# FORD MOTOR COMPANY—TAB 2

# MOTOR
# AUTO REPAIR MANUAL

## CHRYSLER CORPORATION & FORD MOTOR COMPANY

**55th Edition, Volume 2**

First Printing

---



---


**Published by**

**MOTOR**

**Hearst Books/Business Publishing Group,**
**A Division of The Hearst Corp.**

**5600 Crooks Road, Troy, MI 48098**

Printed in the U.S.A.



ISBN 0-87851-742-1

# VEHICLE IDENTIFICATION

## TABLE OF CONTENTS



## CHRYSLER EXCEPT IMPORTS & 1989 MEDALLION

### V.I.N. DEFINED

**1st POSITION**
**COUNTRY**
1 = United States
2 = Canada
3 = Mexico
4 = United States

**2nd POSITION**
**MAKE**
A = Imperial
B = Dodge
C = Chrysler
D = Plymouth
E = Eagle
E = Fargo
P = Plymouth

**3rd POSITION**
**VEHICLE TYPE**
3 = Passenger Car
4 = Multipurpose Vehicle
7 = Truck

**4th POSITION**
**RESTRAINT SYSTEM**
A = Air Bag
B = Manual Belts
C = Automatic Belts
D = 1-3000 LB
E = 3001-4000 LB
F = 4001-5000 LB
G = 5001-6000 LB
X = Air Bag - Manual Passenger
Y = Air Bag - Automatic Passenger

**5th POSITION**
**CARLINE SERIES**
**1983-88**
A = Daytona, Laser
B = Gran Fury Salon
C = LeBaron, Town & Ctry, Limo
D = Aries
E = 600
F = Fifth Avenue, Newport
G = Diplomat
H = LeBaron GTS, Voyager
J = Caravelle, LeBaron
K = Caravan
M = Horizon, Scamp, Turismo
P = Reliant
S = Cordoba, Sundance, Shadow
T = E Class, New Yorker
U = Dynasty, New Yorker
V = 400, 600
X = Lancer, Mirada
Y = Imperial
Z = Omni, Charger, Rampage
**1989-92**
A = Acclaim, Spirit, LeBaron
B = Premier, Monaco
C = Dynasty, New Yorker Salon
C = New Yorker Landau
G = Daytona, Daytona Shelby
H = Voyager, Grand Voyager
H = Lancer, Lancer Shelby
H = LeBaron 4 Door
H = LeBaron GTS

**5th POSITION (CONTINUED)**
J = LeBaron 2 Door
K = Caravan, Caravan C/V
K = Grand Caravan
K = Reliant, Aries, Caravan
L = Horizon, Omni
M = Gran Fury Salon, Newport
M = Caravelle Salon, Diplomat
M = Fifth Avenue
N = Dynasty (Canada)
P = Shadow, Sundance
S = Laser, Talon
T = Talon (AWD)
Y = New Yorker 5th Avenue
Y = Imperial
Y = Town & Country

**6th POSITION**
**SERIES**
1 = Economy (E)
2 = Low (L)
3 = Medium (M)
4 = High (H)
5 = Eagle Premier LX
5 = Dodge Monaco LE
5 = Premium (P)
6 = Eagle Premier ES
6 = Dodge Monaco ES
6 = Special/Sport (S)
7 = Performance/Image (X)

**7th POSITION**
**BODY STYLE**
**PASSENGER CAR**
1 = 2 Door Sedan/Coupe
2 = 2 Door Hardtop (83)
2 = 4 Door Limousine (84-90)
3 = 4 Door Limousine (83)
3 = 2 Door Hardtop (84-90)
4 = 2 Door Hatchback
4 = 3 Door Hatchback
5 = 2 Door Convertible
6 = 4 Door Sedan
8 = 4 Door Hatchback
9 = 4 Door Wagon
**TRUCK**
0 = Extended Wagon
1 = Wagon
1 = Van
3 = Van
4 = Extended Wagon/Van
5 = Wagon

**8th POSITION**
**ENGINE CODE**
A = 1.6-L4, 2 Barrel
A = 2.2-L4, TC
B = 1.7-L4
C = 2.2-L4, 2 Barrel
C = 2.2-L4, Turbo
D = 2.2-L4, TBI
D = 2.2-L4, EFI
E = 2.2-L4, TC
F = 2.2-L4, High Performance
G = 2.6-L4, 2 Barrel
H = 2.5-L4, TBI
H = 2.5-L4, SPI
H = 3.7-L6, 1 Barrel

**8th POSITION (CONTINUED)**
J = 2.5-L4, Turbo
J = 3.7-L6, 1 Barrel
K = 3.7-L6, 2 Barrel
K = 2.5-L4, EFI
L = 3.8-V6, EFI
L = 3.7-L6, 2 Barrel
L = 2.2-L4, TC
N = 5.2-V8, EFI
O = 2.2-L4, EFI
P = 5.2-V8, 2 Barrel
R = 2.0-L4, MPI
R = 3.3-V6, EFI
R = 5.2-V8, 4 Barrel
S = 5.2-V8, 4 Barrel
T = 1.8-L4, MPI
U = 2.0-L4, MPI Turbo
U = 3.0-V6, MPI
X = 2.2-L4, Propane
Z = 5.2-V8, LP
3 = 3.0-V6, EFI
4 = 5.2-V8, 2 Barrel
7 = 5.2-V8, LP
8 = 2.2-L4, 2 Barrel, High Output

**9th POSITION**
**CHECK DIGIT**

**10th POSITION**
**MODEL YEAR**
D = 1983
E = 1984
F = 1985
G = 1986
H = 1987
J = 1988
K = 1989
L = 1990
M = 1991
N = 1992

**11th POSITION**
**ASSEMBLY PLANT**
A = Outer Drive Assembly
C = Jefferson Assembly
D = Belvidere Assembly
E = Bloomington (DSM)
E = Modina, Italy
F = Newark, NJ
G = St. Louis-1, MO
H = Bramalea, Canada
K = Pillette, Canada
M = Lago, Mexico
N = Sterling Heights, MI
R = Windsor, Canada
S = Warren, MI
T = Toluca-1, Mexico
U = Eurostar
V = Toluca-2, Mexico
W = Clairpointe Assembly
W = Kenosha-1, WI
X = St. Louis-2, MO
Y = Kenosha-2, WI

**12th Thru 17th POSITION**
**PRODUCTION SEQUENCE NUMBER**

# CHRYSLER IMPORTS

## V.I.N. DEFINED

### 1st POSITION
**COUNTRY**

J = Japan
M = Thailand
4 = USA (Diamond Star Motors)

### 2nd POSITION
**MAKE**

B = Dodge
E = Eagle
J = Chrysler
L = Dodge, Thailand
P = Plymouth

### 3rd POSITION
**VEHICLE TYPE**

3 = Passenger Car
4 = MPV
7 = Truck

### 4th POSITION
**G.V.W.R. & RESTRAINT SYSTEM**

**PASSENGER CAR**

A = Air Bag
B = Manual Belts
C = Passive Belts
X = Driver Air Bag

**TRUCK or MPV**

D = 1-3000 LB
E = 3001-4000 LB
F = 4001-5000 LB
G = 5001-6000 LB

### 5th POSITION
**LINE**

**PASSENGER CAR**

A = Colt E, Colt DL
A = Colt Premier
A = Colt 100/Vista (Canada)
C = Conquest TSI
D = Stealth, Stealth ES & R/T
E = Stealth R/T Turbo
G = Colt Vista, 2WD
H = Colt Vista, 4WD
R = 2000 GTX
U = Colt, Colt E
U = Colt 200 (Canada)
U = Colt GT, Summit
U = Summit DL & LX
U = Summit ES
V = Colt DL Wagon, 2WD
W = Colt DL Wagon, 4WD

**TRUCK**

J = Raider
L = Ram 50, Ram 50 Custom
L = Ram 50 Sport
L = Power Ram 50 SE & LE
M = Power Ram 50
M = Power Ram 50 SE & LE
M = Power Ram 50 Custom
M = Power Ram 50 Sport

### 6th POSITION
**SERIES**

1 = (E) Economy (S)
2 = (L) Low (Base)
3 = (M) Medium
4 = (H) High
5 = (P) Premium
6 = (S) Special/Sport

### 7th POSITION
**BODY STYLE**

**PASSENGER CAR**

1 = 2 Door Sedan
4 = 2 Door Hatchback
4 = 3 Door Hatchback
4 = Colt, Colt GL, Summit
6 = 4 Door Sedan
6 = Summit, Summit ES
9 = 4 Door Wagon
9 = 5 Door Wagon

**TRUCK**

3 = Van
4 = Conventional Cab-Short
5 = Club Cab
5 = Extended Cab-Long
9 = Conventional Cab-Long

**MPV**

1 = 4 Door Wagon
1 = 5 Door Wagon
3 = 3 Door Metal Top
4 = 4 Door Wagon

### 8th POSITION
**ENGINE CODE**

A = 1.5L, 3 Valve MPI
B = 2.0L, DOHC MPI
B = 3.0L, 24 Valve
C = 3.0L, DOHC Turbo
D = 2.0L, Gas
E = 2.6L, Gas
F = 1.6L, Turbo
H = 2.6L, Turbo
K = 1.5L, Gas
N = 2.6L, Turbo-Intercooler
P = 1.5L, MPI
R = 2.0L, DOHC MPI
S = 3.0L, MPI-18 Valve
T = 1.8L, MPI
U = 2.0L, DOHC MPI
V = 2.0L, MPI
W = 2.4L, MPI
X = 1.5L, MPI
Y = 1.6L, DOHC MPI
Z = 1.6L, DOHC Turbo

### 9th POSITION
**CHECK DIGIT**

### 10th POSITION
**MODEL YEAR**

H = 1987
J = 1988
K = 1989
L = 1990
M = 1991
N = 1992

### 11th POSITION
**ASSEMBLY PLANT**

A = Misushima-2
E = Bloomington (DSM), USA
J = Nagoya-3
O = Thailand
P = Nagoya-2
U = Mizushima-1
Y = Nagoya-1
Z = Okazaki

### 12th Thru 17th POSITION
**PRODUCTION SEQUENCE NUMBER**

# 1989 MEDALLION

## V.I.N. DEFINED

### 1st POSITION
**COUNTRY**
V = France
1 = USA
2 = Canada

### 2nd POSITION
**MANUFACTURER**
A = AMC
B = AMC Canada, LTD.
F = Renault
X = Eagle

### 3rd POSITION
**VEHICLE TYPE**
C = Multipurpose Vehicle
E = Export Left Hand Drive
F = Export Right Hand Drive
M = Passenger Car
1 = Passenger Car

### 4th POSITION
**ENGINE CODE**
A = 1.1-4 Cyl, 1 Barrel
B = 2.5-4 Cyl, 2 Barrel
C = 4.2-6 Cyl, 2 Barrel
D = 1.4-4 Cyl, 1 Barrel
F = 2.2-4 Cyl, MPI
J = 3.0-6 Cyl, MPI
V = 2.0-4 Cyl, 1 Barrel
Y = 2.5-4 Cyl, 1 Barrel
Z = 2.5-4 Cyl, TBI

### 5th POSITION
**TRANSMISSION/TRANSFER CASE**
A = Auto-Column/None
B = Auto-Floor/None
C = Auto-Floor/Full Time
D = Auto-Floor/Full Time
F = Auto-Floor/None
G = 4 Speed-Floor/Full Time
H = 4 Speed-Floor/Part Time
H = 5 Speed-Floor/None
K = Auto-Floor/Part Time
M = 4 Speed-Floor/None
N = 5 Speed-Floor/Part Time
P = 5 Speed-Floor/Full Time
P = Auto-Column/None
T = Auto-Column/None
W = 5 Speed-Floor/None

### 6th & 7th POSITION
**BODY TYPE**
05 = 4 Door Sedan, Concord
06 = 2 Door Sedan, Concord
08 = 4 Door Wagon, Concord
35 = 4 Door Sedan, Eagle
36 = 2 Door Sedan, Eagle
38 = 4 Door Wagon, Eagle
43 = 2 Door Liftback, Spirit
45 = 4 Door Sedan, Medallion
46 = 2 Door Sedan, Spirit
48 = 4 Door Wagon, Medallion
53 = 2 Door Liftback, SX-4
55 = 4 Door Sedan, Premier
56 = 2 Door Sedan, Kammback

### 8th POSITION
**RESTRAINT SYSTEM/TRIM**
B = Manual Belt, Deluxe
C = Manual Belt, Luxury
E = Manual Belt, Deluxe 7 Pass.
0 = Base Manual
5 = DL Manual
7 = Limited Manual
7 = Manual Belt, Eurosport (ES)
9 = Manual Belt, Luxury (LX)

### 9th POSITION
**CHECK DIGIT**

### 10th POSITION
**MODEL YEAR**
B = 1981
C = 1982
D = 1983
E = 1984
F = 1985
G = 1986
H = 1987
J = 1988
K = 1989

### 11th POSITION
**PLANT CODE**
A = Bramalea
B = Brampton
K = Kenosha
2 = Maubeuge
5 = Haren

### 12th Thru 17th POSITION
**PRODUCTION SEQUENCE NUMBER**

# FORD MOTOR CO.

## V.I.N. DEFINED

### 1st POSITION
**COUNTRY**

1 = United States
2 = Canada
3 = South America
3 = Mexico
4 = United States
6 = Australia
9 = Brazil
J = Japan
K = Korea
L = Taiwan
W = Germany

### 2nd POSITION
**MAKE**

B = Ford
C = Ford
C = Imported Truck
F = Ford
F = Mazda
F = Mercury
L = Lincoln
M = Mercury
N = Continental
N = Ford
Z = Ford

### 3rd POSITION
**TYPE**

A = Passenger Car
A = Imported Mercury Tracer
B = Bus
B = Passenger Car
C = Truck, Stripped Chassis
C = Basic, Stripped Chassis
D = Incomplete Vehicle
E = Passenger Car
F = Equiped Without Power Train
F = Imported, Incomplete Truck
H = Incomplete Vehicle
I = Passenger Car
J = Incomplete Vehicle
J = Passenger Car
J = Imported Car, Festiva
M = Multi Purpose Vehicle
N = Passenger Car
P = Passenger Car, Imported
R = Passenger Car
T = Truck, Complete
V = Passenger Car
0 = Imported - Fiesta
1 = Imported - Merker/Scorpio
1 = Passenger Car, Imported
2 = Courier - Complete
3 = Incomplete Vehicle
4 = Multi Purpose Vehicle
4 = Courier - Incomplete
6 = Imported - Festiva

### 4th POSITION
**RESTRAINT SYSTEM**

B = Active Belts
C = Air Bags & Active Belts
D = Active Belts
L = Air Bags & Active Belts
P = Passive & Active Belts

### 5th POSITION
**IDENTIFICATION**

M = Lincoln/Mercury Make
P = Passenger Car (81-89)
P = Ford Make (90-92)
T = Imported & Non-Ford Built

### 6th & 7th POSITION
**BODY SERIES NUMBER**

See The Following Three Pages

### 8th POSITION
**ENGINE CODE**

A = 2.3-L4, EFI/OHC
B = 3.3-V6, 1 Barrel
C = 2.2-L4, EFI (89-92)
C = 3.8-V6, 2 Barrel (84-86)
C = 3.8-V6, EFI (87-90)
C = 3.8-V6, Supercharged (90)
D = 4.2-V8, 2 Barrel (80-82)
D = 2.3-L4, EFI/Turbo (83)
D = 2.5-L4, CFI (86-90)
E = 5.0-V8, EFI/High Output
F = 5.0-V8, CFI/EFI
G = 5.8-V8, 2 Barrel
H = 1.3-L4, EFI, Mazda
H = 2.0-L4, Diesel
J = 1.9-L4, SEFI
K = 1.3-L4, 2-V, Mazda
L = 2.4-V6, Diesel/Turbo (84-85)
L = 2.2-L4, EFI/TC (89-92)
M = 5.0-V8, CFI or EFI/High Output
M = 2.3-L4, EFI (91-92)
N = 2.5-L4, EFI
P = 2.3-L4, EFI/TC
R = 2.3-L4, HSC (83-85)
R = 2.2-L4, EFI/Turbo (89-90)
R = 3.8-V6, OHV
S = 2.3-L4, HSC/CFI/High Output/EFI
T = 2.3-L4, EFI/Turbo/IC
T = 5.0-V8, EFI (91-92)
U = 3.0-V6, EFI
V = 2.9-V6, Fuel Injected
W = 2.3-L4, EFI/Turbo
W = 4.6-V8, EFI (91-92)
X = 3.3-V6, Fuel Injected
X = 2.3-L4, HSC/CFI/EFI
Y = 3.0-V6, SHO/EFI
Z = 1.6-L4, EFI/Mazda (91-92)
1 = 1.3-L4, Fuel Injected
2 = 1.6-L4, Fuel Injected
3 = 3.8-V6, CFI
3 = 3.8-V6, 2 Barrel (Canada)
4 = 1.6-L4, FI/High Output (83-85)
4 = 3.8-V6, EFI/SEFI (87-92)
5 = 1.6-L4, EFI/Mazda
6 = 1.6-L4, EFI/Turbo
6 = 2.3-L4, Propane
6 = 1.6-L4, EFI/TC/Mazda (91-92)
7 = 1.6-L4, Methanol/High Output
8 = 1.6-L4, EFI/Turbo
8 = 1.8-L4, EFI/Mazda
9 = 1.9-L4, CFI

### 9th POSITION
**CHECK DIGIT**

### 10th POSITION
**MODEL YEAR**

B = 1981
C = 1982
D = 1983
E = 1984
F = 1985
G = 1986
H = 1987
J = 1988
K = 1989
L = 1990
M = 1991
N = 1992

### 11th POSITION
**ASSEMBLY PLANT**

A = Atlanta, GA
B = Oakville, Ontario, Canada
E = Mahwah
E = Niehl, West Germany
F = Dearborn, MI
G = Chicago, IL
H = Lorain, OH
J = Los Angeles, CA
J = Monterrey
K = Kansas City, MO
M = West Germany
N = Norfolk, VA
P = Twin Cities, MN
R = Hermosillo, Mexico
R = San Jose, CA
S = Allen Park, MI
T = Metuchen, WI
T = Edison
U = Louisville, KY
W = Wayne, MI
X = St. Thomas, Canada
Y = Wixom, MI
Z = St. Louis, MO
2 = Taiwan
5 = Flat Rock, MI
6 = Kia, Korea
8 = Broadmeadows, Australia

### 12th Thru 17th POSITION
**PRODUCTION SEQUENCE NUMBER**

# FORD MOTOR CO.

## V.I.N. DEFINED

### A BODY - FORD FULL SIZE

**1982-86**

31 = Type - 54D, LTD "S" 4 Door
32 = Type - 66H, LTD 2 Door
33 = Type - 54H, LTD 4 Door
33 = Type - 54K, LTD Crown Vic 4 Door
34 = Type - 66K, LTD Crown Vic 2 Door
37 = Type - 74D, LTD "S" Station Wagon
38 = Type - 74H, LTD Station Wagon
39 = Type - 74K, LTD Country Squire Wagon
42 = Type - 66K, LTD Crown Vic 2 Door
43 = Type - 54K, LTD Crown Vic 4 Door
44 = Type - 74D, LTD "S" Station Wagon

**1987-92**

70 = Type - 66K, LTD Crown Vic 2 Door-Base
71 = Type - 66K, LTD Crown Vic 2 Door-LX
72 = Type - 54K, LTD Crown Vic 4 Door-S
73 = Type - 54K, LTD Crown Vic 4 Door-Base
74 = Type - 54K, LTD Crown Vic 4 Door-LX
75 = Type - 74K, LTD Crown Vic Wagon-S
75 = Type - 54K, LTD Crown Viv 4 Door-Touring
76 = Type - 74K, LTD Crown Vic Wagon-Base
77 = Type - 74K, LTD Crown Vic Wagon-LX
78 = Type - 74K, LTD Country Squire Wagon-Base
79 = Type - 74K, LTD Country Squire Wagon-LX

### A BODY - MERCURY FULL SIZE

**1982**

81 = Type - 54H, Marquis 4 Door
82 = Type - 66K, Marquis Brougham 2 Door
83 = Type - 54K, Marquis Brougham 4 Door
84 = Type - 66L, Grand Marquis 2 Door
85 = Type - 54L, Grand Marquis 4 Door
87 = Type - 74H, Marquis Station Wagon
88 = Type - 74K, Colony Park Wagon

**1983-86**

93 = Type - 66K, Grand Marquis 2 Door
94 = Type - 74K, Grands Marquis Wagon
95 = Type - 54K, Grand Marquis 4 Door

**1987-92**

71 = Type - 66K, 2 Door-GS
72 = Type - 66K, 2 Door-LS
74 = Type - 54K, 4 Door-GS
75 = Type - 54K, 4 Door-LS
78 = Type - 74K, Colony Park Wagon-GS
79 = Type - 74K, Colony Park Wagon-LS

### B BODY - FORD TEMPO

**1984-86**

18 = Type - 66D, 2 Door-Base
19 = Type - 66D, 2 Door-GL
20 = Type - 66D, 2 Door-GLX
21 = Type - 54D, 4 Door-Base
22 = Type - 54D, 4 Door-GL
23 = Type - 54D, 4 Door-GLX

**1987-92**

30 = Type - 66D, 2 Door-L
31 = Type - 66D, 2 Door-GL
32 = Type - 66D, 2 Door-LX
33 = Type - 66D, 2 Door-Sport GLS
34 = Type - 66D, 2 Door-(AWD)
35 = Type - 54D, 4 Door-L, (AWD)
36 = Type - 54D, 4 Door-GL
37 = Type - 54D, 4 Door-LX
38 = Type - 54D, 4 Door-Sport GLS
39 = Type - 54D, 4 Door-LX, (AWD)

### B BODY - MERCURY TOPAZ

**1984-86**

71 = Type - 66D, 2 Door-Base
72 = Type - 66D, 2 Door-GS
73 = Type - 66D, 2 Door-LS
74 = Type - 54D, 4 Door-Base
75 = Type - 54D, 4 Door-GS
76 = Type - 54D, 4 Door-LS

**1987-92**

30 = Type - 66D, 2 Door-L
31 = Type - 66D, 2 Door-GS, (AWD)
32 = Type - 66D, 2 Door-LS
33 = Type - 66D, 2 Door-Sport, (AWD)
35 = Type - 54D, 4 Door-L
36 = Type - 54D, 4 Door-GS, (AWD)
37 = Type - 54D, 4 Door-LS, (AWD)
38 = Type - 54D, 4 Door-Sport, (AWD)

### BT BODY - FORD FESTIVA

**1988-92**

05 = Type - 61, 2 Door-L
06 = Type - 61, 2 Door-GL
07 = Type - 61, 2 Door-LX

### C BODY - FORD EXP

**1982-86**

01 = Type - 67D, 3 Door Hatchback

**Continued On Next Page**

# FORD MOTOR CO.

## V.I.N. DEFINED

### C BODY - MERCURY LN7

**1982**

61 = Type - 67D, 3 Door Hatchback

**1983**

51 = Type - 67D, 3 Door Hatchback

### DC BODY - LINCOLN CONTINENTAL

**1982-92**

97 = Type - 54D, 4 Door-Base/Executive
98 = Type - 54D, 4 Door-Givenchy/Signature

### DT BODY - LINCOLN TOWN CAR

**1982**

92 = Type - 54D, 4 Door

**1983-86**

96 = Type - 54D, 4 Door

**1987-92**

81 = Type - 54D, 4 Door-Base/Executive
82 = Type - 54D, 4 Door-Signature
83 = Type - 54D, 4 Door-Cartier

### E BODY - FORD TAURUS

**1986**

29 = Type - 54D, 4 Door
29 = Type - 74D, 4 Door Wagon

**1987-92**

50 = Type - 54D, 4 Door-L
51 = Type - 54D, 4 Door-MT5
52 = Type - 54D, 4 Door-GL
53 = Type - 54D, 4 Door-LX
54 = Type - 54D, 4 Door-SHO
55 = Type - 74D, 4 Door Wagon-L
56 = Type - 74D, 4 Door Wagon-MT5
57 = Type - 74D, 4 Door Wagon-GL
58 = Type - 74D, 4 Door Wagon-LX

### E BODY - MERCURY SABLE

**1986**

87 = Type - 54D, 4 Door
88 = Type - 74D, 4 Door Wagon

**1987-92**

50 = Type - 54D, 4 Door-GS
53 = Type - 54D, 4 Door-LS
55 = Type - 74D, 4 Door Wagon-GS
58 = Type - 74D, 4 Door Wagon-LS

### F BODY - FORD MUSTANG

**1982**

10 = Type - 66B, 2 Door Sedan
13 = Type - 61H, 3 Door Hatchback Ghia
16 = Type - 61B, 3 Door Hatchback Sedan

**1983-86**

26 = Type - 66B, 2 Door Sedan
27 = Type - 66B, Convertable
28 = Type - 61B, 3 Door Hatchback Ghia

**1987-92**

40 = Type - 66B, 2 Door Sedan-LX
41 = Type - 61B, 2 Door Hatchback-LX
42 = Type - 61B, 2 Door Hatchback-GT
44 = Type - 66B, Convertible-LX
45 = Type - 66B, Convertible-GT

### F BODY - MERCURY COUGAR

**1982**

76 = Type - 66D, 2 Door Except XR7
77 = Type - 54D, 4 Door
90 = Type - 66D, 2 Door XR7

**1983-86**

92 = Type - 66D, 2 Door Sedan

**1987-92**

60 = Type - 66D, 2 Door-LS
62 = Type - 66D, 2 Door-XR7

### G BODY - FORD GRANADA

**1982**

26 = Type - 66D, 2 Door
27 = Type - 54D, 4 Door
28 = Type - 74D, 4 Door Wagon

### G BODY - FORD LTD

**1983-86**

39 = Type - 54D, 4 Door
40 = Type - 74D, 4 Door Wagon

### G BODY - MERCURY MARQUIS

**1983-86**

89 = Type - 54D, 4 Door
90 = Type - 74D, 4 Door Wagon

### J BODY - MERCURY CAPRI

**1982**

67 = Type - 61D, 3 Door
68 = Type - 61H, 3 Door Ghia

**1983-86**

79 = Type - 61D, 3 Door

### K BODY - LINCOLN MARK

**1982**

95 = Type - 66D, 2 Door
96 = Type - 54D, 4 Door

**1983**

98 = Type - 66D, 2 Door
99 = Type - 54D, 4 Door

**1984-86**

98 = Type - 66D, 2 Door

**1987-92**

91 = Type - 63D, 2 Door-Base
92 = Type - 63D, 2 Door-Blass
93 = Type - 63D, 2 Door-LSC

**Continued On Next Page**

# FORD MOTOR CO.

## V.I.N. DEFINED

### MM BODY - MERCURY TRACER

**1988-89**

11 = Type - 61D, 2 Door
12 = Type - 58D, 4 Door
13 = Type - 74D, 4 Door Wagon

**1991-92**

10 = Type - 54D, 4 Door Notchback-Base
14 = Type - 54D, 4 Door Notchback-LS
15 = Type - 74D, 4 Door Wagon-Base

### MX BODY - MERCURY MERKUR-XR4TI

**1986-89**

80 = Type - 61D, 3 Door Hatchback

### MY BODY - MERCURY MERKUR-SCORPIO

**1988-89**

81 = Type - 58 , 5 Door Hatchback

### P BODY - FORD FAIRMONT

**1982**

20 = Type - 66B, 2 Door
21 = Type - 54B, 4 Door, Futura
22 = Type - 36R, 2 Door, Futura
23 = Type - 74B, 4 Door Wagon, Futura

**1983**

35 = Type - 66B, 2 Door
36 = Type - 54B, 4 Door
37 = Type - 36R, 2 Door Sport Coupe

### P BODY - MERCURY ZEPHYR

**1982**

71 = Type - 54D, 4 Door
72 = Type - 36R, 2 Door Z7

**1983**

86 = Type - 54D, 4 Door
87 = Type - 36R, 2 Door Z7

### S BODY - FORD THUNDERBIRD

**1982**

42 = Type - 66D, 2 Door

**1983-86**

46 = Type - 63D, 2 Door

**1987-92**

60 = Type - 63D, 2 Door-Base
61 = Type - 63D, 2 Door-Sport
62 = Type - 63D, 2 Door-LX
64 = Type - 63D, 2 Door-Turbo/Super Coupe

### SA BODY - MERCURY CAPRI

**1991-92**

01 = Type - 76 , 2 Door Convertible-Base
03 = Type - 76 , 2 Door Convertible-XR2

### ST BODY - FORD PROBE

**1989-92**

20 = Type - 61 , 2 Hatchback-GL
21 = Type - 61 , 2 Hatchback-LX
22 = Type - 61 , 2 Hatchback-GT

### W BODY - FORD ESCORT

**1982**

05 = Type - 61D, 3 Door Hatchback
06 = Type - 58D, 5 Door Hatchback
08 = Type - 74D, 4 Door Liftgate

01 = Type - 61D, 3 Door Hatchback-Turbo
04 = Type - 61D, 2 Door Hatchback
05 = Type - 61D, 2 Door Hatchback-GL
06 = Type - 61D, 2 Door Hatchback-GLX
07 = Type - 61D, 2 Door Hatchback-GT
09 = Type - 74D, 4 Door Wagon
10 = Type - 74D, 4 Door Wagon-GL
11 = Type - 74D, 4 Door Wagon-GLX
13 = Type - 58D, 4 Door Hatchback
14 = Type - 58D, 4 Door Hatchback-GL
15 = Type - 58D, 4 Door Hatchback-LX
31 = Type - 61D, 2 Door Hatchback-L
32 = Type - 61D, 2 Door Hatchback-GL
33 = Type - 61D, 2 Door Hatchback-GT
34 = Type - 74D, 4 Door Wagon-L
35 = Type - 74D, 4 Door Wagon-GL
36 = Type - 58D, 4 Door Hatchback-L
37 = Type - 58D, 4 Door Hatchback-GL

**1987-92**

10 = Type - 61D, 2 Door Hatchback-Pony
11 = Type - 61D, 2 Door Hatchback-LS
12 = Type - 61D, 2 Door Hatchback-GT
13 = Type - 54D, 4 Door Notchback-LX
14 = Type - 58D, 4 Door Hatchback-LX
15 = Type - 74D, 4 Door Wagon-LX
16 = Type - 54D, 4 Door Notchback, LX-E
17 = Type - 67D, 2 Door Coupe-EXP Luxury
18 = Type - 67D, 2 Door Coupe-EXP Sport
20 = Type - 61D, 2 Door Hatchback-Pony
21 = Type - 61D, 2 Door Hatchback-GL
23 = Type - 61D, 2 Door Hatchback-GT
25 = Type - 58D, 4 Door Hatchback-GL
28 = Type - 74D, 4 Door Wagon-GL
88 = Type - 67D, 2 Door Coupe-EXP Base
89 = Type - 67D, 2 Door Coupe-EXP Sport
90 = Type - 61D, 2 Door Hatchback-Pony
91 = Type - 61D, 2 Door Hatchback-LX
93 = Type - 61D, 2 Door Hatchback-GT
95 = Type - 58D, 4 Door Hatchback-LX
98 = Type - 74D, 4 Door Wagon-LX

### W BODY - MERCURY LYNX

**1982**

63 = Type - 61D, 3 Door Hatchback
64 = Type - 58D, 5 Door Hatchback
65 = Type - 74D, 4 Door Liftgate

**1983-86**

51 = Type - 61D, 3 Door Hatchback-L
52 = Type - 61D, 3 Door Hatchback-GS
53 = Type - 61D, 3 Door Hatchback
54 = Type - 61D, 3 Door Hatchback-Base
55 = Type - 61D, 3 Door Hatchback-GS
57 = Type - 61D, 3 Door Hatchback-RS
58 = Type - 61D, 3 Door Hatchback-LS
58 = Type - 74D, 4 Door Wagon-L
59 = Type - 74D, 4 Door Wagon-GS
60 = Type - 74D, 4 Door Wagon-Base
61 = Type - 74D, 4 Door Wagon-GS
63 = Type - 74D, 4 Door Wagon-LS
63 = Type - 58D, 5 Door Hatchback-L
64 = Type - 58D, 5 Door Hatchback-GS
65 = Type - 58D, 5 Door Hatchback-Base
66 = Type - 58D, 5 Door Hatchback-GS
68 = Type - 58D, 5 Door Hatchback-LS

**1987**

20 = Type - 61D, 2 Door Sedan-L
21 = Type - 61D, 2 Door Sedan-GS
22 = Type - 61D, 2 Door Sedan-XR3
25 = Type - 58D, 4 Door Hatchback-GS
28 = Type - 74D, 4 Door Wagon-GS

# SERVICE REMINDER & WARNING LAMP RESET PROCEDURES

**TABLE OF CONTENTS**



# Chrysler Corp./Eagle/AMC

**INDEX**



## ANTI-LOCK WARNING LAMP

This lamp will be illuminated when the ignition switch is placed in the On position. The lamp maybe illuminated for as long as 30 seconds as a bulb and system check. If lamp remains illuminated or comes on while operating the vehicle, a problem in the anti-lock brake system is indicated. When lamp is illuminated, place ignition switch in Off position, then restart engine. If lamp still remains illuminated, the anti-lock brake system should be serviced. The brake system will remain functional, but without the anti-lock function. After servicing the anti-lock brake system the lamp will automatically reset when the ignition switch is cycled to the Off position.

## AIRBAG SYSTEM WARNING LAMP

On models equipped with an airbag system, if the airbag warning lamp illuminates and stays on, diagnosis and repair of the airbag system will be necessary to reset the lamp.

## BRAKE PAD WEAR WARNING LAMP

### EAGLE MEDALLION

When this message is displayed, the disc brake pads should be inspected and replaced as necessary. After completing service, the message will be reset automatically.

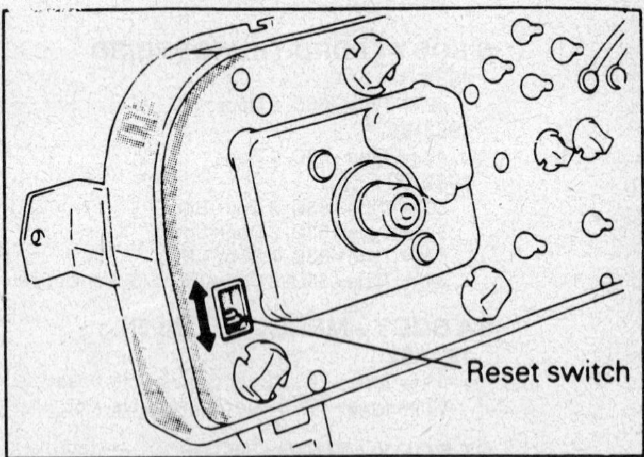


**Fig. 1 EGR or Maintenance Required Lamp reset switch location. 1985–91 Dodge & Plymouth Colt Vista**

## EGR WARNING LAMP

### 1985–87 DODGE & PLYMOUTH COLT VISTA

This lamp will be illuminated every 50,000 miles to indicate interval for EGR system service. After performing EGR system service, the lamp can be reset by moving the reset switch lever located at the rear of the instrument cluster, **Fig. 1.**

# CHECK ENGINE LAMP

## CHRYSLER, DODGE & PLYMOUTH

The Check Engine lamp will be illuminated for approximately 3 seconds after the ignition switch has been placed in the On position as a bulb check. If incorrect or no signals are received by the Single Board Engine Controller (SMEC) from various sensors, the SBEC will illuminate the Check Engine lamp. After diagnosing and servicing the fuel injection system or emission related systems, the SBEC memory will be cleared after approximately 50 to 100 ignition key on-off cycles.

## EAGLE MEDALLION

This lamp will be illuminated during engine starting as a bulb check. Once the engine has started, the lamp should go off. If lamp remains illuminated, the fuel injection and emission control system diagnosis should be performed using tester M.S. 1700. During the diagnosis and repair procedure with tester M.S. 1700, the check engine lamp will be reset.

## DODGE MONACO & EAGLE PREMIER

This lamp will be illuminated during engine starting as a bulb check. Once the engine has started, the lamp should go off. If lamp remains illuminated, the fuel injection and emission control system diagnosis should be performed using tester DRB II. During the diagnosis and repair procedure with tester DRB II, the check engine lamp will be reset.

# CHECK ENGINE OR MALFUNCTION INDICATOR LAMP

## DODGE & PLYMOUTH COLT & EAGLE SUMMIT

This lamp is used to monitor fuel injection and emission control system components for malfunctions. When the ignition switch is placed in the On position, the lamp will illuminate for 2 to 3 seconds as a bulb check. If lamp remains on, a malfunction in the fuel injection or emission control system is indicated. If malfunction is intermittent, the lamp will go off when Electronic Control Unit (ECU) receives a normal signal from the malfunctioning component. If the ECU receives an improper signal from a malfunctioning component for a time longer than that programmed into the ECU, a code will be stored in the ECU memory and the Malfunction Indicator Lamp will be illuminated. After servicing the indicated component, Malfunction Indicator Lamp can be reset by clearing the ECU memory. The ECU memory is cleared by disconnecting the battery ground cable for approximately 10 seconds.

# ELECTRONIC MONITOR

## 1988–89 CHRYSLER LEBARON

This system is an electronic monitor system with sensors, which displays messages on an instrument panel mounted console. If no messages are stored, the message "Monitored Systems OK" will be displayed approximately 6 seconds after ignition switch has been placed in th On position. The system is actuated by depressing the check button located on the front of the message display. When this button is depressed, the system will sound a tone and cycle through the messages and then return to normal operation. If the monitor detects a fault, the component will be noted on the display. The fault messages are as follows:

**BRAKE FLUID LOW**–When this message is displayed, bring brake to proper level. The message will be reset after the ignition switch has been cycled to the Off position.

**COOLANT LEVEL LOW**–When this message is displayed, bring coolant to proper level. The message will be reset after the ignition switch has been cycled to the Off position.

**DISC BRAKE PADS WORN**–When this message is displayed, the disc brake pads should be inspected and replaced as necessary. After completing service, the message will be reset after the ignition switch has been cycled to the Off position.

**DRIVER, PASSENGER OR HATCH AJAR**–Close door or hatch indicated to cancel message.

**ENGINE TEMPERATURE HIGH**–This message will be indicated when an engine overheating condition is encountered. After repairing cause of engine overheating condition or when engine speed is less than 300 RPM, the message will be automatically cancelled.

**EXTERIOR LAMPS ON**–This message will appear when the ignition switch is in Off, Lock or Accessory, the driver's door is open and the light switch is in the On position. This message will be cancelled when light switch is placed in the Off position or the door is closed.

**HEADLAMP, BRAKE OR TAIL LAMP OUT**–The display will be illuminated when brake is applied or light switch is in the On position and a burned out lamp bulb is present. To reset message, replace burned out bulb, then actuate lamp circuit.

**KEY IN IGNITION**–This message will appear when the ignition switch is in the Off, Lock or Accessory position and the driver's door is open. This message will be cancelled when the keys are removed or the door is closed.

**LOW FUEL LEVEL**–When this message is displayed, add fuel to vehicle to reset message.

**LOW OIL PRESSURE**–This message will be displayed when a low engine oil pressure condition exist. If message is encountered with vehicle operating at idle speed, increase engine RPM. If message remains or if message is encountered while operating vehicle, the engine lubricating system should be checked and service immediately. After engine lubricating system has been serviced, the message will be automatically cancelled.

**LOW TRANS PRESSURE**–When this message is displayed, a problem in the automatic transaxle is present. After completing automatic transaxle service, the message will be reset after the ignition switch has been cycled to the Off position.

**VOLTAGE LOW**–When this message is displayed, a problem in the charging or electrical system exist. After servicing, the message will be reset after the ignition switch has been cycled to the Off position.

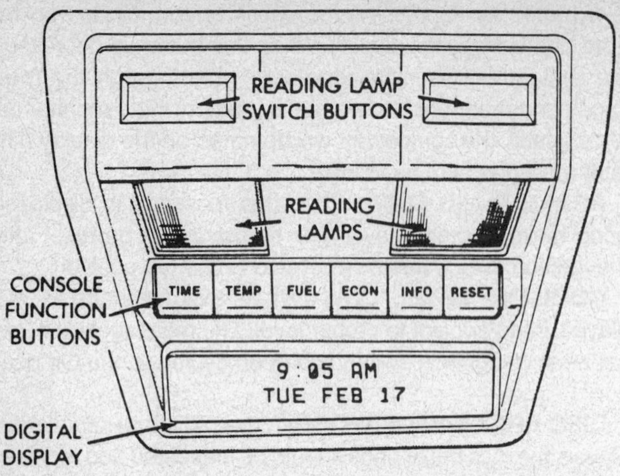


**Fig. 2 Electronic Vehicle Information Center display console. 1988–89 Chrysler New Yorker & Dodge Dynasty**

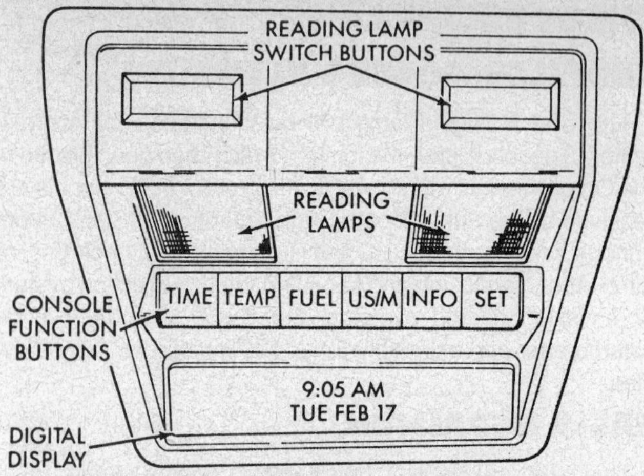


**Fig. 3 Electronic Vehicle Information Center display console. 1990–92 Chrysler New Yorker, Fifth Avenue, Imperial & Dodge Dynasty**

**WASHER FLUID LOW**—When this message is displayed, bring washer fluid to proper level to reset message.

## ELECTRONIC VEHICLE INFORMATION CENTER

### 1988–92 CHRYSLER NEW YORKER & NEW YORKER LANDAU & DODGE DYNASTY, 1990–92 CHRYSLER FIFTH AVENUE & IMPERIAL

On 1988-89 models, this system is a computer controlled monitor system, which displays messages on an overhead console, **Fig. 2.** When the vehicle is started and no faults are present, the display will indicate "MONITORED SYSTEMS OK". If the monitor detects a fault, a tone will be sounded and component will be noted on the display.

On 1990-92 models, the Electronic Vehicle Information Center is a computer controlled warning system which monitors various sensors used on the vehicle. The system supplements the warning indicators in the instrument cluster. When a warning message has been activated, a tone will sound to attract the driver's attention. The warning message will then be displayed on the overhead console, **Fig. 3,** until the condition has been corrected or a new display function is called up. A tone will announce each new warning condition. The warning messages are as follows:

**CHECK ENGINE OIL LEVEL**—When this message is displayed, check engine oil and adjust to proper level. The message will be reset after the ignition switch has been cycled to the Off position.

**CHECK TRANS**—When this message is displayed, a problem in the automatic transaxle is present. After completing automatic transaxle service, the message will be reset after the ignition switch has been cycled to the Off position.

**COOLANT LEVEL LOW**—When this message is displayed, bring coolant to proper level. The message will be reset after the ignition switch has been cycled to the Off position.

**DISC BRAKE PADS WORN**—When this message is displayed, the disc brake pads should be inspected and replaced as necessary. After completing service, the message will be reset after the ignition switch has been cycled to the Off position.

**DRIVER, PASSENGER, LEFT REAR, RIGHT REAR DOOR OR TRUNK AJAR**—Close door to cancel message.

**ENGINE TEMPERATURE CRITICAL**—This message will be indicated when an engine overheating condition is encountered. After repairing cause of engine overheating condition, the message will be automatically cancelled.

**EXTERIOR LAMPS ON**—This message will appear when the ignition switch is in Off, Lock or Accessory, the driver's door is open and the light switch is in the On position. This message will be cancelled when light switch is placed in the Off position or the door is closed.

**HEADLAMP, BRAKE OR TAIL LAMP OUT**—The display will be illuminated when brake is applied or light switch is in the On position and a burned out lamp bulb is present. To reset message, replace burned out bulb, then actuate lamp circuit.

**KEY IN IGNITION**—This message will appear when the ignition switch is in the Off, Lock or Accessory position and the driver's door is open. This message will be cancelled when the keys are removed or the door is closed.

**LOW BRAKE FLUID**—When this message is displayed, bring brake to proper level. The message will be reset after the ignition switch has been cycled to the Off position.

**LOW FUEL LEVEL**—When this message is displayed, add fuel to vehicle. The message will be reset after the ignition switch has been cycled to the Off position.

**LOW OIL PRESSURE**—This message will be displayed when a low engine oil pressure condition exist. If message is encountered with vehicle operating at idle speed, increase engine RPM. If message remains or if message is encountered while operating vehicle, the engine lubricating system should be checked and service immediately. After engine lubricating system has been serviced, the message will be automatically cancelled.

**Fig. 4 Resetting emission or oxygen sensor maintenance reminder switch. 1980 Chrysler, Dodge & Plymouth (mechanical type) & 1980–81 AMC models**

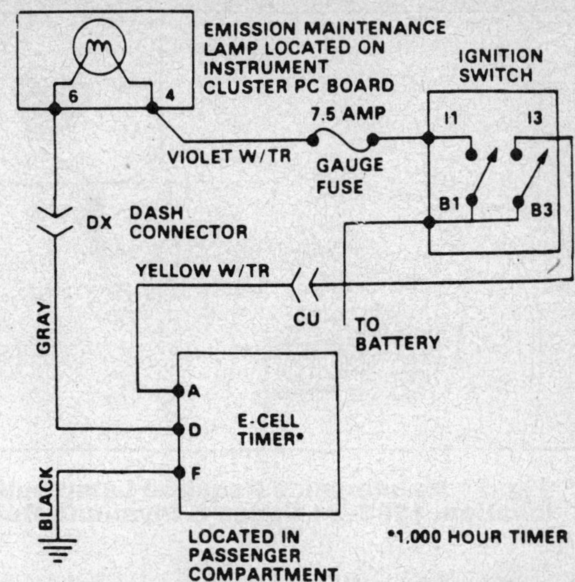


**Fig. 5 Emission maintenance reminder indicator wiring schematic. 1982–83 AMC Concord & Spirit & 1982–87 Eagle**

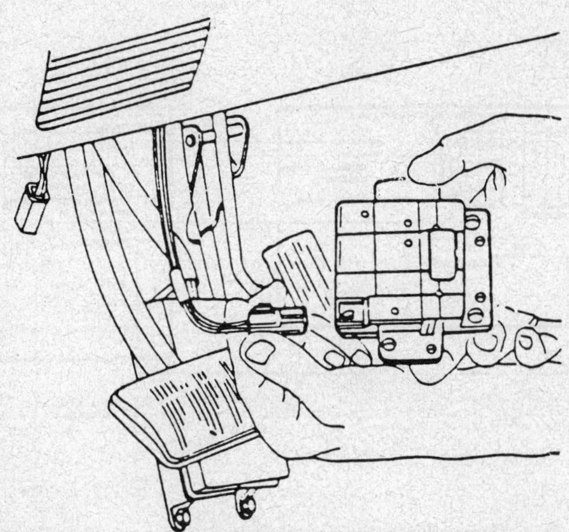

**Fig. 6 Emission maintenance timer replacement. 1988 Eagle except Medallion & Premier**

**SERVICE REMINDER**—This message will be indicated at 7,500 mile or 12 month intervals to indicate that required service is to be performed. After performing the required service, with the Service Reminder message displayed, depress the Vehicle Electronic Information Center Reset button.

**TURN SIGNAL ON**—This message will be indicated when the turn is on and vehicle has traveled a distance over 1/2 mile at a speed above 15 MPH. The message will be reset when the turn signal has been placed in the Off position.

**VOLTAGE IMPROPER**—When this message is displayed, a problem in the charging or electrical system exist. After servicing, the message will be reset after the ignition switch has been cycled to the Off position.

**WASHER FLUID LOW**—When this message is displayed, bring washer fluid to proper level. The message will be reset after the ignition switch has been cycled to the Off position.

# EMISSION MAINTENANCE REMINDER INDICATOR

## 1980–81 AMC CONCORD, EAGLE, PACER & SPIRIT

On 1980-81 models, at 30,000 miles intervals, a warning lamp will be illuminated on the instrument panel to indicate oxygen sensor replacement. After performing the required service, the reminder lamp switch must be reset. The switch is located between the upper and lower speedometer cables in the engine compartment on the lefthand side of the dash panel. Rotate the reset screw located on the switch 1/4 turn counterclockwise, **Fig. 4.**

## 1982–83 AMC CONCORD & SPIRIT & 1982–87 EAGLE

The emission maintenance lamp will, **Fig. 5,** illuminate after 1000 hours of engine operation to indicate that the oxygen sensor must be replaced. After performing the required service, the emission maintenance E-Cell timer must be replaced for the next 1000 hour interval.

This timer is located in the passenger compartment, attached to the wiring harness leading to the MCU. To replace timer, remove printed circuit board, then remove timer from its enclosure and insert replacement timer.

## 1988 EAGLE EXCEPT MEDALLION & PREMIER

The emission maintenance timer will illuminate an indicator lamp on the instrument cluster when vehicle mileage has reached 82,500 miles. At this time, the oxygen sensor and PCV valve should be replaced, in addition to the other required emission maintenance scheduled for this mileage.

**Fig. 7 Maintenance Required Lamp bulb location. 1988–91 Dodge & Plymouth Colt Vista**

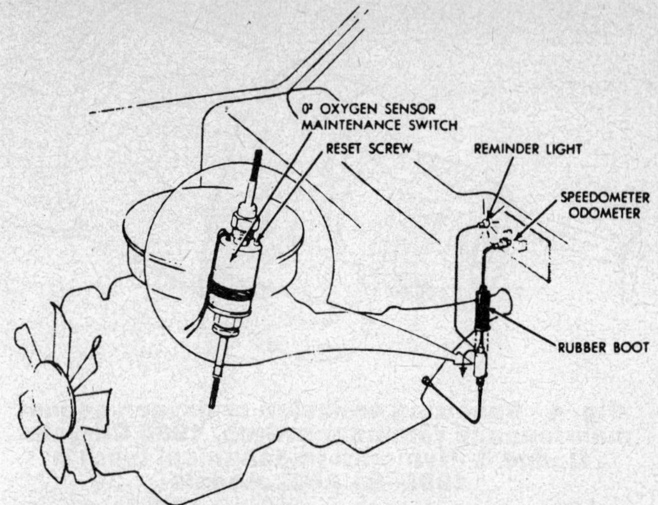


**Fig. 8. Oxygen sensor maintenance reminder system. 1980 Chrysler, Dodge & Plymouth mechanical type**

If the timer should fail before vehicle has accumulated 82,500 miles, the timer and oxygen sensor should both be replaced to maintain a proper sensor replacement interval.

After performing the required service, replace the emission maintenance timer as follows:

1. Remove emission maintenance timer to dash bracket attaching screws. The timer is located on the dash panel to the right of the steering column.
2. Remove timer from bracket, then disconnect electrical connector and remove timer from vehicle, **Fig. 6.**
3. Connect electrical connector to replacement timer, then position timer to mounting bracket and install and tighten attaching screws.

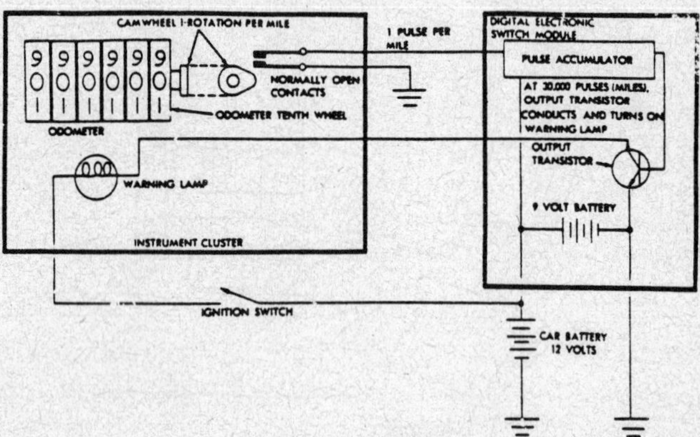


**Fig. 9. Oxygen sensor maintenance reminder system. 1980 Chrysler, Dodge & Plymouth electronic type**

## LOW COOLANT WARNING LAMP

### 1990–92 PLYMOUTH LASER & EAGLE TALON

The Low Coolant Warning Lamp will be illuminated whenever coolant level in the coolant reservoir is below a pre-determined level. Add coolant to bring reservoir to proper level to turn lamp off.

## MAINTENANCE REQUIRED LAMP

### 1988–91 DODGE & PLYMOUTH COLT VISTA

This lamp will be illuminated at 50,000, 80,000, 100,000 and 150,000 miles to indicate interval for emission control system inspection. After performing emission control system inspection at the 50,000, 80,000 or 100,00 mile interval, the lamp can be reset by moving the reset switch lever located at the rear of the instrument cluster, **Fig. 1.** At the 150,000 mile interval, after performing inspection, remove bulb from lamp socket, **Fig. 7.**

## OXYGEN SENSOR MAINTENANCE REMINDER LAMP

### 1980 CHRYSLER, DODGE & PLYMOUTH

At 30,000 miles intervals, a warning lamp will be illuminated on the instrument panel to indicate oxygen sensor replacement. The reminder can either be mechanical, **Fig. 8**, or electronic, **Fig. 9**. After performing the required service, the reminder lamp must be reset.

On the mechanical system, rotate the reset screw located on the switch counterclockwise until it stops, **Fig. 4**.

On the electronic system, remove 9 volt battery from module, which is located under the lefthand side of the instrument panel. Insert a suitable rod into hole on module case to reset switch. After resetting switch, install a replacement 9 volt battery.

# POWER LOSS/LIMIT LAMP

## CHRYSLER, DODGE & PLYMOUTH

The Power Loss/Limit lamp will be illuminated for approximately 3 seconds after the ignition switch has been placed in the On position as a bulb check. If incorrect or no signals are received by the logic module from various sensors, the logic module will illuminate the Power Loss/Limit lamp. After diagnosing and servicing the fuel injection system or EGR system (California models with EGR sensor), the logic module memory can be cleared by disconnecting and reconnecting the battery quick disconnect.

# VEHICLE MAINTENANCE MONITOR (VMM) SYSTEM

## DODGE MONACO & EAGLE PREMIER

This system, **Fig. 10**, monitors regular service and maintenance intervals, engine oil level, engine coolant level, windshield washer fluid level, brake and tail lamps, door ajar, transaxle (models w/4-150 engine) and oil, coolant and washer sensors.

When the vehicle is started and no faults are present, the display will indicate "MONITOR". If the monitor detects a fault, it will be noted on the display. If more than one fault is noted, the fault of the highest priority will be displayed first. The display will then note all existing faults and return to the fault of highest priority. The VMM fault messages are as follows:

a. **DOOR**—Door Ajar—Close door indicated on vehicle outline display to reset monitor.
b. **LAMP**—Brake Or Tail Lamp Outage—The display will be illuminated when brake is applied or light switch is in the On position and a burned out lamp bulb is present. To reset monitor, replace burned out bulb.
c. **COOLANT**—Low Engine Coolant Level—Bringing coolant to proper level will reset monitor.
d. **OIL**—Low Engine Oil Level—The system will check engine oil level approximately 12 minutes after the ignition switch has been placed in the Off position. A low oil level condition must be indicated three consecutive times before the monitor will display "Oil". To reset monitor, add oil to bring to proper level, then while display is indicating the "Oil" message, depress Reset select switch until a beep is noted. Even if Reset select switch is not depressed, the system will automatically reset monitor after three proper oil level readings have been obtained.
e. **WASHER**—Low Washer Fluid Level—Bringing washer fluid to proper level will reset monitor.
f. **TRANS**—Service Transaxle (Models w/4-150 Engine)—Indicates defect in automatic transaxle.
g. **SERVICE**—Perform Required Service and Maintenance—This message will be indicated at 7,500 mile intervals to indicate that required service is to be performed. After performing the required service, depress Reset select switch until a beep is noted.
h. **SENSOR**—This message will be indicated when a defect in the oil, coolant or washer sensor circuit is noted. Refer to "Self-Diagnosis."
i. **MILES (KMS)**—Miles to next scheduled service interval.

### Self-Diagnosis

To diagnosis, depress and hold the Check and List select switches, then place ignition switch in On position. With the instrument cluster switch in the English mode, all diagnosis will be performed automatically in sequence. With the instrument cluster in the Metric mode, the Check select switch will have to be depressed to proceed to the next test. The display will indicate which components are defective or satisfactory, refer to **Fig. 11.** After completing diagnosis, depress Check and List select switches to exit diagnosis mode.

### Troubleshooting

1. If a condition of no display or incorrect information exist, start engine and check the following:
   a. On models less passive restraint check fuses 8 and 19 in fuse panel. On models with passive restraint, check fuses 2 and 8 in fuse panel. Replace any blown fuses.
   b. Using a suitable voltmeter, check terminal Nos. 1 and 5 of connector A, **Fig. 10.** Voltmeter should indicate battery voltage, if not check for open circuit to fuse panel.
   c. Connect a suitable ohmmeter between terminal Nos. 15 and 18 of connector A, **Fig. 10.** Ohmmeter should indicate zero ohms. If a no display condition is present, replace monitor. If a incorrect information condition is present, refer to "Self-Diagnosis." If reading is other than zero ohms, check for open circuit to ground.
   d. With all doors closed, connect an ohmmeter between terminal Nos. 6, 7, 8 and 9 of connector A, **Fig. 10.** Ohmmeter should indicate an infinite reading. If reading is other than infinite, check for short circuit to ground.
2. If monitor fails to change modes, disconnect electrical connector B, **Fig. 10**, and proceed as follows:
   a. With Check select switch depressed, connect ohmmeter between terminal Nos. 2 and 4 of connector B. If ohmmeter reading is zero ohms, proceed to step b. If ohmmeter reading is other than zero ohms, replace mode select switches.
   b. With List select switch depressed, connect ohmmeter between terminal Nos. 2 and 3 of connector B. If ohmmeter reading is zero ohms, proceed to step c. If ohmmeter reading is other than zero ohms, replace mode select switches.
   c. With Reset select switch depressed, connect ohmmeter between terminal Nos. 2 and 5 of connector B. Ohmmeter reading should be zero ohms. If ohmmeter reading is other than zero ohms, replace mode select switches.

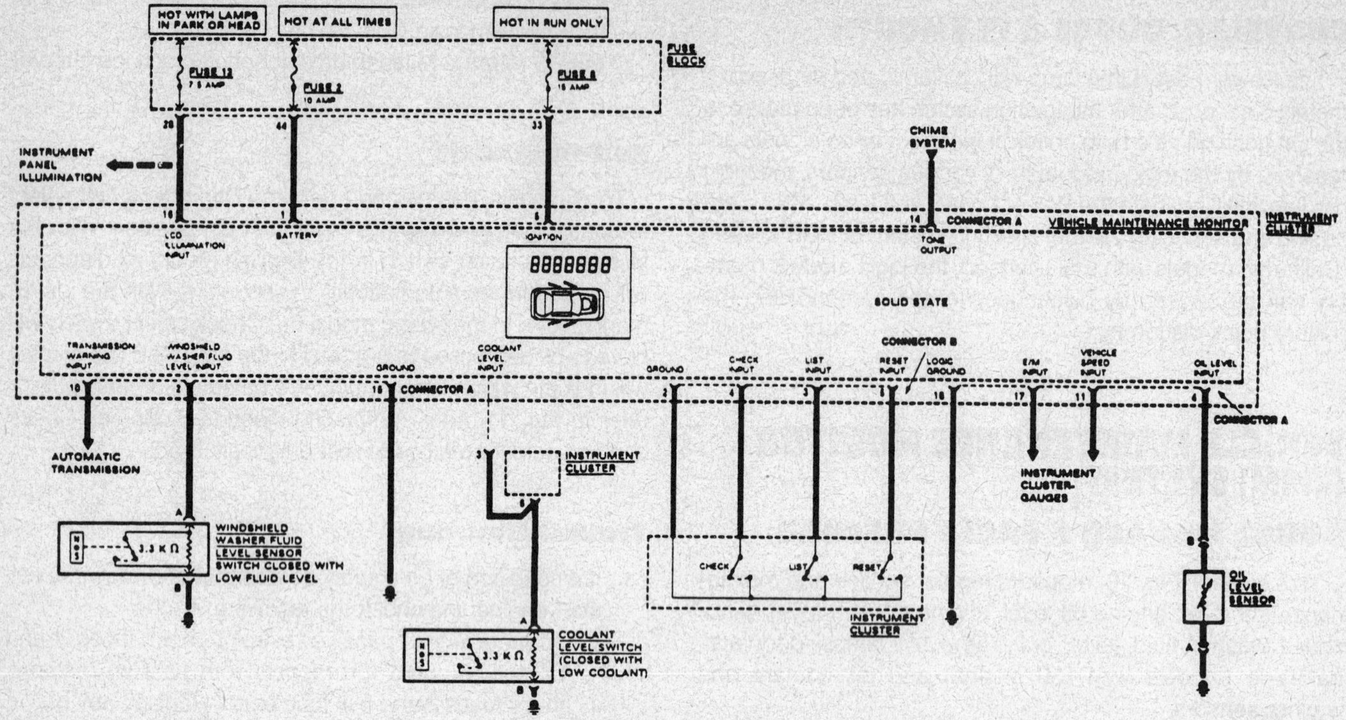


**Fig. 10 Vehicle Maintenance Monitor (VMM) System wiring schematic (Part 1 of 2). Dodge Monaco & Eagle Premier**

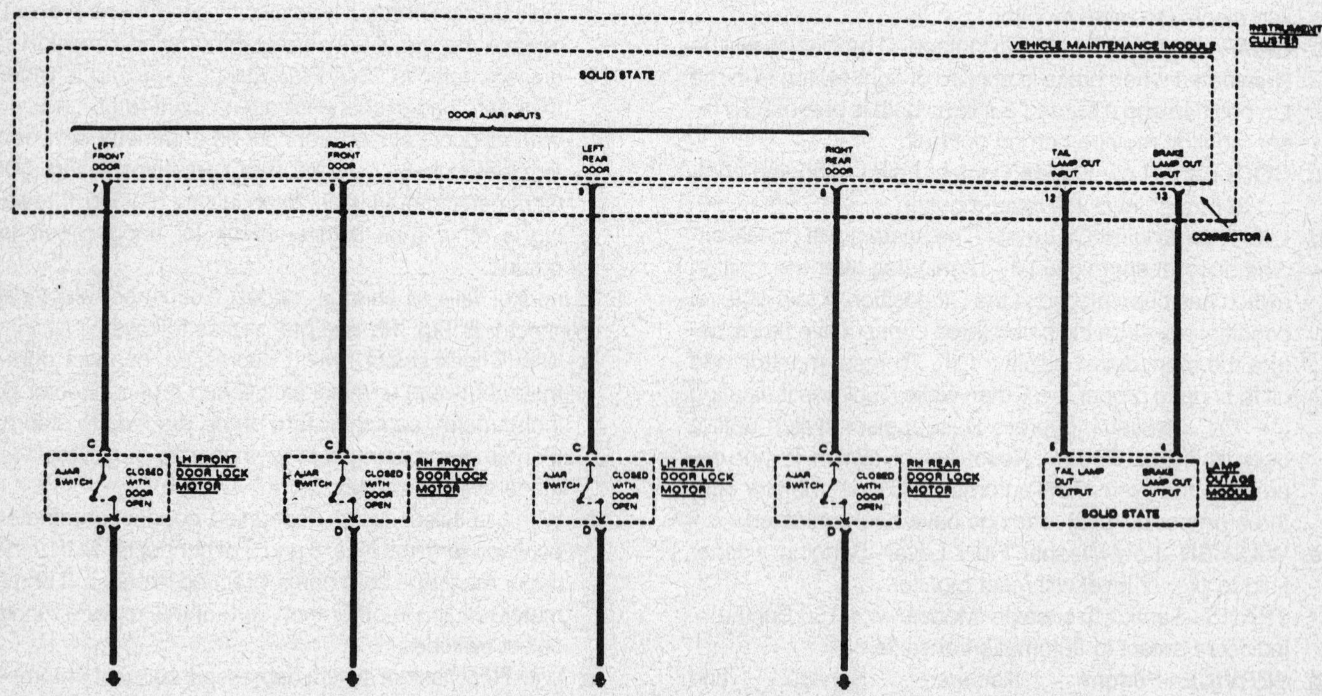


**Fig. 10 Vehicle Maintenance Monitor (VMM) System wiring schematic (Part 2 of 2). Dodge Monaco & Eagle Premier**

**TEST 1** Initially, a number will be displayed on the monitor's screen. This number indicates the version of the maintenance module installed in the vehicle.

**TEST 2**

| In Display | Meaning |
|---|---|
| "CAL O" | Monitor Bad |
| "CAL 1-7" | Monitor OK |
| "CAL F" | Monitor Bad |

**TEST 3** The module internal memory is tested.

| In Display | Meaning |
|---|---|
| "RAM P" | Monitor OK |
| "RAM F" | Monitor Bad |

**TEST 4** The module program is tested.

| In Display | Meaning |
|---|---|
| "ROM P" | Monitor OK |
| "ROM F" | Monitor Bad |

**TEST 5** The monitor's clocks are tested.

| In Display | Meaning |
|---|---|
| "TIME P" | Monitor OK |
| "TIME F" | Monitor Bad |

**TEST 6** The monitor's storage capability is tested.

| In Display | Meaning |
|---|---|
| "NVM P" | Monitor OK |
| "NVM F" | Monitor Bad |

**TEST 7** The monitor's internal synchronization is tested.

| In Display | Meaning |
|---|---|
| "PAR 0" | Monitor OK |
| "PAR N" | Monitor Bad |

**TEST 8** The monitor's display screen is tested.

| In Display | Meaning |
|---|---|
| All Segments ON | Monitor OK |
| All Segments OFF | Monitor OK |
| "0" | Monitor OK |
| "1" | Monitor OK |
| "10" | Monitor OK |
| "100" | Monitor OK |
| "1000" | Monitor OK |
| "10000" | Monitor OK |
| "100000" | Monitor OK |
| "111111" | Monitor OK |
| "122222" | Monitor OK |
| "133333" | Monitor OK |
| "144444" | Monitor OK |
| "155555" | Monitor OK |
| "166666" | Monitor OK |
| "177777" | Monitor OK |
| "188888" | Monitor OK |
| "199999" | Monitor OK |

The graphic segments will light, one at a time, in the following order: the engine symbol, the car outline, right front door, right rear door, rear tail lamps, left rear door, and left front door. Any deviation from the above patterns signifies a bad monitor. Should any of the segments fail to light, the monitor is bad.

**TEST 9** This test can only be performed while the test program is in the manual mode. OIL will flash. Release CHECK button and press and hold LIST button until OIL flashes three times, then release LIST button and OIL will stop flashing. There will be a 30-45 second delay while system is testing. Oil level faults are displayed at this time. The engine oil level is tested.

| In Display | Meaning |
|---|---|
| "OIL H" | Monitor OK, Oil Level Normal |
| "OIL L" | Monitor OK, but Oil Level Is Low |
| "OIL O" | Monitor OK, but Oil Level Sensor Is Open |
| "OIL S" | Monitor OK, but Oil Level Sensor Is Shorted |

**TEST 10** The oil level probe is tested. The intermittent fault can be cleared in diagnostic program by pressing RESET switch while message is displayed.

| In Display | Meaning |
|---|---|
| "OIL IF" | Intermittent Fault With Oil Sensor |
| NO MESSAGE | Monitor OK, Sensor OK |

**TEST 11** The washer fluid level is tested.

| In Display | Meaning |
|---|---|
| "WASH H" | Washer Fluid Level Normal |
| "WASH L" | Washer Fluid Level Low |
| "WASH O" | Washer Fluid Level Probe Open |

**TEST 12** The washer level sensor is tested. The intermittent fault can be cleared in diagnostic program by pressing RESET switch while message is displayed.

| In Display | Meaning |
|---|---|
| "WASHER IF" | Intermittent Fault With Washer Fluid Sensor |
| NO MESSAGE | Monitor OK, Sensor OK |

**TEST 13** The coolant fluid level is tested.

| In Display | Meaning |
|---|---|
| "COOL H" | Coolant Fluid Level Is Normal |
| "COOL L" | Coolant Fluid Level Is Low |
| "COOL O" | Coolant Fluid Level Probe Is Open |

**TEST 14** The coolant fluid level sensor is tested. The intermittent fault can be cleared in diagnostic program by pressing RESET switch while message is displayed.

| In Display | Meaning |
|---|---|
| "COOL IF" | Intermittent Fault With the Coolant Level Sensor |
| NO MESSAGE | Monitor OK, Sensor OK |

**TEST 15** The tail lamp circuit is tested.

| In Display | Meaning |
|---|---|
| "TLO P" | Tail Lamp Circuit OK |
| "TLO F" | Tail Lamp Circuit Open |

**TEST 16** The brake lamp circuit is tested.

| In Display | Meaning |
|---|---|
| "BLO P" | Brake Lamp Circuit OK |
| "BLO F" | Brake Lamp Circuit Open |

**TEST 17** The status of the transmission diagnostic module is tested.

| In Display | Meaning |
|---|---|
| "TRANS P" | Transmission Module OK |
| "TRANS F" | Transmission Module Fault |

**TEST 18** The frequency of the road speed sensor is displayed. When in manual mode, continuous monitoring is possible.

| In Display | Meaning |
|---|---|
| "SPD XXX"* | Frequency of Vehicle Speed Sensor |

*Note: XXX will vary from 0 and increase as vehicle speed increases.

**Fig. 11 Vehicle Maintenance Monitor (VMM) System self diagnosis test chart. Dodge Monaco & Eagle Premier**

# Ford Motor Co.

## INDEX



## ANTI-LOCK WARNING LAMP

This lamp will be illuminated when the ignition switch is placed in the On position. The lamp maybe illuminated for as long as 30 seconds as a bulb and system check. If lamp remains illuminated or comes on while operating the vehicle, a problem in the anti-lock brake system is indicated. When lamp is illuminated, place ignition switch in Off position, then restart engine. If lamp still remains illuminated, the anti-lock brake system should be serviced. The brake system will remain functional, but without the anti-lock function. After servicing the anti-lock brake system, the lamp will automatically be reset when vehicle is operated at a speed over 25 MPH.

## AIRBAG SYSTEM WARNING LAMP

On models equipped with an airbag system, if the airbag warning lamp illuminates and stays on, diagnosis and repair of the airbag system will be necessary to reset the lamp.

## AUXILIARY WARNING INDICATOR & GRAPHIC DISPLAY MODULE

### MERKUR

This system monitors engine oil level, engine coolant level, windshield washer fluid level, brake pad wear, fuel level, seat belt usage, headlamp, brake and tail lamps, door ajar, liftgate ajar and ambient temperature.

When ignition switch is placed in the on position, the graphic display module and all warning indicators will illuminate for 5 seconds. After 5 seconds, all warning lamps should go off and graphic display should indicate outline of vehicle and the two brake lights. The two brake light indications should go out once the brake pedal is depressed. If warning lamps remain illuminated or graphic display indicates a fault, check the following:

The low engine oil warning lamp is used to indicate when engine oil level is 12 mm or more below the specified level. The lamp will be illuminated during engine starting. If oil level is sufficient, the lamp will go off when engine is operating. If oil level is low the lamp will remain on until engine oil is added and the ignition switch is placed in the off position. The module will take approximately 3 minutes to reset. If the engine is started during this period, the last recorded reading will be displayed.

The Low Coolant Warning Lamp will be illuminated whenever coolant level in the coolant recovery bottle is below the specified mark. Raise coolant level in recovery bottle to turn lamp off.

The low fuel warning lamp will be illuminated whenever fuel level drops below 1.4 gals. Add fuel to vehicle to turn lamp off.

The Washer Fluid Warning Lamp will be illuminated whenever fluid drops below the specified reservoir level. Raise washer fluid level in reservoir to turn lamp off.

The brake pad wear warning lamp will be illuminated when disc brake pads wear down to 1.5 mm. At 1.5 mm a wire loop in the brake pad is exposed and severed, which in turn illuminates the brake pad warning lamp. To turn lamp off, replace brake pads.

Air temperature is monitored by a sensor located on the righthand side of the vehicle behind the front bumper. The signal from the sensor is evaluated by the control assembly, which controls the low air temperature (ICE) indication on the graphic display. When air temperature is approximately 39°F, the ICE indication will be illuminated in yellow. When temperature drops to 32°F the triangle located around the ICE indication will be illuminated in red. If a short circuit in wiring between sensor and control assembly is present, the ICE indication on the graphic will flash. If an open circuit between the sensor and control assembly exist, the triangle will flash.

The graphic display will indicate when doors and liftgate are closed (green) and when doors and liftgate are ajar (red). To cancel door or liftgate ajar indication, close door or liftgate indicated.

The graphic will also indicate lamp bulb outage. Replacement of lamp bulb indicated will turn off graphic display indicator. A lamp out indication will also be present if an open or circuit in lamp wiring is present.

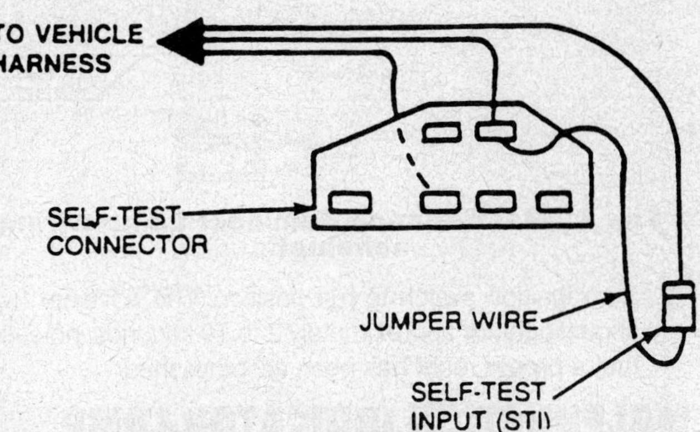


**Fig. 1 Jumper wire connections for resetting Check Engine Lamp**

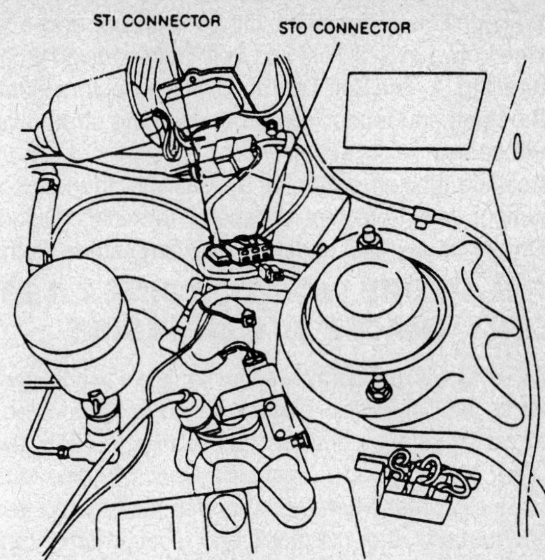


**Fig. 2 STI connector location. 1988–90 Festiva**

# CHECK ENGINE LAMP

## EXCEPT CAPRI, FESTIVA, MERKUR, PROBE w/2.2L ENGINE & 1991 ESCORT/TRACER w/1.8L ENGINE

### 1987–91 Models Equipped w/EEC-IV

This lamp will be illuminated when the ignition switch is placed in the On position. After engine is started the lamp should go off, unless a problem has been detected by the EEC-IV system. After diagnosis and repair, the Check Engine/MIL lamp will automatically reset when stored codes are cleared from the EEC-IV system memory. After diagnosis and repair, EEC-IV memory may be cleared of stored codes as follows:

1. With ignition switch in the Off position, connect a jumper wire between Self Test and Self Test Input (STI) connectors, **Fig. 1.** On Ford Crown Victoria, Mercury Grand Marquis and Lincoln Town Car models, the Self Test and STI connectors are gray in color and are located on the front of lefthand fender apron, near the Electronic Engine Control (EEC) relay. On Ford Mustang models, the Self Test and STI connectors are gray in color and are located on the lefthand fender apron. On Ford Tempo, 1987-90 Escort and Mercury Lynx and Topaz, the Self Test connector is gray in color and the STI connector is black in color and they are both located on the righthand fender apron near the front of the strut tower. On Ford Taurus and Mercury Sable, the Self Test and STI connectors are gray in color and are located on the righthand fender apron near the front of the engine in the area of the AIR pump and alternator. On 1987-88 Ford Thunderbird and Mercury Cougar, the Self Test and STI connectors are gray in color and are located on the lefthand fender apron near the strut tower. On 1989-91 Ford Thunderbird and Mercury Cougar, the Self Test and STI connectors are gray in color and are located on the righthand fender apron near the strut tower. On 1987 Lincoln Mark VII & 1987-89 Continental, the Self Test and STI connectors are gray in color and are located on the righthand side of fender apron near the ignition coil. On 1988-91 Lincoln Continental, the Self Test and STI connectors are attached to the Electronic Control Assembly, which is located in the engine compartment at the center of the firewall below the TFI ignition module.
2. Position ignition switch in On position, then disconnect jumper wire from test connector terminals. Disconnect jumper as soon as check engine lamp starts flashing.

## FESTIVA

The Check Engine Indicator lamp will be illuminated when the ignition switch in in the Run position with engine not operating. When the engine is started, the Check Engine lamp should go off. If lamp remains on, a service code has been stored in the EEC-IV self test system memory. After diagnosis and repair, the self test memory may be cleared of stored codes as follows:

1. With ignition switch in the off position, connect a jumper wire between Self Test Input (STI) connector terminal and ground. The STI connector is located in the engine compartment at the rear lefthand side, **Fig. 2.**
2. Position ignition switch in On position, then disconnect and reconnect jumper wire connected between STI connector and ground.
3. Disconnect jumper from STI connector as soon as check engine lamp stops flashing.
4. Disconnect battery ground cable and depress brake pedal for approximately 5 to 10 seconds.
5. Reconnect battery ground cable.

## MERKUR

This lamp will be illuminated when the ignition switch is placed in the On position. After engine is started the lamp should go off, unless a problem has been detected by the EEC-IV system. After diagnosis and repair, the Check Engine lamp will automatically reset when stored codes are cleared from the EEC-IV system memory. After diagnosis and repair, EEC-IV memory may be cleared of stored codes as follows:

1. With ignition switch in the Off position, connect a jumper wire between Self Test and Self Test Input (STI) connectors, **Fig. 1.** The Self Test and STI connectors located on the righthand fender apron between the strut tower and the battery.
2. Position ignition switch in On position, then disconnect jumper wire from test connector terminals. Disconnect jumper as soon as check engine lamp starts flashing.

### CAPRI, PROBE w/2.2L ENGINE & 1991 ESCORT/TRACER w/1.8L ENGINE

This lamp will be illuminated when the ignition switch is placed in the On position. After engine is started the lamp should go off, unless a problem has been detectedby the system. After diagnosis and repair, the Check Engine lamp will automatically reset when stored codes are cleared from the system memory. After diagnosis and repair, memory may be cleared of stored codes as follows:

1. Disconnect battery ground cable, then depress brake pedal for approximately 5 to 10 seconds.
2. Reconnect battery ground cable.

## LOW COOLANT WARNING SYSTEM

### 1986 LYNX & 1986–90 ESCORT

The Low Coolant Warning Lamp will be illuminated whenever coolant level in the coolant recovery bottle is 1/4 to 3/4 inch or more below the cold full mark. Raise coolant level in recovery bottle to the cold full mark to turn lamp off.

## LOW OIL LEVEL WARNING INDICATOR

This system is used to indicate when engine oil level is 1 1/2 quarts or more below the specified level. The lamp will be illuminated during engine starting. If oil level is sufficient, the lamp will go off when engine is operating. If oil level is low the lamp will remain on until engine oil is added and the ignition switch is placed in the Off position. The module will take approximately 5 minutes to reset. If the engine is started during this period, the last recorded reading will be displayed.

## MAINTENANCE REMINDER INDICATOR

This lamp, **Fig. 3,** is used on some not equipped with electronic engine controls. The lamp will be illuminated after approximately 2000 engine starts (60,000 miles of vehicle operation). After performing the required emission control service, the lamp maybe reset as follows:

1. Turn ignition switch to Off position.
2. Install a suitable screwdriver through the .2 inch hole labeled Reset, then lightly press down and hold.
3. While pressing screwdriver down, turn ignition switch to run position. The advisory lamp will then come on. Hold screwdriver down for approximately 5 seconds.
4. Remove screwdriver and note advisory lamp. Lamp should go out within 2 to 10 seconds indicating that a reset has occurred. If lamp does not go out, repeat procedure. Turn ignition switch to Off position.

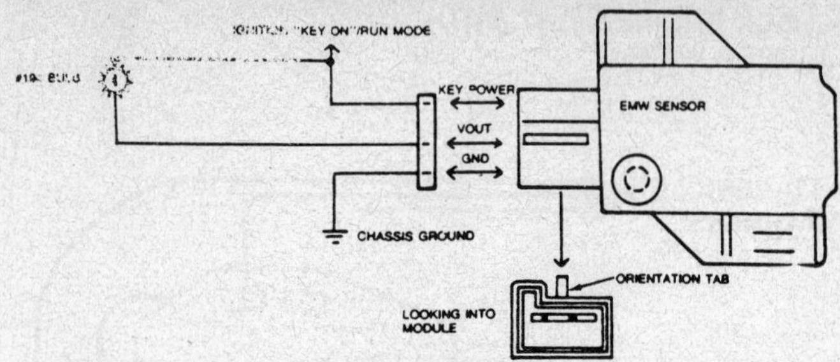


**Fig. 3 Maintenance Reminder Lamp wiring schematic**

5. Turn ignition switch to run position. The advisory lamp should light for approximately 2 to 10 seconds indicating that a proper reset has been accomplished.

## MALFUNCTION INDICATOR LAMP (MIL)

### EXCEPT 1988–89 TRACER

Refer to "Check Engine Lamp, Except Festiva & Merkur" for lamp reset procedure.

### 1988–89 TRACER

The malfunction indicator lamp is used only on EFI models. This lamp indicates a malfunction in the Electronic Engine Control system. If a malfunction occurs, the lamp will illuminate. The malfunction detected may or may not be a noticeable driveability problem. The lamp will be automatically reset during diagnosis and repair of the system.

This indicator system monitors the following:

1. Air Temperature sensor (ACT).
2. Barometric Pressure (BP) sensor.
3. Clutch switch, manual transaxle.
4. Engine coolant temperature (ECT) sensor.
5. Engine coolant temperature (ECT) switch.
6. Exhaust gas oxygen (EGO) sensor.
7. Ignition coil (–) terminal.

## MULTIPLE FUNCTION WARNING INDICATOR

### 1987–89 MUSTANG GT

This system monitors engine oil, cooling system, fuel and washer reservoir levels for low fluid level conditions. During engine starting the lamps will be illuminated for approximately 3 seconds as a bulb check out. After approximately 3 seconds, when the bulb check is completed, low fluid level conditions will be verified, if present.

The low engine oil warning lamp is used to indicate when engine oil level is 1 1/2 quarts or more below the specified level. The lamp will be illuminated during engine starting. If oil level is sufficient, the lamp will go off when engine is operating. If oil level is low the lamp will remain on until engine oil is added and the ignition switch is placed in the Off position. The module will take approximately 90 to 150 seconds to reset. If the engine is started during this period, the last recorded reading will be displayed.

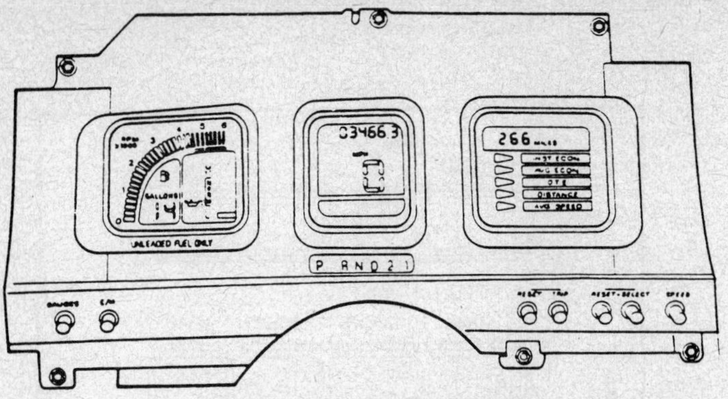


Fig. 4 Trip & reset button locations. 1985–88 Cougar & Thunderbird

RESET SWITCH ACCESS HOLE
OK CHANGE SOON NOW
OIL CHANGE
LOW WASHER OIL LOW
LOW RADIATOR FUEL LOW
FLUID LEVELS

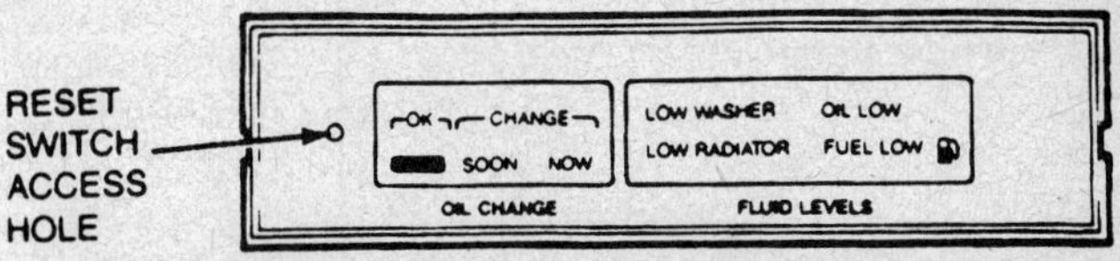

Fig. 5 Oil change interval indicator reset switch access hole location. 1989–91 Cougar & Thunderbird

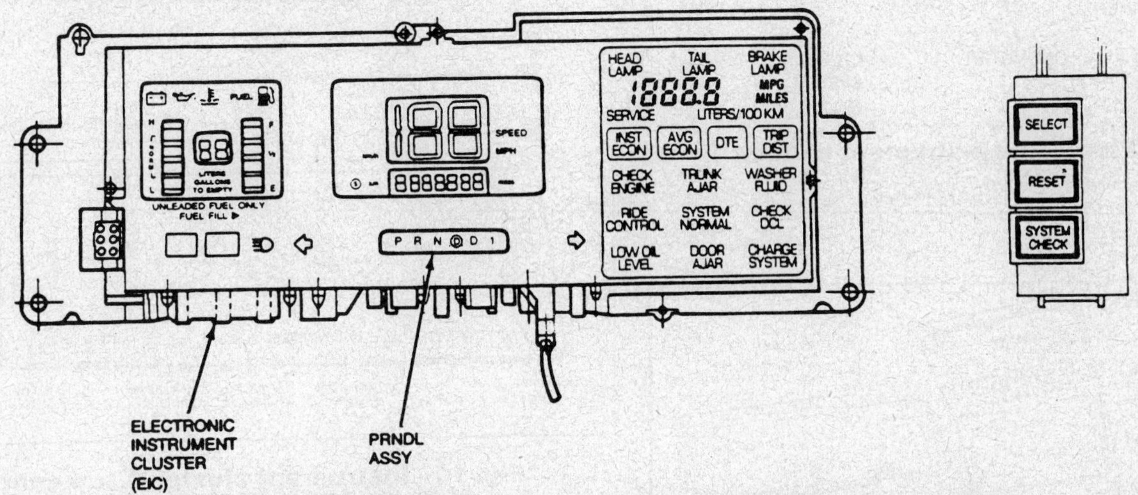


Fig. 6 Instrument cluster & message center. 1988–91 Continental

The Low Coolant Warning Lamp will be illuminated whenever coolant level in the coolant recovery bottle is below the cold full mark. Raise coolant level in recovery bottle to the cold full mark to turn lamp off.

The low fuel warning lamp will be illuminated whenever fuel level is 1/8 tank capacity or less. Add fuel to vehicle to turn lamp off.

The Washer Fluid Warning Lamp will be illuminated whenever reservoir level is below 1/3 capacity. Raise washer fluid level in reservoir to turn lamp off.

# SERVICE INTERVAL REMINDER

## 1985–88 COUGAR & THUNDERBIRD

At approximately 5,000 or 7,500 miles, depending on engine installation, the word Service will appear on the display for approximately 1 1/2 miles to indicate time for service interval. After completing the required service, reset service interval reminder by depressing and holding the Trip and Trip Reset buttons until three beeps are heard, **Fig. 4.**

## 1989–91 COUGAR & THUNDERBIRD

At approximately 7,500 miles, for models less super charged engine, the engine oil change indicator on the Vehicle Maintenance Monitor will indicate an oil change is needed. On models with super charged engine, the need for engine oil change will be indicated at 5,000 miles. After completing the required service, the oil change indicate can be reset by depressing the reset switch, **Fig. 5.** The reset switch is accessed through a switch access hole located to the left of the oil change indicator on the monitor display.

## 1988–91 LINCOLN CONTINENTAL

After performing the require interval service, the service interval reminder mileage display on the instrument cluster can be reset as follows:

1. Depress System Check button on instrument panel, service interval reminder mileage should be displayed on fuel computer display, **Fig. 6.**
2. Depress Reset button, the service interval reminder mileage should start flashing.
3. Depress Reset and System Check buttons at the same time to reset mileage.

## PROBE

### Electronic Instrument Cluster

At 7,500 mile intervals, a Service Check message will be displayed under the System Scanner nomenclature on the in-

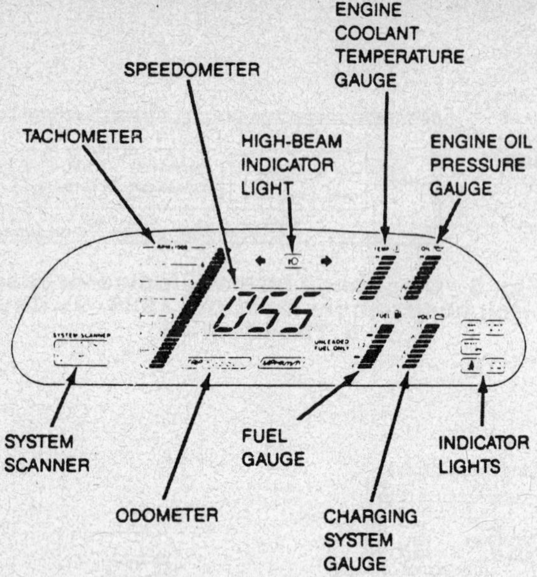


**Fig. 7 Electronic instrument cluster. Probe**

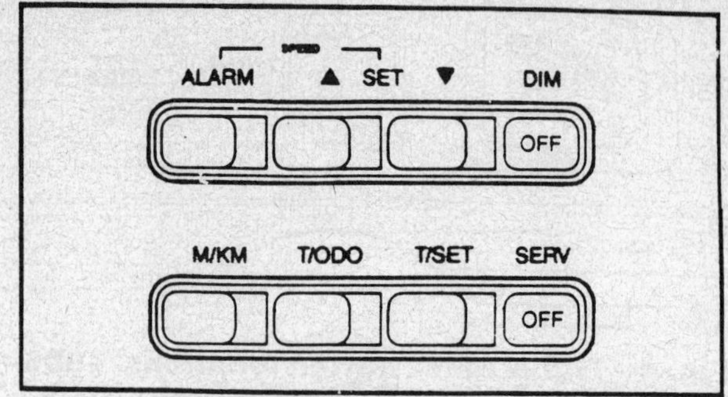


**Fig. 8 Speed alarm keyboard. Probe**

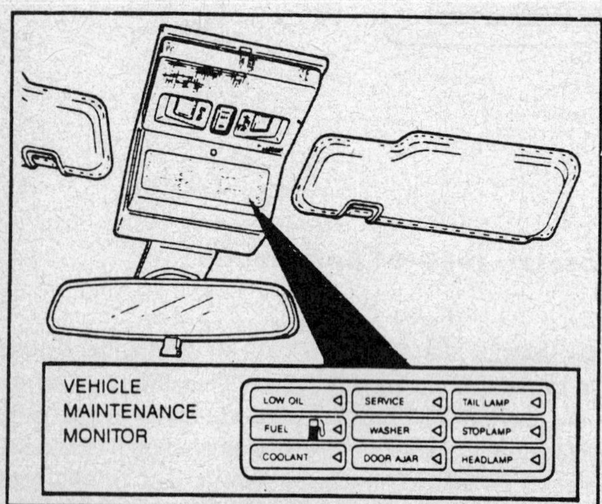


**Fig. 9 Vehicle maintenance monitor. Probe**

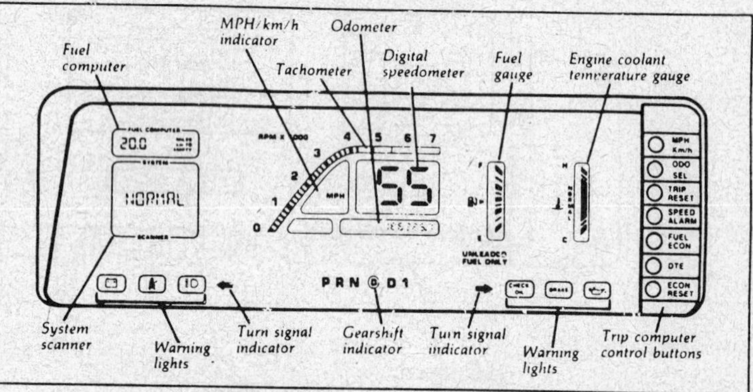


**Fig. 10 Instrument cluster & trip control buttons. 1986–89 Sable & Taurus**

strument cluster for three minutes after engine start, **Fig. 7.** After performing the required interval service, reset the service interval by depressing and holding the Service reset button, located on the speed alarm keyboard, until three tones have sounded, **Fig. 8.**

### Vehicle Maintenance Monitor

On models with Vehicle Maintenance Monitor, at 7,500 mile intervals a Service lamp, located on the overhead map lamp console, will be illuminated for 3 minutes after engine start, **Fig. 9.** After performing the required interval service, reset the service interval. On models with speed alarm keypad, depress and hold the Service reset button, until three tones have sounded. On models less speed alarm keypad, locate reset hole in overhead console, then using a suitable tool depress the reset button located behind the hole.

## 1986–89 SABLE & TAURUS W/ELECTRONIC INSTRUMENT CLUSTER

At 7,200 mile intervals, a Service message will be displayed under the System Scanner nomenclature on the instrument cluster for 30 seconds after engine start, **Fig. 10.** After performing the required interval service, reset the service interval by simultaneously depressing the ODO Sel and Trip Reset buttons located on the instrument panel. The word service will disappear from the display and three tones will sound to indicate the service interval has been reset.

# VEHICLE LIFT POINTS

## TABLE OF CONTENTS



# Chrysler/Eagle

## INDEX



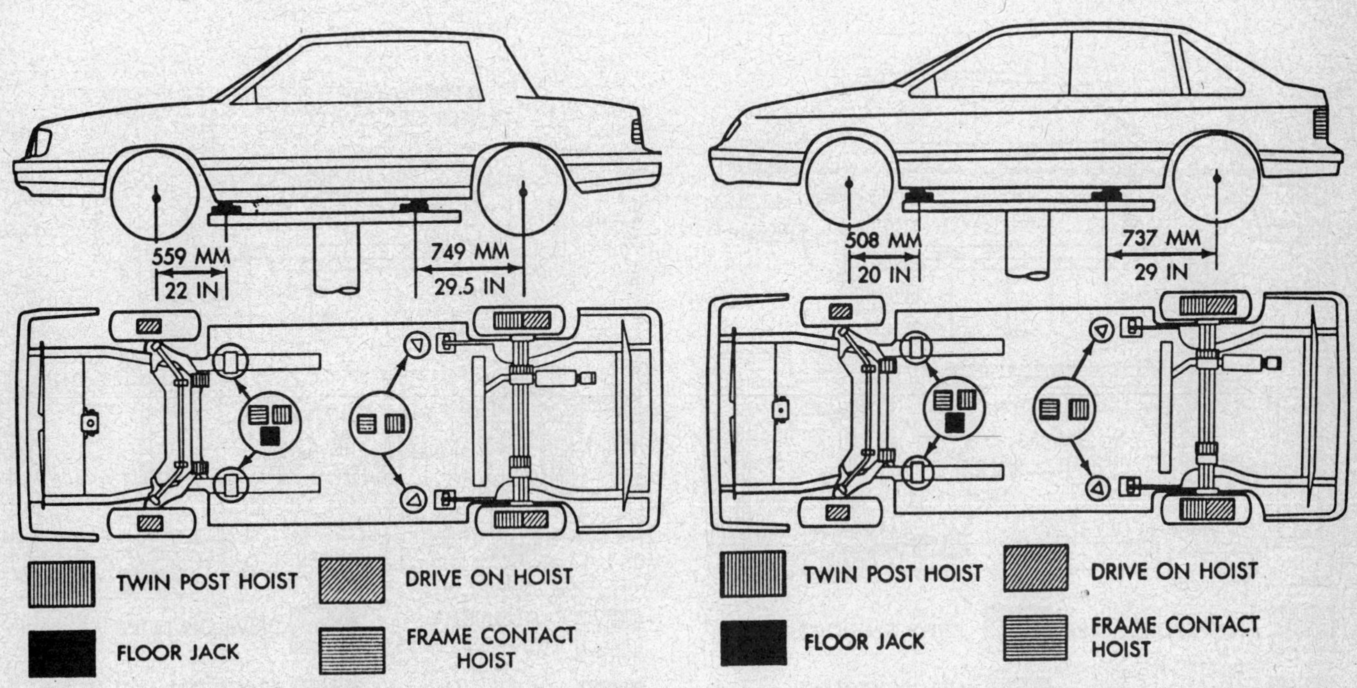


**Fig. 1 Aries & Reliant**

**Fig. 2 Lancer & LeBaron GTS**

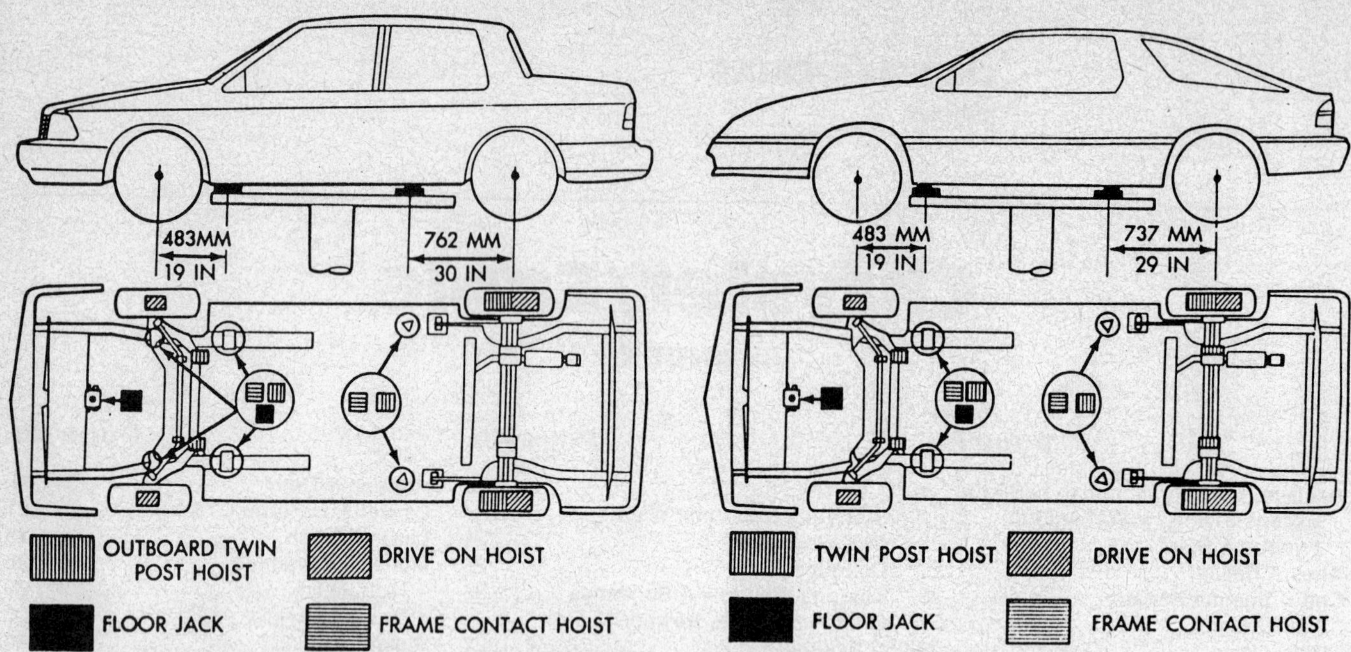


**Fig. 3 Acclaim, Dynasty, Imperial, LeBaron except GTS, New Yorker Fifth Avenue & Spirit**

**Fig. 4 Daytona, Shadow & Sundance**

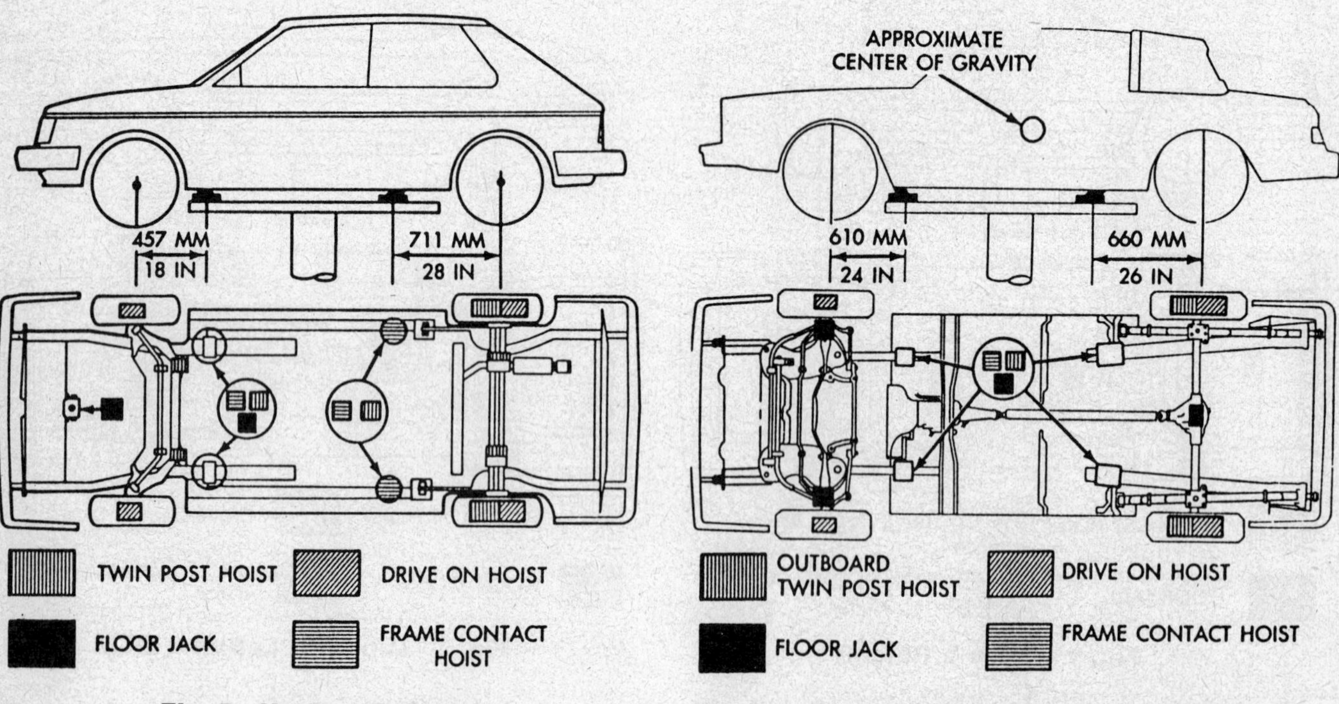


**Fig. 5 Horizon & Omni**

**Fig. 6 Gran Fury Salon, Newport & Fifth Ave**

Fig. 7 Colt & Summit Sedan (Front, Floor Jack)

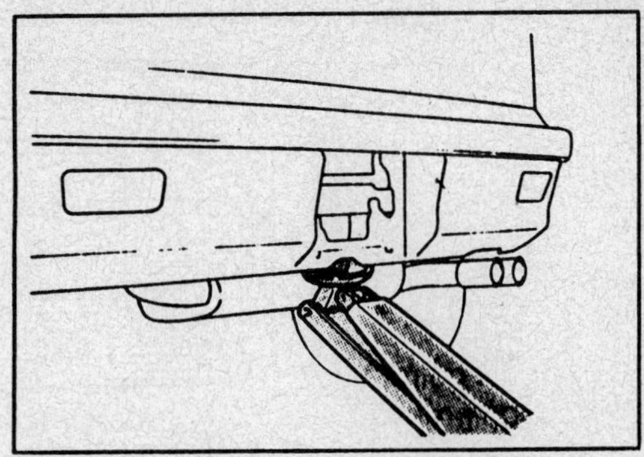

Fig. 8 Colt & Summit Sedan (Rear, Floor Jack)

FRAME CONTACT SUPPORT LOCATION

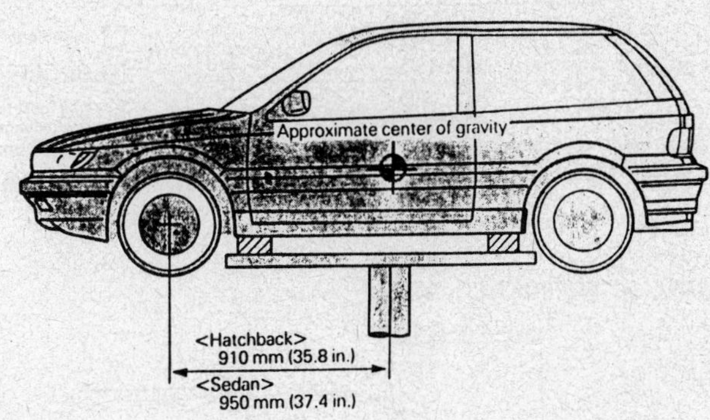


LIFTING, JACKING SUPPORT LOCATION

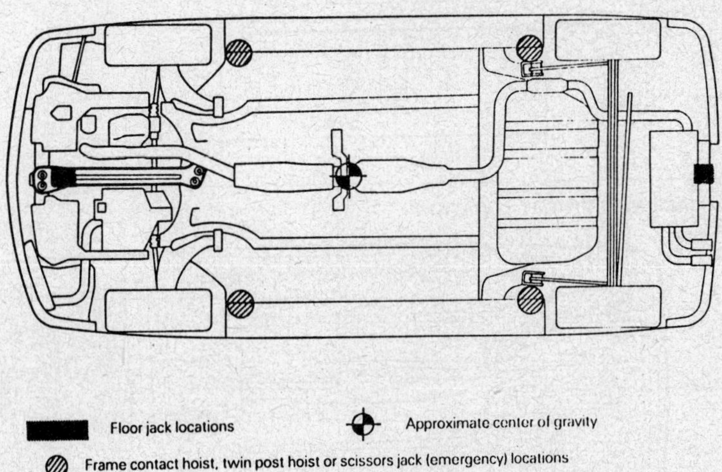


**Caution**

- Never use a jack at the lateral rod or rear suspension assembly.
- In order to prevent scarring the center member, place a piece of cloth on the jack's contact surface (to prevent corrosion caused by damage to the coating).
- Never attempt to position a floor jack on any part of the vehicle underbody.
- Do not attempt to raise one entire side of the vehicle by placing a jack midway between the front and rear wheels. To do so could result in permanent damage to the body.

Fig. 9 Colt & Summit Sedan (Hoist)

# VEHICLE LIFT POINTS

LIFTING, JACKING SUPPORT LOCATION

2WD

4WD

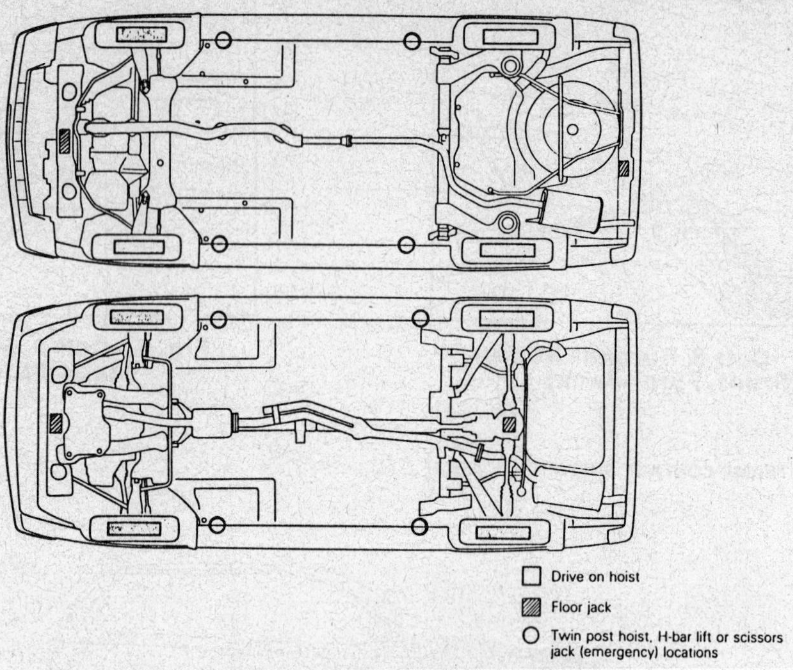

- ☐ Drive on hoist
- ▨ Floor jack
- ○ Twin post hoist, H-bar lift or scissors jack (emergency) locations

**Fig. 10 Colt Vista & Eagle Summit Wagon**

FRAME CONTACT SUPPORT LOCATION

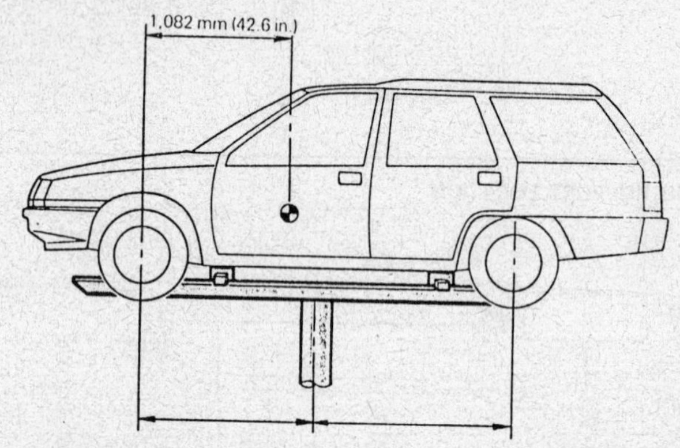


LIFTING, JACKING SUPPORT LOCATION

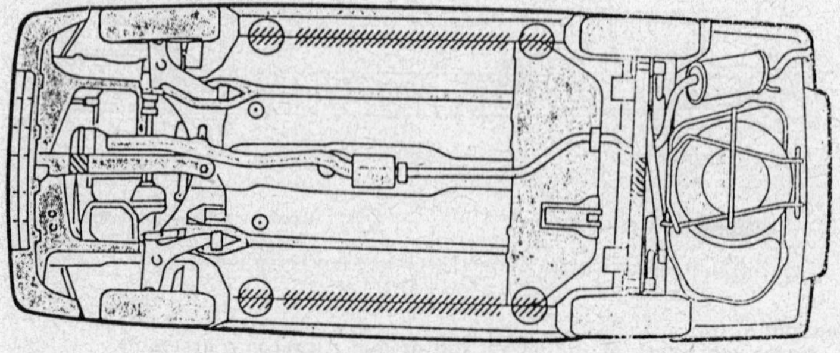

NOTE
Do not support car at locations other than specified support point. Failure to do this will cause damage etc.

- ////// Frame contact hoist
- \\\\\\ Floor jack
- ⊘ Twin post hoist or scissors jack (emergency) locations

**Fig. 11 Colt Wagon**

FRAME CONTACT SUPPORT LOCATION

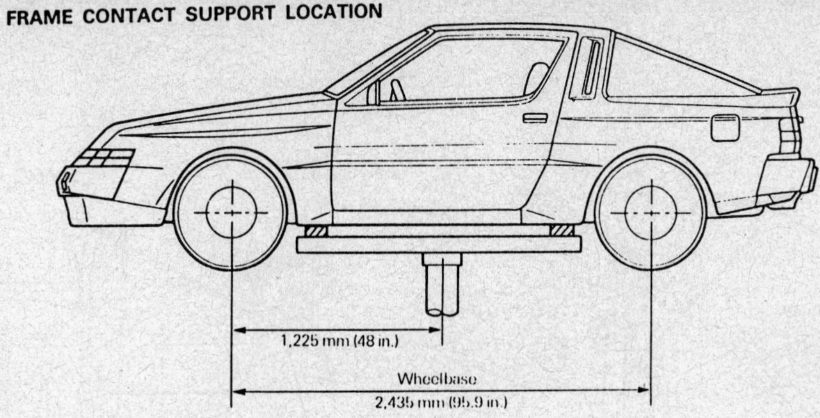


LIFTING, JACKING SUPPORT LOCATION

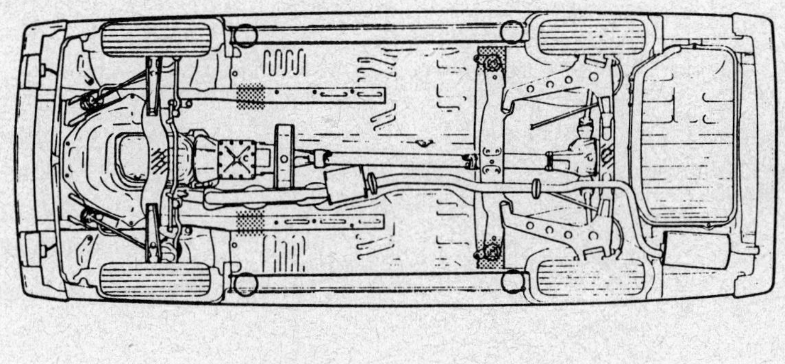

Frame contact hoist

Floor jack

Twin post hoist or scissors jack (emergency) locations

**Fig. 12 Conquest**

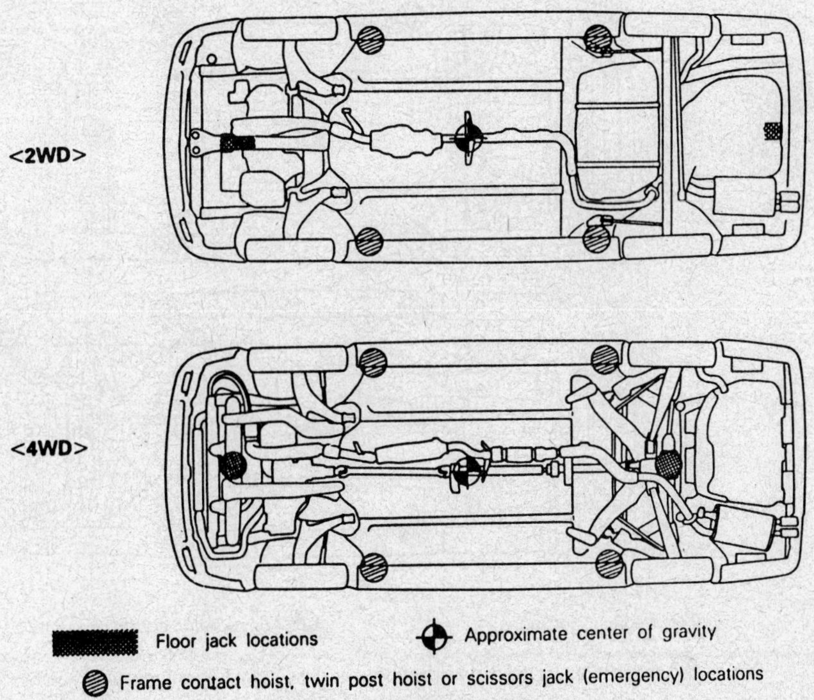


**Fig. 13 Laser & Talon**

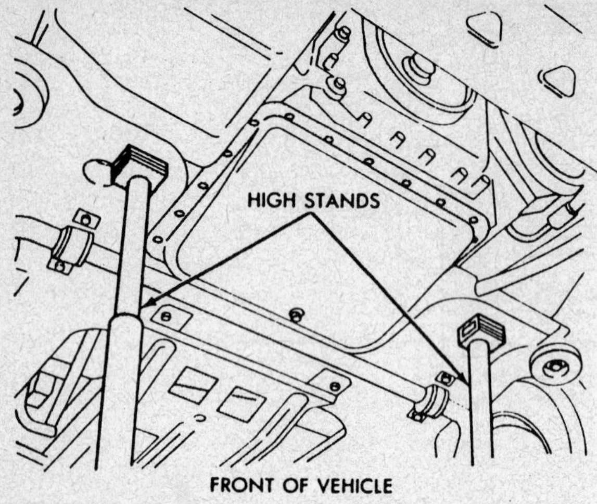

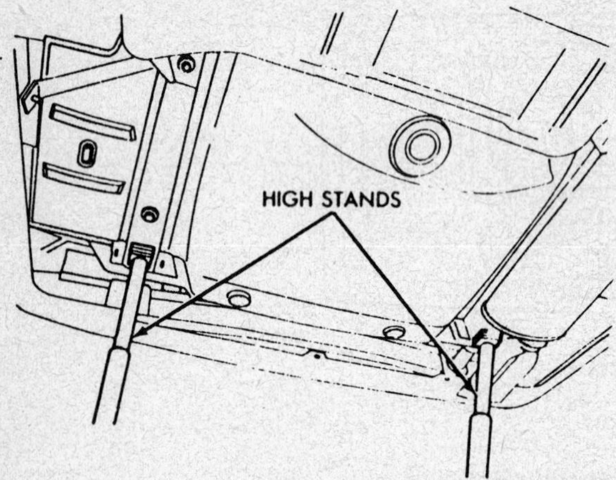

HIGH STANDS
FRONT OF VEHICLE
HIGH STANDS
REAR OF VEHICLE

**Fig. 14 Monaco & Premier (High Stands)**

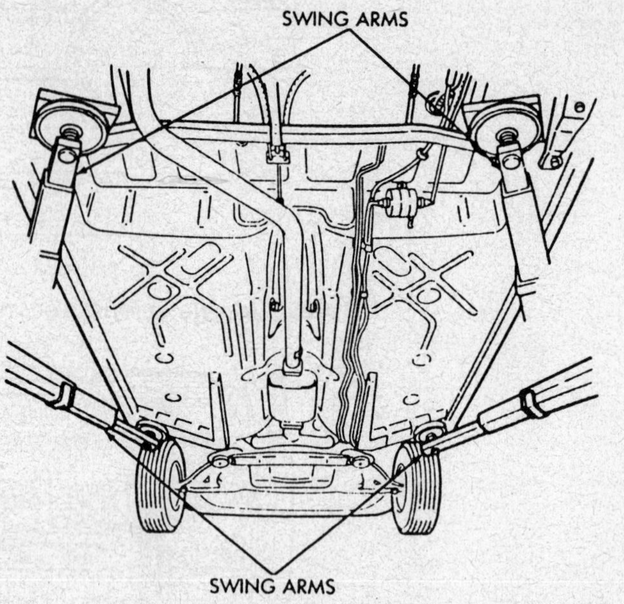

SWING ARMS
SWING ARMS

**Fig. 15 Monaco & Premier (Swing Arm Hoist)**

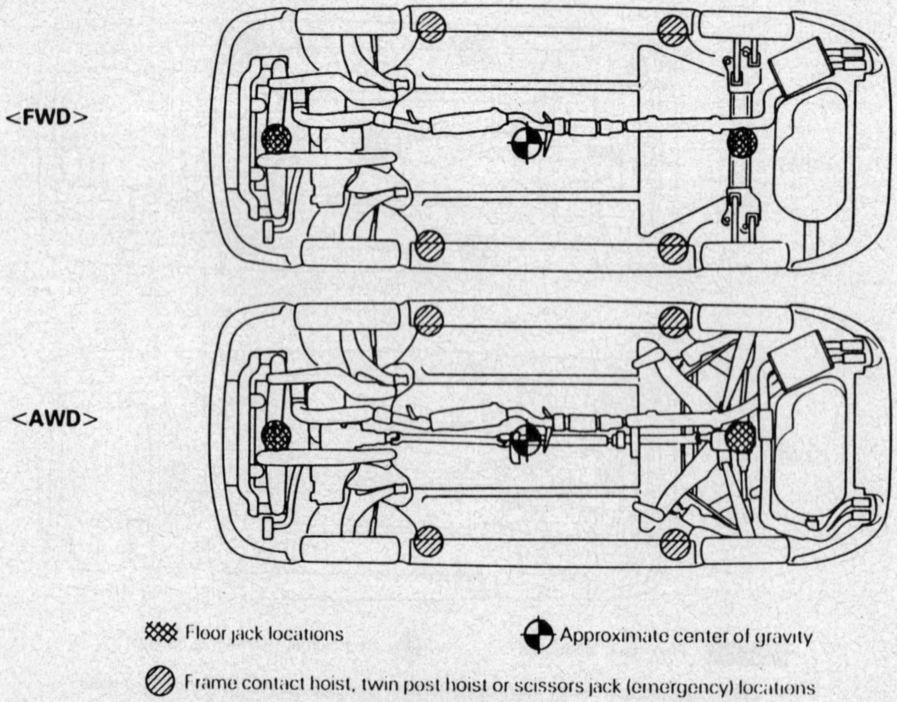

<FWD>
<AWD>
Floor jack locations
Approximate center of gravity
Frame contact hoist, twin post hoist or scissors jack (emergency) locations

**Fig. 16 Stealth**

# Ford Motor Co.

## INDEX



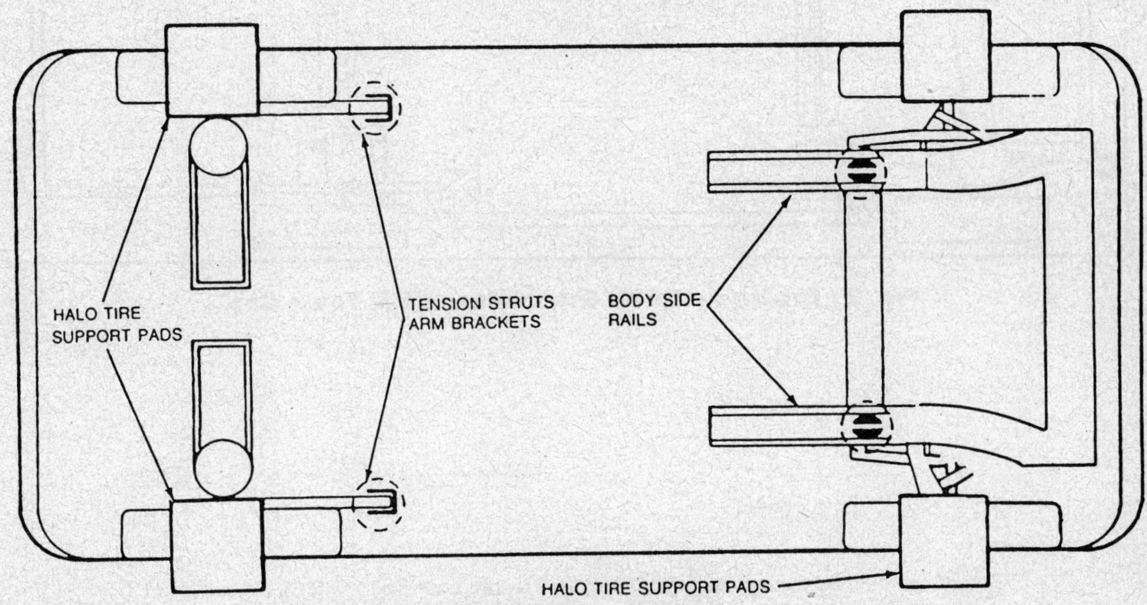


**Fig. 1 Continental**

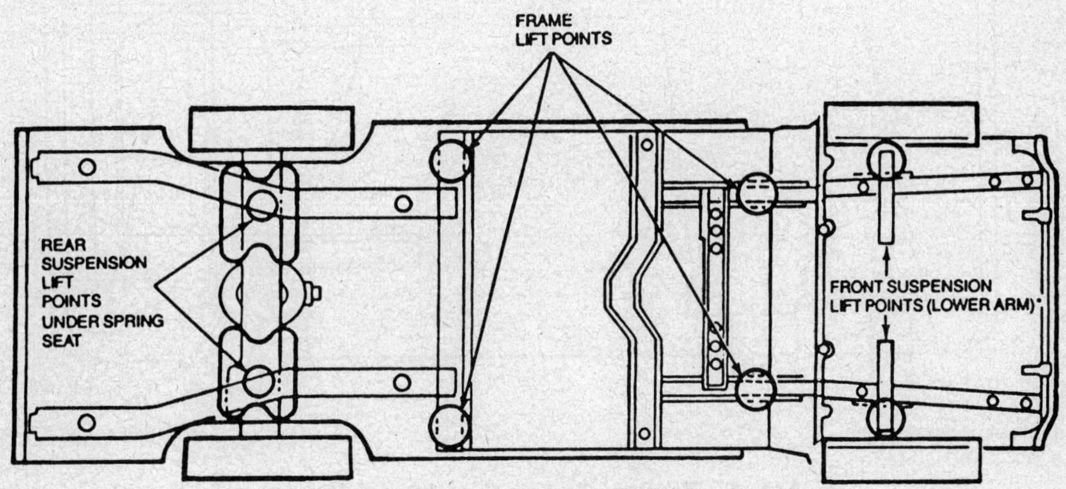


**Fig. 2 Cougar & Thunderbird**

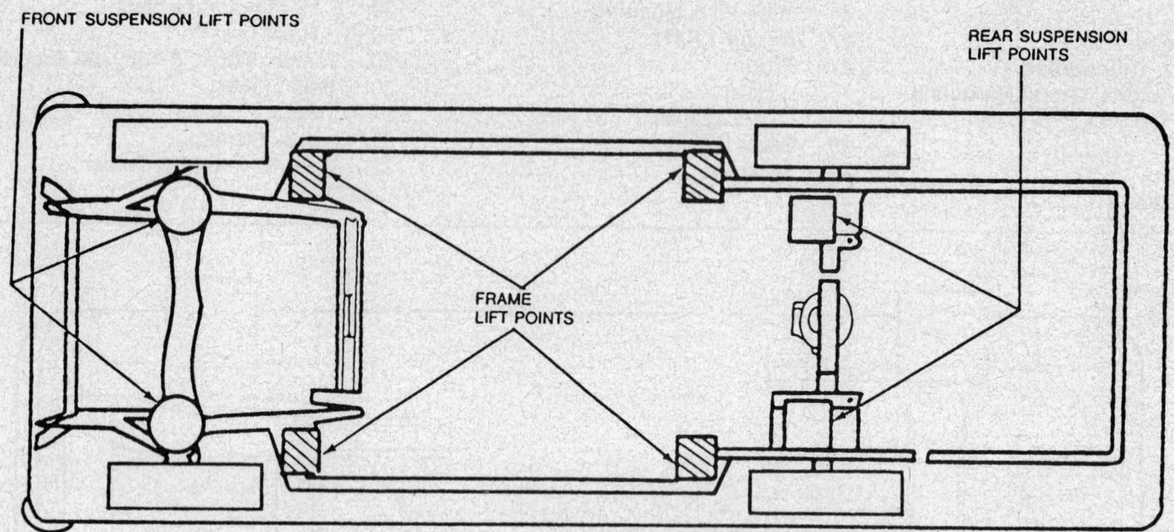


**Fig. 3 Crown Victoria, Grand Marquis & Town Car**

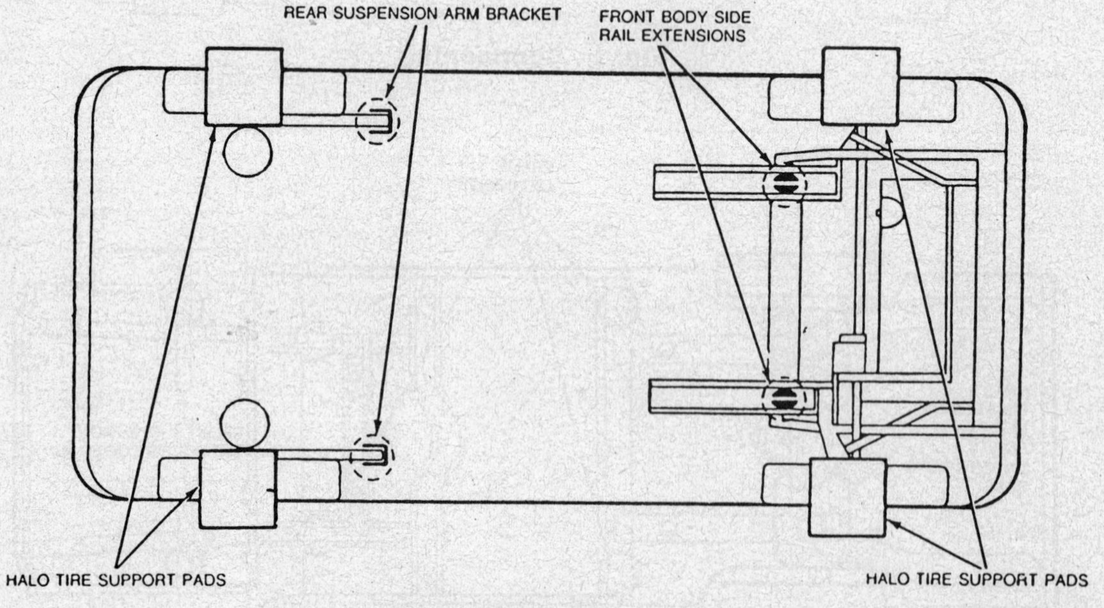


**Fig. 4 Tempo, Topaz & 1989–90 Escort**

FRONT
On both side sills

REAR
On both side sills

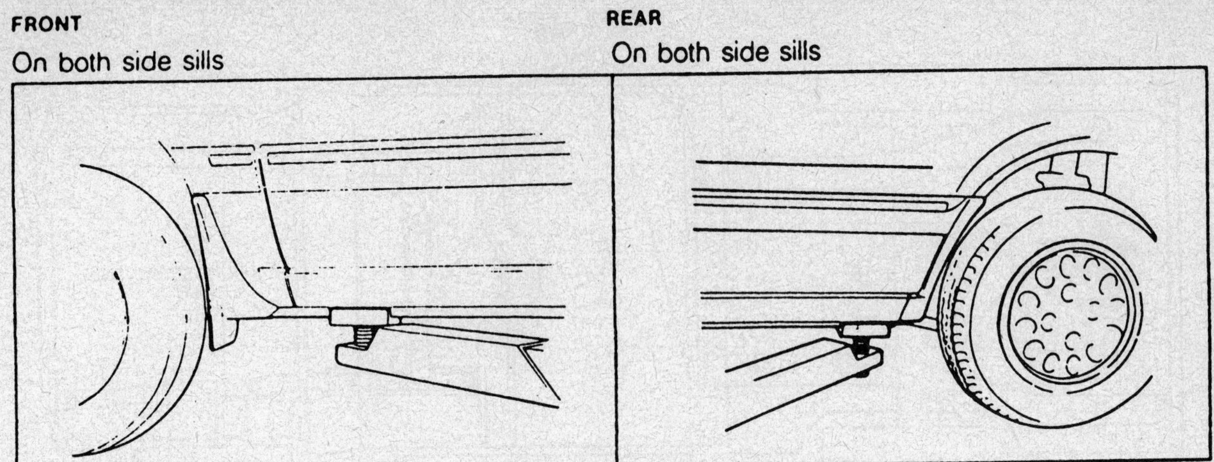

**Fig. 5 Festiva (Hoist)**

FRONT
JACK POSITION:
AT THE FRONT OF THE ENGINE MOUNT MEMBER

SAFETY STAND POSITIONS:
ON BOTH SIDE SILLS (FRONT)

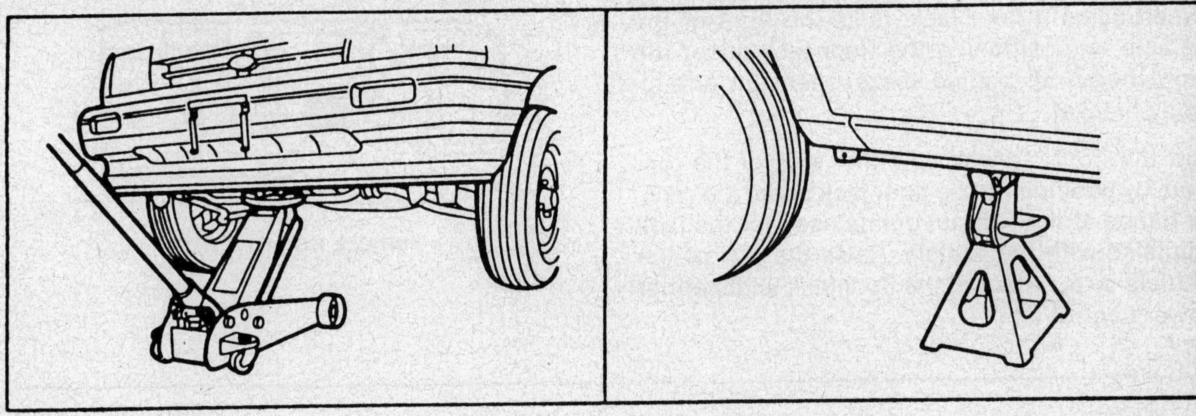

REAR
JACK POSITION:
AT THE CENTER OF THE REAR CROSSMEMBER

SAFETY STAND POSITIONS:
ON BOTH SIDE SILLS (REAR)

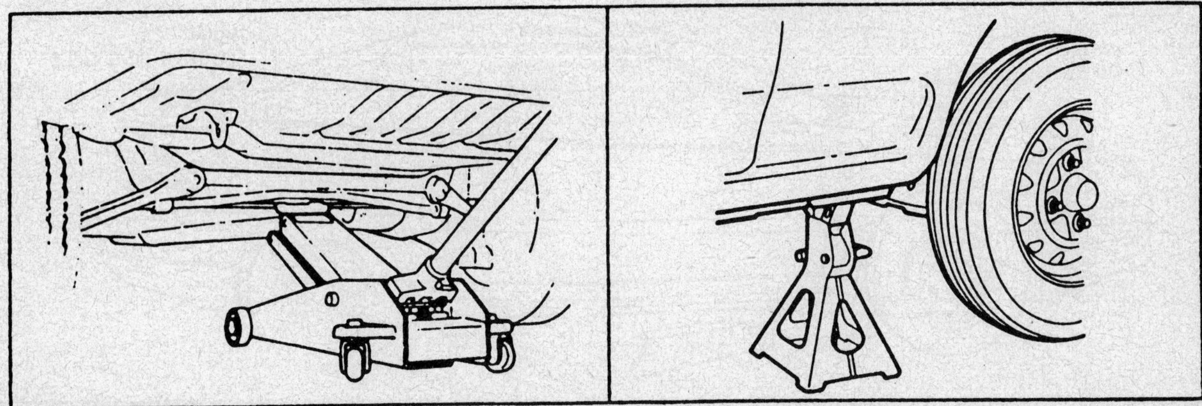

**Fig. 6 Festiva (Jack Stand)**

# VEHICLE LIFT POINTS

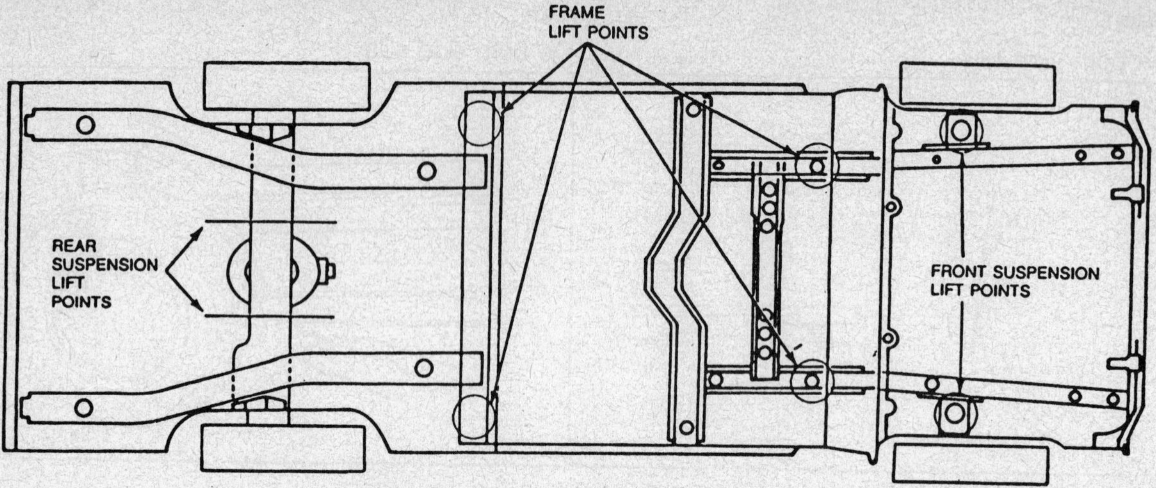


**Fig. 7 Mark VII & Mustang**

When using a floor jack, raise the front of the vehicle by positioning the floor jack under the front body rail behind the suspension arm-to-body bracket.

Lift the front, as well as either side of the rear end, by positioning the floor jack under the rocker flange at the contact points used for the jack supplied with the vehicle. Raise the rear of the vehicle by positioning the floor jack under either lower control arm.

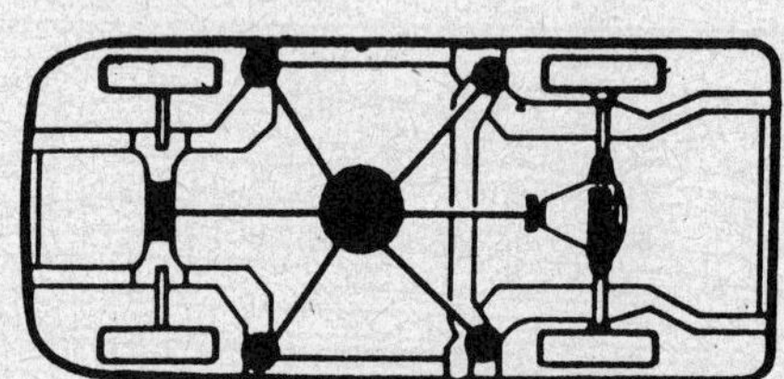

• VEHICLE HOIST POINTS

**Fig. 8 Merkur XR4Ti**

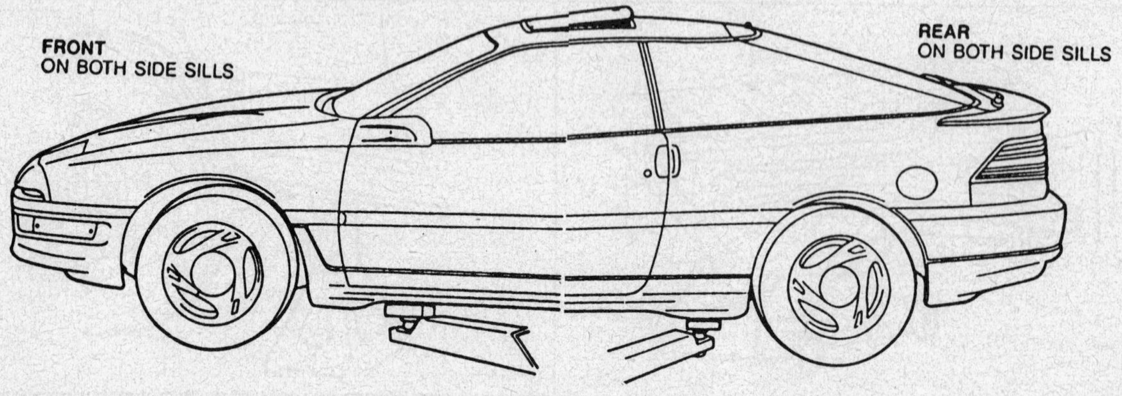


**Fig. 9 Probe (Hoist)**

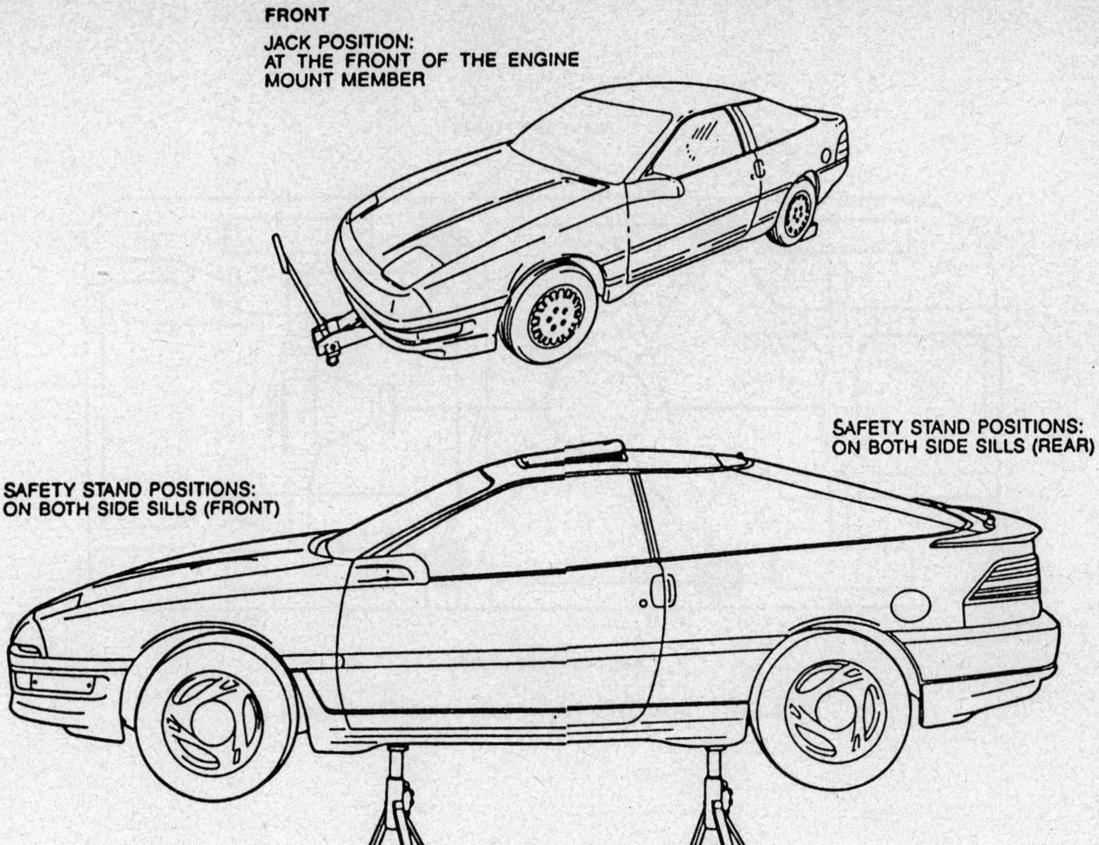


**Fig. 10 Probe (Jack Stands)**

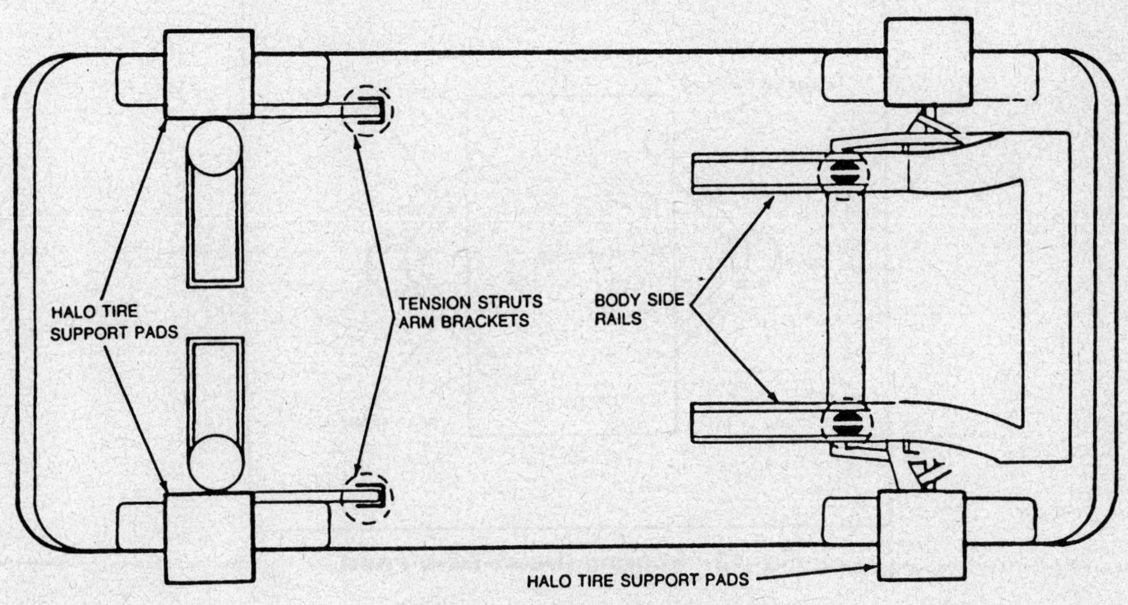


**Fig. 11 Sable & Taurus**

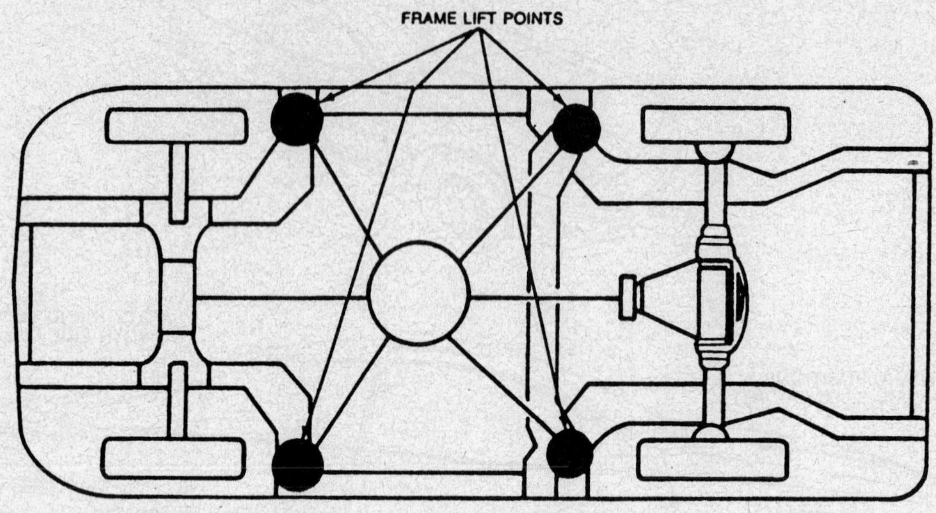


**Fig. 12 Scorpio (Hoist-Frame Contact)**

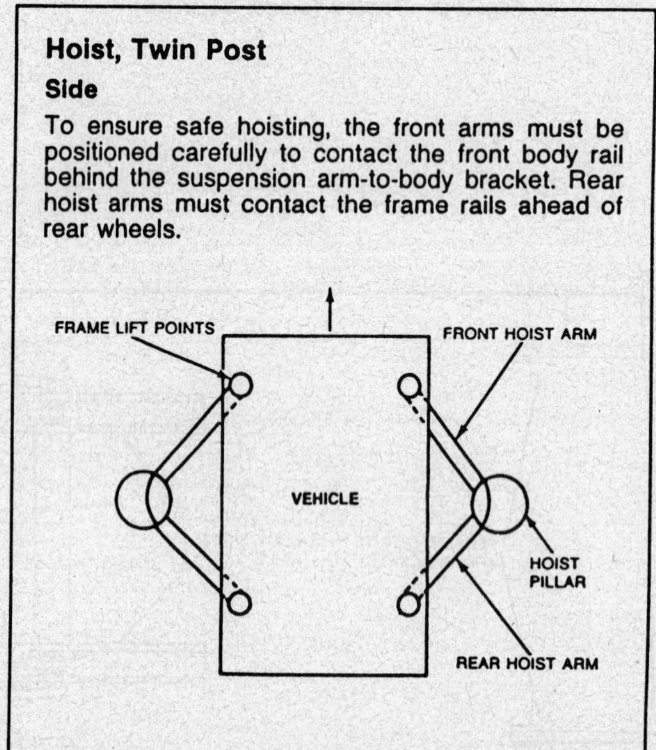

Hoist, Twin Post
Side
To ensure safe hoisting, the front arms must be positioned carefully to contact the front body rail behind the suspension arm-to-body bracket. Rear hoist arms must contact the frame rails ahead of rear wheels.
FRAME LIFT POINTS
FRONT HOIST ARM
VEHICLE
HOIST PILLAR
REAR HOIST ARM


**Fig. 13 Scorpio (Hoist-Twin Post)**

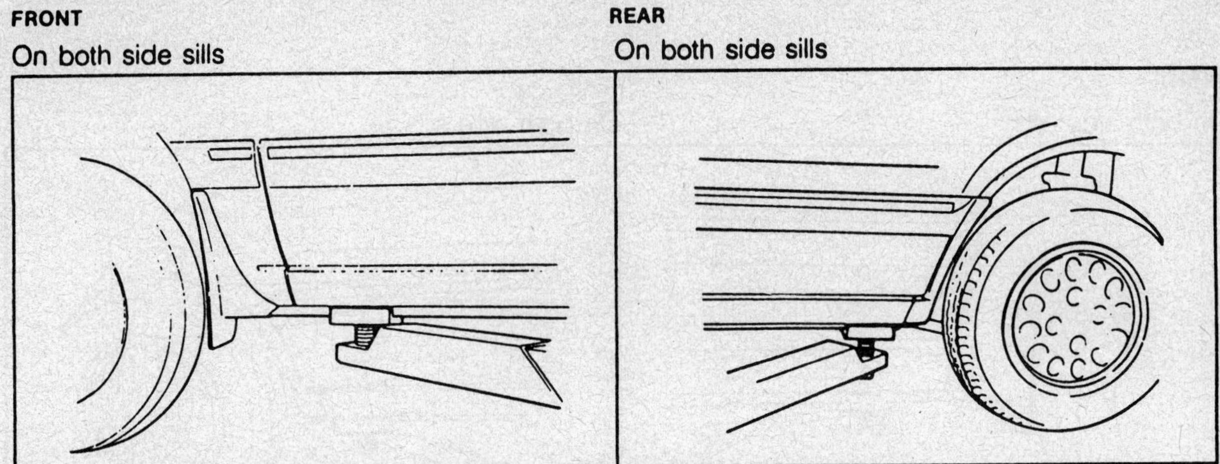


**Fig. 14 1989 Tracer (Hoist)**

**FRONT**
JACK POSITION:
AT THE FRONT OF THE ENGINE MOUNT MEMBER

SAFETY STAND POSITIONS:
ON BOTH SIDE SILLS (FRONT)

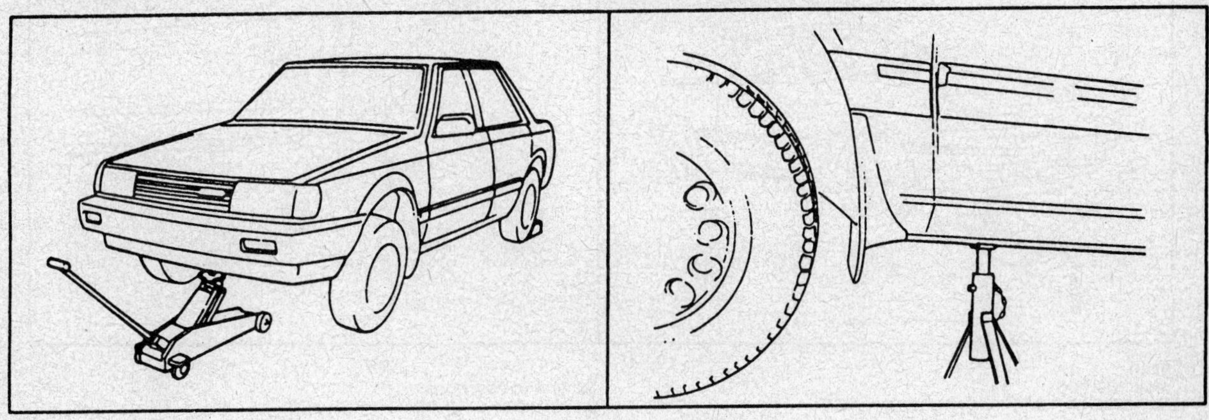

**REAR**
JACK POSITION:
AT THE CENTER OF THE REAR CROSSMEMBER

SAFETY STAND POSITIONS:
ON BOTH SIDE SILLS (REAR)

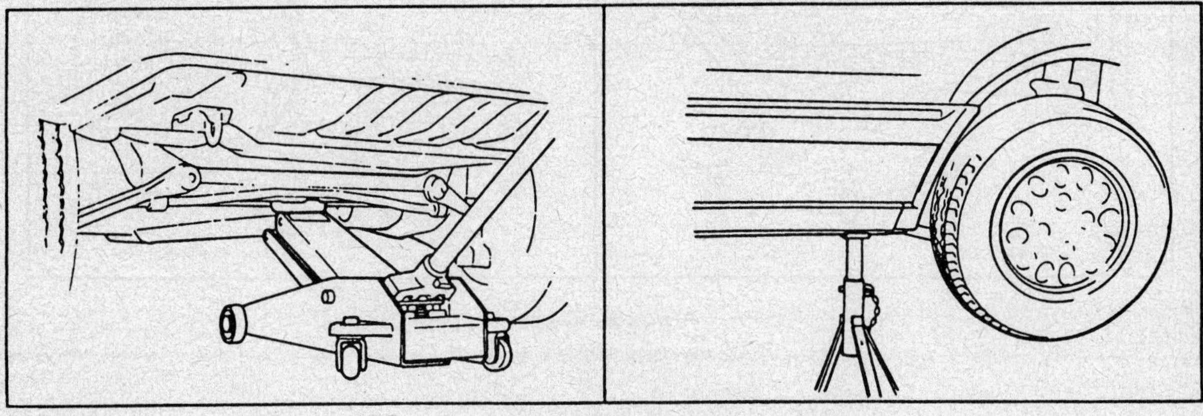

**Fig. 15 1989 Tracer (Jack Stands)**

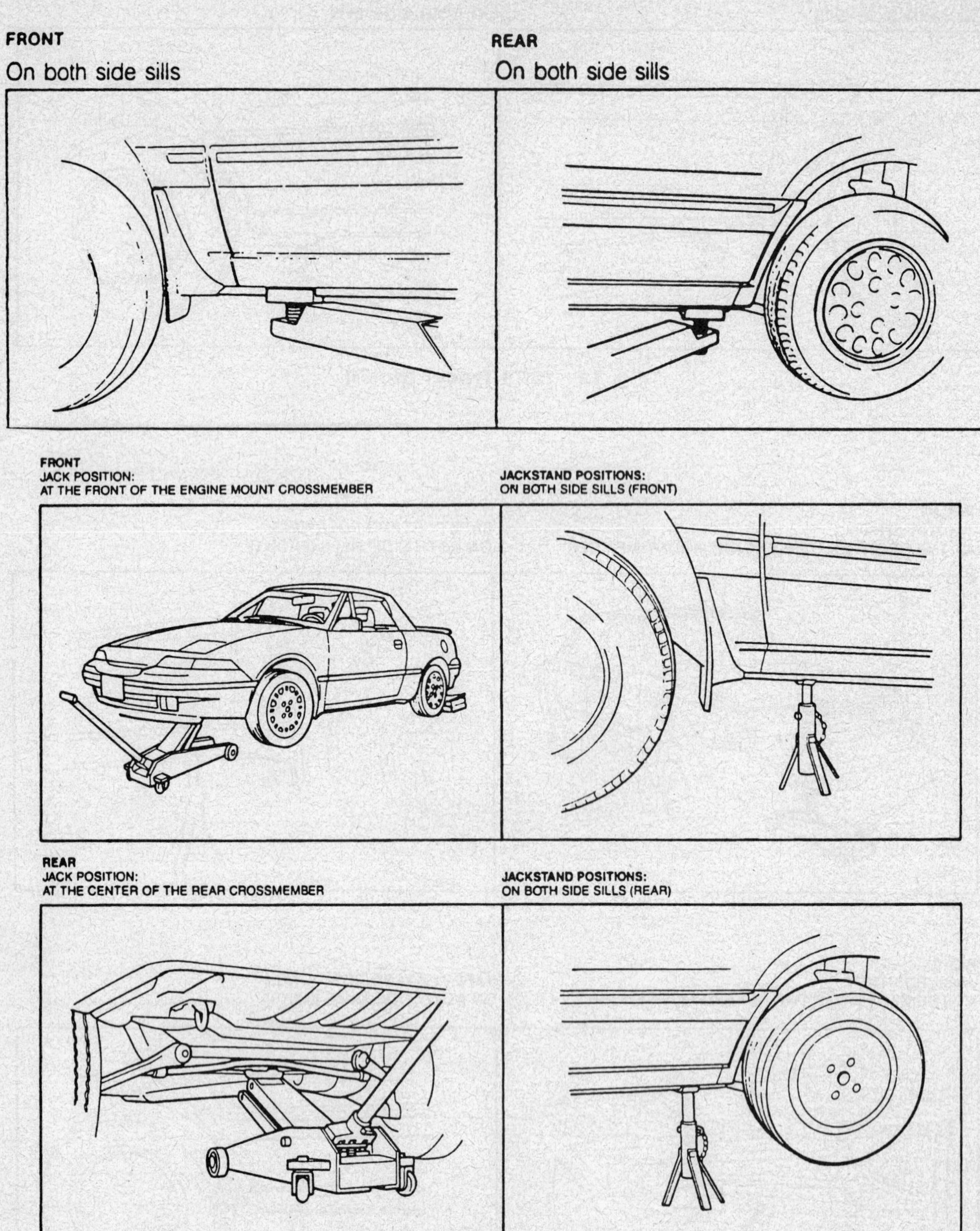
FRONT
On both side sills
REAR
On both side sills
FRONT
JACK POSITION:
AT THE FRONT OF THE ENGINE MOUNT CROSSMEMBER
JACKSTAND POSITIONS:
ON BOTH SIDE SILLS (FRONT)
REAR
JACK POSITION:
AT THE CENTER OF THE REAR CROSSMEMBER
JACKSTAND POSITIONS:
ON BOTH SIDE SILLS (REAR)

**Fig. 16 Capri**

**Lifting**

When lifting a vehicle, always position the hoist lifting pads so that they are in contact with the side sills.

**CAUTION: Never allow the vehicle to be lifted by the trailing links.**

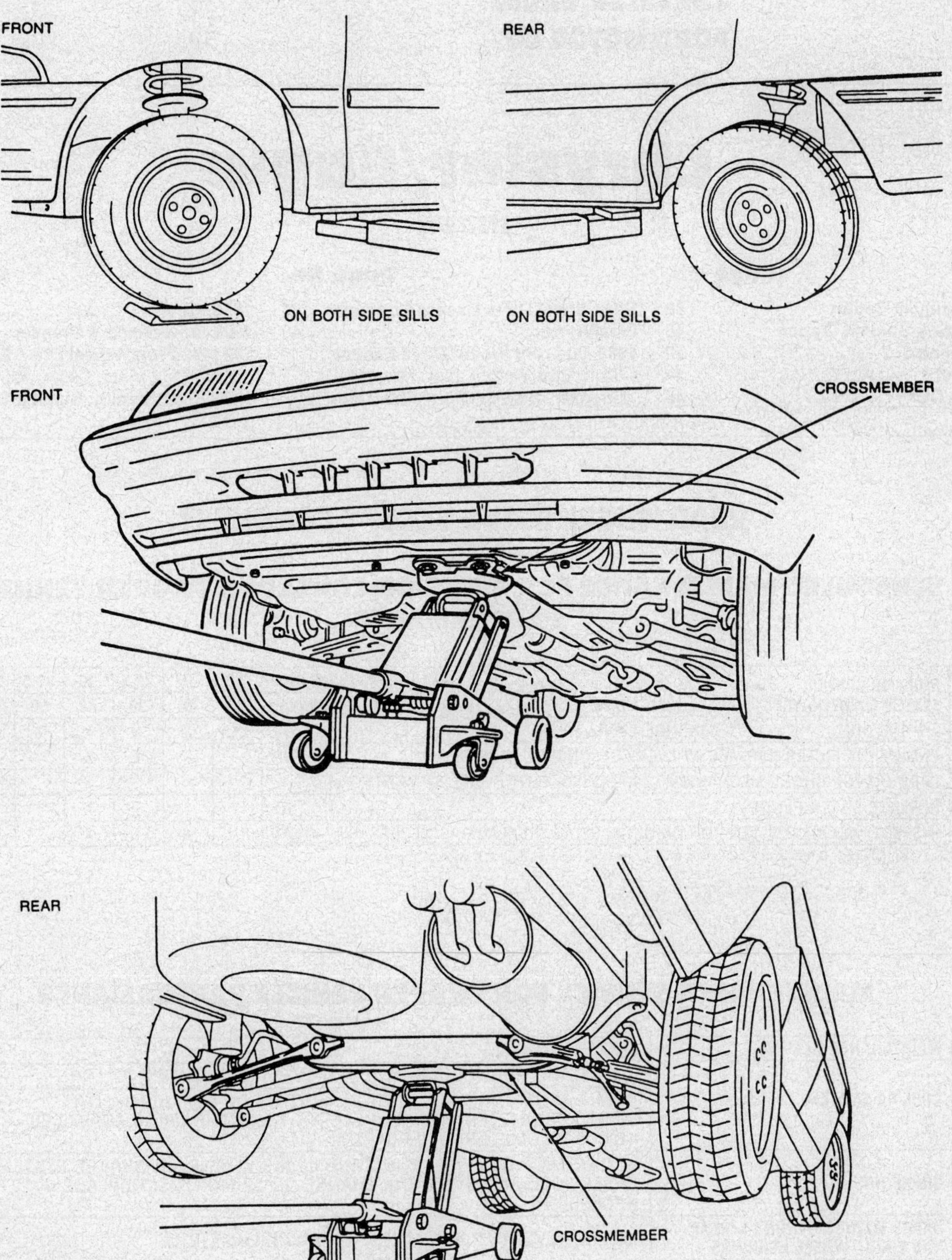


**Fig. 17 1991–92 Escort & Tracer**

# VEHICLE MAINTENANCE SCHEDULES

TABLE OF CONTENTS



# Chrysler/Eagle

INDEX



## REAR WHEEL DRIVE EXCEPT CONQUEST

### SCHEDULED MAINTENANCE FOR EMISSION CONTROL & PROPER VEHICLE PERFORMANCE

| EMISSION CONTROL SYSTEM MAINTENANCE | SERVICE INTERVALS | MILEAGE IN THOUSANDS | 7.5 | 15 | 22.5 | 30 | 37.5 | 45 |
|---|---|---|---|---|---|---|---|---|
| | | KILOMETERS IN THOUSANDS | 12 | 24 | 36 | 48 | 60 | 72 |
| ENGINE OIL | CHANGE EVERY 12 MONTHS | OR | X | X | X | X | X | X |
| ENGINE OIL FILTER REPLACE AT EVERY SECOND OIL CHANGE (1) | | OR | | X | | X | | X |
| CARBURETOR CHOKE MECHANISM — APPLY SOLVENT EVERY 12 MONTHS | | | | | | X | | |
| REPLACE SPARK PLUGS | | AT | | | | X | | |
| INSPECT AND ADJUST TENSION ON DRIVE BELTS, REPLACE AS NECESSARY | | AT | | X | | X | | X |

(1) Note: If mileage is less than 7,500 miles each 12 months, replace oil filter at each oil change.

### MAINTENANCE SERVICE FOR PROPER VEHICLE PERFORMANCE

| MAINTENANCE SERVICE | SERVICE INTERVALS |
|---|---|
| COOLING SYSTEM | CHECK AND SERVICE AS REQUIRED EVERY 12 MONTHS |
| | DRAIN, FLUSH AND REFILL AT 36 MONTHS OR 52,500 MILES - 84 000 KILOMETERS . . . AND EVERY 24 MONTHS OR 30,000 MILES - 48 000 KILOMETERS THEREAFTER |
| BRAKE HOSES | INSPECT FOR DETERIORATION AND LEAKS WHENEVER BRAKES SYSTEM IS SERVICED AND EVERY OIL CHANGE OR 12 MONTHS. REPLACE IF NECESSARY. |
| BRAKE LININGS - FRONT & REAR AND FRONT WHEEL BEARINGS | INSPECT EVERY 22,500 MILES - 36 000 KILOMETERS |
| TIE ROD ENDS & BALL JOINTS | LUBRICATE EVERY 3 YEARS OR 30,000 MILES - 48 000 KILOMETERS |

## SEVERE SERVICE MAINTENANCE

| | |
|---|---|
| ENGINE OIL | CHANGE EVERY 3 MONTHS OR 3,000 MILES - 4 800 KILOMETERS |
| ENGINE OIL FILTER | REPLACE AT EVERY SECOND OIL CHANGE |
| BRAKE LININGS . . . FRONT & REAR AND FRONT WHEEL BEARINGS | INSPECT EVERY 9,000 MILES - 14 400 KILOMETERS |
| UNIVERSAL JOINTS & FRONT SUSPENSION BALL JOINTS | INSPECT AT EVERY OIL CHANGE |
| TIE ROD ENDS | LUBRICATE EVERY 18 MONTHS OR 15,000 MILES - 24 000 KILOMETERS |
| ENGINE AIR FILTER | INSPECT AND REPLACE IF REQUIRED EVERY 15,000 MILES - 24 000 KILOMETERS |
| AUTOMATIC TRANSMISSION | CHANGE FLUID, FILTER, AND ADJUST BAND EVERY 15,000 MILES - 24 000 KILOMETERS |
| MANUAL TRANSMISSION | CHANGE FLUID AND CLEAN PAN MAGNET EVERY 15,000 MILES - 24 000 KILOMETERS |
| AXLE OIL | CHANGE AT 36,000 MILES - 58 000 KILOMETERS |

## CHASSIS LUBRICATION

| Component<br>Wipe All Fittings Clean Before Lubricating | No. of Fittings | Lubricant |
|---|---|---|
| Suspension Ball Joints | 4 | 3 years or 48 000 km (30,000 miles) |
| Tie Rod Ball Joints | 4 | 3 years or 48 000 km (30,000 miles) |
| Steering Gear Arm | 1 | 3 years or 48 000 km (30,000 miles) |

# 1989–90 FRONT WHEEL DRIVE EXCEPT COLT, COLT VISTA, LASER, MONACO, PREMIER, STEALTH, SUMMIT & TALON

## SCHEDULED MAINTENANCE FOR EMISSION CONTROL & PROPER VEHICLE PERFORMANCE

| EMISSION CONTROL SYSTEM MAINTENANCE | SERVICE INTERVALS | MILEAGE IN THOUSANDS | 7.5 | 15 | 22.5 | 30 | 37.5 | 45 |
|---|---|---|---|---|---|---|---|---|
| | | KILOMETERS IN THOUSANDS | 12 | 24 | 36 | 48 | 60 | 72 |
| ENGINE OIL (EXCEPT TURBO) CHANGE EVERY 12 MONTHS | | OR | X | X | X | X | X | X |
| ENGINE OIL (TURBO) CHANGE EVERY 6 MONTHS | | OR | X | X | X | X | X | X |
| ENGINE OIL FILTER REPLACE AT EVERY SECOND OIL CHANGE (1) | | OR | | X | | X | | X |
| REPLACE SPARK PLUGS | | AT | | | | X | | |
| INSPECT AND ADJUST TENSION ON DRIVE BELTS, REPLACE AS NECESSARY | | AT | | X | | X | | X |

(1) Note: If mileage is less than 7,500 miles each 12 months, replace oil filter at each oil change.

## GENERAL MAINTENANCE SERVICE FOR PROPER VEHICLE PERFORMANCE

| MAINTENANCE SERVICE | SERVICE INTERVALS |
|---|---|
| COOLING SYSTEM | CHECK AND SERVICE AS REQUIRED EVERY 12 MONTHS<br>DRAIN, FLUSH AND REFILL AT 36 MONTHS OR 52,500 MILES - 84 000 KILOMETERS . . . AND EVERY 24 MONTHS OR 30,000 MILES - 48 000 KILOMETERS THEREAFTER |
| BRAKE HOSES | INSPECT FOR DETERIORATION AND LEAKS WHENEVER BRAKES SYSTEM IS SERVICED AND EVERY OIL CHANGE OR 12 MONTHS. REPLACE IF NECESSARY. |
| BRAKE LININGS - FRONT & REAR AND REAR WHEEL BEARINGS | INSPECT EVERY 22,500 MILES - 36 000 KILOMETERS |
| TIE ROD ENDS & BALL JOINTS | LUBRICATE EVERY 3 YEARS OR 30,000 MILES - 48 000 KILOMETERS |
| DRIVE SHAFT BOOTS | INSPECT FOR DETERIORATION AND LEAKS EVERY OIL CHANGE. REPLACE IF NECESSARY |

## SEVERE SERVICE MAINTENANCE

| | |
|---|---|
| **ENGINE OIL** | CHANGE EVERY 3 MONTHS OR 3,000 MILES - 4 800 KILOMETERS |
| **ENGINE OIL FILTER** | REPLACE AT EVERY SECOND OIL CHANGE |
| **BRAKE LININGS . . . FRONT & REAR AND REAR WHEEL BEARINGS** | INSPECT EVERY 9,000 MILES - 14 400 KILOMETERS |
| **UNIVERSAL JOINTS & FRONT SUSPENSION BALL JOINTS** | INSPECT AT EVERY OIL CHANGE |
| **TIE ROD ENDS** | LUBRICATE EVERY 18 MONTHS OR 15,000 MILES - 24 00 KILOMETERS |
| **ENGINE AIR FILTER** | INSPECT AND REPLACE IF REQUIRED EVERY 15,000 MILES - 24 000 KILOMETERS |
| **AUTOMATIC TRANSAXLE** | CHANGE FLUID, FILTER, AND ADJUST BAND EVERY 15,00 MILES - 24 000 KILOMETERS |
| **MANUAL TRANSAXLE** | CHANGE FLUID AND CLEAN PAN MAGNET EVERY 15,000 MILES - 24 00 KILOMETERS |

## CHASSIS LUBRICATION

| **Component** | **No. of Fittings** | **Lubricant** |
|---|---|---|
| Suspension Ball Joints (Lower) | 2* | 30,000 miles (48 000 km) or 3 years. |
| Tie Rod Ball Joints** | 2* | 30,000 miles (48 000 km) or 3 years |
| *Be sure all fittings are clean before lubricating | | **Except AL-Body with manual steering |

# COLT & SUMMIT SEDAN

## SCHEDULED MAINTENANCE FOR EMISSION CONTROL & PROPER VEHICLE PERFORMANCE

| Emission Control System Maintenance | Service Intervals | Kilometers in Thousands | 24 | 48 | 72 | 80 | 96 |
|---|---|---|---|---|---|---|---|
| | | Mileage in Thousands | 15 | 30 | 45 | 50 | 60 |
| Check and Adjust Valve Clearance (Intake and Exhaust Valves of 4G1 Engine, and Jet Valves only. Except Engine with both Auto-Lash Adjuster and Non-Jet Valve) | | at | X | X | X | | X |
| Check Fuel System (Tank, Line, Connections and Fuel Filler Cap) for Leaks Every 5 Years | | or | | | | X | |
| Replace Fuel Hoses and Vapor Hoses Every 5 Years | | or | | | | X | |
| Replace Air cleaner Element | | at | | X | | | X |
| Replace Spark Plugs | | at | | X | | | X |

## SEVERE SERVICE MAINTENANCE

| Maintenance Item | Service to be Performed | Mileage Intervals Kilometers in Thousands (Miles in Thousands) | | | | | | | | | Severe Usage Conditions | | | | | | |
|---|---|---|---|---|---|---|---|---|---|---|---|---|---|---|---|---|---|
| | | 12 (7.5) | 24 (15) | 36 (22.5) | 48 (30) | 60 (37.5) | 72 (45) | 80 (50) | 84 (52.5) | 96 (60) | A | B | C | D | E | F | G |
| Air Cleaner Element | Replace | More Frequently | | | | | | | | | X | | | | X | | |
| Spark Plugs | Replace | | X | | X | | X | | | X | | X | | X | | | |
| Engine Oil | Change Every 3 Months or | Every 4,800 Km (3,000 Miles) | | | | | | | | | X | X | X | X | | | X |
| Engine Oil Filter | Replace Every 6 Months or | Every 9,600 Km (6,000 Miles) | | | | | | | | | X | X | X | X | | | X |
| Disc Brake Pads | Inspect for Wear | More Frequently | | | | | | | | | X | | | | | X | |
| Rear Drum Brake Linings and Rear Wheel Cylinders | Inspect for Wear and Leaks | More Frequently | | | | | | | | | X | | | | | X | |

Severe usage conditions

A – Driving in dusty conditions
B – Trailer towing or police, taxi, or commercial type operation
C – Extensive idling
D – Short-trip operation at freezing temperatures (engine not thoroughly warmed up)
E – Driving in sandy areas
F – Driving in salty areas
G – More than 50% operation in heavy city traffic during hot weather above 32°C (90°F)

## GENERAL MAINTENANCE SERVICE FOR PROPER VEHICLE PERFORMANCE

| General Maintenance | | Service Intervals | | Kilometers in Thousands | 24 | 48 | 72 | 80 | 96 |
|---|---|---|---|---|---|---|---|---|---|
| | | | | Mileage in Thousands | 15 | 30 | 45 | 50 | 60 |
| Timing Belt | | Replace | at | | | | | | X |
| Drive Belt (for Water Pump and Alternator) | | Replace | at | | | X | | | X |
| Engine Oil | <N/A> | Change Every Year | or | | Every 12,000 km (7,500 miles) | | | | |
| | <T/C> | Change Every 6 Months | or | | Every 8,000 km (5,000 miles) | | | | |
| Engine Oil Filter | <N/A> | Change Every Year | or | | X | X | X | | X |
| | <T/C> | Change Every Year | or | | Every 16,000 km (10,000 miles) | | | | |
| Manual Transaxle Oil | | Inspect Oil Level | at | | | X | | | X |
| Automatic Transaxle Oil | | Inspect Oil Level Every Year | or | | X | X | X | | X |
| | | Change Oil | | | | X | | | X |
| Engine Coolant | | Replace Every 2 Years | or | | | X | | | X |
| Disc Brake Pads | | Inspect for Wear Every Year | or | | X | X | X | | X |
| Drum Brake Linings and Rear Wheel Cylinders | | Inspect for Wear and Leaks Every 2 Years | or | | | X | | | X |
| Brake Hoses | | Check for Deterioration or Leaks Every Year | or | | X | X | X | | X |
| Ball Joint and Steering Linkage Seals | | Inspect for Grease Leaks and Damage Every 2 Years | or | | | X | | | X |
| Drive Shaft Boots | | Inspect for Grease Leaks and Damage Every Year | or | | X | X | X | | X |
| Rear Wheel Bearings | | Lubricate Grease Every 2 Years | or | | | X | | | X |
| Exhaust System (Connection Portion of Muffler, Pipings and Converter Heat Shields) | | Check and Service as Required Every 2 Years | or | | | X | | | X |

# COLT VISTA & SUMMIT WAGON

## SCHEDULED MAINTENANCE FOR EMISSION CONTROL & PROPER VEHICLE PERFORMANCE

**2WD**

| Emission Control System Maintenance | Service Intervals | Kilometers in Thousands | 24 | 48 | 72 | 80 | 96 |
|---|---|---|---|---|---|---|---|
| | | Mileage in Thousands | 15 | 30 | 45 | 50 | 60 |
| Check Fuel System (Tank, Line and Connections and Fuel filler Cap) for Leaks Every 5 Years | | or | | | | × | |
| Replace Fuel Hoses and Vapor Hoses Every 5 Years | | or | | | | × | |
| Replace Air Cleaner Element | | at | | × | | | × |
| Replace Spark Plugs | | at | | × | | | × |

**4WD**

| Emission Control System Maintenance | Service Intervals | Kilometers in Thousands | 12 | 24 | 36 | 48 | 60 | 72 | 80 | 84 | 96 | 108 | 120 | 128 | 132 | 144 | 156 | 160 | 168 | 180 | 192 |
|---|---|---|---|---|---|---|---|---|---|---|---|---|---|---|---|---|---|---|---|---|---|
| | | Mileage in Thousands | 7.5 | 15 | 22.5 | 30 | 37.5 | 45 | 50 | 52.5 | 60 | 67.5 | 75 | 80 | 82.5 | 90 | 97.5 | 100 | 105 | 112.5 | 120 |
| Check Fuel System (Tank, Line and Connections and Fuel Filler Cap) for Leaks Every 5 Years | | or | | | | | | | × | | | | | | | | | × | | | |
| Replace Vacuum Hoses, Secondary Air Hoses, Crankcase Ventilation Hoses and Water Hoses Every 5 Years | | or | | | | | | | | | × | | | | | | | | | | × |
| Replace Fuel Hoses and Vapor Hoses Every 5 Years | | or | | | | | | | × | | | | | | | | | × | | | |
| Replace Air Cleaner Element | | at | | | | × | | | | | × | | | | | × | | | | | × |
| Clean Crankcase Emission-control System (PCV Valve)* | | at | | | | | | | | | | | | × | | | | | | | |
| Check Evaporative Emission-control System (except Canister)* for Leaks and Clogging Every 5 Years | | or | | | | | | | | | × | | | | | | | | | | × |
| Replace Canister* | | at | | | | | | | | | | | | | | | | × | | | |
| Replace Spark Plugs | | at | | | | × | | | | | × | | | | | × | | | | | × |
| Replace Ignition Cables* Every 5 Years | | or | | | | | | | | | × | | | | | | | | | | × |
| Replace EGR Valve* | | at | | | | | | | × | | | | | | | | | × | | | |
| Replace Oxygen Sensor* | | at | | | | | | | | | | | | × | | | | | | | |

NOTE
*: Except for California

## GENERAL MAINTENANCE SERVICE FOR PROPER VEHICLE PERFORMANCE

| General Maintenance | Service Interval | | Kilometers in Thousands | 12 | 24 | 36 | 48 | 60 | 72 | 84 | 96 |
|---|---|---|---|---|---|---|---|---|---|---|---|
| | | | Mileage in Thousands | 7.5 | 15 | 22.5 | 30 | 37.5 | 45 | 52.5 | 60 |
| Timing Belt (Including the Balancer Belt) | Replace | | at | | | | | | | | × |
| Drive Belt (for Water Pump and Alternator) | Replace | | at | | | | × | | | | × |
| Engine Oil | Change Every Year | | or | × | × | × | × | × | × | × | × |
| Engine Oil Filter | Change Every Year | | or | | × | | × | | × | | × |
| Manual Transaxle Oil | Check Oil Level | | at | | | | × | | | | × |
| Transfer Case* | Check Oil Level | | at | | | | × | | | | × |
| Automatic Transaxle Fluid | Inspect Fluid Level Every Year | | or | | × | | × | | × | | × |
| | Change Fluid | | at | | | | × | | | | × |
| Engine Coolant | Replace Every 2 Years | | or | | | | × | | | | × |
| Front Disc Brake Pads | Inspect for Wear Every Year | | or | | × | | × | | × | | × |
| Drum Brake Linings and Rear Wheel Cylinders | Inspect for Wear and Leaks Every 2 years | | or | | | | × | | | | × |
| Brake Hoses | Check for Deterioration or Leaks Every Year | | or | | × | | × | | × | | × |
| Ball Joint and Steering Linkage Seals | Inspect for Grease Leaks and Damage Every 2 Years | | or | | | | × | | | | × |
| Drive Shaft Boots | Inspect for Grease Leaks and Damage Every Years | | or | | × | | × | | × | | × |
| Rear Axle* | With LSD | Change Oil | at | | | | × | | | | × |
| | Without LSD | Inspect Oil Level | at | | | | × | | | | × |
| Rear Wheel Bearings | Lubricate Grease Every 2 Years | | or | | | | × | | | | × |
| Propeller Shaft Joint* | Lubricate Grease Every 2 Years | | or | | | | × | | | | × |
| Exhaust System (Connection Portion of Muffler, Pipings and Converter Heat Shields) | Check and Service as Required Every Years | | or | | | | × | | | | × |

NOTE
LSD :Limited-slip Differential
*: 4WD

## SEVERE SERVICE MAINTENANCE

| Maintenance Item | Service to be Performed | Mileage Intervals Kilometers in Thousands (Miles in Thousands) | | | | Severe Usage Conditions | | | | | | | |
|---|---|---|---|---|---|---|---|---|---|---|---|---|---|
| | | 24 (15) | 48 (30) | 72 (45) | 96 (60) | A | B | C | D | E | F | G | H |
| Engine Oil | Change Every 3 Months or | Every 4,800 km (3,000 miles) | | | | × | × | × | × | | | × | |
| Engine Oil Filter | Replace Every 6 Months or | Every 9,600 km (6,000 miles) | | | | × | × | × | × | | | × | |
| Air Cleaner Element | Replace | More Frequently | | | | × | | | | × | | | |
| Crankcase Emission-control System* | Check and Clean as Required | More Frequently | | | | × | | | | | | | |
| Spark Plugs | Replace at | × | × | × | × | | × | | × | | | | |
| Front Disc Brake Pads | Inspect for Wear | More Frequently | | | | × | | | | | × | | |
| Rear Drum Brake Linings and Rear Wheel Cylinders | Inspect for Wear and Leaks | More Frequently | | | | × | | | | | × | | |
| Manual Transaxle and Transfer Case* | Change Oil at | | × | | × | | × | | | | | × | × |

NOTE
*: 4WD

Severe usage conditions

A–Driving in dusty conditions
B–Trailer towing, or police, taxi, or commercial type operation
C–Extensive idling
D–Short-trip operation at freezing temperatures (engine not thoroughly warmed up)
E–Driving in sandy areas
F–Driving in salty areas
G–More than 50% operation in heavy city traffic during hot weather above 32°C (90°F)
H–Driving on off-road

# COLT WAGON

## SCHEDULED MAINTENANCE FOR EMISSION CONTROL & PROPER VEHICLE PERFORMANCE

### 2WD

| Emission Control System Maintenance | Service Intervals | Kilometers in Thousands | 24 | 48 | 72 | 80 | 96 |
|---|---|---|---|---|---|---|---|
| | | Mileage in Thousands | 15 | 30 | 45 | 50 | 60 |
| Check Valve Clearance; Adjust as Required | | at | X | X | X | | X |
| Check Fuel System (Tank, Pipe Line and Connections and Fuel Filler Cap) for Leaks Every 5 Years | | or | | | | X | |
| Replace Fuel Hoses and Vapor Hoses Every 5 Years | | or | | | | X | |
| Replace Air Cleaner Element | | at | | X | | | X |
| Replace Spark Plugs | | at | | X | | | X |

### 4WD

| Emission Control System Maintenance | Service Intervals | Kilometers in Thousands | 24 | 36 | 48 | 60 | 72 | 80 | 84 | 96 | 108 | 120 | 132 | 144 | 156 | 160 | 168 | 180 | 192 |
|---|---|---|---|---|---|---|---|---|---|---|---|---|---|---|---|---|---|---|---|
| | | Mileage in Thousands | 15 | 22.5 | 30 | 37.5 | 45 | 50 | 52.5 | 60 | 67.5 | 75 | 82.5 | 90 | 97.5 | 100 | 105 | 112.5 | 120 |
| Check Fuel System (Tank, Pipe Line and Connection and Fuel Filler Cap) for Leaks Every 5 Years | or | | | | | | | X | | | | | | | | X | | | |
| Replace Vacuum Hoses, Secondary Air Hoses, Crankcase Ventilation Hoses and Water Hoses Every 5 Years | or | | | | | | | | | X | | | | | | | | | X |
| Replace Fuel Hoses and Vapor Hoses Every 5 years | or | | | | | | | X | | | | | | | | X | | | |
| Replace Air Cleaner Element | at | | | | X | | | | | X | | | | X | | | | | X |
| Clean Crankcase Emission Control System (PCV Valve)* | | Every 128,000 Km (80,000 Miles) | | | | | | | | | | | | | | | | | |
| Check Evaporative Emission Control System (Except Canister) for Leaks and Clogging* Every 5 years | or | | | | | | | | | X | | | | | | | | | X |
| Replace Canister* | at | | | | | | | | | | | | | | | X | | | |
| Replace Spark Plugs | at | | | | X | | | | | X | | | | X | | | | | X |
| Replace Ignition Cables* Every 5 Years | or | | | | | | | | | X | | | | | | | | | X |
| Replace EGR Valve* | at | | | | | | | X | | | | | | | | X | | | |
| Replace Oxygen Sensor* | | Every 128,000 Km (80,000 Miles) | | | | | | | | | | | | | | | | | |

NOTE:
* Cars for Federal

## GENERAL MAINTENANCE SERVICE FOR PROPER VEHICLE PERFORMANCE

| General Maintenance | Service Intervals | Kilometers in Thousands | 24 | 48 | 72 | 80 | 96 |
|---|---|---|---|---|---|---|---|
| | | Mileage in Thousands | 15 | 30 | 45 | 50 | 60 |
| Timing Belt | Replace | at | | | | | X |
| Drive Belt (for Water Pump and Alternator) | Replace | at | | X | | | X |
| Engine Oil | Change Every Year | or | Every 12,000 Km (7,500 Miles) | | | | |
| Engine Oil Filter | Change Every Year | or | X | X | X | | X |
| Manual Transaxle Oil or *Manual Transaxle and Transfer Oil | Inspect Oil Level | at | | X | | | X |
| Automatic Transaxle Fluid | Inspect Fluid Level Every Year | or | X | X | X | | X |
| | Change Fluid | at | | X | | | X |
| Engine Coolant | Replace Every 2 Year | or | | X | | | X |
| Front Disc Brake Pads | Inspect for Wear Every Year | or | X | X | X | | X |
| Rear Drum Brake Linings and Rear Wheel Cylinders | Inspect for Wear and Leaks Every 2 Years | or | | X | | | X |
| Brake Hoses | Check for Deterioration or Leaks Every Year | or | X | X | X | | X |
| Ball Joint and Steering Linkage Seals | Inspect for Grease Leaks and Damage Every 2 Years | or | | X | | | X |
| Drive Shaft Boots | Inspect for Grease Leaks and Damage Every Year | or | X | X | X | | X |
| Rear Wheel Bearings | Lubricate Grease Every 2 Years | or | | X | | | X |
| *Rear Axle — With LSD | Change Oil | at | | X | | | X |
| *Rear Axle — Without LSD | Inspect Oil Level | at | | X | | | X |
| *Propeller Shaft Joint | Lubricate Grease Every 2 Years | or | | X | | | X |
| Exhaust System (Connection Portion of Muffler, Pipings and Converter Heat Shields) | Check and Service as Required Every 2 Years | or | | X | | | X |

NOTE
* 4WD vehicles only

## SEVERE SERVICE MAINTENANCE

| Maintenance Item | Service to be Performed | | Mileage Intervals Kilometers in Thousands (Miles in Thousands) | | | | Severe Usage Conditions | | | | | | | |
|---|---|---|---|---|---|---|---|---|---|---|---|---|---|---|
| | | | 24 (15) | 48 (30) | 72 (45) | 96 (60) | A | B | C | D | E | F | G | H |
| Engine Oil | Change Every 3 Months | or | Every 4,800 Km (3,000 Miles) | | | | X | X | X | X | | | X | |
| Engine Oil Filter | Replace Every 6 Months | or | Every 9,600 Km (6,000 Miles) | | | | X | X | X | X | | | X | |
| Air Cleaner Element | Replace | | More Frequently | | | | X | | | | X | | | |
| *Crankcase Emission-Control System | Check and Clean as Required | | More Frequently | | | | X | | | | | | | |
| Spark Plugs | Replace | at | X | X | X | X | | X | | X | | | | |
| Front Disc Brake Pads | Inspect for Wear | | More Frequently | | | | X | | | | | X | | |
| Rear Drum Brake Linings and Rear Wheel Cylinders | Inspect for Wear and Leaks | | More Frequently | | | | X | | | | | X | | |
| *Manual Transaxle and Transfer Oil | Change Oil | at | | X | | X | | X | | | | | X | X |

NOTE:
*4WD vehicles only

Severe usage conditions

A – Driving in dusty conditions
B – Trailer towing, police, taxi, or commercial type operation
C – Extensive idling
D – Short-trip operation at freezing temperatures (engine not thoroughly warmed up)
E – Driving in sandy areas
F – Driving in salty areas
G – More than 50% operation in heavy city traffic during hot weather above 32°C (90°F)
H – Driving off road

# CONQUEST

## SCHEDULED MAINTENANCE FOR EMISSION CONTROL & PROPER VEHICLE PERFORMANCE

| Emission Control System Maintenance | Service Intervals | Kilometers in Thousands | 24 | 48 | 72 | 80 | 96 |
|---|---|---|---|---|---|---|---|
| | | Mileage in Thousands | 15 | 30 | 45 | 50 | 60 |
| Check Jet Valve Clearances, Adjust as Required | | | X | X | X | | X |
| Replace Fuel Filter Every 5 Years | | | | | | X | |
| Check Fuel System (Tank, Pipe Line and Connections and Fuel Filler Cap) for Leaks Every 5 Years | | or | | | | X | |
| Replace Fuel Hoses and Vapor Hoses Every 5 Years | | or | | | | X | |
| Replace Air Cleaner Element | | at | | X | | | X |
| Replace Spark Plugs | | at | | X | | | X |

## GENERAL MAINTENANCE SERVICE FOR PROPER VEHICLE PERFORMANCE

| General Maintenance | Service Intervals | | Kilometers in Thousands | 24 | 48 | 72 | 80 | 96 |
|---|---|---|---|---|---|---|---|---|
| | | | Mileage in Thousands | 15 | 30 | 45 | 50 | 60 |
| Drive Belt (for Water Pump and Alternator) | Replace | at | | | X | | | X |
| Engine Oil | Change Every 6 Months | or | | Every 8,000 Km (5,000 Miles) | | | | |
| Engine Oil Filter | Change Every Year | or | | Every 16,000 Km (10,000 Miles) | | | | |
| Manual Transmission Oil | Inspect Oil Level | at | | | X | | | X |
| Engine Coolant | Replace Every 2 Years | or | | | X | | | X |
| Disc Brake Pads | Inspect for Wear Every Year | or | | X | X | X | | X |
| Brake Hoses | Check for Deterioration or Leaks Every Year | or | | X | X | X | | X |
| Ball Joint and Steering Linkage Seals | Inspect for Grease Leaks and Damage Every 2 Years | or | | | X | | | X |
| Drive Shaft Boots | Inspect for Grease Leaks and Damage Every Year | or | | X | X | X | | X |
| Front Wheel Bearings | Lubricate Grease Every 2 Years | or | | | X | | | X |
| Rear Axle | Change Oil | at | | | X | | | X |
| Exhaust System (Connection Portion of Muffler, Pipings and Converter Heat Shields) | Check and Service as Required Every 2 Years | or | | | X | | | X |

## SEVERE SERVICE MAINTENANCE

| Maintenance Item | Service to be Performed | Mileage Intervals Kilometers in Thousands (Miles in Thousands) | | | | Severe Usage Conditions | | | | | | | |
|---|---|---|---|---|---|---|---|---|---|---|---|---|---|
| | | 24 (15) | 48 (30) | 72 (45) | 96 (60) | A | B | C | D | E | F | G | H |
| Air Cleaner Element | Replace | More Frequently | | | | X | | | | X | | | |
| Spark Plugs | Replace | Every 24,000 Km (15,000 Miles) | | | | | X | | X | | | | |
| Engine Oil | Change Every 3 Months or | Every 4,800 Km (3,000 Miles) | | | | X | X | X | X | | | X | |
| Engine Oil Filter | Replace Every 6 Months or | Every 9,600 Km (6,000 Miles) | | | | X | X | X | X | | | X | |
| Disc Brake Pads | Inspect for Wear | More Frequently | | | | X | | | | | X | | |
| Automatic Transmission fluid | Change Fluid | Every 48,000 Km (30,000 Miles) | | | | | X | | | | | X | X |

Severe usage conditions

A – Driving in dusty conditions
B – Trailer towing or police, taxi, or commercial type operation
C – Extensive idling
D – Short-trip operation at freezing temperatures (engine not thoroughly warmed up)
E – Driving in sandy areas
F – Driving in salty areas
G – More than 50% operation in heavy city traffic during hot weather above 32°C (90°F)
H – Driving off-road

# LASER & TALON

## SCHEDULED MAINTENANCE FOR EMISSION CONTROL & PROPER VEHICLE PERFORMANCE

| No. | Emission Control System Maintenance | Service Intervals | | 24 | 48 | 72 | 80 | 96 |
|---|---|---|---|---|---|---|---|---|
| | | | Kilometers in Thousands | 24 | 48 | 72 | 80 | 96 |
| | | | Mileage in Thousands | 15 | 30 | 45 | 50 | 60 |
| 1 | Check Fuel System (Tank, Line and Connections and Fuel Filler Cap) for Leaks Every 5 Years | | or | | | | X | |
| 2 | Replace Fuel Hoses and Vapor Hoses Every 5 Years | | or | | | | X | |
| 3 | Replace Air Cleaner Element | | at | | X | | | X |
| 4 | Replace Spark Plugs | | at | | X | | | X |

## GENERAL MAINTENANCE SERVICE FOR PROPER VEHICLE PERFORMANCE

| No. | General Maintenance | | Service Intervals | | 24 | 48 | 72 | 80 | 96 |
|---|---|---|---|---|---|---|---|---|---|
| | | | | Kilometers in Thousands | 24 | 48 | 72 | 80 | 96 |
| | | | | Mileage in Thousands | 15 | 30 | 45 | 50 | 60 |
| 5 | Timing Belt (Including the Balancer Belt) | | Replace | at | | | | | X |
| 6 | Drive Belt (for Water Pump and Alternator) | | Replace | at | | X | | | X |
| 7 | Engine Oil | Non-Turbo | Change Every Year | or | Every 12,000 km (7,500 miles) | | | | |
| | | Turbo | Change Every 6 Months | | Every 8,000 km (5,000 miles) | | | | |
| 8 | Engine Oil Filter | Non-Turbo | Change Every Year | or | X | X | X | | X |
| | | Turbo | Change Every Year | | Every 16,000 km (10,000 miles) | | | | |
| 9 | Manual Transaxle Oil | | Inspect Oil Level | at | | X | | | X |
| 10 | Automatic Transaxle Fluid | | Inspect Fluid Level Every Year | or | X | X | X | | X |
| | | | Change Fluid | at | | X | | | X |
| 11 | Engine Coolant | | Replace Every 2 Years | or | | X | | | X |
| 12 | Disc Brake Pads | | Inspect for Wear Every Year | or | X | X | X | | X |
| 13 | Brake Hoses | | Check for Deterioration or Leaks Every Year | or | X | X | X | | X |
| 14 | Ball Joint and Steering Linkage Seals | | Inspect for Grease Leaks and Damage Every 2 Years | or | | X | | | X |
| 15 | Drive Shaft Boots | | Inspect for Grease Leaks and Damage Every Year | or | X | X | X | | X |
| 16 | Rear Axle <4WD> | With LSD | Change Oil | | | X | | | X |
| | | Without LSD | Inspect Oil Level | | | X | | | X |
| 17 | Exhaust System (Connection Portion of Muffler, Pipings and Converter Heat Shields) | | Check and Service as Required Every 2 Years | or | | X | | | X |

NOTE
LSD: Limited-slip differential

## SEVERE SERVICE MAINTENANCE

| Maintenance Item | Service to be Performed | Mileage Intervals Kilometers in Thousands (Miles in Thousands) | | | | | | | | | Severe Usage Conditions | | | | | | |
|---|---|---|---|---|---|---|---|---|---|---|---|---|---|---|---|---|---|
| | | 12 (7.5) | 24 (15) | 36 (22.5) | 48 (30) | 60 (37.5) | 72 (45) | 80 (50) | 84 (52.5) | 96 (60) | A | B | C | D | E | F | G |
| Air Cleaner Element | Replace | More Frequently | | | | | | | | | X | | | | X | | |
| Spark Plugs | Replace | | X | | X | | X | | | X | | X | | X | | | |
| Engine Oil | Change Every 3 Months or | Every 4,800 km (3,000 miles) | | | | | | | | | X | X | X | X | | | X |
| Engine Oil Filter | Replace Every 6 Months or | Every 9,600 km (6,000 miles) | | | | | | | | | X | X | X | X | | | X |
| Disc Brake Pads | Inspect for Wear | More Frequently | | | | | | | | | X | | | | | X | |

Severe usage conditions
- A–Driving in dusty conditions
- B–Trailer towing or police, taxi, or commercial type operation
- C–Extensive idling
- D–Short trip operation at freezing temperatures (engine not thoroughly warmed up)
- E–Driving in sandy areas
- F–Driving in salty areas
- G–More than 50% operation in heavy city traffic during hot weather above 32°C (90°F)

## 1989 PREMIER

Required Maintenance

| Miles (Thousands) | 7.5 | 15 | 22.5 | 30 | 37.5 | 45 | 52.5 | 60 | 67.5 | 75 | 82.5 |
|---|---|---|---|---|---|---|---|---|---|---|---|
| Kilometers (Thousands) | 12 | 24 | 36 | 48 | 60 | 72 | 84 | 96 | 108 | 120 | 132 |
| 1. Oil — Change | • | • | • | • | • | • | • | • | • | • | • |
| 2. Oil Filter — Change | • | • | • | • | • | • | • | • | • | • | • |
| 3. Air Filter — Replace | | | | • | | | | • | | | |
| 4. Spark Plugs — Replace[1] | | | | • | | | | • | | | |
| 5. Fuel Filter — Replace | | | | • | | | | • | | | |
| 6. Transaxle Fluid — Check | • | • | • | • | • | • | • | • | • | • | • |
| — Replace | | | | • | | | | • | | | |

INSPECTION AND SERVICE SHOULD ALSO BE PERFORMED ANYTIME A MALFUNCTION IS OBSERVED OR SUSPECTED. RETAIN ALL RECEIPTS.

[1]**Required EPA Designated Emission-Related Maintenance Item.**

NOTE: For mileage beyond that indicated on the charts, you should continue to have maintenance services performed every 7 months or 7,500 miles (12 000 km).

Recommended Vehicle Maintenance

| Miles (Thousands) | 7.5 | 15 | 22.5 | 30 | 37.5 | 45 | 52.5 | 60 | 67.5 | 75 | 82.5 |
|---|---|---|---|---|---|---|---|---|---|---|---|
| Kilometers (Thousands) | 12 | 24 | 36 | 48 | 60 | 72 | 84 | 96 | 108 | 120 | 132 |
| 7. Differential Fluid — Check | | | | • | | | | • | | | |
| 8. Cooling System — Change | | | | • | | | | • | | | |
| 9. Drive Belts | | •[2] | | • | | •[2] | | • | | | |
| 10. Hoses & Connections | | • | | • | | • | | • | | • | |
| 11. Front End, Suspension, Steering | | • | | • | | • | | • | | • | |
| 12. Brakes | | • | | • | | • | | • | | | |
| 13. Body Components | | | | • | | | | • | | | |
| 14. Battery | | | | • | | | | • | | | |
| 15. Ignition System — Inspect | | | | • | | | | • | | | |
| 16. Evaporative System — Inspect | | | | • | | | | • | | | |

INSPECTION AND SERVICE SHOULD ALSO BE PERFORMED ANYTIME A MALFUNCTION IS OBSERVED OR SUSPECTED. RETAIN ALL RECEIPTS.

[2]Except with 2.5L engine.

NOTE: For mileage beyond that indicated on the charts, you should continue to have maintenance services performed every 7 months or 7,500 miles (12 000 km).

## 1990–92 MONACO & PREMIER

**SCHEDULED MAINTENANCE** FOR EMISSION CONTROL AND VEHICLE PERFORMANCE. Inspection and service should be performed when malfunction is suspected.

| SERVICE – Kilometers x 1000 | 12 | 24 | 36 | 48 | 60 | 72 |
|---|---|---|---|---|---|---|
| – Miles x 1000 | 7.5 | 15 | 22.5 | 30 | 37.5 | 45 |
| CHANGE ENGINE OIL 12 Months or | X | X | X | X | X | X |
| REPLACE ENGINE OIL FILTER | X | X | X | X | X | X |
| INSPECT ENGINE AIR FILTER | | X | | X | | X |
| REPLACE SPARK PLUGS (mileage only) | | | | X | | |
| INSPECT DRIVE BELTS (service as required) | | X | | X | | X |

| GENERAL MAINTENANCE | | | | | | |
|---|---|---|---|---|---|---|
| INSPECT BRAKE LININGS<br>All wheels - service as required | | | X | | | X |
| GREASE TIE ROD ENDS at 3 years or | | | | X | | |
| GREASE BALL JOINTS AT 3 years or | | | | X | | |
| INSPECT DRIVE SHAFT BOOTS for leaks | X | X | X | X | X | X |
| INSPECT BRAKE HOSES at every oil change and whenever brakes are serviced | | | | | | |
| INSPECT COOLING SYSTEM every 12 months | | | | | | |
| FLUSH AND WINTERIZE COOLING SYSTEM every 30 months or 48,000 km (30,000 miles) | | | | | | |
| INSPECT AND LUBRICATE REAR WHEEL BEARINGS | | | X | | | X |

**SEVERE SERVICE MAINTENANCE** driving in stop/go conditions, long idling periods, frequent short trips, operating at sustained high speeds in temperatures above 32°C (90°F).

| Kilometers x 1000 | 4.8 | 9.6 | 14 | 19 | 24 | 29 | 34 | 38 | 43 | 48 | 53 | 58 | 62 | 67 | 72 | 77 |
|---|---|---|---|---|---|---|---|---|---|---|---|---|---|---|---|---|
| Mileage x 1000 | 3 | 6 | 9 | 12 | 15 | 18 | 21 | 24 | 27 | 30 | 33 | 36 | 39 | 42 | 45 | 48 |
| CHANGE OIL[1] 6 months | X | X | X | X | X | X | X | X | X | X | X | X | X | X | X | X |
| REPLACE OIL FILTER | X | | X | | X | | X | | X | | X | | X | | X | |
| REPLACE AIR FILTER<br>Inspect and replace if required | | | | | X | | | | | X | | | | | X | |
| INSPECT BALL JOINTS | X | X | X | X | X | X | X | X | X | X | X | X | X | X | X | X |
| INSPECT CV JOINTS | X | X | X | X | X | X | X | X | X | X | X | X | X | X | X | X |
| CHANGE TRANS FLUID<br>Adjust bands at time of fluid and filter change | | | | | X | | | | | X | | | | | X | |
| LUBRICATE TIE ROD ENDS<br>Every 18 months or mileage specified | | | | | X | | | | | X | | | | | X | |
| INSPECT BRAKE LININGS<br>All wheels - replace as necessary | | | X | | | X | | | X | | | X | | | X | |

[1]Three months if SG service engine oil is used.

## STEALTH

### SCHEDULED MAINTENANCE SERVICES FOR EMISSION CONTROL AND PROPER VEHICLE PERFORMANCE

Inspection and services should be performed any time a malfunction is observed or suspected. Retain receipts for all vehicle emission services to protect your emission warranty.

| No. | Emission Control System Maintenance | Service Intervals | | Kilometers in Thousands | 24 | 48 | 72 | 80 | 96 |
|---|---|---|---|---|---|---|---|---|---|
| | | | | Mileage in Thousands | 15 | 30 | 45 | 50 | 60 |
| 1 | Check Fuel System (Tank, Line and Connections and Fuel Filler Cap) for Leaks Every 5 Years | | | or | | | | X | |
| 2 | Check Fuel Hoses for Leaks or Damage Every 2 Years | | | or | | X | | | X |
| 3 | Replace Air Cleaner Element | | | at | | X | | | X |
| 4 | Replace Spark Plugs | at | SOHC | | | X | | | X |
| | | | DOHC | | | | | | X |

### GENERAL MAINTENANCE SERVICE FOR PROPER VEHICLE PERFORMANCE

| No. | General Maintenance | | Service Intervals | Kilometers in Thousands | 24 | 48 | 72 | 80 | 96 |
|---|---|---|---|---|---|---|---|---|---|
| | | | | Mileage in Thousands | 15 | 30 | 45 | 50 | 60 |
| 5 | Timing Belt | | Replace | at | | | | | X |
| 6 | Drive Belt (for Alternator) | | Inspect for Tension | at | | X | | | X |
| 7 | Engine Oil | Non-Turbo | Change Every Year | or | Every 12,000 km (7,500 miles) | | | | |
| | | Turbo | Change Every 6 Months | | Every 8,000 km (5,000 miles) | | | | |
| 8 | Engine Oil Filter | Non-Turbo | Change Every Year | or | X | X | X | | X |
| | | Turbo | Change Every Year | | Every 16,000 km (10,000 miles) | | | | |
| 9 | Manual Transaxle Oil | | Inspect Oil Level | at | | X | | | X |
| 10 | Automatic Transaxle Fluid | | Inspect Fluid Level Every Year | or | X | X | X | | X |
| | | | Change Fluid | at | | X | | | X |
| 11 | Engine Coolant | | Replace Every 2 Years | or | | X | | | X |
| 12 | Disc Brake Pads | | Inspect for Wear Every Year | or | X | X | X | | X |
| 13 | Brake Hoses | | Check for Deterioration or Leaks Every Year | or | X | X | X | | X |
| 14 | Ball Joint and Steering Linkage Seals | | Inspect for Grease Leaks and Damage Every 2 Years | or | | X | | | X |
| 15 | Drive Shaft Boots | | Inspect for Grease Leaks and Damage Every Year | or | X | X | X | | X |
| 16 | Rear Axle <AWD> | With LSD | Change Oil | | | X | | | X |
| | | Without LSD | Inspect Oil Level | | | X | | | X |
| 17 | Exhaust System (Connection Portion of Muffler, Pipings and Converter Heat Shields) | | Check and Service as Required Every 2 Years | or | | X | | | X |

NOTE
LSD: Limited-slip differential

## SCHEDULED MAINTENANCE UNDER SEVERE USAGE CONDITIONS

The maintenance items should be performed according to the following table:

| Maintenance Item | Service to be Performed | Mileage Intervals Kilometers in Thousands (Miles in Thousands) | | | | | | | | | Severe Usage Conditions | | | | | | |
|---|---|---|---|---|---|---|---|---|---|---|---|---|---|---|---|---|---|
| | | 12 (7.5) | 24 (15) | 36 (22.5) | 48 (30) | 60 (37.5) | 72 (45) | 80 (50) | 84 (52.5) | 96 (60) | A | B | C | D | E | F | G |
| Air Cleaner Element | Replace | More Frequently | | | | | | | | | X | | | | X | | |
| Spark Plugs | Replace | | X | | X | | X | | | X | | X | | X | | | |
| Engine Oil | Change Every 3 Months or | Every 4,800 Km (3,000 Miles) | | | | | | | | | X | X | X | X | | | X |
| Engine Oil Filter | Replace Every 6 Months or | Every 9,600 Km (6,000 Miles) | | | | | | | | | X | X | X | X | | | X |
| Disc Brake Pads | Inspect for Wear | More Frequently | | | | | | | | | X | | | | | X | |

Severe usage conditions

- A Driving in dusty conditions
- B Police, taxi, or commercial type operation
- C Extensive idling
- D Short trip operation at freezing temperatures (engine not thoroughly warmed up)
- E Driving in sandy areas
- F Driving in salty areas
- G More than 50% operation in heavy city traffic during hot weather above 32°C (90°F)

# 1991–92 FRONT WHEEL DRIVE EXCEPT COLT, COLT VISTA, LASER, MONACO, PREMIER, STEALTH, SUMMIT & TALON

**SCHEDULED MAINTENANCE** FOR EMISSION CONTROL AND VEHICLE PERFORMANCE. Inspection and service should be performed when malfunction is suspected.

| SERVICE – km x 100 | 12 | 24 | 36 | 48 | 60 | 72 |
|---|---|---|---|---|---|---|
| – Miles x 1000 | 7.5 | 15 | 22.5 | 30 | 37.5 | 45 |
| CHANGE ENGINE OIL Every 6 Months* | X | X | X | X | X | X |
| REPLACE ENGINE OIL FILTER** | X | | X | | X | |
| INSPEGT ENGINE AIR FILTER | | X | | X | | X |
| REPLACE SPARK PLUGS, Mileage Only | | | | X | | |
| INSPECT DRIVE BELTS, Service As Required | | X | | X | | X |
| DRIVER SUPPLEMENTAL AIRBAG SYSTEM — INSPECT EVERY 3 YEARS OR 48,000 km (30,000 MILES). CORRECT AS NECESSARY: · SYSTEM COMPONENTS FOR DAMAGE OR DETERIORATION · DIAGNOSTIC UNIT FOR STORED MALFUNCTION MESSAGES · READINESS INDICATOR (**AIRBAG** LAMP) FUNCTION | | | | X | | |

* 4,800 km (3,000 miles) or 3 months if SG service engine oil is used in a turbocharged engine.
** If mileage is less than 12,000 km (7,500 miles), change filter at every oil change.

| **GENERAL MAINTENANCE** | | | | | | |
|---|---|---|---|---|---|---|
| INSPECT BRAKE LININGS of All Wheels; Service as Required | | | X | | | X |
| GREASE TIE ROD ENDS at 3 Years or | | | | X | | |
| GREASE BALL JOINTS at 3 Years or | | | | X | | |
| INSPECT DRIVE SHAFT BOOTS for Leaks | X | X | X | X | X | X |
| INSPECT BRAKE HOSES at Every Oil Change and Whenever Brakes are Serviced | | | | | | |
| INSPECT COOLING SYSTEM Every 12 Months | | | | | | |
| FLUSH AND WINTERIZE COOLING SYSTEM Every 36 Months or 83,000 km (52,000 miles) | | | | | | |
| INSPECT AND LUBRICATE REAR WHEEL BEARINGS | | | X | | | X |
| TIRE ROTATION at | X | 24,000 km (15,000 miles) Thereafter | | | | |

**SEVERE SERVICE MAINTENANCE**: Driving in Stop/Go Conditions, Long Idling Periods, Frequent Short Trips, Operating at Sustained High Speeds in Temperatures Above 32°C (90°F).

| km x 1000 | 4.8 | 9.6 | 14 | 19 | 24 | 29 | 34 | 38 | 43 | 48 | 53 | 58 | 62 | 67 | 72 | 77 |
|---|---|---|---|---|---|---|---|---|---|---|---|---|---|---|---|---|
| Miles x 1000 | 3 | 6 | 9 | 12 | 15 | 18 | 21 | 24 | 27 | 30 | 33 | 36 | 39 | 42 | 45 | 48 |
| CHANGE OIL***-6 Months | X | X | X | X | X | X | X | X | X | X | X | X | X | X | X | X |
| REPLACE OIL FILTER | X | | X | | X | | X | | X | | X | | X | | X | |
| REPLACE AIR FILTER; Inspect and Replace if Required | | | | | X | | | | | X | | | | | X | |
| INSPECT BALL JOINTS | X | X | X | X | X | X | X | X | X | X | X | X | X | X | X | X |
| INSPECT CV JOINTS | X | X | X | X | X | X | X | X | X | X | X | X | X | X | X | X |
| CHANGE TRANSMISSION FLUID; Adjust Bands at Time of Fluid and Filter Change | | | | | X | | | | | X | | | | | X | |
| LUBRICATE TIE ROD ENDS Every 18 Months or Mileage Specified | | | | | X | | | | | X | | | | | X | |
| INSPECT BRAKE LININGS of All Wheels; Replace as Required | | | X | | | X | | | X | | | X | | | X | |

*** 3 months if SG service engine oil is used.

# Ford Motor Co.

## INDEX



## TEMPO, TOPAZ & 1989–90 Escort

### NORMAL SERVICE MAINTENANCE

| SERVICE INTERVAL Perform at the months or distances shown, whichever comes first. Miles x 1000 | 3 | 6 | 9 | 12 | 15 | 18 | 21 | 24 | 27 | 30 | 33 | 36 | 39 | 42 | 45 | 48 | 51 | 54 | 57 | 60 |
|---|---|---|---|---|---|---|---|---|---|---|---|---|---|---|---|---|---|---|---|---|
| Kilometers x 1000 | 4.8 | 9.6 | 14.4 | 19.2 | 24 | 28.8 | 33.6 | 38.4 | 43.2 | 48 | 52.8 | 57.6 | 62.4 | 67.2 | 72 | 76.8 | 81.6 | 86.4 | 91.2 | 96 |
| **EMISSION CONTROL SERVICE** | | | | | | | | | | | | | | | | | | | | |
| Change Engine Oil and Oil Filter (every 3 months) or | X | X | X | X | X | X | X | X | X | X | X | X | X | X | X | X | X | X | X | X |
| Spark Plugs: Replace | | | | | | | | | | X | | | | | | | | | | |
| Inspect Accessory Drive Belt(s) | | | | | | | | | | X | | | | | | | | | | X |
| Replace Air Cleaner Filter① | | | | | | | | | | X | | | | | | | | | | X |
| Replace Crankcase Emission Filter① | | | | | | | | | | X | | | | | | | | | | X |
| Replace Engine Coolant, (every 36 months) or | | | | | | | | | | X | | | | | | | | | | X |
| Check Engine Coolant Protection, Hoses and Clamps | ANNUALLY | | | | | | | | | | | | | | | | | | | |
| **GENERAL MAINTENANCE** | | | | | | | | | | | | | | | | | | | | |
| Inspect Exhaust Heat Shields | | | | | | | | | | X | | | | | | | | | | X |
| Change Automatic Transaxle Fluid② | | | | | | | | | | X | | | | | | | | | | X |
| Inspect Disc Brake Pads and Rotors (Front)③ | | | | | | | | | | X | | | | | | | | | | X |
| Inspect Brake Linings and Drums (Rear)③ | | | | | | | | | | X | | | | | | | | | | X |
| Inspect and Repack Rear Wheel Bearings④ | | | | | | | | | | X | | | | | | | | | | X |

① If operating in severe dust, more frequent intervals may be required — consult your dealer.

② Change automatic transaxle fluid if your driving habits frequently include one or more of the following conditions:
- Operation during HOT WEATHER (above 32°C (90°F)).
- Towing a trailer or using a car top carrier.
- Police, taxi or door-to-door delivery service.

③ If your driving includes continuous stop and go driving or driving in mountainous areas, more frequent intervals may be required.

④ Replace rear wheel bearings at 100,000 miles (160,930 km).

### SEVERE SERVICE MAINTENANCE

| SERVICE INTERVALS Perform at the months or distances shown, whichever comes first. Miles x 1000 | 7.5 | 15 | 22.5 | 30 | 37.5 | 45 | 52.5 | 60 |
|---|---|---|---|---|---|---|---|---|
| Kilometers x 1000 | 12 | 24 | 36 | 48 | 60 | 72 | 84 | 96 |
| **EMISSIONS CONTROL SERVICE** | | | | | | | | |
| Change Engine Oil and Oil Filter (Every 6 Months) or 7500 miles whichever occurs first | X | X | X | X | X | X | X | X |
| Replace Spark Plugs | | | | X | | | | X |
| Change crankcase emission filter | | | | X | | | | X |
| Inspect Accessory Drive Belt(s) | | | | X | | | | X |
| Replace Air Cleaner Filter① | | | | X① | | | | X① |
| Change Engine Coolant Every 36 Months or | | | | X | | | | X |
| Check Engine Coolant Protection, Hoses and Clamps | ANNUALLY | | | | | | | |
| **GENERAL MAINTENANCE** | | | | | | | | |
| Check Exhaust Heat Shields | | | | X | | | | X |
| Inspect Disc Brake Pads and Rotors (Front)② | | | | X② | | | | X② |
| Inspect Brake Linings and Drums (Rear)② | | | | X② | | | | X② |
| Inspect and Repack Rear Wheel Bearing③ | | | | X③ | | | | X③ |

①If operating in severe dust, more frequent intervals may be required. Consult your dealer.
②If your driving includes continuous stop-and-go driving or driving in mountainous areas, more frequent intervals may be required.
③Replace rear wheel bearings at 100,000 miles (160,930 km).

# CONTINENTAL

## NORMAL SERVICE MAINTENANCE

| SERVICE INTERVALS Perform at the months or distances shown, whichever comes first. Miles x 1000 / Kilometers x 1000 | 7.5 / 12 | 15 / 24 | 22.5 / 36 | 30 / 48 | 37.5 / 60 | 45 / 72 | 52.5 / 84 | 60 / 96 |
|---|---|---|---|---|---|---|---|---|
| **EMISSIONS CONTROL SERVICE** | | | | | | | | |
| Replace Engine Oil and Oil Filter Every 6 Months OR | X | X | X | X | X | X | X | X |
| Replace Spark Plugs | | | | X | | | | X |
| Replace Crankcase Filter① | | | | X | | | | X |
| Inspect Accessory Drive Belt(s) | | | | X | | | | X |
| Replace Air Cleaner Filter① | | | | X | | | | X |
| Replace Engine Coolant Every 36 Months OR | | | | X | | | | X |
| Check Engine Coolant Protection, Hoses and Clamps | ANNUALLY | | | | | | | |
| **GENERAL MAINTENANCE** | | | | | | | | |
| Check Exhaust Heat Shields | | | | X | | | | X |
| Inspect Disc Brake Pads and Rotors (Front and Rear) | | | | X② | | | | X② |
| Inspect and Repack Rear Wheel Bearing | | | | X | | | | X |
| Rotate Tires | X | | X | | X | | X | |

① If operating in severe dust, more frequent intervals may be required. Consult your dealer.

② If your driving includes continuous stop-and-go driving or driving in mountainous areas, more frequent intervals may be required.

X All items designated by an X must be performed in all states.

## SEVERE SERVICE MAINTENANCE

| SERVICE INTERVAL Perform at the months or distances shown, whichever comes first. Miles x 1000 / Kilometers x 1000 | 3 / 4.8 | 6 / 9.6 | 9 / 14.4 | 12 / 19.2 | 15 / 24 | 18 / 28.8 | 21 / 33.6 | 24 / 38.4 | 27 / 43.2 | 30 / 48 | 33 / 52.8 | 36 / 57.6 | 39 / 62.4 | 42 / 67.2 | 45 / 72 | 48 / 76.8 | 51 / 81.6 | 54 / 86.4 | 57 / 91.2 | 60 / 96 |
|---|---|---|---|---|---|---|---|---|---|---|---|---|---|---|---|---|---|---|---|---|
| **EMISSION CONTROL SERVICE** | | | | | | | | | | | | | | | | | | | | |
| Replace Engine Oil and Oil Filter Every 3 months OR | X | X | X | X | X | X | X | X | X | X | X | X | X | X | X | X | X | X | X | X |
| Replace Spark Plugs | | | | | | | | | | X | | | | | | | | | | X |
| Inspect Accessory Drive Belt(s) | | | | | | | | | | X | | | | | | | | | | X |
| Replace Air Cleaner Filter ① | | | | | | | | | | X | | | | | | | | | | X |
| Replace Crankcase Filter ① | | | | | | | | | | X | | | | | | | | | | X |
| Replace Engine Coolant Every 36 Months OR | | | | | | | | | | X | | | | | | | | | | X |
| Check Engine Coolant Protection, Hoses and Clamps | ANNUALLY | | | | | | | | | | | | | | | | | | | |
| **GENERAL MAINTENANCE** | | | | | | | | | | | | | | | | | | | | |
| Inspect Exhaust Heat Shields | | | | | | | | | | X | | | | | | | | | | X |
| Change Automatic Transaxle Fluid ② | | | | | | | | | | ② | | | | | | | | | | ② |
| Inspect Disc Brake Pads and Rotors Front and Rear | | | | | | | | | | X③ | | | | | | | | | | X③ |
| Inspect and Repack Rear Wheel Bearings | | | | | | | | | | X | | | | | | | | | | X |
| Rotate Tires | | X | | | | | X | | | | | X | | | | | X | | | |

① If operating in severe dust, more frequent intervals may be required — consult your dealer.

② Change automatic transaxle fluid if your driving habits frequently include one or more of the following conditions:
- Operation during HOT WEATHER (above 32°C (90°F)).
- Towing a trailer or using a car top carrier.
- Police, taxi or door-to-door delivery service.

③ If your driving includes continuous stop and go driving or driving in mountainous areas, more frequent intervals may be required.

X All items designated by an X must be performed in all states.

## COUGAR & THUNDERBIRD

### NORMAL SERVICE MAINTENANCE

| SERVICE INTERVALS Perform at the months or distances shown, whichever comes first. Miles x 1000 | 7.5 | 15 | 22.5 | 30 | 37.5 | 45 | 52.5 | 60 |
|---|---|---|---|---|---|---|---|---|
| Kilometers x 1000 | 12 | 24 | 36 | 48 | 60 | 72 | 84 | 96 |
| **EMISSIONS CONTROL SERVICE** | | | | | | | | |
| Supercharged Engines — Change Oil and Filter | As Indicated by the Vehicle Maintenance Monitor, But Not Beyond Every 5,000 Miles (8 000 km) or 6 Months, Whichever Comes First | | | | | | | |
| Replace Engine Oil and Oil Filter As Indicated by the Vehicle Maintenance Monitor (if equipped), But Not Beyond Every 6 Months or 7,500 Miles Whichever Occurs First — Except Supercharged | X | X | X | X | X | X | X | X |
| Replace Spark Plugs — Except Supercharged | | | | X | | | | X |
| Replace Spark Plugs — Platinum Type Supercharged | | | | | | | | X |
| Check Supercharger Lubricant | | | | X | | | | X |
| Replace Crankcase Emission Filter① | | | | X | | | | X |
| Inspect Accessory Drive Belt(s) | | | | X | | | | X |
| Replace Air Cleaner Filter① | | | | X | | | | X |
| Replace Engine Coolant Every 36 Months OR | | | | X | | | | X |
| Check Engine Coolant Protection, Hoses and Clamps | ANNUALLY | | | | | | | |
| **GENERAL MAINTENANCE** | | | | | | | | |
| Check Exhaust Heat Shields | | | | X | | | | X |
| Inspect Disc Brake Pads and Rotors (Front and Rear Super Coupe/XR7)② | | | | X | | | | X |
| Inspect Brake Linings and Drums (Rear)② | | | | X | | | | X |
| Rotate Tires | X | | X | | X | | X | |

① If operating in severe dust, more frequent intervals may be required. Consult your dealer.
② If your driving includes continuous stop-and-go driving or driving in mountainous areas, more frequent intervals may be required.

### SEVERE SERVICE MAINTENANCE

| SERVICE INTERVAL Perform at the months or distances shown, Miles x 1000 | 3 | 6 | 9 | 12 | 15 | 18 | 21 | 24 | 27 | 30 | 33 | 36 | 39 | 42 | 45 | 48 | 51 | 54 | 57 | 60 |
|---|---|---|---|---|---|---|---|---|---|---|---|---|---|---|---|---|---|---|---|---|
| whichever comes first. Kilometers x 1000 | 4.8 | 9.6 | 14.4 | 19.2 | 24 | 28.8 | 33.6 | 38.4 | 43.2 | 48 | 52.8 | 57.6 | 62.4 | 67.2 | 72 | 76.8 | 81.6 | 86.4 | 91.2 | 96 |
| **EMISSION CONTROL SERVICE** | | | | | | | | | | | | | | | | | | | | |
| Replace Engine Oil and Oil Filter Every 3 Months OR | X | X | X | X | X | X | X | X | X | X | X | X | X | X | X | X | X | X | X | X |
| Replace Spark Plugs | | | | | | | | | | X | | | | | | | | | | X |
| Replace Spark Plugs (Supercharged use Platinum Type) | | | | | | | | | | | | | | | | | | | | X |
| Check Supercharger Lubricant | | | | | | | | | | X | | | | | | | | | | X |
| Inspect Accessory Drive Belt(s) | | | | | | | | | | X | | | | | | | | | | X |
| Replace Air Cleaner Filter① | | | | | | | | | | X | | | | | | | | | | X |
| Replace Engine Coolant, EVERY 36 Months OR | | | | | | | | | | X | | | | | | | | | | X |
| Check Engine Coolant Protection, Hoses and Clamps | ANNUALLY | | | | | | | | | | | | | | | | | | | |
| **GENERAL MAINTENANCE** | | | | | | | | | | | | | | | | | | | | |
| Inspect Exhaust Heat Shields | | | | | | | | | | X | | | | | | | | | | X |
| Change Automatic Transmission Fluid② | | | | | | | | | | X | | | | | | | | | | X |
| Inspect Brake Pads and Rotors (front)③ (Front and Rear — Super Coupe/XR7)③ | | | | | | | | | | X | | | | | | | | | | X |
| Inspect Brake Linings and Drums (Rear)③ | | | | | | | | | | X | | | | | | | | | | X |
| Rotate Tires | | X | | | | | X | | | | | X | | | | | X | | | |

① If operating in severe dust, more frequent intervals may be required. Consult your dealer.
② Change automatic transmission fluid if your driving habits frequently include one or more of the following conditions:
- Operation during hot weather (above 32°C (90°F)) carrying heavy loads and in hilly terrain.
- Towing a trailer or using a car top carrier.
- Police, taxi or door-to-door delivery service.
- Vehicle accumulates 5,000 miles (8 000 km) or more per month or is used in CONTINUOUS stop-and-go service.

③ If your driving includes continuous stop-and-go driving or driving in mountainous areas, more frequent intervals may be required.
X All items designated by an X must be performed in all states.

# CROWN VICTORIA, GRAND MARQUIS & TOWN CAR

## NORMAL SERVICE MAINTENANCE

| SERVICE INTERVALS Perform at the months or distances shown, whichever comes first. Miles x 1000 / Kilometers x 1000 | 7.5 / 12 | 15 / 24 | 22.5 / 36 | 30 / 48 | 37.5 / 60 | 45 / 72 | 52.5 / 84 | 60 / 96 |
|---|---|---|---|---|---|---|---|---|
| **EMISSIONS CONTROL SERVICE** | | | | | | | | |
| Replace Engine Oil and Filter (Every 6 Months) OR 7,500 Miles Whichever Occurs First | X | X | X | X | X | X | X | X |
| Replace Spark Plugs | | | | X | | | | X |
| Replace Crankcase Emission Filter① | | | | X | | | | X |
| Inspect Accessory Drive Belt(s) | | | | X | | | | X |
| Replace Air Cleaner Filter① | | | | X | | | | X |
| Replace PCV Valve and Crankcase Emission Filter — 5.0L Engine | | (X) | | (X) | | (X) | | X |
| Check/Clean Choke Linkage (5.8L only) | | | | X | | | | X |
| Change Engine Coolant Every 36 Months OR | | | | X | | | | X |
| Check Engine Coolant Protection, Hoses and Clamps | ANNUALLY | | | | | | | |
| **GENERAL MAINTENANCE** | | | | | | | | |
| Check Exhaust Heat Shields | | | | X | | | | X |
| Lube Suspension (Lincoln) | | X③ | | X | | X③ | | X |
| Lubricate Steering Linkage (Lincoln) | | X | | X | | X | | X |
| Inspect Disc Brake Pads and Rotors (Front)② | | | | X | | | | X |
| Inspect Brake Linings and Drums (Rear)② | | | | X | | | | X |
| Inspect and Repack Front Wheel Bearings | | | | X | | | | X |
| Rotate Tires | X | | X | | X | | | X |

① If operating in severe dust, more frequent intervals may be required. Consult your dealer.
② If your driving includes continuous stop-and-go driving or driving in mountainous areas, more frequent intervals may be required.
③ All vehicles except Lincoln Town Car.
X All items designated by an X must be performed in all states.
(X) This item not required to be performed, however, Ford recommends that you also perform maintenance on items designated by an (X) in order to achieve best vehicle operation. Failure to perform this recommended maintenance will not invalidate the vehicle emissions warranty or manufacturer recall liability.

## SEVERE SERVICE MAINTENANCE

| SERVICE INTERVAL Perform at the months or distances shown, whichever comes first. Miles × 1000 / Kilometers × 1000 | 3 / 4.8 | 6 / 9.6 | 9 / 14.4 | 12 / 19.2 | 15 / 24 | 18 / 28.8 | 21 / 33.6 | 24 / 38.4 | 27 / 43.2 | 30 / 48 | 33 / 52.8 | 36 / 57.6 | 39 / 62.4 | 42 / 67.2 | 45 / 72 | 48 / 76.8 | 51 / 81.6 | 54 / 86.4 | 57 / 91.2 | 60 / 96 |
|---|---|---|---|---|---|---|---|---|---|---|---|---|---|---|---|---|---|---|---|---|
| **EMISSION CONTROL SERVICE** | | | | | | | | | | | | | | | | | | | | |
| Replace Engine Oil and Oil Filter Every 3 Months OR | X | X | X | X | X | X | X | X | X | X | X | X | X | X | X | X | X | X | X | X |
| Replace Spark Plugs | | | | | | | | | | X | | | | | | | | | | X |
| Inspect Accessory Drive Belt(s) | | | | | | | | | | X | | | | | | | | | | X |
| Replace PCV Valve and Crankcase Emission Filter (5.0L Engine) | | | | | (X) | | | | | (X) | | | | | (X) | | | | | |
| Replace Air Cleaner Filter① | | | | | | | | | | X | | | | | | | | | | X |
| Replace Crankcase Emission Filter① (5.8L Engine) | | | | | | | | | | X | | | | | | | | | | X |
| Check/Clean Choke Linkage (5.8L Engine) | | | | | | | | | | X | | | | | | | | | | X |
| Replace Engine Coolant, EVERY 36 Months OR | | | | | | | | | | X | | | | | | | | | | X |
| Check Engine Coolant Protection, Hoses and Clamps | ANNUALLY | | | | | | | | | | | | | | | | | | | |
| **GENERAL MAINTENANCE** | | | | | | | | | | | | | | | | | | | | |
| Inspect Exhaust Heat Shields | | | | | | | | | | X | | | | | | | | | | X |
| Change Automatic Transmission Fluid② | | | | | | | | | | X | | | | | | | | | | X |
| Lubricate Suspension (Lincoln) | | | | | | | | | | X | | | | | | | | | | X |
| Lubricate Steering Linkage (Lincoln) | | | | | X | | | | | X | | | | | X | | | | | X |
| Inspect Disc Brake Pads and Rotors③ | | | | | | | | | | X | | | | | | | | | | X |
| Inspect Brake Linings and Drums (Rear) (Lincoln)③ | | | | | | | | | | X | | | | | | | | | | X |
| Inspect and Repack Front Wheel Bearings | | | | | | | | | | X | | | | | | | | | | X |
| Rotate Tires | | X | | | | | X | | | | | X | | | | | X | | | |

① If operating in severe dust, more frequent intervals may be required. Consult your dealer.
② Change automatic transmission fluid if your driving habits frequently include one or more of the following conditions:
- Operation during hot weather (above 32°C (90°F)) carrying heavy loads and in hilly terrain.
- Towing a trailer or using a car top carrrier.
- Police, taxi or door to door delivery service.

③ If your driving includes continuous stop-and-go driving or driving in mountainous areas, more frequent intervals may be required.
X All items designated by an X must be performed in all states.
(X) This item not required to be performed, however, Ford recommends that you also perform maintenance on items designated by an (X) in order to achieve best vehicle operation. Failure to perform this recommended maintenance will not invalidate the vehicle emissions warranty or manufacturer recall liability.

# FESTIVA

## NORMAL SERVICE MAINTENANCE

| MILES × (1000) | 7.5 | 15.0 | 22.5 | 30.0 | 37.5 | 45.0 | 52.5 | 60.0 |
|---|---|---|---|---|---|---|---|---|
| KILOMETERS × (1000) | 12 | 24 | 36 | 48 | 60 | 72 | 84 | 96 |
| **EMISSION CONTROL SERVICE** | | | | | | | | |
| Change Engine Oil (whichever occurs first) Every 6 Months or | X | X | X | X | X | X | X | X |
| Change Engine Oil Filter (whichever occurs first) Every 6 Months or | X | X | X | X | X | X | X | X |
| Spark Plugs: Inspect/Clean | | (2) | | | | (2) | | |
| Replace | | | | X | | | | X |
| Check Idle Speed | | X | | X | | X | | X |
| Inspect Cooling System Every 12 Months or | | X | | X | | X | | X |
| Replace Engine Coolant Every 36 Months or | | | | X | | | | X |
| Check Accessory Drive Belts | | | | X | | | | X |
| Replace Air Cleaner Element | | | | (1) | | | | (1) |
| Replace Fuel Filter | | | | X | | | | X |
| Replace Engine Timing Belt | | | | | | | | X |
| **GENERAL MAINTENANCE** | | | | | | | | |
| Inspect Brake Lines and Connections | | X | | X | | X | | X |
| Inspect Clutch Pedal | | X | | X | | X | | X |
| Inspect Front Disc Brakes | | X | | X | | X | | X |
| Inspect Drum Brakes | | | | X | | | | X |
| Inspect Safety Belts, Buckles, Retrators, & Anchors | | X | | X | | X | | X |
| Inspect Steering Linkage, Rack Guides & Tie Rod Ends | | X | | X | | X | | X |
| Tighten Bolts & Nuts on Chassis & Body | | X | | | | X | | |
| Inspect Steering Operations & Gear Housing | | | | X | | X | | X |
| Inspect Rack Seal Boots | | | | X | | | | X |
| Inspect Front Suspension Ball Joints | | | | X | | | | X |
| Inspect Drive Shaft Dust Boots | | | | X | | | | X |
| Inspect Exhaust System Heat Shield | | | | X | | | | X |
| Inspect Fuel Lines | | | | (2) | | | | X |
| Inspect Transaxle, Change Rod Boots | | | | | | X | | |
| Lubricate Front and Rear Wheel Bearings | | | | | | | | X |

(1) If operating in severe dusty conditions, ask your dealer for proper replacement interval.
(2) Recommended, but not required.

## SEVERE SERVICE MAINTENANCE

| MILES × (1000) | 3 | 6 | 9 | 12 | 15 | 18 | 21 | 24 | 27 | 30 | 33 | 36 | 39 | 42 | 45 | 48 | 51 | 54 | 57 | 60 |
|---|---|---|---|---|---|---|---|---|---|---|---|---|---|---|---|---|---|---|---|---|
| KILOMETERS × (1000) | 4.8 | 9.6 | 14. | 19. | 24. | 28. | 33. | 38. | 43. | 48. | 52. | 57. | 62. | 67. | 72. | 76. | 81. | 86. | 91. | 96. |
| **EMISSION CONTROL SERVICE** | | | | | | | | | | | | | | | | | | | | |
| Change Engine Oil (whichever occurs first) Every 3 Months or | X | X | X | X | X | X | X | X | X | X | X | X | X | X | X | X | X | X | X | X |
| Change Engine Oil Filter (whichever occurs first) Every 3 Months or | X | X | X | X | X | X | X | X | X | X | X | X | X | X | X | X | X | X | X | X |
| Spark Plugs: Inspect/Clean | | X | | X | | X | | X | | | | X | | X | | X | | X | | |
| Replace | | | | | | | | | | X | | | | | | | | | | X |
| Check Idle Speed | | | | | X | | | | | X | | | | | X | | | | | X |
| Inspect Cooling System Every 12 Months or | | | | | X | | | | | X | | | | | X | | | | | X |
| Replace Engine Coolant Every 36 Months or | | | | | | | | | | X | | | | | | | | | | X |
| Check Accessory Drive Belts | | | | | | | | | | X | | | | | | | | | | X |
| Replace Air Cleaner Element | | | | | | | | | | (1) | | | | | | | | | | (1) |
| Replace Fuel Filter | | | | | | | | | | X | | | | | | | | | | X |
| Replace Engine Timing Belt | | | | | | | | | | | | | | | | | | | | X |
| **GENERAL MAINTENANCE** | | | | | | | | | | | | | | | | | | | | |
| Inspect Brake Lines, Connections & Hoses | | | | | X | | | | | X | | | | | X | | | | | X |
| Inspect, Adjust Clutch Pedal | | | | | X | | | | | X | | | | | X | | | | | X |
| Inspect Front Disc Brakes | | | | | X | | | | | X | | | | | X | | | | | X |
| Inspect Rear Drum Brakes | | | | | | | | | | X | | | | | | | | | | X |
| Inspect Safety Belts, Buckles, Retractors & Anchors | | | | | X | | | | | X | | | | | X | | | | | X |
| Inspect Steering Linkage, Rack Guides, & Tie Rod Ends | | | | | X | | | | | X | | | | | X | | | | | X |
| Tighten Bolts & Nuts on Chassis & Body | | | | | X | | | | | | | | | | X | | | | | |
| Inspect Steering Operations and Gear Housing | | | | | | | | | | X | | | | | X | | | | | X |
| Inspect Rack Seal Boots | | | | | | | | | | X | | | | | | | | | | X |
| Inspect Front Suspension Ball Joints | | | | | | | | | | X | | | | | | | | | | X |
| Inspect Drive Shaft Dust Boots | | | | | | | | | | X | | | | | | | | | | X |
| Inspect Exhaust System Heat Shield | | | | | | | | | | X | | | | | | | | | | X |
| Inspect Fuel Lines | | | | | | | | | | (2) | | | | | | | | | | X |
| Inspect Transaxle, Change Rod Boots | | | | | | | | | | | | | | | X | | | | | |
| Lubricate Front and Rear Wheel Bearings | | | | | | | | | | | | | | | | | | | | X |

(1) If operating in severe dusty conditions, ask your dealer for proper replacement interval.
(2) Recommended, but not required.

# MUSTANG

## NORMAL SERVICE MAINTENANCE

| SERVICE INTERVALS Perform at the months or distances shown, whichever comes first. Miles x 1000 | 7.5 | 15 | 22.5 | 30 | 37.5 | 45 | 52.5 | 60 |
|---|---|---|---|---|---|---|---|---|
| Kilometers x 1000 | 12 | 24 | 36 | 48 | 60 | 72 | 84 | 96 |
| **EMISSIONS CONTROL SERVICE** | | | | | | | | |
| Replace Engine Oil and Filter Every 6 Months OR 7,500 Miles Whichever Occurs First | X | X | X | X | X | X | X | X |
| Replace Spark Plugs | | | | X | | | | X |
| Replace Crankcase Emission Filter① | | | | X | | | | X |
| Inspect Accessory Drive Belt(s) | | | | X | | | | X |
| Replace Air Cleaner Filter① | | | | X | | | | X |
| Replace PCV Valve and Crankcase Emission Filter — 5.0L | | (X) | | (X) | | (X) | | X |
| Replace Engine Coolant Every 36 Months OR | | | | X | | | | X |
| Check Engine Coolant Protection, Hoses and Clamps | ANNUALLY | | | | | | | |
| **GENERAL MAINTENANCE** | | | | | | | | |
| Check Exhaust Heat Shields | | | | X | | | | X |
| Lube Tie Rods | | X③ | | X | | X③ | | X |
| Inspect Disc Brake Pads and Rotors② | | | | X | | | | X |
| Inspect Brake Linings and Drums (Rear)② | | | | X② | | | | X② |
| Inspect and Repack Front Wheel Bearings | | | | X | | | | X |
| Rotate Tires | X | | X | | X | | X | |

① If operating in severe dust, more frequent intervals may be required. Consult your dealer.
② If your driving includes continuous stop-and-go driving or driving in mountainous areas, more frequent intervals may be required.
③ All vehicles.
X All items designated by an X must be performed in all states.
(X) This item not required to be performed, however, Ford recommends that you also perform maintenance on items designated by an (X) in order to achieve best vehicle operation. Failure to perform this recommended maintenance will not invalidate the vehicle emissions warranty or manufacturer recall liability.

## SEVERE SERVICE MAINTENANCE

| SERVICE INTERVAL Perform at the months or distances shown, whichever comes first. Miles × 1000 | 3 | 6 | 9 | 12 | 15 | 18 | 21 | 24 | 27 | 30 | 33 | 36 | 39 | 42 | 45 | 48 | 51 | 54 | 57 | 60 |
|---|---|---|---|---|---|---|---|---|---|---|---|---|---|---|---|---|---|---|---|---|
| Kilometers × 1000 | 4.8 | 9.6 | 14.4 | 19.2 | 24 | 28.8 | 33.6 | 38.4 | 43.2 | 48 | 52.8 | 57.6 | 62.4 | 67.2 | 72 | 76.8 | 81.6 | 86.4 | 91.2 | 96 |
| **EMISSION CONTROL SERVICE** | | | | | | | | | | | | | | | | | | | | |
| Replace Engine Oil and Oil Filter Every 3 Months OR | X | X | X | X | X | X | X | X | X | X | X | X | X | X | X | X | X | X | X | X |
| Replace Spark Plugs | | | | | | | | | | X | | | | | | | | | | X |
| Inspect Accessory Drive Belt(s) | | | | | | | | | | X | | | | | | | | | | X |
| Replace PCV Valve and Crankcase Emission Filter — 5.0L | | | | | (X) | | | | | (X) | | | | | (X) | | | | | X |
| Replace Air Cleaner Filter① | | | | | | | | | | X | | | | | | | | | | X |
| Replace Engine Coolant, EVERY 36 Months OR | | | | | | | | | | X | | | | | | | | | | X |
| Check Engine Coolant Protection, Hoses and Clamps | ANNUALLY | | | | | | | | | | | | | | | | | | | |
| **GENERAL MAINTENANCE** | | | | | | | | | | | | | | | | | | | | |
| Inspect Exhaust Heat Shields | | | | | | | | | | X | | | | | | | | | | X |
| Change Automatic Transmission Fluid② | | | | | | | | | | X | | | | | | | | | | X |
| Lubricate Tie Rods | | | | | | | | | | X | | | | | | | | | | X |
| Inspect Disc Brake Pads and Rotors② | | | | | | | | | | X | | | | | | | | | | X |
| Inspect Brake Linings and Drums (Rear)③ | | | | | | | | | | X | | | | | | | | | | X |
| Inspect and Repack Front Wheel Bearings | | | | | | | | | | X | | | | | | | | | | X |
| Rotate Tires | | X | | | | | X | | | | | X | | | | | X | | | |

① If operating in severe dust, more frequent intervals may be required. Consult your dealer.
② Change automatic transmission fluid if your driving habits frequently include one or more of the following conditions:
- Operation during hot weather (above 32°C (90°F)) carrying heavy loads and in hilly terrain.
- Towing a trailer or using a car top carrrier.
- Police, taxi or door to door delivery service.

③ If your driving includes continuous stop-and-go driving or driving in mountainous areas, more frequent intervals may be required.
X All items designated by an X must be performed in all states.
(X) This item not required to be performed, however, Ford recommends that you also perform maintenance on items designated by an (X) in order to achieve best vehicle operation. Failure to perform this recommended maintenance will not invalidate the vehicle emissions warranty or manufacturer recall liability.

# PROBE

## NORMAL SERVICE MAINTENANCE

| MILES X (000) | 7.5 | 15 | 22.5 | 30.0 | 37.5 | 45.0 | 52.5 | 60.0 |
|---|---|---|---|---|---|---|---|---|
| KILOMETERS X (000) | 12 | 24 | 36 | 48 | 60 | 72 | 84 | 96 |
| **EMISSION CONTROL SERVICE** | | | | | | | | |
| Non-Turbocharged Change Engine Oil & Oil Filter | X | X | X | X | X | X | X | X |
| Turbocharged Replace Engine Oil & Oil Filter | EVERY 5,000 MILES (8,000 km) OR 6 MONTHS, WHICHEVER OCCURS FIRST | | | | | | | |
| Replace Spark Plugs: Turbocharged | | (3) | | X | | (3) | | X |
| Non-Turbocharged | | | | X | | | | X |
| Inspect Cooling System Every 12 Months or | | X | | X | | X | | X |
| Replace Engine Coolant Every 36 Months or | | | | X | | | | X |
| Inspect Accessory Drive Belts | | | | X | | | | X |
| Replace Air Cleaner Element (2) | | | | X | | | | X |
| Replace Fuel Filter | | | | | | | | X |
| Replace Engine Timing Belt (1) | | | | | | | | (1) |
| **GENERAL MAINTENANCE** | | | | | | | | |
| Inspect Brake Lines and Connections | | X | | X | | X | | X |
| Inspect Front Disc Brakes | | X | | X | | X | | X |
| Inspect Drum Brakes | | | | X | | | | X |
| Tighten Bolts & Nuts on Chassis & Body | | X | | | | X | | |
| Inspect Steering Operation & Gear Linkage | | | | X | | | | X |
| Inspect Front Suspension Ball Joints | | | | X | | | | X |
| Inspect Driveshaft Dust Boots | | | | X | | | | X |
| Inspect Exhaust System Heat Shield | | | | X | | | | X |
| Inspect Fuel Lines | | | | (3) | | | | X |

(1) Replacement of the timing belt is required at every 60,000 miles (96,000 km). Failure to replace the timing belt may result in damage to the engine.

(2) If operating in severe dust, more frequent intervals may be required. Consult your dealer.

(3) This item not required to be performed, however, Ford recommends that you perform maintenance on this item in order to achieve best vehicle operation. Failure to perform this recommended maintenance will not invalidate the vehicle emissions warranty or manufacturer recall liability.

## SEVERE SERVICE MAINTENANCE

| MILES X (000) | 3 | 6 | 9 | 12 | 15 | 18 | 21 | 24 | 27 | 30 | 33 | 36 | 39 | 42 | 45 | 48 | 51 | 54 | 57 | 60 |
|---|---|---|---|---|---|---|---|---|---|---|---|---|---|---|---|---|---|---|---|---|
| KILOMETERS X (000) | 4.8 | 9.6 | 14. | 19. | 24. | 28. | 33. | 38. | 43. | 48. | 52. | 57. | 62. | 67. | 72. | 76. | 81. | 86. | 91. | 96. |
| **EMISSION CONTROL SERVICE** | | | | | | | | | | | | | | | | | | | | |
| Change Engine Oil & Oil Filter (whichever occurs first) Every 3 Months or | X | X | X | X | X | X | X | X | X | X | X | X | X | X | X | X | X | X | X | X |
| Replace Spark Plugs: Turbocharged | | | | | (3) | | | | | X | | | | | (3) | | | | | X |
| Non-turbocharged | | | | | | | | | | X | | | | | | | | | | X |
| Inspect Cooling System Every 12 Months or | | | | | X | | | | | X | | | | | X | | | | | X |
| Replace Engine Coolant Every 36 Months or | | | | | | | | | | X | | | | | | | | | | X |
| Inspect Accessory Drive Belts | | | | | | | | | | X | | | | | | | | | | X |
| Air Cleaner Element: Inspect/Clean | | | | | (3) | | | | | | | | | | (3) | | | | | |
| Replace (2) | | | | | | | | | | X | | | | | | | | | | X |
| Replace Fuel Filter | | | | | | | | | | | | | | | | | | | | X |
| Replace Engine Timing Belt (1) | | | | | | | | | | | | | | | | | | | | X |
| **GENERAL MAINTENANCE** | | | | | | | | | | | | | | | | | | | | |
| Inspect Brake Lines, Connections & Hoses | | | | | X | | | | | X | | | | | X | | | | | X |
| Inspect Front Disc Brakes | | | | | X | | | | | X | | | | | X | | | | | X |
| Inspect Rear Drum Brakes | | | | | | | | | | X | | | | | | | | | | X |
| Tighten Bolts & Nuts on Chassis & Body | | | | | X | | | | | | | | | | X | | | | | |
| Inspect Steering Operations and Linkage | | | | | | | | | | X | | | | | | | | | | X |
| Inspect Front Suspension Ball Joints | | | | | | | | | | X | | | | | | | | | | X |
| Inspect Drive Shaft Dust Boots | | | | | | | | | | X | | | | | | | | | | X |
| Inspect Exhaust System Heat Shield | | | | | | | | | | X | | | | | | | | | | X |
| Inspect Fuel Lines | | | | | | | | | | (3) | | | | | | | | | | X |
| Change automatic transaxle fluid | | | | | | | | | | (4) | | | | | | | | | | (4) |

(1) Replacement of the timing belt is required at every 60,000 miles (96,000 km). Failure to replace the timing belt may result in damage to the engine.

(2) If operating in severe dust, more frequent intervals may be required. Consult your dealer.

(3) This item not required to be performed, however, Ford recommends that you perform maintenance on this item in order to achieve best vehicle operation. Failure to perform this recommended maintenance will not invalidate the vehicle emissions warranty or manufacturer recall liability.

(4) Change automatic transaxle fluid if your driving habits frequently include one or more of the following conditions:
- Operation during hot weather (above 90ºF, 32ºC) carrying heavy loads and in hilly terrain.
- Towing a trailer or using a car top carrier.
- Police, taxi or door-to-door delivery service.

# SCORPIO

## NORMAL SERVICE MAINTENANCE

| SERVICE INTERVALS Perform at the months or distances shown, whichever comes first. | | | | | | | | | |
|---|---|---|---|---|---|---|---|---|---|
| | Miles x 1000 | 7.5 | 15 | 22.5 | 30 | 37.5 | 45 | 52.5 | 60 |
| | Kilometers x 1000 | 12 | 24 | 36 | 48 | 60 | 72 | 84 | 96 |
| **EMISSIONS CONTROL SERVICE** | | | | | | | | | |
| Change Engine Oil and Oil Filter (every 6 months) or | | X | X | X | X | X | X | X | X |
| Replace Spark Plugs | | | | | X | | | | X |
| Change Crankcase Filter | | | | | X | | | | X |
| Inspect Accessory Drive Belt(s) | | | | | X | | | | X |
| Replace Air Cleaner Filter① | | | | | X① | | | | X① |
| Change Engine Coolant (every 36 months) or | | | | | X | | | | X |
| Check Engine Coolant Protection, Hoses and Clamps | | ANNUALLY | | | | | | | |
| **GENERAL MAINTENANCE** | | | | | | | | | |
| Check Exhaust Heat Shields | | | | | X | | | | X |
| Inspect Disc Brake Pads and Rotors (Front)② | | | | | X② | | | | X② |
| Inspect Brake Linings and Drums (Rear)② | | | | | X② | | | | X② |
| Inspect and Repack Rear Wheel Bearing | | | | | X | | | | X |

①If operating in severe dust, more frequent intervals may be required. Consult your dealer.

②If your driving includes continuous stop-and-go driving or driving in mountainous areas, more frequent intervals may be required.

## SEVERE SERVICE MAINTENANCE

| SERVICE INTERVAL Perform at the months or distances shown, whichever comes first. | | | | | | | | | | | | | | | | | | | | | |
|---|---|---|---|---|---|---|---|---|---|---|---|---|---|---|---|---|---|---|---|---|---|
| | Miles x 1000 | 3 | 6 | 9 | 12 | 15 | 18 | 21 | 24 | 27 | 30 | 33 | 36 | 39 | 42 | 45 | 48 | 51 | 54 | 57 | 60 |
| | Kilometers x 1000 | 4.8 | 9.6 | 14.4 | 19.2 | 24 | 28.8 | 33.6 | 38.4 | 43.2 | 48 | 52.8 | 57.6 | 62.4 | 67.2 | 72 | 76.8 | 81.6 | 86.4 | 91.2 | 96 |
| **EMISSION CONTROL SERVICE** | | | | | | | | | | | | | | | | | | | | | |
| Change Engine Oil (every 3 months) or | | X | X | X | X | X | X | X | X | X | X | X | X | X | X | X | X | X | X | X | X |
| Change Engine Oil Filter (every 3 months) or | | X | X | X | X | X | X | X | X | X | X | X | X | X | X | X | X | X | X | X | X |
| Spark Plugs | | | | | | | | | | | X | | | | | | | | | | X |
| Inspect Accessory Drive Belt(s) | | | | | | | | | | | X | | | | | | | | | | X |
| Replace Air Cleaner Filter ① | | | | | | | | | | | X① | | | | | | | | | | X① |
| Replace Crankcase Filter ① | | | | | | | | | | | X① | | | | | | | | | | X① |
| Replace Engine Coolant (every 36 months) or | | | | | | | | | | | X | | | | | | | | | | X |
| Check Engine Coolant Protection, Hoses and Clamps | | ANNUALLY | | | | | | | | | | | | | | | | | | | |
| **GENERAL MAINTENANCE** | | | | | | | | | | | | | | | | | | | | | |
| Inspect Exhaust Heat Shields | | | | | | | | | | | X | | | | | | | | | | X |
| Change Automatic Transaxle Fluid ② | | | | | | | | | | | ② | | | | | | | | | | ② |
| Inspect Disc Brake Pads and Rotors (Front) | | | | | | | | | | | X③ | | | | | | | | | | X③ |
| Inspect Brake Linings and Drums ③ | | | | | | | | | | | ③ | | | | | | | | | | ③ |
| Inspect and Repack Rear Wheel Bearings | | | | | | | | | | | X | | | | | | | | | | X |

① If operating in severe dust, more frequent intervals may be required — consult your dealer.

② Change automatic transaxle fluid if your driving habits frequently include one or more of the following conditions:
- Operation during HOT WEATHER (above 32°C (90°F)).
- Towing a trailer or using a car top carrier.
- Police, taxi or door-to-door delivery service.

③ If your driving includes continuous stop and go driving or driving in mountainous areas, more frequent intervals may be required.

# TAURUS & SABLE

## NORMAL SERVICE MAINTENANCE

| SERVICE INTERVALS<br>Perform at the months or distances shown, whichever comes first. Miles x 1000 / Kilometers x 1000 | 7.5<br>12 | 15<br>24 | 22.5<br>36 | 30<br>48 | 37.5<br>60 | 45<br>72 | 52.5<br>84 | 60<br>96 |
|---|---|---|---|---|---|---|---|---|
| **EMISSIONS CONTROL SERVICE** | | | | | | | | |
| Replace Engine Oil and Oil Filter Every 6 Months OR | X | X | X | X | X | X | X | X |
| Replace Spark Plugs 2.5L, 3.0L, 3.8L | | | | X | | | | X |
| 3.0L SHO Platinum Plugs | | | | | | | | X |
| Replace Cam Belt and Adjust Valve Lash — 3.0L SHO | | | | | | | | X |
| Replace Crankcase Filter — Four Cylinder Engine Only | | | | X | | | | X |
| Inspect Accessory Drive Belt(s) | | | | X | | | | X |
| Replace Air Cleaner Filter① | | | | X | | | | X |
| Replace Engine Coolant Every 36 Months OR | | | | X | | | | X |
| Check Engine Coolant Protection, Hoses and Clamps | ANNUALLY | | | | | | | |
| **GENERAL MAINTENANCE** | | | | | | | | |
| Inspect Battery Fluid Level (SHO only) ③ | | | X | | | X | | |
| Check Exhaust Heat Shields | | | | X | | | | X |
| Inspect Disc Brake Pads and Rotors (Front) (Front and Rear — SHO) ② | | | | X② | | | | X② |
| Inspect Brake Linings and Drums (Rear)② | | | | X② | | | | X② |
| Inspect and Repack Rear Wheel Bearing | | | | X | | | | X |
| Rotate Tires | X | | X | | X | | X | |

① If operating in severe dust, more frequent intervals may be required. Consult your dealer.

② If your driving includes continuous stop-and-go driving or driving in mountainous areas, more frequent intervals may be required.

X All items designated with an "X" must be performed in all states.

③ If operating in temperatures above 32°C (90°F) check more often.

## SEVERE SERVICE MAINTENANCE

| SERVICE INTERVAL Perform at the months or distances shown, whichever comes first. Miles x 1000 | 3 | 6 | 9 | 12 | 15 | 18 | 21 | 24 | 27 | 30 | 33 | 36 | 39 | 42 | 45 | 48 | 51 | 54 | 57 | 60 |
|---|---|---|---|---|---|---|---|---|---|---|---|---|---|---|---|---|---|---|---|---|
| Kilometers x 1000 | 4.8 | 9.6 | 14.4 | 19.2 | 24 | 28.8 | 33.6 | 38.4 | 43.2 | 48 | 52.8 | 57.6 | 62.4 | 67.2 | 72 | 76.8 | 81.6 | 86.4 | 91.2 | 96 |
| **EMISSION CONTROL SERVICE** | | | | | | | | | | | | | | | | | | | | |
| Replace Engine Oil and Oil Filter Every 3 Months OR | X | X | X | X | X | X | X | X | X | X | X | X | X | X | X | X | X | X | X | X |
| Spark Plugs 3.0L SHO Platinum Plugs | | | | | | | | | | | | | | | | | | | | X |
| 2.5L, 3.0L, 3.8L | | | | | | | | | | X | | | | | | | | | | X |
| Inspect Accessory Drive Belt(s) | | | | | | | | | | X | | | | | | | | | | X |
| Replace Air Cleaner Filter ① | | | | | | | | | | X | | | | | | | | | | X |
| Replace Crankcase Filter Four Cylinder Engines Only ① | | | | | | | | | | X | | | | | | | | | | X |
| Replace Cam Belt and Adjust Valve Lash — 3.0L SHO | | | | | | | | | | | | | | | | | | | | X |
| Replace Engine Coolant Every 36 Months OR | | | | | | | | | | X | | | | | | | | | | X |
| Check Engine Coolant Protection, Hoses and Clamps | ANNUALLY | | | | | | | | | | | | | | | | | | | |
| **GENERAL MAINTENANCE** | | | | | | | | | | | | | | | | | | | | |
| Inspect Exhaust Heat Shields | | | | | | | | | | X | | | | | | | | | | X |
| Change Automatic Transaxle Fluid (2.5L, 3.0L, 3.8L) ② | | | | | | | | | | X | | | | | | | | | | X |
| Inspect Disc Brake Pads and Rotors (Front) ③ (Front and Rear — SHO) | | | | | | | | | | X | | | | | | | | | | X |
| Inspect Brake Linings and Drums ③ | | | | | | | | | | X | | | | | | | | | | X |
| Inspect Battery Fluid Level (SHO only) ④ | | | | | | | | X | | | | | | | | X | | | | |
| Inspect and Repack Rear Wheel Bearings | | | | | | | | | | X | | | | | | | | | | X |
| Rotate Tires | | X | | | | | X | | | | | X | | | | | X | | | |

① If operating in severe dust, more frequent intervals may be required — consult your dealer.

② Change automatic transaxle fluid if your driving habits frequently include one or more of the following conditions:
- Operation during HOT WEATHER (above 32°C (90°F)).
- Towing a trailer or using a car top carrier.
- Police, taxi or door-to-door delivery service.

③ If your driving includes continuous stop and go driving or driving in mountainous areas, more frequent intervals may be required.

X All items designated with an "X" must be performed in all states.

④ If operating in temperatures above 32°C (90°F) check more often.

## 1989 TRACER

## NORMAL SERVICE MAINTENANCE

| MILES × (000) | 7.5 | 15 | 22.5 | 30.0 | 37.5 | 45.0 | 52.5 | 60.0 |
|---|---|---|---|---|---|---|---|---|
| KILOMETERS × (000) | 12 | 24 | 36 | 48 | 60 | 72 | 84 | 96 |
| **EMISSION CONTROL SERVICE** | | | | | | | | |
| Change Engine Oil (whichever occurs first) Every 6 Months or | X | X | X | X | X | X | X | X |
| Change Engine Oil Filter (whichever occurs first) Every 6 months or | X | X | X | X | X | X | X | X |
| Spark Plugs: Inspect/Clean | | X | | | | X | | |
| Replace | | | | X | | | | X |
| Adjust Engine Valve Clearance | | X | | X | | X | | X |
| Inspect Cooling System Every 12 Months or | | X | | X | | X | | X |
| Replace Engine Coolant Every 36 Months or | | | | X | | | | X |
| Check Accessory Drive Belts | | | | X | | | | X |
| Replace Air Cleaner Element | | | | (1) | | | | (1) |
| Replace Fuel Filter | | | | | | | | X |
| Replace Engine Timing Belt | | | | | | | | X |
| **GENERAL MAINTENANCE** | | | | | | | | |
| Inspect Brake Lines and Connections | | X | | X | | X | | X |
| Inspect Clutch Pedal | | X | | X | | X | | X |
| Inspect Front Disc Brakes | | X | | X | | X | | X |
| Inspect Drum Brakes | | | | X | | | | X |
| Inspect Seat Belts, Buckles, Retractors, & Anchors | | X | | X | | X | | X |
| Inspect Steering Linkage, Rack Guides, & Tie Rod Ends | | X | | X | | X | | X |
| Tighten Bolts & Nuts on Chassis & Body | | X | | | | X | | |
| Inspect Steering Operations & Gear Housing | | | | X | | X | | X |
| Inspect Rack Seal Boots | | | | X | | | | X |
| Inspect Front Suspension Ball Joints | | | | X | | | | X |
| Inspect Drive Shaft Dust Boots | | | | X | | | | X |
| Inspect Exhaust System Heat Shield | | | | X | | | | X |
| Inspect Fuel Lines | | | | (2) | | | | X |
| Inspect Transaxle Change Rod Boots | | | | | | X | | |
| Lubricate Front and Rear Wheel Bearings | | | | | | | | X |
| Change Automatic Transaxle Fluid | | | | (3) | | | | (3) |

(1) If operating in severe dusty conditions, ask your dealer for proper replacement interval.

(2) Recommended, but not required.

(3) If your vehicle accumulates 5,000 miles (8,000 kilometers) or more per month, or is used in continuous stop-and-go service, change the fluid every 30,000 miles (48,000 kilometers).

# CAPRI

## NORMAL SERVICE MAINTENANCE

**CUSTOMER MAINTENANCE SCHEDULE A**

Follow this Schedule if your driving habits MAINLY include one or more of the following conditions:

- Short trips of less than 10 miles (16 km) when outside temperatures remain below freezing.
- Operating in severe dust conditions.
- Operating during hot weather, in stop-and-go "rush hour" traffic.
- Extensive idling, such as police, taxi or door-to-door delivery service.

| SERVICE INTERVAL Perform at the months or distances shown, whichever comes first. Miles x 1000 | 3 | 6 | 9 | 12 | 15 | 18 | 21 | 24 | 27 | 30 | 33 | 36 | 39 | 42 | 45 | 48 | 51 | 54 | 57 | 60 |
|---|---|---|---|---|---|---|---|---|---|---|---|---|---|---|---|---|---|---|---|---|
| Kilometers x 1000 | 4.8 | 9.6 | 14 | 19 | 24 | 28 | 33 | 38 | 43 | 48 | 52 | 57 | 62 | 67 | 72 | 76 | 81 | 86 | 91 | 96 |
| **EMISSION CONTROL SERVICE** | | | | | | | | | | | | | | | | | | | | |
| Change Engine Oil and Oil Filter (whichever occurs first) Every 3 Months or | X | X | X | X | X | X | X | X | X | X | X | X | X | X | X | X | X | X | X | X |
| Replace Spark Plugs: Turbocharged | | | | | ④ | | | | | X | | | | | ④ | | | | | X |
| Non-Turbocharged | | | | | | | | | | X | | | | | | | | | | X |
| Check Engine Coolant Protection, Hoses and Clamps | ANNUALLY | | | | | | | | | | | | | | | | | | | |
| Replace Engine Coolant Every 36 Months or | | | | | | | | | | X | | | | | | | | | | X |
| Check Accessory Drive Belts | | | | | | | | | | X | | | | | | | | | | X |
| Inspect Air Cleaner Filter | | | | | X(5) | | | | | | | | | | X(5) | | | | | |
| Replace Air Cleaner Element | | | | | | | | | | X(1) | | | | | | | | | | X(1) |
| Replace Fuel Filter | | | | | | | | | | | | | | | | | | | | X |
| Replace Engine Timing Belt | EVERY 60,000 MILES (96,000 km) | | | | | | | | | | | | | | | | | | | |
| Check Engine Idle Speed | | | | | | | | | | X(4) | | | | | | | | | | X(4) |
| **GENERAL MAINTENANCE** | | | | | | | | | | | | | | | | | | | | |
| Rotate Tires | | X | | | | | X | | | | | X | | | | | X | | | |
| Inspect Brake Lines, Connections & Hoses | | | | | | | | | | X | | | | | | | | | | X |
| Inspect Clutch Pedal Operation | | | | | | | | | | X | | | | | | | | | | X |
| Inspect Front and Rear Disc Brakes | | | | | X | | | | | X | | | | | X | | | | | X |
| Inspect Safety Belts, Buckles, Retractors & Anchors | | | | | | | | | | X | | | | | | | | | | X |
| Inspect Steering Linkage, Rack Guides & Tie Rod Ends | | | | | | | | | | X | | | | | | | | | | X |
| Tighten Bolts & Nuts on Chassis & Body | | | | | | | | | | X | | | | | | | | | | X |
| Inspect Steering Operations, Gear Housing and Rack Seal Boots | | | | | | | | | | X | | | | | X | | | | | X |
| Inspect Front Suspension Ball Joints | | | | | | | | | | X | | | | | | | | | | X |
| Inspect Half Shaft Dust Boots | | | | | | | | | | X | | | | | | | | | | X |
| Inspect Exhaust System Heat Shield | | | | | | | | | | X | | | | | | | | | | X |
| Inspect Fuel Lines | | | | | | | | | | 2 | | | | | | | | | | |
| Lubricate Rear Wheel Bearings | | | | | | | | | | X | | | | | | | | | | X |
| Change Automatic Transaxle Fluid | | | | | | | | | | 3 | | | | | | | | | | 3 |

1 If operating in severe dusty conditions, consult dealer for proper replacement interval.

2 Recommended, but not required.

3 Change automatic transaxle fluid if your driving habits frequently include one or more of the following conditions:
- Operation during hot weather (above 90°F, 32°C), carrying heavy loads and in hilly terrain.
- Police, taxi or door-to-door delivery service

4 This item not required to be performed, however, Ford recommends that you perform maintenance on this item in order to achieve best vehicle operation. Failure to perform this recommended maintenance will not invalidate the vehicle emissions warranty or manufacturer recall liability.

This maintenance is required in all states except California. However, we recommend that it also be performed on California vehicles.

## SEVERE SERVICE MAINTENANCE

**CUSTOMER MAINTENANCE SCHEDULE B**

Follow maintenance Schedule B if, generally, you drive your vehicle on a daily basis for more than 10 miles (16 km) and NONE OF THE UNIQUE DRIVING CONDITIONS SHOWN IN SCHEDULE A APPLY TO YOUR DRIVING HABITS.

| **SERVICE INTERVAL** Perform at the months or distances shown, whichever comes first. | | 7.5 | 15 | 22.5 | 30 | 37.5 | 45 | 52.5 | 60 |
|---|---|---|---|---|---|---|---|---|---|
| | **Miles x 1000** | 7.5 | 15 | 22.5 | 30 | 37.5 | 45 | 52.5 | 60 |
| | **Kilometers x 1000** | 12 | 24 | 36 | 48 | 60 | 72 | 84 | 96 |
| **EMISSION CONTROL SERVICE** | | | | | | | | | |
| Change Engine Oil & Filter (whichever occurs first) Every 6 Months or | | X | X | X | X | X | X | X | X |
| Turbocharged Vehicles Replace Engine Oil & Filter | | EVERY 5,000 MILES (8,000 KM) OR 6 MONTHS WHICHEVER OCCURS FIRST | | | | | | | |
| Replace Spark Plugs: | Turbocharged | | ③ | | X | | ③ | | X |
| | Non-Turbocharged | | | | X | | | | X |
| Check Engine Coolant Protection, Hoses and Clamps | | ANNUALLY | | | | | | | |
| Replace Engine Coolant Every 36 Months or | | | | | X | | | | X |
| Check Accessory Drive Belts | | | | | X | | | | X |
| Replace Air Cleaner Element | | | | | X① | | | | X① |
| Replace Fuel Filter | | | | | | | | | X |
| Replace Engine Timing Belt | | REPLACE EVERY 60,000 MILES (96,000 km) | | | | | | | |
| Check Engine Idle Speed | | | | | X③ | | | | X③ |
| **GENERAL MAINTENANCE** | | | | | | | | | |
| Inspect Brake Lines and Connections | | | | | X | | | | X |
| Inspect Clutch Pedal Operation | | | | | X | | | | X |
| Inspect Front and Rear Disc Brakes | | | X | | X | | X | | X |
| Inspect Safety Belts, Buckles, Retractors & Anchors | | | | | X | | | | X |
| Inspect Steering Linkage, Rack Guides & Tie Rod Ends | | | | | X | | | | X |
| Tighten Bolts & Nuts on Chassis & Body | | | | | X | | | | X |
| Inspect Steering Operations, Gear Housing and Rack Seal Boots | | | | | X | | | | X |
| Inspect Front Suspension Ball Joints | | | | | X | | | | X |
| Inspect Half Shaft Dust Boots | | | | | X | | | | X |
| Inspect Exhaust System Heat Shield | | | | | X | | | | X |
| Inspect Fuel Lines | | | | | ② | | | | X |
| Lubricate Rear Wheel Bearings | | | | | X | | | | X |
| Rotate Tires | | X | | X | | X | | X | |

① If operating in severe dust, more frequent intervals may be required. Consult your dealer.
② Recommended, but not required.
③ This item not required to be performed, however, Ford recommends that you perform maintenance on this item in order to achieve best vehicle operation. Failure to perform this recommended maintenance will not invalidate the vehicle emissions warranty or manufacturer recall liability.

# 1991–92 ESCORT & TRACER

## NORMAL SERVICE MAINTENANCE

Follow maintenance **Schedule A** if your driving habits **MAINLY** include one or more of the following conditions:

- Short trips of less than 10 miles (16 km) when outside temperatures remain below freezing.
- Towing a trailer, or using a car-top carrier.
- Operating in severe dust conditions.
- Operating during hot weather in stop-and-go "rush hour" traffic.
- Extensive idling, such as police, taxi or door-to-door delivery service.

| PERFORM AT THE MONTHS OR DISTANCES SHOWN, WHICHEVER OCCURS FIRST | | | | | | | | | | | | | | | | | | | | |
|---|---|---|---|---|---|---|---|---|---|---|---|---|---|---|---|---|---|---|---|---|
| MILES x 1000 | 3 | 6 | 9 | 12 | 15 | 18 | 21 | 24 | 27 | 30 | 33 | 36 | 39 | 42 | 45 | 48 | 51 | 54 | 57 | 60 |
| KILOMETERS x 1000 | 4.8 | 9.6 | 14.4 | 19.2 | 24 | 28.8 | 33.6 | 38.4 | 43.2 | 48 | 52.8 | 57.6 | 62.4 | 67.2 | 72 | 76.8 | 81.6 | 86.4 | 91.2 | 96 |
| **EMISSION CONTROL SERVICE** | | | | | | | | | | | | | | | | | | | | |
| Change engine oil and oil filter (every 3 months) OR 3,000 miles whichever occurs first | x | x | x | x | x | x | x | x | x | x | x | x | x | x | x | x | x | x | x | x |
| Replace spark plugs | | | | | | | | | | x | | | | | | | | | | x |
| Inspect accessory drive belt(s) | | | | | | | | | | x | | | | | | | | | | x |
| Inspect air cleaner filter (1.8L only) | | | | | x(4) | | | | | | | | | | x(4) | | | | | |
| Replace air cleaner filter (all engines) (1) | | | | | | | | | | x(1) | | | | | | | | | | x(1) |
| Replace crankcase ventilation filter (1) (1.9L only) | | | | | | | | | | x(1) | | | | | | | | | | x(1) |
| Replace engine coolant EVERY 36 months OR | | | | | | | | | | x | | | | | | | | | | x |
| Check engine coolant protection, hoses and clamps | ANNUALLY | | | | | | | | | | | | | | | | | | | |
| Engine timing belt (1.8L only) | REPLACE EVERY 60,000 MILES (96 000 Km) | | | | | | | | | | | | | | | | | | | x |

| MILES x 1000 | 3 | 6 | 9 | 12 | 15 | 18 | 21 | 24 | 27 | 30 | 33 | 36 | 39 | 42 | 45 | 48 | 51 | 54 | 57 | 60 |
|---|---|---|---|---|---|---|---|---|---|---|---|---|---|---|---|---|---|---|---|---|
| KILOMETERS x 1000 | 4.8 | 9.6 | 14.4 | 19.2 | 24 | 28.8 | 33.6 | 38.4 | 43.2 | 48 | 52.8 | 57.6 | 62.4 | 67.2 | 72 | 76.8 | 81.6 | 86.4 | 91.2 | 96 |
| **GENERAL MAINTENANCE** | | | | | | | | | | | | | | | | | | | | |
| Inspect exhaust heat shields | | | | | | | | | | x | | | | | | | | | | x |
| Change automatic transaxle fluid | | | | | | | | | | (2) | | | | | | | | | | (2) |
| Inspect disc brake pads and rotors (3) | | | | | | | | | | x(3) | | | | | | | | | | x(3) |
| Inspect brake linings and drums (3) | | | | | | | | | | x(3) | | | | | | | | | | x(3) |
| Inspect and repack rear wheel bearings | | | | | | | | | | x | | | | | | | | | | x |
| Rotate tires | | x | | | | | x | | | | | x | | | | | x | | | |
| Inspect clutch pedal operation | | | | | | | | | | x | | | | | | | | | | x |
| Inspect halfshaft dust boots | | | | | | | | | | x | | | | | | | | | | x |
| Inspect brake line hoses and connections | | | | | | | | | | x | | | | | | | | | | x |
| Inspect front suspension ball joints | | | | | | | | | | x | | | | | | | | | | x |
| Inspect bolts and nuts on chassis and body | | | | | | | | | | x | | | | | | | | | | x |
| Inspect steering operation and linkage | | | | | | | | | | x | | | | | | | | | | x |

(1) If operating in severe dust, more frequent intervals may be required, consult your dealer.

(2) Change automatic transmission fluid if your driving habits frequently include one or more of the following conditions:
- Operation during hot weather (above 90°F, 32°C), carrying heavy loads and in hilly terrain.
- Towing a trailer or using a car-top carrier.
- Police, taxi or door-to-door delivery service.

(3) If your driving includes continuous stop-and-go driving or driving in mountainous areas, more frequent intervals may be required.

(4) This maintenance is required in all states except California. However, we recommend that it also be performed on California vehicles.

## SEVERE SERVICE MAINTENANCE

Follow maintenance **Schedule B** if, generally, you drive your vehicle on a daily basis for more than 10 miles (16 km) and **NONE OF THE DRIVING CONDITIONS SHOWN IN SCHEDULE A APPLY TO YOUR DRIVING HABITS.**

| PERFORM AT THE MONTHS OR DISTANCES SHOWN, WHICHEVER OCCURS FIRST | | | | | | | | |
|---|---|---|---|---|---|---|---|---|
| MILES x 1000 | 7.5 | 15 | 22.5 | 30 | 37.5 | 45 | 52.5 | 60 |
| KILOMETERS x 1000 | 12 | 24 | 36 | 48 | 60 | 72 | 84 | 96 |
| **EMISSION CONTROL SERVICE** | | | | | | | | |
| Change engine oil and oil filter — every 6 months OR 7,500 miles, whichever occurs first | x | x | x | x | x | x | x | x |
| Replace spark plugs | | | | x | | | | x |
| Change crankcase ventilation filter (1) (1.9L only) | | | | x(1) | | | | x(1) |
| Inspect accessory drive belt(s) | | | | x | | | | x |
| Replace air cleaner filter (1) | | | | x(1) | | | | x(1) |
| Replace engine coolant (every 36 months) OR | | | | x | | | | x |
| Check engine coolant protection, hoses and clamps | ANNUALLY | | | | | | | |
| Engine timing belt (1.8L only) | REPLACE EVERY 60,000 MILES (96 000 Km) | | | | | | | x |

| MILES x 1000 | 7.5 | 15 | 22.5 | 30 | 37.5 | 45 | 52.5 | 60 |
|---|---|---|---|---|---|---|---|---|
| KILOMETERS x 1000 | 12 | 24 | 36 | 48 | 60 | 72 | 84 | 96 |
| **GENERAL MAINTENANCE** | | | | | | | | |
| Check exhaust heat shields | | | | x | | | | x |
| Inspect disc brake pads and rotors (2) | | | | x(2) | | | | x(2) |
| Inspect brake linings and drums (2) | | | | x(2) | | | | x(2) |
| Inspect and repack rear wheel bearings | | | | x | | | | x |
| Rotate tires | x | | x | | x | | x | |
| Inspect halfshaft dust boots | | | | x | | | | x |
| Inspect steering operation and linkage | | | | x | | | | x |
| Inspect front suspension ball joints | | | | x | | | | x |
| Inspect brake line hoses and connections | | | | x | | | | x |
| Inspect bolts and nuts on chassis and body | | | | x | | | | x |
| Inspect clutch pedal operation (if equipped) | | | | x | | | | x |

(1) If operating in severe dust, more frequent intervals may be required. Consult your dealer.
(2) If your driving includes continuous stop-and-go driving or driving in mountainous areas, more frequent intervals may be required.

# ELECTRICAL SYMBOL IDENTIFICATION

TABLE OF CONTENTS

Page No.



# Chrysler/Eagle

| | LEGEND OF SYMBOLS USED ON WIRING DIAGRAMS | | |
|---|---|---|---|
| + | POSITIVE | →≫— | CONNECTOR |
| − | NEGATIVE | ⟶ | MALE CONNECTOR |
| | GROUND | | FEMALE CONNECTOR |
| | FUSE | | DENOTES WIRE CONTINUES ELSEWHERE |
| | GANG FUSES WITH BUSS BAR | | DENOTES WIRE GOES TO ONE OF TWO CIRCUITS |
| | CIRCUIT BREAKER | | SPLICE |
| | CAPACITOR | J2 2 | SPLICE IDENTIFICATION |
| Ω | OHMS | | THERMAL ELEMENT (BI- |
| | RESISTOR | TIMER | TIMER |
| | VARIABLE RESISTOR | | MULTIPLE CONNECTOR |
| | SERIES RESISTOR | | OPTIONAL WIRING WITH / WIRING WITHOUT |
| | COIL | | "Y" WINDINGS |
| | STEP UP COIL | 88:88 | DIGITAL READOUT |
| | OPEN CONTACT | | SINGLE FILAMENT LAMP |
| | CLOSED CONTACT | | DUAL FILAMENT LAMP |

**Fig. 1 1989–91 Chrysler & Eagle Models Except Colt, Colt Vista, Conquest, Laser, Medallion, Stealth, Summit & Talon (Part 1 Of 2)**

| | | | |
|---|---|---|---|
| | CLOSED SWITCH | | L.E.D. — LIGHT EMITTING DIODE |
| | OPEN SWITCH | | THERMISTOR |
| | CLOSED GANGED SWITCH | | GAUGE |
| | OPEN GANGED SWITCH | | SENSOR |
| | TWO POLE SINGLE THROW SWITCH | | FUEL INJECTOR |
| | PRESSURE SWITCH | #36 | DENOTES WIRE GOES THROUGH 40 WAY DISCONNECT |
| | SOLENOID SWITCH | #19 STRG COLUMN | DENOTES WIRE GOES THROUGH 25 WAY STEERING COLUMN CONNECTOR |
| | MERCURY SWITCH | INST PANEL #14 | DENOTES WIRE GOES THROUGH 25 WAY INSTRUMENT PANEL CONNECTOR |
| | DIODE OR RECTIFIER | ENG #7 | DENOTES WIRE GOES THROUGH GROMMET TO ENGINE COMPARTMENT |
| | BY-DIRECTIONAL ZENER DIODE | | DENOTES WIRE GOES THROUGH GROMMET |
| | MOTOR | | HEATED GRID ELEMENTS |
| | ARMATURE AND BRUSHES | | |

**Fig. 1 1989–91 Chrysler & Eagle Models Except Colt, Colt Vista, Conquest, Laser, Medallion, Stealth, Summit & Talon (Part 2 Of 2)**

| | | | | | |
|---|---|---|---|---|---|
| Battery | Body ground | Single bulb | Resistor | Diode | Capacitor |
| Fuse | Equipment ground | Dual bulb | Variable resistor | Zener diode | Crossing of wires without connection |
| Fusible link | ECU interior ground | Speaker | Coil | Transistor | Crossing of wires with connection |
| Connector (Female side / Male side) | Motor | Horn | Pulse generator | Buzzer | Chime |
| Thyristor | Piezoelectric device | Thermistor | Light emitting diode | Photo diode | Photo transistor |

**Fig. 2 Colt, Colt Vista, Conquest, Laser, Summit, Stealth & Talon**

# ELECTRICAL SYMBOL IDENTIFICATION

| | LEGEND OF SYMBOLS USED ON WIRING DIAGRAMS | | |
|---|---|---|---|
| + | POSITIVE | | CONNECTOR |
| − | NEGATIVE | | MALE CONNECTOR |
| | GROUND | | FEMALE CONNECTOR |
| | FUSE | | DENOTES WIRE CONTINUES ELSEWHERE |
| | GANG FUSES WITH BUSS BAR | | DENOTES WIRE GOES TO ONE OF TWO CIRCUITS |
| | CIRCUIT BREAKER | | SPLICE |
| | CAPACITOR | J2 2 | SPLICE IDENTIFICATION |
| Ω | OHMS | | THERMAL ELEMENT |
| | RESISTOR | TIMER | TIMER |
| | VARIABLE RESISTOR | | MULTIPLE CONNECTOR |
| | SERIES RESISTOR | | OPTIONAL WIRING WITH / WIRING WITHOUT |
| | COIL | | "Y" WINDINGS |
| | STEP UP COIL | 88:88 | DIGITAL READOUT |
| | OPEN CONTACT | | SINGLE FILAMENT LAMP |
| | CLOSED CONTACT | | DUAL FILAMENT LAMP |
| | CLOSED SWITCH | | L.E.D. — LIGHT EMITTING DIODE |
| | OPEN SWITCH | | THERMISTOR |
| | CLOSED GANGED SWITCH | | GAUGE |
| | OPEN GANGED SWITCH | | SENSOR |
| | TWO POLE SINGLE THROW SWITCH | | FUEL INJECTOR |
| | PRESSURE SWITCH | #36 | DENOTES WIRE GOES THROUGH BULKHEAD DISCONNECT |
| | SOLENOID SWITCH | #19 STRG COLUMN | DENOTES WIRE GOES THROUGH STEERING COLUMN CONNECTOR |
| | MERCURY SWITCH | INST PANEL #14 | DENOTES WIRE GOES THROUGH INSTRUMENT PANEL CONNECTOR |
| | DIODE OR RECTIFIER | ENG #7 | DENOTES WIRE GOES THROUGH GROMMET TO ENGINE COMPARTMENT |
| | BY-DIRECTIONAL ZENER DIODE | | DENOTES WIRE GOES THROUGH GROMMET |
| | MOTOR | | HEATED GRID ELEMENTS |
| | ARMATURE AND BRUSHES | | |

**Fig. 3 1992 Chrysler & Eagle Models Except Colt, Colt Vista, Laser, Stealth, Summit & Talon**

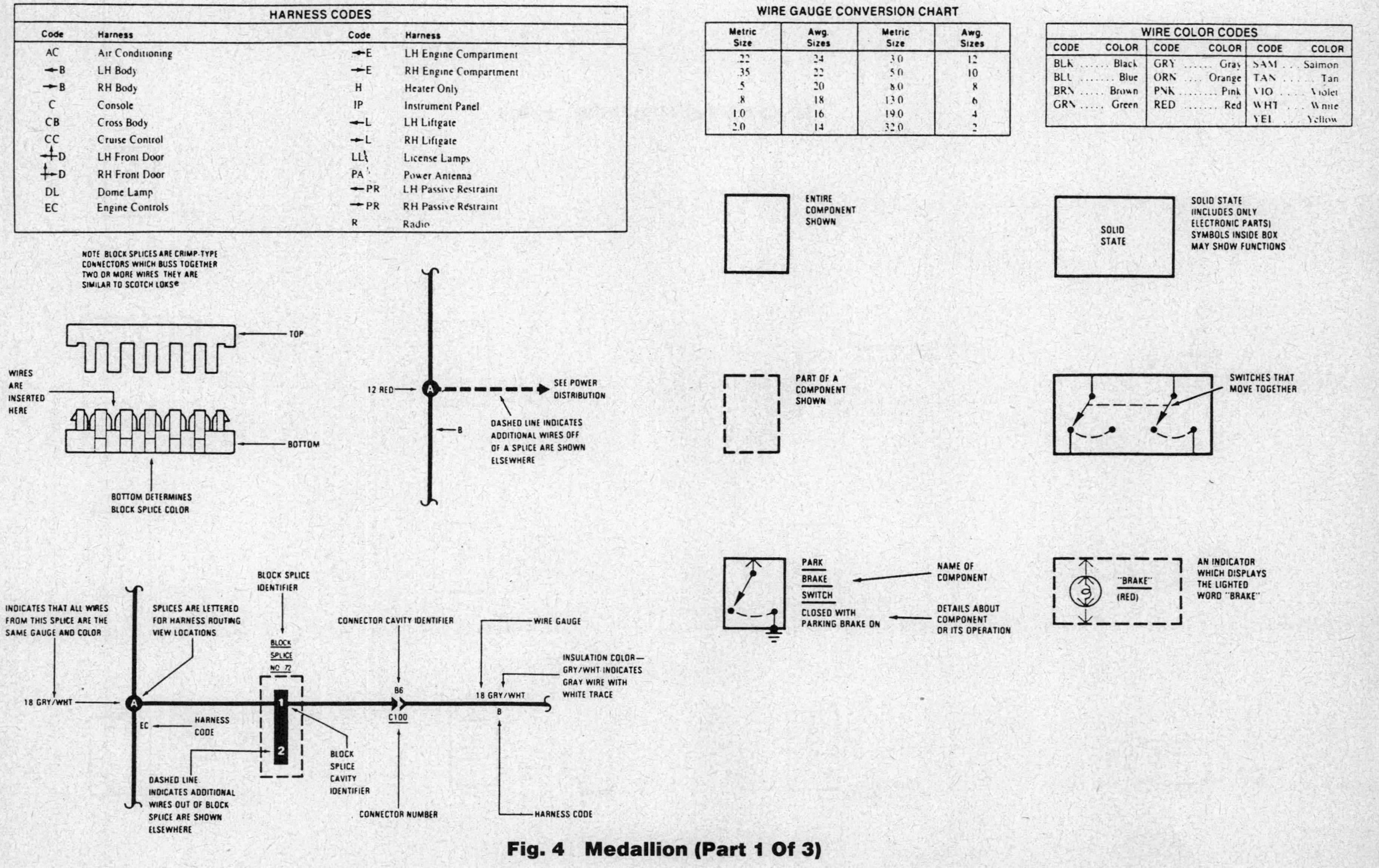

HARNESS CODES

| Code | Harness | Code | Harness |
|---|---|---|---|
| AC | Air Conditioning | ←E | LH Engine Compartment |
| ←B | LH Body | →E | RH Engine Compartment |
| →B | RH Body | H | Heater Only |
| C | Console | IP | Instrument Panel |
| CB | Cross Body | ←L | LH Liftgate |
| CC | Cruise Control | →L | RH Liftgate |
| -+D | LH Front Door | LL | License Lamps |
| +-D | RH Front Door | PA | Power Antenna |
| DL | Dome Lamp | ←PR | LH Passive Restraint |
| EC | Engine Controls | →PR | RH Passive Restraint |
| | | R | Radio |

WIRE GAUGE CONVERSION CHART

| Metric Size | Awg. Sizes | Metric Size | Awg. Sizes |
|---|---|---|---|
| .22 | 24 | 3.0 | 12 |
| .35 | 22 | 5.0 | 10 |
| .5 | 20 | 8.0 | 8 |
| .8 | 18 | 13.0 | 6 |
| 1.0 | 16 | 19.0 | 4 |
| 2.0 | 14 | 32.0 | 2 |

WIRE COLOR CODES

| CODE | COLOR | CODE | COLOR | CODE | COLOR |
|---|---|---|---|---|---|
| BLK | Black | GRY | Gray | SAM | Salmon |
| BLU | Blue | ORN | Orange | TAN | Tan |
| BRN | Brown | PNK | Pink | VIO | Violet |
| GRN | Green | RED | Red | WHT | White |
| | | | | YEL | Yellow |

NOTE BLOCK SPLICES ARE CRIMP-TYPE CONNECTORS WHICH BUSS TOGETHER TWO OR MORE WIRES THEY ARE SIMILAR TO SCOTCH LOKS®
TOP
WIRES ARE INSERTED HERE
BOTTOM
BOTTOM DETERMINES BLOCK SPLICE COLOR
12 RED
A
SEE POWER DISTRIBUTION
B
DASHED LINE INDICATES ADDITIONAL WIRES OFF OF A SPLICE ARE SHOWN ELSEWHERE
ENTIRE COMPONENT SHOWN
SOLID STATE
SOLID STATE (INCLUDES ONLY ELECTRONIC PARTS) SYMBOLS INSIDE BOX MAY SHOW FUNCTIONS
PART OF A COMPONENT SHOWN
SWITCHES THAT MOVE TOGETHER
PARK BRAKE SWITCH
CLOSED WITH PARKING BRAKE ON
NAME OF COMPONENT
DETAILS ABOUT COMPONENT OR ITS OPERATION
"BRAKE" (RED)
AN INDICATOR WHICH DISPLAYS THE LIGHTED WORD "BRAKE"
INDICATES THAT ALL WIRES FROM THIS SPLICE ARE THE SAME GAUGE AND COLOR
18 GRY/WHT
SPLICES ARE LETTERED FOR HARNESS ROUTING VIEW LOCATIONS
BLOCK SPLICE IDENTIFIER
BLOCK SPLICE NO 72
EC
HARNESS CODE
1
2
DASHED LINE INDICATES ADDITIONAL WIRES OUT OF BLOCK SPLICE ARE SHOWN ELSEWHERE
BLOCK SPLICE CAVITY IDENTIFIER
CONNECTOR CAVITY IDENTIFIER
B6
C100
CONNECTOR NUMBER
WIRE GAUGE
18 GRY/WHT
B
INSULATION COLOR— GRY/WHT INDICATES GRAY WIRE WITH WHITE TRACE
HARNESS CODE

Fig. 4 Medallion (Part 1 Of 3)

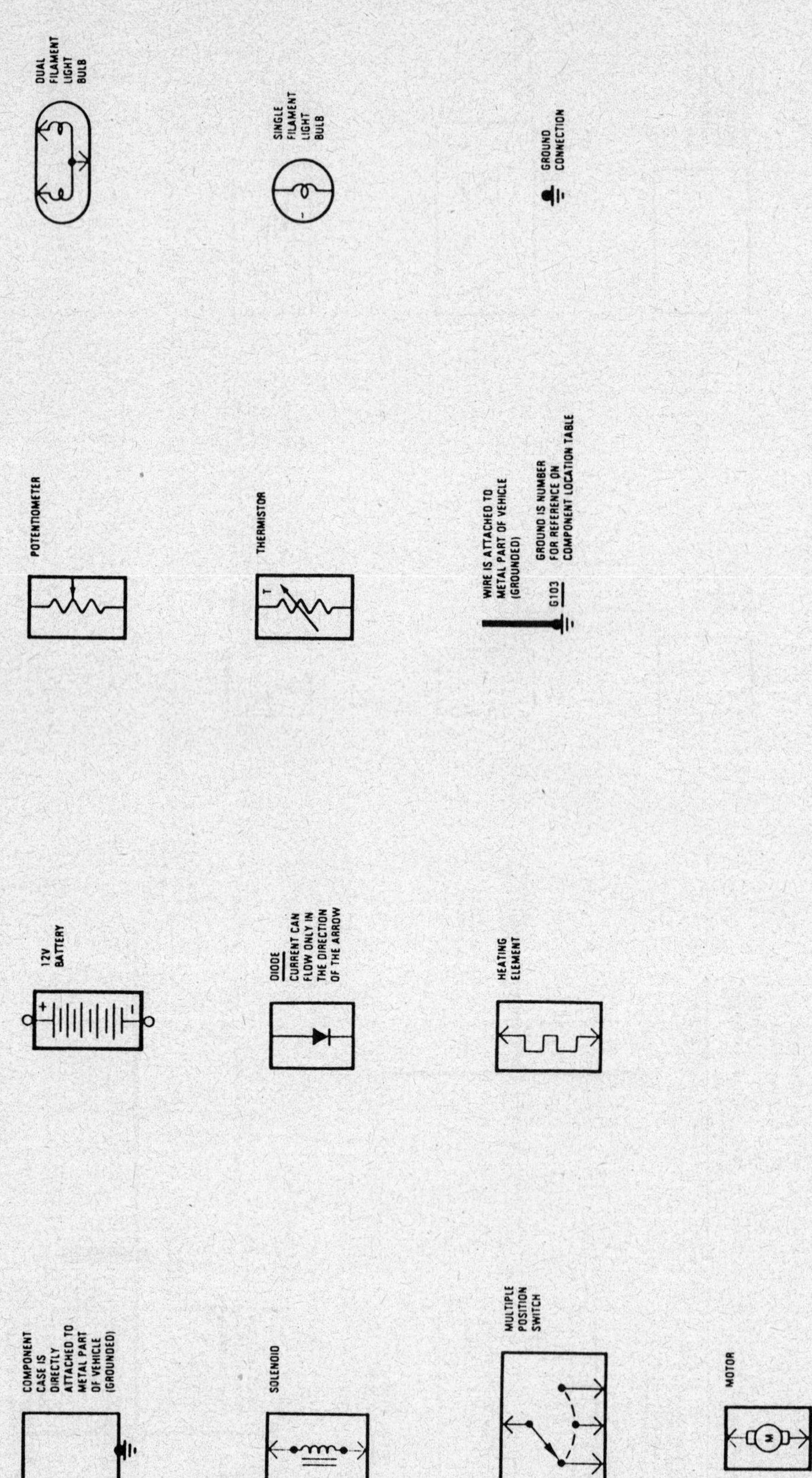


**Fig. 4 Medallion (Part 2 Of 3)**

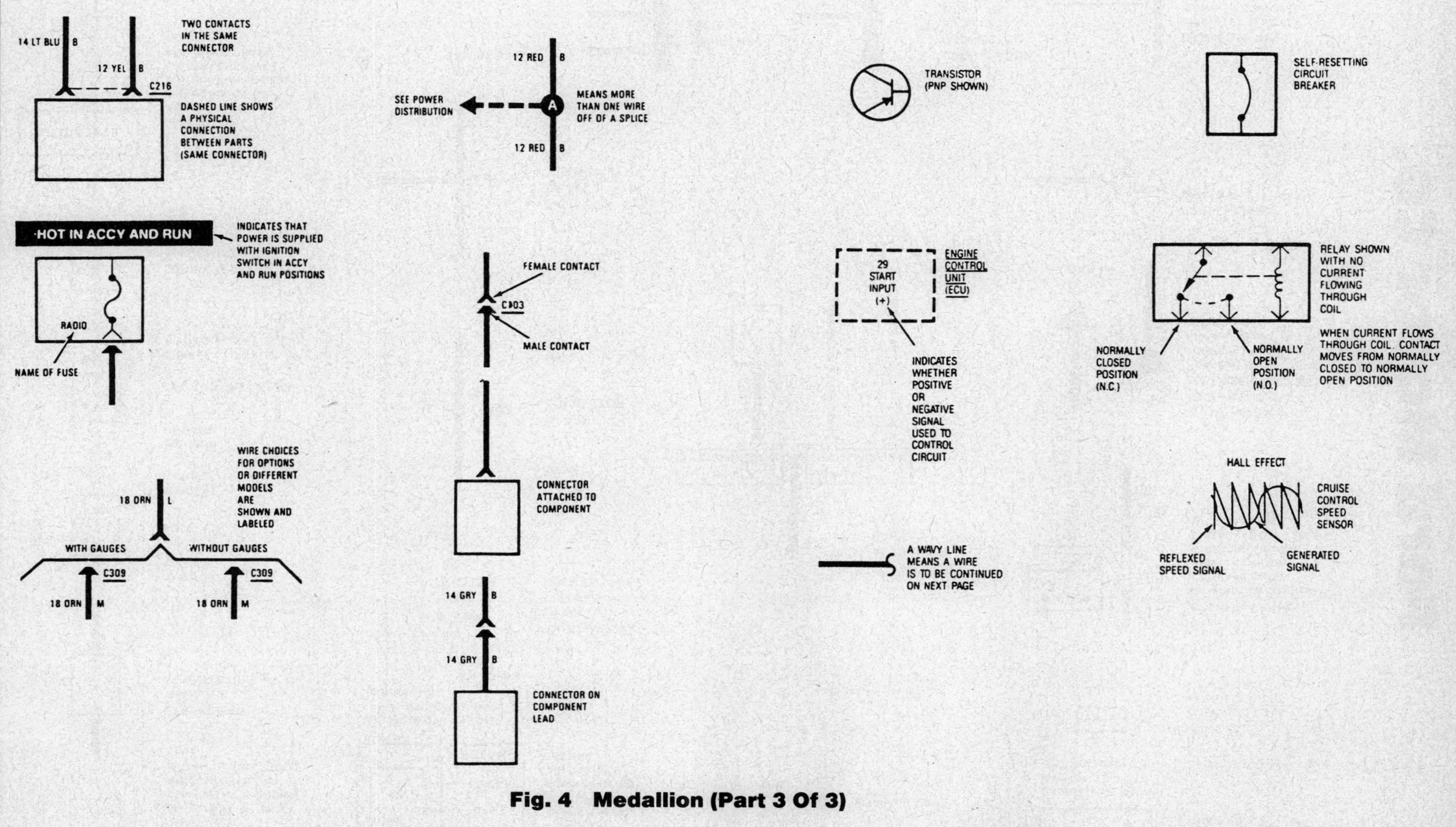


**Fig. 4 Medallion (Part 3 Of 3)**

# Ford Motor Co.

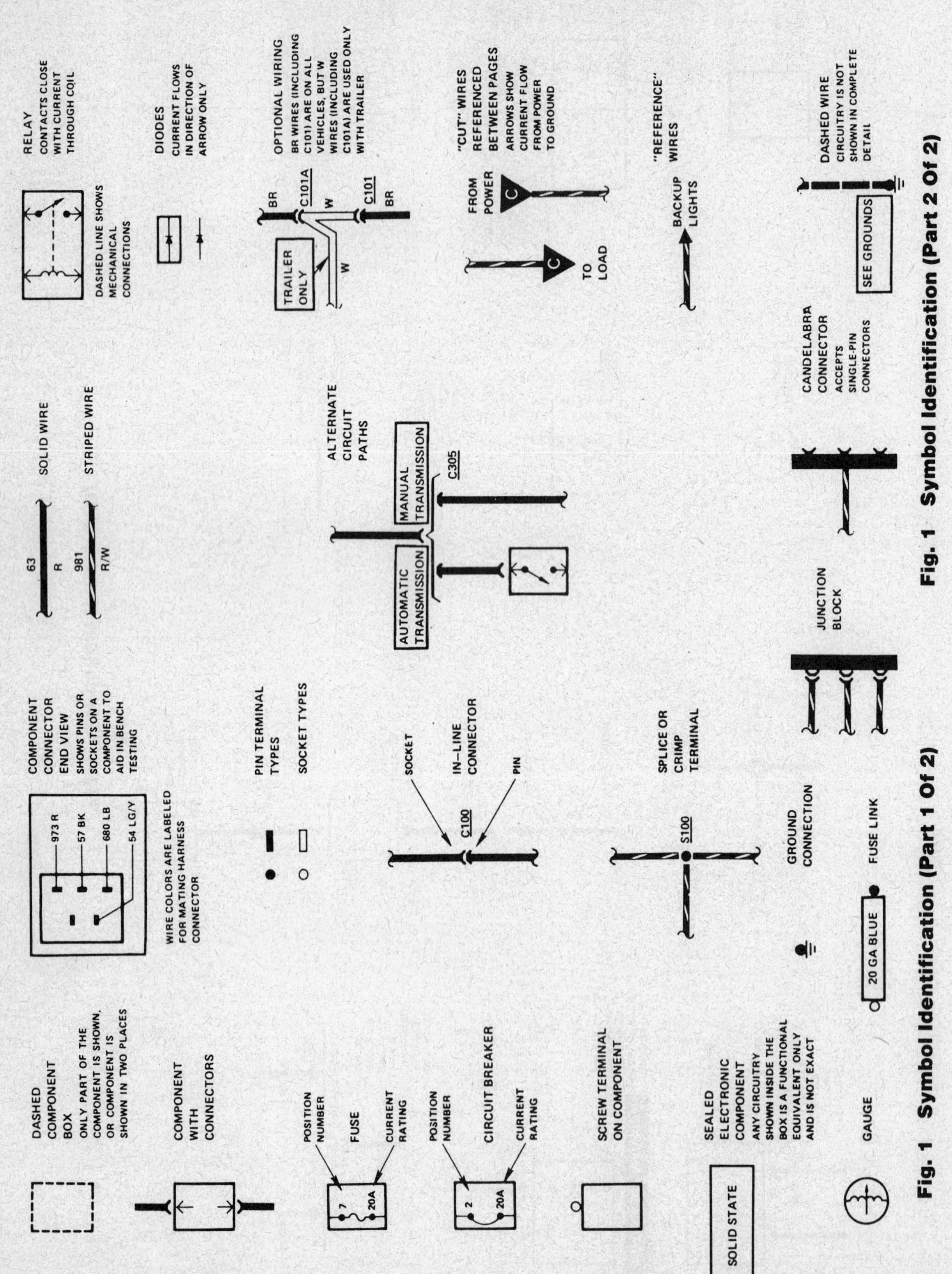
DASHED COMPONENT BOX
ONLY PART OF THE COMPONENT IS SHOWN, OR COMPONENT IS SHOWN IN TWO PLACES
COMPONENT WITH CONNECTORS
POSITION NUMBER
FUSE
CURRENT RATING
7
20A
POSITION NUMBER
CIRCUIT BREAKER
CURRENT RATING
2
20A
SCREW TERMINAL ON COMPONENT
SEALED ELECTRONIC COMPONENT
ANY CIRCUITRY SHOWN INSIDE THE BOX IS A FUNCTIONAL EQUIVALENT ONLY AND IS NOT EXACT
SOLID STATE
GAUGE
973 R
57 BK
680 LB
54 LG/Y
COMPONENT CONNECTOR END VIEW
SHOWS PINS OR SOCKETS ON A COMPONENT TO AID IN BENCH TESTING
WIRE COLORS ARE LABELED FOR MATING HARNESS CONNECTOR
PIN TERMINAL TYPES
SOCKET TYPES
SOCKET
C100
PIN
IN-LINE CONNECTOR
S100
SPLICE OR CRIMP TERMINAL
GROUND CONNECTION
20 GA BLUE
FUSE LINK
63
R
SOLID WIRE
981
R/W
STRIPED WIRE
ALTERNATE CIRCUIT PATHS
MANUAL TRANSMISSION
C305
AUTOMATIC TRANSMISSION
JUNCTION BLOCK
CANDELABRA CONNECTOR
ACCEPTS SINGLE-PIN CONNECTORS
RELAY
CONTACTS CLOSE WITH CURRENT THROUGH COIL
DASHED LINE SHOWS MECHANICAL CONNECTIONS
DIODES
CURRENT FLOWS IN DIRECTION OF ARROW ONLY
BR
C101A
W
C101
BR
TRAILER ONLY
W
OPTIONAL WIRING
BR WIRES (INCLUDING C101) ARE ON ALL VEHICLES, BUT W WIRES (INCLUDING C101A) ARE USED ONLY WITH TRAILER
FROM POWER
C
C
TO LOAD
"CUT" WIRES REFERENCED BETWEEN PAGES
ARROWS SHOW CURRENT FLOW FROM POWER TO GROUND
BACKUP LIGHTS
"REFERENCE" WIRES
SEE GROUNDS
DASHED WIRE
CIRCUITRY IS NOT SHOWN IN COMPLETE DETAIL

**Fig. 1 Symbol Identification (Part 1 Of 2)**

**Fig. 1 Symbol Identification (Part 2 Of 2)**

# CHRYSLER CORPORATION/EAGLE

# CHRYSLER CORPORATION/EAGLE

# CHRYSLER REAR WHEEL DRIVE EXCEPT CONQUEST

**NOTE:** The Following Models Are Covered In This Chapter: CHRYSLER–Fifth Avenue (1989); DODGE–Diplomat (1989); PLYMOUTH–Gran Fury (1989).

## INDEX OF SERVICE OPERATIONS

**NOTE:** Refer To Rear Of This Manual For Manufacturer's Special Service Tool Suppliers.

## INDEX OF SERVICE OPERATIONS —Continued



# Specifications

## GENERAL ENGINE SPECIFICATIONS

| Year | Engine Liter/CID① | Engine VIN Code② | Fuel System | Bore & Stroke | Comp. Ratio | Net H.P. @ RPM③ | Maximum Torque Ft. Lbs. @ RPM | Normal Oil Pressure Psi. |
|---|---|---|---|---|---|---|---|---|
| **CHRYSLER** | | | | | | | | |
| 1989 | 5.2L/V8-318 | P | 6280, 2 Bbl.④ | 3.91 x 3.31 | 9.0 | 140 @ 3600 | 265 @ 2000 | 30–80 |
| **DODGE** | | | | | | | | |
| 1989 | 5.2L/V8-318⑤ | P | 6280, 2 Bbl.④ | 3.91 x 3.31 | 9.0 | 140 @ 3600 | 265 @ 2000 | 30–80 |
| | 5.2L/V8-318⑥ | S | 4 Bbl.⑦ | 3.91 x 3.31 | 8.4 | 175 @ 4000 | 250 @ 3200 | 30–80 |
| **PLYMOUTH** | | | | | | | | |
| 1989 | 5.2L/V8-318⑤ | P | 6280, 2 Bbl.④ | 3.91 x 3.31 | 9.0 | 140 @ 3600 | 265 @ 2000 | 30–80 |
| | 5.2L/V8-318⑥ | S | 4 Bbl.⑦ | 3.91 x 3.31 | 8.4 | 175 @ 4000 | 250 @ 3200 | 30–80 |

①—CID-Cubic Inch Displacement.
②—The eighth digit in the VIN denotes engine code.
③—Ratings are net-as installed in vehicle.
④—Holley.
⑤—Except police package.
⑥—Police package.
⑦—Rochester quadrajet.

## TUNE UP SPECIFICATIONS

| Year & Engine/ VIN Code ① | Spark Plug Gap | Ignition Timing BTDC: Firing Order Fig. ② | Ignition Timing BTDC: Man. Trans. | Ignition Timing BTDC: Auto. Trans. | Ignition Timing BTDC: Mark Fig. | Curb Idle Speed③: Man. Trans. | Curb Idle Speed③: Auto Trans. | Fast Idle Speed: Man. Trans. | Fast Idle Speed: Auto. Trans. | Fuel Pump Pressure Psi. |
|---|---|---|---|---|---|---|---|---|---|---|
| **1989** | | | | | | | | | | |
| 5.2L/V8-318/P 2 Bbl. | .035 | A | — | 7 | B | — | 680N | — | 1700④ | 5.75–7.25 |
| 5.2L/V8-318/S 4 Bbl | .035 | A | — | 16 | B | — | 750N | — | 1450④ | 5.75–7.25 |

①—The eighth digit of the Vehicle Identification Number (V.I.N.) denotes engine code.
②—Before disconnecting wires from distributor cap, determine location of No. 1 wire in cap, as distributor position may have been altered from that shown at the end of this chart.
③—N: Neutral.
④—With stop screw on second highest step of fast idle cam.

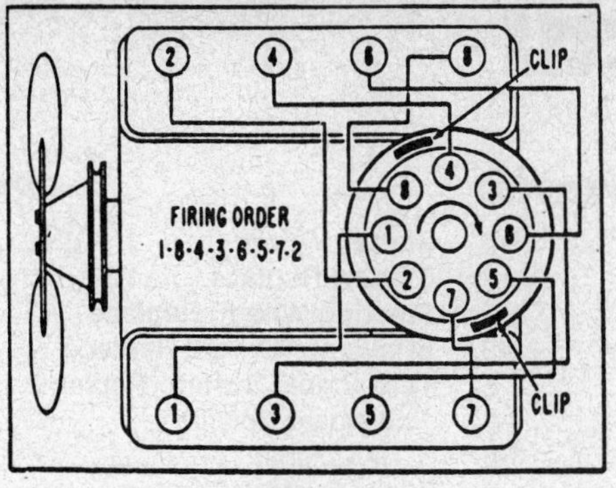

Fig. A

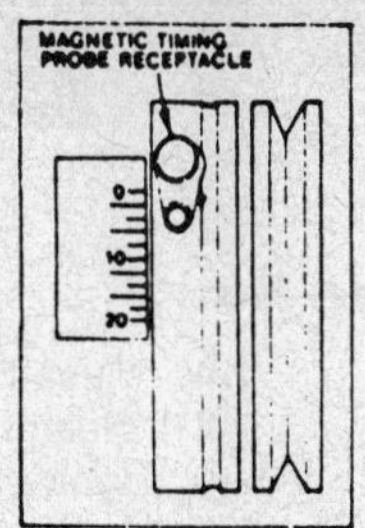

Fig. B

## WHEEL ALIGNMENT SPECIFICATIONS

**NOTE: See that riding height is correct before checking wheel alignment.**

| Year | Model | Caster Angle, Degrees | | Camber Angle, Degrees | | | | Toe-In, Inch | Toe-Out on Turns, Degrees | |
|---|---|---|---|---|---|---|---|---|---|---|
| | | | | Limits | | Desired | | | | |
| | | Limits | Desired | Left | Right | Left | Right | | Outer Wheel | Inner Wheel |
| **CHRYSLER** | | | | | | | | | | |
| 1989 | All | +1¼ to +3¾ | +2½ | −¼ to +1¼ | −¼ to +1¼ | +½ | +½ | 0 to 5/16 | 18 | 20 |
| **DODGE** | | | | | | | | | | |
| 1989 | All | +1¼ to +3¾ | +2½ | −¼ to +1¼ | −¼ to +1¼ | +½ | +½ | 0 to 5/16 | 18 | 20 |
| **PLYMOUTH** | | | | | | | | | | |
| 1989 | All | +1¼ to +3¾ | +2½ | −¼ to +1¼ | −¼ to +1¼ | +½ | +½ | 0 to 5/16 | 18 | 20 |

## COOLING SYSTEM & CAPACITY DATA

| Year | Model or Engine/VIN | Cooling Capacity, Qts. | | Radiator Cap Relief Pressure, Psi. | Thermo. Opening Temp. | Fuel Tank Gals. | Engine Oil Refill Qts. ① | Auto. Trans. Qts. ② | Rear Axle Oil Pints |
|---|---|---|---|---|---|---|---|---|---|
| | | Less A/C | With A/C | | | | | | |
| **CHRYSLER** | | | | | | | | | |
| 1989 | Fifth Avenue 5.2L/V8-318/P | 15½③ | 15½③ | 16 | 195 | 18 | 4 | 8.15⑤ | ④ |
| **DODGE** | | | | | | | | | |
| 1989 | Diplomat 5.2L/V8-318/P | 15½③ | 15½③ | 16 | 195 | 18 | 4 | 8.15⑤ | ④ |
| **PLYMOUTH** | | | | | | | | | |
| 1989 | Gran Fury 5.2L/V8-318/P | 15½③ | 15½③ | 16 | 195 | 18 | 4 | 8.15⑤ | ④ |

①—Add 1 qt. with filter change.
②—Approximate. Make final check with dipstick.
③—Heavy duty cooling system, 16½ qts.
④—With 7¼ inch ring gear, 2.5 pts.; with 8¼ inch ring gear, 4.4 pts.
⑤—Add an additional ¼ qt. with auxiliary cooler.

## LUBRICANT DATA

| Year | Model | Lubricant Type | | | | | |
|---|---|---|---|---|---|---|---|
| | | Tranmission | | | | | |
| | | Manual | Automatic | Transfer Case | Rear Axle | Power Steering | Brake System |
| 1989 | All | — | 7176① | — | API GL-5② | 4318055① | DOT 3 |

①—Mopar part No.
②—On Sure-Grip differentials add 4 ounces of friction modifier Mopar part No. 4318060 or equivalent.

# Electrical

## INDEX



## AIRBAG SYSTEM DISARMING

**On models with airbag restraint system, battery ground cable must be disconnected and isolated before performing this procedure. Failure to do so may result in accidental deployment and personal injury.**

## FUSE PANEL & FLASHER LOCATION

The fuse panel is located to the left side of the steering column under the instrument panel.

The turn signal and hazard flashers are located on the fuse panel.

## STARTER

### REPLACE

1. Disconnect ground cable at battery.
2. Remove cable at starter.
3. Disconnect wires at solenoid.
4. Remove one stud nut and one bolt attaching starter motor to flywheel housing.
5. Slide transmission oil cooler bracket off stud (if so equipped).
6. Remove starter motor and removable seal.
7. Reverse above procedure to install. **When tightening attaching bolt and nut be sure to hold starter away from engine to insure proper alignment.**

## DISTRIBUTOR

### REPLACE

#### REMOVAL

1. Disconnect distributor pickup lead wires from wiring connector, then remove distributor cap.
2. Mark position of rotor on distributor body and engine block surface so that distributor can be installed in the same position.
3. Remove hold-down and bolt and lift distributor from engine.

#### INSTALLATION

1. Position distributor in engine. Ensure O-ring is in groove of distributor housing. Align rotor marks previously scribed on distributor housing.
2. If engine was cranked after distributor was removed from engine, proceed as follows:
   a. Rotate crankshaft to bring No. 1 piston up on its compression stroke and align timing mark on crankshaft pulley with 0 (TDC) mark on timing cover.
   b. With distributor O-ring in place, hold distributor over mounting pad.
   c. Rotate rotor to a position just ahead of the No. 1 distributor cap terminal.
   d. Position distributor in engine.
3. Engage tongue of distributor shaft with slot in distributor oil pump gear.
4. Connect distributor pickup lead wires at wiring connectors.
5. Set ignition timing.

## AIRBAG MODULE

### REPLACE

**Battery ground cable must be disconnected and isolated before performing this procedure. Failure to do so may result in accidental deployment and personal injury.**

1. Disconnect battery ground cable.
2. Using nut remover No. 6239 or equivalent, remove four tamper-proof nuts attaching airbag module to steering wheel.
3. Lift module high enough to remove clockspring connecting wire, then remove module.
4. Reverse procedure to install. **Torque** nuts to 95 inch lbs.

## STEERING WHEEL

### REPLACE

**Battery ground cable must be disconnected and isolated before performing this procedure. Failure to do so may result in accidental deployment and personal injury.**

1. Disconnect battery ground cable.
2. **On models equipped with airbag restraint systems,** remove airbag module as outlined under "Airbag Module, Replace." Remove clockspring set screw from steering wheel, then place it in clockspring to ensure clockspring positioning.
3. **On models less airbag restraint systems,** remove horn pad from steering wheel, then disconnect wiring connectors from horn.
4. **On all models,** remove steering wheel retaining nut, then steering wheel using suitable puller. **Do not bump or hammer on steering shaft to remove wheel as damage to shaft may result.**
5. Reverse procedure to install, noting the following:
   a. Install steering wheel with master serration in hub aligned with missing spline on end of steering shaft.
   b. **Torque** retaining nut to 45 ft. lbs.

## TURN SIGNAL SWITCH

### REPLACE

#### STANDARD COLUMN

**On models with airbag restraint system, battery ground cable must be disconnected and isolated before performing this procedure. Failure to do so may result in accidental deployment and personal injury.**

1. Disconnect battery ground cable.
2. **On models with airbag restraint system,** remove airbag module as outlined under "Airbag Module, Replace."
3. **On all models,** remove steering wheel as outlined under "Steering Wheel, Replace."
4. Remove wiring protector from steering column, then disconnect turn signal switch electrical connector.
5. Remove lock housing cover, then wash/wipe switch assembly.
6. Remove turn signal switch upper bearing retainer screws, then pull

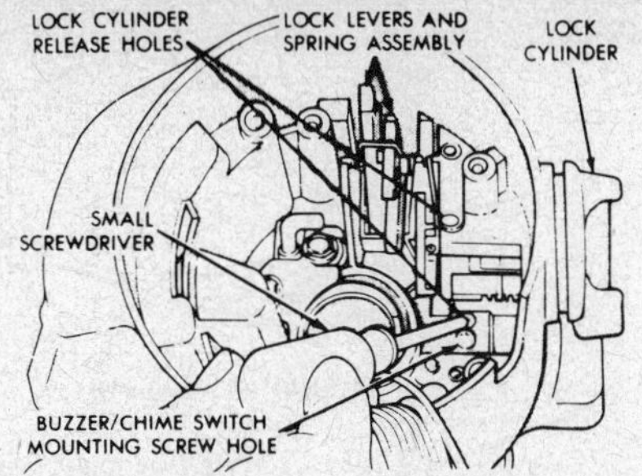


**Fig. 1 Ignition lock removal. Models w/standard tilt column**

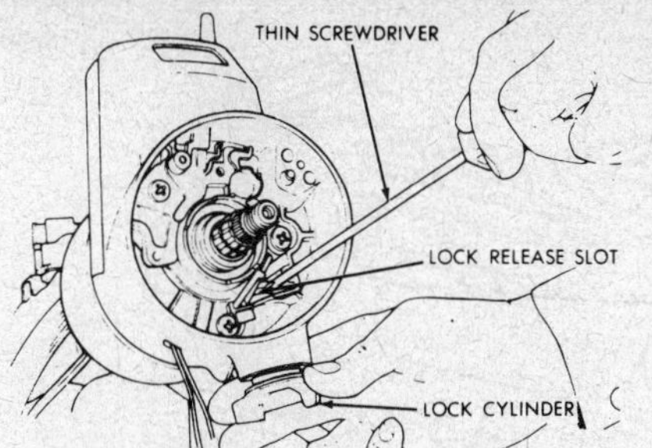


**Fig. 2 Ignition lock removal. Models w/tilt column**

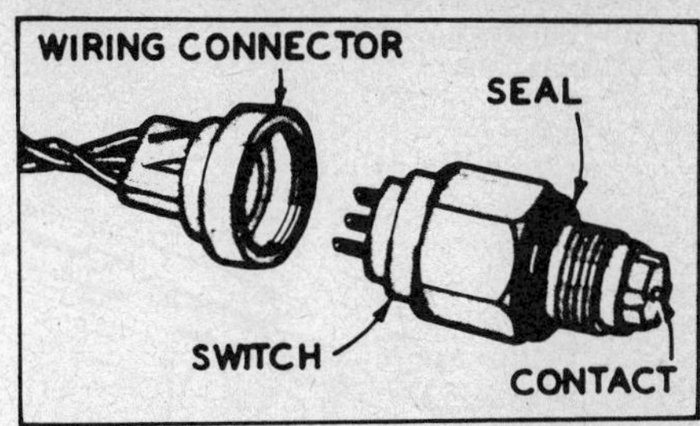


**Fig. 3 Neutral safety switch**

switch from steering column, while carefully guiding wires up through column opening.

7. Reverse procedure to install.

## TILT COLUMN

**On models with airbag restraint system, battery ground cable must be disconnected and isolated before performing this procedure. Failure to do so may result in accidental deployment and personal injury.**

1. Disconnect battery ground cable.
2. **On models with airbag restraint system,** remove airbag module as outlined under "Airbag Module, Replace."
3. **On all models,** remove steering wheel as outlined under "Steering Wheel, Replace."
4. Remove wiring protector, tilt lever, hazard warning knob and ignition key lamp assembly.
5. Pull knob off wash/wipe switch, then pull hider up stalk and remove sleeve attaching screws. Remove sleeve from wash/wipe switch.
6. Rotate shaft in wiper switch to full clockwise position, then remove shaft.
7. Remove cover from lock plate. Depress lock plate with lock plate depressor No. C-4156, then pry out retaining ring.
8. Remove lock plate, canceling cam and upper bearing spring.
9. Remove switch actuator screw and arm.
10. Remove turn signal attaching screws, then place shift bowl in Low position.
11. Pull switch from steering column, while carefully guiding wires up through column opening.
12. Reverse procedure to install.

# IGNITION SWITCH & LOCK

## REPLACE

### STANDARD COLUMN

**On models with airbag restraint system, battery ground cable must be disconnected and isolated before performing this procedure. Failure to do so may result in accidental deployment and personal injury.**

1. Remove turn signal switch as outlined under "Turn Signal Switch, Replace."
2. Remove ignition key lamp assembly retaining screw and the assembly.
3. Remove snap ring from upper end of steering shaft.
4. Remove bearing housing to lock housing retaining screws, then bearing housing from shaft.
5. Remove lock plate spring and lock plate from steering shaft.
6. Remove buzzer/chime switch retaining screw, then switch.
7. Remove ignition switch attaching screws, then ignition switch.
8. Remove dimmer switch mounting screws, then disengage switch from actuator rod.
9. Remove bellcrank attaching screws, then slide bellcrank up until ignition switch actuator rod can be disconnected.
10. Place lock cylinder in the Lock position and remove key. With a suitable tool, depress spring loaded lock retainer and pull lock cylinder from housing bore, **Fig. 1.**
11. Reverse procedure to install.

### TILT COLUMN

**On models with airbag restraint system, battery ground cable must be disconnected and isolated before performing this procedure. Failure to do so may result in accidental deployment and personal injury.**

1. Remove turn signal switch as outlined under "Turn Signal Switch, Replace."
2. Remove key lamp assembly.
3. Place lock cylinder in the Lock position and remove key. With a suitable tool, depress spring loaded lock retainer and pull lock cylinder from housing bore, **Fig. 2.**
4. Remove buzzer/chime switch using a stiff wire. Hook bent on end of wire should be inserted in exposed loop of wedge spring. Ensure spring does not fall into column. **If wedge spring falls into column, complete disassembly is required to retrieve spring.**
5. Remove housing cover attaching screws, then housing cover.
6. If necessary wash/wipe switch and pivot pin can be removed. Also tilt lever opening shield and dimmer switch actuator rod may be remove from cap.
7. Place column in full Up position. Remove tilt spring retainer. Insert screwdriver in opening, press in approximately 3/16 inch and turn approximately 1/8 turn counterclockwise until ears align with grooves in housing and remove spring and guide.
8. Push upper steering shaft in sufficiently to remove steering shaft inner race seat and inner race.
9. With ignition switch in Accessory position, remove ignition switch mounting screws, then ignition switch.
10. Reverse procedure to install.

# IGNITION SWITCH

## ADJUST

**On models with airbag restraint system, battery ground cable must be disconnected and isolated before performing this procedure. Failure to do so may result in accidental deployment and personal injury.**

1. Disconnect battery ground cable.
2. Place transmission in Park and ignition lock in the lock position.
3. If switch was not removed from column, loosen two mounting bolts and insert a lock pin into hole on switch marked lock. If switch was removed from column, pin switch in the lock position, then place switch into rod and rotate 90 degrees over mounting holes. Loosely install mounting bolts. Replacement switches are supplied with locking pins.
4. Apply light upward pressure to align rod and switch and hold switch in this position while tightening retaining bolts. Remove locking pin.
5. Remove lock pin from switch.
6. Reverse procedure to install.

# LIGHT SWITCH

## REPLACE

**On models with airbag restraint system, battery ground cable must be disconnected and isolated before performing this procedure. Failure to do so may result in accidental deployment and personal injury.**

1. Disconnect battery ground cable.
2. Remove cluster bezel.
3. Remove switch mounting plate attaching screws and pull switch and plate assembly outward.
4. Depress headlight switch stem, then depress release button and pull knob and stem from switch.
5. Remove switch mounting nut, then disconnect electrical connector and remove switch.

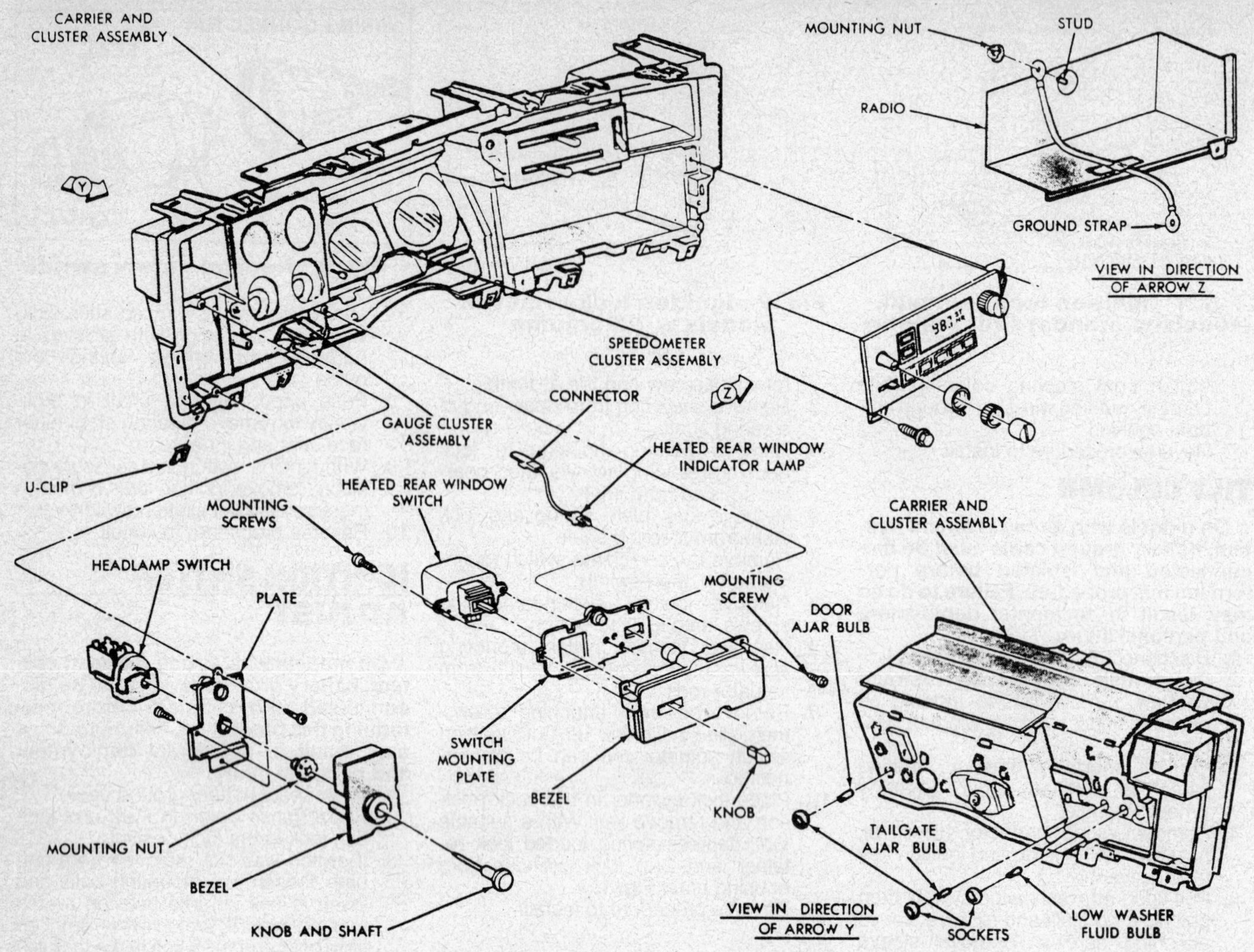


**Fig. 4 Instrument cluster. Diplomat, Fifth Avenue & Gran Fury**

6. Reverse procedure to install.

## STOPLAMP SWITCH
### REPLACE

1. Disconnect battery ground cable.
2. Disconnect wiring from switch and remove switch from brake pedal bracket.
3. Reverse procedure to install.

## NEUTRAL SAFETY & BACK-UP SWITCH
### REPLACE

1. Unscrew switch from transmission case, allowing fluid to drain into a container, **Fig. 3.**
2. Move shift lever to Park and then to Neutral positions and inspect to see that switch operating lever is centered in switch opening in case.
3. Screw switch into transmission case and **torque** to 24 ft. lbs.
4. Add fluid to proper level.
5. Check to see that switch operates only in Park and Neutral.

## INSTRUMENT CLUSTER
### REPLACE

**On models with airbag restraint system, battery ground cable must be disconnected and isolated before performing this procedure. Failure to do so may result in accidental deployment and personal injury.**

1. Disconnect battery ground cable.
2. Remove lower panel assembly.
3. Remove left lower reinforcement by removing two screws located at left end.
4. Remove gear shift indicator.
5. Remove steering column toe plate mounting bolts and upper steering column mounting nuts, then lower the steering column.
6. Disconnect speedometer cable.
7. Remove two mounting screws and detach fuse block from mid-reinforcement.
8. Remove one screw attaching radio to mid-reinforcement.
9. Remove four upper and four lower cluster mounting screws, **Fig. 4.**
10. Pull cluster out from instrument panel and disconnect wire connectors, control cables and vacuum harness, then remove cluster assembly.
11. Reverse procedure to install.

## WINDSHIELD WIPER MOTOR
### REPLACE

1. Disconnect battery ground cable.
2. Remove cowl screen.
3. Remove drive crank arm retaining nut and drive crank. Disconnect wiring to motor.
4. Unfasten and remove wiper motor.
5. Reverse procedure to install.

## WINDSHIELD WIPER TRANSMISSION
### REPLACE

1. Disconnect battery ground cable.
2. Remove top plastic screen.
3. Remove arm and blade assemblies.
4. Remove drive crank from motor by removing the attaching nut.
5. Remove pivot mounting nut and washer.

6. Reverse procedure to install.

## WINDSHIELD WIPER SWITCH

### REPLACE

Refer to "Turn Signal Switch, Replace" for wiper switch replacement on standard columns or "Ignition Switch & Lock, Replace" for wiper switch replacement on tilt columns.

## RADIO

### REPLACE

**On models with airbag restraint system, battery ground cable must be disconnected and isolated before performing this procedure. Failure to do so may result in accidental deployment and personal injury.**

**When installing radio, be sure to adjust antenna trimmer for peak performance.**

1. Disconnect battery ground cable.
2. Remove instrument cluster bezel, then the radio mounting screws.
3. Pull radio from panel and disconnect all wiring, then remove radio from vehicle.
4. Reverse procedure to install.

## HEATER CORE

### REPLACE

**On models with airbag restraint system, battery ground cable must be disconnected and isolated before performing this procedure. Failure to do so may result in accidental deployment and personal injury.**

1. Disconnect battery ground cable, then drain cooling system.
2. Discharge refrigerant system.
3. Remove air cleaner, then disconnect heater hoses from heater core. Install plugs in heater core tubes to prevent coolant from spilling when removing unit.
4. Remove H valve, then cap refrigerant lines to prevent dirt and moisture from entering.
5. Remove instrument cluster bezel assembly.
6. Remove instrument panel upper cover, steering column cover and right intermediate side cowl trim panel.
7. Remove lower instrument panel.
8. Remove instrument center to lower reinforcement.
9. Remove floor console, if equipped.
10. Remove right center air distribution duct.
11. Disconnect locking tab on defroster distribution duct.
12. Disconnect blower motor resistor block wire connector.
13. Disconnect vacuum lines from water valve and vacuum source tee.
14. Remove wiring from heater-A/C unit and vacuum lines from inlet air housing, then disconnect vacuum harness coupling.
15. Remove nuts from heater-A/C housing mounting studs on engine side of dash panel.
16. Remove hanger strap from plenum stud above heater-A/C unit housing, then tilt evaporator housing back to clear dash panel and remove housing from vehicle.
17. Remove servo motor from shaft, then top cover screws and the cover.
18. Remove heater core from housing.
19. Reverse procedure to install.

## EVAPORATOR CORE

### REPLACE

**On models with airbag restraint system, battery ground cable must be disconnected and isolated before performing this procedure. Failure to do so may result in accidental deployment and personal injury.**

1. Disconnect battery ground cable, then drain cooling system.
2. Discharge refrigerant system.
3. Remove air cleaner, then disconnect heater hoses from heater core. Install plugs in heater core tubes to prevent coolant from spilling when removing unit.
4. Remove H valve, then cap refrigerant lines to prevent dirt and moisture from entering.
5. Remove instrument cluster bezel assembly.
6. Remove instrument panel upper cover, steering column cover and right intermediate side cowl trim panel.
7. Remove lower instrument panel.
8. Remove instrument center to lower reinforcement.
9. Remove floor console, if equipped.
10. Remove right center air distribution duct.
11. Disconnect locking tab on defroster distribution duct.
12. Disconnect blower motor resistor block wire connector.
13. Disconnect vacuum lines from water valve and vacuum source tee.
14. Remove wiring from heater-A/C unit and vacuum lines from inlet air housing, then disconnect vacuum harness coupling.
15. Remove nuts from heater-A/C housing mounting studs on engine side of dash panel.
16. Remove hanger strap from plenum stud above heater-A/C unit housing, then tilt evaporator housing back to clear dash panel and remove housing from vehicle.
17. Remove servo motor from shaft, then top cover screws and the cover.
18. Remove evaporator core from housing.
19. Reverse procedure to install.

## BLOWER MOTOR

### REPLACE

**On models with airbag restraint system, battery ground cable must be disconnected and isolated before performing this procedure. Failure to do so may result in accidental deployment and personal injury.**

The blower motor is accessible from under right side of instrument panel.

1. Disconnect battery ground cable.
2. Disconnect blower motor feed wire, then remove blower motor housing to heater-A/C housing attaching nuts and separate blower motor housing from upper housing.
3. Remove blower motor plate attaching screws, then remove wire grommet, mounting plate and blower motor and wheel as an assembly.
4. Reverse procedure to install.

# Engine

## INDEX



## AIRBAG SYSTEM DISARMING

**On models with airbag restraint system, battery ground cable must be disconnected and isolated before performing this procedure. Failure to do so may result in accidental deployment and personal injury.**

## ENGINE MOUNTS
### REPLACE

Refer to **Fig. 1.** when performing this procedure.

1. Disconnect throttle linkage at transmission and at carburetor.
2. Raise hood and position fan to clear radiator hose and radiator top tank.
3. Remove torque nuts from insulator studs.
4. Raise engine just enough to remove front engine mount.
5. Reverse above to install.

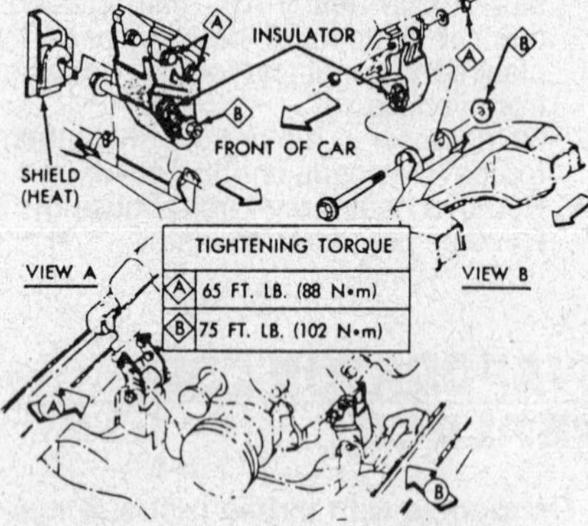


**Fig. 1 Exploded view of engine mounts**

## ENGINE
### REPLACE

1. Scribe a line on hinge brackets on hood to assure proper adjustments when installing, then remove hood.
2. Remove battery, drain cooling system, remove all hoses, fan shroud, disconnect oil cooler lines and remove radiator.
3. **On models with A/C,** remove compressor from mounting bracket and position on right fender. **Do not tilt compressor when removed from mounting bracket. Before installing compressor turn pulley several revolutions by hand to ensure all oil is back in compressor oil sump.**
4. **On all models,** remove distributor cap, vacuum lines and wiring.
5. Remove carburetor, linkage, starter wires and oil pressure wire.
6. Disconnect power steering hoses, if equipped.
7. Remove starter, alternator, charcoal canister and horns.
8. Disconnect exhaust pipe at manifold, then remove bell housing bolts and inspection plate.
9. Mark converter and drive plate to aid in installation, then remove torque converter drive plate bolts.
10. Support transmission with suitable stand. Attach C-clamp on bottom front of torque converter, to assure that converter remains properly positioned in transmission housing.
11. Disconnect engine from torque converter drive plate.
12. Attach engine lifting fixture.
13. Remove engine front mounting bolts, then raise and work engine out of chassis.
14. Reverse procedure to install.

## ROCKER ARMS
### REPLACE

#### REMOVAL

1. Disconnect spark plug wires, then remove closed ventilation system and evaporation control system from cylinder head cover.
2. Remove cylinder head cover and gasket, then rocker shaft bolts and retainers.
3. Remove rocker arm and shaft assembly.

#### INSTALLATION

If rocker arm assemblies are disassembled refer to **Fig. 2,** for rocker arm identification and **Fig. 3,** for positioning on shaft.

1. Install rocker shaft assemblies with notch on end facing inward toward the center of the engine and toward front of engine on the left bank and to the rear on the right bank, make sure to install long stamped steel retainers in the number two and four positions, **Fig. 3. The rocker arm shafts should be torqued down slowly to specifications, starting with the centermost bolts. Allow 20 minutes tappet bleed down time, after installation of the rocker shafts, before engine operation.**
2. Install cylinder head cover and torque to specifications.
3. Install closed crankcase ventilation system and evaporation control system.

## CYLINDER HEAD & INTAKE MANIFOLD
### REPLACE

1. Drain cooling system and disconnect battery ground cable.
2. Remove alternator, carburetor air cleaner and fuel line, then disconnect accelerator linkage.
3. Remove vacuum control hose and distributor cap and wires.
4. Disconnect coil wires, heat indicator wire, heater and bypass hoses.
5. Remove closed ventilation and evaporation control systems, then cylinder head covers.
6. Remove intake manifold, coil and carburetor as an assembly.
7. Remove exhaust manifolds.
8. Remove rocker arm and shaft assemblies as outlined under "Rocker Arms, Replace."
9. Remove pushrods. **During disassembly note location of pushrods so they can be installed in the**

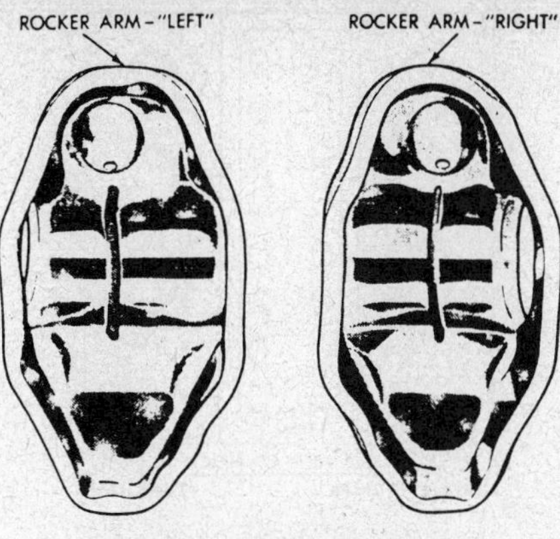


Fig. 2 Rocker arm identification

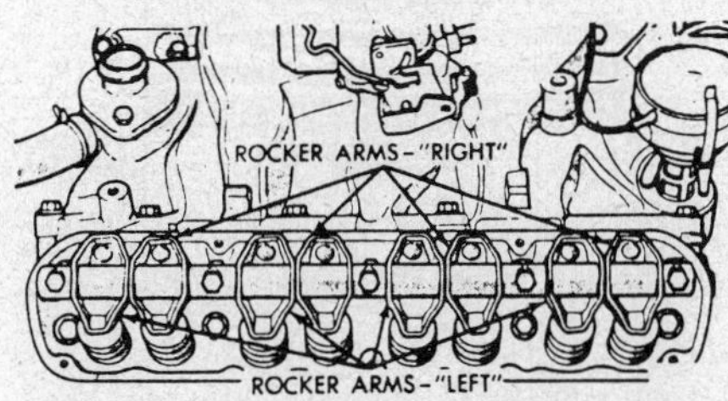


Fig. 3 Rocker arm and shaft assembly installed

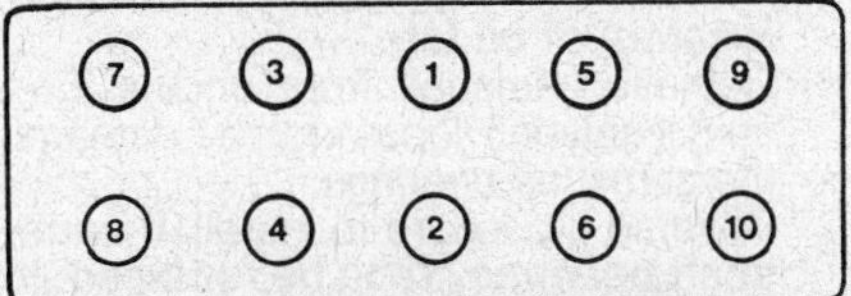

Fig. 4 Cylinder head tightening sequence

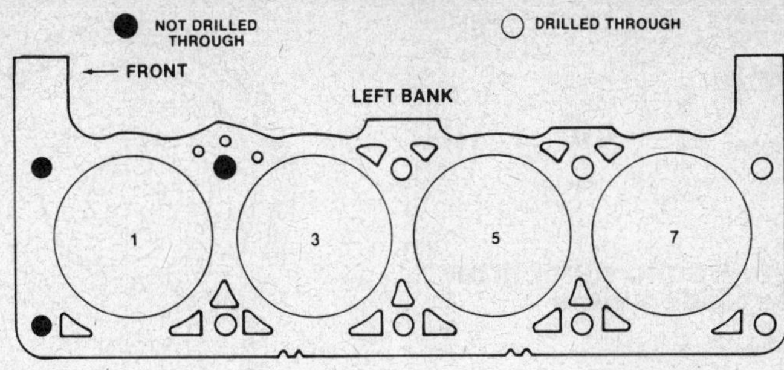


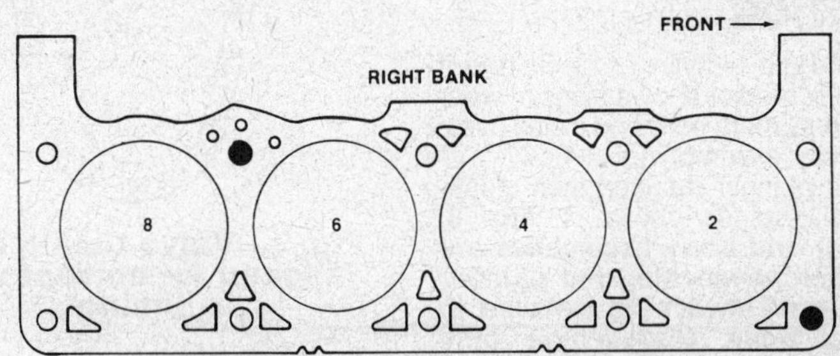


Fig. 5 Cylinder head bolt hole identification

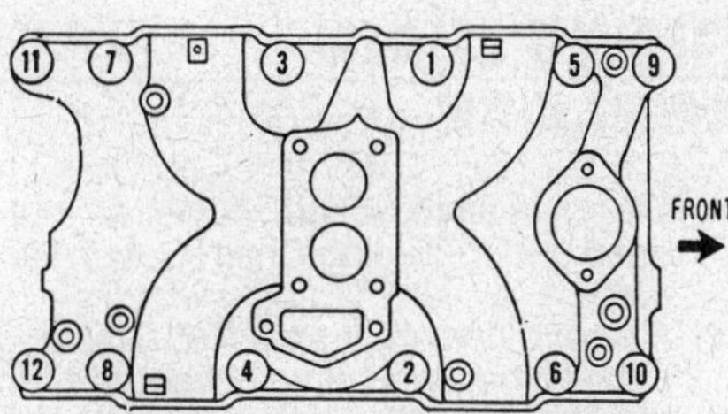


Fig. 6 Intake manifold tightening sequence

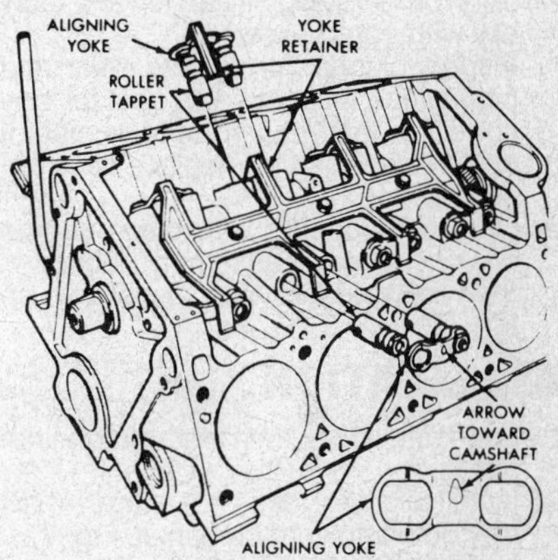


Fig. 7 Hydraulic roller lifter installation

**same position.**

10. Remove cylinder head bolts and cylinder heads.
11. Reverse procedure to install, noting the following:
    a. Install cylinder heads and tighten bolts to specifications in sequence shown in **Fig. 4. 5.2L/V8-318 engines have cylinder head bolt holes drilled through the block into the water jacket in certain locations, Fig. 5. Cylinder head bolts in these locations must have sealer 4057989 or equivalent applied to the threads to prevent engine coolant leakage. Ensure old sealer is cleaned from the threads before applying new sealer.**
    b. Install intake manifold, tighten all bolts finger tight, then torque bolts to specification in sequence shown in **Fig. 6.**

# VALVES

## ADJUST

This engine is equipped with roller type hydraulic tappets. No adjustment is required.

# VALVE ARRANGEMENT

## FRONT TO REAR

5.2L/V8-318.............. E-I-I-E-E-I-I-E

# VALVE LIFT SPECIFICATIONS

| Engine | Year | Int. | Exh. |
|---|---|---|---|
| 5.2L/V8-318 | 1989 | .373 | .400 |

# VALVE TIMING SPECIFICATIONS

## INTAKE OPENS BEFORE TDC

| Engine | Year | Degrees |
|---|---|---|
| 5.2L/V8-318 | 1989 | 10 |

# VALVE GUIDES

Valves operate in guide holes bored directly in the cylinder head. When valve stem-to-guide clearance becomes excessive, valves with oversize stems of .005, .015 and .030 inch are available for service replacement. When necessary to install valves with oversize stems the valve bores should be reamed to provide the proper operating clearance.

# VALVE LIFTERS

## REPLACE

### REMOVAL

1. Remove valve covers, rocker shaft assemblies, pushrods and intake manifold as outlined in "Cylinder Head & Intake Manifold, Replace."
2. Remove yoke retainer and aligning yokes, **Fig. 7.**
3. Insert puller No. C-4129 or equivalent through opening in cylinder head, seat puller securely in head of lifter, then pull lifter from bore. **If more than one lifter is to be removed, identify lift-**

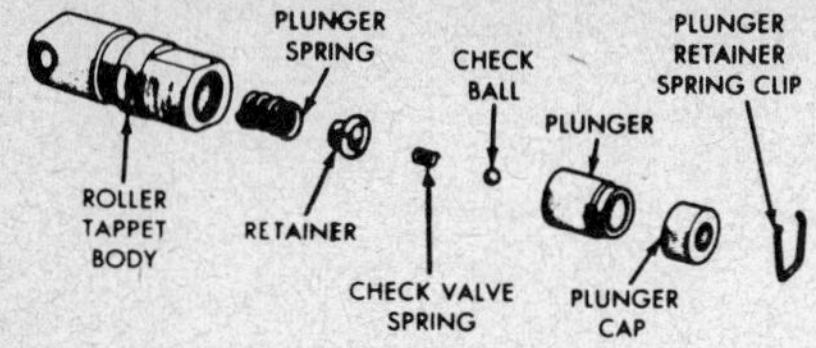


**Fig. 8 Hydraulic roller lifter exploded view**

ers to ensure reinstallation in original position.

## INSPECTION

1. Inspect bore in cylinder block, and if bore is scored or shows signs of wear or sticking, ream bore and install oversized lifter assembly.
2. Pry out plunger retainer, then disassemble lifter as shown in **Fig. 8. Plunger and body assemblies are not interchangeable, and plunger valve must always be installed in original body. Disassemble only one lifter at a time to avoid mixing components.**
3. Clean components with solvent suitable for removing all varnish and blow dry with compressed air.
4. Inspect plunger for scoring, wear and pitting, and inspect valve seat for any condition that may prevent seating. If any defect is found, replace lifter assembly.
5. Coat components with clean engine oil or suitable assembly lubricant, then reassemble lifter as shown in **Fig. 8.**

## INSTALLATION

1. Lubricate lifters, then install in original bores.
2. Install aligning yokes ensuring that arrow points toward camshaft, **Fig. 7.**
3. Install yoke retainers and torque screws to specifications.
4. Reverse remaining procedure to complete installation, start engine and run at approximately 15000 RPM until it reaches normal operating temperature. **To prevent engine damage, do not run engine above fast idle until all lifters have filled with oil and become quiet.**

## TIMING CHAIN COVER
### REPLACE

1. Drain cooling system, then remove radiator, fan and shroud, all drive belts.
2. Remove water pump, then power steering pump.
3. Remove crankshaft pulley from vibration damper, then vibration damper.
4. Remove fuel lines and fuel pump.
5. Loosen oil pan bolts and remove front bolt at each side.
6. Remove chain case cover and gasket, using extreme caution to avoid damaging oil pan gasket otherwise oil pan will have to be removed. It is normal to find particles of neoprene collected between crankshaft seal retainer and oil slinger.
7. Reverse procedure to install.

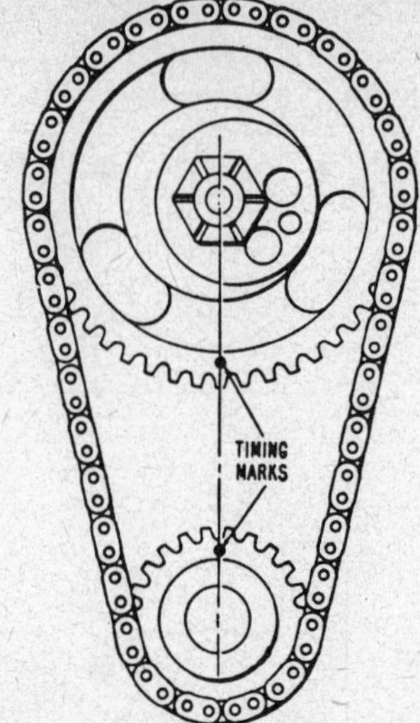


**Fig. 9 Valve timing marks aligned for correct valve timing**

## TIMING CHAIN
### REPLACE

1. Remove timing chain cover as outlined under "Timing Chain Cover, Replace."
2. Remove camshaft sprocket attaching cup washer, fuel pump eccentric, then timing chain with crankshaft and camshaft sprockets.
3. To install chain and sprockets, lay both the camshaft and crankshaft sprockets on the bench. Position the sprockets so that the timing marks are next to each other. Place the chain on both sprockets, then push the gears apart as far as the chain will permit. Use a straightedge to form a line through the exact centers of both gears. The timing marks must be on this line, **Fig. 9.**
4. Slide the chain with both sprockets on the camshaft and crankshaft at the same time; then recheck the alignment. **Use holding tool No. C-3509 to prevent camshaft from contacting welch plug in rear of engine block. Remove distributor and oil pump-distributor drive gear. Position tool against rear side of cam gear and attach tool with distributor retainer plate bolt.**

## CAMSHAFT
### REPLACE

1. Remove intake manifold as outlined under "Cylinder Head & Intake Manifold, Replace."
2. Remove timing chain as outlined under "Timing Chain, Replace."
3. Remove distributor and lift out oil pump/distributor drive shaft.

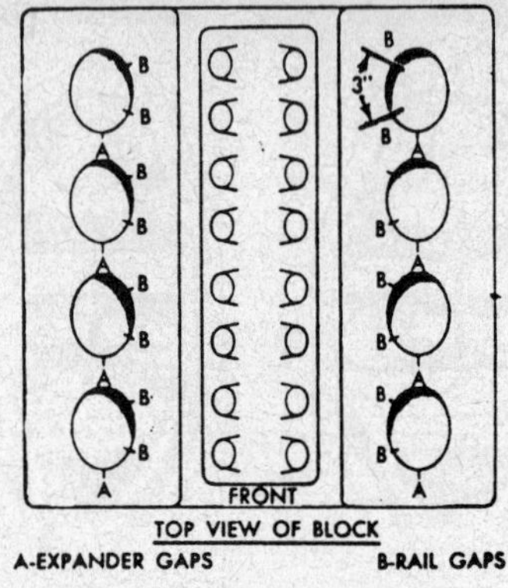


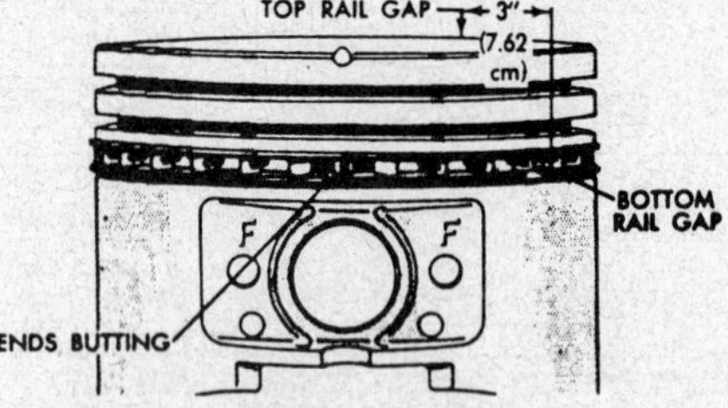


**Fig. 10 Piston ring installation.**

4. Remove camshaft thrust plate. **Note location of oil tab.**
5. Remove camshaft from engine. Ensure camshaft lobes do not damage the camshaft bearings.
6. Reverse procedure to install. **If camshaft bearings are to be replaced, it is recommended that the engine be removed from the chassis and the crankshaft taken out in order that any chips or foreign material may be removed from the oil passages.**

## PISTON & ROD, ASSEMBLE

When installing piston and rod assemblies in the cylinders, align ring rail gaps and expander gaps as shown in **Fig. 10.** Ensure ID mark on each compression ring is facing toward top of the piston.

Immerse the piston head and rings in clean engine oil and, with a suitable piston ring compressor, insert the piston and rod assembly into the bore. Tap the piston down into the bore, using the handle of a hammer.

Refer to **Fig. 11,** for piston specifications.

## PISTONS, PINS & RINGS

Pistons are available in standard sizes and the following oversize: .020 inch.

Pins are available in the following oversizes: .003, .008 inch.

Rings are available in the standard and oversizes.

## MAIN & ROD BEARINGS

Main bearings are furnished in standard

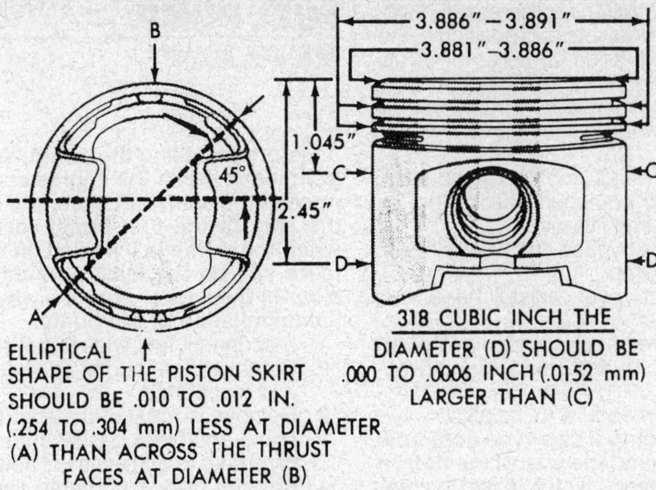


**Fig. 11 Piston measurements**

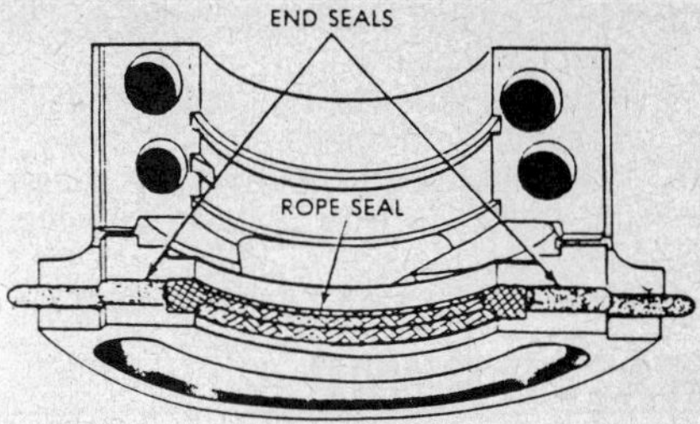


**Fig. 12 Installing seal ends**

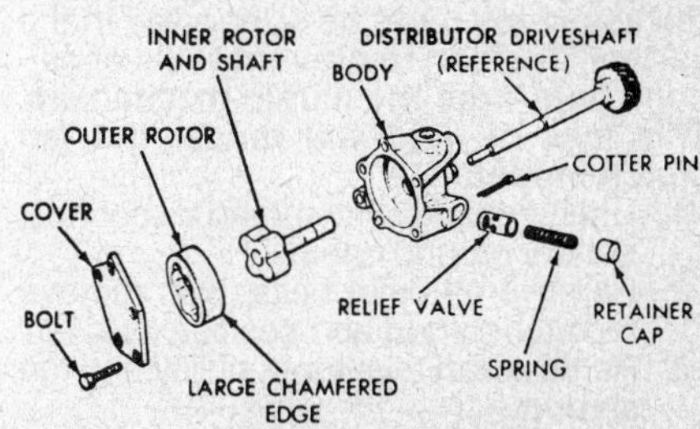


**Fig. 13 Oil pump**

sizes and the following undersizes: .001, .002, .003, .010, .012 inch.

Rod bearings are furnished in standard sizes and the following undersizes: .001, .002, .003, .010, .012 inch.

# REAR MAIN BEARING OIL SEAL
## REPLACE

The 5.2L/V8-318 engine has cap seals in addition to lower seal secured by rear main bearing cap. Cap seal with yellow paint is installed, narrow sealing edge up, into right side of bearing cap with bearing cap in engine position. Cap seals must be flush with shoulder of bearing cap to prevent oil leakage.

1. Remove oil pan as outlined under "Oil Pan, Replace."
2. Remove lower rope seal half from bearing cap.
3. Install new lower seal half in cap, seating seal in cap groove with suitable driver.
4. Cut ends of seal flush with cap surface.
5. Lightly lubricate lower seal surface with engine oil.
6. Install cap side seals, **Fig. 12,** ensuring that seal identified with yellow paint is on the right side.
7. Using seal replacer No. KD-492 or equivalent, replace upper seal. **Trim frayed ends of upper seal after installation, if necessary.**
8. Install bearing cap and torque bolts to specifications.
9. Reinstall oil pump and pan, fill engine and check for leaks.

# OIL PAN
## REPLACE

1. Disconnect battery ground cable and remove engine oil level dipstick.
2. Raise vehicle and drain crankcase.
3. Remove exhaust crossover pipe, then disconnect and lower center link.
4. Remove starter and starter mounting stud.
5. Remove torque converter inspection cover.
6. Remove oil pan attaching bolts and oil pan.
7. Reverse procedure to install, torquing all bolt/nuts to specifications.

# OIL PUMP
## REPLACE

Remove oil pan as outlined, then remove pump from rear main bearing cap. Reverse procedure to install, torquing retaining bolts to specifications.

# OIL PUMP SERVICE

After removing the pump from the engine, it should be disassembled, cleaned and inspected for wear, **Fig. 13.**

1. To remove the relief valve, remove the cotter pin and drill a 1/8 inch hole into the relief valve retainer cap and install a self-threading sheet metal screw.
2. Clamp screw into vise and tap on housing lightly with a soft hammer to remove the retaining cap. Discard retainer cap, then remove the relief valve spring and valve.
3. Remove the oil pump cover and lockwashers.
4. Remove pump rotor, shaft and lift out outer rotor.
5. Mating surface of the pump cover should be smooth. If scratched or grooved, replace the pump.
6. Lay a straightedge across the cover. If a .0015 inch feeler gauge can be inserted between the cover and the straightedge, replace the pump.
7. Measure thickness and diameter of outer rotor. If rotor thickness is .825 inch or less, or if the diameter of rotor is 2.429 inches or less, replace outer rotor.
8. If the inner rotor is .825 inch or less, replace the inner rotor and shaft assembly.
9. Slide outer rotor into pump body with large chamfer edge installed toward pump body. Press rotor to one side with fingers and measure clearance between rotor and body with a feeler gauge. If the measurement is .014 inch or greater, replace the pump.
10. Place the inner rotor and shaft into the pump body. If clearance between the rotors is .008 inch or greater, replace the shaft and both rotors.
11. Place a straightedge across the face of the pump between bolt holes. If a feeler gauge of .004 inch or greater can be inserted, replace the pump.
12. Check the oil pump relief valve plunger for scoring and free operation in the bore. Small marks may be removed with 400-grit sand paper.
13. The relief valve spring should have a free length of approximately 1 61/64 inch and should test between 19.5 and 20 pounds when compressed to 1 11/32 inch. If not, replace the spring.

# BELT TENSION DATA

| Belt | New Lbs. | Used Lbs. |
|---|---|---|
| All | 125 | 80 |

# COOLING SYSTEM BLEED

This engine does not require a specified bleed procedure. After filling cooling system, run engine to operating temperature with radiator/pressure cap off. Air will then be automatically bled through cap opening.

# THERMOSTAT
## REPLACE

1. Drain cooling system.
2. Remove thermostat housing bolts, then the housing.
3. Remove thermostat and discard gasket.

4. Clean gasket sealing surfaces and install new gasket.
5. Install thermostat by centering in intake manifold opening.
6. Install thermostat housing and attaching bolts. **Torque** bolts to 200 inch lbs.
7. Fill cooling system as necessary.

## WATER PUMP
### REPLACE

**When it becomes necessary to remove a fan clutch of the silicone type, the assembly must be supported in the vertical position to prevent leaks of silicone fluid from the clutch mechanism. This loss of fluid will render the fan clutch inoperative.**

1. Drain cooling system and disconnect battery ground cable.
2. Remove all drive belts, then remove radiator shroud and position over fan.
3. Remove fan assembly, pulley and fan shroud.
4. Remove alternator adjusting strap and mounting bolts and position alternator aside.
5. Remove A/C compressor with mounting brackets and position aside, if equipped. Keep compressor in upright position.
6. Remove power steering pump mounting bolts and position pump aside, if equipped.
7. Remove air pump and mounting brackets, if equipped. Disconnect air hose at pump fittings.
8. Disconnect bypass and heater hoses at water pump.
9. Disconnect lower radiator hose from pump.
10. Remove remaining water pump attaching bolts and remove pump assembly.
11. Reverse procedure to install.

**When replacing a cup-type core hole plug in an engine, the size of the hole in the cylinder head, water jacket or rear bearing bore for the camshaft should be checked. At these locations a 1/16 inch oversize hole is sometimes bored in production and an oversize core plug installed. Core plugs 1/16 inch oversize are available for replacement should they be required at these locations.**

## FUEL PUMP
### REPLACE

**Before installing the pump, it is good practice to crank the engine so that the nose of the camshaft eccentric is out of the way of the fuel pump rocker arm when the pump is installed. In this way there will be the least amount of tension on the rocker arm, thereby easing the installation of the pump.**

1. Disconnect fuel lines from fuel pump.
2. Remove fuel pump attaching bolts and fuel pump.
3. Remove all gasket material from the pump and block gasket surfaces. Apply sealer to both sides of new gasket.
4. Position gasket on pump flange and hold pump in position against its mounting surface. Make sure rocker arm is riding on camshaft eccentric.
5. Press pump tight against its mounting. Install retaining screws and tighten them alternately.
6. Connect fuel lines. Then operate engine and check for leaks.

## TIGHTENING SPECIFICATIONS

***Torque Specifications Are For Clean And Lightly Lubricated Threads Only. Dry Or Dirty Threads Produce Increased Friction Which Prevents Accurate Measurement Of Tightness.**

| Year | Component | Torque/Ft. Lbs. |
|---|---|---|
| 1989 | A/C Compressor Bracket To Water Pump Bolt | 30 |
| | A/C Compressor Support Bolts | 30 |
| | A/C Compressor To Bracket Nut | 50 |
| | Camshaft Sprocket Lockbolt | 50 |
| | Alternator Adjusting Bolt | 200① |
| | Alternator Pivot Nut | 30 |
| | Camshaft Sprocket Locknut | 50 |
| | Camshaft Thrust Plate | 210① |
| | Chain Case Cover | 35 |
| | Clutch Housing | ② |
| | Connecting Rod Nut | 45 |
| | Cylinder Head Bolt | 105 |
| | Cylinder Head Cover | 95① |
| | Distributor Clamp Bolt | 200 |
| | Engine Front Mount To Engine Nut | 65 |
| | Engine Front Mount To Frame Nut | 75 |
| | Engine Rear Mount Crossmember To Frame Nut | 75 |
| | Engine Rear Mount Insulator To Extension | 50 |
| | Engine Rear Mount To Crossmember Nut | 50 |
| | Exhaust Manifold Bolt | 20 |
| | Exhaust Manifold Nut | 15 |
| | Exhaust Pipe Flange Nut | 24 |
| | Fan Blade Attaching Bolts | 200① |
| | Flex Plate To Convertor | 270① |
| | Flex Plate To Crankshaft | 55 |
| | Flywheel To Crankshaft | 55 |
| | Fuel Pump Bolts | 30 |
| | Intake Manifold Bolts | 40 |

*Continued*

## TIGHTENING SPECIFICATIONS—Continued

| Year | Component | Torque/Ft. Lbs. |
|---|---|---|
| 1989 | Main Bearing Cap | 85 |
| | Oil Filter Adapter Screw | 30 |
| | Oil Filter Attaching Adapter | 30 |
| | Oil Pan Drain Plug | 20 |
| | Oil Pan Screw | 200① |
| | Oil Pressure Gauge Sending Unit | 60① |
| | Oil Pump Attaching Bolt | 30 |
| | Oil Pump Cover Bolt | 95① |
| | Rocker Shaft Bracket Bolt | 200① |
| | Spark Plug | 30 |
| | Starter Mounting Bolt | 50 |
| | Temperature Gauge Sending Unit | 60① |
| | Vibration Damper | 100 |
| | Water Pump To Housing | 30 |
| | Yoke Retainer | 200① |

①—Inch lbs.
②—3/8 inch bolt, 30 ft. lbs.; 7/16 inch bolt, 50 ft. lbs.

# Rear Axle & Propeller Shaft

## INDEX



## INTEGRAL TYPE REAR AXLE

The integral type rear axles, **Figs. 1 and 2,** have drive pinions mounted in two opposing tapered roller bearings which are preloaded by a spacer positioned between them. The differential is also supported by two tapered roller bearings. A threaded differential bearing adjuster is located in each bearing pedestal cap to eliminate differential side play, adjust and maintain ring and pinion backlash and provide a means of obtaining differential bearing preload.

Axles are retained by means of a C washer which is installed into a groove in the inner end of the axle shaft inside the differential unit.

A removable stamped steel cover, bolted to the rear of the carrier, permits inspection and service of the differential without removal of the complete axle assembly from the vehicle.

**7¹/₄ and 8¹/₄ inch axle differentials have balanced side and pinion gears. Any attempt to mix these side or pinion gears with previously manufactured ones will result in lock up or excessive differential backlash. Side and pinion gears must be replaced as a set.**

## AXLE SHAFT

### REPLACE

1. Raise and support vehicle, then remove wheel assembly and brake drum.
2. Loosen differential housing cover and drain lubricant. Remove cover, **Figs. 1 and 2.**
2. Turn differential case to make pinion shaft lock screw accessible and remove lock screw and shaft.
3. Push axle shaft inward toward center of car and remove C washer from groove in axle shaft, **Fig. 3.**
4. Remove axle shaft from housing, being careful not to damage the axle bearing, which will remain in the housing.
5. The axle bearing and/or seal can now be removed if necessary.
6. Reverse procedure to install.

## REAR AXLE

### REPLACE

1. Raise vehicle and support front of rear springs with floor stands.
2. Drain lubricant from differential housing.
3. Remove rear wheels. **Do not remove brakes drums.**
4. Disconnect brake lines at wheel cylinders. Cap brake line fittings to prevent loss of fluid.
5. Disconnect parking brake cables.
6. Mark propeller shaft universal joint and pinion flanges for reassembly, then remove propeller shaft.
5. Disconnect shock absorbers from spring plate studs, then loosen rear spring U-bolt nuts and remove U-bolts.
6. Remove axle assembly from vehicle.
7. Reverse procedure to install.

## PROPELLER SHAFT

### REPLACE

1. Remove both rear universal joint roller and bushing assembly clamps from pinion yoke. Do not disturb retaining strap holding roller assemblies on cross.
2. Lower front of vehicle slightly to prevent loss of transmission oil and pull propeller shaft out as an assembly.
3. To install, carefully slide yoke into splines on transmission output shaft.
4. Align rear of propeller shaft with pinion yoke and position roller and bushing assemblies into seats of pinion yoke.
5. Install bushing clamps and tighten clamp bolts to 170 inch lbs.

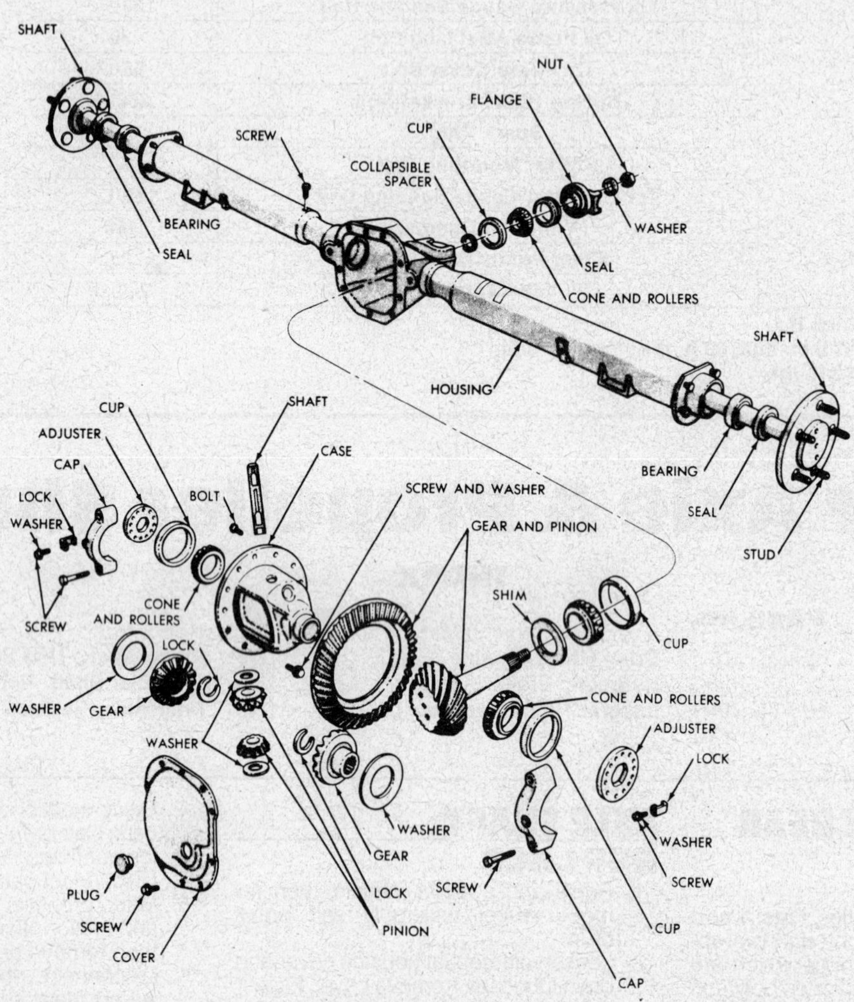


**Fig. 1 Integral carrier rear axle exploded view. Models w/7¼ inch ring gear**

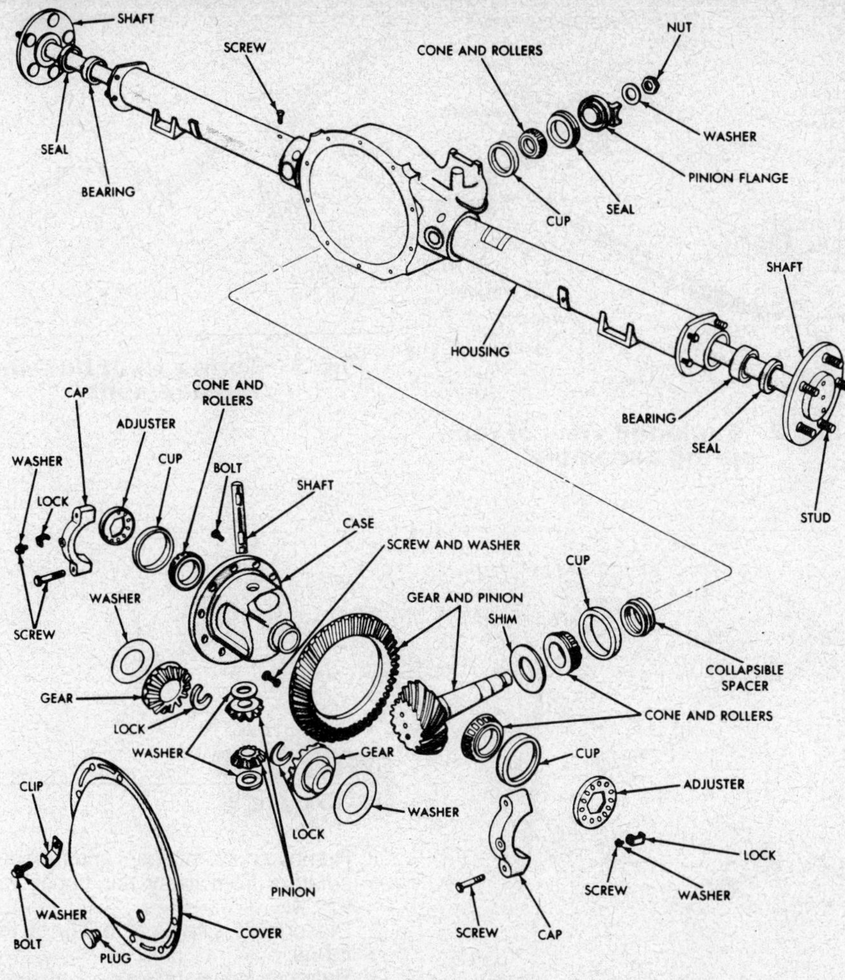


**Fig. 2 Integral carrier rear axle exploded view. Models w/8¼ inch ring gear**

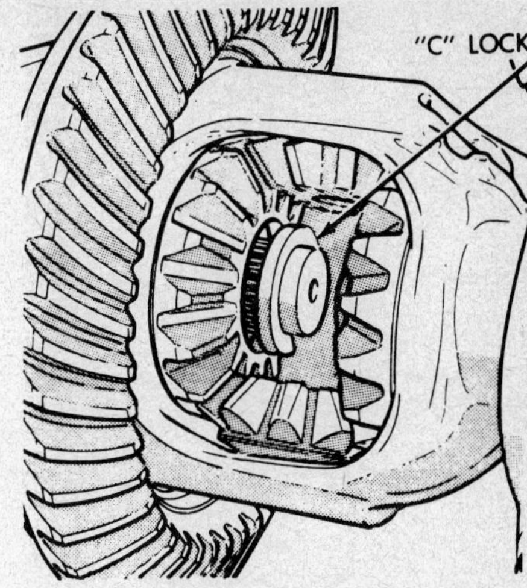


**Fig. 3 Axle shaft 'C' lock installation**

# Rear Suspension

## INDEX



## SHOCK ABSORBER REPLACE

1. Raise and support vehicle.
2. Using floor stands under axle assembly, raise axle to relieve load on shock absorber.
3. Remove shock absorber lower nut, retainer, and bushing from spring plate.
4. Remove shock absorber upper nut and bolt, then shock absorber from vehicle.
5. Reverse procedure to install, torquing all bolts/nut to specifications.

## LEAF SPRING & BUSHINGS REPLACE

1. Raise and support vehicle.
2. Using floor stands under axle assembly, raise axle to relieve load on shock absorber.
3. Disconnect shock absorber at spring plate, then sway bar link at spring plate, if equipped.
4. Remove U-bolts and spring plate, **Fig. 1.**
5. Remove spring front hanger to body mount bracket nuts, **Fig. 2.**
6. Remove rear shackle bolts, lower spring, thus pulling spring front hanger bolts out of holes.
7. Remove front hanger and rear shackle from spring.
8. To replace pivot bushings, proceed as follows:
   a. Bend or remove metal from bushing flange, then bend two locking tabs away from spring eye on opposite side.
   b. Remove bushing a shown in **Fig. 3.**
8. Reverse procedure to install.

## LEAF SPRING SERVICE

To replace interliners, remove spring

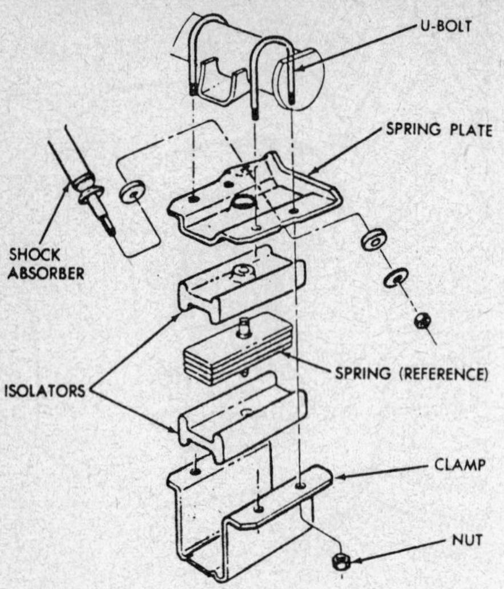


**Fig. 1 Rear spring isolator**

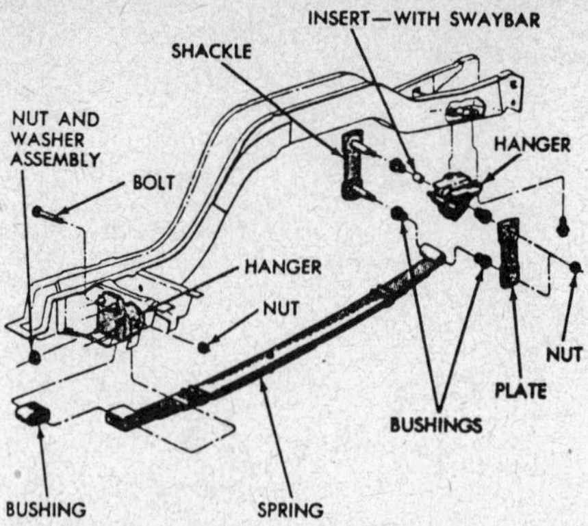

**Fig. 2 Exploded view of rear spring assembly**

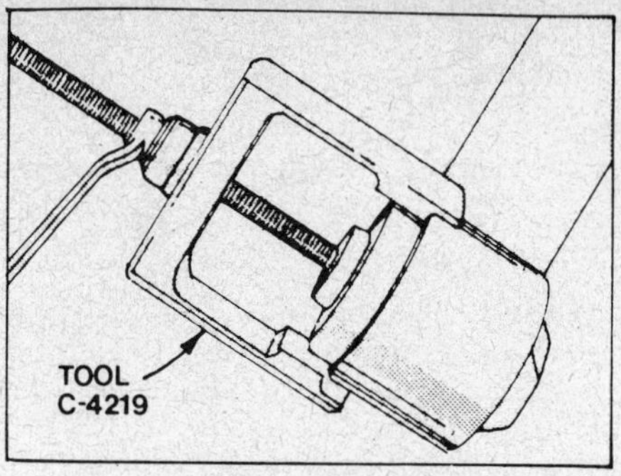

**Fig. 3 Spring pivot bushing replacement**

alignment clips and discard alignment clips. Separate spring leaves with a screwdriver or other suitable tool and remove interliners. Thoroughly clean spring surfaces before installation of new interliners.

To replace zinc interleaves, clamp spring in a vise and remove center bolt. Open vise carefully, allowing spring to expand. Interleaves can now be serviced. Install a drift through spring center bolt holes and clamp spring in a vise. Remove drift and install center bolt.

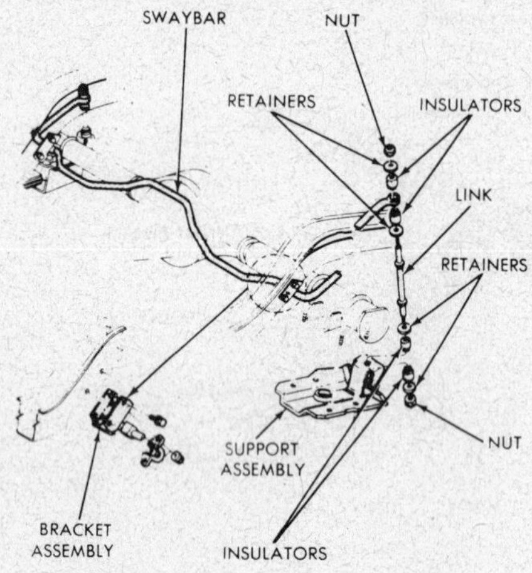


**Fig. 4 Sway bar installation**

## SWAY BAR REPLACE

1. Remove nuts, retainers and rubber insulators from sway bar upper links, **Fig. 4.**
2. Disconnect sway bar brackets from frame.
3. Remove link from support assembly and replace insulators. Reverse procedure to install.

## TIGHTENING SPECIFICATIONS

| Year | Component | Torque/ft. lbs. |
|---|---|---|
| 1989 | Spring Center Bolt Nut | 40 |
| | Spring Front Hanger Nut | 35 |
| | Spring Pivot Bolt And Nut | 105 |
| | Spring Rear Hanger | 35 |
| | Spring Shackle Nut | 35 |
| | Spring U-Bolt Nut | 45 |
| | Shock Absorber Upper Nut | 70 |
| | Shock Absorber Lower Nut | 35 |
| | Sway Bar Shaft Bracket Screws | 100① |
| | Sway Bar Link Nuts | 200① |
| | Wheel Lug Nuts | 85 |

①—Inch lbs.

# Front Suspension & Steering

INDEX



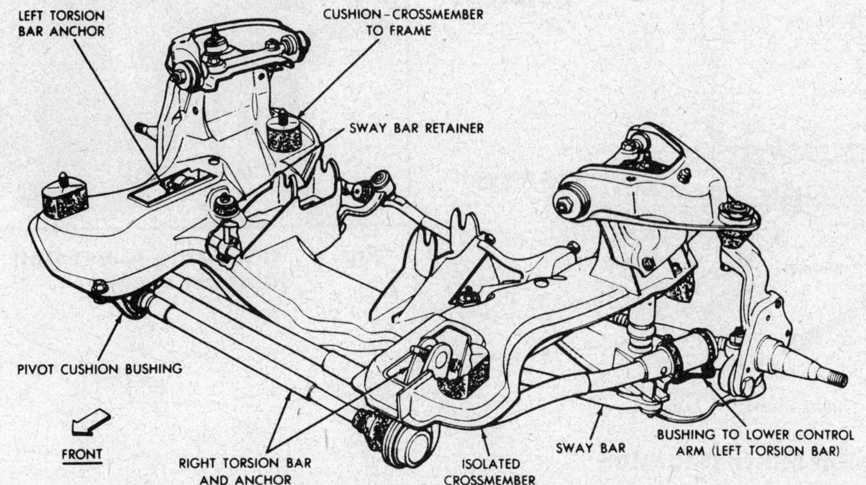


**Fig. 1 Transverse torsion bar front suspension**

## FRONT SUSPENSION

### TRANSVERSE TORSION BAR FRONT SUSPENSION

This front suspension, **Figs. 1 and 2**, incorporates two transverse torsion bars which react on the outboard end of the lower control arms. The torsion bars are anchored in the front crossmember opposite the affected wheel. The torsion bars are mounted parallel to the front crossmember through a pivot cushion bushing, attached to the crossmember, and turns and extends rearward to the lower control arm. The torsion bar ends are provided with an isolated bushing, bolted to the lower control arm and sway bar, which acts as the lower control arm strut.

Riding height is controlled by the torsion bar adjusting bolts on the anchor end of the torsion bar. The right torsion bar is adjusted from the left side and the left torsion bar is adjusted from the right side.

The torsion bar assembly incorporates the pivot cushion bushing, **Fig. 3** and bushing to lower control arm. The lower control arm inner ends are bolted to the crossmember and pivots through bushings.

Caster and camber settings are made by loosening the upper control arm pivot bar bolt nuts and adjusting as necessary.

## WHEEL BEARINGS ADJUST

1. Tighten adjusting nut to 20-25 ft. lbs. while rotating wheel.
2. Back off adjusting nut 1/4 turn.
3. Finger tighten adjusting nut while rotating wheel, then align nut lock with cotter pin slot and install cotter pin.
4. The resulting adjustment should be .001-.003 end play.

## WHEEL BEARINGS REPLACE

1. Raise car and remove front wheels.
2. Remove grease cap, cotter pin, locknut and bearing adjusting nut.
3. Remove bolts that attach caliper to steering knuckle.
4. Slowly slide caliper up and away from disc and support caliper on steering knuckle arm. **Do not allow caliper to hang by brake hose.**
5. Remove thrust washer and outer bearing cone. Remove hub and disc assembly. Grease retainer and inner bearing can now be removed.
6. Reverse procedure to install.

## CHECKING BALL JOINTS FOR WEAR

### UPPER BALL JOINT

1. Position a suitable jack under lower control arm and raise wheel and tire assembly clear of floor, then remove wheel cover and wheel bearing dust cover and cotter pin.
2. Tighten wheel bearing adjusting nut just enough to remove all play between hub, bearings and spindle.
3. Lower jack positioned under lower control arm to allow tire to lightly contact floor.
4. Grasp top of tire and move wheel and tire assembly inward and outward. While moving tire inward and outward, check for movement at ball joints between steering knuckle and upper control arm.
5. If any lateral movement is present, the upper ball joint should be replaced.
6. After completing upper ball joint check, readjust wheel bearing as described under "Wheel Bearings, Adjust."

### LOWER BALL JOINT

**If loose ball joints are suspected, first make sure the front wheel bearings are properly adjusted and that the control arms are tight.**

1. Raise front of vehicle and place jack stands underneath each lower control arm as far out as possible. **The upper control arms must not contact the rubber rebound bumpers.**
2. With weight of vehicle on lower control arms, attach dial indicator onto lower control arm, **Fig. 4.**
3. Place dial indicator plunger tip against ball joint housing and zero dial indicator.
4. Using a pry bar under the center of the tire, raise and lower the tire and measure the axial travel of the ball joint housing with respect to the ball joint. If the axial travel is .030 inch or more than specified, the ball joint should be replaced.

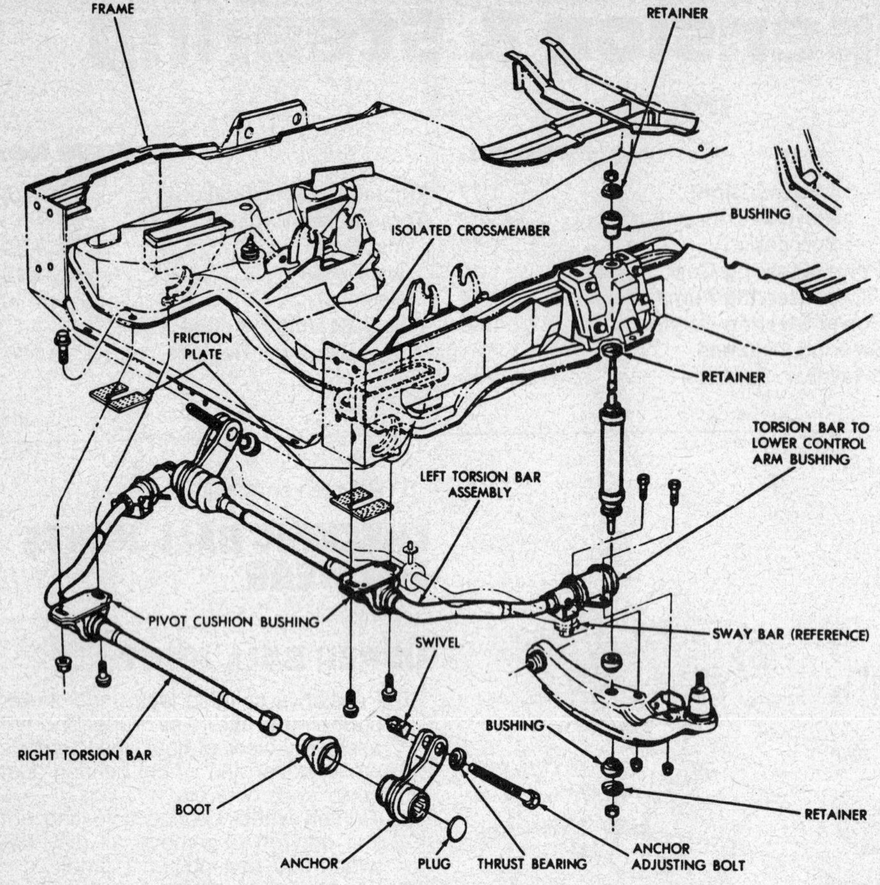


Fig. 2 Transverse torsion bar installation

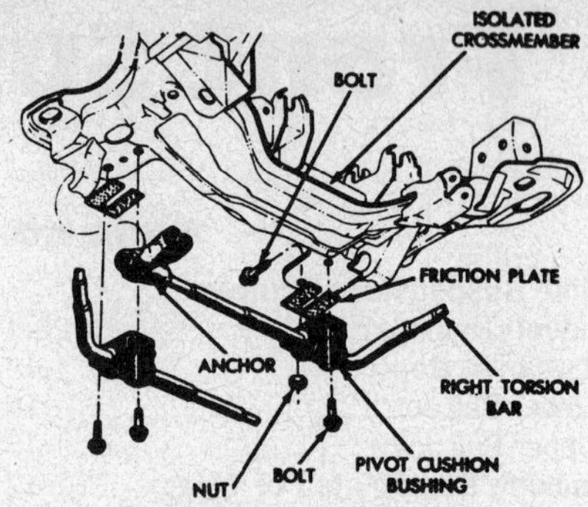


Fig. 3 Pivot cushion bushing & torsion bars

Fig. 4 Checking lower ball joint for wear

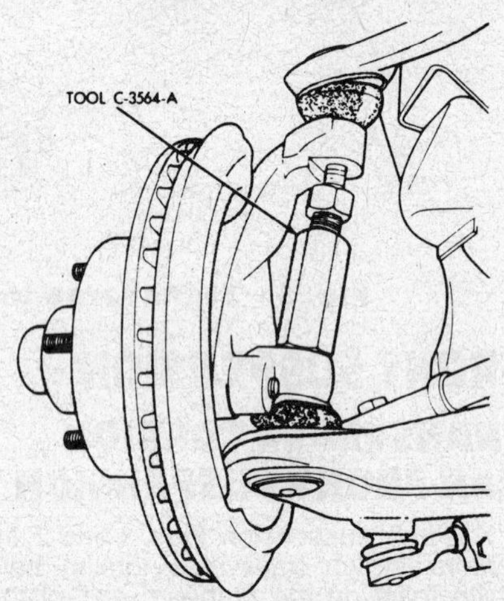


Fig. 5 Removing upper ball joint stud

# BALL JOINTS

## REPLACE

### UPPER BALL JOINT

1. Place ignition switch in the Off position.
2. Using a suitable jack raise front of vehicle and position a jack stand under lower control arm as close to wheel and tire assembly as possible. Check to ensure that jack stand is not in contact with brake splash shield. Also check to ensure that rubber rebound bumper is not in contact with frame. **The torsion bar will remain in the loaded position.**
3. Remove wheel and tire assembly.
4. Remove cotter pin and nut from lower ball joint stud. Position tool No. C3564-A over lower ball joint stud, **Fig. 5,** allowing tool to rest on knuckle arm, then set tool securely against upper ball joint stud.
5. Tighten tool to apply pressure against upper ball joint stud, then strike knuckle with hammer to loosen stud.
6. Remove tool, then detach upper ball joint from knuckle. **Support knuckle and brake assembly to prevent damage to lower ball joint and brake hoses.**
7. Remove upper ball joint from upper control arm, using socket No. C3560.
8. Reverse procedure to install. Thread upper ball joint into control arm as far as possible by hand. Torque upper ball joint into control arm to specifications. After tightening lower ball joint stud nut, install cotter pin. **Ball joint seals should be replaced whenever they have been removed.**

### LOWER BALL JOINT

1. Place ignition switch in the Off position.
2. Raise vehicle and support so front suspension is in the full rebound position. Position jack stands under front frame for additional support.
3. Remove wheel and tire assembly, then remove disc brake caliper and support with wire hook to prevent brake hose from becoming damaged.
4. Remove disc brake hub and rotor assembly and splash shield, then disconnect shock absorber at lower mounting.
5. Release load on torsion bar by rotating adjusting bolt counterclockwise.
6. Remove upper and lower ball joint stud nuts and cotter pin, then position tool No. C3564-A over upper ball joint stud so that tool is resting on steering knuckle, **Fig. 5.**
7. Rotate threaded portion of tool to lock it against lower ball joint stud. Tighten tool to place pressure on lower ball joint stud, then strike steering knuckle with a hammer to loosen stud. Remove tool and disconnect lower ball joint.
8. Use press adaptor No. C4212 to press ball joint from lower control arm.
9. Position replacement ball joint on lower control arm, then press into control arm using press adaptor No. C4212.
10. Install seal over lower ball joint. Use adaptor No. C4039 to press retainer portion of seal until it is locked in position.
11. Position lower ball joint to steering knuckle, then install upper and lower stud nuts and torque to specifications. After tightening stud nuts, install cotter pin.
12. Place tension on torsion bar by rotating adjusting bolt clockwise.
13. Install disc brake assembly and wheel and tire assembly, then adjust front wheel bearing as described under "Wheel Bearings, Adjust."

14. Lubricate ball joint, then lower vehicle and adjust vehicle riding height.

## TORSION BAR REPLACE

### REMOVAL

1. Raise vehicle and support so front suspension is in full rebound position.
2. Rotate anchor adjusting bolts located in frame crossmember, counterclockwise to release load on both torsion bars. Then, remove anchor adjusting bolt from torsion bar to be removed.
3. Raise lower control arms until 2 7/8 inch clearance is obtained between crossmember ledge at jounce bumper and the torsion bar end bushing and support lower arms at this height. **This procedure will align the sway bar and the lower control arm attaching points for disassembly and component realignment and attachment during assembly.**
4. Remove sway bar to control arm attaching bolt and retainers, then the two bolts securing torsion bar end bushing to lower control arm.
5. Remove two bolts securing torsion bar pivot cushion bushing to crossmember, then the torsion bar and anchor assembly from crossmember.
6. Separate anchor from torsion bar.

### INSPECTION

1. Inspect seal for damage and replace, if necessary.
2. Inspect bushing to lower control arm and pivot cushion bushing. Inspect seals on cushion bushing for cuts, tears or severe deterioration that may allow moisture to enter under cushion. If corrosion is evident, replace torsion bar assembly.
3. Inspect torsion bars for paint damage and touch up, if necessary.
4. Clean anchor hex openings and torsion bar hex ends.
5. Inspect torsion bar adjusting bolt and swivel for damage or corrosion and replace, if necessary.

### INSTALLATION

1. Slide balloon seal over torsion bar end with cupped end facing toward hex.
2. Lubricate torsion bar hex end with suitable lubricant, then install hex end into anchor bracket. With the torsion bar in horizontal position, the anchor bracket ears should be positioned nearly straight upward. Position swivel into anchor bracket ears.
3. Install torsion bar anchor bracket assembly into crossmember anchor retainer, then the anchor adjusting bolt and bearing.
4. Install two bolt and washer assemblies securing pivot cushion bushing to crossmember. Leave assemblies loose enough to install friction plates.
5. With lower control arms supported as outlined in step 3 under "Removal," install the two bolt and nut assemblies securing torsion bar bushing to lower control arm and torque nuts to specification.
6. Ensure that torsion bar anchor bracket is fully seated in crossmember. Then install friction plates between crossmember and pivot cushion bushing with open end of slot to rear and bottomed out on mounting bolt. Torque cushion bushing bolts to specification. Place balloon seal over anchor bracket.
7. Install new bolt through sway bar, retainer cushions and sleeve and attach to lower control arm end bushing, then torque bolt to specifications.
8. Rotate anchor adjusting bolt clockwise to load torsion bar.
9. Lower vehicle and adjust riding height.

## SWAY BAR REPLACE

1. Raise and support front of vehicle. **Sway bar to lower control arm attaching points are aligned only when lower control arms are at design height. If frame contact or twin post hoist is used, release load on torsion bar by turning adjuster bolts counterclockwise, then raise lower control arms until clearance between crossmember ledge and torsion bar to lower control arm bushing is 2 7/8 inches. Support lower control arms with jack stand during sway bar removal and installation.**
2. With lower control arms properly supported, remove sway bar to torsion bar bushing attaching bolts, retainers, cushions and sleeves.
3. Remove retainer assembly strap bolts and retainer straps, then remove sway bar.
4. Reverse procedure to install. Inspect cushions and bushings for excessive wear or deterioration and replace as necessary.

## POWER STEERING GEAR REPLACE

1. Disconnect battery ground cable.
2. Remove steering column.
3. Disconnect fluid hoses from steering gear and support free ends above pump to avoid loss of fluid. Plug fittings on gear.
4. Disconnect steering arm from gear with suitable puller.
5. Disconnect exhaust system from exhaust manifolds, then remove starter and heat shield from engine.
6. Remove gear to frame retaining bolts or nuts and remove gear.
7. Reverse procedure to install.

## POWER STEERING PUMP REPLACE

1. Loosen power steering pump mounting and locking bolts, then remove drive belt.
2. Disconnect pressure and return lines at power steering pump.
3. Remove pump mounting bolts, then remove pump and mounting bracket.
4. Reverse procedure to install.

## TIGHTENING SPECIFICATIONS

| Year | Component | Torque/ft. lbs. |
|---|---|---|
| 1989 | Ball Joint Stud Nut | 100 |
| | Ball Joint To Control Arm | 125 |
| | Idler Arm Bolt Nut | 70 |
| | Lower Control Arm Pivot Shaft Nut | 75 |
| | Rebound & Jounce Bumpers | 200① |
| | Shock Absorber Nut (Lower) | 35 |
| | Shock Absorber Nut (Upper) | 25 |
| | Steering Knuckle Bolts/Nuts | 160 |
| | Sway Bar Cushion Bolt | 65 |
| | Sway Bar Link Retainer Nut | 100① |
| | Sway Bar Strap Nut | 30 |
| | Tie Rod End | 40 |

*Continued*

## TIGHTENING SPECIFICATIONS—Continued

| Year | Component | Torque/ft. lbs. |
|---|---|---|
| 1989 | Tie Rod Sleeve Clamps | 150① |
| | Torsion Bar Bushing To Lower Control Arm Bolt/Nut | 70 |
| | Torsion Bar Pivot Cushion Retainer Nut/Bolt | 85 |
| | Upper Control Adjusting Bolt Nut | 150 |
| | Upper Control Arm Pivot Bushing Nut | 110 |
| | Wheel Lug Nuts | 85 |

①—Inch lbs.

# Wheel Alignment

## INDEX



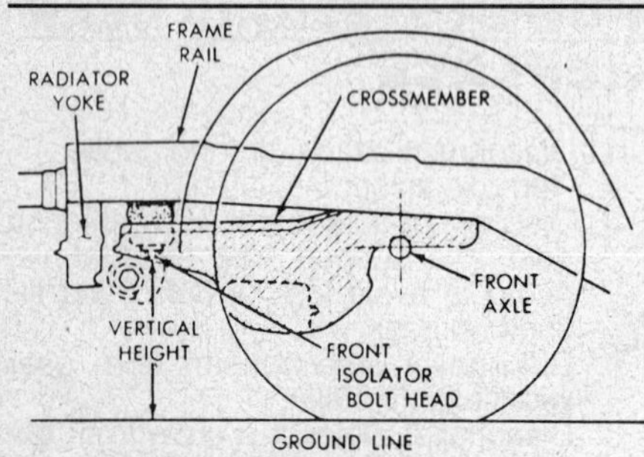


Fig. 1 Measuring front suspension height

## RIDING HEIGHT

### ADJUST

**Front suspension heights must be measured with the recommended tire pressures, with no passenger or luggage compartment load. Vehicle should have a full tank of gasoline or equivalent weight compensation. Car must be on a level surface.**

**Before taking measurements, grasp the bumpers at the center (rear bumper first) and jounce the car up and down several times. Jounce the car at the front bumper the same number of times and release the bumper at the same point in the cycle each time.**

1. Ride height is measured from the head of the front suspension front crossmember insulator bolt to ground, **Fig. 1.**
2. If necessary, turn torsion bar adjusting bolt clockwise to increase height and counterclockwise to decrease height.
3. After completing adjustment, jounce vehicle and recheck riding height. Both sides must be measured even though only one side may have been adjusted. Front vehicle height should not vary more than 1/4 inch from the specified riding height. Riding height should also be within 1/4 inch side to side.

| Year | Model | Height |
|---|---|---|
| CHRYSLER | | |
| 1989 | Fifth Avenue | 12½ inch |
| DODGE | | |
| 1989 | Diplomat | 12½ inch |

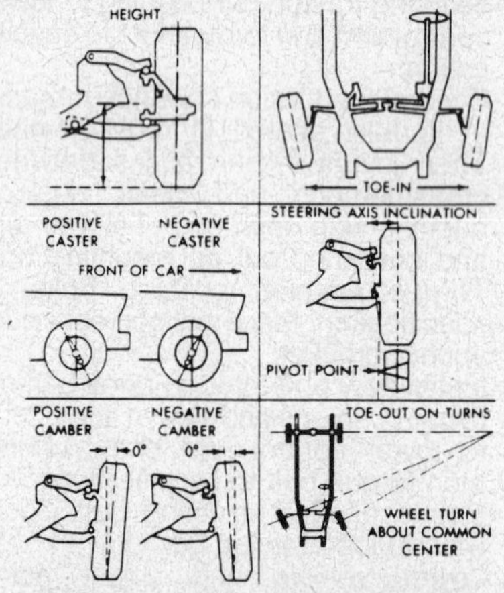


Fig. 2 Alignment factors

| PLYMOUTH | | |
|---|---|---|
| 1989 | Gran Fury | 12½ inch |

## CASTER & CAMBER

### ADJUST

**Front suspension height must be checked and corrected as necessary before performing wheel alignment.**

1. Record initial camber and caster readings before loosening pivot bar bolt nuts, **Fig. 2.**
2. Remove all foreign material from exposed threads of pivot bar adjusting bolt nuts, then loosen nuts slightly holding pivot bar.
3. Adjusting claw No. C-4576 is required to adjust caster and camber. When performing adjustments, the camber settings should be held as close as possible to the "desired" setting, and the caster setting should be held as nearly equal as possible on both wheels, **Fig. 3.**

There may be cases when the vehicle may not have sufficient positive camber adjustment. Upper control arm plate spacers are available that will allow more positive camber adjustment, if required. If this condition is encountered, use spacer 1-4014352 for front suspension upper control arm front pivot support and spacer 1-4014353 for the rear pivot support. To install spacers, proceed as follows:

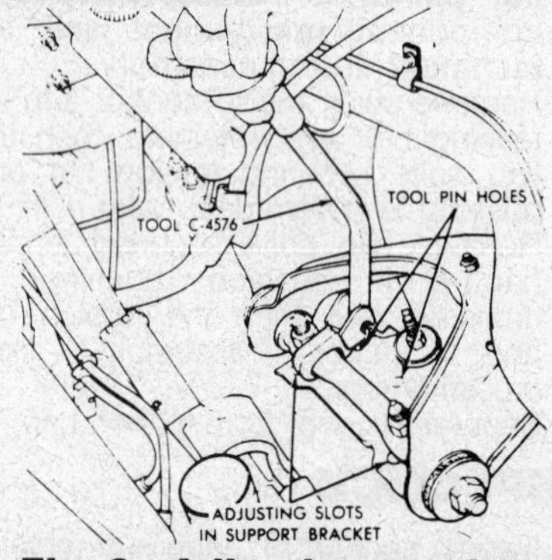


Fig. 3 Adjusting camber & caster using claw No. C-4576

1. Loosen but do not remove caster/camber adjustment nut.
2. Raise vehicle and remove wheel and tire assembly.
3. Loosen but do not remove shock absorber upper mounting nut.
4. Remove two support plate bolts at front end of plate, then loosen two rear bolts enough to slide front spacer between support plate and frame.
5. Align holes in spacer with holes in support plate and frame.
6. Insert two front bolts and start threads. Do not tighten.
7. Repeat steps 4 through 6 for rear spacer.
8. **Torque** the four support plate bolts to 65 ft. lbs. and the shock absorber upper nut to 25 ft. lbs.
9. Lower vehicle and adjust alignment on side that spacers were installed.

## TOE-IN

### ADJUST

With the front wheels in straight ahead position, loosen the clamps at each end of both adjusting tubes. Adjust toe-in by turning the tie rod sleeve which will "center" the steering wheel spokes. If the steering wheel was centered, make the toe-in adjustment by turning both sleeves an equal amount. Position the clamps so they are on the bottom and tighten bolts to 15 ft. lbs.

# CHRYSLER FRONT WHEEL DRIVE EXCEPT COLT, COLT VISTA, LASER, MONACO & STEALTH

**NOTE:** The following models are covered in this chapter: CHRYSLER– Imperial (VIN Y, 1990-92), LeBaron (VIN J, 1989-92), LeBaron GTS (VIN H, 1989), LeBaron Landau (VIN A, 1990-92), New Yorker Fifth Avenue (VIN Y, 1990-92), New Yorker Landau (VIN C, 1989-90), New Yorker Sedan (VIN C, 1991-92), DODGE– Aries (VIN K, 1989), Daytona (VIN G, 1989-92), Dynasty (VIN C, 1989-92), Lancer (VIN H, 1989), Omni (VIN L, 1989-90), Shadow (VIN P, 1989-92), Spirit (VIN A, 1989-92) PLYMOUTH– Acclaim (VIN A, 1989-92), Horizon (VIN L, 1989-90), Reliant (VIN K, 1989), Sundance (VIN P, 1989-92).

## INDEX OF SERVICE OPERATIONS

**NOTE:** Refer To Rear Of This Manual For Vehicle Manufacturer's Special Service Tool Suppliers.

## INDEX OF SERVICE OPERATIONS—Continued



# Specifications

## GENERAL ENGINE SPECIFICATIONS

| Year | Engine CID①/Liter | Engine VIN Code ② | Fuel System | Bore and Stroke Inch (Millimeters) | Compression Ratio | Net HP @ RPM ③ | Maximum Torque Ft. Lbs @ R.P.M. | Normal Oil Pressure Psi. @ 2000 RPM |
|---|---|---|---|---|---|---|---|---|
| 1989 | 2.2L/4-135 | C,D | T.B.I.⑧ | 3.44 x 3.62 (87.5 x 92) | 9.5 | 93 @ 4800 | 122 @ 3200 | 25—80 |
| | 2.2L/4-135④ | A,E | E.F.I.⑦ | 3.44 x 3.62 (87.5 x 92) | 8.1 | 174 @ 5200 | 200 @ 2400 | 25-80 |
| | 2.5L/4-153 | K | T.B.I.⑧ | 3.44 x 4.09 (87.5 x 104) | 8.9 | 100 @ 4800 | 135 @ 2800 | 25-80 |
| | 2.5L/4-153④ | J | E.F.I.⑦ | 3.44 x 4.09 (87.5 x 104) | 7.8 | 150 @ 4800 | 180 @ 2000 | 25-80 |
| | 3.0L/V6-181 | 3 | E.F.I.⑦ | 3.59 x 2.99 (91.1 x 76) | 8.85 | 141 @ 5000 | 171 @ 2800 | 25-80 |
| 1990 | 2.2L/4-135 | D | E.F.I.⑦ | 3.44 x 3.62 (87.5 x 92) | 9.5 | 93 @ 4800 | 122 @ 3200 | 25-80⑤ |
| | 2.2L/4-135④ | C | T.B.I.⑦ | 3.44 x 3.62 (87.7 x 92) | 8.1 | 174 @ 5200 | 210 @ 2400 | 25-80⑤ |
| | 2.5L/4-153 | K | E.F.I.⑧ | 3.44 x 4.09 (87.5 x 104) | 8.9 | 100 @ 4800 | 135 @ 2800 | 25-80⑤ |
| | 2.5L/4-153④ | J | T.B.I.⑦ | 3.44 x 4.09 (87.5 x 104) | 7.8 | 150 @ 4800 | 180 @ 2000 | 25-80⑤ |
| | 3.0L/V6-181 | 3 | E.F.I.⑦ | 3.59 x 2.99 (91.1 x 76) | 8.9 | 141 @ 5000 | 171 @ 2800 | 25-80⑤ |
| | 3.3L/V6-202 | R | E.F.I.⑦ | 3.66 x 3.19 (93 x 81) | 9.8 | 147 @ 4800 | 183 @ 3600 | 30-80⑤ |

Continued

# GENERAL ENGINE SPECIFICATIONS–Continued

| Year | Engine CID①/Liter | Engine VIN Code ② | Fuel System | Bore and Stroke Inch (Millimeters) | Compression Ratio | Net HP @ RPM ③ | Maximum Torque Ft. Lbs @ R.P.M. | Normal Oil Pressure Psi. @ 2000 RPM |
|---|---|---|---|---|---|---|---|---|
| 1991–92 | 2.2L/4-135 | D | T.B.I.⑧ | 3.44 x 3.62 (87.5 x 92) | 9.5 | 93 @ 4800 | 122 @ 3200 | 25–80⑤ |
| | 2.2L/4-135④ | A | M.P.I⑥ | 3.44 x 3.62 (87.5 x 92) | 8.1 | 174 @ 5200 | 211 @ 2800 | 25–80⑤ |
| | 2.5L/4-153 | K | T.B.I.⑧ | 3.44 x 4.09 (87.5 x 104) | 8.9 | 100 @ 4800 | 135 @ 2000 | 25–80⑤ |
| | 2.5L/4-153④ | J | M.P.I⑥ | 3.44 x 4.09 (87.5 x 104) | 7.8 | 150 @ 4800 | 180 @ 2000 | 25–80⑤ |
| | 3.0L/V6-181 | 3 | E.F.I.⑦ | 3.59 x 2.99 (91 x 76) | 8.85 | 141 @ 5000 | 170 @ 2800 | 25–80⑤ |
| | 3.3L/V6-202 | R | E.F.I.⑦ | 3.66 x 3.19 (93 x 81) | 8.9 | 147 @ 4800 | 185 @ 3600 | 30–80⑤ |
| | 3.8L/V6-231 | L | E.F.I.⑦ | 3.78 x 3.43 (96 x 87) | 8.9 | 151 @ 4400 | 204 @ 3200 | 30–80⑤ |

①—CID-cubic inch displacement.
②—The 8th digit of the VIN denotes engine code.
③—Ratings are net-as installed in vehicle.
④—Turbocharged engine.
⑤—At 3000 RPM.
⑥—Multi-port fuel injection.
⑦—Electronic fuel injection.
⑧—Throttle body injection.

# TUNE UP SPECIFICATIONS

| Year & Engine/ V.I.N. Code① | Spark Plug Gap | Ignition Timing BTDC: Firing Order Fig. ② | Ignition Timing BTDC: Man. Trans. | Ignition Timing BTDC: Auto. Trans. | Ignition Timing BTDC: Mark Fig. | Curb Idle Speed③: Man. Trans. | Curb Idle Speed③: Auto Trans. | Fast Idle Speed: Man. Trans. | Fast Idle Speed: Auto. Trans. | Fuel Pump Pressure Psi. |
|---|---|---|---|---|---|---|---|---|---|---|
| **1989** | | | | | | | | | | |
| 2.2L/4-135 (C, D) | .035 | C | 12⑨ | 12⑨ | D | 850 | 850N | ⑥ | ⑥ | 13.5–15.5⑦ |
| 2.2L/4-135 Turbo I (E) | .035 | C | 12⑨ | 12⑨ | D | 850 | 850N | ⑥ | ⑥ | 53–57⑧ |
| 2.2L/4-135 Turbo II (A) | .035 | C | 12⑨ | 12⑨ | D | 900 | 900N | ⑥ | ⑥ | 53–57⑧ |
| 2.5L/4-153 (K) | .035 | C | 12⑨ | 12⑨ | D | 850 | 850N | ⑥ | ⑥ | 13.5–15.5⑦ |
| 3.0L/V6-181 (3) | .041 | F | — | 12 | E | — | 700N | — | ⑥ | 46–50⑧ |
| **1990** | | | | | | | | | | |
| 2.2L/4-135 (D) | .035 | C | 12⑨ | 12⑨ | D | 850 | 850N | ⑥ | ⑥ | 13.5–15.5⑦ |
| 2.2L/4-135 Turbo IV (C) | .035 | C | 12⑨ | 12⑨ | D | 900 | 900N | ⑥ | ⑥ | 53–57⑧ |
| 2.5L/4-153 (K) | .035 | C | 12⑨ | 12⑨ | D | 850 | 850N | ⑥ | ⑥ | 13.5–15.5⑦ |
| 2.5L/4-153 Turbo I (J) | .035 | C | 12⑨ | 12⑨ | D | 900 | 900N | ⑥ | ⑥ | 53–57⑧ |
| 3.0L/V6-181 (3) | .041 | F | 12⑨ | 12⑨ | E | 700 | 700N | ⑥ | ⑥ | 46–50⑧ |
| 3.3L/V6-202 (R) | .050 | A④ | ⑤ | ⑤ | ⑩ | — | 750N | — | ⑥ | 46–50⑧ |
| **1991–92** | | | | | | | | | | |
| 2.2L/4-135 (D) | .035 | C | 12⑨ | 12⑨ | D | 850 | 850N | ⑥ | ⑥ | 39⑧ |
| 2.2L/4-135 Turbo III (A) | .035 | B④ | ⑤ | ⑤ | ⑩ | 750 | 750N | ⑥ | ⑥ | 53–57⑧ |
| 2.5L/4-153 (K) | .035 | C | 12⑨ | 12⑨ | D | 850 | 850N | ⑥ | ⑥ | 55⑧ |
| 2.5L/4-153 Turbo I (J) | .035 | C | 12⑨ | 12⑨ | D | 900 | 900N | ⑥ | ⑥ | 48⑧ |
| 3.0L/V6-181 (3) | .041 | F | 12⑨ | 12⑨ | E | 700 | 700N | ⑥ | ⑥ | 48⑧ |
| 3.3L/V6-202 (R) | .050 | A④ | ⑤ | ⑤ | ⑩ | — | 750N | — | ⑥ | 48⑧ |
| 3.8L/V6-231 (L) | .050 | A④ | ⑤ | ⑤ | ⑩ | — | 750N | — | ⑥ | 48⑧ |

①—The eighth digit of the Vehicle Identification Number (V.I.N.) denotes engine code.
②—Before removing wires from distributor cap, determine location of No. 1 wire in cap, as distributor position may have been altered from that shown at the end of this chart.
③—N: Neutral.
④—Direct Ignition System (DIS).
⑤—Direct Ignition System (DIS), not adjustable.
⑥—Idle speeds are controlled by the Automatic Idle Speed (AIS) motor.
⑦—Loosen gas cap to release pressure in tank. Ground one injector terminal with a jumper wire. Connect the remaining injector terminal to the battery positive post using a jumper wire for no longer than 10 seconds, this will release system pressure. Remove fuel intake hose from throttle body & connect a suitable fuel pressure tester between fuel filter hose & throttle body. Check fuel pressure with engine running.
⑧—Loosen gas cap to release pressure in tank. Ground one terminal of any injector with a jumper wire. connect remaining terminal of injector to the battery positive post using a jumper for no longer that 10 seconds, this will release fuel system pressure. Remove cover from service valve on fuel rail. Connect a suitable fuel pressure tester to service valve. Check fuel pressure with engine running.
⑨—Check ignition timing with coolant sensor wire disconnected.
⑩—Equipped w/crankshaft position sensor.

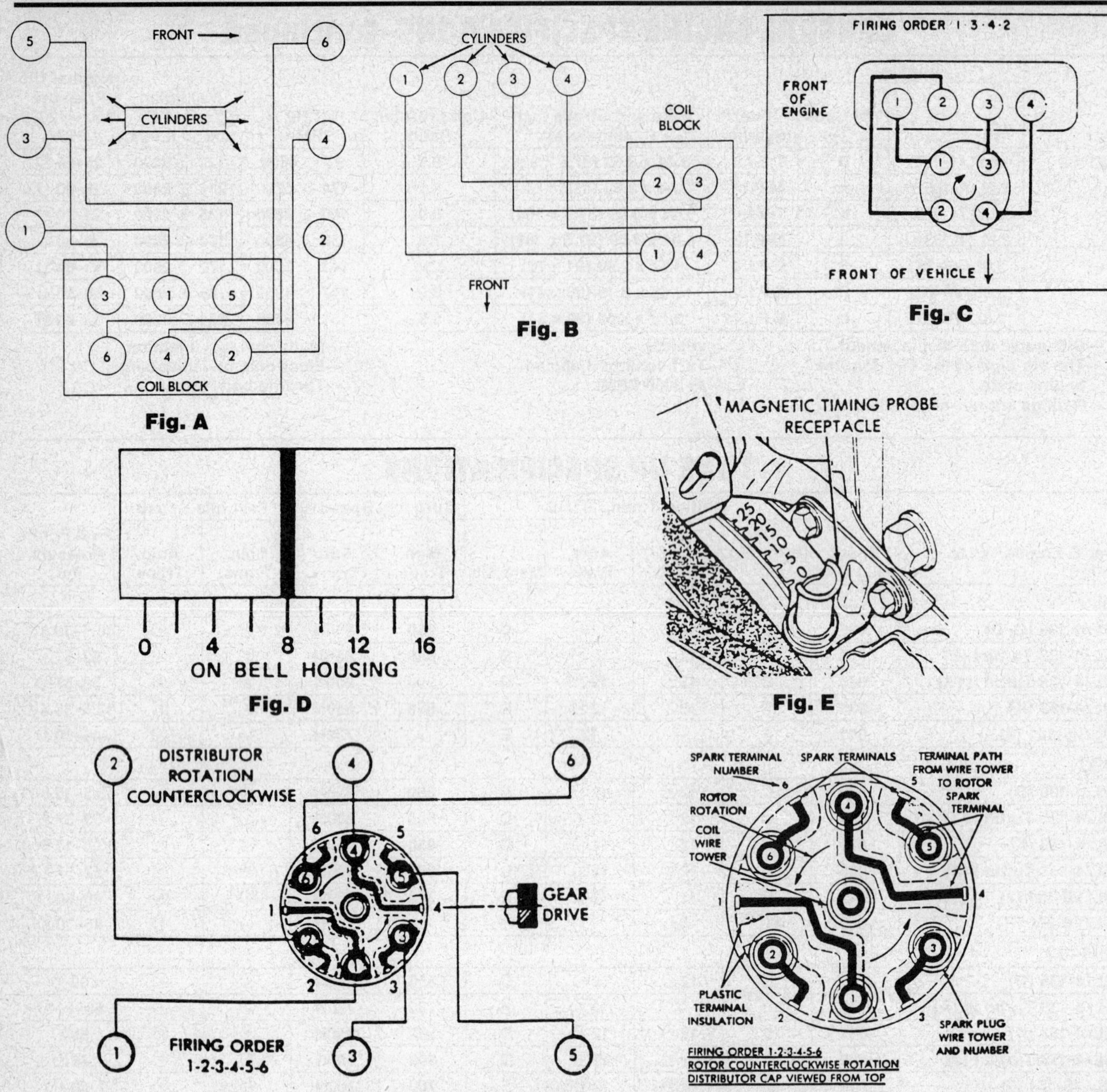


## WHEEL ALIGNMENT SPECIFICATIONS

| Year | Model | Camber Angle, Degrees: Limits, Left | Limits, Right | Desired, Left | Desired, Right | Toe In Inch | Camber ③ |
|---|---|---|---|---|---|---|---|
| 1989-92 | All ① | −1/4 to +3/4 ⑧ | −1/4 to +3/4 ⑧ | +5/16 | +5/16 | ④ | ⑤ |
| | Horizon & Omni ② | −1 1/4 to −1/4 | −1 1/4 to −1/4 | −1/2 | −5/16 | ⑥ | ⑤ |
| | Except Horizon & Omni ② | −1 1/4 to +1/4 | −1 1/4 to +1/4 | 0 to -1 | 0 to -1 | ⑦ | ⑤ |

① —Front wheel alignment.
② —Rear wheel alignment.
③ —Reference only, non adjustable.
④ —7/32" in to 1/8" out (.4° in to .2° out).
⑤ —All except Horizon, Omni, wagon, Imperial & Fifth Avenue w/air suspension, 1.2°; Horizon & Omni, 1.4°; wagon, .9°; Imperial & Fifth Avenue w/air suspension, 1.3°.
⑥ —3/16" out to 13/32" inch (.40 out to .8° in).
⑦ —5/16" out to 5/16" inch (.60 out to .60° in).
⑧ —Except 1990–92 New Yorker Fifth Avenue and Imperial models w/air suspension; −5/16 to +1/2

# COOLING SYSTEM & CAPACITY DATA

| Year | Model or Engine (VIN)① | Cooling Capacity | | Radiator Cap Relief Pressure, Lbs. | Thermo. Opening Temp. Deg. F | Fuel Tank Gals. | Engine Oil Refill Qts. | Transaxle Oil | |
|---|---|---|---|---|---|---|---|---|---|
| | | Less A/C Qts. | With A/C Qts. | | | | | 4 & 5 Speed Pts. | Auto. Trans. Qts. ② |
| 1989 | 2.2L/4-135(D) | 9 | 9 | 16 | 195 | ③ | 4④ | ⑤ | ⑧ |
| | 2.2L/4-135(C) Turbo | 9 | 9 | 16 | 195 | 14 | 4④ | ⑤ | ⑧ |
| | 2.5L/4-153(K) | 9 | 9 | 16 | 195 | ⑨ | 4④ | ⑤ | ⑥ |
| | 3.0L/V6-181(3) | 9.5 | 9.5 | 16 | 195 | 16 | 4④ | — | ⑥ |
| 1990 | 2.2L/4-135(D) | 9 | 9 | 16 | 195 | ③ | 4④ | ⑤ | ⑧ |
| | 2.2L/4-135(C) Turbo | 9 | 9 | 16 | 195 | 14 | 4④ | ⑤ | ⑧ |
| | 2.5L/4-153(K) | 9 | 9 | 16 | 195 | ⑨ | 4④ | ⑤ | ⑥ |
| | 2.5L/4-153(J) Turbo | 9 | 9 | 16 | 195 | ⑨ | 4④ | ⑤ | ⑥ |
| | 3.0L/V6-181(3) | 9.5 | 9.5 | 16 | 195 | 16 | 4④ | — | ⑥ |
| | 3.3L/V6-201(R) | 9.5 | 9.5 | 16 | 195 | 16 | 4④ | — | ⑥ |
| 1991 | 2.2L/4-135(A,D) | 9 | 9 | 16 | 195 | 14 | 4⑦ | 4.8 | ⑥ |
| | 2.5L/4-153(J,K) | 9 | 9 | 16 | 195 | ⑩ | 4⑦ | 4.8 | ⑥ |
| | 3.0L/V6-181(3) | 9.5 | 9.5 | 16 | 195 | ⑩ | 4⑦ | 4.8 | ⑥ |
| | 3.3L/V6-201(R) | 9.5 | 9.5 | 16 | 195 | 16 | 4⑦ | — | ⑥ |
| | 3.8L/V6-231(L) | 9.5 | 9.5 | 16 | 195 | 16 | 4⑦ | — | ⑥ |
| 1992 | 2.2L/4-135(A,D) | 9 | 9 | 16 | 195 | 14 | 4⑦ | 4.8 | ⑥ |
| | 2.5L/4-153 | 9 | 9 | 16 | 195 | ⑩ | 4⑦ | 4.8 | ⑥ |
| | 3.0L/V6-181(3,V) | 9.5 | 9.5 | 16 | 195 | ⑩ | 4⑦ | 4.8 | ⑥ |
| | 3.3L/V6-201(R) | 9.5 | 9.5 | 16 | 195 | 16 | 4⑦ | — | ⑥ |
| | 3.8L/V6-231(L) | 9.5 | 9.5 | 16 | 195 | 16 | 4⑦ | — | ⑥ |

①—The eighth digit of Vehicle Identification Number (VIN) denotes engine code.
②—Approximate. Make final check with dipstick.
③—Horizon & Omni 13 Gals.; others, 14 gals.
④—With or without filter change.
⑤—A525 five spd man. transaxle, 4.6 pts.; A520 & A555 five spd. man. transaxle, 4.8 pts.
⑥—Approximate refill capacity, 4 qts. Total capacity, A413 auto. transaxle, except fleet less lock up, 8.9 qts.; fleet, 9.2 qts.; lock up, 8.5 qts. A604 auto. transaxle, 9.1 qts.
⑦—Add ½ qt. w/filter change.
⑧—Approximate refill capacity, 4 qts. Total capacity, except commercial applications, 8.9 qts.; commercial applications, 9.2 qts.
⑨—Except Acclaim, Dynasty, New Yorker & Spirit, 14 gals.; Acclaim, Dynasty, New Yorker & Spirit, 16 gals.
⑩—Except Acclaim, Dynasty & Spirit, 14 gals.; Acclaim, Dynasty & Spirit, 16 gals.

# LUBRICANT DATA

| Year | Model | Lubricant Type | | | |
|---|---|---|---|---|---|
| | | Transaxle | | | |
| | | Manual | Automatic | Power Steering | Brake System |
| 1989 | All | SF-SF/CC SAE 5W-30 | ① | ② | DOT 3 |
| 1990–92 | All | SG-SG/CD SAE 5W-30 | ① | ③ | DOT 3 |

①—Mopar ATF Type 71760 or Dexron II/Mercon.
②—Mopar PN 4318055, or equivalent.
③—Mopar PN 4549617, or equivalent.

# Electrical

## INDEX



## AIRBAG SYSTEM DISARMING

1. Place ignition switch in lock position.
2. Disconnect and tape battery ground cable connector.
3. **Wait at least 1 minute after disconnecting battery ground cable before doing any further work on vehicle. The SRS system is designed to retain enough voltage to deploy airbag for a short time even after battery has been disconnected.**
4. After repairs are complete, reconnect battery ground cable.
5. From passenger side of vehicle, turn ignition switch to On position.
6. SRS warning light should illuminate for 6 to 8 seconds, then remain off for at least 45 seconds to indicate if SRS system is functioning correctly.
7. If SRS indicator does not perform as described refer to the "Passive Restraint Systems" section.

## FUSE PANEL & FLASHER LOCATION

On all models, the fuse panel is located under the instrument panel to the left of the steering column.

On Horizon and Omni models, the hazard and turn signal flashers are located on the fuse panel. On all models except Acclaim, Dynasty, Imperial, Lancer, LeBaron GTS, LeBaron Landau, New Yorker Fifth Avenue, New Yorker Landau, Shadow, Spirit and Sundance the hazard flasher is located on the fuse panel and the turn signal flasher is clipped to the instrument panel, below the fuse panel.

On Lancer, LeBaron GTS, Dynasty, New Yorker Landau, New Yorker Fifth Avenue, Imperial, 1989 Shadow and Sundance, and 1989 Spirit and Acclaim models, the hazard and turn signal flashers are located on the relay module.

On 1991-92 Shadow and Sundance models, the hazard flasher is located on the relay module and the turn signal flasher is attached to the center A/C duct.

On 1991-92 Spirit, Acclaim and LeBaron Landau models, the hazard flashe r is located on the relay module and the turn signal flasher is attached to the left side A/C duct.

## STARTER REPLACE

### 2.2L/4-135 & 2.5L/4-153 ENGINES

1. Disconnect battery ground cable.
2. Remove starter to flywheel housing and rear bracket to engine or transaxle attaching bolts.
3. **On models equipped with 2.2L/4-135 engine,** loosen air pump tube at exhaust manifold, then position tube bracket away from starter motor.
4. **On all models,** remove heat shield clamp and heat shield, if equipped.
5. Disconnect starter cable at starter motor and solenoid leads at solenoid, then remove starter motor.
6. Reverse procedure to install.

### 3.0L/V6-181, 3.3L/V6-202 & 3.8L/V6-231 ENGINES

1. Disconnect battery ground cable.
2. Remove three starter motor attaching bolts from transaxle bellhousing.
3. Remove two wire connector terminal nuts from starter, then disconnect wire connector and remove starter.
4. Reverse procedure to install.

## DISTRIBUTOR REPLACE

### REMOVAL

1. Disconnect distributor lead wires from electrical connector.
2. Loosen distributor cap retaining screws, then remove distributor cap.
3. Rotate crankshaft until rotor is pointing in the direction of the engine block, then scribe a line on block for assembly reference.
4. Remove distributor hold-down bolt,

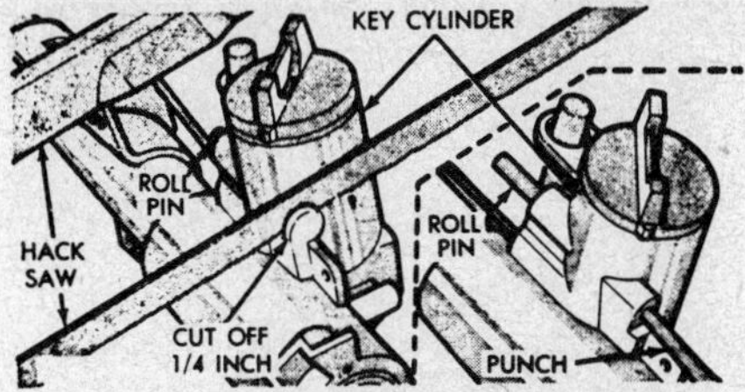


**Fig. 1 Ignition lock cylinder retaining pin removal**

then carefully lift distributor from engine.

## INSTALLATION

1. Position distributor into engine with gasket installed on base of distributor.
2. Engage distributor drive gear with camshaft drive gear so distributor rotor aligns with scribe mark made during removal.
3. If engine was cranked while distributor was removed, proceed as follows:
   a. Rotate crankshaft until No. 1 piston is at top dead center of compression stroke.
   b. Rotate distributor rotor to No. 1 distributor cap terminal position.
   c. Install distributor into engine, engaging distributor drive gear with camshaft. The rotor should be properly positioned under distributor cap No. 1 terminal.
4. Install distributor cap, then distributor hold-down.
5. Connect distributor lead wires to electrical connector.
6. Adjust ignition timing to specifications.

# IGNITION LOCK REPLACE

**Disable airbag as outlined under "Airbag System Disarming." After prodedure has been completed, rearm airbag system as outlined under "Airbag System Disarming."**

## MODELS LESS TILT COLUMN

### 1989 Horizon & Omni

1. Remove steering wheel as outlined under "Steering Wheel, Replace," then column covers and turn signal switch.
2. With a hacksaw blade, cut upper 1/4 inch from retainer pin boss, **Fig. 1.**
3. Using a suitable drift, drive roll pin from housing and remove lock cylinder.
4. Insert new cylinder into housing, ensuring that it engages lug or ignition switch driver.
5. Install roll pin.
6. Check for proper operation.

### 1989–90 Models Except 1989 Horizon & Omni; 1990 Dynasty, Daytona, Imperial, LeBaron, New Yorker Landau & Fifth Avenue

1. Disconnect battery ground cable.

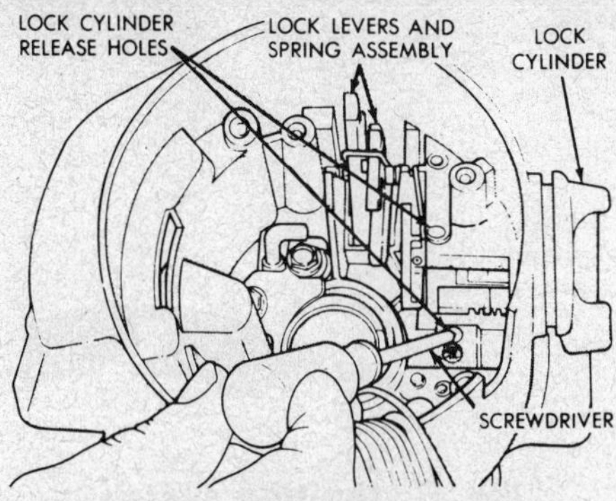


**Fig. 2 Ignition lock cylinder removal**

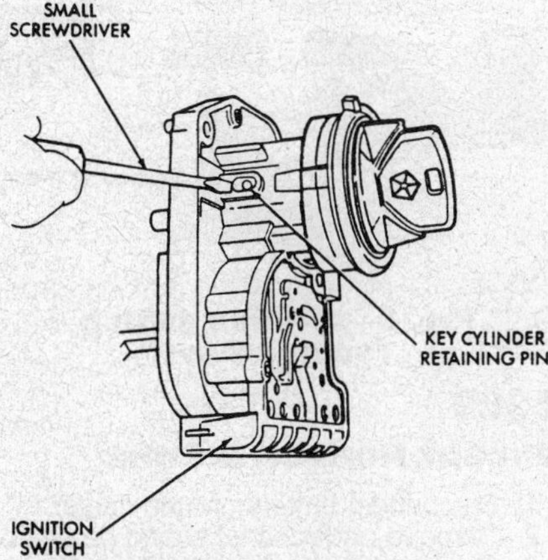


**Fig. 4 Releasing ignition lock cylinder retaining pin**

2. Remove turn signal switch as described under "Turn Signal Switch, Replace."
3. Disconnect horn and ignition key lamp ground wires, then remove ignition key lamp attaching screw and lamp.
4. Remove four screws attaching upper bearing housing to lock housing and the snap ring from upper end of steering shaft, then the upper bearing housing.
5. Remove lock plate spring and lock plate from steering shaft.
6. Position lock cylinder in Lock position and remove ignition key.
7. Remove key warning buzzer attaching screws and buzzer.
8. Remove two screws attaching ignition switch to steering column, then rotate switch 90° and slide from rod.
9. Remove two screws attaching dimmer switch, then disengage dimmer switch from actuator rod.
10. Remove two bellcrank attaching screws, then slide bellcrank up into lock housing until it can be disconnected from ignition switch actuator rod.
11. With lock cylinder in Lock position, insert a small diameter screwdriver into lock cylinder release holes and push inward until spring loaded lock cylinder retainers release, **Fig. 2.**
12. Grasp lock cylinder and pull from lock housing bore.
13. Reverse procedure to install. The lock cylinder and ignition switch must be in the Lock position.

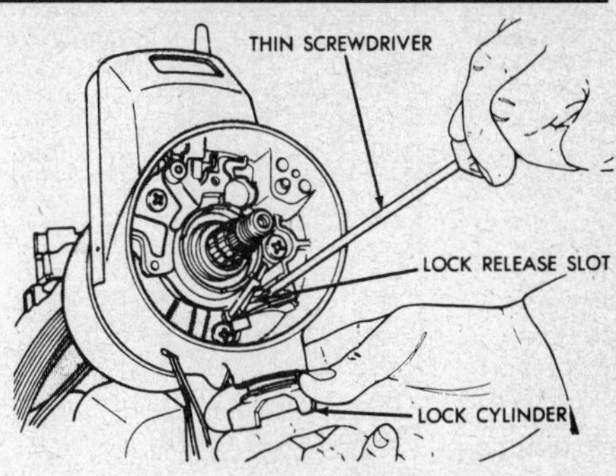


**Fig. 3 Ignition lock cylinder removal**

### 1990 Dynasty, Daytona, Imperial, LeBaron, New Yorker Landau & Fifth Avenue

Refer to "Models w/Tilt Column,"" 1990-92" for replacement procedure.

### 1991–92

Refer to "Models w/Tilt Column,"" 1990-92" for replacement procedure.

## MODELS w/TILT COLUMN

### 1989

1. Disconnect battery ground cable.
2. Remove turn signal switch as described under "Turn Signal Switch, Replace."
3. Remove ignition key lamp.
4. Position ignition lock cylinder in Lock position, then remove ignition key.
5. Insert a thin screwdriver into lock cylinder release slot and depress spring latch which releases lock cylinder, then grasp lock cylinder and remove from column, **Fig. 3.**
6. Reverse procedure to install.

### 1990–92

On these models, the ignition lock and ignition switch are removed as an assembly.

1. Disconnect battery ground cable.
2. Remove tilt lever.
3. Remove three Torx column cover attaching screws, then the upper and lower column covers.
4. Using tamper proof Torx bit tool No. 440-TX20H or equivalent, remove three ignition switch mounting screws.
5. Carefully pull switch away from column. Release two connector locks on seven terminal wiring connector, then disconnect from ignition switch.
6. Release connector lock on four terminal connector, then disconnect from ignition switch.
7. Remove ignition lock from ignition switch as follows:
   a. With key inserted and switch in Lock position, use a small screwdriver to depress ignition lock re-

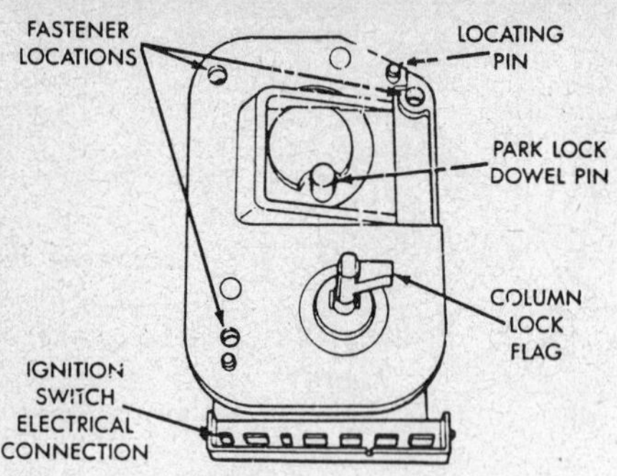


**Fig. 5 Ignition switch, rear view**

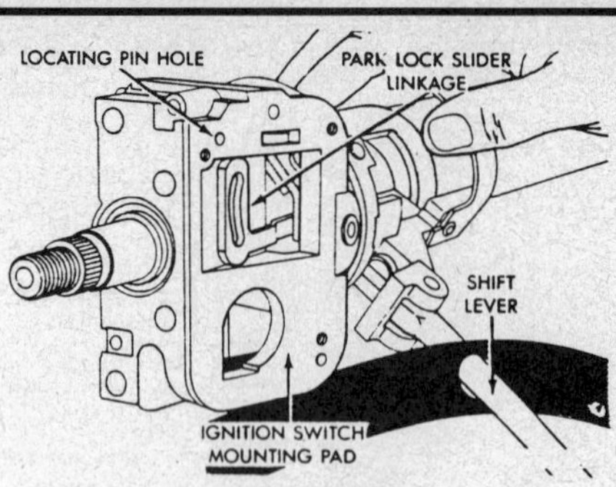


**Fig. 6 Ignition switch mounting pad**

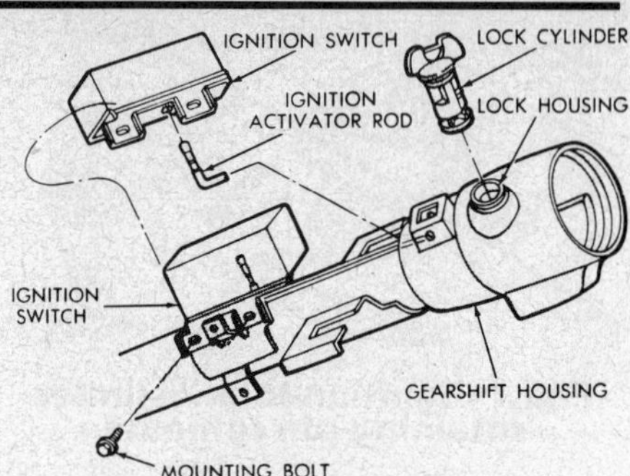


**Fig. 7 Ignition switch replacement**

taining pin flush with lock cylinder surface, **Fig. 4.**

b. Rotate key clockwise to Off position. Ignition lock should now be unseated from ignition switch assembly. **Do not attempt to remove ignition lock at this time.**
c. With ignition lock in unseated position (lock bezel approximately 1/8 inch above halo light ring), rotate key counterclockwise to Lock position, then remove key.
d. Remove ignition lock from ignition switch.

8. Reverse procedure to install, noting the following:
   a. Connect two wiring connectors to ignition switch. Ensure switch locking tabs are fully seated in connectors.
   b. Install ignition switch on steering column.
   c. **On column shift models,** shift lever must be in P position and park lock dowel pin on ignition switch assembly must engage with column park lock slider linkage, **Figs. 5 and 6.**
   d. **On all models,** verify ignition switch is in Lock position (flag parallel with ignition switch terminals).
   e. Apply a dab of suitable grease to flag and pin, then position park lock link and slider to mid-travel.
   f. Position ignition switch against lock housing face. Ensure pin is inserted into park link contour slot.
   g. Install ignition switch retaining screws and **torque** to 12-22 inch lbs.
   h. With ignition lock and switch in Lock position, insert ignition lock into ignition switch until it bottoms.
   i. Insert key, then while carefully pushing ignition lock toward ignition switch, turn key clockwise to Run position.
   j. Check for proper operation on ignition switch in all positions.

# IGNITION SWITCH
## REPLACE

**Disable airbag as outlined under "Airbag System Disarming." After prodedure has been completed, rearm airbag system as outlined under "Airbag System Disarming."**

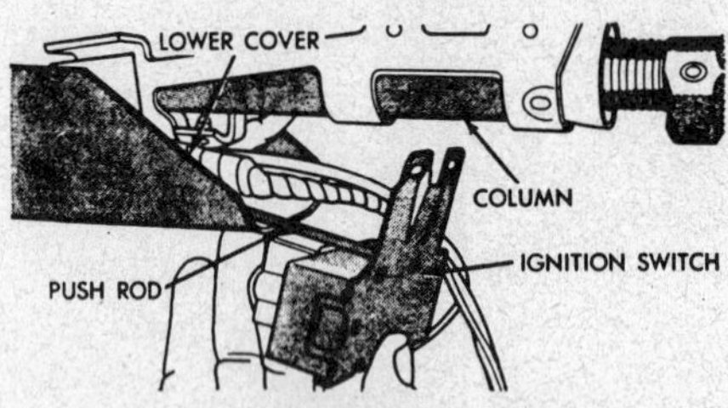


**Fig. 8 Ignition switch replacement**

### 1989

#### Except Horizon & Omni

1. Disconnect battery ground cable.
2. Remove under panel sound deadner.
3. Disconnect speed control switch.
4. Remove two switch attaching screws, then rotate switch 90° and pull up to disengage switch from rod, **Fig. 7.**
5. Reverse procedure to install. When installing new switch push up gently on switch relieve slack in rod system.

#### Horizon & Omni

1. Disconnect battery ground cable.
2. Remove connector from ignition switch.
3. Place ignition lock in Lock position and remove key.
4. Remove two ignition switch mounting screws and permit switch and pushrod to drop below column jacket, **Fig. 8.**
5. Rotate switch 90° for removal of switch from pushrod.
6. Position ignition switch in Lock position, second detent from top of the switch.
7. Place switch at right angle to column and insert pushrod.
8. Align switch on bracket and loosely install screws.
9. With a light rearward load on switch, tighten attaching screws.
10. Connect ignition switch wiring connector and battery ground cable.
11. Check for proper operation.

### 1990

#### Acclaim, Horizon, LeBaron Landau, Omni, Shadow, Spirit & Sundance Less Tilt Column

1. Disconnect battery ground cable.
2. **On Horizon and Omni models,** remove lower instrument panel and pad assembly.
3. **On Acclaim, LeBaron Landau, Shadow, Spirit and Sundance models,** remove lower steering column cover.
4. **On all models,** remove steering column cover.
5. Lower steering column for access to ignition switch. Refer to procedure outlined under "Steering Column" section.
6. Remove two screws attaching ignition switch steering column.
7. Rotate switch 90° and pull up to disengage from ignition switch rod.
8. Reverse procedure to install, noting the following:
   a. Rotate switch 90° and push down to engage ignition switch rod.
   b. Install two ignition switch attaching screws but do not tighten.
   c. Adjust ignition switch by carefully pushing up on switch to take up slack in rod system. **This must be done with ignition lock in Lock position and key removed.**

#### Dynasty, Daytona, Imperial, LeBaron Coupe/Convertible, New Yorker Fifth Avenue & New Yorker Landau w/Standard & Tilt Columns, Acclaim, LeBaron Landau, Shadow, Spirit & Sundance w/Tilt Column

On these models, the ignition lock and ignition switch are removed as an assembly. Refer to procedure outlined under "Ignition Lock, Replace."

### 1991–92

On these models, the ignition lock and ignition switch are removed as an assembly. Refer to procedure outlined under "Ignition Lock, Replace."

# HEADLAMP SWITCH
## REPLACE

**Disable airbag as outlined under "Airbag System Disarming." After prodedure has been completed, rearm airbag system as outlined under "Airbag System Disarming."**

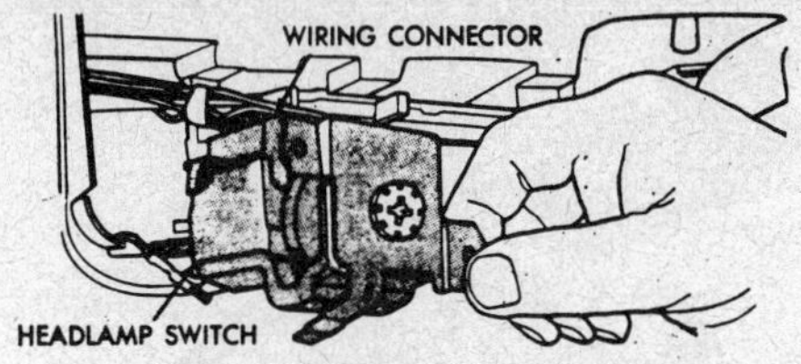


**Fig. 9 Light switch replacement (Typical)**

## 1989

### Except Horizon, Omni, Lancer, LeBaron GTS, 1989 Dynasty & New Yorker Except New Yorker Turbo

1. Disconnect battery ground cable, then place gearshift lever in 1 position.
2. Remove left upper and lower instrument cluster bezel attaching screws, then detach bezel from five retaining clips. Remove bezel.
3. Remove three screws attaching headlamp switch retainer plate to instrument panel.
4. Pull headlamp switch and retainer plate rearward and disconnect wire connector, then depress button on switch and remove switch knob and stem.
5. Remove switch retainer plate escutcheon, then the nut attaching switch to plate.
6. Reverse procedure to install.

### Horizon & Omni

1. Disconnect battery ground cable.
2. Reach under instrument panel and depress light switch knob release button, then pull light switch knob and shaft from switch.
3. Remove four bezel attaching screws and bezel.
4. Remove switch attaching screws and disconnect electrical connector from switch, **Fig. 9.**
5. Remove switch from panel.
6. Reverse procedure to install.

### Lancer & LeBaron GTS

1. Disconnect battery ground cable.
2. Remove cluster bezel attaching screws, then the cluster bezel.
3. Remove headlight and accessory switch module attaching screws, then pull module assembly away from dash panel and disconnect all electrical connectors.
4. Depress button on bottom of headlight switch, then remove switch knob and stem.
5. Remove switch assembly to switch module attaching screws.
6. Remove switch assembly from module, then switch assembly retaining plate from switch.
7. Reverse procedure to install.

### 1989 Dynasty & New Yorker (Except Turbo)

1. Remove cluster bezel.
2. Remove four module mounting screws, then disconnect wiring connectors.
3. Reverse procedure to install.

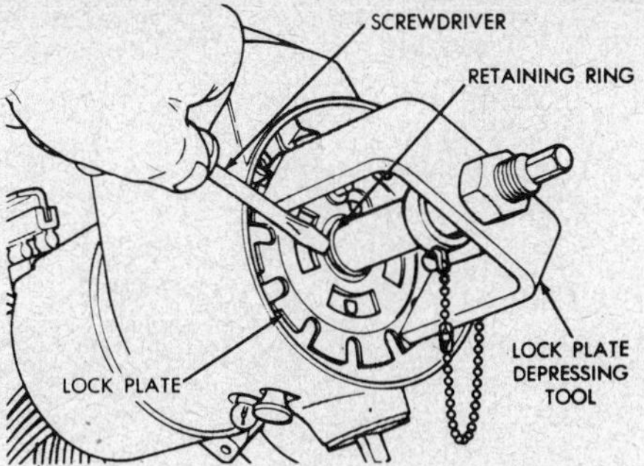


**Fig. 10 Lock plate removal**

## 1990–92

### Except Daytona & LeBaron Coupe/Convertible

1. Disconnect battery ground cable.
2. Remove left trim bezel as follows:
   a. Pull bezel rearward until retaining clips disengage.
3. Remove three headlight switch attaching screws.
4. Pull switch assembly and wiring away from instrument panel, then disconnect wiring connector.
5. Disconnect escutcheon from mounting plate.
6. Unscrew bracket retainer nut attaching switch to bracket, then remove switch.
7. Reverse procedure to install.

### Daytona & LeBaron Coupe/Convertible

1. Disconnect battery ground cable.
2. Remove switch pod assembly. Refer to procedure outlined under "Instrument Cluster, Replace."
3. Remove turn signal lever by pulling straight out of pod.
4. Remove five pod inner panel attaching screws, then the inner panel.
5. Remove turn signal switch to gain access to headlight switch. Refer to procedure outlined under "Turn Signal Switch, Replace."
6. Disconnect headlight switch linkage from buttons.
7. Remove switch mounting screws, then the switch.
8. Reverse procedure to install, noting the following:
   a. Latch switch linkage in up position.
   b. Insert dimmer shaft into dimmer knob while aligning switch in switch pod.
   c. Unlatch linkage and connect to push buttons.
   d. Check all switch modes for proper operation.

# TURN SIGNAL SWITCH REPLACE

**Disable airbag as outlined under "Airbag System Disarming." After prodedure has been completed, rearm airbag system as outlined under "Airbag System Disarming."**

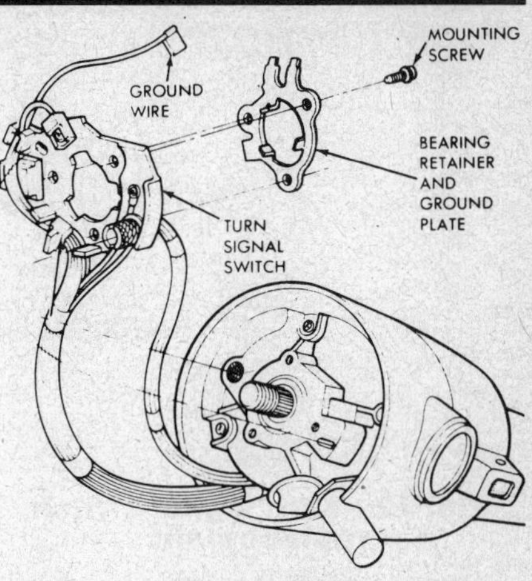


**Fig. 11 Turn signal switch replacement**

For models not covered in this section refer to "Multi-Function Switch, Replace" for replacement procedures.

## 1989

### Except Horizon & Omni

1. Disconnect battery ground cable.
2. Remove horn button and switch and steering wheel nut, then the steering wheel as outlined under "Steering Wheel, Replace."
3. Remove instrument panel lower bezel and steering column cover.
4. **On models with tilt steering column,** remove transaxle gearshift indicator, then two nuts attaching steering column to lower panel. Remove four attaching bolts, then the bracket from column.
5. **On models less tilt column,** position gearshift lever into its full clockwise position. On models with tilt column, place gearshift lever to its midway position.
6. **On models with tilt column,** carefully remove plastic cover from lock plate, then depress lock plate with lock plate depressing tool No. C-4156 or equivalent and remove snap ring, **Fig. 10.** Remove lock plate, canceling cam and upper bearing spring from steering shaft.
7. **On all models,** remove turn signal lever attaching screws and lever. On models with speed control allow lever to hang from column.
8. Remove turn signal switch and upper bearing attaching screws. Carefully remove turn signal switch, while guiding wire up through column opening, **Fig. 11.**
9. Reverse procedure to install.

### HORIZON & OMNI

### Removal

1. Disconnect battery ground cable.
2. Remove horn button or horn pad, then the horn switch.
3. Remove steering wheel nut and steering wheel as outlined under "Steering Wheel, Replace."

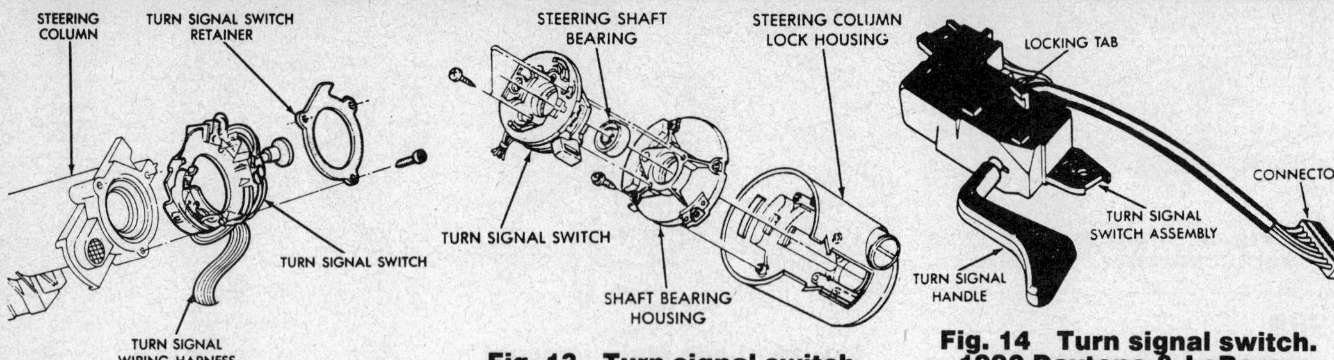


**Fig. 12 Turn signal switch replacement**

**Fig. 13 Turn signal switch replacement**

**Fig. 14 Turn signal switch. 1990 Daytona & LeBaron Coupe/Convertible**

4. Remove four screws from lower steering column cover and cover.
5. Remove screw securing washer-wiper switch and position switch aside.
6. Disconnect turn signal and hazard warning wiring connector, disengage wiring harness from support bracket and remove vinyl tape securing key in buzzer wires to turn signal harness.
7. Remove three turn signal switch retainer screws, **Fig. 12.**
8. Remove turn signal and hazard warning switch while guiding wiring harness out from column.

### Installation

1. Guide wiring harness downward through column until switch is properly seated.
2. Install switch retainer and three screws.
3. Snap plastic harness retainer into support bracket, connect harness connector and tape key in buzzer wires to harness.
4. Install washer-wiper switch and retaining screw.
5. Install lower steering column cover.
6. Install steering wheel, horn switch and horn button.
7. Connect battery ground cable.

## 1990

### ACCLAIM, HORIZON, LEBARON LANDAU, OMNI, SHADOW, SPIRIT & SUNDANCE LESS TILT COLUMN

### Removal

**Removal and installation of steering wheel requires use of DRB II readout tool or equivalent to perform an air bag system check. Perform system check before connecting battery ground cable.**

1. Disconnect battery ground cable.
2. Remove steering wheel as outlined under "Steering Wheel, Replace."
3. Remove sound deadening insulation panel below steering column, if equipped.
4. Remove lower instrument panel bezel.
5. Remove wiring trough by prying out plastic retainer buttons.
6. **On column shift models,** position shift lever in full clockwise position.
7. **On all models,** disconnect turn signal switch wiring connector.
8. Remove screw attaching wiper/washer switch to turn signal switch pivot. Leave turn signal lever (control stalk) in it's installed position.
9. Remove three screws attaching turn signal switch to upper bearing housing, **Fig. 13.**
10. Tape wiring harness connector to wiring harness.
11. Remove turn signal and hazard warning switch while guiding wiring harness out from column.

### Installation

1. Lubricate turn signal switch pivot with Lubriplate or equivalent light lubricant.
2. Tape turn signal switch wiring harness connector to wiring harness, insert connector through opening in steering column, then guide wiring harness downward through column until switch is properly seated.
3. Position switch into place on upper bearing housing, then install three attaching screws and tighten securely.
4. Position turn signal lever to turn signal pivot, then install screw through pivot and tighten securely. **Ensure dimmer switch rod is in control stalk pocket.**
5. Connect turn signal switch wiring harness connector, then install wiring trough to column.
6. Install steering wheel as outlined under "Steering Wheel, Replace."
7. Install sound deadening panel, if equipped.
8. Install lower instrument panel bezel.
9. **Before connecting battery ground cable, perform air bag system check as outlined under "Steering Wheel, Replace."**

### DAYTONA & LEBARON COUPE/CONVERTIBLE

On these models, the turn signal switch is located on the left side of the instrument panel switch pod.

1. Disconnect battery ground cable.
2. Remove switch pod assembly from instrument panel. Refer to procedure outlined under "Instrument Cluster, Replace."
3. Pull out on turn signal lever to remove, **Fig. 14.**
4. Remove two screws from bottom of switch pod assembly.
5. Loosen five screws on bracket inside of switch pod assembly, then remove switch pod inner plastic.
6. Unclip pigtail to lower printed circuit board, then disconnect harness connector.
7. Slide switch out of slot at end of headlamp switch.
8. Reverse procedure to install.

## MULTI-FUNCTION SWITCH

## REPLACE

**Disable airbag as outlined under "Airbag System Disarming." After prodedure has been completed, rearm airbag system as outlined under "Airbag System Disarming."**

### Removal

The multi-function switch contains electrical circuitry for turn signal, cornering lamps, hazard warning, headlamp dimmer, windshield wiper, pulse wipe and windshield washer switching. This switch is mounted to the lefthand side of the steering column. Should any function of the switch fail, the entire switch assembly, **Fig. 15,** must be replaced.

1. Disconnect battery ground cable.
2. Remove tilt lever, then upper and lower steering column covers.
3. Remove multi-function switch tamper proof attaching screws.
4. Carefully pull switch away from steering column. Loosen electrical connector screw. Screw will remain in connector.
5. Disconnect electrical connector from multi-function switch, then remove switch.

### Installation

1. Install electrical connector to switch and **torque** retaining screw to 17 inch lbs.
2. Mount multi-function switch on column and **torque** attaching screws to 17 inch lbs.
3. Install upper and lower steering column covers and **torque** attaching

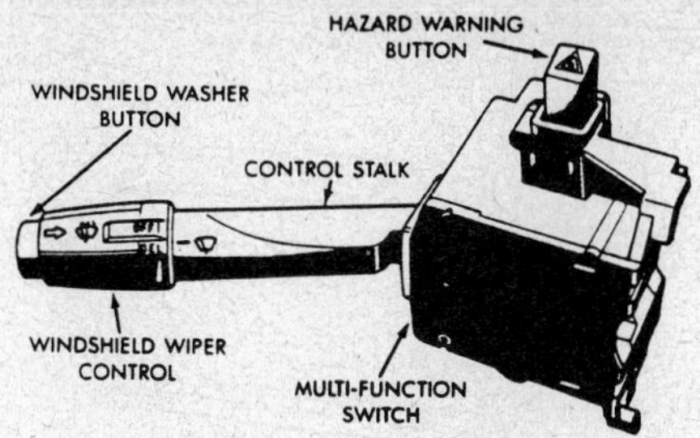


**Fig. 15 Multi-function switch**

screws to 17 inch lbs.
4. Install tilt lever.
5. Connect battery ground cable.
6. Check all functions of switch for proper operation.

# DUAL-FUNCTION SWITCH

## REPLACE

**Disable airbag as outlined under "Airbag System Disarming." After prodedure has been completed, rearm airbag system as outlined under "Airbag System Disarming."**

### 1990–92 DAYTONA & LEBARON COUPE/CONVERTIBLE

On these models, the dual-function switch **Fig. 16** contains circuits for hazard warning switching and turn signal cancellation. The switch is mounted on the left-hand side of the steering column.

#### Removal

1. Disconnect battery ground cable.
2. **On models with tilt column,** remove tilt lever.
3. **On all models,** remove upper and lower steering column covers.
4. Remove tamper proof screws attaching switch to steering column.
5. Carefully pull switch away from column. Release connector lock on wiring connector, remove connector from switch, then remove the switch.

#### Installation

1. Install wiring connector to switch. Ensure switch locking tab is fully seated in wiring connector.
2. Mount switch on column and **torque** attaching screws to 17 inch lbs.
3. Install upper and lower steering column covers and **torque** attaching screws to 17 inch lbs.
4. **On models with tilt column,** install tilt lever.
5. **On all models,** connect battery ground cable.
6. Check all functions of switch for proper operation.

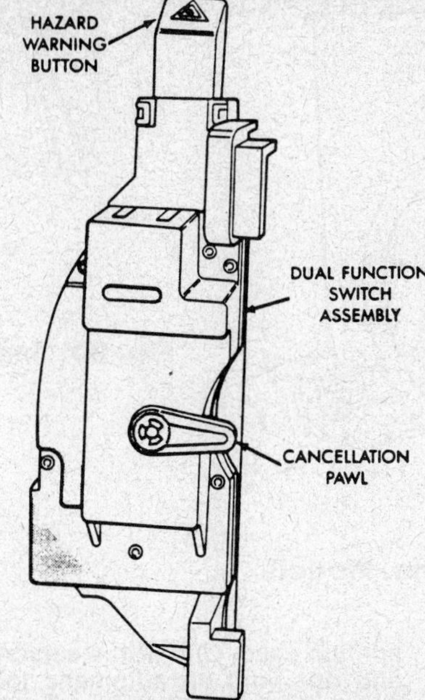


**Fig. 16 Dual-function switch. 1990 Daytona & LeBaron Coupe/Convertible**

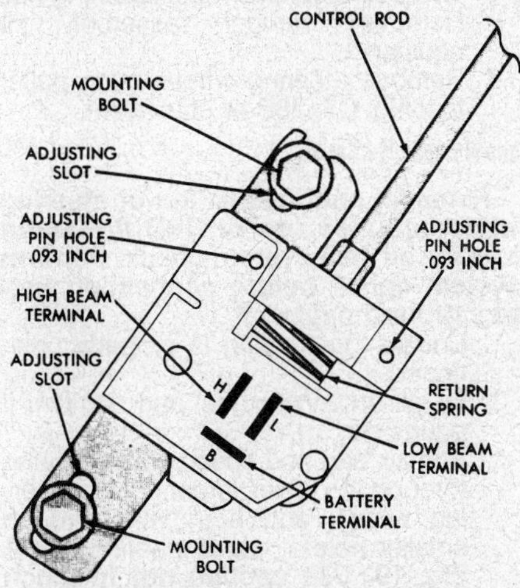


**Fig. 18 Dimmer switch installation**

# DIMMER SWITCH

## REPLACE

**Disable airbag as outlined under "Airbag System Disarming." After prodedure has been completed, rearm airbag system as outlined under "Airbag System Disarming."**

### 1989

#### EXCEPT HORIZON & OMNI

#### Models Less Tilt Column

1. Disconnect battery ground cable, then disconnect electrical connector from switch.
2. Remove two screws attaching switch to column, **Fig. 17.**

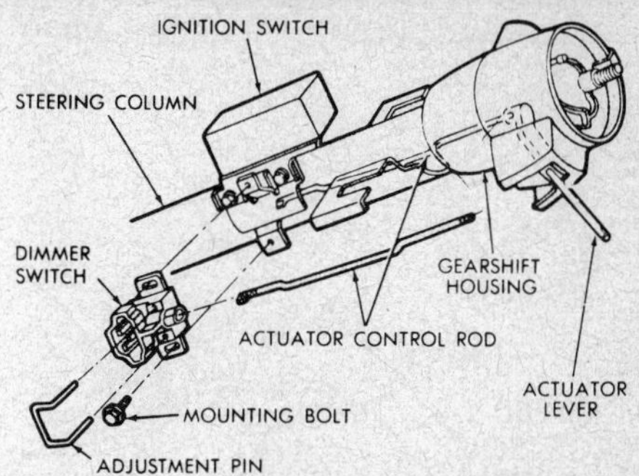


**Fig. 17 Dimmer switch replacement**

3. Reverse procedure to install. During installation, gently push up on switch to take up slack on rod.

#### Models w/Tilt Column

Refer to "Horizon & Omni" for "Dimmer Switch, Replace procedure."

#### HORIZON & OMNI

1. Disconnect battery ground cable, then disconnect connector from switch.
2. Remove two switch mounting screws and disengage switch from pushrod, **Fig. 18.**
3. To install switch, firmly seat pushrod into switch, then compress switch until two .093 inch drill shanks can be inserted into alignment holes. Position upper end of pushrod in pocket of washer/wiper switch. **This can be done by feel, or if necessary, by removing lower column cover.**
4. Apply a light rearward pressure on switch, then install screws and remove drills. **The switch should click when lever is lifted, and again as lever returns, just before it reaches its stop in the down position.**
5. Reconnect wiring connector to switch and connect battery ground cable.

### 1990

#### Except Acclaim, Horizon, LeBaron, Spirit, & Omni Less Tilt Column

On these models, the dimmer switch is contained within the multi-function switch. Refer to procedure outlined under ""Multi-Function Switch, Replace."

#### Acclaim, Horizon, LeBaron, Spirit, & Omni Less Tilt Column

1. Disconnect battery ground cable.
2. Remove lower steering column cover, then disconnect switch electrical connector.
3. Remove two screws attaching dimmer switch to mounting plate, disengage switch from control rod, then remove the switch.
4. Position new switch, install two attaching screws but do not tighten.
5. Insert control rod, then insert adjustment pin in switch hole to lock switch in adjustment position, **Fig. 17.**
6. Adjust switch by carefully pushing up

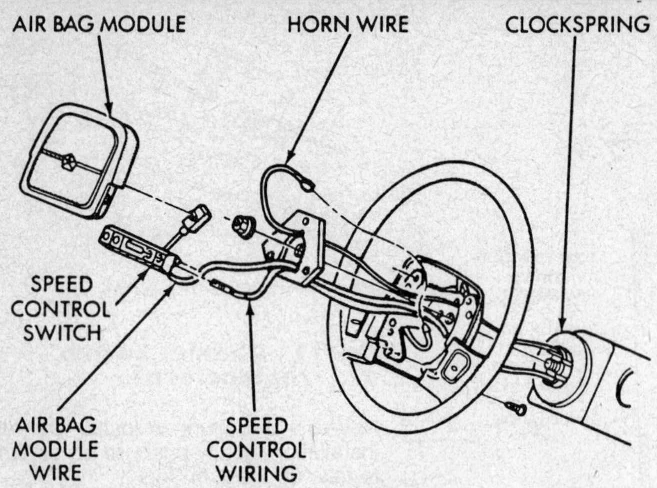


**Fig. 19 Steering wheel components. Models w/air bag**

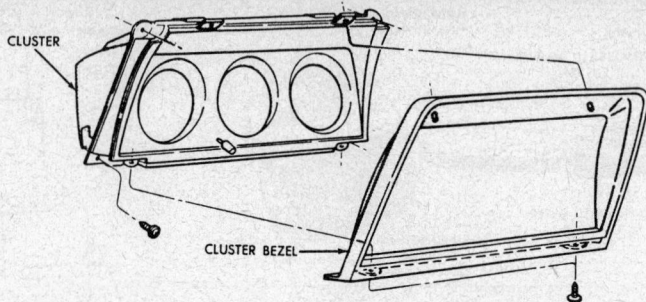

**Fig. 20 Instrument cluster & bezel. Horizon & Omni**

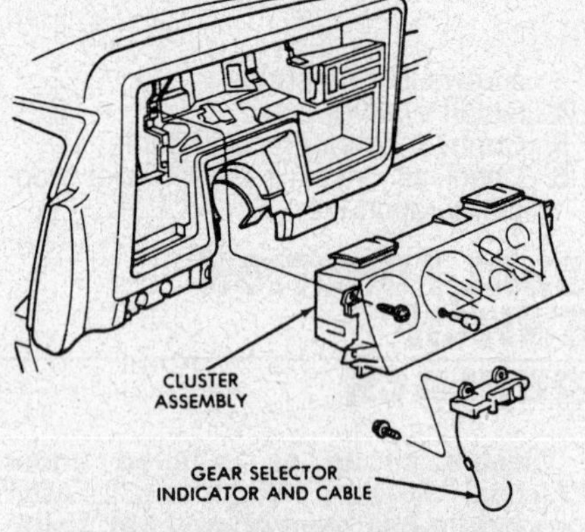


**Fig. 21 Instrument cluster GTS; 1989 Dynasty & New Yorker assembly. 1989 Lancer & LeBaron**

on switch to take up control rod slack.

7. Tighten switch attaching screws, then remove adjustment pin.
8. Connect dimmer switch electrical connector, then install steering column cover.
9. Connect battery ground cable.

## 1991–92

On these models, the dimmer switch is contained within the multi-function switch. Refer to procedure outlined under "Multi-Function Switch, Replace."

# STEERING WHEEL REPLACE

## MODELS w/AIRBAG

**Disable airbag as outlined under "Airbag System Disarming." After prodedure has been completed, rearm airbag system as outlined under "Airbag System Disarming."**

**Removal and installation of steering wheel requires use of DRB II readout tool for air bag system check. Perform system check before connecting battery ground cable.**

### Removal

1. Disconnect battery ground cable.
2. Ensure wheels are in straight ahead position and column is locked in place.
3. Using a 10 mm thinwall socket, remove four nuts attaching air bag module from back side of steering wheel, **Fig. 19.**
4. Lift air bag module, then disconnect electrical connector by spreading apart external latching arms and prying up on connector.
5. Remove speed control switch, if equipped.
6. If equipped, remove clockspring setscrew from storage location on steering wheel, then install screw in clockspring to maintain clockspring position. Screw is on a plastic tether. **There are two types of clocksprings used. One with a setscrew and one with an automatic lock, which engages when steering wheel is removed. Automatic locking clocksprings can be identified by lack of setscrew and tether strap.**
7. Remove steering wheel retaining nut.
8. Remove damper assembly, if equipped.
9. Remove steering wheel using puller tool No. C3428B or equivalent.

### Installation

**Removal and installation of steering wheel requires use of DRB II readout tool for air bag system check. Perform system check before connecting battery ground cable.**

1. Ensure clockspring is properly positioned.
2. Install steering wheel and damper, if equipped.
3. Pull air bag and speed control wiring through the lower, larger hole in steering wheel; and horn wire through smaller hole at top of steering wheel, **Fig. 19. Use caution not to pinch wires.**
4. Install steering wheel retaining nut and **torque** to 45 ft. lbs.
5. Move clockspring setscrew to steering wheel storage location, if equipped.
6. Install speed control switch, if equipped.
7. Connect clockspring wiring connector to air bag module. **To ensure complete connection, latching arms must be visibly on top of connector housing.**
8. Install four air bag module attaching nuts and **torque** to 80-100 inch. lbs.
9. **Before connecting battery ground cable, perform air bag system check as follows:**
   a. Connect DRB II readout tool to air bag system diagnostic module (ASDM) diagnostic 6-way connector, located at right side of console.
   b. From passenger side of vehicle, turn ignition key to On position. Exit vehicle with DRB II.
   c. Ensure no one is inside vehicle, then connect negative battery cable.
   d. Using DRB II, read and record active fault data.
   e. Read and record any stored faults.
   f. If any faults are present, refer to procedure outlined under "Passive Restraint System" section.
   g. Erase stored faults if no active fault codes are present.
   h. With ignition key in On position ensure no one is inside vehicle.
   i. From passenger side of vehicle, turn ignition key to Off then On position and observe instrument panel air bag warning light. Light should go out after six to eight seconds, indicating system is operating correctly. **If air bag warning light does not illuminate, or goes on and stays on, there is a system malfunction. Refer to procedure outlined under "Passive Restraint System" section.**

## MODELS LESS AIRBAG

1. Disconnect battery ground cable.
2. Remove horn pad assembly, then the steering wheel retaining nut.
3. Remove steering wheel using puller tool No. C-3428B or equivalent.
4. Reverse procedure to install, noting the following:
   a. Position steering wheel master serration over missing tooth on

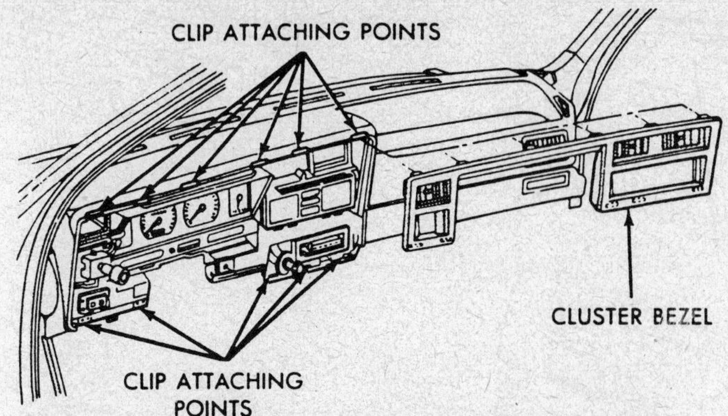


**Fig. 22 Instrument cluster bezel. 1989–90 Acclaim, Spirit & 1990 LeBaron Landau**

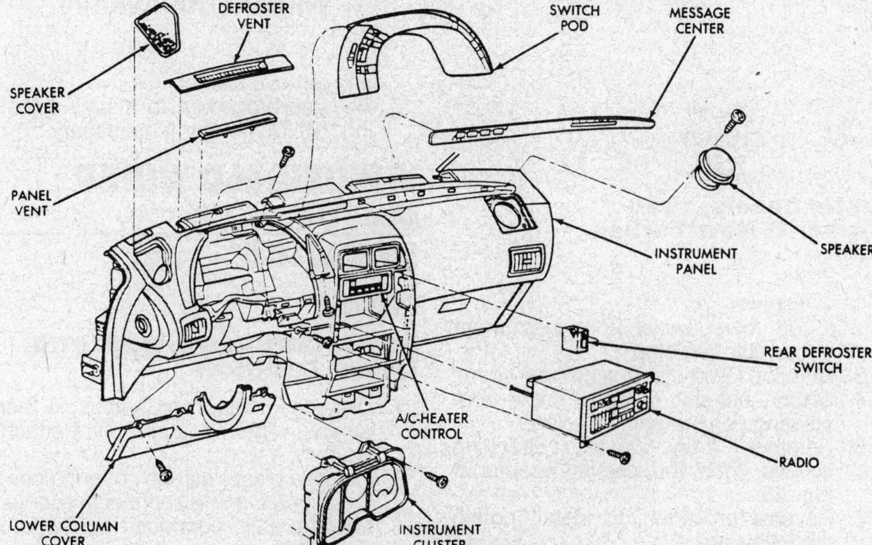


**Fig. 23 Instrument panel components. 1990 Daytona & LeBaron Coupe/Convertible**

steering shaft.

b. **Torque** steering wheel retaining nut to 45 ft. lbs.

## INSTRUMENT CLUSTER REPLACE

**Disable airbag as outlined under "Airbag System Disarming." After prodedure has been completed, rearm airbag system as outlined under "Airbag System Disarming."**

### HORIZON & OMNI

1. Disconnect battery ground cable.
2. Remove two lower cluster bezel retaining screws, **Fig. 20.**
3. Allow bezel to drop slightly, then remove bezel.
4. Remove four screws securing instrument cluster and pull cluster away from dash.
5. Disconnect electrical connectors and speedometer cable, then remove cluster.
6. Reverse procedure to install.

### 1989 DAYTONA & 1989 LEBARON (EXCEPT GTS)

1. Disconnect battery ground cable.
2. Remove screws securing cluster bezel and bezel.
3. Remove four screws securing cluster and pull cluster away from dash.
4. Disconnect electrical connectors and speedometer cable, if equipped, then remove cluster.
5. Reverse procedure to install.

### 1989 LANCER, LEBARON GTS, DYNASTY & NEW YORKER

1. Disconnect battery ground cable.
2. Place gear selector lever in lowest position, then remove instrument cluster bezel attaching screws and bezel.
3. Remove lower steering column cover, then disconnect gear selector cable at steering column shift housing.
4. Remove mask and lens assembly.
5. Remove speedometer assembly, then disconnect speedometer cable.
6. Remove cluster assembly attaching screws, then pull cluster assembly away from dash panel.
7. Disconnect all electrical connectors from cluster assembly, then remove cluster, **Fig. 21.**
8. Reverse procedure to install.

### 1989–90 SHADOW & SUNDANCE

1. Disconnect battery ground cable.
2. Unscrew trip reset knob, then remove screws securing cluster bezel and bezel.
3. Remove four screws securing cluster and pull cluster away from dash.
4. Disconnect electrical connectors and speedometer cable, if equipped, then remove cluster.
5. Reverse procedure to install.

### 1989 ARIES & RELIANT

1. Disconnect battery ground cable, then place gearshift lever in 1 position.
2. Remove six cluster bezel retaining screws and snap bezel out of retaining clips.
3. Remove trip reset knob, then the mask from retaining clips.
4. Remove rearward screws from upper dash pad, lift rearward edge of upper dash pad and remove two screws from top of cluster and bottom two cluster retaining screws.
5. Disconnect all connectors and slide the cluster out of dash.
6. Reverse procedure to install.

### ACCLAIM, SPIRIT & 1990–92 LEBARON LANDAU

1. Disconnect battery ground cable.
2. Remove cluster bezel as follows:
   a. **On column shift models,** place shift lever in N position.
   b. **On models with tilt column,** adjust tilt to lowest position.
   c. **On all models,** pull cluster bezel rearward to disengage 11 retaining clips, then remove cluster bezel, **Fig. 22.**
3. **On column shift models,** proceed as follows:
   a. Remove lower steering column cover.
   b. Disconnect shift indicator wire.
4. **On all models,** remove four screws attaching cluster to base panel.
5. Pull cluster rearward, reach behind cluster and disconnect wiring harness.
6. Remove cluster assembly.
7. Reverse procedure to install, adjusting shift indicator cable on column shift models.

### 1990–92 DAYTONA & LEBARON COUPE/CONVERTIBLE

1. Disconnect battery ground cable.
2. Remove switch pod assembly as fol-

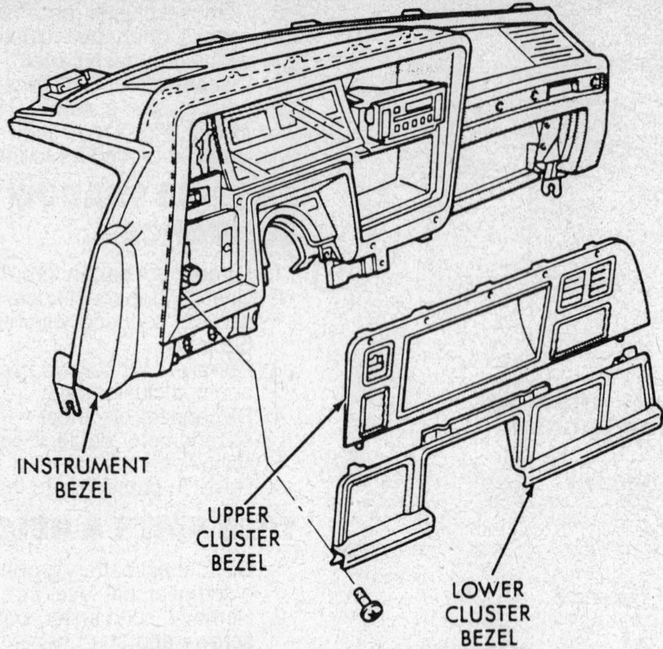


**Fig. 24 Instrument cluster bezels. 1990 Dynasty, Imperial, New Yorker & New Yorker Fifth Avenue**

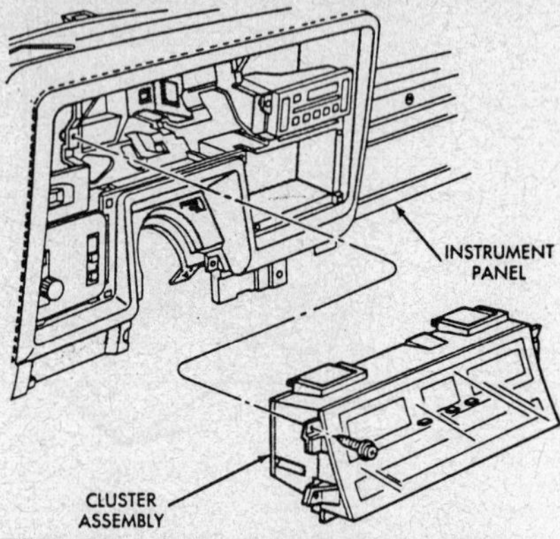


**Fig. 25 Instrument cluster assembly. 1990 Dynasty, Imperial, New Yorker & New Yorker Fifth Avenue**

lows:

a. Pry up edge of panel vent grille, using a straightedge to disengage retaining clips, then remove grille, **Fig. 23.**
b. Remove two attaching screws located under panel vent grille.
c. Remove two outboard attaching screws located under switch pod assembly.
d. Pull switch pod rearward to remove and simultaneously disconnect all wiring connections.
e. Remove switch pod assembly.

3. **On models with tilt column,** remove tilt lever.
4. **On all models,** remove upper and lower steering column covers.
5. Remove cluster trim bezel by pulling rearward to disengage retaining clips.
6. Remove four cluster attaching screws and pull cluster rearward.
7. Tilt cluster to disconnect all wiring connectors and turbo gauge hose, if equipped, then remove cluster assembly.
8. Reverse procedure to install.

## 1990–92 DYNASTY, IMPERIAL, NEW YORKER & NEW YORKER FIFTH AVENUE

1. Disconnect battery ground cable.
2. Remove upper and lower cluster bezels as follows:
   a. Move shift lever to Low position.
   b. Remove five Torx upper bezel attaching, **Fig. 24.**
   c. Lift upper bezel over steering wheel to remove.
   d. Remove four lower bezel attaching screws.
   e. Lift lower bezel from instrument panel to remove.
3. Remove lower steering column cover.
4. Disconnect shift indicator cable from steering column shift housing.
5. Remove four cluster attaching screws, then the cluster assembly, **Fig. 25.**
6. Reverse procedure to install, noting the following:
   a. Install cluster assembly while routing shift indicator cable through base panel.
   b. Place shift lever in N.
   c. Pull shift indicator cable so pointer is between R and N, then allow cable to snap back.
   d. Connect shift indicator cable to shift housing, then place shift lever in P.

## 1991–92 SHADOW & SUNDANCE

1. Disconnect battery ground cable.
2. Remove cluster bezel attaching screws and bezel.
3. **On models with column shift**, proceed as follows:
   a. Remove lower steering column cover and place gear selector in neutral or park position.
   b. Remove PRNDL cable eyelet from column actuating arm.
   c. Release lock bar on column insert and remove insert from column.
   d. Secure insert and cable out of the way.
4. **On all models,** remove rear window and radio bezels.
5. Remove cluster attaching screws and pull cluster from dash.
6. Disconnect two electrical connectors and remove cluster.
7. Reverse procedure to install, adjusting PRNDL pointer if necessary.

# WINDSHIELD WIPER MOTOR

## REPLACE

### FRONT

#### Aries, Caravelle, Daytona, Laser, Lebaron

1. Disconnect battery ground cable, then remove wiper arms and pivot attaching nuts.
2. Remove plastic screen covering cowl, if equipped, and disconnect reservoir hose from "T" connector on Daytona and Laser.
3. Remove wiper motor cover and disconnect electrical connectors to motor.
4. Push pivots downward into plenum chamber, then pull motor outward to clear mounting stud. Move wiper motor toward driver's side of vehicle as far as possible and pull righthand pivot and link assembly through opening, then move motor toward passenger side of vehicle and remove wiper motor, and lefthand pivot and link assembly.
5. Remove nut from end of motor shaft, then the motor crank.
6. Reverse procedure to install.

#### Horizon & Omni

1. Remove wiper arm assemblies.
2. Remove nuts from left and right pivots.
3. Remove wiper motor plastic cover.
4. Disconnect wiper motor wiring harness.
5. Remove three bolts from wiper motor mounting bracket.
6. Disengage pivots from cowl top mounting positions.
7. Remove wiper motor, cranks, pivots and drive link assembly from cowl plenum chamber.
8. Remove wiper motor from drive crank

linkage.
9. Reverse procedure to install.

### Acclaim, Dynasty, Imperial, LeBaron Landau, New Yorker, New Yorker Fifth Avenue & Spirit; Lancer, Lebaron GTS, Shadow & Sundance

1. Disconnect battery ground cable.
2. Remove wiper arms, then the plastic cowl cover.
3. Remove pivot mounting stud retaining nuts and disconnect wiper motor wiring connector.
4. Remove motor mounting bracket retaining bolts, then the motor assembly from cowl plenum.
5. Reverse procedure to install.

## REAR

### Aries, Reliant, LeBaron, Executive, Lancer & Town & Country

1. Disconnect battery ground cable.
2. Remove wiper arm and blade assembly.
3. Remove wiper motor cover, then disconnect wire connector from motor.
4. Remove four screws attaching wiper motor bracket to liftgate, then the wiper motor.
5. Reverse procedure to install.

### Daytona & Laser

1. Disconnect battery ground cable.
2. Raise wiper arm, release latch and remove arm assembly.
3. Remove inner trim panel and disconnect electrical connector to motor.
4. Remove grommet from liftgate glass.
5. Remove 2 screws securing motor and the motor.
6. Reverse procedure to install.

### Horizon & Omni

1. Disconnect battery ground cable and remove wiper arm assembly.
2. Remove pivot shaft nut, bezel and seal.
3. Remove wiper motor cover and disconnect electrical connector to motor.
4. Remove screws securing wiper motor and motor.
5. Reverse procedure to install.

# WIPER SWITCH
# REPLACE

**Disable airbag as outlined under "Airbag System Disarming." After prodedure has been completed, rearm airbag system as outlined under "Airbag System Disarming."**

On models equipped with a multi-function switch refer to "Multi-Function Switch, Replace."

## 1989

## FRONT

### Except Horizon & Omni

1. Disconnect battery ground cable and

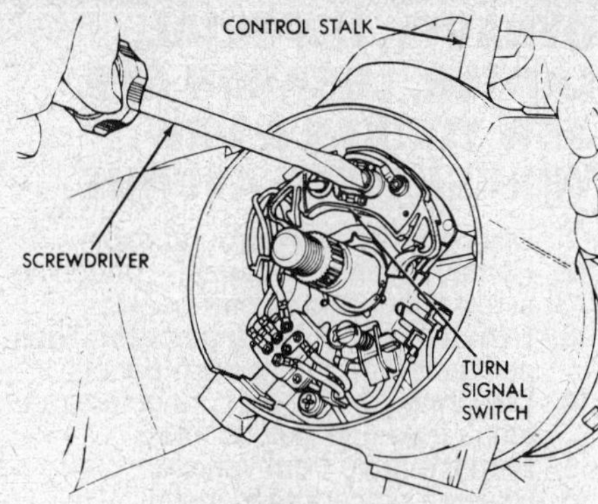


**Fig. 26 Windshield wiper switch removal**

remove steering wheel as outlined under "Steering Wheel, Replace."
2. **On models equipped with intermittent wiper system,** remove two screws attaching turn signal lever cover to lock housing and the turn signal lever cover.
3. **On all models,** remove screw attaching windshield wiper switch and switch, **Fig. 26.**
4. Reverse procedure to install.

### Horizon & Omni

1. Disconnect battery ground cable.
2. Disconnect wiper switch and turn signal switch wiring harness connectors.
3. Remove lower column cover.
4. Remove horn button.
5. Place ignition lock in Off position and turn steering wheel so access hole in hub area is at 9 o'clock position.
6. With a suitable screwdriver, loosen turn signal lever screw through access hole.
7. Disengage dimmer pushrod from wiper switch.
8. Unsnap wiring clip and remove wiper switch.
9. Reverse procedure to install.

## REAR

### Except Horizon, Omni, Lancer & LeBaron GTS

1. Disconnect battery ground cable.
2. Remove cluster bezel, then seven lower trim bezel attaching screws.
3. Remove trim bezel by unsnapping two retaining clips.
4. Disconnect switch assembly electrical connector.
5. Remove two switch attaching screws and the switch.
6. Reverse procedure to install.

### Horizon & Omni

1. Disconnect battery ground cable.
2. Depress two spring clips on top of bezel, using a thin blade screwdriver.
3. Tip bezel rearward and pull out switch assembly.
4. Remove switch and lamp electrical connector, then the switch assembly.
5. Reverse procedure to install.

### Lancer & LeBaron GTS

1. Disconnect battery ground cable.
2. Remove headlight and accessory switch module from instrument panel.
3. Remove two rear wiper and washer switch attaching screws from module, then the switch.
4. Reverse procedure to install.

## 1990

## FRONT

### Acclaim, Horizon, LeBaron Landau, Omni, Shadow, Spirit & Sundance Less Tilt Column

**Removal and installation of steering wheel requires use of DRB II readout tool for air bag system check. Perform system check before connecting battery ground cable.**

1. Disconnect battery ground cable.
2. Remove steering wheel as outlined under" Steering Wheel, Replace."
3. Remove two screws attaching turn signal lever cover to lock housing, then remove turn signal lever cover.
4. Remove screw attaching wiper/washer switch, then the switch.
5. Reverse procedure to install, referring to "Steering Wheel, Replace" when installing steering wheel:

### Daytona & LeBaron Coupe/Convertible

1. Disconnect battery ground cable.
2. Remove switch pod assembly. Refer to procedure outlined under "Instrument Cluster, Replace."
3. Remove five screws attaching inner switch pod panel, then remove the inner panel.
4. Disconnect switch linkage from buttons.
5. Remove switch mounting screws, then the switch.
6. Reverse procedure to install, noting the following:
   a. Secure switch linkage in up position.
   b. Insert switch into switch pod, then install attaching screws.
   c. Connect linkage to buttons.
   d. Check all switch modes for proper operation.

## REAR

### Horizon & Omni

1. Disconnect battery ground cable.
2. Remove console upper bezel.
3. Pull console lower bezel until retaining clips disengage, but do not disconnect wiring.
4. Unsnap switch from underside of bezel, disconnect switch wiring, then remove switch.
5. Reverse procedure to install.

# RADIO
# REPLACE

**Disable airbag as outlined under "Airbag System Disarming." After prodedure has been completed, rearm airbag system as outlined under "Airbag System Disarming."**

**Fig. 27 Blower motor replacement. Horizon & Omni less A/C**

## DAYTONA, LASER & LEBARON

1. Disconnect battery ground cable.
2. **On 1989 models,** remove two screws securing bottom of console bezel, then lift bezel from console.
3. **On 1990-92 models,** remove center instrument panel bezel by pulling rearward.
4. **On all models,** remove two screws securing radio and pull radio away from console.
5. Disconnect electrical connectors and antenna lead, then remove radio.
6. Reverse procedure to install.

## 1989 HORIZON, OMNI

1. Disconnect battery ground cable.
2. Remove right bezel attaching screws and open glove box.
3. Remove bezel, guiding right end around glove box as needed.
4. Remove radio mounting screws.
5. Pull radio from panel and disconnect wiring, ground strap and antenna lead from radio.
6. Remove radio from vehicle.
7. Reverse procedure to install.

## 1990 HORIZON & OMNI

1. Remove console upper bezel (snaps out).
2. Remove lower console bezel, but do not disconnect wiring.
3. Remove radio attaching screws.
4. Pull radio rearward, disconnect antenna lead, ground strap and electrical connectors, then remove radio.
5. Reverse procedure to install.

## 1989 ARIES, CARAVELLE, EXECUTIVE, LEBARON EXCEPT GTS, NEW YORKER, RELIANT

1. Disconnect battery ground cable.
2. Remove left instrument bezel attaching screws, then the bezel.
3. Remove two radio and radio bezel to base panel attaching screws.
4. Pull radio through front face of base panel, then disconnect electrical connectors, antenna lead and ground strap.
5. Remove radio from vehicle.
6. Reverse procedure to install.

## DYNASTY, IMPERIAL, LANCER, LEBARON GTS, NEW YORKER & NEW YORKER FIFTH AVENUE

1. Disconnect battery ground cable.
2. Remove cluster bezel attaching screws, then the cluster bezel.
3. Remove radio attaching screws, then pull radio away from dash panel.
4. Disconnect electrical connectors, antenna lead and ground strap.
5. Remove radio from vehicle.
6. Reverse procedure to install.

## SHADOW & SUNDANCE

1. Remove center module bezel.
2. Remove lower center module cover if equipped with base console. Remove right console sidewall if equipped with full console.
3. Remove mounting screws and the radio from instrument panel. Disconnect wiring and remove ground straps.
4. Reverse procedure to install.

## ACCLAIM & SPIRIT; 1991–92 LEBARON LANDAU

1. Disconnect battery ground cable.
2. Remove center bezel by pulling straight back to disengage from the five retaining clips.
3. Remove radio attaching screws.
4. Pull radio from panel and disconnect wiring, ground strap and antenna lead from radio, then remove radio.
5. Reverse procedure to install.

# BLOWER MOTOR REPLACE

**Disable airbag as outlined under "Airbag System Disarming." After prodedure has been completed, rearm airbag system as outlined under "Airbag System Disarming."**

## 1989

### LESS A/C

#### Except Horizon & Omni

1. Perform steps 1 through 14 as outlined under "Heater Core, Replace."
2. Remove blower motor to heater housing attaching screws and the blower motor.
3. Remove clamp retaining blower motor wheel to shaft, the two nuts attaching retainer plate to blower motor and the plate.
4. Reverse procedure to install.

#### Horizon & Omni

1. Disconnect battery ground cable.
2. Disconnect blower motor wiring connector.
3. Remove left heater outlet duct.
4. Remove screws retaining blower motor mounting plate to heater unit.
5. Remove blower motor assembly, **Fig. 27.**
6. Reverse procedure to install.

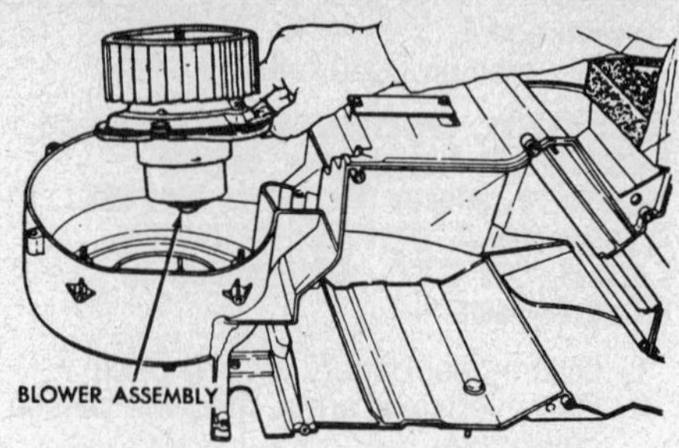


**Fig. 28 Blower motor replacement. 1989 models with A/C**

### WITH A/C

1. Disconnect battery ground cable.
2. Remove three screws securing glove box to instrument panel and glove box.
3. Disconnect blower motor feed and ground wires. Remove wires from retaining clip on recirculating housing.
4. Disconnect blower motor vent tube from A/C unit.
5. Loosen recirculation door actuator from bracket and remove actuator from housing. Do not disconnect vacuum lines.
6. Remove seven screws securing recirculating housing to A/C unit, then the housing.
7. Remove three blower motor mounting flange nuts and blower motor, **Fig. 28.**
8. Reverse procedure to install.

## 1990–92

1. Disconnect battery ground cable.
2. Remove glove box.
3. **On models with A/C,** disconnect two vacuum lines from recirculating air door actuator.
4. **On all models,** disconnect blower lead wire connector.
5. Remove two screws from top of blower motor, attaching it to the heater A/C unit cover.
6. Remove five screws from around blower housing, then separate blower housing from heater A/C unit, **Fig. 29.**
7. Remove three screws attaching blower motor and wheel to unit housing, then separate blower assembly from unit housing.

# HEATER CORE REPLACE

**Disable airbag as outlined under "Airbag System Disarming." After prodedure has been completed, rearm airbag system as outlined under "Airbag System Disarming."**

## HORIZON & OMNI

### 1989

#### Less A/C

1. Disconnect battery ground cable, then

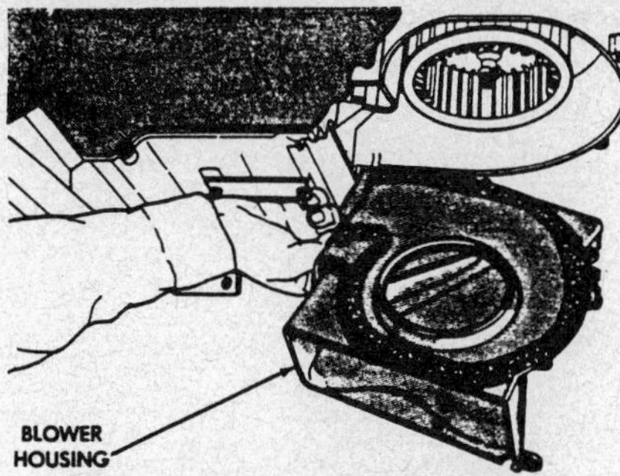


**Fig. 29 Blower housing (Typical)**

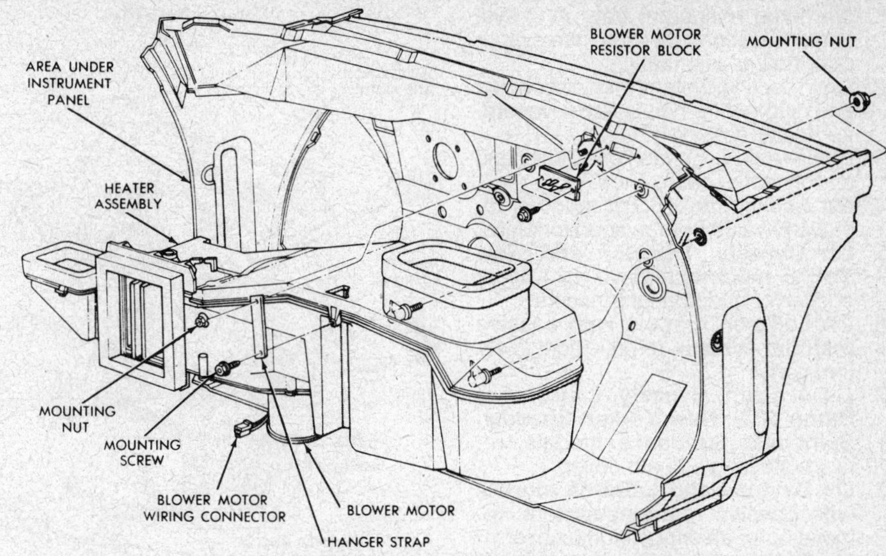


**Fig. 30 Heater assembly. 1989 Horizon, Omni less A/C**

drain cooling system.

2. Disconnect blower motor electrical connector, then remove ashtray.
3. Depress red color coded tab on end of temperature control cable, and pull control cable out of receiver on heater assembly.
4. Remove glove box and door assembly.
5. Disconnect heater hoses and plug heater core tube openings.
6. Remove two heater assembly to dash panel attaching nuts, **Fig. 30.**
7. Disconnect blower resistor electrical connector, then remove heater support brace to instrument panel attaching screws.
8. Remove heater support bracket nut, then disconnect strap from plenum stud and lower heater assembly from under instrument panel.
9. Depress yellow color coded tab on end of mode door control cable out of receiver on heater assembly.
10. Move heater unit toward right side of vehicle, then out from under instrument panel.
11. Remove left heater outlet duct attaching screws, then the heater outlet duct.
12. Remove four blower motor mounting plate attaching screws, then the blower motor assembly.
13. Remove four outside air and defroster door cover attaching screws, then the door cover.
14. Remove defroster door assembly, then lift defroster door control rod out of heater assembly.
15. Remove 8 heater core cover attaching screws, then the core cover.
16. Slide heater core up and out of heater assembly.
17. Reverse procedure to install.

### With A/C

1. Disconnect battery ground cable, then drain cooling system and discharge A/C system.
2. Disconnect blend air door cable and disengage from clip on heater air duct.
3. Remove glove box and door assembly.
4. Remove center bezel attaching screws, then the center bezel.
5. Remove center distribution duct and defroster duct adapter.
6. Disconnect heater hoses and A/C lines. Plug heater core tube openings.
7. Disconnect vacuum lines at engine and water valve.
8. Remove four dash retaining nuts, then the right side cowl trim panel.
9. Remove right instrument panel pivot bracket attaching screw, then two screws attaching lower instrument panel at steering column.
10. Remove panel top cover.
11. Remove all but left panel to fenceline attaching screw, then pull carpet from under A/C unit as far rearward as possible.
12. Remove support strap attaching nut and blower motor ground cable, then support heater unit with hands and remove strap from its plenum stud, **Fig. 31.**
13. Lift and pull evaporator heater assembly rearward to clear dash panel and liner. The panel will also have to be pulled rearward to allow assembly clearance.
14. Remove evaporator heater assembly from dash panel, taking care to prevent dash panel attaching studs from hanging up in dash liner.
15. Place evaporator heater assembly on workbench, then remove nut from mode door actuator arm on top cover.
16. Remove two retaining clips from front edge of cover, then the mode door actuator to cover attaching screws and mode door actuator.
17. Remove 15 heater unit cover attaching screws, then the cover. Lift mode door out of heater assembly.
18. Remove heater core tube retaining bracket attaching screw, then lift core from heater assembly.
19. Reverse procedure to install.

### 1990

1. Disconnect battery ground cable.
2. **On models with A/C,** discharge A/C system.
3. **On all models,** drain cooling system.
4. **On models with A/C,** remove H-valve.
5. **On all models,** disconnect heater hoses from heater core. Plug heater core tubes to prevent spillage.
6. **On models with A/C,** remove A/C drain tube.
7. **On all models,** disconnect vacuum lines from water valve and vacuum supply nipple.
8. Remove heater A/C unit housing to dash panel attaching nuts.
9. Remove radio assembly. Refer to procedure outlined under "Radio, Replace."
10. Remove console assembly.
11. Remove lower instrument panel.
12. Remove right backing plate from under steering column.
13. Remove both side instrument panel to floor console brace fasteners and position braces aside without disconnecting wiring connectors.
14. Remove air bag diagnostic module from mounting. Do not disconnect wiring connector. Remove module bracket from floor.
15. Remove air distribution duct.
16. Remove defroster duct adapter.
17. Remove hanger strap from unit housing and position aside to the left.
18. Disconnect heater A/C blower motor and vacuum connections.
19. Disconnect air blend door control cable from unit housing, then the cable from clip on air duct.
20. Disconnect antenna cable from retaining clip on unit housing.
21. Move passenger seat as far rearward as possible, then remove unit housing from vehicle.
22. Remove heater A/C unit top cover, **Fig. 32.**
23. Remove heater core-to-dash panel seal from core tubes, then remove heater core.
24. Reverse procedure to install.

## EXCEPT HORIZON & OMNI

### 1989

1. Disconnect battery ground cable, then

discharge refrigerant from A/C system and disconnect lines from evaporator heater assembly.
2. Drain cooling system, then disconnect and plug heater hoses from evaporator heater assembly.
3. Remove A/C condensate drain and disconnect vacuum lines.
4. **On Acclaim and Spirit models,** remove H-valve from evaporator plate.
5. **On Dynasty, LeBaron and New Yorker models,** remove right upper and lower underpanel silencers.
6. **On LeBaron models with passive restraint system,** remove right lower trim panel.
7. **On Acclaim, Dynasty, Lancer, LeBaron GTS, New Yorker, Shadow, Spirit and Sundance models,** remove steering column cover.
8. **On Daytona and LeBaron models with passive restraint system,** remove outer steering column cover.
9. **On Acclaim, Dynasty, New Yorker, Spirit models and LeBaron models with passive restraint system,** remove left underpanel silencer.
10. **On Acclaim and Spirit models,** remove right underpanel silencer pad.
11. **On Daytona and LeBaron models with passive restraint system,** remove hood release and parking brake release handles from inner steering column cover, then remove the cover.
12. **On all models,** slide front bench seat or right front bucket seat back as far as possible.
13. **On Acclaim, Shadow, Spirit and Sundance models,** remove right A-pillar trim.
14. **On all models,** remove right cowl side trim. On LeBaron models, unfasten lower end of right A-pillar trim to allow removal of side trim.
15. Remove glove box. **If necessary, remove right instrument panel reinforcement to allow glove box removal.**
16. **On Acclaim and Spirit models,** proceed as follows:
    a. Disconnect vacuum lines from air door actuator and electrical connector from blower motor.
    b. Remove relay panel from above glove compartment opening, then disconnect A/C vacuum line connector and radio noise capacitors.
    c. Remove left windshield pillar trim cover and left lower side cowl side trim cover.
    d. Remove hood release handle mechanism attaching screws, then disconnect parking brake release mechanism connecting rod.
    e. Remove Instrument center bezel, then the radio and heater controls.
    f. Remove cigar lighter and message center/trip computer, if equipped.
17. **On Daytona and LeBaron models,** proceed as follows:
    a. Remove forward console bezel, side trim and lower carpet panels.
    b. Loosen floor console and move rearward, then remove forward console.
    c. **On models with passive restraint system,** remove instrument panel-to-floor reinforcement.
18. **On Shadow and Sundance models,** proceed as follows:
    a. Remove center bezel, then the lower center module cover.
    b. Remove floor console, then the instrument panel brace from steering column opening.
    c. Remove instrument panel support bracket from below glove box opening.
    d. Remove ashtray, then the radio assembly and panel top cover.
    e. Remove three right side instrument panel attaching screws below windshield.
19. **On Aries and Reliant models,** remove floor console.
20. **On Lancer and LeBaron GTS models,** remove front and rear consoles.
21. **On Dynasty and New Yorker models,** remove ashtray assembly.
22. **On Aries, Reliant, Shadow and Sundance models,** pull lower right side of instrument panel rearward.
23. **On all models,** remove center distribution and defroster adapter ducts.
24. **On Dynasty, Lancer, LeBaron GTS, New Yorker, Shadow and Sundance models,** disconnect relay module electrical connector.
25. **On Shadow and Sundance models,** remove instrument panel-to-evaporator heater assembly bracket, then the lower air distribution duct.
26. **On Aries and Reliant,** remove audible message center, then the brace securing right side cowl to plenum.
27. **On all models,** disconnect blower motor electrical connector, then the demister hoses from top of evaporator heater assembly.

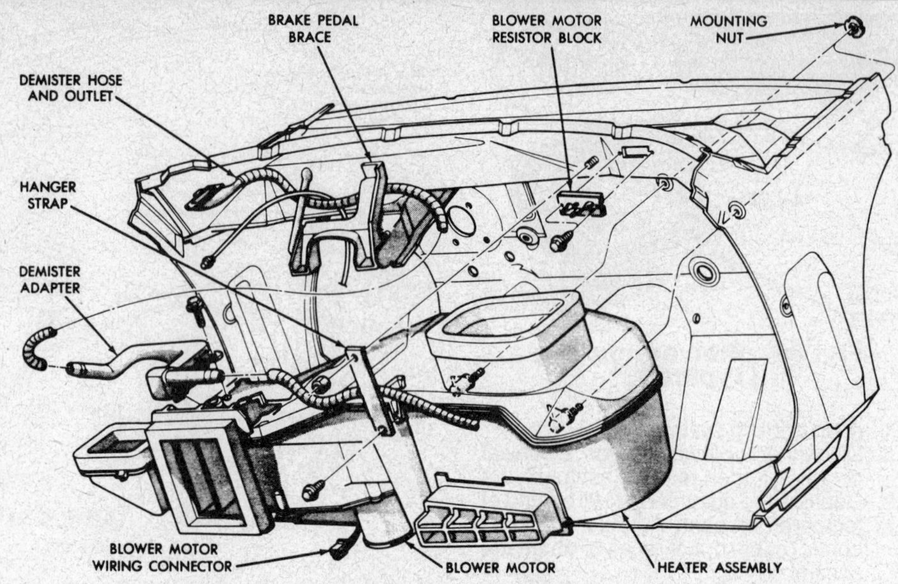


**Fig. 31 Heater assembly. Horizon & Omni with A/C**

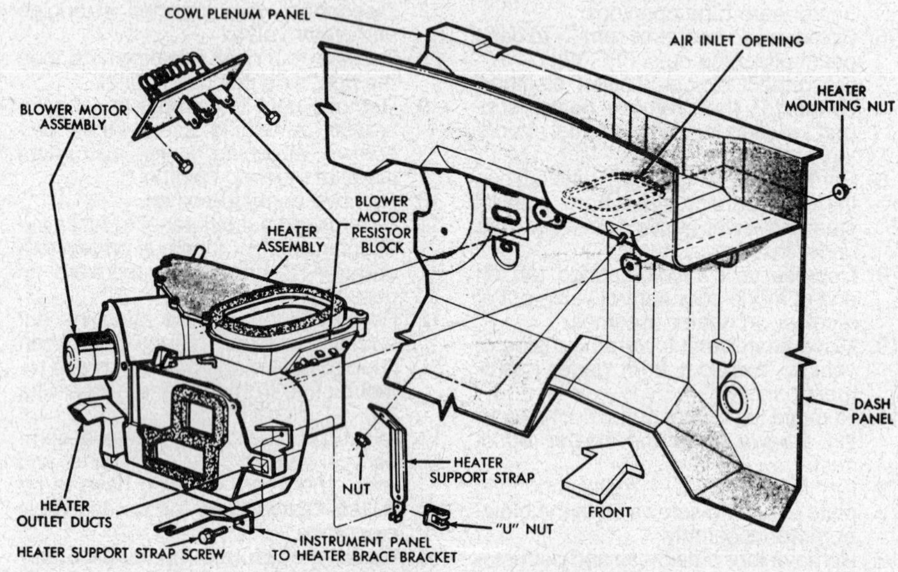


**Fig. 32 Heater assembly**

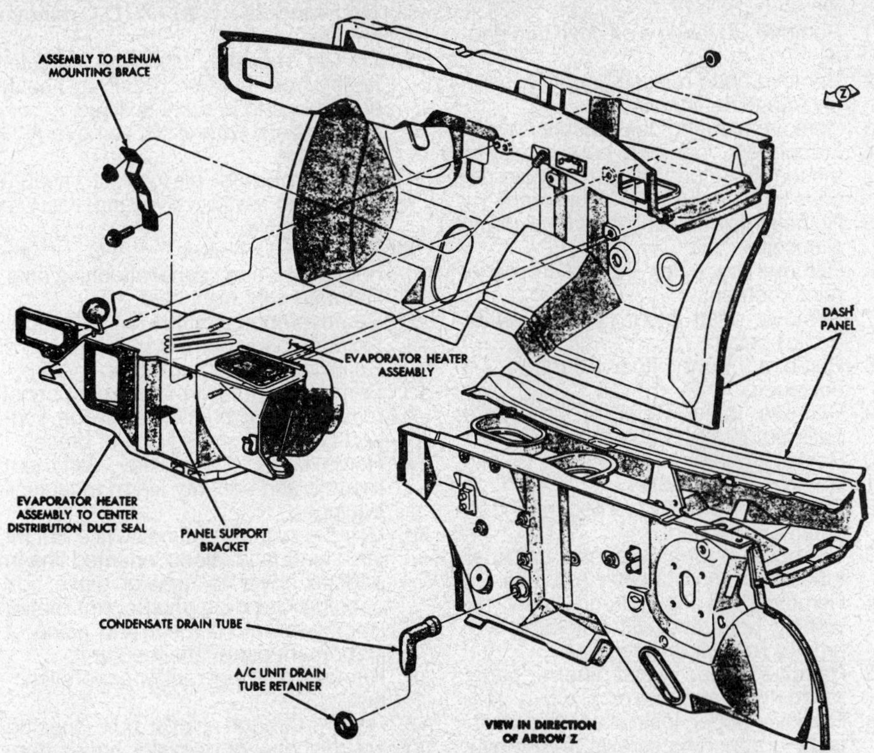


**Fig. 33 Heater assembly. Models less A/C except Horizon & Omni**

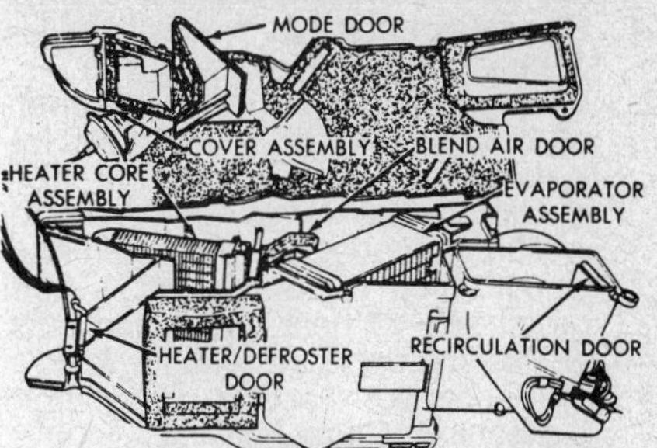


**Fig. 34 Heater assembly. 1989 Daytona, Lancer & less A/C LeBaron GTS**

28. **On models less automatic temperature control,** proceed as follows:
    a. Disconnect temperature control cable flag from bottom of evaporator heater assembly.
    b. Unfasten cable from left side of heat distribution duct.
    c. Disconnect vacuum lines from evaporator heater assembly.
29. **On models with automatic temperature control,** disconnect instrument panel wiring harness from rear of ATC unit.
30. **On Dynasty, Lancer, LeBaron GTS and New Yorker models,** disconnect fuse block and right 25-way connector from instrument panel.
31. **On Acclaim and Spirit models,** proceed as follows:
    a. Remove steering column attaching bolts and allow steering wheel to rest on front seat, then remove upper instrument panel defroster cover.
    b. Remove upper instrument panel attaching screws under windshield opening, then loosen left lower instrument panel attaching screw and remove right instrument panel attaching screw.
32. **On all models,** unfasten antenna cable from clip on evaporator heater assembly.
33. **On all models except Dynasty, Lancer, LeBaron GTS and New Yorker,** fold carpet back from right side of floor.
34. **On all models,** remove four evaporator heater assembly attaching nuts from engine compartment side.
35. Remove lower screw from hanger strap, then rotate the strap aside.
36. Pull evaporator heater assembly rearward until mounting studs are cleared, then lower unit, **Figs. 33 and 34.**
37. **On Shadow and Sundance models,** remove demister adapter from top of unit.
38. **On Shadow and Sundance models,** slide assembly up from under instrument panel while pulling lower right side of panel rearward.
39. **On all models except Acclaim, Shadow, Spirit and Sundance,** pull lower right side of instrument panel rearward and rotate assembly while pulling from under instrument panel.
40. **On all models,** place evaporator heater unit on bench, then remove evaporator heater unit top cover.
41. Remove expansion valve seal and retaining screw from under sealing plate, then lift heater core out of assembly.
42. Reverse procedure to install.

### 1990–92 Dynasty, Imperial, New Yorker, New Yorker Fifth Avenue, Shadow & Sundance

1. Disconnect battery ground cable.
2. **On models with A/C,** discharge A/C system, then disconnect refrigerant lines from heater A/C unit housing.
3. **On all models,** drain cooling system, then disconnect heater hoses from heater core. Tape heater core tubes to prevent leakage during removal.
4. **On models with A/C,** remove A/C drain hose.
5. **On all models,** disconnect vacuum lines.
6. **On Dynasty and New Yorker models,** remove righthand upper and lower underpanel silencers.
7. **On Dynasty, New Yorker, Shadow and Sundance models,** remove steering column cover.
8. **On Dynasty and New Yorker models,** remove lefthand underpanel silencer.
9. **On all models,** position front seat or right front seat as far back as possible.
10. **On Shadow and Sundance models,** remove right A-pillar trim and right cowl side trim.
11. **On all models,** remove glove box.
12. **On Dynasty and New Yorker models,** remove right instrument panel reinforcement.
13. **On Shadow and Sundance models,** proceed as follows:
    a. Remove right instrument panel roll up screw.
    b. Remove center bezel.
    c. Remove lower center module cover.
    d. Remove floor console.
    e. Remove instrument panel support brace (from steering column opening to right cowl side at bottom of instrument panel).
    f. Remove instrument panel to support bracket (below glove box opening).
    g. Remove ash receiver.
    h. Remove radio. Refer to procedure outlined under "Radio, Replace."
    i. Remove instrument panel top cover.
    j. Remove three right side instrument panel-to-fence attaching screws (below windshield).
14. **On Dynasty and New Yorker models,** remove ash receiver.
15. **On Shadow and Sundance models,** pull right lower side of instrument panel rearward.
16. **On all models,** remove center distribution and defroster adapter ducts.
17. **On Dynasty, New Yorker, Shadow and Sundance models,** disconnect relay module.
18. **On Shadow and Sundance models,** proceed as follows:
    a. Remove instrument panel to heater A/C unit housing bracket.
    b. Remove lower air distribution duct.
19. **On all models,** disconnect blower motor wire connector.

20. Disconnect demister hoses from top of heater A/C unit housing.
21. **On models less automatic temperature control (ATC),** proceed as follows:
    a. Disconnect temperature control flag from bottom of heater A/C unit, then disconnect cable from left side of heat distribution duct. Position cable aside to the left.
    b. Disconnect vacuum lines from heater A/C unit housing.
22. **On models with ATC,** disconnect instrument panel wiring from rear face of ATC unit.
23. **On Dynasty and New Yorker models,** disconnect righthand 25-way connector and fuse block from instrument panel.
24. **On all models except Dynasty and New Yorker,** fold right side floor carpet back.
25. **On all models,** remove four heater A/C unit housing attaching screws from inside engine compartment.
26. Remove heater A/C unit housing strap lower screw and position strap aside.
27. Move heater A/C unit housing rearward until clear of mounting studs, then lower the unit.
28. **On Shadow and Sundance models,** remove demister adapter from top of heater A/C unit.
29. **On all models,** pull lower right side of instrument panel rearward.
30. **On all models except Shadow and Sundance,** rotate heater A/C unit while pulling from instrument panel.
31. **On Shadow and Sundance models,** slide heater A/C unit from under instrument panel.
32. **On all models,** remove heater A/C unit top cover, **Fig. 32.**
33. Remove heater core-to-dash panel seal from core tubes, then remove heater core.
34. Reverse procedure to install.

### Acclaim, LeBaron Landau & Spirit

1. Disconnect battery ground cable.
2. Remove glove box.
3. **On models with A/C,** disconnect two vacuum lines from recirculating air door actuator.
4. **On all models,** disconnect blower lead wire connector.
5. Remove two screws from top of blower motor, attaching it to the heater A/C unit cover.
6. Remove five screws from around blower housing, then separate blower housing from heater A/C unit, **Fig. 29.**
7. Remove three screws attaching blower motor and wheel to unit housing, then separate blower assembly from unit housing.
8. Remove relay panel above glove box opening.
9. Through glove compartment opening, disconnect A/C vacuum line and radio noise capacitor connectors, as equipped.
10. Remove left windshield pillar trim cover.
11. Remove left lower side cowl trim panel.
12. Remove hood release handle assembly attaching screws.
13. Remove steering column trim covers.
14. Disconnect parking brake release mechanism connecting rod (gain access through fuse panel opening).
15. Remove lower left instrument panel silencer.
16. Remove lower left instrument panel reinforcement.
17. Remove instrument panel center (radio) bezel.
18. Remove front floor console, if equipped.
19. Remove radio. Refer to procedure outlined under "Radio, Replace."
20. Remove heater A/C control.
21. Remove cigar lighter.
22. Remove message center/trip computer, if equipped.
23. Disconnect side window demister tubes from top of heater A/C unit.
24. Remove steering column upper attaching bolts and allow steering column to rest on drivers seat.
25. Remove upper instrument panel (defroster outlet) cover.
26. Remove upper instrument panel attaching attaching screws from below windshield opening.
27. Loosen, but do not remove, left lower cowl-to-instrument panel attaching screw.
28. Carefully pull instrument panel away from dash panel on right side of vehicle and allow instrument panel to rest on passenger seat. **Protect passenger seat using a suitable cover.**
29. Drain cooling system, disconnect heater hoses from heater core, then plug heater core tubes to prevent spillage.
30. **On models with A/C,** proceed as follows:
    a. Discharge A/C system, then disconnect refrigerant lines from H-valve at dash panel on righthand side of vehicle. Seal refrigerant lines.
    b Remove H-valve from evaporator plate. Seal H-valve to prevent contamination.
    c. Remove A/C drain tube.
31. **On all models,** remove heater A/C unit-to-dash panel attaching nuts.
32. From inside of vehicle, pull heater A/C unit housing rearward to clear dash panel silencer, then remove from vehicle.
33. Remove heater A/C unit top cover, **Fig. 32.**
34. Remove heater core-to-dash panel seal from core tubes, then remove heater core.
35. Reverse procedure to install.

### Daytona & LeBaron Coupe/Convertible

1. Disconnect battery ground cable.
2. **On models with A/C,** discharge A/C system.
3. **On all models,** drain cooling system.
4. **On models with A/C,** remove H-valve.
5. **On all models,** disconnect heater hoses from heater core. Plug heater core tubes to prevent spillage.
6. **On models with A/C,** remove A/C drain tube.
7. **On all models,** disconnect vacuum lines from water valve and vacuum supply nipple.
8. Remove heater A/C unit housing-to-dash panel attaching nuts.
9. Remove right front seat.
10. Remove right side cowl trim panel.
11. Remove body computer.
12. Remove glove box module.
13. Remove right lower instrument panel reinforcement bracket, then the support bracket from left end of brace.
14. Remove radio capacitor, lamp-out module and security alarm module, if equipped.
15. Using a suitable cutting device, cut instrument panel along indented line in padded cover to right of glove box opening. **Cut only plastic, not metal.** Remove reinforcement and piece of instrument panel attached to it.
16. Remove both side under panel silencers.
17. Reach through glove box opening and disconnect demister hoses from top of heater A/C unit housing.
18. Disconnect antenna cable.
19. Disconnect blower motor wiring connectors.
20. Disconnect blend air door control cable from unit housing and position aside.
21. Roll floor carpet back from under unit housing far enough to avoid interference with unit housing removal.
22. Remove lower steering column cover and reinforcement.
23. Remove lower reinforcement support bracket from the side of steering column opening to the left of radio.
24. Remove air distribution duct and defroster adapter through opening at left side of instrument panel.
25. Remove hanger strap from unit housing and position aside to the left.
26. Remove unit housing from under right side of instrument panel.
27. Remove heater A/C unit top cover, **Fig. 32.**
28. Remove heater core-to-dash panel seal from core tubes, then remove heater core.
29. Reverse procedure to install.

## EVAPORATOR CORE REPLACE

**Disable airbag as outlined under "Airbag System Disarming." After prodedure has been completed, rearm airbag system as outlined under "Airbag System Disarming."**

1. Remove heater A/C housing as outlined under "Heater Core, Replace."
2. Remove evaporator core from housing.
3. Reverse procedure to install.

# 2.2L/4-135 & 2.5L/4-153 Engines

## INDEX



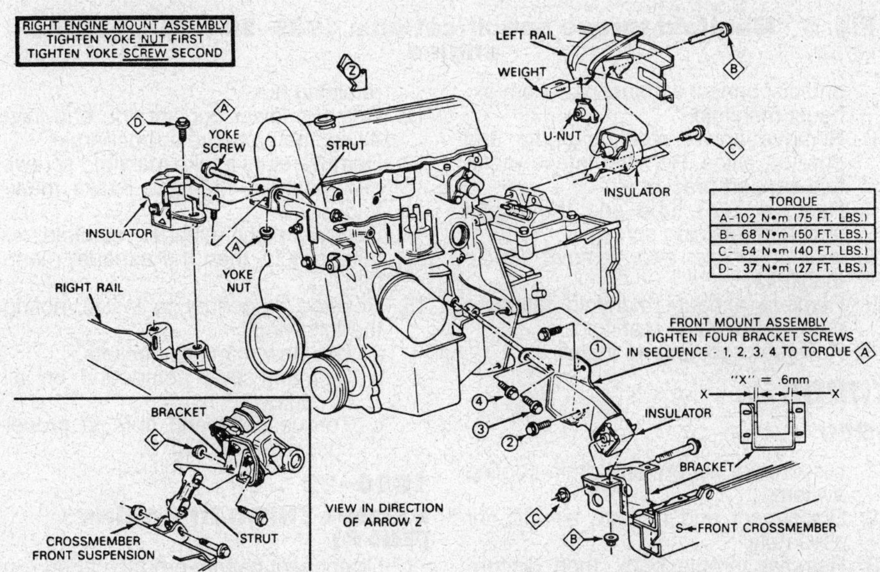


**Fig. 1 Engine mounts. 1989–90**

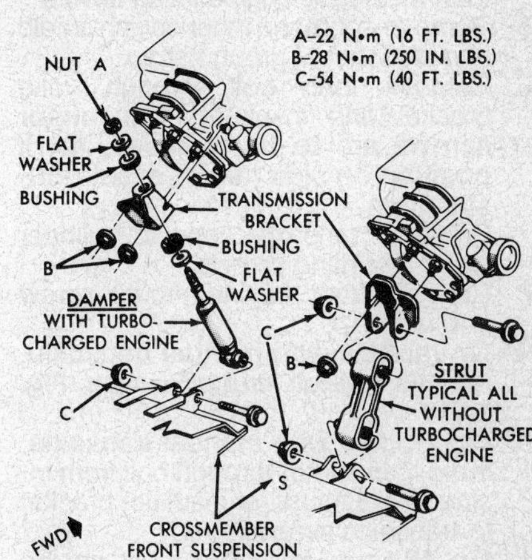


**Fig. 2 Anti roll strut & damper**

## AIRBAG SYSTEM DISARMING

**This system is a complex, electro-mechanical unit. Before attempting to diagnose, remove or install any airbag system components, you must first disable the airbag system as follows:**

1. Place ignition switch in lock position.
2. Disconnect and tape battery ground cable connector.
3. **Wait at least 1 minute after disconnecting battery ground cable before doing any further work on vehicle. The SRS system is designed to retain enough voltage to deploy airbag for a short time even after battery has been disconnected.**
4. After repairs are complete, reconnect battery ground cable.
5. From passenger side of vehicle, turn ignition switch to On position.
6. SRS warning light should illuminate for 6 to 8 seconds, then remain off for at least 45 seconds to indicate if SRS system is functioning correctly.
7. If SRS indicator does not perform as described refer to the "Passive Restraint Systems" section.

## ENGINE MOUNTS

**When positioning the engine, check driveshaft length as outlined in the "Front Suspension & Steering Section" under "Driveshaft Length, Adjust." The engine mounts incorporate slotted bolt holes to permit side-to-side positioning of the engine thereby affecting the length of the driveshaft. Failure to properly position engine may result in extensive damage to the engine.**

Refer to **Fig. 1 and 2** when replacing the engine mounts.

## ENGINE REPLACE

**Disable airbag as outlined under "Airbag System Disarming." After prodedure has been completed, rearm airbag system as outlined under "Airbag System Disarming."**

1. Disconnect battery ground cable.
2. Scribe alignment marks on hood and hood hinge, then remove hood.
3. Drain cooling system, then disconnect radiator hoses from radiator and engine.
4. Remove air cleaner, radiator and fan assembly.
5. Remove A/C compressor from

mounting bracket and position aside with hoses attached, if equipped.

6. Remove power steering pump from mounting bracket and position aside with hoses attached, if equipped.
7. Drain crankcase and remove oil filter.
8. Disconnect wire connectors at alternator, carburetor and engine.
9. Disconnect fuel line, heater hose and accelerator cable.
10. Remove alternator from mounting bracket and position aside.
11. **On models equipped with manual transaxle,** disconnect clutch cable, then remove transaxle lower cover.
12. **On all models,** disconnect exhaust pipe from exhaust manifold, then remove starter motor.
13. **On models equipped with automatic transaxle,** remove transaxle case lower cover and place alignment marks on flex plate and torque converter. Remove converter to flex plate attaching screws. Attach a C-clamp to front lower portion of converter housing to retain torque converter in housing when engine is being removed.
14. **On all models,** install a suitable transmission holding fixture and attach a suitable engine lifting device.
15. Remove righthand inner splash shield and disconnect ground strap.
16. Remove long bolt through yoke bracket and insulator. **If insulator screws are to be removed, mark position on side rail for exact reinstallation.**
17. Remove transaxle case to cylinder block mounting screws.
18. Remove front engine mount screw and nut.
19. **On models with manual transaxle,** remove anti-roll strut or damper, **Fig. 2.**
20. **On models with manual transaxle,** remove insulator through bolt from inside wheel house, or insulator bracket to transaxle screws.
21. **On all models,** carefully lift engine from vehicle.
22. Reverse procedure to install.

# INTAKE & EXHAUST MANIFOLD REPLACE

## EXCEPT TURBO

**Before servicing the fuel pump, fuel lines, fuel filter, throttle body or fuel injectors, the fuel system pressure must be released as outlined under "Fuel System Pressure Release."**

1. Disconnect battery ground cable and drain coolant system.
2. Remove air cleaner and disconnect all vacuum and fuel lines and electrical connectors from carburetor or throttle body.
3. Disconnect throttle linkage, then remove power steering pump drive belt.
4. Disconnect power brake vacuum hose from manifold, if equipped.
5. Disconnect hoses from water crossover, then raise and support vehicle and disconnect exhaust pipe from exhaust manifold.
6. Remove power steering pump and position aside. Remove intake manifold support bracket.
7. Remove EGR tube and the intake manifold retaining screws.
8. Lower vehicle and remove intake manifold.
9. Remove exhaust manifold retaining nuts and exhaust manifold.
10. Reverse procedure to install.

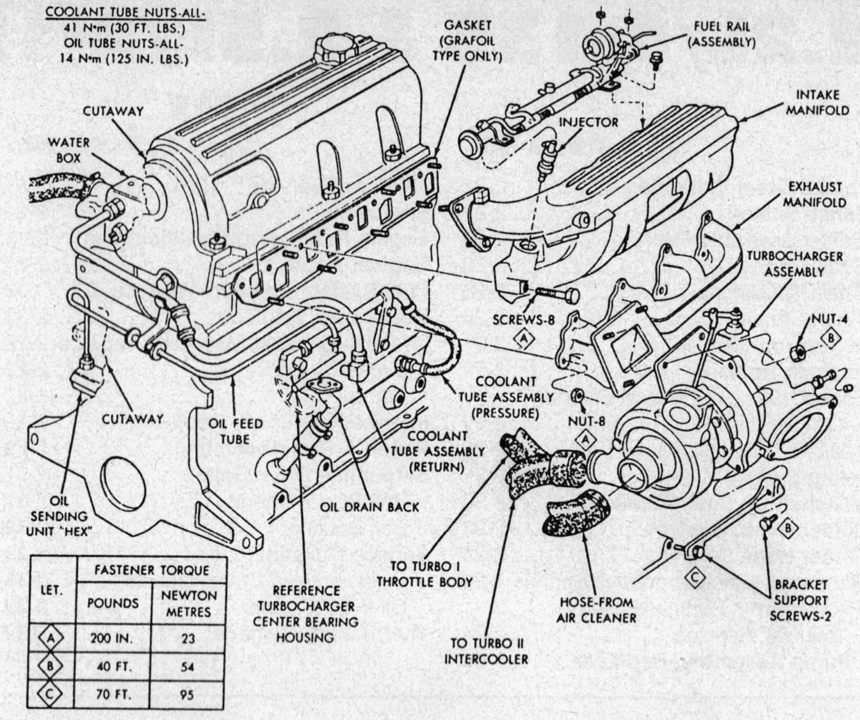


| LET. | FASTENER TORQUE | |
|---|---|---|
| | POUNDS | NEWTON METRES |
| A | 200 IN. | 23 |
| B | 40 FT. | 54 |
| C | 70 FT. | 95 |

**Fig. 3 Manifold torque specifications. 1989–90 turbocharged engine**

## TURBO

### 1989

1. Disconnect battery and drain cooling system.
2. Disconnect and remove air cleaner assembly.
3. Remove throttle body, then disconnect PCV and all hoses and throttle linkages from manifolds.
4. Remove fuel injector rail **Fig. 3.**
5. Remove front engine mount through bolt and rotate engine forward away from cowl.
6. Remove coolant and oil lines from turbocharger, then remove wastegate rod-to-gate retaining clip.
7. Remove turbo retaining nuts, then disconnect oxygen sensor electrical connector and vacuum lines.
8. Raise and support vehicle, then remove the right front wheel and tire assembly.
9. Remove turbo to block support bracket, then the driveshaft assembly **Fig. 3.**
10. Separate oil drain back tube from turbo housing and remove fitting.
11. Disconnect exhaust pipe from turbo, then the remaining turbo to manifold retaining nut.
12. Remove lower coolant line and inlet fitting, then remove turbocharger.
13. Remove eight intake manifold screws and washers, then the intake manifold.
14. Remove eight exhaust manifold retaining nuts, then the exhaust manifold.
15. Reverse procedure to install, noting the following:
    a. Use new manifold gaskets.
    b. Use anti-seize compound on all threads.
    c. Torque bolts and nuts to proper specifications, **Fig. 3.**

### 1990–92

#### Except Turbo III Engines (VIN A)

1. Disconnect battery ground cable.
2. Remove air cleaner and throttle cable.
3. Disconnect automatic idle speed (AIS) motor and throttle position sensor (TPS) connectors.
4. Disconnect vacuum hoses from throttle body.
5. Disconnect detonation sensor, fuel injector and charge temperature sensor connectors.
6. Loosen tube nut on fuel pressure regulator. **Wrap shop towels around hoses to catch any gasoline spillage.**
7. Open fuel tube clip and remove fuel tube.
8. Disconnect vacuum hoses from fuel pressure regulator, then remove fuel pressure regulator attaching nuts and regulator.
9. Remove PCV, brake booster and vacuum vapor harness from intake manifold.

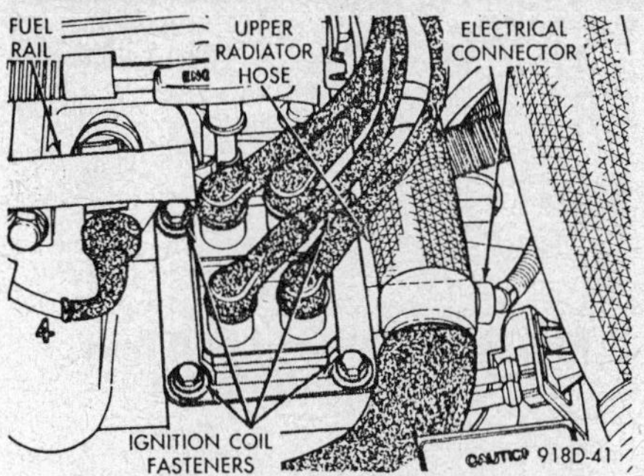


**Fig. 4 Direct Ignition System (DIS) coil location.**

10. Disconnect knock sensor connector, then remove fuel rail to intake manifold attaching screws.
11. Remove fuel rail and injector assembly by pulling rail so injectors come straight out of their ports.
12. Remove front engine mount through bolt and rotate engine forward away from cowl.
13. Remove coolant and oil lines from turbocharger, then remove wastegate rod-to-gate retaining clip.
14. Remove turbo retaining nuts, then disconnect oxygen sensor electrical connector and vacuum lines.
15. Raise and support vehicle, then remove the right front wheel and tire assembly.
16. Remove turbo to block support bracket, then the driveshaft assembly **Fig. 3.**
17. Separate oil drain back tube from turbo housing and remove fitting.
18. Disconnect exhaust pipe from turbo, then remove remaining turbo to manifold retaining nut.
19. Remove lower coolant line and inlet fitting, then remove turbocharger.
20. Remove eight intake manifold screws and washers, then the intake manifold.
21. Remove eight exhaust manifold retaining nuts, then the exhaust manifold.
22. Reverse procedure to install, noting the following:
    a. Use new manifold gaskets.
    b. Use anti-seize compound on all threads.
    c. Torque bolts and nuts to proper specifications, **Fig. 3.**

### Turbo III Engines (VIN A)

1. Disconnect battery ground cable.
2. Remove fresh air duct from air filter housing.
3. Remove radiator hose to cylinder head, **Fig. 3**
4. Remove Direct Ignition System (DIS) Coils from intake manifold, **Fig. 4**
5. Remove throttle and speed control cables.
6. Disconnect intercooler to throttle body outlet hose.
7. Disconnect vacuum hoses from throttle body and remove harness.
8. Disconnect automatic idle speed (AIS) motor and throttle position sensor connectors.

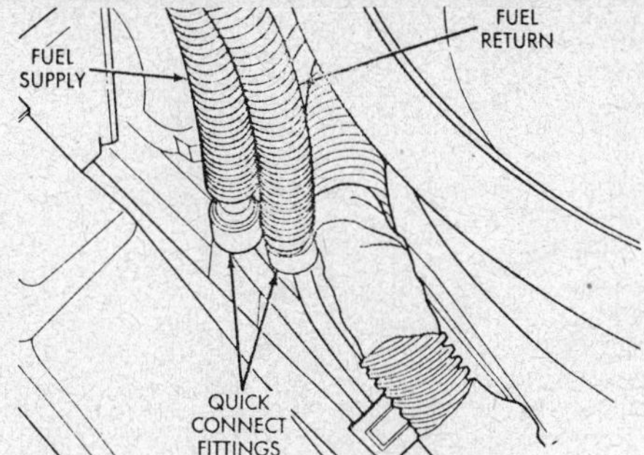


**Fig. 5 Fuel supply & return hose connections**

9. Remove PCV breather/separator box and vacuum harness, brake booster, vacuum vapor harness and fuel pressure regulator harness from intake manifold.
10. Disconnect fuel injector and charge temperature wiring connector.
11. Remove fuel supply and return hose quick connect at fuel tube assembly, **Fig. 5. Wrap shop towels around hoses to catch any gasoline spillage.**
12. Remove front engine mount through bolt and rotate engine forward away from cowl.
13. Remove coolant and oil lines from turbocharger, then remove wastegate rod-to-gate retaining clip.
14. Remove turbo retaining nuts, then disconnect oxygen sensor electrical connector and vacuum lines.
15. Raise and support vehicle, then remove the right front wheel and tire assembly.
16. Remove turbo to block support bracket, then the driveshaft assembly **Fig. 3.**
17. Separate oil drain back tube from turbo housing and remove fitting.
18. Disconnect exhaust pipe from turbo, then the remaining turbo to manifold retaining nut.
19. Remove lower coolant line and inlet fitting, then remove turbocharger.
20. Remove eight intake manifold screws and washers, then the intake manifold.
21. Remove eight exhaust manifold retaining nuts, then the exhaust manifold.
22. Reverse procedure to install, noting the following:
    a. Use new manifold gaskets.
    b. Use anti-seize compound on all threads.
    c. Torque bolts and nuts to proper specifications, **Fig. 3.**

## CYLINDER HEAD REPLACE

### EXCEPT 1991–92 TURBO III ENGINE (VIN A)

**Before servicing the fuel pump, fuel lines, fuel filter, throttle body or fuel injectors, the fuel system pressure must be released as outlined under "Fuel System Pressure Release."**

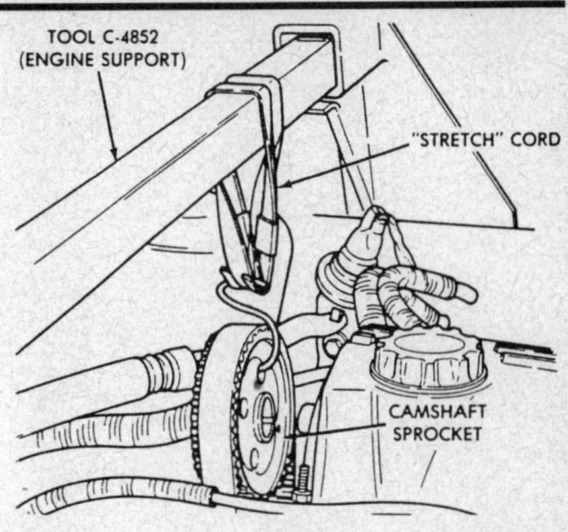


**Fig. 6 Suspending camshaft sprocket**

Removal and installation of cylinder head requires separation of camshaft sprocket from camshaft. In order to maintain camshaft, intermediate shaft and crankshaft timing, the timing belt is left indexed on the camshaft sprocket while the assembly is suspended under light tension, **Fig. 6.**

When removing camshaft sprocket from camshaft, adequate tension on sprocket and belt assembly must be maintained to prevent the timing belt from disengaging from the intermediate or crankshaft timing sprockets. **Failure to maintain adequate tension on timing belt may result in incorrect engine timing.**

#### Removal

1. Release fuel system pressure.
2. Disconnect battery ground cable, then drain cooling system.
3. Remove air cleaner and disconnect all vacuum lines, electrical wiring and fuel lines from throttle body.
4. Disconnect throttle linkage.
5. **On models with power steering,** loosen power steering pump, then remove power steering belt.
6. **On all models,** disconnect power brake vacuum hose from intake manifold.
7. Disconnect water hoses from water crossover.
8. Raise and support vehicle, then disconnect exhaust pipe from exhaust manifold.
9. Lower vehicle, remove power steering pump assembly and position aside.
10. Disconnect dipstick tube from thermostat housing, then rotate bracket from stud. **Do not bend bracket.**
11. Remove solid mount compressor bracket as shown, **Fig. 7.**
12. Remove cylinder head cover attaching bolts, then the cover.
13. Remove cylinder head bolts in sequence shown in **Fig. 8,** then the cylinder head assembly.

#### Inspection

1. Ensure cylinder head is flat within .004 inch (0.1 mm).
2. Inspect camshaft journals for scoring.

#### Installation

**Always use the specific head gasket**

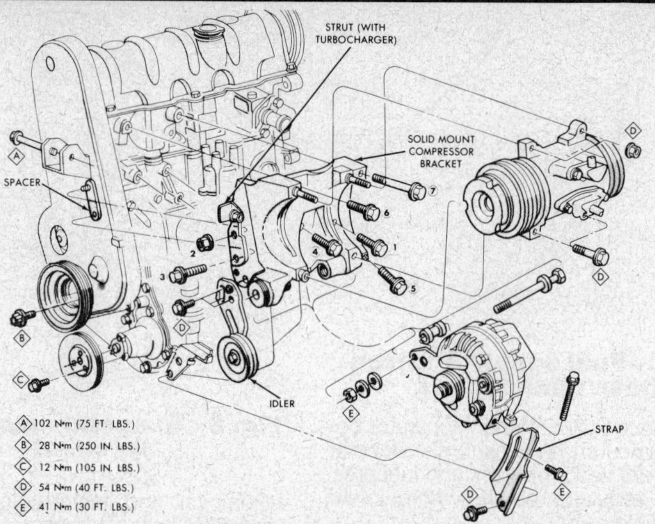


**Fig. 7 Accessory & solid mount compressor bracket**

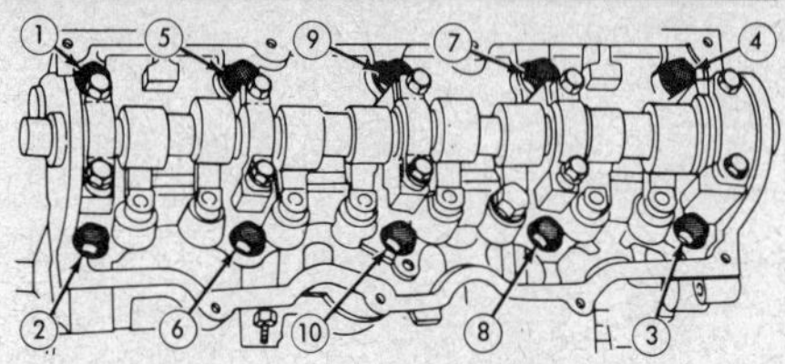

**Fig. 8 Cylinder head bolt removal sequence**

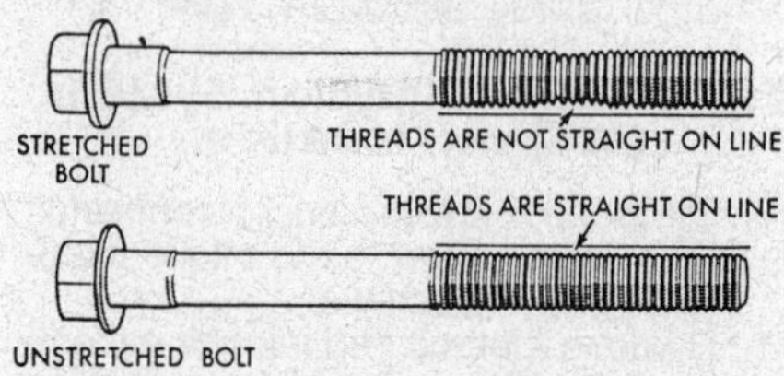


**Fig. 9 Checking cylinder head bolts**

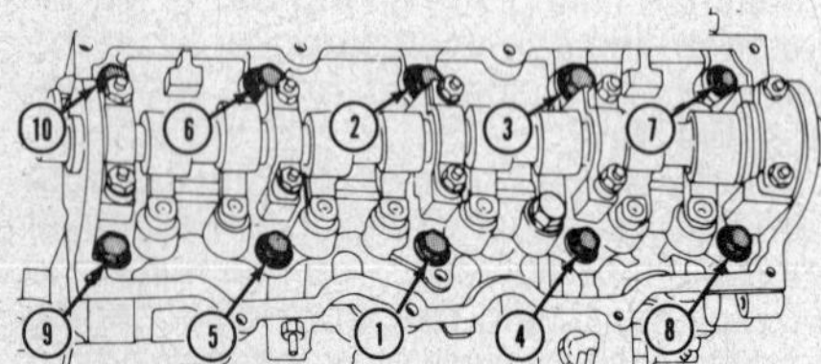

**Fig. 10 Cylinder head bolt tightening sequence. Except 1991–92 2.2L/4-135 Turbo III engine (VIN A)**

**for the engine's year and displacement since they are not interchangeable.**

Ensure proper head bolts are used. This bolt can be identified by an "11" stamped on bolt head. These bolts are used on all engines. Do not intermix 10 and 11 mm head bolts, as stripping of threads or cracking of the block may result. Inspect bolts to determine if they are stretched, Fig. 9. If all bolt threads are not straight on line, replace bolt.

1. Position cylinder head on block.
2. Refer to tightening sequence, **Fig. 10**, and tighten cylinder head bolts in 4 steps as follows:
   a. **Torque** all bolts 45 ft. lbs.
   b. **Torque** all bolts to 65 ft. lbs.
   c. **Torque** all bolts again to 65 ft. lbs.
   d. Tighten each bolt an additional 1/4 turn (90°), noting bolt torque. **If bolt torque is not over 90 ft. lbs. after tightening an additional 1/4 turn, bolt should be replaced.**
3. Reverse remaining removal installation procedure to complete installation, torquing all bolts to specifications.

### 1991–92 TURBO III ENGINE (VIN A)

#### Removal

**Before servicing the fuel pump, fuel lines, fuel filter, throttle body or fuel injectors, the fuel system pressure must be released as outlined under "Fuel System Pressure Release."**

1. Remove intake and exhaust manifold and outlined under "Intake & Exhaust Manifold, Replace."
2. Remove timing belt as outlined under "Timing Belt, Sprockets & Oil Seals."
3. Remove solid mount compressor bracket as shown, **Fig. 7.**
4. Remove cylinder head bolts.

#### Inspection

1. Ensure cylinder head is flat within .004 inch (0.1 mm).
2. Inspect camshaft journals for scoring.

#### Installation

**The Turbo III head gasket is not the same gasket as used on the 2.5L/4-153 turbo engine.**

**Head bolt diameter is 11 mm. These bolts are unique to this engine application and are not interchangeable with other engines. Cylinder head bolts should be examined before use. If the threads are necked down the bolts should be replaced, Fig. 9.**

1. Position cylinder head on block.
2. Refer to tightening sequence, **Fig. 11**, and tighten cylinder head bolts in 4 steps as follows:
   a. **Torque** all bolts 45 ft. lbs.
   b. **Torque** all bolts to 65 ft. lbs.
   c. **Torque** all bolts again to 65 ft. lbs.
   d. Tighten each bolt an additional 1/4 turn (90°), noting bolt torque. **If bolt torque is not over 90 ft. lbs. after tightening an additional 1/4 turn, bolt should be replaced.**
3. Reverse remaining removal installation procedure to complete installation, torquing all bolts to specifications.

## CYLINDER HEAD SERVICE

### ROCKER ARM & HYDRAULIC LASH ADJUSTER, REPLACE

#### Except 1991–92 Turbo III Engine (VIN A)

1. Remove valve cover.

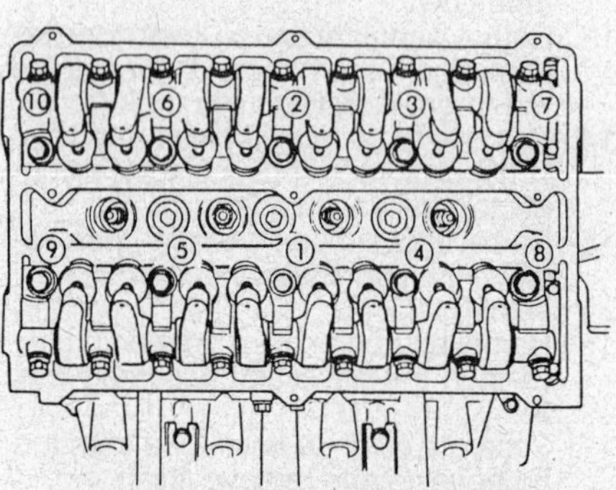

**Fig. 11 Cylinder head tightening sequence. 1991–92 2.2L/4-135 Turbo III engine (VIN A).**

2. Rotate cam until base circle is in contact with rocker arm. Depress valve spring using tool No. 4682 or equivalent and slide rocker arm out. Keep rocker arms in order for assembly.
3. Remove hydraulic lash adjuster.
4. Reverse procedure to install.

#### 1991–92 Turbo III Engine (VIN A)

1. Remove ignition cable and valve covers.
2. Remove rocker arm shaft(s) in sequence shown in **Fig. 12.**
3. Slide rocker off shaft, keeping arms in order for assembly.
4. Remove hydraulic lash adjusters.
5. Reverse procedure to install using tightening sequence shown in **Fig. 13.**

## REMOVING & INSTALLING VALVE SPRINGS

### EXCEPT 1991–92 TURBO III ENGINE (VIN A)

#### Cylinder Head Off Engine

1. Using valve spring compressor tool No. 4682 or equivalent, compress valve spring enough to remove and install valve bead locks, **Fig. 14.**

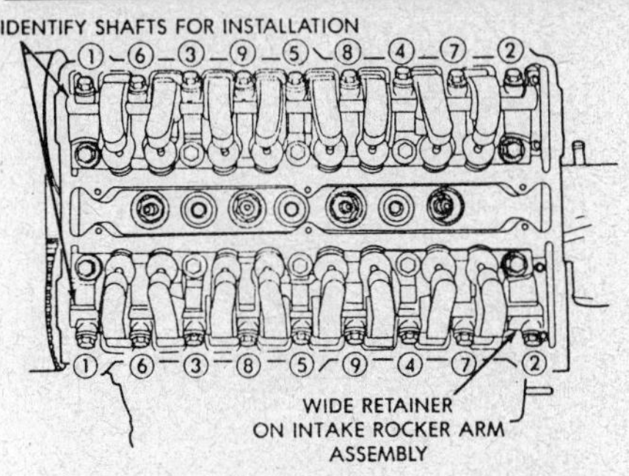


**Fig. 12 Rocker arm shaft loosing sequence. 1991–92 2.2L/4-135 Turbo III engine (VIN A).**

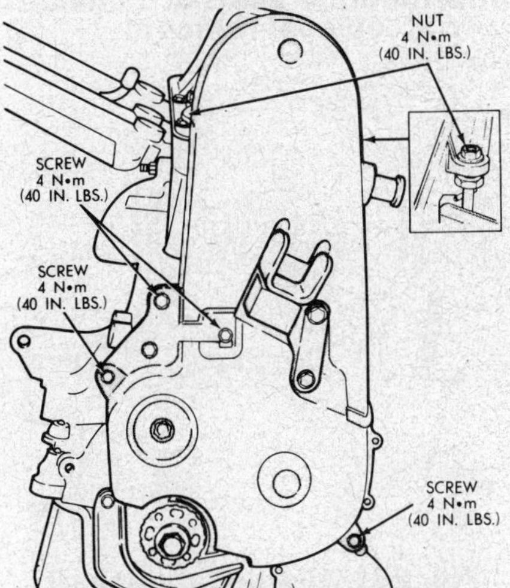


**Fig. 15 Timing belt cover removal. Except 1991–92 2.2L/4-135 Turbo III engine (VIN A)**

### Cylinder Head On Engine

1. Rotate crankshaft until piston is at TDC on compression stroke.
2. Apply 90-100 psi of compressed air into spark plug hole of valve being removed.
3. Using valve spring compressor tool No. 4683 or equivalent tool, compress valve spring enough to remove valve stem locks.
4. Remove valve spring and spring seat.
5. Remove valve seal.

### 1991–92 TURBO III ENGINE (VIN A)

1. Remove cylinder head as outlined under "Cylinder Head, Replace."
2. Compress valve springs using valve spring compressor tool No. C-3422-B and adapter Nos. 6537 and 6537 or equivalent.
3. Remove valve retaining locks, valve spring retainers, valve stem seals and valve springs.
4. Reverse procedure to install.

# VALVES

## ADJUST

Hydraulic valve lifters are used; no adjustment is necessary.

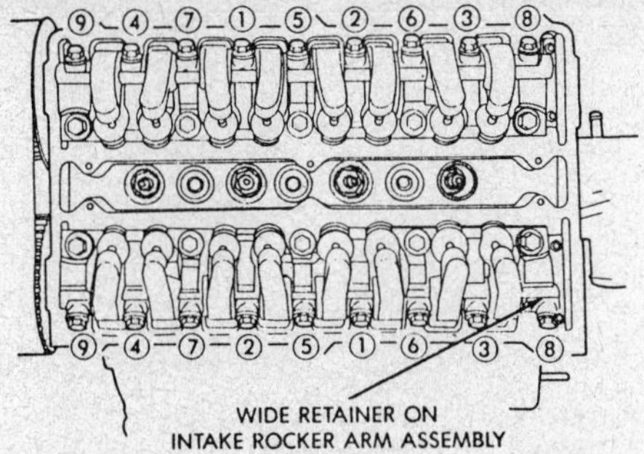


**Fig. 13 Rocker arm shaft tightening sequence. 1991–92 2.2L/4-135 Turbo III engine (VIN A).**

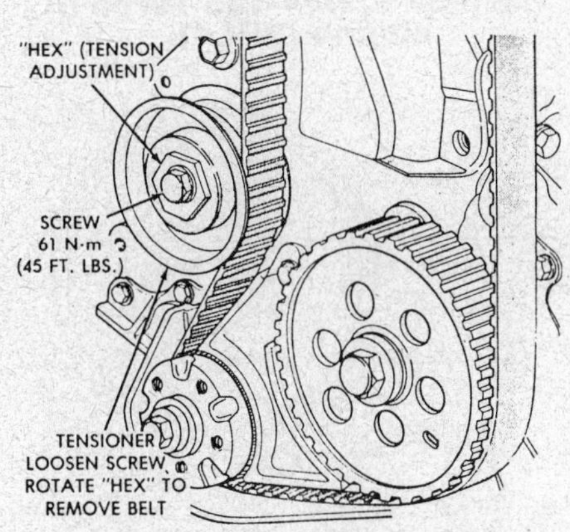


**Fig. 16 Timing Belt Tensioner. Except 1991–92 Turbo III Engine (VIN A)**

# VALVE LIFT SPECIFICATIONS

| Engine | Year | Lift |
|---|---|---|
| 2.2L/4-135(1) | 1989–92 | .430 |
| 2.2L/4-135(2) | 1991–92 | .250 |

(1)—Except 1991-92 Turbo III engine (VIN A).
(2)—1991-92 Turbo III engine (VIN A).

# VALVE TIMING

| Engine | Year | Degrees(1) Intake (2) | Exhaust (4) |
|---|---|---|---|
| 2.2L/4-135 | 1989–92 | 0 | 44 |
| | 1989–90 | 8(3) | 40 |
| | 1991–92 | 25(3) | 16 |
| 2.5L/4-153 | 1989–92 | 4 | 40 |
| 2.5L/4-153 Turbo | 1989–92 | 8(3) | 40 |

(1)—Valve opening specification.
(2)—Before Top Dead Center.
(3)—After Top Dead Center.
(4)—Before Bottom Dead Center.

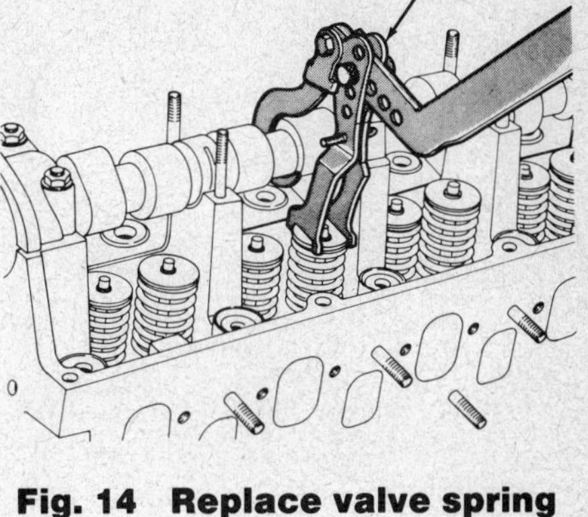


**Fig. 14 Replace valve spring**

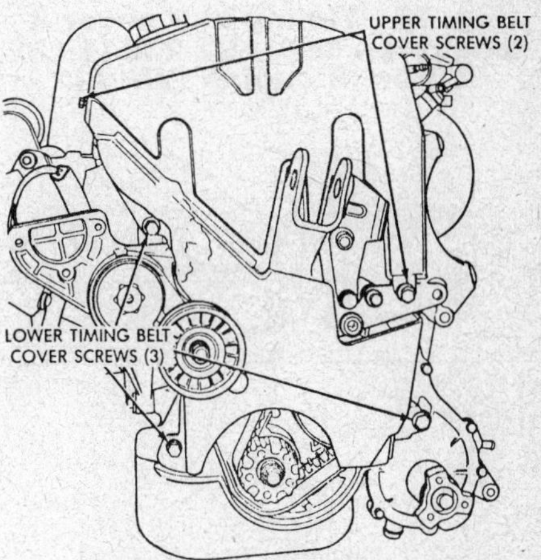


**Fig. 17 Timing belt cover removal. 1991–92 2.2L/4-135 Turbo III engine (VIN A).**

# TIMING BELT, SPROCKETS & OIL SEALS

## TIMING BELT & COVER

### Except 1991–92 Turbo III Engine (VIN A)

1. Raise and support vehicle, then remove right inner splash shield.
2. Remove engine drive belts, then the crankshaft pulley and water pump pulley retaining bolts.
3. Remove crankshaft and water pump pulleys.
4. Lower vehicle, then remove nuts securing cover to cylinder head and cylinder block, **Fig. 15.**
5. Position a suitable jack under engine, then remove right hand engine mount bolt and raise engine slightly.
6. Rotate crankshaft to align timing marks as outlined under "Crankshaft and Intermediate Shaft Timing," and ensure camshaft is aligned as outlined under "Camshaft Timing."
7. Loosen timing belt tensioner, then remove timing belt, **Fig. 16.**
8. Ensure crankshaft and intermediate shaft timing marks are aligned, install timing belt as outlined under "Camshaft Timing," then reverse remaining procedure to complete installation.

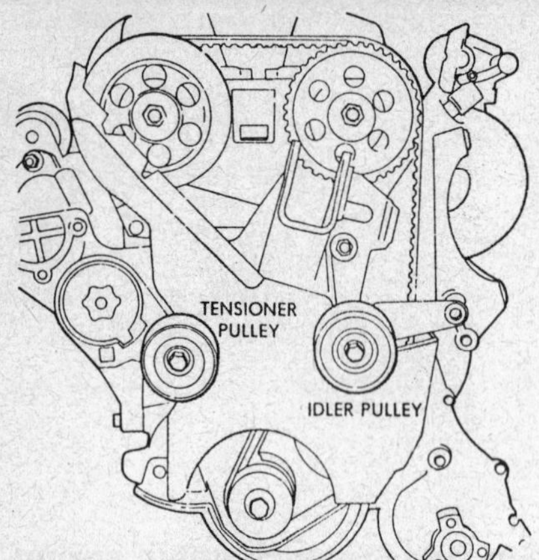


**Fig. 18 Timing belt cover & tensioner. 1991–92 2.2L/4-135 Turbo III engine (VIN A).**

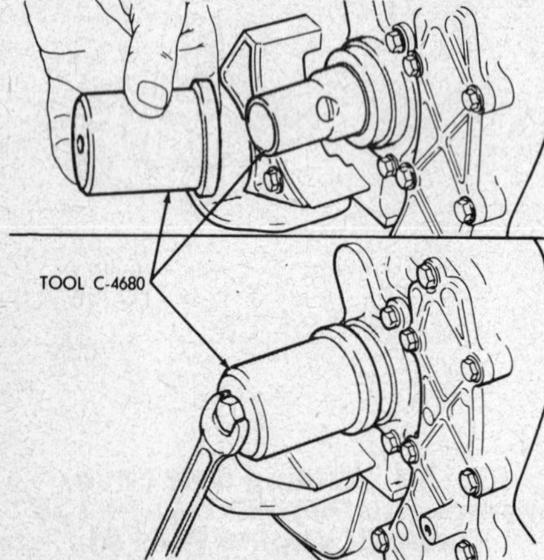


**Fig. 21 Crankshaft, intermediate shaft & camshaft oil seal installation**

### 1991–92 Turbo III Engine (VIN A)

1. Remove PCV tube and upper timing belt cover screws and cover, **Fig. 17.**
2. Remove accessory drive belt.
3. Raise and support vehicle and remove righthand wheel and inner splash shield.
4. Remove water pump and crankshaft pulleys.
5. Remove lower accessory drive belt idler and tensioner pulley, **Fig. 18.**
6. Remove lower timing belt cover screws and cover.
7. Lower vehicle.
8. Lift engine with engine support tool No. 4852 or equivalent and separate right engine mount.
9. Raise and support vehicle. Remove lower accessory drive belt idler pulley bracket assembly, **Fig. 19.**
10. Loosen timing belt tensioner, remove timing belt and idler pulley.
11. Install timing belt as outlined under " Camshaft Timing," then reverse remaining procedure to complete installation.

## CRANKSHAFT SPROCKET

1. With timing belt removed from engine, remove crankshaft sprocket bolt.
2. Remove crankshaft sprocket using a suitable puller.

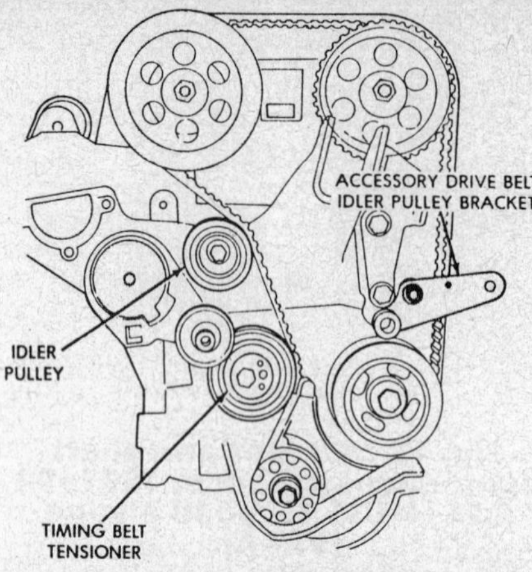


**Fig. 19 Removing timing belt. 1991–92 2.2L/4-135 Turbo III engine (VIN A).**

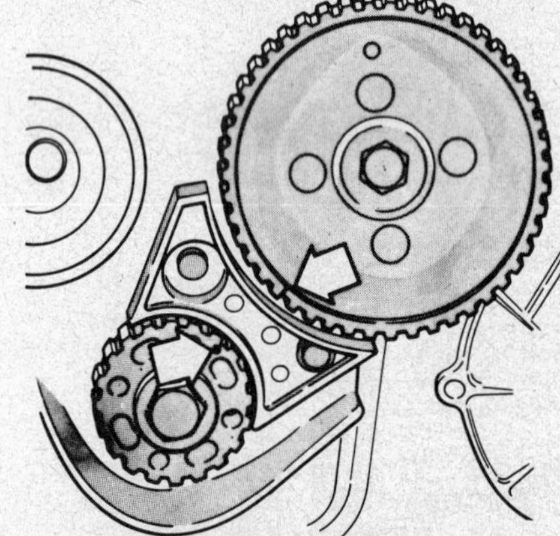
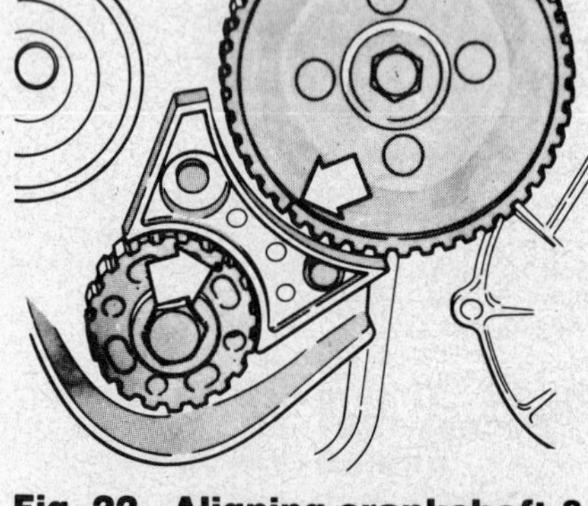

**Fig. 22 Aligning crankshaft & intermediate shaft timing marks**

## FRONT CRANKSHAFT, INTERMEDIATE SHAFT & CAMSHAFT OIL SEAL SERVICE

Refer to **Figs. 20 and 21** for removal and installation of crankshaft, intermediate shaft or camshaft seals.

The replacement seal for early built 2.2L/4-135 engines will also be rubber backed with arrows indicating direction of rotation and location in the head marked on seal. The seals must be installed as indicated.

On the 1991-92 Turbo III engine (VIN A), it will be necessary to remove the righthand engine mount.

## CRANKSHAFT & INTERMEDIATE SHAFT TIMING

1. Rotate crankshaft and intermediate shaft until markings on sprockets are aligned, **Fig. 22.**

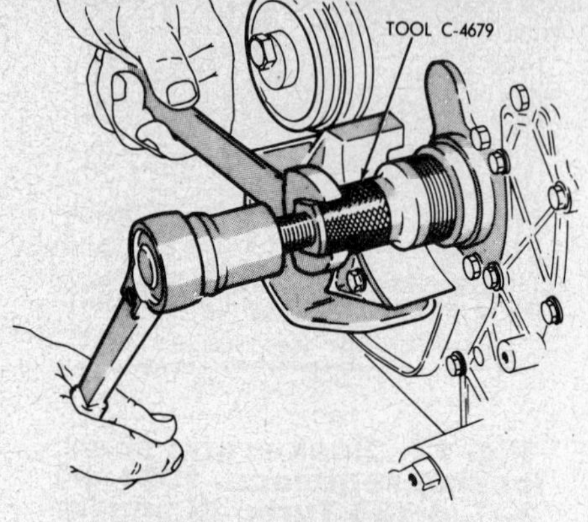


**Fig. 20 Crankshaft, intermediate shaft & camshaft oil seal removal**

**Fig. 23 Aligning camshaft timing marks. Except 1991–92 2.2L/4-135 Turbo III engine (VIN A)**

## CAMSHAFT TIMING

### Except 1991–92 Turbo III Engine (VIN A)

1. Rotate camshaft until arrows on hub are aligned with No. 1 camshaft cap to cylinder head line, **Fig. 23.** Small hole must be located along vertical center line.
2. Install timing belt. Refer to procedure outlined under "Adjusting Timing Belt Tension" for proper timing belt adjustment.
3. Rotate crankshaft two full revolutions and recheck timing. **Do not allow oil or solvents to contact timing belt since they will deteriorate the rubber and cause tooth slippage.**

### 1991–92 Turbo III Engine (VIN A)

1. Remove air cleaner duct and the ignition cable cover.
2. Remove valve covers and loosen rocker arm assemblies about three turns, **Fig. 12.**
3. Align and pin both intake and exhaust cam sprockets with 3/16 drills or pin punches, **Fig. 24. Accessory shaft does not need to be timed.**
4. Install a dial indicator in No. 1 spark plug hole.
5. Rotate crankshaft until No. 1 cylinder

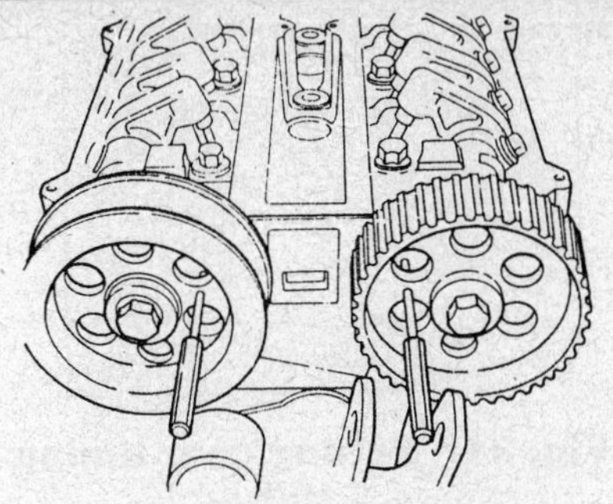
Fig. 24 Camshafts pinned into position. 1991–92 2.2L/4-135 Turbo III engine (VIN A).

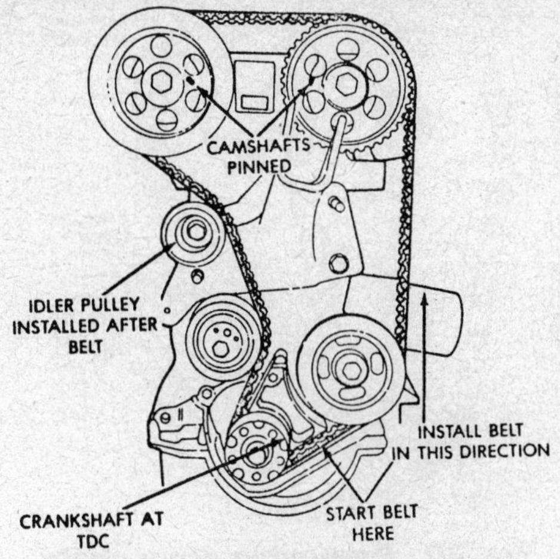

Fig. 25 Aligning camshafts and crankshaft timing marks. 1991–92 2.2L/4-135 Turbo III engine (VIN A).

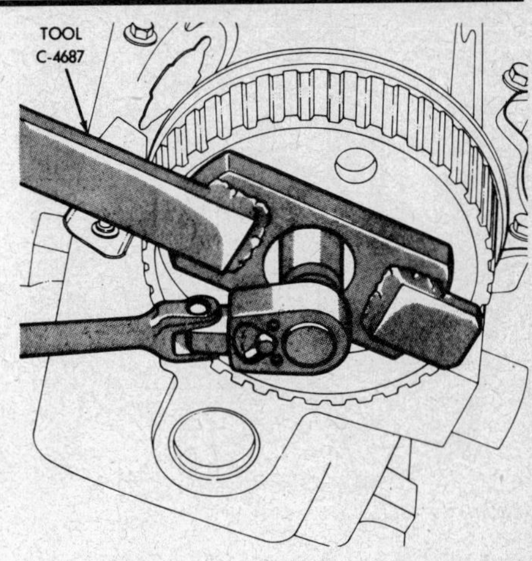

Fig. 26 Camshaft & intermediate shaft sprocket replacement

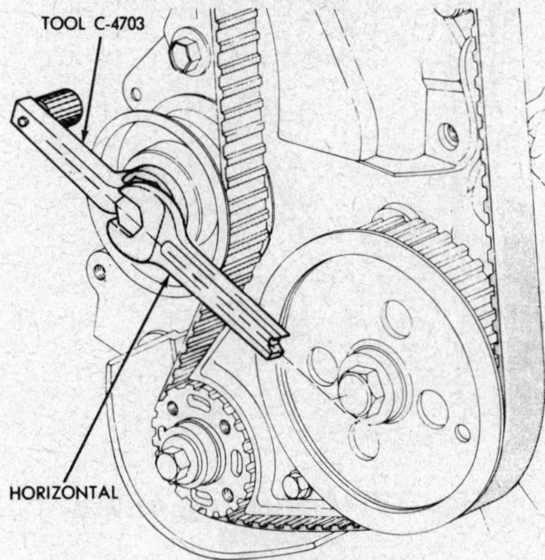

Fig. 27 Adjusting timing belt tension

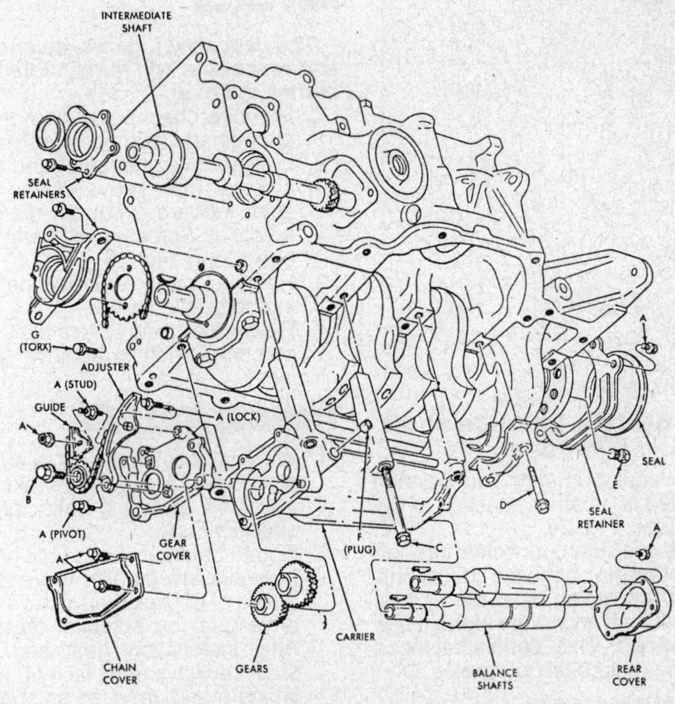

Fig. 28 Crankshaft, intermediate & balance shaft assemblies.

is at top dead center. Mark the engine block for TDC reference.

6. Install timing belt and idler pulley in sequence shown in **Fig. 25.**
7. Remove dial indicator and drills or pins from camshaft sprockets.
8. Install belt tensioner gauge on timing belt between camshaft pulleys and adjust tension to 110 ft. lbs.
9. Rotate crankshaft clockwise two full turns and check alignment of camshaft and crankshaft. **Do not rotate crankshaft counterclockwise or attempt to rotate engine using cam or accessory shaft attaching screw.**
10. Check belt tension, adjust if necessary.
11. Torque rocker arm shafts in sequence shown to specification, **Fig. 13.**
12. Install valve covers, spark plug, ignition cable and ignition cable covers.

## CAMSHAFT & INTERMEDIATE SHAFT SPROCKET, REPLACE

Refer to **Fig. 26** for removal and installation of intermediate shaft sprocket.

## ADJUSTING TIMING BELT TENSION

### Except 1991–92 Turbo III Engine (VIN A)

1. Remove spark plugs then rotate crankshaft to TDC position.
2. Loosen tensioner locknut using belt tensioner tool No. C-4703 or equivalent, **Fig. 27.**
3. Reset belt tension so that belt tensioning tool axis is within 15° of horizontal.
4. Rotate crankshaft two revolutions in clockwise direction and position at TDC, then tighten tensioner locknut.

### 1991–92 Turbo III Engine (VIN A)

1. Remove timing belt upper and lower cover as outlined under "Timing Belt, Sprockets & Oil Seals."
2. Install belt tensioner gauge on timing belt between camshaft pulleys and adjust tension to 110 ft. lbs.
3. Rotate crankshaft clockwise two full turns and check alignment of camshaft and crankshaft. **Do not rotate crankshaft counterclockwise or attempt to rotate engine using cam or accessory shaft attaching screw.**
4. Check belt tension, adjust if necessary.

## BALANCE SHAFTS

The 2.5L/4-153, 1990 2.2L/4-135 Turbo IV and 1991-92 2.2L/4-135 Turbo III

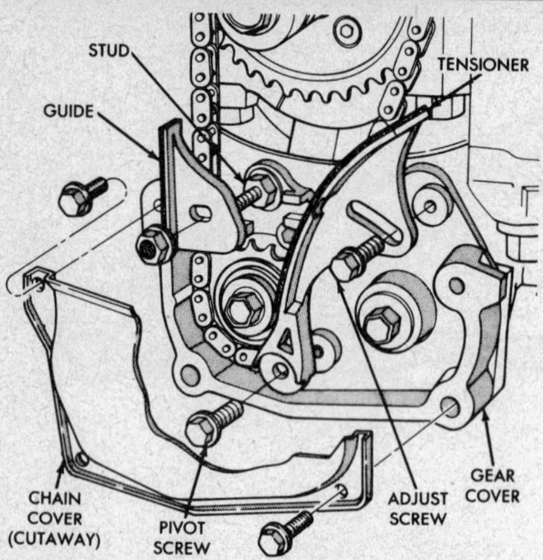


**Fig. 29 Removing chain cover, guide & tensioner**

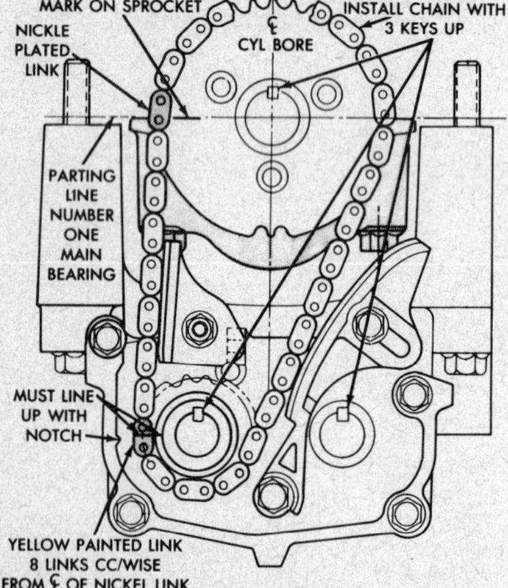


**Fig. 32 Setting balance shaft timing**

engines are equipped with two balance shafts installed in a carrier attached to the lower crankcase, **Fig. 28.**

The shafts are interconnected through gears to rotate in opposite directions. These gears are driven by a short chain from the crankshaft and rotate at two times crankshaft speed. This counterbalances certain engine reciprocating masses.

## SHAFT, REPLACE

1. Remove oil pan, oil pickup, timing belt cover, belt, crankshaft belt sprocket and front crankshaft oil seal retainer.
2. Remove chain cover, guide and tensioner, **Fig. 29.**
3. Remove balance shaft gear and chain sprocket retaining screws and crankshaft chain sprocket Torx screws, then the chain and sprocket assembly, **Fig. 30.**
4. Remove double-ended gear cover retaining stud, then the cover and balance shaft gears.
5. Remove carrier rear cover and balance shafts.
6. Remove six carrier to crankshaft attaching bolts to separate carrier.
7. Reverse procedure to install, then adjust crankshaft to balance shaft gear timing.

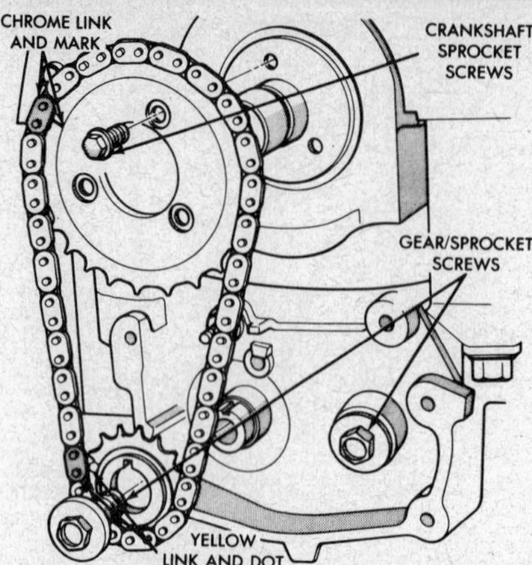


**Fig. 30 Removing drive chain & sprockets**

## CARRIER ASSEMBLY, REPLACE

**The gear cover, gears, balance shafts and rear cover will remain intact during carrier removal.**

1. Remove chain cover and driven balance shaft chain sprocket screw.
2. Loosen tensioner pivot and adjusting screws, then move driven balance shaft inboard (through) driven chain sprocket. Sprocket will hang in lower chain loop, **Fig. 28.**
3. Remove carrier to crankshaft attaching bolts and carrier.
4. Reverse procedure to install, then adjust crankshaft to balance shaft timing.

## TIMING, ADJUST

1. With balance shafts installed in carrier, position carrier on crankshaft and install six attaching bolts, torquing to specifications.
2. Rotate balance shafts until both shaft keyways are parallel to vertical centerline of engine, then install short hub drive gear on sprocket driven shaft. After installation, gear and balance shaft keyways must face up with gear timing marks meshed as shown, **Fig. 31.**
3. Install gear cover and torque double ended stud/washer fastener to specifications.
4. Install crankshaft sprocket and torque socket head Torx screws to specifications.
5. Rotate crankshaft until number one cylinder is at top dead center (TDC). The timing marks on chain sprocket should line up with parting line on left side of number one main bearing cap, **Fig. 32.**
6. Place chain over crankshaft sprocket so that nickel plated link of chain is over timing mark on crankshaft sprocket, **Fig. 32.**
7. Place balance shaft sprocket into timing chain so that timing mark on sprocket (yellow dot) mates with yellow painted or nickel plated link on chain.
8. With balance shaft keyways at 12 o'clock, slide balance shaft sprocket onto nose of balance shaft. Balance shaft may have to be pushed in slightly to allow for clearance. **Balance shaft timing is correct if the timing mark on sprocket, painted link and arrow on side of gear cover are aligned.**
9. If sprockets are timed correctly, install balance shaft bolts, torquing to specifications. A wood block placed between crankcase and crankshaft counterbalance will prevent gear rotation.

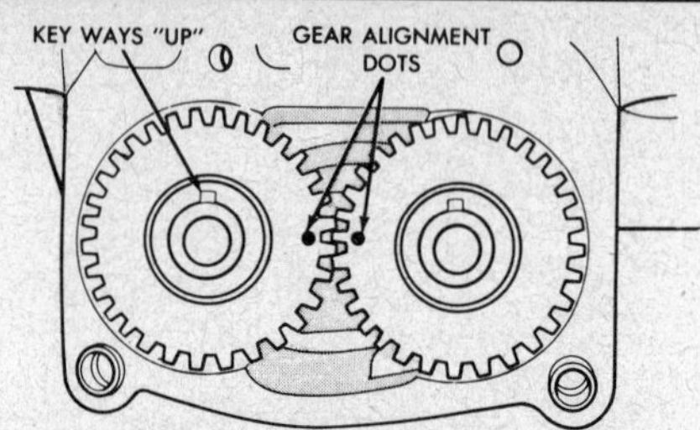


**Fig. 31 Setting gear timing**

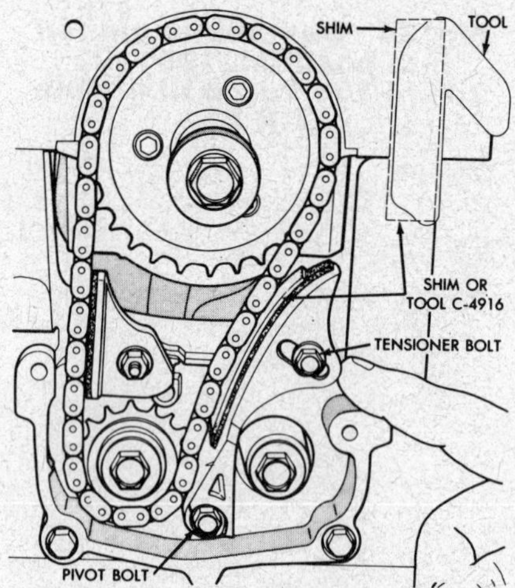


**Fig. 33 Adjusting chain tension**

## CHAIN TENSIONING

1. Install chain tensioner loosely assembled.
2. Place a .039 inch thick by 2.75 inch long shim or tool No. C-4916 between tensioner and chain, push tensioner and shim up against chain and apply firm pressure directly behind adjustment slot to take up all slack. Chain must have shoe radius contact as shown, **Fig. 33.**
3. With load applied, tighten top tensioner bolt first, then bottom pivot bolt, torquing both to specifications, then remove shim.
4. Position guide on double ended stud, ensuring tab on guide fits into slot on gear cover, then install nut/washer assembly, torquing to specifications.
5. Install carrier covers, torquing screws to specifications.

| Intermediate Shaft Journal and Bushing Sizes | |
|---|---|
| **Intermediate Shaft** | |
| Large Journal | 42.670/42.695 mm (1.679/1.680 in.) |
| Small Journal | 19.670/19.695 mm (.774/.775 in.) |
| Bushing-Bore Diameter | |
| Large Bushing | 42.730/42.750 mm (1.682/1.683 in.) |
| Small Bushing | 19.720/19.750 mm (.776/.777 in.) |
| Maximum Clearance Allowed | |
| Large | .035/.080 mm (.0013/.003 in.) |
| Small | .025/.080 mm (.0009/.003 in.) |

**Fig. 34 Intermediate shaft journal specifications.**

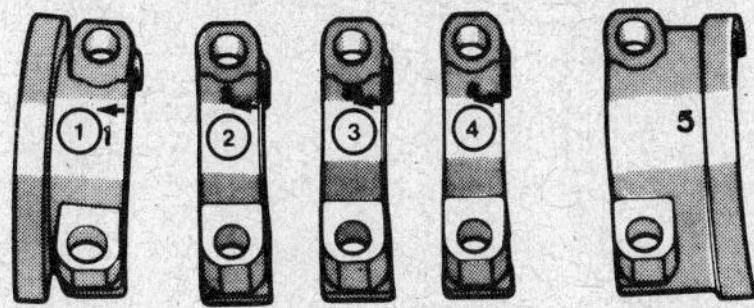


**Fig. 37 Camshaft bearing cap installation**

# INTERMEDIATE SHAFT
## REPLACE

On models with conventional ignition systems, remove distributor as outlined under "Distributor, Replace" in the "Electrical" section.

1. Remove oil pump assembly as outlined under"Oil Pump, Replace."
2. Remove intermediate shaft sprocket and seal as outlined under "Timing Belt, Sprockets & Oil Seals."
3. Remove retainer plate attaching screws.
4. Remove retainer.
5. Remove intermediate shaft.
6. Remove intermediate shaft front bushing using tool No. C-4697-2.
7. Remove intermediate shaft rear bushing using tool No. C-4686-2.
8. Measure intermediate shaft, if not within specifications shown in **Fig. 34** replace parts as needed.
9. Reverse procedure to install, noting the following:
   a. Install rear intermediate shaft bushing using tool No. C-4686-1 until tool is flush with block.
   b. Install front intermediate shaft bushing using tool No. C-4697-1 until tool is flush with block.
   c. Lubricate distributor drive gear when installing.
   d. Apply Form-In-Place gasket material as shown in **Fig. 35** and install intermediate shaft retainer.
   e. Refer to "Timing Belt, Sprockets & Oil Seals" for timing of intermediate shaft.

# CAMSHAFT
## REPLACE

Removal and installation of camshaft requires separation of camshaft sprocket from camshaft. In order to maintain camshaft, intermediate shaft and crankshaft timing, the timing belt is left indexed on the camshaft sprocket while the assembly is suspended under light tension, **Fig. 36.**

When removing camshaft sprocket from camshaft, adequate tension on sprocket

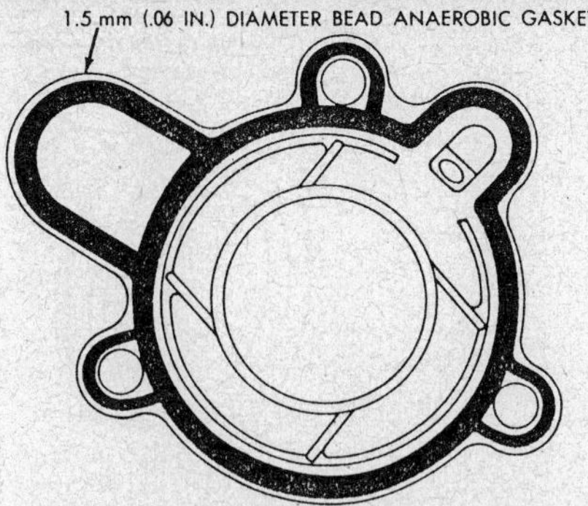


**Fig. 35 Sealing intermediate shaft retainer**

and belt assembly must be maintained to prevent the timing belt from disengaging from the intermediate or crankshaft timing sprockets. **Failure to maintain adequate tension on timing belt may result in incorrect engine timing.**

### EXCEPT 1991–92 TURBO III ENGINE (VIN A)

1. Mark rocker arms to ensure installation in original position.
2. Evenly loosen camshaft bearing bolts in sequence shown in **Fig. 36,** until all bolts have been loosened 3-4 turns.
3. Tap rear of camshaft with suitable mallet to break caps free.
4. Continue loosening bearing cap bolts, ensuring camshaft does not cock, then remove bearing caps and camshaft. **Loosen bearing cap bolts evenly. If camshaft cocks in bearing bores, bearing surfaces may be damaged.**
5. With caps removed from engine, check oil holes for obstructions. **Some engines may be equipped with oversize camshaft bearings. Engines with oversize camshaft bearings can be identified by green markings on cylinder head and camshaft at AIR pump side of engine.**
6. Check camshaft lobe height in center (contact area) and on shoulders of lobe. If difference in reading exceeds .010 inch (.25 mm), camshaft should be replaced.
7. Install rocker arms in original positions, then position camshaft in bearing saddles of cylinder head.
8. Apply suitable sealant to No. 1 and No. 5 bearing cap.
9. Align caps in proper sequence, with No. 1 cap at timing belt end and No. 5 cap at flywheel end of engine, and ensure arrow on caps 1, 2, 3 and 4 point toward timing belt, **Fig. 37. Install caps before installing camshaft seals.**
10. Torque cap bolts to specifications. Torque cap bolts evenly in crossing pattern to ensure camshaft remains properly aligned.
11. Install camshaft seals as outlined.

### 1991–92 TURBO III ENGINE (VIN A)

Cylinder head must be removed from

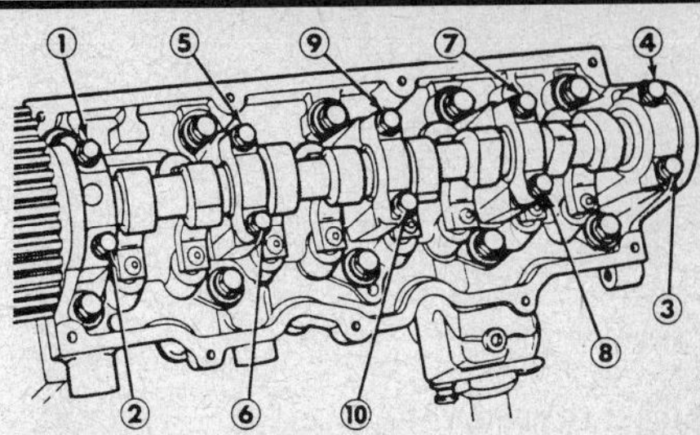


**Fig. 36 Camshaft bearing cap removal**

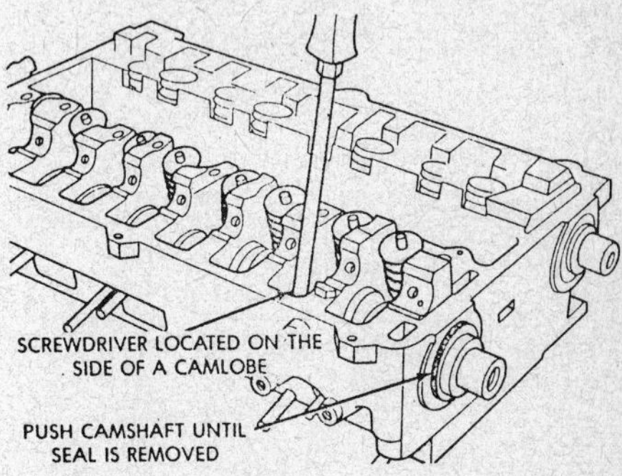


**Fig. 38 Removing camshaft oil seal. 1991–92 2.2L/4-135 Turbo III engine (VIN A).**

vehicle before removal of camshafts is possible.

1. Mark rocker arms to ensure installation in original position.
2. Evenly loosen camshaft bearing bolts in sequence shown in **Fig. 12,** until all bolts have been removed.
3. Remove thrust plates from rear of camshafts. **Thrust plates are not the same thickness and cannot be interchanged. The intake camshaft uses a wider thrust plate than the exhaust.**
4. Before camshafts can be removed the cam seal must be removed first. **Use care not to damage seal surface of the camshaft.**
5. Using a screwdriver placed against the side of the cam lobe, push the cam out of the head, **Fig. 38.** The cam seal will be pushed out by the cam.
6. Slide the camshaft out of cylinder head using care not to scratch bearing surfaces in the head.
7. Check camshaft lobe height in center (contact area) and on shoulders of lobe. If difference in reading exceeds .010 inch (.25 mm), camshaft should be replaced.
8. Lubricate camshaft journals with clean engine oil and carefully install camshaft into head.
9. Install thrust plates and tighten to specification.
10. Install new cam seals.

# PISTON & ROD ASSEMBLY

When installing piston and rod assembly, valve cut must face toward manifold

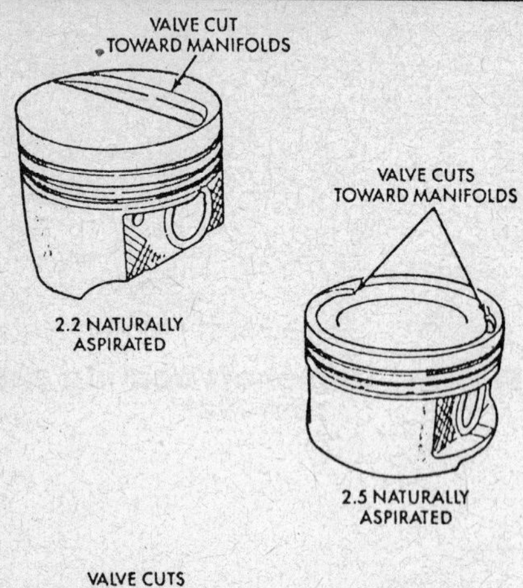


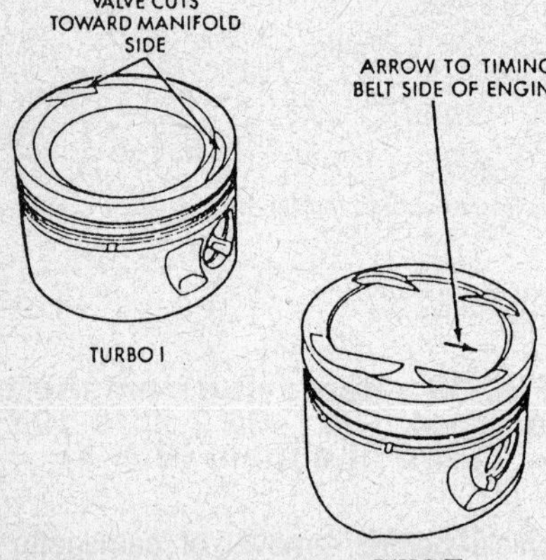


Fig. 39 Piston & connecting rod assembly

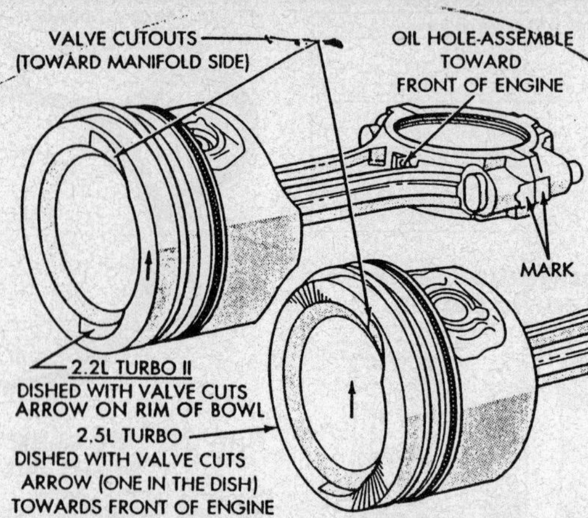


Fig. 40 Piston & connecting rod assembly. 1989 turbo models

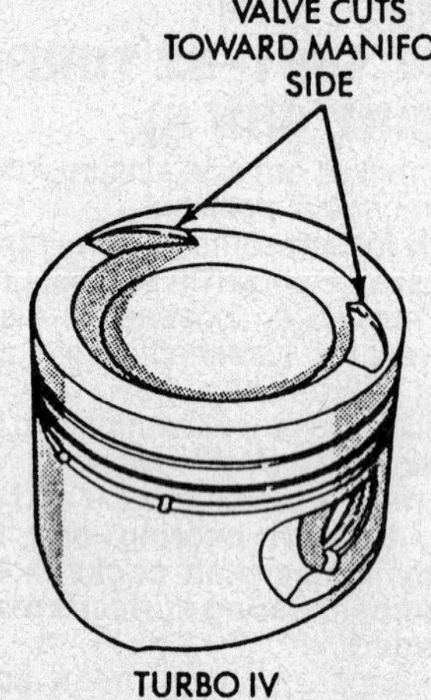


Fig. 41 Piston & connecting rod assembly. 1990 turbo models

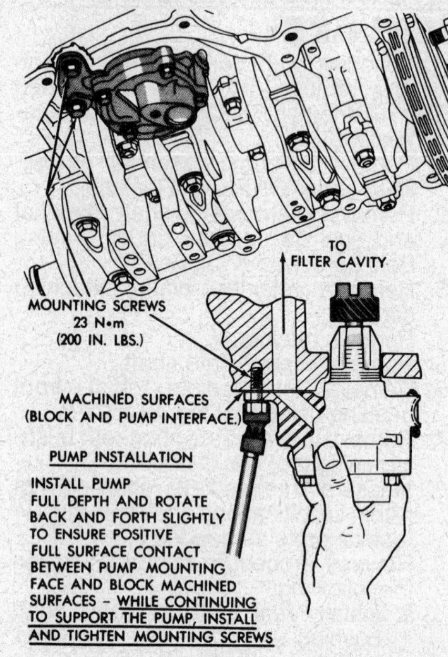


Fig. 42 Oil pump replacement

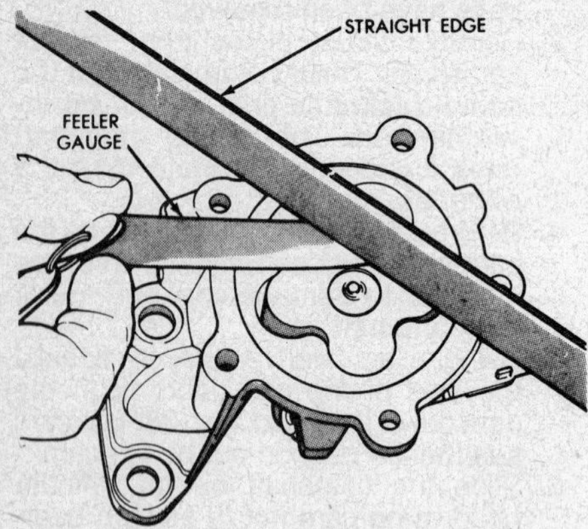


Fig. 43 Measuring oil pump endplay

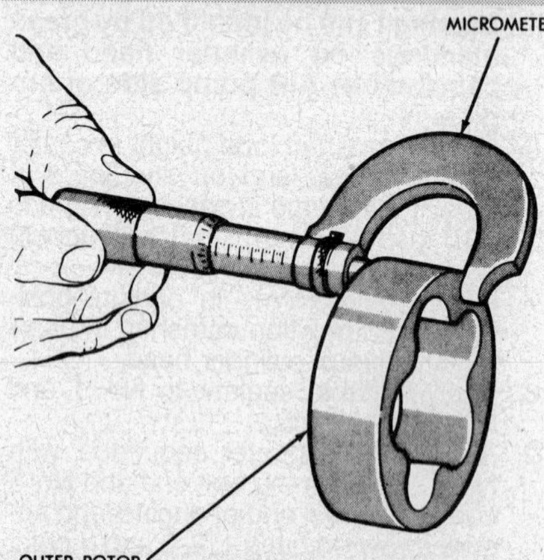


Fig. 44 Measuring oil pump outer rotor thickness

side of engine, **Fig. 39 through 41.** Turbocharged engine pistons will have an arrow or dimple toward front of engine. Oil hole on connecting rod must face timing belt side of engine.

Connecting rod side clearance should be .005-.013 inch. On 1989 models, there is a maximum limit of .015 inch.

## CRANKSHAFT OIL SEAL REPLACE

1. Remove transaxle assembly.
2. Remove flywheel or flex plate from rear of crankshaft.
3. Pry out rear seal with a suitable tool. Use care not to nick or damage crankshaft flange seal surface or retainer bore.
4. Reverse procedure to install, noting the following:
   a. Use seal pilot tool C-4681 when installing seal.
   b. Lightly coat seal outside dimension with Loctite Stud N' Bearing Mount or equivalent.

## OIL PUMP ASSEMBLY REPLACE

1. With oil pan removed, remove two screws securing oil pump to cylinder block assembly, **Fig. 42.**
2. Apply suitable sealant to pump to block interface.
3. Lubricate oil pump rotor and shaft and the drive gear.
4. Install pump full depth and rotate back and forth slightly to ensure proper positioning and alignment through full surface contact of pump and block machined interface surfaces. **Pump must be held in fully seated position while installing screws.**

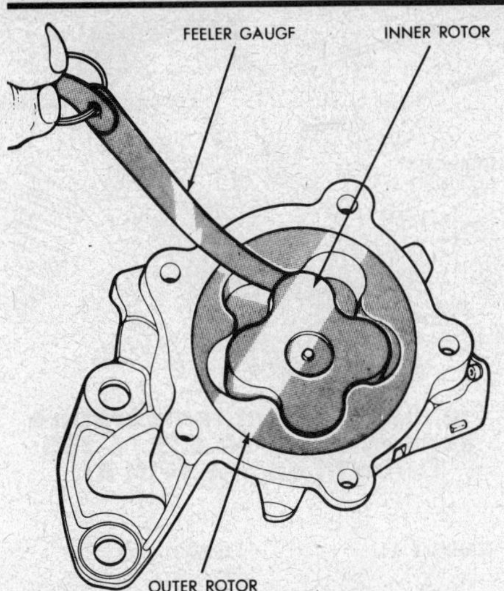


**Fig. 45 Measuring clearance between oil pump rotors**

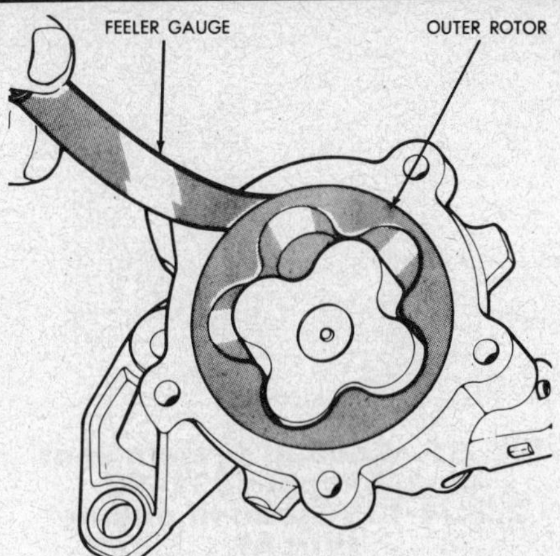


**Fig. 46 Measuring oil pump outer rotor clearance**

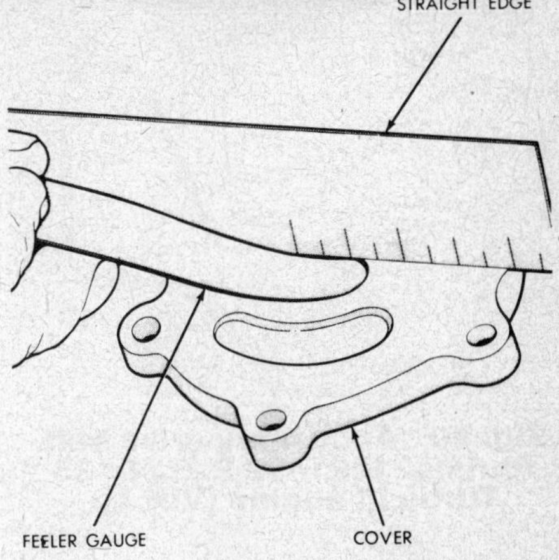


**Fig. 47 Measuring oil pump cover clearance**

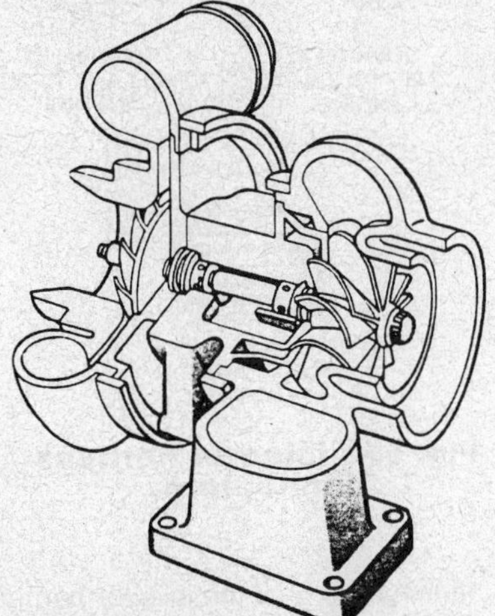

**Fig. 48 Section view of Garret-AiResearch T3 type turbocharger**

5. Torque attaching screws to specifications.

## OIL PUMP SERVICE

1. Measure the following oil pump clearances:
   a. Endplay, **Fig. 43,** should be .0010-.0035 inch.
   b. Outer rotor specifications, **Fig. 44.** Thickness should be .9435 inch minimum and 2.469 inches minimum diameter. Install outer rotor with chamfered edge in pump body.
   c. Clearance between rotors, **Fig. 45,** should be .008 inch maximum.
   d. Outer rotor clearance, **Fig. 46,** should be .014 inch maximum.
   e. Oil pump cover, **Fig. 47,** clearance should be .003 inch maximum.
   f. Oil pressure relief valve spring free length should be 1.95 inches.

## TURBOCHARGER

The turbocharged engine is similar to the standard 2.2L/4-135 engine. However, many components have been upgraded in order to withstand more than fifty percent higher power output generated by the turbocharger. This upgrading includes more durable intake and exhaust valve materials, better sealing piston rings, a larger capacity oil pump, select-fit bearings, and a revised camshaft. Dished piston tops are incorporated to lower the compression ratio.

The turbocharged engine integrates a Garrett-AiResearch T-3 center housing and wastegate assembly with a Chrysler built compressor and turbine housing, and exhaust outlet elbow, **Fig. 48.** The wastegate is calibrated to regulate maximum boost pressure at 7.5 psi. Turbo boost begins at 1200 RPM, rises to 7.2 psi at 2050 RPM, and peaks at 7.5 psi at 6000 RPM.

This turbocharger also incorporates a water cooled turbine end shaft bearing which lowers bearing temperatures, especially after a hot shut-off, to increase durability of the turbocharger, **Fig. 49.**

The 1990 2.2L/4-135 Turbo IV engines use a Variable Nozzle Turbocharger (VNT) to increase torque across the engines power band and reduce turbo lag. The VNT has 12 aerodynamic movable vanes, each of which pivots around the turbine wheel. A unison ring moves the vanes to adjust the flow of exhaust to the turbine wheel.

The VNT incorporates a two-chamber vane actuator that combines an upper chamber to control boost, a lower chamber to control part-throttle actuation and electronic software to control the system. The actuator uses either manifold vacuum or turbocharger boost pressure as the power source to move the vanes, depending on operating conditions. In many instances of normal driving, both chambers function simultaneously for optimum vane position.

Three electrical solenoids apply the appropriate vacuum or pressure signals to the actuator. The solenoids are operated by the engine control computer. The VNT also incorporates a 360° water-jacketed turbine bearing housing to increase turbocharger durability.

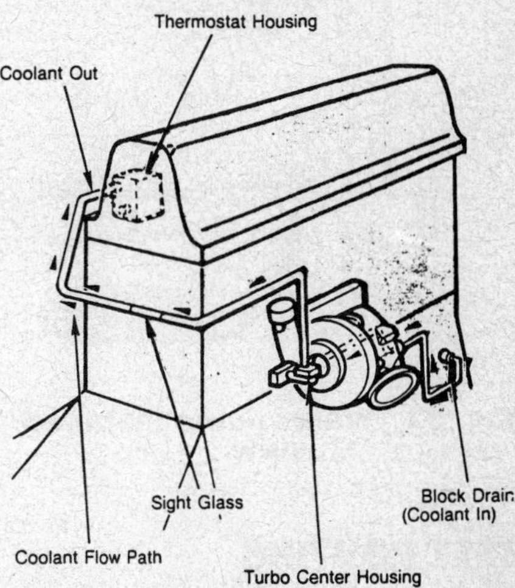


**Fig. 49 Turbocharger water cooling system**

## BELT TENSION DATA

| Belt | New Lbs. | Used Lbs. |
|---|---|---|
| **1989** | | |
| **Air Cond.** | 105 | 80 |
| **Alternator** | 115 | 80 |
| **Power Steer.** | 105 | 80 |
| **1990–92①** | | |
| **Air Cond.** | 125 | 80 |
| **Alternator** | 130 | 80 |
| **Power Steer.** | 105 | 80 |

①—Except 1991–92 2.2L/4-135 Turbo III engine (VIN A).

## SERPENTINE DRIVE BELTS

### BELT REPLACEMENT

#### 1991–92 2.2L/4-135 Turbo III Engine

1. Raise vehicle on hoist.
2. Remove right front splash shield.
3. Release tension by rotating tensioner clockwise, **Fig. 50.**
4. Reverse procedure to install.

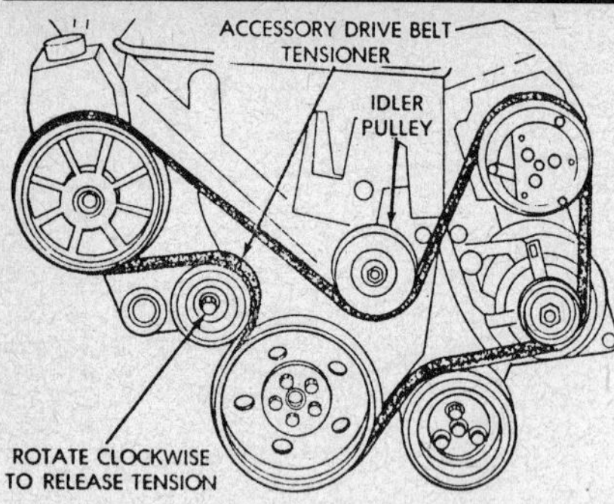


**Fig. 50 Accessory drive belt routing. 1991–92 2.2L/4-135 Turbo III engine (VIN A).**

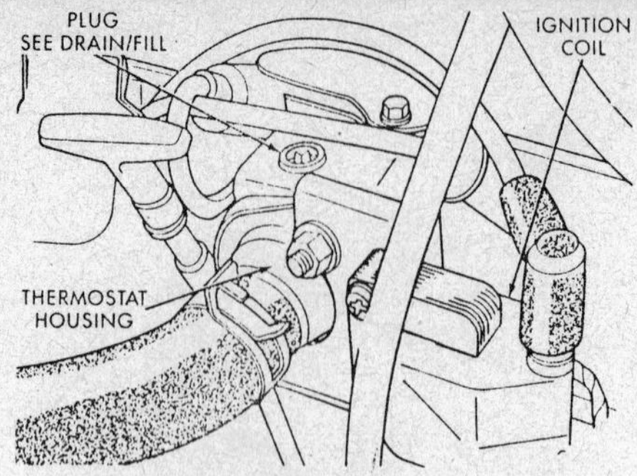


**Fig. 51 Cooling system vent plug. Except 1991–92 2.2L/4-135 Turbo III engine (VIN A).**

**Fig. 52 Coolant temperature sensor. 1991–92 2.2L/4-135 Turbo III engine (VIN A).**

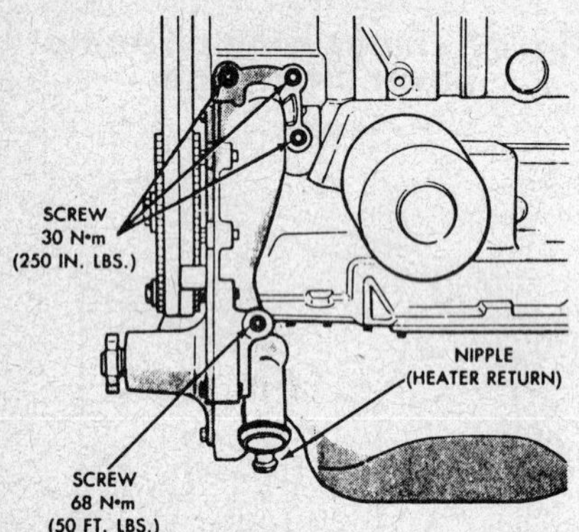


**Fig. 53 Water pump installed view**

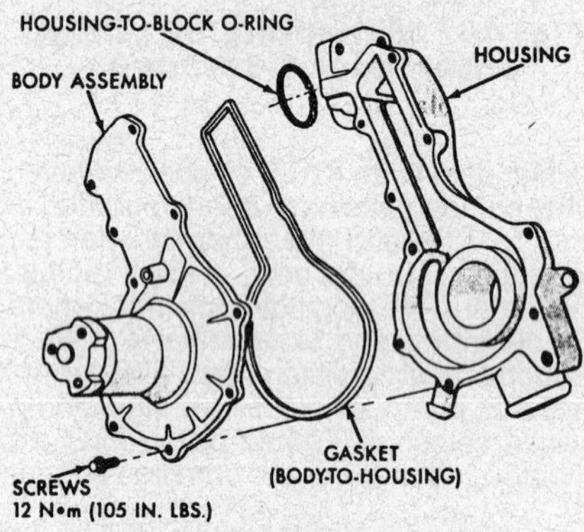


**Fig. 54 Water pump components**

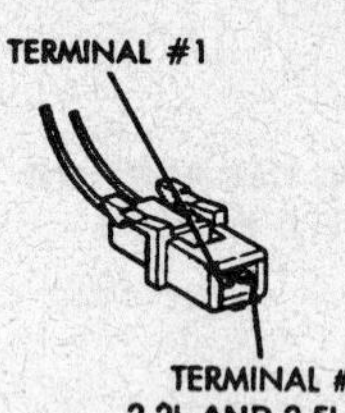

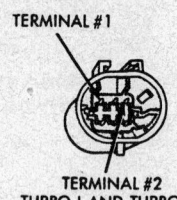

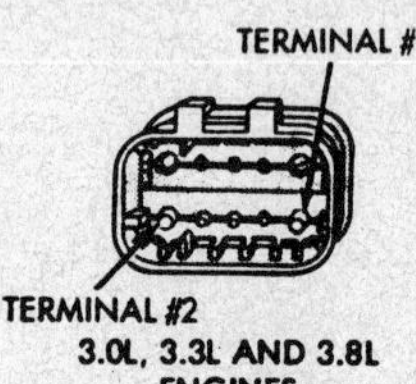


**Fig. 55 Injector harness connectors.**

## BELT ROUTING

### 1991–92 2.2L/4-135 Turbo III Engine

Refer to **Fig. 50** for serpentine drive belt routing.

## COOLING SYSTEM BLEED

The cooling system on except Turbo III engines requires venting by removal of the plug on top of the water box, **Fig. 51.** On the Turbo III engines, venting requires removing the coolant temperature sensor on top of the thermostat housing, **Fig. 52.**

Fill the system with the recommended 50 percent mixture of antifreeze and water until mixture reaches the vent holes, then tighten the vent plug, on except Turbo III engines, or coolant temperature sensor, on Turbo III engines, to specifications. Continue to fill cooling system until full.

## WATER PUMP

### REPLACE

1. Disconnect battery ground cable.
2. Drain cooling system, and remove upper radiator hose.
3. Remove A/C compressor from mounting brackets and position aside with refrigerant lines attached, if equipped.
4. Remove alternator.
5. Disconnect lower radiator hose, bypass hose. Remove four water pump to engine attaching screws and water pump, **Figs. 53 and 54.**
6. Reverse procedure to install.

## THERMOSTAT

### REPLACE

1. Drain coolant system down to thermostat level.
2. Remove thermostat housing bolts and housing.
3. Remove thermostat, discard gasket and clean both gasket sealing surfaces.
4. Reverse procedure to install. Dip new gasket in water and ensure to center thermostat in water box on gasket.

## FUEL SYSTEM PRESSURE RELEASE

Before servicing the fuel pump, fuel lines, fuel filter, throttle body or fuel injectors, the fuel system pressure must be released as follows:

1. Loosen fuel filler cap to release fuel tank pressure.
2. Disconnect injector wiring harness from engine harness.
3. Connect a jumper wire to ground terminal No. 1 of the injector harness to engine ground, **Fig. 55.**
4. Connect a jumper wire to the positive terminal No. 2 of the injector harness and touch the battery positive post for no longer then 5 seconds. This releases system pressure.
5. Remove jumper wires and continue fuel system service.

## FUEL PUMP

### REPLACE

1. Relieve fuel pump pressure, refer to "Fuel Pressure, Relief"for proper procedure, then disconnect battery ground cable.
2. Remove fuel tank filler cap, then fuel filler tube to to quarter panel attaching screws.
3. Raise and support vehicle, then remove draft tube cap on sending unit and siphon fuel from tank.
4. Disconnect all fuel lines and electrical connections to fuel tank.
5. Place suitable jack under fuel tank, then loosen retaining strap attaching bolts and lower tank from vehicle.
6. Loosen lock ring attaching fuel pump using brass drift and hammer by gently tapping lock ring sideways, then remove fuel pump and O-ring from tank.
7. Reverse procedure to install. Do not overtighten O-ring. **Torque** fuel strap nuts to 21 ft. lbs.

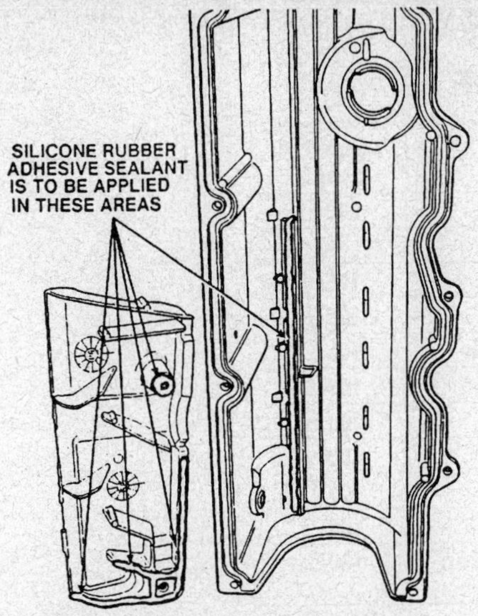


**Fig. 56 Applying silicone rubber adhesive sealant**

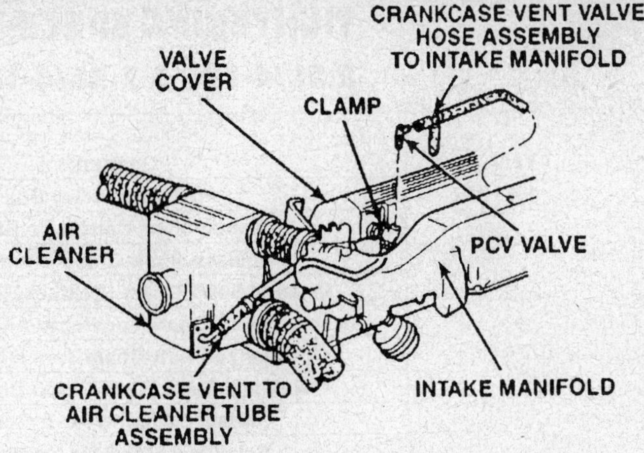


**Fig. 57 PCV system. Turbo I & Turbo II engines**

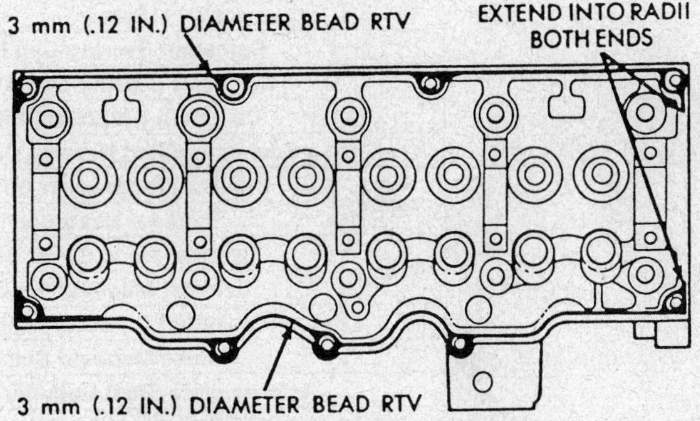


**Fig. 58 Applying silicone rubber adhesive (RTV) sealant**

# SERVICE BULLETINS

## OIL IN AIR CLEANER

Some 1989-90 models with 2.2L/4-135 Turbo I and Turbo IV engines may have engine oil leaking from the bottom of the air cleaner housing. To verify the condition, remove the air cleaner element and check for oil saturation of the air filter and breather elements. If oil saturation is present, proceed as follows:

1. The following parts are required for repair:
   a. Cylinder head cover gasket, part No. 4343882.
   b. Air Cleaner Element, part No. 4342801 or equivalent, for all models.
   c. Breather Element, part No. 4306914 or equivalent, for all models.
   d. Silicone Rubber Adhesive Sealant, part No. 4318025 or equivalent, for all models.
2. Remove cylinder head cover.
3. Remove baffle plate by removing two bolts from the back of the cylinder head cover, then pry the baffle from the cover. **The silicone rubber sealant adheres well, requiring some force to separate the baffle plate from the cover.**
4. **On all models,** clean old sealant off of baffle plate and cylinder head cover.
5. Apply silicone rubber adhesive sealant on the baffle plate and cylinder head cover as shown, **Fig. 56.**
6. Press baffle into cylinder head cover using caution not to damage the nipple.
7. Remove crankcase vent-to-air cleaner tube assembly, PCV valve and intake manifold hose assembly, **Fig. 57.**
8. Remove air cleaner and breather elements and discard.
9. Install new air cleaner and breather elements.
10. Install cylinder head cover. Torque bolts to specifications.
11. Clean and install PCV system, **Fig. 57.**

## CYLINDER HEAD COVER OIL LEAK

On 1989-90 models with a 2.2L/4-135 or 2.5L/4-153 EFI engine that are diagnosed as having an oil leak at the cylinder head cover gasket will require to have the original cover replaced with a cover that uses RTV sealant instead of a gasket.

To correct the oil leak problem, obtain the Cylinder Head Cover Kit No. 5241066, and replace the cylinder head cover. The original components, cover, gasket and fasteners, are not to be interchangeable and should be discarded. The original fasteners are too long to be used with the RTV type valve cover.

Use the following replacement procedure:

1. Remove fuel tube and wiring bracket fasteners.
2. Remove timing belt cover. Refer to "Timing Belt, Sprockets & Oil Seals" for procedure.
3. Remove existing cylinder head cover and gasket.
4. Clean cylinder head cover mating surfaces and apply RTV sealant, part No. 4318025, to cylinder head cover rail, **Fig. 58.**
5. Install cylinder head cover and seals, using the four stud/washers at each corner of cylinder head and the five screws/washers in remaining holes.
6. **Torque** the cover screws to 105 inch lbs. then install timing belt cover and fuel tube and wiring bracket fasteners.

# TIGHTENING SPECIFICATIONS

## 2.2L/4-135 & 2.5L/4-153 ENGINE

| Year | Component | Torque/ft. lbs. |
|---|---|---|
| 1989–92 | Air Pump Pulley Bolt⑥ | 250① |
| | Balance Shaft Carrier To Block Bolt | 40 |
| | Balance Shaft Chain Snubber Nut | 105① |
| | Balance Shaft Chain Snubber Stud & Washer | 105① |
| | Balance Shaft Chain Tensioner Adjustment Screw | 105① |
| | Balance Shaft Chain Tensioner Screw | 105① |
| | Balance Shaft Front Chain Cover Screw | 105① |
| | Balance Shaft Gear & Sprocket | 250① |
| | Balance Shaft Gear Cover Screw | 105① |
| | Balance Shaft Rear Cover Screw | 105① |
| | Balance Shaft Sprocket To Crankshaft Torx Drive Cap Screw | 130① |
| | Camshaft Bearing Cap Bolt | 215① |
| | Camshaft Bearing Cap Nut⑨ | 165① |
| | Camshaft Sprocket Bolt⑨ | 65 |
| | Connecting Rod Bearing Cap Nut | 40④ |
| | Crankshaft Sprocket Bolt⑨ | ③ |
| | Cylinder Head Bolt | ② |
| | Cylinder Head Cover Bolt | 105① |
| | Exhaust Manifold Nut⑨ | 200① |
| | Front Crankshaft Oil Seal Retainer Screw | 105① |
| | Intake Manifold Bolt | 200① |
| | Intermediate Shaft Retainer Screw | 105① |
| | Intermediate Shaft Sprocket Bolt⑨ | 65 |
| | Lower Timing Belt Cover Screw⑨ | 40① |
| | Main Bearing Cap Bolt | 30④ |
| | Oil Pan Drain Plug | 240① |
| | Oil Pan Screw⑨ | ⑤ |
| | Oil Pump Cover Screw | 105① |
| | Oil Pump Mounting Screw | 200① |
| | Oil Pump Strainer To Cover Screw | 250① |
| | Oil Pump Strainer To Maincap Screw | 105① |
| | Rear Crankshaft Oil Seal Retainer Screw | 105① |
| | Spark Plug⑨ | 26 |
| | Thermostat Housing Screw⑨ | 250① |
| | Upper Timing Belt Cover Screw | 40① |
| | Water Pump Housing Screw (Lower) | 40 |
| | Water Pump Housing Screw (Upper) | 250① |
| 1991–92 | Camshaft Thrust Plate Retaining Nut⑦ | 72① |
| | Connecting Rod Bearing Cap Nut⑦ | 50 |
| | Camshaft Sprocket Bolt⑦ | 47 |
| | Crankshaft Sprocket Bolt⑦ | 80 |
| | Intermediate Shaft Sprocket Bolt⑦ | 53 |
| | Lower Timing Belt Cover⑦ | 72① |
| | Exhaust Manifold Studs⑦ | 210① |
| | Oil Pan Bolts⑦ | ⑧ |
| | Rocker Arm Shaft Retaining Bolts⑦ | 210① |
| | Rocker Cover Bolts⑦ | 115① |
| | Spark Plugs⑦ | 220① |
| | Thermostat Housing Bolts⑦ | 210① |
| | Timing Belt Idler Pulley Bolt⑦ | 39 |
| | Timing Belt Tensioner Pulley Bolt⑦ | 39 |

Continued

①—Inch lbs.
②—Refer to text.
③—1989 models, 50 ft. lbs.; 1990 models, 90 ft. lbs.
④—After reaching specified torque, turn an additional 1/4 turn to achieve proper tightness.
⑤—M6 screws, 105 inch lbs,; M8 screws, 200 inch lbs.
⑥—1989-90 models only.
⑦—1991-92 2.2L/4-135 Turbo III Engine (VIN A).
⑧—M6 screws, 220 inch lbs,; M8 screws, 260 inch lbs.
⑨—Except 1991-92 2.2L/4-135 Turbo III Engine (VIN A).

# 3.0L/V6-181 Engine

## INDEX



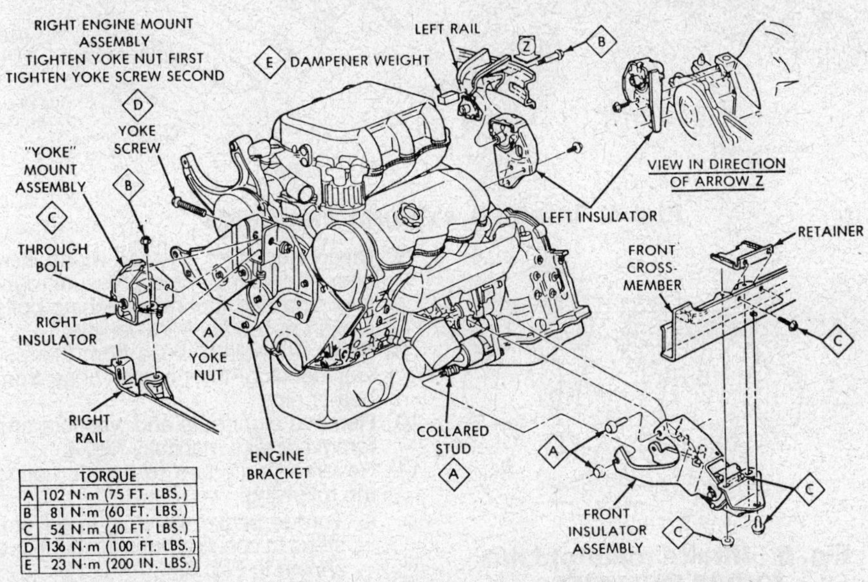

**Fig. 1 Engine mounting**

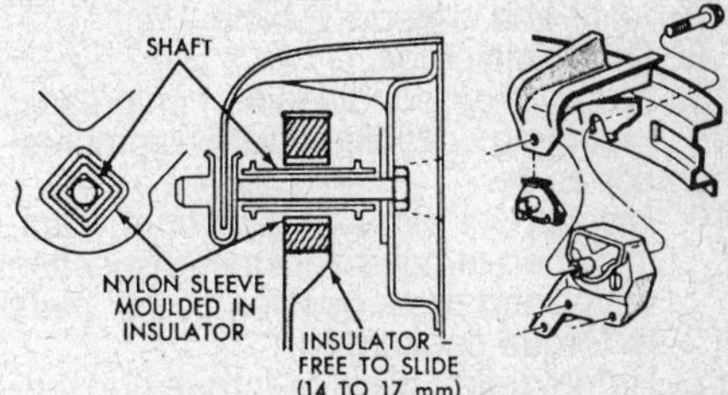

**Fig. 2 Left insulator movement**

## AIRBAG SYSTEM DISARMING

**This system is a complex, electro-mechanical unit. Before attempting to diagnose, remove or install any airbag system components, you must first disable the airbag system as follows:**

1. Place ignition switch in lock position.
2. Disconnect and tape battery ground cable connector.
3. **Wait at least 1 minute after disconnecting battery ground cable before doing any further work on vehicle. The SRS system is designed to retain enough voltage to deploy airbag for a short time even after battery has been disconnected.**
4. After repairs are complete, reconnect battery ground cable.
5. From passenger side of vehicle, turn ignition switch to On position.
6. SRS warning light should illuminate for 6 to 8 seconds, then remain off for at least 45 seconds to indicate if SRS system is functioning correctly.
7. If SRS indicator does not perform as described refer to the "Passive Restraint Systems" section.

## ENGINE MOUNTS
### REPLACE

The left engine mount insulator is sleeved to provide lateral movement adjustment with engine weight removed or not, **Figs. 1 and 2**..

1. Loosen the right engine mount vertical attaching bolt with the engine and transaxle supported with a suitable jack to relieve load on motor mounts.
2. Loosen the front engine mount bracket to front crossmember bolts.
3. Pry the engine right or left to attain proper driveshaft length.
4. **Torque** right engine mount insulator vertical bolts to 60 ft. lbs. and front engine mount bolts to 40 ft. lbs.
5. Center the left engine mount insulator and recheck driveshaft length.

## ENGINE
### REPLACE

**Disable airbag as outlined under "Airbag System Disarming." After prodedure has been completed, rearm airbag system as outlined under "Airbag System Disarming."**

**Before servicing the fuel pump, fuel lines, fuel filter, throttle body or fuel injectors, the fuel system pressure must be released as outlined under "Fuel System Pressure Release."**

1. Disconnect battery ground cable.

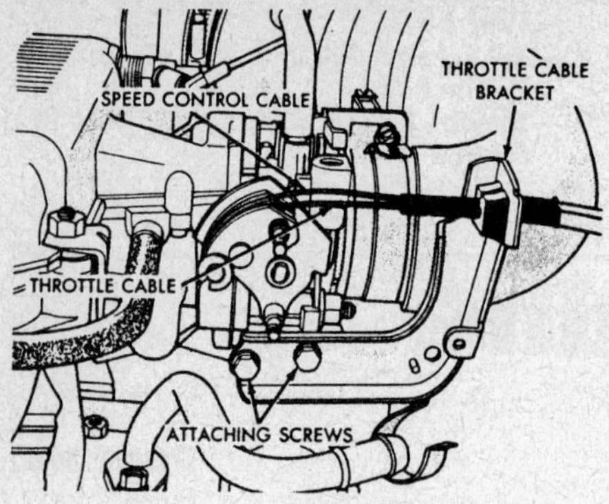


**Fig. 3 Throttle cable**

2. Mark hood hinge locations and remove hood.
3. Drain cooling system, then disconnect all electrical connections.
4. Remove coolant hoses, radiator and fan assembly.
5. Relieve fuel pressure as outlined under "Fuel System Pressure Release."
6. Disconnect fuel lines, then unhook the accelerator cable.
7. Remove air cleaner assembly, then raise and support vehicle.
8. Drain engine oil.
9. Remove air conditioning compressor mounting bolts and position compressor aside.
10. Disconnect exhaust pipe from manifold, then remove transaxle inspection cover and mark position of flex plate to torque converter.
11. Remove flex plate-to-torque converter attaching screws and clamp bottom of converter housing to prevent converter from moving.
12. Remove power steering attaching bolts and position pump aside.
13. Remove two lower transaxle-to-block screws, then the starter. Lower vehicle to ground.
14. Install suitable transmission holding fixture, then install engine lifting hoist and support engine.
15. Remove upper transaxle case to block bolts.
16. Mark position of right engine mount insulator on right rail supports, then remove insulator-to-rails screws.
17. Remove front engine mount through bolt and nut.
18. Remove left engine mount insulator through bolt or insulator bracket-to-transaxle screws.
19. Carefully lower engine from vehicle.
20. Reverse procedure to install, tightening flex plate and axle to block bolts to specifications.

# INTAKE & EXHAUST MANIFOLD
## REPLACE

**Before servicing the fuel pump, fuel lines, fuel filter, throttle body or fuel injectors, the fuel system pressure must be released as outlined under "Fuel System Pressure Release."**

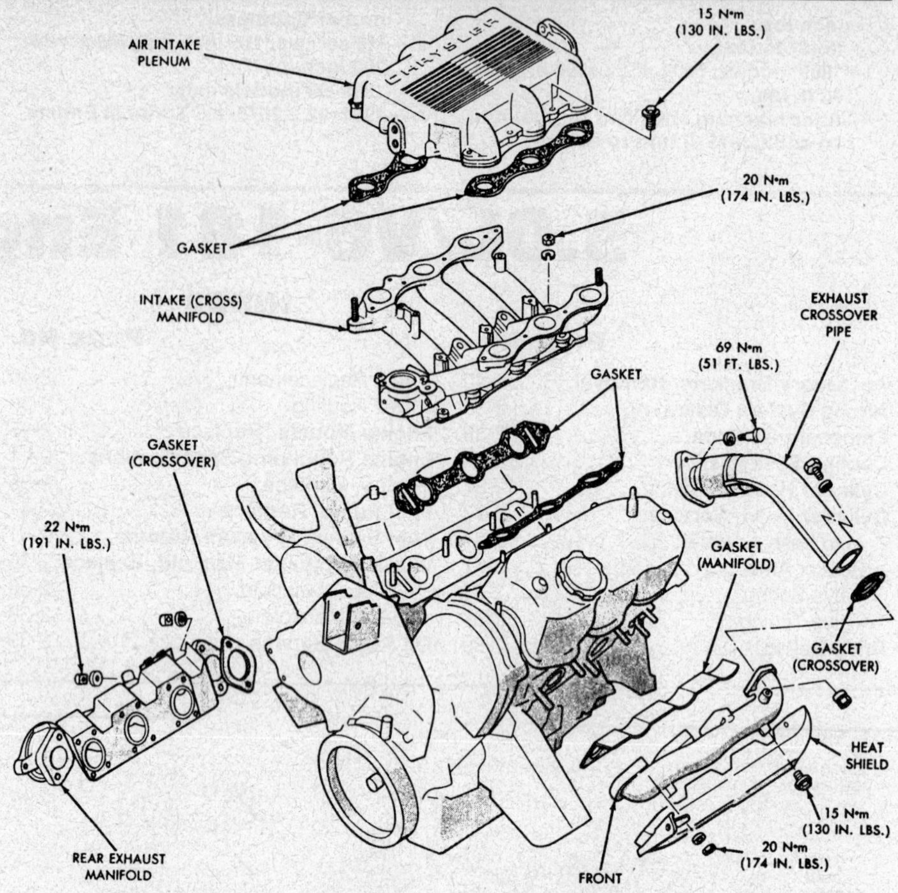


**Fig. 4 Intake & exhaust manifolds**

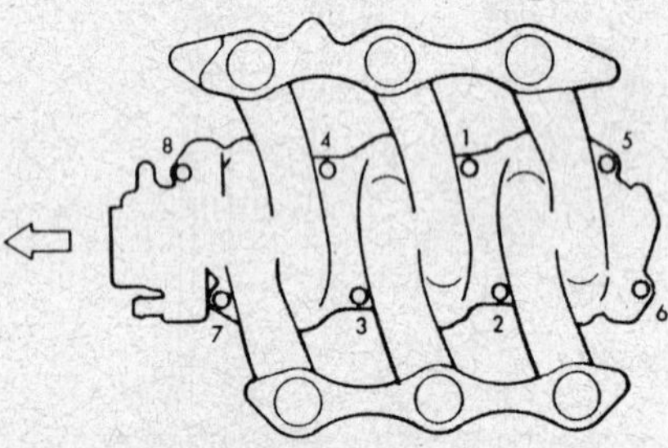


**Fig. 5 Intake manifold nut torque sequence**

## INTAKE MANIFOLD

1. Disconnect battery negative cable then relieve fuel system pressure as outlined under "Fuel System Pressure Release."
2. Drain cooling system, then remove air cleaner to throttle body hose.
3. Remove throttle cable and transaxle kickdown linkage, **Fig. 3**, then remove all wiring connectors and vacuum hoses from throttle body.
4. Remove PCV and brake booster hoses, and EGR tube flange from air intake plenum.
5. Mark and remove all necessary wiring and vacuum connectors.
6. Remove fuel hoses from fuel rail.
7. Remove eight intake plenum to intake manifold hold-down bolts and remove plenum.
8. Disconnect fuel injector wiring harness, then remove fuel pressure regulator and and fuel rail attaching bolts and lift assembly from vehicle.
9. Separate radiator hose from thermostat housing, then heater hose from heater pipe.
10. Remove eight nuts and washers and remove intake manifold, **Fig. 4.**
11. Reverse procedure to install, noting the following:
    a. Torque intake manifold in several steps to specifications in sequence shown in **Fig. 5.**
    b. Ensure injector holes are clean and lubricate injector O-rings with a drop of clean oil before installation.
    c. Torque fuel rail retaining bolts and fuel regulator retaining bolts to specifications.
    d. Torque intake plenum bolts to specifications according to sequence shown in **Fig. 6.**

## EXHAUST MANIFOLD

1. Raise and support vehicle, then disconnect exhaust pipe from rear exhaust manifold.
2. Disconnect EGR tube from rear manifold, then disconnect oxygen sensor lead wire.
3. Disconnect exhaust crossover pipe from manifolds, **Fig. 7,** then remove rear manifold-to-cylinder head retaining bolts and the manifold.

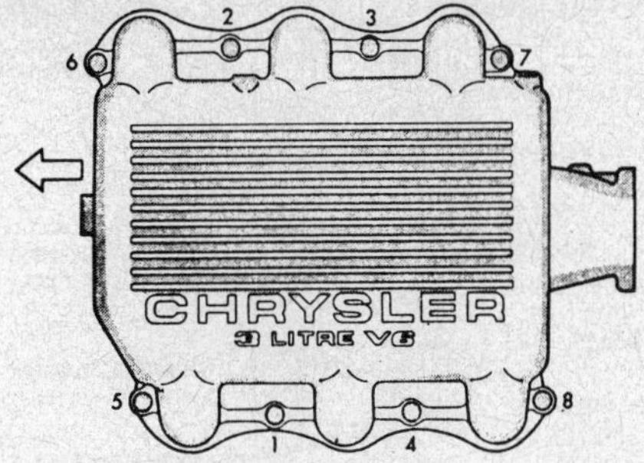


Fig. 6 Intake plenum torque sequence

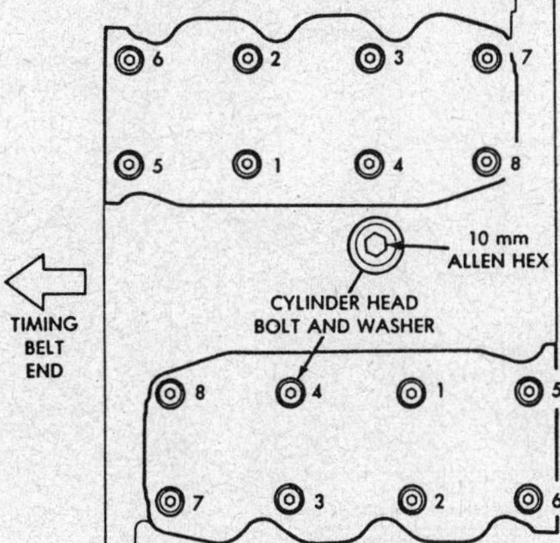


Fig. 9 Cylinder head bolt torque sequence

4. Lower vehicle, then remove heat shield from front manifold.
5. Remove crossover pipe to front exhaust manifold bolts, then the front exhaust manifold retaining nuts and manifold.
6. Reverse procedure to install, noting the following:
   a. Torque rear exhaust manifold, exhaust pipe, crossover pipe and front exhaust manifold to specifications.

## CYLINDER HEAD REPLACE

**Before servicing the fuel pump, fuel lines, fuel filter, throttle body or fuel injectors, the fuel system pressure must be released as outlined under "Fuel System Pressure Release."**

1. Remove camshaft and rocker arm, and upper intake manifold assemblies as previously described.
2. Remove distributor, then the exhaust manifolds and crossover as previously described.
3. Remove cylinder head bolts in sequence shown in **Fig. 8**, then remove cylinder head.
4. Inspect cylinder head before installing. Cylinder head must be flat within .002 inch.
5. Reverse procedure to install. Torque head bolts to specifications in two or three steps in sequence shown in **Fig. 9.**

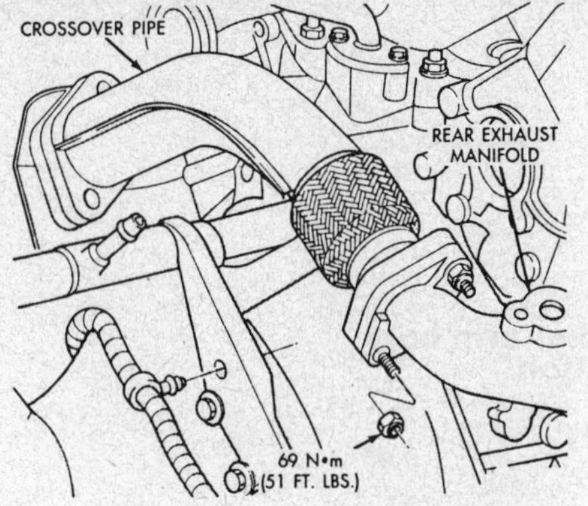


Fig. 7 Crossover pipe

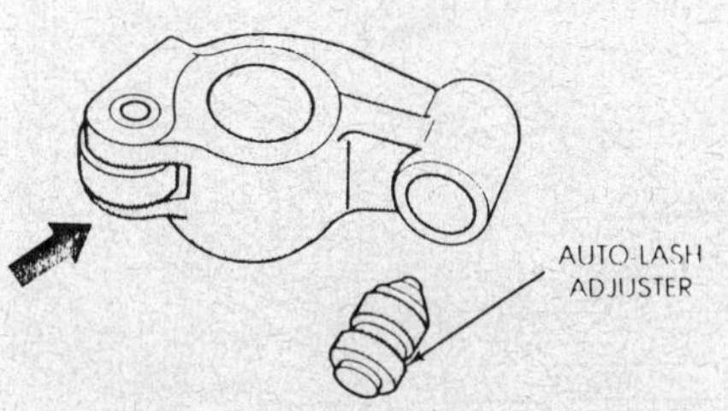


Fig. 10 Auto lash adjuster

## CYLINDER HEAD, SERVICE

### AUTO LASH ADJUSTER

Automatic lash adjusters are used, no adjustment is needed, **Fig. 10.**

#### Functional Check

1. Inserting a small wire through the air bleed hole in the rocker arm, **Fig. 11,** and very lightly push the auto adjuster ball check down.
2. While lightly holding check ball down, move rocker up and down to check for freeplay.
3. If no freeplay is present, replace adjuster. **Do not disassemble the auto lash adjuster.**

### VALVE SPRING, REPLACE

1. Remove cylinder heads as outlined under "Cylinder Head, Replace."
2. Remove rocker arm shafts and camshafts as outlined under "Camshaft, Replace."
3. Using a suitable valve spring compressor tool, compress valve spring and remove spring retainer locks, retainer, valve spring, spring seat and valve stem seal.
4. Reverse procedure to install.

### ROCKER ARM, REPLACE

1. Remove rocker arm shaft as outlined under "Camshaft, Replace."
2. Inspect rocker arm mounting portion of shafts for wear or damage.
3. Check oil holes for clogging.
4. Reverse procedure to install.

**SERVICE BULLETIN:** Some 1990

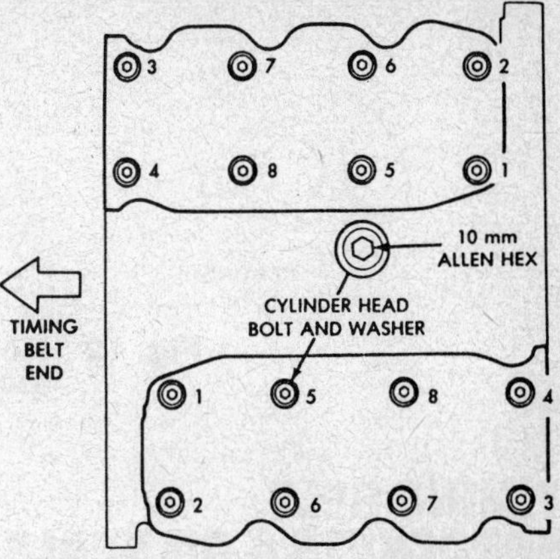


Fig. 8 Cylinder head bolt removal sequence

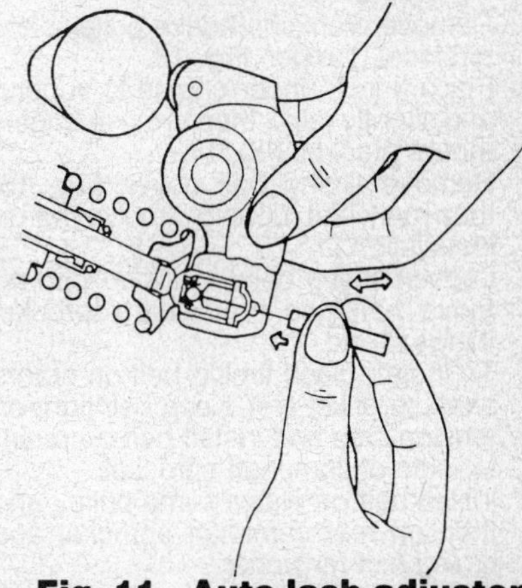

Fig. 11 Auto lash adjuster check

3.0L/V6-181 engines built before engine code 7-370 may exhibit a valve train ticking noise. This noise can occur at any engine temperature. This condition may be the result of a rocker arm casting burr in the area of the rocker arm shaft bore.

To correct this condition, remove the appropriate cylinder head cover. carefully move rocker arms, one at a time, away from cam shaft bearing cap. Inspect rocker arm surface that contacts the cam shaft bearing cap for casting burrs as shown in **Fig. 12.** If no burrs are found perform "Functional Check" as outlined under "Auto Lash Adjuster." If Burrs are found, proceed as follows:

1. Remove and disassemble rocker arm shafts as outlined under "Rocker Arm, Replace."
2. Using an oil stone or 500 grit wet/dry sandpaper soaked in oil, remove casting burr from rocker arm.
3. Thoroughly clean rocker arm and shafts to remove all traces of abrasive material.
4. Reverse procedure to install and ensure proper operation.

## VALVE TIMING

| | Degrees① | |
|---|---|---|
| **Year** | **Intake②** | **Exhaust③** |
| **1989–92** | **19** | **57** |

**①—Valve opening specification.**
**②—Before Top Dead Center.**
**③—Before Bottom Dead Center.**

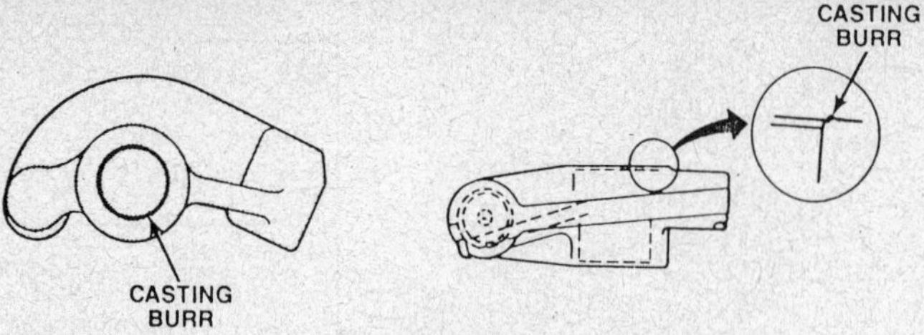


**Fig. 12 Rocker arm burr location**

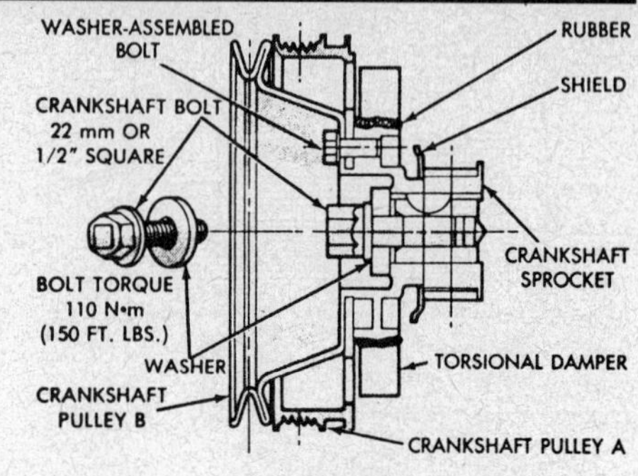


**Fig. 13 Crankshaft pulley assembly**

# TIMING BELT, SPROCKETS & OIL SEALS

## TIMING BELT, REMOVAL

1. Remove crankshaft drive pulleys and torsional damper, **Fig. 13.**
2. Place a jack under engine to support and slightly raise, then remove engine mount bracket, **Fig. 14.**
3. Remove timing belt cover, **Fig. 15,** then mark belt running direction for re-installation.
4. Loosen timing belt tensioner, then remove belt and crankshaft sprocket flange shield.
5. To install, place timing belt on crankshaft sprocket first. Keep belt tight on tension side and install belt on radiator side of camshaft sprocket.
6. Install belt on water pump pulley and then on rear camshaft sprocket and timing belt tensioner.
7. Rotate engine at the front camshaft sprocket, turning in opposite direction to tension the tension side of belt, then check that all timing marks line up, **Fig. 16.**
8. Install crankshaft sprocket flange, loosen tensioner bolt and turn crankshaft two full turns in clockwise direction.
9. Recheck timing marks, then torque tensioner lock bolt to specifications.
10. Reassemble belt cover, brackets and pulleys in reverse order of removal.

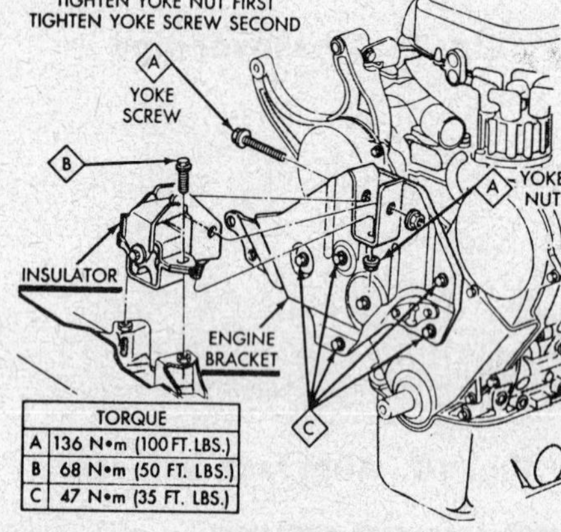


| TORQUE | |
|---|---|
| A | 136 N•m (100 FT. LBS.) |
| B | 68 N•m (50 FT. LBS.) |
| C | 47 N•m (35 FT. LBS.) |

**Fig. 14 Right engine mount & bracket**

BRACKET HARNESS CLIP
COVER (REAR REFERENCE)
REAR COVER D BOLTS
BRACKET HARNESS CLIP
A
B
UPPER REAR COVER
C
LOWER COVER
UPPER FRONT COVER (OUTER)

| TORQUE ALL-14 N•m (115 IN. LBS.) | | | |
|---|---|---|---|
| A | M6×20 | C | M6×25 |
| B | M6×55 | D | M6×10 |

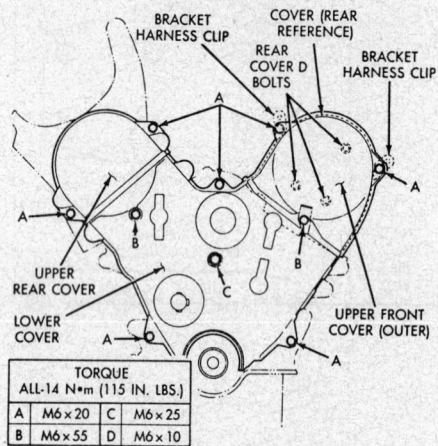

**Fig. 15 Timing belt cover**

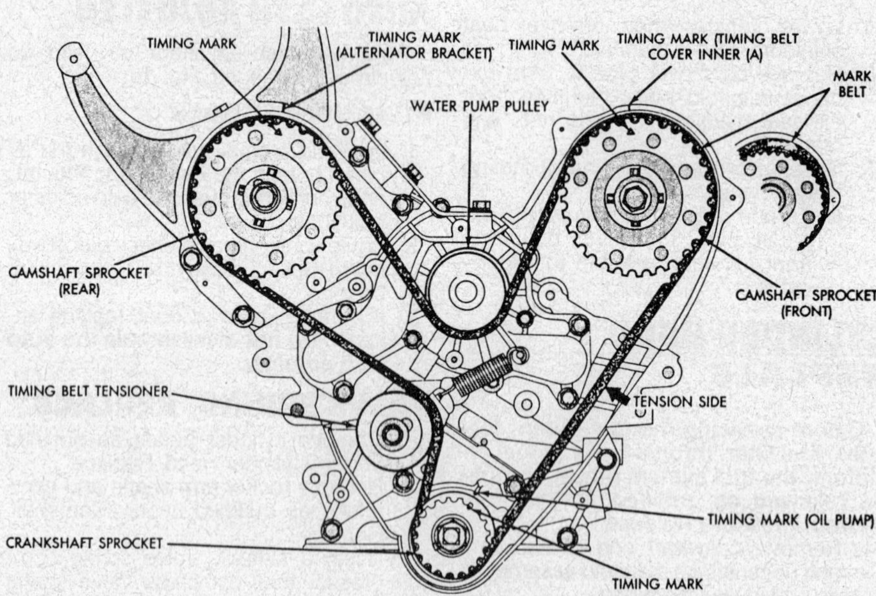


**Fig. 16 Timing belt & pulleys**

## CAMSHAFT & CRANKSHAFT SPROCKET

1. After timing belt has been removed, pull crankshaft sprocket off crankshaft, **Fig. 13.**
2. Hold camshaft with sprocket holding tool No. MB990775 or equivalent, **Fig. 17,** and remove sprocket bolt.
3. Reverse procedure to install, torque retaining bolts to specifications.

## CAMSHAFT & CRANKSHAFT OIL SEAL

Refer to **Figs. 18, 19 and 20** for seal removal and installation.

## CAMSHAFT TIMING

1. Install camshaft and crankshaft sprockets as shown in **Fig. 16,**
2. Follow steps 5 through 9 in "Timing Belt, Removal" section.

# CAMSHAFT REPLACE

**Before servicing the fuel pump, fuel lines, fuel filter, throttle body or fuel injectors, the fuel system pressure must be released as outlined under "Fuel System Pressure Release."**

1. Install auto lash adjuster retainer tool No. MD998443 or equivalent, **Fig. 21.**
2. Remove distributor extension, then loosen camshaft bearing caps without removing bolts from caps.
3. Remove rocker arm, rocker shafts and bearing cap as an assembly.
4. Inspect camshaft for scored journals, or any abnormal wear. Cam lobe height should be 1.595-1.615 inch on 1989 models or 1.604-1.624 inch on 1990-92 models.

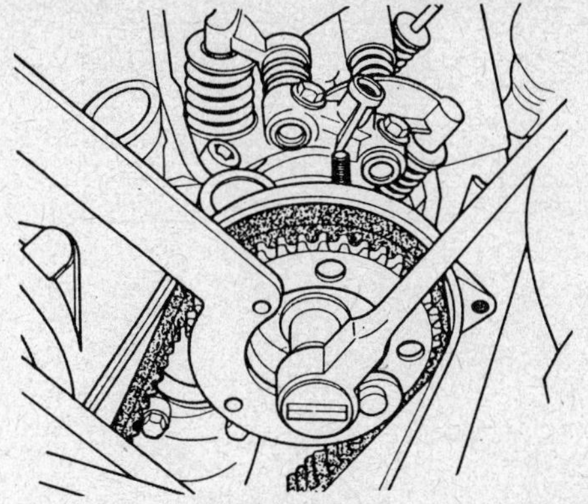

Fig. 17 Camshaft sprocket

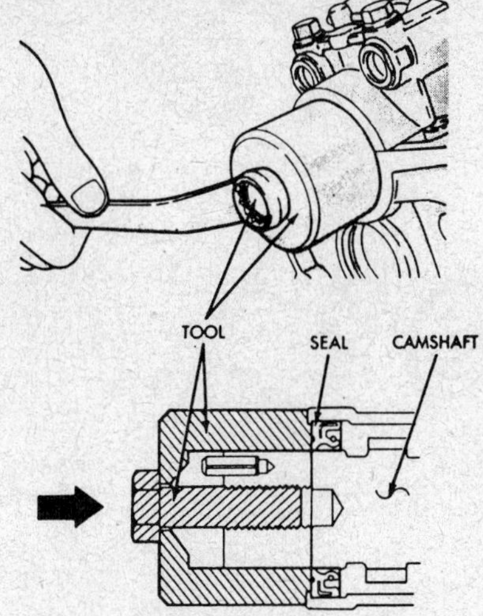


Fig. 18 Camshaft oil seal

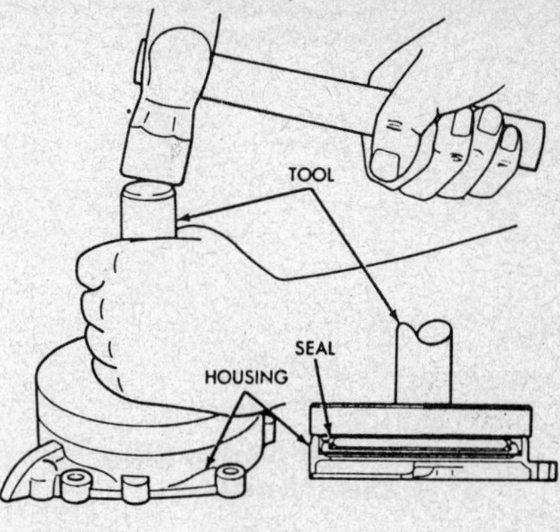


Fig. 19 Crankshaft rear oil seal

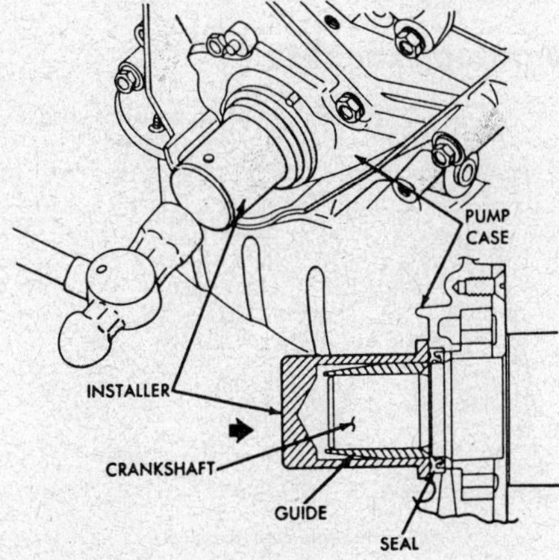


Fig. 20 Crankshaft front oil seal

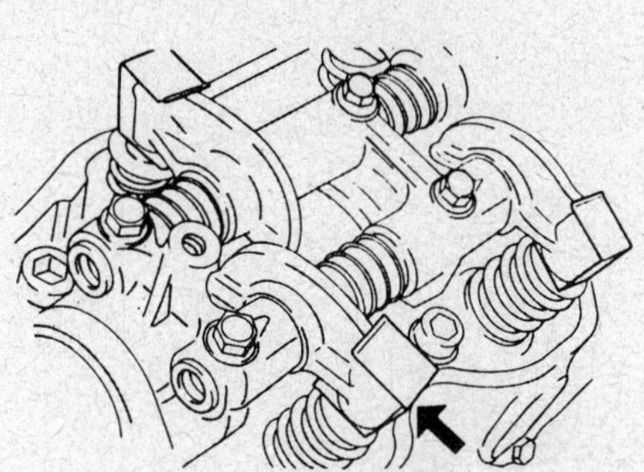

Fig. 21 Lash adjuster retainers

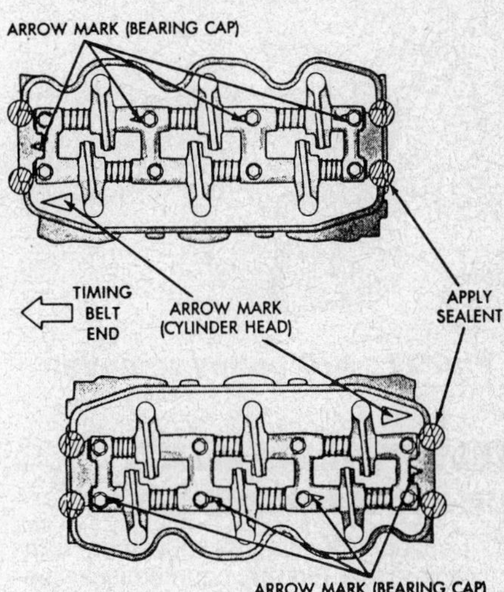


Fig. 22 Camshaft bearing cap installation

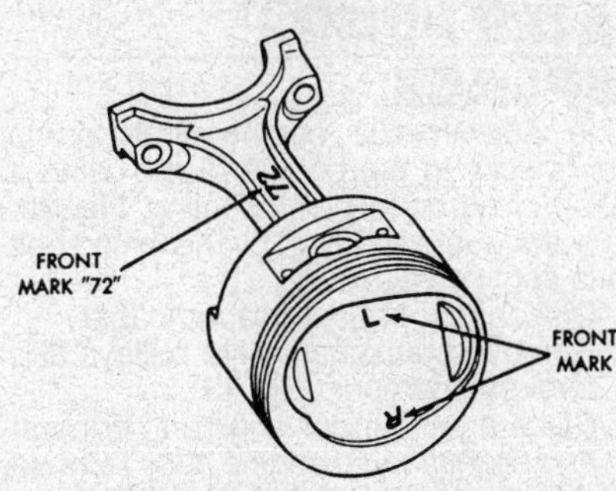


Fig. 23 Piston & rod assembly

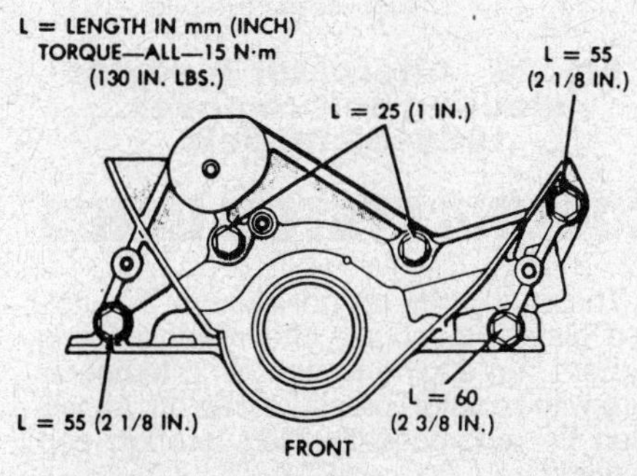


Fig. 24 Oil pump assembly

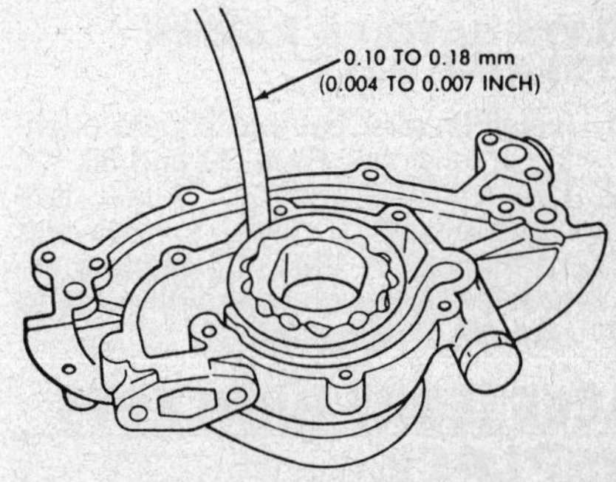


Fig. 25 Oil pump rotor-to-case clearance

5. Lubricate camshaft journals and cams with engine oil before installation, then install bearing cap ends with sealant applied as shown in **Fig. 22.**
6. Install rocker arm shaft with arrow mark on bearing cap and mark on cylinder head pointing in the same direction, **Fig. 22.**
7. **Torque** bearing cap bolts to 85 inch lbs. in the following order; 3, 2, 1, 4.
8. Repeat step 7 and **torque** to 180 inch lbs., then install distributor drive adapter assembly.
9. Install new camshaft oil seal, **Fig. 18,** then a new end plug with tool No. MB998306.

# PISTON & ROD ASSEMBLY

When installing piston and rod assemblies, cylinders 1, 3 and 5 should have the "R" facing forward, and cylinders 2, 4 and 6 should have the "L" facing forward. The connecting rod must always have the "72" mark facing forward, **Fig. 23.**

Connecting rod bearing clearance should be .001-.003 inch and rod side clearance should be .004-.010 inch.

# OIL PUMP SERVICE

1. Remove five retaining bolts holding oil pump to block, **Fig. 24.**
2. Check pump condition and perform checks according to **Figs. 25 and 26.**
3. Install pump with proper length bolts in correct position and torque to specifications, **Fig. 24.**

# DRIVE BELTS

## BELTS ROUTING

Refer to **Figs. 27 through 30** for drive belt routing.

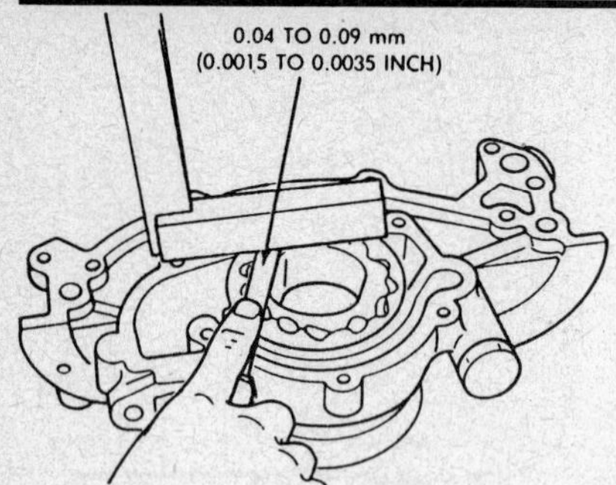


**Fig. 26 Oil pump side clearance**

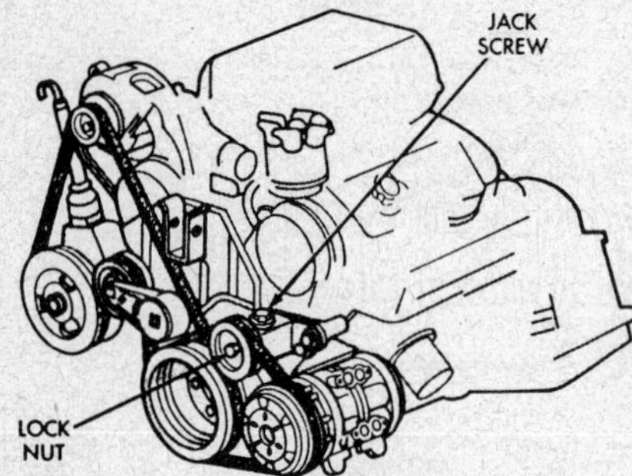


**Fig. 27 A/C pulley removal**

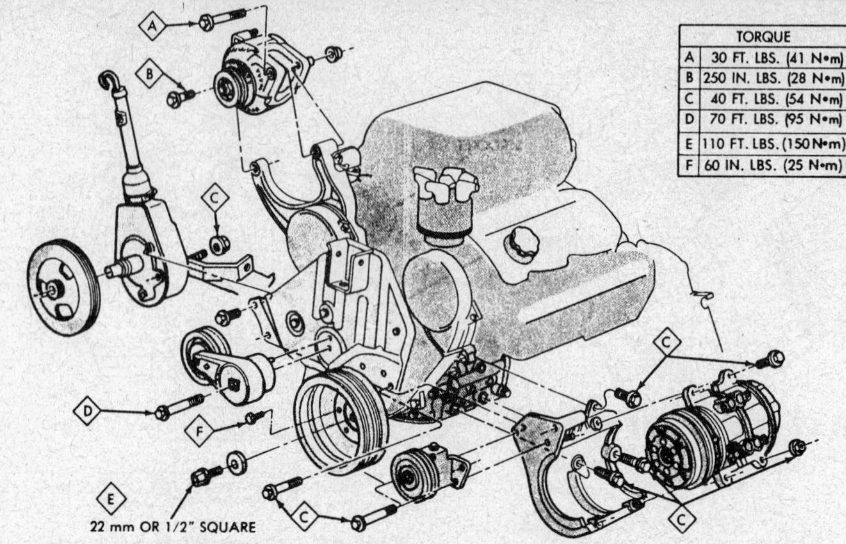

TORQUE
A 30 FT. LBS. (41 N•m)
B 250 IN. LBS. (28 N•m)
C 40 FT. LBS. (54 N•m)
D 70 FT. LBS. (95 N•m)
E 110 FT. LBS. (150 N•m)
F 60 IN. LBS. (25 N•m)
22 mm OR 1/2" SQUARE


**Fig. 28 Accessory mounting brackets**

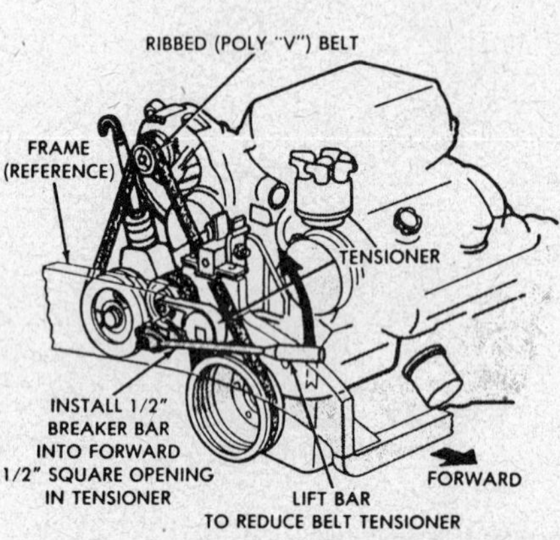


**Fig. 29 Alternator & power steering belt removal. 1989–90 models**

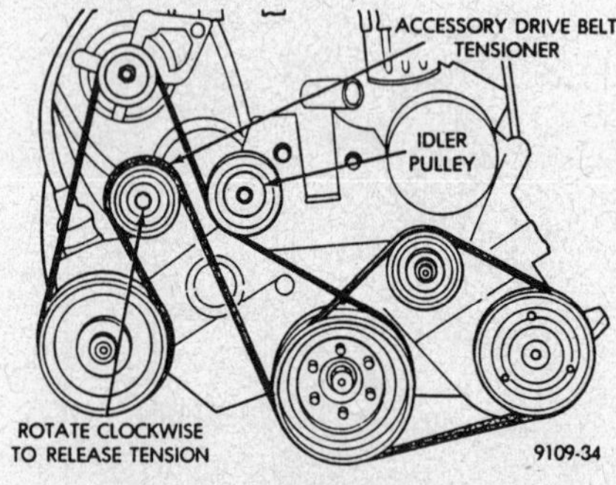


**Fig. 30 Alternator & power steering belt removal. 1990–92 models**

## BELT REPLACEMENT

### AIR CONDITIONING BELT

1. Loosen adjusting locknut, then turn jack-screw, **Fig. 27**, counterclockwise to reduce belt tension and remove belt.
2. When reinstalling belt, adjust belt tension to 5/16 inch deflection between pulleys.

### ALTERNATOR & POWER STEERING BELT

1. Install breaker bar into square opening in tensioner, **Figs. 29 and 30.**
2. **On 1989-90 models,** rotate tensioner counterclockwise to remove or install belt.**On 1991-92, models rotate tensioner counterclockwise to remove or install belt.**

## ACCESSORY BRACKETS

### REPLACE

1. Remove air conditioning compressor to mounting bracket screws and position compressor aside.
2. Remove A/C mounting bracket and adjustable drive belt tensioner retaining bolts.
3. Remove steering pump belt tensioner mounting bolt and automatic belt tensioner.
4. Remove two steering pump to engine mounting bracket screws and rear support locknut, then position power steering pump aside.
5. Reverse procedure to install. Torque bolts to specifications, **Fig. 28.**

## COOLING SYSTEM BLEED

These engines do not require a specified bleed procedure. After filling cooling system, run engine to operating temperature with radiator/pressure cap off. Air will then be automatically bled through cap opening.

## THERMOSTAT

### REPLACE

1. Drain coolant system down to thermostat level.
2. Remove thermostat housing bolts and housing.
3. Remove thermostat, discard gasket and clean both gasket sealing surfaces.
4. Reverse procedure to install, noting the following:
   a. Center thermostat in water box pocket.
   b. Ensure flange is seated correctly in the countersunk portion of intake manifold water box, **Fig. 31.**
   c. Install new gasket and housing.

## WATER PUMP

### REPLACE

The 3.0L/V6-181 engine water pump bolts directly to the engine block, using a gasket for pump-to-block sealing, **Fig. 32.** The water pump is driven by the timing belt and is serviced as a unit.

1. Disconnect battery ground cable.
2. Remove crankshaft drive pulleys and torsional damper, **Fig. 13.**
3. Place a jack under engine to support and slightly raise engine, then remove engine mount bracket, **Fig. 14.**
4. Remove timing belt cover, **Fig. 15,** then mark belt running direction for reinstallation.
5. Loosen timing belt tensioner, then remove belt and crankshaft sprocket flange shield.
6. Drain cooling system.
7. Remove water pump mounting bolts.
8. Separate water pump from water inlet pipe **Fig. 32,** then remove water pump.
9. Reverse procedure to install, noting the following:
   a. Use a new O-ring on water inlet pipe.
   b. Torque water pump mounting bolts to specifications.
   c. Refer to procedure outlined under

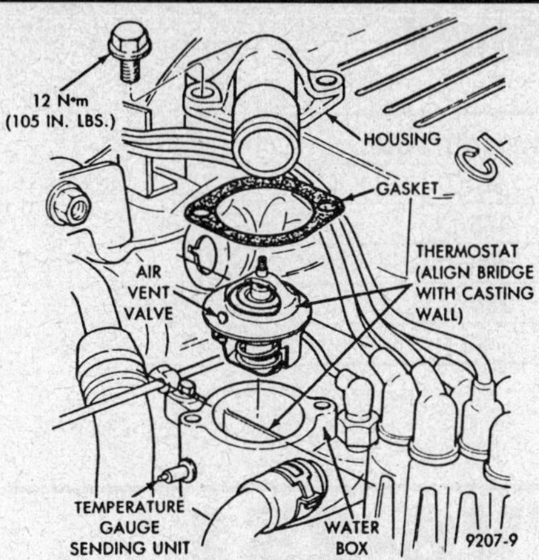


*Fig. 11 Thermostat, Housing, and Water Box—3.0L Engine*

**Fig. 31 Thermostat assembly. 3.0L/V6-181 engine**

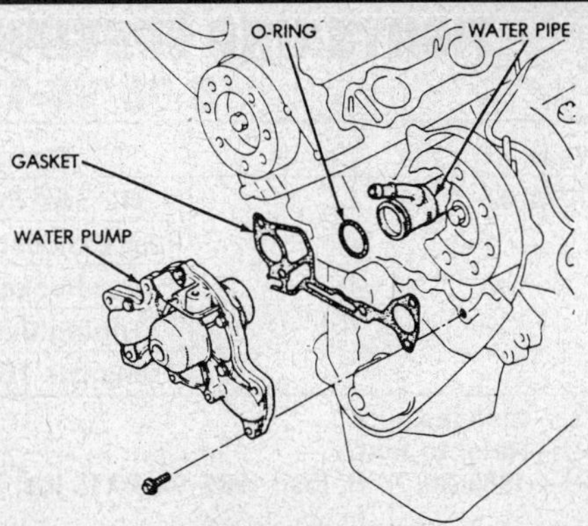


**Fig. 32 Water pump removal & installation**

"Timing Belt, Replace" for timing belt installation and tensioning procedure.

## FUEL SYSTEM PRESSURE RELEASE

1. Loosen fuel tank filler cap.
2. Disconnect injector wiring harness and connect a suitable jumper wire between ground terminal No. 1 and a suitable ground.
3. Connect a second jumper wire between terminal No. 2 of injector harness and battery positive for no longer than five seconds.
4. Remove jumper wires.

## FUEL PUMP REPLACE

Refer to "Fuel Pump, Replace" procedure in the 2.2L/4-135 & 2.5L/4-153 engine chapter.

## TIGHTENING SPECIFICATIONS

### 3.0L/V6-181 ENGINE

| Year | Component | Torque/Ft. Lbs. |
|---|---|---|
| 1989–92 | Alternator Bracket | 250① |
| | Camshaft Bearing Cap | 180① ② |
| | Camshaft Sprocket | 70 |
| | Connecting Rod Cap | 38 |
| | Crankshaft Bearing Cap | 60 |
| | Crankshaft Pulley A (Crankshaft Bolt) | 110 |
| | Crankshaft Pulley B | 250① |
| | Cylinder Head Bolt (Cold) | ③ ② |
| | Distributor Adapter | 120① |
| | Engine Support Bracket | 35 |
| | Exhaust Crossover Pipe | 51 |
| | Exhaust Pipe Shoulder Bolts | 250① |
| | Flex Plat To Torque Convertor | 55 |
| | Front Exhaust Manifold Bolts | 130① |
| | Fuel Pressure Regulator Bolts | 95① |
| | Fuel Rail Bolts | 115① |
| | Intake Manifold Nuts | 174① ② |
| | Intake Plenum Screws | 130① ② |
| | Oil Drain Plug | 30 |
| | Oil Pan | 50① |
| | Oil Pickup | 160① |
| | Oil Pump Assembly | 120① |

*Continued*

## TIGHTENING SPECIFICATIONS—Continued
### 3.0L/V6-181 ENGINE

| Year | Component | Torque/Ft. Lbs. |
|---|---|---|
| 1989–92 | Oil Seal Rear Housing | 95① |
| | Rear Exhaust Manifold Nuts | 175① |
| | Rocker Cover | 88① |
| | Timing Belt Tensioner | 250① |
| | Transaxle To Engine Block | 75 |

①—Inch lbs.
②—Refer to text.
③—1989–90, 70 ft. lbs.; 1991–92, 80 ft. lbs.

# 3.3L/V6-202 & 3.8L/V6-231 Engines

## INDEX



## AIRBAG SYSTEM DISARMING

**This system is a complex, electro-mechanical unit. Before attempting to diagnose, remove or install any airbag system components, you must first disable the airbag system as follows:**

1. Place ignition switch in lock position.
2. Disconnect and tape battery ground cable connector.
3. **Wait at least 1 minute after disconnecting battery ground cable before doing any further work on vehicle. The SRS system is designed to retain enough voltage to deploy airbag for a short time even after battery has been disconnected.**
4. After repairs are complete, reconnect battery ground cable.
5. From passenger side of vehicle, turn ignition switch to On position.
6. SRS warning light should illuminate for 6 to 8 seconds, then remain off for at least 45 seconds to indicate if SRS system is functioning correctly.
7. If SRS indicator does not perform as described refer to the "Passive Restraint Systems" section.

## ENGINE MOUNTS

### REPLACE

Refer to **Fig. 1.** when replacing engine mounts.

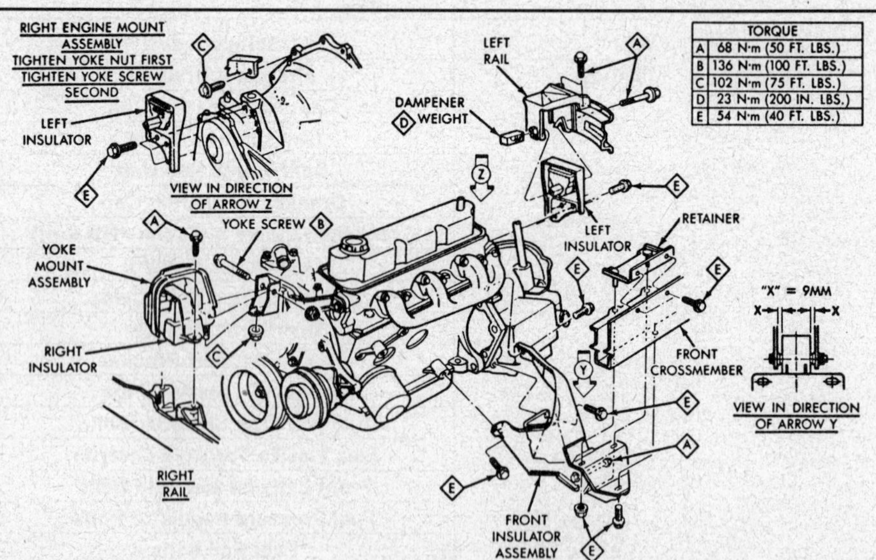


**Fig. 1 Engine mounts**

### ENGINE MOUNT INSULATOR, ADJUST

The left engine mount insulator **Fig. 2** is sleeved to provide lateral movement adjustment with engine weight removed or not.

1. Loosen the right engine mount vertical attaching bolt with the engine and transaxle supported with a suitable jack to relieve load on motor mounts.
2. Loosen the front engine mount bracket to front crossmember bolts.
3. Pry the engine right or left to attain proper driveshaft length.
4. **Torque** right engine mount insulator vertical bolts to 60 ft. lbs. and front engine mount bolts to 40 ft. lbs.

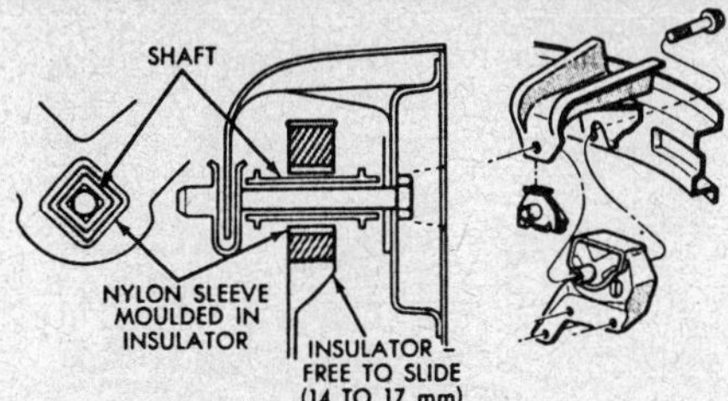


**Fig. 2 Left engine mount insulator**

5. Center the left engine mount insulator and recheck driveshaft length.

# ENGINE

## REPLACE

**Disable airbag as outlined under "Airbag System Disarming." After prodedure has been completed, rearm airbag system as outlined under "Airbag System Disarming."**

**Before servicing the fuel pump, fuel lines, fuel filter, throttle body or fuel injectors, the fuel system pressure must be released as outlined under "Fuel System Pressure Release."**

1. Disconnect battery ground cable.
2. Mark hood hinge locations and remove hood.
3. Drain cooling system, then disconnect all electrical connections.
4. Remove coolant hoses, radiator and fan assembly.
5. Relieve fuel pressure as follows:
   a. Loosen fuel tank filler cap.
   b. Disconnect injector wiring harness and connect a suitable jumper wire between ground terminal No. 1 and a suitable ground.
   c. Connect a second jumper wire between terminal No. 2 of injector harness and battery positive for no longer than five seconds.
   d. Remove jumper wires.
6. Disconnect fuel lines, then unhook the accelerator cable.
7. Remove air cleaner assembly, then raise and support vehicle.
8. Drain engine oil.
9. Remove air conditioning compressor mounting bolts and position compressor aside.
10. Disconnect exhaust pipe from manifold, then remove transaxle inspection cover and mark position of flex plate to torque converter.
11. Remove flex plate-to-torque converter attaching screws and clamp bottom of converter housing to prevent converter from moving.
12. Remove power steering attaching bolts and position pump aside.
13. Remove two lower transaxle to block screws, then the starter. Lower vehicle to ground.
14. Disconnect vacuum lines and ground strap.
15. Install suitable transmission holding fixture, then install engine lifting hoist and support engine.
16. Remove upper transaxle case to block bolts.

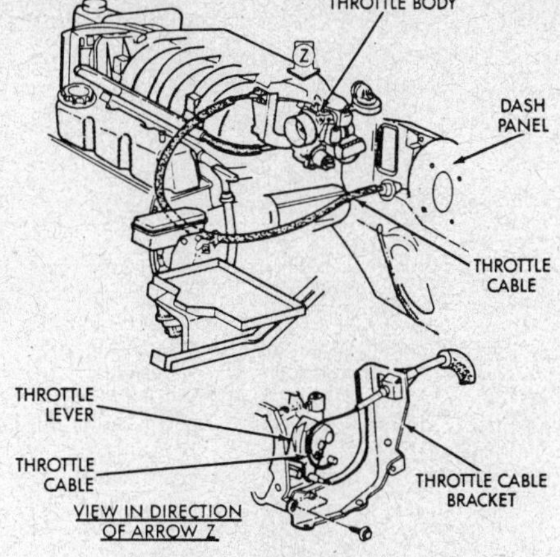


**Fig. 3 Throttle cable**

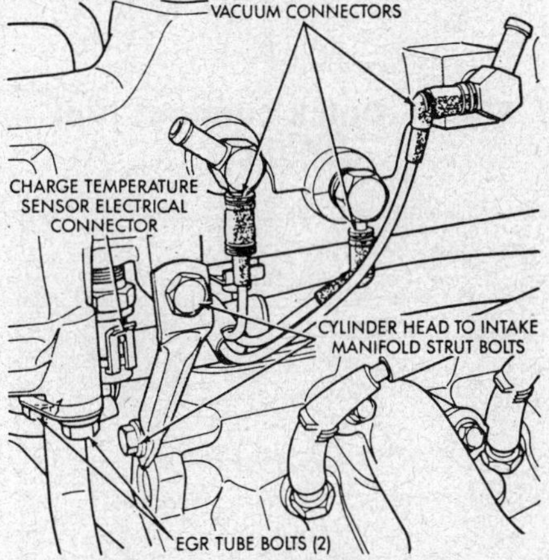


**Fig. 5 Air intake plenum electrical & vacuum connections**

17. Refer to **Fig. 1** and separate engine mount/insulators as follows:
    a. Mark position of right insulator on right rail supports, then remove insulator- to-rail screws.
    b. Remove front engine through bolt and nut.
    c. Remove left insulator through bolt from inside wheelwell or insulator bracket-to-transaxle screws.
18. Remove engine from vehicle.
19. Reverse procedure to install, noting the following:
    a. **Torque** transaxle-to-cylinder block bolts to 75 ft. lbs.
    b. **Torque** flex plate-to-torque converter bolts to 55 ft. lbs.

# INTAKE & EXHAUST MANIFOLDS

## REPLACE

**Before servicing the fuel pump, fuel lines, fuel filter, throttle body or fuel injectors, the fuel system pressure must be released as outlined under "Fuel System Pressure Release."**

## INTAKE MANIFOLD

### Removal

1. Disconnect battery ground cable.

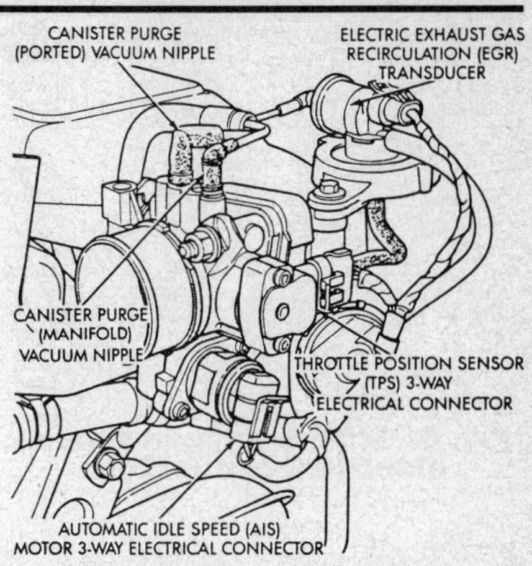


**Fig. 4 Throttle body electrical & vacuum connections**

2. Relieve fuel pressure as outlined under "Fuel System Pressure Release."
3. Drain cooling system, then remove air cleaner and throttle body hose assembly.
4. Disconnect throttle cable from throttle body, **Fig. 3,** then disconnect wiring harness from throttle cable bracket.
5. Disconnect automatic idle speed (AIS) motor and throttle position sensor (TPS) wiring connectors from throttle body, **Fig. 4.**
6. Disconnect vacuum harness from throttle body, **Fig. 4.**
7. Disconnect PCV and brake booster hoses from air intake plenum, **Fig. 5.**
8. Disconnect EGR tube flange from intake plenum, **Fig. 5.**
9. Disconnect charge temperature sensor (CTS) electrical connector, then the vacuum harness connectors from intake plenum, **Fig. 5.**
10. Remove cylinder head to intake plenum strut, **Fig. 5.**
11. Disconnect manifold absolute pressure (MAP) sensor and heated oxygen sensor electrical connectors, **Fig. 6.**
12. Remove engine mounted ground strap.
13. Disconnect fuel hose quick disconnect fittings from fuel rail by pushing in on plastic rings on ends of fittings, **Fig. 7.** Carefully pull fittings from fuel rail. **Wrap a shop towel around hoses to catch any fuel spillage,**
14. Remove direct ignition system (DIS) coil and alternator bracket to intake manifold bolt, **Fig. 8.**
15. Remove intake plenum bolts, **Fig. 9,** then rotate plenum back over rear valve cover.
16. Cover intake manifold with a suitable cover.
17. Disconnect vacuum harness connector from fuel pressure regulator.
18. Remove fuel tube retainer bracket screw and fuel rail attaching bolts, **Fig. 10.** Spread retainer bracket to provide fuel tube removal clearance.
19. Disconnect fuel rail injector wiring clip from alternator bracket.

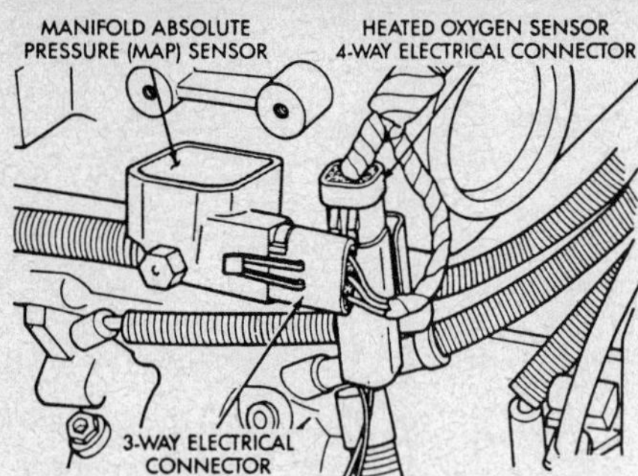


**Fig. 6 MAP & oxygen sensor electrical connectors**

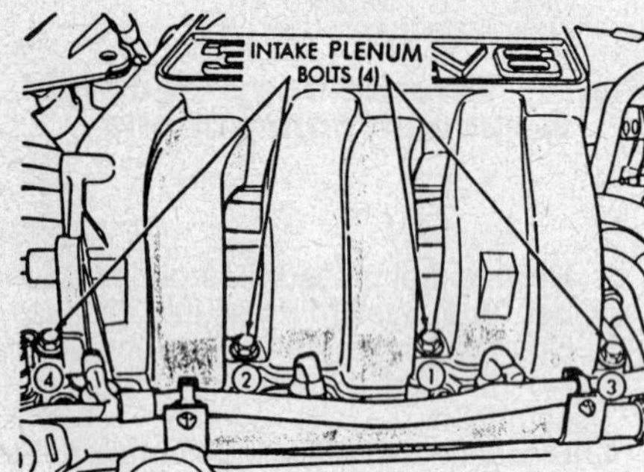


**Fig. 9 Intake plenum bolt removal & tightening sequence**

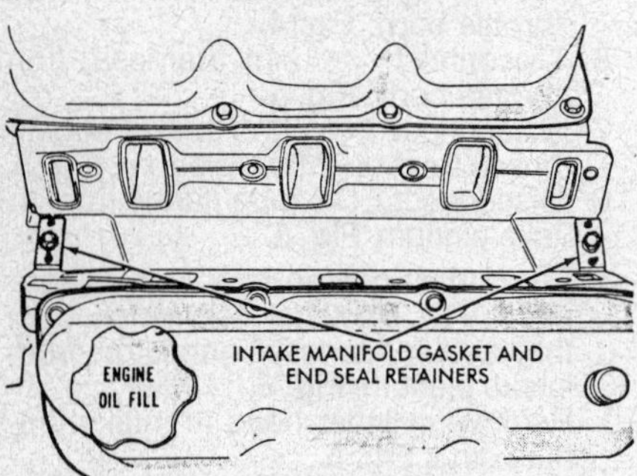


**Fig. 12 Intake manifold end seal retainers**

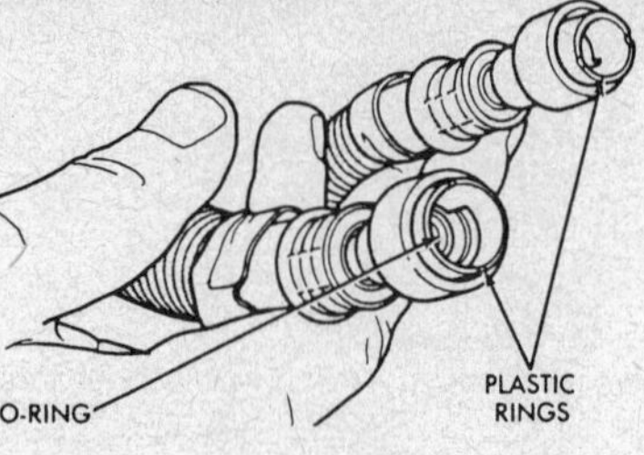


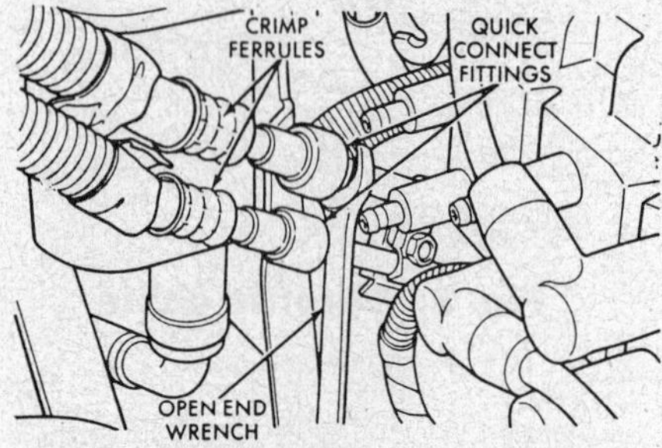


**Fig. 7 Quick connect fuel fittings**

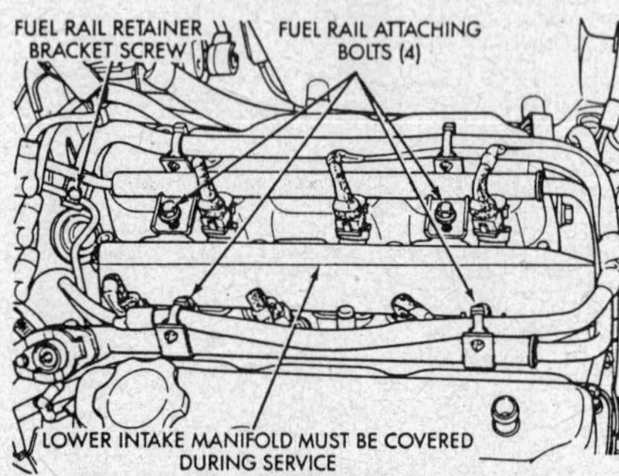


**Fig. 10 Fuel rail attaching bolts**

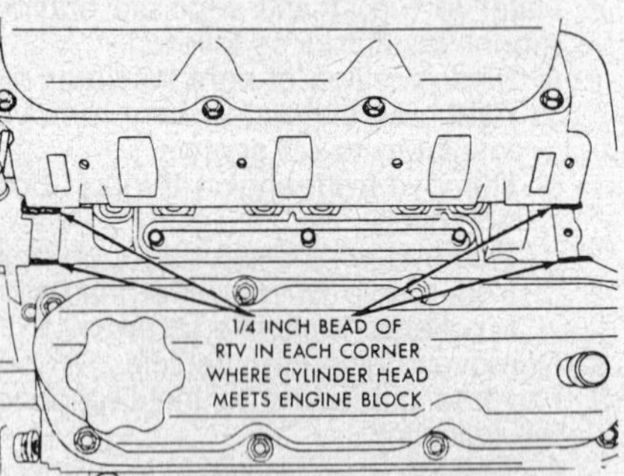


**Fig. 13 Applying sealant to intake manifold gasket**

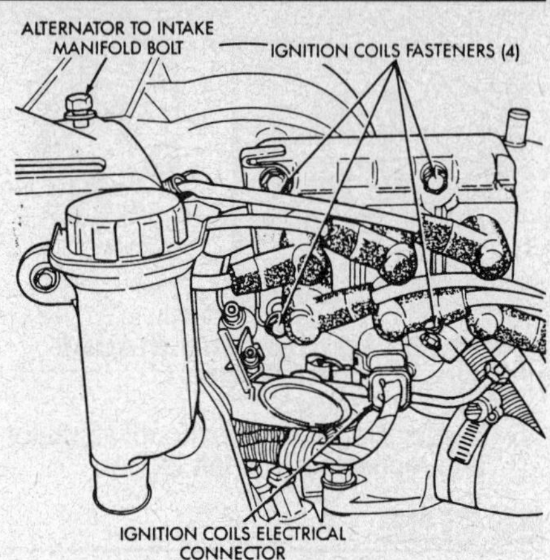


**Fig. 8 DIS ignition coil**

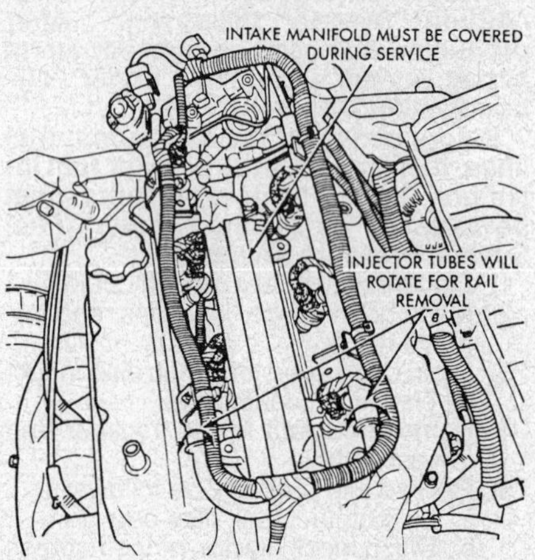


**Fig. 11 Removing fuel rail**

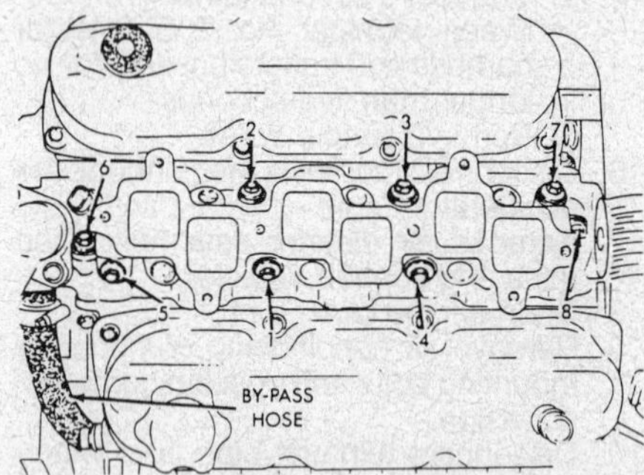


**Fig. 14 Intake manifold bolt tightening sequence**

20. Disconnect cam sensor, coolant temperature sensor and engine temperature sensor connectors.
21. Disconnect fuel injector wiring clip from intake manifold water tube.
22. Remove fuel rail. Use caution not to damage injector O-rings when removing from ports, **Fig. 11.**
23. Remove upper radiator hose, bypass hose and rear intake manifold hose.
24. Remove intake manifold bolts, then the intake manifold.
25. Remove intake manifold seal retainers, **Fig. 12,** then the intake manifold gasket.

### Installation

1. Clean all surfaces of cylinder block and cylinder heads.
2. Apply a drop approximately 1/4 inch in diameter of rubber sealer, part No. 4318025 or equivalent, on each of the four manifold to cylinder head gasket corners, **Fig. 13.**
3. Carefully install intake manifold gasket and end seal retainers, **Fig. 12.** Torque end seal retainer screws to specifications. **Intake manifold gasket is made of very thin metal and may cause personal injury, handle with care.**
4. Install intake manifold and retaining bolts and **torque** to 10 inch lbs. Retorque to specifications in sequence shown in **Fig. 14,** then torque again to specifications. **After intake manifold is in place, inspect to ensure seals are in place.**
5. Ensure injector holes are clean and all plugs are removed.
6. Lube injector O-rings with clean engine oil to ease installation.
7. Position the tip of each injector into ports. Push assembly into place until injectors are fully seated in ports, **Fig. 11.**
8. Install four fuel rail attaching bolts and torque to specifications.
9. Install fuel tube retaining bracket screw and torque to specifications, **Fig. 10.**
10. Connect cam sensor, coolant temperature sensor and engine temperature sensor connectors.
11. Install fuel injector harness wiring

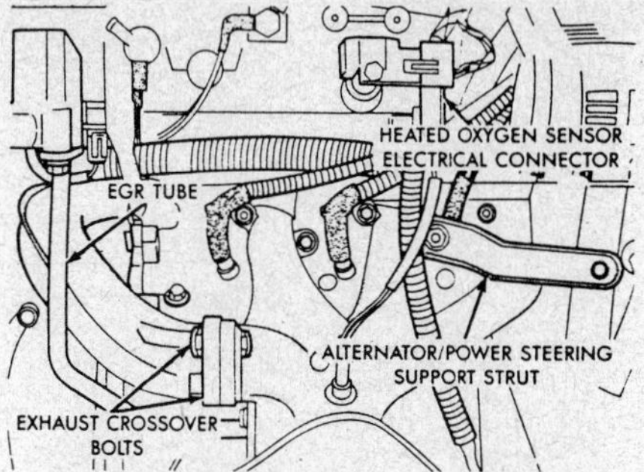


**Fig. 15 EGR tube, oxygen sensor connector & alternator/power steering strut**

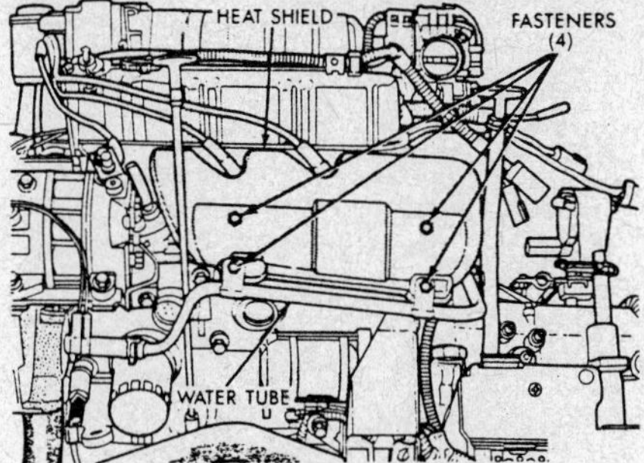


**Fig. 16 Front exhaust manifold heat shield**

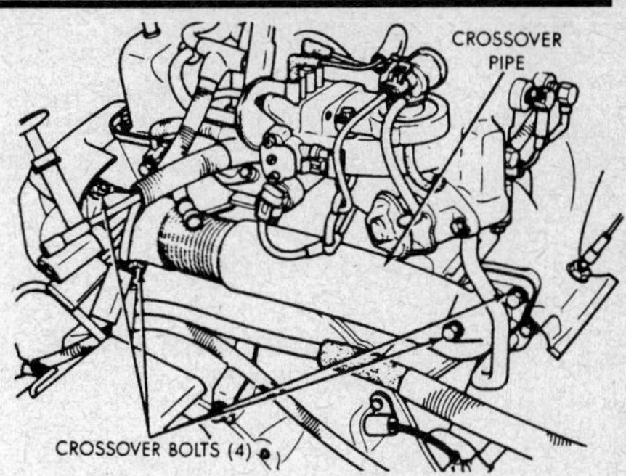


**Fig. 17 Crossover pipe & bolts**

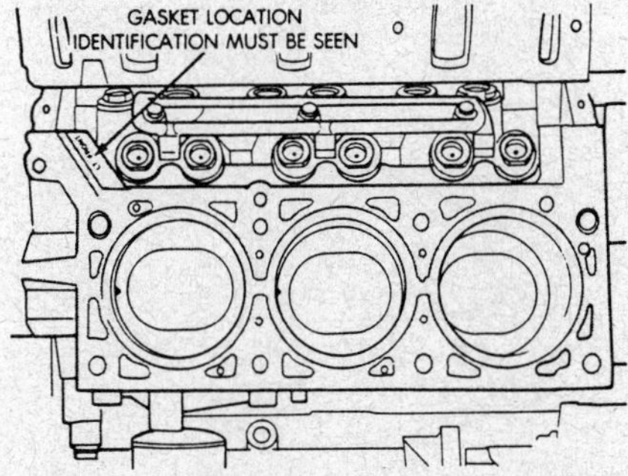


**Fig. 18 Installing head gasket**

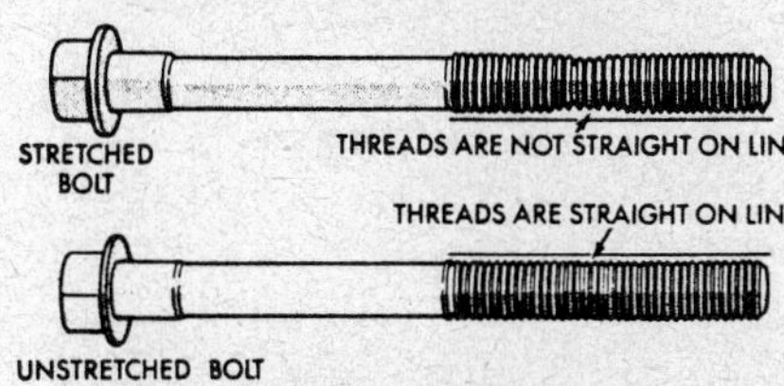


**Fig. 19 Checking cylinder head bolts**

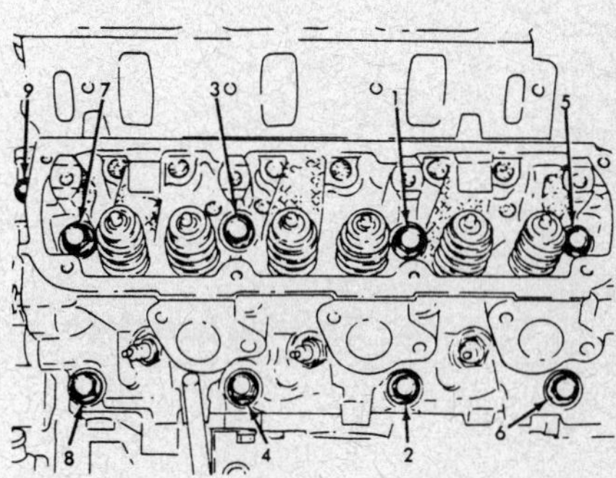


**Fig. 20 Cylinder head bolt tightening sequence**

clips on alternator bracket and intake manifold water tube.

12. Connect fuel pressure regulator vacuum line.
13. Remove covering from intake manifold and clean surface.
14. Install a new plenum gasket on intake manifold, position plenum on intake manifold and install bolts finger tight.
15. Install alternator bracket to intake manifold bolt, then the cylinder head to intake manifold strut bolts. **Do not torque.**
16. Torque plenum bolts to specifications in sequence shown in **Fig. 9.**
17. Torque alternator bracket to intake manifold bolt to specifications.
18. Torque cylinder head to intake manifold strut bolt to specifications.
19. Connect engine ground strap, MAP and heated oxygen sensor electrical connectors, **Fig. 6.**
20. Connect CTS electrical connector, then the vacuum harness to intake plenum, **Fig. 5.**
21. Using a new gasket, connect EGR tube flange to intake manifold and torque to specifications.
22. Attach wiring harness to hole in throttle cable bracket.
23. Connect AIS and TPS wiring connectors, **Fig. 4.**
24. Connect vacuum harness to throttle body, **Fig. 4.**
25. Install DIS coils. Torque fasteners to specifications, **Fig. 8.**
26. Install fuel hose quick connector fittings to fuel rail. Push fittings onto rail until they click into place. Fuel supply fitting is 5/16 inch and fuel return fitting is 1/4 inch, **Fig. 7.**
27. Install throttle cable, **Fig. 3.**
28. Install air cleaner and hose assembly, then connect battery ground cable and fill cooling system.

## EXHAUST MANIFOLD

### Removal

1. Disconnect battery ground cable.
2. Raise and support vehicle, then disconnect exhaust pipe from rear (cowl side) exhaust pipe at articulated joint.
3. Separate EGR tube from rear manifold, then disconnect heated oxygen sensor connector, **Fig. 15.**
4. Remove alternator/power steering support strut, **Fig. 15.**
5. Remove bolts attaching crossover pipe to exhaust manifold, **Fig. 15.**
6. Remove bolts attaching rear manifold to cylinder head, then the manifold.
7. Lower vehicle, then remove screws attaching heat shield to front manifold, **Fig. 16.**
8. Remove bolts attaching crossover pipe to front exhaust manifold, **Fig. 17,** then the nuts attaching manifold to cylinder head. Remove front exhaust manifold assembly.

### Installation

1. Install rear exhaust manifold and torque attaching bolts to specifications.
2. Connect exhaust pipe to rear exhaust manifold and **torque** shoulder bolt to specifications.
3. Connect crossover pipe to rear exhaust manifold and torque bolt to specifications, then connect oxygen sensor electrical connector, **Fig. 15.**
4. Install EGR tube and alternator/power steering strut, **Fig. 15.**
5. Install front exhaust manifold and connect exhaust crossover, **Fig. 17.**
6. Install front exhaust manifold heat shield and **torque** attaching screws to specifications.
7. Connect battery ground cable.

## CYLINDER HEADS REPLACE

**Before servicing the fuel pump, fuel lines, fuel filter, throttle body or fuel injectors, the fuel system pressure must be released as outlined under "Fuel System Pressure Release."**

### REMOVAL

1. Disconnect battery ground cable, then drain cooling system.
2. Remove intake manifold and throttle body. Refer to procedure outlined under 'Intake and Exhaust Manifolds, Replace."
3. Disconnect coil wires, sending unit wire, heater hoses and by-pass hose.
4. Remove closed ventilation system, evaporation control system and cylinder head covers.
5. Remove exhaust manifolds. Refer to procedure outlined under "Intake and Exhaust Manifolds, Replace."
6. Remove rocker arm and shaft assemblies. Remove pushrods noting position for installation in their original locations.
7. Remove nine bolts attaching each cylinder head, then the cylinder head assemblies.

### INSPECTION

Inspect all surfaces with a straightedge if there is any reason to suspect leakage. If out of flatness exceeds .00075 inch (.019

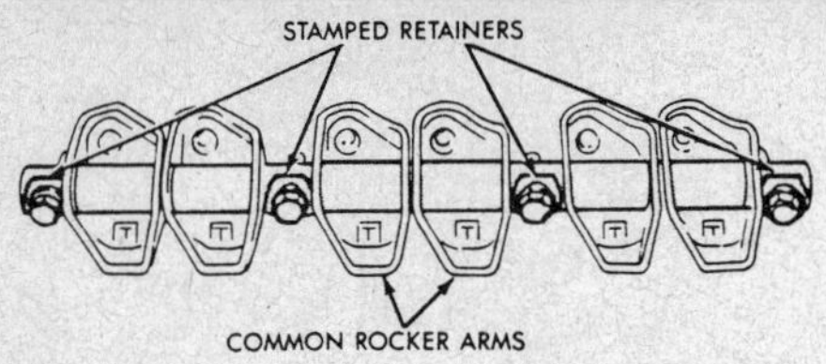


**Fig. 21 Rocker arm shaft retainers**

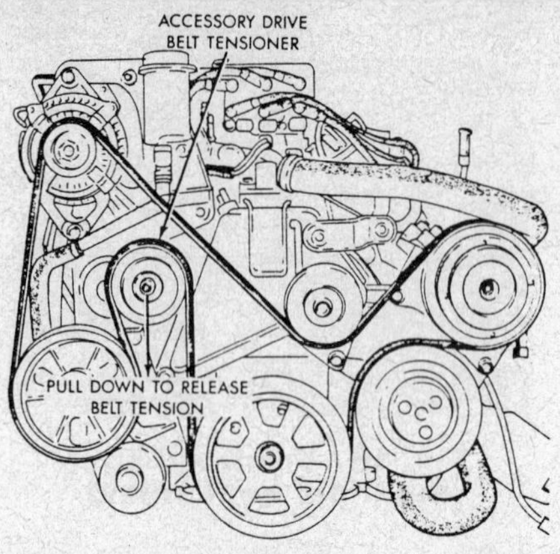


**Fig. 22 Accessory drive belt routing**

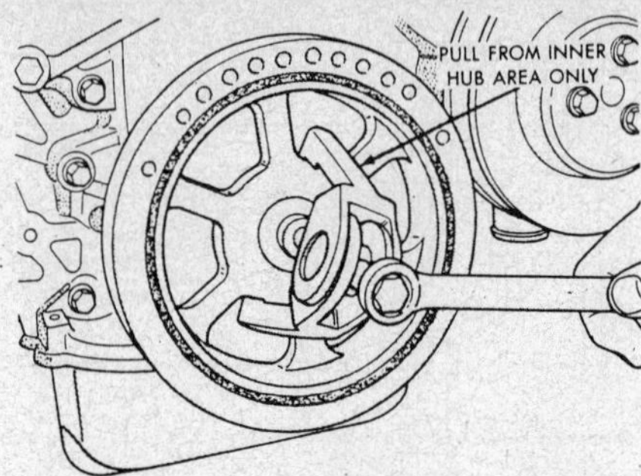


**Fig. 23 Removing crankshaft pulley**

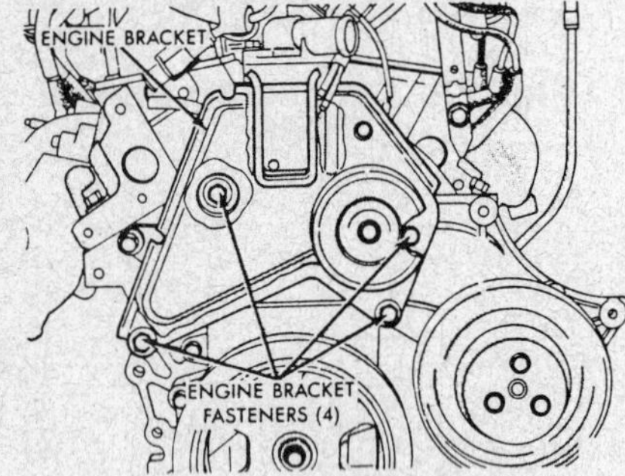


**Fig. 24 Engine bracket**

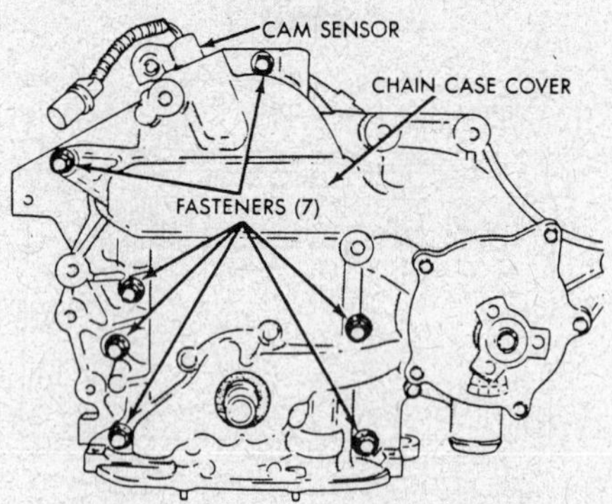


**Fig. 25 Timing case cover**

mm) times the span length in inches in any direction, replace the head.

As an example, if a 12 inch span is .004 inch (.019 mm) out of flat, allowable is 12 x .00075 inch (.019 mm) equals .009 inch (.22 mm). This amount of out of flat is acceptable.

## INSTALLATION

1. Clean all surfaces of cylinder heads and cylinder block.
2. Install new head gaskets on cylinder block, **Fig. 18.**
3. Install cylinder heads on cylinder block.
4. Examine cylinder head bolts for stretching as shown, **Fig. 19.** Replace any bolts that are stretched.
5. Torque cylinder head bolts in sequence shown in **Fig. 20,** as follows:
   a. **Torque** all bolts to 45 ft. lbs.
   b. **Torque** all bolts to 65 ft. lbs.
   c. **Torque** all bolts again to 65 ft. lbs.
   d. Turn each bolt an additional 1/4 turn, noting bolt torque. **If bolt torque is not over 90 ft. lbs. after tightening an additional 1/4 turn, bolt should be replaced.**
6. Install pushrods, rocker arm and shaft assemblies with stamped steel retainers positioned as shown, **Fig. 21.** Torque to specifications.
7. Install new cylinder head cover gaskets, then install cylinder head covers. Torque to specifications.
8. Reverse remaining removal procedure to complete installation.

# AUTO LASH ADJUSTER

Automatic lash adjusters are used, no adjustment is needed.

# VALVE LIFT SPECIFICATIONS

| Engine | Year | Lift |
|---|---|---|
| 3.3L/V6-202 | 1990-92 | .400 |
| 3.8L/V6-231 | 1991-92 | .400 |

# VALVE TIMING

1. Remove front valve cover and all six spark plugs.
2. Rotate engine until the No. 2 piston is at top dead center (TDC) of compression stroke.
3. Install a degree wheel on the crankshaft pulley.
4. Using proper adapter, install a dial into No. 2 spark plug hole. Using the indicator to find TDC on compression stroke.
5. Position degree wheel to zero.
6. Remove dial indicator from spark plug hole.
7. Place a .200 inch (5.08 mm) spacer between the valve stem tip of No. 2 intake valve and rocker arm pad. Allow tappet to bleed down to give a solid tappet effect.
8. Install a dial indicator so plunger contacts the No. 2 intake valve spring retainer as nearly perpendicular as possible. Zero the indicator.
9. Rotate the engine clockwise until intake valve ahs lifted .010 inch (.254 mm). **Do not turn crankshaft any further clockwise as intake valve may bottom and result in serious damage.**
10. Degree wheel should read 3° before top dead center (BTDC) to 4° after top dead center (ATDC).

# TIMING CHAIN COVER, OIL SEAL & CHAIN SERVICE

## TIMING CHAIN COVER REMOVAL

1. Disconnect battery ground cable.
2. Drain cooling system.
3. Support engine, then remove right engine mount.
4. Raise and support vehicle, then drain engine oil.
5. Remove oil pan and oil pump pick up. **It may be necessary to remove transaxle inspection cover.**
6. Remove accessory drive belt as follows:
   a. Remove right front wheel and tire assembly, then the inner splash shield.
   b. Release belt tension by rotating the tensioner clockwise, **Fig. 22,** then remove accessory drive belt.
7. Remove A/C compressor and position aside.
8. Remove A/C compressor mounting bracket.
9. Using a suitable puller, remove crankshaft pulley as shown, **Fig. 23. Pull from inner hub area only.**
10. Remove idler pulley from engine bracket, then the engine bracket, **Fig. 24.**
11. Remove cam sensor from chain case cover, then the chain case cover, **Fig. 25.**

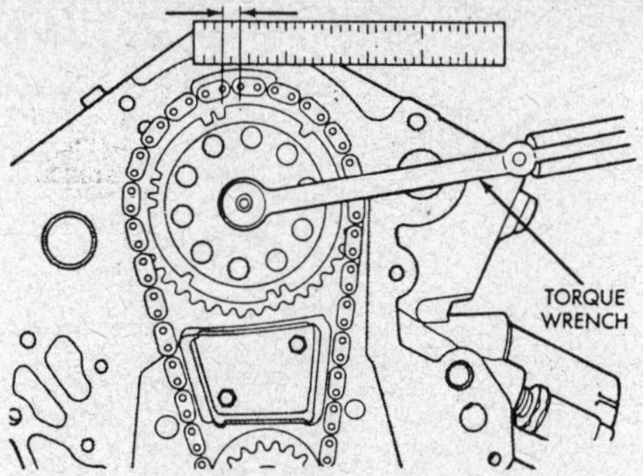

**Fig. 26 Measuring timing chain movement**

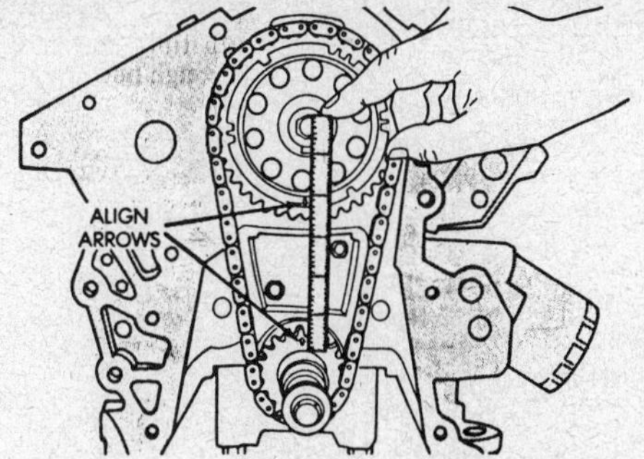

**Fig. 27 Aligning timing marks**

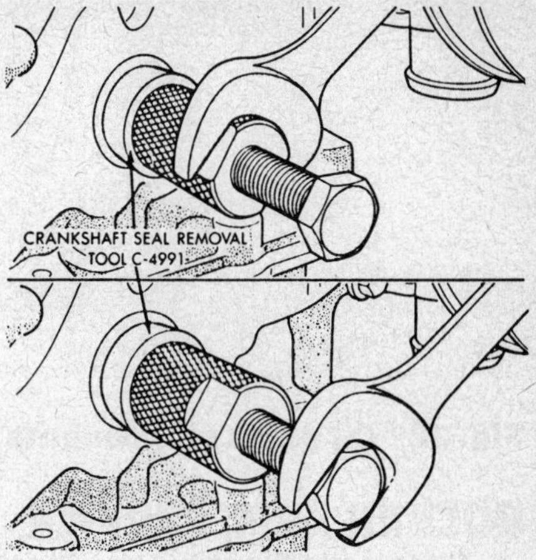

**Fig. 28 Removing crankshaft oil seal**

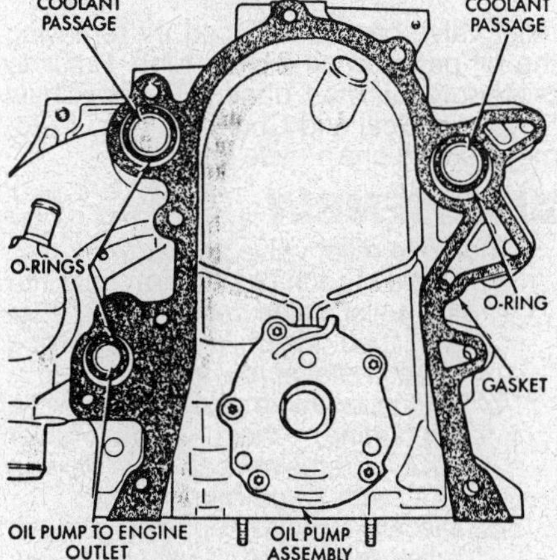

**Fig. 29 Timing case cover gasket & O-rings**

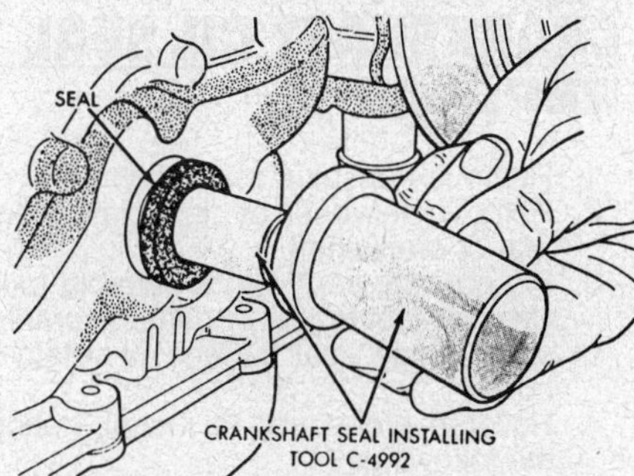

**Fig. 30 Installing crankcase oil seal**

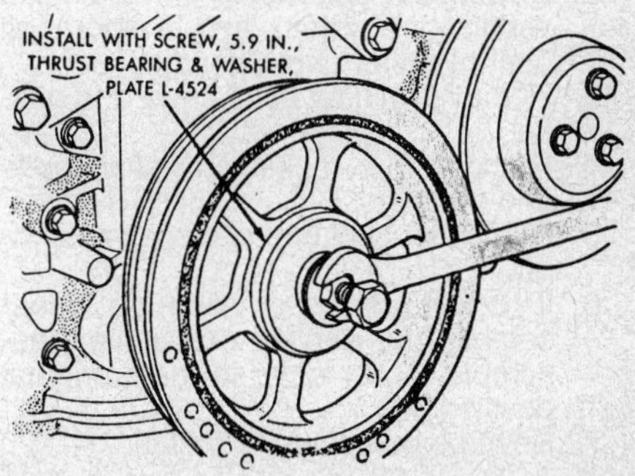

**Fig. 31 Installing crankshaft pulley**

## TIMING CHAIN INSPECTION

1. Place a scale next to timing chain so that chain movement can be measured.
2. Install a torque wrench and socket over camshaft sprocket, then apply torque in direction of crankshaft rotation to take up chain slack. Apply 30 ft. lbs of torque with cylinder heads installed or 15 ft. lbs of torque with cylinder heads removed. **With torque applied to camshaft sprocket bolt, crankshaft should not be allowed to move. It may be necessary to block crankshaft to prevent rotation.**
3. Holding a scale with dimension reading even with edge of a chain link, apply the specified torque in the reverse direction and note amount of chain movement, **Fig. 26.**
4. If timing chain movement exceeds 1/8 inch (3.175 mm), chain must be replaced.

## TIMING CHAIN, REPLACE

1. Remove camshaft sprocket attaching cup washer, then remove timing chain with crankshaft and camshaft sprockets.
2. Install new timing chain around both sprockets.
3. Turn crankshaft and camshaft to align keyway locations in both sprockets.
4. Lift sprocket and chain, keeping sprockets tight against chain in position described.
5. Slide both sprockets with chain evenly over their respective shafts, then use a straightedge to check alignment of timing marks, **Fig. 27.**
6. Install cup washer and camshaft sprocket bolt. Torque bolt to specifications.
7. Check camshaft endplay. Endplay should measure .002-.006 inch (.051-.0152 mm) with a new thrust plate or up to .010 inch (.254 mm) with a used thrust plate, on 1990 engines and .005-.012 inches on 1991-92 engines. If camshaft endplay is not as specified, replace thrust plate.
8. Install timing chain snubber.

## TIMING CHAIN COVER INSTALLATION & OIL SEAL REPLACEMENT

1. Ensure mating surfaces of chain case cover are clean and free of burrs. **Crankshaft oil seal must be removed to ensure correct oil pump engagement.**
2. Remove crankshaft oil seal using crankshaft removal tool No. C-4991 or equivalent, as shown in **Fig. 28. Use caution not to damage crankshaft seal surface of cover.**
3. Install a new cover gasket and new O-rings, **Fig. 29.**
4. Rotate crankshaft so that oil pump drive flats are vertical.
5. Position oil pump inner rotor so that mating flats are in the same position as crankshaft drive flats, **Fig. 29.**
6. Install cover onto crankshaft. **Ensure oil pump is correctly engaged on crankshaft or severe damage may result.**
7. Install chain case cover screws and torque to specifications.
8. Install crankshaft oil seal as follows:
   a. Position seal into opening with seal spring towards inside of engine.
   b. Install seal until flush with cover using seal crankshaft seal installing tool No. C-4992 or equivalent, **Fig. 30.**
9. Install crankshaft pulley using thrust bearing/washer plate tool No. L-4524 or equivalent and a 5.9 inch screw, **Fig. 31.** Torque crankshaft pulley bolt to specifications.
10. Install engine bracket, **Fig. 24** and **torque** attaching screws to 40 ft. lbs.
11. Install idler pulley on engine bracket.
12. Install cam sensor.
13. Install A/C compressor mounting bracket, then the A/C compressor.
14. Install accessory drive belt, **Fig. 22.**
15. Install right front inner splash shield, then the wheel and tire assembly.
16. Install oil pump pickup, oil pan and transaxle inspection cover, if removed.
17. Install engine mount.
18. Fill crankcase with oil to proper level.
19. Fill cooling system.
20. Connect battery ground cable.

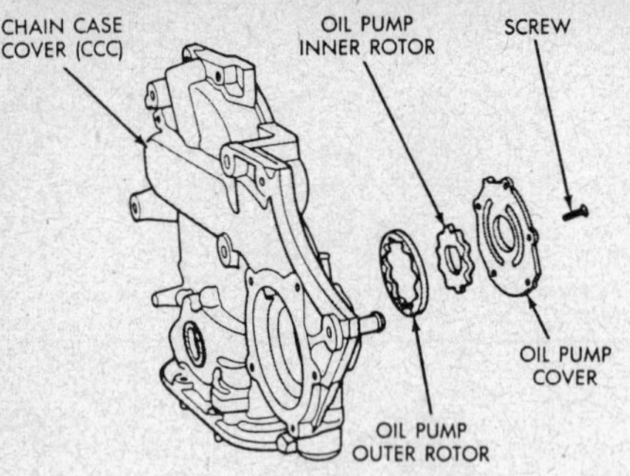


**Fig. 32 Oil pump components**

RELIEF VALVE
SPRING
RETAINER CAP

**Fig. 33 Oil pressure relief valve components**

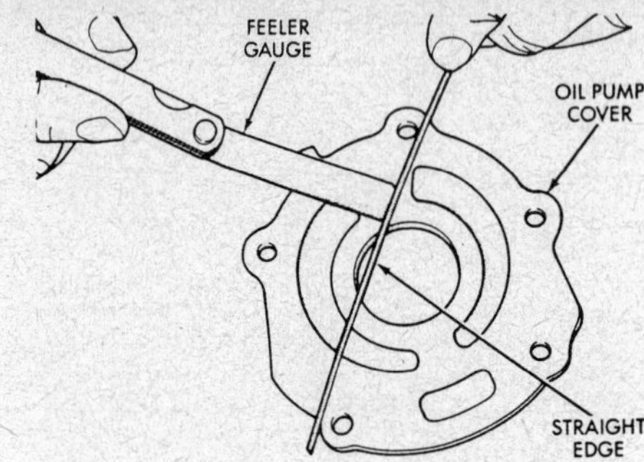


**Fig. 34 Measuring oil pump cover flatness**

# ROCKER ARM, SERVICE

1. Remove intake manifold as outlined under "Intake & Exhaust Manifolds, Replace."
2. Disconnect spark plug wires, closed ventilation system and evaporation control system from head cover.
3. Remove cylinder head cover and gasket.
4. Remove four rocker arm shaft bolts and retainers.
5. Remove rocker arm and shaft assembly.
6. If rocker arm assemblies are disassembled for service or cleaning, assemble rocker arms in there original position.
7. Reverse procedure to install.

# VALVE SPRING REPLACE

1. Remove cylinder heads as outlined under "Cylinder Head, Replace."
2. Remove rocker arm shafts and camshafts as outlined under "Rocker Arm, Service."
3. Using a suitable valve spring compressor tool, compress valve spring and remove spring retainer locks, retainer, valve spring, spring seat and valve stem seal.
4. Reverse procedure to install.

# CAMSHAFT REPLACE

**Before servicing the fuel pump, fuel lines, fuel filter, throttle body or fuel injectors, the fuel system pressure must be released as outlined under "Fuel System Pressure Release."**

1. Remove intake manifold, cylinder head covers, cylinder heads, timing chain cover and timing chain as previously outlined.
2. Remove rocker arm and shaft assemblies, pushrods and tappets. Identify each component so component will be replaced in its original location.
3. Remove camshaft thrust plate.
4. Install a long bolt into front of camshaft to aid in camshaft removal.
5. Remove the camshaft, using care not to damage cam bearing.
6. Reverse procedure to install, torquing all attaching bolts to specifications.

# CRANKSHAFT OIL SEAL REPLACE

1. Remove transaxle assembly.
2. Remove flywheel or flex plate from rear of crankshaft.
3. Pry out rear seal with a suitable tool. Use care not to nick or damage crankshaft flange seal surface or retainer bore.
4. Reverse procedure to install, noting the following:
   a. Use seal pilot tool C-4681 when installing seal.
   b. Lightly coat seal outside dimension with Loctite Stud N' Bearing Mount or equivalent.

**SERVICE BULLETIN:** Some 1990 3.3L/V6-202 engines may exhibit an oil leak at the rear of the engine. This leak may be misdiagnosed as a rear crankshaft seal or oil pan leak. This leak may be the result of one or more of the four untapped holes in the rear crankshaft flange being drilled too deep.

If the oil leak is from this condition, the following procedure involves installing four cap plugs in the crankshaft flange. Obtain four cap plugs part No. T3075032 and Stud N' Bearing Mount part No. 4318032, and proceed as follows:

1. Remove transaxle as outlined under "Transaxle Replace" in the "Clutch & Manual transaxle" section for manual transaxles or "Automatic Transaxle" section for automatic transaxles.
2. Remove flywheel or flex plate from rear of crankshaft.
3. Thoroughly clean and dry the four untapped holes in the crankshaft flange.
4. Lightly coat the outside diameter of one cap plug with Stud N' Bearing Mount.
5. Using a 5/16 inch diameter blunt nose punch, drive the cup plug into one of the holes until the end of the plug is slightly below the surface of the flange.
6. Repeat steps 4 and 5 for the three remaining holes.
7. Install the flywheel or flex plate then install the transaxle.

# OIL PUMP SERVICE

It is necessary to remove the oil pan, oil pickup and chain case cover (CCC) to service oil pump rotors, **Fig. 32.** The oil pump relief valve can be serviced by removing the oil pan and oil pickup tube. Refer to procedure outlined under "Timing Chain Cover, Oil Seal and Chain Service" to remove timing chain case cover.

## DISASSEMBLY

1. Remove relief valve as follows:
   a. Drill a 1/8 inch (3.175 mm) hole into the relief valve retainer cap, **Fig. 33,** then insert a self-threading sheet metal screw into cap.
   b. Clamp screw in a vise, then while supporting chain case cover (CCC), remove cap by tapping CCC with a soft hammer.
   c. Discard retainer cap, then remove relief spring and relief valve, **Fig. 33.**
2. Remove oil pump cover screws, then lift off cover, **Fig. 32.**
3. Remove pump rotors, **Fig. 32.**
4. Wash all parts in a suitable solvent and inspect for damage or wear.

## INSPECTION & REPAIR

1. Clean all parts thoroughly. Mating surfaces of CCC should be smooth. Replace pump cover if scratched or grooved.
2. Lay a straightedge across pump cover surface, **Fig. 34.** If a .003 inch (.076 mm) feeler gauge can be inserted between cover and straightedge, cover should be replaced.
3. Measure thickness and diameter of outer rotor, **Fig. 35.** If outer rotor thickness measures .3005 inch (7.36 mm) or less, or if the diameter is 3.141 inches (79.78 mm) or less, replace outer rotor.
4. If inner rotor thickness, **Fig. 36,** measures .301 inch (7.64 mm) or less, replace inner rotor and shaft assembly.
5. Install outer rotor into CCC, press one side with fingers and measure clearance between outer rotor and CCC, **Fig. 37.** If measurement is .022 inch (56 mm) or more, replace CCC only if outer rotor is within specifications.
6. Install inner rotor into CCC, then measure clearance between inner and outer rotors, **Fig. 38.** If clearance measured between rotors is .008 inch (.203 mm) or more, replace both rotors.
7. Place a straightedge across face of CCC between bolt holes, **Fig. 39.** If a

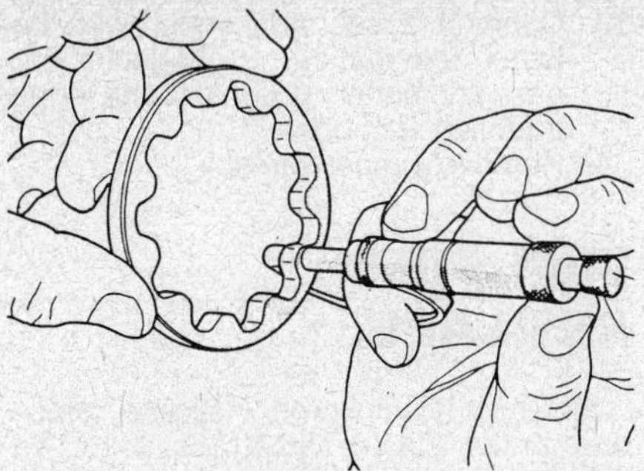

Fig. 35 Measuring outer rotor thickness

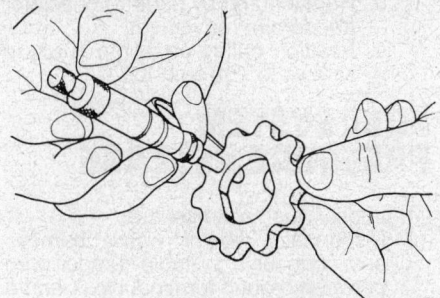

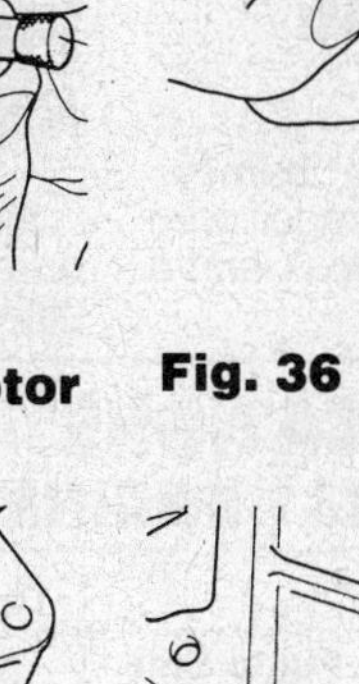

Fig. 36 Measuring inner rotor thickness

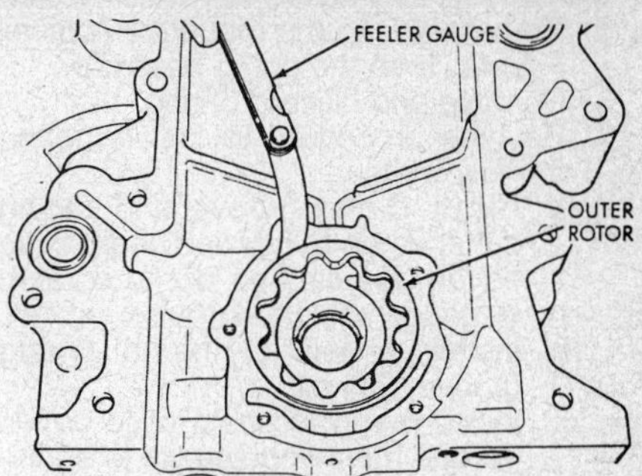


Fig. 37 Measuring outer rotor clearance in case

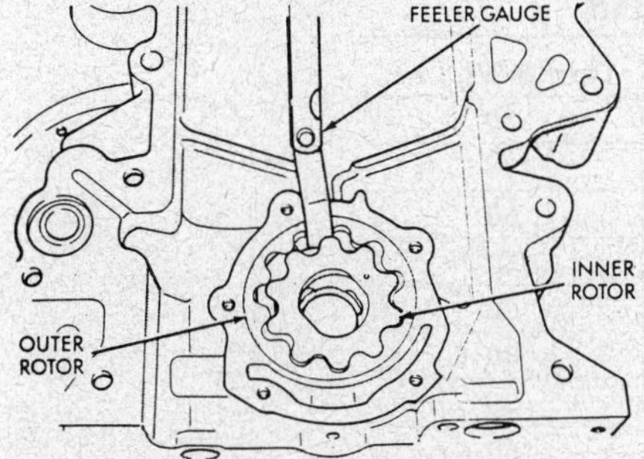


Fig. 38 Measuring clearance between rotors

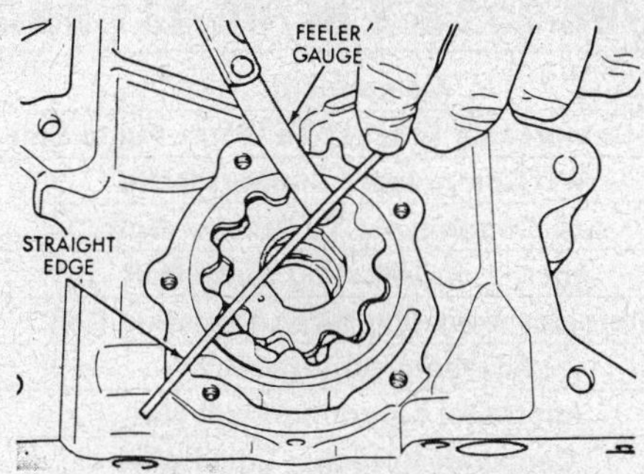


Fig. 39 Measuring clearance between rotors & case

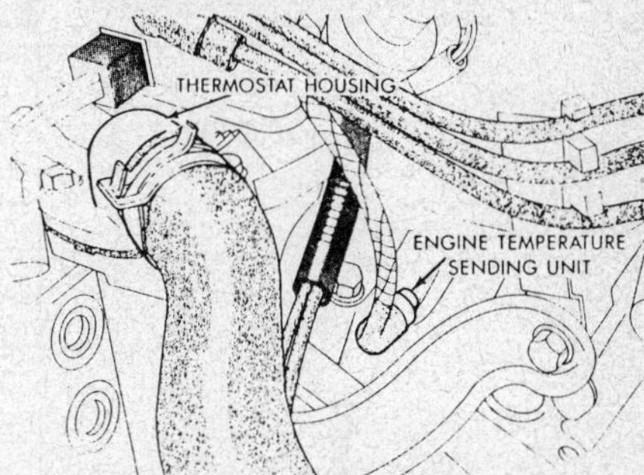


Fig. 40 Coolant temperature sensor location

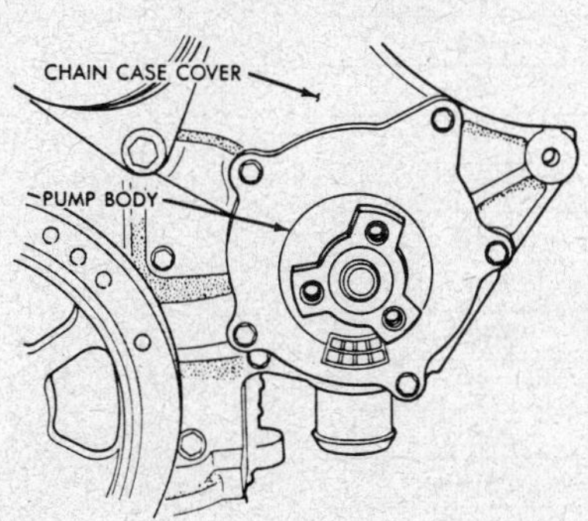


Fig. 41 Water pump installed view

feeler gauge of .004 inch (.102 mm) or more can be inserted between rotors and straightedge, replace pump assembly.

8. Inspect oil pressure relief valve plunger for scoring and free operation in it's bore. Small marks can be removed with 400-grit wet or dry sand paper.
9. Relief valve spring has a free length of approximately 1.95 inch (49.5 mm) and should test between 19.5-20.5 pounds when compressed to 1 1/32 inch (34 mm). Replace spring that does not meet specifications.

## ASSEMBLY & INSTALLATION

1. Assemble oil pump as shown, **Figs. 32 and 33,** using new parts as required.
2. Torque oil pump cover screws to specifications.
3. Prime oil pump prior to installation by filling rotor cavity with engine oil.
4. Refer to procedure outlined under "Timing Chain Cover, Oil Seal and Chain Service" to install timing chain case cover.

# SERPENTINE DRIVE BELT

## DRIVE BELT ROUTING

Refer to **Fig. 22** for serpentine drive belt routing.

## BELT REPLACEMENT

1. Raise vehicle on hoist.
2. Remove right front splash shield.
3. Release tension by rotating tensioner clockwise, **Fig. 22.**
4. Reverse procedure to install.

# COOLING SYSTEM BLEED

The cooling system on the 3.3L/V6-202 and 3.8L/V6-231 engines requires venting by removing the coolant temperature sensor on top of the thermostat housing, **Fig. 40.**

Fill the system with the recommended 50 percent mixture of antifreeze and water until mixture reaches the vent holes, then tighten coolant temperature sensor to specifications. Continue to fill cooling system until full.

# THERMOSTAT

## REPLACE

1. Drain coolant system down to thermostat level.

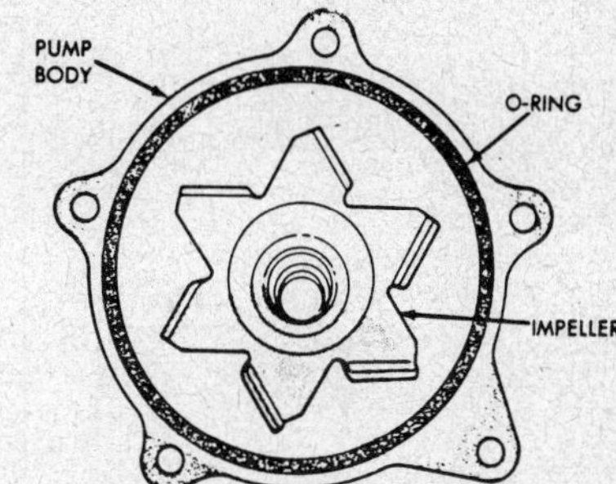


Fig. 42 Water pump body

2. Remove thermostat housing bolts and housing.
3. Remove thermostat, discard gasket and clean both gasket sealing surfaces.
4. Reverse procedure to install. Dip new gasket in water and ensure to center thermostat in recess.

# WATER PUMP

## REPLACE

1. Disconnect battery ground cable.
2. Remove accessory drive belt as follows:
   a. Remove right front wheel and tire assembly, then the inner splash shield.
   b. Release belt tension by rotating the tensioner clockwise, **Fig. 22,** then remove accessory drive belt.
3. Drain cooling system.
4. Remove three pump pulley bolts, then the pulley.

5. Remove five pump mounting screws, **Fig. 41,** then the pump assembly.
6. Remove and discard O-ring.
7. Reverse procedure to install, noting the following:
   a. Clean O-ring groove and O-ring surfaces on pump and chain case cover. Use caution not to scratch or gouge sealing surfaces.
   b. Install a new O-ring in O-ring groove, **Fig. 42.**
   c. Install pump to chain case cover. Torque mounting screws to specifications.
   d. Rotate pump by hand to check for freedom of movement.
   e. Position pulley on pump. **Torque** screws to 250 inch lbs.

## FUEL SYSTEM PRESSURE RELEASE

1. Loosen fuel tank filler cap.
2. Disconnect injector wiring harness and connect a suitable jumper wire between ground terminal No. 1 and a suitable ground.
3. Connect a second jumper wire between terminal No. 2 of injector harness and battery positive for no longer than five seconds.
4. Remove jumper wires.

## FUEL PUMP REPLACE

Refer to "Fuel Pump, Replace" procedure in the 2.2L/4-135 & 2.5L/4-153 engine chapter.

## TIGHTENING SPECIFICATIONS
### 3.3L/V6-202 & 3.8L/V6-231 ENGINE

| Year | Component | Torque/Ft. Lbs. |
|---|---|---|
| 1990–92 | A/C Compressor Bracket To Water Pump Bolt | 30 |
| | A/C Compressor Support Bolts | 30 |
| | A/C Compressor To Bracket Bolt | 50 |
| | Alternator Adjusting Strap Bolt | 200① |
| | Alternator Adjusting Strap Mounting Bolt | 30 |
| | Alternator Bracket Bolt | 30 |
| | Alternator Mounting Pivot Nut | 30 |
| | Camshaft Sprocket Lockbolt | 40 |
| | Camshaft Thrust Plate | 105① |
| | Chain Case Cover Bolt | ② |
| | Connecting Rod Nut | 40③ |
| | Crankshaft Bolt (Vibration Damper) | 40 |
| | Crankshaft Pulley Screw To Crankshaft | 40 |
| | Cylinder Head Bolt | ④ |
| | Cylinder Head Cover Bolts | 105① |
| | Cylinder Head To Intake Manifold Bolts | 40 |
| | DIS Coil Fasteners | 105① |
| | EGR Tube Flange | 200① |
| | Exhaust Crossover Pipe Flange Nut/Bolt | 25 |
| | Exhaust Manifold Screw | 200① |
| | Exhaust Pipe Shoulder Bolts | 250① |
| | Front Exhaust Manifold Heat Shield Screws | 200① |
| | Fuel Rail Bolts | 200① |
| | Fuel Rail Tube Bracket Bolts | 35 |
| | Intake Manifold Plenum Bolt | 250① |
| | Intake Manifold Bolt | 200① ④ |
| | Intake Manifold Gasket Retaining Screw | 105① |
| | Main Bearing Cap Bolt | 30③ |
| | Oil Filter Attaching Stud | 30 |
| | Oil Level Sensor Plug | 20 |
| | Oil Pan Drain Plug | 20 |
| | Oil Pan Screw | 105① |
| | Oil Pressure Gauge Sending Unit | 60① |
| | Oil Pump Cover Bolt T-30 | 105① |
| | Oil Pump Pick-Up Tube Screw | 250① |
| | Rocker Shaft Bracket Bolt | 250① |
| | Spark Plug | 30 |
| | Starter Mounting Bolt | 50 |
| | Tappet Retainer Yoke Screw | 105① |
| | Temperature Gauge Sending Unit | 60① |
| | Timing Chain Snubber Screw | 105① |
| | Water Pump To Chain Case Cover Bolt | 105① |

*Continued*

## TIGHTENING SPECIFICATIONS—Continued

①—Inch lbs.
②—M8 bolts, 20 ft. lbs.; M10 bolts, 40 ft. lbs.
③—Turn an additional 1/4 turn after reaching specified torque.
④—Refer to text.

# Clutch & Manual Transaxle

## INDEX



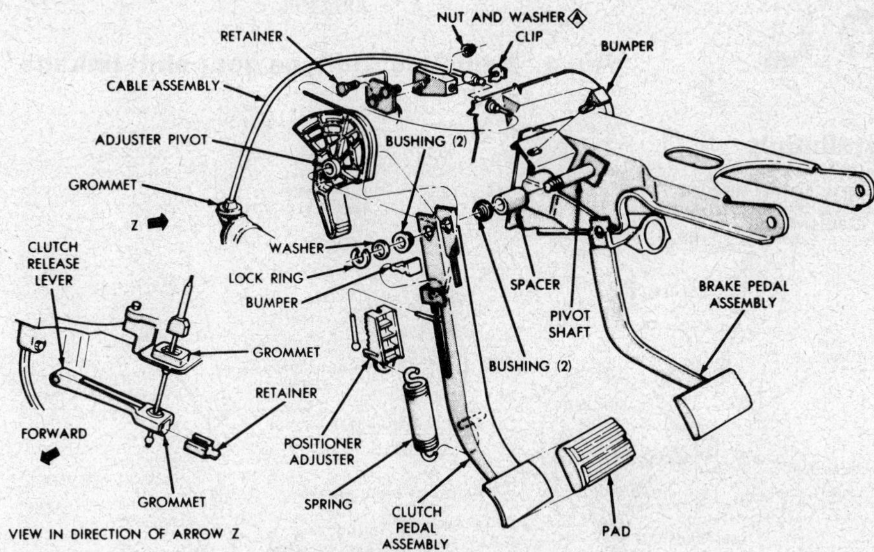


**Fig. 1 Clutch cable routing**

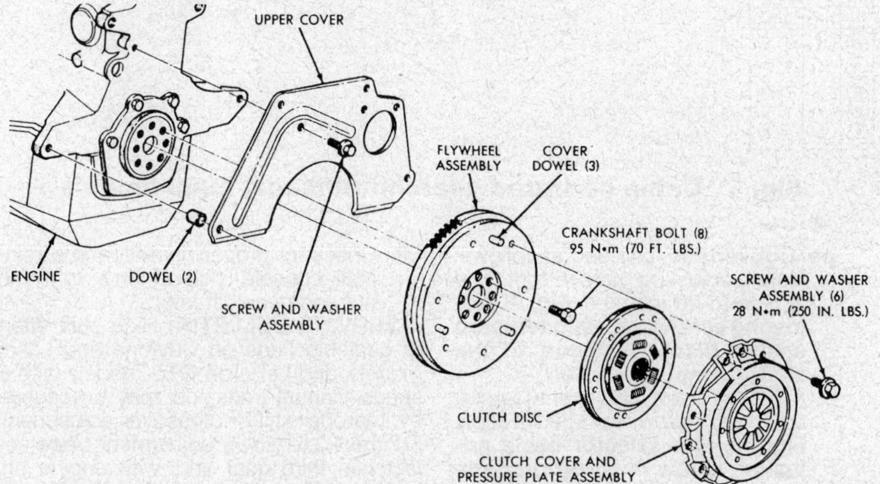


**Fig. 2 Clutch assembly**

## CLUTCH
## ADJUST

The clutch release cable, **Fig. 1,** cannot be adjusted. When the cable is properly routed, the spring between clutch pedal and positioner adjuster will hold clutch cable in proper position. An adjuster pivot is used to hold release cable in place to ensure complete clutch release when clutch pedal is depressed.

## CLUTCH
## REPLACE

1. Remove transaxle as outlined under "Manual Transaxle, Replace" procedure.
2. Mark relationship between clutch cover and flywheel for reference during reassembly, then insert suitable clutch disc aligning tool through clutch disc hub.
3. Gradually loosen clutch cover attaching bolts, then remove pressure plate and cover assembly and disc from flywheel.
4. Remove clutch release shaft and slide release bearing assembly off input shaft seal retainer. Remove fork from release bearing thrust plate.
5. Reverse procedure to install. Align reference marks made during disassembly, then using a clutch disc alignment tool, install disc, plate and cover to flywheel. Refer to **Fig. 2** for torque specifications.

## GEARSHIFT LINKAGE
## ADJUST

### ROD LINKAGE

1. Remove lockpin from transaxle selector shaft housing, **Fig. 3.**
2. Reverse lockpin so long end is facing downward, and insert pin into same threaded hole while pushing selector shaft into selector housing.
3. Raise and support vehicle then loosen clamp bolt that secures gearshift tube to gearshift rod.
4. Check that gearshift connector slides and rotates freely in gearshift tube.
5. Position shifter mechanism connector assembly so that isolator is contacting upstanding flange, while rib on isolator is aligned fore and aft with hole in blocker bracket. Hold connector isolator in this position and torque clamp bolt on gearshift tube to specification. No significant force should be placed on linkage during this procedure, **Fig. 4.**

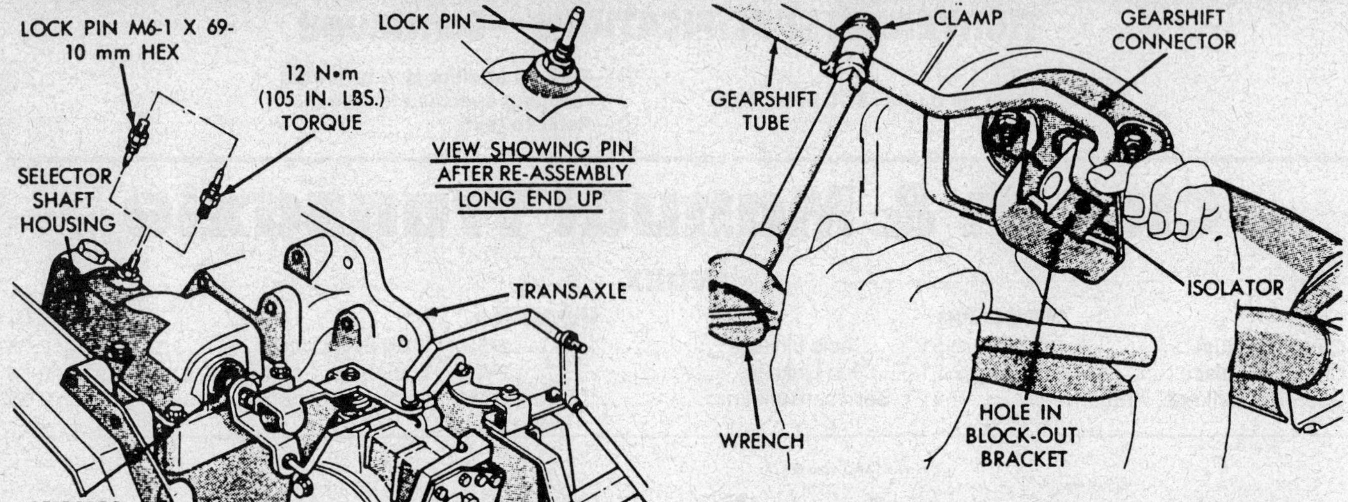


**Fig. 3 Lockpin removal & installation**

**Fig. 4 Adjusting rod-type gear shift linkage**

6. Lower vehicle, remove lockpin from selector shaft housing and reinstall lockpin in reversed position. Torque pin to specification.
7. Check for proper operation.

## CABLE LINKAGE

### 1989

1. Remove lockpin from transaxle selector shaft housing, **Figs. 3 and 5.**
2. Reverse lockpin so long end is down, and insert lockpin into same threaded hole while pushing selector shaft in 1-2 neutral position.
3. Remove gearshift knob, retaining nut and pull-up ring.
4. **On all models except Daytona and Laser,** remove console attaching screws and console.
5. **On Daytona and Laser models,** remove console as follows:
   a. Remove front seat assemblies.
   b. Remove two forward console bezel attaching screws and bezel.
   c. Remove carpet retaining clips from console.
   d. Remove console attaching bolts and screws.
   e. Disconnect electrical connectors from console, then remove console from vehicle.
6. **On LeBaron GTS, Lancer, Aries, Reliant, Shadow and Sundance models,** proceed as follows:
   a. Fabricate two cable adjusting pins as shown in **Fig. 6.**
   b. Adjust selector cable and torque adjusting screw to specification, **Fig. 7. The selector cable adjusting screw must be properly torqued.**
   c. Adjust crossover cable and torque adjusting screw to specification, **Fig. 8. The crossover cable adjusting screw must be properly torqued.**
7. **On Daytona & LeBaron Coupe/Convertible,** proceed as follows:
   a. Install adjusting screw tool and tighten to 20 inch lbs. **Fig. 9. Adjusting screw tool, with tethered spacer block, is taped to the shifter support bracket.**
   b. Adjust selector cable and torque adjusting screw to specification, **Fig. 10. The selector cable adjusting screw must be properly torqued.**
   c. Adjust crossover cable and torque adjusting screw to specification, **Fig. 11. The crossover cable adjusting screw must be properly torqued.**
8. **On all models,** remove lockpin from selector shaft housing and reinstall lockpin so long end is up in selector shaft housing, **Fig. 3.**

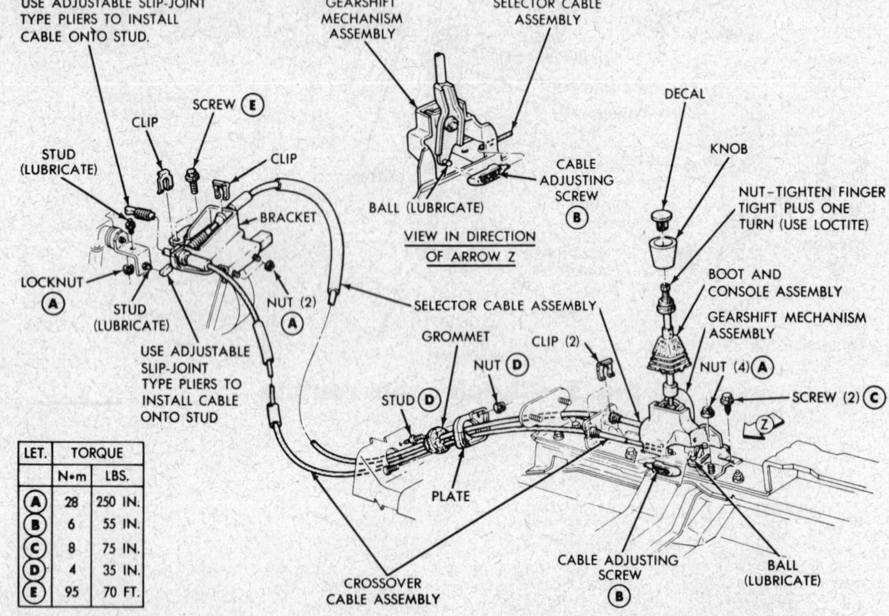


| LET. | TORQUE | |
|---|---|---|
| | N•m | LBS. |
| A | 28 | 250 IN. |
| B | 6 | 55 IN. |
| C | 8 | 75 IN. |
| D | 4 | 35 IN. |
| E | 95 | 70 FT. |

**Fig. 5 Cable operated gearshift linkage. 1989 models**

9. Check for proper operation and reinstall console, pull-up ring, retaining nut and gearshift knob.

**SERVICE BULLETIN:** High shift effort or gear blockage on Daytona and Laser models, and LeBaron GTS models with 5 speed manual transaxle, may be caused by improper shifter crossover adjustment. To check crossover adjustment place selector in third gear and, with engine off, make rapid shifts between second and third gears while applying moderate (approximately 20 lbs.) preload toward reverse/neutral position. Place selector in second gear and make slow shifts between first and second gears while applying minimal crossover preload toward reverse/neutral position. Obstruction or total blockage of a gear during above tests, after initial synchronizer line-up, indicates an

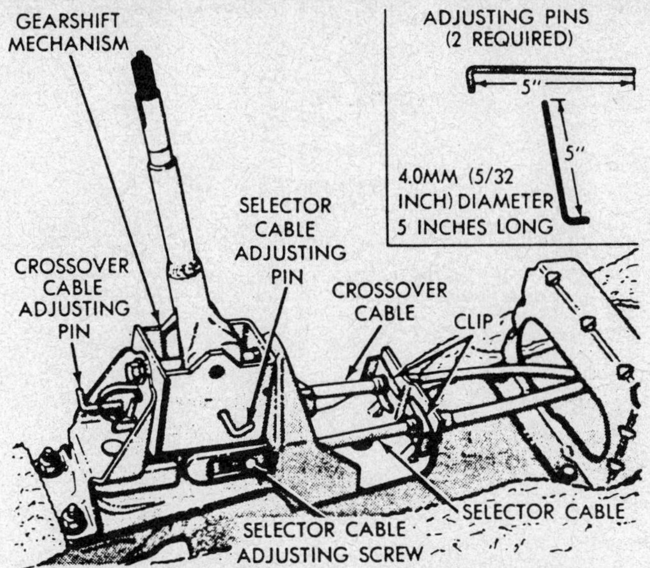


**Fig. 6 Cable adjusting pins. 1989 Except Daytona & LeBaron Coupe/Convertible**

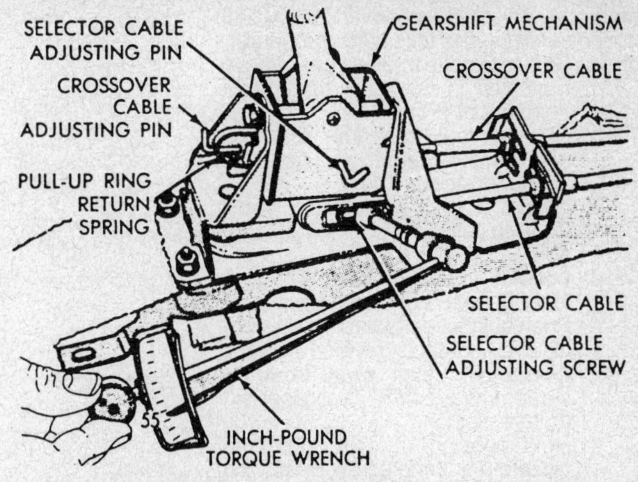


**Fig. 7 Adjusting selector cable. 1989 Except Daytona & LeBaron Coupe/Convertible**

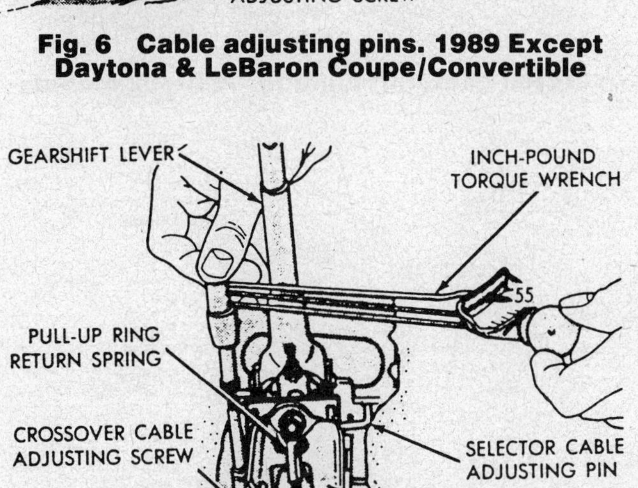


**Fig. 8 Adjusting crossover cable. 1989 Except Daytona & LeBaron Coupe/Convertible**

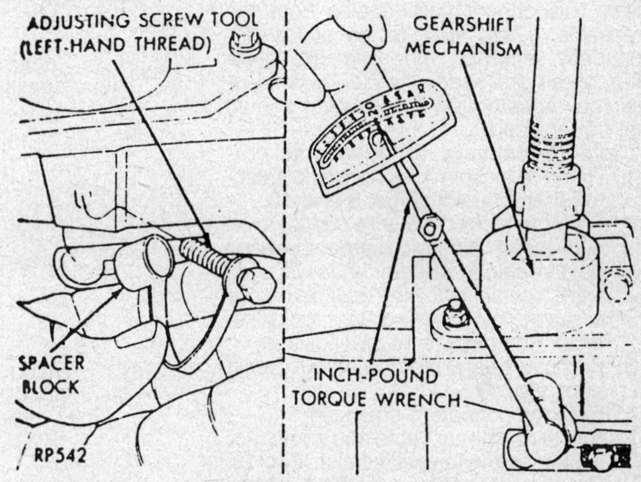


**Fig. 9 Cable adjusting screw tool. 1989 Daytona & LeBaron Coupe/Convertible**

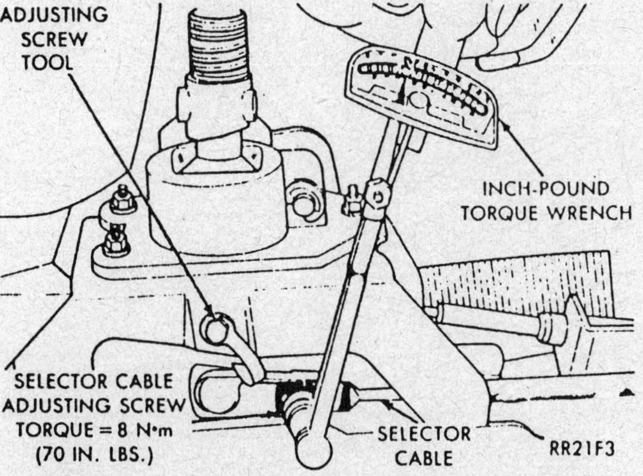


**Fig. 10 Adjusting selector cable. 1989 Daytona & LeBaron Coupe/Convertible**

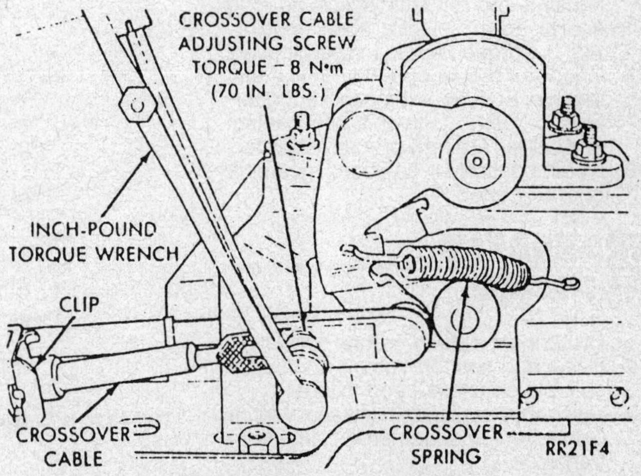


**Fig. 11 Adjusting crossover cable. 1989 Daytona & LeBaron Coupe/Convertible**

improperly adjusted crossover gate. Adjust crossover using the following procedure:

a. Shift transaxle into first gear. Leave transaxle in first gear throughout adjustment procedure.
b. Slide driver's seat fully rearward and remove carpet pad from left side of floor console.
c. Locate crossover adjusting screw through left side opening of console.
d. Loosen adjusting screw until shift lever is free in crossover direction.
e. Push shift lever toward reverse until lever contacts reverse lockout, then move lever away from reverse toward fifth gear approximately 1/8 inch.
f. Hold position of shift lever and **torque** adjusting screw to 55 inch lbs.
g. Replace carpet, then recheck operation of shifter.

### 1990–92

Before replacing the gearshift selector or crossover cable for a hard shifting condition, disconnect both cables from the transaxle. Then, from inside of vehicle, manually operate the gearshift lever through all gear ranges. If the gearshift lever moves smoothly, the cable(s) should not be replaced.

**Selector cable is not adjustable.**

1. Remove lockpin from transaxle selector shaft housing, **Figs. 3 and 12.**
2. Reverse lockpin so long end is down and insert pin into same threaded hole. A hole in selector shaft will align with lockpin, allowing lockpin to be screwed into housing. This locks selector shaft in 3-4 neutral position.
3. Remove gearshift knob and gearshift boot, **Fig. 12.**
4. Remove console, if equipped.
5. Adjust crossover cable and torque adjusting screw to specification, **Fig. 13. Crossover cable adjusting screw must be properly torqued. Ensure crossover bellcrank does not move when tightening adjusting screw.**
6. Remove lockpin from selector shaft housing and reinstall lockpin so long end is up in selector shaft housing, **Fig. 3.** Torque lockpin to specification.
7. Check for proper operation in first and reverse. Ensure reverse lockout operates properly. Gearshift mechanism and cables are now properly adjusted.
8. Install console, if equipped, gearshift boot and knob.

## TRANSAXLE

## REPLACE

1. Disconnect battery ground cable.
2. Raise and support vehicle and install suitable engine support fixture.
3. Disconnect gearshift linkage, clutch cable and speedometer cable from transaxle.
4. Remove front wheel and tire assemblies.
5. Remove left front splash shield, then

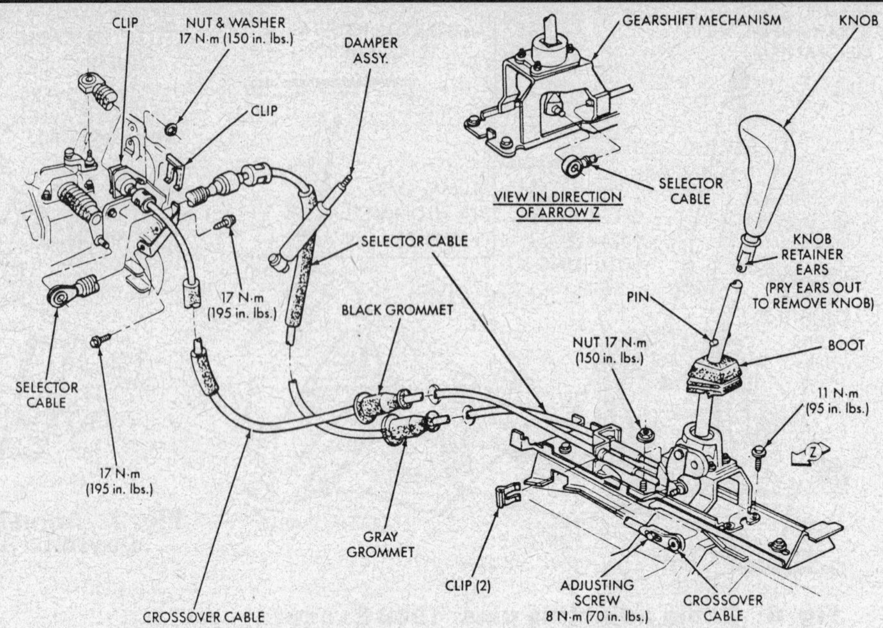


**Fig. 12 Cable operated gearshift linkage. 1990–92 models**

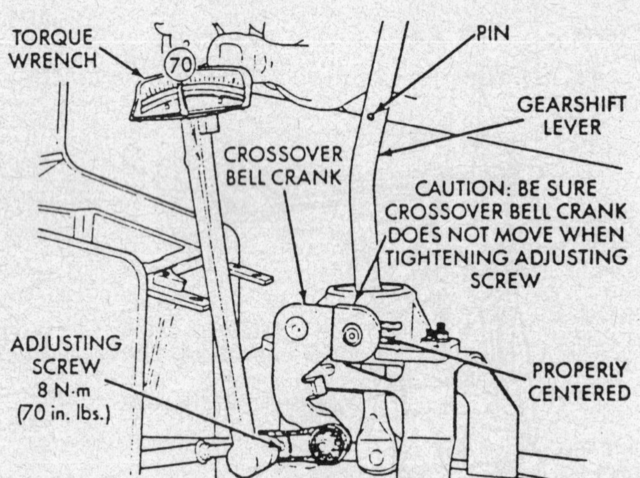


**Fig. 13 Adjusting crossover cable. 1990–92 models**

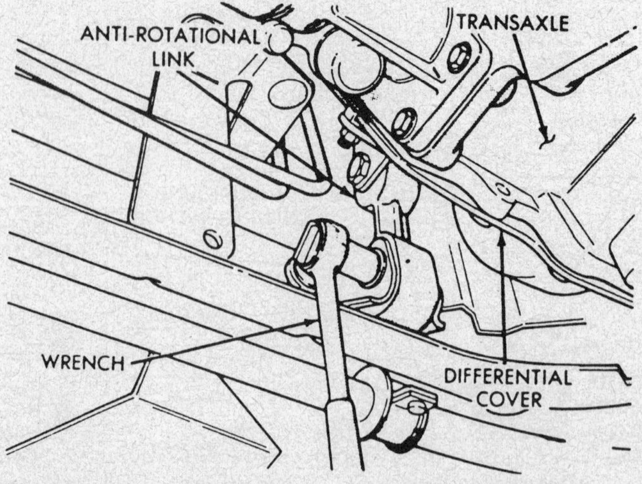


**Fig. 14 Removing anti-rotational link**

the impact bracket from transaxle if so equipped.
6. Refer to "Driveshafts, Replace" to disconnect driveshafts.
7. Support transaxle and remove upper clutch housing bolts.
8. Remove left engine mount from transaxle noting location of bolts.
9. Remove anti-rotational link, **Fig. 14. Do not remove bracket from transaxle.**
10. Remove transaxle-to-engine attaching bolts.
11. Move engine and transaxle toward left side of vehicle until mainshaft clears clutch and lower and remove transaxle.
12. Reverse procedure to install. When installing left engine mount, refer to "Engine Mount, Replace" section.

## SERVICE BULLETINS

### SLIPPING CLUTCH

**On 1989 Dodge Daytona, Chrysler LeBaron Coupe and Convertible models built between 11-16-08 through 11-28-17,** flywheel attaching bolts may not have had the necessary sealing adhesive applied to their threads.

This may result in engine oil leaking past bolt threads, then onto clutch. then slipping. If this condition is suspect, proceed as follows:

1. Remove transaxle as outlined in "Manual Transaxle, Replace."
2. Inspect heads of eight flywheel to crankshaft attaching bolts.
3. Correct flywheel bolts heads are orange. If so, reinstall clutch and transmission assembly.
4. If bolts heads are not orange, replace bolts with proper bolts Part No. 6501197, then **torque,** bolts to 70 ft. lbs.
5. If clutch facings are contaminated with oil, replace clutch.
6. Ensure inside of clutch housing, flywheel and pressure plate are free of oil residue.
7. Reinstall clutch and transaxle assembly.

## TIGHTENING SPECIFICATIONS

| Year | Component | Torque/Ft. Lbs. |
|---|---|---|
| 1989–92 | Anti-Rotational Strut Bracket To Stud Nut | 17 |
| | Back-Up Lamp Switch | 20 |
| | Case To Engine Block Bolt | 70 |
| | Crossover Cable Adjusting Screw | 70① |
| | Flywheel To Crankshaft Bolt | 70 |
| | Gearshift Housing To Case Bolt | 21 |
| | Gearshift Tube Clamp Bolt | 170① |
| | Mount To Block And Case Bolt | 70 |
| | Pressure Plate To Flywheel Bolt | 21 |
| | Selector Cable Adjusting Screw | 70① |
| | Selector Shaft Lockpin | 105① |
| | Shift Linkage Adjusting Pin | 9 |
| | Strut To Block Bolt | 70 |
| | Strut To Case Bolt | 70 |

①—Inch lbs.

# Rear Axle & Suspension

## INDEX



## REAR AXLE

## REPLACE

### EXCEPT HORIZON & OMNI

1. Raise and support vehicle, support rear axle, and remove rear wheels.
2. Disconnect parking brake cable at connector and cable housing at floor pan bracket, **Fig. 1.**
3. Disconnect brake tube assembly from brake line on trailing arm support bracket, and remove lock.
4. **On models equipped with automatic load leveling system,** disconnect link from sensor to track bar.
5. **On all models,** disconnect shock absorbers and track bar at rear axle. Support track bar end.
6. Lower axle until spring and isolator assemblies, **Fig. 2,** come free and can be removed.
7. Support pivot ends of trailing arms and remove pivot bracket bolts. Lower and remove axle from vehicle.
8. Reverse procedure to install. Torque brake tube assembly to hose fitting and other components to specifications.

### HORIZON & OMNI

1. Raise and support vehicle.
2. Remove wheels.
3. Remove brake fitting and retaining clips securing flexible brake line.
4. Remove parking brake cable adjusting connection nut, **Fig. 3.**
5. Release parking brake cables from bracket by slipping ball-end of cables

through brake connectors.

6. Pull parking brake cable through bracket.
7. Remove brake drums.
8. Remove brake assembly and spindle retaining bolts, **Fig. 4.**
9. Position spindle aside using a piece of wire.
10. **Support axle and suspension with a suitable jack.**
11. Remove shock absorber mounting bolts.
12. Remove trailing arm to hanger bracket mounting bolt.
13. Lower rear axle from vehicle.
14. Reverse procedure to install. Bleed brake system.

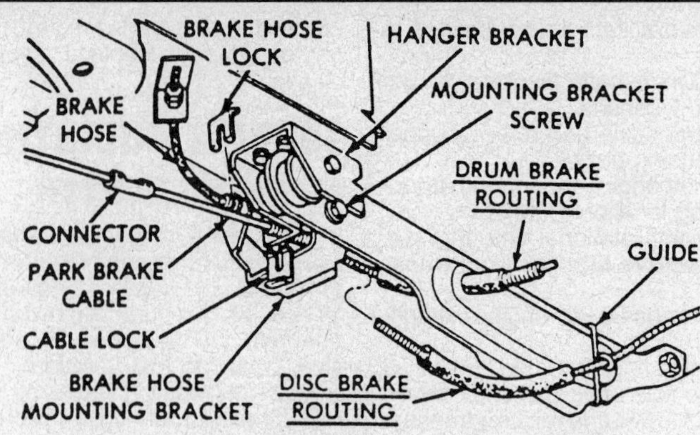


**Fig. 1 Parking brake cable & brake tube assemblies. Except Horizon & Omni**

# SHOCK ABSORBER & COIL SPRING

## REPLACE

## EXCEPT HORIZON & OMNI

### Removal

1. Raise and support vehicle.
2. Support axle assembly and remove wheel and tire assemblies.
3. **On models with air shocks,** disconnect air lines. On all models, remove both upper and lower shock absorber attaching bolts, then the shock absorbers.
4. **On models equipped with automatic load leveling system,** remove link from track bar to sensor.
5. **On all models,** lower axle assembly until spring and spring upper isolator can be removed, **Fig. 2.**

### Installation

1. Position jounce bumper to rail, install and **torque** attaching screws to 70 inch lbs.
2. Install isolator over jounce bumper and install spring.
3. Raise axle and install shock absorbers. Loosely assemble lower shock absorber attaching bolts and torque upper attaching bolts to specifications. On models with load leveling system, attach link to track bar.
4. With suspension supporting vehicle, torque shock absorber lower attaching screws to specifications.

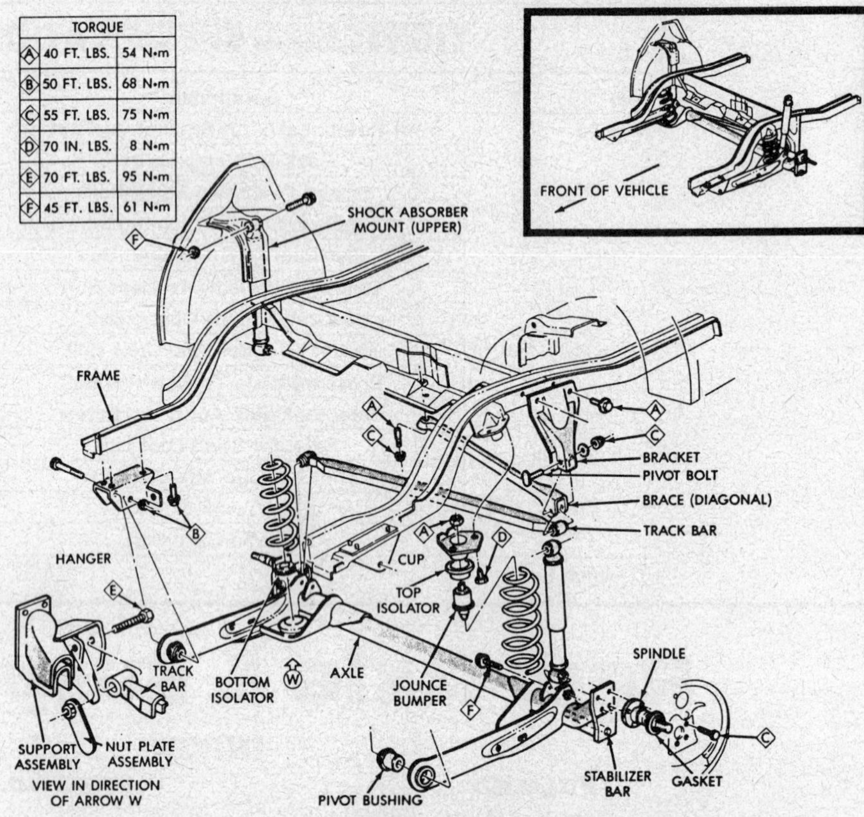

| TORQUE | | |
|---|---|---|
| A | 40 FT. LBS. | 54 N•m |
| B | 50 FT. LBS. | 68 N•m |
| C | 55 FT. LBS. | 75 N•m |
| D | 70 IN. LBS. | 8 N•m |
| E | 70 FT. LBS. | 95 N•m |
| F | 45 FT. LBS. | 61 N•m |



**Fig. 2 Rear axle & suspension assembly. Models except Horizon & Omni**

## HORIZON & OMNI

### Replacement

1. Remove upper shock absorber mounting protective cap, located inside vehicle at upper rear wheelwell area. On two door models, remove lower rear quarter trim panel for access.
2. Remove upper shock absorber mounting nut, isolator retainer and upper isolator, **Fig. 4.**
3. Raise and support vehicle.
4. Remove shock absorber lower mounting bolt.
5. Remove shock absorber and coil spring assembly from vehicle.
6. Reverse procedure to install.

### Service

1. Install coil spring retractor tool No. L-4838 or equivalent, on coil spring and support in a vise, **Fig. 5.** Grip four or five coils of the spring in the retractors. Also, do not extend retractors more than 9¼ inches.
2. Tighten retractors evenly until spring pressure is released from upper spring seat.
3. Hold flat end of pushrod and loosen retaining nut. **Ensure that spring is properly compressed before loosening retaining nut since personal injury may result.**
4. Remove lower isolator, pushrod sleeve and upper spring seat.
5. Remove shock absorber from coil spring.
6. Remove jounce bumper and dust shield from pushrod, **Fig. 6.**
7. Remove lower spring seat. **Fig. 6.**
8. Reverse procedure to assemble.

# REAR WHEEL BEARING

## ADJUST

1. **Torque** adjusting nut to 270 inch lbs. while rotating wheel.
2. Stop wheel and loosen adjusting nut, **Fig. 7.**
3. Tighten adjusting nut finger tight. End-play should be .001-.003 inch.
4. Install castle lock with slots aligned with cotter pin hole.
5. Install cotter pin and grease cap.

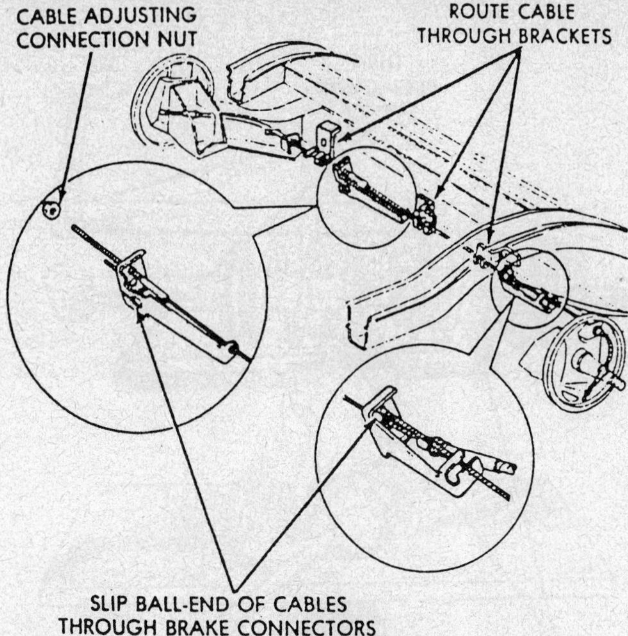


**Fig. 3 Parking brake cable assemblies. Horizon & Omni**

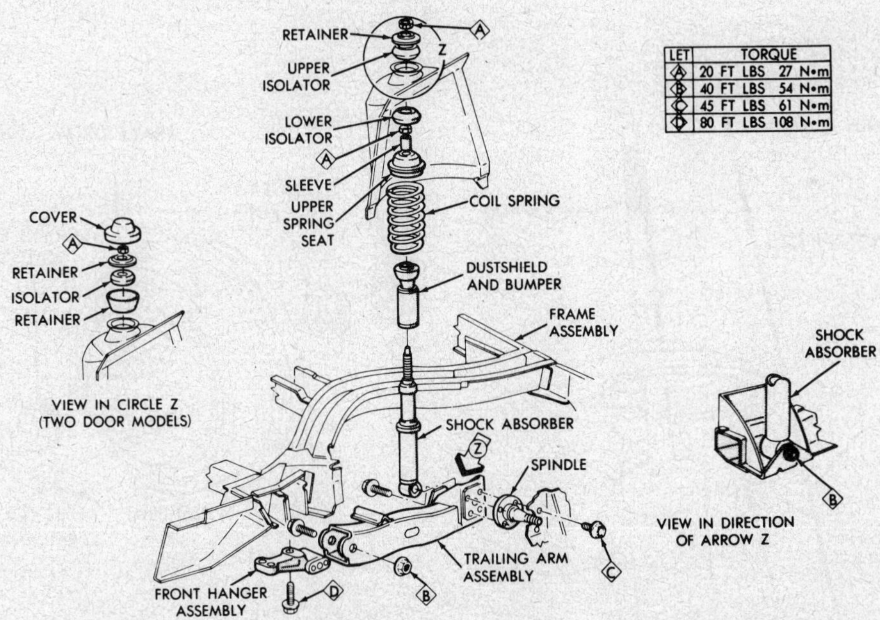


**Fig. 4 Rear axle & suspension assembly. Horizon & Omni**

# SERVICE BULLETIN
## REAR SUSPENSION NOISE

On some **1989-91 Dynasty, New Yorker, Imperial & Fifth Avenue models,** there may be a noise from the rear suspension due to the pivot bushing to hanger bracket interference. If noise is present proceed as follows:

1. With vehicle suspension at ride height, on a drive-on hoist if possible, loosen the hanger bracket to frame bolts.
2. Jounce vehicle.
3. Hanger brackets may move inboard or may need a push. If brackets have moved inboard, **torque** hanger bracket to frame rail bolts to 55 ft. lbs. while vehicle is at ride height.
4. Road test vehicle and if noise is still present replace both pivot bushings.

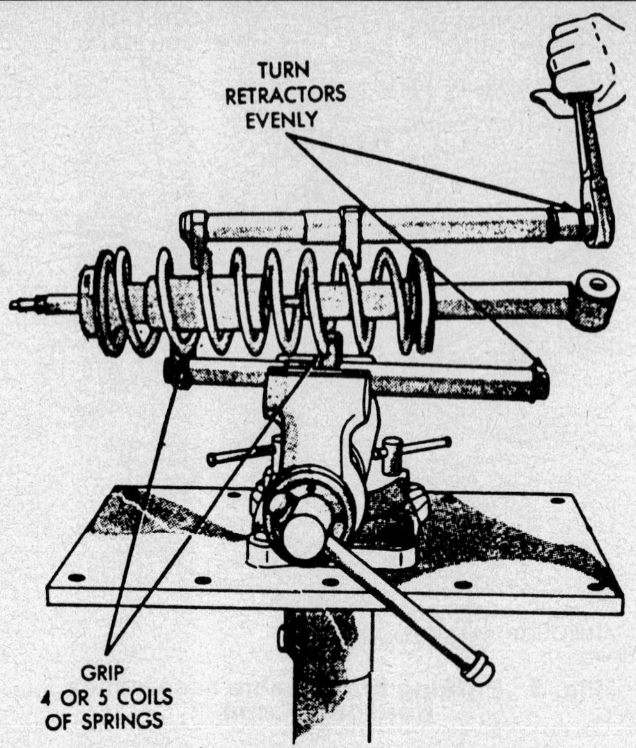


**Fig. 5 Retracting coil spring**

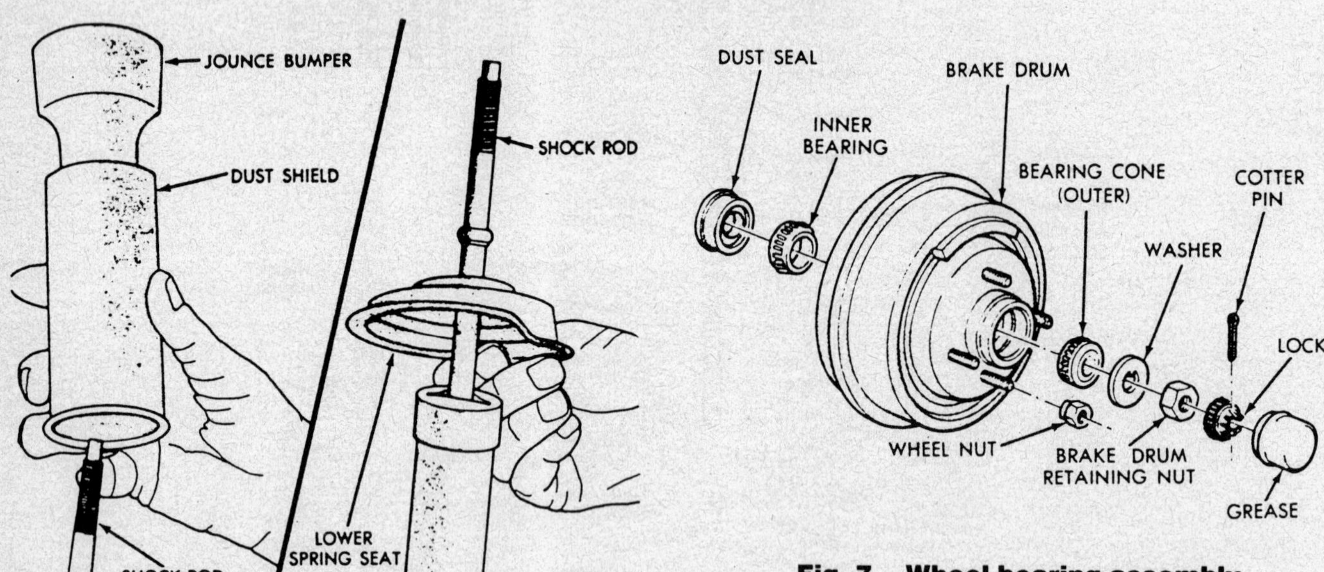


**Fig. 6 Jounce bumper, dust shield & lower spring seat replacement**

**Fig. 7 Wheel bearing assembly**

## TIGHTENING SPECIFICATIONS

| Year | Component | Torque/Ft. Lbs. |
|---|---|---|
| | Brake Tube To Hose Fitting | 140③ |
| | Isolator Cup Screws | 70③ |
| | Spindle Mounting Bolts | 55 |
| | Shock Absorber Lower Mounting Bolts① | 40 |
| | Shock Absorber Mounting Nut② | 45 |
| | Shock Absorber Mounting Nuts① | 20 |
| | Strut Damper To Knuckle Leg① | 45④ |
| | Strut Damper To Knuckle Leg② | 75④ |
| | Sway Bar Bushing And Cushion Bolt⑤ ⑦ | 30 |
| | Sway Bar Bushing And Cushion Bolt① ⑦ | 25 |
| | Sway Bar Bushing And Cushion Bolt⑥ ⑦ | 40 |
| | Sway Bar Bushing And Cushion Bolt⑧ | 40 |
| | Track Bar Brace/Body Stud② | 40 |
| | Track Bar Brace To Stud Nut② | 55 |
| | Track Bar Mounting Bracket To Rail Bolts② | 40 |
| | Track Bar To Axle Attaching Bolts② | 70 |
| | Track Bar To Mounting Bracket Bolt② | 55 |
| | Trailing Arm To Hanger Bracket Mounting Bracket Bolts | 40 |
| | Wheel Nuts | 95 |

①—Horizon & Omni.
②—All models except Horizon & Omni.
③—Inch lbs.
④—After reaching specified torque turn an additional 90°.
⑤—All except Horizon, Omni, New Yorker, New Yorker Landau & Dynasty.
⑥—New Yorker, New Yorker Landau & Dynasty.
⑦—1989–90 models.
⑧—1991–92 models.

# Front Suspension & Steering

## INDEX



## DESCRIPTION

These models use a MacPherson type front suspension with vertical shock absorber struts attached to the upper fender reinforcement and steering knuckle, **Fig. 1.** The lower control arms are attached inboard to a crossmember and outboard to the steering knuckle through a ball joint to provide lower steering knuckle position. During steering maneuvers, the strut and steering knuckle rotate as an assembly.

The driveshafts are attached inboard to the transaxle output drive flanges and outboard to the driven wheel hub.

## HUB & BEARING REPLACE

If there is movement noted on one or both wheels but no bearing noise, measure movement at wheel outer rim diameter with a dial gauge. The maximum allowable movement on a 13 inch wheel at the rim lip is .020 inch, on a 14 inch wheel .023 inch and .025 inch on a 15 inch wheel. Do not replace bearings for looseness if movement is as specified. Also do not over torque the axle retaining nut beyond 180 ft. lbs. to minimize bearing freeplay.

**Service procedures that involve hub removal require a new hub bearing be installed.**

### PRESSED-IN TYPE

#### Removal

1. Remove steering knuckle as outlined under "Steering Knuckle, Replace."
2. Using tool kit No. C-4811 or equivalent, remove hub from bearing as follows:
   a. Back out one of the bearing retainer screws, then install bracket between screw head and retainer, **Fig. 2.**
   b. Place thrust button inside hub bore.

c. Install two screws firmly into tapped brake adapter extensions, then the nut and washer on adapter screw.
d. Tighten screw to remove hub from bearing.

3. Remove three screws and bearing retainer from knuckle.
4. Pry bearing seal from machined recess in knuckle.
5. Press bearing out of knuckle using tool No. C-4811 or equivalent.

## Installation

1. Press new bearing into knuckle using tool No. C-4811 or equivalent.
2. Install new seal and bearing retainer. Torque retainer screws to specification.
3. Press hub into bearing using tool No. C-4811 or equivalent.
4. Install new bearing seal using seal installer tool No. C-4698 or equivalent.

## BOLT-IN TYPE

Some models use a bolt-in type hub and bearing assembly. This unit is serviced as a complete assembly and is attached to the steering knuckle by four mounting screws that are removed from the rear of the steering knuckle.

1. Remove steering knuckle as outlined under "Steering Knuckle, Replace."
2. Remove four hub and bearing assembly attaching screws from rear of steering knu ckle.
3. Remove hub and bearing assembly. **Replacement of grease seal is recommended whenever this service is performed.**
4. Install new hub and bearing assembly in steering knuckle and torque screws in a cross pattern to specification. **Knuckle and bearing mounting surfaces must be smooth and free of foreign material and nicks.**
5. Install new seal using seal installer tool No. C-4698 or equivalent.
6. **During any service procedures where knuckle and driveshaft are separated, clean seal and wear sleeve, then lubricate both parts.** Lubricate full circumference of seal and wear sleeve with Mopar Multi-Purpose Lubricant, part No. 4318063 or equivalent, as shown in **Fig. 3.**
7. Install steering knuckle as outlined under ""Steering Knuckle, Replace."

1. FRONT SUSPENSION CROSSMEMBER
2. FRONT PIVOT BOLT
3. LOWER CONTROL ARM
4. SWAY ELIMINATOR SHAFT ASSEMBLY
5. LOWER ARM BALL JOINT ASSEMBLY
6. STEERING GEAR
7. TIE ROD ASSEMBLY
8. DRIVESHAFT
9. STEERING KNUCKLE
10. STRUT DAMPER ASSEMBLY
11. COIL SPRING
12. UPPER SPRING SEAT
13. REBOUND STOP
14. UPPER MOUNT ASSEMBLY
15. JOUNCE BUMPER
16. DUST SHIELD

**Fig. 1 Front suspension**

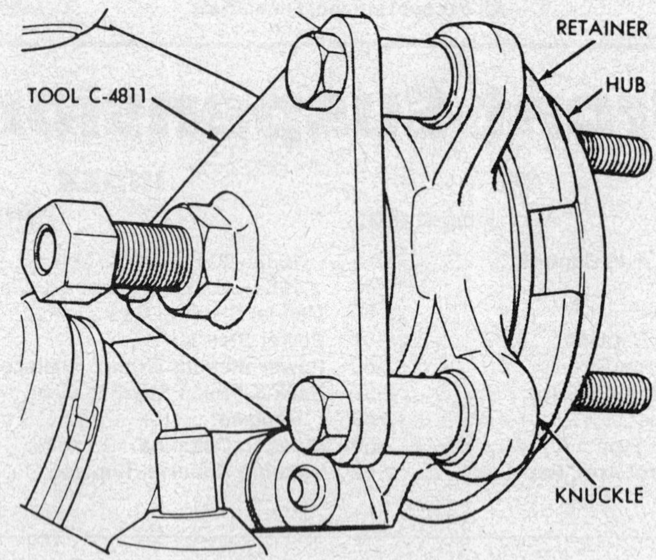


**Fig. 2 Hub removal**

# BALL JOINTS

The lower control arm ball joints operate with no freeplay. The ball joint is pressed into the lower control arm. Ball joints can be pressed from lower control arm using a $1^{1}/_{16}$ inch deep socket and tool No. C-4699-2. When pressing ball joint into lower control arm, use tool Nos. C-4699-1 and C-4699-2. Install ball joint seal using a $1^{1}/_{2}$ socket and tool No. C-4699-2. **On some models the ball joint is welded to the lower control arm. On these models the ball joint and lower control arm must be replaced as an assembly.**

## BALL JOINT INSPECTION

With weight of vehicle resting on wheel and tire assembly, attempt to move grease fitting with fingers, **Fig. 4.** Do not use a tool or added force to attempt to move grease fitting. If grease fitting moves freely, then ball joint is worn and should be replaced.

# STRUT DAMPER ASSEMBLY REPLACE

## REMOVAL

1. Raise and support vehicle, then remove front wheels.
2. Mark position of camber adjusting cam for proper alignment during installation, **Fig. 5.**
3. Mark outline of strut on knuckle for

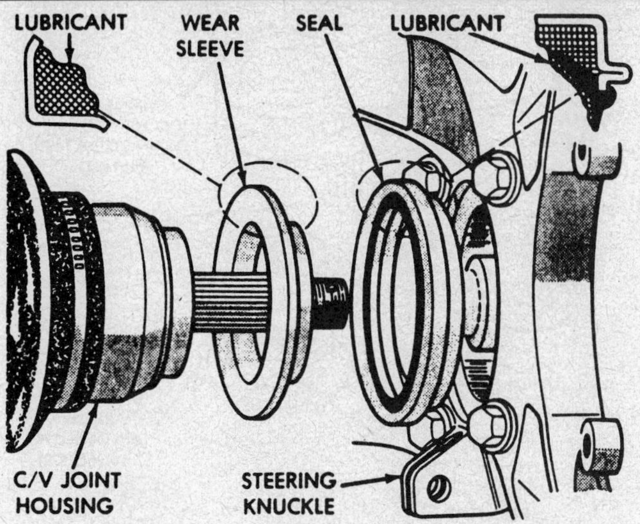

**Fig. 3 Lubricating seal & wear sleeve**

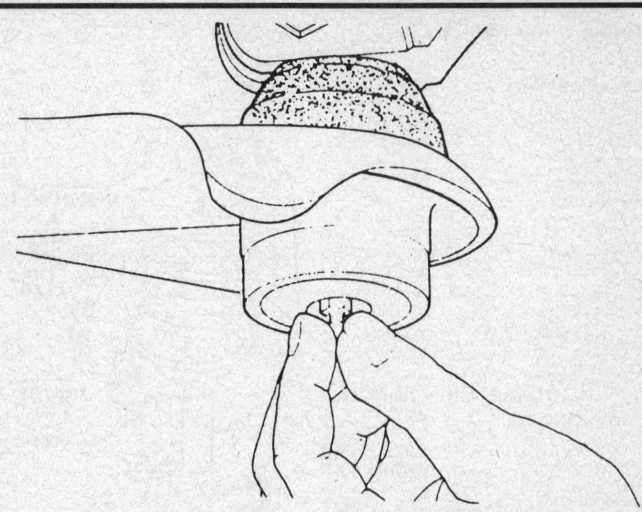
**Fig. 4 Checking ball joint for wear**

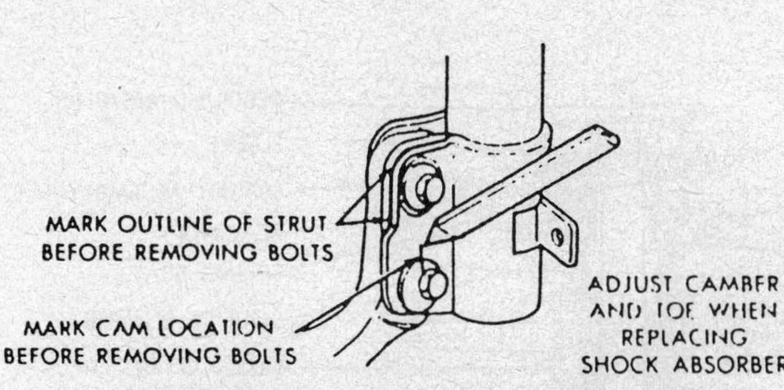

**Fig. 5 Marking strut for installation**

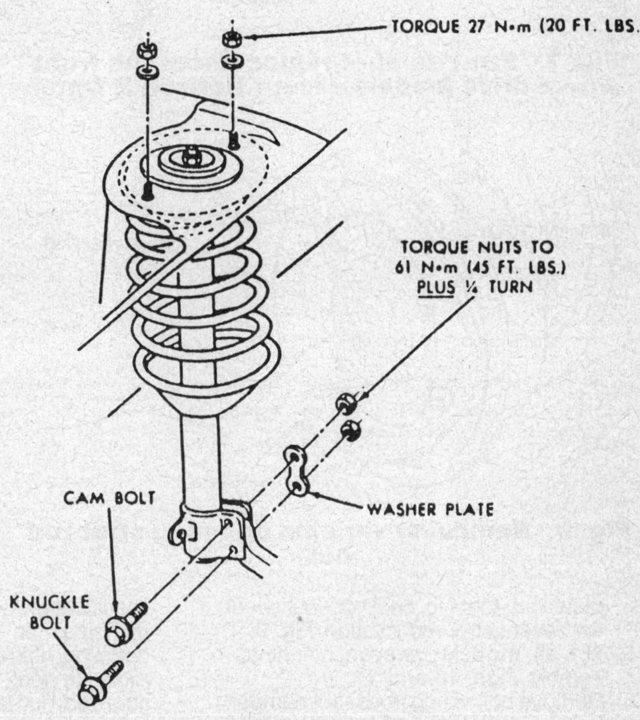

**Fig. 6 Strut damper replacement. Horizon & Omni**

proper alignment during installation, **Fig. 5.**

4. Remove cam bolt, knuckle bolt or bolts, washer plate or plates and brake hose to damper bracket attaching screw, **Figs. 6 and 7.**
5. **On 1990 models with variable damping,** disconnect electrical connector from upper strut rod by pinching the two latching arms, then pulling connector straight off of rod end, **Fig. 8. Do not rotate connector.**
6. **On all models,** remove strut damper to fender shield attaching nut and washer assemblies.
7. Remove strut damper from vehicle.

## INSTALLATION

1. Position strut assembly into fender reinforcement, then install retaining nuts and washers and torque to specification.
2. Position steering knuckle and washer plate to strut, then install cam and through bolts.
3. Install brake hose retainer on damper, then index alignment marks made during removal.
4. Position a four inch or larger C-clamp on steering knuckle and strut, then tighten clamp just enough to eliminate any looseness between strut and knuckle. Check alignment of marks made during removal. Torque cam bolt nuts to specifications, then advance nuts an additional ¼ turn.
5. Remove C-clamp, then install wheel and tire assembly. Torque wheel nuts to specification.
6. **On 1990 models with variable damping,** attach electrical connector to top of strut rod, using caution to align key-way (wire should point toward vehicle center line), **Fig. 8.** Connector is correctly installed when both latching fingers engage in strut stem.

## COIL SPRING REPLACE

1. Remove strut damper assembly as outlined previously.
2. Using tool spring compressor tool No. 4838 or equivalent, compress coil spring.
3. **On all except 1990 models with variable damping,** remove strut rod nut while holding strut rod to prevent rotation.
4. **On 1990 models with variable damping,** hold strut rod retaining

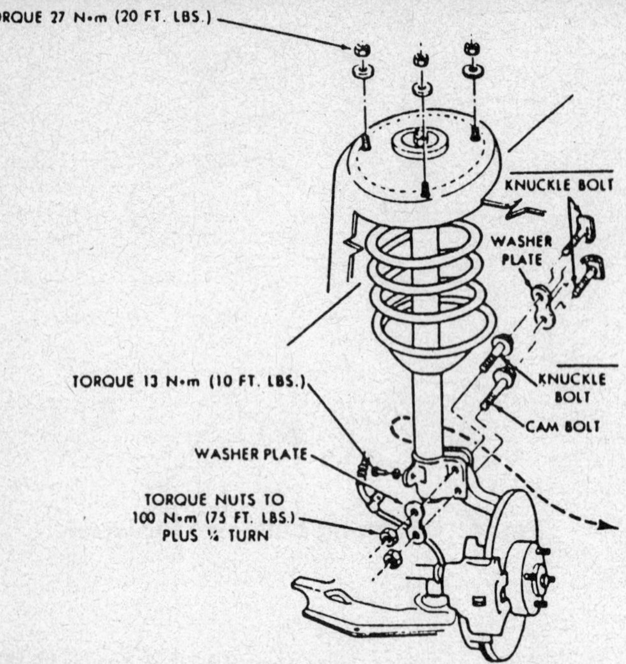


Fig. 7 **Strut damper replacement. All front wheel drive models except Horizon & Omni**

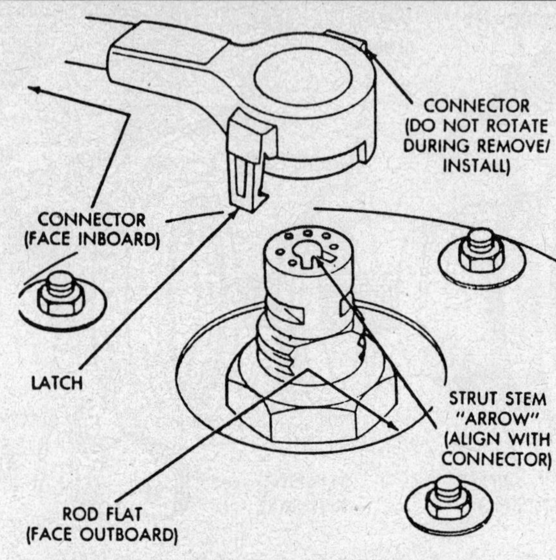


**Fig. 8 Variable strut damper electrical connector**

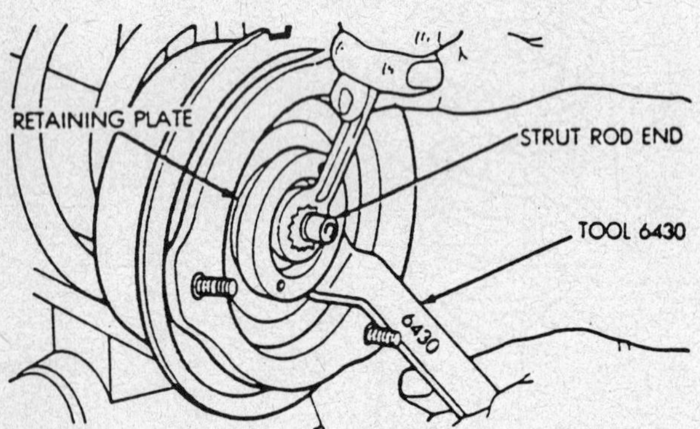


**Fig. 9 Removing variable damping strut rod nut**

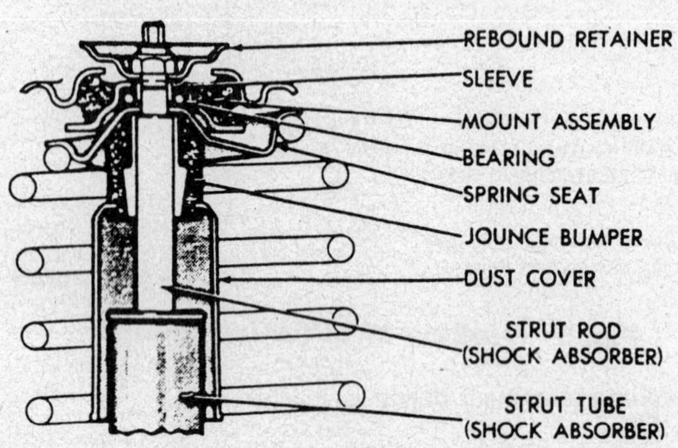


**Fig. 10 Strut damper assembly. Horizon & Omni**

plate with tool No. 6430 or equivalent to prevent strut rod rotation, **Fig. 9.**

5. **On all models,** remove mount assembly, **Figs. 10 and 11.**
6. Remove coil spring from strut damper.
7. Inspect mount assembly for deterioration of rubber isolator, retainers for cracks and distortion and bearings for binding.
8. Install bumper dust shield assembly.
9. Install spring and seat, upper spring retainer, bearing and spacer, mount assembly, rebound bumper and retainer and rod nut. Position spring upper retainer tab or notch correctly with respect to bottom bracket, Figs. 12 and 13.
10. **On 1990 models with variable damping,** align strut rod electrical connector as follows:
    a. Align flat on strut rod and one retaining stud on mount within 15° in opposite direction from spring seat alignment notch, **Fig. 14.**
11. **On all models,** torque strut rod nut to specification on models less variable damping. On models with variable damping, hold retaining plate and strut rod with tool No. 6340 and torque strut rod nut to specification. **Do not release spring compressor before torquing nut.**
12. Remove spring compressor tool.

# SWAY BAR REPLACE

## REMOVAL

1. Raise and support front of vehicle.
2. Remove nuts, bolts and retainers.
3. Remove sway bar.

## INSTALLATION

1. Position crossmember bushings on bar with curved surface up and split to front of vehicle. Set upper clamps onto crossmember bushings, lift bar assembly into crossmember and install lower clamps and bolts.
2. Position retainers at control arms, then insert bolts and install nuts.
3. With lower control arms raised to design height, tighten bolts to specification.

# LOWER CONTROL ARM REPLACE

## 1989–90 HORIZON & OMNI

### Removal

1. Raise and support vehicle.
2. Remove front inner pivot through bolt, rear stub strut nut, retainer and bushing and the ball joint to steering knuckle clamp bolt, **Fig. 15.**
3. Separate the ball joint from steering knuckle by prying between ball stud retainer and lower control arm. **Removing steering knuckle from vehicle after releasing from ball joint can separate inner C/V joint.**

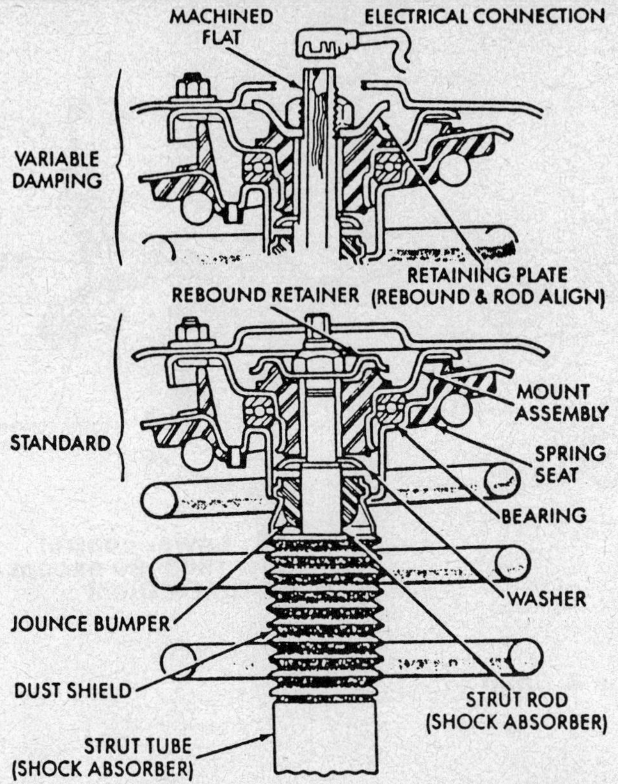


**Fig. 11 Strut damper assembly. All models except Horizon & Omni**

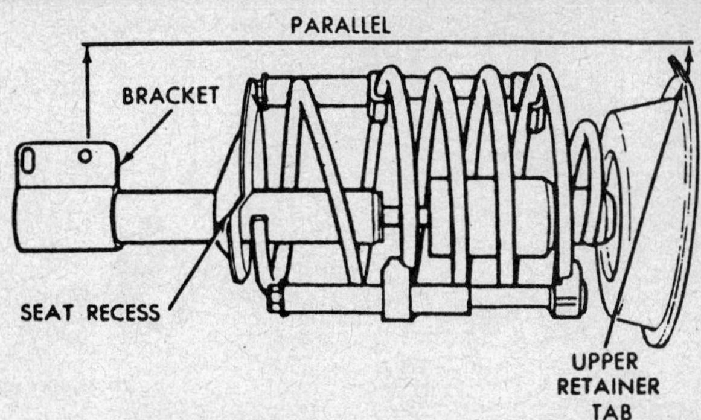


**Fig. 12 Spring seat & retainer position. 1989 models except Horizon & Omni**

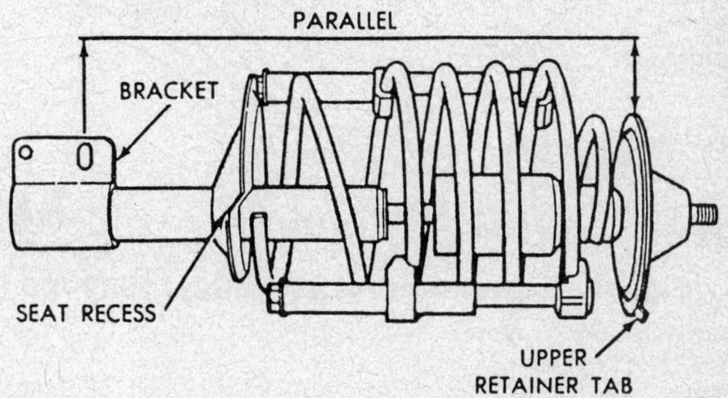


**Fig. 13 Spring seat & retainer position. 1989 Horizon & Omni & all 1990 models**

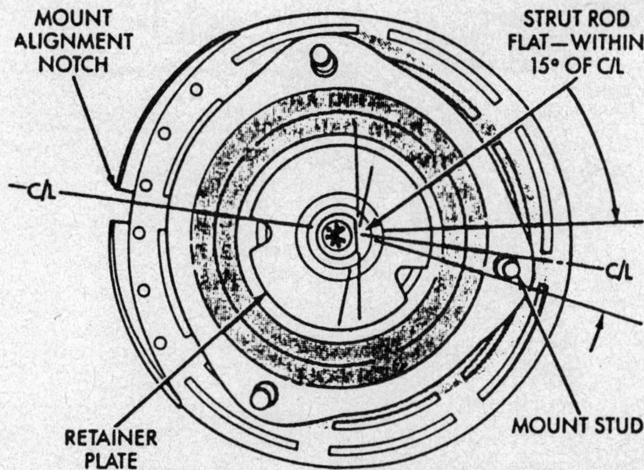


**Fig. 14 Aligning variable damping strut rod electrical connector**

4. Remove sway bar to control arm nut and reinforcement. Rotate control arm over sway bar. Remove rear stub strut bushing, sleeve and retainer.

### Installation

1. Install retainer, bushing and sleeve on stub strut.
2. Position control arm over sway bar and install rear stub strut and front pivot into crossmember.
3. Install front pivot bolt and loosely assemble nut, **Fig. 15.**
4. Install stub strut bushing and retainer and loosely assemble nut.
5. Install ball joint stud into steering knuckle, then the clamp bolt. Torque bolt to specification.
6. Place sway bar bracket stud through control arm and install retainer and nut. Torque nut to specifications.
7. Lower vehicle and with suspension supporting vehicle, torque front pivot bolt and stub strut nut to specification.

## 1989–92 EXCEPT HORIZON & OMNI

The lower control arm is serviced as a complete assembly with pivot bushings and ball joint.

### Removal

1. Raise and support vehicle.
2. Remove front and rear inner pivot through bolt and ball joint to steering knuckle clamp bolt, **Fig. 16.**
3. Separate ball joint from steering knuckle. **Removing steering knuckle from vehicle after releasing from ball joint can separate inner C/V joint.**
4. Remove sway bar to control arm end bushing retainer nuts and rotate control arm over sway bar. Remove stub strut retainer. Inspect lower control arm for distortion and check bushings for deterioration.

### Installation

1. Position control arm over sway bar, then install pivot bolts and loosely assemble nuts.
2. Install ball joint stud into steering knuckle, then install clamp bolt. Torque bolt to specification.
3. Install sway bar end bushing to control arm, then install retainer bolts. Torque to specifications.
4. Lower vehicle and with suspension supporting vehicle, torque pivot bolts to specification.

## STEERING KNUCKLE REPLACE

### REMOVAL

1. Remove wheel hub cotter pin, locknut and spring washer.
2. Loosen hub nut with brakes applied,

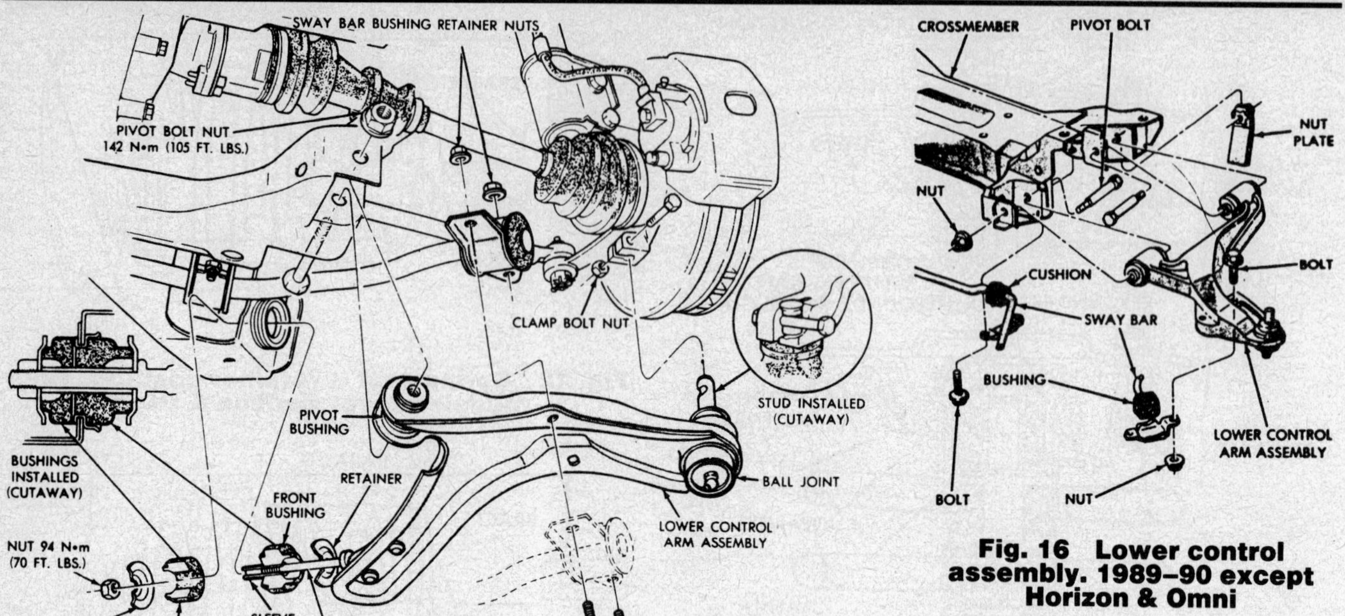


**Fig. 15 Lower control assembly. 1989–90 Horizon & Omni**

**Fig. 16 Lower control assembly. 1989–90 except Horizon & Omni**

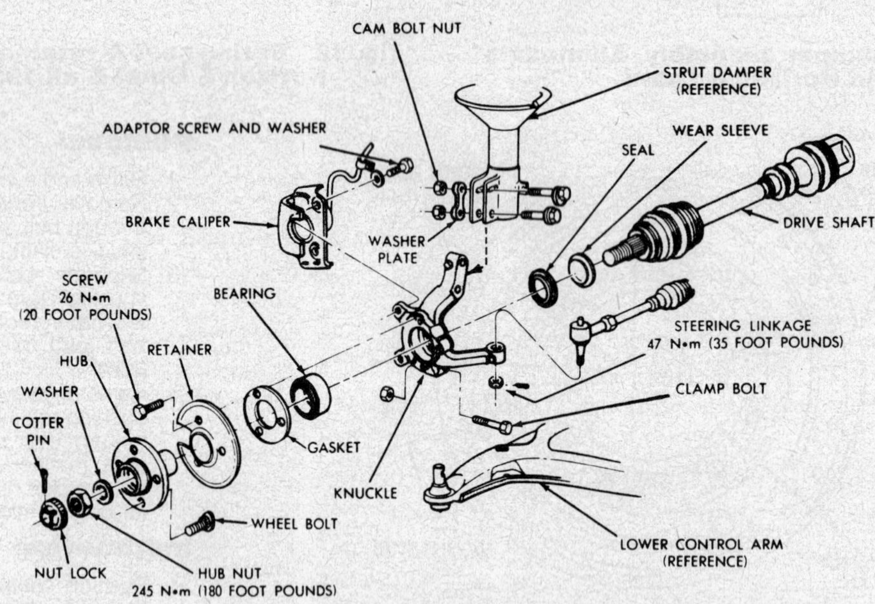


**Fig. 17 Steering knuckle assembly**

**Fig. 17. The hub and driveshaft are splined together through the knuckle and retained by hub nut.**

3. Raise and support vehicle.
4. Remove front wheel and the hub nut. Ensure that splined driveshaft is free to separate from spline in hub during knuckle removal. **A pulling force on the shaft can separate the inner C/V joint.** Tap lightly with a brass drift, if required.
5. Disconnect tie rod end from steering arm with puller tool No. C-3894-A or equivalent.
6. Disconnect brake hose retainer from strut damper.
7. Remove clamp bolt securing ball joint stud into steering knuckle and brake caliper adapter screw and washer assemblies.
8. Support caliper with a piece of wire. **Do not hang by brake hose.**
9. Remove rotor.
10. Separate ball joint stud from knuckle assembly, then pull knuckle out and away from driveshaft. **Do not permit driveshaft to hang after separating steering knuckle from vehicle.**

## INSTALLATION

1. Place steering knuckle on lower ball joint stud and driveshaft through hub.
2. Install and torque ball joint to steering knuckle clamp bolt to specification.
3. Install tie rod end into steering arm and torque nut to specifications. Install cotter pin.
4. Install rotor.
5. Install caliper over rotor and position adapter to steering knuckle. Install adapter to knuckle bolts and **torque** to 160 ft. lbs.
6. Attach brake hose retainer to strut

damper and torque screw to specification.
7. Install washer and hub nut, then with brakes applied, torque hub nut to specification.
8. Install spring washer, locknut and new cotter pin.

## RACK & PINION STEERING GEAR

### REPLACE

1. Raise and support vehicle, then remove front wheels.
2. Remove tie rod ends with a suitable puller.
3. Disconnect engine damper strut from crossmember, if equipped.
4. Remove four front suspension crossmember attaching bolts, then lower the crossmember using a transmission jack, so that steering gear can be disconnected from steering column.
5. Disconnect lower stub shaft from from steering gear coupling. **Do not remove roll pin.**
6. **On models with power steering,** disconnect hoses from steering gear.
7. **On all models,** remove bolts attaching steering gear to crossmember, then remove steering gear from crossmember.
8. Reverse procedure to install, noting the following:
   a. Using an assistant, from inside of vehicle, guide steering column coupling onto steering gear. **On models with manual steering, ensure master serrations are aligned.**
   b. **Right rear crossmember bolt is a pilot bolt that correctly locates crossmember. Tighten this bolt first. Torque** all crossmember attaching bolts to 90 ft. lbs.
   c. Torque bolts attaching steering gear to crossmember to specifications.
   d. Check for oil leaks.
   e. Adjust toe. Refer to procedure to outlined under "Wheel Alignment."

## POWER STEERING PUMP

### REPLACE

1. Disconnect vapor separator hose from carburetor or throttle body, then the two wires from A/C clutch cycling switch, if equipped.
2. Remove power steering pump drive belt adjusting bolt and nut, then the nut attaching pump end hose bracket, if equipped.
3. Raise and support vehicle, then remove nut attaching pump pressure hose bracket to crossmember.
4. Disconnect pressure hose from steering gear and allow fluid to drain into a suitable container.
5. Remove drive belt splash shield, then disconnect both pressure and return hoses at power steering pump. Cap hoses and fittings to prevent entry of dirt.
6. Remove lower stud nut and pivot bolt from power steering pump, then lower the vehicle.
7. Remove belt from pump, then move pump rearward to clear mounting bracket and remove adjusting bracket.
8. Rotate pump so pulley faces rear of vehicle, then lift pump assembly from vehicle.
9. Reverse procedure to install.

## TIGHTENING SPECIFICATIONS

| Year | Component | Torque/Ft. Lbs. |
|---|---|---|
| 1989–92 | Brake Hose To Damper Screw | 10 |
| | Cam Bolt Nuts⑤ | 46⑥ |
| | Cam Bolt Nuts⑦ | 75⑥ |
| | Control Arm Clamp Bolt | ⑩ |
| | Control Arm Front Pivot Bolt⑪ | 95 |
| | Control Arm Pivot Bolts⑬ | 125 |
| | Control Arm Stub Strut Nut⑪ | 70 |
| | Crossmember Bolts | 90⑫ |
| | Hub & Bearing Retaining Screws⑮ | 45⑯ |
| | Hub Bearing Retainer Screw⑭ | 20 |
| | Hub Nut | 180 |
| | Manual Steering Gear Clamp And Housing Pad Bolts | 17-25 |
| | Manual Steering Gear Tie Rod End Locknut | 45-65 |
| | Manual Steering Gear Tie Rod End Nut | 25-50 |
| | Power Steering Gear Inner Tie Rod | 70 |
| | Power Steering Gear Tie Rod End Locknut | 55 |
| | Power Steering Gear Tie Rod End Nut | 38 |
| | Power Steering Gear To Crossmember Bolts | 50 |
| | Power Steering Pressure Hose Locating Bracket | 9 |
| | Power Steering Pressure Hose Tube Nuts | 25 |
| | Power Steering Pump Bracket Mounting Fasteners | ① |
| | Power Steering Pump Discharge Fitting | ② |
| | Power Steering Pump Relief Valve Ball Seat | 4③ |
| | Power Steering Return Tube Locating Bracket | 21 |
| | Power Steering Return Tube Nut | 25 |
| | Steering Column Clamp Bolt | 105④ |
| | Steering Column Clamp Stud Nut | 20④ |
| | Steering Column Clamp Stud | 105④ |
| | Steering Gear To Crossmember Bolts | 50 |
| | Steering Wheel To Steering Shaft Nut | 45 |

*Continued*

## TIGHTENING SPECIFICATIONS—Continued

| Year | Component | Torque/Ft. Lbs. |
|---|---|---|
| 1989–92 | Strut Damper To Knuckle Leg⑤ | 45⑥ |
| | Strut Damper To Knuckle Leg⑦ | 75⑥ |
| | Strut Retaining Nuts | 20 |
| | Strut Rod Bolts⑧ | 55 |
| | Strut Rod Bolts⑨ | 75 |
| | Sway Bar Bushing And Cushion Bolt⑤ | 25 |
| | Sway Bar Bushing And Cushion Bolt⑦ | 40 |
| | Wheel Nuts | 95 |

①—M8 bolts, 21 ft. lbs.; M10 bolts and nuts, 30 ft. lbs.; M10 stud, 35 ft. lbs.
②—Saginaw pump, 40 ft. lbs; ZF pump, 37 ft. lbs.
③—Saginaw pump.
④—Inch lbs.
⑤—Horizon and Omni.
⑥—Turn an additional 1/4 turn after reaching specified torque.
⑦—All models except Horizon and Omni.
⑧—Except variable damping.
⑨—Variable damping.
⑩—On 1989–90 models, 70 ft. lbs.; On 1991–92 models, 105 ft. lbs.
⑪—1989–90 Horizon & Omni.
⑫—Refer to text.
⑬—1989–92 except Horizon & Omni.
⑭—Pressed in type.
⑮—Bolt on type.
⑯—Torque screws in a cross pattern.

# Wheel Alignment

## INDEX

Page No.



## FRONT WHEEL ALIGNMENT

Prior to wheel alignment ensure tires are at recommended pressure, are of equal size and have approximately the same wear pattern. Check front wheel and tire assembly for radial runout and inspect lower ball joints and steering linkage for looseness. Check front and rear springs for sagging or damage. Front suspension inspections should be performed on a level floor or alignment rack with fuel tank at capacity and vehicle free of luggage and passenger compartment load. The vehicle should be bounced an equal number of times from the center of the bumper alternately, first from the rear, then the front, releasing at bottom of down cycle.

### CASTER

The caster angle on these models cannot be adjusted.

### CAMBER

To adjust camber, loosen the cam and through bolts, **Figs. 1 and 2.** On all models except 1989 Lancer and LeBaron, Shadow and Sundance and Dynasty, Imperial, New

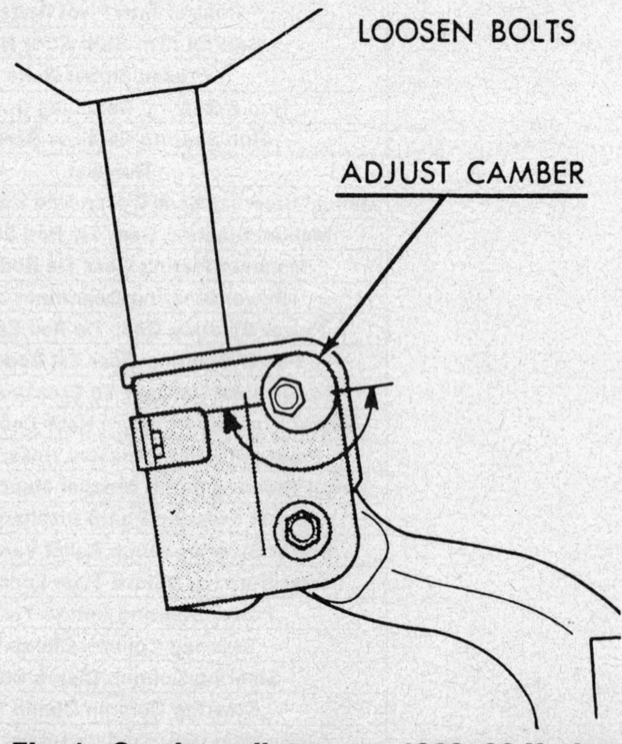


**Fig. 1 Camber adjustment. 1989–90 Horizon & Omni**

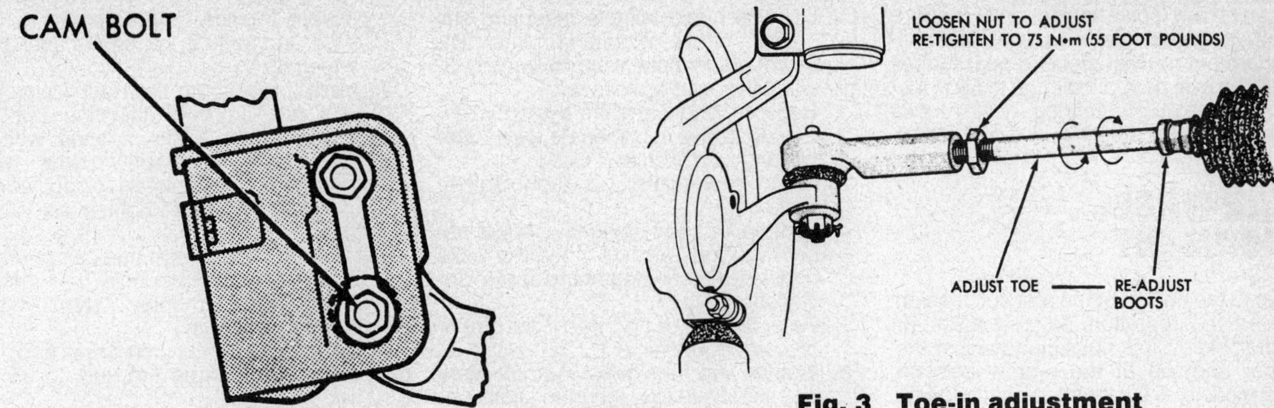


Fig. 2 Camber adjustment. All except Horizon & Omni

Fig. 3 Toe-in adjustment

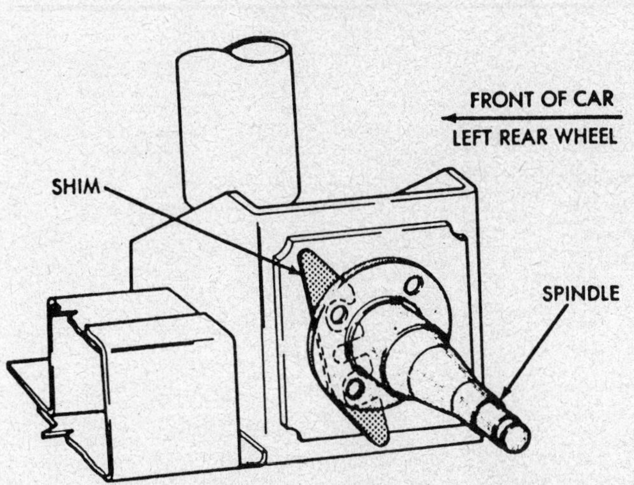


Fig. 4 Shim installation for toe-out

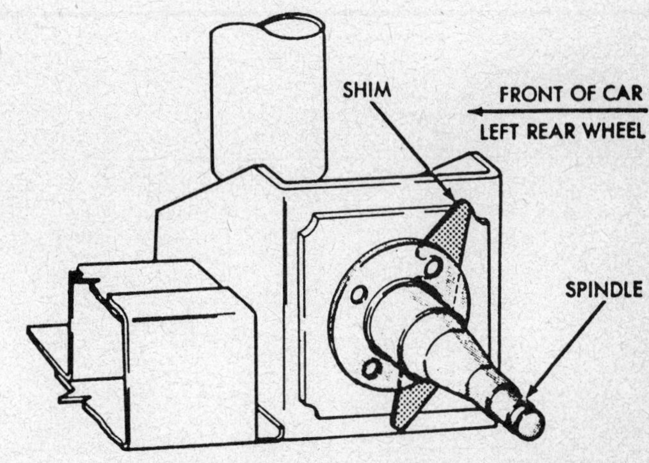


Fig. 5 Shim installation for toe-in

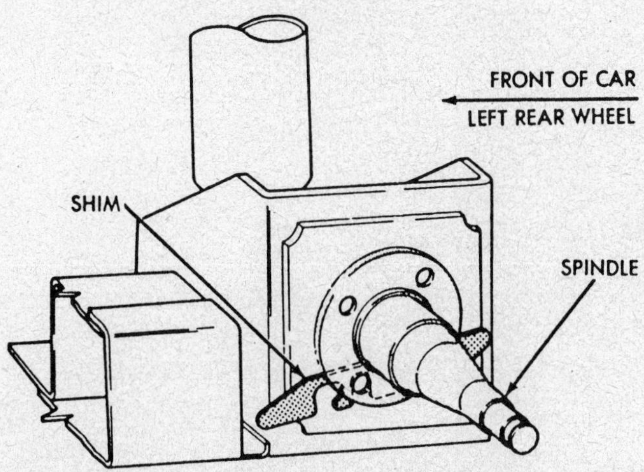


Fig. 6 Shim installation for negative camber

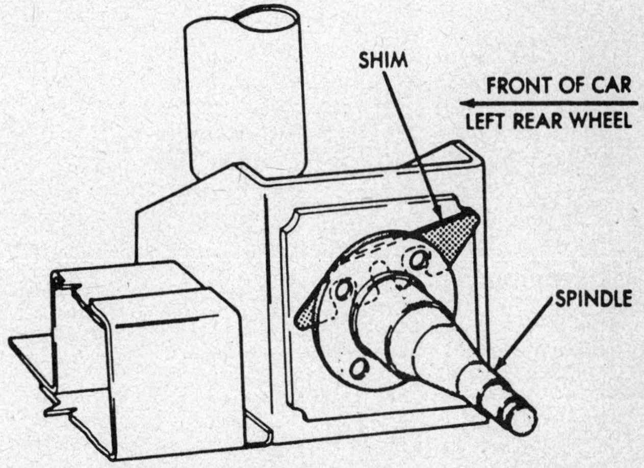


Fig. 7 Shim installation for positive camber

Yorker and New Yorker Fifth Avenue, rotate cam bolt to move top of wheel in or out to obtain specified camber angle. On 1989 Lancer and LeBaron, Shadow and Sundance and Dynasty, Imperial, New Yorker and New Yorker Fifth Avenue, loosen knuckle bolts just enough to allow movement between strut and knuckle, then push or pull tire to obtain specified camber angle. On 1989-90 Horizon and Omni, **torque** cam bolt nuts to 45 ft. lbs., then advance nuts an additional 1/4 turn. On all models except Horizon and Omni, **torque** nuts to 75 ft. lbs., then advance an additional 1/4 turn.

## TOE-IN

To adjust toe-in, center steering wheel and hold in position with a suitable tool.

Loosen tie rod locknuts and rotate the rod, **Fig. 3,** to adjust toe-in to specifications. Use care not to twist steering gear rubber boots. **Torque** tie rod locknuts to 55 ft. lbs. Adjust position of steering gear rubber boots. Remove steering wheel holding tool.

## REAR WHEEL ALIGNMENT

Due to the design of the rear suspension and the incorporation of stub axles or wheel spindles, it is possible to adjust the camber and toe of the rear wheels on these models. Adjustment is controlled by adding shims approximately .010 inch thick between the spindle mounting surface and spindle mounting plate. The amount of adjustment is approximately .3° per shim. Proceed as follows:

1. Remove wheel and tire assembly.
2. Pry off grease cap, then remove cotter pin and castle lock.
3. Remove adjusting nut, then remove brake drum.
4. Loosen, but do not remove brake assembly and spindle mounting bolts enough to allow clearance for shim installation, **Fig. 3.**
5. Refer to **Figs. 4 through 7** for proper placement of shims.
6. Tighten the four brake support plate and spindle to axle mounting bolts until snug, **torque** bolts on all models except Imperial and Dynasty to 55 ft.lbs. and to 80 ft. lbs. on Dynasty and Imperial.
7. Install brake drum, then install washer and nut. **Torque** adjusting nut to 20-25 ft. lbs. while rotating wheel, then back off adjusting nut with wrench to to completely release bearing preload. Finger tighten adjusting nut.
8. Position locknut with one pair of slots inline with cotter pin hole, then install cotter pin. Endplay should be 0.001-0.003 inch.
9. Install grease cap, then wheel and tire assembly. **Torque** lug nuts to 95 ft. lbs.
10. Re-check alignment specifications.

# DODGE MONACO & EAGLE PREMIER

## INDEX OF SERVICE OPERATIONS

**NOTE:** Refer To Rear Of This Manual For Vehicle Manufacturer's Special Service Tool Suppliers.

## INDEX OF SERVICE OPERATIONS—Continued



# Specifications

## GENERAL ENGINE SPECIFICATIONS

| Year | Engine Liter/CID① | Engine VIN Code ② | Fuel System | Bore and Stroke Inch (Millimeters) | Compression Ratio | Net HP @ RPM ③ | Maximum Torque Ft. Lbs @ R.P.M. | Normal Oil Pressure Psi. |
|---|---|---|---|---|---|---|---|---|
| 1989–90 | 2.5L/4-150 | H | TBI④ | 3.876 x 3.188 (98 x 80) | 9.2 | 111 @ 4750 | 142 @ 2500 | 55–65⑤ |
| 1989–92 | 3.0L/V6-180 | U | TBI④ | 3.660 x 2.870 (93 x 73) | 9.3 | 150 @ 5000 | 171 @ 3750 | 60⑥ |

①—CID-cubic inch displacement.
②—8th digit of the VIN denotes engine code.
③—Ratings are net-as installed in vehicle.
④—Throttle body injection.
⑤—3500 RPM.
⑥—4000 RPM.

## TUNE UP SPECIFICATIONS

| Year & Engine/ VIN Code ① | Spark Plug Gap | Ignition Timing BTDC② Firing Order Fig. ③ | Ignition Timing Man. Trans. | Ignition Timing Auto. Trans. | Mark Fig. | Curb Idle Speed Man. Trans. | Curb Idle Speed Auto Trans. | Fast Idle Speed Man. Trans. | Fast Idle Speed Auto. Trans. | Fuel Pump Pressure, Psi. |
|---|---|---|---|---|---|---|---|---|---|---|
| **1989–90** | | | | | | | | | | |
| 2.5L/4-150(H) | .035 | A | — | ④ | D | — | ④ | — | ④ | 14.5⑨ |
| 3.0L/V6-182(U) | .035 | B | ④ | ④ | E | ④ | ④ | ④ | ④ | 29⑦ |
| **1991–92** | | | | | | | | | | |
| 3.0L/V6-182(U)⑤ | .035 | B | ④ | ④ | E | ④ | ④ | ④ | ④ | 29⑦ |
| 3.0L/V6-182(U)⑥ | .035 | C | ④ | ④ | E | ⑧ | ⑧ | ④ | ④ | 43⑦ |

①—Eighth digit of the Vehicle Identification Number (VIN) denotes engine code.
②—BTDC: Before Top Dead Center.
③—Before disconnecting wires from distributor cap, determine location of No. 1 wire in cap, as distributor position may have been altered from that shown at the end of this chart.
④—Computer controlled, non-adjustable.
⑤—Early 1991 models.
⑥—Late 1991 models and 1992 models with Direct Ignition System.
⑦—Remove filler cap from fuel tank. Position shop towel around tub e & fitting, then using a suitable tool disconnect black fuel supply line from fuel rail. Connect a suitable fuel pressure test gauge between tube & fuel rail. Start engine & check fuel pressure.
⑧—With transaxle in Neutral, 625–725N RPM; with transaxle in Drive, 565–665 RPM.
⑨—With engine cool, position shop towel near throttle body test port plug, then remove test port plug from throttle body. The test port is located on the throttle body on the side of the fuel pressure regulator near the fuel return connection. Connect a suitable fuel pressure test gauge to test port, the start engine & check fuel pressure.

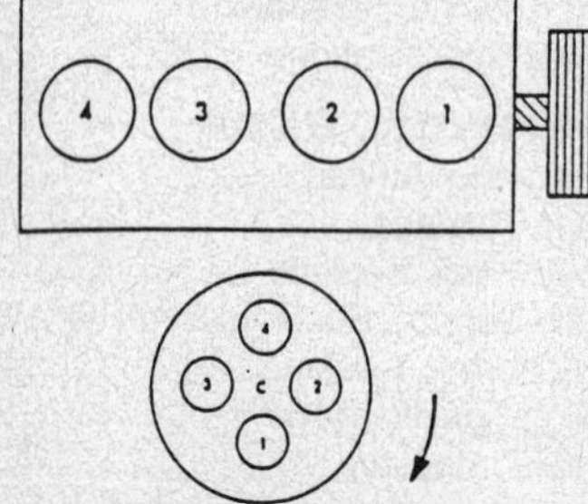


Fig. A

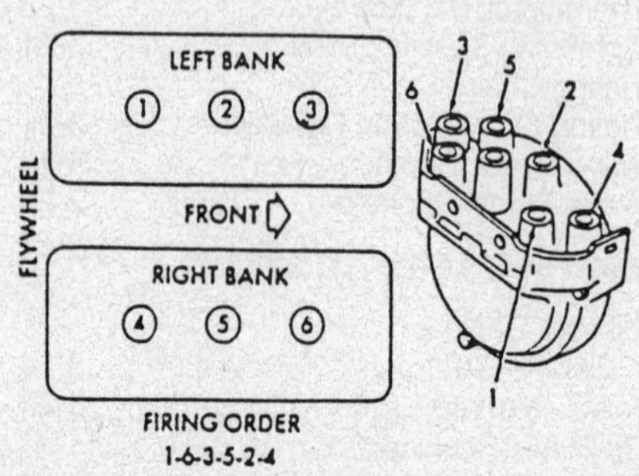


Fig. B

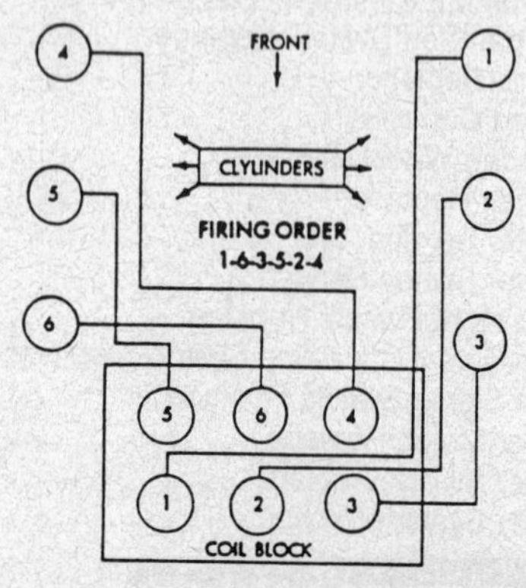


Fig. C

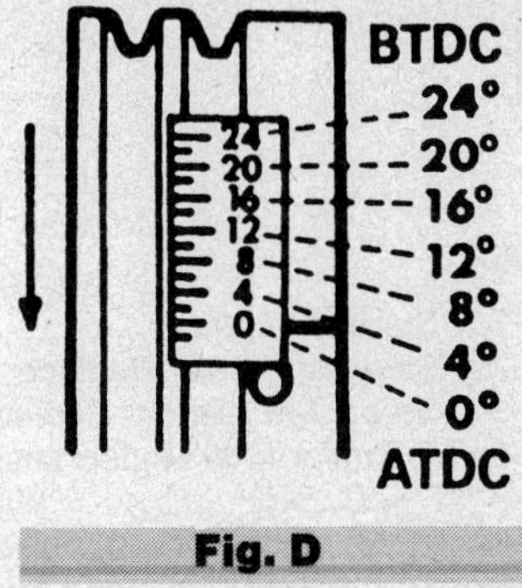


Fig. D

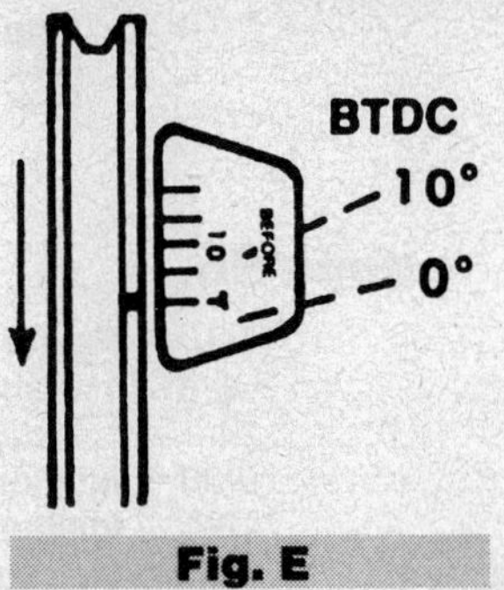


Fig. E

## FRONT WHEEL ALIGNMENT SPECIFICATIONS

| Year | Model | Caster Angle, Degrees | | Camber Angle, Degrees | | | | Toe-Out Per Wheel, Inch |
|---|---|---|---|---|---|---|---|---|
| | | | | Limits | | Desired | | |
| | | Limits | Desired | Left | Right | Left | Right | |
| 1988–89 | Premier | +1.32 to +2.82 | +2.07 | −.08 to +.58 | −.08 to +.58 | +.25 | +.25 | ① |
| 1990–92 | All | +1.5 to +2.5 | +2 | −.17 to +.83 | −.17 to +.83 | +.33 | +.33 | 0 |

①—Toe-out per wheel, 1/16 inch.

## REAR WHEEL ALIGNMENT SPECIFICATIONS

| Year | Model | Camber Angle, Degrees | | | | Toe-In, Inch |
|---|---|---|---|---|---|---|
| | | Limits | | Desired | | |
| | | Left | Right | Left | Right | |
| 1988–89 | All | −.4 to −.93 | −.4 to −.93 | −.67 | −.67 | ① |
| 1990–92 | All | −1 to 0 | −1 to 0 | −.5 | −.5 | 0 |

①—1/32 to 1/4 inch toe-in.

## COOLING SYSTEM & CAPACITIES DATA

| Year | Model or Engine (VIN)① | Cooling Capacity | | Radiator Cap Relief Pressure, Lbs. | Thermo. Opening Temp. Deg. F | Fuel Tank Gals. | Engine Oil Refill Qts. | Transaxle Oil | |
|---|---|---|---|---|---|---|---|---|---|
| | | Less A/C Qts. | With A/C Qts. | | | | | 5 Speed Pts. | Auto. Trans. Qts. ② |
| 1989 | 2.5L/4-150(H) | 8.6 | 8.6 | 17.4 | 195 | 17 | 5③ | — | ④ |
| | 3.0L/V6-182(U) | 8.6 | 8.6 | 17.4 | 190 | 17 | 6③ | — | ⑤ |
| 1990 | 2.5L/4-150(H) | 8.6 | 8.6 | 17.4 | 195 | 17 | 5③ | — | ④ |
| | 3.0L/V6-182(U) | 8.6 | 8.6 | 17.4 | 190 | 17 | 6③ | 6.3 | ④⑤ |
| 1991–92 | 3.0L/V6-182(U) | 9.5 | 9.5 | 17.4 | 190 | 17 | 6③ | — | ⑥ |

①—The eighth digit of Vehicle identification number (VIN) denotes engine code.
②—Approximate. Make final check with dipstick.
③—Includes filter.
④—AR-4 Automatic Transaxle, fluid change only, 2.8 qts.; total capacity, 5.6 qts., use Universal or Mercon Type fluid. Differential, .89 qts., use 75W-140 hypoid gear lubricant.
⑤—ZF-4 Automatic Transaxle, fluid change only, 2.8 qts.; total capacity, 7.4 qts., use Mercon Type fluid. Differential, .66 qts., use 75W-140 hypoid gear lubricant.
⑥—Fluid change only, 4 qts.; total capacity, 7.4 qts., use Mercon Type fluid. Differential, .43 qts., use 75W-140 hypoid gear lubricant.

## LUBRICANT DATA

| Year | Model | Lubricant Type | | | | |
|---|---|---|---|---|---|---|
| | | Transaxle | | | | |
| | | Manual | Automatic | Rear Axle | Power Steering | Brake System |
| 1989–92 | All | — | Mercon | 75W-140② | ① | DOT 3 |

①—Use Mopar 82200946 or equivalent power steering fluid.
②—Synthetic type lubricant.

# Electrical

INDEX



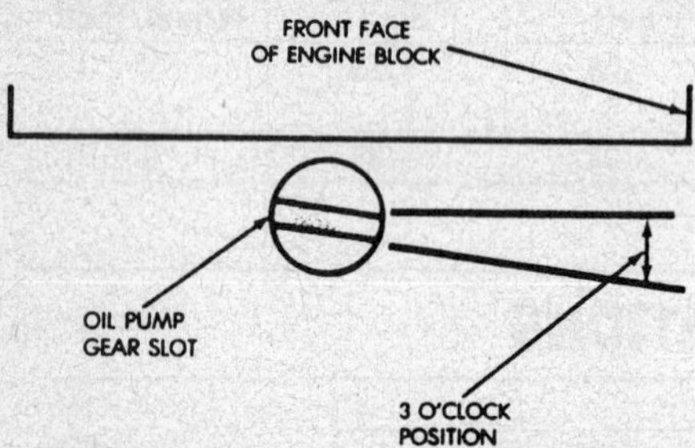


**Fig. 1 Positioning oil pump gear slot. 2.5L/4-150 engine.**

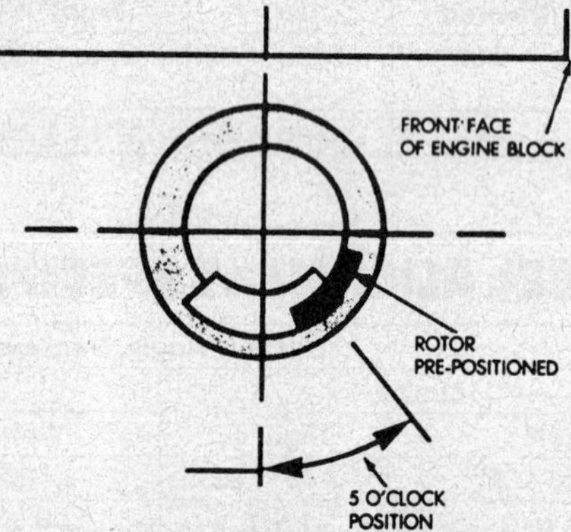


**Fig. 2 Rotor position during distributor installation. 2.5L/4-150 engine.**

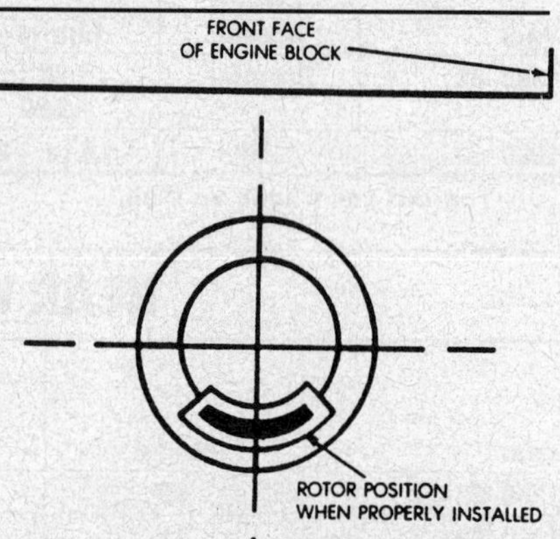


**Fig. 3 Rotor position once distributor is fully engaged. 2.5L/4-150 engine.**

## FUSE PANEL & FLASHER LOCATION

The fuse panel is located in the engine compartment, on the left inner fenderwell.

The flasher is integral with headlamp/turn signal module.

## STARTER REPLACE

1. Disconnect battery ground cable.
2. Disconnect two wires from starter solenoid.
3. Remove starter attaching bolts, then the starter motor and mounting plate.
4. Reverse procedure to install.

## DISTRIBUTOR REPLACE

### 2.5L/4-150 ENGINE

#### Removal

1. Remove distributor cap, leaving ignition coil and spark plug wires attached.
2. Scribe a mark on distributor housing inline with the tip of the rotor.
3. Scribe another mark on the distributor housing near the retaining clamp, continuing mark onto the engine block.
4. Remove distributor retaining bolt and clamp, then the distributor.

#### Installation

1. Clean the distributor mounting area and replace gasket in counterbore of cylinder block.
2. Position distributor in cylinder block.
3. If engine was not rotated while distributor was removed, proceed as follows:
   a. Align rotor tip with scribe mark on distributor housing, then turn rotor approximately 1/8 turn counterclockwise past mark.
   b. **Ensure distributor shaft fully engages oil pump drive gear shaft.** It may be necessary to slightly crank engine while exerting downward pressure on distributor to fully engage distributor shaft with oil pump drive gear shaft.
   c. Slide distributor shaft down into engine, aligning scribed mark on housing with corresponding mark on cylinder block.
   d. Install distributor hold-down clamp, then the bolt.
4. If engine was rotated while distributor was removed, proceed as follows:
   a. Remove No. 1 spark plug.
   b. Hold a finger over No. 1 spark plug hole and rotate engine until compression is felt, then continue slowly rotating engine until timing mark on vibration damper is at TDC. **Do not rotate engine backward to perform this task.**
   c. Using a flat screwdriver, rotate oil pump gear until gear slot on oil pump shaft is slightly past 3 o'clock position, **Fig. 1.**
   d. With distributor cap removed, install distributor with rotor located at 5 o'clock position, **Fig. 2.**
   e. Fully engage distributor into engine. At this time rotor should be at 6 o'clock position, **Fig. 3.**
   f. Install distributor hold-down clamp, then the bolt.

## STEERING WHEEL REPLACE

1. Disconnect battery ground cable.
2. Remove horn pad and disconnect horn button.
3. Disconnect two wires and remove horn button.
4. Noting position of reference mark on the end of the steering shaft, remove steering wheel nut and slide steering wheel off shaft.
5. Disconnect cruise control electrical connector if equipped, then remove steering wheel.
6. Reverse procedure to install.

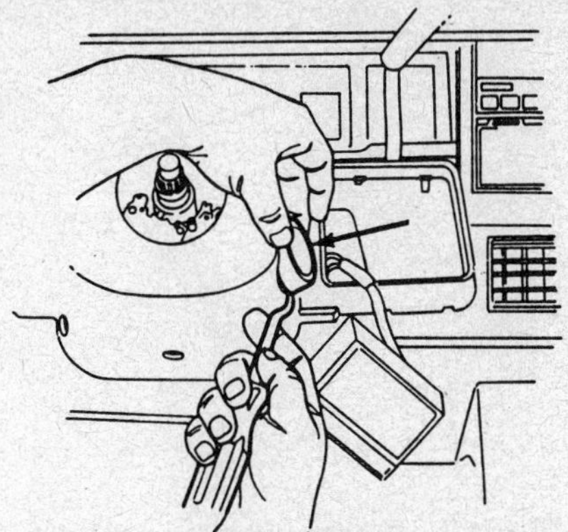

Fig. 4 Removing ignition switch trim ring

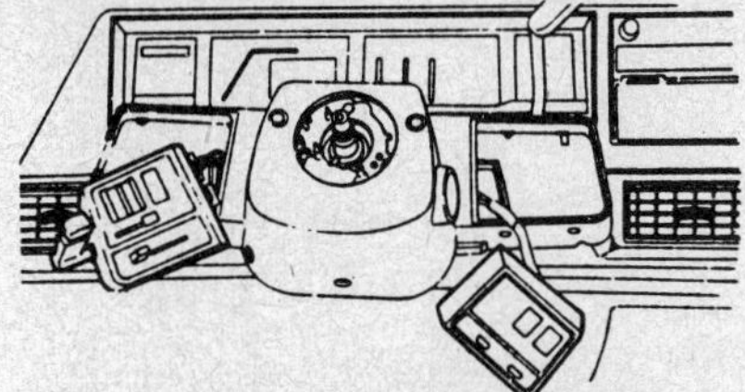

Fig. 5 Removing headlight & A/C-heater pods

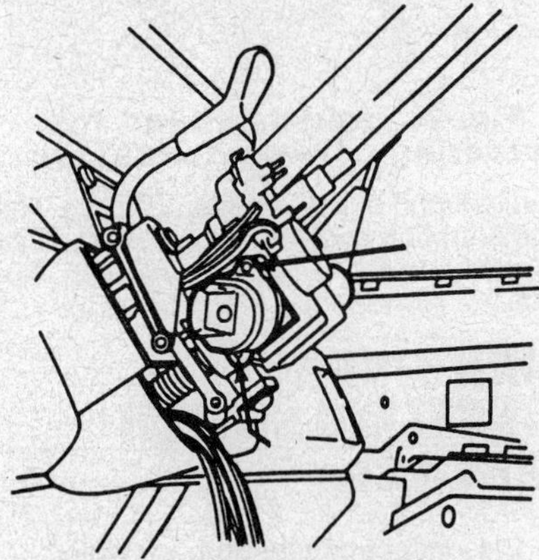

Fig. 7 Ignition switch retaining screws

Fig. 6 Removing key lock cylinder

## IGNITION LOCK
### REPLACE

1. Remove steering wheel, refer to "Steering Wheel Replace."
2. Remove turn signal canceler cam by unhooking tabs and sliding canceler off steering column. **If vehicle is equipped with tilt wheel, remove tilt wheel control arm.**
3. Remove upper and lower headlight pod retaining screws. **There are two small retaining clips on the headlight and A/C-heater pods that may fall off when pod is removed.**
4. Remove A/C-heater housing pod retaining screws, then carefully remove pod back.
5. Carefully remove headlight and A/C-heater pod.
6. Remove ignition switch trim ring by prying it away from pod housing, **Fig. 4.**
7. Remove retaining screws and the headlight pod back.
8. Remove screws from housing, then pass pods through openings in pod housing and remove housing, **Fig. 5.**
9. Place key in unmarked position lining up key with groove in lock cylinder housing, **Fig. 6.**
10. Press locking tab from underneath as shown, **Fig. 6,** then remove lock cylinder.
11. Reverse procedure to install, ensuring steering wheel is aligned with reference mark on steering shaft. **Torque** steering wheel nut to 52 ft. lbs.

## IGNITION SWITCH
### REPLACE

1. Disconnect battery ground cable.
2. Remove screws and instrument panel lower cover.
3. Unfasten horn button and disconnect wires to remove.
4. Noting position of reference mark on the end of the steering shaft, remove steering wheel nut and slide steering wheel off shaft.
5. Disconnect electrical connector and remove steering wheel.
6. Remove turn signal canceler cam by unhooking tabs and sliding canceler off steering column. **If vehicle is equipped with tilt wheel, remove tilt wheel control arm.**
7. Remove upper and lower headlight pod retaining screws. **There are two small retaining clips on the headlight and A/C-heater pods that may fall off when pod is removed.**
8. Remove A/C-heater housing pod retaining screws, then carefully remove pod back.
9. Carefully remove headlight and A/C-heater pod.
10. Remove ignition switch trim ring by prying it away from pod housing, **Fig. 4.**
11. Remove retaining screws and the headlight pod back.
12. Remove screws from housing, then pass pods through openings in pod housing and remove housing, **Fig. 5.**
13. Remove screw, then separate and remove lower column shroud.
14. Remove upper column shroud attaching screws and the shroud.
15. Remove ignition switch retaining screws and separate ignition switch from lock cylinder housing, **Fig. 7.**
16. Cut tie straps, then remove screw and wire harness anchor.
17. Loosen hold-down nut in center of steering column connector.
18. Separate pod connectors from steering column connector by placing a flat blade screwdriver between the connectors to disengage locking tab.
19. Push on the wire side of headlight pod connector and slide the connector out of channels of steering column connector.
20. Remove ignition switch and harness.
21. Reverse procedure to install, ensuring steering wheel is aligned with reference mark on steering shaft. **Torque** steering wheel nut to 52 ft. lbs.

## NEUTRAL START SWITCH
### REPLACE

1. Disconnect neutral switch harness connector in engine compartment.
2. Raise and support vehicle, then remove splash shield.
3. Remove bolt attaching switch bracket to transaxle case, then the switch from case.
4. Remove neutral switch and harness from vehicle.
5. Reverse procedure to install, **torquing** switch bracket to 90 inch lbs.

## STOP LIGHT SWITCH
### REPLACE

#### 1989 MODELS LESS CRUISE CONTROL

1. Disconnect switch electrical connectors.
2. Remove pushrod bolt, then the switch.
3. Reverse procedure to install.

#### EXCEPT 1989 MODELS LESS CRUISE CONTROL

1. Disconnect switch electrical connectors.
2. Unseat switch retainer, then remove stop light switch.
3. Reverse procedure to install, noting the following:
   a. Ensure tabs on switch and retainer are aligned.
   b. Depress brake pedal and push in switch until housing is fully seated against switch bracket, release pedal and lightly pull up against internal master cylinder stop.

## HEADLAMP POD
### REPLACE

1. Disconnect battery ground cable.

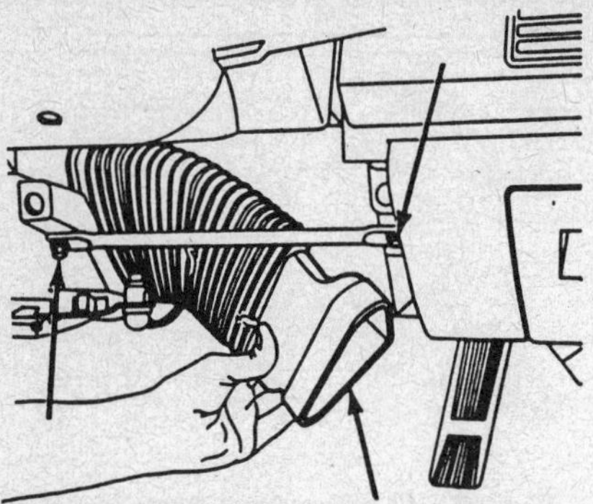

Fig. 8 Air duct & support bar

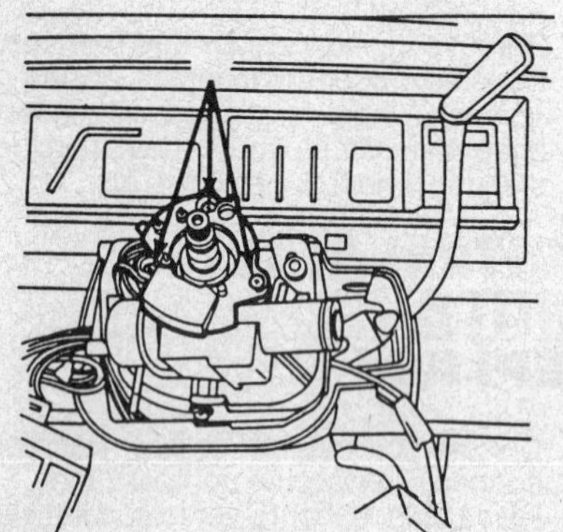

Fig. 11 Turn signal canceling switch

2. Remove screws and instrument panel lower cover.
3. Remove screws and support bar, then pull air duct out of the way, **Fig. 8.**
4. Remove tie straps, loosen hold-down nut in center of steering column connector, and separate steering column connector, **Fig. 9.**
5. Separate headlight pod connector from steering column connector by placing a flat blade screwdriver between the connectors to disengage locking tab.
6. Push on wire side of headlight pod connector and slide connector out of channels of steering column connector.
7. Remove upper and lower retaining screws from pod.
8. Gently pull pod wires out through housing enough to expose the two screws and remove screws, **Fig. 10.**
9. Remove rear of pod housing, then gently pull pod forward and pull harness out through housing to remove pod.
10. Reverse procedure to install.

# TURN SIGNAL SWITCH
## REPLACE

The turn signal switch is located in the headlight pod on the steering column. The turn signal and pod are serviced as an assembly. Refer to "Headlight Pod, Replace."

# DIMMER SWITCH
## REPLACE

The dimmer switch is located in the headlight pod on the steering column. The dimmer switch and pod are serviced as an assembly. Refer to "Headlight Pod, Replace."

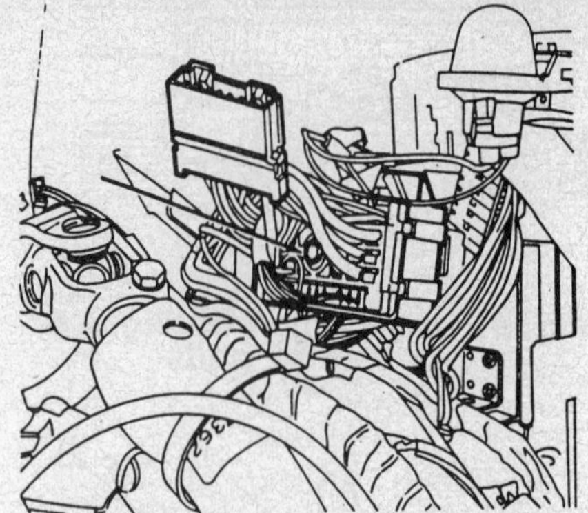

Fig. 9 Hold-down nut for steering column connector

# TURN SIGNAL CANCELING SWITCH
## REPLACE

1. Disconnect battery ground cable.
2. Remove screws and instrument panel lower cover.
3. Unfasten horn button and disconnect wires to remove.
4. Noting position of reference mark on the end of the steering shaft, remove steering wheel nut and slide steering wheel off shaft.
5. Disconnect electrical connector and remove steering wheel.
6. Remove turn signal canceler cam by unhooking tabs and sliding canceler off steering column. **If vehicle is equipped with tilt wheel remove tilt wheel control arm.**
7. Remove upper and lower headlight pod retaining screws. **There are two small retaining clips on the headlight and A/C-heater pods that may fall off when pod is removed.**
8. Remove A/C-heater housing pod retaining screws, then carefully remove pod back.
9. Carefully remove headlight and A/C-heater pod.
10. Remove ignition switch trim ring by prying it away from pod housing, **Fig. 4.**
11. Remove retaining screws and the headlight pod back.
12. Remove screws from housing, then pass pods through openings in pod housing and remove housing, **Fig. 5.**
13. Remove screw, then separate and remove lower column shroud.
14. Remove upper column shroud retaining screws and the shroud.
15. Remove screws to free turn signal canceling switch, then disconnect canceling switch connector and remove switch, **Fig. 11.**
16. Reverse procedure to install, ensuring steering wheel is aligned with reference mark on the steering shaft. **Torque** steering wheel nut to 52 ft. lbs.

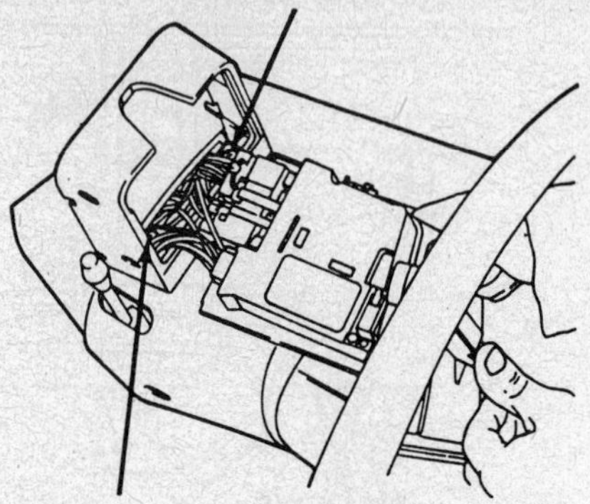

Fig. 10 Removing headlight pod back

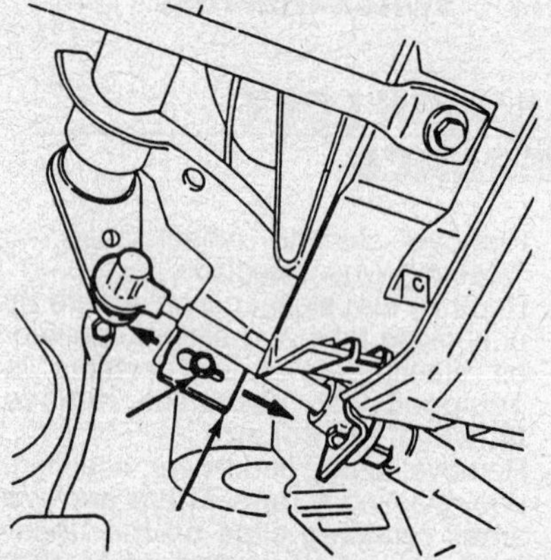

Fig. 12 Shift indicator cable anchor

# INSTRUMENT CLUSTER
## REPLACE
### REMOVAL

1. Disconnect battery ground cable.
2. Loosen screw that holds shift indicator anchor bracket in place.
3. Remove shift indicator cable anchor by sliding to keyhole position, **Fig. 12.**
4. Remove wire from rear of gearshift lever pulley.
5. Remove instrument cluster bezel retaining screws and the bezel, then remove cluster retaining screws.
6. Move gearshift lever to "1" position, then tilt cluster forward and disconnect electrical connectors.
7. Remove screws and instrument panel lower cover, then remove cluster.

### INSTALLATION

1. Guide shift indicator wire into instrument panel and down to shift linkage.
2. Connect electrical connectors and install cluster with screws.
3. Loop shift indicator wire over pulley and install shift cable anchor onto screw, **Fig. 13.**
4. Move gearshift lever to neutral position and check position of shift indicator. If pointer is not aligned with N on display, slide anchor until indicator is correct. Tighten screw and check for proper positioning of indicator in all positions, **Fig. 13.**

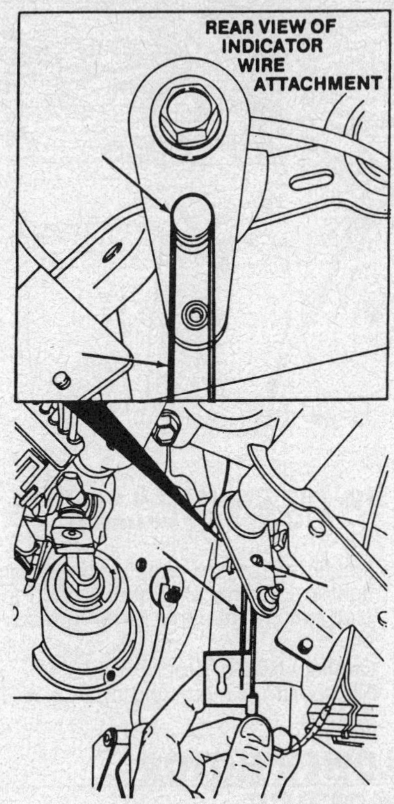


**Fig. 13 Removing wire from gearshift lever pulley**

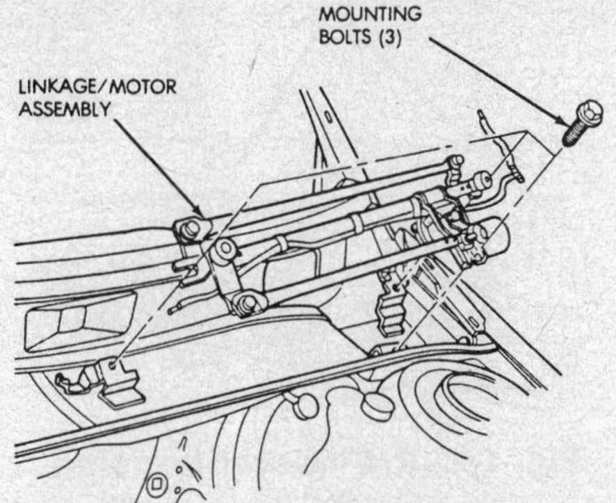


**Fig. 14 Wiper assembly replacement**

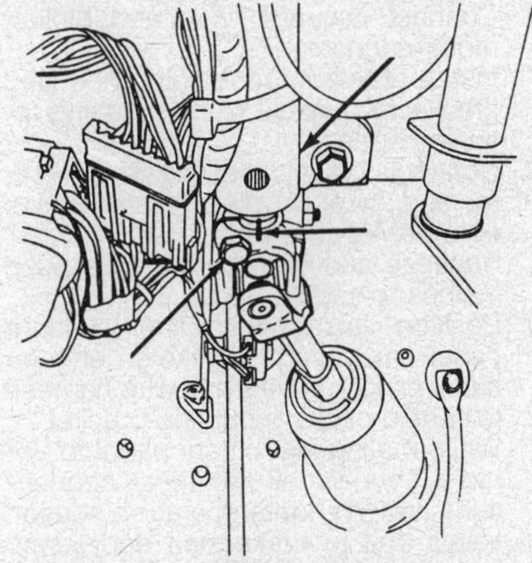

**Fig. 16 Steering column shaft & intermediate shaft**

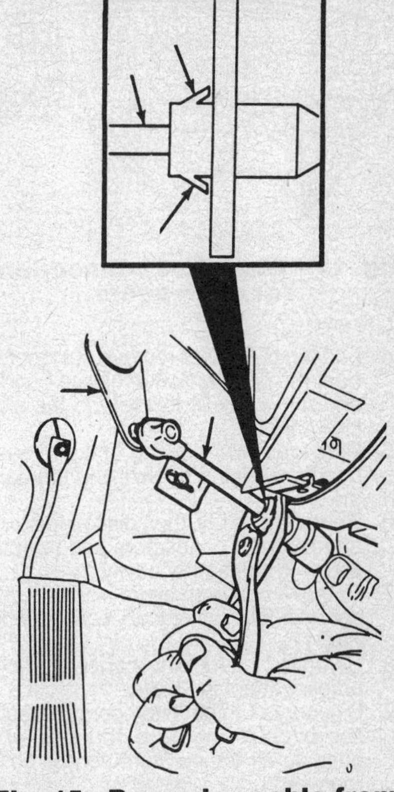

**Fig. 15 Removing cable from column mounting bracket**

5. Install bezel and instrument panel lower trim cover.

# WIPER SWITCH
## REPLACE

The wiper switch is located in the headlight pod on the steering column. The wiper switch and pod are serviced as an assembly. Refer to "Headlight Pod, Replace."

# WIPER MOTOR & LINKAGE
## REPLACE

1. Lift up on drivers side wiper arm, then bend retainer tab fully from wiper arm.
2. Remove drivers wiper arm assembly from arm shaft, then disconnect center and drivers washer hoses.
3. Lift up on passengers side wiper arm, then bend retainer tab fully from wiper arm.
4. Remove passengers wiper arm assembly from arm shaft.
5. Remove cowl screen hold-down bolts, then turn cowl screen locking screws 1/4 turn.
6. Remove left screen by sliding toward rear of car.
7. Using suitable fork, remove ball end of link by lifting upward.
8. Move linkage to maximum right position.
9. Hold motor crank arm, then remove center shaft locknut and spacer.
10. Remove motor crank arm from shaft, then the depressed park linkage.
11. Remove three wiper motor mounting bolts, then disconnect motor electrical connectors.
12. Disconnect washer hose at base of center tee fitting.
13. Remove wiper motor and linkage assembly, **Fig. 14.**
14. Reverse procedure to install, noting the following:
    a. **Torque** crank arm to motor shaft to 16 ft. lbs.
    b. Install center wiper arm onto shaft so that tip of blade is 0-2.5 inches.
    c. Install left wiper arm onto shaft so that tip of blade is 1.5-3.75 inches above grille.
    d. Cycle wipers once allowing them to park. Ensure wipers rest in park position.

# RADIO
## REPLACE

1. Disconnect battery ground cable.
2. Remove instrument cluster bezel.
3. Remove screws and pull radio forward and out of instrument panel.
4. Disconnect electrical connector, ground wire and antenna wire, then remove radio.
5. Reverse procedure to install.

# HEATER CORE
## REPLACE

### REMOVAL

1. Disconnect battery ground cable.
2. Remove instrument panel lower trim cover retaining screws and the cover.
3. Remove instrument panel support rod retaining screws and the rod.
4. Remove steering column wiring harness bulkhead connector retaining screw.
5. Disconnect automatic transaxle shift cable from lever with a screwdriver.
6. Compress cable retainer tangs with pliers and slide cable out of column mounting bracket, **Fig. 15.**
7. Loosen screw securing anchoring bracket in place, then move bracket to key hole position and remove it from its mounting bracket.
8. Lift indicator wire off of pulley.
9. Pull sleeve down to expose steering column universal joint.
10. Make a reference mark on steering column shaft and intermediate shaft and remove bolt from intermediate shaft, **Fig. 16.**
11. Remove bolts and nuts that hold steering column to instrument panel/brake sled.
12. Carefully lower steering column assembly to vehicle floor, then separate steering column shaft from intermediate shaft and remove column assembly from vehicle.
13. Remove defroster grille and remove bolts under grille.

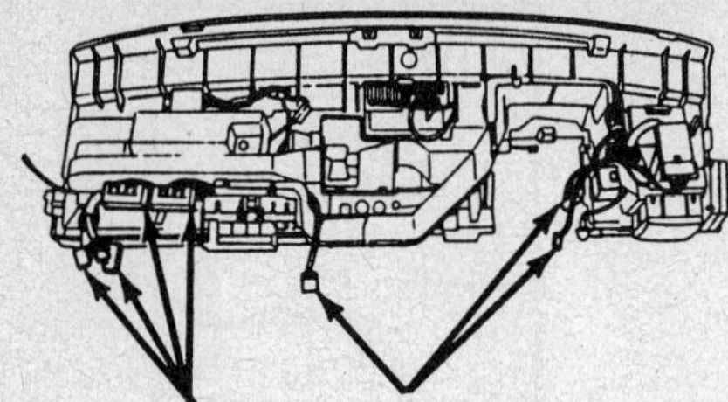

**Fig. 17 Electrical connections for dash panel**

14. Loosen but do not remove nut located near the parking brake release handle and nut which is located on the side kick panel.
15. Remove lower parking brake release handle retaining screws and the handle.
16. Remove ashtray, then disconnect cigarette lighter connectors and remove screw from ashtray cavity.
17. Remove bolt from brake sled and disconnect all electrical connections, **Fig. 17.**
18. Remove instrument panel to floor bracket attaching bolts.
19. Disconnect interior temperature sensor by pressing tabs together and pushing air temperature sensor hose rearward.
20. Carefully lift up and rearward to disengage and remove instrument panel, then remove floor duct extension.
21. Drain cooling system and discharge A/C system.
22. Squeeze and slide heater core hose clamps off of heater core tubes towards engine and carefully pry heater hoses off of heater core tubes. **Heater core tubes are made of plastic and may break if too much pressure is applied.**
23. Disconnect coolant level switch connector, then remove coolant reservoir retaining strap and move reservoir aside.
24. Disconnect blower motor electrical connector and vacuum hose.
25. Disconnect refrigerant lines from dash panel using appropriate tools from tool kit No. MS-1979 or equivalent.
26. Remove nuts holding A/C-heater housing to firewall.
27. From inside vehicle, remove nuts holding A/C-heater housing, **Fig. 18.**
28. Carefully pull A/C-heater housing rearward and remove from vehicle.
29. Release plastic tabs and remove heater core.

## INSTALLATION

1. Install heater core by gently pushing until core snaps into place.
2. Position A/C-heater housing to dash panel. Ensure drain tube extends through its opening in upper floor and blower motor connector and vacuum line extends through dash panel, **Fig. 19.**
3. Ensure ECU connectors are to right of drain tube and install nuts on inside of vehicle.

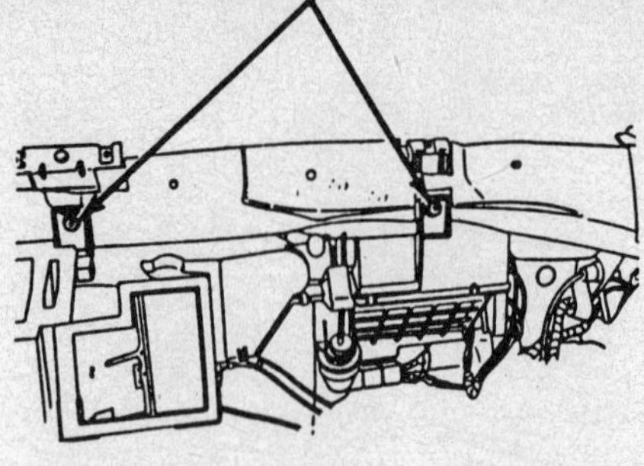

**Fig. 18 A/C-heater housing**

4. Install floor duct extension.
5. Install new O-rings on refrigerant lines and lubricate with a suitable refrigerant oil, then press each line into its connector until it snaps into place.
6. Connect vacuum hose and blower motor connector.
7. Install coolant reservoir mounting bracket and install reservoir using retaining strap.
8. Connect coolant level switch connector and carefully slide heater hoses onto heater core tubes.
9. Squeeze and slide heater core hose clamps to secure hoses.
10. Position instrument panel. Ensure panel mounting brackets engage studs on kick panels and wire harness is behind center mounting bracket.
11. While mating instrument panel to vehicle, connect all electrical connections and interior temperature sensor.
12. Install bolt to brake sled and screw into ashtray cavity.
13. Install bolts to center support bracket, connect cigarette lighter connectors and install ashtray.
14. Tighten nut located near parking brake release handle and nut which is located on passenger side kick panel.
15. Install parking brake release handle.
16. Install bolts and the defroster grille.
17. Position and install steering column shaft in intermediate steering shaft U-joint. Align two shafts using reference marks made during removal.
18. Install, but do not tighten, U-joint bolt.
19. Lift steering column into position and install nuts and bolts that attach column to instrument panel. **Torque** bolts to 35 ft. lbs.
20. Tighten bolt in intermediate steering shaft U-joint.
21. Move plastic sleeve back into position and snap shift cable into mounting bracket.
22. Snap shift cable head onto mounting ball in shift arm.
23. Loop the shift indicator wire over the pulley and position anchoring bracket over screw.
24. Move gearshift lever to neutral position and check position of shift indicator. If pointer is not aligned with N on display, slide anchor until indicator is correct. Tighten screw and check for proper positioning of indicator in all positions, **Fig. 13.**
25. Install bulkhead connector and connector attaching screw and connect column connector.

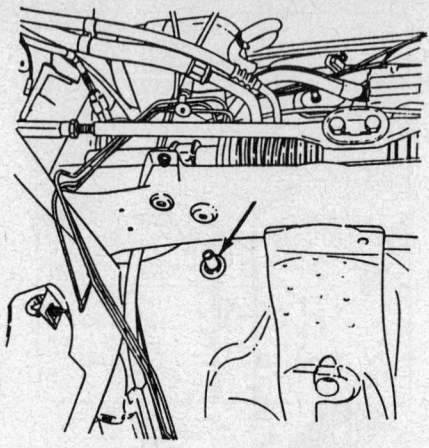

**Fig. 19 Drain tube position A/C-heater housing**

26. Install instrument panel support rod, tighten rod attaching screws and install instrument panel lower trim cover.
27. Connect battery ground cable.
28. Fill cooling system and charge A/C system.

# BLOWER MOTOR
## REPLACE

1. Disconnect coolant level switch electrical connector.
2. Remove coolant reservoir retaining strap and move reservoir aside.
3. Remove coolant reservoir mounting bracket bolts and the bracket.
4. Pry off retaining clip and disconnect wires from blower motor.
5. Remove blower motor mounting screws and the blower motor.
6. Reverse procedure to install.

# EVAPORATOR CORE
## REPLACE

1. **On models equipped with knee bolster,** remove ash tray, then ash tray receiver retaining screw.
2. Disconnect cigar lighter electrical connector.
3. Remove two front console to bracket retaining screws.
4. Remove three armrest assembly to console retaining screws, then the armrest.
5. Remove two rear of console to bracket retaining screws.
6. Remove seat belt guide from inside console.
7. Remove console.
8. Remove two pivot bracket to knee bolster retaining bolts.
9. Loosen two pivot bracket retaining screws. **Do not remove retaining screws.**
10. Remove one screw and two Torx bolts retaining forward console bracket to floor.
11. Slide forward console bracket rearward.

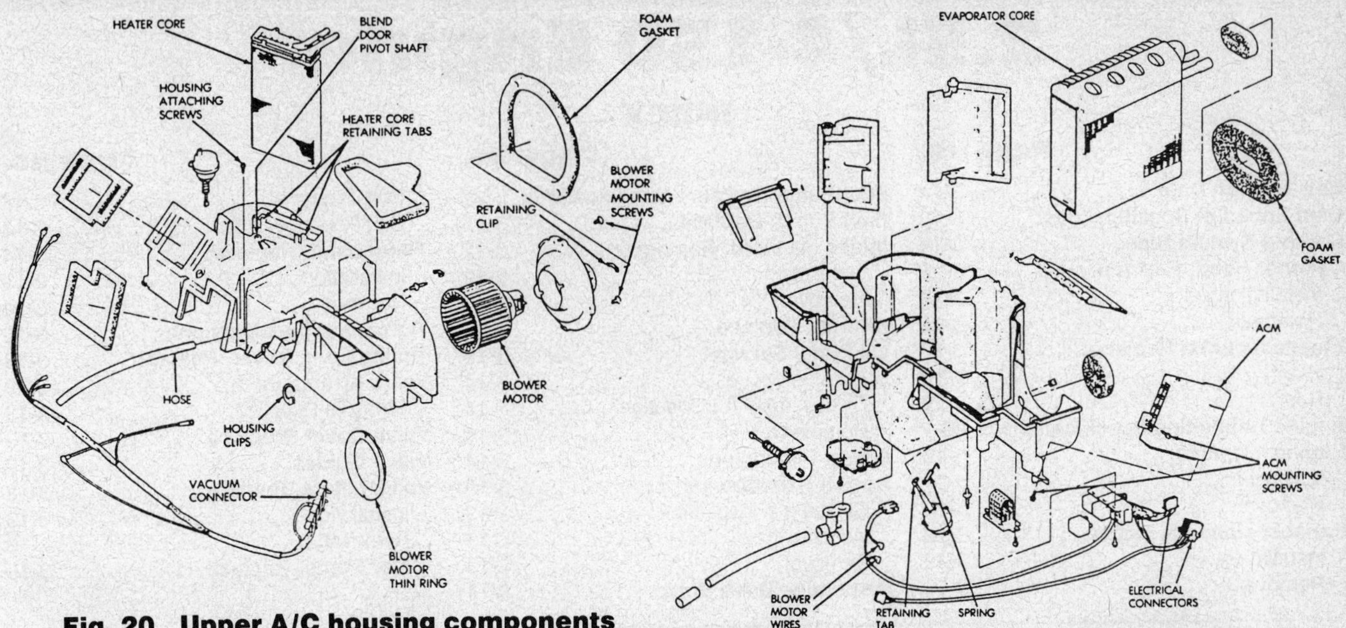


**Fig. 20 Upper A/C housing components**

**Fig. 21 Lower A/C housing components**

12. Remove two knee bolster to instrument panel retaining screws from center of knee bolster.
13. Remove one knee bolster retaining screw located to left of steering column.
14. Remove one air duct to knee bolster retaining screw.
15. Remove garnish molding retaining screw located at bottom of instrument panel.
16. Remove four retaining nuts at ends of knee bolster.
17. Move knee bolster toward rear of vehicle enough to gain access to the two parking brake release handle retaining screws.
18. Remove brake handle retaining screws, then the knee bolster.
19. Remove heater core, refer to "Heater Core Replace."
20. Remove vacuum and electrical connectors from A/C control module, **Fig. 20.**
21. Remove A/C module retaining screws, then the module.
22. Unlock retaining tab and remove motor arm from door pivot arm.
23. Remove spring and clear vacuum line from motor.
24. Release heater core retaining tabs, then remove core, **Fig. 20.**
25. Remove foam gaskets, then disconnect blower motor electrical connector.
26. Remove blower motor.
27. Remove upper to lower housing attaching screws and clips.
28. Separate upper and lower housing halves.
29. Remove evaporator core, **Fig. 21.**
30. Reverse procedure to install. **Add three ounces of refrigerant oil if evaporator core is replaced.**

# 2.5L/4-150 Engine

## INDEX



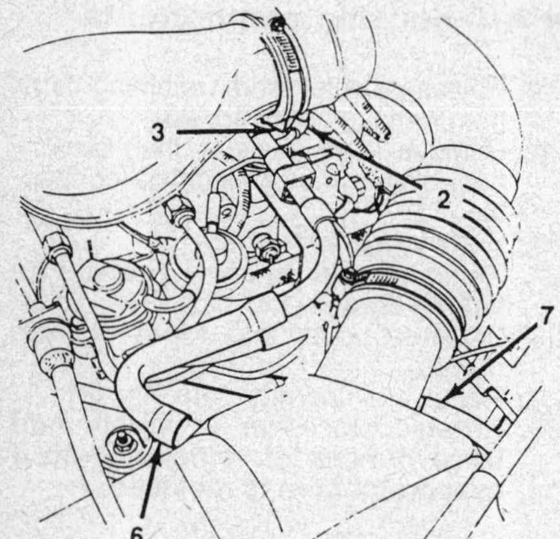


**Fig. 1 Routing of vacuum lines & hoses**

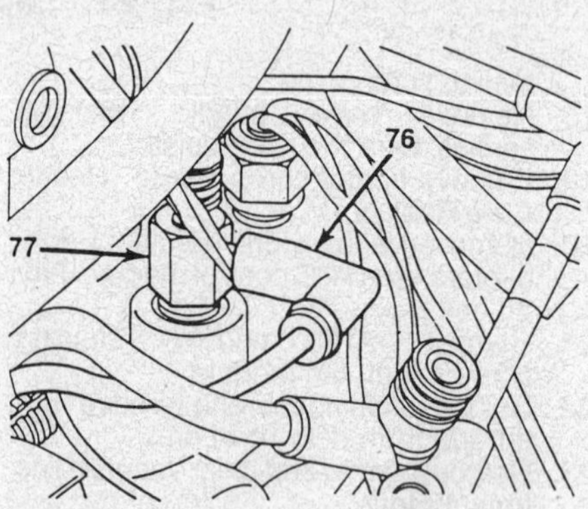


**Fig. 2 Intake vacuum port**

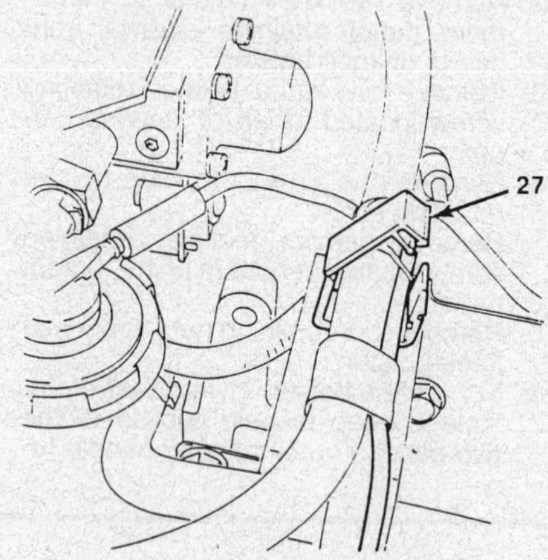


**Fig. 3 Molded vacuum assembly**

## ENGINE MOUNTS REPLACE

### FRONT

1. Disconnect battery ground cable, then remove top engine mount nuts.
2. Raise and support vehicle, then remove bottom engine mount nuts.
3. Raise engine enough to remove engine mount. It may be necessary to disconnect engine pitch restrictor.
4. Reverse procedure to install.

### REAR

1. Disconnect battery ground cable, then raise and support vehicle.
2. Remove underbody splash shield, then the exhaust bracket.
3. Support transaxle with suitable jack.
4. Remove crossmember bolts that attach side of transaxle crossmember to engine cradle.
5. Remove rear mount bolt that attaches rear mount to crossmember, then the crossmember.
6. Remove rear mount bracket from case.
7. Reverse procedure to install.

## ENGINE REPLACE

### REMOVAL

1. Position vehicle on side mount hoist or lift from under tires.
2. Disconnect both battery cables.
3. Drain cooling system.
4. Remove air bonnet and tube and disconnect vacuum lines (2 and 3), **Fig. 1.**
5. Remove crankcase ventilation and evaporative emissions canister hoses (6 and 7) from air cleaner.
6. Using finger pressure, unfasten accelerator and cruise control cables and position aside.
7. Disconnect hot air tube and hot air door vacuum line from air cleaner.
8. Disconnect air cleaner attaching clips and remove air cleaner.
9. Remove battery hold-down bracket and the battery.
10. Remove fuel tank filler cap to relieve pressure, then reinstall the cap.
11. Disconnect black fuel supply line and gray fuel return line from throttle body.
12. Disconnect vacuum hose from vacuum port on the intake manifold and vacuum hose (76) from EGR transducer (77), **Fig. 2.**
13. Disconnect vacuum hoses from EGR solenoid on driver's side of engine compartment.
14. Disconnect CCV hose from valve cover.
15. Unfasten clamp and position aside molded vacuum manifold assembly (27), **Fig. 3.**
16. Disconnect MAP sensor vacuum line (21), then HEVAC vacuum reservoir vacuum hose (22). Unfasten bulkhead screw, then (23) pull bulkhead connector (24) and position aside, **Fig. 4.**
17. Disconnect hose from vacuum brake booster.
18. Unfasten heater hoses, upper radiator hoses and coolant expansion bottle

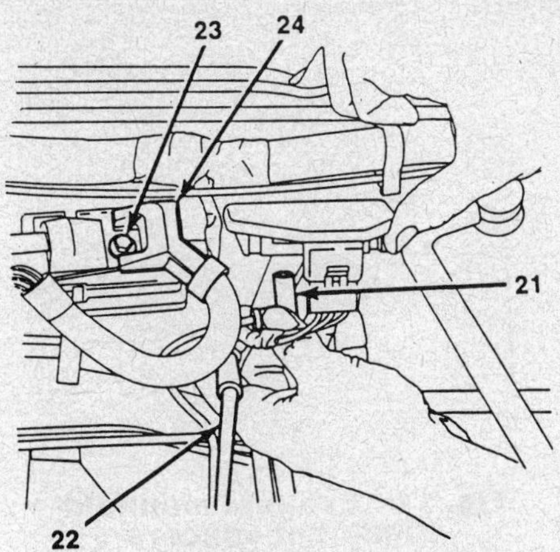

**Fig. 4 Bulkhead connector**

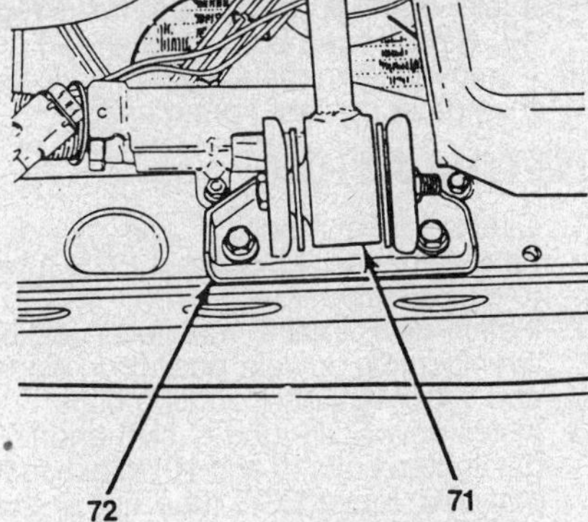

**Fig. 5 Pitch restrictor to crossmember**

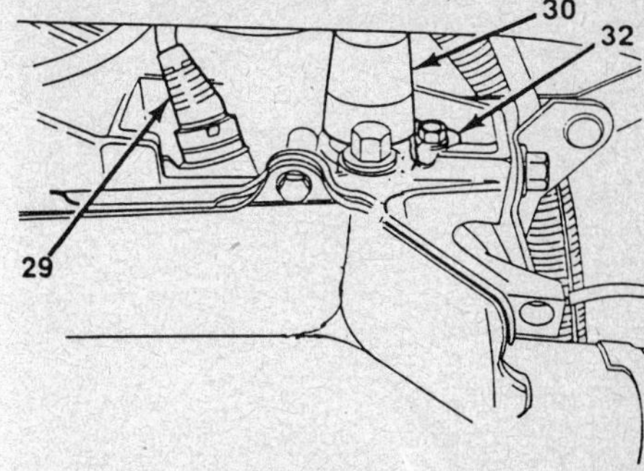

**Fig. 6 Multi-function switch at transmission**

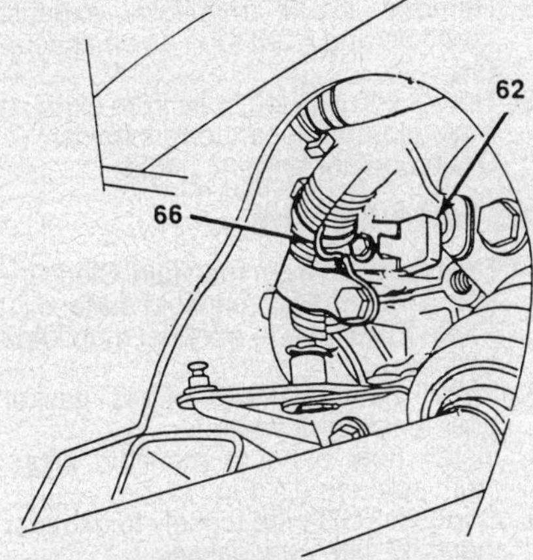

**Fig. 7 Sensor & ground wire at transmission**

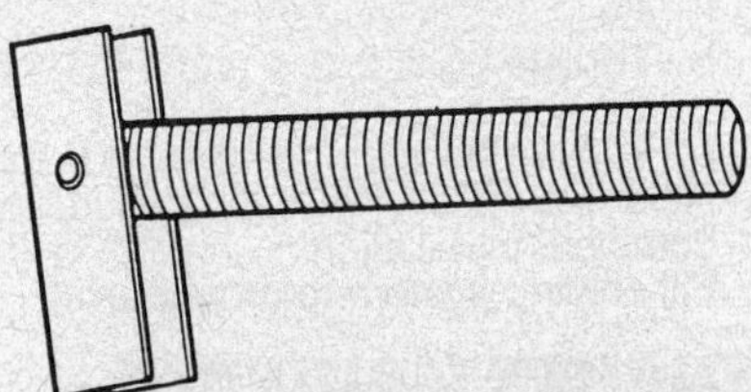
**Fig. 8 Cradle to dolly attaching bolt**

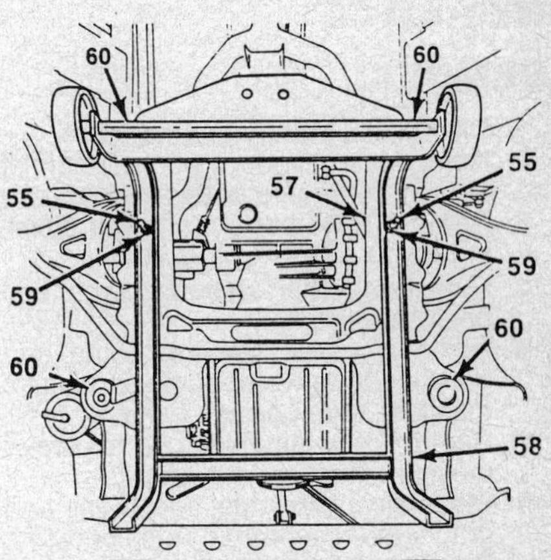

**Fig. 9 Cradle to vehicle installation**

hoses and position aside.

19. Disconnect coil wire from MPA module.
20. Remove power steering pivot and attaching bolts and position power steering pump aside.
21. Disconnect lower radiator hose from radiator.
22. Disconnect wires from starter and ground wire from starter mounting bolt.
23. Disconnect A/C wire connector (50), then compressor mounting bolts (51) and position compressor aside.
24. Disconnect alternator connector and output wire.
25. Disconnect oil pressure sender wire and TPS electrical connector.
26. Raise and support vehicle.
27. Remove front tire and wheel assemblies.
28. Unfasten brake caliper and position aside, leaving hydraulic lines attached.
29. Remove hub nut on both sides.
30. Remove steering knuckle to strut attaching nuts on both sides of vehicle. **Bolts are splined and must not be turned.**
31. Separate strut to steering knuckle by removing lower strut bolts from both sides of vehicle.
32. Raise vehicle further and remove four bolts securing transmission shield.
33. Using a suitable screwdriver, disconnect transmission shift cable from linkage arm, then remove shifter cable bracket.
34. Disconnect exhaust system from catalytic converter.
35. Remove engine splash shield and disconnect oil level sensor connector.
36. Disconnect pitch restrictor (71) from bracket on body front lower crossmember, then remove bracket (72), **Fig. 5.**
37. Remove solenoid and unfasten wire harness attached to dipstick tube and position aside.
38. Disconnect TCU electrical connector (29) from transmission.
39. Disconnect multi-function switch (30) from transmission by removing retainer (32), **Fig. 6.**
40. Disconnect sensor (62) and ground wire (66) and position aside, **Fig. 7.**
41. Position sub-frame dolly (Mot 1040.99), wheels toward rear of vehicle. Install dolly (58) to cradle by inserting special attaching bolts (55), **Fig. 8.** into holes of cradle (57) and tighten nuts (59) **Fig. 9.**
42. Lower hoist until dolly rests on floor, then remove four cradle mounting bolts (60).
43. Raise vehicle off engine.
44. To position dolly for installation, draw the outline of dolly legs and center of wheels.

## INSTALLATION

To position engine/transmission under vehicle, install floor jack under front bar of dolly, then jack front legs of dolly one inch off ground and move dolly to outline marks.

1. Lower vehicle onto cradle until it contacts cradle bolt pads. **Cradle bolts must be installed with rubber spacers between the body and metal washers.**
2. Install cradle mounting bolts and tighten to specifications.
3. Raise vehicle and connect steering knuckle to strut using splined strut bolts. Tighten to specifications. **Bolts are splined and must not be tightened.**
4. Install hub nut and tighten to specifications.
5. Install disk brake pads and calipers.
6. Raise vehicle further and remove sub-frame dolly.
7. Refer to "Removal" procedure to complete installation, noting the following:
   a. Tighten front engine support bracket bolts to lower body crossmember to specifications.
   b. Tighten attaching nuts and bolts to specifications.
   c. Finger tighten power steering pivot bolt and rear mounting bolts, then tighten to specifications.
   d. Fill cooling system to specifications.

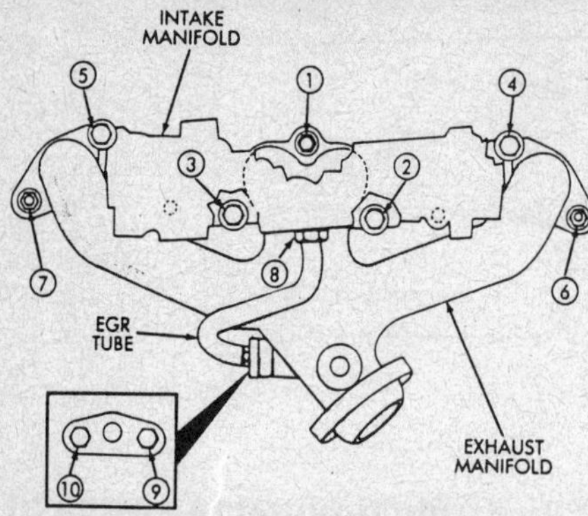


**Fig. 10 Intake & exhaust manifold bolt sequence**

# INTAKE MANIFOLD
## REPLACE
### REMOVAL

1. Disconnect battery ground cable.
2. Remove throttle body bonnet/air inlet hose from throttle body air cleaner.
3. Remove drive belt from power steering pump.
4. Unfasten power steering pump and position aside.
5. Remove power steering pump and brackets from water pump and intake manifold, then position aside.
6. Remove fuel tank filler cap to relieve pressure, then reinstall cap.
7. Disconnect black fuel supply line and gray return line from throttle body.
8. Disconnect accelerator cable from throttle body and hold-down bracket.
9. With finger pressure, disconnect cruise control connector from throttle body.
10. Unfasten electrical connectors for throttle position sensor, idle speed control motor, coolant temperature sensor from thermostat, coolant temperature sensor from intake manifold, fuel injector, air temperature sensor and oxygen sensor.
11. Disconnect crankcase ventilation vacuum hose and MAP sensor vacuum hose connector from throttle body.
12. Disconnect vacuum hose (76) from vacuum port (77) on the intake manifold, **Fig. 2.**
13. Disconnect vacuum hose from EGR transducer.
14. Disconnect vacuum hoses from EGR solenoid on driver's side of engine compartment.
15. Disconnect CCV hose from valve cover.
16. Remove molded vacuum harness.
17. Disconnect vacuum brake booster hose from intake manifold.
18. Loosen EGR tube nut from intake manifold and remove bolts securing EGR tube to exhaust manifold.
19. Install Mot. 453.01 clamps to heater hoses at front and rear of intake manifold.
20. Remove heater hose clamps and disconnect hoses from intake manifold.
21. Remove bolts (2, 3, 4 and 5) securing intake manifold to cylinder head **Fig. 10.**, then loosen bolts (1, 6 and 7).
22. Remove intake manifold and gaskets, then drain coolant from manifold.

### INSTALLATION

1. Clean intake manifold and cylinder head surfaces. Also clean EGR tube to exhaust manifold.
2. Install new intake manifold gasket over locating dowels, position in place and finger tighten mounting bolts.
3. Install new EGR tube gasket and finger tighten bolts (9 and 10) to exhaust manifold, leave EGR tube nut at the manifold finger tightened.
4. Tighten intake manifold bolts **Fig. 10**, in the following sequence:
   a. **Torque** bolts 1, 6, 7 and 8 to 30 ft. lbs.
   b. **Torque** bolts 2, 3, 4 and 5 to 23 ft. lbs.
   c. **Torque** bolts 9 and 10 to 14 ft. lbs.
5. Refer to "Removal" procedure to complete installation.
6. Fill cooling system to proper level.

# EXHAUST MANIFOLD
## REPLACE
### REMOVAL

1. Disconnect battery ground cable.
2. Remove air cleaner bonnet/inlet hose from throttle body and air cleaner.
3. Loosen EGR tube nut from intake manifold and bolts from the exhaust manifold.
4. Disconnect exhaust down pipe from exhaust manifold.
5. Remove power steering pump and brackets from water pump and intake manifold, then position aside.
6. Remove fuel tank filler to relive pressure, then reinstall cap.
7. With finger pressure, disconnect cruise control connector from throttle body.
8. Disconnect electrical connectors for throttle position sensor, idle speed control motor, coolant temperature sensor from thermostat, coolant temperature sensor from intake manifold, fuel injector, air temperature sensor and oxygen sensor, then position harness aside.
9. Disconnect crankcase ventilation vacuum hose and MAP sensor vacuum hose connector from throttle body.
10. Disconnect vacuum hose from vacuum port on intake manifold.
11. Disconnect vacuum hose from EGR transducer, also vacuum hoses from EGR solenoid on drivers side of engine compartment.
12. Disconnect CCV hose from valve cover.
13. Remove molded vacuum harness.
14. Disconnect vacuum brake booster hose from intake manifold.
15. Loosen EGR tube nut from intake manifold and remove bolts securing EGR tube to exhaust manifold.
16. Install Mot. 453.01 clamps to heater hoses at front and rear of intake manifold.

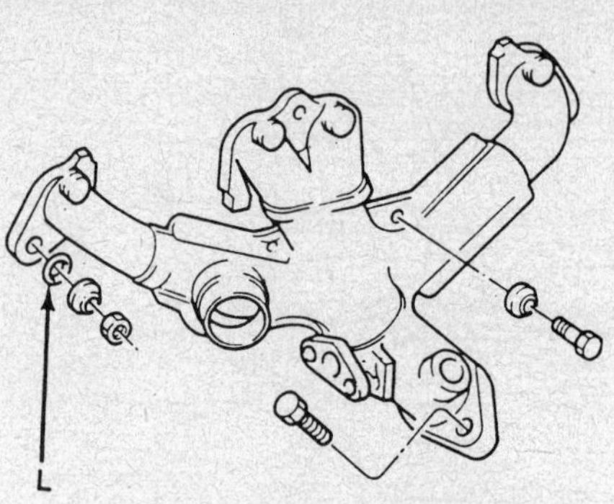


**Fig. 11 Exhaust manifold alignment spacers**

17. Remove heater hose clamps and disconnect hoses from intake manifold.
18. Remove intake manifold, exhaust manifold and EGR tube as an assembly.
19. Remove EGR tube bolts from exhaust manifold and separate manifolds.
20. Drain coolant from manifold.

### INSTALLATION

1. Drain coolant from manifold. Clean intake and exhaust manifold surface.
2. Clean EGR tube to exhaust manifolds surface.
3. Install new intake manifold gasket over locating dowels.
4. Install new exhaust manifold alignment spacers (L), **Fig. 11.**
5. Connect EGR tube loosely to exhaust manifold with new gasket.
6. Position manifold in place and finger tighten mounting bolts.
7. **Torque** bolts in sequence as follows, **Fig. 10.**:
   a. Bolts 1, 6, 7 and 8, to 30 ft. lbs.
   b. Bolts 2, 3, 4 and 5 to 23 ft. lbs.
   c. Bolts 9 and 10 to 14 ft. lbs.
8. Refer to "Removal" procedure to complete installation. **Torque** exhaust down pipe bolts to 25 ft. lbs.
9. Fill cooling system to proper level.

# CYLINDER HEAD
## REPLACE
### REMOVAL

1. Disconnect battery ground cable and drain cooling system.
2. Remove A/C drive belt, then unfasten compressor and position aside.
3. Remove A/C compressor bracket to cylinder head attaching bolts and loosen bracket to block attaching bolts.
4. Disconnect upper radiator and heater hose from thermostat housing.
5. Remove valve cover as described under "Valve Cover, Replace."
6. To avoid damage, alternately loosen then remove two cap screws from each rocker arm bridge and pivot assembly.
7. Remove the bridges, pivots and rocker arms and place on bench in order removed.

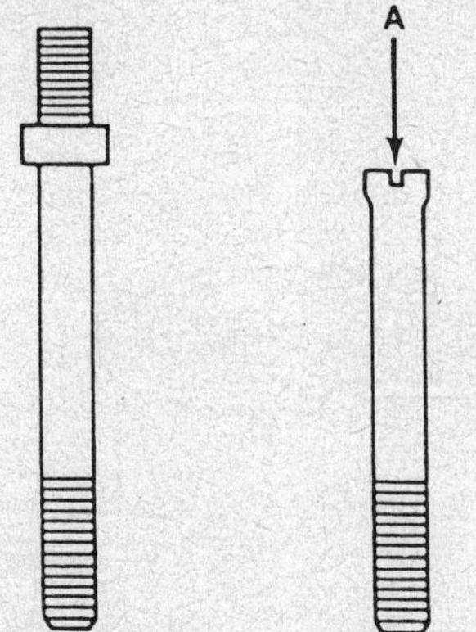


**Fig. 12 Cylinder head alignment dowels**

8. Remove intake and exhaust manifolds, as described under "Exhaust Manifold, Replace" and "Intake Manifold, Replace."
9. Remove cylinder head bolts, cylinder head and gasket.

### INSTALLATION

To ease installation, fabricate two used head bolts as alignment dowels. Cut the head off one bolt and cut a slot (A) in the second bolt, **Fig. 12.**

1. Insert one dowel in bolt hole No. 10, the other in bolt hole No. 8. Place cylinder head gasket with numbers facing up on dowels, then install cylinder head.
2. Install remaining head bolts except No. 7. Coat threads of No. 7 with Loctite or suitable sealant, then install bolt.
3. Remove dowels and install head bolts No. 8 and 10.
4. **Torque** bolts in sequence to 22 ft. lbs., **Fig. 13.**
5. **Torque** bolts in sequence to 45 ft. lbs.
6. Recheck all bolts ensuring the torque is 45 ft. lbs.
7. In sequence **torque** all bolts except No. 7 to 110 ft. lbs. and No. 7 to 100 ft. lbs.
8. Install pushrods, rocker arms, pivots and bridges in the order removed.
9. Refer to "Removal" procedure to complete installation, noting the following:
   a. Tighten A/C compressor mounting bracket to cylinder head and block and A/C compressor to bracket to specifications.
   b. Fill cooling system to proper level.

## VALVE ARRANGEMENT

### FRONT TO REAR

2.5L/4-150 . . . . . . . . . . . . . . . E-I-I-E-E-I-I-E

## CAM LOBE LIFT SPECIFICATIONS

Intake. . . . . . . . . . . . . . . . . . . . . . . . .240inch
Exhaust. . . . . . . . . . . . . . . . . . . . . . .250inch

## VALVE COVER REPLACE

1. Remove cooling system air bleed hose holders.
2. Disconnect crankcase ventilation vacuum hose from valve cover.
3. Disconnect fresh air inlet hose from valve cover.
4. Remove cover mounting bolts and the cover. **Break cover seal completely before prying upward.**
5. Reverse procedure to install. Clean cylinder head and valve cover surfaces before installing.

## VALVE LIFTERS REPLACE

### REMOVAL

1. Remove valve cover as previously described.
2. Remove bridge and pivot assemblies, then the rocker arms by alternately loosening each capscrew, one turn at a time. **Ensure all components are removed and installed in the same order.**
3. Remove pushrods, then the lifters through pushrod openings in cylinder head with suitable tool.
4. Inspect valve lifters and camshaft lobes for wear and replace if necessary. **Retain lifters in order of removal.**

### INSTALLATION

1. Apply suitable oil conditioner to lifters, then install lifters using a suitable tool.
2. Install pushrods in same location as they were removed.
3. Tighten capscrews loosely, one turn at a time with rocker arms, bridge and pivot assemblies in proper position, then tighten to specifications.
4. Pour remaining oil conditioner over valve assembly and let remain with engine oil for at least 1000 miles.
5. Install valve cover.

## ROCKER ARM SERVICE

### REMOVAL

1. Remove valve cover.
2. Alternately loosen each bridge and pivot assembly capscrew one turn at a time.
3. Remove capscrews, bridges, pivot assemblies and pushrods, then set on bench in sequence removed.

### CLEANING & INSPECTION

1. Clean components with cleaning solvent and use compressed air to blow out oil passages in rocker arms and pushrods.
2. Inspect pivot surface area of rocker arms. Replace if any are scuffed, pitted or excessively worn.
3. Inspect valve stem to tip contact surface of rocker arm and replace if pitted.

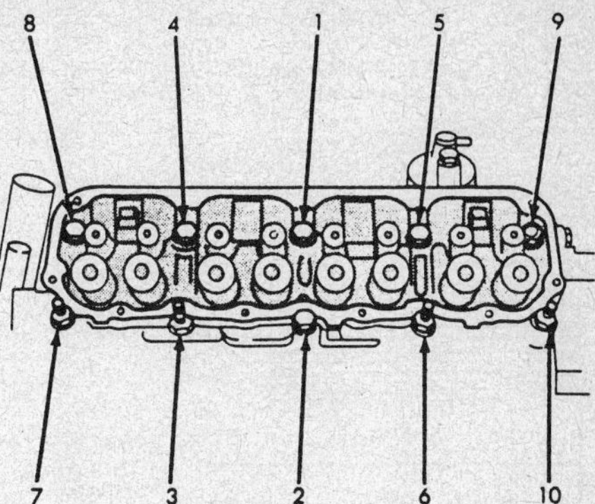


**Fig. 13 Cylinder head torque sequence**

4. Inspect pushrod end for excessive wear, also check corresponding hydraulic lifter. If worn, replace as necessary.
5. Inspect length of pushrod and cylinder head for abnormal wear and correct condition if required.

### INSTALLATION

1. Apply suitable oil conditioner to pushrods. then install pushrods into center of lifter.
2. Lubricate area of rocker arm that the pivot contacts and install rocker arms, pivots and bridge to location removed.
3. Tighten capscrews alternately one turn at a time to specifications.
4. Install valve cover.

## VALVE GUIDES

Valve guides are an integral part of the cylinder head and are not replaceable. When the valve stem guide clearance is excessive, the valve guide bores must be reamed oversize. Service valves with oversize stems are available in .003 inch and .015 inch increments. Corresponding oversize valve stem seals are also available and must be used with valve having .015 oversize stems.

If valve guides are reamed oversized, the valve seats must be reground after to ensure that the valve seat is concentric to the valve guide.

## TIMING CASE COVER REPLACE

1. Disconnect battery ground cable.
2. Remove vibration damper, the the fan shroud assembly.
3. Remove water pump pulley, then the accessory drive brackets that are attached to timing case cover.
4. Remove A/C compressor (if equipped) and alternator bracket assembly from cylinder head. Position aside.
5. Remove timing case cover attaching bolts, then the case cover front seal and gasket from engine.
6. Cut off oil pan side gasket end tabs and oil pan front seal tabs flush with front face of cylinder block. Remove gasket tabs.

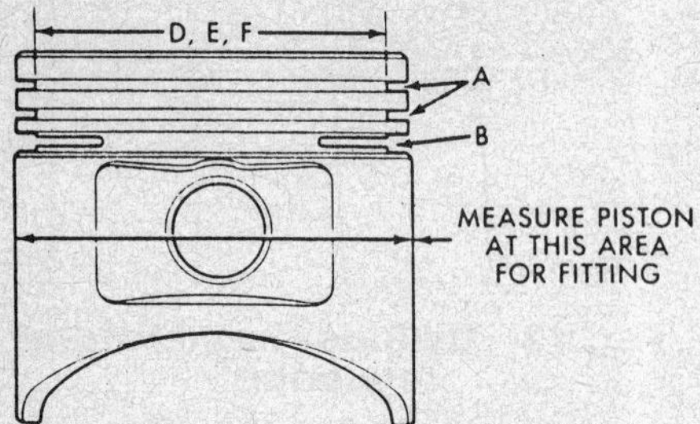


**Fig. 14 Piston dimensions**

7. Reverse procedure to install.

# PISTON DIMENSIONS

Refer to **Fig. 14**, for piston dimensions.

# OIL PAN REPLACE

1. Disconnect battery ground cable.
2. Raise and support vehicle.
3. Remove oil pan drain plug, then drain engine oil.
4. Disconnect exhaust downpipe at exhaust manifold.
5. Disconnect exhaust hanger at converter, then lower pipe.
6. Remove starter.
7. Remove converter/flywheel housing access cover.
8. Remove oil pan attaching bolts, then remove pan and discard gasket.
9. Reverse procedure to install.

# OIL PUMP SERVICE

## REMOVAL

1. Remove oil pan.
2. Remove oil pump to cylinder block retaining bolts. **If oil tube or strainer is disturbed or moved, a replacement tube and strainer must be replaced.**

## DISASSEMBLY & INSPECTION

1. Remove pump cover retaining screws and the cover.
2. Position Plastigage across the full width of each gear, **Fig. 15,** then reinstall pump cover and tighten to specifications.
3. Remove cover and compare compressed Plastigage with scale on envelope. Gear end clearance should be .002-.006 inch. Replace oil pump if clearance is excessive.
4. Insert a feeler gauge between each gear tooth and pump body inner wall, **Fig. 16.** Gear to pump body clearance should be .002-.004. Replace idler gear, shaft and drive gear assembly if clearance is excessive.
5. Remove pickup tube and screen assembly to check pressure relief valve. Remove cotter pin, then slide spring retainer, spring and pressure relief valve plunger out of pump body. If plunger binds during removal, clean or replace as necessary. **Relief valve plungers are available in standard or .010 inch oversizes.**

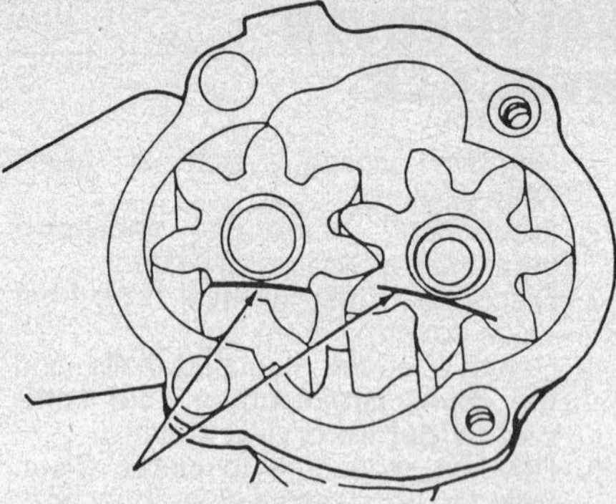

**Fig. 15 Oil pump gear end clearance**

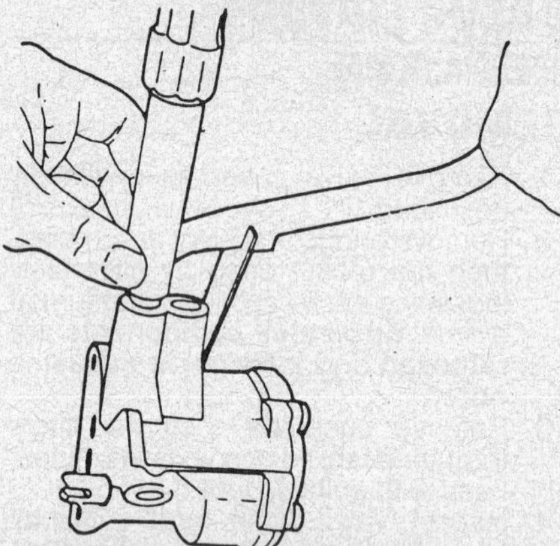

**Fig. 17 Oil pump pickup tube & screen installation**

## ASSEMBLY

1. Install relief valve plunger, spring, retainer and cotter pin.
2. If pickup tube and screen assembly was removed, install replacement assembly as follows:
   a. Apply a light coat of suitable sealant to end of pickup tube.
   b. Drive tube into pump body using tool No. J-21882, **Fig. 17.** Ensure support bracket is aligned properly.
3. Install idler shaft, idler gear and drive gear assembly.
4. Fill pump with petroleum jelly and apply a thin bead of Loctite to top of pump housing.
5. Install pump cover and pump cover retaining screws, torque to specifications. Spin drive gearshaft to ensure free movement.

# BELT TENSION DATA

| Belt | New, Lbs. | Used, Lbs. |
|---|---|---|
| Accessory | 180–200 | 140–160 |

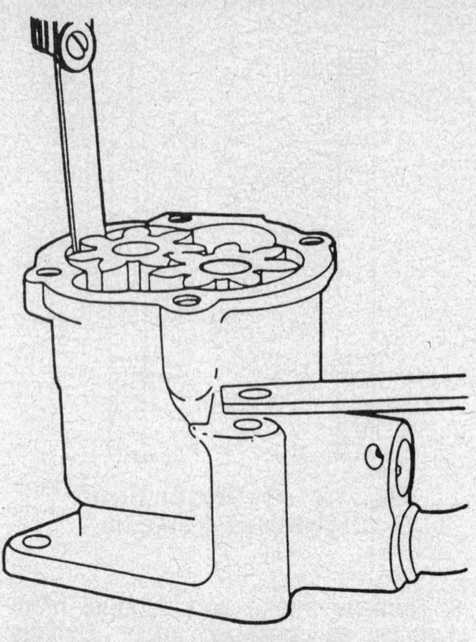

**Fig. 16 Oil pump gear to body clearance**

# SERPENTINE DRIVE BELTS

## BELT ROUTING

Accessory drives are driven by one serpentine belt. When replacing the belt, ensure correct routing is followed, **Figs. 18 and 19.** If belt is routed incorrectly, the water pump could turn in the opposite direction and cause engine to overheat.

## BELT, REPLACE

1. Disconnect battery ground cable.
2. Loosen power steering locknut.
3. Loosen power steering pump pivot bolt.
4. Loosen power steering pump rear attaching bolts.
5. Loosen adjusting bolt, then remove belt.
6. Reverse procedure to install.

# COOLING SYSTEM BLEED

This engine does not require a specific bleed procedure. After filling cooling system, run engine to operating temperature with radiator/pressure cap off. Air will then be automatically bled through cap opening.

# THERMOSTAT REPLACE

## REMOVAL

Do not remove pressure cap while engine is hot or under pressure. Ensure coolant does not drip onto accessory drive belt or drive pulley. If it does, flush with clean water.

1. Drain coolant into a clean container for reuse. Drain until level is below the thermostat housing.
2. Disconnect coolant temperature sensor wire connector from sensor on

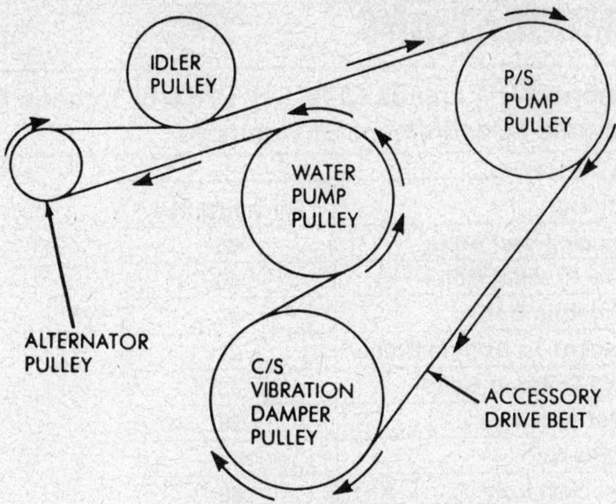


**Fig. 18 Serpentine belt routing. Less A/C**

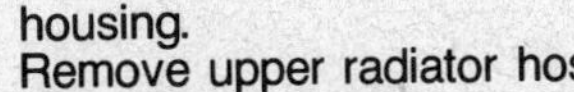

housing.

3. Remove upper radiator hose and intake manifold hoses.
4. Remove retaining bolt, housing, gasket and thermostat.
5. Clean mating surfaces of housing and intake manifold. Ensure that draincock is closed.

## INSTALLATION

1. Install thermostat into recess in cylinder head, ensuring that "TO RAD", stamped on thermostat, is pointing in right direction and air bleed valve pointing up.
2. Install new gasket and thermostat housing. Ensure that thermostat is seated properly in recess.
3. Install two retaining bolts, then tighten to specifications.
4. Install upper radiator hose, intake hoses and ensure draincock is closed.
5. Connect temperature sensor connector and fill cooling system with proper 50/50 mixture of antifreeze, then replace pressure cap.
6. Start engine and run until warm. Check for leaks, then recheck coolant level. Fill as necessary, the radiator and reserve.

## WATER PUMP REPLACE

1. Remove electric cooling fan assembly.
2. Loosen and remove accessory drive belt.
3. Remove water pump pulley mounting bolts.

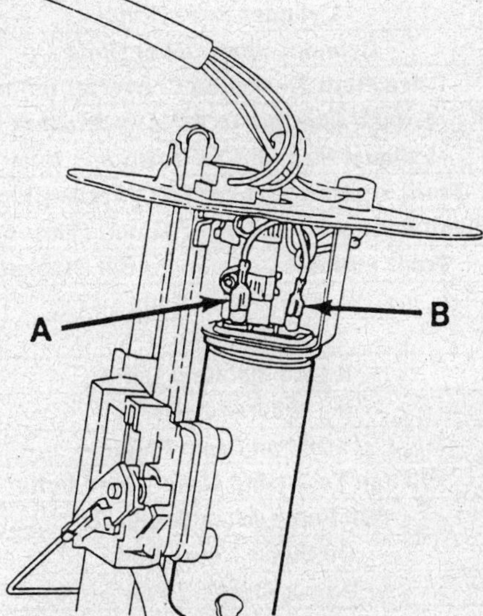


**Fig. 20 Fuel pump removal**

4. Drain coolant from system, then disconnect radiator and heater hoses from pump.
5. Remove water pump attaching bolts and the pump.
6. Clean and inspect cylinder block surface.
7. Reverse procedure to install. Tighten attaching nuts and bolts to specifications. Fill cooling system to proper level.

## FUEL PUMP REPLACE

1. The fuel pump/sender unit is located in the fuel tank. Remove fuel tank as follows:
   a. Disconnect battery ground cable.
   b. Remove fuel tank filler cap to relieve fuel tank pressure, then install fuel tank filler cap.

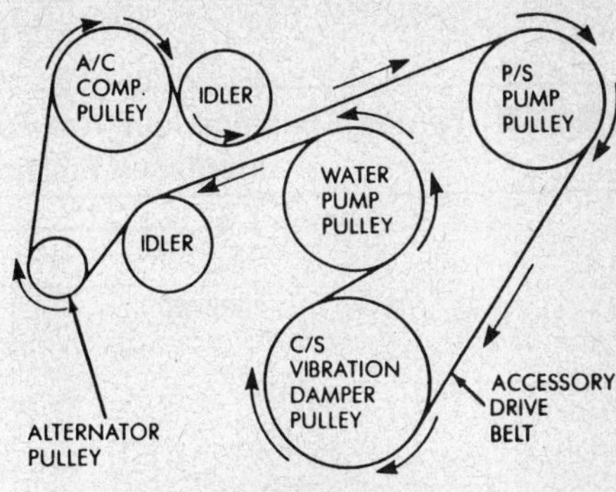


**Fig. 19 Serpentine belt routing. With A/C**

   c. Raise and support vehicle.
   d. Remove right rear wheel and tire assembly, then the splash shield from wheel well.
   e. Remove ground wire retaining screw.
   f. Loosen hose clamp and disconnect fuel tank vent hose from fuel tank filler neck.
   g. Slide fuel tank vent hose out of retaining clip.
   h. Loosen and remove nut securing fuel tank support strap. Push other end of strap up and out left side frame rail.
   i. Place transmission jack under fuel tank to support it while removing tank.
   j. Disconnect quick-connect fittings from fuel filler inlet nipple tube, wrap in suitable shop towel, then apply pressure to retainer tabs and pulling fitting back. Note that retainer stays on nipple.
   k. Pull black hose toward fuel tank and through hole in body.
   l. Disconnect fuel pump/sending unit electrical connector.
   m. Disconnect fuel tank to evaporator canister vapor tube at hose and gray hose.
   n. Remove fuel tank attaching bolts. Lower fuel tank on transmission jack two to three inches. Tip fuel tank down on jack while lowering it out of vehicle.
   o. Lower tank and remove it from transmission jack.
2. Remove fuel pump/sender assembly attaching screws.
3. Disconnect electrical connectors (A) and (B) from terminals on top of fuel pump, **Fig. 20.**
4. Remove fuel pump hold down bracket attaching nut, bracket, gasket and bolt.
5. Disconnect hose clamp at inlet port of fuel pump.
6. Remove hose clamp and pull fuel pump out. Retain gasket for installation.
7. Reverse procedure to install.

## TIGHTENING SPECIFICATIONS

**NOTE:** Torque Specifications Are For Clean And Lightly Lubricated Threads Only. Dry Or Dirty Threads Produce Increased Friction Which Prevents Accurate Measurement Of Tightness.

| Year | Component | Torque/ft. lbs. |
|---|---|---|
| 1989–90 | A/C Bracket To Block/Head Bolts | 30 |
| | A/C Compressor To Bracket Bolts | 20 |
| | Alternator Adjusting Bolt | 20 |
| | Alternator Mounting Bracket To Engine Bolts | 28 |
| | Alternator Mounting To Head Bolts | 33 |
| | Alternator Pivot Bolt/Nut | 28 |
| | Block Heater Nut | 16② |
| | Camshaft Sprocket Bolt | 80 |
| | Connecting Rod Bolt Nuts | 33 |
| | Crankshaft Main Bearing Bolts | 80 |
| | Crankshaft Pulley To Damper Nut | 20 |
| | Cylinder Head Bolts | ① |
| | Cylinder Head Cover Bolts | 70② |
| | Drive Plate To Torque Converter Bolts | 40 |
| | Engine Support To Support Bracket | 75 |
| | Exhaust Manifold To Downpipe Nuts | 23 |
| | Front Support Bracket To Cylinder Block | 45 |
| | Front Support Cushion To Mount (Thru Bolt) | 48 |
| | Front Support Cushion To Sill Bracket | 30 |
| | Fuel Pump Bolts | 16 |
| | Hub Nut | 181 |
| | Intake Manifold Bolts | ① |
| | Oil Pan Bolts | ③ |
| | Oil Pan Drain Plug | 25 |
| | Oil Pan To Timing Case Cover Bolts | 11 |
| | Oil Pump Attaching Bolts | ④ |
| | Oil Pump Cover Bolts | 70② |
| | Power Steering Pump | 20 |
| | Rear Support To Cushion To Bracket Bolts | 32 |
| | Rocker Arm Assembly To Cylinder Head | 19 |
| | Starter Motor Ground | 31 |
| | Starter Motor To Cylinder Block | 33 |
| | Thermostat Housing | 13 |
| | Timing Case To Cylinder Block Bolts | 62② |
| | Vibration Damper Bolt | 80 |
| | Water Pump | 13 |
| | Water Pump Pulley | 20 |
| | Wheel Lug Nuts | 63 |

①—Refer to text for procedure.
②—Inch lbs.
③—1/4 inch bolts, 7 ft. lbs; 5/16 inch bolts, 11 ft. lbs.
④—Short bolts, 10 ft. lbs; long bolts, 17 ft. lbs.

# 3.0L/V6-180 Engine

## INDEX



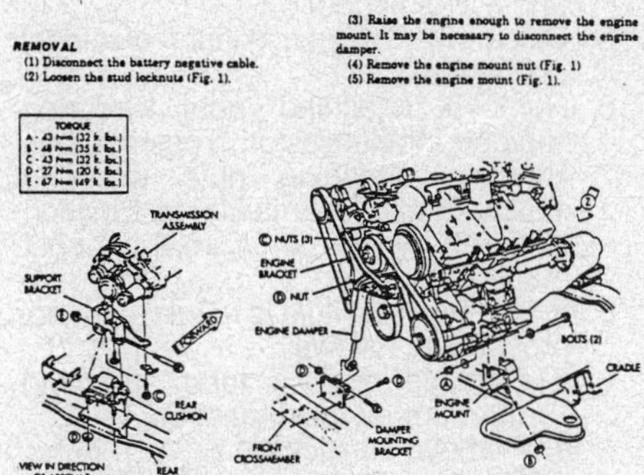


**Fig. 1 Engine mounts**

## ENGINE MOUNT REPLACE

### FRONT

1. Disconnect battery ground cable.
2. Loosen stud locknuts.
3. Install suitable engine lifting equipment.
4. Raise engine slightly, then engine mount attaching nut and mount, **Fig. 1.**
5. Reverse procedure to install.

### REAR

1. Disconnect battery ground cable.
2. Raise and support vehicle.
3. Remove underbody splash shield.
4. Using suitable jack stand, support transaxle assembly.
5. Remove crossmember to engine cradle attaching bolts.
6. Remove rear mount to support bracket attaching nut and bolt.
7. Remove exhaust down pipe.
8. Remove crossmember and rear cushion.
9. Remove bracket attaching bolts, then bracket.
10. Reverse procedure to install.

## ENGINE DAMPER REPLACE

1. Disconnect battery ground cable.
2. Remove damper bracket attaching locknut and bolt.
3. Remove front engine bracket attaching nut and bolt, then remove damper.
4. Reverse proceaure to install.

## ENGINE REPLACE

**The engine and transaxle are removed as an assembly. This procedure must be performed on a side mount hoist.**

1. Disconnect negative then positive battery cables, then drain cooling system.
2. Remove throttle body plenum attaching screws, then remove hose from idle speed regulator.
3. Loosen hose clamp and remove throttle body plenum.
4. Disconnect crankcase ventilation hose and evaporative emissions canister hose from air cleaner.
5. Remove air sensor vacuum hose from air cleaner, then disconnect distributor coil wire and position aside.
6. Disconnect cruise control and accelerator cables from throttle arm, **Fig. 2.** Do not use any tools to disconnect connectors.
7. Apply pressure to tabs on accelerator and cruise control cables and push them through attaching bracket. Set cable unit to side of engine compartment.
8. Disconnect hot air tube from air cleaner.
9. Disconnect air cleaner attaching clips and remove air cleaner.
10. Remove battery hold-down clamp and the battery.
11. Remove fuel tank filler cap to relieve pressure, then reinstall cap.

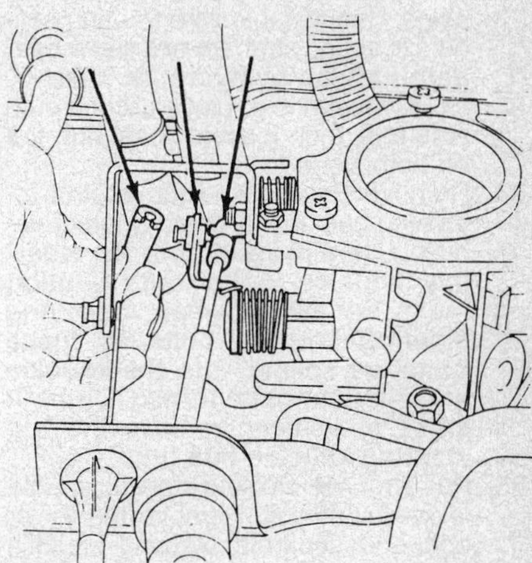

**Fig. 2 Disconnect cables from throttle arm**

12. Disconnect black fuel supply tube from fuel rail and gray fuel return tube from fuel pressure regulator by applying pressure to retaining tabs and pulling apart.
13. Disconnect vacuum hoses from EGR solenoid.
14. Disconnect MAP sensor vacuum line and Hevac vacuum reservoir hose.
15. Remove bulkhead attaching screw and disconnect bulkhead connector. Position connector on top of engine.
16. Disconnect electrical connector from dash panel and remove vacuum booster hose from brake vacuum booster.
17. Disconnect coolant lines from dash panel and coolant bottle.
18. Disconnect radiator hoses from water pump and position aside.
19. Disconnect front engine shock absorber from engine bracket. Push shock up against cooling fan.
20. Open driver's door and remove bottom instrument panel section under steering wheel.

21. Disconnect shifter cable from arm on steering column.
22. Apply pressure to tabs on side cable housing and pull cable through holding bracket.
23. Raise and support vehicle, then remove splash shield below alternator.
24. Disconnect knock sensor, oil level sensor, oil pressure sender and alternator electrical connectors.
25. Disconnect alternator output wire from back of alternator.
26. Disconnect wire harness clip from back of alternator and position aside.
27. Loosen accessory drive belt pivot bolt, locking bolt and adjusting bolt to loosen drive belt.
28. Remove power steering pump and pump reservoir mounting bolts.
29. Lower vehicle.
30. Unfasten A/C compressor and position aside, leaving refrigerant lines attached.
31. Raise and support vehicle, then remove front tires.
32. Unfasten brake calipers and position aside. Use suitable wire to hang calipers in spring strut. **Do not allow calipers to hang by hydraulic hose.**
33. Hold wheel hub in place using a suitable tool, then loosen wheel hub nut on both sides.
34. Remove steering knuckle to strut attaching bolt nuts on both sides of vehicle. **Use a brass drift to tap steering knuckle bolts out. Caution must be taken when removing steering knuckle bolts as these bolts are splined into the knuckle and should not be turned. On both sides of vehicle, remove the top steering knuckle bolt first.**
35. Pull strut out, pivoting steering knuckle on lower bolt. Remove the lower bolt and separate steering knuckle from strut.
36. Disconnect battery negative cable and solenoid wire from starter.
37. Remove middle starter attaching bolt and disconnect ground cable.
38. Remove sub-frame shield attaching bolts, and the shield.
39. Disconnect oxygen sensor electrical connector and catalytic converter from Y-pipe.
40. Pull shifter cable grommet down, then grasp cable and pull it through hole in body.
41. Install Mot. 1040.99 sub-frame dolly or equivalent to engine cradle. Install attaching bolts into cradle, **Fig. 3.** Push large end of channel iron up. Insert bolt into holes in cradle. Adjust bolt until channel iron lays flat in hole. Adjust remaining bolts in same manner.
42. Install engine dolly to cradle with dolly wheels toward rear of vehicle. Ensure arms at front of dolly are pointing up toward cradle. Install dolly to cradle by lifting dolly up and lining up holes in dolly with bolts just installed in cradle. Tighten attaching nuts.
43. Lower hoist until dolly rests on floor, then remove cradle mounting bolts.
44. Ensure all hoses, vacuum lines and wire harnesses are positioned so as not to snag or catch when vehicle is lifted off engine.
45. Slowly raise vehicle off engine.
46. Draw outline of dolly legs and center line of wheels on floor. Once dolly is repositioned under vehicle, it can be correctly positioned so that it aligns with vehicle at installation.
47. Reverse procedure to install.

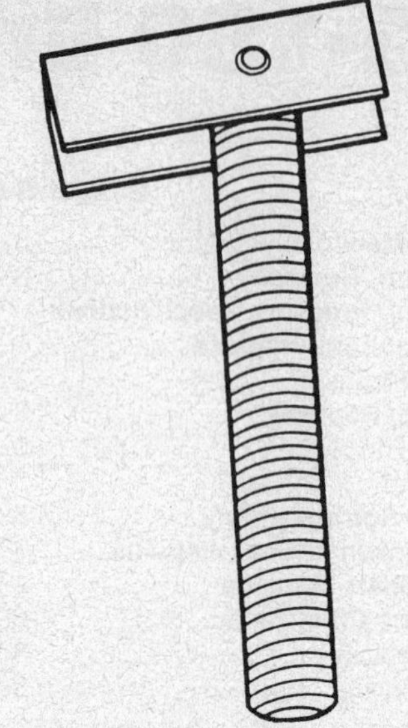

**Fig. 3 Engine cradle-to dolly bolt**

## INTAKE MANIFOLD
## REPLACE

1. Disconnect battery ground cable.
2. Remove throttle body plenum.
3. Disconnect transmission kickdown cable from throttle body.
4. Disconnect accelerator cable and cruise control cable connector. **Do not use tools to disconnect cable or connectors.**
5. Disconnect brake vacuum booster hose.
6. Disconnect vacuum connection from throttle body adapter.
7. Disconnect Throttle Position Sensor (TPS) connector.
8. Disconnect idle air bypass hose from throttle body adapter.
9. Disconnect Hevac reservoir vacuum hose from fitting on throttle body adapter.
10. Disconnect EGR tube.
11. Disconnect EGR valve transducer vacuum hose.
12. Disconnect air temperature sensor wire connector, located behind idle air bypass hose.
13. Tag each fuel injector connector with number of corresponding injector, then disconnect fuel injector wire harness from injectors and position aside.
14. Disconnect CCV vacuum hose from fitting between Nos. 2 and 3 runners.
15. Remove fuel tank filler cap to relieve fuel tank pressure, then install fuel tank filler cap.
16. Place shop towels under fuel tubes. Disconnect fuel supply tube from fuel rail and fuel return tube from fuel pressure regulator using M.S. 1999 fuel line disconnect tool. Slide tool onto nipple and push forward into quick-connector until handle stops on connector casing. Remove fuel tubes and position aside.
17. Remove intake manifold attaching bolts and the intake manifold.
18. Remove and discard O-rings in cylinder heads.
19. Reverse procedure to install.

## EXHAUST MANIFOLD
## REPLACE

1. Disconnect battery ground cable.
2. Disconnect EGR tube from right side exhaust manifold.
3. Raise and support vehicle.
4. Disconnect catalytic converter from Y-pipe by removing attaching nuts. Remove converter by pulling back and out of hanger.
5. Disconnect oxygen sensor electrical connector.
6. Remove attaching nuts securing Y-pipe to transmission crossmember.
7. Remove attaching nuts securing Y-pipe to exhaust manifolds. Position Y-pipe back and away from exhaust manifolds.
8. If right side manifold is to be removed, proceed as follows:
   a. Remove dipstick tube attaching nut from exhaust manifold.
   b. Remove dipstick tube.
   c. Remove remaining exhaust manifold attaching nuts.
   d. Remove manifold and gasket.
9. If left side manifold is to be removed, proceed as follows:
   a. Remove hot air tube heat stove.
   b. Disconnect starter wires and ground cable.
   c. Remove lower exhaust manifold attaching nuts and the starter heat shield.
   d. Remove remaining exhaust manifold attaching nuts.
   e. Remove manifold and gasket.
10. Reverse procedure to install, noting the following:
    a. Exhaust manifold gaskets have a ring on one side. Install gaskets with ring toward cylinder head and tabs toward oil pan.
    b. Tighten attaching nuts and bolts to specifications.

## VALVE COVER
## REPLACE

### RIGHT SIDE

#### Removal

1. Disconnect battery ground cable.
2. Loosen accessory drive belt.
3. Remove spark plug wire holder.
4. Unfasten A/C compressor and position aside, leaving refrigerant lines attached.

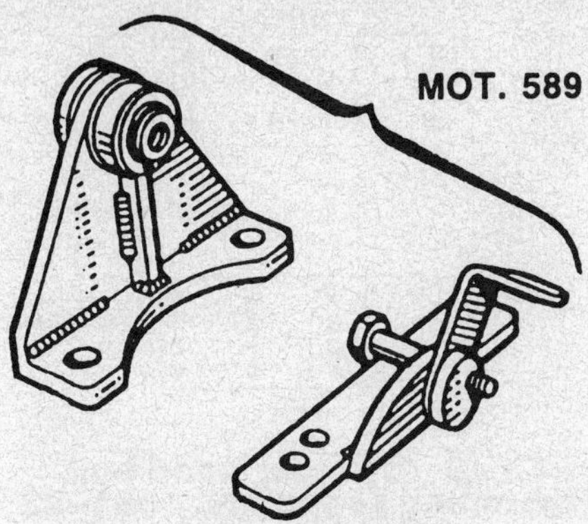


**Fig. 4 Camshaft sprocket removal tool**

5. Remove valve cover attaching bolts.
6. Remove cover and old gasket.

### Installation

1. Clean cylinder head and valve head mating surfaces.
2. Apply a light coating of gasket sealer to cylinder head mating surfaces.
3. Install valve head cover with new gasket.
4. Install spark plug holder.
5. Install valve cover attaching bolts and torque to specifications.
6. Install A/C compressor.
7. Install accessory drive belt.
8. Connect battery ground cable.

## LEFT SIDE

### Removal

1. Disconnect battery ground cable.
2. Disconnect throttle body plenum/air inlet hose assembly from throttle body and air cleaner.
3. Remove vacuum brake booster hose from throttle body.
4. Disconnect Crankcase Ventilation (CCV) fresh air hose from valve head cover.
5. Disconnect CCV vacuum hose from valve head cover.
6. Disconnect and remove air cleaner.
7. Remove power steering reservoir attaching bolts and position reservoir aside.
8. Disconnect accelerator cable from throttle body retainer bracket and position aside.
9. Remove idle speed regulator bracket attaching bolts from rear of valve cover.
10. Remove spark plug wire holder.
11. Remove valve head cover attaching bolts.
12. Remove cover and old gasket.

### Installation

1. Clean cylinder head and valve head cover mating surfaces.
2. Apply a light coating of gasket sealer to cylinder head mating surfaces.
3. Install valve head cover and new gasket.
4. Install valve cover attaching bolts and torque to specifications.
5. Install spark plug wire holder.
6. Install idle speed regulator bracket to rear of valve head cover.
7. Connect accelerator cable and cruise control cable to retainer bracket and throttle body.
8. Install power steering pump reservoir.
9. Install air cleaner.
10. Install CCV fresh air hose and vacuum hose.
11. Connect vacuum brake booster hose.
12. Connect throttle body plenum/air inlet hose assembly to air cleaner and throttle body.
13. Connect battery ground cable.

# CYLINDER HEAD REPLACE

**Cylinder head must be cool prior to removal to avoid cylinder head distortion.**

## RIGHT SIDE

### Removal

1. Disconnect battery ground cable and drain cooling system.
2. Remove intake and exhaust manifolds from cylinder head as previously described.
3. Remove valve cover as described under "Valve Cover, Replace."
4. Remove spark plug wires from cylinder head.
5. Remove top alternator mounting bracket.
6. Remove timing case attaching bolts in cylinder head and inline bolts directly below. **Timing chain and sprocket must be held in place. If chain and sprocket slip, timing case must be removed and chain tensioners released.**
7. Turn engine over until camshaft sprocket dowel is straight up.
8. Attach tool No. Mot. 589 or 7317 or equivalent, to timing case cover, **Fig. 4.** Secure with two short cylinder head cover bolts.
9. Position adjusting lever (B) behind camshaft sprocket. Thread bolt (A) through front of tool, sprocket and into lever. Push lever up as far as possible and tighten bolt, **Fig. 5.**
10. Remove plug in front of timing case cover to gain access to camshaft sprocket bolt, then remove cylinder head attaching bolts.
11. Remove rocker arm shaft assembly. Install one head bolt in center and tighten two turns. Remove camshaft cover and gasket from rear of cylinder head.
12. Loosen camshaft thrust plate screw. Pull plate up and torque screw to allow camshaft to move back as sprocket bolt is removed.
13. Loosen camshaft sprocket bolt and pull camshaft back until bolt is out of camshaft, then slide camshaft back away from sprocket.
14. Insert a drift punch into front and rear cylinder head bolt holes on exhaust manifold side of head. Tap dowels down below head gasket. **Do not lift or pry cylinder head straight up as this will cause cylinder liners to come up and out of block.**

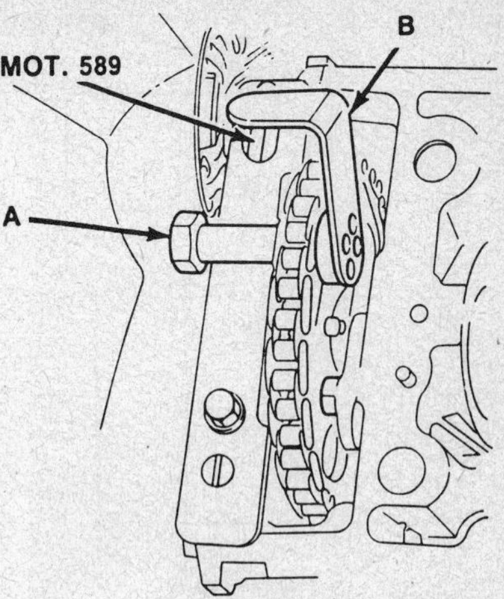


**Fig. 5 Camshaft sprocket removal**

15. Position a piece of wood against rear intake manifold side of cylinder head and strike with a hammer. Repeat procedure for front exhaust manifold.
16. Remove cylinder head bolts, cylinder head and cylinder head gasket.
17. Install tool No. 7315 or Mot. 588 or equivalent liner clamps, between cylinder liners to hold them in place.
18. Use tool No. 7314 or Mot. 587 or equivalent to remove cylinder head locating dowels, **Fig. 6.**
19. Place lint free shop towels in tops of cylinder bores.
20. Remove tool No. 7315 or Mot. 588 or equivalent liner hold-down clamps, to clean cylinder block, then reinstall liner clamps.
21. Clean cylinder block and cylinder head mating surfaces.
22. Check liner protrusion.
23. **On 1989-90 models,** liner should protrude between .0051 and .0078 inch.
24. **On 1991-92 models,** liner should protrude between .002 and .005 inch.

### Installation

1. Trim timing case cover gasket flush with cylinder head surface.
2. Cut sections from new gaskets and attach them to the timing case cover. Apply a suitable weather strip adhesive and allow to dry.
3. Install .118 inch (3 mm) pin punches into holes in block below locating dowel bolt holes. Push dowels in holes until they contact pin punches.
4. Remove shop towels from cylinder bores.
5. Install new cylinder head gasket over alignment dowels.
6. Apply a thin coat of gasket sealer to cylinder head mating surface.
7. Install cylinder head.
8. Install timing case cover to cylinder head attaching bolts and tighten finger tight.
9. Position camshaft into sprocket. Align dowel with slot in camshaft. Install sprocket bolt and tighten finger tight.

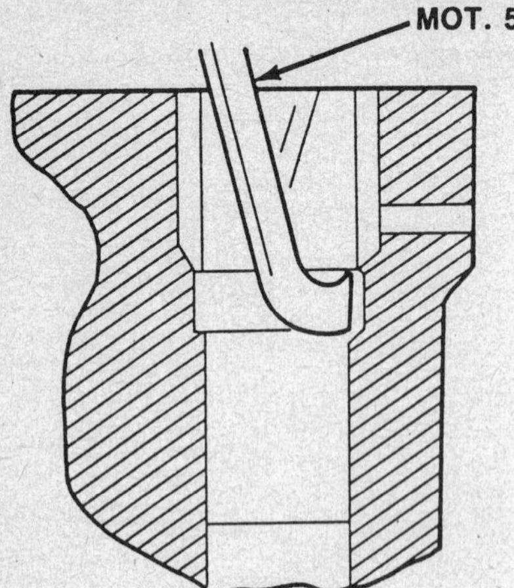


**Fig. 6 Cylinder head locating dowel removal**

10. Remove support bracket assembly.
11. Loosen camshaft thrust plate bolt and slide plate into groove in cylinder head. Tighten to specifications.
12. Remove pin punches.
13. Install rocker shaft assembly and cylinder head bolts.
14. Torque cylinder head bolts as follows:
    a. Torque cylinder head bolts in sequence shown in **Figs. 7 and 8**, to 44 ft. lbs.
    b. **On 1989-90 models,** loosen bolt No. 1 completely, then **torque** bolt to 15 ft. lbs.
    c. **On 1991-92 models,** loosen bolt No. 1 completely, then **torque** bolt to 30 ft. lbs.
    d. **On all models,** place graduated disc tool No. 7321 or equivalent, between socket and torque wrench. Turn graduated disc clockwise until locking stem rests against a solid object which will prevent disc from turning.
    e. **On 1989-90 models,** angle torque bolt No. 1 to 104-108°.
    f. **On 1991-92 models,** angle torque bolt No. 1 to 160-200°.
    g. **On all models,** repeat procedure for remaining bolts in sequence.
15. Tighten timing case cover attaching bolts to specifications.
16. Torque camshaft sprocket bolt to specifications.
17. Install valve covers, as described under "Valve Covers, Replace."
18. Install intake and exhaust manifolds, as previously described.
19. Apply Loctite to threads of timing case cover plug and install plug in timing case cover.
20. Install spark plug wires.
21. Connect alternator bracket.
22. Fill and bleed cooling system.
23. Install accessory drive belt.
24. Connect battery ground cable.
25. **On 1989-90 models,** start vehicle and run for 15 minutes (without a load) at 1800 to 2000 RPM.
26. **On 1989-90 models,** turn engine off and allow to cool, then angle torque all cylinder head bolts an additional 45° in tightening sequence.

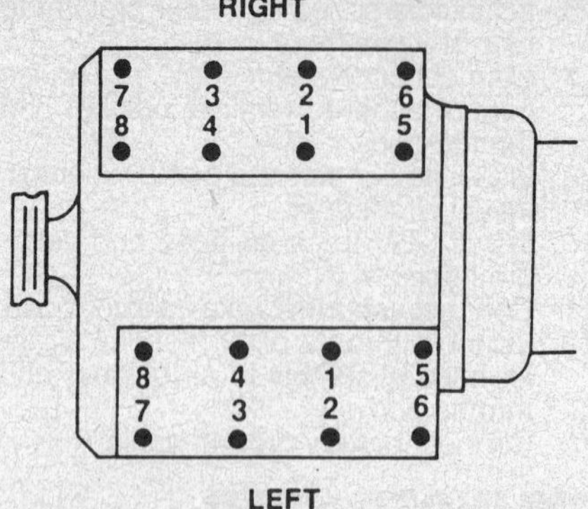


**Fig. 7 Cylinder head bolt tightening sequence. 1989–90**

27. **On 1989-90 models,** use a torque wrench to verify that each bolt has at least 52 ft. lbs. of torque.

## LEFT SIDE

### Removal

1. Disconnect battery ground cable and drain cooling system.
2. Remove intake and exhaust manifolds from cylinder head as previously described.
3. Remove valve head cover as described under "Valve Head Cover, Replace."
4. Remove spark plug wires from spark plugs.
5. Remove distributor cap, rotor and dust shield.
6. Turn engine over until camshaft sprocket dowel is straight up. **Timing chain and sprocket must be held in place. If chain and sprocket slip, timing case must be removed and chain tensioners released.**
7. Attach tool No. Mot. 589 or 7317 or equivalent, to support camshaft sprocket and chain while removing cylinder head cover. Remove bolt and adjusting lever from tool bracket and position aside. Secure with two short cylinder head cover bolts.
8. Thread bolt through bracket, sprocket and into adjusting lever. Pull lever up and tighten bolt.
9. Loosen camshaft thrust plate attaching bolt. Pull thrust plate up and away from camshaft. Tighten bolt.
10. Remove timing case cover from cylinder head attaching bolts.
11. Place a wrench on crankshaft pulley nut to prevent engine from turning over.
12. Position suitable tool into camshaft sprocket bolt and remove bolt.
13. Remove cylinder head attaching bolts.
14. Remove rocker shaft assembly.
15. Install one cylinder head bolt into middle bolt hole and tighten two full turns.
16. Insert a drift punch into front and rear cylinder head bolt holes on exhaust manifold side of head. Tap dowels down below head gasket. **Do not lift or pry cylinder head straight up as this will cause cylinder liners to come up and out of block.**

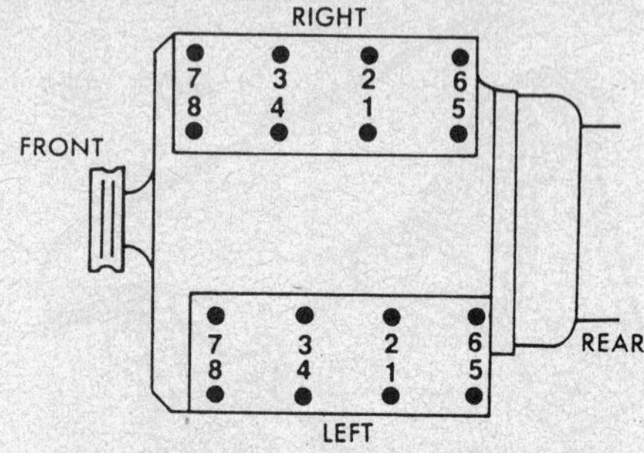


**Fig. 8 Cylinder head bolt tightening sequence. 1991–92**

17. Position a piece of wood against rear intake manifold side of cylinder head and strike with a hammer. Repeat procedure on all sides of cylinder head until head is loose.
18. Remove cylinder head bolt, cylinder head and cylinder head gasket.
19. Use tool No. 7314 or Mot. 587 or equivalent, to remove cylinder head locating dowels.
20. Place lint free shop towels in tops of cylinder bores.
21. Install tool No. 7315 or Mot. 588 or equivalent liner clamps between cylinder liners to hold them in place.
22. Clean cylinder block and cylinder head mating surfaces.
23. Check liner protrusion.
24. **On 1989-90 models,** liner should protrude between .0051 and .0078 inch.
25. **On 1991-92 models,** liner should protrude between .002 and .005 inch.

### Installation

1. Trim timing case cover gasket flush with cylinder head surface.
2. Cut sections from new gaskets and attach to timing case cover. Apply a suitable weather strip adhesive and allow to dry.
3. Install .118 inch (3 mm) pin punches into holes in block below locating dowel bolt holes. Push dowels in holes until they contact pin punches.
4. Remove shop towels from cylinder bores.
5. Install new cylinder head gasket over alignment dowels.
6. Apply a thin coat of gasket sealer to cylinder head mating surface.
7. Install cylinder head.
8. Install timing case cover to cylinder head attaching bolts and tighten finger tight.
9. Position camshaft into sprocket. Align dowel with slot in camshaft. Install sprocket bolt and tighten finger tight.
10. Remove support bracket assembly.
11. Loosen camshaft thrust plate bolt and slide plate into groove in cylinder head. Retorque camshaft thrust plate bolt to specifications.
12. Remove pin punches.
13. Install rocker shaft assembly and cylinder head bolts.
14. Torque cylinder head bolts as follows:
    a. Torque cylinder head bolts in sequence shown, **Figs. 7 and 8,** to

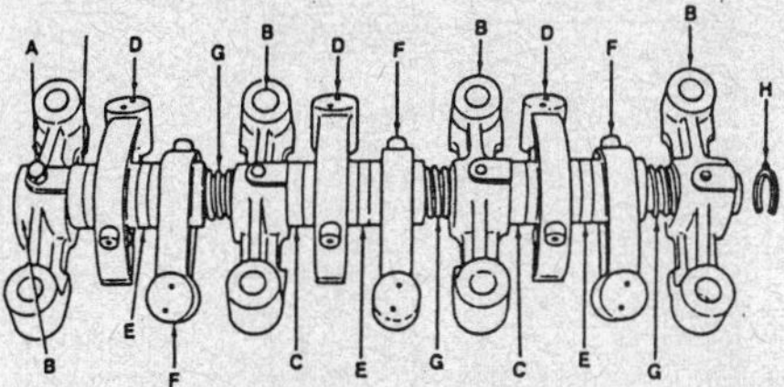


**Fig. 9 Rocker shaft assembly**

44 ft. lbs.

b. **On 1989-90 models,** loosen bolt No. 1 completely, then **torque** bolt to 15 ft. lbs.

c. **On 1991-92 models,** loosen bolt No. 1 completely, then **torque** bolt to 30 ft. lbs.

d. **On all models,** place graduated disc Mot. 591.03 between socket and torque wrench. Turn graduated disc clockwise until locking stem rests against a solid object which will prevent disc from turning.

e. Angle torque bolt No. 1 to 104-108°.

f. Repeat procedure for remaining bolts in sequence.

15. Tighten timing case cover attaching bolts to specifications.
16. Torque camshaft sprocket bolt to specifications.
17. Install valve covers, as described under "Valve Covers, Replace."
18. Install intake and exhaust manifolds as previously described.
19. Install distributor cap, rotor and dust shield.
20. Install spark plug wires.
21. Fill and bleed cooling system.
22. Connect battery ground cable.
23. **On 1989-90 models,** start vehicle and run for 15 minutes (without a load) at 1800 to 2000 RPM.
24. **On 1989-90 models,** turn engine off and allow to cool, then angle torque all cylinder head bolts an additional 45° in tightening sequence.
25. **On 1989-90 models,** use a torque wrench to verify that each bolt has at least 52 ft. lbs. of torque.

## ROCKER SHAFT
## REPLACE

Left and right rocker shaft assemblies are identical and can be installed on either cylinder head, however, when reusing these assemblies always install shaft on original cylinder head.

Oil galley plugs in ends of rocker shafts are pressed in and are not replaceable. When disassembling shaft, position parts aside in order of removal.

1. Remove lock screw (A), pedestal (B) and thick spacer (C), **Fig. 9.**
2. Remove rocker arm with automatic lash adjuster on right (D).
3. Remove thin spacer (E).
4. Remove rocker arm with automatic lash adjuster on left (F).
5. Remove spring (G), then the circlip from end of rocker shaft (H).
6. Reverse procedure to assemble and install. Torque attaching screw to specifications.

## CAMSHAFT
## REPLACE

The engine is equipped with dual camshafts. The right and left camshafts are not the same and cannot be interchanged. The camshafts can be identified by the location of the lobes, **Fig. 10.** On left-hand camshaft (A) both lobes (B) for each cylinder are on the same side. On right-hand camshaft (C) the lobes (D) for each cylinder are on opposite sides. The camshafts are removed and installed from the rear of the cylinder heads.

### REMOVAL

1. Remove camshaft cover from rear of cylinder head.
2. Loosen camshaft retainer attaching bolt and slide retainer up and out of the groove in camshaft. Tighten bolt.
3. Carefully slide camshaft out rear of cylinder head.

### INSTALLATION

1. Lubricate and install camshaft from rear of cylinder head.
2. Loosen bolt and slide retainer into groove at front of camshaft. Tighten to specifications.
3. Check camshaft endplay using a feeler gauge or dial indicator. Endplay must measure .0030-.0055 inch.
4. Install cover with a new gasket at rear of cylinder head. Apply a light coating of Loctite to attaching bolt and tighten to specifications.

## TIMING CHAIN COVER
## REPLACE

1. Remove valve covers as described under," Valve Cover, Replace."
2. Hold camshaft sprocket in place and remove distributor drive/camshaft sprocket bolt.
3. Pull distributor drive forward and off of camshaft sprocket.
4. Remove timing cover attaching bolt.
5. Place a pry bar between cylinder block and boss on front cover and carefully remove cover.
6. Remove gaskets.
7. Reverse procedure to install.

## TIMING CHAIN

### INSPECTION

Check timing chain and sprocket for wear. If either side has excessive wear, replace timing chains, sprockets, guide shoes and tensions for both sides.

1. Remove valve head cover as described under,"Valve Head Cover, Replace."
2. Pull up on top of timing chain. This produces a gap between the bottom of the timing chain and the bottom area between two sprocket teeth. A maximum clearance of .067 inch must be maintained. A gap of .067 inch corresponds to a travel of .866 inch by the timing chain tensioner plunger.
3. Insert the solid end of a number 51 drill bit (.067 inch diameter) to gauge size of gap. If drill bit does not fit into gap, wear is not excessive and components can be reused. If drill bit fits into gap between timing chain and sprocket teeth the following components must be replaced: timing chain shoes, tensioners, guides, sprockets and tensioner shoes.

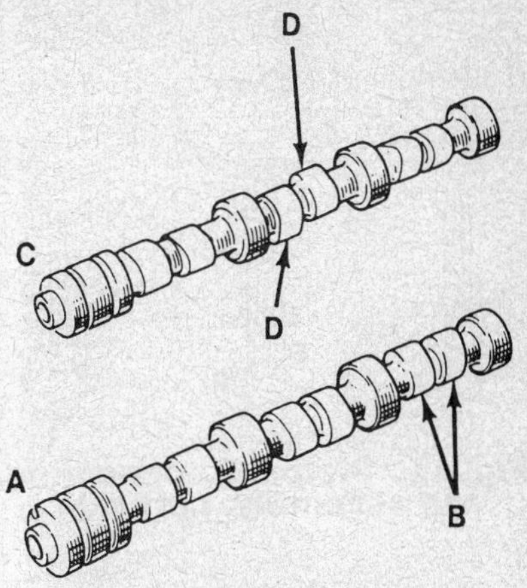


**Fig. 10 Camshaft identification**

### REPLACEMENT

When removing timing chains, tensioners, guides, sprockets, and tensioner shoes, keep left and right sides separated. Components must be returned to their original positions.

1. Remove bolt attaching right side camshaft sprocket to camshaft.
2. Remove right side timing chain tensioner and let tensioner shoe hang down.
3. Remove right side timing chain, then the camshaft sprocket and timing chain guide.
4. Remove right side tensioner shoe.
5. Remove left side timing chain tensioner and timing chain.
6. Remove left side camshaft sprocket, then the timing chain guide and tensioner.
7. Remove tensioner filters.
8. Reverse procedure to install. Install timing chain cover as described under, "Timing Chain Cover, Replace."

## PISTON & ROD ASSEMBLY

When installing left bank pistons 1, 2 and 3, shoulder on connecting rod large end must be opposite arrow on piston crown, **Fig. 11.** On right bank pistons 4, 5 and 6, shoulder must be on same side as arrow on piston crown, **Fig. 12.**

Install left bank connecting rod/piston assemblies 1, 2 and 3 with arrow on crown

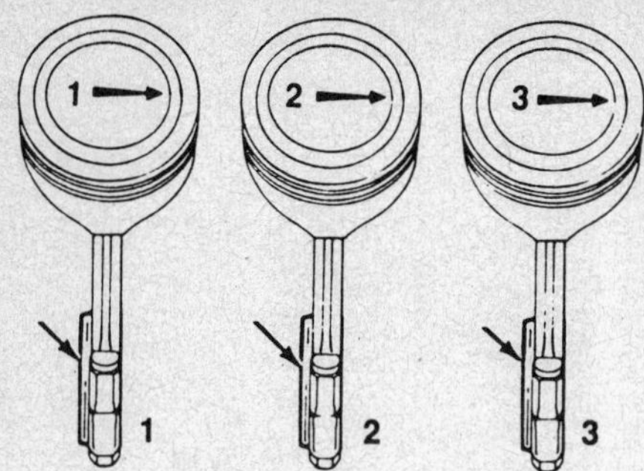

**Fig. 11 Piston & connecting rod assembly. Left side**

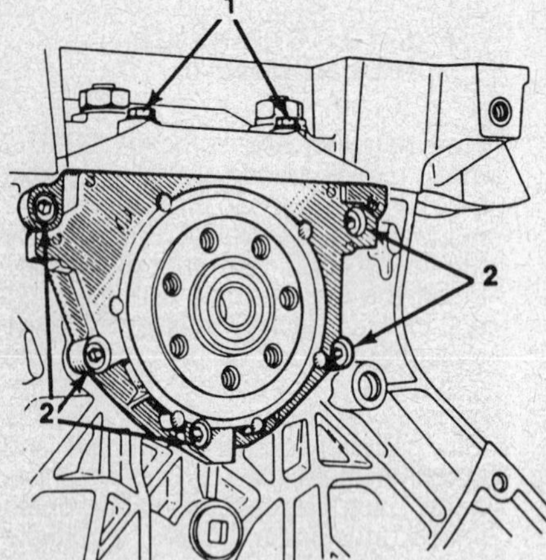

**Fig. 14 Rear crankshaft seal removal**

of piston pointing toward crankshaft pulley end and shoulder of connecting rod pointing to flywheel end of engine. Install right bank connecting rod/piston assemblies 4, 5 and 6 with arrows on crown of piston and shoulder of connecting rod facing crankshaft pulley end of engine, **Fig. 13.**

# REAR CRANKSHAFT SEAL

## REPLACE

1. Remove two attaching bolts from lower casing (1), **Fig. 14.**
2. Remove seal housing attaching bolts(2), **Fig. 14.**
3. Remove seal housing and gasket.
4. Remove old seal from housing.
5. Use new gasket and install seal housing to cylinder block.
6. Loosely install all attaching bolts including casing to seal housing bolts.
7. Tighten seal housing to block bolts first, then tighten lower casing to seal housing bolts.
8. Tighten attaching bolts to specifications.
9. Lightly oil inner and outer edges of new seal.
10. Place new seal on tool No. 6482 or equivalent seal installer.
11. Install new seal by gently tapping end of tool No. 6482 or equivalent until

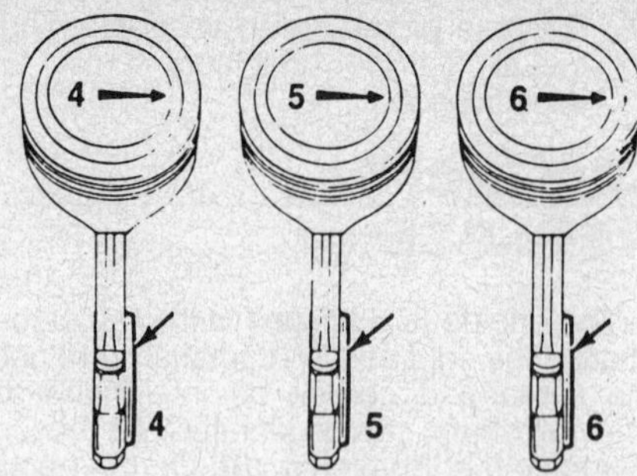

**Fig. 12 Piston & connecting rod assembly. Right side**

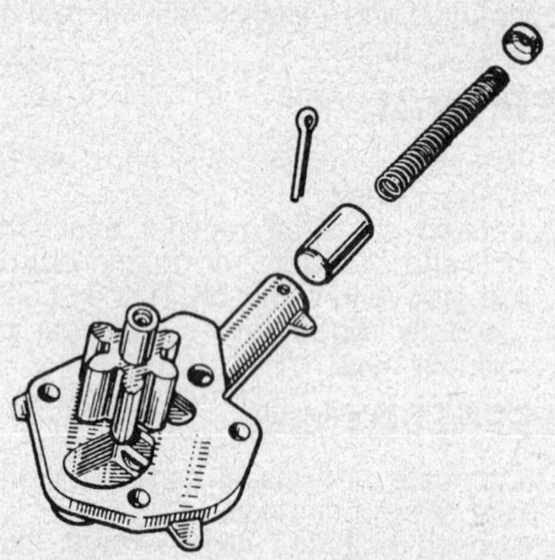

**Fig. 15 Oil pump removal**

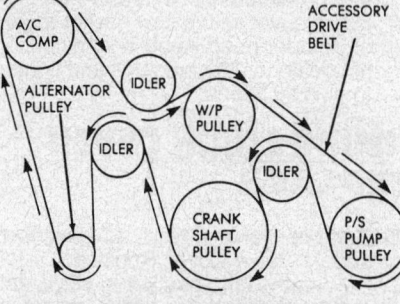

**Fig. 17 Serpentine drive belt installation. With A/C**

tool stops.

12. Remove tool No. 6482 or equivalent, turning tool while pulling out.

# OIL PAN

## REPLACE

1. Drain engine oil.
2. Remove oil pan attaching screws, then the oil pan and gasket.
3. Clean pan and gasket surfaces.
4. Install new gasket and reinstall pan.
5. Install oil pan attaching screws and torque to specifications.
6. Refill engine oil.

# OIL PUMP

## REPLACE

### REMOVAL

1. Remove timing cover and rotate

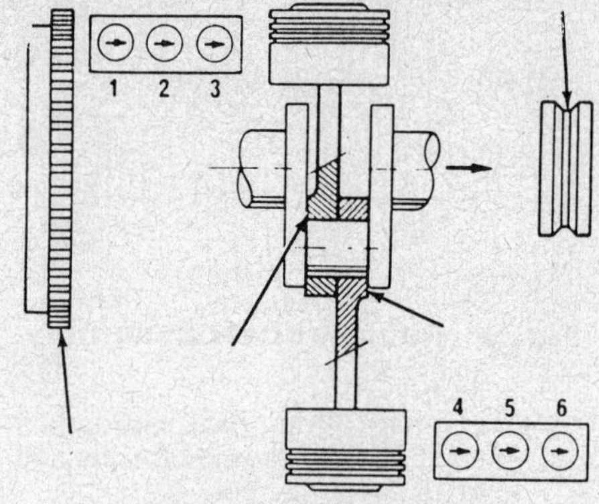

**Fig. 13 Piston & connecting rod installation**

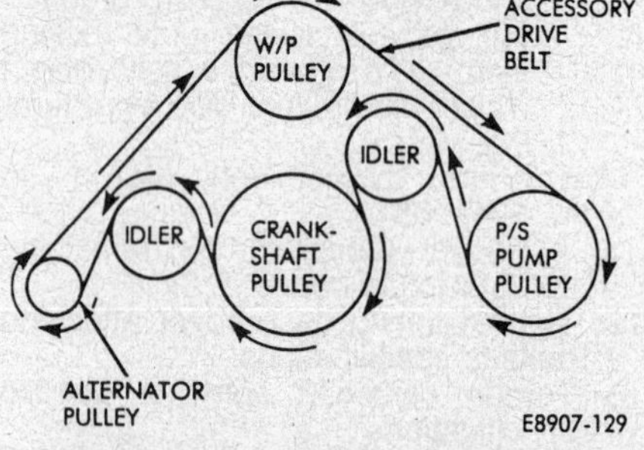


**Fig. 16 Serpentine drive belt installation. Less A/C**

crankshaft until key is pointing up.

2. Remove oil pump sprocket attaching bolts.
3. Clean thread lock from attaching bolts.
4. Remove chain sprocket and chain.
5. Remove oil pump cover attaching bolts and then the cover.
6. Remove split key from oil pump cover and remove retainer, spring and relief valve, **Fig. 15.** Check condition of all parts. If any part shows excessive wear, the complete oil pump must be replaced.

### INSTALLATION

1. Apply clean engine oil and install relief valve, spring and retainer into oil pump cover. When installing relief valve, open end must face spring.
2. Install split key.
3. Lubricate driven gear idler shaft with clean engine oil and install gear over idler shaft.
4. Install pump cover and pump cover retaining screws and torque screws to specifications.
5. Prime oil pump by squirting oil through hole below oil filter connector.
6. Fill oil filter with clean engine oil and install on engine.
7. After timing chains have been installed, install oil pump sprocket and chain. Apply Loctite to threads of sprocket attaching bolts and tighten to specifications.

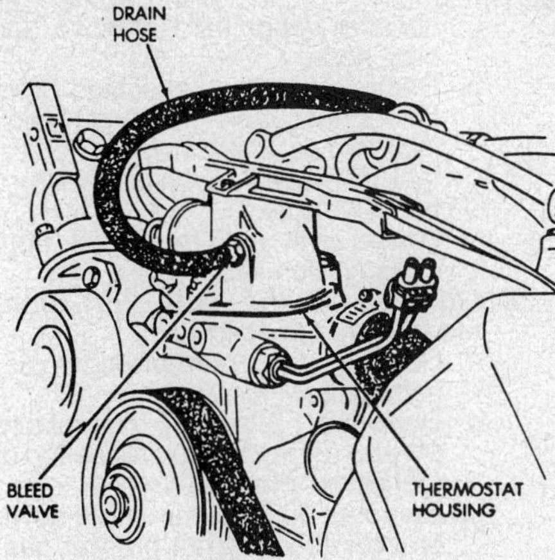


**Fig. 18 Thermostat housing air bleed valve**

## BELT TENSION DATA

| Belt | New, Lbs. | Used, Lbs. |
|---|---|---|
| Accessory | 180–200 | 140–160 |

## SERPENTINE DRIVE BELTS

### BELT ROUTING

The serpentine drive belt must be installed as shown to ensure correct water pump rotation, **Figs. 16 and 17.** Incorrect routing of drive belt can cause engine to overheat. When a new accessory drive belt is installed, it must be tensioned after 7500 miles of use.

### BELT, REPLACE

1. Disconnect battery ground cable.
2. Raise and support vehicle.
3. Remove splash shield below alternator.
4. Loosen alternator pivot bolt.
5. Loosen locking bolt.
6. Loosen adjusting bolt until belt can be removed from alternator pulley.
7. Lower vehicle.
8. Remove engine damper mounting bracket attaching locknuts, then push bracket toward engine.
9. Remove accessory drive belt.
10. Reverse procedure to install.

## COOLING SYSTEM BLEEDING

1. Attach a .250 inch ID hose approximately 48 inches long to the bleed valve on the thermostat housing, **Fig. 18.** Route hose away from accessory drive belt and pulleys.
2. Place other end of hose into a clean container. **The hose will prevent coolant from contacting the accessory drive belt and drive pulleys.**
3. Open bleed valve, then slowly fill coolant pressure bottle until a steady stream of coolant flows from hose attached to bleed valve.

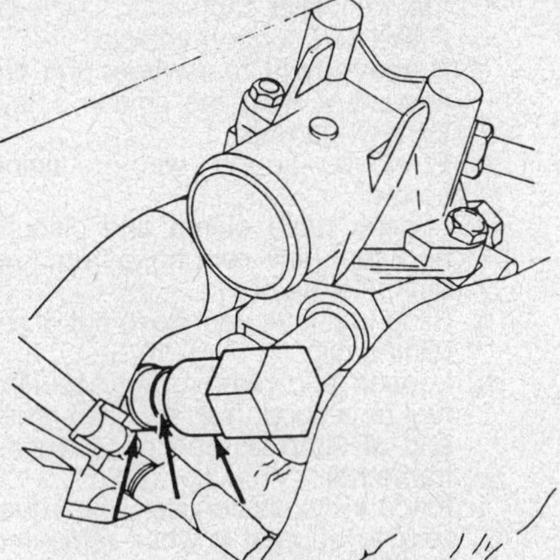

**Fig. 19 Heater tube locking sleeve removal**

4. Close bleed valve and continue filling to the Full mark of the coolant pressure bottle.
5. Install cap tightly on coolant pressure bottle, then remove hose from bleed valve.
6. Start and run engine until upper radiator hose is warm.
7. Turn engine off, then reattach drain hose to bleed valve on thermostat housing.
8. Open bleed valve until a steady stream of coolant flows from hose.
9. Close bleed valve and remove hose.
10. Ensure coolant level in coolant pressure bottle is at or slightly above the Full mark. **The Full mark on the coolant pressure bottle is the correct coolant level for a cold engine. A hot engine will normally have a coolant level higher than the full mark.**

## THERMOSTAT REPLACE

### REMOVAL

Do not remove pressure cap while engine is hot or under pressure. Ensure coolant does not drip onto accessory drive belt or drive pulley. If it does, flush with clean water.

1. Drain coolant into a clean container for reuse. Drain until level is below the thermostat housing.
2. Disconnect coolant temperature sensor wire from sensor.
3. Remove spark plug wire holder from top of thermostat housing and place a shop towel over belts and pulleys.
4. Leave upper radiator hose connected. Remove two retaining bolts, housing, gasket and thermostat.
5. Clean mating surfaces, ensuring that thermostat well is clear of blockage.

### INSTALLATION

1. Install thermostat with air bleed valve to rear of well and flat disk to bottom of thermostat well.
2. Install new gasket, then housing. Install retaining bolts and tighten to specifications.

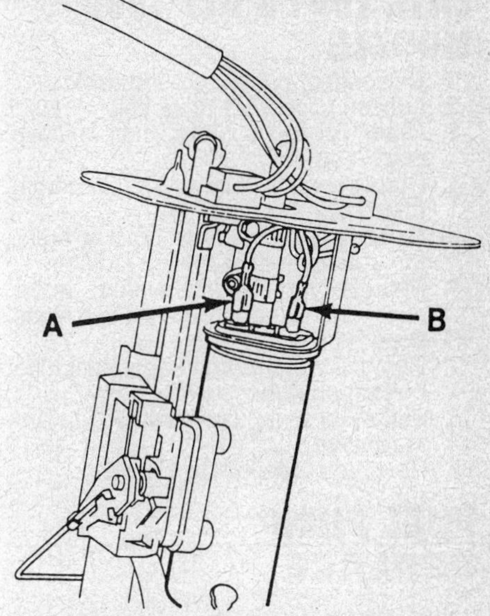


**Fig. 20 Fuel pump removal. 1989–90 & early 1991**

3. Close radiator drain, then fill radiator and bleed cooling system. Start engine, running until warm.
4. Check for leaks, then recheck level. Refill as necessary. Check reserve bottle.

## WATER PUMP REPLACE

### 1989–90 & EARLY 1991 MODELS

1. Disconnect battery ground cable.
2. Loosen accessory drive belt from alternator.
3. Attach a 1/4 inch hose to radiator drain. Open radiator drain, remove coolant bottle cap and drain radiator.
4. Remove spark plug wire holder from top of thermostat housing.
5. Remove engine damper mounting bracket attaching nuts and push bracket toward radiator.
6. Position belt away from water pump.
7. Remove upper and lower radiator hoses from water pump.
8. Disconnect coolant temperature sensor.
9. Loosen water pump hose clamps from cylinder heads. Do not remove hoses.
10. Loosen heater hose clamps and connecting hose at rear of water pump.
11. Remove heater tube locking sleeve from elbow connector, **Fig. 19.**
12. Remove water pump top attaching bolts.
13. Using a box wrench remove water pump lower attaching bolt.
14. Grasp bottom of water pump pulley, pull out and up to remove water pump.
15. Reverse procedure to install.

### LATE 1991 & ALL 1992 MODELS

1. Disconnect battery ground cable.
2. Loosen accessory drive belt.
3. Drain cooling system, then remove engine cover.
4. Remove spark plug wire retainer from thermostat housing.
5. Remove front damper bracket bolts, then push bracket toward radiator.
6. Remove radiator hose from water rack and thermostat, then bypass hose from water rack.
7. Remove water pump upper attaching bolts, then remove lower bolt.
8. Pull water pump outward and upward to remove.
9. Reverse procedure to install.

## FUEL PUMP

### REPLACE

1. The fuel pump/sender unit is located in the fuel tank. Remove fuel tank as follows:
   a. Disconnect battery ground cable.
   b. Remove fuel tank filler cap to relieve fuel tank pressure, then install fuel tank filler cap.
   c. Raise and support vehicle.
   d. Remove right rear wheel and tire assembly, then the splash shield from wheelwell.
   e. Remove ground wire retaining screw.
   f. Loosen hose clamp and disconnect fuel tank vent hose from fuel tank filler neck.
   g. Slide fuel tank vent hose out of retaining clip.
   h. Loosen and remove nut securing fuel tank support strap. Push other end of strap up and out left side frame rail.
   i. Place transmission jack under fuel tank to support it while removing tank.
   j. Disconnect quick-connect fittings from fuel filler inlet nipple tube, wrap in suitable shop towel, then apply pressure to retainer tabs and pulling fitting back. Note that retainer stays on nipple.
   k. Pull black hose toward fuel tank and through hole in body.
   l. Disconnect fuel pump/sending unit electrical connector.
   m. Disconnect fuel tank to evaporator canister vapor tube at hose and gray hose.
   n. Remove fuel tank attaching bolts. Lower fuel tank on transmission jack two to three inches. Tip fuel tank down on jack while lowering it out of vehicle.
   o. Lower tank and remove it from transmission jack.
2. **On 1989-90 and early 1991 models**, proceed as follows:
   a. Remove fuel pump/sender assembly from fuel tank
   b. Disconnect electrical connectors (A) and (B) from terminals on top of fuel pump, **Fig. 20.**
   c. Remove fuel pump hold-down bracket attaching nut, bracket, gasket and bolt.
   d. Disconnect hose clamp at inlet port of fuel pump.
   e. Remove hose clamp and pull fuel pump out. Retain gasket for installation.
3. **On late 1991 and all 1992 models,** loosen fuel pump module clamp, then remove fuel pump and sender assembly.
4. **On all models,** reverse procedure to install.

## TIGHTENING SPECIFICATIONS

**NOTE:** Torque Specifications Are For Clean And Lightly Lubricated Threads Only. Dry Or Dirty Threads Produce Increased Friction Which Prevents Accurate Measurement Of Tightness.

| Year | Component | Torque Ft. Lbs. |
|---|---|---|
| 1989–91 | A/C Compressor Mounting Bolt | 20 |
| | Air Cleaner Hose Clamp | 30① |
| | Alternator Locking Bolt | 20 |
| | Alternator Pivot Bolt | 37 |
| | Camshaft Sprocket Bolt | 59 |
| | Camshaft Thrust Plate Mounting Bolt | 9 |
| | Connecting Rod Nut | 35 |
| | Crankshaft Pulley Nut | 133 |
| | Crankshaft Rear Seal Housing Bolt | 9 |
| | Cylinder Head Bolt | ② |
| | Cylinder Head Cover Bolt | 9 |
| | Cylinder Head Rear Cover Bolt | 53① |
| | Differential Cover Bolt | 20 |
| | Distributor Cap Mounting Bolt | 80① |
| | Distributor Rotor Mounting Bolt | 26① |
| | Engine Cradle Bolt | 92 |
| | Engine Damper Bottom Locknut | 20 |
| | Engine Damper Top Nut | 32 |
| | Engine Mount Nut | 48 |
| | Engine Mount Stud Locknut | 48 |
| | Fuel Tank | 12 |
| | Halfshaft To Brake Hub Nut | 181 |
| | Idle Pulley To Timing Cover Bolt | 30 |
| | Oil Baffle Bearing Mounting Bolt | 13 |
| | Oil Baffle Mounting Bolt | 9 |

Continued

## TIGHTENING SPECIFICATIONS—Continued

| Year | Component | Torque Ft. Lbs. |
|---|---|---|
| | Oil Pan Drain Plug | 22 |
| | Oil Pan Mounting Bolt | 9 |
| | Oil Pump Cover Bolt | 9 |
| | Oil Pump Sprocket Bolt | 53① |
| | Oil Pump Sump To Block Bolt | 9 |
| | Power Steering Pump Front Bracket/Rear Bracket Nut | 30 |
| | Power Steering Pump Front Bracket/Timing Case Bolt | 20 |
| | Power Steering Pump Rear Mounting Bracket Stud Bolt | 30 |
| | Power Steering Pump Rear Mounting Bolt | 20 |
| | Rear Cushion To Support Bracket | 49 |
| | Rear Cushion To Exhaust Bracket | 23 |
| | Rocker Shaft Locknut | 53① |
| | Splash Shield (Underbody) | 21 |
| | Starter Motor Mounting Bolt | 31 |
| | Thermostat Housing | 9 |
| | Timing Case Cover | 9 |
| | Timing Chain Guide | 53① |
| | Timing Chain Tensioner Bolt | 53① |
| | Timing Chain Tensioner Shoe Bolt | 9 |
| | Torque Converter To Driveplate | 24 |
| | Transaxle Mounting & Alignment Stud | 48 |
| | Transaxle Support Bracket Stud | 30 |
| | Water Pump | 13 |

①—Inch lbs. ②—Refer to text for procedure.

# Rear Axle & Suspension

## INDEX



## REAR AXLE
### REPLACE

1. Raise and support vehicle.
2. Remove rear wheel and tire assemblies.
3. Disconnect shock absorbers from axle.
4. Loosen adjustment nuts to allow balls on end of parking brake cables to pass through access holes. Remove cables from body support.
5. Disconnect brake hoses from metal brake lines and axle.
6. Position supporting jack under axle assembly and remove attaching bolts.
7. Remove axle assembly by lowering support jack.
8. Reverse procedure to install.

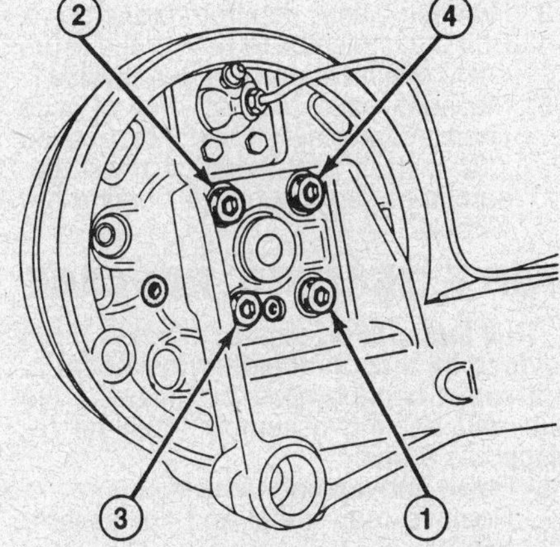


**Fig. 1 Axle shaft bolt torque sequence**

## REAR AXLE SHAFT
### REPLACE

1. Raise and support vehicle.
2. Remove rear wheel and tire assembly.
3. Remove and discard safety nuts securing brake drum to axle shaft hub.
4. Remove plastic hub cover using suitable screwdriver.
5. Remove brake drum from axle shaft hub.
6. Remove and discard axle shaft hub locknut.
7. Remove axle shaft hub from axle shaft using a suitable puller if necessary.
8. Remove axle shaft to rear axle attaching bolts.
9. Remove brake backing plate to axle

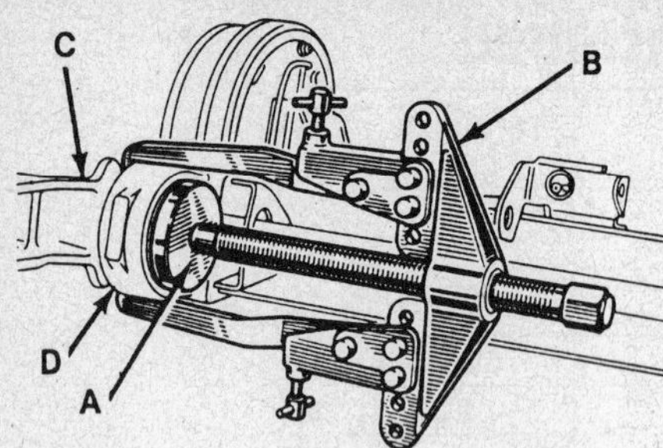


**Fig. 2 Rear axle bushing removal**

shaft attaching bolt.

10. Remove axle shaft from trailing arm.
11. Reverse procedure to install, noting the following:
    a. Tighten axle shaft to rear axle attaching bolts in sequence shown, **Fig. 1,** to specifications.
    b. Torque brake backing plate to axle shaft attaching bolt to specifications.
    c. Install and torque new axle shaft hub locknut and torque to specifications.
    d. Install brake drum and new safety nuts to axle shaft hub.

## REAR AXLE SUPPORT BUSHING

## REPLACE

### REMOVAL

1. Remove rear axle assembly as previously described.
2. Remove torsion bars from axle as described under, "Torsion Bar, Replace."
3. Install component (A) from T.Ar.1056, bushing remover set, and a two jaw extractor (B) on axle, **Fig. 2.**
4. Drive support bracket and bushing from rear axle.
5. To remove bushing from support bracket, weld a 1.02 inch nut to inside of bushing. This nut is used as a backup to drive bushing from support bracket.
6. Using a suitable hydraulic press and bearing splitter tool, drive bushing from support bracket with a suitable socket. Do not reuse bushing after removal.

### INSTALLATION

1. Position new bushing into rear axle.
2. Using driver tool and bushing receiving cup from T.Ar.1056, draw bushing into axle until flush with outside edge of axle.
3. Position support bracket to axle for proper bushing preload, **Fig. 3.** Before pressing support bracket (A) to axle bushing, it must be properly positioned. Adjust support bracket so that dimension "X" measures 27/32–29/32 inch.
4. Position straightedge along top of support bracket where it attaches to body at points (D), **Fig. 3.**
5. After support bracket is positioned to axle, press support bracket to rear axle using T.Ar.1056.
6. Press support bracket until left and right support brackets are at a distance of 51.87-51.98 inch. This measurement is taken between left and right support bracket bolt holes.
7. Install torsion bars to axle as described under, "Torsion Bar, Replace."
8. Install rear axle assembly into vehicle as previously described.

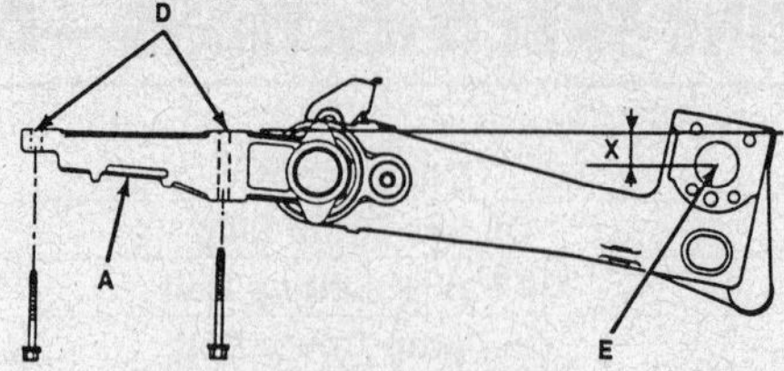


**Fig. 3 Axle support bracket**

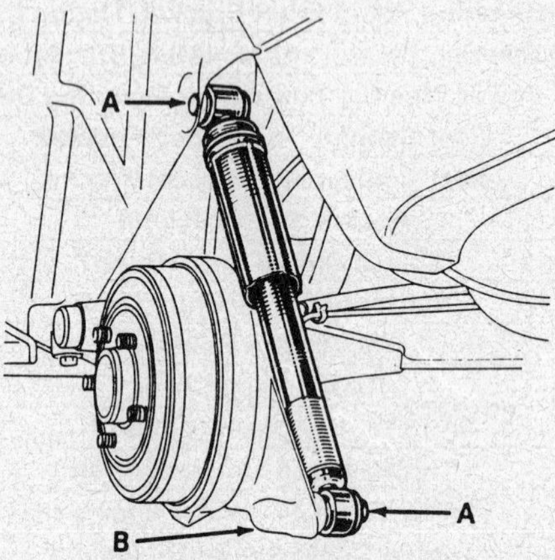


**Fig. 5 Shock absorber bolt location**

## HUB & BEARING SERVICE

### BEARING INSPECTION

1. Raise and support vehicle.
2. Remove rear wheel and tire assembly.
3. Remove plastic cap from brake drum.
4. Bolt dial indicator to rear brake drum using dial indicator adapter ROU541.
5. Measure axial play at end of axle shaft. Axial play should not exceed .001 inch. If play exceeds this measurement, replace hub & bearing assembly.

### HUB & BEARING, REPLACE

**This installation procedure has been revised by a Technical Service Bulletin.**

If wheel bearing must be replaced, the hub and bearing assembly must be replaced as a unit.

1. Raise and support vehicle.
2. Remove rear wheel and tire assembly.
3. Remove safety nuts securing brake drum to axle shaft hub.
4. Remove plastic hub cover using suitable screwdriver.
5. Remove brake drum from axle shaft hub.
6. Remove axle shaft hub locknut.
7. Remove wheel hub and bearing assembly from vehicle.
8. Reverse procedure to install noting the following:
    a. Torque new hub nut to specifications.
    b. Install O-ring (PN 454339) to hub and bearing cap to eliminate water or dust entering rear wheel bearing, **Fig. 4.**
    c. Install brake drum to hub using new safety nuts.

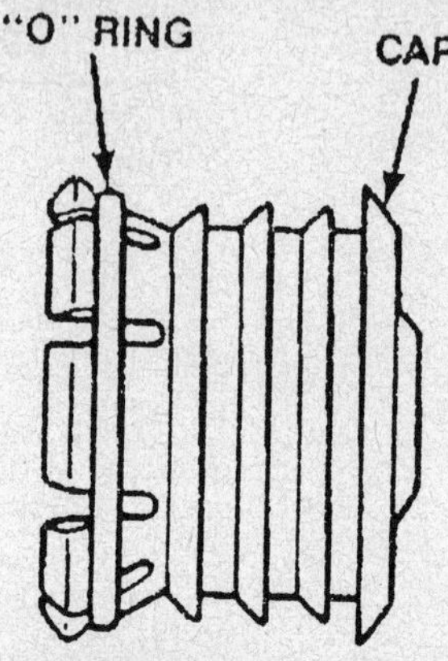


**Fig. 4 Hub & bearing O-ring installation**

## SHOCK ABSORBER

## REPLACE

1. Raise and support vehicle. **Do not support vehicle weight under V-shaped channel on axle.**
2. Raise and support control arm at point B, **Fig. 5,** to relieve tension from shock absorber.
3. Remove shock absorber attaching bolts, then lower shock absorber from vehicle.
4. Reverse procedure to install. Torque upper and lower attaching bolt.

## TORSION BAR

## REPLACE

### REMOVAL

1. Raise and support vehicle. **Do not support vehicle weight under V-shaped channel on axle. Axle weight must be supported at point A, Fig. 6,** using a suitable jack.
2. Remove both rear wheel and tire assemblies.
3. Remove rear shock absorbers as previously described.
4. Remove protective caps (A) and (B), **Fig. 7,** from both sides of vehicle.
5. Remove clips from ends of suspension and anti-sway bars using a suitable screwdriver.
6. Note alignment mark D, **Fig. 8,** on suspension bar mount and make a reference mark (position E) on lower

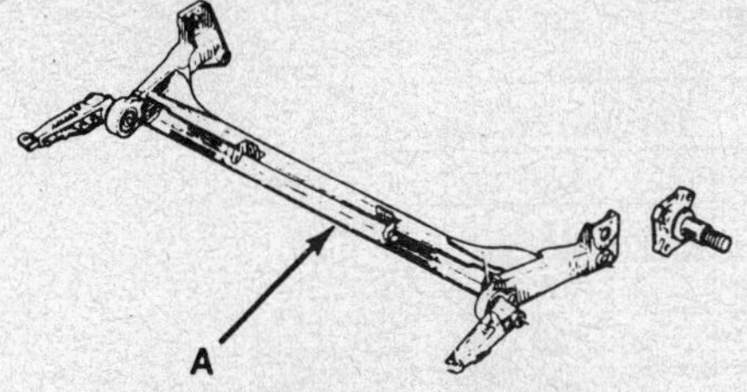


**Fig. 6 Hydraulic jack positioning point**

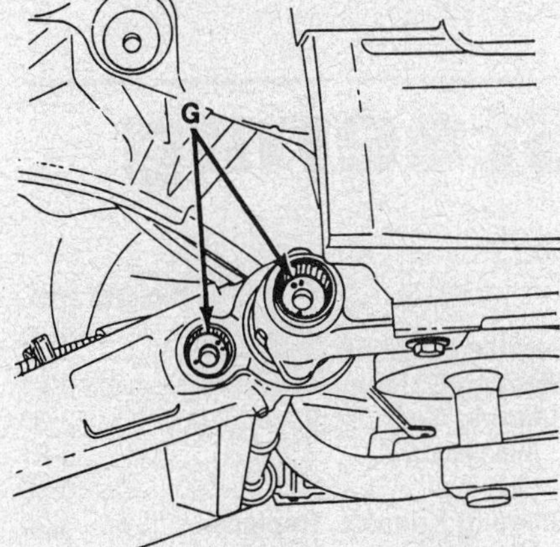


**Fig. 9 Torsion bar reference & location marks**

control arm as shown.

7. Note and record positions of marks G, **Fig. 9,** on all four torsion bars relative to marks D and E. Location of marks on torsion bars (position G) will vary depending on application.
8. Lower rear axle, then pull suspension bars using a suitable slide hammer until splines disengage.
9. Pull anti-sway bars out using a suitable slide hammer. **The rear axle assembly will be damaged if a load is applied to jack supporting the axle.**
10. Support axle at point L, **Fig. 10,** then loosen bolts (M) approximately four turns and bolts (N) approximately ten turns.
11. Lower jack until axle has dropped approximately one inch.
12. Remove suspension bars, then the torsion bar connecting link from vehicle.

## INSTALLATION

1. Install torsion bars into rear axle. **Do not engage splines at this time. Ensure torsion bars are installed in original position.**
2. Raise axle and torque rear axle mounting bolts to specifications.
3. Position rear trailing arms as follows:
   a. Adjust dimension X, **Fig. 11,** on each of two tools Sus.Lm.02 to $17\frac{15}{16}$ inches.
   b. Loosely install bolt (C) and spacer

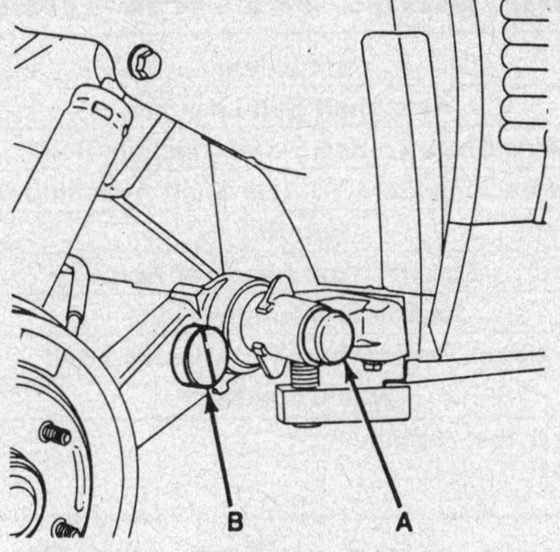


**Fig. 7 Anti-sway bar protective end caps**

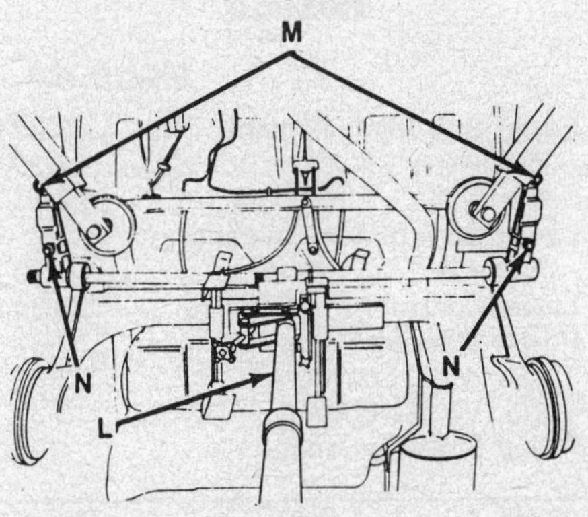


**Fig. 10 Axle attaching bolt locations**

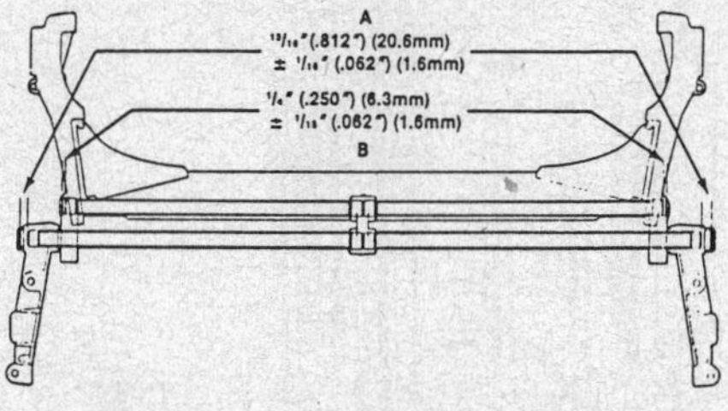


**Fig. 12 Torsion bar spline dimensions**

(A) from tool set No. T.Ar. 1056 into rear lower shock absorber mounting hole.

4. Apply a suitable lubricant to torsion bar splines and install torsion bars in original position. Ensure recorded marks G, D, and E are properly aligned to avoid added stress to bars.
5. Use recorded marks to position anti-sway bar G into mounting.
6. Install connecting link to splines of anti-sway bar G. Ensure connecting link is centered in V-shaped channel in axle.
7. Install anti-sway bar D in outer mounting and secure in connecting link.
8. Install both suspension bars through

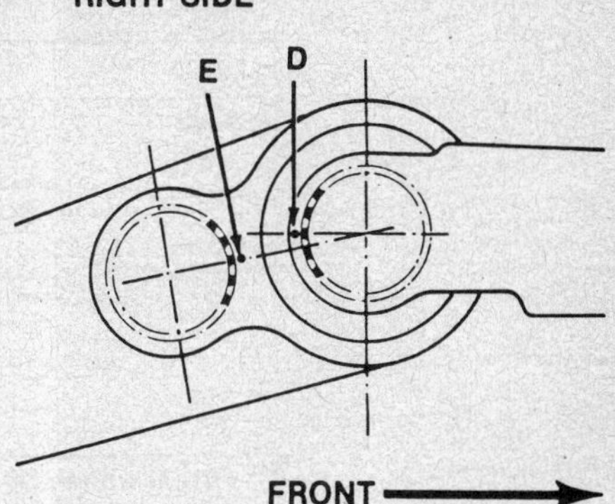


**Fig. 8 Lower control arm reference marks**

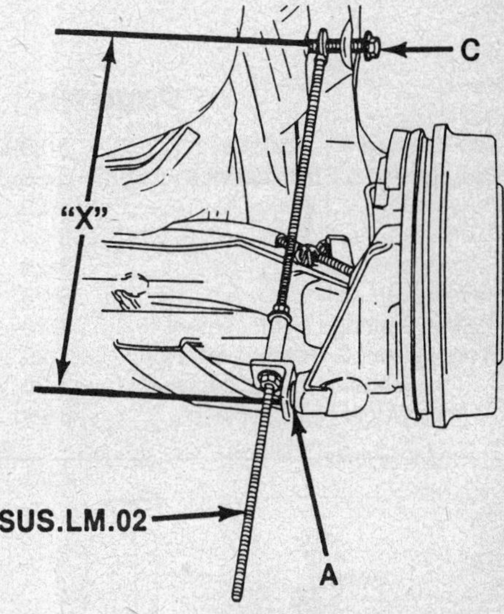


**Fig. 11 Axle spacing tool position**

outer mounting and secure in connecting link. **Ensure all torsion bars are installed in original position. If splines are difficult to engage, slightly twist link as necessary using suitable pliers on the connecting link.**

9. Remove threaded rod tools from vehicle, then install shock absorbers.
10. Install clips and protective caps on end of torsion bars.
11. Center torsion bars in mountings as follows:
    a. Tap ends of suspension bars until outer end of bar protrudes $\frac{3}{4}$-$\frac{7}{8}$ inch from outer edge of mount on both sides, **Fig. 12, using a large brass drift. Do not hammer directly on torsion bar splines.**
    b. Tap ends of anti-sway bars until outer end of bar protrudes $\frac{3}{16}$-$\frac{5}{16}$ inch from outer edge of mount on both sides, **Fig. 12. Do not hammer directly on torsion bar splines.**
12. Install wheel and tire assemblies.

## TIGHTENING SPECIFICATIONS

| Year | Component | Torque/Ft. Lbs. |
|---|---|---|
| 1989–92 | Axle Shaft Hub Locknut | 123 |
| | Axle Shaft-To-Rear Axle Attaching Bolts | 47 |
| | Brake Backing Plate-To-Axle Shaft Attaching Bolt | 12 |
| | Hub Nut | 123 |
| | Lower Shock Absorber Bolt | 85 |
| | Rear Axle Mounting Bolts | 68 |
| | Upper Shock Absorber Attaching Bolt | 60 |
| | Wheel Lug Nut | ① |

①—Steel wheel; 54-72 ft. lbs, aluminum wheel; 80-100 ft. lbs.

# Front Suspension & Steering

## INDEX



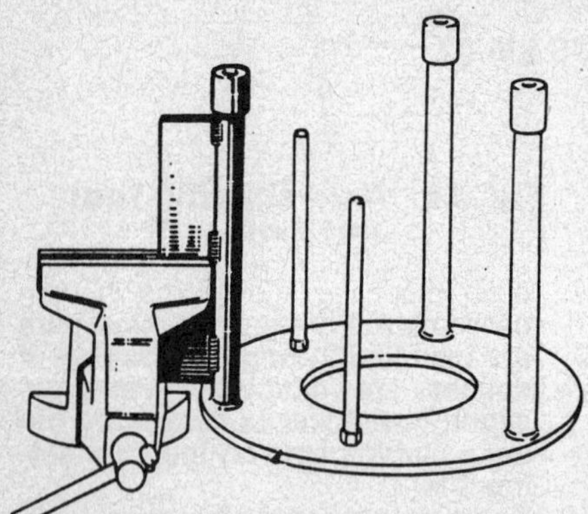

Fig. 1 Spring removal tool lower plate

## COIL SPRING & STRUT SERVICE

### REMOVAL

1. Raise and support vehicle. **Ensure vehicle weight is not supported under front lower control arms.**
2. Remove front tire and wheel assemblies.
3. Remove outer tie rod end securing nut, then the tie rod using suitable tool.
4. Remove three strut to body attaching nuts.
5. Remove securing nuts from bottom of shock absorber.
6. Remove lower shock absorber mounting bolts.
7. To prevent damage, wrap boot then press down on lower control arm and guide assembly out.

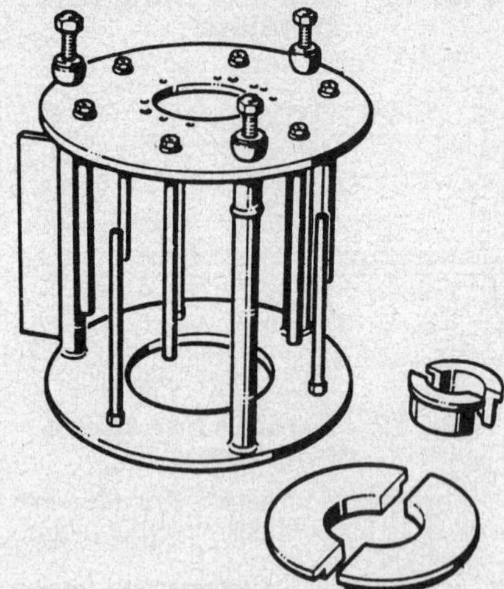

Fig. 2 Installing lower adapter plates

### DISASSEMBLY

Suspension Tool Kit No. 1052.99 is supplied with various adapter plates for different models. Eagle Premier models use adapter plates stamped R-21.

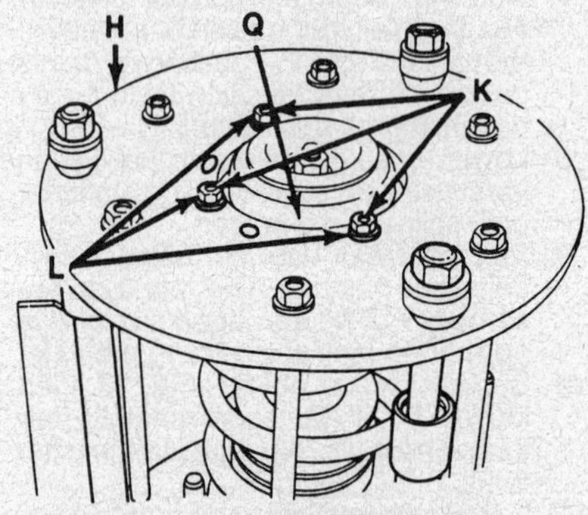


Fig. 3 Installing top adapter plate

1. Place lower plate from spring removal tool into a vise, **Fig. 1.**
2. Place lower adapter plates (G) into lower plate, **Fig. 2.**
3. Place smaller adapter plates (F) around lower part of strut assembly and properly seat into lower plate that is secured in the vise.
4. Install top adapter plate (H), **Fig. 3,** onto strut assembly and rotate strut to align with holes on plate. Install three 5/16 inch by 1.5 inch bolts (L & K) in length through top plate and tighten to cushion (Q).
5. Threading rods into mounts, slowly compress coil spring to approximately 13/32 inch.
6. Relieve spring tension evenly by loos-

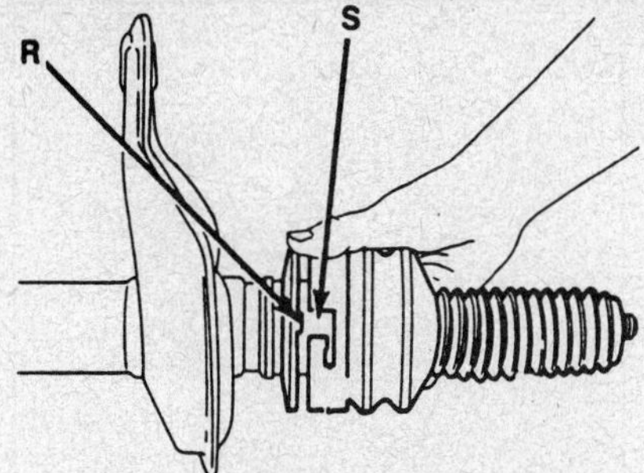


Fig. 4 Removing jounce bumper and dust boot

ening threaded bolts and remove spring.

## STRUT CARTRIDGE REPLACEMENT

**To avoid damage to strut assembly, mount strut in strut clamping vise No. YA-457 or equivalent.**

1. Align tab (R) with opening (S) on jounce bumper, then remove jounce bumper and dust boot, **Fig. 4.**
2. Remove pressed-on cap. Use care to avoid damaging threads.
3. Remove 7/16 to 31/64 from top of strut body using a suitable cutting tool.
4. Remove and discard strut cartridge, then pour residual oil from strut body.
5. Remove excess metal from inside of strut tube caused by cutting operation.
6. Install new cartridge and threaded cap. Torque threaded cap to specifications.

## ASSEMBLY

1. Install dust boot over strut body, **Fig. 5.**
2. Inspect rubber isolator tubes for any wear and replace if necessary.
3. Rotate spring on strut assembly so it bottoms into stop. Spring should be separated by isolator tubes.
4. Place spring retainer on top of spring so it bottoms on end of spring.
5. Install pivot bearing on top of spring retainer.
6. Place strut cushion on top of pivot bearing.
7. Place lower adapter plates (G) into lower plate, **Fig. 2.**
8. Place smaller adapter plates (F) around lower part of strut assembly and properly seat into lower plate that is secured in the vise.
9. Install top adapter plate (H), **Fig. 3,** onto strut assembly and rotate strut to align with holes on plate, install three 5/16 inch by 1.5 inch bolts (L) in length through top plate and tighten down.
10. Threading rods (M) into mounts (N) slowly compress adapter plate evenly until strut shaft appears through upper plate.
11. Install rebound cup and torque to specifications.
12. Remove from tool and install in vehicle.

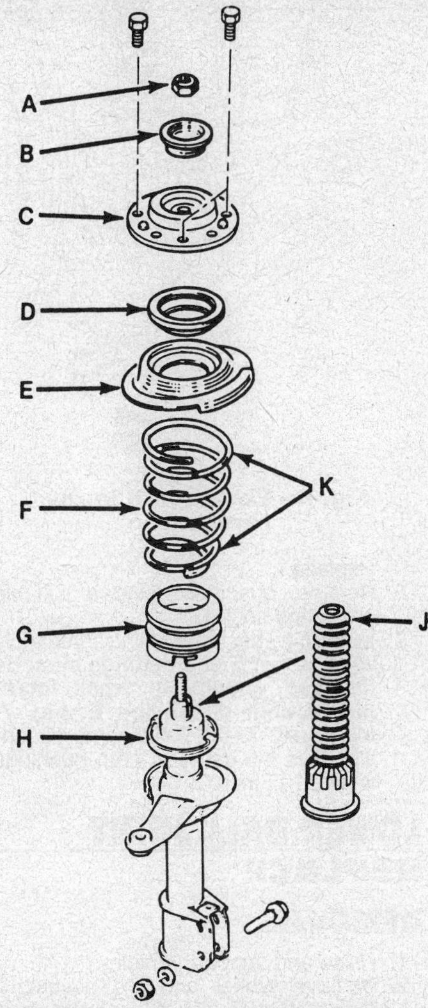


**A-Locknut**
**B-Rebound Cup**
**C-Strut Cushion**
**D-Pivot Bearing**
**E-Spring Seat**
**F-Coil Spring**
**G-Jounce Bumper**
**H-Shock Absorber**
**J-Dust Boot**
**K-Rubber Spring Isolator Tubes**

Fig. 5 Exploded view of spring strut assembly

## INSTALLATION

1. Position spring/strut assembly on vehicle and finger tighten strut to body nuts.
2. Install lower mounting bolts and nuts, torquing nuts to specifications. **Bolts are splined and must not be tightened.**
3. Install upper mounting bolts and torque to specifications.
4. Install tie rod end to strut nut and torque to specifications.
5. Install wheel and tire assembly, lower vehicle.

## ANTI-SWAY BAR REPLACE

1. Remove anti-sway bar clamp bolts and nuts, then the anti-sway bar.

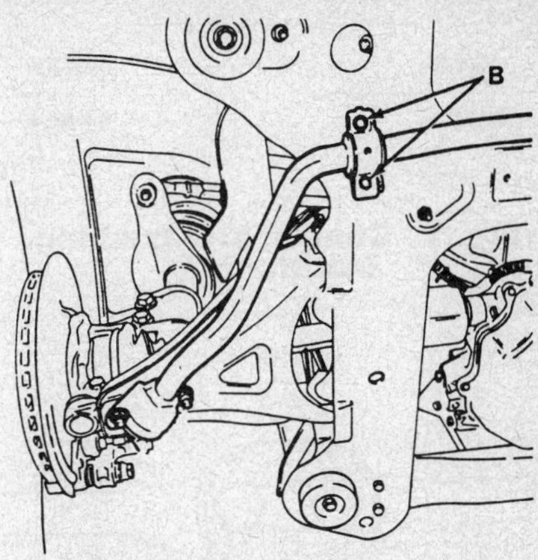


Fig. 6 Stabilizer bar inboard bracket bolts

2. Temporarily install one nut to retain lower ball joint.
3. Check anti-sway bar bushings for damage or excessive wear and replace if necessary.
4. Reverse procedure to install. Torque inner and outer anti-sway bar clamp to specifications.

## FRONT WHEEL & BEARING SERVICE

Hub and bearing are serviced separately. The hub can be replaced without removing bearing from steering knuckle. In order to replace bearing from steering knuckle, the wheel hub must be removed as an assembly. If bearing components are worn or damaged, replace complete assembly.

## FRONT WHEEL HUB, REPLACE

### Removal

1. Raise and support vehicle.
2. Remove wheel and tire assembly, then unfasten brake caliper and position aside.
3. Remove hub nut and the hub using a suitable tool.
4. If replacing hub, remove bearing race using a suitable tool.

### Installation

1. If necessary, install new bearing race in hub using a suitable press.
2. Lubricate bearing surface of hub with suitable chassis grease.
3. Insert hub on end of driveshaft and tap with a brass hammer so driveshaft extends past hub.
4. Install driveshaft nut and torque to specifications.
5. Install brake rotor and caliper, then the wheel and tire assembly.

## FRONT WHEEL BEARING, REPLACE

### Removal

1. Remove hub as described under

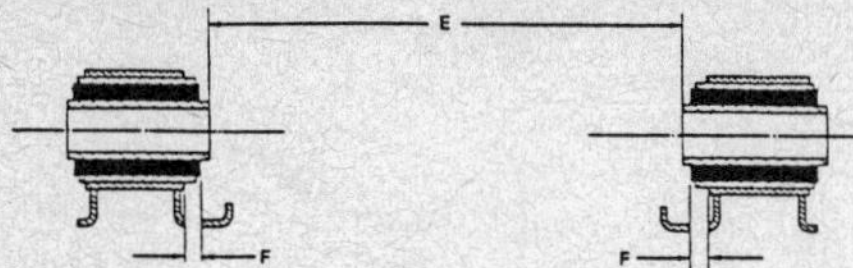


**Fig. 7 Control arm bushing installation**

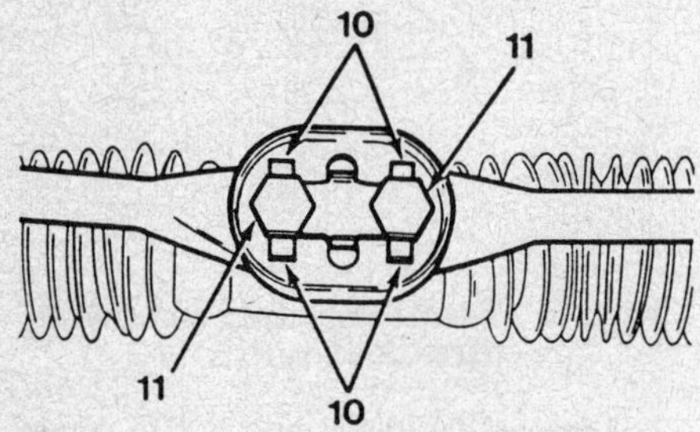


**Fig. 10 Tie rod attaching bolt lock tabs**

"Front Wheel Hub, Replace."

2. Remove bearing assembly to steering knuckle attaching bolts, then the bearing assembly.
3. If necessary, remove bearing outer race using a suitable press and puller. **Bearing race and bearing should be replaced as a set.**

### Installation

1. Pack new bearing with suitable grease.
2. Install bearing race in bearing.
3. Press other bearing race into front wheel hub.
4. Place bearing assembly in steering knuckle, then torque attaching bolt to specifications.
5. Install front wheel hub.

## LOWER CONTROL ARM REPLACE

1. Raise and support vehicle.
2. Remove wheel and tire assembly, then protect driveshaft boot with shop towel.
3. Loosen stabilizer bar inboard bracket bolts (B), **Fig. 6.**
4. Remove stabilizer bar outboard mounting brackets.
5. Remove keybolt from lower ball joint.
6. Remove control arm to engine cradle attaching bolts, then the control arm.
7. Inspect lower control arm bushings for damage or excessive wear and replace if necessary.
8. Reverse procedure to install. Torque ball joint keybolt nut and control arm to engine cradle bolt to specifications.

## LOWER CONTROL ARM BUSHING REPLACE

1. Remove lower control arm as described under "Lower Control Arm, Replace."
2. Remove bushings using a suitable press and socket.
3. Install new bushings using same tools used for removal. **Bushings must be installed equally in small increments until dimension E, Fig. 7,** measures 7.461-7.499 and dimension F is the same at both bushings within .197 inch.

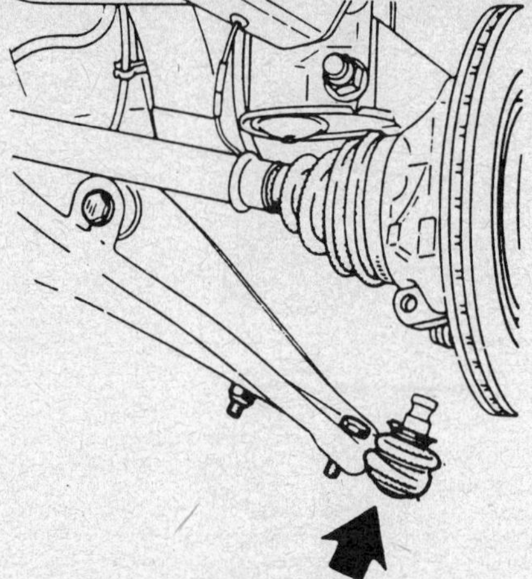

**Fig. 8 Lower ball joint removal**

## LOWER BALL JOINT REPLACE

### REMOVAL

1. Raise and support vehicle.
2. Remove wheel and tire assembly, then protect driveshaft boot with shop towel.
3. Loosen stabilizer bar inner bracket bolts and remove outer mounting brackets.
4. Remove lower ball joint keybolt, then loosen lower control arm bolts.
5. Lower stabilizer bar, then with brass or plastic mallet, tap out ball joint in direction of arrow, **Fig. 8.**

### INSTALLATION

1. Install new ball joint in lower control arm and finger tighten bolts.
2. Insert ball stud in steering knuckle. Torque ball joint keybolt and nut to specifications.
3. Finger tighten stabilizer bar outer mounting brackets.
4. With vehicle weight supported by wheels, torque inner and outer stabilizer bar mounting brackets to specifications.

## STEERING KNUCKLE REPLACE

**When removing steering knuckle, the front wheel hub and wheel bearing assembly can be removed as an assembly.**

### REMOVAL

1. Raise and support vehicle.

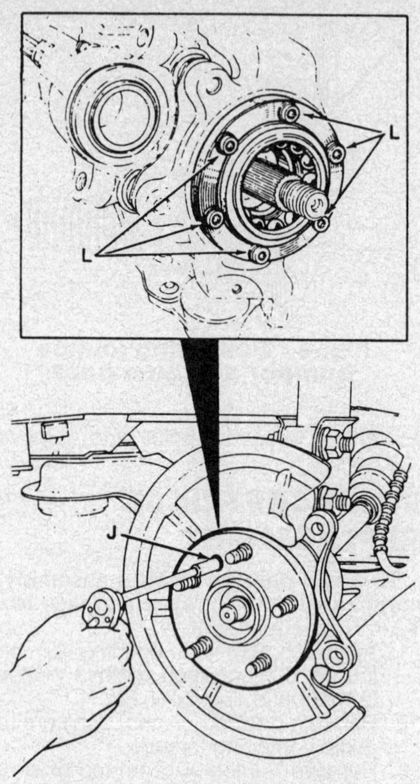


**Fig. 9 Removing wheel bearing attaching bolts**

2. Remove wheel and tire assembly, then protect driveshaft boot with shop towel.
3. Unfasten brake caliper and position aside, leaving hydraulic lines attached.
4. Remove driveshaft center nut and the rotor.
5. Remove wheel bearing to steering knuckle attaching bolts (L) through access hole (J) in front hub, **Fig. 9.**
6. Remove front hub and wheel bearing assembly using a suitable tool.
7. Remove ball joint keybolt and separate ball joint from knuckle.
8. Remove steering knuckle to strut attaching bolts, then the steering knuckle assembly.

### INSTALLATION

1. Position ball joint in steering knuckle, then install ball joint keybolt and nut.
2. Install steering knuckle to strut attaching bolts.
3. Place front hub and wheel bearing assembly over driveshaft. Using access hole in wheel hub, attach wheel bearing to steering knuckle and torque to specifications.
4. Torque driveshaft nut to specifications.
5. Install brake rotor and caliper.

## STEERING GEAR REPLACE

### REMOVAL

1. Remove instrument panel lower cov-

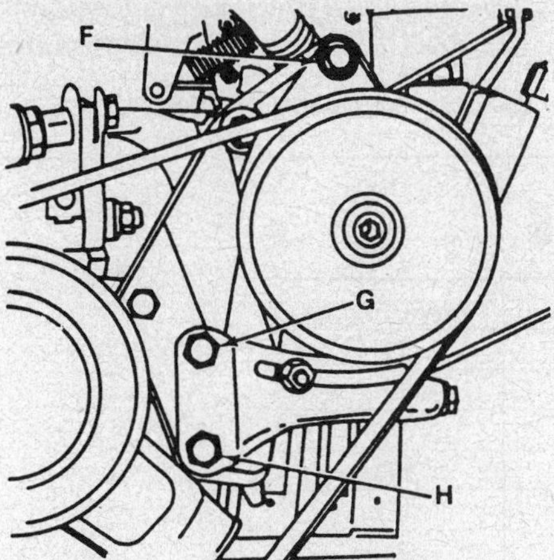


Fig. 11 Power steering attaching bolts

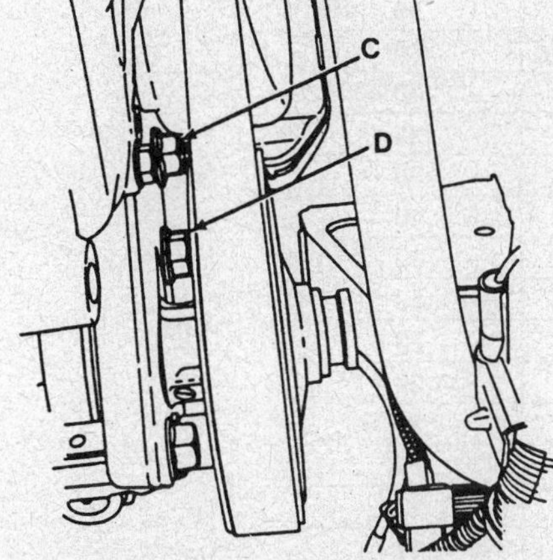


Fig. 12 Power steering bracket bolts (Part 3 of 3)

er.
2. Unfasten steering shaft boot flange and slide upward for access of U-joint.
3. Mark intermediate shaft and steering shaft for installation reference.
4. Remove shaft through bolt.
5. In engine compartment, pry out splash shield clips using a suitable screwdriver.
6. Fold back lock tab (10) on bolts (11) that attach tie rods to steering rack, then loosen bolts one or two turns, **Fig. 10.**
7. Remove power steering pump lines from rubber mounting block and disconnect lines from steering gear. **Replace O-rings on disconnected lines during installation.**
8. Remove mounting nut.
9. Raise and support vehicle.
10. Remove left front wheel and tire assembly, then disconnect tie rod ends from steering knuckles using a suitable tool.
11. Remove three bolts attaching steering gear to vehicle body and slide steering gear assembly through access opening in left fender panel.

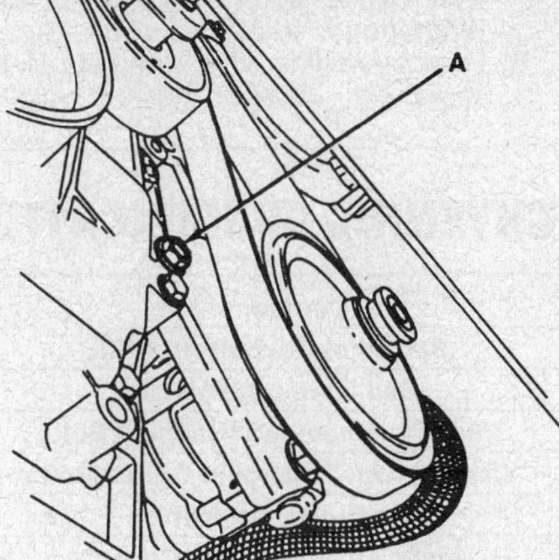


Fig. 12 Power steering bracket bolts (Part 1 of 3)

## INSTALLATION

1. Attach tie rods to steering gear. Do not tighten completely at this time.
2. Install gear assembly through access opening in left fender panel and install gear to body mounting bolts and nuts.
3. Connect tie rod ends to steering knuckle, torque retaining nut to specifications.
4. Connect fluid lines with new O-rings to steering gear.
5. Install fluid lines into rubber mounting block.
6. Torque tie rod to steering gear attaching bolts to specifications, then bend lock tabs over tie rod bolt heads.
7. Align and connect intermediate shaft and steering gear shaft with reference marks made during removal.
8. Install and torque intermediate shaft coupling bolt to specifications.
9. Install steering shaft boot.
10. Fill power steering system to proper level.

# POWER STEERING PUMP REPLACE

## 2.5L/4-150 ENGINE

1. Disconnect battery ground cable.
2. Loosen pump drive belt.
3. Disconnect return hose and high pressure hose from pump.
4. Remove pump mounting bolts and the pump.
5. Reverse procedure to install, noting the following:
   a. Install and tighten attaching bolts (F, G & H) as indicated in **Fig. 11,** then remaining bolts. **Torque** bracket to intake manifold and water pump bolts to 30 ft. lbs. and all other bolts to 20 ft. lbs.
   b. Fill pump reservoir to proper level.

## 3.0L/V6-180 ENGINE

### Removal

1. Raise and support vehicle.
2. Remove underbody splash pan, then

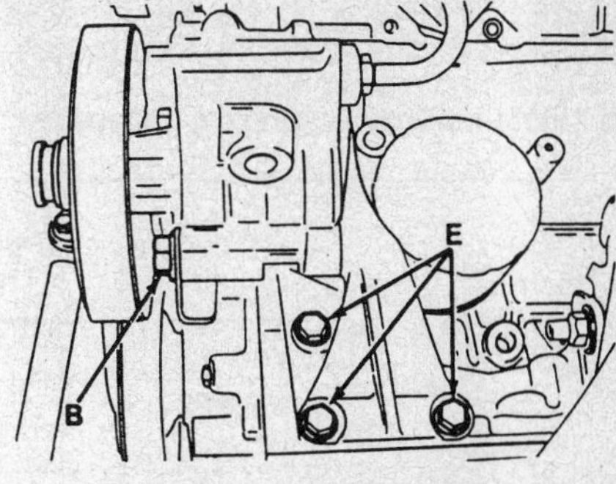


Fig. 12 Power steering bracket bolts (Part 2 of 3)

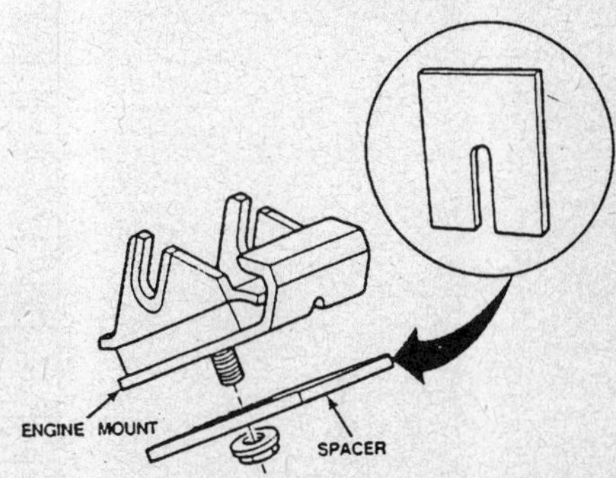


Fig. 13 Engine mount spacer installation

loosen drive belt.
3. Disconnect high pressure hose from pump.
4. Remove all pump bracket bolts, then the pump and bracket as an assembly.

### Installation

1. Install pump assembly on engine.
2. Tighten pump bracket bolts and nuts A through E, **Fig. 12.** in alphabetical order. **Torque** rear bracket to reservoir bolt to 20 ft. lbs., front bracket to rear bracket stud to 15 ft. lbs. and all other nuts and bolts to 30 ft. lbs.
3. Connect return hose and pressure hose to pump.
4. Install and adjust drive belt.
5. Install underbody splash shield.
6. Lower vehicle and fill pump to proper level.

# SERVICE BULLETINS

Some 1989-90 models may experience an interference condition of the lower control arm with the right inner CV joint boot. This condition may occur when the vehicle is at or near full suspension travel.

Inspect the right inner CV boot near the large band clamp, if the boot is cut or damaged, proceed as follows:

1. Disconnect battery ground cable.
2. Loosen both engine mount attaching nuts.
3. Raise engine enough to install spacer under right engine mount. Place spacer so opening of shim slot is pointed toward center of vehicle, **Fig.**

13.
4. Lower engine to spacer, then **torque** attaching nuts to 48 ft. lbs.
5. **Installation of engine mount spacer may cause an interference of the hinge cover with the hood.**
6. Remove engine cover, then cut 1/4 to 3/8 inch off each of the four engine support and reinstall engine cover.
7. If boot is cut or da,aged, replace as required.
8. Connect battery ground cable.

## TIGHTENING SPECIFICATIONS

| Year | Component | Torque/Ft. Lbs. |
|---|---|---|
| 1989–92 | Ball Joint Keybolt And Nut | 77 |
| | Ball Joint Keybolt Nut | 77 |
| | Bearing Assembly Attaching Bolts | 11 |
| | Control Arm To Engine Cradle Bolts | 103 |
| | Driveshaft Nut | 181 |
| | Inner Anti-Sway Bar Clamps | 21 |
| | Inner Stabilizer Bar Mounting Brackets | 21 |
| | Intermediate Shaft Coupling Bolt | 25 |
| | Lower Mounting Bolts | 123 |
| | Outer Anti-Sway Bar Clamps | 60 |
| | Outer Stabilizer Bar Mounting Brackets | 60 |
| | Power Steering Bracket To Bracket Lower Nut/Stud | 30 |
| | Power Steering Bracket To Bracket Upper Nut | 30 |
| | Power Steering Bracket To Upper Stud | 15 |
| | Power Steering Front Bracket To Rear Bracket | 30 |
| | Power Steering Front Bracket To Timing Cover | 20 |
| | Power Steering Rear Bracket To Sump | 30 |
| | Rebound Cup Locknut | 59 |
| | Strut Rebound Cup | 73 |
| | Tie Rod End-To-Strut Nut | 27 |
| | Tie Rod Ends To Steering Knuckle Nuts | 35 |
| | Tie Rod-To-Steering Gear Attaching Bolts | 55 |
| | Upper Mounting Nuts | 17 |
| | Wheel Bearing To Steering Knuckle Bolts | 11 |
| | Wheel Lug Nut | ① |

①—Steel wheel; 54-72 ft. lbs, aluminum wheel; 80-100 ft. lbs.

# Wheel Alignment

## INDEX



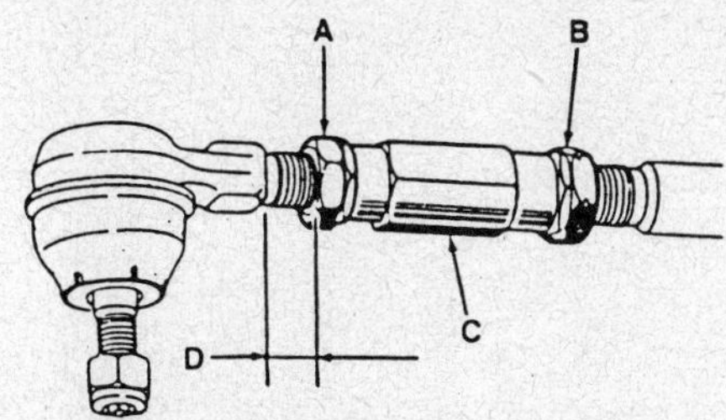


**Fig. 1 Toe-out adjustment**

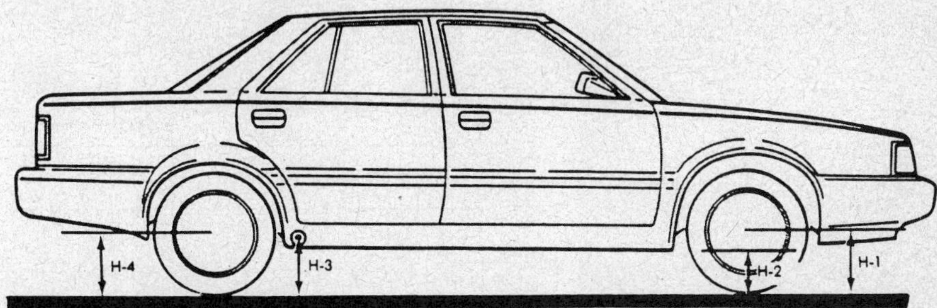


**Fig. 2 Measuring vehicle height (Part 1 of 2)**

## PRELIMINARY INSPECTION

Prior to front end alignment, check vehicle for proper tire size and inflation. Also check wheel and tire radial lateral runout. Steering and suspension components should be inspected for damage and replaced if necessary. Wheel bearing endplay and brake operation should be corrected if necessary. Center steering gear as follows:

1. Support vehicle on alignment rack.
2. Turn steering wheel completely to the left, then completely to the right and count number of turns to the stop.
3. Turn steering wheel to the left one-half the number of turns counted.
4. If steering wheel needs to be centered, adjust after toe adjustment. Refer to "Steering Wheel Alignment."

## FRONT WHEEL ALIGNMENT

### CASTER & CAMBER

Caster and camber built-in angles are not adjustable. A difference of more than one degree between left and right caster or camber angles may result in pulling to one side, or tire wear. Inspection and replacement of damaged suspension and steering parts should be performed to correct alignment angles. Brake drag or an under inflated tire, can also cause the vehicle to pull.

Bounce vehicle several times and check alignment angles of caster and camber then. Repair or replace vehicle suspension parts if alignment is out of specifications.

### TOE-OUT

Front wheel toe-out is adjusted only after the steering gear has been centered. Excessive toe-out will wear the inner edge of tires. Insufficient toe-out will wear outer edge of tires. To adjust toe-out, turn tie rods in or out.

**Fig. 2 Measuring vehicle height (Part 2 of 2)**

1. Loosen tie rod locknut (A - righthand threads), then (B - lefthand threads), **Fig. 1.**
2. Turn adjusting sleeve (C) to required length, ensuring both tie rod ends have an equal amount of threads showing.
3. **Torque** locknuts and to 26 ft. lbs.

### RIDE HEIGHT

1. Measure height H-1 and H-4 from wheel hub horizontal centerline to surface on right and left sides of vehicle, **Fig. 2.**
2. Measure height H-2 from engine cradle at wheel hub vertical centerline to surface.
3. Measure height H-3 from front torsion bar horizontal centerline to surface, **Fig. 2.**
4. Compare height measurements from each side of vehicle, as follows:
   a. Subtract H-2 from H-1, measurement should be 3.36 to 3.98 inches.
   b. Subtract H-3 from H-4, measurement should be 1.25 to 1.87 inches.

## SERVICE BULLETINS

### PREMATURE TIRE WEAR

Some 1989 Premier models may experience premature tire wear on either the front or rear or both which may be evident by visual inspection and/or sound, may be the result of static toe adjustment.

To repair this condition, adjust the toe alignment to the following specifications. For front toe adjustment follow the standard procedures.

1. Loosen the four Torx head bolts attaching the rear axle/torsion bar assembly to the shaft and flange assembly (drum brakes) or the trailing arm to the brake and spindle assembly (disc brakes), at least three (3) full turns.
2. Remove and discard the two front upper and lower bolts.
3. Install two new bolts (part No. J0762039). **To make this toe adjustment it will be necessary to use shim (part No. 5205114) Modified as shown in Fig. 3.**
4. Slide modified shim between the rear axle/torsion bar assembly and back side of brake support plate (drum brakes), or trailing arm and back side of brake and spindle assembly (disc brakes). Tighten bolts enough to hold shim in position. **If necessary, it is permissible to install one additional shim on each side to bring the toe within specifications.**
5. Remove and discard the two rear upper and lower bolts.
6. Install two new bolts (part No. J0762039).
7. **Torque** all four bolts to 48 ft. lbs.
8. Repeat operation on other side.

FRONT WHEEL CURB TOE SPECIFICATIONS

| o | Degrees | X minus Y in. | X minus Y mm. |
|---|---|---|---|
| | 0° ± 0.15° | 0" ± 0.1278" | 0 ± 3.246 mm. |

REAR WHEEL CURB TOE SPECIFICATIONS

| o | Degrees | M minus N in. | M minus N mm. |
|---|---|---|---|
| | 0° ± 0.23° | 0" ± 0.1960" | 0 ± 4.9777 mm. |

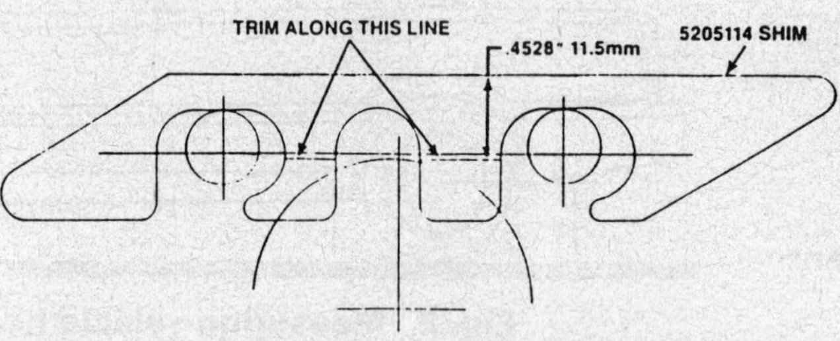


**Fig. 3 Modified shim**

# EAGLE MEDALLION

## INDEX OF SERVICE OPERATIONS

**NOTE:** Refer To The Rear Of This Manual For Vehicle Manufacturer's Special Tool Suppliers.

## INDEX OF SERVICE OPERATIONS—Continued



# Specifications

## GENERAL ENGINE SPECIFICATIONS

| Year | Engine | | Fuel System | Bore & Stroke | Compression Ratio | Net H.P. @ RPM③ | Maximum Torque Ft. Lbs. @ RPM | Normal Oil Pressure Psi |
|---|---|---|---|---|---|---|---|---|
| | Liter/CID① | VIN Code② | | | | | | |
| 1989 | 2.2L/4-132 | F | Fuel Inj.④ | 3.46 x 3.50 | 9.2 | 103 @ 5000 | 124 @ 2500 | 44⑤ |

①—CID: Cubic Inch Displacement.
②—The fourth digit of the VIN denotes engine code.
③—Ratings are net, as installed in vehicle.
④—Multi-point electronic fuel injection system.
⑤—At 3000 RPM.

## TUNE UP SPECIFICATIONS

| Year & Engine/ VIN | Spark Plug Gap | Ignition Timing BTDC① | | | | Curb Idle Speed | | Fast Idle Speed | | Fuel Pressure Psi |
|---|---|---|---|---|---|---|---|---|---|---|
| | | Firing Order Fig. | Man. Trans. | Auto. Trans. | Mark Fig. | Man. Trans. | Auto. Trans. | Man. Trans. | Auto. Trans. | |
| **1989** | | | | | | | | | | |
| 2.2L/4-132(F) | .035 | A | ② | ② | ③ | ④ | ④ | ④ | ④ | 36⑤ |

①—BTDC: Before Top Dead Center.
②—Controlled by the ECU (Electronic Control Unit).
③—Equipped with crankshaft position sensor, located at flywheel end of engine.
④—Controlled by idle speed regulating valve.
⑤—Position a shop towel around hose connection. Disconnect fuel hose located between fuel pressure regulator & fuel rail, then connect a suitable fuel pressure gauge.

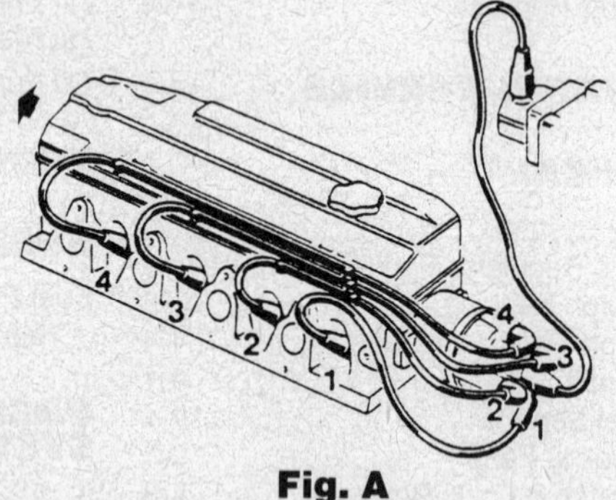


Fig. A

## FRONT WHEEL ALIGNMENT SPECIFICATIONS

*The specifications listed below are for unloaded vehicles

| Year | Model | Caster Angle, Degrees ① ③ | | Camber Angle, Degrees ③ | | Toe-Out Angle (Inches) | | King Pin Inclination (Degrees) ③ | |
|---|---|---|---|---|---|---|---|---|---|
| | | Limits | Desired | Limits | Desired | Per Wheel | Total Over Two Wheels | Limits | Desired |
| 1989 | All | ② | ② | 0 to +1 | +½ | .078 to .125 | .04 to .12 | 12⅙ to 13⅙ | 12⅔ |

①—Vehicle ride height must be checked and, if necessary adjusted before checking front wheel alignment.
②—3½° when vehicle ride height is 1.38 inch, 3° when vehicle ride height is 2.17 inch, 2½° when vehicle ride height is 2.95 inch, 2° when vehicle ride height is 3.74 inch or 1½° when vehicle ride height is 4.53 inch.
③—Not adjustable.

## REAR WHEEL ALIGNMENT SPECIFICATIONS

*The specifications listed below are for unloaded vehicles

| Year | Model | Camber Angle, (Degrees) ① | | Toe-In (Inch) ① |
|---|---|---|---|---|
| | | Limits | Desired | |
| 1989 | All | -2/3 to -1/6 | -2/3 | .078–.197 |

①—Not adjustable.

## COOLING SYSTEM & CAPACITY DATA

| Year | Model | Cooling Capacity Qts. | | Radiator Cap Relief Pressure, Lbs. | Thermo. Opening Temp. | Fuel Tank Gals. | Engine Oil Refill Qts. | Transaxle Oil | |
|---|---|---|---|---|---|---|---|---|---|
| | | Less A/C | With A/C | | | | | 5 Speed Pints | Auto. Trans. Qts.① |
| 1989 | All | ② | ② | — | 192 | 17.4 | 5¼③ | 4.8 | ④ |

①—Approximate, make final check with dipstick.
②—Models with automatic transaxle, 7.1 qts.; models with manual transaxle, 6.75 qts.
③—With filter change.
④—Oil pan only, 2.6 qts.; total capacity, 6.3 qts.

## LUBRICANT DATA

| Year | Model | Lubricant Type | | | | | |
|---|---|---|---|---|---|---|---|
| | | Transaxle | | Transfer Case | Rear Axle | Power Steering | Brake System |
| | | Manual | Automatic | | | | |
| 1989 | All | API GL-5 | Dexron II | — | — | 8993342① | Dot 3 |

①—Chrysler/Eagle Part No.

# Electrical

## INDEX



## STARTER
### REPLACE

1. Disconnect battery ground cable.
2. Remove starter motor mounting bracket attaching bolts, then the mounting bracket.
3. Disconnect starter solenoid electrical connectors.
4. Remove starter motor rear mounting bolts (E), **Fig. 1.**
5. Remove remaining starter mounting bolts (C).
6. Remove starter and locating bushing (B).
7. Reverse procedure to install.

## IGNITION SWITCH & LOCK
### REPLACE

1. Disconnect battery ground cable.
2. Remove attaching screws from lower steering column cover.
3. **On vehicles equipped with cruise control, pull down wire (B), Fig. 2, located on the forward edge of the lower cover. This will pull the spring loaded commutator brush back into its housing. If the commutator brush is not pulled into its housing before the lower cover is removed, the brush will be broken off.**
4. **On all models,** remove upper and lower steering column covers.
5. Remove attaching screws and lower instrument panel cover.
6. Remove ignition switch cover.
7. Disconnect two wire electrical connectors (one black and one gray).
8. Remove ignition switch attaching screw.
9. Turn ignition switch to the unmarked (arrow) position (H), **Fig. 3.**
10. Push on locking tabs (E), **Fig. 4,** and remove switch. Remove switch by feeding the wires through the lock cylinder bore.
11. To disconnect the tumbler from the electrical switch, remove two attaching screws securing assembly together and separate assembly.
12. Reverse procedure to install. **Vehicles equipped with cruise control, note the following:**
    a. Pull down on wire located at the forward edge of the lower cover.

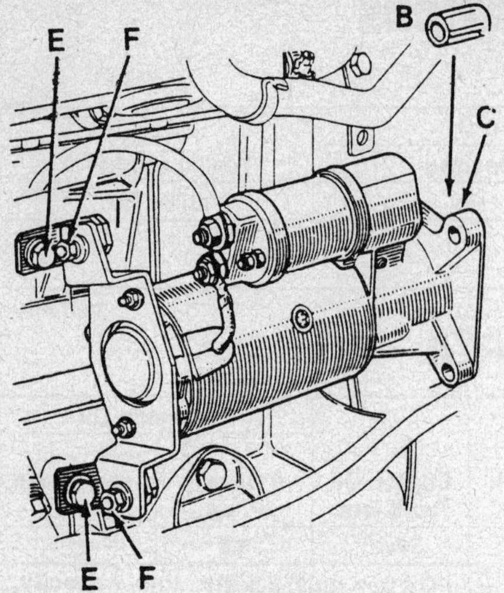


Fig. 1 Starter motor Installation

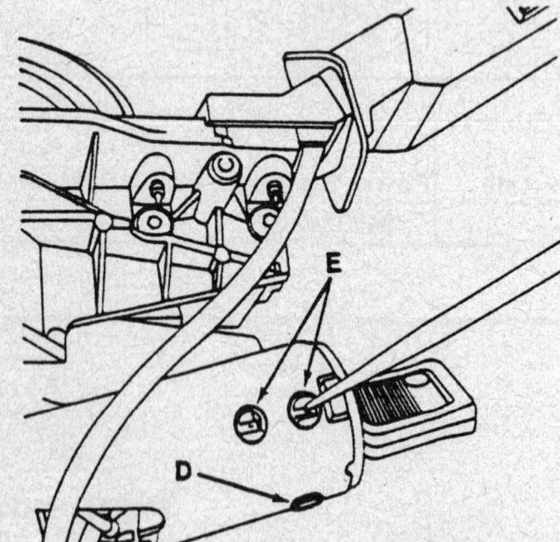


Fig. 4 Ignition switch retaining tab locations

b. This will put the spring loaded commutator brush back into its housing.
c. If the commutator brush is not pulled into its housing, the commutator brush will be broken off.

## COMBINATION SWITCH REPLACE

1. Disconnect battery ground cable.
2. Remove attaching screws from lower steering column cover.
3. **On models equipped with cruise control, pull down on wire (B), Fig. 2, located at the forward edge of the lower cover. This will pull the spring loaded commutator brush back into its housing. If the commutator brush is not pulled into its housing before the lower cover is removed, the brush will be broken off.**
4. **On all models,** remove upper and

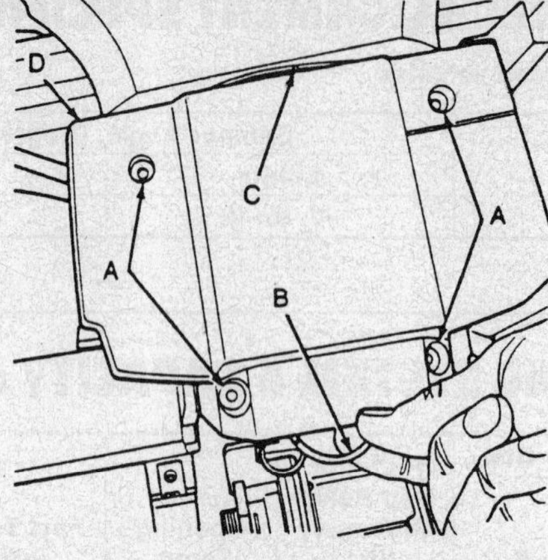


Fig. 2 Cruise control commutator brush wire location

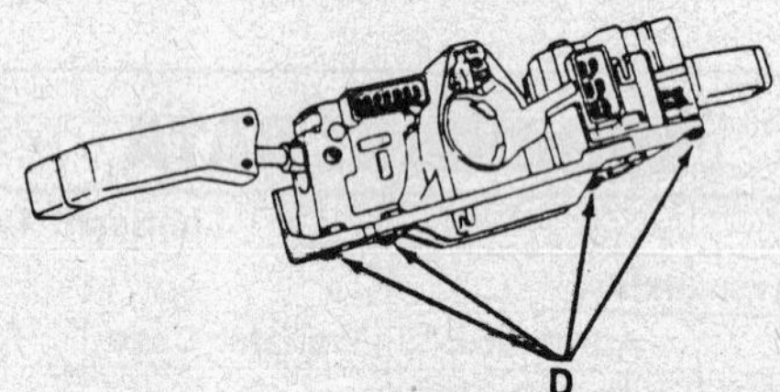


Fig. 5 Attaching screw locations for switch removal

lower steering housing column covers.

5. If only one switch requires replacement (the combination switch includes the light switch, turn signal and windshield wiper switch), remove attaching screws (D), **Fig. 5**, securing that particular switch.
6. Disconnect electrical connectors.
7. If the entire switch assembly requires replacement, proceed as follows:
   a. Remove attaching screws located on either side of the steering wheel cover.
   b. Remove steering wheel trim cover.
   c. Place an alignment mark on the steering wheel and shaft before removing steering wheel.
   d. Loosen but do not remove steering wheel locknut.
   e. Do not use a hammer to tap against the end of the steering column. The inner column will collapse if struck.
   f. Grasp steering wheel and give it a quick pull.
   g. When the steering wheel comes loose, remove steering wheel locknut and steering wheel.
   h. Remove attaching screw (A), **Fig. 6,** and switch holder bracket.
8. Reverse procedure to install, noting the following:
   a. When installing steering wheel, place two drops of Loctite 271 or equivalent onto steering wheel locknut threads.
   b. **On models equipped with cruise**

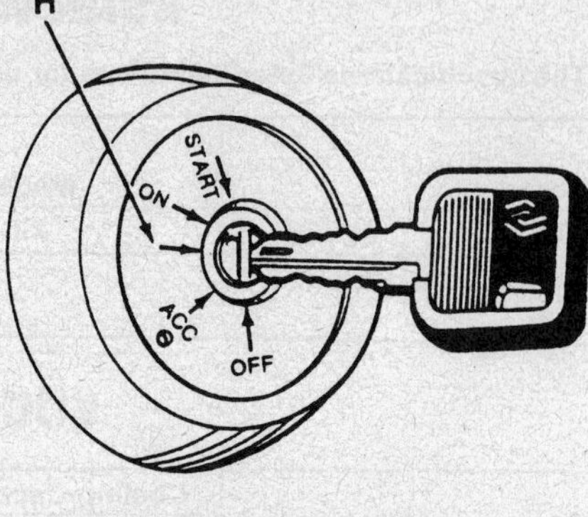


Fig. 3 Position ignition lock for replacement

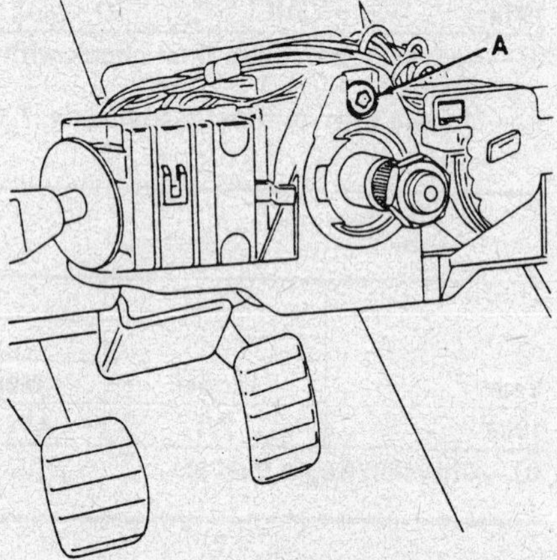


Fig. 6 Combination switch holder attaching screw location

**control, pull down on wire located at the forward edge of the lower cover. This will pull the spring loaded commutator brush back into its housing. If the commutator brush is not pulled into its housing before the lower cover is removed/installed, the brush will be broken off.**

   c. **Torque** steering wheel retaining nut to 30 ft. lbs.

## INSTRUMENT CLUSTER REPLACE

1. Disconnect battery ground cable.
2. Remove trim shield attaching screws (A), **Fig. 7.**
3. Depress holding tabs using a suitable screwdriver and remove glare shield, **Fig. 7.**
4. Open fuse panel.
5. Disconnect speedometer cable by working through the fuse panel opening.
6. Remove attaching screws, then lift instrument cluster, in direction of arrow to release tabs and pull cluster forward, **Fig. 8.**
7. Reverse procedure to install.

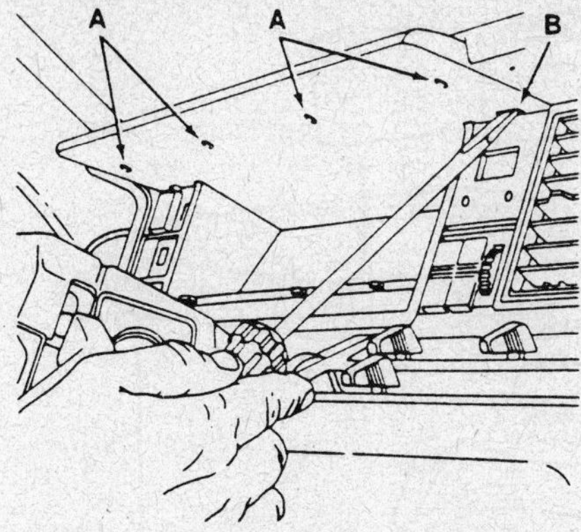

Fig. 7 Instrument cluster trim shield removal

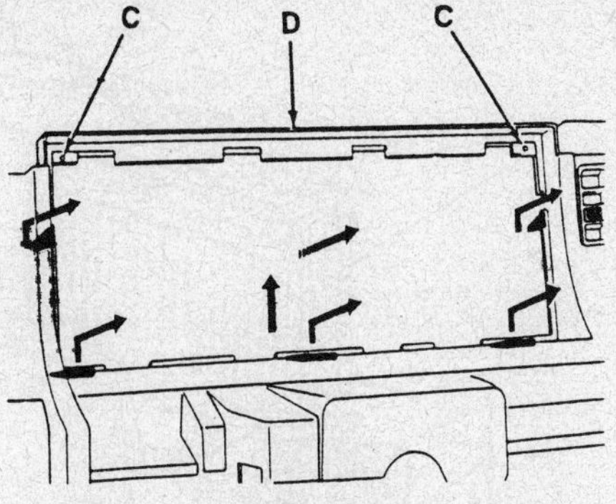

Fig. 8 Instrument cluster removal

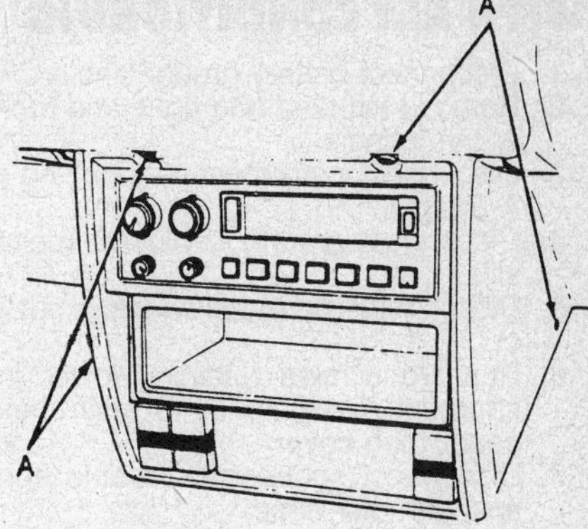

Fig. 9 Radio trim panel attaching screw locations

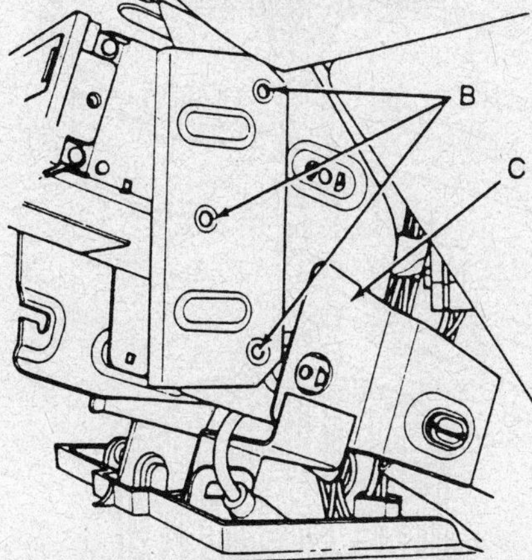

Fig. 10 Radio rivet locations

## STEERING WHEEL
### REPLACE

1. Remove steering wheel trim cover.
2. Place an alignment mark on the steering wheel and shaft before removing steering wheel.
3. Loosen but do not remove steering wheel locknut.
4. Do not hammer against the end of the steering column. The inner column will collapse if struck.
5. Grasp steering wheel and give it a quick pull.
6. When the steering wheel comes loose, remove steering wheel locknut and steering wheel.
7. Reverse procedure to install, noting the following:
   a. When installing steering wheel, place two drops of Loctite 271 or equivalent onto steering wheel locknut threads.
   b. **Torque** steering wheel retaining nut to 30 ft. lbs.

## RADIO
### REPLACE

1. Disconnect battery ground cable.
2. Open glove compartment door.
3. Remove four radio trim panel attaching screws (A), **Fig. 9**,then remove trim panel.
4. Using a 5/32 inch drill bit, remove rivets (B) from both sides of radio, then remove anti-theft brackets (C), **Fig. 10.**
5. Remove Torx head bolt retaining radio assembly to instrument panel.
6. Pull radio outward, then disconnect electrical connectors and antenna lead.
7. Remove radio assembly.
8. Reverse procedure to install. When installing radio, use 3/16 inch short shank rivets.

## WIPER MOTOR & LINKAGE
### REPLACE
#### FRONT

1. Disconnect battery ground cable.
2. Remove wiper blade arms by removing attaching nuts.
3. Remove front cowl panel by removing two attaching screws (D) and by turning the five remaining attaching screws (C), 1/4 turn counterclockwise, **Fig. 11.**
4. Remove attaching screws and windshield wiper assembly.
5. Disconnect electrical connector.
6. Remove attaching nut from wiper link.
7. Remove wiper motor attaching screws, then the motor.
8. Reverse procedure to install. Ensure motor is in Park position prior to installation.

#### REAR

1. Disconnect battery ground cable.
2. Remove clips securing left rear interior trim panel (with washer reservoir) and pull trim panel off.
3. Disconnect electrical connector.
4. Lift up spray nozzle cover.
5. Remove wiper arm.
6. Remove rear motor attaching bolts, then the motor.
7. Reverse procedure to install.

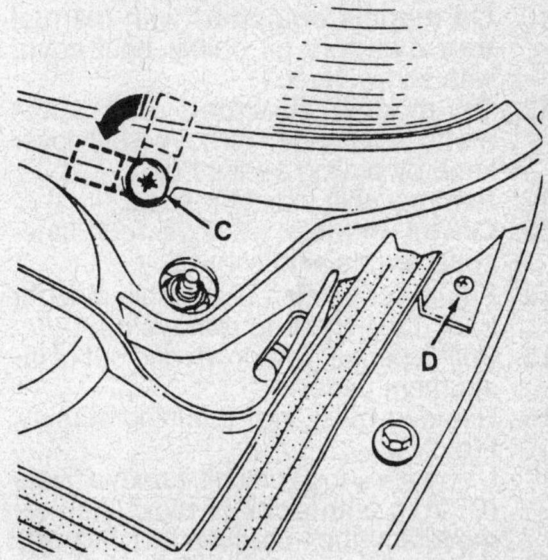

Fig. 11 Cowl panel removal

## BLOWER MOTOR
### REPLACE

1. Disconnect battery ground cable.
2. Remove glove compartment door straps.
3. Lower glove compartment door and release retaining clips, then remove door.
4. Remove inner glove compartment.
5. Disconnect ventilator outlet from righthand side of blower housing.
6. Remove blower motor attaching screws and blower motor, **Figs. 12 and 13.**
7. Reverse procedure to install.

## HEATER CORE
### REPLACE
#### LESS AIR CONDITIONING

1. Disconnect battery ground cable.
2. Remove heater housing assembly.
3. Remove heater core to blower motor attaching screws.
4. Spread the four attaching clips and remove heater core by pulling upward. **Use care when removing heater core as not to damage heater core fins, Figs. 12 and 13.**
5. Reverse procedure to install.

### WITH AIR CONDITIONING

1. Disconnect battery ground cable.
2. Remove lefthand and righthand rocker trim panels.
3. Disconnect instrument panel wiring at A-pillars.
4. Disconnect ground cables at rocker sills.
5. Disconnect fuse panel and door buzzer.
6. Remove screws retaining lower instrument panel cover to instrument panel, then cover.
7. Disconnect speedometer cable from speedometer head.
8. Remove console retaining screws.
9. Open glove box door and pull edge of console out to free it from instrument panel.
10. **On models equipped with manual transaxle,** pry off shifter boot cover with screwdriver.
11. **On models equipped with automatic transaxle,** remove shift lever knob by pulling straight up.
12. Remove shift indicator bezel.
13. **On all models,** remove four inner console retaining screws.
14. Pull lower section of console straight back, then lift up to remove it.
15. Pull upper section down and out of instrument panel.
16. Remove radio trim retaining screws, **Fig. 9.**
17. Using a 5/32 inch drill bit, remove rivets (B) from both sides of radio, then remove anti-theft brackets (C), **Fig. 10.**
18. Remove retaining screw from heater control.
19. Remove heater control knobs by pulling straight up.
20. Lower heater control panel, then disconnect the two cables and electrical connections.
21. Remove upper and lower steering column covers. **On vehicles equipped with cruise control, pull down wire (B), Fig. 2, located on the forward edge of the lower cover. This will pull the spring loaded commutator brush back into its housing. If the commutator brush is not pulled into its housing before the lower cover is removed, the brush will be broken off.**
22. Remove bolt and nut at steering joint connection under dash.
23. Remove four hex head bolts and one large Torx head bolt holding steering column in place.
24. Pull steering column forward slightly, then column will drop down.
25. Disconnect steering column wiring harness from dash harness.
26. Remove steering column.
27. Remove attaching bolts at each corner of dash panel, then remove dash panel assembly.
28. Clamp off heater hoses in engine compartment.
29. Disconnect heater hoses from heater core.
30. Remove heater blower housing to the cowl panel.
31. Remove heater blower housing by pulling it rearward.
32. Remove two retaining screws that retain heater core to blower housing.
33. Spread the four retaining clips, then remove heater core assembly.
34. Reverse procedure to install.

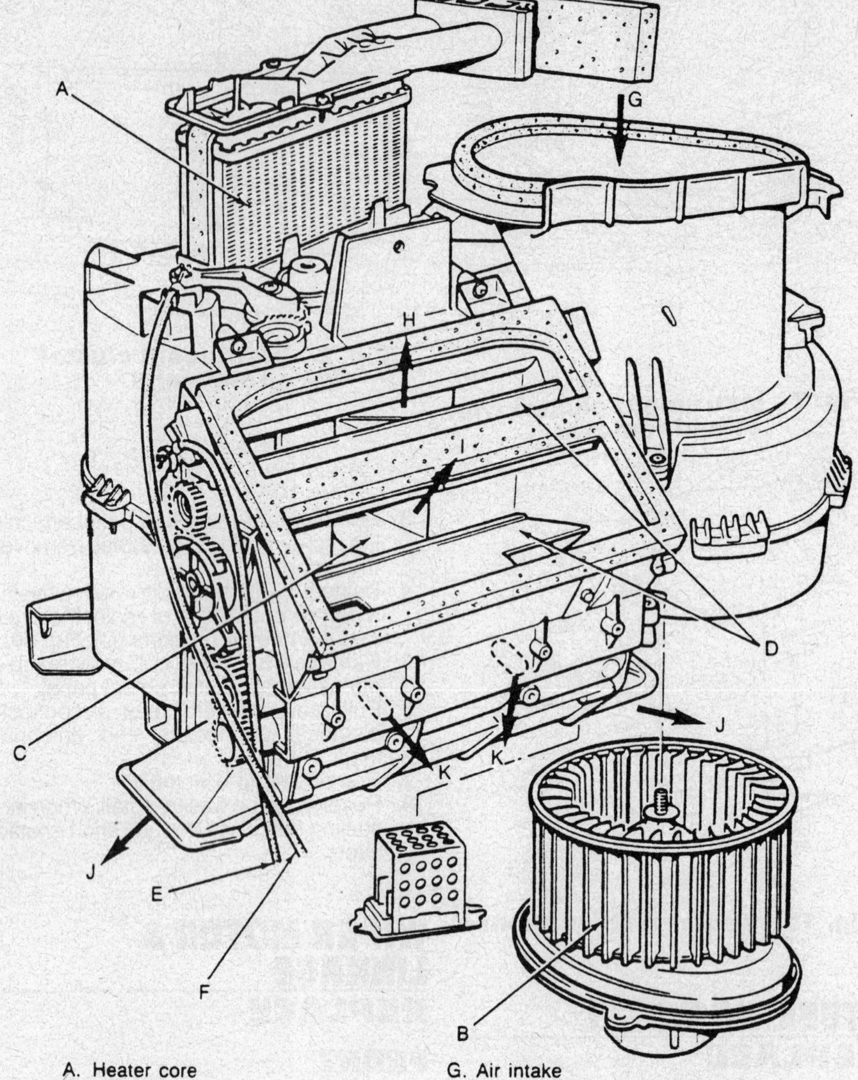


A. Heater core
B. Heater fan
C. Hot air/cold air door
D. Up/down distribution doors
E. Air distribution cable
F. Blend air cable
G. Air intake
H. Windshield defroster outlet
I. Instrument panel ventilator outlet
J. Lower ventilator outlets
K. Rear seat ventilator outlets (on certain models)

**Fig. 12 Heater assembly components**

## EVAPORATOR CORE REPLACE

1. Disconnect battery ground cable.
2. Remove lefthand and righthand rocker trim panels.
3. Disconnect instrument panel wiring at A-pillars.
4. Disconnect ground cables at rocker sills.
5. Disconnect fuse panel and door buzzer.
6. Remove screws retaining lower instrument panel cover to instrument panel, then cover.
7. Disconnect speedometer cable from speedometer head.
8. Remove console retaining screws.
9. Open glove box door and pull edge of console out to free it from instrument panel.
10. **On models equipped with manual transaxle,** pry off shifter boot cover with screwdriver.
11. **On models equipped with automatic transaxle,** remove shift lever knob by pulling straight up.
12. Remove shift indicator bezel.
13. **On all models,** remove four inner console retaining screws.
14. Pull lower section of console straight back, then lift up to remove it.

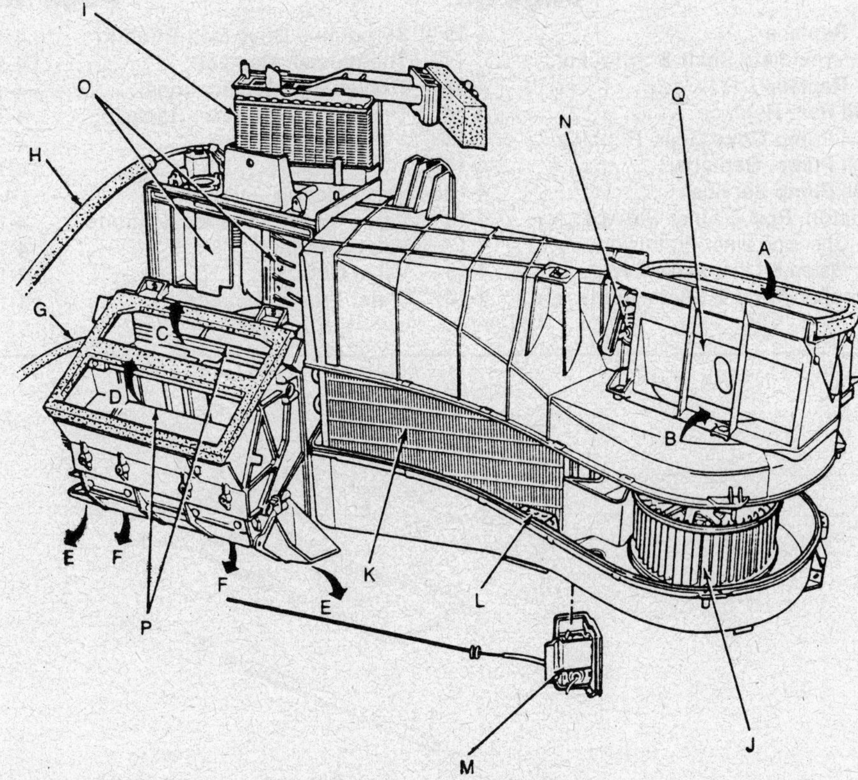


**Fig. 13 A/C & heater assembly components**

15. Pull upper section down and out of instrument panel.
16. Remove radio trim retaining screws, **Fig. 9.**
17. Using a 5/32 inch drill bit, remove rivets (B) from both sides of radio, then remove anti-theft brackets (C), **Fig. 10.**
18. Remove retaining screw from heater control.
19. Remove heater control knobs by pulling straight up.
20. Lower heater control panel, then disconnect the two cables and electrical connections.
21. Remove upper and lower steering column covers. **On vehicles equipped with cruise control, pull down wire (B), Fig. 2, located on the forward edge of the lower cover. This will pull the spring loaded commutator brush back into its housing. If the commutator brush is not pulled into its housing before the lower cover is removed, the brush will be broken off.**
22. Remove bolt and nut at steering joint connection under dash.
23. Remove four hex head bolts and one large Torx head bolt holding steering column in place.
24. Pull steering column forward slightly, then column will drop down.
25. Disconnect steering column wiring harness from dash harness.
26. Remove steering column.
27. Remove attaching bolts at each corner of dash panel, then remove dash panel assembly.
28. Clamp off heater hoses in engine compartment.
29. Disconnect heater hoses from heater core.
30. Purge air conditioning system of freon.
31. Disconnect air conditioning hoses from expansion valve.
32. Remove evaporator housing retaining screws from inside passenger compartment.
33. Remove vacuum reservior from its bracket on the engine compartment side of dash panel.
34. Remove two heater/evaporator housing retaining nuts from engine compartment side.
35. Remove heater/evaporator housing assembly from vehicle, **Fig. 13.**
36. Remove all retaining screws from heater/evaporator housing.
37. Remove heater core assembly.
38. Remove retaining clips from heater/evaporator housing.
39. Mark air blend door gears for reassembly. Gently pry up on gear assemblies, to disengage gear from door assembly.
40. Separate housing halves, then lift evaporator core from housing. **Use care to guide the capillary tube out of the evaporator core.**
41. Reverse procedure to install.

# Engine

## INDEX



## ENGINE REPLACE

1. Disconnect battery ground cable.
2. Mark hood hinge area and remove hood.
3. Remove grille attaching screws, then the grille.
4. Remove radiator support attaching screws, face panel, support and panel assembly.
5. **On models equipped with air conditioning, slowly and carefully discharge refrigerant from system.**
6. Disconnect radiator lower hose and drain coolant from radiator. **Drain coolant into a suitable container.**
7. Disconnect upper radiator hose.
8. Disconnect heater hoses at the heater core.
9. Disconnect coil, alternator and starter electrical connectors and cables.
10. Remove engine ground straps.
11. Label, then disconnect all vacuum hoses.
12. Disconnect fuel supply and return lines from fuel rail.
13. Disconnect accelerator cable from throttle plate and valve cover.
14. Disconnect throttle plate cover hoses.
15. **On models equipped with manual transaxle, disconnect clutch cable from bracket and release lever on the clutch housing.**
16. Remove ignition TDC sensor from clutch or converter housing.
17. Disconnect and remove ECU top cover as follows:
    a. Remove plastic screw from cover mounting stud.
    b. Disconnect electrical connector.
    c. Loosen upper and lower attaching clips, then place ECU top cover and electrical connectors/wires aside on the engine.
18. Remove air cleaner assembly.
19. Disconnect cooling fan and thermo switch electrical connectors.
20. Remove exhaust head pipe to exhaust manifold attaching bolts.
21. Raise and support vehicle.
22. Remove underbody splash shield attaching bolts, then the splash shield.
23. **On models equipped with automatic transaxle, cut tie straps securing BVA module wires to the engine harness. Disconnect module and position aside.**
24. Loosen and remove power steering drive belt. Remove pump attaching bolts and position pump assembly aside.
25. Remove exhaust head pipe mounting bolt. Remove two spring loaded attaching bolts connecting head pipe to converter pipe. Separate converter pipe from head pipe.
26. Remove radiator cooling fan.

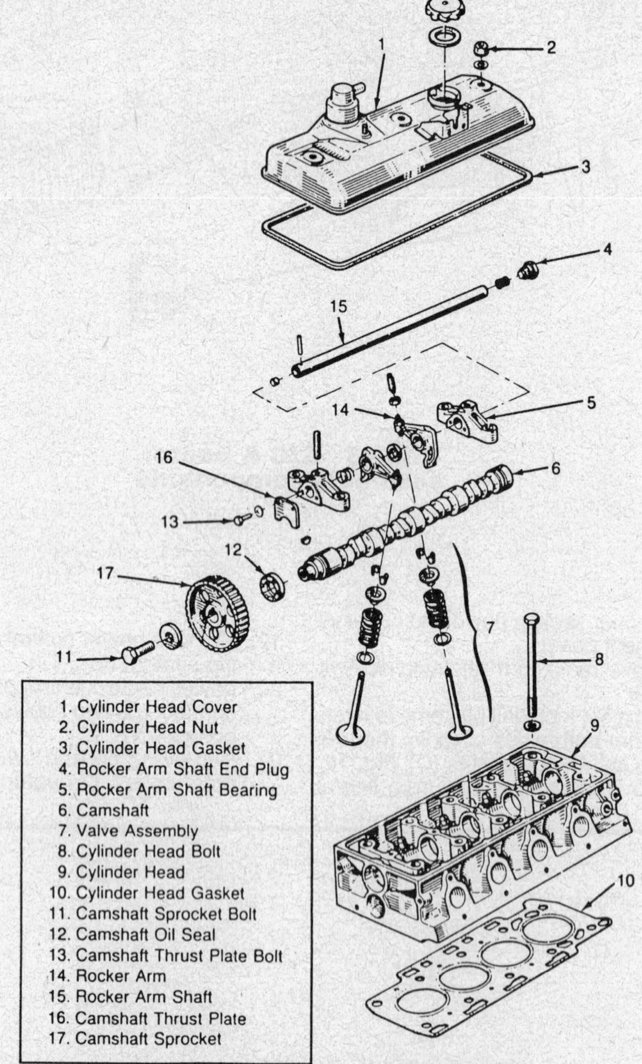


**Exploded view of cylinder head**

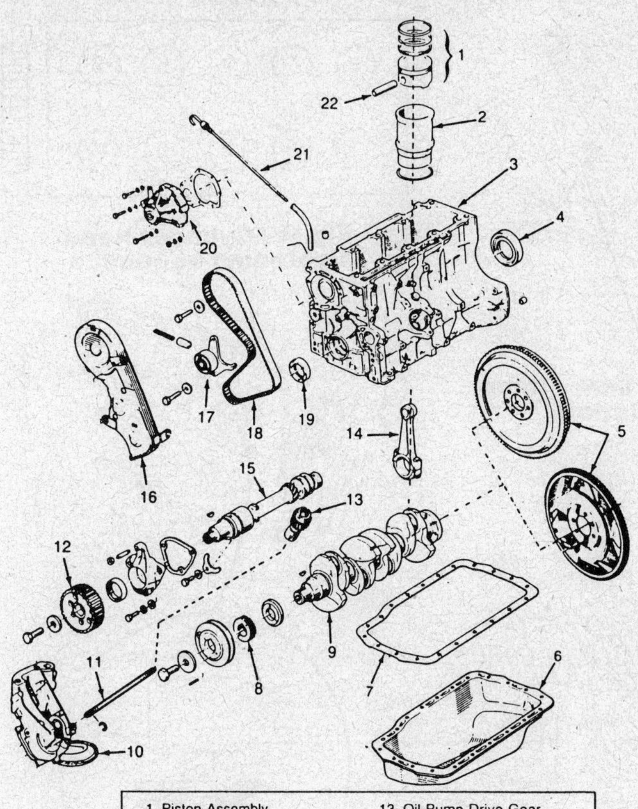

1. Piston Assembly
2. Cylinder Liner
3. Cylinder Block
4. Crankshaft Oil Seal (Rear)
5. Flywheel/Drive Plate
6. Oil Pan
7. Oil Pan Gasket
8. Crankshaft Sprocket
9. Crankshaft
10. Oil Pump
11. Oil Pump Drive Shaft
12. Intermediate Shaft Sprocket
13. Oil Pump Drive Gear
14. Connecting Rod
15. Intermediate Shaft
16. Timing Belt Cover
17. Timing Belt Tensioner
18. Timing Belt
19. Crankshaft Oil Seal (Front)
20. Water Pump
21. Oil Level Dip Stick
22. Piston Pin

**Exploded view of engine block components**

**Engine oiling system**

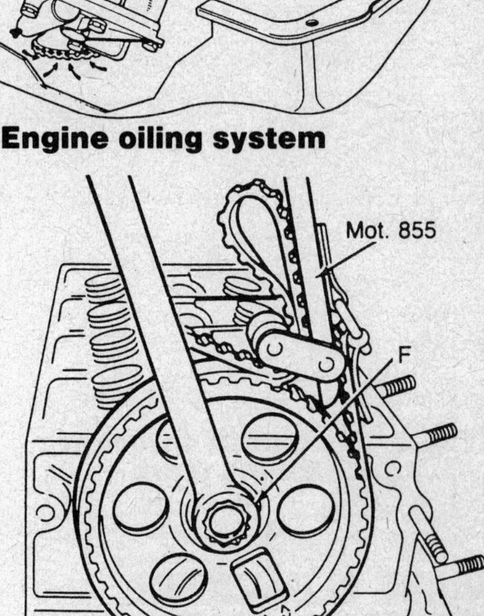


**Fig. 1 Camshaft sprocket bolt removal & installation**

27. **On models equipped with A/C, remove radiator, condenser and cooling fan as an assembly.**
28. **On models equipped with automatic transaxle, remove starter motor. Mark position of torque converter and flex plate for assembly. Remove converter attaching bolts working through starter opening.**
29. Remove engine to transaxle bellhousing attaching bolts, then lower vehicle.
30. Remove as follows:
    a. Attach a suitable chain to engine and engine hoist.
    b. Attach one end of chain to engine lifting eye.
    c. Wrap other end of chain around coolant outlet housing located at the front of the engine. **If it appears that the lifting chain may contact either of the housing sensors, remove the sensors before lifting the engine.**
    d. Remove nuts attaching engine mount cushions to engine cradle.
    e. Raise engine off cradle and pull it forward until clear of transaxle assembly.
    f. Lift engine assembly up and out of engine compartment at approximately a 15° angle.
    g. Position suitable supports under the transaxle immediately after removing the engine. Do not allow transaxle the remain unsupported.
31. Reverse procedure to install.

# CYLINDER HEAD
## REPLACE

1. Disconnect battery ground cable.
2. Remove drive belts from engine, then drain cooling system
3. Remove crankshaft pulley attaching bolt, then remove pulley.
4. Remove intake and exhaust manifolds and brackets.
5. Remove timing belt as described under "Timing Belt, Replace."
6. Remove cylinder head cover.
7. Using tool No. Mot. 855 to hold camshaft sprocket in position, loosen and remove camshaft sprocket attaching bolt, then remove camshaft sprocket, **Fig. 1.**
8. Remove all cylinder head attaching bolts except bolt (G), **Fig. 2.** Loosen bolt (G) one turn.
9. Place a wooden block on cylinder head at position (H), **Fig. 2,**then tap wooden block with hammer to loosen cylinder head from cylinder liners.
10. Remove remaining cylinder head bolt, then remove cylinder head.
11. Install clamp tool Mot. 588 or equivalent on cylinder block to hold cylinder liners in position, **Fig. 3.**
12. Reverse procedure to install. **Torque** cylinder bolts in sequence shown in **Fig. 4** to **torque** listed at the end of this section. When installing timing belt, refer to "Timing Belt, Replace" procedure.

# VALVE TIMING
## INTAKE OPENS BEFORE TDC

| Engine | Year | Degrees |
|---|---|---|
| 2.2L/4-132 | 1989 | 12 |

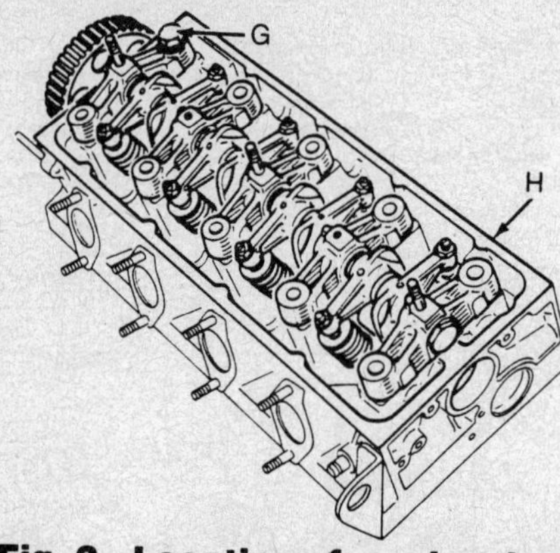


**Fig. 2 Locations for releasing cylinder head from cylinder liners**

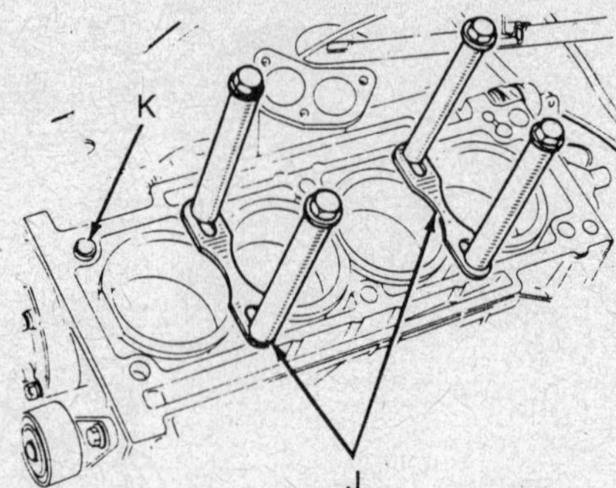


**Fig. 3 Cylinder liner clamp tool installation**

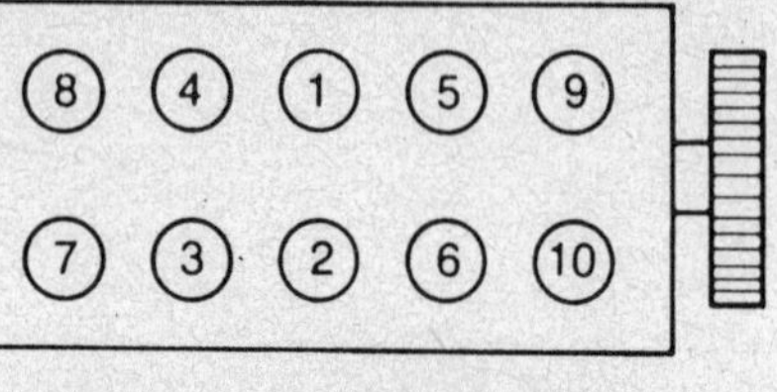


**Fig. 4 Cylinder head tightening sequence**

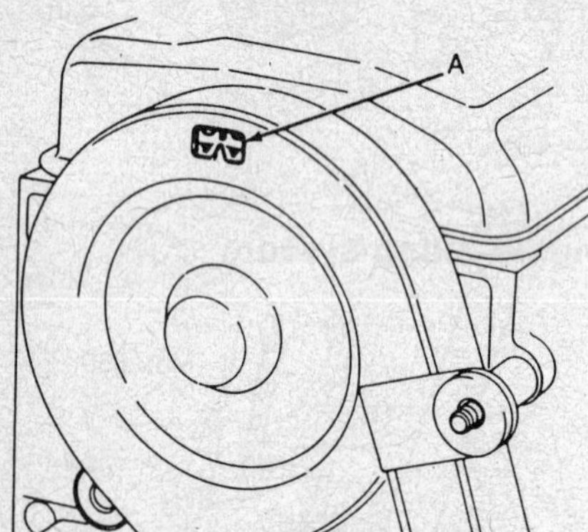


**Fig. 5 Camshaft sprocket front timing mark**

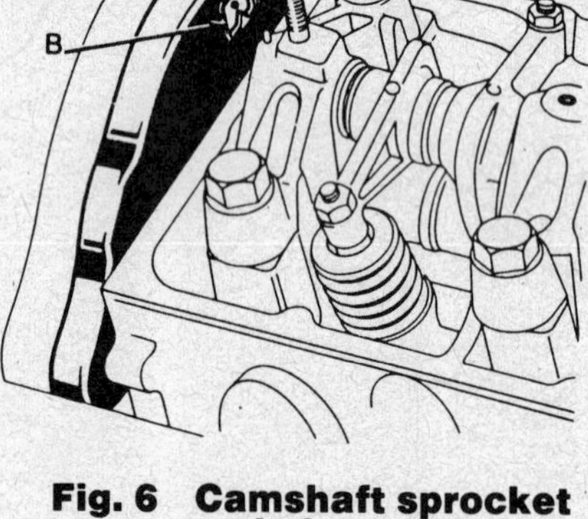


**Fig. 6 Camshaft sprocket rear timing mark**

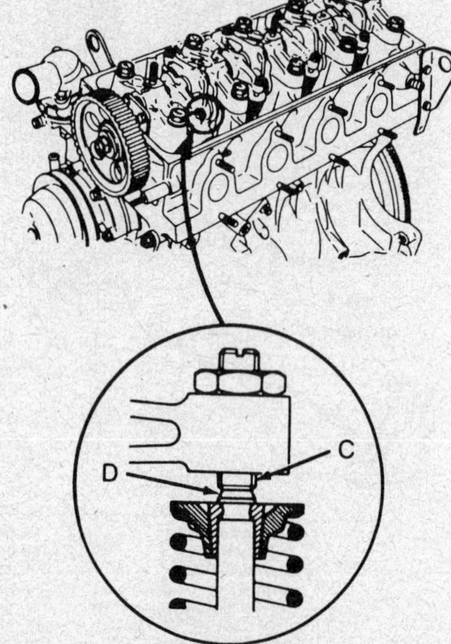


**Fig. 7 Checking rocker arm to valve stem alignment**

**Fig. 8 Valve guide installed depth**

# VALVE CLEARANCE SPECIFICATIONS

| Engine | Year | Int. | Exh. |
|---|---|---|---|
| 2.2L/4-132 | 1989 | .005C | .009C |

# VALVES

## ADJUST

**It should be noted that cylinders on this engine are numbered from rear to front, with No. 1 cylinder located at the flywheel end.**

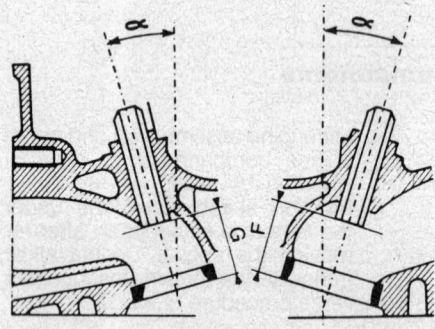

1. Remove cylinder head cover.
2. Rotate crankshaft in clockwise direction, until camshaft sprocket timing mark is aligned with front timing belt cover pointer (A), **Fig. 5**. Ensure timing mark is for No. 1 cylinder TDC, not No. 4 cylinder.
3. Rotate crankshaft sprocket clockwise until first mark on rear of camshaft sprocket is aligned with pointer on rear timing belt cover (B), **Fig. 6.**
4. Check and adjust valve clearance for No. 2 cylinder intake and No. 4 cylinder exhaust valves. **When adjusting valves, ensure adjusting screw (C) is properly aligned with valve stem (D), Fig. 7. If not, check rocker arm and adjusting screw for damage and wear and replace as necessary.**
5. Rotate crankshaft in clockwise direction until the second mark on rear of camshaft sprocket is aligned with pointer on rear timing belt cover. Check and adjust valve clearance for No. 1 cylinder intake and No. 2 cylinder exhaust valves.
6. Rotate crankshaft in clockwise direction until the third mark on rear of camshaft sprocket is aligned with pointer on rear timing belt cover. Check and adjust valve clearance for No. 3 cylinder intake and No. 1 cylinder exhaust valves.
7. Rotate crankshaft in clockwise direction until the fourth mark on rear of camshaft sprocket is aligned with pointer on rear timing belt cover. Check and adjust valve clearance for No. 4 cylinder intake and No. 3 cylinder exhaust valves.
8. After completing adjustment, reinstall cylinder head cover.

# VALVE GUIDES

Valve guide are available in standard size and over sizes of .519 inch and .525 inch. The valve guides are press fit to the cylinder head. Replacement valve guides should be pressed into the cylinder head from the bottom. Press intake valve guides into cylinder head until clearance (F), **Fig. 8,** between bottom of cylinder head and bottom of valve guide is 1.22 inches. Press exhaust valve guide in until clearance (G), **Fig. 8**, is 1.29 inches. After completing installation, valve guides should be reamed to .315 inch.

# ROCKER ARMS & SHAFT

## REPLACE

1. Remove cylinder head.
2. Remove camshaft thrust plate (A), **Fig. 9.**
3. Remove end plug (B) and filter (C) from rocker shaft, **Fig. 9.**

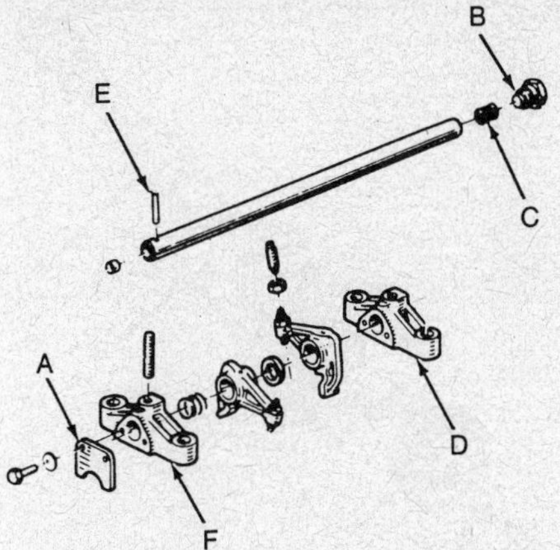


Fig. 9 Rocker arms & shaft

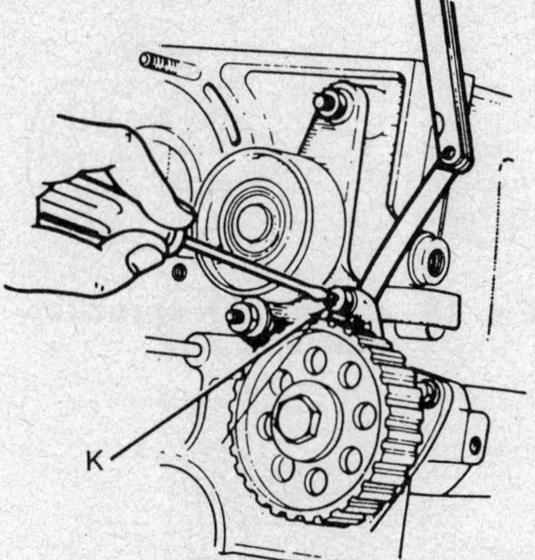


Fig. 10 Checking intermediate shaft cover to timing belt tensioner clearance

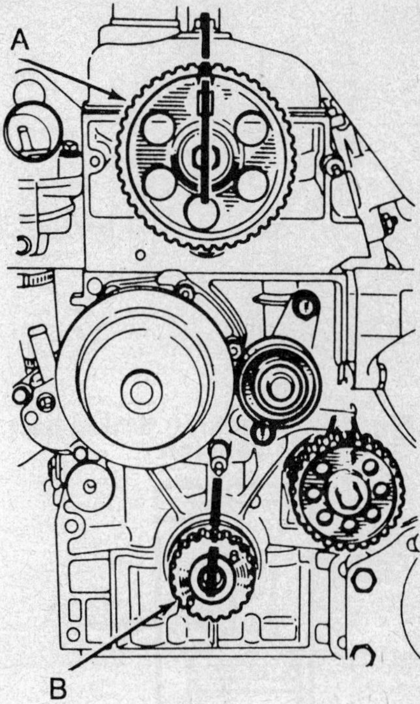


Fig. 11 Positioning camshaft & crankshaft sprocket timing marks

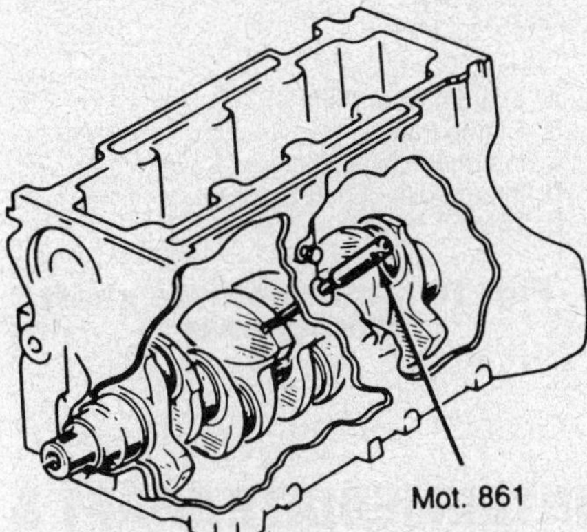


Fig. 12 Tool No. Mot. 861 installation

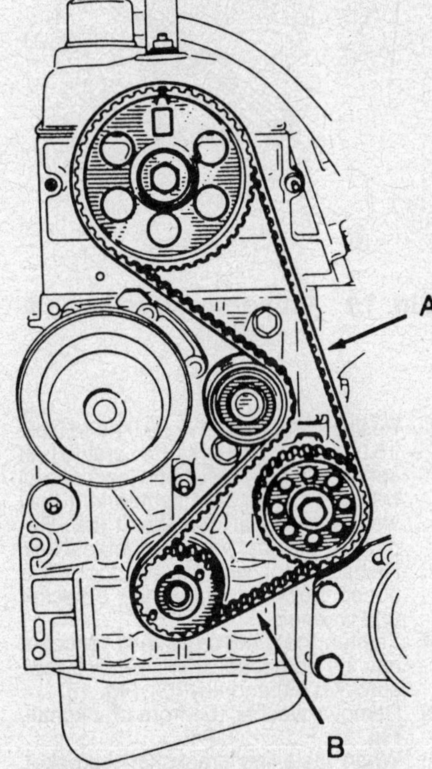


Fig. 13 Timing belt tension

4. Remove No. 1 rocker shaft bearing housing (D), **Fig. 9.**
5. Remove retaining pin (E), then remove No. 5 rocker shaft bearing housing (F), **Fig. 9.**
6. Remove remaining rocker arms and bearing housings.
7. Reverse procedure to install. It should be noted that rocker shaft bearing housings Nos. 1, 2, 3, and 4 are identical. The No. 5 rocker shaft bearing housing has two threaded bore for the camshaft thrust plate and a bore for the retaining pin. When installing rocker arm components, ensure pin is properly seated in No. 5 bearing housing. Intake and exhaust rocker arms are identical.

## TIMING BELT & COVER REPLACE

Whenever the timing belt has broken or slipped significantly, a possibility of internal engine damage is present.

### REMOVAL

1. Disconnect battery ground cable.
2. Remove drive belts from engine.
3. Remove crankshaft pulley attaching bolt, then remove pulley.
4. Remove timing belt cover, then loosen timing belt tensioner and remove timing belt.

### INSTALLATION

**Prior to timing belt installation, intermediate shaft cover to timing belt tensioner clearance should be checked to prevent movement of timing belt during tensioning. Using a suitable feeler gauge measure clearance. Clearance should be .004 inch. If necessary adjust by turning adjusting screw (K), Fig. 10.**

1. Position camshaft sprocket timing mark and crankshaft sprocket key way as shown in **Fig. 11.**
2. Remove access plug from side of cylinder block and insert tool Mot. 861 or equivalent into slot on crankshaft throw, **Fig. 12.**
3. Loosen crankshaft tensioner bolts, then position tensioner pulley toward water pump and tighten bolts.
4. Install timing belt over sprockets, then loosen timing belt tensioner bolts. The timing belt should be tight at positions A and B, **Fig. 13.**
5. Tighten timing belt tension bolts, then position timing belt cover over sprockets.
6. Check alignment of camshaft sprocket timing mark with pointer on timing belt cover (A), **Fig. 5.**
7. Adjust timing belt tension as follows:
   a. Remove tool No. Mot. 861 from cylinder block, then install access plug.
   b. Rotate crankshaft two turns in clockwise direction.
   c. Remove timing belt cover and loosen timing belt tensioner bolts approximately 1/4 turn.
   d. Tighten the lower timing belt tensioner bolt, then the upper timing belt tensioner bolt.
   e. Check timing belt tension using tool Ele. 346 or equivalent, **Fig. 14.** Timing belt deflection should be .216 to .276 inch.
   f. Install timing belt cover.
8. Install crankshaft pulley. Prior to installation, apply Loctite 515 or equivalent to crankshaft pulley to sprocket

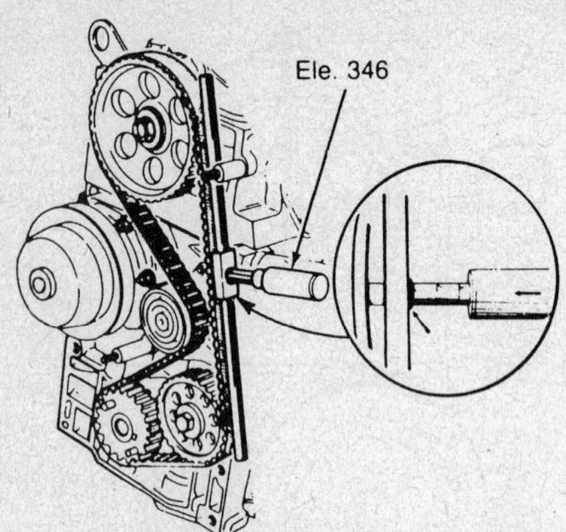


**Fig. 14 Checking timing belt tension**

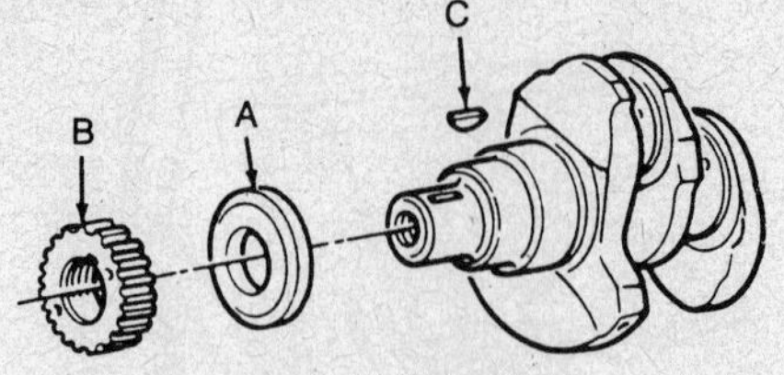


**Fig. 15 Crankshaft sprocket, washer & key**

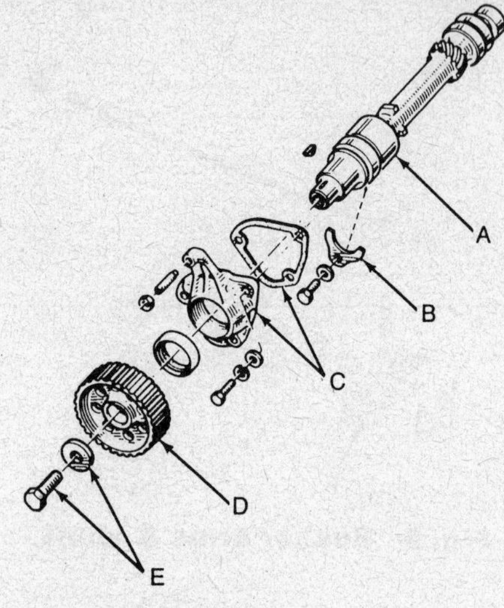


A. Intermediate Shaft
B. Clamp Plate
C. Intermediate Gasket and Cover
D. Intermediate Shaft Sprocket
E. Washer and Bolt

**Fig. 16 Intermediate shaft components**

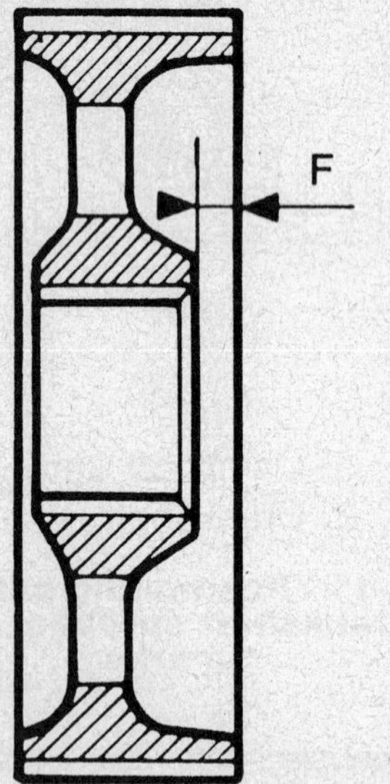


**Fig. 17 Positioning intermediate shaft sprocket**

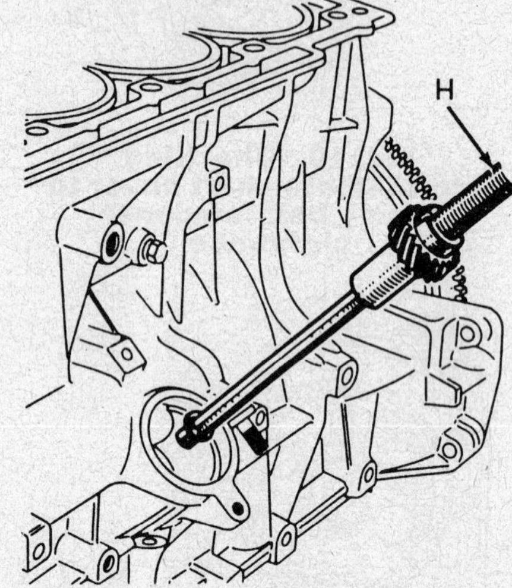


**Fig. 18 Oil pump drive gear & shaft**

mating surface. When tightening crankshaft pulley attaching bolt, use tool No. Mot. 582 or equivalent to hold flywheel in position.

9. Install drive belts.
10. Connect battery ground cable.

## CAMSHAFT SPROCKET
### REPLACE

1. Remove timing belt as described under "Timing Belt, Replace."
2. Using tool No. Mot. 855 or equivalent to hold camshaft sprocket in position, remove camshaft sprocket attaching bolt, **Fig. 1.**
3. Remove camshaft sprocket from camshaft.
4. Reverse procedure to install. Torque camshaft sprocket attaching bolt to torque listed at the end of this section.

## CRANKSHAFT SPROCKET
### REPLACE

1. Remove timing belt as described under "Timing Belt, Replace."
2. Position tool Nos. B.Vi. 28.01 and Rou. 15.01 or equivalents to crankshaft sprocket washer. Position jaws of tool behind washer, then tighten tool until washer stops at crankshaft key. Remove tools after washer contacts key.
3. Reinstall tool, with jaws of tool positioned between crankshaft sprocket and washer.
4. Tighten tool until crankshaft sprocket can be removed, then remove tool, sprocket (B) and key (C), **Fig. 15.**
5. Remove washer (D) from crankshaft, **Fig. 15.**
6. When installing crankshaft sprocket, the chamfered side of the sprocket should face the washer.

## CAMSHAFT
### REPLACE

1. Remove cylinder head as described under "Cylinder Head, Replace."
2. Remove rocker arms as described under "Rocket Arms and Shaft, Replace."
3. Using a suitable tool, carefully pry camshaft oil seal from cylinder head.
4. Remove camshaft from cylinder head.
5. Reverse procedure to install. Lubricate camshaft seal with engine oil prior to installation. Use tool No. Mot. 791.10 to install camshaft oil seal.

## INTERMEDIATE SHAFT & SPROCKET
### REPLACE

1. Remove timing belt as described under "Timing Belt, Replace."
2. Remove oil pump drive gear as described under "Oil Pump Drive Gear, Replace."
3. Using tool No. Mot. 855 or equivalent to hold intermediate shaft sprocket in position, remove sprocket retaining bolt.
4. Remove intermediate shaft sprocket and key, **Fig. 16.**
5. Remove cover retaining bolts, cover and gasket.
6. Remove clamp plate attaching bolt and clamp plate.
7. Remove intermediate shaft.
8. Reverse procedure to install. noting the following:
   a. If intermediate shaft cover seal is to be replaced, lubricate seal lips with engine oil and install seal with tool No. Mot. 790 or equivalent.
   b. When installing intermediate shaft sprocket, position side of sprocket with the wider hub offset toward the engine block, **Fig. 17.**
   c. Intermediate shaft cover to timing belt tensioner clearance must be adjusted to prevent movement of timing belt during tensioning. Using a suitable feeler gauge measure clearance. Clearance should be .004 inch. If necessary adjust by turning adjusting screw (K), **Fig. 10.**

Fig. 19 Piston & rod assembly

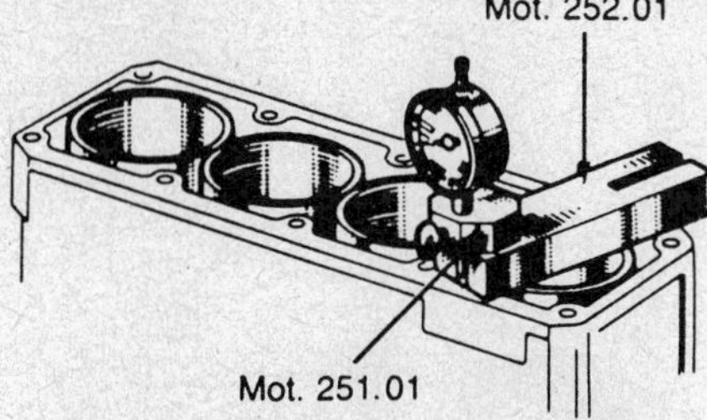

Fig. 20 Measuring cylinder liner protrusion

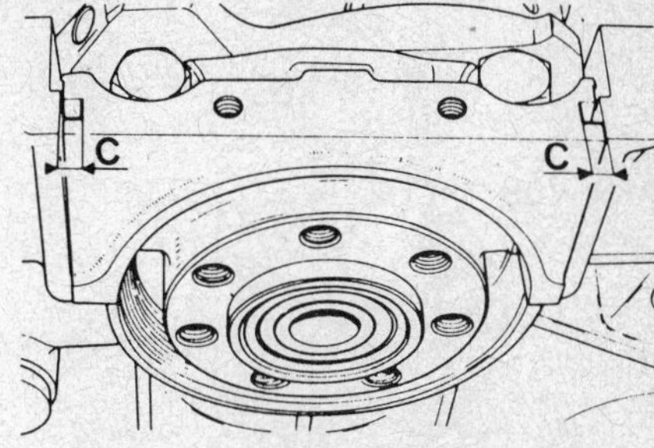

Fig. 21 Measuring main bearing cap to engine block clearance

## OIL PUMP DRIVE GEAR
### REPLACE

1. Remove oil pump drive gear cover plate.
2. Using a suitable threaded rod, remove oil pump drive gear and shaft, **Fig. 18.**
3. Reverse procedure to install. Ensure oil pump shaft properly engages oil pump and that drive gear is properly meshed.

## PISTON, ROD & LINER SERVICE

The pistons and liners are serviceable without removing the engine from the vehicle. Pistons and liners are available in standard size only and are matched sets. **Do not mix the pistons or liners during assembly.**

To remove the piston assemblies, remove the cylinder head and oil pan.

Assemble pistons to rods with the arrow on the piston facing toward the flywheel end of engine and oil hole on the connecting rod facing away oil filter side of engine, **Fig. 19.**

Liner protrusion must be checked prior to the final assembly of the piston and liners in the block. The liners must protrude slightly above the block to insure proper sealing by the head gasket and the head. All engine blocks are fitted with O-rings for sealing. Liner protrusion cannot be changed in blocks fitted with O-rings. However, the protrusion should be checked to ensure proper cylinder and head sealing.

### CHECKING LINER PROTRUSION

1. Install liners in block without O-ring seal.
2. Install dial indicator in gauge block Mot. 251.01 and tighten screw clamp, **Fig. 20.**
3. Place thrust plate Mot. 252.01 across each cylinder liner, **Fig. 20,** and measure liner protrusion above block with dial indicator. Liner protrusion should be between .003 to .006 inch.
4. If liner protrusion is not within specifications, measure protrusion of replacement liner to determine whether liner or cylinder block is defective, and replace components as needed.
5. When protrusion of all liners is within specifications, arrange liners so that the difference in protrusion between adjacent liners does not exceed .002 inch, and so that the protrusions are stepped down from the No. 1 cylinder to the No. 4 cylinder.
6. After the liner protrusion has been checked, remove the liners from the block and assemble the piston, rod and liner assemblies as outlined.

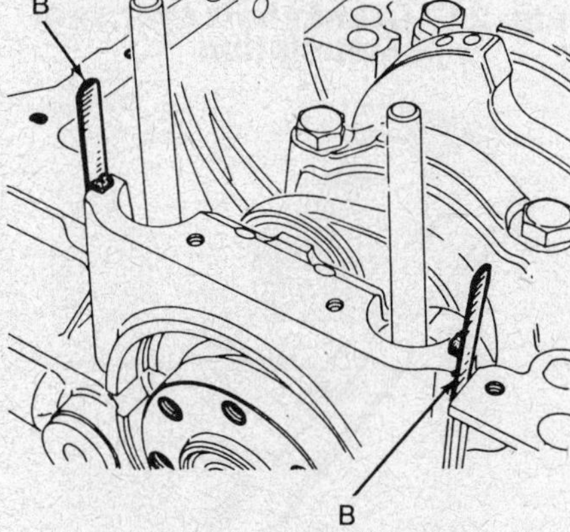

Fig. 22 Positioning shim stock on side of main bearing cap

### PISTON & LINER ASSEMBLY

1. Install new O-ring seal onto each liner, ensuring O-ring is not twisted.
2. Assemble pistons, rods, piston rings and bearing inserts, noting matching marks and installation position.
3. Lubricate the pistons and rings with engine oil.
4. Compress rings with suitable tool and insert piston and connecting rod assemblies through bottom of liner, ensuring machined sides of the connecting rod bearing end are parallel with the flat edge on the top of the liner.
5. Lubricate connecting rod journals and bearing inserts in connecting rod and cap, then install the piston liner assemblies into the block. Ensure O-ring is not twisted. Mount as follows:
   a. Number 1 piston at the flywheel/flex plate end.
   b. Oil hole on the connecting rod facing oil filter side of engine.
   c. Arrow on piston must face towards the flywheel/flex plate.

## CRANKSHAFT FRONT OR REAR OIL SEAL
### REPLACE

1. If front seal is to be replaced, remove crankshaft sprocket as described under "Crankshaft Sprocket, Replace."
2. If rear seal is to be replaced, remove transaxle and flywheel from vehicle.
3. If either or both seals are to be replaced, remove oil pan as described under "Oil Pan, Replace."
4. Remove main bearing cap bolts, then remove main bearing cap.
5. Remove side seals from main bearing cap.
6. Install main bearing cap on cylinder block without side seals.
7. Measure clearance (C), **Fig. 21,** between cylinder block and main bearing cap. If clearance is .197 inch or less use a .201 inch thick side seal. If clearance is more than .197 inch, use a .212 inch thick side seal.
8. Remove main bearing cap from cylinder block.
9. Insert replacement seal into side slots on main bearing cap, with grooves facing outward. Seal should protrude approximately .008 inch from cap.
10. Lubricate side seal with engine oil.
11. Position a .001 inch thick piece of shim stock (B) to each side of main bearing cap, then position main bearing cap to engine, **Fig. 22.**
12. Remove shim stock, then check to ensure each side seal is protruding .008 inch from bearing cap surface.
13. Install and **torque** main bearing cap bolts to specification.
14. Side seal ends should protrude .020 to .028 inch from cylinder block surface and trim as necessary.
15. Install crankshaft oil seal. For front seal use tool No. Mot. 789 or equivalent, **Fig. 23.** For rear seal use tool No. Mot. 788 or equivalent, **Fig. 24.** If seal surface on crankshaft is worn, install a .06 inch thick washer between tool and seal to position seal rearward. Lubricate seal lip with engine oil.
16. Install oil pan and crankshaft sprocket and/or transaxle and flywheel.

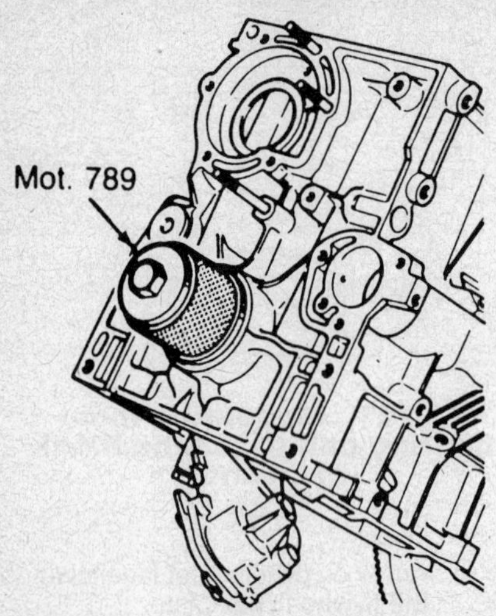


Fig. 23 Crankshaft front seal installation

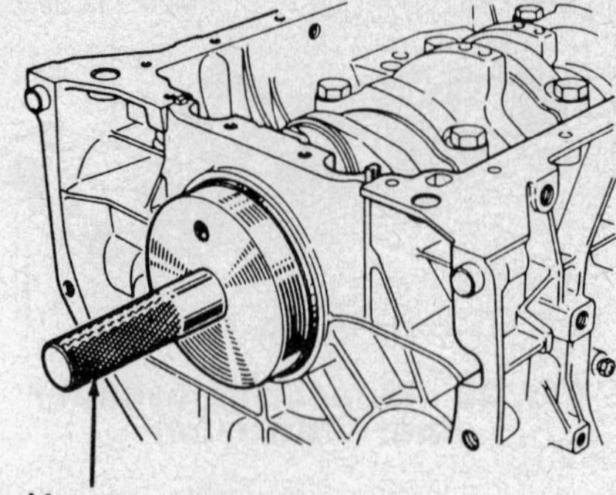


Fig. 24 Crankshaft rear seal installation

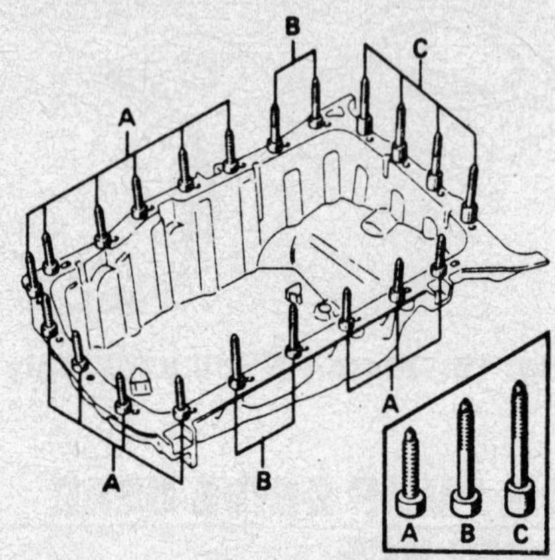


Fig. 25 Oil pan attaching bolt locations

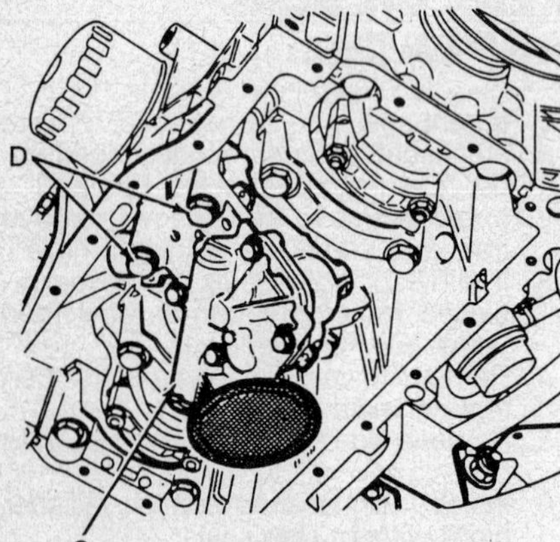


Fig. 26 Oil pump attaching bolt locations

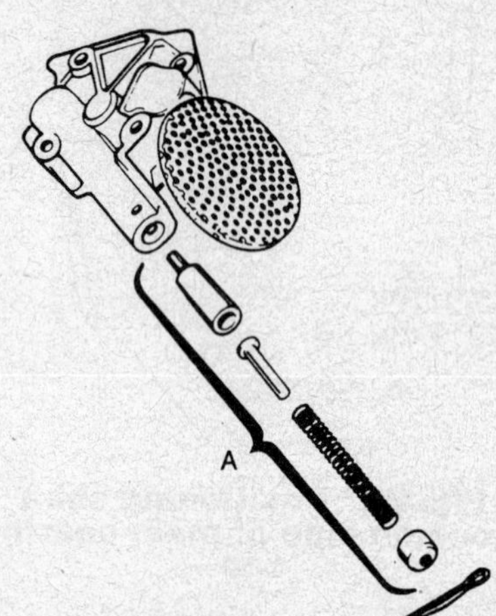


Fig. 27 Oil pump relief valve assembly

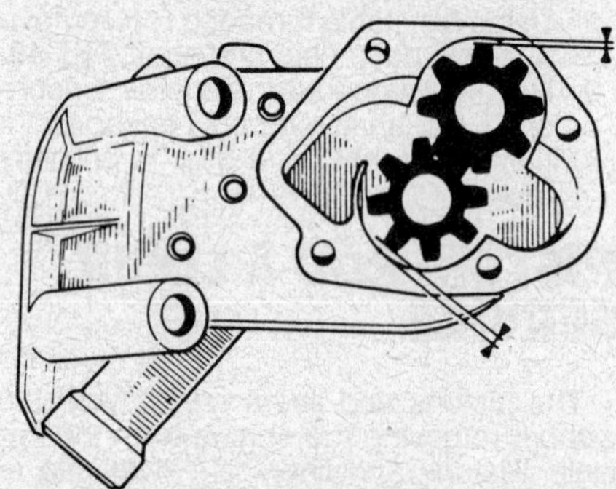

Fig. 28 Measuring oil pump gear to housing clearance

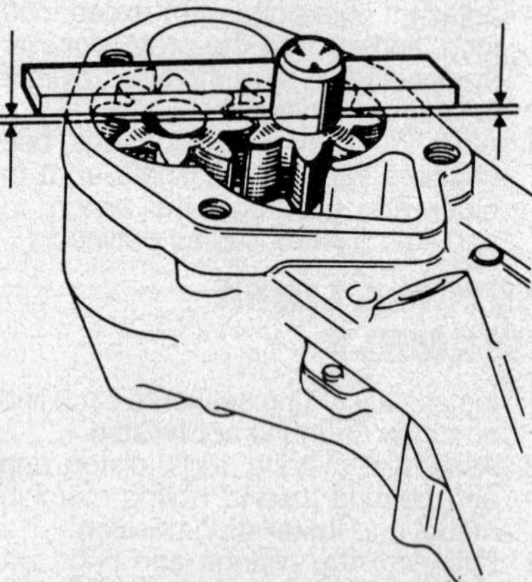

Fig. 29 Measuring oil pump gear to cover clearance

## OIL PAN
### REPLACE

1. Disconnect battery ground cable.
2. Raise and support vehicle.
3. Remove underbody splash shield.
4. Drain oil from engine.
5. Remove engine mount cushion attaching nuts.
6. Install oil drain plug and lower vehicle.
7. Raise hood and place engine support tool MS 1900 or equivalent, onto inner fender panel flanges.
8. Attach a suitable chain to engine lifting eyes and onto tool support screw.
9. Tighten support screw until there is enough clearance to remove oil pan assembly.
10. Using a suitable tool, remove oil pan attaching bolts, then the oil pan.
11. Clean pan and engine block gasket surface.
12. Reverse procedure to install. Note the following:
    a. Do not apply any type of sealant compound to the new gasket, oil pan or engine block. The new oil pan gasket must be installed dry.
    b. Three different length oil pan attaching bolts (A, B, C) are used, **Fig. 25.**
    c. Install attaching bolts in proper location as shown.
    d. First install all oil pan attaching bolts (in proper location) finger tight.
    e. Tighten the bolts attaching oil pan to the clutch/converter housing first.
    f. Tighten the remaining attaching bolts.
    g. **Torque** all bolts to specification.

## OIL PUMP
### REPLACE

1. Drain crankcase, then remove oil pan as described under "Oil Pan, Replace."
2. Remove oil pump attaching bolts (D), then remove oil pump (C), **Fig. 26.**
3. Reverse procedure to install. Ensure oil pump drive gear shaft properly engages oil pump.

## OIL PUMP SERVICE

1. Remove oil pump pressure relief valve from pump housing, **Fig. 27.**
2. Remove oil pump housing cover.
3. Measure gear to housing clearance, **Fig. 28.** Clearance should be .002 to .005 inch.
4. Measure gear to cover clearance, **Fig. 29.** Clearance should be .001 to .004 inch.
5. Replace any worn components, then reassemble.

## WATER PUMP
### REPLACE

1. Disconnect battery ground cable.

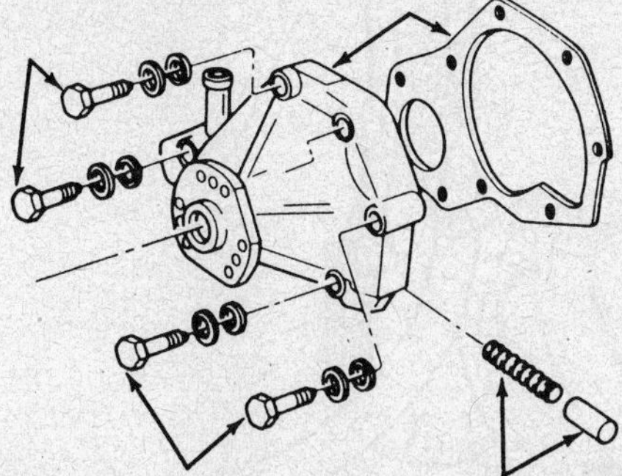

Fig. 30 Water pump assembly

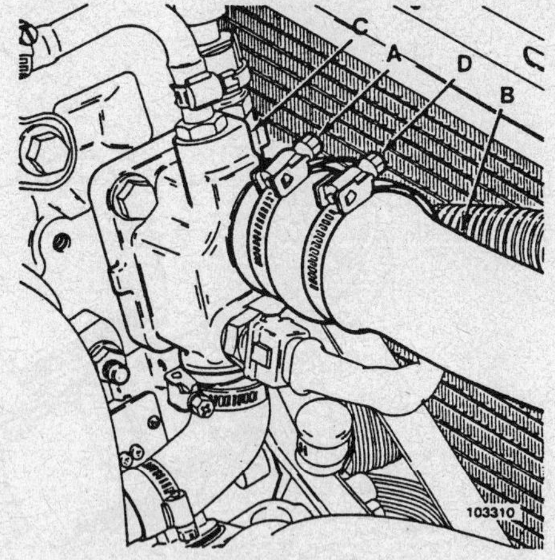


Fig. 31 Thermostat retaining clamps

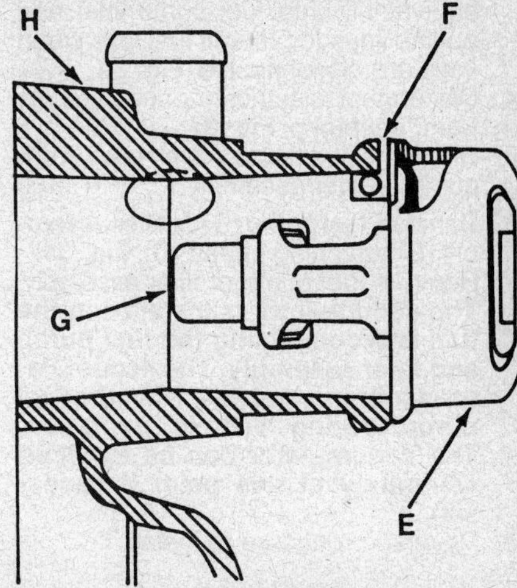


Fig. 32 Thermostat installation

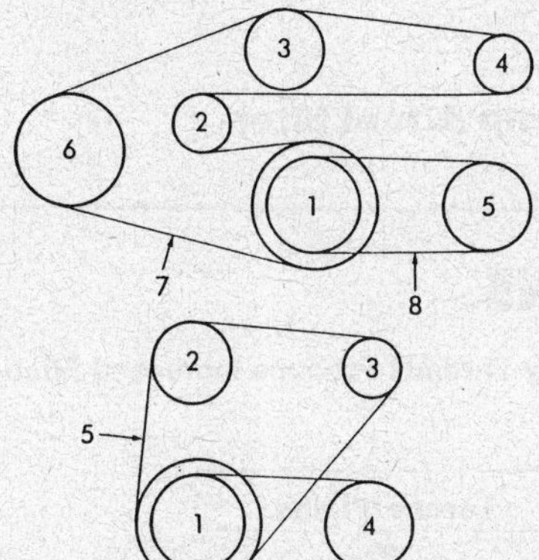


With A/C
1. Crankshaft
2. Idler
3. Water pump
4. Alternator
5. Power steering pump
6. A/C compressor
7. Tension measuring point for serpentine belt
8. Tension measuring point for power steering belt.

Without A/C
1. Crankshaft
2. Water pump
3. Alternator
4. Power steering pump
5. Tension measuring point for serpentine belt
6. Tension measuring point for power steering belt

Fig. 33 Serpentine drive belt routing

2. Mark hood hinge area and remove hood.
3. Disconnect radiator lower hose and drain coolant into a suitable container.
4. Remove radiator assembly, condenser and cooling fans.
5. Carefully and slowly discharge refrigerant from A/C system.
6. Loosen power steering pump drive belt.
7. Loosen serpentine drive belt adjustment bolt and nut. Loosen belt and remove from water pump assembly.
8. Remove timing belt cover attaching bolts, then the cover.
9. Remove water pump pulley bolt, then the pulley from pump shaft.
10. Remove pump attaching bolts. Remove pump and gasket, **Fig. 30.**
11. Reverse procedure to install.

## THERMOSTAT
## REPLACE

1. Disconnect lower radiator hose and drain coolant into suitable container.
2. Loosen upper radiator hose clamp (A), **Fig. 31,** then disconnect upper hose from engine.
3. Loosen thermostat retaining clamp (D), **Fig. 31,** then remove thermostat from upper hose.
4. Install thermostat in upper hose with thermostat check ball (F) positioned at the top and valve (G) toward the housing, **Fig. 32.**
5. Tighten thermostat retaining clamp, then install upper and lower hoses to engine.
6. Fill cooling system as necessary, then bleed system as described under "Cooling System Bleed."

## COOLING SYSTEM BLEED

1. Ensure all hose connections are secure.
2. Open cooling system bleed screws located at upper radiator hose and heater core inlet hose. **On models with automatic transaxle, a bleed screw is also located in the oil cooler upper coolant hose.**
3. Add coolant through expansion tank until a steady stream of coolant is emitted from the bleed screws.
4. Close bleed screws, then start engine and operate at 1500 RPM.
5. Check level in expansion tank and add coolant as necessary to bring to maximum level.
6. Install pressure cap on expansion tank and operate engine until cooling operates.
7. Check level in expansion tank and add coolant as necessary.

## BELT TENSION DATA

| Belt | New Lbs. | Used Lbs. |
|---|---|---|
| Serpentine Drive Belt | 180–200 | 140–160 |
| Power Steer. | 100–120 | 65–85 |

## SERPENTINE DRIVE BELT ROUTING

Refer to **Fig. 33,** for proper routing when installing serpentine drive belt. When adjusting belt tension, power steering belt tension must be adjusted prior to serpentine belt tension to ensure both belts are properly adjusted.

## FUEL PUMP, FILTER & ACCUMULATOR
## REPLACE

**The fuel pump and filter assembly are located on the passenger side of the vehicle. They are mounted on a plate to the floor pan ahead of the fuel tank and rear axle assembly. The fuel pump, filter and accumulator can be serviced separately.**

1. Disconnect battery ground cable.
2. Raise and support vehicle.
3. Install tool clamps Mot. 453.01 or

equivalent, onto fuel pump inlet and outline lines to prevent fuel loss when lines are disconnected, **Fig. 34.**

4. Disconnect electrical connectors (A) from fuel pump, **Fig. 34.**
5. Disconnect and cap fuel lines from pump or filter assembly.
6. Remove fuel pump (D) or filter assembly (E) attaching straps (C), **Fig. 34.**
7. Remove fuel pump or filter assembly. **The accumulator is installed in the fuel line connecting the fuel pump and filter assembly. The accumulator dampens fuel flow from the fuel pump during vehicle operation. The accumulator can be serviced separately at this point if necessary.**
8. Reverse procedure to install.

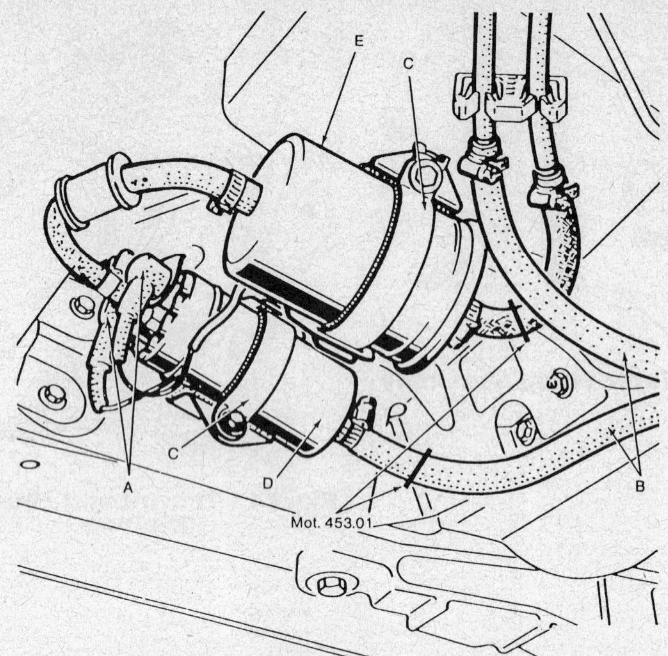


**Fig. 34 Fuel pump & fuel filter**

## TIGHTENING SPECIFICATIONS

***Torque Specifications Are For Clean And Lightly Lubricated Threads Only. Dry Or Dirty Threads Produce Increased Friction Which Prevents Accurate Measurement Of Tightness.**

| Year | Component | Torque/Ft. lbs. |
|---|---|---|
| 1989 | Camshaft Sprocket Bolt | 37 |
| | Connecting Rod Bolts | 46 |
| | Crankshaft Pulley Bolt | 96 |
| | Cylinder Head Bolts | 69 |
| | Cylinder Head Cover Nuts | 3.6 |
| | Engine To Transaxle Bolts | 37 |
| | Flex Plate Bolts | 50 |
| | Flywheel Bolts | 44 |
| | Intermediate Shaft Sprocket Bolt | 37 |
| | Main Bearing Cap Bolts | 69 |
| | Oil Pan Screws | 7.4 |
| | Oil Pump Bolts | 33 |
| | Rocker Arm Shaft Plug | 15 |
| | Spark Plug | 11 |
| | Timing Belt Tensioner Bolts | 18 |
| | Torque Converter To Flex Plate | 22 |

# Clutch & Manual Transaxle

## INDEX



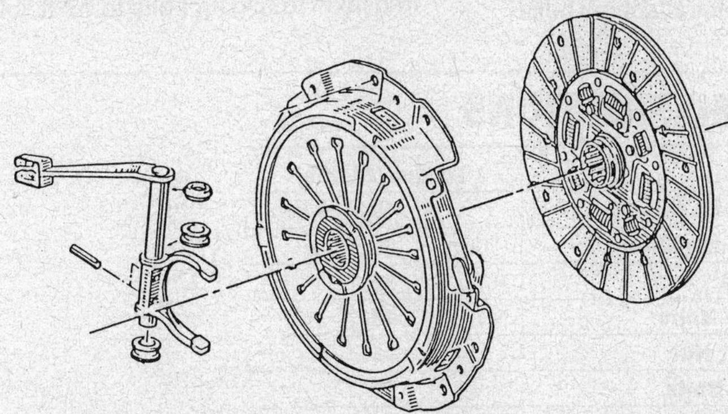

**Fig. 1 Clutch, pressure plate & release fork**

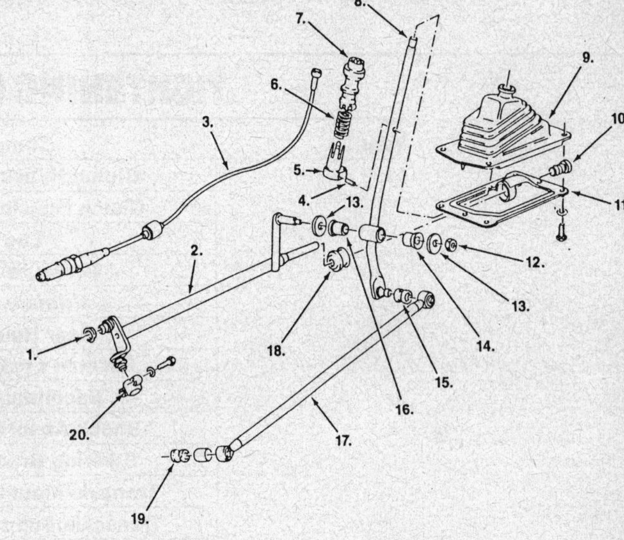

1. Bushing
2. Shift Rod
3. Reverse Lockout Cable
4. Roll Pin
5. Reverse Lockout Base
6. Lockout Spring
7. Reverse Lockout Handle
8. Shift Lever
9. Inner Shift Boot
10. End Piece
11. Base Plate
12. Shift Lever Nut
13. Washer
14. Outer Bushing
15. Isolator, Shift Rod-to-Shift Lever
16. Inner Bushing
17. Shift Rod
18. Isolator, End Piece
19. Isolator, Shift Rod End
20. Retainer Cup

**Fig. 2 Manual shift linkage**

## CLUTCH CABLE
### ADJUST

The clutch cable is adjusted by pulling upward and rearward on the clutch pedal, and then releasing. This will momentarily disengage the pedal cam and sector, allowing the adjusting spring to take up cable slack.

## CLUTCH
### REPLACE

1. Remove transaxle from vehicle.
2. Install a suitable flywheel locking tool, then remove pressure plate attaching bolts.
3. Remove pressure plate, release bearing assembly and clutch disc, **Fig. 1.**
4. Reverse procedure to install. **When installing clutch disc, long side of hub should face pressure plate. Torque** pressure plate attaching bolts to 18 ft. lbs.

## MANUAL SHIFT LINKAGE

The shift linkage, **Fig. 2,** is not adjustable. If problems in shifting are encountered, the linkage rods, bushings, insulators and other components should be checked for wear and damage. Any worn or damaged components should be replaced.

## MANUAL TRANSAXLE
### REPLACE

1. Disconnect battery ground cable.
2. Disconnect flex hose from heat tube and remove attaching bolt.
3. Remove bracket attaching bolt located at rear of engine.
4. Remove remaining heat tube and tube bracket attaching bolts and nuts. The remaining bolts/nuts are located under the intake manifold.
5. Remove TDC sensor to clutch housing attaching bolts, then the sensor.
6. Remove steering bracket.
7. **On models with A/C, carefully and slowly discharge refrigerant from system.**
8. Disconnect and cap A/C lines from connector block and retainer. Remove retainer.
9. Remove crossmember attaching bolts.
10. Raise and support vehicle.
11. Remove front tire and wheel assembly.
12. Using tool T.Av. 476 or equivalent, disconnect passenger side tie rod ball stud from steering knuckle. **Run the tie rod ball joint nut to the end of the ball stud before installing tool. This will protect the stud threads when loosening the stud.**
13. Remove passenger side steering tie rod.
14. Loosen coolant expansion tank attaching strap. Pull tank out from strap and position aside.
15. Place engine support tool M.S. 1900 or equivalent, onto fender flanges. Attach a suitable chain onto engine and support tool. Take up chain slack but do not lift engine.
16. Remove exhaust head pipe to exhaust manifold attaching bolts.
17. Label, then disconnect all electrical connectors and vacuum lines from transaxle assembly or which may prevent the transaxle from being removed from vehicle.
18. Remove exhaust head pipe to converter attaching bolts. Remove exhaust hanger nut.
19. Disconnect head pipe from converter.
20. Support transaxle assembly, then remove crossmember.
21. Disconnect clutch control cable.
22. Remove steering knuckle upper mount attaching bolt. Loosen but do not remove lower bolt.
23. Remove driveshaft roll pins.
24. Swing each rotor and steering knuckle assembly outward, then slide driveshafts off transaxle side gear stub shafts.
25. Remove plastic cover attached to bottom of transaxle.

26. Remove transaxle drain plug and drain lubricant from transaxle.
27. Disconnect reverse lockout cable from transaxle.
28. Disconnect shift rod from lever.
29. Remove crossover bracket bolts, then the shift rod from bracket.
30. Disconnect speedometer cable.
31. Disconnect ground strap from transaxle.
32. Support transaxle using a suitable jack.
33. Remove transaxle support cushion attaching nuts.
34. Remove two transaxle mount bracket to transaxle attaching bolts. Remove brackets.
35. Using support tool M.S. 1900 or equivalent, raise engine.
36. Disconnect wire harness electrical connectors.
37. Remove starter motor attaching bolts, then the starter motor.
38. Lower engine enough for access to the the clutch housing attaching bolts.
39. Remove clutch housing to engine attaching bolts/nuts.
40. Pull transaxle assembly straight back until clutch shaft clears pressure plate, then lower and remove transaxle.
41. Reverse procedure to install. **Torque** transaxle to engine bolts to 37 ft. lbs.

## TIGHTENING SPECIFICATIONS

| Year | Component | Torque/Ft. lbs. |
|---|---|---|
| 1989 | Clutch Housing Bolts (8mm) | 18 |
| | Clutch Housing Bolts (10mm) | 25 |
| | Lug Bolts | 66 |
| | Pressure Plate Bolts | 18 |
| | Primary Shaft Nut | 96 |
| | Rear Housing Bolts | 11 |
| | Reverse Lockout Cable Nut | 15 |
| | Secondary Shaft Nut | 110 |
| | Shock Absorber Lower Nuts | 148 |
| | Steering Bracket Lock Nuts | 26 |
| | Tranaxle Mounting Bracket Bolt | 30 |
| | Transaxle Support Cushion Nuts | 30 |
| | Transaxle to Engine Bolts | 37 |

# Rear Axle & Suspension

## INDEX



## REAR AXLE ASSEMBLY REPLACE

**The torsion bars do not require removal from the axle assembly to necessitate rear axle removal.**

1. Disconnect battery ground cable.
2. Raise and support vehicle.
3. Remove rear tire and wheel assembly.
4. Remove shock absorbers.
5. Disconnect parking brake cable from rear wheels.
6. Disconnect and cap brake lines.
7. Disconnect brake compensator linkage from axle assembly.
8. Support axle assembly using a suitable jack.
9. Remove axle assembly attaching bolts.
10. Lower and remove axle assembly from vehicle.
11. Reverse procedure to install. Check bearing play as follows:
    a. Install a suitable dial indicator onto rear brake drum.
    b. Measure axial play at the end of the axle shaft.
    c. Axial play should not exceed .001 inch.
    d. If axial play exceeds specified amount, replace brake drum hub bearing.

## REAR WHEEL BEARING SERVICE

**Before removing hub bearing, check bearing axial play. Bolt a dial indicator onto the rear brake drum using dial indicator adapter Rou.541 or equivalent. Measure axial play at the end of the axle shaft. Axial play should not exceed .001 inch. If measurement obtained exceeds specification, replace hub bearing.**

### REMOVAL

1. Raise and support vehicle.
2. Remove wheel(s).
3. Remove screws attaching brake drum to axle shaft hub.
4. Remove brake drum from axle shaft hub.
5. Using a suitable screwdriver, remove plastic hub cover.
6. Remove axle shaft hub locknut.
7. Remove axle shaft hub from axle shaft. **If necessary use tool T.Av. 1050 or equivalent, to remove hub.**
8. Remove bearing retaining clip (F) from machined groove (G) on axle shaft hub, **Fig. 1.** Using a suitable section of pipe (H, approximately 1.92 inch outside diameter) and a press, remove wheel bearing (E) from hub.

### INSTALLATION

**Do not install a used bearing. When installing bearing onto axle shaft hub, do not apply press load directly to the center bearing race. Apply load to the outer portion of the bearing only.**

1. Thoroughly clean hub assembly.
2. Using a suitable press and a section of pipe (A, approximately 2 inches in diameter), press bearing (B) into hub assembly, **Fig. 2.**
3. Install a new bearing retaining clip.

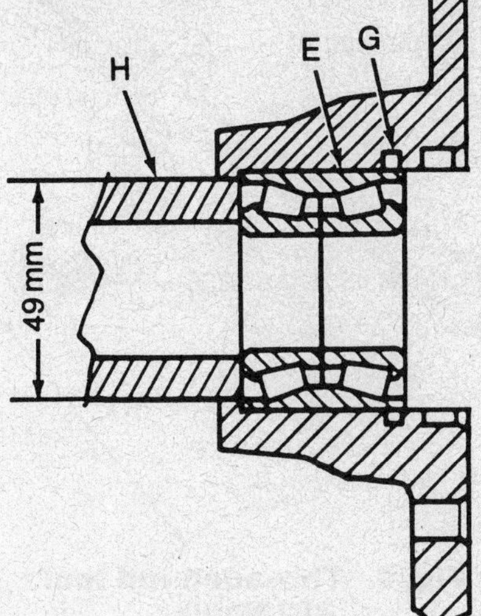


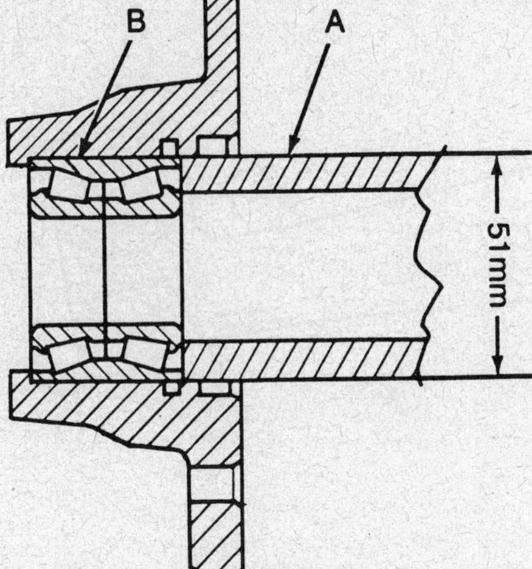


Fig. 2 Rear wheel bearing installation

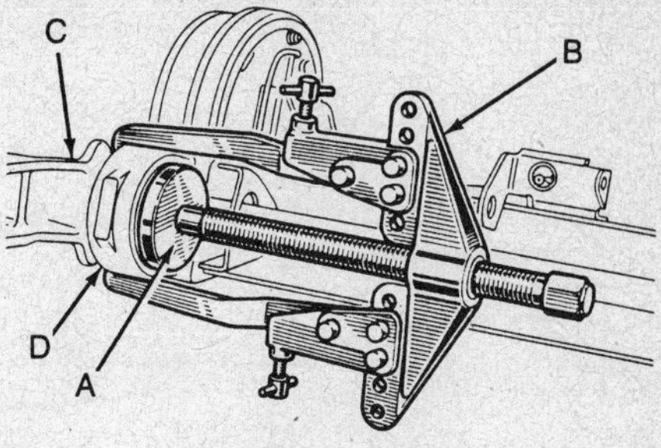

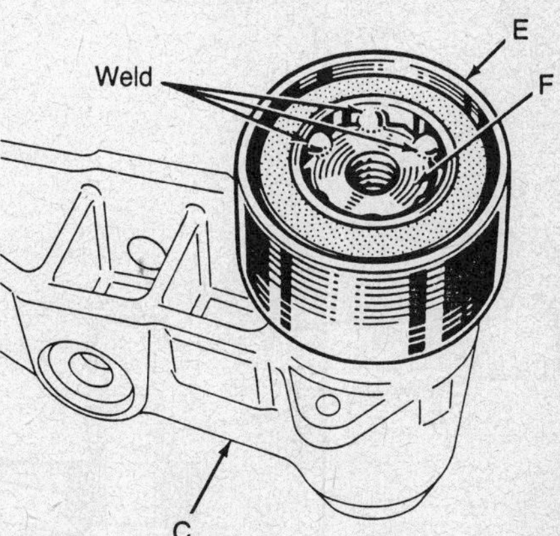


Fig. 3 Installing extractor tool onto axle pivot arm

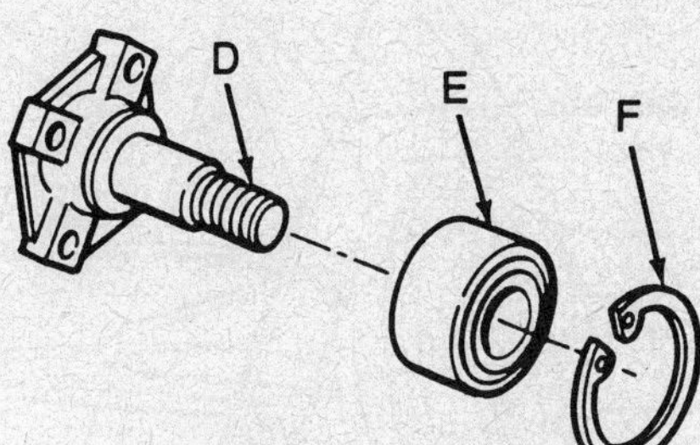


Fig. 1 Axle shaft hub assembly

4. Lightly lubricate axle shaft and install axle shaft hub onto axle shaft.
5. Install and tighten a new axle shaft hub locknut.
6. Install brake drum and attaching screws.
7. Install plastic hub cover.
8. Install wheel(s).
9. Check brakes from proper operation.
10. Lower vehicle.

# AXLE PIVOT ARM SERVICE

## REMOVAL

1. Remove rear axle assembly from vehicle as described previously.
2. Remove torsion bars from vehicle.
3. Install tool component (A) from tool T.Ar. 1056 or equivalent and a two jaw extractor (B) onto axle assembly (D), **Fig. 3.**
4. Drive axle pivot arm (C) and bushing from rear axle assembly, **Fig. 4.**
5. Remove bushing (E) from axle pivot arm (C). **A piece of metal (a 26 mm nut would be acceptable) and must be welded to the inside of the bushing, Fig. 4. The nut is used as a back-up to drive the bushing from the axle pivot arm.**
6. Using a suitable press and bearing splitter tool, J-22912-01 or equivalent, drive bushing from axle pivot arm. **When driving bushing, use a suitable section of pipe or socket to prevent damage. Do not reuse bushing after it has been removed.**

## INSTALLATION

1. Position bushing into rear axle assembly.
2. Using tool T.Ar. 1056 or equivalent, draw bushing into axle until it is flush with the outer edge of the axle. Position pivot arm to the axle for proper bushing preload. Before pressing the axle pivot arm (A) onto the axle bushing (B), it must be properly positioned. Position a straight edge along the top of the axle pivot arm where it attaches to the body at points (D), **Fig. 5.** Move the pivot arm until dimension X is approximately .275 inch. Take measurement from the center line of the axle shaft (E) to the straightedge on the axle pivot arm mounting points.
3. With pivot arm correctly positioned to the axle assembly, press pivot arm to the rear axle using tool T.Ar. 1056 or equivalent.
4. Press axle pivot arm until dimension Y is 50.5 inches. Dimension Y is taken between the left and right pivot arms at bolt holes (F).
5. Install rear axle assembly into assembly as described previously.
6. Install torsion bars into axle.

# AXLE SHAFT

## REPLACE

1. Raise and support vehicle.
2. Remove tire and wheel assembly.
3. Remove brake drum to axle shaft hub attaching screws, then the brake drum.
4. Remove brake drum from axle shaft hub.
5. Using a suitable screwdriver, pry off plastic hub cover.
6. Remove axle shaft hub locknut.
7. Remove axle shaft hub from axle shaft.



Fig. 4 Removing bushing from axle pivot arm

8. Remove axle shaft to rear axle attaching bolts.
9. Remove bolt attaching brake backing plate to axle shaft.
10. Remove axle shaft.
11. Reverse procedure to install.

# SHOCK ABSORBER

## REPLACE

**Never raise vehicle from under the V shaped channel on the rear axle.**

1. Raise and support vehicle.
2. Lift control arm to relieve tension from shock absorber. **The shock absorber mounting bolts are not interchangeable. Mark location of bolt before removing.**
3. Remove upper and lower shock absorber attaching bolts, then the shock absorber.
4. Reverse procedure to install.

# TORSION BAR SERVICE

## REMOVAL

**Never raise vehicle from under the V shaped channel on the rear axle.**

1. Raise and support vehicle.
2. Remove both rear tire and wheel assemblies.
3. Remove shock absorbers.
4. Remove dust caps covering ends of torsion bar by prying them off.
5. Mark and note splined positions of torsion bars before removal. Remove

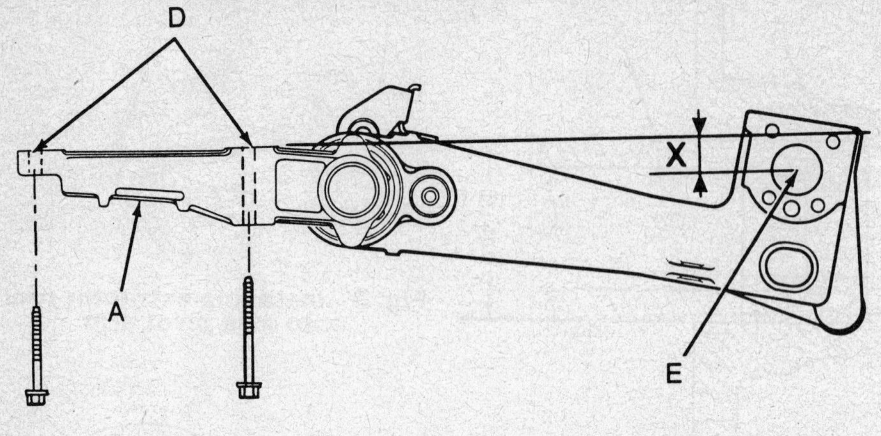


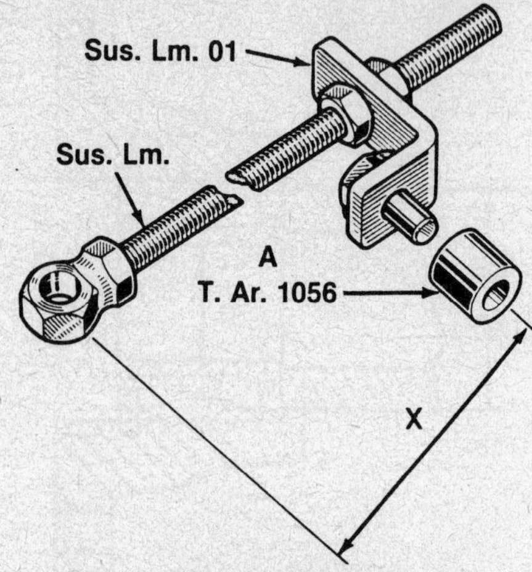


Fig. 6 Threaded rod tool assembly

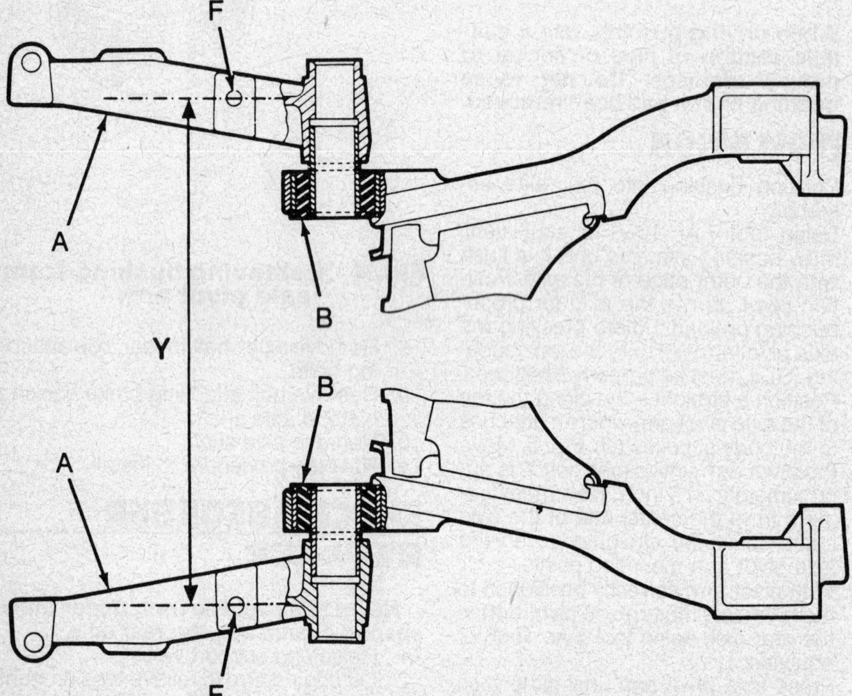


Fig. 5 Axle pivot arm bushing & pivot arm alignment

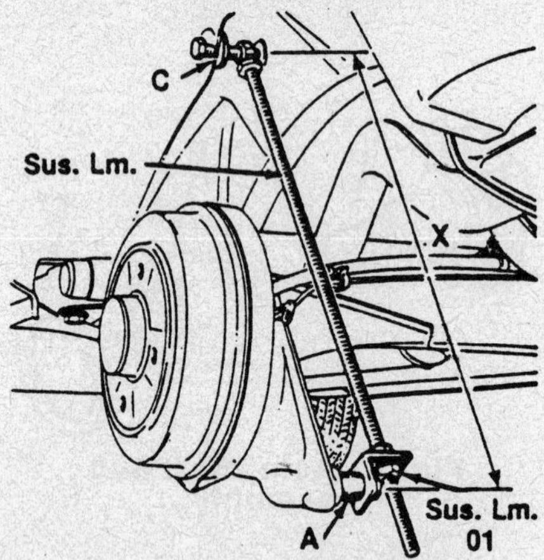


Fig. 7 Installing threaded rod tool assembly in place of shock absorber

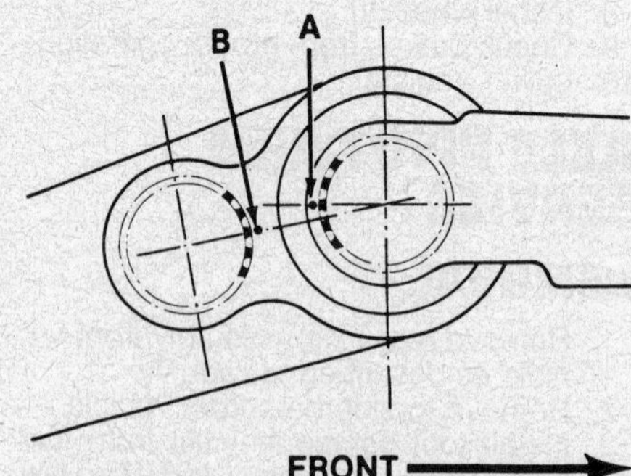


Fig. 8 Suspension bars mounting hole stamping marks

suspension bar or anti-sway bar (stabilizer bar).

6. Remove torsion bar connecting link only if all four torsion bars are being removed.

## INSTALLATION

### 1 To 3 Bars

**Before the torsion bars are installed, the rear trailing arms must be properly positioned.** To accomplish this, proceed as follows:

1. Tools Sus.Lm, Sus.Lm. 01 and T.Ar. 1056 are required.
2. Adjust bracket tool Sus.Lm.01 until dimension X is obtained.
3. **On sedan models dimension X should be 19.37 inch and on wagon models dimension X should be 18.97 inch, Fig. 6.**
4. Position tool assembly in place of the shock absorber and bolt it to point (C), **Fig. 7.**
5. Slip spacer (A) into lower shock absorber mounting hole.
6. The suspension bar mounting holes have a stamped mark A which enables the suspension bars to be initially positioned. An additional mark B must be made on the lower control arm for the anti-sway bar, **Fig. 8.** Place a ruler on the center line of the two mounting holes and place a mark (B) at the bottom of a tooth on the lower control (C), **Fig. 9.** Ensure letter on the torsion bar matches the position it is being installed into. The left-hand bar is marked G and the right-hand bar is marked D, **Figs. 10 and 11.**
7. Apply lubricant No. 8993630 or equivalent, onto splines on the torsion bar and their mounting holes. Align torsion bar indexing mark to the mounting hole.

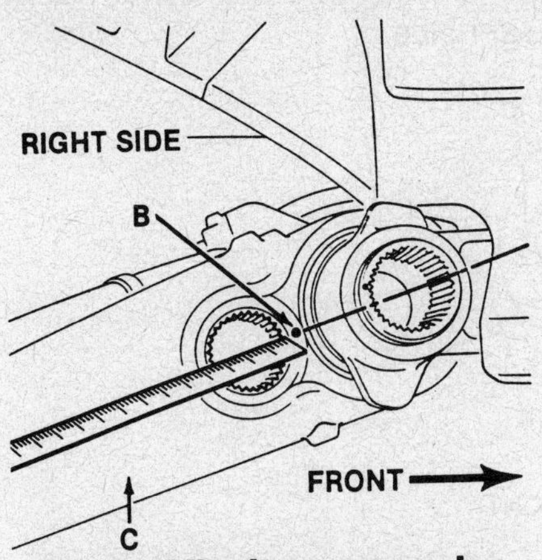


**Fig. 9 Aligning suspension bar & lower control arm tooth marks**

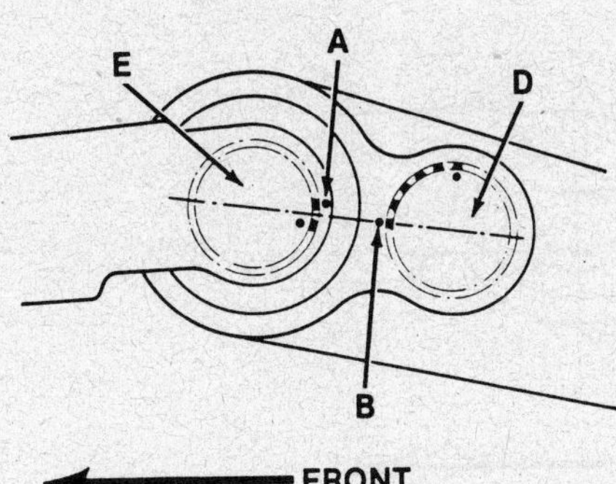


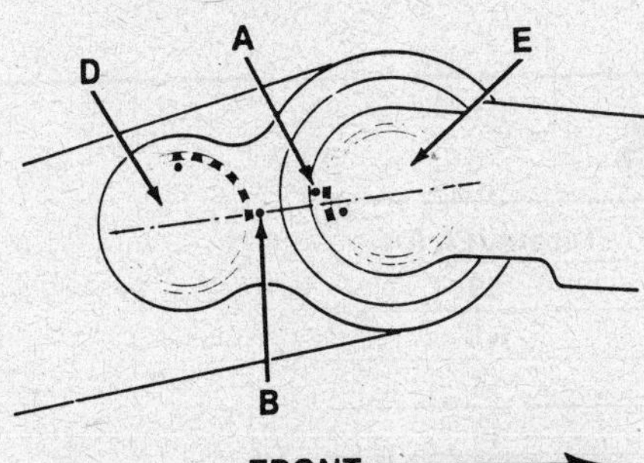


**Fig. 12 Positioning anti-sway & suspension bars (torsion bar installation) 1 to 3 bars. Sedan models**

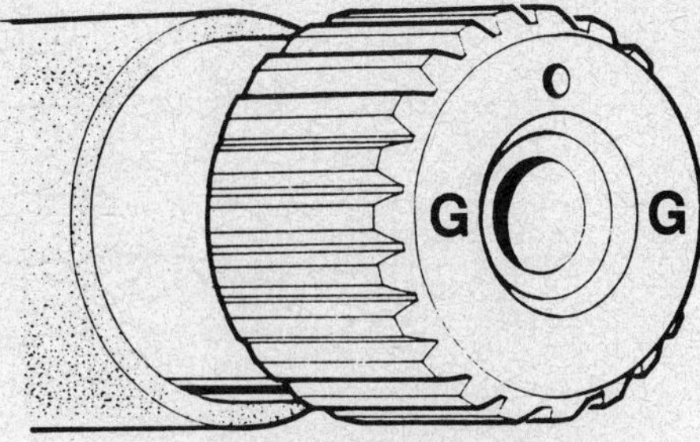


**Fig. 10 Lefthand bar identification letter G**

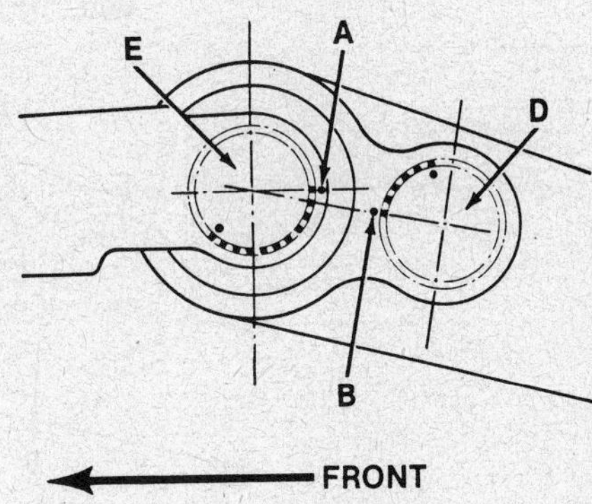


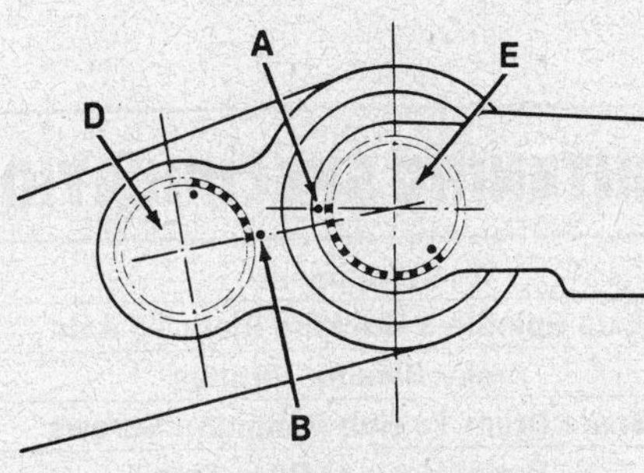


**Fig. 13 Positioning anti-sway & suspension bars (torsion bar installation) 1 to 3 bars. Wagon models**

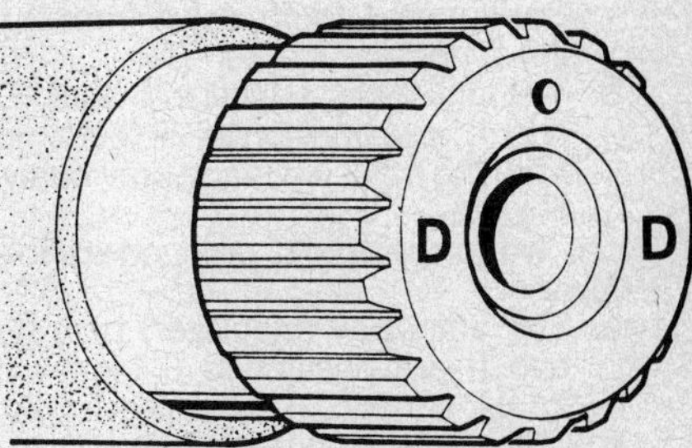


**Fig. 11 Righthand bar identification letter D**

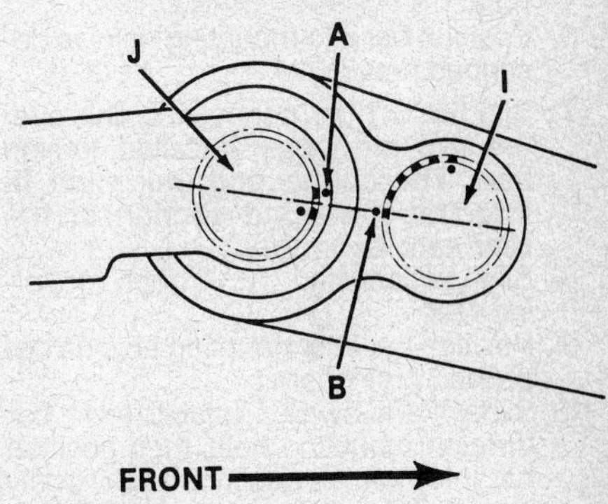


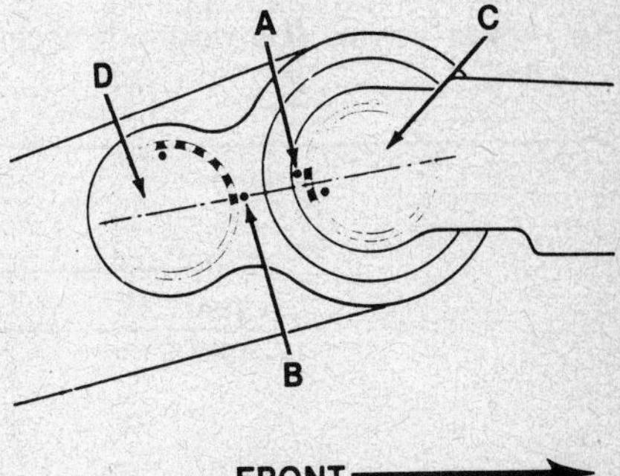


**Fig. 14 Positioning anti-sway & suspension bars (torsion bar installation) all 4 bars. Sedan models**

8. **On sedan models,** proceed as follows:
   a. The anti-sway (stabilizer) bar (D) is positioned 5 teeth up from the mark (B) made previously, **Fig. 12.**
   b. The suspension bar (E) is positioned 1 tooth down from the initial position marked (A).
9. **On wagon models,** proceed as follows:
   a. The anti-sway (stabilizer) bar (D) is positioned 5 teeth up from the mark (B) made previously.
   b. The suspension bar (E) is positioned 10 teeth down from the initial position mark (A), **Fig. 13.** Do not use a hammer to drive in torsion bars (other than brass) as damage to the splines will result.
10. When the bars are properly aligned, push into place. A brass hammer may be used for this purpose.
11. Remove threaded rod.
12. Install tire and wheel assemblies.
13. Lower vehicle.
14. Check and adjust vehicle height as required.

### All 4 Bars

**Before installing torsion bars, the rear trailing arms must be properly positioned.** To accomplish this, proceed as follows:

1. Tools Sus.Lm, Sus.Lm. 01 and T.Ar. 1056 are required.
2. Refer to steps 1 through 7 under "1 To 3 Bars."

3. **On sedan models,** proceed as follows:
   a. The suspension bars (J and C) are positioned 1 tooth down from the initial position marked (A).
   b. The anti-sway (stabilizer) bars (D and I) are positioned 5 teeth up from the mark (B) made previously, **Fig. 14.**
4. **On wagon models,** proceed as follows:
   a. The anti-sway (stabilizer) bars (D and I) are positioned 5 teeth up from the mark (B) made previously.
   b. The suspension bars (J and C) are positioned 10 teeth down from the initial position mark (A), **Fig. 15.**
5. With anti-sway and suspension bars properly positioned, slide anti-sway (stabilizer) bar through the mounting hole.
6. Position bar into mounting hole as described previously.
7. Slip torsion bar connecting link over the two previously installed torsion bars. **The connecting link must fit into the V shaped section of the rear axle assembly.**
8. Slide suspension bar through mounting hole.
9. Position bar into mounting hole as described previously.
10. Slide anti-sway (stabilizer) bar through mounting hole, then position bar into hole as described previously and slide into connecting link. **If it is difficult to align the torsion bars, the connecting link can be slightly twisted to facilitate alignment of the torsion bars.**
11. Remove threaded rod tool assembly, install wheels, lower vehicle and check vehicle ride height.
12. Adjust vehicle ride height, if necessary.

WAGON LEFT SIDE

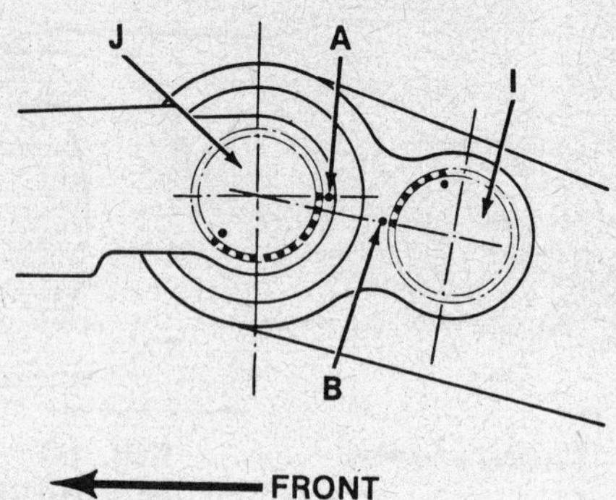


WAGON RIGHT SIDE

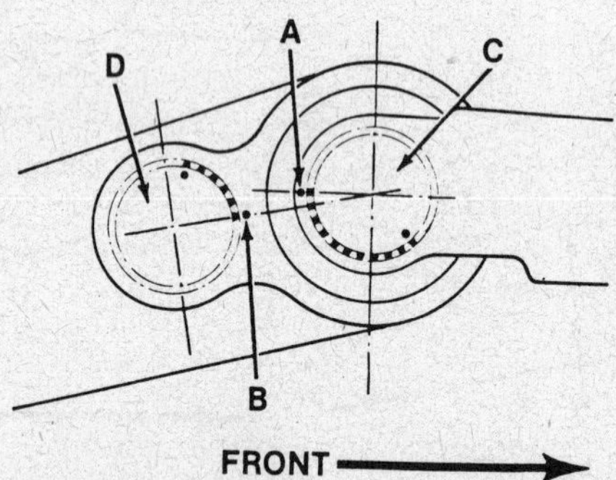


**Fig. 15 Positioning anti-sway & suspension bars (torsion bar installation) all 4 bars. Wagon models**

## TIGHTENING SPECIFICATIONS

| Year | Component | Torque/Ft. lbs. |
|---|---|---|
| 1989 | Axle Spindle & Backing Plate To Axle | 55 |
| | Brake Bleeder Fittings | 5.8 |
| | Brake Drum To Hub Retaining Screws | 14 |
| | Brake Hose At Rear Axle | 10 |
| | Master Cylinder Brake Line Fittings | 10 |
| | Master Cylinder To Power Brake Unit Nuts | 10 |
| | Pivot Arm Bolts | 63 |
| | Power Brake Unit To Dash Panel Nuts | 15 |
| | Rear Hub Attaching Spindle Nut | 118 |
| | Shock Absorber Lower Attachment | 63 |
| | Shock Absorber Upper Attachment | 59 |
| | Wheel Lug Nuts | 66 |

# Front Suspension & Steering

## INDEX



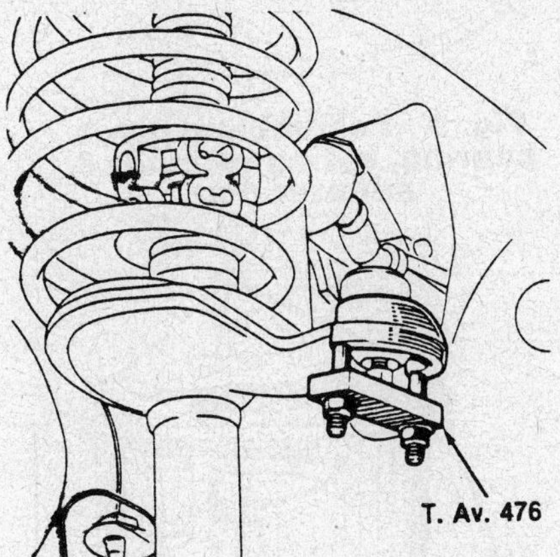


**Fig. 1 Using tool T.Av.476 to remove outer tie rod end**

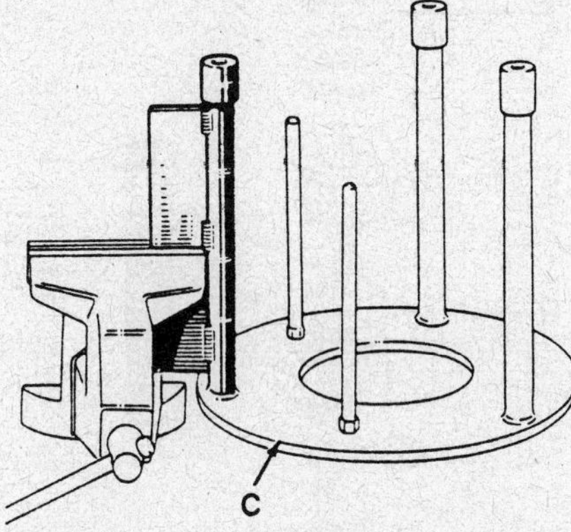


**Fig. 2 Lower adapter plate assembly**

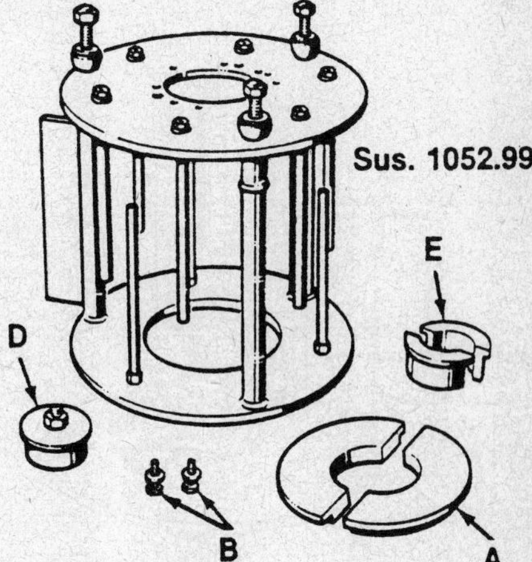


**Fig. 3 Using tool Sus.1052.99**

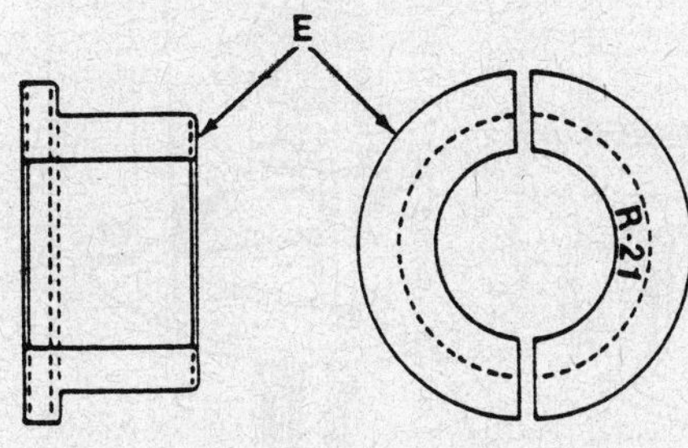


**Fig. 4 Adapter plates R-21**

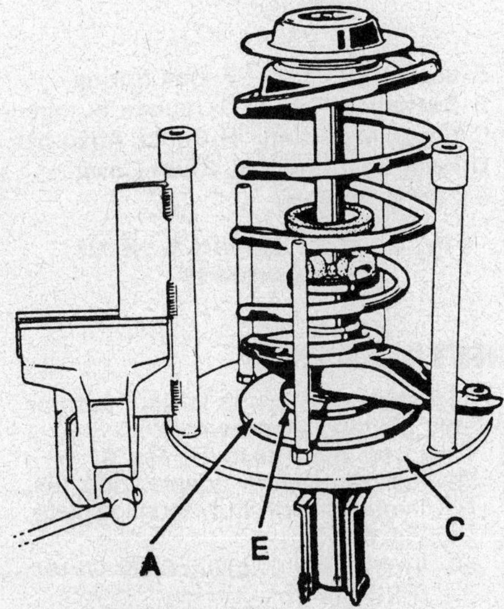


**Fig. 5 Placing coil spring/strut assembly into tool**

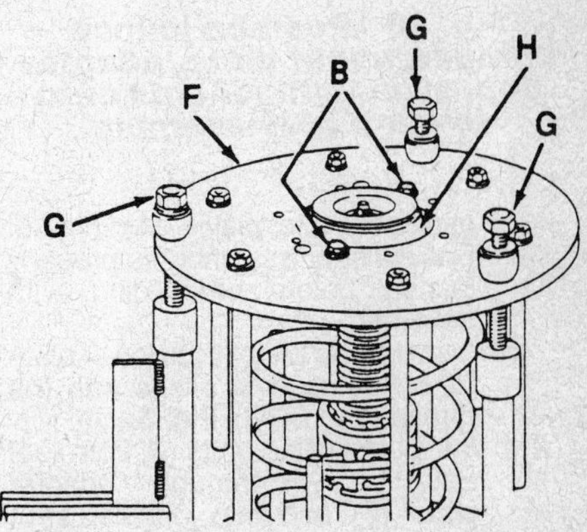


**Fig. 6 Installing upper plate to lower plate & aligning plates using threaded rods**

## COIL SPRING & STRUT SERVICE

### REMOVAL

**Do not support vehicle weight using the lower control arms or damage may result.**

1. Disconnect battery ground cable.
2. Raise and support vehicle.
3. Remove tire and wheel assembly.
4. Using tool T.Av.476 or equivalent, remove outer tie rod, **Fig. 1.**
5. Remove two attaching bolts securing lower portion of strut. The attaching bolts are splined and require the use of a brass of lead mallet for removal. **Prior to removing the two lower strut attaching bolts, ensure front suspension is hanging free. There should be no pressure or tension on any front suspension component.**
6. Remove upper attaching bolts.
7. Press on lower control arm and guide strut/coil spring assembly past the drive axle to prevent the strut from coming into contact with the driveshaft boot.
8. To separate coil spring from strut, proceed as follows:
   a. Place the lower plate (C) from tool Sus.1052.99 into a suitable vise, **Fig. 2.**
   b. Place lower adapter plates (A, shoulder facing downward) into the lower plate (C), **Fig. 3.** Tool set Sus.1052.99 is supplied with different adapter plates (E) to fit various Renault models. For use on the Eagle Medallion, locate and use adapter stamped R-21 and shaped as shown in **Fig. 4.**
   c. Place adapter plates (E) around the lower portion of the strut assembly, then position lower strut

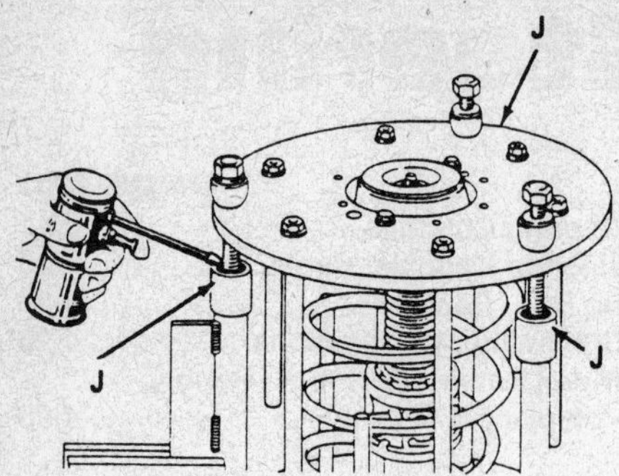


Fig. 7 Applying oil to points (J)

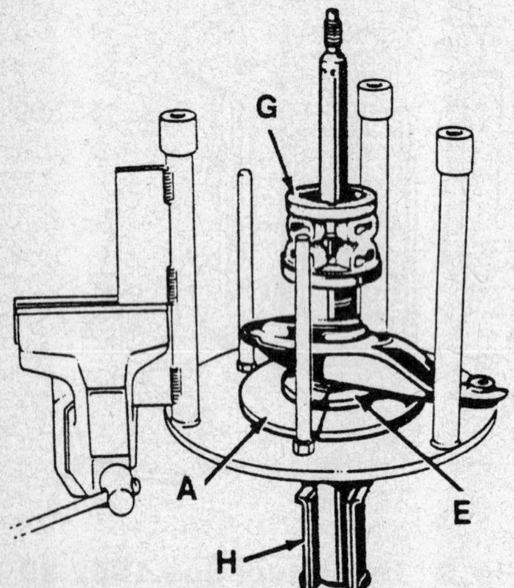


Fig. 10 Position jounce bumper, upper plate, adapter cup, strut components onto lower plate assembly

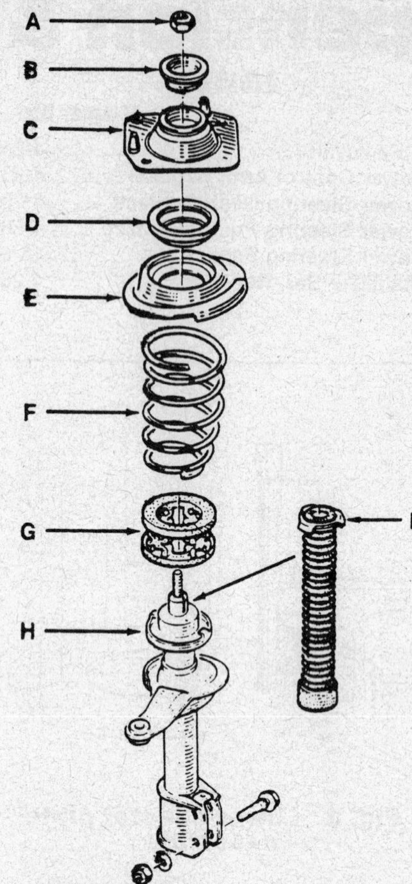


A-Locknut
B-Bearing
C-Shock Mounting
D-Pivot Bearing
E-Spring Retainer
F-Coil Spring
G-Jounce Bumper
H-Shock Absorber
I -Dust Cover

Fig. 8 Coil spring & strut components

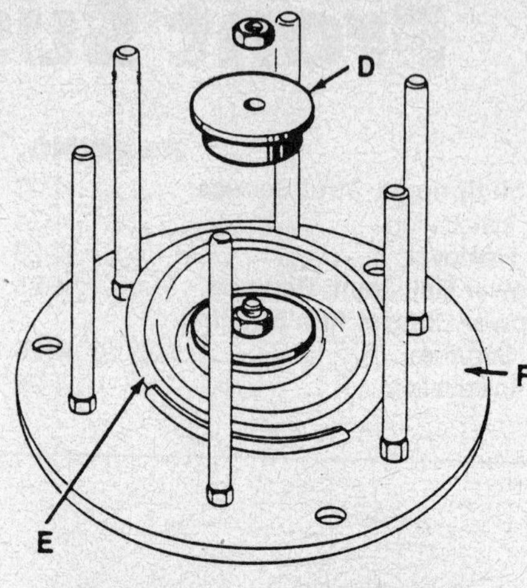


Fig. 9 Assembling pivot bearing, spring retainer & adapter cup

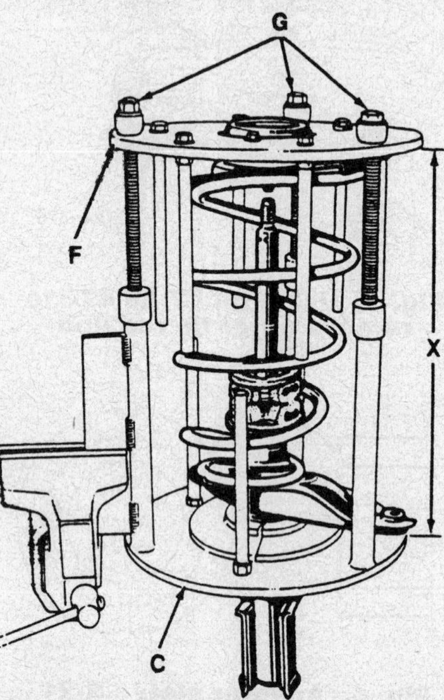


Fig. 11 Obtaining dimension X

assembly into plates (A), **Fig. 5.** Ensure strut assembly is properly seated before proceeding with next step.

d. Install upper plate (F) to lower plate (C) while aligning plates with the threaded rods (G), **Fig. 6.**
e. Install attaching bolts (B, from tool Sus.1052.99) through adapter plate (F) and into original strut mounting plate (H), **Fig. 6.** The upper plate (F) has multiple mounting holes used for various Renault models. Install bolts (B) through holes stamped R-21.
f. Liberally apply clean oil to points indicated (J) as shown in **Fig. 7.** The tool Sus.1052.99 is under extreme tension and oil application is necessary.
g. Using threaded rods (G), slowly compress the upper plate (F) approximately .393 inches.
h. Using a suitable Allen wrench, remove strut locknut.
i. Using the threaded rods (G), slowly remove all tension from coil spring.
j. Remove upper plate and strut components A through I, **Fig. 8.**

## INSTALLATION

1. To attach coil spring to strut assembly, proceed as follows:
   a. Invert upper plate (F), **Fig. 9.**
   b. Insert bolt from adapter cup (D), through top of strut mounting plate, **Fig. 9.**
   c. Invert strut mounting plate on upper plate.
   d. Assemble (in order) the pivot bearing and spring retainer (E) using adapter cup (D). Install nut onto adapter cup finger tight.
   e. Position strut (H) into adapter plates (A) and (E). Position jounce bumper (G), **Fig. 10.**
   f. Place upper plate (F), with adapter cup (D) and strut components, onto lower plate (C). The upper portion of the coil spring must be rotated to fit the "stop" located on the spring retainer.
   g. Using the threaded rods (G), slowly compress upper plate (F) until dimension X is 15.70 inches, **Fig. 11.** Ensure upper portion of the coil spring is located in the stop on the spring retainer.
   h. Remove adapter cup (D) from the strut assembly.
   i. Continue to tighten threaded rods (G) until the threaded portion of the strut shaft has passed through the upper plate (F) enough to install the locknut, **Fig. 11.** If difficulty is experienced in bringing the strut shaft through the strut mounting, position a suitable screwdriver into the hex hole in the top end of the shaft for alignment.
   j. Install bearing and locknut.
   k. Tighten lock nut, then slowly release tension from the threaded rods until all tension is relieved from the coil spring.

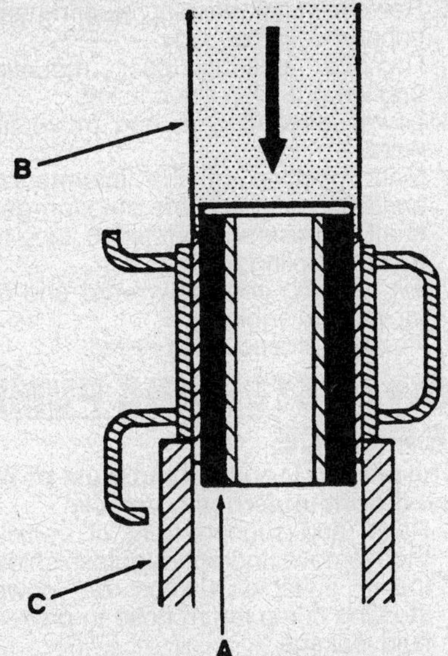


**Fig. 12 Using driver/receiver for bushing removal**

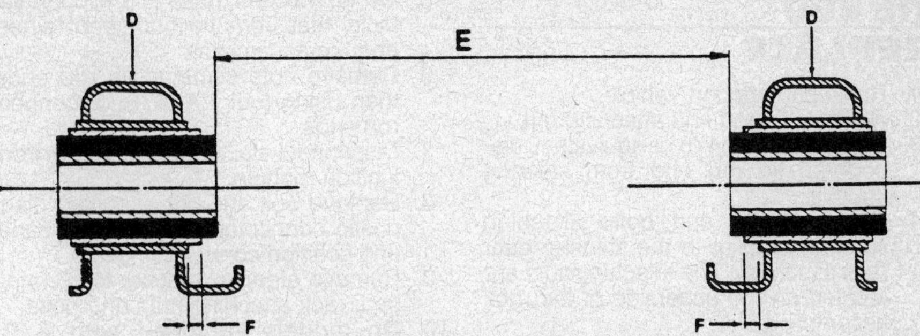


**Fig. 13 Obtaining dimension E**

l. Remove upper plate (F) from strut assembly.
m. Remove strut assembly from lower plate.

2. To install coil spring/strut assembly, proceed as follows:
   a. Install strut assembly in position using the three upper attaching bolts. Finger tighten bolts.
   b. When installing do not damage driveshaft boot.
   c. Install outer tie rod end.
   d. Install lower attaching bolts.
   e. Install upper attaching bolts.
   f. Since the outer tie rod end is attaching to the strut body, check toe measurement if the strut has been replaced.

## STABILIZER BAR
### REPLACE

**Vehicle weight must rest on wheels for easier removal of bar.**

1. Remove stabilizer bar bracket to body attaching bolts.
2. Remove stabilizer bar bracket to control arm attaching nuts. **The nuts and bolts securing the stabilizer bar lower bracket also retains the lower ball joint(s). Replace a nut on one of the two bolts to ensure ball joint does not move out of position.**
3. Check condition of stabilizer bar bushings and replace, if necessary.
4. Reverse procedure to install. Coat all new bushings using lubricant No. 8993630 or equivalent.

## LOWER BALL JOINT
### REPLACE

1. Disconnect stabilizer bar from both lower control arms. The bracket bolts and nuts also secure the lower ball joints to the arms. Replace a nut on one of the two attaching bolts after removing the bracket(s).
2. Raise and support vehicle.
3. Remove wheel(s).
4. Remove lower ball joint key bolt and nut.
5. Loosen but do not remove bolts attaching lower control arm to the engine cradle.
6. Remove and retain plastic washer located on lower ball joint.
7. Remove ball joint attaching bolts, then the ball joint.
8. Reverse procedure to install.

## LOWER CONTROL ARM
### REPLACE

**Remove nuts from stabilizer bar mounting bracket bolts and slide bracket off the bolts. Disconnect the brackets from both lower control arms. The bracket bolts and nuts also secure the lower ball joints to the control arms. Replace a nut on one of the two bolts after removing the bracket.**

1. Move stabilizer bar downward and away from the lower control arm.
2. Raise and support vehicle.
3. Remove wheel(s).
4. Remove lower ball joint key bolt and nut.
5. Remove bolts attaching lower control arm to the engine cradle, then the control arm.
6. Retain plastic washer located on the lower ball joint.
7. Reverse procedure to install.

## LOWER CONTROL ARM BUSHING SERVICE
### REMOVAL

1. Using a suitable press, drive bushings (A), **Fig. 12,** out.
2. Use suitable size sockets of sections of pipe as a bushing driver (B) and a bushing receiver (C), **Fig. 12.**
3. The driver (B) outside diameter should be 1.34 inches.
4. The receiver (C) inside diameter should be 1.42 inches.

### INSTALLATION

Install replacement bushings using a suitable press and the same bushing driver/receiver tools used during removal. The control arm bushing are not identical and should not be interchanged from one side to the next. **Press the bushings (D), Fig. 13, into the control arm equally and in small increments. Dimension (E) must be 7.48 inches plus or minus .019 inch. Dimension (F) must be the same at both bushing locations.**

## WHEEL BEARING & HUB ASSEMBLY
### REPLACE

1. Raise and support vehicle.
2. Remove wheel(s).
3. Remove brake rotor and caliper assembly.
4. Tie caliper to the spring or strut. Do not allow the brake line to support weight of the caliper.
5. Using toll Rou.604.01 or equivalent to secure wheel hub, remove driveshaft attaching nut.
6. Remove bolts attaching bearing to the steering knuckle.
7. Remove hub and bearing from knuckle and driveshaft assembly.
8. Reverse procedure to install.

## STEERING KNUCKLE
### REPLACE

1. Raise and support vehicle.
2. Remove wheel, brake caliper and rotor assemblies. Secure caliper to the strut or spring. Do not allow the brake hose to support the weight of the caliper.
3. Using tool Rou.604.01 or equivalent to secure wheel hub, remove driveshaft attaching nut.
4. Remove wheel bearing and hub as an assembly.
5. Remove steering knuckle to strut attaching bolts and the lower ball joint key bolt and nut.
6. Disconnect ball joint from steering knuckle and remove steering knuckle. Do not damage driveshaft boot when removing steering knuckle.
7. Reverse procedure to install.

## TIE ROD

### REPLACE

1. Raise and support vehicle.
2. Remove tie rod end attaching nut.
3. Using tool T.Av.476 or equivalent, disconnect tie rod end from steering knuckle.
4. Remove nuts and bolts attaching steering bracket to the steering gear rack assembly. The attaching nuts are located on the underside of the rack assembly.
5. Remove nuts and bolts attaching tie rod to the steering bracket.
6. Remove tie rod assembly.
7. Reverse procedure to install.

## POWER STEERING GEAR

### REPLACE

1. Disconnect battery ground cable.
2. Remove instrument panel lower cover attaching screws, then the lower cover.
3. Remove steering shaft coupling pinch bolt. Mark position of coupling and steering shaft.
4. **On models equipped with A/C, carefully and slowly discharge refrigerant from system.**
5. **On all models,** raise and support vehicle, then remove both front wheel and tire assemblies.
6. Remove nuts securing tie rod ends, then using tool T.Av.476, disconnect rod ends.
7. Disconnect electrical connectors from ignition module.
8. Remove bolt and nut attaching diagnostic connectors to the dash panel and position connectors aside.
9. Remove steering bracket to steering gear rack attaching nuts and bolts.
10. **On models equipped with A/C, disconnect and cap lines from the expansion valve. Remove bolt attaching retainer to the side sill and position lines aside. A/C hoses and lines are under extreme pressure. Before disconnecting hoses and lines, ensure A/C system is completely discharged of refrigerant.**
11. **On all models,** remove crossmember attaching bolts, then the crossmember.
12. Install tool Mot.453.01 or equivalent, onto power steering pump reservoir hoses to prevent fluid leakage.
13. Remove power steering hose bracket and disconnect power steering hoses from gear assembly.
14. Remove nuts attaching steering gear support collar to body.
15. Remove steering gear mounting bracket nut, then the bracket.
16. Lower steering gear and move forward.
17. Mark position of the intermediate shaft coupling and the steering gear shaft for assembly reference, then remove coupling pinch bolt.
18. Tilt steering gear downward and remove from vehicle.
19. Reverse procedure to install.

## POWER STEERING PUMP

### REPLACE

**The power steering pump must be removed from underneath vehicle.**

1. Raise and support front of vehicle, then remove underbody splash shield.
2. Install suitable clamps on power steering pump return hose to prevent fluid leakage.
3. Remove power steering pump drive belt.
4. Disconnect power steering pump pressure and return lines at pump.
5. Remove power steering pump to bracket attaching bolts, then remove power steering pump.
6. Reverse procedure to install.

## TIGHTENING SPECIFICATIONS

| Year | Component | Torque/Ft. lbs. |
|---|---|---|
| 1989 | Disc Brake Caliper Attaching Bolts | 74 |
| | Driveshaft Nut | 184 |
| | Lower Ball Joint Pinch Bolt | 44 |
| | Lower Ball Joint Retaining Bolts & Nuts | 59 |
| | Lower Control Arm Top Cradle Bolts | 59 |
| | Stabilizer Bar Mounting Bracket | 22 |
| | Steering Gear Rack To Bracket Bolts & Nuts | 30 |
| | Steering Knuckle To Strut Bolts | 148 |
| | Steering Rear Mounting Bolts | 37 |
| | Steering Shaft Coupling Pinch Bolts | 19 |
| | Strut Upper Nut | 44 |
| | Strut Upper Mounting To Strut Tower Nuts | 18 |
| | Tie Rod End Adjusting Sleeve Lock Nuts | 26 |
| | Tie Rod To Bracket Bolts & Nuts | 26 |
| | Upper Ball Joint Nut | 30 |
| | Wheel Bearing To Knuckle Bolts | 15 |
| | Wheel Lug Nuts | 66 |

# Wheel Alignment

INDEX



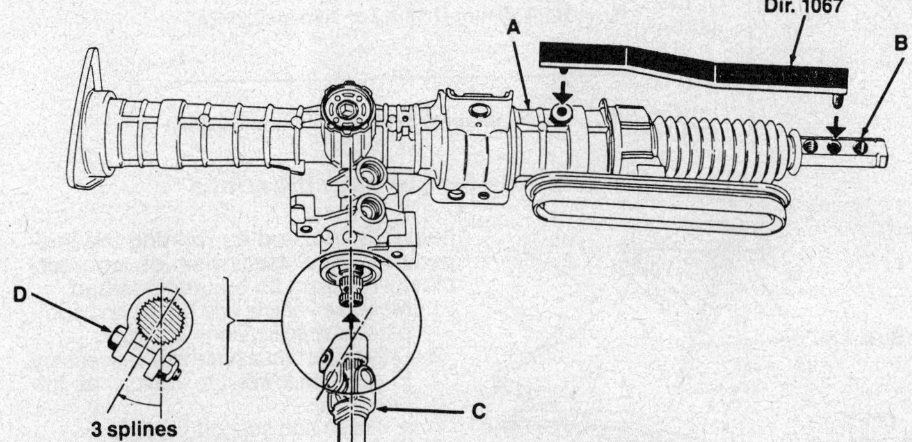


**Fig. 1 Positioning centering tool Dir.1067 onto gear housing and rack assembly**

## DESCRIPTION & PRELIMINARY INFORMATION

**Before proceeding with any check/adjustment procedure, ensure vehicle ride height is checked and/or adjusted as described previously. Also the following information is for front wheel alignment only. Rear wheel alignment is factory set and cannot be adjusted.**

### CASTER & CAMBER ANGLES

Caster and camber are built-in angles and are not adjustable. If either angle is incorrect, it will be necessary to inspect and/or replace the suspension or steering component contributing to the incorrect angle. Refer to "Alignment Diagnosis."

The relationship between left and right caster/camber angle is critical. A side-to-side difference of more than 1° may result in a pull to one side.

If the vehicle pulls to one side, the condition usually is a result of excessive camber or insufficient caster on the pulling side. Incorrect caster/camber is not the only cause of vehicle pull. Brake drag, a damaged or under inflated tire, body damage or damage to the steering components can all cause a pulling condition.

### TOE-OUT ANGLE

The front suspension is set/adjusted for front wheel toe-out. The toe setting ia adjusted only after the steering gear has been locked in a centered position using tool Dir.1067 or equivalent. Refer to "Toe-Out, Adjust" for service procedure.

To identify a incorrect toe condition, excessive toe-out will wear the inner edge of each front tire. Insufficient toe-out (or a toe-in condition), will wear the outer edge of each front tire.

## ALIGNMENT DIAGNOSIS

**The following information outlines the general causes of incorrect front alignment angles since caster/camber angles are not adjustable.**

### INCORRECT CASTER ANGLE

The possible cause(s) for incorrect caster angles are as follows:

1. Bent lower control arm.
2. Bent frame rails.
3. Bent or damaged body components.
4. Loose or worn lower control arm bushings.

### INCORRECT CAMBER ANGLE

The possible cause(s) for incorrect camber angles are as follows:

1. Bent lower control arm.
2. Bent frame rails.
3. Bent or damaged body components.
4. Loose or worn lower ball joint.
5. Loose or worn lower control arm bushings.

### TOE ANGLE INCORRECT BY MORE THAN 1/4 INCH (TOTAL TOE)

The possible cause(s) for incorrect toe angle exceeding 1/4 inch are as follows:

1. Bent or damaged steering knuckle.
2. Bent tie rod end.
3. Worn or loose tie rod end.
4. Worn or loose lower control arm bushings.

## FRONT WHEEL ALIGNMENT CHECKS

Perform the front wheel alignment procedures in the following sequence: Preliminary Inspection, Steering Gear Centering, Alignment Angles Check, Toe Setting Adjust, and Steering Wheel Centering.

Perform the preliminary inspection before the vehicle is on an alignment rack. Center the steering gear and check alignment angles with the vehicle placed on an alignment rack.

### PRELIMINARY INSPECTION

1. Ensure tires are of the same size and properly inflated.
2. Inspect tread surfaces and note type and degree of wear.
3. Measure and adjust vehicle ride height.
4. Check braking operation. Correct problems before alignment adjustment.
5. Check front wheel bearing end play.
6. Check wheel radial and lateral run-out.

### STEERING GEAR CENTERING

1. Remove bolts and nuts attaching steering bracket to the rack assembly and move bracket (and tie rods) aside.
2. Place centering tool Dir.1067, **Fig. 1**, onto gear housing (A) and rack assembly (B) as shown. **Ensure centering studs on tool are firmly seated.**
3. With tool installed, the steering gear will automatically be centered and locked in position.
4. Check position of the steering shaft

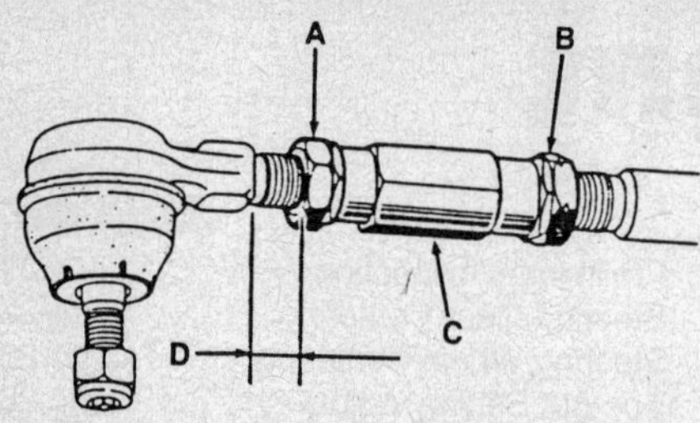

Fig. 2 Toe-out adjustment

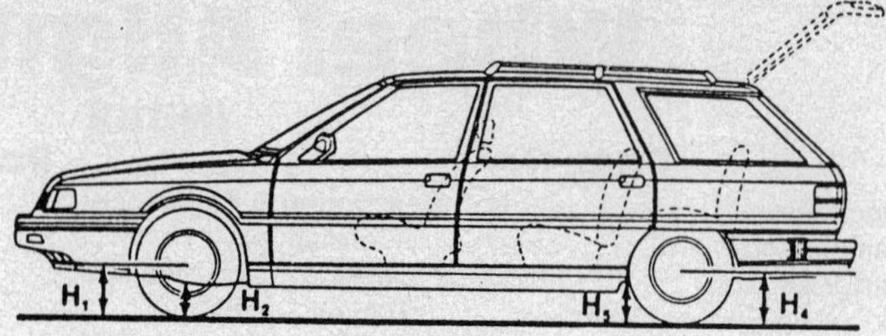


| | REAR |
|---|---|
| L48 (SEDAN) | $H_4 - H_5$ = 30mm (1.18in.) ± 7.5mm (0.295in.) |
| K48A (WAGON) | $H_4 - H_6$ = 10mm (0.393in.) ± 7.5mm (0.295in.) |

**Fig. 3 Vehicle ride height specifications**

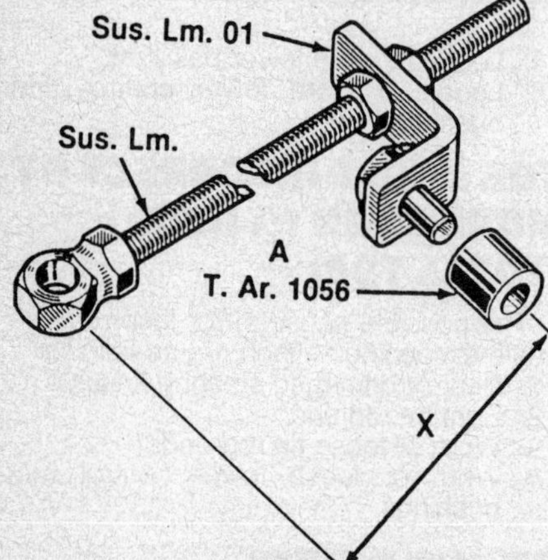

**Fig. 4 Threaded rod tool assembly**

coupling (C), **Fig. 1.** The coupling pinch bolt (D) must be located at the coupling underside and positioned 3 splines away from a horizontal position. Adjust coupling position, if necessary.

## ALIGNMENT ANGLES CHECK

1. Jounce vehicle front end several times to settle the suspension components.
2. Check alignment angles in the following sequence: Caster, Camber and Toe-Out.
3. If the alignment angles are within specifications proceed to "Toe-Out Setting, Adjust."
4. If caster, camber or toe-out are not within specified limits, it will be necessary to repair or replace the steering, suspension or body component causing the incorrect alignment.
5. Remove tool Dir.1067 and install steering bracket onto the steering gear rack assembly.
6. Center the steering wheel, if necessary. Refer to "Steering Wheel Centering."
7. Remove vehicle from alignment rack.

## TOE-OUT SETTING, ADJUST

1. Loosen tie rod locknut (A), **Fig. 2**, and steering arm locknut (B). **Locknut (A) has righthand threads. Locknut (B) has lefthand threads.**
2. Turn each adjusting sleeve (C) inward or outward to obtain the required toe-out reading.
3. The number of threads (D) visible at each tie rod end should be approximately the same.
4. **Torque** locknuts (A) and (B) to 26 ft. lbs. **Do not allow the adjusting sleeve (C) to rotate while tightening the locknuts.**

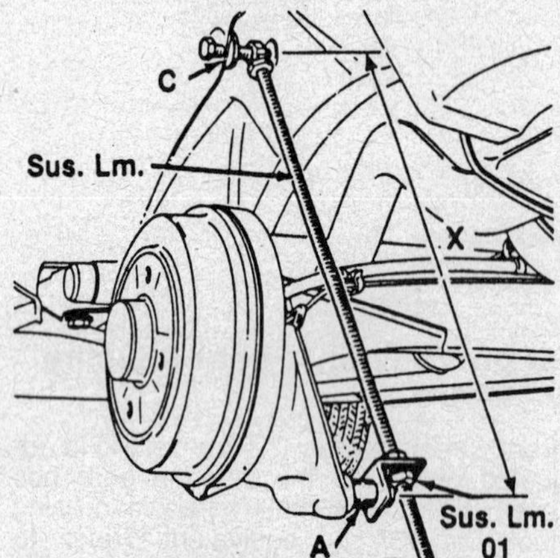

**Fig. 5 Installing threaded rod tool assembly in place of shock absorber**

## STEERING WHEEL CENTERING

Do not use the tie rod adjusting sleeves to center the steering wheel. The correct method of centering the steering wheel is to remove the steering wheel and center it on the steering shaft as necessary. After centering, **torque** steering wheel attaching nut to 30 ft. lbs.

## VEHICLE RIDE HEIGHT ADJUST

**Only the rear suspension height is adjustable. If front suspension ride height is not within specification, check suspension for worn and damaged components. The vehicle rear ride height is adjusted by rotating the suspension bars clockwise or counterclockwise from its original position.**

1. Measure vehicle ride height and compare to specifications in **Fig. 3.**
2. Determine measurement necessary to raise or lower the vehicle, as follows:
   a. Raise and support vehicle.
   b. Remove both rear wheels.
   c. Remove shock absorbers as described previously.
   d. **Install, then adjust threaded rod tool Sus.Lm (A) with tool Sus.Lm.01 bracket until dimension X is 19.37 inches on sedan models or 18.97 inches on wagon models, Fig. 4.**
   e. Position tool assembly in place of the shock absorber and attach it at point C, **Fig. 5.** The spacer (A) from tool set T.Ar.1056 or equivalent must also be used.
   f. Slip spacer (A) into the lower shock absorber mounting hole.
   g. Mark position of the suspension torsion bars before removal.
   h. Using a suitable tool, remove suspension bar. **Do not attempt to change the vehicle ride height by use of the anti-sway (stabilizer) bars.**
   i. To raise vehicle ride height, lengthen the threaded rod to position the torsion bar to the next available spline.
   j. To lower the vehicle ride height, shorten the threaded rod to position the torsion bar to the next available spline.
   k. One spline change is equal to .118 inch.
   l. After obtaining correct vehicle ride height measurement, remove threaded rod tool and install shock absorber.
   m. Install wheels, remove supports and lower vehicle.
   n. Check vehicle ride height, adjust if necessary.

# EAGLE TALON & PLYMOUTH LASER

## INDEX OF SERVICE OPERATIONS

**NOTE:** Refer To Rear Of This Manual For Vehicle Manufacturer's Special Service Tool Suppliers.



*Continued*

## INDEX OF SERVICE OPERATIONS—Continued



# Specifications

## GENERAL ENGINE SPECIFICATIONS

| Year | Engine Liter/CID① | Engine VIN② | Fuel System | Bore and Stroke, Inch | Compression Ratio | Net HP @ RPM ③ | Maximum Torque Ft. Lbs @ RPM | Normal Oil Pressure psi @ RPM |
|---|---|---|---|---|---|---|---|---|
| 1990–92 | 1.8L/4-107 | T | MPI④ | 3.17 x 3.39 | 9.0 | 92 @ 5000 | 105 @ 3500 | 11.4 @ 700 |
| | 2.0L/4-122⑤ | R | MPI④ | 3.35 x 3.46 | 9.0 | 135 @ 6000 | 125 @ 5000 | 11.4 @ 750 |
| | 2.0L/4-122⑥ | U | MPI④ | 3.35 x 3.46 | 7.8 | 190 @ 6000 | 203 @ 3000 | 11.4 @ 750 |

①—CID-cubic inch displacement.
②—Eighth digit of VIN denotes engine code.
③—Ratings are net as installed in vehicle.
④—Multi-point injection.
⑤—Except turbocharged.
⑥—Turbocharged.

## TUNE UP SPECIFICATIONS

| Year | Liter/CID① | VIN② | Spark Plug Gap, Inch | Ignition Timing, °BTDC③ Firing Order | Firing Order Fig. | Man. Trans. | Auto. Trans. | Mark Fig. | Curb Idle Speed, RPM Man. Trans. | Auto. Trans. | Fuel Pump Pressure, psi |
|---|---|---|---|---|---|---|---|---|---|---|---|
| 1990–92 | 1.8L/4-107 | T | .039-.043 | 1-3-4-2 | A | 5④⑦ | 5④ | B | 700⑥ | 700⑥ | 38④ |
| | 2.0L/4-122⑧ | R | .039-.043 | 1-3-4-2 | A | 5⑤⑦ | 5⑤⑦ | B | 750⑥ | 750⑥ | 36-38⑤ |
| | 2.0L/4-122⑨ | U | .028-.031 | 1-3-4-2 | A | 5⑤⑦ | 5⑤⑦ | B | 750⑥ | 750⑥ | 27⑤ |

①—CID-Cubic inch displacement.
②—Eighth digit of VIN denotes engine code.
③—BTDC-Before top dead center.
④—At 700 RPM.
⑤—At 750 RPM.
⑥—±100 RPM.
⑦—With jumper wire connected between ignition timing adjustment connector and ground. Refer to Fig. C for 1.8L engines and Fig. D for 2.0L engines.
⑧—Except turbocharged.
⑨—Turbocharged.

*Continued*

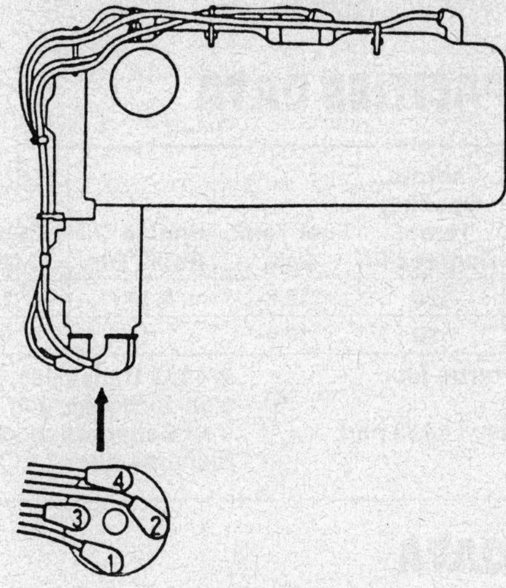

Fig. A.

Fig. B.

Fig. D.

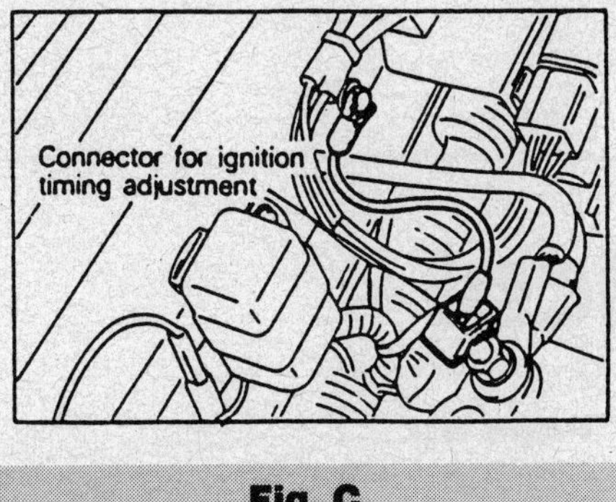


Fig. C.

## WHEEL ALIGNMENT SPECIFICATIONS

| Year | Model | Camber Angle, Degrees | | Caster Angle, Degrees | | Toe In Inch |
|---|---|---|---|---|---|---|
| | | Limits | Desired | Limits | Desired | |
| **Front** | | | | | | |
| 1990–92 | ① | −4/15 to +11/15 | +7/30 | +1 5/6 to +2 5/6 | +2 1/3 | 0④ |
| | ② | −5/12 to +7/12 | +1/12 | +1 1/10 to +2 9/20 | +2 3/10 | 0④ |
| | ③ | −1/3 to +2/3 | +1/6 | +1 1/5 to +2 4/5 | +2 3/10 | 0④ |
| **Rear** | | | | | | |
| 1990–92 | ⑤ | −1 1/4 to −1/4 | −3/4 | — | — | 0⑥ |
| | ③ | −2 1/20 to −1 1/20 | −1 11/20 | — | — | .14⑥ |

①—Two wheel drive models w/1.8L engine.
②—Two wheel drive models w/2.0L engine.
③—Four wheel drive models.
④—Plus or minus .12 inch.
⑤—Two wheel drive models.
④—Plus or minus .118 inch.

Continued

## COOLING SYSTEM & CAPACITIES DATA

| Year | Liter/CID① | VIN Code | Cooling Capacity Less A/C, Qts. | Cooling Capacity With A/C, Qts. | Radiator Cap Relief Pressure, Lbs. | Thermo. Opening Temp., Degrees F. | Fuel Tank, Gals. | Engine Oil Refill, Qts. | Transmission Oil 5 Speed, Qts. | Transmission Oil Auto. Trans., Qts. |
|---|---|---|---|---|---|---|---|---|---|---|
| 1990–92 | 1.8L/4-107 | T | 6.6 | 6.6 | 11-15 | 190 | 15.9 | 4.1② | 1.9 | ④ |
| | 2.0L/4-122 | R,U | 7.6 | 7.6 | 11-15 | 190 | 15.9 | ⑤ | ③ | ④ |

①—CID-Cubic inch displacement.
②—Includes filter.
③—Except turbo, 1.9 pints; turbo two wheel drive, 2.3 pints; turbo four wheel drive, 2.4 pints.
④—F4A22 transaxle, 6.4 qts.; F4A33 and W4A33 transaxles, 7.4 qts.
⑤—Non-turbocharged models, 4.6 Qts.; Turbocharged models, 4.8 Qts. Includes filter.

## LUBRICANT DATA

| Year | Model | Lubricant Type: Transaxle Manual | Transaxle Automatic | Transfer Case | Rear Axle | Power Steering | Brake System |
|---|---|---|---|---|---|---|---|
| 1990–92 | All | API GL-4 | ① | API GL-4 | API GL-5 | ① | Dot 3 |

①—Dexron or Dexron II automatic transmission fluid type 7176, Dia ATF SP.

# Electrical

## INDEX



## FUSE PANEL & FLASHER LOCATION

The fuse panel is located under the driver's side instrument panel.

The flasher is located under the driver side instrument panel.

## STARTER
### REPLACE

1. Remove battery and battery tray.
2. Disconnect speedometer cable from transaxle.
3. **On 1.8L engine models,** remove manifold bracket.
4. **On all models,** disconnect electrical connectors.
5. Remove starter attaching bolts, then the starter.
6. Reverse procedure to install.

## DISTRIBUTOR
### REPLACE

1. Disconnect battery ground cable.
2. Remove spark plug cables from distributor, **keep plug wires in order for installation.**
3. Remove distributor hold-down bolt, then the distributor.
4. Reverse procedure to install noting the following:
   a. Turn the crankshaft so that the No. 1 cylinder is at top dead center.
   b. Align distributor housing and gear mating marks, **Fig 1.**
   c. Install distributor to engine while aligning fine cut groove of distributor installation flange with center of distributor installation stud.

## IGNITION LOCK
### REPLACE

1. Remove upper and lower steering column covers.
2. Insert key in steering lock cylinder, turn to Accessory position.
3. Using Phillips screwdriver, push lockpin **Fig. 2,** of steering lock cylinder inward and pull lock cylinder out of housing.
4. Reverse procedure to install.

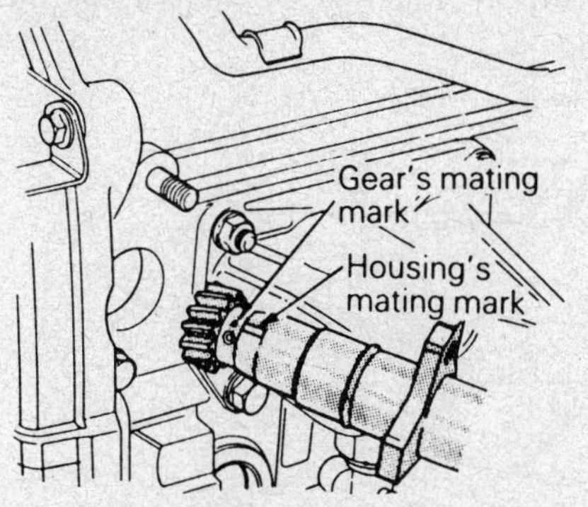


Fig. 1 Aligning distributor

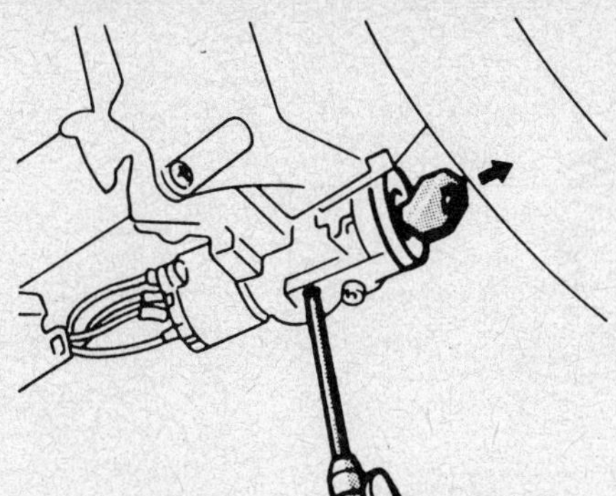

Fig. 2 Ignition lock release

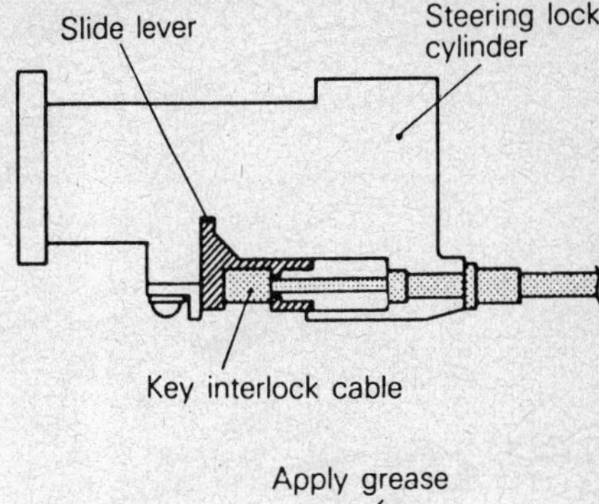


Fig. 4 Installing slide lever

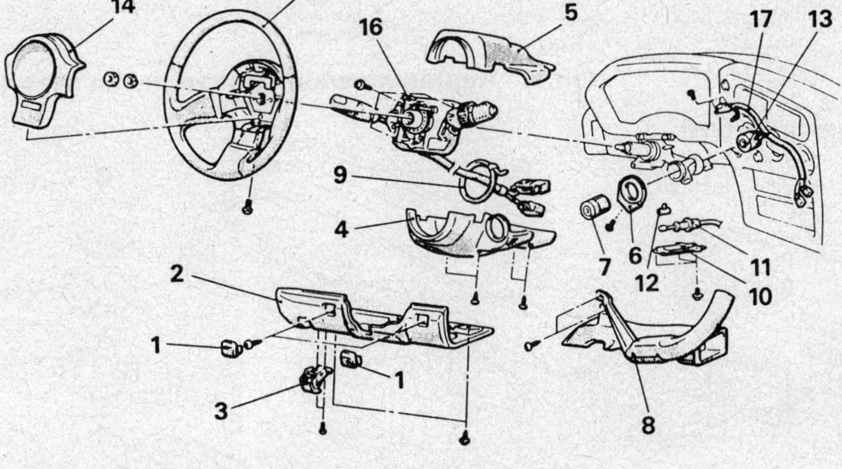


1. Plug
2. Knee protector
3. Hood lock release handle
4. Column cover lower
5. Column cover upper
6. Ignition key illumination light
7. Steering lock cylinder
8. Lap cooler duct and shower duct
9. Cable band
10. Cover*
11. Key interlock cable*
12. Slide lever*
13. Ignition switch segment
14. Horn pad
15. Steering wheel
16. Column switch
17. Key reminder switch segment

NOTE
* indicates vehicles with A/T safety-lock system.

Fig. 3 Removing ignition switch

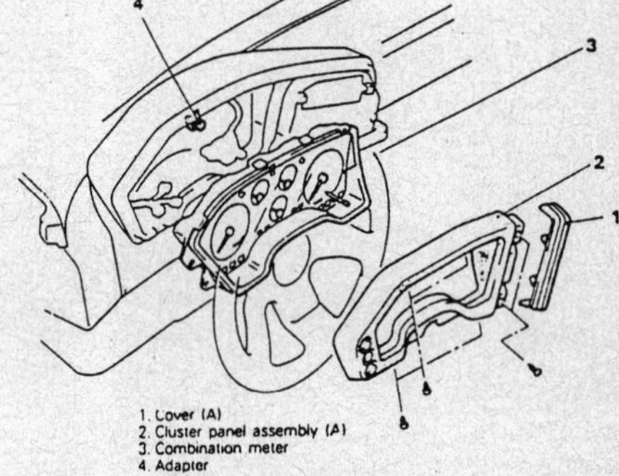


Fig. 5 Replacing pop-up and dimmer switches

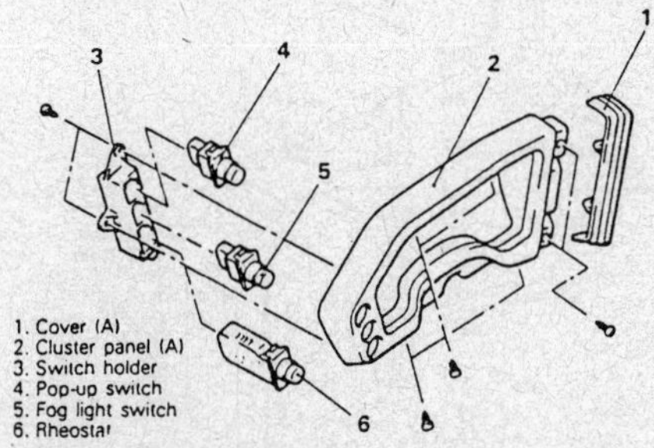


Fig. 6 Steering wheel removal

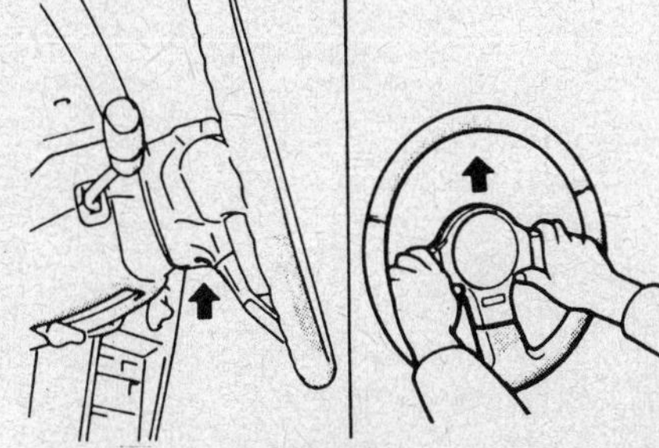

Fig. 7 Replacing instrument cluster

## IGNITION SWITCH
## REPLACE

Remove ignition switch in numbered sequence, **Fig. 3,** noting the following:

1. With key removed, install slide lever to steering lock cylinder.
2. Connect key interlock cable to slide lever and steering lock cylinder as shown **Fig. 4.**
3. Apply coating of multi-purpose grease where shown, **Fig. 4.**
4. Remove horn pad attaching screw, then the horn pad by pressing upward.
5. Remove steering wheel using wheel puller. **Do not use hammer as this may damage collapsible mechanism.**
6. Reverse procedure to install.

## HEADLAMP SWITCH
## REPLACE

Refer to "Column Switch, Replace" for procedure.

## COLUMN SWITCH
## REPLACE

Remove column switch in numbered sequence, **Fig. 3,** noting the following:

1. Remove horn pad attaching screw, then the horn pad by pressing upward.
2. Remove steering wheel using wheel puller. **Do not use hammer as this may damage collapsible mechanism.**
3. Reverse procedure to install.

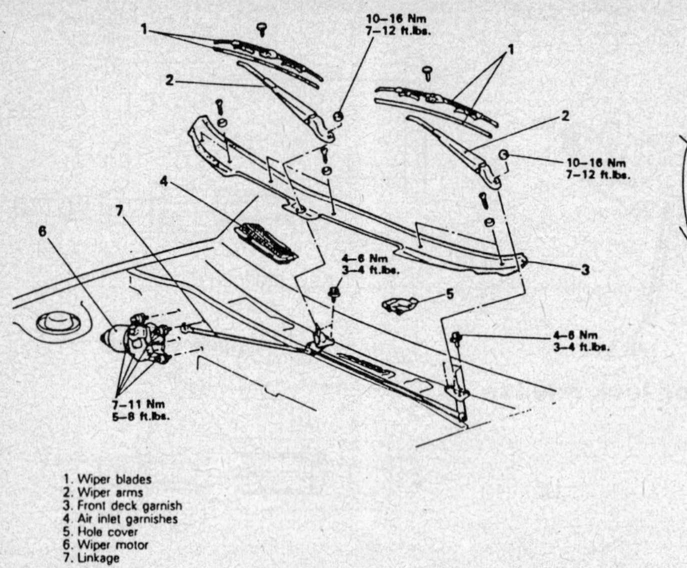


1. Wiper blades
2. Wiper arms
3. Front deck garnish
4. Air inlet garnishes
5. Hole cover
6. Wiper motor
7. Linkage

**Fig. 8 Replacing wiper transmission (Front)**

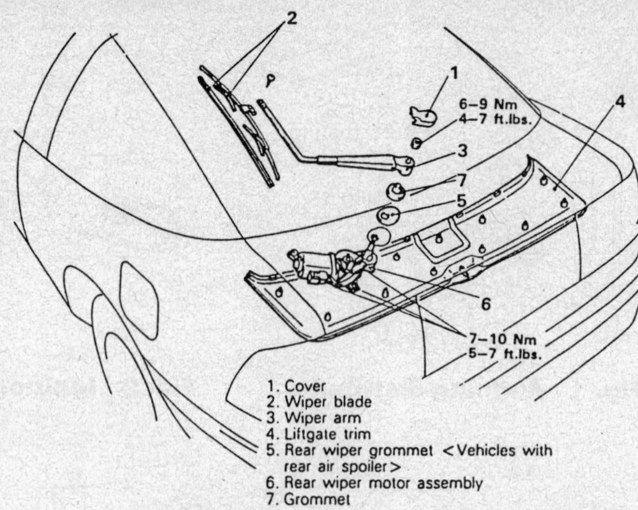


1. Cover
2. Wiper blade
3. Wiper arm
4. Liftgate trim
5. Rear wiper grommet <Vehicles with rear air spoiler>
6. Rear wiper motor assembly
7. Grommet

**Fig. 9 Replacing wiper transmission (Rear)**

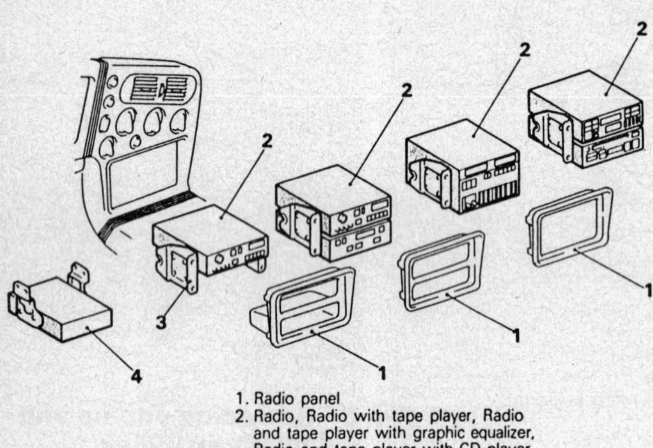

1. Radio panel
2. Radio, Radio with tape player, Radio and tape player with graphic equalizer, Radio and tape player with CD player.
3. Radio bracket
4. Amplifier

**Fig. 10 Replacing radio**

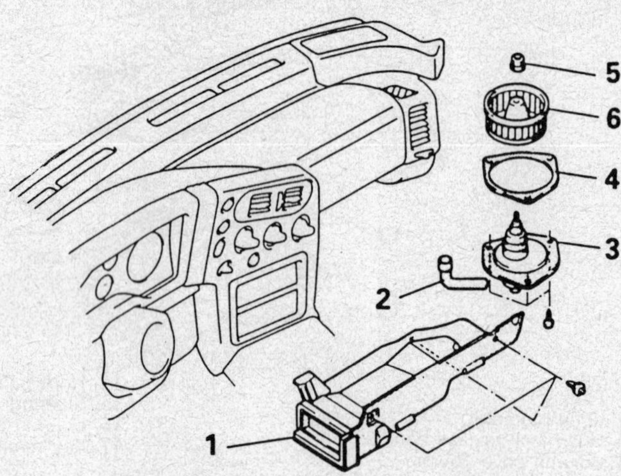

1. Shower duct R.H. <if so equipped>
2. Hose
3. Blower motor assembly
4. Packing
5. Fan installation nut
6. Fan

**Fig. 11 Replacing blower motor**

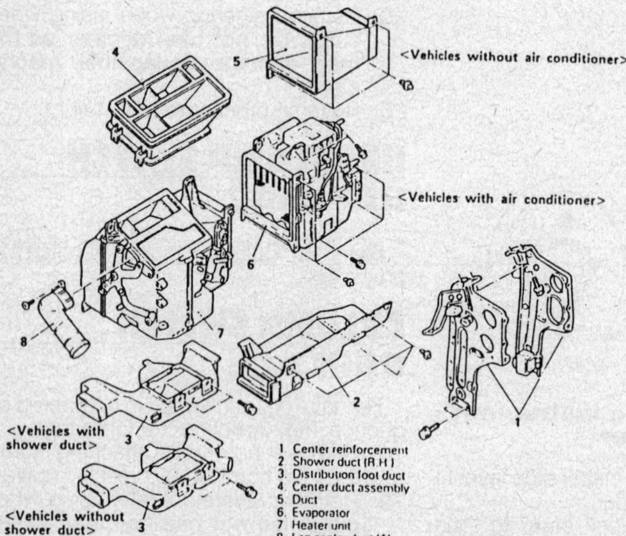


1. Center reinforcement
2. Shower duct (R.H.)
3. Distribution foot duct
4. Center duct assembly
5. Duct
6. Evaporator
7. Heater unit
8. Lap cooler duct (A)

**Fig. 12 Exploded view of heater unit**

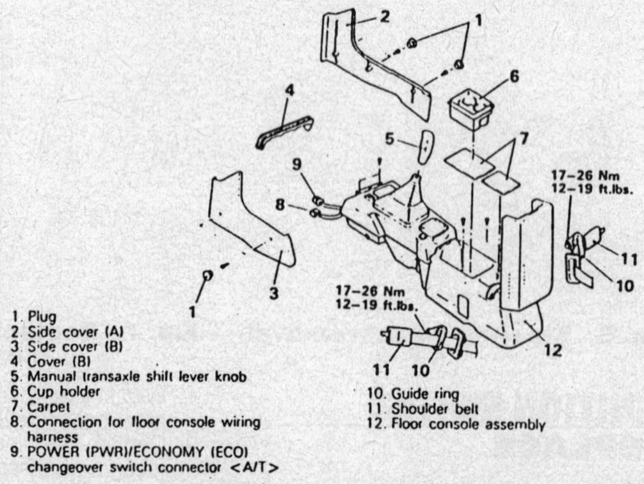


1. Plug
2. Side cover (A)
3. Side cover (B)
4. Cover (B)
5. Manual transaxle shift lever knob
6. Cup holder
7. Carpet
8. Connection for floor console wiring harness
9. POWER (PWR)/ECONOMY (ECO) changeover switch connector <A/T>
10. Guide ring
11. Shoulder belt
12. Floor console assembly

**Fig. 13 Floor console removal**

**Fig. 14 Removing heater core plate**

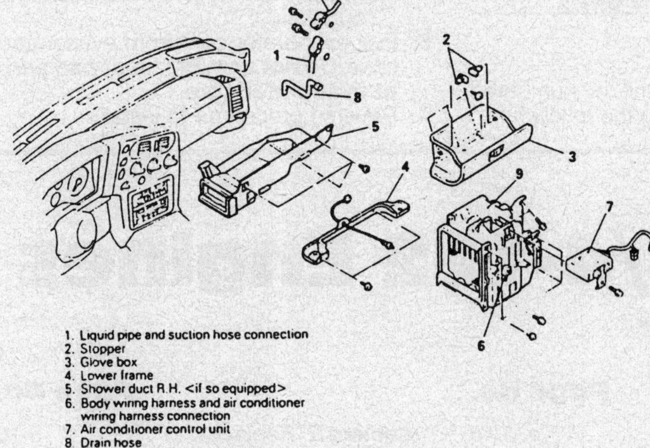


**Fig. 15 Replacing evaporator**

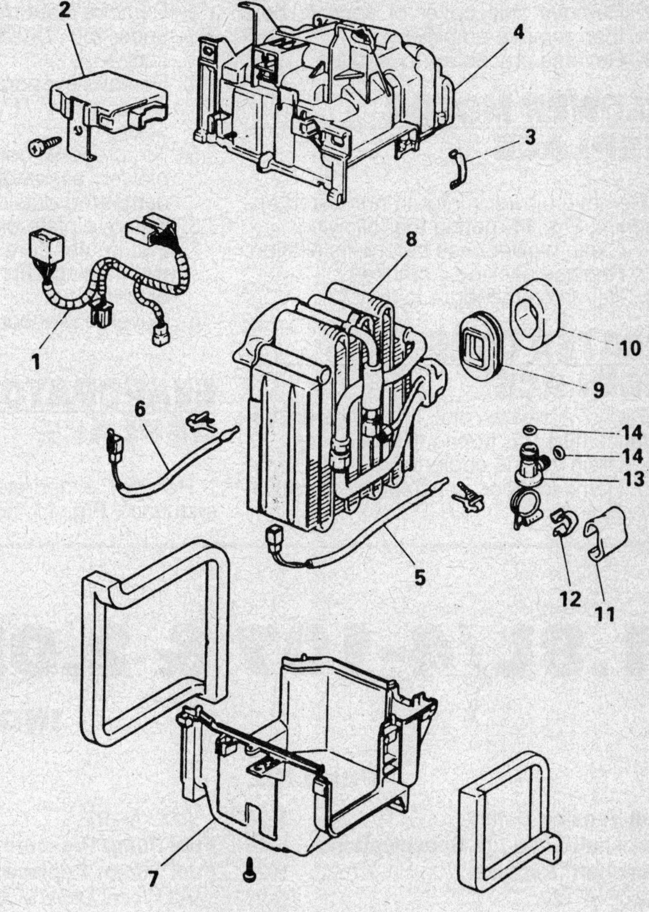

1. Wiring harness
2. Air conditioner control unit
3. Clips
4. Evaporater case (upper)
5. Air inlet sensor
6. Air thermo sensor
7. Evaporater case (lower)
8. Evaporater assembly
9. Grommet
10. Insulator
11. Rubber insulator
12. Clip
13. Expansion valve
14. O-ring

**Fig. 16 Exploded view of evaporator unit**

## POP-UP, FOG LAMP & DIMMER SWITCH

### REPLACE

Remove pop-up, fog lamp and dimmer switches in numbered sequence, **Fig. 5.**. Reverse procedure to install.

## STEERING WHEEL

### REPLACE

1. Remove horn pad attaching screw, then the horn pad by pressing upward, **Fig. 6.**
2. Remove steering wheel using wheel puller. **Do not use hammer as this may damage the collapsible mechanism.**
3. Reverse procedure to install.

## INSTRUMENT CLUSTER

### REPLACE

Remove instrument cluster in numbered sequence, **Fig. 7,** noting the following:

1. When removing adapter, disconnect speedometer cable at transaxle end of cable.
2. To remove adapter, pull speedometer cable slightly toward vehicle interior, then release lock by turning adapter.
3. Reverse procedure to install.

## WINDSHIELD WIPER MOTOR & TRANSMISSION

### REPLACE

#### FRONT

Remove front windshield wiper motor and transmission in numbered sequence, **Fig. 8,** noting the following:

1. Mark position of wiper arms before removal.
2. When mounting wiper arms check identification marks. Dr indicates driver side, As indicates passenger side.
3. Install wiper arm to pivot shaft so when in stop position wiper blades will be 1 inch from deck garnish.
4. Reverse procedure to install.

#### REAR

Remove rear windshield wiper motor and transmission in numbered sequence, **Fig. 9,** noting the following:

1. Using plastic trim tool, remove clip mounting areas on back of liftgate, then remove trim.
2. Install grommet with arrow positioned up.
3. Install wiper arm to pivot shaft so that blade will stop 1 inch from end liftgate glass.
4. Reverse procedure to install.

## RADIO

### REPLACE

Remove radio in numbered sequence, **Fig. 10,** noting the following:

1. Use plastic trim tool to pry lower part of radio panel out of console.

2. Remove side cover of console box, then remove amplifier.
3. Reverse procedure to install.

## BLOWER MOTOR REPLACE

Remove blower motor in numbered sequence, **Fig. 11,** noting the following:

1. Clean blower case before installation.
2. Replace packing if cracked.
3. Reverse procedure to install.

## HEATER CORE REPLACE

Remove heater unit in numbered sequence, **Fig. 12,** noting the following:

1. Drain engine coolant.
2. Remove floor console as shown in **Fig. 13.**
3. Remove instrument panel as outlined under the "Dash Panel Service" section.
4. Remove evaporator assembly as outlined under "Evaporator Core, Replace."
5. To prevent bolts from falling into blower assembly, set air selection damper to outside air introduction.
6. Remove plate on heater unit **Fig. 14.**
7. Pull heater core from heater unit. **Do not damage fin or pad part of heater core.**
8. Reverse procedure to install.

## EVAPORATOR CORE REPLACE

Remove evaporator unit in numbered sequence, **Fig. 15,** noting the following:

1. Drain engine coolant.
2. Remove floor console as shown in **Fig. 13.**
3. Remove instrument panel as outlined under the "Dash Panel Service" section.
4. To prevent bolts from falling into blower assembly, set air selection damper to outside air introduction.
5. Remove evaporator core from case, **Fig. 16,** noting the following:
   a. Remove case clips using a flat blade screw driver covered with shop towel to prevent damage to case.
   b. Remove expansion valve by using two wrenches, one inlet side, one outlet side.
6. Pull evaporator core from evaporator case. **Do not damage fin or pad part of evaporator core.**
7. Reverse procedure to install.

# 1.8L/4-107 & 2.0L/4-122 Engines

## INDEX



## ENGINE MOUNT REPLACE

Remove engine mount in numbered sequence, **Fig. 1,** noting the following:

1. Slightly raise and support engine, removing weight of engine from mount.
2. **On 1.8L/4-107 engines,** bracket (2) is not used.
3. **On all engines,** inspect insulators for damage or cracks and replace as necessary.
4. Check brackets and replace if deformed or damaged.
5. When installing mounting stoppers, ensure arrow on stopper faces center of engine.
6. Reverse procedure to install.

## ENGINE ROLL STOPPER, REPLACE

Remove engine roll stoppers in numbered sequence, **Fig. 2,** noting the following:

1. Slightly raise and support engine, removing weight of engine from mount.
2. Inspect insulators for damage or cracks and replace as necessary.
3. Check brackets and replace if deformed or damaged.
4. Discard and replace front roll stopper bracket installation nuts. When installing new nuts, first snug nuts to bolts, then lower engine and torque to specifications once weight of engine is applied to mount.
5. **On 1990 models,** when installing rear roll stopper bracket on models with automatic transmission, ensure clearance of insulator is as shown in **Fig. 3.** Specification given is with engine weight removed from mount.
6. **On 1991-92 models,** when installing rear roll stopper bracket on models with automatic transmission, ensure distance between center hole and lower edge of bracket is as shown in **Fig. 4.**
7. **On all models,** install front roll stopper bracket with hole positioned as shown in **Fig. 5.**
8. When installing front roll stopper bracket, ensure distance between center hole of insulator and lower edge of bracket is as shown, **Fig. 6.**
9. Reverse procedure to install.

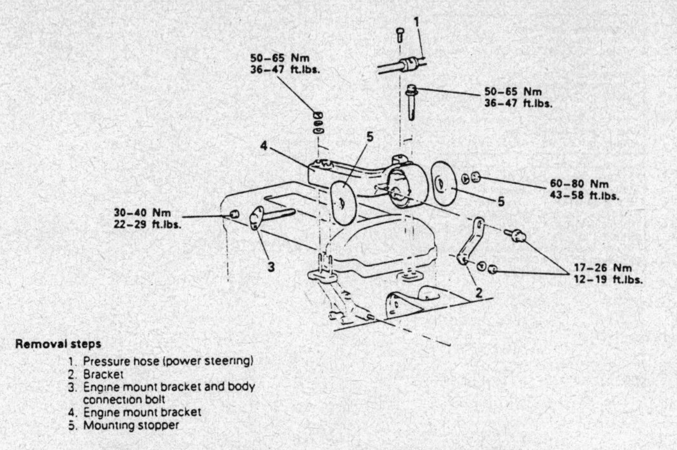


**Fig. 1 Engine mount assembly**

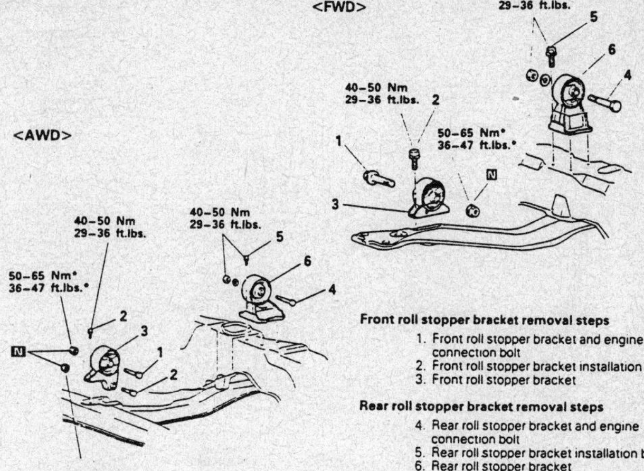


N : Non-reusable parts
For tightening locations indicated by the * symbol, first tighten temporarily, and then make the final tightening with the entire weight of the engine applied to the vehicle body.

**Fig. 2 Engine roll stopper assemblies**

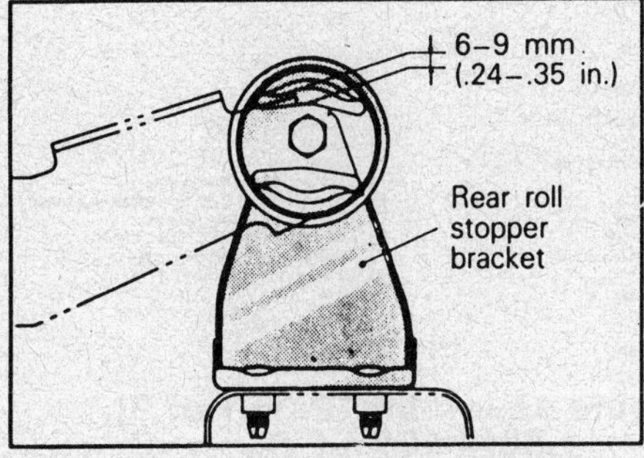


**Fig. 3 Rear roll stopper bracket insulator clearance. 1990**

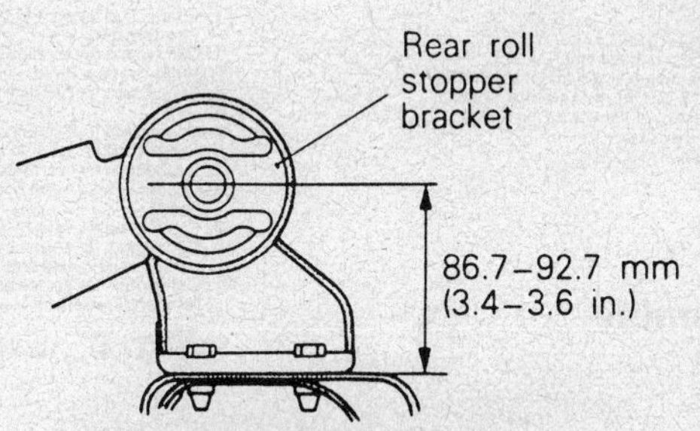


**Fig. 4 Rear roll stopper bracket clearance. 1991–92**

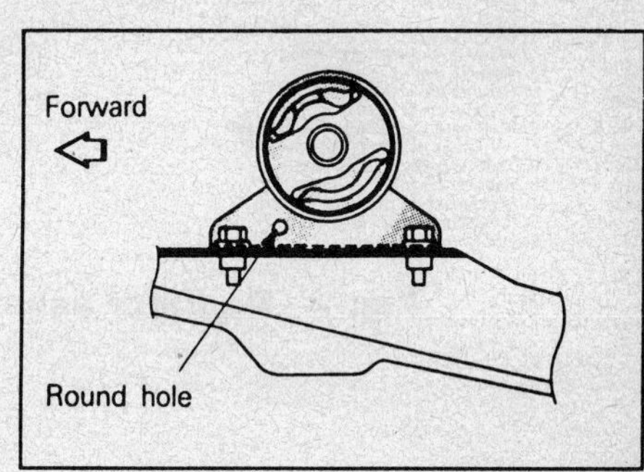


**Fig. 5 Installing front roll stopper bracket**

**Fig. 6 Checking front roll stopper bracket insulator clearance**

## ENGINE REPLACE

1. Relieve fuel system pressure as follows:
   a. Disconnect fuel pump harness connector at fuel tank.
   b. Start engine and let it run until it stalls, then turn ignition switch to off.
   c. Disconnect negative battery cable.
   d. Reconnect fuel pump harness connector.
2. Remove hood.
3. Drain coolant as follows:
   a. Place instrument panel temperature control lever in Hot position.
   b. Carefully remove radiator cap.
   c. Remove radiator drain plug.
4. Remove transaxle assembly. On models with automatic transaxle, refer to "Transaxle, Replace" in the "Automatic Transaxle" section. On models with manual transaxle, refer to "Manual Transaxle, Replace" in the "Clutch & Manual Transaxle" section.
5. Remove radiator in numbered sequence as shown in **Fig. 7,** noting the following:
   a. Prior to removing radiator hoses, mark hose clamps in relation to hose for installation reference.
   b. After disconnecting transaxle cooler lines on models with automatic transaxle, plug or cover end of line to prevent entry of dirt or foreign material.
6. Remove engine in numbered sequence, referring to **Fig. 8** on models with 1.8L/4-107 engine and **Fig. 9** on models with 2.0L/4-122 engine, noting the following:
   a. Remove power steering pump from bracket with hoses attached, then secure pump out of the way with a piece of wire.
   b. Remove air conditioner compressor from bracket with hoses attached, then secure compressor out of the way with a piece of wire.
   c. Using a suitable engine hoist, slightly raise engine, then remove engine mount bracket.
7. Reverse procedure to install.

## INTAKE MANIFOLD REPLACE

### REMOVAL

Remove intake manifold in numbered sequence, referring to **Fig. 10** on

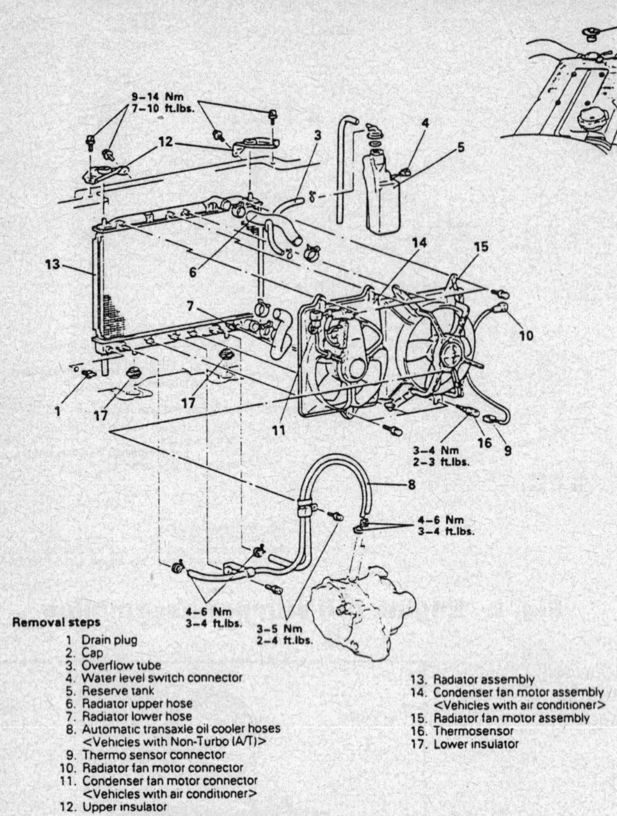


**Removal steps**

1. Drain plug
2. Cap
3. Overflow tube
4. Water level switch connector
5. Reserve tank
6. Radiator upper hose
7. Radiator lower hose
8. Automatic transaxle oil cooler hoses <Vehicles with Non-Turbo (A/T)>
9. Thermo sensor connector
10. Radiator fan motor connector
11. Condenser fan motor connector <Vehicles with air conditioner>
12. Upper insulator
13. Radiator assembly
14. Condenser fan motor assembly <Vehicles with air conditioner>
15. Radiator fan motor assembly
16. Thermosensor
17. Lower insulator

**Fig. 7 Radiator assembly**

**Pre-removal Operation**
- Eliminating Fuel Pressure in Fuel Line (Refer to GROUP 14–Service Adjustment Procedures.)
- Removal of Engine Hood
- Draining of Engine Coolant (Refer to GROUP 0–Maintenance Service.)
- Removal of the Transaxle Assembly (Refer to GROUP 21–Transaxle Assembly.)
- Removal of the Radiator (Refer to GROUP 7–Radiator.)

**Post-installation Operation**
- Installation of the Radiator (Refer to GROUP 7–Radiator.)
- Installation of the Transaxle Assembly (Refer to GROUP 21–Transaxle Assembly.)
- Refilling of Engine Coolant (Refer to GROUP 0–Maintenance Service.)
- Installation of Engine Hood

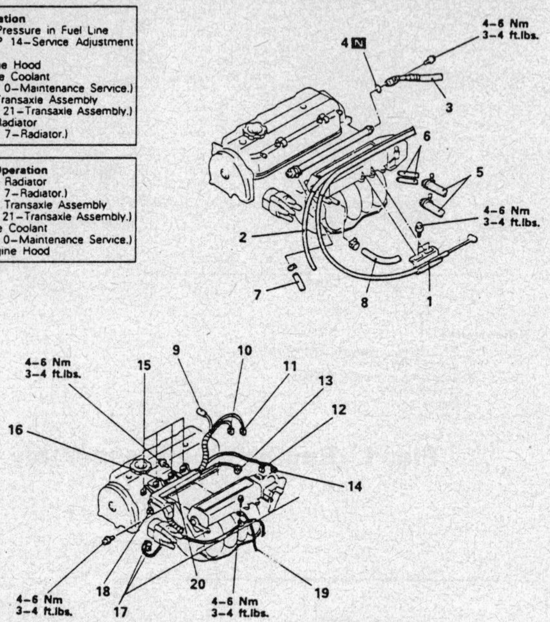

**Removal steps**

1. Connection for accelerator cable or throttle cable
2. Connection for accelerator cable (Auto-cruise control)
3. Connection for fuel high pressure hose
4. O-ring
5. Connection for heater hoses
6. Connection for vacuum hoses
7. Connection for fuel return hose
8. Connection for brake booster vacuum hose
9. Connection for oxygen sensor
10. Connection for engine coolant temperature gauge unit
11. Connection for engine coolant temperature sensor
12. Connection for ISC
13. Connection for TPS
14. Connection for MPS
15. Connection for fuel injectors
16. Connection for EGR temperature sensor
17. Connection for distributor
18. Connection for CRC filter
19. Connection for ground cable
20. Control wiring harness

N : Non-reusable parts

**Fig. 8 Engine assembly (Part 1 of 2). 1.8L/4-107**

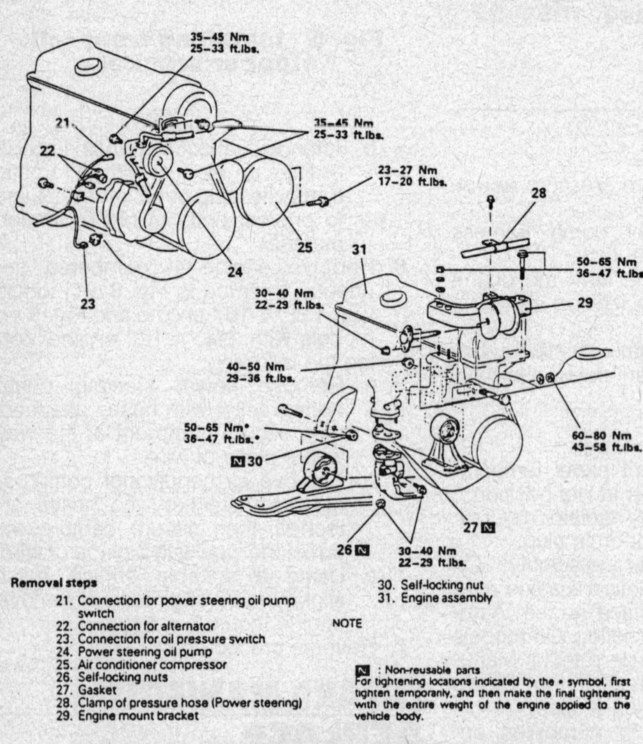


**Removal steps**

21. Connection for power steering oil pump switch
22. Connection for alternator
23. Connection for oil pressure switch
24. Power steering oil pump
25. Air conditioner compressor
26. Self-locking nuts
27. Gasket
28. Clamp of pressure hose (Power steering)
29. Engine mount bracket
30. Self-locking nut
31. Engine assembly

NOTE

N : Non-reusable parts
For tightening locations indicated by the * symbol, first tighten temporarily, and then make the final tightening with the entire weight of the engine applied to the vehicle body.

**Fig. 8 Engine assembly (Part 2 of 2). 1.8L/4-107**

**Pre-removal Operation**
- Eliminating Fuel Pressure in Fuel Line (Refer to GROUP 14–Service Adjustment Procedures.)
- Removal of Engine Hood
- Draining of Engine Coolant (Refer to GROUP 7–Service Adjustment Procedures.)
- Removal of the Transaxle Assembly (Refer to GROUP 21–Transaxle Assembly.)
- Removal of the Radiator (Refer to GROUP 7–Radiator.)
- Removal of Under Cover Left

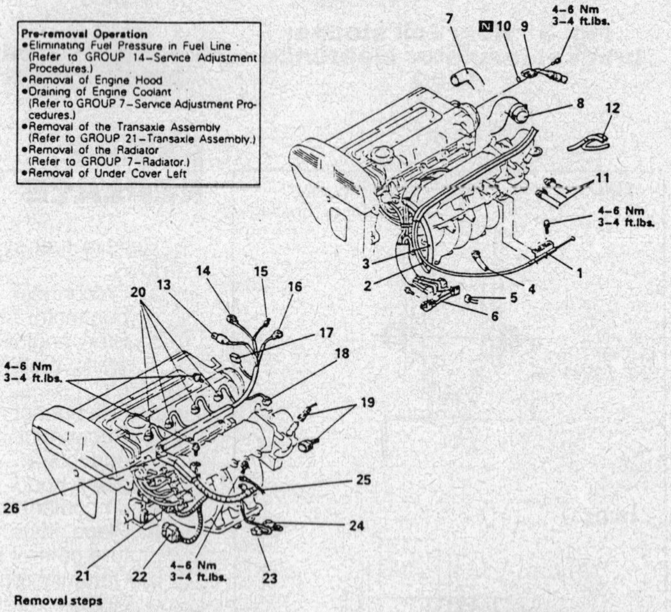

**Removal steps**

1. Connection for accelerator cable or throttle cable
2. Connection for accelerator cable (Auto-cruise control)
3. Connection for fuel return hose
4. Connection for brake booster vacuum hose
5. Connection for solenoid valve (Turbo)
6. Solenoid valve bracket (Turbo)
7. Connection for air hose A (Turbo)
8. Connection for air hose C (Turbo)
9. Connection for fuel high pressure hose
10. O-ring
11. Connection for heater hoses
12. Connection for vacuum hoses
13. Connection for oxygen sensor
14. Connection for engine coolant temperature sensor
15. Connection for engine coolant temperature gauge unit
16. Connection for engine coolant temperature switch (Air conditioner)
17. Connection for crank angle sensor
18. Connection for TPS
19. Connection for ISC and idle switch
20. Connection for fuel injectors
21. Connection for ignition coil
22. Connection for power transistor
23. Connection for knock sensor (Turbo)
24. Connection for EGR temperature sensor (California vehicles only)
25. Connection for ground cable
26. Control wiring harness

N : Non-reusable parts

**Fig. 9 Engine assembly (Part 1 of 2). 2.0L/4-122**

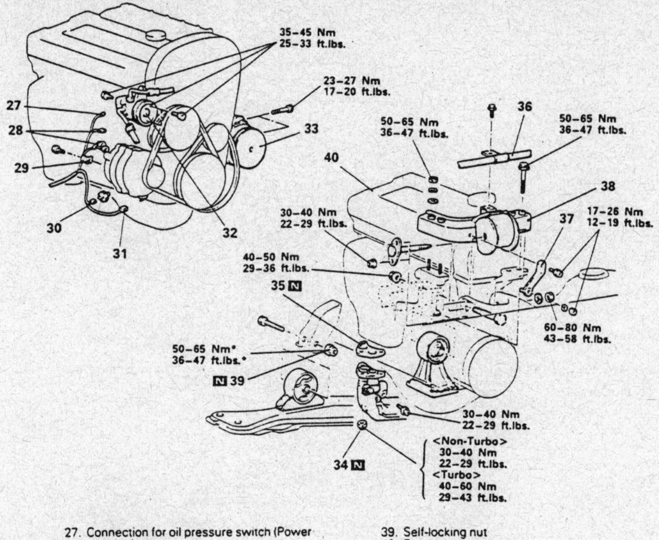


27. Connection for oil pressure switch (Power steering)
28. Connection for alternator
29. Alternator wiring harness clamp
30. Connection for oil pressure switch
31. Connection for oil pressure gauge unit
32. Power steering oil pump
33. Air conditioner compressor
34. Self-locking nuts
35. Gasket
36. Pressure hose (Power steering)
37. Bracket
38. Engine mount bracket
39. Self-locking nut
40. Engine assembly

N : Non-reusable parts
For tightening locations indicated by the * symbol, first tighten temporarily, and then make the final tightening with the entire weight of the engine applied to the vehicle body.

**Fig. 9 Engine assembly (Part 2 of 2). 2.0L/4-122**

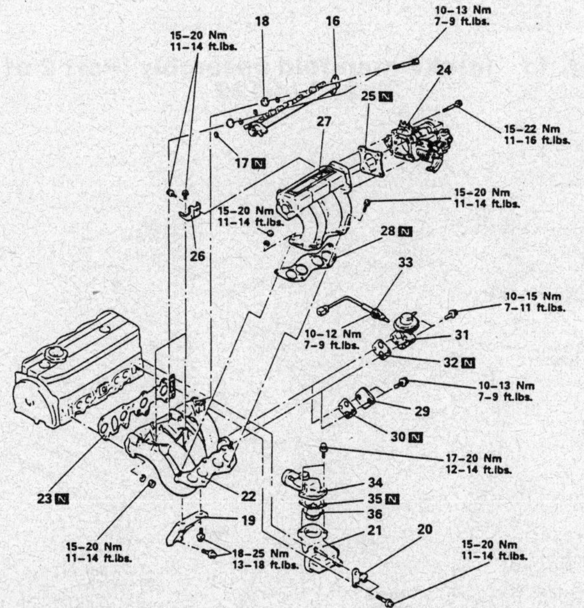


**Removal steps**

16. Delivery pipe, fuel injector and pressure regulator
17. Insulator
18. Insulator
19. Intake manifold stay
20. Engine hanger
21. Thermostat housing
22. Intake manifold
23. Intake manifold gasket
24. Throttle body assembly
25. Gasket
26. Air intake plenum stay
27. Air intake plenum
28. Air intake plenum gasket
29. Cover <Vehicles for Federal and Canada>
30. Gasket <Vehicles for Federal>
31. EGR valve <Vehicles for California>
32. EGR gasket <Vehicles for California>
33. EGR temperature sensor <Vehicles for California>
34. Water outlet fitting
35. Gasket
36. Thermostat

N : Non-reusable parts

**Fig. 10 Intake manifold assembly (Part 2 of 2). 1.8L/4-107**

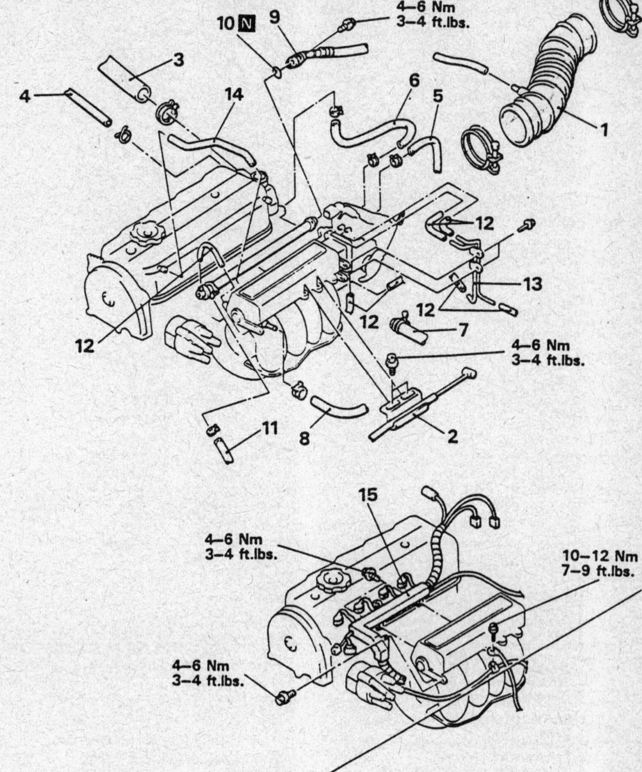


**Removal steps**

1. Air intake hose
2. Connection for accelerator cable
3. Connection for radiator upper hose
4. Connection for overflow tube
5. Connection for water by-pass hose
6. Water hose
7. Connection for heater hose
8. Connection for brake booster vacuum hose
9. Connection for fuel high pressure hose
10. O-ring
11. Connection for fuel return hose
12. Connection for vacuum hoses
13. Vacuum pipe
14. PCV hose
15. Connection for control harness

N : Non-reusable parts

**Fig. 10 Intake manifold assembly (Part 1 of 2). 1.8L/4-107**

1.8L/4-107 engines and **Fig. 11** on 2.0L/4-122 engines, noting the following:

1. Drain coolant as follows:
   a. Place instrument panel temperature control lever in Hot position.
   b. Carefully remove radiator cap.
   c. Remove radiator drain plug.
2. **On 1.8L/4-107 engines,** when removing upper radiator hose, mark hose clamp in relation to hose for assembly reference.
3. **On all models,** before disconnecting high pressure fuel line, relieve fuel system pressure as follows:
   a. Disconnect fuel pump harness connector at fuel tank.
   b. Start engine and let it run until it stalls, then turn ignition switch to off.
   c. Disconnect negative battery cable.
   d. Reconnect fuel pump harness connector.
4. Remove delivery pipe, fuel injector and regulator as an assembly.

## INSPECTION

Inspect intake manifold and air intake plenum (if equipped) as follows:

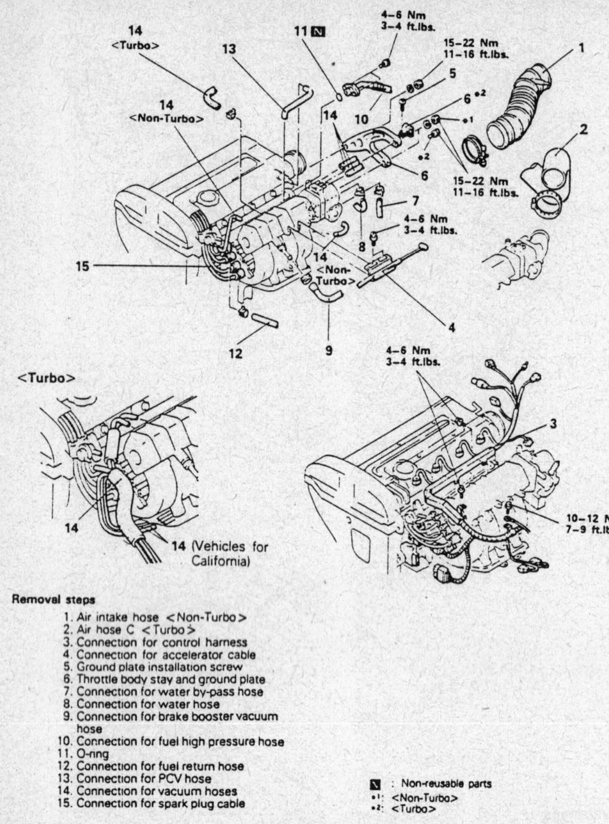


**Removal steps**

1. Air intake hose <Non-Turbo>
2. Air hose C <Turbo>
3. Connection for control harness
4. Connection for accelerator cable
5. Ground plate installation screw
6. Throttle body stay and ground plate
7. Connection for water by-pass hose
8. Connection for water hose
9. Connection for brake booster vacuum hose
10. Connection for fuel high pressure hose
11. O-ring
12. Connection for fuel return hose
13. Connection for PCV hose
14. Connection for vacuum hoses
15. Connection for spark plug cable

N : Non-reusable parts
*1: <Non-Turbo>
*2: <Turbo>

**Fig. 11 Intake manifold assembly (Part 1 of 2). 2.0L/4-122**

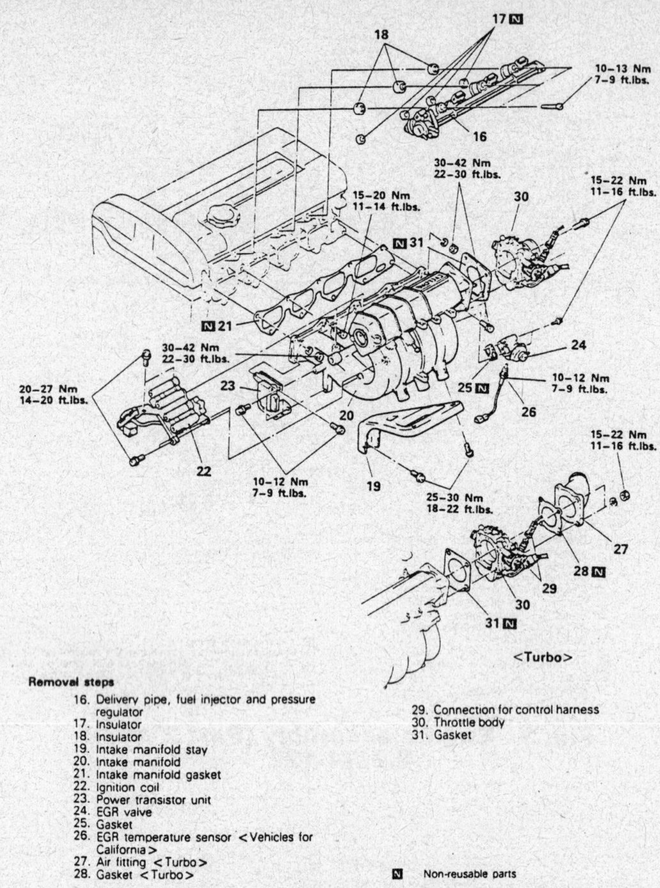


**Removal steps**

16. Delivery pipe, fuel injector and pressure regulator
17. Insulator
18. Insulator
19. Intake manifold stay
20. Intake manifold
21. Intake manifold gasket
22. Ignition coil
23. Power transistor unit
24. EGR valve
25. Gasket
26. EGR temperature sensor <Vehicles for California>
27. Air fitting <Turbo>
28. Gasket <Turbo>
29. Connection for control harness
30. Throttle body
31. Gasket

N Non-reusable parts

**Fig. 11 Intake manifold assembly (Part 2 of 2). 2.0L/4-122**

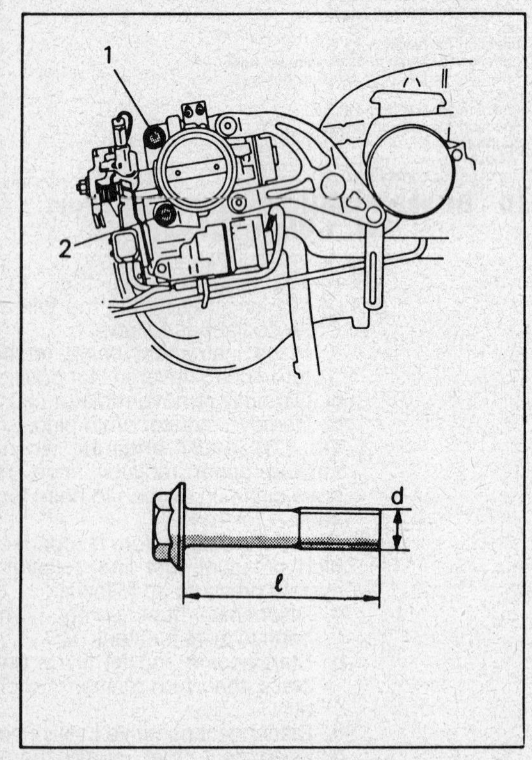

| No. | d × ℓ mm (in.) |
|---|---|
| 1 | 8 × 30 (.31 × 1.18) |
| 2 | 8 × 55 (.31 × 2.16) |

**Fig. 12 Throttle body attaching bolts. 2.0L/4-122**

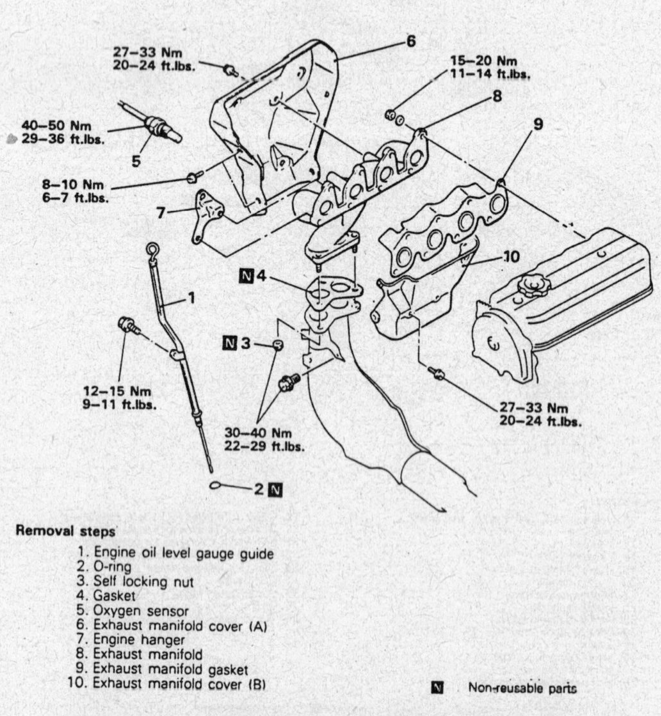


**Removal steps**

1. Engine oil level gauge guide
2. O-ring
3. Self locking nut
4. Gasket
5. Oxygen sensor
6. Exhaust manifold cover (A)
7. Engine hanger
8. Exhaust manifold
9. Exhaust manifold gasket
10. Exhaust manifold cover (B)

N Non-reusable parts

**Fig. 13 Exhaust manifold assembly. 1.8L/4-107**

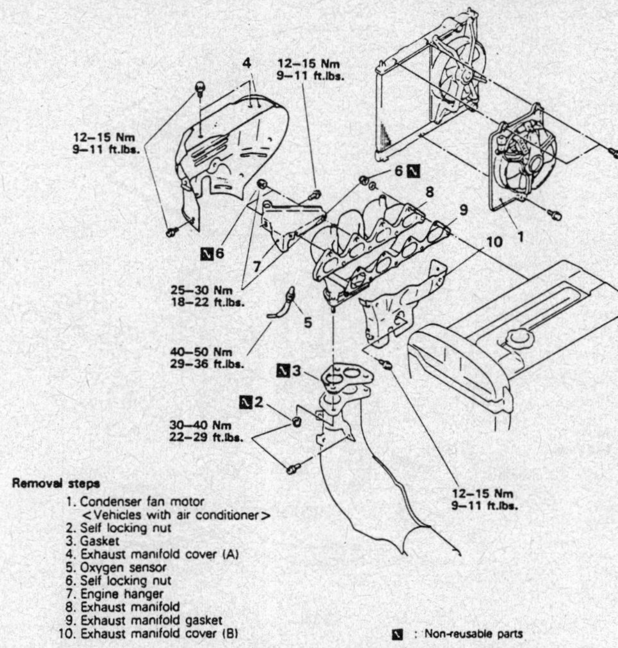


**Fig. 14 Exhaust manifold assembly. 2.0L/4-122 except turbo**

Removal steps
1. Condenser fan motor assembly <Vehicles with air conditioner>
2. Oxygen sensor connector
3. Engine oil level gauge guide
4. O-ring
5. Connection for air intake hose
6. Connection for vacuum hose
7. Connection for vacuum hose
8. Connection for air hose A
9. Heat protector A
10. Heat protector B
11. Power steering oil pump
12. Oil pump bracket
13. Self-locking nut
14. Engine hanger
15. Eye bolt
16. Gasket
17. Connection for water hose
18. Connection for water pipe B
19. Self-locking nut
20. Gasket
21. Exhaust manifold
22. Exhaust manifold gasket
23. Ring
24. Gasket

: Non-reusable parts

**Fig. 15 Exhaust manifold assembly. 2.0L/4-122 turbo**

1. Check for damage, cracks or defects.
2. Ensure coolant and jet air passages are clear.
3. Check installation surfaces with a straightedge. Replace if deflection exceeds .012 inch.

## INSTALLATION

Reverse removal procedure to install. On 2.0L/4-122 engines, when installing throttle body, refer to bolt length chart, **Fig. 12.**

# EXHAUST MANIFOLD REPLACE

Remove exhaust manifold in numbered sequence, referring to **Fig. 13** on 1.8L/4-107 engines, **Fig. 14** on non-turbocharged 2.0L/4-122 engines and **Fig. 15** on turbocharged 2.0L/4-122 engines, noting the following:

1. **On 2.0L/4-122 turbocharged engine,** drain engine oil and coolant prior to removing exhaust manifold. To drain coolant, proceed as follows:
   a. Place instrument panel temperature control lever in Hot position.
   b. Carefully remove radiator cap.
   c. Remove radiator drain plug.
2. **On all models,** use oxygen sensor socket No. MD998703 or equivalent to remove oxygen sensor.
3. **On 2.0L/4-122 turbocharged engine,** leave power steering hoses attached when disconnecting power steering pump. Position pump out of the way and secure with a piece of wire.
4. **On all models,** reverse procedure to install. On 2.0L/4-122 turbocharged engine, apply machine oil to inner surface pipe flare prior to installing water pipe (18), **Fig. 15.**

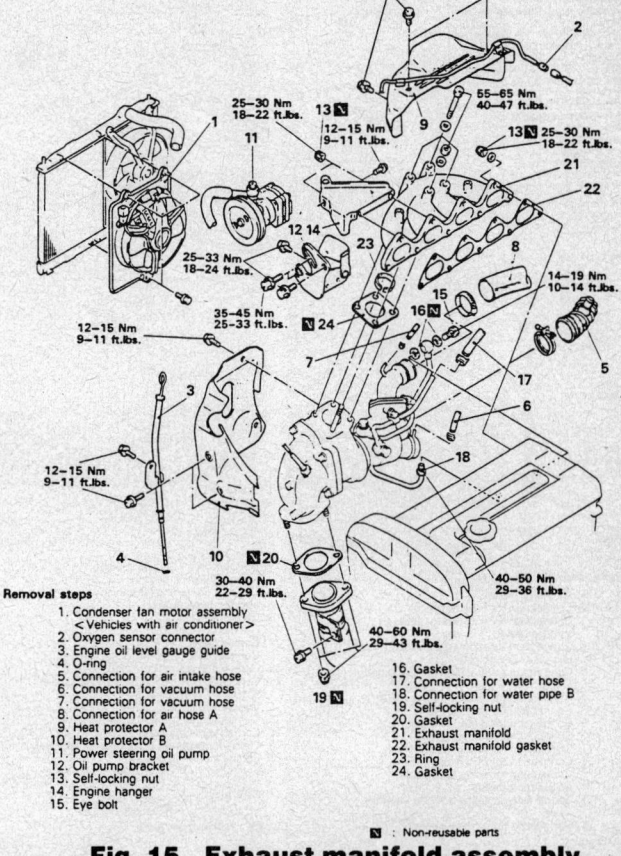

# CYLINDER HEAD REPLACE

## 1.8L/4-107

### Removal

Remove cylinder head in numbered sequence, **Fig. 16,** noting the following:

1. Before disconnecting high pressure fuel line, relieve fuel system pressure as follows:
   a. Disconnect fuel pump harness connector at fuel tank.
   b. Start engine and let it run until it stalls, then turn ignition switch to off.
   c. Disconnect negative battery cable.
   d. Reconnect fuel pump harness connector.
2. Before removing upper radiator hose, mark hose clamp in relation to hose for assembly reference, then drain coolant as follows:
   a. Place instrument panel temperature control lever in Hot position.
   b. Carefully remove radiator cap.
   c. Remove radiator drain plug.
3. To remove engine mount bracket, slightly raise and support engine, removing weight of engine from mount.
4. Remove camshaft sprocket as follows:
   a. Turn crankshaft clockwise and align timing marks, **Fig. 17. Do not turn crankshaft counterclockwise.**
   b. Remove camshaft sprocket with timing belt attached, then lay sprocket and belt on timing belt front lower cover. **Do not rotate crankshaft once camshaft sprocket is removed.**
5. Using cylinder head bolt wrench No. TW-10B or equivalent, remove cylinder head bolts in sequence as shown in **Fig. 18.**

### Installation

Reverse removal procedure to install, noting the following:

1. Install cylinder head gasket as follows:
   a. Using a suitable scraper, remove old gasket material from cylinder block, using care not to allow old gasket material to fall into cylinder or passages.
   b. Clean head and block surfaces which come in contact with head gasket.
   c. Place head gasket on block with identification mark at top front. **Do not apply sealant to head gasket.**
2. When installing cylinder head, torque head bolts to specifications in two or three steps and in order as shown in **Fig. 19.**
3. When installing semi-circular packing, apply liberal amount of gasket sealant onto circumference of packing.
4. When installing high pressure fuel line (5), apply small amount of gasoline to

**Pre-removal Operation**
- Eliminating Fuel Pressure in Fuel Line (Refer to GROUP 14—Service Adjustment Procedures.)
- Draining of Engine Coolant (Refer to GROUP 7—Service Adjustment Procedures.)

**Post-installation Operation**
- Filling of Engine Coolant (Refer to GROUP 7—Service Adjustment Procedures.)
- Engine Adjustment (Refer to P.9-24.)

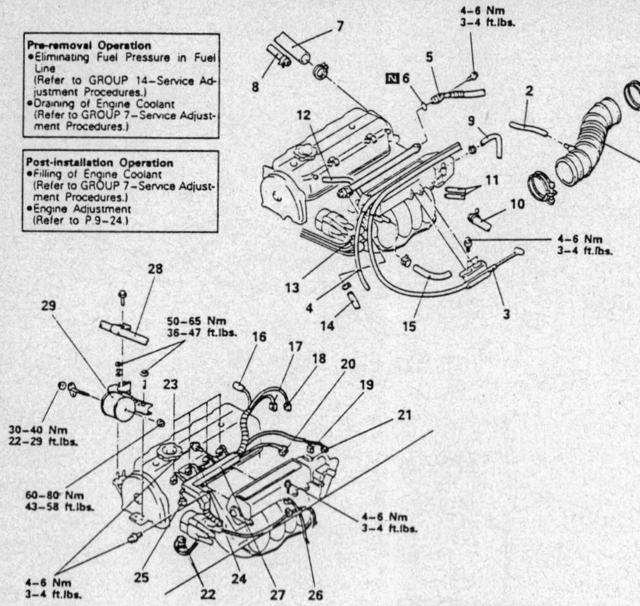

**Removal steps**
1. Air intake hose
2. Connection for breather hose
3. Connection for accelerator cable or throttle cable
4. Connection for accelerator cable (Auto-cruise control)
5. Connection for fuel high pressure hose
6. O-ring
7. Connection for radiator upper hose
8. Connection for water hose
9. Connection for water by-pass hose
10. Connection for heater hose
11. Connection for vacuum hose
12. Connection for PCV hose
13. Connection for spark plug cable
14. Connection for fuel return hose
15. Connection for brake booster vacuum hose
16. Connection for oxygen sensor
17. Connection for engine coolant temperature gauge unit
18. Connection for engine coolant temperature sensor
19. Connection for ISC
20. Connection for TPS
21. Connection for MPS
22. Connection for distributor
23. Connection for injector
24. Connection for EGR temperature sensor (California vehicles only)
25. Connection for CRC filter
26. Connection for ground cable
27. Control wiring harness
28. Clamp for pressure hose (Power steering)
29. Engine mounting bracket

(4) N : Non-reusable parts

**Fig. 16 Cylinder head removal (Part 1 of 2). 1.8L/4-107**

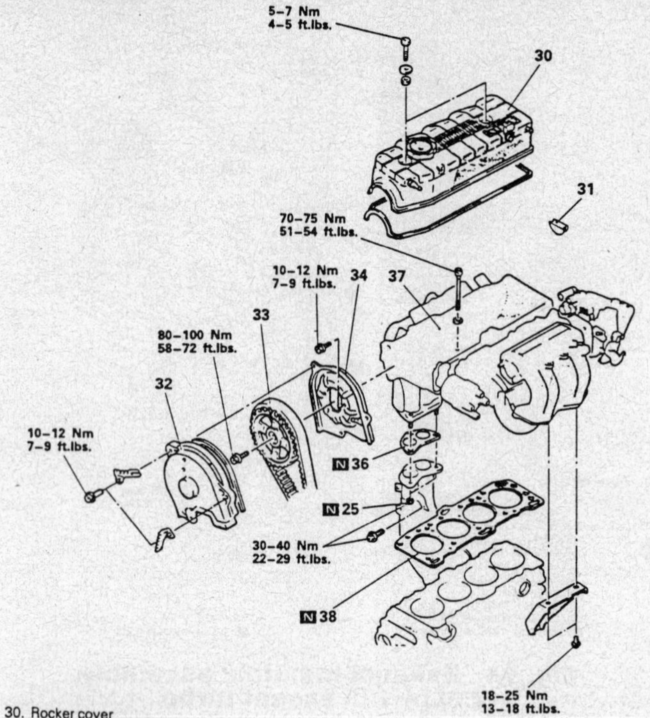

30. Rocker cover
31. Semi-circular packing
32. Timing belt front upper cover
33. Camshaft sprocket
34. Timing belt rear upper cover
35. Self-locking nuts
36. Gasket
37. Cylinder head assembly
38. Cylinder head gasket

N : Non-reusable parts

**Fig. 16 Cylinder head removal (Part 2 of 2). 1.8L/4-107**

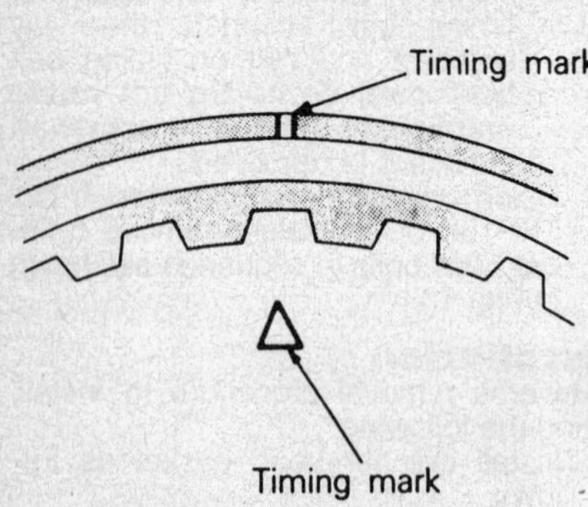


**Fig. 17 Timing mark alignment. 1.8L/4-107**

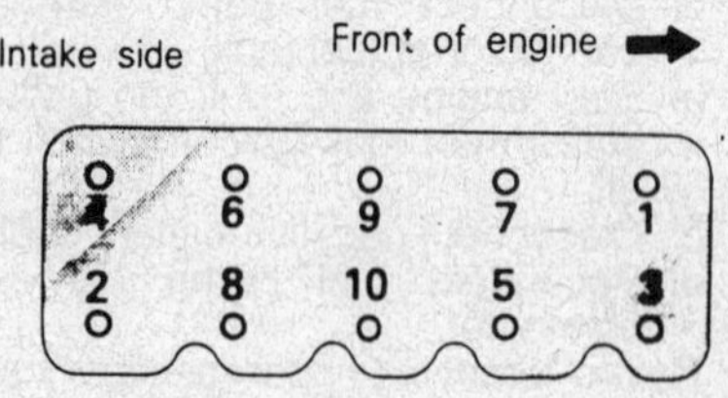


**Fig. 18 Head bolt removal sequence. 1.8L/4-107**

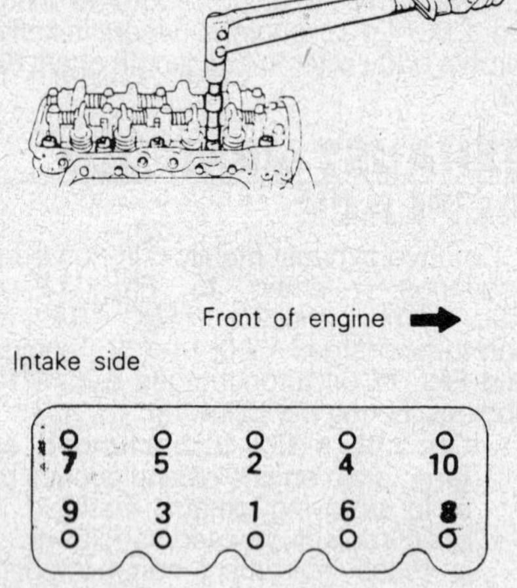


**Fig. 19 Head bolt tightening sequence. 1.8L/4-107**

hose union. Use care to avoid damaging O-ring.

## 2.0L/4-122

### Removal

Remove cylinder head in numbered sequence, **Fig. 20**, noting the following:

1. Before disconnecting high pressure fuel line, relieve fuel system pressure as follows:
   a. Disconnect fuel pump harness connector at fuel tank.
   b. Start engine and let it run until it stalls, then turn ignition switch to off.
   c. Disconnect negative battery cable.
   d. Reconnect fuel pump harness connector.
   e. Cover fuel line connection with rags to prevent spraying of fuel during disconnection.
2. Before removing upper radiator hose, mark hose clamp in relation to hose for assembly reference, then drain coolant as follows:
   a. Place instrument panel temperature control lever in Hot position.
   b. Carefully remove radiator cap.
   c. Remove radiator drain plug.
3. Refer to "Timing Belt, Replace" when removing timing belt.
4. Using cylinder head bolt wrench No. MD998051 or equivalent, remove cylinder head bolts in sequence as shown in **Fig. 21**.

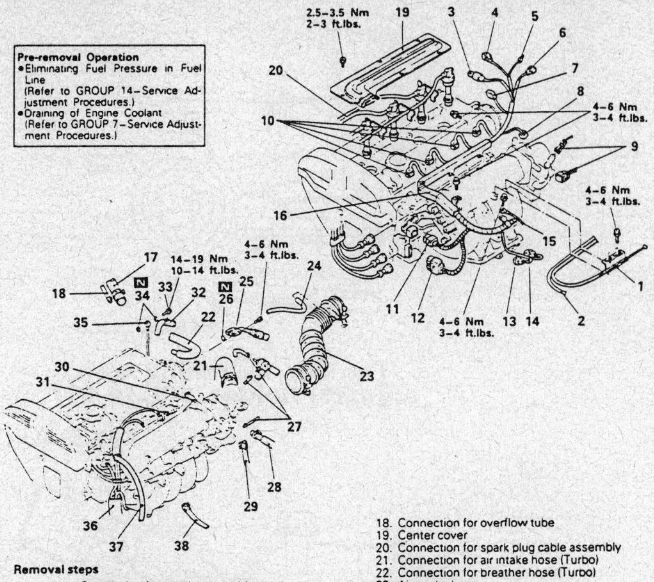

**Pre-removal Operation**
- Eliminating Fuel Pressure in Fuel Line (Refer to GROUP 14–Service Adjustment Procedures.)
- Draining of Engine Coolant (Refer to GROUP 7–Service Adjustment Procedures.)

**Removal steps**
1. Connection for accelerator cable or throttle cable
2. Connection for accelerator cable (Auto-cruise control)
3. Connection for oxygen sensor
4. Connection for engine coolant temperature sensor
5. Connection for engine coolant temperature gauge unit
6. Connection for engine coolant temperature switch (air conditioner)
7. Connection for crank angle sensor
8. Connection for TPS
9. Connection for ISC and idle switch
10. Connection for fuel injector
11. Connection for ignition coil
12. Connection for power transistor
13. Connection for knock sensor (Turbo)
14. Connection for EGR temperature sensor (California vehicles only)
15. Connection for ground cable
16. Control wiring harness
17. Connection for radiator upper hose
18. Connection for overflow tube
19. Center cover
20. Connection for spark plug cable assembly
21. Connection for air intake hose (Turbo)
22. Connection for breather hose (Turbo)
23. Air intake hose
24. Connection for breather hose
25. Connection for fuel high pressure hose
26. O-ring
27. Connection for vacuum hoses
28. Connection for heater hose
29. Connection for water by-pass hose
30. Connection for PCV hose
31. Connection for vacuum hose (Turbo)
32. Connection for water hose (Turbo)
33. Eye-bolt (Turbo)
34. Gasket (Turbo)
35. Connection for oil pipe (Turbo)
36. Connection for vacuum hoses (Turbo)
37. Connection for fuel return hose
38. Connection for brake booster vacuum hose

N : Non-reusable parts

Fig. 20 Cylinder head removal (Part 1 of 2). 2.0L/4-122

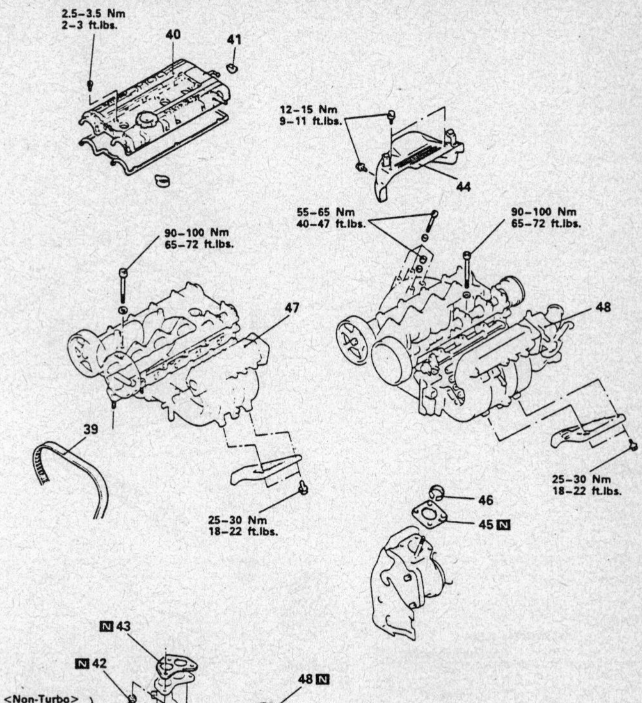

39. Timing belt
40. Rocker cover
41. Semi-circular packing
42. Self locking nuts
43. Gasket (Non-Turbo)
44. Heat protector (Turbo)
45. Gasket (Turbo)
46. Ring (Turbo)
47. Cylinder head assembly
48. Cylinder head gasket

N : Non-reusable parts

Fig. 20 Cylinder head removal (Part 2 of 2). 2.0L/4-122

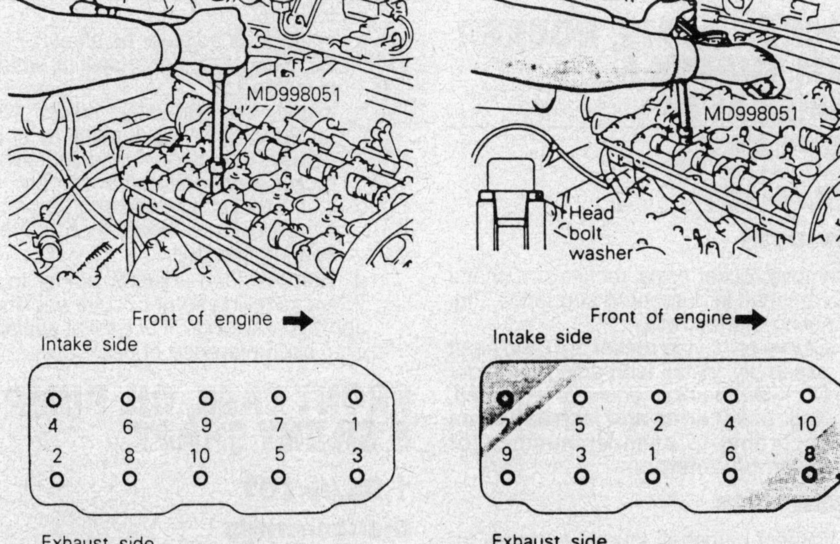


Fig. 21 Head bolt removal sequence. 2.0L/4-122

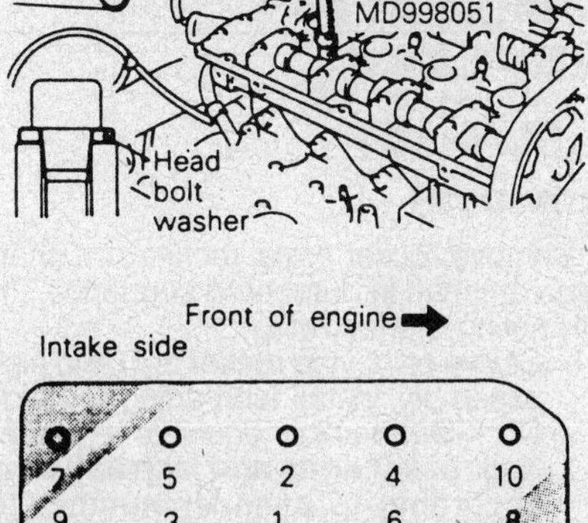


Fig. 22 Head bolt tightening sequence. 2.0L/4-122

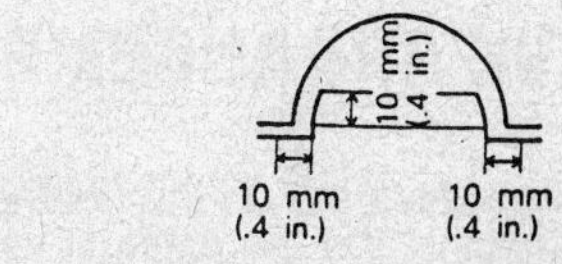


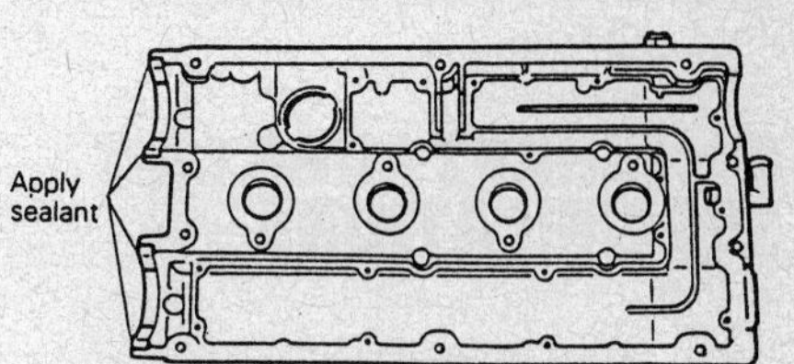


Fig. 23 Installing rocker cover. 2.0L/4-122

## Installation

Reverse removal procedure to install, noting the following:

1. Install cylinder head gasket as follows:
   a. Using a suitable scraper, remove old gasket material from cylinder block, using care not to allow old gasket material to fall into cylinder or passages.
   b. Clean head and block surfaces that come in contact with head gasket.
   c. Place head gasket on block with identification mark at top front. **Do not apply sealant to head gasket.**
2. When installing cylinder head, install head bolt washers, then torque head bolts to specifications in two or three steps and in order as shown in **Fig. 22.**
3. When installing semi-circular packing, apply liberal amount of gasket sealant onto circumference of packing.
4. When installing rocker cover, apply gasket sealant to area as shown in **Fig. 23.**
5. Refer to "Timing Belt, Replace" when installing timing belt.
6. When installing high pressure fuel line (5), apply small amount of gasoline to hose union. Use care to avoid damaging O-ring.

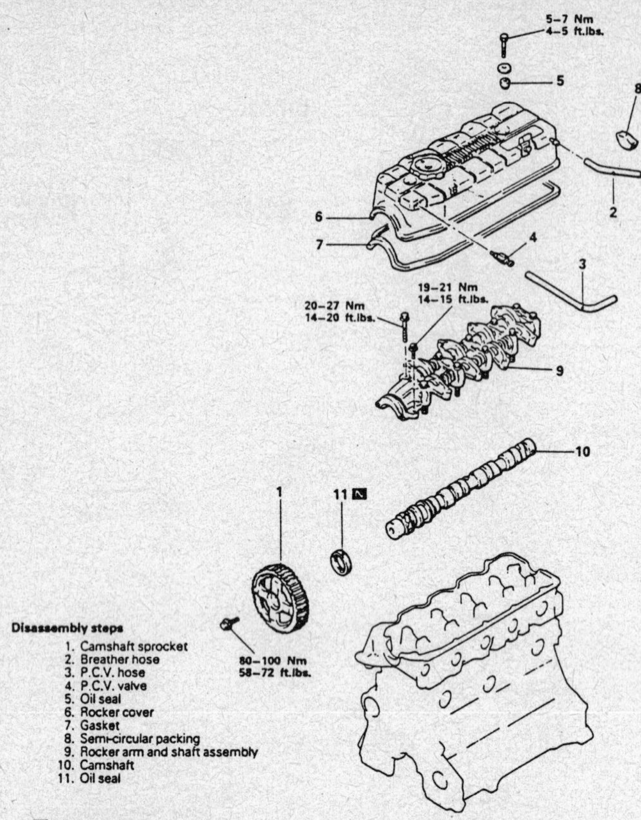


**Fig. 24 Rocker arms, rocker arm shafts & camshaft assembly. 1.8L/4-107**

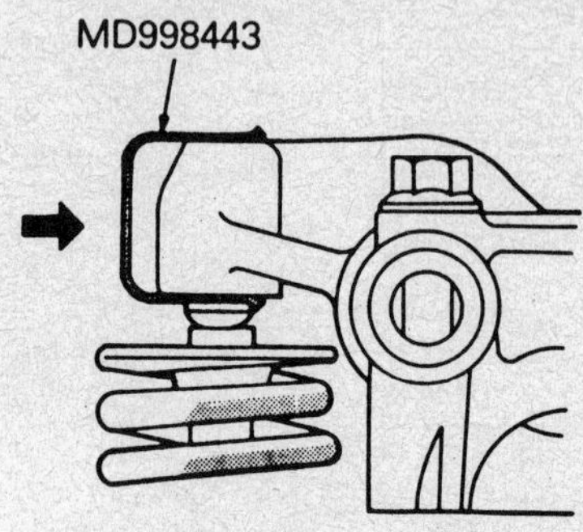


**Fig. 25 Installing lash adjuster holder. 1.8L/4-107**

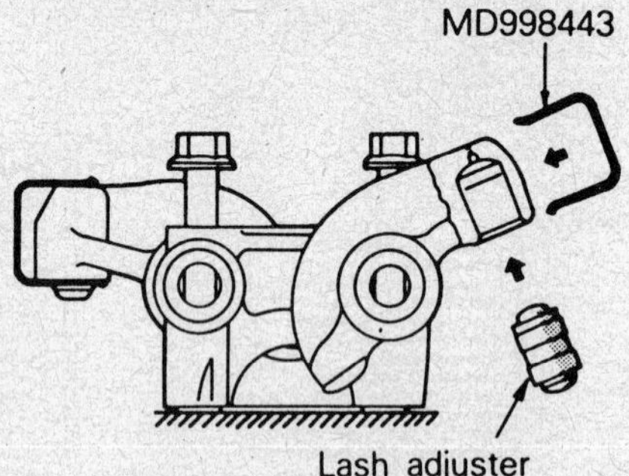


**Fig. 26 Installing lash adjuster. 1.8L/4-107**

# VALVE ARRANGEMENT

Intake valves are on the righthand side of the engine and the exhaust valves are on the left hand side of the engine.

# CAMSHAFT LOBE LIFT SPECIFICATIONS

| Year | Intake Lobe | Exhaust Lobe |
|---|---|---|
| 1.8L/4-107 | | |
| 1990–92 | 1.4138 | 1.4138 |
| 2.0L/4-122 | | |
| 1990 | 1.3974 | 1.3858 |
| 1991–92 | ① | ① |

**①—Models w/manual transmissions, 1.3974 inches; models w/automatic transmissions, 1.3858 inches.**

# VALVES

## ADJUST

Hydraulic lash adjusters are used; no adjustment is necessary.

# ROCKER ARMS, ROCKER ARM SHAFTS & CAMSHAFT

## REPLACE

### 1.8L/4-107

#### Removal

Remove rocker arms, rocker arm shafts and camshaft in numbered sequence, **Fig. 24**, noting the following:

1. Before removing rocker arm and shaft assembly, install lash adjuster holder No. MD998443 or equivalent, **Fig. 25. Tag rocker arms and lash adjusters according to cylinder number for assembly reference.**

#### Inspection

1. Inspect camshaft journal surfaces for damage or seizure, replacing as necessary. If journal is seized, check cylinder head for possible damage.
2. Check camshaft cams for wear or damage, replacing as necessary. Ensure lobe height is within specifications.

#### Installation

Reverse removal procedure to install, noting the following:

1. Install oil seal (11) as follows:
   a. Apply engine oil to oil seal lip.
   b. Using seal installation tool No. MD998364 or equivalent, drive oil seal into cylinder head.
2. Install rocker arm and shaft assembly as follows:
   a. Install lash adjuster as shown, **Fig. 26,** using care not to spill oil which is inside it.
   b. Install lash adjuster holder No. MD998443 or equivalent to hold adjuster in place while installing rocker arm and shaft assembly.
   c. Install rocker arm and shaft assembly on cylinder head, then tighten bearing cap bolt.
   d. Remove lash adjuster holder tool.
3. When installing semi-circular packing, apply liberal amount of gasket sealant onto circumference of packing.

# FRONT CASE, OIL PUMP & SILENT SHAFT

### 1.8L/4-107

#### Disassembly

Disassemble front case, oil pump and silent shaft in numbered sequence, **Fig. 27,** noting the following:

1. Use oil pressure switch socket No. MD998054 or equivalent to remove oil pressure switch.
2. Remove oil pan as outlined under "Oil Pan & Oil Screen, Replace."
3. When removing oil pump driven gear flange bolt, insert a Phillips screwdriver into plug hole on left side of cylinder block, **Fig. 28,** to block the silent shaft.
4. If front case will not come loose from

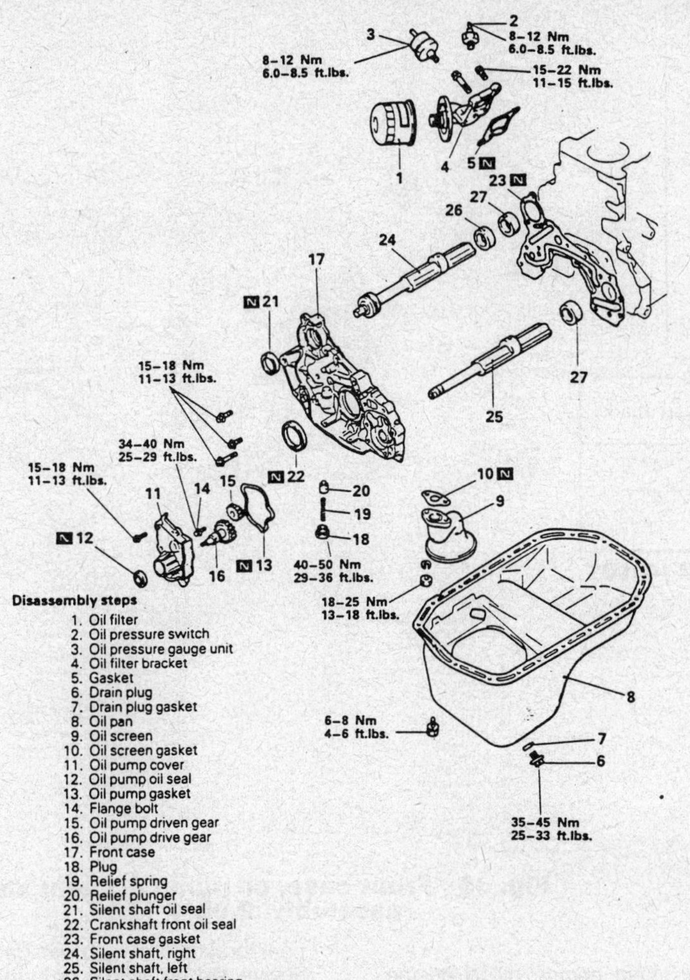


**Fig. 27 Front case, oil pump & silent shaft assembly. 1.8L/4-107**

**Fig. 28 Removing flange bolt. 1.8L/4-107**

**Fig. 29 Removing front case. 1.8L/4-107**

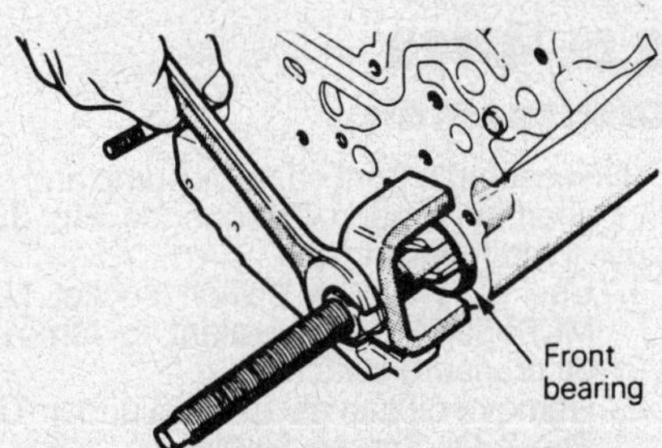


**Fig. 30 Removing silent shaft front bearings. 1.8L/4-107**

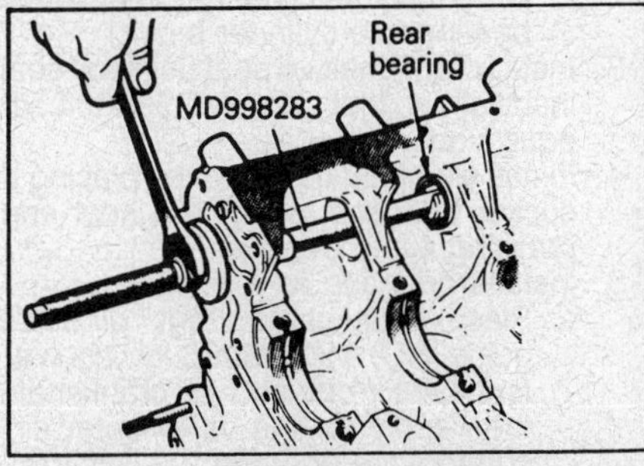


**Fig. 31 Removing silent shaft rear bearing. 1.8L/4-107**

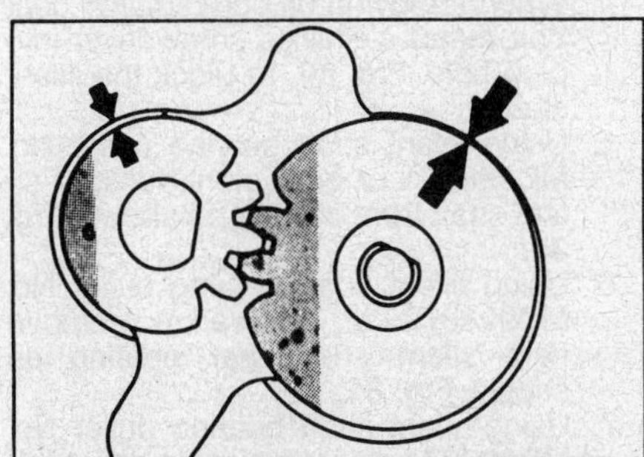

**Fig. 32 Checking oil pump tip clearance. 1.8L/4-107**

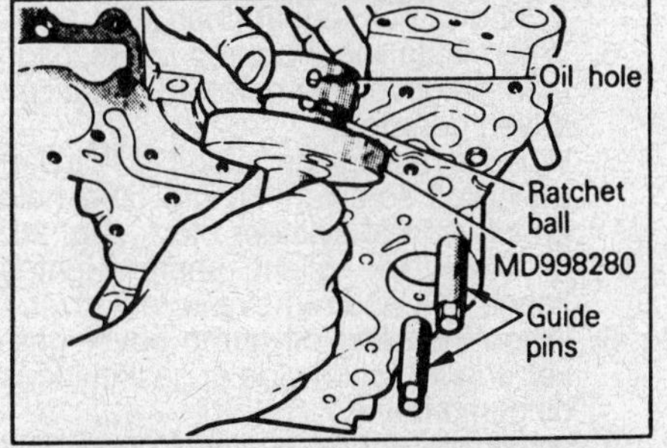


**Fig. 33 Installing silent shaft front bearing. 1.8L/4-107**

block once all attaching bolts are removed, insert a flat screwdriver into slot as shown in **Fig. 29**, and pry case away from block. **Do not pry in any other location on case.**

5. Using silent shaft bearing puller MD998282 or equivalent, remove silent shaft front bearings as shown, **Fig. 30.**
6. Using silent shaft bearing puller MD998283 or equivalent, remove silent shaft rear bearings as shown, **Fig. 31.**

## Inspection

1. Inspect silent shaft for the following:
   a. Clogged oil passages.
   b. Seized or damaged journal.
   c. Ensure oil clearance is within specifications. Clearance should be as follows: right front, .0012-.0024 inch; right rear, .0020-.0036 inch; left front, .0008-.0021 inch; left rear, .0020-.0036 inch.
2. Inspect front case for the following:
   a. Clogged oil passages.
   b. Damaged or seized left silent shaft front bearing section.
   c. Cracks or other signs of damage on case.
3. Test oil switch as follows:
   a. Connect an ohmmeter between switch terminal and switch body.
   b. If ohmmeter reads no continuity, replace switch. If ohmmeter reads continuity, proceed to step c.

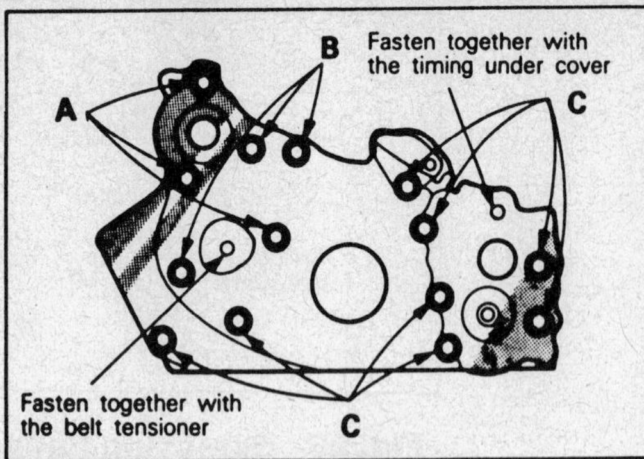


| Code | Bolt size (diameter x length) mm (in.) | Head mark |
|---|---|---|
| A | 8 x 20 (.32 x .79) | "4" |
| B | 8 x 25 (.32 x .98) | "4" |
| C | 8 x 40 (.32 x 1.57) | "4" |

**Fig. 34 Front case attaching bolts. 1.8L/4-107**

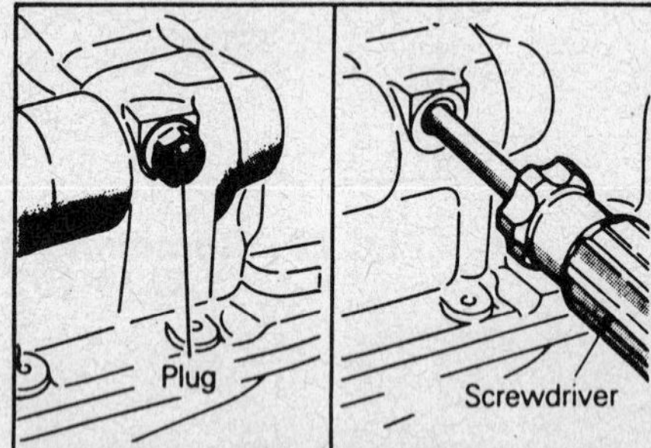


**Fig. 36 Blocking silent shaft for oil pump sprocket removal**

Disassembly steps

1. Drain plug
2. Gasket
3. Oil filter
4. Oil cooler bolt (Turbo)
5. Oil cooler (Turbo)
6. Oil pressure switch
7. Harness assembly
8. Oil pressure gauge unit
9. Oil pan
10. Oil screen
11. Gasket
12. Oil filter bracket
13. Gasket
14. Relief plug
15. Gasket
16. Relief spring
17. Relief plunger
18. Plug cap
19. O-ring
20. Driven gear bolt
21. Front case
22. Gasket
23. Oil seal
24. Silent shaft oil seal
25. Crankshaft front oil seal
26. Oil pump cover
27. Oil pump driven gear
28. Oil pump drive gear
29. Left silent shaft
30. Right silent shaft
31. Silent shaft front bearings
32. Right silent shaft rear bearing
33. Left silent shaft rear bearing
34. Check valve (Turbo)
35. Gasket (Turbo)
36. Oil jet (Turbo)
37. Gasket (Turbo)

N : Non-reusable parts

**Fig. 35 Front case, oil pump & silent shaft assembly. 2.0L/4-122**

c. Insert a fine wedge into oil switch hole. Ohmmeter should read no continuity when wedge is slightly pressed into hole, If ohmmeter reads continuity, replace switch.

4. Inspect oil pump as follows:
   a. Install oil pump gears in front case and check tip clearance in location shown, **Fig. 32.**
   b. Check side clearance of gears.
   c. Check for for ridge wear on surface of oil pump cover.
5. Inspect oil relief plunger. Ensure plunger slides smoothly and spring is functional.

### Assembly

Reverse removal procedure to install, noting the following:

1. When installing silent shaft rear bearing, apply clean engine oil to engine block bearing hole and to outer circumference of bearing. Using bearing installation tool No. MD998286 or equivalent and a hammer, drive bearing into cylinder block.
2. Install silent shaft front bearing as follows:
   a. Using bearing installation tool set No. MD998280 or equivalent, install two guide pins (included in set) into threaded holes of cylinder block, **Fig. 33,**
   b. Place bearing onto bearing installer, locking ratchet ball of tool into hole in bearing, **Fig. 33.**
   c. Apply clean engine oil to engine block bearing hole and to outer circumference of bearing.
   d. Place installation tool on guide pins, then using a hammer, drive bearing into cylinder block.
3. Install crankshaft oil seal using oil seal installation tool No. MD998304 or equivalent.
4. Install silent shaft oil seal by placing a socket over the top of the seal and pressing it into the case.
5. Install front case as follows:
   a. Place crankshaft front oil seal guide NO. MD998285 or equivalent over front end of crankshaft, then apply engine oil to outer circumference of guide.
   b. Install front case over top of guide, onto cylinder block.
   c. Install case attaching bolts, referring to bolt length chart, **Fig. 34.**
6. When installing oil pump gears, align mark on drive gear notch with mark on driven gear tooth.
7. When installing flange bolt (14), insert a Phillips screwdriver into plug hole on left side of cylinder block, **Fig. 28,** to block the silent shaft. Tighten flange bolt and remove screwdriver.
8. When installing oil pump cover gasket, ensure round side of gasket faces oil pump cover.
9. Install oil pan as outlined under "Oil Pan & Oil Screen, Replace."
10. When installing oil pressure switch, coat threads of switch with gasket adhesive. **Do not allow hole in end of switch to be covered with adhesive.** Install switch using oil pressure switch socket No. MD998054 or equivalent.

## 2.0L/4-122

### Disassembly

Disassemble front case, oil pump and silent shaft in numbered sequence, **Fig. 35,** noting the following:

1. Use oil pressure switch socket No. MD998054 or equivalent to remove oil pressure switch.
2. Remove oil pan as outlined under "Oil Pan & Oil Screen, Replace."
3. Use plug cap socket No. MD998162 or equivalent to remove front case plug cap (17).
4. When removing oil pump driven gear bolt, insert a Phillips screwdriver into plug hole, **Fig. 36,** to block the silent shaft.
5. Using silent shaft bearing puller No. MD998371 or equivalent, remove silent shaft front bearing as shown, **Fig. 30.**
6. Using silent shaft bearing puller No. MD998372 or equivalent, remove right silent shaft rear bearing as shown, **Fig. 31.**
7. Using silent shaft bearing puller No. MD998374 or equivalent, remove left silent shaft rear bearing as shown, **Fig. 37.**

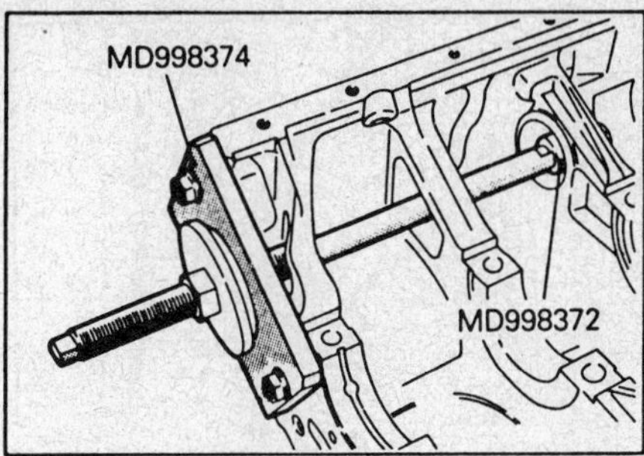


Fig. 37 Removing left silent shaft rear bearing. 2.0L/4-122

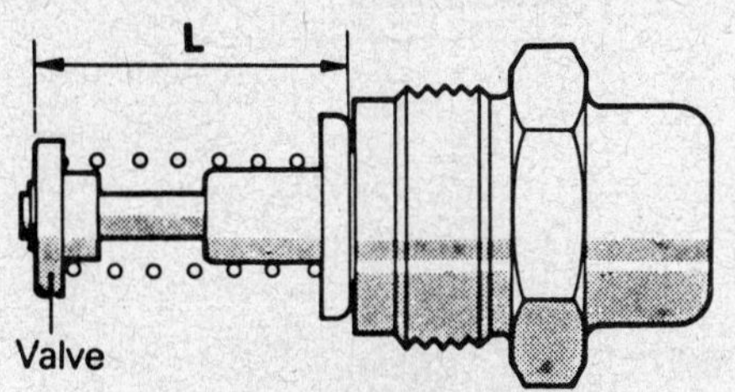


Fig. 38 Oil cooler bypass valve. 2.0L/4-122

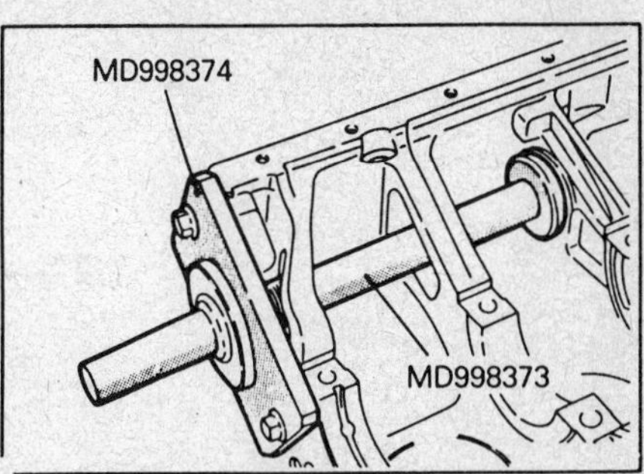


Fig. 39 Installing left silent shaft rear bearing. 2.0L/4-122

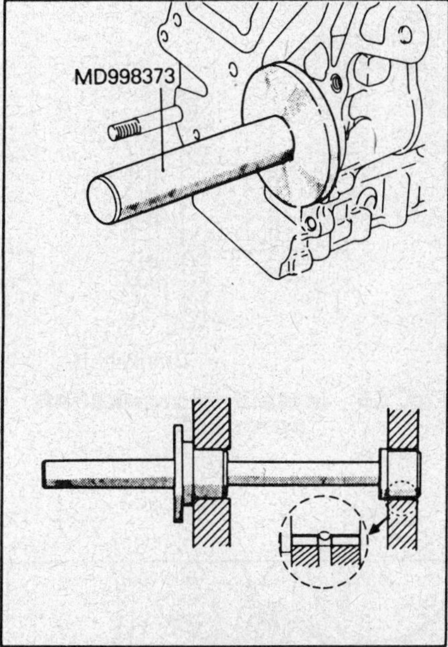


Fig. 40 Installing right silent shaft rear bearing. 2.0L/4-122

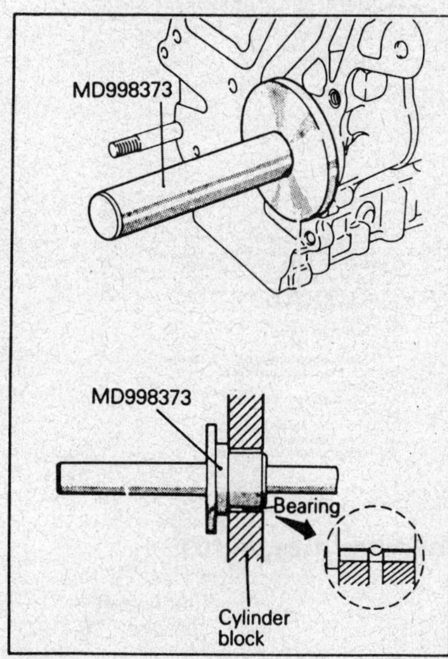


Fig. 41 Installing silent shaft front bearing. 2.0L/4-122

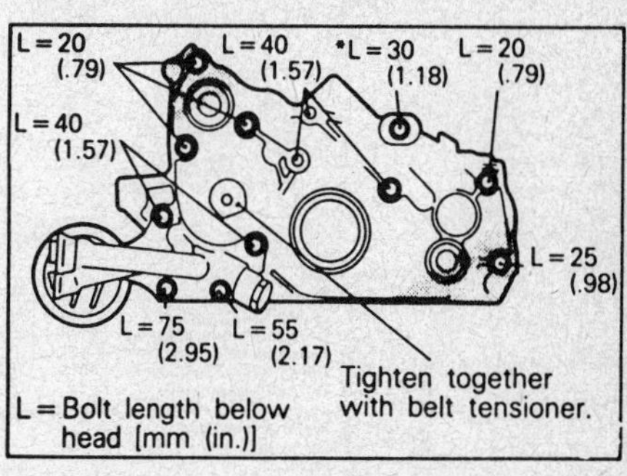


Fig. 42 Front case attaching bolts. 2.0L/4-122

## Inspection

1. Inspect front case for the following:
   a. Clogged oil passages.
   b. Damaged or seized left silent shaft front bearing section.
   c. Cracks or other signs of damage on case.
2. Inspect oil seal lip for wear or damage, replacing as necessary.
3. Test oil switch as follows:
   a. Connect an ohmmeter between switch terminal and switch body.
   b. If ohmmeter reads no continuity, replace switch. If ohmmeter reads continuity, proceed to step c.
   c. Insert a fine wedge into oil switch hole. Ohmmeter should read no continuity when wedge is slightly pressed into hole, If ohmmeter reads continuity, replace switch.
4. **On models with turbocharged engine,** inspect oil cooler bypass valve as follows:
   a. Ensure valves move smoothly.
   b. Measure dimension L on bypass valve, **Fig. 38.** At room temperature, dimension L should be 1.358 inch.
   c. Dip valve in engine oil heated to 212°F. Dimension L should now be at least 1.570 inch.
5. **On all models,** inspect oil pump as follows:
   a. Install oil pump gears in front case and rotate gears, ensuring smooth rotation without excessive looseness.
   b. Check for for ridge wear on surface of oil pump cover.
   c. Check drive gear and driven gear tip clearance.
   d. Check side clearance of gears.
6. Inspect silent shaft for the following:
   a. Clogged oil passages.
   b. Seized or damaged journal.
   c. Ensure oil clearance is within specifications. Clearance should be as follows: right front, .0008-.0024 inch; right rear, .0008-.0021 inch; left front, .0002-.0036 inch; left rear, .0017-.0033 inch.
7. Inspect oil jet and check valve for clogging or damage.

## Assembly

Reverse removal procedure to install, noting the following:

1. When installing oil jet, ensure nozzle is installed toward the piston.
2. When installing left silent shaft rear bearing, apply clean engine oil to engine block bearing hole and to outer circumference of bearing. Using bearing installation tool No. MD998374 or equivalent, **Fig. 39,** install bearing into cylinder block.
3. When installing right silent shaft rear bearing, apply clean engine oil to engine block bearing hole and to outer circumference of bearing. Using bearing installation tool No. MD998373 or equivalent, **Fig. 40,** install bearing into cylinder block. **Ensure oil hole in bearing is aligned with oil hole in cylinder block.**
4. When installing silent shaft front bearing, apply clean engine oil to engine block bearing hole and to outer circumference of bearing. Using bearing installation tool No. MD998373 or equivalent, **Fig. 41,** install bearing into cylinder block. **Ensure oil hole in bearing is aligned with oil hole in cylinder block.**
5. When installing oil pump gears, coat gears with clean engine oil, then align mark on drive gear notch with mark on driven gear tooth.
6. Install crankshaft oil seal using oil seal installation tool No. MD998375 or equivalent.
7. Install oil seal (22) and silent shaft oil seal (23) by placing a socket over the

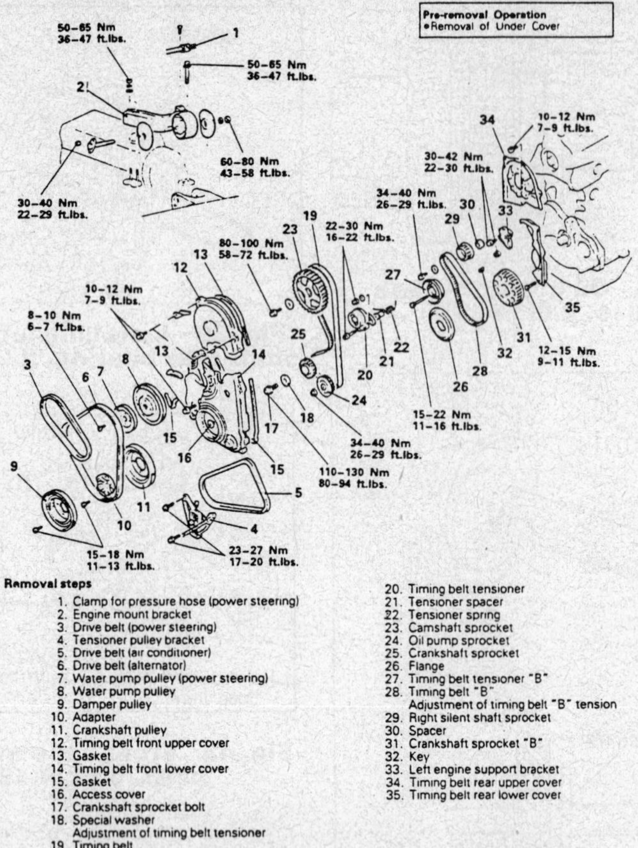


**Fig. 43 Timing belt assembly. 1.8L/4-107**

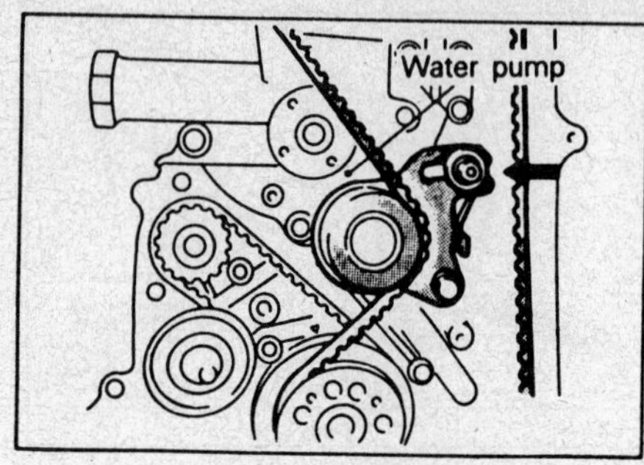


**Fig. 44 Timing belt tensioner. 1.8L/4-107**

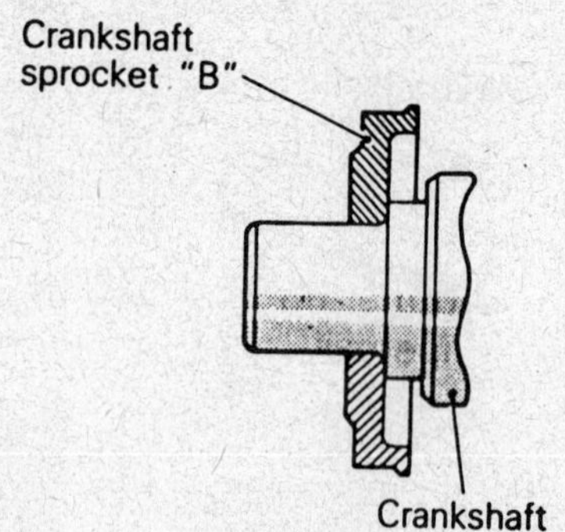


**Fig. 45 installing crankshaft sprocket**

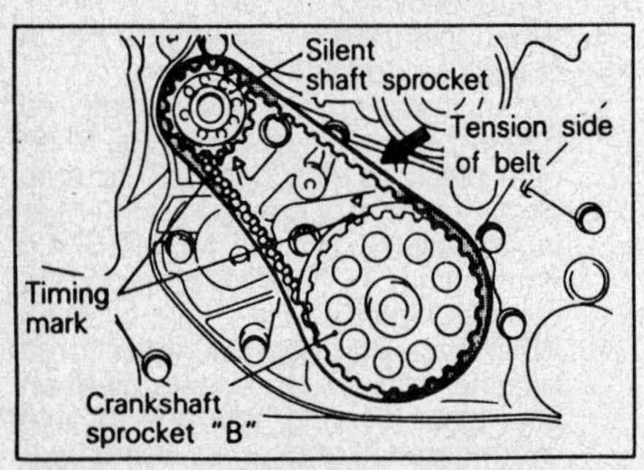


**Fig. 46 Aligning crankshaft sprocket B and silent shaft sprocket timing marks. 1.8L/4-107**

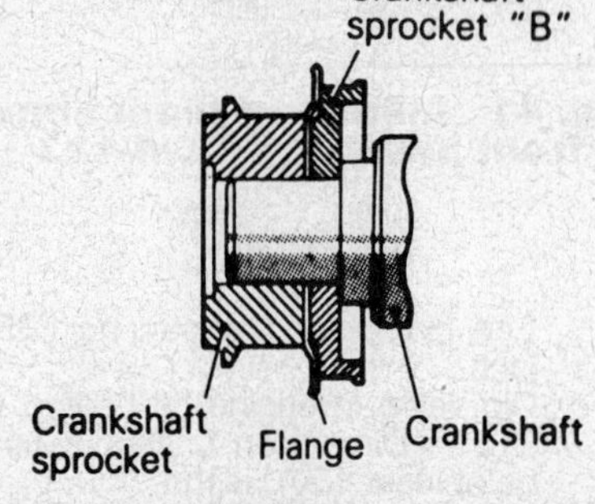


**Fig. 47 Installing crankshaft sprocket flange**

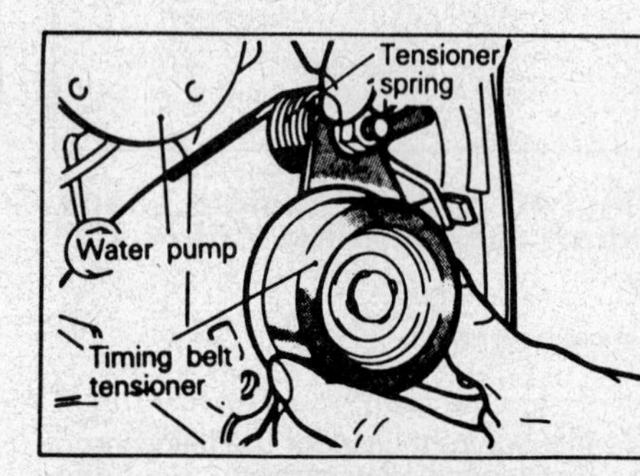


**Fig. 48 Installing timing belt tensioner & spring. 1.8L/4-107**

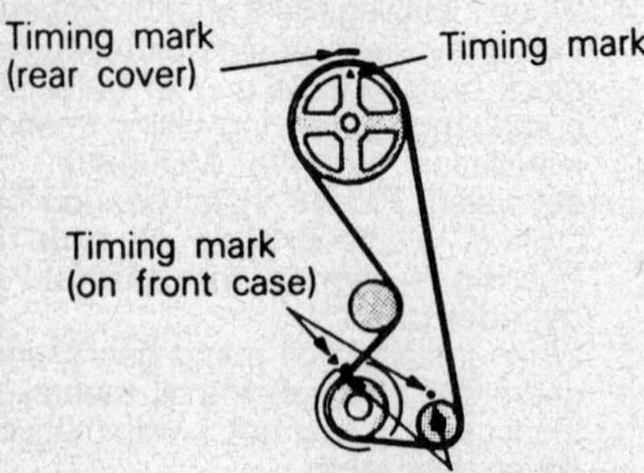


**Fig. 49 Aligning camshaft sprocket, crankshaft sprocket and oil pump sprocket timing marks. 1.8L/4-107**

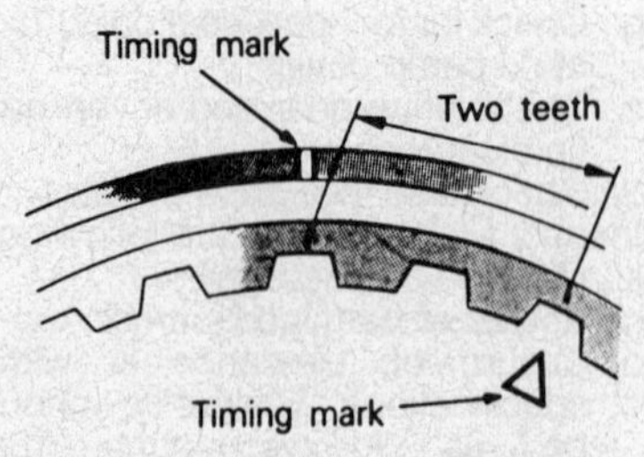


**Fig. 50 Adjusting timing belt tension. 1.8L/4-107**

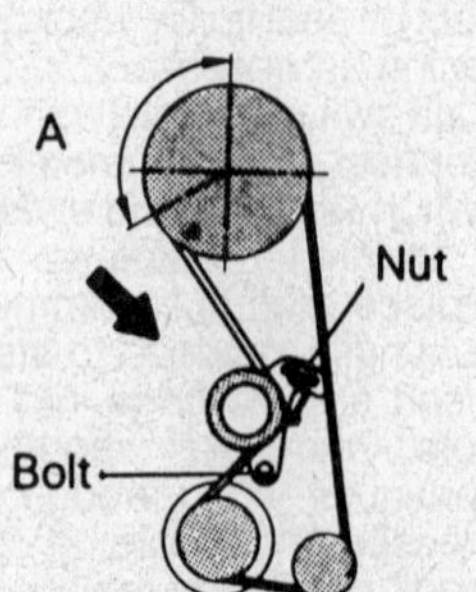


**Fig. 51 Tightening tensioner. 1.8L/4-107**

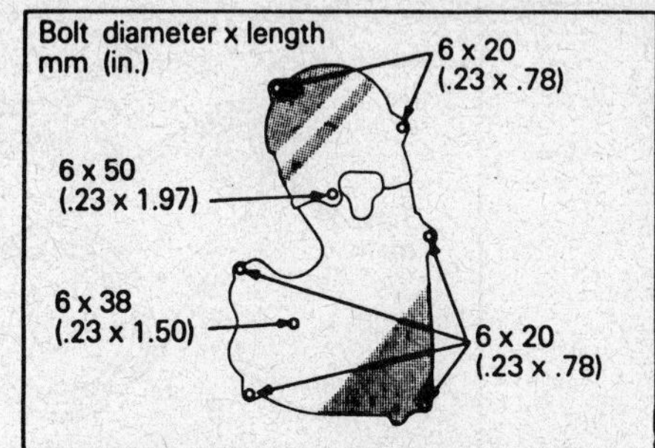


**Fig. 52 Timing belt cover attaching bolts. 1.8L/4-107**

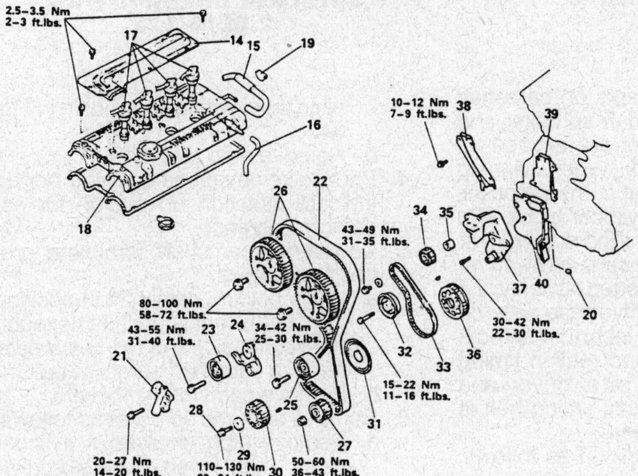


**Installation steps**

40. Timing belt rear left cover (lower)
39. Timing belt rear left cover (upper)
38. Timing belt rear right cover
37. Left engine support bracket
36. Crankshaft sprocket "B"
35. Spacer
34. Silent shaft sprocket
33. Timing belt "B"
Adjustment of timing belt "B" tension
32. Tensioner "B"
31. Flange
30. Crankshaft sprocket
29. Special washer
28. Crankshaft sprocket bolt
27. Oil pump sprocket
26. Camshaft sprocket
25. Idle pulley
21. Auto tensioner
24. Tensioner arm
23. Tensioner pulley
22. Timing belt
Adjustment of timing belt tension
20. Plug rubber
19. Semi-circular packing
18. Rocker cover
17. Connection for spark plug cables
16. PCV hose
15. Breather hose
14. Center cover
13. Timing belt front lower cover
12. Timing belt front upper cover
11. Crankshaft pulley
10. Water pump pulley (power steering)
9. Water pump pulley
8. Drive belt (air conditioner)
7. Tensioner pulley bracket
6. Drive belt (power steering)
5. Drive belt (alternator)
4. Return pipe clamp bolt (power steering)
3. Engine mount bracket
2. Bracket
1. Clamp for pressure hose (power steering)

**Fig. 53 Timing belt assembly (Part 2 of 2). 2.0L/4-122**

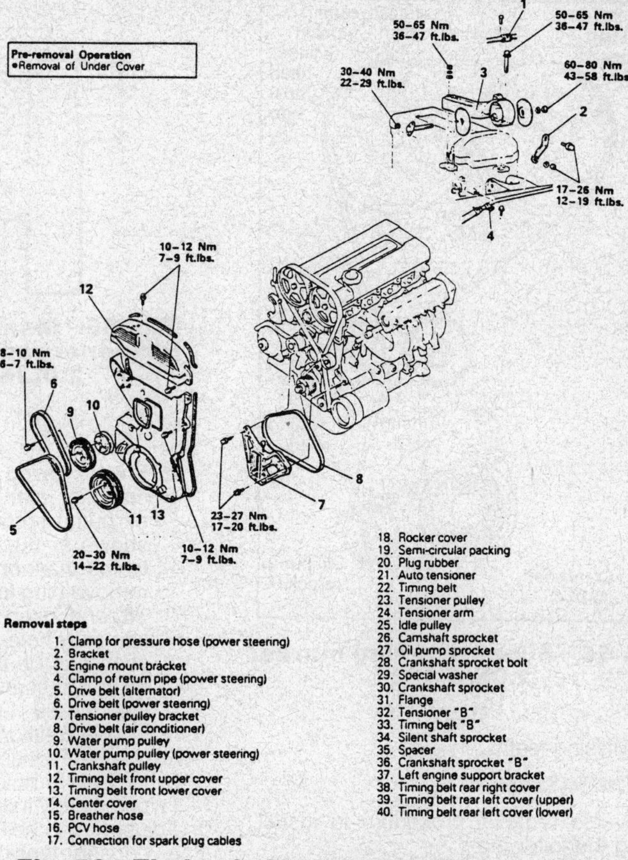


**Fig. 53 Timing belt assembly (Part 1 of 2). 2.0L/4-122**

top of the seal and pressing it into the case.

8. Install front case as follows:
   a. Place crankshaft front oil seal guide No. MD998285 or equivalent over front end of crankshaft, then apply engine oil to outer circumference of guide.
   b. Install front case over top of guide, onto cylinder block. Temporarily tighten all bolts except the filter bracket attaching bolts, referring to bolt length chart, **Fig. 42.**
   c. Install oil filter bracket and the four attaching bolts.
   d. Tighten all bolts to specifications.
9. When installing driven gear bolt (19), insert a Phillips screwdriver into plug hole on left side of cylinder block, **Fig. 36,** to block the silent shaft.
10. When installing plug cap, place a new O-ring into groove of case, then use plug cap socket No. MD998162 or equivalent to tighten cap.
11. Install oil pan as outlined under "Oil Pan & Oil Screen, Replace."
12. When installing oil pressure switch, coat threads of switch with gasket adhesive. **Do not allow hole in end of switch to be covered with adhesive.** Install switch using oil pressure switch socket No. MD998054 or equivalent.

## TIMING BELT REPLACE 1.8L/4-107

### Removal

Remove timing belt in numbered sequence as shown in **Fig. 43,** noting the following:

1. To remove engine mounting bracket, slightly raise and support engine, removing weight of engine from mount.
2. Before removing timing belt (19), proceed as follows:
   a. Turn crankshaft clockwise and align timing marks, **Fig. 17. Do not turn crankshaft counterclockwise.**
   b. Mark timing belt to indicate direction of rotation for assembly reference.
   c. Loosen bolt and spacer nut on timing belt tensioner, move tensioner towards water pump as shown in **Fig. 44,** then hand tighten tensioner in this position.
3. Remove oil pump sprocket as follows:
   a. Remove plug on side of cylinder block, then insert Phillips screwdriver into hole to block left silent shaft, **Fig. 36.**
   b. Remove oil pump sprocket nut, then the sprocket.
4. Before removing timing belt B (28), mark back of belt to indicate direction of rotation for assembly reference.

### Inspection

Inspect timing belts and replace if any of the following conditions exist:

1. Hardened or cracked back surface.
2. Cracked or separated canvas.
3. Cracked tooth bottom.
4. Cracked side.
6. Abnormal wear.

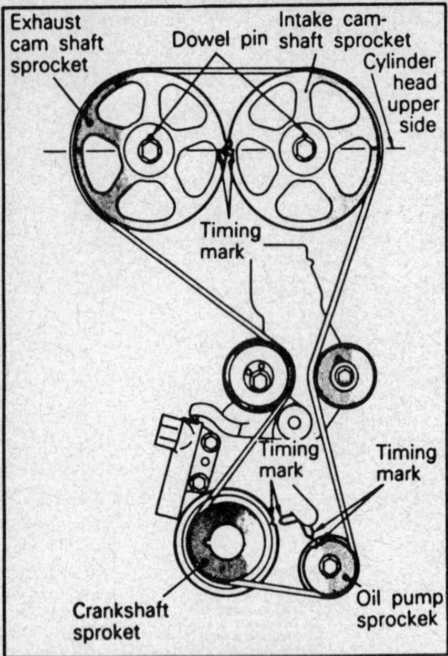


**Fig. 54 Aligning timing marks. 2.0L/4-122**

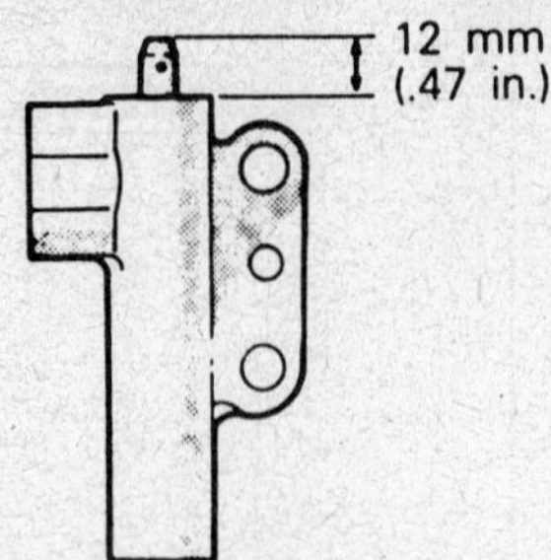


**Fig. 55 Measuring auto tensioner rod protrusion. 2.0L/4-122**

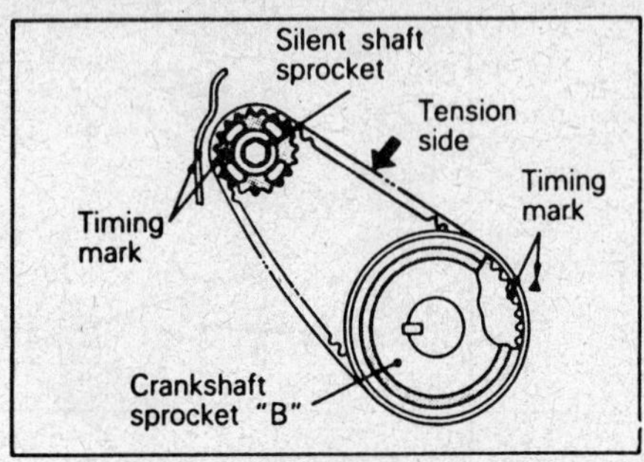


**Fig. 56 Aligning crankshaft sprocket B and silent shaft sprocket timing marks. 2.0L/4-122**

7. Missing teeth.

### Installation

Reverse removal procedure to install, noting the following:

1. Install crankshaft sprocket B (31) as shown in **Fig. 45.**
2. When installing spacer (30), apply a thin coating of engine oil to outside of spacer, then install spacer with chamfered end facing oil seal. **Failure to install chamfered end toward oil seal may result in oil leakage.**
3. Before installing timing belt B, ensure mark on crankshaft sprocket and mark on silent shaft sprocket are aligned as shown in **Fig. 46.** Install belt and adjust tension as follows:
   a. Temporarily install timing belt B tensioner with the flange toward the front of the engine and the center of the tensioner pulley to the left and above center of the attaching bolt.
   b. While holding the tensioner in your hand, apply pressure on the timing belt until the tension side of the belt is taut, then tighten tensioner bolt.
   c. To check tension, depress the tension side of the belt with your finger. Belt deflection should be .20-.28 inch.
4. Install flange (26) in direction as shown in **Fig. 47.**
5. Install the tensioner spring, tensioner spacer, timing belt tensioner and timing belt as follows:
   a. Install tensioner spring, tensioner spacer and timing belt tensioner.
   b. Place upper end of tensioner spring against water pump body, **Fig 48,** then move tensioner fully toward water pump and temporarily secure.
   c. Ensure timing marks on camshaft sprocket, crankshaft sprocket and oil pump sprocket are aligned as shown in **Fig. 49.** When aligning timing mark on oil pump sprocket, remove plug in cylinder block, **Fig. 36,** and insert Phillips screwdriver into plug hole. Ensure screwdriver shaft can be inserted at least 2.4 inches. If screwdriver can only be inserted .80-1.00 inch, turn sprocket one rotation and realign timing marks. Reinsert screwdriver and leave it in hole until timing belt is completely installed.
6. Adjust timing belt tension as follows:
   a. Loosen tensioner mounting nut. This will apply tension to timing belt.
   b. Ensure each sprocket is still aligned with timing marks.
   c. Turn crankshaft clockwise distance of two teeth on camshaft sprocket, **Fig. 50. Do not rotate crankshaft counterclockwise.**
   d. Apply enough force on tensioner in direction of arrow so that no portion of belt raises out above pulley in area A, **Fig. 51.**
   e. Tighten tensioner installation bolt, then the tensioner spacer nut. **Do not tighten nut first, as belt will be thrown out of adjustment.**
   f. Check clearance between outside of belt and cover by pulling outward on belt between camshaft sprocket and oil pump sprocket. Deflection should be .40 inch.
7. When installing timing belt front lower and front upper covers, note location and size of attaching bolts as shown in **Fig. 52.**

## 2.0L/4-122

### Removal

Remove timing belt in numbered sequence as shown in **Fig. 53,** noting the following:

1. To remove engine mount bracket, slightly raise and support engine, removing weight of engine from mount.
2. Before removing alternator drive belt, loosen water pump pulley mounting bolts.
3. Remove auto tensioner as follows:
   a. Turn crankshaft clockwise and align timing marks as shown in **Fig. 54.**
   b. Remove auto tensioner.
4. Prior to removal, mark timing belt to indicate direction of rotation for assembly reference.
5. To remove camshaft sprockets, proceed as follows:
   a. While holding camshaft in position with a crescent wrench at hexagon between No. 2 and No. 3 journals, remove camshaft sprocket bolt.
   b. Remove camshaft sprockets.
6. Remove oil pump sprocket as follows:
   a. Remove plug on side of cylinder block, then insert Phillips screwdriver into hole to block left silent shaft, **Fig. 36.**
   b. Remove oil pump sprocket nut, then the sprocket.

### Inspection

Inspect timing belts and replace if any of the following conditions exist:

1. Hardened or cracked back surface.
2. Cracked or separated canvas.
3. Cracked tooth bottom.
4. Cracked side.
6. Abnormal wear.
7. Missing teeth.

Inspect tensioner pulley and idler pulley. Replace pulleys if binding, excessive play, abnormal noise or grease leakage occurs while turning.

Inspect auto tensioner for weak tension, leakage and rod end wear or damage. Check rod protrusion, **Fig. 55.** If protrusion exceeds .47 inch, replace auto tensioner.

### Installation

Reverse removal procedure to install, noting the following:

1. Install crankshaft sprocket B (36) as shown in **Fig. 45.**
2. When installing spacer (35), apply a thin coating of engine oil to outside of spacer, then install spacer with chamfered end facing oil seal. **Failure to install chamfered end toward oil seal may result in oil leakage.**
3. Before installing timing belt B, ensure mark on crankshaft sprocket B and mark on silent shaft sprocket are aligned as shown in **Fig. 56.** Install belt and adjust tension as follows:
   a. Temporarily install timing belt B

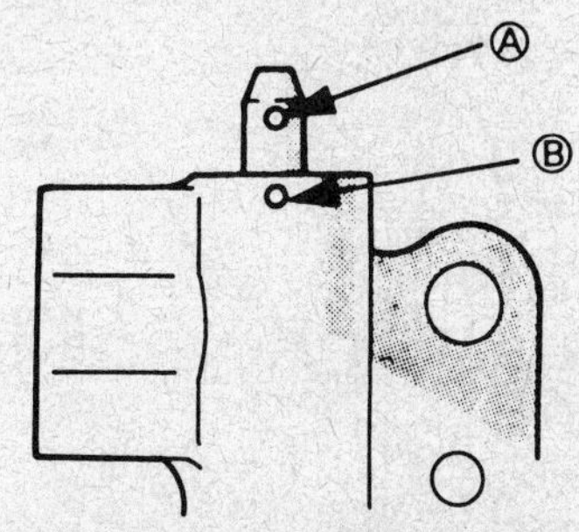


**Fig. 57 Retracting auto tensioner rod. 2.0L/4-122**

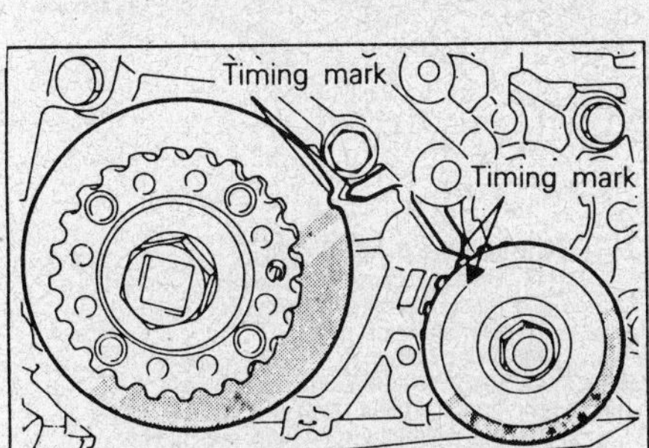


**Fig. 60 Aligning crankshaft sprocket & oil pump sprocket timing marks. 2.0L/4-122**

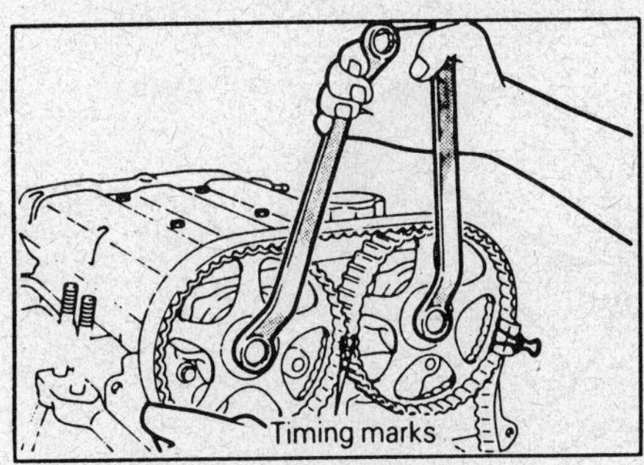


**Fig. 62 Installing timing belt. 2.0L/4-122**

tensioner with the flange toward the front of the engine and the center of the tensioner pulley to the left and above center of the attaching bolt.

b. While holding the tensioner in your hand, apply pressure on the timing belt until the tension side of the belt is taut, then tighten tensioner bolt.

c. To check tension, depress the tension side of the belt with your finger. Belt deflection should be .20-.28 inch.

4. Install flange (31) and crankshaft sprocket (30) in direction as shown in **Fig. 47.**

5. When installing oil pump sprocket, install a Phillips screwdriver into plug hole, **Fig. 36,** to block the left silent shaft, then install oil pump sprocket and attaching bolt.

6. To install camshaft sprockets, hold

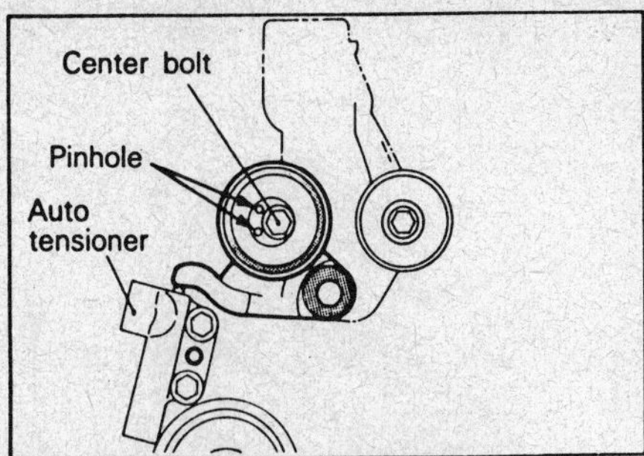


**Fig. 58 Installing tensioner pulley. 2.0L/4-122**

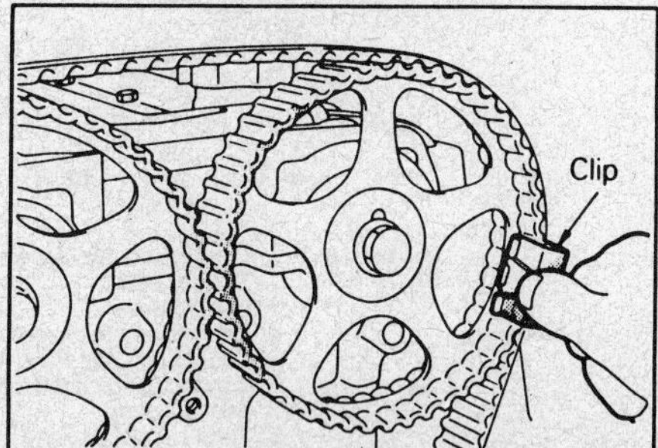


**Fig. 61 Retaining timing belt to intake camshaft sprocket. 2.0L/4-122**

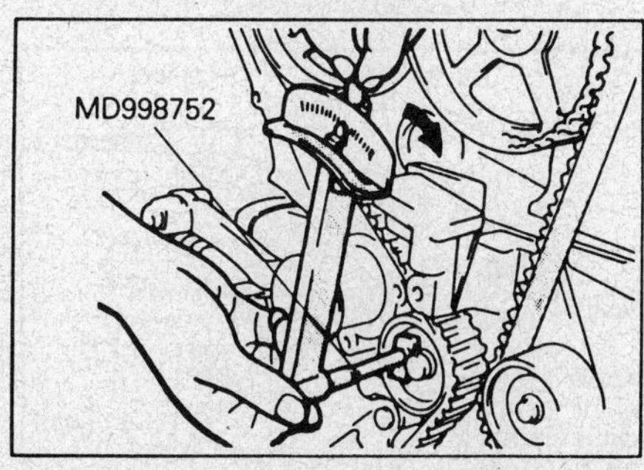


**Fig. 63 Adjusting timing belt tension. 2.0L/4-122**

camshaft in position with a crescent wrench at hexagon between No. 2 and No. 3 journals, remove camshaft sprocket bolt, then install sprocket and attaching bolt.

7. When installing auto tensioner, if rod is in fully extended position, reset as follows:

a. Using a soft-jawed vise, clamp the auto tensioner in a level position. **If plug protrudes from bottom of tensioner, place a flat washer around it to prevent damage from vise.**

b. Slowly close vise until set hole (A) in tensioner rod is aligned with set hole (B) in tensioner cylinder, **Fig. 57.**

c. Insert a piece of wire through the set holes, then install auto tensioner. **Leave wire installed in tensioner.**

8. Install the tensioner pulley with pinhole in pulley shaft to left of center bolt, **Fig. 58.** Hand tighten center bolt.

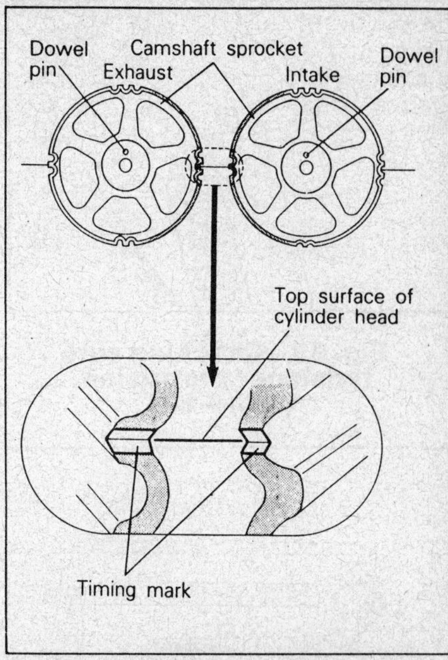


**Fig. 59 Aligning exhaust & intake camshaft sprocket timing marks. 2.0L/4-122**

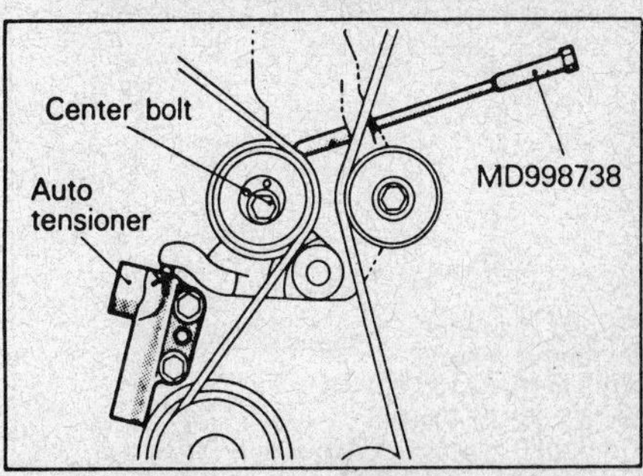


**Fig. 64 Installing auto tensioner tool. 2.0L/4-122**

9. Install timing belt as follows:

a. Turn camshaft sprockets so dowel pins are on top, then align timing marks so they face each other, parallel with the top surface of the cylinder head, **Fig. 59.**

b. Align crankshaft sprocket timing mark, then the oil pump sprocket timing mark as shown in **Fig. 60.** Ensure oil pump sprocket is installed correctly by removing plug in cylinder block, **Fig. 36,** then inserting a Phillips screwdriver into plug hole. Ensure screwdriver shaft can be inserted at least 2.4 inches. If screwdriver can only be inserted .80-1.00 inch, turn sprocket one rotation and realign timing marks. Reinsert screwdriver and leave it in the hole.

c. Thread timing belt over intake-side camshaft sprocket and clip belt onto sprocket as shown, **Fig. 61.** Using two wrenches, feed timing belt over exhaust-side sprocket, **Fig. 62,** then clip belt onto exhaust-side sprocket.

d. Thread timing belt over idler pulley,

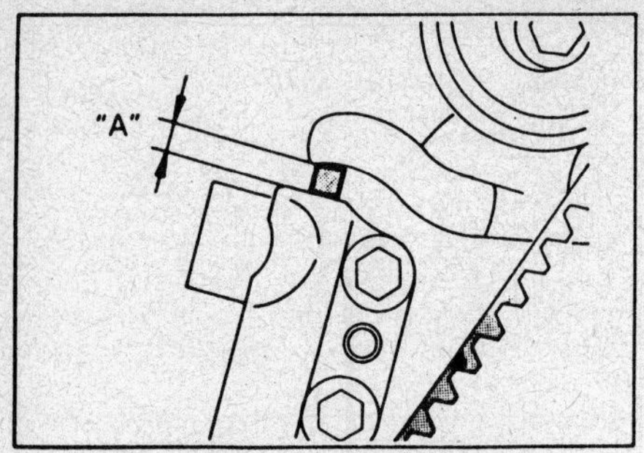


Fig. 65 Checking auto tensioner protrusion. 2.0L/4-122

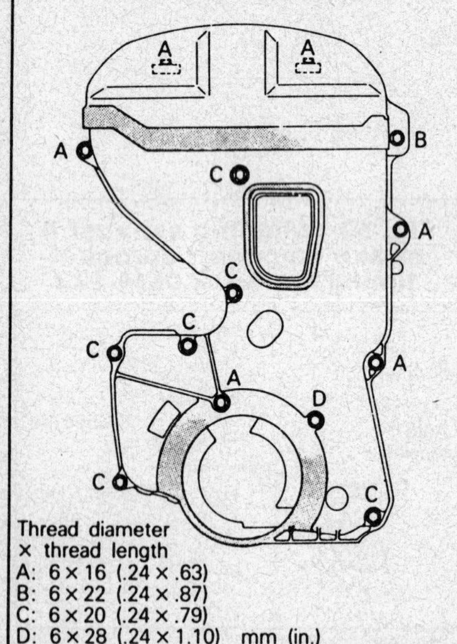


Fig. 66 Timing belt cover attaching bolts. 2.0L/4-122

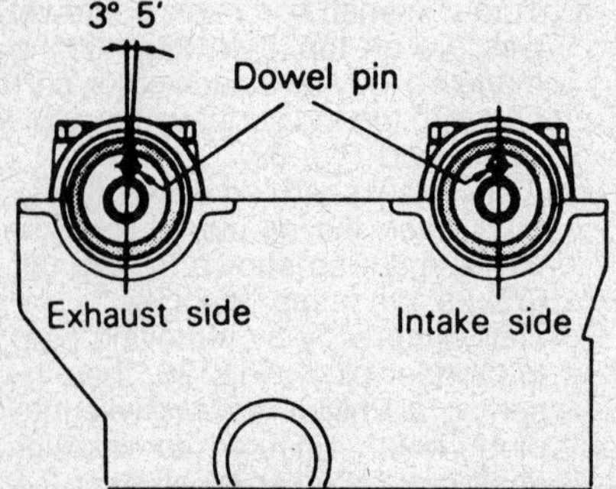


Fig. 68 Installing camshafts. 2.0L/4-122

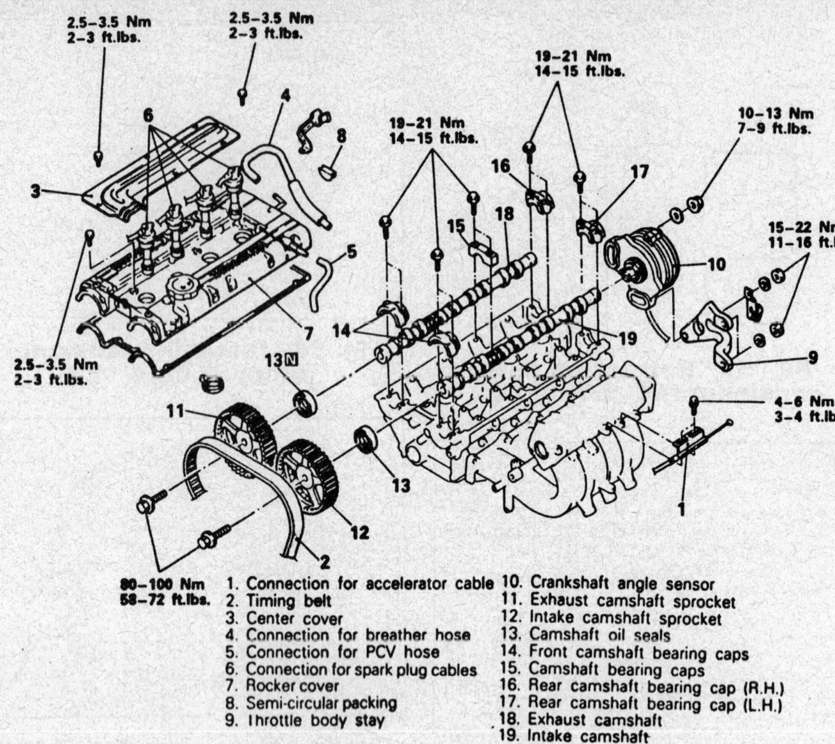


Fig. 67 Camshaft assembly. 2.0L/4-122

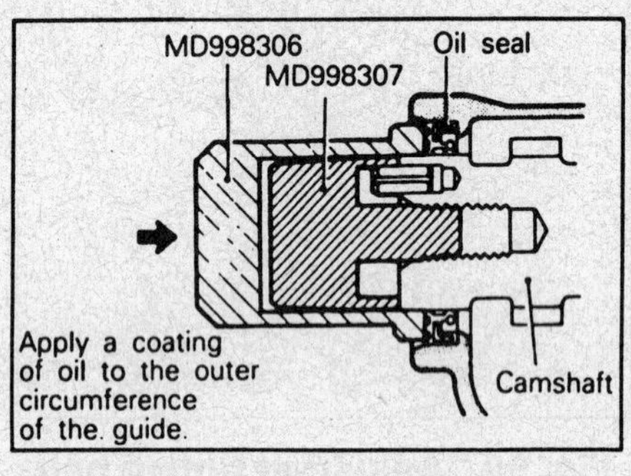


Fig. 69 Installing camshaft oil seal. 2.0L/4-122

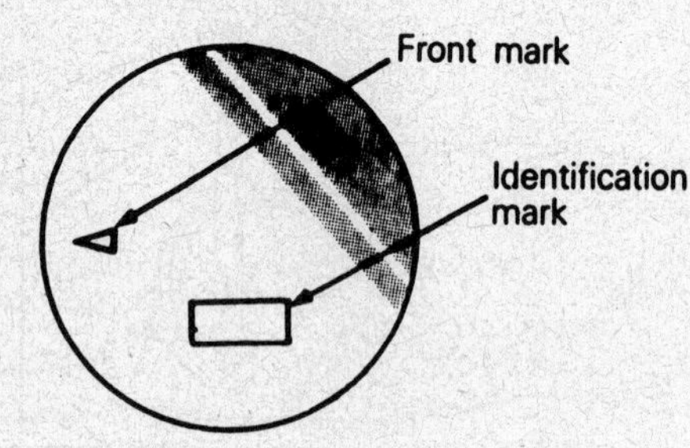


Fig. 70 Top view of piston

oil pump pulley sprocket, crankshaft pulley sprocket and tensioner pulley, then remove clips.

e. Lift tensioner pulley toward top and center of engine, then tighten center bolt.
f. Ensure all timing marks are aligned, then remove screwdriver inserted into plug hole.

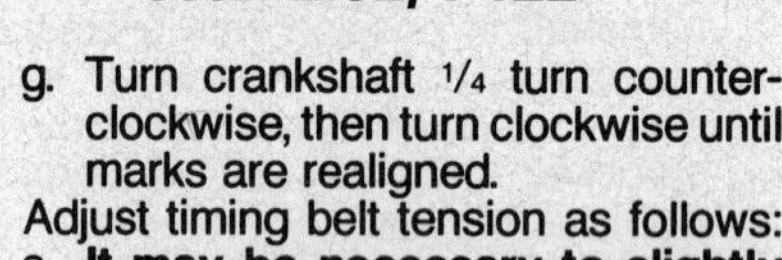

g. Turn crankshaft 1/4 turn counterclockwise, then turn clockwise until marks are realigned.

10. Adjust timing belt tension as follows:
    a. **It may be necessary to slightly raise and support engine to provide adequate body clearance during this step.** Loosen auto tensioner center bolt and install auto tensioner installation tool No. MD998752 or equivalent and a torque wrench as shown in **Fig. 63.** Apply 22.2-24.6 inch lbs. torque, then while holding tensioner pulley with installation tool, tighten center bolt.
    b. Screw auto tensioner installation tool MD998738 or equivalent into left engine support bracket until it contacts tensioner arm, **Fig. 64.** Screw tool in slightly more, then remove piece of wire installed into auto tensioner. Remove installation tool.
    c. Rotate crankshaft clockwise two complete turns, then let tensioner set for 15 minutes. After time has expired, measure distance between tensioner arm and tensioner body (A), **Fig. 65.** Clearance should be .15-.18 inch. If clearance is not as specified, repeat steps 10A, 10B and 10C until clearance is within specifications.
    d. If clearance does not exist between tensioner arm and body, reinstall installation tool MD998738 or equivalent, screwing tool in until it contacts tensioner arm. Once the tool contacts tensioner arm, screw in further (2.5-3 turns) until tensioner pushrod is moved back and tensioner arm contacts tensioner body. Remove installation tool.
    e. Install rubber plug into timing belt rear cover.
11. When installing semi-circular packing, apply liberal amount of gasket sealant

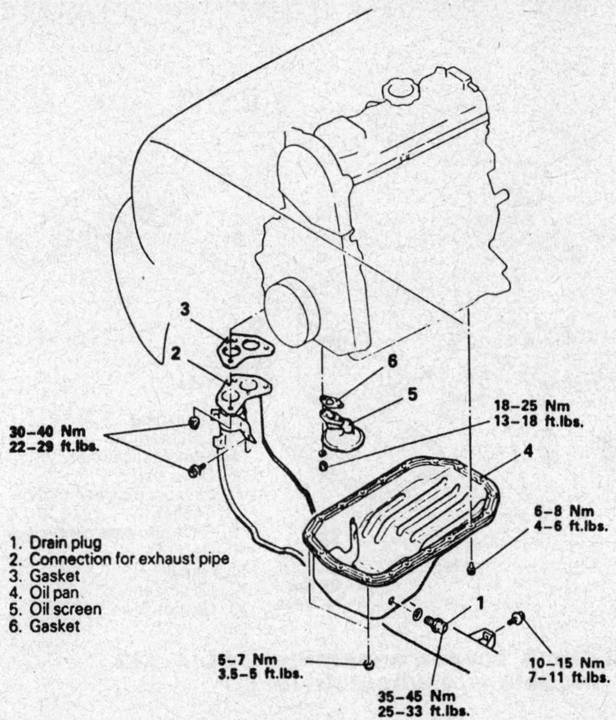


**Fig. 71 Oil pan & screen assembly. 1.8L/4-107**

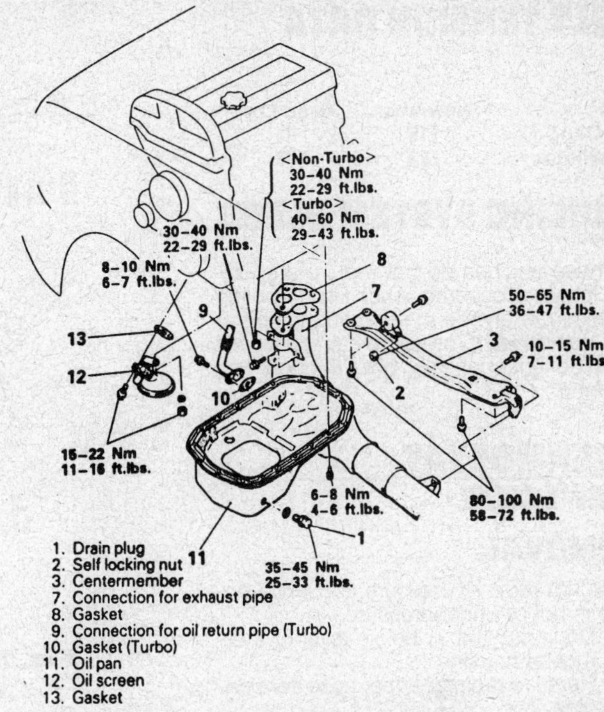


**Fig. 72 Oil pan & screen assembly. 2.0L/4-122 models w/2 wheel drive**

onto circumference of packing.

12. When installing rocker cover, apply gasket sealant to area as shown in **Fig. 23.**
13. Refer to **Fig. 66** when installing timing belt upper and lower cover attaching bolts.

# CAMSHAFT

## REPLACE

## 2.0L/4-122

### Removal

Remove camshaft in numbered sequence, **Fig. 67,** noting the following:

1. Remove timing belt as outlined under "Timing Belt, Replace."
2. Remove camshaft sprockets as follows:
   a. While holding camshaft in position with a crescent wrench at hexagon between No. 2 and No. 3 journals, remove camshaft sprocket bolt.
   b. Remove camshaft sprockets.
3. Remove camshaft oil seals using a suitable screwdriver.
4. Remove camshaft bearing caps by loosening installation bolts in two or three steps. If bearing cap is difficult to remove, gently tap on the rear portion of the camshaft with a plastic hammer.

### Installation

Reverse removal procedure to install, noting the following:

1. Install the camshafts on the cylinder head. **Ensure intake side camshaft is installed on intake side and exhaust side camshaft is installed on exhaust side.** Intake side camshaft has a slot machined in the back end to drive the crank angle sensor. Once installed, the camshaft dowel pins should be in the positions as shown in **Fig. 68.**
2. When installing camshaft bearing caps, tighten evenly, in two or three steps.
3. When installing camshaft oil seal, use oil seal guide tool No. MD998307 and oil seal installation tool No. MD998306 or equivalents as shown, **Fig. 69.**
4. Install crank angle sensor as follows:
   a. Ensure mating mark on housing of crank angle sensor is aligned with notch in plate.
   b. Ensure crank angle sensor does not move when tightening attaching nut.
5. When installing semi-circular packing, apply liberal amount of gasket sealant onto circumference of packing.
6. When installing rocker cover, apply gasket sealant to area as shown in **Fig. 23.**

# PISTON & ROD ASSEMBLY

When installing piston and rod assembly, arrow on top of piston must face toward timing belt side of engine, **Fig. 70.**

# OIL PAN & OIL SCREEN

## REPLACE

### REMOVAL

Remove oil pan and oil screen in numbered sequence, referring to **Fig. 71** on all models with 1.8L/4-107 engine, **Fig. 72** on two wheel drive models with 2.0L/4-122 engine and **Fig. 73** on four wheel drive models with 2.0L/4-122 engine, noting the following:

1. Once all oil pan bolts are removed, use oil pan separator No. MD998727 or equivalent and a hammer to loosen pan. **Do not use a screwdriver or a chisel to perform this task, as damage to oil pan flange may result.**
2. Remove pan by placing a brass bar at corner of separator tool and striking it with a hammer.

### INSPECTION

Replace the oil pan if damaged or cracked. Ensure screen is not clogged, cracked or damage.

### INSTALLATION

Reverse removal procedure to install. When installing oil pan, ensure mating surfaces are clean, then apply gasket adhesive into groove in oil pan flange. Do not allow adhesive to cover bolt holes.

## BELT TENSION DATA

| Belt | New Lbs. | Used Lbs. |
|---|---|---|
| Air Cond. | 115 | 80 |
| Alternator | 132 | 88 |

## COOLING SYSTEM BLEED

These engines do not require a specified bleed procedure. After filling cooling system, run engine to operating temperature with radiator/pressure cap off. Air will then be automatically bled through cap opening.

## THERMOSTAT REPLACE

### REMOVAL

Do not remove pressure cap while engine is hot or under pressure.

1. Drain coolant to below level of thermostat housing.
2. Remove radiator upper hose from engine.
3. Remove two retaining bolts, water outlet fitting, gasket and thermostat.
4. Clear mating surfaces and close drain.

### INSTALLATION

1. Reverse removal procedures to install.
2. Install thermostat so that the flange seats in recess of intake manifold and thermostat case, **Fig. 74.**
3. Install retaining bolts, **torquing** to 12-14 ft. lbs.
4. Ensure that drain is closed, then refill coolant. Replace cap, start engine until warm. Check of leaks, then recheck coolant and fill if necessary.

## WATER PUMP REPLACE

### 1.8L/4-107

Remove water pump in numbered sequence, **Fig. 75,** noting the following:

1. Remove lower engine compartment cover.
2. Drain engine coolant as follows:
   a. Place instrument panel temperature control lever in Hot position.
   b. Carefully remove radiator cap.
   c. Remove radiator drain plug.
3. To remove engine mount bracket, slightly raise and support engine, removing weight of engine from mount.
4. Before removing water pump drive belt, loosen water pump pulley installation bolt.
5. Remove rocker cover, timing belt covers, timing belt and timing belt B as outlined under "Timing Belt, Replace."

#### Installation

Reverse removal procedure to install, noting the following:

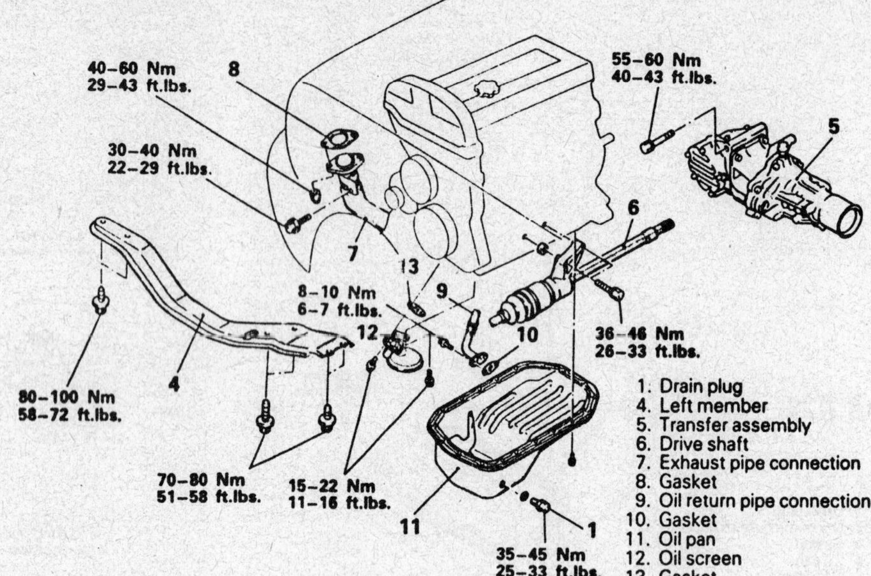


**Fig. 73 Oil pan & screen assembly. 2.0L/4-122 models w/4 wheel drive**

1. Coat the O-ring (26) with water to ease installation.
2. Refer to bolt length chart, **Fig. 76,** when installing water pump attaching bolts.

### 2.0L/4-122

Remove water pump in numbered sequence, **Fig. 77,** noting the following:

1. Remove lower engine compartment cover.
2. Drain engine coolant as follows:
   a. Place instrument panel temperature control lever in Hot position.
   b. Carefully remove radiator cap.
   c. Remove radiator drain plug.
3. To remove engine mount bracket, slightly raise and support engine, removing weight of engine from mount.
4. Remove automatic tensioner, timing belt and timing belt B as outlined under "Timing Belt, Replace."

#### Installation

Reverse removal procedure to install, noting the following:

1. Coat the O-ring (26) with water to ease installation.
2. Refer to bolt length chart, **Fig. 78,** when installing water pump attaching bolts.

## FUEL PUMP REPLACE

### TWO WHEEL DRIVE MODELS

#### Removal

Remove fuel pump in numbered sequence, **Fig. 79,** noting the following:

1. Remove fuel from fuel tank into a suitable container.
2. Cover fuel line connection with rags to prevent spraying of fuel when disconnecting high pressure fuel line.
3. Loosen the two self-locking nuts (3) to the end of the stud bolt.
4. After disconnecting the lateral rod and body (5), lower the lateral rod and suspend from axle beam using a piece of wire.

#### Installation

Reverse removal procedure to install, noting the following:

1. Install overfill limiter in the direction as shown, **Fig. 80.**
2. When installing fuel gauge unit, align the two positioning projections as shown, **Fig. 81.** Ensure bend in float assembly is pointed to left during installation.
3. When installing fuel pump, O-ring and attaching bolt, proceed as follows:
   a. Align three positioning projections of packing with holes in fuel pump.
   b. Install lowest holding bolt first, ensuring O-ring is not pinched.
4. Tighten self-locking nuts until rear end of tank band contacts body.

### ALL WHEEL DRIVE MODELS

#### Removal

Remove fuel pump in numbered sequence, **Fig. 82.** When disconnecting high pressure fuel line, over fuel line connection with rags to prevent spraying of fuel.

#### Installation

Reverse removal procedure to install, noting the following:

1. When installing fuel pump and fuel gauge unit assembly, align three positioning projections of packing with holes in pump and gauge assembly.

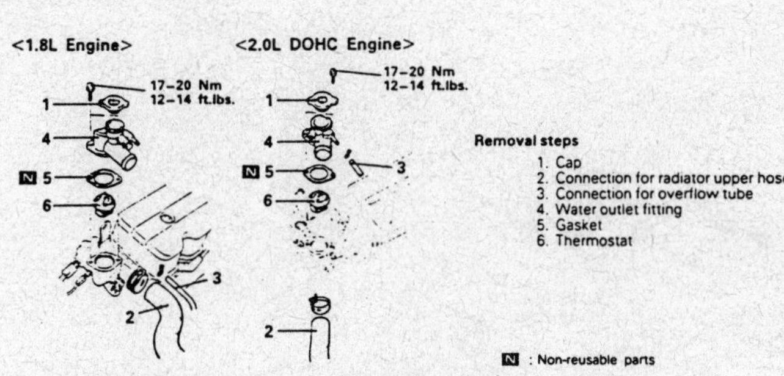


**Fig. 74 Thermostat replacement**

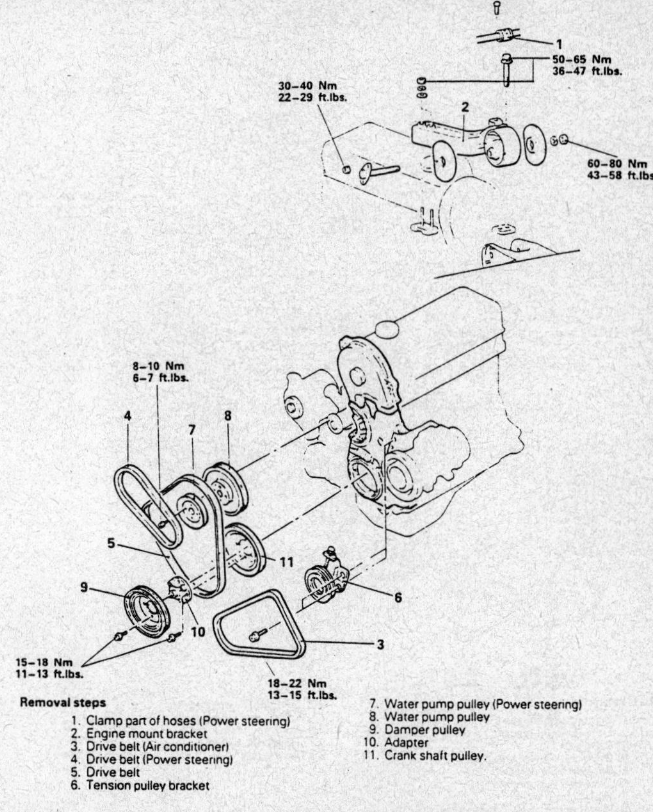


**Fig. 75 Water pump assembly (Part 1 of 2). 1.8L/4-107**

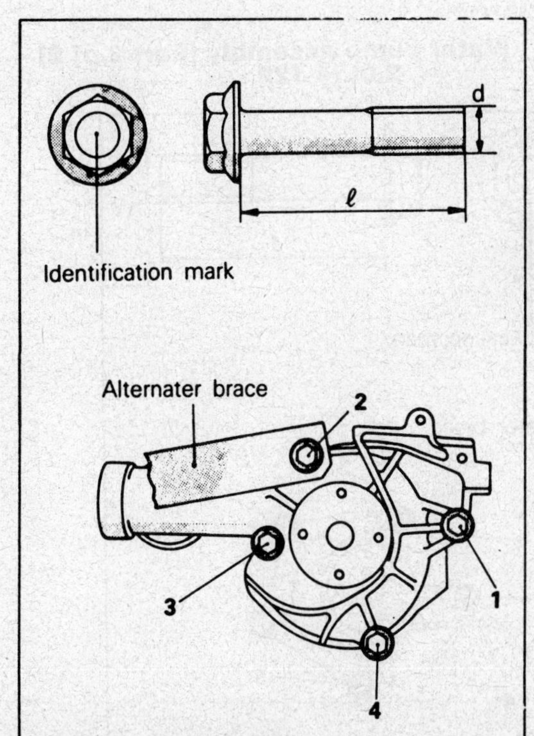


| No. | Identification mark | Bolt diameter (d) x length (ℓ) mm (in.) | Torque Nm (ft.lbs.) |
|---|---|---|---|
| 1 | 4 | 8 x 28 (.31 x 1.1) | 12–15 (9–10) |
| 2 | 7 | 8 x 70 (.31 x 2.76) | 20–27 (15–19) |
| 3 | 4 | 8 x 55 (.31 x 2.17) | 12–15 (9–10) |
| 4 | 4 | 8 x 28 (.31 x 1.1) | |

**Fig. 76 Water pump attaching bolts. 1.8L/4-107**

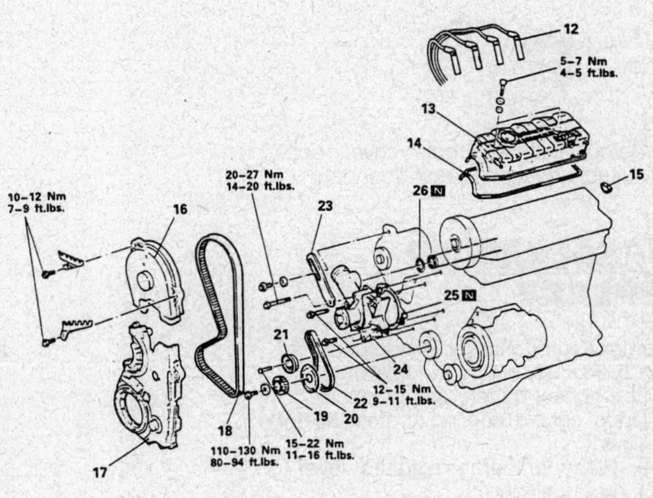


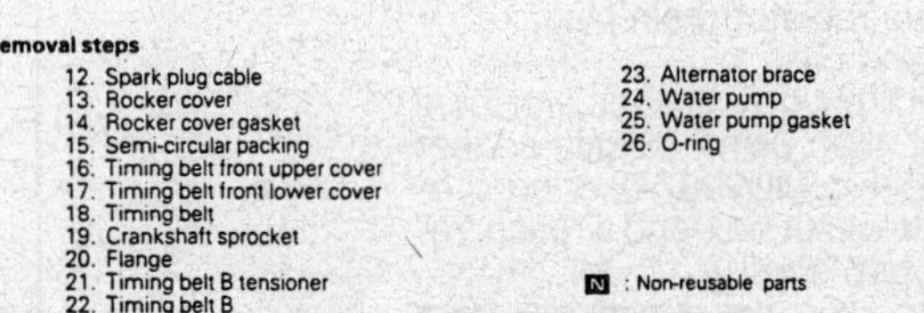

Removal steps

12. Spark plug cable
13. Rocker cover
14. Rocker cover gasket
15. Semi-circular packing
16. Timing belt front upper cover
17. Timing belt front lower cover
18. Timing belt
19. Crankshaft sprocket
20. Flange
21. Timing belt B tensioner
22. Timing belt B
23. Alternator brace
24. Water pump
25. Water pump gasket
26. O-ring

N : Non-reusable parts

**Fig. 75 Water pump assembly (Part 2 of 2). 1.8L/4-107**

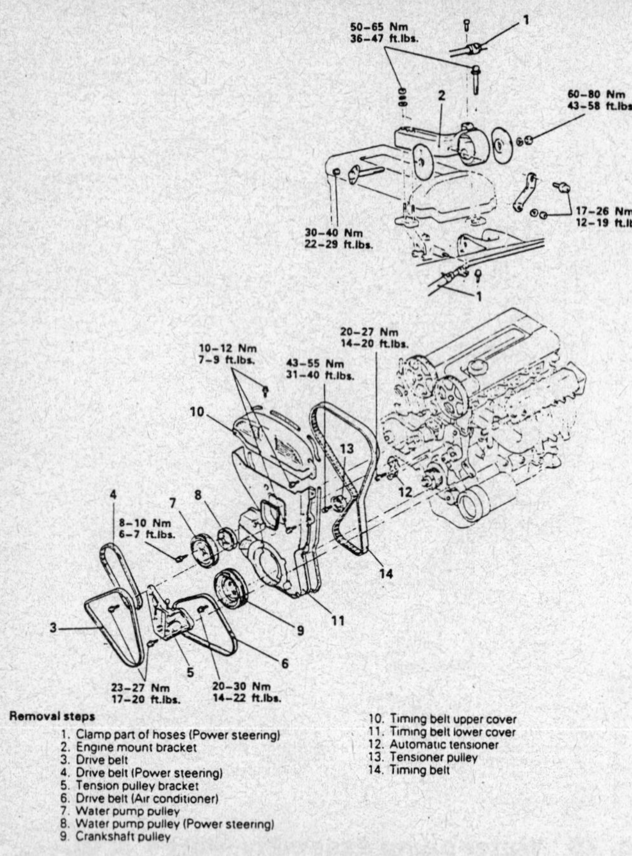


**Fig. 77 Water pump assembly (Part 1 of 2). 2.0L/4-122**

2. Before installing hole cover, apply suitable sealant to rear floor pan.

## TURBOCHARGER
## REPLACE

Remove turbocharger in numbered sequence, **Fig. 83,** noting the following.

1. Disconnect battery ground cable.
2. Drain engine cooling system as follows:
   a. Place temperature control lever in hot position.
   b. Carefully remove radiator cap.
   c. Remove radiator drain plug.
3. Drain engine oil.
4. Disconnect oxygen sensor electrical connector, then using oxygen sensor socket tool No. MD998748 or equivalent and an offset box-end wrench, remove oxygen sensor.
5. Remove power steering pump from bracket with hoses attached, then secure pump aside with a piece of wire.
6. Remove turbocharger assembly with water pipes A and B and oil pipe attached. **After disconnecting oil**

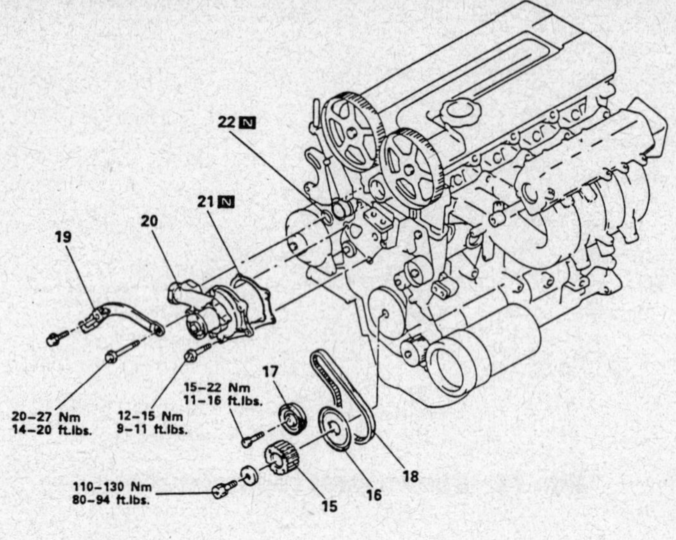


15. Crankshaft sprocket
16. Flange
17. Timing belt B tensioner
18. Timing belt B
19. Alternator brace
20. Water pump
21. Water pump gasket
22. O-ring

N : Non-reusable parts

**Fig. 77 Water pump assembly (Part 2 of 2). 2.0L/4-122**

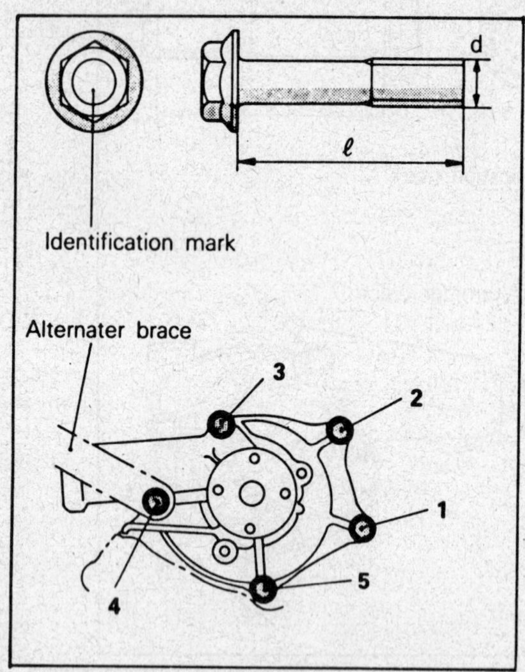


| No. | Identification mark | Bolt diameter (d) x length (ℓ) mm (in.) | Torque Nm (ft.lbs.) |
|---|---|---|---|
| 1 | 4 | 8 x 14 (.31 x .55) | 12–15 (9–10) |
| 2 | 4 | 8 x 22 (.31 x .87) | |
| 3 | 4 | 8 x 30 (.31 x 1.18) | |
| 4 | 7 | 8 x 65 (.31 x 2.56) | 20–27 (15–19) |
| 5 | 4 | 8 x 28 (.31 x 1.10) | 12–15 (9–10) |

**Fig. 78 Water pump attaching bolts. 2.0L/4-122**

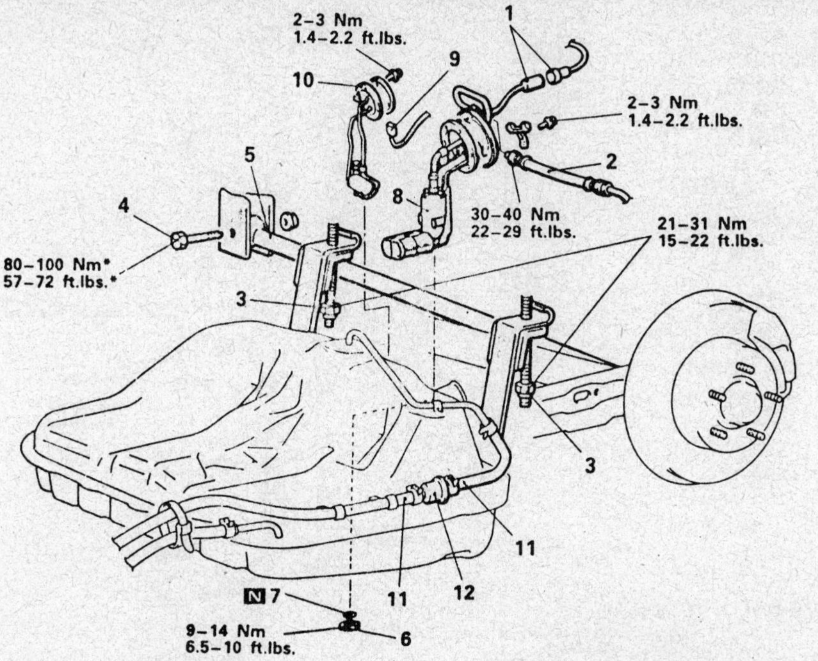


**Fuel pump removal steps**

1. Connection for fuel pump connector
2. High pressure fuel hose
3. Self locking nut
4. Lateral rod attaching bolt
5. Lateral rod and body connection
6. Bolt
7. O-ring
8. Electric fuel pump

**Fuel gauge unit removal steps**

3. Self locking nut
4. Lateral rod attaching bolt
5. Lateral rod and body connection
9. Connection for fuel gauge unit connector
10. Fuel gauge unit

**Overfill limiter removal steps**

11. Connection for vapor hose
12. Overfill limiter (Two-way valve)

**Fig. 79 Fuel pump assembly. Models w/2 wheel drive**

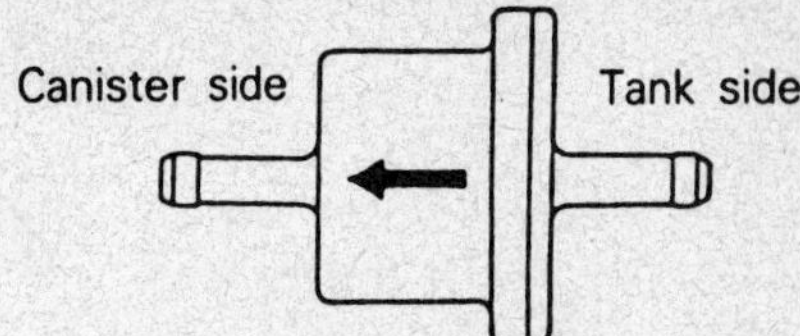


**Fig. 80 Fuel tank overfill limiter**

Positioning projection

**Fig. 81 Installing fuel gauge unit**

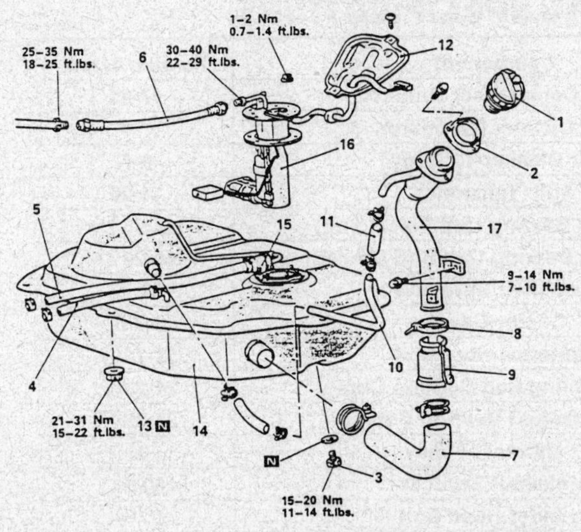


**Removal steps**

1. Fuel tank cap
2. Packing
3. Drain plug
4. Return hose
5. Vapor hose
6. High pressure fuel hose
7. Fuel filler hose
8. Cable band
9. Protector
10. Vapor pipe
11. Vapor hose
12. Hole cover
13. Self-locking nut
14. Fuel tank
15. Overfill limiter (Two-way valve)
16. Fuel pump and fuel gauge unit assembly
17. Fuel filler neck

N : Non-reusable parts

**Fig. 82 Fuel pump assembly. Models w/4 wheel drive**

**pipe, ensure foreign material does not enter oil passage hole of turbocharger.**

7. Reverse procedure to install, noting the following:
   a. Prior to installing turbocharger assembly, pour a small quantity of clean engine oil into oil supply pipe fitting hole in turbocharger.
   b. Clean alignment surfaces of turbocharger. **Use caution not to allow gasket or other foreign material to enter oil passage hole.**
   c. Use new gaskets, locknuts and O-rings.
   d. Install oxygen sensor using oxygen sensor socket tool No. MD998748 or equivalent and an offset box-end wrench, then connect oxygen sensor electrical connector.

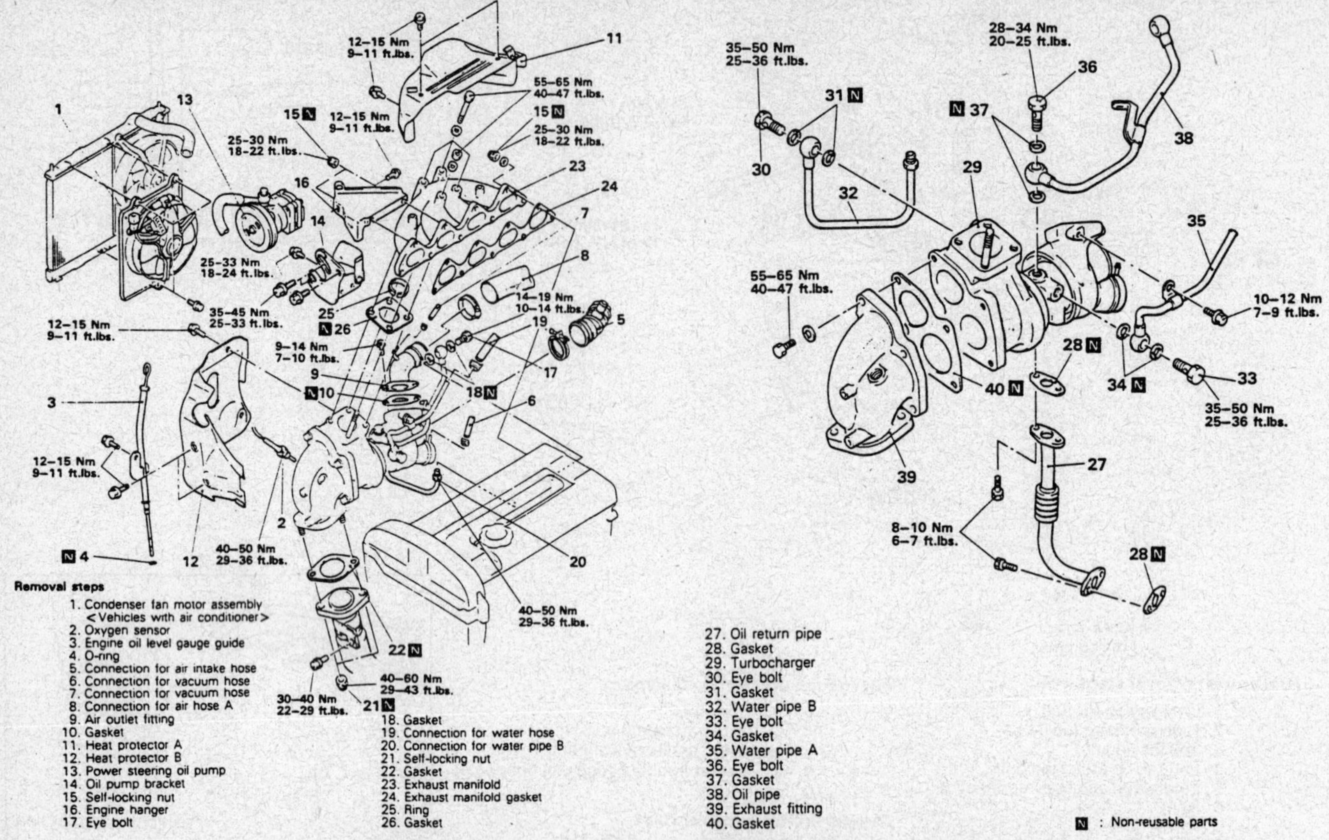


**Fig. 83 Turbocharger assembly (Part 1 of 2). 2.0L/4-122**

**Fig. 83 Turbocharger assembly (Part 2 of 2). 2.0L/4-122**

# TIGHTENING SPECIFICATIONS

| Year | Component | Torque/ft. lbs. |
|---|---|---|
| 1990–92 | A/C Compressor Bracket | 17-20 |
| | Air Cleaner Resonator | 7-9 |
| | Air Cleaner-to-Body | 6-7 |
| | Auto Tensioner | 14-20 |
| | Camshaft Bearing Cap Bolt (Long) | 14-15 (1) |
| | Camshaft Bearing Cap Bolt (Short) | 14-20 (1) |
| | Camshaft Sprocket | 58-72 |
| | Center Cover | 2-3 (11) |
| | Centermember Bolt | 58-72 (11) |
| | Connecting Rod Bearing Cap | 24-25 (1) |
| | Crankshaft Bearing Cap | 37-39 (1) |
| | Crankshaft Pulley | (2) |
| | Crankshaft Sprocket | 80-94 |
| | Cylinder Head Bolt | (3) (4) |
| | Distributor | 7-9 (1) |
| | Driveplate | 94-101 |
| | EGR Valve | (5) |
| | Electric Fuel Pump (Bolt) | 6.5-10 |
| | Electric Fuel Pump (Screws) | 1.4-2.2 |
| | Engine Coolant Temperature Sensor | 15-29 (11) |
| | Engine Cooler Pipe-to-Front Case | 29-33 (11) |
| | Engine Mount Bracket Nut | 36-47 |
| | Engine Mount Bracket-to-Body | 36-51 |

*Continued*

# TIGHTENING SPECIFICATIONS—Continued

| Year | Component | Torque/ft. lbs. |
|---|---|---|
| 1990–92—Cont'd | Engine Mount Insulator Nut (Large) | 43-58 |
| | Engine Mount Insulator Nut (Small) | 22-29 |
| | Engine Oil Cooler Mounting Nut | 6-9 ⑪ |
| | Engine Oil Hose Mounting Nut | 2-4 ⑪ |
| | Exhaust Manifold-to-Engine | 18-22 |
| | Exhaust Manifold-to-Turbocharger (Turbo) | 40-47 ⑪ |
| | Exhaust Pipe Clamp Bolt | 22-29 |
| | Exhaust Pipe Support Bracket | 22-30 |
| | Exhaust Pipe-to-Hanger | 7-11 |
| | Exhaust Pipe-to-Manifold (Non-Turbo) | 22-29 |
| | Exhaust Pipe-to-Manifold (Turbo) | 29-43 ⑪ |
| | Eye Bolt (Engine Oil Cooler Side) | 22-25 ⑪ |
| | Eye Bolt (Oil Filter Bracket Side) | 29-33 ⑪ |
| | Flywheel | 94-101 |
| | Front Case | 14-16 |
| | Front Roll Stopper Bracket-to-Body | 40-54 |
| | Front Roll Stopper Bracket-to-Centermember | 29-36 |
| | Front Roll Stopper Insulator Nut | 36-47 |
| | Fuel Gauge Unit | 1.4-2.2 |
| | Fuel Tank Self-Locking Nut | 57-72 |
| | Heat Shield-to-Exhaust Manifold | 9-11 ⑪ |
| | Intake Manifold Stay Bolt | ⑥ |
| | Intake Manifold-to-Engine (M8) | 11-14 |
| | Intake Manifold-to-Engine (M10) | 22-30 |
| | Intercooler Air Bypass Valve | 11-16 ⑪ |
| | Intercooler Air Pipe B | 9-11 ⑪ |
| | Intercooler-to-Body | 9-11 ⑪ |
| | Left Engine Support Bracket | 22-30 |
| | Oil Filter Bracket | 11-16 |
| | Oil Level Gauge Mounting Bolt | 9-11 |
| | Oil Pan (bolts) | 4-6 |
| | Oil Pan (nuts) | 3.5-5 |
| | Oil Pan Drain Plug | 25-33 |
| | Oil Pipe-to-Engine (Turbo) | 10-14 ⑪ |
| | Oil Pressure Gauge Unit | 6-9 |
| | Oil Pressure Switch | 6-9 |
| | Oil Pump Cover | 29-36 |
| | Oil Pump Driven Gear | 25-29 |
| | Oil Pump Sprocket | ⑦ |
| | Oil Return Pipe-to-Oil Pan (Turbo) | 6-7 ⑪ |
| | Oil Screen | 11-16 |
| | Oxygen Sensor | 29-36 ⑪ |
| | Power Steering Bracket | 25-33 |
| | Radiator Upper Insulator | 7-10 |
| | Relief Plug | 11-13 |
| | Rocker Cover | 2-3 |
| | Silent Shaft Sprocket | ⑧ |
| | Tensioner Pulley Bracket | 17-20 |
| | Thermo Valve | 14-28 ① |
| | Thermosensor-to-Radiator | 2-3 |
| | Throttle Body | ⑨ |
| | Throttle Position Sensor | 1.1-1.8 |
| | Timing Belt B Tensioner Bolt | 11-16 |
| | Timing Belt Front Cover | 7-9 |

*Continued*

## TIGHTENING SPECIFICATIONS—Continued

| Year | Component | Torque/ft. lbs. |
|---|---|---|
| 1990-92—Cont'd | Timing Belt Idle Pulley | 25-30 |
| | Timing Belt Rear Cover | 7-9 |
| | Timing Belt Tensioner Pulley | ⑩ |
| | Transaxle Mount Insulator Nut | 43-58 |
| | Transaxle Mount-to-Body | 29-36 |
| | Wastegate Actuator | 7-9⑪ |
| | Water Outlet | 12-14⑪ |
| | Water Pipe-to-Engine | 10-14⑪ |
| | Water Pipe-to-Turbocharger | 25-36⑪ |
| | Water Pump Bolt (4T) | 9-11 |
| | Water Pump Bolt (7T) | 14-20 |
| | Water Pump Pulley | 6-7 |

①—1.8L/4-107 Engine.
②—1.8L/4-107 Engine, 11-13 ft. lbs.; 2.0L/4-122, 14-22 ft. lbs.
③—1.8L/4-107 Engine, 51-54 ft. lbs.; 2.0L/4-122, 65-72 ft. lbs.
④—Tighten in two or three steps. See text for sequence.
⑤—1.8L/4-107 Engine, 7-11 ft. lbs.; 2.0L/4-122, 11-16 ft. lbs.
⑥—1.8L/4-107 Engine, 13-18 ft. lbs.; 2.0L/4-122, 18-22 ft. lbs.
⑦—1.8L/4-107 Engine, 26-29 ft. lbs.; 2.0L/4-122, 36-43 ft. lbs.
⑧—1.8L/4-107 Engine, 25-29 ft. lbs.; 2.0L/4-122, 31-35 ft. lbs.
⑨—1.8L/4-107 Engine, 7-9 ft. lbs.; 2.0L/4-122, 11-16 ft. lbs.
⑩—1.8L/4-107 Engine, 16-22 ft. lbs.; 2.0L/4-122, 31-40 ft. lbs.
⑪—2.0L/4-122 Engine.

# Clutch & Manual Transaxle

## INDEX



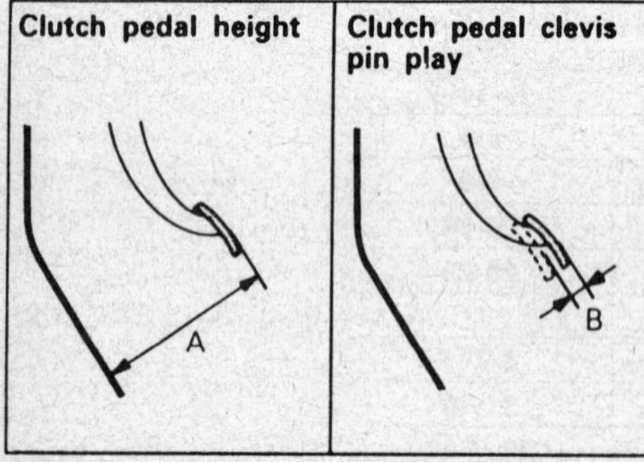


Fig. 1 Clutch pedal inspection

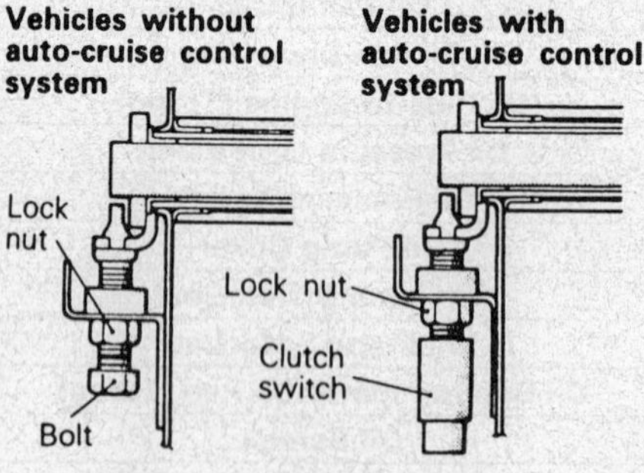


Fig. 2 Clutch pedal adjustment

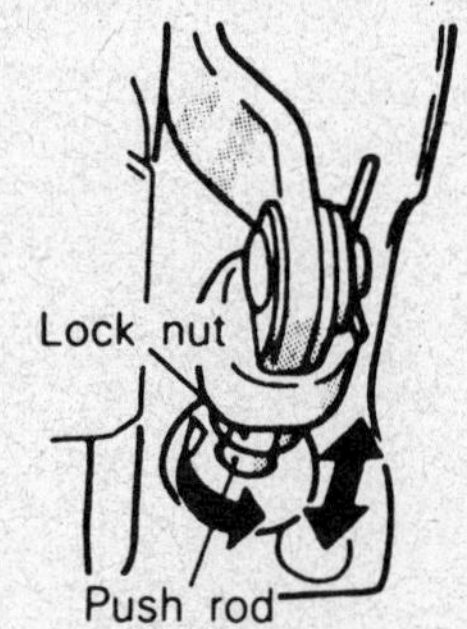


Fig. 3 Adjusting pushrod

## CLUTCH PEDAL

### ADJUST

1. Measure clutch pedal height or clevis pin play as shown, **Fig. 1.**
2. If height is higher than 6.93-7.13 inches, proceed as follows:
   a. **On models less auto-cruise system,** adjust bolt until pedal height is correct, **Fig. 2,** then secure by tightening locknut.
   b. **On models with auto-cruise,** disconnect clutch switch connector. Turn switch until pedal height is correct, **Fig. 2,** then secure by tightening locknut.
3. **On all models,** if pedal height is lower than 6.93-7.13 inches, proceed as follows:
   a. Loosen bolt or clutch switch and turn pushrod until pedal height is correct, **Fig. 3. Do not move pushrod toward master cylinder.**
   b. After adjustment, tighten bolt or clutch switch to reach pedal stopper, then lock with locknut.
4. If clevis pin play is not .04-.12 inch, proceed as follows:
   a. Turn pushrod until clevis pin play is correct.
5. Ensure interlock switch is as shown **Fig. 4,** when clutch pedal is fully de-

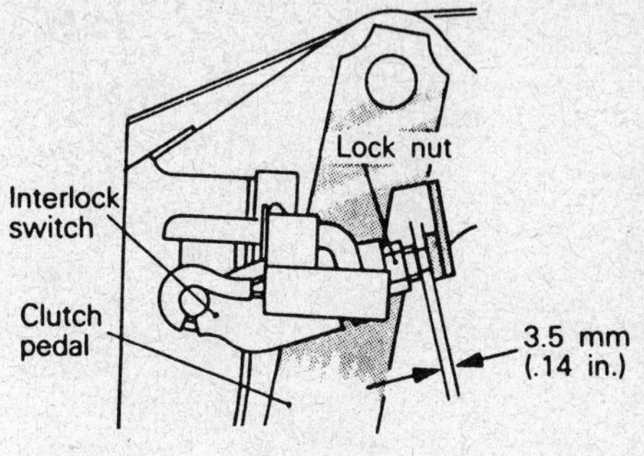


**Fig. 4 Adjusting interlock switch**

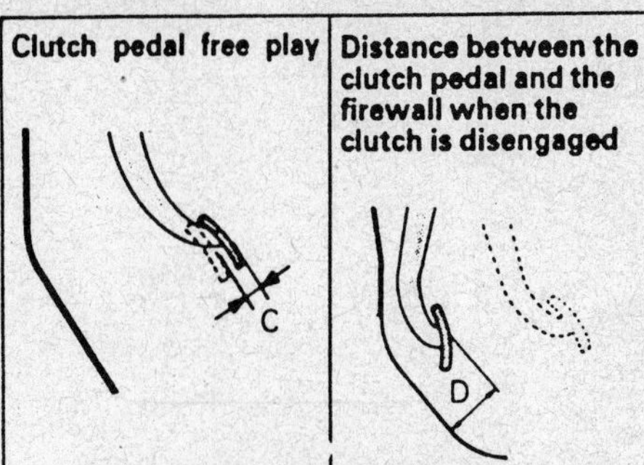


**Fig. 5 Confirming clutch pedal operation**

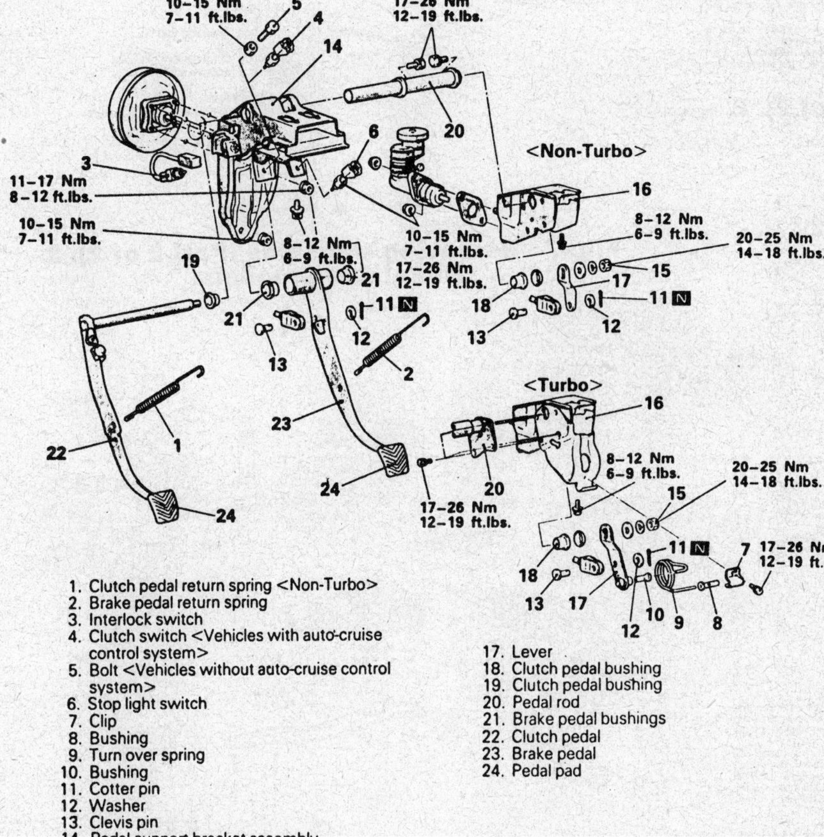


1. Clutch pedal return spring <Non-Turbo>
2. Brake pedal return spring
3. Interlock switch
4. Clutch switch <Vehicles with auto-cruise control system>
5. Bolt <Vehicles without auto-cruise control system>
6. Stop light switch
7. Clip
8. Bushing
9. Turn over spring
10. Bushing
11. Cotter pin
12. Washer
13. Clevis pin
14. Pedal support bracket assembly
15. Clutch pedal mounting nut
16. Clutch pedal bracket
17. Lever
18. Clutch pedal bushing
19. Clutch pedal bushing
20. Pedal rod
21. Brake pedal bushings
22. Clutch pedal
23. Brake pedal
24. Pedal pad

**Fig. 6 Removing clutch pedal**

pressed, if necessary adjust.

6. Confirm clutch pedal freeplay **Fig. 5,** is .24 to .51 of inch.
7. Confirm distance between clutch pedal and firewall, when clutch is disengaged **Fig. 5,**is 2.2 inches or more. If distance is not as specified, problem may be the result of air in hydraulic system or faulty master cylinder or clutch.

## CLUTCH PEDAL
### REPLACE

Remove clutch pedal in numbered sequence, **Fig. 6,** noting the following:

1. Remove lap cooler duct, shower duct, and knee protector. Refer to the "Dash Panel" section for procedures.
2. Remove steering column assembly as outlined under "Steering Column, Replace" in the Steering Column" section.
3. Remove relay box.
4. Apply lubricant to the clutch pedal bushings, clevis pin and washer and, on turbo models, bushing No. 8.
5. Reverse procedure to install.

## CLUTCH
### REPLACE

1. Remove transaxle as outlined under "Manual Transaxle, Replace."
2. Diagonally loosen clutch cover bolts in two or three steps.
3. Support clutch cover and remove cover bolts, lowering clutch and clutch cover.
4. Remove clutch bearing return clip, bearing, release fork, fulcrum and release fork boot from transaxle.
5. Reverse procedure to install.

## CLUTCH SLAVE CYLINDER
### REPLACE

1. Drain clutch fluid into a suitable container.
2. Disconnect clutch slave cylinder tube connections.
3. Remove slave cylinder retaining bolts then the slave cylinder.
4. Reverse procedure to install, noting the following:
   a. Apply multi-purpose grease to slave cylinder pushrod where it contacts the release fork.
   b. Bleed hydraulic clutch system as outlined under" Hydraulic Clutch System Bleeding."

## HYDRAULIC CLUTCH SYSTEM BLEEDING

Whenever the any component of the hydraulic clutch system has been removed, bleeding must be performed. Bleed system using bleeder screw located on the clutch slave cylinder.

## MANUAL TRANSAXLE
### REPLACE

Remove transaxle in numbered sequence, **Figs. 7 and 8,** noting the following:

1. Remove battery.
2. **On models with auto-cruise,** remove control actuator and bracket.
3. **On all models,** remove air intake hose.
4. Raise on support vehicle.
5. Drain transaxle oil.
6. Remove clutch release cylinder and clutch oil line bracket bolt, then secure at body side without disconnecting oil line coupling.
7. Disconnect tie rod end and lower ball joint.
8. **On 2 wheel drive models,** disconnect driveshaft as follows:
   a. Insert pry bar between transaxle case and driveshaft, **Fig. 9,** then pry driveshaft from transaxle. **Do not pull on driveshaft, as doing so will damage inboard joint. Do not insert pry bar so deep as to damage oil seal.**

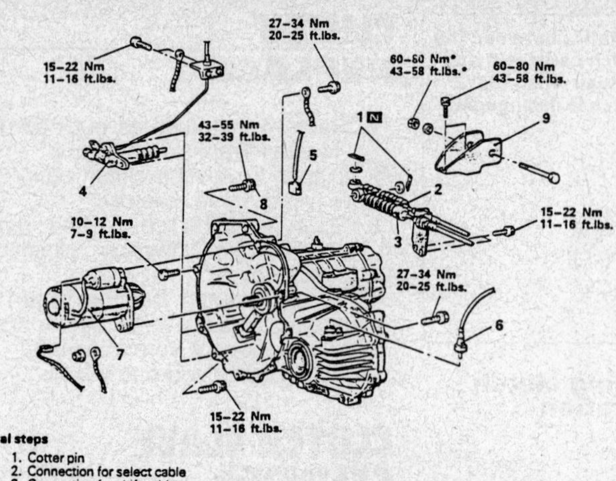


**Removal steps**

1. Cotter pin
2. Connection for select cable
3. Connection for shift cable
4. Connection for clutch release cylinder
5. Backup light switch connector
6. Connection for speedometer cable
7. Starter
8. Transaxle assembly upper part coupling bolt
9. Transaxle mount bracket

N : Non-reusable parts
For tightening locations indicated by the * symbol, first tighten temporarily, and then make the final tightening with the entire weight of the engine applied to the vehicle body.
If the grease has been wiped from the input shaft spline or if the input shaft has been replaced, apply special grease (MOPAR Multi-mileage Lubricant Part No. 2525035 or equivalent) to the input shaft spline.

**Fig. 7 Removing transaxle (Part 1 of 2). 2 wheel drive models**

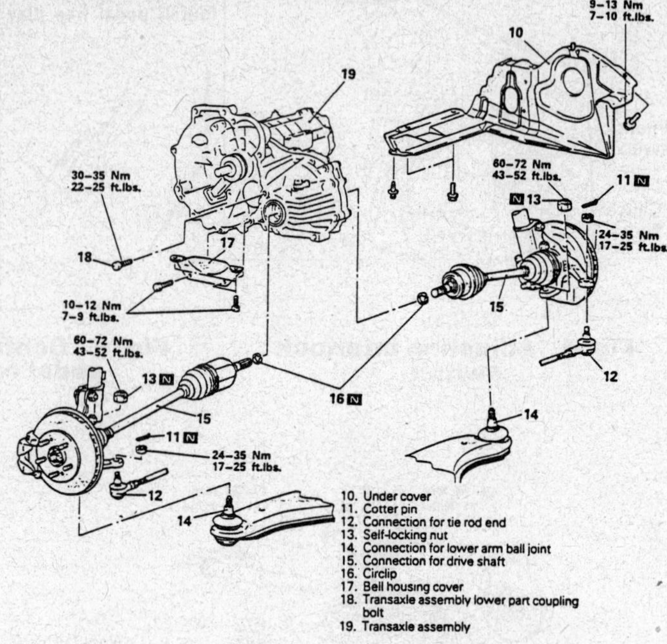


10. Under cover
11. Cotter pin
12. Connection for tie rod end
13. Self-locking nut
14. Connection for lower arm ball joint
15. Connection for drive shaft
16. Circlip
17. Bell housing cover
18. Transaxle assembly lower part coupling bolt
19. Transaxle assembly

N : Non-reusable parts

**Fig. 7 Removing transaxle (Part 2 of 2). 2 wheel drive models**

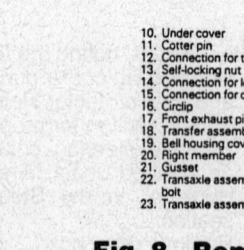

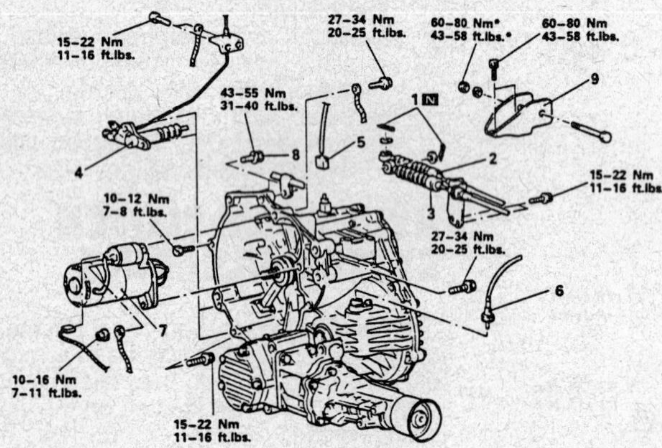


**Removal steps**

1. Cotter pin
2. Connection for select cable
3. Connection for shift cable
4. Connection for clutch release cylinder
5. Backup light switch connector
6. Connection for speedometer cable
7. Starter
8. Transaxle assembly upper part coupling bolt
9. Transaxle mount bracket

N : Non-reusable parts
For tightening locations indicated by the * symbol, first tighten temporarily, and then make the final tightening with the entire weight of the engine applied to the vehicle body.
If the grease has been wiped from the input shaft and center shaft splines or if the input shaft and center shaft have been replaced, apply special grease (MOPAR Multi-mileage Lubricant Part No. 2525035 or equivalent) to the input shaft and center shaft splines.

**Fig. 8 Removing transaxle (Part 1 of 2). 4 wheel drive models**

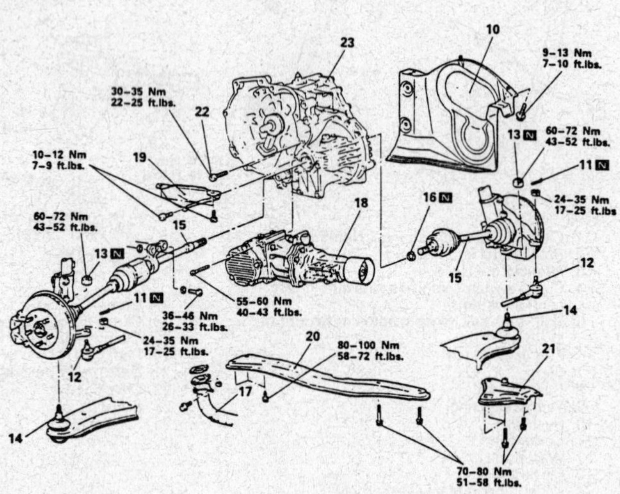


10. Under cover
11. Cotter pin
12. Connection for tie rod end
13. Self-locking nut
14. Connection for lower arm ball joint
15. Connection for drive shaft
16. Circlip
17. Front exhaust pipe
18. Transfer assembly
19. Bell housing cover
20. Right member
21. Gusset
22. Transaxle assembly lower part coupling bolt
23. Transaxle assembly

N : Non-reusable parts

**Fig. 8 Removing transaxle (Part 2 of 2). 4 wheel drive models**

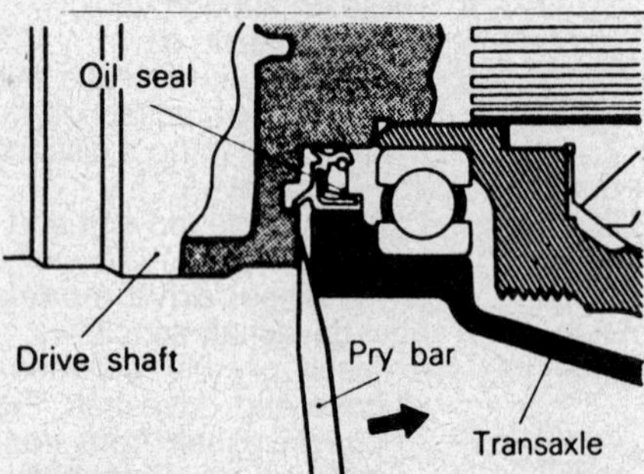


**Fig. 9 Removing driveshaft**

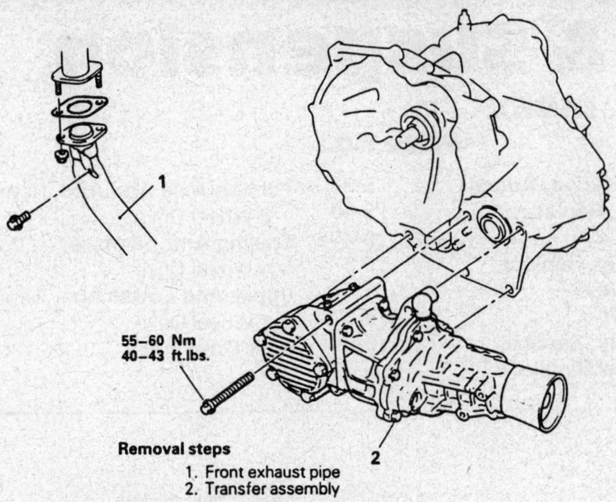
1
55–60 Nm
40–43 ft.lbs.
2
Removal steps
1. Front exhaust pipe
2. Transfer assembly
If the grease has been wiped from the center shaft spline or if the center shaft has been replaced, apply special grease (MOPAR Multi-mileage Lubricant Part No.2525035 or equivalent) to the center shaft spline.

**Fig. 10 Removing transfer case assembly**

b. Secure removed end of driveshaft away from transaxle.

9. **On 4 wheel drive models,** disconnect driveshaft as follows:
   a. **On righthand side,** insert pry bar between transaxle case and driveshaft, **Fig. 9,** then pry driveshaft from transaxle. **Do not pull on driveshaft, as doing so will damage inboard joint. Do not insert pry bar so deep as to damage oil seal.**
   b. **On lefthand side,** lightly tap driveshaft T.J. case with plastic hammer. **Remove driveshaft with hub and knuckle as an assembly.**
   c. Secure removed end of driveshaft away from transaxle.
10. **On 4 wheel drive models,** remove transfer case in numbered sequence, **Fig. 10,** noting the following:
    a. Move transfer case to left and lower from front side of vehicle, then remove propeller shaft.
11. **On all models,** support transaxle assembly using jack, after moving transaxle to right lower away from vehicle.
12. When installing driveshaft ensure inboard joint is straight relative to transaxle.
13. Align serration, then securely insert driveshaft into transaxle.
14. Reverse procedure to install.

## TIGHTENING SPECIFICATIONS

| Year | Component | Torque/ft. lbs. |
|---|---|---|
| 1990–92 | Back-up Lamp Switch | 22-25 |
| | Bearing Retainer Bolt | 11-15 |
| | Bellhousing Cover | 7-9 |
| | Bleeder Plug | 7-9 |
| | Brake Booster Installation Nut | 7-11 |
| | Clutch Cover Assembly | 11-16 |
| | Clutch Pedal Bracket | 6-9 |
| | Clutch Pedal Support Bracket | 6-9 |
| | Clutch Pedal To Support Bracket | 14-18 |
| | Clutch Release Cylinder | 11-16 |
| | Clutch Tube Flare Nut | 9-12 |
| | Drain Plug | 22-25 |
| | Flywheel Bolts | 94-191 |
| | Fulcrum | 25-30 |
| | Input Shaft Locknut | 102-115 |
| | Lower Arm Ball Joint To Knuckle | 43-52 |
| | Poppet Plug | 43-52 |
| | Rear Housing Cover Bolt | 11-15 |
| | Restrict Ball Assembly | 11-15 |
| | Shift And Select Cable To Transaxle | 11-16 |
| | Speedometer Sleeve Bolt | 20-25 |
| | Starter Motor Mounting Bolt | 20-25 |
| | Stop Lamp Switch | 7-11 |
| | Stopper Bracket Bolt | 11-15 |
| | Tie Rod End To Knuckle | 17-25 |
| | Transaxle Bracket | 43-58 |
| | Transaxle Case Tightening Bolt | 26-30 |
| | Transaxle Mounting Bolt (.47 inch) | 32-39 |
| | Transaxle Mounting Bolt (.40 inch) | 22-25 |
| | Transaxle Mounting Bolt (.31 inch) | 7-9 |
| | Transfer Assembly Mounting Bolt | 40-43 |

# Rear Axle & Suspension

## INDEX



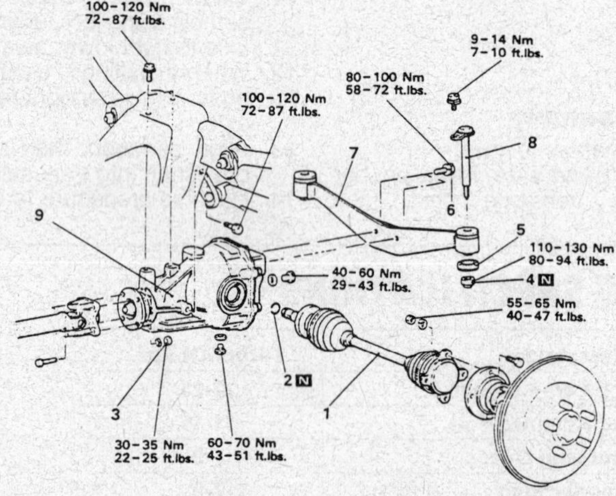


**Fig. 1 Differential carrier assembly**

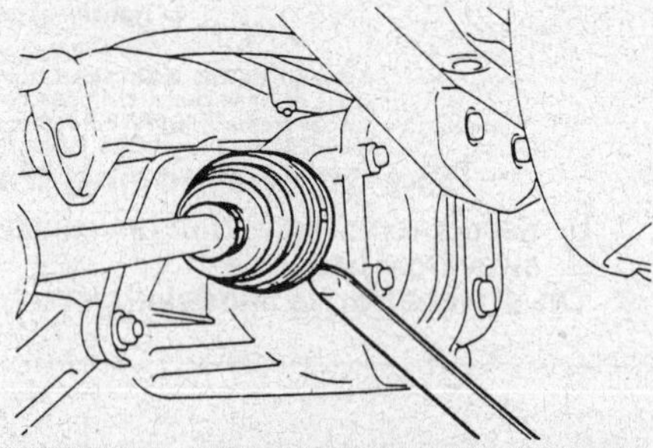

**Fig. 2 Removing driveshaft assembly**

## REAR WHEEL BEARING

### ADJUST

1. To check bearing endplay, proceed as follows:
   a. Place dial gauge against hub surface, then move hub in axial direction.
   b. If endplay exceeds .004 inch, locknut should be tightened.
   c. Torque locknut to specifications.
2. Replace hub bearing unit if adjustment cannot be made to within limit.

## DIFFERENTIAL CARRIER

### REPLACE

1. Replace differential carrier in numbered sequence shown in **Fig. 1,** noting the following:
   a. Driveshaft as outlined under "Driveshaft, Replace."
   b. Mark then disconnect propeller shaft assembly.

## DRIVESHAFT

### REPLACE

1. Remove companion flange to driveshaft bolts.
2. Remove driveshaft from differential carrier using a suitable pry bar, **Fig. 2.**
3. Remove circlip from end of driveshaft.
4. Remove oil seal using a suitable oil seal remover tool.
5. Reverse procedure to install, noting the following:
   a. Install oil seal using suitable oil seal installer tool.
   b. When installing driveshaft, ensure not to damage oil seal by the driveshaft splines.
   c. Install driveshaft with the two part serration on right hand differential side. driveshaft can be identified by the color of the BJ boot band, yellow for left and orange for right.

## REAR AXLE HUB

### REPLACE

### 2 WHEEL DRIVE

Remove rear axle hub in numbered sequence, **Fig. 3,** noting the following:

1. Remove rear speed sensor as follows:
   a. Remove rear toothed rotor, then the clip.
   b. Remove cable band, then the connection to speed sensor.
   c. Remove rear speed sensor and bracket.
2. Suspend caliper assembly with a piece of wire. **Do not hang caliper by brake hose.**
3. Rear hub bearing cannot be disassembled.
4. Press inner race until it contacts with spindle end.
5. Align wheel bearing nut with spindle indentation and crimp.
6. Reverse procedure to install.

## AXLE SHAFT

### REPLACE

### 4 WHEEL DRIVE

Remove rear axle hub in numbered sequence, **Fig. 4,** noting the following:

1. Remove rear speed sensor as follows:
   a. Remove rear toothed rotor, then the clip.
   b. Remove cable band, then the connection to speed sensor.
   c. Remove rear speed sensor and bracket.
2. Suspend caliper assembly with a piece of wire. **Do not hang caliper by brake hose.**
3. Press off bearing using suitable press.
4. Reverse procedure to install.

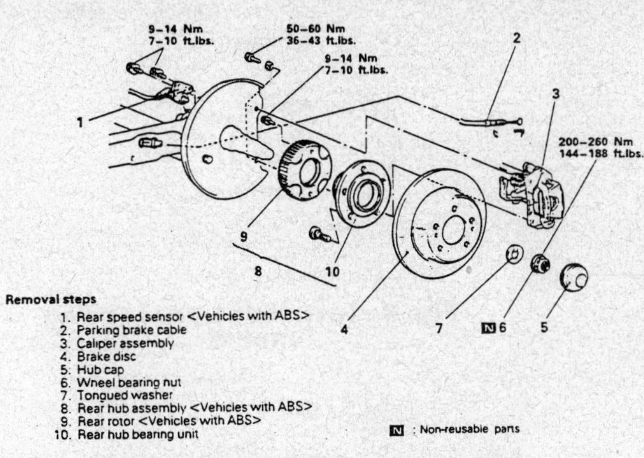


Removal steps
1. Rear speed sensor <Vehicles with ABS>
2. Parking brake cable
3. Caliper assembly
4. Brake disc
5. Hub cap
6. Wheel bearing nut
7. Tongued washer
8. Rear hub assembly <Vehicles with ABS>
9. Rear rotor <Vehicles with ABS>
10. Rear hub bearing unit

N : Non-reusable parts

**Fig. 3 Replacing rear axle hub**

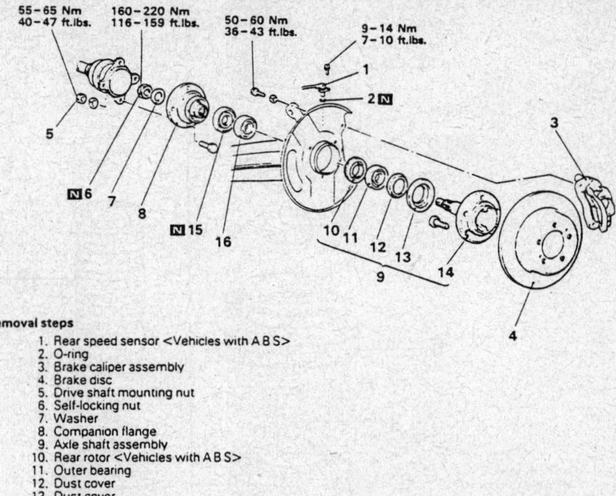


Removal steps
1. Rear speed sensor <Vehicles with A B S>
2. O-ring
3. Brake caliper assembly
4. Brake disc
5. Drive shaft mounting nut
6. Self-locking nut
7. Washer
8. Companion flange
9. Axle shaft assembly
10. Rear rotor <Vehicles with A B S>
11. Outer bearing
12. Dust cover
13. Dust cover
14. Axle shaft
15. Oil seal
16. Inner bearing

N : Non-reusable parts

**Fig. 4 Axle shaft replacement**

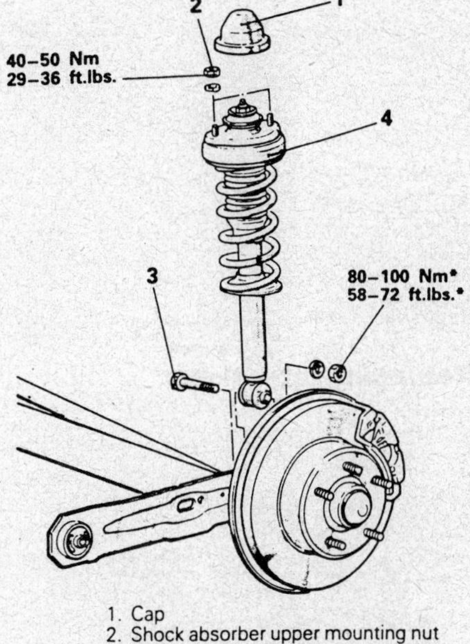


1. Cap
2. Shock absorber upper mounting nut
3. Shock absorber lower mounting bolt
4. Shock absorber

**Fig. 5 Removing shock absorber assembly (2WD)**

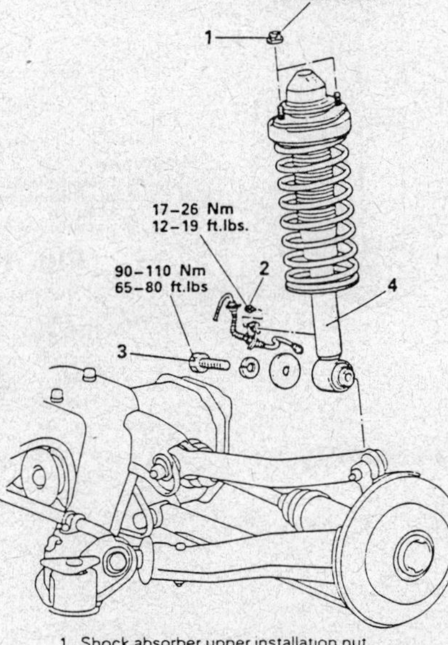


1. Shock absorber upper installation nut
2. Brake tube bracket installation bolt
3. Shock absorber lower installation bolt
4. Shock absorber assembly

**Fig. 6 Removing shock absorber assembly (4WD)**

# STRUT ASSEMBLY

## REPLACE

### 2 WHEEL DRIVE

Remove shock absorber assembly in numbered sequence, **Fig. 5,** noting the following:

1. Jack up torsion axle and arm assembly in order to release tension.
2. Place jack at center of axle beam, ensuring jack does not contact lateral rod.
3. Reverse procedure to install.

### 4 WHEEL DRIVE

Remove shock absorber assembly in numbered sequence, **Fig. 6.** Reverse procedure to install.

# STRUT ASSEMBLY

## SERVICE

Disassemble strut assembly in numbered sequence shown in **Fig. 7,** noting the following:

1. Ensure spring is properly seated in upper and lower spring seat when installing.
2. Install strut upper bracket as shown in **Fig. 8,** then tighten strut rod nut to specifications.

# UPPER AND LOWER ARM

## REPLACE

### 4 WHEEL DRIVE

Remove upper and lower arm in numbered sequence, **Fig. 9,** noting the following:

1. Loosen, but do not remove self-locking nut
2. Press fit lower arm bushing until outer edge is flush with lower arm edge.
3. Reverse procedure to install.

# LATERAL ROD

## REPLACE

### 2 WHEEL DRIVE

Remove lateral rod in numbered sequence, **Fig. 10,** noting the following:

1. Install lateral rod mounting bolt from top of axle beam with nut on bottom of lateral rod.
2. Reverse procedure to install.

# TORSION AXLE AND ARM

## REPLACE

### 2 WHEEL DRIVE

Remove torsion axle and arm in numbered sequence, **Fig. 11,** noting the following:

1. Remove rear speed sensor as follows:
   a. Remove rear toothed rotor, then the clip.
   b. Remove cable band, then the connection to speed sensor.
   c. Remove rear speed sensor and bracket.
   d. Reverse procedure to install.
2. Suspend caliper assembly with a piece of wire. **Do not hang caliper by brake hose.**

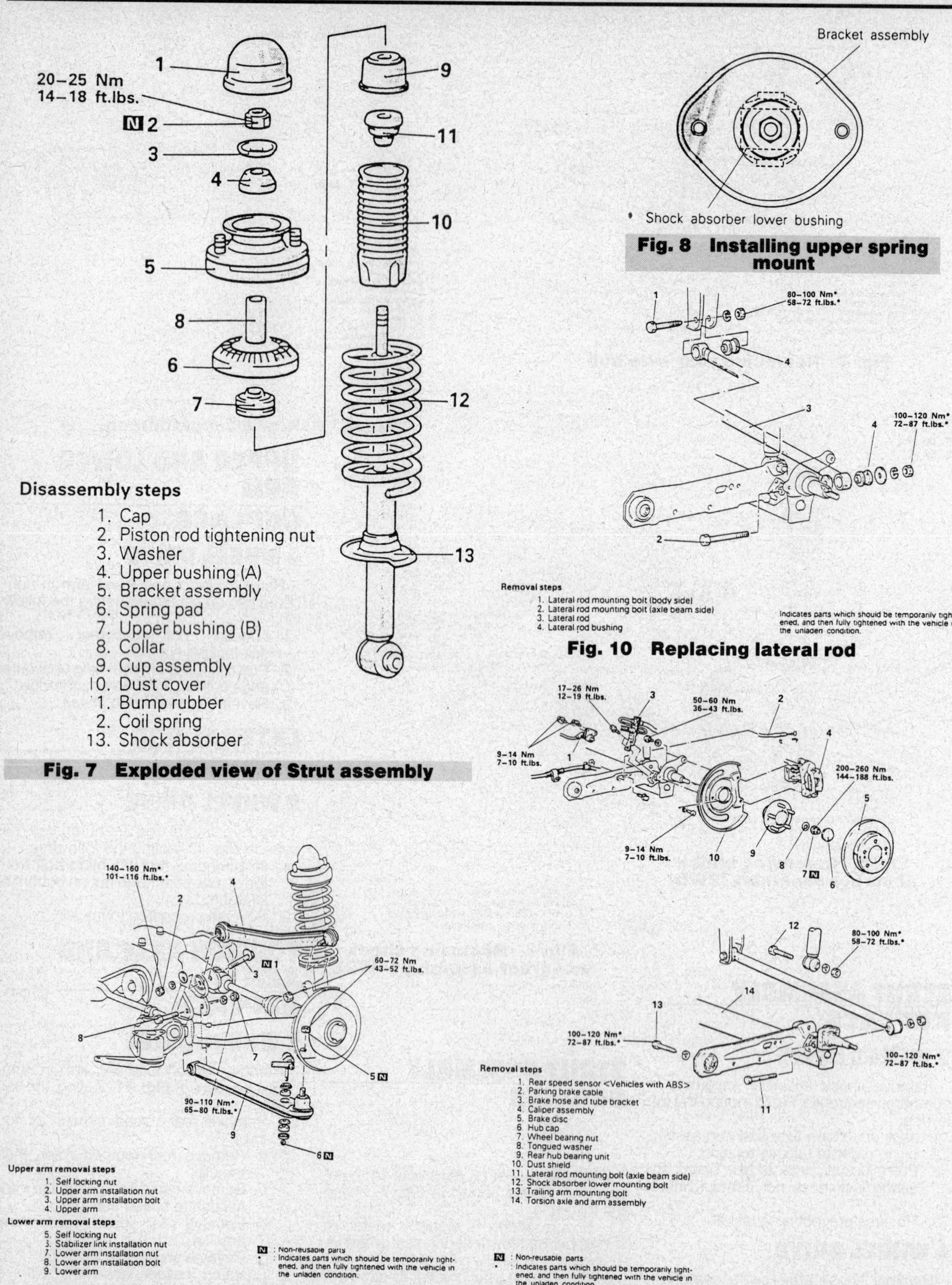


**Disassembly steps**

1. Cap
2. Piston rod tightening nut
3. Washer
4. Upper bushing (A)
5. Bracket assembly
6. Spring pad
7. Upper bushing (B)
8. Collar
9. Cup assembly
10. Dust cover
11. Bump rubber
12. Coil spring
13. Shock absorber

**Fig. 7 Exploded view of Strut assembly**

* Shock absorber lower bushing

**Fig. 8 Installing upper spring mount**

**Removal steps**

1. Lateral rod mounting bolt (body side)
2. Lateral rod mounting bolt (axle beam side)
3. Lateral rod
4. Lateral rod bushing

* Indicates parts which should be temporarily tightened, and then fully tightened with the vehicle in the unladen condition.

**Fig. 10 Replacing lateral rod**

**Upper arm removal steps**

1. Self locking nut
2. Upper arm installation nut
3. Upper arm installation bolt
4. Upper arm

**Lower arm removal steps**

5. Self locking nut
6. Stabilizer link installation nut
7. Lower arm installation nut
8. Lower arm installation bolt
9. Lower arm

N : Non-reusable parts
* : Indicates parts which should be temporarily tightened, and then fully tightened with the vehicle in the unladen condition.

**Fig. 9 Replacing upper and lower arm**

**Removal steps**

1. Rear speed sensor <Vehicles with ABS>
2. Parking brake cable
3. Brake hose and tube bracket
4. Caliper assembly
5. Brake disc
6. Hub cap
7. Wheel bearing nut
8. Tongued washer
9. Rear hub bearing unit
10. Dust shield
11. Lateral rod mounting bolt (axle beam side)
12. Shock absorber lower mounting bolt
13. Trailing arm mounting bolt
14. Torsion axle and arm assembly

N : Non-reusable parts
* : Indicates parts which should be temporarily tightened, and then fully tightened with the vehicle in the unladen condition.

**Fig. 11 Replacing torsion axle and arm assembly**

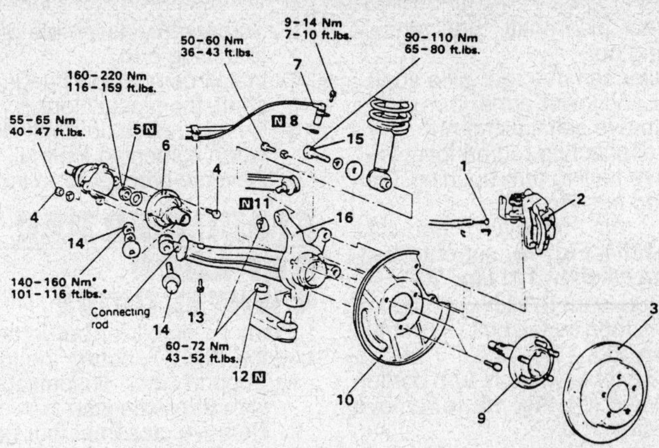


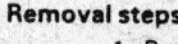

**Removal steps**

1. Parking cable end
2. Rear brake assembly
3. Rear brake disc
4. Drive shaft and companion flange installation bolt, nut
5. Self locking nut
6. Companion flange
7. Rear speed sensor <Vehicles with ABS>
8. O-ring
9. Rear axle shaft
10. Dust shield
11. Self locking nut (upper arm)
12. Self locking nut (lower arm)
13. Parking brake cable and rear speed sensor installation bolt
14. Trailing arm installation bolt, nut
15. Rear shock absorber installation bolt
16. Trailing arm

N : Non-reusable parts
* : Indicates parts which should be temporarily tightened, and then fully tightened with the vehicle in the unladen condition.

**Fig. 12 Replacing trailing arm**

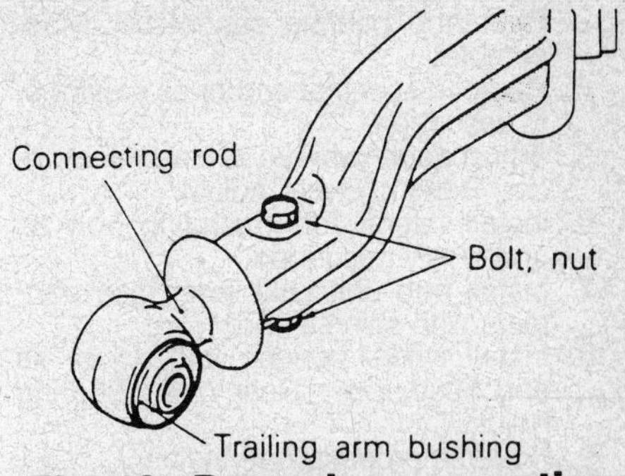

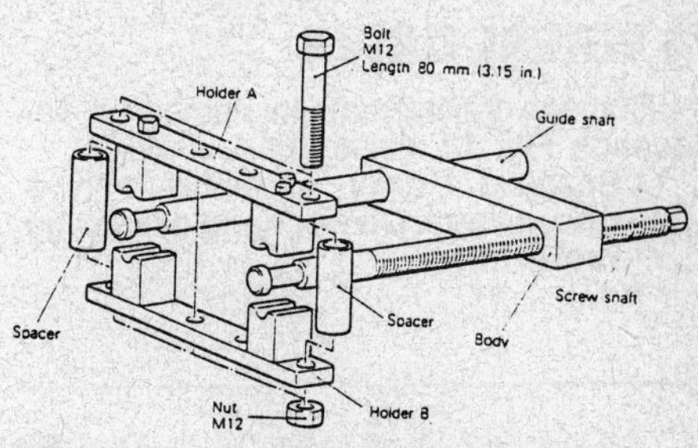


**Fig. 13 Removing connecting rod**

Bolt
M12
Length 80 mm (3.15 in.)
Holder A
Guide shaft
Screw shaft
Spacer
Spacer
Body
Nut
M12
Holder B

**Fig. 14 Rod remover tool No. MB991254**

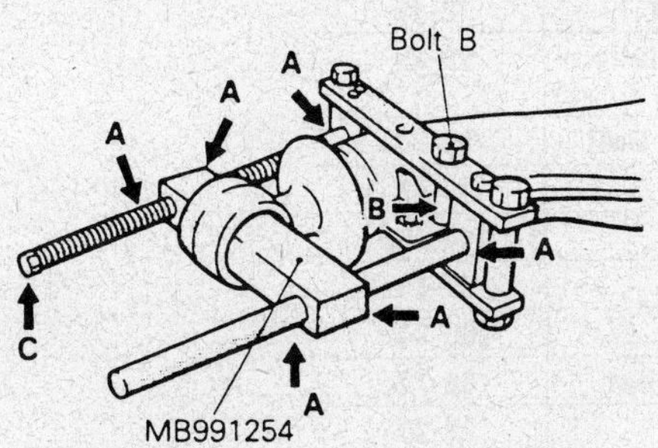

**Fig. 15 Lubrication points**

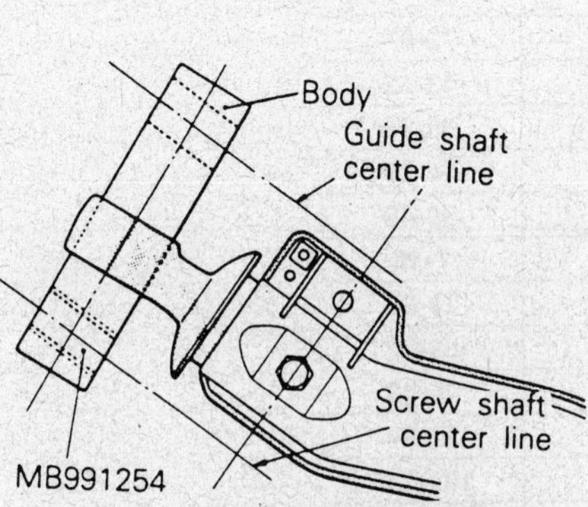


**Fig. 16 Installing rod remover tool No. MB991254**

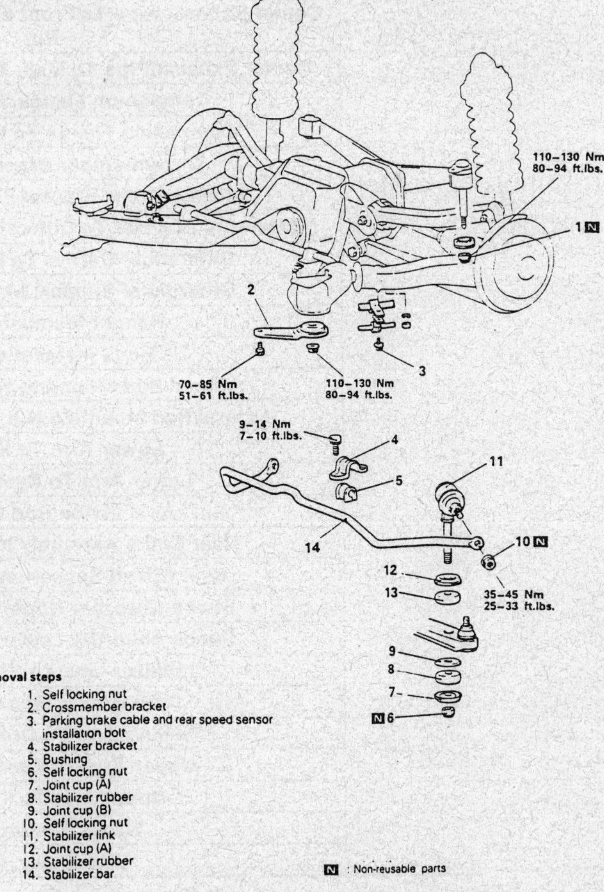


**Fig. 17 Replacing stabilizer bar**

3. Rear hub bearing cannot be disassembled.
4. Remove shock absorber as previously described.
5. Adjust parking brake as described under "Parking Brake Adjust."
6. Install lateral rod mounting bolt as previously described.
7. Install hub unit until inner race contacts with spindle end.
8. Install wheel bearing and adjust as described under "Rear Wheel Bearing Adjust."
9. Reverse procedure to install.

## TRAILING ARM
## REPLACE

### 4 WHEEL DRIVE

Remove trailing arm in numbered sequence, **Fig. 12,** noting the following:

1. Suspend caliper assembly with a piece of wire. **Do not hang caliper by brake hose.**
2. Secure rear axle shaft, then remove self locking nut.
3. Using puller, remove rear axle shaft.
4. On upper and lower arms, loosen, but do not remove self locking nut.
5. Replace connecting rod as follows:
   a. Remove trailing arm bushing, then bolt and nut, **Fig. 13.**
   b. Using rod remover tool No. MB991254, **Fig. 14,** set onto trailing arm as shown in **Fig. 15.**
   c. Apply lubricant to sliding portion of tool (A), then install bolt (B) in trailing arm, **Fig. 15,**
   d. Using suitable wrench, turn portion as marked (C), **Fig. 15,** to remove connection rod.
   e. Installation of body should be performed with screw shaft and guide shaft center lines aligned as shown in **Fig. 16.**
   f. Apply soapy water to rubber portion of connection rod.
   g. Reverse procedure to press fit, torquing bolt to specifications.
6. Temporarily assemble rear axle shaft to trailing arm.
7. Install companion flange to rear axle shaft, then install locking nut.
8. Ensure rear axle shaft does not turn when tightening locknut.
9. Reverse procedure to install.

## STABILIZER BAR
## REPLACE
### 4 WHEEL DRIVE

Remove stabilizer bar in numbered sequence, **Fig. 17,** noting the following:

1. Support rear suspension assembly with transaxle jack.
2. Remove crossmember brackets.
3. Lower transaxle jack slightly, maintaining gap between rear suspension and body.
4. Ensure stabilizer link ball joint starting torque is 15-28 inch lbs. If starting torque exceeds upper limit, replace link.
5. Reverse procedure to install.

## TIGHTENING SPECIFICATIONS

| Year | Component | Torque/ft. lbs. |
|---|---|---|
| 1990–92 | Brake Tube Bracket To Rear Shock Absorber | 12-19 |
| | Center Exhaust Pipe To Front Exhaust Pipe Installation Nut | 22-29 |
| | Center Exhaust Pipe To Main Muffler Installation Bolt | 29-36 |
| | Companion Flange To Driveshaft | 40-47 |
| | Companion Flange To Rear Axle Shaft | 116-159 |
| | Crossmember Bracket To Body | 51-61 |
| | Crossmember Bracket To Crossmember | 80-94 |
| | Differential Carrier To Differential Support Member | 58-72 |
| | Differential Carrier To Propeller Shaft | 22-25 |
| | Differential Support Member To Body | 80-94 |
| | Hanger Installation Bolt | 7-11 |
| | Hook Installation Bolt | 7-11 |
| | Lateral Rod Mounting Nut (Body Side) | 58-72 |
| | Lateral Rod Mounting Nut (Axle Beam Side) | 72-87 |
| | Lower Arm To Knuckle | 43-52 |
| | Lower Arm To Crossmember | 65-80 |
| | Piston Rod Nut | 14-18 |
| | Rear Brake Assembly Installation Bolt | 36-43 |
| | Rear Speed Sensor Installation Bolt | 7-10 |
| | Shock Absorber Upper Mounting Nut | 29-36 |
| | Shock Absorber Lower Mounting Nut | 58-72 |
| | Stabilizer Link To Stabilizer Bar | 25-33 |
| | Trailing Arm Mounting Bolt | 72-87 |
| | Trailing Arm To Crossmember | 101-116 |
| | Upper Arm To Crossmember | 101-116 |
| | Upper Arm To Knuckle | 43-52 |
| | Wheel Bearing Nut | 144-188 |
| | Wheel Lug Nuts | 87-101 |

# Front Suspension & Steering

## INDEX



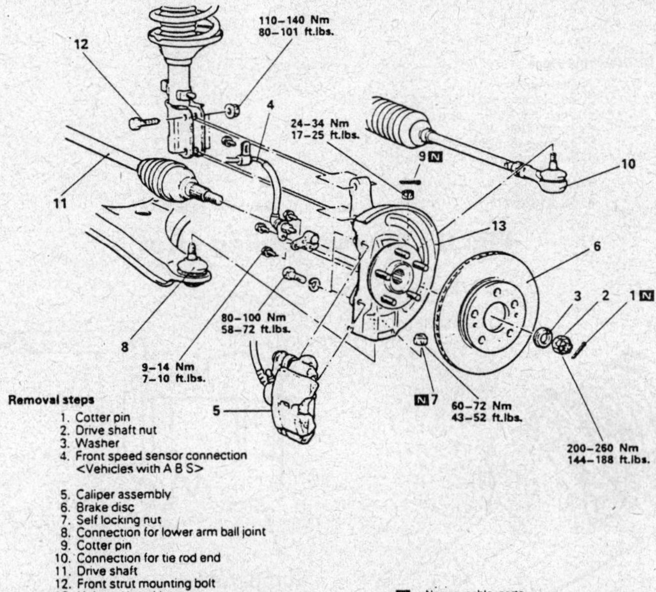


**Fig. 1 Removing hub & knuckle assembly**

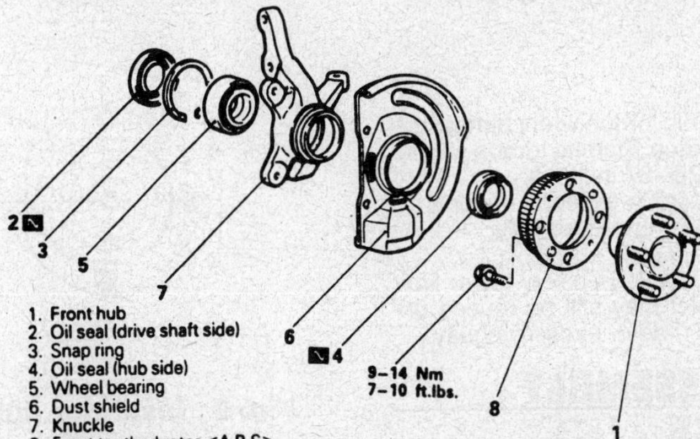


**Fig. 3 Disassembling hub and knuckle**

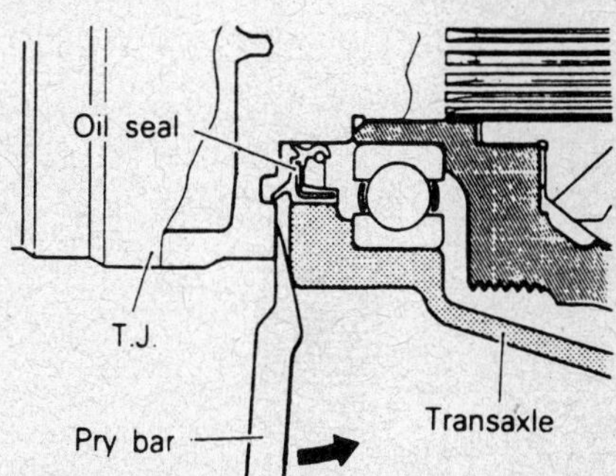


**Fig. 2 Removing driveshaft**

## STEERING KNUCKLE & HUB ASSEMBLY REPLACE

### REMOVAL

Remove knuckle and hub assembly in numbered sequence, **Fig. 1,** noting the following:

1. Loosen driveshaft nut with vehicle on floor and brakes applied.
2. Remove speed sensor mounting bolts, then the sensor. **Use care not to damage pole piece at tip of speed sensor and the toothed edge of the rotor.**
3. Remove and suspend caliper assembly using a piece of wire.
4. Insert pry bar between transaxle case and driveshaft, **Fig. 2,** then pry driveshaft from transaxle. **Do not pull on driveshaft.**

### DISASSEMBLY & ASSEMBLY

Disassemble knuckle and hub assembly in numbered sequence, **Fig. 3,** noting the following:

1. Use knuckle arm bridge tool No. MB991001 or equivalent, to separate hub from knuckle. **Do not strike with hammer, as bearing damage could occur.**
2. Remove oil seal from knuckle.
3. Using puller, remove wheel bearing inner race from front hub. It may be necessary to crush oil seal so puller will catch inner race.
4. Remove snap ring from knuckle.
5. Remove bearings from knuckle.
6. Fill wheel bearings with grease, applying thin coating of grease to knuckle and bearing surfaces.
7. With wheel bearing inner race removed, press in bearing using oil seal installer tool No. MB990985 or equivalent.
8. Install wheel bearing inner race to wheel bearing.
9. Drive hub side of oil seal into knuckle until flush with knuckle end surface.
10. Mount hub assembly to knuckle and torque to specifications.
11. Rotate hub assembly to seat bearing.
12. Measure wheel bearing starting torque; torque should be 16 inch lbs.
13. Measure endplay of hub; Endplay should be .008 inch.

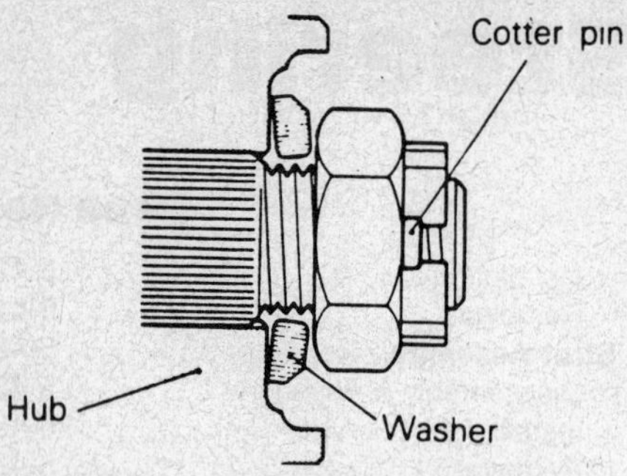


Fig. 4 Installing washer

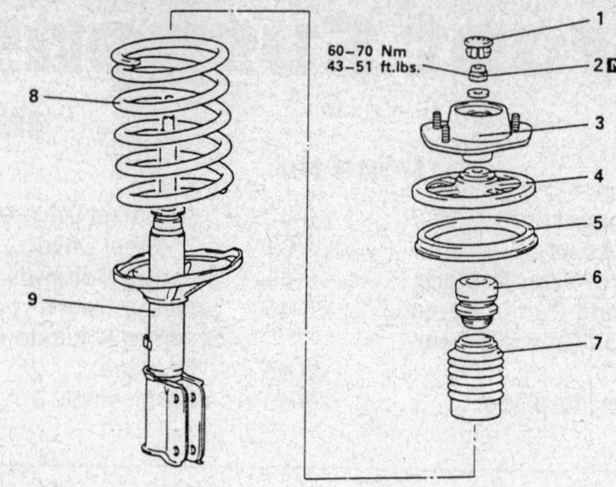


Disassembly steps
1. Dust cover
2. Self-locking nut
3. Strut insulator
4. Spring seat, upper
5. Spring pad, upper
6. Bump rubber
7. Dust cover
8. Coil spring
9. Strut assembly

N : Non-reusable parts

Fig. 6 Disassembling strut

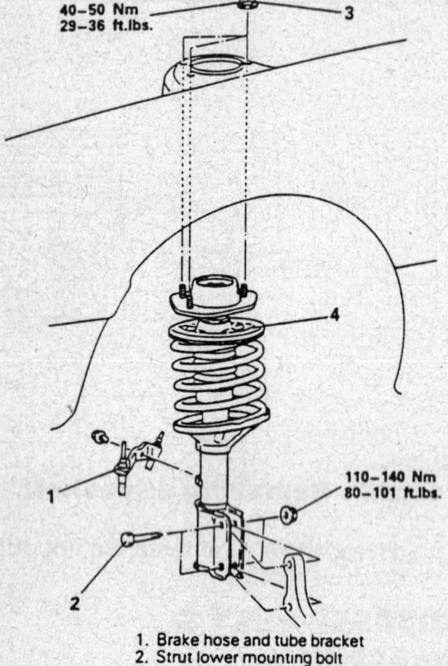


1. Brake hose and tube bracket
2. Strut lower mounting bolt
3. Strut upper mounting nut
4. Strut assembly

Fig. 5 Removing strut assembly

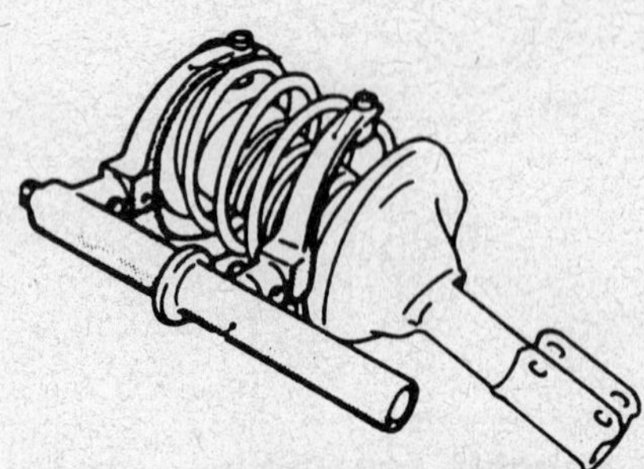

Fig. 7 Compressing spring

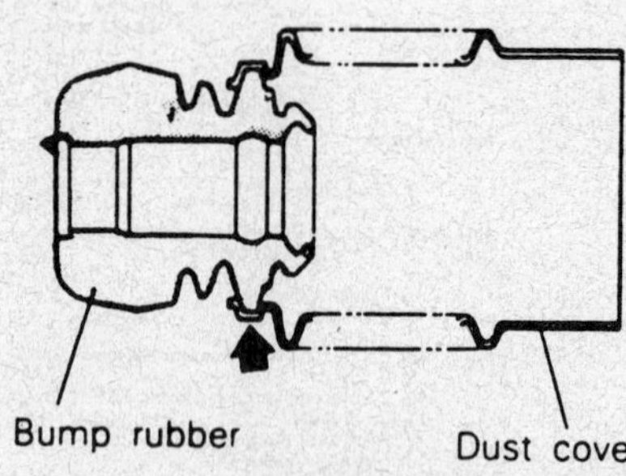


Fig. 8 Installing dust cover

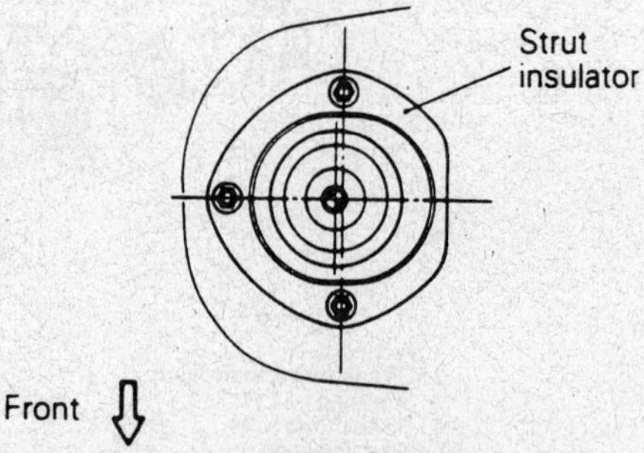

Fig. 9 Insulator position

14. If starting torque and hub endplay are not within specification, it is possible that assembly has not been installed correctly. Repeat disassembly and assembly procedure.

## INSTALLATION

Reverse removal procedure to install, noting the following:

1. Install washer and wheel bearing nut in direction shown, **Fig. 4.**
2. After installing wheel, lower vehicle to ground, then final tighten wheel bearing nut.
3. If cotter pin holes do not match, **torque** nut up to 188 ft. lbs.

# BALL JOINT, INSPECTION

Check ball joint for correct starting torque as follows:

1. Several times deflect ball joint stud from side to side.
2. Mount two nuts on ball joint, then using a suitable torque wrench measure starting torque. Starting torque should be within 26–87 inch lbs.
3. If starting torque exceeds upper limit, replace lower arm assembly.
4. If starting torque is below lower limit, the ball joint may still be reused unless it has drag or excessive play.

# STRUT ASSEMBLY REPLACE

## REMOVAL

Remove strut assembly in numbered sequence, **Fig. 5**, noting the following:

1. Do not pry brake hose and line away from strut.

## DISASSEMBLY & ASSEMBLY

Disassemble strut in numbered sequence, **Fig. 6**, noting the following:

1. Compress coil spring **Fig. 7**, then remove locknut.
2. Join dust cover and bump rubber, **Fig. 8.**
3. Line up holes in spring upper and lower seats.

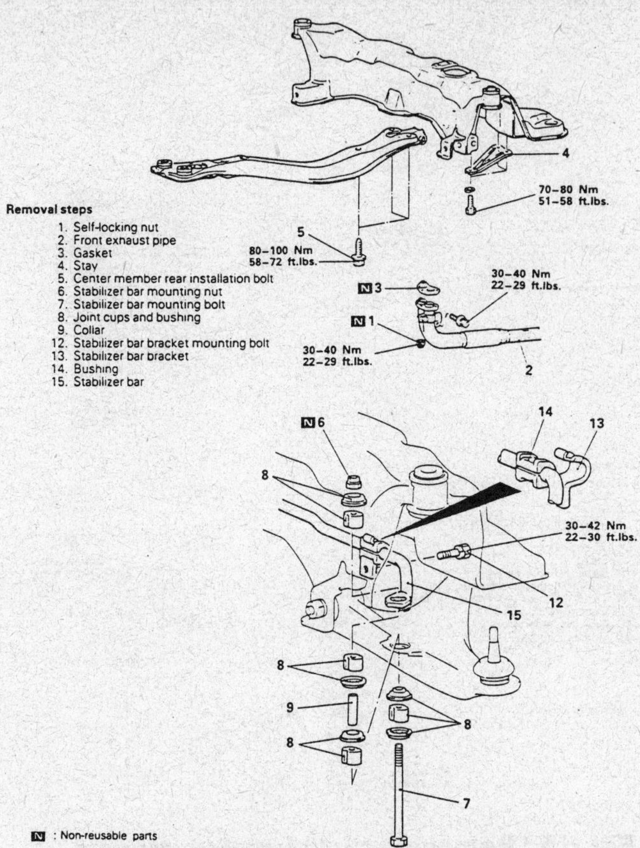


**Fig. 10 Removing stabilizer bar (2WD models). Rubber bushing type**

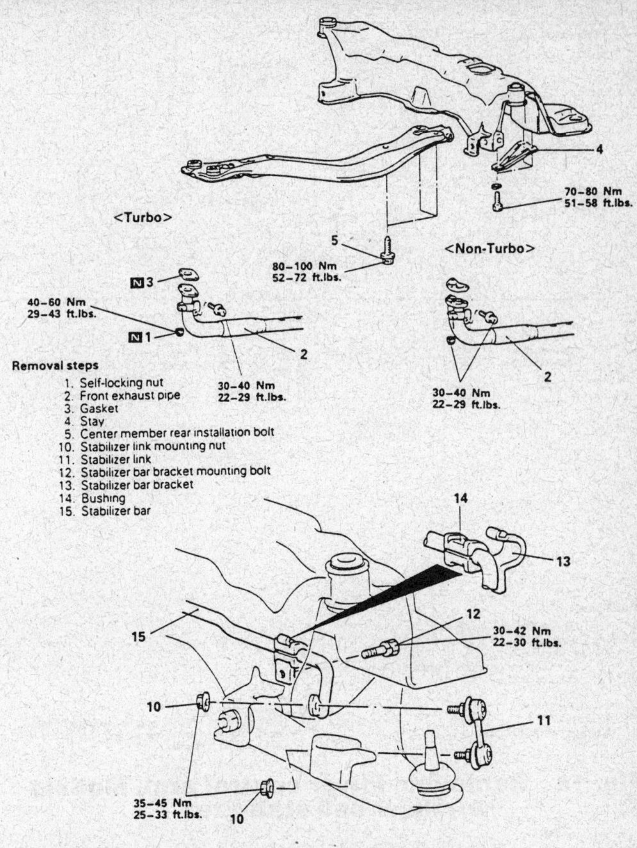


N : Non-reusable parts

**Fig. 11 Removing stabilizer bar (2WD models). Pillow-ball type**

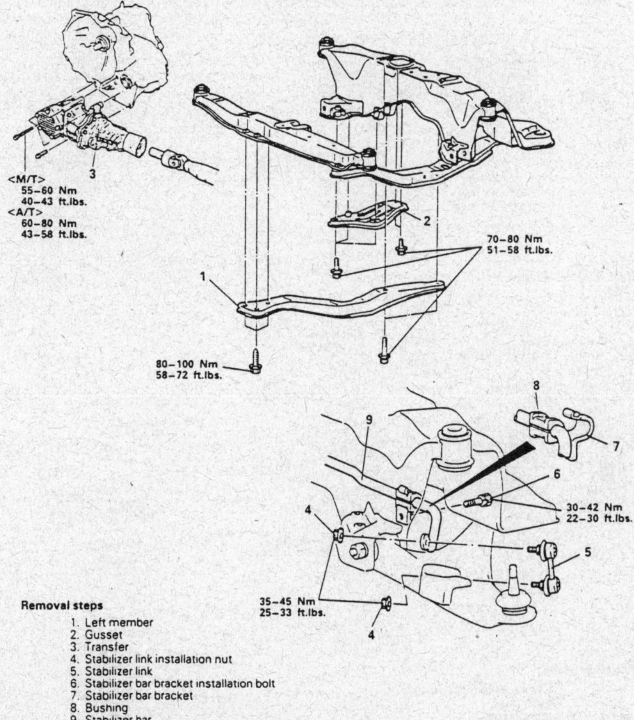


**Fig. 12 Removing stabilizer bar. 4WD models**

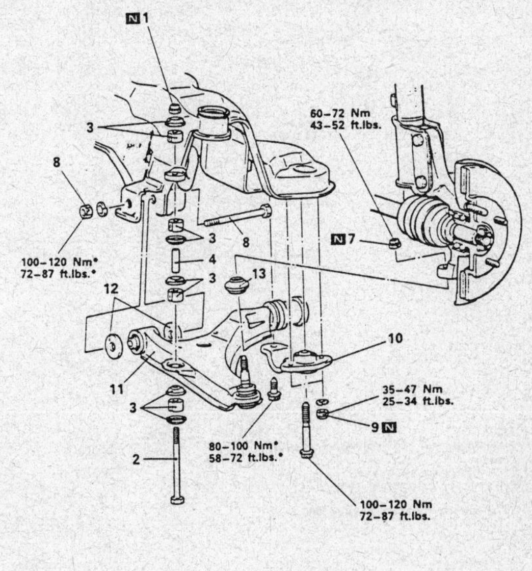


Removal step
1. Stabilizer bar mounting nut
2. Stabilizer bar mounting bolt
3. Joint cups and bushing
4. Collar
7. Self-locking nut
8. Lower arm mounting nut and bolt
9. Self-locking nut
10. Clamp
11. Lower arm
12. Stopper
13. Ball joint dust cover

N : Non-reusable parts
* : Indicates parts which should be temporarily tightened, and then fully tightened with the vehicle in the unladen condition.

**Fig. 13 Removing lower control arm. Models w/rubber bushing stabilizer**

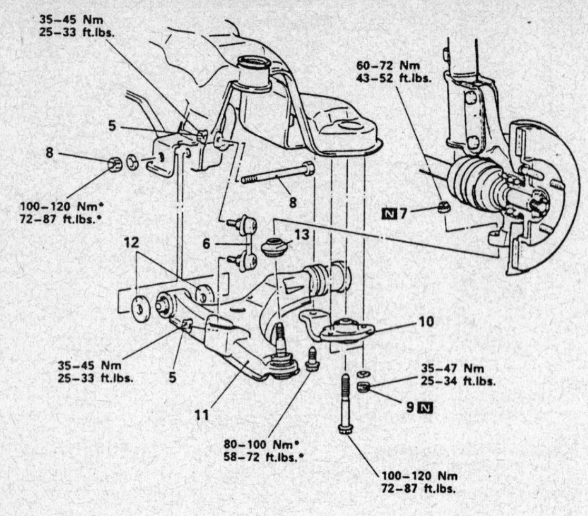


Removal step

5. Stabilizer link mounting nut
6. Stabilizer link
7. Self-locking nut
8. Lower arm mounting nut and bolt
9. Self-locking nut
10. Clamp
11. Lower arm
12. Stopper
13. Ball joint dust cover

N : Non-reusable parts
* : Indicates parts which should be temporarily tightened, and then fully tightened with the vehicle in the unladen condition.

**Fig. 14 Removing lower control arm. Models w/pillow-ball stabilizer**

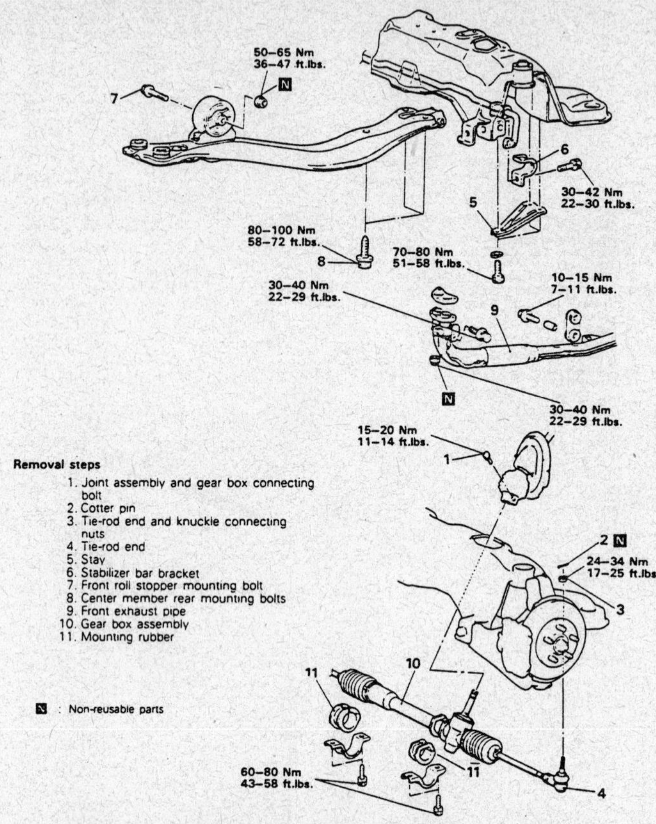


Removal steps

1. Joint assembly and gear box connecting bolt
2. Cotter pin
3. Tie-rod end and knuckle connecting nuts
4. Tie-rod end
5. Stay
6. Stabilizer bar bracket
7. Front roll stopper mounting bolt
8. Center member rear mounting bolts
9. Front exhaust pipe
10. Gear box assembly
11. Mounting rubber

N : Non-reusable parts

**Fig. 15 Removing rack & pinion. Models w/manual steering**

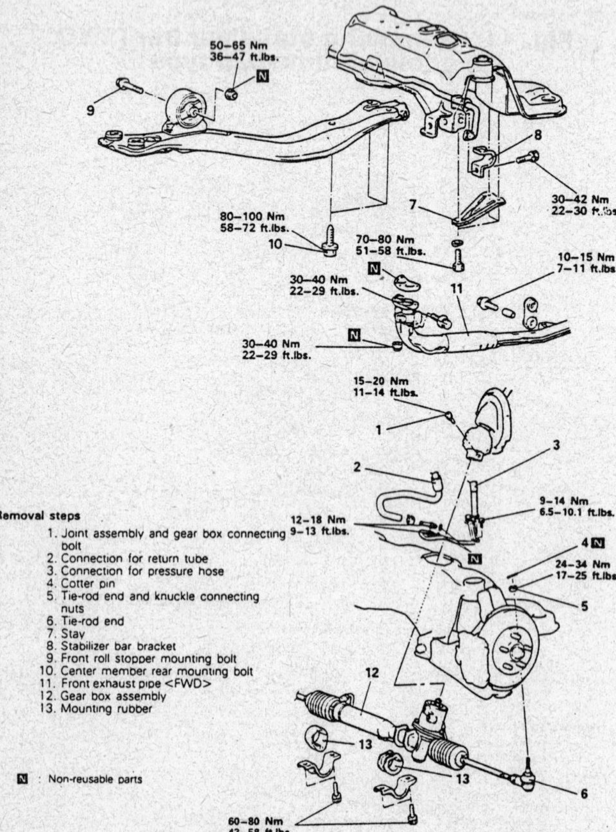


Removal steps

1. Joint assembly and gear box connecting bolt
2. Connection for return tube
3. Connection for pressure hose
4. Cotter pin
5. Tie-rod end and knuckle connecting nuts
6. Tie-rod end
7. Stay
8. Stabilizer bar bracket
9. Front roll stopper mounting bolt
10. Center member rear mounting bolt
11. Front exhaust pipe <FWD>
12. Gear box assembly
13. Mounting rubber

N : Non-reusable parts

**Fig. 16 Removing rack & pinion. Models w/power steering**

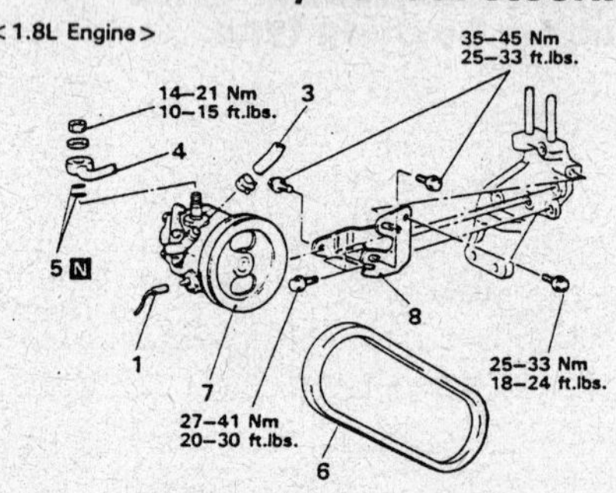


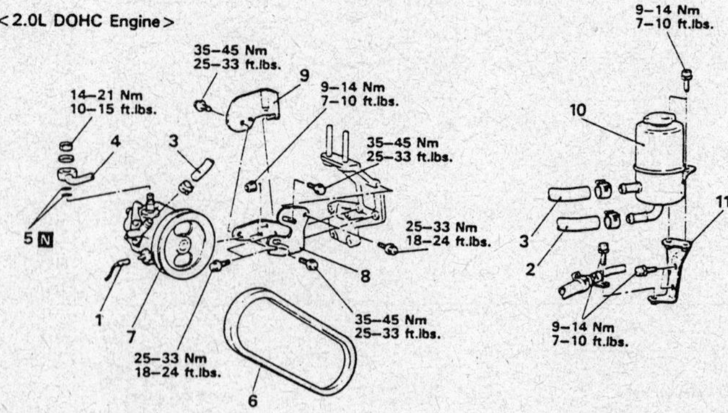


Removal steps

1. Pressure switch connector
2. Return hose
3. Suction hose
4. Pressure hose
5. O-ring
6. V-belt
7. Oil pump
8. Oil pump bracket
9. Heat protector <2.0L DOHC Engine>
10. Oil reservoir
11. Reservoir bracket

N : Non-reusable parts

**Fig. 17 Removing power steering pump**

## INSTALLATION

Reverse removal procedure to install, noting the following:

1. Install strut assembly insulator as shown, **Fig. 9.**

## STABILIZER BAR REPLACE

### 2 WHEEL DRIVE

Remove stabilizer bar in numbered sequence, **Figs. 10 & 11,** noting the following:

1. Front exhaust pipe must be removed.
2. Pull both ends of stabilizer bar to rear of driveshaft.
3. Move right side of bar until it clears lower arm.
4. Pull stabilizer bar out right side.
5. Check stabilizer bar ball joint starting torque; torque should be 15-28 inch lbs. If starting torque exceeds specified torque, replace stabilizer link.
6. Reverse procedure to install.

### ALL WHEEL DRIVE MODELS

Remove stabilizer bar in numbered sequence, **Fig. 12,** noting the following:

1. Disconnect coupling of knuckle and lower arm on right side.
2. Pull sides of bar between driveshaft and lower arm.
3. Reverse procedure to install.

## LOWER CONTROL ARM REPLACE

Remove lower control arm in numbered sequence, **Figs. 13 and 14,** noting the following:

1. Check ball joint starting torque; torque should be 26–87 inch lbs. If reading exceeds specified amount, replace lower arm assembly.
2. Reverse procedure to install.

## RACK & PINION STEERING GEAR REPLACE

Remove rack & pinion in numbered sequence, **Figs. 15 & 16,** noting the following:

1. Turn rack completely to right, the disconnect gearbox from crossmember.
2. While tilting gearbox downward, remove from left side.
3. Reverse procedure to install.

## POWER STEERING PUMP REPLACE

Remove steering pump in numbered sequence, **Fig. 17,** noting the following:

1. Remove reservoir cap and disconnect return hose to drain fluid.
2. Raise and support vehicle.
3. Disconnect high tension cable, then turn crank engine to drain fluid from gearbox.
4. Cover alternator (located under oil pump) if any hoses are removed
5. When connecting pressure hose, ensure slit contacts oil pump guide bracket.

## TIGHTENING SPECIFICATIONS

| Year | Component | Torque/ft. lbs. |
|---|---|---|
| 1990–92 | Caliper Assembly Mounting Bolt | 58-72 |
| | Center Bearing Bracket | 26-33 |
| | Center Member To Body | 58-72 |
| | Driveshaft Nut | 144-188 |
| | End Plug | 36-51 |
| | Feed Tubes | 9-13 |
| | Front Exhaust Pipe Clamp | 22-29 |
| | Front Roll Stopper Bracket To Center Member | 29-36 |
| | Front Speed Sensor Bracket | 7-10 |
| | Front Toothed Rotor | 7-10 |
| | Gearbox To Bracket To Crossmember | 43-58 |
| | Heat Protector Installation Nut | 7-10 |
| | Hub Assembly To Knuckle | 144-188 |
| | Joint Assembly | 11-14 |
| | Knuckle To Ball Joint | 43-52 |
| | Knuckle To Strut Assembly | 80-101 |
| | Lower Arm Clamp To Crossmember (Nut) | 25-34 |
| | Lower Arm Clamp To Crossmember (Bolt) | 58-72 |
| | Lower Arm To Crossmember | 72-87 |
| | Oil Pump To Bracket | 25-33 |
| | Oil Reservoir Bracket Installation Bolt | 7-10 |
| | Oil Reservoir Installation Bolt | 7-10 |
| | Pinion And Valve Assembly To Self-Locking Nut | 14-22 |
| | Pressure Hose To Gearbox | 9-13 |
| | Pressure Hose To Oil Pump | 10-15 |
| | Return Tube To Gearbox | 9-13 |
| | Stabilizer Bar Bracket | 22-30 |
| | Stabilizer Link | 25-33 |
| | Stay To Crossmember | 51-58 |
| | Strut Top End Nut | 43-51 |

*Continued*

## TIGHTENING SPECIFICATIONS—Continued

| Year | Component | Torque/ft. lbs. |
|---|---|---|
| | Strut Upper Mounting Nut | 29-39 |
| | Terminal Assembly To Pump Body | 18-22 |
| | Tie Rod End Ball Joint | 17-25 |
| | Tie Rod End To Rack | 58-72 |
| | Wheel Lug Nuts | 87-101 |

# Wheel Alignment

INDEX



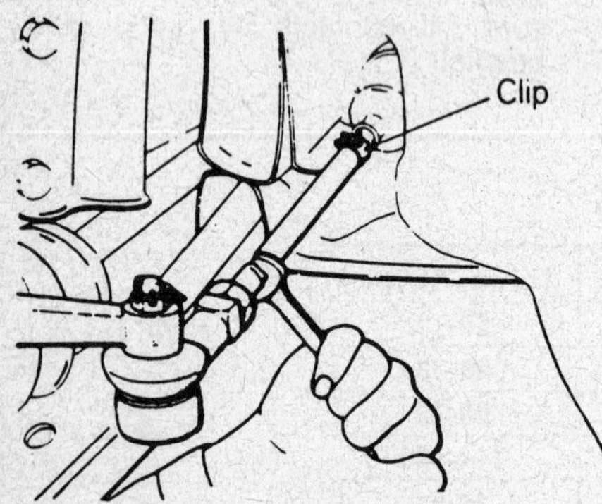


Fig. 1 Adjusting toe-in.

## FRONT WHEEL ALIGNMENT

Prior to wheel alignment, ensure tires are at recommended pressure, are of equal size and have approximately the same wear pattern. Check front wheel and tire assembly for radial runout and inspect lower ball joints and steering linkage for looseness. Check front and rear springs for sagging or damage. Front suspension inspections should be performed on a level floor or alignment rack with fuel tank at capacity and vehicle free of luggage and passenger compartment load. The vehicle should be bounced an equal number of times from the center of the bumper alternately, first from the rear, then the front, releasing at the bottom of down cycle.

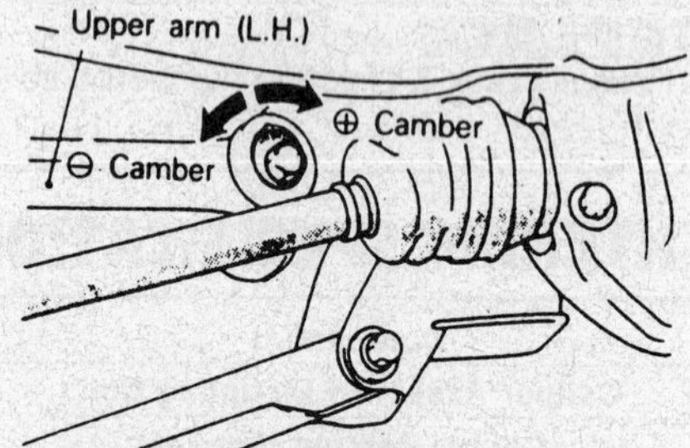


Fig. 2 Adjusting rear wheel camber. 4 wheel drive

### CASTER & CAMBER

Caster and camber are preset at the factory and cannot be adjusted. If caster or camber are not within specifications, replace bent or damaged components.

### TOE-IN

Adjust toe-in by undoing clips and turning each tie rod turnbuckle an equal amount in opposite directions, **Fig. 1.** Toe will move out as the left turnbuckle is turned toward front of vehicle and the right turnbuckle is turned toward rear of vehicle. For each half turn, toe-in will increase or decrease .24 inch.

## REAR WHEEL ALIGNMENT

### 2 WHEEL DRIVE

Camber and toe-in are preset at the factory and cannot be adjusted. If camber or toe-in are not within specifications, replace bent or damaged components.

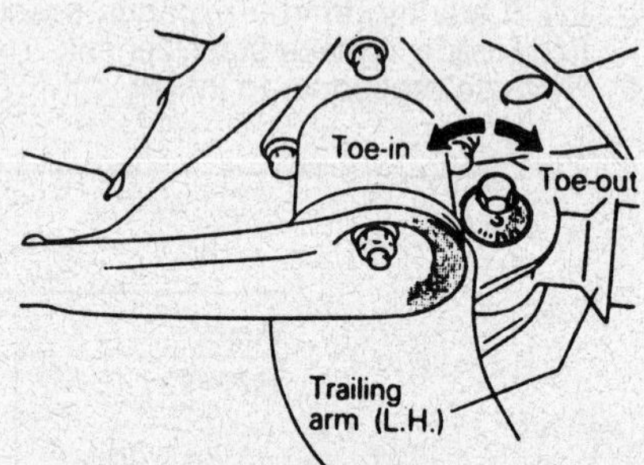


Fig. 3 Adjusting rear wheel toe-in. 4 wheel drive

### 4 WHEEL DRIVE

#### CAMBER

**Always adjust toe-in following a camber adjustment, toe in will vary .035 inch for every camber scale adjustment.**

1. Measure camber using a camber/caster/kingpin gauge.
2. If camber is not within specifications, adjust by moving the mounting bolt located on the crossmember side of the arm, **Fig. 2.**

#### TOE-IN

1. Measure toe-in using a toe-in gauge.
2. If toe-in is not within specifications, adjust by moving the mounting bolts located on the crossmember side of the trailing arm, **Fig. 3.**

# COLT, COLT VISTA, COLT WAGON, CONQUEST, SUMMIT & SUMMIT WAGON

## INDEX OF SERVICE OPERATIONS

**NOTE:** Refer To The Rear Of This Manual For Vehicle Manufacturer's Special Tool Suppliers.

# INDEX OF SERVICE OPERATIONS—Continued

# Specifications

## GENERAL ENGINE SPECIFICATIONS

| Year | Engine Liter/CID① | Engine VIN Code② | Fuel System | Bore & Stroke | Comp. Ratio | Net Horsepower @ RPM③ | Maximum Torque Ft. Lbs. @ RPM | Normal Oil Pressure Psi. |
|---|---|---|---|---|---|---|---|---|
| 1989 | 1.5L/4-89.6 | X | MPI | 2.97 x 3.23 | 9.4 | 81 @ 5500 | 91 @ 3500 | 11.4④ |
| | 1.6L/4-97.4⑤ | Y | MPI | 3.03 x 3.39 | 9.0 | 113 @ 6500 | 99 @ 5000 | 11.4④ |
| | 1.6L/4-97.4⑤ ⑥ | Z | MPI | 3.03 x 3.39 | 8.0 | 135 @ 6000 | 141 @ 3000 | 11.4④ |
| | 1.8L/4-107 | T | MPI | 3.17 x 3.39 | 9.0 | 87 @ 5000 | 102 @ 3000 | 11.4④ |
| | 2.0L/4-121.9 | V | MPI | 3.35 x 3.46 | 8.5 | 96 @ 5000 | 119 @ 3500 | 11.4④ |
| | 2.6L/4-156⑥ ⑦ | N | ECI | 3.59 x 3.86 | 7.0 | 188 @ 5000 | 234 @ 2500 | 11.4④ |
| 1990 | 1.5L/4-89.6⑧ | X | MPI | 3.23 x 3.23 | 9.4 | 81 @ 5500 | 113 @ 6500 | 11.4④ |
| | 1.5L/4-89.6⑨ | X | MPI | 2.97 x 3.23 | 9.4 | 75 @ 5500 | 87 @ 2500 | 11.4④ |
| | 1.6L/4-97.4⑤ | Y | MPI | 3.03 x 3.39 | 9.2 | 113 @ 6500 | 99 @ 5000 | 11.4④ |
| | 1.8L/4-107 | T | MPI | 3.17 x 3.39 | 9.0 | 87 @ 5000 | 102 @ 3000 | 11.4④ |
| | 2.0L/4-121.9 | V | MPI | 3.35 x 3.46 | 8.5 | 96 @ 5000 | 113 @ 3500 | 11.4④ |
| 1991 | 1.5L/4-89.6 | A | MPI | 2.97 x 3.23 | 9.2 | 92 @ 6000 | 93 @ 3000 | 11.4④ |
| | 2.0L/4-121.9 | V | MPI | 3.35 x 3.46 | 8.5 | 96 @ 5000 | 113 @ 3500 | 11.4④ |
| 1992 | 1.5L/4-89.6 | A | MPI | 2.97 x 3.23 | 9.2 | 92 @ 6000 | 93 @ 3000 | 11.4④ |
| | 1.8L/4-111.9 | D | MPI | 3.19 x 3.50 | 9.5 | 113 @ 6000 | 116 @ 4500 | 11.4④ |
| | 2.4L/4-143.5 | W | MPI | 3.40 x 3.94 | 8.5 | 116 @ 5000 | 136 @ 3500 | 11.4④ |

ECI—Electronic Control Fuel Injection System.
MPI—Multi-Point Fuel Injection System.
①—CID: Cubic inch displacement.
②—The eighth digit of the VIN denotes engine code.
③—Ratings are net, as installed in vehicle.
④—Minimum oil pressure at idle RPM, with oil temperature at 167 to 194°F.
⑤—DOHC engine.
⑥—Turbocharged engine.
⑦—Intercooled turbocharger.
⑧—Colt & Summit.
⑨—Colt wagon.

## TUNE UP SPECIFICATIONS

| Engine/VIN | Spark Plug Gap | Ignition Timing BTDC: Firing Order Fig. | Ignition Timing BTDC: Man. Trans. | Ignition Timing BTDC: Auto. Trans. | Ignition Timing BTDC: Mark Fig. | Curb Idle Speed: Man. Trans. | Curb Idle Speed: Auto. Trans. | Fast Idle Speed: Man. Trans. | Fast Idle Speed: Auto. Trans. | Fuel Pressure Psi |
|---|---|---|---|---|---|---|---|---|---|---|
| **1989** | | | | | | | | | | |
| 1.6L/4-97.4/Z | .030 | A | 5N | 5P | B | 750N | 750N | — | — | ①② |
| 2.6L/4-156/N③ | .041 | C | 10N | 10N | D | 850N④ | 850P④ | ④ | ④ | 35-38⑤ |
| 2.6L/4-156/N⑥ | .041 | C | 10N⑦ | 10N⑦ | D | 850N④ | 850P④ | ④ | ④ | 35-38⑤ |
| **1989–90** | | | | | | | | | | |
| 1.5L/4-89.6/X | .041 | E | 5N⑦ | 5P⑦ | B | 750N④ | 750P④ | ④ | ④ | ②⑧ |
| 1.6L/4-97.4/Y | .041 | A | 5N | 5P | B | 750N | 750N | — | — | ①② |
| 1.8L/4-107/T | .041 | E | 5⑦ | 5⑦ | B | 700N④ | 700P④ | ④ | ④ | ②⑧ |
| **1989–91** | | | | | | | | | | |
| 2.0L/4-121.9/V MPI | .041 | E | 5N⑦ | 5N⑦ | B | 700N④ | 700P④ | ④ | ④ | ②⑧ |
| **1991–92** | | | | | | | | | | |
| 1.5L/4-89.6/A | .041 | F | 5N⑦ | 5P⑦ | B | 750N④ | 750P④ | ④ | ④ | ②⑧ |
| **1992** | | | | | | | | | | |
| 1.8L/4-111.9/D | .041 | — | 5⑨ | 5⑨ | B | 750N⑨ | 750N⑨ | ④ | ④ | ②⑧ |
| 2.4L/4-143.5/W | .041 | E | 5⑨ | 5⑨ | B | 750N⑨ | 750N⑨ | ④ | ④ | ②⑧ |

*Continued*

BTDC—Before top dead center.
N—Neutral.
P—Park.
①—Disconnect fuel pump electrical connector, located at fuel tank under rear seat cushion. Start engine & operate until it stalls. Disconnect battery ground cable, then reconnect fuel pump electrical connector. Place shop towels around fuel high pressure hose at fuel delivery pipe side, then disconnect hose. Remove throttle body stay bracket, then install suitable fuel pressure gauge between fuel delivery pipe & high pressure hose. Connect battery ground cable and check fuel pressure with engine idling.
②—Vacuum hose connected to pressure regulator, 38 psi; vacuum hose disconnected from pressure regulator, 47-50 psi.
③—Except High Altitude.
④—Controlled by Idle Speed Control (ISC).
⑤—Disconnect fuel pump electrical connector, located under rear seat cushion. Start engine & operate until it stalls. Disconnect battery ground cable, then reconnect fuel pump electrical connector. Place shop towels around fuel high pressure hose at fuel mixer, then disconnect hose. Install suitable fuel pressure gauge between fuel mixer & high pressure hose. Connect battery ground cable and check fuel pressure with engine idling.
⑥—High Altitude.
⑦—With jumper wire connected between ignition timing adjustment connector & ground. Refer to Figs. G through L.
⑧—Disconnect fuel pump electrical connector, located at fuel tank. Start engine & operate until it stalls. Disconnect battery ground cable, then reconnect fuel pump electrical connector. Place shop towels around fuel high pressure hose at fuel delivery pipe side, then disconnect hose. Install suitable fuel pressure gauge between fuel delivery pipe & high pressure hose. Connect battery ground cable and check fuel pressure with engine idling.

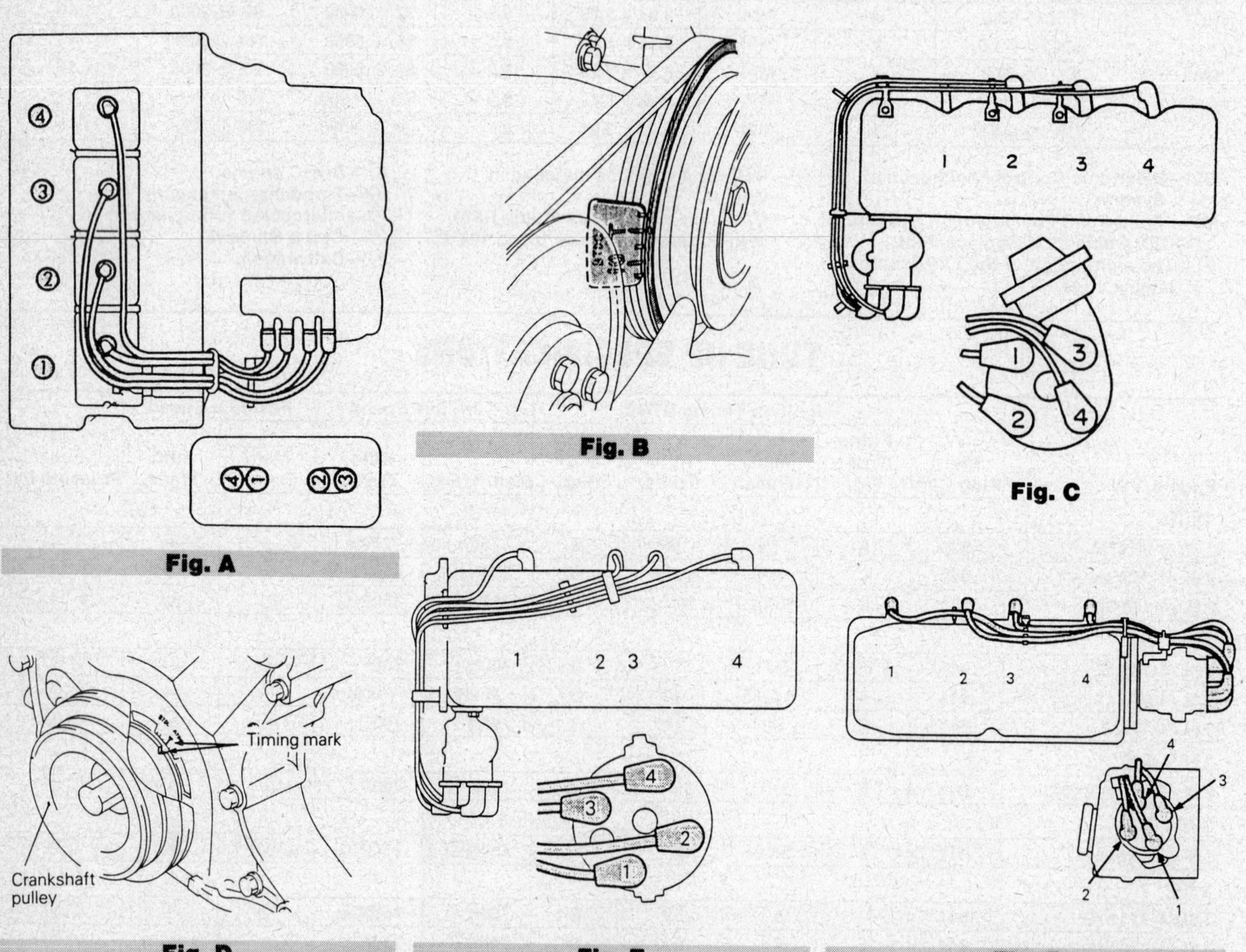


Fig. A

Fig. B

Fig. C

Fig. D

Fig. E

Fig. F

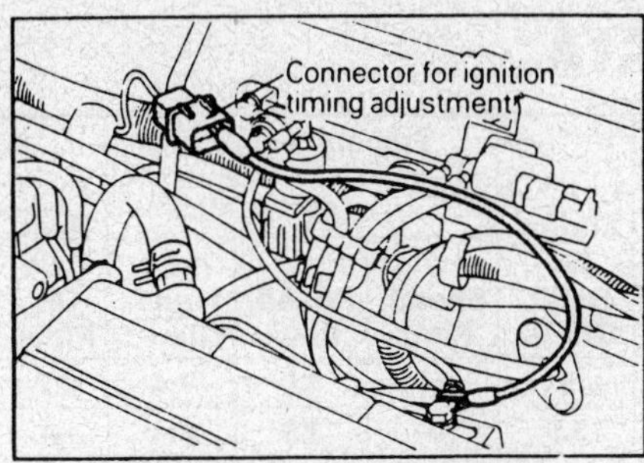


**Fig. G Ignition timing adjustment connector. Colt & Summit 1.5L engines**

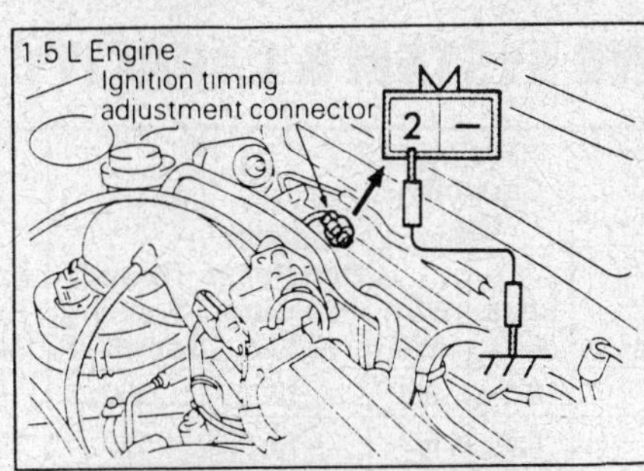


**Fig. H Ignition timing adjustment connector. Colt wagon 1.5L engines**

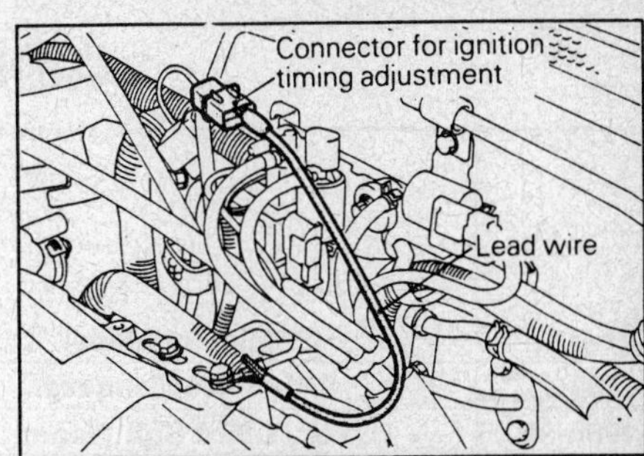


**Fig. I Ignition timing adjustment connector. Colt & Summit 1.6L engines**

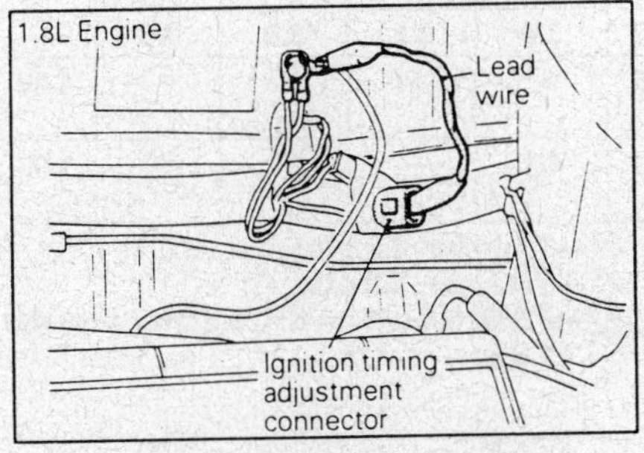


**Fig. J Ignition timing adjustment connector. Colt wagon 1.8L engines**

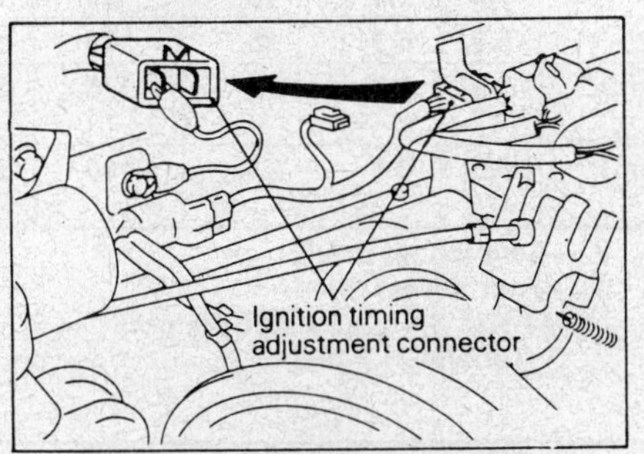


**Fig. K Ignition timing adjustment connector. Colt Vista 2.0L engines**

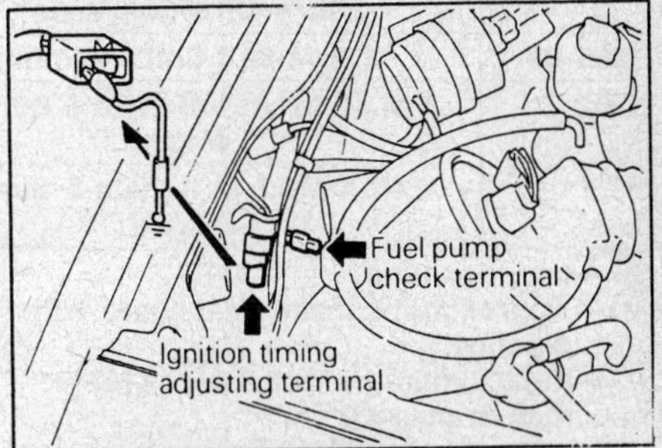


**Fig. L Ignition timing adjustment connector. Conquest 2.6L engines, High Altitude**

# FRONT WHEEL ALIGNMENT SPECIFICATIONS

| Year | Model | Caster Angle, Degrees | | Camber Angle, Degrees | | | | Toe-In |
|---|---|---|---|---|---|---|---|---|
| | | Limits | Desired | Left | Right | Left | Right | |
| 1989 | Conquest | +5 1/3 to +6 1/3 | +5 5/6 | −1 to 0 | −1 to 0 | −1/2 | −1/2 | ① |
| 1989–90 | Colt Wagon②③ | +1/6 to +1 1/6 | +2/3 | −1/2 to +1/2 | −1/2 to +1/2 | 0 | 0 | ④ |
| | Colt Wagon②⑤ | +5/6 to +1 5/6 | +1 1/3 | −1/2 to +1/2 | −1/2 to +1/2 | 0 | 0 | ④ |
| | Colt Wagon⑥ | +1/2 to +1 1/2 | +1 | −1/2 to +1/2 | −1/2 to +1/2 | 0 | 0 | ④ |
| 1989–91 | Colt Vista② | +3/10 to +1 3/10 | +4/5 | −1/12 to +11/12 | −1/12 to +11/12 | +5/12 | +5/12 | ④ |
| | Colt Vista⑥ | +1/3 to +1 1/3 | +5/6 | +1/3 to +1 1/3 | +1/3 to +1 1/3 | +5/6 | +5/6 | ④ |
| 1989–92 | Colt | +1 5/6 to +2 5/6 | +2 1/3 | −1/2 to +1/2 | −1/2 to +1/2 | 0 | 0 | ④ |
| | Summit | +1 5/6 to +2 5/6 | +2 1/3 | −1/2 to +1/2 | −1/2 to +1/2 | 0 | 0 | ④ |

①—.2 inch toe in to .2 inch toe-out.
②—2WD.
③—Less power steering.
④—.12 inch toe in to .12 inch toe-out.
⑤—With power steering.
⑥—4WD.

# REAR WHEEL ALIGNMENT SPECIFICATIONS

| Year | Model | Camber Degrees | | Toe In, Inch |
|---|---|---|---|---|
| | | Limits | Desired | |
| 1989 | Conquest | −3/4 to +1/4 | −1/4 | ① |
| 1989–90 | Colt | −1 1/6 to −1/6 | −2/3 | ② |
| | Summit | −1 1/6 to −1/6 | −2/3 | ② |
| | Colt Wagon③ | −7/12 to +7/12 | 0 | ② |
| | Colt Wagon④ | 0 | 0 | 0 |
| 1989–91 | Colt Vista③ | −1 1/10 to 0 | −7/12 | 0 |
| | Colt Vista④ | −1/2 to +1/2⑤ | 0⑤ | 0 |
| 1991–92 | Colt | −1 1/4 to −1/12 | −2/3 | ② |
| | Summit | −1 1/4 to −1/12 | −2/3 | ② |

①—.08 inch toe in to .08 inch toe-out.
②—.18 inch toe in to .18 inch toe-out.
③—2WD.
④—4WD.
⑤—Difference between left & right, 1/2°.

# COOLING SYSTEM & CAPACITY DATA

| Year | Engine or Model | Cooling Capacity, Qts. Less A/C | Cooling Capacity, Qts. With A/C | Radiator Cap Relief Pressure, Lbs. | Thermo. Opening Temp. °F. | Fuel Tank Gals. | Engine Oil Refill, Qts. ① | Transmission Oil 4 Speed, Pints | Transmission Oil 5 Speed, Pints | Transmission Oil Auto. Trans., Qts. ② | Rear Axle Oil, Pints |
|---|---|---|---|---|---|---|---|---|---|---|---|
| 1989 | 2.6L/4-156 Conquest | 9.5 | 9.5 | 13 | 190 | 19.8 | 5 | — | 4.8 | 7.4 | 2.7 |
| 1989–90 | 1.5L/4-89.6 Colt Wagon | 5.3 | 5.3 | 13 | 190 | 12.4 | 3.5 | — | 3.8 | 6.1 | — |
| | 1.6L/4-97.4 Colt & Summit | 5.3 | 5.3 | 13 | 190 | 13.2 | 4.6 | — | ③ | 6.5 | — |
| | 1.8L/4-107 Colt Wagon | 5.3 | 5.3 | 13 | 190 | 12.4 | 4 | — | 4.7 | 6.1 | — |
| 1989–91 | 2.0L/4-121.9 Colt Vista④ | 7.4 | 7.4 | 13 | 190 | 13.2 | 4.2 | — | 5.2 | 6.1 | — |
| | 2.0L/4-121.9 Colt Vista⑤ | 7.4 | 7.4 | 13 | 190 | 14.5 | 4.2 | — | 4.4⑧ | — | 1.5 |
| 1989–92 | 1.5L/4-89.6 Colt & Summit | 5.3 | 5.3 | 13 | 190 | 13.2 | 3.6 | 3.6 | 3.8 | 6.5 | — |
| 1992 | 1.8L/4-111.9 Colt Vista & Summit Wagon | 6.3 | 6.3 | 9.2 | 170 | 14.5 | 4 | — | ⑥ | ⑨ | 1.48 |
| | 2.4L/4-143.5 Colt Vista & Summit Wagon | 6.8 | 6.8 | 9.2 | 190 | 14.5 | 4.1 | — | 4.8⑦ | ⑨ | 1.48 |

①—Includes filter.
②—Approximate, make final check with dipstick.
③—KM206 man. trans, 3.8 pts.; KM210 man. trans., 4.4 pts.
④—Two wheel drive.
⑤—Four wheel drive.
⑥—FWD, 3.8 pts.; AWD, 4.8 pts.; transfer, 1.2 pts.
⑦—Transfer, 1.2 pts.
⑧—Transfer, 1.4 pts.
⑨—FWD, 6.4 qts.; AWD, 6.9 qts.; transfer, 1.2 pts.

# LUBRICANT DATA

| Year | Model | Lubricant Type: Transmission Manual | Transmission Automatic | Transfer Case | Rear Axle | Power Steering | Brake System |
|---|---|---|---|---|---|---|---|
| 1989–92 | All | API GL4 | ① | API GL4 | API GL4 | ① | DOT 3 |

①—Mopar ATF plus automatic transmission fluid type 7176/Dextron or Dextron II.

# Electrical

## INDEX



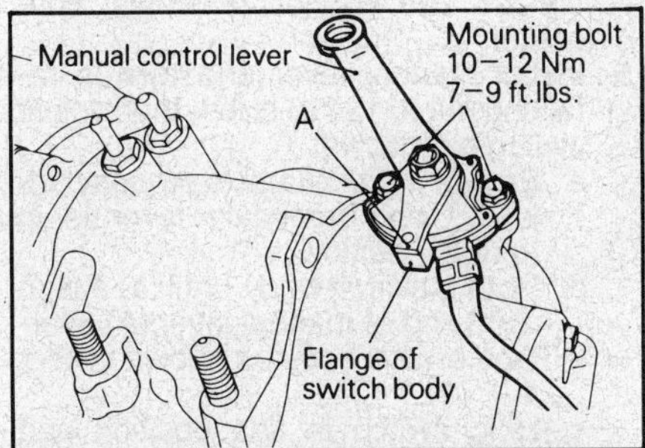


**Fig. 1 Neutral safety switch adjustment. Colt, Colt Vista, Colt Wagon & Summit**

## FUSE PANEL LOCATION

The fuse panel is located behind the instrument panel access cover to the left of the steering column.

## FLASHER LOCATION

### COLT & SUMMIT

The flasher unit is located on the fuse panel, behind instrument panel access cover to left of steering column.

### COLT VISTA

The flasher unit is located on the relay panel, behind instrument panel to left of steering column.

### CONQUEST

The flasher unit is located on the relay panel, under far left hand side of instrument panel.

## STARTER REPLACE

1. Disconnect battery ground cable.
2. **On models w/1.5L engines,** remove air cleaner and intake manifold stay, as needed, to gain access to starter.
3. Disconnect starter wiring.
4. Remove starter mounting bolts, then remove starter motor.
5. Reverse procedure to install.

## DISTRIBUTOR REPLACE

### REMOVAL

1. Disconnect battery ground cable.
2. Disconnect distributor wiring harness, then remove distributor cap with ignition cables attached and position aside.
3. **On 2.6L engines,** disconnect vacuum hose.
4. Remove mounting bolt, then the distributor.

### INSTALLATION

1. Rotate crankshaft until piston of No.1 cylinder is at top dead center on compression stroke.

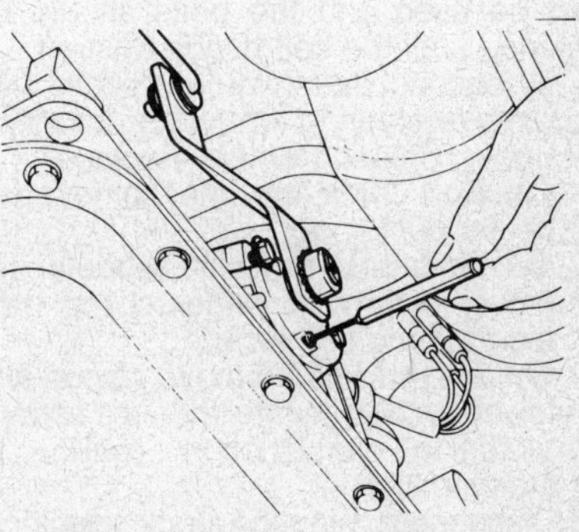

**Fig. 2 Neutral safety switch adjustment. Conquest**

2. Align mating mark line on distributor housing with corresponding mating mark hole on distributor gear.
3. Install distributor onto cylinder head while aligning mating mark on distributor attaching flange with center of cylinder head distributor flange stud.
4. Install mounting nut, then vacuum hose(s), wiring harness and distributor cap.
5. Check and reset ignition timing if necessary.

## IGNITION LOCK REPLACE

### EXCEPT COLT WAGON

The heads of the bolts securing the steering lock assembly shear off when the

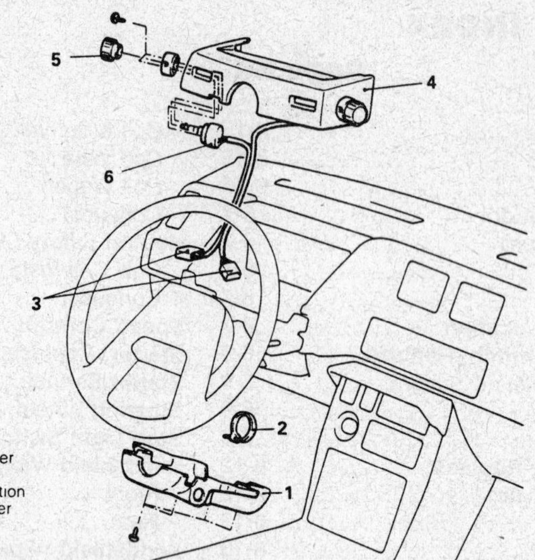


**Fig. 3 HeadLamp switch replacement. Colt Wagon**

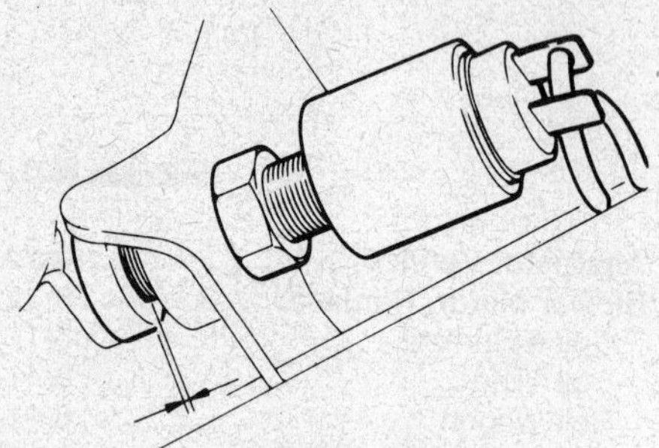

**Fig. 4 Adjusting stoplamp switch clearance**

bolts are tightened. Replacement of the steering lock assembly may require that the steering column be removed, as these bolts must be cut or slotted to permit removal with a screwdriver. When the lock assembly is installed, new shear bolts must be used and the bolts should be tightened until the bolt heads twist off.

1. Disconnect battery ground cable, then remove steering wheel as described under "Steering Wheel, Replace."
2. **On Colt Vista models,** remove lap heater duct.
3. **On Colt and Summit models,** remove instrument under cover, then the foot and lap ducts.
4. **On all models,** remove upper and lower column covers, then the screws attaching combination switch to steering lock.
5. Disconnect steering lock electrical connector, then use a suitable tool to cut grooves in heads of attaching bolts and remove screws using a screwdriver.
6. Remove steering lock.
7. Reverse procedure to install.

## COLT WAGON

The heads of the bolts securing the steering lock assembly shear off when the bolts are tightened. Replacement of the steering lock assembly may require that the steering column be removed, as these bolts must be cut or slotted to permit removal with a screwdriver. When the lock assembly is installed, new shear bolts must be used and the bolts should be tightened until the bolt heads twist off.

1. Disconnect battery ground cable, then remove steering wheel as described under "Steering Wheel, Replace."
2. Remove lower cover and lower column cover, then the knobs from wiper/washer and headlight switches.
3. Remove wiper/washer and headlight switch attaching screws, then the upper cover.
4. Remove screws attaching column switch to steering lock.
5. Disconnect steering lock electrical connector, then use a suitable tool to cut grooves in heads of attaching bolts and remove screws using a screwdriver.
6. Remove steering lock.
7. Reverse procedure to install.

# IGNITION SWITCH
## REPLACE

Ignition switch may be replaced without removing steering lock.

1. Disconnect battery ground cable.
2. **On Colt and Summit models,** remove knee protector, then the upper and lower column covers.
3. **On Colt Vista models,** remove upper and lower column covers.
4. **On Colt Wagon and Conquest models,** remove lower column cover.
5. **On all models,** remove band securing electrical connector, then disconnect electrical connector.
6. **On 1991-92 Colt and Summit with automatic transmission,** remove interlock cable cover, then disconnect interlock cable, spring and slide lever.
7. **On all models,** remove screws attaching ignition switch to ignition lock, then the switch from lock assembly.
8. Reverse procedure to install.

# CLUTCH SWITCH
## REPLACE

1. Disconnect clutch switch electrical connector.
2. Remove locknut, then the clutch switch.
3. Reverse procedure to install.

# NEUTRAL SAFETY SWITCH
## REPLACE

### COLT, COLT VISTA, COLT WAGON & SUMMIT

1. Place selector lever in neutral position.
2. Hold transaxle shift lever and remove retaining nut, then remove manual lever.
3. Disconnect switch electrical connector and remove retaining screws, then remove switch from transaxle.
4. Install replacement switch over selector shaft, loosely install retaining screws and connect electrical connector.
5. Install manual lever and **torque** retaining nut to 13-15 ft. lbs., then adjust switch as follows:
   a. Ensure shift linkage is properly adjusted and transaxle lever is in neutral position.
   b. Rotate switch body until .472 inch wide end of manual lever (A) overlaps switch body as shown in **Fig. 1.**
   c. Hold switch in this position and **torque** retaining screws to 7–9 ft. lbs.
   d. Check operation of selector and switch, and ensure that starter only engages with selector in park or neutral.

### CONQUEST

1. Place selector lever in neutral position, then raise and support vehicle.
2. Hold transmission selector lever and remove retaining nut, then remove manual lever.
3. Disconnect switch electrical connector and remove retaining screws, then remove switch from transmission.
4. Install replacement switch over selector shaft, loosely install retaining screws and connect electrical connector.
5. Install manual lever and **torque** retaining nut to 22-29 ft. lbs., then adjust switch as follows:
   a. Ensure shift linkage is properly adjusted and transaxle lever is in neutral (vertical) position, then re-

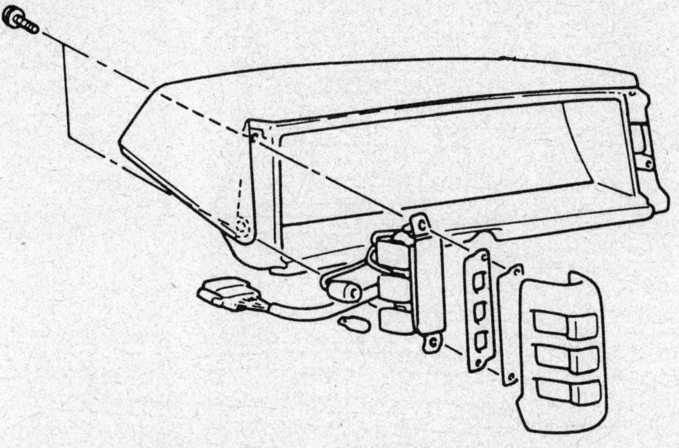

**Fig. 5 Cluster switch replacement. Conquest**

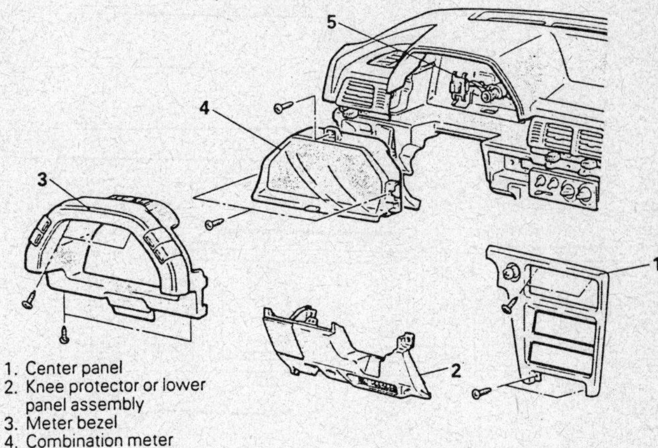


**Fig. 6 Instrument cluster. Colt & Summit**

move screw from switch alignment hole, **Fig. 2.**

b. Rotate switch body until .079 inch gauge rod can be inserted through alignment hole and switch rotor, then **torque** switch retaining screws equally to 4-5 ft. lbs.
c. Remove gauge pin and install screw, lower vehicle, then ensure that starter only engages with selector lever in park or neutral.

## HEADLAMP SWITCH REPLACE

### COLT, COLT VISTA & SUMMIT

Refer to "Combination Switch, Replace" for procedure.

### COLT WAGON

1. Disconnect battery ground cable and remove lower steering column cover.
2. Remove strap securing switch harness to column, then disconnect switch electrical connector.
3. Remove upper steering column cover, place light switch in the Off position, then pull off switch knob.
4. Remove switch to upper cover attaching screws, then remove switch from cover, **Fig. 3.**
5. Reverse procedure to install.

### CONQUEST

Refer to "Cluster Switch, Replace" for procedure.

## STOP LIGHT SWITCH REPLACE

1. Disconnect battery ground cable.
2. Disconnect electrical connector from brake lamp switch.
3. Remove retaining nut from bracket and then remove switch.
4. Reverse procedure to install. Ensure brake pedal height is correct, then adjust switch to obtain a clearance of .02 to .04 inch between switch housing and pedal stopper with pedal released, **Fig. 4.**

## COLUMN SWITCH REPLACE

### COLT WAGON & CONQUEST

On Colt Wagon models, the column switch includes the turn signal and headlight dimmer switches. On Conquest models, the column switch includes the turn signal, headlight dimmer and wiper/washer switches.

1. Disconnect battery ground cable.
2. Remove steering wheel as described under "Steering Wheel, Replace.
3. Remove lower steering column cover, then the cable .
4. Remove wiring harness retaining straps, then disconnect electrical connectors.
5. Remove column switch assembly.
6. Reverse procedure to install, noting the following:
   a. Ensure column switch is properly aligned with steering shaft center.
   b. Attach switch wiring along column tube as close to center line as possible.
   c. Retain wiring using suitable retaining straps to prevent contact with other parts.

## CLUSTER SWITCH REPLACE

### CONQUEST

The cluster switch includes the headlight, hazard, fog light and headlight pop-up switches.

1. Disconnect battery ground cable.
2. Remove instrument cluster bezel attaching screws, then pull cover outward and disconnect switch electrical connectors and remove cover, **Fig. 5.**
3. Remove screws attaching switch to cluster cover, then remove switch.
4. Reverse procedure to install.

## COMBINATION SWITCH REPLACE

### COLT, COLT VISTA & SUMMIT

The combination switch includes the headlight, headlight dimmer, turn signal and wiper/washer switches.

1. Disconnect battery ground cable.
2. Remove steering wheel as described under "Steering Wheel, Replace."
3. **On Colt and Summit models,** remove knee protector.
4. **On all models,** remove upper and lower column covers.
5. Remove wiring harness retaining straps, then disconnect electrical connectors.
6. Remove attaching screws, then the combination switch assembly.
7. Reverse procedure to install.

## STEERING WHEEL REPLACE

1. Disconnect battery ground cable.
2. Remove steering wheel horn pad, then remove steering wheel to column shaft attaching nut.
3. Using a suitable puller, remove steering wheel.
4. Reverse procedure to install. **Torque** steering wheel to column shaft attaching nut to 25 to 33 ft. lbs.

## INSTRUMENT CLUSTER REPLACE

### COLT & SUMMIT

1. Disconnect battery ground cable.
2. Remove instrument panel lower center trim panel, **Fig. 6.**
3. Remove instrument panel lower left hand trim panel.
4. Remove instrument cluster bezel.
5. Remove instrument cluster attaching

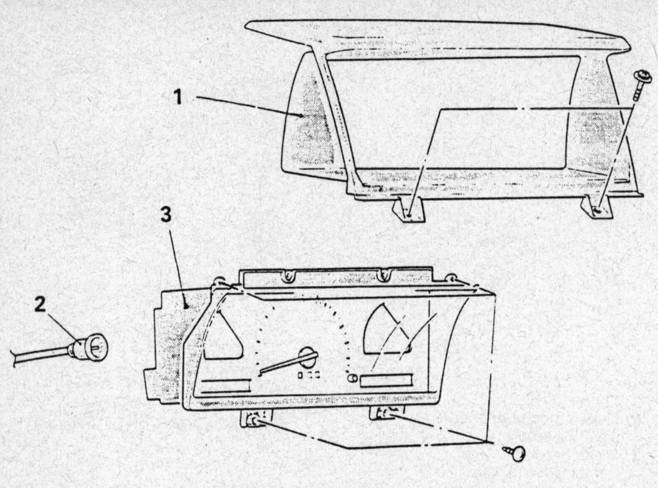


1. Meter hood
2. Speedometer cable connection
3. Meter assembly

**Fig. 7 Instrument cluster. Colt Wagon**

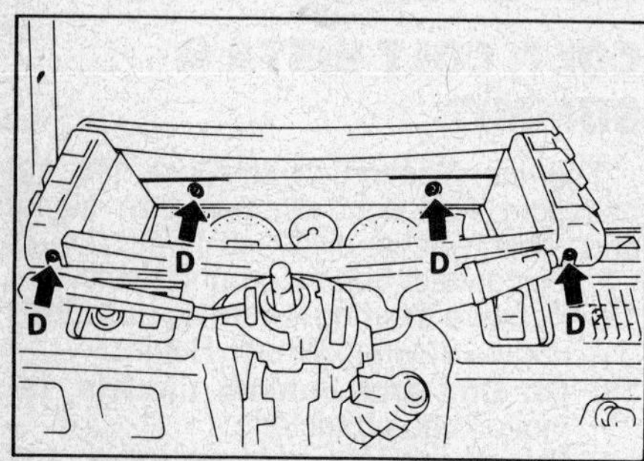


**Fig. 9 Instrument cluster bezel removal. Conquest**

screws, pull cluster slightly outward and disconnect speedometer cable and electrical connectors.

6. Remove instrument cluster assembly.
7. Reverse procedure to install.

## COLT WAGON

1. Disconnect battery ground cable.
2. Remove 2 retaining screws from bottom of cluster bezel, release upper retaining clips and remove cluster bezel.
3. Remove instrument cluster attaching screws, then tilt cluster outwards and disconnect speedometer cable and electrical connectors, **Figs. 7.**
4. Remove instrument cluster.
5. Reverse procedure to install.

## COLT VISTA

1. Disconnect battery ground cable.
2. Remove cluster bezel cover using suitable tool, then remove bezel attaching screws and bezel, **Fig. 8.**
3. Remove instrument cluster retaining screws and pull cluster away from instrument panel.
4. Disconnect speedometer cable and electrical connectors, then remove instrument cluster.
5. Reverse procedure to install.

## CONQUEST

1. Disconnect battery ground cable.
2. Remove instrument cluster bezel attaching screws, **Fig. 9.**
3. While pulling both edges at lower side of bezel outward, lift bezel upward and out, then disconnect cluster switch and remove bezel.
4. Remove instrument cluster upper attaching nuts, then the lower attaching screws.
5. Pull lower part of case slightly outward, then disconnect speedometer cable.
6. Disconnect electrical connectors, then the wiring harness at body side of panel.
7. Remove instrument cluster from vehicle.
8. Reverse procedure to install.

# WINDSHIELD WIPER MOTOR

## REPLACE

### FRONT

1. Disconnect battery ground cable.
2. Remove wiper motor attaching bolts or nuts, pull motor out slightly and disconnect linkage. **If it is necessary to remove crank arm, mark relationship of crank arm to motor prior to removal to ensure proper stop angle after installation.**
3. Remove wiper motor.
4. Reverse procedure to install. When installing crank arm on wiper motor, ensure reference marks made during removal are aligned.



1. Bezel Cover
2. Cluster Bezel
3. Cluster Screws
4. Speedometer Cable
5. Harness Connector
6. Instrument Cluster

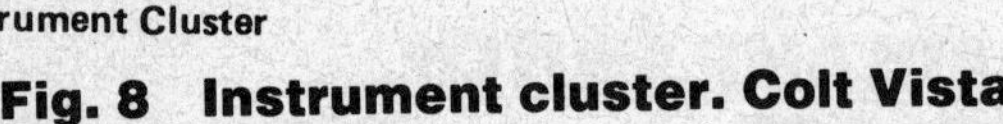

**Fig. 8 Instrument cluster. Colt Vista**

### REAR

1. Disconnect battery ground cable.
2. Remove wiper arm from shaft, then the washers and grommets, noting position for installation.
3. Remove liftgate trim panel, then disconnect wiper motor electrical connector.
4. Remove wiper motor attaching screws, then the motor from liftgate.
5. Reverse procedure to install. Mount wiper arm so that when motor is in park position distance between tip of blade and lower window molding is .6-1 inch on Colt Vista or 1.8-2.2 inches on Colt Wagon and Conquest.

# WINDSHIELD WIPER TRANSMISSION

## REPLACE

1. Disconnect battery ground cable, then remove wiper arm and blade assemblies from pivots.
2. **On Conquest models,** remove pivot locknut shield caps, then the pivot locknuts.
3. **On models except Conquest,** remove front deck garnishes, then the pivot lock and attaching nuts.
4. **On all models,** remove wiper motor as described under "Windshield Wiper Motor, Replace."
5. Remove wiper transmission assembly.
6. Reverse procedure to install, noting the following:

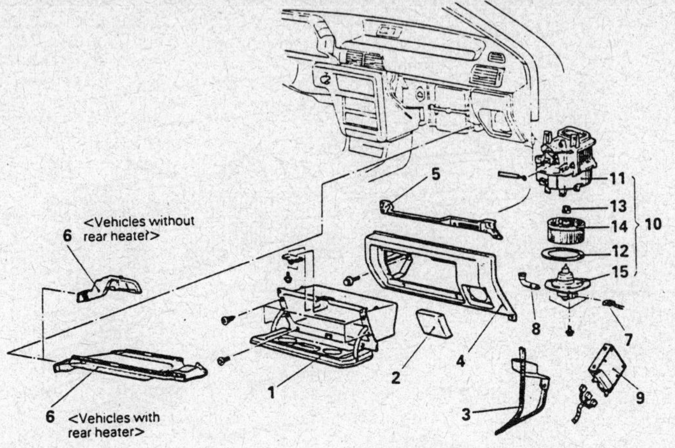


1. Glove box
2. Speaker cover
3. Cowl side trim, R.H.
4. Knee protector, R.H.
5. Glove box frame
6. Lap heater duct <vehicles without rear heater> or shower duct <vehicles with rear heater>
7. Blower motor connector
8. Hose
9. MPI control unit
10. Blower motor assembly
11. Blower case
12. Packing
13. Fan installation nut
14. Fan
15. Blower motor

**Fig. 10 Blower motor replacement. Colt & Summit**

1. Lower glove box
2. Reinforcement
3. Upper glove box
4. Absorber bracket <2WD
5. Air selection control wire
6. Duct
7. Blower assembly

**Fig. 11 Blower motor replacement. Colt Vista**

a. Mount wiper arms so that when motor is in park position distance between wiper blade and bottom of windshield is .6 inch on left side and .8 inch on right side for Colt Wagon, 1.2 inch on left side and 1 inch on right side for Colt Vista, .5 inch on both sides for Conquest.

# WINDSHIELD WIPER SWITCH

## REPLACE

### FRONT

#### Colt, Colt Vista & Summit

Refer to "Combination Switch, Replace" for procedure.

#### Colt Wagon

1. Disconnect battery ground cable and remove lower steering column cover.
2. Remove strap securing switch harness to column, then disconnect switch electrical connector.
3. Remove upper steering column cover, place wiper switch in the Off position, then pull off switch knob.
4. Remove switch to upper cover attaching screws, then remove switch from cover.
5. Reverse procedure to install.

#### Conquest

Refer to "Column Switch, Replace."for procedure.

### REAR

#### Colt & Summit

1. Insert suitable tool behind switch, compress lock tab and pry switch from instrument panel. Taking care not to mar garnish or instrument panel.
2. Disconnect electrical connector and remove switch.
3. Reverse procedure to install.

#### Colt Wagon

The rear windshield wiper switch is incorporated in the front windshield wiper switch. Refer to "Front" for procedure.

#### Colt Vista & Conquest

1. Insert suitable tool behind switch garnish, compress lock tab and pry switch and garnish assembly from instrument panel, taking care not to mar garnish or instrument panel.
2. Disconnect electrical connector and remove switch. **On Conquest models, compress tabs on side of switch and remove switch from garnish.**
3. Reverse procedure to install.

# BLOWER MOTOR

## REPLACE

### COLT & SUMMIT

Refer to **Fig. 10** during replacement procedure.

1. Disconnect battery ground cable, then remove glove box assembly.
2. Remove righthand speaker cover, cowl side trim and knee protector.
3. Remove glove box frame, then the lap heater duct on models without rear heater or shower duct on models with rear heater.
4. Disconnect blower motor electrical connector, then the drain hose.
5. Remove MPI control unit, then the blower motor from blower motor assembly.
6. Reverse procedure to install.

### COLT VISTA

Refer to **Fig. 11** during replacement procedure.

1. Disconnect battery ground cable, then remove lower glove box.
2. Remove reinforcement, then the upper glove box.
3. **On 2WD models,** remove absorber bracket.
4. **On all models,** disconnect blower motor electrical connector, then remove blower motor attaching bolts and blower motor.
5. Reverse procedure to install.

### COLT WAGON

Refer to **Fig. 12** during replacement procedure.

1. Disconnect battery ground cable, then remove glove box.
2. Disconnect blower motor electrical connector, then remove blower motor attaching bolts and blower motor.
3. Reverse procedure to install.

### CONQUEST

Refer to **Fig. 13** during replacement procedure.

1. Disconnect battery ground cable.
2. Remove instrument panel under cover, then the glove box.
3. Disconnect blower motor electrical connector.
4. Remove blower motor attaching screws, then the blower motor.
5. Reverse procedure to install.

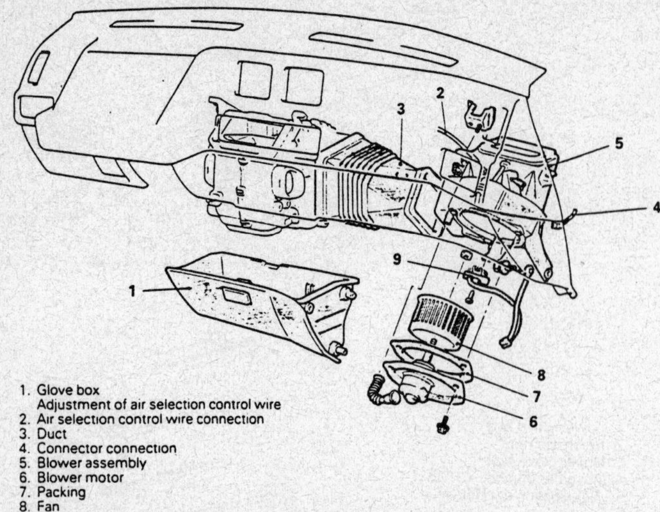

1. Glove box
   Adjustment of air selection control wire
2. Air selection control wire connection
3. Duct
4. Connector connection
5. Blower assembly
6. Blower motor
7. Packing
8. Fan
9. Resistor

**Fig. 12 Blower motor replacement. Colt Wagon**

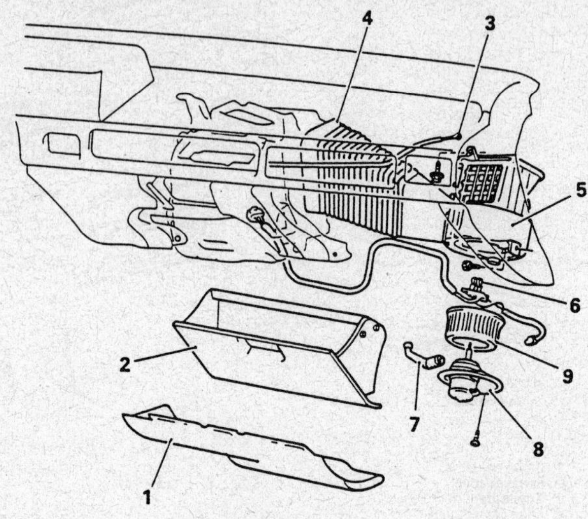

1. Under cover
   Adjustment of air selection control wire
2. Glove box
3. Air selection control wire connection
4. Duct (vehicles without air conditioner) or duct joint (vehicles with air conditioner)
5. Blower assembly
6. Resistor
7. Hose
8. Blower motor
9. Blower

**Fig. 13 Blower motor replacement. Conquest**

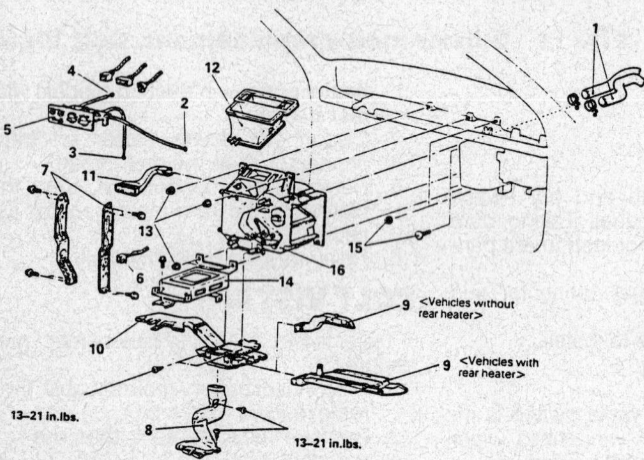


1. Connection for the heater hoses
2. Connection for the air selection control wire
3. Connection for the temperature control wire
4. Connection for the mode selection control wire
5. Heater control assembly
6. MPI control relay connector
7. Instrument panel center stay assembly
8. Rear heater duct A
9. Lap heater duct <vehicles without rear heater> or shower duct <vehicles with rear heater>
10. Foot duct
11. Lap duct
12. Center ventilation duct
13. Heater unit mounting nuts
14. ELC-4 A/T control unit
15. Evaporator mounting nuts, clips
16. Heater unit

**Fig. 14 Heater core replacement. Colt & Summit**

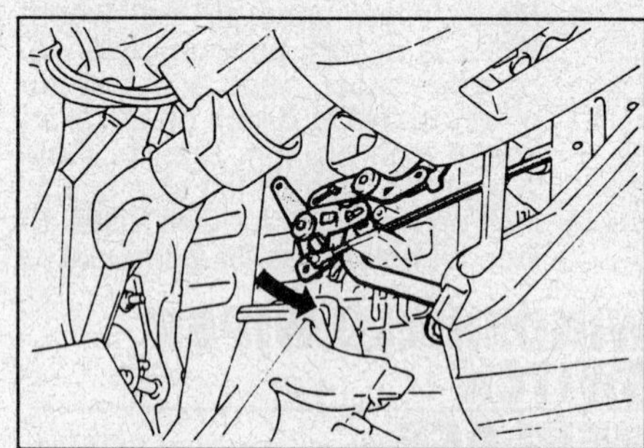

**Fig. 15 Positioning mode selection damper lever. Colt & Summit**

# HEATER CORE REPLACE

## COLT & SUMMIT

Refer to **Fig. 14** during replacement procedure.

1. Disconnect battery ground cable.
2. Set temperature lever at the extreme hot position, then drain engine coolant and disconnect heater hoses.
3. Remove front seats and floor console, then the instrument panel as described in "Dash Panel Service" section.
4. Disconnect air selection, temperature control and mode selection control wires.
5. Remove heater control assembly, then disconnect MPI relay connector.
6. Remove instrument panel center stay assembly.
7. **On models with rear heater,** remove rear heater and shower ducts.
8. **On models less rear heater,** remove lap heater duct.
9. **On all models,** remove foot, lap and center ventilation ducts, then the heater unit mounting nuts.
10. **On models with ELC-4 automatic transmission,** remove ELC-4 A/T control unit.
11. **On models with A/C,** remove evaporator mounting nuts and clips, then pull evaporator outward to allow access to heater unit. **Be careful not to damage liquid pipe or suction hose.**
12. **On all models,** remove heater unit.
13. Remove side plate and heater core fastening clips from heater unit, then pull out heater core from heater unit.
14. Reverse procedure to install, noting the following:
    a. Place mode selector lever in vent position, then with mode selection damper lever pulled outward in direction indicated by arrow in **Fig. 15,** connect mode selection control wire to lever and secure outer cable using clip.
    b. Place temperature control lever in "COOL" position, then with blend air damper lever pressed completely downward in direction indi-

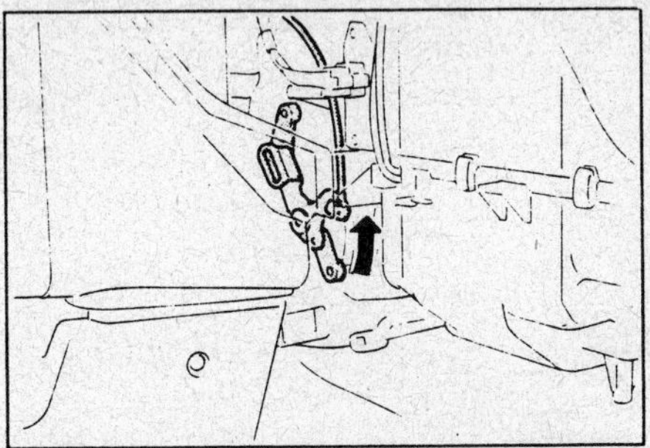

Fig. 16 Positioning blend air damper lever. Colt & Summit

Fig. 17 Positioning air selection damper lever. Colt & Summit

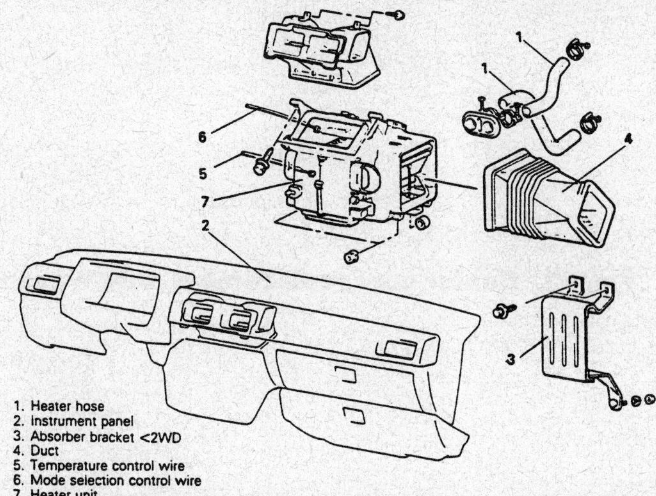


Fig. 18 Heater core replacement. Colt Vista

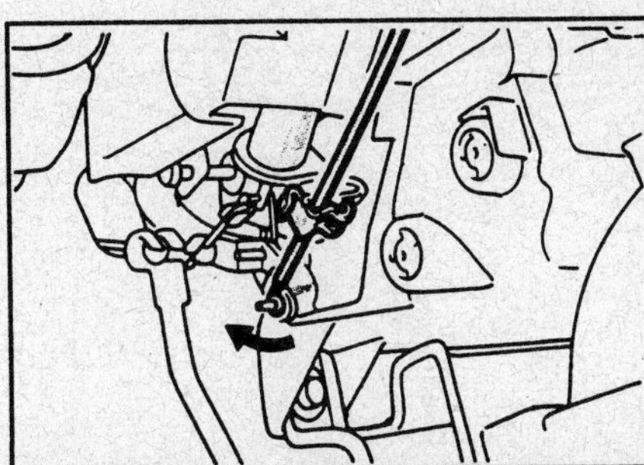

Fig. 19 Positioning mode selection damper lever. Colt Vista & Wagon

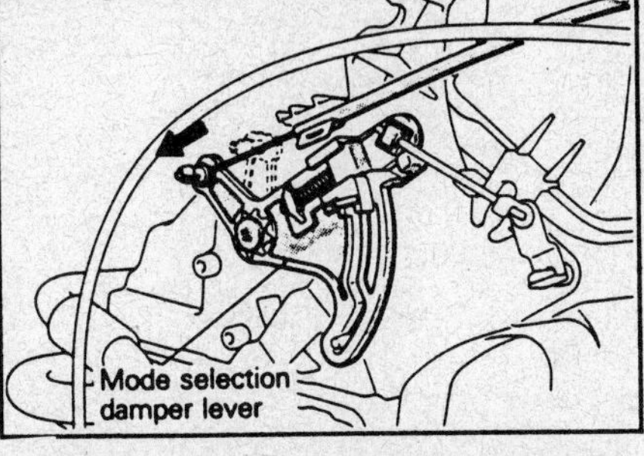


Fig. 20 Positioning water valve control lever. Colt Vista

cated by arrow in **Fig. 16,** connect temperature control wire to lever and secure outer cable using clip.
  c. Place air selection lever in recirculation position, then set air selection damper lever as it contacts stopper as shown in **Fig. 17,** connect air selection control wire to lever and secure outer cable using clip.

## COLT VISTA

Refer to **Fig. 18** during replacement procedure.

1. Disconnect battery ground cable.
2. Place temperature control lever in warm position, then drain cooling system and disconnect heater hoses.
3. Remove instrument panel as described in "Dash Panel Service" section.
4. **On 2WD models,** remove absorber bracket.
5. **On all models,** remove heater duct, then disconnect temperature control air and mode selection wires.
6. Remove heater unit.
7. Remove water valve link, joint hose clamps, joint hose and screws from heater unit, then the heater core from heater unit.
8. Reverse procedure to install, noting the following:
   a. Place mode selector lever in defrost/vent position, then with mode selection damper lever pressed inward in direction indicated by arrow in **Fig. 19,** connect mode selection control wire to lever and secure outer cable using clip.
   b. Place temperature control lever in "COOL" position, then with water valve control lever pressed inward in direction indicated by arrow in **Fig. 20,** connect temperature control wire to lever and secure outer cable using clip.
   c. Place air selection lever in recirculation position, then with air selection damper lever pressed inward in direction indicated by arrow in **Fig. 21,** connect air selection control wire to lever and secure outer cable using clip.

## COLT WAGON

Refer to **Fig. 22** during replacement procedure.

1. Disconnect battery ground cable.
2. Place temperature control lever in warm position, then drain cooling system and disconnect heater hoses.
3. Remove instrument panel as described in "Dash Panel Service" section.
4. Remove heater and center ventilation ducts, then disconnect air selection, temperature control and mode selection wires.
5. Remove heater unit.
6. Remove water valve cover, joint hose clamp, joint hose, screws and piping clamp from heater unit, then the heater core from heater unit.
7. Reverse procedure to install, noting the following:
   a. Place mode selector lever in defrost/vent position, then with mode selection damper lever pressed inward in direction indicated by arrow in **Fig. 19,** connect mode selection control wire to lever and secure outer cable using clip.
   b. Place temperature control lever in "COOL" position, then with water valve control lever pressed inward in direction indicated by arrow in **Fig. 23,** connect temperature control wire to lever and secure outer cable using clip.
   c. Place air selection lever in recirculation position, then with air selection damper lever pressed inward in direction indicated by arrow in **Fig. 24,** connect air selection control wire to lever and secure outer cable using clip.

## CONQUEST

Refer to **Fig. 25** during replacement procedure.

1. Disconnect battery ground cable.
2. Place temperature control lever in warm position, then drain cooling system and disconnect heater hoses.
3. Remove floor console, then the instru-

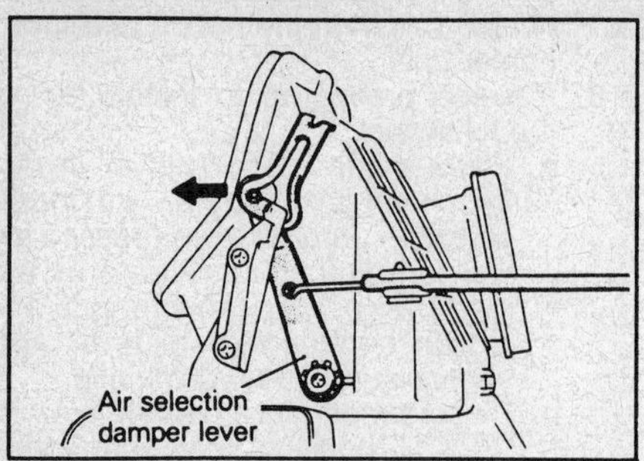


**Fig. 21 Positioning air selection damper lever. Colt Vista**

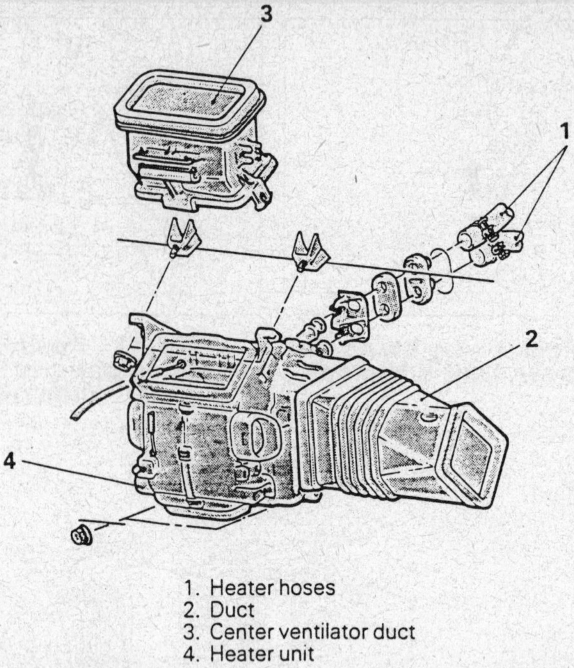

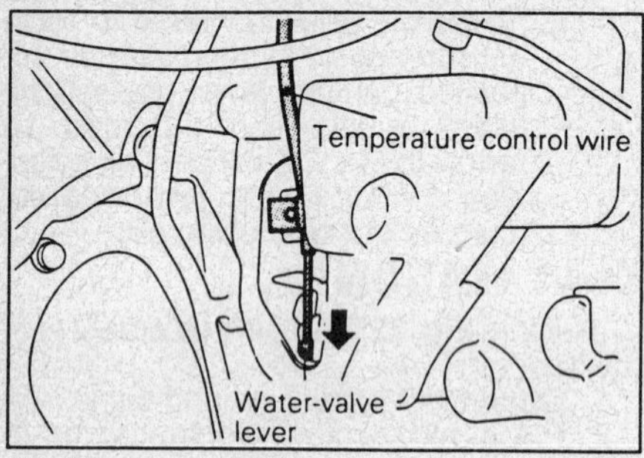


**Fig. 23 Positioning water valve control lever. Colt Wagon**

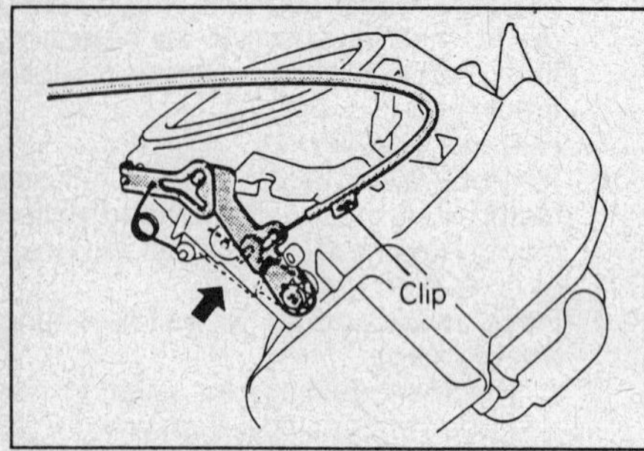


**Fig. 24 Positioning air selection damper lever. Colt Wagon**

1. Heater hoses
2. Duct
3. Center ventilator duct
4. Heater unit

**Fig. 22 Heater core replacement. Colt Wagon**

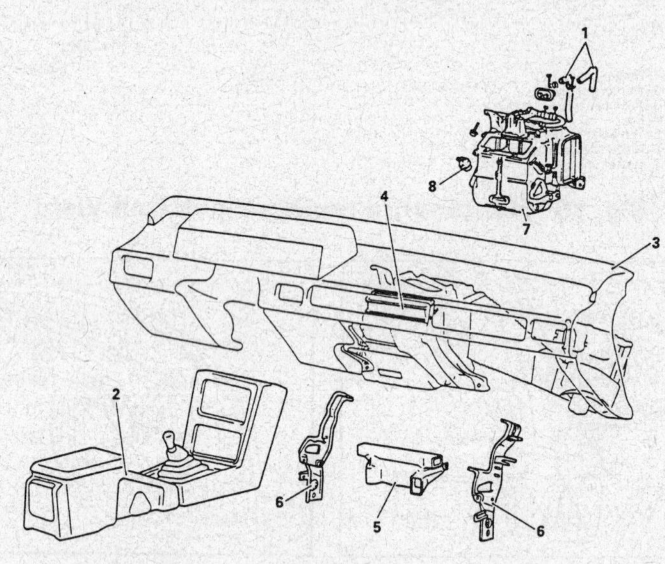

1. Water hoses
2. Floor console
3. Instrument panel
4. Center ventilator duct
5. Lap heater duct
6. Center reinforcement
7. Heater unit
8. Blower relay

**Fig. 25 Heater core replacement. Conquest**

ment panel as described in "Dash Panel Service" section.

4. Remove center ventilator and lap heater ducts, then the center reinforcement.
5. Disconnect mode selection, temperature control and air selection cables.
6. Remove heater unit.
7. Unlock water valve lever clip, then disconnect link for blend air damper from water valve lever.
8. Remove pipe clamp, joint hose clamp, joint hose and screws, then the water valve.
9. Remove plate, then the heater core from heater unit. **It may be necessary to remove damper lever to allow clearance for heater core removal.**
10. Reverse procedure to install, noting the following:
    a. Place mode selector lever in defrost/vent position, then with mode selection damper lever pressed in direction indicated by arrow in **Fig. 26,** connect mode selection control wire to lever and secure outer cable using clip.
    b. Place temperature control lever in "COOL" position, then with blend air damper lever pressed in direction indicated by arrow in **Fig. 27,** connect temperature control wire to lever and secure outer cable using clip.
    c. Place air selection lever in recirculation position, then with air selection damper lever pressed in direction indicated by arrow in **Fig. 28,** connect air selection control wire to lever and secure outer cable using clip.

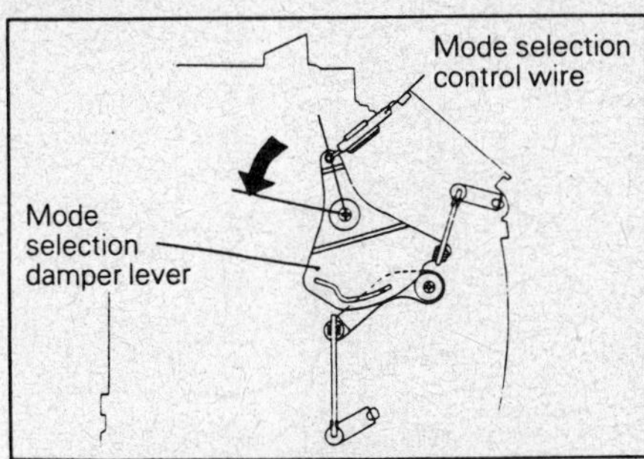


**Fig. 26 Positioning mode selection damper lever. Conquest**

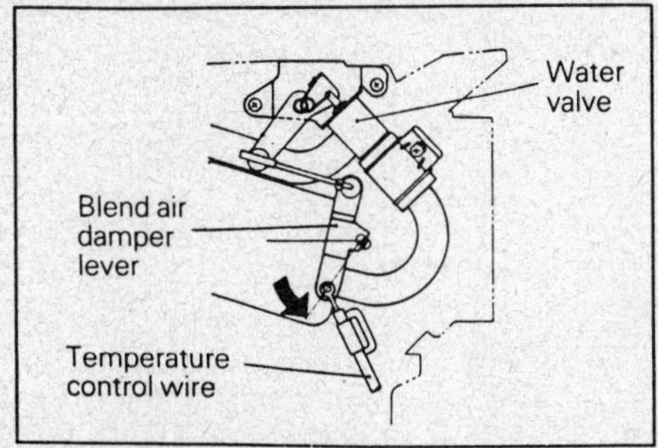


**Fig. 27 Positioning blend air damper lever. Conquest**

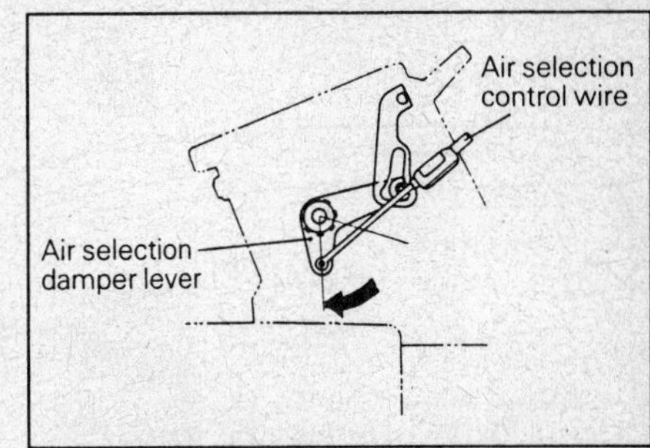


**Fig. 28 Positioning air selection damper lever. Conquest**

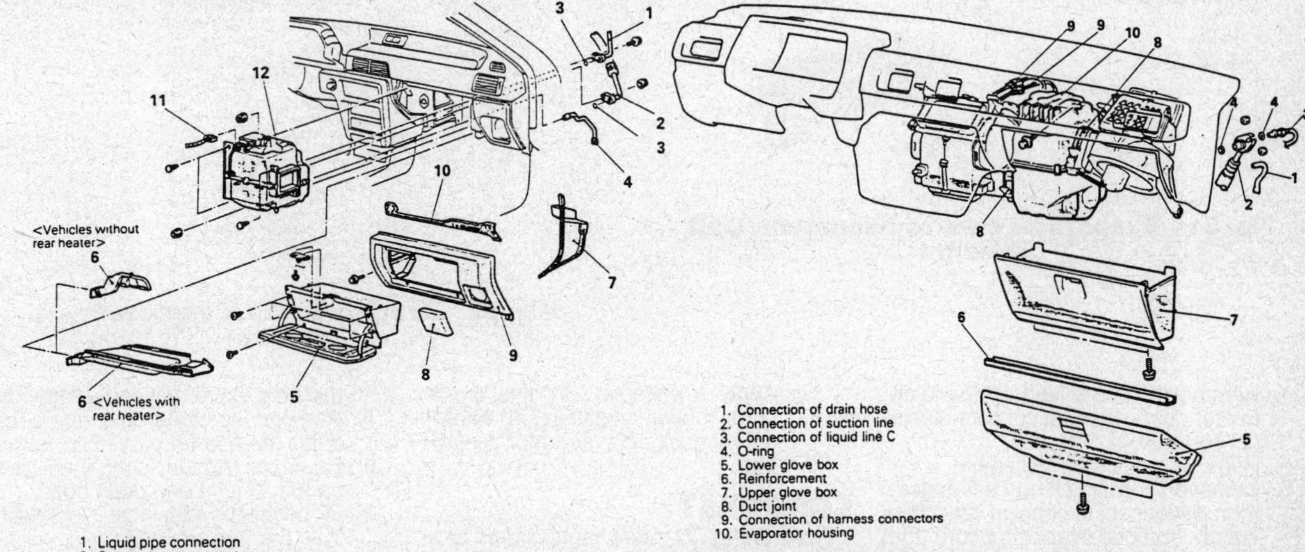


1. Liquid pipe connection
2. Suction hose connection
3. O-rings
4. Drain hose
5. Glove box
6. Lap heater duct <vehicles without rear heater> or shower duct <vehicles with rear heater>
7. Cowl side trim
8. Speaker cover
9. Knee protector, R.H.
10. Glove box frame
11. Connection of the connector (12P) for auto compressor control unit
12. Evaporator

**Fig. 29 Evaporator core replacement. Colt & Summit**

1. Connection of drain hose
2. Connection of suction line
3. Connection of liquid line C
4. O-ring
5. Lower glove box
6. Reinforcement
7. Upper glove box
8. Duct joint
9. Connection of harness connectors
10. Evaporator housing

**Fig. 30 Evaporator core replacement. Colt Vista**

# EVAPORATOR CORE REPLACE

## COLT & SUMMIT

Refer to **Fig. 29** during replacement procedure.

1. Disconnect battery ground cable, then discharge refrigerant from A/C system as described in "Air Conditioning" section.
2. Remove canister from canister bracket in engine compartment and set aside, then disconnect liquid pipe and suction hose and cap fittings.
3. Remove evaporator drain hose, then the glove box assembly.
4. Remove lap heater duct on models less rear heater or shower duct on models with rear heater.
5. Remove righthand cowl side trim, speaker cover and knee protector.
6. Remove glove box frame, then disconnect electrical connector from evaporator.
7. Remove evaporator assembly.
8. Remove clips attaching case halves, then disconnect expansion valve flare nut and remove evaporator core from case.
9. Reverse procedure to install. Apply compressor oil to O-rings and expansion valve of evaporator assembly.

## COLT VISTA

Refer to **Fig. 30** during replacement procedure.

1. Disconnect battery ground cable, then discharge refrigerant from A/C system as described in "Air Conditioning" section.
2. Disconnect liquid pipe and suction hose and cap fittings.
3. Remove evaporator drain hose, then the lower glove box, reinforcement and upper glove box.
4. Disconnect duct joint and electrical connectors.
5. Remove evaporator assembly.
6. Remove clips attaching case halves, then disconnect expansion valve flare nut and remove evaporator core from case.
7. Reverse procedure to install. Apply compressor oil to O-rings and expansion valve of evaporator assembly.

## COLT WAGON

Refer to **Fig. 31** during replacement procedure.

1. Disconnect battery ground cable, then discharge refrigerant from A/C system as described in "Air Conditioning" section.
2. Disconnect liquid pipe and suction hose and cap fittings.
3. Remove evaporator drain hose, then the glove box and dash insert.

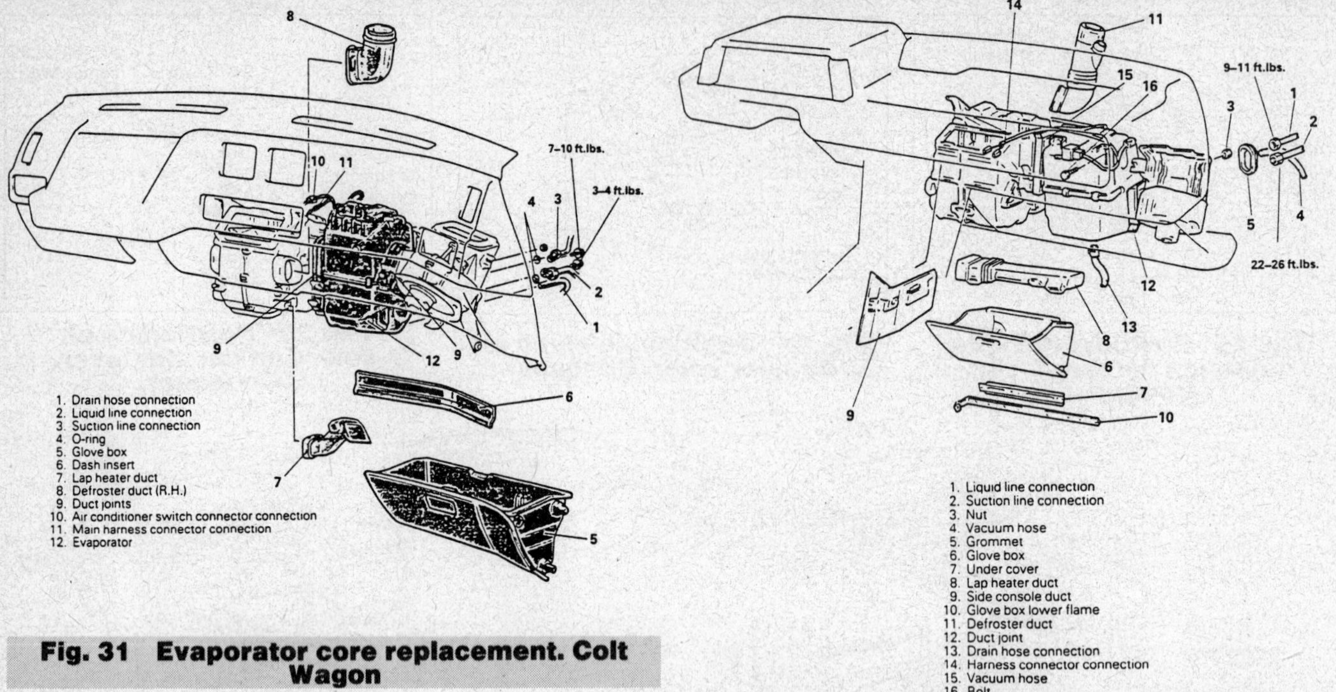


**Fig. 31 Evaporator core replacement. Colt Wagon**

**Fig. 32 Evaporator core replacement. Conquest**

4. Remove lap heater and righthand defroster ducts, then disconnect electrical connectors.
5. Remove evaporator assembly.
6. Remove clips attaching case halves, then disconnect expansion valve flare nut and remove evaporator core from case.
7. Reverse procedure to install, noting the following:
   a. Apply compressor oil to O-rings and expansion valve of evaporator assembly.
   b. Install thermistor securely to clip located at fin of evaporator assembly.
   c. Apply a suitable adhesive grommets, rubber insulation and electrical harness on evaporator assembly.

## CONQUEST

Refer to **Fig. 32** during replacement procedure.

1. Disconnect battery ground cable, then discharge refrigerant from A/C system as described in "Air Conditioning" section.
2. Disconnect liquid pipe and suction hose and cap fittings, then remove nut from evaporator.
3. Remove vacuum hose and grommet, then the glove box and under cover.
4. Remove lap heater and side console ducts, then lower glove box frame.
5. Remove defroster duct, then disconnect duct joint and drain hose.
6. Disconnect electrical connectors, then the vacuum hose.
7. Remove bolt, then the evaporator assembly.
8. Remove clips attaching case halves, then disconnect expansion valve flare nut and remove evaporator core from case.
9. Reverse procedure to install. Apply compressor oil to O-rings and expansion valve of evaporator assembly.

# 1.5L/4-89.6 & 1.6L/4-97.4 Engines

## INDEX



## ENGINE

### REPLACE

The engine and transaxle must be removed as an assembly.

1. Scribe reference marks between hood and hood hinges, then remove hood.
2. Relieve fuel pressure as follows:
   a. With engine running, disconnect fuel pump connector.
   b. Allow engine to deplete fuel supply, then turn ignition Off. **Failure to relieve fuel system pressure prior to disconnecting fuel system components may cause fire or personal injury.**
3. Disconnect battery cables, then remove battery and battery tray.
4. Remove air cleaner and engine undercover, if equipped.
5. Drain cooling system into suitable container.
6. **On models with automatic transaxle,** disconnect transaxle cooling hoses from transaxle.
7. **On all models,** disconnect heater and the upper and lower radiator hoses from engine, then disconnect cooling fan motor and remove radiator.
8. Mark and disconnect necessary vacuum hoses and engine/transaxle wiring that would interfere with engine removal.
9. Disconnect accelerator cable and brake booster vacuum hose.
10. **On models with manual transaxle,** disconnect control cable or clutch tube.
11. **On models with automatic transaxle,** disconnect automatic transaxle control cable. **Handle control cable very carefully so as not to bend inner cable.**
12. **On all models,** disconnect speedometer cable.
13. **On models equipped with power steering,** remove power steering pump and hoses as an assembly leaving hoses connected, then use wire to secure pump.
14. **On all models,** raise and support vehicle.
15. **On models equipped with A/C,** remove compressor belt, then remove compressor mounting bolts and compressor leaving refrigerant lines connected. Disconnect compressor wiring, then use wire to secure compressor and hose assembly.
16. **On models with manual transaxle,** remove shift control rod and extension rod from transaxle. Use wire to secure rods out of the way.
17. **On all models,** disconnect front exhaust pipe from exhaust manifold.
18. Drain engine oil into suitable container. **On models with turbocharged engines,** remove oil cooler lines from engine.
19. **On all models,** disconnect stabilizer bar from lower control arm.
20. Loosen, but do not remove ball joint stud attaching nut, then disconnect ball joint from steering knuckle using puller tool No. MB991113 or equivalent.
21. Loosen, but do not remove tie rod end attaching nut, then disconnect tie rod end from steering knuckle using puller tool No. MB991113 or equivalent.
22. Drain transaxle oil.
23. **On models equipped with driveshaft center bearing,** remove snap ring securing center bearing, then using plastic hammer, lightly tap D.O.J. (double offset joint) outer race to remove driveshaft from transaxle. Remove center bearing.
24. **On models not equipped with driveshaft center bearing,** insert suitable pry bar between transaxle case and driveshaft, then pry driveshaft from transaxle case. **Do not insert pry bar too deep or oil seal will be damaged. Do not pull on drive axle and do not overextend CV joints, as joints will be damaged.**
25. **On all models,** cover transaxle holes to prevent entry of dirt and replace drive axle circlips.
26. Use wire to secure driveshafts out of the way.
27. Attach suitable engine lifting device, then raise lift enough to tension equipment.
28. Remove front roll stopper insulator bolt, then the rear roll stopper insulator bolt.
29. Remove left mount insulator attaching nut. **Do not remove bolt.**
30. Raise engine/transaxle assembly enough to remove weight from mounts.
31. Remove blind cover from inside right fender shield, then remove transaxle mount bracket bolt.
32. Remove left mount insulator bolt, then while directing transaxle side down, remove engine/transaxle assembly from vehicle.
33. Separate engine from transaxle as follows:
    a. Remove starter motor.
    b. **On models with automatic transaxle,** remove bolts securing torque converter to drive plate.
    c. **On all models,** remove engine-to-transaxle attaching bolts, then remove transaxle assembly.
34. Reverse procedure to install.

## CYLINDER HEAD

### REPLACE

#### 1.5L/4-89.6

1. Disconnect battery ground cable and drain cooling system.

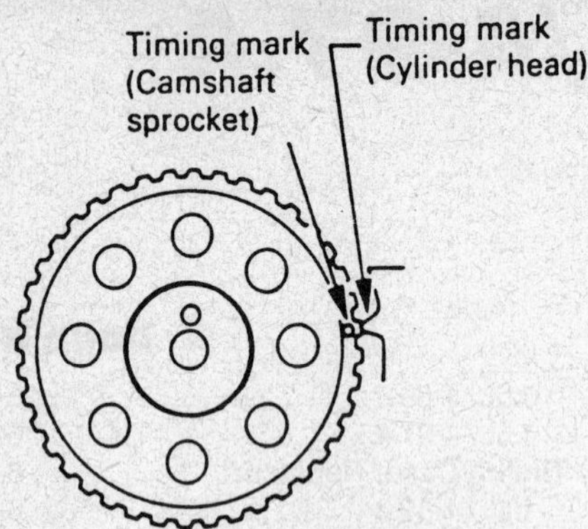


**Fig. 1 Camshaft timing marks. 1.5L/4-89.6 engines**

2. Disconnect breather and secondary air hose, then remove air cleaner assembly, air intake duct and hot air duct.
3. Disconnect accelerator cable from throttle lever and brackets.
4. Disconnect upper radiator, heater and water hoses, fuel hoses and the brake booster hose.
5. **On models with automatic transaxle,** disconnect throttle cable from engine. **On models with manual transaxle,** disconnect clutch cable and secure aside.
6. **On all models,** mark and disconnect necessary electrical connectors and vacuum hoses, release harness clips and secure harnesses aside to prevent damage.
7. Disconnect ignition coil high tension lead, then remove distributor cap and plug wires.
8. Support engine as needed, then remove left engine mount bracket from cylinder head.
9. Remove exhaust manifold covers and disconnect exhaust pipe from manifold.
10. Remove engine oil dipstick and plug opening.
11. Remove upper timing belt cover, rocker arm cover and the gasket.
12. Rotate crankshaft in normal direction of rotation (clockwise) to bring No. 1 cylinder to top dead center compression stroke. The No. 1 cylinder is at top dead center compression stroke when the mark on the upper timing undercover is aligned with the mark on the camshaft sprocket, **Fig. 1.**
13. Place an alignment mark on timing belt, in line with mark on camshaft sprocket timing mark, **Fig. 1.**
14. Remove camshaft sprocket attaching bolt, then detach sprocket from camshaft with timing belt attached. Position camshaft sprocket on lower belt cover or suspend sprocket and belt from hood to maintain proper timing alignment. **Do not rotate crankshaft after removing sprocket from camshaft.**
15. Remove cylinder head attaching bolts in sequence shown in **Fig. 2.** Loosen bolts evenly, in three steps, to prevent cylinder head warpage, then remove cylinder head and gasket. Take care not to dislodge camshaft sprocket during cylinder head removal.

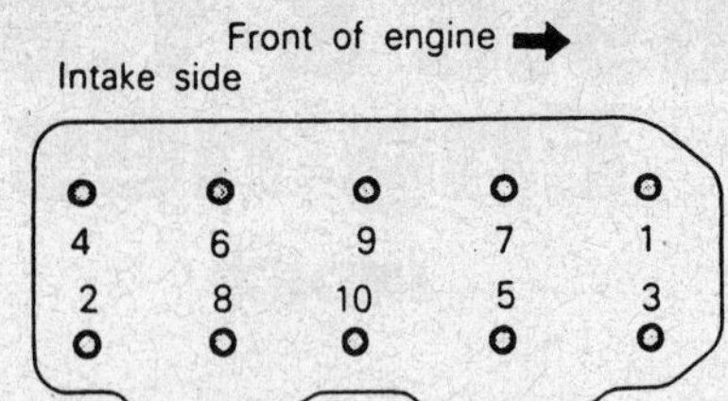


**Fig. 2 Cylinder head bolt loosening sequence**

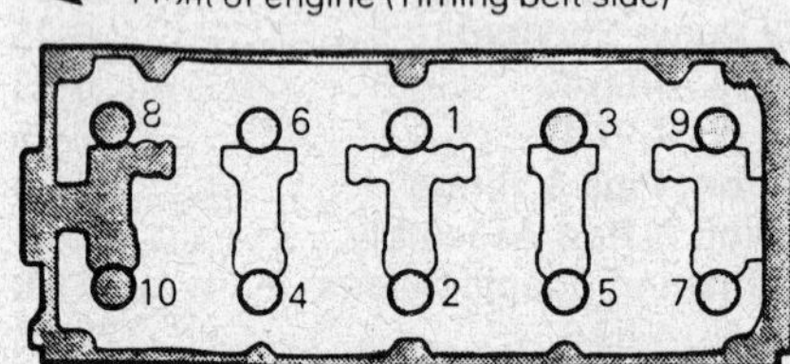


**Fig. 4 Cylinder head bolt tightening sequence. 1991–92 1.5L/4-89.6 engines**

16. Reverse procedure to install, noting the following:
   a. Do not apply sealer to cylinder head gasket. Install gasket with I.D. mark toward timing belt.
   b. Prior to installing cylinder head on engine, ensure crankshaft and camshaft timing marks are aligned.
   c. Tighten cylinder head bolts in sequence shown in **Figs. 3 and 4.** Tighten bolts in two steps to ensure proper seating of cylinder head to cylinder block.
   d. After cylinder head has been installed, adjust timing belt tension and valve clearance as outlined.

## 1.6L/4-97.4

1. Relieve fuel pressure as follows:
   a. With engine running, disconnect fuel pump connector.
   b. Allow engine to deplete fuel supply, then turn ignition Off. **Failure to release pressure prior to disconnecting fuel lines may cause fire or personal injury.**
2. Disconnect battery ground cable, drain cooling system, then disconnect upper radiator hose.
3. Disconnect engine cooling fan motor electrical connector, then remove radiator.
4. Disconnect accelerator cable from throttle body.
5. Disconnect breather hose and purge hose from air intake hose.
6. Remove two turbocharger air hoses.
7. Disconnect air bypass hose from air intake hose, then remove air intake hose.

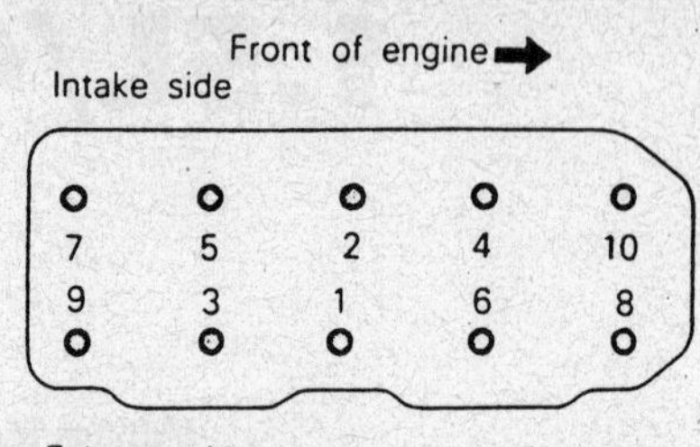


**Fig. 3 Cylinder head bolt tightening sequence. 1989–90 1.5L/4-89.6 & 1.6L/4-97.4 engines**

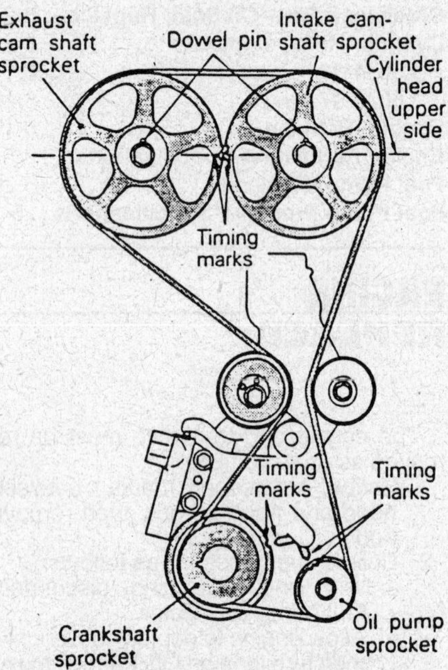


**Fig. 5 Aligning timing marks. 1.6L/4-97.4 engines**

8. Disconnect air flow sensor electrical connector, then remove air cleaner assembly.
9. Mark and disconnect necessary electrical connectors and vacuum hoses, release harness from clips and secure aside.
10. Disconnect fuel hoses, heater hoses and the brake booster hose.
11. Remove engine center cover, then disconnect connections for fuel injectors, spark plug wires and control wiring harness.
12. Remove timing belt as follows:
   a. Remove undercover.
   b. Using a wood block and a jack, place wood block on engine oil pan and raise engine only enough to relieve tension on top engine mount, then remove mount and bracket.
   c. Remove engine drive belts. **Prior to removing water pump drive belt, loosen water pump pulley bolts.**
   d. Remove crankshaft pulley.
   e. Remove upper and lower timing covers.

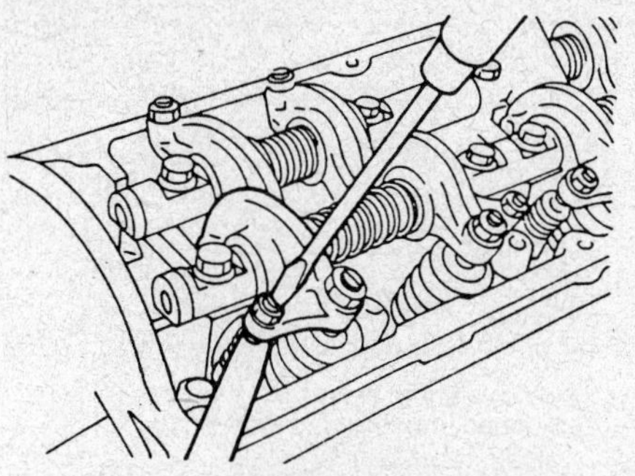

**Fig. 6 Adjusting jet valve clearance**

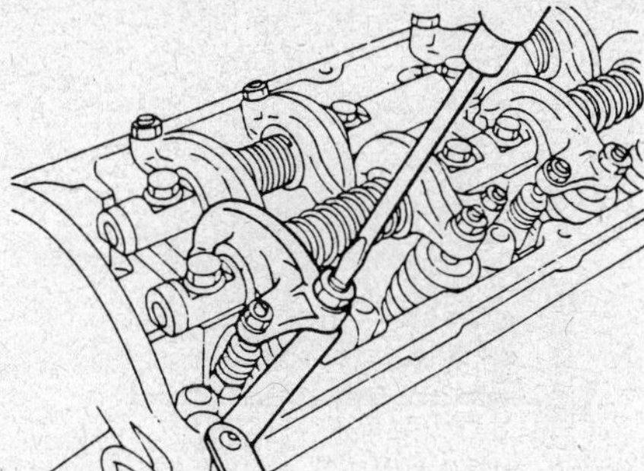

**Fig. 7 Adjusting valve clearance**

| Size mm (in.) | Size mark | Cylinder head hole size mm (in.) |
|---|---|---|
| 0.05 (.002) O.S. | 5 | 12.050 – 12.068 (.4744 – .4751) |
| 0.25 (.010) O.S. | 25 | 12.250 – 12.268 (.4823 – .4830) |
| 0.50 (.020) O.S. | 50 | 12.500 – 12.518 (.4921 – .4928) |

**Fig. 8 Valve guide & guide bore oversizes**

f. Remove tensioner pulley and bracket.
g. Disconnect PCV hose, then remove rocker cover.
h. Rotate crankshaft clockwise to bring No. 1 cylinder to top dead center compression stroke. **Rotate crankshaft only in clockwise direction.** The No. 1 cylinder is at top dead center compression stroke when the timing marks on camshaft sprockets are aligned with upper surface of cylinder head and dowel pins on camshaft sprockets are facing up as shown, **Fig. 5.**
i. Remove auto tensioner.
j. Mark timing belt indicating direction of rotation, then remove timing belt.

13. Remove heat shield, then disconnect water pipe from cylinder head.
14. Disconnect and plug oil return line from turbocharger.
15. Remove tension rod from between cylinder head and intake housing.
16. Disconnect exhaust pipe from turbocharger.
17. Remove bolts attaching intake manifold to support.
18. Using wrench tool No. MD998051 or equivalent, remove cylinder head attaching bolts in sequence as shown, **Fig. 2.** Loosen head bolts evenly, in two or three steps to prevent cylinder head warpage. When removing cylinder head use care not to disturb the camshaft sprockets. After removing cylinder head, clean gasket surfaces on head and block.
19. Remove intake and exhaust manifolds.
20. Reverse procedure to install, noting the following:

a. Ensure new cylinder head gasket has proper identification mark for engine. Position gasket with identification mark facing up and towards front of engine.
b. Tighten cylinder head bolts in sequence as shown, **Fig. 3. Ensure head bolt washers are correctly installed.**
c. Ensure camshaft and crankshaft timing marks are correctly aligned.
d. When installing rocker cover, apply sealant No. 4318034 or equivalent to semi-circular packing.

# VALVE LASH SPECIFICATIONS

| Engine | Year | Clearance Inch Int. | Clearance Inch Exh. | Jet Valve |
|---|---|---|---|---|
| All | 1989–91 | .006H | .010H | — |

**H: Hot.**

# VALVE TIMING

## INTAKE OPENS BTDC

| Engine | Year | Degrees |
|---|---|---|
| 1.5L/4-89.6 | 1989–90 | 18.5 |
| | 1991 | 14.5 |
| 1.6L/4-97.4 | 1989–90 | 21 |

# VALVES

## ADJUST

**On models equipped with jet valve, the jet valve must be adjusted before adjusting the intake valve.** 1.6L/4-97.4 Turbo engines are equipped with hydraulic lash adjusters with no provision for adjustment.

## JET VALVE

1. Following procedure for intake and exhaust valve adjustment, position No. 1 cylinder at top dead center compression stroke.
2. Loosen intake valve adjusting screw at least two turns, then loosen jet valve adjusting screw locknut.
3. Rotate jet valve adjusting screw counterclockwise and insert a .010 inch (.25mm) feeler gauge between jet valve stem and adjusting screw, **Fig. 6.**
4. Tighten jet valve adjusting screw until it contacts the feeler gauge blade, then while holding adjusting screw in position, tighten locknut.
5. After jet valve adjustment has been completed, adjust intake valve clearance. Continue to follow intake and exhaust valve adjustment procedure and adjust jet valves as necessary.

## INTAKE & EXHAUST VALVES

1. With engine at operating temperature, remove rocker arm cover.
2. Disconnect high tension lead from ignition coil.
3. While observing rocker arms on No. 4 cylinder, rotate crankshaft clockwise until the exhaust valve is closing and the intake valve has just to open. Ensure timing mark on crankshaft pulley is aligned with "T" mark on lower timing cover case. At this position the No. 1 cylinder is at top dead center compression stroke. Check and adjust valve clearance for both intake and exhaust valves of No. 1 cylinder, intake valve of No. 2 cylinder and exhaust valve of No. 3 cylinder. If valve clearance is not as specified, adjust valves as follows:
   a. Loosen rocker arm locknut.
   b. Turn adjusting screw while measuring clearance with a feeler gauge, **Fig. 7,** until screw contacts feeler gauge.
   c. Intake valve clearance should be .006 inch (.15mm) and exhaust valve clearance should be .010 inch (.25mm) with engine hot.
   d. Hold adjusting screw in place and tighten locknut.
4. Rotate crankshaft clockwise 360 degrees then check and adjust valve clearance for exhaust valve of No. 2 cylinder, intake valve of No. 3 cylinder and intake and exhaust valves of No. 4 cylinder.
5. After completing adjustment, install rocker arm cover and connect ignition coil high tension lead.

# VALVE GUIDES

## REPLACE

1. Press old valve guide from cylinder head toward lower surface using the special valve guide tool and press.
2. Ream each valve guide bore in cylinder head to the O.D. of replacement valve guide, **Fig. 8. Never use a valve guide of the same size as the removed guide.**

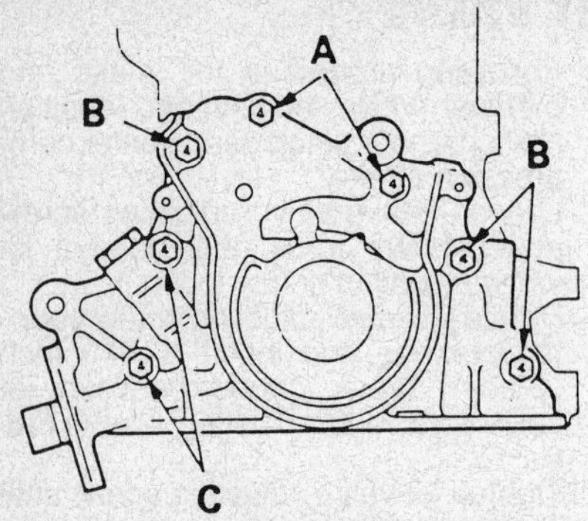


**Fig. 9 Timing case cover bolt locations. 1989–90 1.5L/4-89.6 engines**

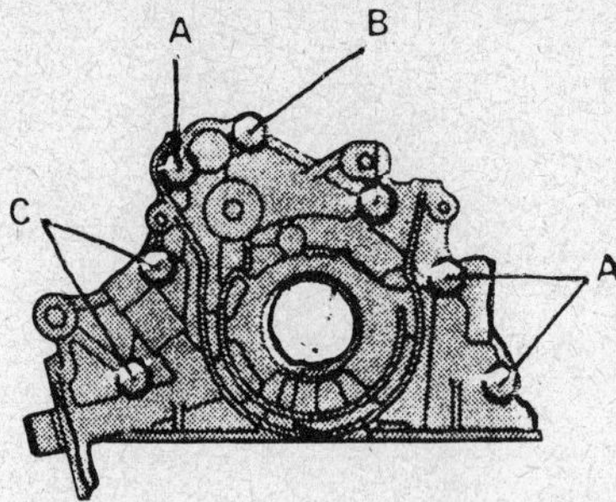


**Fig. 10 Timing case cover bolt locations. 1991–92 1.5L/4-89.6 engines**

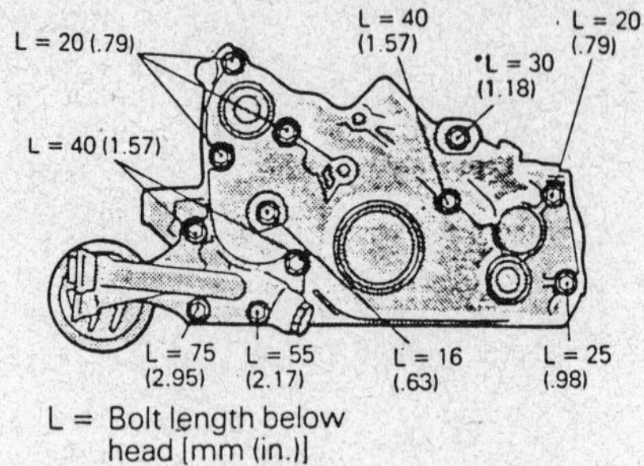


**Fig. 11 Timing case cover bolt lengths & locations. 1.6L/4-97.4 engine**

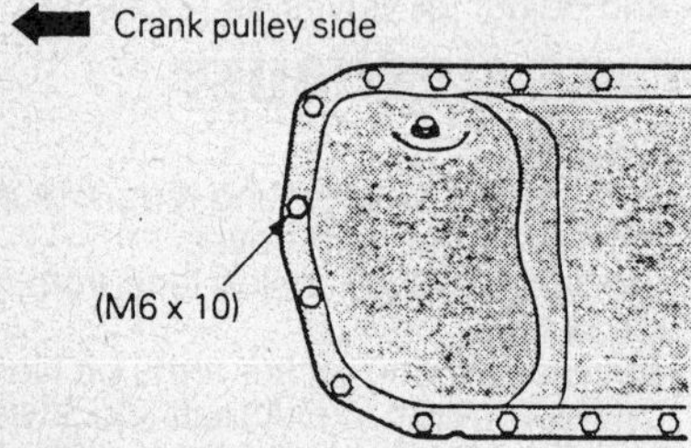


**Fig. 12 Oil pan bolt location. 1.6L/4-97.4 engine**

3. Install new valve guide using special valve guide and stopper tools and press.
4. **On all engines except 1991 1.5L/4-89.6,** note that valve guides for intake and exhaust are of different lengths. Intake guides are 1.791 inches (45.5mm) long, exhaust guides are 1.988 inches (50.5mm) long. **On 1991 1.5L/4-89.6 engine,** intake length is 1.732 inches and exhaust is 1.949 inches.
5. After installation of new valve guides, insert valve and ensure it slides freely, then check for proper clearance. If clearance is not correct, ream valve guide until proper clearance is obtained. Refer to "Valve Specifications" for stem to guide clearance.

# TIMING CASE REPLACE

## 1.5L/4-89.6

1. Remove timing belt as outlined under "Timing Belt, Replace."
2. Remove oil pan and oil screen, then the timing case.
3. Reverse procedure to install. When installing timing case attaching bolts, refer to **Figs. 9 and 10,** and note that bolts installed in location A are 1.18 inches in length, bolts installed in location B are .79 inches in length and bolts installed in location C are 2.36 inches in length. When installing oil seal, lubricate seal lips with engine oil, then position seal on crankshaft and tap into timing case using seal installer tool No. MD998304 or equivalent. Before installing oil pan, apply sealer at the four front timing case and rear oil seal case to cylinder block mating surfaces.

## 1.6L/4-97.4

1. Remove timing belt as outlined under "Timing Belt, Replace."
2. Drain crankcase, then remove oil filter and disconnect oil pressure switch connector.
3. Remove oil pan attaching bolts, then drive in oil pan gasket cutter tool No. MD998727 or equivalent, between cylinder block and oil pan. Break gasket seal using the tool, then remove oil pan.
4. Remove oil pickup screen and gasket.
5. Remove oil filter adapter attaching bolts, then the oil filter adapter.
6. Remove front case attaching bolts, noting length and position for installation, then remove front case and oil pump as an assembly.
7. Reverse procedure to install noting the following:
   a. If front crankshaft seal is to be replaced, install using seal installer tool No. MD998375 or equivalent.
   b. Install guide tool No. MD998285 or equivalent, on front end of crankshaft and apply a light coat of oil to outer circumference of the tool. Install front case assembly and gasket and temporarily tighten bolts. When installing bolts, refer to **Fig. 11,** for bolt length and position.
   c. Install oil filter adapter and gasket, torquing bolts to specifications.
   d. Tighten front case attaching bolts, then remove guide tool.
   e. When installing oil pan, apply a .16 inch (4mm) wide bead of sealant to entire circumference of oil pan flange. Note difference in bolt length shown in **Fig. 12.**

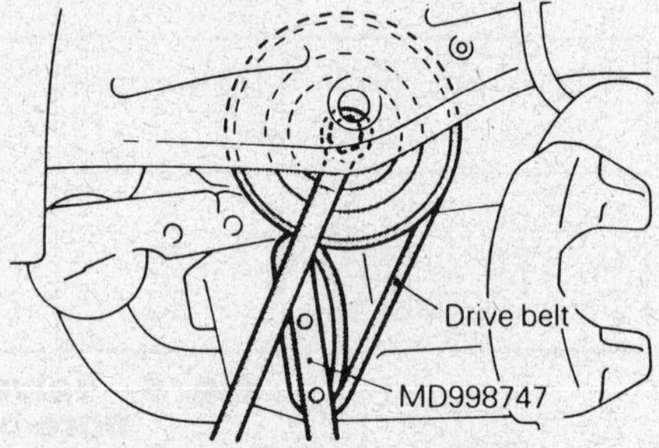


**Fig. 13 Timing belt removal. 1.5L/4-89.6 engine**

# TIMING BELT REPLACE

## 1.5L/4-89.6

### Removal

1. Remove battery ground cable.
2. Disconnect breather and secondary air hoses, then remove air cleaner assembly, air intake duct and heated air duct as needed.
3. Disconnect accelerator cable and oxygen sensor lead, and remove spark plug wires as needed.
4. Remove accessory drive belts.
5. Support engine as needed, then remove left engine mount bracket.
6. Remove power steering pump, if equipped and water pump pulleys.
7. Remove rocker arm cover, gasket and packing, and the upper timing belt cover.
8. **On 1991-92 models,** using special tool No. MD998747 and discarded drive belt, stop rotation of crankshaft pulley, remove A/C and crankshaft pulley, **Fig. 13.**
9. **On all models,** rotate crankshaft in normal direction of rotation (clockwise) until timing marks are aligned, **Fig. 14,** loosen belt tensioner bolts and move timing belt tensioner fully toward the water pump, then tighten bolts to hold tensioner.
10. Remove timing belt. If the timing belt is to be reused, place an arrow mark indicating turning direction (direction of engine rotation) to ensure the belt is installed in the same direction as before.

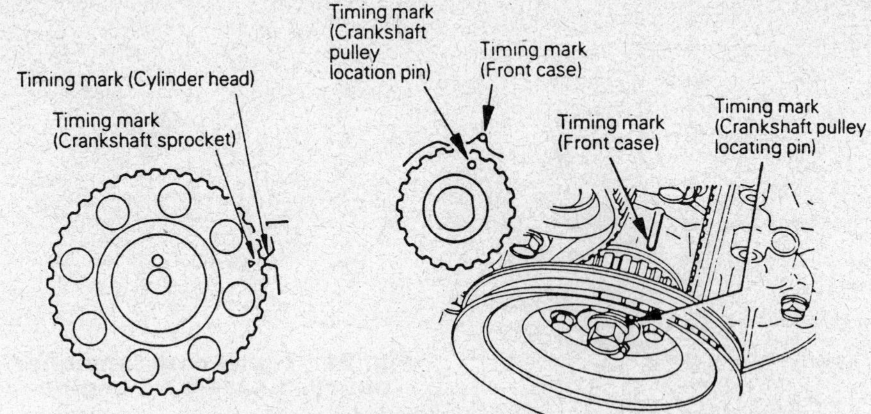


**Fig. 14 Camshaft & crankshaft sprocket timing marks. 1.5L/4-89.6 engines**

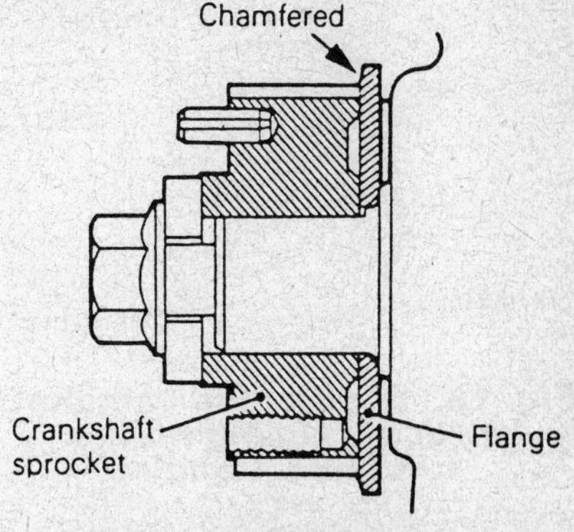


**Fig. 15 Installing flange & crankshaft sprocket. 1.5L/4-89.6 engines**

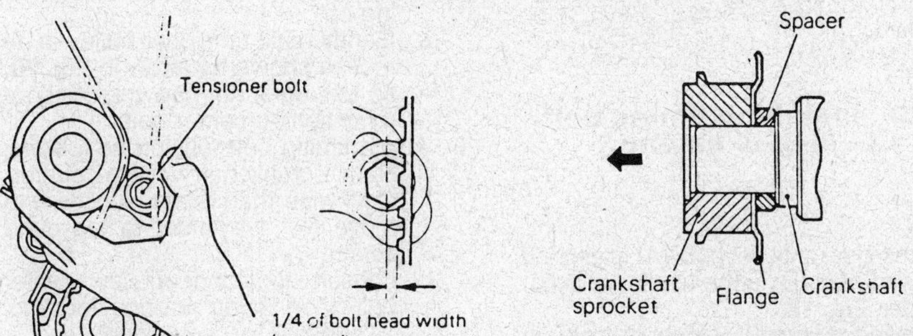


**Fig. 16 Checking timing belt tension. 1.5L/4-89.6 engines**

**Fig. 17 Installing crankshaft sprocket and flange. 1.6L/4-97.4 engine**

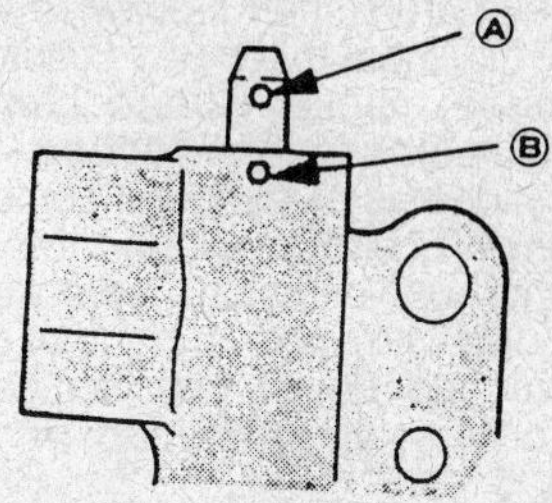


**Fig. 18 Aligning auto tensioner rod. 1.6L/4-97.4 engine**

11. Remove camshaft sprocket, crankshaft sprocket and flange, and timing belt tensioner as needed.
12. Inspect belt and replace if any of the following conditions are noted:
    a. Hardened back surface rubber. With back surface glossy, non-elastic and so hard that no mark is produced when fingernail is forced into surface.
    b. Cracked back surface rubber.
    c. Cracked or separated canvas.
    d. Cracks at tooth bottom or side of belt.

### Installation

1. Install flange and crankshaft sprocket as shown in **Fig. 15.**
2. Tighten crankshaft sprocket bolt.
3. Install camshaft sprocket.
4. Install timing belt tensioner as follows:
    a. Mount tensioner, spring and spacer, then temporarily tighten pivot bolt.
    b. Temporarily tighten the adjusting bolt, then install bottom end of the spring into front case.
    c. Secure tensioner to the position nearest the water pump.
5. Ensure timing marks are aligned, **Fig. 14.**
6. Install timing belt over crankshaft sprocket, then the camshaft sprocket, keeping tension side of belt tight as belt is installed. If used belt is installed, ensure belt is installed in original direction.
7. Apply counterclockwise force to camshaft sprocket to tighten tension side of belt, ensuring that timing marks remain aligned.
8. Install crankshaft pulley to prevent belt from slipping off sprocket, then adjust belt tension as follows:
    a. Loosen tensioner bolts to allow tensioner to bear against belt, then tighten adjusting bolt and pivot bolt. **Tighten adjusting bolt first to prevent tensioner from rotating away from belt.**
    b. Rotate crankshaft clockwise one full revolution, then realign crankshaft sprocket timing mark with pointer. **Crankshaft must be rotated smoothly, in clockwise direction. Do not apply any force other than spring force of tensioner to timing belt.**
    c. Loosen tensioner pivot and adjusting bolts. then tighten adjuster bolt and pivot bolt. **Tighten adjusting bolt first to prevent tensioner from rotating away from belt.**
    d. Check belt tension by holding belt as shown in **Fig. 16,** and applying thumb pressure to tension side of belt. Tension is correct when tooth of belt covers approximately 1/4 the width of the tensioner adjuster bolt.
    e. Rotate crankshaft clockwise, one full revolution and ensure timing marks line up.
9. Reverse remaining procedure to complete installation, then adjust valve clearances as outlined.

## 1.6L/4-97.4

### Removal

1. Disconnect battery ground cable.
2. Disconnect accelerator cable from throttle body.
3. Remove undercover.
4. Using a wood block and a jack, place wood block on engine oil pan and raise engine only enough to relieve tension on top engine mount, then remove mount and bracket.
5. Remove engine drive belts. **Prior to removing water pump drive belt, loosen water pump pulley bolts.**
6. Remove crankshaft pulley.
7. Remove upper and lower timing covers.
8. Remove tensioner pulley and bracket.
9. Disconnect PCV and breather hoses, then remove center cover, spark plug

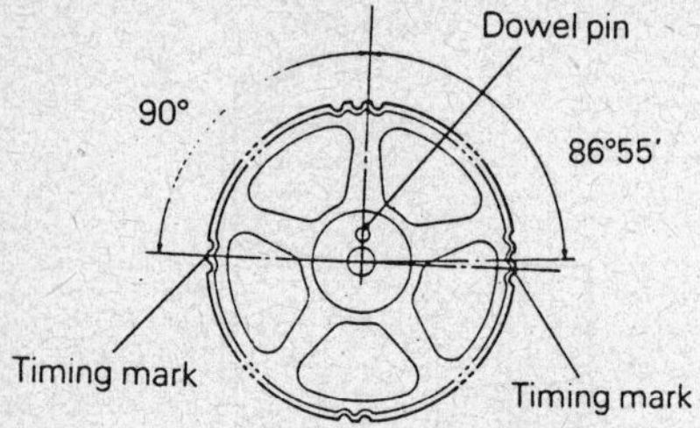


**Fig. 19 Positioning camshaft sprocket timing marks. 1.6L/4-97.4 engine**

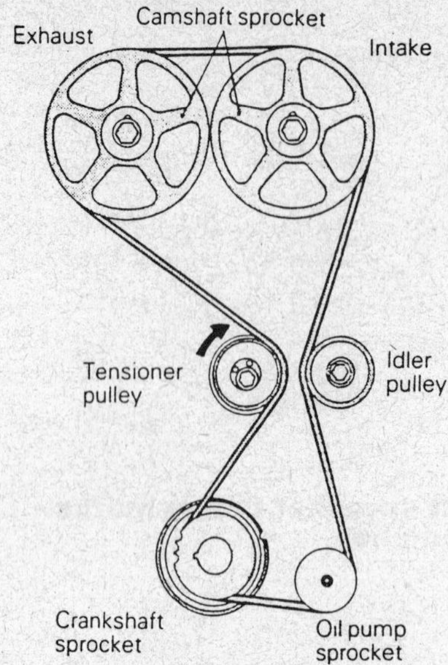


**Fig. 20 Installing timing belt. 1.6L/4-97.4 engine**

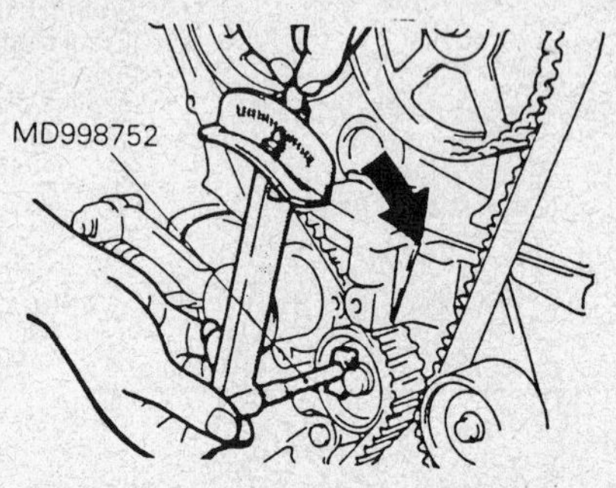


**Fig. 21 Tightening tensioner pulley. 1.6L/4-97.4 engine**

wires and rocker cover.

10. Rotate crankshaft clockwise to bring No. 1 cylinder to top dead center compression stroke. **Rotate crankshaft only in clockwise direction.** The No. 1 cylinder is at top dead center compression stroke when the timing marks on camshaft sprockets are aligned with upper surface of cylinder head and dowel pins on camshaft sprockets are facing up as shown, **Fig. 5.**
11. Remove auto tensioner and pulley.
12. Remove timing belt. If timing belt is to be reused, mark timing belt indicating direction of rotation.
13. Remove crankshaft sprocket spacer and flange, camshaft sprockets, oil pump sprocket and timing belt tensioner as needed.
14. Inspect belt and replace if any of the following conditions are noted:
    a. Hardened back surface rubber with back surface glossy, non-elastic and so hard that no mark is produced when fingernail is forced into surface.
    b. Cracked back surface rubber.
    c. Cracked or separated canvas.
    d. Cracks at tooth bottom or side of belt.

## Installation

1. Install spacer, flange and crankshaft sprocket. **Ensure crankshaft sprocket and flange are correctly installed as shown in Fig. 17.**
2. Install oil pump sprocket, torquing attaching nut to specifications.
3. Install camshaft sprockets. Using a wrench, hold the camshaft at the hexagonal portion (between No. 2 and No. 3 journals) and tighten attaching bolt. **Locking the camshaft sprocket with a tool may damage the sprocket.**
4. Install auto tensioner. If tensioner rod is fully extended, proceed as follows:
    a. Position auto tensioner level in a soft jawed vise. If plug at bottom of tensioner protrudes, apply a plain washer to prevent the plug from direct contact with vise.
    b. Slowly push tensioner rod in, using the vise, until set hole (A) is aligned with hole (B) in the tensioner cylinder, **Fig. 18.**
    c. Insert a wire .055 inch (1.4mm) in diameter into the set holes, then remove auto tensioner from the vise.
    d. Install auto tensioner. **Leave the wire installed in the auto tensioner.**
5. Install tensioner pulley onto tensioner arm, position the hole in pulley shaft to the left of the center bolt, then tighten center bolt finger tight.
6. Rotate camshaft sprockets so that their dowel pins are located on top, then align the timing marks facing each other with the top surface of cylinder head, **Fig. 6.** When exhaust camshaft is released, it will rotate one tooth in the counterclockwise direction. This should be taken into account when installing timing belt on sprockets. **The camshaft sprockets are interchangeable and have two sets of timing marks. When the sprocket is mounted on the exhaust camshaft, use the timing mark on the right with dowel pin hole on top. For the intake sprocket, use the mark on the left with dowel pin hole on top, Fig. 19.**
7. Align camshaft sprocket and oil pump sprocket timing marks as shown, **Fig. 5.**
8. Install timing belt as follows:
    a. Install timing belt around intake camshaft sprocket, **Fig. 20,** and retain using a suitable spring clip.
    b. Install timing belt around exhaust camshaft sprocket, aligning timing marks with cylinder head top surface using two wrenches. Retain belt in position using a suitable spring clip.
    c. Install timing belt around idler pulley, oil pump sprocket, crankshaft sprocket and tensioner pulley.
    d. Remove spring clips retaining timing belt.
    e. Gently raise tensioner pulley in direction shown by arrow in **Fig. 20,** so belt does not sag, then temporarily tighten center bolt.
9. Adjust timing belt tension as follows:
    a. Rotate crankshaft 1/4 turn counterclockwise, then rotate clockwise to move No. 1 cylinder to top dead center.
    b. Loosen tensioner pulley center bolt, then using wrench tool No. MD998752 or equivalent, and a torque wrench, apply a **torque** of 1.88-2.03 ft. lbs., **Fig. 21.** Use a torque wrench capable of measurement within a range of 0-2.2 ft. lbs. If vehicle body interferes with torque wrench, use a jack to slightly raise engine.
    c. Holding tensioner pulley with the tool, tighten tensioner pulley center bolt.
    d. Screw set screw tool No. MD998738 or equivalent, into left engine support bracket until end of tool makes contact with tensioner arm, **Fig. 22.** Turn the tool enough to relieve tension on auto tensioner rod, then remove set wire previously installed in auto tensioner.
    e. Remove set screw tool.
    f. Rotate crankshaft clockwise two complete turns, then let sit for 15 minutes.
    g. Measure clearance (A) between tensioner arm and auto tensioner body, **Fig. 23.** If clearance is not .15-.18 inch (3.8-4.5mm), repeat steps a-g until clearance is correct.
    h. If clearance (A) cannot be measured with engine in vehicle, screw in set screw tool No. MD998738 or equivalent, until end of tool makes contact with tensioner arm.
    i. Starting in this position, count the number of turns of the tool required to bring tensioner arm in contact with auto tensioner body. Ensure contact is made within 2.5-3 turns.
    j. Install rubber plug into timing belt rear cover.

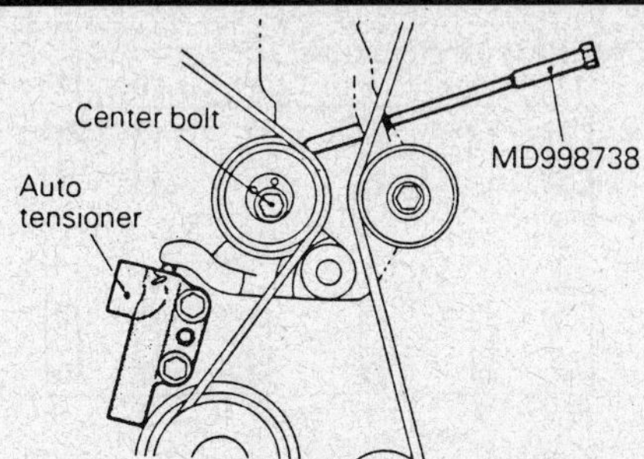


**Fig. 22 Adjusting timing belt tension. 1.6L/4-97.4 engine**

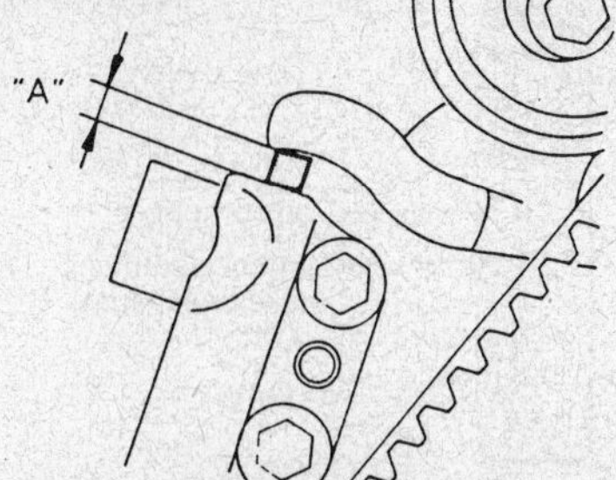


**Fig. 23 Checking timing belt tension. 1.6L/4-97.4 engine**

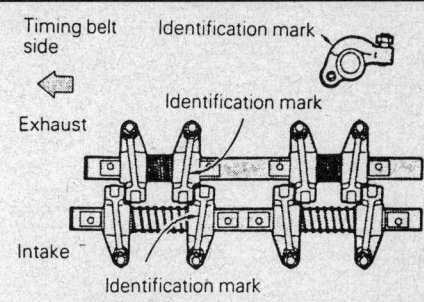

**Fig. 24 Rocker arm & shaft assembly installation. 1989–90 1.5L/4-89.6 engines**

10. Reverse procedure to install remaining components, noting the following:
    a. When installing rocker cover, apply sealant No. 4318034 or equivalent to semi-circular packing.

# CAMSHAFT, ROCKER ARMS & SHAFTS

## REPLACE

### 1.5L/4-89.6

#### Removal

1. Disconnect battery ground cable.
2. **On 1991-92 models,** remove the distributor, refer to "Distributor, Replace" in the Electrical Section.
3. **On all models,** disconnect breather hose and secondary air hose.
4. Remove air cleaner and timing belt cover.
5. Rotate crankshaft in normal direction of rotation (clockwise) to bring No. 1 cylinder to top dead center compression stroke. The No. 1 cylinder is at top dead center compression stroke when the mark on the upper timing undercover is aligned with the mark on the camshaft sprocket, **Fig. 1.**
6. Move timing belt tensioner fully toward the water pump assembly and temporarily secure it.
7. Remove camshaft sprocket attaching bolt, then detach sprocket from camshaft with timing belt attached. Position camshaft sprocket on lower belt cover or suspend sprocket and belt from hood to maintain proper timing alignment. **Do not rotate crankshaft after removing sprocket from camshaft.**
8. Remove rocker cover and gasket, and note position of camshaft.
9. Remove rocker shaft assembly and cylinder head rear cover.
10. Remove camshaft thrust case tightening bolt, thrust case, camshaft and oil seal. Remove assembly toward transaxle side of cylinder head.
11. **On 1991-92 models,** remove oil seal, exhaust side, then intake side rocker arm assembly and camshaft.

#### INSTALLATION

#### 1989–90

1. Check camshaft journals for wear. If journals are badly worn, replace camshaft.
2. Install camshaft thrust case and thrust plate to camshaft end and firmly tighten attaching bolt. Check camshaft endplay. Endplay should be .002-.008 inch. If endplay exceeds specified value, replace thrust case and recheck endplay.
3. If endplay is still not within specification, check rear end of camshaft journal for wear. If badly worn, replace camshaft.
4. Lubricate camshaft journal and thrust portions of camshaft with clean engine oil.
5. Insert camshaft into cylinder head and rotate camshaft to position noted during disassembly (TDC on compression stroke for No. 1 cylinder).
6. Insert camshaft thrust case with the threaded hole facing upward. Align threaded hole with bolt hole in the cylinder head. Install and firmly tighten attaching bolt.
7. Install rear gasket and cover. Firmly tighten bolts.
8. Using guide tool No. MD998307 and seal installer tool No. MD998306 or equivalents, install camshaft oil seal. Lubricate external surface of seal completely with engine oil.
9. Ensure seal is completely seated.
10. Install camshaft sprocket and timing belt, and ensure timing marks are aligned, **Fig. 1.** Tighten camshaft sprocket bolt.
11. Install rocker arm and shaft assembly, **Fig. 24.** Both intake and exhaust rocker arms have identification marks stamped on the side of the rocker arm at the valve end. Rocker arms marked 1 and 3 can be installed at cylinder locations 1 and 3. Rocker arms marked 2 and 4 can be installed at cylinder locations 2 and 4. Also note that rocker arm springs for exhaust rocker arms have a free length of 1.85 inches (47mm), while those for intake rocker arms have a free length of 3.03 inches (77mm). Tighten rocker arm shaft bolts.
12. Temporarily set valve clearances to specifications with the engine cold. Valve clearance specifications for cold engine are as follows:
    a. If equipped, jet valve, .007 inch (.17mm).
    b. Intake valve, .003 inch (.07mm).
    c. Exhaust valve, .007 inch (.17mm)
13. Install gasket in rocker cover groove, then temporarily install rocker cover.
14. Start and operate engine at idle speed until normal operating temperature is reached and adjust valve clearances. With engine hot, if equipped, adjust jet valve clearance to specifications.
15. Install rocker cover.
16. Reverse remaining procedure to complete installation, torquing rocker cover bolts to specifications.

#### 1991–92 Models

1. Check camshaft journals for wear. If journals are badly worn, replace camshaft.
2. Lubricate, then install camshaft so dowel on camshaft is straight up in cylinder head, **Fig. 25.**
3. Install the intake, then exhaust side rocker arm assemblies. Torque the rocker arm shaft bolts in an even pattern to specifications.
4. Lubricate the surface of oil seal and end of camshaft. Using guide tool No. MD998307 and seal installer tool No. MD998306 or equivalents, install camshaft oil seal. Ensure seal is completely seated.
5. Install camshaft sprocket and timing belt, and ensure timing marks are aligned, **Fig. 1. Torque** camshaft sprocket bolt to specifications.
6. Temporarily set valve clearances to specifications with engine cold.
7. Install gasket in rocker cover groove, then temporarily install rocker cover.
8. Start and operate engine at idle speed until normal operating temperature is reached and adjust valve clearances.
9. Install rocker cover, torque bolts to specifications.
10. Install remaining hoses.

### 1.6L/4-97.4

#### Removal

1. Disconnect battery ground cable.
2. Disconnect accelerator cable from throttle body.
3. Remove timing belt as follows:
    a. Remove undercover.
    b. Using a wood block and a jack, place wood block on engine oil pan and raise engine only enough to relieve tension on top engine mount, then remove mount and bracket.

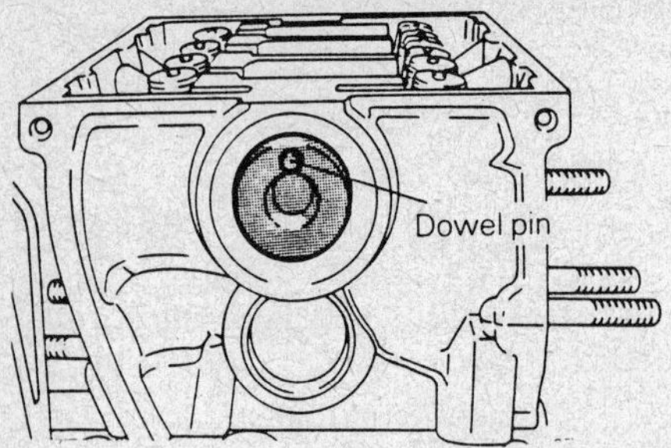


**Fig. 25 Camshaft installation. 1.5L/4-89.6 engines**

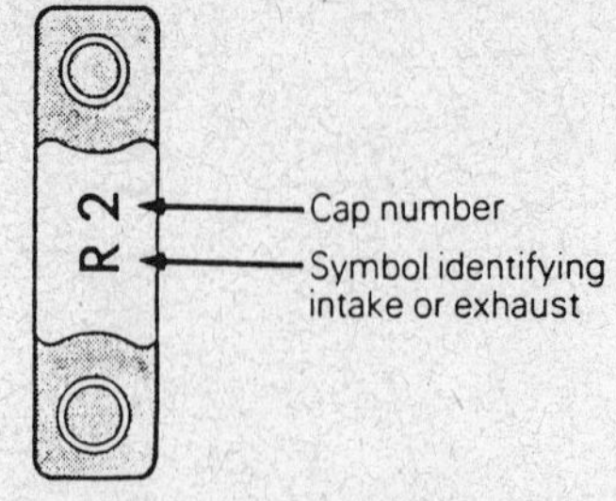


**Fig. 26 Camshaft bearing cap identification. 1.6L/4-97.4 engines**

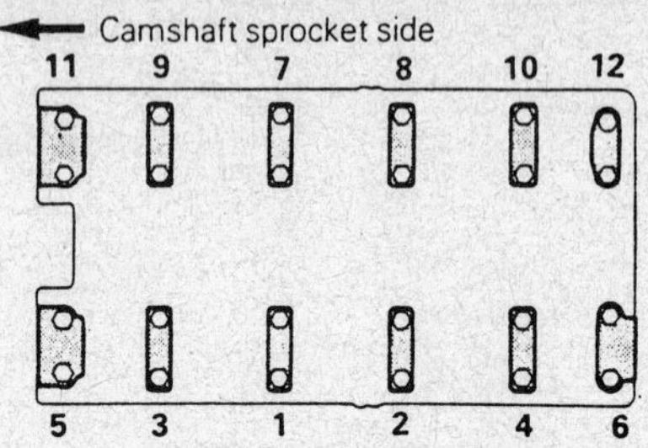


**Fig. 27 Camshaft bearing cap tightening sequence. 1.6L/4-97.4 engines**

c. Remove engine drive belts. **Prior to removing water pump drive belt, loosen water pump pulley bolts.**
d. Remove crankshaft pulley.
e. Remove upper and lower timing covers.
f. Remove tensioner pulley and bracket.
g. Disconnect PCV and breather hoses, then remove center cover, spark plug wires and rocker cover.
h. Rotate crankshaft clockwise to bring No. 1 cylinder to top dead center of compression stroke. **Rotate crankshaft only in clockwise direction.** The No. 1 cylinder is at top dead center of compression stroke when the timing marks on camshaft sprockets are aligned with upper surface of cylinder head and dowel pins on camshaft sprockets are facing up as shown, **Fig. 5.**
i. Remove auto tensioner.
j. Mark timing belt indicating direction of rotation, then remove timing belt.

4. Remove throttle body support bracket.
5. Remove crankshaft angle sensor from rear of intake camshaft.
6. Remove camshaft sprockets as follows:
   a. Using a wrench at the hexagonal part of the camshaft (to prevent the camshaft from turning) loosen, then remove the camshaft sprocket bolts and camshaft sprockets.
7. Using a screwdriver or suitable tool, remove camshaft oil seals. **Use caution not to damage front camshaft bearing caps or camshafts.**
8. Loosen camshaft bearing cap bolts in two or three steps, then remove bolts and bearing caps. **If bearing caps are difficult to remove, use a plastic hammer to lightly tap the rear part ot the camshaft, then remove bearing caps.**
9. Remove intake and exhaust camshafts.
10. Remove rocker arms.

### Installation

1. Check camshaft journals and replace if damage or seizure is evident.
2. Check camshaft lobes and replace if excessive wear or damage are evident. Measure camshaft lobe height. Minimum lobe height is as follows: intake lobes; 1.3661 inches (34.700mm), exhaust lobes; 1.3546 inches (34.407mm). Replace camshaft if lobe height is below minimum value.
3. Check rocker arms and replace if damage or seizure is evident.
4. Install rocker arms.
5. Apply engine oil to journals and lobes of camshafts, then install camshafts on cylinder head. **Ensure camshafts are correctly installed. The intake camshaft has a slit on the rear end for driving the crankshaft angle sensor. Also ensure dowel pins on sprocket ends are positioned on the top.**
6. Install camshaft bearing caps. Bearing caps 2-5 are the same shape. Check identification marks on bearing caps to determine correct location, **Fig. 26.** "L" indicates intake camshaft side; "R" indicates exhaust camshaft side. No. 1 bearing caps are marked only "L" or "R". **Ensure rocker arms are correctly mounted on lash adjusters and valve stem ends.**
7. Tighten camshaft bearing caps in sequence shown in **Fig. 27,** in two or three stages by torquing progressively.
8. Install guide tool No. MD998307 or equivalent, on camshaft, then apply oil to camshaft oil seal and insert the oil seal along the guide tool until it contacts cylinder head, **Fig. 28.** Using installer tool No. MD998306 or equivalent, press oil seal into cylinder head, then remove the tools.
9. Install camshaft sprockets, torquing attaching bolts to specifications.
10. Install crankshaft angle sensor as follows:
    a. Position dowel pin on intake camshaft on the top.
    b. Align punch mark on crankshaft angle sensor housing with notch in plate as shown in **Fig. 29.**
    c. Install crankshaft angle sensor on cylinder head.
11. Reverse remaining procedure to complete installation, noting the following:
    a. Ensure camshaft and crankshaft timing marks are correctly aligned.
    b. When installing rocker cover, apply sealant No. 4318034 or equivalent to semi-circular packing.

## PISTON & ROD ASSEMBLY

The piston and rod is assembled with the indented arrow on the piston and the embossed numeral on the rod facing toward front of engine, **Fig. 30.**

## PISTON, PINS & RINGS

Pistons and rings are available in standard size and oversizes of .010, .020, .030 and .039 inch. Oversize pins are not available.

## MAIN & ROD BEARINGS

Main and rod bearings are available in undersizes of .010, .020 and .030 inch.

The main bearing caps are installed with arrows facing front of engine.

## CRANKSHAFT REAR OIL SEAL

### REPLACE

1. Remove transmission, clutch assembly and flywheel or flex plate, as equipped.
2. Remove rear oil seal case and separate: oil seal, case and separator, if equipped. **Fig. 31.**
3. Drive in oil seal from inside of case, using suitable tool, **Fig. 32.** Ensure the oil seal plate fits properly in the inner contact surface of the seal case, if equipped.
4. Install separator with the oil hole facing the bottom of the case, if equipped.
5. Apply engine oil to oil seal lips.
6. Install the oil seal case in the cylinder block.

## OIL PAN

### REPLACE

On some models it may be necessary to remove engine from vehicle to gain ac-

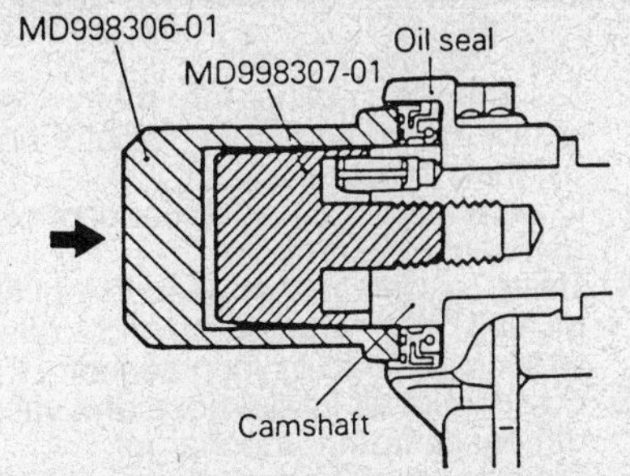

**Fig. 28 Installing camshaft oil seals. 1.6L/4-97.4 engines**

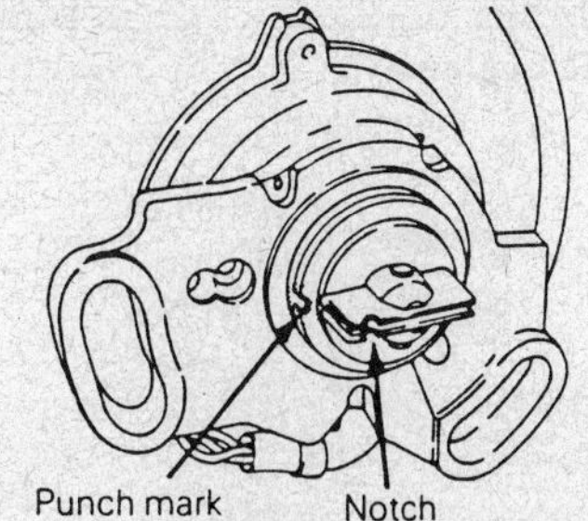

**Fig. 29 Aligning crankshaft angle sensor. 1.6L/4-97.4 engines**

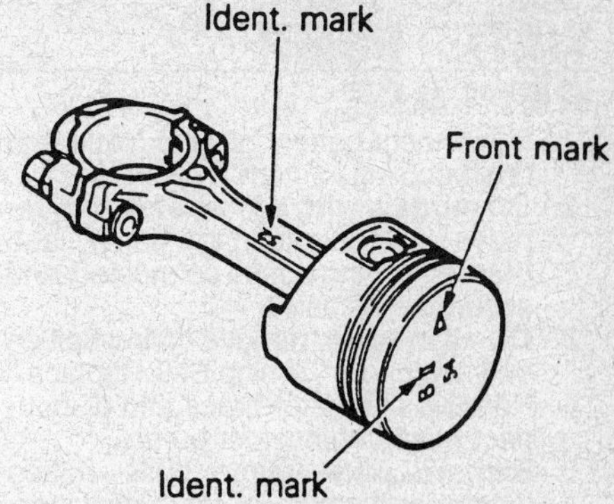

**Fig. 30 Piston & rod assembly**

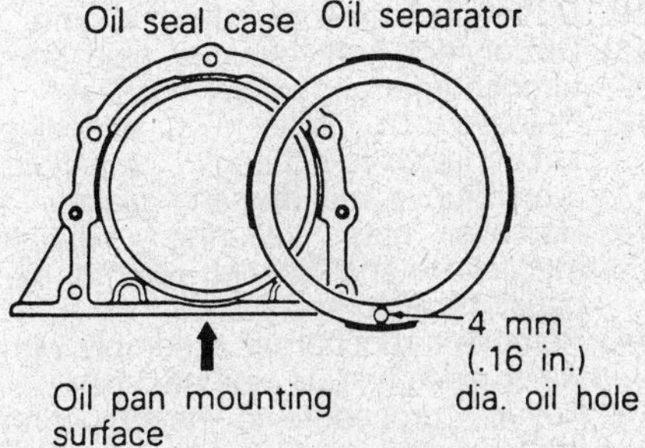

**Fig. 31 Disassembled view of oil seal case**

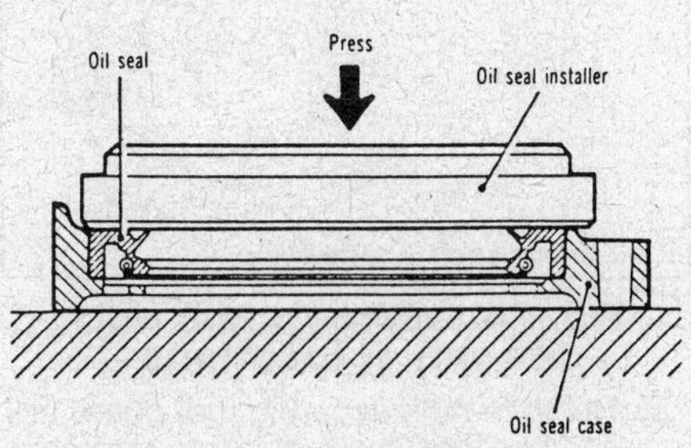

**Fig. 32 Installing rear seal into case**

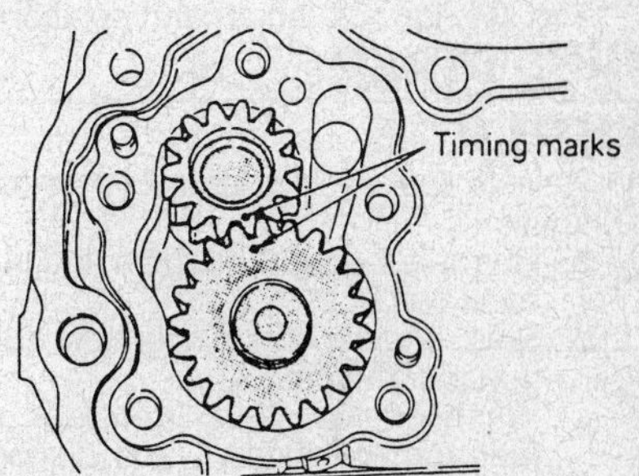

**Fig. 33 Aligning oil pump gear timing marks. 1.6L/4-97.4 engine**

cess to oil pan.

1. Raise and support vehicle, remove engine splash pan, if equipped, then drain crankcase.
2. Remove the oil pressure sender unit, if necessary, and **on turbocharged models,** disconnect oil drain hose and remove oil drain pipe.
3. **On all models,** remove the oil pan bolts, then using oil pan gasket cutter tool No. MD998727 or equivalent, break seal of oil pan gasket and remove oil pan.
4. Remove oil pump pickup if necessary.
5. Reverse procedure to install.

## OIL PUMP REPLACE

To remove oil pump pickup, refer to "Oil Pan, Replace."

### 1.5L/4-89.6

1. Remove timing case as outlined under "Timing Case, Replace."
2. Remove oil pump cover, then the inner and outer gears from front case. Mark outer gear surface facing timing case so it can be installed in the same direction.
3. Remove relief valve plug, spring and valve.
4. Reverse procedure to install. Lubricate oil pump internal components with engine oil before installing. After installing oil pump cover, check to ensure oil pump gears rotate smoothly.

### 1.6L/4-97.4

1. Remove timing case as outlined under "Timing Case, Replace."
2. Remove oil pump cover, then drive and driven gears from front case.
3. Reverse procedure to install, noting the following:
   a. Lubricate oil pump internal components with engine oil prior to installation.
   b. Align drive and driven gear timing marks as shown, **Fig. 33.**
   c. Ensure oil pump gears rotate smoothly.

## OIL PUMP SERVICE

### 1.5L/4-89.6

Using a feeler gauge clearance between oil pump outer gear and pump housing. Clearance should be .0039-.0079 inch. Check clearance between outer gear and pump crescent. Clearance should be .0087-.0173 inch. Check clearance between inner gear and crescent. Clearance should be .0083-.0134 inch. Using a straight edge and feeler gauge, measure gear side clearance. Gear endplay should be .0016-.0039 inch.

### 1.6L/4-97.4

Using a feeler gauge clearance between oil pump drive gear and pump housing. Clearance should be .0063-.0083 inch. Check clearance between driven gear and pump housing. Clearance should be .0051-.0071 inch. Using a straight edge and feeler gauge, measure gear side clearance. Drive gear side clearance should be .0031-.0055 inch. Driven gear side clearance should be .0024-.0047 inch.

## BELT TENSION DATA

| Component | Belt Tension New Lbs. | Belt Tension Used Lbs.① |
|---|---|---|
| **1.5L/4-89.6** | | |
| **Alternator** | **110—154** | **88** |
| **A/C** | ②③ | ②③ |
| **P.S.** | ②④ | ②④ |
| **1.6L/4-97.4** | | |
| **Alternator** | **110—154** | **88** |
| **A/C** | ②⑤ | ②⑤ |
| **P.S.** | ②⑥ | ②⑥ |

①—**A new belt run 30 minutes is used.**
②—**Belt deflection with a pressure of 22 lbs. applied.**
③—**.16-.24.**
④—**.2-.4.**
⑤—**.35-.43.**
⑥—**.2-.4.**

## COOLING SYSTEM BLEED

These engines do not require a specified bleed procedure. After filling cooling system, run engine to operating temperature with radiator/pressure cap off. Air will then be automatically bled through cap opening.

# WATER PUMP

## REPLACE

1. Disconnect battery ground cable and drain cooling system.
2. **On models with power steering,** remove power steering pump and bracket leaving hoses connected, and secure pump aside.
3. **On all models.** remove timing belt as outlined under "Timing Belt, Replace."
4. Remove alternator brace and disconnect hoses from water pump.
5. Remove water pump bolts, noting length and position for installation, then remove water pump, gasket and O-ring.
6. Reverse procedure to install. Refer to **Fig. 34**, for bolt length and position.

# FUEL PUMP

## REPLACE

1. Relieve fuel system pressure as follows:
   a. Remove rear seat cushion and pull back carpet.
   b. Start engine and disconnect fuel pump connector.
   c. When engine stops from lack of fuel, turn off ignition and disconnect battery ground cable.
2. Remove fuel tank cap, raise and support rear of vehicle and drain fuel into suitable container.
3. Disconnect filler hose from tank, support tank with suitable jack and remove nuts securing tank straps.
4. Lower fuel tank, then mark and disconnect fuel hoses, vapor hoses and electrical connectors.

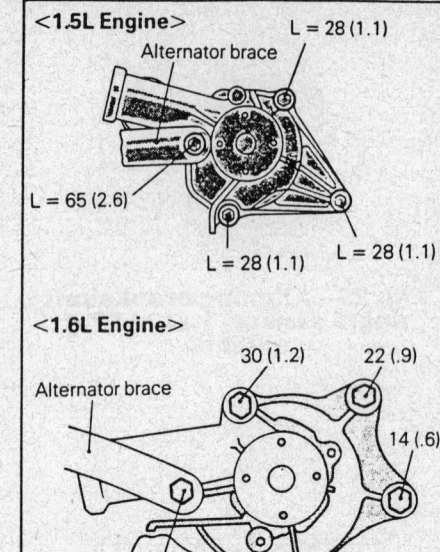

**Fig. 34 Water pump bolt lengths & locations**

5. Remove nuts securing fuel pump assembly, then the fuel pump and gasket.
6. Reverse procedure to install.

# TURBOCHARGER

## REPLACE

### 1.6L/4-97.4

1. Disconnect battery ground cable, then drain cooling system.
2. Disconnect cooling fan motor connector, upper and lower radiator hoses, then remove radiator.
3. Drain engine oil, then disconnect oxygen sensor connector.
4. Using oxygen sensor wrench tool No. MD998748 or equivalent, and a offset wrench, remove oxygen sensor.
5. Disconnect air intake hose and vacuum hoses from turbocharger.
6. Disconnect air hose from front of turbocharger.
7. Remove exhaust manifold heat shield and turbocharger heat shield.
8. Remove engine hanger.
9. Remove eye bolt, gasket and water hose connection from water pipe.
10. Disconnect water pipe from engine.
11. Disconnect front exhaust pipe from turbocharger and remove gasket.
12. Remove bolts attaching turbocharger-to-exhaust manifold, then remove seal ring and gasket.
13. Remove nuts securing exhaust manifold-to-engine, then remove exhaust manifold and gasket.
14. Remove turbocharger assembly with water pipes and oil pipe attached.
15. Reverse procedure to install, noting the following:
    a. Prior to installing turbocharger assembly, pour a small quantity of clean engine oil into oil supply pipe fitting hole in turbocharger.
    b. Prior to installing water inlet pipe, apply machine oil to inner surface of pipe flare.
    c. Refill cooling system and engine oil to specifications.

# TIGHTENING SPECIFICATIONS

## 1.5L/4-89.6

| Year | Component | Torque/Ft. Lbs. |
|---|---|---|
| 1989–92 | Camshaft Sprocket Bolt | 47-54 |
| | Connecting Rod Cap Nuts | ① |
| | Crankshaft Pulley Bolts | 9-11 |
| | Crankshaft Sprocket | 51-72 |
| | Cylinder Head Bolts, Engine Cold | 51-54 |
| | Cylinder Head Bolts, Engine Hot | 58-61② |
| | Exhaust Manifold Nuts & Bolts | 11-14 |
| | Flex Plate Bolts | 94-101 |
| | Flywheel Bolts | 94-101 |
| | Front Case Bolt | 9-11 |
| | Intake Manifold Nuts & Bolts | ③ |
| | Jet Valve Assembly | 13-15 |
| | Main Bearing Cap Bolts | 36-40 |
| | Oil Pan Bolts | 4-6 |
| | Oil Pan Drain Plug | 26-32 |
| | Oil Pressure Switch | 11-16 |
| | Oil Pump Cover | 6-7 |
| | Oil Pump Relief Valve Plug | 29-36 |
| | Oil Screen | 11-16 |

*Continued*

## TIGHTENING SPECIFICATIONS—Continued

| Year | Component | Torque/Ft. Lbs. |
|---|---|---|
| 1989-92 | Rocker Arm Cover Bolts | 1.1-1.4 |
| | Rocker Arm Shaft | ④ |
| | Spark Plug | 15-21 |
| | Timing Belt Cover Upper & Lower | 7-9 |
| | Timing Belt Tensioner | 14-20 |
| | Water Pump To Engine | ⑤ |

①—1989-90, 23-25 ft. lbs; 1991-92, 14.5 ft. lbs., then tighten an additional 1/4 turn.
②—1989-90 models.
③—1989-90, 13-18 ft. lbs; 1991-92, 11-14 ft. lbs.
④—1989-90, 15-19 ft. lbs; 1991-92, 21-25 ft. lbs.
⑤—Bolts w/head marked 4, 9-10 ft. lbs.; bolts w/head marked 7, 15-19 ft. lbs.

## 1.6L/4-97.4

| Year | Component | Torque/Ft. Lbs. |
|---|---|---|
| 1989-90 | Camshaft Bearing Caps | ② |
| | Camshaft Sprocket Bolt | 58-72 |
| | Connecting Rod Cap Nuts | 36-38 |
| | Crankshaft Pulley Bolts | 14-22 |
| | Crankshaft Sprocket | 80-94 |
| | Cylinder Head Bolts, Engine Cold | 65-72 |
| | Cylinder Head Bolts, Engine Hot | 72-80 |
| | Exhaust Manifold Nuts & Bolts | 18-22 |
| | Exhaust Manifold To Turbocharger | 40-47 |
| | Flex Plate Bolts | 94-101 |
| | Flywheel Bolts | 94-101 |
| | Front Case | ③ |
| | Intake Manifold Nuts & Bolts | ④ |
| | Main Bearing Cap Bolts | 47-51 |
| | Oil Pan Bolts | 4-6 |
| | Oil Pan Drain Plug | 25-33 |
| | Oil Pressure Switch | 6-8 |
| | Oil Pump Cover | 11-13 |
| | Oil Pump Relief Valve Plug | 14-20 |
| | Oil Pump Sprocket | 25-29 |
| | Oil Screen | 11-16 |
| | Rocker Arm Cover Bolts | 2-3 |
| | Spark Plug | 15-21 |
| | Timing Belt Cover Upper & Lower | 7-9 |
| | Timing Belt Tensioner | 15-19 |
| | Water Pump To Engine | ① |

①—Bolts w/head marked 4, 9-10 ft. lbs.; bolts w/head marked 7, 15-19 ft. lbs.
②—8 x 65 mm bolts, 14-15 ft. lbs.; 6 x 20 mm bolts, 5.8-8.6 ft. lbs.
③—M8 x 30 bolts, 20-26 ft. lbs.; except M8 x 30 bolts, 14-20 ft. lbs.
④—M8 bolt, 11-14 ft. lbs.; M10 bolts, 22-30 ft. lbs.

# 1.8L/4-107 Engine

INDEX



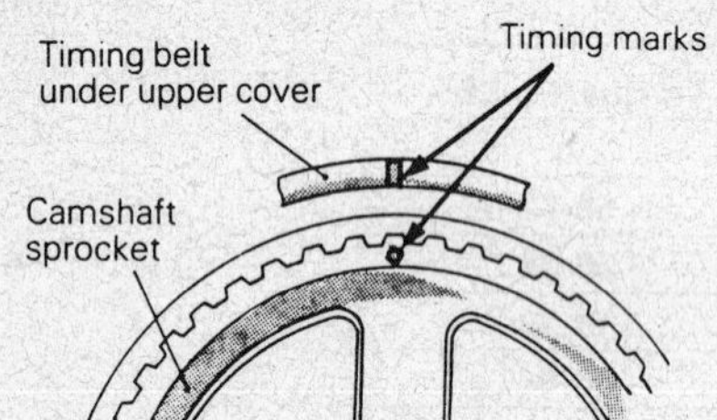


**Fig. 1 Aligning camshaft sprocket timing marks**

## ENGINE REPLACE

1. Scribe reference marks between hood and hood hinges, then remove hood.
2. Relieve fuel pressure as follows:
   a. With engine running, disconnect fuel pump connector.
   b. Allow engine to deplete fuel supply, then turn ignition Off.
3. Disconnect battery cables, then remove battery and battery tray.
4. Remove air cleaner and engine under cover.
5. Drain cooling system, engine crankcase and transaxle fluid.
6. On automatic transaxle models, disconnect transaxle cooling hoses from transaxle.
7. Disconnect heater and the upper and lower radiator hoses from engine, then remove radiator.
8. Mark and disconnect necessary vacuum hoses and engine/transaxle wiring that would interfere with engine removal.
9. Disconnect accelerator cable and brake booster vacuum hose.
10. On models with manual transaxle, disconnect clutch tube.
11. On automatic transaxle models, disconnect control cable. **Handle control cable very carefully so as not to bend inner cable.**
12. On all models, disconnect speedometer cable.
13. Remove power steering pump and hoses as an assembly leaving hoses connected, then use wire to secure pump.
14. Raise and support vehicle.
15. If equipped with A/C, remove compressor belt, then remove compressor mounting bolts and compressor leaving refrigerant lines connected. Disconnect compressor wiring, then use wire to secure compressor and hose assembly.
16. Remove front exhaust pipe.
17. Disconnect stabilizer bar from lower control arm.
18. Loosen, but do not remove ball joint stud attaching nut, then disconnect ball joint from steering knuckle using tool MB991113.
19. Loosen, but do not remove tie rod end attaching nut, then disconnect tie rod end from steering knuckle using tool MB991113.
20. Insert suitable pry bar between transaxle case and drive shaft, then pry drive shaft from transaxle case. **Do not insert pry bar too deep or oil seal will be damaged. Do not pull on drive axle and do not overextend CV joints, as joints will be damaged.**
21. Cover transaxle holes to prevent entry of dirt and replace drive axle circlips.
22. Use wire to secure drive shafts out of the way.
23. Attach suitable engine lifting device, then raise lift enough to tension equipment.
24. Remove front roll stopper insulator bolt, then the rear roll stopper insulator bolt.
25. Remove left mount insulator attaching nut. **Do not remove bolt.**
26. Raise engine/transaxle assembly enough to remove weight from mounts.
27. Remove blind cover from inside right fender shield, then remove transaxle mount bracket bolt.
28. Remove left mount insulator bolt, then while directing transaxle side down, remove engine/transaxle assembly from vehicle.
29. Reverse procedure to install.

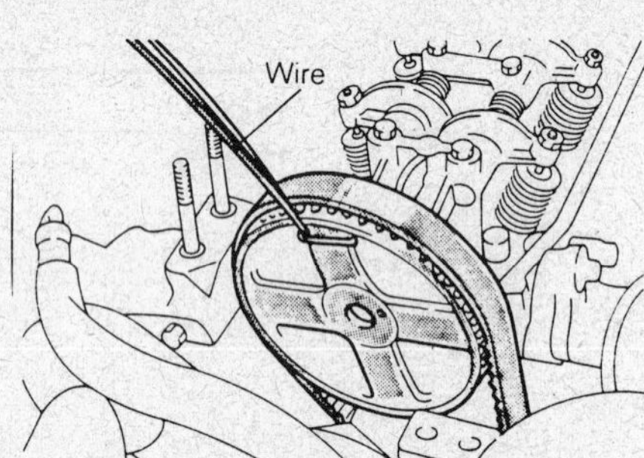


**Fig. 2 Securing camshaft sprocket**

## CYLINDER HEAD REPLACE

1. Disconnect battery ground cable, then drain cooling system.
2. Remove air cleaner, then disconnect control cables from throttle lever and bracket.
3. Disconnect exhaust pipe from manifold.
4. Disconnect upper radiator hose and heater hoses as needed.
5. Disconnect spark plug wires.
6. Remove power steering pump attaching bolts and drive belt, then position pump aside.
7. Mark and disconnect necessary electrical connectors and vacuum hoses, release harness clamps, then position harness aside to prevent damage.
8. Remove timing belt upper cover, then the rocker arm cover.
9. Rotate crankshaft in normal direction of rotation until No. 1 cylinder is at top dead center and camshaft and crankshaft timing marks are aligned, **Fig. 1.**
10. Place a chalk mark between timing belt and camshaft sprocket, then remove camshaft sprocket bolt, separate sprocket from camshaft, leaving belt in place on sprocket. Secure sprocket and belt with wire, **Fig. 2.** Ensure sprocket does not disengage from belt and fall, and maintain ten-

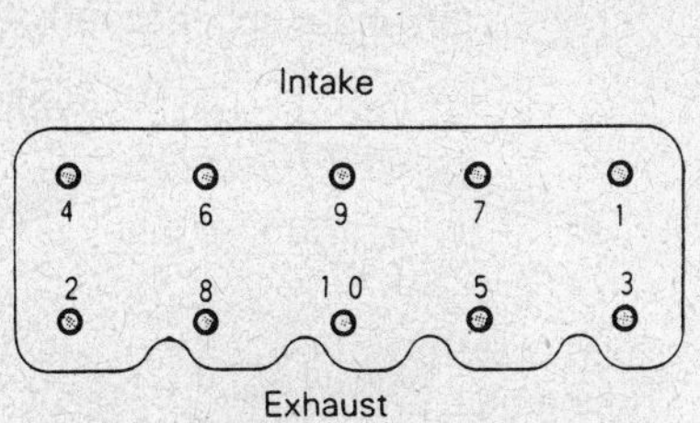


**Fig. 3 Cylinder head bolt loosening sequence**

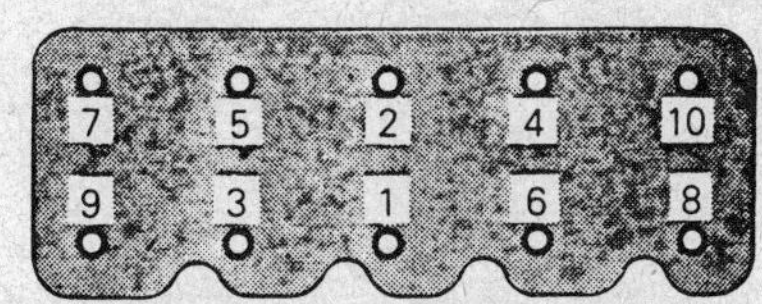


**Fig. 4 Cylinder head bolt tightening sequence**

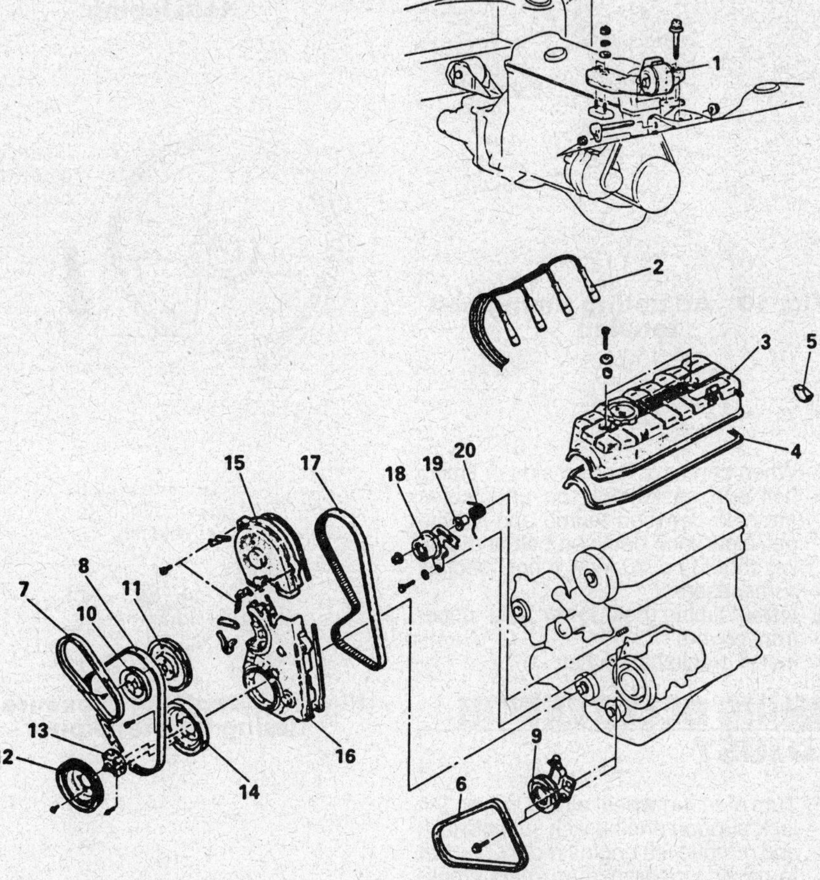

1. Left mount bracket
2. Spark plug cable
3. Rocker cover
4. Rocker cover gasket
5. Semi-circular packing
6. Drive belt (Air conditioner)
7. Drive belt (Power steering)
8. Drive belt (Alternator)
9. Tensioner pulley bracket
10. Water pump pulley
11. Water pump pulley
12. Damper pulley
13. Adapter
14. Crankshaft pulley
Adjustment of the valve clearance
15. Timing belt front upper cover
16. Timing belt front lower cover
Adjustment of timing belt
17. Timing belt
18. Timing belt tensioner
19. Tensioner spacer
20. Tensioner spring

**Fig. 5 Timing belt components**

sion on belt to maintain proper timing. **Do not rotate crankshaft after sprocket is removed from camshaft.**

11. Remove cylinder head attaching bolts in sequence shown, **Fig. 3.** Loosen bolts evenly in three steps, to prevent cylinder head warpage, then remove cylinder head and gasket. Take care not to dislodge camshaft sprocket during cylinder head removal.
12. Reverse procedure to install. Install cylinder head bolts and tighten in sequence, **Fig. 4.**

# VALVE LASH SPECIFICATIONS

| | | Clearance Inch | |
|---|---|---|---|
| **Engine** | **Year** | **Int.** | **Exh.** |
| **1.8L/4-107** | **1989–92** | ① | ① |

**①—Equipped with hydraulic valve lash adjusters.**

# VALVE TIMING

## INTAKE OPENS BTDC

| Engine | Year | Degrees |
|---|---|---|
| 1.8L/4-107 | 1989–91 | 20 |

# VALVES

## ADJUST

**These engines use hydraulic lash adjusters. No adjustments are required.**

# TIMING BELT

## REPLACE

### REMOVAL

1. Disconnect battery ground cable.
2. Remove left hand engine mounting bracket, **Fig. 5.**
3. **On models with power steering, remove power steering pump pulley.**
4. **On all models, remove crankshaft pulley, then the cover assembly.**
5. Rotate crankshaft in normal direction of rotation until No. 1 cylinder is at top dead center and camshaft and crankshaft timing marks are aligned, **Fig. 6.**
6. Loosen tensioner bolt, then slide tensioner toward water pump and tighten bolt, **Fig. 7.**
7. Mark direction of rotation on timing belt, then remove belt, **Fig. 6.**

### INSTALLATION

1. Install timing belt tensioner spring, then install tensioner and tighten adjusting nut. The tensioner spring should be positioned so that upper end of spring is against water pump body. Push on tensioner to align mounting bolt holes, then install mounting bolt.
2. Loosen tensioner mounting nut and bolt and push tensioner toward water pump as far as possible. Then tighten nut to secure tensioner in this position.
3. Check to ensure all timing marks are aligned, **Fig. 6,** and position timing belt over crankshaft sprocket. Then install timing belt over oil pump sprocket and camshaft sprocket. When installing timing belt, ensure tension side of belt is tight.
4. Loosen tensioner nut and bolt, then push tensioner toward adjusting nut to mesh belt and camshaft sprocket. Retighten nut and bolt.

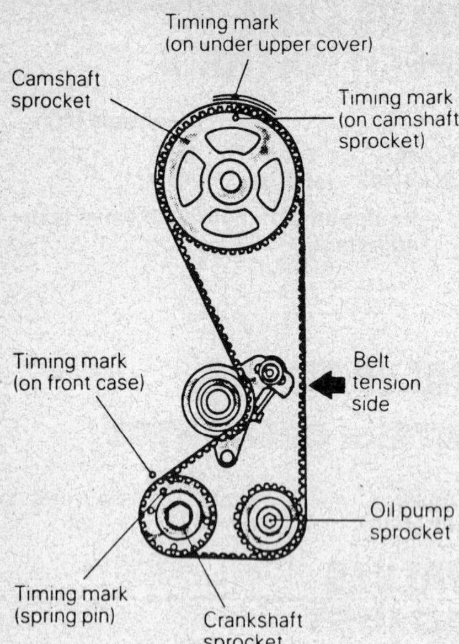


**Fig. 6 Valve timing marks**

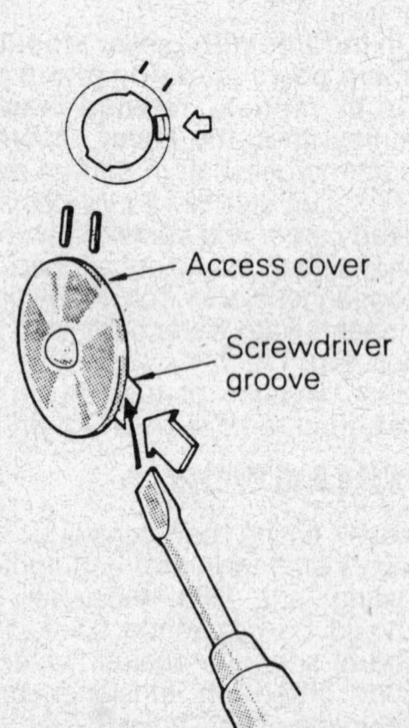


**Fig. 9 Timing belt tension adjustment access covers**

5. Check to ensure all timing marks are aligned, then rotate crankshaft one revolution in the normal direction of rotation. Crankshaft should be rotated smoothly and timing belt should not be pushed or twisted while crankshaft is being rotated. This procedure is performed to apply tension to the tension side of the timing belt.
6. Loosen tensioner bolt and nut, then tighten tensioner adjusting nut and mounting bolt. This procedure is performed to apply tension to loose side of timing belt.

**Fig. 7 Positioning timing belt tensioner**

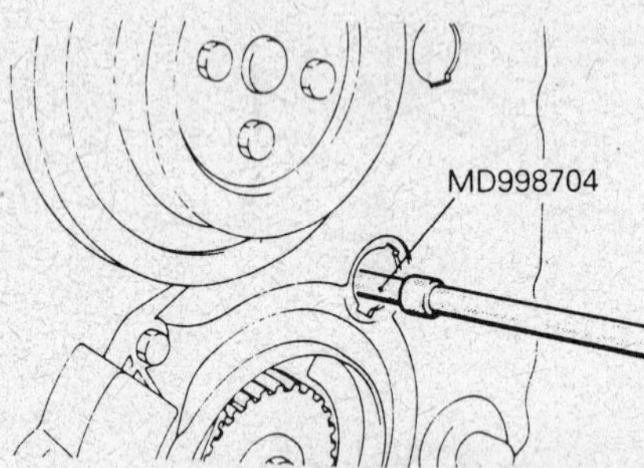


**Fig. 10 Adjusting timing belt tension**

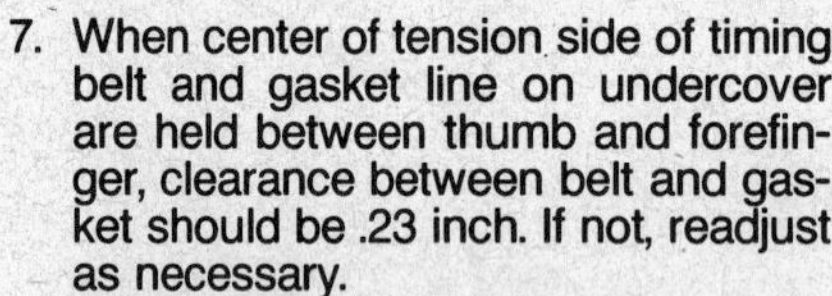

7. When center of tension side of timing belt and gasket line on undercover are held between thumb and forefinger, clearance between belt and gasket should be .23 inch. If not, readjust as necessary.
8. Install timing belt lower and upper front covers.
9. Install crankshaft pulley.

## TIMING BELT TENSION ADJUST

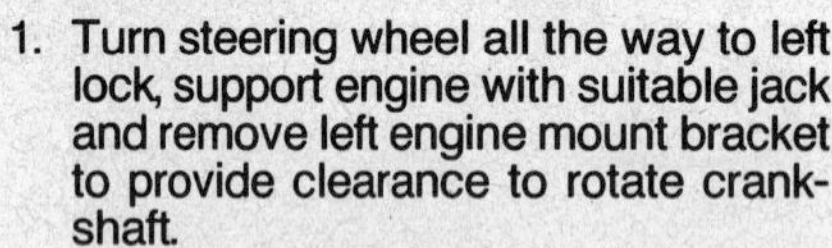

1. Turn steering wheel all the way to left lock, support engine with suitable jack and remove left engine mount bracket to provide clearance to rotate crankshaft.
2. Remove timing belt upper front cover and the spark plugs.
3. Rotate crankshaft clockwise (normal direction of rotation) and inspect timing belt. If belt is satisfactory, continue rotating crankshaft until No. 1 Cylinder is at TDC on compression stroke and timing mark on camshaft sprocket is aligned with mark on belt cover, Fig. 1.
4. Rotate crankshaft clockwise until mark on camshaft sprocket is 2 teeth away from mark on cover, **Fig. 8.**. **Do not rotate crankshaft counterclockwise, as belt tension will be adversely affected.**
5. Remove accessory drive belts and pulleys as needed, then the two adjusting port covers, inserting a screwdriver into slot on timing belt cover and prying timing port covers off, **Fig. 9.**

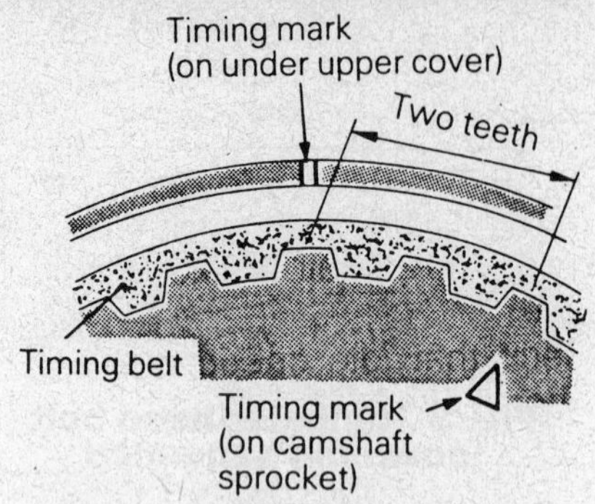


**Fig. 8 Positioning camshaft sprocket for timing belt tensioning**

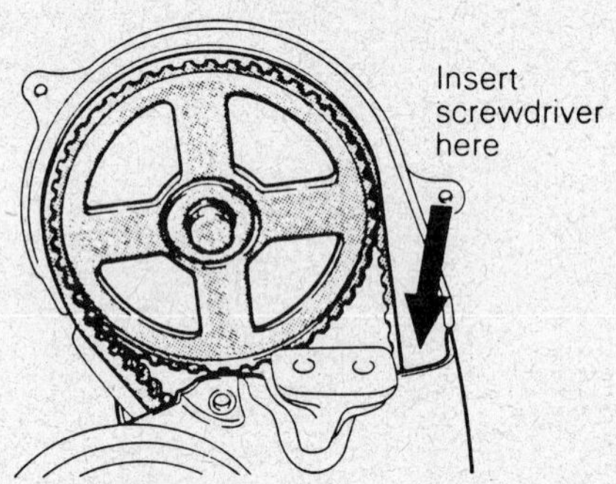


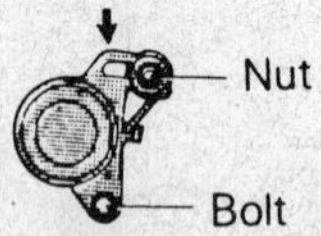


**Fig. 11 Applying pressure to timing belt tensioner**

6. Insert tool No. MD998704 or equivalent, through adjusting port, loosen timing belt tensioner nut and bolt 180 to 200 degrees, **Fig. 10. Do not loosen bolt or nut more than 200 degrees, as fastener may fall out into cover.**
7. Check to ensure that tensioner is not sticking, by inserting a screwdriver through opening on top of lower timing belt cover and pushing tensioner toward timing belt, **Fig. 11.** Release tensioner and remove screwdriver. Spring tension of the timing belt tensioner will automatically adjust the timing belt.
8. Tighten tensioner lower bolt, then the slot side nut. Always tighten lower bolt first to prevent tensioner from rotating out of position.
9. Install adjusting port covers, then install timing belt upper front cover.

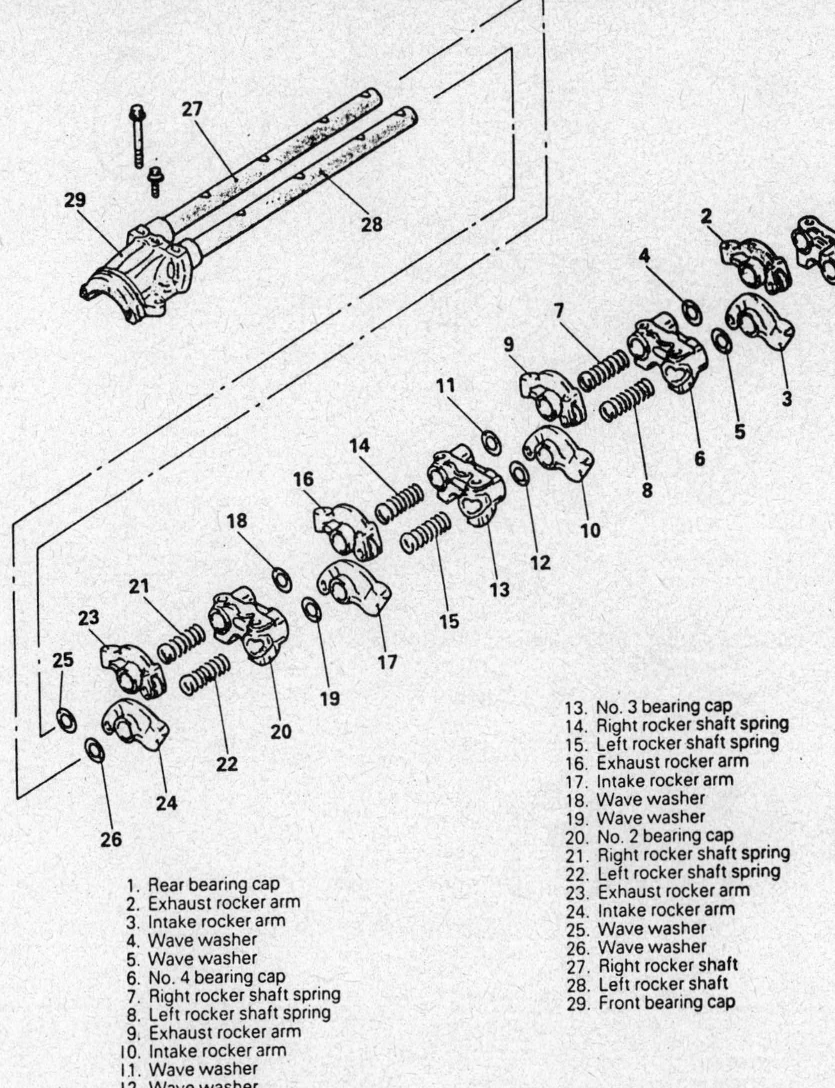


**Fig. 12 Rocker arm & shaft assembly**

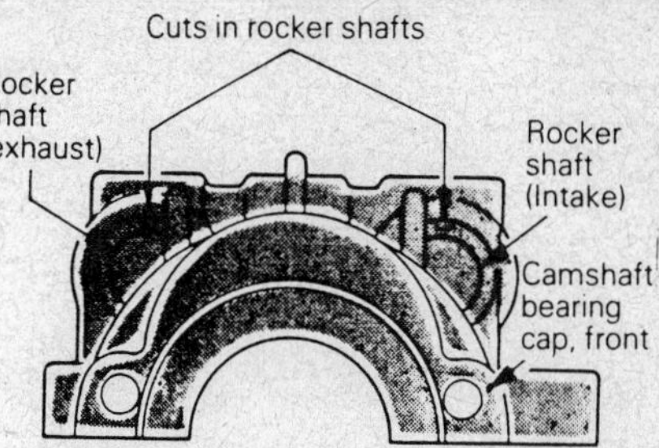


**Fig. 13 Positioning rocker shaft in front bearing cap**

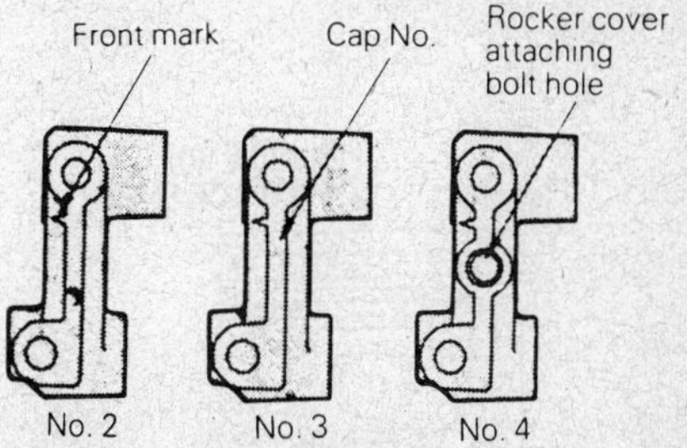


**Fig. 14 Camshaft bearing cap Nos. 2, 3 & 4 identification**

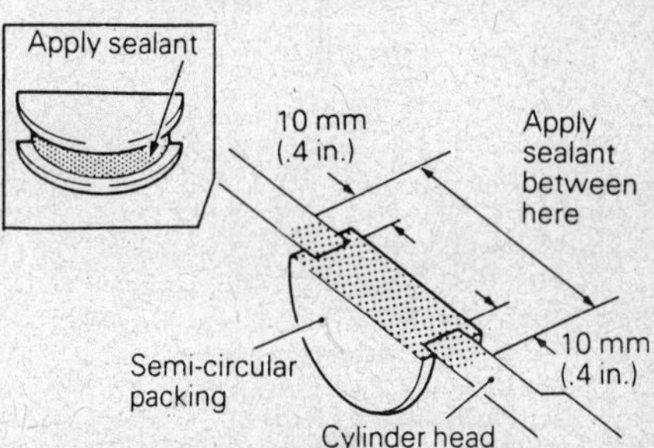


**Fig. 15 Semi-circular gasket installation**

# CAMSHAFT, ROCKER ARMS & SHAFT
## REPLACE

1. Disconnect battery ground cable.
2. Remove breather hose and P.V.C. hose from rocker cover.
3. Remove rocker cover, then the gasket.
4. Rotate crankshaft in normal direction of rotation until No. 1 cylinder is at top dead center and camshaft and crankshaft timing marks are aligned.
5. Place a chalk mark between timing belt and camshaft sprocket, then remove camshaft sprocket bolt, separate sprocket from camshaft, leaving belt in place on sprocket. Secure sprocket and belt with wire, **Fig. 2.** Ensure sprocket does not disengage from belt and fall, and maintain tension on belt to maintain proper timing. **Do not rotate crankshaft after sprocket is removed from camshaft.**
6. Prior to removal of rocker arm and rocker shaft assembly, install hydraulic lash adjuster holder tool No. MD998443 or equivalent, to ensure the hydraulic lash adjuster is not allowed to fall.
7. Remove semicircular packing, then the oil seal.
8. Remove rocker arm and shaft assembly, then the hydraulic lash adjuster.
9. Remove camshaft.
10. Reverse procedure to install, noting the following:
    a. Assemble rocker arms to rocker shafts, then install on cylinder head, **Fig. 12.**
    b. Apply engine oil to inside diameter of rocker before assembly.
    c. Ensure cuts on rocker arm shafts are facing upward, **Fig. 13.** Refer to **Fig. 14,** for identification of Nos. 2, 3 and 4 bearing caps.
    d. Apply suitable sealer to semi-circular packing, **Fig. 15.**
    e. When valve cover is installed, apply suitable gasket sealant, Fig. 16.

# PISTON & ROD ASSEMBLY

The piston and rod is assembled with the indented arrow on the piston and the embossed numeral on the rod facing toward front of engine, **Fig. 17.**

# PISTON, PINS & RINGS

Pistons and rings are available in standard sizes and oversizes of .010, .020, .030 and .039 inch. Oversize pins are not available.

# CRANKSHAFT REAR OIL SEAL
## REPLACE

1. Remove transmission, clutch assembly and flywheel or flex plate, as equipped.

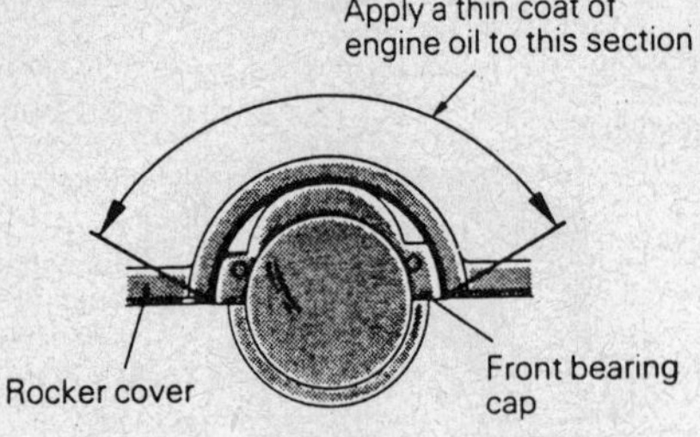


**Fig. 16 Rocker arm cover installation**

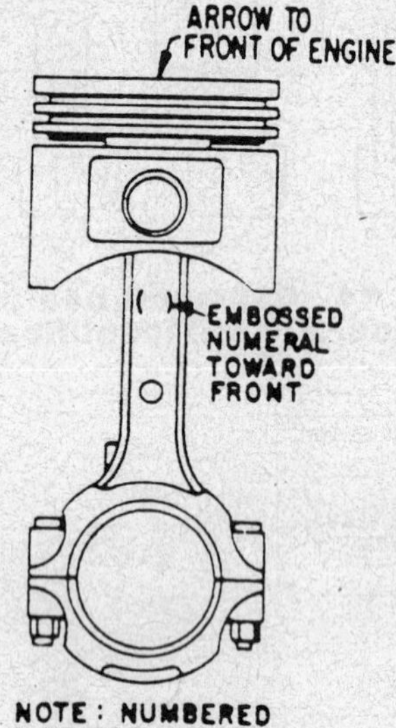


**Fig. 17 Piston & rod assembly**

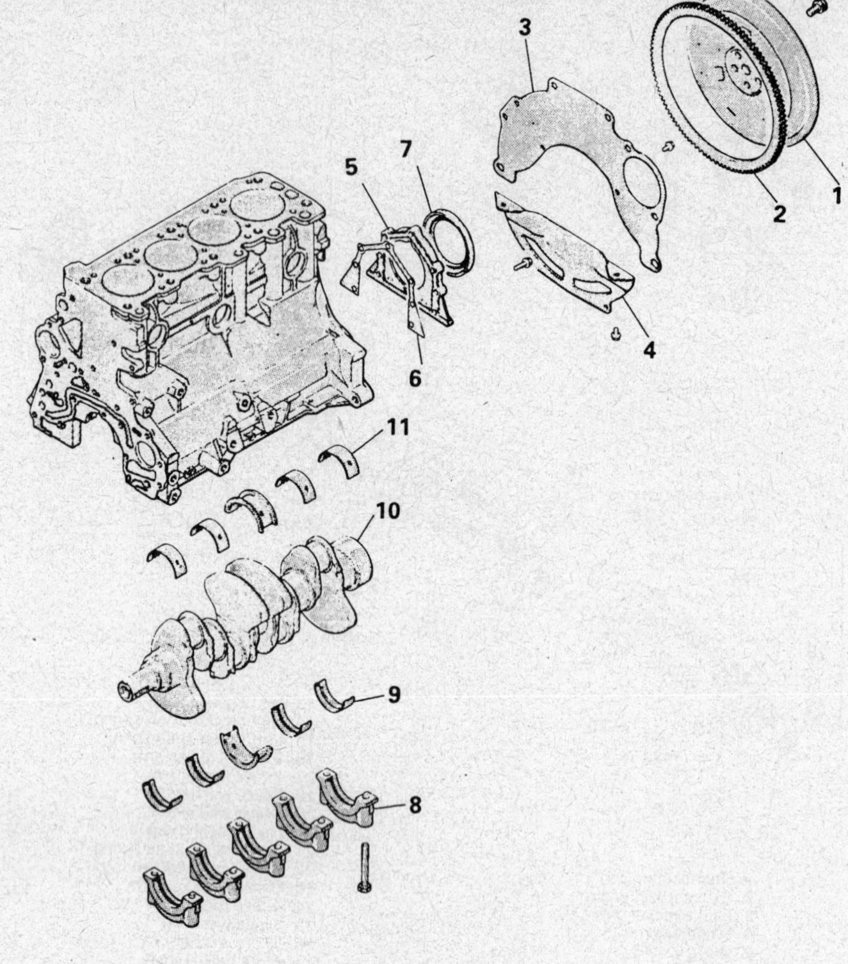


1. Flywheel
2. Ring gear
3. Rear plate
4. Bell housing cover
5. Oil seal case
6. Gasket
7. Rear oil seal
8. Bearing cap
9. Lower bearing
10. Crankshaft
11. Upper bearing

**Fig. 18 Crankshaft rear oil seal replacement**

2. Remove rear oil seal case and separate: oil seal, case and separator, if equipped. **Fig. 18.**
3. Drive in oil seal from inside of case, using suitable tool. Ensure the oil seal plate fits properly in the inner contact surface of the seal case, if equipped.
4. Install separator with the oil hole facing the bottom of the case, if equipped.
5. Apply engine oil to oil seal lips.
6. Install the oil seal case in the cylinder block.

# OIL PAN
## REPLACE

1. Raise and support vehicle, remove engine splash pan, if equipped, then drain crankcase.
2. Remove the oil pressure sender unit, if necessary.
3. Remove the oil pan bolts and remove oil pan, **Fig. 19.**
4. Remove oil pump pickup if necessary.
5. Reverse procedure to install.

# OIL PUMP
## REPLACE

To remove oil pump pickup, refer to "Oil Pan, Replace."

1. Remove timing belt as outlined under "Timing Belt, Replace", then remove timing belt rear cover.
2. Remove oil pump cover, then the inner and outer gears from front case. Mark outer gear surface facing timing case so it can be installed in the same direction, **Fig. 19.**
3. Remove relief valve plug, spring and valve.
4. Reverse procedure to install. Lubricate oil pump internal components with engine oil before installing. After installing oil pump cover, check to ensure oil pump gears rotate smoothly.

# OIL PUMP SERVICE

Check oil pump rotor to housing clearances and cover, **Fig. 20.** Side clearance should be .0024 to .0047 inch. Tip clearance should be .0016 to .0017 inch. Body clearance should be .0039 to .0063 inch. Drive shaft to cover clearance should be .0008 to .0020 inch.

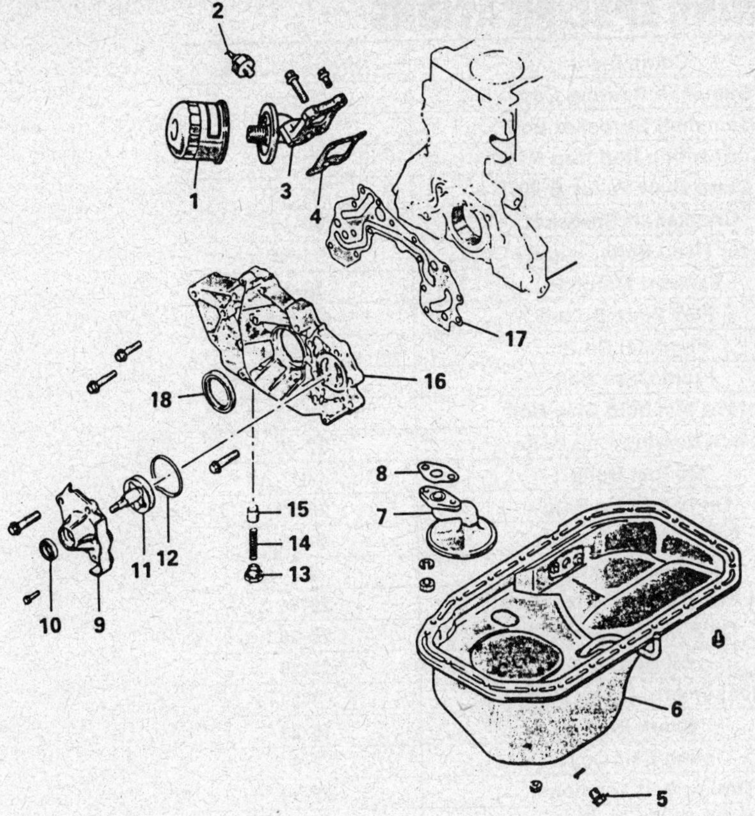


1. Oil filter
2. Oil pressure switch
3. Oil filter bracket
4. Gasket
5. Drain plug
6. Oil pan
7. Oil screen
8. Oil screen gasket
9. Oil pump cover
10. Oil seal
11. Oil pump rotor assembly
12. Oil pump gasket
13. Plug
14. Relief spring
15. Relief plunger
16. Front case
17. Front case gasket
18. Crankshaft oil seal

**Fig. 19 Oil pan & oil pump replacement**

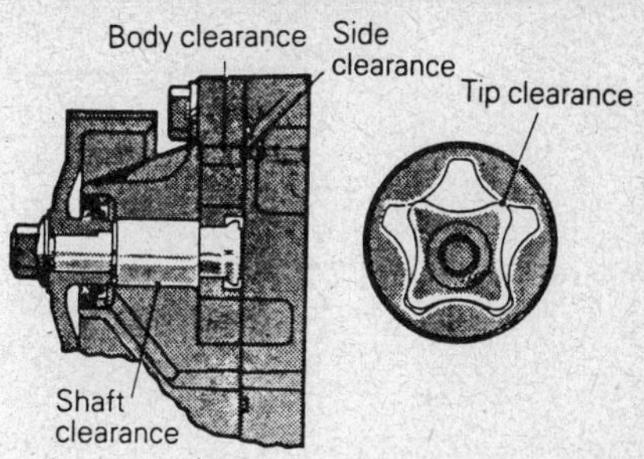


**Fig. 20 Checking oil pump clearances**

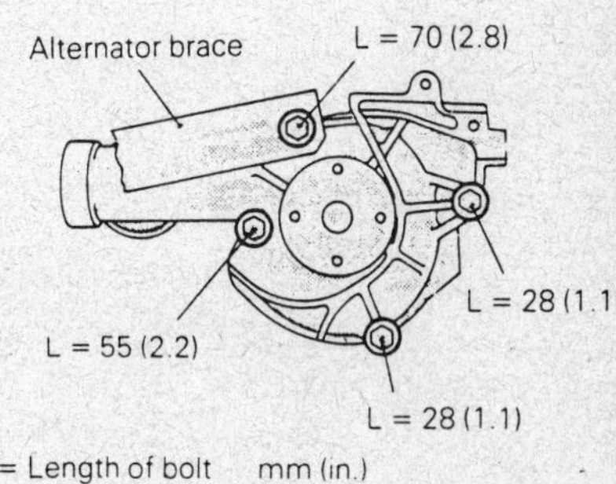


**Fig. 21 Water pump bolt installation**

# BELT TENSION DATA

| Component | Belt Tension New Lbs. | Belt Tension Used Lbs.① |
|---|---|---|
| Alternator | 110—154 | 88 |
| A/C | ②③ | ②③ |
| P.S. | ②④ | ②④ |

**①—A new belt run 30 minutes is used.**
**②—Belt deflection with a pressure of 22 lbs. applied.**
**③—.16–.24.**
**④—.2–.4.**

# COOLING SYSTEM BLEED

These engines do not require a specified bleed procedure. After filling cooling system, run engine to operating temperature with radiator/pressure cap off. Air will then be automatically bled through cap opening.

# WATER PUMP REPLACE

1. Disconnect battery ground cable and drain cooling system.
2. **On models with power steering, remove power steering pump and bracket leaving hoses connected, and secure pump aside.**
3. **On all models.** remove timing belt as outlined under "Timing Belt, Replace."
4. Remove alternator brace and disconnect hoses from water pump.
5. Remove water pump bolts, noting length and position for installation, then remove water pump, gasket and O-ring.
6. Reverse procedure to install. Refer to **Fig. 21,** for bolt length and position.

# FUEL PUMP REPLACE

1. Relieve fuel system pressure as follows:
   a. Start engine and disconnect fuel pump connector.
   b. When engine stops from lack of fuel, turn off ignition and disconnect battery ground cable.
2. Remove fuel tank cap, raise and support rear of vehicle and drain fuel into suitable container.
3. Disconnect filler hose from tank, support tank with suitable jack and remove nuts securing tank straps.
4. Lower fuel tank, then mark and disconnect fuel hoses, vapor hoses and electrical connectors.
5. Remove nuts securing fuel pump assembly, then the fuel pump and gasket.
6. Reverse procedure to install.

## TIGHTENING SPECIFICATIONS

| Year | Component | Torque/Ft. Lbs. |
|---|---|---|
| 1989–92 | Camshaft Bearing Caps | ② |
| | Camshaft Sprocket Bolt | 58-72 |
| | Connecting Rod Cap Nuts | 24-25 |
| | Crankshaft Pulley Bolts | 11-13 |
| | Crankshaft Sprocket | 80-94 |
| | Cylinder Head Bolts, Engine Cold | 51-54 |
| | Exhaust Manifold | 18-22 |
| | Flex Plate Bolts | 94-101 |
| | Flywheel Bolts | 94-101 |
| | Front Case Bolt | 11-13 |
| | Intake Manifold Stay Bolt | 15-22 |
| | Main Bearing Cap Bolts | 37-39 |
| | Oil Pan Bolts | ① |
| | Oil Pan Drain Plug | 26-32 |
| | Oil Pressure Switch | 6-8.5 |
| | Oil Pump Cover | 6-7 |
| | Oil Pump Relief Valve Plug | 29-36 |
| | Oil Pump Sprocket | 25-28 |
| | Oil Screen | 11-15 |
| | Rocker Arm Cover Bolts | 4-5 |
| | Spark Plug | 15-21 |
| | Timing Belt Cover | 7-9 |
| | Timing Belt Tensioner | 22-30 |
| | Water Pump To Engine | ③ |

①—Bolt, 4–6 ft. lbs.; nut, 4–5 ft. lbs.
②—8 x 15 mm bolts, 14–15 ft. lbs.; 6 x 20 mm bolts, 7.5–8.5 ft. lbs.
③—Bolt heads marked 4, 9–11 ft. lbs.; bolt heads marked 7, 14–20 ft. lbs.

# 2.0L/4-121.9 Engine

## INDEX



## ENGINE REPLACE

Prior to engine removal, start engine, disconnect electric fuel pump connector and allow engine to run out of fuel to relieve residual fuel system pressure. **Failure to relieve fuel system pressure prior to disconnecting fuel system components may cause fire or personal injury.**

### 2WD MODELS

1. Remove battery, then the engine ground, radiator fan motor connector, engine harness connector and battery tray.
2. Remove battery tray installation bracket, then drain engine coolant and transmission fluid.
3. Discharge A/C refrigerant, then drain the power steering fluid.
4. Remove radiator reservoir tank, then the windshield washer reservoir.
5. Disconnect transaxle oil cooler hoses on vehicles equipped with automatic transaxles, then plug hose openings.
6. Disconnect upper and lower radiator hoses from engine side, then the heater hoses.
7. Remove firewall ground cable, then the air cleaner.
8. Disconnect brake booster vacuum hose, then the high tension cables

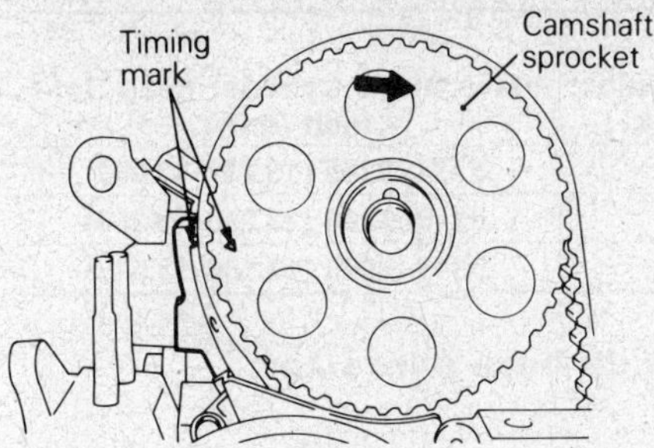


**Fig. 1 Camshaft timing marks**

from coil and spark plugs.

9. On vehicles with manual transaxles, disconnect clutch cable from transaxle.
10. On vehicles with automatic transaxles, disconnect control cable from transaxle and transaxle mounting bracket.
11. On all models, disconnect speedometer cable from transaxle, then the accelerator cable from engine.
12. Disconnect right fender engine ground, then the A/C hoses from compressor, if equipped. **Cap compressor and hose openings to prevent foreign matter from entering.**
13. Disconnect power steering hoses from pump, then the pressure switch connector, if equipped.
14. Disconnect alternator electrical connector, then the oil pressure switch.
15. Remove vacuum control unit and solenoid valve attaching screws, then disconnect electrical connector.
16. Disconnect purge control valve hoses, then loosen canister body clamp and remove hoses.
17. Disconnect fuel return hose from carburetor, then the main hose from fuel filter.
18. Raise and support vehicle, then disconnect and support front exhaust pipe.
19. On vehicles with manual transaxle, remove shift rod, then the extension and range selector cable.
20. On all models, disconnect left and right strut bars, then the stabilizer bars from lower arms.
21. Remove left and right lower arms to No. 2 crossmember attaching bolts, then the drive shaft from transaxle. **Plug case openings to prevent foreign matter from entering and replace driveshaft retaining ring after each removal.**
22. Secure lower arms and drive shaft to No. 2 crossmember, then attach a suitable lifting device to engine.
23. Slightly raise engine, then remove left mount insulator nut.
24. Remove front roll insulator nut and heat protector bolt then the rear roll insulator protector bolt.
25. Remove left mount insulator to fender attaching bolt, then the power steering oil reservoir, if equipped.
26. Remove cap from right inner fender shield, the insulator bracket attaching bolts and bracket, then remove, in sequence, the select control valve attaching bolts and valve, wiring connector and vacuum hoses.
27. Lift engine until no weight is applied to mountings, then remove insulator bolts from rear roll stopper, front roll bracket and left mount bracket.
28. Remove engine/transaxle assembly from vehicle.
29. Reverse procedure to install.

## 4WD MODELS

1. Disconnect battery cables, then remove battery, battery tray and battery tray support bracket.
2. Disconnect power steering and engine oil pressure switch connectors.
3. Disconnect alternator wiring, then remove the air cleaner.
4. Disconnect coil high tension lead, distributor wiring and engine ground strap from the firewall.
5. Remove windshield washer tank.
6. Disconnect power brake booster hose, then identify and remove all vacuum hoses and electrical connectors from engine.
7. Drain engine coolant into suitable container, then remove reservoir container.
8. Disconnect radiator upper and lower hoses from engine, then remove radiator assembly.
9. Disconnect heater hoses from engine, then the accelerator cable and speed control cable (if equipped) from carburetor.
10. Disconnect speedometer cable.
11. Discharge A/C system (if equipped), then disconnect A/C hoses from compressor. **Cap all open ends of A/C system to prevent entry of dirt and foreign matter.**
12. Disconnect power steering hose from pump, fuel return hose from carburetor and main fuel line at fuel filter.
13. Disconnect shift control cables from transaxle case, then raise and support vehicle.
14. Remove engine/transaxle lower protection plate and cover.
15. Drain transmission and transfer case oil into suitable container.
16. Disconnect front exhaust pipe from manifold.
17. Remove driveshaft, then the clutch slave cylinder. Disconnect clutch hydraulic tubes.
18. Remove front drive shafts as outlined under "Front Suspension & Steering Section."
19. Remove transfer extension stopper bracket.
20. Lower vehicle to floor, then remove top engine to body coupling bracket nuts. **Do not remove coupling bracket bolt at this time.**
21. Remove select control valves from transaxle insulator bracket, then the transaxle mounting insulator nut. Do not remove bolt at this time.
22. Remove front roll insulator installation nut, then the rear insulator to engine coupling nut.
23. Remove front grille, bridge panel and A/C condenser, if equipped.

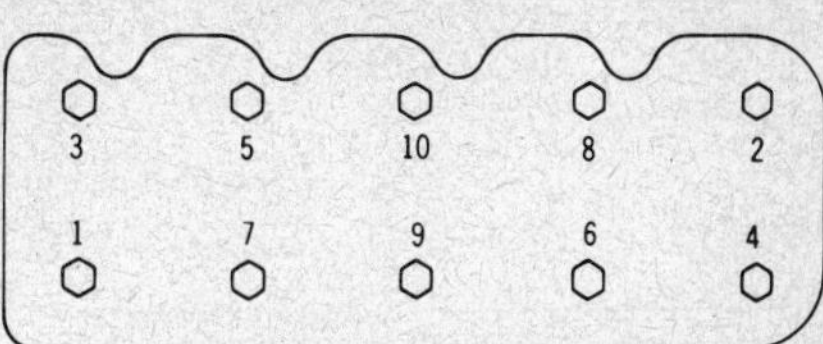


**Fig. 2 Cylinder head bolt loosening sequence**

24. Attach suitable engine lifting equipment to engine/transaxle assembly, then lift engine/transaxle assembly enough to relieve pressure on engine mounts. Remove mounting bolts.
25. Remove engine/transaxle assembly from vehicle.
26. Reverse procedure to install.

## CYLINDER HEAD REPLACE

1. Disconnect battery ground cable and drain cooling system.
2. Remove air cleaner and disconnect control cables from throttle lever and bracket.
3. Disconnect exhaust pipe from manifold.
4. Disconnect upper radiator hose and heater hoses and bypass hose.
5. Disconnect spark plug wires.
6. Remove power steering pump mounting bolts and drive belt, then secure pump aside leaving hoses connected.
7. Mark and disconnect necessary electrical connectors and vacuum hoses, release harness clamps and secure harness aside to prevent damage.
8. Remove timing belt upper cover and rocker arm cover.
9. Rotate crankshaft in normal direction of rotation until No. 1 cylinder is at TDC and crankshaft and camshaft timing marks are aligned, **Fig. 1.**
10. Place chalk mark between timing belt and camshaft sprocket, remove camshaft sprocket bolt, separate sprocket from camshaft leaving belt in place on sprocket, then secure sprocket and belt on lower timing cover. Take care that sprocket does not disengage from belt and fall, and maintain tension on belt to maintain proper timing. **Do not rotate crankshaft after sprocket is removed from camshaft.**
11. Remove cylinder head attaching bolts in sequence shown in **Fig. 2.** Loosen bolts evenly, in three steps, to prevent cylinder head warpage, then remove cylinder head and gasket. Take care not to dislodge camshaft sprocket during cylinder head removal.
12. Reverse procedure to install, noting the following:
    a. Do not apply sealer to cylinder head gasket. Ensure that proper I.D. mark is on gasket and install with mark towards cylinder head.
    b. Prior to installing cylinder head on engine, ensure that crankshaft and camshaft timing marks are aligned.
    c. When installing cylinder head, tighten bolts in sequence shown in

8 6 1 3 9
10 4 2 5 7

**Fig. 3 Cylinder head bolt tightening sequence**

| Engine | Valve Guide Oversize Inch (mm) | Valve Guide Mark | Valve Guide Cylinder Head Bore Inch (mm) |
|---|---|---|---|
| 2.0L/4-121.9 | .002 (.05) | 5 | .5138-.5145 (13.050-13.068) |
| | .010 (.25) | 25 | .5216-.5224 (13.250-13.268) |
| | .020 (.50) | 50 | .5315-.5323 (13.500-13.518) |

**Fig. 4 Valve guide & guide bore oversizes**

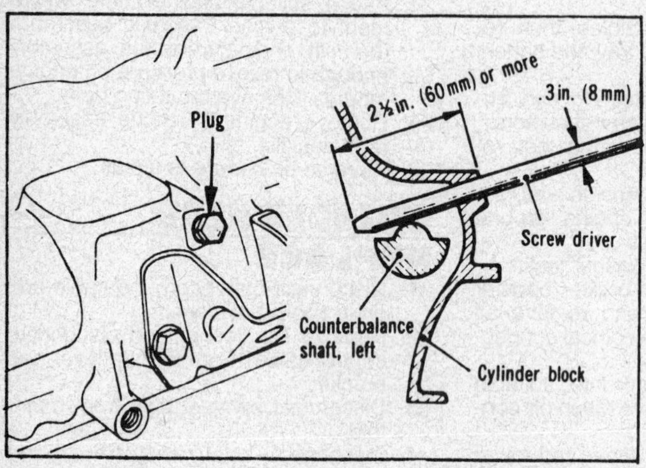


**Fig. 5 Locking left silent shaft**

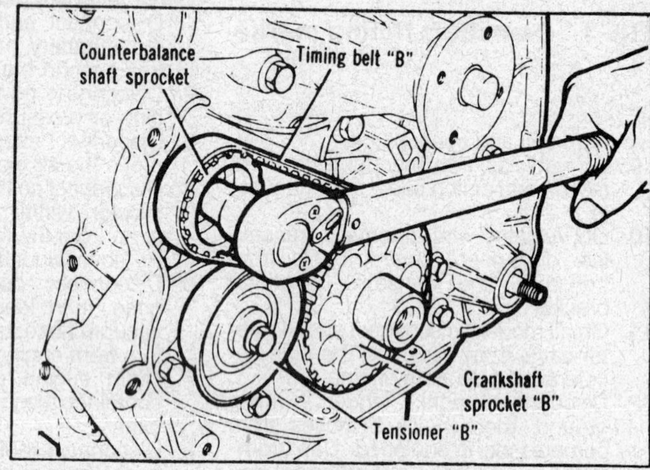


**Fig. 6 Silent shaft timing belt (B) & tensioner**

**Fig. 3.** Tighten bolts in two steps to ensure proper seating of cylinder head to cylinder block.

d. After cylinder head has been installed, adjust timing belt tension and valve clearance as outlined.
e. When installing rocker cover, apply sealant No. 4318034 or equivalent to semicircular packing.

# VALVE LASH SPECIFICATIONS

| Engine | Year | Clearance Inch Int. | Exh. |
|---|---|---|---|
| 2.0L/4-121 | 1989-92 | ① | ① |

**H: Hot.**
**①—Equipped with hydraulic lash adjusters, no adjustment.**

# VALVE TIMING

## INTAKE OPENS BTDC

| Engine | Year | Degrees |
|---|---|---|
| 2.0L/4-121 | 1989-92 | 19 |

# VALVES

## ADJUST

### INTAKE & EXHAUST VALVES

On these engines, the intake and exhaust valves are equipped with hydraulic lash adjusters with no provision for adjustment.

# VALVE GUIDES

## REPLACE

1. Press old valve guide from cylinder head toward lower surface using push rod from valve guide replacement kit, tool No. MD998115.
2. Ream each valve guide bore in cylinder head to the O.D. of replacement valve guide, **Fig. 4.**
3. Press fit new valve guide into top of cylinder head using tool No. MD998115. This tool installs valve guide to a predetermined height. If a standard size valve guide has been removed, replacement valve guide should be oversized. New valve guide should be installed at room temperature.
4. After installation of new valve guides, insert valve and check for proper stem to guide clearance. If clearance is not correct, ream guide until proper clearance is obtained.

# TIMING CASE

## REPLACE

1. Remove timing belt as described under "Timing Belt, Replace."
2. Remove camshaft sprocket, crankshaft sprocket and flange.
3. Remove timing belt tensioner.
4. Remove oil pump sprocket. When the oil pump sprocket nut is removed, first remove plug at bottom of left side of cylinder block, then insert a suitable screwdriver to keep the left counterbalance shaft in position, **Fig. 5.**
5. Loosen counterbalance shaft sprocket mounting bolt then remove tensioner "B," **Fig. 6,** and timing belt "B."
6. Remove crankshaft sprocket "B," **Fig. 6,** and the counterbalance shaft sprocket.
7. Remove timing belt upper under and lower under covers.
8. Remove water pump.
9. Remove cylinder head assembly.
10. Remove oil pan, oil screen and oil pump cover.
11. Insert a screwdriver through plug hole in left side of cylinder block to hold counterbalance shaft in position, then loosen oil pump driven gear mounting bolt, **Fig. 7.**
12. Remove timing case with left counterbalance shaft attached.
13. Reverse procedure to install. Refer to "Timing Belt, Replace" procedure for timing belt installation.

# TIMING BELT

## REPLACE

### REMOVAL

1. Remove crankshaft pulley(s), then the timing belt upper and lower front covers.
2. Rotate crankshaft in normal direction of rotation and align timing marks as shown in **Fig. 8,** then remove crankshaft sprocket attaching bolt.
3. Loosen main tensioner pivot and disengage spring from boss on water

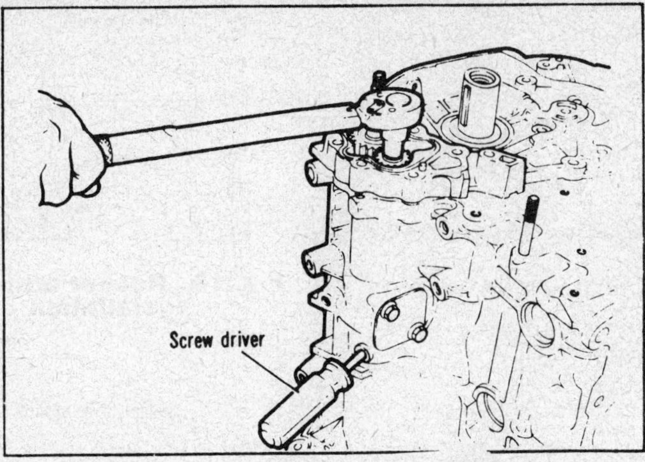


**Fig. 7 Oil pump driven gear removal**

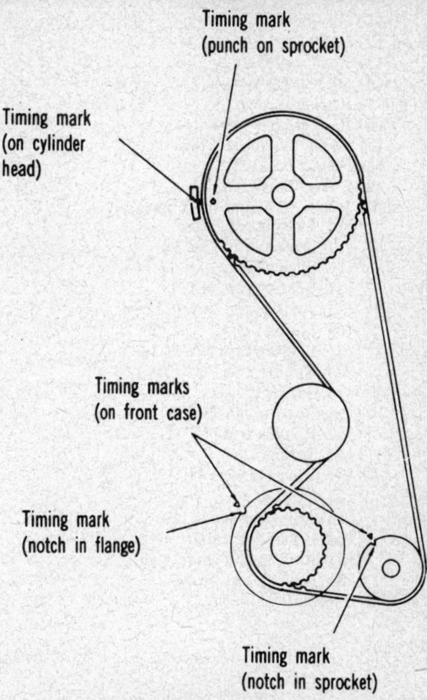


**Fig. 8 Crankshaft, camshaft & oil pump timing marks**

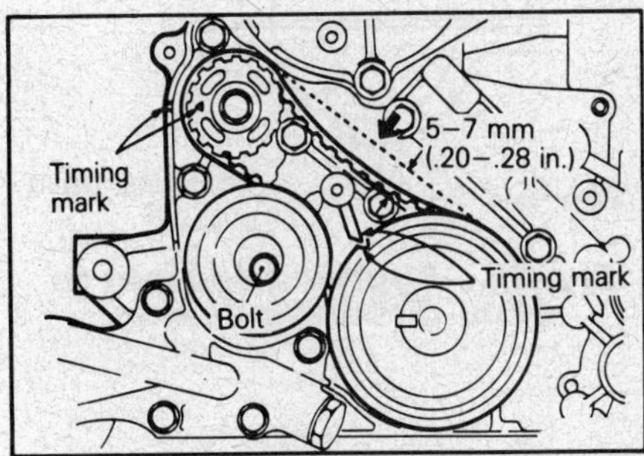


**Fig. 9 Aligning silent shaft & crankshaft sprocket timing marks**

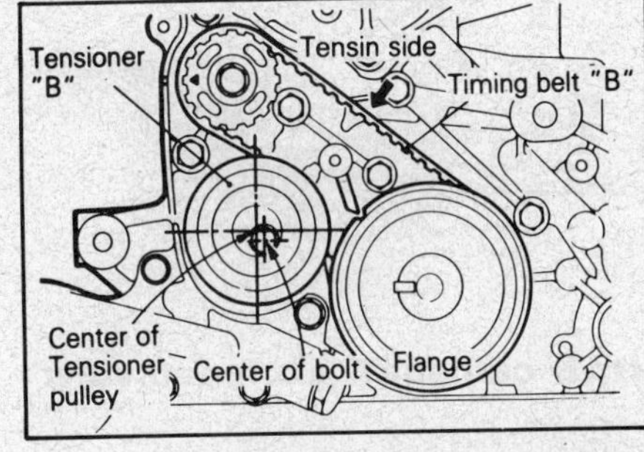


**Fig. 10 Installing silent shaft belt tensioner**

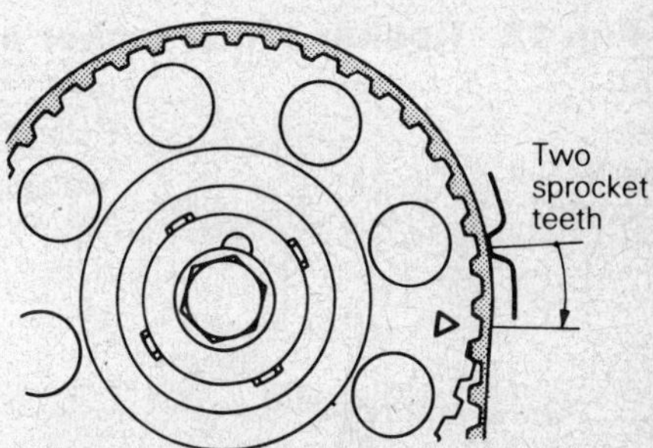


**Fig. 11 Positioning camshaft sprocket for timing belt adjustment**

pump, then remove tensioner assembly.

4. Remove main timing belt from crankshaft, camshaft and oil pump sprockets. If belt is to be reused, place chalk mark on belt indicating direction of rotation.
5. Remove camshaft sprocket, then the crankshaft sprocket and flange.
6. Remove plug from lower left hand side of cylinder block, then insert a screwdriver into hole to hold silent shaft in position while removing oil pump sprocket nut, **Fig. 5.** Use a screwdriver with shaft diameter of .3 inch which can be inserted at least 2.4 inches.
7. Loosen right hand silent shaft sprocket bolt until it can be rotated by hand, then remove silent shaft belt tensioner and silent shaft timing belt. If belt is to be reused, place chalk mark on belt indicating direction of rotation.
8. Remove crankshaft sprocket, then the right hand silent shaft sprocket and spacer.
9. Inspect timing belts, sprocket and tensioners for wear and damage.

## INSTALLATION

1. Install crankshaft sprocket inner sprocket with raised lip toward inside.
2. Coat silent shaft spacer with oil and install spacer with chamfer toward inside, then install right hand silent shaft sprocket and tighten attaching bolt.
3. Install and adjust silent shaft timing belt (B) as follows:
   a. Align crankshaft and silent shaft sprocket timing marks with marks on timing case, **Fig. 9.**
   b. Install silent shaft timing belt (B) over crankshaft and silent shaft sprockets. When installing timing belt, ensure tension side of belt has no slack. If used belt is installed, ensure belt is installed in original position.
   c. Install silent shaft belt tensioner (B), assembling tensioner so that pulley is to left of installation bolt and pulley flange faces front of engine, **Fig. 10.**
   d. Raise tensioner toward belt by hand and apply sufficient pressure so that tension side of belt is taut, then tighten tensioner bolt. **Ensure tensioner does not rotate with bolt as it is tightened, as excessive tension will be placed on belt.**
   e. Ensure timing marks are still aligned and check belt tension. There should be approximately .20-.28 inch (5-7 mm) slack on tension side of belt when belt is moved by hand.
4. Install crankshaft sprocket flange with raised side facing out, then install crankshaft sprocket.
5. Install oil pump sprocket and align timing mark, **Fig. 8.** With oil pump sprocket timing marks aligned, insert a screwdriver with a shaft diameter of .3 inch into hole in left hand side of cylinder block, **Fig. 5.** If screwdriver can be inserted 2.4 inches or more, alignment is correct. If screwdriver can be inserted only 1 inch, rotate oil pump sprocket one revolution and realign timing marks. Check to ensure that screwdriver can be inserted 2.4 inches or more. This check is performed to ensure that silent shaft and oil pump sprocket are properly positioned. Leave screwdriver inserted in hole until after timing belt has been installed.
6. Tighten oil pump sprocket bolt, ensuring that timing marks remain aligned.
7. Install main timing belt tensioner, attach top side of tensioner spring to protrusion on water pump, move tensioner as far as possible toward water pump and tighten tensioner bolts.
8. Install camshaft sprocket and align timing marks, **Fig. 8.**

(1) Oil filler cap
(2) Bolt (2)
(3) Washer (2)
(4) Oil seal (2)
(5) Rocker cover
(6) Rocker cover gasket
(7) Semi-circular packing
(8) Flange bolt (2)
(9) Flange bolt (10)
(10) Rocker arm and shaft assembly
-(1) Bearing cap, rear
-(2) Rocker arm "D" (2)
-(3) Spring (2)
-(4) Bearing cap, No. 4
-(5) Rocker arm "C" (2)
-(6) Spring (2)
-(7) Bearing cap, No. 3
-(8) Rocker arm "C" (2)
-(9) Spring (2)
-(10) Bearing cap, No. 2
-(11) Rocker arm "C" (2)
-(12) Spring
-(13) Wave washer
-(14) Nut (8)
-(15) Adjusting screw (8)
-(16) Rocker arm shaft, left
-(17) Rocker arm shaft, right
-(18) Bearing cap, front
(11) Camshaft

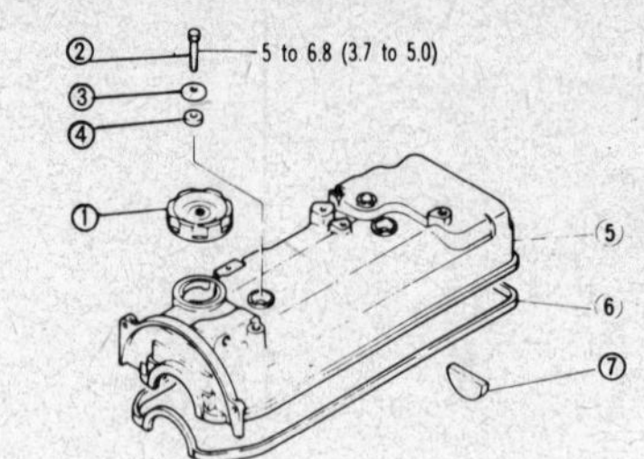


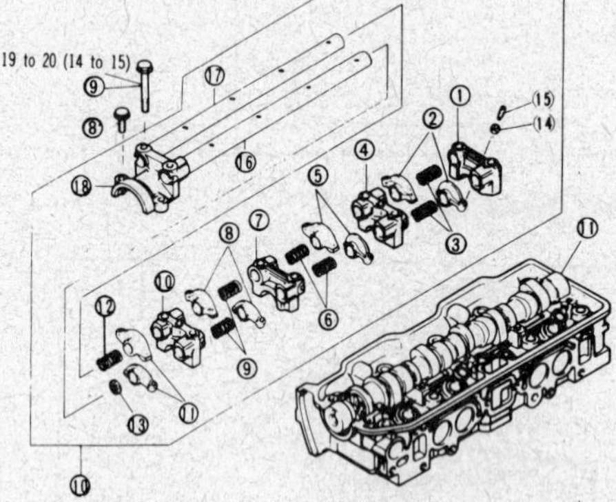


Tightening torque: Nm (ft-lbs)

**Fig. 12 Rocker arms, rocker shafts & camshaft exploded view**

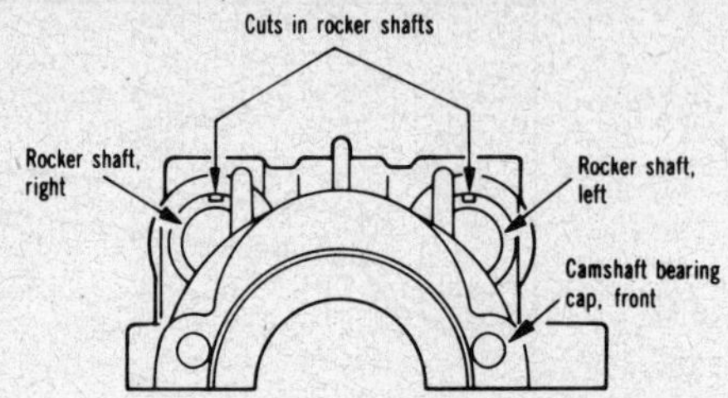


**Fig. 13 Rocker arm shaft installation**

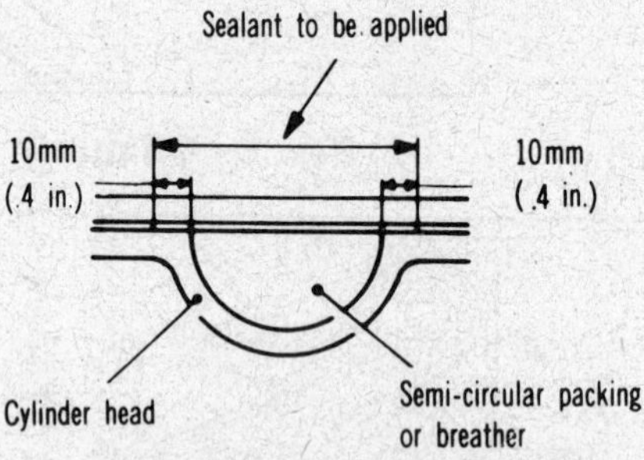


**Fig. 16 Applying sealant to semi-circular packing**

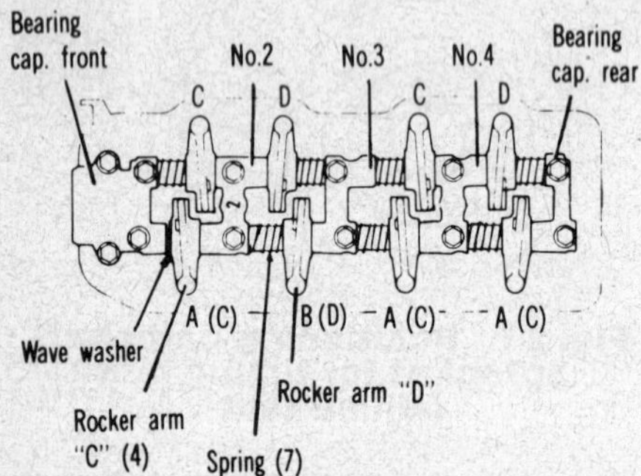


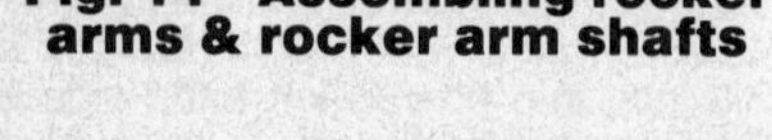

**Fig. 14 Assembling rocker arms & rocker arm shafts**

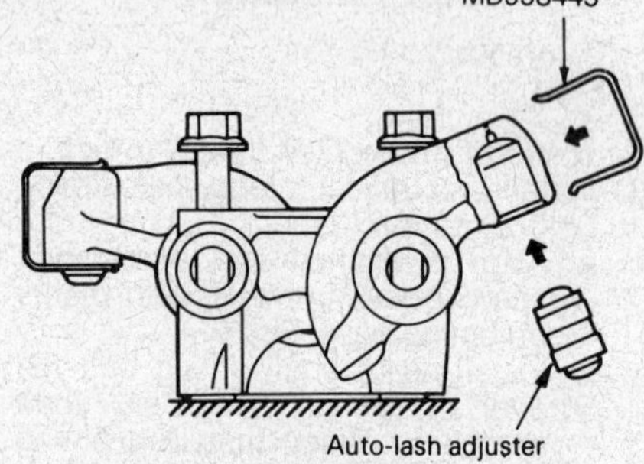


**Fig. 15 Hydraulic lash adjuster & retaining clip installation**

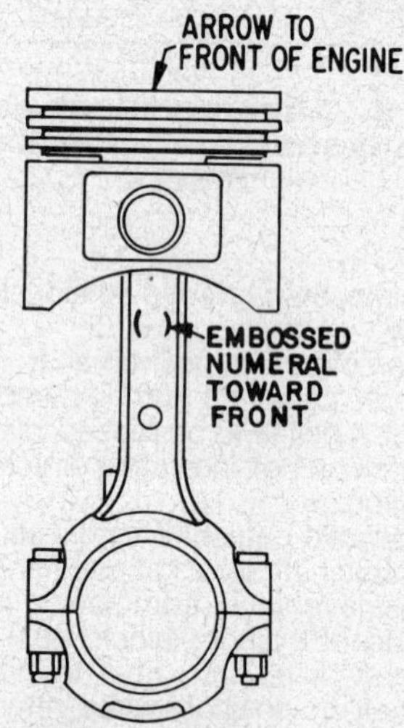


**Fig. 17 Piston & rod assembly**

9. Install and adjust main timing belt as follows:
   a. Install timing belt, first over the crankshaft sprocket, then the oil pump and camshaft sprockets, holding belt tight so there is no slack on tension side of belt. Apply counterclockwise force on camshaft sprocket to aid in tensioning belt, and ensure that all timing marks remain aligned.
   b. Loosen tensioner bolts, allowing tensioner to spring to apply force to timing belt.
   c. Remove screwdriver from hole in left side of block, then rotate crankshaft clockwise until mark on camshaft sprocket is moved 2 teeth away from mark on cylinder head. **Do not rotate crankshaft counterclockwise or place pressure on belt to test tension.**
   d. Press tensioner toward belt until timing belt is fully seated on camshaft sprocket, then tighten tensioner adjuster bolt and pivot bolt. Belt should engage approximately 225° of crankshaft sprocket. When tightening tensioner bolts, always tighten adjuster bolt first, then the pivot bolt, to prevent tensioner from rotating out of position.
   e. Press belt toward outer edge of cover between oil pump and camshaft sprockets, squeezing belt and edge of cover with thumb and forefinger, then check clearance between back of belt and cover. Belt tension is correct when clearance is approximately .55 inch (14 mm).
   f. Rotate crankshaft clockwise, 2 full turns, align crankshaft timing mark with mark on cover, and ensure oil pump and camshaft sprocket timing marks are properly aligned, **Fig. 8.**
10. Ensure camshaft sprocket bolt is properly tightened, the reverse remaining procedure to complete installation.

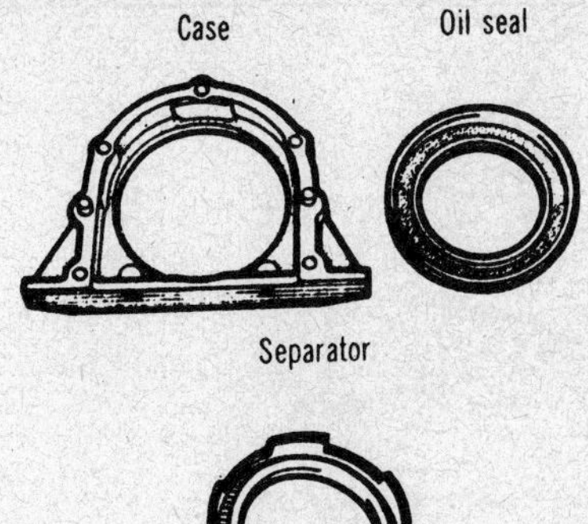


**Fig. 18 Disassembled view of rear seal**

# TIMING BELT TENSION

## ADJUST

On These engines, the timing belt tension may be adjusted without removing the timing cover through adjustment ports located on the cover.

1. Remove timing belt upper front cover and the spark plugs.
2. Rotate crankshaft clockwise (normal direction of rotation) and inspect timing belt. If belt is satisfactory, continue rotating crankshaft until No. 1 Cylinder is at TDC on compression stroke and timing mark on camshaft sprocket is aligned with mark on belt cover or cylinder head.
3. Rotate crankshaft clockwise until mark on camshaft sprocket is 2 teeth away from mark on cover or cylinder head, **Fig. 11.** This causes spring pressure of No. 2 exhaust valve to apply specific tension to tension timing belt. **Do not rotate crankshaft counterclockwise, as belt tension will be adversely affected.**
4. Remove accessory drive belts and pulleys as needed, then the two adjusting port covers, inserting a screwdriver into slot on timing belt cover and prying timing port covers off.
5. Insert 14 mm socket through adjusting port, loosen timing belt tensioner nut and bolt 1/2-3/4 turn. **Do not loosen bolt or nut more than 3/4 turn, as fastener may fall out into cover.**
6. Check to ensure that tensioner is not sticking, by inserting a screwdriver through opening on top of lower timing belt cover and pushing tensioner toward timing belt. Release tensioner and remove screwdriver. Spring tension of the timing belt tensioner will automatically adjust the timing belt.
7. Tighten tensioner adjuster bolt, then the pivot bolt. Always tighten slotted adjuster bolt or nut first to prevent tensioner from rotating out of position.
8. Install adjusting port covers, then install timing belt upper front cover.

# CAMSHAFT, ROCKER ARMS & SHAFTS

## REPLACE

### REMOVAL

1. Disconnect battery ground cable and remove air cleaner.
2. Disconnect spark plug wires and remove accessory drive belts, as needed.
3. Mark and disconnect necessary electrical connectors and vacuum hoses, then remove timing belt upper cover and rocker arm cover.
4. Rotate crankshaft in normal direction of rotation until No. 1 cylinder is at TDC and crankshaft and camshaft timing marks are aligned, **Fig. 1.**
5. Place chalk mark between timing belt and camshaft sprocket, remove camshaft sprocket bolt, separate sprocket from camshaft leaving belt in place on sprocket, then secure sprocket and belt on lower timing cover. Take care that sprocket does not disengage from belt and fall, and maintain tension on belt to maintain proper timing. **Do not rotate crankshaft after sprocket is removed from camshaft.**
6. Evenly loosen camshaft bearing cap/rocker arm retaining bolts in crossing pattern, remove bearing caps and rocker shafts as an assembly, then remove camshaft.
7. Disassemble components in numerical order, **Fig. 12,** noting position for installation.

### INSTALLATION

1. Coat camshaft with suitable assembly lubricant and position cam in head, with camshaft aligned so that valves for No. 1 cylinder are closed (TDC on compression stroke).
2. Insert rocker shafts into front bearing cap, with cuts on front of rocker shaft facing upward, **Fig. 13.**
3. Apply engine oil to I.D. of rocker arms prior to assembly. Assemble rocker arms, springs and remaining bearing caps on rocker shafts, **Fig. 14,** in positions noted during disassembly.
4. On models with hydraulic lash adjusters, insert each adjuster into rocker arm taking care not to spill fluid from adjuster. Retain adjusters using suitable clips, **Fig. 15,** to prevent them from falling out during installation.
5. On all models, install assembly onto cylinder head and evenly tighten bolts in crossing pattern until bearing caps are seated. When caps are seated, torque bolts to specifications in crossing pattern.
6. Install sleeve over camshaft and press oil seal into place using suitable driver.
7. Install camshaft sprocket and timing belt, then ensure timing marks are properly aligned.
8. On models less hydraulic valve lash adjusters, adjust valve clearance, then temporarily install rocker cover.

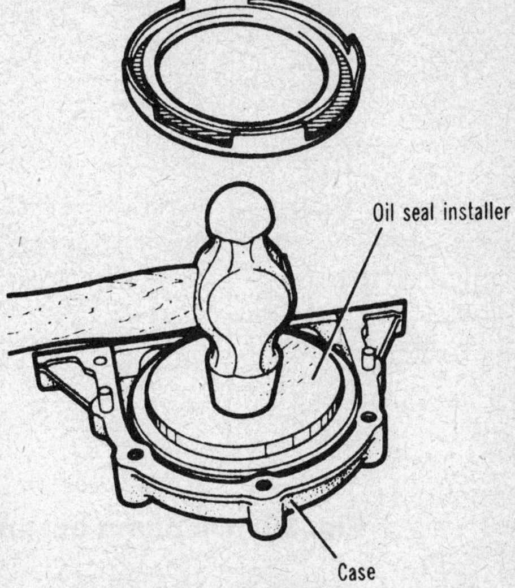


**Fig. 19 Installing rear seal into case**

9. Reverse remaining procedure to complete installation, then check timing belt tension as outlined. On models less hydraulic valve lash adjusters, after engine reaches normal operating temperature, recheck valve clearances and adjust as needed.
10. When installing rocker cover after checking valve clearances, apply suitable sealer to semi-circular packing and cylinder head, **Fig. 16,** then install rocker cover.

# PISTON & ROD ASSEMBLY

This piston and rod is assembled with the indented arrow on the piston and the embossed numeral on the rod facing toward front of engine, **Fig. 17.**

# PISTON, PINS & RINGS

Pistons and rings are available in standard size and oversizes of .010, .020, .030 and .039 inch. Oversize pins are not available.

# MAIN & ROD BEARINGS

Main and rod bearings are available in undersizes of .010, .020 and .030 inch.

The main bearing caps are installed with arrows facing front of engine.

# CRANKSHAFT REAR OIL SEAL

## REPLACE

1. Remove transmission, clutch assembly and flywheel or flex plate, as equipped.
2. Remove rear oil seal case and separate into three parts: oil seal, separator and case, **Fig. 18.**
3. Drive in oil seal from inside of case,

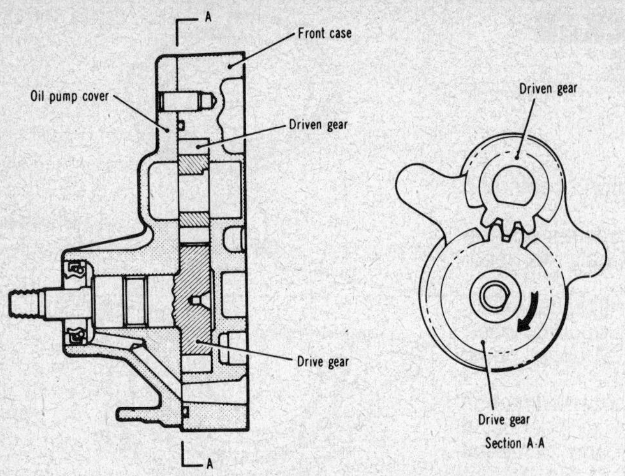


**Fig. 20 Oil pump assembly**

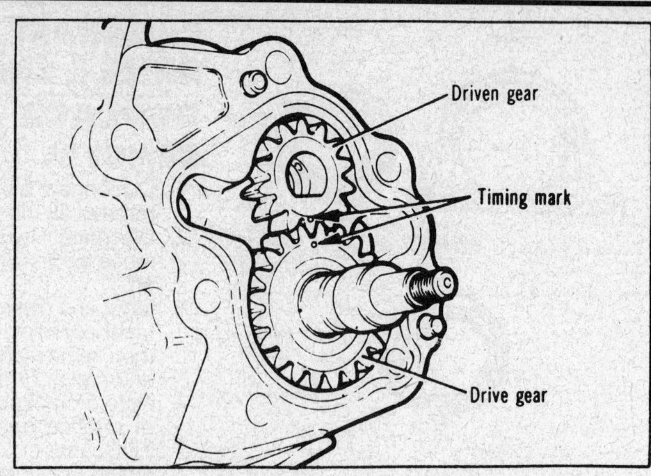


**Fig. 21 Oil pump gear timing marks**

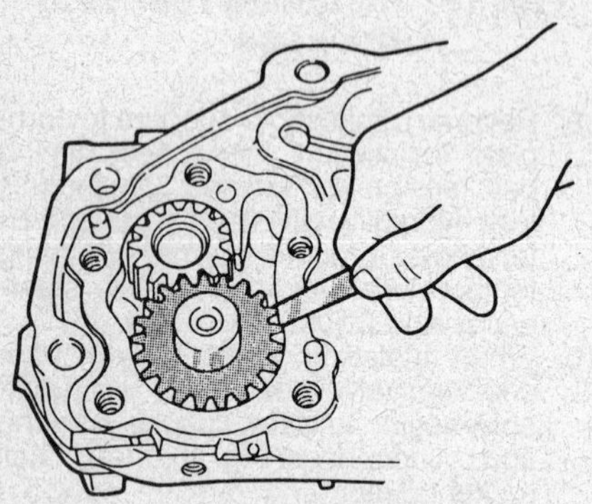

**Fig. 22 Checking oil pump drive gear to housing clearance**

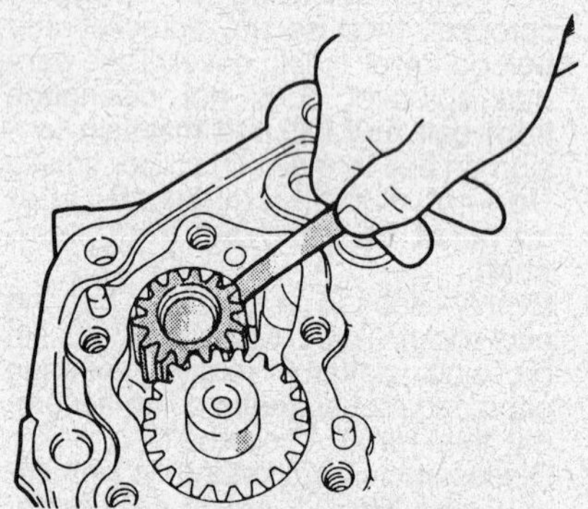

**Fig. 23 Checking oil pump driven gear to housing clearance**

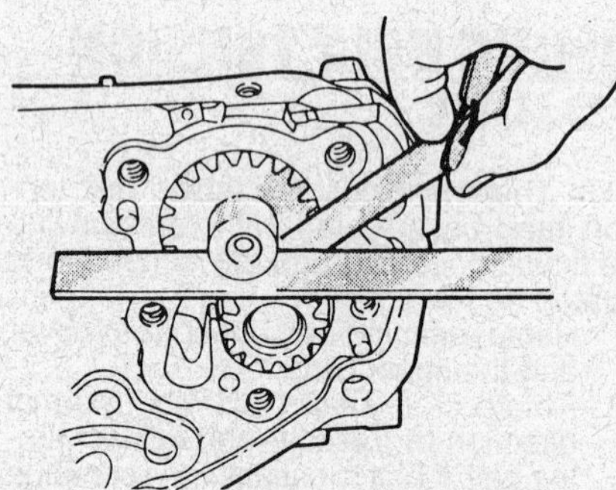

**Fig. 24 Checking oil pump gear side clearance**

using suitable tool, **Fig. 19.** Ensure the oil seal plate fits properly in the inner contact surface of the seal case, if equipped.

4. Install separator with the oil hole facing the bottom of the case, if equipped.
5. Apply engine oil to oil seal lips.
6. Install the oil seal case in the cylinder block.

## OIL PAN REPLACE

On some models it may be necessary to remove engine from vehicle to gain access to oil pan.

1. Raise and support vehicle, remove engine splash pan, if equipped, then drain crankcase.
2. Remove the oil pressure sender unit, if necessary, and on turbocharged models, disconnect oil drain hose and remove oil drain pipe.
3. Remove the oil pan bolts and oil pan.
4. Remove oil pump pickup if necessary.
5. Reverse procedure to install.

## OIL PUMP REPLACE

To remove oil pump pickup, refer to "Oil Pan, Replace."

The oil pump is of the gear type, **Fig. 20.** The oil pump is also used to drive the left counterbalance shaft. The oil pump drive gear has a sprocket driven by a timing belt. The counterbalance shaft is mounted to the oil pump driven gear and rotates in the opposite direction of crankshaft rotation.

1. Remove timing case as outlined under "Timing Case, Replace" procedure.
2. Remove oil pump gears and left counterbalance shaft from case.
3. Install oil pump gear in timing case, aligning timing marks, **Fig. 21.**
4. Insert left counterbalance shaft into driven gear.

## OIL PUMP SERVICE

With drive and driven gears positioned in front case, check drive gear to gear pocket clearance, using a suitable feeler gauge, **Fig. 22.** Clearance should be .0063 to .0083. Check driven gear to gear pocket clearance, using feeler gauge, **Fig. 23.** Clearance should be .0051 to .0071. Using a straight edge and feeler gauge, measure gear side clearance, **Fig. 24.** Side clearance should be .0031 to .0055 for drive gear and .0024 to .0047 for driven gear.

## BELT TENSION DATA

| | Belt Tension | |
|---|---|---|
| **Component** | **New Lbs.** | **Used Lbs.**① |
| **Alternator** | **110—154** | **88** |
| **A/C** | ②③ | ②③ |
| **P.S.** | ②④ | ②④ |

**①—A new belt run 30 minutes is used.**
**②—Belt deflection with a pressure of 22 lbs. applied.**
**③—.35-.43.**
**④—.3-.4.**

## COOLING SYSTEM BLEED

These engines do not require a specified bleed procedure. After filling cooling system, run engine to operating temperature with radiator/pressure cap off. Air will then be automatically bled through cap opening.

## WATER PUMP
### REPLACE

1. Disconnect battery ground cable and drain cooling system.
2. Remove fan shroud, then disconnect lower radiator hose.
3. Remove drive belt cooling fan and pulley.
4. Place No. 1 piston at top dead center, compression stroke.
5. Remove camshaft pulley, timing belt covers, timing belt, camshaft sprocket, upper under cover and timing belt tensioner.
6. Remove water pump mounting bolts and the water pump.
7. Reverse procedure to install. Refer to **Fig. 25,** for water pump attaching bolt identification and installation.

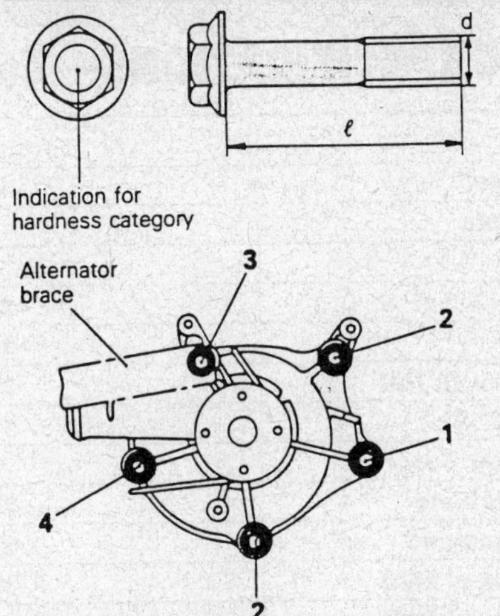


| No. | Hardness category (Head mark) | d×ℓ mm (in.) |
|---|---|---|
| 1 | 4T | 8×20 (.31×.79) |
| 2 | 4T | 8×30 (.31×1.18) |
| 3 | 7T | 8×65 (.31×2.26) |
| 4 | 4T | 8×40 (.31×1.57) |

**Fig. 25 Water pump attaching bolt identification & installation**

## FUEL PUMP
### REPLACE

1. Relieve fuel system pressure as follows:
   a. Start engine and disconnect electric fuel pump connector. Connector is located inside rear compartment.
   b. When engine stops from lack of fuel, turn off ignition and disconnect battery ground cable.
2. Push fuel pump/sending unit lead and grommet through floor and remove fuel tank cap.
3. Raise and support rear of vehicle, drain fuel tank into suitable container and disconnect filler hose.
4. On 2WD models, remove spare tire carrier assembly.
5. Support tank with suitable jack and remove nuts securing tank straps.
6. Lower tank, mark and disconnect fuel hoses, vapor hoses and electrical connectors, then remove tank.
7. Remove nuts or bolts securing pump, then withdraw pump assembly from tank.
8. Reverse procedure to install.

## TIGHTENING SPECIFICATIONS

| Component | Torque Ft. Lbs. |
|---|---|
| **1989–92** | |
| **Camshaft Bearing Cap Bolts** | **15-19** |
| **Camshaft Sprocket** | **58-72** |
| **Connecting Rod Cap Nuts** | **37-38** |
| **Coolant Temperature Switch** | **9-13** |
| **Crankshaft Pulley** | **15-21** |
| **Crankshaft Sprocket** | **80-94** |
| **Cylinder Head, Engine Cold** | **65-72** |
| **Cylinder Head, Engine Hot** | **73-79** |
| **Exhaust Manifold** | **11-15** |
| **Flex Plate** | **94-101** |
| **Flywheel** | **94-101** |
| **Front Case Bolts** | **15-19** |
| **Intake Manifold** | **11-15** |
| **Jet Valve** | **—** |
| **Main Bearing Cap Bolts** | **37-39** |
| **Oil Pan** | **4-6** |
| **Oil Pan Drain Plug** | **26-32** |
| **Oil Pressure Switch** | **5.8-9** |
| **Oil Pump Cover** | **11-13** |
| **Oil Pump Driven Gear Bolt** | **25-28** |
| **Oil Pump Relief Valve** | **29-36** |
| **Oil Pump Sprocket** | **37-43** |
| **Oil Screen** | **11-15** |

*Continued*

## TIGHTENING SPECIFICATIONS—Continued

| Component | Torque Ft. Lbs. |
|---|---|
| Pressure Plate To Flywheel | 11-15 |
| Rocker Arm Adjusting Nuts | 6-7 |
| Rocker Cover | 4-5 |
| Silent Shaft Sprocket | 25-28 |
| Spark Plug | 15-21 |
| Timing Belt Tensioner Bolt Or Nut | 32-29 |
| Timing Belt Tensioner "B" Bolt | 11-15 |
| Timing Belt Upper & Lower Covers | 7-9 |
| Torque Converter To Flex Plate | 33-38 |
| Transaxle To Engine, Automatic | 31-40 |
| Transaxle To Engine, Manual 2WD | 32-39 |
| Transaxle To Engine, Manual 4WD | ② |
| Water Pump Pulley | 6-7 |
| Water Pump To Engine | ① |

①—M8 x 65 mm bolts, 15–19 ft. lbs.; M8 x 20 mm, M8 x 30 mm & M8 x 40 bolts mm, 9–10 ft. lbs.

②—M 10 bolts, 31–40 ft. lbs.; M8 bolts, 22–25 ft. lbs.

# 2.6L/4-156 Engine

Page No.



## ENGINE REPLACE

1. Disconnect battery ground cable.
2. Drain cooling system, crankcase, transaxle and clutch release system, and remove engine under cover.
3. Mark position of hood hinges, then remove hood.
4. Release residual fuel pressure as follows:
   a. Remove high floor side panel from luggage compartment.
   b. Start engine and disconnect electrical connector from fuel tank sending unit (fuel pump connector).
   c. When engine stops from lack of fuel, turn off ignition. **Failure to release pressure prior to disconnecting fuel lines may cause fire or personal injury.**
5. Remove air cleaner and heat protector, then disconnect oxygen sensor electrical connector and remove intercooler inlet and outlet hoses, if equipped.
6. Disconnect brake booster hose and heater hoses.
7. Remove accessory drive belts. On models with A/C and/or power steering, remove compressor and power steering pump mounting bolts, then secure assemblies aside, leaving hoses connected.
8. Disconnect exhaust pipe from catalytic converter.
9. Disconnect and plug oil cooler and transaxle cooler lines, if equipped, disconnect radiator hoses, then remove radiator assembly.
10. Disconnect accelerator, cruise control and kickdown cables, as equipped.
11. Disconnect and plug fuel lines and clutch slave cylinder hose.
12. Disconnect coil high tension lead and speedometer cable.
13. Mark and disconnect necessary electrical connectors and vacuum hoses from both engine and transmission, then secure harnesses aside to prevent damage.
14. Remove shift knob and spool release lever, console cover, inner and rear console boxes, console side covers and the front console box, then remove shifter assembly.
15. Raise and support vehicle, mark installation position of propeller shaft companion flange, then remove propeller shaft.
16. Remove front engine mount nuts and loosen but do not remove rear mount nuts and bracket bolts.
17. Lower vehicle and attach suitable lifting equipment to engine.
18. Support transmission with suitable jack, then remove rear engine mount and bracket assembly.
19. Remove engine and transmission assembly from vehicle.
20. Reverse procedure to install.

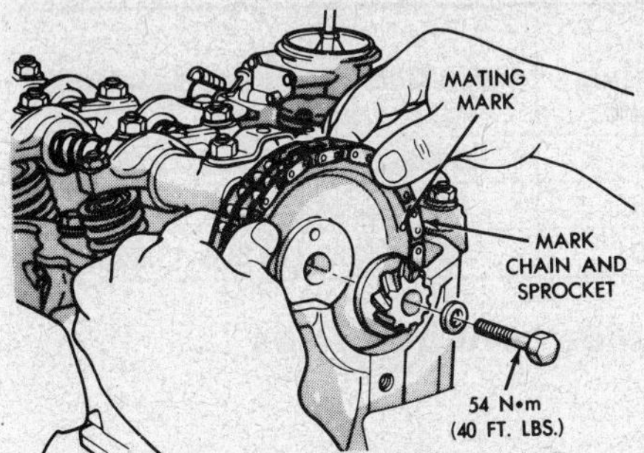


**Fig. 1 Camshaft sprocket & timing chain timing mark alignment**

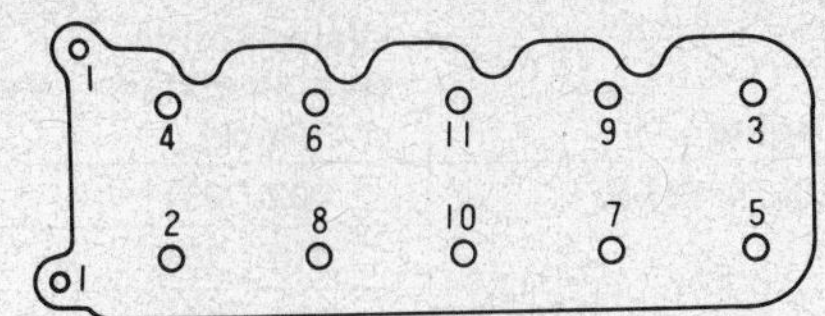


**Fig. 2 Cylinder head bolt loosening sequence**

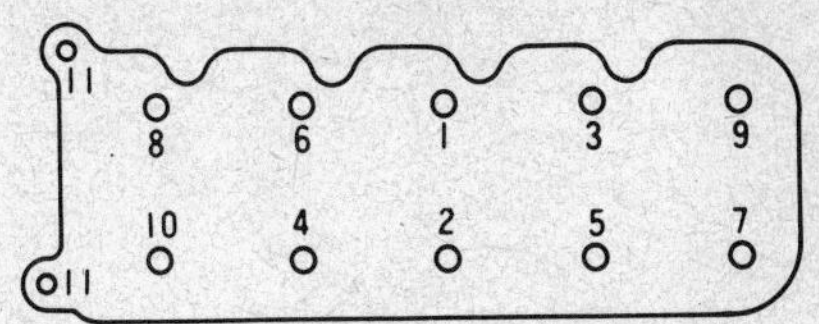


**Fig. 3 Cylinder head bolt tightening sequence**

# CYLINDER HEAD

## REPLACE

1. Release residual fuel pressure as follows:
   a. Start engine, then disconnect electrical connector from fuel pump.
   b. When engine stops from lack of fuel, turn off ignition. **Failure to release pressure prior to disconnecting fuel lines may cause fire or personal injury.**
2. Disconnect battery ground cable and drain crankcase and cooling system.
3. On models with A/C, loosen compressor drive belt tensioner and remove drive belt.
4. On all models, remove master cylinder and turbocharger heat shields and disconnect oxygen sensor lead from harness connector.
5. Remove air cleaner assembly.
6. On models with intercooler, proceed as follows:
   a. Disconnect intercooler hoses from turbocharger and air inlet tube.
   b. Disconnect boost sensor hose.
   c. Disconnect electrical connector from air intake temperature sensor on air intake tube.
7. On all models, disconnect upper radiator hose and remove air intake tube.
8. Remove secondary air cleaner, then disconnect PCV hose.
9. Disconnect control cables from throttle lever and brackets.
10. Remove bolt securing boost sensor tube.
11. Remove rocker arm cover, gasket and semi-circular packing.
12. Rotate crankshaft clockwise until No. 1 cylinder is at TDC on compression stroke and camshaft sprocket timing mark and plated link on timing chain are aligned as shown in **Fig. 1.**
13. Remove distributor cap and spark plug wires, mark position of distributor rotor and installation position of distributor, then remove distributor. **Do not rotate crankshaft with distributor removed.**
14. Disconnect fuel hoses, water hoses and brake booster hose.
15. Mark and disconnect necessary electrical connectors and vacuum hoses, release harness clips and secure harness aside to prevent damage.
16. Remove dipstick tube and O-ring seal, and plug opening.
17. Disconnect and plug turbocharger oil lines.
18. Disconnect water hoses from turbocharger, if equipped, and disconnect exhaust pipe.
19. Remove camshaft sprocket bolt and distributor drive gear.
20. Separate camshaft sprocket leaving timing chain on sprocket, then seat sprocket and chain assembly on sprocket holder inside timing cover. Maintain tension on chain and do not allow chain to come off sprocket. **Do not rotate crankshaft with camshaft sprocket removed.**
21. Remove cylinder head attaching bolts in sequence shown in **Fig. 2.** Loosen bolts evenly, in three steps, to prevent cylinder head warpage, then remove cylinder head and gasket. Take care not to dislodge camshaft sprocket during cylinder head removal.
22. Reverse procedure to install, noting the following:
   a. Do not apply sealer to cylinder head gasket. Apply a thin bead of sealer at joint between timing cover and cylinder block. Ensure that proper I.D. mark is on gasket and install with mark at front of engine and facing up.
   b. Prior to installing cylinder head on engine, ensure that crankshaft and camshaft timing marks are aligned.
   c. Tighten cylinder head bolts in sequence shown in **Fig. 3.** Tighten bolts in two steps to ensure proper seating of cylinder head to cylinder block.
   d. Install sprocket and chain on camshaft, then the distributor drive gear and sprocket bolt. Ensure that timing marks are aligned, **Fig. 1.**
   e. Install distributor, aligning matching marks made during disassembly.
   f. When installing rocker cover, apply 3M sealant 8660 or equivalent to semi-circular packing.

# VALVE LASH SPECIFICATIONS

| | Clearance Inch | | |
|---|---|---|---|
| **Engine** | **Int.** | **Exh.** | **Jet Valve** |
| **2.6L/4-156** | ① | ① | **.010H** |

**H:Hot.**
**①—Hydraulic valve lash adjusters, no adjustment.**

# VALVE TIMING

## INTAKE OPEN BTDC

| Engine | Year | Degrees |
|---|---|---|
| 2.6L/4-156 | 1989 | 25 |

# VALVES

## ADJUST

### INTAKE & EXHAUST VALVES

On 2.6L/4-156 engines, the intake and exhaust valves are equipped with hydraulic lash adjusters with no provision for adjustment. However, the jet valve requires periodic adjustment.

### JET VALVE

Position No. 1 cylinder at top dead center compression stroke. Loosen jet valve adjusting screw locknut. Back off jet valve adjusting screw and insert a suitable feeler gauge between jet valve stem and adjusting screw, **Fig. 4.** Tighten jet valve adjusting screw until it contacts the feeler gauge blade, then while holding screw in position, tighten locknut. Position remaining cylinders at top dead center and repeat jet valve adjustment procedure.

# VALVE GUIDES

## REPLACE

1. Press old valve guide from cylinder head toward lower surface using push rod from valve guide replacement kit, tool No. MD998115 and a suitable press.
2. Ream each valve guide bore in cylinder head to the O.D. of replacement valve guide, **Fig. 5.**
3. Press fit new valve guide into top of cylinder head using tool No. MD998115. This tool installs valve guide to a predetermined height. If a standard size valve guide has been removed, replacement valve guide should be oversized. New valve guide should be installed at room temperature.
4. After installation of new valve guides, insert valve and check for proper clearance. If clearance is not correct, ream guide until proper clearance is obtained. Refer to "Valve Specifications" for stem to guide clearance.

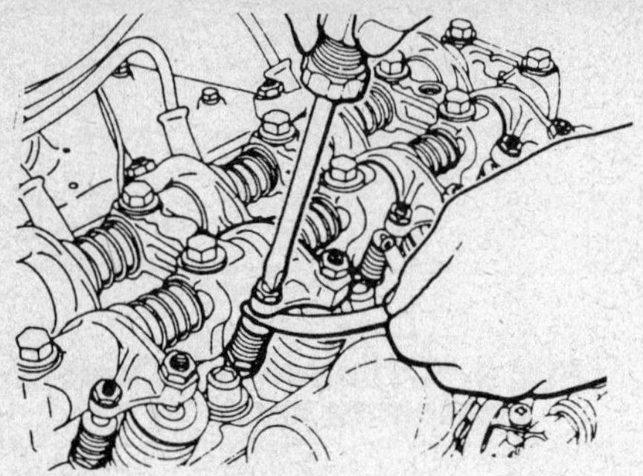

Fig. 4 Adjusting jet valve clearance

| Engine | Valve Guide Oversize Inch (mm) | Valve Guide Mark | Valve Guide Cylinder Head Bore Inch (mm) |
|---|---|---|---|
| 2.0L/4-121.9 | .002 (.05) | 5 | .5138-.5145 (13.050-13.068) |
| | .010 (.25) | 25 | .5216-.5224 (13.250-13.268) |
| | .020 (.50) | 50 | .5315-.5323 (13.500-13.518) |

Fig. 5 Valve guide & guide bore oversizes

# TIMING CASE

## REPLACE

1. Disconnect battery cables, then drain cooling system.
2. Remove fan shroud, then disconnect upper and lower radiator hoses and remove radiator.
3. Raise and support front of vehicle, then remove lower splash shield.
4. Drain crankcase, then remove oil pan attaching bolts and oil pan.
5. Position No. 1 cylinder at top dead center compression stroke.
6. Remove fan, water pump pulley, alternator and crankshaft pulley.
7. Remove air cleaner, then detach spark plug wire at spark plugs and remove distributor.
8. Remove rocker arm cover, then remove two front cylinder head bolts and air cleaner vent tube attaching bolt.
9. Disconnect heater hose, then remove timing case cover attaching bolts and timing case cover.
10. Reverse procedure to install. Apply sealer to timing case cover to cylinder head mating surfaces. Also apply sealer to oil pan side of oil pan gasket and to the four timing case covers and rear seal case to cylinder block mating surfaces.

# TIMING CHAIN

## REPLACE

### REMOVAL

1. Remove timing chain case as outlined under "Timing Case, Replace."
2. Remove chain guides "A," "B" and "C," **Fig. 6.**
3. Remove sprocket "B" locking bolts, **Fig. 6.**
4. Remove crankshaft sprocket "B," counterbalance shaft sprocket "B" and chain "B," **Fig. 6.**
5. Remove crankshaft sprocket, camshaft sprocket and timing chain, **Fig. 7,** Depress tensioner as chain is removed.

### INSTALLATION

1. Rotate crankshaft to place No. 1 piston at top dead center, compression stroke.
2. Install camshaft sprocket and crankshaft sprocket on timing chain. When the sprockets are installed, ensure the mating marks of the chain and sprockets are properly aligned. The mating marks on the sprockets are punched marks on the corresponding teeth. The marks on the chain are two plated links, **Fig. 7.**
3. Install camshaft sprocket on camshaft and align the keyway of the crankshaft sprocket with the key of the crankshaft, then install sprocket on crankshaft. Ensure timing marks are properly aligned.
4. Install crankshaft sprocket "B," **Fig. 6,** on the crankshaft.
5. Install two counterbalance shaft sprockets "B" on chain "B," aligning the mating marks. The mating marks on sprockets are punched marks on the corresponding teeth. The mating marks on the chain are three plated links, **Fig. 8.**
6. Install chain "B" on crankshaft sprocket, then the two counterbalance shaft sprockets "B" and tighten the lock bolts.
7. Install chain guides "A," "B" and "C," **Fig. 8,** and loosely install mounting bolts.
8. Tighten chain guides "A" and "C" mounting bolts.
9. Shake right and left sprockets "B" to collect chain slack at point "P," **Fig. 8.** Adjust position of chain guide "B" so when the chain is pulled in direction of arrow "Y," **Fig. 8,** the clearance between chain guide "B" and the links of chain "B" will be .04-.14 inch. Tighten chain guide "B" mounting bolts.
10. Install timing case gasket and case.
11. Install oil screen and oil pan.
12. Install crankshaft pulley.

# TIMING CHAIN TENSION

## ADJUST

On these engines, the timing chain tension may be adjusted without removing the timing cover through adjustment ports located on the cover.

1. Remove adjusting port cover located at center timing chain cover under water pump.
2. Loosen timing chain guide retaining bolt (B), **Fig. 9.**
3. With finger, push downward on timing chain guide projection as far as possible and tighten retaining bolt (B). Then install timing port cover and gasket. **Use only finger pressure to push downward on timing chain guide projection. Do not use a screwdriver or other tool to push downward on guide, as timing chain tension will be excessive.**

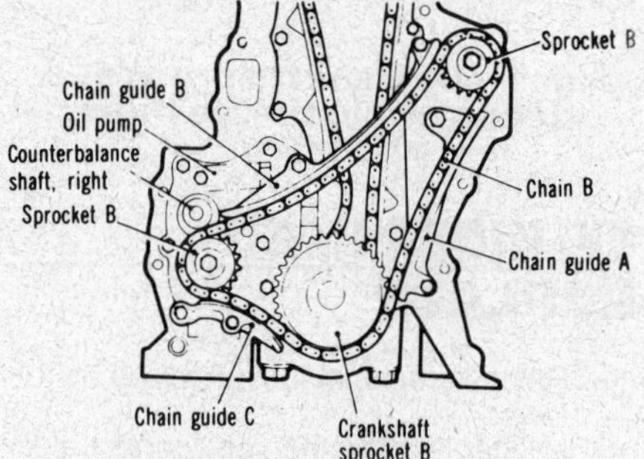


Fig. 6 Counterbalance shaft drive system

# CAMSHAFT, ROCKER ARMS & SHAFTS

## REPLACE

### REMOVAL

1. If rocker assembly and camshaft are being removed with cylinder head in place, proceed as follows:
   a. Remove necessary hoses cables and wiring to permit rocker cover removal, then remove cover and gasket.
   b. Rotate crankshaft clockwise until No. 1 cylinder is at TDC on compression stroke and camshaft sprocket timing mark and plated link on timing chain are aligned as shown in **Fig. 1.**
   c. Remove distributor cap and spark plug wires, mark position of distributor rotor and installation position of distributor, then remove distributor. **Do not rotate crankshaft with distributor removed.**
   d. Remove camshaft sprocket bolt and distributor drive gear.
   e. Separate camshaft sprocket leaving timing chain on sprocket, then seat sprocket and chain assembly on sprocket holder inside timing cover. Maintain tension on chain and do not allow chain to come off sprocket. **Do not rotate crankshaft with camshaft sprocket removed.**
2. Evenly loosen bolts securing camshaft bearing caps in crossing pattern, then remove caps, rockers and rocker shafts as an assembly. **These engines are equipped with hydraulic**

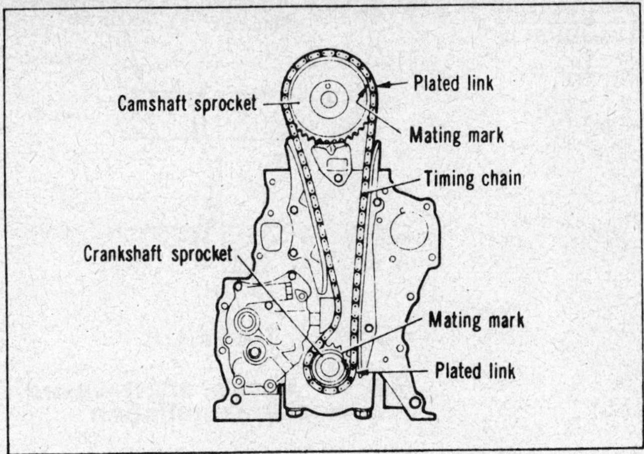


**Fig. 7 Timing chain installation**

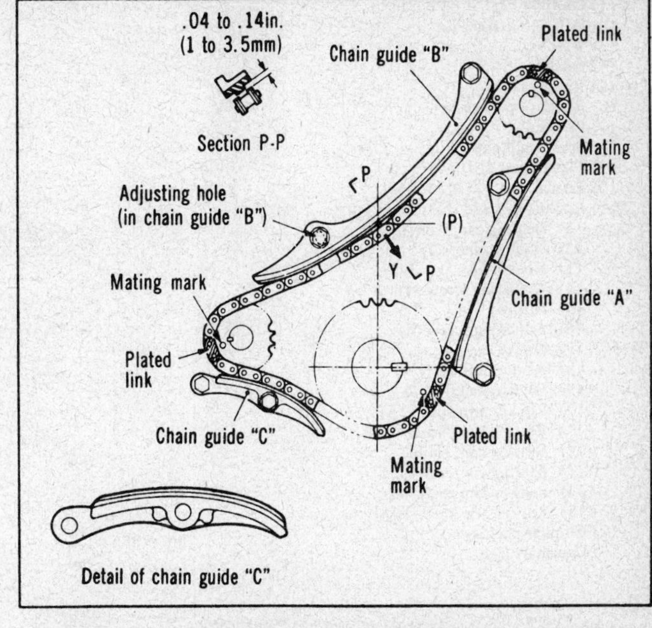


**Fig. 8 Counterbalance shaft drive chain & tensioner installation**

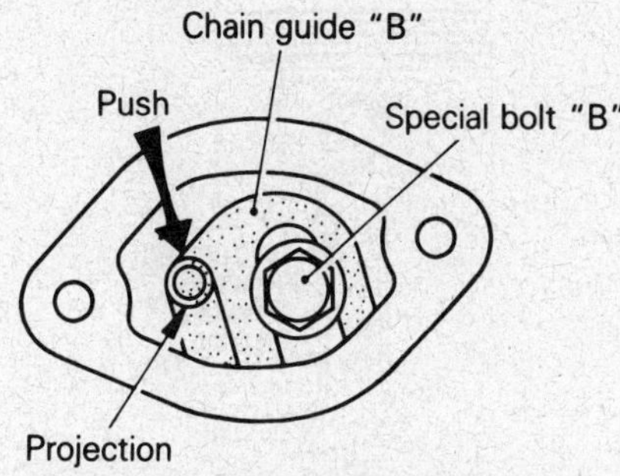


**Fig. 9 Counterbalance shaft timing chain adjustment**

**lash adjusters, install suitable retainer clips over adjusters, Fig. 10, prior to removing rocker assembly.**

3. Remove parts in numerical order as shown, **Fig. 11.**

## INSTALLATION

1. Insert left and right rocker shafts into front bearing cap, noting that rear end of intake shaft (left) has a notch.
2. Align mating mark of rocker arm shaft front end with mating mark of front bearing cap, then insert and tighten shaft to bearing cap attaching bolts.
3. Install waved washers as shown, **Fig. 12,** then assemble rocker arm and shaft assembly as shown, **Fig. 13.**
4. Lubricate camshaft lobes and bearing journals with engine oil, then position camshaft on cylinder head and align camshaft so that intake and exhaust valves for No. 1 cylinder will be fully closed (TDC on compression stroke for No. 1 cylinder).
5. Apply sealant to O.D. of circular packing, then assemble circular packing to cylinder head as shown, **Fig. 14.**
6. Install rocker assembly onto cylinder head, then torque bearing cap bolts to specifications.
7. Install camshaft sprocket and timing chain assembly, and the distributor drive gear, then ensure timing marks are properly aligned and torque sprocket bolt to specifications.

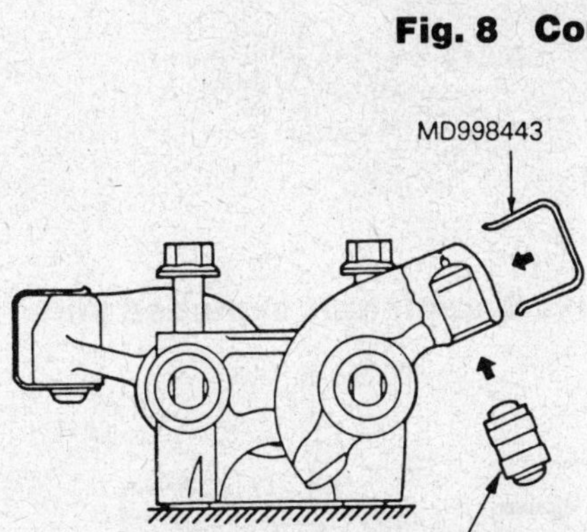


**Fig. 10 Hydraulic lash adjuster & retaining clip installation**

8. Reverse procedure to complete installation, noting the following:
   a. Install distributor, aligning matching marks made during disassembly.
   b. Install semi-circular packing to front of cylinder head, then apply a suitable sealant to top of packing.
   c. Install rocker cover and gasket.

## PISTON & ROD ASSEMBLY

This piston and rod is assembled with the indented arrow on the piston and the embossed numeral on the rod facing toward front of engine, **Fig. 15.**

## PISTON, PINS & RINGS

Pistons and rings are available in standard size and oversizes of .010, .020, .030 and .039 inch. Oversize pins are not available.

## MAIN & ROD BEARINGS

Main and rod bearings are available in undersizes of .010, .020 and .030 inch.

The main bearing caps are installed with arrows facing front of engine.

## CRANKSHAFT REAR OIL SEAL

### REPLACE

1. Remove transmission, clutch assembly and flywheel or flex plate, as equipped.
2. Remove rear oil seal case and separate into three parts: oil seal, separator and case, **Fig. 16.**
3. Drive in oil seal from inside of case, using suitable tool, **Fig. 17.** Ensure the oil seal plate fits properly in the inner contact surface of the seal case, if equipped.
4. Install separator with the oil hole facing the bottom of the case, if equipped.
5. Apply engine oil to oil seal lips.
6. Install the oil seal case in the cylinder block.

## OIL PAN

### REPLACE

1. Raise and support vehicle, remove engine splash pan, if equipped, then drain crankcase.
2. Remove the oil pressure sender unit, if necessary, and on turbocharged models, disconnect oil drain hose and remove oil drain pipe.
3. Remove the oil pan bolts and oil pan.
4. Remove oil pump pickup if necessary.
5. Reverse procedure to install.

(1) Oil filler cap
(2) Bolt – 8 x 40 (2)
(3) Washer (2)
(4) Oil seal (2)
(5) Rocker cover
(6) Rocker cover gasket
(7) PCV valve
(8) Semi-circular packing
(9) Flange bolt (10)
(10) Flange bolt – 8 x 25 (2)
(11) Rocker arm and shaft assembly
-(1) Bearing cap, front
-(2) Wave washer (2)
-(3) Rocker arm "A" (4)
-(4) Adjusting screw (4)
-(5) Nut (4)
-(6) Adjusting screw (8)
-(7) Nut (8)
-(8) Rocker arm "C" (4)
-(9) Bearing cap, No. 2
-(10) Rocker arm spring (6)
-(11) Bearing cap, No. 3
-(12) Bearing cap, No. 4
-(13) Bearing cap, rear
-(14) Rocker arm shaft, left
-(15) Rocker arm shaft, right
(12) Circular packing
(13) Camshaft

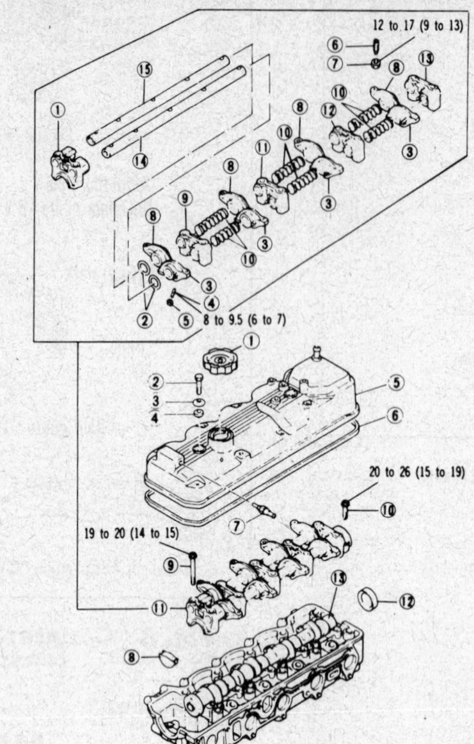


Tightening torque Nm (ft-lbs)

**Fig. 11 Rocker arms, rocker shafts & camshaft exploded view**

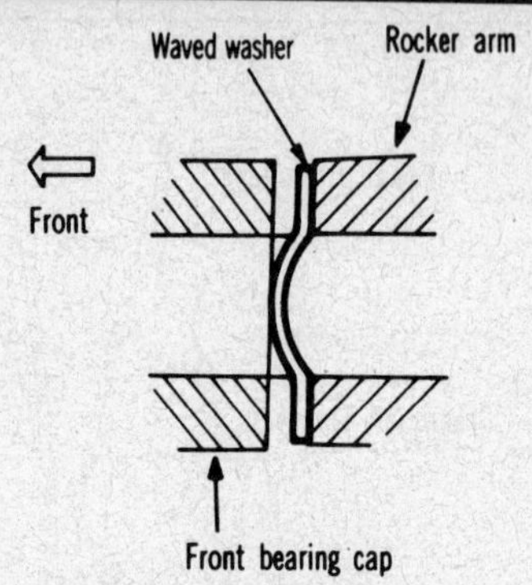


**Fig. 12 Rocker shaft waved washer installation**

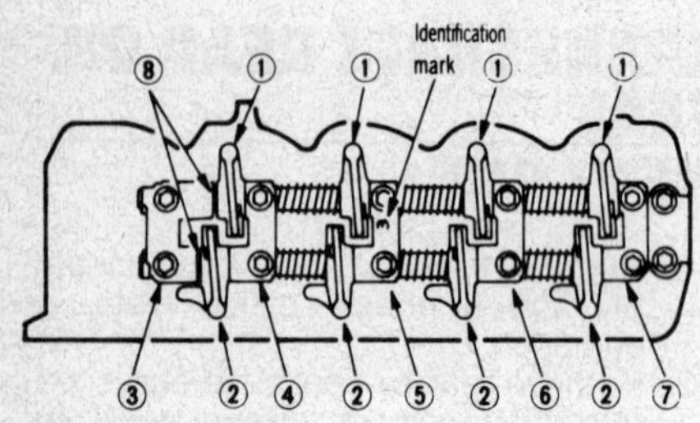


(1) Rocker arm "C"
(2) Rocker arm "A"
(3) Front bearing cap
(4) No. 2 bearing cap
(5) No. 3 bearing cap
(Inscribed mark 3 on top surface)
(6) No. 4 bearing cap
(Rocker screw hole on top surface)
(7) Rear bearing cap
(8) Waved washer

**Fig. 13 Assembling rocker arms & rocker arm shafts**

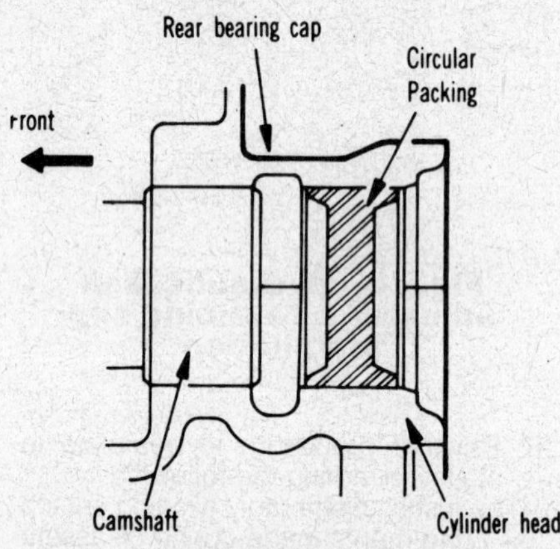


**Fig. 14 Semicircular packing installation**

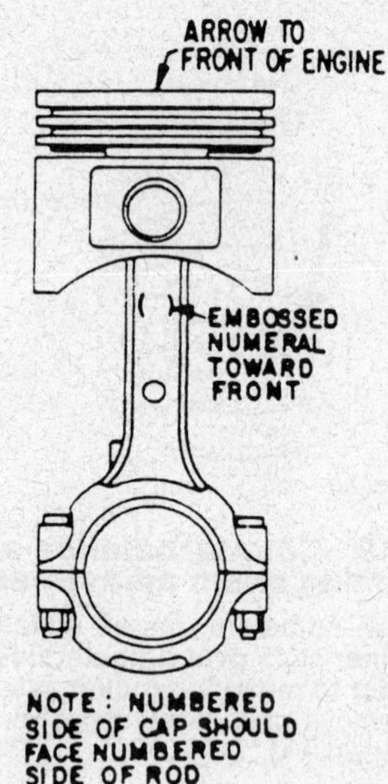


**Fig. 15 Piston & rod assembly**

# OIL PUMP REPLACE

The oil pump is of the gear type, **Fig. 18**, and is also used to drive the right counterbalance shaft. The oil pump drive gear has a sprocket driven by a chain. The counterbalance shaft is mounted to the oil pump driven gear and rotates in the opposite direction of crankshaft rotation.

1. Remove timing chain as outlined under "Timing Chain, Replace" procedure.
2. Remove bolt locking oil pump driven gear to right balancer shaft, then the oil pump mounting bolts.
3. Remove the oil pump assembly.
4. When installing the oil pump, be sure that the keyway of the oil pump driven gear fits the Woodruff key at the end of the balancer shaft and that the key does not go out of the keyway. After the oil pump assembly has been correctly installed, firmly tighten the oil pump mounting bolts. Next, tighten the balancer shaft and driven gear mounting bolts. If the fit of the Woodruff key and driven gear is too tight,

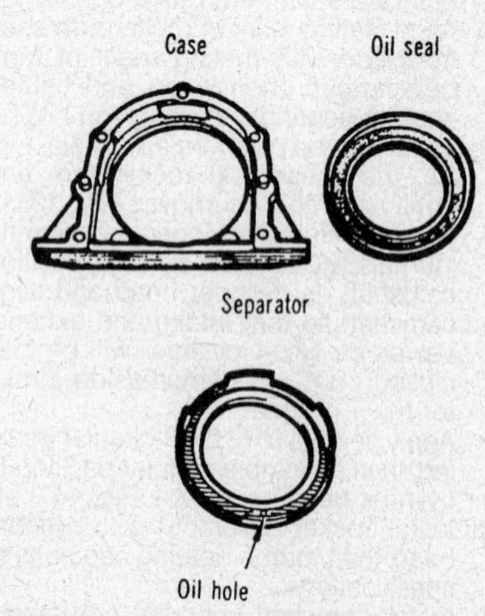


**Fig. 16 Disassembled view of rear seal**

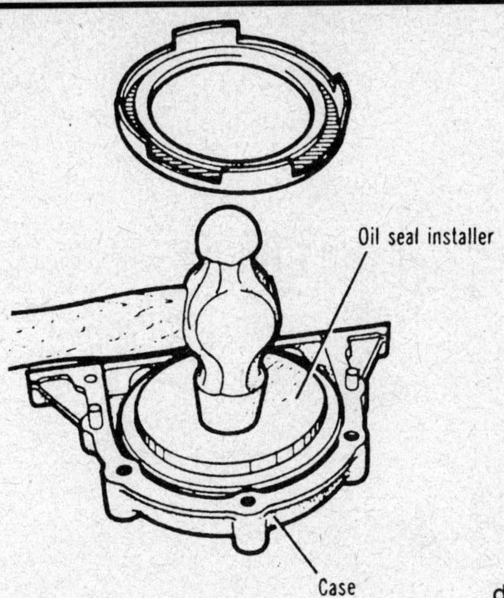


**Fig. 17 Installing rear seal into case**

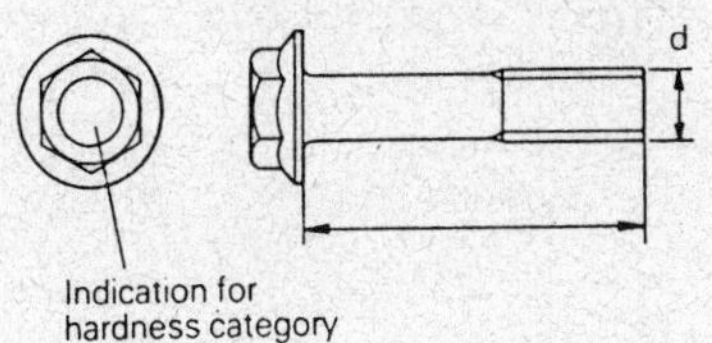


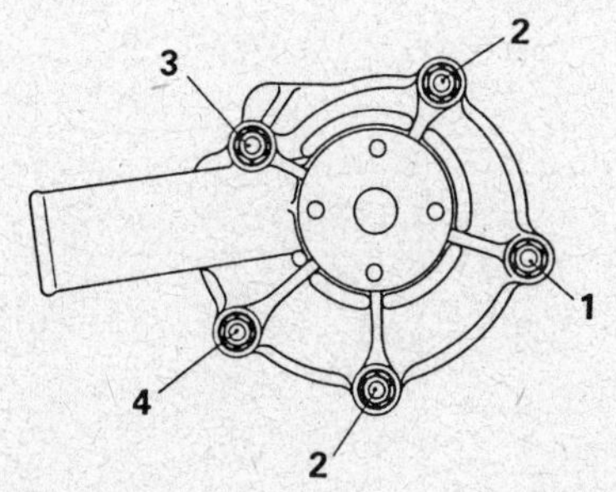


| No. | Hardness category (Head mark) | d x ℓ mm (in.) |
|---|---|---|
| 1 | 4T | 8 x 23 (.31 x .90) |
| 2 | 4T | 8 x 28 (.31 x 1.10) |
| 3 | 4T | 8 x 88 (.31 x 3.46) |
| 4 | 4T | 8 x 78 (.31 x 3.07) |

**Fig. 19 Water pump attaching bolt identification & installation.**

first insert the balancer shaft into the oil pump, temporarily tighten the bolt and insert the balancer shaft and oil pump as an assembly in the cylinder block. **Fill the oil pump with a sufficient amount of engine oil (more than .6 cu. inch) prior to installation.**

# OIL PUMP SERVICE

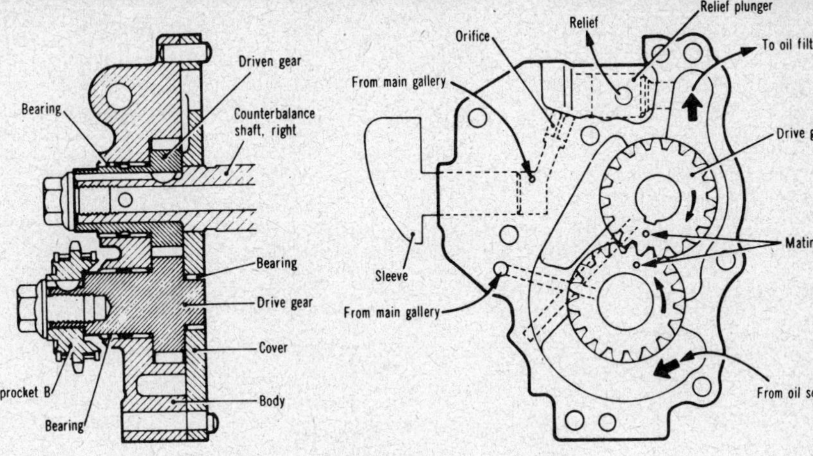


**Fig. 18 Oil pump assembly**

Using a feeler gauge, check oil drive and driven gear to housing gear tip clearance. Clearance should be .0043-..0059 inch. Using a straight edge and feeler gauge, check gear side clearance. Gear side clearance should be .0016-.0039 inch for driven gear and .0020-,0043 inch for drive gear.

# BELT TENSION DATA

| Engine | Component | Deflection In Inch① |
|---|---|---|
| 2.6L/4-156 | Alternator | .28-.39 |
| — | A/C | ② |
| — | P.S. | .35—.47 |

**①—Belt deflection with a pressure of 22 lbs. applied.**

**②—New, .5-.6; Used, .7-.8, a new belt run 30 minutes is used.**

# COOLING SYSTEM BLEED

These engines do not require a specified bleed procedure. After filling cooling system, run engine to operating temperature with radiator/pressure cap off. Air will then be automatically bled through cap opening.

# WATER PUMP
## REPLACE

1. Drain cooling system, then disconnect battery ground cable.
2. Remove fan shroud, then disconnect lower radiator hose.
3. Remove drive belt, cooling fan and pulley.
4. Remove water pump mounting bolts and the water pump.
5. Reverse procedure to install, refer to **Fig. 19**, for water pump attaching bolt identification and installation.

# FUEL PUMP
## REPLACE

1. Remove high floor side panel from luggage compartment floor, then the fuel pump connector access panel.
2. Start engine, then disconnect fuel pump and gauge sending unit electrical connectors.
3. When engine stops from lack of fuel, turn off ignition and disconnect battery ground cable.
4. Remove fuel tank cap, raise and support rear of vehicle and drain fuel into suitable container.
5. Remove left rear wheel and fuel pipe cover, then mark and disconnect fuel and vapor hoses.
6. Disconnect fuel filler and breather hoses from tank.
7. Support fuel tank and remove retaining bolts, then lower tank from vehicle.
8. Remove fuel pump from tank.
9. Reverse procedure to install.

# TURBOCHARGER
## REPLACE

1. Drain crankcase and cooling system.
2. Remove heat shield, then disconnect oxygen sensor electrical connector and remove oxygen sensor.
3. Disconnect secondary air pipe from catalytic converter, **Fig. 20.**
4. On models less intercooler, remove air intake pipe and O-ring.
5. On models with intercooler, remove air and boost hoses.
6. On all models, disconnect vacuum hose from air intake hose, if equipped, then remove air intake hose.
7. Remove catalytic converter to turbocharger attaching nuts.
8. Remove oil pipe, gasket and bracket bolt from turbocharger. Cap turbocharger opening.
9. Disconnect two coolant pipes from turbocharger.
10. Disconnect oil hose from return pipe, then remove oil pipe clamp.
11. Remove turbocharger attaching nuts, then remove turbocharger charger.
12. Remove oil return pipe from turbocharger.
13. Reverse procedure to install. Prior to connecting oil pipe, pour a small amount of engine oil into turbocharger.

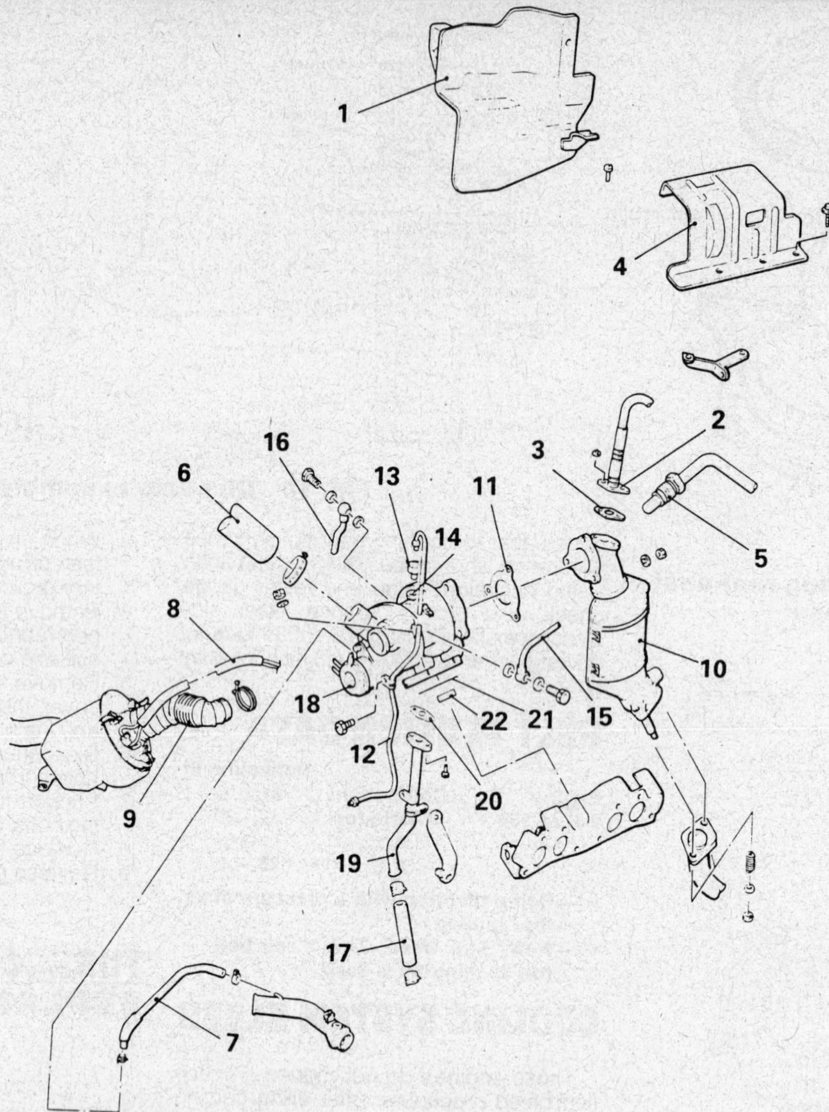


1. Heat protector
2. Oxygen sensor
3. Gasket
4. Heat protector
5. Secondary air pipe
6. Air hose A
7. Boost hose
8. Vacuum hose connection
9. Air intake hose
10. Catalytic converter
11. Gasket
12. Oil pipe
13. Oil pipe joint
14. Gasket
15. Water pipe A
16. Water pipe B
17. Oil hose
18. Turbocharger
19. Oil return pipe
20. Gasket
21. Gasket
22. Ring

**Fig. 20 Turbocharger replacement**

# TIGHTENING SPECIFICATIONS

| Year | Component | Torque/Ft. Lbs. |
|---|---|---|
| 1989 | Camshaft Bearing Cap Bolts | 14-15 |
| | Camshaft Sprocket Bolt | 37-43 |
| | Chain Guide Access Cover Bolts | 7.5-8.5 |
| | Chain Guide Upper Bolt | 6-7 |
| | Chain Guide Lower Bolt | 11-15 |
| | Connecting Rod Cap Nuts | 33-34 |
| | Coolant Temperature Sender | 22-28 |
| | Crankshaft Pulley Bolts | 80-94 |
| | Cylinder Head Bolts, Engine Cold | ① |
| | Cylinder Head Bolts, Engine Hot | ② |
| | Engine Mount Front Insulator To Engine | 9.4-14 |
| | Engine Mount Front Insulator To Crossmember | 22-29 |
| | Engine Mount Rear Insulator To Engine | 14-17 |
| | Engine Mount Rear Insulator To Engine Support Bracket | 9.4-14 |
| | Engine Oil Cooler Eye Bolt | 22-25 |
| | Engine Support Bracket To Body | 7.2 |
| | Engine Support Bracket Bolts | 37-43 |
| | Exhaust Manifold Nuts & Bolts | 11-14 |
| | Flex Plate Bolts | 94-101 |
| | Flywheel Bolts | 94-101 |
| | Intake Manifold Nuts & Bolts | 11-14 |
| | Intercooler Air Hose Band | 2-4 |
| | Jet Valve Assembly | 13-15 |
| | Main Bearing Cap Bolts | 55-61 |
| | Oil Pan Bolts | 4.5-5.5 |
| | Oil Pan Drain Plug | 26-32 |
| | Oil Pressure Switch | 11-15 |
| | Oil Pump Cover | 7.5-8.5 |
| | Oil Pump Driven Gear Bolts | 44-50 |
| | Oil Pump Mounting Bolt | 7.5-8.5 |
| | Oil Pump Relief Valve Plug | 22-32 |
| | Oil Pump Screen | 11-15 |
| | Oil Pump Sprocket Bolt | 44-50 |
| | Pressure Plate To Flywheel | 11-15 |
| | Rocker Arm Adjusting Nuts | 6-7 |
| | Rocker Arm Cover Bolts | 4-5 |
| | Silent Shaft Chamber Cover Bolts | 4-5 |
| | Silent Shaft Sprocket Bolt | 44-50 |
| | Spark Plug | 15-21 |
| | Thrust Plate Bolt | 7.5-8.5 |
| | Timing Chain Cover Bolts | 9-10 |
| | Torque Converter To Flex Plate | 42-46 |
| | Transaxle To Engine, Automatic | 31-39 |
| | Transaxle To Engine, Manual | 31-40 |
| | Turbocharger Oil Pipe Flare Nut | 13-17 |
| | Water Pump Pulley | 7.5-8.5 |
| | Water Pump To Timing Chain Case | 9-10 |

① —Refer to bolt tightening sequence. Bolt Nos. 1 to 10, 65–72 ft. lbs.; bolt No. 11, 11–15 ft. lbs.

② —Refer to bolt tightening sequence. Bolt Nos. 1 to 10, 73–79 ft. lbs.; bolt No. 11, 11–15 ft. lbs.

# Clutch, Manual Transaxle/Transmission & Transfer Assembly



## CLUTCH PEDAL
### ADJUST

Refer to **Fig. 1** for clutch pedal height, freeplay and pedal height at clutch release point specifications.

### CABLE RELEASE SYSTEM

1. Measure clutch pedal height (A), **Fig. 2.** If height is not within specifications, check pedal bracket for damage and wear and repair as needed.
2. Measure clutch pedal freeplay (B), **Fig. 2.**
3. If freeplay is not within specifications, turn outer cable adjusting nut at toeboard until clutch cable free play is within .20-.24 inch, **Fig. 3.**
4. Depress clutch pedal several times, then check clutch pedal to floorboard clearance at clutch release point (C), **Fig. 4.**
5. If clutch pedal to floorboard clearance at release point is less than specified, check clutch assembly and release mechanism and repair as needed.
6. **On Colt and Summit models,** ensure that when clutch pedal is depressed all the way, 5.9 inches, interlock switch switches over from On to Off, **Fig. 5.**
7. If necessary, loosen locknut and adjust.

### HYDRAULIC RELEASE SYSTEM

1. Measure clutch pedal height (A), **Fig. 2.**
2. If not within specifications, adjust as follows:
   a. **On models less cruise control,** loosen locknut and turn adjusting bolt to bring height within specifications.
   b. **On models with cruise control,** loosen locknut and turn clutch switch to bring height within specifications.
3. Measure clutch pedal clevis pin play (B), **Fig. 2,** should be .04-.12 inch.

| Year | Model | Pedal Height (A) Inch | Freeplay (B) Inch | Release Point (C) Inch① |
|---|---|---|---|---|
| 1989 | Conquest② | 7.4–7.6 | .2–.5 | 1.4 |
| 1989–90 | Colt & Summit | 6.70–6.89 | .24–.55 | 2.8 |
| | Colt Wagon | 6.3–6.5 | .24–.55 | 2.76 |
| 1989–91 | Colt Vista | 7.1–7.3 | .24–.51 | 2.17 |
| 1991–92 | Colt & Summit② | 6.61–6.73 | .24–.51 | 2.8 |
| | Colt & Summit③ | 6.61–6.73 | .80–1.18 | 3.2 |

①—Minimum.
②—Hydraulic release.
③—Cable release.

**Fig. 1 Clutch pedal adjustment specifications**

4. If not within specifications, adjust clutch master cylinder push rod as necessary to bring play within specifications. **Do not press push rod into master cylinder when adjusting clevis pin clearance.**
5. **On Colt and Summit models,** ensure that when clutch pedal is depressed all the way, 5.9 inches, interlock switch switches over from On to Off, **Fig. 5.** If necessary, loosen locknut and adjust.
6. **On all models,** measure clutch pedal free play (B), **Fig. 2,** and clutch pedal to floorboard clearance at clutch release point (C), **Fig. 4.**
7. If clearance and/or free play are not within specifications, hydraulic system requires bleeding or clutch is faulty.

## CLUTCH
### REPLACE

1. Remove transmission or transaxle as described under "Manual Transmission/Transaxle, Replace."
2. With suitable clutch disc guide inserted in center hole to prevent clutch disc from dropping, evenly loosen bolts holding clutch cover assembly in a crossing pattern, then remove clutch cover assembly.
3. Remove clutch disc.
4. Reverse procedure to install, noting the following:
   a. Clean surface of flywheel thoroughly with fine sandpaper or crocus cloth and ensure that all oil or greasee has been removed.
   b. Apply a small amount of multi-purpose grease to clutch disc and input shaft splines and groove of release bearing.
   c. Torque clutch cover bolts to specifications.

## SLAVE CYLINDER
### REPLACE

1. Drain clutch fluid, then disconnect hydraulic line.
2. **On Colt, Colt Wagon and Summit models with 1.5L/4-89.6 or 1.6L/4-97.4 except Turbo engines,** remove snap ring and clevis pin securing slave cylinder to clutch fork.
3. **On all models,** remove attaching bolts, then the slave cylinder.
4. Reverse procedure to install, noting the following:
   a. Apply multi-purpose greasee to clevis pin or push rod contact surfaces as equipped.
   b. Torque attaching bolts to specifications.
   c. Bleed hydraulic system and adjust clutch pedal.

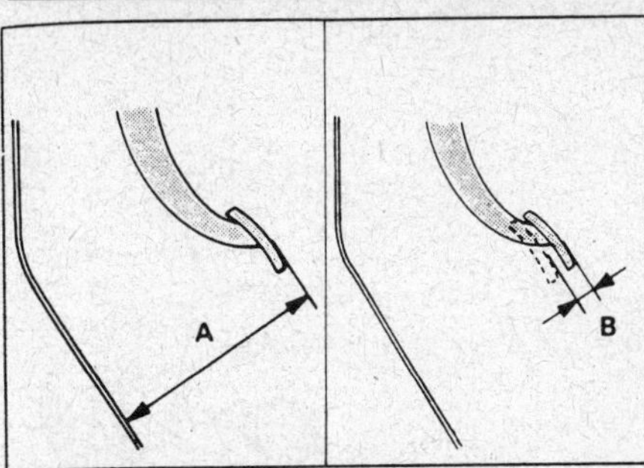


**Fig. 2 Clutch pedal height (A), freeplay & clevis pin play (B) measurements**

## CLUTCH BLEED PROCEDURE

1. Connect a suitable hose to bleeder screw at slave cylinder, then loosen bleeder screw.
2. Push pedal down slowly until all air is expelled, hold clutch pedal down until bleeder screw is retightened.
3. Refill master cylinder as necessary.

## MANUAL TRANSMISSION /TRANSAXLE

## REPLACE

### COLT & SUMMIT

Refer to **Fig. 6** during replacement procedures.

1. Disconnect battery ground cable, then remove the battery and battery tray.
2. Remove air cleaner assembly, then the air pipe and air hose on turbocharged models.
3. Drain transaxle oil, then remove tension rod on 1.6L/4-97.4 engines.
4. Disconnect clutch cable or slave cylinder as equipped and secure at body side, then the backup lamp switch electrical connector and speedometer cable.
5. Remove starter motor, transaxle upper attaching bolts, transaxle mounting bracket and under cover.
6. Disconnect tie rod ends and lower ball joints using steering linkage puller MB990635 or equivalent, then remove drive shafts as follows:
   a. **On models less turbocharger,** insert a pry bar between transaxle case and drive shaft and pry drive shaft from transaxle. Secure to body with wire.
   b. **On models with turbocharger lefthand side,** disconnect drive shaft and inner shaft assembly by tapping on tripod joint case with a plastic hammer. Secure to body with wire. **Do not tap on center bearing, damage may result.**
   c. **On models with turbocharger righthand side,** refer to step 6a.
7. **On all models,** remove bell housing cover and transaxle lower attaching bolts.

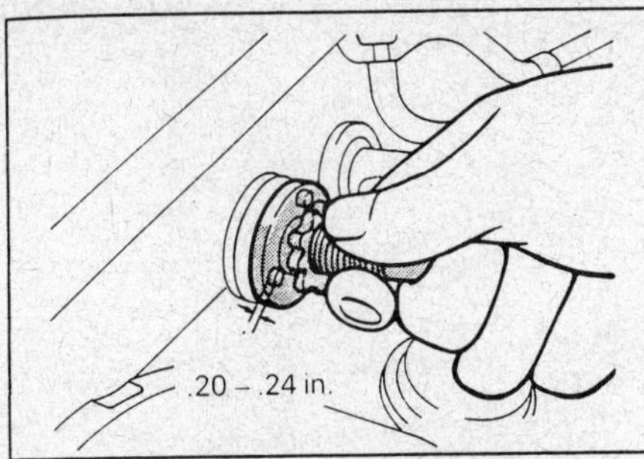


**Fig. 3 Clutch cable adjustment**

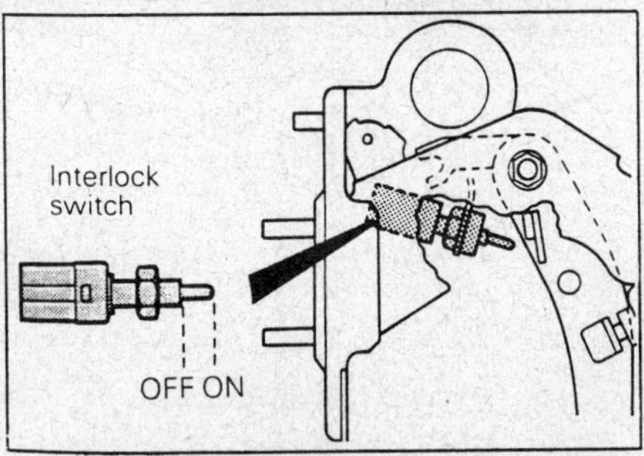


**Fig. 5 Checking interlock switch adjustment. Colt & Summit**

8. Support transaxle assembly on a suitable transaxle jack, then move assembly to right, lower and remove from vehicle.
9. Reverse procedure to install. Torque attaching bolts to specifications.

### COLT VISTA

Refer to **Fig. 7** during replacement procedures.

#### 2WD Models

1. Remove hood and righthand under cover, then drain transaxle oil and clutch fluid.
2. Remove drain and filler plugs, then disconnect main fusible link from battery tray.
3. Remove battery, battery tray and under bracket.
4. Remove air cleaner assembly, then disconnect clutch slave cylinder hydraulic line, if equipped.
5. Disconnect clutch cable, if equipped, speedometer cable and back-up lamp wiring harness from transaxle.
6. Disconnect electrical connectors from starter, then remove starter and upper transaxle to engine attaching bolts.
7. Remove dust cover, then disconnect stabilizer and righthand strut bars.
8. Insert two large screwdrivers between transaxle case and drive shaft and pry drive shaft from transaxle. Secure to body with wire.
9. Remove bell housing cover, then attach a chain to engine hooks and lift engine enough to relieve pressure on mounting bracket insulators, support transaxle with a suitable transaxle jack and remove mounting bracket.
10. Slide transaxle assembly to right, lower and remove from vehicle.
11. Reverse procedure to install. Bleed clutch hydraulic system, if equipped and torque attaching bolts to specifications.

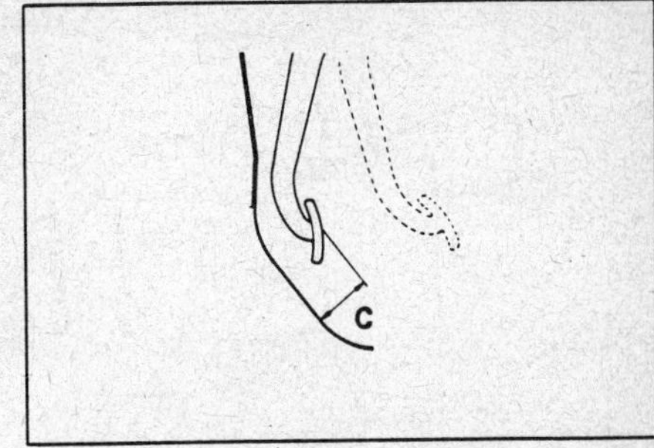


**Fig. 4 Clutch release point measurement**

#### 4WD Models

Engine and transaxle must be removed as an assembly. Refer to **Fig. 8** when removing transaxle from engine.

1. Remove engine and transaxle assembly as described under "Engine, Replace in "2.0L/4-121.9 Engine" section, then remove transaxle from engine as follows:
   a. Remove select control valve and vacuum tank assembly, then disconnect back up light switch, select switch and engage switch electrical connectors.
   b. Remove actuator and starter motor, then the bell housing cover.
   c. Remove transaxle to engine attaching bolts, then separate transaxle from engine.
2. Reverse procedure to install. Torque attaching bolts to specifications.

### COLT WAGON

#### 2WD Models

Refer to **Fig. 9** during replacement procedures.

1. Remove righthand under cover, then drain transaxle oil and clutch fluid.
2. Remove drain and filler plugs, then the air cleaner, battery and battery tray.
3. Disconnect clutch slave cylinder hydraulic line, shift cable, select cable, back-up light electrical connector, ground cable and speedometer cable.
4. Remove starter motor, then disconnect stabilizer bar.
5. Disconnect tie rod ends and lower ball joints using steering linkage puller MB991113 or equivalent, then insert a pry bar between transaxle case and drive shaft and pry drive shaft from transaxle. Secure to body with wire.
6. Mark bottom of roll rod for reference during re-installation, then remove.
7. Support transaxle assembly on a suitable transaxle jack, remove mount bracket, then move assembly to right, lower and remove from vehicle.
8. Reverse procedure to install. Torque attaching bolts to specifications.

#### 4WD Models

Engine and transaxle must be removed as an assembly.

1. Tension rod
2. Control cable connection
3. Clutch cable connection
   <Cable control type>
4. Clutch release cylinder connection
   <Hydraulic control type>
5. Backup lamp switch connector connection
6. Speedometer cable connection
7. Starter motor
8. Transaxle assembly upper connecting bolt
9. Transaxle mounting bracket
10. Under cover
11. Tie rod end connection
12. Lower arm ball joint connection
13. Drive shaft connection
14. Drive shaft and inner shaft assembly connection
15. Bell housing cover
16. Transaxle assembly lower connecting bolt
17. Transaxle assembly

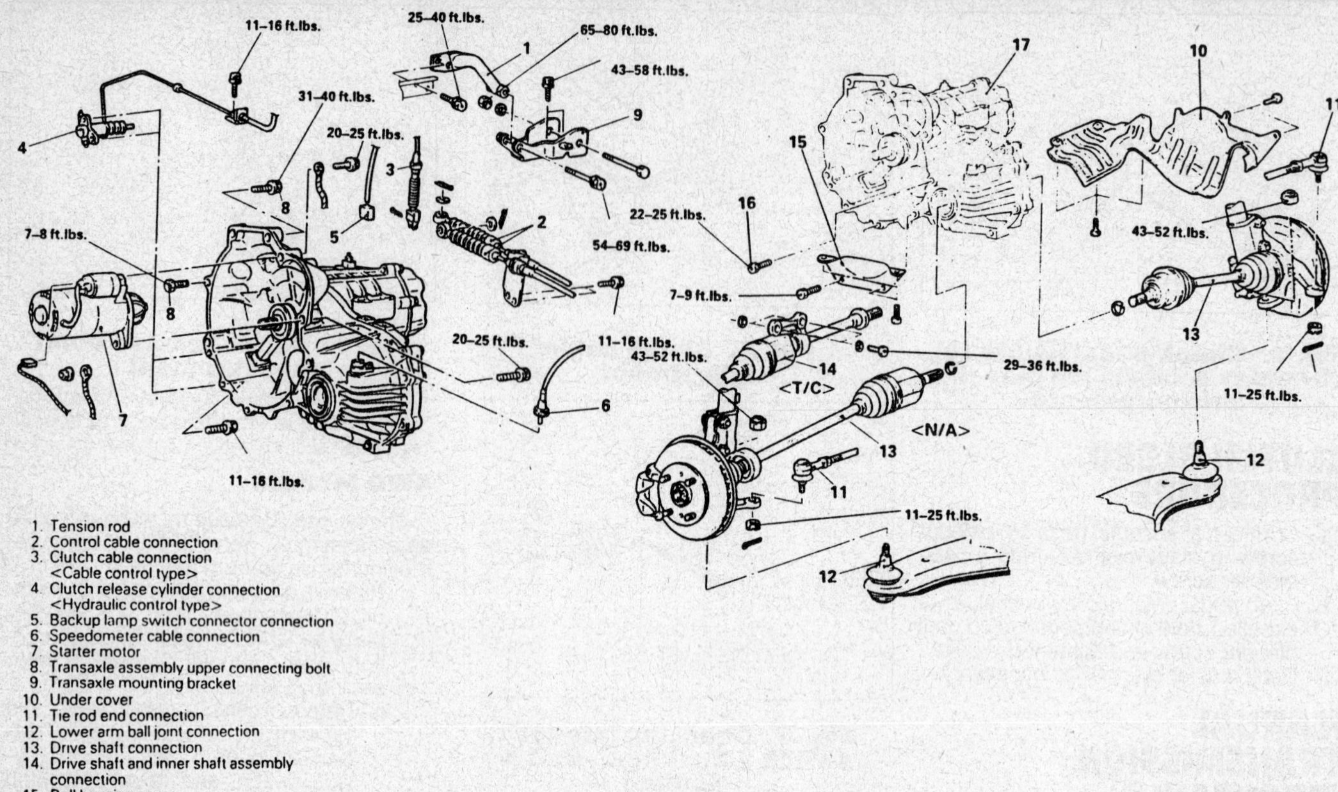

**Fig. 6 Transaxle assembly removal. Colt & Summit**

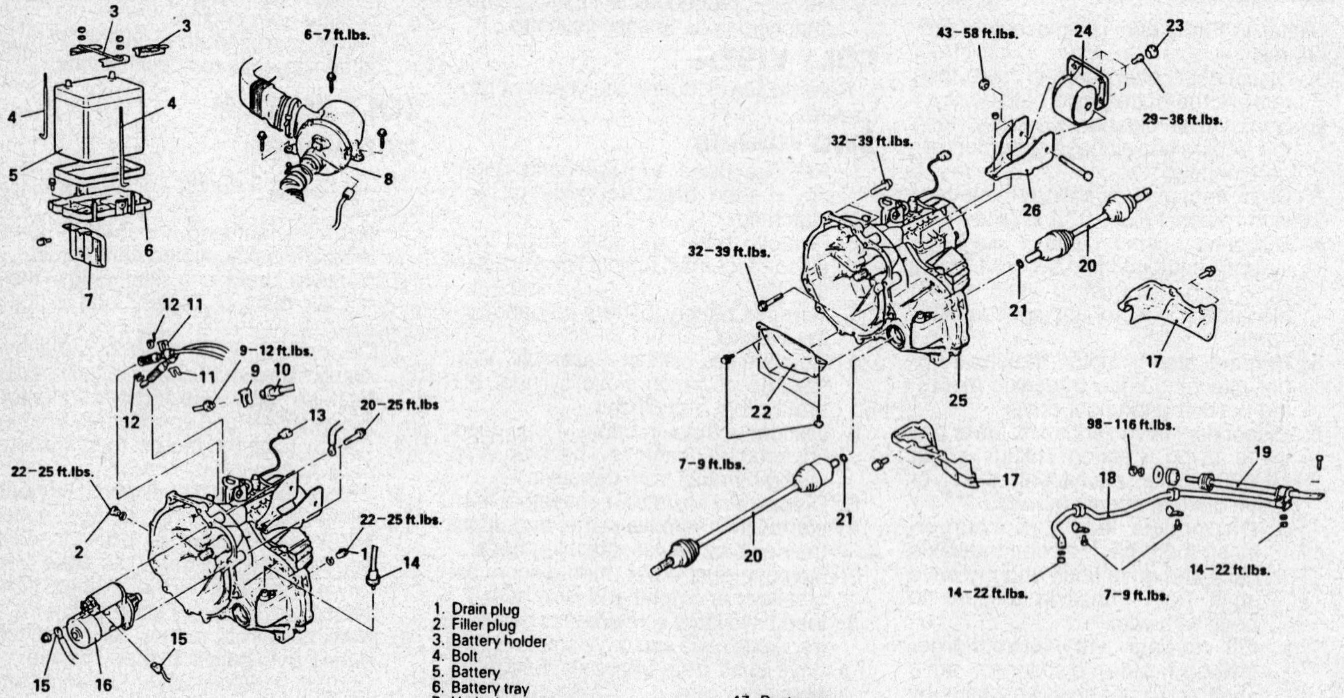

1. Drain plug
2. Filler plug
3. Battery holder
4. Bolt
5. Battery
6. Battery tray
7. Under bracket
8. Air cleaner case assembly
9. Clip
10. Clutch tube connection
11. Clip
12. Cotter pin
13. Back up light switch harness connection
14. Speedometer cable connection
15. Starter motor harness connection
16. Starter motor
17. Dust cover
18. Stabilizer
19. Strut bar (R.H.)
20. Drive shaft
21. Circlip
22. Bell housing cover
23. Cap
24. Transaxle mounting bracket
25. Transaxle assembly
26. Transaxle bracket

**Fig. 7 Transaxle assembly removal. 2WD Colt Vista**

1. Engine and Transaxle
2. Select control valve and vacuum tank assembly
3. Back up light switch connector connection
4. Select switch connector connection
5. Engage switch connector connection
6. Actuator
7. Starter motor
8. Bell housing cover
9. Transaxle assembly

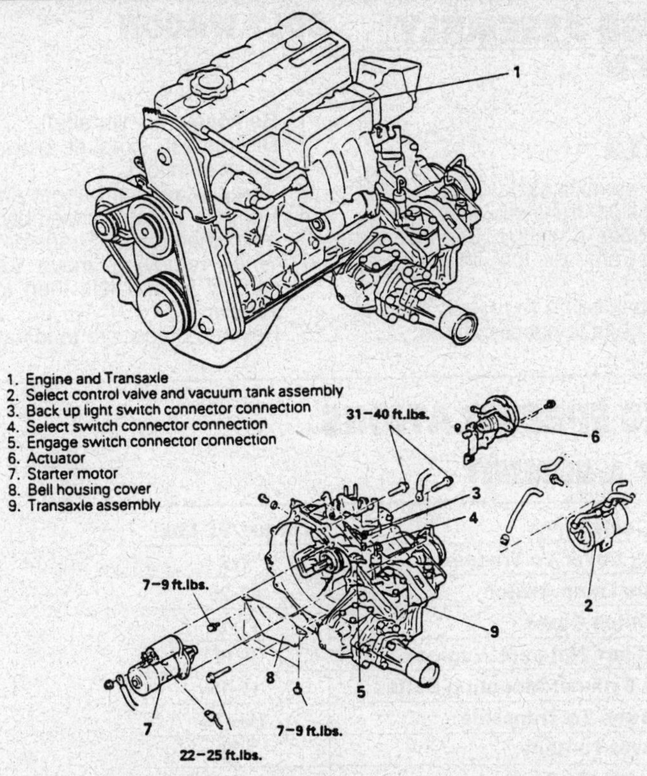

**Fig. 8 Transaxle assembly removal. 4WD Colt Vista**

1. Remove engine and transaxle assembly as described under "Engine, Replace in "1.8L/4-107 Engine" section, then remove transaxle from engine as follows:
   a. Remove transaxle to engine attaching bolts, then separate transaxle from engine.
2. Reverse procedure to install. Torque attaching bolts to specifications.

## CONQUEST

1. Disconnect battery ground cable.
2. Remove gearshift lever assembly as follows:
   a. Remove gearshift knob, spool release levers and rear console box trim plate.
   b. Remove rear console liner and the rear console box.
   c. Remove console side covers, front console box and shift boot retainer ring.
   d. Ensure shifter is in neutral, remove bolts securing gearshift assembly, disconnect stopper plate from extension housing, then lift gearshift assembly off extension housing.
3. Place a suitable insulator at rear of cylinder head to prevent damage, then raise and support vehicle.
4. Drain transmission, then remove propeller shaft.

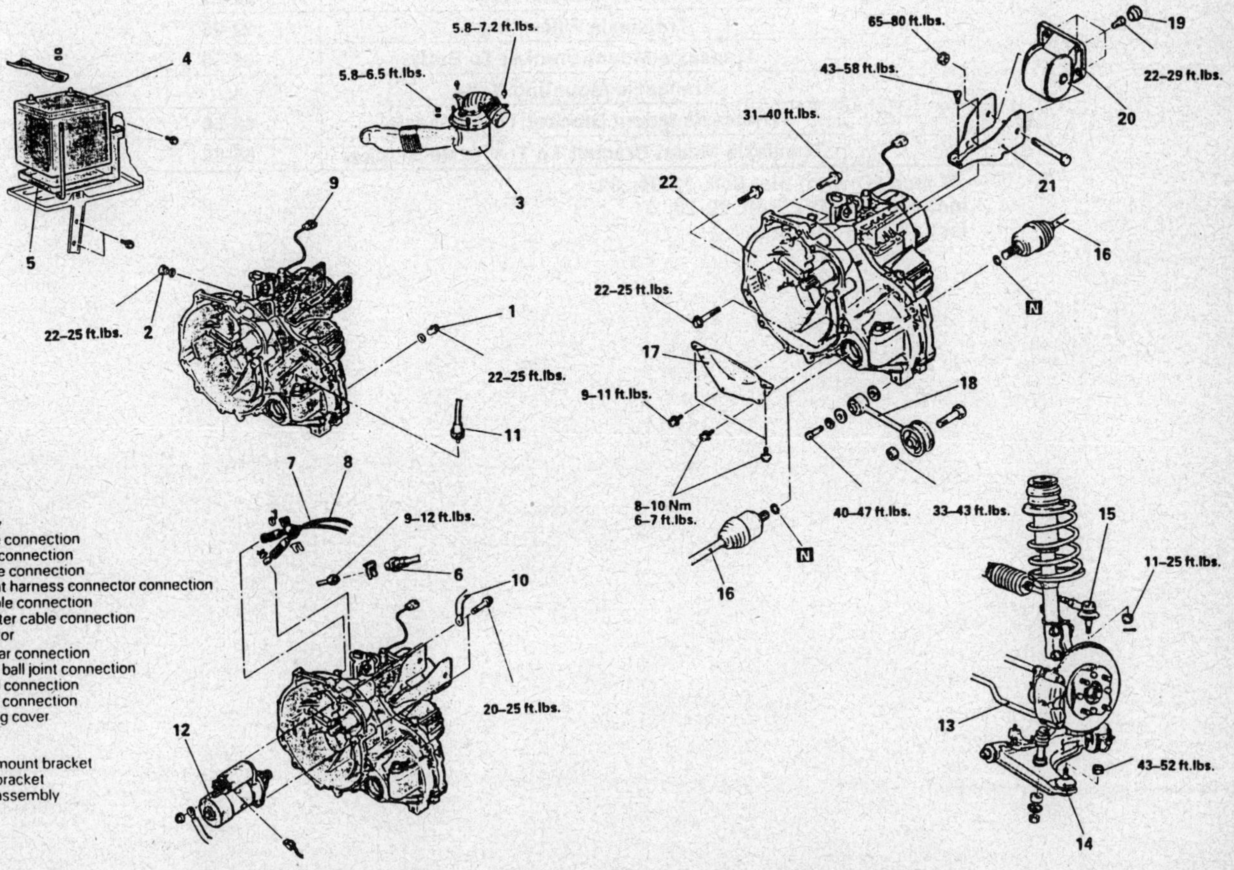

1. Drain plug
2. Filler plug
3. Air cleaner
4. Battery
5. Battery tray
6. Clutch tube connection
7. Shift cable connection
8. Select cable connection
9. Backup light harness connector connection
10. Ground cable connection
11. Speedometer cable connection
12. Starter motor
13. Stabilizer bar connection
14. Lower arm ball joint connection
15. Tie rod end connection
16. Drive shaft connection
17. Bell housing cover
18. Roll rod
19. Cap
20. Transaxle mount bracket
21. Transaxle bracket
22. Transaxle assembly

**Fig. 9 Transaxle assembly removal. 2WD Colt Wagon**

5. Disconnect speedometer cable and back-up light switch wiring harness.
6. Remove clutch release cylinder, bell-housing cover and starter motor.
7. Using suitable jack, support transmission.
8. Remove transmission to engine attaching bolts.
9. Remove engine support bracket, insulator assembly, and ground cable.
10. Lower jack and remove transmission from under vehicle.
11. Reverse procedure to install. Torque attaching bolts to specifications.

## TRANSFER ASSEMBLY REPLACE

### COLT VISTA

1. Remove transaxle as described under "Transmission/transaxle, Replace.
2. Remove bolts attaching transfer assembly to transaxle, then the transfer assembly.
3. Reverse procedure to install. Torque attaching bolts to specifications.

### COLT WAGON

1. Remove propeller shaft.
2. Disconnect exhaust pipe from exhaust manifold.
3. Remove transfer hanger and bracket.
4. Remove transfer assembly attaching bolts, then remove transfer assembly. When removing, move transfer assembly toward left, then lower from vehicle.
5. Reverse procedure to install.

## TIGHTENING SPECIFICATIONS

### COLT & SUMMIT

| Year | Component | Torque/Ft. Lbs. |
|---|---|---|
| 1989–92 | Bell Housing Cover To Transaxle | 7-9 |
| | Backup Lamp Switch | 22-25 |
| | Clutch Cover | 11-15 |
| | Clutch Tube Flare Nut (1.6L Engine) | 9-12 |
| | Clutch Release Cylinder Mounting Bolts | 11-15 |
| | Clutch Tube To Transaxle | 11—16 |
| | Lever To Body | 7-10 |
| | Shift Lever To Bracket | 14-20 |
| | Speedometer Sleeve Bolt | 2.5-3.5 |
| | Starter Mounting Bolts | 20-25 |
| | Transaxle Case Tightening Bolt | 26-30 |
| | Transaxle Drain Plug | 22-25 |
| | Transaxle Filler Plug | 22-25 |
| | Transaxle Mount Bracket To Body | 65-80 |
| | Transaxle Mounting Bolts | ① |
| | Transaxle Mount Bracket To Transaxle | 43-58 |
| | Transaxle Mount Bracket To Transaxle Bracket | 65-80 |

①—.47 inch (12 mm) Dia. Bolt, 32–39; .39 inch (10 mm) Dia. Bolt, 22–25; .31 inch (8 mm) Dia. Bolt, 7–9.

*Continued*

# TIGHTENING SPECIFICATIONS—Continued

## COLT WAGON 2WD

| Year | Component | Torque/Ft. Lbs. |
|---|---|---|
| 1989–90 | Backup Lamp Switch | 22-25 |
| | Bellhousing Installation Bolt | ① |
| | Clutch Cover | 11-15 |
| | Clutch Release Cylinder Mounting Bolts | 11-15 |
| | Clutch Release Cylinder To Union Bolt | 14—18 |
| | Clutch Tube Flare Nut | 9-12 |
| | Lever To Body | 7-10 |
| | Roll Rod To Roll Rod Bracket | 33-43 |
| | Roll Rod To Transaxle | 43-51 |
| | Shift Lever To Bracket | 14-20 |
| | Speedometer Sleeve Bolt | 2.5-3.5 |
| | Starter Mounting Bolts | 20-25 |
| | Transaxle Case Tightening Bolt | 26-30 |
| | Transaxle Mount Bolt | ② |
| | Transaxle Mount Bracket To Body | 22-29 |
| | Transaxle Mount Bracket To Transaxle | 43-58 |

①—.31 inch (8 mm) Dia. Bolt, 9–11; .23 inch (6 mm) Dia. Bolt, 6–7.

②—.31 inch (8 mm) Dia. Bolt, 31-40; .39 inch (10 mm) Dia. Bolt, 22–25.

## COLT WAGON 4WD

| Year | Component | Torque/Ft. Lbs. |
|---|---|---|
| 1989–90 | Backup Lamp Switch | 22-25 |
| | Bellhousing Cover Mounting Bolts | 4-7 |
| | Engine To Transaxle Mounting Bolt | ① |
| | Extension Housing Mounting Bolt | 11-15 |
| | Oil Filler Plug | 22-25 |
| | Oil Drain Plug | 22-25 |
| | Shift Cable Bracket Mounting Bolt | 11-15 |
| | Speedometer Mounting Bolt | 2.5-3.5 |
| | Starter Mounting Bolts | 16-23 |
| | Transaxle Case Mounting Bolts | 26-30 |
| | Transfer Axle Mount Bracket Mounting Bolt | 43-57 |
| | Transfer Case Adapter Mounting Bolt | 26-30 |
| | Transfer Case Mounting Bolts | 40-43 |
| | Transfer Cover Mounting Bolt | 11-15 |

①—.39 inch (10 mm) Dia. Bolt, 32-39; .31 inch (8 mm) Dia. Bolt, 16-23; .23 inch (6 mm) Dia. Bolt, 8-9.

## COLT VISTA 2WD

| Year | Component | Torque/Ft. Lbs. |
|---|---|---|
| 1989–91 | Backup Lamp Switch | 22-25 |
| | Bellhousing Cover Bolts | 7-9 |
| | Clutch Tube Flare Nut | 9-12 |
| | Oil Filler Plug | 22-25 |
| | Oil Drain Plug | 22-25 |
| | Shift Lever To Bracket | 14-20 |
| | Speedometer Sleeve Bolt | 2.5-3.5 |
| | Starter Mounting Bolts | 20-25 |
| | Transaxle Bracket | 29-36 |
| | Transaxle Mounting Bracket | 20-25 |
| | Transaxle To Engine | 43-58 |

*Continued*

## TIGHTENING SPECIFICATIONS—Continued

### COLT VISTA 4WD

| Year | Component | Torque/Ft. Lbs. |
|---|---|---|
| 1989–91 | Backup Lamp Switch | 22-25 |
| | Bellhousing Cover Mounting Bolts | 7-9 |
| | Clutch Tube Flare Nut | 9-12 |
| | Extension Housing | 11-15 |
| | Indicator Lamp Switch | 22 |
| | Oil Filler Plug | 22-25 |
| | Oil Drain Plug | 22-25 |
| | Shift Lever To Bracket | 14-20 |
| | Transaxle Extension Stopper Bracket | 22-29 |
| | Transaxle Mounting Bracket | 40-43 |
| | Transfer Case Bolts | |

### CONQUEST

| Year | Component | Torque/Ft. Lbs. |
|---|---|---|
| 1989 | Backup Lamp Switch | 22 |
| | Clutch To Flywheel | 11-15 |
| | Clutch Tube Flare Nut | 9.4-12.3 |
| | Oil Drain Plug | 26-32 |
| | Oil Filler Plug | 22-25 |
| | Propeller Shaft Flange Yoke Attaching Bolts | 36-40 |
| | Rear Engine Mount To Transmission Bolt | 14-17 |
| | Rear Engine Mount To Body Bolt | 7 |
| | Release Cylinder To Transmission Case | 22-30 |
| | Starter Bolts | 16-23 |
| | Transmission Mounting Bolts | 31-40 |
| | Transmission To Engine | 32-39 |

# Rear Axle & Suspension

Page No.



## REAR AXLE REPLACE

### COLT WAGON w/4WD

1. Raise and support rear of vehicle at body, then remove wheel and tire assembly. Support rear axle using a suitable jack.
2. Disconnect propeller shaft from rear axle companion flange, **Fig. 1.**
3. Remove brake drums, then remove brake shoes.
4. Disconnect parking brake cables from rear axle housing and parking brake levers.
5. Remove stabilizer bar link nuts.
6. Remove stabilizer bar bracket bolts, then remove stabilizer bar.
7. Remove load sensing proportioning valve bracket bolt.
8. Remove shock absorber lower attaching bolts.
9. Remove lateral rod to axle housing attaching bolt.
10. Disconnect brake line fittings from rear axle.
11. Remove upper and lower arm to axle housing attaching bolts.
12. Carefully lower rear axle assembly and remove coil springs.

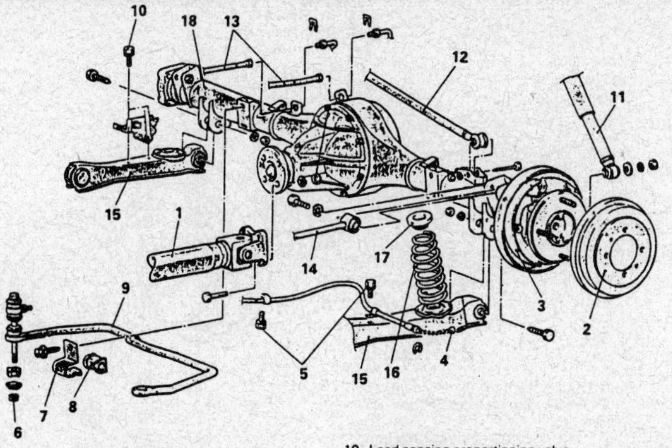

1. Propeller shaft
2. Brake drum
3. Shoe assembly
4. Parking brake cable connection
5. Parking brake cable attaching bolt
6. Self-locking nut
7. Fixture
8. Bushing
9. Stabilizer bar
10. Load sensing proportioning valve bracket mounting bolt
11. Shock absorber connection
12. Lateral rod connection
13. Rear brake tube connection
14. Upper arm connection
15. Lower arm connection
16. Coil spring
17. Spring seat
18. Axle assembly

**Fig. 1 Rear axle & suspension. Colt Wagon w/4WD**

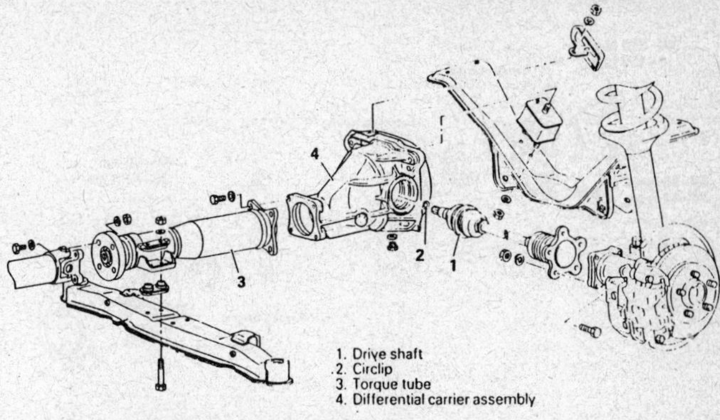


**Fig. 2 Drive axle replacement. Conquest**

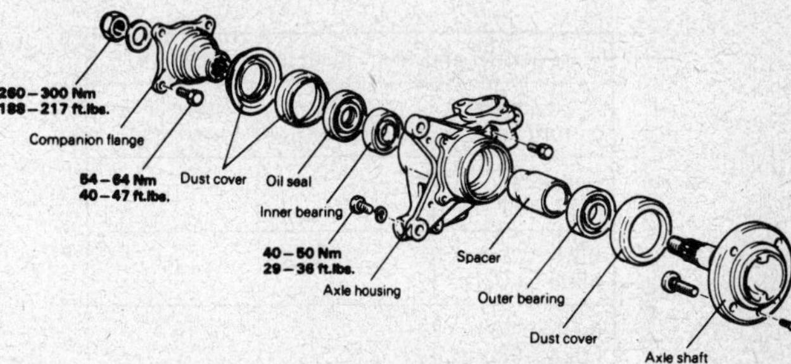


**Fig. 4 Axle housing exploded view. Conquest**

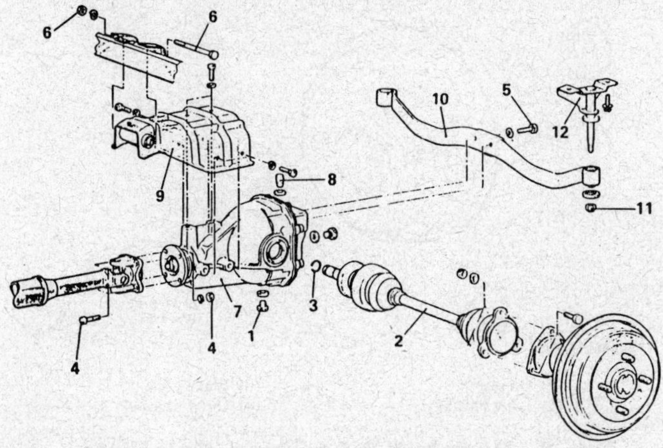

1. Drain plug
2. Drive shaft
3. Circlip
4. Rear propeller shaft and differential carrier coupling bolt and nut
5. Differential carrier rear mounting bolt
6. Differential carrier front mounting bolt and nut
7. Differential carrier
8. Vent plug
9. Differential front support bracket
10. Differential rear support
11. differential rear support mounting nut
12. Differential mount stopper

**Fig. 3 Drive axle replacement. Colt Vista w/4WD**

13. Remove rear axle assembly from vehicle.
14 Reverse procedure to install.

# DIFFERENTIAL ASSEMBLY

## REPLACE

### CONQUEST

1. Drain gear oil into suitable container.
2. Remove drive axles, **Fig. 2.**
3. Remove torque tube as follows:
   a. Remove driveshaft.
   b. Apply parking brake, then loosen torque tube companion flange attaching nut. Loosen nut only. Do not remove.
   c. Remove torque tube to differential attaching bolts, then the torque tube to front support attaching bolts.
   d. Using a suitable slide hammer, remove extension shaft spline from spline coupling.
   e. Remove slide hammer, then pull torque tube assembly out towards rear.
4. Remove rear support insulator to crossmember attaching nuts, then the rear support to rear support insulator attaching nuts.
5. Raise differential carrier assembly with suitable jack, then disconnect differential carrier from rear support insulators.
6. Remove carrier.
7. Reverse procedure to install.

### COLT VISTA w/4WD

1. Drain gear oil into suitable container.
2. Remove drive axles, **Fig. 3.**
3. Disconnect driveshaft from companion flange.
4. Remove differential front support bracket to crossmember attaching bolt.
5. Remove differential rear support to differential carrier attaching bolts, then remove differential carrier.
6. Remove front support bracket and differential cover.
7. Reverse procedure to install.

# REAR AXLE SHAFT & BEARING

## REPLACE

### CONQUEST

1. Raise and support rear of vehicle.
2. Remove rear wheel and tire assembly, then disconnect parking brake cable from rear brake caliper.
3. Remove rear caliper assembly, caliper support and rotor. Support caliper assembly with suitable piece of wire to prevent damage to brake hose.
4. Remove four drive axle to companion flange attaching bolts, then disconnect the drive axle.
5. Remove axle housing from lower control arm and strut assembly.
6. Position axle housing in suitable vise, then loosen companion flange nut and washer.
7. Using suitable hammer free axle shaft from bearings, then remove nut, companion flange and axle shaft, **Fig. 4.**

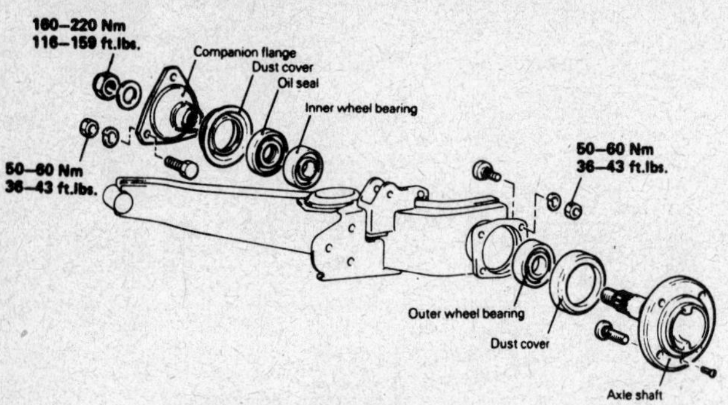


**Fig. 5 Axle housing exploded view. Colt Vista w/4WD**

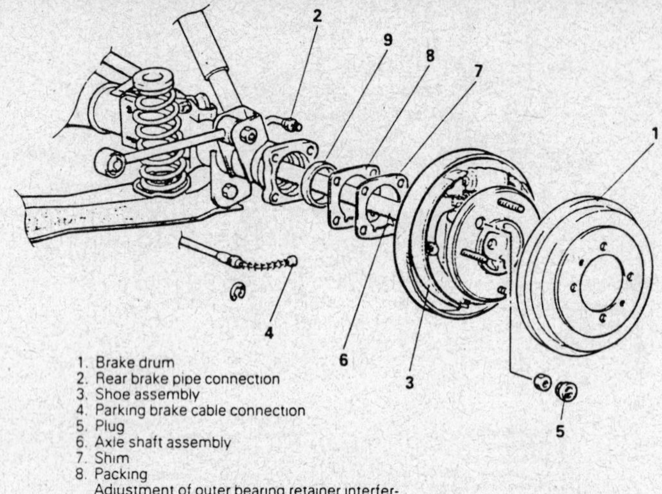


**Fig. 6 Rear axle shaft & bearing. Colt Wagon w/4WD**

| Packing and shim selection procedure | | |
|---|---|---|
| Clearance mm (in.) | Number of packings | Number of shims |
| Less than 0.2 (.008) | 0 | 0 |
| 0.2 to 0.5 (.008 to .02) | 1 | 0 |
| 0.5 to 0.75 (.02 to .03) | 2 | 0 |
| 0.75 to 1.0 (.03 to .04) | 2 | 1 |
| 1.00 to 1.25 (.04 to .05) | 2 | 2 |

**Fig. 7 Rear axle bearing shim & packing selection chart. Colt Wagon w/4WD**

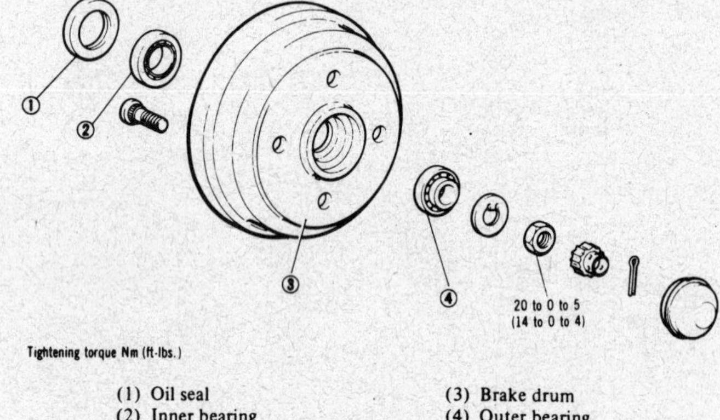


**Fig. 8 Rear hub & bearings. Colt Vista**

8. Remove dust covers, then using spanner wrench tool No. C-4381 and bearing puller tool No. C-293-PA, remove rear axle bearings.
9. Press fit new outer bearing to axle shaft. The seal side of outer bearing should face the flange side of the axle shaft.
10. Apply suitable greasee to axle housing inside surface, then press fit inner bearing with seal side facing companion flange.
11. Install oil seal with suitable seal installer until seal contacts edge of axle housing.
12. Install axle housing, the apply suitable oil to seal lip.
13. Assemble axle housing using **Fig. 4** for reference.
14. Measure axle axial endplay with dial indicator. If endplay exceeds .031 inch, replace bearing.

## COLT VISTA W/4WD

1. Raise and support rear of vehicle.
2. Remove rear wheel and tire assembly, then the brake drum.
3. Remove three bolts securing drive axle to companion flange, then disconnect drive axle.
4. Remove companion flange nut and washer, **Fig. 5**.
5. Using suitable axle puller, remove axle shaft from inner arm.
6. Remove inner arm from rear suspension.
7. Using suitable press, remove dust covers and wheel bearings from axle shaft and inner arm.
8. Install replacement outer dust cover on axle shaft using suitable tool and plastic hammer. Install dust cover with concave side facing towards companion flange side of axle shaft.
9. Apply suitable greasee to outer bearing seal inner lip circumference, the install outer bearing with suitable press. Install bearing with seal surface facing companion flange side of axle shaft.
10. Using suitable press, install replacement inner bearing in inner arm, then using suitable seal installer and plastic hammer, install replacement oil seal.
11. Press axle shaft into inner arm.
12. Assemble axle housing using **Fig. 5** for reference.
13. Measure axle axial endplay with dial indicator. If endplay exceeds .031 inch, replace bearing.

## 1989–91 COLT WAGON W/4WD

1. Raise and support rear of vehicle, then remove wheel and tire assembly.
2. Remove rear brake drum, then remove brake shoes.
3. Disconnect brake line from wheel cylinder. Cap brake line and wheel cylinder fitting.
4. Disconnect parking brake cable from lever at backing plate.
5. Through holes in axle shaft flange remove bearing retainer attaching nuts, **Fig. 6**.
6. Using tool a suitable puller, remove axle shaft from rear axle housing.
7. Press bearing assembly from axle shaft as necessary.
8. Using a suitable puller, remove oil seal from axle housing as necessary.
9. Reverse procedure to install. When installing replacement oil seal, apply suitable greasee to axle housing to seal contact area. Also apply greasee to oil seal lip. Install seal using bearing installer tool Nos. MB990938 and MB990935 or equivalent. Prior to in-

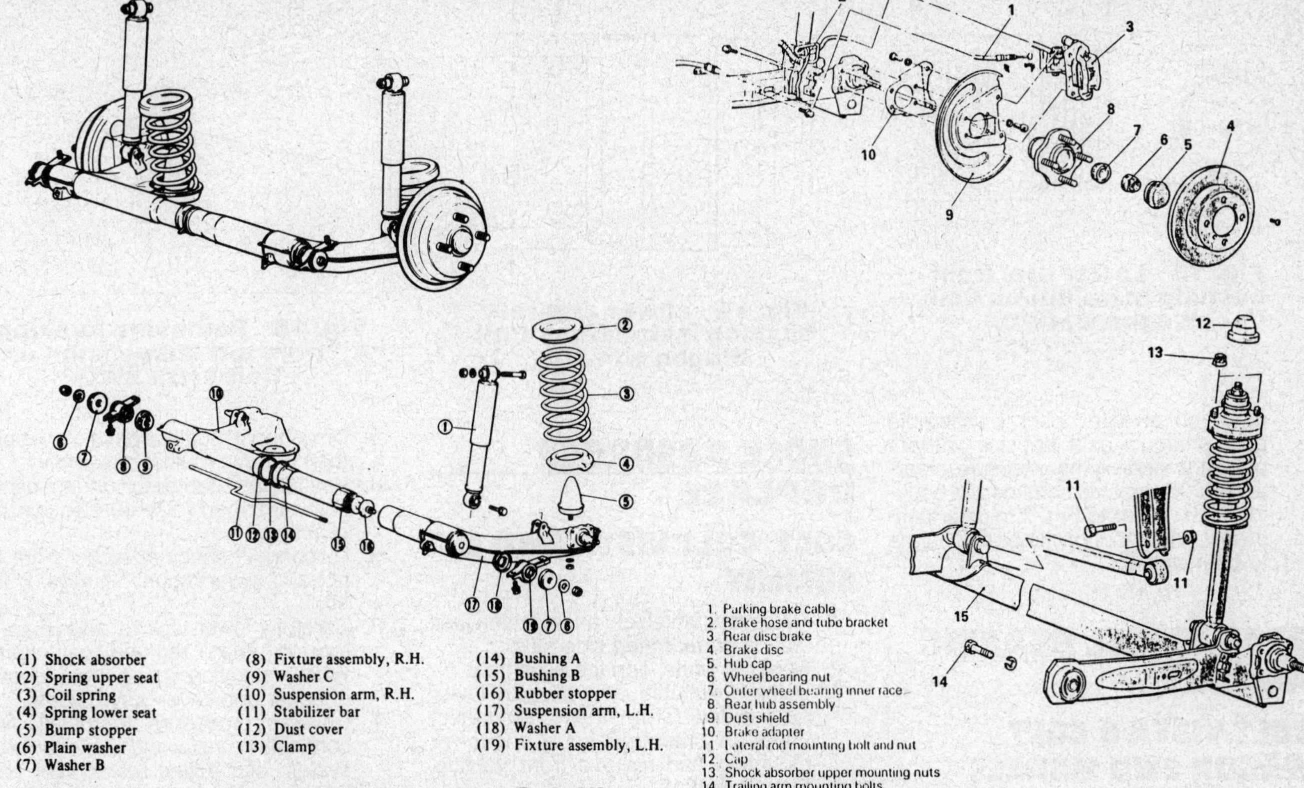

(1) Shock absorber
(2) Spring upper seat
(3) Coil spring
(4) Spring lower seat
(5) Bump stopper
(6) Plain washer
(7) Washer B
(8) Fixture assembly, R.H.
(9) Washer C
(10) Suspension arm, R.H.
(11) Stabilizer bar
(12) Dust cover
(13) Clamp
(14) Bushing A
(15) Bushing B
(16) Rubber stopper
(17) Suspension arm, L.H.
(18) Washer A
(19) Fixture assembly, L.H.

**Fig. 9 Coil spring rear suspension. Colt Vista 2WD**

1. Parking brake cable
2. Brake hose and tube bracket
3. Rear disc brake
4. Brake disc
5. Hub cap
6. Wheel bearing nut
7. Outer wheel bearing inner race
8. Rear hub assembly
9. Dust shield
10. Brake adapter
11. Lateral rod mounting bolt and nut
12. Cap
13. Shock absorber upper mounting nuts
14. Trailing arm mounting bolts
15. Rear suspension assembly

**Fig. 10 Coil spring rear suspension. 1989–91 Colt Hatchback & Sedan & Summit**

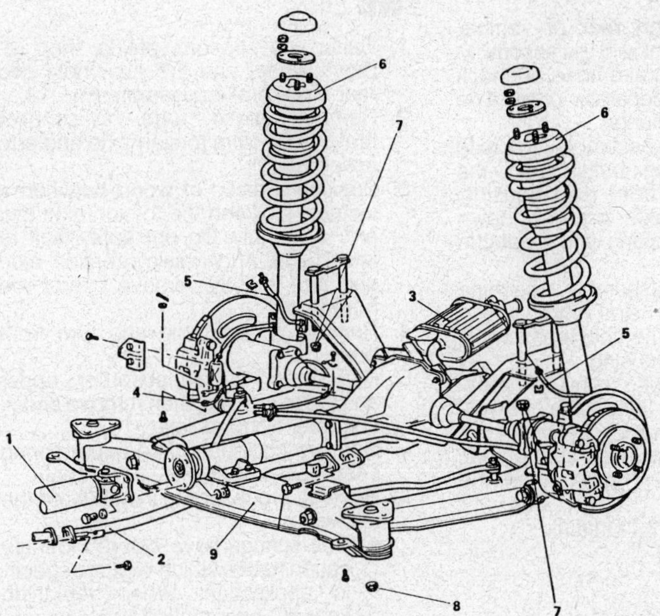

1. Propeller shaft
2. Center exhaust pipe
3. Main muffler
   Parking brake cable adjustment
4. Parking brake cable connection
5. Rear brake hose connection
6. Strut assembly connection
7. Crossmember mounting nut (Self-locking nut)
8. Pin assembly to front support mounting nut (Self-locking nut)
9. Suspension assembly

**Fig. 11 Coil spring rear suspension. Conquest**

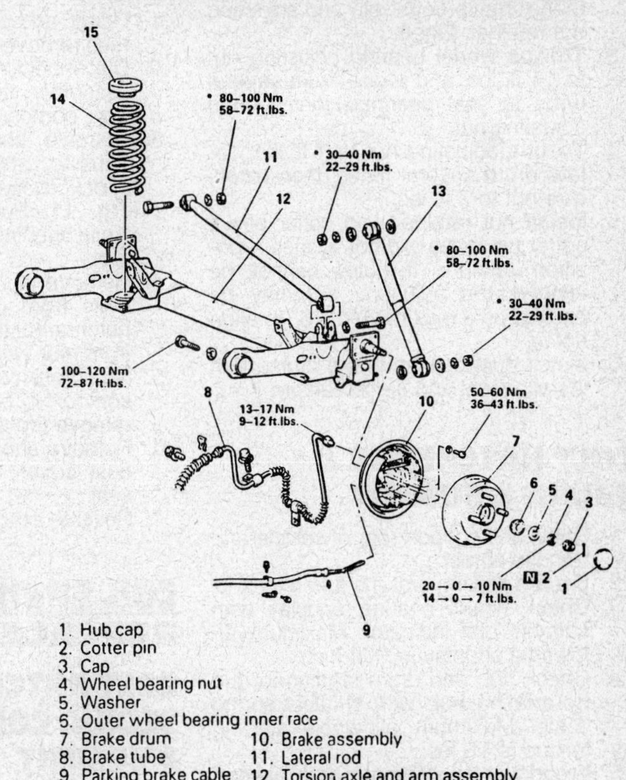


1. Hub cap
2. Cotter pin
3. Cap
4. Wheel bearing nut
5. Washer
6. Outer wheel bearing inner race
7. Brake drum
8. Brake tube
9. Parking brake cable
10. Brake assembly
11. Lateral rod
12. Torsion axle and arm assembly
13. Shock absorber assembly
14. Coil spring
15. Upper spring seat

**Fig. 12 Coil spring rear suspension. Colt Wagon 2WD**

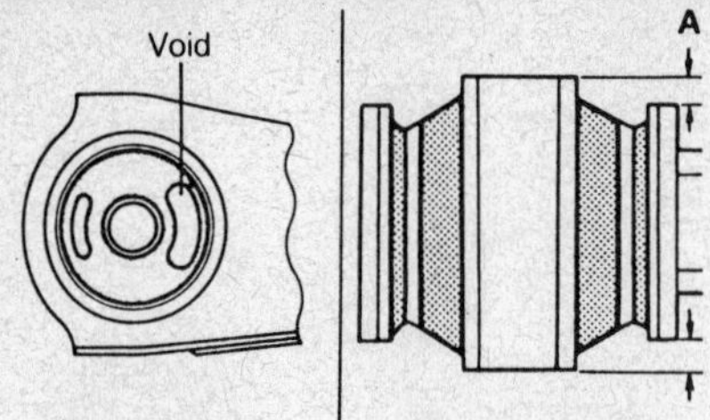


Fig. 13 Lower arm front bushing installation. Colt Wagon w/4WD.

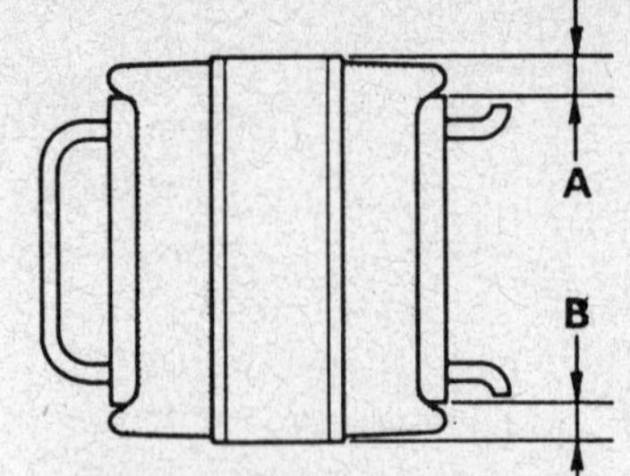


Fig. 14 Lower arm rear bushing installation. Colt Wagon w/4 WD

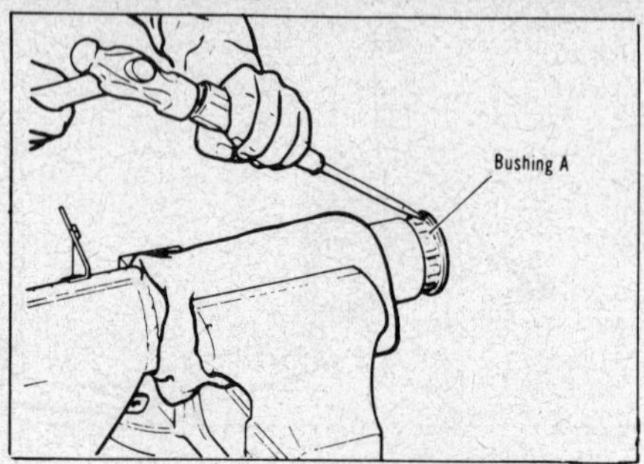


Fig. 15 Removing bushing "A" from left suspension arm. Colt Vista 2WD

stallation of axle bearing, assemble axle shaft to axle housing without packings and shims. Measure clearance between axle housing and backing plate. Refer to **Fig. 7** to determine proper amount of packings and shims to be installed.

# REAR WHEEL BEARING ADJUST

## COLT VISTA & COLT WAGON 2WD MODELS

1. Raise and support rear of vehicle, then remove wheel and tire assembly.
2. Remove dust cap from brake drum, then remove cotter pin and adjusting nut retainer, **Fig. 8.**
3. **Torque** wheel bearing adjusting nut to 14 ft. lbs. and rotate drum several turns to seat bearings, then loosen adjusting nut.
4. **Torque** adjusting nut to 7 ft. lbs., rotate drum several times, then **retorque** nut to 7 ft. lbs.
5. Install nut retainer and cotter pin. If cotter pin holes are not aligned reposition retainer. If holes cannot be aligned, the adjusting nut may be backed off a maximum of 15° to align holes.
6. Install dust cap on brake drum, then install wheel and tire assembly.

## COLT HATCHBACK & SEDAN & SUMMIT

1. Raise and support rear of vehicle and remove wheel.
2. Ensure parking brake is fully released.
3. Check wheel bearing endplay with suitable dial indicator. Maximum allowable endplay is .008 inch.
4. Check hub and drum starting torque by rotating hub with suitable spring scale. Maximum allowable starting torque is 4.9 lbs.
5. If endplay or starting torque exceed limits, loosen bearing retaining nut, then **retorque** nut to 108 to 145 ft. lbs. for 1989-91 models.
6. If endplay or starting torque are still not within limits, replace wheel bearings as needed.

# SHOCK ABSORBER REPLACE

## COLT, COLT VISTA 2WD & SUMMIT

1. Raise rear of vehicle and position jack stands under frame side rails.
2. Remove wheel and tire assembly.
3. Using a suitable jack, support lower suspension arm, then disconnect shock absorber from upper and lower mounting and remove from vehicle, **Figs. 9 and 10.**
4. Reverse procedure to install.

## CONQUEST

1. Raise and support rear of vehicle, then remove wheel and tire assembly.
2. Disconnect rear brake hose at shock assembly, then separate drive axle from companion flange.
3. Remove shock assembly to axle housing attaching bolts, then the shock assembly from axle housing, **Fig. 11.** Push axle housing down while opening coupling with a suitable tool.
4. Remove shock assembly attaching bolts from under side trim in rear hatch area, then the shock assembly from rear wheel housing.
5. Compress coil spring using compressor tool No. L-4514 or equivalent, then remove top end nut.
6. Remove shock insulator, spring seat, dust cover, rubber helper, then the seat.
7. Reverse procedure to install.

# COIL SPRING REPLACE

## COLT HATCHBACK & SEDAN, COLT VISTA 2WD & SUMMIT

1. Raise rear of vehicle and position jackstands under frame side rails to support body.
2. Remove wheel and tire assembly, then remove rear drum brake assembly.
3. Disconnect muffler from exhaust pipe, then remove muffler assembly.
4. Position a suitable jack under suspension arm, then raise suspension arm slightly.
5. Disconnect shock absorber from upper and lower mounting, **Figs. 9 and 10.**
6. Carefully lower jack to relieve spring tension, then remove coil spring. When removing spring, note location of upper and lower spring seats.
7. Reverse procedure to install. After completing installation, bleed brake system and adjust rear wheel bearings.

## COLT WAGON

### 2WD

1. Raise and support vehicle, then remove wheel and tire assembly and rear drum brake assembly, **Fig. 12.**
2. Remove brake tube. Disconnect brake hose from torsion axle and arm assembly.
3. Position a piece of wood between a suitable jack and the torsion axle and arm assembly. Do not apply jack to lateral rod. After raising torsion axle and arm slightly, remove lateral rod from body.
4. Remove torsion axle and arm from body.
5. Disconnect shock absorber upper and lower mounts, then remove shock absorber from vehicle.
6. Remove coil spring and upper spring seat. Note location of spring seats.
7. Reverse procedure to install. Note the following:
   a. Coil springs have colored identification marks which indicate specific application. When replacing springs, ensure that replacement springs are appropriately marked.
   b. After completing installation, bleed brake system and adjust rear wheel bearings.

### 4WD

1. Raise and support rear of vehicle at body, then remove wheel and tire assembly. Support rear axle using a suitable jack.
2. Remove stabilizer bar link nut, **Fig. 1.**
3. Remove load sensing proportioning valve mounting bracket bolt.

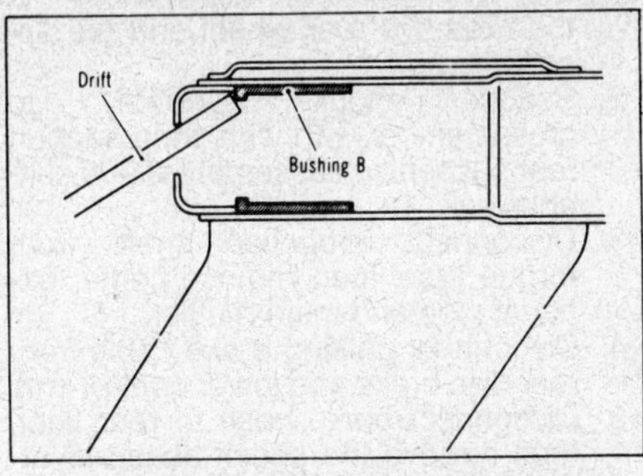


**Fig. 16 Removing bushing "B" from left suspension arm. Colt Vista 2WD**

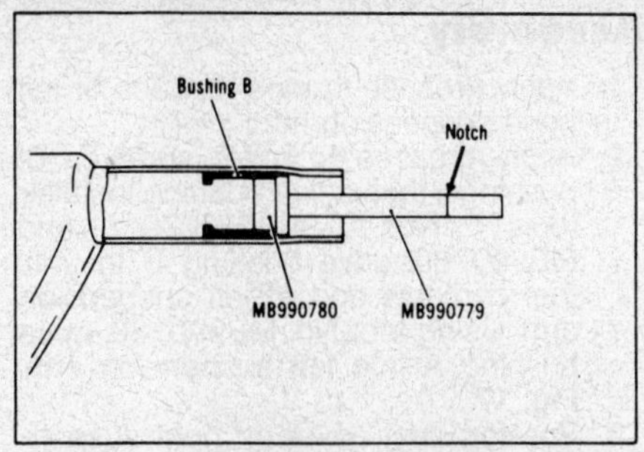


**Fig. 17 Installing bushing "B" into left suspension arm. Colt Vista 2 WD**

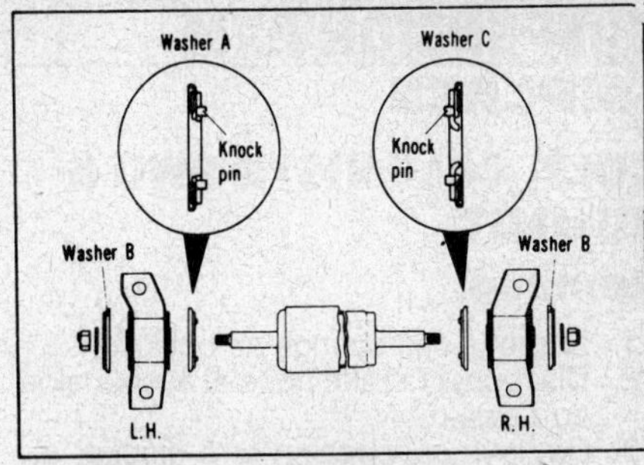


**Fig. 18 Installing mounting bracket components. Colt Vista 2WD**

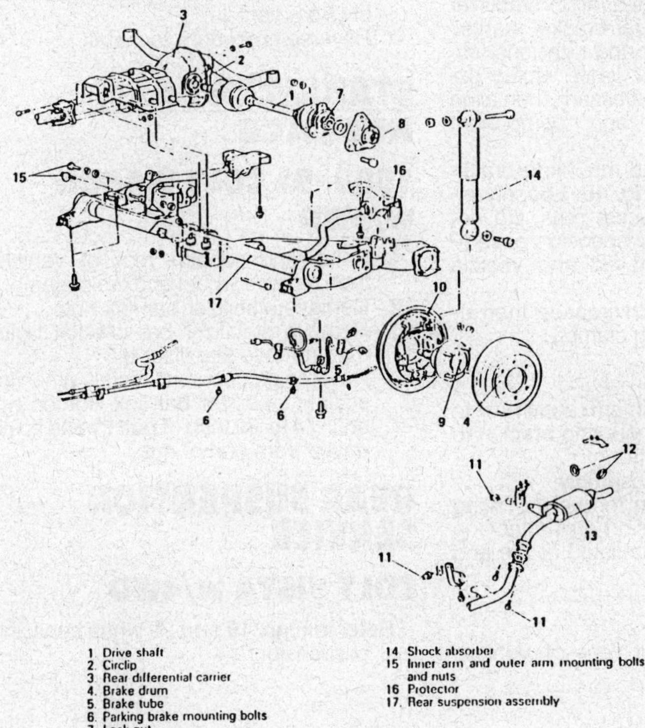


**Fig. 19 Rear suspension removal & installation. Colt Vista w/4WD**

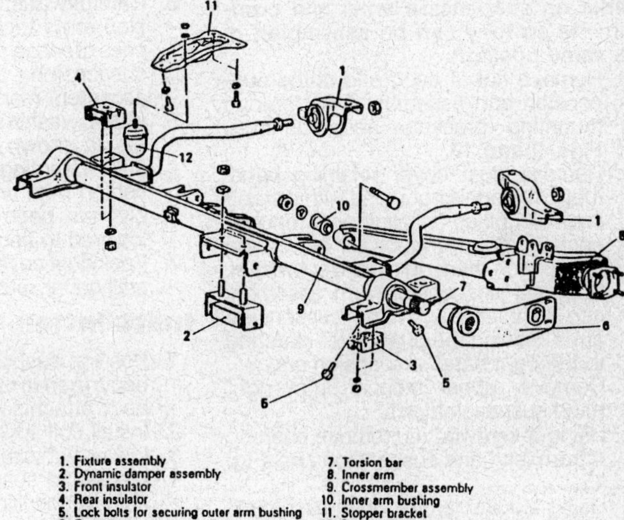


**Fig. 20 Rear suspension disassembly & assembly. Colt Vista w/4WD**

4. Remove lateral rod to axle housing attaching bolt.
5. Remove shock absorber lower attaching bolt.
6. Carefully lower jack positioned under rear housing until coil spring can be removed.
7. Reverse procedure to install.

## CONTROL ARMS REPLACE

### CONQUEST

1. Raise and support rear of vehicle, then remove wheel and tire assembly.
2. Disconnect parking brake cable from lower control arm, then remove the stabilizer bar.
3. Remove lower control arm to axle housing attaching bolts, then the lower arm to front support attaching bolts, **Fig. 11.**
4. Remove lower control arm to crossmember attaching bolts, then the lower control arm from vehicle.
5. Reverse procedure to install. Apply a coat of suitable greasee to shaft cutout between lower control arm and axle housing. Install shaft with identification mark facing downward.

## 1989–91 COLT WAGON W/4WD

### Lower Arm

1. Remove coil spring as described under "Coil Spring, Replace."
2. Remove lower arm to axle and body bracket attaching bolts, then remove lower arm, **Fig. 1.**
3. When replacing lower arm bushings, refer to **Figs. 13 and 14,** for installation dimensions.
4. Reverse procedure to install.

### Upper Arm

1. Raise and support rear of vehicle, then remove wheel and tire assembly.
2. Remove upper arm to axle housing and body bracket bolts, then remove upper arm, **Fig. 1.**
3. Reverse procedure to install.

## SUSPENSION ARM REPLACE

### COLT, COLT VISTA 2WD & SUMMIT

#### Removal

1. Remove coil springs as outlined.
2. Disconnect brake hose at suspension arm assembly.
3. Remove suspension arm bracket attaching bolts at each side of arm, then remove right and left hand suspension arms as an assembly, **Figs. 9 and 10.**

#### Disassembly

**Before disassembly, place alignment marks on suspension arms and components so they can be assembled in the same position.**

1. Remove nut at each end of the suspension arm assembly, then remove mounting brackets and bushings, **Figs. 9 and 10.**
2. Remove dust cover retaining band, then on models equipped with a stabilizer bar, place an alignment mark at each end of the stabilizer bar in line with punch mark on stabilizer bracket.
3. Separate suspension arm assembly into right and left hand suspension arms, leaving the dust cover attached to the right hand suspension arm.
4. Remove rubber stopper from right hand suspension arm.
5. Using a screwdriver, remove bushing A from left hand suspension arm, **Fig. 15.**
6. Using a suitable drift, drive bushing B from left hand suspension arm, **Fig. 16.**
7. Inspect all components for wear and damage and replace as necessary.

#### Assembly

1. Apply greasee to inner surface of left hand suspension arm.
2. Apply greasee to outer surfaces of bushings, then using bushing installer tools Nos. MB990779 and MB990780, drive bushing B in until tool contacts end of left suspension arm. Using tool No. MB990780, drive bushing A into left suspension arm, **Fig. 17.**
3. Position dust cover on right suspension arm, then coat suspension arm with greasee from shoulder at mounting bracket end approximately 15.7 inches toward center of arm and install rubber stopper.
4. On models equipped, align stabilizer bar and stabilizer bar bracket marks.
5. Carefully push left and right suspension arms together, while wiping excess greasee as necessary, then align suspension arm and component alignment marks.
6. Install washers and mounting brackets as shown in **Fig. 18.** Loosely install mounting bracket nuts. Do not tighten nuts until suspension assembly has been installed and vehicle lowered to floor.
7. Pack dust cover with greasee, then install cover retaining clamp.

#### Installation

1. Position suspension arm assembly to body, then install mounting bracket to body attaching bolts.
2. Install coil spring assembly.
3. Lower vehicle, then torque mounting bracket to suspension arm attaching nuts to specification listed at the end of this section.

### CONQUEST

1. Raise and support rear of vehicle, then remove rear wheel and tire assemblies.
2. Secure shock assembly to crossmember with wire, then support rear suspension assembly with a suitable jack.
3. Disconnect propeller shaft from torque tube, then remove center exhaust pipe and main muffler.
4. Disconnect parking brake cable from rear disc brake and lower control arm.
5. Disconnect brake hose at rear floor, then remove the shock absorber attaching nuts.
6. Remove crossmember attaching nuts, then the front support attaching nuts and bolts.
7. Slowly lower rear suspension assembly from vehicle.
8. Reverse procedure to install.

## STABILIZER BAR REPLACE

### 1989–91 COLT WAGON w/4WD

1. Raise and support rear of vehicle, then remove wheel and tire assembly.
2. Remove stabilizer bar link nuts.
3. Remove stabilizer bar bracket bolts, then remove stabilizer bar.
4. Reverse procedure to install. When installing stabilizer bar link, tighten nut until .74 to .82 inch of bolt thread is exposed from end of nut.

## REAR SUSPENSION SERVICE

### COLT VISTA w/4WD

Refer to **Figs. 19 and 20** when servicing rear suspension.

## TIGHTENING SPECIFICATIONS

### COLT & SUMMIT

| Year | Component | Torque/Ft. Lbs. |
|---|---|---|
| 1988–92 | Brake Adapter, Disc Brakes | 36-43 |
| | Dust Shield To Trailing Arm | 36-43 |
| | Lateral Rod To Axle | 58-72 |
| | Lateral Rod To Body | 58-72 |
| | Piston Rod Nut | 14-22 |
| | Shock Unit Lower Attachment | 58-72 |
| | Shock Unit Upper Attachment | 18-25 |
| | Suspension Arm, Left To Right Hand | 58-72 |
| | Suspension Arm To Body | 36-51 |
| | Trailing Arm | 98-108 |
| | Wheel & Tire Assembly | 65-80 |
| | Wheel Bearing Nut | 108-145 |

*Continued*

# TIGHTENING SPECIFICATIONS—Continued

## COLT WAGON 2WD

| Year | Component | Torque/Ft. Lbs. |
|---|---|---|
| 1989–90 | Lateral Rod To Axle | 58-72 |
| | Lateral Rod To Body | 58-72 |
| | Load Sensing Proportioning Valve | 7-10 |
| | Master Cylinder Attaching Nuts | 6-9 |
| | Power Brake Unit Attaching Nuts | 6-9 |
| | Shock Unit Lower Attachment | 22-29 |
| | Shock Unit Upper Attachment | 22-29 |
| | Trailing Arm | 72-87 |
| | Wheel & Tire Assembly | 65-80 |

## COLT WAGON 4WD

| Year | Component | Torque/Ft. Lbs. |
|---|---|---|
| 1989–90 | Bracket To Lateral Rod | 9-11 |
| | Lateral Rod To Axle | 58-72 |
| | Lateral Rod To Body | 58-72 |
| | Lower Arm | 94-108 |
| | Master Cylinder Attaching Nuts | 6-9 |
| | Propeller Shaft To Pinion Flange | 22-25 |
| | Shock Unit Lower Attachment | 22-29 |
| | Shock Unit Upper Attachment | 22-29 |
| | Upper Arm | 94-108 |
| | Upper Arm Bracket | 36-51 |
| | Wheel & Tire Assembly | 65-80 |

## COLT VISTA 2WD

| Year | Component | Torque/Ft. Lbs. |
|---|---|---|
| 1989–91 | Shock Unit Lower Attachment | 58-80 |
| | Shock Unit Upper Attachment | 58-80 |
| | Suspension Arm, Left To Right Hand | 87-108 |
| | Suspension Arm To Body | 94-108 |
| | Wheel & Tire Assembly | ① |

①—Steel wheel, 50–57 ft. lbs.; aluminum wheel, 65–80 ft. lbs.

*Continued*

# TIGHTENING SPECIFICATIONS—Continued

## COLT VISTA 4WD

| Year | Component | Torque/Ft. Lbs. |
|---|---|---|
| 1989–91 | Axle Shaft To Companion Flange | 116-159 |
| | Crossmember Support To Body | 58-87 |
| | Differential Front Support Bracket To Crossmember | 87-101 |
| | Differential Rear Support To Differential Carrier | 43-65 |
| | Drive Shaft To Axle Shaft Flange | 40-47 |
| | Dynamic Damper Nuts | 14-20 |
| | Extension Rod To Fixture | 72-101 |
| | Fixture Assembly To Body | 36-50 |
| | Front Insulator To Crossmember Bracket | 7-11 |
| | Inner Arm Nut | 51-65 |
| | Master Cylinder Attaching Nuts | 6-9 |
| | Outer Arm Bushing Lock Bolts | 16-22 |
| | Outer & Inner Arm Attaching Bolts | 58-72 |
| | Outer & Inner Arm Toe Adjusting Nut | 87-101 |
| | Power Brake Unit Attaching Nuts | 6-9 |
| | Shock Absorber To Body | 58-80 |
| | Shock Absorber To Inner Arm | 58-80 |
| | Stopper Bracket To Body | 22-36 |
| | Stopper Bracket To Bumper Stop | 14-22 |
| | Wheel & Tire Assembly | ① |

①—Steel wheel, 50–57 ft. lbs.; aluminum wheel, 65–80 ft. lbs.

## CONQUEST

| Year | Component | Torque/Ft. Lbs. |
|---|---|---|
| 1989 | Front Support Lower Stopper Bolt To Body | 29-36 |
| | Front Support Nut To Pin Assembly | 51-61 |
| | Lower Control Arm Locking Pin | 11-14 |
| | Lower Control Arm To Axle Housing | 80-94 |
| | Lower Control Arm To Crossmember | 94-108 |
| | Lower Control Arm To Front Support | 94-108 |
| | Pin Assembly | 51-61 |
| | Propeller Shaft To Pinion Flange | 36-43 |
| | Rear Support To Differential Carrier | 36-51 |
| | Stabilizer Bar To Front Support | 22-29 |
| | Stabilizer Bar To Lower Control Arm | 7-14 |
| | Strut Unit Lower Attachment | 36-51 |
| | Strut Unit Upper Attachment | 18-25 |
| | Support Insulator To Crossmember | 18-22 |
| | Support Insulator To Rear Support | 22-25 |
| | Wheel & Tire Assembly | 65-80 |

# Front Suspension & Steering

## INDEX



## HUB & WHEEL BEARING REPLACE

### CONQUEST

1. Raise and support front of vehicle and remove wheel.
2. Remove bolts securing caliper support to steering knuckle, remove caliper and support as an assembly leaving hose connected and suspend caliper from front spring, taking care not to damage brake hose.
3. Remove hub cap, cotter pin, and pin retainer.
4. Remove hub nut, washer and outer bearing, then remove hub and rotor assembly from spindle.
5. Scribe matching marks between hub and rotor. On models less intercooler, remove bolts securing brake rotor to hub, then separate hub and rotor. On models with intercooler, remove retaining clips and bolts, then separate rotor from hub.
6. Remove oil seal and inner bearing, then drive bearing outer races from hub using suitable [illegible].
7. Clean hub and bearings with suitable solvent and blow dry with compressed air. Inspect components noting the following:
   a. Check fit of bearing outer races in hub. If bearings have "spun" and races are loose in hub, hub should be replaced.
   b. Inspect bearings and replace if damaged, scored or excessively worn.
8. Install inner and outer bearing outer races in hub using suitable driver, then pack center of hub with greasee.
9. Install brake rotor on hub and align matching marks. On models less intercooler tighten nuts. On models with intercooler, install hub bolts and secure rotor with retaining clips.
10. Pack wheel bearings, working greasee through rollers from wide end of bearing with palm of hand. Keep bearings covered until installation.
11. Install inner wheel bearing in hub, then press new seal into hub using suitable driver.
12. Coat seal lips with greasee, mount hub assembly on spindle.
13. Install outer bearing, washer and nut, then adjust wheel bearings as outlined.
14. Install caliper assembly.

## HUB & KNUCKLE REPLACE

### COLT, COLT VISTA, COLT WAGON & SUMMIT

1. With vehicle on ground, remove cotter pin and loosen hub to drive shaft retaining nut.
2. Raise and support front of vehicle, then remove wheel and tire assembly, then remove hub to driveshaft nut and washer.
3. Remove front brake assembly from hub, then using suitable puller, disconnect tie rod end from steering knuckle.
4. Using axle shaft puller tool No. CT-1003 or equivalent, detach driveshaft from hub.
5. Disconnect steering knuckle from strut, then remove knuckle and hub as an assembly.
6. Reverse procedure to install. After installing brake assembly, bleed brake system.

## WHEEL BEARINGS ADJUST

### CONQUEST

After installing bearings and wheel hub, **torque** nut to 14.5 ft. lbs. to seat all parts then loosen nut. **Torque** nut to 4 ft. lbs. and after installing cap, install cotter pin. If the holes do not align after shifting the position of installed cap, loosen nut until a flute on nut aligns with cotter pin hole in spindle. Do not back off nut more than 15 degrees.

## LOWER BALL JOINT INSPECTION

1. Raise front of vehicle until both wheels are suspended.
2. Have an assistant shake bottom edge of tire in and out and inspect lower end of knuckle and lower control arm for movement.
3. If movement is observed, replace lower control arm assembly. Refer to "Lower Control Arm, Replace." for proper procedure.

## LOWER BALL JOINT REPLACE

### COLT, COLT WAGON & SUMMIT

With load removed from lower ball joint, check starting torque with inch lb. wrench. If starting torque is not 21.7-86.8 inch lbs., replace lower control arm and ball joint as an assembly. Refer to "Lower Control Arm, Replace" for procedure.

### COLT VISTA & CONQUEST

To replace lower ball joints, refer to "Lower Control Arm, Replace."

## STRUT REPLACE

### COLT, COLT WAGON & SUMMIT

1. Raise and support front of vehicle.
2. Remove brake hose bracket to strut attaching screws, then the bracket.
3. Remove strut to knuckle attaching bolts.
4. Remove dust cover from top of strut.
5. Remove strut assembly attaching nuts, **Figs. 1 through 3,** then the strut.
6. Reverse procedure to install.

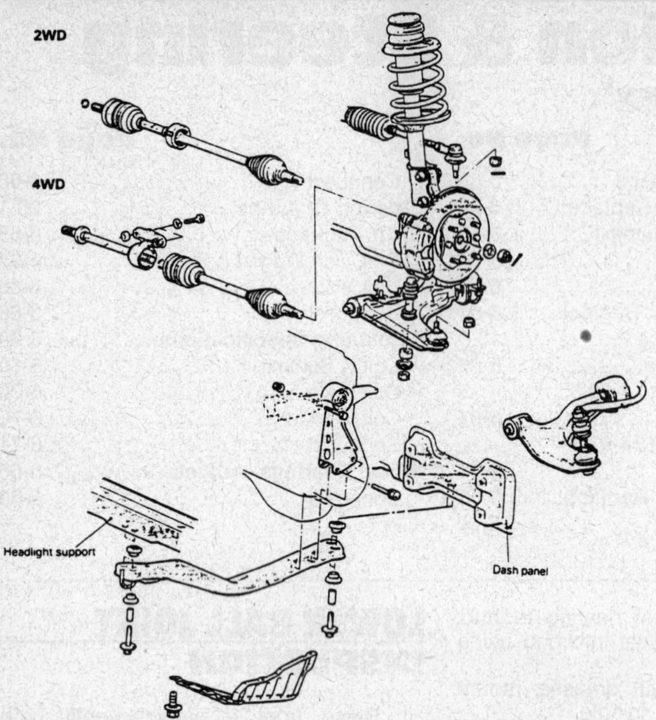


Fig. 1 Front suspension. Colt Wagon

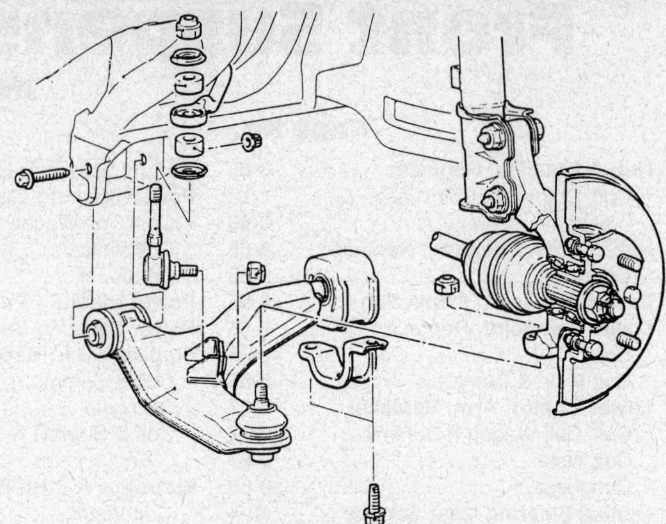

Fig. 2 Front suspension. Colt & Summit w/1.5L/4-89.6 engine

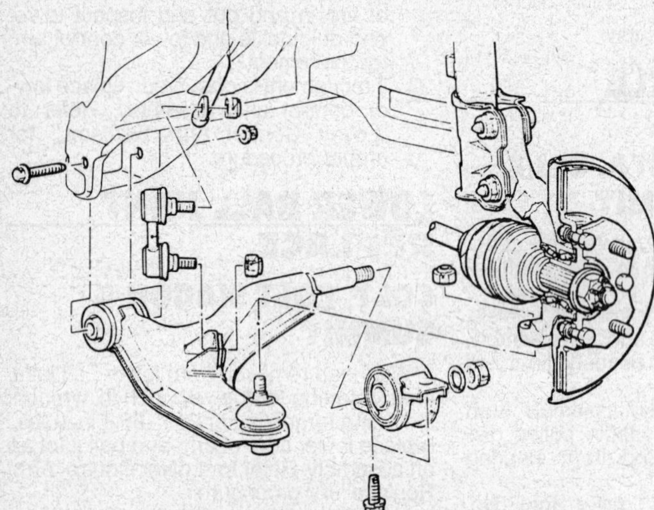

Fig. 3 Front suspension. Colt & Summit w/1.6L/4-97.4 engine

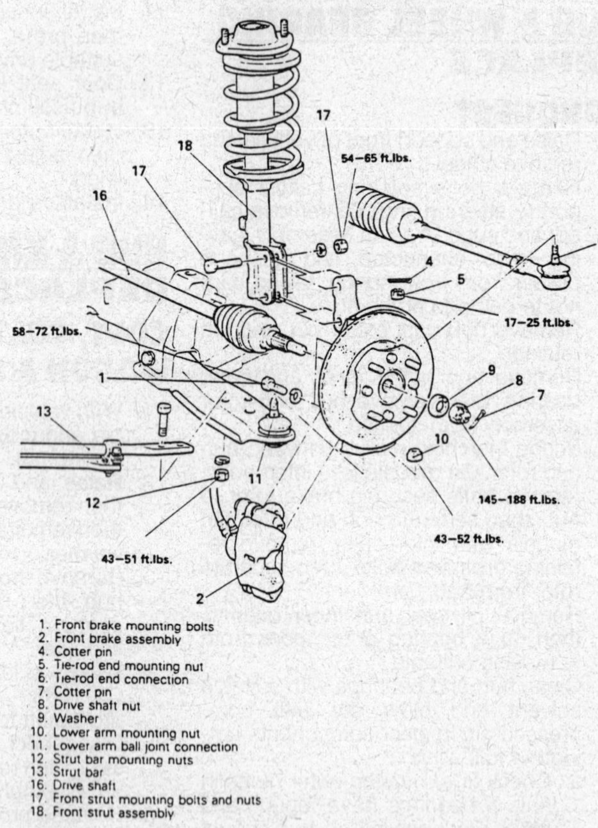


Fig. 4 Front suspension. Colt Vista 2WD

## COLT VISTA

1. Raise and support front of vehicle, then remove wheel and tire assembly.
2. Remove brake hose bracket from strut assembly, then the strut assembly from knuckle.
3. Remove strut insulator to strut housing panel attaching bolts, then remove strut from wheel housing, **Figs. 4 and 5.**
4. Reverse procedure to install.

## CONQUEST

1. Raise and support front of vehicle.
2. Remove wheel, tire, brake caliper, rotor and dust cover from steering knuckle.
3. Remove knuckle arm to strut attaching bolts, then separate knuckle arm and strut, **Fig. 6.**
4. Remove strut to body attaching nuts, then the strut.
5. Reverse procedure to install.

# STABILIZER & STRUT BAR

## REPLACE

### CONQUEST

1. Disconnect strut bars from lower control arms, then from strut bar bracket.
2. Disconnect stabilizer bar from lower control arm, then from frame.
3. Remove strut bar and/or stabilizer bar from vehicle.
4. Reverse procedure to install. Tighten stabilizer bar bushing attaching nuts until distance from top of threads to top of nuts is .59-.67 inch.
5. Tighten strut bar attaching nut until distance between the end of strut bar and the front surface of the locknut is 3.09 inches.

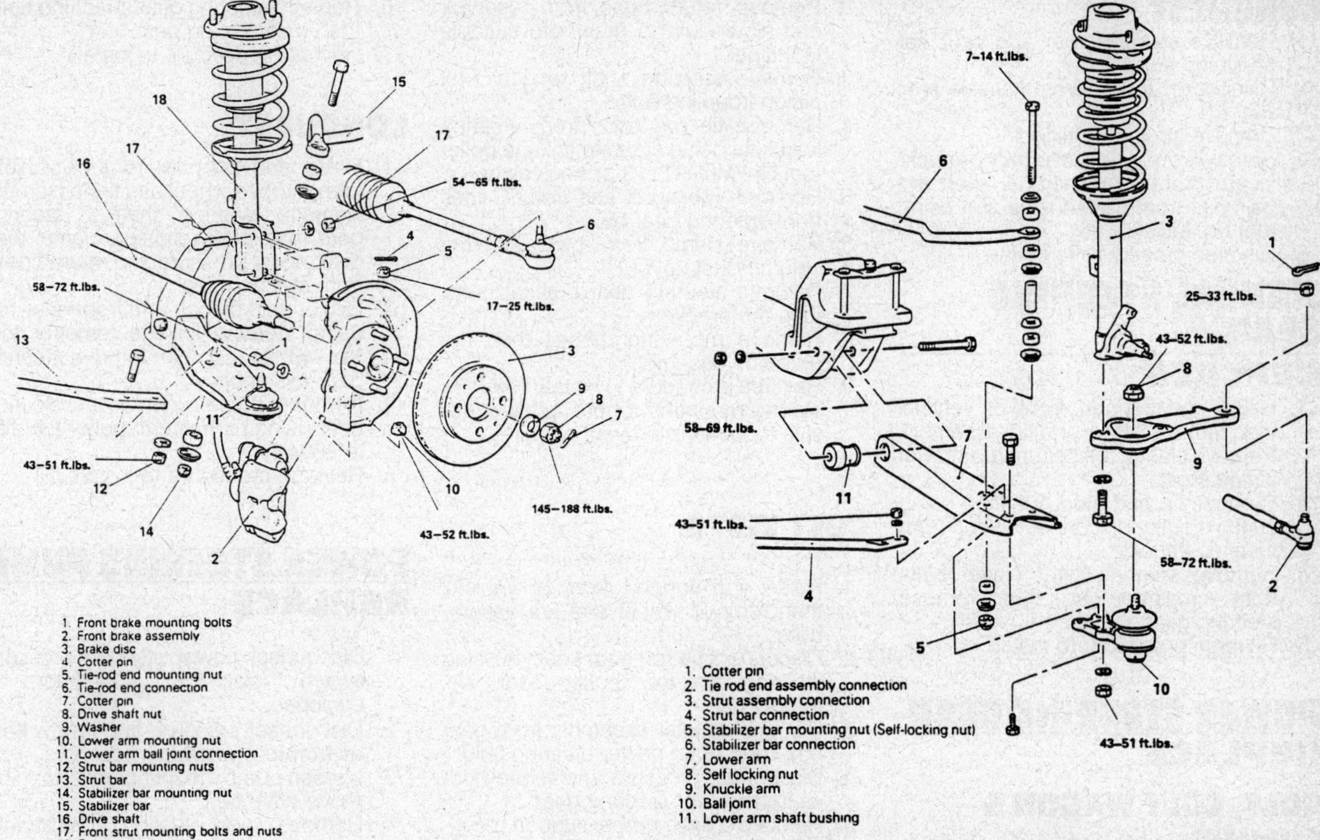


**Fig. 5 Front suspension. Colt Vista w/4WD**

**Fig. 6 Front suspension. Conquest**

### COLT VISTA

1. Disconnect stabilizer bar from lower control arm, then from frame.
2. Disconnect strut bars from lower control arms, then from frame.
3. Remove strut bar and/or stabilizer bar from vehicle.
4. Reverse procedure to install. Tighten stabilizer bar to frame bushing attaching nuts until distance from top of threads to top of nuts is .31-.39 inch. Tighten stabilizer bar to lower arm bushing attaching nuts until distance from top of threads to top of nuts is .31-.39 inch on two wheel drive models, or .51-.59 inch on four wheel drive models.
5. Tighten strut bar attaching nut until distance between the end of strut bar and the front surface of the locknut is 3.07 inches.

## STABILIZER BAR REPLACE

### COLT & SUMMIT w/1.5L/4-89.6 ENGINE

1. Raise and support vehicle, then remove under cover attaching bolt and the under cover. Remove the center member as well.
2. Remove stabilizer bar to lower control arm mounting bolt, nut and hardware.
3. Remove stabilizer bar bracket mounting bracket bolts, then the bracket and stabilizer bar.
4. Reverse procedure to install. Tighten stabilizer bar to lower control arm bushing attaching nuts until distance from top of threads to top of nuts is .83-.91 inch.

### COLT & SUMMIT w/1.6L/4-97.4 ENGINE

1. Remove cotter pin and nut, then separate tie rod end from steering knuckle using steering linkage puller tool No. MD990635 or equivalent. Suspend tie rod from chassis with cord.
2. Remove center member rear attaching bolts, then remove roll stopper mounting bolts.
3. Remove stabilizer link lock nuts. Use a suitable Allen wrench to hold link stud in position when removing lock nut.
4. Remove stabilizer bar link.
5. Remove stabilizer bar mounting bolts, then remove stabilizer bar through steering gear access provided in body.
6. Reverse procedure to install. When installing stabilizer link, tighten nut until .12 to .20 inch of stud thread protrudes above nut.

## LOWER CONTROL ARM REPLACE

### COLT, COLT WAGON & SUMMIT

1. Raise and support vehicle.
2. Remove center member. On all models, remove chassis under cover, then disconnect stabilizer bar from lower control arm.
3. Disconnect ball joint from steering knuckle, **Figs. 1 through 3.**
4. Loosen lower control arm to chassis attaching bolts, then remove lower control arm.
5. Replace ball joint dust cover.
6. Reverse procedure to install.

### COLT VISTA

1. Remove stabilizer bar to lower control arm attaching bolts, then the strut bar to lower control arm attaching bolts.
2. Loosen ball joint stud, then disconnect ball joint from knuckle, **Figs. 4 and 5.**
3. Remove lower arm from No. 2 crossmember. **Ball joint dust cover must be replaced during installation.**
4. Reverse procedure to install.

### CONQUEST

1. Remove stabilizer bar and strut bar attaching bolts.
2. Disconnect tie rod from knuckle arm, **Fig. 6.**
3. Remove strut as outlined.
4. Remove lower control arm and knuckle arm from crossmember, then the ball joint from the knuckle arm using tool No. MB990635.
5. Reverse procedure to install.

## MANUAL STEERING GEAR

### REPLACE

1. Raise and support front of vehicle, then remove wheel and tire assembly.
2. Remove clamp bolt securing joint with pinion shaft.
3. Remove tie end stud nut, then using suitable puller disconnect tie rod from steering knuckle.
4. Remove steering gear clamp bolts from crossmember, then remove steering gear.
5. Reverse procedure to install.

## POWER STEERING GEAR

### REPLACE

#### COLT, COLT WAGON & SUMMIT

1. Raise and support front of vehicle.
2. Remove return hose from reservoir and allow fluid to drain into suitable container.
3. Remove steering shaft to gear box pinion coupling bolt.
4. Remove tie rod ends from steering knuckles using steering linkage puller tool No. MB991113 or equivalent.
5. Remove pressure and return lines from steering gear box.
6. Remove clamp from lower steering column dust cover.
7. Remove steering gear bracket bolts, then the brackets.
8. Remove mounting rubber, then the gear box assembly.
9. Reverse procedure to install. When installing mounting rubber, apply adhesive to joints to prevent opening.

#### COLT VISTA

1. Raise and support front of vehicle, then remove wheel and tire assemblies.
2. Disconnect tie rod from knuckle using steering linkage puller tool No. MB991113.
3. Disconnect joint assembly from gear box, then drain power steering fluid.
4. Disconnect pressure and return hoses from power steering gear.
5. Remove crossmember support bracket attaching bolts, then the support bracket from No. 2 crossmember.
6. Remove steering gear attaching bolts, then the steering gear.
7. Reverse procedure to install.

#### CONQUEST

1. Raise and support front of vehicle, then remove wheel and tire assembly.
2. Remove steering shaft to steering gear mainshaft retaining clamp, then disconnect pressure and return hoses from steering gear.
3. Disconnect pitman arm from relay rod using steering linkage remover tool No. MB991113, then remove steering gear assembly.
4. Remove pitman arm from steering gear using pitman arm puller tool No. C-3894-A.
5. Reverse procedure to install.

## POWER STEERING PUMP

### REPLACE

1. Disconnect power steering pressure switch electrical connector, if equipped.
2. Disconnect pressure and return hoses from power steering pump.
3. Loosen pump mounting bolts, then remove drive belt.
4. Remove power steering pump attaching bolts, then remove pump.
5. Reverse procedure to install.

# TIGHTENING SPECIFICATIONS

## COLT & SUMMIT

| Year | Component | Torque Ft. Lbs. |
|---|---|---|
| 1989-92 | Caliper To Knuckle | 58-72 |
| | Center Bearing Bracket To Engine | 26-33 |
| | Center Member Rear Mounting Bolt | 43-58 |
| | Connector To Power Steering Pump Body | 36-51 |
| | Driveshaft Nut | 144-188 |
| | Hub To Brake Rotor | 36-43 |
| | Knuckle To Strut Assembly | 80-94 |
| | Lower Arm Ball Joint | 43-52 |
| | Lower Arm Bushing B Mounting Nut | 90-112① |
| | Lower Arm Front Mounting Nut | 69-87 |
| | Lower Arm Rear Mounting Bolt | 43-58 |
| | Power Steering Cooler Tube Clamp Bolt | 2-3 |
| | Power Steering Cooler Tube To Body | 7-10 |
| | Power Steering Cooler Tube To Hood Stay | 3-4 |
| | Power Steering Gear End Plug | 36-51 |
| | Power Steering Gear Feed Tubes | 9-13 |
| | Power Steering Gear Pinion And Valve Assembly To Locknut | 14-22 |
| | Power Steering Gear Valve Housing Bolts | 12-19 |
| | Power Steering Pressure Hose To Pressure Tube | 22-29 |
| | Power Steering Pressure Hose To Pump | 10-15 |
| | Power Steering Pressure Tube To Steering Gear | 9-13 |
| | Power Steering Pump Bracket To Engine | 18-24 |
| | Power Steering Pump Cover To Pump Body | 13-16 |
| | Power Steering Pump Heat Shield | 7-10 |
| | Power Steering Pump Reservoir Bolt | 7-10 |
| | Power Steering Pump Reservoir Bracket Bolt | 7-10 |
| | Power Steering Pump To Pump Bracket | 33-40 |
| | Power Steering Return Tube To Steering Gear | 9-13 |
| | Power Steering Suction Connector To Pump Body | 4-7 |
| | Rack Support Cover Locknut | 36-51 |
| | Rear Roll Stopper Mounting Nut | 33-43 |
| | Stabilizer Bar Mounting Bolt | 12-19 |
| | Stabilizer Link Mounting Nut | 40-51 |
| | Steering Column Lower Bracket | 6-9 |
| | Steering Column Upper Bracket | 6-9 |
| | Steering Gear To Body | 43-58 |
| | Steering Shaft Dust Cover | 2.6-3.6 |
| | Steering Shaft Joint To Steering Gear | 11-14 |
| | Steering Wheel Locknut | 25-33 |
| | Strut Top End Nut | 43-57 |
| | Strut Upper Mounting Nut | 25-33 |
| | Terminal Assembly To Power Steering Pump Body | 18-22 |
| | Tie Rod End Ball Joint | 11-25 |
| | Tie Rod End Locknut | 25-36 |
| | Tie Rod End To Rack | 58-72 |
| | Top Cover Locknut | 36-51 |

①—1989-91 models w/1.6L engine.

*Continued*

# TIGHTENING SPECIFICATIONS-CONTINUED

## COLT WAGON

| Year | Component | Torque Ft. Lbs. |
|---|---|---|
| 1989–90 | Caliper To Knuckle | 58-72 |
| | Center Bearing Bracket To Engine | 26-33 |
| | Center Member To Body | 43-58 |
| | Hub To Brake Disc | 36-43 |
| | Knuckle To Strut | 54-65 |
| | Lower Arm Ball Joint | 43—52 |
| | Lower Arm Bushing Support Bracket To Body | 43-58 |
| | Lower Arm Shaft To Body | 116-137 |
| | Lower Arm To Shaft | 69-87 |
| | Roll Stopper Bracket To Center Member | 33-43 |
| | Stabilizer Bar Bracket To Body | 12-19 |
| | Strut To Body | 25-36 |
| | Strut Upper Nut | 33-43 |
| | Tie Rod End | 11-25 |
| | Wheel Bearing | 144-188 |
| | Wheel & Tire Assembly | 65-80 |

## COLT VISTA

| Year | Component | Torque Ft. Lbs. |
|---|---|---|
| 1989–91 | Center Bearing Bracket Mounting Bolt | 29-40 |
| | Center Member Front Mounting Bolt | 22-29① |
| | Center Member Rear Mounting Nut | 54-72① |
| | Connector To Power Steering Pump Body | 29-43 |
| | Driveshaft Mounting Nut | 145-188 |
| | Dust Cover Mounting Bolt | 6-8② |
| | Flare Nuts Of Power Steering Gear Feed Tube | 9-13 |
| | Front Brake Assembly To Knuckle | 58-72 |
| | Front Exhaust Pipe To Catalytic Converter Bolt | 29-43① |
| | Front Hub To Brake Rotor | 36-43 |
| | Front Roll Bracket To No. 1 Crossmember | 29-36 |
| | Hanger Bracket Mounting Bolt | 7.2-14① |
| | Lower Arm Ball Joint To Knuckle | 43-52 |
| | Lower Arm Shaft | 58-69① |
| | Lower Arm Shaft | 80-101② |
| | No. 1 Crossmember To Body Side Member | 69-87 |
| | No. 2 Crossmember To Side Members | 58-72 |
| | Power Steering Cooler Tube To Body | 5.0-7.9 |
| | Power Steering Cooler Tube To Grill Bracket | 6.5-10.1 |
| | Power Steering Gear End Plug | 36-51 |
| | Power Steering Gear Pinion Housing Locknut | 72-108① |
| | Power Steering Gear Self-Locking Nut | 14-22 |
| | Power Steering Hose Clamp Attaching Bolts | 6-9 |
| | Power Steering Pressure Hose To Connector | 12-19② |
| | Power Steering Pressure Hose To Connector | 29-36① |
| | Power Steering Pressure Hose To Steering Gear | 9-13 |
| | Power Steering Pump Brace Bolt | 18-24 |

*Continued*

# TIGHTENING SPECIFICATIONS-CONTINUED

| Year | Component | Torque Ft. Lbs. |
|---|---|---|
| 1989–91 | Power Steering Pump Bracket | 14-20 |
| | Power Steering Pump Cover | 13-16 |
| | Power Steering Pump Guide Bracket Locknut | 22-29① |
| | Power Steering Pump Oil Reservoir | 6-9 |
| | Power Steering Pump Reservoir Bracket | 6-9 |
| | Power Steering Pump Support Bolt | 14-20 |
| | Power Steering Return Hose To Steering Gear | 9-13 |
| | Power Steering Return Hose To Steering Gear | 9-13 |
| | Rear Insulator To Center Member | 22-29① |
| | Rear Roll Insulator To Engine Bracket | 22-29② |
| | Rear Roll Stopper Bracket To No. 2 Crossmember | 43-58② |
| | Stabilizer Bar Hanger Bracket | 7-9 |
| | Stabilizer Bar To Stabilizer Bar Hanger | 14-22② |
| | Steering Column Mounting Bolts | 6-9 |
| | Steering Gear End Housing Clamp | 43-58 |
| | Steering Gear Housing Clamp | 43-58 |
| | Steering Gear Mounting Bolts | 43-58 |
| | Steering Rack Support Cover Locknut | 36-39 |
| | Steering Shaft Joint To Steering Gear | 11-14 |
| | Steering Shaft To Joint Assembly | 11-14 |
| | Steering Wheel Mounting Nut | 25-33 |
| | Strut Assembly To Knuckle | 54-64 |
| | Strut Bar To Lower Arm | 43-51 |
| | Strut Bar To No. 1 Crossmember | 98-116 |
| | Strut Insulator To Piston Rod | 43-51 |
| | Strut Insulator To Wheelhouse | 22-29 |
| | Suction Connector To Power Steering Pump Body | 4-7 |
| | Terminal Assembly To Power Steering Pump Body | 18-22 |
| | Tie Rod End Ball Joint To Knuckle | 17-25 |
| | Tie Rod End Locknut | 36-39 |
| | Tie Rod End To Steering Rack | 58-72 |
| | Transfer Extension Stopper Bracket To No. 2 Crossmember | 22-29① |
| | Transfer Extension Stopper Mounting Bolts | 6-9① |
| | Transfer Extension Stopper Mounting Nuts | 6-9① |

①—Four wheel drive models.
②—Two Wheel drive models.

## CONQUEST

| Year | Component | Torque Ft. Lbs. |
|---|---|---|
| 1989 | Crossmember To Body | 43-58 |
| | Disc Cover To Strut Assembly | 6-9 |
| | Engine Mount Bracket To Crossmember | 22-29 |
| | Front Hub To Brake Disc | 25-29 |
| | Idler Arm Attaching Nut | 29-43 |
| | Idler Arm Support And Frame | 25-29 |
| | Knuckle Arm To Ball Joint | 43-52 |
| | Knuckle Arm To Strut Assembly | 58-72 |
| | Lower Arm Shaft Bolt | 58-69 |
| | Lower Arm To Ball Joint | 43-51 |
| | Pitman Arm To Steering Gear | 94-108 |

*Continued*

# TIGHTENING SPECIFICATIONS-CONTINUED

| Year | Component | Torque Ft. Lbs. |
|---|---|---|
| 1989 | Power Steering Pressure Hose | 22-29 |
| | Power Steering Pump Brace Bolt | 10-15 |
| | Power Steering Pump Connector | 36-51 |
| | Power Steering Pump Cover | 13-16 |
| | Power Steering Pump Reservoir | 6-9 |
| | Power Steering Pump Suction Connector | 4-7 |
| | Power Steering Return Hose | 29-36 |
| | Relay Rod To Idler Arm | 25-33 |
| | Relay Rod To Pitman Arm | 25-33 |
| | Shock Absorber Ring Nut | 101-108 |
| | Stabilizer Bar Bracket | 6-9 |
| | Stabilizer Bar To Lower Control Arm | 7-14 |
| | Steering Column Support Plate | 6.5-10 |
| | Steering Column Tube Clamp | 3.6-6.0 |
| | Steering Gear Adjusting Bolt Locknut | 22-33 |
| | Steering Gear Attaching Bolts | 25-29 |
| | Steering Gear Breather Plug | 2-3 |
| | Steering Gear Locknut | 130-166① |
| | Steering Gear Side Cover | 33-40 |
| | Steering Gear Valve Housing | 33-40 |
| | Steering Shaft To Steering Gear Bolt | 14-18 |
| | Steering Wheel Locknut | 25-33 |
| | Stopper Bolt Locknut For Adjustment Of Steering Angle | 14 |
| | Strut Assembly To Brake Assembly | 58-72 |
| | Strut Bar Bracket To Frame | 25-33 |
| | Strut Bar To Lower Control Arm | 43-51 |
| | Strut Bar To Strut Bar Bracket | 54-61 |
| | Strut Insulator To Body | 18-25 |
| | Strut Top End Nut | 43-51 |
| | Tie Rod End Socket Relay Rod | 25-33 |
| | Tie Rod End Stud | 36-40 |
| | Tie Rod End To Knuckle Arm | 25-33 |
| | Tie Rod End | 25-33 |
| | Tilt Link Cover | 6.5-10 |

①—If special tool is used to measure torque, torque to 98-127 ft. lbs.

# Wheel Alignment

INDEX



## PRELIMINARY CHECK

1. Road test vehicle noting any abnormal steering or handling characteristics.
2. Ensure tires are the proper type, correctly inflated and that tires on each axle are the same size.
3. Inspect ball joints, suspension arms, bushings and tie rods, and repair or replace any component that is damaged or excessively worn.
4. Ensure wheel run-out is not excessive, and that wheel bearings are properly adjusted.
5. Jounce vehicle several times to settle suspension.
6. Place vehicle on suitable alignment rack following manufacturer's instructions.
7. Check and correct alignment angles in the following sequence: Rear toe and camber, caster, front camber and front toe.
8. Correct any angle that is not within specifications. If no adjustment is possible, check for damaged or worn suspension components and/or damaged or distorted chassis and correct as needed.

## FRONT WHEEL ALIGNMENT

### CASTER

#### Colt, Colt Wagon & Summit

Caster is pre-set at the factory and is not adjustable. If caster is out of specifications, replace bent, worn or otherwise damaged parts.

#### Colt Vista & Conquest

Caster normally requires no adjustment. However, slight adjustments can be made by moving the strut bar nut. After adjustment, ensure that variation between left and right sides is less than 1/2°.

### CAMBER

The specified camber is built into the steering knuckle, which is part of the strut assembly, and no adjustment is provided.

### TOE-IN

#### Colt, Colt Wagon, Conquest & Summit

On Colt, Colt Wagon and Summit models, remove outer bellows clamp from tie rod before adjusting toe. After completing adjustment, reinstall clamp.

The amount of toe-in of the left front wheel is reduced by turning the tie rod turnbuckle toward the front of the car and the amount of toe-in on the right front wheel is reduced by turning it toward the rear of the the car. After adjustment, the difference in length between the two tie rods should not exceed .2 inch (5 mm).

#### Colt Vista

Adjust toe-in by removing the left and right tie rod turnbuckle retaining clips, then turning the left and right turnbuckles the same amount in opposite directions. To reduce toe-in, turn the left turnbuckle toward the front of the vehicle and the right turnbuckle toward the rear of the vehicle. For each half turn of the turnbuckle, toe-in will be adjusted by approximately .24 inch.

## REAR WHEEL ALIGNMENT

### CAMBER

Rear camber is pre-set during vehicle assembly and cannot be adjusted. If camber is not within specifications, check for worn or damaged suspension component, and damaged or deformed floor pan or body and repair as needed.

### TOE-IN

#### Colt, Colt Wagon & Summit

Rear toe is pre-set during vehicle assembly and cannot be adjusted. If toe is not within specifications, check for worn or damaged suspension components, and damaged or deformed floor pan or body and repair as needed.

#### Colt Vista

Toe is adjustable by rotating the outer and inner arm mounting bolts. If toe-in is not within specifications, rotate left and right outer arm and inner arm bolts, each by the same amount, to perform adjustment. An adjustment of approximately .08 inch (2 mm) will be made when the outer arm and inner arm bolts are turned the equivalent of 1 alignment mark.

#### Conquest

Toe-in is adjusted by rotating the lower control arm mounting bolts as follows:

1. Loosen locknut while holding mounting bolt.
2. Rotate mounting bolts until toe is within specifications. Movement of 1 graduation will change toe by approximately .08 inch (2 mm). **Rotate left and right mounting bolts equally.**
3. Tighten locknut and recheck setting.
4. Repeat adjustment until toe setting is equal for both wheels and total toe is within specifications.

# VEHICLE RIDE HEIGHT SPECIFICATIONS

| Year | Model | Height In Inches ① | |
|---|---|---|---|
| | | Front Bumper To Ground | Rear Bumper To Ground |
| 1989 | Conquest | 14 | 14.6 |
| 1989–90 | Colt Wagon | 9.3 | 11 |
| 1989–91 | Colt Vista 2WD | 15 | 15 |
| | Colt Vista 4WD | 17.5 | 17.5 |
| 1989–92 | Colt & Summit ② | 23.5 ③ | 25 ③ |
| | Colt & Summit ④ | 23.5 ③ | 21 ③ |

① —If not within specifications, check suspension components for wear and damage.
② —Hatchback.
③ —Measured in degrees from bottom center of wheel to bottom of bumper.
④ —Sedan.

# DODGE STEALTH

## INDEX OF SERVICE OPERATIONS

**NOTE:** Refer To Rear Of This Manual For Vehicle Manufacturer's Special Service Tool Suppliers.

# Specifications

## GENERAL ENGINE SPECIFICATIONS

| Year | Engine | | Fuel System | Bore and Stroke | Compression Ratio | Net H.P. @ RPM | Maximum Torque Ft. Lbs. @ RPM | Normal Oil Pressure Pounds |
|---|---|---|---|---|---|---|---|---|
| | Liter/CID | VIN Code | | | | | | |
| 1991-92 | 3.0L/V6-181① | S | MPI② | 3.58 x 2.99 | 8.9 | 164 @ 5500 | 185 @ 4000 | 11.4③ |
| | 3.0L/V6-181④ | B | MPI② | 3.58 x 2.99 | 10.0 | 222 @ 6000 | 201 @ 4500 | 11.4③ |
| | 3.0L/V6-181⑤ | C | MPI② | 3.58 x 2.99 | 8.0 | 300 @ 6000 | 307 @ 2500 | 11.4③ |

①—Single over head cam.
②—Multi port fuel injection.
③—Minimum at 700 RPM.
④—Dual over head cam, except turbocharged.
⑤—Dual over head cam, turbocharged.

## TUNE UP SPECIFICATIONS

| Year & Engine, VIN Code | Spark Plug Gap | Ignition Timing BTDC | | | | Curb Idle Speed | | Fast Idle Speed | | Fuel Pump Pressure |
|---|---|---|---|---|---|---|---|---|---|---|
| | | Firing Order Fig. | Man. Trans. | Auto. Trans. | Mark Fig. | Man. Trans. | Auto Trans. | Man. Trans. | Auto. Trans. | |
| **1991-92** | | | | | | | | | | |
| 3.0L/V6-181, S④ | .39-.43 | A② | 5① | 5① | C | 600-800 | 600-800 | ⑧ | ⑧ | 47-50③ |
| 3.0L/V6-181, B⑤ | .39-.43 | B② | 5① | 5① | ⑦ | 600-800 | 600-800 | ⑧ | ⑧ | 47-50③ |
| 3.0L/V6-181, C⑥ | .39-.43 | B② | 5① | 5① | ⑦ | 600-800 | 600-800 | ⑧ | ⑧ | 43-45③ |

①—With ignition timing adjusting terminal grounded.
②—Firing order, 1-2-3-4-5-6.
③—With vacuum hose disconnected at curb idle speed.
④—Single over head cam.
⑤—Dual over head cam, except turbocharged.
⑥—Dual over head cam, turbocharged.
⑦—Equipped with a crankshaft position sensor.
⑧—Dual Controlled by idle speed Control.

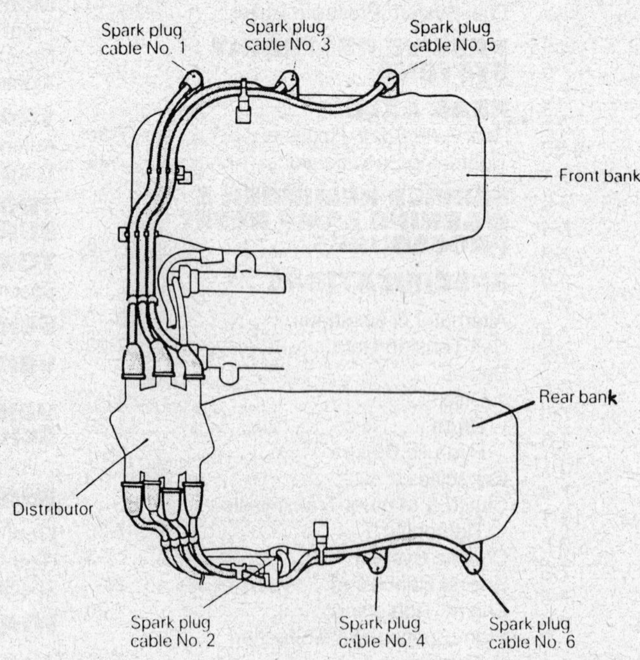


**Fig. A**

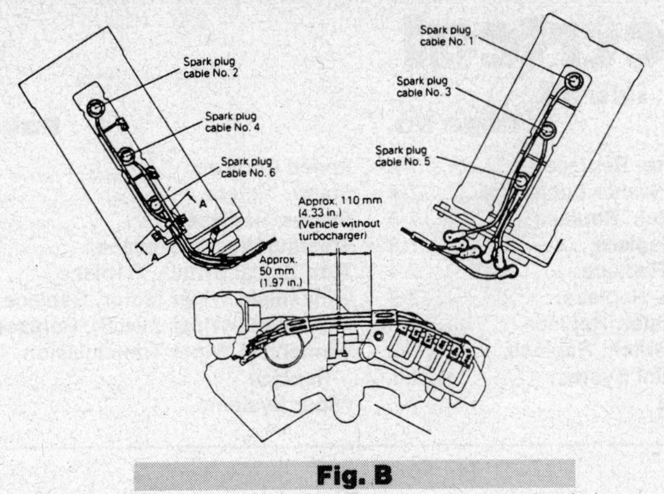


Fig. B

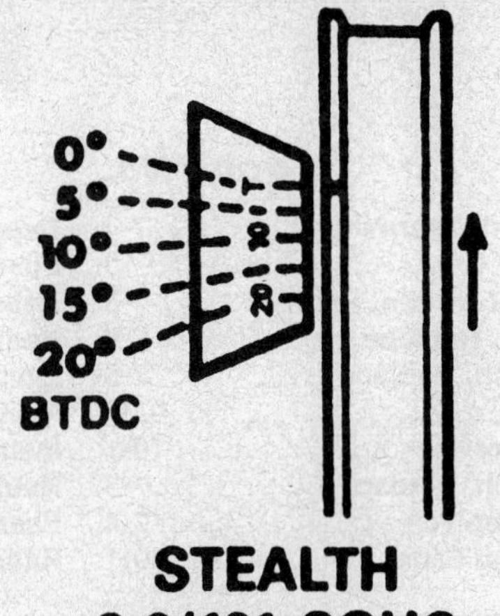


Fig. C

# WHEEL ALIGNMENT SPECIFICATIONS

| Year | Model | Caster Angle, Degrees | | Camber Angle, Degrees | | Toe-In Inch |
|---|---|---|---|---|---|---|
| | | Limits | Desired | Limits | Desired | |
| **Front** | | | | | | |
| 1991-92 | All | +3.42 to +4.42 | +3.92 | −.5 to +.5 | 0 | 0 |
| **Rear** | | | | | | |
| 1991-92 | FWD | — | — | −.5 to +.5 | 0 | −.08 to +.10 |
| 1991-92 | AWD | — | — | −1/3 to +2/3 | 0 | −.08 to +.10 |

# COOLING SYSTEM & CAPACITY DATA

| Year | Engine/VIN | Cooling Capacity, Qts. | | Radiator Cap Relief Pressure, Lbs. | Thermo. Opening Temp. | Fuel Tank Gals. | Engine Oil Refill Qts. | Transaxle Oil | |
|---|---|---|---|---|---|---|---|---|---|
| | | Less A/C | With A/C | | | | | Manual Transaxle Pts. | Auto. Transaxle Qts. |
| 1991-92 | 3.0L/V6-181, S | 8.5 | 8.5 | 11–15 | 180 | 19.8 | 4.2① | ② | 7.9 |
| | 3.0L/V6-181, B | 8.5 | 8.5 | 11–15 | 170 | 19.8 | 4.2① | ② | 7.9 |
| | 3.0L/V6-181, C | 8.5 | 8.5 | 11–15 | 170 | 19.8 | 4.2① | ② | 7.9 |

①—Add .5 quart for filter and/or oil cooler.

②—Front wheel drive, 2.4 quarts; All wheel drive, 2.5 quarts.

# LUBRICANT DATA

| Year | Model | Lubricant Type | | | | | |
|---|---|---|---|---|---|---|---|
| | | Transaxle | | | | | |
| | | Manual | Automatic | Transfer Case | Rear Axle | Power Steering | Brake System |
| 1991-92 | All | API GL-4 | Dia ATF SP① | API GL-4 | API GL-5 | ② | ③ |

①—Automatic transmission fluid type 7176 or equivalent.

②—Dexron or Dexron II automatic transmission fluid type 7176 or equivalent.

③—Dot 3 or Dot 4 brake fluid or equivalent.

# Electrical

## INDEX



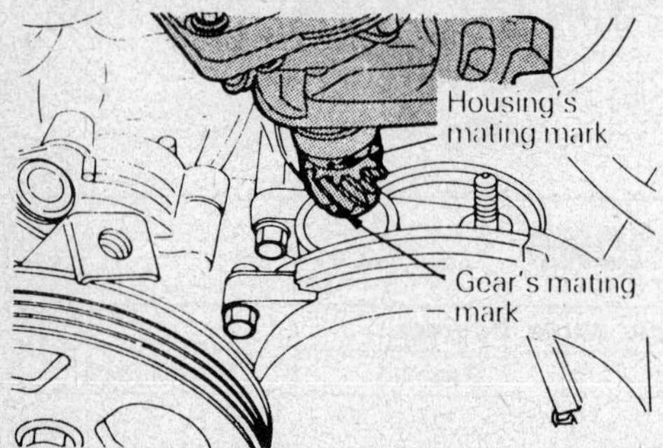


**Fig. 1 Distributor alignment**

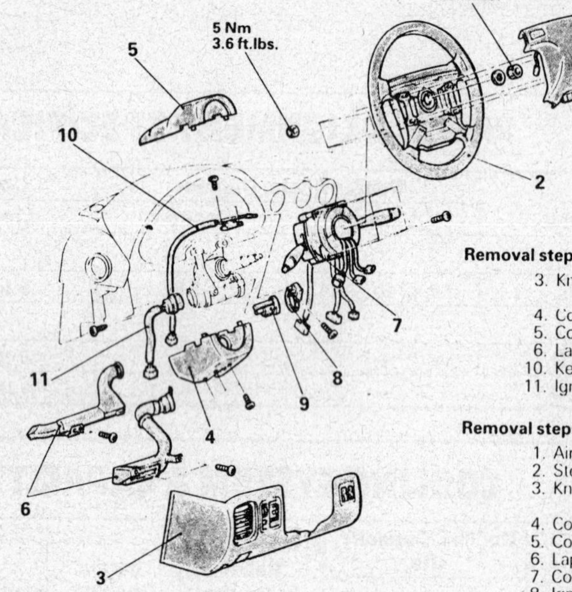


**Fig. 2 Ignition lock & ignition switch**

## AIRBAG SYSTEM DISARMING

1. Place ignition switch in lock position.
2. Disconnect and tape battery ground cable connector.
3. **Wait at least 1 minute after disconnecting battery ground cable before doing any further work on vehicle.** The SRS system is designed to retain enough voltage to deploy airbag for a short time even after battery has been disconnected.
4. After repairs are complete, reconnect battery ground cable.
5. From passenger side of vehicle, turn ignition switch to On position.
6. SRS warning light should illuminate for 6 to 8 seconds, then remain off for at least 45 seconds to indicate if SRS system is functioning correctly.
7. If SRS indicator does not perform as described refer to the "Passive Restraint Systems" section.

## FUSE PANEL & FLASHER LOCATIONS

The fuse panel is located under the instrument panel to the left of the steering column.

The turn signal and hazard flasher unit is located to the lower left of the steering column near the drivers door assembly.

## STARTER REPLACE

1. Disconnect battery ground cable.
2. Disconnect starter motor electrical connector.
3. Remove starter motor bracket attaching bolt.
4. Remove starter motor attaching nut, then remove starter motor assembly.
5. Reverse procedure to install. **Torque** starter motor bracket attaching bolt to 22 ft. lbs.

## DISTRIBUTOR REPLACE

1. Disconnect battery ground cable.
2. Disconnect spark plug wires.
3. Remove distributor assembly attaching nut, then remove distributor.
4. Reverse procedure to install, noting the following:
   a. Rotate crankshaft that No. 1 cylinder is at compression top dead center (TDC).
   b. Align distributor housing and gear mating marks, **Fig. 1.**
   c. **Torque** distributor assembly attaching nut to 11 ft. lbs.

## IGNITION LOCK REPLACE

1. Disable airbag as outlined under "Airbag System, Disarming."
2. Remove steering wheel as outlined under "Steering Wheel, Replace."
3. Remove instrument panel lower knee protector attaching screws.
4. Remove ignition lock cylinder as shown in **Fig. 2,** noting the following:
   a. Remove steering column cover upper to lower attaching screws,

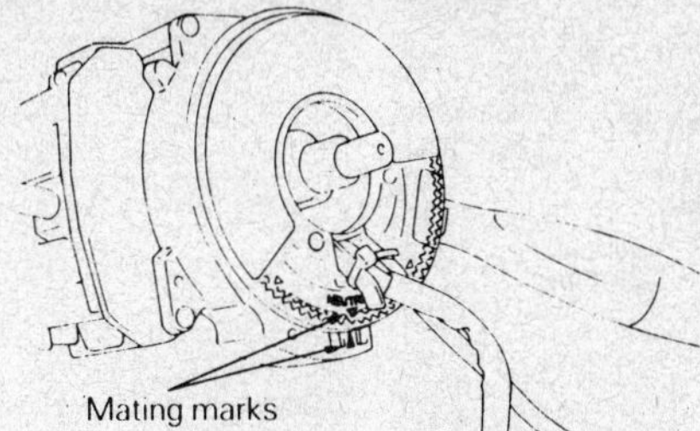


**Fig. 3 Steering wheel clock spring alignment**

then carefully unsnap upper steering column cover from lower.
b. To remove steering lock cylinder insert ignition key and place in "ACC" position.
c. Using suitable Phillips head screwdriver, press lockpin inward to release lock cylinder.
5. Reverse procedure to install, noting the following:
a. Align "Neutral" mark of clock spring with mating marks, **Fig. 3. If clock spring is not properly aligned, steering wheel may not be completely rotational, or flat cable within clock spring may be severed obstructing normal SRS operation which may cause personal injury.**
b. Enable airbag as outlined under "Airbag System, Disarming."

## IGNITION SWITCH
### REPLACE

1. Disable airbag as outlined under "Airbag System, Disarming."
2. Remove instrument panel lower knee protector attaching screws.
3. Remove ignition switch as shown in **Fig. 2,** noting the following:
a. Remove steering column cover upper to lower attaching screws, then carefully unsnap upper steering column cover from lower.
4. Reverse procedure to install, enabling airbag as outlined under "Airbag System, Disarming."

## NEUTRAL START SWITCH
### REPLACE

1. Disconnect battery ground cable.
2. Disconnect neutral switch electrical connector.
3. Remove neutral switch assembly.
4. Reverse procedure to install. Adjust as follows:
a. Place selector lever in "Neutral" position.
b. Place manual control lever in "Neutral" position.
c. Turn switch body, ensuring manual control lever end is aligned with opening in switch body flange.
d. **Torque** switch attaching bolts to 7-9 ft. lbs.

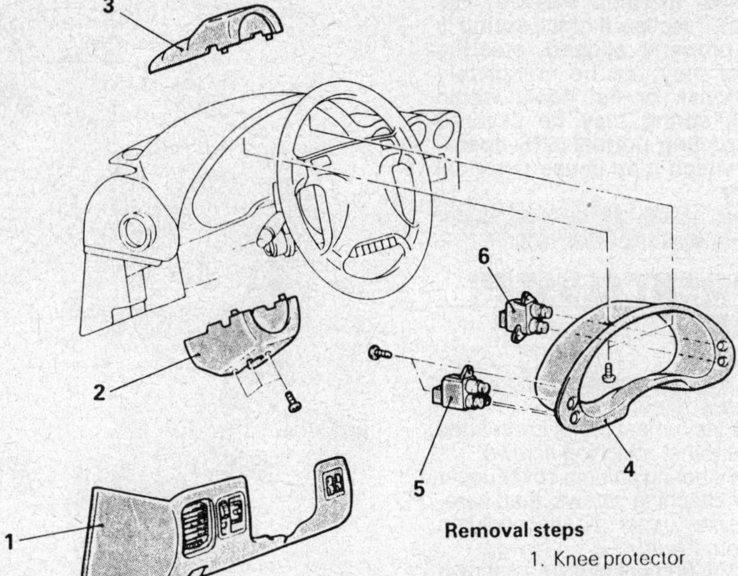


**Fig. 4 Headlight switch assembly**

## HEADLAMP SWITCH
### REPLACE

1. Disable airbag as outlined under "Airbag System, Disarming."
2. Disconnect battery ground cable.
3. Remove instrument panel lower knee protector attaching screws.
4. Remove headlamp switch as shown in **Fig. 4,** noting the following:
a. Remove steering column cover upper to lower attaching screws, then carefully unsnap upper steering column cover from lower.
5. Reverse procedure to install enabling airbag as outlined under "Airbag System, Disarming."

## BACK-UP LIGHT SWITCH
### REPLACE

1. Disconnect battery ground cable.
2. Disconnect back-up switch electrical connector.
3. Remove back-up light switch and gasket from transaxle assembly.
4. Reverse procedure to install. **Torque** switch assembly to 22-25 ft. lbs.

## TURN SIGNAL SWITCH
### REPLACE

Refer to "Column Switch, Replace" for turn signal switch replace procedure.

## COLUMN SWITCH
### REPLACE

1. Disable airbag as outlined under "Airbag System, Disarming."
2. Disconnect battery ground cable.
3. Remove steering wheel as outlined under "Steering Wheel, Replace."
4. Remove turn signal switch as shown in **Fig. 5,** noting the following:
a. Remove steering column cover upper to lower attaching screws, then carefully unsnap upper steering column cover from lower.
5. Reverse procedure to install, enabling airbag as outlined under "Airbag System, Disarming."

## DIMMER SWITCH
### REPLACE

Refer to "Column Switch, Replace," for dimmer switch replacement.

## STEERING WHEEL
### REPLACE

1. Disable airbag as outlined under "Airbag System, Disarming."
2. Remove air bag module and airbag clock spring as outlined in the "Passive Restraints" section. **Do not use excessive force to disconnect clock spring. Store airbag assembly in dry place with pad cover face up.**
3. Remove steering wheel attaching nut.
4. Using suitable steering wheel removal tool, remove steering wheel. **Do not use hammer to remove steering wheel as damage may occur.**
5. Reverse procedure to install, noting the following:
a. **Torque** steering wheel attaching nut to 29 ft. lbs.
b. Install clock spring and airbag as

outlined in the "Passive Restraints" section. **If clock spring is not properly aligned, steering wheel may not be completely rotational, or flat cable within clock spring may be severed obstructing normal SRS operation which may cause personal injury.**

c. Enable airbag as outlined under "Airbag System, Disarming."

## INSTRUMENT CLUSTER
### REPLACE

1. Disable airbag as outlined under "Airbag System, Disarming."
2. Remove instrument panel lower knee protector panel attaching screws.
3. Remove steering column cover upper to lower attaching screws, then carefully unsnap upper steering column cover from lower.
4. Remove instrument cluster as shown in **Fig. 6**, noting the following:
   a. **On models equipped with mechanical speedometer,** disconnect speedometer cable at transaxle, then pull toward interior, then disconnect instrument cluster speedometer adapter by turning right or left.
5. Reverse procedure to install, enabling airbag as outlined under "Airbag System, Disarming."

## WINDSHIELD WIPER MOTOR
### REPLACE

1. Disconnect battery ground cable.
2. Remove wiper arm attaching bolt, then remove wiper arm.
3. Unsnap hole cover assembly, **Fig. 7.**
4. Disconnect wiper motor electrical connector.
5. Remove wiper motor attaching bolts, then remove wiper motor.
6. Reverse procedure to install. **Torque** wiper motor attaching bolts to 7 ft. lbs. **Torque** wiper arm attaching nuts to 9.4 ft. lbs.

## WINDSHIELD WIPER TRANSMISSION
### REPLACE

1. Disconnect battery ground cable.
2. Remove wiper blade, then remove wiper arm attaching nut, **Fig. 7.**
3. Remove front deck attaching screws, then remove front deck.
4. Remove RH air inlet assembly.
5. Unsnap hole cover assembly.
6. Remove wiper motor attaching bolts, then position wiper motor aside.
7. Remove wiper transmission attaching bolts, then remove wiper transmission assembly.
8. Reverse procedure to install. **Torque** linkage attaching bolts to 4 ft. lbs. **Torque** wiper motor attaching bolts to 7 ft. lbs. **Torque** wiper arm attaching nuts to 9.4 ft. lbs.

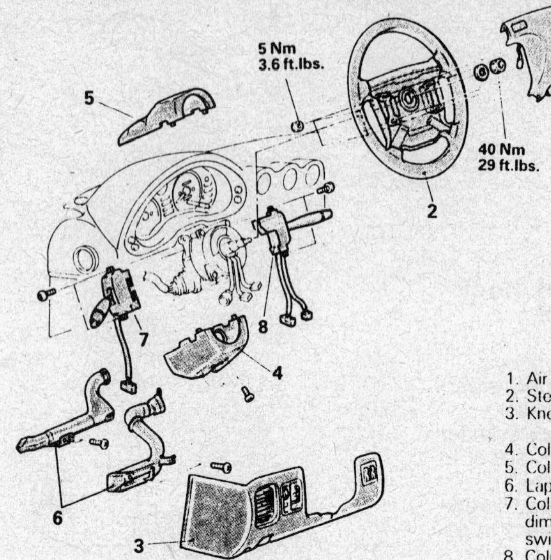


1. Air bag module
2. Steering wheel
3. Knee protector
4. Column cover lower
5. Column cover upper
6. Lap cooler duct and foot shower duct
7. Column switch left (For lighting switch, dimmer/passing switch and turn signal switch)
8. Column switch right (For wiper and washer switch)

**Fig. 5 Steering column switch replacement**

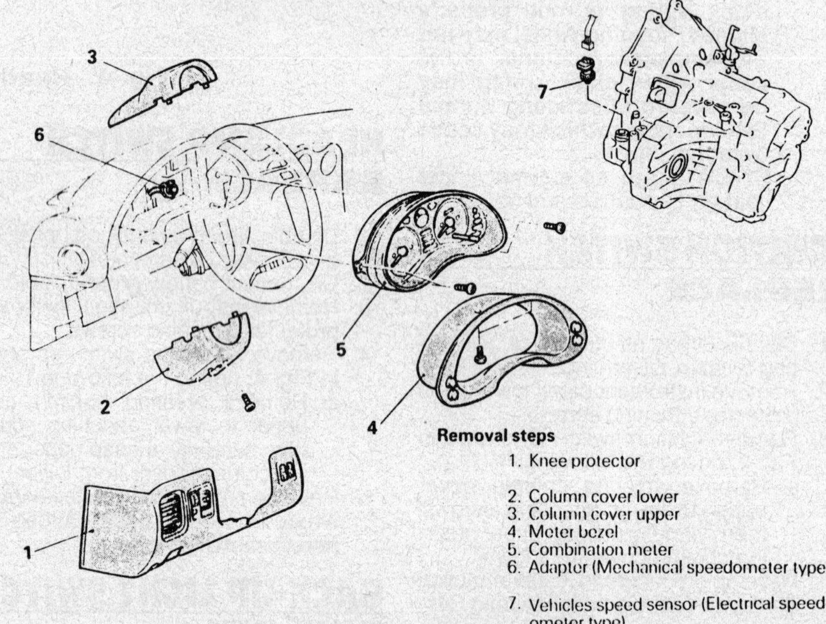


**Fig. 6 Instrument cluster**

## WINDSHIELD WIPER SWITCH
### REPLACE

Refer to "Column Switch, Replace," for wiper switch replacement.

## RADIO
### REPLACE

**Disable airbag as outlined under "Airbag System, Disarming" before performing the following operation.**

1. Disconnect battery ground cable.
2. Remove radio assembly as shown in **Fig. 8.**
3. Remove front console assembly as shown in **Fig. 9.**
4. Reverse procedure to install, enabling airbag as outlined under "Airbag System, Disarming."

## BLOWER MOTOR
### REPLACE

**Disable airbag as outlined under "Airbag System, Disarming" before performing the following operation.**

1. Disconnect battery ground cable.
2. Remove glove compartment attaching screws, then carefully push sides inward to remove.

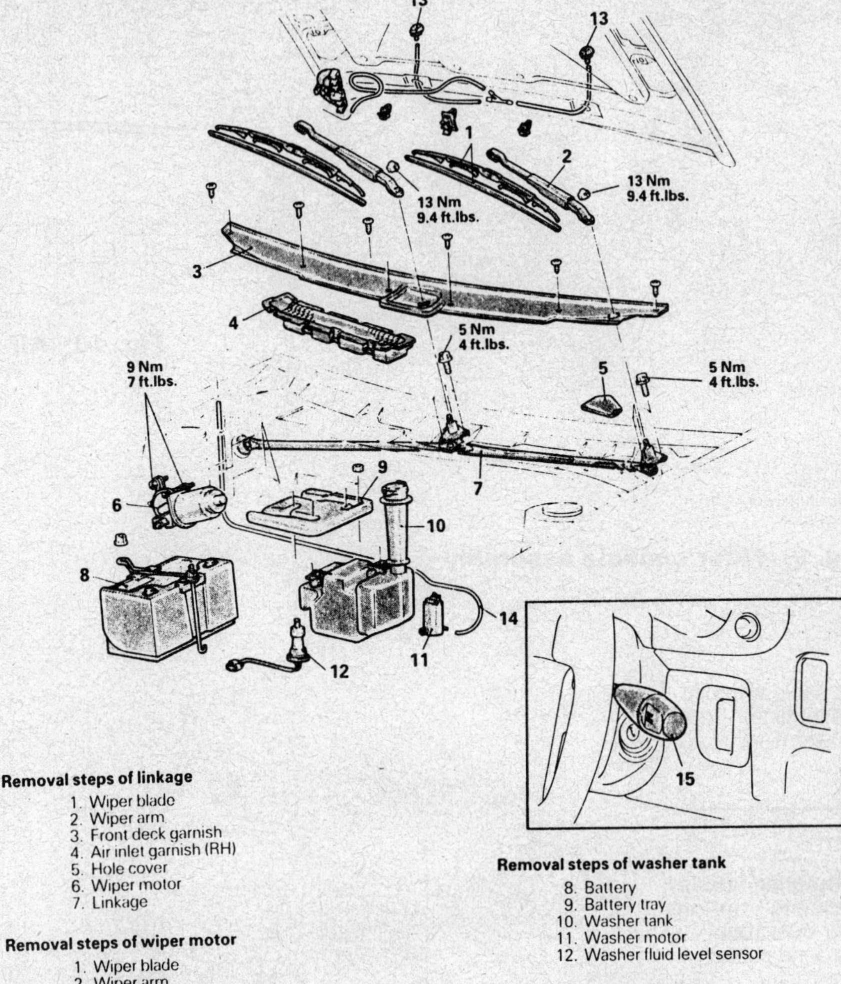


**Removal steps of linkage**

1. Wiper blade
2. Wiper arm
3. Front deck garnish
4. Air inlet garnish (RH)
5. Hole cover
6. Wiper motor
7. Linkage

**Removal steps of wiper motor**

1. Wiper blade
2. Wiper arm
5. Hole cover
6. Wiper motor

**Removal of column switch (wiper washer switch)**

15. Column switch

**Removal steps of washer tank**

8. Battery
9. Battery tray
10. Washer tank
11. Washer motor
12. Washer fluid level sensor

**Removal steps of washer tube**

8. Battery
9. Battery tray
13. Washer nozzle
14. Washer tube

**Fig. 7 Windshield wiper motor & transmission assembly**

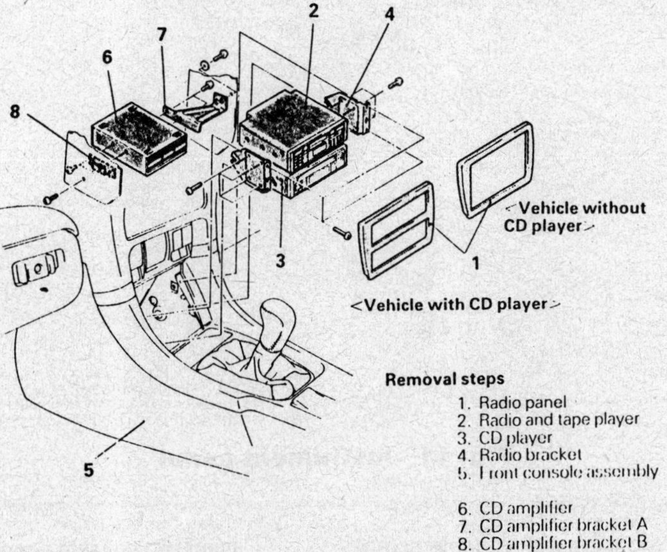


**Removal steps**

1. Radio panel
2. Radio and tape player
3. CD player
4. Radio bracket
5. Front console assembly
6. CD amplifier
7. CD amplifier bracket A
8. CD amplifier bracket B

**Fig. 8 Radio assembly**

3. Remove glove compartment latch attaching screws.
4. Remove four glove compartment outer case attaching screws.
5. Remove four right lower cover attaching screws.
6. Disconnect lower frame electrical connector, then remove lower frame attaching screws.
7. **On models equipped with A/C,** remove evaporator attaching bolt and nut.
8. **On all models,** disconnect air selection control wire at blower motor case.
9. Remove side frame attaching screws.
10. Disconnect blower motor electrical connectors.
11. Remove blower case attaching nuts, then remove blower motor case.
12. Remove blower motor attaching bolt, then remove blower motor.
13. Reverse procedure to install, noting the following:
    a. Position air selection control lever as in **Fig. 10.**
    b. Press air selection damper inward, then connect inner cable of air selection wire to air selection lever,

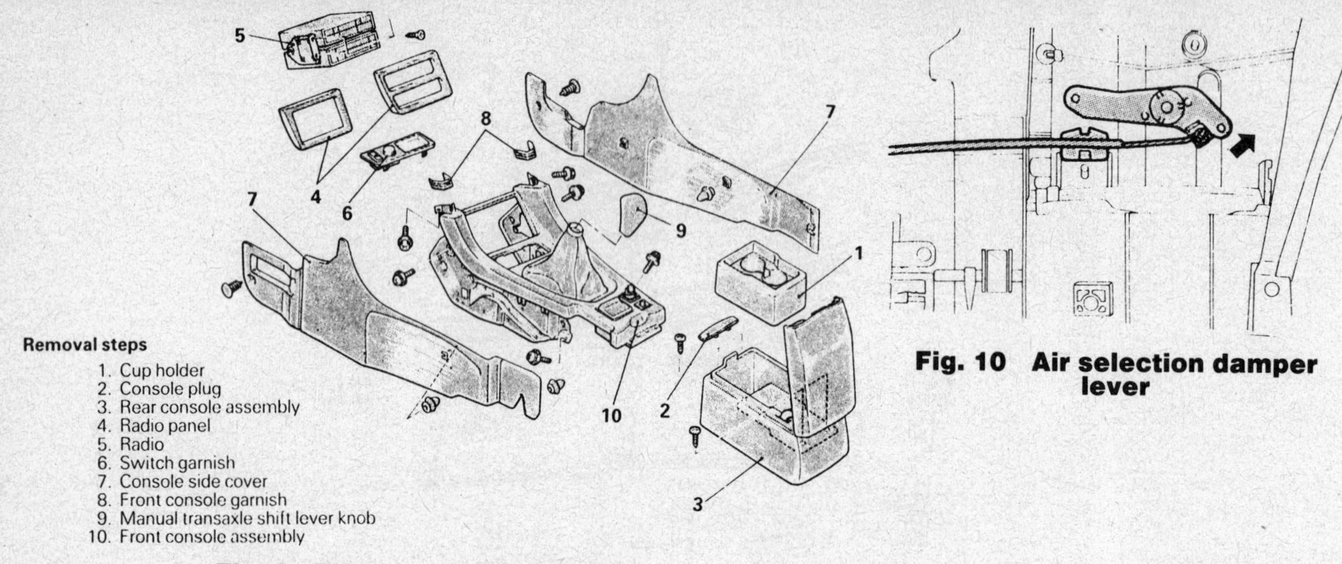


**Fig. 9 Floor console assembly**

**Fig. 10 Air selection damper lever**

then secure outer cable with clip.

c. Enable airbag as outlined under "Airbag System, Disarming."

## HEATER CORE REPLACE

**Disable airbag as outlined under "Airbag System, Disarming" before performing the following operation.**

1. Disconnect battery ground cable.
2. Drain cooling system.
3. Remove floor console as shown in **Fig. 9.**
4. Remove instrument panel as shown in **Fig. 11.**
5. Remove heater core as shown in **Fig. 12,** noting the following:
   a. **On models equipped with A/C,** set inside/outside air selection damper to position that permits outside air introduction to prevent evaporator assembly attaching to enter the blower assembly.
6. Reverse procedure to install, enabling airbag as outlined under "Airbag System, Disarming."

## EVAPORATOR CORE REPLACE

**Disable airbag as outlined under "Airbag System, Disarming" before performing the following operation.**

1. Discharge air conditioning system.
2. Remove battery cables, then remove battery assembly.
3. Remove evaporator case assembly as shown in **Fig. 13,** noting the following:
   a. Cap hoses and pipes to prevent entry of contaminates.
4. Disassemble evaporator case as shown in **Fig. 14,** noting the following:
   a. Disconnect evaporator cover attaching clips with suitable screwdriver covered with shop towel to prevent damage.
   b. Loosen expansion valve flare nut using two suitable wrenches.
5. Reverse procedure to install, enabling airbag as outlined under "Airbag System, Disarming."

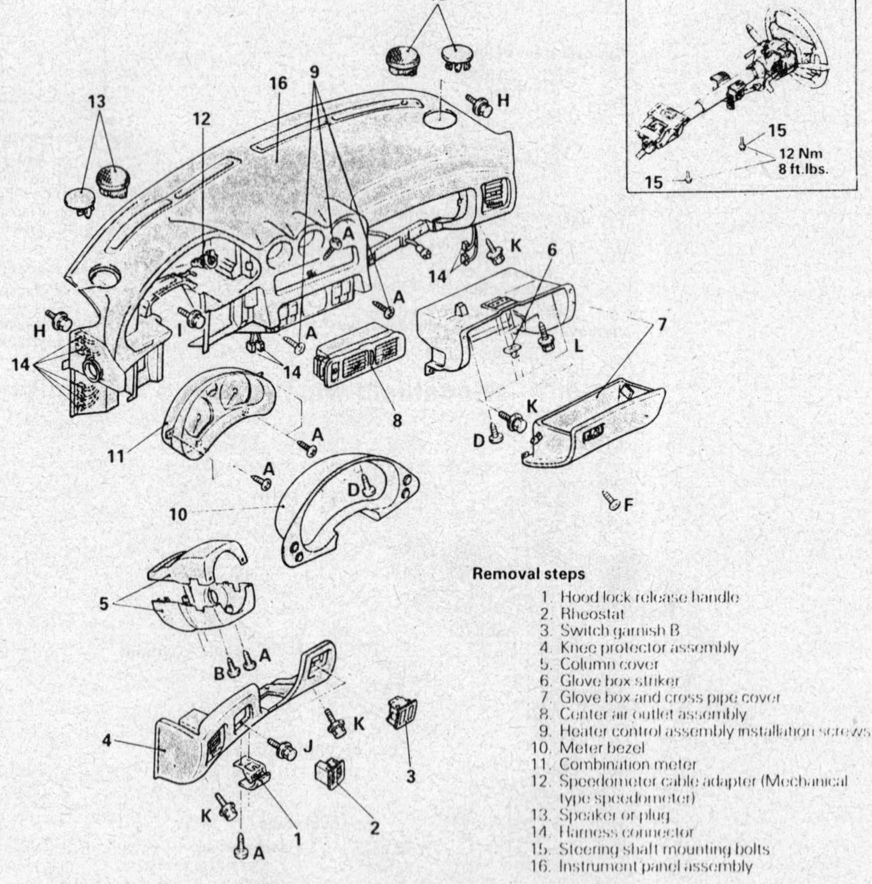


**Fig. 11 Instrument panel**

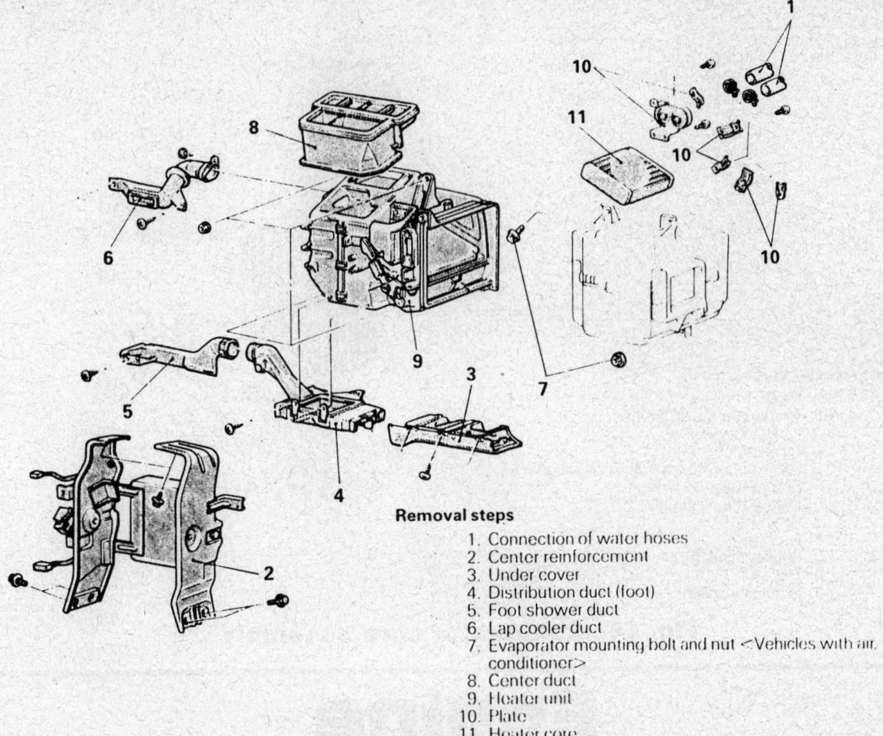


**Fig. 12 Heater core assembly**

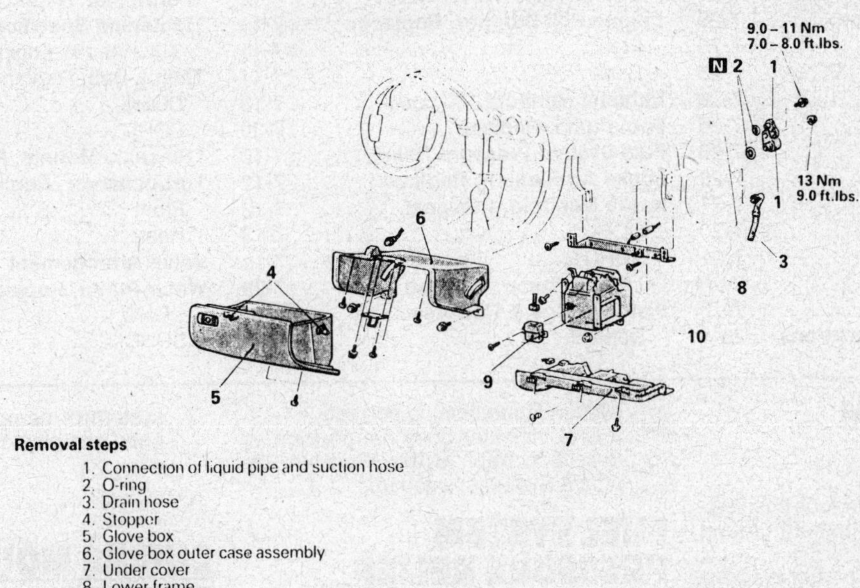


**Fig. 13 Evaporator case assembly**

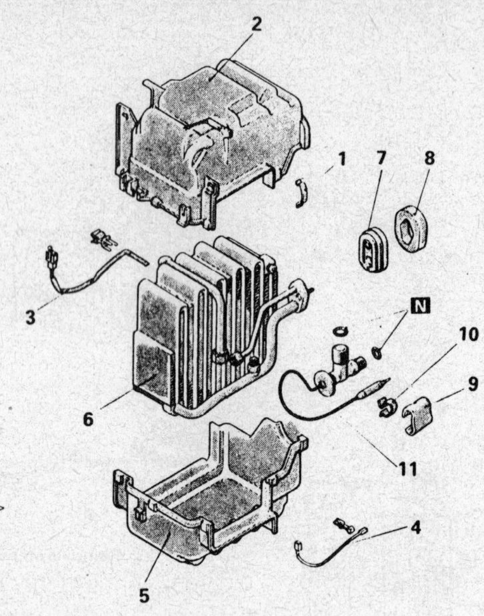


**Disassembly steps**

1. Clips
2. Evaporater case (upper)
3. Fin thermo sensor
4. Air inlet sensor
   <Vehicles with manual air conditioner>
5. Evaporator case (lower)
6. Evaporator assembly
7. Grommet
8. Insulator
9. Rubber insulator
10. Clip
11. Expansion valve

**Fig. 14 Evaporator core assembly**

# Engine

## INDEX



## AIRBAG SYSTEM DISARMING

1. Place ignition switch in lock position.
2. Disconnect and tape battery ground cable connector.
3. **Wait at least 1 minute after disconnecting battery ground cable before doing any further work on vehicle.** The SRS system is designed to retain enough voltage to deploy airbag for a short time even after battery has been disconnected.
4. After repairs are complete, reconnect battery ground cable.
5. From passenger side of vehicle, turn ignition switch to On position.
6. SRS warning light should illuminate for 6 to 8 seconds, then remain off for at least 45 seconds to indicate if SRS system is functioning correctly.
7. If SRS indicator does not perform as described refer to the "Passive Restraint Systems" section.

## FUEL SYSTEM PRESSURE RELIEF

**To reduce the risk of fire and personal injury, it is necessary to relieve the fuel system pressure before servicing fuel system components.**

1. Remove fuel gauge sending unit cover in luggage compartment.
2. Disconnect fuel pump harness connector.
3. Start engine and allow to run.
4. After engine stop by itself, turn ignition switch to Off position.
5. Connect fuel pump harness after fuel system or components service have been completed.

## ENGINE MOUNTS REPLACE

1. Raise and support engine using suitable support tool.
2. Remove engine mount in order shown in **Fig. 1,** noting the following:
   a. Remove actuator and position aside.
3. Reverse procedure to install, noting the following:
   a. When installing engine mounting bracket, align arrow on mounting stopper as shown in **Fig. 2.**

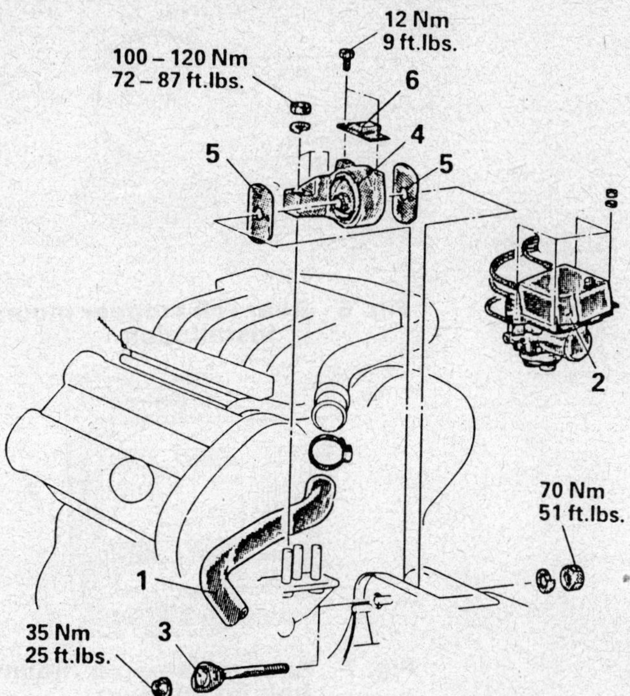


1. Connection for air hose G <Turbo>
2. Cruise control pump and link assembly <Vehicles with Cruise Control>
3. Engine mount bracket and body connection bolt
4. Engine mount bracket
5. Mounting stopper
6. Dynamic damper <DOHC>

**Fig. 1 Engine mount replacement**

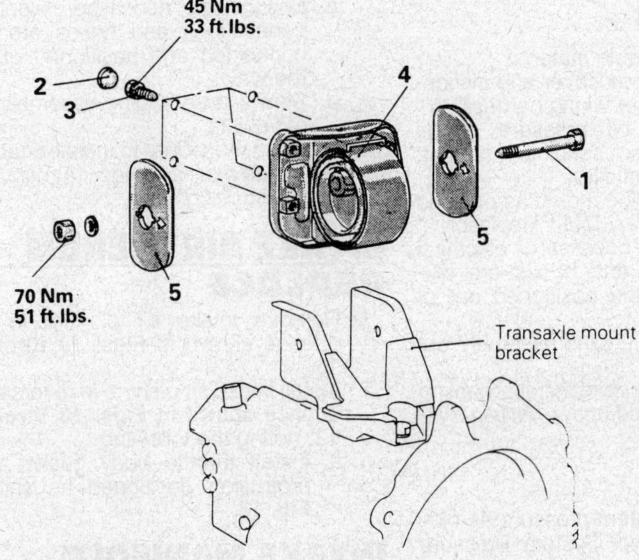


**Removal steps**

1. Transaxle mount bracket and transaxle connection bolt
2. Cap
3. Transaxle mount bracket installation bolt
4. Transaxle mount bracket
5. Mounting stopper

**Fig. 3 Transaxle mount replacement**

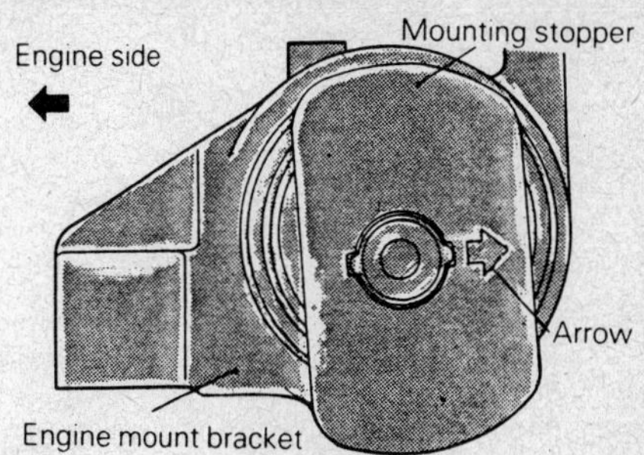


**Fig. 2 Installing engine mount**

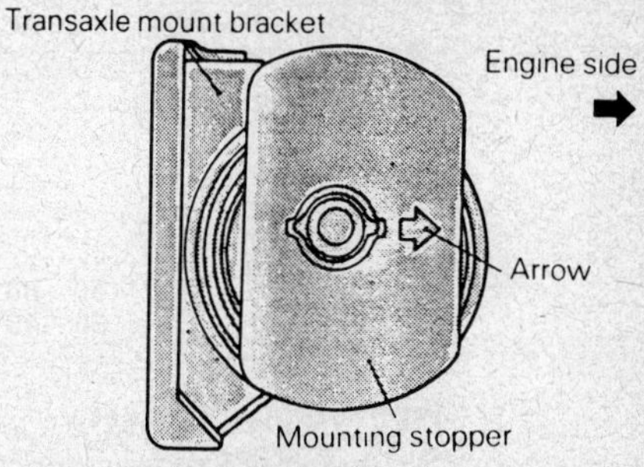

Transaxle mount bracket

Engine side

Arrow

Mounting stopper

**Fig. 4 Installing transaxle mount**

# TRANSAXLE MOUNTS REPLACE

1. Raise and support transaxle using suitable support tool.
2. Remove air cleaner assembly.
3. Remove transaxle mount in order shown in **Fig. 3.**
4. Reverse procedure to install, noting the following:
   a. When installing transaxle mounting bracket, align arrow on mounting stopper as shown in **Fig. 4.**

# ENGINE ROLL STOPPER REPLACE

## FRONT

1. **On models with turbocharger,** remove A/C condenser cooling fan assembly.
2. **On models with turbocharger,** remove left catalytic converter.
3. Remove front engine roll stopper in order shown in **Fig. 5.**
4. Reverse procedure to install.

## REAR

1. **On models with turbocharger,** remove A/C condenser cooling fan assembly.
2. **On models with turbocharger,** remove left catalytic converter.
3. **On all models,** remove rear roll stopper in order shown in **Fig. 5,** noting the following:
   a. Slightly raise rear roll stopper bracket while turning roll stopper as shown in **Fig. 6.**
4. Reverse procedure to install, noting the following:
   a. Install rear roll stopper bracket as shown in **Fig. 6.**

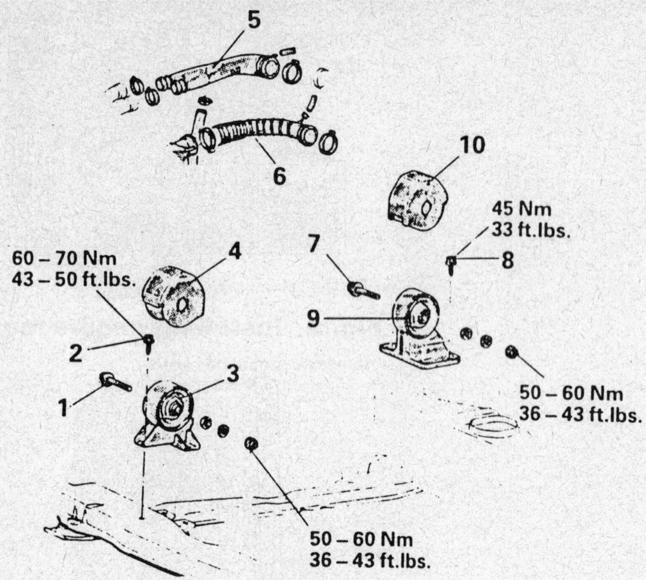


**Front stopper bracket**

1. Front roll stopper bracket and engine connection bolt
2. Front roll stopper bracket installation bolt
3. Front roll stopper bracket
4. Heat protector <Turbo>

**Rear roll stopper bracket**

5. Air hose A <Turbo>
6. Air intake hose C <Turbo>
7. Rear roll stopper bracket and engine connection bolt
8. Rear roll stopper bracket installation bolt
9. Rear roll stopper bracket
10. Heat protector <Turbo>

**Fig. 5 Engine roll stopper replacement**

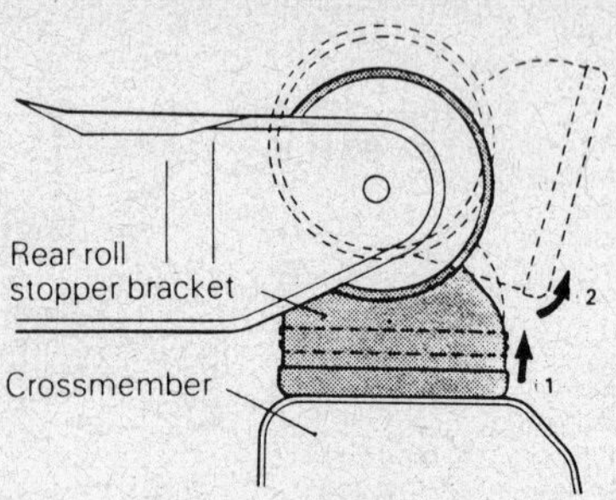


**Fig. 6 Rear roll stopper mount installation**

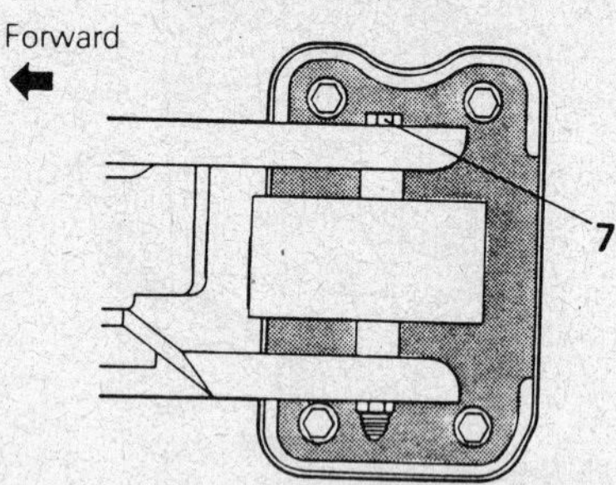


**Fig. 7 Rear roll stopper mount bolt installation**

b. Install through bolt as shown in **Fig. 7.**

# ENGINE
## REPLACE

**Disable airbag as outlined under "Airbag System, Disarming" before performing the following operation.**

### SOHC

1. Relieve fuel system pressure as outlined under "Fuel System Pressure Relief."
2. Mark and remove hood assembly.
3. Disconnect and remove cruise control pump and link assembly.
4. Drain cooling system.
5. Remove front exhaust pipes.
6. Remove transaxle as outlined under "Manual Transaxle, Replace" in the "Clutch & Manual Transaxle" section.
7. Remove radiator assembly.
8. Remove engine assembly in order shown in **Fig. 8,** noting the following:
   a. Disconnect power steering pump and A/C compressor with hoses attached. Support aside with rope or other suitable material.
   b. Open relay box cover and disconnect alternator wiring harness.
   c. Disconnect oil pressure gauge connector from sending unit located near the oil filter.
   d. Remove engine mount as outlined under "Engine Mount, Replace."
   e. Ensure all necessary electrical connections and hoses are disconnected and positioned out of the way.
   f. Slowly raise engine assembly out of vehicle.
9. Reverse procedure to install, enabling airbag as outlined under "Airbag System, Disarming."

### DOHC

1. Relieve fuel system pressure as outlined under "Fuel System Pressure Relief."
2. Mark and remove hood assembly.
3. Disconnect and remove cruise control pump and link assembly.
4. **On turbocharged models,** remove air hose and air pipe.
5. **On all models,** remove front exhaust pipes.
6. Remove transaxle as outlined under "Manual Transaxle, Replace" in the "Clutch & Manual Transaxle" section.
7. Remove radiator assembly.
8. Remove engine assembly in order shown in **Fig. 9,** noting the following:
   a. Disconnect power steering pump and A/C compressor with hoses attached. Support aside with rope or other suitable material.
   b. Remove engine mount as outlined under "Engine Mount, Replace."
   c. Ensure all necessary electrical connections and hoses are disconnected and positioned out of the way.
   d. Slowly raise engine assembly out of vehicle.
9. Reverse procedure to install, enabling airbag as outlined under "Airbag System, Disarming."

# INTAKE AIR PLENUM
## REPLACE

1. Remove intake air plenum in sequence shown in **Figs. 10 through 12.**
2. Install intake air plenum in reverse sequence shown in **Figs. 10 through 12,** noting the following:
   a. Install throttle body gasket with protrusion positioned as shown, **Fig. 13.**

# INTAKE MANIFOLD
## REPLACE

### SOHC

1. Relieve fuel system pressure as outlined under "Fuel System Pressure Relief."
2. Drain engine coolant.
3. Remove intake air plenum as outlined under "Intake Air Plenum, Replace."

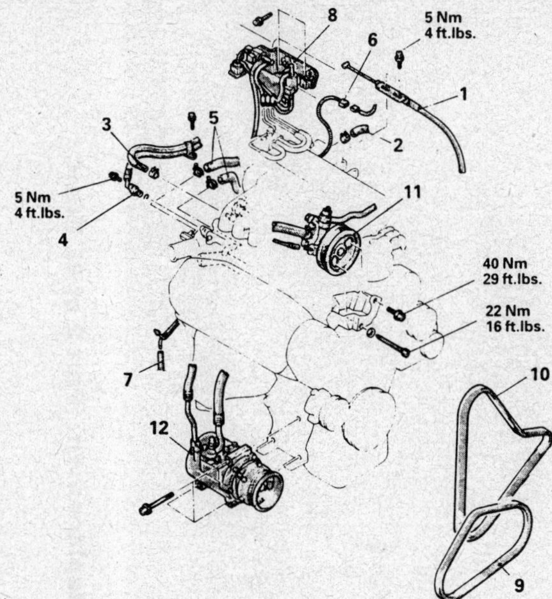


1. Connection of accelerator cable
2. Connection of brake booster vacuum hose
3. Connection of fuel return hose
4. Connection of fuel high pressure hose
5. Connection of heater hose
6. Connection of EGR temperature sensor <Vehicles for California>
7. Connection of vaper hose
8. Solenoid valve assembly
9. Drive belt (air conditioner)
10. Drive belt (alternator and power steering)
11. Power steering oil pump
12. Air conditioner compressor

**Fig. 8 Engine replacement (Part 1 of 2). SOHC**

13. Connection of ISC
14. Connection of TPS
15. Connection of injector harness
16. Connection of engine coolant temperature switch (Air conditioner)
17. Connection of engine coolant temperature sensor
18. Connection of engine coolant temperature gauge unit
19. Connection of fuel injectors
20. Connection of power transistor
21. Connection of distributer
22. Connection of ignition coil
23. Connection of condenser
24. Connection of ground cable
25. Connection of relay box and engine control harness.
26. Connection of oil pressure gauge unit

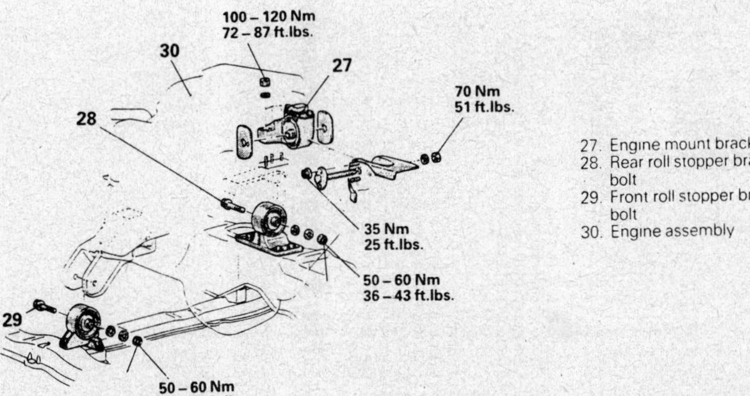


27. Engine mount bracket
28. Rear roll stopper bracket mount bolt
29. Front roll stopper bracket mount bolt
30. Engine assembly

**Fig. 8 Engine replacement (Part 2 of 2). SOHC**

4. Remove intake manifold in sequence shown in **Fig. 14,** noting the following:
   a. Disconnect delivery pipe with injectors attached.
5. Reverse procedure to install, noting the following:
   a. Install intake manifold gasket with adhesive coated side toward the intake manifold.
   b. Apply lubricant to the intake manifold nuts and tighten to specification.

## DOHC

1. Relieve fuel system pressure as outlined under "Fuel System Pressure Relief."
2. Drain engine coolant.
3. Remove intake air plenum as outlined under "Intake Air Plenum, Replace."
4. Remove intake manifold in sequence shown in **Fig. 15.**
5. Reverse procedure to install, noting the following:
   a. Install intake manifold gaskets with protrusion position as shown, **Fig. 16.**
   b. **On turbocharged models, torque** intake manifold front bank nuts to 2.2-3.6 ft. lbs.
   c. **On turbocharged models, torque** intake manifold rear bank nuts to 9-11 ft. lbs.
   d. **On turbocharged models, torque** intake manifold front bank nuts to 9-11 ft. lbs.
   e. **On turbocharged models,** repeat steps c and d one more time.
   f. **On except turbocharged models,** lubricate intake manifold nuts and tighten to specification.

# EXHAUST MANIFOLD

## REPLACE

1. **On except turbocharged models,** remove front exhaust pipe.
2. **On DOHC models less turbocharged,** remove condenser fan motor assembly.
3. **On turbocharged models,** remove turbocharger as outlined under "Turbocharger, Replace."
4. Remove exhaust manifold in sequence shown in **Figs. 17 through 19.**
5. **On except turbocharged models,** reverse procedure shown in **Figs. 17 and 18** to install.
6. **On turbocharged models,** install exhaust manifold in reverse sequence shown in **Fig. 19,** noting the following:
   a. **Torque** exhaust manifold nuts marked A to 22 ft. lbs., **Fig. 20.**
   b. **Torque** exhaust manifold nuts marked B to 34-38 ft. lbs., **Fig. 20.**
   c. Back off exhaust manifold nuts marked B to a **torque** value of 7 ft. lbs.
   d. **Torque** exhaust manifold nuts marked B to 21-22 ft. lbs.
   e. Install exhaust manifold stay with it resting on exhaust manifold, fit it along with exhaust manifold over the studs.

*Continued on page 7-19*

1. Connection of accelerator cable
2. Connection of brake booster vacuum hose
3. Connection of booster vacuum hose <Turbo>
4. Connection of fuel return hose
5. Connection of fuel high pressure hose
6. Connection of ground cable
7. Solenoid valve assembly
8. Connection of vapor hose
9. Connection of heater hose
10. Connection of EGR temperature sensor <Vehicles for California>
11. Drive belt (Alternator and air conditioner)
12. Drive belt (Power steering)
13. Connection of alternator harness
14. Connection of oxygen sensor <Turbo>
15. Air conditioner compressor
16. Power steering oil pump
17. Connection of oil pressure switch (Power steering)
18. Connection of oil cooler pipes <Turbo>

**Fig. 9 Engine Replacement (Part 1 of 2). DOHC**

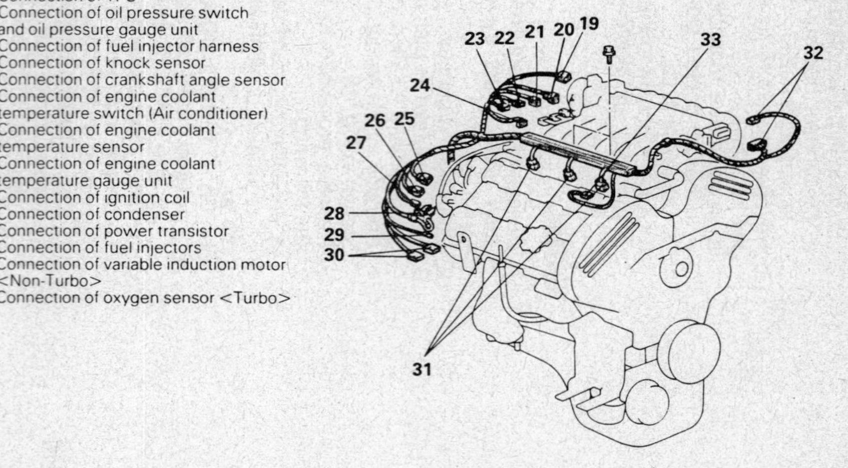


19. Connection of ISC
20. Connection of TPS
21. Connection of oil pressure switch and oil pressure gauge unit
22. Connection of fuel injector harness
23. Connection of knock sensor
24. Connection of crankshaft angle sensor
25. Connection of engine coolant temperature switch (Air conditioner)
26. Connection of engine coolant temperature sensor
27. Connection of engine coolant temperature gauge unit
28. Connection of ignition coil
29. Connection of condenser
30. Connection of power transistor
31. Connection of fuel injectors
32. Connection of variable induction motor <Non-Turbo>
33. Connection of oxygen sensor <Turbo>

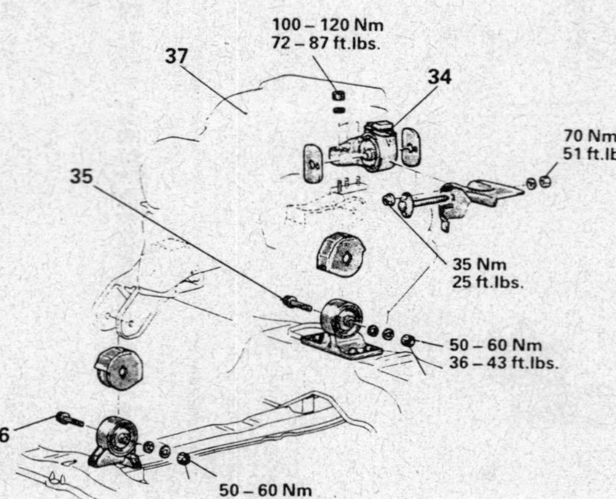


34. Engine mounting bracket
35. Rear roll stopper bracket and engine connection bolt
36. Front roll stopper bracket and engine connection bolt
37. Engine assembly

**Fig. 9 Engine Replacement (Part 2 of 2). DOHC**

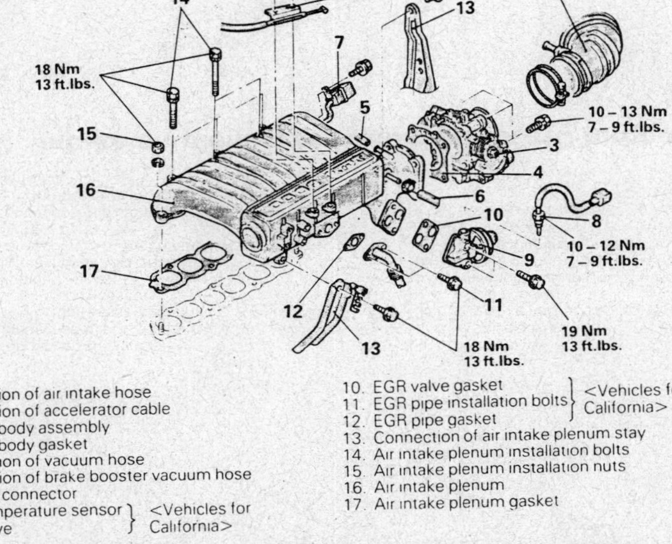


1. Connection of air intake hose
2. Connection of accelerator cable
3. Throttle body assembly
4. Throttle body gasket
5. Connection of vacuum hose
6. Connection of brake booster vacuum hose
7. Harness connector
8. EGR temperature sensor } <Vehicles for
9. EGR valve } California>
10. EGR valve gasket } <Vehicles for
11. EGR pipe installation bolts } California>
12. EGR pipe gasket }
13. Connection of air intake plenum stay
14. Air intake plenum installation bolts
15. Air intake plenum installation nuts
16. Air intake plenum
17. Air intake plenum gasket

**Fig. 10 Intake air plenum replacement. SOHC**

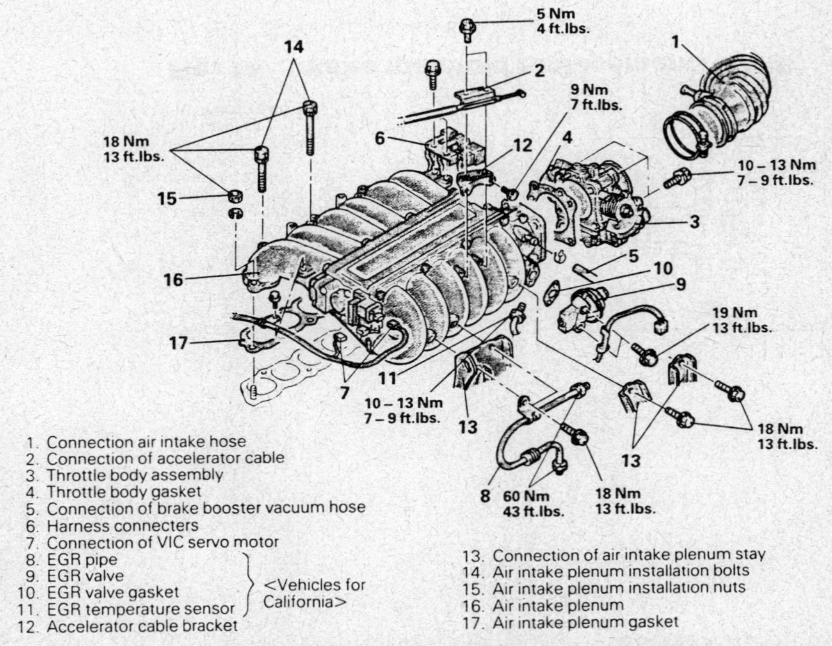


1. Connection air intake hose
2. Connection of accelerator cable
3. Throttle body assembly
4. Throttle body gasket
5. Connection of brake booster vacuum hose
6. Harness connecters
7. Connection of VIC servo motor
8. EGR pipe }
9. EGR valve } <Vehicles for
10. EGR valve gasket } California>
11. EGR temperature sensor }
12. Accelerator cable bracket
13. Connection of air intake plenum stay
14. Air intake plenum installation bolts
15. Air intake plenum installation nuts
16. Air intake plenum
17. Air intake plenum gasket

**Fig. 11 intake air plenum replacement. DOHC except turbocharged**

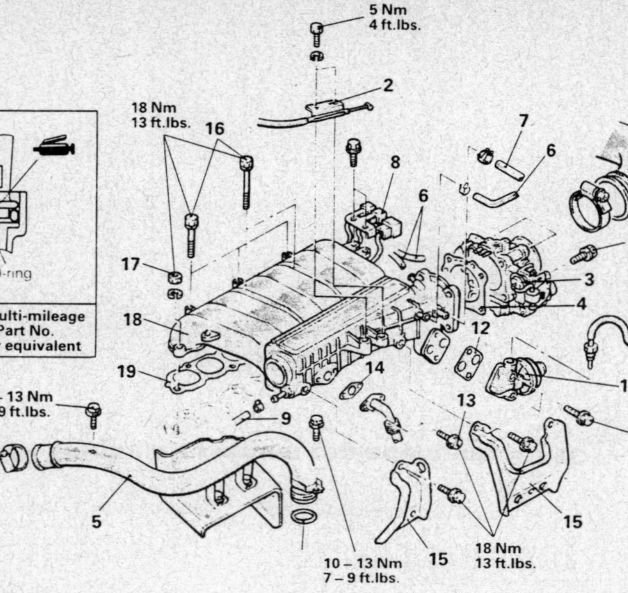


1. Connection air hose A
2. Connection of accelerator cable
3. Throttle body assembly
4. Throttle body gasket
5. Air pipe A
6. Connection of vacuum hose
7. Connection of brake booster vacuum hose
8. Harness connecter
9. Connection of clutch booster vacuum hose
10. EGR temperature sensor <Vehicles for California>
11. EGR valve
12. EGR valve gasket
13. EGR pipe installation bolts
14. EGR pipe gasket
15. Connection of air intake plenum stay
16. Air intake plenum installation bolts
17. Air intake plenum installation nuts
18. Air intake plenum
19. Air intake plenum gasket

**Fig. 12 Intake air plenum replacement. DOHC turbocharged**

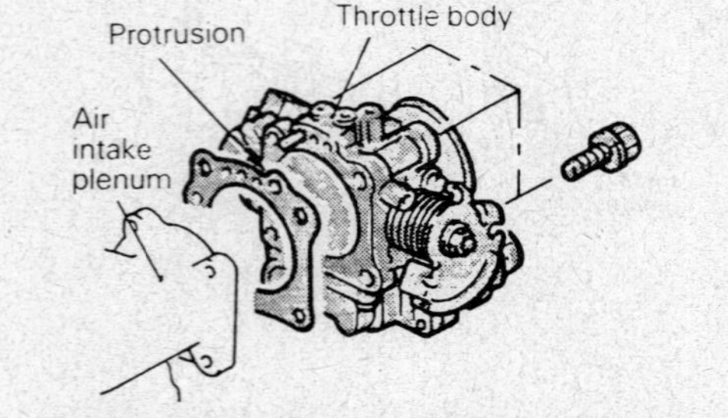


**Fig. 13 Installing throttle body gasket**

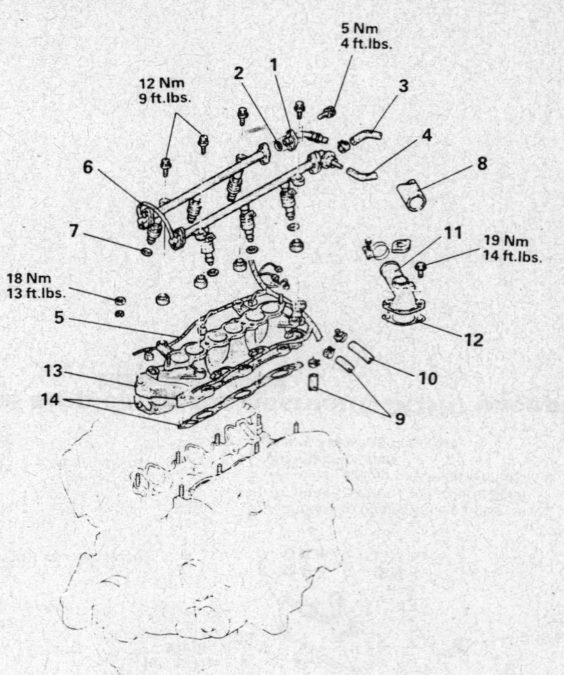


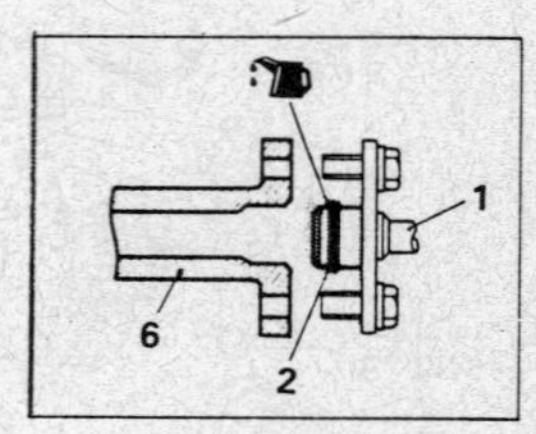

1. Connection for high-pressure fuel hose
2. O-ring
3. Connection for fuel return hose
4. Connection for vacuum hoses
5. Wiring harness connector
6. Delivery pipe (with injectors)
7. Insulators
8. Connection for radiator upper hose
9. Connection for heater hose
10. Connection for water hose
11. Water outlet fitting
12. Water outlet fitting gasket
13. Intake manifold
14. Intake manifold gasket

**Fig. 14 Intake manifold replacement. SOHC**

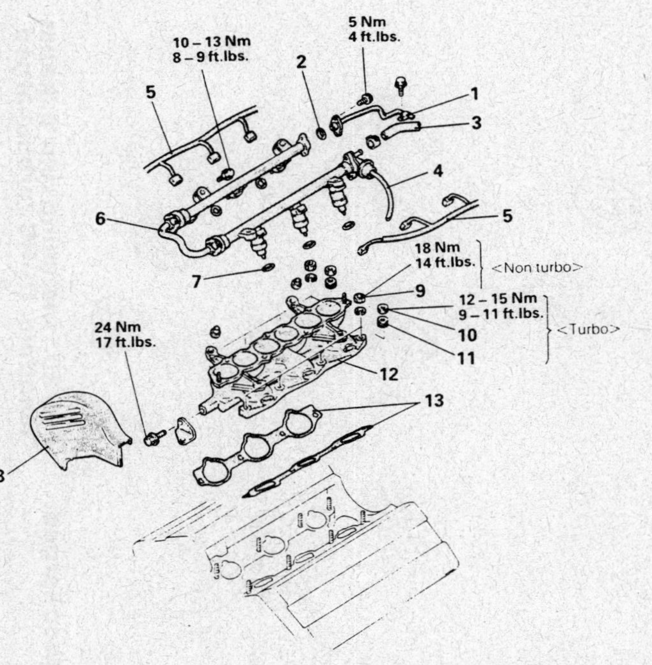

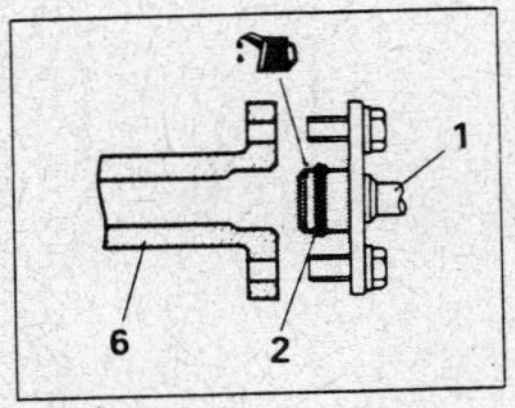

1. Connection for high-pressure fuel hose
2. O-ring
3. Connection for fuel return hose
4. Connection for vacuum hoses
5. Connection for injector connector
6. Delivery pipe (with injectors)
7. Insulators
8. Timing belt upper cover
9. Intake manifold mounting nut <Non turbo>
10. Intake manifold mounting nut <Turbo>
11. Cone disc spring <Turbo>
12. Intake manifold
13. Intake manifold gasket

**Fig. 15 Intake manifold replacement. DOHC**

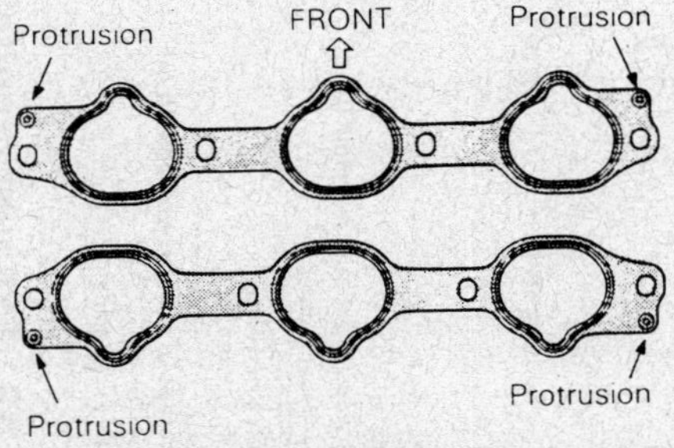

Protrusion FRONT Protrusion

Protrusion Protrusion

**Fig. 16 Installing intake manifold gaskets. DOHC**

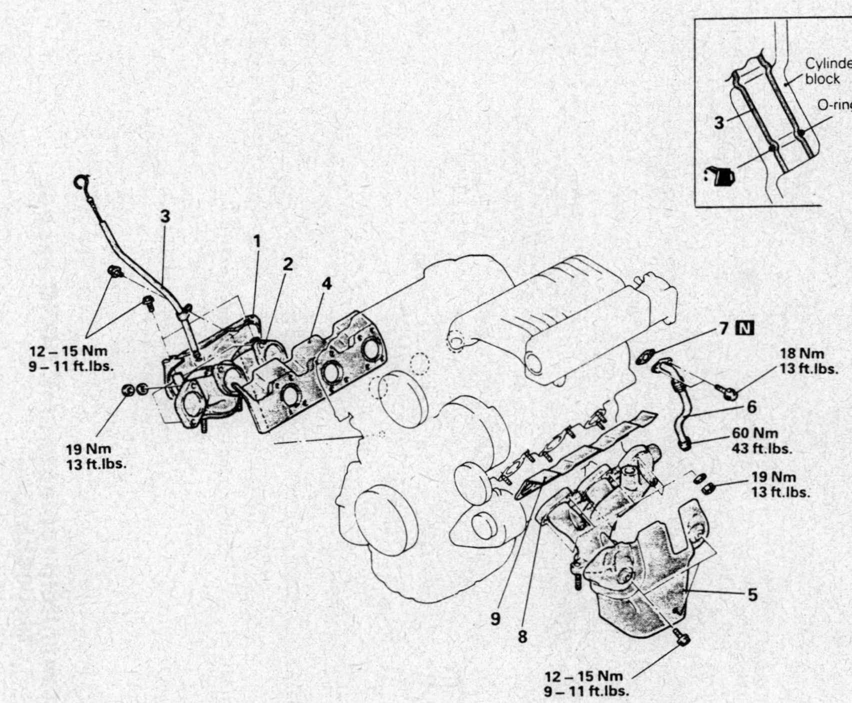


**Removal steps of exhaust manifold (front)**

1. Heat protector
2. Exhaust manifold (front)
3. Oil level gauge guide
4. Gasket

**Removal steps of exhaust manifold (rear)**

5. Heat protector
6. EGR pipe <Vehicles for California>
7. EGR gasket <Vehicles for California>
8. Exhaust manifold (rear)
9. Gasket

**Fig. 17 Exhaust manifold replacement. SOHC**

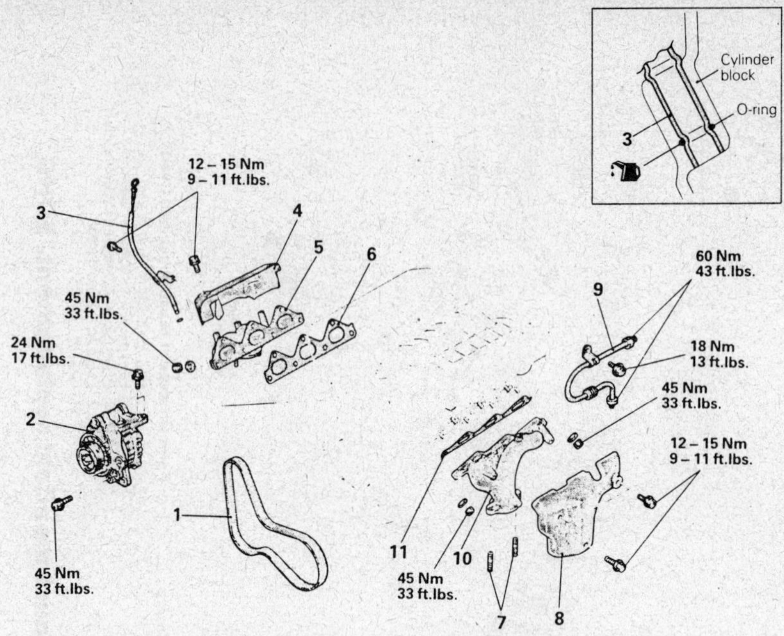


**Removal steps of exhaust manifold (front)**

1. Drive belt (Alternator)

   Service Adjustment procedures)
2. Alternator assembly
3. Oil level gauge guide
4. Heat protector
5. Exhaust manifold (front)
6. Gasket

**Removal steps of exhaust manifold (rear)**

7. Stud
8. Heat protector
9. EGR pipe <Vehicles for California>
10. Exhaust manifold (rear)
11. Gasket

**Fig. 18 Exhaust manifold replacement. DOHC except turbocharged**

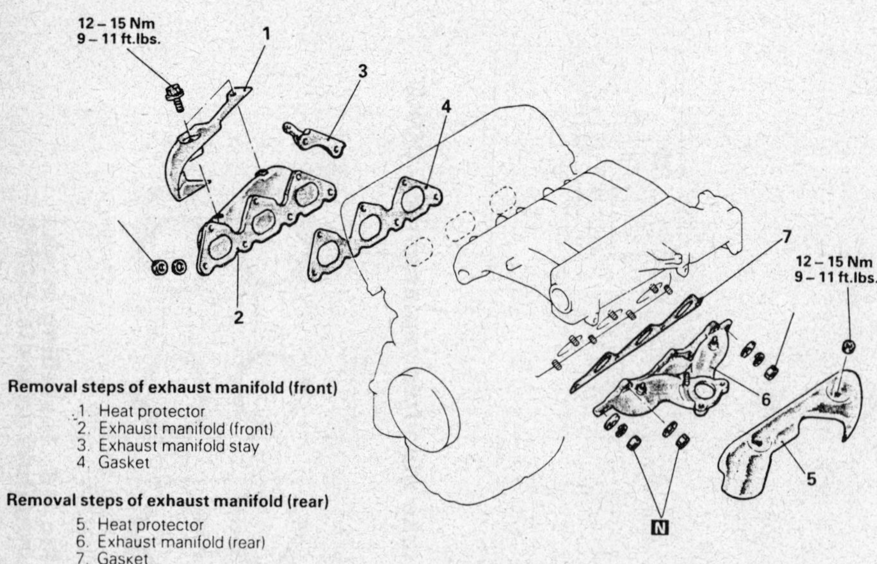


**Removal steps of exhaust manifold (front)**

1. Heat protector
2. Exhaust manifold (front)
3. Exhaust manifold stay
4. Gasket

**Removal steps of exhaust manifold (rear)**

5. Heat protector
6. Exhaust manifold (rear)
7. Gasket

**Fig. 19 Exhaust manifold replacement. DOHC turbocharged**

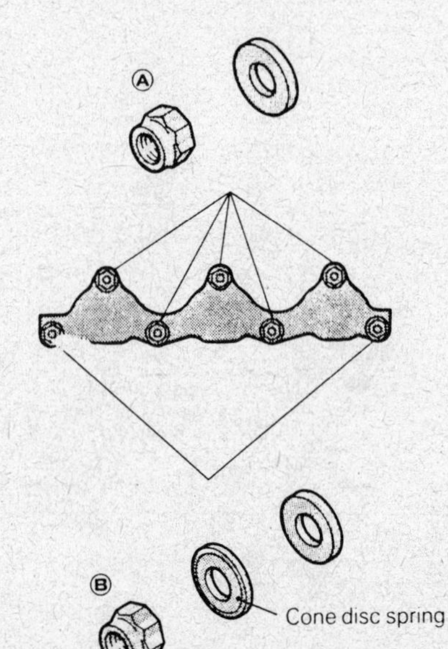


**Fig. 20 Installing rear exhaust manifold. DOHC turbocharged**

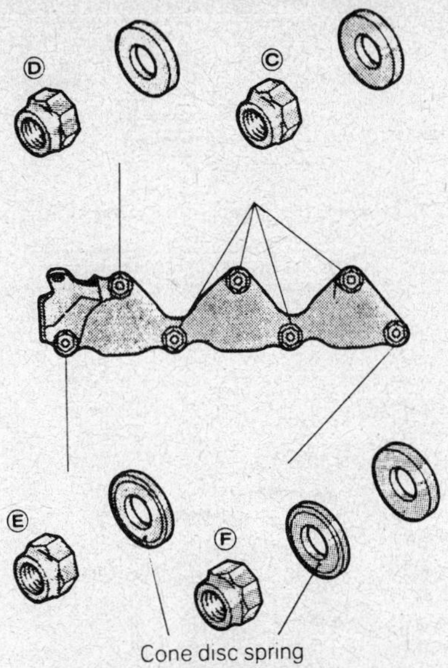


**Fig. 21 Installing front exhaust manifold. DOHC turbocharged**

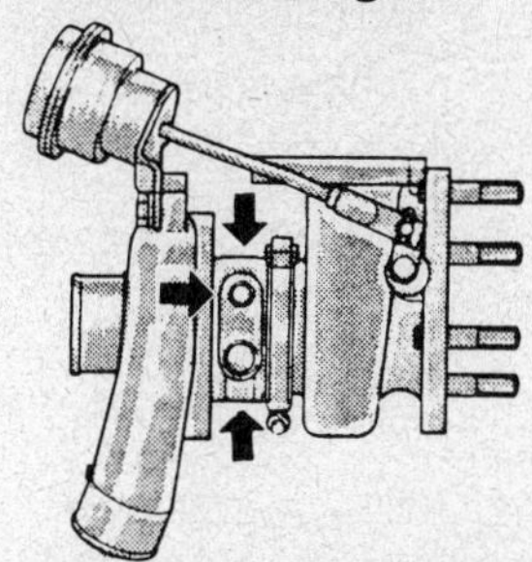

**Fig. 23 Cleaning turbocharger. DOHC turbocharged**

f. **Torque** exhaust manifold nuts marked C to 22 ft. lbs., **Fig. 21.**
g. Temporarily tighten turbocharger to exhaust manifold.
h. **Torque** nut marked D to 22 ft. lbs., **Fig. 21.**
i. **Torque** exhaust manifold nuts marked E and F to 34-38 ft. lbs., **Fig. 21.**
j. Back off exhaust manifold nuts marked E and F to a **Torque** value of 7 ft. lbs.
k. **Torque** exhaust manifold nuts marked E and F to 21-22 ft. lbs., **Fig. 21.**

## TURBOCHARGER REPLACE

### FRONT

1. Remove radiator assembly and transmission stay bracket.
2. Remove front exhaust pipe assembly.
3. Remove front turbocharger in sequence shown in **Fig. 22,** noting the following:

1. Air hose C
2. Air intake hose B
3. Air hose D
4. Air hose A
5. Air hose B
6. Air pipe B
7. Air hose E
8. Air pipe C
9. Drive belt
10. Alternator assembly
11. Engine oil level gauge guide
12. Heat protector B
13. Water pipe A
14. Water pipe B
15. Connection of oxygen sensor
16. Turbocharger & fitting assembly
17. Gasket
18. Ring
19. Oxygen sensor
20. Turbocharger stay
21. Exhaust fitting
22. Gasket
23. Oil return pipe
24. Turbocharger assembly
25. Air conditioner compressor
26. Tension pulley bracket
27. Air conditioner compressor bracket
28. Oil pipe

**Fig. 22 Turbocharger replacement, front. DOHC turbocharged**

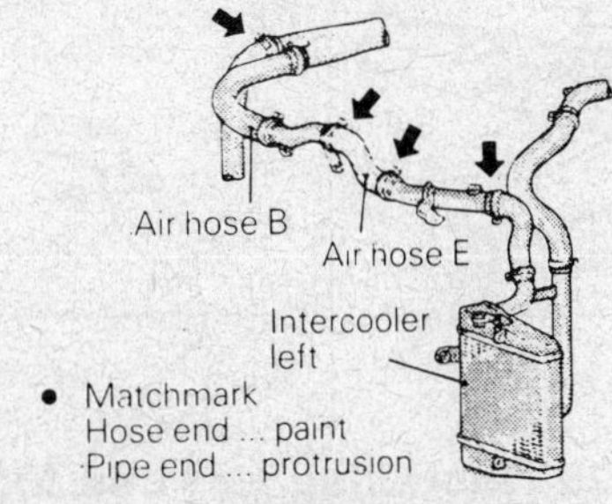


**Fig. 24 Installing air hose E/5 & B. DOHC turbocharged**

a. Disconnect oxygen sensor connector and remove using oxygen wrench remover tool No. MD998770, or equivalent.
b. Disconnect A/C compressor with hoses attached. Position aside using suitable support wire.

4. Reverse procedure to install, noting the following:
   a. Clean points marked in **Fig. 23.** and supply clean engine oil into oil pipe installation hole.
   b. Install oxygen sensor using oxygen sensor wrench tool No. MD998770, or equivalent.
   c. Align marks on air hose E/5 and B indicated by arrows in **Fig. 24** and seat completely into stepper portion of pipe or until seated.
   d. Align marks on air hose D/1 and C indicated by arrows in **Fig. 25** and seat completely into stepper portion of pipe or until seated.
   e. Align and engage air intake hose notches mark with an arrow in **Fig. 26** until fully seated.

### REAR

1. Drain engine cooling system.
2. Remove front exhaust pipe.

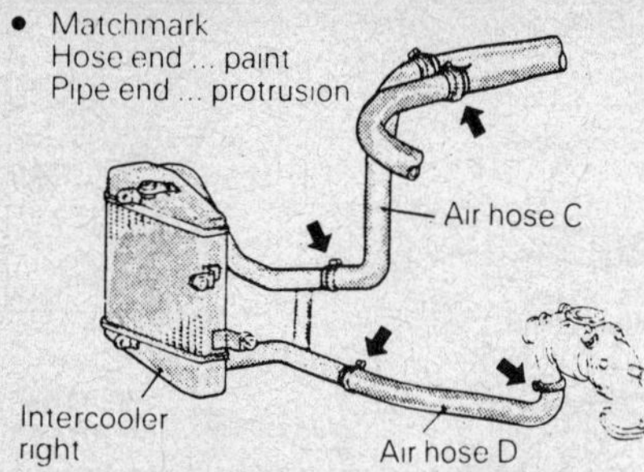


**Fig. 25 Installing air hose D/1 & C. DOHC turbocharged**

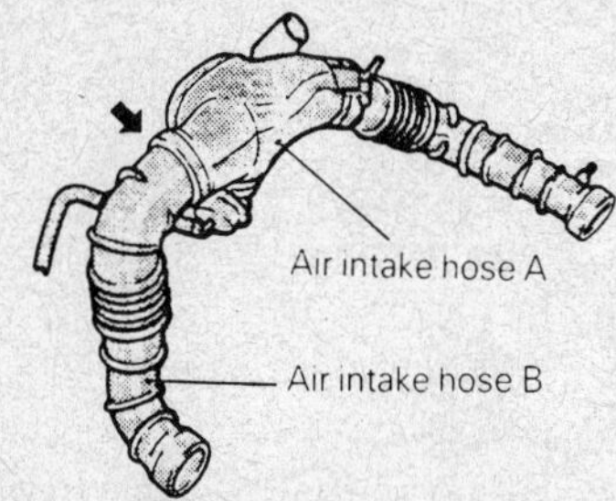


**Fig. 26 Installing intake hose, front. DOHC turbocharged**

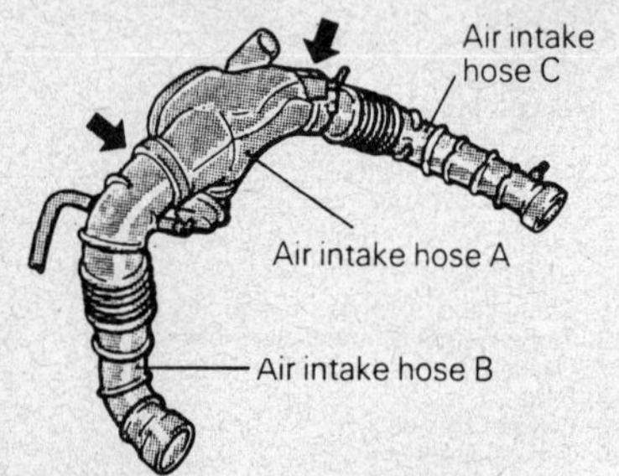


**Fig. 28 Installing air intake hose, rear. DOHC turbocharged**

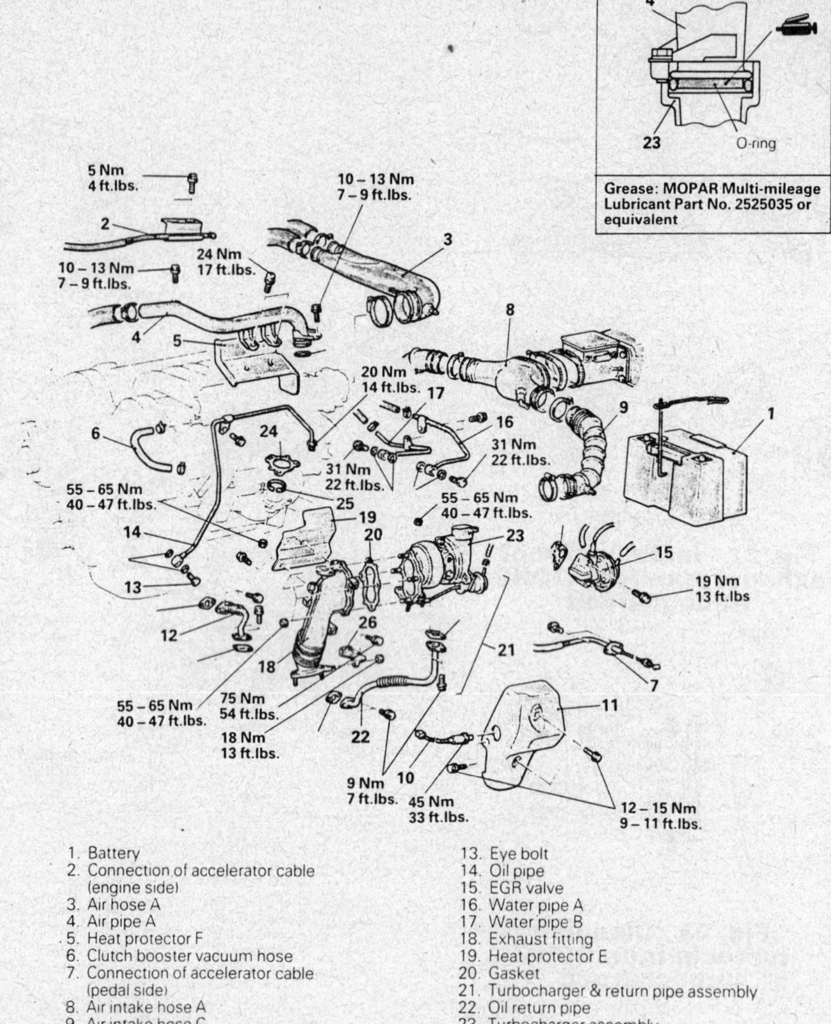


1. Battery
2. Connection of accelerator cable (engine side)
3. Air hose A
4. Air pipe A
5. Heat protector F
6. Clutch booster vacuum hose
7. Connection of accelerator cable (pedal side)
8. Air intake hose A
9. Air intake hose C
10. Oxygen sensor
11. Heat protector D
12. EGR pipe
13. Eye bolt
14. Oil pipe
15. EGR valve
16. Water pipe A
17. Water pipe B
18. Exhaust fitting
19. Heat protector E
20. Gasket
21. Turbocharger & return pipe assembly
22. Oil return pipe
23. Turbocharger assembly
24. Gasket
25. Ring
26. Exhaust fitting stay

**Fig. 27 Turbocharger replacement, rear. DOHC turbocharged**

3. Remove rear turbocharger in sequence shown in **Fig. 27**, noting the following:
   a. Disconnect oxygen sensor connector and remove using oxygen wrench remover tool No. MD998770, or equivalent.
4. Reverse procedure to install, noting the following:
   a. Clean points marked in **Fig. 23.** and supply clean engine oil into oil pipe installation hole.
   b. Install oxygen sensor using oxygen sensor wrench tool No. MD998770, or equivalent.
   c. Align and engage air intake hose notches mark with an arrow in **Fig. 28** until fully seated.
   d. Align marks on air pipe A/3 and A indicated by arrows in **Fig. 29** and seat completely into stepper portion of pipe or until seated.

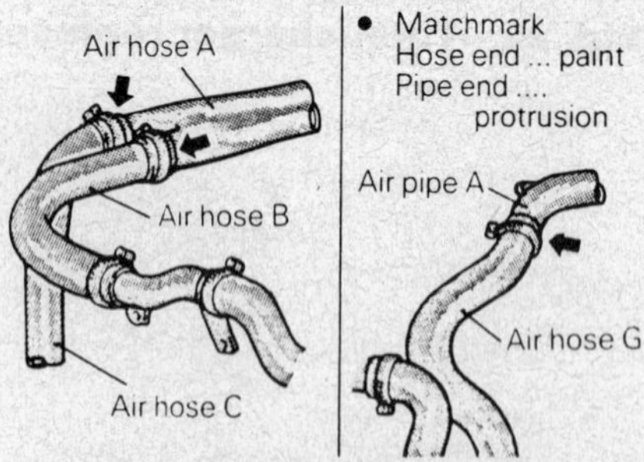


**Fig. 29 Installing air hose A/3 & A. DOHC turbocharged**

# CYLINDER HEAD REPLACE

## SOHC

1. Remove exhaust manifold as outlined under "Exhaust Manifold, Replace."
2. Remove intake manifold as outlined under "Intake manifold, Replace."
3. Remove timing belt as outlined under "Timing Belt, Replace."
4. Remove cylinder head in sequence shown in **Figs. 30 and 31,** noting the following:
   a. Remove camshaft sprockets as outlined under "Camshaft Oil Seal, Replace."
5. Reverse procedure to install, noting the following:
   a. Ensure cylinder head gasket has proper identification mark for engine.
   b. Install marking on cylinder head gasket upward and toward the front.
   c. Tighten cylinder head bolts in sequence to specification in several steps, **Fig. 32.**

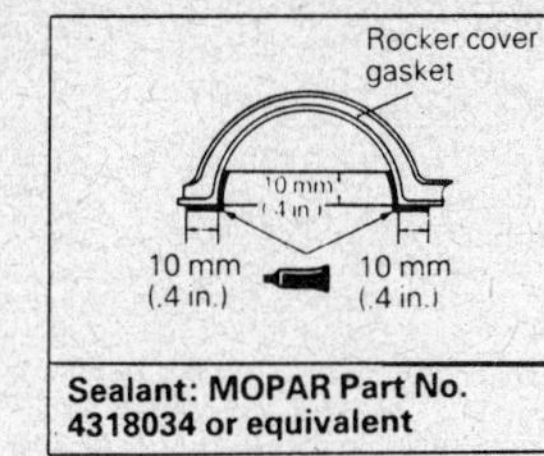


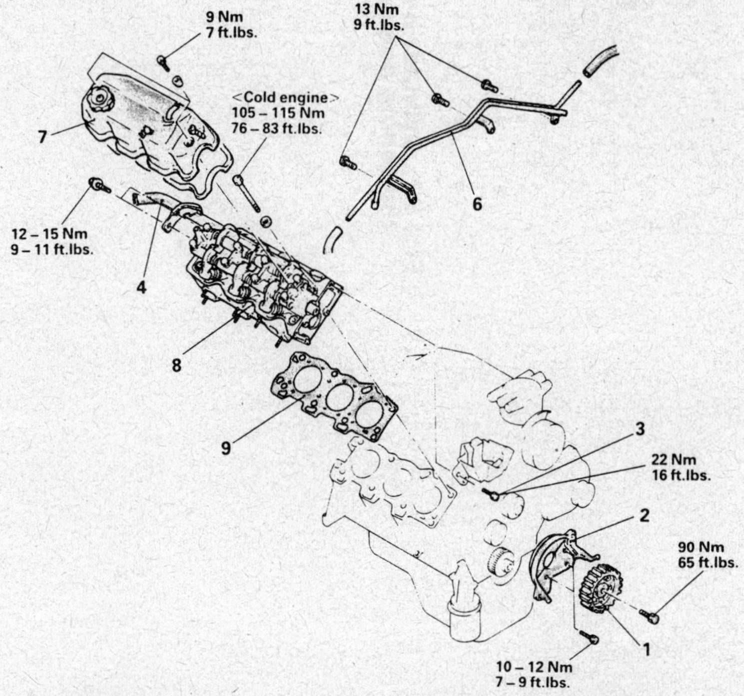


**Fig. 30 Cylinder head replacement, front bank. SOHC**

## DOHC

1. Drain engine cooling system.
2. Remove intake manifold as outlined under "Intake manifold, Replace."
3. **On turbocharged models,** remove turbocharger as outlined under "Turbocharger, replace."
4. Remove exhaust manifold as outlined under "Exhaust Manifold, Replace."
5. Remove timing belt as outlined under "Timing Belt, Replace."
6. Remove cylinder head in sequence shown in **Fig. 33,** noting the following:
   a. Remove camshaft sprockets as outlined under "Camshaft Oil Seal, Replace."
7. Reverse procedure to install, noting the following:
   a. Ensure cylinder head gasket has proper identification mark for engine.
   b. Install marking on cylinder head gasket upward and toward the front.
   c. Tighten cylinder head bolts in sequence to specification in several steps, **Fig. 32.**

# VALVE ARRANGEMENT

The exhaust valves are on the outboard side of the cylinder head and the intake valves are on the inboard side of the cylinder head.

# CAMSHAFT LOBE LIFT SPECIFICATIONS

| Engine | Camshaft | Standard Value, Inch | Limit, Inch |
|---|---|---|---|
| SOHC | Intake | 1.6240 | 1.6430 |
| | Exhaust | 1.6240 | 1.6430 |
| DOHC | Intake | 1.3972 | 1.3776 |
| | Exhaust | 1.3858 | 1.3661 |

# TIMING BELT REPLACE

Replace timing belt every 60,000 miles or every five years to prevent cylinder head, valve train or piston damage.

## SOHC

1. Remove lefthand front and side undercover.
2. Disconnect and remove cruise control pump and link assembly.
3. Raise and support engine assembly to take weight off engine mounts.
4. Remove timing belt in order shown in **Fig. 34,** noting the following:
   a. Disconnect power steering pump and A/C compressor with hoses attached. Support aside with rope or other suitable material.
   b. Remove engine mount as outlined under "Engine Mount, Replace.
   c. Remove engine mount bracket in sequence shown in **Fig. 35,** lubricating reamer bolt indicated by arrow then remove bolt slowly. **Reamer bolt is sometimes heat seized on engine support bracket.**
   d. Remove crankshaft pulley using end yoke holder tool No. MB990767 and crankshaft pulley holder tool No. MB998719, or equivalent, as shown in **Fig. 36.**
   e. Align timing marks prior to timing belt removal.
   f. Mark rotation direction on timing belt for installation if belt is to be reused.
   g. Loosen timing belt tensioner bolt and turn tensioner counterclockwise and tighten tensioner bolt.
   h. Remove timing belt.
5. Reverse procedure to install, noting the following:
   a. Align timing marks on camshaft and crankshaft sprockets, **Fig. 37.**
   b. Install timing belt on crankshaft first, then working counterclockwise position belt over one camshaft sprocket, water pump pulley, other camshaft sprocket then over belt tensioner, **Fig. 38.**
   c. Apply force counterclockwise to rear camshaft sprocket. Ensure timing marks are aligned.
   d. Attach front flange then loosen timing belt tensioner bolt and allow tensioner to tighten belt using spring force.
   e. Using crankshaft wrench tool No. MD998716, or equivalent, turn crankshaft two turns clockwise.
   f. Re-align timing marks and tighten timing belt tensioner bolt to specification.
   g. Measure belt tension using a suitable belt tension gauge tool on timing belt opposite side of tensioner, **Fig. 39.**. Belt tension should be 46.3-68.3 ft. lbs.
   h. Install timing cover bolts as shown in **Fig. 40.**
   i. Install engine support bracket bolts in sequence shown in **Fig. 41.**

## DOHC

### Removal

1. Remove lefthand front and side undercover.
2. Disconnect and remove cruise control pump and link assembly.

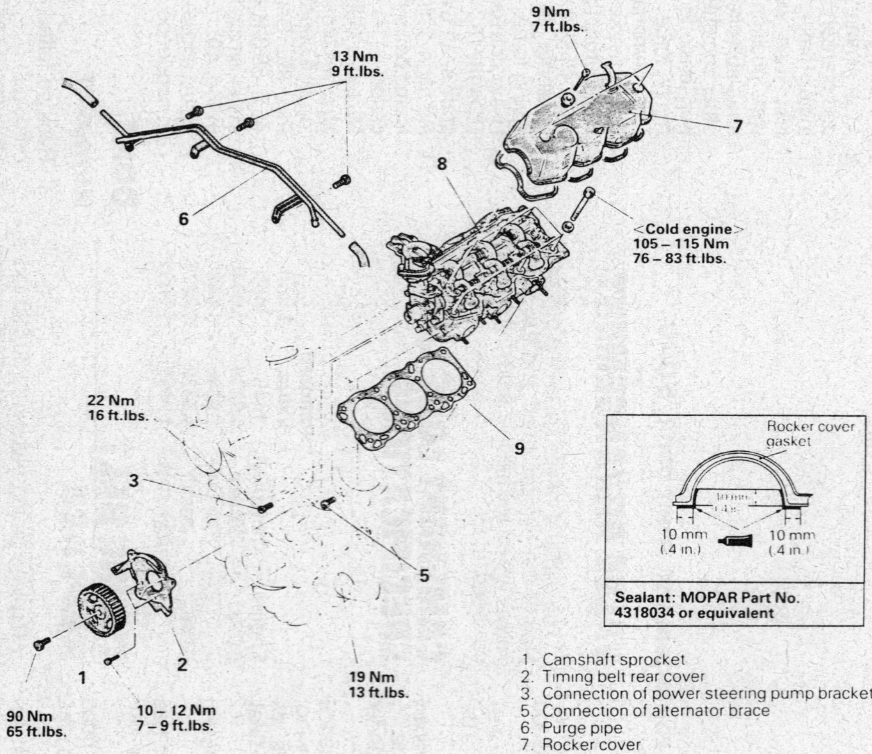

Rear bank
9 Nm
7 ft.lbs.
13 Nm
9 ft.lbs.
<Cold engine>
105 – 115 Nm
76 – 83 ft.lbs.
22 Nm
16 ft.lbs.
19 Nm
13 ft.lbs.
90 Nm
65 ft.lbs.
10 – 12 Nm
7 – 9 ft.lbs.
1
2
3
5
6
7
8
9
Rocker cover gasket
10 mm (.4 in.)
10 mm (.4 in.)
Sealant: MOPAR Part No. 4318034 or equivalent

1. Camshaft sprocket
2. Timing belt rear cover
3. Connection of power steering pump bracket
5. Connection of alternator brace
6. Purge pipe
7. Rocker cover
8. Cylinder head assembly
9. Cylinder head gasket

**Fig. 31 Cylinder head replacement, rear bank. SOHC**

MD998051
Head bolt washer
6 2 3 7
5 1 4 8
Front bank
Timing belt side
8 4 1 5
7 3 2 6
Rear bank

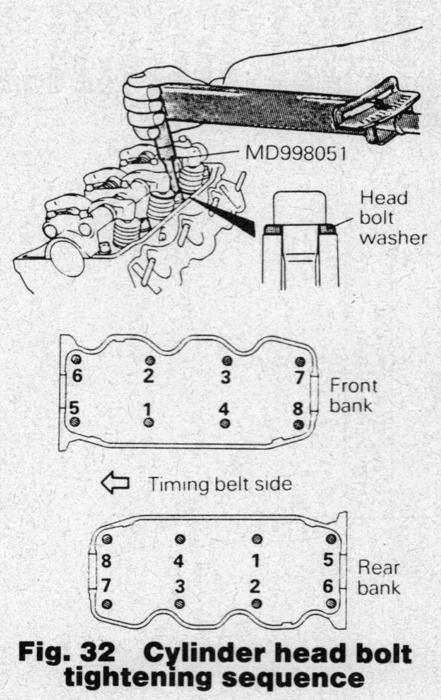

**Fig. 32 Cylinder head bolt tightening sequence**

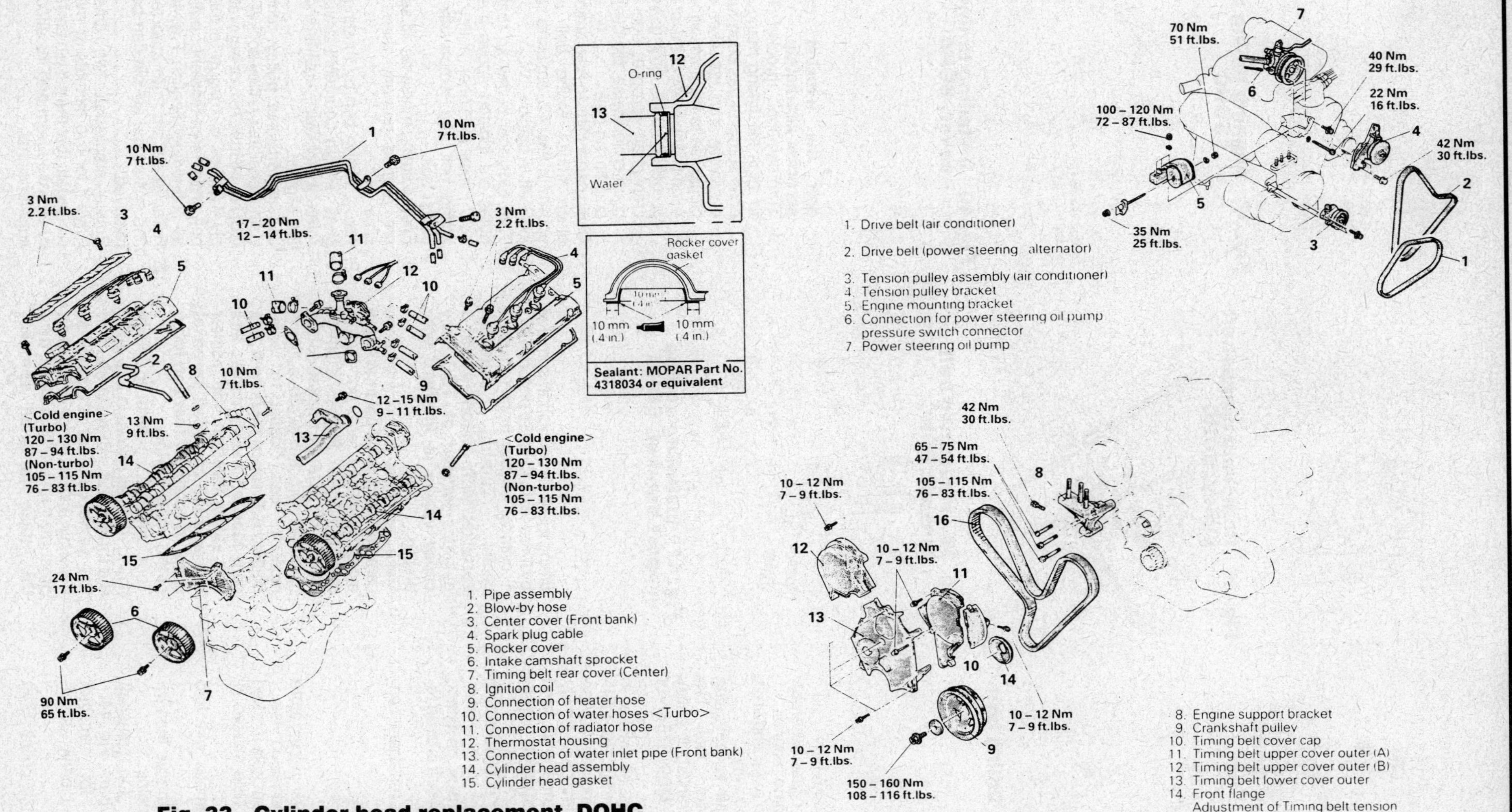


**Fig. 33 Cylinder head replacement. DOHC**

**Fig. 34 Timing belt replacement. SOHC**

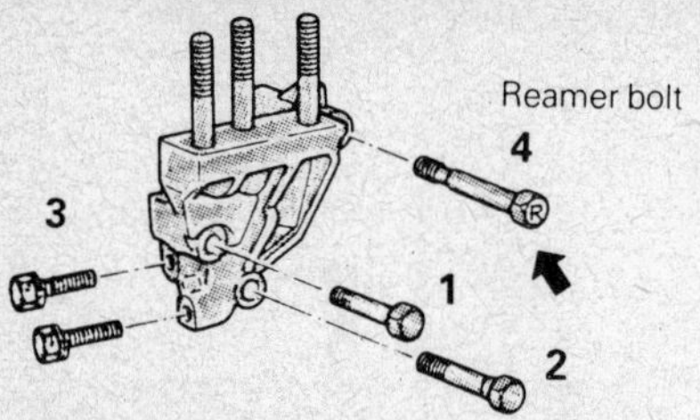


**Fig. 35 Removing engine support bracket. SOHC**

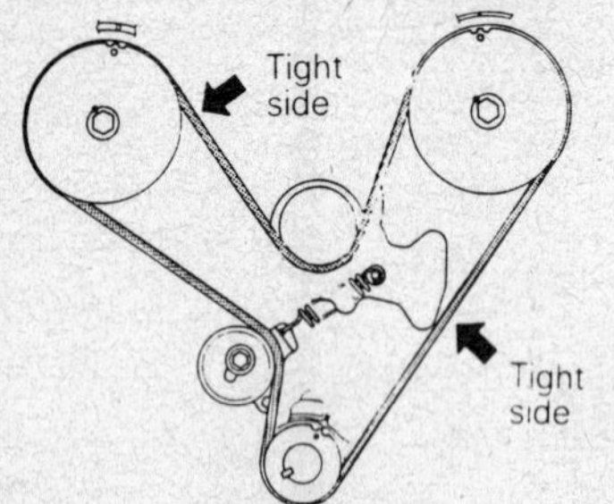


**Fig. 38 Installing timing belt. SOHC**

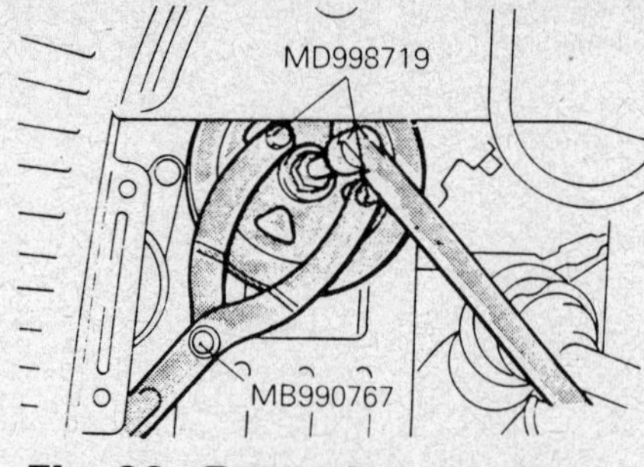


**Fig. 36 Removing crankshaft pulley. SOHC**

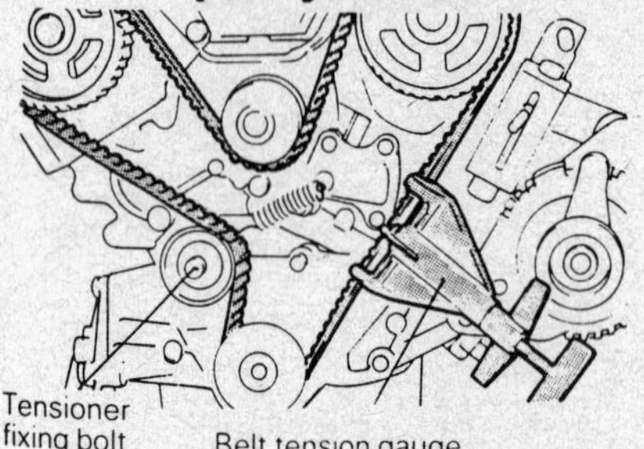


**Fig. 39 Measuring belt tension. SOHC**

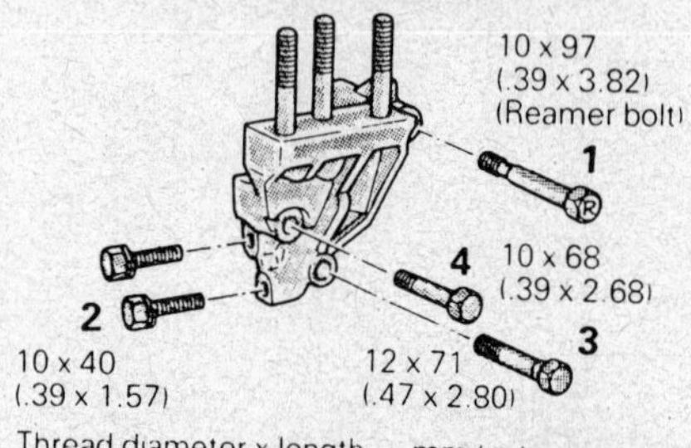


**Fig. 41 Installing engine support bracket. SOHC**

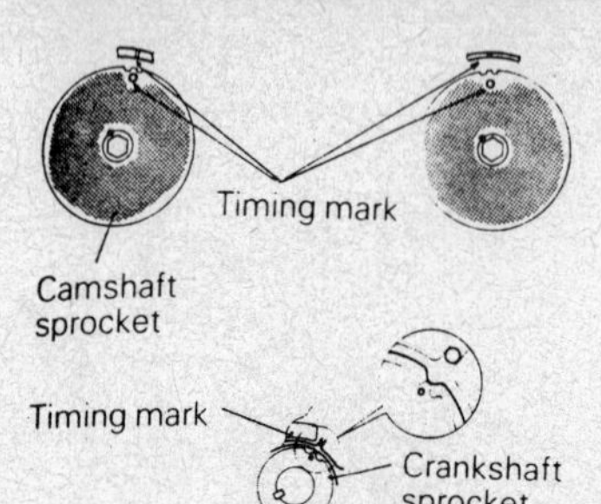


**Fig. 37 Aligning timing marks. SOHC**

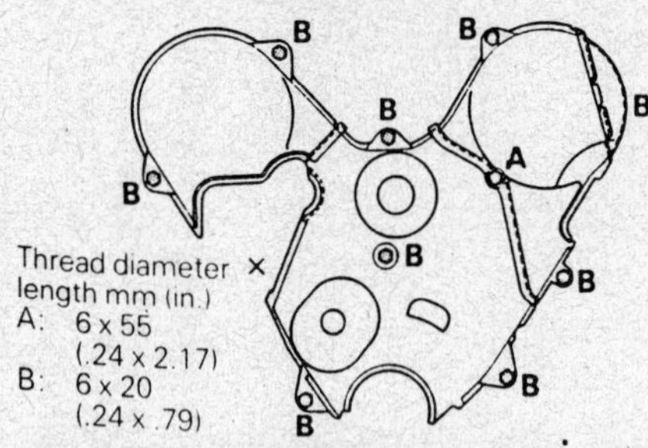


**Fig. 40 Installing timing belt cover. SOHC**

3. Remove alternator assembly.
4. Raise and support engine assembly to take weight off engine mounts.
5. Remove timing belt in order shown in **Fig. 42,** noting the following:
   a. Remove crankshaft pulley using end yoke holder tool No. MB990767 and crankshaft pulley holder tool No. MB998754, or equivalent.
   b. Remove engine mount bracket in sequence shown in **Fig. 35,** lubricating reamer bolt indicated by arrow then remove bolt slowly. **Reamer bolt is sometimes heat seized on engine support bracket.**
   c. Align timing marks prior to timing belt removal.
   d. Mark rotation direction on timing belt for installation if belt is to be reused.
   e. Loosen timing belt tensioner center bolt.
   f. Remove timing belt.

## Installation

1. Reset auto tensioner by placing auto tensioner level in a soft jawed vise.
2. Push rod inward until set hole marked A is aligned with set hole marked B, **Fig. 43.**
3. Insert a .055 inch diameter wire into set holes.
4. Remove tensioner from vise then install tensioner onto engine.
5. Align timing marks for camshaft sprockets on the rear bank, **Fig. 44.**
6. Align timing marks for camshaft sprockets on the front bank, as follows:
   a. Install the crankshaft pulley. Shift timing mark on crankshaft sprocket by three teeth to lower piston in No. 1 cylinder slightly from top dead center. **Turning camshaft sprocket with piston in No. 1 cylinder located at TDC may cause valves to interfere with piston.**
   b. Make sure that timing marks on camshaft sprockets for intake and exhaust valves are not within range marked A, **Fig. 45.** If timing mark is within range marked A, turn camshaft sprocket to move timing mark to area closest to range marked A. **In range marked A, the cam lobe on the camshaft lifts the valve through the rocker arm and the camshaft sprocket is apt to rotate by reaction force of the valve spring.**
   c. Turn camshaft sprocket to locate timing mark as shown in **Fig. 46. If the intake and exhaust valves of the same cylinder lift simultaneously, interference with each other may result. Therefore, turn the intake camshaft sprocket and the exhaust camshaft sprocket alternately.**
   d. Turn camshaft sprocket clockwise to align the timing marks. If camshaft sprocket has been turned excessively, turn sprocket counterclockwise to align timing marks.
   e. Align timing mark of the crankshaft sprocket. Shift timing mark of crankshaft sprocket one tooth in counterclockwise direction to install timing belt.
7. Using paper clips to hold timing belt in place, install timing belt in order shown in **Fig. 47,** ensuring not to allow belt to slack.
8. Turn tensioner pulley so that its pin holes are located above the center bolt. Press tensioner pulley against timing belt and temporarily tighten center bolt.
9. Ensure timing marks on all sprockets are aligned properly then remove clips.
10. Adjust timing belt by rotating crankshaft 1/4 turn counterclockwise, then rotate it clockwise until timing marks are aligned.
11. Loosen tensioner pulley center bolt. Using tensioner pulley socket wrench tool No. MB998767, or equivalent, apply 7.2 ft.lbs of **torque** to the timing belt and tighten tensioner pulley center bolt to specification, **Fig. 48.**
12. Remove set pin from auto tensioner and ensure the set pin can be easily removed.
13. Rotate crankshaft two times and leave it for five minutes or more. Ensure again that the set pin can be easily removed from and installed to the auto tensioner.

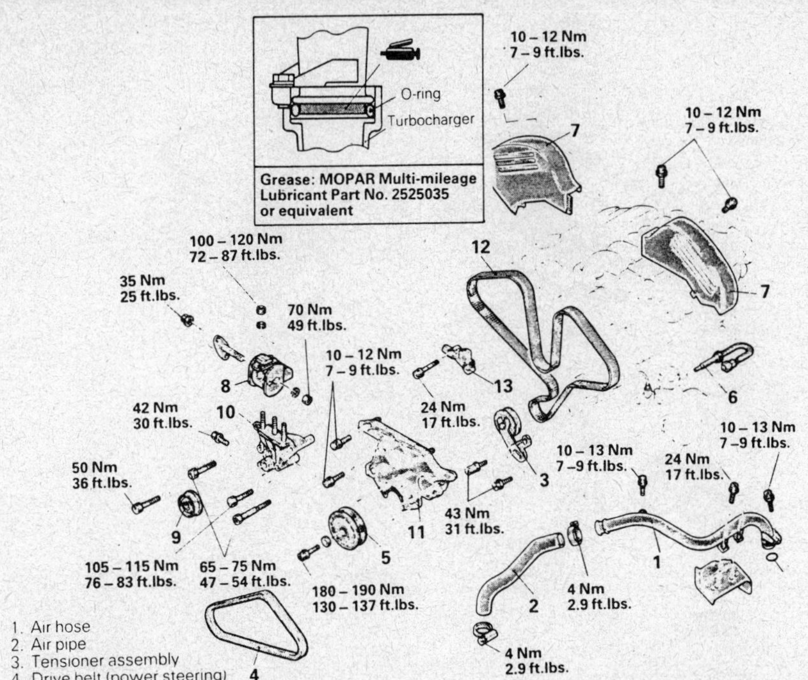


1. Air hose
2. Air pipe
3. Tensioner assembly
4. Drive belt (power steering)
5. Crankshaft pulley
6. Brake fluid level sensor
7. Timing belt upper cover
8. Engine mount bracket
9. Idler pulley (alternator / air conditioner)
10. Engine support bracket
11. Timing belt lower cover
    Adjustment of timing belt tension
12. Timing belt
13. Auto tensioner

**Fig. 42 Removing timing belt. DOHC**

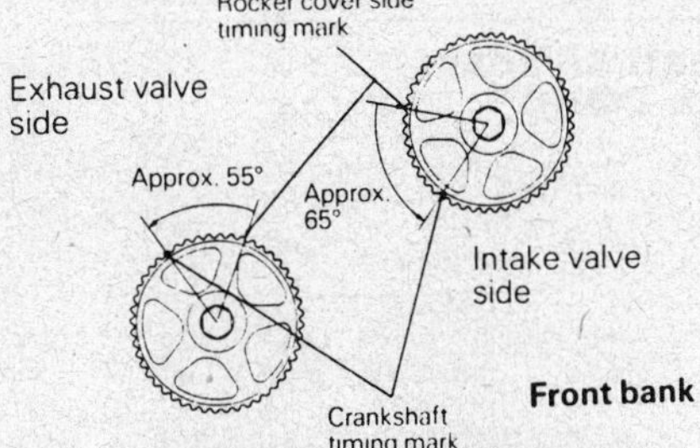


**Fig. 46 Positioning camshaft sprockets. DOHC**

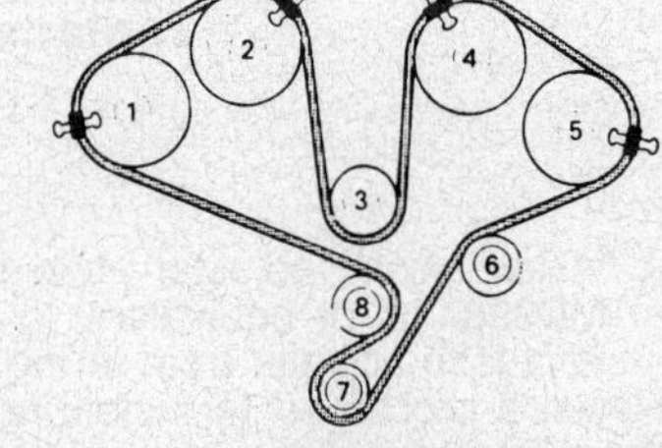
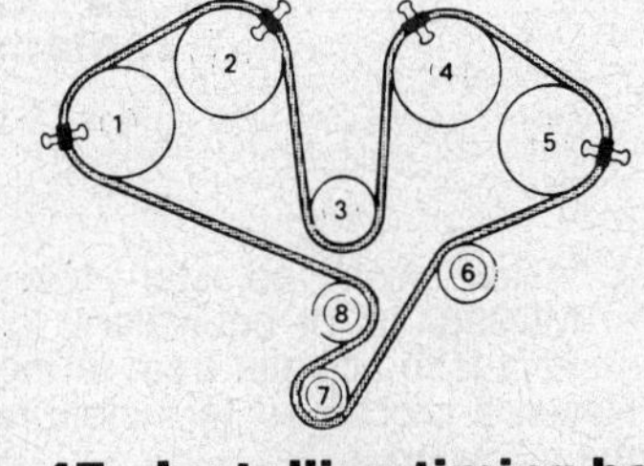

**Fig. 47 Installing timing belt. DOHC**



**Fig. 49 Tightening tensioner pulley bolt. DOHC**

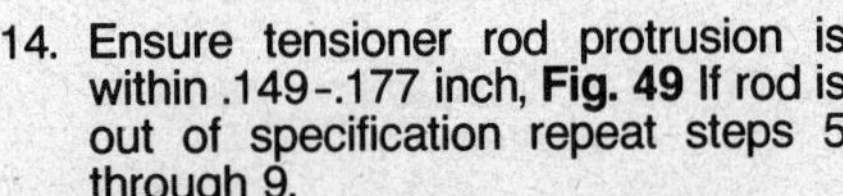

14. Ensure tensioner rod protrusion is within .149-.177 inch, **Fig. 49** If rod is out of specification repeat steps 5 through 9.
15. Ensure timing marks are aligned on all sprockets.
16. Install lower timing belt cover bolts as shown in **Fig. 50.**
17. Install engine support bracket bolts in sequence shown in **Fig. 51.**
18. Reverse remaining removal procedure to install.

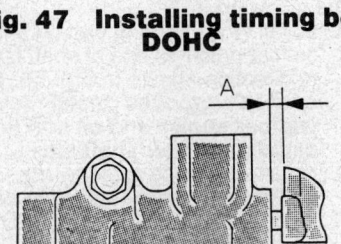

## CAMSHAFT OIL SEAL REPLACE

### SOHC

1. Remove timing belt as outlined under "Timing Belt, Replace."

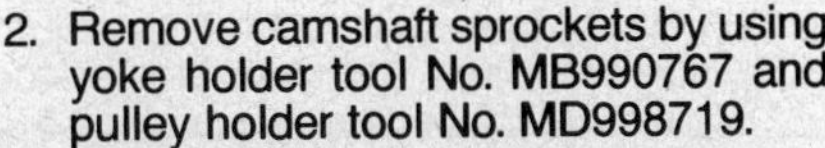

2. Remove camshaft sprockets by using yoke holder tool No. MB990767 and pulley holder tool No. MD998719.
3. Remove timing belt rear covers.
4. Remove oil seal by using a suitable pry tool.
5. Reverse procedure to install, noting the following:

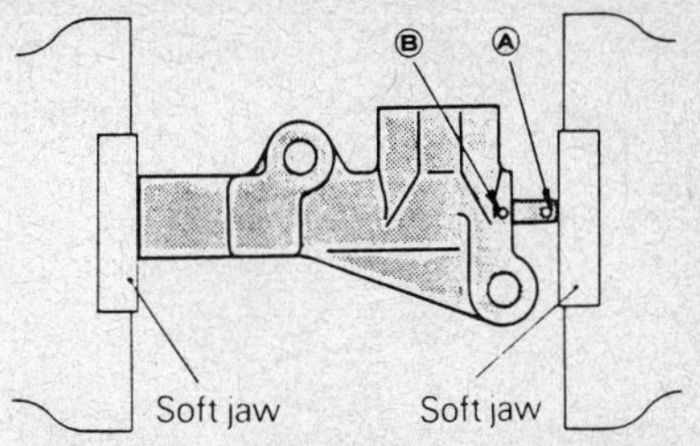


**Fig. 43 Aligning set holes. DOHC**

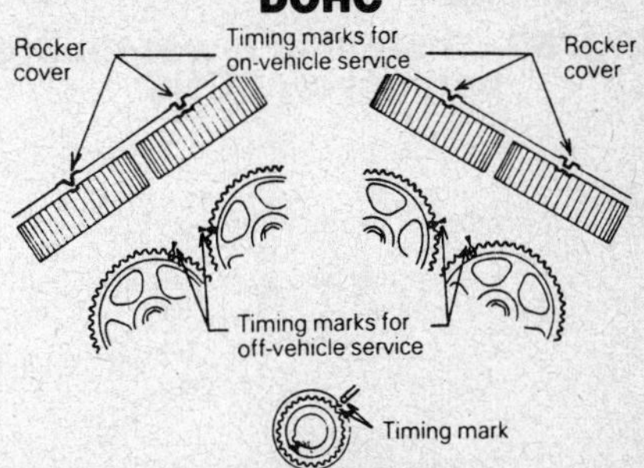


**Fig. 44 Aligning timing marks. DOHC**

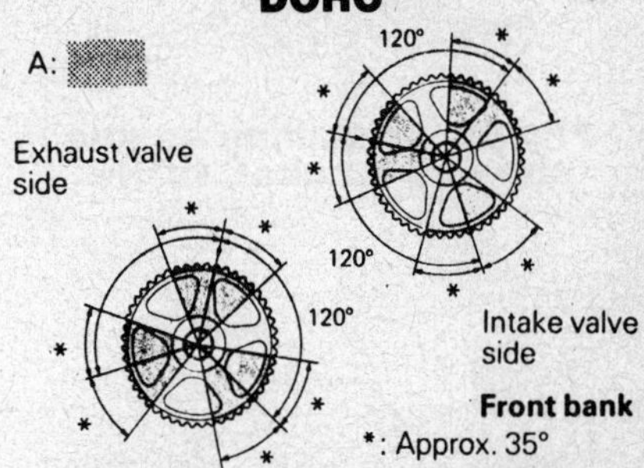


**Fig. 45 Rear camshaft alignment position. DOHC**

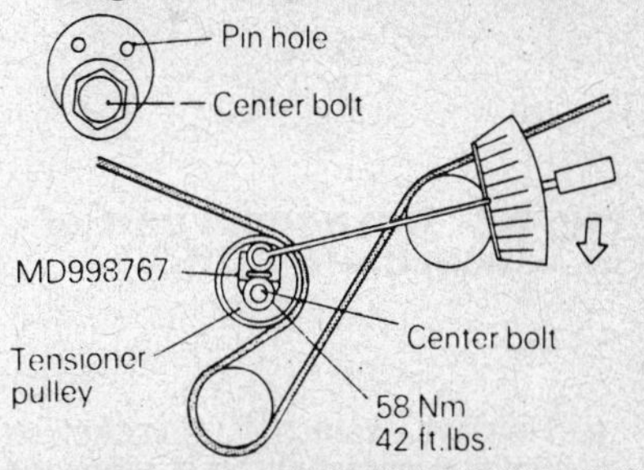


**Fig. 48 Measuring rod protrusion**

a. Install oil seal using seal installer tool No. MD998713, or equivalent.

### DOHC

1. Remove timing belt as outlined under "Timing Belt, Removal."
2. Remove intake manifold as outlined under "Intake Manifold, Replace."
3. Remove camshaft oil seals in sequence shown in **Fig. 52,** noting the following:

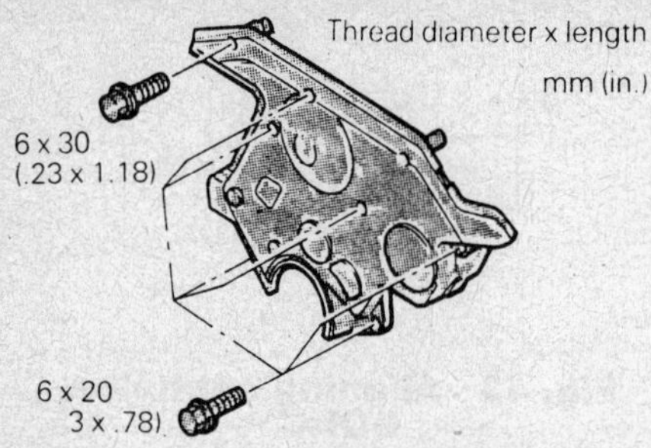


**Fig. 50 Installing lower timing belt cover. DOHC**

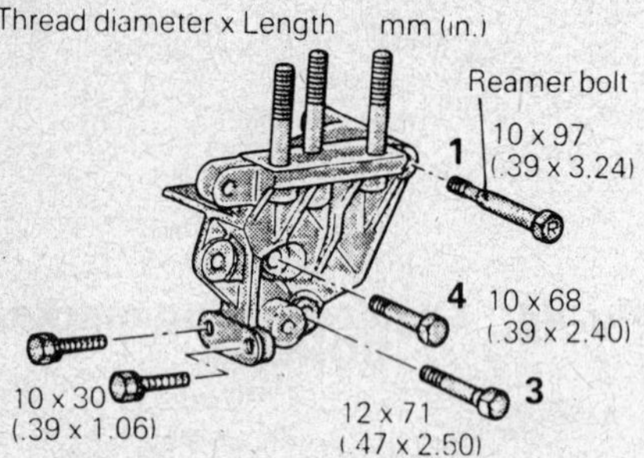


**Fig. 51 Installing engine support bracket. DOHC**

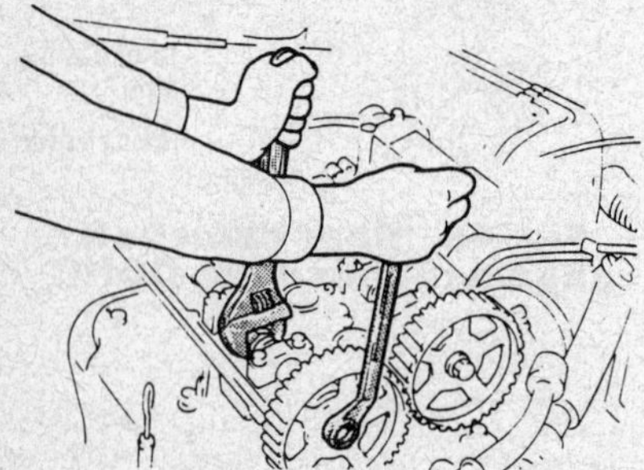

**Fig. 53 Hexagonal part of camshaft. DOHC**

a. Remove camshaft sprocket by holding camshaft on the hexagonal part and removing sprocket bolt, **Fig. 53.**
b. Cut out a portion of the camshaft seal then pry out seal using a suitable pry tool.

4. Reverse procedure to install, noting the following:
   a. Install camshaft oil seal using seal installer tool No. MD998671.
   b. Tighten rocker covers in sequence shown in **Fig. 54.** Rocker cover bolts are color code, front bank bolts are black and read bank bolts are green.

# CAMSHAFT

## REPLACE

### SOHC

1. Remove camshaft in sequence shown in **Fig. 55,** noting the following:

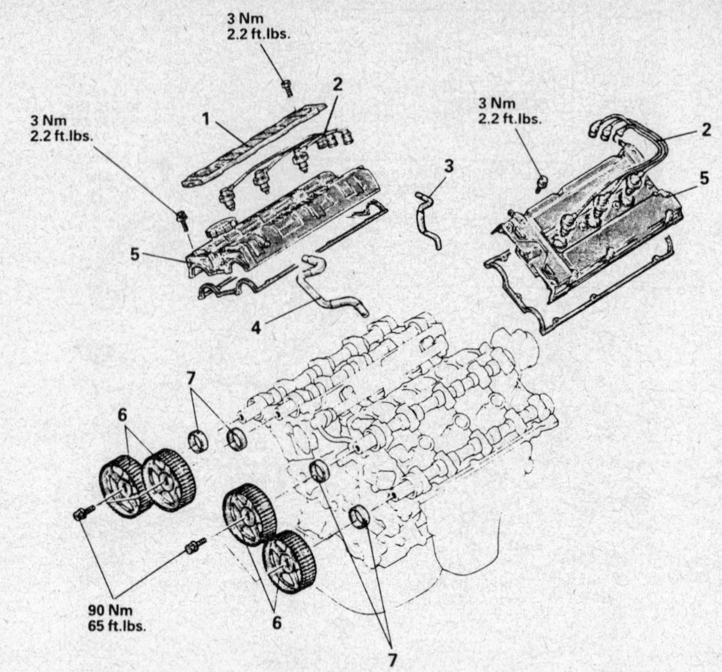


1. Center cover (front bank)
2. Connection for spark plug cables
3. Connection for breather hose
4. Connection for PCV hose
5. Rocker cover
6. Camshaft sprocket
7. Camshaft oil seals

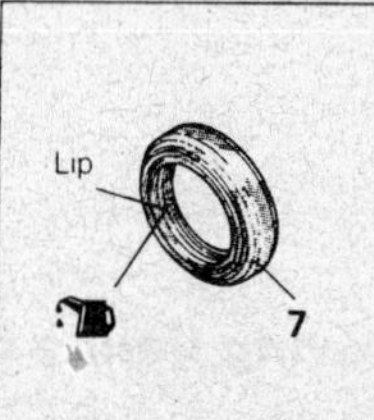


Rocker cover gasket
10 mm (.4 in.)
10 mm (.4 in.)
10 mm (.4 in.)
Sealant: MOPAR Part No. 4318034 or equivalent

**Fig. 52 Camshaft oil seal replacement. DOHC**

a. Install lash adjuster tool No. MD998443, or equivalent, to prevent lash adjuster from falling out.

2. Reverse procedure to install, noting the following:
   a. Install No. 1 bearing cap on shafts so that notch on end of shaft faces in direction shown in **Fig. 56. Ensure oil grooves faces downward as shown and oil port is located on rocker shaft side.**
   b. Install remaining bearing caps on shaft with arrow mark on each bearing cap points in same direction as No. 1 bearing cap.
   c. Immerse lash adjuster in clean diesel fuel.
   d. Using a small wire, move plunger up and down several times while pushing down lightly on check ball in order to bleed out air.
   e. Install lash adjuster into rocker arms, using care not to spill out diesel fuel, then retain lash adjuster with lash adjuster retainer tool No. MD998443, or equivalent, **Fig. 57.**
   f. Apply a small amount of sealant to areas shown, **Fig. 58.**
   g. Install rocker arm shaft assembly bearing cap arrow marks in same

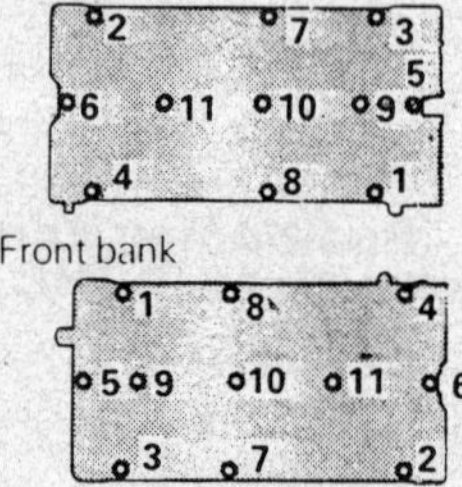


**Fig. 54 Installing rocker cover. DOHC**

direction as arrow mark on cylinder head.
   h. Tighten bearing cap bolts to specification, then remove lash adjuster tool.
   i. Install circular packing using seal installer tool No. MD998306, or equivalent.
   j. Install camshaft oil seal and sprocket.

### DOHC

1. Remove camshaft in sequence shown in **Fig. 59.**

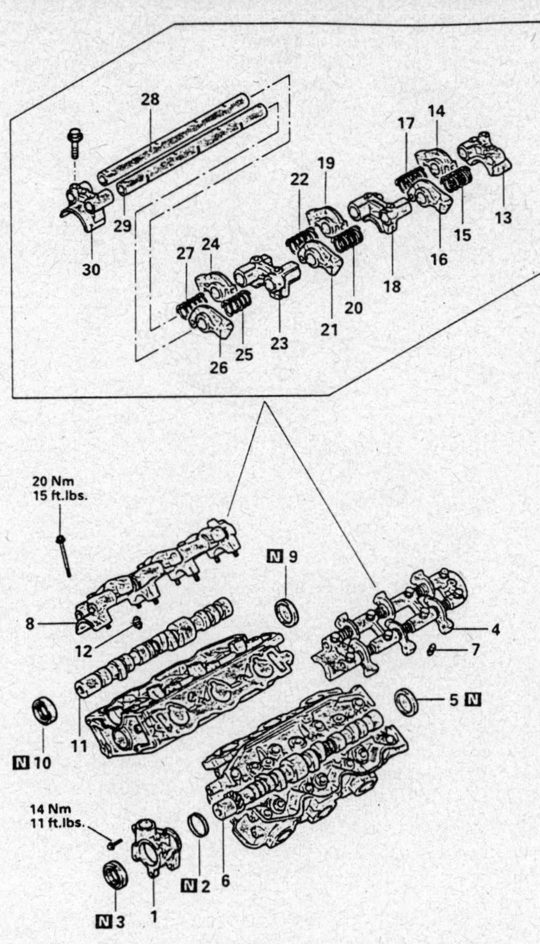


**Removal steps**

1. Distributor adaptor
2. O-ring
3. Camshaft oil seal
4. Rocker arm and shaft assembly (rear)
5. Circular packing
6. Camshaft (rear)
7. Lash adjuster
8. Rocker arm and shaft assembly (front)
9. Circular packing
10. Camshaft oil seal
11. Camshaft (front)
12. Lash adjuster
13. Bearing cap No. 4
14. Rocker arm (B)
15. Spring
16. Rocker arm (A)
17. Spring
18. Bearing cap No. 3
19. Rocker arm (B)
20. Spring
21. Rocker arm (A)
22. Spring
23. Bearing cap No. 2
24. Rocker arm (B)
25. Spring
26. Rocker arm (A)
27. Spring
28. Rocker arm shaft (B)
29. Rocker arm shaft (A)
30. Bearing cap No. 1

**Installation steps**

30. Bearing cap No. 1
29. Rocker arm shaft (A)
28. Rocker arm shaft (B)
27. Spring
26. Rocker arm (A)
25. Spring
24. Rocker arm (B)
23. Bearing cap No. 2
22. Spring
21. Rocker arm (A)
20. Spring
19. Rocker arm (B)
18. Bearing cap No. 3
17. Spring
16. Rocker arm (A)
15. Spring
14. Rocker arm (B)
13. Bearing cap No. 4
11. Camshaft (front)
12. Lash adjuster
8. Rocker arm and shaft assembly (front)
9. Circular packing
10. Camshaft oil seal
6. Camshaft (rear)
7. Lash adjuster
4. Rocker arm and shaft assembly (rear)
5. Circular packing
2. O-ring
1. Distributor adaptor
3. Camshaft oil seal

**Fig. 55 Camshaft replacement. SOHC**

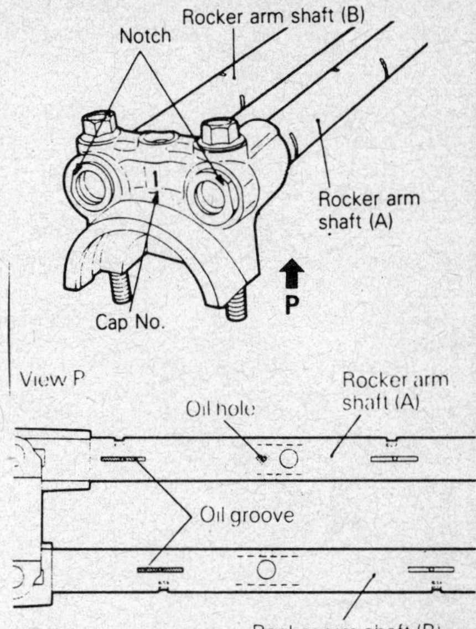


**Fig. 56 Installing rocker arm shafts. SOHC**

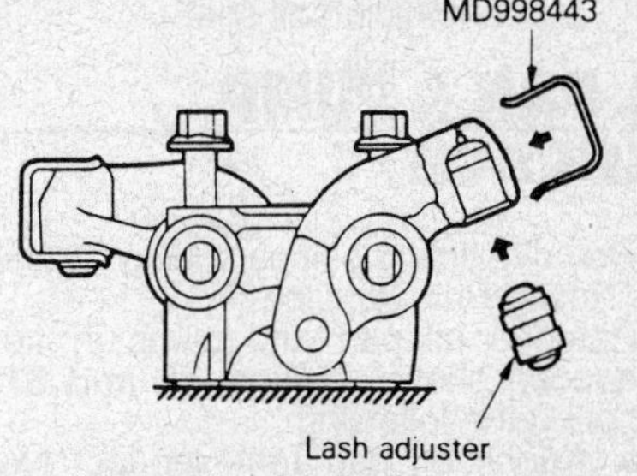


**Fig. 57 Installing lash adjuster**

2. Install camshaft in reverse sequence shown in **Fig. 59,** noting the following:
   a. Immerse lash adjuster in clean diesel fuel.
   b. Using a small wire, move plunger up and down several times while pushing down lightly on check ball in order to bleed out air.
   c. Install lash adjuster into rocker arms, using care not to spill out diesel fuel, then retain lash adjuster with lash adjuster retainer tool No. MD998443, or equivalent, **Fig. 57.**
   d. Turn crankshaft to bring No. 1 cylinder to TDC.
   e. Install intake camshaft, marked V, and exhaust camshaft, marked C, onto the cylinder head with dowel pins as shown in **Fig. 60.**
   f. Install bearing caps, on proper camshaft, with arrow mark pointing in same direction as arrow mark on cylinder head.
   g. Tighten bearing cap bolts to specification in several steps.
   h. Install circular packing using seal installer tool No. MD998762, or equivalent.
   i. Install camshaft oil seal and sprocket.

# PISTON, RINGS & ROD ASSEMBLY
## REPLACE

1. Remove piston and rod assembly as outlined under **Fig. 61,** noting the following:
   a. Mark large end of connecting rod with cylinder number.
   b. Inspect side clearance between piston ring and ring groove. If side clearance is not as specified in "Engine Rebuilding Specifications," replace rings or piston or both.
2. Reverse procedure to install, noting the following:
   a. Arrange piston rings as shown in **Fig. 62.**
   b. Pistons for SOHC engines are identified for front and rear banks, **Fig. 63.**
   c. Align connecting rod marks made during disassembly when assembling cod on crankshaft.

# CRANKSHAFT
## REPLACE

1. Replace crankshaft, flywheel and driveplate and shown in **Fig. 64,** noting the following when assembling:
   a. Install main bearings half with an oil groove on the cylinder block and the other half with no oil groove on the bearing cap side.
   b. Install thrust bearings with the groove side facing outward on No. 3 journal.
   c. Install bearing cap and tighten cap bolts to specification.
   d. Apply engine oil to thread and bearing surface of each bearing cap stay bolts. **Bearing cap stays A and B differ in shape, install in correct order, Fig. 65.**
   e. Temporarily tighten bolts on cylinder block side.
   f. Torque bolts on bearing cap side to specification.
   g. Torque bolts on cylinder block side to specification.

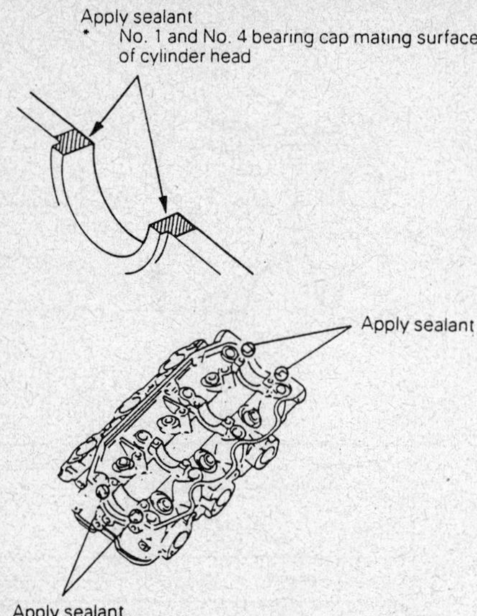


**Fig. 58 Sealing camshaft. SOHC**

h. Using seal installation tool No. MD998718 or equivalent, install rear crankshaft oil seal.

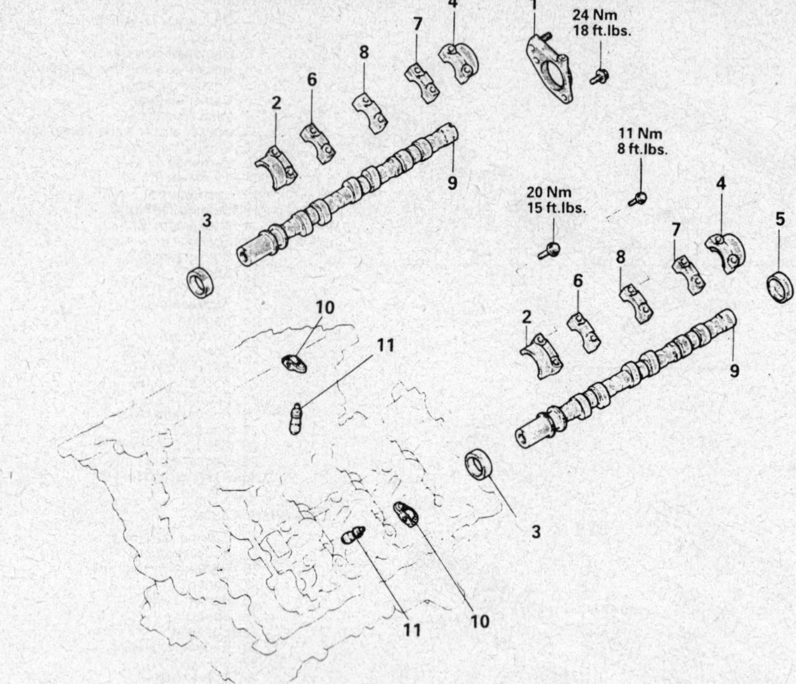


| Removal steps | Installation steps |
|---|---|
| 1. Crank angle sensor adaptor | 11. Lash adjuster |
| 2. Bearing cap front | 10. Rocker arm |
| 3. Oil seal | 9. Camshaft |
| 4. Bearing cap rear | 8. Bearing cap No. 3 |
| 5. Circular packing | 7. Bearing cap No. 4 |
| 6. Bearing cap No. 2 | 6. Bearing cap No. 2 |
| 7. Bearing cap No. 4 | 4. Bearing cap rear |
| 8. Bearing cap No. 3 | 2. Bearing cap front |
| 9. Camshaft | 5. Circular packing |
| 10. Rocker arm | 3. Oil seal |
| 11. Lash adjuster | 1. Crank angle sensor adaptor |

**Fig. 59 Camshaft replacement. DOHC**

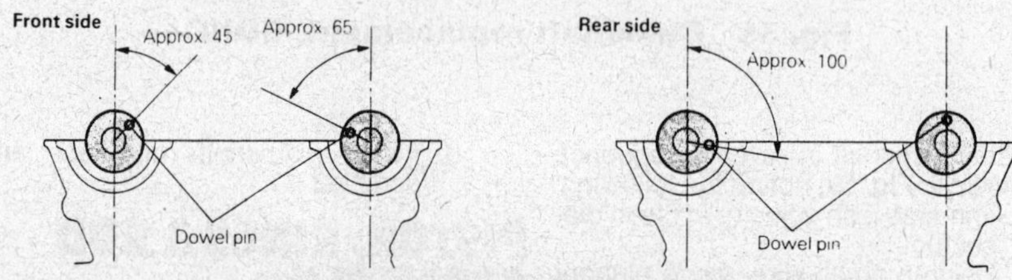


**Fig. 60 Installing camshafts. DOHC**

## OIL PAN & PUMP REPLACE

1. Remove timing belt as outlined under "Timing Belt, Replace."
2. Remove oil pan and pump in sequence shown in **Figs. 66 and 67**, noting the following:
   a. Knock oil pan remover tool No. MD998727 in deeply between oil pan and cylinder block.
   b. Hitting side of tool, slide and remove oil pan.
3. Reverse procedure to install, noting the following:
   a. Install oil pump seal using seal installer tool No. MD998717, or equivalent.
   b. Apply a bead of sealant around flange of oil pan and tighten oil pan bolts in sequence to specification, **Fig. 68.**

## BELT TENSION DATA

| Engine, VIN | Component | New① | Used① |
|---|---|---|---|
| 3.0L/V6-181, S | Alternator & Power Steering Pump | .157–.197 | .236–.315 |
| 3.0L/V6-181, S | A/C Compressor | .256–.275 | .275–.335 |
| 3.0L/V6-181, B & C | A/C Compressor & Alternator | .138–.157 | .157–.196 |
| 3.0L/V6-181, B & C | Alternator | .138–.157 | .157–.196 |
| 3.0L/V6-181, B & C | Power Steering Pump | .354–.433 | .354–.433 |

①—Deflection Inch

## SERPENTINE DRIVE BELTS

### BELT ROUTING

Refer to **Fig. 69** for belt routing.

## THERMOSTAT REPLACE

**Do not remove pressure cap while engine is hot or under pressure.**

1. Drain coolant to level below thermostat housing.
2. **On turbo models,** remove air intake hoses one (1) and two (2), **Fig. 70.**
3. **On non-turbo engines,** remove air intake hose (3).
4. **On DOHC models,** remove lower radiator hose (4), three housing retaining bolts. housing (5), gasket (8) and thermostat (9).
5. **On SOHC models,** remove upper radiator hose (6), two housing retaining bolts, housing (7), gasket (8) and thermostat (9).

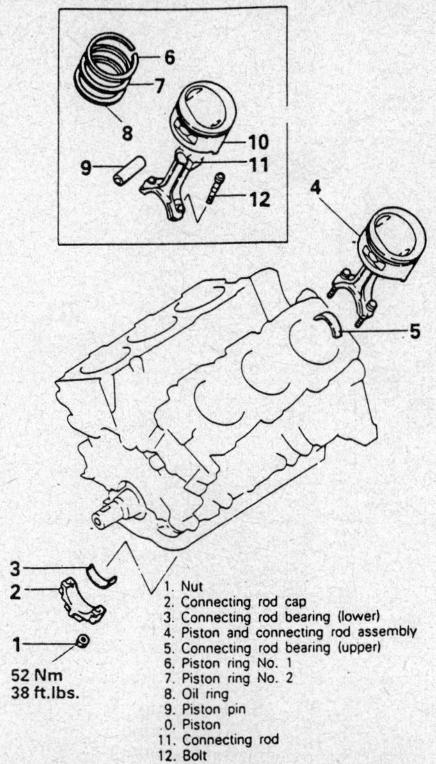


**Fig. 61 Piston, rings & rod assembly**

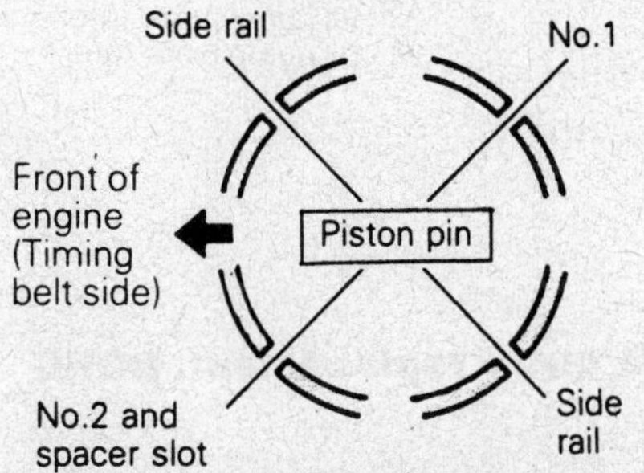


**Fig. 62 Piston ring alignment position**

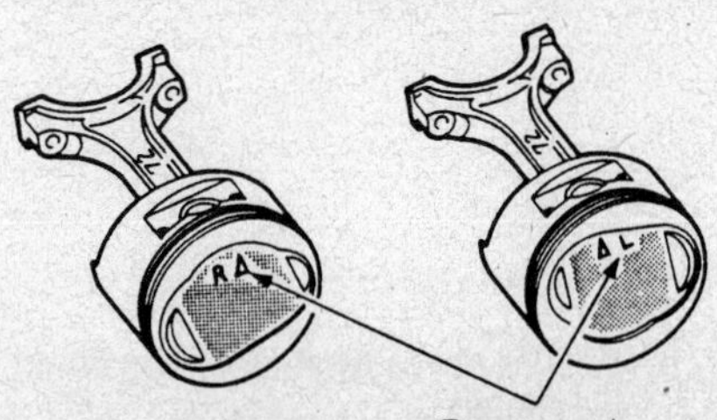


**Fig. 63 Piston installation direction. SOHC**

6. Clean mating surfaces and close drain.
7. Reverse removal procedures to install.
8. Refer to **Fig. 71,** before installing thermostat.
9. Ensure that drain is closed, then refill coolant. Replace cap, start engine until warm. Check of leaks, then recheck coolant and fill if necessary.

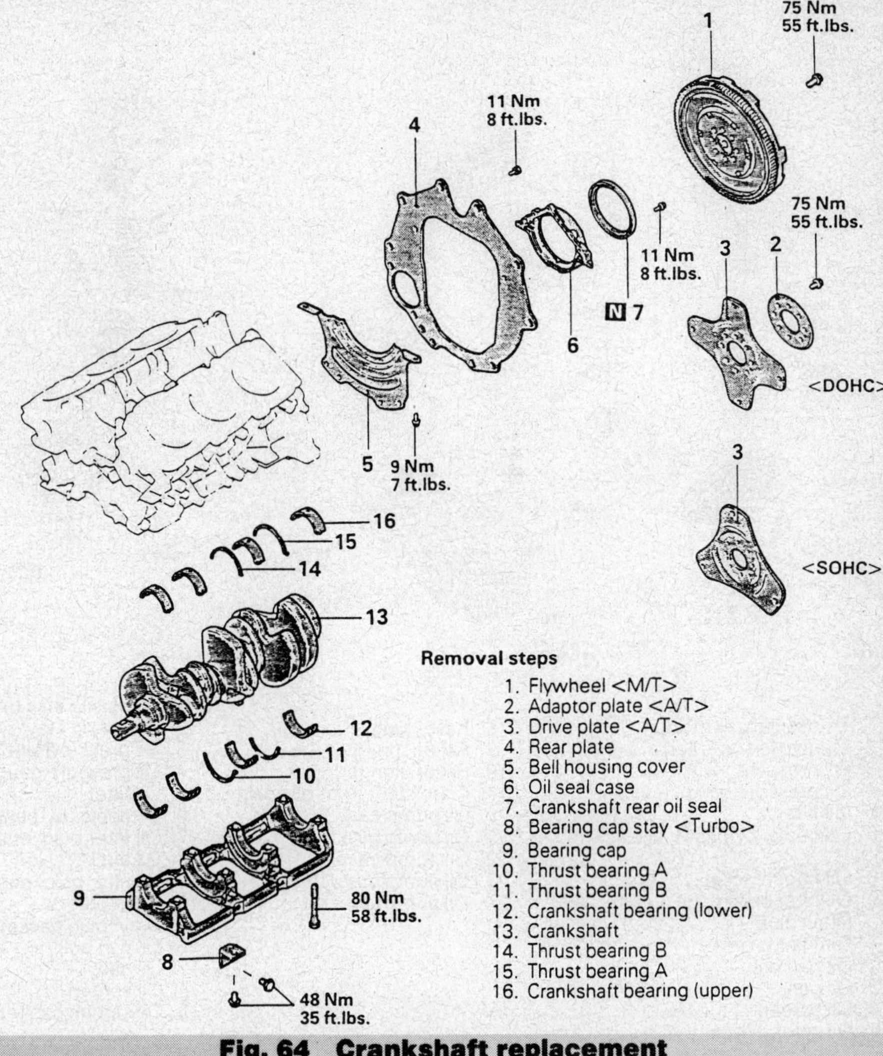


**Fig. 64 Crankshaft replacement**

## COOLING SYSTEM BLEED

These engines do not require a specified bleed procedure. After filling cooling system, run engine to operating temperature with radiator/pressure cap off. Air will then be automatically bled through cap opening.

## WATER PUMP REPLACE

### SOHC

1. Drain engine cooling system.
2. Remove timing belt as outlined under "Timing Belt, Replace."
3. Replace water pump in sequence shown in **Fig. 72,** noting the following:
   a. **On models with automatic transaxle,** insert O-ring to water inlet pipe and coat outer circumference of O-ring with water.
   b. **On models with manual transaxles,** insert O-ring to water inlet pipe A and coat outer circumference of O-ring with water.

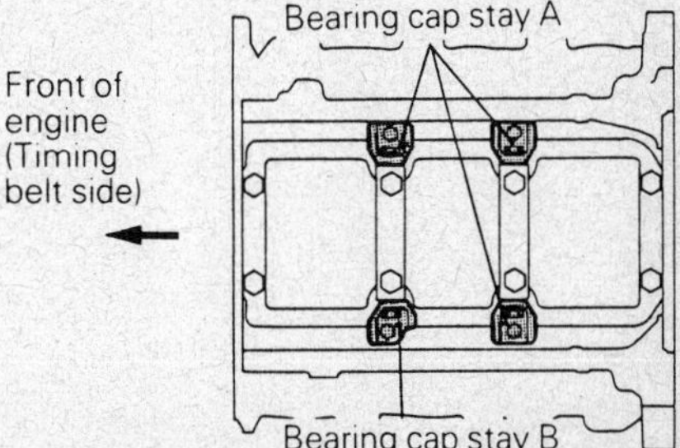


**Fig. 65 Main bearing cap stays**

   c. **On models with manual transaxles,** insert O-ring to water inlet pipe B and coat outer circumference of O-ring with water.

### DOHC

1. Drain engine cooling system.
2. Remove power transistor assembly.
3. Remove timing belt as outlined under "Timing Belt, Replace."
4. Replace water pump in sequence shown in **Fig. 73,** noting the following:

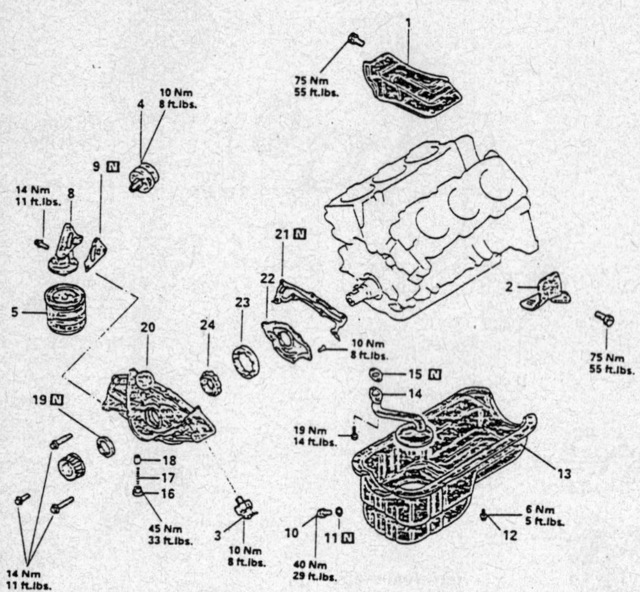


1. Transaxle stay (front)
2. Transaxle stay (rear)
3. Oil pressure switch
4. Oil pressure gauge unit
5. Oil filter
6. Oil cooler by-pass valve <Turbo>
8. Oil filter bracket
9. Oil filter bracket gasket
10. Drain plug
11. Drain plug gasket
12. Oil pan bolt
13. Oil pan
14. Oil screen
15. Oil screen gasket
16. Relief plug
17. Relief spring
18. Relief plunger
19. Crankshaft front oil seal
20. Oil pump case
21. Oil pump gasket
22. Oil pump cover
23. Oil pump outer rotor
24. Oil pump inner rotor

**Fig. 66 Oil pan & pump replacement. SOHC**

1. Transaxle stay (front)
2. Transaxle stay (rear)
3. Oil pressure switch
4. Oil pressure gauge unit
5. Oil filter
6. Oil cooler by-pass valve <Turbo>
7. Oil filter bracket stay <DOHC>
8. Oil filter bracket
9. Oil filter bracket gasket
10. Drain plug
11. Drain plug gasket
12. Oil pan bolt
13. Oil pan
14. Oil screen
15. Oil screen gasket
16. Relief plug
17. Relief spring
18. Relief plunger
19. Crankshaft front oil seal
20. Oil pump case
21. Oil pump gasket
22. Oil pump cover
23. Oil pump outer rotor
24. Oil pump inner rotor

**Fig. 67 Oil pan & pump replacement. DOHC**

a. Install water pump bolts as shown in **Fig. 74.**
b. Replace O-ring at both ends of water inlet pipe and coat new O-rings with water to aid in installation.

## FUEL PUMP
## REPLACE

1. Release fuel system pressure as outlined under "Fuel System Pressure Release."
2. Drain fuel tank into a suitable container.
3. Remove fuel pump and sending unit in numbered sequence shown in **Fig. 75,** noting the following:
   a. Before disconnecting high pressure fuel lines, cover connections with a rag to prevent residual fuel from splashing.
   b. Secure pump side nut of fuel line connections then loosen line side nut.
4. Reverse procedure to install, noting the following:
   a. Align three projections of packings with holes in fuel pump and fuel gauge unit assembly.
   b. Ensure not to twist fuel lines when tightening.
   c. Install overfill limiter valve in correct direction, **Fig. 76.**
   d. After installation, check for fuel leaks.

## TIGHTENING SPECIFICATIONS

### 3.0L/V6-181 ENGINE

For engine tightening specifications, refer to individual repair procedure or illustrations.

Tightening sequence of flange bolts (bottom view)

12 8 4 1 5 9
16 13
15 4
11 7 3 2 6 10

Front of engine (Timing belt side)

**Fig. 68 Installing oil pan**

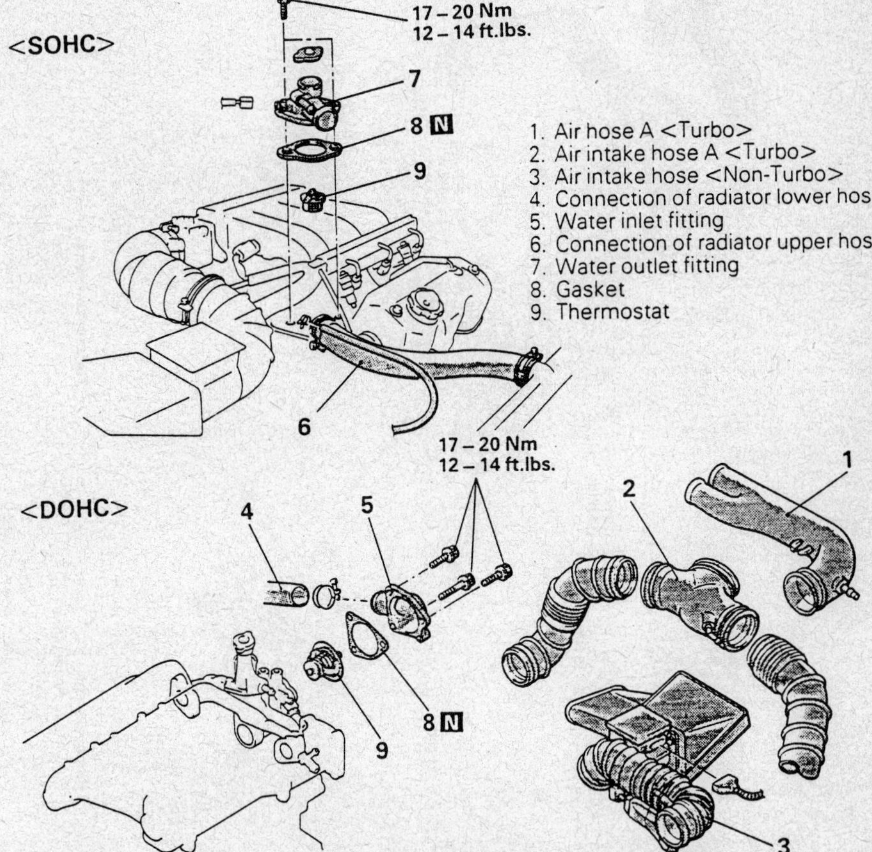


**Fig. 70 Thermostat replacement procedure**

<SOHC>

Power steering pump pulley

Tension pulley

Tension pulley

Alternator pulley

Air conditioner compressor pulley

Crankshaft pulley

<DOHC<Vehicle without air conditioner>

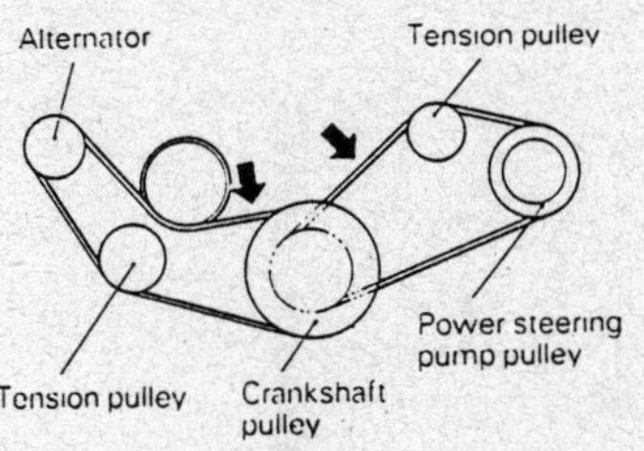


<Vehicle with air conditioner>

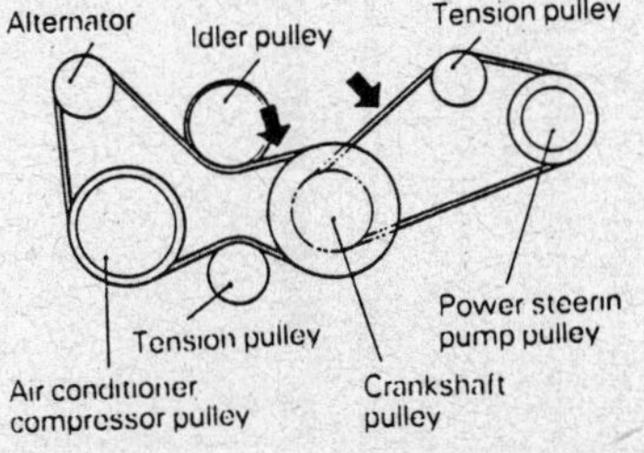


**Fig. 69 Drive belt routing**

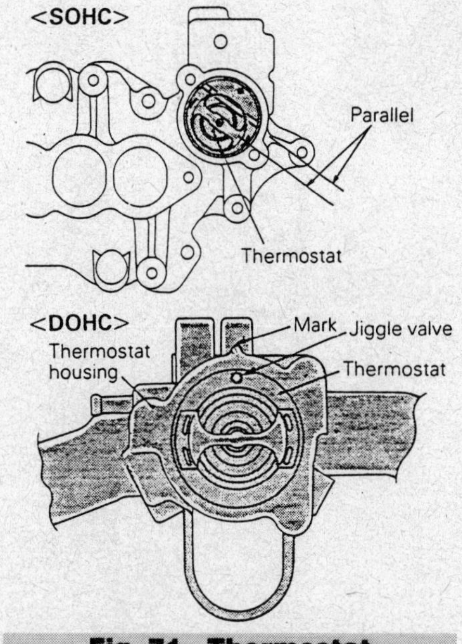


**Fig. 71 Thermostat installation direction**

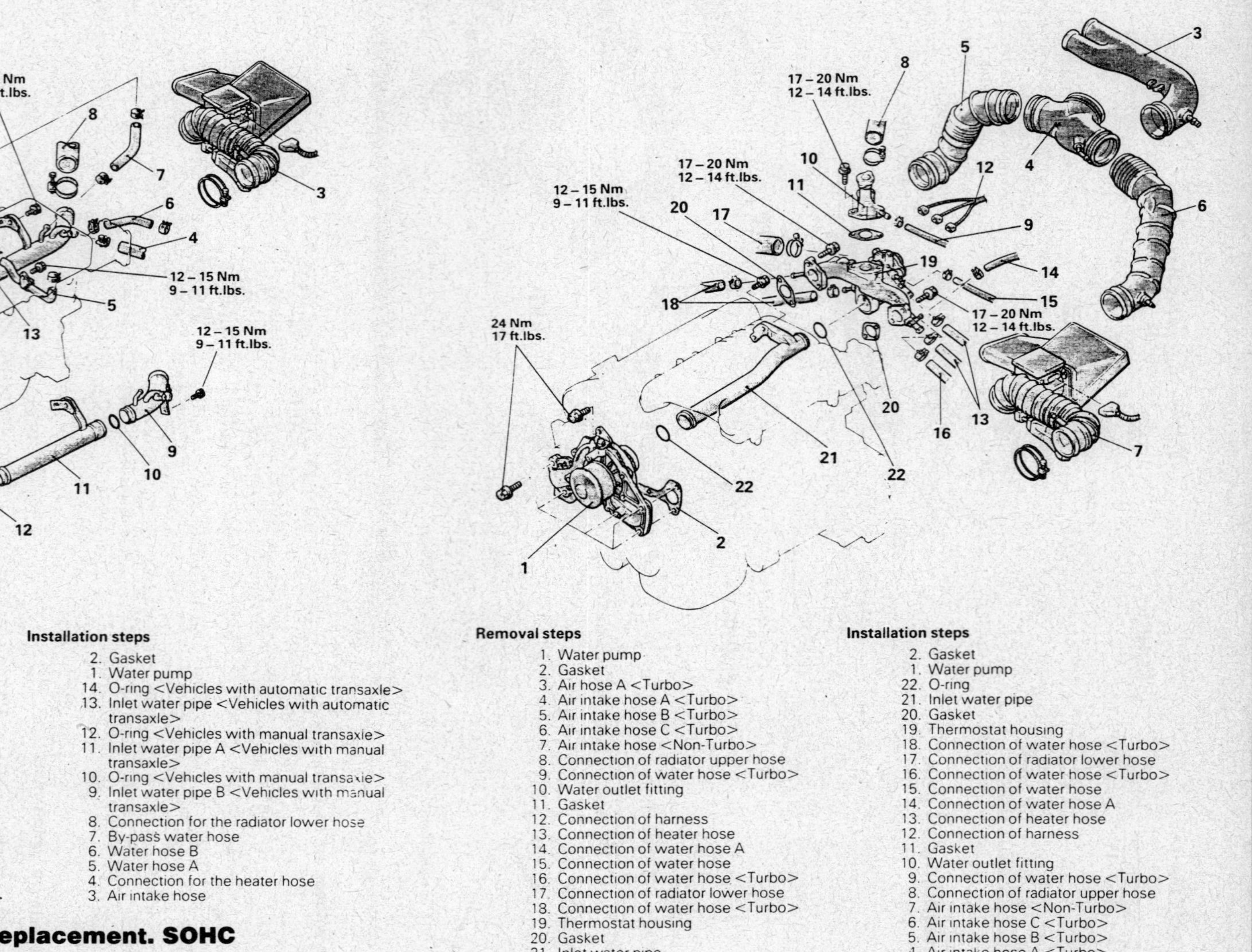


**Removal steps**

1. Water pump
2. Gasket
3. Air intake hose
4. Connection of the heater hose
5. Water hose A
6. Water hose B
7. By-pass water hose
8. Connection of the radiator lower hose
9. Inlet water pipe B <Vehicles with manual transaxle>
10. O-ring <Vehicles with manual transaxle>
11. Inlet water pipe A <Vehicles with manual transaxle>
12. O-ring <Vehicles with manual transaxle>
13. Inlet water pipe <Vehicles with automatic transaxle>
14. O-ring <Vehicles with automatic transaxle>

**Installation steps**

2. Gasket
1. Water pump
14. O-ring <Vehicles with automatic transaxle>
13. Inlet water pipe <Vehicles with automatic transaxle>
12. O-ring <Vehicles with manual transaxle>
11. Inlet water pipe A <Vehicles with manual transaxle>
10. O-ring <Vehicles with manual transaxle>
9. Inlet water pipe B <Vehicles with manual transaxle>
8. Connection for the radiator lower hose
7. By-pass water hose
6. Water hose B
5. Water hose A
4. Connection for the heater hose
3. Air intake hose

**Fig. 72 Water pump replacement. SOHC**

**Removal steps**

1. Water pump
2. Gasket
3. Air hose A <Turbo>
4. Air intake hose A <Turbo>
5. Air intake hose B <Turbo>
6. Air intake hose C <Turbo>
7. Air intake hose <Non-Turbo>
8. Connection of radiator upper hose
9. Connection of water hose <Turbo>
10. Water outlet fitting
11. Gasket
12. Connection of harness
13. Connection of heater hose
14. Connection of water hose A
15. Connection of water hose
16. Connection of water hose <Turbo>
17. Connection of radiator lower hose
18. Connection of water hose <Turbo>
19. Thermostat housing
20. Gasket
21. Inlet water pipe
22. O-ring

**Installation steps**

2. Gasket
1. Water pump
22. O-ring
21. Inlet water pipe
20. Gasket
19. Thermostat housing
18. Connection of water hose <Turbo>
17. Connection of radiator lower hose
16. Connection of water hose <Turbo>
15. Connection of water hose
14. Connection of water hose A
13. Connection of heater hose
12. Connection of harness
11. Gasket
10. Water outlet fitting
9. Connection of water hose <Turbo>
8. Connection of radiator upper hose
7. Air intake hose <Non-Turbo>
6. Air intake hose C <Turbo>
5. Air intake hose B <Turbo>
4. Air intake hose A <Turbo>
3. Air hose A <Turbo>

**Fig. 73 Water pump replacement. DOHC**

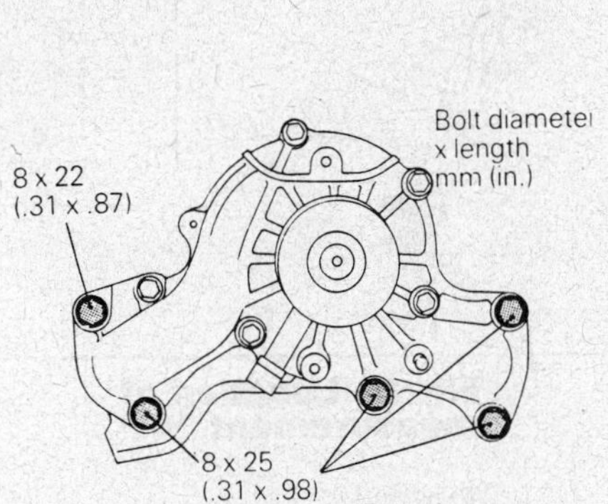


Fig. 74 Installing water pump bolts. DOHC

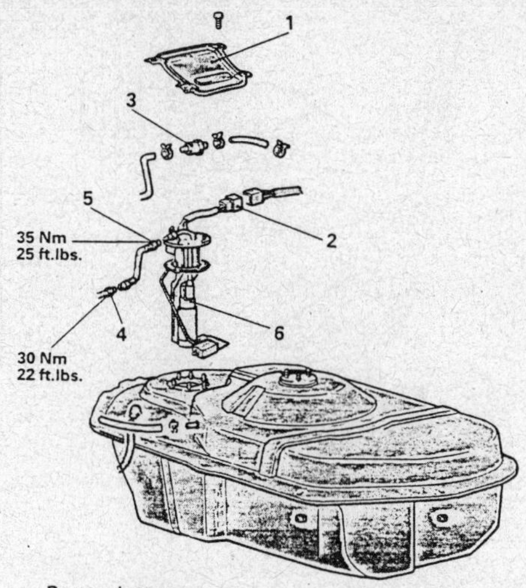


Removal steps

1. Fuel gauge cover
2. Fuel pump and fuel gauge unit assembly connector
3. Overfill limiter (Two-way valve)
4. High pressure fuel hose connection (body side)
5. High pressure fuel hose connection (fuel pump side)
6. Fuel pump and fuel gauge unit assembly

Fig. 75 Fuel pump replacement procedure

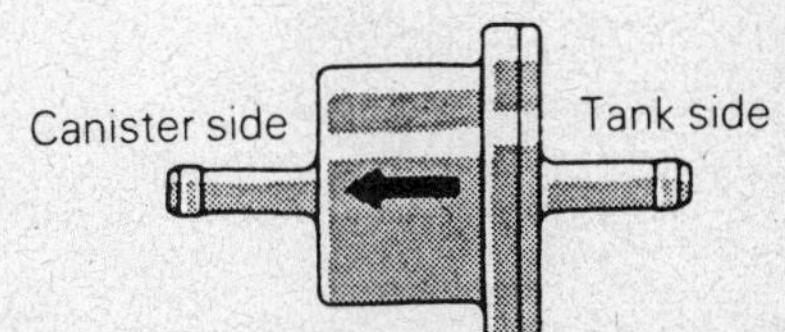


Fig. 76 Overflow limiter valve installation

# Clutch & Manual Transaxle

## INDEX



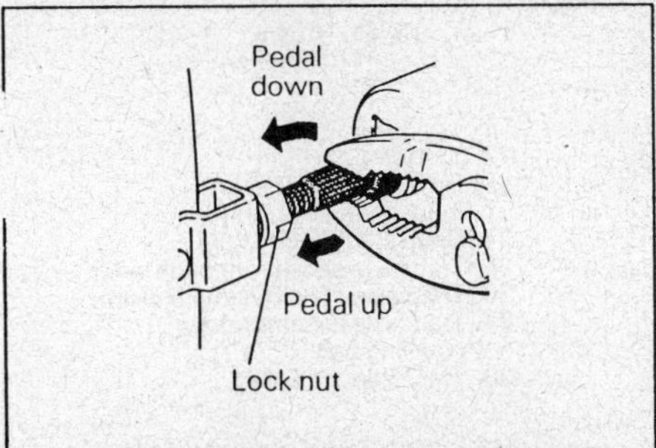


Fig. 1 Clutch pedal height pushrod adjustment

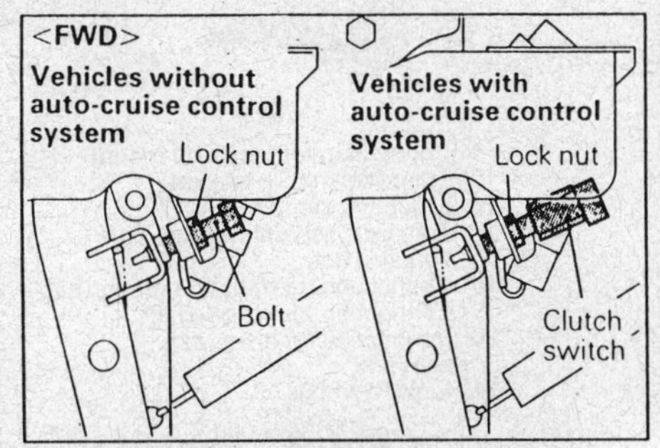


Fig. 2 Clutch pedal height adjusters

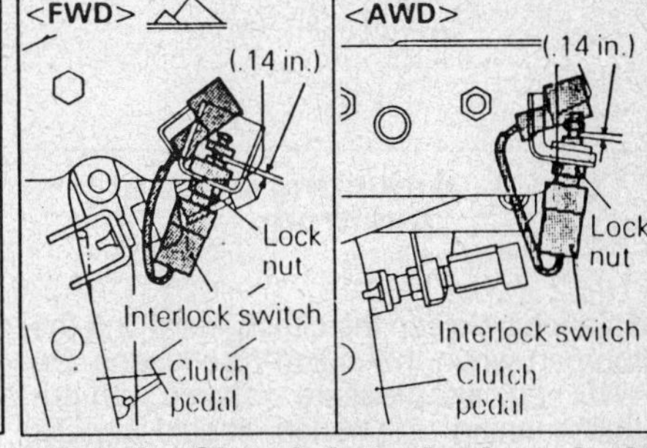


Fig. 3 Clutch interlock switch

## CLUTCH PEDAL HEIGHT ADJUST

To determine if the pedal height requires adjustment, measure the distance from the floor pan to the upper center of pedal pad. The distance should be 6.97-7.17 inches.

If pedal height is lower than specified, loosen bolt or clutch switch, then turn the pushrod to adjust clutch pedal to specification **Fig. 1.** After making the adjustment, adjust the bolt or clutch switch to reach the pedal stopper and tighten locknut. If pedal height is higher than specified, use the following procedure:

1. **On vehicles less cruise control,** turn and adjust bolt located at top of pedal so that pedal height is within specification **Fig. 2,** then secure by tightening locknut.
2. **On vehicles equipped with cruise control,** disconnect clutch switch connector, then turn switch to adjust pedal height **Fig. 2.** Tighten switch locknut.
3. Ensure that clutch interlock switch is as shown in **Fig. 3,** when clutch pedal is fully depressed. If switch is not as shown, loosen locknut and adjust.

## CLUTCH PEDAL FREEPLAY ADJUSTMENT

On AWD vehicles, depress clutch pedal two to three times with the engine off to eliminate booster negative pressure before testing pedal freeplay.

To determine if the pedal freeplay is not within specification, depress clutch pedal by hand until clutch resistance is felt. Measure the distance between upper pedal height and where resistance is felt. Freeplay should be .24-.51 inches. After pedal freeplay has been checked, measure the

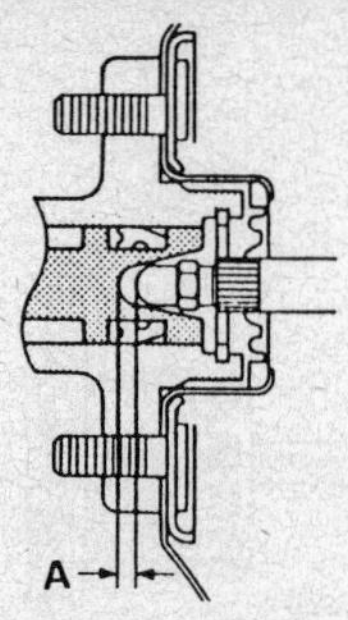


**Fig. 4 Clutch booster piston to pushrod clearance**

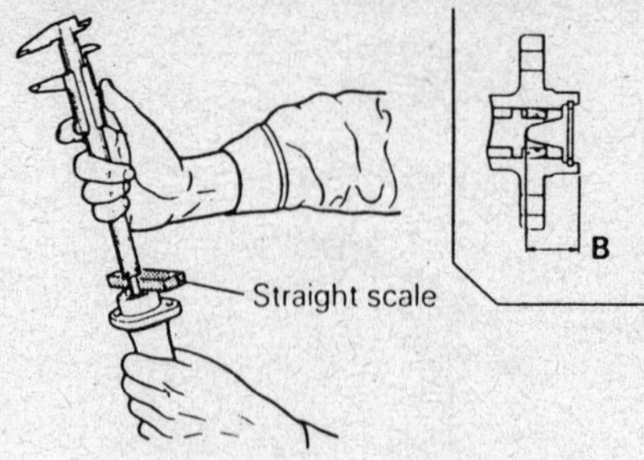


**Fig. 5 Location of measurement "B"**

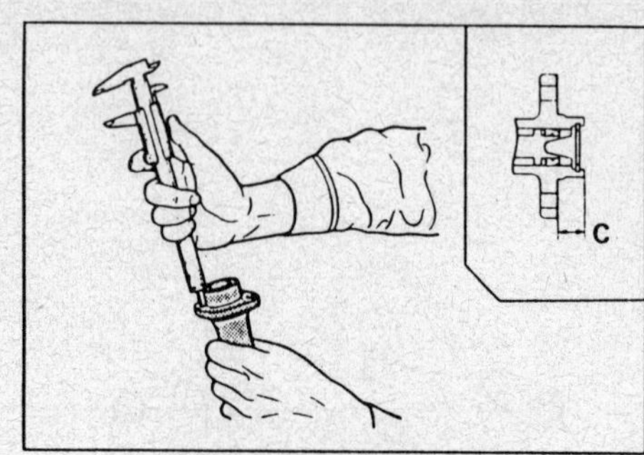


**Fig. 6 Location of measurement "C"**

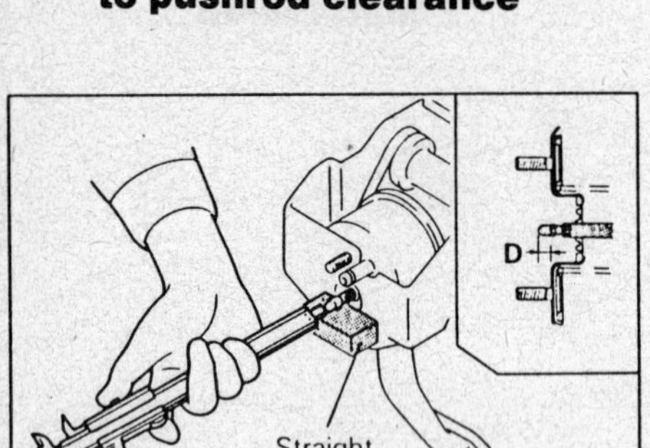


**Fig. 7 Location of measurement "D"**

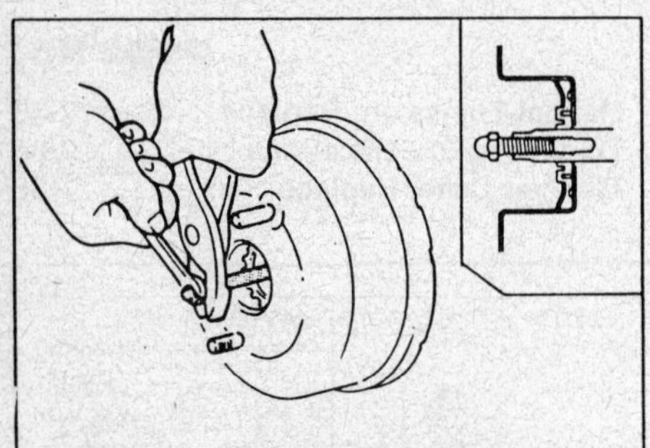

**Fig. 8 Adjusting booster pushrod**

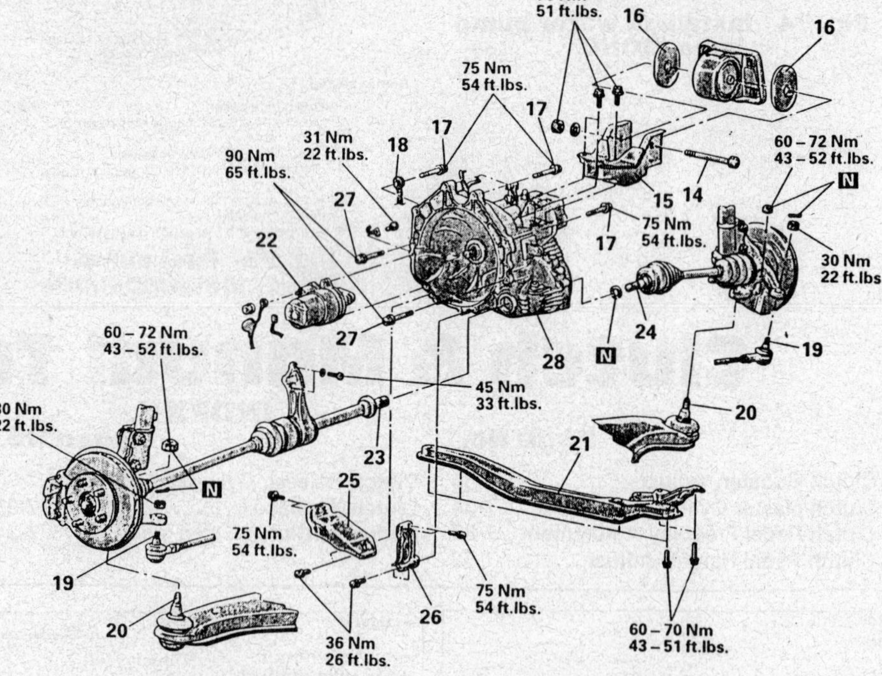


14. Connection for transaxle mount
15. Transaxle mount bracket
16. Mounting stopper
17. Transaxle assembly upper part coupling bolt
18. Connection for transaxle ground cable
19. Connection for tie rod end
20. Connection for lower arm ball joint
21. Right member
22. Starter
23. Drive shaft (Left side), Inner shaft assembly
24. Drive shaft (Right side)
25. Transaxle stay (Front bank side)
26. Transaxle stay (Rear bank side)
27. Transaxle assembly lower part coupling bolt
28. Transaxle assembly

**Fig. 9 Exploded view of component locations**

distance between the clutch pedal and the floorpan when the clutch disengages. On AWD vehicles, measure distance with engine running. Clearance should be 2.2 inches or greater.

If the pedal freeplay and/or clutch disengagement clearance is not within specification, bleed the clutch hydraulic system.

# HYDRAULIC CLUTCH BLEED

The clutch hydraulic system must be bled whenever the pressure line is disconnected or system component replacement is required.

**The fluid in the reservoir must be maintained at the 3/4 level or higher during air bleeding.**

1. Remove bleeder cap from slave cylinder and attach vinyl hose to bleeder screw, then place other end of hose in container.
2. Slowly pump clutch pedal several times.
3. With clutch pedal depressed, loosen bleeder screw to release trapped air.
4. Tighten bleeder screw.
5. Repeat steps 2 through 4 until no air bubbles appear in fluid.

# CLUTCH MASTER CYLINDER

## REPLACE

1. Drain fluid from clutch hydraulic system.
2. Disconnect fluid sensor connector from brake master cylinder.
3. Disconnect brake lines from brake master cylinder, then vacuum hose.
4. Working from inside vehicle, remove clevis pin retaining brake booster pushrod to brake pedal.
5. Remove four brake booster retaining bolts from brake pedal support bracket.
6. Remove brake master cylinder and booster assembly from engine compartment.
7. Disconnect clutch pressure line from master cylinder.
8. **On AWD vehicles,** working form inside engine compartment, remove clutch master cylinder retaining bolts.
9. **On FWD models,** working from inside vehicle, remove master cylinder

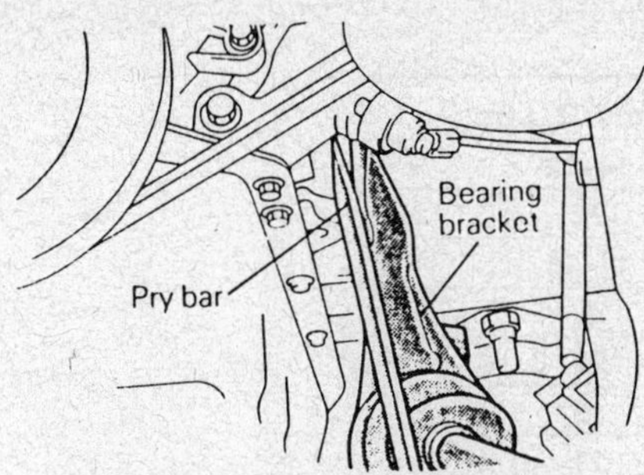


**Fig. 10 View of lefthand driveshaft bearing bracket**

retaining nuts.

10. **On all models,** remove clutch master cylinder from engine compartment.
11. Reverse procedure to install, **Torque** clutch master cylinder retaining nuts to 9 ft. lbs. **Torque** brake master cylinder retaining nuts to 10 ft. lbs.

## CLUTCH RELEASE CYLINDER

### REPLACE

1. Remove air cleaner and intake hose assembly from vehicle.
2. **On AWD models,** remove vacuum pipe from above battery.
3. **On all models,** remove battery, then battery tray assembly from vehicle.
4. Remove windshield washer reservoir from vehicle.
5. Disconnect pressure line from release cylinder, then plug line to prevent leakage.
6. Remove release cylinder retaining bolts, then cylinder.
7. Reverse procedure to install. **Torque** slave cylinder retaining bolts to 13 ft. lbs. Bleed clutch and brake hydraulic systems.

## CLUTCH BOOSTER

### ADJUST

Refer to **Fig. 4** when adjusting clearance between clutch booster pushrod and piston.

1. Measure and record dimensions B, C and D, **Figs. 5 through 7.**
2. Using measured values obtained in step one, add measurements C and D, then subtract that measurement from measurement B, this will give you dimension A in **Fig. 4.** Dimension A should be between .0082-.0181 inches.
3. If clearance is not within specification, adjust the pushrod length by turning the adjustable end of pushrod, **Fig. 8.** Improper clearance may cause excessive clutch drag.

## CLUTCH

### REPLACE

1. Remove transaxle as described under "Manual Transaxle, Replace" procedure.
2. Mark position of clutch cover to flywheel for reference during installation.
3. Diagonally loosen clutch cover retaining bolts, loosen bolts one or two turns at a time, to avoid bending cover flange.
4. Apply MOPAR Multi-mileage Lubricant (part No. 2525035) or equivalent to parts as follows:
   a. Apply a thin coating of to release arm fulcrum and point of contact with release bearing.
   b. To end of the release cylinders, pushrod and to pushrod hole in release fork.
   c. Pack inner surface of clutch release bearing and groove. **Do not leave excess lubricant on bearing which may be thrown onto clutch disc, causing clutch disc contamination and/or slippage.**
   d. Apply a thin coating of to clutch disc inner splines.
5. Using a universal clutch disc alignment tool, position clutch disc to flywheel.
6. Install clutch cover assembly. Tighten bolts a little at a time, working in a diagonal sequence. **Torque** bolts to 11-15 ft. lbs.

## MANUAL TRANSAXLE

### REPLACE

1. Drain transaxle fluid.
2. **On vehicles equipped with SOHC engine,** drain engine coolant.
3. Remove front wheel and tire assemblies.
4. **On all models,** working from inside front inner fenderwells, remove engine splash shields.
5. **On AWD models,** remove vacuum pipe assembly from above battery.
6. **On all models,** remove battery and battery tray assembly.
7. Remove windshield washer reservoir from vehicle.
8. Disconnect air flow sensor.
9. Remove air duct hose and air cleaner cover from engine.
10. **On vehicles equipped with SOHC engine,** remove upper and lower radiator hoses.
11. **On all models,** disconnect pressure line from release cylinder, then plug pressure line.
12. Disconnect ground strap from transaxle.
13. Disconnect back-up light switch electrical connector located above transaxle.
14. Disconnect speedometer cable at transaxle assembly.

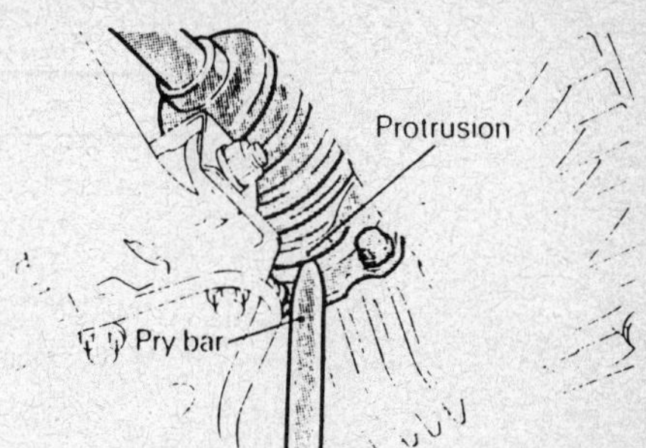


**Fig. 11 Location of righthand driveshaft protrusion**

15. Raise and support vehicle.
16. Raise and support transaxle assembly with floor jack or equivalent, then remove transaxle mount insulator bolt, mount bracket and mounting stopper.
17. Disconnect front tie rod ends from steering knuckles.
18. Disconnect steering knuckle from lower control arm.
19. Remove right member, then starter assembly **Fig. 9.**
20. Remove lefthand bearing bracket retaining bolts, **Fig. 10.**
21. Insert a pry bar between bearing bracket and engine block, then pry lefthand driveshaft assembly from transaxle.
22. Remove lefthand driveshaft, hub and inner shaft from vehicle as a assembly.
23. Insert pry bar to protrusion shown in **Fig. 11** to remove righthand driveshaft assembly from transaxle.
24. **On AWD models,** remove driveshaft retaining bolts, then midship bearing retaining bolts and driveshaft from vehicle.
25. **On all models,** support transaxle with transmission jack or equivalent, then remove transaxle assembly lower coupling bolt.
26. Remove transaxle from vehicle.
27. Reverse procedure to install. **Torque** all bolts to specification.

## TRANSFER CASE

### REPLACE

1. Drain transaxle assembly.
2. Remove active front venturi skirt from vehicle.
3. Remove front exhaust pipe and main muffler assembly from vehicle.
4. Remove driveshaft retaining bolts, then midship bearing retaining bolts and driveshaft from vehicle.
5. Remove five transfer case retaining bolts, then transfer case.
6. Reverse procedure to install. **Torque** all bolts to specification.

## TIGHTENING SPECIFICATIONS

| Year | Component | Torque/ft. Lbs. |
|---|---|---|
| 1991-92 | Back-Up Lamp Switch | 14–22 |
| | Brake Pedal Shaft | 22 |
| | Clutch Cover Bolt | 11–15 |
| | Clutch Master Cylinder Bolt | 9 |
| | Clutch Pedal Bolt | 22 |
| | Clutch Release Cylinder | 13 |
| | Clutch Tube Bolt | 11 |
| | Clutch Vacuum Line Bolt | 11–13 |
| | Flywheel Bolt | 55 |
| | RH Member Bolt | 43–51 |
| | Starter Cover Bolt | 7 |
| | Stop Lamp Switch | 10 |
| | Tie Rod End | 22 |
| | Transaxle Coupling Bolt | 65 |
| | Transaxle Mount | 33 |
| | Transaxle Stay | 54 |
| | Transfer Case To Transaxle | 64 |

# Rear Axle & Suspension

## INDEX



## REAR AXLE SHAFT

### REPLACE

1. Remove rear axle shaft as shown in **Fig. 1,** noting the following:
   a. **On models equipped with ABS brake system,** remove rear speed sensor attaching nut. **Ensure speed sensor tip and toothed edge of rotor do not strike other parts, as damage may result.**
   b. **On all models,** remove caliper assembly then suspend using suitable wire.
   c. Using tool No. C 3281 or equivalent, secure axle shaft, then remove companion flange self-locking nut.
   d. **On models equipped with ABS brake system,** using tool No. P 334 or equivalent, remove rear rotor from axle shaft assembly.
   e. **On all models,** using tool No. P334 or equivalent, remove outer bearing and dust shield assembly.
   f. Using tool No. C 4171 or equivalent, remove inner bearing and seal from axle housing.
2. Reverse procedure to install, noting the following:
   a. Using tool No. C 4171 or equivalent, press fit inner bearing onto axle housing.
   b. Using tool No. MB990641 or equivalent, press oil seal onto axle housing with oil seal depression facing upward, and until it contacts shoulder on inside of axle housing. Using suitable plastic hammer, lightly tap top and circumference of tool press fitting oil seal gradually and evenly.
   c. Using tool No. MB990799 or equivalent, press fit dust shield until it contacts with axle shaft shoulder. Using suitable plastic hammer, lightly tap top and circumference of tool press fitting oil seal gradually and evenly.
   d. Apply multipurpose grease around circumference of inner side of outer bearing seal lip.
   e. Using tool No. P 334 or equivalent, press fit outer bearing to axle shaft, ensuring bearing seal lip surface faces axle shaft flange.
   f. **On models equipped with ABS brake systems,** using tool No. P 334 or equivalent, press fit rotor to axle shaft with rear rotor groove toward axle shaft flange.
   g. **On all models,** using tool No. C3281 or equivalent, secure axle shaft, then tighten companion flange self-locking nut.

## DRIVESHAFT

### REPLACE

1. Remove driveshaft as shown in **Fig. 2,** noting the following:
   a. Using suitable tool, remove driveshaft from differential carrier. **Ensure differential carrier oil seal is not damaged by driveshaft spline.**
2. Reverse to install, noting the following:
   a. Using tool Nos. C4171 and MB991380 or equivalents, install oil seal.
   b. **Ensure differential carrier oil seal is not damaged by driveshaft spline.**
   c. **On models equipped with Limited Slip Differential (LSD) a Viscus Coulping Unit (VCU) has a tow part serration, ensure installation on correct side.**
   d. Driveshaft LH boot band color on ball joint side is white, RH side is blue.

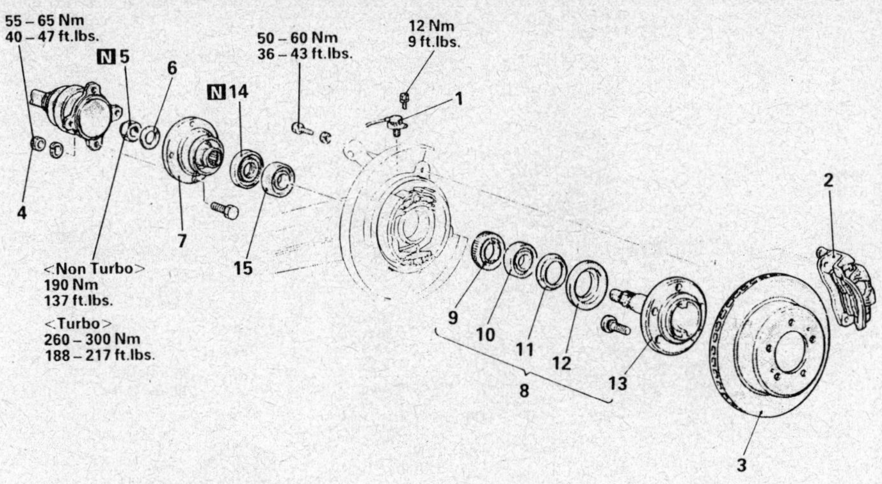


Removal steps

1. Rear speed sensor <Vehicles with A.B.S.>
2. Brake caliper assembly
3. Brake disc
4. Drive shaft mounting nut
5. Self-locking nut
6. Washer
7. Companion flange
8. Axle shaft assembly
9. Rear rotor <Vehicles with A.B.S.>
10. Outer bearing
11. Dust shield
12. Dust shield
13. Axle shaft
14. Oil seal
15. Inner bearing

**Fig. 1 Rear axle shaft assembly**

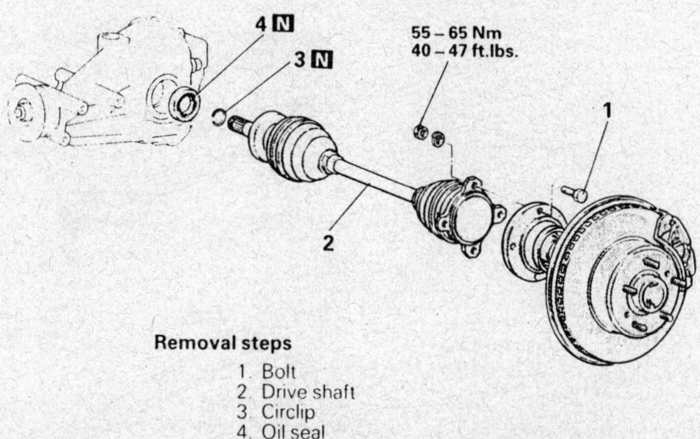


**Fig. 2 Rear driveshaft assembly**

# DIFFERENTIAL CARRIER REPLACE

1. Drain differential gear oil.
2. Remove main muffler assembly as follows:
   a. Remove main muffler and center exhaust pipe attaching bolts and gasket.
   b. Remove rubber hanger attaching bolts.
   c. Remove main muffler assembly.
3. Remove differential carrier as shown in **Fig. 3,** noting the following:
   a. Using suitable tool, remove driveshaft from differential carrier. **Ensure differential carrier oil seal is not damaged by driveshaft spline.**
   b. Mark differential companion flange and propeller shaft flange yoke for installation alignment.
   c. Support propeller shaft with suitable wire.
   d. Hold bottom of differential carrier, then remove rear wheel oil pump through mounting hole, then remove differential carrier.
4. Reverse procedure to install, noting the following:
   a. Install rear wheel oil pump through mounting hole, then install differential carrier.
   b. Align flange yoke and companion flange mating mark, then install propeller shaft.

**SERVICE BULLETIN:** Some 1991 AWD models built prior to August 20, 1991, may experience a drivetrain rear end noise on hard acceleration in 1st or 2nd gear. This noise may be caused by a driveshaft misalignment. Align rear driveshaft as follows:

1. Raise and support vehicle.
2. Remove insulator locking nuts on both center bearing insulators.
3. Inspect 1st center bearing insulator to see if shims have been installed. If shims have been installed, remove shims from 1st center bearing insulator and install onto 2nd bearing insulator.
4. If no shims were installed, install two 1/8 inch shims onto 2nd center bearing insulator.
5. Install locking nuts and **torque** to 22 ft. lbs.

# FRONT WHEEL DRIVE

## CONTROL ARMS & ASSIST LINK, REPLACE

1. Remove shock absorber assembly as outlined under "Shock Absorber, Replace."
2. Remove upper arm, lower arm and assist link as shown in **Fig. 4,** noting the following:
   a. Using tool No. MB990635 or equivalent, disconnect upper arm, lower arm and assist link from knuckle assembly. Suspend tool with suitable rope to prevent dropping.
   b. Loosen ball joint attaching nut, do not remove.
3. Reverse procedure to install.

## TRAILING ARM, REPLACE

1. Remove trailing arm as shown in **Fig. 5,** noting the following:
   a. Using tool No. MB990635 or equivalent, disconnect upper arm, lower arm and assist link from knuckle assembly. Suspend tool with suitable rope to prevent dropping.
   b. Loosen ball joint attaching nut, do not remove.
2. Reverse procedure to install, noting the following:
   a. Hold stabilizer link ball studs with suitable wrench, tighten self-locking nut so protrusion of stabilizer link is within .197-.276 inch.

## HUB & BEARING ASSEMBLY, REPLACE

1. Remove rear hub and bearing assembly as shown in **Fig. 6,** noting the following:
   a. **On models equipped with ABS brake system,** remove rear speed sensor attaching nut. **Ensure speed sensor tip and toothed edge of rotor do not strike other parts, as damage may result.**

b. **On all models,** remove caliper assembly then suspend using suitable wire.
c. **On models equipped with ABS brake system, do not scratch or scar toothed surface of rotor, if rotor is deformed it may not be able to accurately sense wheel rotation speed and the system may perform normally.**

2. Reverse procedure to install, noting the following:
   a. Align wheel bearing attaching nut with spindle indentation, then crimp.

## SHOCK ABSORBER, REPLACE

1. Remove interior rear side trim panel to gain access to shock assembly.
2. Remove upper shock absorber attaching nut.
3. Remove ECS electrical connector.
4. Remove shock absorber upper cap.
5. Raise and support vehicle.
6. Remove brake line clamp attaching bolt.
7. Remove shock absorber lower attaching bolt, then remove shock assembly.
8. Reverse procedure to install. Tighten to specifications.

## COIL SPRING, REPLACE

1. Remove shock absorber assembly as outlined under "Shock Absorber, Replace."
2. Remove coil spring as shown in **Fig. 7,** noting the following:
   a. Using tool No. C-4838 or equivalent, compress spring, then remove piston rod attaching nut.
3. Reverse procedure to install, noting the following:
   a. Using tool No. L-4514 or equivalent, compress spring, install on shock absorber assembly, align coil spring in spring seat.
   b. Install new piston rod attaching nut, then tighten to specifications.

## STABILIZER BAR, REPLACE

1. Remove stabilizer bar as shown in **Fig. 8.**
2. Reverse procedure to install, noting the following:
   a. Hold stabilizer link ball studs with suitable wrench, tighten self-locking nut so protrusion of stabilizer link is within .197-.276 inch.
   b. Align LH stabilizer bar bushing with stabilizer bar marking end, then temporarily tighten attaching bolts.
   c. Install RH stabilizer bar bushing and bracket, then temporarily tighten attaching bolts.
   d. Install stabilizer bar to stabilizer link then tighten bracket attaching bolt to specifications.

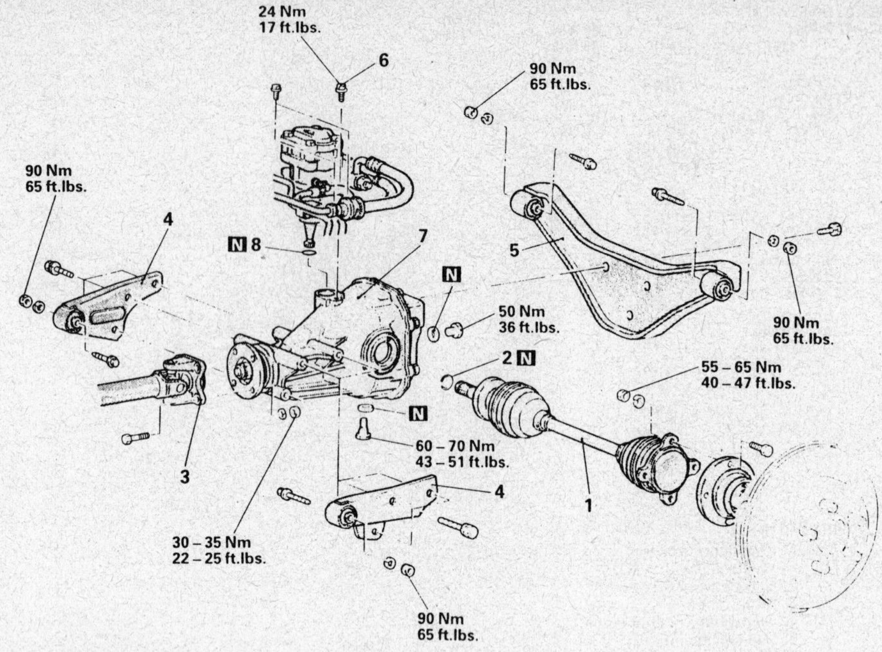


**Removal steps**

1. Drive shaft
2. Circlip
3. Propeller shaft connection
4. Differential support assembly
5. Differential support member assembly
6. Rear wheel oil pump installation bolt
7. Differential carrier
8. O-ring

**Fig. 3 Rear differential carrier assembly**

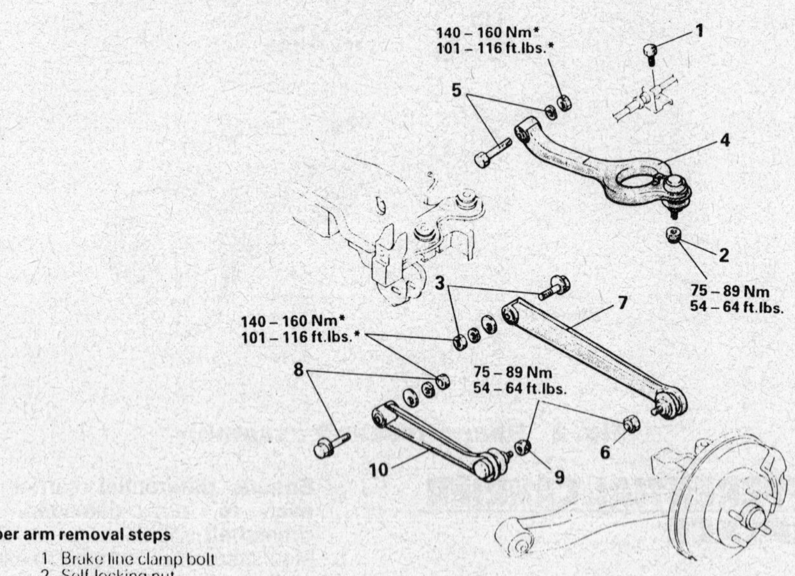


**Upper arm removal steps**

1. Brake line clamp bolt
2. Self-locking nut
3. Upper arm mounting bolt and nut
4. Upper arm

**Lower arm removal steps**

5. Lower arm mounting bolt and nut
6. Self-locking nut
7. Lower arm

**Assist link removal steps**

8. Assist link mounting bolt and nut
9. Self-locking nut
10. Assist link

**Fig. 4 Upper & lower control arms & assist link. FWD**

Removal steps

1. Brake caliper mounting bolt
2. Brake caliper
3. Brake line clamp bolt
4. Rear brake disc
5. Hub cap
6. Wheel bearing nut
7. Hub assembly
8. Parking brake cable clamp bolt
9. Parking brake cable end
10. Rear speed sensor clamp bolt (ABS)
11. ABS speed sensor (ABS)
12. Backing plate
13. Stabilizer link mounting nut
14. Self-locking nut
15. Shock absorber mounting bolt (upper)
16. Self-locking nut
17. Self-locking nut
18. Trailing arm mounting bolt and nut
19. Trailing arm assembly

**Fig. 5 Trailing arm assembly. FWD**

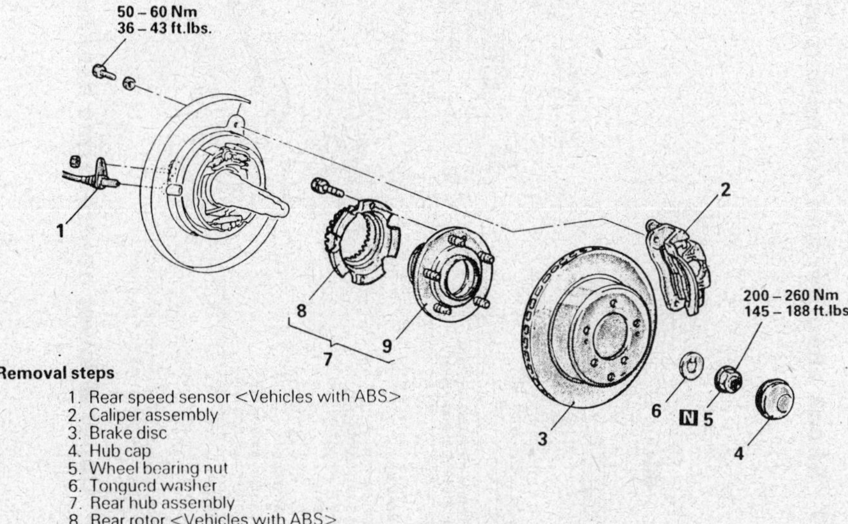


Removal steps

1. Rear speed sensor <Vehicles with ABS>
2. Caliper assembly
3. Brake disc
4. Hub cap
5. Wheel bearing nut
6. Tongued washer
7. Rear hub assembly
8. Rear rotor <Vehicles with ABS>
9. Rear hub unit bearing

Caution
Rear hub unit bearing cannot be disassembled.

**Fig. 6 Rear hub & bearing assembly. FWD**

# ALL WHEEL DRIVE

## CONTROL ARM, REPLACE

1. Remove control arms as shown in **Fig. 9,** noting the following:
   a. Using tool No. MB990635 or equivalent, disconnect upper arm ball joint from knuckle assembly. Suspend tool with suitable rope to prevent dropping.
   b. Loosen ball joint attaching nut, do not remove.
   c. Lower lower control arm at crossmember side. Using tool MB990635 or equivalent, disconnect lower arm ball joint from knuckle assembly.
   d. Loosen ball joint attaching nut, do not remove.
2. Reverse procedure to install, noting the following:
   a. Hold stabilizer link ball studs with suitable wrench, tighten self-locking nut so protrusion of stabilizer link is within .197-.276 inch.

## TRAILING ARM, REPLACE

1. Remove trailing arm as shown in **Fig. 10,** noting the following:
   a. Using tool No. C3281 or equivalent, secure rear axle, then remove self-locking nut.
   b. Using tool Nos. C637 and CT 1003 or equivalent, remove rear axle shaft.
   c. Using tool No. MB990635 or equivalent, disconnect ball joint from knuckle assembly. Suspend tool with suitable rope to prevent dropping.
   d. Loosen ball joint attaching nut, do not remove.
2. Reverse procedure to install.

## SHOCK ABSORBER, REPLACE

1. Remove interior rear side trim panel to gain access to shock assembly.
2. Remove upper shock absorber attaching nut.
3. Remove ECS electrical connector.
4. Remove shock absorber upper cap.
5. Raise and support vehicle.
6. Remove shock absorber lower attaching bolt, then remove shock assembly.
7. Reverse procedure to install. Tighten to specifications.

## COIL SPRING, REPLACE

1. Remove shock absorber assembly as outlined under "Shock Absorber, Replace."
2. Remove coil spring as shown in **Fig. 11,** noting the following:
   a. Using tool No. C-4838 or equivalent, compress spring, then remove piston rod attaching nut.
3. Reverse procedure to install, noting the following:
   a. Using tool No. L-4514 or equivalent, compress spring, install on

**Disassembly steps**

1. Piston rod tightening nut
2. Washer
3. Upper bushing (A)
4. Bracket assembly
5. Upper spring pad
6. Upper bushing (B)
7. Collar
8. Cup assembly
9. Dust cover
10. Bump rubber
11. Coil spring
12. Shock absorber

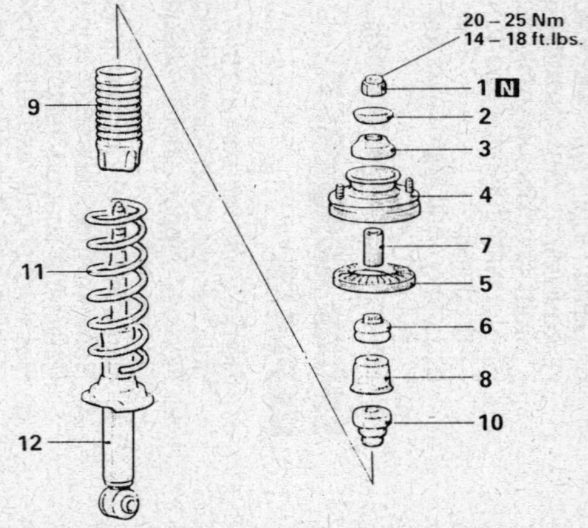

20 – 25 Nm
14 – 18 ft.lbs.
1 N
2
3
4
7
5
6
8
10
9
11
12

**Fig. 7 Shock absorber and coil spring assembly. FWD**

40 Nm
29 ft.lbs.
8
40 Nm
29 ft.lbs.
1
2
3
12
9
10
11
7
6
5
4

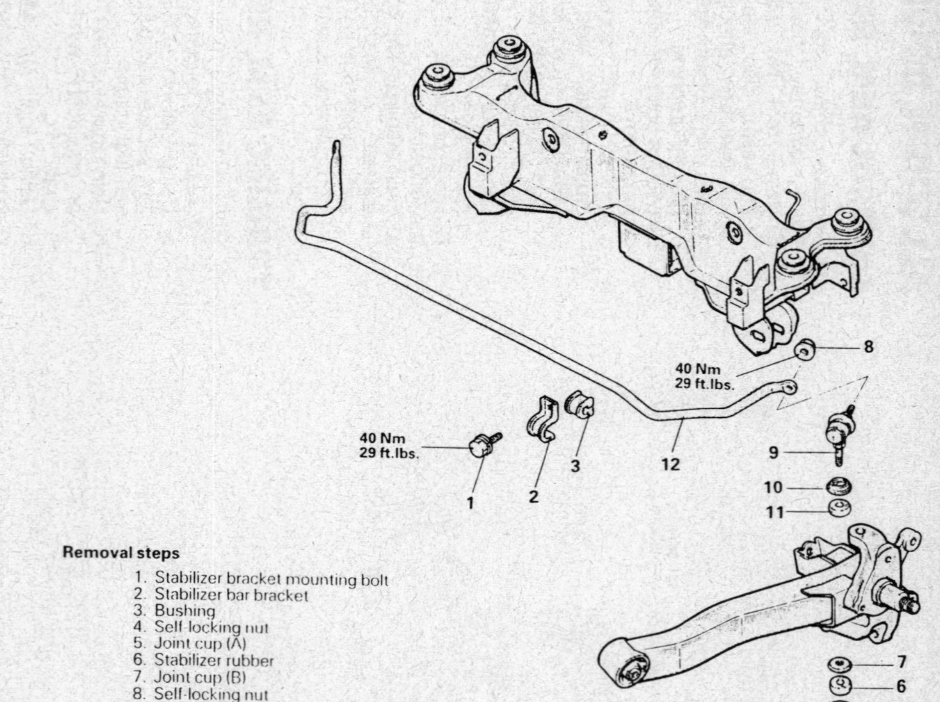

**Removal steps**

1. Stabilizer bracket mounting bolt
2. Stabilizer bar bracket
3. Bushing
4. Self-locking nut
5. Joint cup (A)
6. Stabilizer rubber
7. Joint cup (B)
8. Self-locking nut
9. Stabilizer link
10. Joint cup (A)
11. Stabilizer rubber
12. Stabilizer bar

**Fig. 8 Stabilizer bar assembly. FWD**

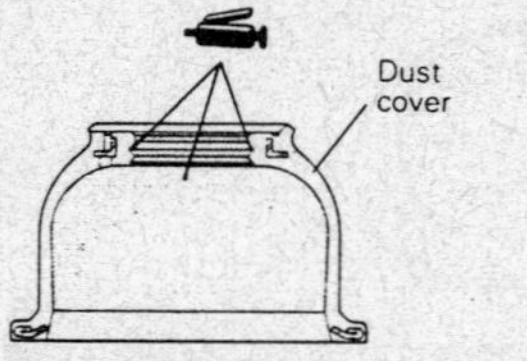

Dust
cover

**Grease: MOPAR Multi-mileage Lubricant Part No. 2525035 or equivalent**

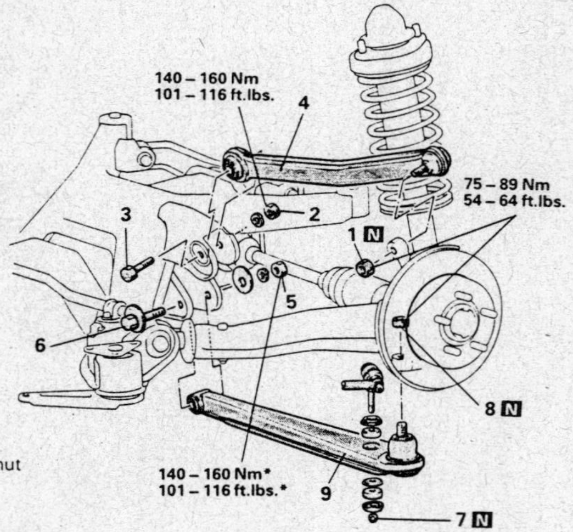

140 – 160 Nm
101 – 116 ft.lbs.
4
3
2
1 N
75 – 89 Nm
54 – 64 ft.lbs.
5
6
8 N
140 – 160 Nm*
101 – 116 ft.lbs.*
9
7 N

**Upper arm removal steps**

1. Self-locking nut
2. Upper arm mounting nut
3. Upper arm mounting bolt
4. Upper arm

**Lower arm removal steps**

5. Lower arm mounting nut
6. Lower arm mounting bolt
7. Stabilizer link to lower arm coupling nut
8. Self-locking nut
9. Lower arm

NOTE
For tightening points marked with *, first temporarily tighten and then ground the vehicle to torque to specification where the vehicle is empty.

**Fig. 9 Upper & lower control arms assembly. AWD**

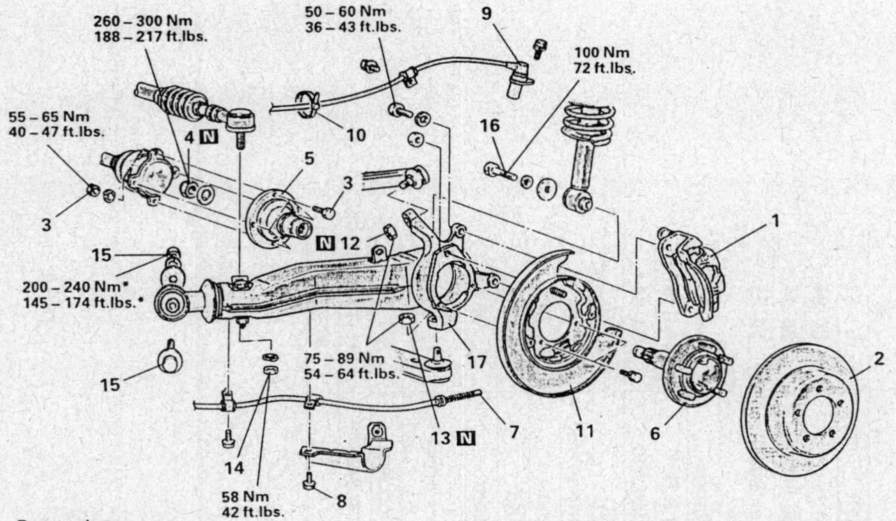

Removal steps

1. Rear brake caliper assembly
2. Rear brake disc
3. Drive shaft to companion flange mounting bolt and nut
4. Self-locking nut
5. Companion flange
6. Rear axle shaft
7. Parking brake cable end
8. Parking brake cable clamp bolt
9. Rear speed sensor (ABS)
10. Rear speed sensor cable and parking brake cable bands (ABS)
11. Dust shield
12. Self-locking nut (upper arm)
13. Self-locking nut (lower arm)
14. Tie rod end mounting nut
15. Trailing arm mounting bolt and nut
16. Rear shock absorber mounting bolt
17. Trailing arm

NOTE
For tightening points marked with *, first temporarily tighten and then ground the vehicle to torque to specification where the vehicle is empty.

**Fig. 10 Trailing arm assembly. AWD**

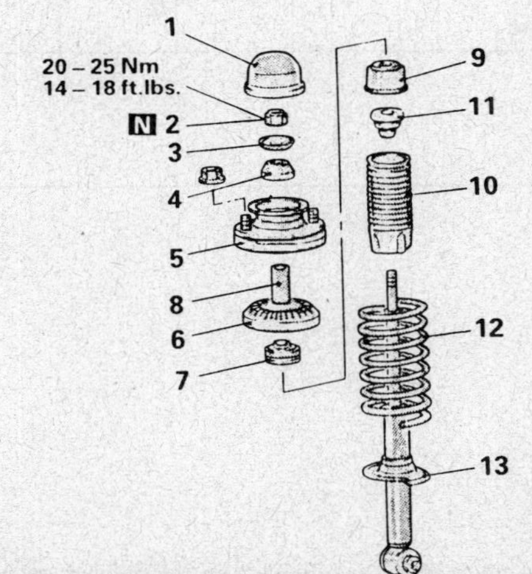


Disassembly steps

1. Cap
2. Piston rod tightening nut
3. Washer
4. Upper bushing (A)
5. Bracket assembly
6. Spring pad
7. Upper bushing (B)
8. Collar
9. Cup assembly
10. Dust cover
11. Bump rubber
12. Coil spring
13. Shock absorber

**Fig. 11 Shock absorber & coil spring assembly. AWD**

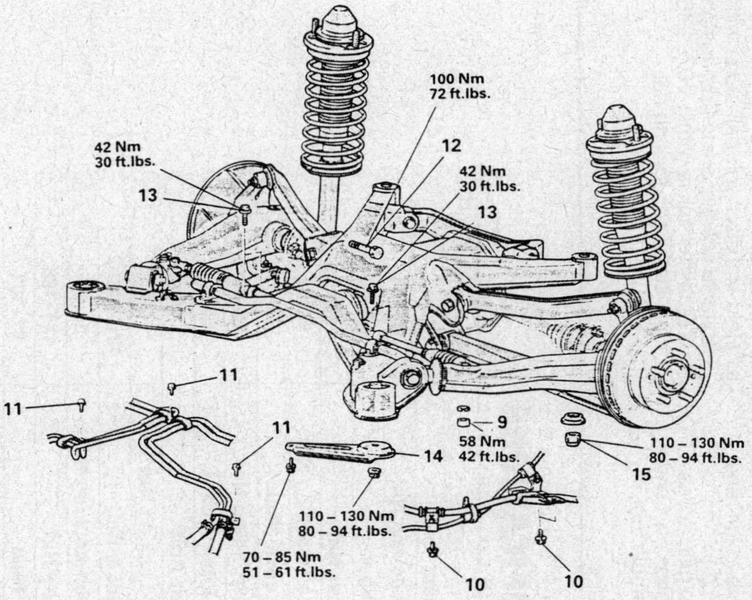

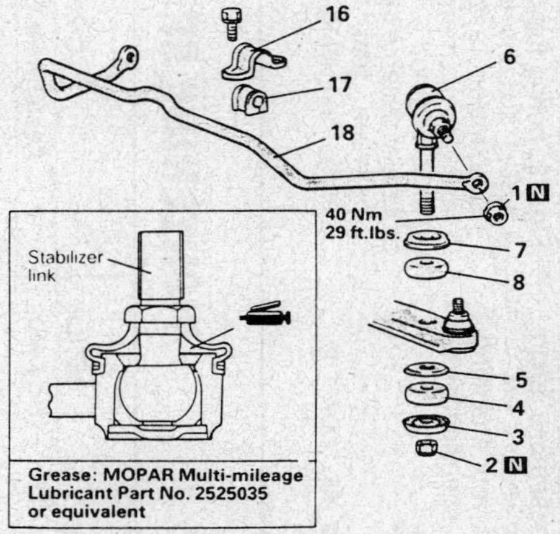

Removal steps

1. Self-locking nut*
2. Self-locking nut*
3. Joint cup A*
4. Stabilizer rubber*
5. Joint cup B*
6. Stabilizer link*
7. Joint cup A*
8. Stabilizer rubber*
9. Tie rod end mounting nut*
10. Parking brake cable bracket mounting bolt*
11. 4WS piping fixing bolt <4WS>
12. Rear shock absorber mounting bolt
13. Power cylinder mounting bolt <4WS>
14. Crossmember bracket*
15. Crossmember mounting nut*
16. Stabilizer bracket*
17. Bushing*
18. Stabilizer bar

NOTE
Parts marked with * are symmetrical.

**Fig. 12 Stabilizer bar assembly. AWD**

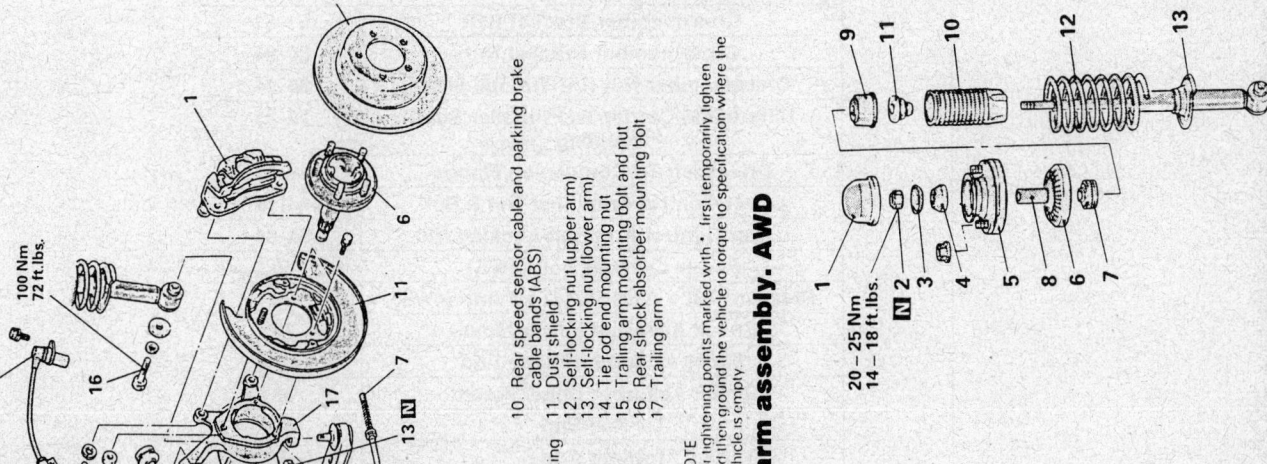

shock absorber assembly, align coil spring in spring seat.

b. Install new piston rod attaching nut, then tighten to specifications.

## STABILIZER BAR, REPLACE

1. Remove stabilizer bar as shown in **Fig. 12,** noting the following:
   a. Using suitable jack, support rear suspension assembly, then remove crossmember bracket and attaching nut.
   b. Lower suitable jack, to gain access between rear suspension and body, then using a suitable tool, remove stabilizer bar.
2. Reverse procedure to install, noting the following:
   a. Hold stabilizer link ball studs with suitable wrench, ensure protrusion of stabilizer link is within .197-.276 inch, install self-locking nut.

## TIGHTENING SPECIFICATIONS

| Year | Model | Component | Torque/Ft. Lbs. |
|---|---|---|---|
| 1991-92 | FWD | Assist Arm Self-Locking Nut | 54-64 |
| | | Brake Caliper | 36-43 |
| | | Crossmember Nut | 65 |
| | | Lower Control Arm Self-Locking Nut | 54-64 |
| | | Shock Absorber Lower Mount | 65① |
| | | Shock Absorber Piston Rod Nut | 14-18 |
| | | Shock Absorber Upper Mount | 33 |
| | | Stabilizer Bar Bolt | 29 |
| | | Stabilizer Bar Self-Locking Nut | 29 |
| | | Trailing Arm Nut & Bolt | 101-116① |
| | | Upper Control Arm Self-Locking Nut | 54-64 |
| | | Wheel Bearing Nut | 145-188 |
| | | Wheel Lug Nuts | 87-101 |
| | AWD | ABS Cable Attaching Bolt | 9 |
| | | ABS Rear Speed Sensor Bolt | 9 |
| | | Brake Caliper Bolt | 36-43 |
| | | Center Bearing Nut | 22 |
| | | Crossmember Bracket Bolt | 51-61 |
| | | Crossmember Bracket Nut | 80-94 |
| | | Crossmember Nut (Differential Side) | 80-94 |
| | | Differential Carrier To Propeller Shaft Coupling | 22-25 |
| | | Driveshaft To Companion Flange | 40-47 |
| | | Lower Control Arm Inner Nut & Bolt | 101-116① |
| | | Lower Control Arm Self-Locking Nut | 54-64 |
| | | Power Cylinder Bolt (4WS) | 30 |
| | | Pressure Tube Assembly To Pump (4WS) | 25 |
| | | Shock Absorber Lower Mount | 72 |
| | | Shock Absorber Piston Rod | 14-18 |
| | | Shock Absorber Upper Mount | 33 |
| | | Tie Rod End | 42 |
| | | Trailing Arm | 145-174① |
| | | Upper Control Arm Self-Locking Nut | 54-64 |
| | | Upper Control Arm Inner Nut & Bolt | 101-116① |
| | | Wheel Lug Nuts | 87-101 |

①—Tighten temporarily, then tighten to specifications once vehicle is unladen.

# Front Suspension & Steering

## INDEX



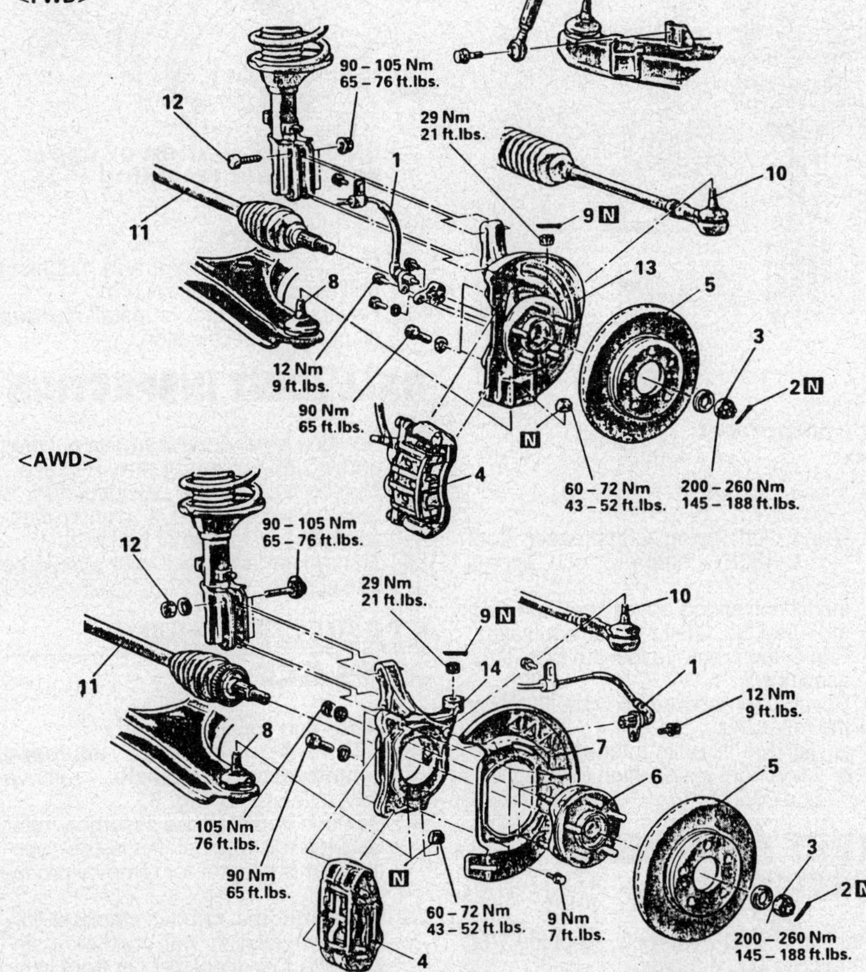


1. Front speed sensor connection <Vehicles with A.B.S.>
2. Cotter pin
3. Drive shaft nut
4. Caliper assembly
5. Brake disc
6. Front hub unit bearing
7. Dust shield
8. Lower arm ball joint connection
9. Cotter pin
10. Tie rod end connection
11. Drive shaft
12. Front strut mounting bolt
13. Hub and knuckle
14. Hub

**Fig. 1 Exploded view of front suspension components**

## AIRBAG SYSTEM DISARMING

1. Place ignition switch in lock position.
2. Disconnect and tape battery ground cable connector.
3. **Wait at least 1 minute after disconnecting battery ground cable before doing any further work on vehicle.** The SRS system is designed to retain enough voltage to deploy airbag for a short time even after battery has been disconnected.
4. After repairs are complete, reconnect battery ground cable.
5. From passenger side of vehicle, turn ignition switch to On position.
6. SRS warning light should illuminate for 6 to 8 seconds, then remain off for at least 45 seconds to indicate if SRS system is functioning correctly.
7. If SRS indicator does not perform as described refer to the "Passive Restraint Systems" section.

## WHEEL BEARING

### ADJUST

Bearing preload is pre-set to the specified value by design and cannot be adjusted.

## STEERING KNUCKLE

### REPLACE

1. Raise and support vehicle.
2. Remove wheel and tire assembly.
3. Remove vehicle speed sensor retaining bolt from knuckle assembly, then suspend sensor.
4. Remove hub nut cotter pin, then hub nut.
5. Remove caliper retaining bolts, then suspend caliper out of way.
6. Remove front hub unit bearing retaining bolts from rear of steering knuckle assembly, then press driveshaft from hub unit and backing plate **Fig. 1.**
7. Remove tie rod end from steering knuckle assembly.
8. Press lower ball joint assembly from steering knuckle.
9. Suspend driveshaft assembly with wire, then swing steering knuckle clear of driveshaft assembly.

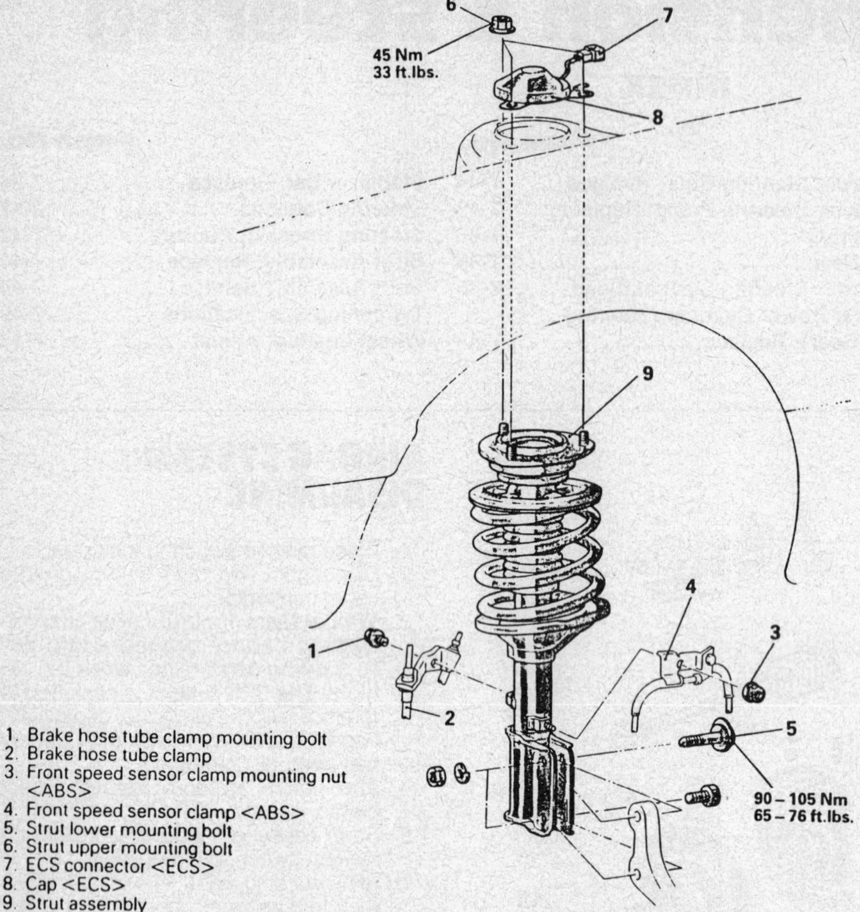


**Fig. 2 Front strut component location**

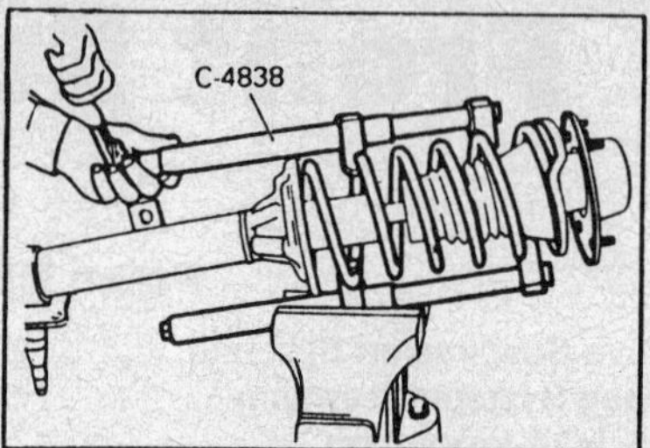


**Fig. 3 Installation of spring compressor tool**

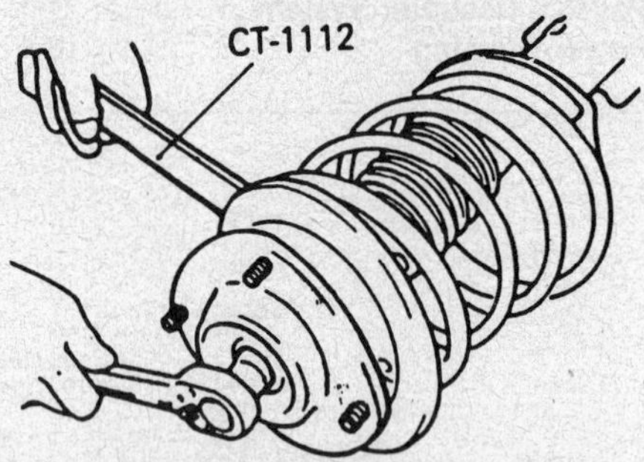


**Fig. 4 Installation of upper spring seat retaining tool**

10. Remove steering knuckle to strut retaining bolts, then steering knuckle.
11. Reverse procedure to install. **Torque** all bolts to specification.

## HUB & BEARING UNIT
### REPLACE

Refer to the "Steering Knuckle, Replacement" procedure in this section to perform hub and bearing unit replacement.

## STRUT ASSEMBLY
### REPLACE

1. Raise and support vehicle, then remove wheel and tire assembly.
2. Remove brake hose clamp retaining bolt, then brake hose from strut assembly.
3. Remove front speed sensor retaining nut from strut assembly, then position clamp aside.
4. Remove lower strut to steering knuckle retaining bolts.
5. Working from inside engine compartment, disconnect ECS connector, **Fig. 2.**
6. Remove upper strut retaining bolts, then strut assembly.
7. Using Coil Spring Compressor (tool No. C-4838) compress coil spring, **Fig. 3.**
8. Install coil spring upper seat retaining tool (tool No. CT-1112) or equivalent, **Fig. 4,** then remove locknut from strut assembly.
9. Reverse procedure to install noting the following:
   a. **Torque** all bolts to specification.
   b. Align front suspension to specification.

## STRUT ASSEMBLY SERVICE

Refer to "Strut Assembly, Replace" for strut service procedures.

## LOWER CONTROL ARM
### REPLACE

1. Remove upper and lower stabilizer link mounting nuts, then stabilizer link, **Fig. 5.**
2. Remove lower ball joint to steering knuckle retaining nut, then press ball joint from steering knuckle assembly.
3. Remove lower control arm clamp mounting bolts.
4. Remove lower control arm mounting bolt, then lower control arm.
5. Reverse procedure to install. **Torque** all bolts to specification.

## BALL JOINT INSPECTION

1. Remove lower control arm as outlined under "Lower Control Arm, Replace."
2. Tighten two nuts on ball joint stud.
3. Using a suitable torque wrench, measure starting torque of ball joint.
4. Starting torque of ball joint should be 86-191 inch lbs.

## STABILIZER BAR
### REPLACE

1. Raise and support vehicle.
2. **On AWD models equipped w/automatic transaxle,** remove transaxle stay B, **Fig. 6.**
3. Remove transfer case assembly, refer to "Clutch & Manual Transaxle" section in this chapter for removal procedure.
4. **On all models,** remove stabilizer link.
5. Remove stabilizer bar bracket retaining bolts, then stabilizer bar from vehicle.
6. Reverse procedure to install. Torque all bolts to specification.

## POWER STEERING GEAR
### REPLACE

1. Disarm airbag as outlined under "Airbag System Disarming."
2. Center front wheels and remove ignition key. **Failure to do so mat damage SRS clock spring and render**

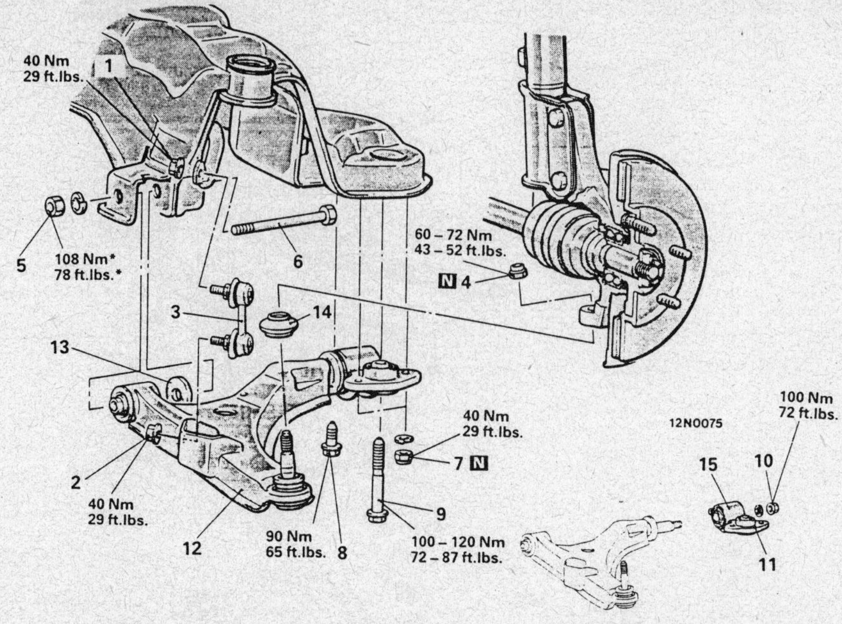


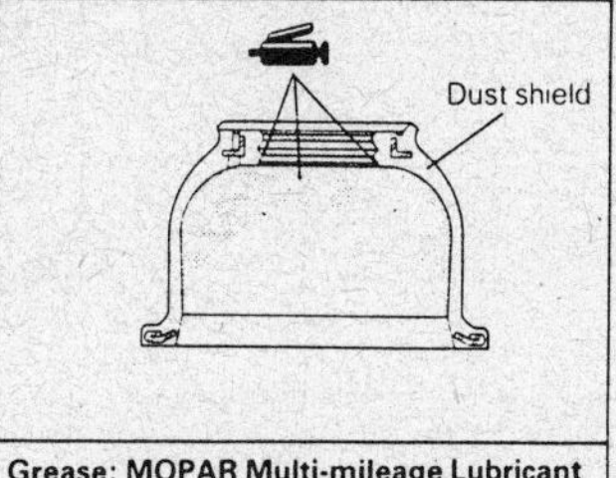


Grease: MOPAR Multi-mileage Lubricant Part No. 2525035 or equivalent

**Removal steps**

1. Stabilizer link mounting nut (stabilizer bar side)
2. Stabilizer link mounting nut (lower arm side)
3. Stabilizer link
4. Self-locking nut connecting lower arm ball joint to knuckle
5. Lower arm mounting nut
6. Lower arm mounting bolt
7. Clamp mounting self-locking nut
8. Clamp mounting bolt (small)
9. Clamp mounting bolt (large)
10. Lower arm clamp mounting self-locking nut
11. Lower arm mounting clamp
12. Lower arm
13. Stopper
14. Dust shield
15. Rod bushing

NOTE
For tightening points marked with *, first temporarily tighten them, then ground the vehicle and torque to specification where the vehicle is empty.

**Fig. 5 Lower control arm replace**

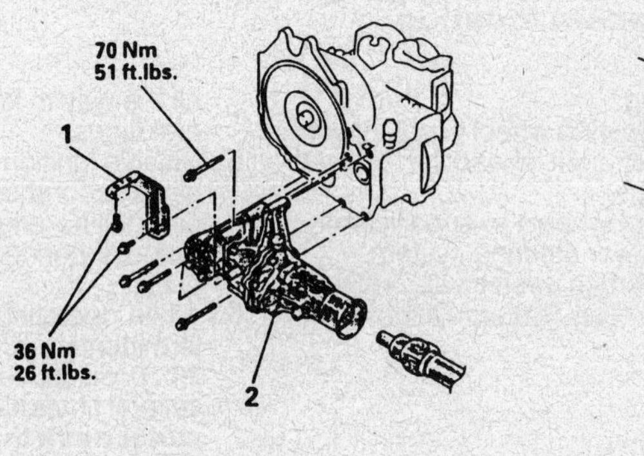


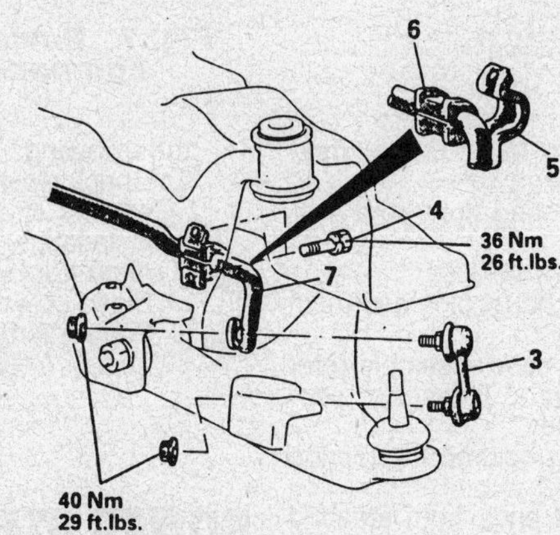


1. Transmission stay B
   <AWD vehicles with automatic transaxle>
2. Transfer (AWD)
3. Stabilizer link
4. Stabilizer bar bracket mounting bolt
5. Stabilizer bar bracket
6. Bushing
7. Stabilizer bar

**Fig. 6 Location of transaxle "Stay B"**

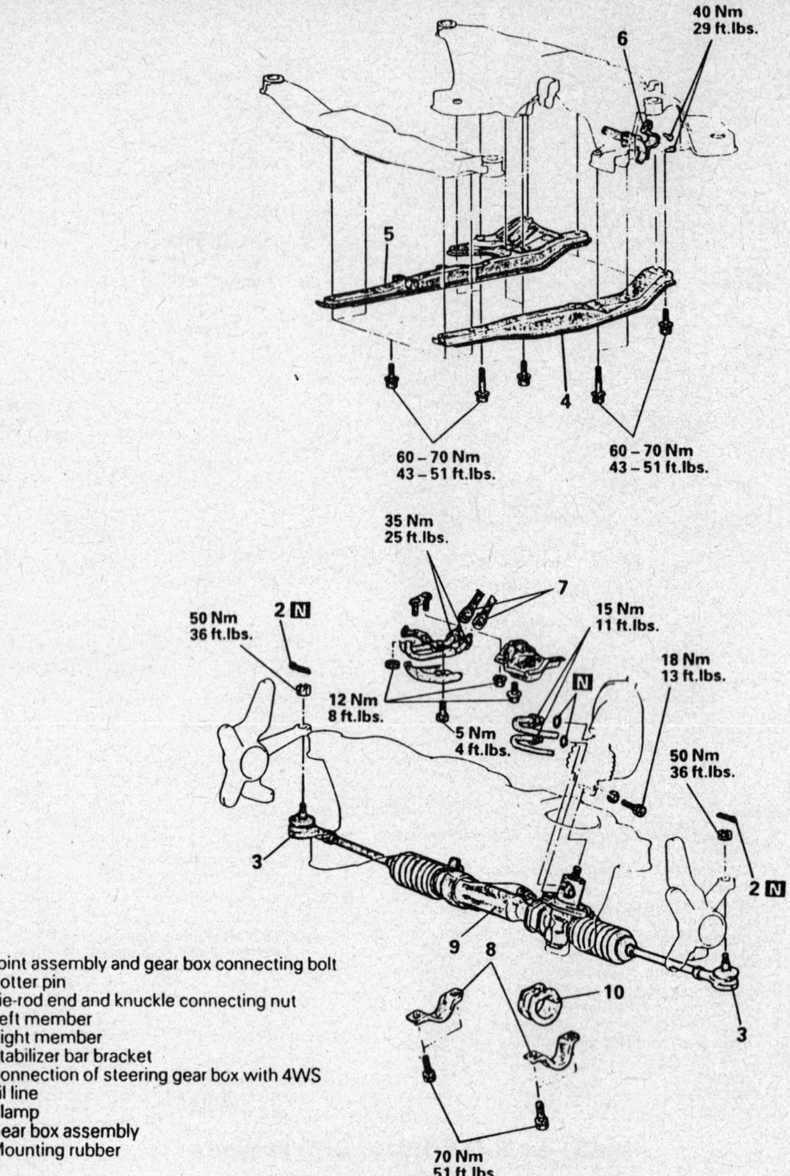


**Fig. 7 Power steering gear component location**

**the SRS system inoperative, risking serious injury.**

3. Drain power steering fluid from system.
4. Raise and support vehicle.
5. Remove front exhaust pipe and main muffler assembly.
6. Remove transfer case assembly, refer to "Clutch & Manual Transaxle" section in this chapter.
7. Remove steering column to steering gear pinch bolt.
8. Separate tie rod ends from steering knuckle assemblies.
9. Support engine and transaxle assembly with transmission jack, then remove left member and right member, **Fig. 7.**
10. Disconnect pressure lines from steering gear assembly.
11. Remove steering gear retaining clamps, then steering gear.
12. Reverse procedure to install, noting the following:
    a. Check steering wheel position with wheels straight ahead for correct installation.
    b. Align front wheels to specification.
    c. Bleed power steering system.
    d. Enable airbag system as outlined under "Airbag System Disarming."

## POWER STEERING SYSTEM BLEED

1. Raise and support vehicle.
2. Fill power steering pump to specification with recommended fluid.
3. Manually turn power steering pump by hand three or four revolutions.
4. Turn steering wheel with engine off, all the way to left and to the right several times.
5. Disable ignition system, on SOHC engines ground coil high tension cable. On DOHC engines disconnect wire harness connector at Distributor coil pack.
6. While operating the starter motor intermittently, turn steering wheel to full left position, then full right position several times. **Do not operate starter motor more than 15-20 seconds at a time without sufficient cool down time.**
7. Connect ignition system wiring, then start engine. Run at idle only.
8. Recheck fluid level, then turn steering wheel to full left and to full right positions.
9. Ensure fluid level and composition of fluid in reservoir has not changed while engine is running or with engine stopped.

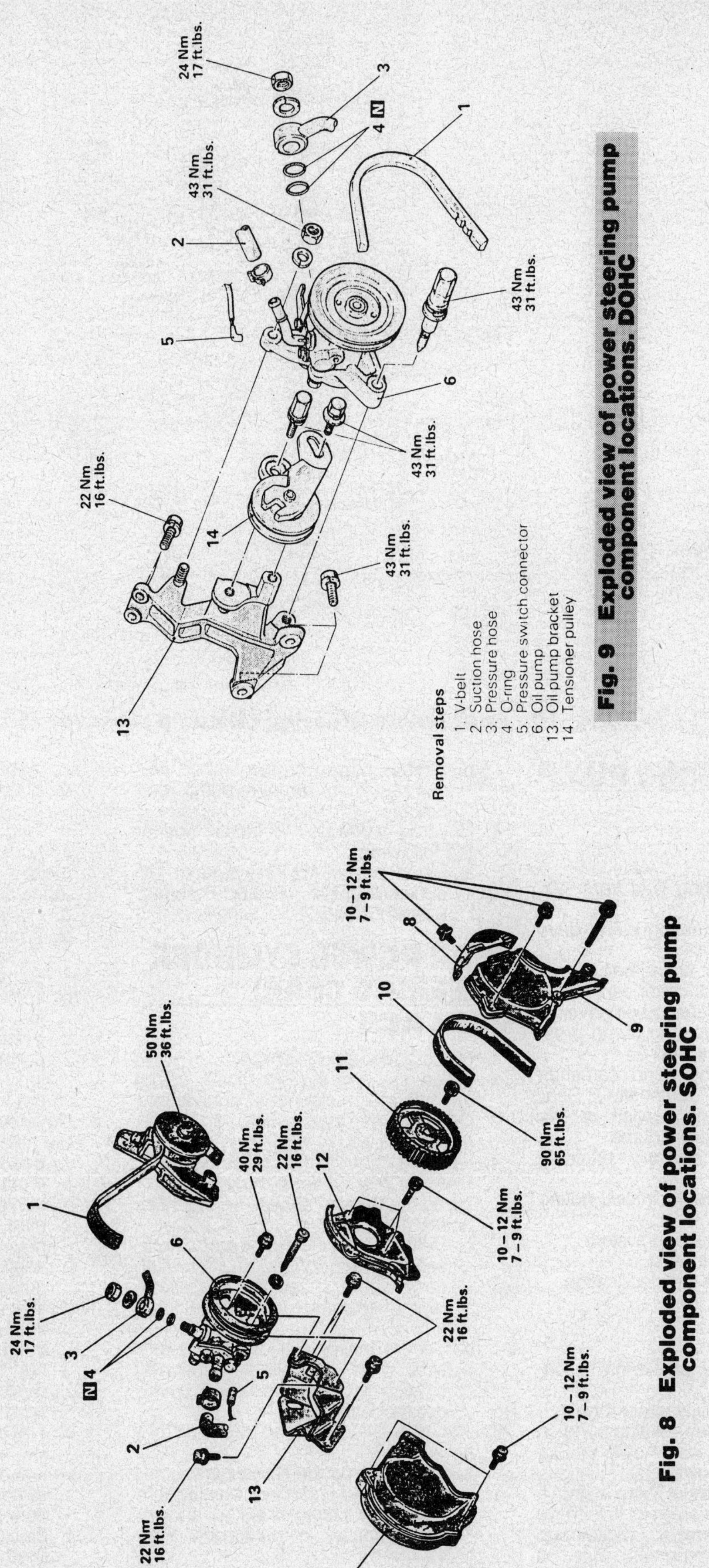


**Fig. 8 Exploded view of power steering pump component locations. SOHC**

Removal steps

1. V-belt
2. Suction hose
3. Pressure hose
4. O-ring
5. Pressure switch connector
6. Oil pump
13. Oil pump bracket
14. Tensioner pulley

**Fig. 9 Exploded view of power steering pump component locations. DOHC**

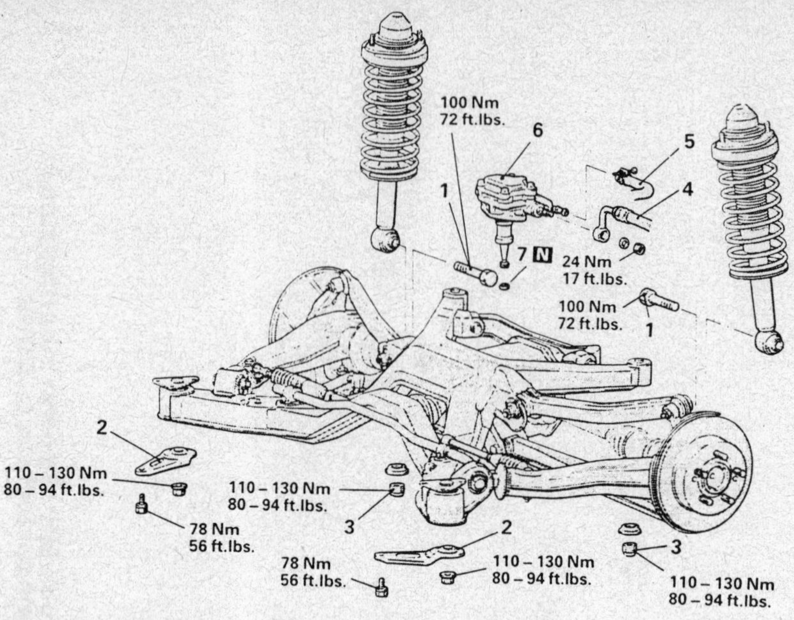


**Fig. 10 Rear power steering oil pump removal**

# POWER STEERING PUMP REPLACE

## FRONT

1. Drain power steering fluid from system.
2. Remove power steering pump drive belt.
3. Remove right front timing belt cover.
4. Remove timing belt cover cap.
5. Remove left front timing belt cover.
6. Remove power steering pump pressure hoses, **Figs. 8 and 9.**
7. Remove timing belt and camshaft sprocket, refer to "Camshaft Oil Seal, Replace" in engine section of this chapter for these procedures.
8. Remove power steering retaining bolts, then pump.
9. Reverse procedure to install, noting the following:
   a. Bleed power steering system.
   b. Adjust drive belt tension.
   c. Torque all bolts to specification.

## REAR

1. Drain power steering fluid into a suitable container.
2. Remove main muffler assembly.
3. Remove rear power steering pump in numbered sequence shown in **Fig. 10,** noting the following:
   a. Support differential case using a suitable transmission jack, then remove crossmember bracket and crossmember mounting nuts on the differential side.
   b. Slightly lower crossmember assembly, then remove pump assembly.
4. Reverse procedure to install, noting the following:
   a. Bleed power steering system as outlined under "Power Steering System Bleed."

# REAR POWER CYLINDER (STEERING GEAR) REPLACE

1. Raise and support vehicle.
2. Clean steering system piping using suitable steam cleaner or equivalent.
3. Drain steering system fluid into a suitable container.
4. Remove main muffler assembly.
5. Remove rear power cylinder in numbered sequence shown in **Fig. 11,** noting the following:
   a. Before removing the crossmember self-locking nut, support differential case with a suitable transmission jack , then remove the self-locking nut.
   b. Secure power cylinder on tie rod side with a suitable spanner wrench and remove power cylinder mounting nut.
6. Inspect the tie rod swing torque as follows:
   a. Swing tie rod ten times, hard.
   b. Point tie rod end down, then attach a suitable spring scale as shown and measure swing torque, **Fig. 12.**
   c. If swing torque is more than 26 inch lbs., replace the tie rod.
   d. If swing torque is less than 4 inch lbs., the ball joint may be reused as long as it operates smoothly and is not loose.
7. Inspect power cylinder slide resistance as follows:
   a. Place piston in neutral position.
   b. Wrap wire around tie rod end, then measure slide resistance using a suitable spring scale, **Fig. 13.**
   c. If slide resistance is more than 15 lbs., replace the power cylinder.
   d. If resistance is less than 15 lbs., the power cylinder may be reused as long as it slides smoothly and is not loose.
8. Reverse procedure to install, noting the following:
   a. Secure power cylinder to crossmember.
   b. Move power cylinder piston rod over its full stroke to determine its neutral position.
   c. Align tie rod ends and installation holes at trailing arm.
   d. When tie rod ends and the installation holes on the trailing arm do not meet, loosen tie rod end securing nut, then adjust the length. **The dust cover fastener clip should be removed for this.**
   e. The difference between lengths of left and right tie rods should be less than .039 inch. **The threads of the tie rod ends may be used as a guide for this.**
   f. Bleed the Steering system as outlined under "Power Steering System Bleed."

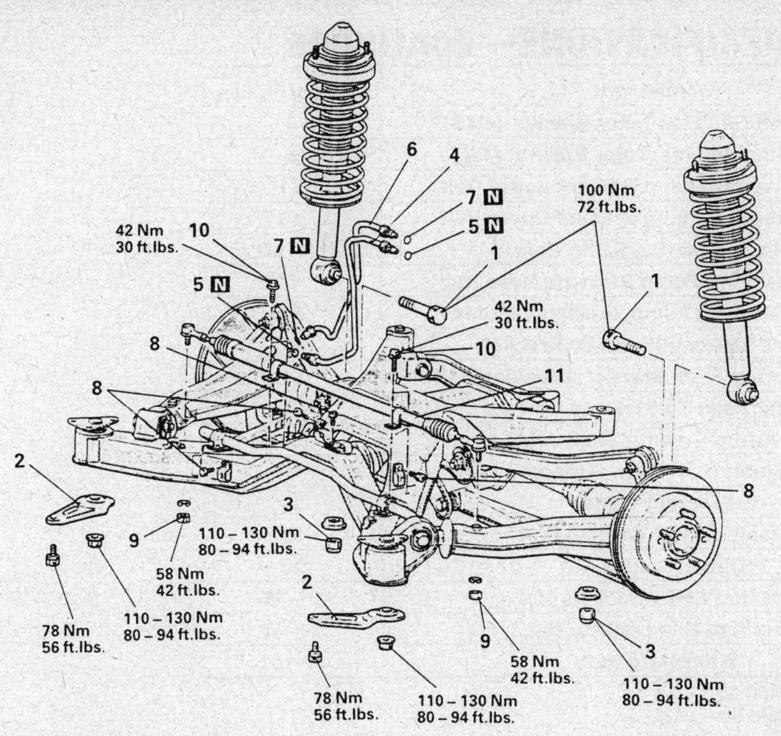


Removal steps

1. Rear shock absorber lower mounting bolt
2. Crossmember bracket
3. Crossmember mounting nut (on differential side)
4. Pressure tube (RL)
5. O-ring
6. Pressure tube (RR)
7. O-ring
8. Oil line clamp bolt
9. Tie rod end nut
10. Power cylinder installation bolt
11. Power cylinder

Fluid line flared nut
15 Nm
11 ft.lbs.

**Fig. 11 Rear power cylinder removal**

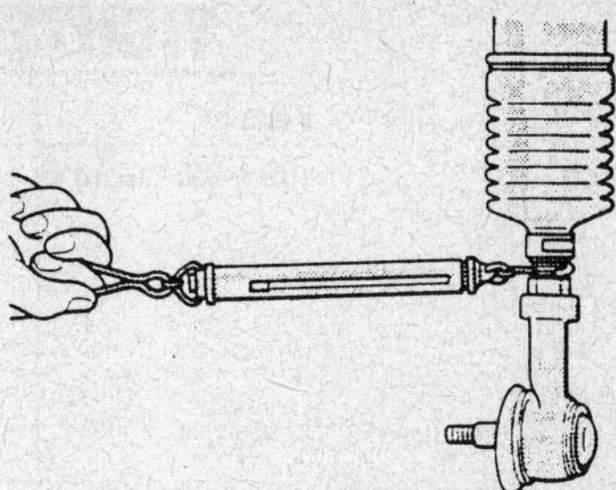

**Fig. 12 Measuring swing torque**

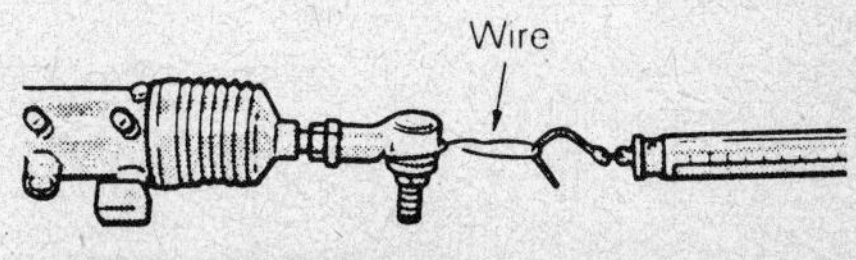


**Fig. 13 Measuring slide resistance of power cylinder**

# TIGHTENING SPECIFICATIONS

| Year | Component | Torque/Ft. Lbs. |
|---|---|---|
| 1991-92 | Airbag Module | 4 |
| | Axle Shaft Nut | 145–188 |
| | Crossmember Attaching Bolt | 43–51 |
| | Crossmember Attaching Nut | 58–72 |
| | Crossmember Lower Plate Self-Locking Nut | 65 |
| | Dust Plate Bolt (AWD) | 7 |
| | Front Brake Caliper | 65 |
| | Front Roll Stopper Bolt | 43–51 |
| | Front Speed Sensor Attaching Bolt | 9 |
| | Front Strut Lower Mount Bolt | 65–76 |
| | Front Strut Piston Rod Nut | 56 |
| | Inner Shaft Bracket Bolt | 33 |
| | Lower Ball Joint Nut | 43–52 |
| | Lower Ball Joint To Steering Knuckle Nut | 43–52 |
| | Lower Control Arm Clamp Long Bolt | 72–87 |
| | Lower Control Arm Clamp Mounting Nut | 72 |
| | Lower Control Arm Clamp Nut | 29 |
| | Lower Control Arm Clamp Short Bolt | 65① |
| | Lower Control Arm Nut | 72–87① |
| | Power Steering Gearbox Line Fittings (4WS) | 25 |
| | Power Steering Line Fitting | 11 |

*Continued*

## TIGHTENING SPECIFICATIONS—Continued

| Year | Component | Torque/Ft. Lbs. |
|---|---|---|
| 1991-92—Cont'd | Power Steering Line Inner Bracket (4WS) | 4 |
| | Power Steering Line Outer Bracket (4WS) | 8 |
| | Power Steering Pump Bracket Lower Bolt | 31 |
| | Power Steering Pump Bracket Upper Bolt | 16 |
| | Power Steering Pump Plug | 18–22 |
| | Power Steering Pump Pressure Hose Nut | 17 |
| | Power Steering Pump Tensioner Pulley | 31 |
| | Power Steering Pump To Bracket | 31 |
| | Power Steering Rack Bracket Attaching Bolts | 51 |
| | Power Steering Rack To Steering Column Linkage | 13 |
| | Steering Column Shaft Joint | 13 |
| | Steering Column Support | 8 |
| | Steering Wheel | 29 |
| | Stabilizer Bar Bracket Bolt | 26 |
| | Stabilizer Link Nut | 29 |
| | Tie Rod End Attaching Nut | 21–36 |
| | Tie Rod End Locking Nut | 36–40 |
| | Wheel Lug Nuts | 87-101 |

①—Tighten temporarily, tighten to specifications when vehicle is unladen.

# Wheel Alignment

## INDEX



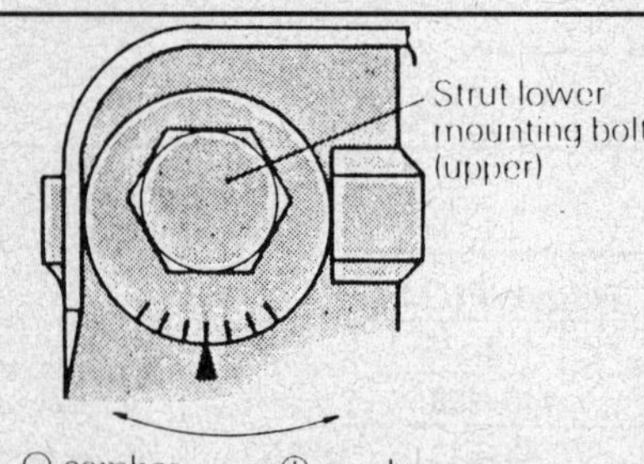


**Fig. 1 Front camber adjustment**

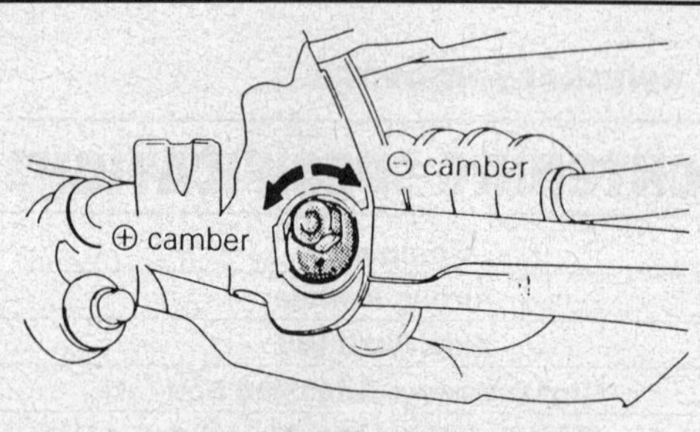


**Fig. 2 Rear camber adjustment**

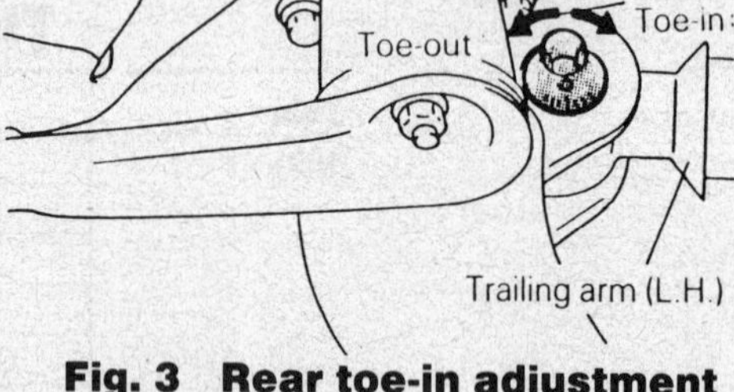


**Fig. 3 Rear toe-in adjustment**

## FRONT WHEEL ALIGNMENT

Adjust front toe-in after front camber has been adjusted. One camber graduation change changes toe by about .02 inch.

### CAMBER

To adjust camber, turn strut lower mounting bolt (upper), **Fig. 1.** One graduation is equivalent to about .33° in camber.

### CASTER

Caster has been factory adjusted to the standard value and requires no adjustment.

### TOE-IN

Adjust toe-in by releasing tie rod clips, then turning right and left tie rod jam nut, in opposite directions, and equal amount.

## REAR WHEEL ALIGNMENT

### FWD

Adjust rear toe-in after rear camber has been adjusted. On models equipped with 4WS, disconnect 4WS tie rod end from trailing arm prior to making adjustments.

#### Camber

To adjust camber, turn lower control arm mounting bolt on the crossmember side, **Fig. 2.** At the left wheel turn the mounting bolt clockwise to indicate negative camber, at the right wheel turn the mounting bolt right to indicate positive camber. One graduation changes camber by about .2°. **Adjust eccentric cam bolt within 90° from central position.**

#### Toe-In

To adjust toe-in, turn right and left trailing arm mounting bolts on the crossmember side, the same amount. At the left wheel turn the mounting bolt clockwise to indicate toe-in, at the right wheel turn the mounting bolt clockwise to indicate toe-out, **Fig. 3.** One graduation changes toe by about .08 inch.

### AWD

#### Camber

1. Measure camber with a camber/caster/kingpin gauge.
2. Adjust camber by moving mounting bolt located on crossmember side of lower arm. One graduation changes camber by about 1/5°.

# AIR CONDITIONING

## TABLE OF CONTENTS



# System Testing

## INDEX



## GENERAL PRECAUTIONS

The freon refrigerant used is also known as R-12. It is odorless and colorless both as a gas and a liquid. Since it boils (vaporizes) at −21.7°F, it will usually be in a vapor state when being handled in a repair shop. But if a portion of the liquid coolant should come in contact with the hands or face, note that its temperature momentarily will be at least −22°F.

**Protective goggles should be worn when opening any refrigerant lines. If liquid coolant does touch the eyes, bathe eyes quickly in cold water, then apply a bland disinfectant oil to eyes. See an eye doctor.**

**When checking a system for leaks with a torch type leak detector, do not breathe vapors coming from flame. Do not discharge refrigerant in an area of a live flame. A poisonous phosgene gas is produced when R-12 is burned. While the small amount of gas produced by a leak detector is not harmful unless inhaled directly at the flame, the quantity of refrigerant released into the air when a system is purged can be extremely dangerous if allowed to come in contact with an open flame. Thus, when purging a system, ensure that the discharge hose is routed to a well ventilated place where no flame is present. Under these conditions the refrigerant will be quickly dissipated into the surrounding air.**

**Never allow the temperature of refrigerant drums to exceed 125°F. The resultant increase in temperature will cause a corresponding increase in pressure which may cause the safety plug to release or the drum to burst.**

**If it is necessary to heat a drum of refrigerant when charging a system, the drum should be placed in water that is no hotter than 125°F. Never use a blow torch or other open flame. If possible, a pressure release mechanism should be attached before the drum is heated.**

When connecting and disconnecting service gauges on A/C system, ensure that gauge hand valves are fully closed and that compressor service valves, if equipped, are in the back-seated (fully counterclockwise) position. Do not disconnect gauge hoses from service port adapters, if used, while gauges are connected to A/C system. To disconnect hoses, always remove adapter from service port. Do not disconnect hoses from gauge manifold while connected to A/C system, as refrigerant will be rapidly discharged.

After disconnecting gauge lines, check the valve areas to be sure service valves are correctly seated and Schraeder valves, if used, are not leaking.

## EXERCISE SYSTEM

An important fact most owners ignore is that A/C units must be used periodically. Manufacturers caution that when the air conditioner is not used regularly, particularly during cold months, it should be turned on for a few minutes once every two or three weeks while the engine is running. This keeps the system in good operating condition.

Checking out the system for effects of disuse before the onset of summer is one of the most important aspects of A/C servicing.

First clean out the condenser core, mounted in all cases in front of the radiator. All obstructions, such as leaves, bugs and dirt, must be removed, as they will reduce heat transfer and impair the efficiency of the system. Make sure the space between the condenser and the radiator is also free of foreign matter.

Ensure evaporator water drain is open. The evaporator cools and dehumidifies the air before it enters the passenger compartment; there, the refrigerant is changed from a liquid to a vapor. As the core cools the air, moisture condenses on it but is prevented from collecting in the evaporator by the water drain.

## PERFORMANCE TEST

### CHRYSLER EXCEPT LASER, MONACO, STEALTH & IMPORTS

Air temperature in test room must be 70°F minimum for this test.

1. Connect tachometer and manifold gauge set to vehicle.
2. Set control to MAX A/C, temperature lever on full cool and blower on High.
3. Start engine and adjust to idle to 1000 RPM with A/C clutch engaged. Engine should be at normal operating temperature. Doors and windows should be closed.
4. Insert thermometer in left center A/C outlet and operate the engine for five

minutes. The A/C clutch may cycle depending on ambient conditions.

5. With A/C clutch engaged, compare discharge air temperature to A/C performance temperature chart, **Figs. 1 and 2.**
6. Disconnect vacuum line from heater water control valve. Observe valve arm for movement as line is disconnected. If arm does not move, service heater control valve as necessary. If arm moves satisfactory, plug vacuum line.
7. Operate A/C for two minutes and take discharge air temperature readings. If temperature increased by more than 5°F, check blend air door for correct operation. If temperature does not increase more than 5°F, compare discharge air temperature, suction and discharge pressures with values in the performance chart corresponding with the ambient temperature. Connect vacuum line.
8. If discharge air temperature fails to meet specifications further diagnosis of air conditioning system should be performed

| Ambient Temperature | 21°C (70°F) | 26.5°C (80°F) | 32°C (90°F) | 37.5°C (100°F) | 43°C (110°F) |
|---|---|---|---|---|---|
| Discharge Air Temperature Center Panel Outlet | 2-8°C (35-46°F) | 4-10°C (39-50°F) | 7-13°C (44-55°F) | 10-17°C (50-62°F) | 13-21°C (56-70°F) |
| Compressor Discharge Pressure | 965 1448 kPag (140 210 psig) | 1240 1620 kPag (180 235 psig) | 1448 1860 kpag (210 270 psig) | 1655 2137 kPag (240 310 psig) | 1930 2413 kPag (280 350 psig) |
| Evaporator Suction Pressure | 69 165 kPag (10 24 psig) | 110 207 kPag (16 30 psig) | 138 248 kPag (20 36 psig) | 172 296 kPag (25 43 psig) | 207 359 kPag (30 52 psig) |

**Fig. 1 Performance temperature chart. Chrysler w/fixed displacement compressor**

| Ambient Temperature | 21°C (70°F) | 26.5°C (80°F) | 32°C (90°F) | 37.5°C (100°F) |
|---|---|---|---|---|
| Discharge Air Temperature Center Panel Outlet | 2-8°C (35-46°F) | 4-10°C (39-50°F) | 7-13°C (44-55°F) | 10-17°C (50-62°F) |
| Compressor Discharge Pressure | 965 1448 kPag (140 210 psig) | 1240 1620 kPag (180 235 psig) | 1448 1860 kpag (210 270 psig) | 1655 2137 kPag (240 310 psig) |
| Evaporator Suction Pressure | 69 234 kPag (10 30-35 psig) | 110 260 kPag (16 38 psig) | 138 290 kPag (20 42 psig) | 172 331 kPag (25 48 psig) |

**Fig. 2 Performance temperature chart. Chrysler w/variable displacement compressor**

NORMAL CLUTCH CYCLE RATE PER MINUTE

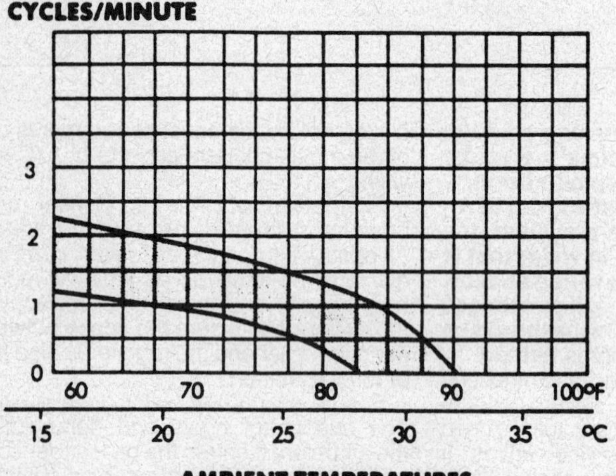


NORMAL CENTER REGISTER DISCHARGE TEMPERATURES

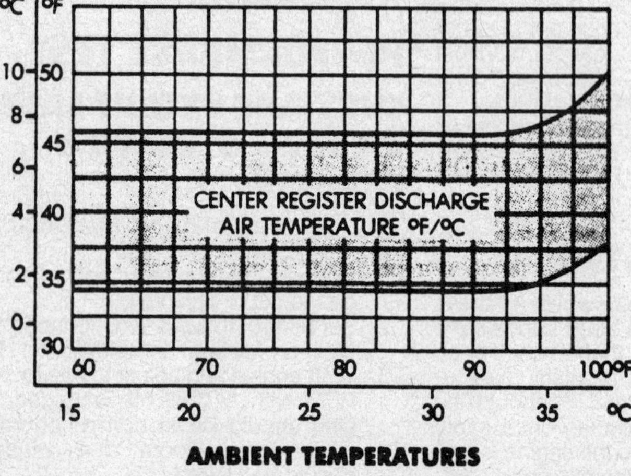


THESE CONDITIONAL REQUIREMENTS FOR THE FIXED ORIFICE TUBE CYCLING CLUTCH SYSTEM TESTS MUST BE SATISFIED TO OBTAIN ACCURATE PRESSURE READINGS.

- STABILIZED IN CAR TEMPERATURE @ 70°F TO 80°F (21°C TO 27°C)
- MAXIMUM A/C (RECIRCULATING AIR)
- MAXIMUM BLOWING SPEED
- 1500 ENGINE RPM FOR 10 MINUTES

NORMAL FIXED ORIFICE TUBE CYCLING CLUTCH REFRIGERANT SYSTEM PRESSURES

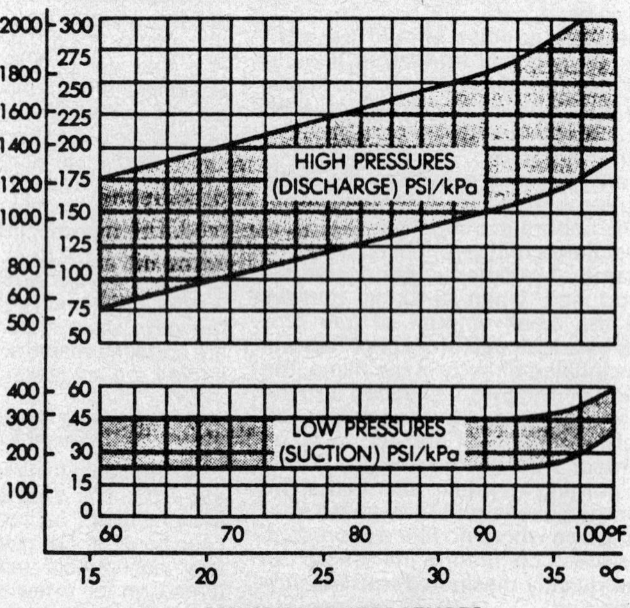


**Fig. 3 A/C preliminary diagnosis test. Monaco & Eagle Premier**

TOTAL CLUTCH
CYCLE TIME — SECONDS

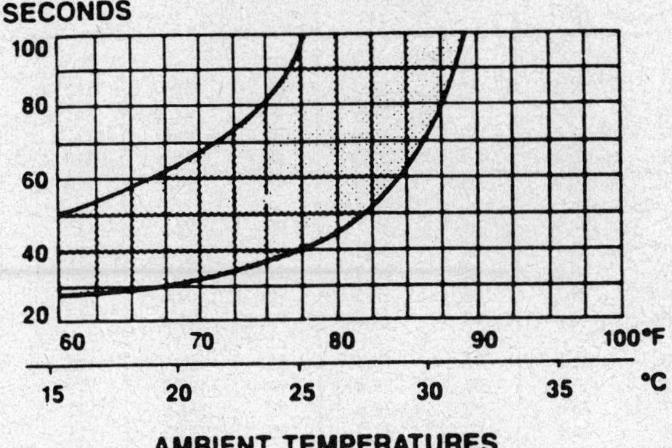


NORMAL CLUTCH
OFF TIME — SECONDS

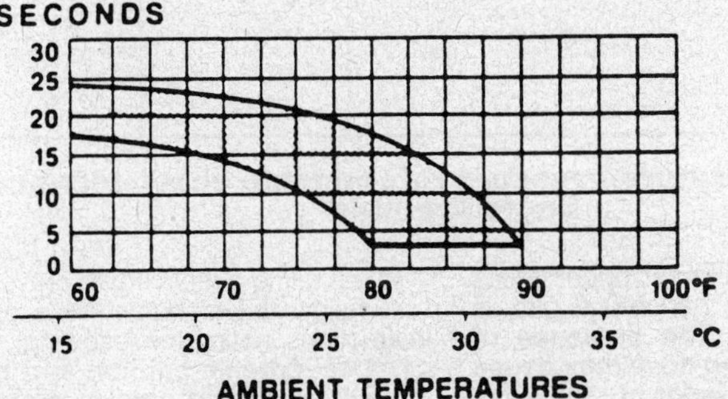


**THESE CONDITIONAL REQUIREMENTS FOR THE FIXED ORIFICE TUBE CYCLING CLUTCH SYSTEM TESTS MUST BE SATISFIED TO OBTAIN ACCURATE PRESSURE READINGS.**

- Stabilized in Car Temperature @ 70°F to 80°F (21°C to 27°C)
- Maximum A/C (Recirculating Air)
- Maximum Blowing Speed
- 1500 Engine RPM For 10 Minutes

NORMAL CLUTCH
ON TIME — SECONDS

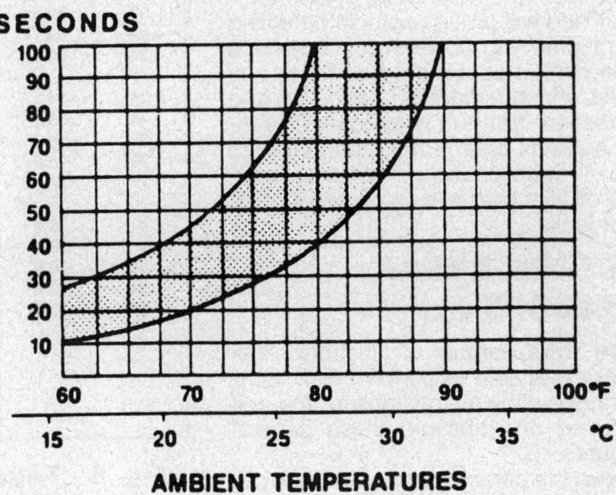


**Fig. 4 A/C Clutch Cycle Time Chart. Monaco & Eagle Premier**

## MONACO & EAGLE PREMIER

Diagnosis of the refrigerant system is performed by analyzing the clutch cycle time rate. Refer to **Figs. 3 through 5** for testing of the A/C system.

## COLT, COLT VISTA & EAGLE SUMMIT

1. Connect a suitable manifold gauge set and tachometer.
2. Position air temperature controls as follows:
   a. Select air conditioner.
   b. Position mode selection lever to "Face."
   c. Position temperature control lever to "Max" cooling.
   d. Position air selection lever to "Recirc."
   e. Position blower lever to high.
3. Start engine, then adjust RPM to 1000 with compressor clutch engaged.
4. Vehicle doors should be closed, windows up and engine should be at normal operating temperature.
5. Insert a thermometer in the left center vent and allow engine to run for 20 minutes.
6. Note the discharge temperature and compare with chart **Figs. 6 and 7. Reading should be taken with compressor clutch engaged.**

## CONQUEST

1. Connect a suitable manifold gauge set and tachometer.
2. Press auto. mode button on A/C control panel, then reset control buttons to max. cooling in manual mode as follows:
   a. Place mode selection button in the face position.
   b. Place temperature control buttons in max. cooling position.
   c. Place air selection button in the "Recirc" position.
   d. Place blower switch to high position.
3. Start engine, then adjust RPM to 1000 with compressor clutch engaged.
4. Vehicle doors should be closed, windows up and engine should be at normal operating temperature.
5. Insert a thermometer in the left center vent and allow engine to run for 20 minutes.
6. Note the discharge temperature and compare with chart **Fig. 7. Reading should be taken with compressor clutch engaged.**

## LASER, STEALTH & EAGLE TALON

1. Connect a suitable manifold gauge set and tachometer.
2. Set controls of air conditioner as follows:
   a. Air conditioning switch to A/C On position.
   b. Place mode selection lever in Face position.
   c. Place temperature control lever in Max. cooling position.
   d. Place air selection lever in Recirculation position.
   e. Place blower switch to high position.
3. Start engine, then adjust idle to 1000

RPM with compressor clutch engaged.

4. Vehicle doors should be closed, windows up and engine should be at normal operating temperature.
5. Insert a thermometer in the left center vent and allow engine to run for 20 minutes.
6. Note the discharge temperature and compare with chart **Figs. 8 and 9. Reading should be taken with compressor clutch engaged.**

## LEAK TESTS

Testing the refrigerant system for leaks is one of the most important phases of troubleshooting. One or more of the methods outlined will prove useful in detecting leaks or checking connections if service work is performed. Before beginning any leak test, attach a manifold gauge set and note pressure. If little or no pressure is indicated, a partial charge must be installed. Check all connections, compressor head gasket, oil filler plug and compressor shaft seal for leaks.

## ELECTRONIC LEAK DETECTORS

There are a number of electronic leak detectors available to perform leak tests. Refer to operating instructions for the unit being used and observe these general procedures:

1. Move the detector probe one inch per second in areas of suspected leaks.
2. Position the probe below the test point, as refrigerant gas is heavier than air.
3. Be sure to check service access gauge port valve fittings, particularly when valve caps are missing, as dirt accumulations can destroy the sealing area of valve core when manifold gauge set is attached. Replace missing valve caps after cleaning valve core area. **Valve caps should only be finger tightened. Using pliers to tighten valve caps may distort sealing surface of valve.**
4. Check for leaks in manifold gauge set and hoses, as well as the rest of the system.

## FLAME-TYPE (HALIDE) LEAK DETECTORS

**When using flame-type detectors, avoid inhaling fumes produced by burning refrigerant. Do not use this type detector where concentrations of combustible or explosive gases, dusts or vapors may exist.**

1. Adjust detector flame as low as possible to obtain maximum sensitivity. Be sure copper element is cherry red and not burned away. The flame will be almost colorless.
2. Slowly move detector along areas of suspected leaks. A slight leak will cause the flame to change to a bright yellow-green color. A significant leak will be indicated by a brilliant blue flame. Position detector under areas being tested as refrigerant gas is heavier than air. **The presence of dust in the pickup hose may cause a change in the color of the flame. If not recognized, a false diagnosis could be made. Store leak detector in a clean place and ensure hose is free of dust before leak testing.**
3. Check for leaks in the manifold gauge set and hoses, as well as the rest of the system.
4. Use a small fan to ventilate areas where the leak detector indicates refrigerant constantly. These areas are contaminated with refrigerant and must be ventilated before leak can be pinpointed.

| TEMP. °F | PRESS. PSI | TEMP. °F | PRESS. PSI | TEMP. °F | PRESS. PSI | TEMP. °F | PRESS. PSI | TEMP. °F | PRESS. PSI |
|---|---|---|---|---|---|---|---|---|---|
| 0 | 9.1 | 35 | 32.5 | 60 | 57.7 | 85 | 91.7 | 110 | 136.0 |
| 2 | 10.1 | 36 | 33.4 | 61 | 58.9 | 86 | 93.2 | 111 | 138.0 |
| 4 | 11.2 | 37 | 34.3 | 62 | 60.0 | 87 | 94.8 | 112 | 140.1 |
| 6 | 12.3 | 38 | 35.1 | 63 | 61.3 | 88 | 96.4 | 113 | 142.1 |
| 8 | 13.4 | 39 | 36.0 | 64 | 62.5 | 89 | 98.0 | 114 | 144.2 |
| 10 | 14.6 | 40 | 36.9 | 65 | 63.7 | 90 | 99.6 | 115 | 146.3 |
| 12 | 15.8 | 41 | 37.9 | 66 | 64.9 | 91 | 101.3 | 116 | 148.4 |
| 14 | 17.1 | 42 | 38.8 | 67 | 66.2 | 92 | 103.0 | 117 | 151.2 |
| 16 | 18.3 | 43 | 39.7 | 68 | 67.5 | 93 | 104.6 | 118 | 152.7 |
| 18 | 19.7 | 44 | 40.7 | 69 | 68.8 | 94 | 106.3 | 119 | 154.9 |
| 20 | 21.0 | 45 | 41.7 | 70 | 70.1 | 95 | 108.1 | 120 | 157.1 |
| 21 | 21.7 | 46 | 42.[illegible] | 71 | 71.4 | 96 | 109.8 | 121 | 159.3 |
| 22 | 22.4 | 47 | 43.6 | 72 | 72.8 | 97 | 111.5 | 122 | 161.5 |
| 23 | 23.1 | 48 | 44.6 | 73 | 74.2 | 98 | 113.3 | 123 | 163.8 |
| 24 | 23.8 | 49 | 45.6 | 74 | 75.5 | 99 | 115.1 | 124 | 166.1 |
| 25 | 24.6 | 50 | 46.6 | 75 | 76.9 | 100 | 116.9 | 125 | 168.4 |
| 26 | 25.3 | 51 | 47.6 | 76 | 78.3 | 101 | 118.8 | 126 | 170.7 |
| 27 | 26.1 | 52 | 48.7 | 77 | 79.2 | 102 | 120.6 | 127 | 173.1 |
| 28 | 26.8 | 53 | 49.8 | 78 | 81.1 | 103 | 122.4 | 128 | 175.4 |
| 29 | 27.6 | 54 | 50.9 | 79 | 82.5 | 104 | 124.3 | 129 | 177.8 |
| 30 | 28.4 | 55 | 52.0 | 80 | 84.0 | 105 | 126.2 | 130 | 182.2 |
| 31 | 29.2 | 56 | 53.1 | 81 | 85.5 | 106 | 128.1 | 131 | 182.6 |
| 32 | 30.0 | 57 | 55.4 | 82 | 87.0 | 107 | 130.0 | 132 | 185.1 |
| 33 | 30.9 | 58 | 56.6 | 83 | 88.5 | 108 | 132.1 | 133 | 187.6 |
| 34 | 31.7 | 59 | 57.1 | 84 | 90.1 | 109 | 135.1 | 134 | 190.1 |

**Fig. 5 Temperature-pressure relationship chart. Monaco & Eagle Premier**

## FLUID LEAK DETECTORS

Apply leak detector solution around joints to be tested. A cluster of bubbles will form immediately if there is a leak. A white foam that forms after a short while will indicate an extremely small leak. In some confined areas such as sections of the evaporator and condenser, electronic leak detectors will be more useful.

## DISCHARGING SYSTEM

The use of refrigerant recovery and recycling stations allows the recovery and reuse of refrigerant after contaminants and moisture have been removed.

When using a recovery or recycling station, follow the manufacturer's operating instructions, noting the following:

1. **Use extreme caution and observe all safety and service precautions related to use of refrigerants.**
2. Connect refrigerant recycling station hose(s) to vehicle A/C service port(s) and recovery station inlet fitting. Hoses used should have shut off devices or check valve within 12 inches of hose ends to minimize introduction of air into recycling station and to minimize amount of refrigerant released when hose(s) is disconnected.
3. Turn recycling station On to start recovery process. Allow recycling station to pump refrigerant from A/C system until station pressure gauge indicates vacuum.
4. After vehicle A/C system has been evacuated, close station inlet valve, if equipped.
5. Turn station Off. On some stations the pump will automatically be turned Off by a low pressure switch.
6. Allow vehicle A/C system to remain closed for approximately two minutes. Observe vacuum level indicated on gauge. If pressure does not rise, disconnect recycling station hose(s).
7. If system pressure rises, repeat steps 3 through 6 until vacuum level remains stable for two minutes.
8. Service A/C system as necessary, then evacuate and recharge A/C system.

| Garage ambient temperature °C (°F) | 21 (70) | 26.5 (80) | 32 (90) | 37.5 (100) | 40.6 (105) |
|---|---|---|---|---|---|
| Discharge air temperature °C (°F) | 1.7 – 4.4 (35 – 40) | 1.7 – 5.0 (35 – 41) | 1.7 – 5.6 (35 – 42) | 1.7 – 6.1 (35 – 43) | 1.7 – 6.7 (35 – 44) |
| Compressor discharge pressure kPa (psi) | 928 – 1,322 (132 – 188) | 1,069 – 1,547 (152 – 220) | 1,209 – 1,772 (172 – 252) | 1,336 – 1,969 (190 – 280) | 1,406 – 2,109 (200 – 300) |
| Evaporator suction pressure kPa (psi) | 127 – 148 (18 – 21) | 131 – 162 (18.6 – 23) | 134 – 176 (19 – 25) | 135 – 188 (19.2 – 26.8) | 136 – 194 (19.4 – 27.6) |

**Fig. 6 Performance temperature chart. 1989 Colt & Eagle Summit**

| Garage ambient temperature °C (°F) | 21 (70) | 26.7 (80) | 32.2 (90) | 37.8 (100) | 43.3 (110) |
|---|---|---|---|---|---|
| Discharge air temperature °C (°F) | 2.8 – 4.4 (37 – 40) | 3.3 – 5.0 (38 – 41) | 3.8 – 5.6 (39 – 42) | 4.4 – 7.2 (40 – 45) | 4.4 – 7.8 (40 – 46) |
| Compressor discharge pressure kPa (psi) | 758 – 1,310 (110 – 190) | 896 – 1,517 (130 – 220) | 1,103 – 1,793 (160 – 260) | 1,310 – 1,999 (190 – 290) | 1,517 – 2,206 (220 – 320) |
| Compressor suction pressure kPa (psi) | 131 – 165 (19 – 24) | 138 – 179 (20 – 26) | 145 – 186 (21 – 27) | 152 – 193 (22 – 28) | 159 – 200 (23 – 29) |

**Fig. 7 Performance temperature chart. Colt Vista, Conquest & 1990–91 Colt, Eagle Summit**

| Garage ambient temperature °C (°F) | 21 (70) | 26.7 (80) | 32.2 (90) | 37.8 (100) | 43.3 (110) |
|---|---|---|---|---|---|
| Discharge air temperature °C (°F) | 2.0–8.0 (35.6–46.4) | 2.0–8.0 (35.6–46.4) | 2.0–8.0 (35.6–46.4) | 4.0–11.0 (39.2–51.8) | 6.0–14.0 (42.8–57.2) |
| Compressor discharge pressure kPa (psi) | 900–1,300 (128–186) | 1,000–1,400 (142–199) | 1,100–1,500 (156–212) | 1,300–1,700 (186–242) | 1,500–1,900 (212–270) |
| Compressor suction pressure kPa (psi) | 50–150 (7.1–21.3) | 80–180 (11.4–25.6) | 100–200 (14.2–28.4) | 130–230 (18.5–32.7) | 150–250 (21.3–35.6) |

**Fig. 8 Performance temperature chart. Laser & Eagle Talon**

| Garage ambient temperature °C (°F) | 21 (70) | 26.7 (80) | 32.2 (90) | 37.8 (100) | 43.3 (110) |
|---|---|---|---|---|---|
| Discharge air temperature °C (°F) | 0.0 – 3.0 (32.0 – 37.4) | 1.0 – 4.0 (33.8 – 39.2) | 1.0 – 4.0 (33.8 – 39.2) | 1.0 – 4.0 (33.8 – 39.2) | 2.0 – 5.0 (35.6 – 41.0) |
| Compressor discharge pressure kPa (psi) | 690 – 740 (98.1 – 105.3) | 780 – 830 (110.9 – 118.1) | 870 – 920 (123.7 – 130.9) | 1,080 – 1,130 (153.6 – 160.7) | 1,210 – 1,260 (172.1 – 179.2) |
| Compressor suction pressure kPa (psi) | 130 – 190 (18.5 – 27.5) | 130 – 190 (18.5 – 27.5) | 130 – 190 (18.5 – 27.5) | 130 – 190 (18.5 – 27.5) | 130 – 190 (18.5 – 27.5) |

**Fig. 9 Performance temperature chart. Stealth**

# EVACUATING SYSTEM

## USING VACUUM PUMP

Vacuum pumps suitable for removing air and moisture from A/C systems are commercially available. A specification for system pump-down used here is 26 to 29½ inches vacuum. This reading can be attained at or near sea level only. For each 1000 feet of altitude this operation is being performed, the reading will be 1 inch vacuum lower. As an example, at 5000 feet elevation, only 21-24½ inches of vacuum can be obtained.

**The system must be completely discharged before it can be evacuated. Damage to vacuum pump may result if pressurized refrigerant is allowed to enter.**

1. With gauges connected into system, remove cap from vacuum hose connector. Install center hose from gauge manifold to vacuum pump connector. Mid-position high and low side compressor service valves (if used). Open high and low side gauge manifold hand valves.
2. Operate vacuum pump a minimum of 30 minutes for air and moisture removal. Watch compound gauge that system pumps down into a vacuum. System will reach 26-29½ inches vacuum in not over 5 minutes. If system does not pump down, check all connections and leak-test if necessary.
3. Close gauge manifold hand valves and shut off vacuum pump.
4. Check ability of system to hold vacuum. Watch compound gauge to see that gauge does not rise at a faster rate than 1 inch vacuum every 4 or 5 minutes. If compound gauge rises at too rapid a rate, install partial charge and leak-test. Then evacuate system as outlined above.
5. If system holds vacuum, charge system with refrigerant.

## USING CHARGING STATION

A vacuum pump is built into the charging station and is constructed to withstand repeated and prolonged use without damage. Complete moisture removal from the system is possible only with a vacuum pump constructed for the purpose.

**The system must be completely discharged before it can be evacuated. Damage to the vacuum pump may result if pressurized refrigerant is allowed to enter.**

1. Connect hose to vacuum pump if system was discharged through charging station.
2. Open high and low side gauge valves of charging station.
3. Connect station into 110-volt current.
4. Engage "Off-On" switch to vacuum pump according to directions of specific station being used.

5. System should pump down into a 28-29 1/2 inches vacuum in not more than 5 minutes. If system fails to meet this specification, repair as necessary.
6. Operate pump a minimum of 30 minutes to remove all air and moisture.
7. Close high and low side gauge valves. Open switch to turn off pump.
8. Check ability of system to hold vacuum by watching compound gauge to see that it does not rise at a rate higher than 1 inch of vacuum every 4 or 5 minutes. If rise rate is not within specifications, repair system as necessary. If rise rate is within specifications, charge system with refrigerant.

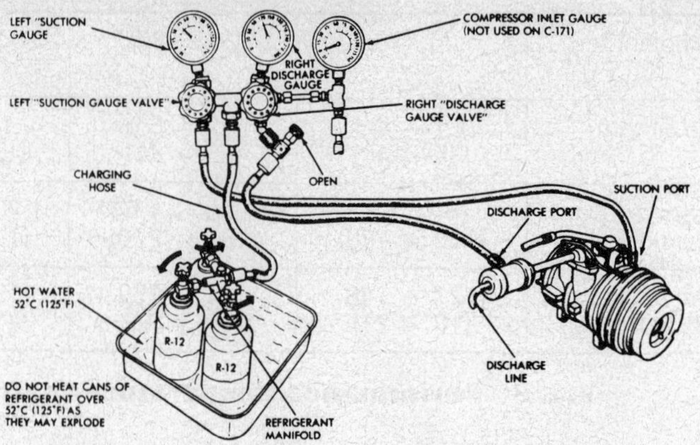

**Fig. 10 Complete charging of system**

# CHARGING THE SYSTEM

## EXCEPT MONACO, EAGLE MEDALLION & PREMIER

### Charging w/14 Ounce Cans

**Never use cans to charge into high pressure side of system (compressor discharge port) or into system at high temperature, as high system pressure transferred into charging can may cause it to explode.**

1. Attach center hose from manifold gauge set to refrigerant dispensing manifold. Turn refrigerant manifold valves completely counterclockwise to open fully, and remove protective caps from refrigerant manifold.
2. Screw refrigerant cans into manifold, ensuring gasket is in place and in good condition. **Torque** can and manifold nuts to 6-8 ft. lbs.
3. Turn refrigerant manifold valves clockwise to puncture cans, and close manifold valves, **Fig. 10.**
4. Loosen charging hose at gauge set manifold and turn a refrigerant valve counterclockwise to release refrigerant and purge air from charging hose. When refrigerant gas escapes from loose connection, retighten hose.
5. Fully open all refrigerant manifold valves being used and place refrigerant cans into pan of hot water at 125°F to aid transfer of refrigerant gas. **Do not heat refrigerant cans over 125°F as they may explode. Place water pan and refrigerant cans on scale and note weight.**
6. **On Colt, Colt Vista, Conquest & Eagle Summit,** connect a jumper wire across cycling clutch switch terminals. This will engage clutch to compressor.
7. **On all models,** start engine and turn A/C On, then index blower switch to low position.
8. Low pressure cut-out switch will prevent clutch from engaging until refrigerant is added to system. If clutch does engage, replace switch before continuing.
9. Charge through suction side of system by slowly opening suction manifold valve. Adjust valve so charging pressure does not exceed 50 psi.
10. Adjust engine speed to fast idle of 1300 RPM on 1989 models or 1400-1550 RPM for 1990-1991 models.
11. After specified refrigerant charge has entered system, close gauge set manifold valves, refrigerant manifold valves, and reconnect wiring.

### Charging w/Bulk Refrigerant Supply

Charging system with liquid on compressor discharge side is no longer recommended due to safety reasons.

## EAGLE MEDALLION

### Using Multi-Refrigerant Can Opener

1. Connect pressure gauge and manifold assembly No. J-23575 or equivalent. Keep both service valves in mid-position.
2. Close both gauge hand valves and disconnect service hose from vacuum pump.
3. Connect service hose to center of refrigerant can opener. Close valves on dispenser.
4. Attach refrigerant cans to opener. Refer to A/C Data Table for proper weight of refrigerant for vehicle being serviced. On Semi-Automatic Climate Control Systems, install a jumper wire across the two terminals of the cycling pressure switch harness connector.
5. Open one petcock valve and loosen center service hose at gauge to allow refrigerant to purge air from hose. Tighten hose and close petcock valve.
6. Open suction gauge hand valve and one petcock valve. Do not open high pressure gauge hand valve.
7. Start engine and set A/C system controls to maximum cooling position. Compressor will help pull refrigerant gas into suction side of system. **Refrigerant cans can be placed in pan of water no hotter than 125°F to aid charging process.**
8. When first can is empty, open next valve to continue charging until specified amount of refrigerant is in system. Frost line on can may be used as a guide when specifications call for using part of full can. If a scale is available, weigh cans before and during charging procedure to ensure accurate filling.
9. When system is fully charged, close suction gauge hand valve and all petcock valves, and remove jumper wire if applicable.
10. Operate system for 5-10 minutes to allow it to stabilize and to determine if system cycles properly.
11. After checking operation of system, back-seat suction and discharge service valves to normal operating position by turning valves fully counterclockwise.
12. Loosen pressure gauge and manifold assembly service hoses to release refrigerant trapped in hoses. Remove pressure gauge and manifold assembly and install dust caps on fittings.

### Using Charging Station J-23500-01

1. After discharging and evacuating system, close low pressure valve on charging station. Fully open lefthand refrigerant control valve at base of cylinder and high pressure valve on charging station and allow required charge of refrigerant to enter high side of system. When full charge has entered system, close refrigerant control valve and high pressure valve on charging station. **If bubbles appear in the sight glass, tilt the charging station back momentarily. Do not permit level of liquid to drop below zero mark on cylinder sight glass.**
2. After charging is completed, close manifold gauges and check high and low pressures and system operation. **Read gauges with high and low pressure valves closed on charging station. Low pressure gauge can be damaged if both high and low pressure valves are opened.**
3. Close all valves on charging station and close refrigerant drum valve when all operations are finished.
4. After completing operational check, back-seat suction and discharge service valves to their normal operating position by turning them fully counterclockwise.

5. Disconnect high and low pressure charging hoses from compressor.
6. Open valve on top of cylinder to remove remaining refrigerant as charging cylinder is not designed to store refrigerant.
7. Replace quick seal caps on compressor service valves.

### MONACO & EAGLE PREMIER

**Never use cans to charge into high pressure side of system (compressor discharge port) or into system at high temperature, as high system pressure transferred into charging can may cause it to explode.**

1. Attach center hose from manifold gauge set to refrigerant dispensing manifold. Turn refrigerant manifold valves completely counterclockwise to open fully, and remove protective caps from refrigerant manifold.
2. Screw refrigerant cans into manifold, ensuring gasket is in place and in good condition.
3. Turn refrigerant manifold valves clockwise to puncture cans, and close manifold valves, **Fig. 10.**
4. Loosen charging hose at gauge set manifold and turn a refrigerant valve counterclockwise to release refrigerant and purge air from charging hose. When refrigerant gas escapes from loose connection, retighten hose.
5. Fully open all refrigerant manifold valves being used and place refrigerant cans into pan of hot water at 125°F to aid transfer of refrigerant gas. **Do not heat refrigerant cans over 125°F as they may explode. Place water pan and refrigerant cans on scale and note weight.**
6. Connect a jumper wire across cycling clutch switch terminals.
7. Open Manifold gauge low side valve and allow refrigerant to be drawn into system.
8. When no more refrigerant is being drawn into system, start engine and set controls to Max A/C, then select the high blower position.
9. Allow remaining refrigerant to be drawn into system, then close the manifold low side valve and refrigerant supply valve.
10. Remove jumper wire from clutch cycling pressure switch, then reconnect connector.
11. Operate system until pressures stabilize and normal operation is verified.

# System Servicing

## INDEX



## OIL CHARGE

### CHRYSLER EXCEPT LASER, MONACO, STEALTH & IMPORTS

A new service fixed displacement type compressor contains 7.25 ounces of refrigerant oil. A new service variable displacement type compressor contains 8.7 ounces of refrigerant oil. Before installing replacement compressor, drain oil from replacement and failed compressors (drain oil from suction port). Add same amount of oil to replacement compressor as drained from failed compressor.

When other air conditioning system components are replaced add the following quantities of 500 viscosity refrigerant oil: Evaporator, 2 ounces; Condenser, 1 ounce; Filter-Drier, 1 ounce.

### COLT VISTA (DR1015C) COMPRESSORS

When replacing system components, add the following quantities of refrigerant oil: Compressor, 1.5 ounces; Condenser, .5 ounce; Evaporator, .8 ounce; Line, .5 ounce.

### CONQUEST (DR6148) COMPRESSOR

When replacing system components, add the following quantities of refrigerant oil: Compressor, 3.9 ounces; Condenser, .8 ounce; Evaporator, 1.2 ounces; Line, .5 ounce.

### COLT & EAGLE SUMMIT (FX105V) COMPRESSOR

When replacing system components, add the following quantities of refrigerant oil: Compressor, 2.8 ounces; Condenser, .5 ounce; Evaporator, 1.7 ounces; Line, .35 ounce.

### MONACO & EAGLE PREMIER (SD-709) COMPRESSOR

When replacing system components, add the following quantities of refrigerant oil: Compressor, amount drained from failed unit, plus 1 ounce; Accumulator/Drier, amount drained from failed unit, plus 1 ounce; Condenser, 1 ounce; Evaporator, 3 ounces.

### EAGLE MEDALLION

When replacing system components, add the following quantities of refrigerant oil: Compressor, amount drained from failed unit, plus 1 ounce; Condenser, 1 ounce.

### LASER & EAGLE TALON (10PA17) COMPRESSOR

When replacing system components, add the following quantities of refrigerant oil: Compressor, 1 ounce; Condenser, .7 ounce; Evaporator, 1 ounce; Line, .3 ounce; Receiver/Drier, .3 ounce.

### STEALTH (FX-105VS) COMPRESSOR

Before installing replacement compressor, drain oil from replacement and failed compressors (drain oil from suction port). Add same amount of oil to replacement compressor as drained from failed compressor.

When other air conditioning system components are replaced add the following quantities of 500 viscosity refrigerant oil: Evaporator, 2.4 ounces; Condenser, .3 ounce; Receiver-Drier, .2 ounce; Piping, .3 ounce.

## OIL LEVEL CHECK

**The oil level of these compressors should be checked whenever refrigerant has been lost due to leakage or through normal system servicing.**

### MONACO, EAGLE MEDALLION & PREMIER

Mounting angle will affect reading on dipstick. This procedure is designed for compressor removed from vehicle and on flat surface.

1. Remove oil filler plug and, looking through plug hole, turn front clutch plate to position piston connecting rod in center of oil filler plug hole, **Fig. 1.**
2. Insert dipstick J-29642-12 through oil filler plug hole to the right of piston connecting rod until dipstick stop contacts compressor housing, **Fig. 2.**

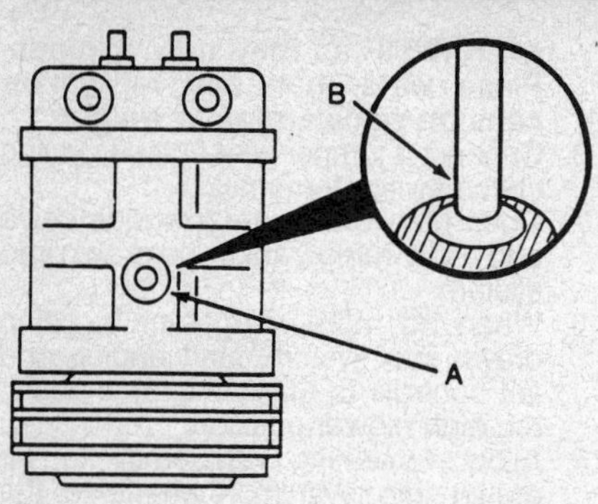


**Fig. 1 Positioning compressor connecting rod. Monaco, Eagle Medallion & Premier**

3. Remove dipstick and note number of increments covered. When properly filled, the compressor should contain between four and six increments of oil for Medallion or six and eight increments of oil for Premier.
4. Adjust oil level as necessary and install oil fill plug.

## CHARGING VALVE LOCATION

### CHRYSLER

#### FWD Except Colt, Colt Vista, Laser & Monaco

All low side valve are located on the compressor or on suction line near compressor. All high side valves are located on the discharge line between compressor and condenser.

#### RWD Except Conquest & Stealth

All charging low side valves are located on the compressor and all high side valves are located on the muffler.

#### Colt, Colt Vista & Laser

Low side valve is located on top of the compressor. High pressure valve is located on compressor discharge line.

#### Conquest

Low side valve and high side valves are located on the compressor.

#### Monaco

Low side valve is located on top of accumulator/drier. High pressure valve is located on compressor discharge line.

#### Stealth

Low side charging valves are located on the compressor and high side valves are located high pressure line.

### EAGLE

#### Eagle Premier

Low side valve is located on top of accumulator/drier. High pressure valve is located on compressor discharge line.

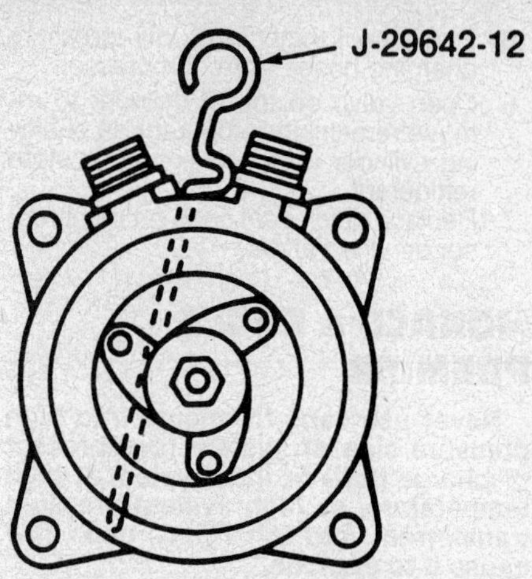


**Fig. 2 Checking compressor oil level with dipstick J-29642-12. Monaco, Eagle Medallion & Premier**

#### Eagle Medallion

Low side valve is located on the suction line. High pressure valve is located on compressor discharge line.

#### Eagle Summit & Talon

Low side valve is located on top of the compressor. High pressure valve is located on compressor discharge line.

# A/C Data Table

| Year | Model | Refrigerant Capacity, Lbs. | Refrigerant Oil | | | Compressor Clutch Air Gap, Inch |
|---|---|---|---|---|---|---|
| | | | Viscosity | Total System Capacity, Ounces | Compressor Oil Level Check | |
| **CHRYSLER EXCEPT IMPORTS** | | | | | | |
| 1989 | RWD | 2.56 | 500 | 7.25 | ① | .020-.035 |
| 1989-91⑥ | FWD | 2.37 | 500 | ② | ① | ③ |
| 1990-91 | Laser | 2.00 | 500 | 2.7 | ① | .014-.026 |
| 1990-91 | Monaco | 2.25 | 500 | 6-8⑤ | ④ | .016-.031 |
| 1991 | Stealth | 2.12 | 500 | 4.75-6.1 | ① | .01-.02 |
| **CHRYSLER IMPORTS** | | | | | | |
| 1989-91 | Colt | 2.25 | 500 | 5.0 | ① | .010-.020 |
| 1989-91 | Colt Vista | 2.0 | 500 | 2.7 | ① | .016-.028 |
| 1989 | Conquest | 1.81 | 500 | 5.7 | ① | .020-.030 |
| **EAGLE** | | | | | | |
| 1989 | Medallion | 1.8 | 500 | 4-6⑤ | ④ | .016-.031 |
| 1989-91 | Premier | 2.25 | 500 | 6-8⑤ | ④ | .016-.031 |
| 1989-91 | Summit | 2.25 | 500 | 5.0 | ① | .010-.020 |
| 1990-91 | Talon | 2.00 | 500 | 2.7 | ① | .014-.026 |

① —Note that "Oil Level" cannot be checked. Refer to total capacity in ounces.
② —Fixed displacement compressor, 7.25 ounces; Variable displacement compressor, 8.7 ounces.
③ —Fixed displacement compressor, .020-.035 inches; Variable displacement compressor, .035 inches.
④ —Refer to text for procedure.
⑤ —Measured in dipstick increments.
⑥ —Except Laser, Monaco & Stealth.

# ENGINE COOLING FANS

TABLE OF CONTENTS



# Variable Speed Fans

INDEX



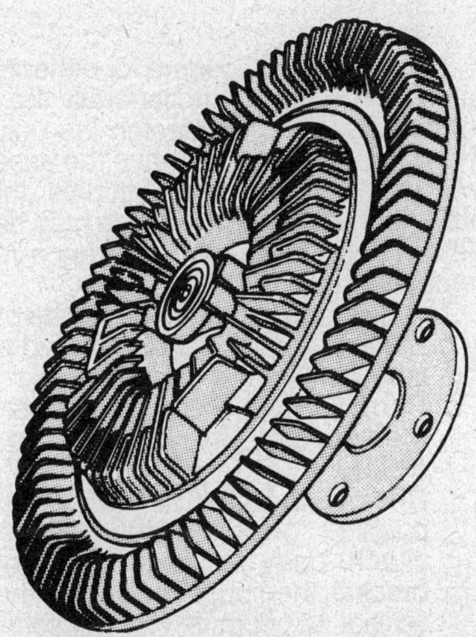

**Fig. 1 Fan drive clutch**

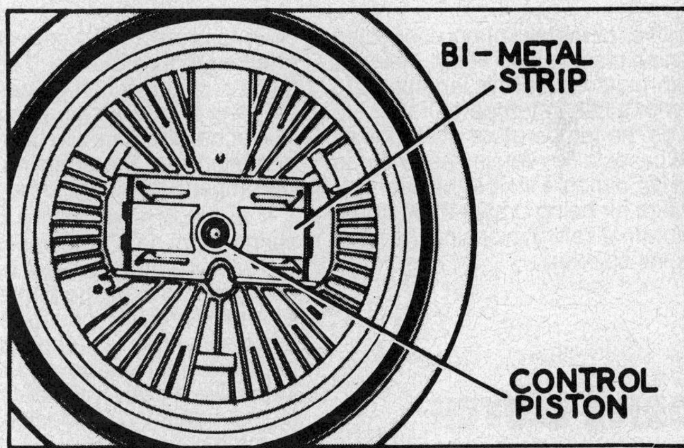


**Fig. 2 Variable-speed fan with flat bi-metal thermostatic spring**

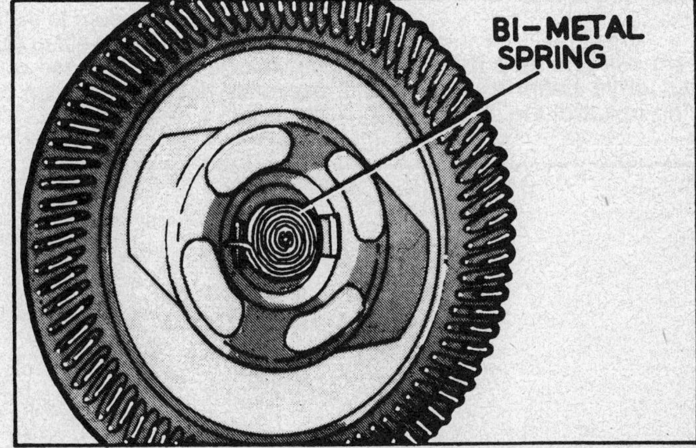


**Fig. 3 Variable-speed fan with coiled bi-metal thermostatic spring**

## DESCRIPTION

The fan drive clutch, **Fig. 1,** is a fluid coupling containing silicone oil. Fan speed is regulated by the torque-carrying capacity of the silicone oil. The more silicone oil in the coupling the greater the fan speed, and the less silicone oil the slower the fan speed.

Two types of fan drive clutches are in use. On the cast cover type, **Fig. 2,** a bi-metallic strip and control piston on the front of the fluid coupling regulates the amount of silicone oil entering the coupling. The bi-metallic strip bows outward with an increase in surrounding temperature and allows a piston to move outward. The piston opens a valve regulating the flow of silicone oil into the coupling from a reserve chamber. The silicone oil is returned to the reserve chamber through a bleed hole when the valve is closed.

On the stamped cover type, **Fig. 3,** a

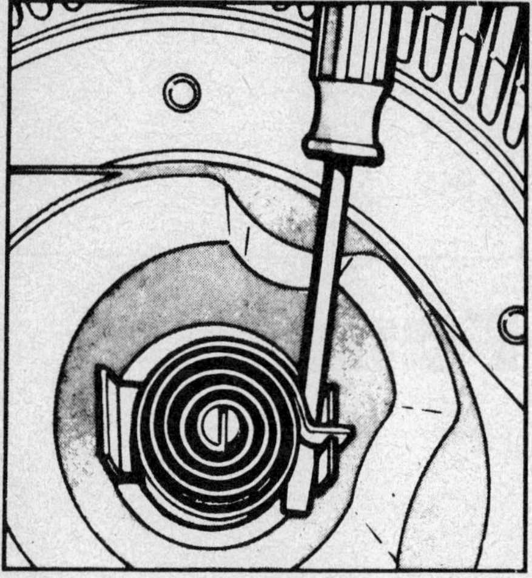

**Fig. 4 Disconnecting bi-metal spring**

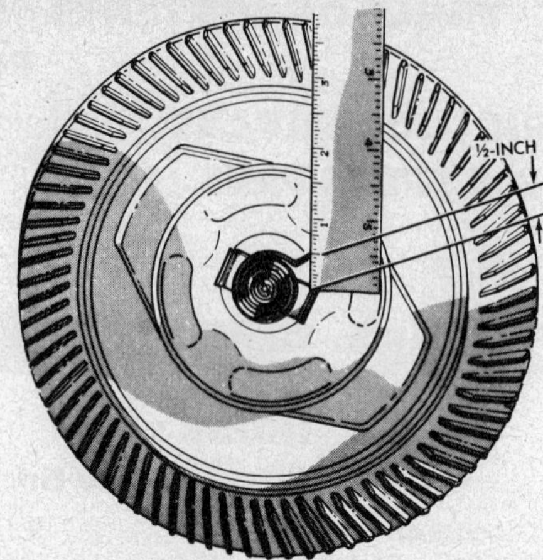


**Fig. 5 Checking spring & shaft rotation**

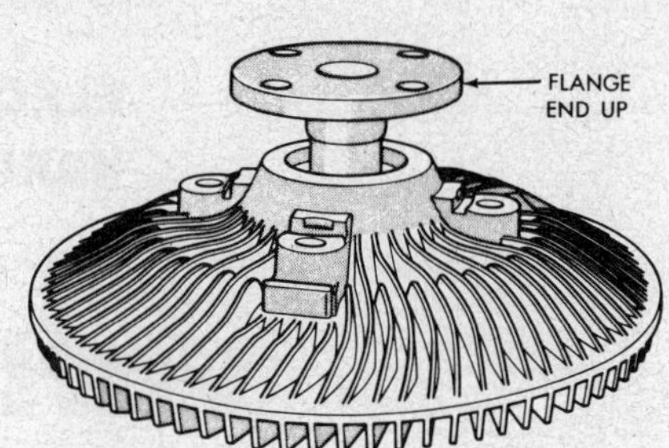


**Fig. 6 Proper position for storage of fan drive clutch**

heat-sensitive, bi-metal spring connected to an opening plate brings about a similar result. Both units cause the fan speed to increase with a rise in temperature and to decrease as the temperature goes down.

In some cases a flex-fan is used instead of a fan drive clutch. Flexible blades vary the volume of air being drawn through the radiator, automatically increasing the pitch at low engine speeds.

## FAN DRIVE CLUTCH TEST

**Do not operate engine until the fan has been first checked for possible cracks and separations.**

Run the engine at a fast idle speed (1000 RPM) until normal operating temperature is reached. This process can be speeded up by blocking off the front of the radiator with cardboard. Regardless of temperatures, the unit must be operated for at least five minutes immediately before being tested.

Stop the engine, then using a glove or a cloth to protect the hand, check the effort required to turn the fan. If considerable effort is required, it can be assumed that the coupling is operating satisfactorily. If very little effort is required to turn the fan, it is an indication that the coupling is not operating properly and should be replaced.

If the clutch fan is the coiled bi-metal spring type on Eagle models, it may be tested while the vehicle is being driven. To check, disconnect the bi-metal spring, **Fig. 4,** and rotate 90° counterclockwise. This disables the temperature-controlled free-wheeling feature and the clutch performs like a conventional fan. If this cures the overheating condition, replace the clutch fan.

To test Chrysler Corp. vehicles, stop engine, disconnect the bi-metal spring, **Fig. 4,** and rotate counterclockwise until a stop is felt. Measure the gap between end of coil and housing clip, **Fig. 5.** The gap should be ½ inch. If not, replace fan clutch.

## SERVICE

**To prevent silicone fluid from draining into fan drive bearing, store with flange facing upward, Fig. 6.**

The removal procedure for either type of fan clutch assembly is generally the same for all cars. Merely unfasten the unit from the water pump and remove the assembly from the car. On some models, the fan shroud or upper radiator hose may have to be removed to provide clearance for fan removal.

The unit shown in **Fig. 2,** may be partially disassembled for inspection and cleaning as follows:

1. Remove four retaining capscrews, then separate the fan from the drive clutch.
   Remove the metal strip on the front by pushing one end toward the fan clutch body to clear the retaining bracket, then push the strip to the side so that its opposite end will spring out of place.
3. Remove the control piston, then check the piston for free movement of the coupling device. If the piston sticks, clean with emery cloth. If the bi-metal strip is damaged, replace the clutch assembly.
4. Reverse procedure to install.

The coil spring type of fan clutch cannot be disassembled, serviced or repaired. If assembly does not function properly, replace with a new unit.

# Electric Cooling Fans

**NOTE: Wire Code Identification And Symbol Identification Located In Front Of This Manual Can Be Used As An Aid When Using Wiring Circuits Found In This Section.**

## INDEX



## EXCEPT COLT, COLT VISTA, CONQUEST, EAGLE MEDALLION & SUMMIT

### DESCRIPTION

#### Except New Yorker Salon, Dynasty, Fifth Avenue & Imperial w/V6 Engine & Laser/Talon, Monaco/Premier & Stealth

Fan control is accomplished two ways. The fan will alway runs when the A/C compressor clutch is engaged or when the engine coolant temperature set limit has been exceeded and the engine controller turns on the fan through the fan relay.

Switching through the engine controller provides fan control for the following conditions:

1. The fan will not run during engine cranking until the engine starts, regardless what the engine temperature is.
2. The Fan will always run when the A/C compressor clutch is engaged.
3. The fan will run at vehicle speeds above 40 mph only if coolant temperature reaches 230°F and will turn off when temperatures drops to 220°F. At speeds below 40 mph the fan switches on at 210°F and off at 200°F.
4. To help prevent steaming, the fan will run below 60°F ambient temperatures with coolant temperature between 100-195° and engine at idle and then only for three minutes.

#### New Yorker Salon, Dynasty, Fifth Avenue & Imperial w/V6 Engine

Fan control is accomplished based on coolant temperature and A/C head pressure.

The fan will go on when:

1. Coolant temperature reaches 210°F and turn off at 200°F regardless of vehicle speed.
2. When A/C system is engaged.
3. When A/C compressor head pressure reaches 220 psi and turn off when head pressure reaches 160 psi.

#### Laser/Talon

With the A/C compressor clutch is disengaged, the ignition switch in On position and engine coolant temperature above 185°F, the thermosensor contacts close. This causes current to flow through the radiator fan motor relay coil, thermosensor and ground causing the radiator fan motor relay to contacts to close. Current flows through the radiator fan motor relay contacts, radiator fan motor and ground causing the radiator fan motor to opetate.

When the A/C compressor clutch is engaged and the thermosensor is On, when the engine coolant temperature reaches 185°F, the condenser fan as well as the radiator fan will operate.

Refer to **Fig. 1** for other fan operation mode conditions.

#### Monaco/Premier

The fan(s) will turn On when the contacts of the cooling fan relay close and supply battery voltage to the motor from a fuse link. There is only one fan relay that controls both fans. The cooling fan will turn On if engine coolant temperature is above 220°F or if the A/C compressor clutch is engaged, which will cause both fans operate.

#### Stealth

Refer to **Fig. 2** for fan operation mode conditions.

### DIAGNOSIS

Refer to **Figs. 3 through 34**, for coolant fan wiring diagrams.

| Switch conditions | | Fan rotating condition | |
|---|---|---|---|
| Air conditioner switch | Thermo sensor | Cooling (radiator) fan | Condenser fan |
| LO (0V) | OFF | OFF | OFF |
| LO (0V) | ON | HIGH | OFF |
| HI (12V) | OFF | LOW | LOW |
| HI (12V) | ON | HIGH | HIGH |

NOTE
The thermo sensor is ON when the temperature reaches 85°C (185°F) or more.

**Fig. 1 Fan operation mode conditions. Laser/Talon**

| Switch conditions | | | | Fan revolving operation condition | |
|---|---|---|---|---|---|
| Air conditioner switch | Thermo sensor | | Engine coolant temperature switch (for air conditioner cut-off) OFF at 115 ± 3°C (239 ± 5°F) or over, ON at 108°C (226°F) or less | Radiator fan motor | Condenser fan motor |
| | For radiator fan ON at 85 ± 4°C (185 ± 7°F) or more OFF at 77°C (171°F) or less | For condenser fan ON at 95 ± 4°C (203 ± 7°F) or more OFF at 87°C (189°F) or less | | | Condenser fan motor operates in HIGH only when it receives input from condenser fan motor relay (HI) and (LO) |
| OFF | OFF | OFF | | OFF | OFF |
| | ON | OFF | | LOW | OFF |
| | | ON | | HIGH | LOW |
| ON | OFF | OFF | | LOW | LOW |
| | ON | OFF | ON | LOW | LOW |
| | | ON | | HIGH | HIGH |
| | | | OFF | HIGH | LOW |

**Fig. 2 Fan operation mode conditions. Stealth**

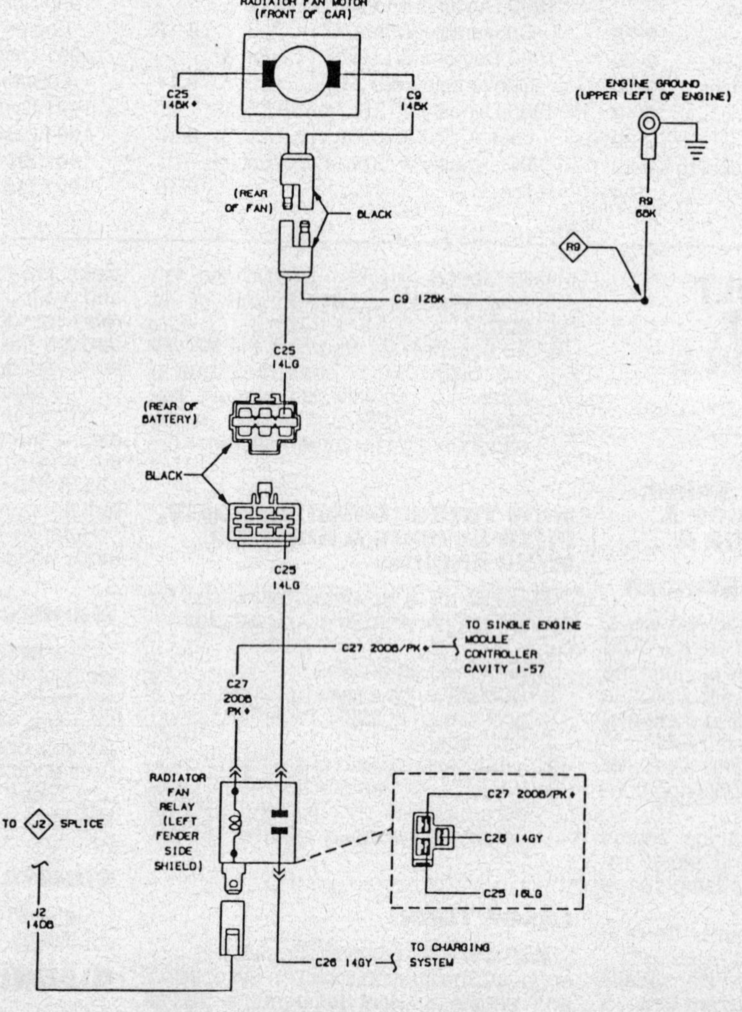


**Fig. 3 Coolant fan relay wiring diagram. 1989 Aries & Reliant less A/C**

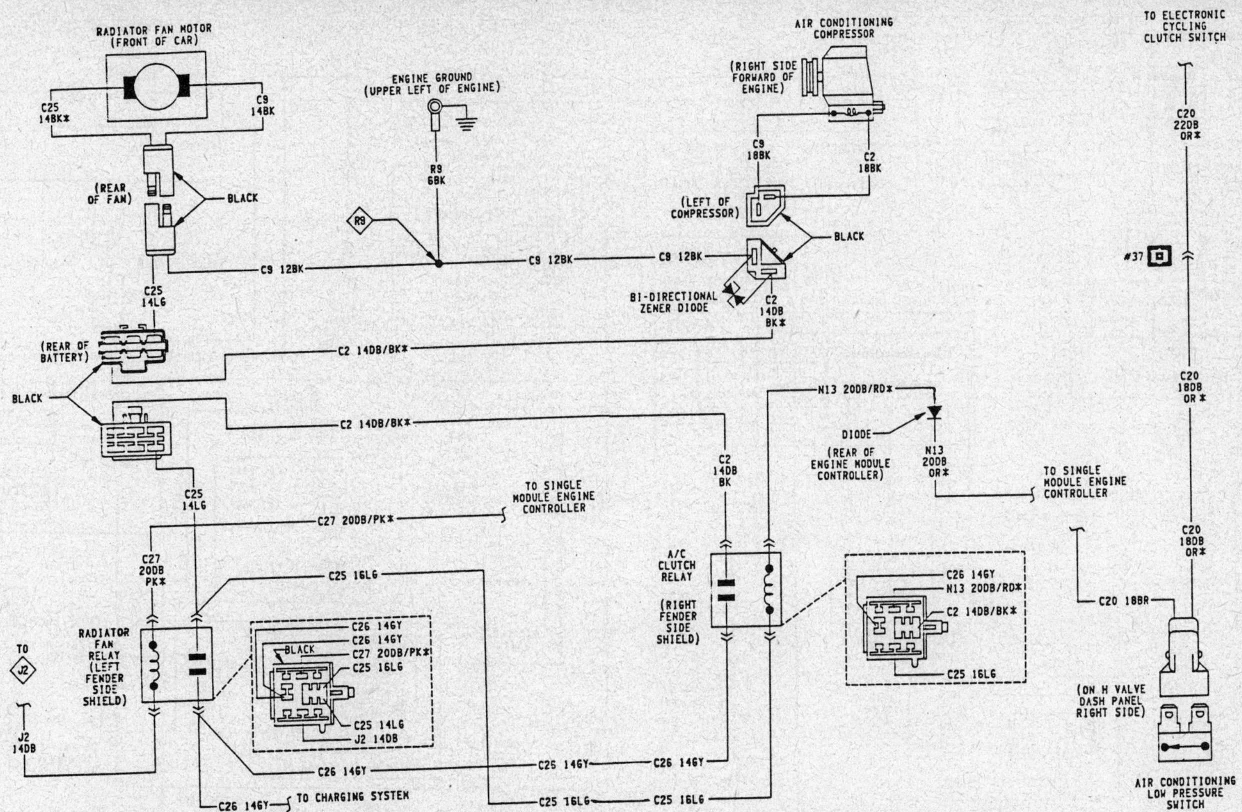


**Fig. 4 Coolant fan relay wiring diagram. 1989 Aries & Reliant w/air conditioning**

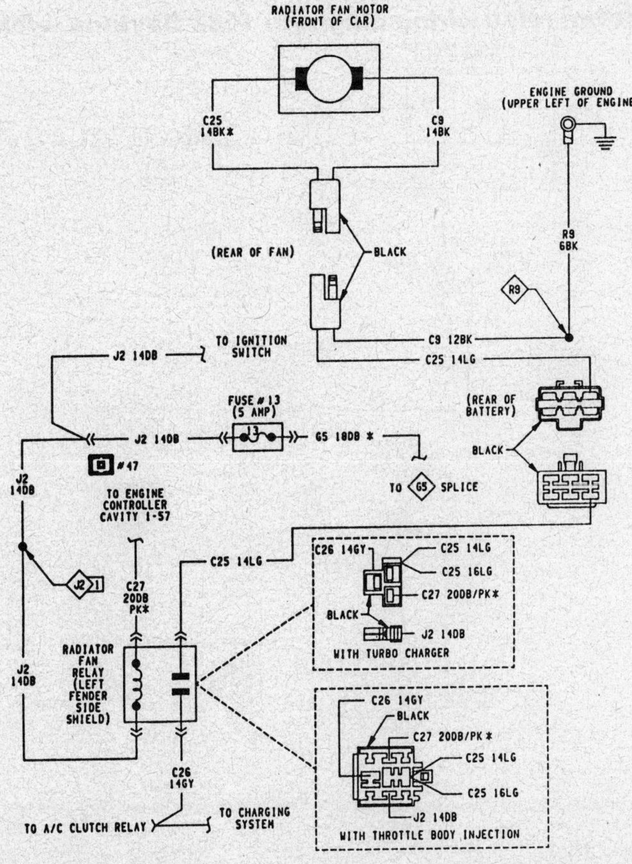


**Fig. 5 Coolant fan relay wiring diagram. 1989 Daytona less A/C**

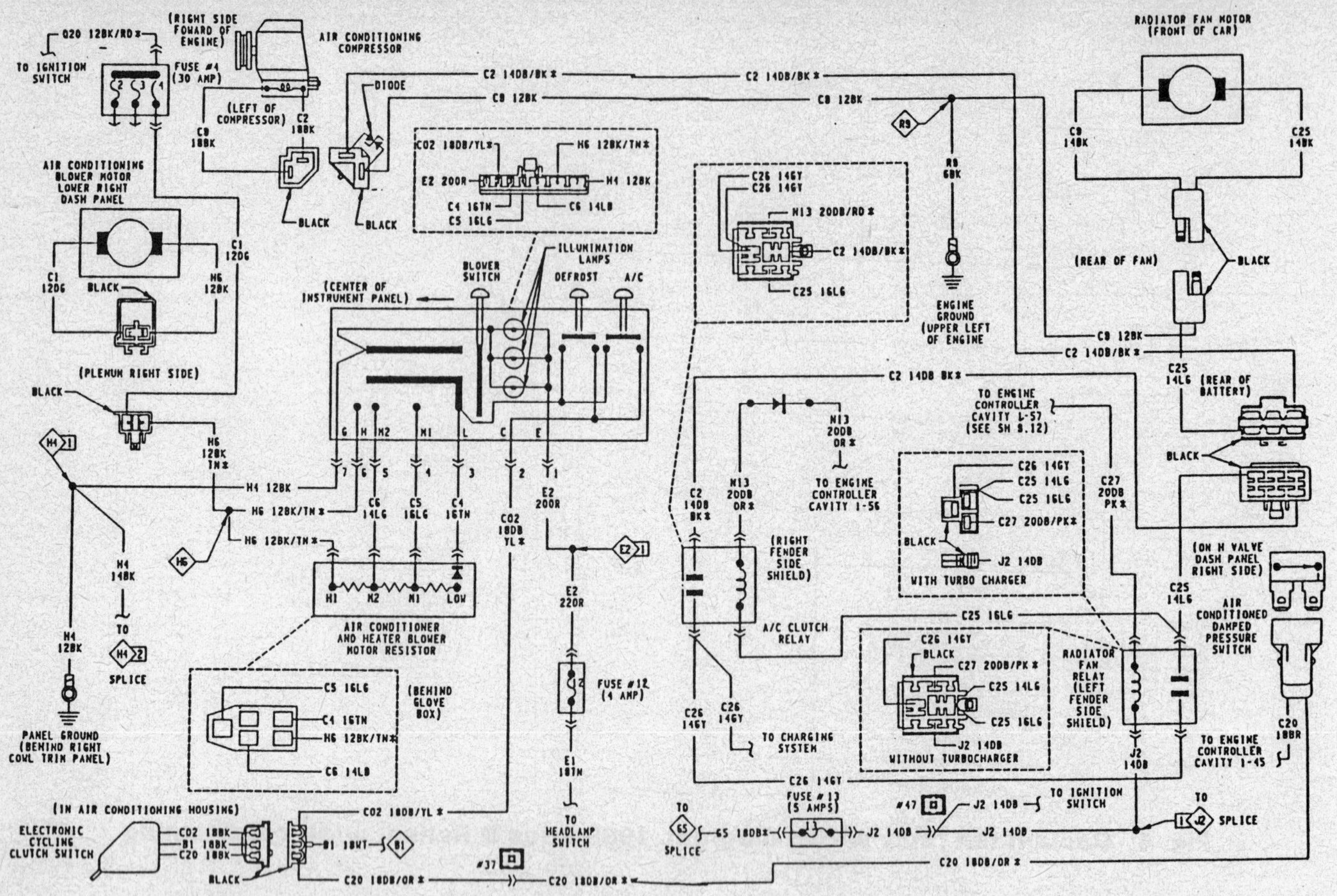

Fig. 6 Coolant fan relay wiring diagram. 1989 Daytona w/air conditioning

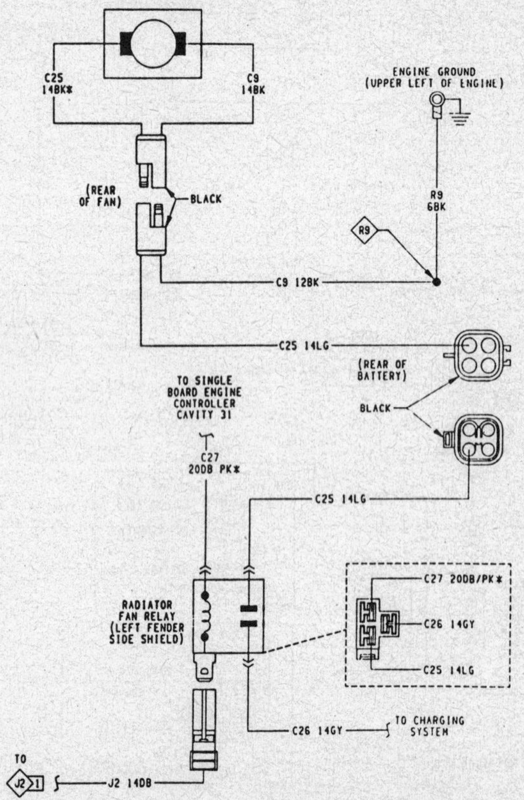


Fig. 7 Coolant fan relay wiring diagram. 1989 Omni & Horizon less A/C

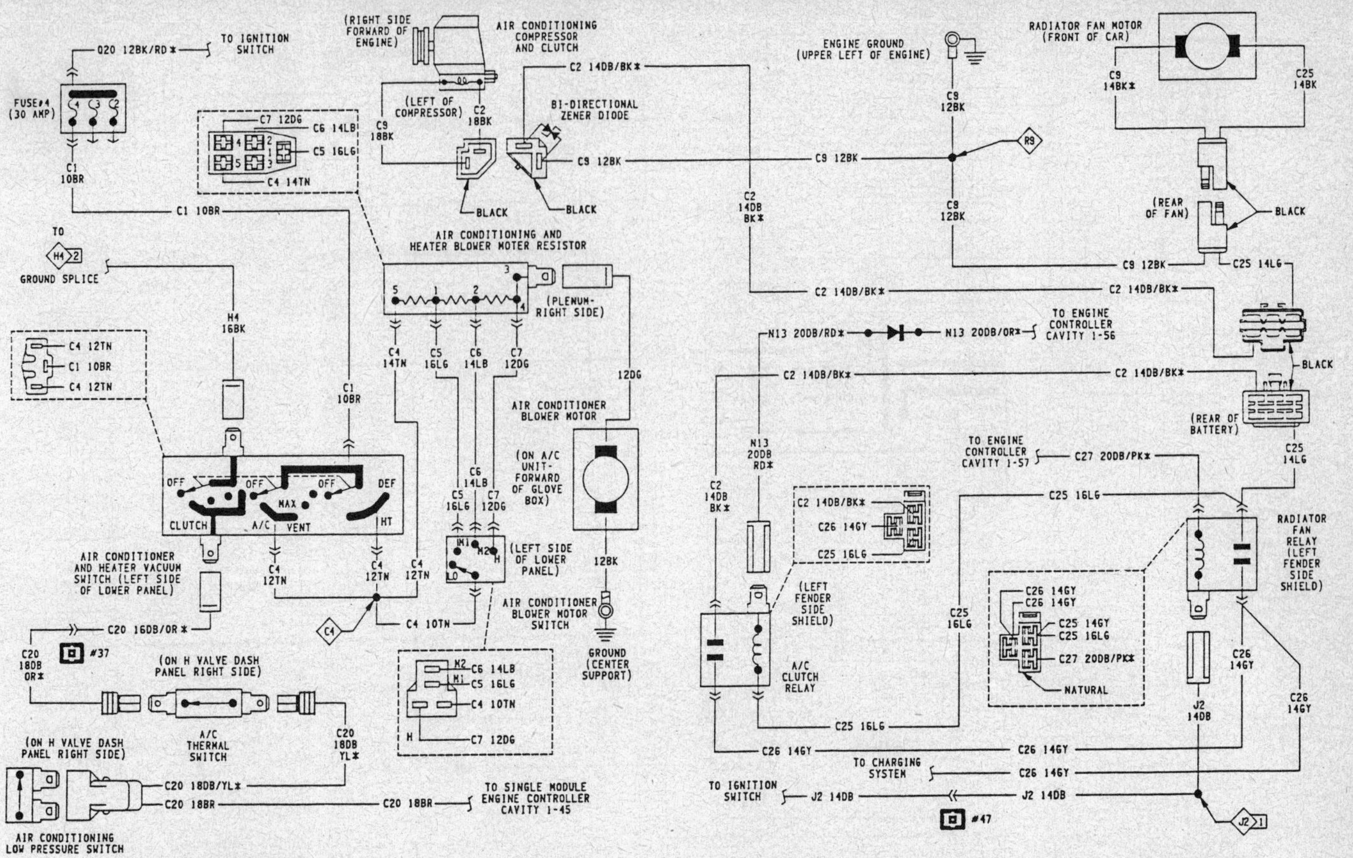

**Fig. 8 Coolant fan relay wiring diagram. 1989-90 Omni & Horizon w/air conditioning**

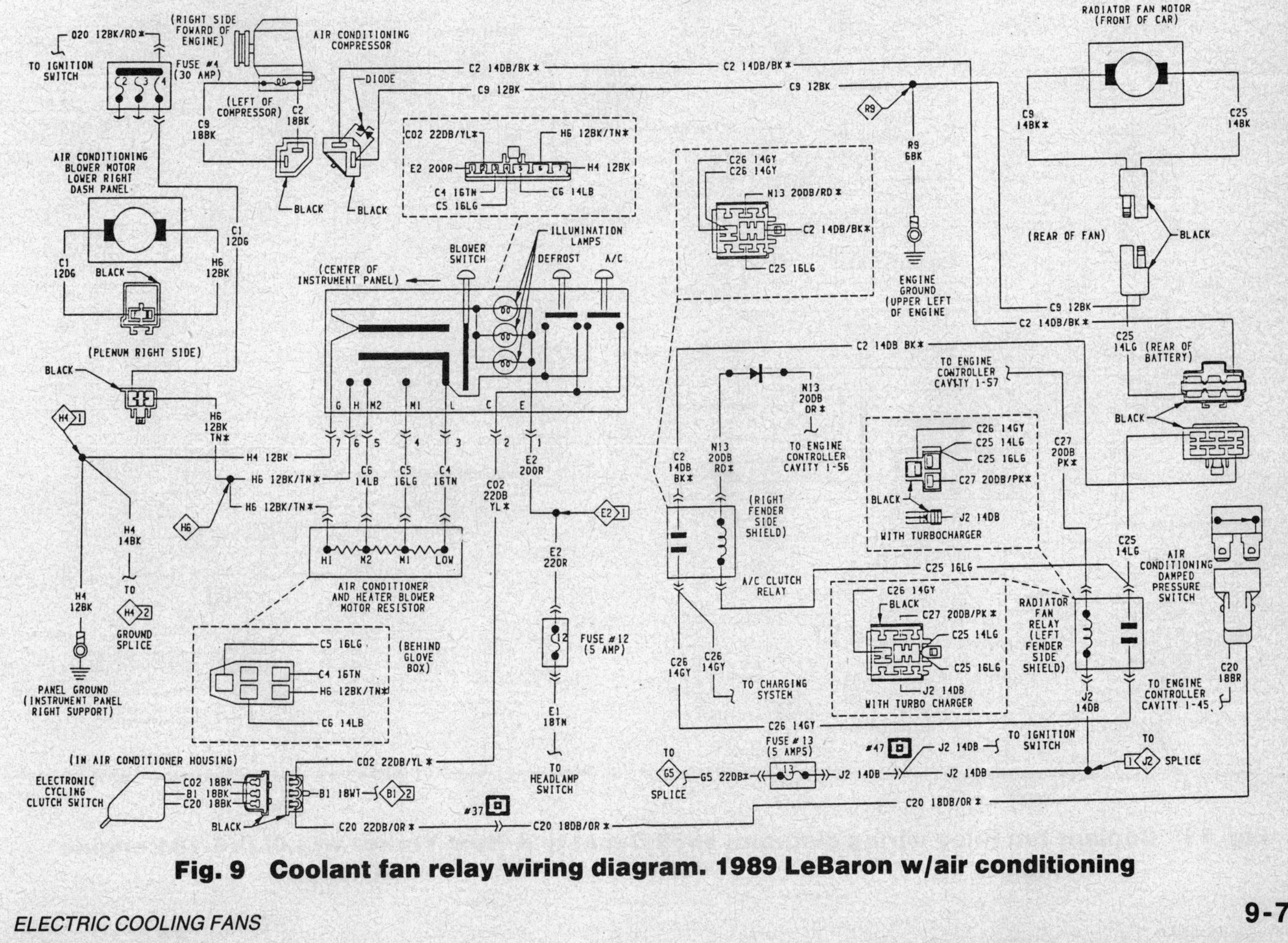

**Fig. 9 Coolant fan relay wiring diagram. 1989 LeBaron w/air conditioning**

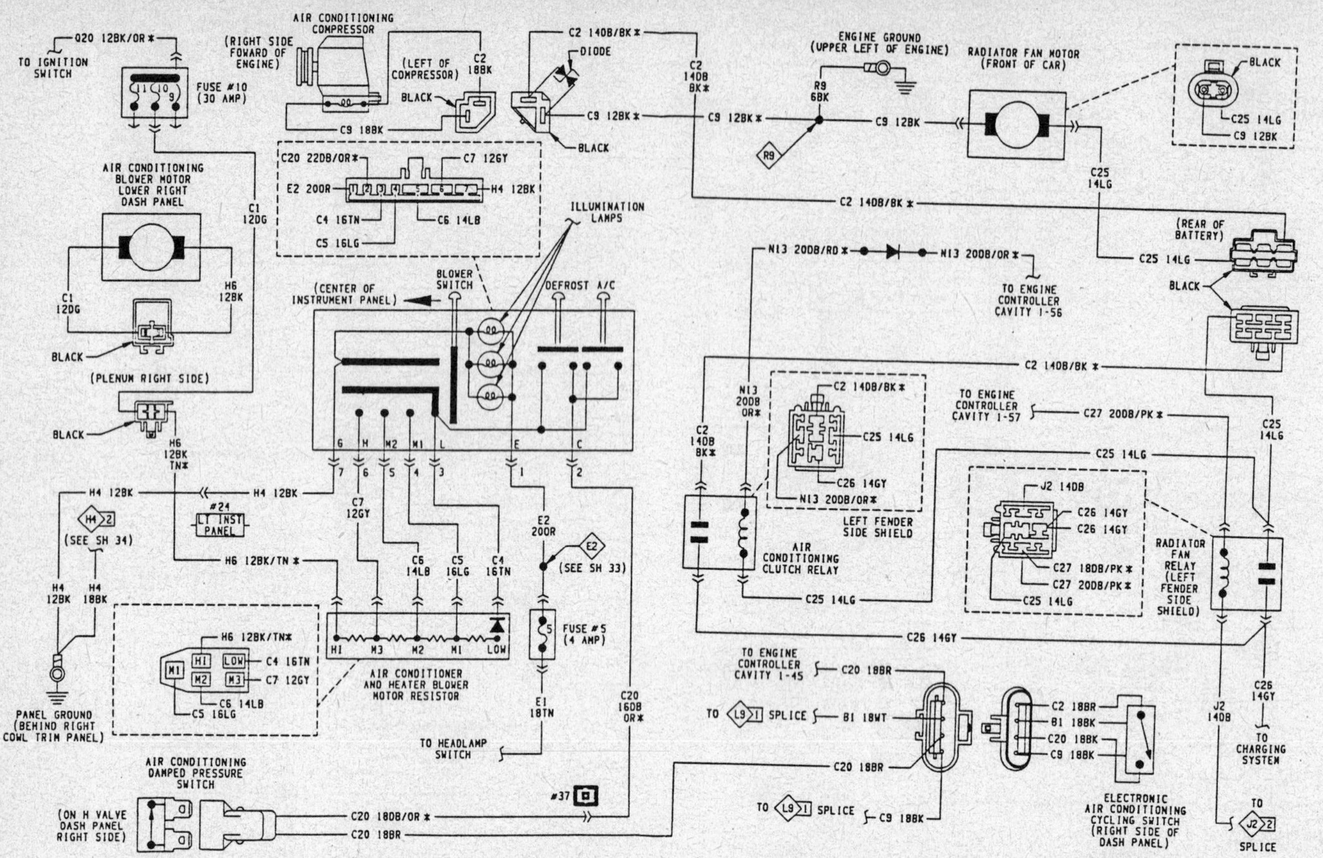

**Fig. 10 Coolant fan relay wiring diagram. 1989 Dynasty w/2.5L/4-153 engine**

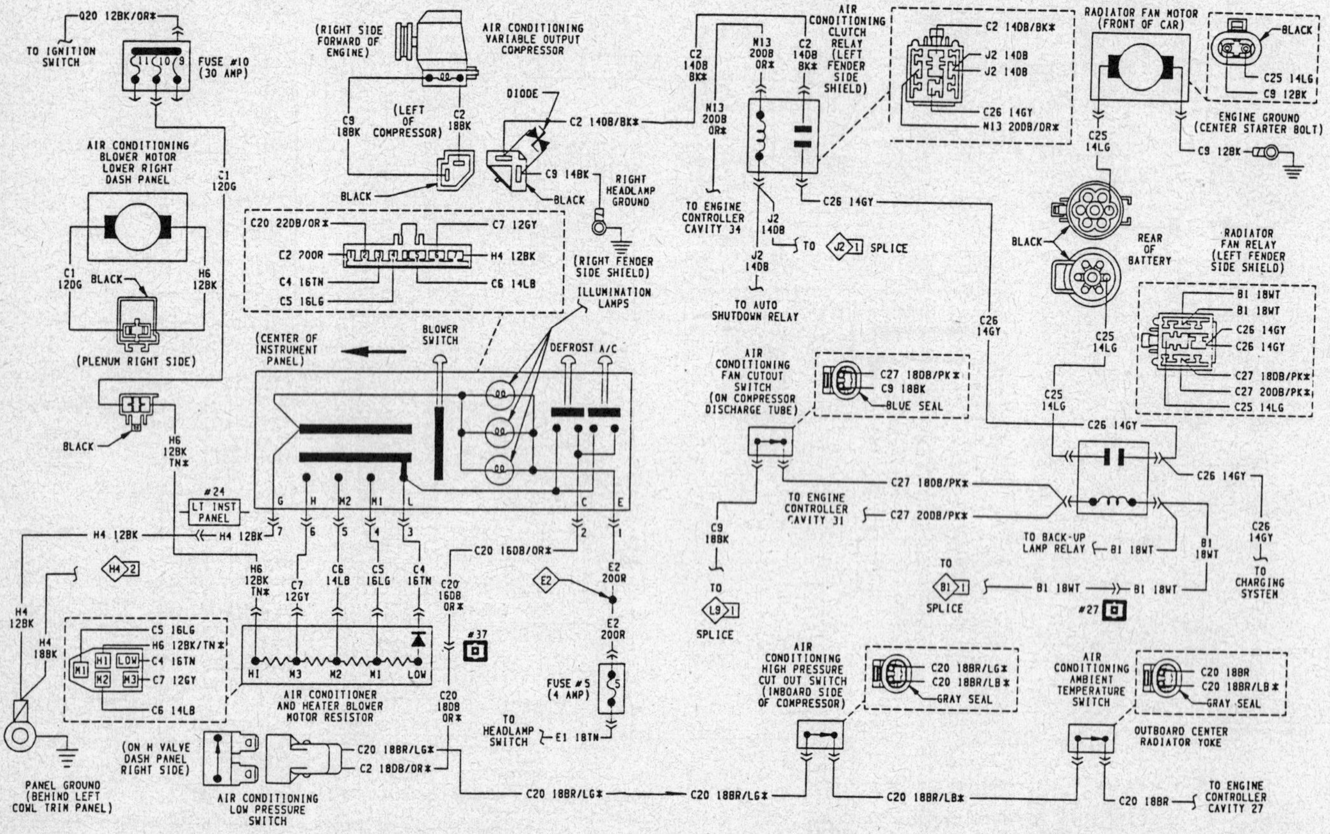

**Fig. 11 Coolant fan relay wiring diagram. 1989 Dynasty & New Yorker w/3.0L/V6-181 engine**

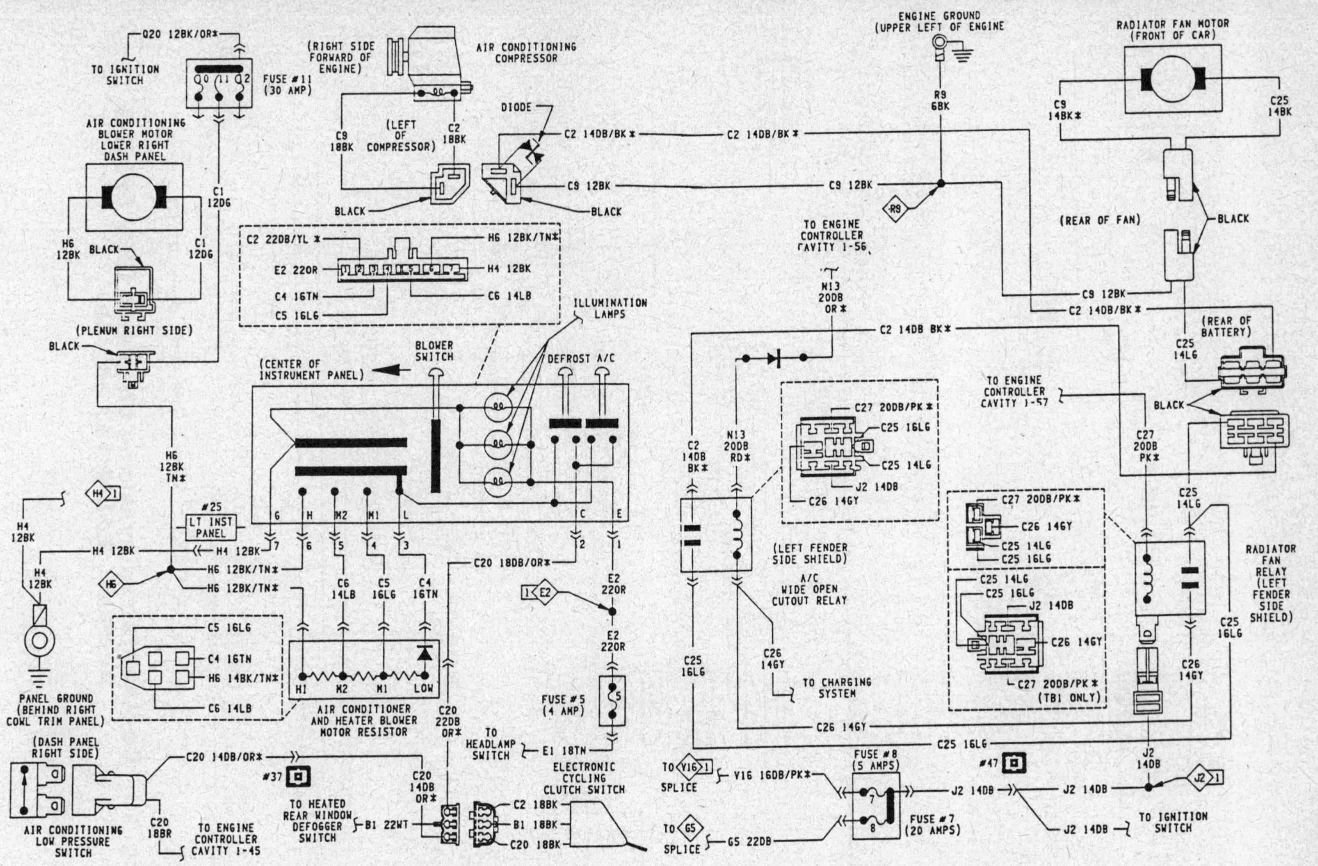

Fig. 12 Coolant fan relay wiring diagram. 1989 LeBaron GTS & Lancer

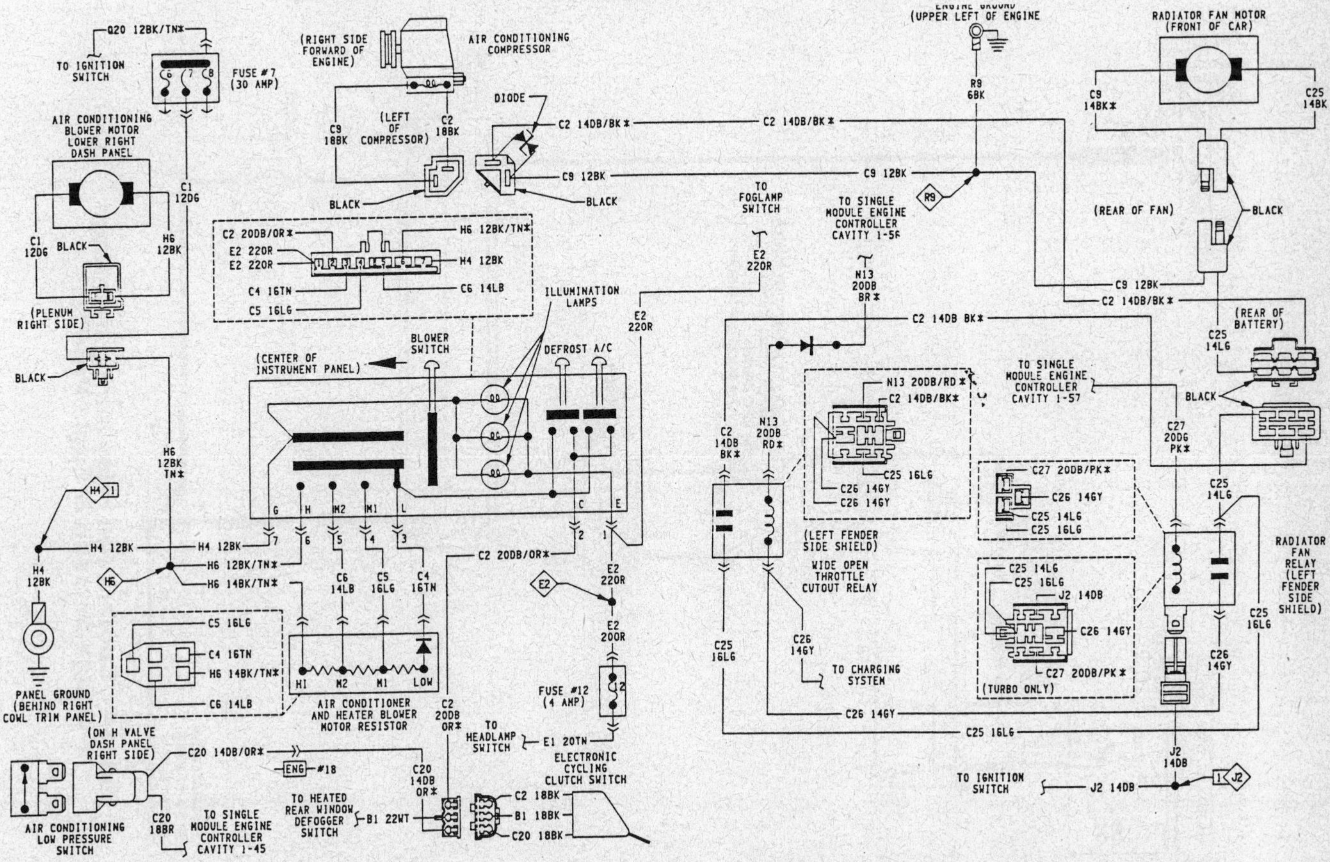

Fig. 13 Coolant fan relay wiring diagram. 1989 Shadow & Sundance with A/C

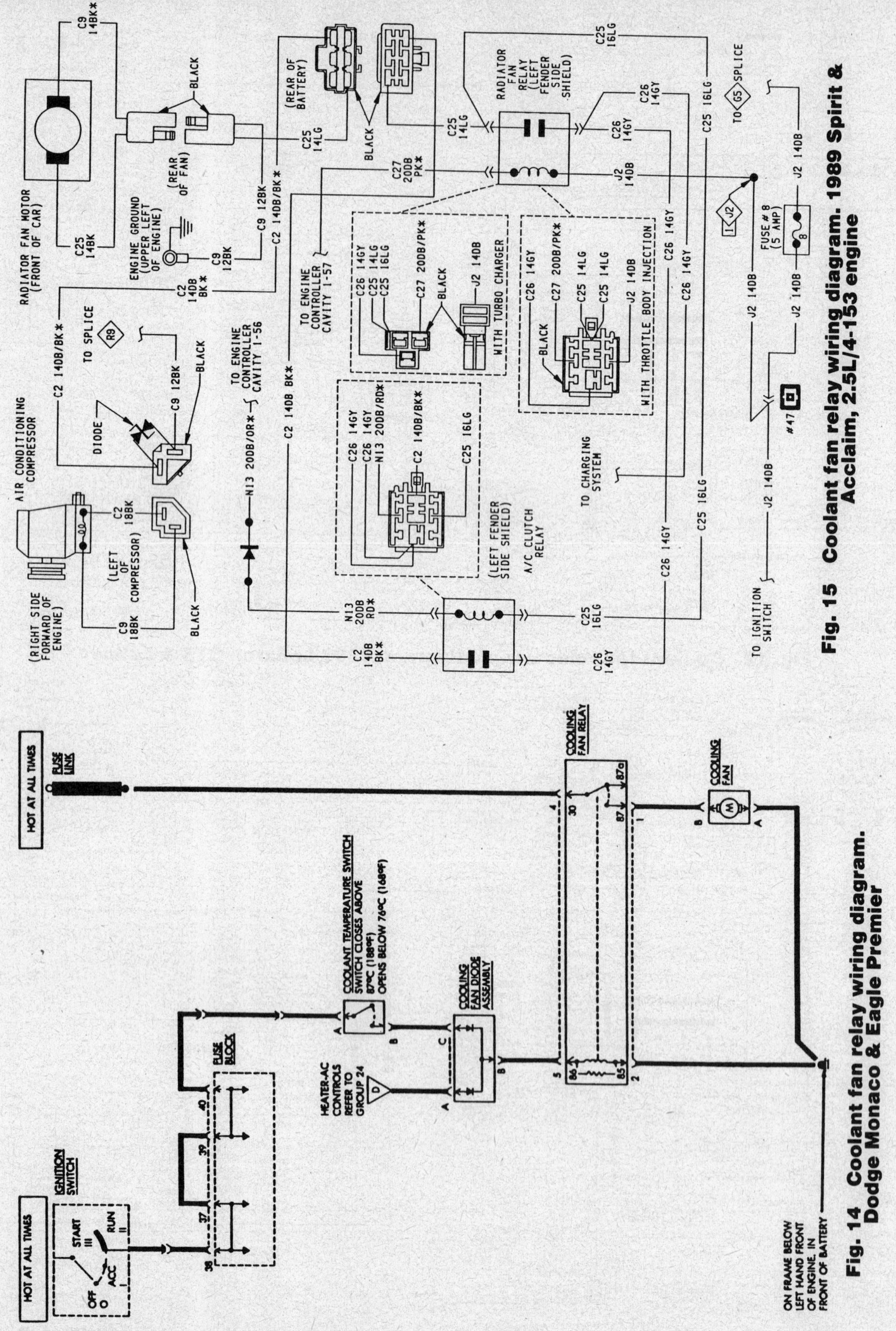


**Fig. 15** Coolant fan relay wiring diagram. 1989 Spirit & Acclaim, 2.5L/4-153 engine

**Fig. 14** Coolant fan relay wiring diagram. Dodge Monaco & Eagle Premier

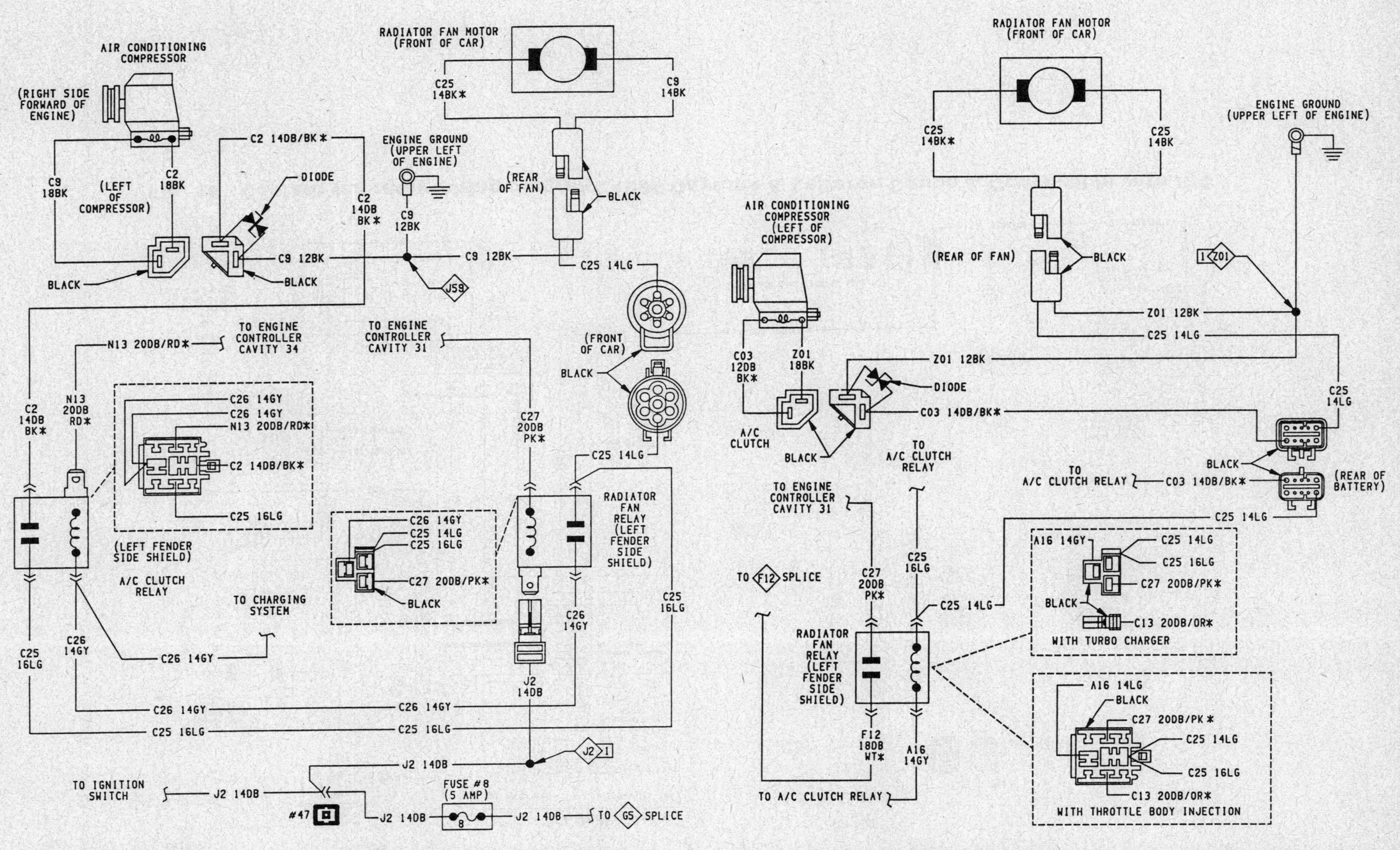


**Fig. 16 Coolant fan relay wiring diagram. 1989 Spirit & Acclaim, 3.0L/V6-181 engine**

**Fig. 17 Coolant fan relay wiring diagram. 1990 Daytona & LeBaron Coupe & Convertible less A/C**

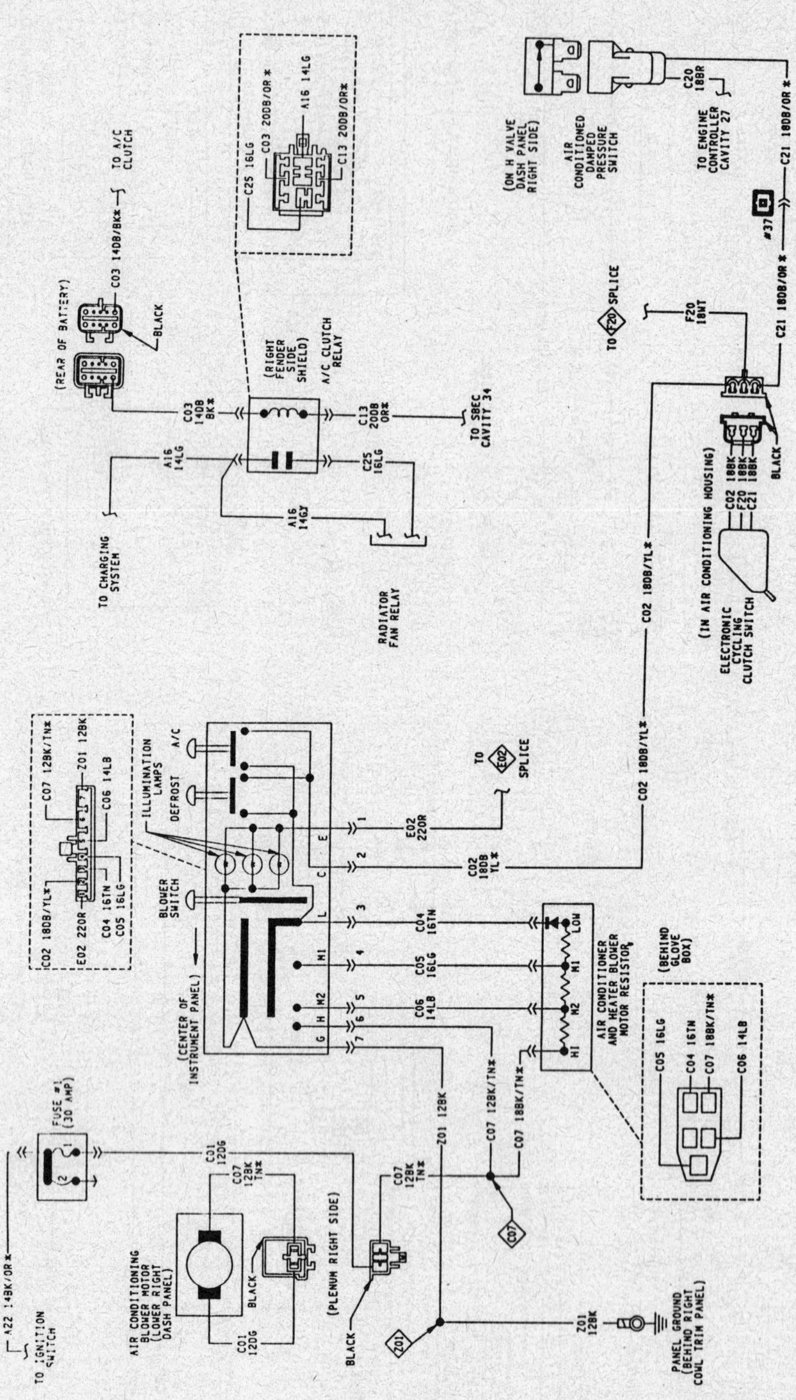


**Fig. 18 Coolant fan relay wiring diagram. 1990 Daytona & LeBaron Coupe & Convertible with A/C**

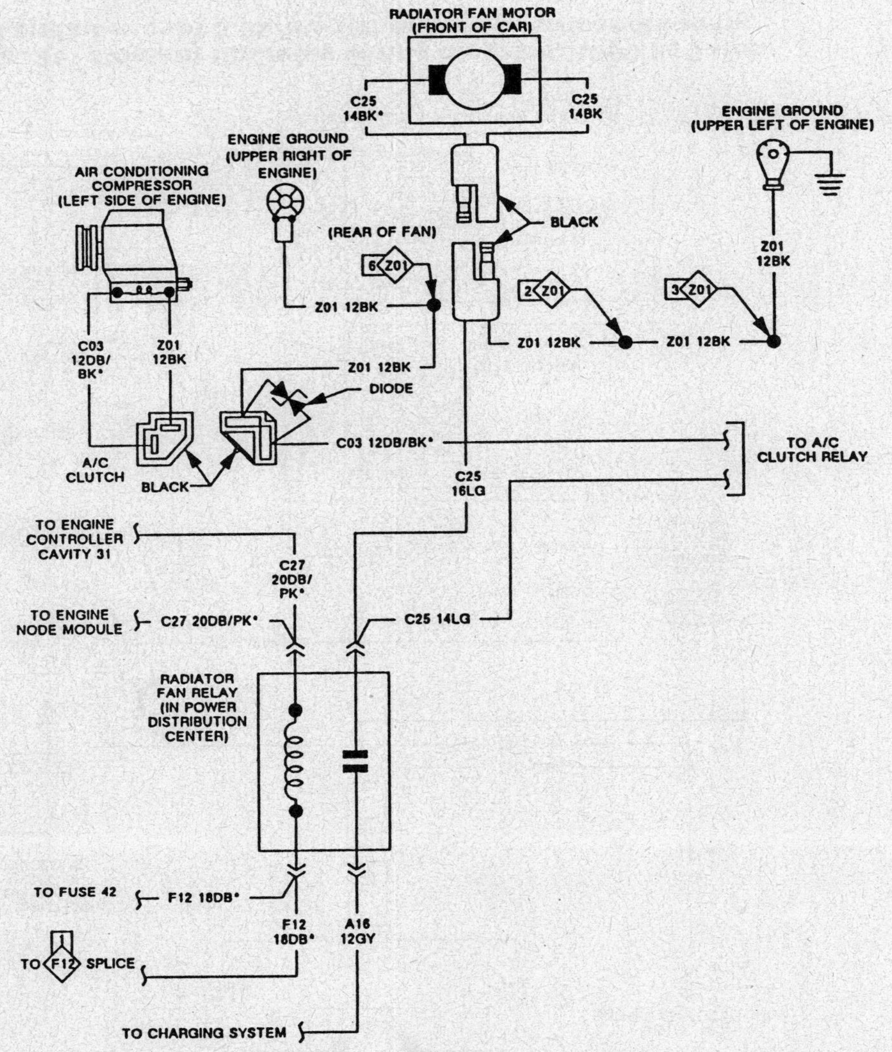


**Fig. 19 Cooling Fan Wiring Circuit. 1991 Daytona, LeBaron Coupe & LeBaron Convertible**

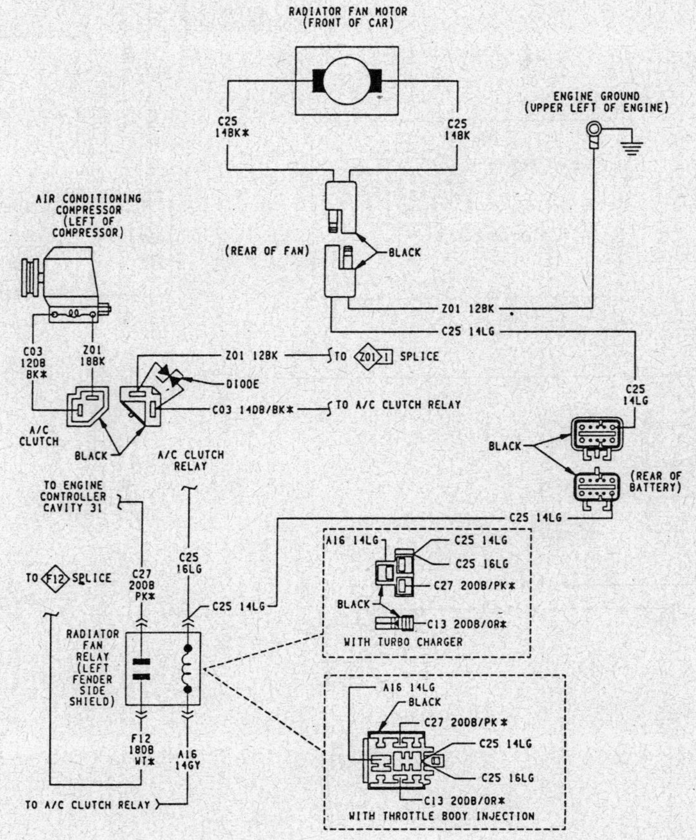


**Fig. 20 Coolant fan relay wiring diagram. 1990 LeBaron Landau w/3.0L/V6-181 engine & A/C**

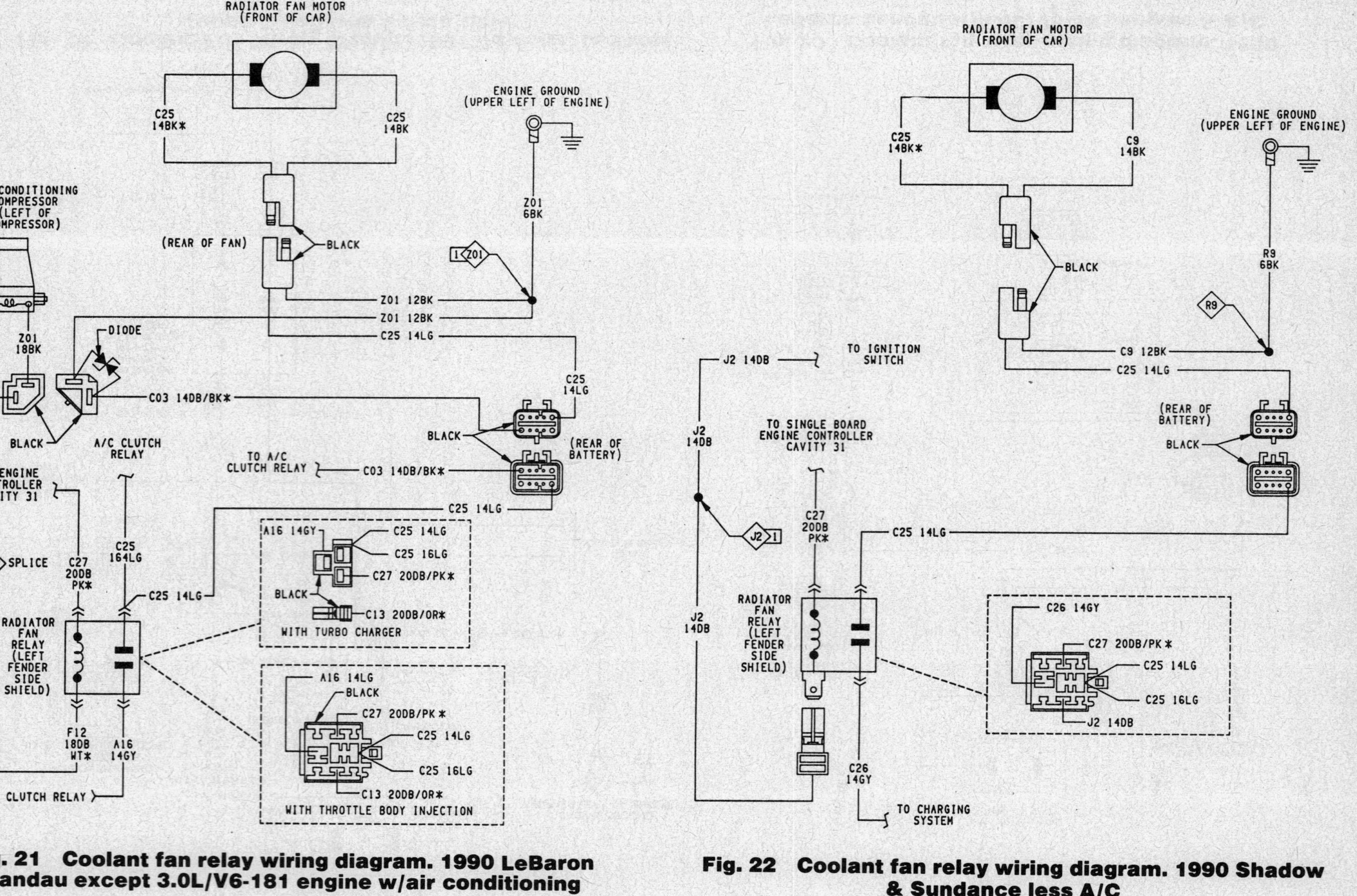


**Fig. 21 Coolant fan relay wiring diagram. 1990 LeBaron Landau except 3.0L/V6-181 engine w/air conditioning**

**Fig. 22 Coolant fan relay wiring diagram. 1990 Shadow & Sundance less A/C**

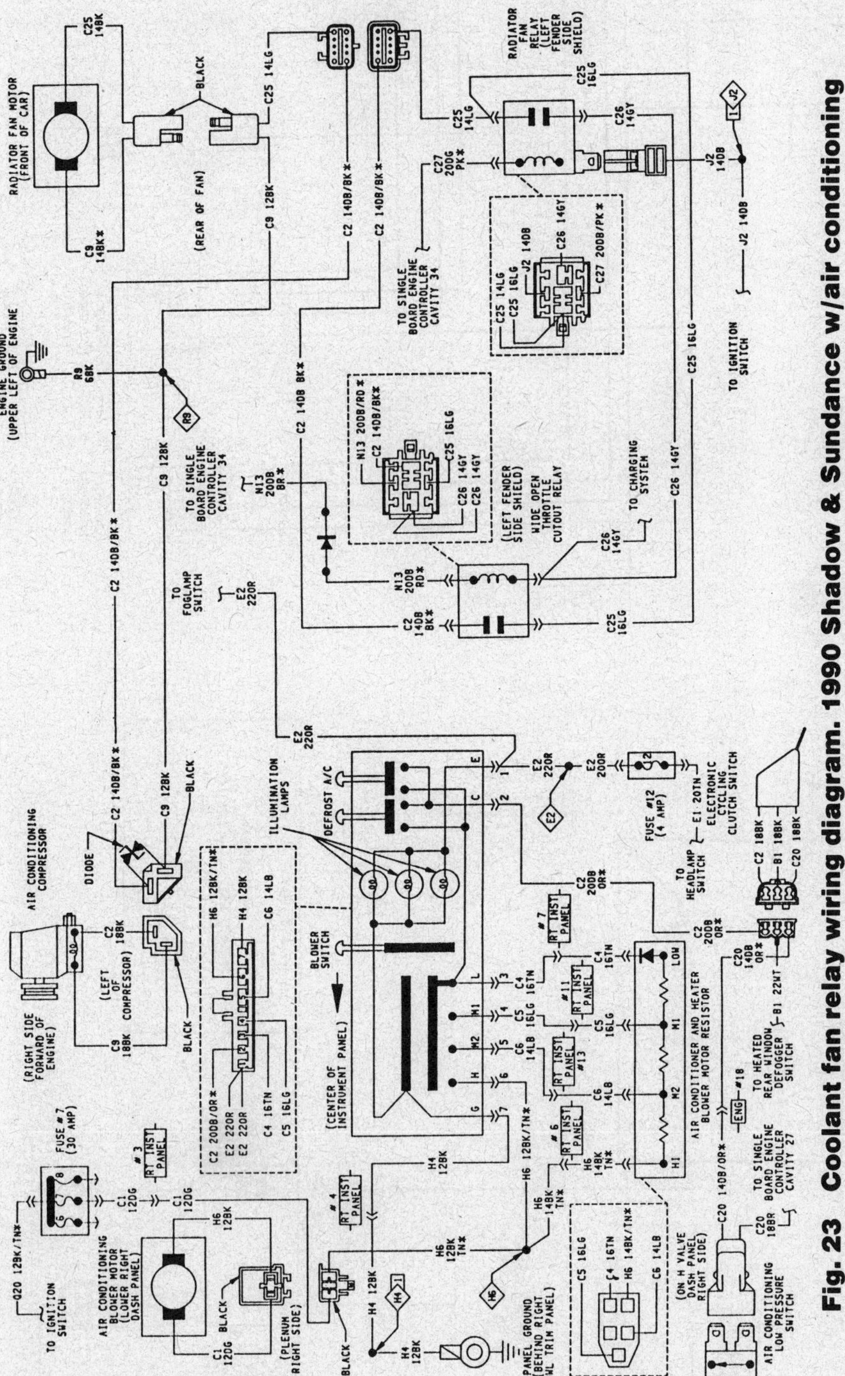


**Fig. 23 Coolant fan relay wiring diagram. 1990 Shadow & Sundance w/air conditioning**

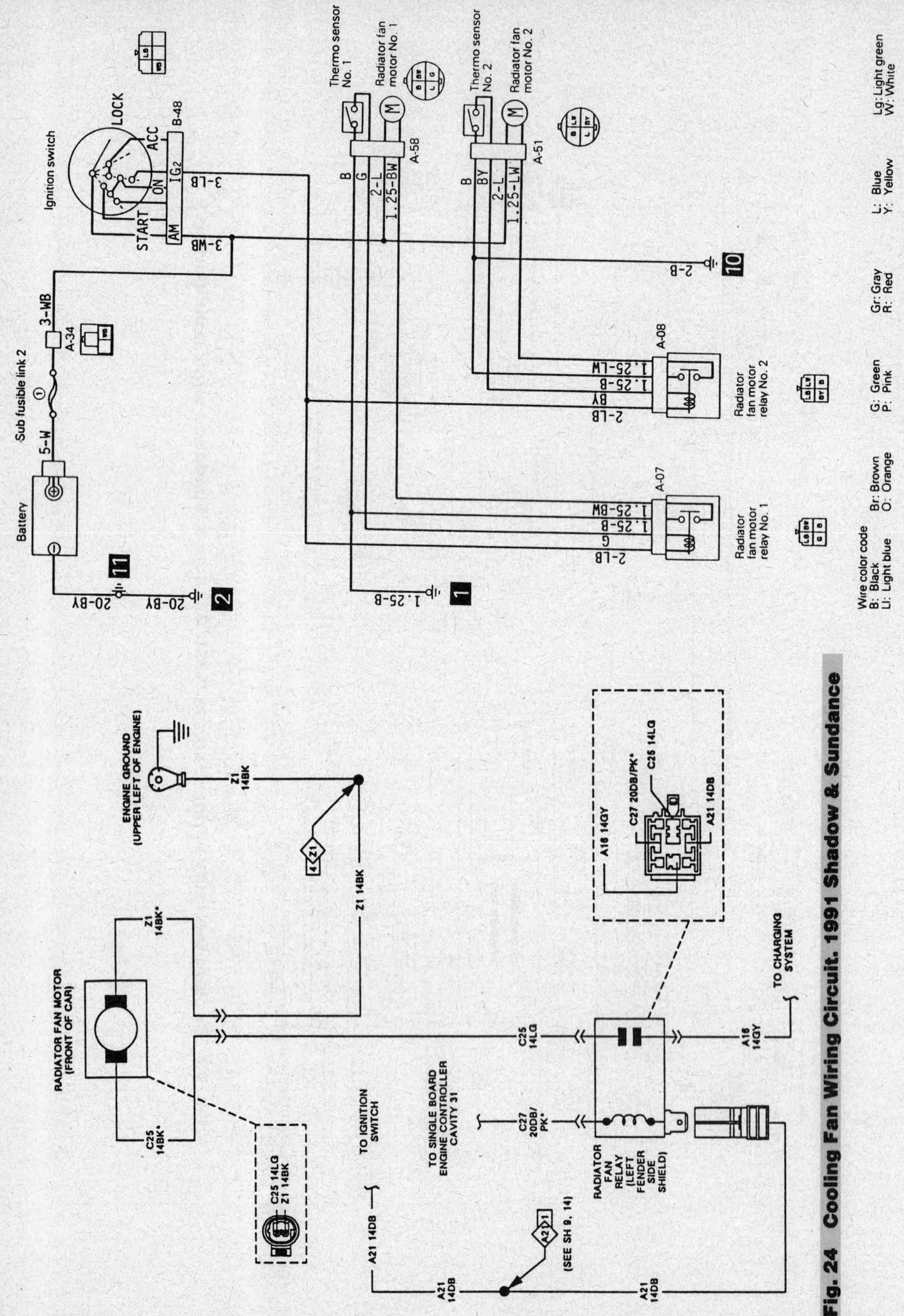


**Fig. 24A Coolant fan relay wiring diagram. Conquest.**

**Fig. 24 Cooling Fan Wiring Circuit. 1991 Shadow & Sundance**

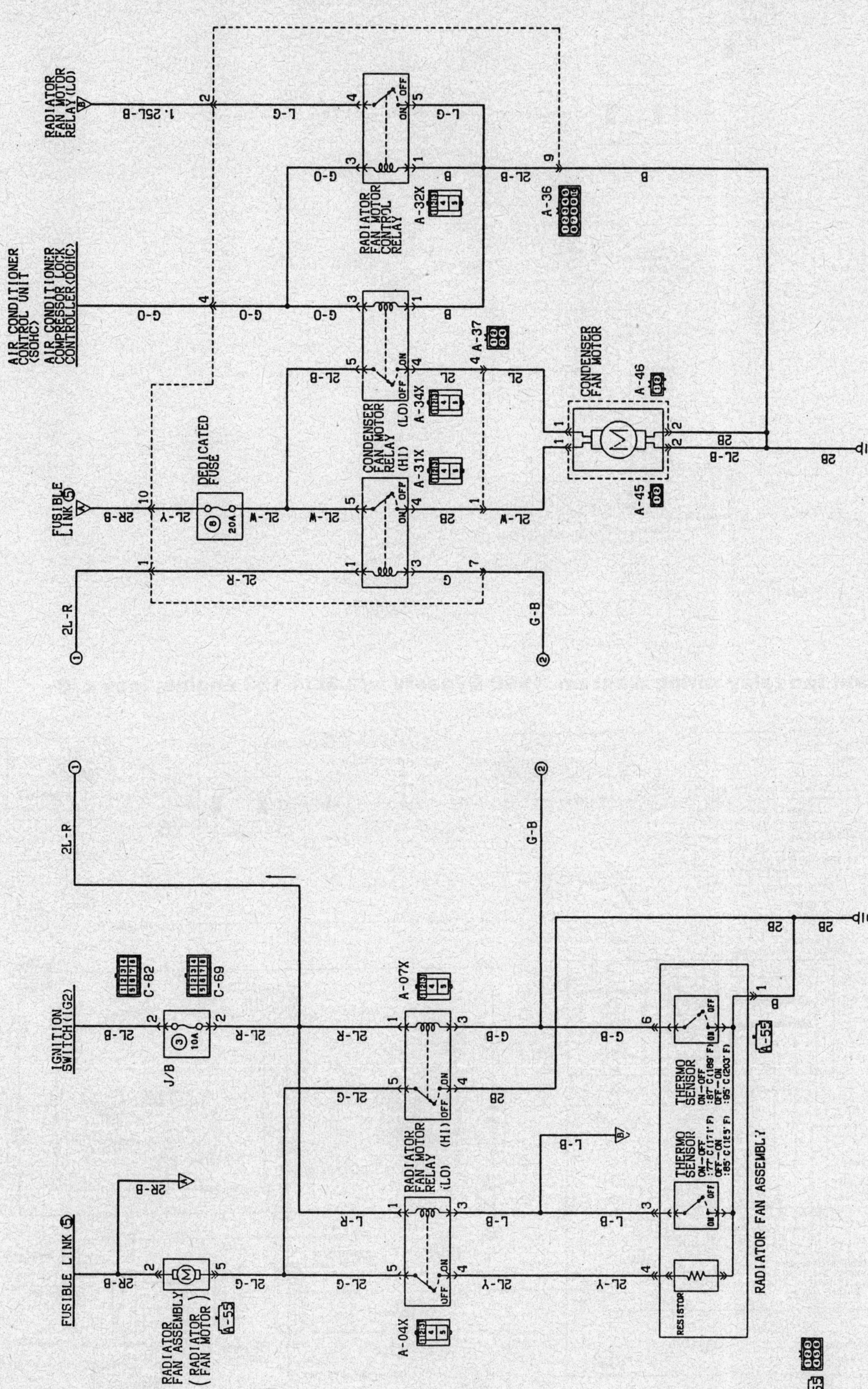


Fig. 25 Cooling Fan Wiring Circuit. Stealth

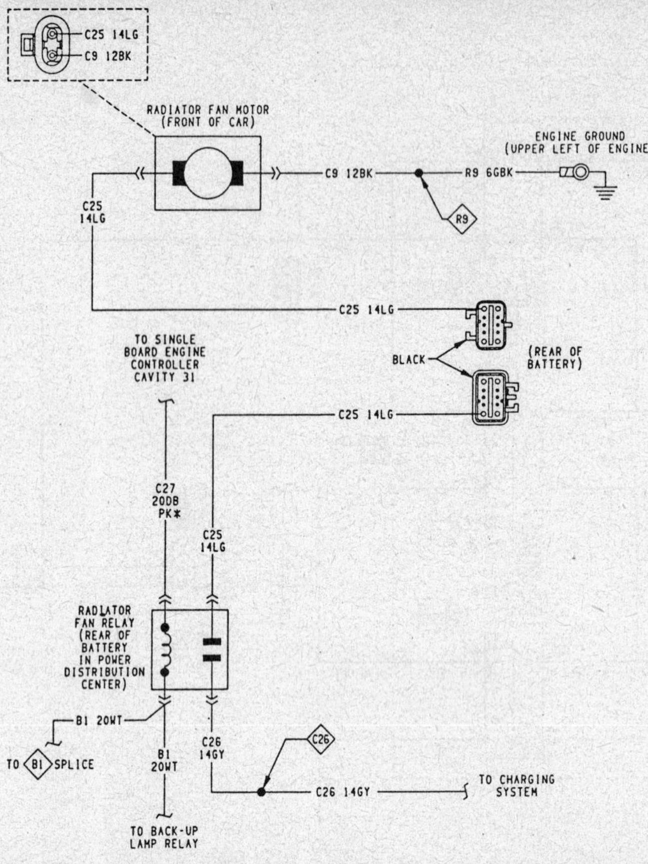


**Fig. 26 Coolant fan relay wiring diagram. 1990 Dynasty w/2.5L/4-153 engine, less A/C**

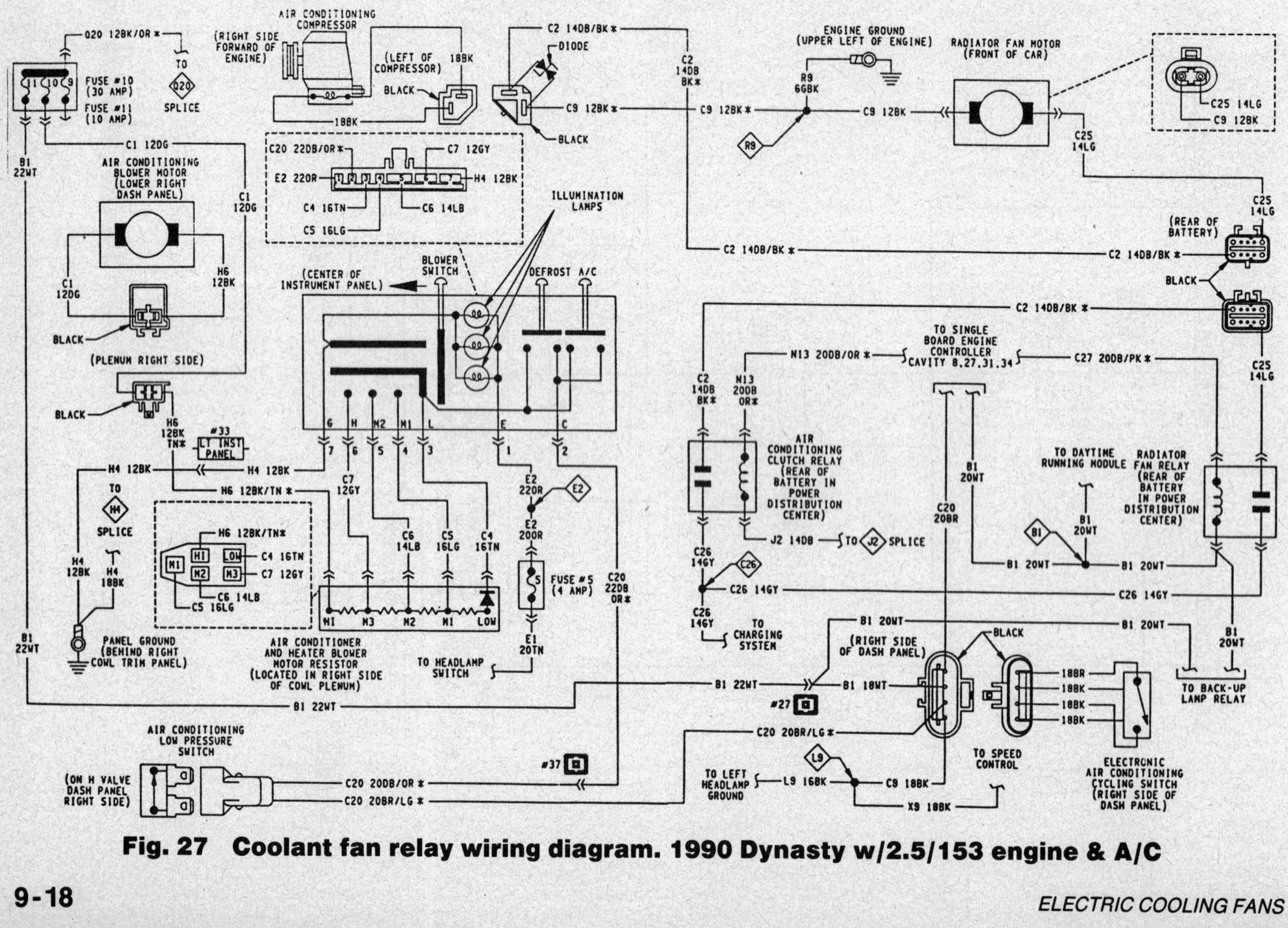

**Fig. 27 Coolant fan relay wiring diagram. 1990 Dynasty w/2.5/153 engine & A/C**

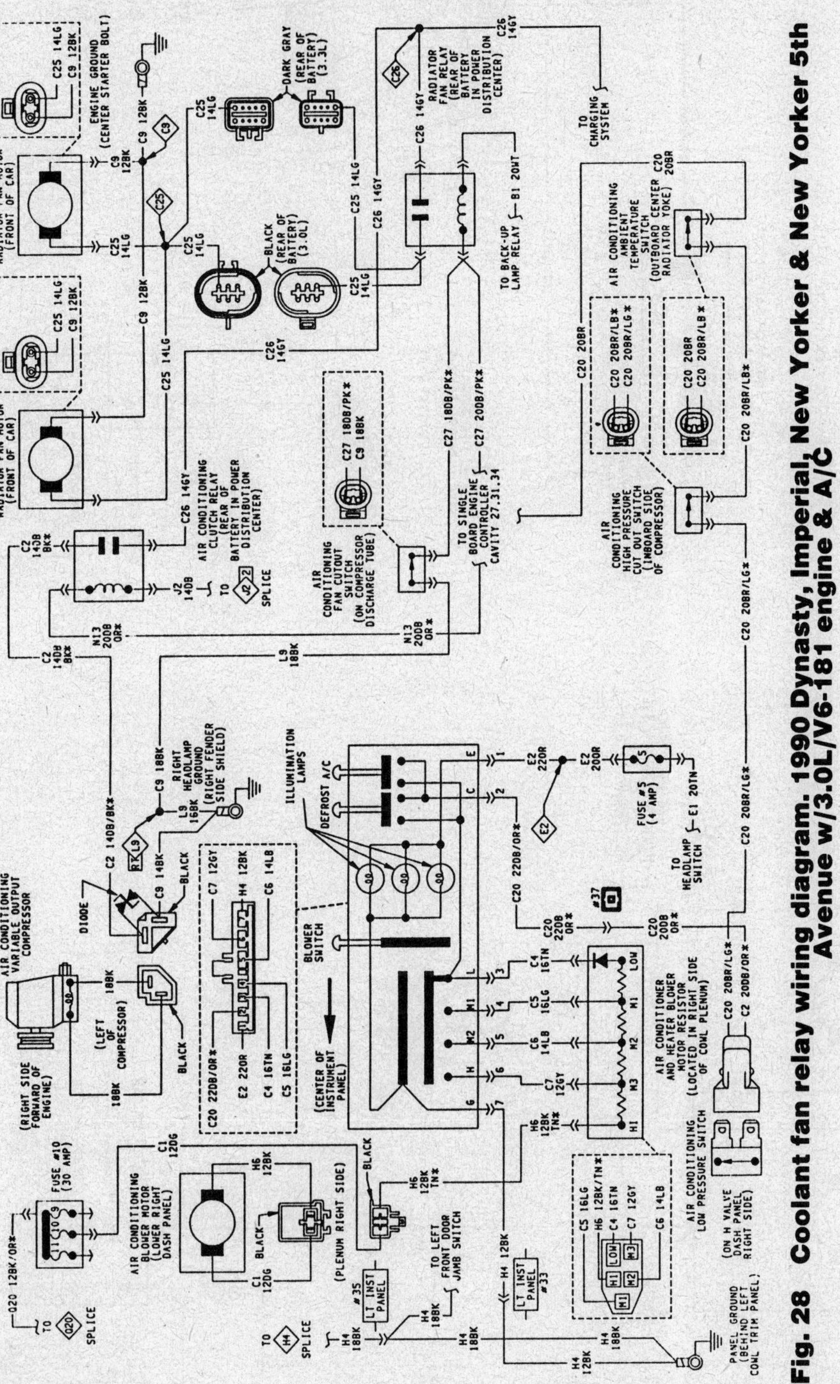


**Fig. 28 Coolant fan relay wiring diagram. 1990 Dynasty, Imperial, New Yorker & New Yorker 5th Avenue w/3.0L/V6-181 engine & A/C**

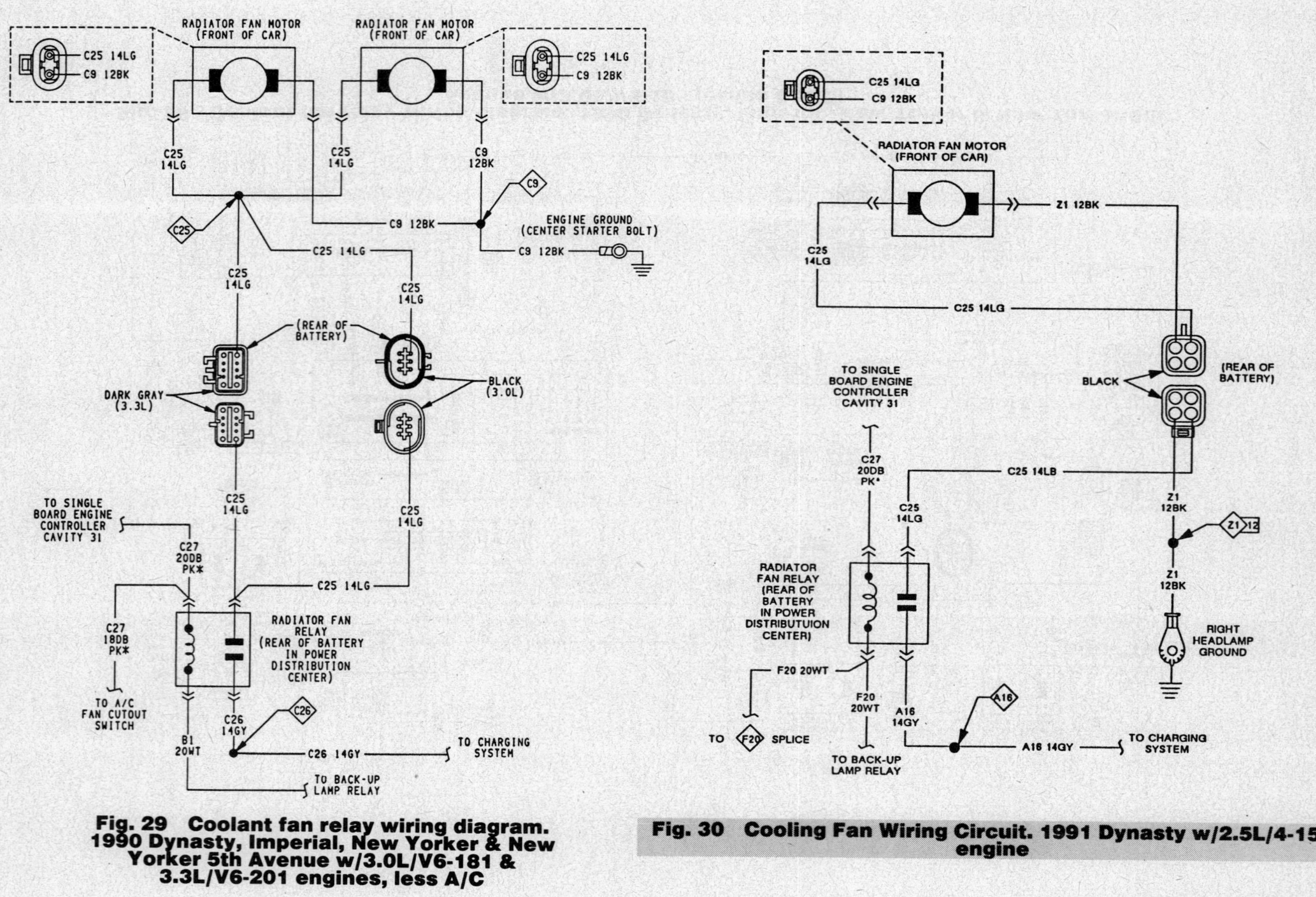


**Fig. 29 Coolant fan relay wiring diagram. 1990 Dynasty, Imperial, New Yorker & New Yorker 5th Avenue w/3.0L/V6-181 & 3.3L/V6-201 engines, less A/C**

**Fig. 30 Cooling Fan Wiring Circuit. 1991 Dynasty w/2.5L/4-153 engine**

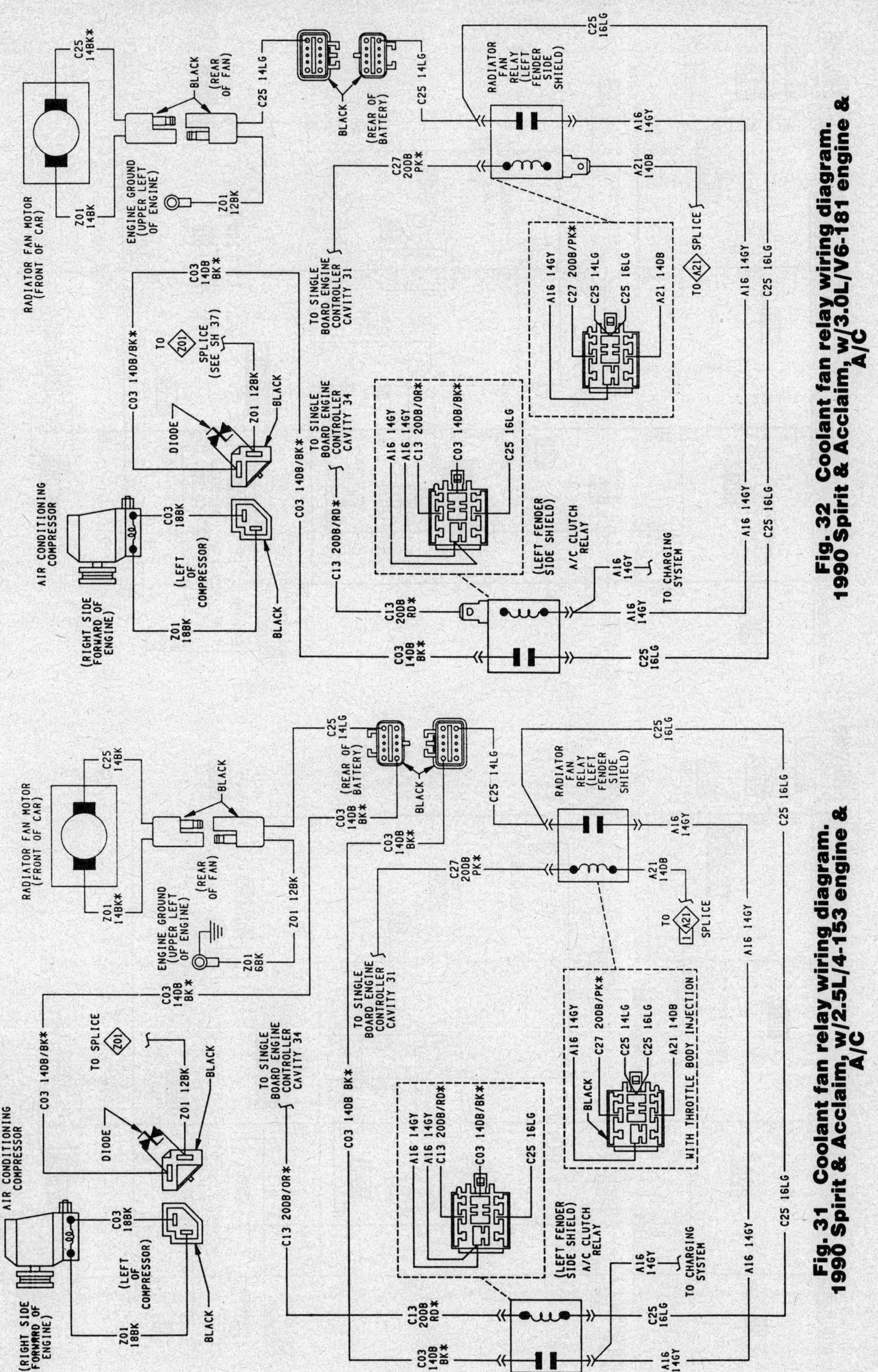


**Fig. 32 Coolant fan relay wiring diagram. 1990 Spirit & Acclaim, w/3.0L/V6-181 engine & A/C**

**Fig. 31 Coolant fan relay wiring diagram. 1990 Spirit & Acclaim, w/2.5L/4-153 engine & A/C**

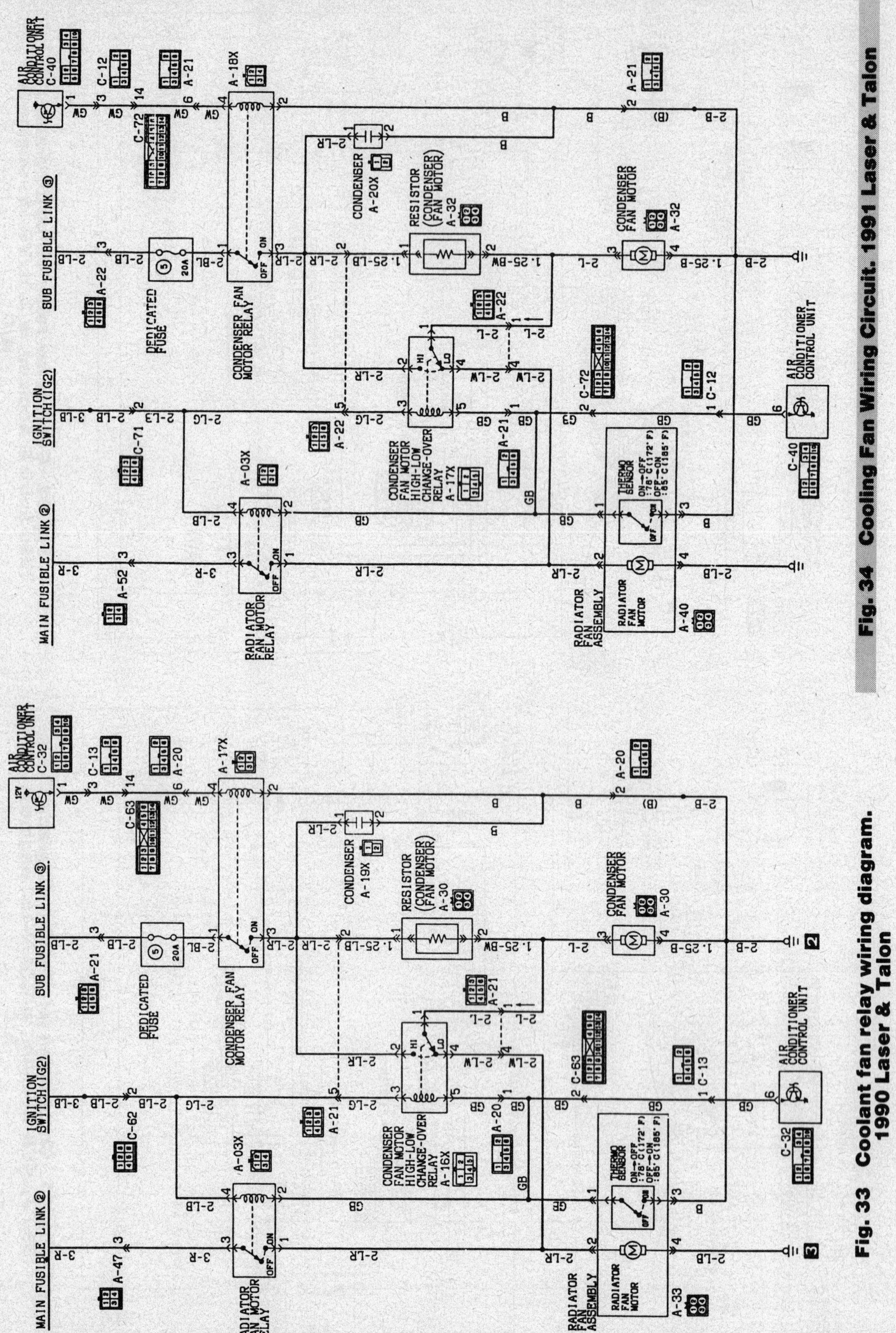

**Fig. 34 Cooling Fan Wiring Circuit. 1991 Laser & Talon**

**Fig. 33 Coolant fan relay wiring diagram. 1990 Laser & Talon**

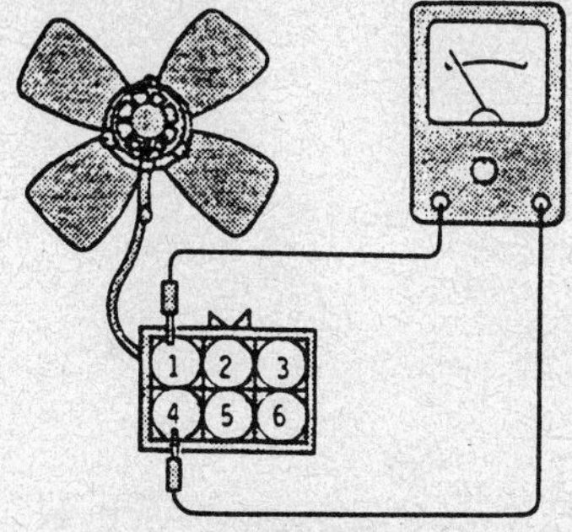


Fig. 35 Radiator fan connector terminals. Stealth

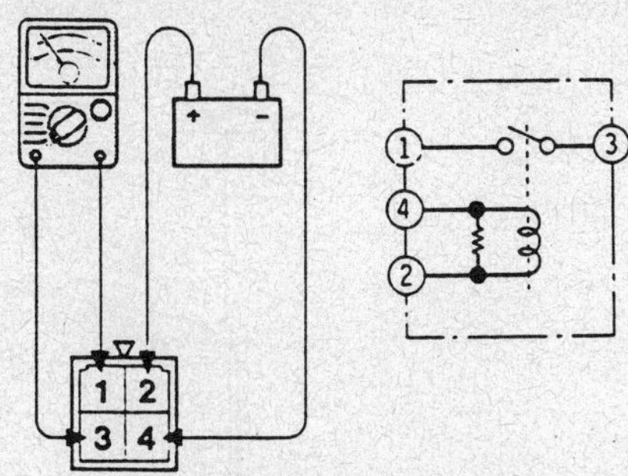


Fig. 36 Radiator fan motor relay. Laser/Talon & Stealth

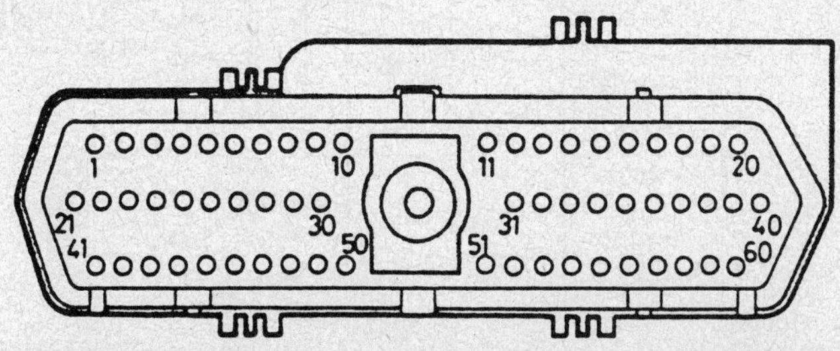


Fig. 37 Engine controller 60-way connector. Except Laser/Talon, Stealth & Monaco Premier

## COOLANT TEMPERATURE SENSOR

1. With key Off, disconnect coolant temperature sensor connector.
2. Measure resistance between sensor terminals.
3. If resistance is not 700-1000 ohms at temperature of 200°F, replace sensor.

## COOLANT TEMPERATURE SWITCH

### Stealth

1. Place sensor in hot water up to mounting thread.
2. Check for continuity between terminals on sensor.
3. If no continuity exists with water temperature at 234-244°F, replace sensor.

## THERMO SENSOR

### Laser/Talon

1. Place sensor in hot water up to mounting thread.
2. Check for continuity between terminals on sensor.
3. If no continuity exists with water temperature at 180-190°F or at 172°F or less, replace sensor.

## RADIATOR FAN RESISTOR

### Stealth

1. Measure resistance between connector terminals 1 and 4 of radiator fan connector, **Fig. 35.**
2. If resistance is not .29-.35 ohms, replace resistor.

## RADIATOR FAN MOTOR RELAY

### Laser/Talon & Stealth

1. Remove radiator fan relay from relay box located at RH side of engine compartment.
2. Check for continuity between terminals 1 and 3, **Fig. 36.** If continuity exists, replace relay.
3. Check for continuity between terminals 2 and 4. If no continuity exists, replace relay.
4. Supply battery voltage to terminals 2 and 4. Check for continuity between terminals 1 and 3. If no continuity exists, replace relay.

## ELECTRIC FAN MOTOR

Disconnect wire connector from fan motor terminal, then connect a 14 gauge jumper wire from battery to fan motor terminal. If fan motor does not operate properly, replace fan motor.

## ELECTRIC FAN MOTOR CIRCUIT TEST

### Except Laser/Talon, Monaco/Premier, Stealth

1. Run engine to normal operating temperature.
2. Check wiring connector in C25, C9 and C26 for proper engagement.
3. Connect diagnostic read out tool DRB II to diagnostic connector. Check for fault codes.
4. If fault code 88,12,35,55 is detected, proceed to step 5.
5. With ignition switch in Run position, test for battery voltage at fan relay single pin connector. If battery voltage is detected, proceed to step 7.
6. If voltage reads at zero to one volt, proceed to step 7.
7. With ignition switch in Off position, disconnect the 60-way connector from engine controller and return ignition switch to Run position. Test for battery voltage at terminal 31 of 60-way connector, **Fig. 37.** If battery voltage exists and female terminal is not damaged, replace engine controller. If no battery voltage exists, repair open or short in circuit C27.
8. With ignition switch in Off position, disconnect 60-way connector from engine controller and return ignition switch to Run position. Test for battery voltage at single pin connector on fan relay. If battery voltage exists, replace engine controller. If voltage is zero to one volt proceed to step 9.
9. With ignition switch in Run position, test for battery voltage at wire C27 in 3-way connector of fan relay. If battery voltage exists, replace fan relay. If voltage is zero to one, repair open or short in circuit C27.
10. Turn ignition switch Off, connect 60-way connector and test system.

### 1989–90 Monaco/Premier

1. Place ignition switch in Run position.
2. Connect a jumper wire between coolant temperature switch terminals A and B.
3. If cooling fan operates, replace cooling fan temperature switch.
4. If cooling fan does not operate, check for voltage at cooling fan relay connector terminal 5.
5. If no battery voltage exists, repair open between terminal 5 and ignition switch.
6. If battery voltage exists, test for voltage at fan relay connector terminal 4.
7. If no voltage exists, repair open between terminal 4 and fuse link G.
8. If voltage exists, check for voltage at fan relay connector terminal 2.
9. If voltage exists, repair open to ground.
10. If no voltage exists, check for voltage at cooling fan condenser terminal 1.
11. If no voltage exists, replace cooling fan relay.
12. If voltage exists, inspect connections at cooling fan motor for clean tight fix.
13. If connections are clean and tight, replace cooling fan.
14. If connections are not clean and tight, clean end reconnect connectors.

### 1991 Monaco/Premier

1. Run engine to normal operating temperature.
2. If fans do not come on, shutoff engine and with ignition in Run position, check for battery voltage at fan connectors.
3. If battery voltage is present and one or both fans do not operate, replace defective fan motor(s).
4. If battery voltage is not present, repair open or short in electrical wiring.

### Laser/Talon

1. Disconnect fan motor connector and connect to battery voltage, observing correct polarity.
2. If fan does not run normally, replace fan motor assembly.

3. If fan is noticeably overheated the system voltage may be too high. Check charging system.

**Stealth**

1. Disconnect fan motor connector and connect to battery voltage, observing correct polarity, to terminals 2 and 5, **Fig. 35.**
2. If fan does not run normally, replace fan motor assembly.
3. If fan is noticeably overheated the system voltage may be too high. Check charging system.

## SYSTEM SERVICE

### Fan Motor, Replace

1. Disconnect battery negative cable, then disconnect fan motor electrical connector.
2. Remove fan motor, fan and fan shroud or support as an assembly from radiator support.
3. To remove fan blade from motor, support motor and shaft assembly on workbench, then remove fan blade retaining clip. Use caution to prevent bending of motor shaft. **Do not allow fan blades to become bent or damaged in any way.**
4. Reverse procedure to install.

### Coolant Temperature Sensor, Replace

The coolant temperature sensor is located in the thermostat housing. Ensure coolant does not contact accessory drive belt or pulleys. Flush any spilled coolant with water.

1. Drain coolant from cylinder block by removing drain plug, located behind and below exhaust manifold.
2. Disconnect coolant temperature sensor electrical connector, then remove sensor.
3. Reverse procedure to install. Refill cooling system.

# COLT, COLT VISTA & SUMMIT

## DESCRIPTION

The electric cooling fan is controlled by a thermo sensor and a relay, the thermo sensor, is located in the radiator lower tank **Fig. 38.** When coolant temperature reaches approximately 185°F, the thermo sensor contacts close, providing a ground circuit to the fan relay, which provides voltage to the fan motor.

When coolant temperature drops to approximately 178°F, the thermo sensor contacts open, opening the fan relay and shutting off the fan.

## COMPONENT TESTING

Refer to **Figs. 39 through 42,** for coolant fan relay wiring diagrams.

### THERMO SENSOR

1. Remove thermo sensor from radiator.
2. Submerge sensor end of thermo sensor in water as shown in **Fig. 43.**
3. Connect ohmmeter across thermo sensor terminal and casing, then heat water.
4. When water temperature reaches approximately 185°F, the thermo sensor contacts should close and continuity should exist between sensor terminal and casing.
5. Allow water to cool with thermo sensor still submerged. When water temperature drops to approximately 178°F, the thermo sensor contacts should open and continuity should not exist between sensor terminal and casing.

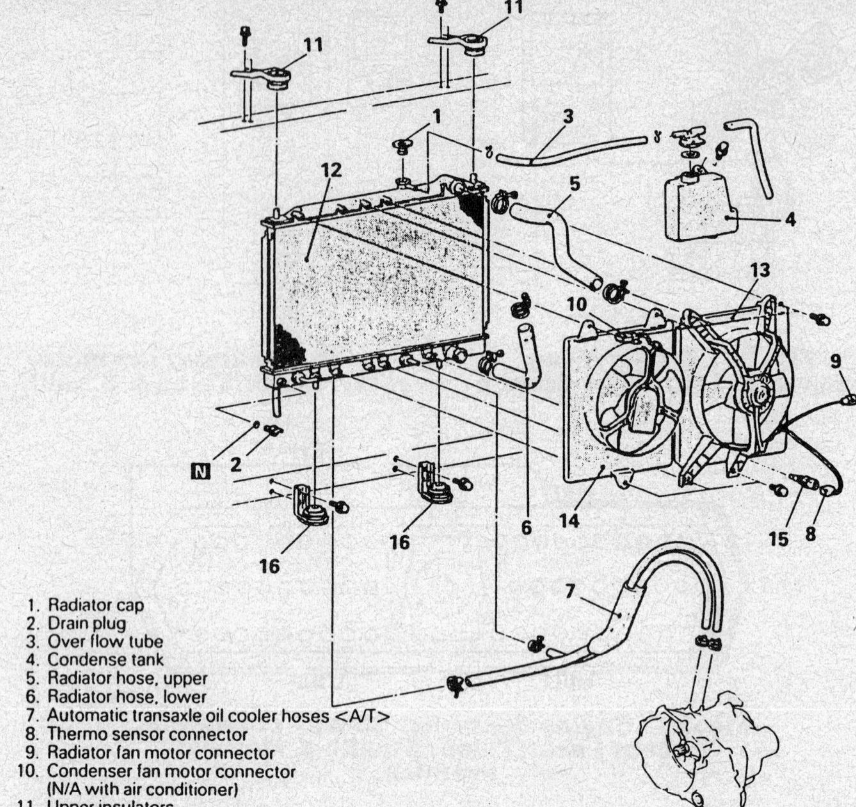


**Fig. 38 Electric cooling fan. Colt, Colt Vista & Summit**

### RELAY TESTING

**On Colt models,** the fan relay is located in the relay box which is located in engine compartment. **On Colt Vista models,** the relay box is located on the right front wheel house.

#### Colt & Eagle Summit

1. Using a suitable ohmmeter, check continuity between relay terminals, when battery voltage is supplied to terminal No. 2 and terminal No. 5 is grounded, **Fig. 44.**
2. With relay de-energized, continuity should exist between terminals No. 1 and No. 3 and between terminals No. 2 and No. 5.
3. With relay energized, continuity should exist between terminals No. 3 and No. 6.
4. If relay performance is not satisfactory, replace as necessary.

#### Colt Vista

1. Remove relay from from relay box, Connect battery power source to terminal No. 2. Using a suitable ohmmeter, check continuity between terminals with terminal No. 4 grounded. Continuity should exist between terminals No. 1 and No. 3, **Fig. 45.**
2. Disconnect power source. Continuity should exist between terminals 2 and 4. There should be no continuity between terminals 1 and 3.
3. If relay performance is not satisfactory, replace as necessary.

## SYSTEM SERVICE

### Fan Motor, Replace

1. Disconnect battery ground cable.
2. Disconnect fan motor electrical connector and thermo sensor electrical connectors.
3. Disconnect condenser fan motor electrical connector, if equipped.
4. Remove upper radiator hose, if equipped with air conditioning.

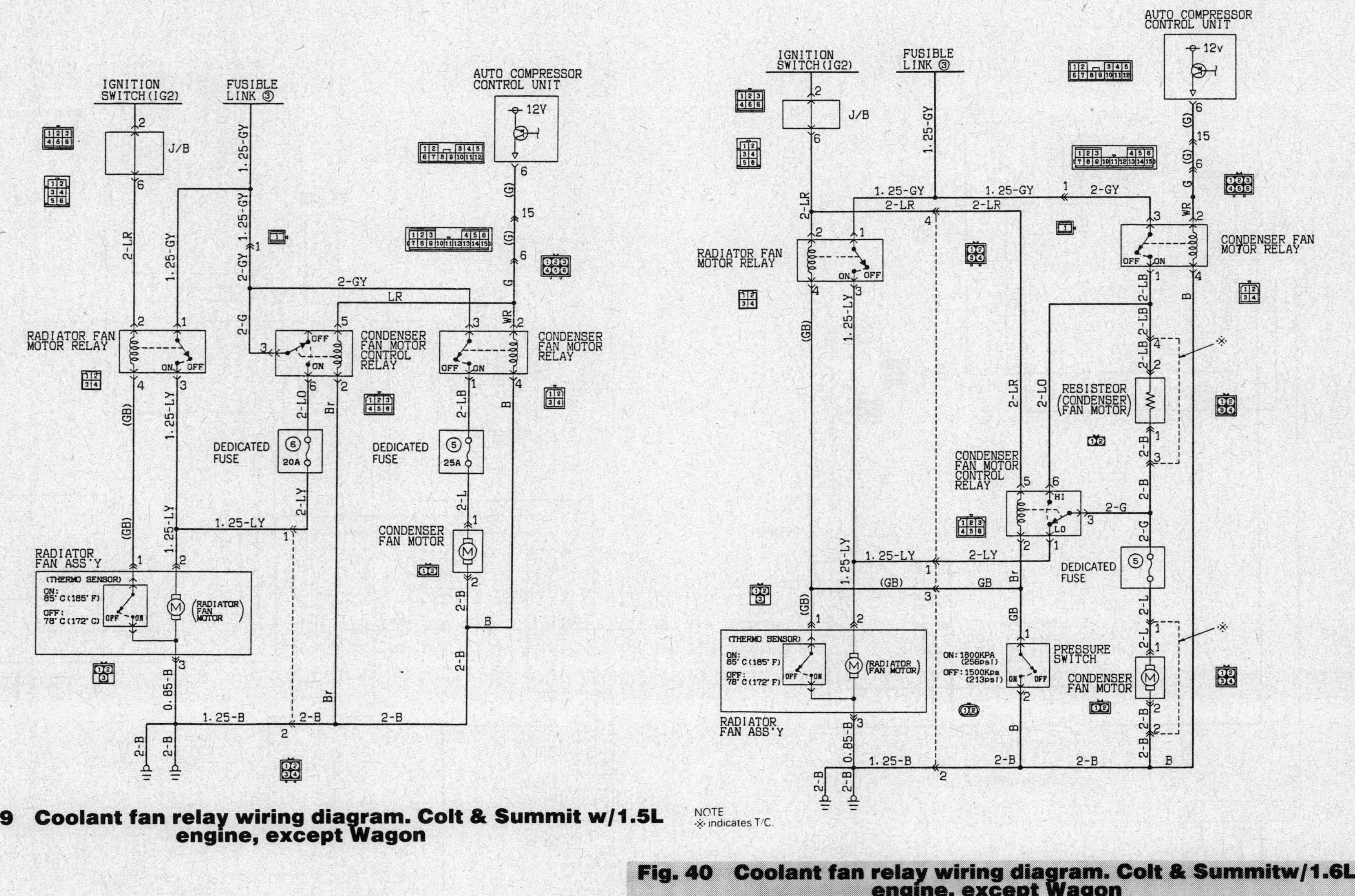


Fig. 39 Coolant fan relay wiring diagram. Colt & Summit w/1.5L engine, except Wagon

Fig. 40 Coolant fan relay wiring diagram. Colt & Summitw/1.6L engine, except Wagon

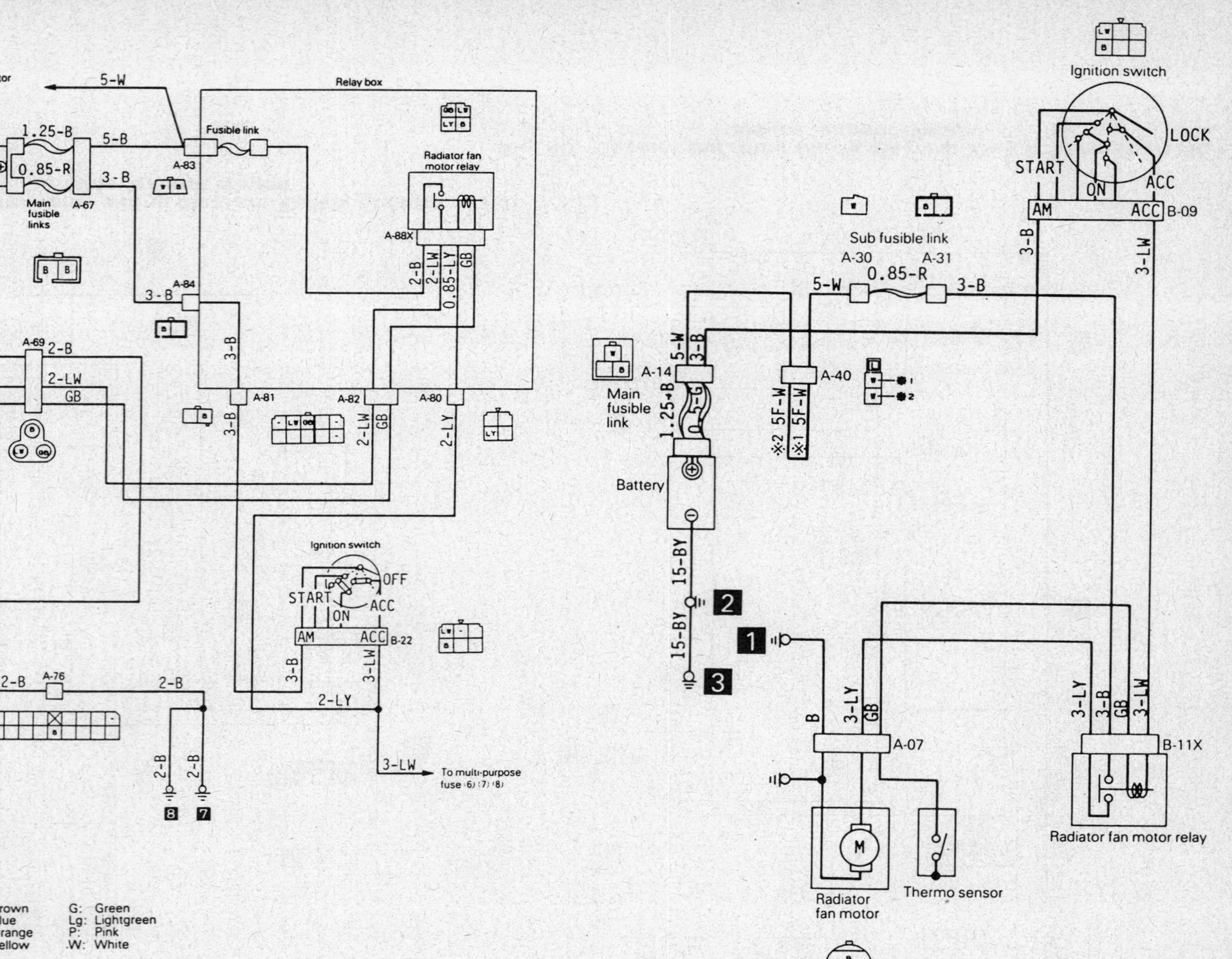


**Fig. 41 Coolant fan relay wiring diagram. Colt Vista**

**Fig. 42 Coolant fan relay wiring diagram. Colt Wagon**

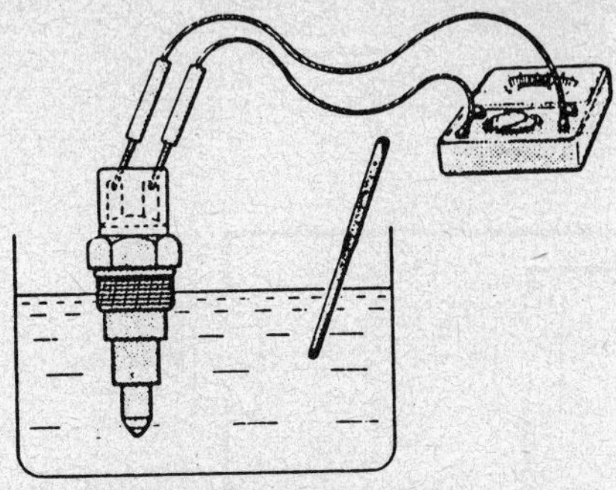

Fig. 43 Testing thermo sensor. Colt, Colt Vista & Summit

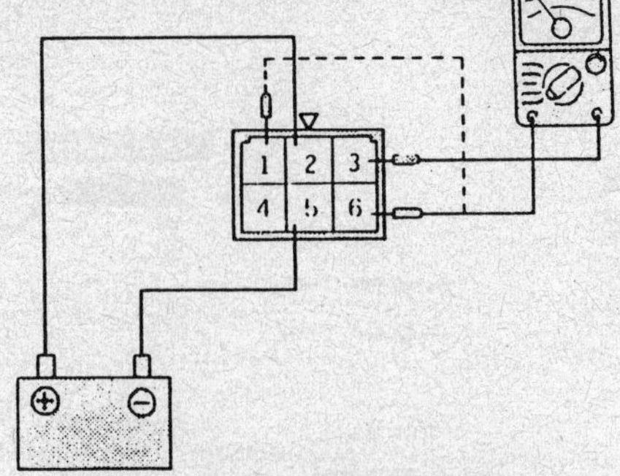

Fig. 44 Testing relay terminal. Colt & Summit

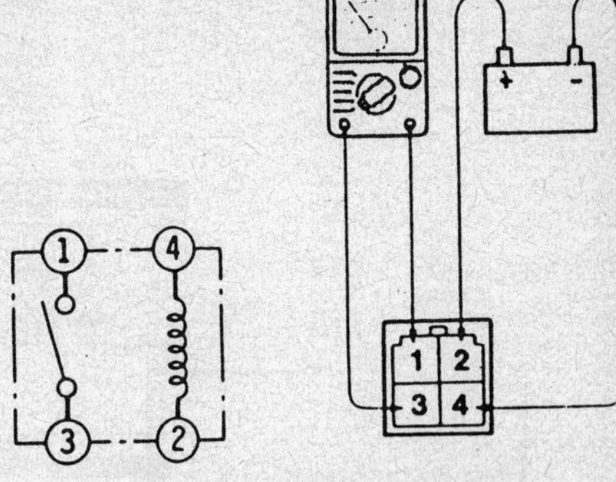

Fig. 45 Testing relay terminal. Colt Vista

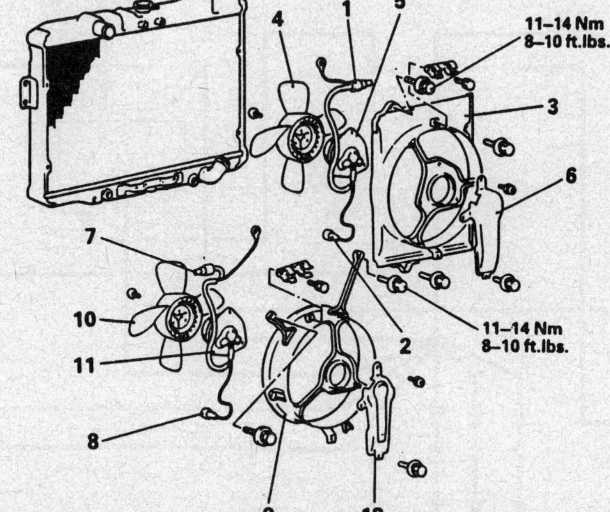


1. Fan motor connection
2. Connector cap
3. Shroud
4. Fan
5. Motor No. 1
6. Air duct

7. Fan motor connection
8. Connector cap
9. Shroud
10. Fan
11. Motor No. 2
12. Air duct

Fig. 46 Electric engine cooling fan. Conquest

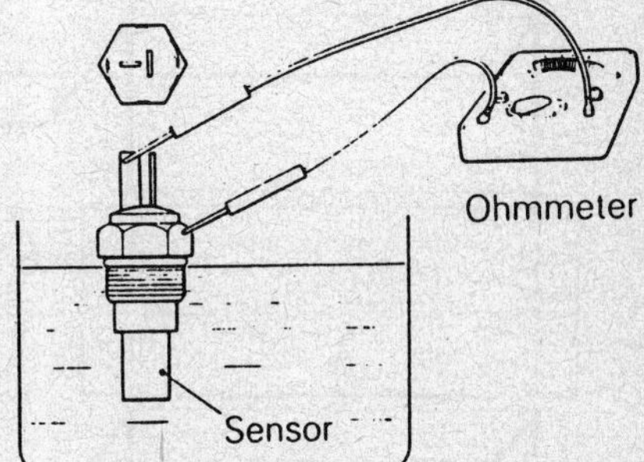


Fig. 47 Testing thermo sensor. Conquest

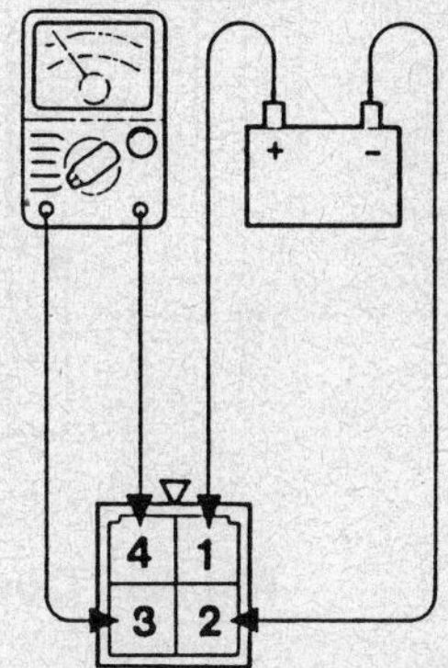

Fig. 48 Testing relay terminal. Conquest

5. Remove fan motor retaining bolts, then the fan motor assembly.
6. Reverse procedure to install.

### Thermo Sensor, Replace

1. Disconnect battery ground cable.
2. Drain coolant from radiator into suitable container.
3. Remove thermo sensor wiring from sensor located in radiator lower tank.
4. Remove sensor from radiator.
5. Reverse procedure to install. **Torque** sensor to 7-14 ft. lbs.

# CONQUEST

## DESCRIPTION

The electric cooling fans are controlled by two thermo sensors and two relays, **Fig. 46.** Both sensors are located in the radiator lower tank. Thermo sensor No. 1 operates when coolant temperature reaches approximately 185°F, causing the thermo sensor contacts to close providing a ground circuit to the fan relay, which provides voltage to fan motor No. 1. Thermo sensor No. 2 operates in the same manner as sensor No. 1, but does not activate fan motor No. 2 until coolant temperature reaches 212°F.

## COMPONENT TESTING

Refer to **Figure 24A** for coolant fan relay wiring diagrams.

### Thermo sensor

1. Remove thermo sensor from radiator.
2. Submerge sensor end of thermo sensor in water as shown in **Fig. 47.**
3. Connect ohmmeter across thermo sensor terminal and casing, then heat water.
4. **On thermo sensor No. 1,** when water temperature reaches approximately 185°F, the thermo sensor contacts should close and continuity should exist between sensor terminal and casing.
5. **On thermo sensor No. 2,** when water temperature reaches approximately 212°F, the thermo sensor contacts should close and continuity should exist between sensor terminal and casing.

### Relay Testing

The fan motor relays are located on the right front wheel house.

1. With relay disconnected, use suitable ohmmeter to check continuity between terminals No. 1 and No. 2, **Fig. 48.** Continuity should exist. Check for continuity between terminals No. 3 and No. 4. Continuity should not exist.
2. Apply battery voltage to terminal No. 1 and ground terminal No. 2, then check for continuity between terminals No. 3 and No. 4. Continuity should exist.
3. If relay does not perform as outlined above, replace.

## SYSTEM SERVICE

### Thermo Sensor, Replace

1. Disconnect battery ground cable.
2. Drain coolant from radiator into suitable container.
3. Disconnect thermo sensor wiring from sensor located in radiator lower tank.

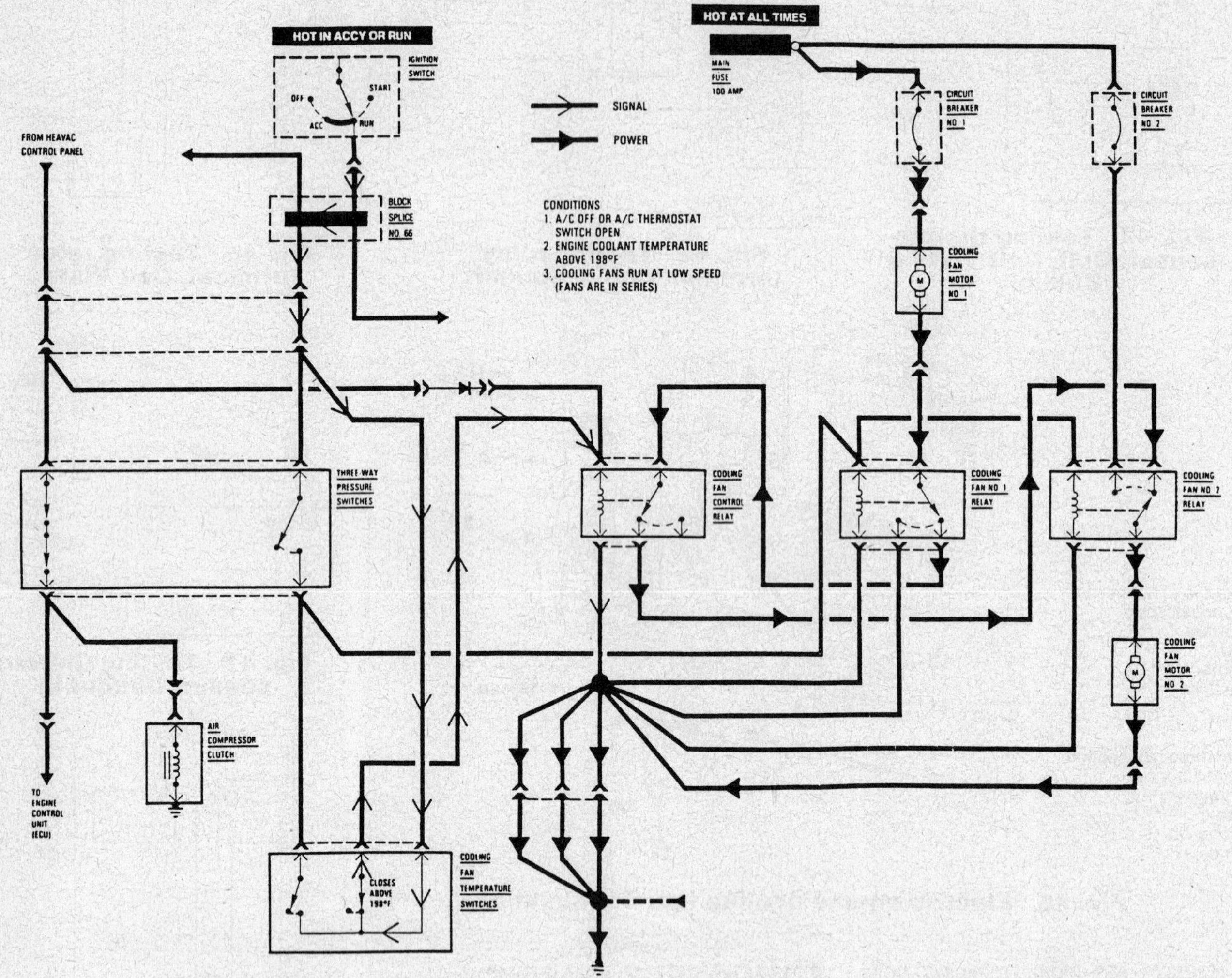


**Fig.49 Coolant fan relay wiring diagram. 1989 Medallion w/air conditioning**

4. Remove sensor from radiator.
5. Reverse procedure to install. **Torque** sensor to 10-12 ft. lbs.

### Fan Motor, Replace

1. Disconnect battery ground cable.
2. Disconnect thermo sensor and fan motor electrical connectors.
3. Remove air duct.
4. Remove shroud retaining bolts, then the radiator fan motor from radiator.
5. Separate fan from fan motor.
6. Reverse procedure to install.

# EAGLE MEDALLION

## DESCRIPTION

Models equipped with air conditioning and/or automatic transaxle are equipped with dual coolant thermo switch/electric cooling fan assemblies.

The radiator fan switch is located within the radiator assembly. The switch allows the cooling fans to operate at high or low speeds depending on coolant temperature.

When coolant temperature is above approximately 198°F, but below 212°F, the radiator fan switch low speed contacts close. This energizes a low speed relay which supplies battery voltage (in series) to each fan for low speed operation. In series, the fans receive approximately one half battery voltage.

When coolant temperature rises above approximately 212°F, the radiator fan high speed switch contacts close. This energizes the two high speed relays, which supply battery voltage (in parallel) to each fan for high speed operation. In parallel, the fans receive full battery voltage.

**On models equipped with air conditioning,** the cooling fan operates continuously while the air conditioning system is being used. Fan speed is varied according to coolant temperature during operation. However, a pressure switch in the air conditioning system will immediately switch the fans to high speed operation, if system pressure exceeds 319 psi.

## SYSTEM SERVICE

Refer to **Figs. 49 and 50,** for coolant fan relay wiring diagrams.

### Electric Cooling Fan, Replace

**Do not loosen cooling system pressure caps, hoses or bleed screws while coolant is hot and system is under pressure. Allow system to cool before servicing the system.**

1. Disconnect battery ground cable.
2. Remove hood, if necessary.
3. Remove grille attaching screws, then the grille.
4. Remove radiator support and face panel attaching screws, then the support and panel.

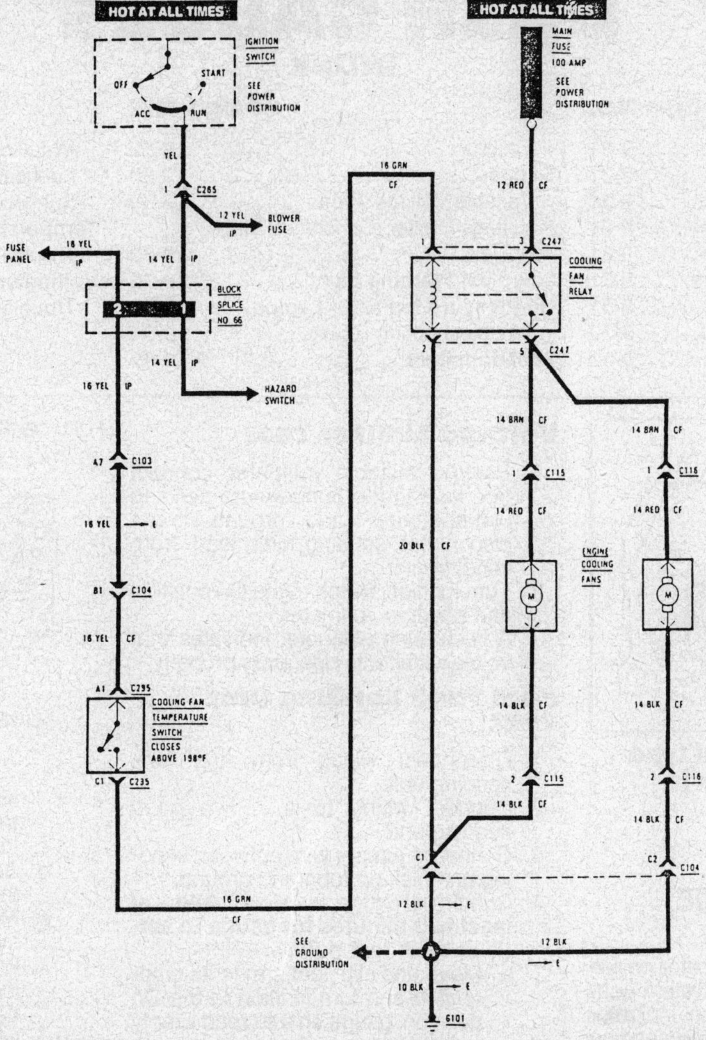


**Fig. 50 Coolant fan relay wiring diagram. 1989 Medallion less A/C**

5. Remove mount attaching screws, then disconnect lower radiator hose. Drain coolant into a suitable container.
6. Remove upper and lower radiator hoses.
7. Disconnect electrical connectors from electric cooling fan and cooling fan thermo switch.
8. Remove fan assembly attaching bolts, then the fan assembly.
9. Reverse procedure to install.

# DASH GAUGES

## INDEX



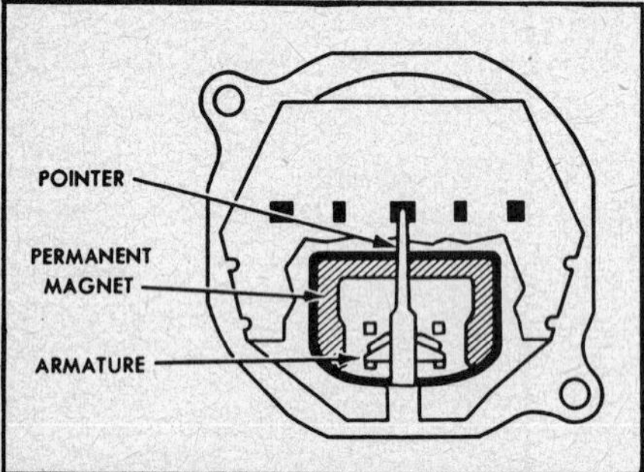


**Fig. 1 Conventional type ammeter (typical)**

# GAUGES

## VOLTAGE LIMITER (CONSTANT VOLTAGE) TYPE

The voltage limiter type indicator gauge is a bi-metal resistance type system consisting of a voltage limiter, an indicator gauge, and a variable resistance sending unit. Current to the system is applied to the gauge terminals by the voltage limiter, which maintains an average pulsating value of 5 volts.

The indicator gauge consists of a pointer which is attached to a wire-wound bi-metal strip. Current passing through the coil heats the bi-metal strip, causing the pointer to move. As more current passes through the coil, heat increases, moving the pointer farther.

The circuit is completed through a sending unit which contains a variable resistor. When resistance is high, less current is allowed to pass through the gauge, and the pointer moves very little. As resistance decreases due to changing conditions in system being monitored, current increases through the gauge coil, causing pointer to move farther.

### DIAGNOSIS & TESTING

Gauge failures are often caused by defective wiring or grounds. The first step in locating trouble should be a thorough inspection of all wiring, terminals and printed circuits. If wiring is secured by clamps, check to see whether the insulation has been severed thereby grounding the wire. In the case of a fuel gauge installation, rust may cause failure by corrosion at the ground connection of the tank unit.

#### Voltage Limiter Test

1. Using a suitable voltmeter, connect one lead to the temperature sending unit and other lead to ground. Do not disconnect sending unit lead from sending unit.
2. Turn ignition switch to the On position and observe voltmeter.
3. A fluctuating voltmeter indicates that voltage limiter is operating properly.

#### Fuel Tank Sending Unit Test

1. Disconnect wiring from fuel tank sending unit.
2. Connect wiring to a known good sending unit.
3. Connect a jumper wire between sending unit pick up tube and ground.
4. Check fuel gauge as follows: **Allow at least two minutes for gauge to settle at each test point.**
   a. Move and clip float arm to its empty stop and turn ignition to the On position, gauge should read Empty or below.
   b. Move and clip float arm to the Full position, gauge should read Full or above.
5. If gauge does not meet specifications, check the following items for possible malfunction:
   a. Wiring and connections between gauge sending unit and multiple connector behind left kick panel.
   b. Wiring and connections between multiple connector and printed circuit board terminals.
   c. Circuit continuity between printed circuit board terminals and gauge terminals. **If the above items are satisfactory, the gauge is defective and must be replaced.**
6. If fuel gauge meets specifications check original fuel tank sending unit as follows:
   a. Remove fuel tank sending unit from fuel tank and connect a jumper wire between sending unit pick up tube and ground.
7. Repeat step 4.
8. If fuel gauge is now within specifications, check the following as possible cause:
   a. Ground wire from sending unit to left side cowl for continuity.
   b. Sending unit deformed. Ensure float arm moves freely and pick up tube is not bent.
   c. Inspect float.
   d. Sending unit improperly installed. Install correctly.
   e. Mounting flange on fuel tank for sending unit deformed.
   f. Fuel tank bottom deformed causing improper positioning of pick-up tube.

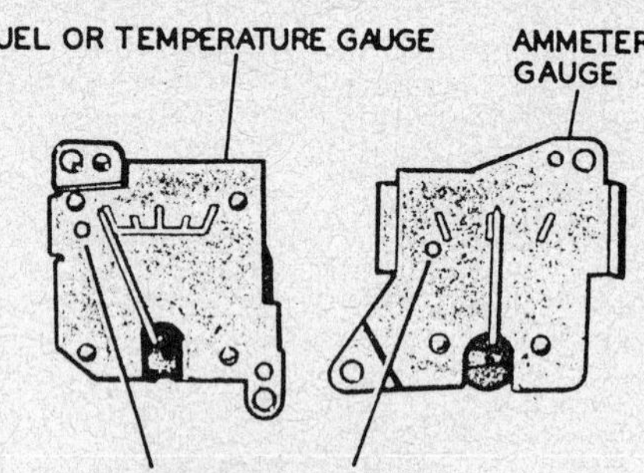


**Fig. 2 Gauge**

#### Oil & Temperature Sending Units

1. Test dash gauge and voltage regulator as outlined above.
2. If system is satisfactory, start engine and allow it to reach operating temperature.
3. If no reading is indicated on the gauge, check the sending unit to gauge wire by removing the wire from the sending unit and momentarily ground this wire to a clean, unpainted portion of the engine.
4. If the gauge still does not indicate, wire is defective. Repair or replace wire.
5. If grounding the new or repaired wire causes the dash gauge to indicate, the sending unit is faulty.

## VARIABLE VOLTAGE TYPE

The variable voltage type dash gauge consists of two magnetic coils to which battery voltage is applied. The coils act on the gauge pointer and pull in opposite directions. One coil is grounded directly to the chassis, while the other coil is grounded through a variable resistor within the sending unit. Resistance through the sending unit determines current flow through its coil, and therefore pointer position.

When resistance is high in the sending unit, less current is allowed to flow through its coil, causing the gauge pointer to move toward the directly grounded coil. When resistance in the sending unit decreases, more current is allowed to pass through its coil, increasing the magnetic field. The gauge pointer is then attracted toward the coil which is grounded through the sending unit.

## AMMETERS

The ammeter is used to indicate current flow into and out of the battery. When electrical accessories in the vehicle draw more current than the alternator can supply, current flows from the battery and the ammeter indicates a discharge (-) condition. When electrical loads of the vehicle are less than alternator output, current is available to charge the battery, and the ammeter indicates a charge (+) condition. If battery is fully charged, the voltage regulator reduces alternator output to meet only immediate vehicle electrical loads. When this happens, the ammeter will read zero.

## VARIABLE VOLTAGE TYPE

A conventional ammeter is connected between the battery and alternator in order to indicate current flow. This type ammeter, **Fig. 1,** consists of a frame to which a permanent magnet is attached. The frame also supports an armature and pointer assembly. Current in this system flows from the alternator through the ammeter, then to the battery or from the battery through the ammeter into the vehicle electrical system, depending on vehicle operating conditions.

When current flow is not present through the ammeter, the magnet holds the pointer armature so the pointer stands centered in the dial. When current passes in either direction through the ammeter, the resulting magnetic field attracts the armature away from the effect of the permanent magnet, giving a reading proportional to the strength of the current flowing.

### Troubleshooting

When the ammeter fails to register correctly, the trouble may be in the alternator, battery, or the wiring from the ammeter to the alternator and battery.

Check connections at the ammeter, ignition switch, battery and alternator. Repair as necessary.

All wires with chafed, burned or broken insulation should be repaired or replaced. After repairs have been made, and all connections are tightened, connect the battery cable and turn ignition switch to the On position. The needle should point slightly to the discharge (-) side.

Start engine and raise engine speed. The ammeter needle should then move to the charge side.

If the ammeter fails to operate correctly, replace the ammeter.

## SHUNT TYPE

The shunt type ammeter is a specially calibrated voltmeter. It's purpose is to read voltage drop across a resistance wire (shunt) between the battery and condition is indicated for an extended period, the battery and charging system should be checked.alternator. The shunt is located in the vehicle wiring or within the ammeter.

When voltage is higher at the alternator end of the shunt, the meter indicates a charge (+) condition. When voltage is higher at the battery end of the shunt, the meter indicates a discharge (−) condition. When voltage is equal at both ends of the shunt, the meter reads zero.

### Troubleshooting

Ammeter accuracy can be determined by comparing reading with an ammeter of known accuracy.

1. With engine stopped and ignition switch in "On" position, turn on headlamps and heater fan. Meter should indicate a discharge (-) condition.
2. If ammeter pointer does not move, check ammeter terminals for proper connection and open circuit in wiring harness. If connections and wiring harness are satisfactory, ammeter is defective.
3. If ammeter indicates a charge (+) condition, wiring harness connections are reversed at ammeter.

## VOLTMETER

The voltmeter gauge measures electrical flow from the battery to indicate battery output tolerances. The voltmeter reading can range from 13.5-14.0 volts under normal operating conditions. If an undercharge or overcharge

## TROUBLESHOOTING

To check voltmeter turn headlights on, then turn key to the On position. Pointer should move to 12.5 volts. If needle movement is not present, check connections from battery to circuit breaker. If connections are tight and meter shows no movement, check wire continuity. If continuity is satisfactory, meter is inoperative and must be replaced.

## ELECTRICAL TEMPERATURE GAUGES

This system consists of a sending unit, located on the cylinder head, electrical temperature gauge and an instrument voltage regulator. As engine temperature increases or decreases, resistance of the sending unit changes, in turn controlling current flow to the gauge. When engine temperature is low, the resistance of the sending unit is high, restricting current flow to the gauge, in turn indicating low engine temperature. As engine temperature increases, resistance of the sending unit decreases, permitting an increased current flow to the gauge, resulting in an increased temperature reading.

## TROUBLESHOOTING

Disconnect terminal from temperature sending unit on engine, then connect test lead of tester C-3826A to terminal and second test lead to ground. Place pointer of gauge tester on E position and turn ignition switch to the On position. The temperature gauge should show C plus or minus 1/8 inch.

Place pointer of tester on the 1/2 position, the gauge should advance to the operating range left of 1/2 position of the dial. Place pointer of the tester in the F position, gauge should advance to H position of the dial. If gauge responds to test correctly, but does not operate when terminal is attached to sending unit, replace gauge.

## ELECTRICAL OIL PRESSURE GAUGES

The oil pressure indicating system consists a instrument voltage regulator, electrical oil pressure gauge and a sending unit which are connected in series. The sending unit consists of a diaphragm, contact and a variable resistor. As oil pressure increases or decreases, the diaphragm actuates the contact on the variable resistor, in turn controlling current flow to the gauge. When oil pressure is low, the resistance of the variable resistor is high, restricting current flow to the gauge, in turn indicating low oil pressure. As oil pressure increases, the resistance of the variable resistor is lowered, increasing current flow to the gauge, resulting in an increased gauge reading.

## TROUBLESHOOTING

Disconnect oil pressure gauge electrical connector from the sending unit, then connect a 12 volt test lamp between the gauge connector and ground, then turn ignition to the On position. If test lamp flashes, the instrument voltage regulator is functioning properly and the gauge circuit is not broken. If the test lamp remains lit, the instrument voltage regulator is defective and must be replaced. If the test lamp does not light, check the instrument voltage regulator for proper ground or an open circuit. Also, check for an open in the instrument voltage regulator to oil pressure gauge wire or in the gauge. **If test lamp flashes and gauge is not accurate, gauge may be out of calibration. Replace gauge.**

## OIL PRESSURE INDICATOR LAMP

A warning lamp on the instrument panel is used in place of the conventional dash indicating gauge to warn the driver when oil pressure is low. The warning lamp is wired in series with the ignition switch and the oil sending unit.

The oil pressure switch contains a diaphragm and contacts. When the ignition switch is turned to the On position, the warning lamp circuit is energized and the circuit is completed through the closed contacts in the pressure switch. When the engine is started, build-up of oil pressure compresses the diaphragm, opening the contacts, thereby breaking the circuit.

## TROUBLESHOOTING

When the ignition is turned on, the oil

pressure warning lamp should light. If the lamp does not light, disconnect the sending unit electrical connector from the engine unit and ground wire to the frame or cylinder block. If the warning lamp still does not light with the ignition switch on, replace the bulb.

If the warning lamp lights when the wire is grounded, check the unit for looseness or improper grounding. If the unit is found to be tight and properly grounded, replace unit.

If the warning lamp remains lit under normal conditions, replace the unit before proceeding further to determine the cause for a low pressure indication.

Under normal conditions, the warning lamp will sometimes light or flicker when the engine is idling. However, the lamp should go out when engine idle is raised.

# TEMPERATURE INDICATOR LAMP

If the engine cooling system is not functioning properly, causing coolant temperature to exceed a predetermined value, the coolant temperature warning lamp will lite.

## TROUBLESHOOTING

If the lamp is not lit when engine is being cranked, check for a defective bulb, open in the light circuit, or a defective ignition switch.

If the lamp is lit when the engine is running, check for overheated cooling system, defective temperature switch, or wiring between lamp and switch for short to ground.

**As a test circuit to check the temperature indicator lamp is functioning properly, a wire which is connected to the ground terminal of the ignition switch is tapped into indicator lamp circuit. When the ignition is in the Start (engine cranking) position, the ground terminal is grounded inside the switch and the lamp will lite. When the engine is started and the ignition switch is in the On position, the test circuit is opened and the temperature lamp is then controlled by the temperature switch.**

# GAUGE ALERT SYSTEM

The fuel, temperature and ammeter gauges are equipped with a Light Emitting Diode (LED) mounted in each of the gauge dials, **Fig. 2.** This diode will illuminate and alert the driver that the system is malfunctioning. The electronic sensor circuit is mounted on the gauge housing. The printed circuit board is permanently attached and is not serviceable. If the LED is malfunctioning, the gauge and the printed circuit board must be replaced as an assembly.

The oil pressure warning switch, mounted on the engine, is controlled by engine oil pressure.

When engine oil pressure is high (normal operating condition) the switch is held in the Off position allowing no current to flow to the oil pressure warning lamp on the instrument panel.

When engine oil pressure is low the switch is in the On position allowing current to flow to the oil pressure warning lamp on the instrument panel causing th instrument panel to be illuminated. When the switch is in the Off position it completes the circuit for the electric choke heater.

## DESCRIPTION

### Fuel Gauge

When the gauge indicator shows approximately 1/8 tank of fuel remaining, the LED will light alerting the driver to a low fuel situation.

### Temperature Gauge

When gauge indicator shows engine temperature approximately 240 to 260° the LED will light alerting the driver to an overheat condition.

### Ammeter Gauge

This LED operates independently of the gauge indicator and monitors system voltage. The LED will alert the driver of three charging system potential malfunctions.

1. A discharging condition, caused by excessive electrical demand on charging system (engine at idle RPM).
2. A weak or defective battery with ignition switch in the On position (before the ignition switch is moved to the Start position).
3. A weak or defective battery with minimum demand on charging system, while vehicle is being used in stop and go driving (intermittent LED illumination occurring).

## TESTING

### Fuel & Temperature LED

Use tester C-3826 for diagnosing systems.

### Ammeter LED

**Proceed with the following test only if the battery and charging system are functioning properly.**

Turn ignition switch to the On position and turn on headlights, windshield wipers and stoplights. This will cause excessive demand on charging system activating the LED immediately or within approximately one minute. If the LED does not light, there is a malfunction in the system. If LED lights, run engine at approximately 2000 RPM, LED should stop emitting light. If the LED continues to emit light there is a malfunction in the system. **In all cases of system malfunctions, the complete gauge must be replaced.**

# SPEEDOMETERS

The following material covers only that service on speedometers which can be performed by the average service man. Repairs on the units themselves are not included as they require special tools and extreme care when making repairs and adjustments and only an experienced speedometer mechanic should attempt such servicing.

The speedometer has two main parts: the indicator head and the speedometer drive cable. When the speedometer fails to indicate speed or mileage, the cable or housing is probably broken.

## SPEEDOMETER CABLE

Most cables are broken due to lack of lubrication or a sharp bend or kink in the housing.

A cable might break because the speedometer head mechanism binds. If such is the case, the speedometer head should be repaired or replaced before a new cable or housing is installed.

A jumpy or noisy pointer condition is due to a dry or kinked speedometer cable. The kinked cable rubs on the housing and winds up, slowing down the pointer. The cable then unwinds and the pointer jumps.

To check for kinks, remove the cable, lay it on a flat surface and twist one end with the fingers. If it turns over smoothly the cable is not kinked. But if part of the cable flops over as it is twisted, the cable is kinked and should be replaced.

## LUBRICATION

The speedometer cable should be lubricated with special cable lubricant every 10,000 miles.

Fill the ferrule on the upper end of the housing with the cable lubricant. Insert the cable in the housing, starting at the upper end. Turn the cable around carefully while feeding it into the housing. Repeat filling the ferrule except for the last six inches of cable. Too much lubricant at this point may cause the lubricant to work into the indicating hand.

## INSTALLING CABLE

During installation, if the cable sticks when inserted in the housing and will not go through, the housing is damaged inside or kinked. Be sure to check the housing from one end to the other. Straighten any sharp bends by relocating clamps or elbows. Replace housing if it is badly kinked or broken. Position the cable and housing so that they lead into the head as straight as possible.

Check the new cable for kinks before installing it. Use wide, sweeping, gradual curves when the cable comes out of the transmission and connects to the head so the cable will not be damaged during its installation.

If inspection indicates that the cable and housing are in good condition, yet pointer action is erratic, check the speedometer head for possible binding.

The speedometer drive pinion should also be checked. If the pinion is dry or its teeth are stripped, the speedometer may not register properly.

The transmission mainshaft nut must be tight or the speedometer drive gear may slip on the mainshaft and cause slow speed readings.

# LOW FUEL WARNING LIGHT

When the ignition is turned to the On position current flows to the low-fuel warning sensor. If the fuel level falls below the preset level, the fuel level sensor, which is normally submerged in fuel, is exposed to air and resistance to the sensor decreases to a low level, in turn causing the warning light to go on.

# STARTER MOTORS & SWITCHES

## TABLE OF CONTENTS



# General Information

## INDEX



## STARTER TROUBLE CHECK-OUT

When trouble develops in the starting motor circuit, and the starter cranks the engine slowly or not at all, several preliminary checks can be made to determine whether the trouble lies in the battery, in the starter, in the wiring between them, or elsewhere. Many conditions besides defects in the starter itself can result in poor cranking performance.

To make a quick check of the starter system, turn on the headlights. They should burn with normal brilliance. If they do not, the battery may be run down.

If the battery is in a charged condition so that lights burn brightly, operate the starting motor. Any one of three things will happen to the lights: they will go out, they will dim considerably or they will stay bright without any cranking action taking place.

### IF LAMP GOES OUT

If the lamps go out as the starter switch is closed, it indicates that there is a poor connection between the battery and starting motor. This poor connection will most often be found at the battery terminals. Correction is made by removing the cable clamps from the terminals, cleaning the terminals and clamps, replacing the clamps and tightening them securely. A coating of corrosion inhibitor (petroleum jelly will do) may be applied to the clamps and terminals to retard the formation of corrosion.

### IF LAMP DIMS

If the lamps dim considerably as the starter switch is closed and the starter operates slowly or not at all, the battery may be run down, or there may be some mechanical condition in the engine or starting motor that is throwing a heavy burden on the starting motor. This imposes a high discharge rate on the battery which causes noticeable dimming of the lamps.

Check the battery state of charge. If it is charged, the trouble probably lies in either the engine or starting motor itself. In the engine, tight bearings or pistons or heavy oil place an added burden on the starting motor. Low temperatures also hamper starting motor performance since it thickens engine oil and makes the engine considerably harder to crank and start. Also, a battery is less efficient at low temperatures.

In the starting motor, a bent armature, loose pole shoe screws or worn bearings, any of which may allow the armature to drag, will reduce cranking performance and increase current draw.

In addition, more serious internal damage is sometimes found. Thrown armature windings or commutator bars, which sometimes occur on overrunning clutch drive starting motors, are usually caused by excessive overrunning after starting. This is the result of such conditions as the driver keeping the starting switch closed too long after the engine has started, the driver opening the throttle too wide in starting, or improper carburetor fast idle adjustment. Any of these subject the overrunning clutch to extra strain so it tends to seize, spinning the armature at high speed with resulting armature damage.

Another cause may be engine backfire during cranking which may result, among other things, from ignition timing being too far advanced.

To avoid such failures, the driver should pause a few seconds after a false start to make sure the engine has come completely to rest before another start is attempted. In addition, the ignition timing should be checked if engine backfiring has caused the trouble.

### LAMP STAYS BRIGHT, NO CRANKING ACTION

This condition indicates an open circuit at some point, either in the starter itself, the starter switch or control circuit. The solenoid control circuit can be eliminated momentarily by placing a heavy jumper lead across the solenoid main terminals to see if the starter will operate. This connects the starter directly to the battery and, if it operates, it indicates that the control circuit is not functioning normally. The wiring and control units must be checked to locate the trouble.

If the starter does not operate with the jumper attached, it will probably have to be removed from the engine so it can be examined in detail.

## CHECKING CIRCUIT WITH VOLTMETER

Excessive resistance in the circuit between the battery and starter will reduce cranking performance. The resistance can be checked by using a voltmeter to measure voltage drop in the circuits while the starter is operated. There are three checks to be made:

1. Voltage drop between car frame and grounded battery terminal post (not cable clamp).
2. Voltage drop between car frame and starting motor field frame.
3. Voltage drop between insulated battery terminal post and starting motor terminal stud (or the battery terminal stud of the solenoid).

Each of these should show no more than one-tenth (0.1) volt drop when the starting motor is cranking the engine. Do not use the starter for more than 30 seconds at a time to avoid overheating it.

If excessive voltage drop is found in any of these circuits, make correction by disconnecting the cables, cleaning the connections carefully, and then reconnecting the cables firmly in place. A coating of petroleum jelly on the battery cables and terminal clamps will retard corrosion. **On some cars, extra long battery cables may be required due to the location of the battery and starter. This may result in somewhat higher voltage drop than the above recommended 0.1 volt. The only means of determining the normal voltage drop in such cases is to check several of these vehicles. Then when the voltage drop is well above the normal figure for all cars checked, abnormal resistance will be indicated and correction can be made as already explained.**

## SOLENOID SWITCHES

The solenoid switch on a cranking motor not only closes the circuit between the battery and the cranking motor but also shifts the drive pinion into mesh with the engine flywheel ring gear. This is done by means of a linkage between the solenoid switch plunger and the shift lever on the cranking motor.

There are two windings in the solenoid; a pull-in winding and a hold-in winding. Both windings are energized when the external control switch is closed. They produce a magnetic field which pulls the plunger in so that the drive pinion is shifted into mesh, and the main contacts in the solenoid switch are closed to connect the battery directly to the cranking motor. Closing the main switch contacts shorts out the pull-in winding since this winding is connected across the main contacts. The magnetism produced by the hold-in winding is sufficient to hold the plunger in, and shorting out the pull-in winding reduces drain on the battery. When the control switch is opened, it disconnects the hold-in winding from the battery. When the hold-in winding is disconnected from the battery, the shift lever spring withdraws the plunger from the solenoid, opening the solenoid switch contacts and at the same time withdrawing the drive pinion from mesh. Proper operation of the switch depends on maintaining a definite balance between the magnetic strength of the pull-in and hold-in windings.

This balance is established in the design by the size of the wire and the number of turns specified. An open circuit in the hold-in winding or attempts to crank with a discharged battery will cause the switch to chatter.

To disassemble the solenoid, remove nuts, washers and insulators from the switch terminal and battery terminal. Remove cover and take out the contact disk assembly.

## STARTER MOTOR SERVICE

To obtain full performance data on a starting motor or to determine the cause of abnormal operation, the starting motor should be submitted to a no-load and torque test. These tests are best performed on a starter bench tester with the starter mounted on it.

From a practical standpoint, however, a simple torque test may be made quickly with the starter in the car. Make sure the battery is fully charged and that the starter circuit wires and terminals are in good condition. Then operate the starter to see if the engine turns over normally. If it does not, the torque developed is below standard and the starter should be removed for further checking.

## STARTER DRIVE TROUBLES

Starter drive troubles are easy to diagnose and they usually cannot be confused with ordinary starter difficulties. If the starter does not turn over at all or if it drags, look for trouble in the starter or electrical supply system. Concentrate on the starter drive or ring gear if the starter is noisy, if it turns but does not engage the engine, or if the starter won't disengage after the engine is started. After the starter is removed, the trouble can usually be located quickly.

Worn or chipped ring gear or starter pinion are the usual causes of noisy operation. Before replacing either or both of these parts try to find out what caused the damage. With the Bendix type drive, incomplete engagement of the pinion with the ring gear is a common cause of tooth damage. The wrong pinion clearance on starter drives of the overrunning clutch type leads to poor meshing of the pinion and ring gear and too rapid tooth wear.

A less common cause of noise with either type of drive is a bent starter armature shaft. When this shaft is bent, the pinion gear alternately binds and then only partly meshes with the ring gear. Most manufacturers specify a maximum of .003 inch radial run-out on the armature shaft.

### WHEN CLUTCH DRIVE FAILS

The overrunning clutch type drive seldom becomes so worn that it fails to engage since it is directly activated by a fork and lever. The only thing that is likely to happen is that, once engaged, it will not turn the engine because the clutch itself is worn out. A much more frequent difficulty and one that rapidly wears ring gear and teeth is partial engagement. Proper meshing of the pinion is controlled by the end clearance between the pinion gear and the starter housing or pinion stop, if used.

On some starters, the solenoids are completely enclosed in the starter housing and the pinion clearance is not adjustable. If the clearance is not correct, the starter must be disassembled and checked for excessive wear of solenoid linkage, shift lever mechanism, or improper assembly of parts.

Failure of the overrunning clutch drive to disengage is usually caused by binding between the armature shaft and the drive. If the drive, particularly the clutch, shows signs of overheating it indicates that it is not disengaging immediately after the engine starts. If the clutch is forced to overrun too long, it overheats and turns a bluish color. For the cause of the binding, look for rust or chewing gum between the armature shaft and the drive, or for burred splines. Excess oil on the drive will lead to gumming, and inadequate air circulation in the flywheel housing will cause rust.

Overrunning clutch drives cannot be overhauled in the field, so they must be replaced. In cleaning, never soak them in a solvent because the solvent may enter the clutch and dissolve the sealed-in lubricant. Wipe them off lightly with kerosene and lubricate them sparingly with SAE 10 or 10W oil.

### WHEN BENDIX DRIVE FAILS

When a Bendix type drive doesn't engage the cause usually is one of three things: either the drive spring is broken, one of the drive spring bolts has sheared off, or the screwshaft threads won't allow the pinion to travel toward the flywheel. In the first two cases, remove the drive by unscrewing the setscrew under the last coil of the drive spring and replace the broken parts. Gummed or rusty screwshaft threads are fairly common causes of Bendix drive failure and are easily cleaned with a little kerosene or steel wool, depending on the trouble. Here again, as in the case of overrunning clutch drives, use light oil sparingly, and be sure the flywheel housing has adequate ventilation. There is usually a breather hole in the bottom of the flywheel housing which should be open.

The failure of a Bendix drive to disengage or to mesh properly is most often caused by gummed or rusty screwshaft threads. When this is not true, look for mechanical failure within the drive itself.

# Starter Motor Specifications

| Model | Engine Liter/ CID | Starter | | Free Speed Test | | | | Cranking Amp Draw Test③ |
|---|---|---|---|---|---|---|---|---|
| | | Make | Type | Power Rating | Amps① | Volts | RPM② | |
| **1989** | | | | | | | | |
| Colt | 1.5L/4-90④ | Mitsubishi | Direct Drive | .7 | 60 | 11.5 | 6500 | — |
| | 1.5L/4-90⑤ | Mitsubishi | Direct Drive | .9 | 60 | 11.5 | 6600 | — |
| | 1.6L/4-97 | Mitsubishi | Gear Reduction | 1.2 | 90 | 11 | 3000 | — |
| Colt Vista | 2.0L/4-122④ | Mitsubishi | Direct Drive | .9 | 60 | 11.5 | 6600 | — |
| | 2.0L/4-122⑤ | Mitsubishi | Gear Reduction | 1.2 | 90 | 11 | 3000 | — |
| Conquest | 2.6L/4-156 | Mitsubishi | Gear Reduction | 1.2 | 100 | 11.5 | 3000 | — |
| Eagle Medallion | 2.22L/4-135 | Paris-Rhone | Direct Drive | — | — | 9.6 | — | 160 |
| Eagle Premier | 2.5L/4-153 | Mitsubishi | Direct Drive | 1.4 | 75 | 11.5 | 2900 | 130 |
| | 3.0L/V6-181 | Mitsubishi | Gear Reduction | — | 80 | 11.2 | 2500 | 130 |
| Eagle Summit | 1.5L/4-90④ | Mitsubishi | Direct Drive | .7 | 60 | 11.5 | 6500 | — |
| | 1.5L/4-90⑤ | Mitsubishi | Direct Drive | .9 | 60 | 11.5 | 6600 | — |
| | 1.6L/4-97 | Mitsubishi | Gear Reduction | 1.2 | 90 | 11 | 3000 | — |
| FWD⑥ | 2.2L/4-135 | Bosch | Gear Reduction | 1.1 | 69 | 11 | 3447 | 150-220 |
| | 2.5L/4-153 | Bosch | Gear Reduction | 1.1 | 69 | 11 | 3447 | 150-220 |
| | 3.0L/V6-18 | 1Bosch | Gear Reduction | 1.1 | 69 | 11 | 3447 | 150-220 |
| | 3.0L/V6-181 | Nippondenso | Direct Drive | 1.4 | 74 | 11 | 3980 | 150-220 |
| RWD⑦ | 5.2L/V8-318 | Nippondenso | Gear Reduction | 1.4 | 82 | 11 | 3625 | 150-220 |
| **1990** | | | | | | | | |
| Colt | ⑧ | Mitsubishi | Direct Drive | .7 | 60 | 11.5 | 6500 | — |
| | ⑨ | Mitsubishi | Direct Drive | .9 | 60 | 11.5 | 6600 | — |
| | ⑩ | Mitsubishi | Direct Drive | .9 | 60 | 11.5 | 6600 | — |
| Colt Vista | 2.0L/4-122④ | Mitsubishi | Direct Drive | .9 | 60 | 11.5 | 6000 | — |
| | 2.0L/4-122⑤ | Mitsubishi | Gear Reduction | 1.2 | 90 | 11 | 3000 | — |
| Colt Wagon | 1.5L/4-90④ | Mitsubishi | Direct Drive | .7 | 60 | 11.5 | 6500 | — |
| | 1.5L/4-90⑤ | Mitsubishi | Direct Drive | .9 | 60 | 11.5 | 6600 | — |
| | 1.8L/4-107 | Mitsubishi | Direct Drive | .9 | 60 | 11.5 | 6600 | — |
| Eagle Premier | 3.0L/V6-181 | Mitsubishi | — | — | 80 | 11.2 | 2500 | — |
| Eagle Summit | ⑧ | Mitsubishi | Direct Drive | .7 | 60 | 11.5 | 6500 | — |
| | ⑨ | Mitsubishi | Direct Drive | .9 | 60 | 11.5 | 6600 | — |
| | ⑩ | Mitsubishi | Direct Drive | .9 | 60 | 11.5 | 6600 | — |
| Eagle Talon | 1.8L/4-107 | Mitsubishi | Direct Drive | .9 | 60 | 11.5 | 6600 | — |
| | 2.0L/4-122 | Mitsubishi | Gear Reduction | 1.2 | 90 | 11 | 3000 | — |
| FWD⑥ | 2.2L/4-135 | Bosch | Gear Reduction | 1.1 | 69 | 11 | 3447 | 150-220 |
| | 2.5L/4-153 | Bosch | Gear Reduction | 1.1 | 69 | 11 | 3447 | 150-220 |
| | 3.0L/V6-181 | Bosch | Gear Reduction | 1.1 | 69 | 11 | 3447 | 150-220 |
| | 3.0L/V6-181 | Nippondenso | Direct Drive | 1.4 | 74 | 11 | 3980 | 150-220 |
| | 3.3L/V6-202 | Nippondenso | Direct Drive | 1.4 | 74 | 11 | 3980 | 150-220 |
| Laser | 1.8L/4-107 | Mitsubishi | Direct Drive | .9 | 60 | 11.5 | 6600 | — |
| | 2.0L/4-122 | Mitsubishi | Gear Reduction | 1.2 | 90 | 11 | 3000 | — |

*Continued*

## STARTER MOTOR SPECIFICATIONS—Continued

| Model | Engine Liter/ CID | Starter | | Free Speed Test | | | | Cranking Amp Draw Test③ |
|---|---|---|---|---|---|---|---|---|
| | | Make | Type | Power Rating | Amps① | Volts | RPM② | |
| **1990–Continued** | | | | | | | | |
| Monaco | 3.0L/V6-181 | Mitsubishi | — | — | 80 | 11.2 | 2500 | — |
| **1991** | | | | | | | | |
| Colt | ⑧ | Mitsubishi | Direct Drive | .7 | 60 | 11.5 | 6500 | — |
| | ⑨ | Mitsubishi | Direct Drive | .9 | 60 | 11.5 | 6600 | — |
| | ⑩ | Mitsubishi | Direct Drive | .9 | 60 | 11.5 | 6600 | — |
| Colt Vista | 2.0L/4-122④ | Mitsubishi | Direct Drive | .9 | 60 | 11.5 | 6600 | — |
| | 2.0L/4-122⑤ | Mitsubishi | Gear Reduction | 1.2 | 90 | 11 | 3000 | — |
| Eagle Premier | 3.0L/V6-181 | Mitsubishi | — | — | 80 | 11.2 | 2500 | — |
| Eagle Summit | ⑧ | Mitsubishi | Direct Drive | .7 | 60 | 11.5 | 6500 | — |
| | ⑨ | Mitsubishi | Direct Drive | .9 | 60 | 11.5 | 6600 | — |
| | ⑩ | Mitsubishi | Direct Drive | .9 | 60 | 11.5 | 6600 | — |
| Eagle Talon | 1.8L/4-107 | Mitsubishi | Direct Drive | .9 | 60 | 11.5 | 6600 | — |
| | 2.0L/4-122 | Mitsubishi | Gear Reduction | 1.2 | 90 | 11 | 3000 | — |
| FWD⑥ | 2.2L/4-135 | Bosch | Gear Reduction | 1.1 | 69 | 11 | 3447 | 150-220 |
| | 2.5L/4-153 | Bosch | Gear Reduction | 1.1 | 69 | 11 | 3447 | 150-220 |
| | 3.0L/V6-181 | Bosch | Gear Reduction | 1.1 | 73 | 11 | 3473 | 150-220 |
| | 3.0L/V6-181 | Nippondenso | Direct Drive | 1.4 | 73 | 11 | 3601 | 150-220 |
| | 3.3L/V6-202 | Nippondenso | Direct Drive | 1.4 | 73 | 11 | 3601 | 150-220 |
| | 3.8L/V6-231 | Nippondenso | Direct Drive | 1.4 | 73 | 11 | 3601 | 150-220 |
| Laser | 1.8L/4-107 | Mitsubishi | Direct Drive | .9 | 60 | 11.5 | 6600 | — |
| | 2.0L/4-122 | Mitsubishi | Gear Reduction | 1.2 | 90 | 11 | 3000 | — |
| Monaco | 3.0L/V6-181 | Mitsubishi | — | — | 80 | 11.2 | 2500 | — |
| Stealth | 3.0L/V6-181 | Mitsubishi | Gear Reduction | 1.2 | 90 | 11 | 3000 | — |

①—Maximum.
②—Minimum.
③—With engine at operating temperature.
④—Manual transmission.
⑤—Automatic transmission.
⑥—Models except Colt, Colt Vista, Laser, Monaco & Stealth.
⑦—Models except Conquest.
⑧—Models w/manual transmission.
⑨—Hatchback models w/automatic transmission.
⑩—Sedan models w/automatic transmission.

# Bosch Starter Motors

## INDEX



## DESCRIPTION

Bosch starters are a direct drive starter, **Fig. 1.** Direct drive starters incorporate an overrunning clutch type starter drive. A solenoid switch is mounted on the starter motor.

The other Bosch starter is a gear reduction starter. This starter uses six permanent magnets in place of conventional wound field magnets to save weight, eliminate field winding to case shorts, and improve cold start performance. The gear reduction system uses a planetary gear train to transmit armature rotation to the pinion shaft. A solenoid switch is mounted on the starter motor drive end shield.

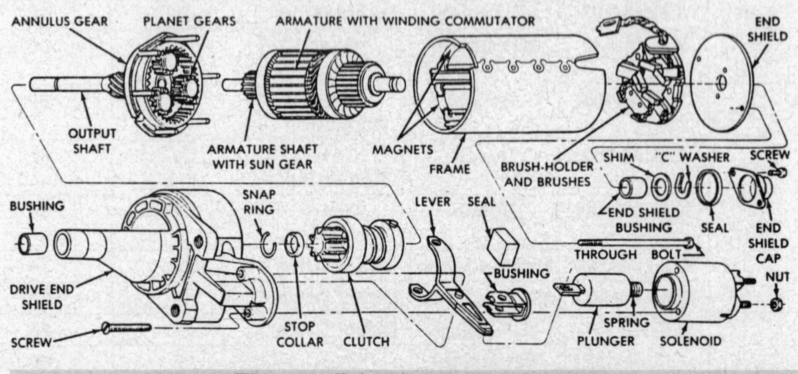


**Fig. 1 Bosch starter motor**

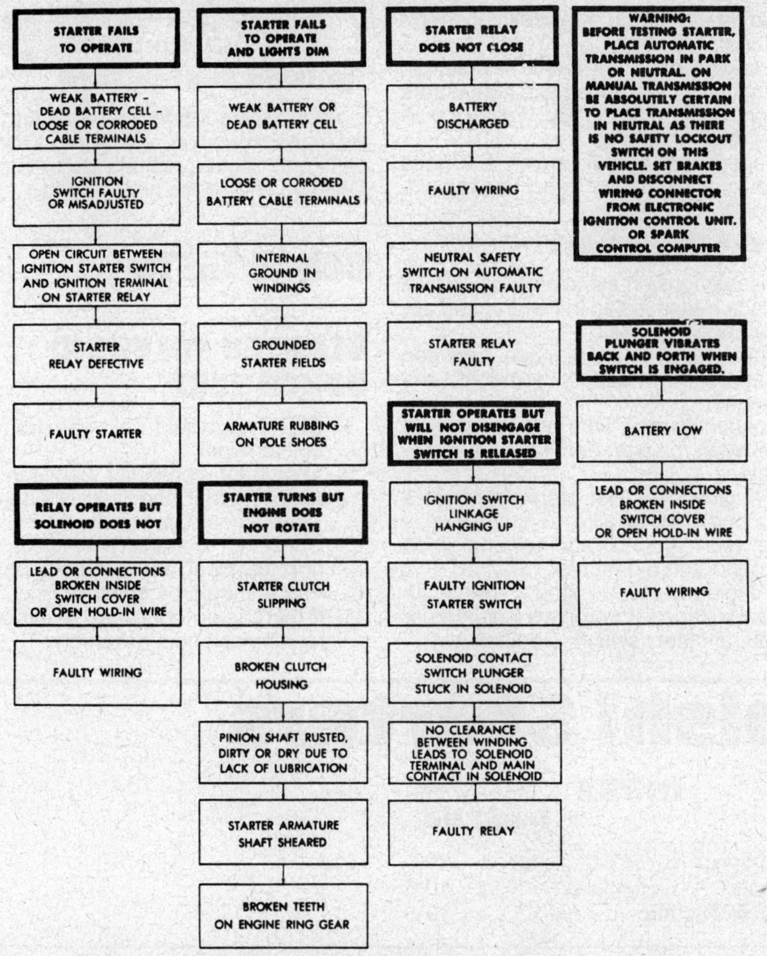


**Fig. 2 Starter motor troubleshooting. 1989**

| SYMPTOM<br>STARTER FAILS TO ENGAGE. NO SOUNDS | SYMPTOM<br>STARTER FAILS TO ENGAGE. SOLENOID OR RELAY CLICKS | SYMPTOM<br>STARTER ENGAGES, FAILS TO TURN ENGINE. DOME LIGHT DIMS | SYMPTOM<br>STARTER ENGAGES DRIVE CLUTCH SPINS OUT | SYMPTOM<br>STARTER DOES NOT DISENGAGE AFTER ENGINE STARTS |
|---|---|---|---|---|
| POSSIBLE CAUSE<br>STARTER CONTROL CIRCUIT FACULTY. SEE GROUP 8W, WIRING DIAGRAMS<br>IGNITION SWITCH MISADJUSED OR FAULTY<br>NEUTRAL SAFETY SWITCH (AUTO TRANS.) FAULTY OR MISADJUSTED<br>GEAR SELECTOR PRNDL SWITCH (A-604 TRANS.) FAULTY<br>STARTER RELAY FAULTY<br>STARTER ASSEMBLY FAULTY | POSSIBLE CAUSE<br>RESISTANCE TOO HIGH IN STARTER FEED CIRCUIT<br>STARTER CONTROL CIRCUIT FAULTY SEE GROUP 8W, WIRING DIAGRAMS<br>STARTER RELAY FAULTY<br>STARTER ASSEMBLY FAULTY | POSSIBLE CAUSE<br>RESISTANCE TOO HIGH IN STARTER FEED CIRCUIT<br>STARTER RELAY FAULTY<br>STARTER ASSEMBLY FAULTY | POSSIBLE CAUSE<br>DRIVE CLUTCH FAULTY<br>BROKEN TEETH ON RING GEAR<br>STARTER ASSEMBLY FAULTY | POSSIBLE CAUSE<br>IGNITION SWITCH MISADJUSTED<br>IGNITION SWITCH FAULTY<br>STARTER RELAY FAULTY<br>STARTER ASSEMBLY FAULTY |

•REFER TO APPROPRIATE GROUP AND SECTION OF THIS MANUAL FOR PROPER SERVICE AND TEST PROCEDURES FOR THE COMPONENTS INVOLVED

**Fig. 3 Starter motor troubleshooting. 1990–91**

## TROUBLESHOOTING

Refer to **Figs. 2 and 3** when troubleshooting the starting system.

## IN-VEHICLE TESTING

**Before starting any tests, ensure that battery is fully charged and that all connections are good then disable ignition** system as follows:

1. **On models with distributor ignition systems,** disconnect ignition coil cable from distributor cap. Connect a suitable jumper wire between coil cable end terminal and a good body ground.
2. **On models with direct ignition system,** disconnect ignition coils electrical connector.

## STARTER FEED CIRCUIT TEST

The following tests will require a suitable volt-ohmmeter tester.

1. Connect tester to battery terminals following manufactures instructions.
2. Disable ignition system.
3. Ensure all electrical accessories are Off, transmission in Park or Neutral and the parking brake is set.
4. Turn ignition switch to Start position and observe tester.
5. If voltage reads above 9.6 volts and amperage draw reads above 250 amps, perform test shown under "Starter Feed Circuit Resistance Test."
6. If voltage reads 12.4 volts or more and amperage reads 0-10 amps, perform test shown under "Starter Control Circuit Test."
7. After starting system problems have been corrected, verify battery state of charge. Disconnect all testing equipment and connect ignition system. Start vehicle several times to ensure that system is operating correctly.

## STARTER FEED CIRCUIT RESISTANCE TEST

The following operation will require a voltmeter accurate to 1/10 of a volt.

1. Disable ignition system.
2. With wiring harnesses and components connected properly, proceed as follows:
   a. Connect positive lead of voltmeter to negative battery post and negative lead to negative battery cable clamp. Turn ignition switch to Start position and observe voltmeter. If voltage is detected, correct poor contact between cable clamp and post.
   b. Connect positive lead of voltmeter to negative battery terminal and negative lead to engine block near battery cable attaching point. Turn ignition switch to Start position and observe voltmeter. If voltage reads above .2 volts, correct poor connection at ground cable attaching point. If voltmeter still reads above .2 volts after correcting poor contacts, replace ground cable.
3. Remove starter heat shield then proceed as follows:
   a. Connect positive voltmeter lead to starter motor housing and negative lead to negative battery terminal. Turn ignition switch to Start position. If voltage reads above .2 volts, correct poor starter to engine ground.

b. Connect positive voltmeter lead to positive battery terminal and negative lead to battery cable terminal on starter solenoid. Turn ignition switch ot Start position. If voltage reads above .2 volts, correct poor contact at battery cable solenoid connection. If reading is still above .2 volts after correcting contact points, replace positive battery cable.

4. If resistance tests detect no feed circuit failures, remove starter motor and perform test under "Bench Test."

## STARTER CONTROL CIRCUIT TEST

The starter control circuit consists of start solenoid, starter relay, ignition switch, neutral safety switch and all related wiring and connections.

### Starter Solenoid Test

1. Disable ignition system.
2. Connect heavy jumper wire on starter relay between battery and solenoid terminals. If engine cranks, perform starter relay test.
3. If engine does not crank or solenoid chatters, check wiring and connectors from relay to starter for loose or corroded connections.
4. Repeat test and, if engine still does not crank properly, repair or replace starter as necessary.

### Starter Relay Test

1. Disable ignition system.
2. Place transmission in Neutral and apply parking brake.
3. Check for battery voltage between starter relay battery terminal and ground.
4. Connect jumper wire on starter relay between battery and ignition terminals.
5. If engine does not crank, connect a second jumper wire to starter relay between ground terminal and good ground and repeat test.
6. If engine cranks in step 4, transmission linkage is improperly adjusted or neutral safety switch is defective.
7. If engine does not crank in step 4, starter relay is defective.

### Ignition Switch Test

After testing starter solenoid and relay, test ignition switch and wiring. Check all wiring for opens or shorts and all connectors for being loose or corroded.

## BENCH TESTS

## STARTER SOLENOID BENCH TEST

1. Disconnect field coil wire from field coil terminal.
2. Check for continuity between solenoid terminal and field coil terminal. There should be continuity.
3. Check for continuity between solenoid terminal and solenoid housing. There should be continuity.
4. If there is no continuity in either test, replace solenoid assembly.

# Mitsubishi Starters

## INDEX



## DESCRIPTION

Mitsubishi starters are either direct drive or gear reduction type. **Fig. 1** is a direct drive starter motor with an overrunning clutch type starter drive. A solenoid switch is mounted on the starter motor. **Fig. 2** is a gear reduction type utilizing a planetary gear assembly to obtain higher rotational speeds with the same torque output.

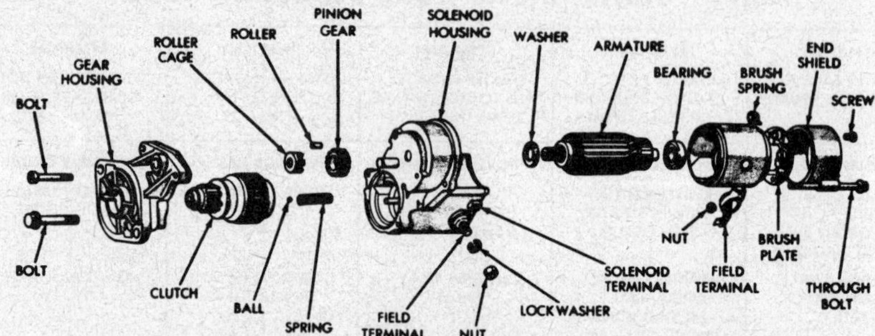


**Fig. 1 Mitsubishi direct drive starter exploded view**

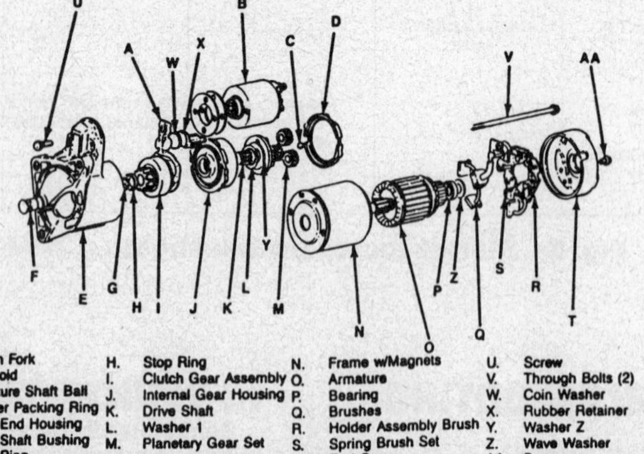


**Fig. 2 Mitsubishi gear reduction starter exploded view**

## DIAGNOSIS

For diagnosis of this starter, refer to "Bosch Starters."

## IN-VEHICLE TESTING

When testing this starter, refer to "Bosch Starters."

# Nippondenso Starters

## INDEX



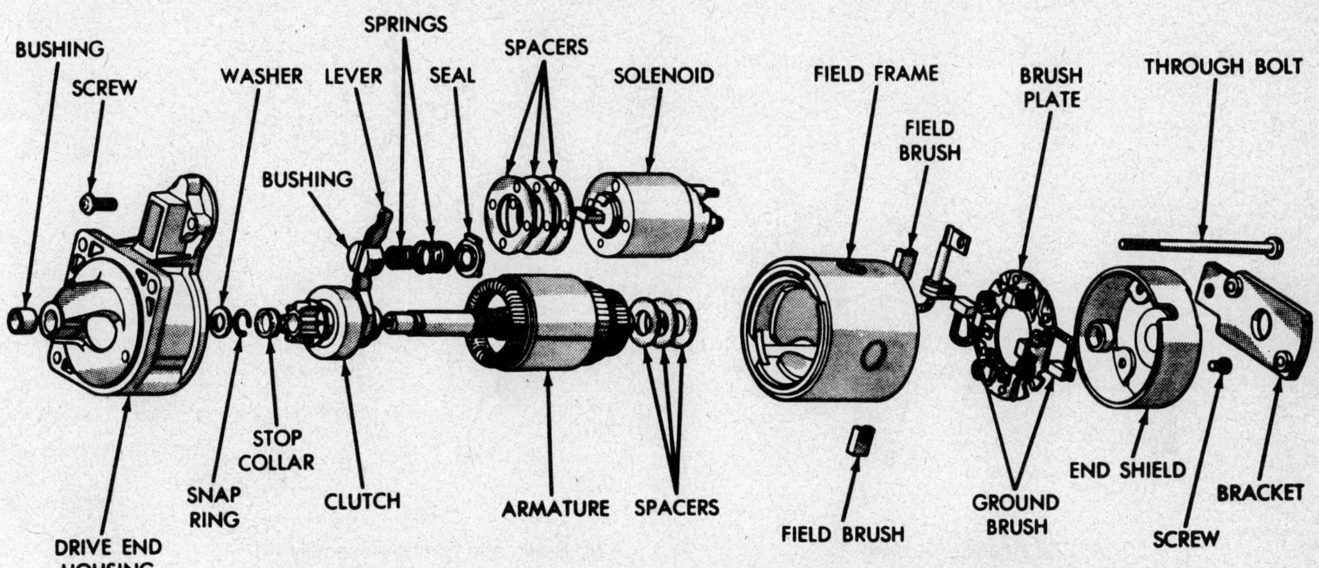


**Fig. 1 Exploded view of Nippondenso direct drive starter**

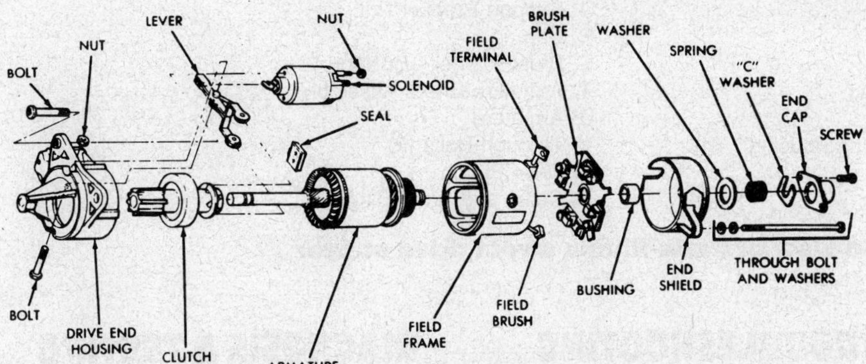


**Fig. 2 Exploded view of Nippondenso reduction gear starter**

## DESCRIPTION

Nippondenso starters, **Figs. 1 and 2,** are either direct drive or reduction gear types. The direct drive starter has an overrunning clutch type starter drive and a solenoid switch is mounted on the starter motor. The structure of the reduction gear type starter differs from that of the direct drive type, but the electrical wiring is the same for both types.

## DIAGNOSIS & TESTING

When diagnosing or testing Nippondenso starters, refer to "Bosch Starters."

# Paris-Rhone Starters

## INDEX



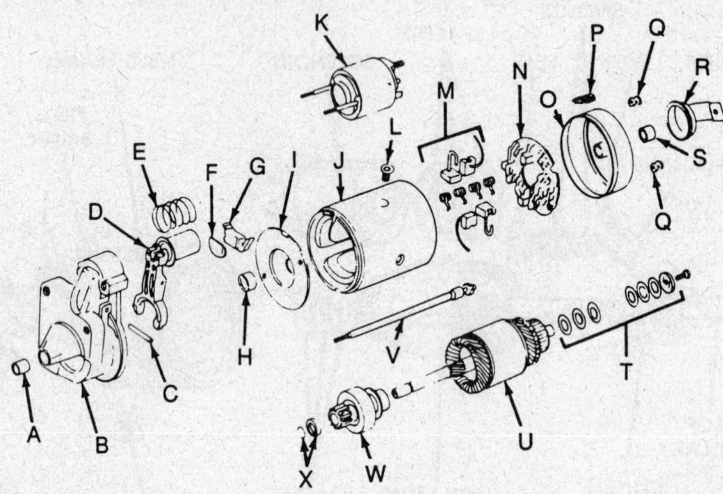


A. End Housing Bushing
B. End Housing
C. Yoke Axle
D. Pinion Yoke and Solenoid Shaft
E. Solenoid Spring
F. Spacer
G. Pad
H. Support Plate Bushing
I. Support Plate
J. Armature-Field Winding Housing
K. Solenoid
L. Pole Shoe Screw (4)
M. Brush and Spring Assembly (4)
N. Brush Holder
O. End Cover
P. Grommet
Q. Support Bracket Nut
R. Cap
S. Brush Holder - Bushing
T. Armature Brake Assembly
U. Armature
V. Through Bolts (2)
W. Drive Pinion
X. Collar and Snap Ring

**Fig. 1 Exploded view of Paris-Rhone direct drive starter**

## DESCRIPTION

Paris-Rhone starter, **Fig. 1**, is a direct drive type. The direct drive starter has an overrunning clutch type starter drive and a solenoid switch is mounted on the starter motor.

## TROUBLESHOOTING

Refer to **Fig. 2** when troubleshooting the starting system.

## DIAGNOSIS & TESTING

When diagnosing or testing Paris-Rhone starters, refer to "Bosch Starters."

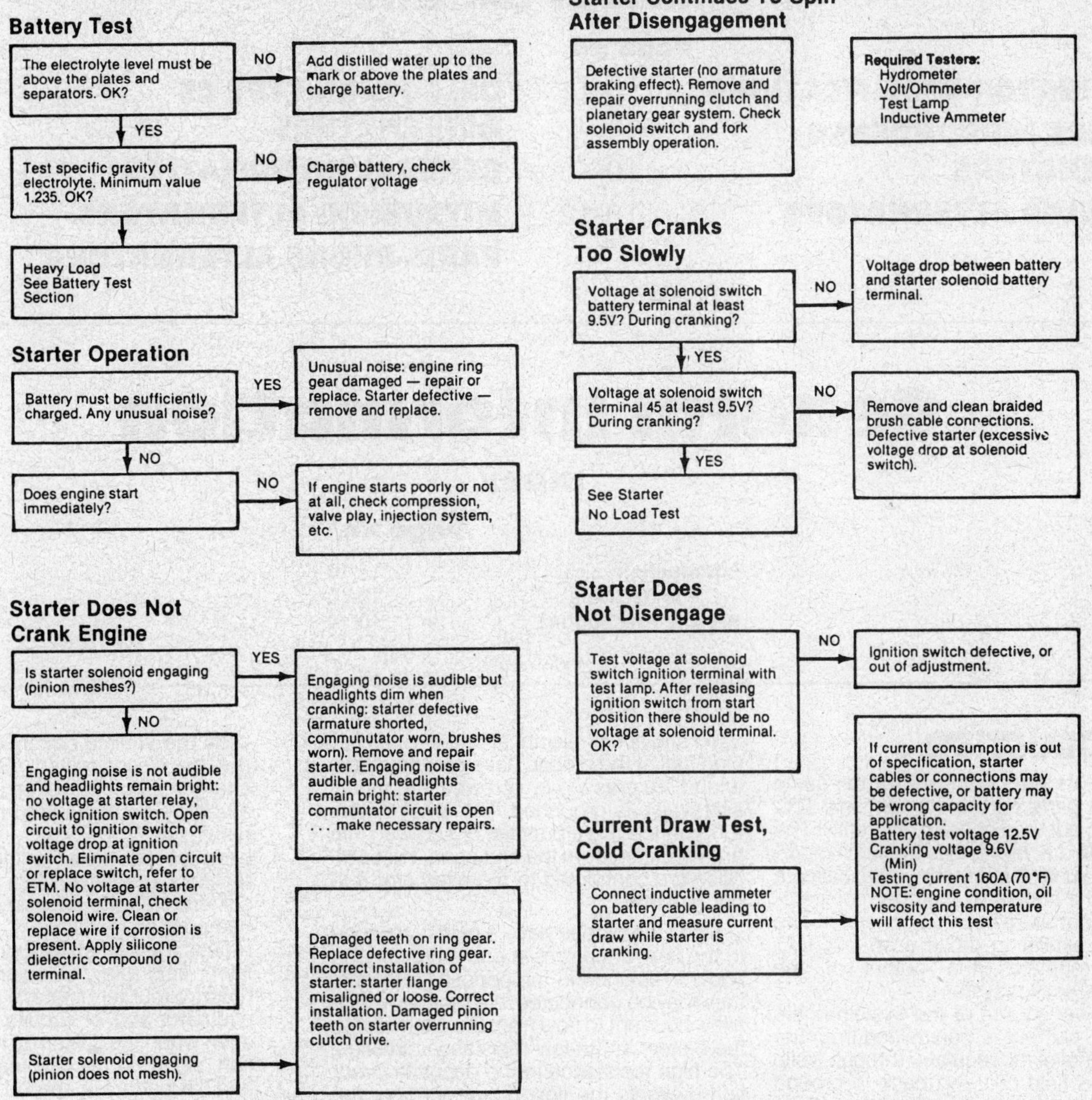


**Fig. 2 Troubleshooting starting system**

# ALTERNATORS

## TABLE OF CONTENTS



# General Information

## INDEX



## INTRODUCTION

Alternators are composed of the same functional parts as the conventional D.C. generator, but they operate differently. The field is called a rotor and is the turning portion of the unit. A generating part, called a stator, is the stationary member, comparable to the armature in a D.C. generator. The regulator, similar to those used in a D.C. system, regulates the output of the alternator-rectifier system.

The power source of the system is the alternator. Current is transmitted from the field terminal of the regulator through a slip ring to the field coil and back to ground through another slip ring. The strength of the field regulates the output of the alternating current. This alternating current is then transmitted from the alternator to the rectifier where it is converted to direct current.

These alternators employ a three-phase stator winding in which the phase windings are electrically 120 degrees apart. The rotor consists of a field coil encased between interleaved sections producing a magnetic field with alternate north and south poles. By rotating the rotor inside the stator the alternating current is induced in the stator windings. This alternating current is rectified (changed to D.C.) by silicon diodes and brought out to the output terminal of the alternator.

### DIODE RECTIFIERS

Six or more silicon diode rectifiers are used and act as electrical one-way valves. One half of the diodes have ground polarity and are pressed or screwed into a heat sink which is grounded. The other diodes (ungrounded) are pressed or screwed into and insulated from the end head. These diodes are connected to the alternator output terminal.

Since the diodes have a high resistance to the flow of current in one direction and a low resistance in the opposite direction, they may be connected in a manner which allows current to flow from the alternator to the battery in the low resistance direction. The high resistance in the opposite direction prevents the flow of current from the battery to the alternator. Because of this feature no circuit breaker is required between the alternator and battery.

## SERVICE PRECAUTIONS

1. Ensure battery polarity is correct when servicing units. Reversed battery polarity will damage rectifiers and regulators.
2. If booster battery is used for starting, be sure to use correct polarity in hook up.
3. When a fast charger is used to charge a vehicle battery, the vehicle battery cables should be disconnected unless the fast charger is equipped with a special alternator protector, in which case the vehicle battery cables need not be disconnected. Also the fast charger should never be used to start a vehicle as damage to rectifiers will result.
4. Lead connections to the grounded rectifiers (negative) should never be soldered, as the excessive heat may damage the rectifiers.
5. Unless the system includes a load relay or field relay, grounding the alternator output terminal will damage the alternator and/or circuits. This is true even when the system is not in operation, since no circuit breaker is used and the battery is applied to the alternator output terminal at all times. The field or load relay acts as a circuit breaker in that it is controlled by the ignition switch.
6. Before making any in-vehicle tests of the alternator or regulator, the battery should be checked and the circuit inspected for faulty wiring or insulation, loose or corroded connections and poor ground circuits.
7. Check alternator belt tension to ensure belt is tight enough to prevent slipping under load.
8. The ignition switch should be off and the battery ground cable disconnected before making any test connections to prevent damage to the system.
9. The vehicle battery must be fully charged or a fully charged battery may be installed for test purposes.

# Alternator Specifications

| Model | Engine | Type | Id. No. | Rated Output Amps |
|---|---|---|---|---|
| **1989** | | | | |
| Colt | 1.5L/4-92 | Mitsubishi | A2T09493 | 75 |
| | 1.6L/4-92⑥ | Mitsubishi | A3T03393 | 75 |
| | 1.6L/4-97⑤ | Mitsubishi | A3T03493 | 65 |
| Colt Vista | 2.0L/4-122 | Mitsubishi | A2T48691 | 65 |
| Conquest | 2.6L/4-156 | Mitsubishi | A2T49977 | 75 |
| Eagle Medallion | 2.22L/4-135 | Paris-Rhone | A14N113 | 61② |
| | 2.22L/4-135 | Paris-Rhone | A14N117 | 76② |
| Eagle Premier | — | Delco | CS130-85 | 61② |
| | — | Delco | CS130-96 | 65② |
| | — | Delco | CS130-105 | 74② |
| Eagle Summit | 1.5L/4-92 | Mitsubishi | A2T09493 | 75 |
| | 1.6L/4-92⑥ | Mitsubishi | A3T03393 | 75 |
| | 1.6L/4-97⑤ | Mitsubishi | A3T03493 | 65 |
| FWD① | 2.2L/4-135 | Nippondenso 75HS | 5233416 | 68② |
| | 2.2L/4-135 | Nippondenso 90HS | 5233418 | 87② |
| | 2.2L/4-135 | Nippondenso 120HS | 5233608 | 98② |
| | 2.5L/4-153 | Nippondenso 75HS | 5233416 | 68② |
| | 2.5L/4-153 | Nippondenso 90HS | 5233418 | 87② |
| | 2.5L/4-153 | Nippondenso 120HS | 5233608 | 98② |
| | 3.0L/V6-181 | Nippondenso 90HS | 5233449 | 87② |
| | 3.0L/V6-181 | Nippondenso 120HS | 5233660 | 98② |
| | — | Bosch | 5233718 | 75② |
| RWD④ | 5.2L/V8-318 | Chrysler 120HS | 5233199 | 98② |
| | 5.2L/V8-318 | Chrysler 90HS | 5233472 | 87② |
| | 5.2L/V8-318 | Nippondenso 120HS | 5233599 | 98② |
| | 5.2L/V8-318 | Nippondenso 90HS | 5227672 | 87② |
| **1990** | | | | |
| Colt | — | Mitsubishi | — | 75 |
| Colt Vista | 2.0L/4-122 | Mitsubishi | A2T48691 | 65 |
| Colt Wagon | 1.5L/4-92 | Mitsubishi | A2T09493 | 75 |
| | 1.8L/4-107 | Mitsubishi | A2T17692 | 75 |
| Eagle Premier | 3.0L/V6-181 | Mitsubishi | — | 65② |
| Eagle Summit | — | Mitsubishi | — | 75 |
| Eagle Talon | 2.0L/4-122⑦ | Mitsubishi | A2T48791 | 65 |
| | 2.0L/4-122⑧ | Mitsubishi | A2T09792 | 75 |
| FWD① | 2.2L/4-135 | Nippondenso 75HS | 4557301 | 68② |
| | 2.2L/4-135 | Nippondenso 90HS | 5234031 | 87② |
| | 2.2L/4-135 | Nippondenso 120HS | 5234208 | 98② |
| | 2.2L/4-135 | Nippondenso 120HS | 5234231 | 98② |
| | 2.5L/4-153 | Nippondenso 75HS | 4557301 | 68② |
| | 2.5L/4-153 | Nippondenso 90HS | 5234031 | 87② |
| | 2.5L/4-153 | Nippondenso 120HS | 5234208 | 98② |
| | 2.5L/4-153 | Nippondenso 120HS | 5234231 | 98② |
| | 3.0L/V6-181 | Nippondenso 90HS | 5234029 | 87② |
| | 3.0L/V6-181 | Nippondenso 120HS | 5234260 | 98② |
| | 3.3L/V6-202 | Nippondenso 90HS | 5234032 | 87② |
| | — | Bosch 90RS | 5234208 | 75② |
| Laser | 2.0L/4-122⑦ | Mitsubishi | A2T48791 | 65 |
| | 2.0L/4-122⑧ | Mitsubishi | A2T09792 | 75 |
| Monaco | 3.0L/V6-181 | Mitsubishi | — | 65② |

*Continued*

## ALTERNATOR SPECIFICATIONS—Continued

| Model | Engine | Type | Id. No. | Rated Output Amps |
|---|---|---|---|---|
| **1991** | | | | |
| Colt | — | Mitsubishi | — | 75 |
| Colt Vista | 2.0L/4-122 | Mitsubishi | A2T48691 | 65 |
| Eagle Premier | 3.0L/V6-181 | Mitsubishi | — | 65② |
| Eagle Summit | — | Mitsubishi | — | 75 |
| Eagle Talon | 2.0L/4-122⑤ | Mitsubishi | — | 65 |
| | 2.0L/4-122⑥ | Mitsubishi | — | 75 |
| FWD① | 2.2L/4-135 | Bosch 90HS | 4557431 | 84② |
| | 2.2L/4-135 | Bosch 90RS | 5234231 | 88② |
| | 2.2L/4-135 | Nippondenso 75HS | 4557301 | 68② |
| | 2.2L/4-135 | Nippondenso 90HS | 5234031 | 87② |
| | 2.5L/4-153 | Bosch 90HS | 4557431 | 84② |
| | 2.5L/4-153 | Bosch 90RS | 5234231 | 88② |
| | 2.5L/4-153 | Nippondenso 75HS | 4557301 | 68② |
| | 2.5L/4-153 | Nippondenso 90HS | 5234031 | 87② |
| | 3.0L/V6-181 | Bosch 90HS | 4557432 | 86② |
| | 3.0L/V6-181 | Nippondenso 90HS | 5234032 | 90② |
| | 3.0L/V6-181 | Nippondenso 120HS | 5234033 | 102② |
| | 3.3L/V6-202 | Nippondenso 90HS | 5234032 | 90② |
| | 3.3L/V6-202 | Nippondenso 120HS | 5234033 | 102② |
| | 3.8L/V6-231 | Nippondenso 90HS | 5234032 | 90② |
| | 3.8L/V6-231 | Nippondenso 120HS | 5234033 | 102② |
| Laser | 2.0L/4-122⑤ | Mitsubishi | — | 65 |
| | 2.0L/4-122⑥ | Mitsubishi | — | 75 |
| Monaco | 3.0L/V6-181 | Mitsubishi | — | 65② |
| Stealth | 3.0L/V6-181⑨ | Mitsubishi | — | 90 |
| | 3.0L/V6-181⑩ | Mitsubishi | — | 110 |

①—Except Colt, Colt Vista, Laser, Monaco & Stealth.
②—At 1250 engine RPM.
③—Minimum.
④—Except Conquest.
⑤—Non-turbocharged manual transmission models.
⑥—All turbocharged engines and non-turbocharged automatic transmission models.
⑦—Manual transmission.
⑧—Automatic transmission.
⑨—SOHC.
⑩—DOHC.

# Chrysler Alternators

## INDEX

**Page No.**



## IN-VEHICLE TESTING

### CHARGING CIRCUIT RESISTANCE TEST

#### EXCEPT UNITS W/REGULATORS IN-ENGINE ELECTRONICS

1. Disconnect battery ground cable. Disconnect "Bat" lead at the alternator.
2. Complete test connections as shown in **Fig. 1.** Do not connect blue J2 lead of wiring connector to ground. Do not spread connector terminals with jumper wire.
3. Connect battery ground cable, start engine and operate at idle.
4. Adjust engine speed and carbon pile to obtain 20 amps in the circuit and check voltmeter reading. Reading should not exceed .5 volts. If a voltage drop is indicated, inspect, clean and tighten all connections in the circuit. A voltage drop test at each connection can be performed to isolate the trouble.

#### UNITS W/REGULATOR IN-ENGINE ELECTRONICS

1. Disconnect battery ground cable and the "Bat" lead from alternator output terminal.
2. Complete test connections as shown in **Fig. 2.**
3. Remove air hose between power module and air cleaner, then the wiring harness electrical connector.
4. Connect a suitable jumper wire from wiring harness connector green wire

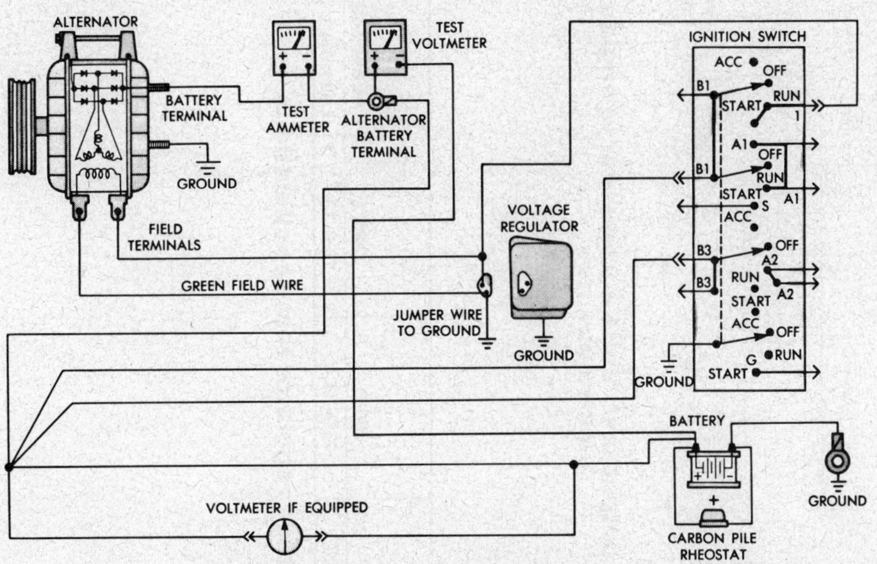


**Fig. 1 Charging circuit resistance test. Except units w/regulator in engine electronics**

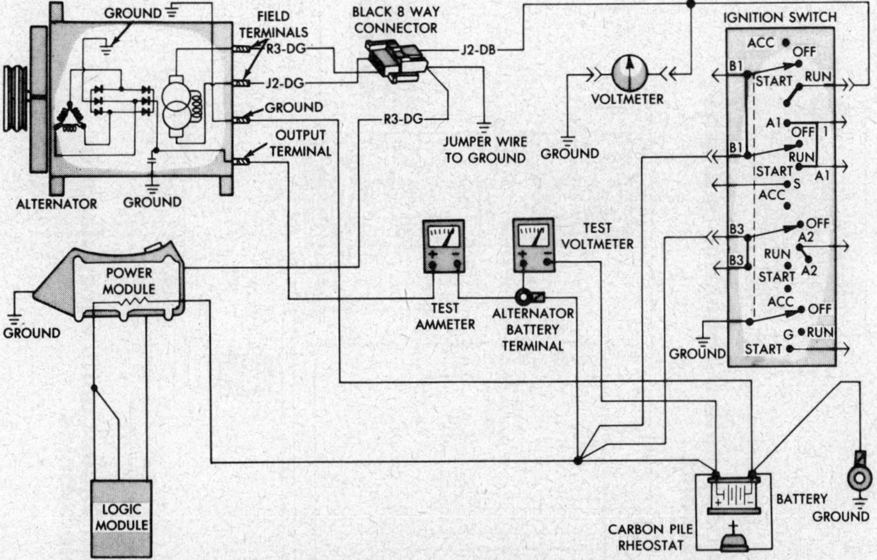


**Fig. 2 Charging circuit resistance test. Units w/regulator in engine electronics**

terminal to ground. **Do not connect blue J2 lead of wiring electrical connector to ground.**

5. Connect battery ground cable, then start engine and operate at idle.
6. Adjust engine speed and carbon pile rheostat to obtain 20 amps in the circuit and check voltmeter reading. Reading should not exceed .5 volts. If a higher voltage drop is indicated, inspect, clean and tighten all connections in the circuit. A voltage drop test at each connection can be performed to isolate the problem.

## CURRENT OUTPUT TEST

### EXCEPT UNITS W/REGULATOR IN-ENGINE ELECTRONICS

1. Disconnect battery ground cable, complete test connections as shown, **Fig. 3,** and start engine and operate at idle. **Do not connect blue J2 lead of wiring electrical connector to ground. Immediately after starting, reduce engine speed to idle.**
2. Adjust the carbon pile and engine speed in increments until a speed of 1250 RPM and 15 volts are obtained. **While increasing speed, do not allow voltage to exceed 16 volts.**
3. Check ammeter reading. Output current should be within specifications.

### UNITS W/REGULATOR IN ENGINE ELECTRONICS

1. Disconnect battery ground cable and "Bat" lead from alternator output terminal.
2. Complete test connections as shown in **Fig. 4.**
3. Remove air hose between power module and air cleaner, then the wiring harness electrical connector.
4. Connect a suitable jumper wire from wiring harness connector green wire terminal to ground. **Do not connect blue J2 lead of wiring electrical connector to ground.**
5. Connect battery ground cable, then start engine and operate at idle.
6. Adjust carbon pile rheostat and engine speed to obtain 15 volts at 1250 RPM. **While increasing engine speed, do not allow voltage to exceed 16 volts.**
7. If ammeter reading is not approximately that of alternator rating, repair or replace alternator.

## VOLTAGE REGULATOR TEST

**Battery must be fully charged for test to be accurate.**

### EXCEPT UNITS W/REGULATOR CONTROLLED BY ENGINE ELECTRONICS

1. Connect test equipment, **Fig 5.**
2. Start and run engine at 1250 RPM with all lights and accessories turned "Off." Voltage should be as specified in **Fig. 6.**
3. It is normal for the vehicle ammeter to indicate an immediate charge, then gradually return to the normal position.
4. If voltage is below limits or is fluctuating, proceed with the following:
   a. Check voltage regulator for proper ground. The ground is obtained through the regulator case to mounting screws, then to the vehicle sheet metal.
   b. With ignition switch "Off," disconnect voltage regulator connector. Turn ignition On and check for battery voltage at the wiring harness terminal. Both green and blue leads should have battery voltage.
   c. If voltage regulator was grounded properly and battery voltage was present at the green and blue leads, replace voltage regulator and repeat test.

### UNITS W/REGULATOR IN-ENGINE ELECTRONICS

Voltage regulator is controlled by Electronic Control Unit.

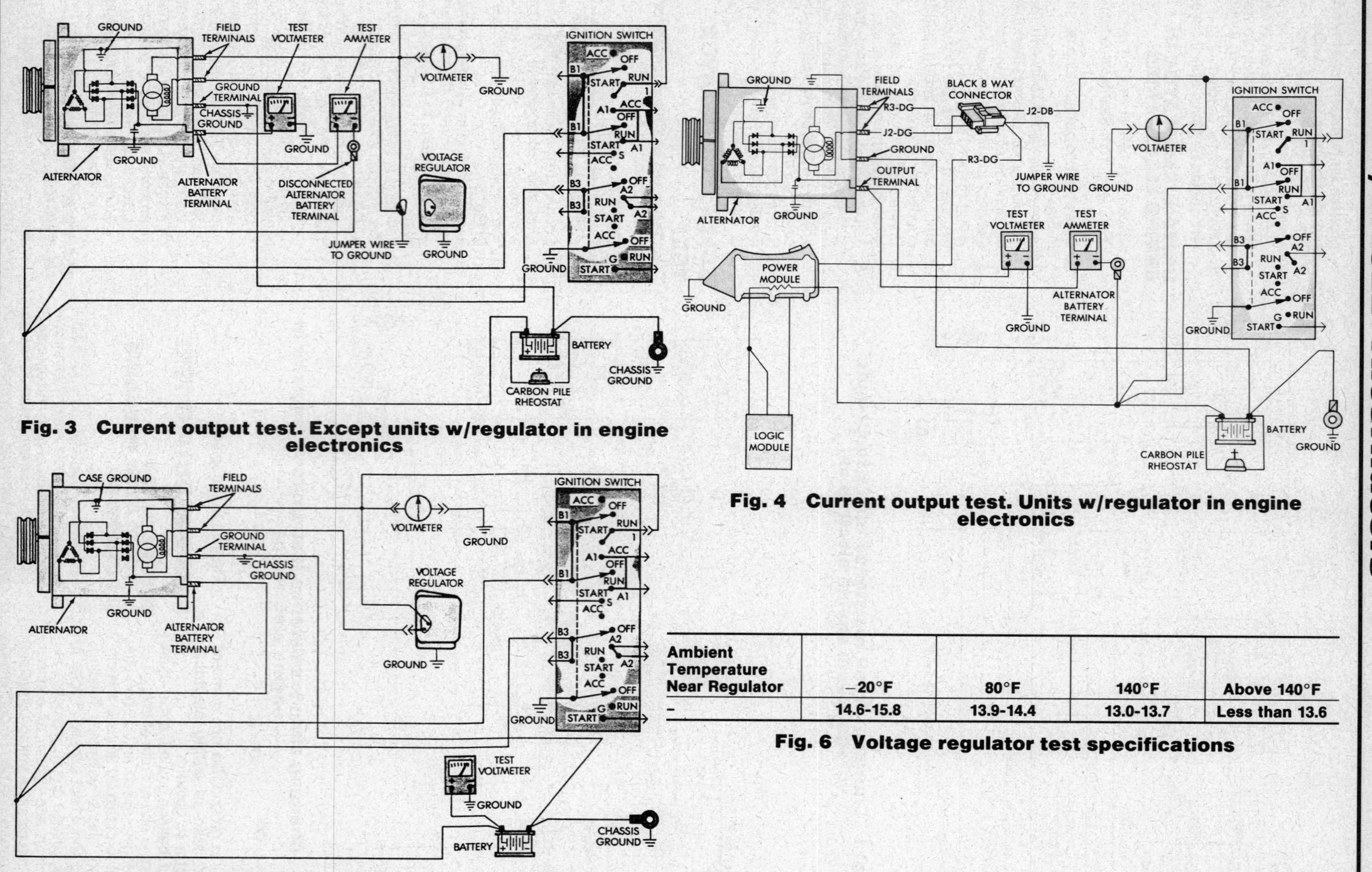


Fig. 3 Current output test. Except units w/regulator in engine electronics

Fig. 4 Current output test. Units w/regulator in engine electronics

Fig. 5 Voltage regulator test. Except units w/regulator in engine electronics

| Ambient Temperature Near Regulator | −20°F | 80°F | 140°F | Above 140°F |
|---|---|---|---|---|
| – | 14.6-15.8 | 13.9-14.4 | 13.0-13.7 | Less than 13.6 |

Fig. 6 Voltage regulator test specifications

# Bosch & Nippondenso Alternators

## INDEX



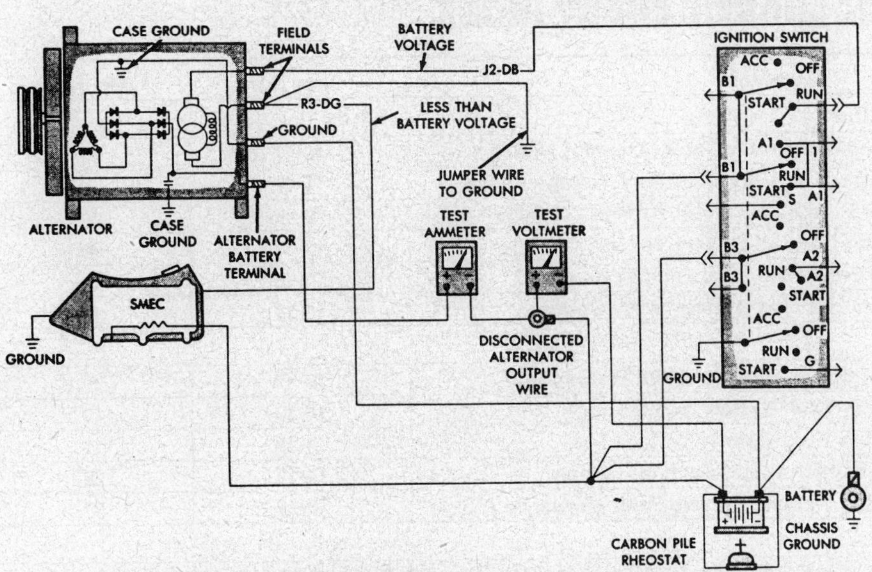


**Fig. 1 Charging circuit resistance test**

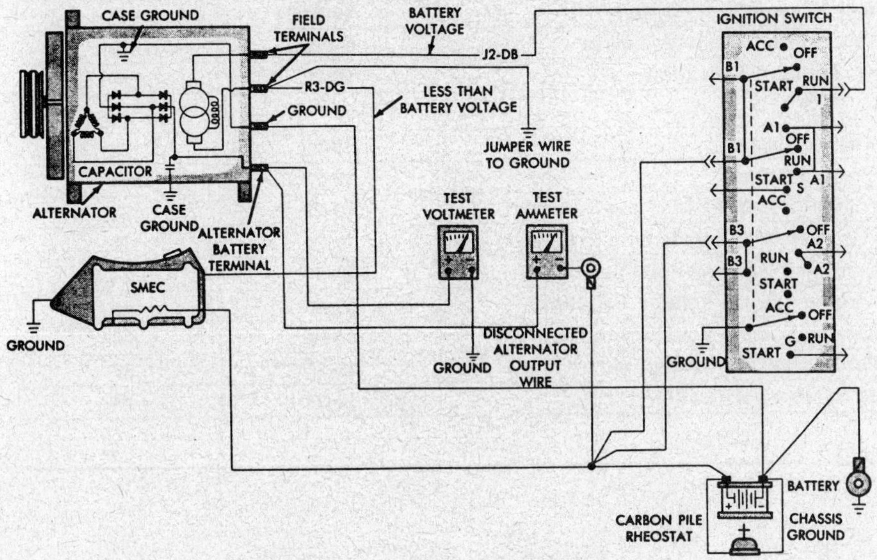


**Fig. 2 Current output test**

## DESCRIPTION

The main components of the alternator are the rotor, stator, rectifier, end shields and drive pulley. Direct current is available at the output "B+" terminal.

Alternator output is controlled by voltage regulator circuitry contained within the power and logic modules of the Engine Controller.

## IN-VEHICLE TESTING

### CHARGING CIRCUIT RESISTANCE TEST

1. Disconnect battery ground cable and the "Bat" lead from alternator output terminal.
2. Complete test connections as shown in **Fig. 1.**
3. Remove air hose between engine controller and air cleaner.
4. **On non-turbo models,** connect a suitable jumper wire from green (R3) terminal to ground. **Do not connect blue J2 circuit to ground. On turbo models,** connect a suitable jumper wire from green R3 lead wire on dash side of black 8 way connector to ground. **Do not connect blue J2 lead of 8 way wiring connector to ground.**
5. **On all models,** connect battery ground cable, then start engine and operate at idle.
6. Adjust engine speed and carbon pile rheostat to obtain 20 amps in the circuit, then check voltmeter reading. Reading should not exceed .5 volts. If a higher voltage drop is indicated, inspect, clean and tighten all connections in the circuit. A voltage drop test at each connection can be performed to isolate the problem.

### CURRENT OUTPUT TEST

1. Disconnect battery ground cable and "Bat" lead from alternator output terminal.
2. Complete test connections as shown in **Fig. 2.**
3. Remove air hose between engine controller and air cleaner.
4. **On non-turbo models,** connect a suitable jumper wire from green (R3) terminal to ground. **Do not connect blue J2 circuit to ground. On turbo models,** models, connect a suitable jumper wire from green R3 lead wire on dash side of black 8 way connector to ground. **Do not connect blue J2 lead of 8 way wiring connector to ground.**
5. **On all models,** connect battery ground cable, then start engine and operate at idle.
6. Adjust carbon pile rheostat and engine speed to obtain 15 volts at 1250 RPM. **While increasing engine speed, do not allow voltage to exceed 16 volts.**

7. If ammeter reading is not within limits shown in "Alternator Specifications" replace alternator.

## ON-BOARD DIAGNOSTIC SYSTEM

The on-board diagnostic system can be used to help determine charging system malfunctions. This system monitors, then stores information that can be retrieved by using a DRBII diagnostic tool. Install DRBII on vehicle and refer to **Figs. 3 through 8,** on except 1989 models with 3.0L/V6-181 engine, **Figs. 9 through 13** on 1989 models with 3.0L/V6-181 engines, **Figs. 14 through 19** on 1990 models and **Figs. 20 through 28** on 1991 models, for proper code diagnostic procedure.

If a diagnostic tool is not available the fault codes can be retrieved by using the "Check Engine" lamp on the instrument cluster. Cycle the ignition switch On-Off-On-Off-On without starting the engine. The light will go on for two seconds as a bulb check, immediately following this will be the fault code. Count the number of flashes, for example flash, pause, flash, flash is fault code 12. Refer to **Figs. 29 through 34,** for fault codes and fault code diagnosis. All fault codes are two digit numbers with a four second pause between different codes.

## DIAGNOSTIC CHART INDEX

| Test No. | Symptom | Page No. | Fig. No. |
|---|---|---|---|
| **1989 Models Except 3.0L/V6-181 Engine** | | | |
| 1 | Checking Charging System For Fault (Trouble) Codes | 10-17 | 3 |
| 2 | Checking For Fault Code 16-Loss Of Battery Voltage Sense | 10-17 | 4 |
| 3 | Checking For Fault Code 46-Battery Voltage Too High | 10-17 | 5 |
| 4 | Checking For Fault Code 47-Battery Voltage Too Low | 10-18 | 6 |
| 5 | Checking For Intermittent Fault Codes | 10-18 | 7 |
| 6 | Checking The Charging System w/No Codes | 10-18 | 8 |
| **1989 Models w/3.0L Engine** | | | |
| 1 | Checking Charging System For Fault Messages | 10-19 | 9 |
| 2 | Checking For Fault-Battery Voltage High | 10-19 | 10 |
| 3 | Checking For Fault-Battery Voltage Low | 10-19 | 11 |
| 4 | Checking For Intermittent Fault Messages | 10-19 | 12 |
| 5 | Checking Charging System With No Fault Messages | 10-19 | 13 |
| **1990** | | | |
| 1 | Testing Battery | 10-20 | 14 |
| 2 | Repairing Fault "Alternator Field Circuit" | 10-20 | 15 |
| 3 | Repairing Fault "Charging Output Low" | 10-21 | 16 |
| 4 | Repairing Fault "Battery Voltage High" | 10-21 | 17 |
| 5 | Checking For Intermittent Fault Messages | 10-21 | 18 |
| VER | Charging System Verification | 10-22 | 19 |
| **1991** | | | |
| 1A | Testing Battery | 10-22 | 20 |
| 1B | Testing Battery | 10-22 | 21 |
| 2A | Repairing Fault "Alternator Field Not Switching Properly" | 10-23 | 22 |
| 2C | Repairing Fault "Alternator Field Not Switching Properly" | 10-24 | 23 |
| 3A | Repairing Fault "Charging System Voltage Too Low" | 10-24 | 24 |
| 4A | Repairing Fault "Charging System Voltage Too High" | 10-24 | 25 |
| 4B | Repairing Fault "Charging System Voltage Too High" | 10-25 | 26 |
| 5A | Checking For Intermittent Problems | 10-25 | 27 |
| VER | Charging System Verification | 10-25 | 28 |

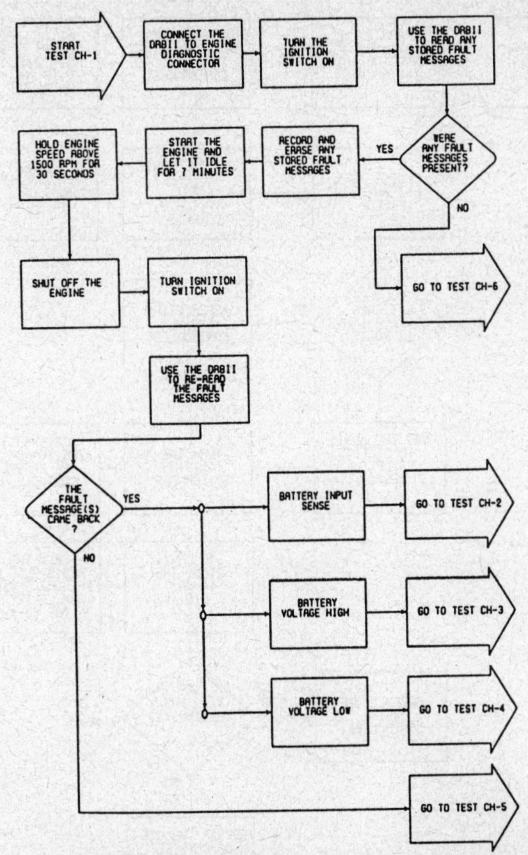


**Fig. 3 Test 1, checking charging system for fault (trouble) codes. 1989 models except 3.0L/V6-181 engine**

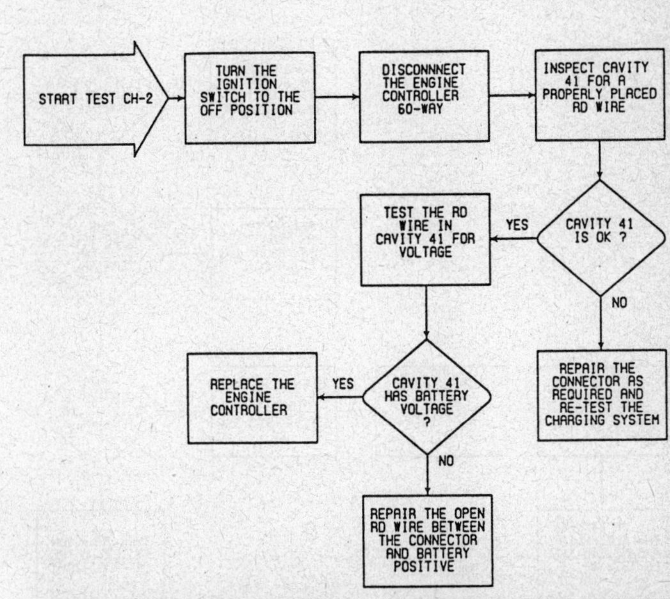


**Fig. 4 Test 2, checking for fault code 16- loss of battery voltage sense. 1989 models except 3.0L/V6-181 engine**

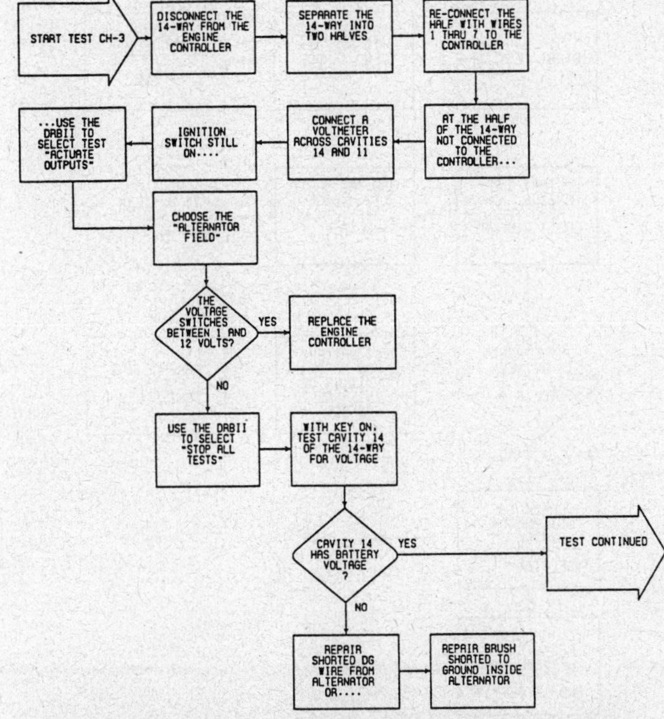


**Fig. 5 Test 3, checking for fault code 46- battery voltage too high (Part 1 of 2). 1989 models except 3.0L/V6-181 engine**

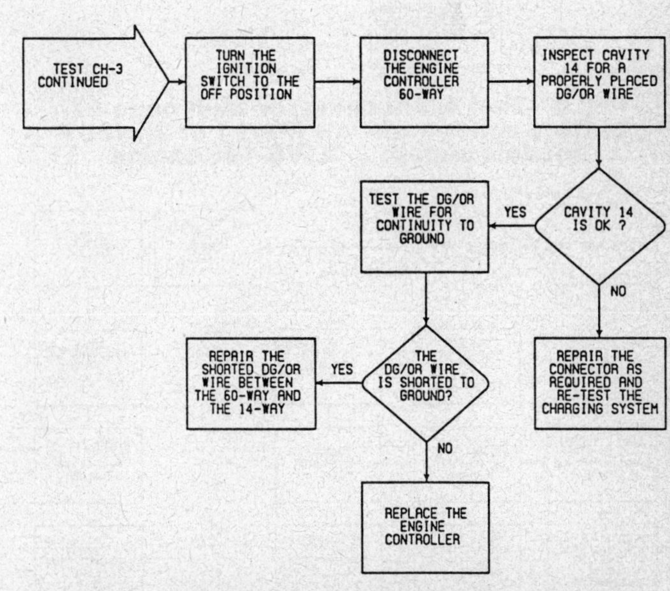


**Fig. 5 Test 3, checking for fault code 46- battery voltage too high (Part 2 of 2). 1989 models except 3.0L/V6-181 engine**

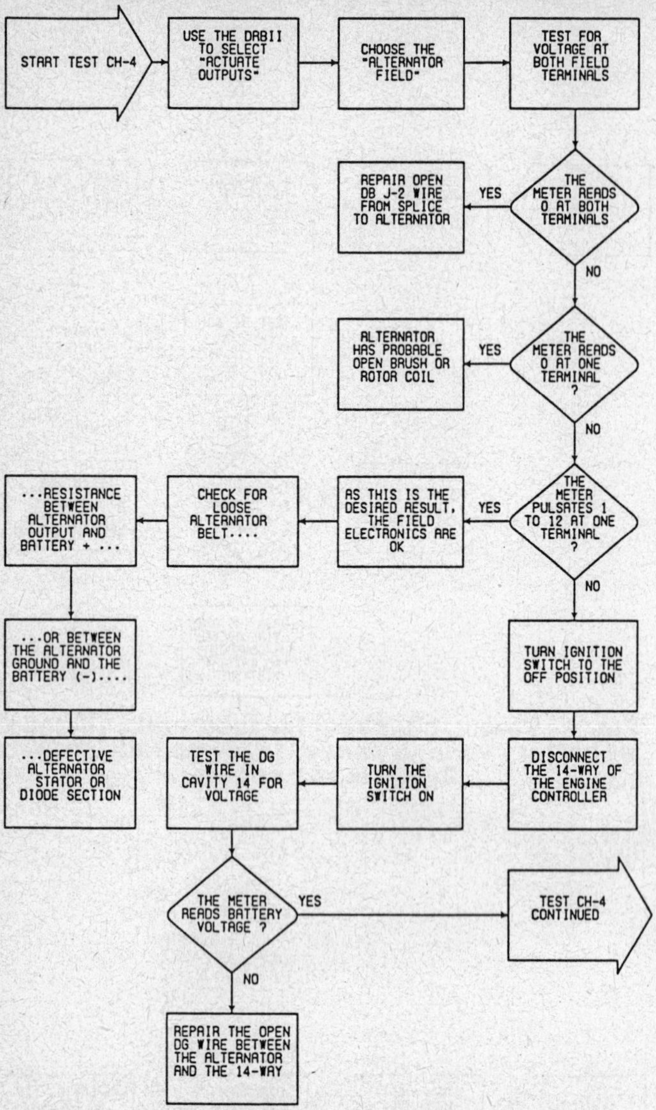

START TEST CH-4
USE THE DRBII TO SELECT "ACTUATE OUTPUTS"
CHOOSE THE "ALTERNATOR FIELD"
TEST FOR VOLTAGE AT BOTH FIELD TERMINALS
THE METER READS 0 AT BOTH TERMINALS
YES
REPAIR OPEN DB J-2 WIRE FROM SPLICE TO ALTERNATOR
NO
THE METER READS 0 AT ONE TERMINAL ?
YES
ALTERNATOR HAS PROBABLE OPEN BRUSH OR ROTOR COIL
NO
THE METER PULSATES 1 TO 12 AT ONE TERMINAL ?
YES
AS THIS IS THE DESIRED RESULT, THE FIELD ELECTRONICS ARE OK
CHECK FOR LOOSE ALTERNATOR BELT....
...RESISTANCE BETWEEN ALTERNATOR OUTPUT AND BATTERY + ...
...OR BETWEEN THE ALTERNATOR GROUND AND THE BATTERY (-)....
...DEFECTIVE ALTERNATOR STATOR OR DIODE SECTION
NO
TURN IGNITION SWITCH TO THE OFF POSITION
DISCONNECT THE 14-WAY OF THE ENGINE CONTROLLER
TURN THE IGNITION SWITCH ON
TEST THE DG WIRE IN CAVITY 14 FOR VOLTAGE
THE METER READS BATTERY VOLTAGE ?
YES
TEST CH-4 CONTINUED
NO
REPAIR THE OPEN DG WIRE BETWEEN THE ALTERNATOR AND THE 14-WAY

**Fig. 6 Test 4, checking for fault code 47-battery voltage too low (Part 1 of 2). 1989 models except 3.0L/V6-181 engine**

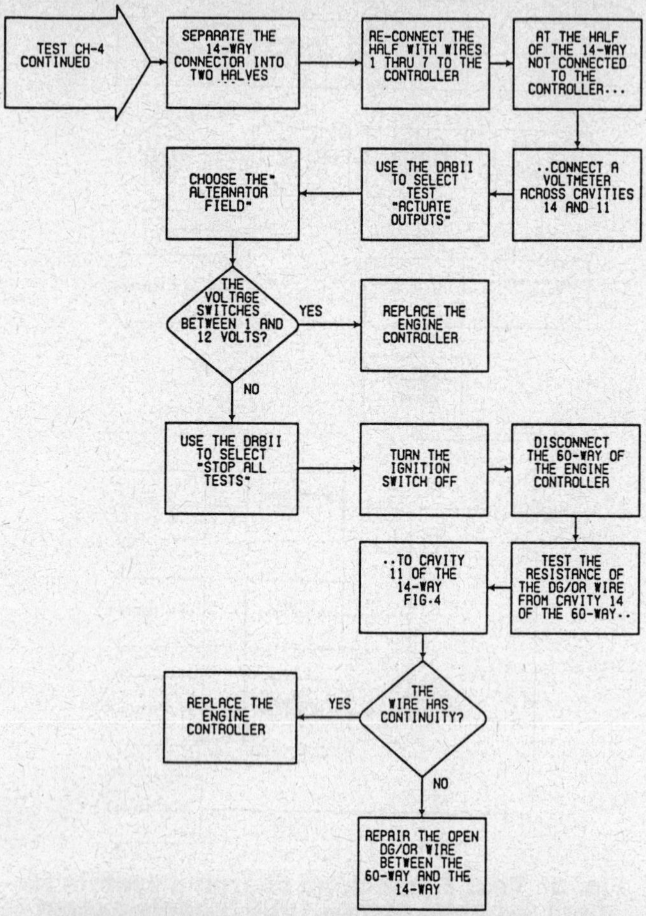

TEST CH-4 CONTINUED
SEPARATE THE 14-WAY CONNECTOR INTO TWO HALVES ...
RE-CONNECT THE HALF WITH WIRES 1 THRU 7 TO THE CONTROLLER
AT THE HALF OF THE 14-WAY NOT CONNECTED TO THE CONTROLLER...
..CONNECT A VOLTMETER ACROSS CAVITIES 14 AND 11
USE THE DRBII TO SELECT TEST "ACTUATE OUTPUTS"
CHOOSE THE "ALTERNATOR FIELD"
THE VOLTAGE SWITCHES BETWEEN 1 AND 12 VOLTS?
YES
REPLACE THE ENGINE CONTROLLER
NO
USE THE DRBII TO SELECT "STOP ALL TESTS"
TURN THE IGNITION SWITCH OFF
DISCONNECT THE 60-WAY OF THE ENGINE CONTROLLER
TEST THE RESISTANCE OF THE DG/OR WIRE FROM CAVITY 14 OF THE 60-WAY..
..TO CAVITY 11 OF THE 14-WAY FIG.4
THE WIRE HAS CONTINUITY?
YES
REPLACE THE ENGINE CONTROLLER
NO
REPAIR THE OPEN DG/OR WIRE BETWEEN THE 60-WAY AND THE 14-WAY

**Fig. 6 Test 4, checking for fault code 47-battery voltage too low (Part 2 of 2). 1989 models except 3.0L/V6-181 engine**

START TEST CH-5
CODE WAS BATTERY INPUT SENSE ?
YES
USE THE DRBII TO READ "SENSOR VOLTAGES"
SELECT "BATTERY VOLTAGE"
WHILE OBSERVING THE DRBII DISPLAY...
WIGGLE THE RD BATTERY SENSE WIRE AT THE CONTROLLER...
...CONTINUING BACK TOWARD THE AUTO SHUT-DOWN RELAY
THE DRBII DISPLAY VOLTAGE WILL CHANGE WHEN THE DEFECT IS MOVED
NO
BATTERY VOLTAGE LOW OR BATTERY VOLTAGE HIGH
USE THE DRBII TO SELECT "ACTUATE OUTPUTS"
CHOOSE "ALTERNATOR FIELD"
CONNECT A VOLTMETER TO THE R3 FIELD TERMINAL
WIGGLE THE DB AND DG WIRE STARTING AT THE ALTERNATOR
CONTINUE WIGGLING BACK TOWARD THE ENGINE CONTROLLER
WHEN THE INTERMITTENT CONNECTION IS MOVED,....
THE VOLTMETER WILL STOP CHANGING FROM 1 TO 12 VOLTS

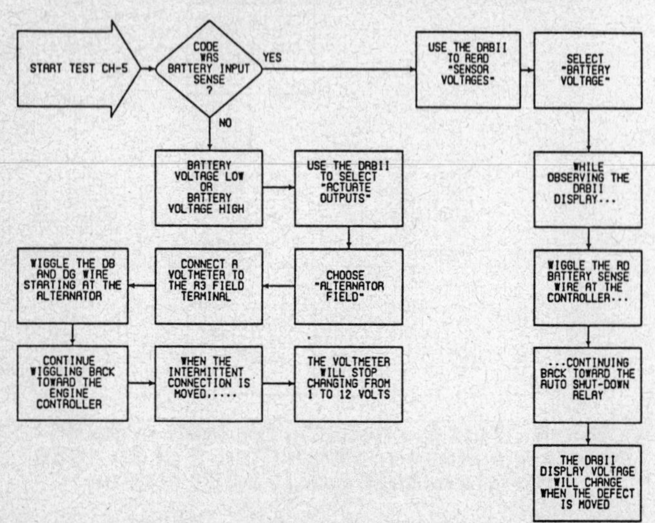

**Fig. 7 Test 5, checking for intermittent fault codes. 1989 models except 3.0L/V6-181 engine**

START TEST CH-6
USE THE DRBII TO SELECT "READ SENSOR VOLTAGES"
CHOOSE BATTERY TEMPERATURE SENSOR
THE VOLTAGE IS BETWEEN .2 AND 3 VOLTS ?
YES
USE THE DRBII TO CHOOSE "BATTERY VOLTAGE"
START THE ENGINE AND READ THE DRBII DISPLAY
NO
REPLACE THE ENGINE CONTROLLER
THE VOLTAGE IS BETWEEN 13 AND 15 VOLTS ?
YES
TEST BATTERY FOR DRAIN CONDITION OR INTERNAL DEFECT
NO
CHECK THE ALTERNATOR STATOR OR DIODE SECTION...
..OR HIGH RESISTANCE BETWEEN THE ALTERNATOR AND BATTERY +

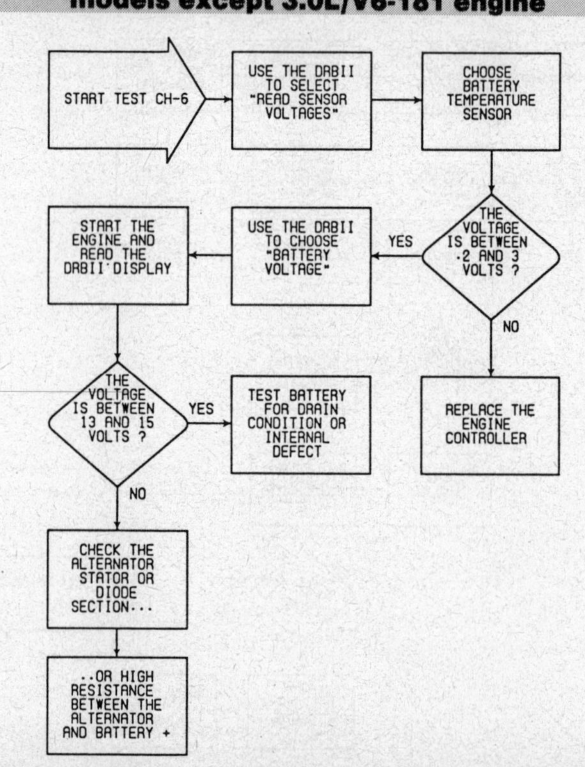

**Fig. 8 Test 6, checking the charging system w/no codes. 1989 models except 3.0L/V6-181 engine**

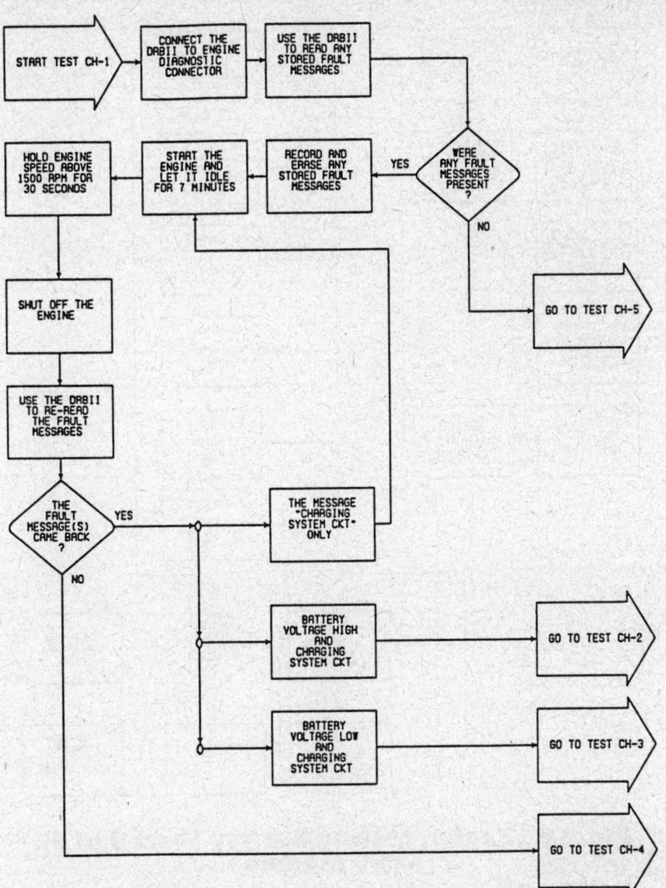


**Fig. 9 Test 1, checking charging system for fault messages. 1989 models w/3.0L engine**

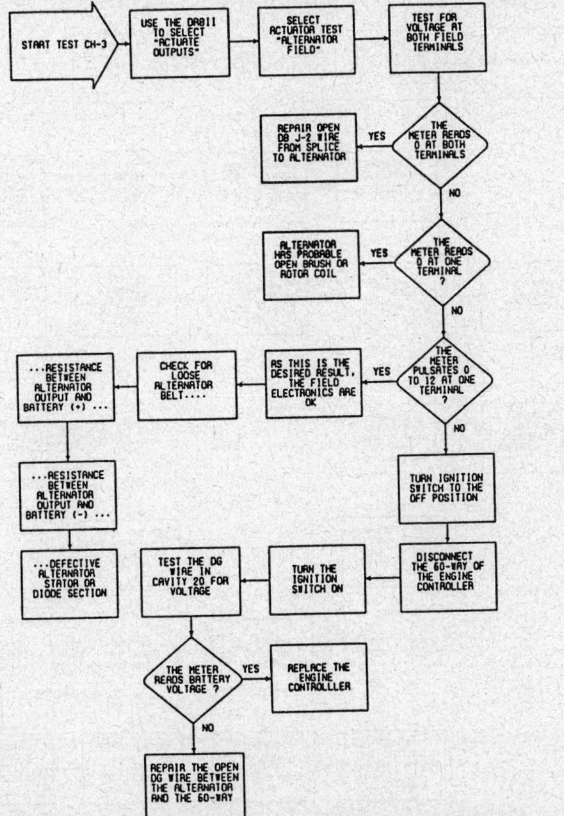


**Fig. 11 Test 3, checking for fault-battery voltage low. 1989 models w/3.0L engine**

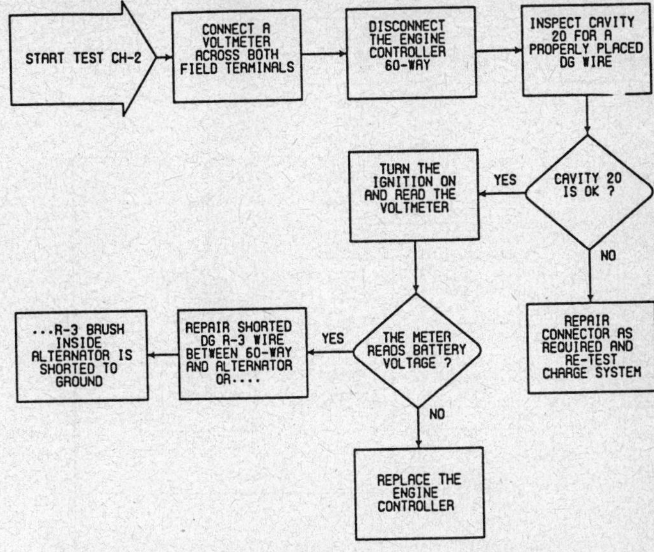


**Fig. 10 Test 2, checking for fault-battery voltage high. 1989 models w/3.0L engine**

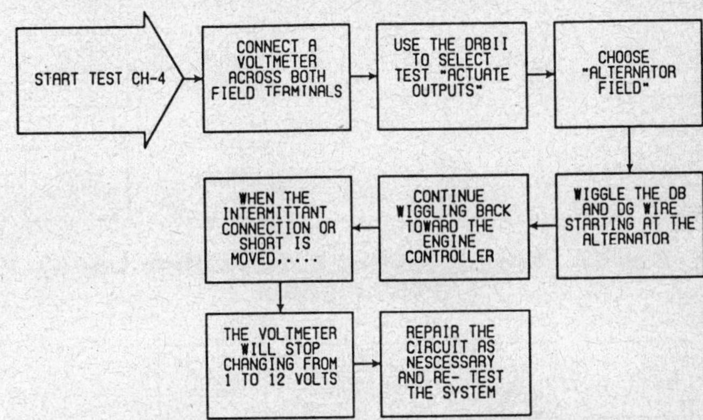


**Fig. 12 Test 4, checking for intermittent fault messages. 1989 models w/3.0L engine**

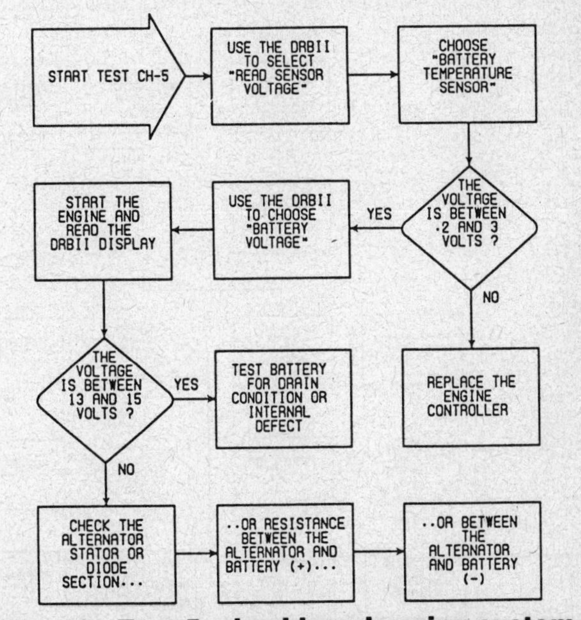


**Fig. 13 Test 5, checking charging system with no fault messages. 1989 models w/3.0L engine**

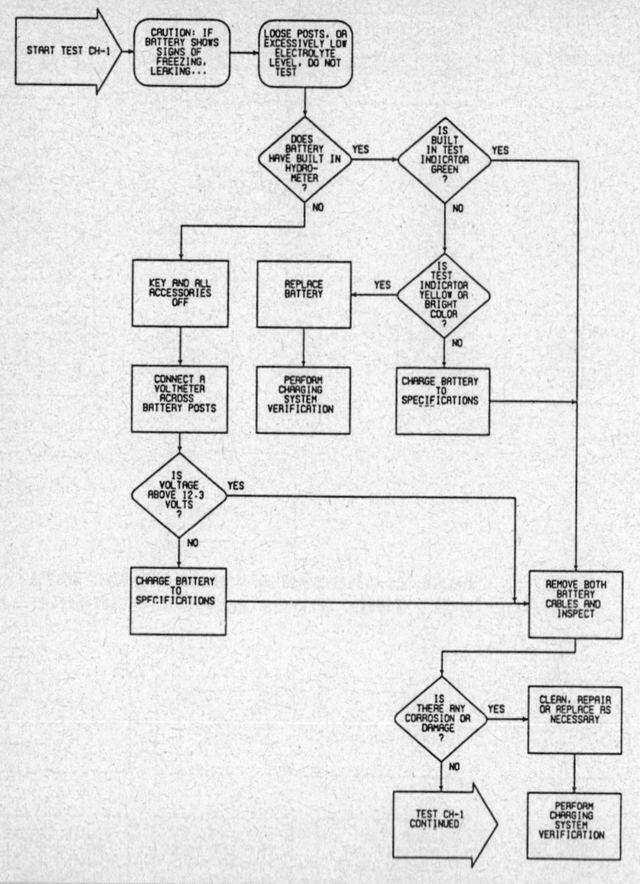


**Fig. 14 Test 1, testing battery (Part 1 of 3). 1990 models**

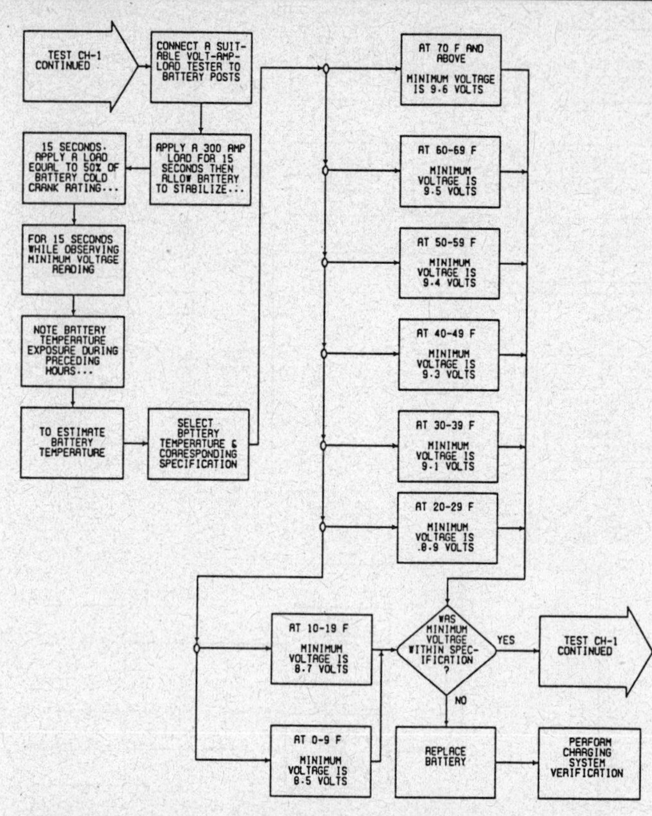


**Fig. 14 Test 1, testing battery (Part 2 of 3). 1990 models**

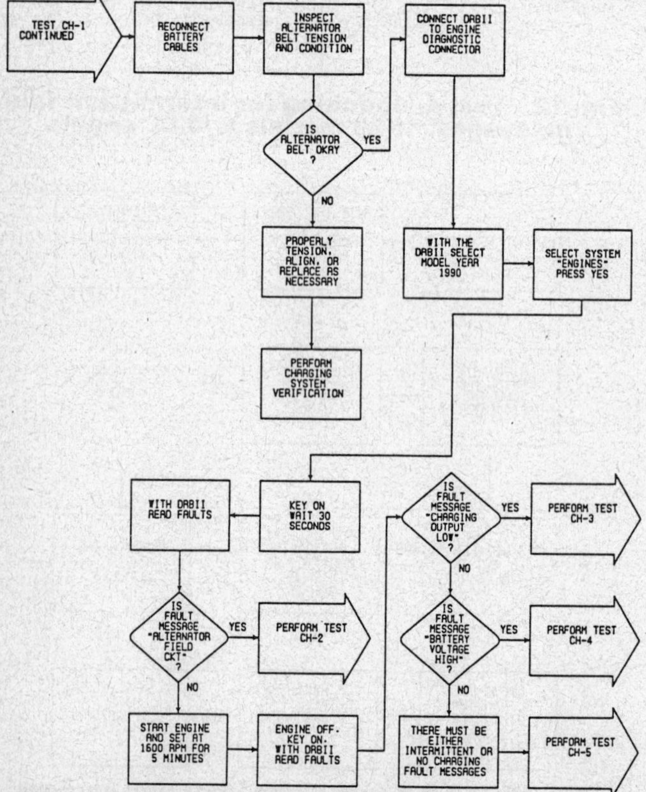


**Fig. 14 Test 1, testing battery (Part 3 of 3). 1990 models**

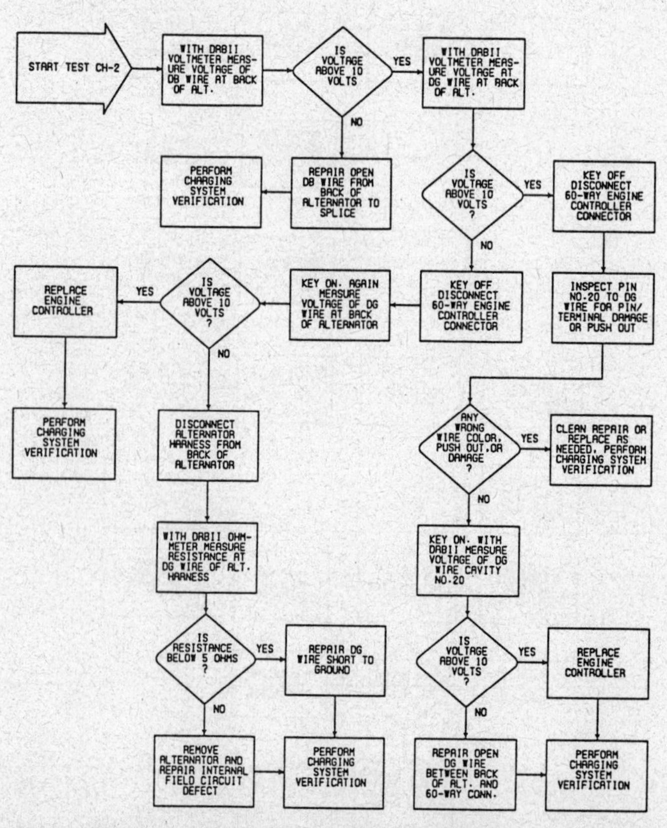


**Fig. 15 Test 2, repairing fault "alternator field circuit." 1990 models**

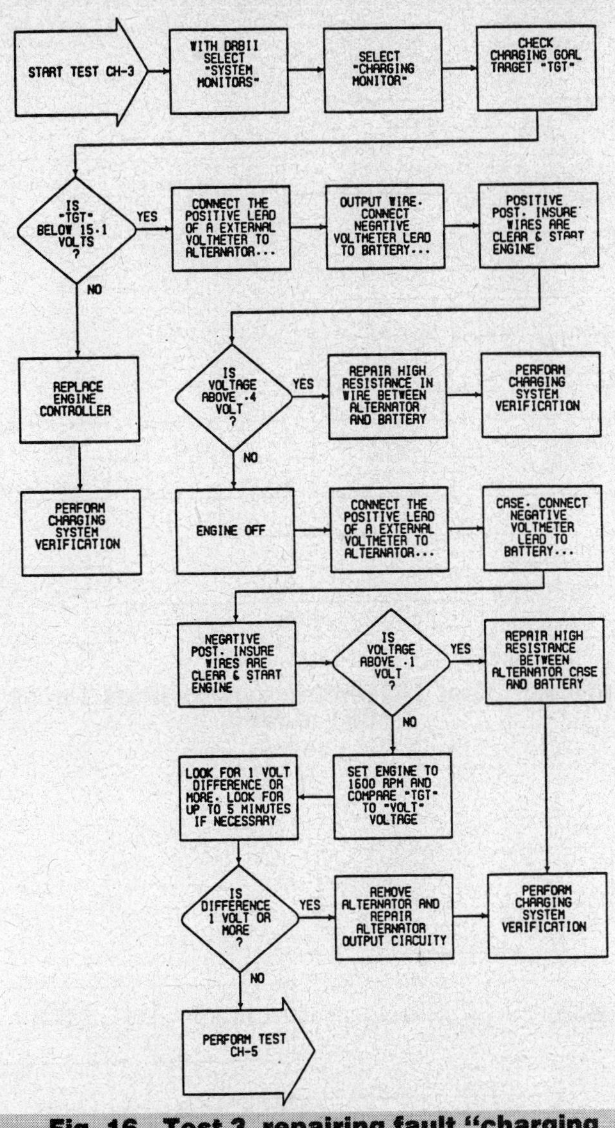


**Fig. 16 Test 3, repairing fault "charging output low." 1990 models**

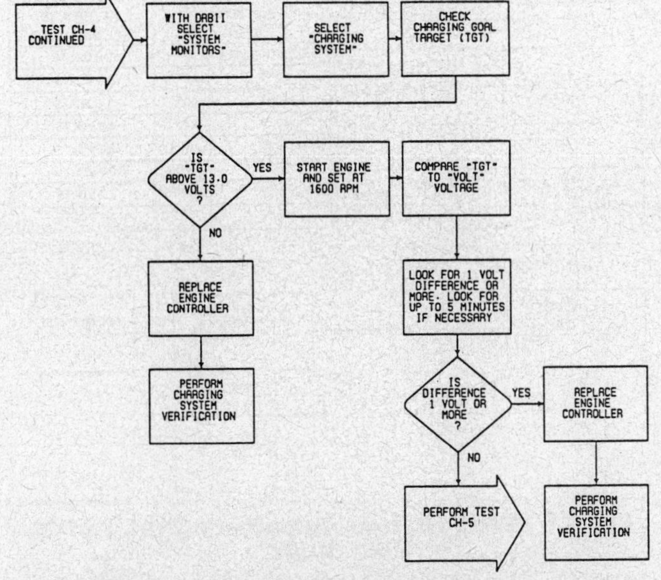


**Fig. 17 Test 4, repairing fault "battery voltage high" (Part 2 of 2). 1990 models**

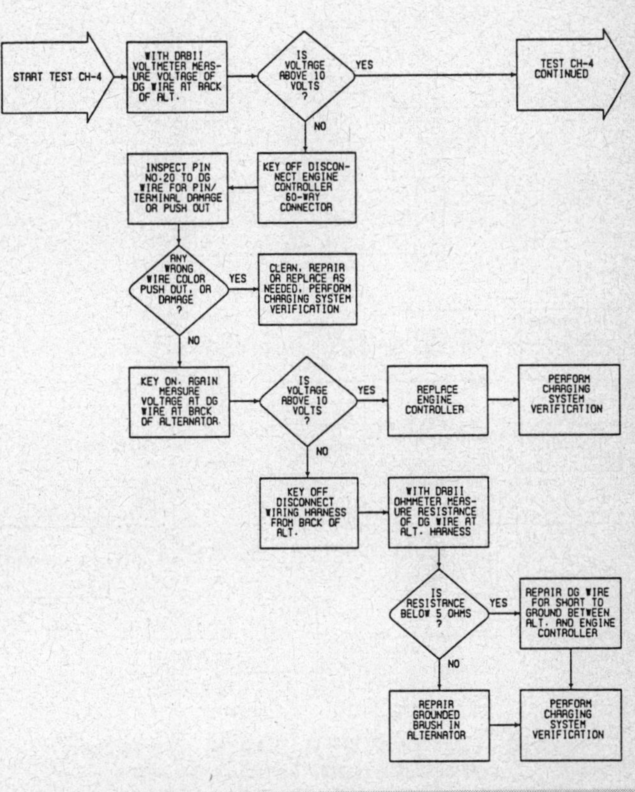


**Fig. 17 Test 4, repairing fault "battery voltage high" (Part 1 of 2). 1990 models**

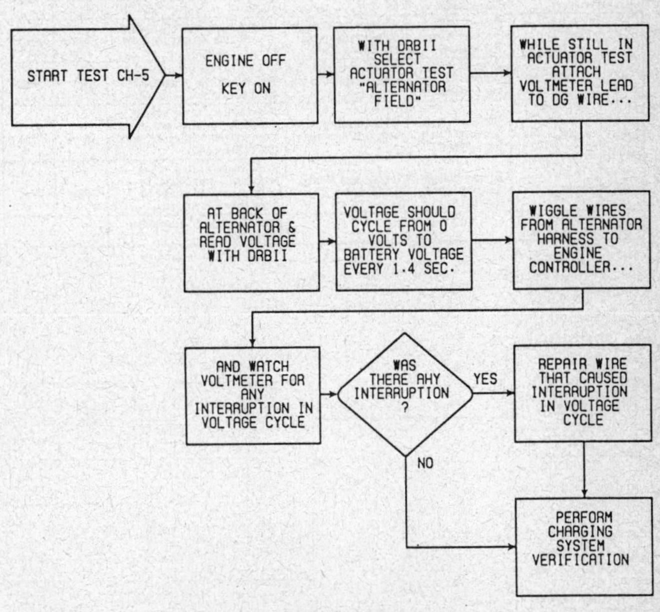


**Fig. 18 Test 5, checking for intermittent fault messages. 1990 models**

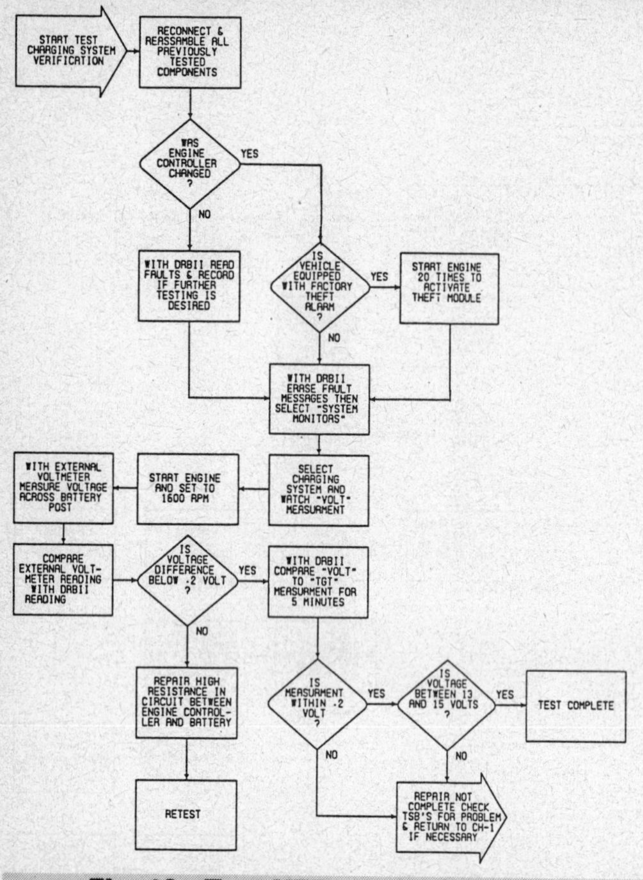


**Fig. 19 Test VER, charging system verification. 1990 models**

| Fault Code | Type | Check Engine Lamp | Circuit | When Monitored By The Logic Module | When Put Into Memory | Actuator Tests Test Code | Sensor Read Tests |
|---|---|---|---|---|---|---|---|
| 12 | Indication | No | Battery Feed to the Engine Controller | All the time when the ignition switch is on. | If the battery feed to the logic module has been disconnected within the last 50-100 engine starts. | None | None |
| 16 | Fault | Yes | Battery Voltage Sensing (Charging System) | All the time after one minutes from when the engine starts. | If the battery sensing voltage drops below 4 volts for more than 13 seconds. | None | Yes |
| 41 | Fault | No | Alternator Field Control (Charging System) | All the time when the ignition switch is on. | If the field control fails to switch properly or excessive alt. field current detected. | Yes | None |
| 46 | Fault | Yes | Battery Voltage Sensing (Charging System) | All the time when the engine is running. | If the battery sense voltage is more than 1 volt above the desired control voltage for more than 13 seconds. | None | Yes |
| 47 | Fault | No | Battery Voltage Sensing (Charging System) | Engine rpm above 1,500 rpm. | If the battery sense voltage is less than 1 volt below the desired control voltage for more than 33 seconds. | None | Yes |
| 55 | Indication | No | | | Indicates end of diagnostic mode. | | |

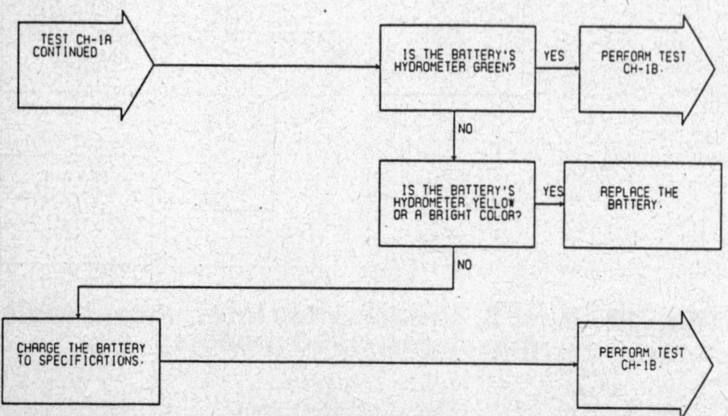


**Fig. 20 Test 1A, testing battery (Part 2 of 2). 1991 models**

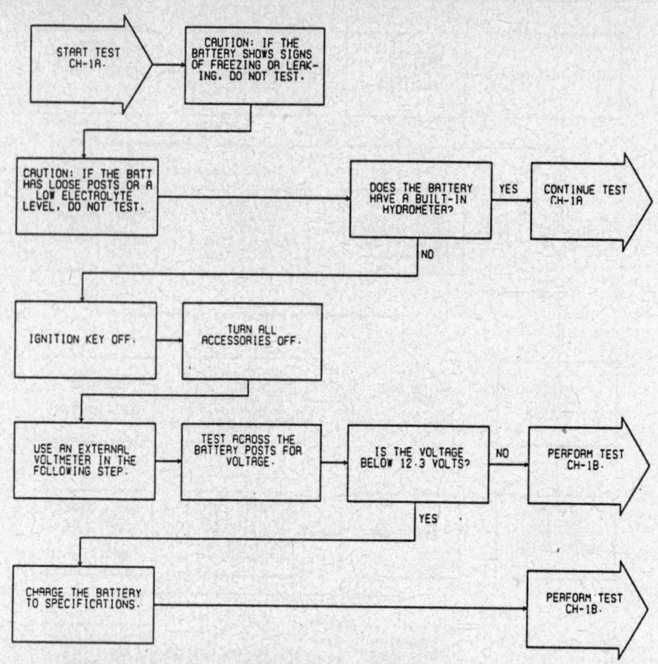


**Fig. 20 Test 1A, testing battery (Part 1 of 2). 1991 models**

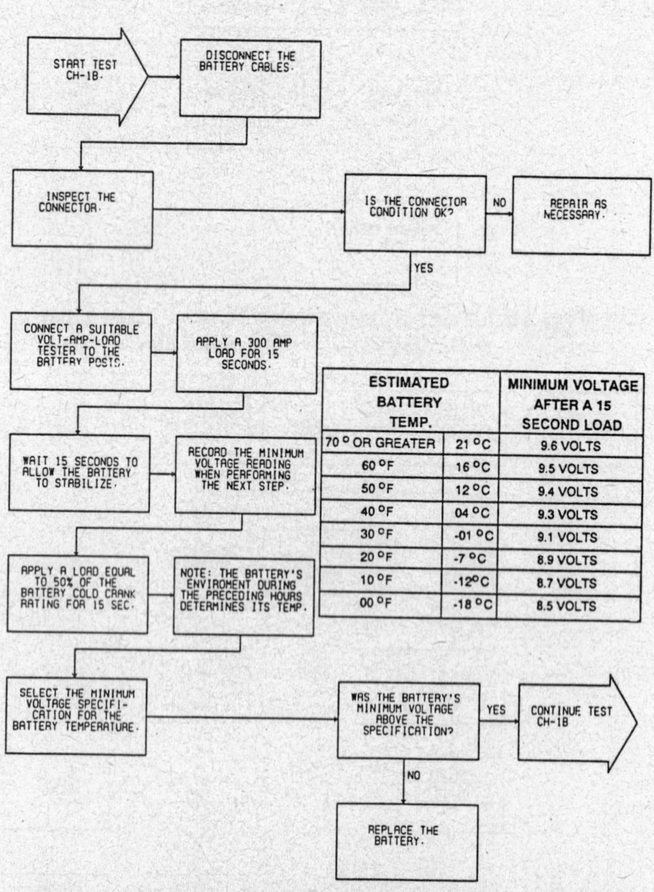


| ESTIMATED BATTERY TEMP. | | MINIMUM VOLTAGE AFTER A 15 SECOND LOAD |
|---|---|---|
| 70 °F OR GREATER | 21 °C | 9.6 VOLTS |
| 60 °F | 16 °C | 9.5 VOLTS |
| 50 °F | 12 °C | 9.4 VOLTS |
| 40 °F | 04 °C | 9.3 VOLTS |
| 30 °F | -01 °C | 9.1 VOLTS |
| 20 °F | -7 °C | 8.9 VOLTS |
| 10 °F | -12°C | 8.7 VOLTS |
| 00 °F | -18 °C | 8.5 VOLTS |

**Fig. 21 Test 1B, testing battery (Part 1 of 3). 1991 models**

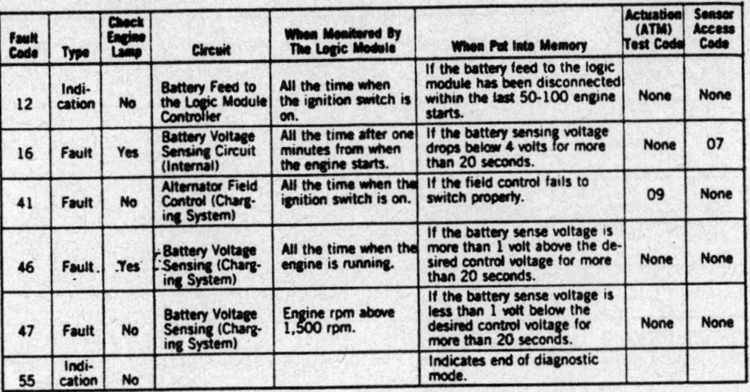

| Fault Code | Type | Check Engine Lamp | Circuit | When Monitored By The Logic Module | When Put Into Memory | Actuation (ATM) Test Code | Sensor Access Code |
|---|---|---|---|---|---|---|---|
| 12 | Indi-cation | No | Battery Feed to the Logic Module Controller | All the time when the ignition switch is on. | If the battery feed to the logic module has been disconnected within the last 50-100 engine starts. | None | None |
| 16 | Fault | Yes | Battery Voltage Sensing Circuit (Internal) | All the time after one minutes from when the engine starts. | If the battery sensing voltage drops below 4 volts for more than 20 seconds. | None | 07 |
| 41 | Fault | No | Alternator Field Control (Charg-ing System) | All the time when the ignition switch is on. | If the field control fails to switch properly. | 09 | None |
| 46 | Fault | Yes | Battery Voltage Sensing (Charg-ing System) | All the time when the engine is running. | If the battery sense voltage is more than 1 volt above the de-sired control voltage for more than 20 seconds. | None | None |
| 47 | Fault | No | Battery Voltage Sensing (Charg-ing System) | Engine rpm above 1,500 rpm. | If the battery sense voltage is less than 1 volt below the desired control voltage for more than 20 seconds. | None | None |
| 55 | Indi-cation | No | | | Indicates end of diagnostic mode. | | |

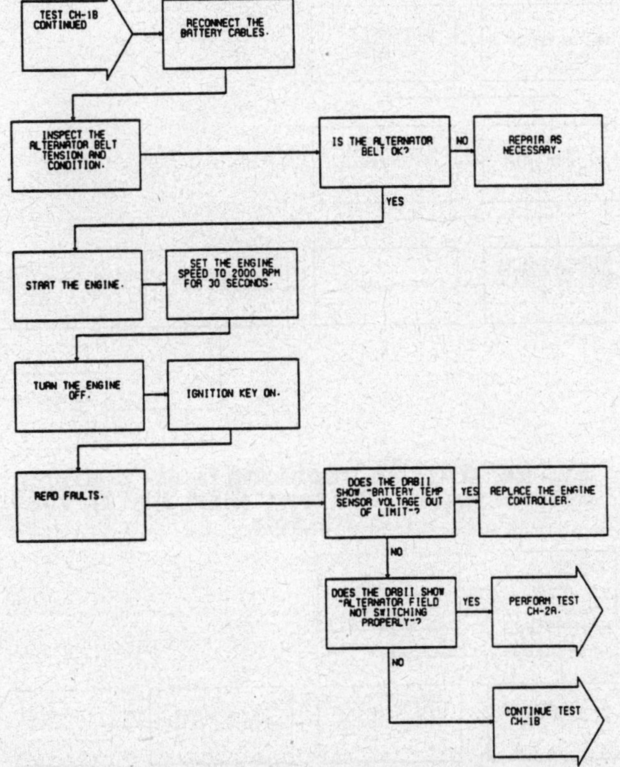


**Fig. 21 Test 1B, testing battery (Part 2 of 3). 1991 models**

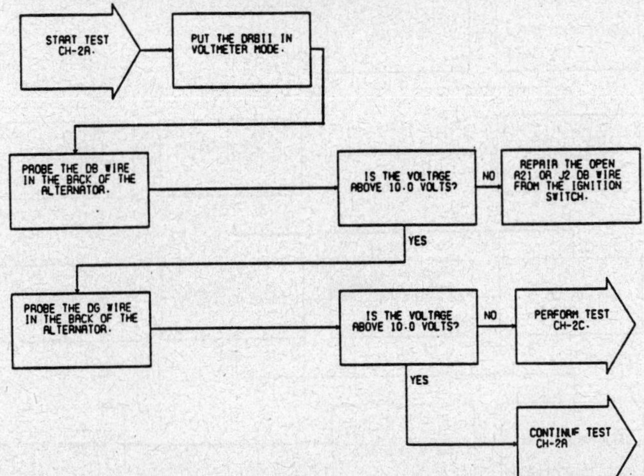


**Fig. 22 Test 2A, repairing fault "alternator field not switching properly" (Part 1 of 2). 1991 models**

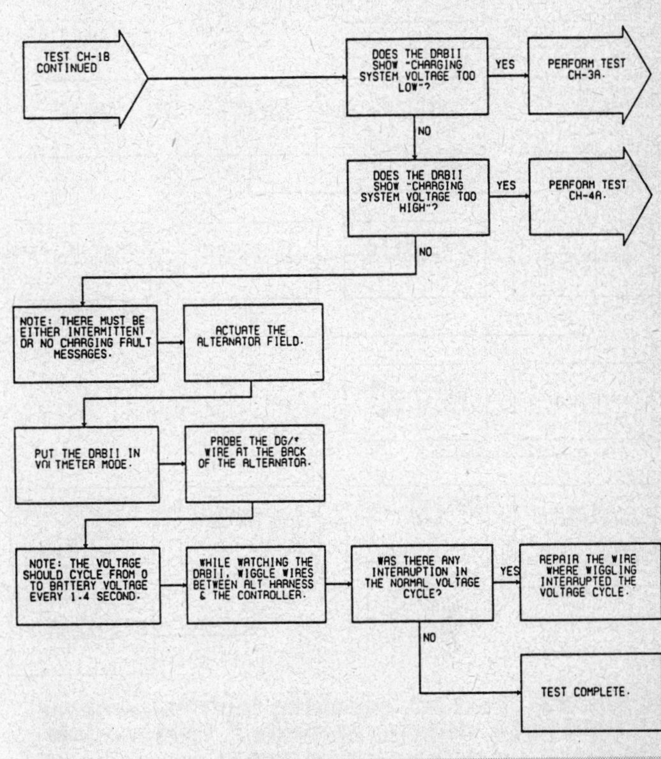


**Fig. 21 Test 1B, testing battery (Part 3 of 3). 1991 models**

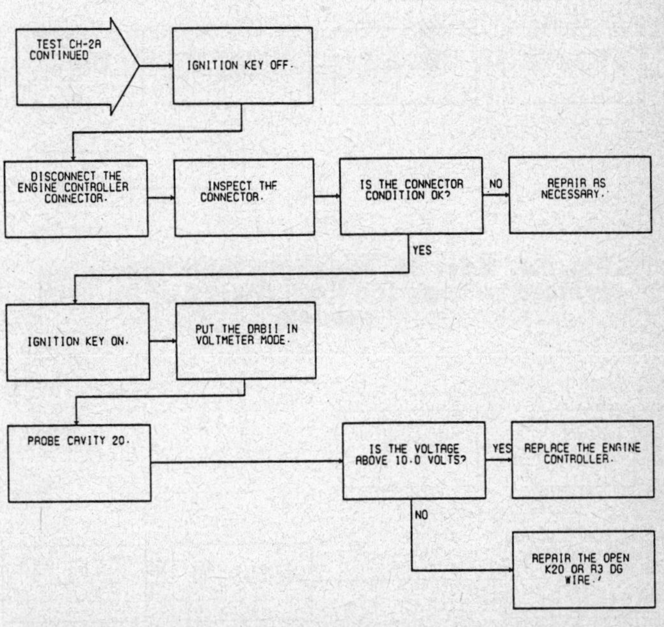


**Fig. 22 Test 2A, repairing fault "alternator field not switching properly" (Part 2 of 2). 1991 models**

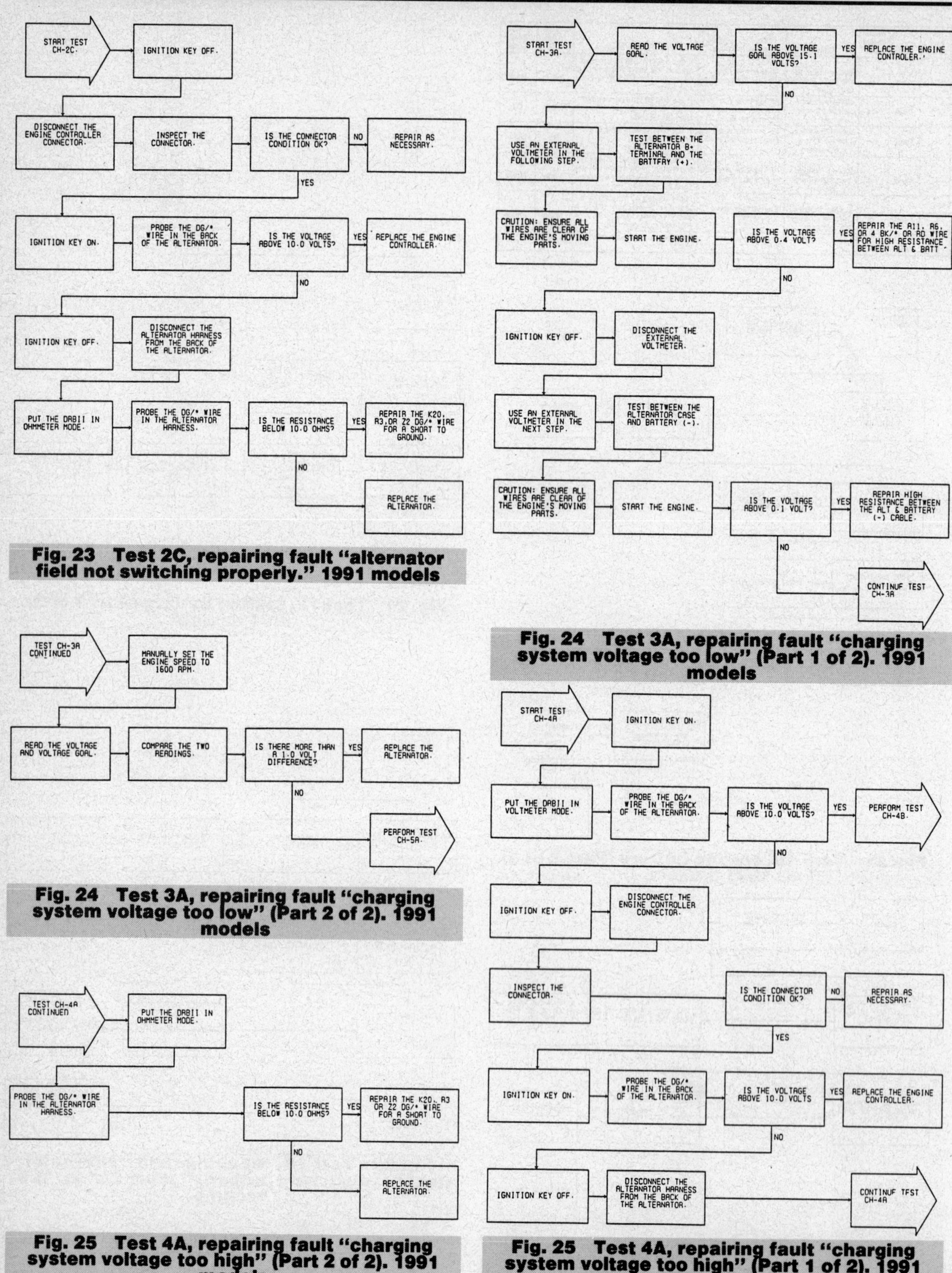


Fig. 23 Test 2C, repairing fault "alternator field not switching properly." 1991 models



Fig. 24 Test 3A, repairing fault "charging system voltage too low" (Part 1 of 2). 1991 models



Fig. 24 Test 3A, repairing fault "charging system voltage too low" (Part 2 of 2). 1991 models



Fig. 25 Test 4A, repairing fault "charging system voltage too high" (Part 1 of 2). 1991 models



Fig. 25 Test 4A, repairing fault "charging system voltage too high" (Part 2 of 2). 1991 models

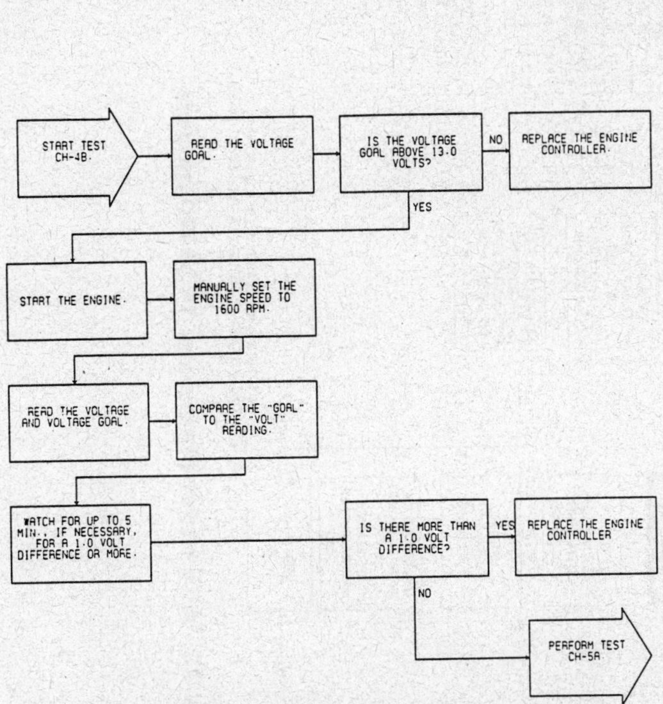


**Fig. 26 Test 4B, repairing fault "charging system voltage too high." 1991 models**

Inspect the vehicle to ensure that all engine components are connected. Reassemble and reconnect components as necessary.

If the engine controller has been changed, do the following:

1. If the vehicle is equipped with a factory theft alarm, start the vehicle at least 20 times so that the alarm system may be activated when desired.

Connect the DRBII to the engine diagnostic connector and erase faults.

Ensure no other speed control problem remains by doing the following:

1. Start the engine.
2. Raise the engine speed to 2000 rpm for at least 30 seconds.
3. Allow the engine to idle.
4. Turn the engine off.
5. Turn ignition key on.
6. With the DRBII, read fault messages. Refer to HELP 1 for assistance.

If the repaired fault has reset, the repair is not complete. Check all pertinent TECHNICAL SERVICE BULLETINS and return to TEST CH-1A if necessary.

If there is another fault, return to TEST CH-1A and follow the path specified by the other fault.

If there are no other faults, the repair is now complete.

**Fig. 28 Test VER, charging system verification. 1991 models**

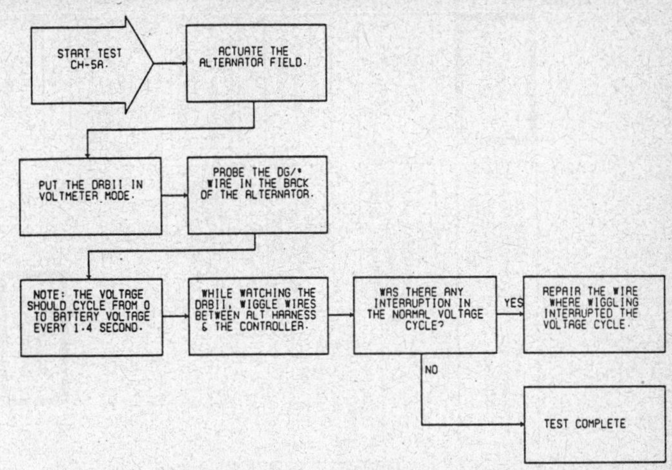


**Fig. 27 Test 5A, checking for intermittent problems. 1991 models**

| Fault Code | Type | Check Engine Lamp | Circuit | When Monitored By The Logic Module | When Put Into Memory | Actuator Tests Test Code | Sensor Read Tests |
|---|---|---|---|---|---|---|---|
| 12 | Indi-cation | No | Battery Feed to the Engine Controller | All the time when the ignition switch is on. | If the battery feed to the logic module has been disconnected within the last 50-100 engine starts. | None | None |
| 16 | Fault | Yes | Battery Voltage Sensing (Charg-ing System) | All the time after one minutes from when the engine starts. | If the battery sensing voltage drops below 4 volts for more than 13 seconds. | None | Yes |
| 41 | Fault | No | Alternator Field Control (Charg-ing System) | All the time when the ignition switch is on. | If the field control fails to switch properly or excessive alt. field current detected. | Yes | None |
| 46 | Fault | Yes | Battery Voltage Sensing (Charg-ing System) | All the time when the engine is running. | If the battery sense voltage is more than 1 volt above the de-sired control voltage for more than 13 seconds. | None | Yes |
| 47 | Fault | No | Battery Voltage Sensing (Charg-ing System) | Engine rpm above 1,500 rpm. | If the battery sense voltage is less than 1 volt below the desired control voltage for more than 33 seconds. | None | Yes |
| 55 | Indi-cation | No | | | Indicates end of diagnostic mode. | | |

**Fig. 29 Alternator fault code. 1989 models w/2.2L & 2.5L engines**

| Fault Code | Type | Check Engine Lamp | Circuit | When Monitored By The Logic Module | When Put Into Memory | Actuation (ATM) Test Code | Sensor Access Code |
|---|---|---|---|---|---|---|---|
| 12 | Indi-cation | No | Battery Feed to the Logic Module Controller | All the time when the ignition switch is on. | If the battery feed to the logic module has been disconnected within the last 50-100 engine starts. | None | None |
| 16 | Fault | Yes | Battery Voltage Sensing Circuit (Internal) | All the time after one minutes from when the engine starts. | If the battery sensing voltage drops below 4 volts for more than 20 seconds. | None | 07 |
| 41 | Fault | No | Alternator Field Control (Charg-ing System) | All the time when the ignition switch is on. | If the field control fails to switch properly. | 09 | None |
| 46 | Fault | Yes | Battery Voltage Sensing (Charg-ing System) | All the time when the engine is running. | If the battery sense voltage is more than 1 volt above the de-sired control voltage for more than 20 seconds. | None | None |
| 47 | Fault | No | Battery Voltage Sensing (Charg-ing System) | Engine rpm above 1,500 rpm. | If the battery sense voltage is less than 1 volt below the desired control voltage for more than 20 seconds. | None | None |
| 55 | Indi-cation | No | | | Indicates end of diagnostic mode. | | |

**Fig. 30 Alternator fault code. 1989 models w/3.0L engine**

| Code | Type | Power Loss Lamp | Circuit | When Monitored By The Logic Module | When Put Into Memory | Actuation (ATM)) Test Code | Sensor Access Code |
|---|---|---|---|---|---|---|---|
| 12 | Indi-cation | No | Battery Feed to the Logic Module | All the time when the ignition switch is on. | If the battery feed to the logic module has been disconnected within the last 50-100 engine starts. | None | None |
| 16 | Fault | Yes | Battery Voltage Sensing (Charg-ing System) | All the time after one minutes from when the engine starts. | If the battery sensing voltage drops below 4 volts for more than 20 seconds. | None | 07 |
| 41 | Fault | No | Alternator Field Control (Charg-ing System) | All the time when the ignition switch is on. | If the field control fails to switch properly. | 09 | None |
| 46 | Fault | Yes | Battery Voltage Sensing (Charg-ing System) | All the time when the engine is running. | If the battery sense voltage is more than 1 volt above the de-sired control voltage for more than 20 seconds. | None | None |
| 47 | Fault | No | Battery Voltage Sensing (Charg-ing System) | Engine rpm above 1,500 rpm. | If the battery sense voltage is less than 1 volt below the desired control voltage for more than 20 seconds. | None | None |
| 55 | Indi-cation | No | | | Indicates end of diagnostic mode. | | |
| 88 | Indi-cation | No | | | Indicates start of diagnostic mode. NOTE: This code must appear first in the diagnostic mode or fault codes will be inaccurate. | | |

**Fig. 31 Alternator fault code. 1989 models w/turbo engine**

| Fault Code | Type | Check Engine Lamp | Circuit | When Monitored By The Logic Module | When Put Into Memory |
|---|---|---|---|---|---|
| 12 | Indi-cation | No | Battery Feed to the Logic Module Controller | All the time when the ignition switch is on. | If the battery feed to the logic module has been disconnected within the last 50-100 engine starts. |
| 41 | Fault | Yes | Alternator Field Control (Charg-ing System) | All the time when the ignition switch is on. | If the field control fails to switch properly. |
| 46 | Fault | Yes | Battery Voltage Sensing (Charg-ing System) | All the time when the engine is running. | If the battery sense voltage is more than 1 volt above the desired control voltage for more than 20 seconds. |
| 47 | Fault | Yes | Battery Voltage Sensing (Charg-ing System) | Engine rpm above 1,500 rpm. | If the battery sense voltage is less than 1 volt below the desired control voltage for more than 20 seconds and active test indicates a starter problem. |
| 55 | Indi-cation | No | | | Indicates end of diagnostic mode. |

**Fig. 32 Alternator fault code. 1990–91 models**

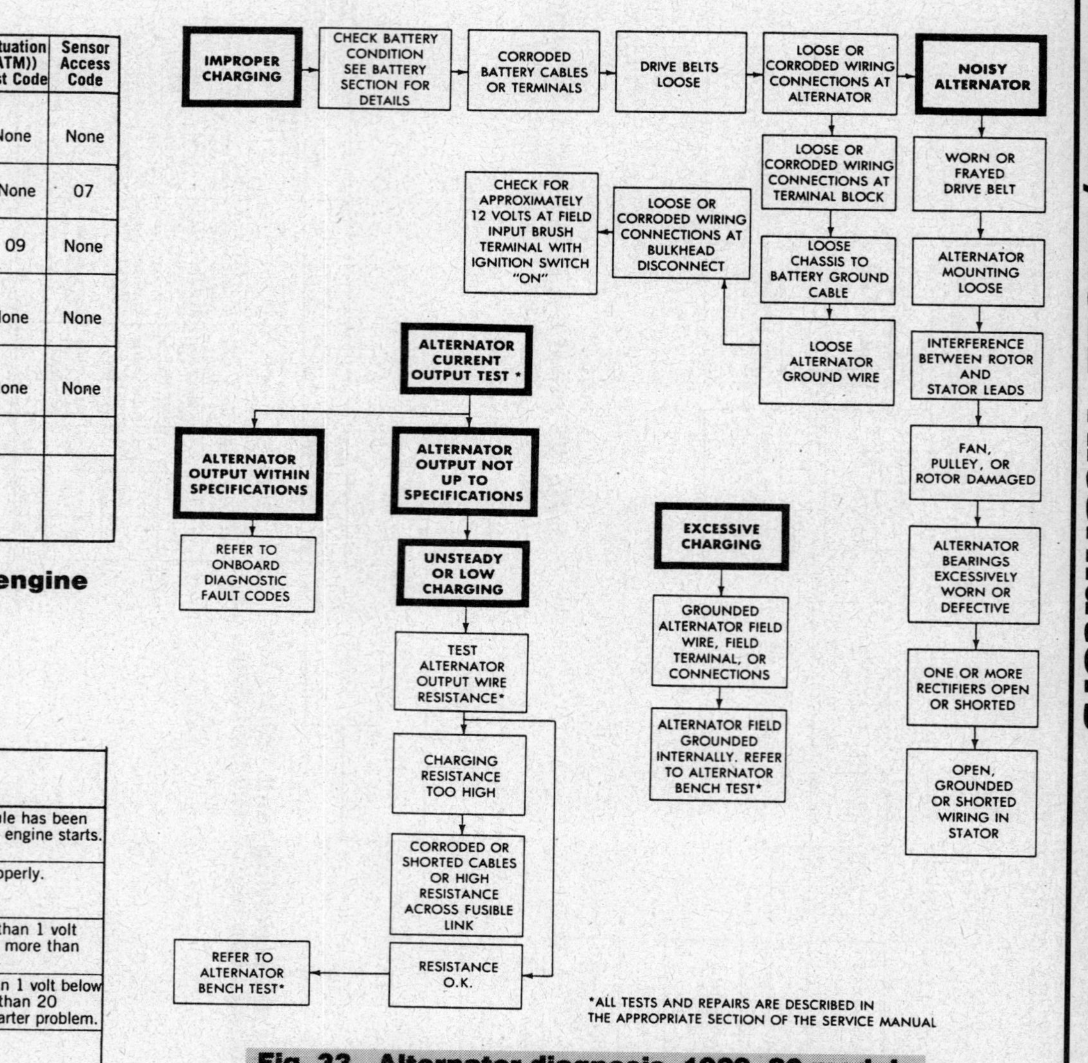


**Fig. 33 Alternator diagnosis. 1989–90 models**

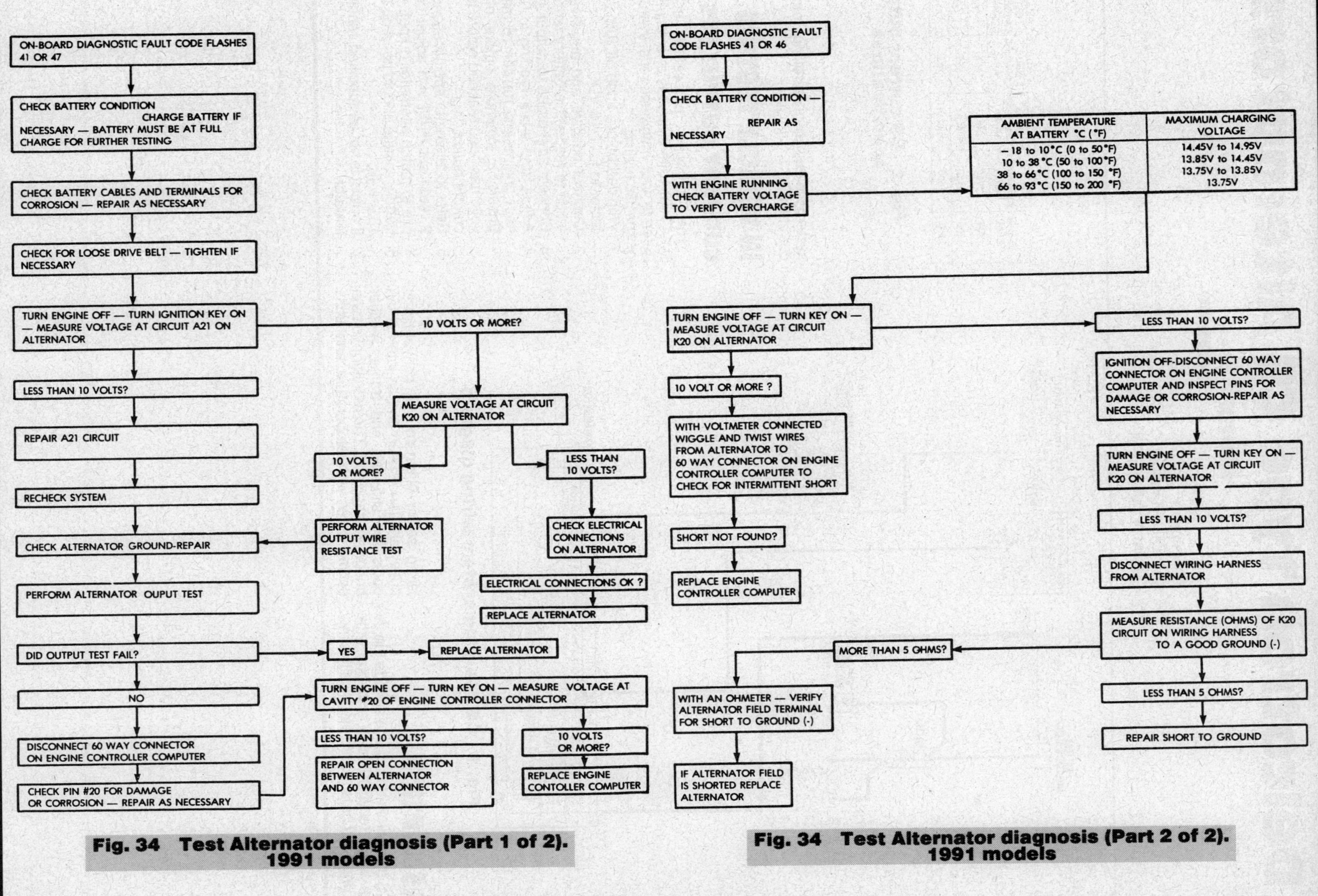


**Fig. 34 Test Alternator diagnosis (Part 1 of 2). 1991 models**

**Fig. 34 Test Alternator diagnosis (Part 2 of 2). 1991 models**

# Delcotron Type CS Alternators

## INDEX



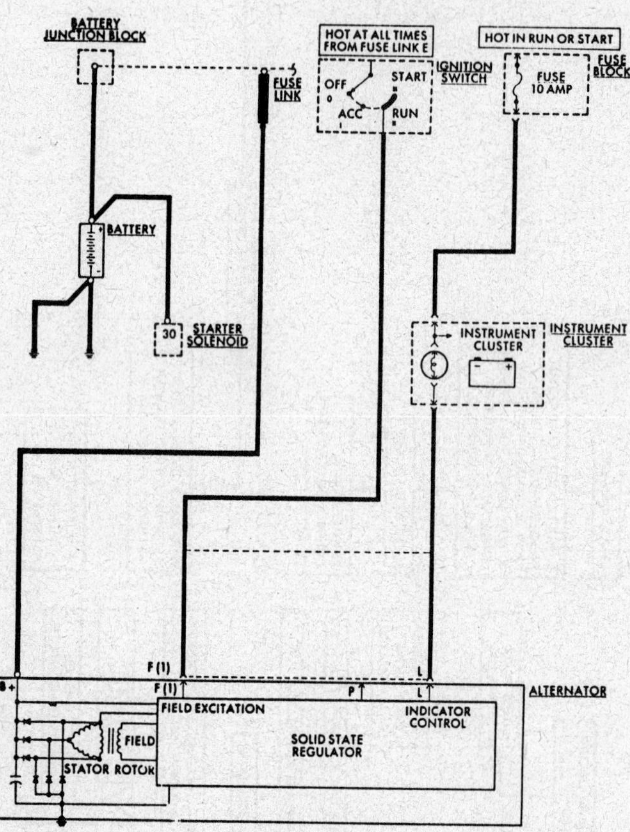


Fig. 1 CS charging system wiring diagram

## DESCRIPTION

CS alternators do not use a diode trio. A delta stator, rectifier bridge, and rotor with slip rings and brushes are electrically similar to earlier alternators. A conventional pulley and fan is used and an internal fan cools the slip ring end frame, rectifier bridge and regulator. The regulator voltage setting varies with temperature, and limits system voltage by controlling rotor field current, **Fig. 1**.

| Engine RPM | Alternator RPM | Delco CS130-85 Amp | Delco CS130-96 Amp | Delco CS130-105 Amp |
|---|---|---|---|---|
| 800 | 2250 | 48A | 51A | 60A |
| 1200 | 3350 | 61A | 65A | 74A |
| 2000 | 5600 | 70A | 78A | 84A |

**Fig. 2 CS current output specifications**

## IN VEHICLE TESTING

### CURRENT OUTPUT TEST

The following procedure uses a S-VAT-40 volts-amps-tester or equivalent. Refer to tool manufacturer's instructions for specific testing.

1. With carbon pile knob off, turn volt selector to EXT-18 VDC.
2. Connect positive and negative load leads to respective battery terminals.
3. Connect amp probe to output lead.
4. Adjust amp meter reading to 0, then start engine and run for 15 minutes. Ensure a minimum output of 13.0 volts has been reached before testing current output.
5. Refer to alternator specifications, **Fig. 2**, then set RPM and adjust carbon pile to match alternator output.
6. Battery voltage should not drop below 13.0 volts.
7. If output is not as specified, replace alternator.

# Mitsubishi Alternators

## INDEX



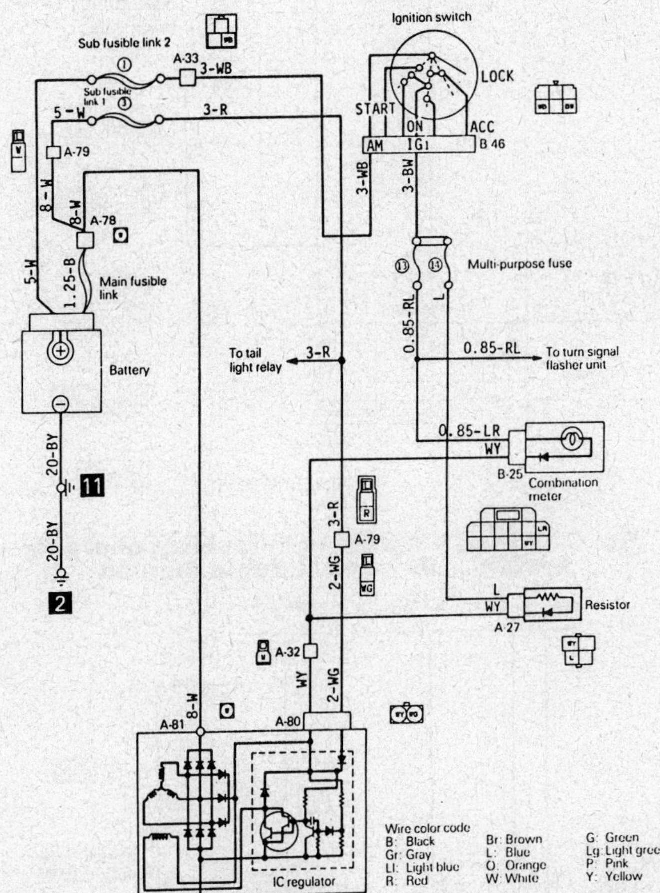


**Fig. 1 Wiring diagram of Mitsubishi charging system. Conquest**

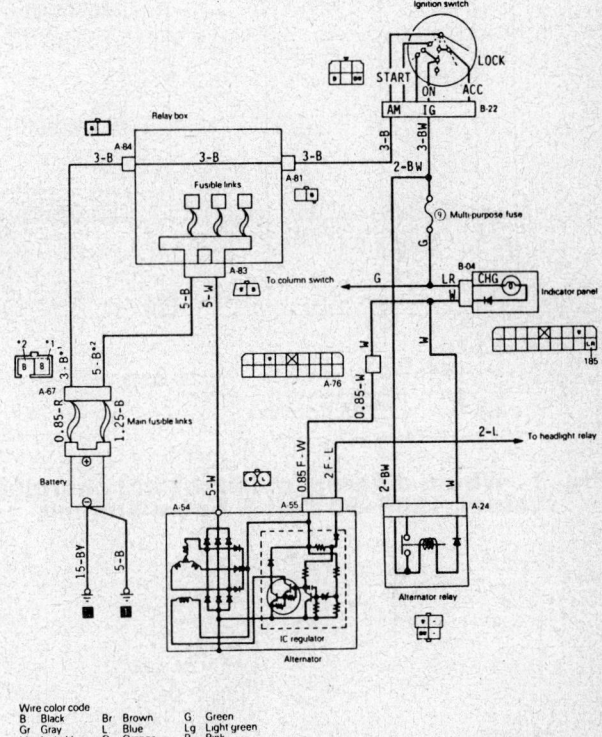

**Fig. 2 Wiring diagram of Mitsubishi charging system. Colt Vista**

## DESCRIPTION

On these units the regulator is incorporated into the alternator rear housing, **Figs. 1 through 11.** The electronic voltage regulator has the ability to vary regulated system voltage upward or downward as temperature changes. No voltage regulated adjustments are required on these units.

## IN-VEHICLE TESTING

### CHARGING VOLTAGE TEST

1. With ignition switch in the Off position, disconnect battery ground cable and connect a digital voltmeter between alternator S terminal, **Fig. 12,** and ground.
2. Disconnect alternator output wire from alternator B terminal, then connect a DC ammeter in series between the B terminal and the disconnected output wire. Connect positive lead of ammeter to B terminal. Connect negative lead to the disconnected output wire.
3. Install engine tachometer and reconnect battery ground cable.
4. Place ignition switch in the On position and note voltmeter. The reading should equal battery voltage. If reading is 0, check for an open circuit in the wire between alternator S terminal and battery positive terminal or a blown fusible link.
5. Start engine, keeping all accessories and lights off. Run engine at a constant 2500 RPM and read voltmeter when alternator output current drops to 10 amps or less.

### ALTERNATOR OUTPUT WIRE VOLTAGE DROP TEST

1. Disconnect battery ground cable.
2. Disconnect alternator output lead from alternator "B" terminal. **Fig. 13,** then connect a DC ammeter between "B" and disconnected output lead. Connect positive lead of ammeter to

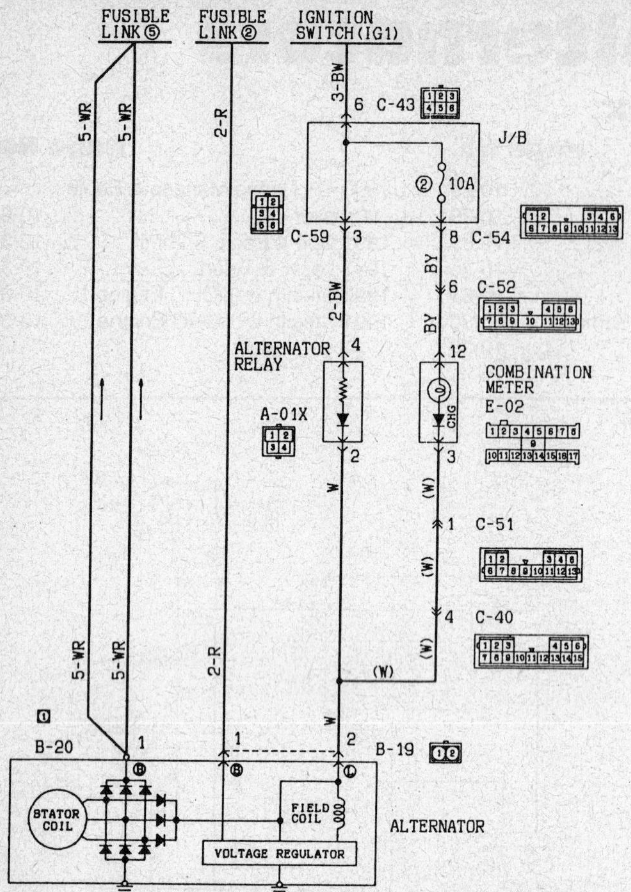


**Fig. 3 Wiring diagram of Mitsubishi charging system. 1989–90 Colt & Eagle Summit**

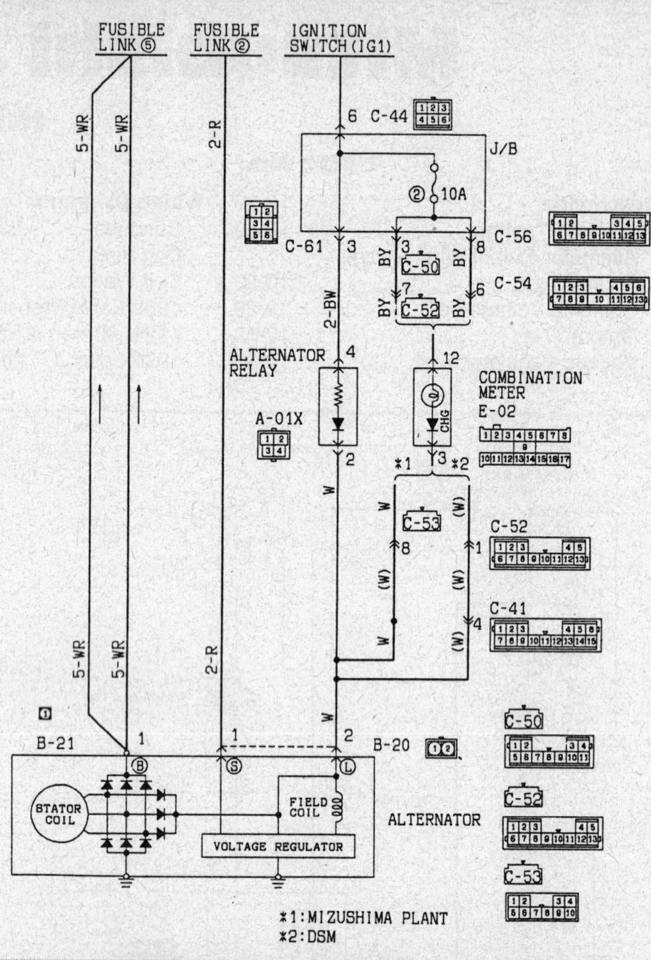


**Fig. 4 Wiring diagram of Mitsubishi charging system. 1991 Colt & Eagle Summit**

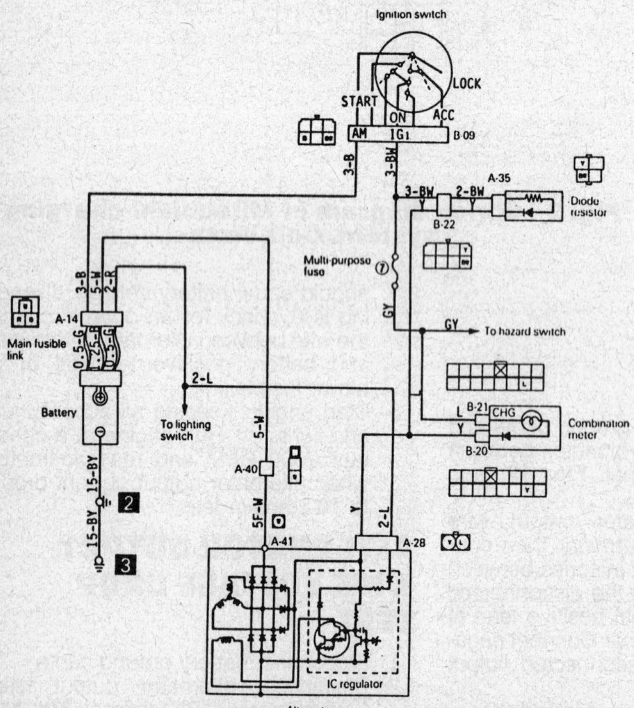


**Fig. 5 Wiring diagram of Mitsubishi charging system. Colt Wagon**

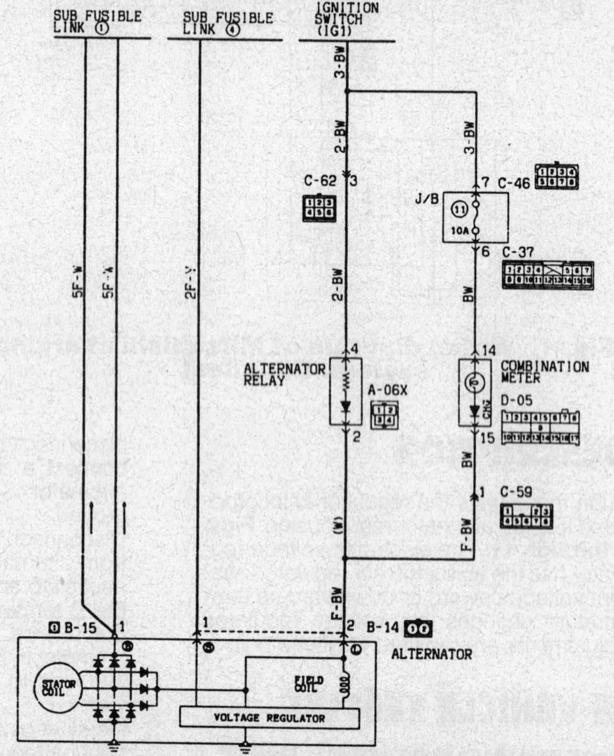


**Fig. 6 Wiring diagram of Mitsubishi charging system. 1990 Laser & Talon**

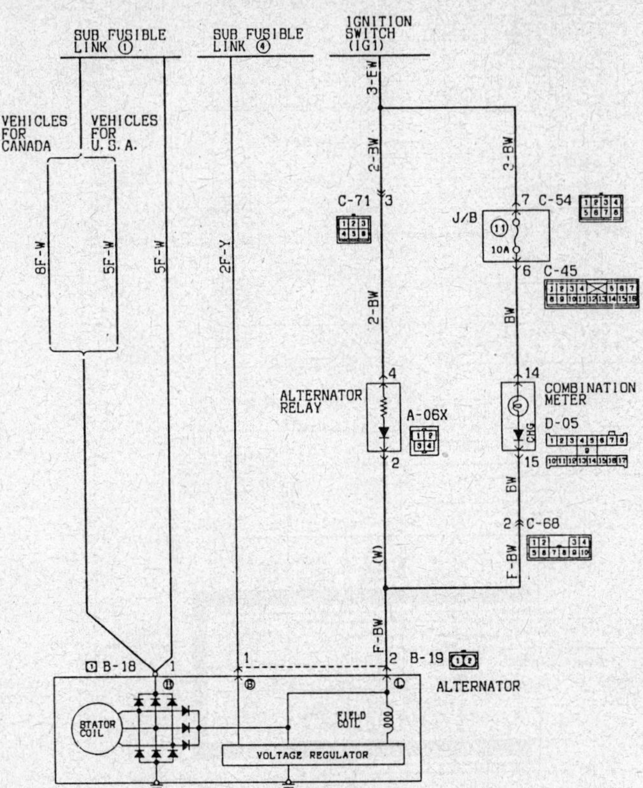


**Fig. 7 Wiring diagram of Mitsubishi charging system. 1991 Laser & Talon**

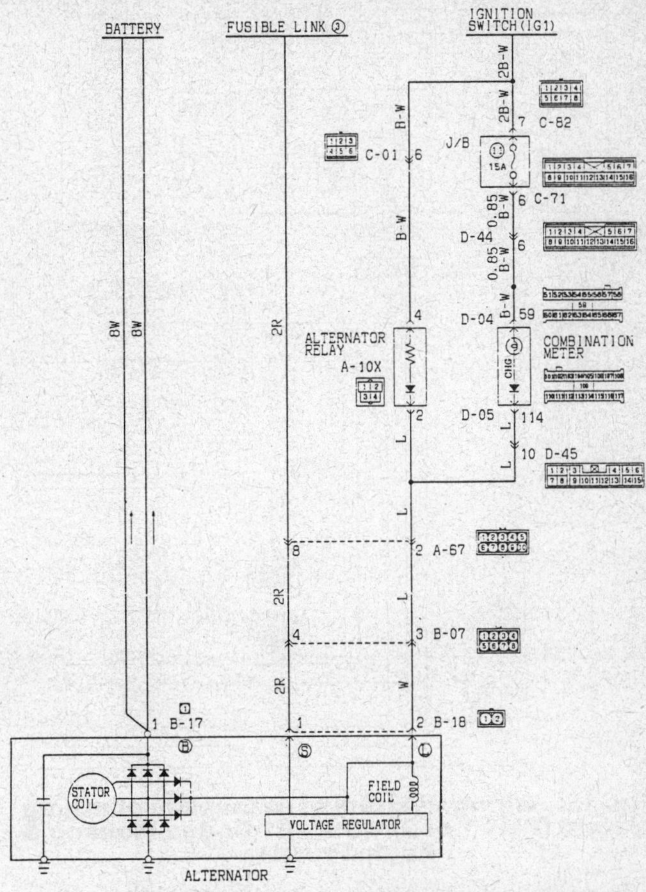


**Fig. 8 Wiring diagram of Mitsubishi charging system. 1991 Stealth w/SOHC engine**

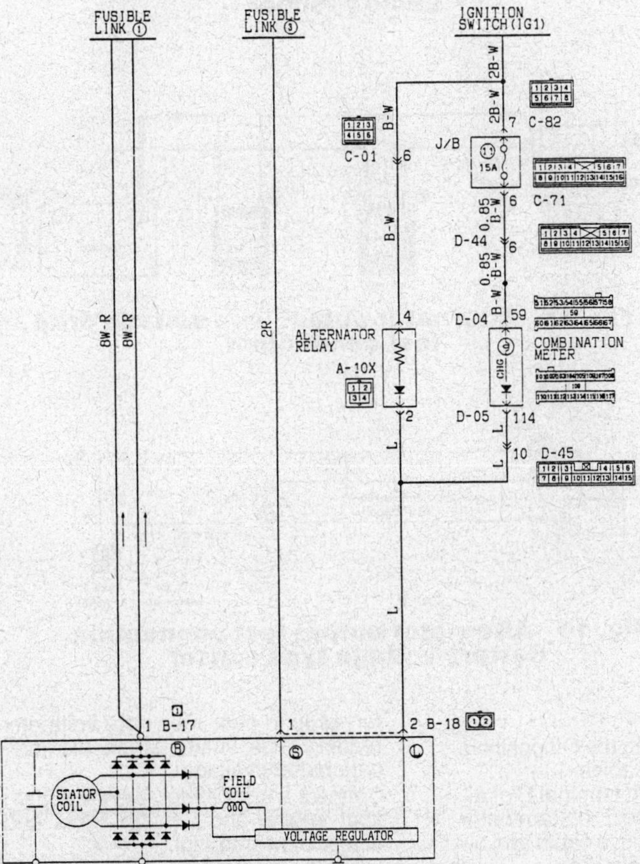


**Fig. 9 Wiring diagram of Mitsubishi charging system. 1991 Stealth w/DOHC engine**

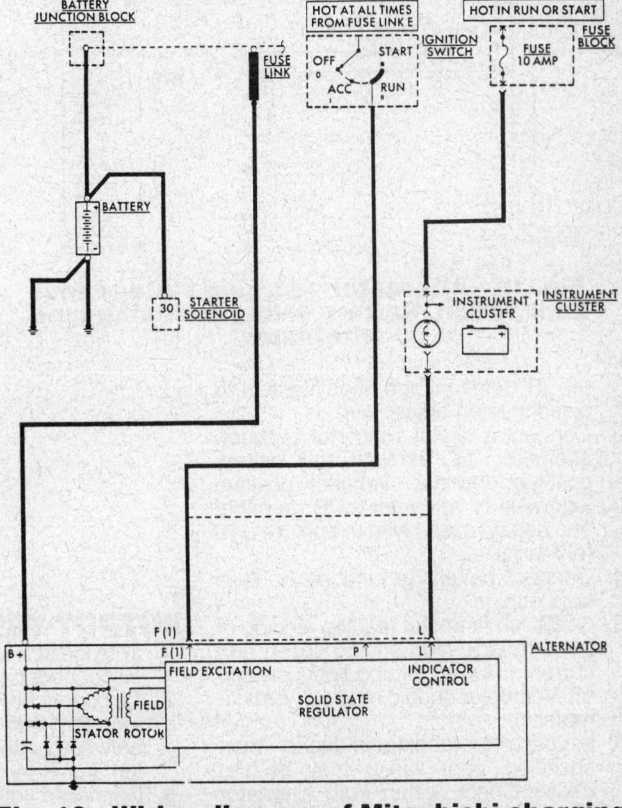


**Fig. 10 Wiring diagram of Mitsubishi charging system. 1989 Eagle Premier**

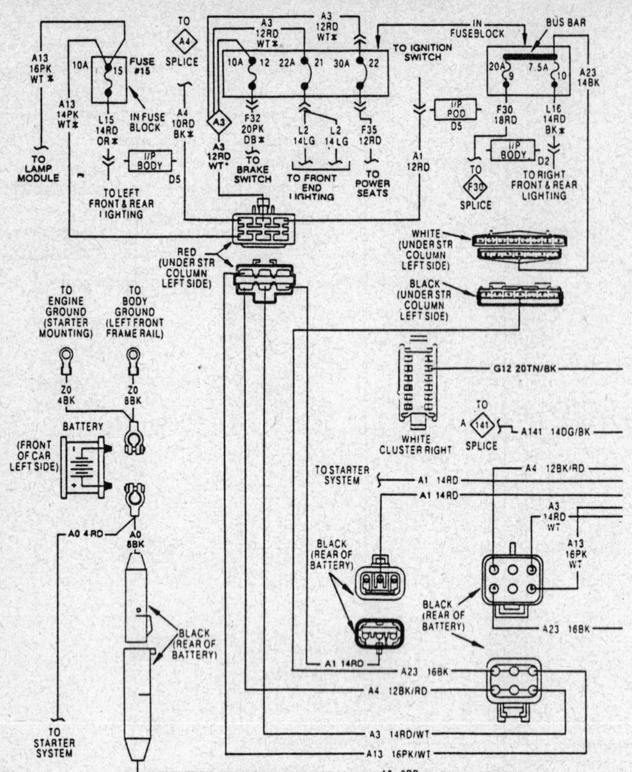


Fig. 11 Wiring diagram of Mitsubishi charging system (Part 1 of 2). 1990–91 Dodge Monaco & Eagle Premier

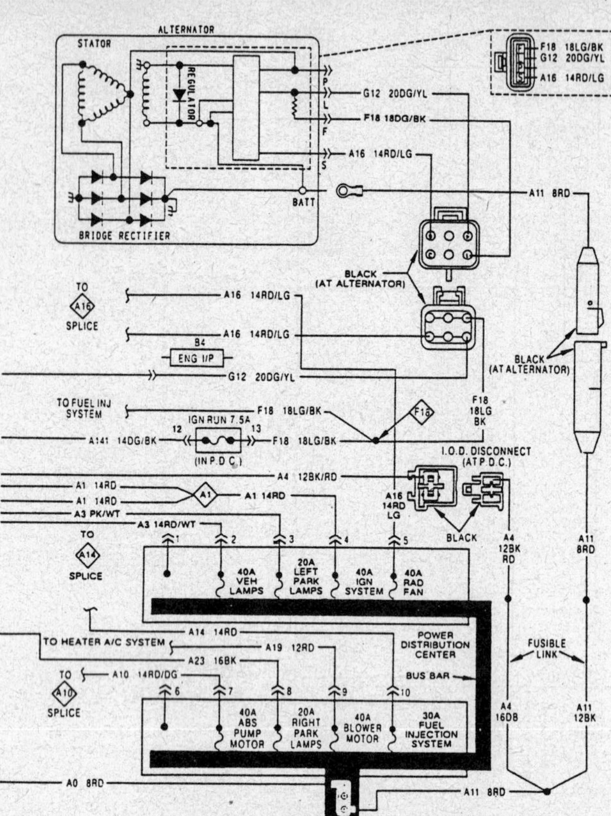


Fig. 11 Wiring diagram of Mitsubishi charging system (Part 2 of 2). 1990–91 Dodge Monaco & Eagle Premier

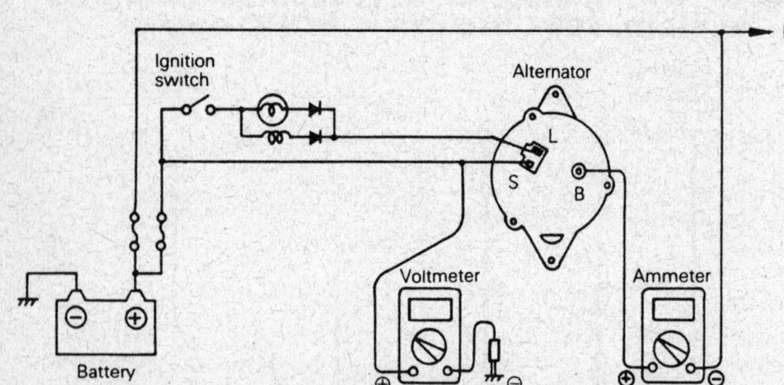


Fig. 12 Alternator charging voltage test connection. Battery voltage sensing type alternator

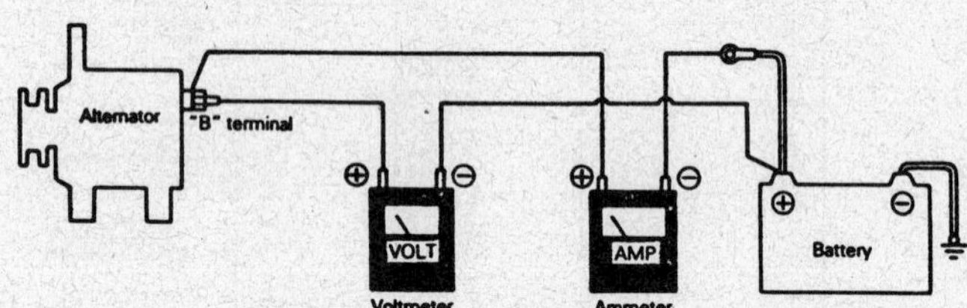


Fig. 13 Alternator output wire voltage drop test connection

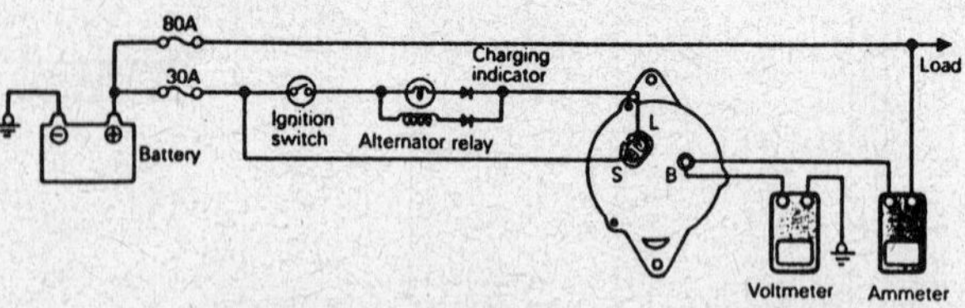


Fig. 14 Alternator output test connection. Battery voltage type sensor

the "B" terminal and negative lead to disconnected output wire.

3. Connect a digital voltmeter between alternator "B" terminal and battery positive terminal. Connect positive lead wire of voltmeter to "B" terminal and negative lead wire to positive battery terminal.
4. Connect battery ground cable, then start engine.
5. Obtain an ammeter reading reading of 20 A by adjusting engine speed and current draw by turning lights on and off. Voltmeter should read 0.2 V maximum.
6. If voltmeter reading is higher than specified, poor wiring may be the cause. Check wiring from alternator "B" terminal to battery for proper connections or signs of overheating.

## OUTPUT TEST

1. With ignition switch in the Off position, disconnect battery cables.
2. Disconnect wire from terminal B of alternator, then connect an ammeter between battery positive cable and alternator B terminal, **Fig. 14.**
3. Connect a voltmeter between B terminal and ground, **Fig. 14.**
4. Connect battery ground cable to battery ground post, then note voltmeter reading. The voltmeter should indicate battery voltage.
5. Connect a tachometer to engine, then start engine and turn on lights and heater blower to high.
6. Operate engine at approximately 2500 RPM and note ammeter reading. Reading must be higher than limit value. Refer specifications on alternator

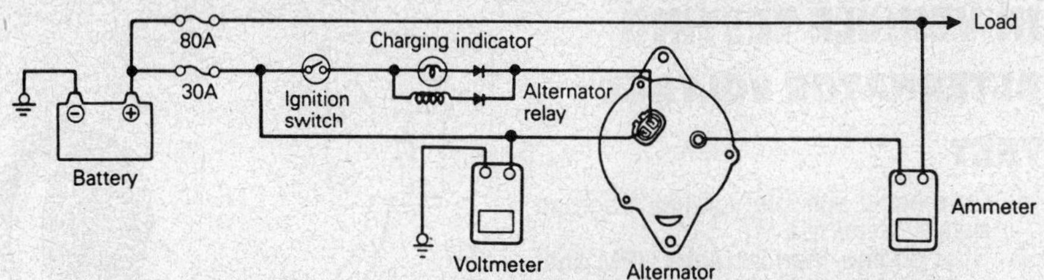


**Fig. 15 Voltage regulator test connections**

nameplate. **After engine has been started, the ammeter reading will gradually decrease as the battery approaches a fully charged condition. Read the ammeter indication at its maximum value while increasing engine RPM.**

## VOLTAGE REGULATOR TEST

1. With ignition switch in the Off position, disconnect battery ground cable and connect a digital voltmeter between alternator S terminal **Fig. 15,** and ground.
2. Disconnect alternator output wire from alternator B terminal, then connect a DC ammeter in series between the B terminal and the output wire. Connect positive lead of ammeter to B terminal. Connect negative lead to the output wire.
3. Install a tachometer per manufacturers instructions, then connect battery ground cable.
4. Place ignition switch in the On position and note voltmeter. The reading should equal battery voltage. If reading is 0, check for an open circuit in the wire between alternator S terminal and battery positive terminal or a blown fusible link.
5. Start engine, keeping all accessories and lights off. Run engine at a constant 2500 RPM and read voltmeter, when alternator output current drops to 10 amps or less, voltage reading should read 13.9-14.9 at 68°F or 13.4-14.6 at 140°F.

# Paris-Rhone Alternators

## INDEX



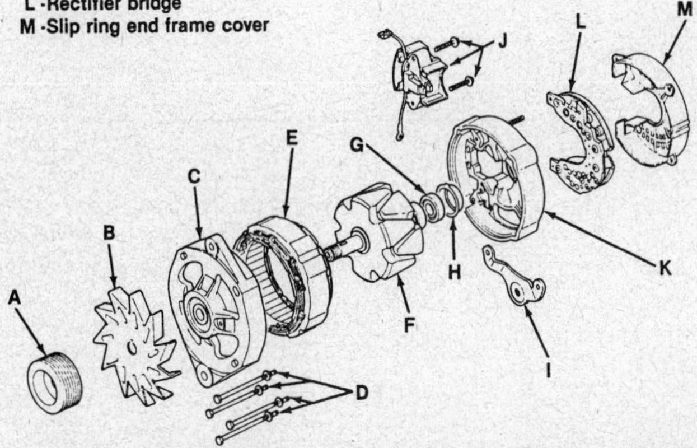


**Fig. 1 Exploded view of alternator assembly**

## DESCRIPTION

The Paris-Rhone alternator, **Fig. 1,** features a solid state built-in regulator that is available in two output capacities. These alternators are available in 60 amp and 70 amp ratings. All regulator components are enclosed in a solid mold with no need or provision for adjustment of the regulator. A rectifier bridge changes A.C. voltage to D.C. voltage which is available at the output terminal.

The alternator warning lamp is mounted on the instrument panel and illuminates when the ignition switch is turned on and goes out after the engine starts. If the lamp remains on or illuminates while the engine is running, a charging system malfunction is indicated.

## TROUBLESHOOTING

### ALTERNATOR LAMP DOES NOT ILLUMINATE W/IGNITION SWITCH ON

1. Check if alternator connector is loose or disconnected.
2. Check ring terminal on alternator case for proper ground.
3. Ground wide terminal on connector, then check bulb by ensuring lamp lights.

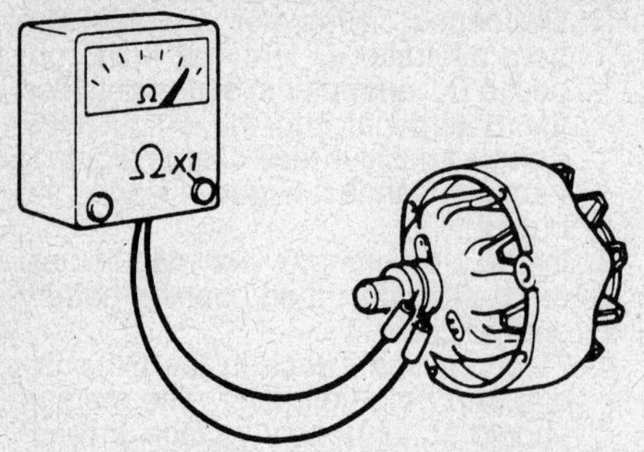


Fig. 2 Testing rotor assembly

## ALTERNATOR LAMP ILLUMINATES W/IGNITION SWITCH ON

1. If warning lamp illuminates when engine is operating, a charging system defect is indicated. Check for loose or broken alternator drive belt, defective alternator or defective regulator.
2. If regulator voltage is less than 12.5 volts, check for defective diodes, an open stator winding, excessive carbon on slip rings and/or worn brushes.

# IN-VEHICLE TESTING

## ALTERNATOR VOLTAGE TEST

1. Connect a suitable voltmeter across battery terminals.
2. Start engine, then increase RPM until voltmeter pointer remains steady. Voltage should be 12.5-15 volts.
3. Turn on as many accessories as possible with, then recheck voltage reading. Reading should be 12.5-15 volts.

## ROTOR TEST

1. Using a suitable ohmmeter, **Fig. 2**, check resistance between the two sections of the rotor slip rings. Take resistance readings at a minimum of four points around slip rings.
2. Resistance should be 2.9-3.5 ohms on 60 amp rotor or 3.0-3.6 ohms on 75 amp rotor. If resistance is not as specified, replace rotor.

## STATOR TEST

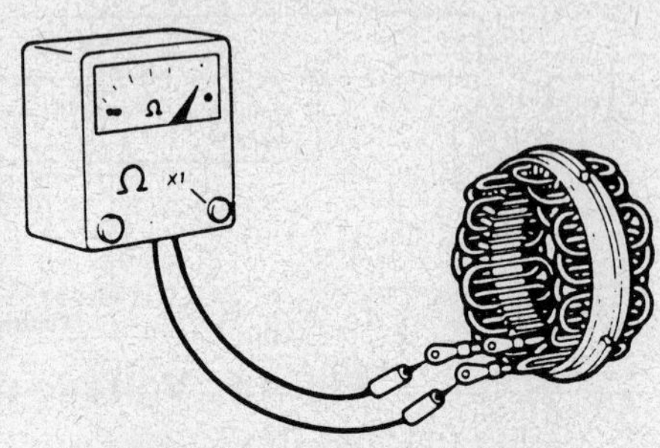


Fig. 3 Testing stator assembly

1. Using a suitable ohmmeter, check resistance across each stator wire connections.
2. Connect test leads to wires A and B, **Fig. 3**, then note resistance.
3. Connect test leads to wires B and C, then note resistance.
4. Connect test leads to wires A and C, then note resistance.
5. Resistance across each stator wire should not exceed .1± .01 ohms. on 60 amp stators or .08 ohms ±.008 ohms on 75 amp stators. Replace stator if resistance is not as specified.

# DISC BRAKES

## TABLE OF CONTENTS



---

# Applications

Type No.

## CHRYSLER

**Conquest:**
- Front:
  - 1989—FS17 .......... 9
- Rear:
  - 1989—AD Type .......... 10

**Fifth Avenue RWD:**
- Front:
  - 1989 .......... 1

**Imperial:**
- Front
  - 1990 .......... 5
  - 1991 .......... 6
- Rear
  - 1990 .......... 3
  - 1991 .......... 12

**LeBaron:**
- Front:
  - 1989 w/14 & 15 Inch Wheels, Except Turbo .......... 4
  - 1989 w/15 & 16 Inch Wheels & Turbo .......... 5
  - 1990-91 w/14 Inch Wheels .......... 4
  - 1990-91 w/15 & 16 Inch Wheels .......... 5
- Rear:
  - 1989-91 .......... 12

**LeBaron GTS:**
- Front:
  - 1989 .......... 4

**LeBaron Landau:**
- Front:
  - 1990 .......... 4
  - 1991 w/14 Inch Wheels .......... 4
  - 1991 w/15 Inch Wheels .......... 5
- Rear:
  - 1990-91 .......... 12

**New Yorker:**
- Front:
  - 1989-90 .......... 5
  - 1991 .......... 6
- Rear:
  - 1989-90 .......... 3
  - 1991 .......... 12

## APPLICATIONS—Continued

| | Type No. |
|---|---|
| **New Yorker Fifth Avenue:** | |
| Front: | |
| 1990 | 5 |
| 1991 | 6 |
| Rear: | |
| 1990 | 3 |
| 1991 | 12 |

### DODGE

| | Type No. |
|---|---|
| **Aries:** | |
| Front: | |
| 1989 2 Door | 2 |
| 1989 4 Door | 4 |
| **Colt:** | |
| Front: | |
| 1989-90 w/1.5L Engine–PFS15 | 9 |
| 1989-90 w/1.6L Engine–AD54 | 8 |
| 1991–MR31S | 13 |
| Rear: | |
| 1989-90 w/1.6L Engine–AD30P | 10 |
| **Colt Vista:** | |
| Front: | |
| 1989-91–AD54 | 8 |
| **Colt Wagon:** | |
| Front: | |
| 1989-90 2WD–PFS15 | 9 |
| 1989-90 4WD–AD54 | 8 |
| **Daytona:** | |
| Front: | |
| 1989 w/14 & 15 Inch Wheels | 4 |
| 1989 w/15 Inch Wheels & Shelby Package & 16 Inch Wheels w/Turbo | 5 |
| 1990 w/14 & 15 Inch Wheels & Rear Drum Brakes | 4 |
| 1990 w/15 & 16 Inch Wheels & Rear Disc Brakes | 5 |
| 1991 w/Rear Drum Brakes | 4 |
| 1991 w/Rear Disc Brakes | 5 |
| Rear: | |
| 1989-91 | 12 |
| **Diplomat:** | |
| Front: | |
| 1989 | 1 |
| **Dynasty:** | |
| Front: | |
| 1989-90 | 5 |
| 1991 | 6 |
| Rear: | |
| 1989-90 | 3 |
| 1991 | 12 |
| **Lancer:** | |
| Front: | |
| 1989 | 4 |
| **Monaco:** | |
| Front: | |
| 1990 | 7 |
| 1991 | 6 |
| Rear: | |
| 1990-91 | 16 |
| **Omni:** | |
| Front: | |
| 1989-90 | 4 |
| **Shadow:** | |
| Front: | |
| 1989 Standard | 2 |
| 1989 ES | 4 |
| 1990-91 | 4 |
| Rear: | |
| 1989-90 | 12 |
| **Spirit:** | |
| Front: | |
| 1989-90 | 4 |
| 1991 w/14 Inch Wheels | 4 |
| 1991 w/15 Inch Wheels | 5 |
| Rear: | |
| 1990-91 | 12 |
| **Stealth:** | |
| Front: | |
| 1991 AWD–MR66Z | 14 |
| 1991 FWD–MR57W | 14 |
| Rear: | |
| 1991 AWD–MR58V | 15 |
| 1991 FWD–MR45V | 15 |

### EAGLE

| | Type No. |
|---|---|
| **Eagle Medallion:** | |
| Front: | |
| 1989 | 11 |
| **Eagle Premier:** | |
| Front: | |
| 1989-90 | 7 |
| 1991 | 6 |
| Rear: | |
| 1989-91 | 16 |
| **Eagle Summit:** | |
| Front: | |
| 1989-90–AD54 | 8 |
| 1991–MR34V | 13 |
| Rear: | |
| 1989-90 w/1.6L Engine–AD30P | 10 |
| **Eagle Talon:** | |
| Front | |
| 1990 Up To April 1989 Production–AD54 | 8 |
| 1990 From March 1989 Production–MR44V | 13 |
| 1991 AWD–MR46V | 13 |
| 1991 FWD–MR44V | 13 |
| Rear | |
| 1990–AD30P | 10 |
| 1991 AWD–AD35P | 10 |
| 1991 FWD–AD30P | 10 |

### PLYMOUTH

| | Type No. |
|---|---|
| **Acclaim:** | |
| Front: | |
| 1989-90 | 4 |
| 1991 w/14 Inch Wheels | 4 |
| 1991 w/15 Inch Wheels | 5 |
| Rear: | |
| 1990-91 | 12 |
| **Colt:** | |
| Front: | |
| 1989-90 w/1.5L Engine–PFS15 | 9 |
| 1989-90 w/1.6L Engine–AD54 | 8 |
| 1991–MR31S | 13 |
| Rear: | |
| 1989-90 w/1.6L Engine–AD30P | 10 |
| **Colt Vista:** | |
| Front: | |
| 1989-91–AD54 | 8 |
| **Colt Wagon:** | |
| Front: | |
| 1989-90 2WD–PFS15 | 9 |
| 1989-90 4WD–AD54 | 8 |
| **Grand Fury:** | |
| Front: | |
| 1989 | 1 |
| **Horizon:** | |
| Front: | |
| 1989-90 | 4 |
| **Laser:** | |
| Front | |
| 1990 Up To April 1989 Production–AD54 | 8 |
| 1990 From March 1989 Production–MR44V | 13 |
| 1991–MR44V | 13 |
| Rear | |
| 1990-91–AD30P | 10 |
| **Reliant:** | |
| Front: | |
| 1989 2 Door | 2 |
| 1989 4 Door | 4 |
| **Sundance:** | |
| Front: | |
| 1989 Standard | 2 |
| 1989 RS | 4 |
| 1990-91 | 4 |
| Rear: | |
| 1989-90 | 12 |

# Troubleshooting

This section covers general troubleshooting procedures for both disc and drum brake systems. Refer to **Figs. 1 through 5** for these procedures.

| Symptom | Probable cause | Remedy |
|---|---|---|
| Vehicle pulls to one side when brakes are applied | Grease or oil on pad or lining surface | Replace |
| | Inadequate contact of pad or lining | Correct |
| | Auto adjuster malfunction | Adjust |
| | Drum eccentricity or uneven wear | Repair or replace as necessary |
| Insufficient braking power | Low or deteriorated brake fluid | Refill or change |
| | Air in brake system | Bleed air |
| | Overheated brake rotor due to dragging of pad or lining | Correct |
| | Grease or oil on pad, or lining surface | Replace |
| | Inadequate contact of pad or lining | Correct |
| | Brake booster malfunction | Correct |
| | Auto adjuster malfunction | Adjust |
| | Clogged brake line | Correct |
| | Proportioning valve malfunction | Replace |
| Increased pedal stroke (Reduced pedal to floorboard clearance) | Air in brake system | Bleed air |
| | Worn lining or pad | Replace |
| | Broken vacuum hose | Replace |
| | Brake fluid leaks | Correct |
| | Auto adjuster malfunction | Adjust |
| | Excessive push rod to master cylinder clearance | Adjust |
| | Faulty master cylinder | Replace |
| Brake drag | Incomplete release of parking brake | Correct |
| | Incorrect parking brake adjustment | Adjust |
| | Worn brake pedal return spring | Replace |
| | Broken rear drum brake shoe return spring | Replace |
| | Lack of lubrication in sliding parts | Lubricate |
| | Improper push rod to master cylinder clearance | Adjust |
| | Faulty master cylinder piston return spring | Replace |
| | Clogged master cylinder return port | Correct |

**Fig. 1 Brake system troubleshooting (Part 1 of 3). Colt, Colt Vista, Colt Wagon, Conquest, Laser, Stealth, Eagle Summit & Talon**

| Symptom | Probable cause | Remedy |
|---|---|---|
| Insufficient parking brake function | Worn brake lining or pads | Replace |
| | Excessive parking brake lever stroke | Adjust the parking brake lever stroke or check the parking brake cable routing |
| | Grease or oil on lining or pad surface | Replace |
| | Auto adjuster malfunction | Adjust |
| | Parking brake cable sticking | Replace |
| | Stuck wheel cylinder or caliper piston | Replace |
| Scraping or grinding noise when brakes are applied | Worn brake linings or pads | Replace |
| | Caliper to wheel interference | Correct or replace |
| | Dust cover to disc interference | Correct or replace |
| | Bent brake backing plate | Correct or replace |
| | Cracked drums or brake disc | Correct or replace |
| Squealing, groaning or chattering noise when brakes are applied | Disc brakes – missing or damaged brake pad shim | Replace |
| | Brake drums and linings, discs and pads worn or scored | Correct or replace |
| | Improper lining parts | Correct or replace |
| | Disc brakes – burred or rusted calipers | Clean or deburr |
| | Dirty, greased, contaminated or glazed linings | Clean or replace |
| | Drum brakes – weak, damaged or incorrect shoe hold-down springs, loose or damaged shoe hold-down pins and springs | Correct or replace |
| | Incorrect brake pedal or booster push rod | Adjust |
| Squealing noise when brakes are not applied | Bent or warped backing plate causing interference with drum | Replace |
| | Improper machining of drum causing interference with backing plate or shoe | Replace drum |
| | Disc brakes – rusted, stuck | Lubricate or replace |
| | Worn, damaged or insufficiently lubricated wheel bearings | Lubricate or replace |
| | Drum brakes – weak, damaged or incorrect shoe-to-shoe spring | Replace |
| | Loose or extra parts in brakes | Retighten |

**Fig. 1 Brake system troubleshooting (Part 2 of 3). Colt, Colt Vista, Colt Wagon, Conquest, Laser, Stealth, Eagle Summit & Talon**

| Symptom | Probable cause | Remedy |
|---|---|---|
| Squealing noise when brakes are not applied | Improper positioning of pads in caliper | Correct |
| | Improper installation of support mounting to caliper body | Correct |
| | Poor return of brake booster or master cylinder or wheel cylinder | Replace |
| | Incorrect brake pedal or booster push-rod | Adjust |
| Groaning, clicking or rattling noise when brakes are not applied | Stones or foreign material trapped inside wheel covers | Remove stones, etc. |
| | Loose wheel nuts | Retighten |
| | Disc brakes – failure of shim | Replace |
| | Disc brakes – loose installation bolt | Retighten |
| | Worn, damaged or dry wheel bearings | Lubricate or replace |
| | Disc brakes – wear on sleeve | Replace |
| | Incorrect brake pedal or booster push-rod | Adjust |

**Fig. 1 Brake system troubleshooting (Part 3 of 3). Colt, Colt Vista, Colt Wagon, Conquest, Laser, Stealth, Eagle Summit & Talon**

| INCIDENTS | POSSIBLE CAUSES |
|---|---|
| Brakes binding or grabbing | · Linings not chamfered<br>· Oil or grease on linings<br>· Caliper seized<br>· Weak return springs |
| Brakes pulsating | · Oval drums<br>· Excessive disc run-out<br>· Discs not of even thickness<br>· Abnormal deposit on discs (corrosion between lining and disc).<br>· Linings cracked or broken |
| Front brakes pulling to one side | · Check front end alignment<br>· Check front axle, suspension and steering<br>· Piston seized*<br>· Tires (worn · incorrect inflation pressure)<br>· Pinched brake-line.<br>*ATTENTION: Pulling to one side indicates a seized piston on the opposite side. |
| Rear brakes pulling to one side | · Incorrect compensator or limiter setting<br>· Piston seized<br>· Incorrect shoe adjustment manual adjustment: shoe too far from drum<br>automatic adjustment: handbrake cable too tight.<br>NOTE: Automatic wear take-up is performed by the brake pedal provided the handbrake cable is not abnormally tight when in off position<br>· Return spring |
| Overheating brakes | · Master cylinder operating clearance insufficient to allow master cylinder to return to neutral position.<br>· Master cylinder operating clearance insufficient to allow master cylinder to return to neutral position.<br>· Piston seized or not returning properly.<br>· Pinched brake line<br>· Handbrake mechanism seized<br>· Incorrect handbrake adjustment |

**Fig. 2 Brake system troubleshooting (Part 1 of 2). Eagle Medallion, Premier & Dodge Monaco**

| INCIDENT | POSSIBLE CAUSES |
|---|---|
| "Hard pedal":<br><br>Great effort Needed and only a slight deceleration noticed in vehicle. | · Power servo defective<br><br>· Linings/pads<br><br>· oily<br>· glazed, not to specification<br>· overheating (due to excessive braking) or not to specification<br>· seized piston<br>· pinched brake line<br>· pads/linings worn: |
| "Soft pedal"<br><br>Note: since the power servo system on current vehicles is very effective, the impression may be given that the pedal is "soft". To find out whether an incident has occurred or the braking system is operating normally, two tests must be performed.<br><br>1. Vehicle moving<br>· Assessment test: relation between pedal travel and vehicle deceleration.<br><br>2. Vehicle stationary with ignition off<br>· Additional test on pedal travel: depress the brake pedal 5 times to empty the brake servo, before assessing the result of the test. | · Air in system: poor bleeding<br><br>· Internal leakage in braking system<br><br>· Lack of fluid in reservoir (external leak in braking system). |
| "Long" pedal travel<br><br>Test to be performed with vehicle stationary and ignition off.<br><br>Note: The brake pedal must be depressed 5 times in order to empty the brake servo before taking account of the test results. | · Incorrect shoe adjustment<br><br>Drum brakes<br><br>· Manual adjustments: shoes too far from drum surface.<br><br>Disc and drum brakes<br><br>· Automatic adjustment: handbrake cable too tight.<br><br>Note: Automatic wear take-up is performed by by the brake pedal, provided the handbrake is not abnormally tight in the off position.<br><br>· Excessively worn pads/linings of pads/linings not symmetrical (or crossed)<br><br>· Excessive master cylinder operating clearance.<br><br>· Brake fluid boiling or has heated up. |
| Pedal "travels to floor"<br><br>Test to be performed on stationary vehicle with ignition off.<br><br>Note: The brake pedal must be depressed 5 times in order to empty the brake servo before taking account of the test results. | · Fluid loss (check for leaks)<br><br>· Faulty sealing cup between the two master cylinder circuits.<br><br>· Brake fluid boiling. |

**Fig. 2 Brake system troubleshooting (Part 2 of 2). Eagle Medallion, Premier & Dodge Monaco**

**BASIC DIAGNOSIS GUIDE**

| SYMPTOM | CHART 1 MISC. COND. | CHART 2 ACTUATION | CHART 3 POWER BRAKES | CHART 4 BRAKE NOISE | CHART 5 WHEEL BRAKES |
|---|---|---|---|---|---|
| BRAKE WARNING LIGHT "ON" | | X | NO | | |
| EXCESSIVE PEDAL TRAVEL | | X | NO | | O |
| PEDAL GOES TO FLOOR | 6O | X | | | |
| STOP LIGHT "ON" WITHOUT BRAKES | 3X | | | | |
| ALL BRAKES DRAG | 5X | O | | | |
| REAR BRAKES DRAG | 2X | NO | NO | | |
| GRABBY BRAKES | | | O | | X |
| SPONGY BRAKE PEDAL | | X | NO | | |
| PREMATURE REAR LOCKUP | 4O | NO | NO | | O |
| EXCESSIVE PEDAL EFFORT | 1X | | O | | |
| ROUGH ENGINE IDLE | | | O | | |
| BRAKE CHATTER (ROUGH) | | NO | NO | | X |
| SURGE DURING BRAKING | | | | | X |
| NOISE DURING BRAKING | | | | X | |
| RATTLE OR CLUNKING NOISE | | NO | | X | |
| PEDAL PULSATES DURING BRAKING | | NO | NO | | X |
| PULL TO RIGHT OR LEFT | | NO | NO | | X |

NO: NOT POSSIBLE CAUSE    X: MOST LIKELY CAUSE    O: POSSIBLE CAUSE

**Fig. 3 Brake system troubleshooting (Part 1 of 6). FWD Chrysler Corp. vehicles**

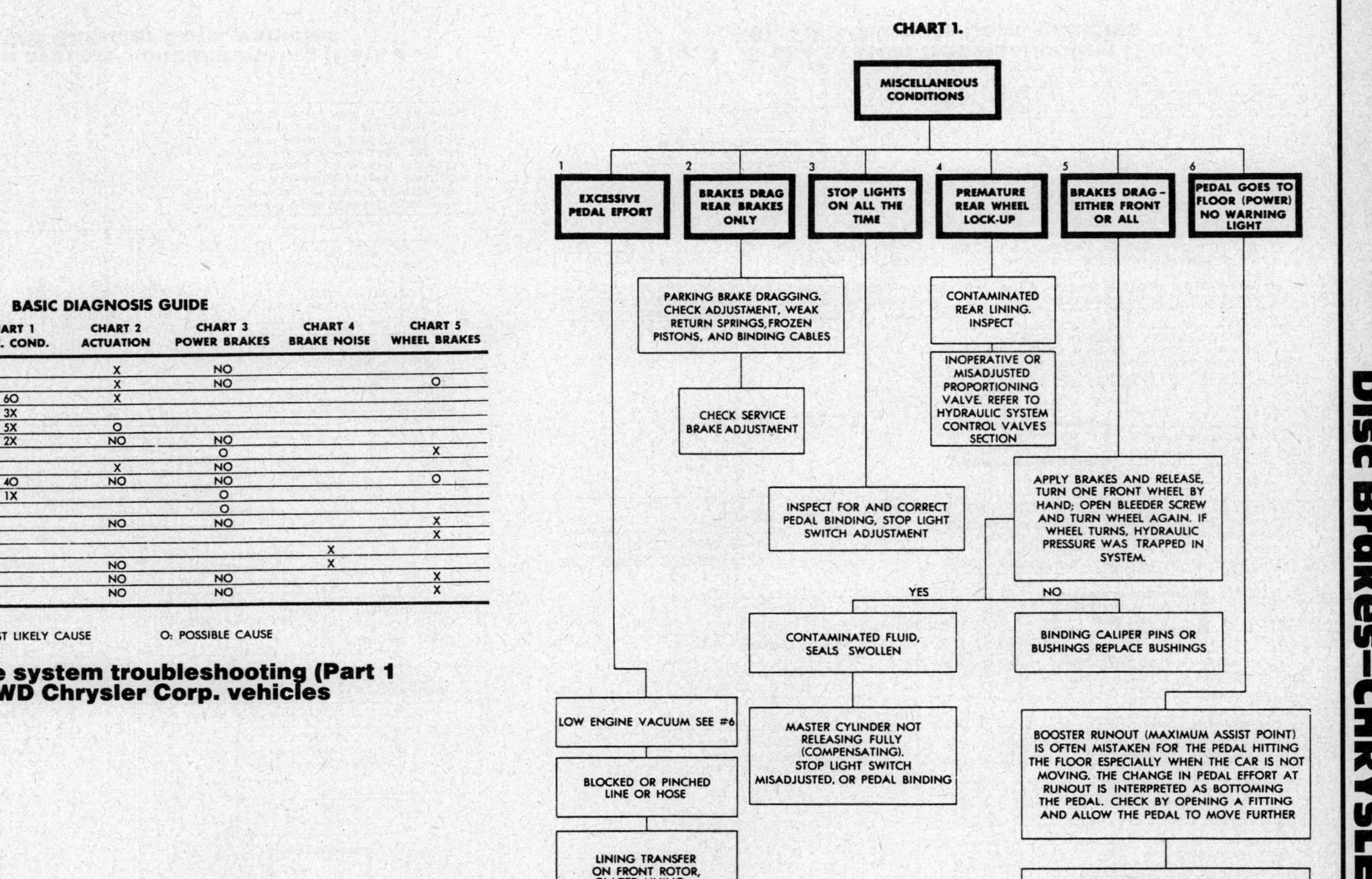


**Fig. 3 Brake system troubleshooting (Part 2 of 6). FWD Chrysler Corp. vehicles**

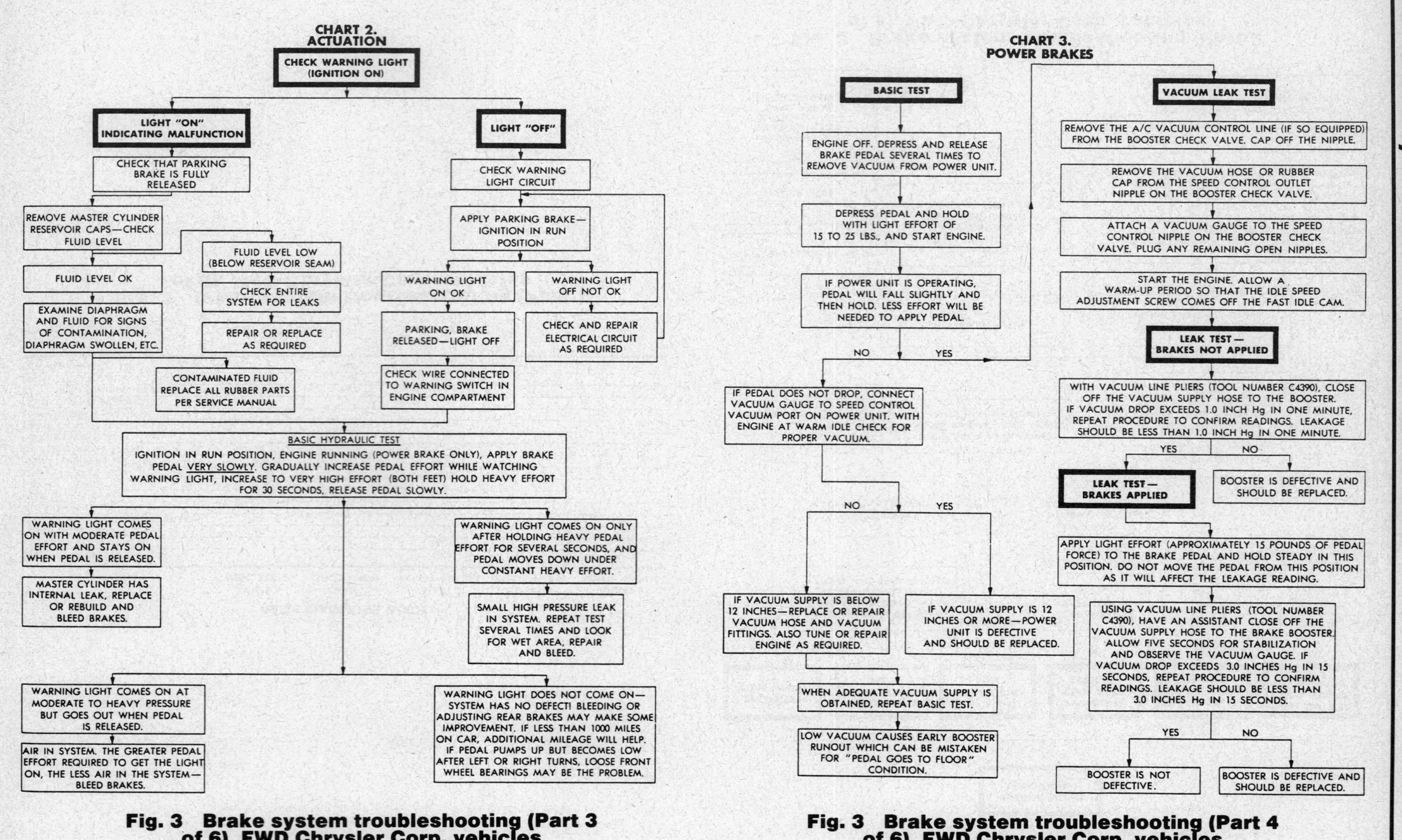

CHART 2.
ACTUATION
CHECK WARNING LIGHT (IGNITION ON)
LIGHT "ON" INDICATING MALFUNCTION
CHECK THAT PARKING BRAKE IS FULLY RELEASED
REMOVE MASTER CYLINDER RESERVOIR CAPS—CHECK FLUID LEVEL
FLUID LEVEL OK
EXAMINE DIAPHRAGM AND FLUID FOR SIGNS OF CONTAMINATION, DIAPHRAGM SWOLLEN, ETC.
FLUID LEVEL LOW (BELOW RESERVOIR SEAM)
CHECK ENTIRE SYSTEM FOR LEAKS
REPAIR OR REPLACE AS REQUIRED
CONTAMINATED FLUID REPLACE ALL RUBBER PARTS PER SERVICE MANUAL
LIGHT "OFF"
CHECK WARNING LIGHT CIRCUIT
APPLY PARKING BRAKE—IGNITION IN RUN POSITION
WARNING LIGHT ON OK
WARNING LIGHT OFF NOT OK
PARKING, BRAKE RELEASED—LIGHT OFF
CHECK AND REPAIR ELECTRICAL CIRCUIT AS REQUIRED
CHECK WIRE CONNECTED TO WARNING SWITCH IN ENGINE COMPARTMENT
BASIC HYDRAULIC TEST
IGNITION IN RUN POSITION, ENGINE RUNNING (POWER BRAKE ONLY), APPLY BRAKE PEDAL VERY SLOWLY. GRADUALLY INCREASE PEDAL EFFORT WHILE WATCHING WARNING LIGHT, INCREASE TO VERY HIGH EFFORT (BOTH FEET) HOLD HEAVY EFFORT FOR 30 SECONDS, RELEASE PEDAL SLOWLY.
WARNING LIGHT COMES ON WITH MODERATE PEDAL EFFORT AND STAYS ON WHEN PEDAL IS RELEASED.
MASTER CYLINDER HAS INTERNAL LEAK, REPLACE OR REBUILD AND BLEED BRAKES.
WARNING LIGHT COMES ON ONLY AFTER HOLDING HEAVY PEDAL EFFORT FOR SEVERAL SECONDS, AND PEDAL MOVES DOWN UNDER CONSTANT HEAVY EFFORT.
SMALL HIGH PRESSURE LEAK IN SYSTEM. REPEAT TEST SEVERAL TIMES AND LOOK FOR WET AREA, REPAIR AND BLEED.
WARNING LIGHT COMES ON AT MODERATE TO HEAVY PRESSURE BUT GOES OUT WHEN PEDAL IS RELEASED.
AIR IN SYSTEM. THE GREATER PEDAL EFFORT REQUIRED TO GET THE LIGHT ON, THE LESS AIR IN THE SYSTEM—BLEED BRAKES.
WARNING LIGHT DOES NOT COME ON—SYSTEM HAS NO DEFECT! BLEEDING OR ADJUSTING REAR BRAKES MAY MAKE SOME IMPROVEMENT. IF LESS THAN 1000 MILES ON CAR, ADDITIONAL MILEAGE WILL HELP. IF PEDAL PUMPS UP BUT BECOMES LOW AFTER LEFT OR RIGHT TURNS, LOOSE FRONT WHEEL BEARINGS MAY BE THE PROBLEM.
CHART 3.
POWER BRAKES
BASIC TEST
ENGINE OFF. DEPRESS AND RELEASE BRAKE PEDAL SEVERAL TIMES TO REMOVE VACUUM FROM POWER UNIT.
DEPRESS PEDAL AND HOLD WITH LIGHT EFFORT OF 15 TO 25 LBS., AND START ENGINE.
IF POWER UNIT IS OPERATING, PEDAL WILL FALL SLIGHTLY AND THEN HOLD. LESS EFFORT WILL BE NEEDED TO APPLY PEDAL.
NO
YES
IF PEDAL DOES NOT DROP, CONNECT VACUUM GAUGE TO SPEED CONTROL VACUUM PORT ON POWER UNIT. WITH ENGINE AT WARM IDLE CHECK FOR PROPER VACUUM.
NO
YES
IF VACUUM SUPPLY IS BELOW 12 INCHES—REPLACE OR REPAIR VACUUM HOSE AND VACUUM FITTINGS. ALSO TUNE OR REPAIR ENGINE AS REQUIRED.
IF VACUUM SUPPLY IS 12 INCHES OR MORE—POWER UNIT IS DEFECTIVE AND SHOULD BE REPLACED.
WHEN ADEQUATE VACUUM SUPPLY IS OBTAINED, REPEAT BASIC TEST.
LOW VACUUM CAUSES EARLY BOOSTER RUNOUT WHICH CAN BE MISTAKEN FOR "PEDAL GOES TO FLOOR" CONDITION.
VACUUM LEAK TEST
REMOVE THE A/C VACUUM CONTROL LINE (IF SO EQUIPPED) FROM THE BOOSTER CHECK VALVE. CAP OFF THE NIPPLE.
REMOVE THE VACUUM HOSE OR RUBBER CAP FROM THE SPEED CONTROL OUTLET NIPPLE ON THE BOOSTER CHECK VALVE.
ATTACH A VACUUM GAUGE TO THE SPEED CONTROL NIPPLE ON THE BOOSTER CHECK VALVE. PLUG ANY REMAINING OPEN NIPPLES.
START THE ENGINE. ALLOW A WARM-UP PERIOD SO THAT THE IDLE SPEED ADJUSTMENT SCREW COMES OFF THE FAST IDLE CAM.
LEAK TEST—BRAKES NOT APPLIED
WITH VACUUM LINE PLIERS (TOOL NUMBER C4390), CLOSE OFF THE VACUUM SUPPLY HOSE TO THE BOOSTER. IF VACUUM DROP EXCEEDS 1.0 INCH Hg IN ONE MINUTE, REPEAT PROCEDURE TO CONFIRM READINGS. LEAKAGE SHOULD BE LESS THAN 1.0 INCH Hg IN ONE MINUTE.
YES
NO
LEAK TEST—BRAKES APPLIED
BOOSTER IS DEFECTIVE AND SHOULD BE REPLACED.
APPLY LIGHT EFFORT (APPROXIMATELY 15 POUNDS OF PEDAL FORCE) TO THE BRAKE PEDAL AND HOLD STEADY IN THIS POSITION. DO NOT MOVE THE PEDAL FROM THIS POSITION AS IT WILL AFFECT THE LEAKAGE READING.
USING VACUUM LINE PLIERS (TOOL NUMBER C4390), HAVE AN ASSISTANT CLOSE OFF THE VACUUM SUPPLY HOSE TO THE BRAKE BOOSTER. ALLOW FIVE SECONDS FOR STABILIZATION AND OBSERVE THE VACUUM GAUGE. IF VACUUM DROP EXCEEDS 3.0 INCHES Hg IN 15 SECONDS, REPEAT PROCEDURE TO CONFIRM READINGS. LEAKAGE SHOULD BE LESS THAN 3.0 INCHES Hg IN 15 SECONDS.
YES
NO
BOOSTER IS NOT DEFECTIVE.
BOOSTER IS DEFECTIVE AND SHOULD BE REPLACED.


**Fig. 3 Brake system troubleshooting (Part 3 of 6). FWD Chrysler Corp. vehicles**

**Fig. 3 Brake system troubleshooting (Part 4 of 6). FWD Chrysler Corp. vehicles**

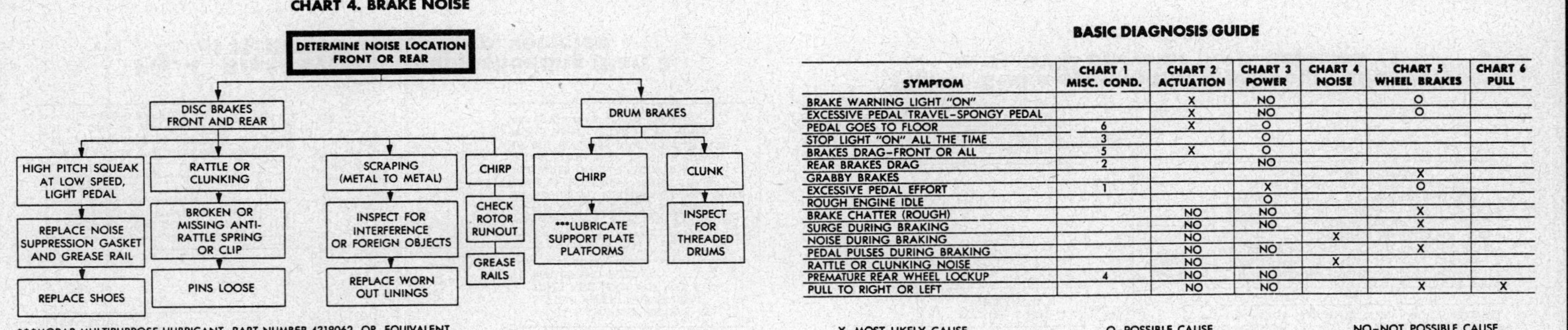

### CHART 4. BRAKE NOISE

DETERMINE NOISE LOCATION FRONT OR REAR
DISC BRAKES FRONT AND REAR
DRUM BRAKES
HIGH PITCH SQUEAK AT LOW SPEED, LIGHT PEDAL
REPLACE NOISE SUPPRESSION GASKET AND GREASE RAIL
REPLACE SHOES
RATTLE OR CLUNKING
BROKEN OR MISSING ANTI-RATTLE SPRING OR CLIP
PINS LOOSE
SCRAPING (METAL TO METAL)
INSPECT FOR INTERFERENCE OR FOREIGN OBJECTS
REPLACE WORN OUT LININGS
CHIRP
CHECK ROTOR RUNOUT
GREASE RAILS
CHIRP
***LUBRICATE SUPPORT PLATE PLATFORMS
CLUNK
INSPECT FOR THREADED DRUMS

***MOPAR MULTIPURPOSE LIUBRICANT, PART NUMBER 4318062, OR EQUIVALENT.

**Fig. 3 Brake system troubleshooting (Part 5 of 6). FWD Chrysler Corp. vehicles**

### BASIC DIAGNOSIS GUIDE

| SYMPTOM | CHART 1 MISC. COND. | CHART 2 ACTUATION | CHART 3 POWER | CHART 4 NOISE | CHART 5 WHEEL BRAKES | CHART 6 PULL |
|---|---|---|---|---|---|---|
| BRAKE WARNING LIGHT "ON" | | X | NO | | O | |
| EXCESSIVE PEDAL TRAVEL-SPONGY PEDAL | | X | NO | | O | |
| PEDAL GOES TO FLOOR | 6 | X | O | | | |
| STOP LIGHT "ON" ALL THE TIME | 3 | | O | | | |
| BRAKES DRAG-FRONT OR ALL | 5 | X | O | | | |
| REAR BRAKES DRAG | 2 | | NO | | | |
| GRABBY BRAKES | | | | | X | |
| EXCESSIVE PEDAL EFFORT | 1 | | X | | O | |
| ROUGH ENGINE IDLE | | | O | | | |
| BRAKE CHATTER (ROUGH) | | NO | NO | | X | |
| SURGE DURING BRAKING | | NO | NO | | X | |
| NOISE DURING BRAKING | | NO | | X | | |
| PEDAL PULSES DURING BRAKING | | NO | NO | | X | |
| RATTLE OR CLUNKING NOISE | | NO | | X | | |
| PREMATURE REAR WHEEL LOCKUP | 4 | NO | NO | | | |
| PULL TO RIGHT OR LEFT | | NO | NO | | X | X |

X–MOST LIKELY CAUSE O–POSSIBLE CAUSE NO–NOT POSSIBLE CAUSE

**Fig. 4 Brake system troubleshooting (Part 1 of 7). RWD Chrysler Corp. vehicles**

### CHART 5. WHEEL BRAKES

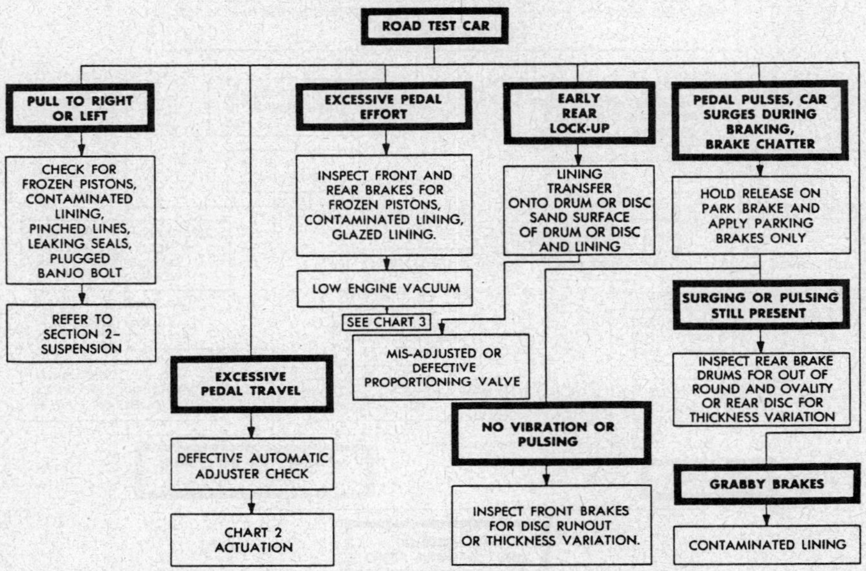

ROAD TEST CAR
PULL TO RIGHT OR LEFT
CHECK FOR FROZEN PISTONS, CONTAMINATED LINING, PINCHED LINES, LEAKING SEALS, PLUGGED BANJO BOLT
REFER TO SECTION 2–SUSPENSION
EXCESSIVE PEDAL TRAVEL
DEFECTIVE AUTOMATIC ADJUSTER CHECK
CHART 2 ACTUATION
EXCESSIVE PEDAL EFFORT
INSPECT FRONT AND REAR BRAKES FOR FROZEN PISTONS, CONTAMINATED LINING, GLAZED LINING.
LOW ENGINE VACUUM
SEE CHART 3
MIS-ADJUSTED OR DEFECTIVE PROPORTIONING VALVE
EARLY REAR LOCK-UP
LINING TRANSFER ONTO DRUM OR DISC SAND SURFACE OF DRUM OR DISC AND LINING
NO VIBRATION OR PULSING
INSPECT FRONT BRAKES FOR DISC RUNOUT OR THICKNESS VARIATION.
PEDAL PULSES, CAR SURGES DURING BRAKING, BRAKE CHATTER
HOLD RELEASE ON PARK BRAKE AND APPLY PARKING BRAKES ONLY
SURGING OR PULSING STILL PRESENT
INSPECT REAR BRAKE DRUMS FOR OUT OF ROUND AND OVALITY OR REAR DISC FOR THICKNESS VARIATION
GRABBY BRAKES
CONTAMINATED LINING

**Fig. 3 Brake system troubleshooting (Part 6 of 6). FWD Chrysler Corp. vehicles**

### BRAKE CHART 1 DIAGNOSIS

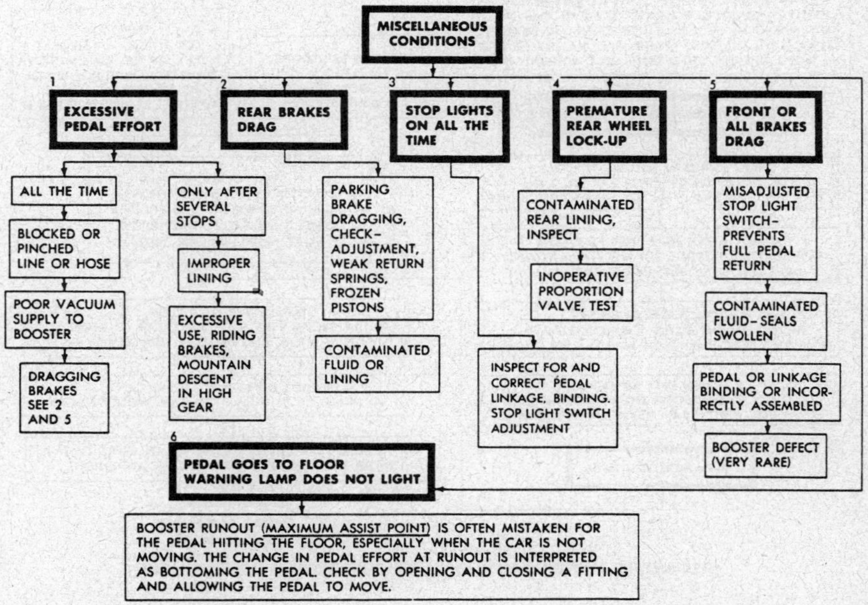

MISCELLANEOUS CONDITIONS
1
EXCESSIVE PEDAL EFFORT
ALL THE TIME
BLOCKED OR PINCHED LINE OR HOSE
POOR VACUUM SUPPLY TO BOOSTER
DRAGGING BRAKES SEE 2 AND 5
ONLY AFTER SEVERAL STOPS
IMPROPER LINING
EXCESSIVE USE, RIDING BRAKES, MOUNTAIN DESCENT IN HIGH GEAR
2
REAR BRAKES DRAG
PARKING BRAKE DRAGGING, CHECK–ADJUSTMENT, WEAK RETURN SPRINGS, FROZEN PISTONS
CONTAMINATED FLUID OR LINING
3
STOP LIGHTS ON ALL THE TIME
INSPECT FOR AND CORRECT PEDAL LINKAGE, BINDING. STOP LIGHT SWITCH ADJUSTMENT
4
PREMATURE REAR WHEEL LOCK-UP
CONTAMINATED REAR LINING, INSPECT
INOPERATIVE PROPORTION VALVE, TEST
5
FRONT OR ALL BRAKES DRAG
MISADJUSTED STOP LIGHT SWITCH–PREVENTS FULL PEDAL RETURN
CONTAMINATED FLUID–SEALS SWOLLEN
PEDAL OR LINKAGE BINDING OR INCORRECTLY ASSEMBLED
BOOSTER DEFECT (VERY RARE)
6
PEDAL GOES TO FLOOR WARNING LAMP DOES NOT LIGHT
BOOSTER RUNOUT (MAXIMUM ASSIST POINT) IS OFTEN MISTAKEN FOR THE PEDAL HITTING THE FLOOR, ESPECIALLY WHEN THE CAR IS NOT MOVING. THE CHANGE IN PEDAL EFFORT AT RUNOUT IS INTERPRETED AS BOTTOMING THE PEDAL. CHECK BY OPENING AND CLOSING A FITTING AND ALLOWING THE PEDAL TO MOVE.

**Fig. 4 Brake system troubleshooting (Part 2 of 7). RWD Chrysler Corp. vehicles**

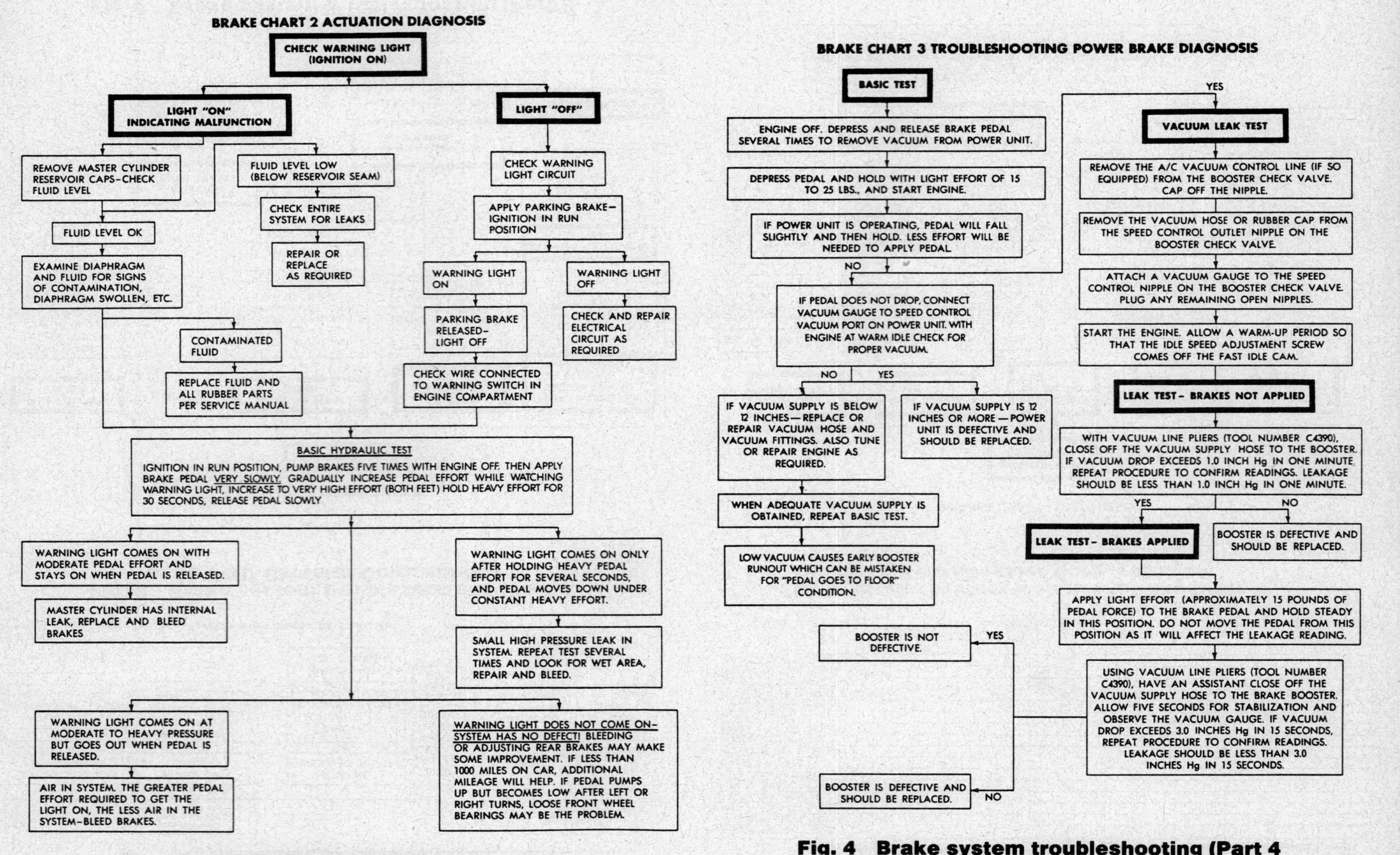


**Fig. 4 Brake system troubleshooting (Part 3 of 7). RWD Chrysler Corp. vehicles**

**Fig. 4 Brake system troubleshooting (Part 4 of 7). RWD Chrysler Corp. vehicles**

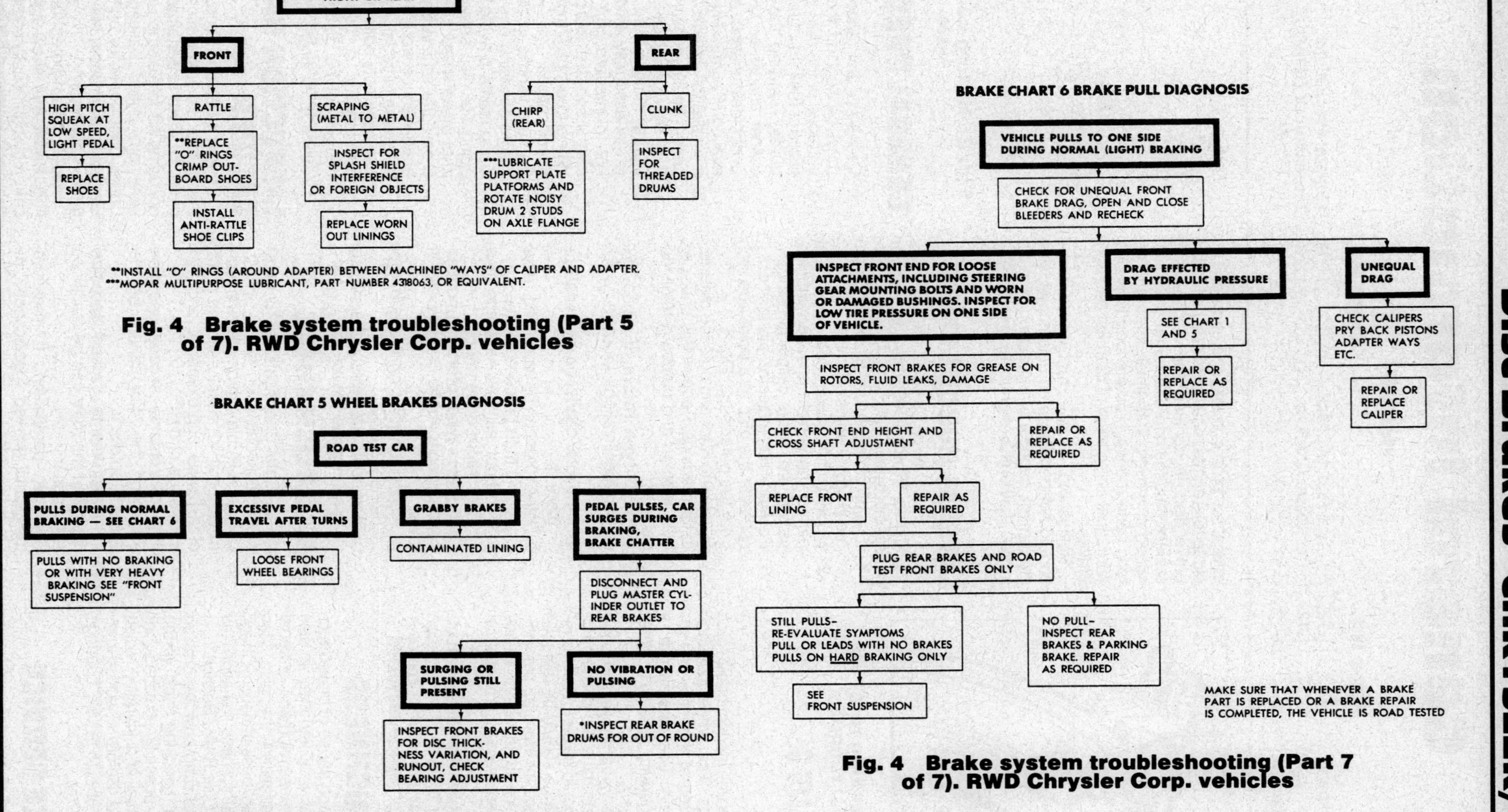


**Fig. 4 Brake system troubleshooting (Part 5 of 7). RWD Chrysler Corp. vehicles**



**Fig. 4 Brake system troubleshooting (Part 6 of 7). RWD Chrysler Corp. vehicles**



**Fig. 4 Brake system troubleshooting (Part 7 of 7). RWD Chrysler Corp. vehicles**

# General Information

## INDEX



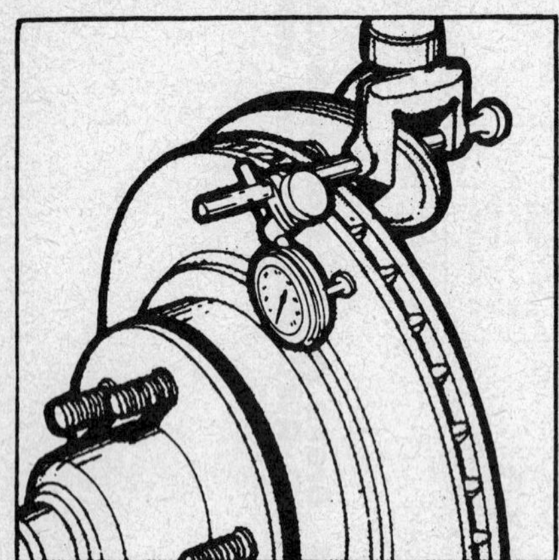

**Fig. 1 Checking rotor for lateral runout**

## BRAKE PADS & CALIPERS

Remove wheels and inspect brake rotor, caliper and linings. The wheel bearings should be inspected at this time and repacked if necessary. Use caution not to contaminate linings with grease or other foreign substances.

If an on-vehicle visual inspection does not adequately determine the condition of the linings, they should be removed and inspected. Brake linings should be replaced if cracked, damaged, or worn as per individual manufacturer limitations. If linings do not require replacement, reinstall in original positions.

Calipers assemblies should be inspected for damage, cracks, fluid leakage through the casting (porosity), or improper operation. Repair or replace as needed.

## BRAKE ROUGHNESS

The most common cause of brake chatter on disc brakes is a variation in disc thickness. If roughness, vibration, or pedal pulsation is experienced the disc may have excessive thickness variation. Check rotor parallelism (thickness variation) as described under "Disc Brake Service."

Excessive lateral runout of the braking disc may cause a "knocking back" of the caliper pistons, possibly creating increased pedal travel and vibration when brakes are applied. Before checking runout, if applicable ensure wheel bearings are adjusted properly.

## DISC BRAKE SERVICE

Maintenance of disc brakes is extremely critical for proper brake operation due to close tolerances required in machining the brake disc. In addition, the disc rubbing surface must be non-directional and maintained at a micro inch finish to control erratic performance, promote long lining life, and equal lining wear of both left and right brakes.

Refinishing of the rubbing surfaces should not be attempted unless precision equipment, capable of measuring in micro inches (millionths of an inch) is available.

## LATERAL RUNOUT CHECK

Refer to "Rotor Specifications" for runout specifications.

1. If applicable, ensure wheel bearings are properly adjusted.
2. Mount a dial indicator to a convenient part of the vehicle (steering knuckle, tie rod, disc brake caliper housing).
3. Position dial indicator plunger so it contacts the disc at a point one inch from the outer edge, **Fig. 1.**
4. Rotate the rotor and note the dial indicator readings. Perform this check on both inboard and outboard rotor faces.
5. **On hub type rotors,** if runout exceeds specifications proceed as follows:
   a. If the rotor cannot be machined, replace it.
   b. If the rotor can be machined, resurface it, then proceed to step c.
   c. If runout still exceeds specifications, replace the rotor.
6. **On hubless type rotors,** if runout exceeds specifications proceed as follows:
   a. Reposition rotor on the hub, then recheck runout.
   b. If runout still exceeds specifications, replace the rotor.

## PARALLELISM CHECK

Refer to "Rotor Specifications" for parallelism specifications.

1. Using a suitable micrometer, measure the rotor at 12 equally spaced points at a radius approximately one inch from edge of disc.
2. If measurements exceed specifications and the rotor cannot be machined, replace it.
3. If measurements exceed specifications and the rotor can be machined, resurface it.
4. Recheck parallelism. If measurements still exceed specifications, replace the rotor.

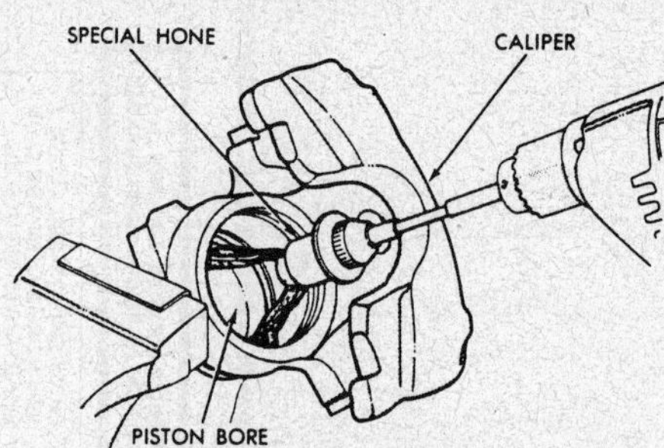


**Fig. 2 Honing caliper piston bore**

## GENERAL PRECAUTIONS

1. Grease or any other foreign material must be kept off the caliper, linings, surfaces of the disc and external surfaces of the hub, during service procedures. Handling the brake disc and caliper should be done in a way to avoid deformation of the disc and nicking or scratching brake linings.
2. If inspection reveals that the rubber piston seals are worn or damaged, they should be replaced.
3. During removal and installation of a wheel assembly, exercise care so as not to interfere with or damage the caliper splash shield or bleeder screw.
4. Wheel bearings should be adjusted to specifications.
5. Be sure vehicle is centered on hoist before servicing any of the front end components to avoid bending or damaging the disc splash shield on full right or left wheel turns.
6. Before the vehicle is moved after any brake service work, be sure to obtain a firm brake pedal.
7. The assembly bolts of the two caliper housings (if a two piece caliper) should not be disturbed unless the caliper requires service.

## INSPECTION OF CALIPER

Should it become necessary to remove the caliper for installation of new parts, clean all parts in denatured alcohol, wipe dry using lint-free cloths. Using an air hose, blow out drilled passages and bores. Check dust boots for punctures or tears. Generally, new boots should be installed upon reassembly.

Inspect piston bores for scoring or pitting. Bores that show light scratches or corrosion can usually be cleaned with crocus cloth. However, bores that have deep scratches or scoring may be honed, provided the diameter of the bore is not increased more than .002 inch. If the bore does not clean up to within this specification, a new caliper housing should be installed. Black stains on the bore walls are caused by piston seals and will do no harm.

When using a hone, **Fig. 2,** be sure to install the hone baffle before honing bore. The baffle is used to protect the hone stones from damage. Use extreme care in cleaning the caliper after honing. Remove all dust and grit by flushing the caliper with denatured alcohol. Wipe dry with clean lint-free cloth and then clean a second time in the same manner.

# Type 1—Kelsey-Hayes Sliding Caliper Disc Brake, Front

## INDEX



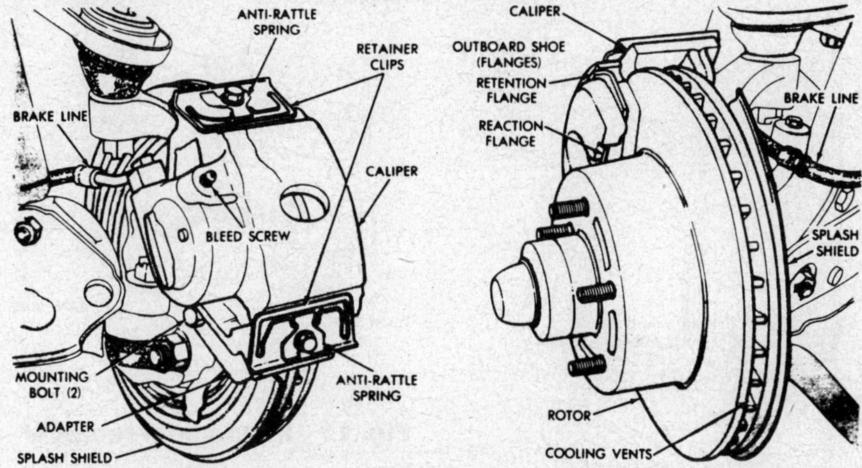


**Fig. 1 Kelsey-Hayes sliding caliper disc brake assembly**

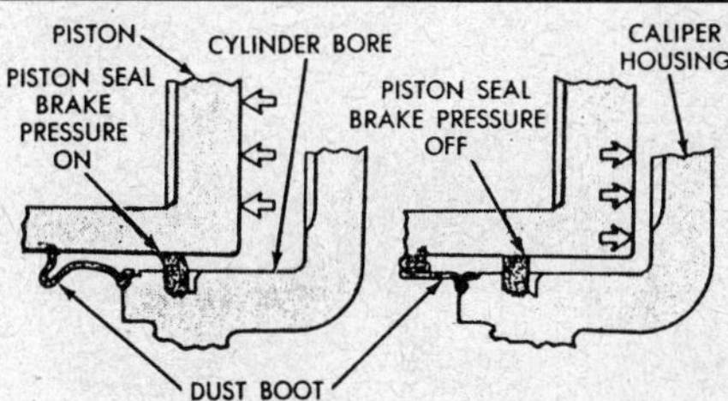


**Fig. 2 Piston seal function**

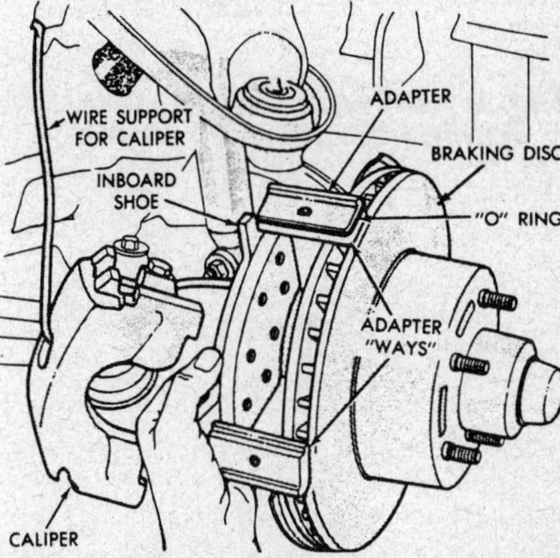


**Fig. 5 Replacing inboard pad**

not let caliper hang on hose.

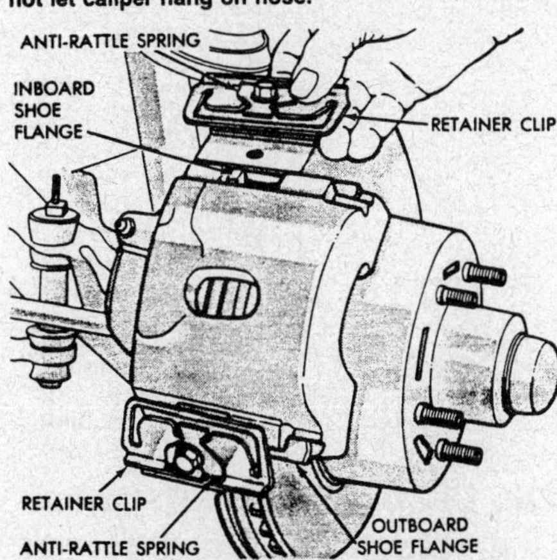


**Fig. 3 Retainer clips & anti-rattle spring replacement**

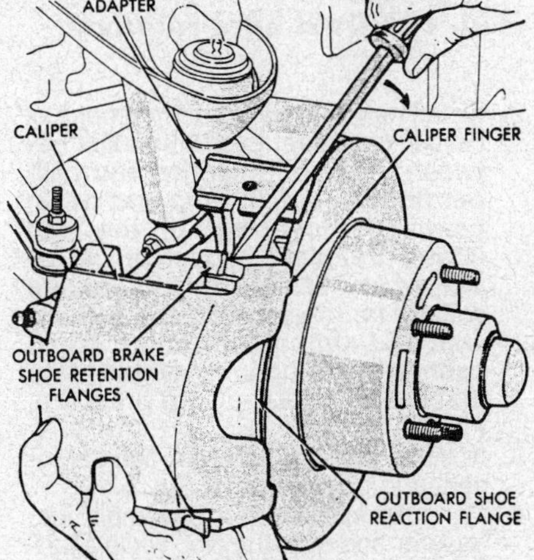


**Fig. 4 Removing outboard pad**

## OPERATION

This sliding caliper single piston system uses a one piece hub and is actuated by the hydraulic system and disc assembly, **Fig. 1.** Alignment and positioning of the caliper is achieved by two machined guides or ways on the adapter, while caliper retaining clips allow lateral movement of the caliper. Outboard pad flanges are used to position and locate the pad on the caliper fingers while the inboard pad is retained by the adapter. Braking force applied onto the outboard pad is transferred to the caliper, while braking force applied onto the inboard pad is transferred directly to the adapter.

A square cut piston seal provides a hydraulic seal between the piston and the cylinder bore, **Fig. 2.** A dust boot with a wiping lip installed in a groove in the cylinder bore and piston prevents contamination in the piston and cylinder bore area. Adjustment between the disc and the pad is obtained automatically by the outward relocation of the piston as the inboard lining wears and inward movement of the caliper as the outboard lining wears.

## CALIPER REMOVAL

**On models equipped with anti-lock brakes, prior to disconnecting any hydraulic lines or fittings, the hydraulic system must be depressurized by pumping the brake pedal a minimum of 25 times with ignition Off.**

1. Raise and support vehicle.
2. Remove front wheel and tire assembly.
3. Remove caliper retaining clips and anti-rattle springs, **Fig. 3.**
4. Remove caliper from disc by slowly sliding caliper assembly out and away from disc. **Support caliper to avoid damage to brake hose.**

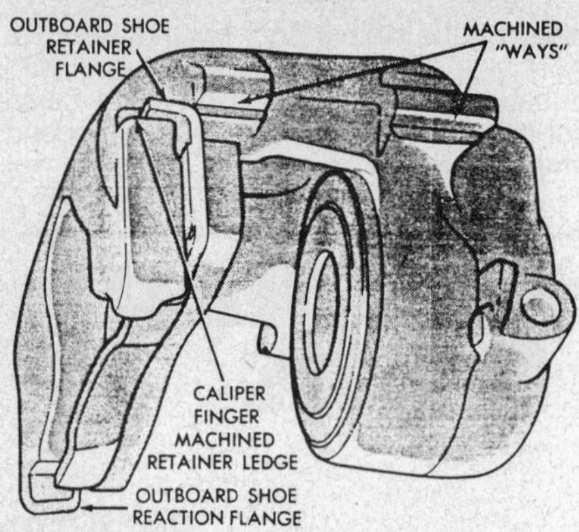


**Fig. 6 Caliper finger & outboard pad retainer flange**

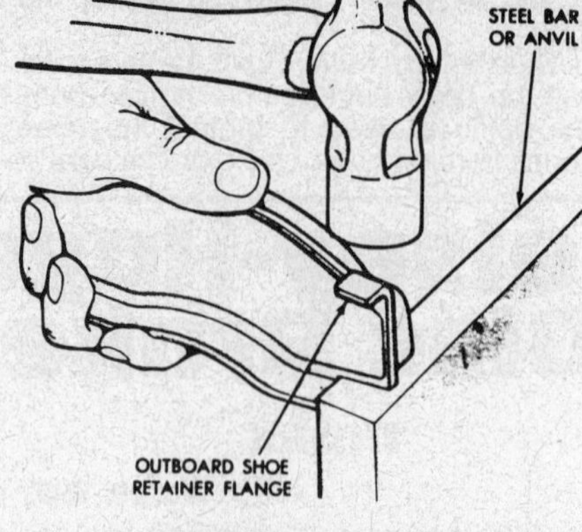


**Fig. 7 Bending outboard pad retaining flange**

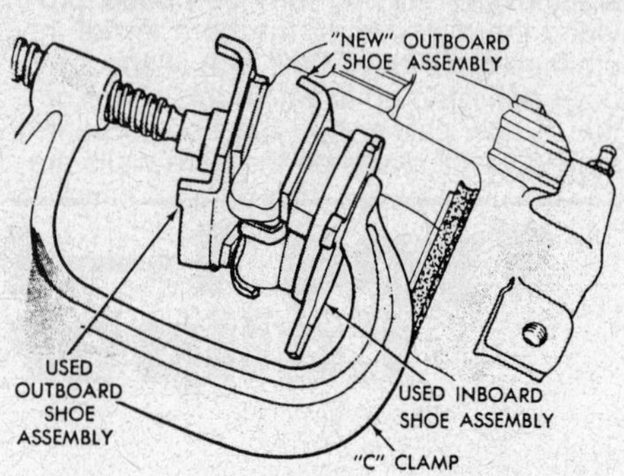


**Fig. 8 Installing outboard pad using C-clamp**

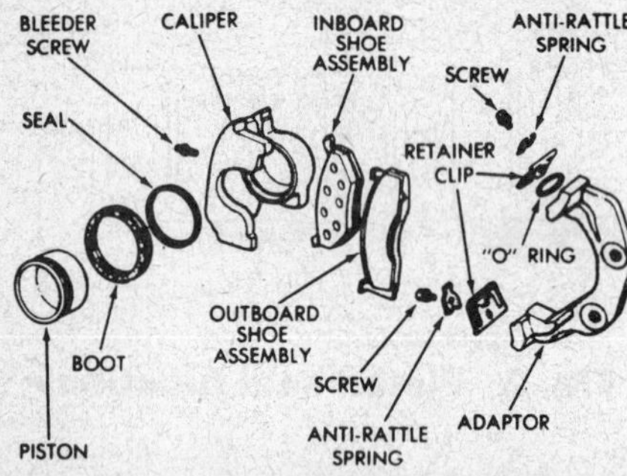


**Fig. 9 Disassembled view of Kelsey-Hayes disc brake**

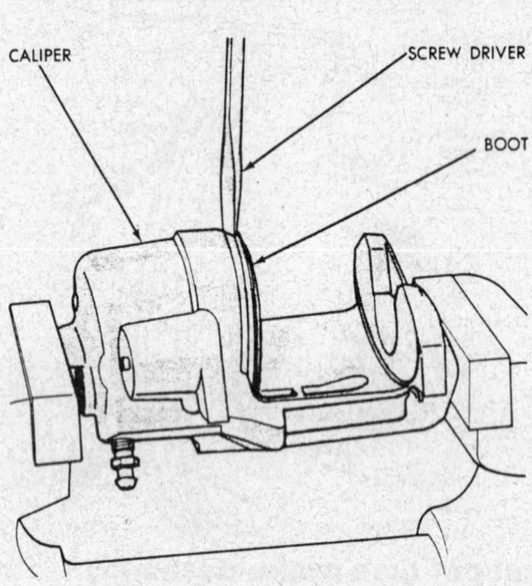


**Fig. 10 Dust boot removal**

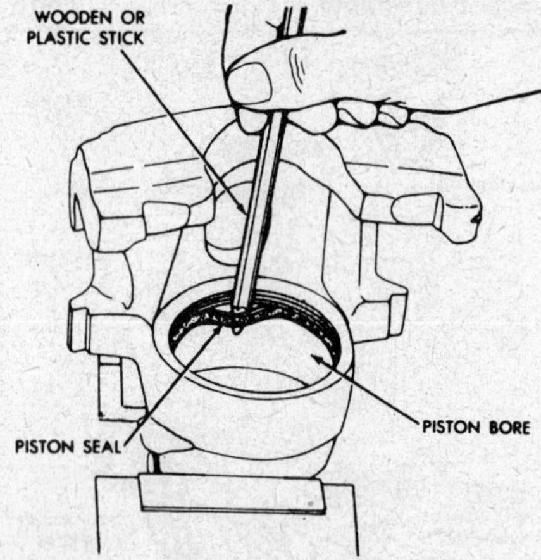


**Fig. 11 Piston seal removal**

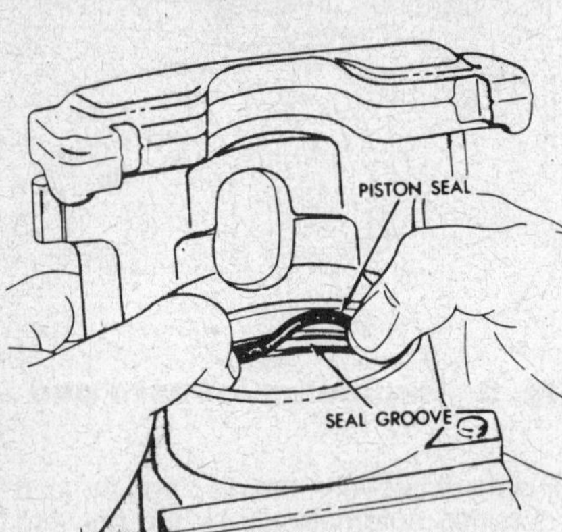
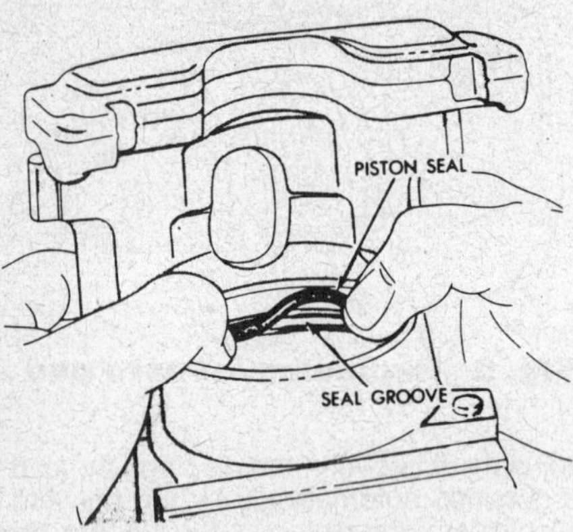


**Fig. 12 Piston seal installation**

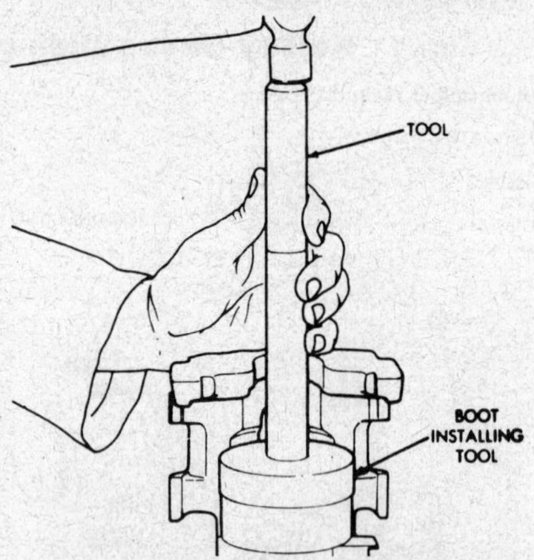


**Fig. 13 Dust boot installation**

## BRAKE PAD REMOVAL

1. Remove caliper assembly as described above.
2. Remove outboard pad by prying between the pad and caliper fingers, **Fig. 4. Support caliper to avoid damage to brake hose.**
3. Remove inboard brake pad from adapter, **Fig. 5.**

## BRAKE PAD INSTALLATION

**Remove approximately 1/3 of brake fluid from reservoir.**

1. Push piston back into bore until bottomed.
2. Install new outboard pad in recess of caliper. **No freeplay should exist between brake pad flanges and caliper fingers, Fig. 6. If up and down (vertical) movement of the pad shows freeplay, pad must be removed and flanges bent to provide a slight interference fit, Fig. 7. Reinstall pad after modification. If pad cannot be finger snapped into place, use light C-clamp pressure, Fig. 8.**
3. Position inboard pad with flanges inserted in adapter ways, **Fig. 5.**
4. Carefully slide caliper assembly into adapter and over the disc while aligning caliper on machined ways of adapter. **Ensure dust boot is not pulled out from groove when piston and boot slide over the inboard pad.**
5. Install anti-rattle springs and retaining clips and torque to specifications. **The inboard pad anti-rattle spring is to be installed on top of the retainer spring plate, Fig 3.**

## CALIPER DISASSEMBLY

1. With caliper and pads removed as described previously, place caliper onto the upper control arm and slowly depress brake pedal to hydraulically push piston from bore, **Fig. 9.** The pedal will fall when piston passes bore opening.
2. Support pedal below first inch of pedal travel to prevent excessive fluid loss.
3. To remove piston from the opposite caliper, disconnect flexible brake line at frame bracket at vehicle side where piston has been removed previously and plug tube to prevent pressure loss. By depressing brake pedal, this piston can also be hydraulically pushed out.

4. Disconnect flexible brake hose from caliper, then mount caliper in a soft-jawed vise. **Excessive vise pressure will distort caliper bore.**
5. Using a suitable screwdriver, remove and discard dust boot, **Fig. 10.**
6. Insert a tool such as a small, pointed wooden or plastic object between the cylinder bore and the seal and work seal out of the groove in the piston bore, **Fig. 11. A metal tool such as a screwdriver should not be used, as it can cause damage to the piston bore or burr the edges of the seal groove.**

## CALIPER INSPECTION

1. Clean all parts with a suitable brake cleaner and blow dry using compressed air.
2. Inspect piston bore for scoring or pitting. If scratches or corrosion cannot be cleaned with crocus cloth, hone bore with suitable brake hone using brake fluid as a lubricant. Do not increase bore more than .002 inch while honing. Replace caliper if corrosion or pitting is excessive.
3. Replace caliper piston if it is excessively pitted, scored or worn, or if honing the caliper bore was necessary.

## CALIPER ASSEMBLY

1. Dip new piston seals in clean brake fluid. Work seal gently into the groove until seal is properly seated, ensuring seal is not twisted or rolled, **Fig. 12. Do not reuse old seals.**
2. Lubricate piston boot generously with clean brake fluid, then position over piston.
3. Install piston into bore and push past seal until piston bottoms in bore.
4. Position dust boot in counterbore and drive boot onto counterbore with tool C-4689 and handle C-4171, **Fig. 13.**
5. Install brake hose to caliper using new seal washers.
6. Install caliper and pads as described under "Brake Pad Installation."

# Type 2—A.T.E. Dual Pin Floating Caliper Disc Brake, Front

### INDEX



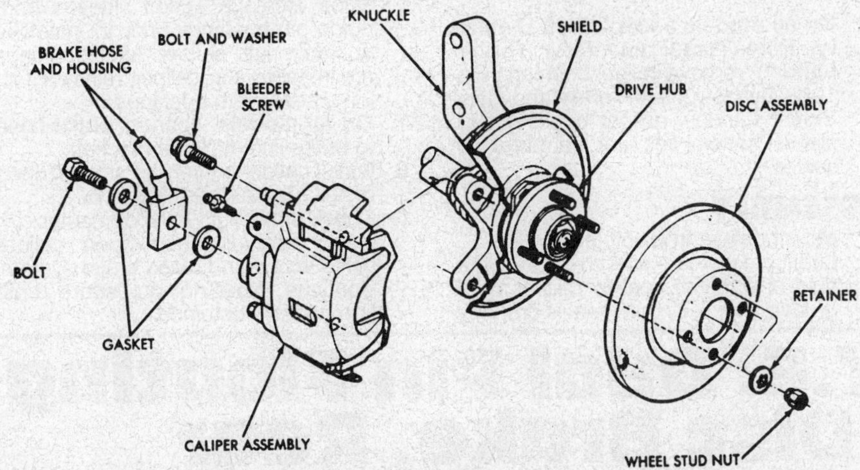


**Fig. 1 A.T.E. dual pin floating caliper front disc brake assembly**

## OPERATION

The single piston floating caliper disc brake assembly consists of the hub and disc brake rotor assembly, caliper, pads, splash shield and adapter, **Fig. 1.**

The caliper assembly floats on two rubber bushings riding on two steel guide pins threaded into the adapter. The bushings are inserted on the inboard portion of the caliper. Two machined abutments on the adapter position and align the caliper fore and aft. Guide pins and bushings control caliper and piston seal movement to assist in maintaining proper pad clearance. All braking force is taken directly by the adapter.

## BRAKE PADS REPLACE

**On models equipped with anti-lock brakes, prior to disconnecting any hydraulic lines or fittings, the hydraulic system must be depressurized by pumping the brake pedal a minimum of 25 times with ignition Off.**

1. Raise and support vehicle.
2. Remove wheel and tire assembly.
3. Remove hold-down spring from caliper assembly by pressing spring outward.
4. Loosen, but do not remove caliper guide pins, then remove caliper from disc. Inboard pad will remain inside caliper. **Support caliper assembly to prevent damage to hydraulic brake hose. Remove caliper guide pins only if bushings or sleeves are to be replaced.**
5. Remove inboard pad from caliper and outboard pad from adapter.
6. Push caliper piston into bore. Remove some brake fluid from master cylinder reservoir to prevent overflowing when piston is pushed into bore.
7. Install new inboard pad into caliper with retainer positioned in piston bore.
8. Install outboard pad onto adapter.
9. Position caliper over brake disc and adapter, then **torque** guide pins to 18-26 ft. lbs.
10. Install hold-down spring, then install tire and wheel assembly and lower vehicle.
11. Check master cylinder reservoir for proper brake fluid lever.

## CALIPER OVERHAUL

### DISASSEMBLY

1. Remove caliper assembly as described under "Brake Pads, Replace."
2. Place a wood block between caliper piston and caliper fingers. With brake hose attached to caliper, **Fig. 2,** carefully depress brake pedal to push piston out of caliper bore. Prop brake pedal to any position below first inch of brake pedal travel to prevent brake fluid loss.
3. If pistons are to be removed from both calipers, disconnect brake hose at

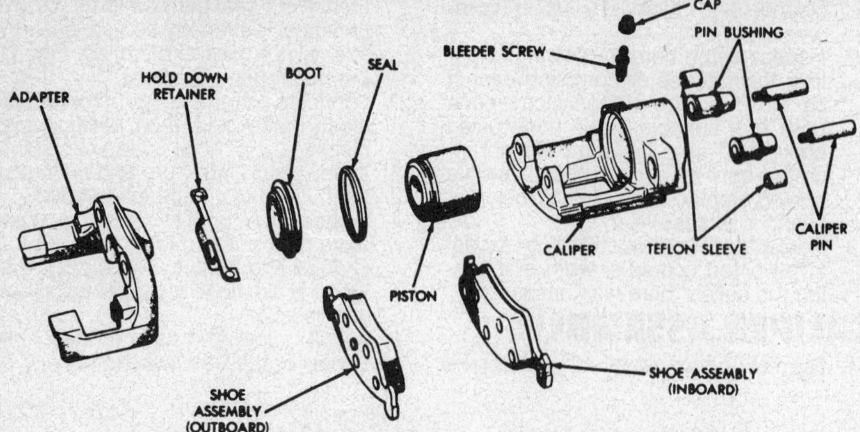


**Fig. 2 Disassembled view of A.T.E. disc brake**

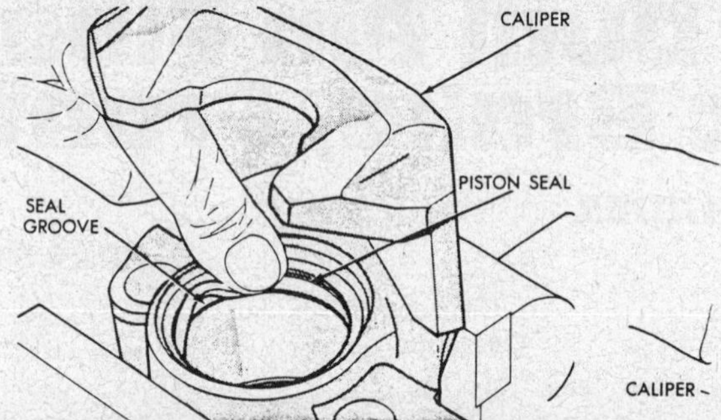


**Fig. 3 Installing piston seal**

frame bracket after removing piston, then cap brake line and repeat procedure to remove piston from other caliper.

4. Disconnect brake hose from caliper.
5. Mount caliper in a soft jawed vise.
6. Support caliper, then remove and discard dust boot.
7. Using a small wooden or plastic stick, remove seal from groove in piston bore and discard. **Do not use a screwdriver or other metal tool, as this may scratch caliper bore.**
8. **On all models except 1988 Dynasty, New Yorker and New Yorker Landau,** remove caliper bushings. On 1988 Dynasty, New Yorker and New Yorker Landau, caliper bushing and sleeve assemblies are permanently sealed.

### ASSEMBLY

1. Mount caliper in a soft jawed vise.
2. Lubricate piston seal with clean brake fluid and install seal in caliper bore groove, **Fig. 3.** Ensure seal is properly seated.

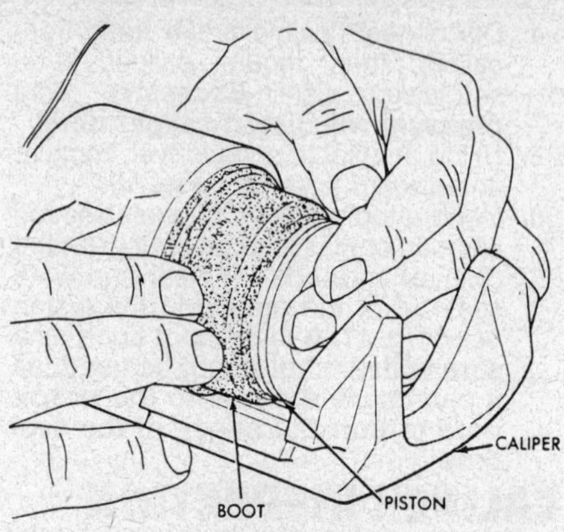


**Fig. 4 Installing caliper piston & dust boot**

3. Lubricate piston boot with clean brake fluid and position over piston.
4. Install piston and boot assembly, pushing it past piston seal until it bottoms into caliper bore.
5. Using a hammer and tool No. C-4689 with C-4171 handle, drive dust boot into counterbore until properly seated, **Fig. 4.**
6. **On models where bushings require replacement,** compress flanges of bushings and install on caliper housing. Ensure bushing flanges extend evenly over caliper housing on both sides. Remove Teflon sleeves from guide pin bushings prior to installing bushings into caliper. After bushings are installed into caliper, reinstall Teflon sleeves into bushings.
7. **On all models,** connect brake hose to brake line at frame bracket.
8. Install caliper on vehicle as described under "Brake Pads, Replace."
9. Check brake fluid level of master cylinder reservoir, then open caliper bleed screw and bleed brake system. Continue bleeding procedure until firm pedal is obtained.

# Type 3—A.T.E. Dual Pin Floating Caliper Disc Brake, Rear

## INDEX



## DESCRIPTION

This single piston, floating caliper rear disc brake assembly, **Fig. 1,** includes a hub assembly, rotor, caliper, pads, an adapter and a mechanically operated parking brake. The caliper has either a 1.299 (33 mm) or 1.42 inch (36 mm) piston located on the inboard side.

The caliper floats on rubber bushings with metal sleeves on two bolts that are threaded into the adapter. Two machined abutments on the adapter position and align the caliper and brake pads for movement fore and aft.

## BRAKE PADS

### REPLACE

**On models equipped with anti-lock brakes, prior to disconnecting any hydraulic lines or fittings, the hydraulic system must be depressurized by pumping the brake pedal a minimum of 25 times with ignition Off.**

### REMOVAL

1. Raise and properly support vehicle.
2. Remove rear wheel and tire assembly, and ensure parking brake is released.
3. Pump brake pedal, then manually pull caliper assembly toward outside of vehicle so that piston will retract.
4. Drive brake pad retainer pin out of caliper, **Fig. 2.**
5. Remove caliper mounting bolts, **Fig. 3,** then the caliper by lifting upward and away from disc. Support caliper with suitable wire. **Do not allow caliper to hang by brake hose.**

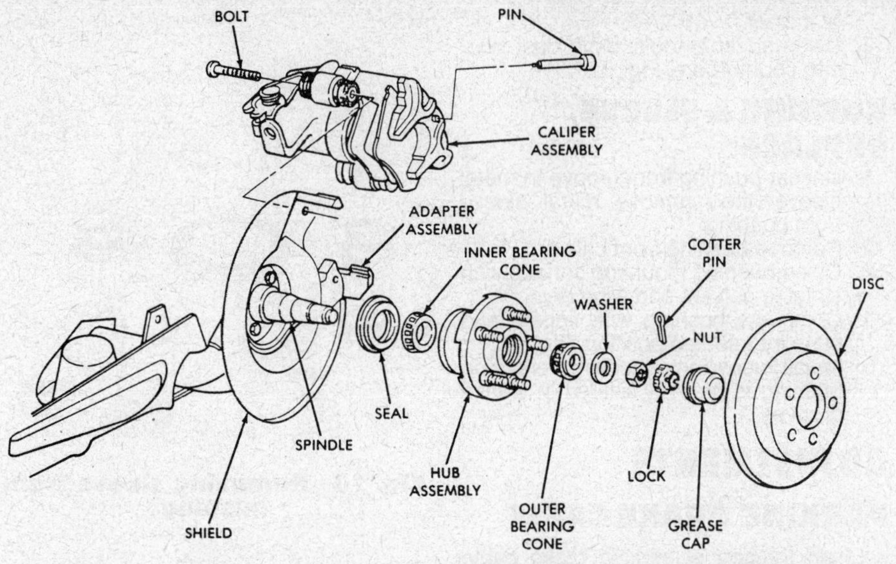


**Fig. 1 A.T.E. floating caliper rear disc brake assembly**

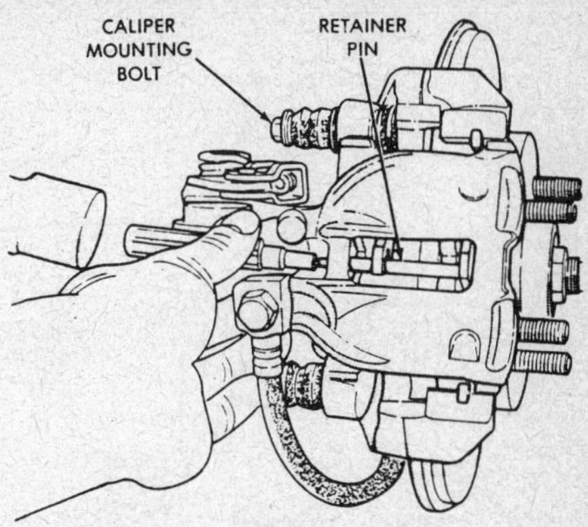


**Fig. 2 Removing brake pad retainer pin**

CALIPER MOUNTING BOLT
CALIPER MOUNTING BOLT
PARKING BRAKE CABLE ASSEMBLY

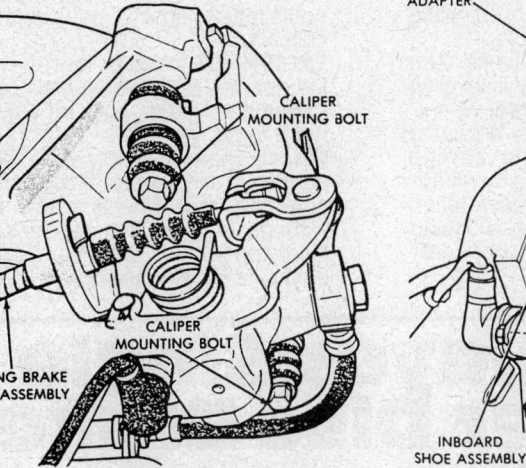

**Fig. 3 Caliper mounting bolt locations**

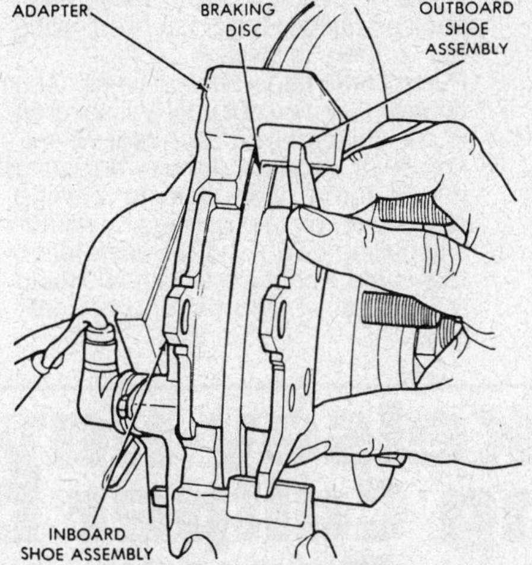
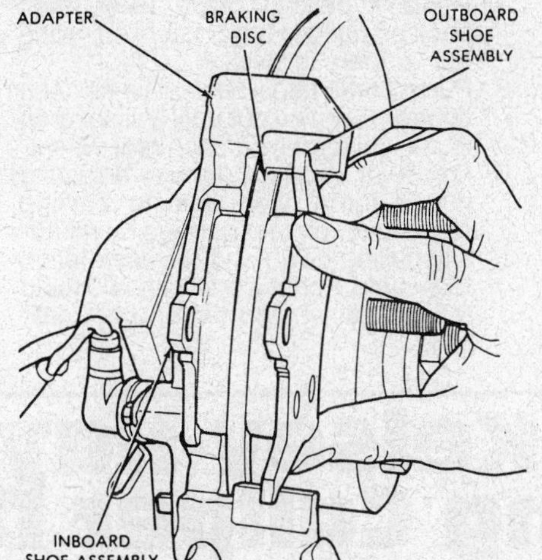


**Fig. 4 Brake pad replacement**

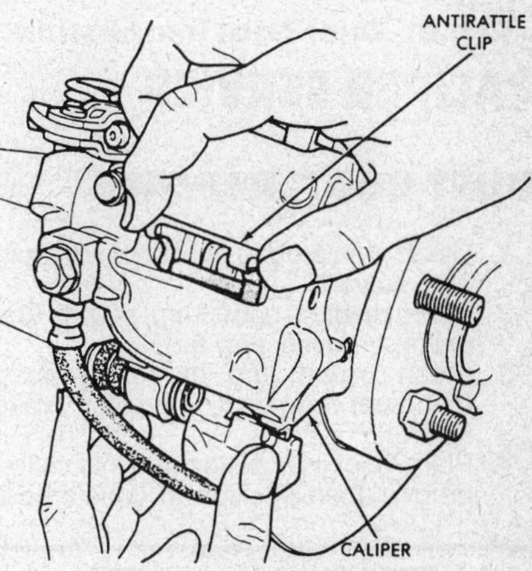


**Fig. 5 Anti-rattle clip installation**

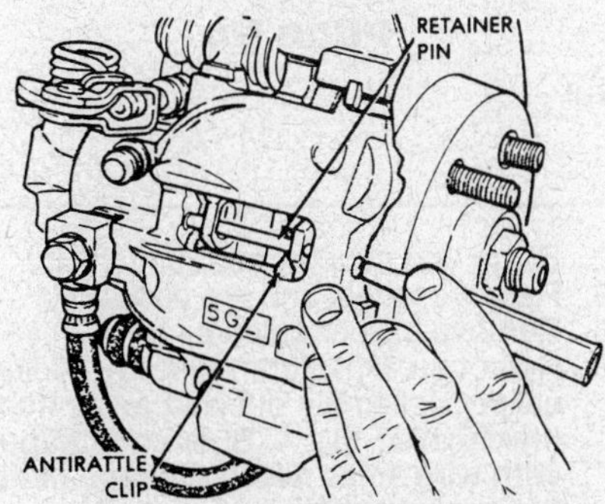


**Fig. 6 Anti-rattle clip & retainer pin positioning**

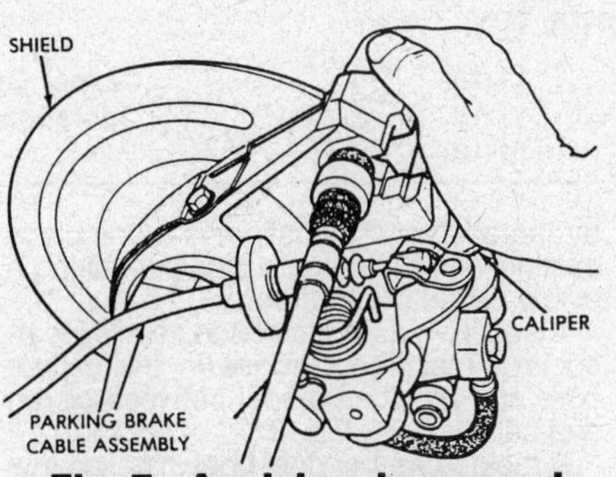


**Fig. 7 Applying downward pressure to caliper**

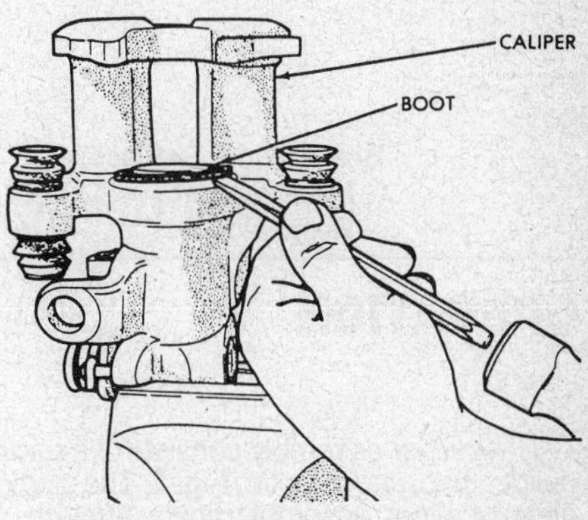


**Fig. 8 Removing dust boot**

6. Remove brake pads and anti-rattle clip.

## INSTALLATION

1. Lubricate adapter ways with suitable grease.
2. Install inboard pad first, then the outboard pad on adapter assembly, **Fig. 4.**
3. Place caliper with lower end inserted first over disc and pads onto adapter. **Do not install mounting bolts at this time.**
4. Insert anti-rattle clip through opening in caliper as shown in **Fig. 5.** Place lower portion of clip in position first, then release. **Ensure clip falls into correct position, Fig. 6.**
5. Install brake pad retainer pin through caliper and pads. Drive into position using hammer and suitable drift, **Fig. 6.**
6. Push down on upper portion of caliper to load anti-rattle clip, **Fig. 7.**
7. Install upper mounting bolt first, then the lower bolt. Torque bolts to specifications.
8. Install wheel and tire assembly, then lower vehicle.

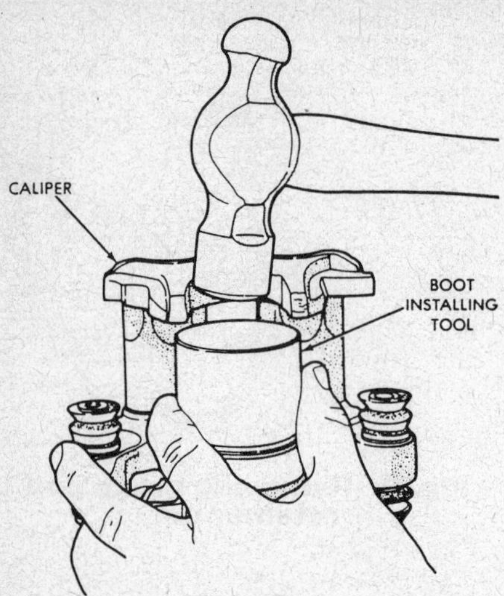


Fig. 9 Dust boot installation

## CALIPER SERVICE

### DUST BOOT, REPLACE

1. Clean area around dust boot with suitable solvent.
2. Remove dust boot from caliper and piston grooves, **Fig. 8.**
3. Clean piston and caliper grooves, then coat new boot with clean brake fluid.
4. Place boot over piston and into piston groove, then position in counterbore of caliper.
5. Using suitable tools, drive dust boot into counterbore, **Fig, 9.**

### BUSHING & SLEEVE, REPLACE

1. Unseat bushing from groove in metal sleeve, then remove metal sleeve from bushing.
2. Remove bushing from caliper.
3. Clean bushing mounting surface with suitable solvent and wipe dry.
4. Compress bushing with fingers and push into seated position, **Fig. 10.**
5. Install sleeve into bushing, ensuring bushing is properly seated in sleeve grooves.

## ADJUSTMENTS

### PARKING BRAKE CABLE

Clean threads of parking brake cable with a wire brush and lubricate prior to loosening adjusting nut.

1. Release parking brake lever, then back off parking brake cable adjusting nut so there is slack in cable.
2. Pump brake pedal several times, then tighten adjusting nut until a slight drag is felt while rotating each rear wheel.
3. **On 1989 models,** loosen adjusting nut 5 turns, then actuate parking brake lever on rear calipers by manually pulling down and releasing each rear cable. Parking brake lever should return against stop pin on both calipers.

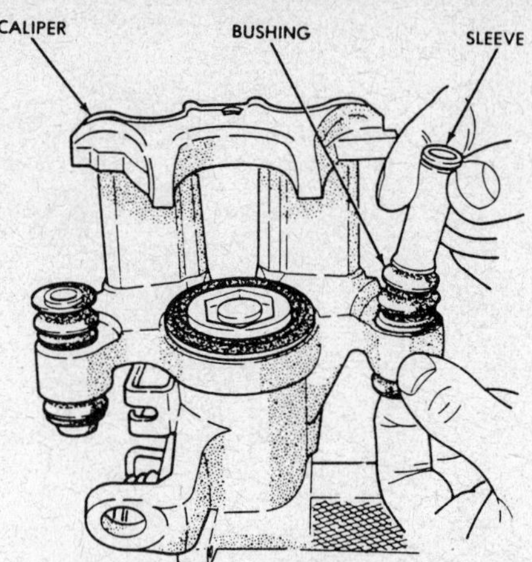


Fig. 10 Removing sleeve from bushing

4. If parking brake lever is not touching stop pins, loosen adjusting nut 1 turn.
5. Repeat steps 3 and 4 until parking brake returns against stop pin on both calipers.
6. **On 1990-91 models,** loosen adjusting nut until both rear wheels can be rotated freely, then back off adjusting nut 2 turns.
7. **On all models,** apply and release parking brake several times and ensure that rear wheels rotate freely without dragging and that actuating levers on both calipers return against stop pins in Off position.

# Type 4—Kelsey-Hayes Single Pin Floating Caliper Disc Brake, Front

INDEX



## OPERATION

The caliper assembly consists of a rotor, caliper, pad, and adapter, **Fig. 1.** The single piston caliper assembly floats through a rubber bushing on a single pin, threaded into the adapter. The bushing is inserted into the inboard portion of the caliper. Two machined abutments on the adapter, position and align the caliper fore and aft. The guide pin and bushing controls the movement of the caliper and the piston seal to assist in maintaining proper pad clearance.

This assembly has three anti-rattle clips. One is on top of the inboard pad, one clip is on the bottom of the outboard pad, and one clip is on top of the caliper, **Fig. 2.**

All of the braking force is taken directly by the adapter. The caliper is a one piece casting with the inboard side containing a single piston cylinder bore.

A square cut rubber piston seal is located in a machined groove in the caliper bore and provides a seal between piston and caliper bore, **Fig. 3.**

A molded rubber dust boot installed in a groove in the cylinder bore and piston keeps contamination from the caliper bore and piston. The boot mounts in the caliper bore and in a groove in the piston, **Fig. 3.**

## BRAKE PADS REPLACE

### REMOVAL

1. Remove brake fluid until reservoir is half full.
2. Raise and support front of vehicle.
3. Remove wheel and tire assembly.
4. Remove caliper guide pin.
5. Remove caliper from disc by sliding caliper assembly out and away from braking disc, **Fig. 4. Suspend caliper with wire so as not to damage flexible brake hose.**
6. Remove outboard brake lining, then lift off rotor and remove inboard brake lining.

### INSTALLATION

1. Lubricate adapter ways with suitable grease.
2. Push piston back into cylinder bore with uniform pressure until it is bottomed.
3. Position inboard pad on adapter, then install rotor.

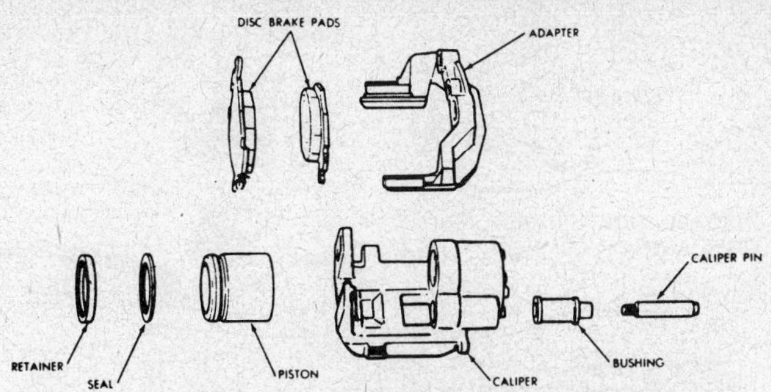


**Fig. 1 Disassembled view of Kelsey-Hayes disc brake**

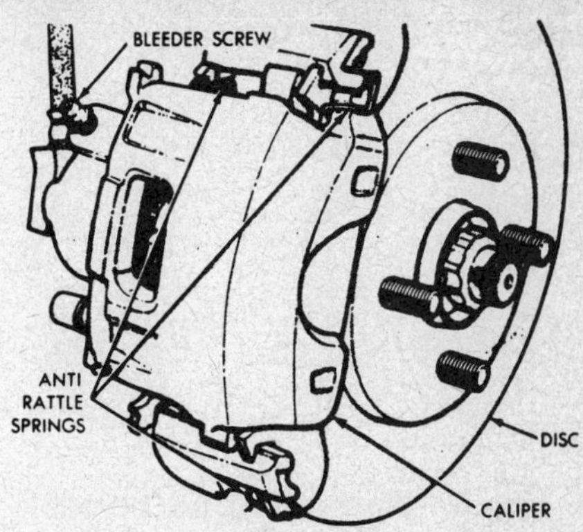


**Fig. 2 Anti-rattle spring location**

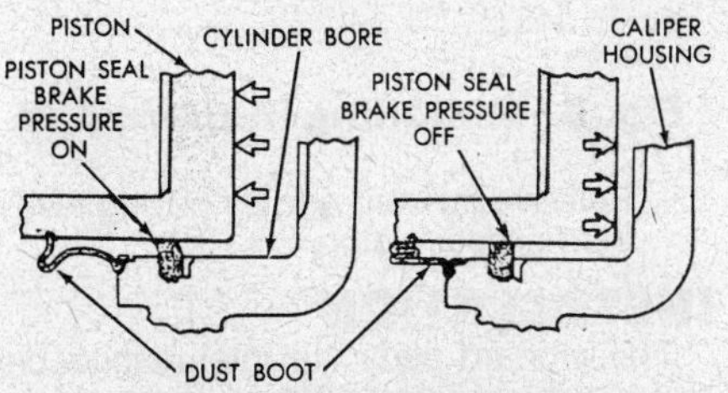


**Fig. 3 Cross-sectional view of piston seal & dust boot**

4. While holding outboard pad in position on adapter, carefully position caliper over disc brake rotor.
5. Lower caliper over rotor and adapter.
6. Install guide pin through bushing, caliper and adapter.
7. Press in on guide pin and thread pin into adapter.
8. Install wheel and tire assembly, then lower vehicle.

## CALIPER OVERHAUL

Refer to "Caliper Overhaul" as described under "Type 2—A.T.E. Dual Pin Floating Caliper Disc Brake, Front" for overhaul procedure.

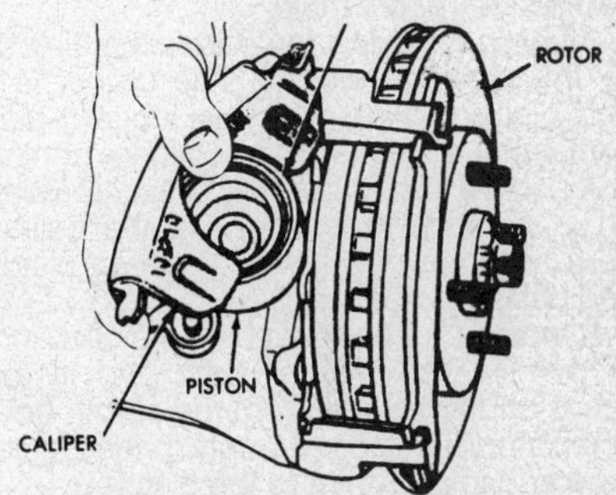


**Fig. 4 Removing caliper**

# Type 5—Kelsey-Hayes Dual Pin Floating Caliper Disc Brake, Front

## INDEX



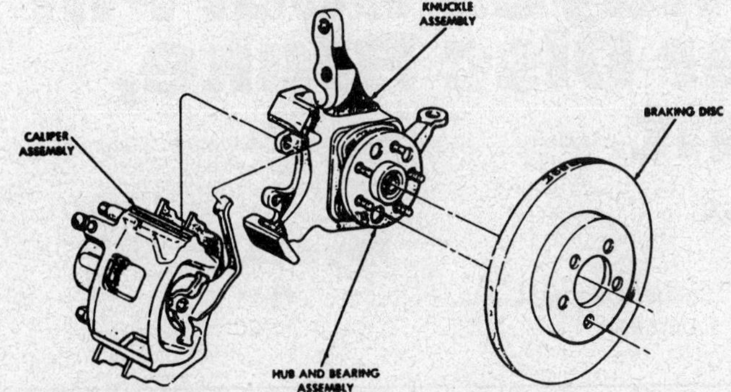


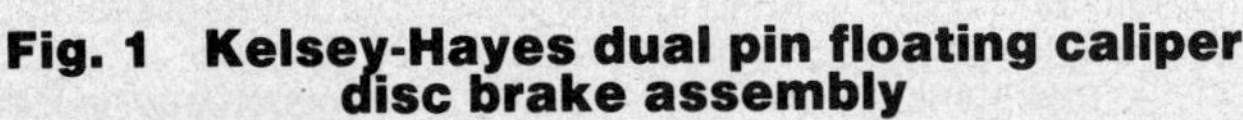

**Fig. 1 Kelsey-Hayes dual pin floating caliper disc brake assembly**

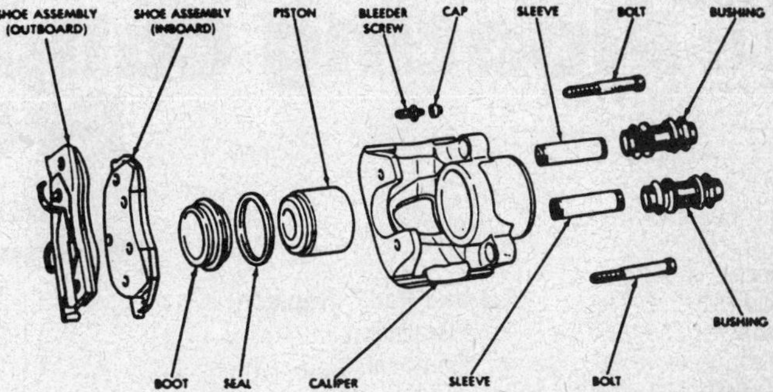


**Fig. 2 Disassembled view of Kelsey-Hayes disc brake**

## OPERATION

The single piston, floating caliper disc brake assembly, **Fig. 1,** consists of the rotor, caliper, pads and the driving hub. The caliper, **Fig. 2,** is mounted through bushings and sleeves by two through bolts threaded into the steering knuckle. Two machined abutments on the steering knuckle position and align the caliper fore and aft. The mounting bolts and bushings control the movement of the caliper and the piston seal to assist in maintaining proper pad clearance.

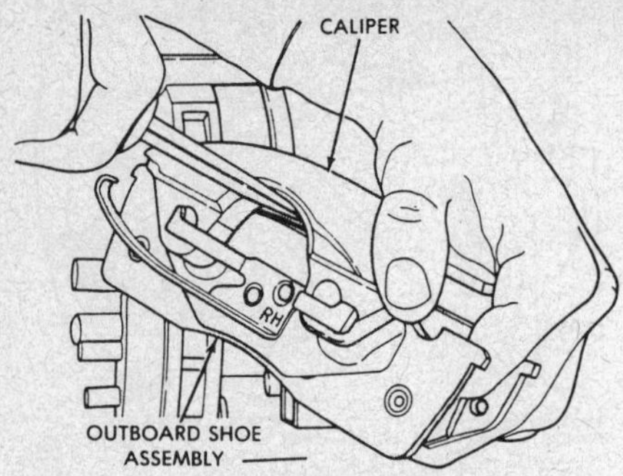


**Fig. 3 Removing outboard pad**

This assembly has an anti-rattle clip attached to the outer pad and an inner pad-piston retainer clip.

All of the braking force is taken directly by the steering knuckle. The caliper is a one piece casting with the inboard side containing a single piston cylinder bore.

A square cut rubber piston seal is located in a machined groove in the caliper bore and provides a seal between piston and caliper bore.

A molded rubber dust boot installed in a groove in the cylinder bore and piston keeps contamination from the caliper bore and piston. The boot mounts in the caliper bore and in a groove in the piston.

## BRAKE PADS

### REPLACE

#### REMOVAL

1. Remove 1/2 of brake fluid from reservoir.
2. Raise and support front of vehicle.
3. Remove wheel and tire assembly.
4. Remove caliper-to-steering knuckle attaching bolts.
5. Remove caliper and brake pads as an assembly by pulling lower end of caliper outward from steering knuckle, then sliding assembly away from braking disc. **Suspend caliper with wire to avoid damaging brake hose.**
6. Remove outboard pad by prying between pad and caliper, **Fig. 3. Support caliper to avoid damage to brake hose.**

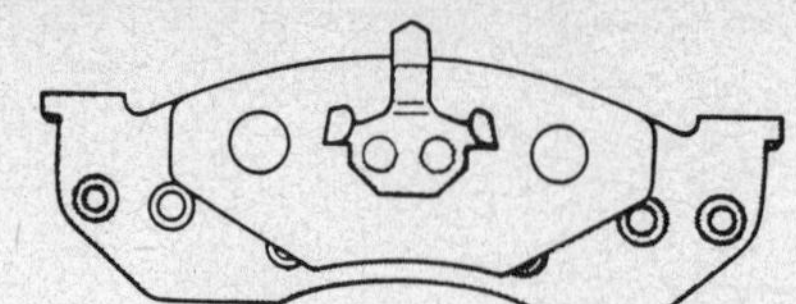


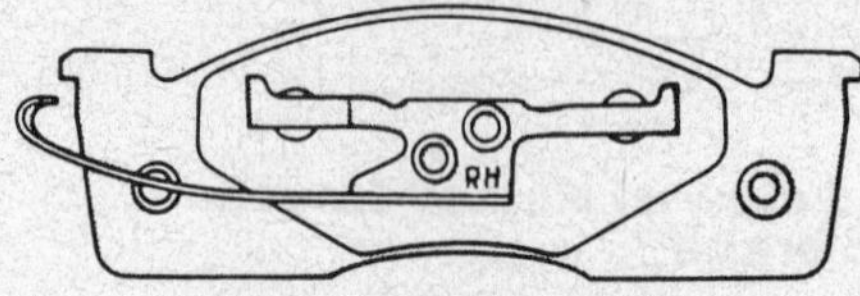


**Fig. 4 Brake pad identification**

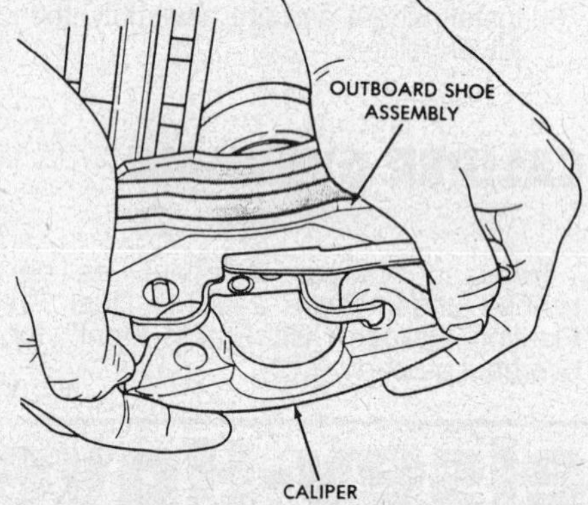


**Fig. 6 Installing outboard pad**

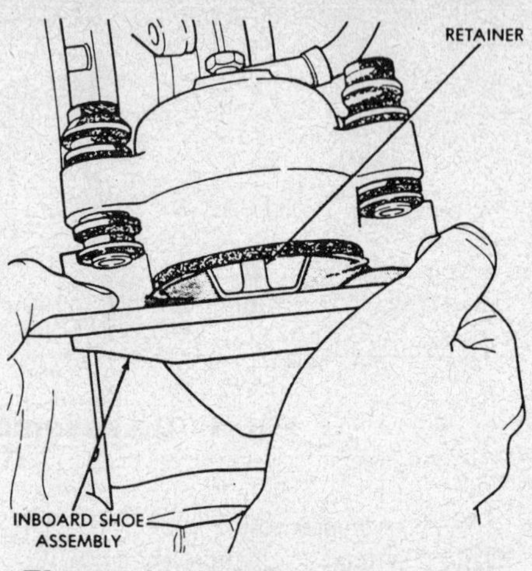


**Fig. 5 Installing inboard pad**

7. Remove inboard pad by pulling away from caliper piston.

#### INSTALLATION

The inboard pads are interchangeable and may be used on either side of vehicle. The outboard pads are not interchangeable and are marked "L" for left side or "R" for right side of vehicle, **Fig. 4.**

1. Lubricate adapter ways with suitable grease.
2. Install inboard pad in caliper, entering retainer into bore of piston, **Fig. 5.**
3. Position properly marked outboard pad hold-down spring into caliper as shown in **Fig. 6.**
4. Lower caliper over braking disc, then install attaching bolts. Torque bolts to specifications.
5. Install tire and wheel assembly and lower vehicle.

## CALIPER OVERHAUL

Refer to "Caliper Overhaul" as described under "Type 2—A.T.E. Dual Pin Floating Caliper Disc Brake, Front" for overhaul procedure.

# Type 6—Kelsey-Hayes Dual Pin Floating Caliper Disc Brake, Front

### INDEX



## OPERATION

The single piston, floating caliper disc brake assembly, **Fig. 1,** consists of the rotor, caliper, pads and the driving hub. The caliper is mounted through bushings and sleeves by two through bolts threaded into an adapter. Two machined abutments on the adapter position and align the caliper fore and aft. The mounting bolts and bushings control the movement of the caliper and the piston seal to assist in maintaining proper pad clearance.

This assembly has an anti-rattle clip attached to the outer pad and an inner pad-piston retainer clip.

All of the braking force is taken directly by the adapter. The caliper is a one piece casting with the inboard side containing a single piston cylinder bore.

A square cut rubber piston seal is located in a machined groove in the caliper bore and provides a seal between piston and caliper bore.

A molded rubber dust boot installed in a groove in the cylinder bore and piston keeps contamination from the caliper bore

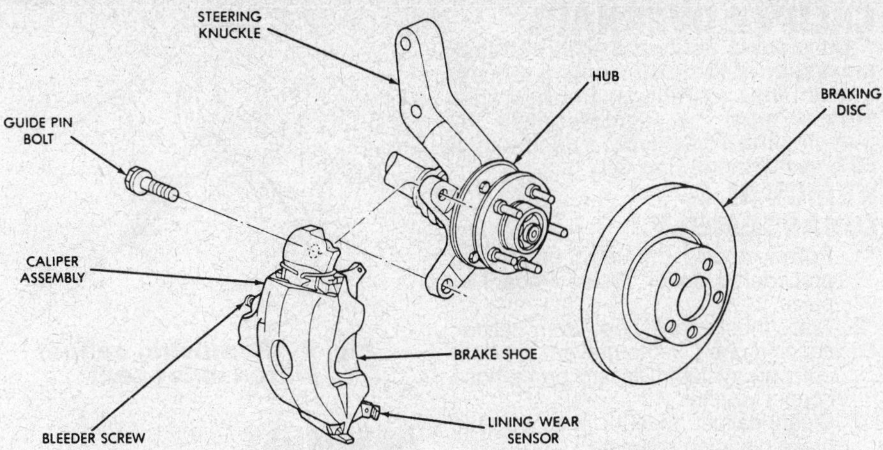


**Fig. 1 Kelsey-Hayes dual pin floating caliper disc brake assembly**

and piston. The boot mounts in the caliper bore and in a groove in the piston.

## BRAKE PADS
## REPLACE
### REMOVAL

1. Remove 1/2 of brake fluid from reservoir.
2. Raise and support front of vehicle.
3. Remove wheel and tire assembly.
4. Remove caliper guide pin bolts, then wedge caliper away from rotor using a screwdriver to break gasket adhesive seals.
5. Remove caliper by slowly sliding assembly out and away from rotor. **Suspend caliper with wire to avoid damaging brake hose.**
6. Remove outboard pad, rotor, then the inboard pad by sliding off of adapter.

### INSTALLATION

1. Lubricate adapter ways with suitable grease.
2. Install inboard pad, rotor, then the outboard pad onto adapter.
3. Lower caliper over rotor and pad assemblies, then install guide pins. Torque pins to specifications.
4. Install tire and wheel assembly and lower vehicle.

## CALIPER OVERHAUL

Refer to "Caliper Overhaul" as described under "Type 2—A.T.E. Dual Pin Floating Caliper Disc Brake, Front" for overhaul procedure.

# Type 7—Dual Pin Sliding Caliper Disc Brake, Front

INDEX



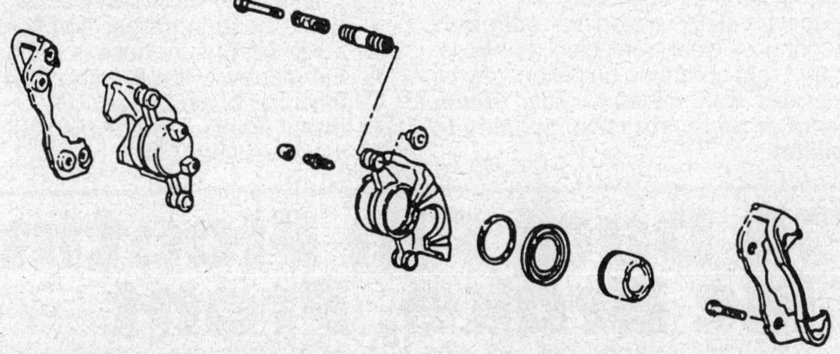

**Fig. 1 Disassembled view of disc brake assembly**

## OPERATION

This dual pin sliding caliper disc brake system uses a rotor mounted on a drive hub, brake pads, a mounting bracket and a single piston caliper, **Fig. 1.**

Two pins which are mounted through sleeves and bushings in the caliper onto a mounting bracket control the movement of the caliper and the piston seal, to assist in maintaining proper pad clearance.

This assembly uses two anti-rattle clips, one mounted on the bottom end of each brake pad.

A molded rubber and metal dust seal protects the piston and caliper bore from corrosion, and is held in place by an inner lip which is seated into a piston groove.

## BRAKE PADS
## REPLACE
### REMOVAL

1. Drain and discard approximately 1/2 of the brake fluid from the master cylinder reservoir.
2. Raise and support vehicle.

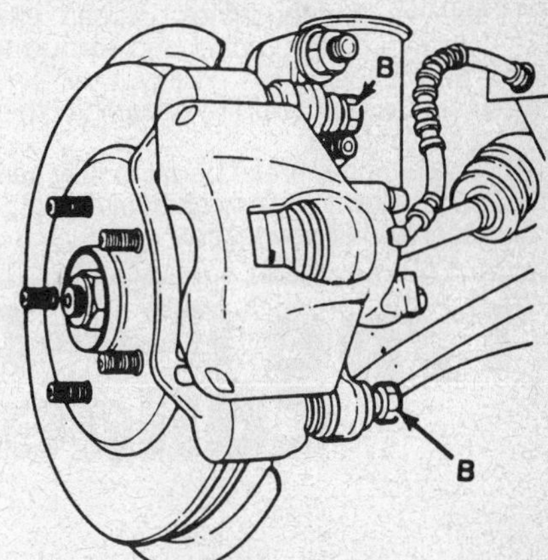


**Fig. 2 Caliper mounting pin locations**

3. Remove wheel and tire assembly.
4. Using a suitable screwdriver, slightly pry piston into caliper bore.
5. Remove caliper mounting pins, **Fig. 2,** then lift caliper from mounting bracket and off rotor. **Suspend caliper with suitable wire to prevent damaging brake hose.**
6. Remove outer brake pad first, then the inner pad, noting position of anti-rattle clips for assembly reference.

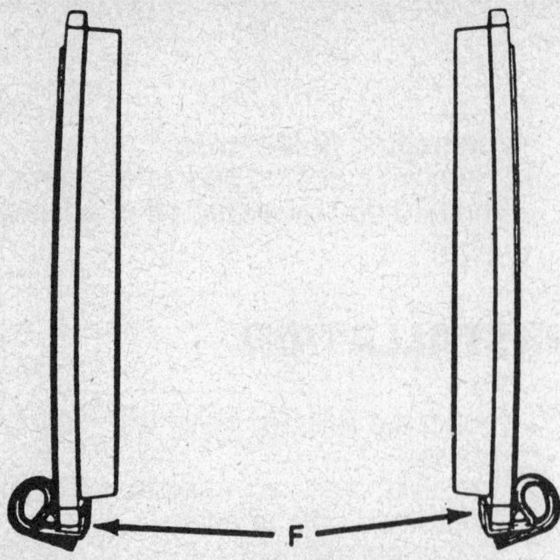


Fig. 3 Anti-rattle clip locations

7. Wipe inside of caliper with dry, clean cloth and inspect piston bore for leakage. If leakage is present, refer to "Caliper Overhaul." **Do not clean caliper with compressed air as damage to the dust boot may result.**

## INSTALLATION

1. Using a C-clamp, push caliper piston back until it is bottomed into cylinder bore.
2. Using a wire brush, thoroughly clean brake pad contact points on caliper mount.
3. Assemble anti-rattle clips on brake pads as shown in **Fig. 3.**
4. Position inner pad on caliper mount first, then the outer pad.
5. Lower caliper over brake pads onto caliper mounting bracket, ensuring brake hose is not twisted.
6. Lubricate mounting pins with suitable grease, then install through caliper sleeves and bushings. Thread pins into mounting bracket and **torque** to 18 1/2 ft. lbs.
7. Install wheel and tire assembly, then lower vehicle.
8. Slowly pump brake pedal to fully seat pads, then top off brake fluid level in reservoir as necessary.

## CALIPER OVERHAUL

**On models equipped with anti-lock brakes, prior to disconnecting any hydraulic lines or fittings, the hydraulic system must be depressurized by pumping the brake pedal a minimum of 25 times with ignition Off.**

### REMOVAL & DISASSEMBLY

1. Follow steps 1 through 5 of removal procedures under "Brake Pads, Replace."
2. Disconnect brake hose from caliper, capping open line to prevent dirt from entering system. Discard brake hose copper washer.
3. Clean caliper exterior with suitable brake cleaning solvent.
4. Drain caliper, then place on clean work surface.
5. Using screwdriver, loosen metal lip of caliper piston dust seal.
6. Place a block of wood between caliper and caliper piston, then using compressed air, gently apply air pressure into caliper fluid inlet hole to ease piston out of bore. **Do not place fingers in front of piston in an attempt to catch or protect it when applying compressed air. This could result in serious injury.**
7. Using a feeler gauge or other suitable tool, remove piston inner seal, **Fig. 4.**

### INSPECTION

1. Inspect caliper bore for scoring or corrosion. Light corrosion and scoring can be removed with brake hone, using brake fluid for lubricant. **Do not attempt to clean caliper bore with any other abrasives.**
2. Clean caliper with suitable brake cleaning solvent, then dry with compressed air.
3. Inspect caliper hardware for corrosion and replace as necessary.
4. Inspect caliper piston for corrosion, scoring or wear, replacing as necessary. Light corrosion on piston may be cleaned with mineral spirits. **Never sand or apply abrasive cleaners to piston.**

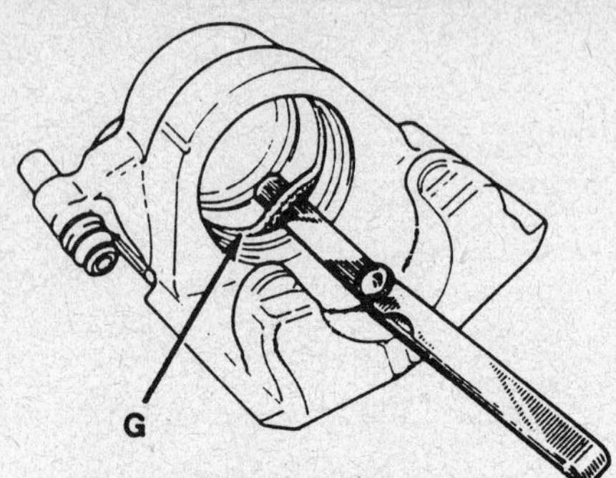


Fig. 4 Removing caliper piston inner seal

### ASSEMBLY

1. Lubricate piston bore and new inner seal with brake fluid, then work seal into caliper bore groove by hand.
2. Lubricate piston with brake fluid, then slide metal portion of new dust seal over open end of piston and pull rearward until seal inner lip seats in piston groove, then push outer portion of seal forward until it is flush with end of piston.
3. Insert piston and seal assembly into bore. Do not unseat inner seal. With a slight rocking motion, bottom piston into bore.
4. Center seal lip into counterbore on caliper, then seat seal into caliper housing using tool No. Fre. KM.02 and adapter No. Fre. ML.02 or equivalents.

### INSTALLATION

1. Position caliper over brake pads onto caliper mounting bracket.
2. Lubricate mounting pins with suitable grease, then install through caliper sleeves and bushings. Thread pins into mounting bracket and **torque** to 18 1/2 ft. lbs.
3. Using a new copper washer, install brake hose in caliper and **torque** to 13 ft. lbs. Ensure hose is not twisted.
4. Fill master cylinder with clean brake fluid and bleed brakes.
5. Install wheel and tire assembly, then lower vehicle.

# Type 8—AD54 Dual Pin Floating Caliper Disc Brake, Front

INDEX

Page No.



## BRAKE PADS
### REPLACE

1. Remove approximately 1/3 of brake fluid from master cylinder.
2. Raise and support vehicle, then remove tire and wheel assembly.
3. Remove lock pin, **Figs. 1 and 2,** then pivot caliper body upward and secure with wire.
4. Remove inner shims, anti-squeak shims, brake pad assemblies and pad clips from support mounting.
5. Press caliper piston into caliper bore with suitable tool.
6. Install upper and lower pad clips, pad assemblies, inner shims and anti-squeak shims into support mounting.
7. Lower caliper body, then install lock pin.
8. Depress brake pedal several times to seat pads, then check and replenish

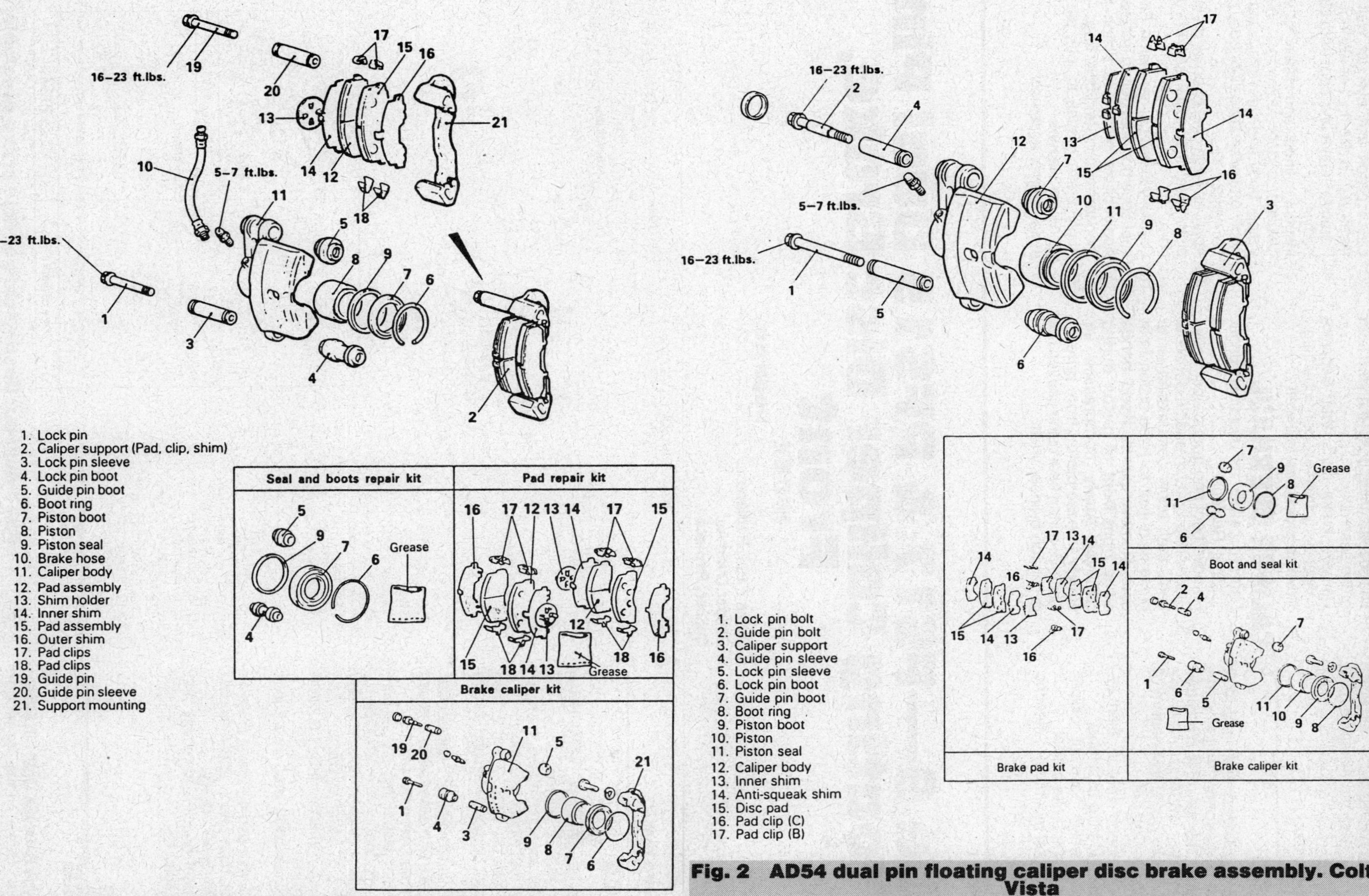


**Fig. 1 AD54 dual pin floating caliper disc brake assembly. 1989–90 Colt w/1.6L engine, 4WD Colt Wagon & Eagle Summit; 1990 Laser & Eagle Talon up to April 1989 production**

**Fig. 2 AD54 dual pin floating caliper disc brake assembly. Colt Vista**

brake fluid as necessary.
9. Install wheel and tire assembly and lower vehicle.

## CALIPER
### REPLACE

**On models equipped with anti-lock brakes, prior to disconnecting any hydraulic lines or fittings, the hydraulic system must be depressurized by pumping the brake pedal a minimum of 25 times with ignition Off.**

1. Raise and support vehicle, then remove wheel and tire assembly.
2. Disconnect brake hose at caliper strut, then at the brake caliper.
3. Remove support mounting to steering knuckle attaching bolts, then the front brake assembly.
4. Remove brake pads, then separate caliper body from support mounting.
5. Reverse procedure to install.

## CALIPER OVERHAUL

1. Remove caliper as described under "Caliper, Replace."
2. Remove boot ring from caliper body.
3. Place shop towel in saddle of caliper body, then apply compressed air to brake fluid inlet to force piston from bore. Remove piston. **Keep hands away from front of piston during removal. Apply compressed air slowly to ease piston from bore.**
4. Remove piston seal using caution not to scratch cylinder walls.
5. Clean piston and cylinder wall surfaces with brake fluid or alcohol.
6. Remove sleeve and boot from caliper body.
7. Inspect cylinder and piston for wear, damage and/or corrosion. Inspect caliper body and sleeve for wear.
8. Apply brake fluid to caliper body cylinder walls.
9. Apply an even coat of brake grease to piston seal, then install seal in caliper bore.
10. Carefully install caliper piston. Ensure seal does not twist during installation.
11. Apply brake grease to piston boot, then install boot and boot ring.
12. Apply brake grease to lock pin and guide pin sleeves.
13. Install caliper assembly.

# Type 9—FS17 & PFS15 Dual Pin Floating Caliper Disc Brake, Front

INDEX



## BRAKE PADS
### REPLACE

1. Remove approximately 1/3 of brake fluid from master cylinder.
2. Raise and support vehicle, then remove tire and wheel assembly.
3. Remove lock pin, **Figs. 1 and 2,** then pivot caliper body upward and secure with wire.
4. Remove inner shims, anti-squeak shims, brake pad assemblies and pad clips from support mounting.
5. Press caliper piston into caliper bore with suitable tool.
6. Install upper and lower pad clips, pad assemblies, inner shims and anti-squeak shims into support mounting.
7. Lower caliper body, then install lock pin.
8. Depress brake pedal several times to seat pads, then check and replenish brake fluid as necessary.
9. Install wheel and tire assembly and lower vehicle.

## CALIPER
### REPLACE

Refer to "Type 8—AD54 Dual Pin Floating Caliper Disc Brake, Front" for procedure.

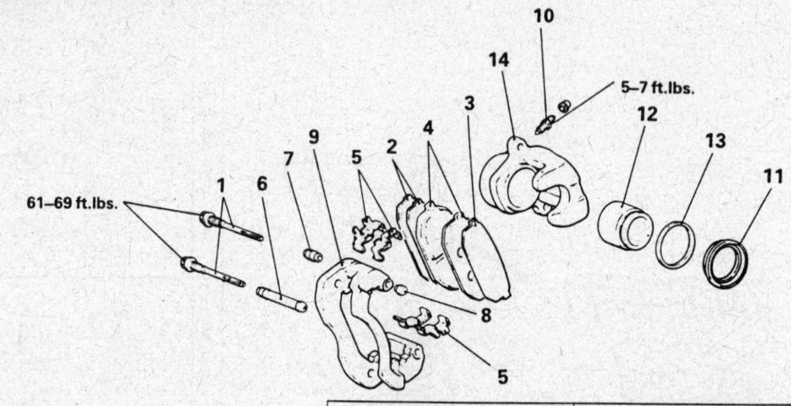


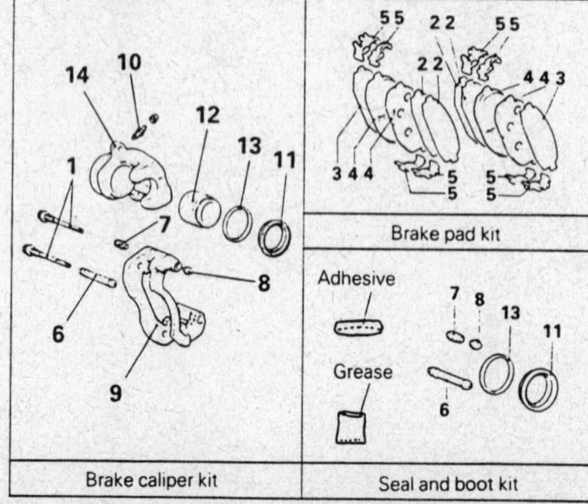


1. Slide pin
2. Inner shim
3. Outer shim
4. Pad assembly
5. Pad retainer
6. Bushing
7. Pin boot
8. Cap
9. Caliper support
10. Bleeder screw
11. Dust boot
12. Piston
13. Piston seal
14. Caliper body

**Fig. 1 FS17 dual pin floating caliper disc brake assembly. Conquest**

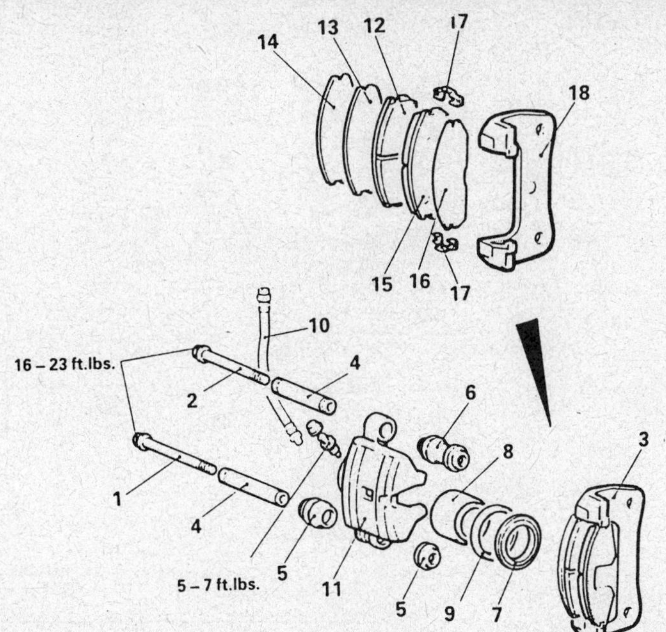


1. Sleeve bolt
2. Sleeve bolt
3. Caliper support (pad, retainer, shim)
4. Sleeve
5. Sleeve boot
6. Bushing
7. Dust boot
8. Piston
9. Piston seal
10. Brake hose
11. Caliper body
12. Pad assembly
13. Anti-squeak shim (inner)
14. Inner shim
15. Pad assembly
16. Anti-squeak shim (outer)
17. Pad retainer
18. Caliper support

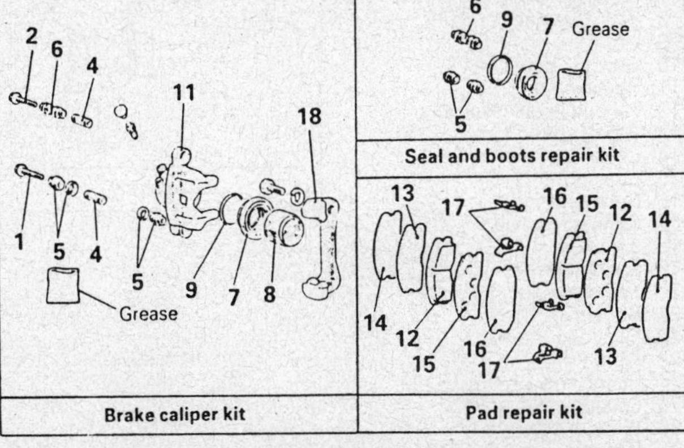


**Fig. 2 PFS15 dual pin floating caliper disc brake assembly. 1989–90 Colt w/1.5L engine & 2WD Colt Wagon**

## CALIPER OVERHAUL

1. Remove caliper assembly as described under "Caliper, Replace."
2. Remove bushing from caliper support using slide pin, then cap and pin boot.
3. Position a shop towel in caliper body, then apply compressed air through the brake hose fitting hole to remove piston and dust boot.
4. Using a suitable screwdriver, remove piston seal.
5. Inspect cylinder and piston for wear or damage and/or corrosion. Inspect caliper body and sleeve for wear.
6. Install new piston seal into cylinder. The piston seal in repair kit is coated with a special grease, do not wipe it off.
7. Apply suitable grease to lip of cylinder, then brake fluid to external surface of piston.
8. Install new dust boot onto piston.
9. Position end of dust boot into caliper body groove and install piston into caliper by hand. Take care not to damage piston. Ensure end of dust boot is fitted into piston groove.
10. Apply a suitable grease to contact surface of slide pin, seat surface of cap for caliper support, and inside surface of pin boot.
11. Install cap and pin boot to caliper support, then apply suitable grease to inside surface of bushing.
12. Apply a suitable adhesive to lip of slide pin bushing, then install bushing into caliper support using slide pin.
13. Apply brake fluid to threads of slide pin and a suitable grease to shank of slide pin, then install caliper body to caliper support.
14. Install caliper assembly.

# Type 10—AD Type, AD30P & AD35P Dual Pin Floating Caliper Disc Brake, Rear

INDEX



## BRAKE PADS

### REPLACE

1. Remove approximately 1/3 of brake fluid from master cylinder.
2. Raise and support vehicle, then remove wheel assembly.
3. Loosen parking brake cable at lever underneath console, then disconnect cable from caliper.
4. Remove lower caliper lock pin, then pivot caliper up and support with wire to prevent damage to brake hose.
5. Remove brake pads, shims and pad clips, **Figs. 1 and 2.**
6. Using piston driver MB990652 or equivalent, thread caliper piston into bore and ensure that piston stopper grooves are aligned as shown in **Fig. 3**, so that they will interlock with projections on pad assembly.
7. Install brake pads, shims and pad clips, then lower caliper and install lock pin.
8. Depress brake pedal several times to seat pads, then check and replenish brake fluid as necessary.

9. Connect parking brake cable, then install wheel and tire assembly and lower vehicle.
10. Adjust parking brake cable as described under "Adjustments."

## CALIPER
## REPLACE

**On models equipped with anti-lock brakes, prior to disconnecting any hydraulic lines or fittings, the hydraulic system must be depressurized by pumping the brake pedal a minimum of 25 times with ignition Off.**

1. Raise and support vehicle, then remove wheel assembly.
2. Disconnect brake hose, then parking brake cable from brake assembly.
3. Remove brake assembly attaching bolts, then brake assembly.
4. Remove brake pads and shims, then separate caliper body from caliper support, **Figs. 1 and 2.**
5. Reverse procedure to install.

## CALIPER OVERHAUL
### AD TYPE

1. Remove caliper assembly as described.
2. Remove guide pin boot, boot retainer, lid and lock pin boot, **Fig. 1.**
3. Remove retaining ring by disengaging cap ring from lever cap groove and sliding lever cap away.
4. Remove parking lever assembly, garter spring, lever cap, cap ring, return spring and connecting link.
5. Unscrew spindle from caliper body, then remove spring washer, spindle seal, boot ring and dust boot.
6. Push out piston from caliper body using a suitable screwdriver, then remove piston seal taking care not to damage caliper bore.
7. Remove parking brake cable bracket, then the bleeder screw.
8. Using bearing remover/installer MB990665 or equivalent, and a suitable vise, press bearings from caliper.
9. Inspect cylinder and piston for wear or damage and/or corrosion. Inspect caliper body and sleeve for wear.
10. Reverse procedure to assemble, noting the following:
    a. Apply grease supplied with seal and boot kit to caliper bearings, then using a suitable vise and bearing remover/installer MB990665 or equivalent, press bearings in until they are flush with caliper body. **Insert bearings so that depressed marks on bearings face outward.**
    b. Coat piston seal and inside surface of cylinder with suitable brake fluid, then install piston seal into cylinder.
    c. Gently install piston assembly into cylinder by hand, being careful not to twist piston assembly.
    d. Apply grease supplied with seal and boot kit to dust boot, then fit dust boot groove in caliper body.
    e. Coat spindle seal with brake fluid, then install spring washers onto spindle as shown in **Fig. 4.**
    f. Coat contact surface of caliper body and spring washers with grease supplied in seal and boot kit, then carefully screw spindle into caliper body until it rotates freely.
    g. Using connecting link installer MB990666 or equivalent, compress spring washers and screw spindle into caliper.
    h. Position connecting link and return spring onto spindle and install lever cap to parking lever assembly, then install assembly into caliper body. Hold parking lever assembly with retaining ring.
    i. Apply grease supplied in seal and boot kit to lever cap and lip, then install lever cap to caliper body.
    j. Coat contact point of caliper support guide pin and inside of lock pin boot with grease supplied in seal and boot kit.
    k. Adjust parking brake cable.

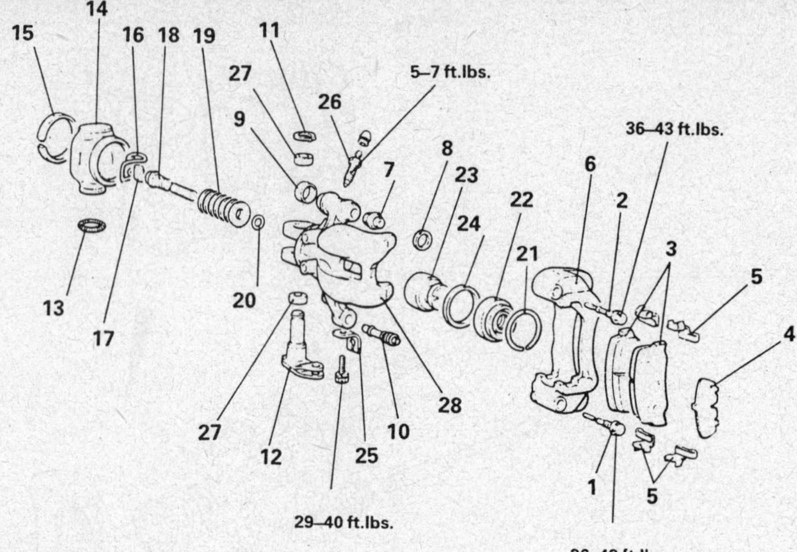


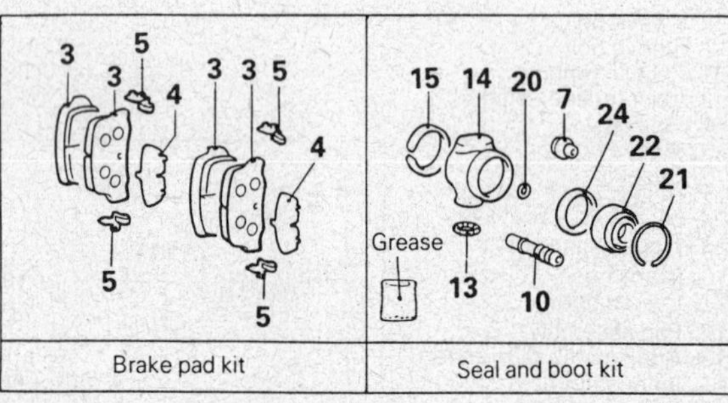


1. Lock pin
2. Guide pin
3. Pad assembly
4. Shim
5. Pad clip
6. Caliper support
7. Guide pin boot
8. Boot retainer
9. Lid
10. Lock pin boot
11. Retaining ring
12. Parking lever assembly
13. Garter spring
14. Lever cap
15. Cap ring
16. Return spring
17. Connecting link
18. Spindle
19. Spring washer
20. Spindle seal
21. Boot ring
22. Dust boot
23. Piston
24. Piston seal
25. Parking cable bracket
26. Bleeder screw
27. Bearing
28. Caliper body

**Fig. 1 AD Type dual pin floating caliper disc brake assembly. Conquest**

### AD30P & AD35P

1. Remove caliper assembly as described under "Caliper Replace."
2. Remove lock pin sleeve, lock pin boot, guide pin boot, boot ring and piston boot, **Fig. 2.**
3. Remove piston assembly using piston driver MB990652 or equivalent to twist piston out of caliper body.
4. Remove piston seal using finger tips. **Do not use flat blade screwdriver or other tool to prevent damage to inner cylinder.**
5. Compress spring case into caliper body using a 3/4 inch steel pipe as shown in **Fig. 5,** then remove snap ring using suitable snap ring pliers.
6. Remove spring case, return spring, stopper plate and stopper.

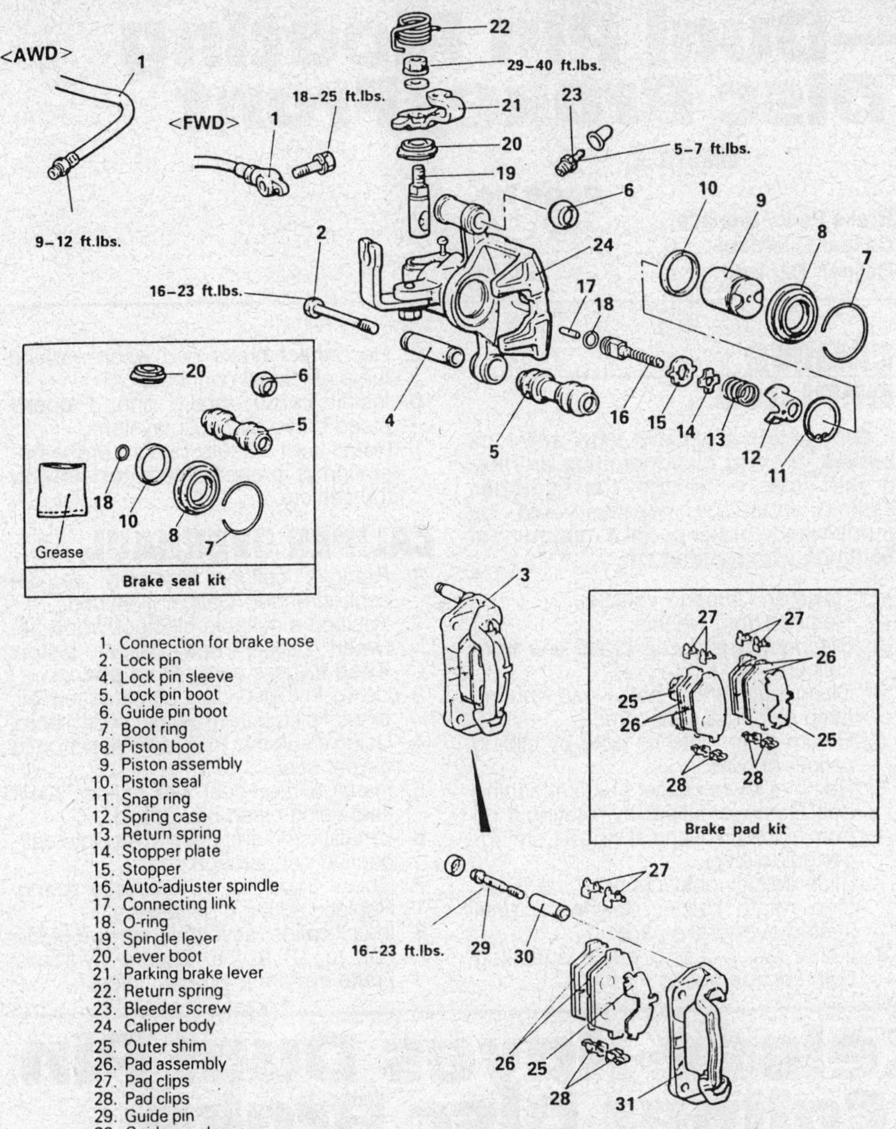


**Fig. 2 AD30P & AD35P dual pin floating caliper disc brake assembly. Laser & Talon & 1989–90 Colt & Summit w/1.6L engine**

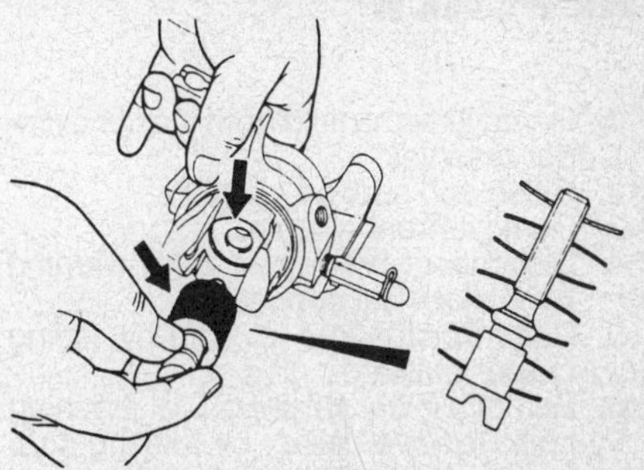


**Fig. 3 Aligning caliper piston stopper grooves**

**Fig. 4 Installation direction of spring washers on spindle. AD Type caliper**

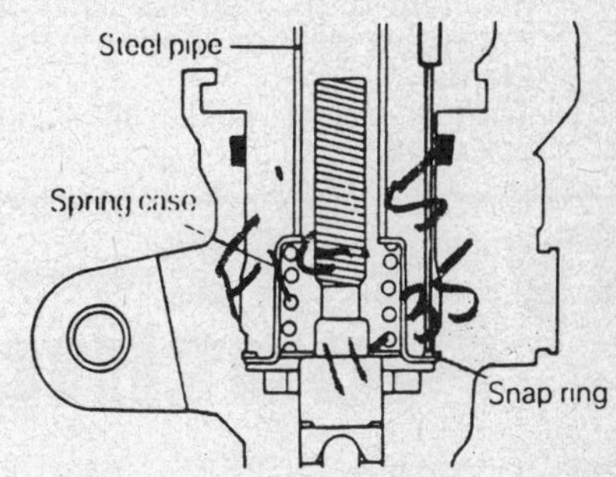


**Fig. 5 Compressing spring case. AD30P & AD35P calipers**

7. Remove auto-adjuster spindle, connecting link, O-ring, spindle lever and lever boot.
8. Remove parking brake lever, return spring and bleeder screw.
9. Inspect the following:
   a. Connecting link and spindle for wear or damage.
   b. Caliper body for rust or cracks.
   c. Spindle lever shaft and piston for rust.
   d. Bearing for wear, piston seal and boot for wear, cracks or deterioration.
10. Reverse procedure to assemble, noting the following:
    a. Apply grease supplied in brake seal kit to lever boot, spindle lever, O-ring, connecting link and auto-adjuster spindle.
    b. Compress spring case into caliper body using a 3/4 inch steel pipe as shown in **Fig. 5**, then install snap ring using suitable snap ring pliers. **Install snap ring to caliper body with opening facing bleeder.**
    c. Apply grease supplied in brake seal kit to cylinder walls, piston seal and piston, then install piston seal into cylinder.
    d. Using piston driver MB990652 or equivalent, press piston into caliper body with stopper grooves aligned, **Fig. 4**.
    e. Apply grease supplied in brake seal kit to piston boot mounting grooves in caliper body and piston, then install piston boot.
    f. Apply grease supplied in brake seal kit to guide pin boot inner surface, lock pin boot inner surface and lock pin sleeve.
    g. Adjust parking brake cable.

# ADJUSTMENTS

## PARKING BRAKE, ADJUST

1. Pull parking brake lever with a force of approximately 45 lbs. while counting number of clicks.
2. Lever should click 4-5 times on models with AD Type calipers and 5-7 times on AD30P and AD35P calipers.
3. If not within specifications, remove console and release parking brake lever, then turn adjusting nut located behind parking brake lever as necessary to bring parking brake within specifications.

# Type 11—Dual Pin Floating Caliper Disc Brake, Front

## INDEX



## BRAKE PADS

### REPLACE

1. Remove some fluid from master cylinder reservoir.
2. Raise and support vehicle.
3. Remove front wheels.
4. Disconnect brake pad wear warning lamp electrical connector.
5. Return piston into its bore by sliding caliper outward.
6. Remove lower caliper guide attaching bolt. Remove caliper by rotating it up from guide pivot and sliding it from upper guide pivot.
7. Remove brake pads.
8. Reverse procedure to install noting the following:
   a. **After removal of brake pads, inspect disc brake rotor. Do not machine rotor. Replace rotor if excessive wear or scoring is evident.**
   b. **Torque** caliper guide attaching bolt to 18 ft. lbs.

## CALIPER

### REPLACE

**On models equipped with anti-lock brakes, prior to disconnecting any hydraulic lines or fittings, the hydraulic system must be depressurized by pumping the brake pedal a minimum of 25 times with ignition Off.**

1. Raise and support vehicle.
2. Remove front wheels.
3. Disconnect and cap brake line from caliper.
4. Disconnect brake pad wear warning lamp electrical connector.
5. Return piston into its bore by sliding caliper outward.
6. Remove lower caliper guide attaching bolt. Remove caliper by rotating it up from guide pivot and sliding it from upper guide pivot.
7. Slide caliper onto upper guide pivot, then rotate caliper downward until seated over brake pads.
8. Install lower caliper guide attaching bolt. **Torque** bolt to 18 ft. lbs.
9. Reconnect brake pad wear warning lamp electrical connector.
10. Install caliper brake line. Properly bleed brake hydraulic system.
11. Install front wheels. Ensure brake operation is proper before test driving the vehicle.

## CALIPER OVERHAUL

1. Remove caliper assembly as described under "Caliper, Replace."
2. Position a suitable block of wood between caliper and caliper piston. **Keep fingers away from piston.**
3. Using low pressure compressed air, extract piston from caliper piston bore.
4. Using a suitable tool, remove piston to caliper seal.
5. Install a new seal into caliper. Coat seal using clean brake fluid.
6. Install piston and dust cover onto caliper. Do not damage seal.
7. Check condition of anti-rattle spring. Replace spring if necessary.
8. Install caliper assembly, **torque** guide bolt to 18 ft. lbs. Ensure hydraulic brake system is properly bled.

# Type 12—Kelsey-Hayes Dual Pin Floating Caliper Disc Brake, Rear

## INDEX



## DESCRIPTION

This single piston, floating caliper rear disc brake assembly, **Fig. 1,** includes a hub assembly, adapter, rotor, caliper, shoes and pads. The parking brake system consists of a small duo-servo brake mounted to an adapter which expands out against the hat section on the inside of the rotor. The caliper has either a 1.338 (34 mm) or 1.42 inch (36 mm) piston located on the inboard side.

The caliper floats on rubber bushings with metal sleeves on two bolts that are threaded into the adapter. Two machined abutments on the adapter position and align the caliper and brake pads for movement fore and aft.

## BRAKE PADS

### REPLACE

1. Raise and support vehicle.
2. Remove rear wheel and tire assembly.
3. Remove caliper retaining bolts, then lift caliper away from adapter rails. **Hang caliper from wire away from rotor.**
4. Remove outer brake pad by prying pad retaining clip over raised area on caliper, then sliding it down and off caliper.
5. Remove inner brake pad by pulling it away from the piston.
6. Retract piston, then reverse procedure to install. Torque caliper retaining bolts to specifications.

## CALIPER OVERHAUL

**On models equipped with anti-lock brakes, prior to disconnecting any hydraulic lines or fittings, the hydraulic system must be depressurized by pumping the brake pedal a minimum of 25 times with ignition Off.**

1. Remove caliper from rotor as described under "Brake Pads, Replace."
2. Place a small piece of wood between piston and caliper fingers, then carefully depress brake pedal to hydraulically push piston out of bore. Prop

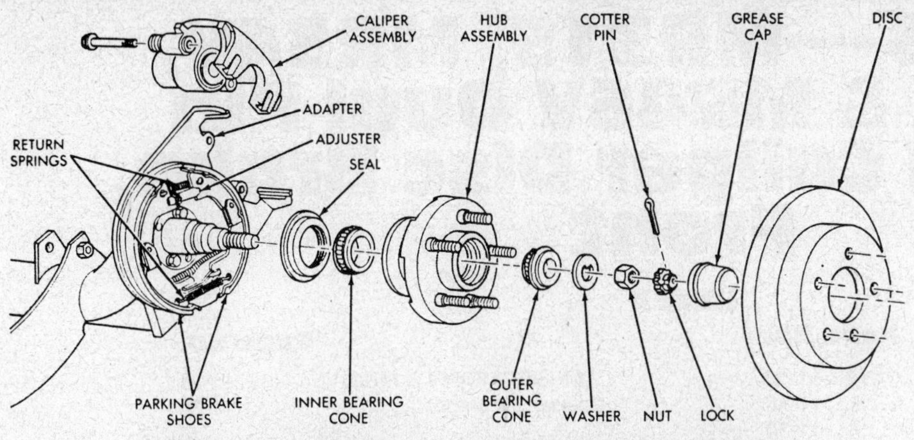


**Fig. 1 Kelsey-Hayes dual pin floating caliper disc brake assembly**

brake pedal to any position below first inch of brake pedal travel to prevent brake fluid loss.

3. If pistons are to be removed from both calipers, disconnect brake hose at frame bracket after removing piston, then cap brake line and repeat procedure to remove piston from other caliper.
4. Disconnect brake hose from caliper.
5. Mount caliper in a soft jawed vise.
6. Support caliper, then remove and discard dust boot.
7. Using a small wooden or plastic stick, remove seal from groove in piston bore and discard. **Do not use a screwdriver or other metal tool, as this may scratch caliper bore.**
8. If necessary, proceed as follows:
   a. Push out and pull inner sleeve from inside of bushing using your fingers, then collapse one side of bushing while pulling on other side to remove bushing from caliper.
9. Using denatured alcohol or equivalent, thoroughly clean piston and caliper grooves, caliper housing and bushing mounting surfaces.
10. Dip new piston seal in clean brake fluid and install in groove in bore.
11. Coat new piston boot with clean brake fluid leaving a generous amount inside boot.
12. Coat piston with clean brake fluid, then position dust boot over piston.
13. Install piston into bore pushing it past piston seal until it bottoms in bore.
14. Position dust boot in counterbore, then using a hammer and installer C-4383-7 or equivalent, drive boot into counterbore of caliper.
15. If necessary, proceed as follows:
    a. Fold bushing in half lengthwise at solid middle section, then using your fingers, insert folded bushing into caliper assembly ensuring solid section of bushing is fully seated in hole. Using a suitable tool, ensure bushing is properly seated.
    b. Install sleeve into one end of bushing until seal area of bushing is past seal groove in sleeve.
    c. Holding coiled end of bushing with one hand, push sleeve through bushing until one end of bushing is fully seated into seal groove on end of sleeve.
    d. Holding sleeve in place, work other end of bushing over end of sleeve and into seal groove. Ensure other end of bushing does not come out of seal groove in sleeve.

## PARKING BRAKE SHOES

### REPLACE

1. Raise and support vehicle.
2. Remove rear wheel and tire assembly.
3. Remove caliper from rotor as described under "Brake Pads, Replace."
4. Remove rotor from hub.
5. Remove grease cap, cotter pin, lock nut, retaining nut, washer, hub and bearings.
6. Using a suitable tool, remove forward hold-down clip.
7. Turn adjuster wheel until adjuster is at its shortest length, then remove adjuster assembly.
8. Remove upper shoe to shoe spring.
9. Pull front shoe away from anchor, then remove front shoe and lower spring.
10. Using a suitable tool, remove rear hold-down clip and shoe.
11. Reverse procedure to install noting the following:
    a. Adjust shoe diameter to 6.75 inches.
    b. Torque wheel bearing adjusting nut to specifications while rotating hub to seat bearings, back off adjusting nut 1/4 turn, then tighten finger tight.
    c. Align nut-to-spindle holes for cotter pin insertion.

## ADJUSTMENTS

### PARKING BRAKE, ADJUST

1. Release parking brake.
2. Raise and support vehicle.
3. Adjust parking brake cable until there is slack in the cable.
4. Tighten adjusting nut until a slight drag is felt when rotating the rear wheels.
5. Back off adjusting nut two full turns past the point when both rear wheels rotate freely.
6. Check parking brake operation.

## SERVICE BULLETINS

### REAR DISC BRAKE NOISE AFTER LIGHT RAIN OR HIGH HUMIDITY

#### 1989–90 Daytona & LeBaron Coupe & Convertible

These vehicles may experience a grinding sound which occurs after a light rain or during high humidity for the first two or three stops. This is likely caused by glazing on the rear disc brake rotors. Replace rear disc pads with pads made from a new formulated material for noise reduction. Part No. 4423667.

# Type 13—MR31S, MR34V, MR44V & MR46V Dual Pin Floating Caliper Disc Brake, Front

## INDEX



## BRAKE PADS
### REPLACE

1. Remove approximately 1/3 of brake fluid from master cylinder.
2. Raise and support vehicle, then remove tire and wheel assembly.
3. Remove guide pin or lower slide pin, **Figs. 1 and 2,** then lift caliper body upward and secure with wire.
4. Remove inner shims, anti-squeak shims, brake pad assemblies and pad clips from support mounting.
5. Press caliper piston into caliper bore with suitable tool.
6. Install upper and lower pad clips, pad assemblies, inner shims and anti-squeak shims into support mounting.
7. Lower caliper body, then install lock pin.
8. Depress brake pedal several times to seat pads, then check and replenish brake fluid as necessary.
9. Install wheel and tire assembly and lower vehicle.

## CALIPER
### REPLACE

Refer to "Type 8—AD54 Dual Pin Floating Caliper Disc Brake, Front" for procedure.

## CALIPER OVERHAUL

### MR31S

1. Remove caliper assembly as described under "Caliper, Replace."
2. Remove upper slide pin, torque member, pin boot and bushing, **Fig. 1.**
3. Position a shop towel in caliper body, then apply compressed air through the brake hose fitting hole to remove piston and dust boot. **Apply air gently.**
4. Remove piston seal using finger tips. **Do not use screwdriver or other tool to prevent damage to inner cylinder.**
5. Reverse procedure to assemble, noting the following:

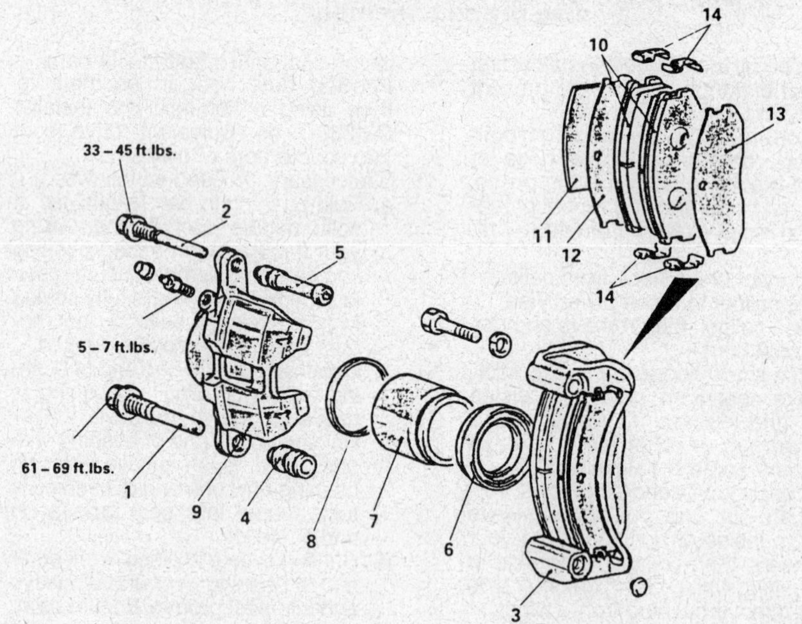


1. Slide pin (M14)
2. Slide pin (M10)
3. Torque member (pad, pad liner, shim)
4. Pin boot
5. Bushing
6. Piston boot
7. Piston
8. Piston seal
9. Caliper body
10. Pad assembly
11. Inner shim
12. Inner shim
13. Outer shim
14. Pad liner

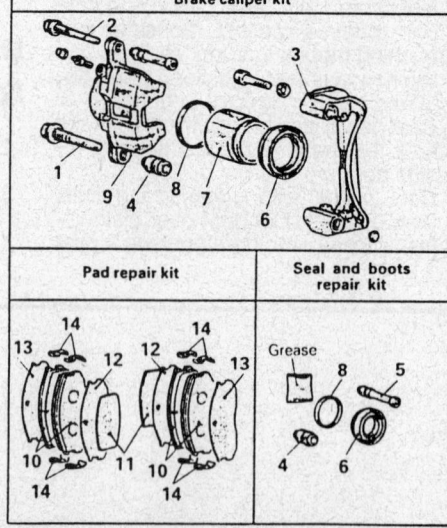

Brake caliper kit

Pad repair kit

Seal and boots repair kit

Grease

**Fig. 1 MR31S dual pin floating caliper disc brake assembly. 1991 Colt**

a. Inspect cylinder and piston for wear or damage and/or corrosion. Inspect caliper body and sleeve for wear.

b. Apply suitable brake fluid to inner cylinder, then install piston seal into cylinder groove. **Do not wipe grease from seal and boot repair**

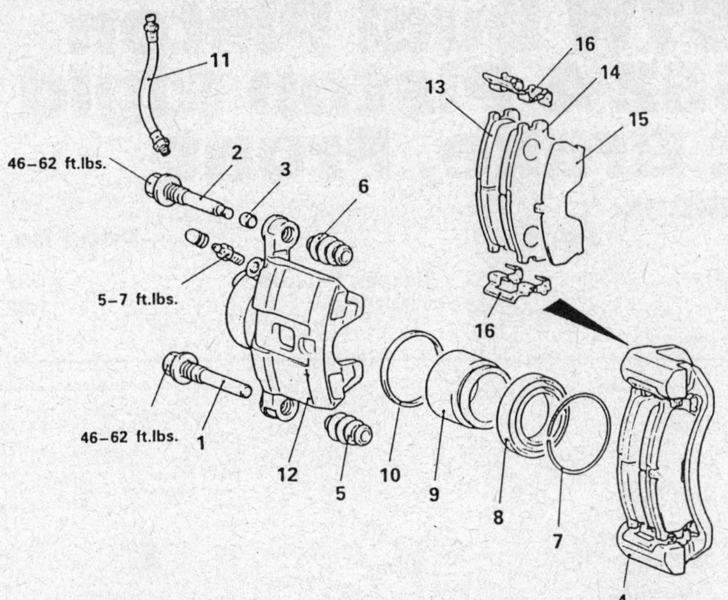


1. Guide pin
2. Lock pin
3. Bushing
4. Caliper support (Pad, clip, shim)
5. Guide pin boot
6. Lock pin boot
7. Boot ring
8. Piston boot
9. Piston
10. Piston seal
11. Brake hose
12. Caliper body
13. Pad and wear indicator assembly
14. Pad assembly
15. Outer shim
16. Clip

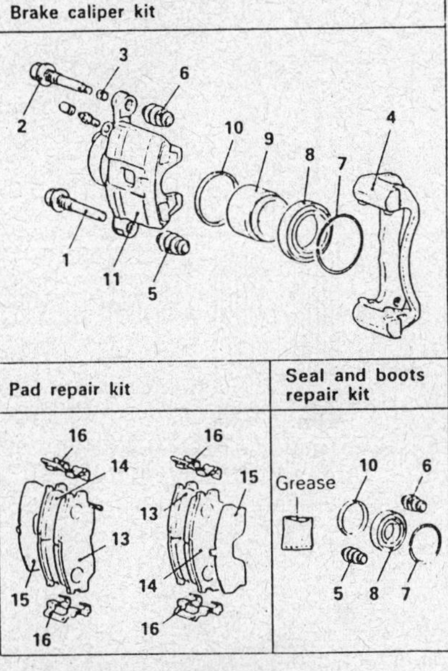


**Fig. 2 MR34V, MR44V & MR46V dual pin floating caliper disc brake assembly. Laser & Talon from May 1989 production & 1991 Summit**

**kit on piston seal.**

c. Apply suitable brake fluid to piston and insert into cylinder without twisting.
d. Fill piston edge with grease from seal and boot repair kit, then install piston boot.
e. Lubricate bushing, pin boot and slide pins with grease from seal and boot repair kit.

## MR34V, MR44V & MR46V

1. Remove caliper assembly as described under "Caliper, Replace."
2. Remove lock pin, bushing, caliper support, guide pin and lock pin boots, **Fig. 2.**
3. Remove boot ring using a suitable flat blade screwdriver.
4. Position a shop towel in caliper body, then apply compressed air through the brake hose fitting hole to remove piston and dust boot. **Apply air gently.**
5. Remove piston seal using finger tips. **Do not use screwdriver or other tool to prevent damage to inner cylinder.**
6. Reverse procedure to assemble, noting the following:
   a. Inspect cylinder and piston for wear or damage and/or corrosion. Inspect caliper body and sleeve for wear.
   b. Apply suitable brake fluid to inner cylinder, then install piston seal into cylinder groove. **Do not wipe grease from seal and boot repair kit on piston seal.**
   c. Apply suitable brake fluid to piston and insert into cylinder without twisting.
   d. Fill piston edge with grease from seal and boot repair kit, then install piston boot.
   e. Lubricate sliding surface of lock pin and guide pin boots, caliper support and bushing with grease from seal and boot repair kit.
   f. Install guide and lock pins with their head marks matched with identification marks on caliper body.

# Type 14—MR57W Dual Piston Floating & MR66Z 4-Piston Rigid Caliper Disc Brake, Front

INDEX



## BRAKE PADS

### REPLACE

### MR57W

1. Remove approximately 1/3 of brake fluid from master cylinder.
2. Raise and support vehicle, then remove tire and wheel assembly.
3. Remove guide pin, **Fig. 1,** then lift caliper body upward and secure with wire.
4. Remove outer shims, brake pad assemblies and pad clips from support mounting.
5. Press caliper piston into caliper bore with suitable tool.
6. Install upper and lower pad clips, pad assemblies and outer shims into support mounting.
7. Lower caliper body, then install guide pin.
8. Depress brake pedal several times to seat pads, then check and replenish brake fluid as necessary.
9. Install wheel and tire assembly and lower vehicle.

### MR66Z

1. Remove approximately 1/3 of brake fluid from master cylinder.
2. Raise and support front of vehicle, then remove tire and wheel assembly.
3. Remove the clip, then while holding cross spring, remove pad pins, **Fig. 2.**
4. Remove brake pad assemblies and shims.
5. Press caliper piston into caliper bore with suitable tool.
6. Apply a suitable multi-purpose grease to both sides of inner shims, then install pad assemblies and shims, pad pins and clip.
7. Depress brake pedal several times to seat pads, then check and replenish brake fluid as necessary.
8. Install wheel and tire assembly and lower vehicle.

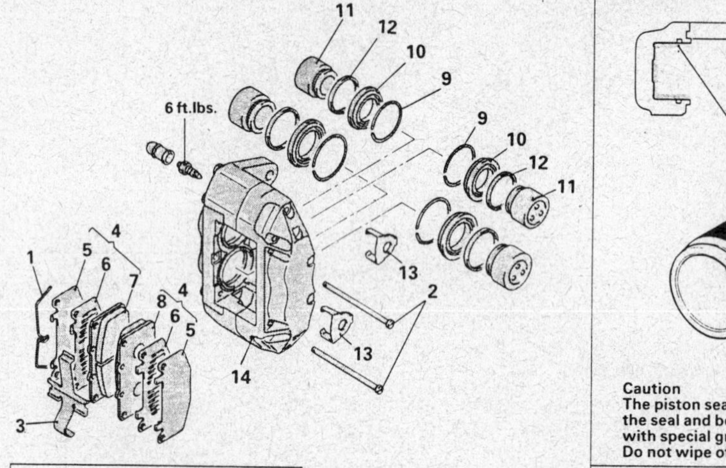


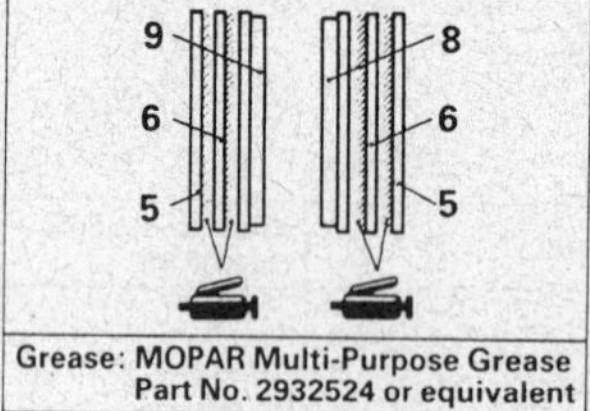

The piston seal contained in the seal and boot kit is coated with special grease.
Do not wipe off the grease.
Brake fluid: MOPAR Brake Fluid/ Conforming to DOT3

Grease: MOPAR Multi-Purpose Grease Part No. 2932524 or equivalent


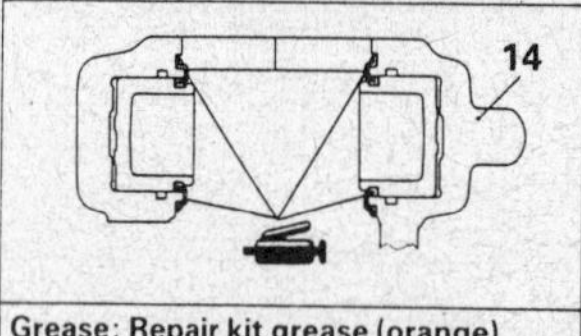


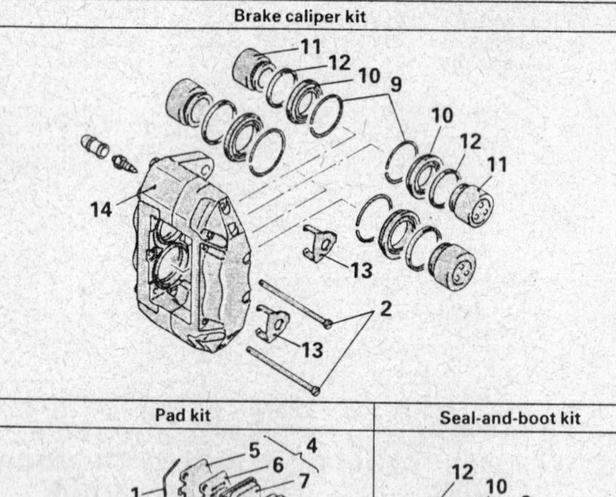


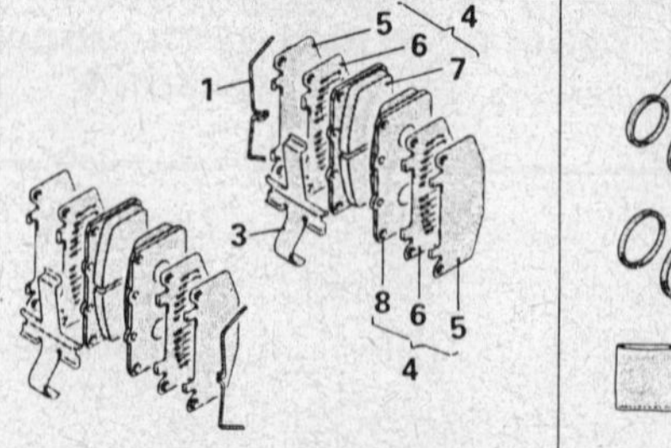


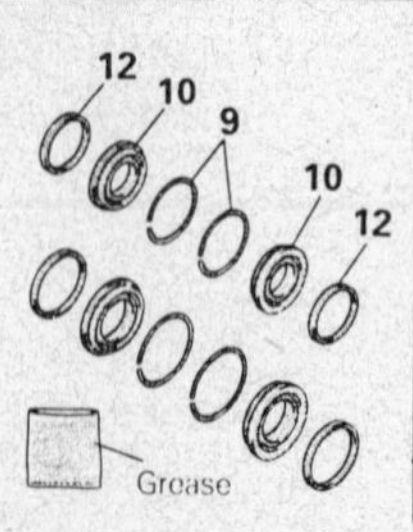


1. Clip
2. Pad pin
3. Cross spring
4. Pad assembly
5. Shim
6. Shim
7. Inner pad (with wear indicator)
8. Outer pad
9. Retaining ring
10. Piston boot
11. Piston
12. Piston seal
13. Washer
14. Caliper body

**Fig. 1 MR57W dual piston floating caliper disc brake assembly. FWD Stealth**

## CALIPER

### REPLACE

**On models equipped with anti-lock brakes, prior to disconnecting any hydraulic lines or fittings, the hydraulic system must be depressurized by pumping the brake pedal a minimum of 25 times with ignition Off.**

### MR57W

Refer to "Type 8—AD54 Dual Pin Floating Caliper Disc Brake, Front" for procedure.

## CALIPER OVERHAUL

### MR57W

1. Remove caliper assembly as described under "Caliper, Replace."
2. Remove lock pin, bushing, caliper support, pin boot and boot ring, **Fig. 1.**
3. Use compressed air to evenly remove the two piston boots and pistons. **Send compressed air gradually,**

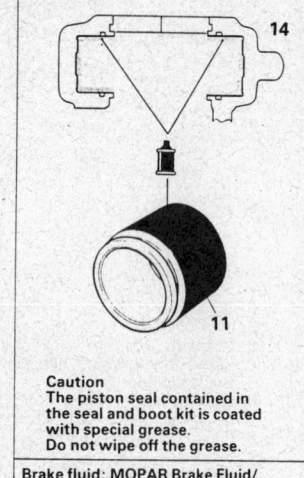

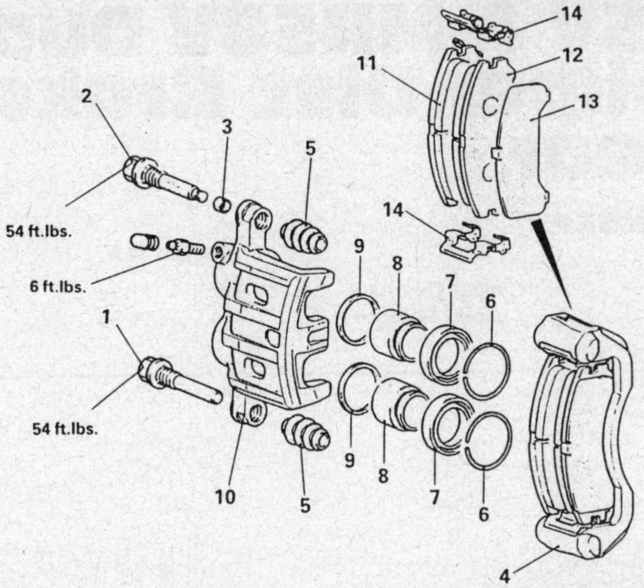


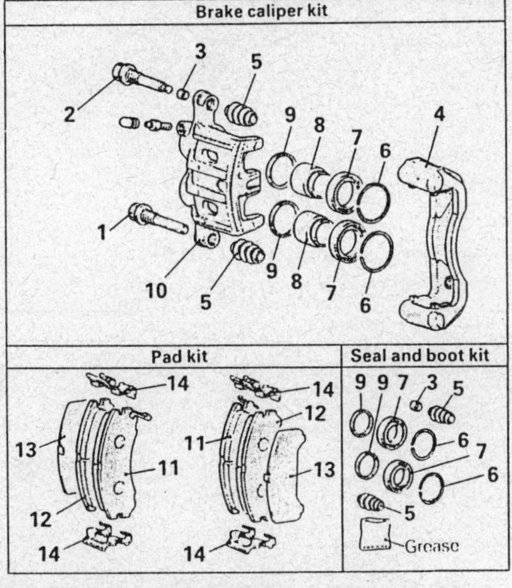


1. Guide pin
2. Lock pin
3. Bushing
4. Caliper support (pad, clip, shim)
5. Pin boot
6. Boot ring
7. Piston boot
8. Piston
9. Piston seal
10. Caliper body
11. Pad & wear indicator
12. Pad assembly
13. Outer shim
14. Clip

**Fig. 2 MR66Z 4-piston rigid caliper disc brake assembly. AWD Stealth**

**using handle of hammer to protect pistons.**

4. Remove piston seal with finger tip to avoid damaging cylinder inner surface.
5. Reverse procedure to assemble, noting the following:
   a. Inspect cylinders and pistons for wear or damage and/or corrosion. Inspect caliper body and sleeve for wear.
   b. Apply suitable brake fluid to inner cylinders, then install piston seals into cylinder groove. **Do not wipe grease from seal and boot repair kit on piston seal.**
   c. Apply suitable brake fluid to pistons and insert into cylinders without twisting.
   d. Fill piston edges with grease from seal and boot repair kit, then install piston boots.
   e. Lubricate sliding surface of guide and lock pins and their boots with grease from seal and boot repair kit.
   f. Install guide and lock pins with their head marks matched with identification marks on caliper body.

## MR66Z

**On models equipped with anti-lock brakes, prior to disconnecting any hydraulic lines or fittings, the hydraulic system must be depressurized by pumping the brake pedal a minimum of 25 times with ignition Off.**

1. Remove pads as described under "Pads, Replace."
2. Disconnect brake hose at brake tube connection and caliper, then remove caliper mounting bolts and caliper.
3. Place caliper on a suitable work bench, remove retaining rings and piston boots, **Fig. 2,** then install a wooden block in center of caliper body and apply compressed air to evenly remove the four pistons. **Keep fingers away from piston area to avoid being pinched. Wear safety glasses to avoid brake fluid from getting into eyes.**
4. Remove piston seals using a suitable screwdriver, then the washers. **Do not damage cylinder inner surface.**
5. Reverse procedure to assemble, noting the following:
   a. Inspect cylinders and pistons for wear or damage and/or corrosion. Inspect caliper body for wear.
   b. Apply suitable brake fluid to inner cylinders, then install piston seals into cylinder groove. **Do not wipe grease from seal and boot repair kit on piston seals.**
   c. Apply suitable brake fluid to pistons and insert into cylinder without twisting.
   d. Fill piston edges with grease from seal and boot repair kit, then install piston boots.

# Type 15—MR45V & MR58V Dual Pin Floating Caliper Disc Brake, Rear

INDEX



## BRAKE PAD
### REPLACE

1. Remove approximately 1/3 of brake fluid from master cylinder.
2. Raise and support vehicle, then remove tire and wheel assembly.
3. Loosen parking brake cable at lever underneath console, then disconnect cable from caliper.
4. Remove lock pin, **Figs. 1 and 2,** then lift caliper body upward and secure with wire.
5. Remove inner and outer shims, brake pad assemblies and pad clips from support mounting.
6. Press caliper piston into caliper bore with suitable tool.
7. Install upper and lower pad clips, pad assemblies and inner and outer shims into support mounting.
8. Lower caliper body, then install lock pin.
9. Depress brake pedal several times to seat pads, then check and replenish brake fluid as necessary.
10. Connect parking brake cable, then install wheel and tire assembly and lower vehicle.
11. Adjust parking brake cable as described under "Adjustments."

## CALIPER
### REPLACE

Refer to "Type 10—AD Type, AD30P & AD35P Dual Pin Floating Caliper Disc Brake, Rear" for procedure.

## CALIPER OVERHAUL

1. Remove caliper assembly as described under "Caliper Replace."
2. **On MR45V caliper,** remove guide pin and bushing, **Fig. 1.**
3. **On both calipers,** remove caliper support, **Figs. 1 and 2.**
4. **On MR58V caliper,** remove sleeve, **Fig. 2.**
5. **On both calipers,** remove pin boots and boot ring.
6. Position a shop towel in caliper body, then apply compressed air through the brake hose fitting hole to remove piston and dust boot. **Apply air gently.**

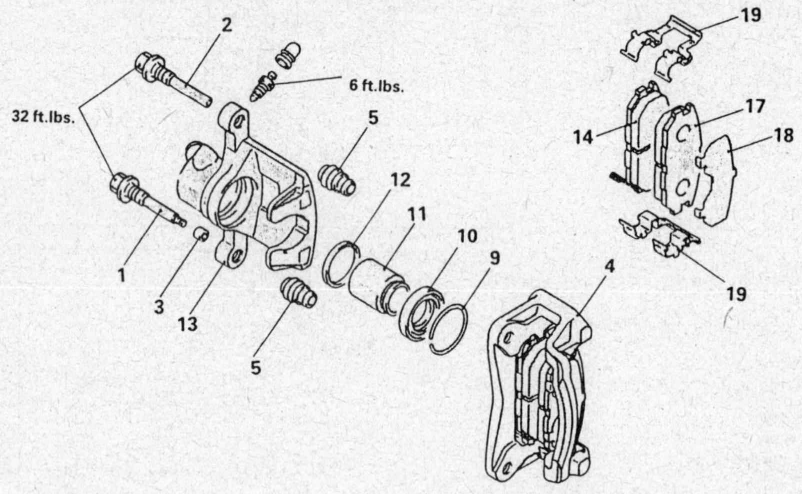


1. Lock pin
2. Guide pin
3. Bushing
4. Caliper support (pad, clip, shim)
5. Pin boot
9. Boot ring
10. Piston boot
11. Piston
12. Piston seal
13. Caliper body
14. Pad and wear indicator assembly
17. Pad assembly
18. Outer shim
19. Clip

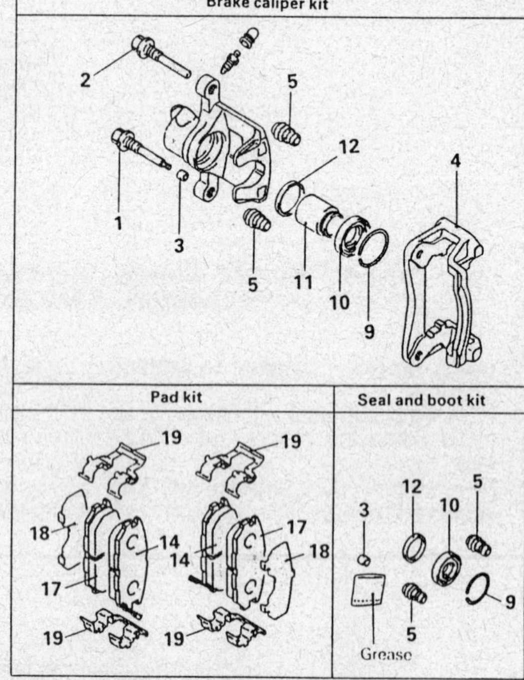


**Fig. 1 MR45V dual pin floating caliper disc brake assembly. FWD Stealth**

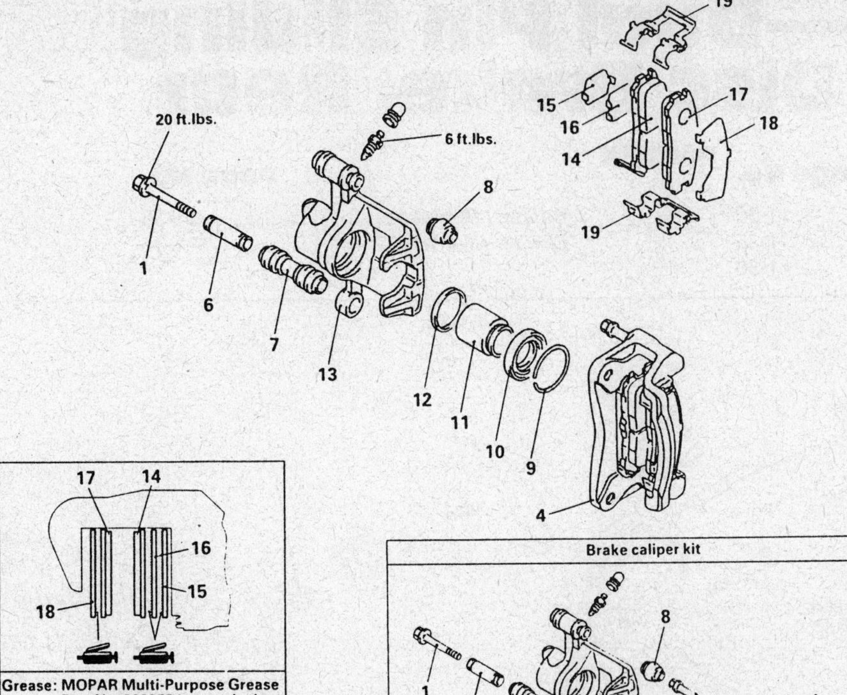


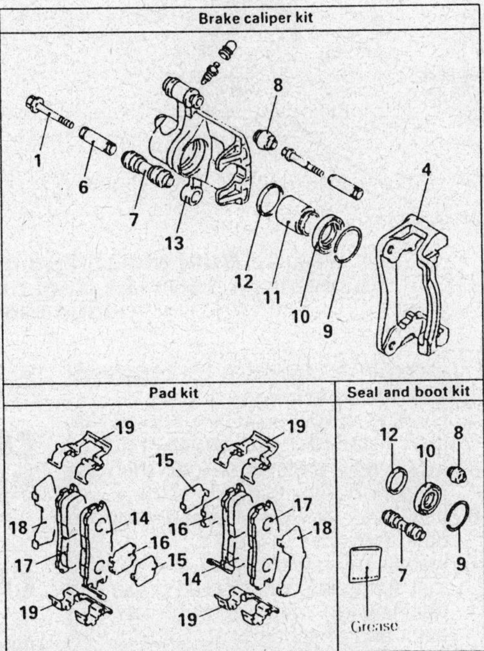


1. Lock pin
4. Caliper support (pad, clip, shim)
6. Sleeve
7. Lock pin boot
8. Guide pin boot
9. Boot ring
10. Piston boot
11. Piston
12. Piston seal
13. Caliper body
14. Pad and wear indicator assembly
15. Inner shim
16. Inner shim
17. Pad assembly
18. Outer shim
19. Clip

**Fig. 2 MR58V dual pin floating caliper disc brake assembly. AWD Stealth**

7. Remove piston seal using finger tips. **Do not use screwdriver or other tool to prevent damage to inner cylinder.**
8. Reverse procedure to assemble, noting the following:
   a. Inspect cylinder and piston for wear or damage and/or corrosion. Inspect caliper body and sleeve for wear.
   b. Apply suitable brake fluid to inner cylinder, then install piston seal into cylinder groove. **Do not wipe grease from seal and boot repair kit on piston seal.**
   c. Apply suitable brake fluid to piston and insert into cylinder without twisting.
   d. Fill piston edge with grease from seal and boot repair kit, then install piston boot.
   e. Lubricate bushing, pin boot and slide pins with grease from seal and boot repair kit.

## ADJUSTMENTS

### PARKING BRAKE, ADJUST

1. Pull parking brake lever with a force of approximately 45 lbs. while counting number of clicks.
2. Lever should click 3-5 times.
3. If not within specifications, remove cup holder and plug, then turn adjusting nut located behind parking brake lever as necessary to bring parking brake within specifications.

# Type 16—Dual Pin Sliding Caliper Disc Brake, Rear

INDEX



## BRAKE PAD

### REPLACE

**On models equipped with anti-lock brakes, prior to disconnecting any hydraulic lines or fittings, the hydraulic system must be depressurized by pumping the brake pedal a minimum of 25 times with ignition Off.**

1. Remove approximately 1/3 of brake fluid from master cylinder.
2. Raise and support vehicle, then remove tire and wheel assembly.
3. Disconnect parking brake cable operating lever return spring, **Fig. 1.**
4. Remove bolt attaching operating lever to caliper, then use a scribe to mark position of operating lever and remove operating lever using a suitable flat blade screwdriver.
5. Disconnect parking brake cable from mounting flange, then remove upper slide pin.
6. Loosen lower slide pin and tilt caliper downward.
7. Remove brake pad retaining pin using a suitable pin punch, then the lower slide pin and lift caliper off rotor and secure with wire.
8. Remove anti-rattle spring, then the brake pads.
9. Remove rotor retaining nuts, then the rotor.
10. Inspect parking brake operating lever return spring, brake pad retaining pin, slide pins and bushings, and replace as necessary.
11. Bottom caliper piston in its bore, then temporarily mount caliper on axle shaft. Install and tighten slide pins just enough to hold caliper in place.
12. Using a 3/8 inch drive extension, ratchet and 7/16 inch deep well socket, insert spanner 6366 or equivalent into deep well socket.
13. Insert spanner tool lugs into matching holes in caliper piston face, and rotate piston in a clockwise direction until fully seated in bore.
14. Remove caliper slide pins and caliper, then install rotor and retaining nuts.
15. Install new pads in caliper, then the caliper on rotor and axle shaft.
16. Install caliper slide pins and torque to specifications.
17. Install anti-rattle spring and ensure that spring is positioned so brake pad retaining pin will go through loops at each end of spring.
18. Insert parking brake cable in mounting flange, then position return spring on caliper and install operating lever on parking brake cable.
19. Pull parking brake lever rearward and install operating lever on caliper.
20. Connect return spring to operating lever first, then hook spring onto caliper with a long screwdriver. **Rounded end of return spring attaches to operating lever and square end goes to caliper.**
21. Install wheel and tire, lower vehicle, then apply brakes several times to seat pads and equalize parking brake adjustment.

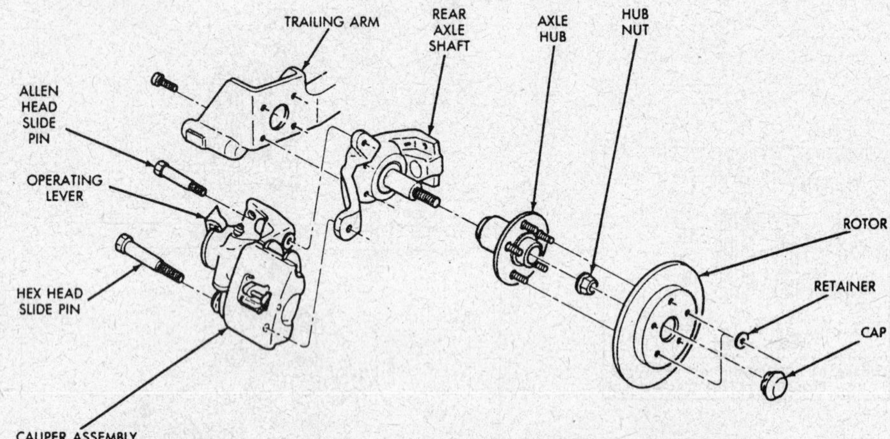


**Fig. 1 Dual pin sliding caliper disc brake assembly. 1989–91 Eagle Premier & 1990–91 Monaco**

## CALIPER

### REPLACE

Refer to "Brake Pads, Replace" for procedure.

## CALIPER OVERHAUL

These calipers are not serviceable, and must be replaced if worn or damaged.

## ADJUSTMENTS

### PARKING BRAKE, ADJUST

1. Apply and release parking brake 5 times to center pads, then press pedal down to first detent (one click).
2. Raise and support vehicle, then tighten adjusting nut until a slight drag is felt at one or both rear wheels when tires are rotated.
3. Loosen adjusting nut one turn, apply parking brake pedal once and release, then check for drag at rear wheels.

# Caliper Specifications

| Year | Model | Caliper Bore Dia. Inch |
|---|---|---|
| **FRONT** | | |
| 1989 | Chrysler Domestic Rear Wheel Drive | 2.754-2.756 |
| | Conquest | 2.250 |
| | Eagle Medallion | 2.125 |
| 1989-90 | Colt① | 2.010 |
| | Colt② | 2.122 |
| | Colt Wagon 2WD | 2.010 |
| | Colt Wagon 4WD | 2.122 |
| | Eagle Premier | 2.244 |
| | Eagle Summit① | 2.010 |
| | Eagle Summit② | 2.122 |
| 1989-91 | Chrysler Domestic Front Wheel Drive | 2.125 |
| | Colt Vista | 2.120 |
| 1990 | Eagle Talon | 2.122 |
| | Monaco | 2.244 |
| 1990-91 | Laser | 2.122 |
| 1991 | Colt | 2.010 |
| 1991 | Eagle Premier | 2.125 |
| 1991 | Eagle Summit | 2.125 |
| 1991 | Eagle Talon AWD | 2.374 |
| 1991 | Eagle Talon FWD | 2.122 |
| 1991 | Monaco | 2.125 |
| 1991 | Stealth AWD | ③ |
| 1991 | Stealth FWD | 1.685 |
| **REAR** | | |
| 1989 | Conquest | 1.625 |
| 1989-90 | Colt② | 1.850 |
| | Dynasty & New Yorker | 1.417 |
| | Eagle Summit② | 1.850 |
| | Shadow & Sundance⑤ | 1.338 |
| | Shadow & Sundance⑦ | 1.417 |
| 1989-91 | Daytona⑤ | 1.338 |
| | Daytona⑥ | 1.417 |
| | LeBaron⑤ | 1.338 |
| | LeBaron⑥ | 1.417 |
| 1990 | Eagle Talon | 1.850 |
| | Imperial & New Yorker Fifth Avenue | ④ |
| | LeBaron Landau | 1.338 |
| 1990-91 | Acclaim & Spirit⑤ | 1.338 |
| | Acclaim & Spirit⑦ | 1.417 |
| | Laser | 1.850 |
| 1991 | Dynasty & New Yorker | 1.338 |
| | Eagle Premier | 1.417 |
| | Eagle Talon AWD | 1.374 |
| | Eagle Talon | 1.850 |
| | Imperial | 1.338 |
| | LeBaron Landau⑤ | 1.338 |
| | LeBaron Landau⑦ | 1.417 |
| | Monaco | 1.417 |
| 1991 | New Yorker Fifth Avenue⑤ | 1.338 |
| | New Yorker Fifth Avenue⑦ | 1.417 |

*Continued*

## CALIPER SPECIFICATIONS—Continued

| Year | Model | Caliper Bore Dia. Inch |
|---|---|---|
| 1991 (cont'd.) | Stealth AWD | 1.500 |
| | Stealth FWD | 1.374 |

①—Models with 1.5L engine.
②—Models with 1.6L engine
③—Two at 1.590 inch & two at 1.685 inch.
④—1.299 inch or 1.417 inch.
⑤—With 14 inch wheels.
⑥—With 15 & 16 inch wheels.
⑦—With 15 inch wheels.

# Rotor Specifications

| Year | Model | Nominal Thickness (Inches) | Minimum Refinish Thickness (Inches) | Thickness Variation Parallelism (Inches) | Lateral Runout (T.I.R.) | Finish (Micro-Inch) |
|---|---|---|---|---|---|---|
| **FRONT** | | | | | | |
| 1989 | Chrysler Domestic Rear Wheel Drive | 1.000-1/010 | .940 | .0005 | .0040 | 15-80 |
| | Conquest | — | .881 | — | .006 | — |
| | Eagle Medallion | .775 | .696① | — | .002 | — |
| 1989–90 | Chrysler Domestic Front Wheel Drive② | .490-.505 | .431 | .0005 | .0050 | 15-80 |
| | Colt③ | .511 | .449 | — | .006 | — |
| | Colt④ | .944 | .882 | — | .006 | — |
| | Colt Wagon 2WD | .511 | .449 | — | .006 | — |
| | Colt Wagon 4WD | .708 | .646 | — | .006 | — |
| | Eagle Premier | .866 | .807 | .001 | .003 | — |
| | Eagle Summit③ | .511 | .449 | — | .006 | — |
| | Eagle Summit④ | .944 | .882 | — | .006 | — |
| 1989–91 | Chrysler Domestic Front Wheel Drive⑤ | .930-.940 | .882 | .0005 | .0050 | 15-80 |
| | Colt Vista 2WD | .708 | .646 | — | .006 | — |
| | Colt Vista 4WD | .944 | .882 | — | .006 | — |
| 1990 | Monaco | .866 | .807 | .001 | .003 | — |
| 1990–91 | Eagle Talon | .944 | .881 | — | .0031 | — |
| | Laser | .944 | .881 | — | .0031 | — |
| 1991 | Colt | .511 | .449 | — | .006 | — |
| 1991 | Eagle Summit | .708 | .646 | — | .006 | — |
| 1991 | Eagle Premier | .944 | .885 | .001 | .003 | — |
| 1991 | Monaco | .944 | .885 | .001 | .003 | — |
| 1991 | Stealth AWD | 1.181 | 1.118 | — | .004 | — |
| 1991 | Stealth FWD | .944 | .881 | — | .004 | — |
| **REAR** | | | | | | |
| 1989 | Conquest | — | .881 | — | .006 | — |
| 1989–90 | Colt④ | .393 | .331 | — | .006 | — |
| | Eagle Summit④ | .393 | .331 | — | .006 | — |
| | Shadow & Sundance | .467-.478 | .409 | .0005 | .005 | 15-80 |
| 1989–91 | Daytona & LeBaron⑥ | .467-.478 | .409 | .0005 | .005 | 15-80 |
| | Daytona & LeBaron⑦ | .856-.876 | .797 | .0005 | .003 | 15-80 |
| | Dynasty & New Yorker | .350-.358 | .339 | .0005 | .003 | 15-80 |
| 1990–91 | Acclaim, LeBaron Landau & Spirit | .467-.478 | .409 | .0005 | .005 | 15-80 |
| | Eagle Talon & Laser | .393 | .331 | — | .0031 | — |
| | Imperial & New Yorker Fifth Avenue | .350-.358 | .339 | .0005 | .003 | 15-80 |
| 1991 | Eagle Premier & Monaco | .393 | .374 | .0005 | .003 | — |
| | Stealth AWD | .787 | .724 | — | .0031 | — |
| | Stealth FWD | .708 | .645 | — | .0031 | — |

①—Do not machine brake disc rotor. Replace brake rotor if excessive wear and/or scoring is evident.
②—Omni & Horizon models.
③—Models with 1.5L engine.
④—Models with 1.6L engine.
⑤—All Except Omni & Horizon models.
⑥—Solid rotor.
⑦—Vented rotor.

# DRUM BRAKES

## TABLE OF CONTENTS



# Applications

| | Type No. |
|---|---|
| **Domestic Front Wheel Drive Models:** | |
| 1989 | 2 |
| 1990-91 | 2 |
| 1990-91 | 3 |
| **Domestic Rear Wheel Drive Models** | 1 |
| **Eagle Premier & Monaco** | 4 |
| **Colt & Eagle Summit:** | |
| 1989-90 | 5 |
| 1991 | 7 |
| **Colt Vista & Colt Wagon** | 6 |
| **Eagle Medallion** | 8 |

# Troubleshooting

Refer to "Troubleshooting" in the "Disc Brake" section for general disc and drum brake troubleshooting procedures.

# General Information

## INDEX



## SERVICE PRECAUTIONS

When working on or around brake assemblies, care must be taken to prevent breathing asbestos dust, as many manufacturers incorporate asbestos fibers in the production of brake linings. During routine service operations, the amount of asbestos dust from brake lining wear is at a low level due to a chemical breakdown during use. A few precautions will minimize exposure.

**Do not sand or grind brake linings unless suitable local exhaust ventilation equipment is used to prevent excessive asbestos exposure.**

1. Wear a suitable respirator approved for asbestos dust use during all repair procedures.
2. When cleaning brake dust from brake parts, use a vacuum cleaner with a highly efficient filter system. If a suitable vacuum cleaner is not available, use a water soaked rag. **Do not use compressed air or dry brush to clean brake parts.**
3. Keep work area clean using same equipment as for cleaning brake parts.
4. Properly dispose of rags and vacuum cleaner bags by placing them in plastic bags.
5. Do not smoke or eat while working on brake systems.
6. Never use any fluid containing mineral oil to clean brake system components. This will damage the rubber caps and seals. If system contamination is suspected, check brake fluid in the reservoir for dirt, discoloration, or separation (breakdown) of the brake fluid into distinct layers. Drain and flush the hydraulic system with clean brake fluid if contamination is suspected.

## GENERAL INSPECTION

### BRAKE DRUMS

Any time the brake drums are removed for brake service, the braking surface diameter should be checked with a suitable brake drum micrometer at several points to determine if they are within the safe oversize limit stamped on the brake drum outer surface. If the braking surface diameter exceeds specifications, the drum must be replaced. If the braking surface diameter is within specifications, drums should be cleaned and inspected for cracks, scores, deep grooves, taper, out of round and heat spotting. If drums are cracked or heat spotted, they must be replaced. Scoring and grooves in the braking surface can only be removed by machining with special equipment, as long as the braking surface is within specifications. Any brake drum showing taper or sufficiently out of round to cause vehicle vibration or noise while braking should also be machined, removing only enough stock to true up the drum.

After a brake drum is machined, wipe the braking surface diameter with a denatured alcohol soaked cloth. If one brake drum is machined, the other should also be machined to the same diameter to maintain equal braking forces.

## BRAKE LININGS & SPRINGS

Inspect brake linings for excessive wear, damage, oil, grease or brake fluid contamination. If any of the above conditions exist, brake linings should be replaced as an axle set to maintain equal braking forces. Examine brake shoe webbing, hold-down and return springs for signs of overheating indicated by a slight blue color. Any component which exhibits overheating signs should be replaced. Overheated springs lose their pull and could cause brake linings to wear out prematurely. Inspect all springs for sags, bends and external damage and replace as necessary.

Inspect hold-down retainers and pins for bends, rust and corrosion. If any of the above is found, replace as required.

## BACKING PLATE

Inspect backing plate shoe contact surface for grooves that may restrict shoe movement and cannot be removed by lightly sanding with emery cloth or other suitable abrasive. If backing plate exhibits above condition, it should be replaced. Also inspect for signs of cracks, warpage and excessive rust, indicating need for replacement.

## ADJUSTER MECHANISM

Inspect all components for rust, corrosion, bends and fatigue. Replace as necessary. On adjuster mechanism equipped with adjuster cable, inspect cable for kinks, fraying or elongation of eyelet and replace as necessary.

## PARKING BRAKE CABLE

Inspect parking brake cable end for kinks, fraying and elongation and replace as necessary. Use a small hose clamp to compress clamp where it enters backing plate to remove.

# Type 1—Duo Servo Drum Brake

### INDEX



## REMOVAL

1. Raise and support rear of vehicle.
2. Remove tire and wheel assembly, then remove brake drum. If brake lining is dragging on brake drum, back off brake adjustment by rotating adjustment screw. **If brake drum is rusted or corroded to axle flange and cannot be removed readily, lightly tap axle flange to drum mounting surface with a suitable hammer.**
3. Using brake spring pliers or equivalent, remove primary and secondary shoe return springs, **Fig. 1.**
4. Remove automatic adjuster cable from anchor plate and unhook from adjuster lever.
5. Remove adjuster cable, overload spring, cable guide and anchor plate.
6. Unhook adjuster lever spring from lever and remove spring and lever.
7. Remove shoe to shoe spring from secondary shoe web, then the primary shoe.
8. Spread shoes apart and remove parking brake strut and spring.
9. Using suitable tool, remove shoe retainers, then the springs and nails.
10. Disconnect parking brake cable from lever and remove brake shoes.
11. Remove parking brake lever from secondary shoe.
12. Clean dirt from brake drum, backing plate and all other components. **Do not use compressed air or dry brush to clean brake parts. Many brake parts contain asbestos fibers which, if inhaled, can cause serious injury. To clean brake parts, use a water soaked rag or a suitable vacuum cleaner to minimize airborne dust.**

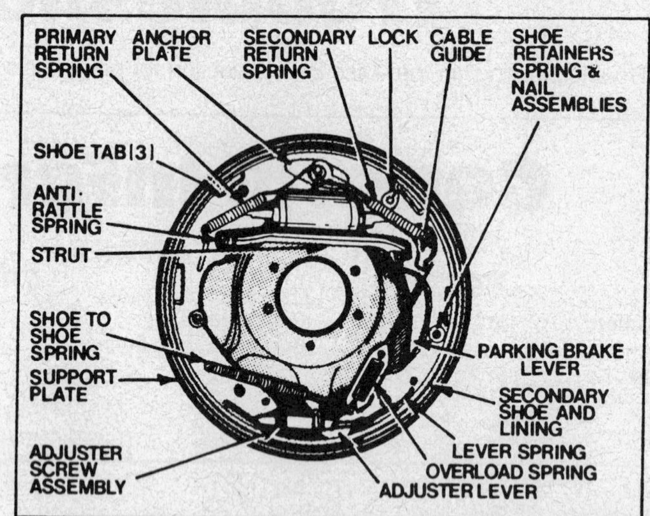


**Fig. 1 Duo servo drum brake assembly. Type 1**

## INSPECTION

Refer to "General Information" at the front of this chapter.

## INSTALLATION

1. Lubricate parking brake lever fulcrum with suitable brake lube, then attach lever to secondary brake shoe. Ensure the lever operates smoothly.
2. Lightly lubricate backing plate shoe contact surfaces with suitable brake lube.
3. Connect parking brake lever to cable and slide secondary brake shoe into position.
4. Connect wheel cylinder link to brake shoe.
5. Slide parking brake lever strut behind axle flange and into parking brake lever slot, then place parking brake anti-rattle spring over strut.

6. Position primary brake shoe on backing plate, then connect wheel cylinder link and parking brake strut.
7. Install anchor plate and position adjuster cable eye over anchor pin.
8. Install primary shoe return spring using brake spring pliers or equivalent.
9. Place protruding hole rim of cable guide in secondary shoe web hole, then holding guide in position, install secondary shoe return spring through cable guide and secondary shoe. Install spring on anchor pin using brake spring pliers or equivalent. **Ensure cable guide remains flat against secondary shoe web during and after return spring installation. Also ensure secondary spring end overlaps primary spring end on anchor pin.**
10. Using suitable pliers, squeeze spring ends around anchor pin until parallel.
11. Install adjuster screw assembly between primary and secondary brake shoes with star wheel on secondary shoe side. **The left side adjuster assembly stud is stamped "L" and is cadmium-plated. The right side adjuster assembly is not stamped and is colored black.**
12. Install shoe to shoe spring, then position adjusting lever spring over pivot pin on shoe web.
13. Install adjusting lever under spring and over pivot pin, then slide lever slightly rearward.
14. Install nails, springs and retainers.
15. Thread adjuster cable over guide and hook end of overload spring in lever. Ensure eye of cable is pulled tight against anchor and in a straight line with guide.
16. Install brake drum, tire and wheel assembly.
17. Adjust brakes. Refer to "Adjustments" for procedure.
18. If any hydraulic connections have been opened, bleed brake system.
19. Check master cylinder fluid level, and replenish as necessary.
20. Check brake pedal for proper feel and return.
21. Lower vehicle and road test. **Do not severely apply brakes immediately after installation of new brake linings or permanent damage may occur to linings, and/or brake drums may become scored. Brakes must be used moderately during first few hundred miles of operation to ensure proper burnishing of linings.**

## SERVICE BRAKE

### ADJUST

1. Each backing plate has two adjusting hole covers; remove the rear cover and turn the adjusting screw upward with a screwdriver or other suitable tool to expand the shoes until a slight drag is felt when the drum is rotated.
2. While holding the adjustment lever out of engagement with the adjusting screw, back off the adjusting screw until wheel rotates freely with no drag.
3. Install wheel and adjusting hole cover. Adjust brakes on remaining wheel in the same manner.
4. If pedal height is not satisfactory, drive the vehicle and ensure sufficient reverse stops until proper pedal height is obtained.

## PARKING BRAKE

### ADJUST

**The following procedure has been revised by a Technical Service Bulletin.**

1. Release parking brake lever and loosen cable adjusting nut to be sure cable is slack.
2. With rear wheel brakes adjusted properly adjusted, tighten cable adjusting nut until a slight drag is felt when the rear wheels are rotated. Then loosen the cable adjusting nut counterclockwise five turns.
3. **On models with four wheel disc brakes,** proceed as follows:
   a. Actuate parking brake lever on rear calipers by manually pulling down and releasing each of the rear parking brake cables located on the underbody.
   b. The parking brake lever should return against stop pin on both rear calipers.
   c. Repeat steps a and b until parking brake lever returns against stop pin on both calipers.
   d. After completing adjustment, apply and release the parking brake. The actuating levers on both calipers must return against the stop pin in the off position and both wheels must rotate freely. Repeat procedure if necessary.
4. **On models less four wheel disc brakes,** proceed as follows:
   a. Back off cable adjusting nut an additional two turns.
   b. Apply and release parking brake several times to be sure rear wheels are not dragging when cable is in released position.

# Type 2 & 3—Kelsey-Hayes & Varga Leading Trailing Drum Brakes

### INDEX



## REMOVAL

1. Raise and support rear of vehicle.
2. Remove tire and wheel assembly, then remove brake drum. If brake lining is dragging on brake drum, back off brake adjustment by rotating adjustment screw.
3. Using suitable pliers, remove adjuster lever spring, **Fig. 1.**
4. Remove adjuster lever.
5. Turn automatic adjuster screw out to expand shoes past wheel cylinder boot.
6. Disconnect parking brake cable from parking brake lever.
7. **On Type 2—Kelsey Hayes,** using suitable tool, remove hold-down springs.
8. Pull brake shoe assembly down and away from anchor plate, then remove brake shoe springs and adjusting screw assembly.
9. **On Type 3—Varga,** remove upper shoe to shoe return spring on leading shoe, **Fig. 2,** leading shoe hold down spring, shoe to shoe spring at anchor plate, then the shoe and adjuster assembly.
10. Remove hold down spring and lower shoe to anchor plate spring for trailing shoe.
11. **On Type 2—Kelsey Hayes,** remove C-clip retaining parking brake lever to trailing brake shoe webbing.
12. **On Type 3—Varga,** remove parking brake lever from trailing shoe by prying retainer tangs apart.
13. Clean dirt from brake drum, anchor plate and all other components. **Do not use compressed air or dry brush to clean brake parts. Many brake parts contain asbestos fibers, which, if inhaled, can cause**

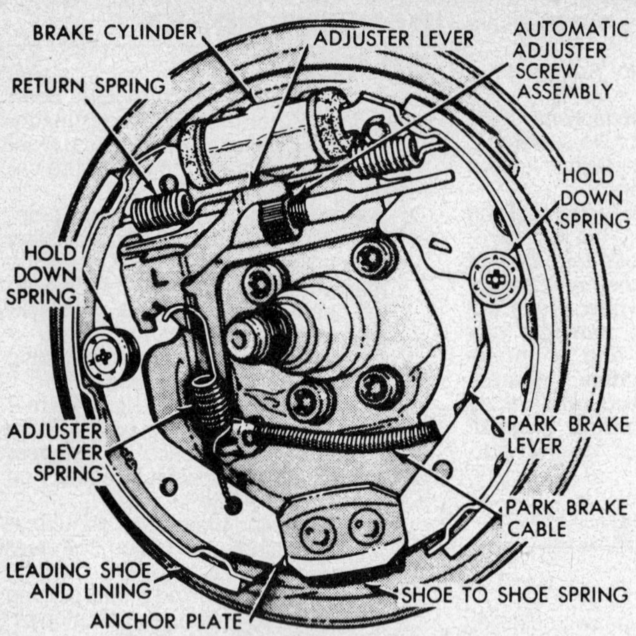


**Fig. 1 Kelsey-Hayes leading trailing drum brake assembly. Type 2**

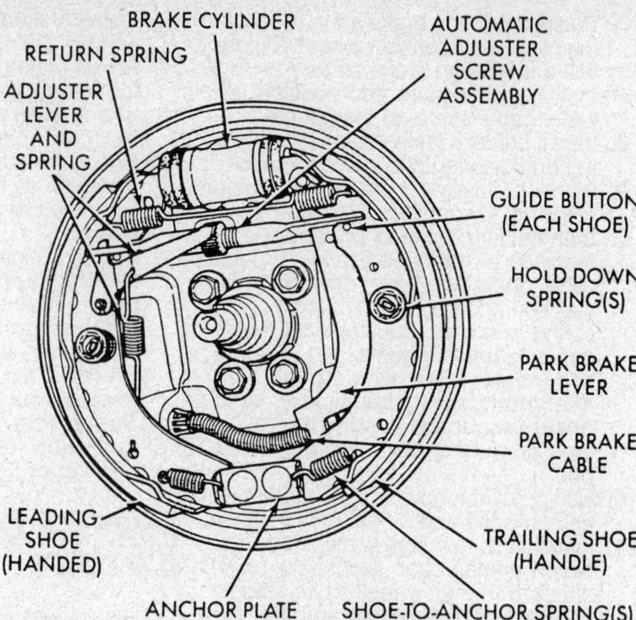


**Fig. 2 Varga leading trailing drum brake assembly. Type 3**

**serious injury. To clean brake parts, use a water soaked rag or a suitable vacuum cleaner to minimize airborne dust.**

## INSPECTION

Refer to "General Information" at the front of this chapter.

## INSTALLATION

### TYPE 2—KELSEY-HAYES

1. Lightly lubricate anchor plate shoe contact surfaces with suitable brake lube.
2. Remove brake drum hub grease seal and bearings, then clean and repack bearings and reinstall. Install new grease seal.
3. Assemble automatic adjuster screw assembly, return spring and shoe-to-shoe spring to brake shoe assembly.
4. Position lining assembly near anchor plate, then assemble parking brake lever to trailing shoe webbing. Secure with C-clip.
5. Install lining assembly onto anchor plate. When positioned, back off adjuster nut to seat brake shoe ends in wheel cylinder.
6. Install hold-down springs.
7. Position adjuster lever, then using suitable pliers, install adjuster lever spring.
8. Install brake drum and bearings. Refer to individual car chapter for wheel bearing adjustment procedure.
9. Adjust brakes. Refer to individual car chapter for procedure.
10. Install tire and wheel assembly.
11. If any hydraulic connections have been opened, bleed brake system.
12. Check master cylinder level, and replenish as necessary.
13. Check brake pedal for proper feel and return.
14. Lower vehicle and road test. **Do not severely apply brakes immediately after installation of new brake linings or permanent damage may occur to linings and/or brake drums may become scored. Brakes must be used moderately during first several hundred miles of operation to ensure proper burnishing.**

### TYPE 3—VARGA

1. Assemble park brake lever and wave washer to trailing shoe, then install retainer and close ends.
2. Install park brake cable in lever of trailing shoe, then attach trailing shoe and leading shoe lower springs to shoes and anchor plate.
3. Position shoes on support plate and install hold down springs.
4. Install automatic adjusters, ends must be above extruded pins in web of shoe. **Left side adjuster has left hand threads and right hand adjuster has right hand threads, do not interchange.**
5. Install upper shoe to shoe spring, then rotate adjuster to to remove free play from adjuster assembly.
6. Install adjuster lever on leading pivot pin and attach short end of adjuster spring in hole of lever and long end in leading shoe hole.
7. Connect park brake cable and adjust shoes so that they do not interfere with drum installation.

## SERVICE BRAKE

## ADJUST

1. Each backing plate has two adjusting hole covers; remove the rear cover and turn the adjusting screw upward with a screwdriver or other suitable tool to expand the shoes until a slight drag is felt when the drum is rotated.
2. While holding the adjustment lever out of engagement with the adjusting screw, back off the adjusting screw until wheel rotates freely with no drag.
3. Install wheel and adjusting hole cover. Adjust brakes on remaining wheel in the same manner.
4. If pedal height is not satisfactory, drive the vehicle and perform sufficient reverse stops until proper pedal height is obtained.

## PARKING BRAKE

## ADJUST

1. Release parking brake lever, then loosen cable adjusting nut and ensure cable is slack.
2. Ensure rear wheel brakes are properly adjusted, then tighten cable adjusting nut until a slight drag is felt when the rear wheels are rotated. Loosen the cable adjusting nut until both rear wheels rotate freely.
3. Back off cable adjusting nut an additional two turns.
4. Apply and release parking brake several times to be sure rear wheels are not dragging when cable is in released position.

# Type 4—Leading Trailing Drum Brake

INDEX



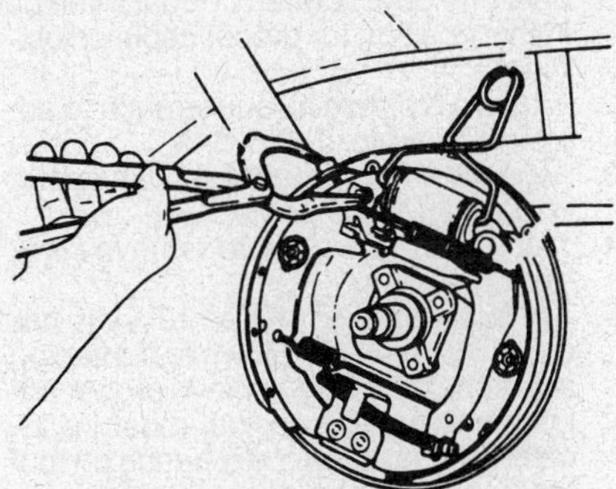

**Fig. 1 Removing upper & lower return springs**

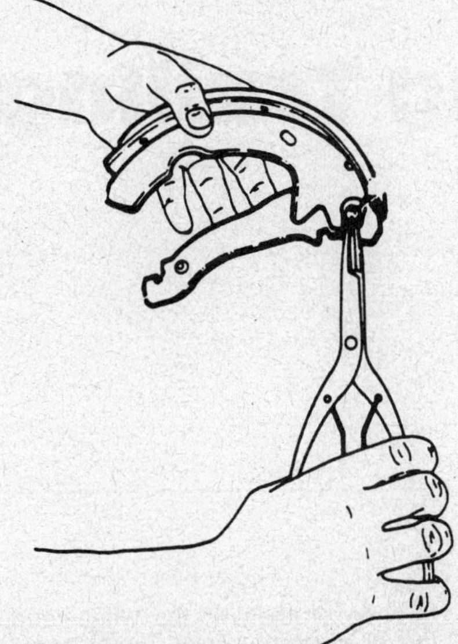

**Fig. 4 Separating park brake lever from primary shoe**

## REMOVAL

1. Raise and support vehicle.
2. Remove rear wheel and tire assembly.
3. Remove brake drum. If brake lining is dragging on brake drum, remove access plug from backing plate and back off brake adjustment by rotating adjustment screw.
4. Install suitable wheel cylinder clamp over ends of wheel cylinder to retain pistons in bore.
5. Remove upper and lower return springs, **Fig. 1**, using suitable brake spring pliers.

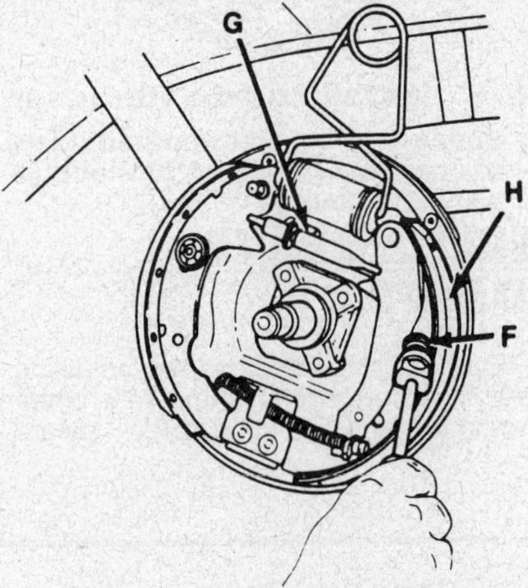


**Fig. 2 Removing primary shoe, hold-down spring & self-adjusting lever**

6. Remove adjuster lever, then the parking brake cable from parking brake lever.
7. Using suitable tool, compress and remove rear hold-down spring (F), then remove self-adjusting screw (G) and primary brake shoe (H), **Fig. 2.**
8. Remove front hold-down spring (J), then the secondary brake shoe (K), **Fig 3.**
9. Using snap ring pliers, remove clip from pivot pin on primary shoe, **Fig 4**, then separate park brake lever from shoe.
10. Clean dirt from backing plate, brake drum and hardware.

## INSPECTION

1. Inspect components for damage and unusual wear. Replace as necessary.
2. Inspect wheel cylinders. Boots which are torn, cut, or heat damaged indicate need for wheel cylinder replacement. Fluid spilling from boot center hole, or wetness around wheel cylinder ends indicates cup leakage and need for wheel cylinder replacement. **A small amount of fluid is always present and is considered normal, acting as a lubricant for the cylinder pistons.**
3. Inspect backing plate for evidence of seal leakage. If leakage exists, refer to individual car chapters for axle seal replacement procedure.
4. Inspect backing plate attaching bolts and ensure they are tight.
5. Check adjuster screw operation. If satisfactory, lightly lubricate adjusting screw and washer with suitable brake lube. If operation is unsatisfactory, replace.
6. Using fine emery cloth or other suitable abrasive, clean rust and dirt from shoe contact surfaces on backing plate. Apply brake lube to contact surfaces and to park brake lever pivot pin.

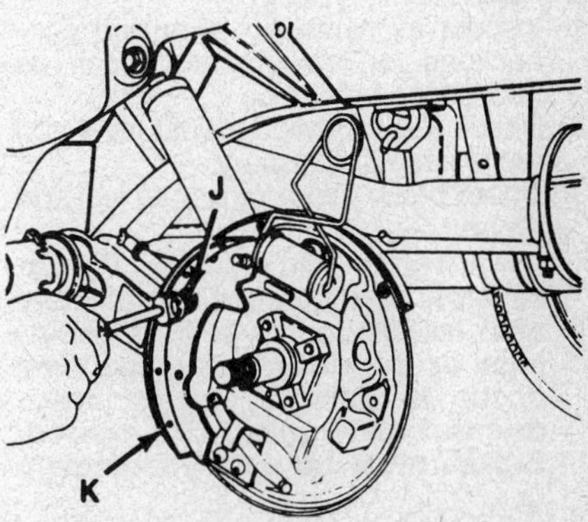


**Fig. 3 Removing secondary shoe & hold-down spring**

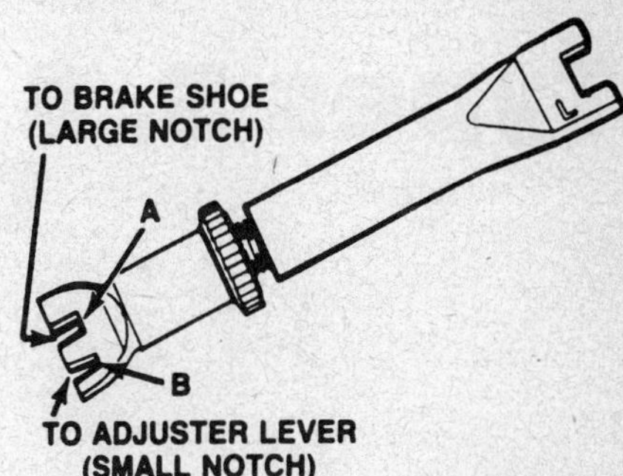


**Fig. 5 Self-adjusting screw notch locations**

## INSTALLATION

1. Install park brake lever on primary brake shoe, compressing clip around pivot pin.
2. Using brake spring pliers, install park brake cable to park brake lever.
3. Install primary brake shoe, hold-down spring and self-adjusting screw.
4. Install secondary brake shoe and hold-down spring. **Ensure shoe is installed into larger (A) of two notches in adjuster lever, Fig. 5.**

5. Remove wheel cylinder clamp, then install adjuster lever (U) to pin (W), **Fig. 6,** and into self-adjusting screw. **Ensure lever is installed into smaller (B) of two notches in adjuster lever, Fig. 5.**
6. Install upper and lower return springs.
7. Ensure brake shoes are centered on backing plate.
8. Install brake drum, wheel and tire assembly.
9. If any hydraulic brake connections have been opened, bleed brake system.
10. Adjust parking brake.
11. Inspect all hydraulic lines and connections for leakage and repair as necessary.
12. Check master cylinder fluid level and replenish as necessary.
13. Check brake pedal for proper feel and return.
14. Lower vehicle and road test. **Do not severely apply brakes immediately after installation of new brake linings or permanent damage may occur to linings, and/or brake drums may become scored. Brakes must be used moderately during first several hundred miles of operation to ensure proper burnishing of linings.**

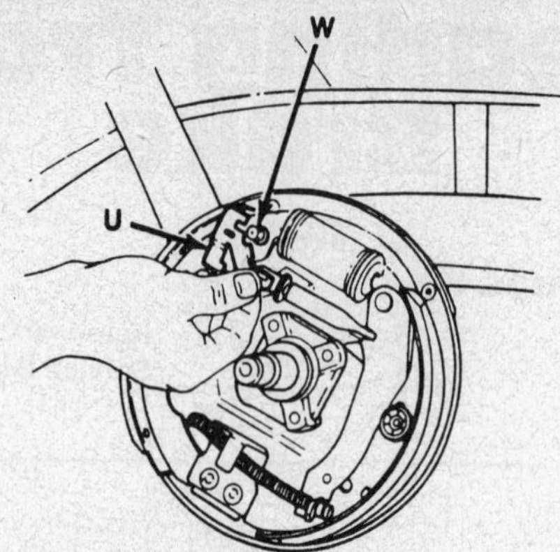


**Fig. 6 Installing adjuster lever**

## SERVICE BRAKE

### ADJUST

1. Each backing plate has two adjusting hole covers; remove the rear cover and turn the adjusting screw upward with a screwdriver or other suitable tool to expand the shoes until a slight drag is felt when the drum is rotated.
2. While holding the adjustment lever out of engagement with the adjusting screw, back off the adjusting screw one complete turn.
3. Install wheel and adjusting hole cover.
4. Lower vehicle and ensure proper brake operation.

## PARKING BRAKE

### ADJUST

1. Push down on parking brake pedal until one click is heard. Pedal must be in this position for proper cable adjustment.
2. Attach a suitable torque wrench to adjusting tool No. J-34651-A.
3. Align notches in tool head with center of parking brake cable.
4. Tighten adjusting nut to remove slack from cable.
5. **Torque** cable to 100-110 inch lbs. using tool J-34651-A while tightening adjustment nut. To achieve proper adjustment, pointer on tool must be located in one of four dark bands on tool face.

# Types 5, 6 & 7—Leading Trailing Drum Brakes

## INDEX

**Page No.**



## BRAKE SERVICE

For drum brake service procedures, refer to **Figs. 1 and 2.**

## SERVICE BRAKES

### ADJUST

These brakes are equipped with self adjusting mechanisms, therefore periodic adjustments are not necessary. If stopping power is insufficient, or if brake pedal travel is excessive, brakes should be cleaned and inspected, and the self-adjusting mechanisms should be checked.

After performing brake service, adjust brake shoes as follows:

1. Ensure shoes are centered on backing plate and measure width of brake shoes using suitable caliper. On Colt Vista models, also measure inside diameter of brake drum.
2. Adjust width of brake shoes to approximately 7.06 inches for Colt. On Colt Vista, adjust brake shoes to a width approximately .060 inch less than inside diameter of brake drum.
3. Install brake drums and adjust parking brake as described.
4. After adjusting parking brake, release parking brake lever and ensure shoe actuating lever is not being pulled by parking brake cable. **If shoe actuating lever is pulled by parking brake cable, self-adjusters will not operate.**

## PARKING BRAKE

### ADJUST

1. Apply parking brake lever with a force of approximately 45 lbs. while counting number of clicks. Lever should click 5-7 times.
2. If not within specifications, release parking brake lever and remove center console, if equipped.
3. Loosen adjusting nut on parking brake lever to free parking brake cables, then depress brake pedal several times to ensure shoe to drum clearance is properly maintained by self-adjusters.
4. Tighten adjusting nut until brake lever can be raised 5-7 notches with a force of approximately 45 lbs. **If adjusting nut is tightened excessively, self-adjuster mechanism will be inoperative.**
5. After adjustment, raise rear of vehicle, ensuring brakes do not drag with parking brake lever released.

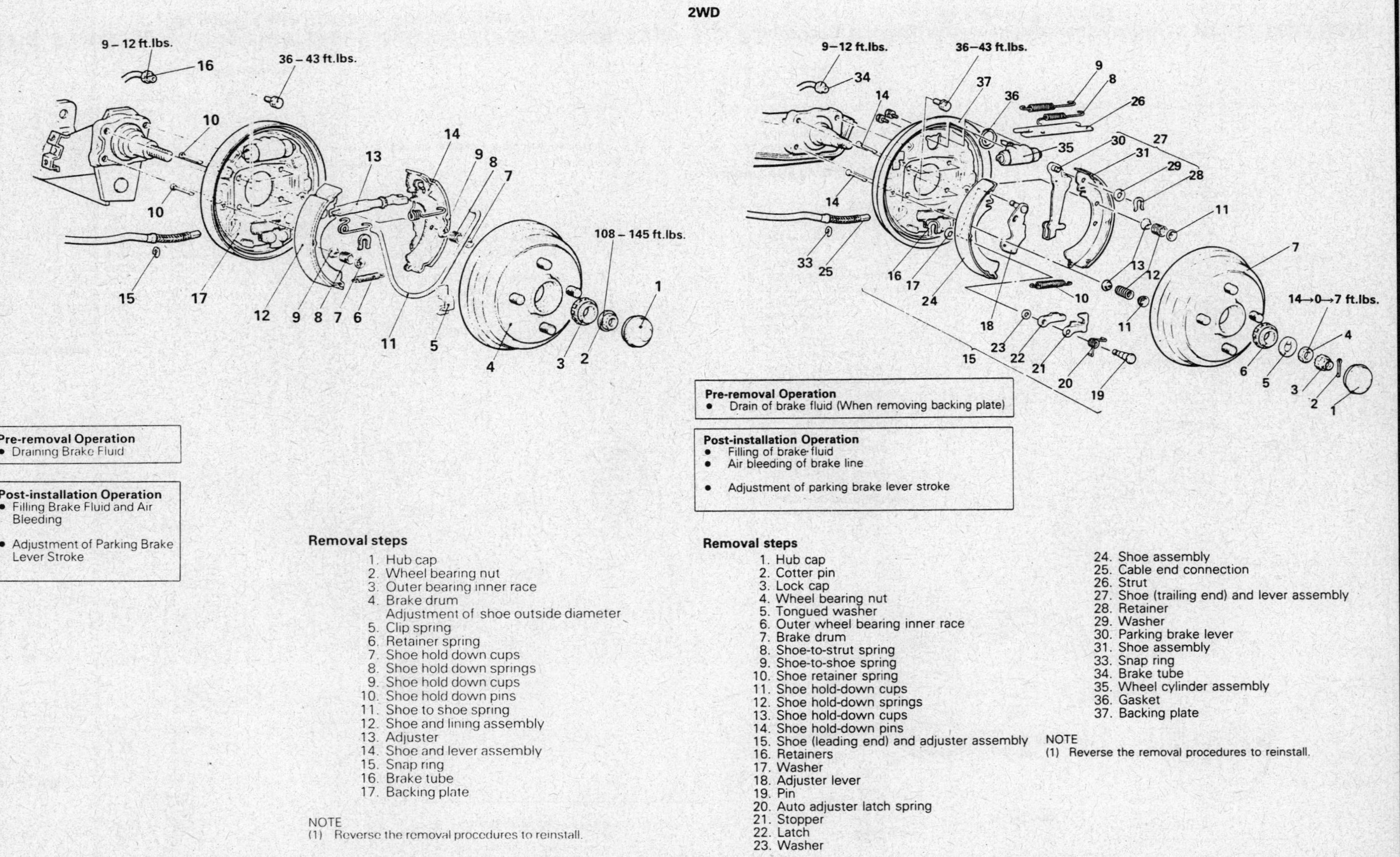
2WD
9 – 12 ft.lbs.
36 – 43 ft.lbs.
108 – 145 ft.lbs.
Pre-removal Operation
• Draining Brake Fluid
Post-installation Operation
• Filling Brake Fluid and Air Bleeding
• Adjustment of Parking Brake Lever Stroke
Removal steps
1. Hub cap
2. Wheel bearing nut
3. Outer bearing inner race
4. Brake drum
Adjustment of shoe outside diameter
5. Clip spring
6. Retainer spring
7. Shoe hold down cups
8. Shoe hold down springs
9. Shoe hold down cups
10. Shoe hold down pins
11. Shoe to shoe spring
12. Shoe and lining assembly
13. Adjuster
14. Shoe and lever assembly
15. Snap ring
16. Brake tube
17. Backing plate
NOTE
(1) Reverse the removal procedures to reinstall.
9–12 ft.lbs.
36–43 ft.lbs.
14→0→7 ft.lbs.
Pre-removal Operation
• Drain of brake fluid (When removing backing plate)
Post-installation Operation
• Filling of brake fluid
• Air bleeding of brake line
• Adjustment of parking brake lever stroke
Removal steps
1. Hub cap
2. Cotter pin
3. Lock cap
4. Wheel bearing nut
5. Tongued washer
6. Outer wheel bearing inner race
7. Brake drum
8. Shoe-to-strut spring
9. Shoe-to-shoe spring
10. Shoe retainer spring
11. Shoe hold-down cups
12. Shoe hold-down springs
13. Shoe hold-down cups
14. Shoe hold-down pins
15. Shoe (leading end) and adjuster assembly
16. Retainers
17. Washer
18. Adjuster lever
19. Pin
20. Auto adjuster latch spring
21. Stopper
22. Latch
23. Washer
24. Shoe assembly
25. Cable end connection
26. Strut
27. Shoe (trailing end) and lever assembly
28. Retainer
29. Washer
30. Parking brake lever
31. Shoe assembly
33. Snap ring
34. Brake tube
35. Wheel cylinder assembly
36. Gasket
37. Backing plate
NOTE
(1) Reverse the removal procedures to reinstall.

**Fig. 1 Leading trailing drum brake assembly. Type 5, 1989–90 Colt & Eagle Summit**

**Fig. 2 Leading trailing drum brake assembly (Part 1 Of 2). Type 6, 2WD Colt Vista & Colt Wagon**

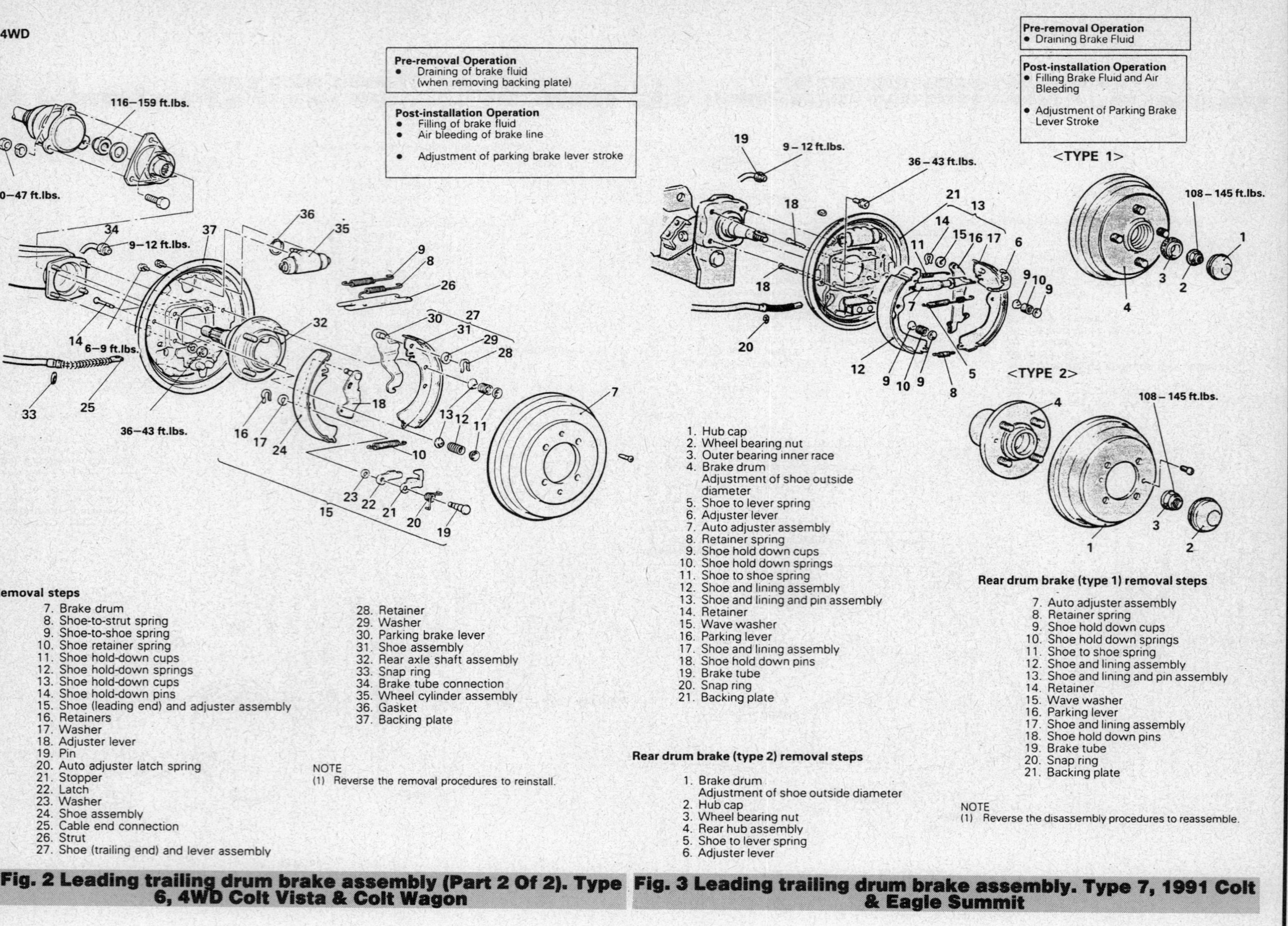


**Pre-removal Operation**
- Draining of brake fluid (when removing backing plate)

**Post-installation Operation**
- Filling of brake fluid
- Air bleeding of brake line
- Adjustment of parking brake lever stroke

**Removal steps**

7. Brake drum
8. Shoe-to-strut spring
9. Shoe-to-shoe spring
10. Shoe retainer spring
11. Shoe hold-down cups
12. Shoe hold-down springs
13. Shoe hold-down cups
14. Shoe hold-down pins
15. Shoe (leading end) and adjuster assembly
16. Retainers
17. Washer
18. Adjuster lever
19. Pin
20. Auto adjuster latch spring
21. Stopper
22. Latch
23. Washer
24. Shoe assembly
25. Cable end connection
26. Strut
27. Shoe (trailing end) and lever assembly
28. Retainer
29. Washer
30. Parking brake lever
31. Shoe assembly
32. Rear axle shaft assembly
33. Snap ring
34. Brake tube connection
35. Wheel cylinder assembly
36. Gasket
37. Backing plate

NOTE
(1) Reverse the removal procedures to reinstall.

**Fig. 2 Leading trailing drum brake assembly (Part 2 Of 2). Type 6, 4WD Colt Vista & Colt Wagon**

**Pre-removal Operation**
- Draining Brake Fluid

**Post-installation Operation**
- Filling Brake Fluid and Air Bleeding
- Adjustment of Parking Brake Lever Stroke

1. Hub cap
2. Wheel bearing nut
3. Outer bearing inner race
4. Brake drum
   Adjustment of shoe outside diameter
5. Shoe to lever spring
6. Adjuster lever
7. Auto adjuster assembly
8. Retainer spring
9. Shoe hold down cups
10. Shoe hold down springs
11. Shoe to shoe spring
12. Shoe and lining assembly
13. Shoe and lining and pin assembly
14. Retainer
15. Wave washer
16. Parking lever
17. Shoe and lining assembly
18. Shoe hold down pins
19. Brake tube
20. Snap ring
21. Backing plate

**Rear drum brake (type 2) removal steps**

1. Brake drum
   Adjustment of shoe outside diameter
2. Hub cap
3. Wheel bearing nut
4. Rear hub assembly
5. Shoe to lever spring
6. Adjuster lever

**Rear drum brake (type 1) removal steps**

7. Auto adjuster assembly
8. Retainer spring
9. Shoe hold down cups
10. Shoe hold down springs
11. Shoe to shoe spring
12. Shoe and lining assembly
13. Shoe and lining and pin assembly
14. Retainer
15. Wave washer
16. Parking lever
17. Shoe and lining assembly
18. Shoe hold down pins
19. Brake tube
20. Snap ring
21. Backing plate

NOTE
(1) Reverse the disassembly procedures to reassemble.

**Fig. 3 Leading trailing drum brake assembly. Type 7, 1991 Colt & Eagle Summit**

# Type 8—Leading Trailing Drum Brake

INDEX



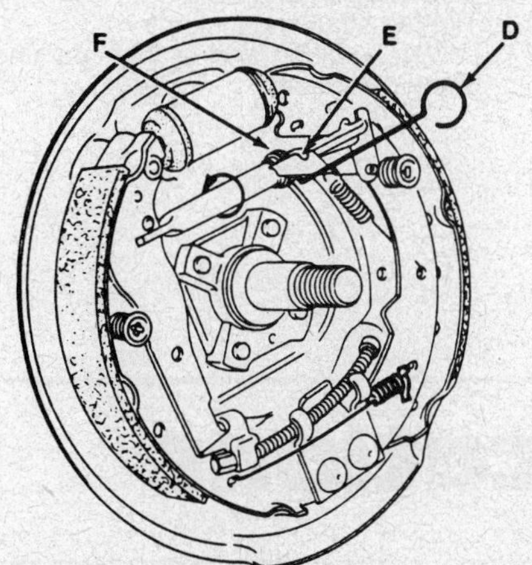


**Fig. 1 Removing brake drum**

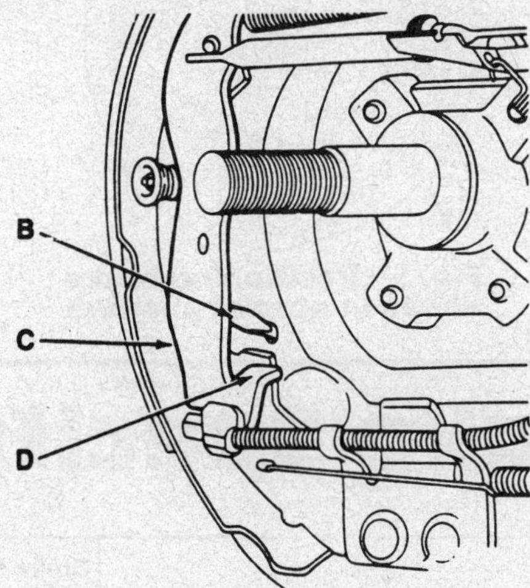


**Fig. 2 Removing brake drum with screwdriver**

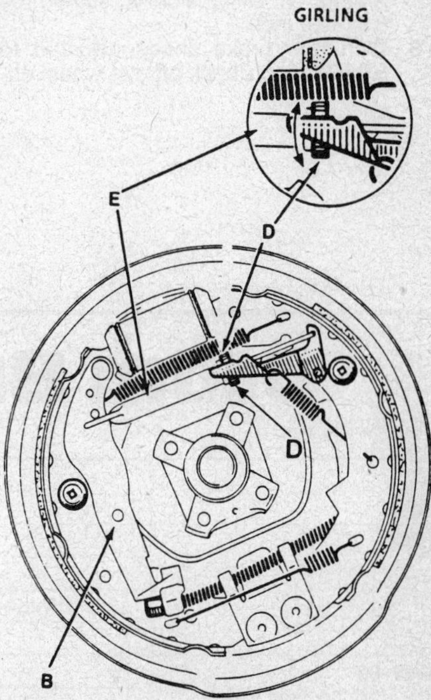


**Fig. 3 Self-adjuster mechanism**

## BRAKE SERVICE

### BRAKE DRUMS, REPLACE

**Both rear brake drum assemblies must have the same inside diameter. If one brake drum is resurfaced, the other brake drum must also be resurfaced. Maximum inside diameter after machining (resurfacing) should be 9.035 inch. Also, do not allow brake dust to fly. Do not use compressed air or dry brush to clean components. Use approved breathing equipment and a water dampened cloth to clean or remove dirt and dust from brake components.**

1. Raise and support vehicle.
2. Remove tire and wheel assemblies.
3. Remove plastic dust cover.
4. Remove the two machine screws and rear brake drum. If brake drum cannot be removed, back off the brake self adjuster. Fabricate a small hook from a piece of coat hanger or heavy wire. Insert the hook tool through one of the bolt hole openings and pull slightly on self adjuster lever while rotating star wheel adjuster using a suitable screwdriver in direction of arrow shown in **Fig. 1.** If brake drum still cannot be removed, loosen the parking brake cables and remove plastic access plug on the rear of the brake backing plate. Insert a suitable screwdriver (B) through access hole and push outward and inward on the parking brake lever (C) so tang (D) will clear the rear brake shoe, **Fig. 2.** This will separate the self adjuster star wheel mechanism from the parking brake lever (C).

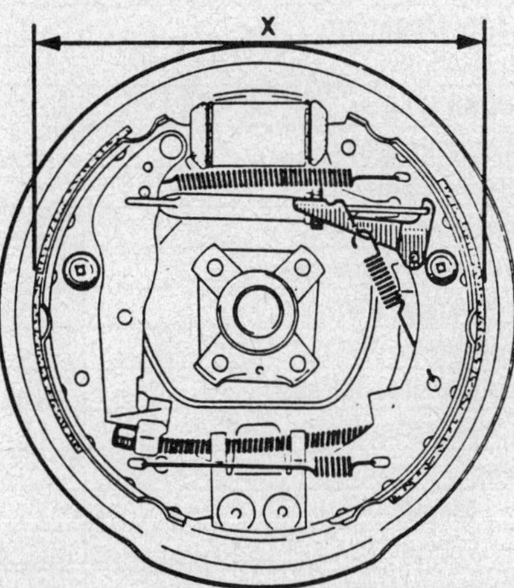


**Fig. 4 Obtaining dimension X**

5. Reverse procedure to install.

### BRAKE SHOES, REPLACE

**Never replace brake linings (shoes) on only one wheel. Replace linings on both sides of axle assembly. Always replace linings with linings of the same make and grade.**

1. Raise and support vehicle.
2. Remove brake drums as described previously.
3. Using a suitable tool, remove upper and lower spring.
4. Install attaching clip Fre. 05 or equivalent, onto wheel cylinder pistons.
5. Remove spring and adjusting lever.
6. Remove hand brake cable from lever.
7. Remove hold down spring and one brake shoe.
8. Remove self adjuster.
9. Remove other shoe hold down spring, then the brake shoe.
10. Using a suitable vacuum cleaner, dust out drums and backing plates.
11. Reverse procedure to install, noting the following:
    a. The internal components of the brakes are different for the lefthand and righthand sides. Do not interchange from side to side.
    b. Lightly grease self adjuster threads and mark it righthand or lefthand.
    c. The end the lefthand adjuster is metallic silver colored and has righthand threads.
    d. The end of the righthand adjuster is gold colored and has lefthand threads.
    e. Adjust brake shoes to 8.97-9.00 inch.

## PARKING BRAKE

### ADJUST

1. Raise and support vehicle.

2. Remove rear tire and wheel assemblies.
3. Remove rear brake drums.
4. Loosen attaching nut at equalizer bracket.
5. Loosen attaching nut to the end of the threaded rod.
6. Verify operation of the self adjuster mechanism (E) by rotating the star wheel adjusters (D) in both directions, **Fig. 3.**
7. Using star wheel adjuster (D), adjust rear brake shoes to obtain dimension X, **Fig. 4.** Dimension X should be 8.97-9.0 inch.
8. With rear brake shoes adjusted to 8.97-9.0 inch, back off star wheel adjuster (D) 5-6 teeth.
9. Verify stop on lever (B), **Fig. 5,** is against brake shoe at point (C).
10. This will verify that the brake cables are returning to their normal position.
11. Install rear brake drums.
12. Install tire and wheel assemblies.
13. Pull up on parking brake lever to the second notch or tooth.
14. Adjust nut on equalizer bracket until both rear wheels are locked.
15. With parking brake lever still on the second notch, back off nut until both rear wheels turn freely.
16. Tighten attaching locknut.
17. Lower vehicle and verify parking brake operation.

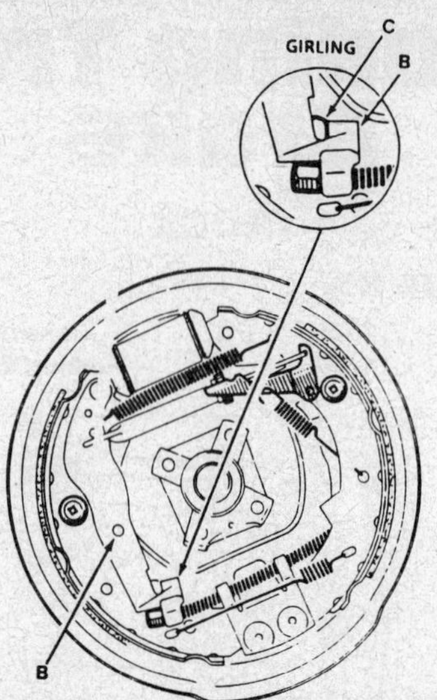


**Fig. 5 Positioning brake shoes in normal position**

# Drum Brake Specifications

| Year | Model | Brake Drum Inside Dia. Inch | Rear Wheel Cylinder Bore Dia. Inch |
|---|---|---|---|
| 1989 | Aries & Reliant | ① | .625 |
| | Lancer & LeBaron GTS | 7.874 | .625 |
| | Diplomat, Fifth Avenue & Grand Fury | ② | .9385 |
| | Eagle Medallion | 8.996 | .866 |
| 1989–90 | Colt | 7.086 | .748 |
| | Colt Wagon | 7.992 | .8125 |
| | Eagle Premier | 8.858 | .944 |
| | Eagle Summit | 7.086 | .748 |
| | Horizon & Omni | 7.874 | .625 |
| 1989–91 | Acclaim & Sundance | 8.661 | .625 |
| | Colt Vista, 2WD | 7.992 | .8125 |
| | Colt Vista, 4WD | 9.000 | .750 |
| | Dynasty & New Yorker | 8.661 | .625 |
| | Shadow & Sundance | 7.874 | .625 |
| 1990–91 | Eagle Premier | 8.858 | .807 |
| | Monaco | 8.858 | .807 |
| 1991 | Colt | 7.086 | .751 |
| | Eagle Summit | 7.086 | .751 |

①—Standard, 7.874 inch; heavy duty, 8.661 inch.
②—Standard, 10.0 inch; heavy duty, 11.0 inch.

# Tightening Specifications

| Year | Component | Torque Ft. Lbs. |
|---|---|---|
| **CHRYSLER DOMESTIC REAR WHEEL DRIVE** | | |
| 1989 | Brake Booster To Dash | 200–250① |
| | Brake Booster Lower Pivot | 18 |
| | Brake Hose To Caliper Banjo Bolt | 30–40 |
| | Brake Line Fittings | 115–170① |
| | Brake Lines To Master Cylinder | 140–230① |
| | Caliper Adapter Mounting Bolts | 130–190 |
| | Caliper Bleed Screw | 80–170① |
| | Caliper Retaining Plate Screws | 170–260① |
| | Caliper Splash Shield Mounting Bolts | 160① |
| | Front Brake Hose To Intermediate Bracket | 75–115① |
| | Master Cylinder To Brake Booster | 170–230① |
| | Support Plate To Rear Axle | 25–60 |
| | Wheel Cylinder Bleed Screws | 60–100① |
| | Wheel Cylinder To Support Plate | 75① |
| | Wheel Lug Nuts | 85 |
| **CHRYSLER DOMESTIC FRONT WHEEL DRIVE②** | | |
| 1989–91 | Bearing Retainer Bolts | 200–300① |
| | Brake Booster To Dash | 200–300① |
| | Brake Hose To Caliper Banjo Bolt | 19–29 |
| | Brake Line Fittings | 115–170① |
| | Caliper Adapter Mounting Bolts | 130–190 |
| | Caliper Bleed Screw | 80–170① |
| | Caliper Guide Pins | 25–35 |
| | Front Brake Hose To Intermediate Bracket | 75–115① |
| | Master Cylinder To Brake Booster | 200–300① |
| | Support Plate To Rear Axle | 45–60 |
| | Wheel Cylinder Bleed Screws | 60–100① |
| | Wheel Cylinder To Support Plate | 75① |
| | Wheel Lug Nuts | 95 |
| **CHRYSLER IMPORTS** | | |
| 1989–91 | Backing Plate Bolts | 36–43 |
| | Brake Booster To Dash⑬ | 8–12 |
| | Brake Booster To Dash③ | 6–9 |
| | Brake Hose To Rear Caliper Banjo Bolt | 18–25 |
| | Bleed Screws | 5–7 |
| | Caliper Support To Front Axle⑭ | 58–72 |
| | Caliper Support To Front Axle④ | 65 |
| | Caliper Support To Rear Axle | 36–43 |
| | Caliper Guide And Lock Pins, Front | ⑤ |
| | Caliper Guide And Lock Pins, Rear | ⑥ |
| | Caliper Sleeve Bolts⑦ | 16–23 |
| | Caliper Slide Pins | ⑧ |
| | Master Cylinder To Brake Booster | 6–9 |
| | Wheel Cylinder | 6–9 |
| | Wheel Lug Nuts | ⑨ |

*Continued*

# Tightening Specifications—Continued

| Year | Component | Torque Ft. Lbs. |
|---|---|---|
| **EAGLE** ⑩ | | |
| 1989 ⑪ | Brake Booster To Dash Nuts | 15 |
| | Bleed Screws | 70 ① |
| | Caliper Guide Bolts | 18 |
| | Caliper Mounting Bolts | 48 |
| | Master Cylinder To Booster Nuts | 10 |
| | Wheel Lug Nuts | 67 |
| 1989–91 ⑫ | Brake Booster To Dash Nuts | 18 |
| | Brake Line Fittings | 11–15 ① |
| | Caliper Mounting Bolts | 70 |
| | Caliper Slide Pins | 15–22 |
| | Master Cylinder To Booster Nuts | 9–13 |
| | Wheel Lug Nuts | 63 |

①—Inch lbs.
②—Except Monaco, refer to Eagle.
③—Conquest.
④—Stealth.
⑤—AD54, 16–23 ft. lbs.; MR34V, 27–36 ft. lbs.; MR44V & MR46V, 46–62 ft. lbs.; MR57W, 54 ft. lbs.
⑥—AD Type, 36–43 ft. lbs.; AD30P & AD35P, 16–23 ft. lbs.; MR45V, 20 ft. lbs.; MR58V, 32 ft. lbs.
⑦—PFS15.
⑧—FS17, 61–69 ft. lbs.; MR31S, M10 33–45 ft. lbs. & M14 61–69 ft. lbs.
⑨—Except Colt Vista with steel wheels, Laser, Stealth & Talon: 65–80 ft. lbs.; Colt Vista with steel wheels: 50–57 ft. lbs.; Laser, Stealth & Talon: 87–101 ft. lbs.
⑩—Refer to Chrysler Imports for Eagle Summit & Talon.
⑪—Medallion.
⑫—Monaco & Premier.
⑬—Except Conquest.
⑭—Except Stealth.

# AUTOMATIC TRANSMISSIONS/TRANSAXLES

## TABLE OF CONTENTS



# Torqueflite Automatic Transmission

## INDEX



## IDENTIFICATION

Transmission identification markings are cast in raised letters and numerals on the lower left side of the bellhousing. There are sufficient variations within each of the main categories to make it necessary to service them by serial number, a stamped seven-digit number appearing on the oil pan side rail.

## DESCRIPTION

These transmissions, **Fig. 1**, combine a torque converter with a fully automatic three speed gear system. The converter housing and transmission case are an integral aluminum casting. The transmission consists of two multiple disc clutches, an overrunning (one-way) clutch, two servos and bands and two planetary gear sets to provide three forward speeds and reverse.

The common sun gear of the planetary gear sets is connected to the front clutch by a driving shell that is splined to the sun gear and to the front clutch retainer.

The hydraulic system consists of a single oil pump and a valve body that contains all the valves except the governor valve.

Venting of the transmission is accomplished by a drilled passage through the upper part of the front pump housing.

The torque converter is attached to the engine crankshaft through a flexible driving plate, and is cooled by circulating the transmission fluid through an oil-to-water type cooler located in the radiator lower tank. A lock-up feature is used on most applications.

The lock-up converter system consists of a lock-up mechanism within the converter, and a lock-up module and switch valve attached to the valve body. The in-

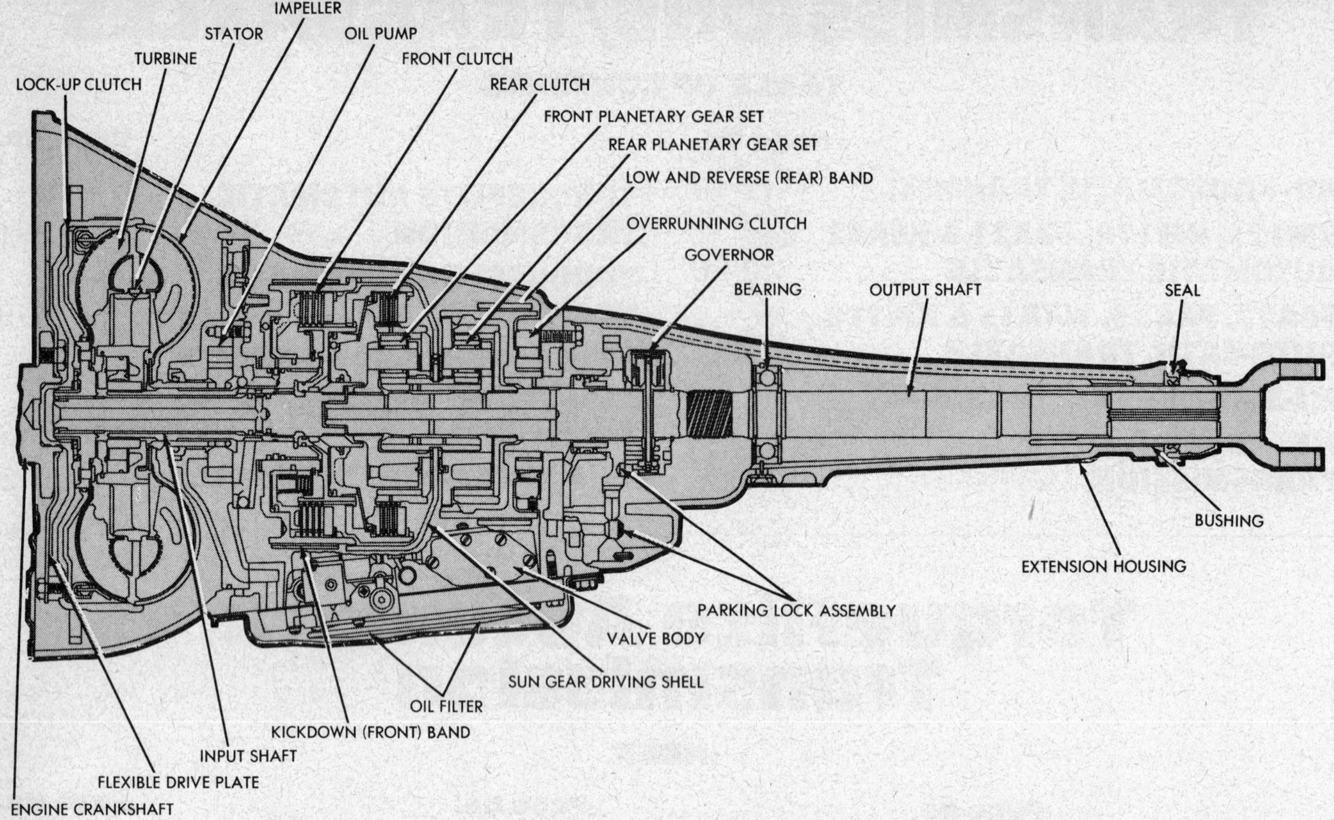


**Fig. 1 Series 904 Torqueflite transmission. 727 models similar**

ternal lock-up mechanism consists of a sliding clutch piston, torsion springs and clutch friction material. The friction material is attached to the front cover, the clutch piston is mounted in the turbine, and the torsion springs are located on the forward side of the turbine. The torsion springs are used to dampen out engine firing impulses, while absorbing the shock loads that occur during lock-up.

When the transmission reaches a predetermined speed, transmission fluid is channeled through the input shaft and into the area between the clutch piston and turbine. The fluid pressure forces the piston against the front cover friction material, locking the turbine to the impeller. When vehicle speed decreases, or the transmission shifts out of direct drive, fluid pressure is released, the clutch piston retracts, and the converter operates in a conventional manner.

Because the lock-up mechanism is completely enclosed within the converter, lock-up converters have a circular decal attached to the front cover stating the converter type and stall ratio.

**Do not attempt to interchange conventional and lock-up convertors. The transmission input shaft and valve body used for lock-up operation are different.**

# MAINTENANCE

## CHECKING OIL LEVEL

To check the oil level, apply the parking brake and operate the engine at idle speed with the transmission in N position.

## CHANGING OIL

Fluid and filter changes or band adjustments are not required for average passenger car use. Severe usage such as police, taxi, trailer towing or prolonged operation in city traffic, requires that fluid and filter be changed and bands adjusted every 15,000 miles.

Whenever the factory fill fluid is changed, only fluids of the type labeled Mopar ATF Plus (Type 7176) should be used. Dexron II automatic transmission fluid should be used only if the recommended fluid is not available.

1. Remove drain plug (if equipped) from transmission oil pan and drain oil. If the oil pan does not have a drain plug, loosen pan bolts and tap pan with a soft mallet to break it loose, permitting fluid to drain.
2. Remove transmission oil pan, replace filter or clean intake screen and pan, adjust bands and reinstall.
3. Add approximately four quarts of automatic transmission fluid through filler tube.
4. Start engine.
5. Allow engine to idle for about two minutes. With parking brake applied, move selector lever momentarily to each position and place in N, then check and adjust fluid level as required.

# TROUBLESHOOTING

## HARSH ENGAGEMENT IN D-1-2-R

1. Engine idle speed too high.
2. Hydraulic pressures too high or too low.
3. Low-reverse band out of adjustment.
4. Accumulator sticking, broken rings or spring.
5. Low-reverse servo, band or linkage malfunction.
6. Worn or faulty front and/or rear clutch.
7. Valve body malfunction or leakage.
8. Throttle linkage sticking or incorrect adjustment.
9. Accumulator broken seal rings, scratched bore, broken or collapsed spring, cracked piston.

## DELAYED ENGAGEMENT IN D-1-2-R

1. Low fluid level.
2. Incorrect manual linkage adjustment.
3. Oil filter clogged.
4. Hydraulic pressures too high or low.
5. Valve body malfunction or leakage.
6. Accumulator sticking, broken rings or spring.

7. Clutches or servos sticking or not operating.
8. Faulty front oil pump.
9. Worn or faulty front and/or rear clutch.
10. Worn or broken input shaft and/or reaction shaft support seal rings.
11. Aerated fluid.
12. Incorrect idle adjustment.
13. Incorrect low and reverse band adjustment.

## RUNAWAY OR HARSH UPSHIFT & 3-2 KICKDOWN

1. Low fluid level.
2. Incorrect throttle linkage adjustment.
3. Hydraulic pressures too high or low.
4. Kickdown band out of adjustment.
5. Valve body malfunction or leakage.
6. Governor malfunction.
7. Accumulator sticking, broken rings or spring.
8. Clutches or servos sticking or not operating.
9. Kickdown servo, band or linkage malfunction.
10. Worn or faulty front clutch.
11. Worn or broken input shaft and/or reaction shaft support seal rings.
12. Aerated oil.
13. Clogged oil filter.

## NO UPSHIFT

1. Low fluid level.
2. Incorrect throttle linkage adjustment.
3. Kickdown band out of adjustment.
4. Hydraulic pressures too high or low.
5. Governor sticking.
6. Valve body malfunction or leakage.
7. Accumulator sticking, broken rings or spring.
8. Clutches or servos sticking or not operating.
9. Faulty oil pump.
10. Kickdown servo, band or linkage malfunction.
11. Worn or faulty front clutch.
12. Worn or broken input shaft and/or reaction shaft support seal rings.
13. Incorrect gearshift linkage adjustment.
14. Governor support seal rings broken or worn.

## DELAYED UPSHIFT

1. Incorrect throttle linkage adjustment.
2. Kickdown band out of adjustment.
3. Governor support seal rings broken or worn.
4. Worn or broken reaction shaft support seal rings.
5. Governor malfunction.
6. Kickdown servo band or linkage malfunction.
7. Worn or faulty front clutch.

## NO KICKDOWN OR NORMAL DOWNSHIFT

1. Incorrect throttle linkage adjustment.
2. Incorrect gearshift linkage adjustment.
3. Kickdown band out of adjustment.
4. Hydraulic pressure too high or low.
5. Governor sticking.
6. Valve body malfunction or leakage.
7. Accumulator sticking, broken rings or spring.
8. Clutches or servos sticking or not operating.
9. Kickdown servo, band or linkage malfunction.
10. Overrunning clutch not holding.
11. Low fluid level.

## ERRATIC SHIFTS

1. Low fluid level.
2. Aerated fluid.
3. Incorrect throttle linkage adjustment.
4. Incorrect gearshift control linkage adjustment.
5. Hydraulic pressures too high or low.
6. Governor sticking.
7. Oil filter clogged.
8. Valve body malfunction or leakage.
9. Clutches or servos sticking or not operating.
10. Faulty oil pump.
11. Worn or broken input shaft and/or reaction shaft support rings.
12. Governor support seal rings broken or worn.
13. Kickdown servo band or linkage malfunction.
14. Worn or faulty front clutch.
15. Incorrect control cable adjustment.

## SLIPS IN FORWARD DRIVE POSITIONS

1. Low oil level.
2. Aerated fluid.
3. Incorrect throttle linkage adjustment.
4. Incorrect gearshift control linkage adjustment.
5. Hydraulic pressures too low.
6. Valve body malfunction or leakage.
7. Accumulator sticking, broken rings or springs.
8. Clutches or servos sticking or not operating.
9. Worn or faulty front and/or rear clutch.
10. Overrunning clutch not holding.
11. Worn or broken input shaft and/or reaction shaft support seal rings.
12. Clogged oil filter.
13. Faulty oil pump.
14. Overrunning clutch worn, broken or seized.
15. Incorrect kickdown band adjustment.
16. Incorrect control cable adjustment.

## SLIPS IN REVERSE ONLY

1. Low fluid level.
2. Aerated fluid.
3. Incorrect gearshift control linkage adjustment.
4. Hydraulic pressures too high or low.
5. Low-reverse band out of adjustment.
6. Valve body malfunction or leakage.
7. Front clutch or rear servo sticking or not operating.
8. Low-reverse servo, band or linkage malfunction.
9. Faulty oil pump.
10. Worn or broken reaction shaft support seal rings.
11. Worn or faulty front clutch.

## SLIPS IN ALL POSITIONS

1. Low fluid level.
2. Hydraulic pressures too low.
3. Valve body malfunction or leakage.
4. Faulty oil pump.
5. Clutches or servos sticking or not operating.
6. Worn or broken input shaft and/or reaction shaft support seal rings.
7. Oil filter clogged.
8. Aerated oil.

## NO DRIVE IN ANY POSITION

1. Low fluid level.
2. Hydraulic pressures too low.
3. Oil filter clogged.
4. Valve body malfunction or leakage.
5. Faulty oil pump.
6. Clutches or servos sticking or not operating.
7. Planetary gear sets broken or seized.
8. Torque converter failure.
9. Incorrect gearshift linkage adjustment.

## NO DRIVE IN FORWARD POSITIONS

1. Hydraulic pressures too low.
2. Valve body malfunction or leakage.
3. Accumulator sticking, broken rings or spring.
4. Clutches or servos sticking or not operating.
5. Worn or faulty rear clutch.
6. Overrunning clutch not holding.
7. Worn or broken input shaft and/or reaction shaft support seal rings.
8. Low fluid level.
9. Planetary gear sets broken or seized.
10. Overrunning clutch worn, broken or seized.
11. Incorrect gearshift linkage adjustment.

**SERVICE BULLETIN:** This condition may be caused by the reaction shaft turning in the reaction shaft support, and blocking the rear clutch passage. When the transmission is disassembled and the rear clutch pack has failed, the reaction shaft and support assembly should be inspected for the following:

a. Reaction shaft turns freely in reaction shaft support.
b. Movement of reaction shaft so rearward end of shaft is not flush with inner surface of support.
c. Reaction shaft bushing damage.
d. Feed holes in reaction shaft blocked.

If any of these conditions exist, the reaction shaft support assembly must be replaced.

## NO DRIVE IN REVERSE

1. Incorrect gearshift control linkage adjustment.
2. Hydraulic pressures too low.
3. Low-reverse band out of adjustment.
4. Valve body malfunction or leakage.
5. Front clutch or rear servo sticking or not operating.
6. Low-reverse servo, band or linkage malfunction.
7. Worn or faulty front and/or rear clutch.
8. Worn or broken reaction shaft support seal rings.
9. Planetary gear sets broken or seized.

## NO LOW GEAR IN D2

1. Governor valve:
   a. Burrs, nicks, scores or binding on weights, shaft and valve.
   b. Collapsed or distorted springs or snap rings.
   c. Cracked or warped body.
   d. Dirty filter.
2. Valve body:
   a. Nicks, scratches or burrs on valves and plugs.
   b. Damaged valve lands or bores.
   c. Collapsed springs.
   d. Damaged or warped mating surfaces.

## DRIVES IN NEUTRAL

1. Incorrect gearshift control linkage adjustment.
2. Valve body malfunction or leakage.
3. Rear clutch worn, faulty, dragging or inoperative.
4. Insufficient clutch plate clearance.
5. Incorrect control cable adjustment.

## DRAGS OR LOCKS

1. Kickdown band out of adjustment.
2. Low-reverse band out of adjustment.
3. Kickdown and/or low-reverse servo, band or linkage malfunction.
4. Front and/or rear clutch faulty.
5. Planetary gear sets broken or seized.
6. Overrunning clutch worn, broken or seized.
7. Hydraulic pressure too low.
8. Valve body: nicks, scratches and burrs on valve and plugs. Rounded edges on valve lands. Scratches on bores, collapsed springs. Nicked or warped mating surfaces.
9. Accumulator, broken seal rings, scratched bore, broken or collapsed spring, cracked piston.

## GRATING, SCRAPING OR GROWLING NOISE

1. Kickdown band out of adjustment.
2. Low-reverse band out of adjustment.
3. Output shaft bearing and/or bushing damaged.
4. Governor support binding or broken seal rings.
5. Oil pump scored or binding.
6. Front and/or rear clutch faulty.
7. Planetary gear sets broken or seized.
8. Overrunning clutch worn, broken or seized.
9. Low fluid level.
10. Clogged oil filter.

## BUZZING NOISE

1. Low fluid level.
2. Pump sucking air.
3. Valve body malfunction.
4. Overrunning clutch inner race damaged.
5. Aerated oil.
6. Governor valve: burrs, nicks, scores or binding on weights, shaft and valve.
7. Collapsed or distorted springs or distorted snap ring. Cracked or warped body. Dirty filter.

## HARD TO FILL, OIL FLOWS OUT FILLER TUBE

1. High fluid level.
2. Breather clogged.
3. Oil filter clogged.
4. Aerated fluid.
5. Clogged lines to cooler.

## TRANSMISSION OVERHEATS

1. Low fluid level.
2. Kickdown band adjustment too tight.
3. Low-reverse band adjustment too tight.
4. Faulty cooling system.
5. Cracked or restricted oil cooler line or fitting.
6. Faulty oil pump.
7. Insufficient clutch plate clearance in front and/or rear clutches.
8. Engine idle too low.
9. Hydraulic pressures too low.
10. Incorrect gearshift linkage adjustment.
11. Kickdown band adjustment too tight.
12. Clogged oil filter.
13. Valve body: Nicks, scratches and burrs on valve and plugs. Rounded edges on valve lands. Scratches on bores, collapsed springs. Nicked or warped mating surfaces.
14. Clogged oil cooler.

## STARTER WILL NOT ENERGIZE IN NEUTRAL OR PARK

1. Incorrect gearshift control linkage adjustment.
2. Faulty or incorrectly adjusted neutral starting switch.
3. Broken lead to neutral switch.
4. Incorrect control cable adjustment.

## SLUGGISH ACCELERATION, EXCESSIVE THROTTLE NEEDED TO MAINTAIN SPEED

1. Low fluid level.
2. Sticking or incorrect throttle linkage adjustment.
3. Faulty torque converter or clutches.
4. Incorrect hydraulic pressures.

## NO LOCK-UP

1. Faulty input shaft, seal ring, locking clutch or torque converter.
2. Sticking fail-safe switch, lock-up valve or switch valve.
3. Faulty oil pump.
4. Leaking turbine hub seal.
5. Sticking governor valve.

## WILL NOT UNLOCK

1. Sticking fail-safe valve, lock-up valve, switch valve or governor valve.
2. Valve body malfunctioning.

## REMAINS LOCKED-UP AT TOO LOW A SPEED IN DRIVE

1. Sticking fail-safe valve, lock-up valve or governor valve.

## LOCKS UP OR DRAGS IN LOW OR SECOND

1. Sticking fail-safe valve.
2. Faulty oil pump.

## STALLS OR IS SLUGGISH IN REVERSE

1. Plugged cooler lines or fittings.
2. Valve body malfunctioning or, faulty oil pump.

## LOUD CHATTER WHILE LOCKING-UP WHEN COLD

1. Leaking turbine hub seal.
2. Faulty torque converter.

## VIBRATIONS AFTER LOCK-UP

1. Throttle linkage improperly adjusted, or sticking governor valve.
2. Engine requires tune up, or otherwise not performing properly.
3. Exhaust system contacting vehicle.

## VIBRATION WHEN VEHICLE IS ACCELERATED IN NEUTRAL

1. Unbalanced torque converter.

## OVERHEATING (OIL BLOWING OUT OF DIPSTICK OR PUMP SEAL)

1. Sticking switch valve.
2. Plugged cooler lines or fittings.

# IN-VEHICLE ADJUSTMENTS

## BANDS, ADJUST

### Kickdown Band

The kickdown band adjusting screw is located on the left side of the transmission case near the throttle lever shaft.

1. Loosen locknut and back off approximately five turns. Check adjusting screw for free turning in transmission case.
2. Using an inch-pound torque wrench, **torque** the band adjusting screw to a reading of 72 inch lbs.
3. Back off adjusting screw 2½ turns.
4. Hold adjusting screw in this position and tighten locknut.

### Low & Reverse Band

1. Raise vehicle, drain transmission and remove oil pan.
2. Inspect fluid for friction material or metal particles which indicate damaged or worn parts.

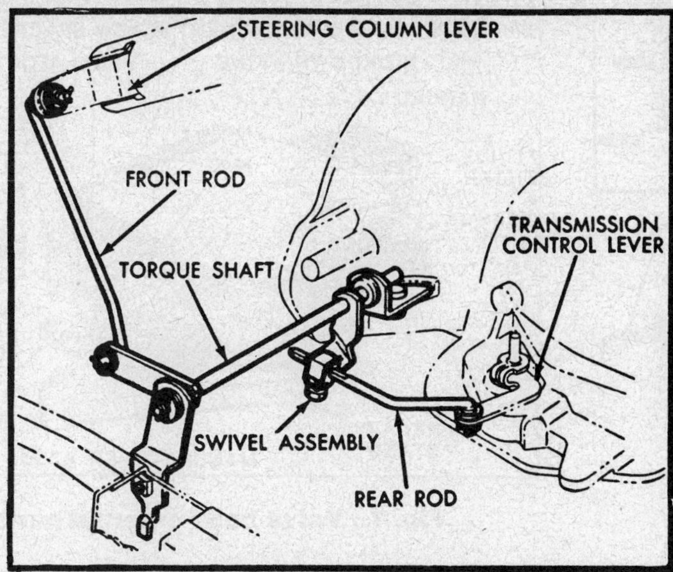


**Fig. 2 Gearshift linkage (typical)**

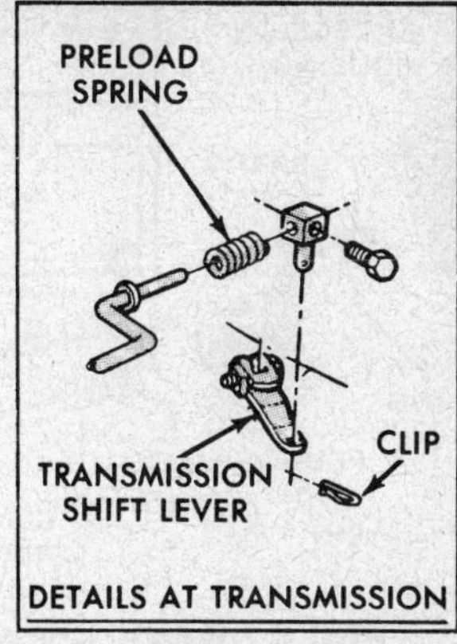


**Fig. 3 Throttle linkage**

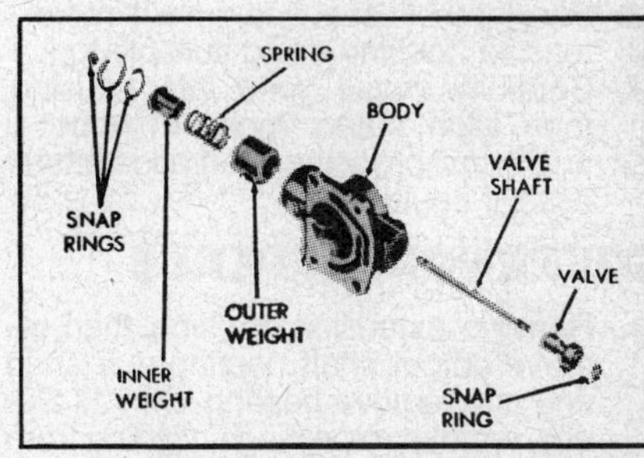


**Fig. 5 Parking lock components**

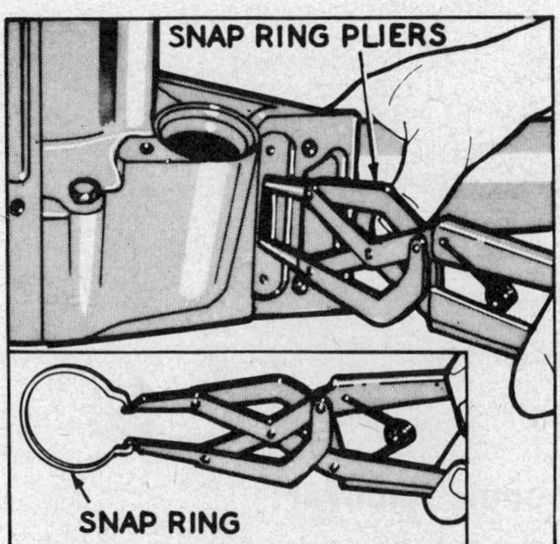


**Fig. 4 Removing or installing extension housing snap ring**

3. Loosen adjusting screw locknut and back off nut approximately five turns. Check adjusting screw for free turning in lever.
4. Using an inch pound torque wrench, **torque** band adjusting screw to 72 inch lbs.
5. Back off adjusting screw 4 turns on A-904 models and 2 turns on A-727 models.
6. Hold adjusting screw and **torque** locknut to 35 ft. lbs., then install oil pan and refill transmission.

## GEARSHIFT CONTROL LINKAGE, ADJUST

1. Loosen adjustable swivel lock bolt, **Fig. 2.**
2. Place selector lever in P and move transmission control lever all the way to rear (in P detent).
3. With both levers still in P position, **torque** swivel clamp screw to 90 inch lbs.

## THROTTLE LINKAGE, ADJUST

**Before proceeding with the adjustment, disconnect the choke rod at the carburetor or block the choke valve wide open. Open the throttle slightly to release the fast idle cam, then return carburetor to the hot idle position.**

Hold or fasten the transmission lever firmly forward against the stop while performing the adjustment to insure a proper adjustment.

1. Support vehicle on hoist and loosen swivel lock screw, **Fig. 3. To insure correct adjustment, swivel must be free to slide along flat end of throttle rod so that preload spring action is not restricted. If necessary, disassemble and clean or repair parts to assure free action.**
2. Hold transmission lever firmly forward against its internal stop and **torque** swivel lock screw to 100 inch lbs. **Adjustment is now finished. Linkage backlash was automatically removed by the preload spring.**
3. Lower vehicle and test linkage operation by moving throttle rod rearward and slowly releasing it making certain that it returns fully.

# IN-VEHICLE REPAIRS

## EXTENSION HOUSING & PARKING LOCK CONTROL ROD, REPLACE

**On some models, it is necessary to unload both torsion bars, remove the left torsion bar, then lower one side of the torsion bar crossmember to provide clearance for extension housing removal.**

1. **On all models,** mark parts for reassembly and remove propeller shaft.
2. Remove speedometer pinion and adapter assembly, then drain about two quarts of fluid from transmission.
3. Remove extension housing to crossmember bolts, then raise transmission with jack and remove crossmember.
4. Remove extension housing to transmission bolts. On console shift models, remove torque shaft lower bracket to extension housing bolts. **On all models, in the following step, the gearshift must be in L therefore positioning the parking lock control rod rearward so it can be disengaged or engaged with the parking lock sprag.**
5. Remove two screws, plate and gasket from bottom of extension housing mounting pad, then spread snap ring from output shaft bearing, **Fig. 4,** and carefully tap extension housing off output shaft bearing.
6. Slide extension housing off shaft to remove parking sprag and spring, then remove snap ring and slide reaction plug and pin assembly out of housing, **Fig. 5.**
7. To replace parking lock control rod, refer procedure outlined under "Valve Body Service."

## OUTPUT SHAFT OIL SEAL, REPLACE

1. Mark propeller shaft to aid in reassembly and remove propeller shaft being careful not to scratch or nick surface on sliding spline yoke.
2. Using a screwdriver and hammer,

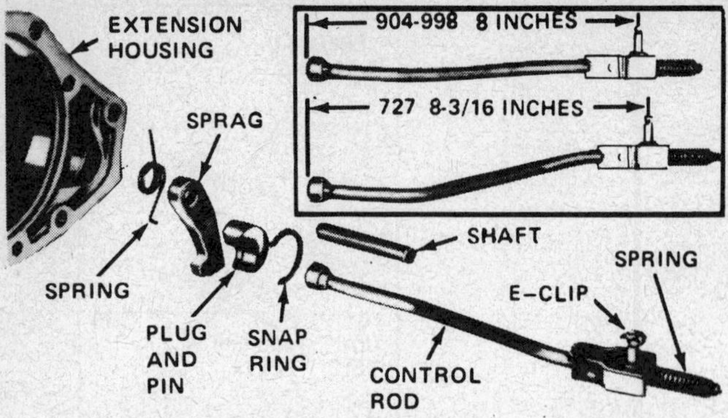


Fig. 6 Governor disassembled

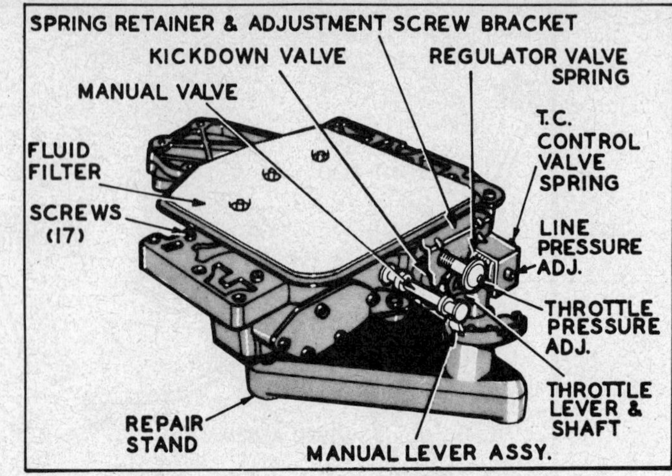


Fig. 7 Valve body external parts

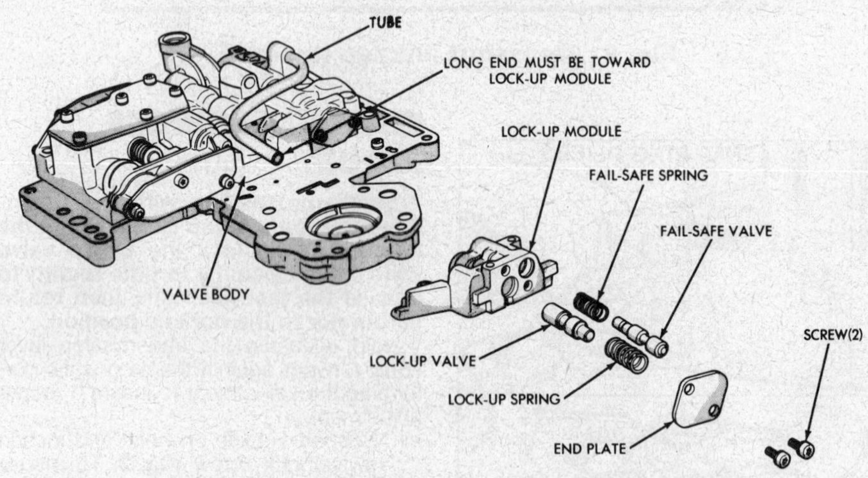


Fig. 8 Lock-up module removal

drive between extension housing and seal and remove seal.

3. Position new seal and drive it into extension housing using suitable tool.
4. Carefully install yoke into housing, then align marks made at removal and install propeller shaft and transfer case, if equipped.

## GOVERNOR, REPLACE

1. Remove extension housing, then remove output shaft bearing rear snap ring and remove bearing. On 727 Series, remove remaining snap ring from shaft.
2. **On all models,** remove snap ring, **Fig. 6,** from weight end of governor valve shaft and remove valve and shaft from governor body.
3. Remove large snap ring from weight end of governor housing, and lift out weight assembly.
4. Remove snap ring from inside governor weight and remove inner weight and spring from outer weight.
5. Remove snap ring from behind governor housing, then slide governor housing and parking brake sprag assembly off output shaft. If necessary, separate governor housing from sprag (four screws) **The primary cause of governor operating failure is due to a sticking governor valve or weights. Rough surfaces may be removed with crocus cloth. Thoroughly clean all parts and check for free movement before assembly.**
6. Reverse procedure to assemble, **torquing** governor body-to-support bolt to 95 inch lbs, and install governor.

## VALVE BODY SERVICE

1. Drain transmission and remove oil pan.
2. Loosen clamp bolts and remove throttle and gear selector levers from manual lever, **Fig. 7.**
3. Remove neutral safety switch and oil filter.
4. Place a drain pan under transmission and remove the ten valve body to transmission bolts. Hold valve body in place while removing bolts.
5. Carefully lower valve body while pulling it forward to disengage parking control rod. **It may be necessary to rotate output shaft to permit parking control rod to clear sprag.**
6. Remove accumulator piston and spring from transmission case. Inspect piston for nicks, scores and wear. Inspect spring for distortion. Inspect rings for freedom in piston grooves and wear or breakage. Replace parts as necessary.
7. Assemble and install valve body, **torquing** valve body attaching bolts to 105 inch lbs.

## LOCK-UP MODULE, REPLACE

1. Remove end plate retaining screws and end plate from module, **Fig. 8.**
2. Remove lock-up spring and valve and fail-safe valve and spring. Tag springs to aid reassembly.
3. Remove lock-up module from valve body.
4. Reverse procedure to install, **torquing** valve body screws to 35 inch lbs.

## TRANSMISSION REPLACE

**The transmission and converter must be removed as an assembly, otherwise, the converter driveplate, front pump bushing and oil seal will be damaged. The driveplate will not support the load; therefore, none of the weight of the transmission should be allowed to rest on the plate during removal.**

1. Disconnect battery ground cable. **Some models will require that the exhaust system be lowered for clearance.**
2. **On all models,** remove engine to transmission struts (if equipped), then disconnect transmission cooler lines and remove starter motor, cooler line bracket and converter access cover.
3. Drain fluid from transmission as outlined under "Maintenance, Changing Oil."
4. Mark converter and driveplate to aid in reassembly. The crankshaft flange bolt circle, inner and outer circle of holes in the driveplate, and the four tapped holes in front face of converter all have one hole offset so these parts will be installed in the original position. This maintains balance of the engine and converter.
5. Remove converter-to-driveplate bolts. Rotate engine clockwise using socket

wrench to gain access to all bolts. **Do not rotate converter or driveplate by prying with a screwdriver or similar tool, as the driveplate might become distorted.**

6. Mark driveshaft to aid in reassembly and remove driveshaft.
7. Disconnect neutral and back-up light switch connector and gearshift and torque shaft assembly from transmission. **When disassembling linkage rods from levers which use plastic grommets as retainers, the grommets should be replaced with new ones.**
8. Disconnect throttle rod from lever at left side of transmission, then remove linkage bellcrank from transmission, if so equipped.
9. Remove oil filler tube and disconnect speedometer cable.
10. Install a suitable fixture or jack that will support engine, then raise transmission slightly with a jack to relieve the load on the supports, and remove the crossmember. **Some models have a torsion bar anchor crossmember that remains in place and requires a careful downward tilt on front of transmission as it is being lowered. If these models have a vibration dampening weight bolted to rear of extension housing, it must be removed.**
11. **On all models,** remove transmission to engine bolts and carefully work transmission and converter assembly rearward off engine block dowels and disengage converter hub from end of crankshaft. Using a small C-clamp on edge of bellhousing, hold converter in place during transmission removal.
12. Remove transmission assembly from under vehicle.
13. Reverse procedure to install, noting the following:
    a. **Torque** transmission-to-engine bolts to 30 ft. lbs.
    b. **Torque** converter-to-driveplate bolts to 270 inch lbs.

## TIGHTENING SPECIFICATIONS

| Component | Torque/Ft. Lbs. |
|---|---|
| Converter Driveplate To Torque Converter Bolt | 270① |
| Cooler Line Fitting | 155① |
| Governor Body To Support Bolt | 105① |
| Kickdown Band Adjusting Screw | 30 |
| Kickdown Lever Shaft Plug | 150① |
| Oil Filler Tube Bracket Bolt | 150① |
| Oil Pan Bolt | 130① |
| Oil Pan Drain Plug | 15 |
| Output Shaft Flange Nut | 175 |
| Output Shaft Support Bolt | 150① |
| Overrunning Cam Clutch Cam Setscrew | 40① |
| Parking Lock Cable Locking Bolt | 10① |
| Parking Lock Cover Pug | 75① |
| Parking Lock lever Shaft Plug | 150① |
| Parking Sprag Cover Bolt | 150① |
| Pressure Test Take-Off Plug | 120① |
| Reaction Shaft Support To Front Pump Bolt | 175① |
| Rear Oil Pump Cover Bolt | 140① |
| Reverse Band Adjusting Screw Locknut | 35 |
| Reverse Band Adjusting Screw Locknut | 25 |
| Speedometer Drive Clamp Screw | 100① |
| Transmission To Engine Bolt | 30 |
| Valve Body Screws | 35① |
| Valve Body To Transmission Case Bolt | 105① |

①—Inch lbs.

# Torqueflite Automatic Transaxle

## INDEX



## IDENTIFICATION

A seven digit part number is stamped on a pad located at the rear of the transaxle on the transaxle oil pan flange. This number must be referred to when servicing the transaxle due to differences in some internal components.

## DESCRIPTION

These transaxles combine a torque converter, automatic 3 speed transaxle, final drive gearing and differential combined into one unit. The torque converter, transaxle and differential assemblies are housed in an integral aluminum diecast housing, Fig. 1. **The differential oil sump is integral with the transaxle sump. Separate filling of the differential is not necessary.**

The torque converter is connected to the crankshaft through a flexible driveplate. Converter cooling is accomplished by an oil-to-water type cooler, located in the radiator side tank. The torque converter cannot be disassembled.

The transaxle consists of two multiple disc clutches, an overrunning clutch, two servos, a hydraulic accumulator, two bands and two planetary gear assemblies to provide three forward and one reverse gear. The sun gear is connected to the front clutch retainer. The hydraulic system consists of an oil pump, and a single valve body which contains all of the valves except the governor valves. Output torque from the main drive gears is transferred through helical gears to the transfer shaft. An integral ring gear on the transfer shaft drives the differential ring gear.

All vehicles except turbocharged models are equipped with a lock-up torque converter. The lock-up mode is activated only in direct drive (3rd gear) and is controlled by the engine control computer. A lock-up solenoid on the valve body transfer plate is powered by the computer to activate torque converter lock-up.

## MAINTENANCE

### ADDING OIL

To check fluid level, apply the parking brake and operate engine at idle speed with transaxle in N or P position. Add fluid as necessary.

### CHANGING OIL

Fluid and filter changes are not required for average passenger car use. Severe usage such as commercial type usage or prolonged operation in city traffic, requires that fluid be changed and bands adjusted every 15,000 miles.

Whenever the factory fill fluid is changed, only fluids of the type labeled Mopar ATF Plus (Type 7176) should be used. Dexron II automatic transmission fluid should be used only if the recommended fluid is not available.

1. Raise vehicle and place a suitable drain pan under transaxle oil pan.
2. Loosen transaxle oil pan attaching bolts and allow fluid to drain, then remove oil pan.
3. Replace oil filter and adjust bands if necessary, then install oil pan and gasket.
4. Add four quarts of approved automatic transaxle fluid through the filler tube.
5. Start engine and allow to idle for at least two minutes, then with parking brake applied move selector lever momentarily to each position. Place selector lever in N or P and check fluid level. Add fluid to bring level to Add mark.
6. Recheck fluid level after transaxle has reached operating temperature. The level should be between Add and Full marks.

## TROUBLESHOOTING

### HARSH ENGAGEMENT FROM NEUTRAL TO DRIVE OR REVERSE

1. High idle speed.
2. Defective or leaking valve body.
3. High hydraulic pressure.
4. Worn or damaged rear clutch.
5. Worn low-reverse band.
6. Planetary gear sets seized or broken.
7. Insufficient clutch plate clearance.
8. Low-reverse band linkage improperly adjusted.

### DELAYED ENGAGEMENT FROM NEUTRAL TO DRIVE OR REVERSE

1. Low hydraulic pressure.
2. Defective or leaking valve body.
3. Low-reverse servo, band or linkage malfunction.
4. Low fluid level.
5. Incorrect gearshift linkage adjustment.
6. Clogged transaxle oil filter.
7. Faulty oil pump.
8. Worn or damaged input shaft seal rings.
9. Aerated fluid.
10. Low idle speed.
11. Worn or damaged reaction shaft support seal rings.
12. Worn or defective front clutch.
13. Worn or defective rear clutch.
14. Overrunning clutch inner race damaged.
15. Insufficient clutch plate clearance.
16. Faulty cooling system.
17. High hydraulic pressure.
18. Governor malfunction.
19. Low-reverse band worn.

### RUNAWAY UPSHIFTS

1. Low hydraulic pressure.
2. Defective or leaking valve body.

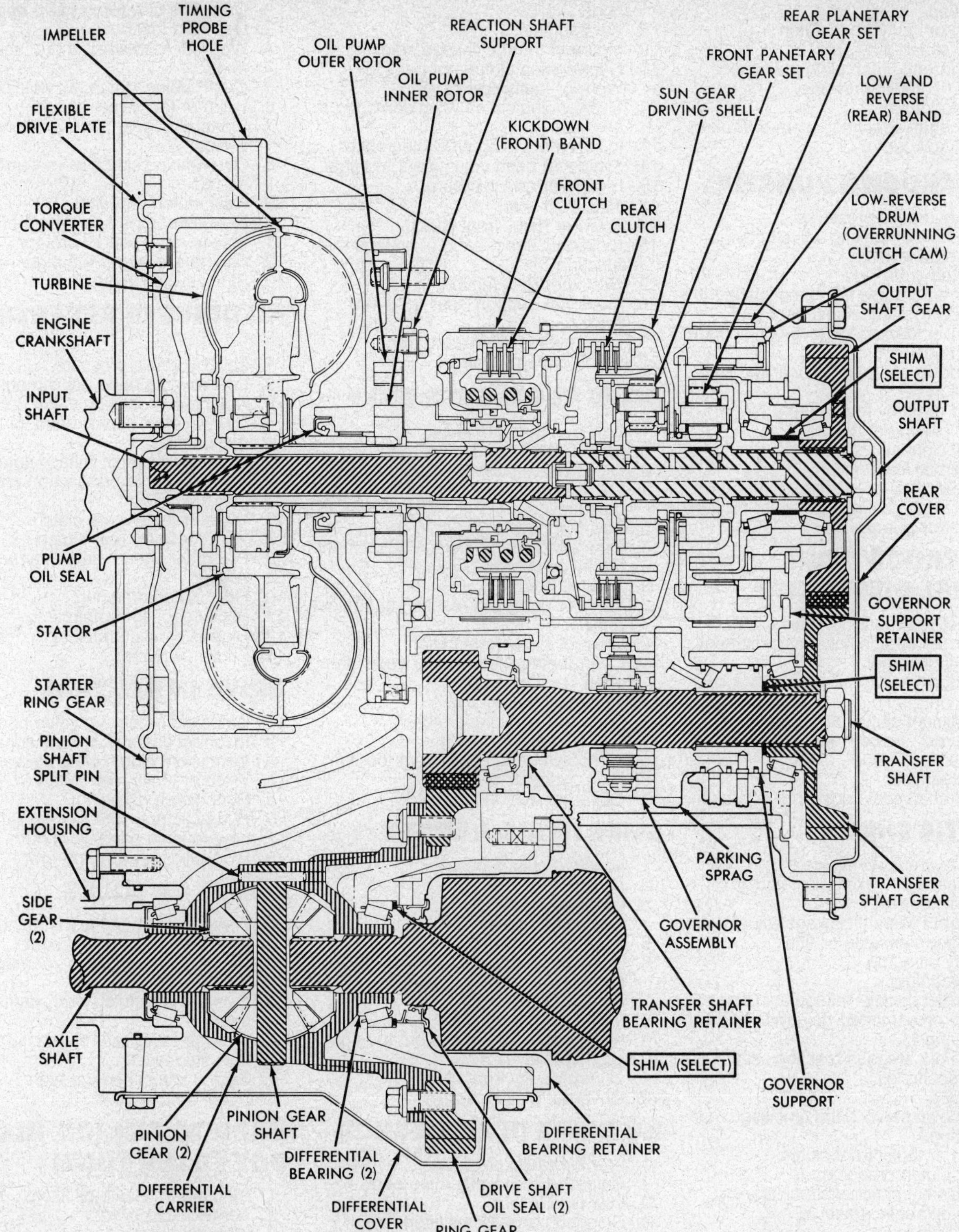


**Fig. 1 Sectional view of Torqueflite automatic transaxle. Typical**

3. Low fluid level.
4. Clogged transaxle oil filter.
5. Aerated fluid.
6. Incorrect throttle linkage adjustment.
7. Worn or damaged reaction shaft support seal rings.
8. Kickdown servo, band or linkage malfunction.
9. Worn or faulty front clutch.
10. Insufficient clutch plate clearance.
11. High fluid level.
12. Governor malfunction.
13. Governor support seal rings worn or broken.
14. Input shaft seal rings worn or broken.
15. Faulty oil pump.

## NO UPSHIFT

1. Low hydraulic pressure.
2. Defective or leaking valve body.
3. Low fluid level.
4. Incorrect gearshift linkage adjustment.
5. Incorrect throttle linkage adjustment.
6. Worn or damaged governor support seal rings.
7. Worn or damaged reaction shaft support seal rings.
8. Faulty governor.
9. Kickdown servo, band or linkage mal-

function.
10. Worn or faulty front clutch.
11. Rear clutch dragging.
12. Insufficient clutch plate clearance.
13. High hydraulic pressure.
14. Aerated fluid.
15. Input shaft seal rings worn or broken.
16. Faulty oil pump.

## 3-2 KICKDOWN RUNAWAY

1. Low hydraulic pressure.
2. Defective or leaking valve body.
3. Low fluid level.
4. Aerated fluid.
5. Incorrect throttle linkage adjustment.
6. Kickdown band adjustment.
7. Worn or damaged governor support seal rings.
8. Kickdown servo, band or linkage malfunction.
9. Worn or faulty front clutch.
10. Rear clutch dragging.
11. Insufficient clutch plate clearance.
12. Governor malfunction.
13. Driveshaft(s) or bushing(s) damaged.
14. Input shaft seal rings worn or broken.
15. Faulty oil pump.

## NO KICKDOWN OR NORMAL DOWNSHIFT

1. Defective or leaking valve body.
2. Incorrect throttle linkage adjustment.
3. Faulty governor.
4. Kickdown servo, band or linkage malfunction.
5. Insufficient clutch plate clearance.
6. Governor support seal rings worn or broken.
7. Aerated fluid.
8. Input shaft seal rings worn or broken.

## ERRATIC SHIFTS

1. Low hydraulic pressure.
2. Defective or leaking valve body.
3. Low fluid level.
4. Incorrect gearshift linkage adjustment.
5. Clogged transaxle oil filter.
6. Faulty oil pump.
7. Aerated fluid.
8. Incorrect throttle linkage adjustment.
9. Worn or damaged governor support seal rings.
10. Worn or damaged reaction shaft support seal rings.
11. Faulty governor.
12. Kickdown servo, band or linkage malfunction.
13. Worn or faulty front clutch.
14. Rear clutch dragging.
15. Insufficient clutch plate clearance.
16. High hydraulic pressure.
17. High fluid level.
18. Governor support seal rings worn or broken.
19. Input shaft seal rings worn or broken.

## SLIPS IN 1, 2 OR DRIVE

1. Low hydraulic pressure.
2. Defective or leaking valve body.
3. Low fluid level.
4. Incorrect gearshift linkage adjustment.
5. Clogged transaxle oil filter.
6. Faulty oil pump.
7. Worn or damaged input shaft seal rings.
8. Aerated fluid.
9. Incorrect throttle linkage adjustment.
10. Overrunning clutch not holding.
11. Worn or faulty rear clutch.
12. Overrunning clutch worn damaged or seized.
13. Insufficient clutch plate clearance.
14. Kickdown band adjustment too tight.
15. High hydraulic pressure.
16. High fluid level.
17. Worn or faulty front clutch.
18. Kickdown servo band or linkage malfunction.
19. Governor malfunction.
20. Governor support seal rings worn or broken.
21. Low-reverse band worn out.
22. Stuck switch valve.

## SLIPS IN REVERSE ONLY

1. Low hydraulic pressure.
2. Low-reverse band adjustment.
3. Defective or leaking valve body.
4. Low-reverse servo, band or linkage malfunction.
5. Low fluid level.
6. Incorrect gearshift linkage adjustment.
7. Faulty oil pump.
8. Aerated fluid.
9. Worn or damaged reaction shaft seal rings.
10. Worn or faulty front clutch.
11. Overrunning clutch inner race damaged.
12. Rear clutch dragging.
13. Worn or faulty rear clutch.
14. Faulty cooling system.
15. Kickdown band adjustment too tight.
16. High hydraulic pressure.
17. Governor malfunction.

## SLIPS IN ALL RANGES

1. Low hydraulic pressure.
2. Defective or leaking valve body.
3. Low fluid level.
4. Clogged transaxle oil filter.
5. Faulty oil pump.
6. Worn or damaged input shaft seal rings.
7. Aerated fluid.
8. Rear clutch dragging.
9. Kickdown band adjustment too tight.
10. High fluid level.
11. worn or faulty front clutch.
12. Governor malfunction.

## NO DRIVE IN ANY RANGE

1. Low hydraulic pressure.
2. Defective or leaking valve body.
3. Low fluid level.
4. Clogged transaxle oil filter.
5. Faulty oil pump.
6. Planetary gear sets damaged or seized.
7. Rear clutch dragging.
8. Kickdown band adjustment too tight.
9. High fluid level.
10. Worn or faulty front clutch.
11. Engine idle speed too high.

## NO DRIVE IN 1, 2 OR DRIVE

1. Low hydraulic pressure.
2. Defective or leaking valve body.
3. Low fluid level.
4. Worn or damaged input shaft seal rings.
5. Overrunning clutch not holding.
6. Worn or faulty rear clutch.
7. Planetary gear sets damaged or seized.
8. Overrunning clutch worn, damaged or seized.
9. Rear clutch dragging.
10. Kickdown band adjustment too tight.
11. Low-reverse band worn out.
12. Engine idle speed too high.
13. Stuck switch valve.

## NO DRIVE IN REVERSE

1. Low hydraulic pressure.
2. Low-reverse band adjustment.
3. Defective or leaking valve body.
4. Low-reverse servo, band or linkage malfunction.
5. Incorrect gearshift linkage adjustment.
6. Worn or damaged reaction shaft support seal rings.
7. Worn or faulty front clutch.
8. Worn or faulty rear clutch.
9. Planetary gear sets damaged or seized.
10. Rear clutch dragging.
11. Faulty cooling system.
12. High hydraulic pressure.
13. Faulty oil pump.

## DRIVE IN NEUTRAL

1. Defective or leaking valve body.
2. Incorrect gearshift linkage adjustment.
3. Insufficient clutch plate clearance.
4. Worn or faulty rear clutch.
5. Rear clutch dragging.
6. Hydraulic pressure too high.
7. Low-reverse band worn out.
8. Hydraulic pressure too low.

## DRAGS OR LOCKS

1. Low-reverse band adjustment.
2. Kickdown band adjustment.
3. Planetary gear sets damaged or seized.
4. Overrunning clutch worn, damaged or seized.
5. Worn or faulty rear clutch.
6. Low fluid level.
7. Engine idle speed too high.
8. Stuck switch valve.

## HARD TO FILL (OIL BLOWS OUT FILLER TUBE)

1. Clogged transaxle oil filter.
2. Aerated fluid.
3. High fluid level.
4. Breather clogged.

## TRANSAXLE OVERHEATS

1. Stuck switch valve.
2. High idle speed.
3. Low hydraulic pressure.
4. Low fluid level.
5. Incorrect gearshift adjustment.
6. Faulty oil pump.
7. Kickdown band adjustment too tight.
8. Faulty cooling system.
9. Insufficient clutch plate clearance.

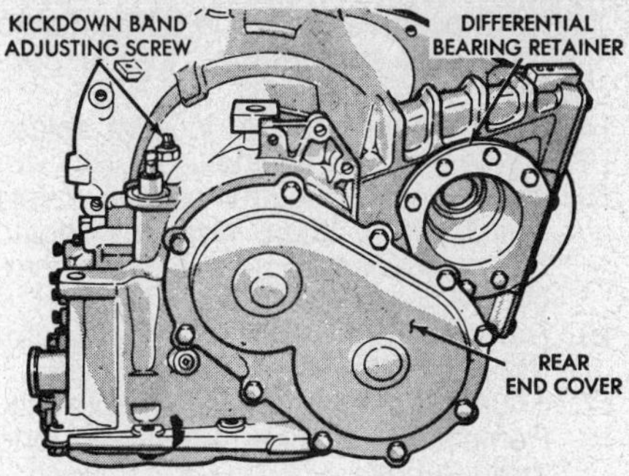


**Fig. 2 Kickdown band adjusting screw location**

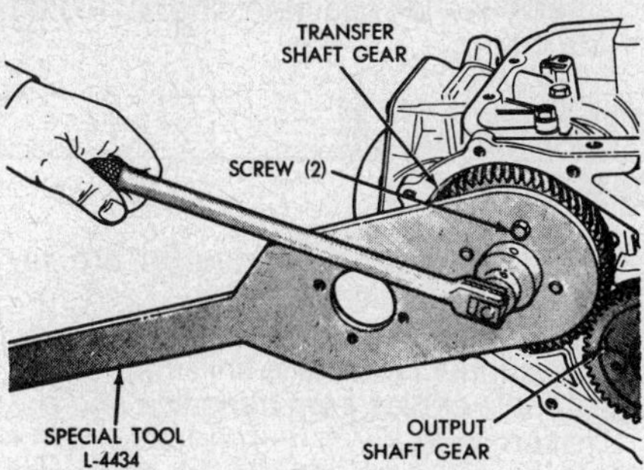


**Fig. 3 Loosening transfer shaft gear retaining nut**

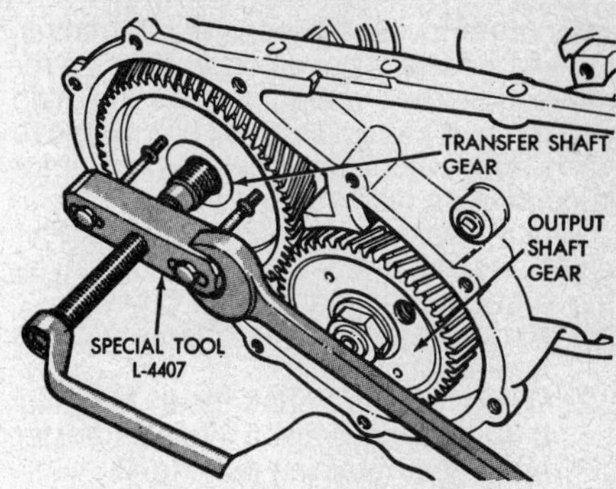


**Fig. 4 Removing transfer shaft gear**

10. Overrunning clutch worn, broken or seized.
11. Planetary gear sets broken or seized.
12. Rear clutch dragging.
13. High hydraulic pressure.
14. Worn or faulty front clutch.
15. Low-reverse servo, band, or linkage malfunction.
16. Defective or leaking valve body.

## HARSH UPSHIFTS

1. Low hydraulic pressure.
2. Incorrect throttle linkage adjustment.
3. Kickdown band adjustment.
4. High hydraulic pressure.
5. Rear clutch dragging.
6. Governor support seal rings worn broken.
7. Driveshaft(s) or bushing(s) damaged.

## DELAYED UPSHIFT

1. Incorrect throttle linkage adjustment.
2. Kickdown band adjustment.
3. Worn or damaged governor support seal rings.
4. Worn or damaged reaction shaft support seal rings.
5. Faulty governor.
6. Kickdown servo, band or linkage malfunction.
7. Worn or faulty front clutch.
8. Driveshaft(s) or bushing(s) damaged.
9. Aerated fluid.
10. Faulty oil pump.

## GRATING, SCRAPING OR GROWLING NOISE

1. Low-reverse band out of adjustment.
2. Kickdown band adjustment.
3. Output shaft bearing or bushing damaged.
4. Planetary gear sets damaged or seized.
5. Overrunning clutch worn, damaged or seized.
6. Worn or faulty rear clutch.
7. Stuck switch valve.

## BUZZING NOISE

1. Defective or leaking valve body.
2. Low fluid level.
3. Aerated fluid.
4. Overrunning clutch inner race damaged.
5. Insufficient clutch plate clearance.
6. Kickdown band adjustment too tight.
7. Faulty governor.
8. Low-reverse band improperly adjusted.

## NO LOCK UP

1. Stuck switch valve.
2. Low hydraulic pressure.
3. Defective or leaking valve body.
4. Low fluid level.
5. Faulty oil pump.
6. Worn or broken input shaft seal rings.
7. Aerated fluid.

# IN-VEHICLE ADJUSTMENTS

## BANDS, ADJUST

### KICKDOWN BAND

1. Loosen locknut and back off nut approximately five turns, **Fig. 2.**
2. Ensure adjusting screw turns freely in transaxle case.
3. Using wrench tool No. C-3880-A and adapter tool No. C-3705 or equivalents, **torque** band adjusting screw to 47-50 inch lbs. If adapter tool No. C-3705 is not used, **torque** adjusting screw to 72 inch lbs.
4. Back off adjusting screw 2½ turns. **Torque** locknut to 35 ft. lbs. while preventing adjusting screw from turning.

### LOW-REVERSE BAND

Before adjustment is attempted, the low-reverse band should be checked for correct end gap as indicated above. To adjust band, proceed as follows:

1. Loosen locknut and back off nut approximately five turns.
2. **Torque** adjusting nut to 41 inch lbs.
3. Back off adjusting nut 3½ turns.
4. **Torque** locknut to 10 ft. lbs.

## GEARSHIFT LINKAGE, ADJUST

When adjusting gear shift linkage, plastic grommets must be replaced.

1. **Set parking brake.**
2. Place selector lever in P position.
3. Raise vehicle, then loosen swivel lock bolt.
4. Move transaxle lever to front detent (P) position.
5. **Torque** swivel lock bolt to 100 inch lbs., then check adjustment. **On models with console shift, apply a minimum forward load of 10 pounds on the console shift lever knob while torquing swivel lock bolt. On some models, it may be necessary to apply the forward load to the transaxle lever while tightening lock bolt.**

## THROTTLE CABLE, ADJUST

1. Perform adjustment with engine at operating temperature, otherwise ensure carburetor is not on fast idle cam by disconnecting choke, if equipped.
2. Loosen cable mounting bracket lock screw.
3. Position mounting bracket with both alignment tabs touching transaxle cast surface.
4. Release cross-lock on cable assembly by pulling the cross-lock upward. **To ensure proper adjustment, the cable must be free to slide all the way toward engine, against its stop, after the cross-lock is released.**
5. Move transaxle throttle control lever fully clockwise against its internal stop, and press cross-lock downward into locked position.
6. **On all models,** reconnect choke, if disconnected, then check cable for freedom of movement by moving throttle control lever.

# IN-VEHICLE REPAIRS

## VALVE BODY, REPLACE

1. Loosen transaxle oil pan attaching bolts and allow transaxle to drain, then remove oil pan.
2. Remove oil filter attaching screws and oil filter.
3. Using a screwdriver, remove E-clip, then remove parking rod.
4. Remove seven valve body attaching bolts, then remove valve body and governor oil tubes.
5. Reverse procedure to install. **Torque** valve body attaching bolts to 105 inch lbs.

## GOVERNOR & TRANSFER SHAFT OIL SEAL, REPLACE

The governor assembly can be removed for reconditioning or replacement without removing the transfer gear cover, transfer gear and governor support. To remove governor, drain transmission fluid and remove transmission oil pan. Remove valve body, unbolt governor from governor support, then remove governor.

When cleaning or assembling the governor assembly, ensure governor valves move freely in governor body bores.

1. Remove rear cover attaching bolts and rear cover.
2. Using transfer shaft gear tool No. L-4434 or equivalent, remove transfer shaft gear retaining nut, **Fig. 3.**
3. Using transfer shaft gear puller tool No. L-4407 or equivalent, remove transfer shaft gear and shim, **Fig. 4.**
4. Remove governor support retainer, then remove low-reverse band anchor pin.
5. Remove governor assembly.
6. Remove transfer shaft retainer snap ring, then using transfer shaft and bearing retainer removal tool No.L-4512 or equivalent and a suitable puller, remove transfer shaft and retainer assembly.
7. Remove transfer shaft retainer from shaft.
8. Using a screwdriver, remove oil seal from transfer shaft retainer.
9. Using suitable tool, tap oil seal into shaft retainer.
10. Reverse procedure to install. **Torque** transfer shaft gear retaining nut to 200 ft. lbs.

## TRANSAXLE REPLACE

**The transaxle and converter are removed as an assembly.**

1. Disconnect battery cables.
2. Disconnect transaxle shift control and throttle cables from transaxle and position aside.
3. Remove upper and lower oil cooler hoses.
4. Support engine with suitable support fixture or engine lifting equipment.
5. Remove three upper bellhousing bolts.
6. Remove hub castle locks, nuts and cotter pins.
7. Raise and support vehicle, then remove front wheels.
8. Remove left splash shield.
9. Remove speedometer adapter, cable and pinion as an assembly.
10. Remove sway bar and both lower ball joint to steering knuckle bolts.
11. Pry lower ball joint from steering knuckle, then remove driveshaft from hub.
12. Remove both driveshafts, supporting both joints at housing.
13. Remove dust cover if equipped, then mark position of torque converter to driveplate and remove torque converter retaining bolts.
14. Remove access plug in right splash shield to rotate engine.
15. Disconnect neutral/park safety switch wire, then remove engine mount bracket from front crossmember.
16. Remove front engine mount insulator through bolt and bellhousing bolts.
17. Support transaxle with a suitable jack.
18. Remove left engine mount and long through bolt.
19. Remove starter.
20. Remove lower bellhousing bolts.
21. Move transaxle away from engine and lower from vehicle. **It may be necessary to pry transaxle away from vehicle between the extension housing and engine block for clearance.**
22. Reverse procedure to install, noting the following:
    a. **Torque** transaxle-to-engine bolts to 70 ft. lbs.
    b. **Torque** starter attaching bolts to 40 ft. lbs.
    c. **Torque** flex plate-to-torque converter bolts to 55 ft. lbs.
    d. **Torque** bellhousing cover bolts to 105 inch lbs.
    e. Fill transaxle to specifications with suitable lubricant, then adjust shift and throttle cables.

## TIGHTENING SPECIFICATIONS

| Component | Torque/Ft. Lbs. |
|---|---|
| Bellhousing Cover Bolt | 105① |
| Connector Assembly Cooler Line | 250① |
| Cooler Hose Connector To Radiator | 110① |
| Differential Bearing Retainer To Case Bolt | 250① |
| Differential Cover To Case Screw Assembly | 165① |
| Differential Extension Housing To Case Bolt | 250① |
| Differential Ring Gear Screw | 70 |
| Flexplate To Crankshaft Bolt | 70 |
| Flexplate To Torque Converter | 55 |
| Front Motor Mount Bolt | 40 |
| Governor Counterweight Screw Assembly | 250① |
| Governor To Support Bolt | 5 |
| Kickdown Band Adjustment Locknut | 35 |
| Left Motor Mount Bolt | 40 |
| Lower Bellhousing Cover Screw Assembly | 105① |
| Manual Cable To Transaxle Case Bolt | 250① |
| Manual Control Lever Screw Assembly | 105① |
| Neutral Safety Switch | 25 |
| Output Shaft Nut | 200 |
| Pressure Check Plug | 45① |
| Pump To Case Bolt Assembly | 275① |
| Reaction Shaft Assembly Bolt | 250① |
| Rear Cover To Case Screw Assembly | 165① |

*Continued*

## TIGHTENING SPECIFICATIONS–Continued

| Component | Torque/Ft. Lbs. |
|---|---|
| Reverse Band Shaft Plug | 5 |
| Speedometer To Extension Screw Assembly | 60① |
| Starter To Transaxle Bellhousing Bolt | 40 |
| Throttle Cable To Transaxle Case Bolt | 105① |
| Throttle Lever To Transaxle Shaft Bolt | 105① |
| Transaxle Oil Pan To Case | 165① |
| Transaxle To Cylinder Block Screw Assembly | 70 |
| Transfer Shaft Nut | 200 |
| Valve Body Filter Screw Assembly | 40① |
| Valve Body Reverse Band Adjusting Locknut | 120① |
| Valve Body Screw Assembly | 40① |
| Valve Body Sprag Retainer To Transfer Case Bolt | 250① |
| Valve Body Transfer Plate Screw Assembly | 40① |
| Valve Body Transfer Plate To Case Screw | 105① |

①—Inch lbs.

# ZF-4 Automatic Transaxle

## INDEX



## IDENTIFICATION

A transaxle identification plate is located on the left side of the case above the oil pan. The information on this plate consists of the build sequence number, manufacturers part number and transaxle type. Refer to these numbers when servicing the transaxle.

## DESCRIPTION

The ZF-4 automatic transaxle, **Fig. 1**, has four forward speeds and one reverse and is used on all Dodge Monaco and Eagle Premier models with V6-180/3.0L engines. Third gear ratio is 1:1. Fourth gear is an overdrive range providing an 0.74:1 gear ratio. **The transmission and differential are not integral and require different lubricants.**

The transaxle consists of a three element torque converter, front mounted oil pump, planetary gear mechanism, roller and sprag clutches, clutch and brake mechanisms and a brake band. The brake band is applied in second and fourth gear ranges by the piston assembly. Transaxle shifting is controlled by a governor valve, a line pressure valve, a throttle pressure regulator valve and a modulator valve. Valve operation is dependent on shift lever position, vehicle speed and throttle position.

## MAINTENANCE

### ADDING OIL

Check fluid level with vehicle cold and sitting on a level surface. With engine idling, shift transaxle through every gear and return to P, then correct level to the Full Cold mark on dipstick.

### CHANGING OIL

The only fluid recommended for use in the ZF-4 transaxle is Mercon automatic transmission fluid. **Do not use any other type of fluid.**

1. Raise and support vehicle.
2. Remove underbody splash shield.
3. Loosen fill tube-to-oil pan attaching nut and drain fluid. Disconnect fill tube from pan.
4. Remove oil pan retaining clamp attaching nuts, then remove retaining clamps and oil pan.
5. Remove oil screen cover bolts, then the cover.
6. Remove oil screen and cover gasket. Clean oil pan, magnet and screen, replacing screen if necessary.
7. Install new O-ring on oil screen. Coat new oil screen cover gasket with petroleum jelly, then install on valve body. Install screen, pressing tabs (Q) into valve body as shown in **Fig. 2.**
8. Install oil screen cover, ensuring oil screen and cover gasket are aligned. Install cover bolts finger tight, referring

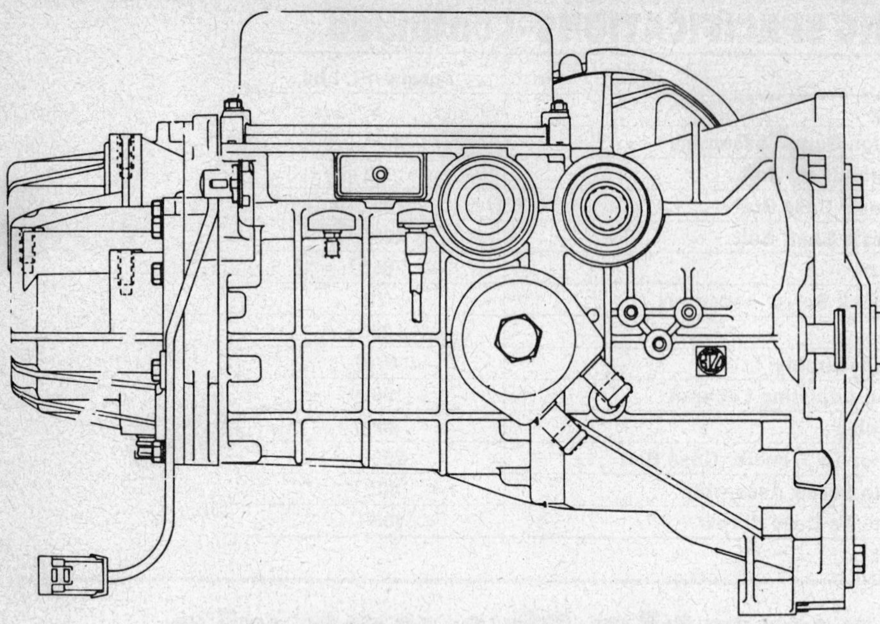

Fig. 1 ZF-4 automatic transaxle

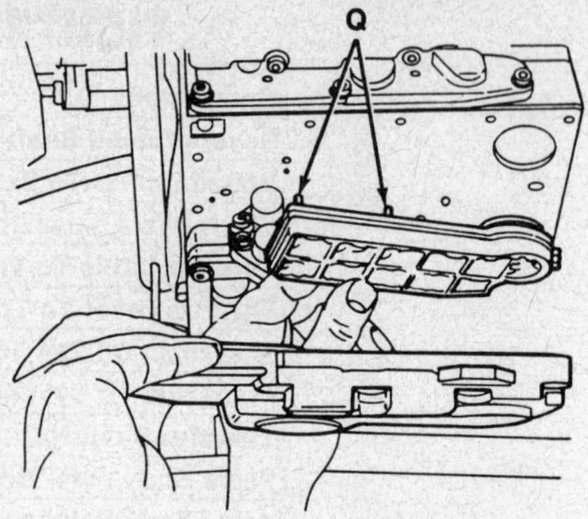


Fig. 2 Installing oil screen

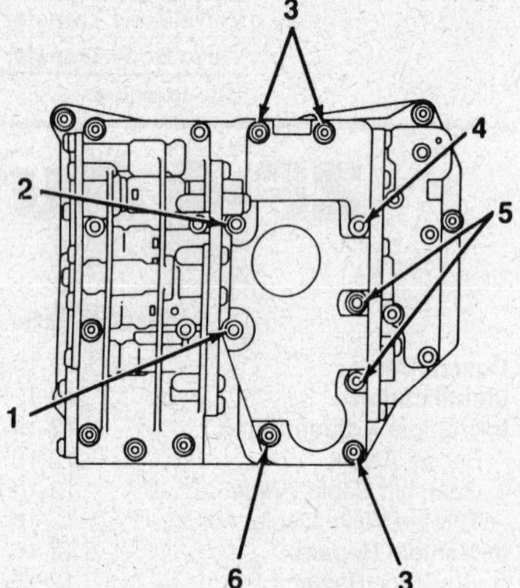


| Bolt No. | Size |
|---|---|
| 1 | M5 x 65 |
| 2 | M5 x 85 |
| 3 | M6 x 75 |
| 4 | M5 x 80 |
| 5 | M5 x 60 |
| 6 | M6 x 83 |

Fig. 3 Oil screen cover bolt installation

to bolt length as shown in **Fig. 3. Torque** M5 bolts to 45 inch lbs. and M6 bolts to 72 inch lbs.

9. Install magnet in oil pan, ensuring it is seated in indentation in pan.
10. Install new gasket on oil pan, then position pan on case. Install pan retaining clamps and attaching nuts on mounting studs. **Torque** clamp nuts to 54 inch lbs.
11. Connect fill tube and attaching nut to oil pan. **Torque** nut to 74 ft. lbs.
12. Install underbody splash shield and lower vehicle.
13. Remove transaxle dipstick and add 2¼ quarts of Mercon automatic transmission fluid through fill tube. Check and adjust fluid level as necessary.

# TROUBLESHOOTING

## DOES NOT ENGAGE IN PARK

1. Shift cable incorrectly adjusted.
2. Excess clearance on detent plate.
3. Detent segment out of position.
4. Park pawl damaged.

## NO REVERSE

1. Shift cable incorrectly adjusted.
2. Oil screen plugged or contaminated.
3. Reverse clutch damaged.
4. First-reverse brake damaged.
5. Governor sticking.
6. Lock-up valve 1 and reverse gear sticking.

## SLIPS ON ACCELERATION FROM STOP

1. 1-2-3 clutch damaged.
2. First-reverse brake damaged.
3. Turbine shaft O-ring or pump starter malfunction.
4. Oil leaking into reverse clutch or piston ring has scored center plate seat.

## CREEPS IN NEUTRAL

1. Shift cable incorrectly adjusted.

## SLUGGISH ACCELERATION, NO POWER

1. Converter valve open.
2. Oil screen plugged.
3. 1-2-3 clutch defective.
4. Roller clutch slips.
5. Shift cable incorrectly adjusted.
6. Throttle or shift valve slipping.

## HARSH ENGAGEMENT FROM NEUTRAL TO DRIVE

1. Accumulator sticking or spring broken.
2. 1-2-3 clutch damaged.

## HARSH ENGAGEMENT FROM PARK OR NEUTRAL TO REVERSE

1. Accumulator inoperative.

## HARSH ENGAGEMENT AT IDLE SPEEDS

1. Accumulator malfunction.
2. Modulator pressure too high.
3. Clutch pack damage.

## NO 1-2 OR 2-1 SHIFT IN DRIVE

1. Governor contaminated, sticking.
2. 1-2 shift valve slips.
3. Forward brake or 2-4 band malfunction.

## NO 2-3 OR 3-2 SHIFT IN DRIVE

1. Governor contaminated, sticking.
2. 2-3 shift valve sticks.
3. 3-4 clutch damaged.
4. Oil supply for 3-4 clutch leaking.

## NO 3-4 OR 4-3 SHIFT IN DRIVE

1. Governor contaminated, sticking.
2. 3-4 valve sticks.
3. Forward brake inoperative.
4. 2-4 band loose.
5. 2-3-4 upshift valve sticks.
6. Position 3-valve sticks.

## NO 1ST GEAR

1. Governor piston sticks.

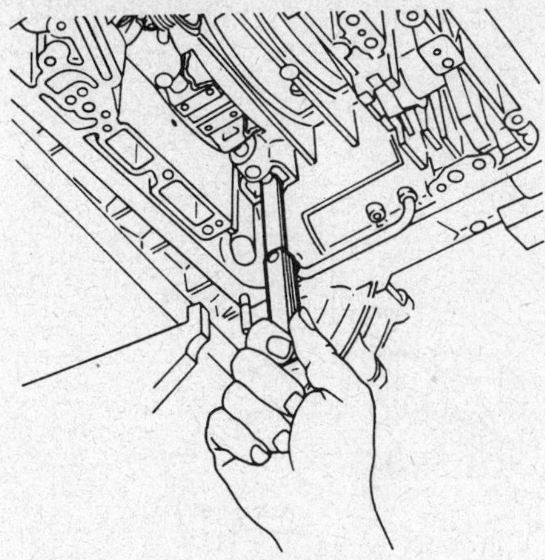

Fig. 4 2-4 band adjustment

2. Leakage in governor assembly.
3. 1-2 shift valve sticks.
4. 2-4 band binds, drags.
5. 2-4 band will not release.

## NO 1ST OR 2ND GEAR

1. Center rectangular ring of governor flange defective.
2. Governor piston sticking.
3. 1-2 and 2-3 shift valves sticking.
4. Closing cap in center plate leaking (reverse clutch always filled with oil).

## SHIFTS 1-3 IN DRIVE, NO 2ND GEAR

1. 2-3 shift valve sticks.
2. 2-3-4 shift valve sticks.
3. 1-2-3 shift valve sticks.

## NO KICKDOWN OR NORMAL DOWNSHIFT

1. Throttle valve cable incorrectly adjusted.
2. Governor sticking.

## KICK DOWNSHIFTS TOO LONG OR HARSH

1. Accumulator malfunction.
2. Modulator pressure incorrect.
3. Clutch pack damage.

## ENGINE OVERSPEED DURING 3-4 SHIFT

1. Orifice control valve sticking.
2. 3-4 traction valve binding.
3. 2-4 band slips.

## ENGINE OVERSPEED DURING 4-3 SHIFT

1. Time control valve and 4-3 downshift valves not coordinated.
2. 1-2-3 clutch damaged.
3. Damper function of 1-2-3 clutch and 4-3 traction valve not functioning properly.

## MANUAL 2ND GEAR DOWNSHIFT, DOWNSHIFT EARLY OR LATE

1. Lock-up valve 2 binding.
2. Governor piston binding.

## NO OVERRUN BRAKING IN MANUAL 1ST GEAR (D1)

1. 2-4 band inoperative.
2. 2-4 band damaged.

## MANUAL 2-1 DOWNSHIFT INCORRECT

**Lock-up valve 1 prevents downshift to 1st gear when speed is 25 mph or more.**

1. Lock-up valve 1 and reverse gear binding.
2. Governor piston binding.

## NO OVERRUN BRAKING IN 1ST GEAR

1. First-reverse brake damaged.

## THROTTLE VALVE CABLE STICKS

1. Cable not attached to cam.
2. Internal friction in cable.
3. Throttle pressure piston sticks.

## NOISY & NO DRIVE OR REVERSE

1. Valve body oil screen plugged.
2. Converter driveplate damaged.
3. Oil pump gears worn or damaged.

## OIL LEAKAGE

1. Oil leaking from converter housing—torque converter leaking at welded seam or pump seal leaking.
2. Leakage between transaxle and oil pan—Oil pan warped, bolts loose or gasket damaged.
3. Leakage between transaxle housing and differential cover—bolts loose.
4. Leakage at transaxle cooler—cooler cracked or split, attaching bolt loose or gasket damaged.
5. Leakage at 2-4 band piston cover—cover O-rings worn or damaged.
6. Leakage from 2-4 band retaining shaft—retaining shaft O-ring damaged.
7. Leakage at output shaft—bolts loose or seal rings damaged.
8. Oil leakage from throttle cable connection in case—cable connector O-ring damaged.
9. Leakage at differential—Output shaft seals or cover seal leaking.
10. Leakage at speedometer sensor—sensor or O-ring damaged.
11. Leakage at breather vents in transmission or differential—transmission or differential overfilled or incorrect fluids used.
12. Leakage at selector shaft—seal ring damaged.

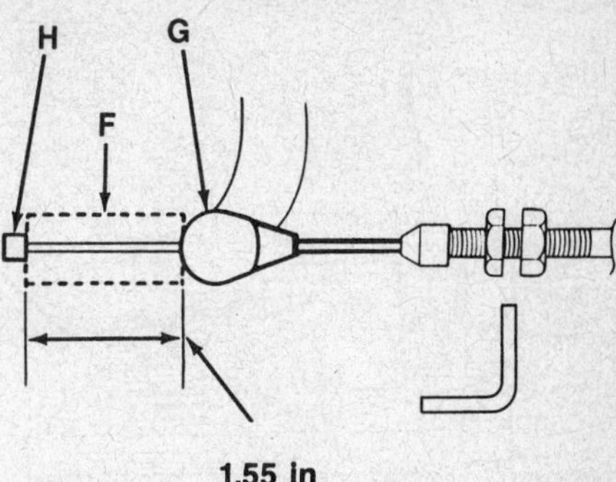


Fig. 5 Throttle valve cable adjustment

## NOISY IN ALL POSITIONS (OIL PUMP)

1. Fluid level too low.
2. Valve body leaking internally.
3. Oil screen plugged.

## NOISY IN ALL POSITIONS

1. Differential or pinion gear bearing adjustment incorrectly set.

# IN-VEHICLE ADJUSTMENTS

## BANDS, ADJUST

### 2-4 Band

1. Remove valve body as outlined under "Valve Body, Replace."
2. Remove band adjusting shim, then measure its thickness.
3. Using a feeler gauge, check clearance between band pin nut and case, **Fig. 4.** Install suitable shim to obtain .049-.059 inch (1.25-1.50 mm) clearance between nut and pin.
4. Install valve body as outlined under "Valve Body, Replace."

## GEARSHIFT CABLE, ADJUST

1. Shift gear selector into P.
2. Raise and support vehicle.
3. Using screwdriver, release cable adjuster clamp.
4. Move gear shift lever into P detent position. P detent is last rearward position.
5. Ensure engagement of park lock by attempting to rotate driveshafts. Driveshafts will not turn when park lock is properly engaged.
6. Lock shift cable into position by pressing adjuster clamp down until it snaps.
7. Lower vehicle. Turn ignition key to L position, then ensure gear selector remains locked in P.
8. Turn ignition key to On position. Ensure engine starts only when shift lever engaged in P or N. **If engine starts in any other position, cable adjustment is incorrect.**
9. Shift gear selector into P. Ensure ignition key can be returned to L position.

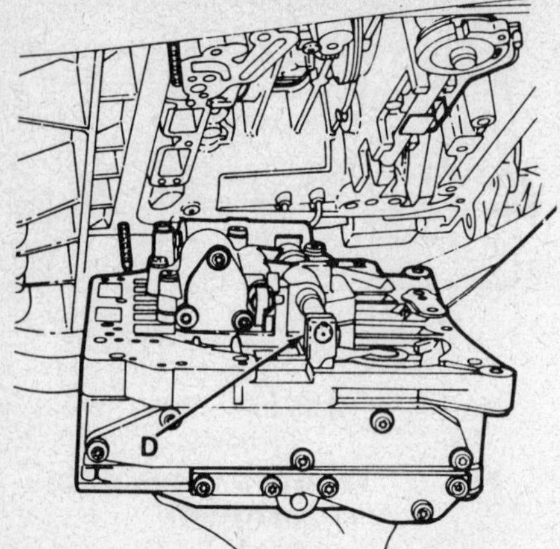


**Fig. 6 Manual valve location**

## THROTTLE VALVE CABLE, ADJUST

1. Loosen throttle valve cable locknuts, then lift threaded cable shank out of engine bracket.
2. Place throttle lever in idle position.
3. Pull cable wire forward, then place 1.55 inch gauge block (F) on wire between cable connector (G) and cable end (H), **Fig. 5.**
4. Pull cable shank rearward to detent position, then insert shank into engine bracket. Tighten locknuts, locking shank into place. **Ensure cable is in detent position, not wide open throttle position.**
5. Remove gauge block and recheck adjustment.

# IN-VEHICLE REPAIRS

## VALVE BODY, REPLACE

1. Shift gear selector into manual first gear position (D1).
2. Raise and support vehicle.
3. Remove underbody splash shield.
4. Loosen fill tube-to-oil pan attaching nut, then drain fluid. Disconnect fill tube from pan.
5. Remove oil pan retaining clamp attaching nuts, then remove retaining clamps and oil pan. **Do not remove oil screen, as valve body is removed with oil screen in place.**
6. Remove valve body attaching bolts, then the valve body.
7. Reverse procedure to install, noting the following:
   a. Place gear shift lever into manual first gear detent (last detent in counterclockwise direction).
   b. Pull throttle cable to wide open throttle position to avoid jamming the throttle cam and piston during valve body installation.
   c. Push manual valve (D), **Fig. 6,** all the way into manual first gear position.
   d. **Torque** valve body attaching bolts to 72 inch lbs.
   e. **Torque** oil pan clamp nuts to 54 inch lbs., **torque** fill tube attaching

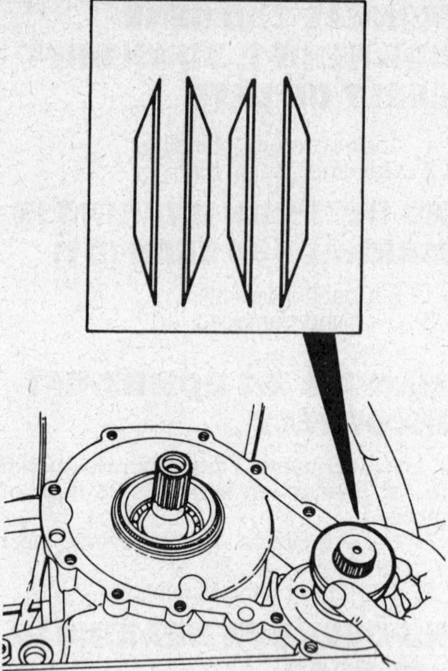

**Fig. 7 Governor spring washers**

nut to 74 ft. lbs.

   f. Remove transaxle dipstick and add 2¼ quarts of Mercon automatic transmission fluid through fill tube. Check and adjust fluid level as necessary.
   g. Adjust throttle valve cable as described under "Throttle Valve Cable, Adjust."

## GOVERNOR, REPLACE

1. Raise and support vehicle.
2. Remove underbody splash shield.
3. Disconnect exhaust pipes.
4. Remove differential drain plug, then drain lubricant.
5. Remove reduction gear case to transaxle attaching bolts, then the reduction gear assembly. Remove gear case gasket.
6. Remove spring washers, **Fig. 7,** noting position for assembly reference.
7. Remove governor cover, then the governor.
8. Remove governor valve attaching bolts, then the valves, **Fig. 8.**
9. Remove one steel and two rubber seals from governor body.
10. Reverse procedure to install, noting the following:
    a. **Torque** governor valve attaching bolts to 8 ft. lbs.
    b. Install new steel and rubber governor seals.
    c. Coat new case-to-transaxle gasket with petroleum jelly and **torque** attaching bolts to 17 ft. lbs.
    d. **Torque** differential drain plug to 18 ft. lbs.
    e. Remove differential fill plug and fill with synthetic type, 75W-140 hypoid gear lubricant. Add lubricant until it flows from fill hole, then install fill plug and **torque** to 37 ft. lbs.

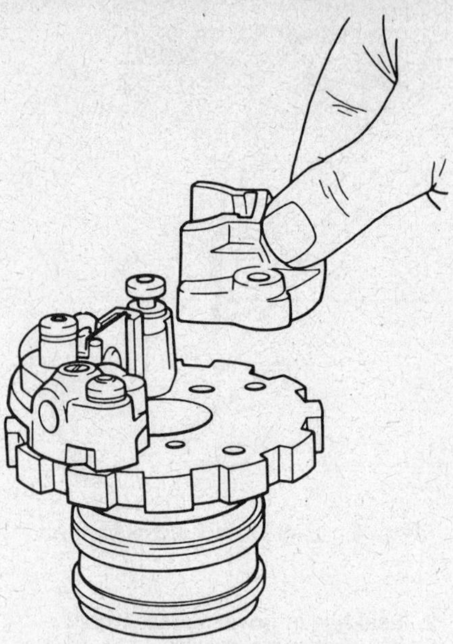

**Fig. 8 Governor valves**

## OUTPUT SHAFT SEAL, REPLACE

### Short Output Shaft

It is necessary to remove differential cover to replace short output shaft inner seal.

1. Raise and support vehicle.
2. Remove differential drain plug, then drain lubricant.
3. Using a suitable punch, remove roll pin attaching driveshaft to output shaft.
4. Using a screwdriver, remove output shaft dust cover.
5. Loosen retaining bolt (C), then pull output shaft and bearing (D) out of differential cover, **Fig. 9.**
6. Using a screwdriver, pry outer seal from cover.
7. Remove differential as follows:
   a. Remove differential fill plug, then the differential cover bolts.
   b. Using suitable jack, raise transaxle as far as possible.
   c. Loosen engine cradle bolts until there is a ½-⅞ inch space between cradle and side sill, as shown in **Fig. 10. Do not completely remove cradle bolts.**
   d. Disconnect oil filler tube, then remove differential cover and ring gear assembly from transaxle case.
8. Using a screwdriver, remove inner seal from case. **Do not damage seal bore with screwdriver when removing seal.**
9. Install new inner seal using seal installer tool No. 6174 and drive handle No. C-6091 or C-4171 or equivalents.
10. Install differential as follows:
    a. Install ring gear assembly.
    b. Install new seal on differential cover, then install cover on transaxle case. **Torque** cover attaching bolts to 17 ft. lbs.
    c. **Torque** engine cradle bolts to 44 ft.

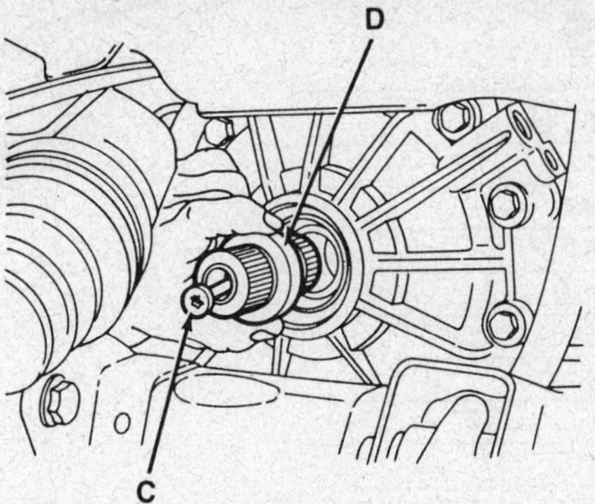


Fig. 9 Removing short output shaft

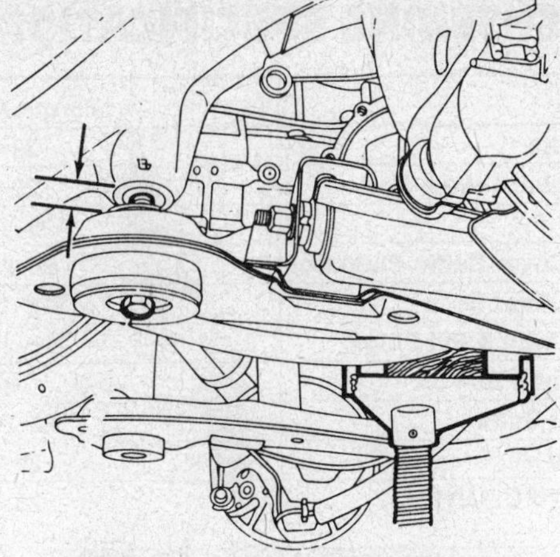

Fig. 10 Lowering engine cradle

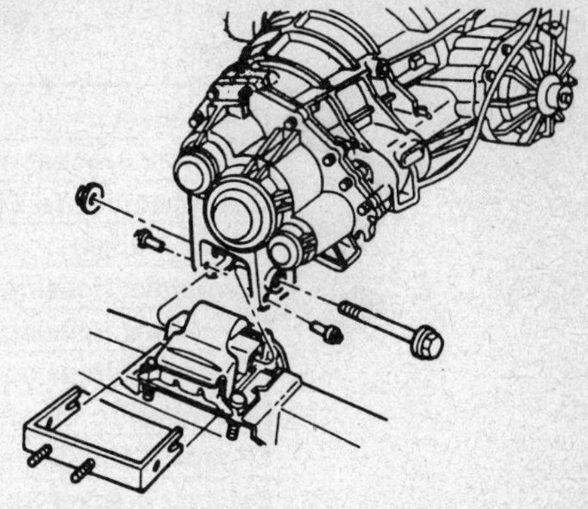

Fig. 11 Rear support bracket assembly

lbs., then remove jack from transaxle.

11. **Ensure output shaft bearing is packed full of suitable grease prior to shaft installation.** Install output shaft and bearing in cover, then install retaining nut and **torque** to 18 ft. lbs.
12. Using seal installer tool No. 6152 or equivalent, install outer seal.
13. Using dust cover installing tool No. 6156 or equivalent and a driver handle, install dust cover over outer seal.
14. Install differential drain plug and **torque** to 18 ft. lbs. Fill differential with synthetic type, 75W-140 hypoid gear lubricant. Add lubricant until it flows from fill hole, then install fill plug and **torque** to 37 ft. lbs.
15. Attach driveshaft to output shaft. Using suitable punch, install driveshaft roll pin.
16. Install underbody splash shield, then lower vehicle.

### Long Output Shaft

1. Raise and support vehicle.
2. Remove differential drain plug, then drain lubricant.
3. Using a suitable punch, remove roll pin attaching driveshaft to output shaft.
4. Using a suitable screwdriver, remove output shaft dust cover.
5. Using seal removal tool No. 6159 and bolt from puller tool No. 6149 or equivalents, remove outer seal.
6. Using snap ring pliers, remove output shaft retaining ring. Remove output shaft and bearing from transaxle case.
7. Using a screwdriver, remove inner seal from case. **Do not damage seal bore with screwdriver when removing seal.**
8. Using seal installer tool No. 6154 or equivalent and a driver handle, install new inner seal.
9. **Ensure output shaft bearing is packed full of suitable grease prior to shaft installation.** Install output shaft and bearing, then the retaining ring.
10. Using seal installer tool No. 6152 or equivalent, install outer seal.
11. Using compressor tool No. 6156 or equivalent and a driver handle, install dust cover.
12. Install differential drain plug and **torque** to 18 ft. lbs. Fill differential with synthetic type, 75W-140 hypoid gear lubricant. Add lubricant until it flows from fill hole, then install fill plug and **torque** to 37 ft. lbs.
13. Attach driveshaft to output shaft. Using suitable punch, install driveshaft roll pin.
14. Install underbody splash shield, then lower vehicle.

## TRANSAXLE REPLACE

1. Disconnect battery cables.
2. Loosen throttle cable adjusting nuts, then remove cable from engine bracket.
3. Raise and support vehicle.
4. Remove front wheel and tire assemblies.
5. Remove steering knuckle-to-strut upper bolts, then loosen, but do not remove lower bolts. **Do not turn bolts,** as they are splined just under bolt head. Hold bolt head with a suitable wrench, then loosen and remove nut. Tilt steering knuckles outward.
6. Remove underbody splash shield.
7. Loosen fill tube-to-oil pan attaching nut and drain transmission fluid, then reinstall nut and **torque** to 74 ft. lbs.
8. Remove both torque converter housing covers, then the converter to driveplate attaching bolts.
9. Using a suitable punch, remove driveshaft roll pins, then disconnect driveshafts from output shafts.
10. Support transaxle with a suitable jack.
11. Remove crossmember-to-side sill attaching nuts.
12. Remove rear cushion to support bracket bolt, then the exhaust pipe bracket attaching bolts, **Fig. 11.**
13. Remove crossmember and rear cushion.
14. Remove support bracket attaching bolts, then the support bracket.
15. Disconnect front exhaust pipe from exhaust manifolds, then remove catalytic converter-to-front pipe attaching nuts. Remove front pipe bracket bolts and nuts.
16. Disconnect oxygen sensor electrical connector.
17. Loosen engine cradle bolts until there is a $1/2$-$7/8$ inch space between cradle and side sill, as shown in **Fig. 10. Do not completely remove cradle bolts or lower cradle more than one inch.**
18. Remove front exhaust pipe.
19. Remove starter attaching bolts, then the starter, plate and dowel.
20. Disconnect shift cable from shift transaxle lever, then remove cable bracket bolts and separate bracket from case. Remove bracket brace rod, then disconnect cable from bracket by squeezing lock tabs.
21. Remove engine timing sensor and attaching bolts.
22. Disconnect and plug transaxle cooler hoses from transaxle cooler.
23. Disconnect speedometer sensor electrical connector.
24. Remove engine-to-transaxle mounting stud nuts and attaching bolts. Pull transaxle away from engine and lower from under vehicle.
25. Reverse procedure to install, noting the following:
    a. Coat torque converter pilot hub with graphite grease prior to installation.
    b. **Torque** engine-to-transaxle attaching bolts, mounting stud nuts and starter attaching bolts to 31 ft. lbs.
    c. **Torque** support bracket to transaxle attaching bolts to 30 ft. lbs. and rear cushion-to-support bracket bolt to 49 ft. lbs.
    d. **Torque** crossmember-to-side sill attaching nuts to 44 ft. lbs. and engine cradle bolts to 92 ft. lbs.
    e. Apply Loctite to driveplate to converter attaching bolts and **torque** to 24 ft. lbs.
    f. **Torque** steering knuckle bolts to 148 ft. lbs.
    g. Fill transaxle with Mercon automatic transmission fluid.
    h. Adjust throttle valve cable as described under "Throttle Valve Cable, Adjust."

## TIGHTENING SPECIFICATIONS

| Component | Torque/Ft. Lbs. |
|---|---|
| Bellcrank Bracket Bolts | 29–33 |
| Crossmember To Engine Cradle Bolts | 29–33 |
| Detent Plunger | 170–184① |
| Differential Housing Cover Baffle Plate Bolt | 84–96① |
| Differential Housing Cover Bolts | 142–158① |
| Differential Housing Drain & Fill Plugs | 170–184① |
| Driveplate To Crankshaft Bolt | ② |
| Engine Timing Sensor Bolts | 68–76① |
| Exhaust Bracket Bolts | 29–33 |
| Exhaust Pipe Flange To Catalytic Converter Nut | 28–32 |
| Exhaust Pipe Flange To Manifold Nuts | 21–25 |
| Fill Tube Bracket Bolt | 12–13 |
| Fluid Cooler Bolts | 22–26 |
| Manual Shaft Lock Plate Bolt | 84–96① |
| Oil Screen Bolts | 43–49① |
| Rear Coverplate Bolts | 142–158① |
| Road Speed Sensor Bracket Bolt | 84–96① |
| Shift Cable Bracket Bolts | 29–33 |
| Shift Cable Bracket Brace Bolts | 168–202① |
| Solenoid Connector Bolt | 84–96① |
| Starter Bolts | 22–26 |
| Starter Shield Nuts | 90–102① |
| Starter Wire Harness Nuts | 75–85① |
| Steering Knuckle Bolts | 140–156 |
| TCU Speed Sensor Bracket Bolt | 84–96① |
| Torque Convertor Bolts | 24 |
| Transaxle Bracket Bolts | 28–30 |
| Transaxle Bracket To Rear Mount Bolt | 46–52 |
| Transaxle Oil Pan Bolts | 84–96① |
| Transaxle Shift Lever Bolt | 96–124① |
| Valve Body Bolts | 43–49① |
| Wheel Lug Nuts | 59–65 |
| Wiring Harness Clamp Bolt | 150① |

①—Inch lbs.
②—40 ft. lbs., then an additional 60°

# AR-4 Automatic Transaxle

## INDEX



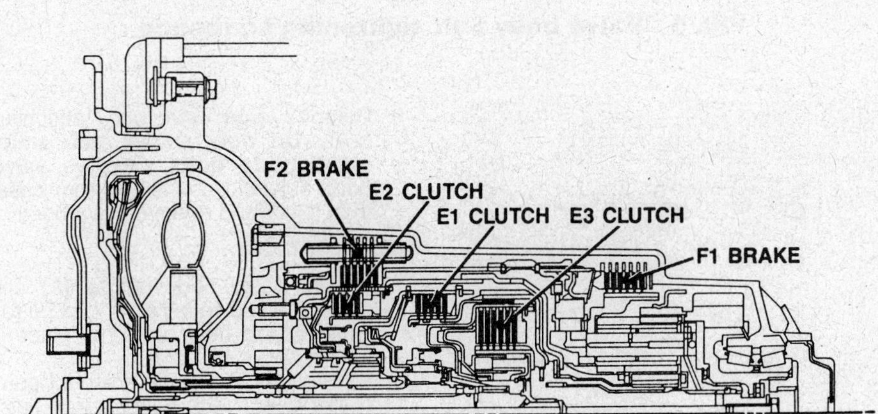


**Fig. 1 AR-4 automatic transaxle**

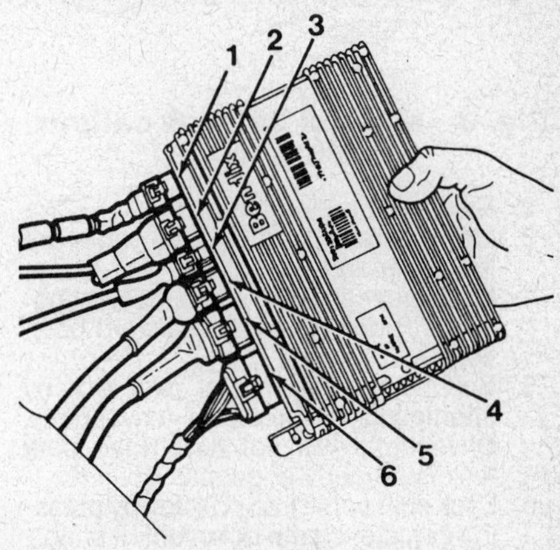


1 - TPS Harness
2 - Speed Sensor Harness
3 - Line Pressure Sensor Harness
4 - Multi-Function Switch Harness
5 - Valve Body Solenoid Harness
6 - Vehicle Wiring Harness

**Fig. 2 Transmission control unit (TCU) & sensor harness locations**

## IDENTIFICATION

A transaxle identification tag is located on the right side of the case next to the oil cooler. The information on this plate provides the fabrication number, manufacturers plant number and transaxle type. Refer to these numbers when servicing the transaxle.

## DESCRIPTION

The AR-4 automatic transaxle, **Fig. 1**, has four forward speeds and one reverse and is used on all Eagle Premier models with 2.5L/4-150 engines. Fourth gear is an overdrive range providing an 0.68:1 gear ratio. **The transmission and differential are not integral and require different lubricants.**

The transaxle consists of a three element torque converter, clutch and brake mechanisms, front mounted oil pump, external oil cooler and an electronically controlled valve body.

The transmission control unit (TCU), **Fig. 2**, controls transaxle shifting. The TCU receives and analyzes input data from the temperature sensor, throttle position sensor, vehicle and engine speed sensors, line pressure sensor and a multi-function switch. Using this data, the TCU transmits shift commands to the valve body solenoids.

## MAINTENANCE

### ADDING OIL

Check fluid with engine idling and vehicle sitting on a level surface. Shift transaxle through every gear and return to P, then correct level to the Full Cold or Full Hot mark on dipstick, depending on fluid temperature.

### CHANGING OIL

Fluid change and oil screen replacement is recommended every 30,000 miles. **Use only Mercon automatic transmission fluid in the AR-4 transaxle.**

1. Raise and support vehicle.
2. Remove underbody splash shield.
3. Remove oil pan drain plug and drain fluid, then remove oil pan bolts and oil pan.
4. Remove two oil screen to valve body attaching bolts, then the screen and gasket.
5. Install screen and new gasket, coating gasket with petroleum jelly. Install screen attaching bolts and **torque** to 46 inch lbs.
6. Clean and dry oil pan, then install new pan gasket. **Do not use any type of sealer on oil pan or gasket.** Ensure gasket mounting spacers are in place, then install pan and attaching bolts, **torquing** bolts to 90 inch lbs.
7. Install new O-ring on oil drain plug, then install plug and **torque** to 177 inch lbs.
8. Install underbody splash shield and lower vehicle. Fill transaxle with Mercon automatic transmission fluid.

## TROUBLESHOOTING

The TCU in the AR-4 transaxle has a self diagnostic program and is programmed for use with the DRB II service diagnostic tester. Use the DRB II tester or equivalent when diagnosis is required, following test equipment manufacturers instructions for diagnostic procedure.

## IN-VEHICLE ADJUSTMENTS

### GEARSHIFT CABLE, ADJUST

1. Shift gear selector into P.

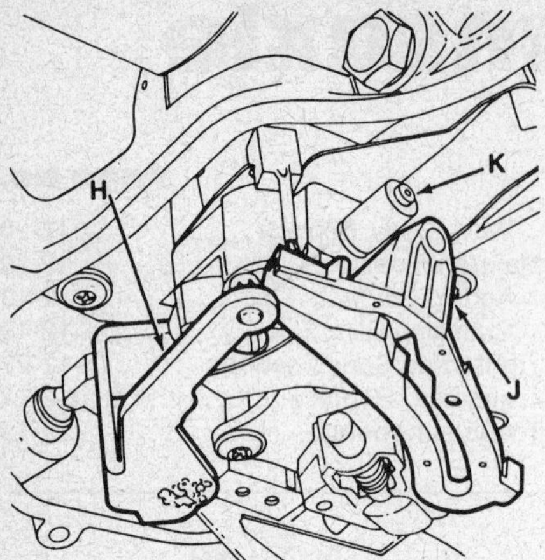


**Fig. 3 Manual valve & caliper removal**

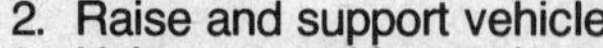

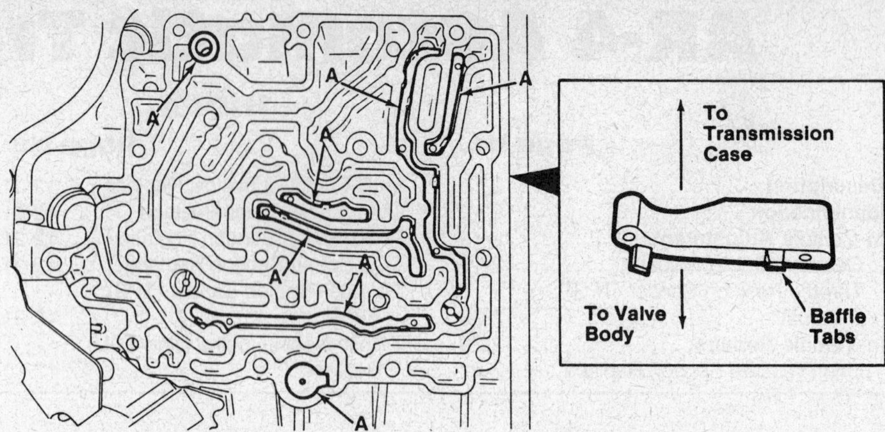


**Fig. 5 Valve body bolt tightening sequence**

2. Raise and support vehicle.
3. Using screwdriver, release cable adjuster clamp.
4. Move gear shift lever into P detent position. P detent is last rearward position.
5. Ensure engagement of park lock by attempting to rotate driveshafts. Driveshafts will not turn when park lock is properly engaged.
6. Lock shift cable into position by pressing adjuster clamp down until it snaps.
7. Lower vehicle. Turn ignition key to L position, then ensure gear selector remains locked in P.
8. Turn ignition key to On position. Ensure engine starts only when shift lever engaged in P or N positions. **If engine starts in any other position, cable adjustment is incorrect.**
9. Shift gear selector in P. Ensure ignition key can be returned to L position.

## THROTTLE POSITION SENSOR (TPS), ADJUST

It is recommended that TPS adjustments be performed using the DRB II tester or equivalent. However, TPS adjustment is possible using a voltmeter No. C4845 or equivalent. **Use the following procedure only if a suitable tester is not available.**

Check input and output voltages at inner four terminal wire connector, marked A, B, C and D. Insert voltmeter test leads through back of wire harness connector. Do not disconnect TPS connector for testing.

1. Disconnect idle speed control (ISC) motor electrical connector. Connect ISC motor exerciser tool No. 7088 or equivalent to ISC motor. Retract ISC plunger until throttle lever contacts idle stop screw and plunger does not contact throttle lever. **Modify electrical connector of tool No. 7088 by cutting a groove in terminal A that is the same size and shape as the grooves in terminals D and B.**
2. Turn ignition key to On position.
3. Check input voltage by connecting negative lead of voltmeter to terminal D and positive lead to terminal A. Note input voltage reading.
4. Check output voltage by disconnecting positive lead from terminal A and connecting it to terminal B. Note output voltage reading.
5. Divide input voltage into output voltage to determine output ratio. Output ratio should be .925-.935.
6. Loosening retaining screws, then pivot TPS to obtain required output ratio as necessary.

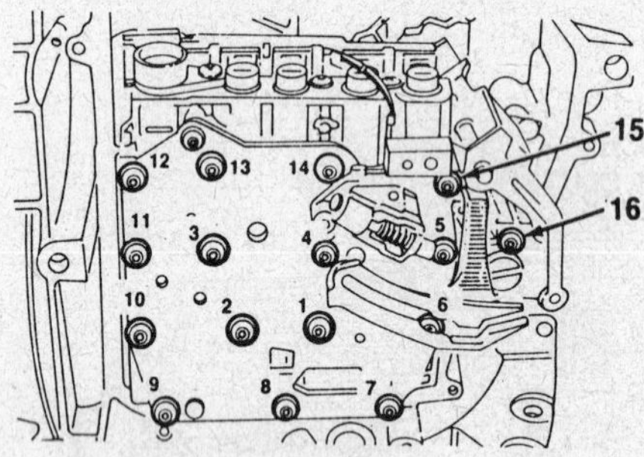


**Fig. 4 Valve body baffle locations**

## IN-VEHICLE REPAIRS

## VALVE BODY, REPLACE

### Removal

1. Raise and support vehicle.
2. Remove underbody splash shield.
3. Remove oil pan drain plug and drain fluid, then remove oil pan bolts and oil pan.
4. Remove two oil screen to valve body attaching bolts, then the screen and gasket.
5. Disconnect solenoid external wire harness connector by squeezing lock ring. **Do not use pliers to squeeze lock ring.** Remove bolt attaching connector to transaxle case.
6. Disconnect shift cable rod from shift lever.
7. Rotate shift arm (H) outward, then disengage caliper (J) from manual valve (K), **Fig. 3.** Remove valve and caliper.
8. Remove large valve body attaching bolts. **Do not remove two small valve body bolts.** Remove valve body solenoid connector from case, then lower and remove valve body.

### Installation

1. Ensure valve body baffles (A) are seated as shown in **Fig. 4.** Use petroleum jelly to hold baffles in place if necessary.
2. Coat new valve body solenoid connector O-ring with transmission fluid, then install it on connector.
3. Raise valve body into position and install solenoid connector into transaxle case. Install valve body attaching bolts finger tight. Ensure valve body is aligned on case, then **torque** bolts to 46 inch lbs. in sequence as shown in **Fig. 5.**
4. Install caliper on manual valve, inserting metal end of caliper first. Swing shift arm over into caliper channel.
5. Install bolt attaching solenoid external wire harness connector to transaxle case, then connect wire harness connector, squeezing lock ring until it snaps into place.
6. Install screen and gasket, coating gasket with petroleum jelly. Install screen attaching bolts and **torque** to 46 inch lbs.
7. Clean and dry oil pan, then install new pan gasket. **Do not use any type of sealer on oil pan or gasket.** Ensure gasket mounting spacers are in place, then install pan and attaching bolts, **torquing** bolts to 90 inch lbs.
8. Install new O-ring on oil drain plug, then install plug and **torque** to 177 inch lbs.
9. Connect shift cable rod to shift lever.
10. Install underbody splash shield and lower vehicle. Fill transaxle with Mercon automatic transmission fluid.

## TRANSMISSION CONTROL UNIT (TCU), REPLACE

1. Remove windshield washer bottle.
2. Unfasten strap that secures TCU to inner fender panel.

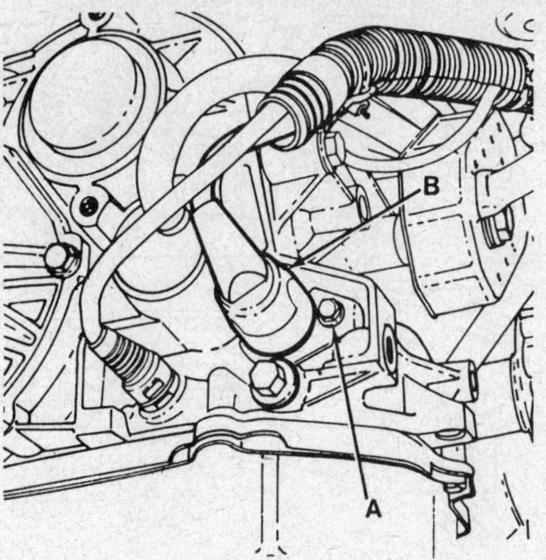


Fig. 6 Multi-function switch

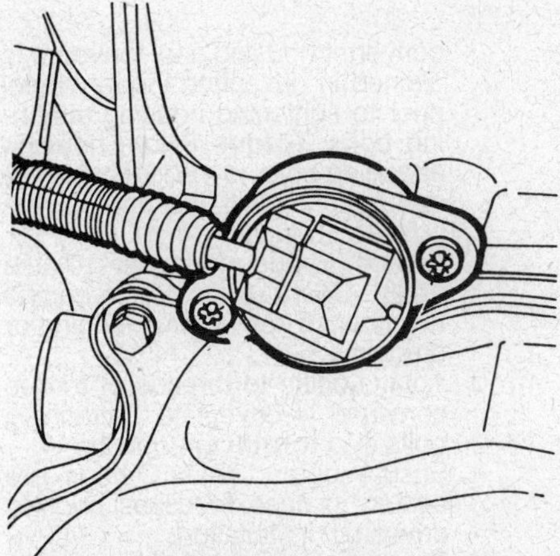

Fig. 9 Line pressure sensor

3. Mark sensor harnesses for installation reference, then disconnect harnesses from TCU, **Fig. 2,** and remove unit.
4. Reverse procedure to install.

## MULTI-FUNCTION SWITCH, REPLACE

1. Raise and support vehicle.
2. Remove switch attaching bolt (A), then pull multi-function switch (B) out of case, **Fig. 6.**
3. Lower vehicle.
4. Remove windshield washer bottle.
5. Disconnect multi-function switch harness (4) from TCU, **Fig. 2,** then remove switch from under vehicle.
6. Reverse procedure to install, coating new switch O-ring with transmission fluid prior to installation. Ensure switch harness is clear of hot or moving components.

## TCU SPEED SENSOR, REPLACE

1. Disconnect TCU speed sensor electrical connector.
2. Remove sensor bracket bolt, then the sensor, **Fig. 7.**
3. Reverse procedure to install, coating new sensor O-ring with transmission fluid prior to installation.

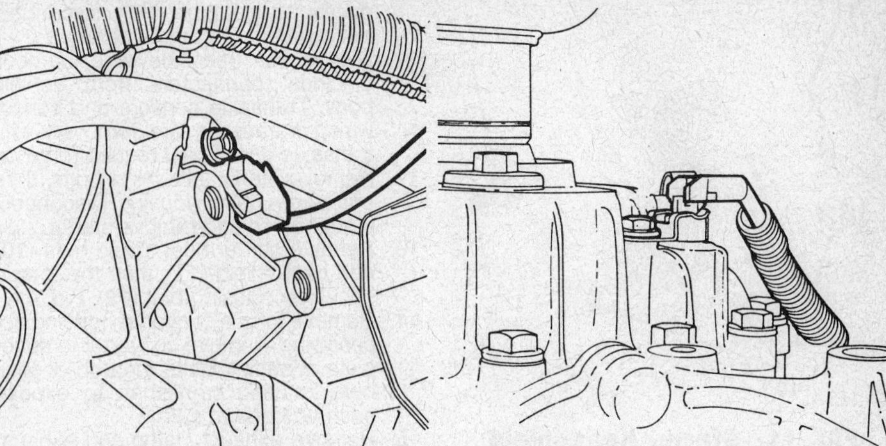

Fig. 7 TCU speed sensor

Fig. 8 Road speed sensor

## ROAD SPEED SENSOR, REPLACE

1. Raise and support vehicle.
2. Remove road speed sensor attaching bolt, then pull sensor out of differential case, **Fig. 8.**
3. Disconnect speed sensor harness (2) from TCU, **Fig. 2,** then remove sensor.
4. Reverse procedure to install, coating new sensor O-ring with transmission fluid prior to installation.

## LINE PRESSURE SENSOR, REPLACE

1. Raise and support vehicle.
2. Remove underbody splash shield.
3. Remove line pressure sensor attaching screws, then the sensor, **Fig. 9.**
4. Lower vehicle.
5. Remove windshield washer bottle.
6. Disconnect line pressure sensor harness (3) from TCU, **Fig. 2,** then remove sensor from under vehicle.
7. Reverse procedure to install, coating new sensor O-ring with transmission fluid prior to installation. Ensure sensor harness is clear of hot or moving components.

## THROTTLE POSITION SENSOR (TPS), REPLACE

1. Disconnect four terminal TPS harness connector from engine harness connector.
2. Remove TPS mounting/adjusting screws.
3. Remove TPS wire harness mounting bracket screws, then the TPS.
4. Reverse procedure to install. Adjust TPS as outlined under "Throttle Position Sensor, Adjust."

## OUTPUT SHAFT SEAL, REPLACE

1. Remove transaxle from vehicle as outlined under "Transaxle, Replace."

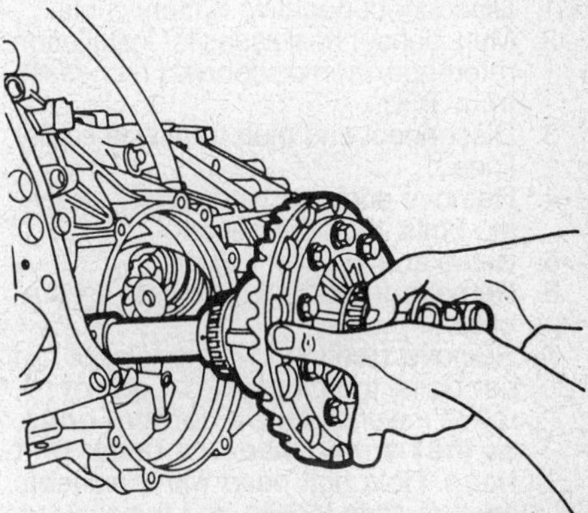

Fig. 10 Removing differential from case

2. Remove differential cover to case attaching bolts.
3. Remove left and right side output shaft O-rings.
4. Pull differential cover from case. **Do not pry cover off.**
5. Using a hammer and a suitable drift, remove left output shaft seal from differential cover.
6. Using seal installer tool No. 6184 or equivalent and a suitable driver handle, install new left output shaft seal. Coat seal lip with petroleum jelly.
7. Remove differential and output shaft assembly from case, **Fig. 10.**
8. Using internal-type puller tool No. 7839 or equivalent and a slide hammer, remove right output shaft seal.
9. Using seal installer tool No. 6185 or equivalent, install right output shaft seal. Coat seal lip with petroleum jelly.
10. Install differential and shaft assembly in case. **Do not damage output shaft seal during differential installation.**
11. Install new O-ring on right output shaft.
12. Install differential cover and attaching bolts. **Torque** bolts to 150 inch lbs.
13. Install new O-ring on left output shaft.
14. Install transaxle as outlined under "Transaxle, Replace."

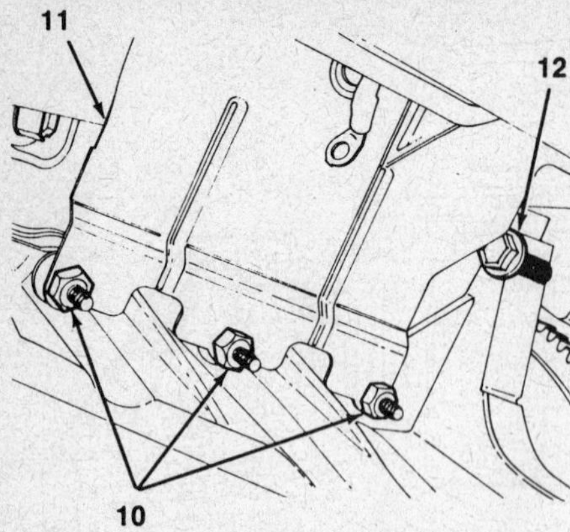


Fig. 11 Starter heat shield

# TRANSAXLE REPLACE

1. Disconnect negative battery cable.
2. Mark sensor harnesses for installation reference, then disconnect harnesses from TCU.
3. Disconnect and plug transaxle cooler lines.
4. Remove engine timing sensor attaching bolts, then the sensor.
5. Raise and support vehicle.
6. Remove front tire and wheel assemblies.
7. Remove steering knuckle-to-strut upper bolts, then loosen, but do not remove lower bolts. **Do not turn bolts, as they are splined just under bolt head.** Hold bolt head with a suitable wrench, then loosen and remove nut. Tilt steering knuckles outward.
8. Remove underbody splash shield.
9. Remove oil pan drain plug and drain transmission fluid, then reinstall plug.
10. Using a suitable punch, remove driveshaft roll pins, then disconnect driveshafts from output shafts.
11. Disconnect transaxle wire harness electrical connectors from vehicle body. Transaxle sensors and sensor wiring harnesses are removed with transaxle and do not require removal.
12. Remove starter attaching bolts, then pull starter out of housing. Disconnect starter wires and remove starter.
13. Remove starter heat shield nuts (10) and heat shield (11), then the torque converter housing bolt (12), **Fig. 11.**
14. Remove torque converter housing access plug. Remove converter to driveplate attaching bolts through access hole, rotating crankshaft to expose each bolt one at a time.
15. Remove exhaust clamp and exhaust bracket attaching bolts, then the bracket.
16. Support transaxle with suitable transmission jack.
17. Remove transaxle crossmember to engine cradle attaching bolts (19). Remove rear mount to crossmember attaching bolt (21), then the crossmember (20), **Fig. 12.**
18. Disconnect shift cable from shift lever. Remove transaxle support brace rod, then the shift cable bracket attaching bolts. Set cable and bracket aside, then remove shift lever and attaching bolts.
19. Remove rear mount bracket to transaxle case attaching bolts, then the bracket.
20. Remove torque converter housing attaching bolts and nuts. Pull transaxle rearward and lower from under vehicle.
21. Reverse procedure to install, noting the following:
    a. Coat torque converter driveplate hub bore with chassis grease prior to installation.
    b. Ensure dowel pins are seated in converter housing and converter is aligned in driveplate trigger wheel prior to tightening housing attaching bolts. **Torque** 8 mm housing attaching bolts to 160 inch lbs., 10 mm bolts to 28 ft. lbs. and 12 mm bolts to 55 ft. lbs.
    c. Ensure torque converter rotates freely. Check transaxle-to-engine alignment if converter is binding or dragging.
    d. Apply Loctite to threads of torque converter-to-driveplate attaching bolts and **torque** to 25 ft. lbs.
    e. Ensure output shaft O-rings are seated in case recesses prior to driveshaft installation.
    f. **Torque** steering knuckle bolts to 148 ft. lbs.
    g. Fill transaxle with Mercon automatic transmission fluid.
    h. Adjust shift cable as outlined under "Gearshift Cable, Adjust."

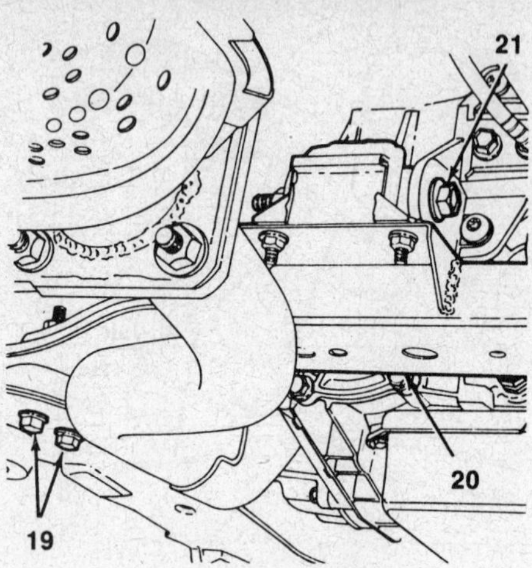


Fig. 12 Removing crossmember

# TIGHTENING SPECIFICATIONS

| Component | Torque/Ft. Lbs. |
|---|---|
| Bellcrank Bracket | 31 |
| Crossmember To Engine Cradle | 31 |
| Detent Plunger | 177① |
| Differential Housing Cover | 177① |
| Differential Housing Cover Baffle Plate | 150① |
| Differential Housing Drain & Fill Plugs | 177① |
| Driveplate To Crankshaft | ② |
| Engine Timing Sensor | 72① |
| Exhaust Bracket | 31 |
| Exhaust Pipe Flange To Catalytic Converter | 30 |
| Exhaust Pipe Flange To Manifold | 23 |
| Fill Tube Bracket | 13 |
| Fluid Cooler | 24 |
| Manual Shaft Lock Plate | 90① |
| Oil Screen | 46① |
| Rear Coverplate | 150① |

Continued

## TIGHTENING SPECIFICATIONS—Continued

| Component | Torque/Ft. Lbs. |
|---|---|
| Road Speed Sensor Bracket | 90① |
| Shift Cable Bracket | 31 |
| Shift Cable Bracket Brace | 185① |
| Solenoid Connector | 90① |
| Starter | 31 |
| Starter Shield | 96① |
| Starter Wire Harness | 80① |
| Steering Knuckle | 148 |
| TCU Speed Sensor Bracket | 90① |
| Transaxle Bracket | 29 |
| Transaxle Bracket To Rear Mount | 49 |
| Transaxle Oil Pan | 90① |
| Transaxle Shift Lever | 110① |
| Wheel Lug Nuts | 63 |
| Wiring Harness Clamp | 150① |

①—Inch lbs. ②—40 ft. lbs., then an additional 60°

# MJ-3 Automatic Transaxle

## INDEX



## IDENTIFICATION

Refer to **Fig. 1,** for transaxle identification. Identification tag is located on bellhousing of transaxle.

## DESCRIPTION

The MJ-3 automatic transaxle has three forward speeds and one reverse and is used on all Eagle Medallion models. The transaxle is electronically controlled by the BVA computer module which is mounted in the engine compartment. The BVA computer interprets information from the road speed sensor, throttle position sensor and the multi-function switch, then converts the information into electrical signals (instructions) to the valve body solenoid valves. These solenoid valves open and close hydraulic passages to change gears.

## MAINTENANCE

### FLUID LEVEL CHECK

The transaxle fluid level can be checked when the fluid is either cold or at normal operating temperature. Check fluid with engine idling and with vehicle on a level surface. Place gear selector into P position and completely apply parking brake. Apply brake pedal and move shift lever through all detents, pausing momentarily in each gear range, then return to P position. Using the dipstick, check fluid level.

With transaxle cold (approximately 60-100°F), fluid level should be between Add and Full marks on the side of dipstick marked Cold. If necessary, add only enough fluid to place fluid level between Add and Full marks. **Do not overfill.**

With transaxle at normal operating temperature (approximately 160-170°F), fluid level should be between Add and Full marks on the side of dipstick marked Hot. Use hot range for reference only. If vehicle has just been driven for a period of time, wait approximately 30 minutes to allow fluid to cool before checking level. If fluid must be added while hot, add only enough to raise level into hot range.

### CHANGING FLUID

Remove dipstick, then the drain plug. Allow fluid to drain as long as possible. Install drain plug using a new seal ring and tighten plug securely. Add fluid through the dipstick tube. Add enough fluid to fill transaxle to proper level. Whenever transaxle fluid is replaced, automatic transaxle fluid additive, part No. 8983 100 034 or equivalent, should be added. This will minimize a fluid foaming condition which occurs during normal vehicle operation. **Do not add more than one bottle of automatic transaxle fluid additive per transaxle fluid change.**

## TROUBLESHOOTING

### CREEP IN NEUTRAL POSITION

1. Incorrect gear selector lever adjustment.
2. Defective E1-E2 clutch assembly.

### CREEP IN DRIVE POSITION

1. Incorrect idle speed adjustment.
2. Incorrectly adjusted or defective accelerator cable.
3. Defective torque converter.

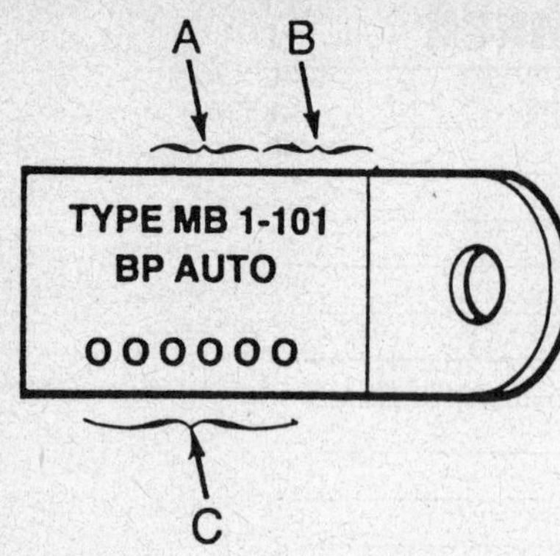


A – Automatic Transaxle Type
B – Type Suffix
C – Fabrication Number

**Fig. 1 Transaxle identification**

## SLIPS DURING DRIVE OR REVERSE

1. Incorrect fluid level.
2. Incorrect fluid pressure (vacuum capsule/modulator incorrectly adjusted).
3. Defective or restricted valve body.
4. Defective or damaged torque converter.

## SLIPS IN DRIVE ONLY

1. Defective or damaged E1-E2 clutch assembly.
2. Worn or damaged free wheel assembly.

## SLIPS DURING SHIFTING

1. Incorrect fluid pressure (vacuum capsule/modulator incorrectly adjusted).
2. Defective or restricted valve body.
3. Restricted oil pump screen.
4. Worn or damaged E1-E2 clutches.
5. Defective F2 brake.

## SURGE DURING DRIVE

1. Incorrect idle speed adjustment.
2. Incorrectly adjusted or damaged accelerator cable.
3. Incorrect fluid level.

## SURGE DURING SHIFTS

1. Incorrect fluid pressure (vacuum capsule/modulator incorrectly adjusted).
2. Defective vacuum capsule (modulator) or hose.
3. Restricted or damaged valve body.

## INCORRECT SHIFT SPEEDS/INTERVALS

1. Incorrectly adjusted or defective accelerator cable.
2. Incorrectly adjusted load potentiometer.
3. Poor electrical connections or defective harness, connectors or grounds.
4. Defective kickdown switch.
5. Defective computer.
6. Defective road speed sensor.

## NO DRIVE IN ANY SHIFT POSITION

1. Incorrectly adjusted gear selector.
2. Incorrect fluid level.
3. Restricted or damaged valve body.
4. Defective oil pump.
5. Restricted oil pump screen.
6. Damaged oil pump shaft or turbine shaft.
7. Defective final drive.
8. Defective converter driveplate or torque converter.
9. Defective E1-E2 clutches.

## NO DRIVE IN D OR 1ST GEAR

1. Defective valve body.
2. Defective E1-E2 clutches.
3. Defective free wheel assembly.

## NO DRIVE IN 3RD OR REVERSE

1. Damaged valve body assembly.
2. Defective E1-E2 clutch assembly.

## NO REVERSE OR ENGINE BRAKING IN 1ST GEAR

1. Defective multi-function switch.
2. Defective valve body.
3. Defective F1 brake.

## NO 1ST SPEED IN DRIVE

1. Poor electrical connections or defective harness, connectors or grounds.
2. Defective solenoid valves.
3. Defective F2 brake.

## NO 2ND SPEED IN DRIVE

1. Poor electrical connections or defective harness, connectors or grounds.
2. Defective valve body.
3. Defective F2 brake.

## NO 3RD SPEED IN DRIVE

1. Poor electrical connections or defective harness, connectors or grounds.
2. Defective computer.
3. Defective solenoid valves.
4. Defective multi-function switch.
5. Defective valve body.

## NO 1ST OR 2ND GEAR HOLD

1. Incorrectly adjusted gear selector lever.
2. Poor electrical connections or defective harness, connectors or grounds.
3. Defective computer.
4. Defective solenoid valves.
5. Defective multi-function switch.
6. Defective valve body.

## REMAINS IN 1ST GEAR w/SELECTOR IN DRIVE

1. Poor electrical connections or defective harness, connectors or grounds.
2. Defective computer.

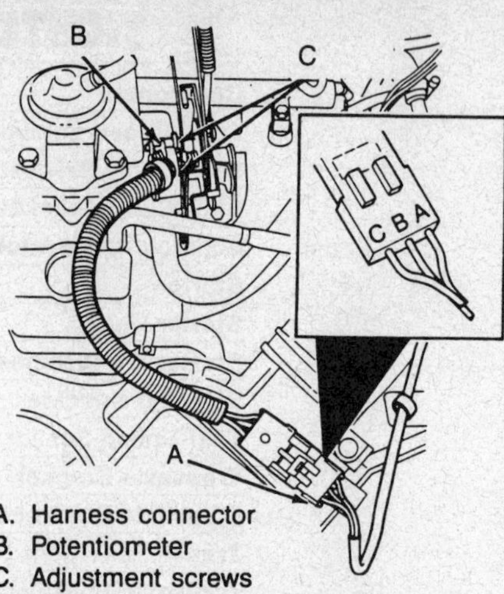


A. Harness connector
B. Potentiometer
C. Adjustment screws

**Fig. 2 Harness connector, throttle position sensor (potentiometer) & adjustment screw assembly**

3. Defective solenoid valves.
4. Defective road speed sensor.
5. Defective valve body.

## REMAINS IN 3RD GEAR w/SELECTOR IN DRIVE

1. Defective fuse.
2. Poor electrical connections or defective harness, connectors or grounds.
3. Defective computer.
4. Defective oil pump.
5. Defective Valve body.

# IN-VEHICLE ADJUSTMENTS

## THROTTLE POSITION SENSOR (TPS), ADJUST

**To perform TPS adjustment procedure, diagnostic tester MS 1700 or equivalent is required.**

1. Verify that throttle is completely opened when accelerator pedal is fully depressed.
2. Turn ignition switch to On position.
3. Check TPS input voltage using a suitable digital volt-ohmmeter as follows:
   a. Insert negative lead of volt-ohmmeter into terminal C of TPS harness connector and positive lead into terminal B of harness connector, **Fig. 2. Do not disconnect harness connector. Insert leads into end of connector and push inward to contact terminals.**
   b. Move throttle plate to wide open position and note voltage reading. Input voltage should be approximately 4.3 volts.
   c. Return throttle plate to closed position.
   d. Remove positive lead from harness connector terminal B and insert it into terminal A.
   e. Move throttle plate to wide open position, then note and record voltage reading.

f. Output voltage should be approximately 3.5-4.5% of the input voltage.
g. Return throttle plate to closed position and determine required TPS output voltage.

4. To determine required TPS output voltage, note example:
   a. Recorded input voltage was 4.2 volts.
   b. 4.2 volts X 4 percent, equals an output voltage of .168 volts.
   c. 4.2 volts X .5 percent, equals an output voltage range variance of ±.021 volts.
   d. Output voltage should be .147-.189 volts.
5. To adjust output voltage, proceed as follows:
   a. Block throttle linkage in wide open position.
   b. Loosen TPS adjustment screws.
   c. Rotate TPS upward or downward to obtain required output voltage.
   d. Tighten TPS screws and check voltage readings. Adjust if necessary.

### SHIFT CABLE, ADJUST

1. If removed, install transaxle right side support bracket attaching bolts and **torque** to 30 ft. lbs.
2. If removed, **torque** two rear engine-to-transaxle cradle attaching bolts to 62 ft. lbs.
3. Unlock cable adjuster clip by popping up the lock tab.
4. Place shift lever in D position.
5. Shift transaxle selector lever completely forward, then back two detent positions.
6. Snap cable end into transaxle outer lever ball stud.
7. With shifter hanging under vehicle, snap adjustment lock into lock position.

## IN-VEHICLE REPAIRS

### SHIFT CABLE, REPLACE

**Removal of the shift mechanism is necessary for this procedure.**

1. Disconnect cable from right side of transaxle support bracket.
2. Using a suitable screwdriver, open bottom shift housing access door.
3. Disconnect cable from lower end of shifter.
4. Remove cable lockpin.
5. Disconnect cable from shifter housing.
6. Reverse procedure to install, then adjust cable.

### MULTI-FUNCTION SWITCH, REPLACE

**This procedure consists of replacing the multi-function switch by cutting the wire harness connecting the computer assembly and multi-function switch. The new multi-function switch service kit includes one multi-function switch with a wire harness and a male connector, one female connector, six male terminals and six seals.**

1. Remove switch from transaxle.
2. Cut harness the same length as replacement harness.
3. On computer side, remove approximately 2.6 inches of outer insulation from cable end. Remove .020 inch of insulation from each wire.
4. Install a seal onto each wire.
5. Install and crimp the six male terminals onto wire ends. **Some computers are connected to the multi-function switch with seven wires. If this is the case, cut yellow or white wire on computer side of harness flush with protective sleeve.**
6. When installing wires into connector, ensure wire color codes are not interchanged.
7. Install connector locking tab.

### ROAD SPEED SENSOR, REPLACE

**This procedure consists of replacing the road speed sensor by cutting the harness connecting the computer and sensor. The new road speed sensor service kit includes one road speed sensor with a wire harness and male connector, one female connector, two male terminals and two seals.**

1. Remove road speed sensor from transaxle.
2. Cut harness the same length as replacement harness.
3. On computer side, remove approximately 1.6 inches of outer insulation from cable end.
4. Remove approximately .20 inch of insulation from each wire.
5. Install a seal onto each wire.
6. Install and crimp two male terminals onto wire ends.
7. When installing wires into connector, ensure wire color codes are not interchanged.
8. Install connector locking tab.

### THROTTLE POSITION SENSOR, REPLACE

1. Remove air filter assembly.
2. Disconnect electrical connector from throttle position sensor.
3. Remove throttle position sensor attaching screws, then the sensor.
4. Reverse procedure to install. Adjust sensor, as required. Refer to procedure outlined under "Throttle Position Sensor, Adjust."

## TRANSAXLE REPLACE

**Install engine support tool No. MS 1900 or equivalent across front of engine compartment. Secure chain around front exhaust manifold port and take up all slack in chain. This will keep engine from tilting forward when transaxle is removed.**

1. Disconnect battery ground cable.
2. Disconnect oxygen sensor electrical connector.
3. Remove hose clamp and tube from lower portion of heat tube.
4. Remove heat tube bracket bolt located at rear of engine.
5. Remove remaining heat tube bracket attaching bolts/nuts, then the heat tube.
6. Remove TDC sensor to converter housing attaching bolts, then the sensor.
7. Remove steering bracket.
8. **On models equipped with air conditioning,** carefully and slowly discharge refrigerant from system.
9. Disconnect and cap air conditioning lines from expansion valve and retainer.
10. **On all models,** remove crossmember to side sill and body attaching bolts.
11. Raise and support vehicle.
12. Remove front tire and wheel assembly.
13. Using ball joint extractor tool No. T.Av.476 or equivalent, disconnect passenger side tie rod ball stud from steering knuckle. Run tie rod ball joint nut to end of ball stud before installing tool.
14. Remove passenger side steering tie rod.
15. Loosen coolant expansion tank attaching strap, then pull tank out of strap and position aside.
16. Remove nuts attaching exhaust pipe to exhaust manifold.
17. Remove two bolts connecting front and rear exhaust pipe sections.
18. Remove front exhaust pipe section from vehicle.
19. Turn crossmember and remove it through wheelwell opening on passenger side of vehicle.
20. Remove steering knuckle upper mount bolt. **Loosen but do not remove lower bolt, as bolts are splined just below the head.**
21. Using roll pin punch tool No. B.Vi.31-01 or equivalent, remove driveshaft roll pins.
22. Swing each rotor and steering knuckle outward, then slide driveshafts off transaxle output shafts.
23. Remove mounting bracket attaching bolts, then the bracket.
24. Disconnect electrical connectors from starter motor.
25. Remove rear starter motor attaching bolts, then the starter and locating bushing.
26. Install driveplate locking tool No. Mot.582 or equivalent, to secure driveplate stationary.
27. Remove torque converter attaching bolts.
28. Remove BVA module from bracket. **Do not remove BVA module from transaxle.**
29. Disconnect and cap transaxle fluid cooler lines from heat exchanger.
30. Disconnect speedometer cable.
31. Using a suitable jack, support transaxle assembly.
32. Lower engine/transaxle cradle by loosening two rear attaching bolts. Lower cradle approximately .590 inch.

33. Using a suitable screwdriver, remove shift cable from shift lever ball stud.
34. Leave shift cable in right side transaxle support bracket, then tie and position bracket aside.
35. Remove ground strap from transaxle.
36. Remove all engine to transaxle attaching bolts.
37. Remove nuts attaching transaxle support cushions to vehicle.
38. Remove bolts attaching two transaxle mount brackets to transaxle, then the brackets.
39. Lower transaxle carefully and guide BVA module and cooler lines out from vehicle.
40. Position torque converter retaining tool No. B.Vi.465 or equivalent, onto front of transaxle to retain torque converter.
41. Reverse procedure to install. Note the following torque specifications:
    a. **Torque** engine to transaxle attaching bolts to 37 ft. lbs.
    b. **Tighten** torque converter attaching bolts to 22 ft. lbs.
    c. **Torque** transaxle mounting bracket bolts to 30 ft. lbs.
    d. **Torque** support cushion attaching nuts to 30 ft. lbs.
    e. **Torque** two rear engine cradle attaching bolts to 62 ft. lbs.
    f. **Torque** cooler lines-to-heat exchanger attaching bolts to 175 inch lbs.
    g. **Torque** upper and lower steering knuckle attaching bolts to 148 ft. lbs.
    h. **Torque** tie rod attaching nuts to 30 ft. lbs.
    i. **Torque** steering tie rods to steering gear bracket attaching bolts/nuts to 25 ft. lbs.
    j. **Torque** steering gear bracket bolts to 30 ft. lbs. **Torque** locknuts to 25 ft. lbs.

## TIGHTENING SPECIFICATIONS

| Component | Torque/Ft. Lbs. |
|---|---|
| Converter To Driveplate Bolt | 20–24 |
| Cooler Line Fitting | 170–180① |
| Driveplate To Crankshaft Bolt | 50–53 |
| Lower Shock Bracket Nut | 143–153 |
| Oil Pan Bracket Bolt | 51–57① |
| Steering Arm Bracket Bolt | 28–32 |
| Steering Arm Bracket Nut | 24–26 |
| Steering Link Ball Joint Nut | 28–32 |
| Tie Rod Bracket Nuts | 24–26 |
| Transaxle Cushion Stud Nut | 28–32 |
| Transaxle To Engine Bolt | 34–40 |
| Vacuum Capsule Hold-Down Bolt | 130–134① |
| Transaxle Mount Bracket To Transaxle Case Bolt | 28–32 |
| Valve Body To Transaxle Case Bolt | 76–84① |
| Wheel Nut | 63–69 |

①—Inch lbs.

# KM171, KM172, F3A21 & F3A22 Automatic Transaxle

## INDEX



## TRANSAXLE IDENTIFICATION

The transmission identification number is located on the vehicle information code plate, which is attached on the fender shield in the engine compartment. The plate indicates model, body code, engine and transmission model number.

## DESCRIPTION

The KM171, KM172, F3A21 & F3A22 are fully automatic three speed transaxles with a lock-up torque converter **Fig. 1.** These transaxles are used on all Colt and Eagle Summit models with 1.5L/4-96 engines and all Colt Vista models.

## TROUBLESHOOTING

### TRANSAXLE

Refer to **Fig. 2** when troubleshooting these transaxles.

### SHIFT LOCK CONTROL SYSTEM

Refer to **Fig. 3,** when troubleshooting the shift lock system.

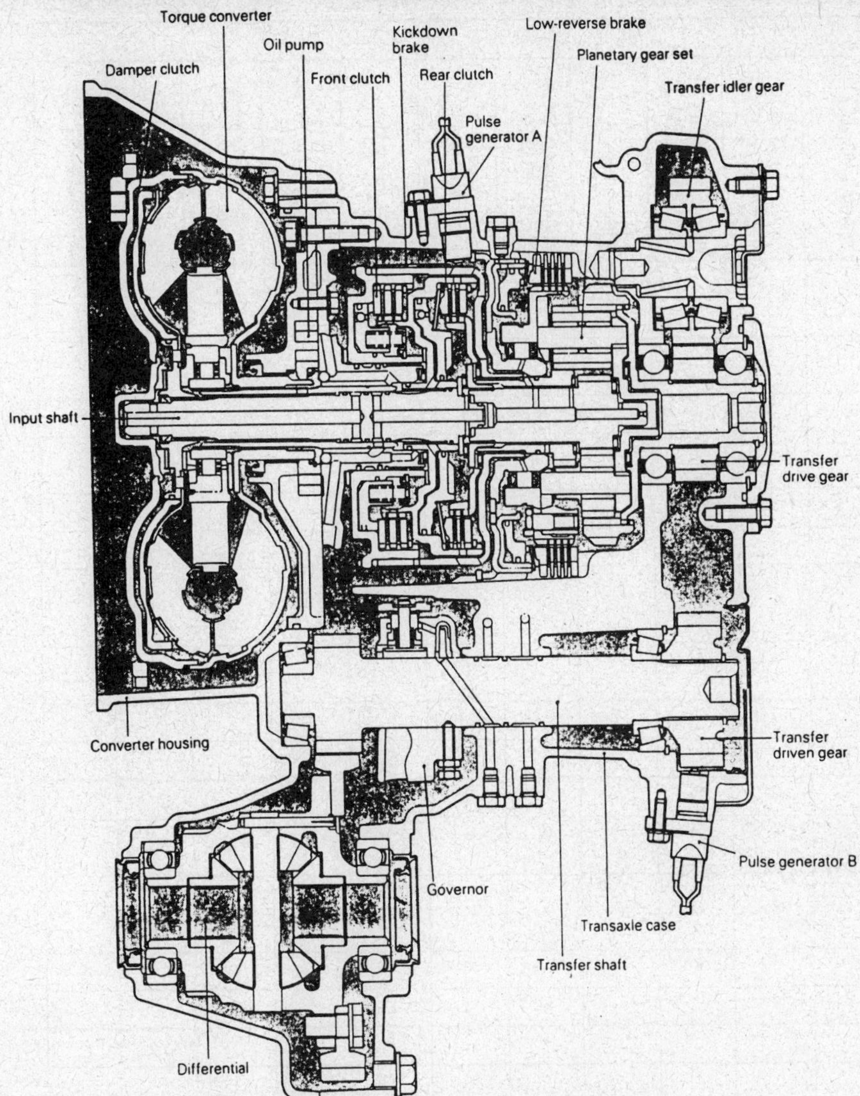


**Fig. 1 KM171 automatic transaxle. (KM172, F3A21 & F3A22 similar)**

# MAINTENANCE

## CHECKING FLUID LEVEL

The vehicle on level surface, start engine and operate at idle speed. With parking brake applied, place selector lever in N, then remove dipstick and check fluid level. Transmission should be at operating temperature when checking fluid level (160-180°F). Fluid level should be between Add and Full lines on dipstick. If necessary, add Dexron II automatic transmission fluid to bring fluid level within Add and Full lines on dipstick.

## CHANGING FLUID

The automatic transaxle fluid should be changed every 30,000 miles on these units. When refilling transaxle, add only Dexron II automatic transaxle fluid.

1. Raise and support front of vehicle, then position drain pan under transaxle and remove drain located at bottom of differential and allow transaxle to drain.
2. Install drain plug, then add 4.2 quarts of the specified automatic transaxle fluid through transaxle dipstick hole.
3. Start engine and check fluid level as outlined under "Checking Fluid Level."

# IN-VEHICLE ADJUSTMENTS

## SHIFT LOCK CABLE

1. With selector lever in "P" position, install end of shift lock cable to shift lock lever.
2. Pull shift lock cable in direction indicated in **Fig. 4** until resistance is felt, then adjust so spring hook projection of shift lock lever is positioned within range "A" in **Fig. 4** relative to spring pin.
3. Move shift lock cable toward lower end of cable attaching bracket and tighten nut.
4. Ensure stop light comes on when brake pedal is depressed.

## THROTTLE CONTROL CABLE, ADJUST

1. Place throttle lever in curb idle position.
2. Raise throttle cable cover (B) upward, then loosen cable lower mounting bracket bolt, **Fig. 5.**
3. Move cable lower mounting bracket until clearance between nipple and top of cable cover (A) is .02-.06 inch, then **torque** cable lower mounting bracket bolt to 9 to 10.5 ft. lbs.
4. With throttle lever in wide open position, pull throttle cable upward to ensure cable has freedom of movement.

# TRANSAXLE REPLACE

## EXCEPT COLT VISTA

1. Disconnect battery cables, then remove battery and battery tray from vehicle.
2. **On turbocharged models,** remove air cleaner case.
3. **On all models,** disconnect kickdown cable from engine and control cable from transaxle.
4. Disconnect inhibitor switch electrical connector, oil cooler lines and speedometer cable from transaxle. **Plug oil cooler lines to prevent contamination.**
5. Disconnect starter motor wiring harness, then remove upper transaxle to engine attaching bolts from transaxle.
6. Remove starter motor attaching bolts and the starter motor.
7. Raise and support vehicle.
8. Remove undercover, then drain transaxle fluid into a suitable container.
9. Disconnect stabilizer bar from lower arm, then unfasten lower arm ball joint connection.
10. Remove right and left driveshafts from transaxle and position aside.
11. Remove bellhousing cover, then the torque converter-to-driveplate attaching bolts. Rotate crankshaft as necessary to gain access to all three bolts. **After removing attaching bolts, push torque converter into transaxle to avoid leaving the converter in the engine.**
12. Support transaxle with a suitable jack, then remove remaining engine to transaxle attaching bolts.
13. Remove transaxle mount insulator bolt, then the mount bracket from transaxle.
14. Slide transaxle to the right, then carefully lower assembly from vehicle.
15. Reverse procedure to install. Install torque converter first to the transaxle, then to the engine.

## COLT VISTA

1. Drain transaxle fluid into a suitable container, then remove transaxle oil level gauge.
2. Disconnect battery cables, then remove battery and battery tray.
3. Remove air cleaner assembly and

| Probable cause | | Symptom: Driving impossible or abnormal (before start) | | | | | | | | | | |
|---|---|---|---|---|---|---|---|---|---|---|---|---|
| | | Starter inoperative | Forward drive impossible | Reverse drive impossible | Engine stalls when shifting from "N" to "D", "R" | Clutch slips in "D" position (stall rpm too high) | Clutch slips in "R" position (stall rpm too high) | Stall rpm too low | Vehicle starts to move in "P" or "N" position | Vehicle starts to move in position midway of "N" and "R" or "N" and "D" | Parking mechanism does not work | Abnormal shock felt when selecting "D", "2", "L" or "R" |
| Engine | 1 Idling rpm abnormal | | | | ⊗ | | | | | | | X |
| Engine | 2 Performance failure | | | | X | | | X | | | | |
| Engine | 3 Throttle control cable inadequately adjusted | | X | X | | X | X | X | | | | X |
| Transaxle proper (power train) | 4 Manual linkage inadequately adjusted | X | ⊗ | ⊗ | | ⊗ | ⊗ | | ⊗ | ⊗ | ⊗ | ⊗ |
| Transaxle proper (power train) | 5 Torque converter failure (including damper clutch for KM171 only) | | X | X | | | | X | | | | |
| Transaxle proper (power train) | 6 Oil pump failure | | X | X | | X | X | | | | | |
| Transaxle proper (power train) | 7 One way clutch failure | | X | | | X | | | | | | |
| Transaxle proper (power train) | 8 Damaged or worn gear or other rotating parts, shim preload inadequately adjusted | | | | | | | | | | | |
| Transaxle proper (power train) | 9 Insufficiently tightened center support | | X | X | | | X | | | | | |
| Transaxle proper (power train) | 10 Parking mechanism failure | | | | | | | | X | | X | |
| Transaxle proper (power train) | 11 Cracked drive plate or loose bolt | | | | | | | | | | | |
| Hydraulic system (including friction elements) | 12 Low fluid level | | ⊗ | ⊗ | | X | X | | | | | |
| Hydraulic system (including friction elements) | 13 Low line pressure (broken seal, leaks, looseness, etc.) | | ⊗ | ⊗ | | ⊗ | ⊗ | | | | | |
| Hydraulic system (including friction elements) | 14 Faulty valve body (valve sticking, poor machining, blowhole, poor adjustment, etc.) | | ⊗ | ⊗ | X | X | X | | X | X | | X |
| Hydraulic system (including friction elements) | 15 Faulty front clutch, piston | | | X | | | X | | | | | X |
| Hydraulic system (including friction elements) | 16 Faulty rear clutch, piston | | ⊗ | | | X | | | | | | X |
| Hydraulic system (including friction elements) | 17 Faulty kickdown band or piston | | | | | | | | | | | |
| Hydraulic system (including friction elements) | 18 Kickdown servo poorly adjusted | | | | | | | | | | | |
| Hydraulic system (including friction elements) | 19 Faulty low reverse brake, piston | | | X | | | | | | | | X |
| Hydraulic system (including friction elements) | 20 O-ring missing in low reverse brake circuit between valve body and case | | | X | | | | | | | | |
| Hydraulic system (including friction elements) | 21 Governor failure | | | | | | | | | | | |
| Electronic control system | 22 Faulty inhibitor switch, open wire, poor adjustemnt | X | | | | | | | | X | | |
| Electronic control system | 23* Faulty throttle position sensor, poor adjustment | | | | | | | | | | | |
| Electronic control system | 24* Pulse generator (A) open wire or shorting | | | | | | | | | | | |
| Electronic control system | 25* Pulse generator (B) open wire or shorting | | | | | | | | | | | |
| Electronic control system | 26* Faulty ignition signal system | | | | | | | | | | | |
| Electronic control system | 27* Damper clutch control solenoid valve open wire (valve closed) | | | | | | | | | | | |
| Electronic control system | 28* Damper clutch solenoid valve shorting, sticking (valve open) | | | | ⊗ | | | | | | | |
| Electronic control system | 29* Coolant temperature sensor faulty | | | | | | | | | | | |
| Electronic control system | 30* Faulty control unit | | | | | | | | | | | |

Remarks: * KM171 only.
⊗ indicates items to be given high priority in inspection.

**Fig. 2 Transaxle troubleshooting chart**

| Symptom | Probable cause | Remedy |
|---|---|---|
| The selector lever can be operated from "P" to "R" without depressing the brake pedal when the ignition key is in the ACC position. | • Damaged shift lock lever, foreign matter caught in the mechanism<br>• Poorly adjusted shift lock cable, broken or disconnected cable<br>• Broken or fatigued return spring of shift lock cable (shift lock lever side) | • Check selector lever bracket assembly and replace if necessary.<br>• Check, adjust or replace shift lock cable. |
| The selector lever cannot be moved from "P" to "R" when the brake pedal is depressed with the ignition key in the ACC position. | • Faulty selector lever assembly<br>• Shift lock cable, key interlock cable, automatic transaxle control cable binding<br>• Poor routing of shift lock cable, key interlock cable<br>• Broken or fatigued return spring of shift lock cable (brake pedal side) | • Check selector lever bracket assembly and replace if necessary.<br>• Check, adjust or replace shift lock cable and key interlock cable.<br>• Check routing of cables.<br>• Replace shift lock cable. |
| The selector lever can be moved from "P" to "R" when the brake pedal is depressed even though the ignition key is in the LOCK position | • Deformed, damaged or worn interlock cam or interlock lever<br>• Poorly adjusted, broken, stretched or disconnected key interlock cable | • Check interlock cam and interlock lever or replace selector lever bracket assembly.<br>• Check, adjust or replace key interlock cable. |
| The selector lever cannot be moved smoothly from "P" to "R". | • Shift lock lever cannot be moved smoothly due to a large amount of play or friction of the fulcrum pin of the shift lock lever.<br>• Poorly adjusted shift lock cable, considerable elongation of inner cable<br>• Poorly adjusted key interlock cable<br>• Broken or fatigued return spring of shift lock cable (brake pedal side)<br>• Interlock cam and interlock lever not sliding smoothly | • Check and adjust shift lock lever, check and replace selector lever bracket assembly.<br>• Check and adjust or replace shift lock cable and key interlock cable. |
| The selector lever cannot be moved from "R" to "P" | • Shift lock lever or interlock cam binding | • Check selector lever bracket assembly, apply grease or replace assembly. |
| The ignition key cannot be turned to LOCK when the selector lever is in the "P" position. | • Damaged interlock cam or interlock lever or foreign matter caught in the mechanism<br>• Poorly adjusted key interlock cable, binding inner cable<br>• Slide lever in key cylinder not sliding smoothly | • Check selector lever bracket assembly and replace if necessary.<br>• Adjust or replace key interlock cable.<br>• Check slide lever and replace if necessary. |
| The ignition key can be turned to LOCK even when the selector lever is at any position other than "P" | • Broken spring pin<br>• Damaged interlock cam<br>• Damaged interlock cover<br>• Poorly adjusted or broken key interlock cable, stretched inner cable<br>• Damaged slide lever | • Replace spring pin.<br>• Check selector lever bracket assembly and replace if necessary.<br>• Check and adjust or replace key interlock cable.<br>• Replace slide lever. |
| The stop light stays ON. | • Poorly adjusted shift lock cable<br>• Broken shift lock cable spring | • Check and adjust or replace shift lock cable. |

**Fig. 3 Shift lock control system troubleshooting**

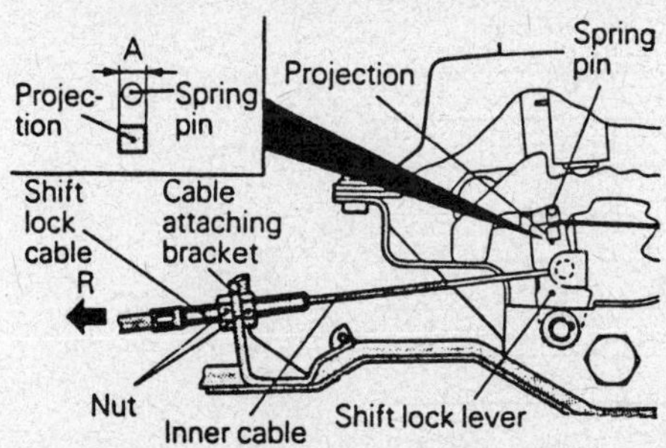


**Fig. 4 Shift lock cable adjustment**

reservoir/windshield washer fluid tank if necessary.

4. Disconnect oil cooling lines from transaxle. Plug lines and openings to prevent contamination.
5. Disconnect throttle control cable, speedometer cable and all electrical connectors from transaxle.
6. Disconnect starter motor wiring and remove starter motor.
7. Raise and support vehicle.

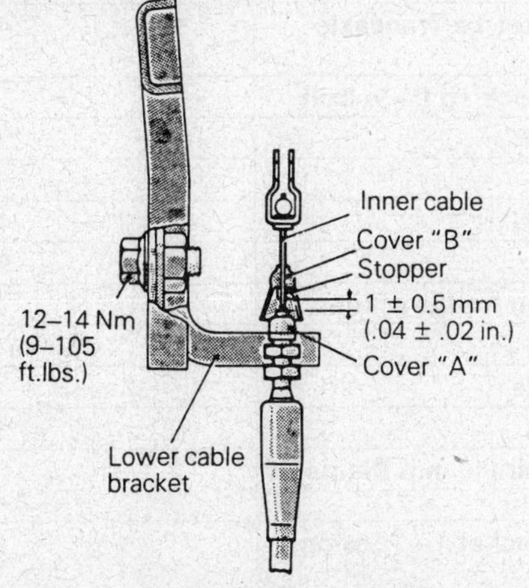


**Fig. 5 Adjusting throttle control cable**

8. Remove dust cover, then the stabilizer bar and strut bar.
9. Remove driveshafts from transaxle as follows:
   a. Loosen ball joint stud nut, then disconnect ball joint from steering

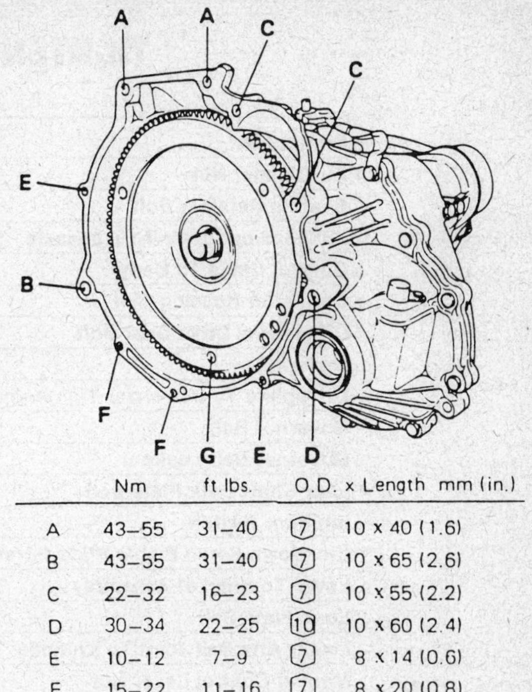


| | Nm | ft.lbs. | O.D. x Length mm (in.) |
|---|---|---|---|
| A | 43–55 | 31–40 | (7) 10 x 40 (1.6) |
| B | 43–55 | 31–40 | (7) 10 x 65 (2.6) |
| C | 22–32 | 16–23 | (7) 10 x 55 (2.2) |
| D | 30–34 | 22–25 | (10) 10 x 60 (2.4) |
| E | 10–12 | 7–9 | (7) 8 x 14 (0.6) |
| F | 15–22 | 11–16 | (7) 8 x 20 (0.8) |
| G | 35–42 | 25–30 | — |

**Fig. 6 Transaxle bolt torque specifications**

knuckle using separating tool No. MB991113 or equivalent.
   b. Loosen tie rod end stud nut, then disconnect tie rod from steering knuckle using separating tool No. MB991113 or equivalent.
   c. Pry righthand driveshaft, then lefthand driveshaft out of transaxle case using two suitable screwdrivers. **Do not insert screwdrivers far enough to damage oil seal.**
10. Remove driveshaft circlips from transaxle case.
11. Remove bellhousing cover attaching bolts and the cover.
12. Remove three torque converter to driveplate attaching bolts, rotating flywheel as necessary. **After removing attaching bolts, push torque converter into transaxle to avoid leaving the converter in the engine.**
13. Remove transaxle mounting bracket as follows:
   a. Scribe hood hinge locations and remove hood.
   b. Lift engine slightly using suitable engine lifting equipment to relieve pressure from mount insulators.
   c. Support lower portion of transaxle with a suitable jack, then remove mounting bracket.
14. Remove transaxle attaching bolts, then slide transaxle to the right and carefully lower assembly from vehicle.
15. Reverse procedure to install, noting the following:
   a. Install torque converter first to transaxle and then to engine.
   b. Fill transaxle to specifications.
   c. Adjust throttle control cable and control cable.
   d. **Torque** other bolts as shown, **Fig. 6.**

## TIGHTENING SPECIFICATIONS

| Component | Torque/Ft. Lbs. |
|---|---|
| Air Cleaner Nut | 6–7 |
| Bearing Retainer Bolt | 11–15 |
| Bellhousing Cover To Transaxle | 7–9 |
| Control Cable To Body | 7–10 |
| Converter Housing Bolt | 14–17 |
| Differential Drive Gear Bolt | 94–101 |
| Driveplate | 94–101 |
| Driveplate To Converter Tightening Bolt | 33–38 |
| Governor Bolt | 6–7 |
| Governor Bolt Locknut | 3–4 |
| Idler Shaft Lock Plate Bolt | 15–19 |
| Inhibitor Switch | 7–9 |
| Kickdown Servo Piston Plate Screw | 4–6 |
| Lever To Bracket Assembly | 10–14 |
| Lock Plate Bolt | 14–20 |
| Lower Arm Ball Joint To Knuckle | 43–52 |
| Manual Control Lever Nut | 12–15 |
| Manual Control Shaft Setscrew | 6–7 |
| Oil Cooler Connector | 11–15 |
| Oil Filter Bolt | 4–5 |
| Oil Pan Bolt | 7–9 |
| Oil Pump Assembly Mounting Bolt | 11–15 |
| One-Way Clutch Outer Race Bolt | 6–7 |
| Planetary Carrier Bolt | 11–15 |
| Pressure Check Plug | 6–7 |
| Pulse Generator Mounting Bolt | 7–9 |
| Pump Housing To Reaction Shaft Support Bolt | 14–20 |
| Transaxle Bracket To Transaxle | 43–58 |
| Transaxle Drain Plug | 22–25 |
| Transaxle Mount Bracket To Body | 29–36 |
| Transaxle Mount Bracket To Transaxle Bracket | 43–58 |
| Speedometer Sleeve Locking Plate Bolt | 2–4 |
| Sprag Rod Support Bolt | 14–20 |
| Stabilizer Bar | 14–22 |
| Starter Motor To Transaxle | 20–25 |
| Strut Bar | 98–116 |
| Tension Rod To Tension Rod Bracket | 25–40 |
| Throttle Cam Bolt | 6–7 |
| Tie Rod End To Knuckle | 11–25 |
| Transaxle Mount Bolt | 31–40 |
| Transaxle Mounting Bolt (10 mm Diameter Bolt) | ① |
| Transaxle Mounting Bracket To Tension Rod | 54–69 |
| Valve Body Assembly Mounting Bolt | 7–9 |
| Valve Body Bolt | 4–5 |

①—KM172, 31–40 ft. lbs.; KM171, 22–25 ft. lbs.

# F4A22, F4A33, W4A33 & KM176 Automatic Transaxle

## INDEX



## TRANSAXLE IDENTIFICATION

The transaxle identification number is located at the top of the bellhousing, **Fig. 1.**

## DESCRIPTION

The Mitsubishi F4A22, F4A33, W4A33 & KM176 is a fully automatic four-speed electronically controlled transaxle. This transaxle is used on Eagle Summit sedans with 1.6L/4-98 non-turbo engine, Eagle Talon, Plymouth Laser and Doodge Stealth.

## TROUBLESHOOTING

### TRANSAXLE

Refer to **Fig. 2** when troubleshooting the transaxle.

### SHIFT LOCK CONTROL SYSTEM

Refer to "KM171, KM172, F3A21, F3A22" transaxle section shift lock control system troubleshooting.

## MAINTENANCE

### CHECKING FLUID LEVEL

With vehicle on level surface, start engine and operate at idle speed. With parking brake applied, move shift lever through each gear, then place selector lever in N. Remove dipstick and check fluid level. Transmission should be at operating temperature when checking fluid level (160-180°F). Fluid level should be within the Hot range on dipstick. If necessary, add Dexron II automatic transmission fluid to bring fluid level within the Hot range.

### CHANGING FLUID

The automatic transaxle fluid should be changed every 30,000 miles on these units. When refilling transaxle, add only Dexron II automatic transaxle fluid.

1. Remove drain plug from bottom of differential and drain fluid into a suitable container.
2. Loosen transaxle oil pan attaching bolts, then tap pan at one corner to break loose and drain fluid into a suitable container.
3. Remove oil pan and drain residual fluid.
4. Inspect oil filter for damage or obstructions and replace if necessary.
5. Install drain plug with a new gasket and **torque** to 22-25 ft. lbs.
6. Clean transaxle case and oil pan mating surfaces, then install oil pan with a new gasket and **torque** attaching bolts to 7.5-8.5 ft. lbs.
7. Add 4.2 quarts Dexron II automatic transmission fluid to transaxle through dipstick hole.
8. Run engine at idle for at least two minutes, then shift transaxle through all ranges and recheck fluid level.
9. Add sufficient fluid to bring level to lower mark on dipstick, then run engine until normal operating temperature is reached. Recheck dipstick and ensure fluid level is within Hot range.

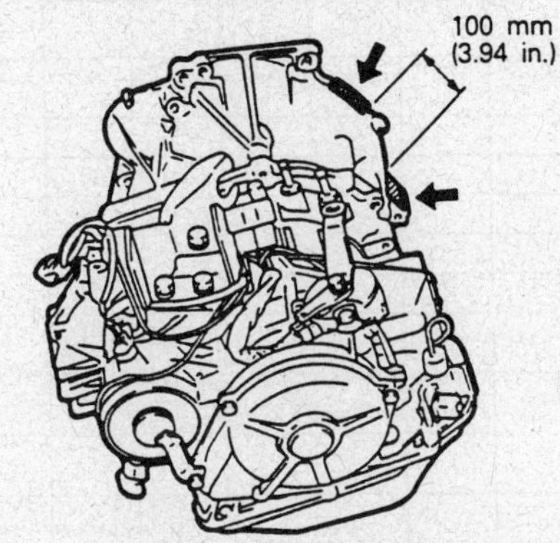


**Fig. 1 Transaxle identification number location**

## IN-VEHICLE ADJUSTMENTS

### INHIBITOR SWITCH & CONTROL CABLE, ADJUST

1. Place selector lever in N range.
2. Loosen two control cable-to-manual control lever adjusting nuts, then place manual control lever in the N position.
3. Rotate inhibitor switch body until alignment holes on the end of manual control lever aligns with switch body flange hole.
4. Tighten two switch attaching bolts without disturbing switch position.
5. Ensure selector lever is shifted to N range, then remove slack from control cable and **torque** adjusting nuts to 7-9 ft.lbs. Ensure proper operation of control lever.

### KICKDOWN SERVO, ADJUST

1. Thoroughly clean kickdown servo cover area.
2. Remove kickdown servo switch, then the snap ring and servo cover.
3. Loosen kickdown servo locknut.
4. Hold kickdown servo piston using kickdown servo wrench tool No. MD998902 or equivalent while **torquing** piston adjusting screw to 7.2 ft. lbs. using socket wrench tool No. MD998901 or equivalent. Back off adjusting screw, **torque** to 3.6 ft. lbs., then back off adjusting screw 2-2 1/4 turns
5. **Torque** locknut to 18-23 ft. lbs. while preventing piston from turning.
6. Install new D-ring into cover, then position cover on case and secure with snap ring.
7. Install kickdown servo switch on cover and **torque** retaining screw to .7-1.0 ft. lbs.

### SHIFT LOCK CONTROL

Refer to "KM171, KM172, F3A21, F3A22" transaxle section for shift lock control adjustment.

| | | Symptom / Probable cause | Driving impossible or abnormal (before start): Starter inoperative | Forward/reverse drive impossible | Forward drive impossible | Reverse drive impossible | Engine stalls when shifting from "N" to "D" or "R" | Clutch slips in "D" position (stall rpm too high) | Clutch slips in "R" position (stall rpm too high) | Stall rpm too low | Vehicle starts to move in "P" or "N" position | Vehicle starts to move in position midway of "N" and "R" or "N" and "D" | Parking mechanism does not work | Abnormal shock felt when selecting "D", "2", "L" or "R" |
|---|---|---|---|---|---|---|---|---|---|---|---|---|---|---|
| Engine | 1 | Idling rpm abnormal | | | | | ⊗ | | | | | | | X |
| Engine | 2 | Performance failure | | | | | X | | | X | | | | |
| Transaxle proper (power train) | 3 | Manual linkage inadequately adjusted | X | ⊗ | ⊗ | ⊗ | | ⊗ | ⊗ | | ⊗ | ⊗ | ⊗ | ⊗ |
| Transaxle proper (power train) | 4 | Torque converter failure (including damper clutch) | | X | X | X | | | | X | | | | |
| Transaxle proper (power train) | 5 | Oil pump failure | | X | X | X | | X | X | | | | | |
| Transaxle proper (power train) | 6 | One way clutch failure | | | X | | | X | | | | | | |
| Transaxle proper (power train) | 7 | Damaged or worn gear or other rotating parts, shim preload inadequately adjusted | | | | | | | | | | | | |
| Transaxle proper (power train) | 8 | Parking mechanism failure | | | | | | | | | X | | X | |
| Transaxle proper (power train) | 9 | Cracked drive plate or loose bolt | | X | | | | | | | | | | |
| Transaxle proper (power train) | 10 | Worn front clutch retainer inside | | | | X | | | X | | | | | |
| Hydraulic system (including friction elements) | 11 | Low fluid level | | ⊗ | ⊗ | X | | X | X | | | | | |
| Hydraulic system (including friction elements) | 12 | Low line pressure (broken seal, leaks, looseness, etc.) | | ⊗ | ⊗ | ⊗ | | ⊗ | ⊗ | | | | | |
| Hydraulic system (including friction elements) | 13 | Faulty valve body (valve sticking, poor machining, blowhole, poor adjustment, etc.) | | ⊗ | ⊗ | X | X | X | X | | X | X | | X |
| Hydraulic system (including friction elements) | 14 | Faulty front clutch, piston | | | | X | | | X | | | | | X |
| Hydraulic system (including friction elements) | 15 | Faulty rear clutch, piston | | | ⊗ | | | X | | | | | | X |
| Hydraulic system (including friction elements) | 16 | Faulty kickdown band or piston | | | | | | | | | | | | |
| Hydraulic system (including friction elements) | 17 | Kickdown servo poorly adjusted | | | | | | | | | | | | |
| Hydraulic system (including friction elements) | 18 | Faulty low reverse brake, piston | | X | | X | | | X | | | | | X |
| Hydraulic system (including friction elements) | 19 | O-ring missing in low reverse brake circuit between valve body and case | | | | X | | | X | | | | | |
| Hydraulic system (including friction elements) | 20 | Faulty end clutch, piston (check ball hole, etc.) | | | | | | | | | | | | |
| Electrical control system | 21 | Faulty inhibitor switch, open wire, poor adjustment | X | | | | | | | | X | X | | X |
| Electrical control system | 22 | Faulty throttle position sensor, poor adjustment | | | | | | | | | | | | X |
| Electrical control system | 23 | Pulse generator (A) open wire or shorting | | | | | | | | | | | | |
| Electrical control system | 24 | Pulse generator (B) open wire or shorting | | | | X | | | | | | | | |
| Electrical control system | 25 | Faulty kickdown servo switch | | | | | | | | | | | | |
| Electrical control system | 26 | Shift control solenoid (A), (B) open wire, shorting, sticking (valve open) | | | | | | | | | | | | |
| Electrical control system | 27 | Faulty ignition signal system | | | | | | | | | | | | |
| Electrical control system | 28 | Poor grounding of ground strap section | | | | | | | | | | | | |
| Electrical control system | 29 | Pressure control solenoid valve open wire or shorting | | | | | | | | | | | | |
| Electrical control system | 30 | Pressure control sticking (valve open) | | ⊗ | ⊗ | ⊗ | | X | X | | | | | |
| Electrical control system | 31 | Damper clutch control solenoid valve open wire (valve closed) | | | | | | | | | | | | |
| Electrical control system | 32 | Damper clutch shorting, sticking (valve open) | | | | | ⊗ | | | | | | | |
| Electrical control system | 33 | OD switch failure | | | | | | | | | | | | |
| Electrical control system | 34 | Faulty accelerator switch, poor adjustment | | | | | | | | | | | | X |
| Electrical control system | 35 | Oil temperature sensor failure | | | | | | | | | | | | |
| Electrical control system | 36 | Vehicle speed sensor (reed switch) failure | | | | | | | | | | | | |
| Electrical control system | 37 | Ignition switch poor contact | | | | | | | | | | | | |
| Electrical control system | 38 | Faulty control unit | | | | | | | | | | | | X |

Remarks: ⊗ indicates items to be given high priority in inspection.

**Fig. 2 Troubleshooting chart (Part 1 of 2)**

| | Shifting failure or shock (after start) | | | | | | | | | | | | | | | | Abnormal noise and others | | | |
|---|---|---|---|---|---|---|---|---|---|---|---|---|---|---|---|---|---|---|---|---|
| | No shifting from 2nd to 3rd | No shifting to 4th | OD switch inoperative | Shifting does not take place according to shift pattern (Shifting itself is possible) | Unsmooth start (starting at 2nd gear, etc.) | High creep and idle vibration | Large shock felt when shifting from 1st to 2nd or from 3rd to 4th | Large shock felt when shifting from 2nd to 3rd or from 4th to 3rd | Large shock felt when shifting up | Large shock felt when shifting down in "D" or "2" | Engine running up when shifting up | Engine running up and large shock when shifting from 3rd to 2nd | Large shock only when cold | Large shock (other than cases listed to left) | Damper clutch inoperative | Abnormal vibration (approx. 1 Hz) in low speed, high load range | Converter housing whining with increasing engine rpm | Mechanical noise (rattling) from converter housing | Abnormal noise from transmission case | Transmission locked at 3rd |
| 1 | | | | | | X | | | | | | | | | | | | | | |
| 2 | | | | | X | | X | X | X | X | | | X | X | | X | | | | |
| 3 | | X | | | X | | | | | | | | | | | | | | | X |
| 4 | | | | | X | | | | | | | | | | X | X | | | | |
| 5 | | | | | | | | | | | | X | | | | | X | | | |
| 6 | | | | | | | | | | | | | | | | | | | | |
| 7 | | | | | | | | | | | | | | | | | | | X | |
| 8 | | | | | | | | | | | | | | | | | | | | |
| 9 | | | | | | | | | | | | | | | | | | X | | |
| 10 | X | X | | | | | | | | | X | X | | | | | | | | X |
| 11 | | | | | | | | | | | | X | | | | | | | | X |
| 12 | | | | | | | | | | | ⊗ | ⊗ | | X | | | | | | X |
| 13 | X | | | X | X | | X | X | X | X | X | X | X | X | X | X | | | | X |
| 14 | X | | | | | | | X | X | | X | | | | | | | | | X |
| 15 | | | | | | | | | | | | | | | | | | | | X |
| 16 | | | | | | | X | | | | X | X | | | | | | | | X |
| 17 | | | | | | | X | | | | X | X | | X | | | | | | |
| 18 | | | | | | | | | | X | | | | | | | | | | X |
| 19 | | | | | | | | | | | | | | | | | | | | X |
| 20 | | ⊗ | | | | | X | | | | X | | | | | | | | | X |
| 21 | | X | | | X | | | | | | | | | | | | | | | X |
| 22 | | | | ⊗ | | | X | X | ⊗ | X | ⊗ | X | | X | X | X | | | | |
| 23 | | | | | | | X | X | X | X | X | X | | X | X | X | | | | X |
| 24 | | | | X | | | | | | | | | | | X | X | | | | X |
| 25 | | | | | | | X | | | | | X | | | | | | | | X |
| 26 | | | | | | | | | | | | | | | | | | | | X |
| 27 | | | | | | | X | X | X | X | X | X | | X | X | | | | | |
| 28 | | | | | | | | | | | | | | | | | | | | X |
| 29 | | | | | | | | | | | | | | | | | | | | X |
| 30 | X | X | | | | | | | | | X | X | | | | | | | | X |
| 31 | | | | | | | | | | | | | | | X | | | | | |
| 32 | | | | | | | | | | | | | | | | X | | | | X |
| 33 | | X | X | | | | | | | | | | | | | | | | | |
| 34 | | | | | X | X | | | | | | | | | X | | | | | |
| 35 | | | | | | | | | | | | | | X | X | X | | | | |
| 36 | | | | | | | | | | | | | | | | | | | | X |
| 37 | | | | X | | | | | | | | | | | | | | | | X |
| 38 | X | X | X | X | X | X | X | X | X | X | X | X | X | X | X | X | | | | X |

**Fig. 2 Troubleshooting chart (Part 2 of 2)**

# TRANSAXLE

## REPLACE

### EXCEPT STEALTH

1. Remove battery, battery tray and air cleaner assembly, then drain transaxle fluid.
2. Disconnect transaxle control cable, fluid cooler lines and shift control solenoid valve connector.
3. Disconnect inhibitor switch, kickdown servo switch connector, pulse generator connector and oil temperature sensor connector, then the speedometer cable.
4. Remove starter assembly, transaxle upper connecting bolt and transaxle mounting bracket.
5. Remove transaxle under-guard, then disconnect tie rod end from steering knuckle using steering linkage puller tool No. MB990635 or equivalent. Loosen the nut but do not remove it.
6. Remove the lower arm ball joint connection using puller tool No. MB990635 or equivalent. Loosen the nut but do not remove it.
7. Insert a pry bar between the transaxle case and the driveshaft and pry driveshaft loose from the case, **Fig. 3.** Do not pull on driveshaft or insert pry bar too deep or oil seal will be damaged. Secure driveshaft away from transaxle with rope or wire.
8. Remove bellhousing cover, driveplate connection and transaxle assembly lower connecting bolt.
9. Support transaxle assembly using a suitable jack, move to the right and lower out of chassis.
10. Reverse procedure to install.

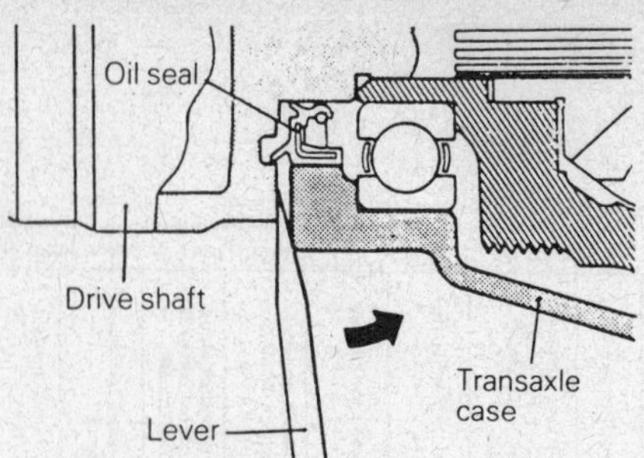


**Fig. 3 Driveshaft removal. All except Stealth**

### STEALTH

1. Disconnect battery ground cable.
2. Drain transaxle fluid.
3. Remove transaxle assembly in numbered sequence shown in **Fig. 4,** noting the following:
   a. Raise transaxle assembly using suitable transmission jack to relieve weight off of mounts, then remove transaxle mount insulator bolt.
   b. Loosen, but do not remove tie rod ends using using ball joint puller tool No. MB991113-01 or equivalent.
   c. Remove left driveshaft bearing bracket bolts and insert pry bar between bearing bracket and cylinder block.
   d. Remove left driveshaft and inner shaft assembly from transaxle. **Remove driveshaft and inner shaft assembly together with hub and knuckle**
   e. Remove right driveshaft by applying pry bar to protrusion, **Fig. 5. Remove driveshaft as an assembly together with hub and knuckle**
   f. Support transaxle assembly with a suitable transaxle stand, then rotate crankshaft and remove four torque converter bolts, **Fig. 6.**

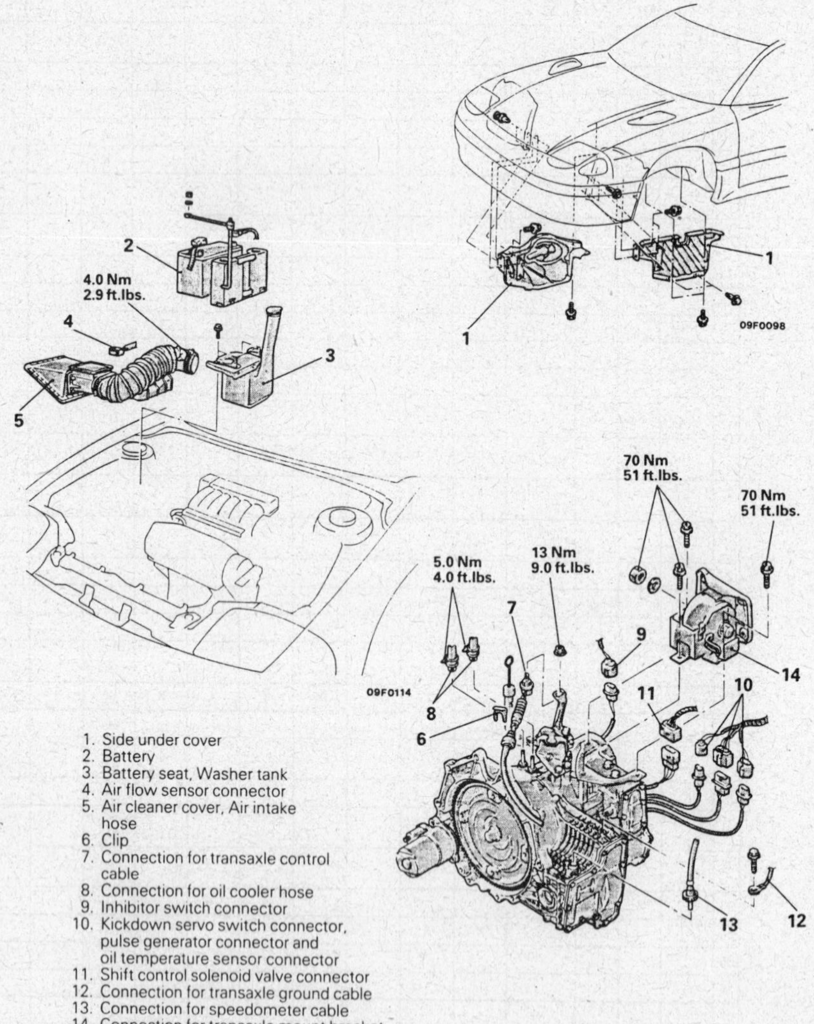


**Fig. 4 Transaxle replacement (Part 1 of 2). Stealth**

   g. After removing bolts, push torque converter toward transaxle.
   h. Remove coupling bolt at bottom of transaxle assembly, then lower transaxle assembly.
4. Reverse procedure to install, noting the following:
   a. Install torque converter to transaxle, then install transaxle.
   b. When connecting transaxle control cable to manual control lever, tighten nut temporarily, then loosen nut and pull cable out slightly and tighten nut.

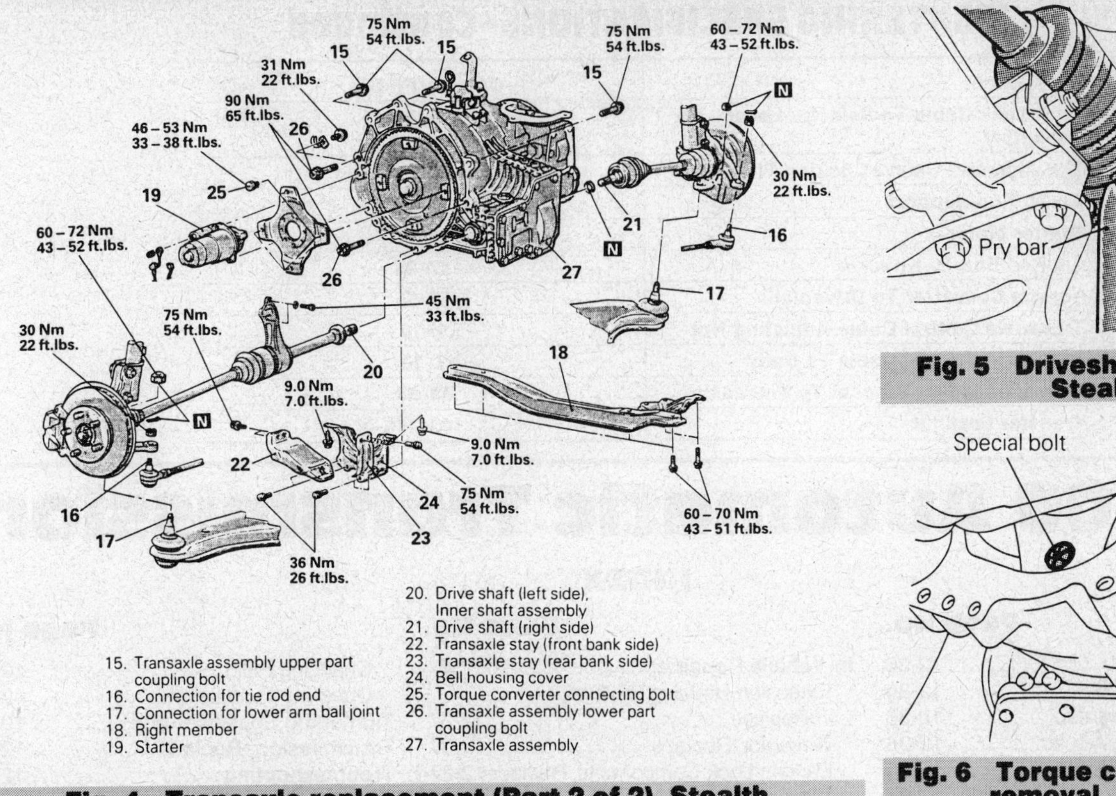


**Fig. 4 Transaxle replacement (Part 2 of 2). Stealth**

**Fig. 5 Driveshaft removal. Stealth**

**Fig. 6 Torque converter bolts removal. Stealth**

# TIGHTENING SPECIFICATIONS

| Component | Torque/Ft. Lbs. |
|---|---|
| Automatic Seat belt Guide Ring | 12–19 |
| Ball Joint To Knuckle | 43-52 |
| Bearing Retainer | 12–15 |
| Bellhousing Cover To Engine | 7-9 |
| Clamp To Body | 3–4 |
| Converter Housing | 14–16 |
| Drain Plug | 22–25 |
| Driveplate To Convertor | 34-38 |
| End Clutch Cover | 5–6 |
| Hose Bracket | 2–4 |
| Inhibitor Switch | 7-9 |
| Lever Assembly To Bracket Assembly | 10–14 |
| Lock Plate | 26–32 |
| Manual Control Lever Nut | 13–15 |
| Manual Control Shaft Setscrew | 6-7 |
| Oil Cooler Hose Clamp | 3-4 |
| Oil Filter | 4-5 |
| Oil Pan | 7-9 |
| Oil Pump Assembly | 14–16 |
| One-Way Clutch Outer Race | 18–25 |
| Pressure Check Plug | 6-7 |
| Pulse Generator | 7-9 |
| Pump Housing To Reaction Shaft Support | 7-9 |
| Selector Lever Assembly | 7–10 |

Continued

## TIGHTENING SPECIFICATIONS–Continued

| Component | Torque/Ft. Lbs. |
|---|---|
| Shift Lock Cable To Selector Lever Assembly | 3–4 |
| Speedometer Sleeve Locking Plate | 2–4 |
| Sprag Rod Support | 15–19 |
| Starter Motor | 20–25 |
| Tie Rod End To Knuckle | 17–25 |
| Torque Converter To Driveplate | 53–55 |
| Transaxle Control Cable Adjusting Nut | 7–10 |
| Transaxle Control Cable To Body | 7–10 |
| Transaxle Mount Bracket To Transaxle | 43–58 |
| Transfer Locknut | 145–166 |

# MR600 Automatic Transmission

## INDEX



## IDENTIFICATION

The transmission identification is located at the top of the bell housing, **Fig. 1**.

## DESCRIPTION

The Jatco MR600 is a fully automatic four speed transmission with a lock-up torque converter and is used on all Conquest **Fig. 2.**

## TROUBLESHOOTING

Refer to **Fig. 3** when troubleshooting the transmission.

## MAINTENANCE

### CHECKING FLUID LEVEL

1. Drive vehicle until normal operating temperature is reached.
2. Park vehicle on a level surface, then block wheels and apply parking brake with engine idling.
3. Move selector lever through all gears, then return to N.
4. Remove dipstick from filler tube, then wipe it clean and insert it back into tube.
5. Remove dipstick again and check fluid level. Fluid should be between the "L and H marks on dipstick.
6. Add Dexron II automatic transmission fluid as necessary.

### CHANGING FLUID

The automatic transmission fluid should be changed every 30,000 miles on these units.

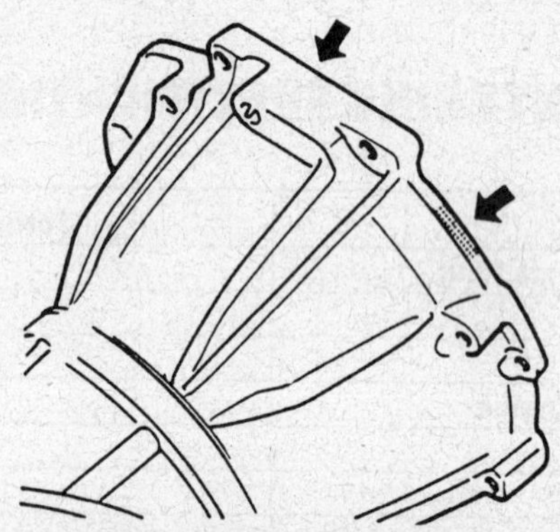

**Fig. 1 Transmission identification**

1. Loosen oil pan attaching bolts, then tap pan at one corner and allow fluid to drain into a suitable container.
2. Remove oil pan and gasket and drain residual fluid from the pan.
3. Install oil pan using a new gasket. **Torque** pan attaching bolts to 4.4-5.7 ft. lbs.
4. Add approximately 5.3 qts. of Dexron II automatic transmission fluid to transmission.
5. Start engine and run at idle for several minutes, then with parking brake applied, shift transmission through all ranges. Add sufficient fluid to bring level to L mark on dipstick.
6. After transmission has reached normal operating temperature, ensure fluid level is between L and H marks on dipstick.

## IN-VEHICLE ADJUSTMENTS

### GEARSHIFT LINKAGE, ADJUST

1. Place selector lever in N position.
2. Loosen lever-to-control rod attaching bolts.
3. Position side lever in N position, then tighten attaching bolts, **Fig. 4.**

### INHIBITOR SWITCH, ADJUST

1. Place manual lever in neutral (vertical) position, then remove screw, **Fig. 5.**
2. Loosen attaching bolts, then insert a .079 inch diameter alignment pin into screw hole.
3. Move switch until alignment pin falls into hole, then **torque** attaching bolts to 3.6-5.1 ft. lbs.
4. Remove alignment pin, then install and tighten screw.

### VACUUM ROD, ADJUST

1. Disconnect vacuum hose from vacuum diaphragm, then remove diaphragm from transmission case.
2. Push vacuum throttle valve as far as possible into valve body, then measure dimension (L), **Fig. 6** using a depth gauge.
3. Refer to chart, **Fig. 7,** and install proper length diaphragm rod.

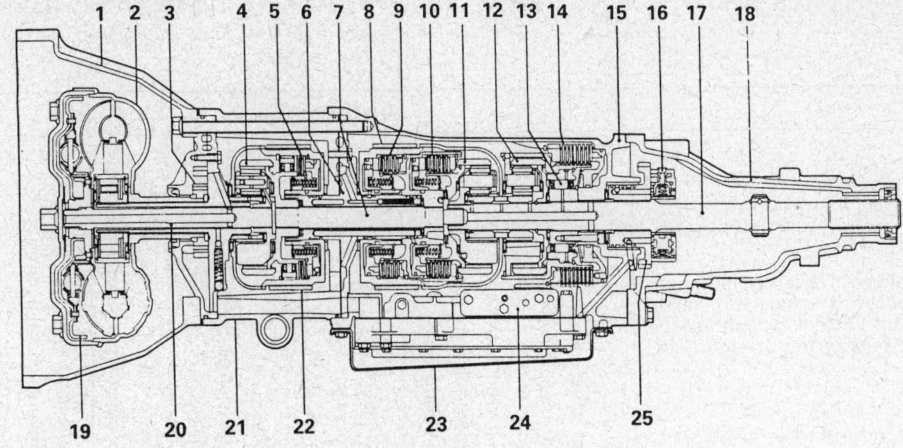


1. Converter housing
2. Torque converter
3. Oil pump
4. O.D. planetary gear
5. Direct clutch
6. Drum support
7. Intermediate shaft
8. Second band brake
9. High-reverse clutch (Front)
10. Forward clutch (Rear)
11. Front planetary gear
12. Rear planetary gear
13. One-way clutch
14. Low-reverse clutch
15. Transmission case
16. Governor valve
17. Output shaft
18. Rear extension
19. Lock-up clutch
20. Input shaft
21. O.D. case
22. O.D. brake band
23. Oil pan
24. Control valve assembly
25. Oil distributor

**Fig. 2 MR600 automatic transmission**

## KICKDOWN SWITCH, ADJUST

The kickdown switch is located on top of the accelerator pedal in the passenger compartment.

1. Loosen locknut, then extend switch until accelerator pedal lever makes contact with switch and the switch clicks.
2. Tighten locknut when switch is properly adjusted. **To avoid part throttle downshifts, do not allow switch to make contact too soon.**

# IN-VEHICLE REPAIRS

## VALVE BODY, REPLACE

### Removal

1. Drain transmission fluid as outlined under "Maintenance, Changing Fluid."
2. Remove downshift solenoid and vacuum diaphragm and rod, **Fig. 8.**
3. Remove valve body attaching bolts and the valve body.

### Installation

1. Move manual shaft to neutral position, then align manual plate with groove in manual valve.
2. Install valve body and **torque** attaching bolts, **Fig. 9**, to 4.0-5.4 ft. lbs.
3. Ensure control lever can be moved to all positions, then install downshift solenoid and vacuum diaphragm and rod. **Ensure diaphragm rod does not interfere with control valve side plate.**
4. Refill transmission as outlined under "Maintenance, Changing Fluid."

## EXTENSION HOUSING OIL SEAL, REPLACE

1. Mark position of propeller shaft for installation reference and remove propeller shaft from transmission.
2. Remove extension housing oil seal using a suitable puller.
3. Apply clean transmission fluid to new seal, then drive seal into place.
4. Apply petroleum jelly to seal lip, then install propeller shaft.

## PARKING LOCK COMPONENTS, REPLACE

1. Drain transmission fluid as outlined under "Maintenance, Changing Fluid."
2. Mark position of propeller shaft for installation reference and remove propeller shaft from transmission.
3. Disconnect speedometer cable from transmission, then remove speedometer sleeve assembly.
4. Support transmission with a suitable jack and wooden block, then remove rear mounting bolts.
5. Remove rear extension housing bolts, then the rear extension housing with mounting.
6. Remove valve body assembly as previously outlined.
7. Inspect parking lock components and replace as necessary.
8. Install valve body, rear extension housing, speedometer sleeve and propeller shaft.
9. Connect speedometer cable to transmission, then refill transmission as outlined under "Maintenance, Changing Fluid."

## GOVERNOR, REPLACE

1. Perform steps 1 through 5 outlined under "Parking Lock Components, Replace."
2. Remove governor attaching bolts and the governor, **Fig. 10.**
3. Reverse procedure to install. **Torque** governor attaching bolts to 3.6-5.1 ft. lbs.
4. Refill transmission as outlined under "Maintenance, Changing Fluid.

# TRANSMISSION REPLACE

1. Disconnect battery ground cable.
2. Loosen oil pan attaching bolts, then tap pan at one corner and allow fluid to drain into a suitable container.
3. Remove oil pan and gasket and drain residual fluid from the pan.
4. Raise and support vehicle.
5. Remove undercover, if equipped.
6. Remove two upper transmission attaching bolts using a suitable tool.
7. Unfasten starter motor and position aside.
8. Remove oil cooler return tube and supply tube bracket from cylinder

| Numbers are arranged in order of probability. Perform inspections starting with number one and working up. Circled numbers indicate that the transmission must be removed from the car | ON CAR | | | | | | | | | | | | | | OFF CAR | | | | | | | | | |
|---|---|---|---|---|---|---|---|---|---|---|---|---|---|---|---|---|---|---|---|---|---|---|---|---|
| | Oil level | Range select linkage | Inhibitor switch and wiring | Vacuum diaphragm and piping | Kickdown solenoid, switch and wiring | Engine idling rpm. | Line pressure | Control valve | Governor | Band servo | Transmission air check | Oil quality | Ignition switch and starter motor | Engine adjustment, brake inspection | Forward clutch (Rear) | High-reverse clutch (Front) | O.D. band brake | 2nd band brake | Low and reverse brake | Oil pump | Oil passage leak | Transmission one-way clutch | High-reverse clutch (Front) check ball | Park linkage |
| Engine does not start in "N", "P" ranges | | 2 | 3 | | | | | | | | | | 1 | | | | | | | | | | | |
| Engine starts in range other than "N" and "P" | | 1 | 2 | | | | | | | | | | | | | | | | | | | | | |
| Transmission noise in "P" and "N" ranges | 1 | | | | | | 2 | | | | | | | | | | | | | ③ | | | | |
| Car moves when changing into "P" range or parking gear does not disengage when shifted out of "P" range | | 1 | | | | | | | | | | | | | | | | | | | | | | ② |
| Car runs in "N" range | | 1 | | | | | | 3 | | | | 2 | | | ④ | | | | | | | | | |
| Car will not run in "R" range (but runs in "D", "2" and "L" ranges). Clutch slips Very poor acceleration | 1 | 2 | | | | | 3 | 5 | | | 6 | 4 | | | ⑨ | ⑧ | | | ⑦ | | ⑩ | | ⑪ | |
| Car braked when shifting into "R" range | | | | | | | | | | 3 | 2 | 1 | | | ④ | | | ⑤ | | | | | | ⑥ |
| Sharp shock in shifting from "N" to "D" range | | | | 2 | | 1 | 3 | 4 | | | | | | | ⑤ | | | | | | | | | |
| Car will not run in "D" range (but runs in "2", "L" and "R" ranges) | | 1 | | | | | 2 | 3 | | | | | | | | | | | | | | ④ | | |
| Car will not run in "D", "L", "2" ranges (but runs in "R" range) Clutch slips Very poor acceleration | 1 | 2 | | | | | 4 | 5 | | | 6 | 3 | | 7 | ⑧ | ⑩ | | | | | ⑨ | | | |
| Clutches or brakes slip somewhat in starting | 1 | 2 | | 6 | | | 3 | 5 | | | 7 | 4 | | | | | | | | ⑧ | ⑨ | | | |
| Excessive creep | | | | | | 1 | | | | | | | | | | | | | | | | | | |
| No creep at all | 1 | 2 | | | | 3 | | 5 | | | | 4 | | | ⑧ | ⑨ | | | | ⑥ | ⑦ | | | |
| Failure to change gear from "1st" to "2nd" | | 1 | | 2 | 3 | | | 5 | 6 | 8 | 7 | 4 | | | | | | ⑨ | | | ⑩ | | | |
| Failure to change gear from "2nd" to "3rd" | | 1 | | 2 | 3 | | | 5 | 6 | 8 | 7 | 4 | | | | ⑨ | | | | | ⑩ | | ⑪ | |
| Failure to change gear from "3rd" to "4th" | | 1 | | 2 | 3 | | | 5 | 6 | 8 | 7 | 4 | | | | | ⑨ | | | | ⑩ | | | |
| Too high a gear change point from "1st" to "2nd", from "2nd" to "3rd", from "3rd" to "4th" | | | | 1 | 2 | | 3 | 5 | 6 | | | 4 | | | | | | | | | ⑦ | | | |
| Gear change directly from "1st" to "3rd" occurs | | | | | | | | 2 | 4 | | 3 | 1 | | | | | | ⑤ | | | ⑥ | | | |
| Gear change directly from "2nd" to "4th" occurs | | | | | | | | 2 | 4 | | 3 | 1 | | | ⑤ | | | | | | ⑥ | | | |

**Fig. 3 Troubleshooting chart (Part 1 of 4)**

| | ON CAR | | | | | | | | | | | | OFF CAR | | | | | | | | | | |
|---|---|---|---|---|---|---|---|---|---|---|---|---|---|---|---|---|---|---|---|---|---|---|---|
| Numbers are arranged in order of probability. Perform inspections starting with number one and working up. Circled numbers indicate that the transmission must be removed from the car | Oil level | Range select linkage | Vacuum diaphragm and piping | Kickdown solenoid, switch and wiring | Line pressure | Engine stall rpm | Control valve | Governor | Band servo | Transmission air check | Oil quality | Engine adjustment, brake inspection | Direct clutch | Forward clutch (Rear) | High-reverse clutch (Front) | O.D. band brake | 2nd band brake | Low and reverse brake | Oil pump | Oil passage leak | Transmission one-way clutch | High-reverse clutch (Front) check ball |
| Too sharp a shock in change from "1st" to "2nd" | . | . | 1 | . | . | 2 | 4 | . | 5 | . | 3 | . | . | . | . | . | ⑥ | . | . | . | . | . |
| Too sharp a shock in change from "2nd" to "3rd" | . | . | 1 | . | 2 | . | 3 | . | 5 | 4 | . | . | . | . | ⑥ | . | . | . | . | . | . | . |
| Too sharp a shock in change from "3rd" to "4th" | . | . | 1 | . | 2 | . | 3 | . | 5 | 4 | . | . | . | . | . | ⑥ | . | . | . | . | . | . |
| Almost no shock or clutches slipping in change from "1st" to "2nd" | 1 | 2 | 3 | . | 4 | . | 6 | . | 8 | 7 | 5 | . | . | . | . | . | ⑨ | . | . | ⑩ | . | . |
| Almost no shock or slipping in change from "2nd" to "3rd" Engine races extremely fast | 1 | 2 | 3 | . | 4 | . | 6 | . | 8 | 7 | 5 | . | . | . | ⑨ | . | . | . | . | ⑩ | . | ⑪ |
| Almost no shock or slipping in change from "3rd" to "4th" | 1 | 2 | 3 | . | 4 | . | 6 | . | 8 | 7 | 5 | . | . | . | . | ⑨ | . | . | . | ⑩ | . | . |
| Car braked by gear change from "1st" to "2nd" | . | . | . | . | . | . | 2 | . | . | . | 1 | . | . | . | ④ | . | . | ③ | . | . | ⑤ | . |
| Car braked by gear change from "2nd" to "3rd" | . | . | . | . | . | . | 3 | . | 2 | . | 1 | . | . | . | . | . | ④ | . | . | . | . | . |
| Car braked by gear change from "3rd" to "4th" | . | . | . | . | . | . | 2 | . | . | . | 1 | . | ③ | . | ④ | . | . | . | . | . | . | . |
| Maximum speed not attained. Acceleration poor | 1 | 2 | . | . | 4 | 5 | 7 | . | 6 | . | 3 | 8 | . | ⑪ | ⑫ | . | ⑨ | ⑩ | ⑬ | . | . | . |
| Failure to change gear from "4th" to "3rd" | . | . | 1 | . | . | . | 3 | 4 | . | 5 | 2 | . | ⑥ | . | ⑦ | ⑧ | . | . | . | ⑨ | . | . |
| Failure to change gear from "3rd" to "2nd" and from "4th" to "2nd" | . | . | 1 | . | . | . | 3 | 4 | 6 | 5 | 2 | . | . | . | ⑦ | ⑩ | ⑧ | . | . | ⑨ | . | . |
| Failure to change gear from "2nd" to "1st" or from "3rd" to "1st" | . | . | 1 | . | . | . | 3 | 4 | 6 | 5 | 2 | . | . | . | . | . | ⑦ | . | . | . | ⑧ | . |
| Gear change shock felt during deceleration by releasing accelerator pedal | . | 1 | 2 | 3 | 4 | . | 5 | 6 | . | . | . | . | . | . | . | . | . | . | . | ⑦ | . | . |
| Too high a change point from "4th" to "3rd", from "3rd" to "2nd", from "2nd" to "1st" | . | 1 | 2 | 3 | 4 | . | 5 | 6 | . | . | . | . | . | . | . | . | . | . | . | ⑦ | . | . |
| Kickdown does not operate when depressing pedal in "3rd" within kickdown car speed | . | . | 2 | 1 | . | . | 4 | 5 | . | . | 3 | . | . | . | . | . | ⑥ | . | . | ⑦ | . | . |
| Kickdown operates or engine overruns when depressing pedal in "3rd" beyond kickdown car speed limit | . | 1 | 2 | . | 3 | . | 5 | 6 | . | 7 | 4 | . | . | . | ⑧ | . | . | . | . | ⑨ | . | . |
| Races extremely fast or slips in changing from "4th" to "3rd" when depressing pedal | . | . | 1 | . | 2 | . | 4 | . | 6 | 5 | 3 | . | ⑦ | . | ⑧ | ⑨ | . | . | . | ⑩ | . | ⑪ |
| Races extremely fast or slips in changing from "3rd" to "2nd" when depressing pedal | . | . | 1 | . | 2 | . | 4 | . | 6 | 5 | 3 | . | . | . | ⑦ | . | ⑧ | . | . | ⑨ | . | ⑩ |

**Fig. 3 Troubleshooting chart (Part 2 of 4)**

| Numbers are arranged in order of probability. Perform inspections starting with number one and working up. Circled numbers indicate that the transmission must be removed from the car | ON CAR | | | | | | | | | | | | | | OFF CAR | | | | | | | | | | | | |
|---|---|---|---|---|---|---|---|---|---|---|---|---|---|---|---|---|---|---|---|---|---|---|---|---|---|---|---|
| | Oil level | Range select linkage | Vacuum diaphragm and piping | Engine idling rpm | Line pressure | Engine stall rpm | Rear lubrication | Control valve | Governor | Band servo | Transmission air check | Oil quality | O.D. cancel switch and wiring | O.D. cancel solenoid | Direct clutch | Forward clutch (Rear) | High-reverse clutch (Front) | O.D. band brake | 2nd band brake | Low and reverse brake | Oil pump | Oil passage leak | Torque converter, one-way clutch | Transmission one-way clutch | Park linkage | Planetary gear | O.D. cancel valve |
| Car will not run in any range | 1 | 2 | . | . | 3 | . | . | 5 | . | . | 6 | 4 | . | . | . | . | . | . | . | . | ⑦ | ⑧ | . | . | ⑨ | . | . |
| Transmission noise in "D", "2", "L" and "R" ranges | 1 | . | . | . | 2 | . | . | . | . | . | . | . | . | . | . | ③ | . | . | . | . | ④ | . | . | ⑤ | . | ⑥ | . |
| Failure to change from "3rd" to "2nd" when changing lever into "2" range | . | 1 | . | . | 2 | . | . | 4 | . | 5 | . | 3 | . | . | . | . | . | . | ⑥ | . | . | ⑦ | . | . | . | . | . |
| Gear change from "2" to "1st" or from "2nd" to "3rd" in "2" range | . | 1 | . | . | 2 | . | . | 3 | . | . | . | . | . | . | . | . | . | . | . | . | . | . | . | . | . | . | . |
| No shock at change from "L" to "2" range or engine races extremely | 1 | 2 | 3 | 4 | . | 5 | . | 7 | . | . | 8 | 6 | . | . | . | . | . | . | ⑨ | . | ⑩ | . | . | . | . | . | . |
| Failure to change from "3rd" to "2nd" when shifting lever into "L" range | . | 1 | . | . | 2 | . | . | 4 | 5 | 7 | 6 | 3 | . | . | . | . | ⑧ | . | ⑨ | . | . | ⑩ | . | . | . | . | . |
| Engine brake does not operate in "L" range | . | 1 | . | . | 2 | . | . | 4 | . | . | 5 | 3 | . | . | . | . | . | . | . | ⑥ | . | ⑦ | . | . | . | . | . |
| Gear change from "1st" to "2nd" or from "2nd" to "3rd" in "L" range | . | 1 | . | . | . | . | . | 2 | . | . | . | . | . | . | . | . | . | . | . | . | . | ③ | . | . | . | . | . |
| Does not change from "2nd" to "1st" in "L" range | 1 | 2 | . | . | . | . | . | 4 | 5 | 6 | 7 | 3 | . | . | . | . | . | . | . | ⑧ | . | ⑨ | . | . | . | . | . |
| Large shock changing from "2nd" to "1st" in "L" range | . | . | 1 | . | . | 2 | . | 4 | . | . | . | 3 | . | . | . | . | . | . | . | ⑤ | . | . | . | . | . | . | . |
| Transmission overheats * | 1 | . | . | . | 3 | 4 | 2 | 6 | . | 8 | 7 | 5 | . | . | . | . | ⑨ | . | ⑩ | ⑪ | ⑫ | ⑬ | ⑭ | . | . | ⑮ | . |
| Oil shoots out during operation White smoke emitted from exhaust pipe during operation | 1 | . | 3 | . | 5 | 6 | 2 | 7 | . | . | 8 | 4 | . | . | . | . | ⑨ | . | ⑩ | ⑪ | ⑫ | ⑬ | ⑭ | . | . | ⑮ | . |
| Offensive smell at oil charging pipe | 1 | . | . | . | . | . | . | . | . | . | . | 2 | . | . | ③ | ④ | ⑤ | ⑥ | ⑦ | ⑥ | ⑦ | ⑧ | ⑨ | . | . | ⑩ | . |
| Transmission shifts to overdrive even if O.D. cancel switch is turned to "ON" | . | . | . | . | . | . | . | . | . | . | . | . | 1 | 2 | . | . | . | . | . | . | . | . | . | . | . | . | ③ |
| Light inside O.D. cancel switch does not glow even if ignition switch is turned to "ON" (engine not started) | . | . | . | . | . | . | . | . | . | . | . | . | 1 | . | . | . | . | . | . | . | . | . | . | . | . | . | . |
| Light inside O.D. cancel switch does not glow even if transmission is shifted to O.D. | . | . | . | . | . | . | . | . | . | . | . | . | 1 | . | . | . | . | . | . | . | . | . | . | . | . | . | . |

**Fig. 3 Troubleshooting chart (Part 3 of 4)**

| Numbers are arranged in order of probability. Perform inspections starting with number one and working up. Circled numbers indicate that the transmission must be removed from the car. | ON CAR | | | OFF CAR | | | | |
|---|---|---|---|---|---|---|---|---|
| | Governor tube | Governor | Line pressure | O-ring in input shaft | Torque converter | Lock-up control valve | Lock-up orifice in oil pump cover | Oil pump |
| Torque converter is not locked up | 1 | 2 | 3 | ④ | ⑨ | ⑥ | ⑦ | ⑤ |
| Lock-up piston slips | | | 1 | ② | ⑤ | | ③ | ④ |
| Lock-up point is extremely high or low | 1 | 2 | | | | ③ | | |
| Engine is stopped at "R", "D", "2" and "L" ranges | | | | | ② | ① | | |
| Transmission overheats | | | 1 | ② | ⑤ | | ③ | ④ |

**Fig. 3 Troubleshooting chart (Part 4 of 4)**

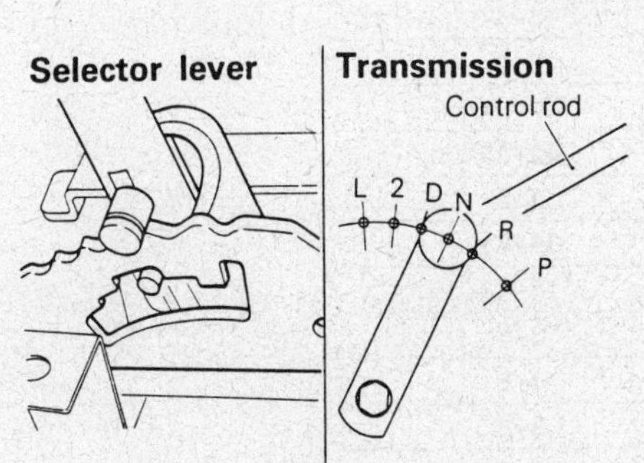


**Fig. 4 Gearshift linkage adjustment**

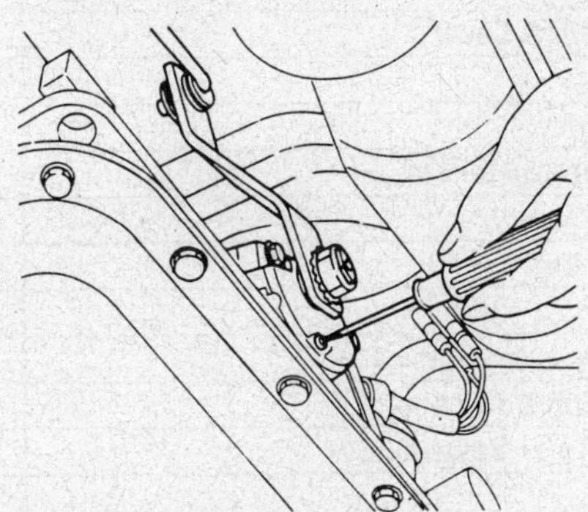

**Fig. 5 Inhibitor switch adjustment**

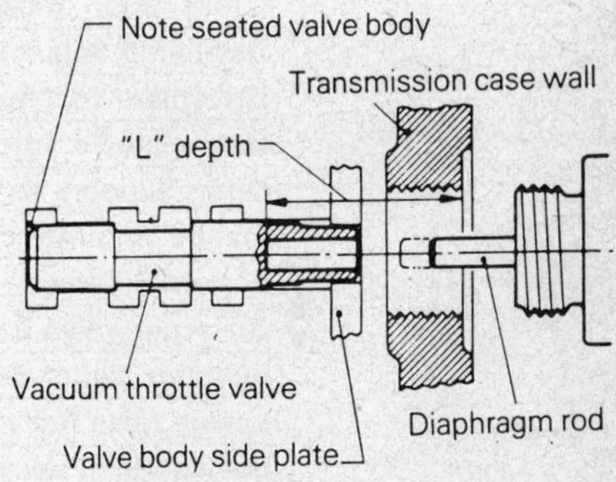


**Fig. 6 Vacuum rod adjustment**

| Measured depth "L" mm (in.) | Rod length mm (in.) | Part number |
|---|---|---|
| Under 25.55 (1.0059) | 29.0 (1.142) | MD610614 |
| 25.65 – 26.05 (1.0098 – 1.0256) | 29.5 (1.161) | MD610615 |
| 26.15 – 26.55 (1.0295 – 1.0453) | 30.0 (1.181) | MD610616 |
| 26.65 – 27.05 (1.0492 – 1.0650) | 30.5 (1.201) | MD610617 |
| Over 27.15 (1.0689) | 31.0 (1.220) | MD610618 |

**Fig. 7 Vacuum rod application chart**

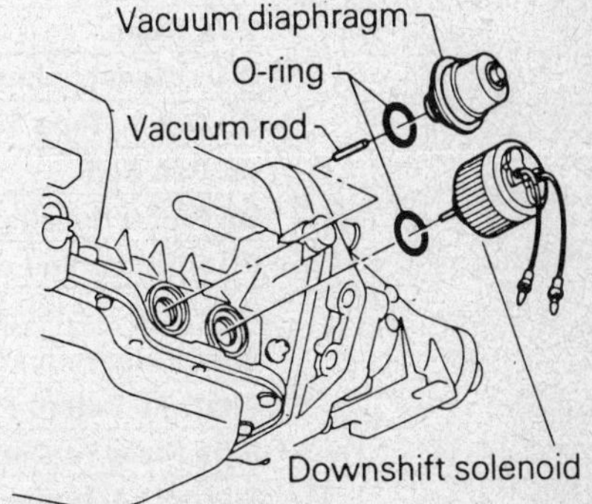


**Fig. 8 Downshift solenoid & vacuum diaphragm removal**

block, then disconnect oil cooler tubes from hoses.

9. Remove bellhousing cover, then the torque converter-to-driveplate attaching bolts. Rotate crankshaft as necessary to gain access to all bolts.
10. Disconnect speedometer cable from transmission.
11. Disconnect control rod and connection lever from cross shaft, then remove the cross shaft assembly.
12. Disconnect ground cable from transmission, then mark position of propeller shaft for installation reference and remove propeller shaft from transmission.
13. Support rear of engine with a suitable jack.
14. Support transmission with a suitable jack, then remove engine support rear bracket.
15. Remove remaining transmission attaching bolts, then carefully lower transmission assembly from vehicle.

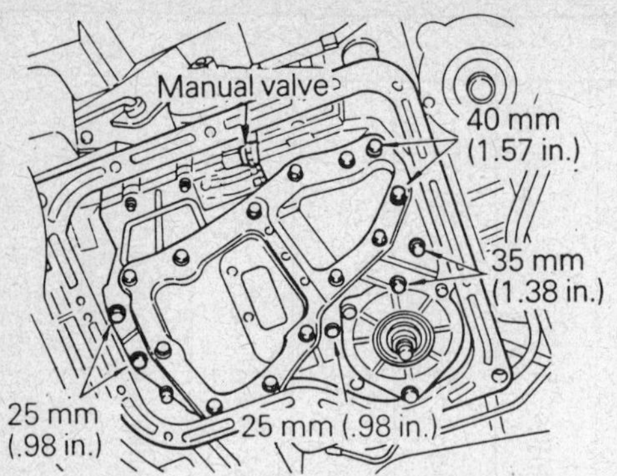


**Fig. 9 Valve body installation**

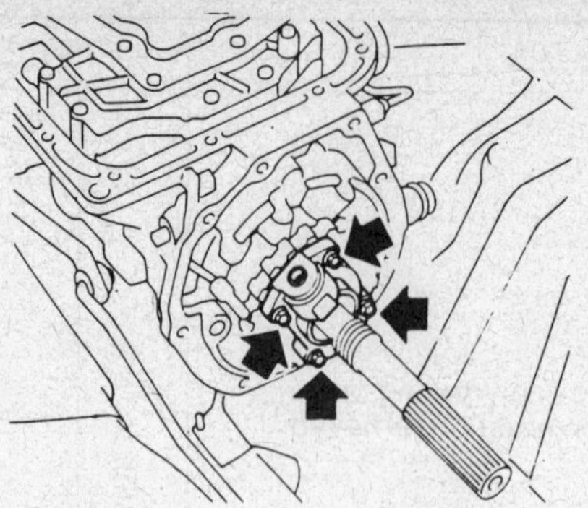

**Fig. 10 Governor removal**

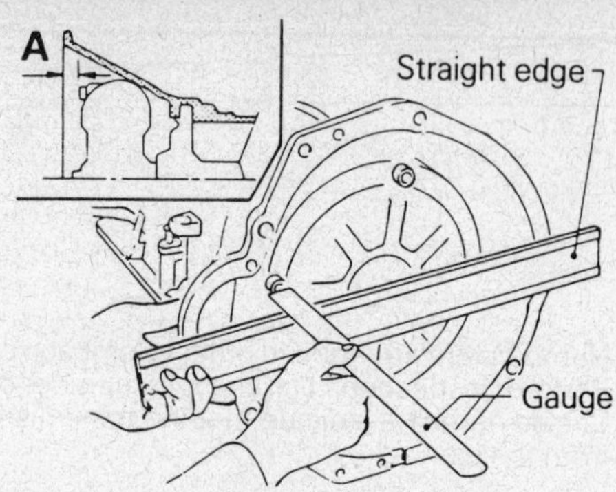


**Fig. 11 Torque converter bolt clearance measurement**

16. Reverse procedure to install, noting the following:
    a. Ensure torque converter bolts dimension (A), **Fig. 11,** measures at least 1.03 inches.
    b. Following installation, adjust inhibitor switch as previously outlined.

# TIGHTENING SPECIFICATIONS

| Component | Torque/Ft. Lbs. |
|---|---|
| Control Valve Body Mounting Bolt | 4–5 |
| Control Valve Reamer Nut | 3.6–5 |
| Converter Housing Mounting Bolt | 33–40 |
| Converter Housing To Engine | 31–39 |
| Cross Shaft To Cross Shaft Lever | 13–17 |
| Downshift Solenoid | 3–4 |
| Driveplate To Crankshaft | 94–100 |
| Driveplate To Torque Converter | 42–46 |
| Drum Support To O.D. Case | 5–6 |
| Flange Yoke Attaching Bolt | 36–43 |
| Governor Tube | 11–13 |
| Governor Valve Body Mounting Bolt | 3–5 |
| Inhibitor Switch Mounting Bolt | 4–5 |
| Lower Valve Body To Upper Valve Body | 1.8–2.5 |
| Manual Shaft Locknut | 22–29 |
| O.D. Servo Cover To Retainer | 3.6–5 |
| O.D. Servo Piston Retainer To O.D. Case | 7–11 |
| O.D. Solenoid | 3 |
| O.D. Stem | 5–7 |
| O.D. Stem Locknut | 11–29 |
| Oil Cooler Pipe To Transmission Case | 22–36 |
| Oil Pan Bolt | 3.6–5 |
| Oil Pump Housing To Oil Pump Cover | 4–6 |
| Oil Strainer To Lower Valve Body | 2–3 |
| One-Way Clutch Inner Race Tightening Bolt | 9–13 |
| Rear Extension Mounting | 14–18 |
| Shaft To Detent Plate | 9 |
| Side Plate To Control Valve Body | 2–2.5 |
| Support Actuator To Rear Extension | 6–8 |
| Test Plug | 4–7 |
| Vacuum Diaphragm | 3 |
| 2nd Piston Stem | ① |
| 2nd Piston Stem Locknut | 11–29 |
| 2nd Servo Piston Retainer To Transmission Case | 5–6 |

①—9–11 ft. lbs., then back off three turns.

# Ultradrive A-604 4-Speed Electronic Automatic Transaxle

## INDEX



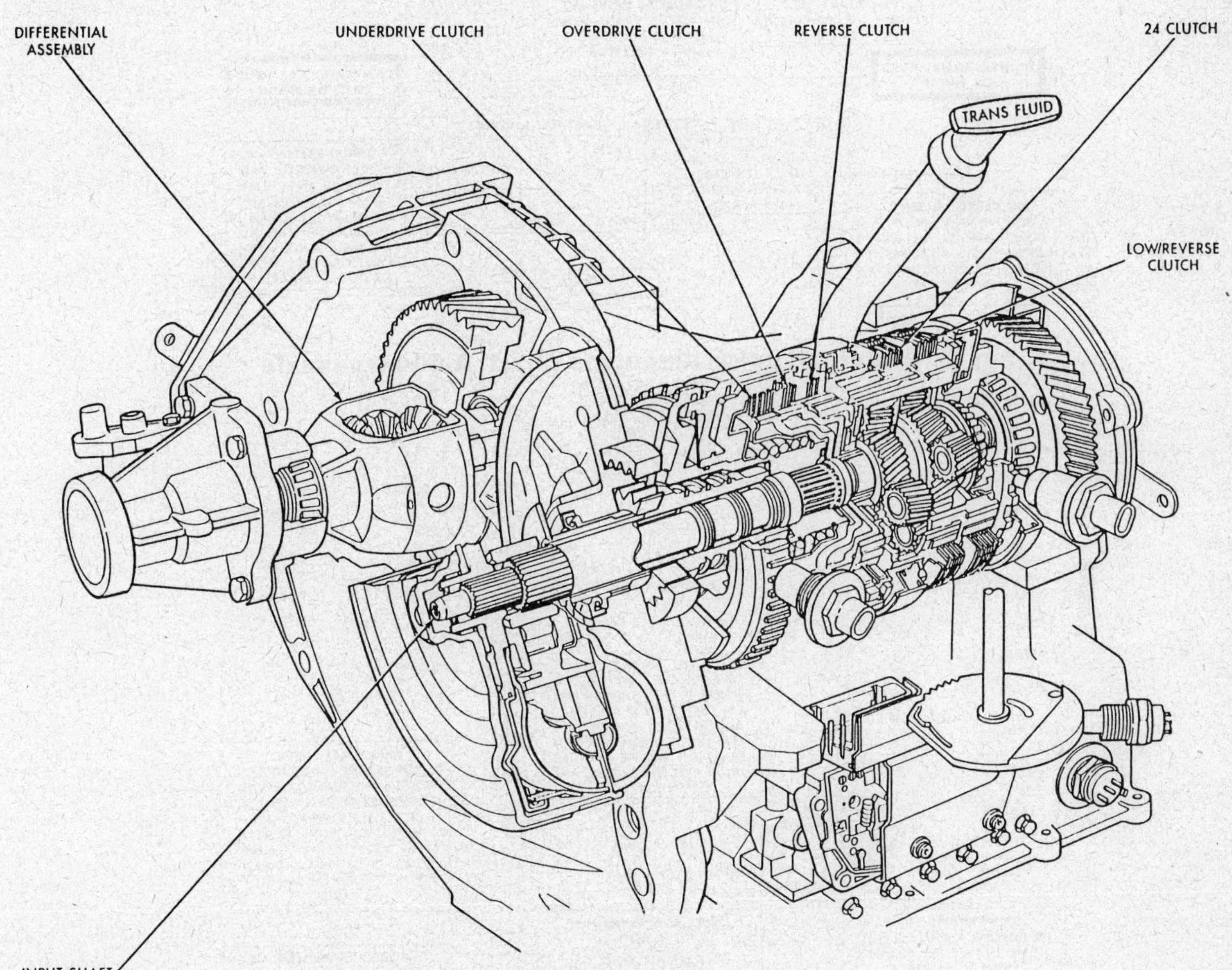


**Fig. 1 Ultradrive A-604 transaxle**

## IDENTIFICATION

During production, the transaxle identification number (TIN) is stamped on a boss located on the transaxle housing. In addition to the TIN, each transaxle carries an assembly part No. which is on a pad just above the oil pan at the rear of the transaxle. This assembly number must be referenced when ordering transaxle replacement parts.

## DESCRIPTION

The A-604 Ultradrive electronic four speed transaxle is a fully adaptive transmission used on Dynasty/New Yorker and Spirit/Acclaim models with V6-181/3.0L engines. The A-604 transaxle uses feedback sensors to adjust functions on a real time basis, similar to electronic anti-lock brake controls.

The A-604 transaxle provides four forward speeds with ratios of 2.84:1, 1.57:1, 1.00:1 and .069:1, and with torque converter lock-up available in second, direct, or overdrive gear. Reverse ratio is 2.21:1. The A-604, **Fig. 1,** consists of three multiple disc input clutches, two multiple disc grounded clutches, four hydraulic accumulators and two planetary gear sets to provide four forward speeds and reverse ratio. Electrical solenoids provide the transmissions shifting control. Sensors on

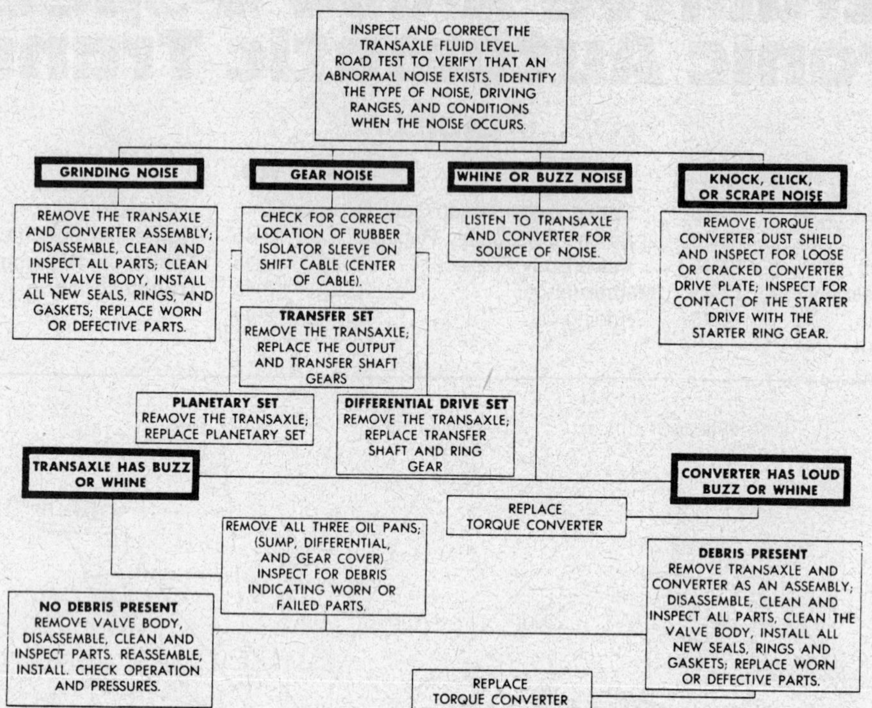


**Fig. 2 Abnormal noise diagnosis chart. A-604 transaxle**

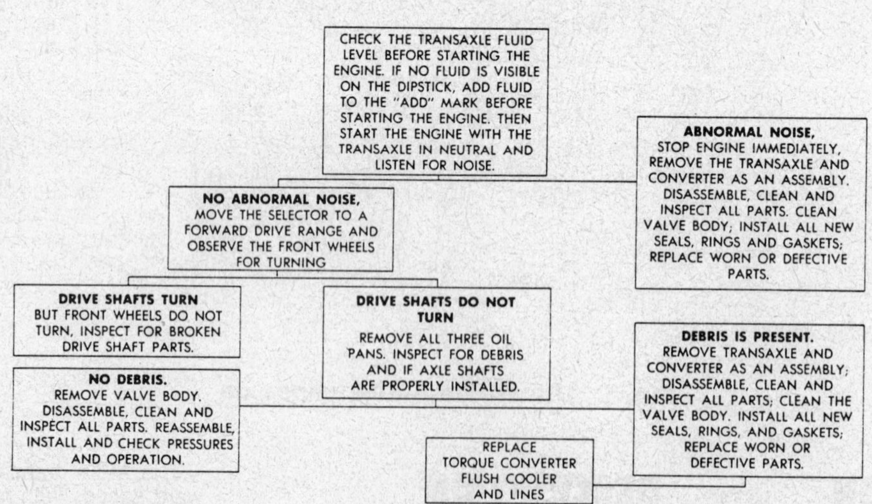


**Fig. 3 Vehicle will not move diagnosis chart. A-604 transaxle**

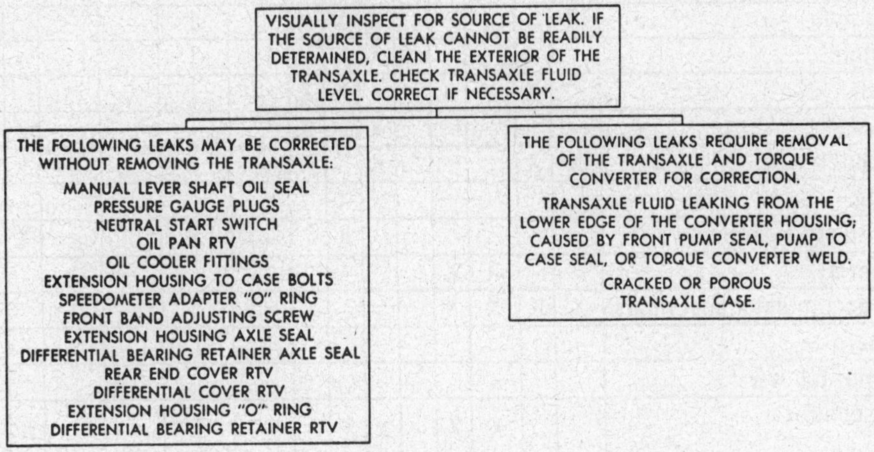

VISUALLY INSPECT FOR SOURCE OF LEAK. IF THE SOURCE OF LEAK CANNOT BE READILY DETERMINED, CLEAN THE EXTERIOR OF THE TRANSAXLE. CHECK TRANSAXLE FLUID LEVEL. CORRECT IF NECESSARY.

THE FOLLOWING LEAKS MAY BE CORRECTED WITHOUT REMOVING THE TRANSAXLE:
MANUAL LEVER SHAFT OIL SEAL
PRESSURE GAUGE PLUGS
NEUTRAL START SWITCH
OIL PAN RTV
OIL COOLER FITTINGS
EXTENSION HOUSING TO CASE BOLTS
SPEEDOMETER ADAPTER "O" RING
FRONT BAND ADJUSTING SCREW
EXTENSION HOUSING AXLE SEAL
DIFFERENTIAL BEARING RETAINER AXLE SEAL
REAR END COVER RTV
DIFFERENTIAL COVER RTV
EXTENSION HOUSING "O" RING
DIFFERENTIAL BEARING RETAINER RTV

THE FOLLOWING LEAKS REQUIRE REMOVAL OF THE TRANSAXLE AND TORQUE CONVERTER FOR CORRECTION.
TRANSAXLE FLUID LEAKING FROM THE LOWER EDGE OF THE CONVERTER HOUSING; CAUSED BY FRONT PUMP SEAL, PUMP TO CASE SEAL, OR TORQUE CONVERTER WELD.
CRACKED OR POROUS TRANSAXLE CASE.

**Fig. 4 Fluid leak diagnosis. A-604 transaxle**

the transmission send control inputs to the electronic control unit located under the hood in a potted, diecast aluminum housing. The system can be diagnosed by accessing information from the electronic control unit memory. The transmission and differential sump have a common oil sump with a communicating opening between the two.

## TROUBLESHOOTING

Before attempting any repair on the A-604 EAT, general engine performance, transmission fluid level and shift linkage must first be checked and adjusted if necessary. For specific symptom diagnosis, refer to **Figs. 2, 3, 4 and 5.**

## MAINTENANCE

### ADDING OIL

Oil level should be checked every six months. To check oil level, start engine and let idle with transaxle in park or neutral for at least one minute. Oil level, when properly filled, will read near the Add mark when oil is cold, (70°F), and in the Hot zone when oil is at normal operating temperature (180°F). Add as necessary.

### CHANGING OIL

Fluid and filter changes are not required for average passenger vehicle usage. If the vehicle is subjected to severe usage, the fluid and filter should be changed at 15,000 mile intervals. The magnet on the inside of the oil pan should also be cleaned with a clean, dry cloth at this time. Fluid and filter change procedure is as follows:

1. Raise vehicle on a suitable hoist and place a wide drain pan container under transaxle oil pan.
2. Loosen pan bolts and tap pan at one corner to break seal and allow fluid to drain, then remove pan.
3. Install new filter and O-ring an bottom of valve body, then clean the oil pan and magnet.
4. Reinstall pan using RTV sealant and **torque** pan bolts to 165 inch lbs.
5. Add four quarts of Mopar ATF Plus Type 7176 or Dexron II automatic transmission fluid through the fill tube.
6. Start engine and allow to idle for at least one minute, then with parking and service brakes applied, move selector lever through it's range, pausing momentarily at each position. Return lever to P or N position.
7. Add fluid to bring level 1/8 inch below the Add mark. Recheck fluid level after transaxle is at normal operating temperature.

## IN-VEHICLE ADJUSTMENTS

### GEARSHIFT LINKAGE ADJUSTMENT

**When it is necessary to disassemble linkage cable from levers, plastic grommet retainers should always be replaced with new grommets.**

1. Place gearshift lever in P position, then loosen clamp bolt on gearshift cable bracket.
2. **On column shift models,** ensure preload adjustment spring engages fork on transaxle bracket.
3. **On all models,** pull the shift lever by hand all the way to the front detent position (P) and **torque** lock screw to 100 inch lbs.

## IN-VEHICLE REPAIRS

### SPEEDOMETER PINION GEAR, REPLACE

1. Remove bolt and washer assembly securing speedometer pinion adapter in the extension housing, then with cable housing connected, carefully work adapter and pinion out of the extension housing.
2. Remove the retainer and pinion from the adapter.
3. If transmission fluid is found in cable housing, install a new speedometer pinion and seal assembly.
4. If transmission fluid is found leaking between the cable and adapter, replace the small O-ring on the cable. Remove the adapter from the cable and replace the O-ring.
5. Clean adapter flange and mating surfaces and install the adapter on the cable, then install pinion on adapter with new large O-ring and install retainer on pinion and adapter. Be sure retainer is properly seated.
6. Install bolt and washer and **torque** to 60 inch lbs.

### SOLENOID ASSEMBLY, REPLACE

1. Remove input speed sensor, **Fig. 6.**
2. Remove sound cover located under input speed sensor opening.
3. Remove solenoid assembly attaching screws, **Fig. 7,** and solenoid assembly.
4. Reverse procedure to install.

### VALVE BODY, REPLACE

1. Raise and support vehicle.
2. Drain transmission fluid as described under "Maintenance."

## DIAGNOSIS CHART "B"

| POSSIBLE CAUSE / CONDITION | HARSH ENGAGEMENT FROM NEUTRAL TO D | HARSH ENGAGEMENT FROM NEUTRAL TO R | DELAYED ENGAGEMENT FROM NEUTRAL TO D | DELAYED ENGAGEMENT FROM NEUTRAL TO R | POOR SHIFT QUALITY | SHIFTS ERRATIC | DRIVES IN NEUTRAL | DRAGS OR LOCKS | GRATING, SCRAPING, GROWLING NOISE | KNOCKING, NOISE | BUZZING NOISE | BUZZING NOISE DURING SHIFTS ONLY | HARD TO FILL, OIL BLOWS OUT FILLER TUBE | TRANSAXLE OVERHEATS | HARSH UPSHIFT | NO UPSHIFT INTO OVERDRIVE | NO LOCKUP | HARSH DOWNSHIFTS | HIGH SHIFT EFFORTS | HARSH LOCKUP SHIFT |
|---|---|---|---|---|---|---|---|---|---|---|---|---|---|---|---|---|---|---|---|---|
| Engine Performance | X | X | | | | X | | | | | | | | | X | | | X | | |
| Worn or faulty clutch(es) | X | X | X | X | | X | X | X | | | | | | | X | X | | X | | |
| —Underdrive clutch | X | | X | | | X | X | X | | | | | | | | | | X | | |
| —Overdrive clutch | | | | | | X | X | X | | | | | | | X | X | | | | |
| —Reverse clutch | | X | | X | | | X | X | | | | | | | | | | | | |
| —2/4 clutch | | | | | | X | | X | | | | | | | X | | | X | | |
| —Low/reverse clutch | X | X | | | | X | | X | | | | | | | | | | X | | |
| Clutch(es) dragging | | | | | | | X | | | | | | | | | | | | | |
| Insufficient clutch plate clearance | | | | | | | X | | | | | | | X | | | | | | |
| Damaged clutch seals | | | X | X | | | | | | | | | | | | | | X | | |
| Worn or damaged accumulator seal ring(s) | X | X | X | X | | | | | | | | | | | | | | X | | |
| Faulty cooling system | | | | | | | | | | | | | | X | | | | | | |
| Engine coolant temp. too low | | | | | | | | | | | | | | | | X | X | | | |
| Incorrect gearshift control linkage adjustment | | | X | X | | X | X | | | | | | | X | | | | | | |
| Shift linkage damaged | | | | | | | | | | | | | | | | | | | X | |
| Chipped or damaged gear teeth | | | | | | | | X | X | | | | | | | | | | | |
| Planetary gear sets broken or seized | | | | | | | | X | X | | | | | | | | | | | |
| Bearings worn or damaged | | | | | | | | X | X | | | | | | | | | | | |
| Driveshaft(s) bushing(s) worn or damaged | | | | | | | | | X | | | | | | | | | | | |
| Worn or broken reaction shaft support seal rings | | | X | X | X | X | | | | | | | | | | | | X | | |
| Worn or damaged input shaft seal rings | | | X | X | | | | | | | | | | | | | X | | | |
| Valve body malfunction or leakage | X | X | X | X | X | X | X | | | | X | | | | | | X | X | X | |
| Hydraulic pressures too low | | | X | X | X | X | | | | | | | | X | X | | X | | | |
| Hydraulic pressures too high | X | X | | | | | | | | | | | | | X | | | X | | |
| Faulty oil pump | | | X | X | | X | | | | | | | | X | | | X | | | |
| Oil filter clogged | | | X | X | X | X | | | | | | | X | | | | | | | |
| Low fluid level | | | X | X | X | X | | | | | X | | | X | | | X | X | | |
| High fluid level | | | | | | | | | | | | | X | X | | | | | | |
| Aerated fluid | | | X | X | X | X | | | | | X | | X | X | | | X | X | | |
| Engine idle speed too low | | | X | X | | | | | | | | | | | | | | | | |
| Engine idle speed too high | X | X | | | | | | | | | | | | X | | | | X | | |
| Normal solenoid operation | | | | | | | | | | | | X | | | | | | | | |
| Solenoid sound cover loose | | | | | | | | | | | | X | | | | | | | | |
| Sticking lockup piston | | | | | | | | | | | | | | | | | | | | X |

**Fig. 5 Symptom diagnosis chart. A-604 transaxle**

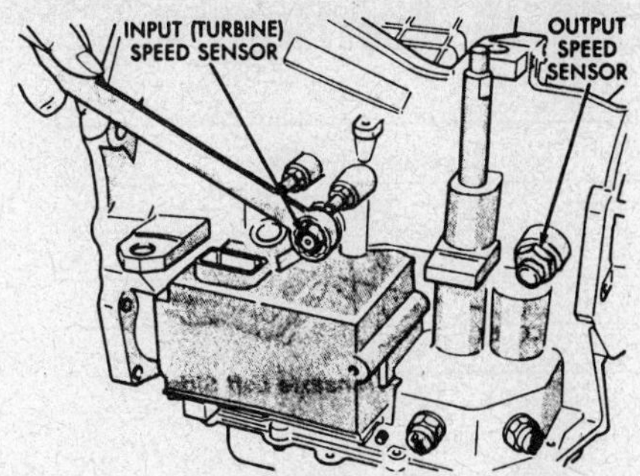


**Fig. 6 Removing input speed sensor**

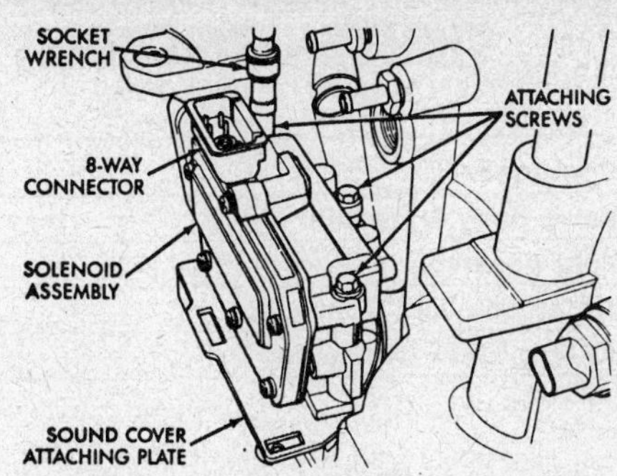


**Fig. 7 Removing solenoid assembly**

3. Remove oil pan attaching bolts and oil pan.
4. Remove oil filter, then the valve body attaching bolts.
5. Push park rod rollers from guide bracket, **Fig. 8,** then remove valve body.
6. Reverse procedure to install noting the following:
   a. Guide park rollers into guide bracket.
   b. **Torque** valve body attaching bolts to 40 inch lbs.
   c. **Torque** oil pan attaching bolts to 14 ft. lbs.

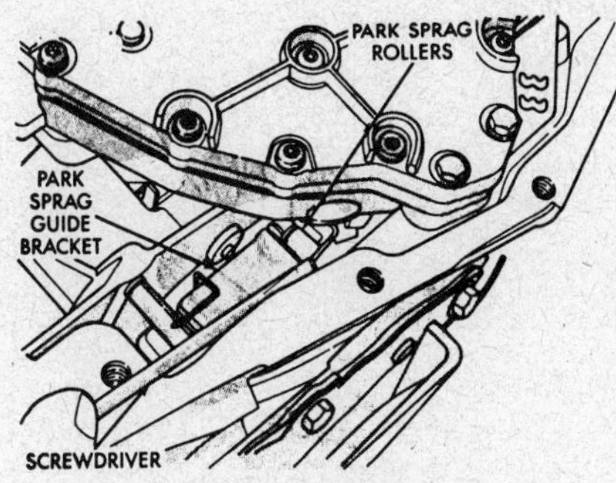


**Fig. 8 Removing park rod rollers from guide bracket**

## TRANSAXLE REPLACE

1. Disconnect battery ground cable.
2. Disconnect throttle linkage and shift control linkage from transaxle.
3. Remove both upper and lower oil cooler hoses.
4. Support engine with suitable engine lifting equipment.
5. Remove bellhousing upper attaching bolts.
6. Raise and support vehicle, then remove front wheels and left splash shield.
7. Remove wheel hub nut and driveshafts.
8. Remove torque converter dust cover, then mark torque converter and driveplate for reference during reassembly.
9. Remove torque converter attaching bolts. Remove plug from access hole in right splash shield to rotate crankcase for bolt removal.
10. Remove N/P switch electrical connector.
11. Remove engine mount bracket from front crossmember, then the front mount insulator through bolt and attaching bolts.
12. Position suitable jack under transaxle, then remove left engine mount.
13. Remove starter, then the remaining bellhousing attaching bolts.
14. Move transaxle away from engine and lower from vehicle.
15. Reverse procedure to install.

## TIGHTENING SPECIFICATIONS

| Component | Torque/Ft. Lbs. |
|---|---|
| Cooler Line Fittings | 9 |
| Differential Cover | 13–14 |
| Differential Ring Cover | 70 |
| Differential Bearing Retainer | 21 |
| Extension Housing | 21 |
| Input Speed Sensor | 20 |
| L/R Clutch Retainer | 3–4 |
| Neutral Safety Switch | 25 |
| Oil Pan To Case | 14 |
| Output Gear Bolt | 200 |
| Output Speed Sensor | 20 |
| Pressure Taps | 4 |
| PRNDL Switch | 25 |
| Pump To Case | 23 |
| Reaction Shaft To Pump | 23 |
| Solenoid Assembly To Case | 8–9 |
| Transfer Plate To case | 8–9 |

## TIGHTENING SPECIFICATIONS–Continued

| Component | Torque/Ft. Lbs. |
|---|---|
| Valve Body & Transfer Plate | 3–4 |
| Vent Assembly | 9 |
| 8-Way Solenoid Connector | 3 |
| 60-Way EATX Connector | 3 |

# FRONT WHEEL DRIVE AXLES

TABLE OF CONTENTS



# Chrysler Except Imports

**NOTE:** For Service Procedures On Dodge Monaco Models, Refer "Eagle Premier" In The "Eagle" Section. For Service Procedures On The Plymouth Laser, Refer To "Eagle Talon" In The "Eagle" Section.

INDEX



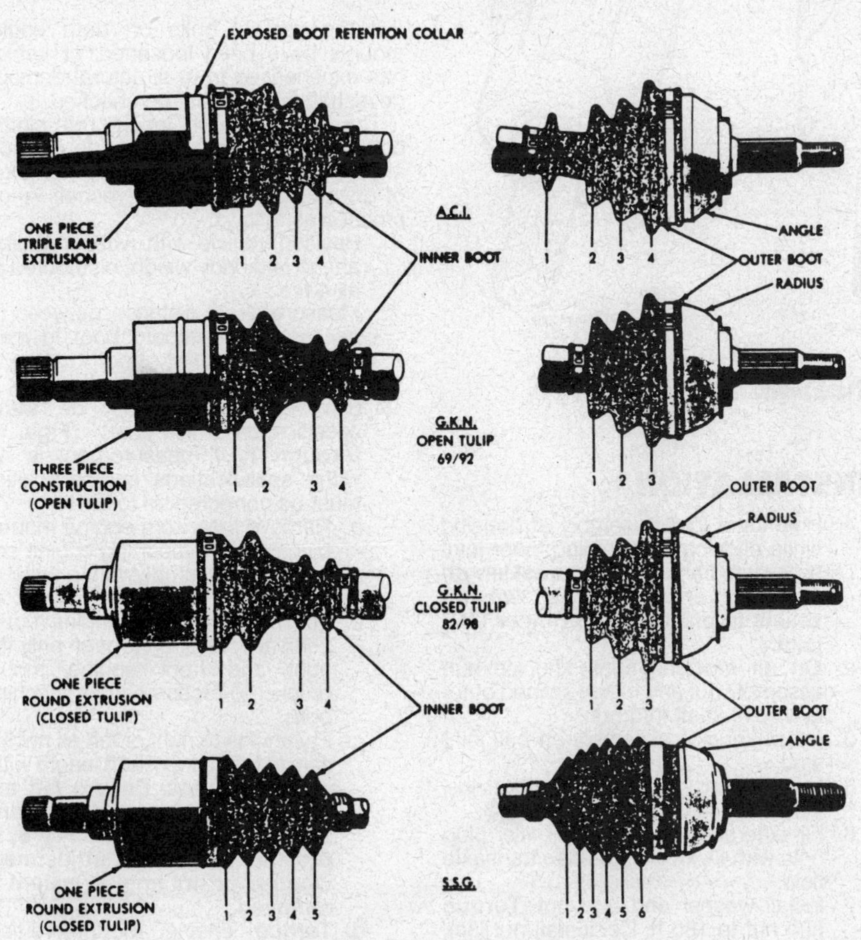


**Fig. 1 Driveshaft identification. 1989–90 models**

## DRIVESHAFT IDENTIFICATION

Driveshafts are identified by manufacturer, **Figs. 1 and 2.** Vehicles can be equipped with any of these assemblies, however they should not be intermixed.

Two different driveshaft systems are used. Some models use an "equal length" system while all others use an "unequal length" system. The "equal length" system has short solid interconnecting shafts of equal length on the left and right sides. The "unequal length" system has a short solid interconnecting shaft on left side with a longer tubular interconnecting shaft on right.

Procedures for installation and removal of driveshafts are essentially the same for all types of assemblies used.

## DRIVESHAFTS REPLACE

### REMOVAL

**Inboard C/V joints have stub shafts splined into differential side gears, or splined into the intermediate shaft on right side of an equal length system. Driveshafts are spring loaded and are retained to side gears by constant spring pressure provided by spring contained in C/V joints.**

1. Remove cotter pin, lock and spring washer, then the hub nut washer and wheel assembly.
2. If removing the righthand driveshaft, speedometer pinion must be removed prior to driveshaft removal, **Fig. 3.**

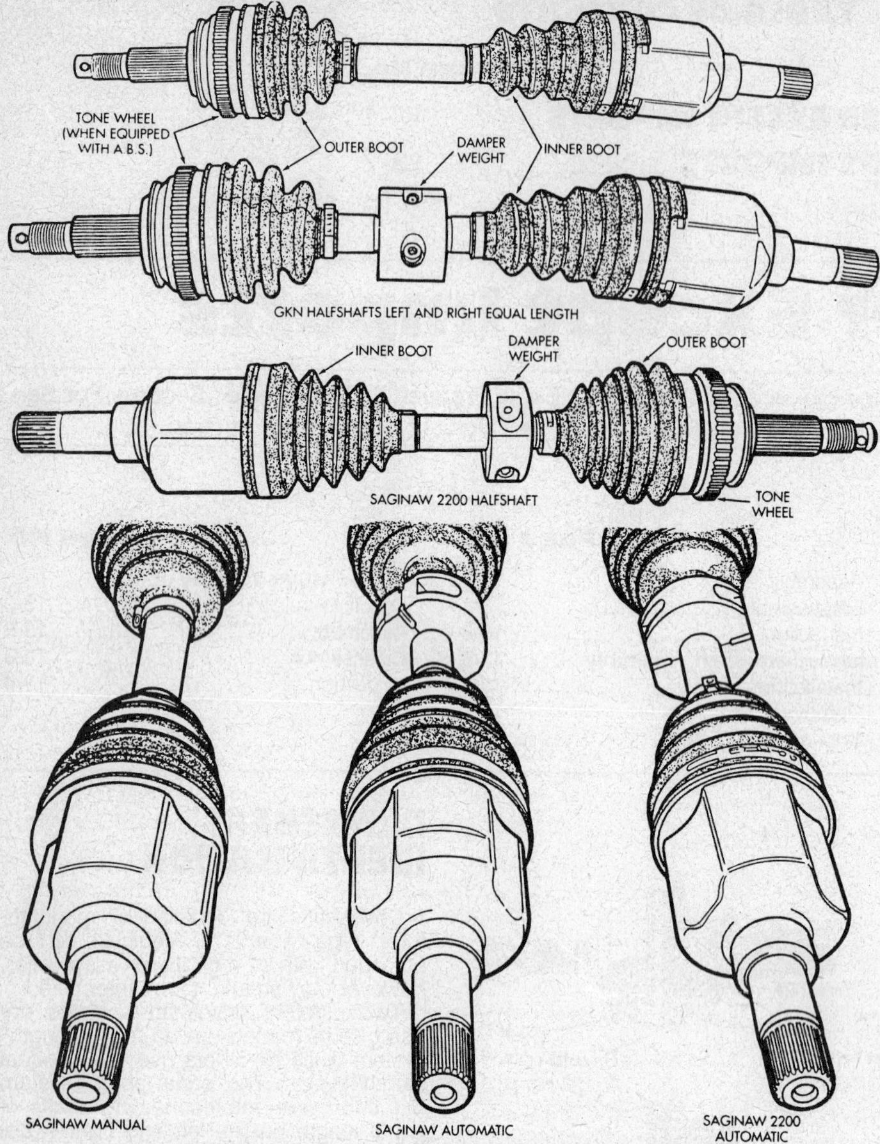


**Fig. 2 Driveshaft identification. 1991 models**

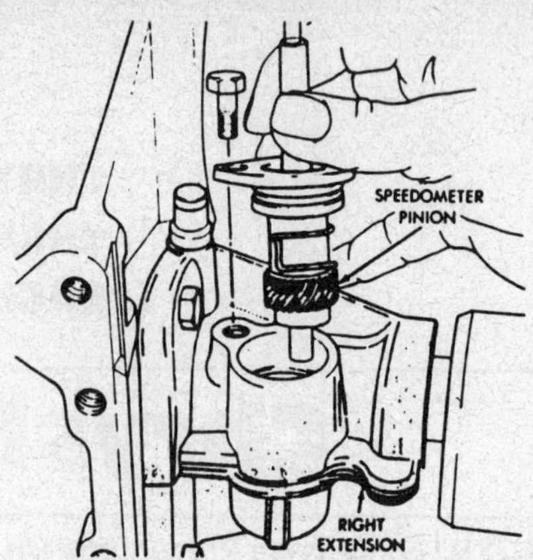


**Fig. 3 Speedometer pinion replacement**

3. Remove clamp bolt securing ball joint clamp bolt to steering knuckle, then separate ball joint stud from steering knuckle. **Do not damage ball joint or C/V joint boots.**
4. Separate outer C/V joint splined shaft from hub by holding C/V housing while moving knuckle/hub assembly away from C/V joint. **Do not damage slinger on outer C/V joint. Do not attempt to remove, repair or replace.**
5. Support assembly at C/V joint housings and remove by pulling outward on the inner C/V joint housing. Do not pull on shaft. **If removing lefthand driveshaft assembly, removal may be aided by inserting a screwdriver blade between differential pinion shaft and carefully prying against end face of stub.**
6. Remove driveshaft assembly from vehicle.

## INSTALLATION

1. Hold inner joint assembly at housing while aligning and guiding inner joint spline into transaxle. **On equal length systems, ensure rubber washer seal is in place on right inner C/V joint.**
2. **On all models,** push knuckle/hub assembly out and install splined outer C/V joint shaft into hub.
3. Install knuckle assembly on ball joint stud.
4. Install clamp bolt. **Torque** to 70 ft. lbs.
5. Install speedometer pinion, **Fig. 3.**
6. Fill differential to bottom of filler plug hole with Dexron automatic transaxle fluid.
7. Install washer and hub nut. **Torque** hub nut to 180 ft. lbs. Install nut lock and cotter pin.
8. If, after attaching driveshaft assembly in vehicle, the inboard boot appears collapsed or deformed, vent the inner boot by inserting a round tipped, small diameter rod between boot and shaft. As venting occurs, the boot will return to normal shape. **After installation of driveshaft, check driveshaft length as outlined in "Driveshaft Length, Adjust."**

## DRIVESHAFT LENGTH ADJUST

If the vertical bolts on both engine mounts have been loosened, or vehicle has experienced front structural damage, driveshaft length must be checked.

The engine mounts incorporate slotted bolt holes to permit side-to-side positioning of the engine, thereby affecting length of driveshaft. To check driveshaft length proceed as follows.

1. Position vehicle with wheels straight ahead and body weight distributed on all 4 tires.
2. Measure direct distance between inner edge of outboard boot to inner edge of inboard boot on both driveshafts, **Fig. 4.**
3. Driveshaft length must be within specifications in chart, **Figs. 4 through 7.** If measurement is not within specifications, engine position must be corrected as follows:
   a. Remove load from engine mounts by carefully supporting engine and transaxle assembly with a suitable jack.
   b. Loosen right and left engine mount vertical bolts, then loosen only the right and front engine mount bracket-to-crossmember attaching bolts.
   c. Pry engine to right or left as necessary to bring driveshaft length within specifications. **Ensure left engine mount is sleeved over long support bolt and shaft, Fig. 8, to provide lateral adjustment whether or not engine weight is removed.**
   d. **Torque** engine mount vertical bolts to 27 ft. lbs. and front and center left engine mount bolts to 40 ft. lbs.

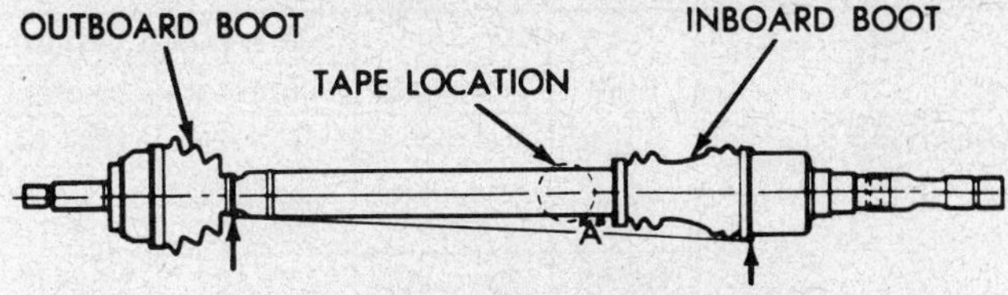


Fig. 4 Measuring driveshaft

| Body | Engine | Driveshaft Identification | | | "A" Dimension | |
|---|---|---|---|---|---|---|
| | | Type | Side | Transaxle | mm | Inch |
| Omni & Horizon | 2.2L | A.C.I. | Right | Auto | 469-478 | 18.5-19.0 |
| | | | Left | N/A | — | — |
| | | 69-92 | Right | Auto | 498-504 | 19.6-19.8 |
| | | | Left | Auto | 208-221 | 8.2- 8.7 |
| | | 69-92 | Right | Manual | 498-504 | 19.6-19.8 |
| | | | Left | Manual | 240-253 | 9.4-10.0 |
| Except Omni, Horizon, Imperial, New Yorker/ 5th Avenue | 2.2L | A.C.I. | Right | All | 477-485 | 18.8-19.1 |
| | | | Left | All | 197-212 | 7.8- 8.3 |
| | | S.S.G. | Right | All | 457-469 | 18.0-18.5 |
| | | | Left | All | 184-200 | 7.2- 7.9 |
| | | 82-98 | Right | All | 481-489 | 18.9-19.2 |
| | | | Left | All | 216-224 | 8.5- 8.8 |
| | 2.5L/3.0L | S.S.G. | Right | All | 457-469 | 18.0-18.5 |
| | | | Left | All | 184-200 | 7.7- 7.9 |
| | | 82.98 | Right | All | 481-489 | 18.9-19.2 |
| | | | Left | All | 216-224 | 8.5- 8.8 |
| Except Omni, Horizon, Imperial, New Yorker, Dynasty | 2.5L Turbo 1 | S.S.G. | Right | Auto | 457-469 | 18.0-18.5 |
| | | | Left | Auto | 184-200 | 7.2- 7.9 |
| | | 82-98 | Right | Auto | 481-489 | 18.9-19.2 |
| | | | Left | Auto | 216-224 | 8.5- 8.8 |
| | | S.S.G. | Right | Manual | 187-196 | 7.4- 7.7 |
| | | | Left | Manual | 187-196 | 7.4- 7.7 |
| | | 82-98 | Right | Manual | 216-224 | 8.5- 8.8 |
| | | | Left | Manual | 216-224 | 8.5- 8.8 |
| Daytona, LeBaron | 2.2L Turbo II | 82-98 | Right | Manual | 216-224 | 8.5- 8.8 |
| | | | Left | Manual | 216-224 | 8.5- 8.8 |
| New Yorker, Dynasty, Imperial | 3.3L | 82-98 | Right | Auto | 481-489 | 18.9-19.2 |
| | | | Left | Auto | 216-224 | 8.5- 8.8 |

Fig. 6 Driveshaft length specifications. 1990 models

| Body | Engine | Driveshaft Identification | | | "A" Dimension | |
|---|---|---|---|---|---|---|
| | | Type | Side | Transaxle | mm | Inch |
| Omni & Horizon | 2.2L | A.C.I. | Right | Auto | 469-478 | 18.5-19.0 |
| | | | Left | N/A | — | — |
| | | 69-92 | Right | Auto | 498-504 | 19.6-19.8 |
| | | | Left | Auto | 208-221 | 8.2- 8.7 |
| | | 69-92 | Right | Manual | 498-504 | 19.6-19.8 |
| | | | Left | Manual | 240-253 | 9.4-10.0 |
| Except Omni, Horizon, Dynasty & New Yorker | 2.2L | A.C.I. | Right | All | 477-485 | 18.8-19.1 |
| | | | Left | All | 197-212 | 7.8- 8.3 |
| | | S.S.G. | Right | All | 457-469 | 18.0-18.5 |
| | | | Left | All | 184-200 | 7.2- 7.9 |
| | | 82-98 | Right | All | 481-489 | 18.9-19.2 |
| | | | Left | All | 216-224 | 8.5- 8.8 |
| | 2.5L | S.S.G. | Right | All | 457-469 | 18.0-18.5 |
| | | | Left | All | 184-200 | 7.7- 7.9 |
| | | 82.98 | Right | All | 481-489 | 18.9-19.2 |
| | | | Left | All | 216-224 | 8.5- 8.8 |
| Except Omni, Horizon, Dynasty & New Yorker | 2.5L Turbo 1 | S.S.G. | Right | Auto | 457-469 | 18.0-18.5 |
| | | | Left | Auto | 184-200 | 7.2- 7.9 |
| | | 82-98 | Right | Auto | 481-489 | 18.9-19.2 |
| | | | Left | Auto | 216-224 | 8.5- 8.8 |
| | | S.S.G. | Right | Manual | 187-196 | 7.4- 7.7 |
| | | | Left | Manual | 187-196 | 7.4- 7.7 |
| | | 82-98 | Right | Manual | 216-224 | 8.5- 8.8 |
| | | | Left | Manual | 216-224 | 8.5- 8.8 |
| Dynasty & New Yorker | 3.0L | 82-98 | Right | Auto | 481-489 | 18.9-19.2 |
| | | | Left | Auto | 216-224 | 8.5- 8.8 |
| Daytona | 2.2L Turbo II | 82-98 | Right | Manual | 216-224 | 8.5- 8.8 |
| | | | Left | Manual | 216-224 | 8.5- 8.8 |

Fig. 5 Driveshaft length specifications. 1989 models

e. **On 1989 New Yorker Landau and Dynasty models, torque** vertical bolts to 60 ft.lbs.

# INNER CONSTANT VELOCITY JOINT SERVICE

## DISASSEMBLY

1. Remove clamp and boot from joint and discard, **Fig. 9.**
2. **On 1989-90 G.K.N. units,** hold housing and lightly compress C/V joint retention spring while bending tabs back with a pair of pliers, **Fig. 10.** Support the housing as the retention spring pushes it from the tripod.
3. **On 1991 G.K.N. units,** Clamp interconnecting bar in a vise and hold C/V joint housing on an angle. Gently pull on housing until one of the rollers is free. Continue to hold housing on an angle and continue to pull on the housing until all roller are free.
4. **On A.C.I. units,** hold housing and lightly compress C/V joint retention spring while bending tabs back with a pair of pliers, **Fig. 11.** Support the housing as the retention spring pushes it from the tripod.
5. **On S.S.G. units,** use a flathead screwdriver to pry wire ring out of groove and slide tripod from housing, **Fig. 12. When removing housing from tripod, hold rollers in place on the trunnion studs to prevent rollers and needle bearings from falling out. After tripod is out of housing, secure rollers in place with tape.**
6. Remove snap ring from end of shaft, then the tripod using a brass drift.

## INSPECTION

Remove grease from assembly and inspect bearing race and tripod components for wear and damage and replace as necessary. On spring loaded joints inspect spring, spring cup and spherical end of connecting shaft for wear and damage and replace as necessary. **Components of spring loaded and non-spring loaded inner C/V joints cannot be interchanged.**

## ASSEMBLY

**Do not use the A.C.I. or G.K.N. boot clamps on the Saginaw hard plastic C/V boots, as these clamps do not have the load capacity to withhold the much greater force needed to clamp plastic boots.**

1. **On right side of equal length systems,** slide rubber seal over stub shaft and into groove.
2. **On all models,** slide small end of boot over shaft. On Tubular type shafts, align boot lip with mark on shaft outer diameter. On solid type shafts, position small end of boot in groove on shaft.
3. Place rubber clamp over groove on boot, if equipped.
4. **On A.C.I and G.K.N. units,** install tripod on shaft with non-chamfered face of tripod body facing shaft retainer groove. On S.S.G. units, place wire ring retainer over interconnecting shaft, then on all models slide tripod on shaft.
5. **On all models,** lock tripod assembly on shaft by installing snap ring in shaft groove.
6. **On G.K.N. units,** distribute two of three provided grease packets into boot and remaining packet into housing, on A.C.I. units, one of two packets into boot and remaining packet into housing, on S.S.G. units, 1/2 of packet into housing and remaining amount into boot.
7. **On all models,** position spring, with spring cup attached to exposed end, into spring pocket, **Fig. 13.** Place a small amount of grease on spring cup, then position housing over tripod. Slip tripod into housing. On G.K.N. units, bend retaining tabs down to original position. On A.C.I. units, reattach boot to hold housing onto shaft without bending back retaining tabs. On S.S.G. units, install tripod wire retaining ring into position. **On all spring units, ensure tripod is securely retained in housing and spring remains centered in housing spring pocket when tripod is installed and seated in spring cup.**
8. **On all units,** position boot over boot retaining groove in housing, then install clamp.

# OUTER CONSTANT VELOCITY JOINT SERVICE

## DISASSEMBLY

1. Cut boot clamps from boot and discard boot and clamps, **Fig. 14.**
2. Clean grease from joint.
3. **On A.C.I. and G.K.N. units,** support shaft in a soft jawed vise, support outer joint and tap with a mallet to dislodge joint from internal circlip installed in a groove at outer end of shaft, **Fig. 15.** Do not remove slinger from housing.
4. **On S.S.G. units,** loosen damper weight bolts and slide weight and boot toward inner joint, then expand circlip with suitable pliers, slide joint from shaft and reinstall damper weight.
5. **On all units,** remove circlip from shaft groove and discard, **Fig. 16.**
6. **On A.C.I. and G.K.N. units,** do not remove heavy lock ring from shaft, **Fig. 16,** unless shaft requires replacement.

| Model | Engine | Side | Transaxle | Driveshaft Length | |
|---|---|---|---|---|---|
| | | | | Millimeters | Inches |
| New Yorker/Salon, Dynasty, Daytona, LeBaron, Shadow & Sundance | 2.2L/4-135 & 2.5L/4-153 | Right | Auto | 452–460 | 17.8–18.1 |
| | | Left | Auto | 188–196 | 7.4–7.7 |
| | | Right | Manual | 453–461 | 17.8–18.1 |
| | | Left | Manual | 196–204 | 7.7–8.0 |
| | 3.0L/V6-181 | Right | Auto | 453–461 | 17.8–18.1 |
| | | Left | Auto | 189–197 | 7.4–7.7 |
| Daytona, LeBaron, Shadow & Sundance | 2.5L/4-153 Turbo | Right | Auto | 453–461 | 17.8–18.1 |
| | | Left | Auto | 189–197 | 7.4–7.7 |
| | | Right | Manual | 189–197 | 7.4–7.7 |
| | | Left | Manual | 196–204 | 7.7–8.0 |
| New Yorker/Salon/Fifth Avenue, Dynasty & Imperial | 3.3L/V6-203 & 3.8L/V6-231 | Right | Auto | 189–197 | 7.4–7.7 |
| | | Left | Auto | 189–197 | 7.4–7.7 |
| LeBaron/Landau, Spirit & Acclaim | 2.5L/4-153, 3.0L/V6-181 & 2.5L/4-153 Turbo | Right | Auto | 434–444 | 17.0–17.5 |
| | | Left | Auto | 176–186 | 6.9–7.3 |
| | 2.5L/4-153 | Right | Manual | 434–444 | 17.0–17.5 |
| | | Left | Manual | 165–175 | 6.5–6.9 |
| | 3.0L/V6-181 | Right | Manual | 453–461 | 17.8–18.1 |
| | | Left | Manual | 196–204 | 7.7–8.0 |
| Daytona & LeBaron | 2.5L/4-153 Turbo | Right | Manual | 165–175 | 6.5–6.9 |
| | | Right | Manual | 165–175 | 6.5–6.9 |
| | 2.2L/4-135 Turbo III | Right | Manual | 194–204 | 7.6–8.0 |
| | | Left | Manual | 194–204 | 7.6–8.0 |

**Fig. 7 Driveshaft length specifications. 1991 models**

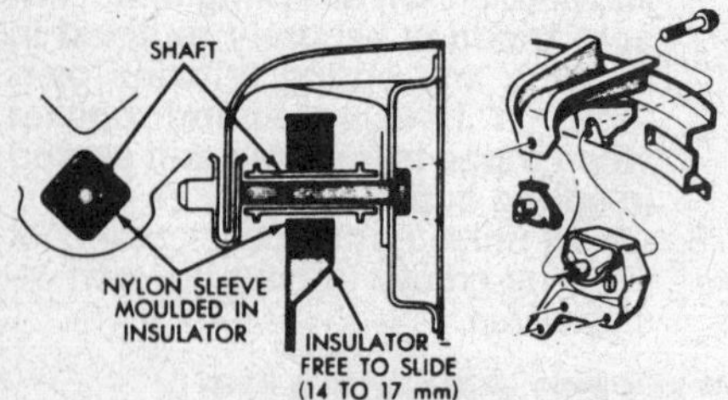


**Fig. 8 Left engine mount adjustment**

7. **On all units,** if constant velocity joint was operating satisfactorily and grease does not appear contaminated, proceed to "Assembly" procedure, Step 8.
8. If constant velocity joint is noisy or badly worn, replace entire unit. The repair kit will include boot, clamps, circlip and lubricant. Clean and inspect joint as outlined in the following steps.
9. Clean surplus grease and mark relative position of inner cross, cage and housing with a dab of paint.
10. Hold joint vertically in a soft jawed vise.
11. Press downward on one side of inner race to tilt cage and remove ball from opposite side, **Fig. 17.** If joint is tight, use a hammer and a brass drift to tap inner race. Do not strike cage. Repeat this step until all six balls are removed. A screwdriver may be used to pry balls loose.

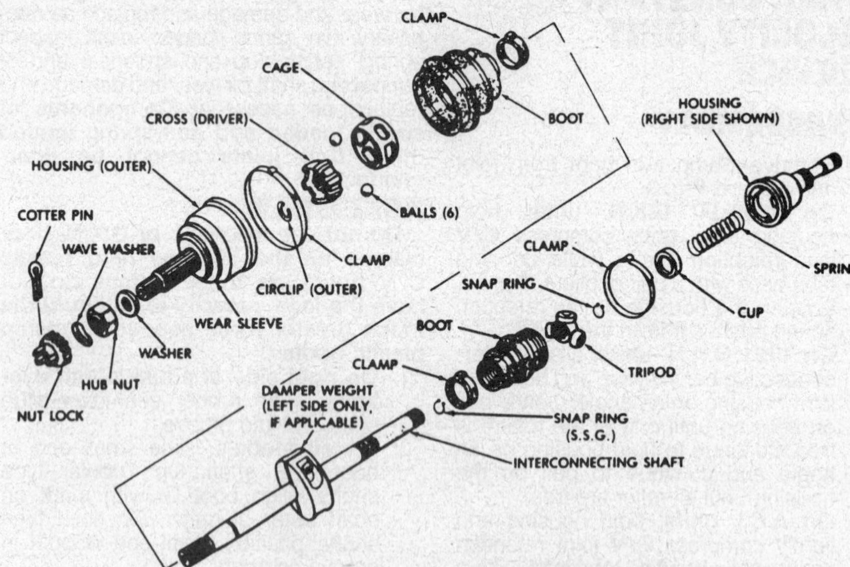


**Fig. 9 Driveshaft components**

12. Tilt cage assembly vertically and position two opposing, elongated cage windows in area between ball grooves. Remove cage and inner race assembly by pulling upward from housing, **Fig. 18.**
13. Rotate inner cross 90 degrees to cage and align one of race spherical lands with an elongated cage window. Raise land into cage window and remove inner race by swinging outward, **Fig. 19.**

## INSPECTION

1. Check housing ball races for excessive wear.
2. Check splined shaft and nut threads for damage.
3. Inspect balls for pitting, cracks, scouring and wear. Dulling of the surface is normal.
4. Inspect cage for excessive wear on inner and outer spherical surfaces, heavy brinnelling of cage, window

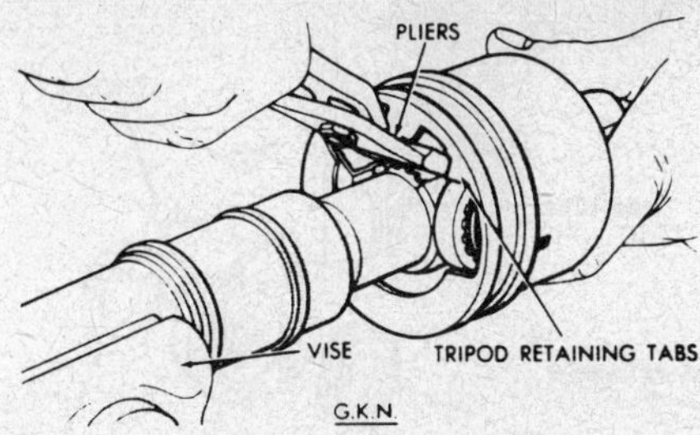


**Fig. 10 Removing tripod from housing. G.K.N. inner C/V joint**

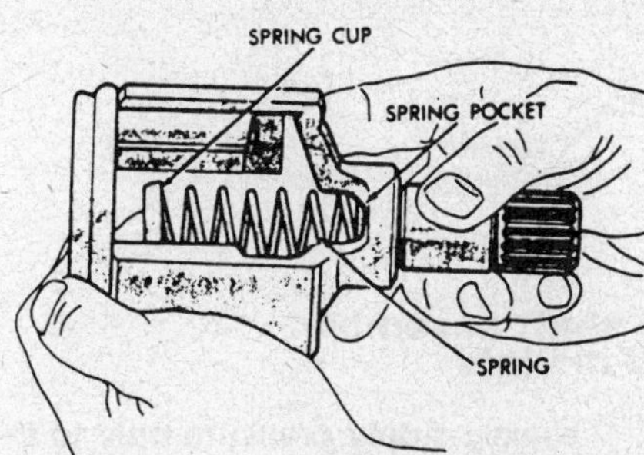


**Fig. 13 C/V joint retention spring**

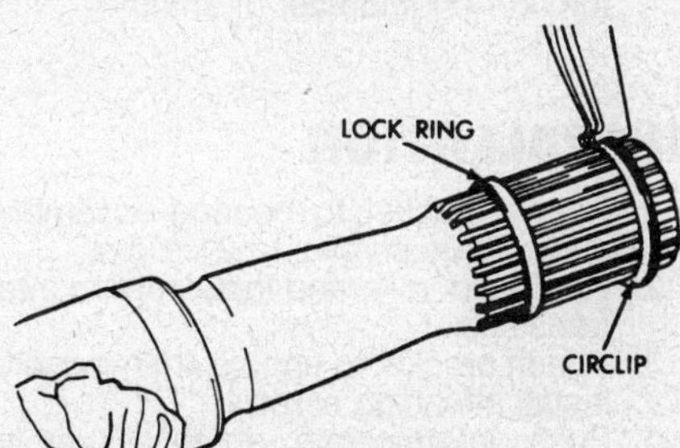


**Fig. 16 Outer C/V joint circlip removal**

cracks and chipping.

5. Inspect inner race (cross) for excessive wear or scouring of ball races.
6. If any of the defects listed in Steps 1 through 5, are found, replace C/V assembly as a unit. **Polished areas in races (cross and housing) and on cage spheres are normal and do not indicate a need for joint replacement unless they are suspected of causing noise and vibration.**

## ASSEMBLY

**Do not use the A.C.I. or G.K.N. boot clamps on the Saginaw hard plastic C/V boots, as these clamps do not have the load capacity to withhold the much greater force needed to clamp plastic boots.**

1. If removed, position wear sleeve on joint housing, then tap sleeve onto housing using seal wear sleeve tool No. C-4698 or equivalent.
2. Lightly oil components, then align marks made during disassembly.

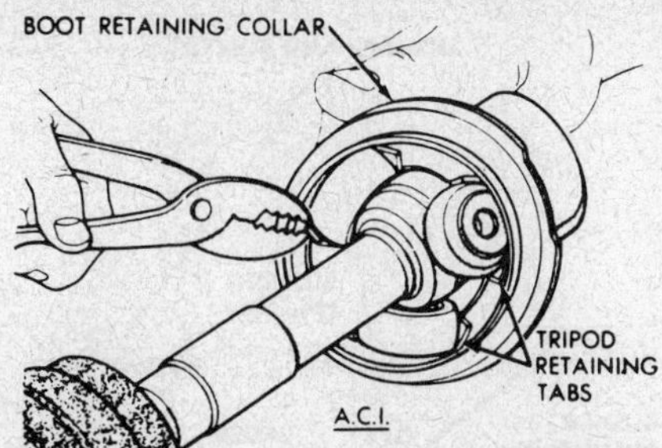


**Fig. 11 Removing tripod from housing. A.C.I. inner C/V joint**

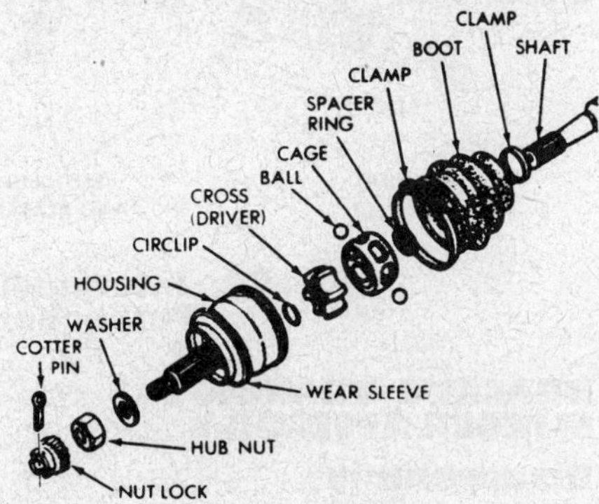


**Fig. 14 Disassembled view of outer C/V joint**

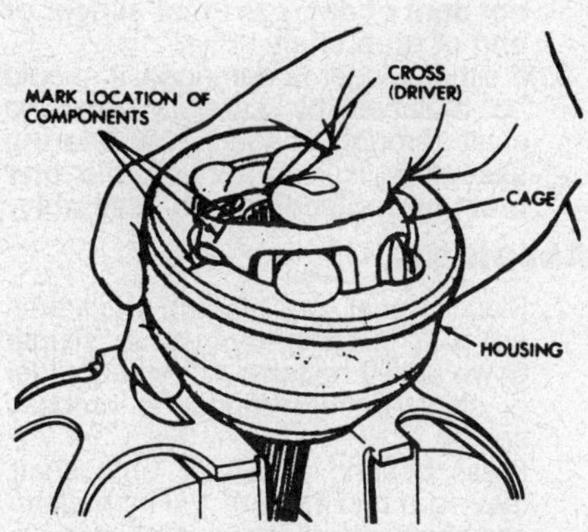


**Fig. 17 Outer C/V joint ball removal**

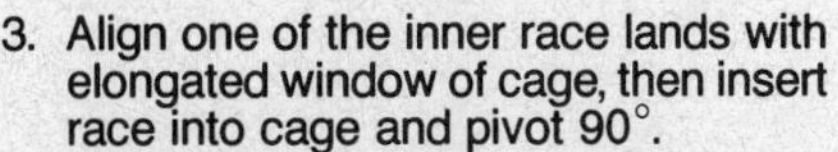

3. Align one of the inner race lands with elongated window of cage, then insert race into cage and pivot 90°.
4. Align elongated cage windows with housing land, then pivot cage 90°.
5. Lubricate ball races with one packet of grease from kit.
6. Tilt cage and inner race assembly and insert balls.
7. With shaft supported in a soft jawed vise, install boot.
8. Install snap ring on shaft. Do not over-expand snap ring during installation.
9. Position joint housing on shaft, then engage by tapping sharply with a soft faced mallet.
10. Ensure snap ring is properly seated by attempting to pull joint from shaft.
11. Locate large end of boot over housing and secures boot clamps.

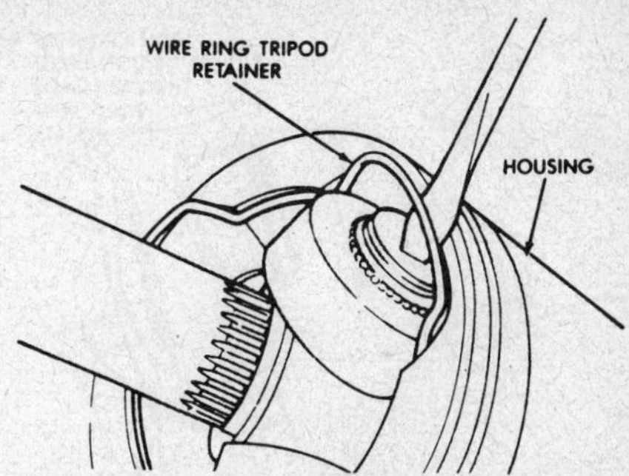


**Fig. 12 Removing tripod from housing. S.S.G. inner C/V joint**

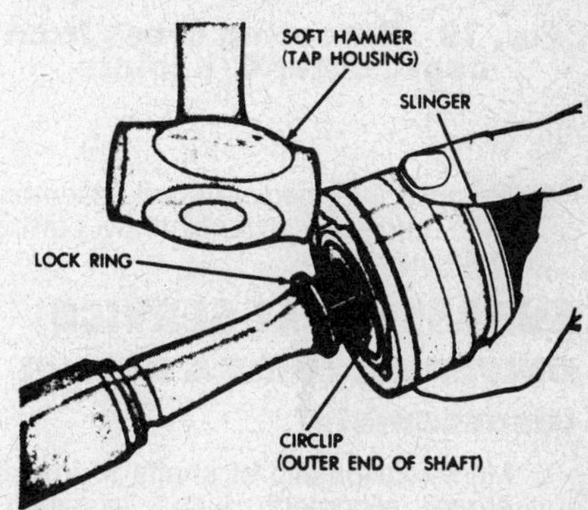


**Fig. 15 Removing outer C/V joint from shaft. Except S.S.G. units**

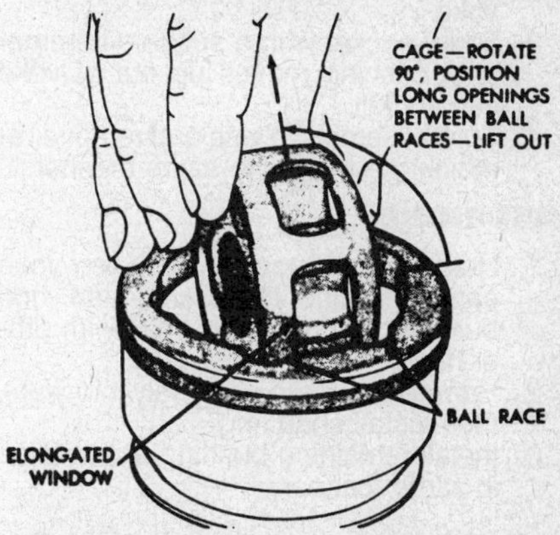


**Fig. 18 Outer C/V joint cage & cross assembly removal**

## INTERMEDIATE SHAFT ASSEMBLY

**The intermediate shaft assembly, Fig. 20, used on front wheel drive equal length systems is the same for manual and automatic transaxles.**

## REMOVAL

1. Remove right driveshaft, referring to "Driveshaft, Replace" procedure.
2. Remove speedometer pinion from extension housing.
3. Remove two screws from bearing assembly bracket to engine block.

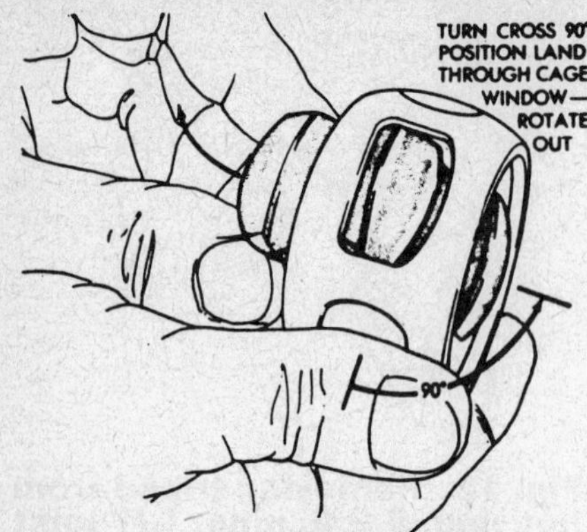


**Fig. 19 Removing cross from cage. Outer C/V joints**

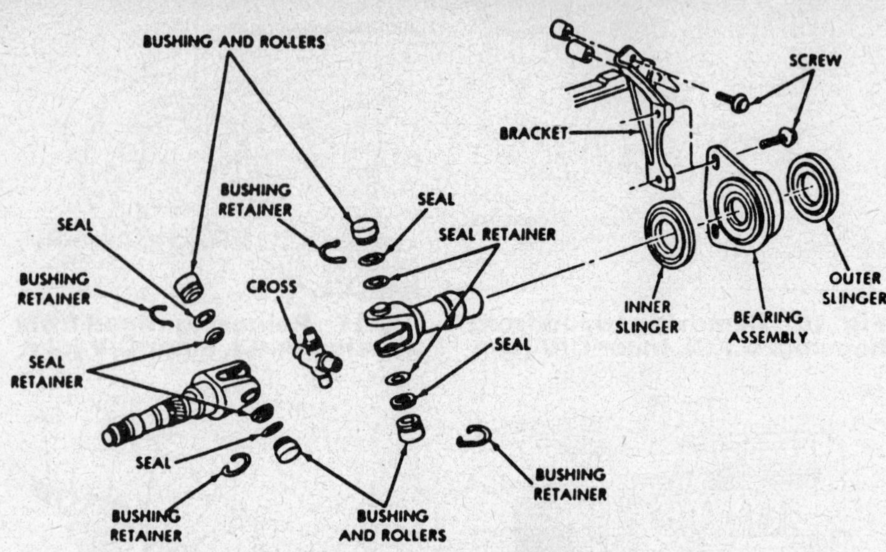


**Fig. 20 Intermediate shaft assembly. Turbocharged models**

4. Remove intermediate shaft assembly from transaxle extension by pulling yoke outward.

## SUBASSEMBLY SERVICE

### UNIVERSAL JOINT & ROLLER

#### Disassembly

1. Mark relationship of shafts to insure proper alignment during assembly. Apply penetrating oil to bushing, then remove snap rings.
2. Support yoke in vise, then position 1 1/8 inch socket over bushing on top of yoke.
3. Strike socket with a suitable hammer until bushing moves up out of yoke into socket.
4. Turn assembly in vise and remove remaining bushings in same manner.

#### Assembly

1. Hold cross in position between yoke ears with one hand and start one bushing assembly into yoke with other hand.
2. Hammer bushing assembly into yoke, then install snap ring.
3. Install remaining bushing assemblies in same manner.

### BRACKET, BEARING & SLINGER ASSEMBLY

#### Disassembly

1. Remove two bearing assembly to support bracket attaching screws, then separate bearing from bracket.
2. Press intermediate shaft out of bearing assembly and outer slinger. **Do not dent or damage inner slinger or end of stub shaft.**
3. If either slinger is damaged, it should be replaced by carefully pressing shaft through slinger. **The bearing assembly is not serviceable and must be replaced as an assembly.**

#### Assembly

1. Place new slinger on stub shaft, then using a suitable tool, drive slinger down until it bottoms out on shoulder of shaft. Ensure slinger is properly seated.
2. Press bearing assembly onto shaft, leaving a minimum of 1/32 inch clearance between slinger and bearing assembly. **Apply pressure only to inner race of bearing assembly during installation.**
3. Press outer slinger into position using a suitable tool. The slinger must bottom out on shoulder of shaft.

## INSTALLATION

1. Attach bracket to bearing assembly and **torque** screws to 21 ft. lbs.
2. Hold stub yoke and install spline into transaxle.
3. Attach bracket to engine, then loosely install attaching screws.
4. Push intermediate shaft assembly into transaxle as far as possible, then **torque** bracket-to-engine attaching screws to 40 ft. lbs.
5. Apply suitable grease inside spline and pilot bore on bearing end of intermediate shaft.
6. Install speedometer pinion, then the right driveshaft. Refer to "Driveshaft, Replace" procedure.

# Chrysler Imports

## INDEX



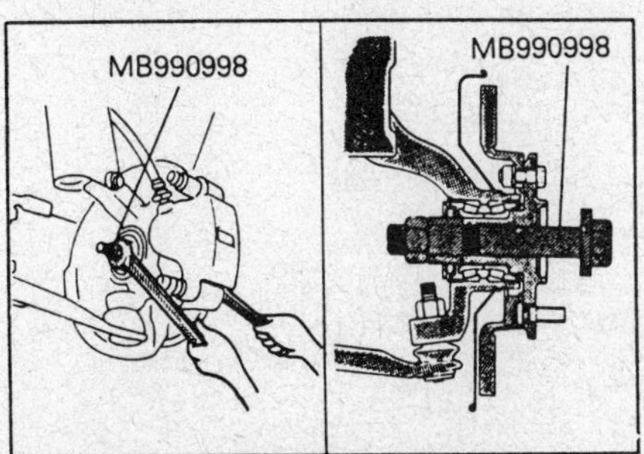


**Fig. 1 Installation wheel bearing support tool**

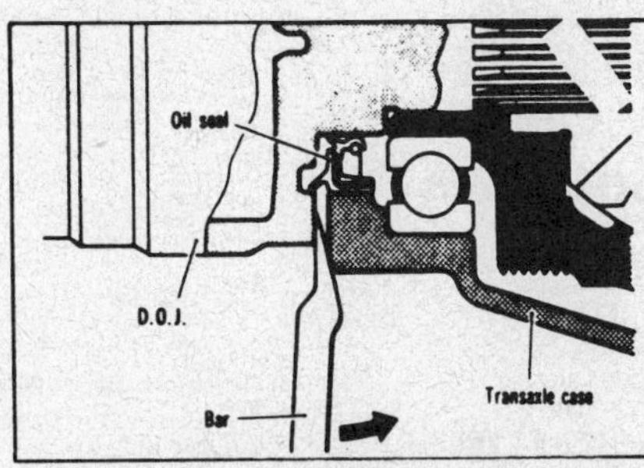


**Fig. 2 Removing front drive axle from transaxle case**

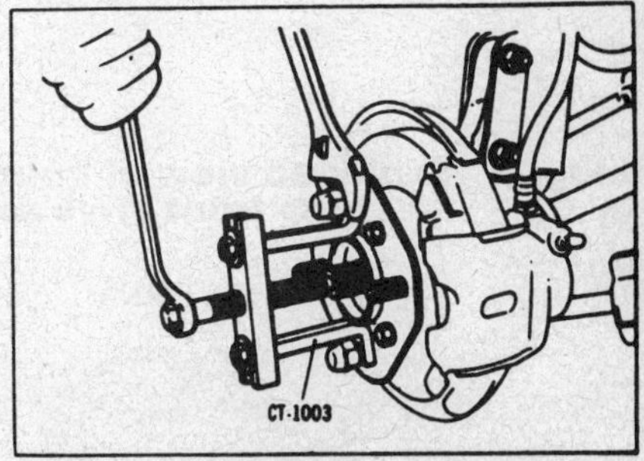


**Fig. 3 Pressing front drive axle from hub**

## FRONT DRIVE AXLE REPLACE

### COLT VISTA w/TWO WHEEL DRIVE

**Do not apply vehicle load to the wheel bearing after removal of the driveshaft. If a load must be applied to the bearing in moving the vehicle, temporarily secure with special tool No. MB990998 or equivalent, Fig. 1.**

1. Remove hub dust cap and loosen drive axle nut, then raise and support front of vehicle and remove wheel and tire assembly.
2. Remove under cover, then remove strut bar and ball joint from lower control arm. **Use care not to damage ball joint dust boot.**
3. Drain transaxle fluid.
4. Insert a suitable pry bar between transaxle case and outer case of double offset joint, then withdraw drive axle, **Fig. 2.** Cover drive axle opening in transaxle. When removing drive axle, support at tripod or double offset joint and pull shaft straight out to prevent damage to boot or joint. After disconnecting drive axle from transaxle, support shaft in proper position. **Pry bar should not be inserted more than .28 inch between transaxle case and outer case of offset joint, as damage to oil seal may result. The double offset joint retainer ring should be replaced whenever the drive axle is removed from transaxle case.**
5. Press drive axle, from hub using axle shaft puller No. CT-1003, **Fig. 3. When pressing drive axle from hub, use care to prevent the spacer from moving out of position.**
6. Reverse procedure to install. Position drive axle so that raised inner diameter of washer is facing nut, then install and **torque** drive axle nut to 145-188 ft. lbs.

### COLT WAGON & COLT VISTA w/FOUR WHEEL DRIVE

**Do not apply vehicle load to the wheel bearing after removal of the driveshaft. If a load must be applied to the bearing in moving the vehicle, temporarily secure with special tool No. MB990998 or equivalent, Fig. 1.**

The following procedure is only for the left side drive axle. Refer to Colt Vista w/Two Wheel Drive for right side drive axle replacement procedure on Colt Vista and Colt & Colt Wagon w/Two Wheel Drive for Colt Wagon procedure.

1. Remove center cap and drive axle nut.
2. Raise and support vehicle, then remove front wheel.
3. Drain transmission fluid.
4. Disconnect lower arm ball joint and knuckle coupling, then remove strut bar and stabilizer bar from lower arm.
5. Remove center bearing snap ring from bearing bracket.
6. Lightly tap double offset joint outer race with a wooden hammer and disconnect drive axle from cardan joint assembly.
7. Disconnect drive axle from bearing bracket.
8. Remove drive axle from hub.
9. Remove bearing bracket attaching bolts, then the bearing bracket.
10. Lightly tap yoke of cardan joint with a wooden hammer and remove it from transaxle assembly.
11. Reverse procedure to install. **Torque** bearing bracket bolts to 29-39 ft. lbs. **Torque** drive axle nut to 145-188 ft. lbs. After installation, ensure boot length is 3.23-3.47 inch.

### COLT & COLT WAGON w/TWO WHEEL DRIVE

**Do not apply vehicle load to the wheel bearing after removal of the driveshaft. If a load must be applied to the bearing in moving the vehicle, temporarily secure with special tool No. MB990998 or equivalent, Fig. 1.**

1. Remove under cover and center member from vehicle, if so equipped.
2. Remove hub nut cotter pin, hub nut and washer, then raise and support vehicle.
3. Remove lower ball joint from steering knuckle, using steering linkage puller No. MB991113 or equivalent.
4. Remove tie rod from steering knuckle using tool No. MB991113 or equivalent.
5. **On drive axles equipped with center bearing,** remove center bearing bracket mounting bolts.
6. **On drive axles not equipped with center bearing,** insert pry bar between transaxle case and drive shaft, then pry drive axle from transaxle case, **Fig. 2.** Remove drive axle from hub using axle shaft puller No. CT-1003 or equivalent, **Fig. 3. Do not pull on drive axle or joints will be damaged. Do not insert pry bar further than necessary or damage to oil seal will result.**
7. **On drive axle equipped with center bearing,** remove driveshaft from hub using shaft remover No. CT-1003 or equivalent. Remove driveshaft and innershaft from transaxle by lightly tapping tripod joint with plastic hammer.

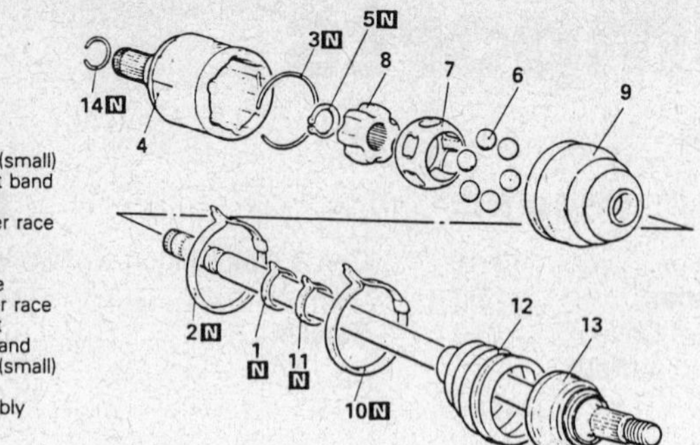

1. Boot band (small)
2. D.O.J. boot band
3. Circlip
4. D.O.J. outer race
5. Snap ring
6. Balls
7. D.O.J. cage
8. D.O.J. inner race
9. D.O.J. boot
10. B.J. boot band
11. Boot band (small)
12. B.J. boot
13. B.J. assembly
14. Circlip

N : Non-reusable parts
B.J. : Birfield Joint
D.O.J. : Double Offset Joint

**Fig. 4 Exploded view of double offset joint type front drive axle**

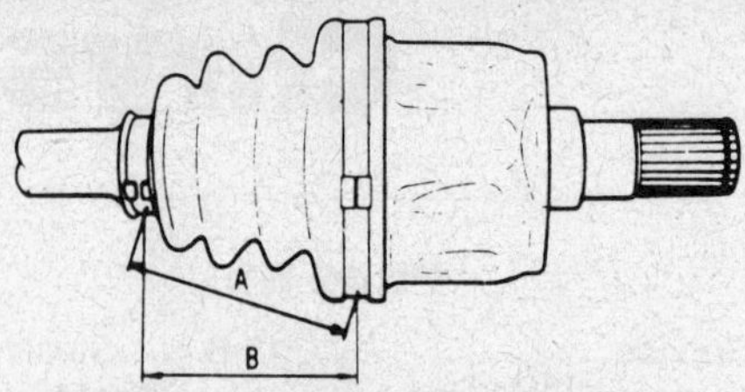


**Fig. 5 Double offset joint or tripod joint boot length measurement**

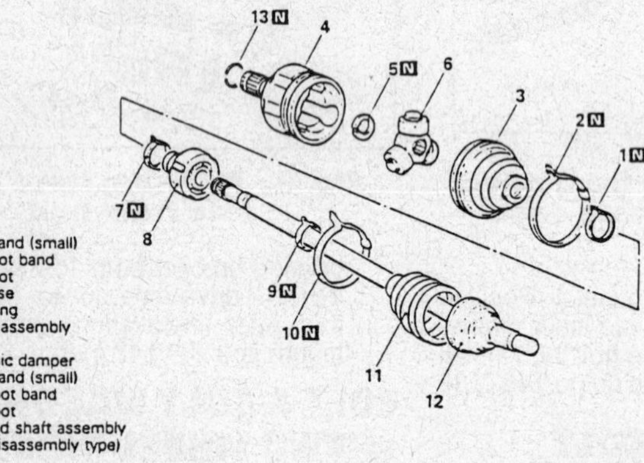

1. Boot band (small)
2. T.J. boot band
3. T.J. boot
4. T.J. case
5. Snap ring
6. Spider assembly
7. Band
8. Dynamic damper
9. Boot band (small)
10. B.J. boot band
11. B.J. boot
12. B.J. and shaft assembly (Non-disassembly type)
13. Circlip

T.J. : Tapered roller bearing
D.O.J.: Double Offset Joint

N : Non-reusable parts

**Fig. 6 Exploded view of tripod type front drive axle. Less innershaft**

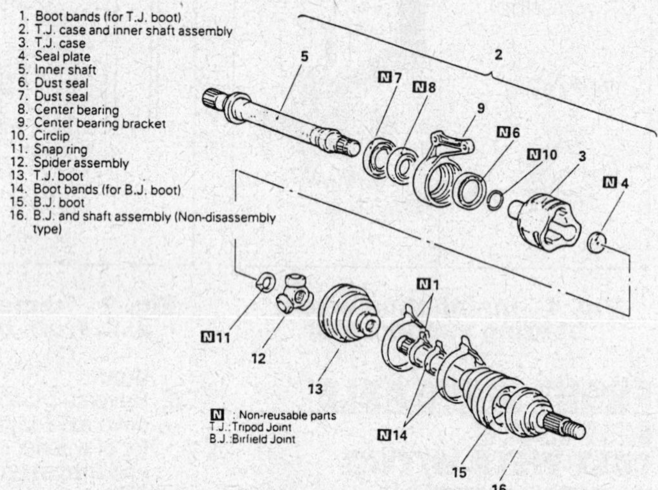

1. Boot bands (for T.J. boot)
2. T.J. case and inner shaft assembly
3. T.J. case
4. Seal plate
5. Inner shaft
6. Dust seal
7. Dust seal
8. Center bearing
9. Center bearing bracket
10. Circlip
11. Snap ring
12. Spider assembly
13. T.J. boot
14. Boot bands (for B.J. boot)
15. B.J. boot
16. B.J. and shaft assembly (Non-disassembly type)

N : Non-reusable parts
T.J.: Tripod Joint
B.J.: Birfield Joint

**Fig. 7 Exploded view of tripod type front drive axle. With innershaft**

**Do not pull on drive axle or joints will be damaged.**

## STEALTH

1. Remove dust cover, cotter pin and driveshaft nut.
2. Raise and support vehicle.
3. Drain transmission oil.
4. Disconnect lower arm ball joint from knuckle, then remove stabilizer and strut bars from lower arm.
5. **On lefthand driveshaft,** remove bearing bracket attaching bolts.
6. **On righthand driveshaft,** insert suitable pry bar between transmission case and driveshaft, then pry driveshaft from transmission. **Do not pull on driveshaft and do not insert pry bar deep enough to damage oil seal.**
7. **On lefthand driveshaft,** if innershaft is hard to remove from transaxle, strike center bearing bracket lightly with a plastic hammer.
8. **On all models,** using tool No. MB990241 or equivalent, remove driveshaft from hub.
9. Reverse procedure to install, noting the following:
   a. Ensure driveshaft washer is correctly installed.
   b. Lower vehicle to ground, then attach and adjust driveshaft nut, **torquing** to 144-188 ft. lbs.
   c. If cotter pin holes do not line up, tighten bolt without exceeding **torque** of 188 ft. lbs., until holes line up.
   d. Install cotter pin. Always use new cotter pins.
   e. Refill transaxle to proper level.

# FRONT AXLE SERVICE
## COLT, COLT WAGON, & COLT VISTA W/TWO WHEEL DRIVE

### DOUBLE OFFSET JOINT TYPE DRIVESHAFT

When servicing the drive axle, do not disassemble the Birfield bell type constant velocity joint, as components on this type joint are precision fitted.

#### Disassembly

1. Remove Double Offset Joint (DOJ) boot bands, then remove circlip using a suitable screwdriver, **Fig. 4.**
2. Remove DOJ outer race from DOJ joint assembly.
3. Remove snap ring, then remove DOJ inner race, cage and balls as an assembly. Clean bearing assembly without disassembling them.
4. Wind tape around drive axle splines, then remove DOJ and Birfield joint boot band and slide boots from drive axle. When inspecting Birfield joint, note amount of grease removed for reassembly.

#### Assembly

A special grease containing Molybdenum is used to lubricate the drive axle double offset joint and the Birfield joint. This special grease is included in the drive axle repair kit and must be used.

1. Wrap tape around drive axle splines to prevent damage to boots, then install Birfield joint and DOJ boots.
2. Apply special grease to DOJ joint assembly.
3. Install DOJ joint assembly on drive axle with chamfered side of cage facing splined end of shaft, then install snap ring.
4. Apply 1.4-2.1 ounces of special Molybdenum grease to double offset joint outer race, then position outer race on drive axle.
5. Apply an additional .7-1.4 ounce of

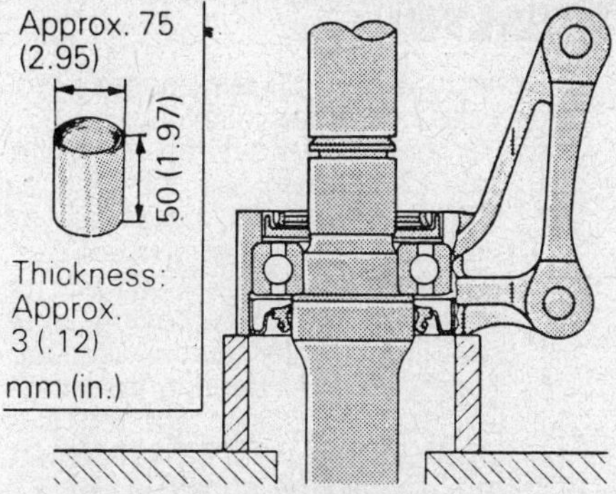


**Fig. 8 Innershaft removal.**

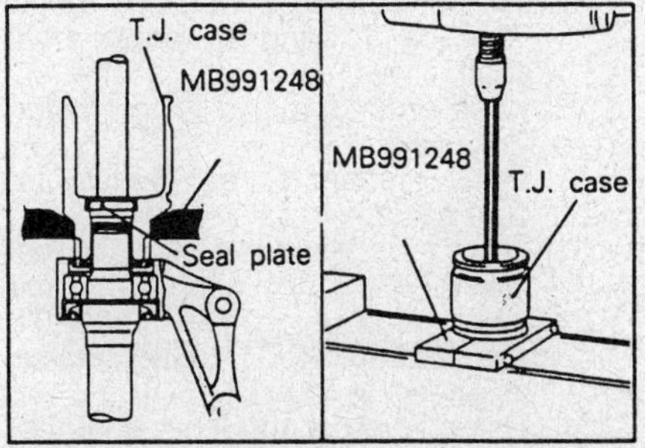


**Fig. 10 Removing innershaft**

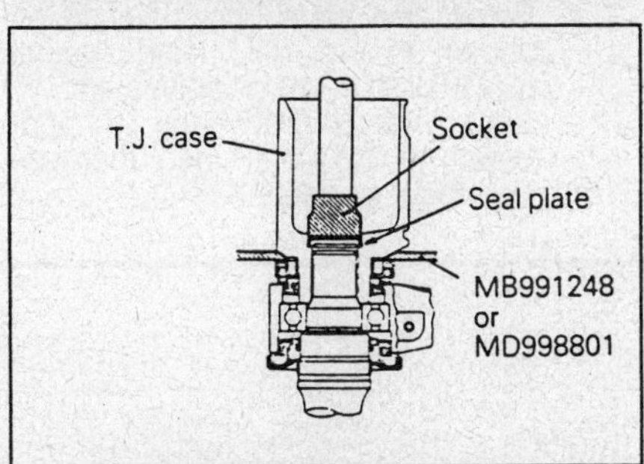


**Fig. 13 Installing seal plate into TJ case. Stealth**

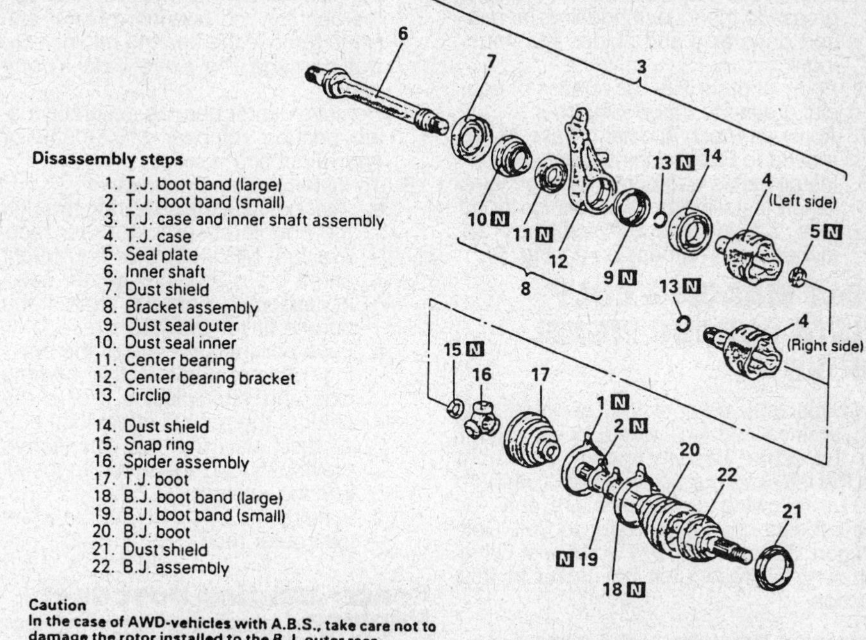


**Fig. 9 Exploded view of front drive axle. Stealth**

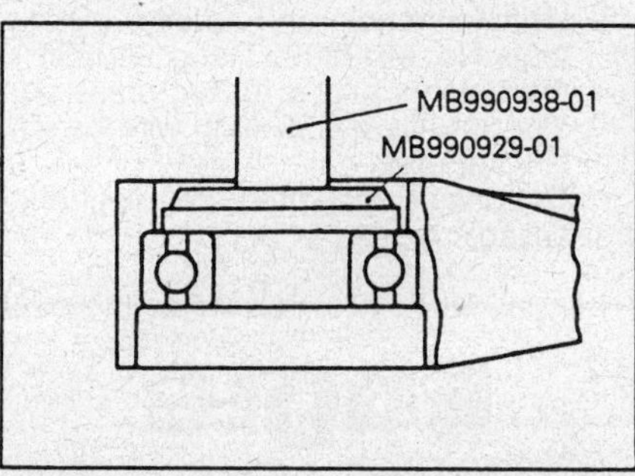


**Fig. 11 Removing center bearing from bracket. Stealth**

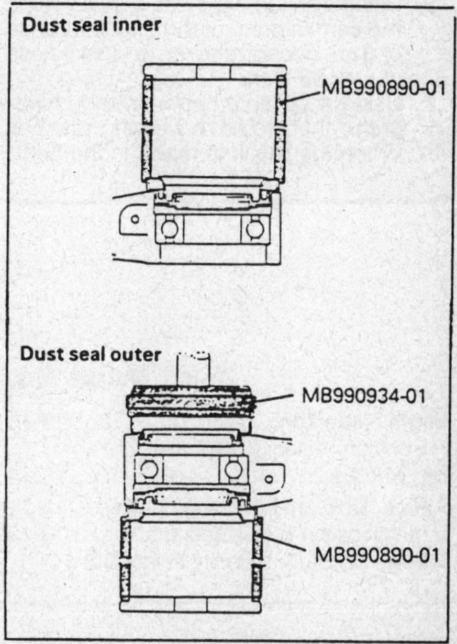


**Fig. 12 Installing dust seals. Stealth**

special Molybdenum grease to DOJ boot, then install clip.

6. Add amount of special Molybdenum grease to Birfield joint as removed during disassembly and inspection.
7. Install boots and boot bands for each joint. When installing boot bands for DOJ, position bands, **Fig. 5,** so that dimension A is 3.5 inches on two wheel drive models or 3.3 inches on four wheel drive models.

## TRIPOD JOINT TYPE DRIVESHAFT

### Disassembly

When servicing the drive axle, do not disassemble the Rzeppa type constant velocity joint, as components of this type joint are precision fitted.

1. Remove boot clamps, then remove boot from tripod joint housing and position on drive axle, **Figs. 6 and 7.**
2. Pull drive axle from tripod joint housing, then remove snap ring and lift tripod joint spider from housing. Clean tripod joint spider and check for wear and damage. Also check joint needle roller bearings for smooth operation. **Do not disassemble tripod joint spider.**
3. Wind tape around drive axle splines, then remove bands for Rzeppa type joint and remove boots from drive axle. If Rzeppa joint is to be reused, do not wipe away grease. Check grease for contamination and clean and replace grease only if necessary. Note amount of grease removed for use during reassembly.
4. **On models with innershaft,** continue disassembly as follows:
   a. Using press and support fixture No. MB991248 or equivalent, press innershaft and seal plate out of Tripod case.
   b. Using two inch steel pipe as support, **Fig. 8,** press innershaft from center bearing support.
   c. Using screwdriver, remove driveshaft side dust seal, then using same steel pipe press out center bearing and differential side dust seal.

### Assembly

A special grease is used to lubricate the drive axle tripod joint and Rzeppa joint. This grease is included in the drive axle repair kit and must be used.

1. Press fit center bearing into center bearing support, then lubricate and press fit dust seals into center bearing.
2. Press fit innershaft into center bearing, then the innershaft assembly into Tripod case.
3. Apply grease to drive axle, then install boots.
4. Position tripod joint spider on drive axle, then install snap ring.

5. Apply 2.8-3.2 ounces of special grease to tripod joint housing, then insert drive axle and spider into housing.
6. Apply another 2.8-3.2 ounces of special grease to tripod joint boot.
7. Apply as much special grease as removed to Rzeppa joint, if necessary.
8. Install bands and boots for each joint. When installing boot bands for tripod joint, bands must be positioned 3.1 inches apart (dimension A), **Fig. 5.**

## COLT WAGON & COLT VISTA w/FOUR WHEEL DRIVE

Driveshafts are identical between two wheel drive and four wheel drive, except for the center bearing support assembly on the left side four wheel drive driveshaft.

The following procedures are only for the left side drive axle. Refer to Colt, Colt Wagon, & Colt Vista w/Two Wheel Drive for service procedures not cover in this section.

### Center Bearing, Replace

1. Remove double offset joint outer race from drive axle.
2. Using a suitable grinder, partially grind the certain point of the circumference of the bearing retainer to a thickness of .04-.06 inch.
3. Using a suitable hammer and chisel, break then remove bearing retainer. When the break is made in the bearing retainer, tap the chisel in between the bearing and bearing retainer and pry to remove the bearing retainer. **Do not damage the drive axle in any way.**
4. Remove center bearing assembly using bearing remover MB990560 or equivalent and a press.
5. To install proceed as follows:
   a. After passing the snap ring through the double offset joint outer race, use tool MB990560 or equivalent and a press to install center bearing assembly onto the shaft of the double offset joint outer race.
   b. Face polished surface of the bearing retainer toward the bearing side and, after placing it onto the shaft of the double offset joint outer face, use the tool mentioned previously and the press to install bearing retainer.
   c. Install drive axle onto double offset joint outer race.

### Center Bearing Dust Seal, Replace

1. Using a suitable screwdriver, remove dust seal from bearing bracket assembly.
2. Using a handle and adapter installer tools No. MB990938 and 990930 or equivalents and a mallet, press dust seal in until seal is flush with bearing bracket end.
3. Coat inside circumference of seal with suitable grease.

## STEALTH

1. Refer to **Fig. 9,** for disassembly procedures noting the following:
   a. Remove inner shaft assembly, with seal plate, from the TJ case as shown in **Fig. 10,** using special tool MB991248 or equivalent.
   b. Use special tool MB990810-01 or equivalent, when removing inner shaft from center bearing bracket.
   c. Remove center bearing from center bracket using special tool MB990938-01, and MB990930-01 or equivalent, as shown in **Fig. 11.**
   d. Wrap splines on driveshaft with tape, so that the TJ and BJ boots are not damaged when removed. Remove TJ and Bj boots from shaft.
2. Reverse procedures to install noting the following:
   a. Apply grease to rear surface of dust seals.
   b. Press inner seal using special tool MB990890-01 or equivalent, and outer seal using MB990934-01, and MB990890-01 or equivalent, as shown in **Fig. 12.**
   c. Install TJ case and inner shaft assembly, applying multi purpose grease to the inner shaft spline.
   d. Press seal plate into TJ case as shown in **Fig. 13,** using special tool MB9911248 or equivalent.
   e. Set distance between TJ boot bands to 3.23-3.47 inch, then secure boot bands.

# Eagle

## INDEX



## EAGLE PREMIER

### DRIVESHAFT, REPLACE

Use caution when servicing driveshafts. Do not strike the end of the shaft or drop it. Inspect C/V boots and replace if damaged or worn.

1. Raise and support vehicle.
2. Remove tire and wheel assembly, then the brake caliper. Do not disconnect brake caliper hose or suspend caliper from hose.
3. Using suitable tool to hold wheel hub in place, remove driveshaft nut.
4. Loosen driveshaft in hub. If driveshaft does not come loose by hand, use hub puller No. T.Av. 1050 or equivalent. **Do not attempt to loosen driveshaft by striking it with a hammer.**
5. Using a punch, remove driveshaft roll pin.
6. Remove steering knuckle-to-strut attaching bolts. **Do not turn bolts, as they are splined just under bolt head.** Hold bolt head with a suitable wrench, then unscrew nut to end of bolt. Tap nut with brass hammer to loosen bolt, then remove nut and slide bolt from knuckle.
7. Tilt steering knuckle out and away from strut, then remove driveshaft.
8. Reverse procedure to install. **Torque** steering knuckle-to-strut attaching nuts to 123 ft. lbs. and driveshaft nut to 181 ft. lbs. Check and adjust transaxle fluid level if necessary.

### INNER CONSTANT VELOCITY JOINT SERVICE

#### Removal & Disassembly

1. Remove driveshaft as described under "Driveshaft, Replace."
2. Cut and remove boot clamps, then slide boot from C/V joint housing, **Fig. 1.** If boot is to be reused, avoid damaging boot when cutting clamps.
3. Remove C/V joint housing by pulling it straight off the tripod.
4. Using snap ring pliers, spread plastic retaining ring (D), then tap tripod off shaft with plastic mallet, **Fig. 2.**
5. Remove boot from shaft. Inspect C/V joint housing, boot, plastic retaining ring, tripod and tripod bearings. Replace worn or damaged components.

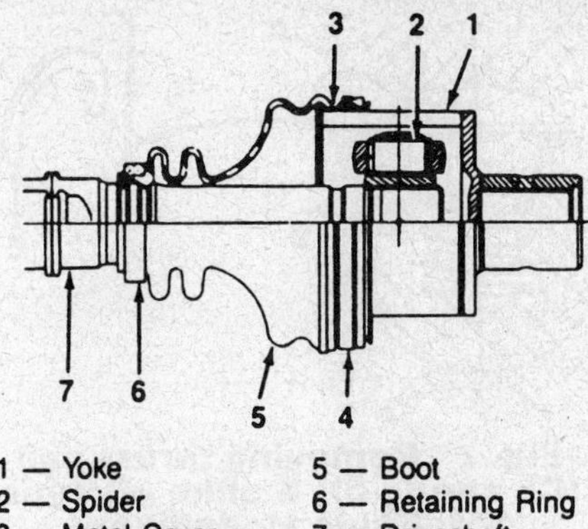


**Fig. 1 Inner C/V joint assembly. Eagle Premier**

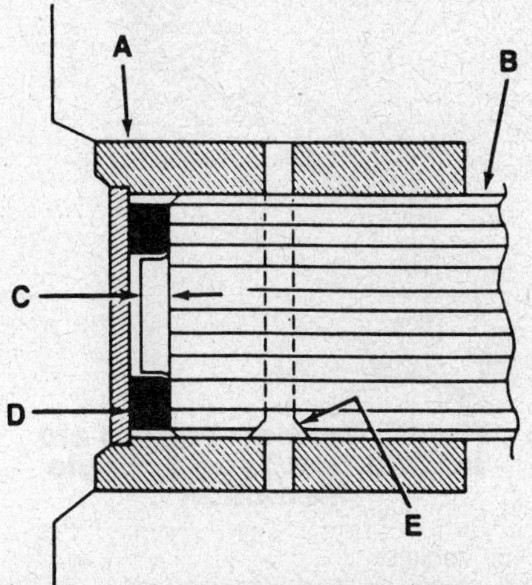


**Fig. 4 Driveshaft identification. Eagle Medallion**

### Assembly & Installation

1. Install new retaining ring by pushing non-tapered end into tripod until it snaps into groove.
2. Install boot on driveshaft.
3. Tap tripod onto driveshaft until retaining ring seats in shaft groove.
4. Lubricate C/V joint housing, tripod bearings and the interior of boot with grease supplied in service kit, then slide housing onto tripod and bearings.
5. Seat boot on housing and driveshaft, then bleed air from boot by inserting a smooth rod (T) between boot and housing, Fig. 3. **Do not damage boot while purging air.**
6. Using boot clamp pliers No. T.Av 1034 or equivalent, install and tighten boot clamps.
7. Install driveshaft as described under "Driveshaft, Replace."

## OUTER CONSTANT VELOCITY JOINT SERVICE

### Removal & Disassembly

1. Remove driveshaft as described under "Driveshaft, Replace."

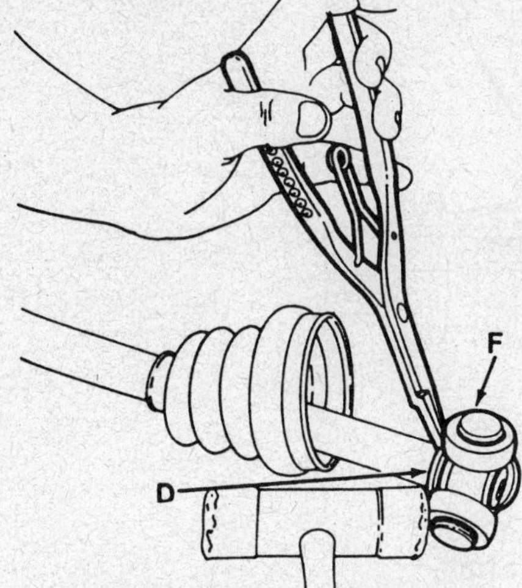


**Fig. 2 Removing trunnion from driveshaft. Eagle Premier**

2. Cut and remove boot clamps, then slide boot rearward for access to plastic retaining ring. If boot is to be reused, avoid damaging boot when cutting clamps.
3. Using snap ring pliers, spread plastic retaining ring, then tap C/V joint with plastic mallet to free shaft from retaining ring.
4. Remove C/V joint, then slide boot off shaft. Inspect retaining ring, and replace if necessary.

### Installation

1. Install new retaining ring with tapered end into C/V joint and segmented end onto driveshaft.
2. Slide boot onto driveshaft.
3. Lubricate C/V joint with grease supplied in service kit. Align driveshaft with plastic retaining ring and C/V joint, then tap joint onto shaft until retaining ring snaps into place.
4. Position boot in clamp groves of C/V joint and driveshaft, then using boot clamps pliers No. T.Av 1034 or equivalent, install and tighten boot clamps.
5. Install driveshaft as described under "Driveshaft, Replace."

# EAGLE MEDALLION

## FRONT DRIVESHAFT SERVICE

### Removal

**Three different types of side gear (output) shafts may be used. Different outer and inner constant velocity joints are used on the driveshafts. After removing the driveshaft boot, identify the type of constant velocity joint used and refer to the appropriate procedures for each joint. Separate service procedures are provided for type 1 and 2 constant velocity outer joints and the type 3 and 4 constant velocity inner joints.**

1. Raise and support vehicle.

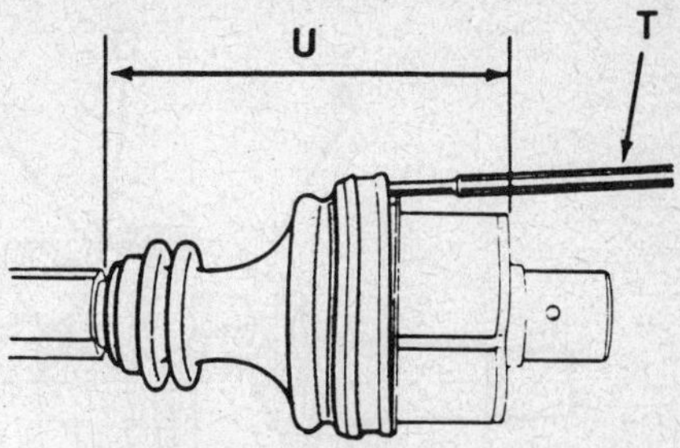


**Fig. 3 Installing inner C/V boot. Eagle Premier**

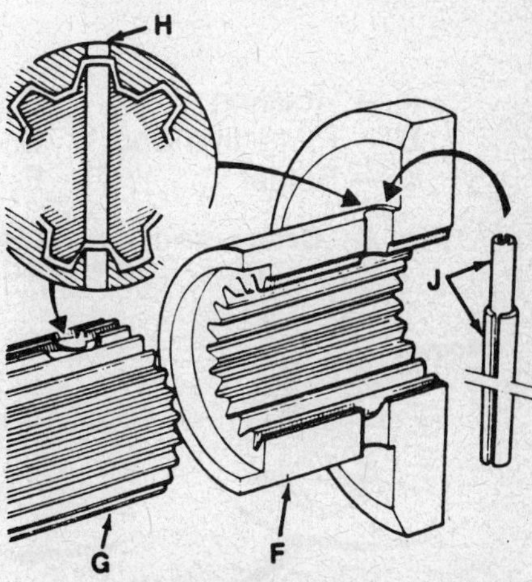


**Fig. 5 Aligning roll pin holes in driveshaft side gear. Eagle Medallion**

2. Remove front wheel and brake caliper assembly. **Secure caliper to the body or spring. Do not allow the brake line to support the weight of the caliper assembly.**
3. Using hub locking bar Rou.604.01 or equivalent to secure hub in position, remove driveshaft attaching nut.
4. Using pin drifts, B.Vi.31.01 or equivalent, remove double roller pins attaching driveshaft to the side gear shaft.
5. Using ball joint extractor T.Av.476 or equivalent, disconnect tie rod end.
6. Remove upper bolt attaching steering knuckle to shock absorber. Loosen but do not remove lower attaching bolt.
7. Tilt brake rotor/steering knuckle assembly outward. **The driveshaft splines are secured to the hub splines with Loctite. Use hub puller T.Av.1050 only to break the shaft loose from the hub for removal. Do not attempt to loosen the shaft with a hammer.**
8. Remove driveshaft as follows:
   a. Position tool T.Av.1050 (only) onto the rotor and hub assembly.
   b. Tighten tool attaching bolt to break the driveshaft splines loose from the hub.
   c. Disconnect the shaft at the transaxle and carefully remove the shaft from the vehicle. Do not damage the driveshaft boot during removal.

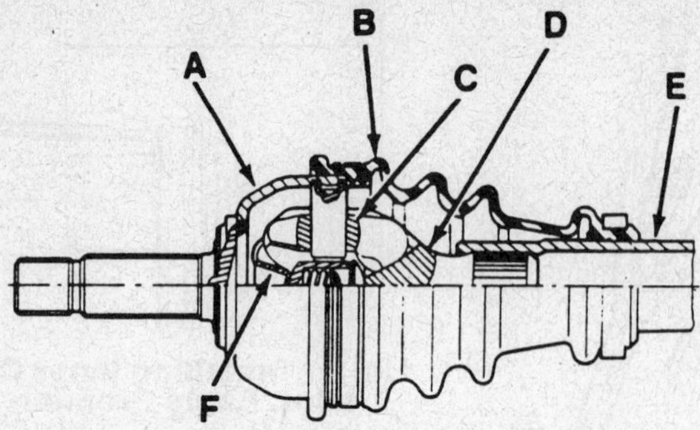


A — Housing
B — Protective Boot
C — Spider
D — Yoke
E — Shaft
F — Starplate

**Fig. 6 Cross-sectional view of type 1 C/V joint. Eagle Medallion**

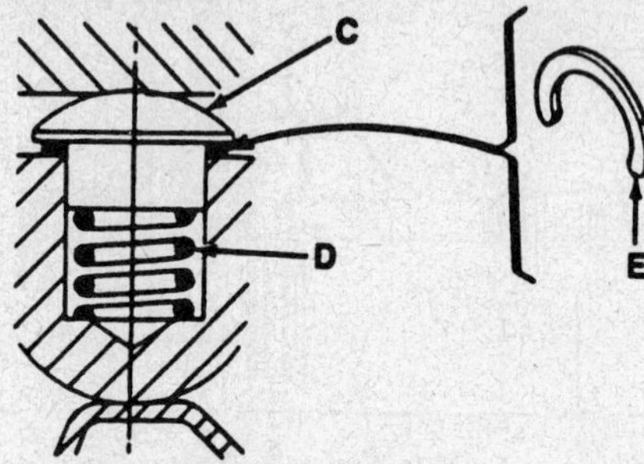


**Fig. 7 Removing thrust ball (C), spring (D) & shim (E) Type 1. Eagle Medallion**

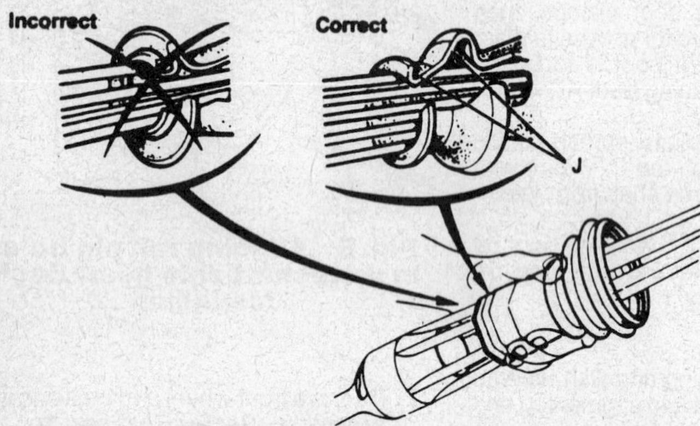


**Fig. 8 Correct boot installation Type 1. Eagle Medallion**

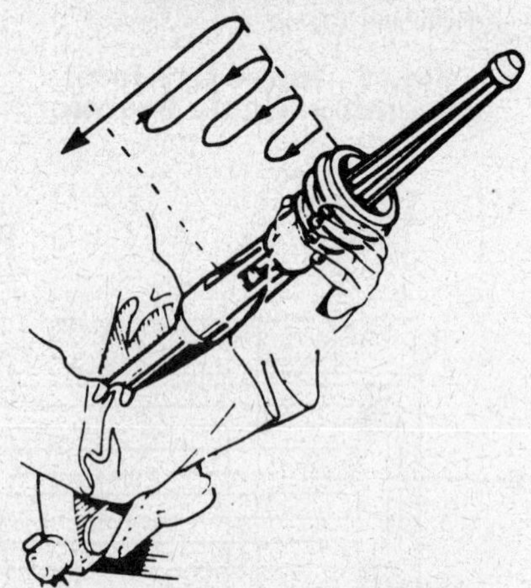

**Fig. 9 Turning boot to aid installation Type 1. Eagle Medallion**

## IDENTIFICATION & INSTALLATION

**Clean driveshaft and hub splines thoroughly using a wire brush. Lubricate seals and splines on the transaxle side gear shaft and driveshaft with clean chassis grease only. Inspect the driveshaft boot. Replace boot if damaged. Before connecting the driveshaft to the transaxle side gear shaft, identify the type of side gear shaft in the transaxle. Three different types are used as described previously.**

Type 1 shafts have a shoulder (C), **Fig. 4,** that is .039 inch (1mm) long. A .118 inch (3mm) thick rubber washer (D) is used between the end of the side gear shaft and driveshaft.

Type 2 shafts have a shoulder (C), **Fig. 4,** that is .118 inch (3mm) long. A .197 inch thick rubber washer (D) is used between the ends of the side gear shaft and driveshaft.

Type 3 shafts do not have a machined shoulder and do not require a rubber washer.

Verify the type of side gear shaft and install the appropriate thickness rubber washer (or no washer in type 3 shafts), before installing.

All of the side gear shaft types have a chamfer (E), **Fig. 4,** machined into one side of the roll pin hole. The chamfer is included to make installation of the double roller pins easier.

To install, proceed as follows:

1. Install driveshaft (F), **Fig. 5,** onto side gear shaft (G).
2. Align roll pin holes (H) in the driveshaft (F) side gear (G).
3. Install driveshaft onto side gear shaft and insert double roll pins (one pin fits inside the other). Position slits into pins 180° apart. Tap pins (J) into place with pin drifts B.Vi.31.01 or equivalent.
4. Seal open ends of the roll pins with silicone sealer after installation.
5. Apply a few drops of Loctite 271 to the driveshaft splines and insert shaft into hub assembly. Use installer tool T.Av.602 of the shafts are difficult to install into hub. **Do not damage the driveshaft boot while installing the shaft.**
6. Apply Loctite 271 onto driveshaft nut and install nut. Using hub locking bar Rou.604.01 or equivalent, tighten nut to 185 ft. lbs.
7. Connect tie rod end to shock arm.
8. Install brake caliper, wheel and lower vehicle.
9. Apply brakes several times to seat pads before moving vehicle.

## CONSTANT VELOCITY JOINT & BOOT SERVICE

### TYPE 1 OUTER C/V JOINT

#### Disassembly

**Refer to Fig. 6 for cross-sectional view of type 1 constant velocity joint assembly.**

1. Remove driveshaft.
2. Cut, then remove boot clamps.
3. Slide boot away from joint and remove as much grease as possible from constant velocity joint. **Do not use cleaning solvents.**
4. Using a suitable screwdriver, lift star plate tabs upward to release the yoke from the spider. Do not bend the tabs.
5. Remove yoke and shaft from constant velocity joint.
6. Remove and retain the thrust ball (C), spring (D) and shim (E) from the spider, **Fig. 7.**
7. Cut the boot in half and remove it from the shaft.
8. Remove all grease from constant velocity joint. **Do not use cleaning solvents.**

#### Assembly

1. Install shaft into a suitable vise. Position shaft so yoke is pointing upward. **Do not attempt to install the boot without using the proper tool for**

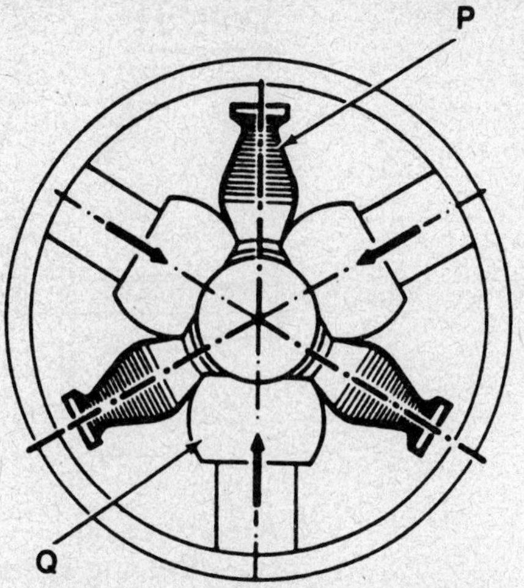

Fig. 11 Roller & star plate installation Type 1. Eagle Medallion

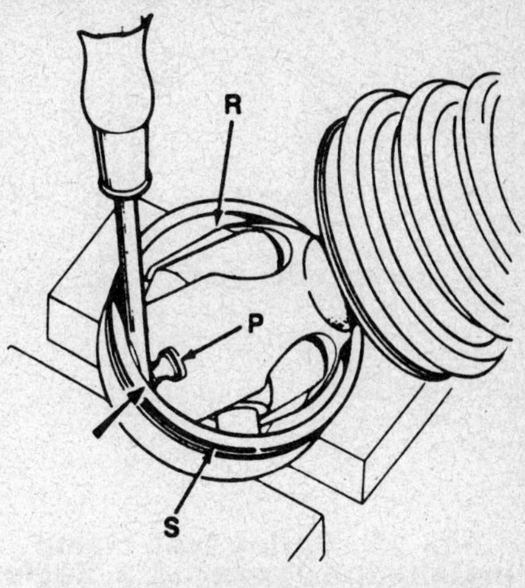

Fig. 12 Inserting shaft yoke into housing Type 1. Eagle Medallion

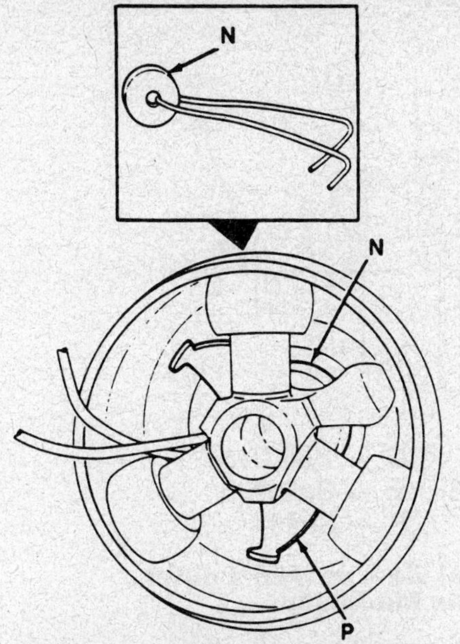


Fig. 10 Tool fabrication to secure spider and star plate Type 1. Eagle Medallion

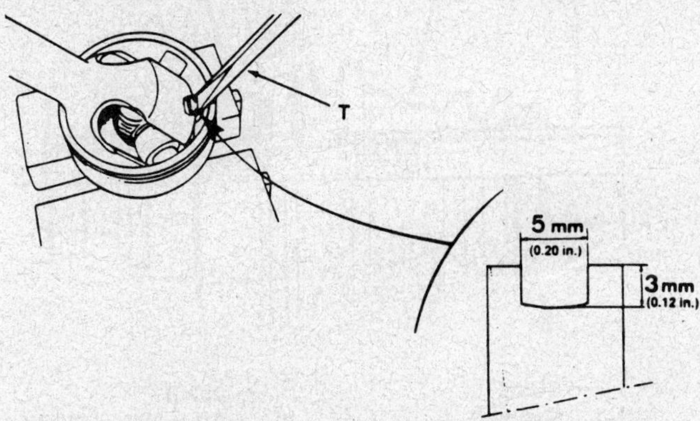


Fig. 13 Installing remaining star plates into yoke Type 1. Eagle Medallion

**that purpose, as the boot can be damaged.**

2. Install expander tool T.Av.586.01 or equivalent onto shaft yoke.
3. Lubricate entire length of expander tool with clean oil.
4. Lubricate inside of the replacement boot with clean oil. Cover the small opening in the replacement boot with your thumb and pour oil into the boot. Spread the oil evenly around the boot interior.
5. Start the boot onto the expander tool.
6. Grip the boot so the first fold (J), **Fig. 8,** will stretch as the boot is worked onto the expander tool.
7. Pull the boot onto the tool as far as possible. Allow the boot to relax and return part way. Ensure the first fold (J) does not slip back. Repeat this procedure three or four times to stretch and expand the boot. **To ease installation, wrap a dry cloth around the boot and use a two handed grip to gradually work the boot onto the tool. Turn the boot back and forth to aid installation, Fig. 9.**
8. When the boot feels most pliable (flexible), use one continuous motion to draw it up to the end of the tool.
9. Slide boot onto shaft and remove expander tool.
10. Lubricate the constant velocity joint components with suitable grease supplied in the service kit. Distribute the grease evenly between boot inner surface, bearing rollers, yoke and housing.
11. Install spring, shim and ball into the spider. **Lubricate these components before installation.**
12. Fabricate and install a spacer (N) under the spider and star plate to hold them upward during assembly. A Spacer can be made from an old shock absorber grommet. Loop a length of wire through it as shown in **Fig. 10,** then insert the spacer under the star plate (P). Move the roller (Q) toward the center and position the star plate arms (P) so that each arm is centered between each spider roller, **Fig. 11.**
13. Insert the shaft yoke (R) into the housing (S), **Fig. 12.**
14. Tilt the shaft and insert one star plate arm (P) into the yoke. Then press the arm into the yoke slot using a screwdriver.
15. Remove spacer from under the star plate by pulling it out with the attached wire.
16. Press the remaining star plate arms into the yoke with a modified screwdriver (T), **Fig. 13.** Grind approximately a .20 by .12 inch notch in the screwdriver tip. Then seat the remaining star plate arms.
17. Ensure each star plate arm is properly seated.
18. Check spider movement. It should move freely in all directions.
19. Lubricate all constant velocity joint components.
20. Position boot into housing and shaft retaining grooves.
21. Purge air from boot. **Do not damage boot when purging air.**
22. Using tool T.Av.1034 or equivalent, install and tighten boot clamps. If a spring type clamp (U), **Fig. 14,** is used at the large end of the boot, use two 1/4 inch drive deep sockets (V) and extensions (W) to spread and install clamp.

## TYPE 2 OUTER C/V JOINT

### Disassembly

**Refer to Fig. 15 for cross-sectional view of type 2 outer constant velocity joint assembly.**

1. Remove clamp at large end of boot.
2. Remove retaining ring (A), **Fig. 16.** Spread ring, tap the ball hub (B) and slide the joint (C) off shaft (D).
3. Remove boot from shaft.
4. Remove as much grease as possible from assembly. **Do not use any cleaning solvents.**

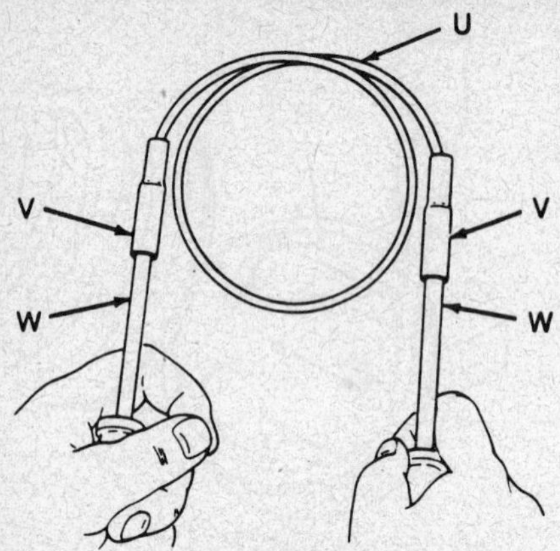


**Fig. 14 Spring type clamp installation Types 1 & 2. Eagle Medallion**

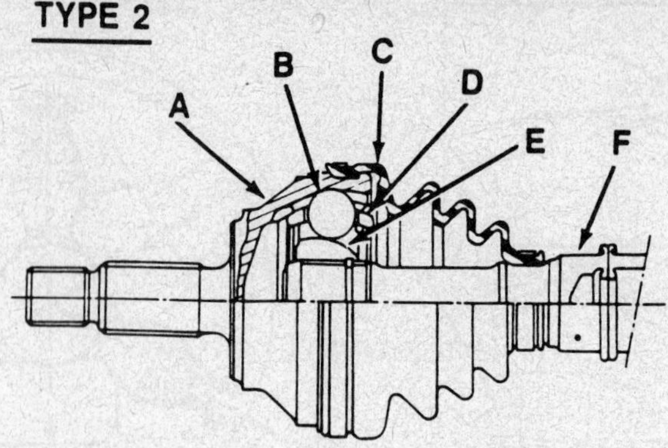


A — Housing
B — Bearing Balls (6)
C — Boot
D — Ball Cage
E — Ball Hub
F — Shaft

**Fig. 15 Cross-sectional view of type 2 outer C/V joint. Eagle Medallion**

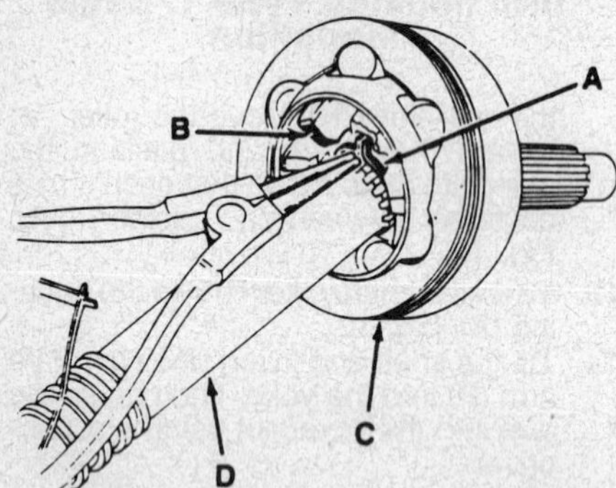


**Fig. 16 Removing retaining ring, ball hub & joint from shaft Type 2. Eagle Medallion**

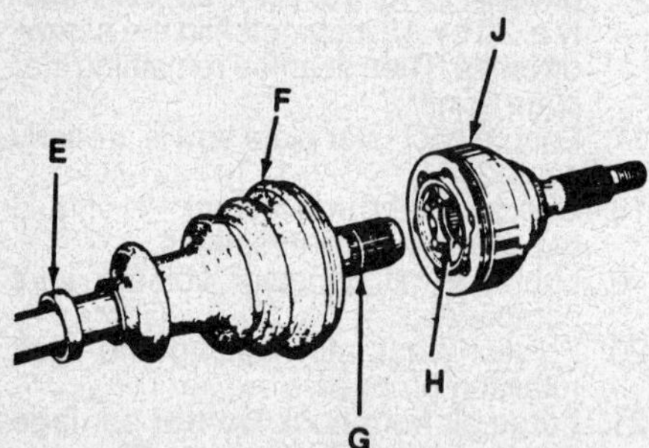


**Fig. 17 Outer joint assembly Type 2. Eagle Medallion**

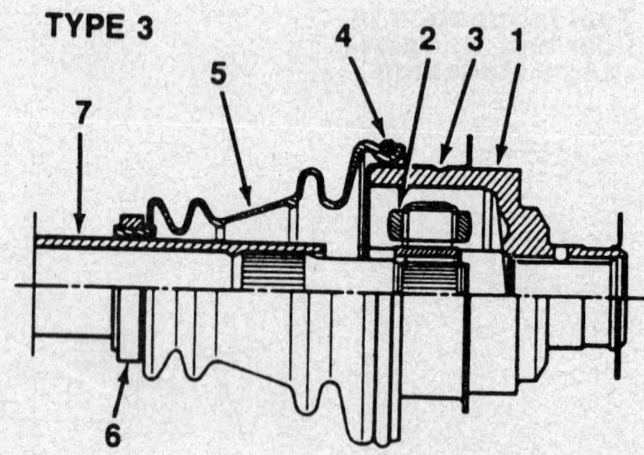


1 — Yoke
2 — Spider
3 — Metal Cover
4 — Retaining Spring
5 — Boot
6 — Retaining Ring
7 — Driveshaft

**Fig. 18 Cross-sectional view of type 3 inner C/V joint. Eagle Medallion**

5. Inspect constant velocity joint. Replace entire joint as an assembly, if required.

### Assembly

1. Install replacement boot retainer (E) and boot (F) onto shaft, **Fig. 17.**
2. Install a replacement retaining ring (A) into constant velocity joint ring groove (H).
3. Lubricate constant velocity joint (J) and interior of boot (F) with suitable grease supplied in the service kit.
4. Install the constant velocity joint (J) onto shaft (G). Ensure retaining ring is completely seated in its groove.
5. Seat boot in constant velocity joint housing and shaft grooves, then install boot clamps.
6. If a spring type clamp (U), **Fig. 14**, is used at the large end of the boot, use two 1/4 inch drive deep sockets (V) and extensions (W) to spread and install clamp.

## TYPE 3 INNER C/V JOINT

### Disassembly

**Refer to Fig. 18 for cross-sectional view of type 3 inner constant velocity joint assembly.**

1. Remove boot retaining spring.
2. Cut boot lengthwise and remove boot from shaft.
3. Using a suitable tool, lift and remove anti-separation plates (C) from joint (B), **Fig. 19.**
4. Remove snap ring securing bearing roller onto shaft.
5. Using a suitable press and press tool U-53P (G), drive bearing rollers (F) off shaft assembly, **Fig. 20.**
6. Clean constant velocity joint assembly. **Do not use cleaning solvents.**
7. If the boot bearing requires replacement, refer to "Inner Constant Velocity Joint Boot Bearing, Replace."

### Assembly

1. Lubricate driveshaft and install replacement boot and boot clamp onto shaft assembly.
2. Using a suitable press, drive replacement bearing roller assembly onto shaft.
3. Install a replacement snap ring onto shaft.
4. Fabricate a wedge to the dimensions shown in **Fig. 21.** The wedge will be used to install the anti-separation plates.
5. Insert wedge between anti-separation plate and yoke.
6. Tap each plate into position and remove wedge.
7. Purge air from boot. **Do not damage**

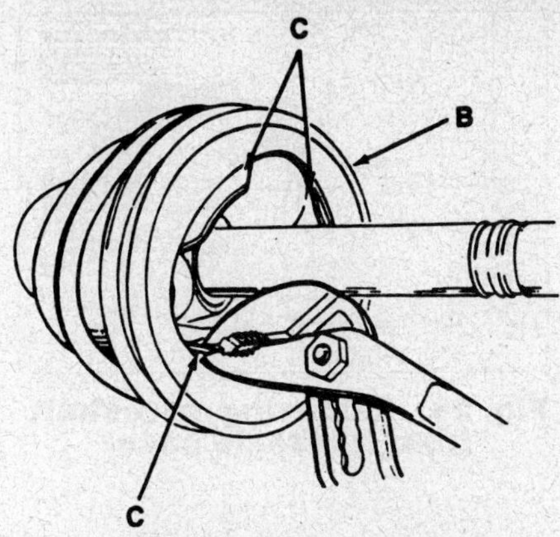


Fig. 19 Removing anti-separation plates from joint Type 3. Eagle Medallion

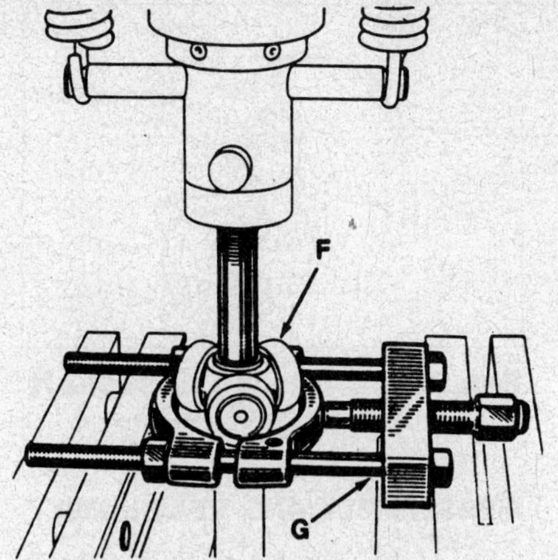


Fig. 20 Pressing bearing rollers from shaft Type 3. Eagle Medallion

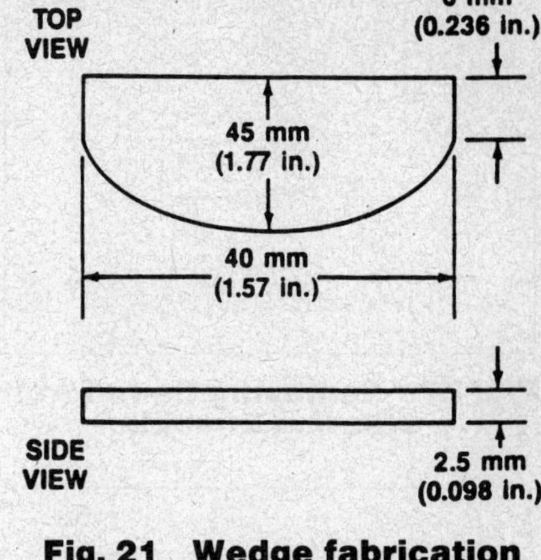


Fig. 21 Wedge fabrication dimensions Type 3. Eagle Medallion

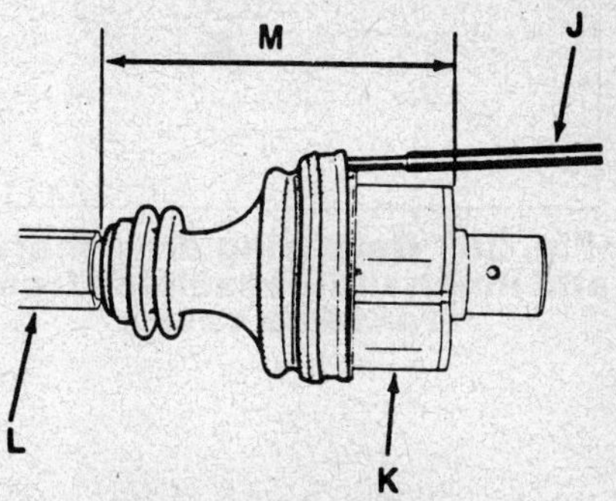


Fig. 23 Obtaining coupling housing distance (M) Type 4. Eagle Medallion

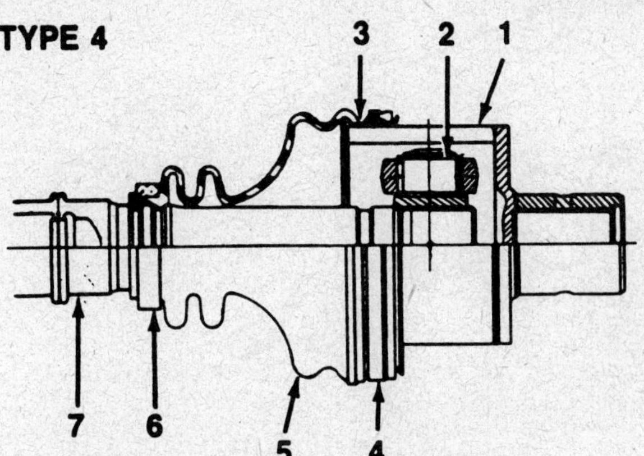


1 — Yoke
2 — Spider
3 — Metal Cover
4 — Retaining Clamp
5 — Boot
6 — Retaining Ring
7 — Driveshaft

Fig. 22 Cross-sectional view of type 4 inner C/V joint. Eagle Medallion

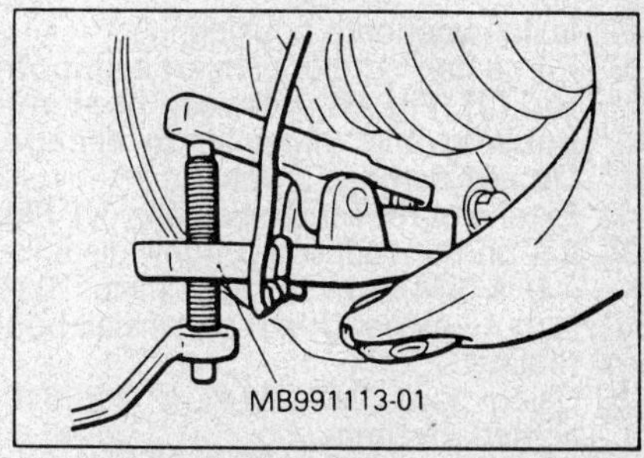


Fig. 26 Removing ball joint from steering knuckle.

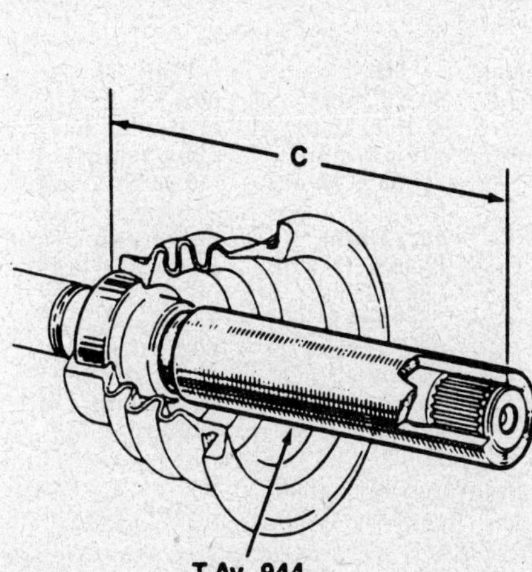


Fig. 24 Pressing boot bearing onto shaft. Eagle Medallion

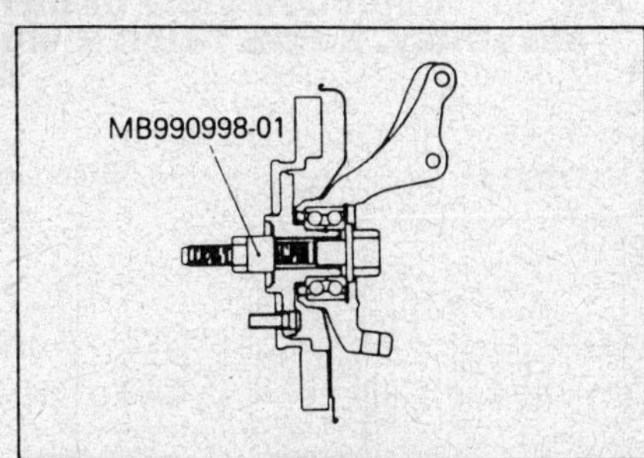


Fig. 25 Installation of wheel bearing support tool.

boot while purging air.

## TYPE 4 INNER C/V JOINT

### Disassembly

**Refer to Fig. 22 for cross-sectional view of type 4 inner constant velocity joint assembly.**

1. Remove boot clamps.
2. Remove yoke by pulling it straight off the bearing rollers.
3. Remove bearing roller snap ring.
4. Using a suitable press and press tool U-53P or equivalent, remove bearing rollers from shaft.
5. Remove boot from shaft.
6. Clean grease from assembly. **Do not use cleaning solvents.**
7. If the boot bearing requires replacement, refer to "Inner Constant Velocity Joint Boot Bearing, Replace."

### Assembly

1. Lubricate driveshaft with suitable grease and install boot and clamp onto shaft.
2. Press bearing rollers onto shaft.
3. Secure rollers using a replacement snap ring or stake rollers in position by center punching the ends of the shaft at three equally spaced points.

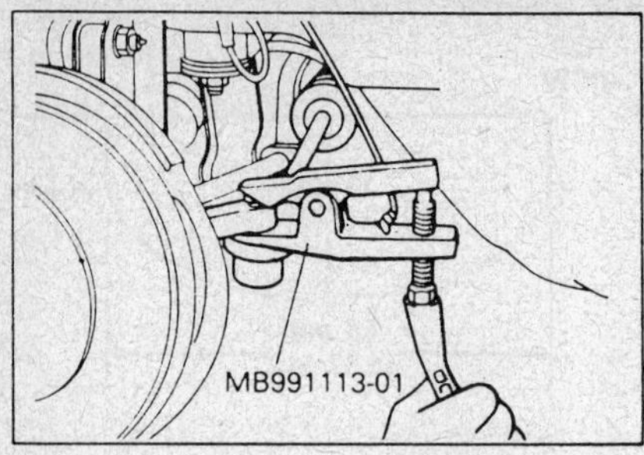


Fig. 27 Removing tie rod from steering knuckle.

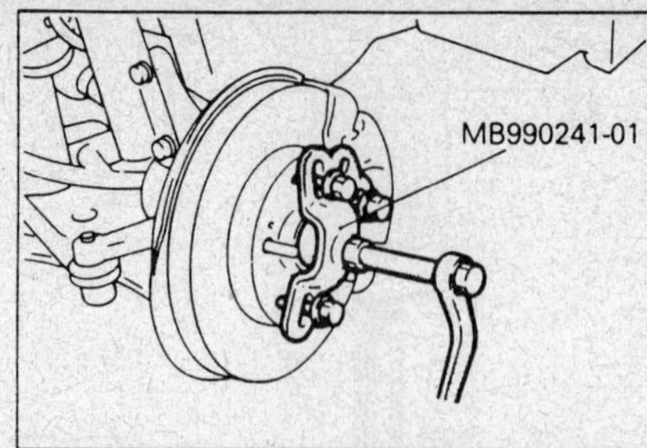


Fig. 28 Removing driveshaft from front hub.

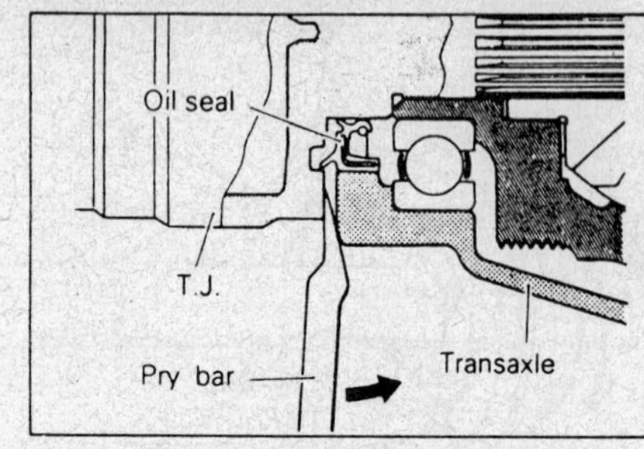


Fig. 29 Removing driveshaft from transaxle case.

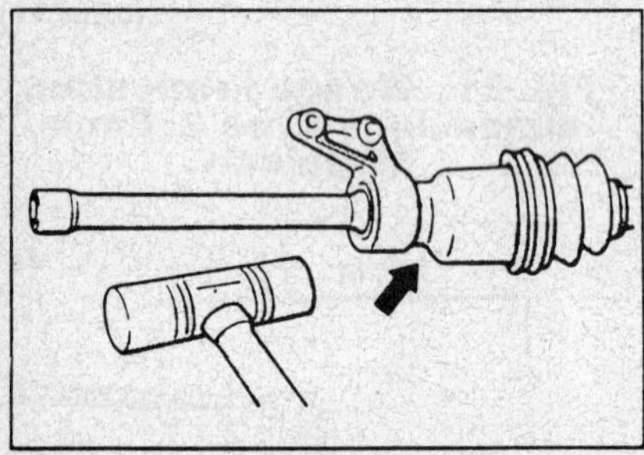

Fig. 30 Removing driveshaft and inner shaft assembly from transaxle case.

4. Lubricate all constant velocity joint components including the boot interior.
5. Install boot onto housing.
6. Purge air from boot. **Insert a smooth rod (J), Fig. 23, between boot and housing and allow air to escape. Do not damage boot.**
7. Extend or retract the housing (K), **Fig. 23,** on the coupling (L) until distance (M) is 6.14 inches plus or minus .039 inch. Remove rod (J) and install boot retainers.
8. Using tool T.Av.1034 or J-22610, tighten retainers.

## INNER CONSTANT VELOCITY JOINT BOOT BEARING, REPLACE

1. Remove constant velocity joint housing and bearing rollers.
2. Remove bearing snap ring.
3. Press bearing and boot off shaft assembly.
4. Using a suitable press and tool T.Av.944 or equivalent, install bearing and boot.
5. Install snap ring.
6. Press boot and bearing onto shaft until tool T.Av.944 bottoms against shaft. At this point, distance (C), **Fig. 24,** should be approximately 5.85 inches. **Do not attempt to install the bearing with a hammer or damage may result.**
7. Assemble constant velocity joint.

### DISASSEMBLY AND REASSEMBLY

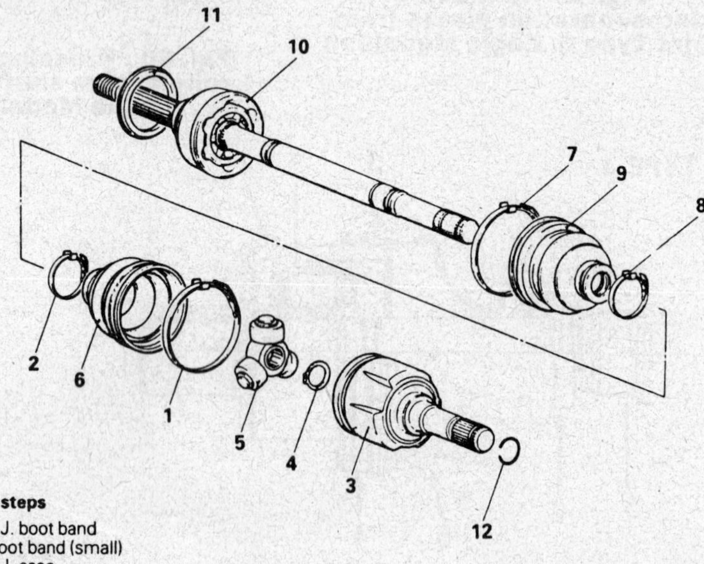


**Disassembly steps**

1. T.J. boot band
2. Boot band (small)
3. T.J. case
4. Snap ring
5. Spider assembly
6. T.J. boot
7. B.J. boot band
8. Boot band (small)
9. B.J. boot
10. B.J. assembly
11. Dust cover
12. Circlip

Fig. 31 Exploded view of birfield joint & tripod type driveshaft assembly. Eagle Talon 2 wheel drive and right side 4 wheel drive.

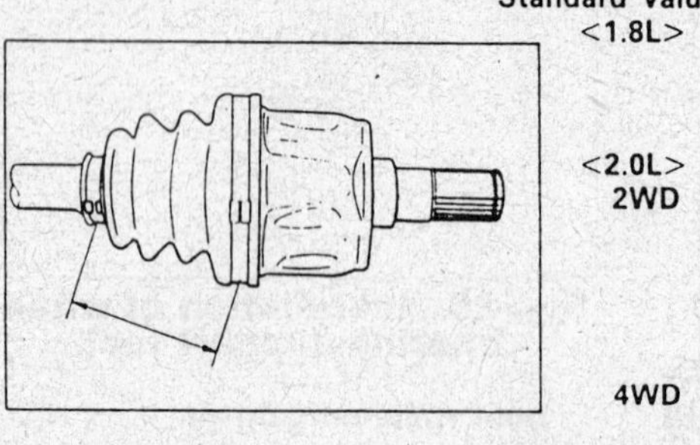

| Standard value: | LH | RH |
|---|---|---|
| <1.8L> | 80±3 mm*1 (3.15±.12 in.) [75±3 mm (2.95±.12 in.)]*2 | 80±3 mm*1 (3.15±.12 in.) [85±3 mm (3.35±.12 in.)]*2 |
| <2.0L> 2WD | 75±3 mm (2.95±.12 in.) [80±3 mm (3.15±.12 in.)]*2 | 80±3 mm (3.15±.12 in.) |
| | 80±3 mm*3 (3.15±.12 in.) | 80±3 mm*3 (3.15±.12 in.) |
| 4WD | 85±3 mm (3.35±.12 in.) | 85±3 mm (3.35±.12 in.) |

NOTE
*1: Vehicles built up to April 1989
*2: Vehicles built from May 1989
*3: <Turbo>

Fig. 32 Tripod joint boot installation. Eagle Talon 2WD & RH shaft 4WD models

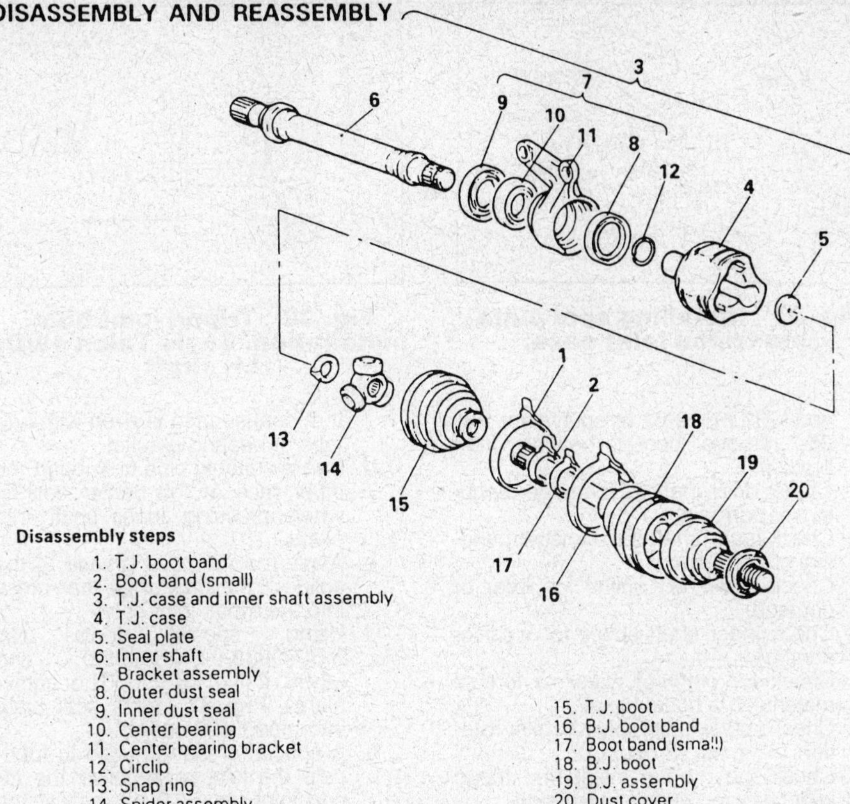


**Fig. 33 Exploded view of birfield joint, tripod type driveshaft & inner shaft assembly. Eagle Talon 4WD, LH shaft**

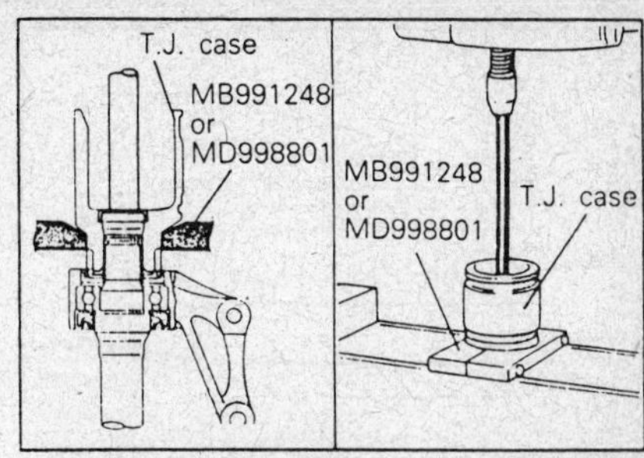


**Fig. 34 Removing inner shaft assembly from tripod joint case**

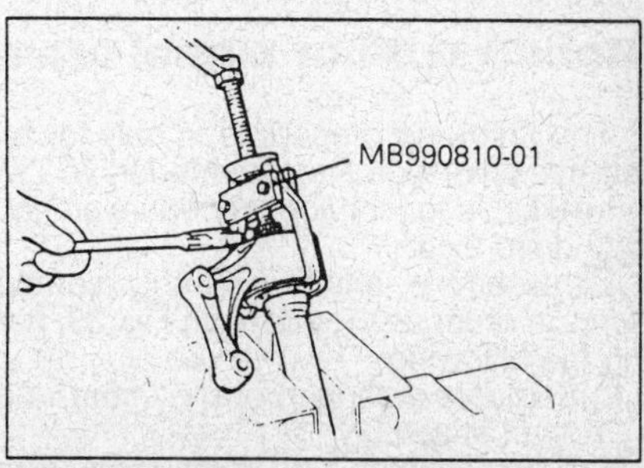


**Fig. 35 Removing inner shaft from center bearing bracket**

# EAGLE TALON

## DRIVESHAFT, REPLACE

### Models w/Two Wheel Drive

**Do not apply vehicle load to the wheel bearing after removal of the driveshaft. If a load must be applied to the bearing in moving the vehicle, temporarily secure with special tool No. MB990998-01 or equivalent, Fig. 25.**

1. Loosen drive axle nut, then raise and support front of vehicle and remove wheel and tire assembly.
2. Using special tool No. MB991113-01, **Fig. 26,** disconnect lower arm ball joint from knuckle.
3. Using special tool No. MB991113-01, **Fig. 27,** disconnect tie rod end from knuckle.
4. Press driveshaft from hub using shaft puller No. MB990241-01, **Fig. 28.**
5. Insert a suitable pry bar between the transaxle case and the driveshaft, and pry the shaft from the transaxle, **Fig. 29. Do not pull on the shaft, as damage to the joint may result. Pry bar should not be inserted too deep, as damage to the oil seal may result.**
6. Reverse procedure to install. Lower vehicle to the ground and tighten knuckle to lower arm ball joint nut, and **torque** axle nut to 188 ft. lbs. maximum.

### Models w/Four Wheel Drive

**Do not apply vehicle load to the wheel bearing after removal of the driveshaft. If a load must be applied to the bearing in moving the vehicle, temporarily secure with special tool No. MB990998-01 or equivalent, Fig. 25.**

The following procedure is only for the left side drive axle. Refer to Models w/Two Wheel Drive for right side drive axle replacement procedure.

1. Loosen drive axle nut, then raise and support front of vehicle and remove wheel and tire assembly.
2. Using special tool No. MB991113-01, **Fig. 26,** disconnect lower arm ball joint from knuckle.
3. Using special tool No. MB991113-01, **Fig. 27,** disconnect tie rod end from knuckle.
4. Press driveshaft and inner shaft assembly from hub using shaft puller No. MB990241-01, **Fig. 28.**
5. Remove driveshaft and inner shaft assembly from transaxle by lightly tapping the tripod joint case with a plastic hammer, **Fig. 30.**
6. Reverse procedure to install. Lower vehicle to the ground, then tighten knuckle to lower arm ball joint nut, and **torque** axle nut to 188 ft. lbs. maximum.

## DRIVESHAFT SERVICE

### Models w/Two Wheel Drive

Disassemble shaft assembly components in order as they appear, **Fig. 31,** noting the following:

1. Remove snap ring from shaft using suitable snap ring pliers.
2. Remove spider assembly from shaft.
3. Clean spider assembly and check for wear or damage. Do not disassemble spider assembly, if the tripod joint case of the shaft assembly is bent, the joint may be damaged. Use care in handling the shaft.
4. Wrap vinyl tape around splines of the shaft to prevent damage to boots during removal.
5. Check driveshaft for damage, bending or corrosion.
6. Check spline for wear or damage.
7. Check for entry of water or foreign material into birfield joint.
8. Check spider assembly for roller rotation, wear, or corrosion.
9. Check the groove inside the tripod joint case for wear or corrosion.
10. Check boots for deterioration, damage, or cracking.
11. Assemble in reverse order of disassembly. A special grease is used to lubricate the joint assemblies. On vehicles built before April 1989, 3.2 oz. or more per joint is required, half at the joint and half in the boot. On vehicles built after April 1989, 3.9 oz. per joint is required.
12. Install bands and boots for each joint. When installing boot bands for tripod joint, set bands at specified distance, **Fig. 32,** in order to adjust the amount of air inside the boot.

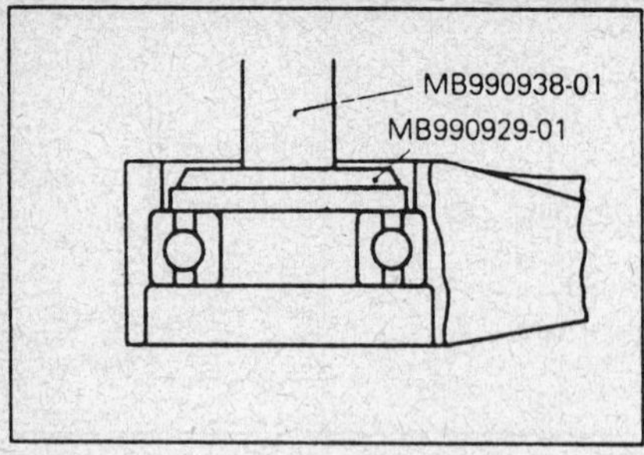


**Fig. 36 Removing center bearing from center bearing bracket.**

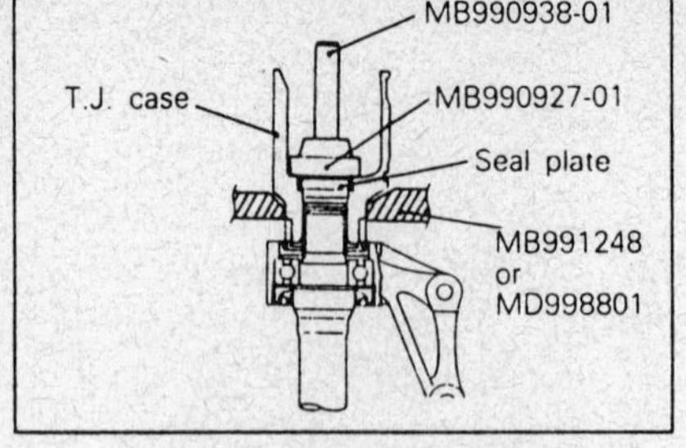


**Fig. 37 Installing seal plate into tripod joint case.**

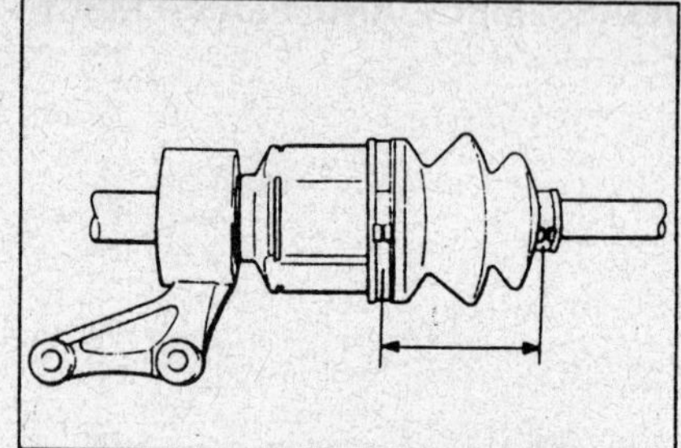

**Fig. 38 Tripod joint boot installation. Eagle Talon 4WD, LH shaft**

### Models w/Four Wheel Drive

The following procedure is only for the left side drive axle. Refer to Models w/Two Wheel Drive for service procedure on right side drive axle.

Disassemble shaft assembly components in order as they appear, **Fig. 33,** noting the following:

1. Separate outer part of shaft from inner shaft assembly.
2. Remove snap ring from shaft using suitable snap ring pliers.
3. Remove spider assembly from shaft.
4. Clean spider assembly and check for wear or damage. Do not disassemble spider assembly, if the tripod joint case of the shaft assembly is bent, the joint may be damaged. Use care in handling the shaft.
5. Wrap vinyl tape around splines of the shaft to prevent damage to boots during removal.
6. Do not disassemble the birfield joint assembly, it is not serviceable.
7. Using special tool No. MB991248 or MD998801 or equivalent, **Fig. 34,** press inner shaft assembly along with seal plate from the tripod joint case.
8. Using special tool No. MB990810-01 or equivalent, **Fig. 35,** remove inner shaft from center bearing bracket.
9. Using special tools No. MB990938-01 and MB990929-01 or equivalent, **Fig. 36,** remove center bearing from bracket.
10. Check driveshaft for damage, bending, or corrosion.
11. Check inner shaft for damage, bending, or corrosion.
12. Check driveshaft spline for wear or damage.
13. Check inner shaft spline for wear or damage.
14. Check for entry of water or foreign material into birfield joint.
15. Check spider assembly for roller rotation, wear, or corrosion.
16. Check the groove inside the tripod joint case for wear or corrosion.
17. Check boots for deterioration, damage, or cracking.
18. Check the center bearing for seizure, discoloration, or roughness of rolling.
19. Check the dust cover for damage or deterioration.
20. Assemble in reverse order, noting the following:
    a. Apply multipurpose grease to the center bearing and inside of the center bearing bracket.
    b. Apply multipurpose grease to the inside lip of the bearing dust seals. Ensure that grease does not adhere to anything outside the lip.
    c. When installing dust seals, ensure that seal surface is even with surface of bearing bracket.
    d. Use a suitable pipe to support the inner race of the center bearing when pressing inner shaft into place.
    e. Apply multipurpose grease to the spline of the inner shaft, then press into the tripod joint case.
    f. Using special tools No. MB990938-01, MB990927-01, and MB991248 or MD998801 or equivalents, **Fig. 37,** press seal plate into tripod joint case.
    g. A special grease is used to lubricate the joint assemblies, the tripod joint uses 3.9 oz., half at the joint and half in the boot. The birfield joint uses 3.2 oz., half at the joint half in the boot. The grease is supplied in the repair kit.
    h. When installing boot bands on the tripod joint, set the bands at a distance of 3.23-3.47 inch, **Fig. 38,** to adjust the amount of air inside the boot.

## EAGLE SUMMIT

Refer to "Colt" in the "Chrysler Imports" section for service procedures on front drive axle.

# ALL WHEEL DRIVE

## INDEX



| Symptom | Probable cause | Remedy |
|---|---|---|
| AXLE SHAFT<br>Noise while wheels are rotating | Brake drag<br>Bent axle shaft<br>Worn or scarred axle shaft bearing | Replace |
| Grease leakage | Worn or damaged oil seal<br>Malfunction of bearing seal | Replace |
| DRIVE SHAFT<br>Noise | Wear, play or seizure of ball joint<br>Excessive drive shaft spline looseness | Replace |
| DIFFERENTIAL (CONVENTIONAL DIFFERENTIAL)<br>Constant noise | Improper final drive gear tooth contact adjustment<br>Loose, worn or damaged side bearing<br>Loose, worn or damaged drive pinion bearing | Correct or replace |
| | Worn drive gear, drive pinion<br>Worn side gear spacer or pinion shaft<br>Deformed drive gear or differential case<br>Damaged gear | Replace |
| | Foreign material | Eliminate the foreign material and check; replace the parts if necessary |
| | Insufficient oil | Replenish |
| Gear noise while driving | Poor gear engagement<br>Improper gear adjustment<br>Improper drive pinion preload adjustment | Correct or replace |
| | Damaged gear | Replace |
| | Foreign material | Eliminate the foreign material and check; replace the parts if necessary |
| | Insufficient oil | Replenish |
| Gear noise while coasting | Improper drive pinion preload adjustment<br>Damaged gear | Correct or replace<br>Replace |
| Bearing noise while driving or coasting | Cracked or damaged drive pinion rear bearing | Replace |
| Noise while turning | Loose side bearing<br>Damaged side gear, pinion gear or pinion shaft | Replace |
| Heat | Insufficient gear backlash<br>Excessive preload | Adjust |
| | Insufficient oil | Replenish |
| Oil leakage | Clogged vent plug | Clean or replace |
| | Cover insufficiently tightened<br>Seal malfunction | Retighten, apply sealant, or replace the gasket |
| | Worn or damaged oil seal | Replace |
| | Excessive oil | Adjust the oil level |
| DIFFERENTIAL (LIMITED SLIP DIFFERENTIAL)<br>Abnormal noise during driving or gear changing | Excessive final drive gear backlash<br>Insufficient drive pinion preload | Adjust |
| | Excessive differential gear backlash | Adjust or replace |
| | Worn spline of a side gear | Replace |
| | Loose companion flange self-locking nut | Retighten or replace |

**Fig. 1 All Wheel Drive (AWD) troubleshooting chart (Part 1 of 2)**

## DESCRIPTION

This system used on Eagle Talon, Stealth, Colt Vista and Colt Wagon models is a full time All Wheel Drive (AWD) system. It has an optional limited slip differential for increased traction. The main components used in this system are the transfer case, rear drive axle, axle shafts and driveshaft.

## TROUBLESHOOTING

Refer to **Fig. 1** when troubleshooting system malfunctions.

## CARRIER INSPECTION BEFORE SERVICE

### REAR AXLE TOTAL BACKLASH

If vehicle vibrates and has a booming sound due to system driveline imbalance. Total axle backlash should be checked. To check backlash, proceed as follows:

1. Place gearshift in neutral, apply parking brake, then raise and support vehicle.
2. Manually turn propeller shaft clockwise as far as it will go and scribe mating mark on companion flange dust cover and differential carrier, **Fig. 2.**
3. Manually turn shaft counterclockwise as far as it will go and measure movement of mating marks.
4. If axle total backlash is less than .2 inch (5 mm), backlash is satisfactory.
5. If backlash is more than .2 inch (5 mm), refer to "Component Service" for adjustment procedures.

### GEAR OIL LEVEL CHECK

1. Remove filler plug and check oil level.
2. If oil level reaches bottom of filler plug hole, oil level is satisfactory.

| Symptom | Probable cause | Remedy |
|---|---|---|
| NOTE<br>In addition to a malfunction of the differential carrier components, abnormal noise can also be caused by the universal joint of the propeller shaft, the axle shafts, the wheel bearings, etc. Before disassembling any parts, take all possibilities into consideration and confirm the source of the noise. | | |
| Abnormal noise when cornering | Damaged differential gears<br>Damaged pinion shaft | Replace |
| | Insufficient gear oil quantity | Replenish |
| Gear noise | Improper final drive gear tooth contact adjustment | Adjust or replace |
| | Incorrect final drive gear backlash<br>Improper drive pinion preload adjustment | Adjust |
| | Damaged, broken, and/or seized tooth surfaces of the drive gear and drive pinion<br>Damaged, broken, and/or seized drive pinion bearings<br>Damaged, broken, and/or seized side bearings<br>Damaged differential case<br>Inferior gear oil | Replace |
| | Insufficient gear oil quantity | Replenish |
| NOTE<br>Noise from the engine, muffler vibration, transaxle, propeller shaft, wheel bearings, tires, body, etc., is easily mistaken as being caused by malfunctions in the differential carrier components. Be extremely careful and attentive when performing the driving test, etc.<br>Test methods to confirm the source of the abnormal noise include: coasting acceleration, constant speed driving, raising the rear wheels on a jack, etc. Use the method most appropriate to the circumstances. | | |
| Gear oil leakage | Worn or damaged front oil seal, or an improperly installed oil seal<br>Damaged gasket | Replace |
| | Loose companion flange self-locking nut | Retighten or replace |
| | Loose filler or drain plug | Retighten or apply adhesive |
| | Clogged or damaged vent plug | Clean or replace |
| Seizure | Insufficient final drive gear backlash<br>Excessive drive pinion preload<br>Excessive side bearing preload<br>Insufficient differential gear backlash<br>Excessive clutch plate preload | Adjust |
| | Inferior gear oil | Replace |
| | Insufficient gear oil quantity | Replenish |
| NOTE<br>In the event of seizure, disassemble and replace the parts involved, and also be sure to check all components for any irregularities and repair or replace as necessary. | | |
| Break down | Incorrect final drive gear backlash<br>Insufficient drive pinion preload<br>Insufficient side bearing preload<br>Excessive differential gear backlash | Adjust |
| | Loose drive gear clamping bolts | Retighten |
| NOTE<br>In addition to disassembling and replacing the failed parts, be sure to check all components for irregularities and repair or replace as necessary. | | |
| The limited slip differential does not function (on snow, mud, ice, etc.) | The limited slip device is damaged | Disassemble, check the functioning, and replace the damaged parts |

**Fig. 1 All Wheel Drive (AWD) troubleshooting chart (Part 2 of 2)**

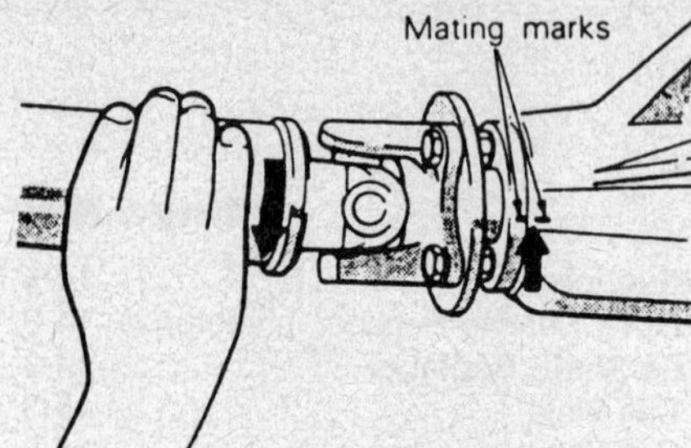


**Fig. 2 Checking rear axle total backlash**

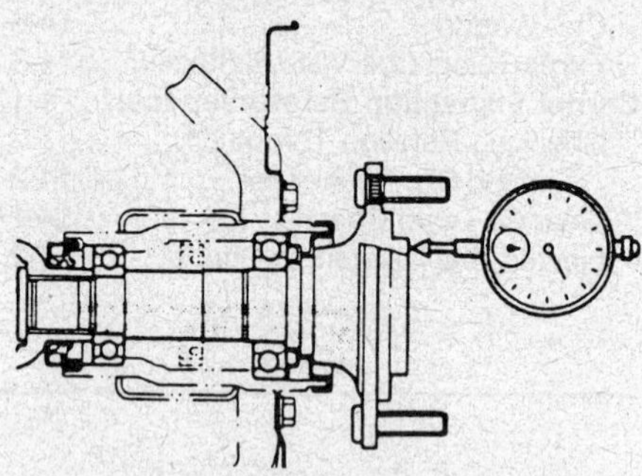

**Fig. 3 Checking rear wheel bearing endplay**

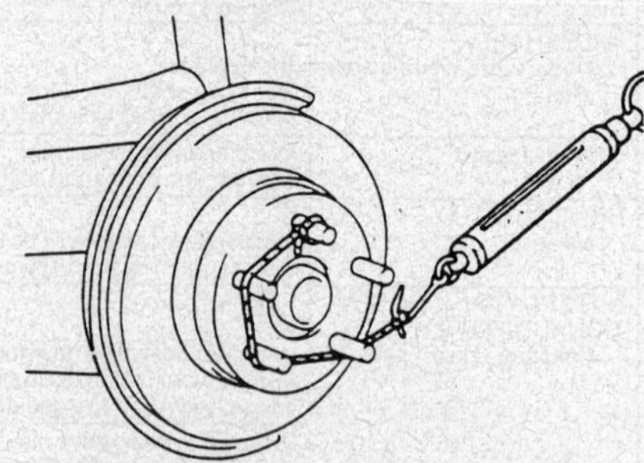

**Fig. 4 Rear wheel bearing rotation sliding resistance check**

3. If level does not reach bottom of filler plug hole, fill differential with MOPAR Hypoid Gear Oil API classification GL-5 or equivalent.

## REAR WHEEL BEARING ENDPLAY CHECK

1. Raise and support vehicle on axle stands.
2. Remove rear wheel and tire assembly, then disconnect parking brake cable from rear brake.
3. Remove caliper assembly and brake disc.
4. Position a dial indicator as shown in **Fig. 3,** and measure endplay when axle is moved in an axial direction.
5. If endplay is less than .031 inch (.8 mm), endplay is satisfactory.
6. If endplay exceeds .031 inch (.8 mm), ensure **torque** of axle shaft companion flange is 116-159 ft. lbs. on except Stealth models and 137 ft. lbs. on Stealth models less turbo or 188-217 ft. lbs. on Stealth models with turbo. If torque is within specification, replace wheel bearing.

## REAR WHEEL BEARING ROTATION SLIDING RESISTANCE CHECK

### Eagle Talon & Stealth

1. Raise and support vehicle.
2. Disconnect driveshaft at companion flange, refer to "Driveshaft, Replace."
3. Remove caliper assembly and suspend with wire.
4. Attach a spring balance to hub bolt, then pull balance at a right angle to bolt, **Fig. 4.** Measure rotation starting torque.
5. If rotation starting torque is less than 6 inch lbs., bearing is satisfactory.
6. If rotation starting torque is more than 6 inch lbs., ensure tightening **torque** of axle shaft companion flange is 116-159 ft. lbs. on Eagle Talon and 137 ft. lbs. on Stealth models less turbo or 188-217 ft. lbs. on Stealth models with turbo. If torque is satisfactory, replace wheel bearing.

## CHECKING ROTATION TORQUE OF LIMITED SLIP DIFFERENTIAL

### Colt Vista & Colt Wagon

1. Set shift lever of transaxle to neutral position, lock front wheels and fully release the parking brake.
2. **On Colt Vista models,** set the 4WD control switch to Off position.
3. **On all models,** raise rear of vehicle so only one wheel is not in contact with ground surface.
4. Remove wheel and mount end yoke holder tool No. MB990767 or equivalent, to hub bolts using hub nuts.
5. Using a suitable torque wrench, measure side gear rotation torque in forward direction.
6. If rotation torque is not 5.06 ft. lbs. or more on Colt Vista models or 1.8 ft. lbs. on Colt Wagon models, disassemble limited slip differential and inspect each component.

| Packing and shim selection procedure | | |
|---|---|---|
| Clearance mm (in.) | Number of packings | Number of shims |
| Less than 0.2 (.008) | 0 | 0 |
| 0.2 to 0.5 (.008 to .02) | 1 | 0 |
| 0.5 to 0.75 (.02 to .03) | 2 | 0 |
| 0.75 to 1.0 (.03 to .04) | 2 | 1 |
| 1.00 to 1.25 (.04 to .05) | 2 | 2 |

**Fig. 5 Packing & shim selection chart. Colt Wagon**

## LIMITED-SLIP DIFFERENTIAL CHECK

1. Block front wheels and move shift lever to neutral.
2. Release parking brake completely, then raise rear wheels and support with rigid jack stand.
3. Disconnect coupling of differential and propeller shaft.
4. Rotate one wheel slowly, ensure wheel on opposite side turns in the same direction.
5. If wheel turns in the opposite direction, replace viscous unit.

# ADJUSTMENTS

## OUTER BEARING RETAINER INTERFERENCE

### Colt Wagon

Adjustment of the outer bearing retainer is required when axle shaft or wheel bearing are replaced, but not required when axle shaft are removed and reinstalled without replacement of components.

1. Install axle shaft into axle housing without installing packings and shims.
2. Temporarily tighten nuts until bearing outer race comes in close contact with axle housing.
3. Measure clearance between axle housing and backing plate.
4. Using chart in **Fig. 5**, determine number and thickness of packing and shims to be used.
5. Install axle shaft assembly.

# AXLE SHAFT REPLACE

## EAGLE TALON & STEALTH

1. Raise and support vehicle, then remove tire and wheel assembly.
2. **On models with Anti-lock Brake System (ABS),** remove ABS sensor and O-ring.
3. **On all models,** remove brake caliper and suspend with wire.
4. Using end yoke holder tool No. MB990767 or equivalent to secure axle shaft, remove companion shaft self-locking nut, **Fig. 6.**
5. Using slide hammer tool No. C-637 and axle puller tool No. CT-1003 or equivalents, remove axle shaft assembly.
6. Reverse procedure to install, on Eagle Talon models, **torque** axle shaft self-locking nut to 116-159 ft. lbs. On Stealth models with turbocharged engines, **torque** axle shaft self-locking nut to 188-217 ft. lbs. on Stealth models with turbo.

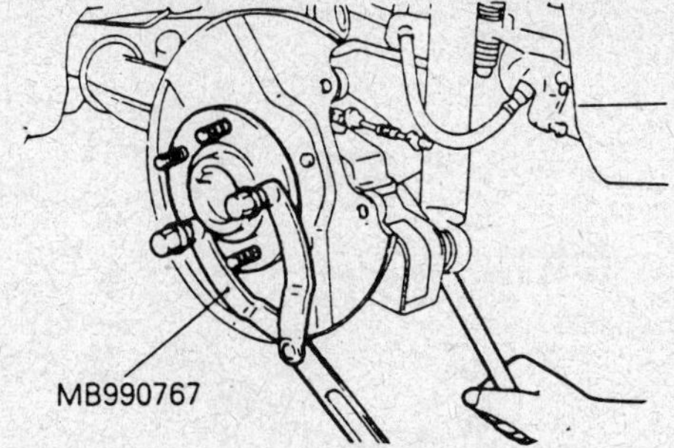


**Fig. 6 Removing axle shaft self-locking nut**

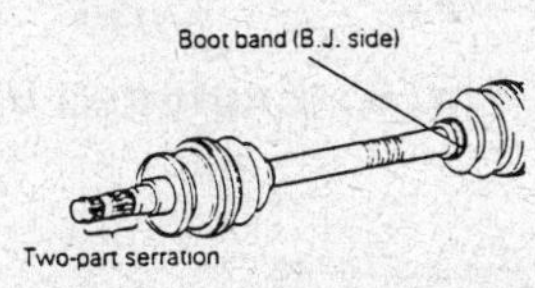


| Item | Drive shaft | |
|---|---|---|
| | LH | RH |
| Boot band (B.J. side) identification color | White | Blue |

**Fig. 8 Driveshaft identification. Stealth**

## COLT VISTA

1. Raise and support vehicle, then remove tire and wheel assembly.
2. Remove brake drum assembly.
3. Remove driveshaft to companion flange bolts.
4. Using end yoke holder tool No. MB990767 or equivalent to secure axle shaft, remove companion shaft self-locking nut, **Fig. 6.**
5. Using slide hammer tool No. C-637 and axle puller tool No. CT-1003 or equivalents, remove axle shaft assembly.
6. Reverse procedure to install, **torque** axle shaft self-locking nut to 116-159 ft. lbs.

## COLT WAGON

1. Raise and support vehicle.
2. Drain brake fluid into a suitable container.
3. Drain differential fluid into a suitable container.
4. Remove brake drum then disconnect rear brake assembly tube.
5. Remove rear brake shoe assembly as outlined under the drum brake section.
6. Disconnect parking brake cable.
7. Pull out axle shaft from housing using axle shaft puller tool No. CTR-1003 or equivalent, and a slide hammer.
8. Remove shim, packing and oil seal.
9. Reverse procedure to install noting the following:
   a. Apply grease to oil seal then install oil seal using oil seal installer tool Nos. MB990938 and MB990935 or equivalent.
   b. Adjust outer bearing retainer interference as outlined under "Bearing Adjust" under "Adjustments."

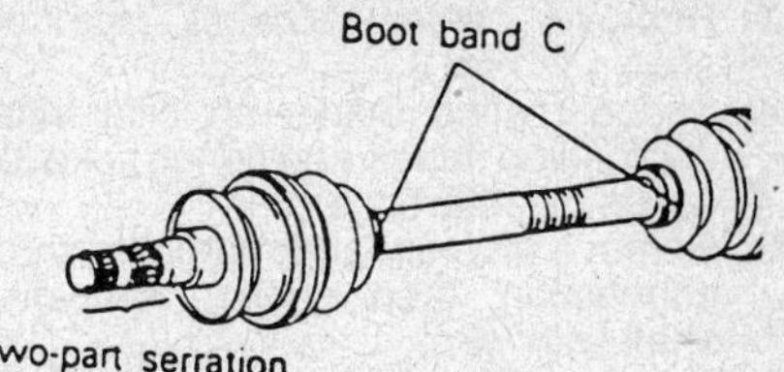


| Item | Drive shaft (left) | Drive shaft (right) |
|---|---|---|
| Boot band C identification color | Yellow | Blue |

**Fig. 7 Driveshaft identification. Eagle Talon**

# DRIVESHAFT REPLACE

1. Raise and support vehicle.
2. Remove companion flange to driveshaft bolts.
3. Using a suitable prying tool, pry driveshaft out of differential carrier.
4. Remove circlip from driveshaft and oil seal from differential carrier.
5. Reverse procedure to install, noting the following:
   a. Use caution to ensure that the differential carrier oil seal is not damaged by the driveshaft spline.
   b. **On Eagle Talon and Stealth models,** driveshafts are of different length. Driveshafts can be distinguished from each other by identification color of boot band C, **Figs. 7 and 8.**
   c. **On all models,** ensure that there is no oil or grease on threaded portion of companion flange and driveshaft attaching bolt and nut **torque** driveshaft to companion flange bolts to 40-47 ft. lbs.

# DIFFERENTIAL CARRIER REPLACE

## EAGLE TALON

1. Remove driveshafts as described in "Driveshaft, Replace."
2. Position a suitable jack under rear axle assembly, then drain differential gear oil.

3. Remove center exhaust pipe as shown in **Fig. 9.**
4. Scribe mating marks on differential companion flange and flange yoke for assembly reference.
5. Remove differential to propeller shaft connection, then support propeller shaft with wire.
6. Remove dynamic damper to differential support member bolts, **Fig. 10.**
7. Remove differential support member bolts, then the carrier.
8. Reverse procedure to install, noting the following:
   a. **Torque** differential support member attaching bolts to 80-94 ft. lbs.
   b. **Torque** dynamic damper to differential support member attaching bolts to 58-72 ft. lbs.
   c. **Torque** propeller shaft to differential carrier attaching bolts to 22-25 ft. lbs.
   d. **Torque** driveshaft to companion flange attaching bolts to 40-47 ft. lbs.

## COLT VISTA

1. Remove driveshafts as described in "Driveshaft, Replace."
2. Position a suitable jack under rear axle assembly, then drain differential gear oil.
3. Scribe mating marks on differential companion flange, propeller shaft flange and flange yoke for assembly reference.
4. Remove differential to propeller shaft connection, then support propeller shaft with wire.
5. Remove differential carrier rear mounting bolt, **Fig. 11.**
6. Remove differential carrier front mounting bolt and nut.
7. Remove differential carrier.
8. Remove differential front support bracket.
9. Reverse procedure to install.

## COLT WAGON

1. Remove axle shaft as outlined under "Axle Shaft, Replace."
2. Remove differential to propeller shaft connection, then support propeller shaft with wire.
3. Remove carrier attaching nuts, **Fig. 12,** and strike lower part of differential carrier assembly with a square piece of lumber several times to remove assembly, **Fig. 13. Loosen, do not remove upper nut to prevent differential from falling.**
4. Reverse procedure to install, noting the following:
   a. When differential carrier is installed, apply semi-drying sealant to differential carrier mounting surface.
   b. **Torque** propeller shaft nuts to 22-25 ft. lbs.

## STEALTH

1. Remove driveshafts as outlined under "Driveshaft, Replace."
2. Position a suitable jack under rear axle assembly, then drain differential gear oil.

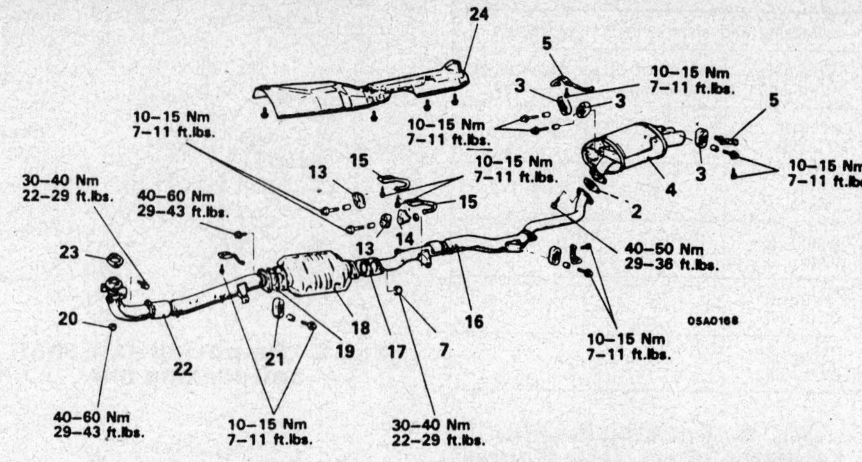


**Fig. 9 Exploded view of exhaust system. Eagle Talon**

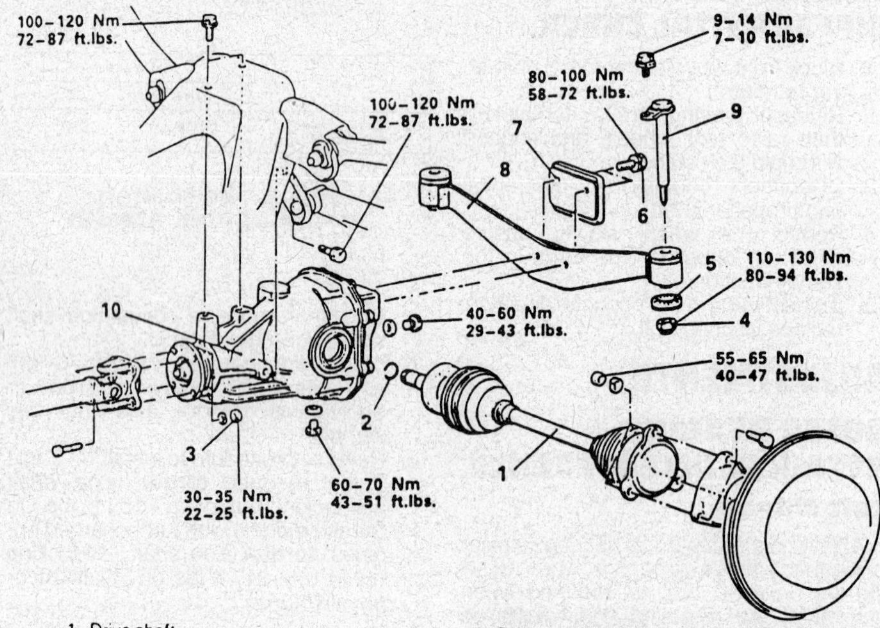


1. Drive shaft
2. Circlip
3. Propeller shaft connection
4. Differential support member installation nut
5. Stopper (lower)
6. Differential support member installation bolts
7. Dynamic damper
8. Differential support member
9. Differential support member installation bolts
10. Differential carrier

**Fig. 10 Removing differential carrier. Eagle Talon**

3. Scribe mating marks on differential companion flange and flange yoke for assembly reference.
4. Remove differential to propeller shaft connection, then support propeller shaft with wire.
5. Remove differential lower and rear support members, **Fig. 14.**
6. Remove rear wheel oil pump retaining bolt.
7. Remove and support rear wheel oil pump then lower differential carrier from vehicle. **Use care not to damage rear wheel oil pump gears.**
8. Reverse procedure to install.

# TRANSFER ASSEMBLY REPLACE

## EAGLE TALON

1. Remove two front exhaust pipe attaching nuts and lower exhaust pipe, **Fig. 15.**
2. Remove transfer assembly mounting bolts.
3. Remove driveshaft by moving transfer assembly to the left and lowering the front side. Suspend driveshaft with a piece of wire.

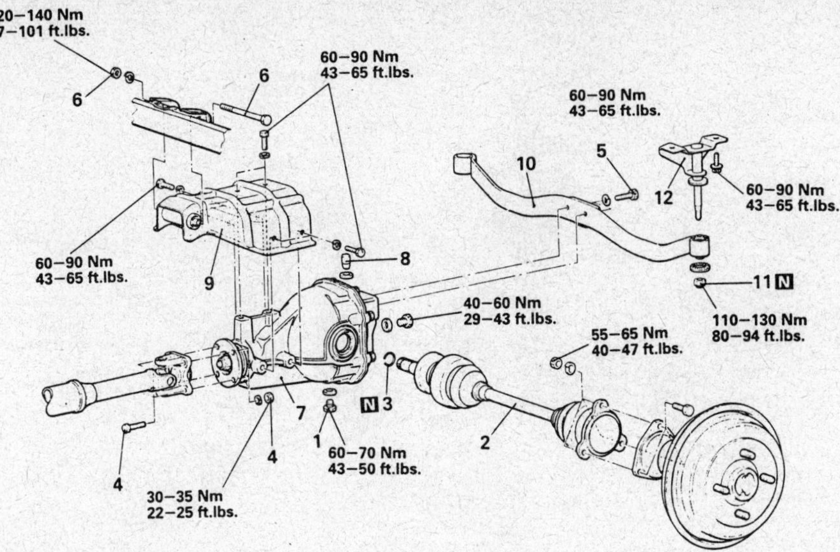


**Removal steps**

1. Drain plug
2. Drive shaft
3. Circlip
4. Rear propeller shaft and differential carrier coupling bolt and nut
5. Differential carrier rear mounting bolt
6. Differential carrier front mounting bolt and nut
7. Differential carrier
8. Vent plug
9. Differential front support bracket
10. Differential rear support
11. differential rear support mounting nut
12. Differential mount stopper

N : Non-reusable parts

**Fig. 11 Removing differential carrier. Colt Vista**

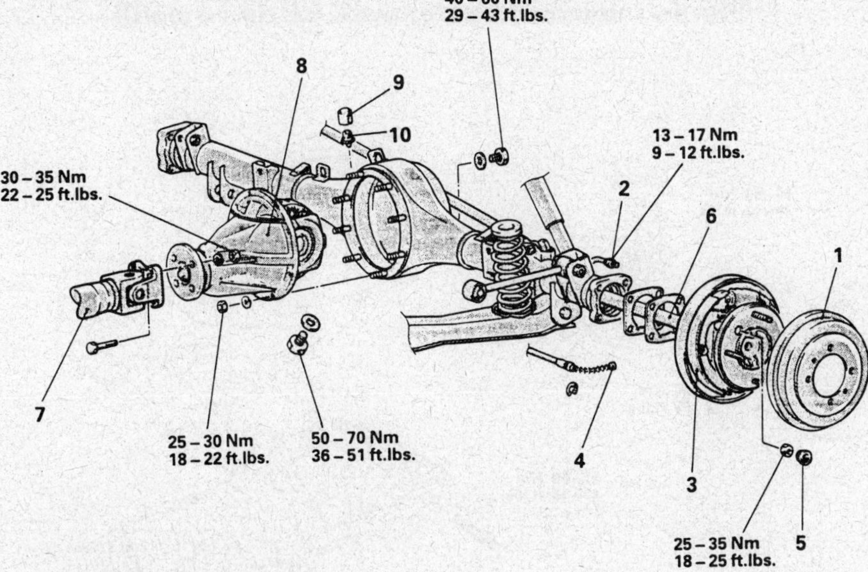


**Removal steps**

1. Brake drum
2. Rear brake pipe connection
3. Shoe assembly
4. Parking brake cable connection
5. Plug
6. Axle shaft assembly
7. Propeller shaft
8. Differential carrier assembly
9. Plug cover
10. Vent plug

**Fig. 12 Removing differential carrier. Colt Wagon**

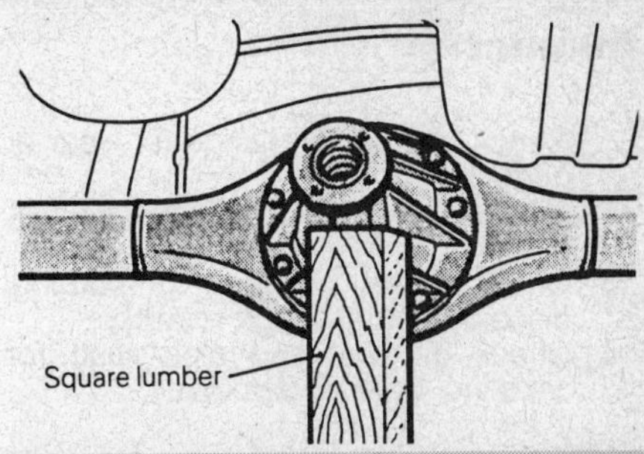


**Fig. 13 Loosening differential carrier. Colt Wagon**

4. Reverse procedure to install, noting the following:
   a. **Torque** transfer assembly mounting bolts to 40-43 ft. lbs.
   b. **Torque** front exhaust pipe attaching nuts to 29-43 ft. lbs.

## COLT VISTA

1. Raise and support vehicle.
2. Remove transaxle and transfer assembly as outlined under "Transaxle, Replace" in the "Colt, Colt Vista, Conquest & Summit" section.
3. Separate transfer assembly from transaxle assembly.
4. Reverse procedure to install.

## COLT WAGON

1. Raise and support vehicle.
2. Remove propeller shaft assembly.
3. Disconnect front exhaust pipe from manifold.
4. Remove transfer hanger and stay, **Fig. 16.**
5. Remove transfer assembly.
6. Reverse procedure to install, **torquing** transfer assembly bolts to 25-30 ft. lbs.

## STEALTH

1. Drain transaxle assembly.
2. Remove active front venturi skirt from vehicle.
3. Remove front exhaust pipe and main muffler assembly from vehicle.
4. Remove driveshaft retaining bolts then midship bearing retaining bolts and driveshaft from vehicle.
5. Remove five transfer case retaining bolts, then transfer assembly.
6. Reverse procedure to install. **Torque** transfer assembly bolts to 64 ft. lbs.

# AXLE SHAFT ASSEMBLY SERVICE

## EAGLE TALON, COLT VISTA & STEALTH

### Disassemble

1. Using bearing removal tool No. MB990560 or equivalent, remove outer bearing and dust cover from axle shaft, **Fig. 17.**
2. Using installer handle tool No. C-4171 and bearing/oil seal removal tool No. MB990928 or equivalents, remove inner bearing and oil seal from axle shaft trailing arm.

### Inspection

1. Check companion flange for wear or damage.
2. Check dust cover for deformation or damage.
3. Check wheel bearings for burning, discoloration or rough rotation.
4. Check oil seal and axle shaft for cracking, wear or damage.

### Assemble

1. Using installer handle tool No. C-4171 and bearing installer tool No. MB990931 or equivalents, press inner bearing onto trailing arm.
2. Apply suitable multipurpose grease to lip of new oil seal. Using oil seal installation tool No. MB990799 and a plastic hammer or equivalents, gradually and evenly press oil seal onto trailing arm with depression of oil seal facing upward, **Fig. 18,** until it contacts shoulder on inside of inner arm.
3. Position inner dust cover as shown in **Fig. 19.** With oil seal installation tool No. MB990799 and plastic hammer or equivalents, gradually and evenly press fit dust cover until it contacts axle shaft shoulder.
4. Position outer dust cover with depression facing upward as shown in **Fig. 20.** With dust cover installation tool No. MB990799 and plastic hammer or equivalents, gradually and evenly press fit dust cover onto axle shaft.
5. Apply multipurpose grease around entire circumference of inner side of outer bearing seal lip. Using bearing installation tool No. MB990560 or equivalent, press fit outer bearing to axle shaft so that the bearing lip surface is facing towards the axle shaft flange as shown in **Fig. 21.**

## COLT WAGON

1. Using a suitable grinder, partially grind inner bearing retainer at one area until thickness becomes .04-.06 inch. **Do not use an oxy-acetylene cutter or similar tool to remove bearing retainer. The resultant heat will weaken axle shaft and might cause it to break.**
2. Using a suitable chisel, make a cut in ground section of inner bearing retainer. **Use care not to damage axle shaft.**
3. Remove bearing using bearing puller tool No. MB990104 or equivalent.
4. Remove outer bearing retainer.
5. Reverse procedure to install, noting the following the following:
   a. Install inner bearing retainer with beveled side facing bearing.
   b. Using suitable press, press fit bearing and bearing retainer onto axle shaft using a force of 17,600 lbs.

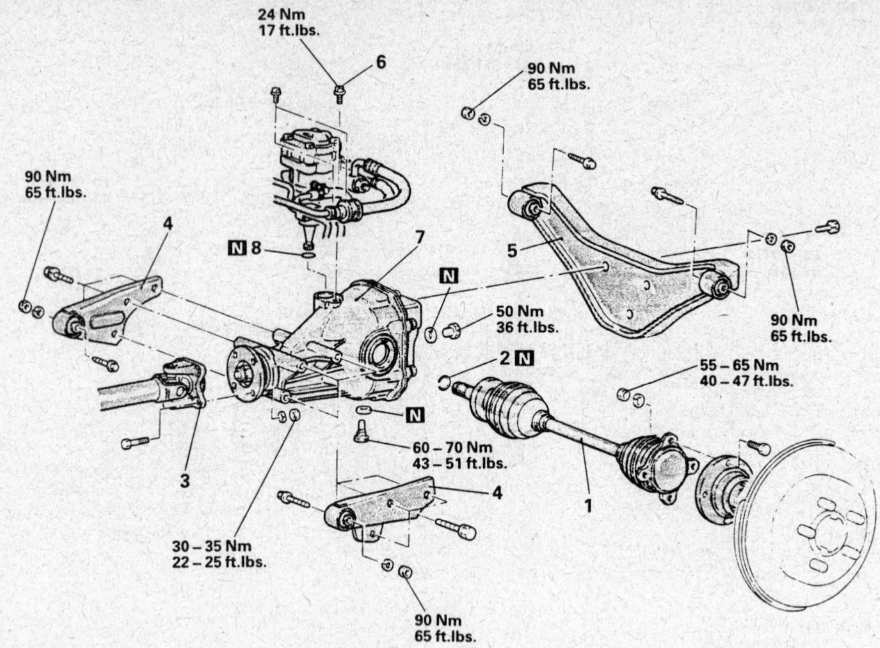


Removal steps
1. Drive shaft
2. Circlip
3. Propeller shaft connection
4. Differential support assembly
5. Differential support member assembly
6. Rear wheel oil pump installation bolt
7. Differential carrier
8. O-ring

**Fig. 14 Removing differential carrier. Stealth**

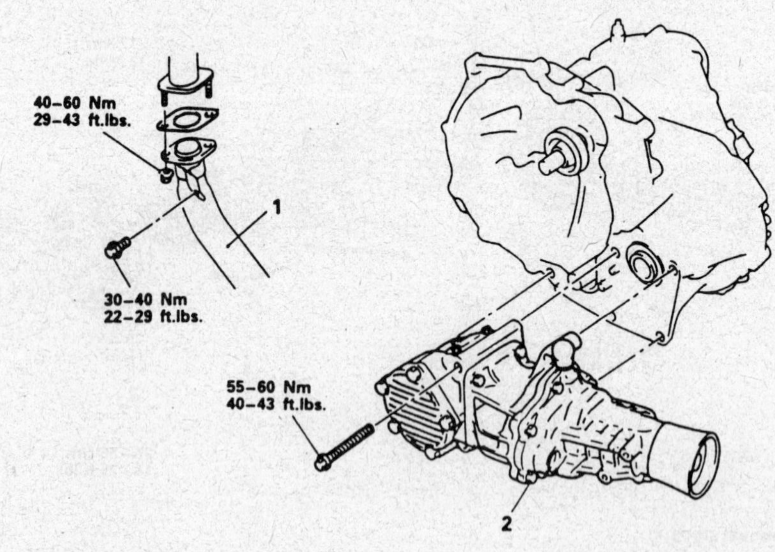


1. Front exhaust pipe connection
2. Transfer assembly

**Fig. 15 Removing transfer assembly. Eagle Talon**

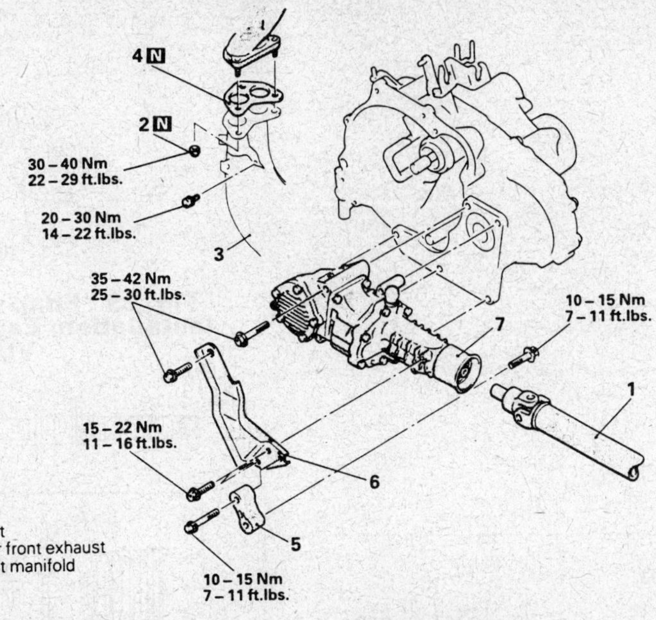


**Removal steps**

1. Propeller shaft
2. Self locking nut
3. Connection for front exhaust pipe to exhaust manifold
4. Gasket
5. Hanger
6. Transfer stay
7. Transfer assembly

**Fig. 16 Removing transfer assembly. Colt Wagon**

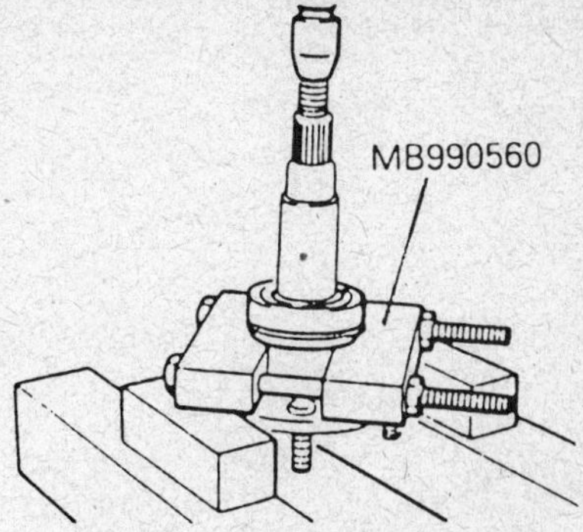


**Fig. 17 Removing outer bearing from axle shaft**

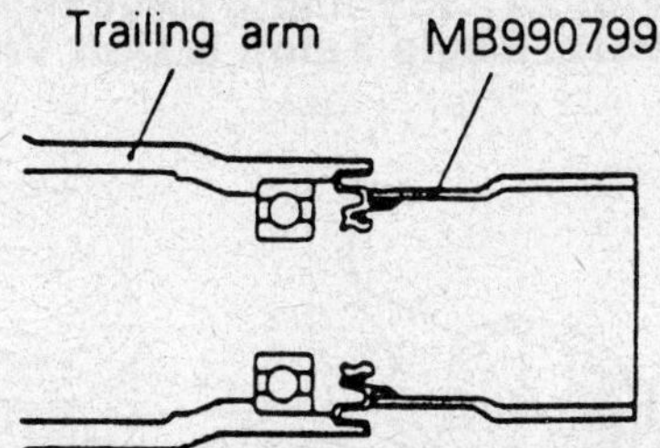


**Fig. 18 Installing oil seal**

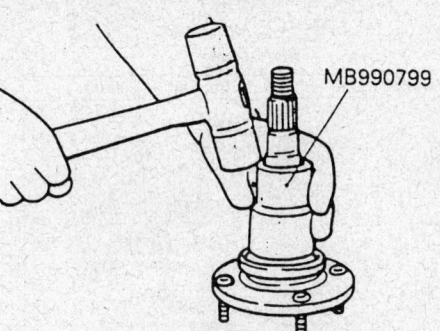

**Fig. 19 Installing inner dust cover**

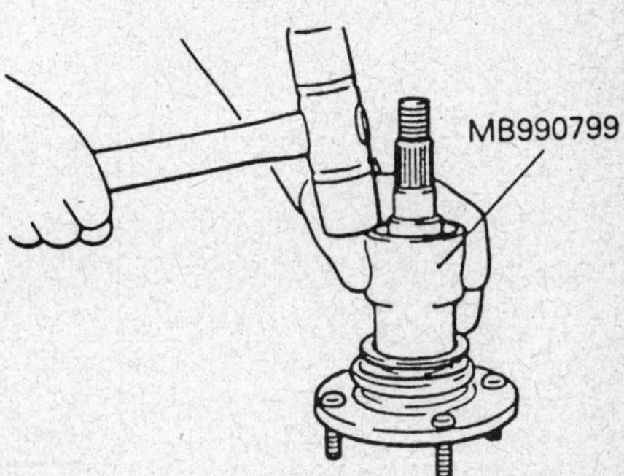


**Fig. 20 Installing outer dust cover**

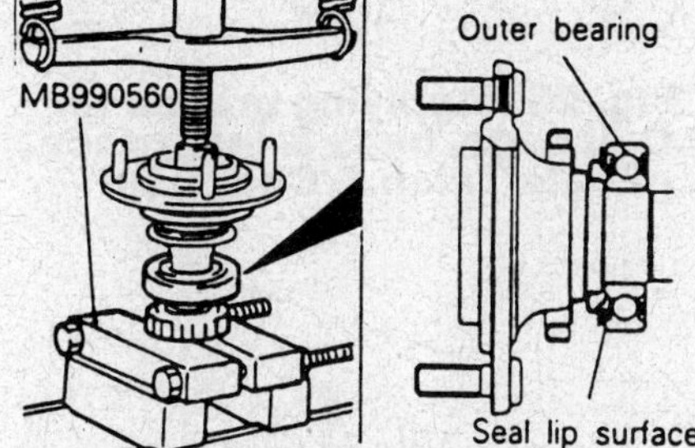


**Fig. 21 Installing outer bearing**

# DRIVESHAFT ASSEMBLY SERVICE

## EAGLE TALON & COLT VISTA

### Disassemble

1. Remove circlip from end of driveshaft, **Fig. 22.**
2. Remove boot bands B and C, then the circlip and D.O.J. outer race.
3. Remove snap ring with suitable snap ring pliers as shown in **Fig. 23,** then D.O.J. inner race, cage and balls as a unit. **Be careful that balls do not drop out of cage. If balls do drop out, press them back into D.O.J. cage with D.O.J. inner race.**
4. Wipe any remaining grease off of driveshaft spline, then remove boot bands A and C.
5. Remove D.O.J. and B.J. boots. **If boots are to be reused, wrap splined portion of driveshaft with vinyl tape before removing boots.**
6. Remove dust cover, driveshaft and B.J. **Do not disassemble B.J.**

### Inspection

1. Check driveshaft for damage, bending or corrosion.
2. Check driveshaft spline for wear or damage.
3. Check B.J. for entry of water or foreign material.
4. Check D.O.J outer race for damage or corrosion.
5. Check D.O.J. cage, balls and inner race for damage, corrosion or wear.

### Assemble

1. Assemble driveshaft and B.J., then install dust cover.
2. Wrap vinyl tape around driveshaft spline, then insert driveshaft in B.J. boot, boot bands A, C, C, B and D.O.J. boot in that sequence, **Fig. 24.**
3. Fill inside of B.J. and B.J. boot with grease included in the driveshaft repair kit. **The grease in the repair kit should be divided into two equal portions for the B.J. and B.J. boot. This is a special type of grease, ensure that no other type of grease comes in contact with the joint.**
4. Secure B.J. boot with boot bands A and C to driveshaft and B.J. **Ensure that B.J. is at a zero angle with driveshaft to ensure the boot contains the correct amount of air.**
5. Apply repair kit grease to D.O.J. cage, balls and inner race as shown in **Fig. 25.**
6. Install cage, balls and inner race onto driveshaft, then using snap ring pliers, fit snap ring securely into groove in shaft,**Fig. 23.**
7. Fill D.O.J. outer race with repair kit grease, then fit driveshaft into D.O.J. outer race.
8. Fill more grease into D.O.J. outer race

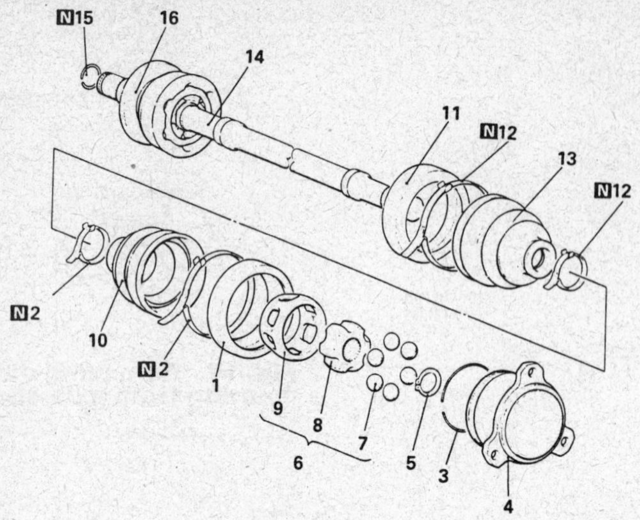


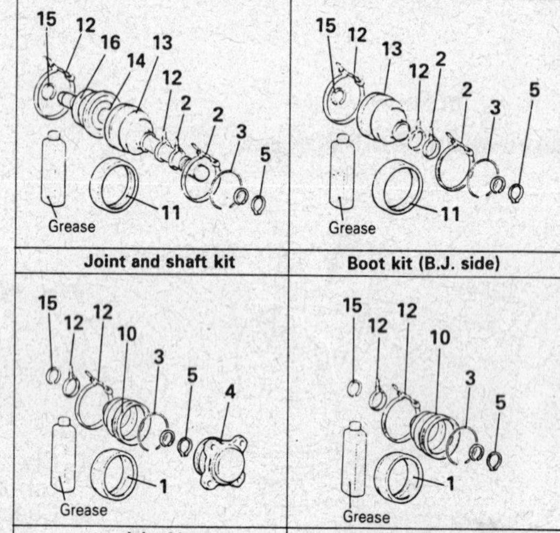


**Disassembly steps**

1. Boot protector
2. Boot band (for D.O.J. boot)
3. Circlip
4. D.O.J. outer race
5. Snap ring
6. D.O.J. cage assembly
7. Ball
8. D.O.J. inner race
9. D.O.J. cage
10. D.O.J. boot
11. Boot protector
12. Boot band (for B.J. boot)
13. B.J. boot
14. B.J. and shaft assembly
15. Circlip
16. Dust cover

N : Non-reusable parts

**Fig. 22 Exploded view of driveshaft. Eagle Talon & Colt Vista**

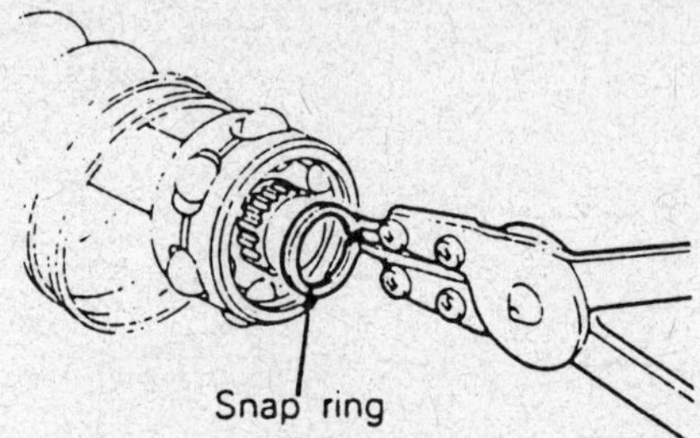


**Fig. 23 Snap ring removal & installation. Eagle Talon & Colt Vista**

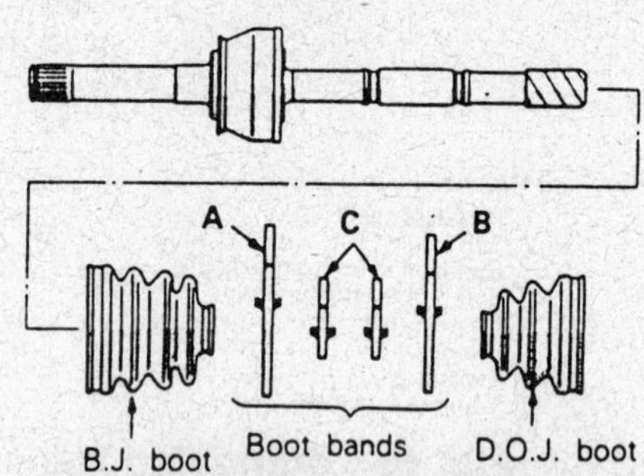


**Fig. 24 Installing driveshaft boots. Eagle Talon & Colt Vista**

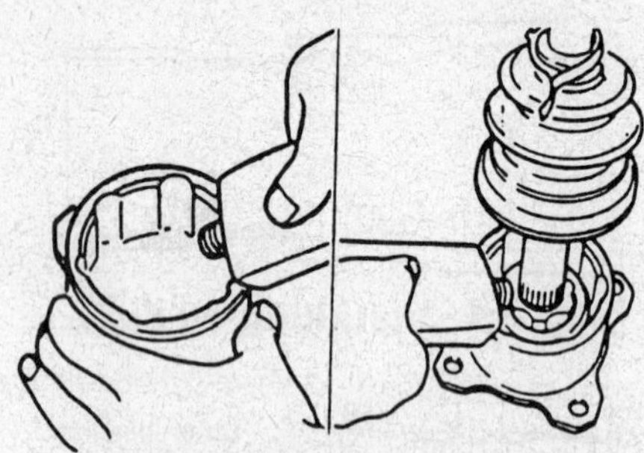

**Fig. 25 Applying grease to D.O.J. cage, balls & inner race. Eagle Talon & Colt Vista**

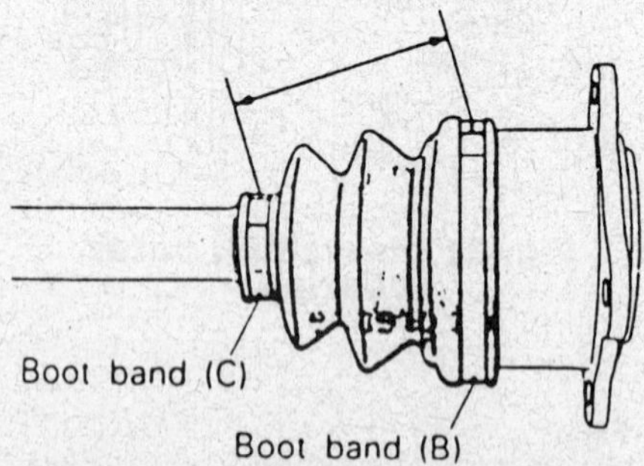


**Fig. 26 Installing driveshaft boot bands. Eagle Talon & Colt Vista**

after it is installed on driveshaft, then install circlip onto D.O.J. outer race.

9. Assemble D.O.J. boot to D.O.J. outer race, then secure boot to driveshaft with boot band C.
10. Place boot band B on D.O.J. boot. **Do not secure boot band B at this time.**
11. Set D.O.J. boot bands from 2¾-3¼ inches apart as shown in **Fig. 26**, then tighten boot band C securely.
12. Pull part of D.O.J. boot away from D.O.J. outer race to allow pressure to escape from boot, then tighten boot band B securely to D.O.J. outer race.

## STEALTH

### Disassembly

1. Remove Tripod Joint (TJ) bands, **Fig. 27.**
2. Remove TJ case.
3. Remove snap ring off TJ end of driveshaft.
4. Remove spider assembly off driveshaft. **Do not disassemble spider assembly.**
5. Wrap vinyl tape around splines of driveshaft then remove TJ boot.
6. Remove Birfield Joint (BJ) bands.
7. Wrap vinyl tape around splines of driveshaft then remove BJ joint boot.
8. Remove BJ joint. **Do not disassemble BJ joint.**

### Inspection

1. Check driveshaft for damage, bending or corrosion.
2. Check driveshaft spline for wear or damage.
3. Check B.J. for entry of water or foreign material.
4. Check spider assembly for roller rotation, wear or corrosion.
5. Check BJ outer race for damage or corrosion.
6. Check boots for damage, cracking or wear.

### Assembly

Reverse disassembly procedure to assemble, noting the following:

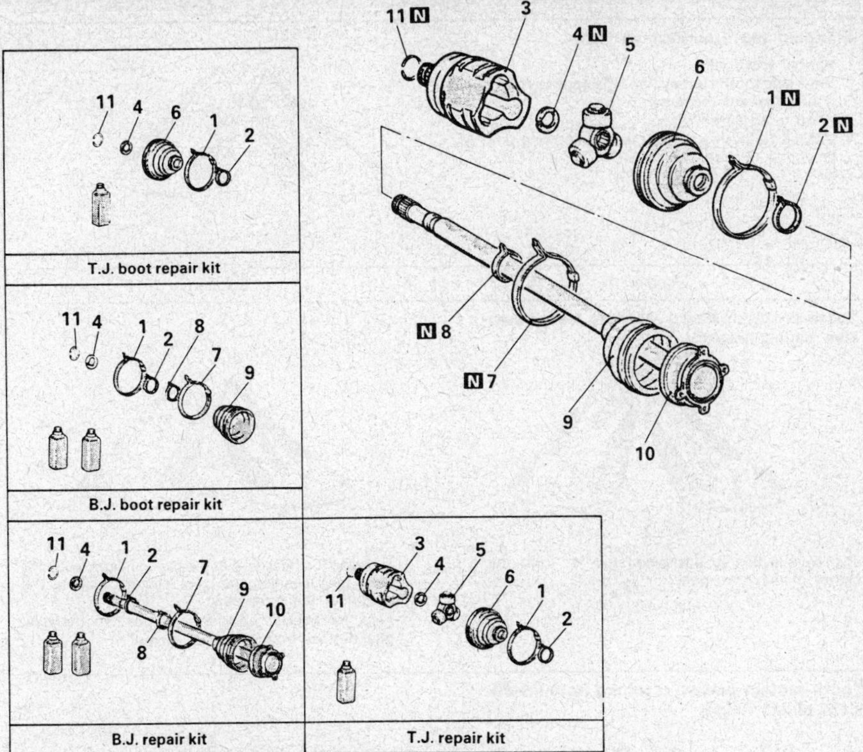


Disassembly steps

1. T.J. boot band (large)
2. T.J. boot band (small)
3. T.J. case
4. Snap ring
5. Spider assembly
6. T.J. boot
7. B.J. boot band (large)
8. B.J. boot band (small)
9. B.J. boot
10. B.J. assembly
11. Circlip

**Fig. 27 Exploded view of driveshaft. Stealth**

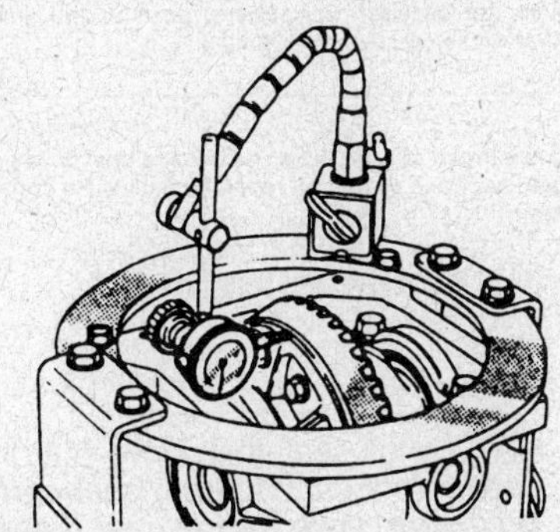

**Fig. 30 Measuring drive gear runout**

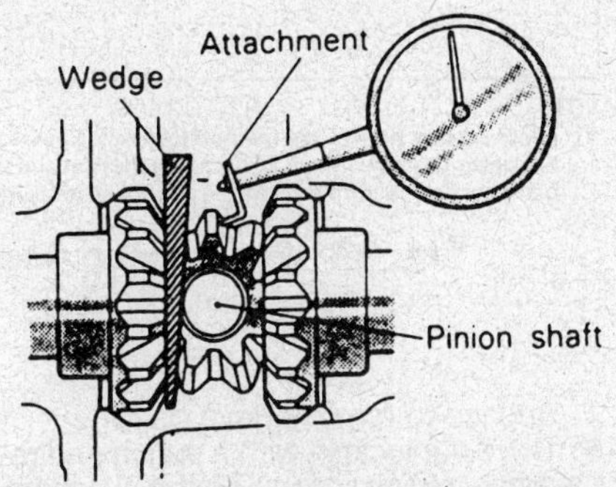


**Fig. 31 Measuring differential gear backlash**

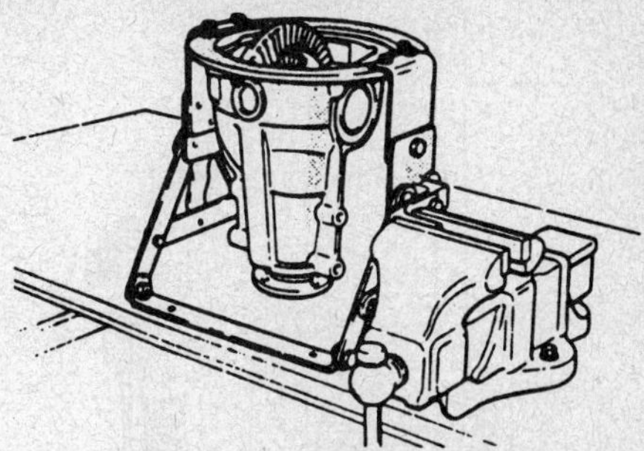

**Fig. 28 Positioning differential carrier in working base**

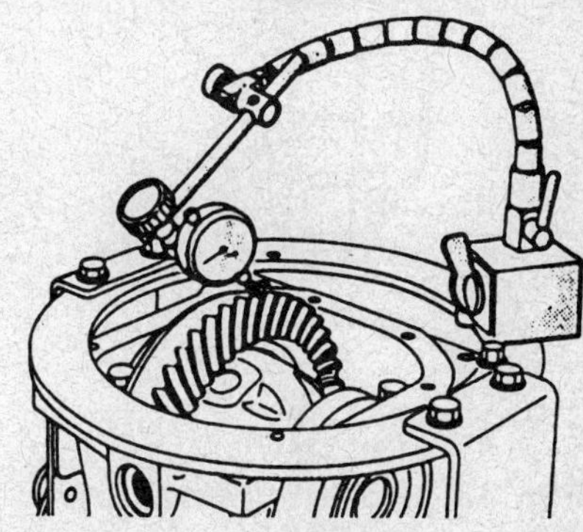

**Fig. 29 Measuring final drive gear backlash**

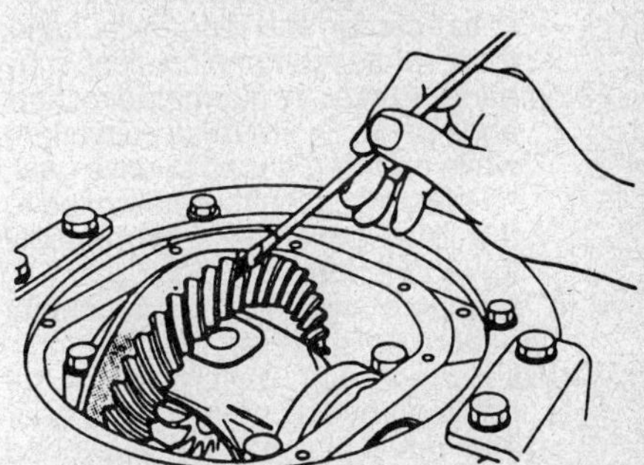

**Fig. 32 Marking final drive gear to check tooth contact**

1. Wrap vinyl tape around spline on driveshaft then install BJ and TJ boots.
2. Fill inside of BJ and BJ boot with half of grease included in repair kit.
3. Secure boot bands with driveshaft at a 0° angle.
4. Apply grease to spider assembly then install spider assembly with chamfered spline end first.
5. Install TJ on driveshaft.
6. Set TJ boot bands 3.35 inch apart to adjust amount of air inside boot then tighten TJ boot band securely.

# DIFFERENTIAL CARRIER SERVICE

## EXCEPT LIMITED SLIP

### PREDISASSEMBLY INSPECTION

1. Support working base in a vise, and attach differential carrier to working base, **Fig. 28.**
2. Check final drive gear backlash as follows:
   a. Lock drive pinion in place, then mount dial indicator as shown in **Fig. 29.**
   b. Measure backlash at four points or more on the circumference of the drive gear. Backlash should be within .004-.006 inch.
3. Mount dial indicator as shown in **Fig. 30,** then measure drive gear runout at the shoulder on the reverse side of drive gear. Runout should not exceed .002 inch.
4. **On except Stealth models,** lock side gear with a wedge as shown in **Fig. 31,** then measure differential gear backlash with dial indicator on pinion gear. Differential gear backlash should not exceed .008 inch.
5. **On all models,** check final drive gear tooth contact as follows:
   a. Apply a thin, uniform coat of machine blue to both surfaces of drive gear teeth as shown in **Fig. 32.**

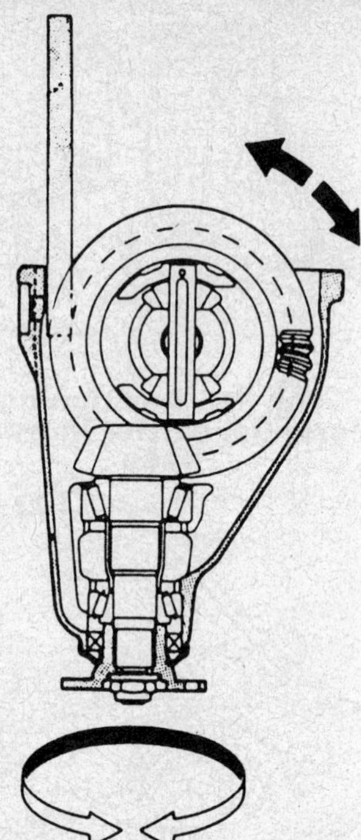

**Fig. 33 Rotating final drive gear**

b. Insert a brass rod between differential carrier and differential case, then rotate companion flange by hand (once in normal direction, and once in reverse direction) while applying a load to drive gear, so that revolution torque applied to the drive pinion is approximately 28-33 inch lbs. **Fig. 33.**

c. Compare and adjust tooth contact pattern as shown in **Fig. 34.**

d. If correct tooth pattern cannot be obtained by adjustment, drive gear and drive pinion have exceeded their usage limit and both gears should be replaced as a set.

**Standard tooth contact pattern**

1 Narrow tooth side
2 Drive-side tooth surface (the side applying power during forward movement)
3 Wide tooth side
4 Coast-side tooth surface (the side applying power during reverse movement)

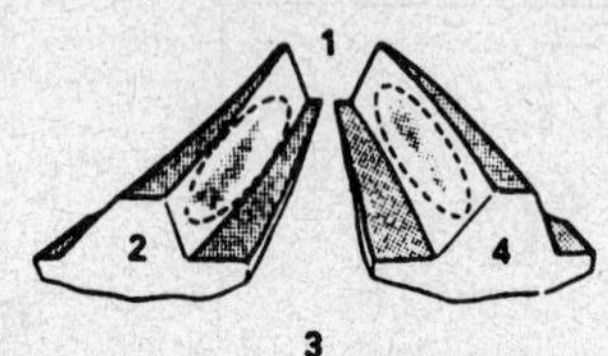


| Problem | Solution |
| --- | --- |
| **Tooth contact pattern resulting from excessive pinion height** 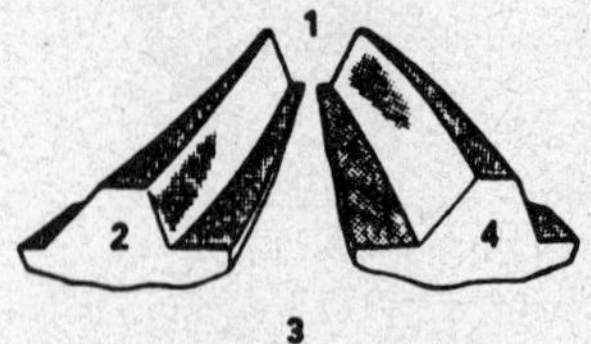 The drive pinion is positioned too far from the center of the drive gear. |  Increase the thickness of the pinion height adjusting shim, and position the drive pinion closer to the center of the drive gear. Also, for backlash adjustment, position the drive gear farther from the drive pinion. |
| **Tooth contact pattern resulting from insufficient pinion height**  The drive pinion is positioned too close to the center of the drive gear. |  Decrease the thickness of the pinion height adjusting shim, and position the drive pinion farther from the center of the drive gear. Also, for backlash adjustment, position the drive gear closer to the drive pinion. |

NOTE
(1) Tooth contact pattern is a method for judging the result of the adjustment of drive pinion height and final drive gear backlash. The adjustment of drive pinion hight and final drive gear backlash should be repeated until tooth contact patterns bear a similarity to the standard tooth contact pattern.

**Fig. 34 Final drive gear & drive pinion adjustment**

## DISASSEMBLE

### Colt Wagon, Colt Vista & Eagle Talon

1. Support working base in a vise, and attach differential carrier to working base.
2. Remove differential cover and vent plug, **Figs. 35 and 36.**
3. Using two hammer shafts or equivalent, slowly and carefully pry differential case assembly out of gear carrier. **Ensure side bearing outer race is not dropped when removing differential case assembly. Keep right and left side bearings separate, so that they do not become mixed at time of reassembly.**
4. Using side bearing puller tool No. MB990810 and side bearing cup tool No. MB990811 or equivalents, pull out side bearing inner races, **Fig. 37.**
5. Scribe mating marks on differential case and drive gear, then loosen drive gear attaching bolts in diagonal sequence to remove drive gear.
6. Drive out lockpin with a punch and remove pinion gears, pinion washers, side gears, side gear spacers and differential case.
7. Scribe mating marks on drive pinion and companion flange. **Mating marks should not be made to contact surfaces of companion flange and propeller shaft.**
8. Using side bearing puller tool No. MB990810 or equivalent, drive out drive pinion together with drive pinion spacer and drive pinion front shims.
9. Mount companion flange attached to taper roller bearing puller tool No. C-293-PA and bearing remover tool C-293-45 or equivalents in a vise as shown in **Fig. 38.** Pull drive pinion rear bearing inner race out of companion flange.
10. Remove drive pinion rear shim used for drive pinion height adjustment and drive pinion.
11. Remove oil seal, then drive out drive pinion front bearing from gear carrier.
12. Drive out drive pinion rear bearing outer race from gear carrier.

### Stealth

Disassemble differential assembly in numbered sequence shown in **Fig. 39,** noting the following:

1. Perform "Inspection Before Disassembly" procedure.
2. Using spanner wrench tool No. MB991367 and pin tool No. MB991385 or equivalent, remove side bearing nut.
3. Using a suitable press, push differential case until it is pressed against the carrier.
4. Remove differential case from press. Insert two spacers in diagonally opposite positions between side bearing outer race to be removed and inner race. Using a press, remove outer race. **Do not allow side bearing to**

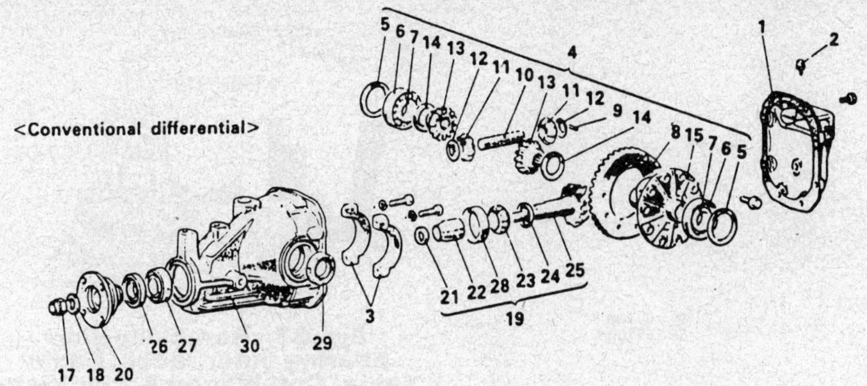


<Limited slip differential>

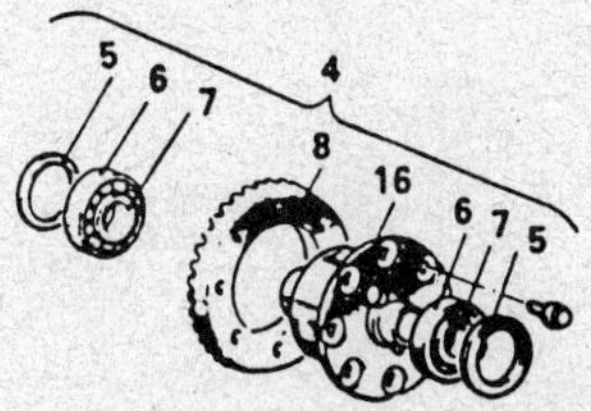


1. Differential cover
2. Vent plug
3. Bearing caps
4. Differential case assembly
5. Side bearing spacers
6. Side bearing outer race
7. Side bearing inner race
8. Drive gear
9. Lock pin
10. Pinion shaft
11. Pinion gears
12. Pinion washers
13. Side gears
14. Side gear spacers
15. Differential case
16. Limited slip differential case assembly
17. Self-locking nut
18. Washer
19. Drive pinion assembly
20. Companion flange
21. Drive pinion front shim (for preload adjustment)
22. Drive pinion spacer
23. Drive pinion rear bearing inner race
24. Drive pinion rear shim (for pinion height adjustment)
25. Drive pinion
26. Oil seal
27. Drive pinion front bearing
28. Drive pinion rear bearing outer race
29. Oil seal
30. Gear carrier

**Fig. 35 Exploded view of differential carrier. Eagle Talon & Colt Vista**

**drop. Keep right and left bearings separate. Use a spacer 1.18 inches long, .39 inch wide and .04-.08 inch high made of copper to prevent damage to bearings.**

5. Pull out side bearing inner races by using suitable bearing puller.
6. Scribe alignment marks on differential case and drive gear. Loosen drive gear bolts in diagonal sequence to remove drive gear.
7. Using end yoke holder tool MB990767-01 or equivalent, remove companion flange self-locking nut.
8. Scribe alignment marks on drive pinion and companion flange. Remove out drive pinion together with drive pinion spacer and shims. **Marks should not be made on contact surfaces of companion flange and shaft.**
9. Pull out drive pinion bearing inner races by using insert tool, pinion carrier bearing puller tool, and side bearing cup remover step plate tool or equivalent.
10. Drive out drive pinion front and rear bearing from gear carrier.

## INSPECTION

1. Check companion flange for wear or damage.
2. Check oil seal for wear or deterioration.
3. Check bearing for wear and discoloration.
4. Check gear carrier for cracks.
5. Check drive pinion and drive gear for wear or cracks.
6. Check side gears, pinion gears and pinion shaft for wear or damage.
7. Check side gear spline for wear or damage.

## ASSEMBLE

### Colt Wagon, Colt Vista & Eagle Talon

1. Apply multipurpose grease to lip of oil seal, then using installer bar tool No. C-4171 and oil seal installer tool No. MB991115 or equivalents, press seal into gear carrier.
2. Using installer handle tool No. C-4171 and bearing installer tool Nos. MB990932 and MB990935 or equivalents, press drive pinion rear and front bearing outer races into gear carrier.
3. Adjust drive pinion height as follows:
   a. Install a pinion height gauge set tool Nos. MB990835 and MB990836 or equivalent and drive pinion front and rear bearing inner races on gear carrier as shown in **Fig. 40. Apply a thin coat of multipurpose grease to mating surface on washer of tool.**
   b. Tighten handle of special tool until standard value of drive pinion turning torque is obtained. On Colt Vista models, specification is 6-9 inch lbs. and on Colt Wagon and Eagle Talon, refer to **Fig. 41.**
   c. Measure drive pinion turning torque (without oil seal).
   d. Position special tool No. MB990835 or equivalent in side bearing seat of gear carrier as shown in **Fig. 42.** Select a drive pinion rear shim of a thickness which corresponds to the gap between special tools. **Clean side bearing seat thoroughly. When positioning special tool, ensure that cut-out sections of tool are in position shown in Fig. 42, and that special tool is in close contact with side bearing seat. When selecting drive pinion rear shims, keep number of drive shims to a minimum.**
   e. Fit selected drive pinion rear shims to drive pinion, then using bearing installer tool No. MB990728 or equivalent, press rear bearing inner race onto drive pinion as shown in **Fig. 43.**
4. Adjust drive pinion preload as follows:
   a. Fit drive pinion front shims between drive pinion spacer and drive pinion front bearing inner race.
   b. **Torque** companion flange to 116-159 ft. lbs. using end yoke holder tool No. MB990767 or equivalent. **Do not install oil seal.**
   c. Using a torque wrench, measure drive pinion turning torque as shown in **Fig. 44.**
   d. Compare measurement. On Colt Vista models, specification is 6-9 inch lbs. and on Colt Wagon and Eagle Talon, refer to **Fig. 41.** If turning torque is not within specification, adjust by replacing drive pinion front shims or drive pinion spacer. **If a number of shims will be required to bring preload within specified value, reduce the number of shims by replacing the spacer.**
   e. Remove companion flange and drive pinion, then drive oil seal into gear carrier front lip. Apply a thin coat of multipurpose grease to the oil seal lip.
   f. Apply a thin coat of multipurpose grease to companion flange washer contacting surface prior to installing drive pinion.
   g. Install drive pinion assembly and companion flange with mating marks aligned, and **torque** companion flange self-locking nut to 116-159 ft. lbs.

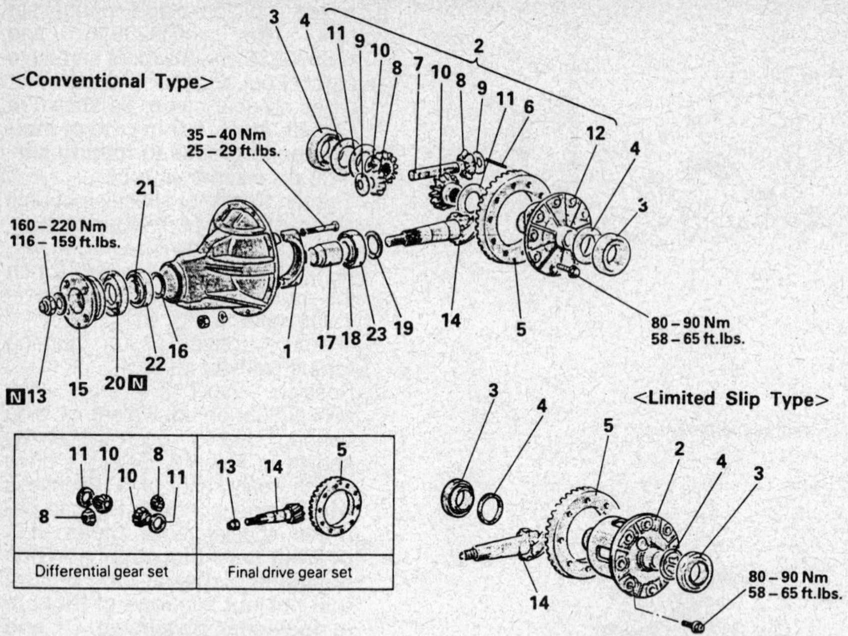


**Disassembly steps**

1. Bearing cap
2. Differential case assembly
3. Side bearing
4. Adjusting shim
5. Drive gear
6. Lock pin
7. Pinion shaft
8. Pinion gear
9. Pinion washer
10. Side gear
11. Side gear spacer
12. Differential case
13. Self-locking nut
14. Drive pinion
15. Companion flange
16. Drive pinion front shim (for preload adjustment)
17. Drive pinion spacer
18. Drive pinion rear bearing inner race
19. Drive pinion rear shim (for pinion height adjustment)
20. Oil seal
21. Drive pinion front bearing
22. Drive pinion front bearing outer race
23. Drive pinion rear bearing outer race

N: Non-reusable parts

**Reassembly steps**

23. Drive pinion rear bearing outer race
22. Drive pinion front bearing outer race
21. Drive pinion front bearing
19. Drive pinion rear shim (for pinion height adjustment)
    Adjustment of pinion height
18. Drive pinion rear bearing inner race
17. Drive pinion spacer
16. Drive pinion front shim (for preload adjustment)
    Adjustment of drive pinion preload
20. Oil seal
15. Companion flange
14. Drive pinion
13. Self-locking nut
12. Differential case
    Adjustment of differential gear backlash <Conventional Type>
11. Side gear spacer
10. Side gear
9. Pinion washer
8. Pinion gear
7. Pinion shaft
6. Lock pin
5. Drive gear
   Adjustment of final drive gear backlash
4. Adjusting shim
3. Side bearing
2. Differential case assembly
1. Bearing cap

**Fig. 36 Exploded view of differential carrier. Colt Wagon**

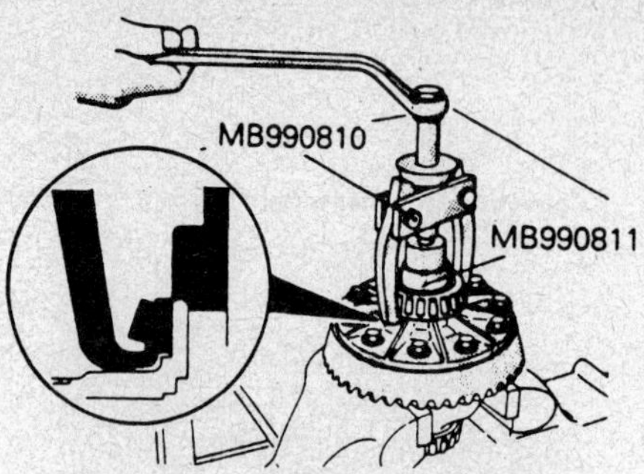


**Fig. 37 Removing side bearing inner races. Eagle Talon, Colt Wagon & Colt Vista**

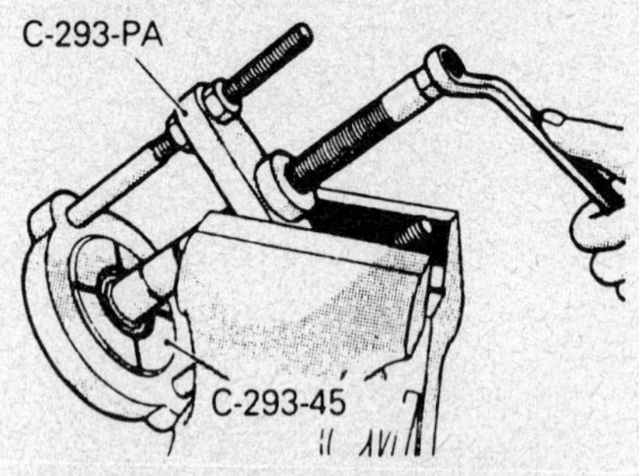


**Fig. 38 Rear bearing inner race removal. Eagle Talon, Colt Wagon & Colt Vista**

h. Measure drive pinion turning torque, and compare with specified value. On Colt Vista models, specification is 6-9 inch lbs. and on Colt Wagon and Eagle Talon, refer to **Fig. 45.** If turning torque is not within specified value, ensure companion flange self-locking nut is tightened within specification and oil seal is correctly installed.

5. Adjust differential gear backlash as follows:
   a. Assemble side gears, side gear spacers, pinion gears and pinion washers into differential case.
   b. Temporarily install pinion shaft. **Do not drive in lockpin at this time.**
   c. While locking side gear with wedge measure differential gear backlash with dial indicator as shown in **Fig. 46.** Measurement should be made for both gears individually.
   d. Gear backlash should not exceed .008 inch (.2 mm). If side gear exceeds limit, adjust by installing thicker side gear spacers.
   e. After adjustment, ensure differential gear rotates smoothly.
   f. If backlash cannot be adjusted, replace side gear and pinion gear as a set.
6. Align pinion shaft lockpin hole with differential case lockpin hole, and drive in lockpin.
7. Stake lockpin with punch at two points as shown in **Fig. 47.**
8. Clean drive gear attaching bolts, then using a M10 X 1.25 tap, remove adhesive adhering to threaded holes of drive gear. Clean remaining material out of drive gear using compressed air.
9. Apply multipurpose adhesive Mopar Loctite No. 271 or equivalent to threaded holes of drive gear.
10. Install drive gear onto differential case with mating marks aligned. **Torque drive gear attaching bolts in a diagonal sequence to 58-65 ft. lbs.**
11. Using bearing installer tool No. MB990728 or equivalent, press side bearing inner races to differential case.
12. Adjust final drive gear backlash as follows:
    a. Install side bearing spacers, which are thinner than those removed, to side bearing outer races and then mount differential case assembly into gear carrier. **Use side bearing spacers with the same thickness for both drive pinion and drive gear sides.**
    b. Push differential case to one side of the gear carrier and measure clearance between gear carrier and side bearing as shown in **Fig. 48.**
    c. Measure thickness of side bearing spacers on one side, then select two pairs of spacers which correspond to that thickness plus one half of clearance plus .002 inch, **Fig. 49.** Install one pair each to drive pinion side and drive gear side.
    d. Install side bearing spacers and differential case assembly to gear carrier as shown in **Fig. 50.**
    e. Tap side bearing spacers with a brass bar to fit them to side bearing outer race.
    f. Align mating marks on gear carrier and bearing cap, then tighten bearing cap.

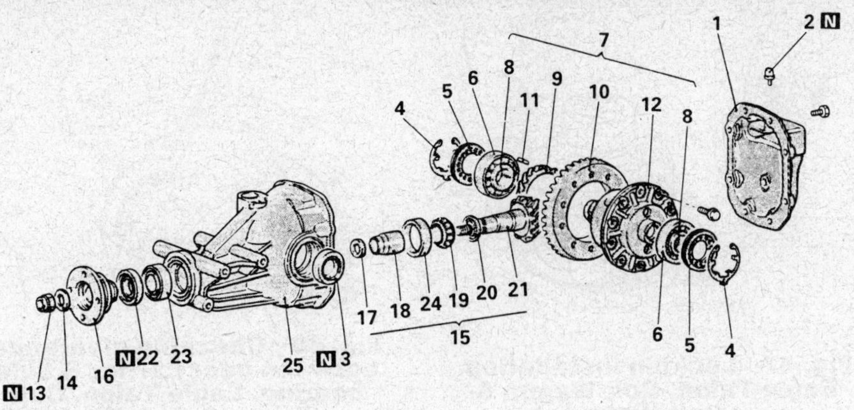

**Disassembly steps**

1. Differential cover assembly
2. Vent plug
3. Oil seal
4. Snap ring
5. Side bearing nut
6. Side bearing outer race
7. Differential case assembly
8. Side bearing inner race
9. Drive gear (for 4WS)
10. Drive gear
11. Spring pin (for 4WS)
12. LSD case
13. Self-locking nut
14. Washer
15. Drive pinion assembly
16. Companion flange
17. Drive pinion front shim (for preload adjustment)
18. Drive pinion spacer
19. Drive pinion rear bearing inner race
20. Drive pinion rear shim (for pinion height adjustment)
21. Drive pinion
22. Oil seal
23. Drive pinion front bearing
24. Drive pinion rear bearing outer race
25. Differential carrier

**Fig. 39 Exploded view of differential carrier. Stealth**

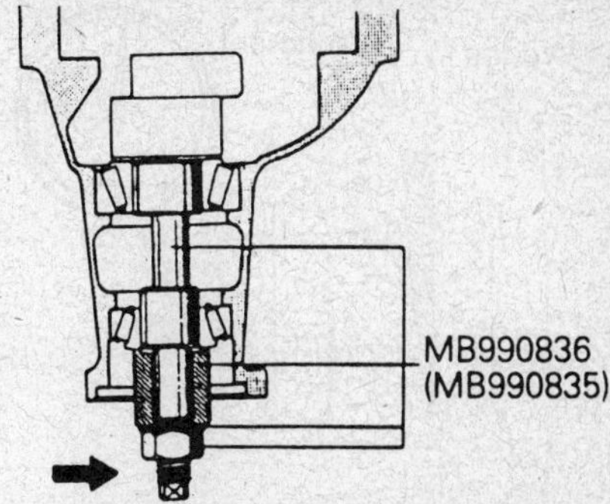


**Fig. 40 Adjusting drive pinion height. Eagle Talon, Colt Wagon & Colt Vista**

| Bearing classification | Bearing lubrication | Rotation torque (starting friction torque) Nm (in.lbs.) |
|---|---|---|
| New | None (with rust-prevention oil) | 0.9–1.2 (8–10) |
| New/reused | Oil application | 0.4–0.5 (3–4) |

NOTE
(1) Gradually tighten the nut of the special tool while checking the drive pinion turning torque.
(2) Because the special tool cannot be turned one turn, turn it several times within the range that it can be turned; then, after fitting to the bearing, measure the rotation torque.

**Fig. 41 Drive pinion turning torque specifications. Without oil seal installed. Eagle Talon & Colt Wagon**

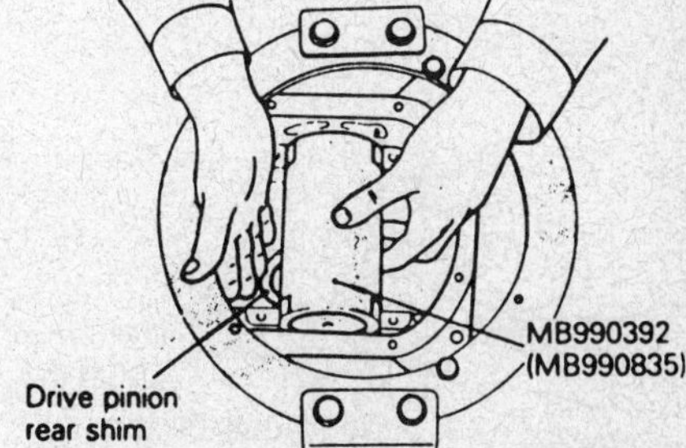


**Fig. 42 Selecting drive pinion adjustment shims. Eagle Talon, Colt Wagon & Colt Vista**

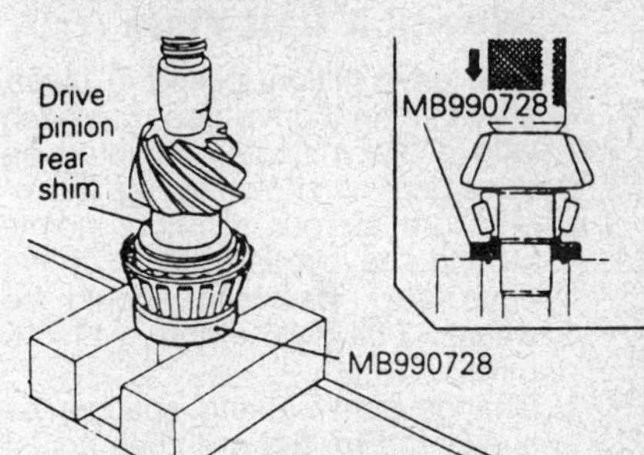

**Fig. 43 Installing drive pinion inner race. Eagle Talon, Colt Wagon & Colt Vista**

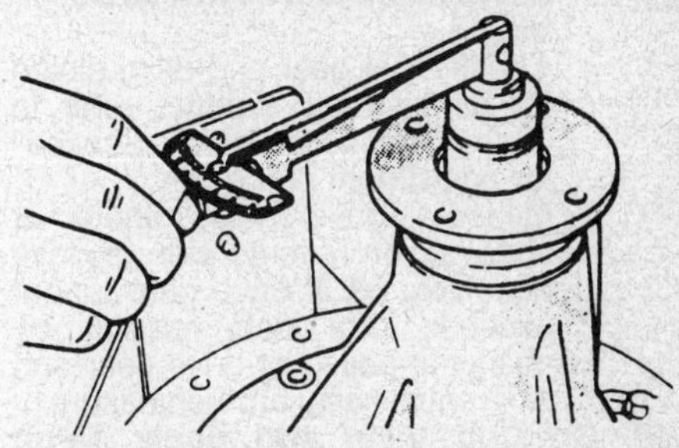

**Fig. 44 Checking drive pinion turning torque. Eagle Talon, Colt Wagon & Colt Vista**

| Bearing classification | Bearing lubrication | Rotation torque (starting friction torque) Nm (in.lbs.) |
|---|---|---|
| New | None (with rust-prevention oil) | 1.0–1.3 (9–11) |
| New/reused | Oil application | 0.5–0.6 (4–5) |

**Fig. 45 Drive pinion turning torque specifications. With oil seal installed. Eagle Talon & Colt Wagon**

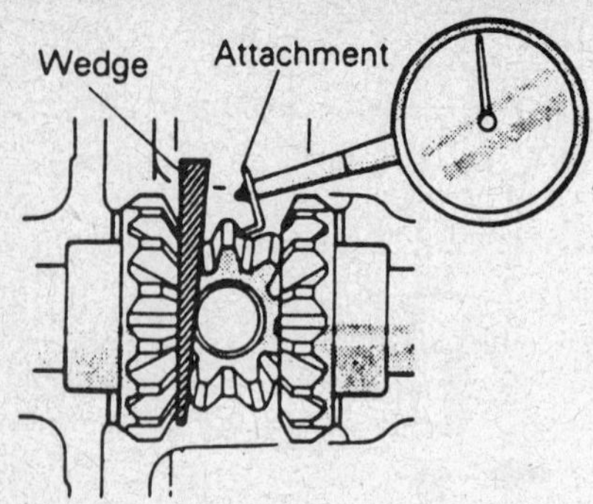


**Fig. 46 Checking differential gear backlash. Eagle Talon, Colt Wagon & Colt Vista**

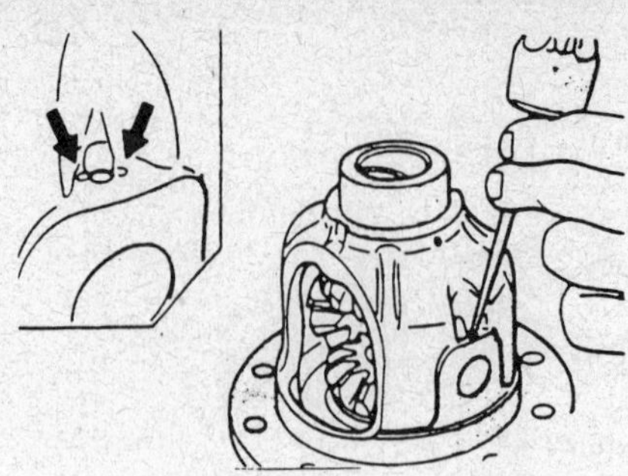

**Fig. 47 Lockpin installation. Eagle Talon, Colt Wagon & Colt Vista**

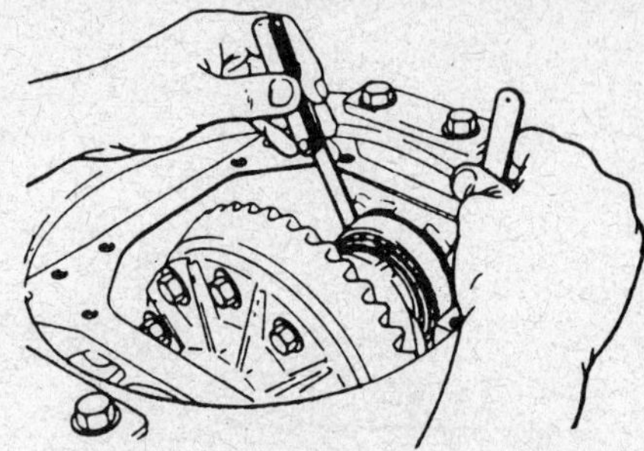

**Fig. 48 Checking clearance between gear carrier & side bearing. Eagle Talon, Colt Wagon & Colt Vista**

$$+\frac{\text{Clearance}}{2}+\begin{matrix}0.05\text{ mm}\\(.002\text{ in.})\end{matrix}$$

= Thickness of the spacer on one side

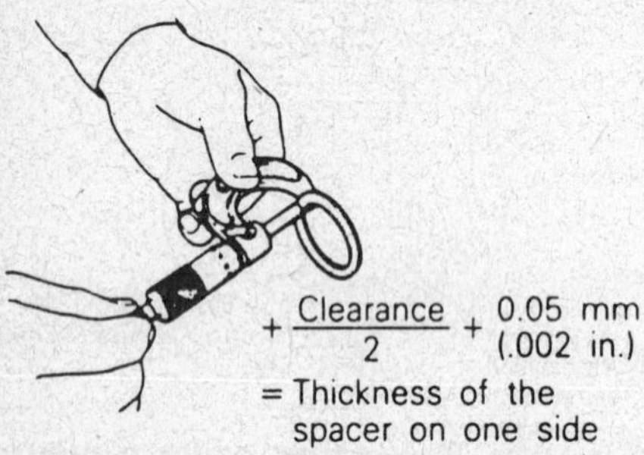

**Fig. 49 Selecting side bearing spacers. Eagle Talon, Colt Wagon & Colt Vista**

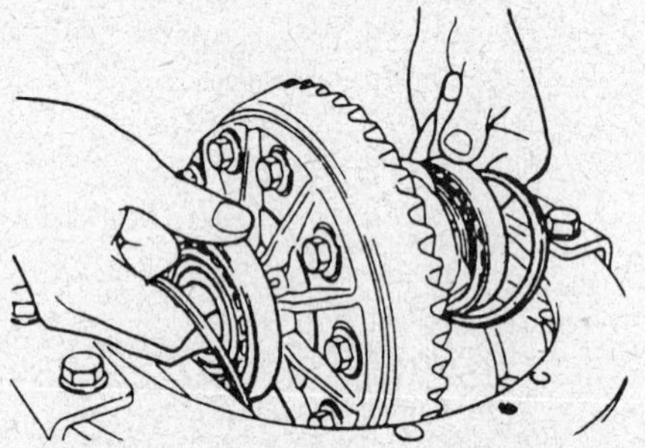

**Fig. 50 Installing side bearing spacers & differential case assembly. Eagle Talon, Colt Wagon & Colt Vista**

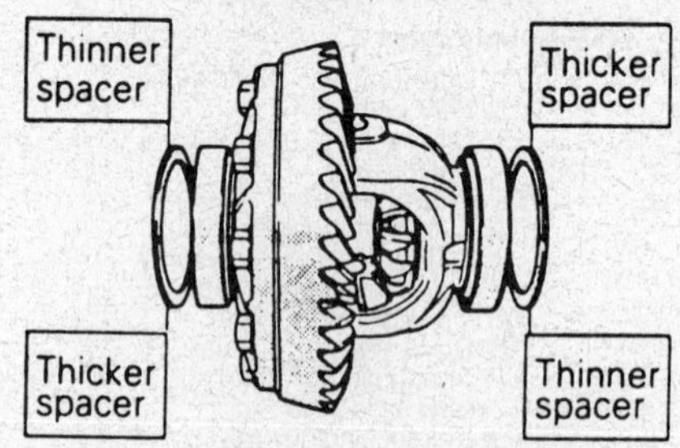


**Fig. 51 Changing side bearing spacers. Eagle Talon, Colt Wagon & Colt Vista**

g. With drive pinion locked in place, measure final drive gear backlash with a dial indicator mounted on drive gear as shown in **Fig. 29.**

h. Measure at four or more points around the circumference of the drive gear, backlash should be within .004-.006 inch (.11-.16 mm).

i. Change side bearing spacers as shown in **Fig. 51,** and then adjust final drive gear backlash between drive gear and drive pinion. **When increasing number of side bearing spacers, use the same number of each, and as few as possible.**

j. Check drive gear and drive pinion for proper tooth contact, refer to "Carrier Inspection Before Service" for adjustment procedure.

k. Measure drive gear runout at shoulder on reverse side of drive gear, **Fig. 30.** If drive gear runout exceeds .002 inch, reinstall by changing phase of drive gear and differential case, and remeasure.

13. **On Colt Vista and Eagle Talon models,** apply a semi-drying sealant to installation surface of differential cover and vent plug, **torque** cover bolts to 22-30 ft. lbs.

## Stealth

Assemble differential carrier in numbered sequence shown in **Fig. 52,** noting the following:

1. **On models w/Four Wheel Steering (4WS),** tap spring pin into differential case to position shown in **Fig. 53,** before press fitting rear wheel oil pump drive gear. Notch on spring should be in position shown.
2. **On all models,** with beveled part of rear wheel oil pump drive gear at inner side, press in drive gear, using rear suspension bushing base tool No. MB990890-01 or equivalent, until drive gear contacts end surface of differential case. Ensure that drive gear and spring pin are flush.
3. Press fit drive pinion rear and front bearing outer races onto gear carrier using handle tool and bearing and oil seal installer tool set No. MB990925 or equivalent. **Use care not to press in outer race at an angle.**
4. Adjust pinion height as follows:
   a. Install special tools as shown in **Fig. 54.**
   b. Tighten handle of tool until the standard value shown in **Fig. 55,** of drive pinion turning torque is obtained.
   c. Measure drive pinion turning torque without oil seal installed.
   d. Position gauge tube tool No. MB990392-01 or equivalent, in side bearing beat of gear carrier then select a drive pinion rear shim of thickness which corresponds to gap between special tools.
   e. Install selected shim on drive pinion and press fit rear bearing inner race using bearing installer tool No. MT215013 or equivalent.
5. Adjust drive pinion preload as follows:
   a. Install drive pinion front shim(s) between pinion spacer and pinion front bearing inner race.
   b. Tighten companion flange to specification using end yoke holder tool. Do not install oil seal.
   c. Ensure drive pinion turning torque is as shown in **Fig. 55.**
   d. If drive pinion turning torque is not within specified range, adjust by replacing drive pinion front shims(s) or drive pinion spacer.
   e. Remove companion flange and drive pinion.
   f. Install oil seal using suitable oil seal installation tool.
   g. Install drive pinion and companion flange aligning marks made during disassembly then tighten companion flange self-locking nut to specification.
   h. Measure pinion turning torque with oil seal installed and ensure that turning torque is no more than one inch lb. greater than what is shown in **Fig. 55.**
6. Adjust differential gear backlash as follows:
   a. Assemble side gears and spacers, pinion gears and washers into differential case.
   b. Temporarily install pinion shaft.
   c. While locking side gear with wedge, measure differential gear backlash with a dial indicator on pinion gear. **The measurement should be made for both pinion gears individually.**
   d. If differential gear backlash exceeds .008 inch, adjust backlash by installing thicker side gear spacers.

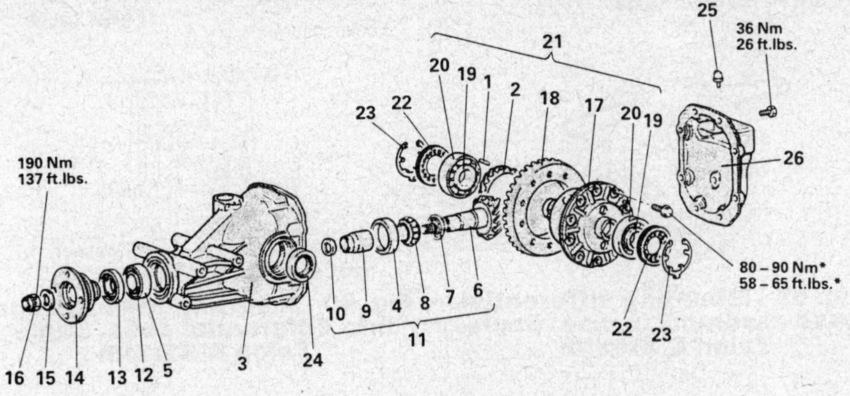


**Reassembly steps**

1. Spring pin (for 4WS)
2. Drive gear (for 4WS)
3. Differential carrier
4. Drive pinion rear bearing outer race
5. Drive pinion front bearing outer race
   Drive pinion height adjustment
6. Drive pinion
7. Drive pinion rear shim
   (for drive pinion height adjustment)
8. Drive pinion rear bearing inner race
9. Drive pinion spacer
   Drive pinion preload adjustment
10. Drive pinion front shim
11. Drive pinion assembly
12. Drive pinion front bearing inner race
13. Oil seal
14. Companion flange
15. Washer
16. Self-locking nut
17. LSD case
18. Drive gear
19. Side bearing inner race
20. Side bearing outer race
    Final drive gear backlash adjustment
21. Differential case assembly
22. Side bearing nut
23. Snap ring
24. Oil seal
25. Vent plug
26. Differential cover assembly

NOTE
*: Tightening torque with oil applied.

**Fig. 52 Assembling differential carrier. Stealth**

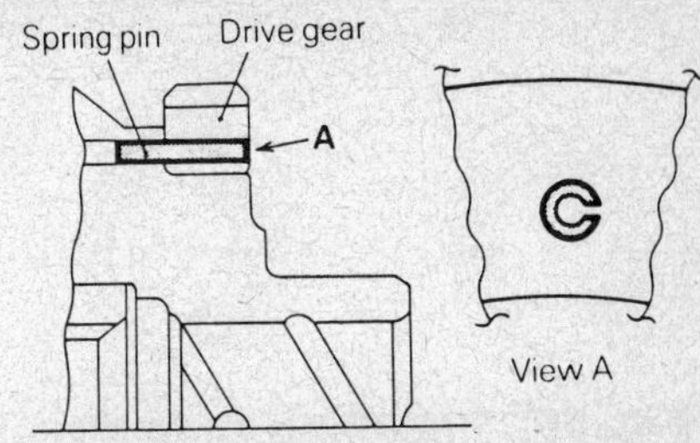


**Fig. 53 Installing spring pin. Stealth**

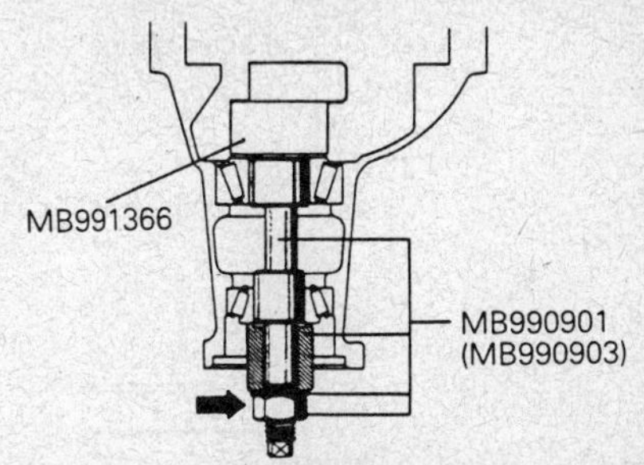


**Fig. 54 Adjusting drive pinion height. Stealth**

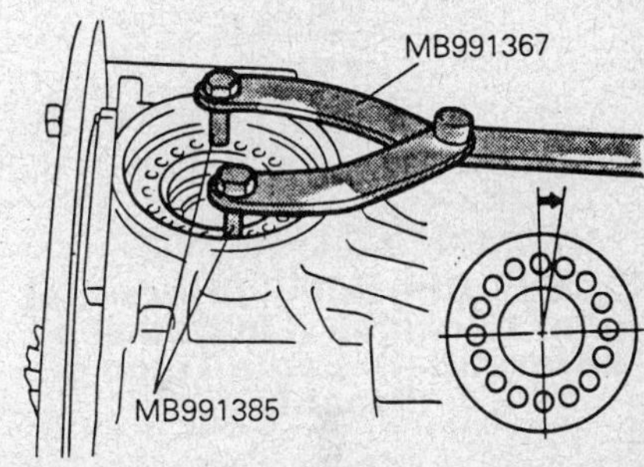


**Fig. 57 Adjusting side bearing nuts. Stealth**

| Bearing classification | Bearing lubrication | Rotation torque Nm (in.lbs.) |
|---|---|---|
| New | None (with rust-prevention oil) | 0.3 – 0.5 (3 – 4) |
| New/reused | Gear oil application | 0.15 – 0.25 (1 – 2) |

NOTE
(1) Gradually tighten the nut of the special tool while checking the drive pinion rotation torque.
(2) Because the special tool cannot be turned one turn, turn it several times within the range that it can be turned; then, after fitting to the bearing, measure the rotation torque.

**Fig. 55 Rotation torque value. Stealth**

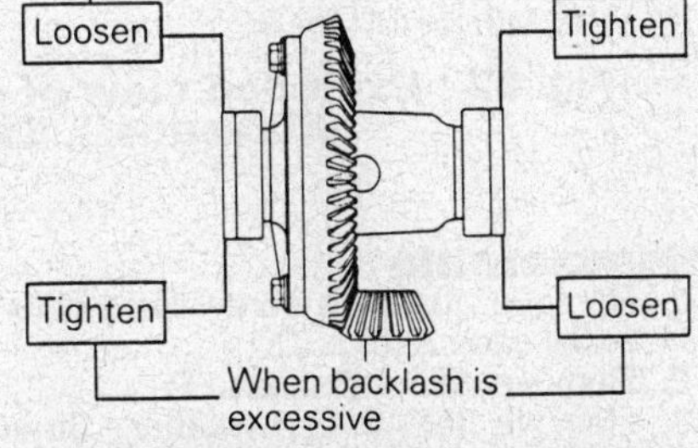


**Fig. 56 Adjusting final gear backlash. Stealth**

e. Measure differential gear backlash again and confirm it is within the specification.
f. After adjustment, ensure that the backlash is less than limit and differential gear rotates smoothly.
g. When adjustment is impossible, replace side gear pinion hears as a set.

7. Align pinion shaft lockpin hole with differential case and install lockpin.
8. Stake lockpin at two points.
9. Clean drive gear attaching bolts.
10. Usa an 10mm x 1.25 tap to remove adhesive from threaded holes of drive gear.
11. Install drive gear onto differential case aligning marks made during disassembly. Tighten bolts in a diagonal sequence.
12. Press side bearing inner races onto differential case.
13. Adjust final drive gear backlash as follows:
    a. Using spanner wrench tool No. MB991367 and pin tool No. MB991385 or equivalent,temporarily tighten side bearing nut until just before preloading.
    b. Measure final drive gear backlash at four or more points on drive gear.
    c. Using spanner wrench and pin tools, adjust backlash until a .004-.006 inch value is reached by turning side bearing nut as shown, **Fig. 56.**
    d. Using the spanner wrench to apply preload, turn down both right and left side bearing nuts on half the distance between centers of two neighboring holes, **Fig. 57.**
    e. Install snap ring at either position shown to lock side bearing nut, **Fig. 58.**
    f. Check drive gear and pinion tooth contact as outlined under "Inspection Before Disassembly."
    g. Measure drive gear runout at shoulder on reverse side of drive gear.
    h. If runout exceeds .002 inch, reinstall by changing the phase of drive gear and differential case, and remeasure.
    i. Using suitable oil seal installer, install oil seal flush with gear carrier end face.

## LIMITED SLIP

### EAGLE TALON & STEALTH

### Predisassembly Inspection

1. Secure differential case assembly in a vise so that differential side gear (right) is facing upward as shown in **Fig. 59.**

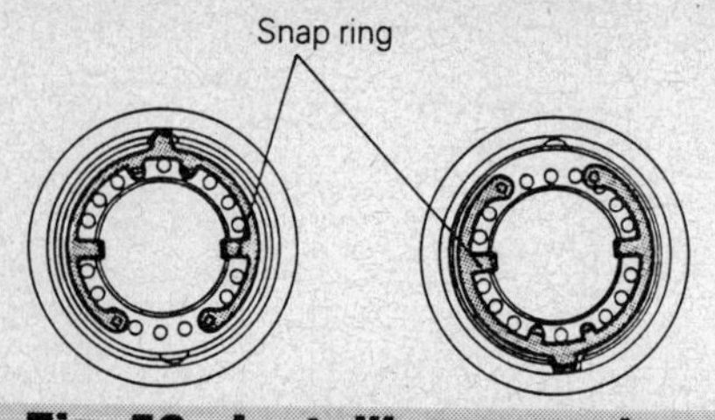


**Fig. 58 Installing snap ring. Stealth**

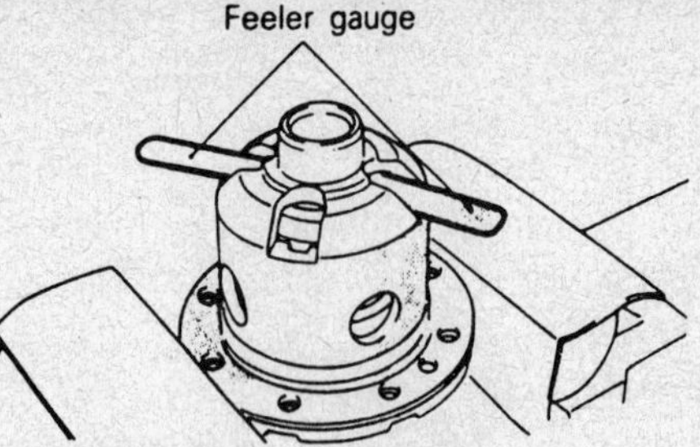


**Fig. 59 Mounting differential case assembly in vise. Eagle Talon & Stealth**

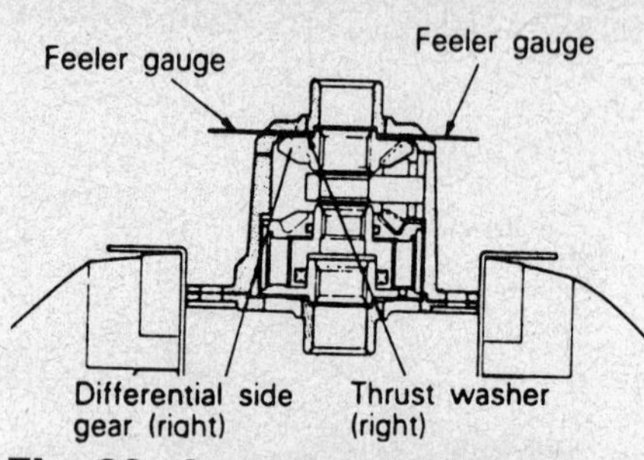


**Fig. 60 Inserting feeler gauge into differential case. Eagle Talon & Stealth**

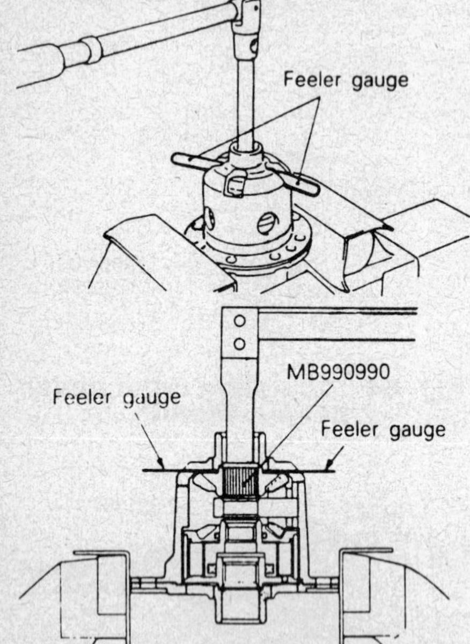


**Fig. 61 Checking differential gear backlash (Limited slip differential). Eagle Talon & Stealth**

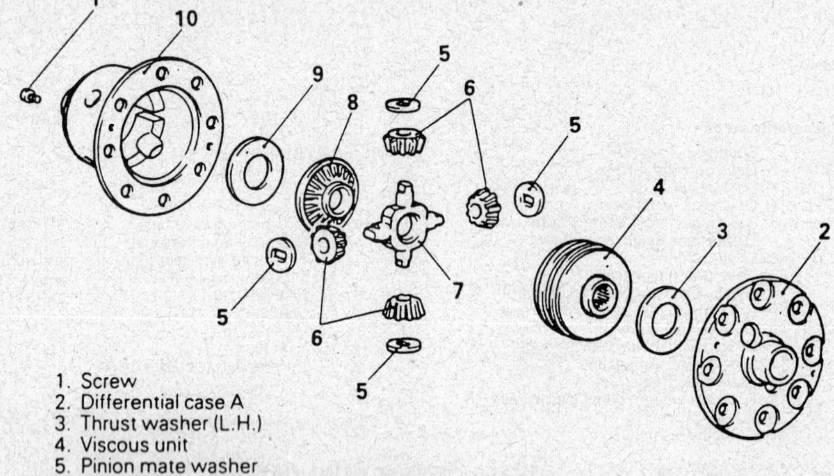


1. Screw
2. Differential case A
3. Thrust washer (L.H.)
4. Viscous unit
5. Pinion mate washer
6. Differential pinion mate
7. Differential pinion shaft
8. Differential side gear (R.H.)
9. Thrust washer (R.H.)
10. Differential case B

**Fig. 62 Exploded view of differential carrier (Limited slip differential). Eagle Talon & Stealth**

2. Insert a .0012 inch (.03 mm) feeler gauge at two places (diagonally) between differential case B and thrust washer, **Fig. 60. Do not insert feeler gauge in oil groove of differential case B.**
3. Insert side gear holding tool No. MB990990 or equivalent at spline part of differential case B (right) and ensure that side gear rotates, **Fig. 61.**
4. Insert a .0035 inch (.09 mm) feeler gauge to replace .0012 inch (.03 mm) feeler gauge.
5. Insert side gear holding tool No. MB990990 or equivalent at spline part of differential case B (right) and ensure that side gear does not rotate, **Fig. 61.**
6. Differential gear backlash (clearance in thrust direction of side gear) should be within .0012-.0035 inch (.03 mm-.09 mm). If clearance in the thrust direction of the side gear is within standard value range, backlash of differential gear is normal.
7. If clearance in thrust direction of side gear is not within specification, remove differential case A and make adjustment by adjusting thickness of the thrust washer (left).

## Disassemble

1. Remove attaching screw from differential case A, **Fig. 62.**
2. Remove differential case B.
3. Remove left thrust washer. **Since thrust washer from left side is of a different thickness than the right side, it will be necessary to mark the washer in some manner for assembly reference.**
4. Remove viscous unit, pinion mate washer, differential pinion mate, pinion shaft and righthand differential side gear.
5. Remove right thrust washer. **Since thrust washer from right side is of a different thickness than the left side, it will be necessary to mark the washer for assembly reference.**

## Inspection

1. Check gears and differential pinion shaft for unusual wear or damage.
2. Check spline part of right side differential gear for stepped wear or damage.
3. Check thrust washer and pinion mate washer for unusual wear of contact surfaces, heat damage or other damage.
4. Check contact surfaces of differential cases A and B for damage or wear, **Fig. 63.**
5. Check spline part of viscous unit for stepped wear or damage, and check contact surface with differential case B.
6. Check left side gear of viscous unit for unusual wear or damage.

## Assemble

1. With pinion mate washer in position shown in **Fig. 64,** install to differential pinion mate to differential pinion shaft, and then install to differential case B.
2. If differential side gear and pinion mate gear have been replaced, select left side thrust washer as follows:
   a. Wash differential side gear and pinion mate gear in unleaded gasoline to remove all foreign material.
   b. Install previously used thrust washers (matching left and right sides), together with gears, viscous unit, pinion mate washer and pinion shaft to differential cases A and B. Using screws, secure temporarily.

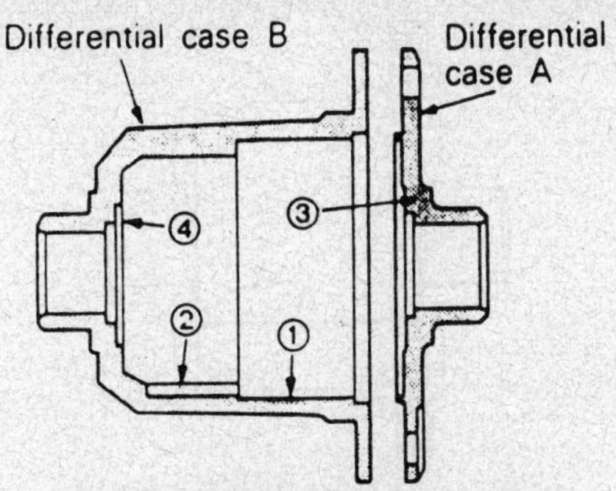

**Fig. 63 Differential case contact surfaces. Eagle Talon & Stealth**

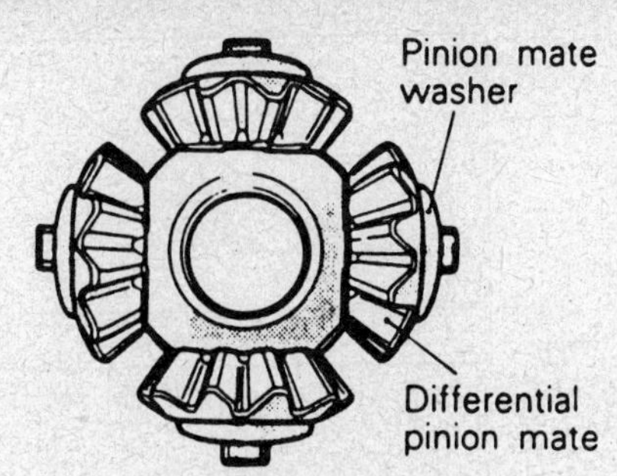


**Fig. 64 Differential pinion mate installation. Eagle Talon & Stealth**

| Thrust washer (left) | |
|---|---|
| Part No. | Thickness mm (in.) |
| MB569243 | 0.8 (.031) |
| | 0.9 (.035) |
| | 1.0 (.039) |
| | 1.1 (.043) |
| | 1.15 (.045) |
| | 1.2 (.047) |
| | 1.25 (.049) |
| | 1.3 (.051) |
| | 1.35 (.053) |
| | 1.4 (.055) |
| | 1.5 (.059) |

**Fig. 65 Thrust washer thickness chart. Eagle Talon & Stealth**

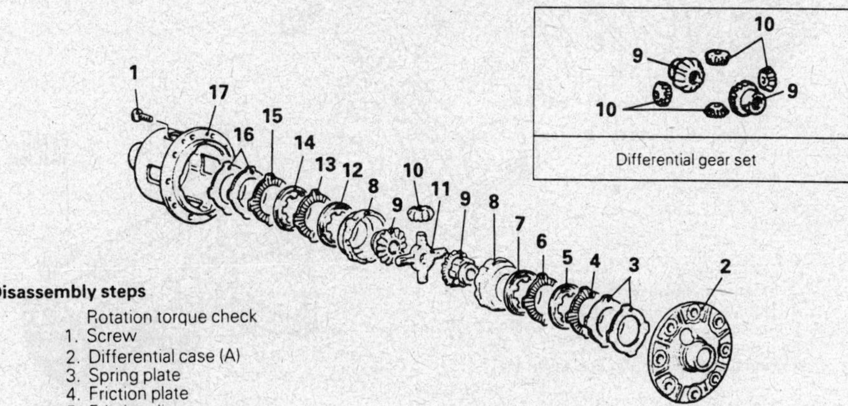


**Disassembly steps**

Rotation torque check
1. Screw
2. Differential case (A)
3. Spring plate
4. Friction plate
5. Friction disc
6. Friction plate
7. Friction disc
8. Pressure ring
9. Side gear
10. Differential pinion gear
11. Differential pinion shaft
12. Friction disc
13. Friction plate
14. Friction disc
15. Friction plate
16. Spring plate
    Adjustment of clutch plate friction force
17. Differential case (B)

**Fig. 66 Exploded view of differential carrier (Limited slip differential). Colt Wagon**

in a vise so that right side differential side gear is facing upward, **Fig. 59. Do not hold differential case to tightly.**

d. Insert a .0012 inch feeler gauge at two places (diagonally) between differential case B and right side thrust washer. **Do not insert feeler gauge in oil groove of differential case B.**

e. Insert side gear holding tool No. MB990990 or equivalent at spline part of differential case B (right) and ensure that side gear does not rotate, **Fig. 61.**

f. Differential gear backlash (clearance in thrust direction of side gear) should be within .0012-.0035 inch (.03 mm-.09 mm). If clearance in the thrust direction of the side gear is within standard value range, backlash of differential gear is normal.

g. If clearance in thrust direction of side gear is not within specification, remove differential case A and make adjustment by selecting appropriate thrust washer from chart shown in **Fig. 65.**

3. After installing thrust washers, align mating marks of differential cases and reassemble.

## COLT WAGON & COLT VISTA
### Predisassembly Inspection

1. Inspect rotation torque of limited slip differential as follows:
   a. Check rotation torque using side gear holding tool set Nos. MB990998 and MB990989 or equivalent.
   b. If rotation torque is not 14-29 ft. lbs. when a used plate is used or 3.6-29 ft. lbs. when a new plate is used, disassemble carrier and correct or replace parts.

### Disassembly

Disassemble differential carrier in numbered sequence shown in **Figs. 66 and 67,** noting the following:

1. Loosen screws of differential case halves uniformly in several steps.
2. Separate differential case halves keeping all internal components on order in which they are removed.
3. Before differential cases are separated, check position of alignment marks.

### Inspection

1. Check side gears, pinion gears and pinion shaft for wear or damage.
2. Check side gear spline for wear or damage.
3. Using a dial indicator, ensure amount of warpage in less than .0031 inch.

### Assembly

Assemble differential carrier in reverse numbered sequence shown in **Figs. 66 and 67,** noting the following:

1. Before assembly, use the following method to adjust clearance between spring plates and differential cases and to adjust endplay of side gear when installing internal components.

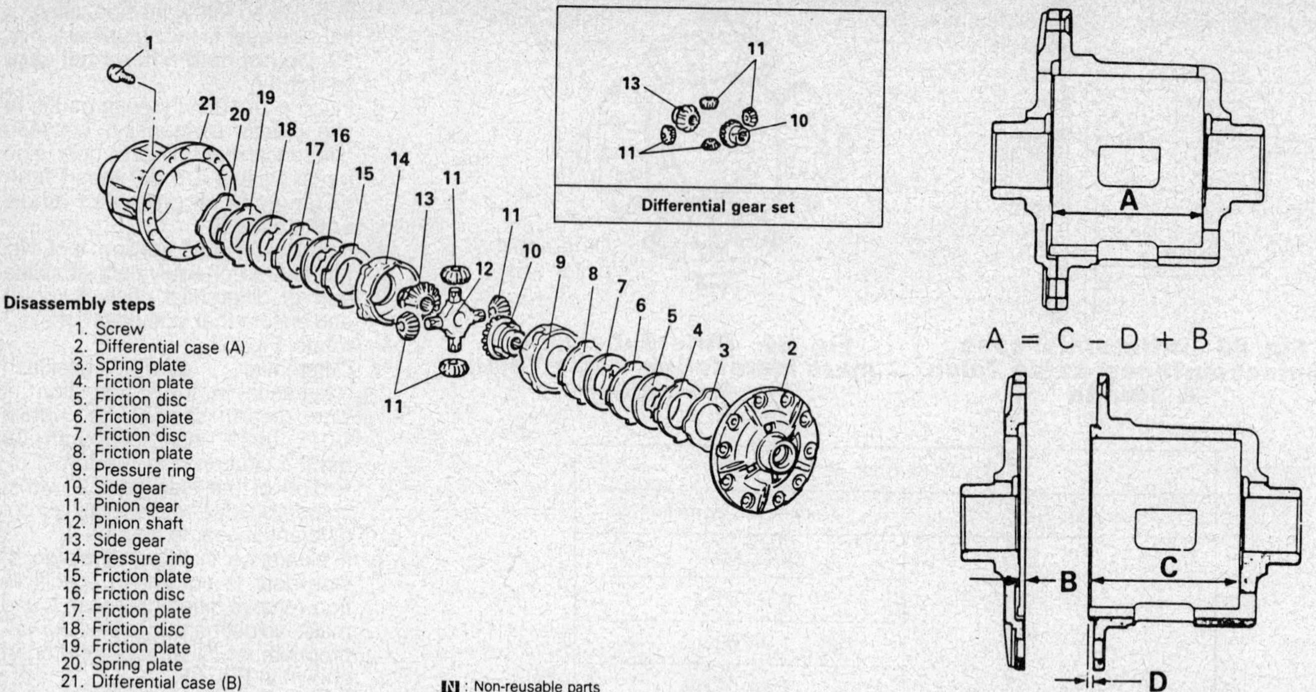


**Fig. 67 Exploded view of differential carrier (Limited slip differential). Colt Vista**

**Fig. 68 Obtaining differential case depth. Colt Wagon & Colt Vista**

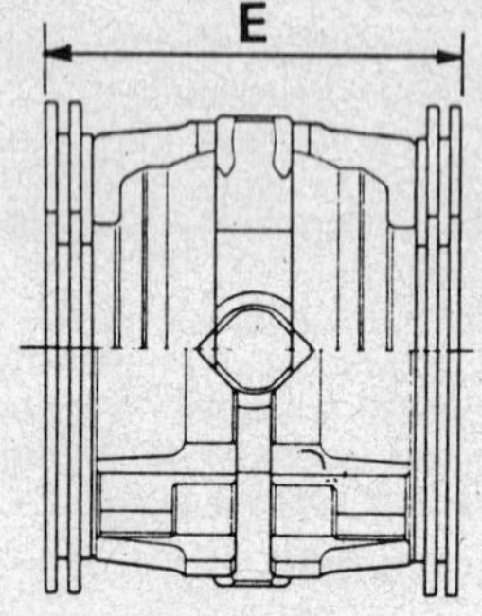


**Fig. 69 Measuring overall width. Colt Wagon & Colt Vista**

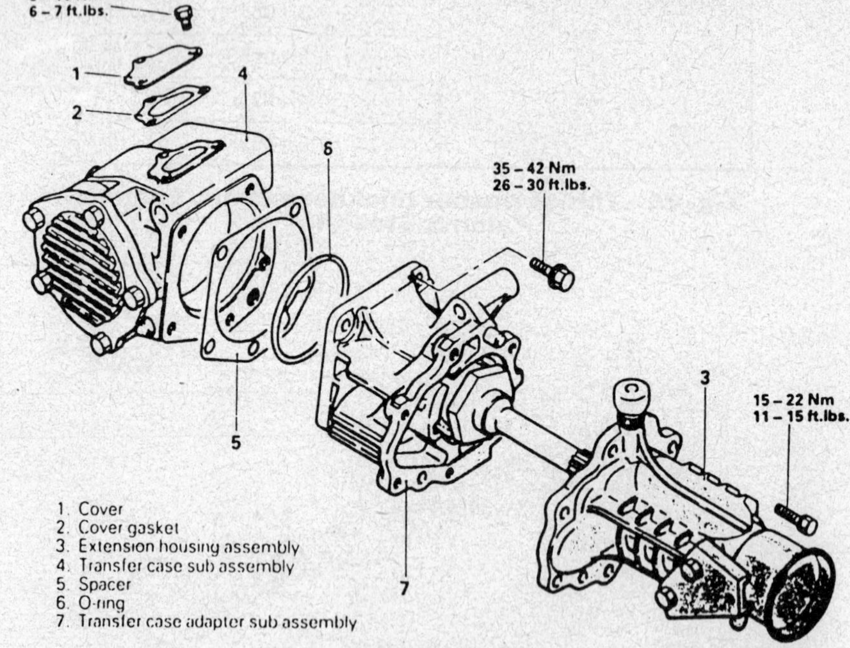


**Fig. 70 Exploded view of transfer assembly. Colt Wagon & Eagle Talon**

a. Obtain differential case depth (A) by subtracting dimension (D) from dimension (C) then adding dimension (B) as shown in **Fig. 68.** This represents distance between clutch plate contact surface when case halves are assembled.
b. Stack spring plates upon another to make a set. Measure and record thickness of left (Lr) and right (Ll) sets. **Select left and right sets to minimize difference in thickness.**
c. Measure thickness of friction discs and friction plates. Record left (Kr) and right (Kr) measurements. **Select left and right sets to minimize difference in thickness.**
d. Obtain thickness difference (X) between right and left clutch plate sets as follows. X = (Lr + Kr) - (Ll + Kl).
e. If difference is more than .0020 inch, replace components as necessary.
f. Assemble pressure rings and their inner parts, friction plates and friction discs together. Measure overall width (E), **Fig. 69.**
g. Obtain clearance (Y) between clutch plate set and differential case as follows. Y = A - (E + Lr + Ll).
h. If clearance (Y) is not .0024-.0098 inch change friction discs.

2. Place each part in differential case as shown in **Figs. 66 and 67.**
3. After assembly, inspect rotation torque as outlined under "Predisassembly Inspection."

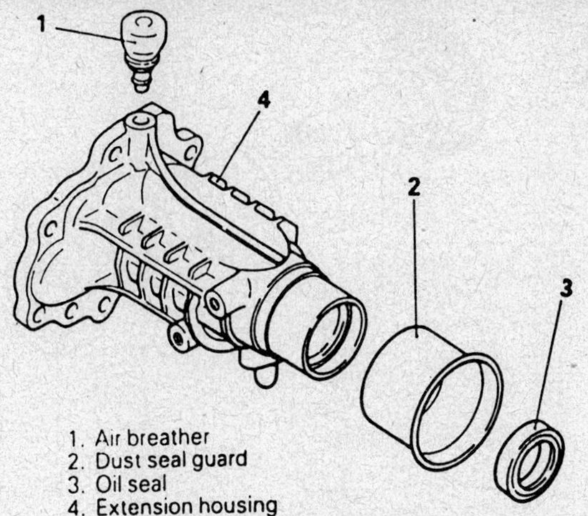


**Fig. 71 Extension housing assembly. Colt Wagon & Eagle Talon**

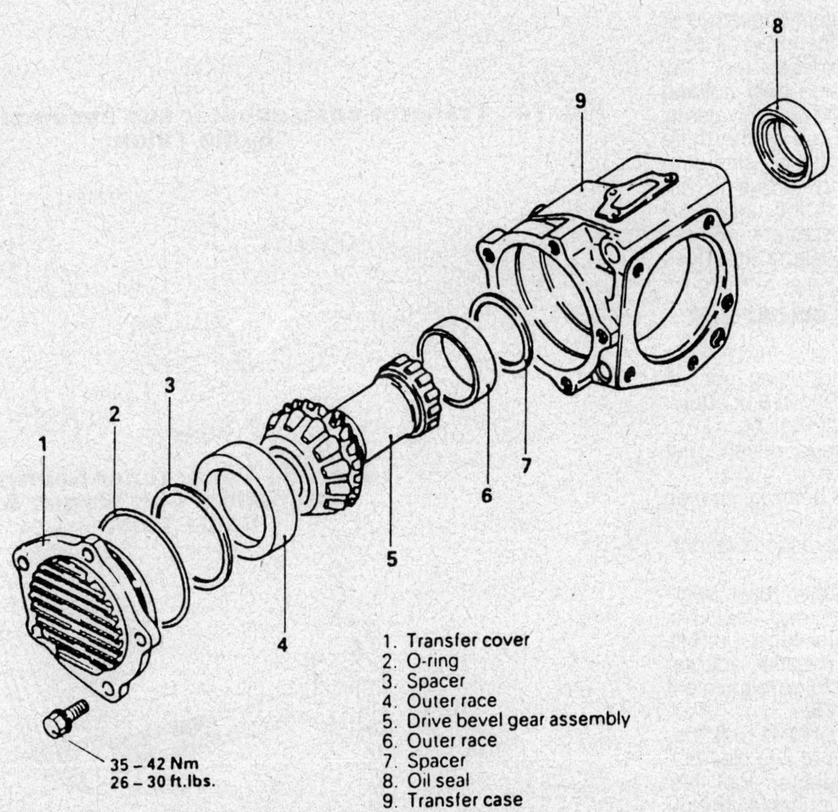


**Fig. 72 Transfer case sub assembly. Colt Wagon & Eagle Talon**

# TRANSFER ASSEMBLY SERVICE

## COLT WAGON & EAGLE TALON

### DISASSEMBLE

1. Remove cover and cover gasket, **Fig. 70.**
2. Remove extension housing assembly and transfer case sub assembly.
3. Remove spacer, O-ring and transfer case adapter sub assembly.

### SUB ASSEMBLY SERVICE

#### Extension Housing Assembly

1. Remove air breather, **Fig. 71.**
2. Remove dust shield guard and oil seal from extension housing assembly.
3. Reverse procedure to assemble, noting the following:
   a. Use oil seal installer MD998304 or equivalent when installing oil seal.
   b. Prior to installing air breather, apply 3M Super Weatherstrip No. 8001 or equivalent to air breather.

#### Transfer Case Sub Assembly

1. Remove transfer cover, **Fig. 72.**

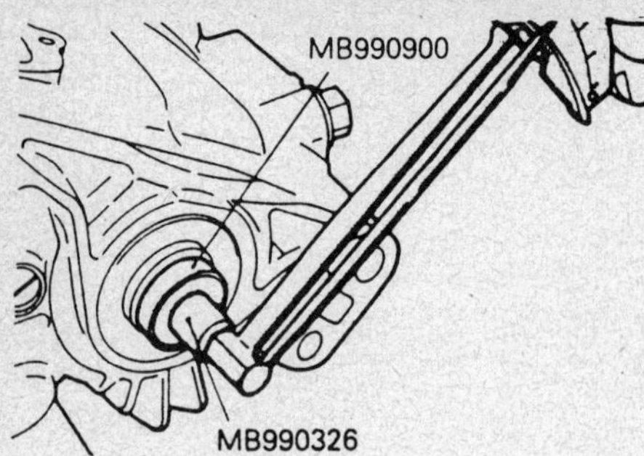


**Fig. 73 Checking turning drive torque of drive bevel gear assembly. Colt Wagon & Eagle Talon**

2. Remove O-ring, spacer and outer race.
3. Remove drive bevel gear assembly, spacer and oil seal.
4. Reverse procedure to assemble, noting the following:
   a. Use oil seal installer MD998323 or equivalent when installing oil seal.
   b. Using preload socket tool No. MB990326 and side gear holding tool No. MB990900 or equivalents, check turning torque of the drive bevel gear assembly as shown in **Fig. 73.** If turning torque is not within 1.23-1.81 ft. lbs., adjust by installing new spacers. Select spacers of nearly same thickness on both sides.

### Transfer Case Adapter Sub Assembly

1. Unstake locknut and using special spanner tool No. MB991013 or equivalent, remove locknut, **Fig. 74.**
2. Using a press, remove driven gear bevel assembly.
3. Remove taper roller bearing, spacer, collar and outer races.
4. Reverse procedure to assemble, noting the following:
   a. When installing taper roller bearing, use installer cap tool No. MD998812, installer tube tool No. MD998814 and installer adapter tool No. MD998820 or equivalent as shown in **Fig. 75.**
   b. **Torque** locknut to 102-115 ft. lbs., then stake locknut at two places.
   c. Using wrench adapter tool No. MD998806 and suitable torque wrench or equivalents, check turning torque of the driven bevel gear assembly as shown in **Fig. 76.** If turning torque is not within 0.72-1.23 ft. lbs., adjust with adjusting spacer.

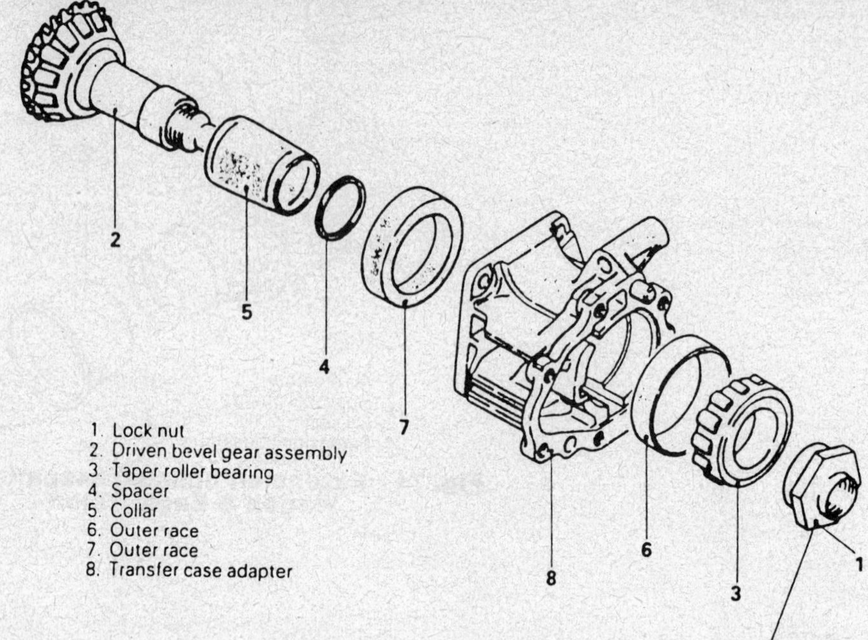


**Fig. 74 Transfer case adapter sub assembly. Colt Wagon & Eagle Talon**

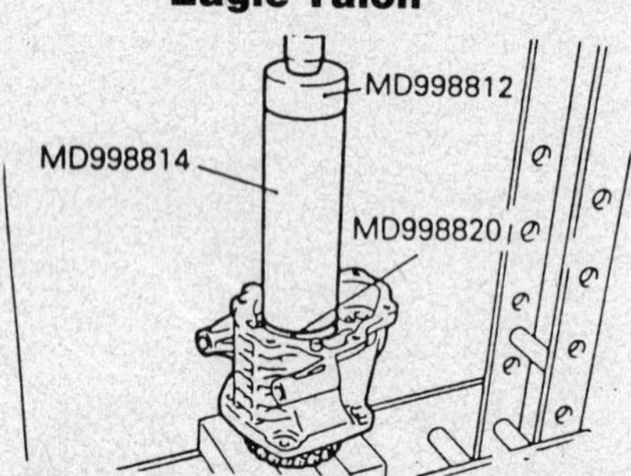


**Fig. 75 Taper roller bearing installation. Colt Wagon & Eagle Talon**

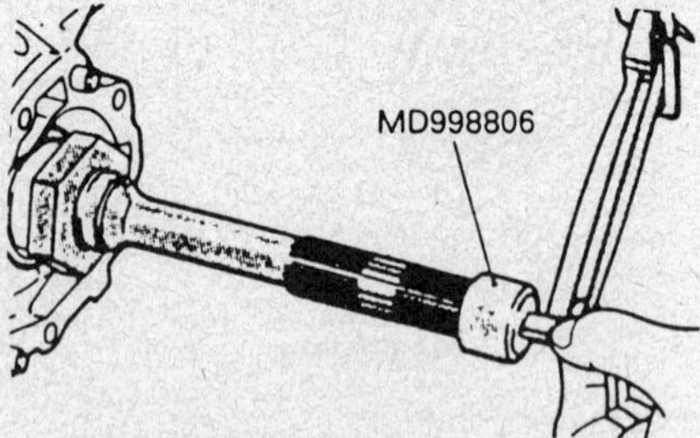


**Fig. 76 Checking turning drive torque of driven bevel gear assembly. Colt Wagon & Eagle Talon**

### Drive Bevel Gear Assembly

1. Using bearing removal tool No. MD998801 or equivalent, remove taper roller bearings and drive bevel gear as shown in **Fig. 77.**
2. Using installer cap tool No. MD998812 and installer adapter tool No. MD998827 or equivalent, install taper roller bearing above drive bevel gear, **Fig. 78.**
3. Using bearing installation tool No. MD998350 or equivalent, install taper roller bearing at opposite end drive bevel gear, **Fig. 78.**

### Driven Bevel Gear Assembly

1. Using bearing removal tool No. MD998801 or equivalent, remove taper roller bearing from driven gear assembly, **Fig. 79.**
2. Use collar to install taper roller bearing onto driven bevel gear.

## COLT VISTA & STEALTH

The transfer assembly used on these models cannot be serviced. If the transfer assembly, other than the extension housing, dust seal guard ot rear oil seal, are found defective complete component replacement is required.

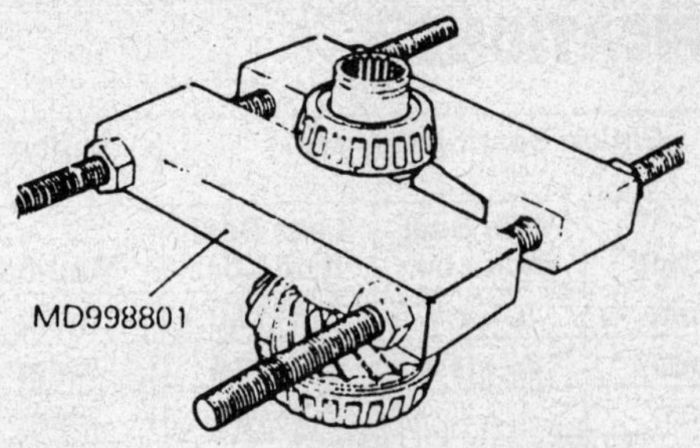


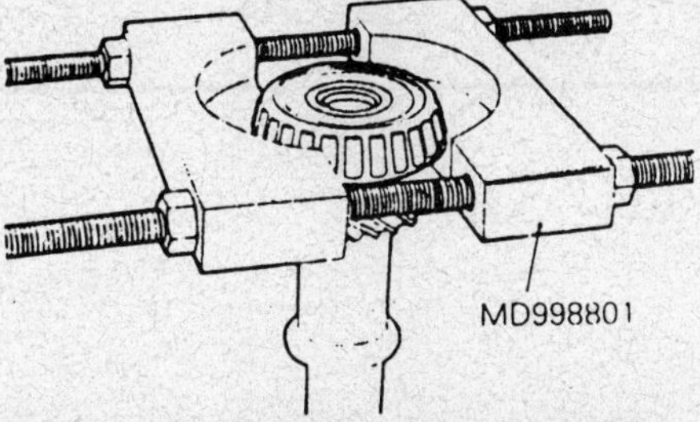


**Fig. 77 Removing taper roller bearings from drive bevel gear assembly. Colt Wagon & Eagle Talon**

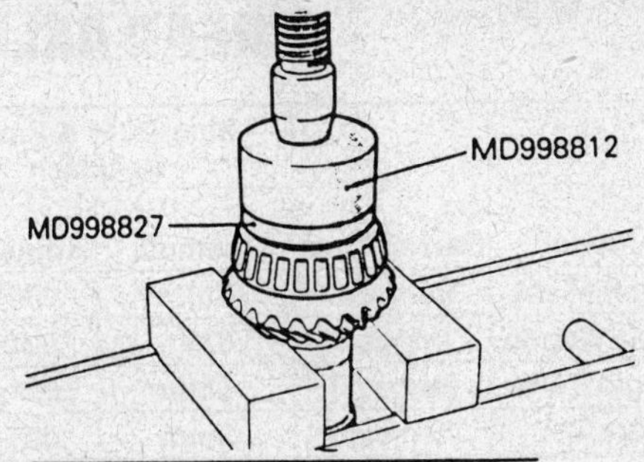


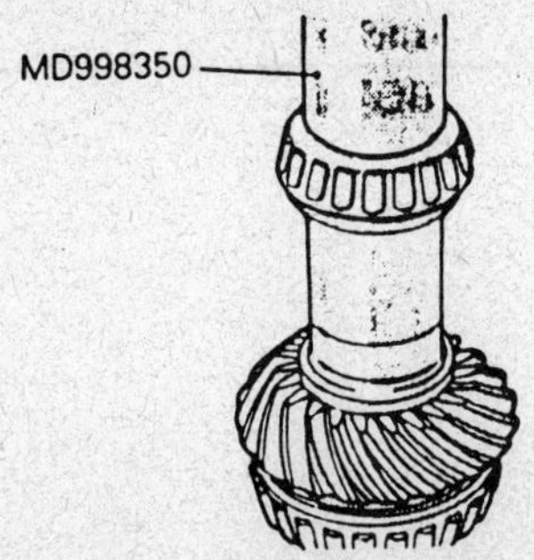


**Fig. 78 Installing taper roller bearings on drive bevel gear assembly. Colt Wagon & Eagle Talon**

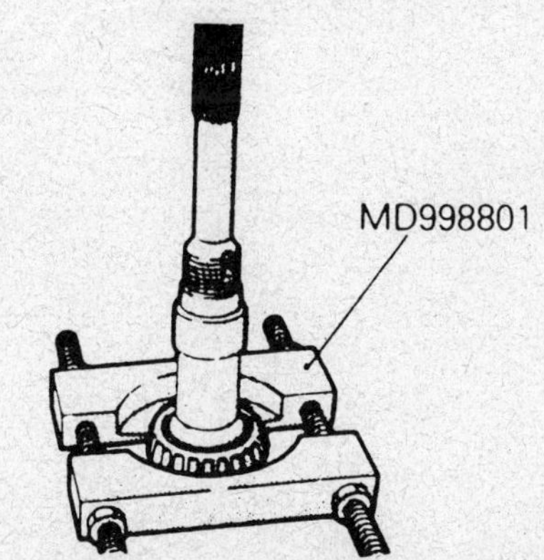


**Fig. 79 Removing taper roller bearings from driven bevel gear assembly. Colt Wagon & Eagle Talon**

## REAR AXLE SPECIFICATIONS

| Year | Model | Carrier Type | Ring Gear & Pinion Backlash | | Pinion Bearing Preload | | | Differential Bearing Preload | |
|---|---|---|---|---|---|---|---|---|---|
| | | | Method | Adjustment | Method | With Seal Inch Lbs. | Less Seal Inch Lbs. | Method | Adjustment |
| 1989–91 | Colt Vista | Removal | Shim | .004–.006 | Shim | 6.1–8.6 | 8.6–11.3 | Shim | .002 |
| 1989–90 | Colt Wagon | Integral | Shim | .004–.006 | Shim | 8.7–11.3 | 7.8–10.4 | Shim | .002 |
| 1990–91 | Eagle Talon | Removal | Shim | .004–.006 | Shim | — | 8–10 | Shim | .002 |
| 1991 | Stealth | Removal | Shim | .004–.006 | Shim | — | 3–4 | Nut | .004–.006 |

# HYDRAULIC BRAKE SYSTEM

## INDEX

**NOTE:** Refer To "Anti-Lock Brakes" Chapter For Procedures Pertaining To ABS Systems Or Rear Brake Lock-Up Control System.



## MASTER CYLINDER APPLICATIONS

**Type No.**

### CHRYSLER EXCEPT COLT, COLT VISTA, COLT WAGON, CONQUEST, LASER, MONACO & STEALTH

**1989:**
Rear Wheel Drive ........ 1
**1989-91:**
Front Wheel Drive ........ 1

### COLT

**1989-91** ........ 7

### COLT VISTA

**1989-91** ........ 4

### COLT WAGON

**1989-90** ........ 6

### CONQUEST

**1989** ........ 5

### LASER

**1990-91** ........ 8

### MONACO

**1990-91** ........ 2

### STEALTH

**1991** ........ 9

### EAGLE MEDALLION

**1989** ........ 3

### EAGLE PREMIER

**1989-91** ........ 2

### EAGLE SUMMIT

**1989-91** ........ 7

### EAGLE TALON

**1990-91** ........ 8

## HYDRAULIC CONTROLS APPLICATIONS

Type No.

### CHRYSLER EXCEPT COLT, COLT VISTA, COLT WAGON, CONQUEST, LASER, MONACO & STEALTH

1989:
Rear Wheel Drive .................... 1

1989-91:
Front Wheel Drive.................... 2

### COLT

1989-91 .............................. 7

Type No.

### COLT VISTA

1989-91:
2WD .............................. 6
4WD .............................. 5

### COLT WAGON

1989-90 .............................. 6

### CONQUEST

1989 .............................. 5

### LASER

1990-91 .............................. 5

### MONACO

1990-91 .............................. 4

Type No.

### STEALTH

1991 .............................. 5

### EAGLE MEDALLION

1989 .............................. 3

### EAGLE PREMIER

1989-91 .............................. 4

### EAGLE SUMMIT

1989-91 .............................. 5

### EAGLE TALON

1990-91 .............................. 5

## FRONT & REAR SPLIT HYDRAULIC BRAKE SYSTEMS

When the brake pedal is depressed, both the primary (front brake) and the secondary (rear brake) master cylinder pistons are moved simultaneously to exert hydraulic fluid pressure on their respective independent hydraulic systems. The fluid displacement of the two master cylinders is proportioned to fulfill the requirements of each of the two independent hydraulic brake systems, **Fig. 1.**

If a failure of a rear (secondary) brake system should occur, initial brake pedal movement causes the unrestricted secondary piston to bottom in the master cylinder bore. Primary piston movement displaces hydraulic fluid in the primary section of the dual master cylinder to actuate the front brake system.

Should the front (primary) brake system fail, initial brake pedal movement causes the unrestricted primary piston to bottom out against the secondary piston. Continued downward movement of the brake pedal moves the secondary piston to displace hydraulic fluid in the rear brake system to actuate the rear brakes.

The increased pedal travel and the increased pedal effort required to compensate for the loss of the failed portion of the brake system provides a warning that a partial brake system failure has occurred. When the ignition switch is turned on, a brake warning light on the instrument panel provides a visual indication that one of the dual brake systems has become inoperative.

Should a failure of either the front or rear brake hydraulic system occur, the hydraulic fluid pressure differential resulting from pressure loss of the failed brake system forces the valve toward the low pressure area to light the brake warning lamp.

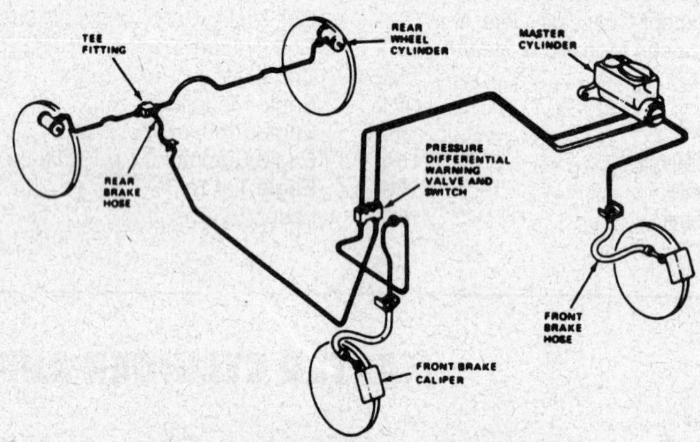


**Fig. 1 Schematic diagram of a hydraulic front & rear split brake system**

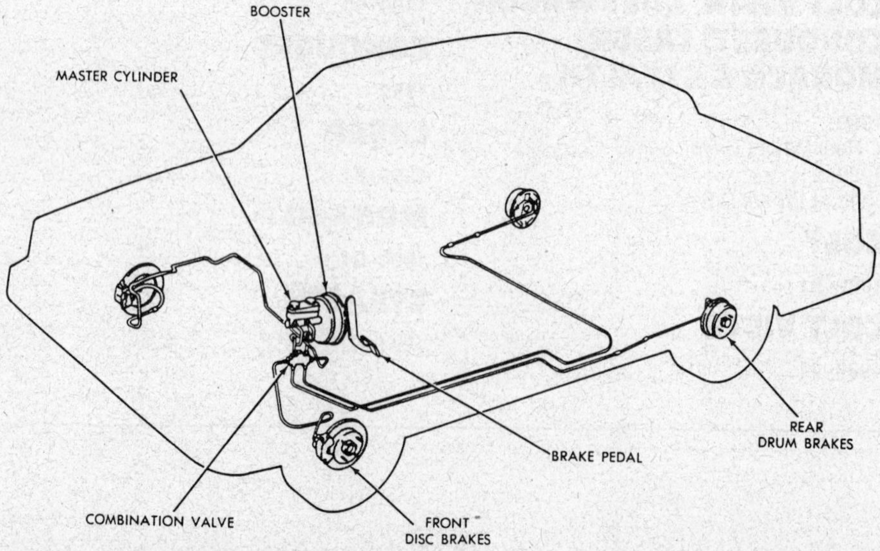


**Fig. 2 Schematic diagram of a hydraulic diagonally split brake system**

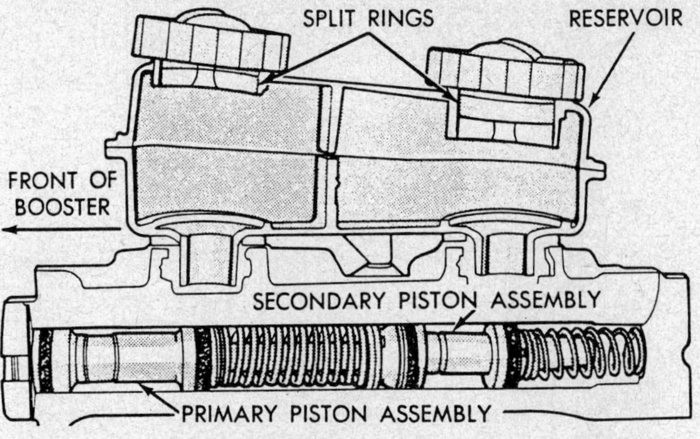


**Fig. 3 Type 1, composite master cylinder**

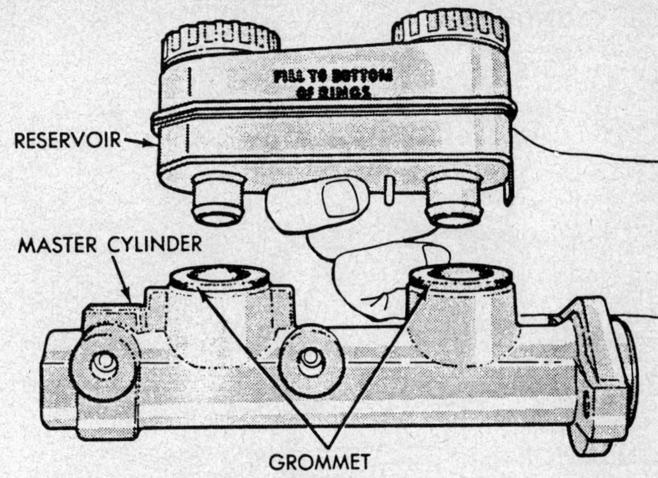


**Fig. 4 Type 1, composite master cylinder reservoir replacement**

# DIAGONALLY SPLIT HYDRAULIC BRAKE SYSTEMS

This system operates on the same principles as conventional front and rear split systems using primary and secondary master cylinders moving simultaneously to exert hydraulic pressure on their respective systems.

The hydraulic brake lines on this system, however, have been diagonally split front to rear (left front to right rear and right front to left rear) in place of separate lines to the front and rear wheels, **Fig. 2.**

In the event of a system failure this would cause the remaining good system to do all the braking on one front wheel and the opposite rear wheel, thus maintaining 50% of the total braking force. The hydraulic pressure loss would result in a pressure differential in the system and cause a warning light on the dashboard to glow as in front and rear split systems.

# TYPE 1—COMPOSITE MASTER CYLINDER

## DESCRIPTION

This master cylinder **Fig. 3,** is comprised of an aluminum body, pistons, springs, O-rings, cup seals, and a reinforced nylon reservoir. The bore of the aluminum body is anodized for durability, and to prevent corrosion and pitting. The reservoir caps contain diaphragms with precision slits for controlled equalization of pressure.

## TESTING

Ensure the master cylinder compensates in both ports by applying the brake pedal lightly (engine running with power brakes) and observing brake fluid squirting up in the reservoir chambers. Due to a baffle incorporated in the master cylinder, only a minor fluid disturbance may be noticed in the rear chamber of the reservoir.

## MASTER CYLINDER, REPLACE

1. Place drain pan under the master cylinder.
2. Using a suitable wrench, disconnect brake lines from the master cylinder. Plug all lines and fittings.
3. Remove master cylinder-to-brake booster attaching nuts.
4. Pull master cylinder outward and away from brake booster.
5. Reverse procedure to install noting the following:
   a. Prior to installing a new or rebuilt master cylinder, it should be bench bled as described under "Hydraulic System Bleeding & Flushing."
   b. **Torque** master cylinder-to-brake booster attaching nuts to 170-230 inch lbs.
   c. **Torque** brake line fittings to 170 inch lbs.

## RESERVOIR, REPLACE

Refer to **Fig. 4** when performing this procedure.

### Removal

1. Remove master cylinder from vehicle as described previously.
2. Thoroughly clean reservoir and housing.
3. Remove reservoir caps, then drain the brake fluid.
4. Clamp housing in a vise.
5. Grasp reservoir by hand, then separate it from the housing by rocking it from side to side. **Do not pry reservoir from the housing.**
6. Remove grommets from housing.

### Installation

1. Install grommets in housing.
2. Apply clean brake fluid to reservoir mounting surface.
3. Position reservoir to housing so wording on reservoir reads from left to right from the front of the housing, **Fig. 4.**
4. Press reservoir into housing while rocking it from side to side. Reservoir is properly seated when bottom of reservoir touches the grommet.
5. Refer to "Hydraulic System Bleeding & Flushing" to bleed the hydraulic system.

## MASTER CYLINDER OVERHAUL

**When disassembling the master cylinder, note the position of all parts as they are removed for proper installation.**

When disassembled, wash all parts in denatured alcohol or clean brake fluid only. Use an air hose to blow out all passages, orifices and valve holes. Air dry and place parts on clean paper or lint-free cloth.

Inspect master cylinder bore for scoring, rust, pitting or etching. Any of these conditions will require replacement of the housing. Never hone the bore of the master cylinder as this will remove the anodized surface. Inspect master cylinder pistons for scoring, pitting or distortion. Replace piston if any of these conditions exist. If either the master cylinder housing or piston is replaced, clean the new parts with denatured alcohol or clean brake fluid, and blow out all passages with air hose.

Examine reservoirs for foreign matter and check all passages for restrictions. If there is any indication of contamination or evidence of corrosion, service the hydraulic system as needed, and flush the entire system as described under "Hydraulic System Bleeding & Flushing."

When reassembling the master cylinder, use all parts contained in the repair kit. Dip all component parts in clean brake fluid, and place them on a clean surface. To prevent faulty operation, when installing seals inspect through side outlet of the dual master cylinder housing to make certain cup lips do not hang up on edge of hole or turn back. A piece of 3/16 inch rod with an end rounded off will be helpful in guiding cups past the hole.

# TYPE 2—RECESSED CARTRIDGE MASTER CYLINDER

## TROUBLESHOOTING

Refer to "Troubleshooting," in "Disc

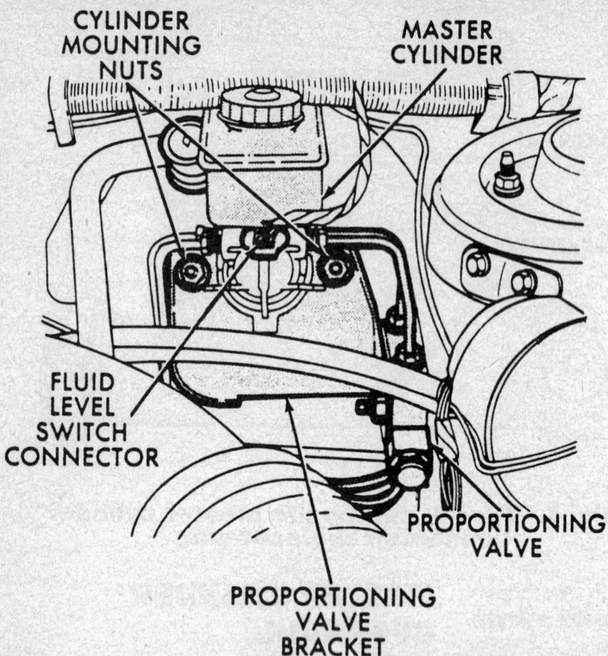


**Fig. 5 Type 2, master cylinder replacement**

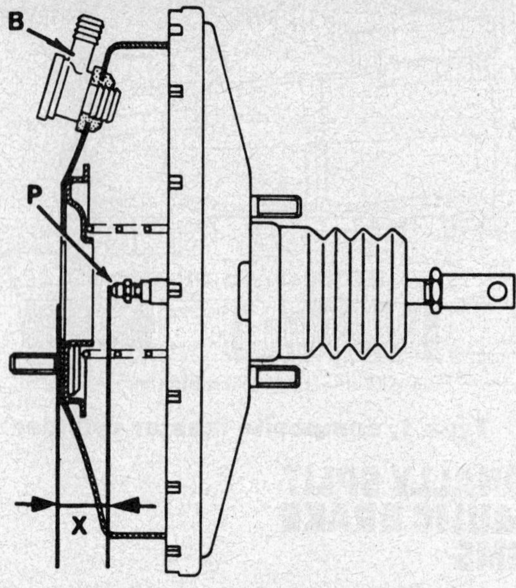


**Fig. 6 Brake booster pushrod depth adjustment. Medallion**

Brakes" for troubleshooting of the hydraulic brake system.

## MASTER CYLINDER, REPLACE

Refer to **Fig. 5,** when replacing master cylinder.

1. Position a drain pan under the master cylinder.
2. Disconnect electrical connector from reservoir, if equipped.
3. Loosen brake lines at top of the proportioning valve, then disconnect brake lines from the master cylinder. Plug all lines and fittings.
4. Remove master cylinder-to-brake booster attaching nuts.
5. Remove proportioning valve mounting bracket.
6. Pull master cylinder outward and away from brake booster.
7. Reverse procedure to install noting the following:
   a. Use caution during master cylinder to brake booster installation. The primary piston protrudes beyond the end cap, and may be damaged if not centered to the booster cavity.
   b. **Torque** brake lines to 11–15 ft. lbs., master cylinder to booster nuts to 9-13 ft. lbs. and proportioning valve bracket to 4-6 ft. lbs.
   c. Bleed hydraulic system as described under "Hydraulic System Bleeding & Flushing."

# TYPE 3—COMPOSITE MASTER CYLINDER

## TESTING

Refer to "Troubleshooting," in "Disc Brakes" for troubleshooting of the hydraulic brake system.

## MASTER CYLINDER, REPLACE

1. Disconnect brake fluid sensor electrical connector from master cylinder reservoir.
2. Position a drain pan under the master cylinder.
3. Remove brake fluid from reservoir.
4. Grasp reservoir by hand, then pull straight up to separate it from the housing.
5. Using a suitable wrench, disconnect brake lines from the master cylinder. Plug all lines and fittings.
6. Remove master cylinder-to-brake booster attaching nuts.
7. Pull master cylinder outward and away from brake booster. Discard booster-to-master cylinder O-ring at the back of the master cylinder.
8. Reverse procedure to install noting the following:
   a. Prior to master cylinder installation, adjust brake booster pushrod to a depth of .878 inch as shown **Fig. 6.**
   b. When installing the reservoir it should click into position when properly seated.
   c. **Torque** master cylinder-to-booster attaching nuts to 10 ft. lbs.
   d. **Torque** brake line fittings to 10 ft. lbs.
   e. Bleed hydraulic system as described under "Hydraulic System Bleeding & Flushing."

# TYPES 4, 5, 6, 7, 8 & 9—COMPOSITE MASTER CYLINDERS

## TESTING

Refer to "Troubleshooting," in "Disc Brakes" for troubleshooting of the hydraulic brake system.

## MASTER CYLINDER, REPLACE

1. **On Stealth models,** disconnect low-pressure hose.
2. **On all models,** disconnect brake fluid sensor electrical connector from master cylinder reservoir.
3. Position a drain pan under the master cylinder, then drain master cylinder.
4. **On models with separately mounted reservoir,** disconnect reservoir hoses from the master cylinder.
5. **On all models,** use a suitable wrench to disconnect brake lines from the master cylinder. Plug all lines and fittings.
6. Remove master cylinder-to-brake booster attaching nuts.
7. **On Colt, Colt Vista and Summit models,** remove proportioning valve.
8. **On all models,** pull master cylinder outward and away from brake booster.
9. Reverse procedure to install noting the following:
   a. Prior to master cylinder installation, check brake booster pushrod-to-primary piston clearance as described under "Adjustments," and adjust if necessary.
   b. Fill master cylinder reservoir, then bleed hydraulic system as described under "Hydraulic System Bleeding & Flushing."
   c. **On all models except Colt Vista and Conquest,** check adjustment of brake pedal as described under "Adjustments," and adjust if necessary.

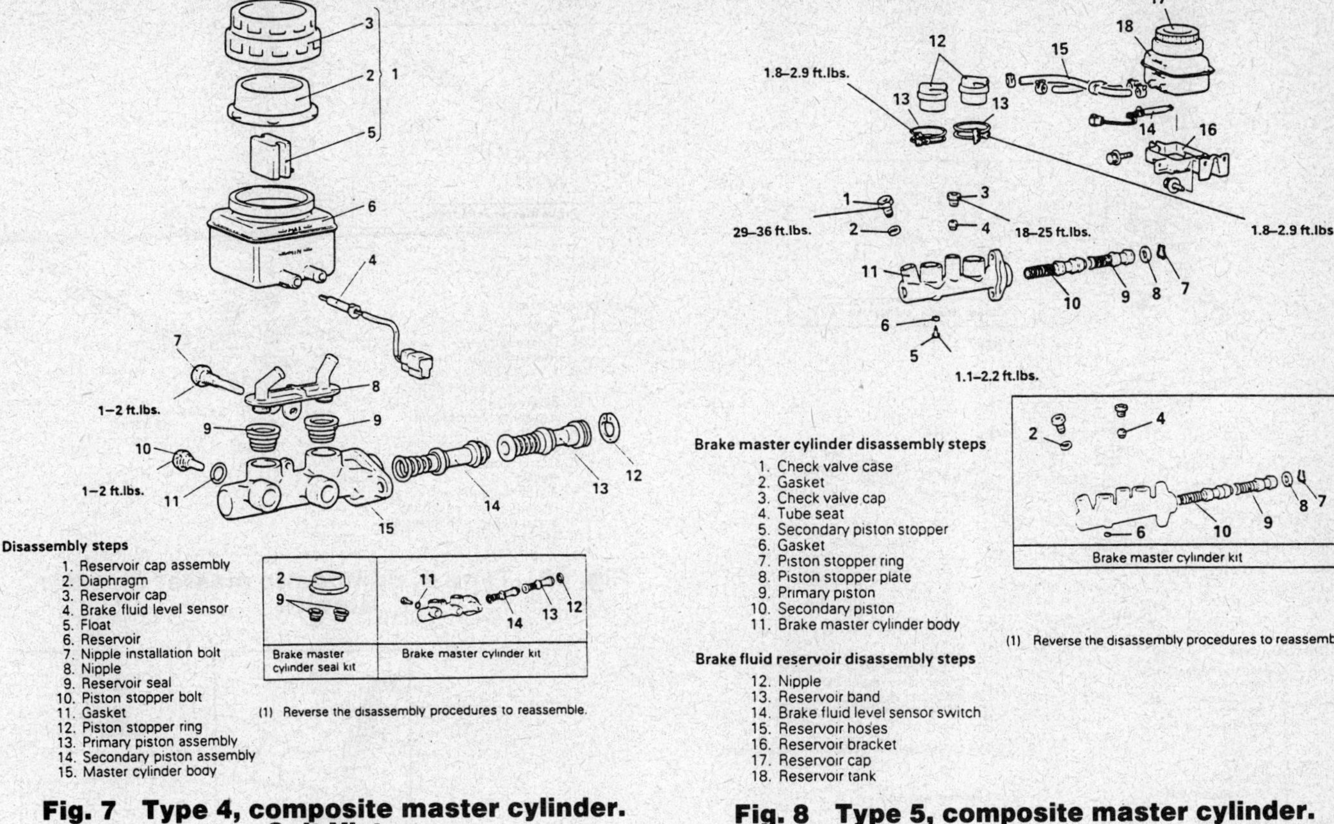


**Fig. 7 Type 4, composite master cylinder. Colt Vista**

**Fig. 8 Type 5, composite master cylinder.**

Brake master cylinder seal kit | Brake master cylinder kit

**Removal steps**

1. Brake fluid level sensor connector connection
2. Brake line connection
3. Reservoir holder assembly
   Adjustment of clearance between brake booster push rod and primary piston
4. Master cylinder
5. Reservoir cap
6. Diaphragm
7. Float
8. Reservoir
9. Nipple
10. Reservoir seal
11. Piston stopper bolt
12. Gasket
13. Piston stopper ring
14. Primary piston assembly
15. Secondary piston assembly

9–12 ft.lbs  1.1–2.2 ft.lbs.  6–9 ft.lbs.

(1) Reverse the removal procedures to reinstall.

**Fig. 9 Type 6, composite master cylinder.**

1–2 ft.lbs.  1–2 ft.lbs.

Brake master cylinder kit

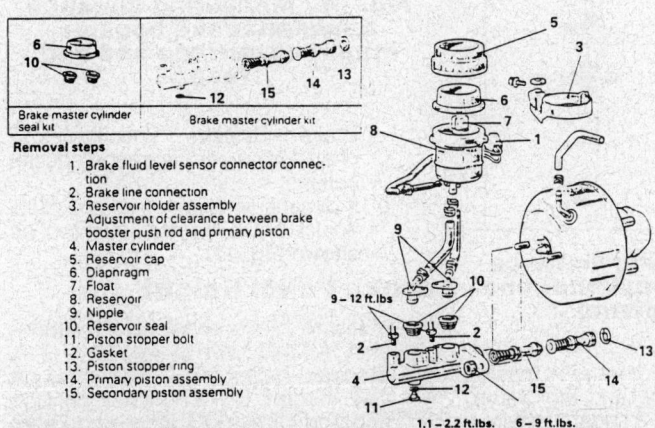

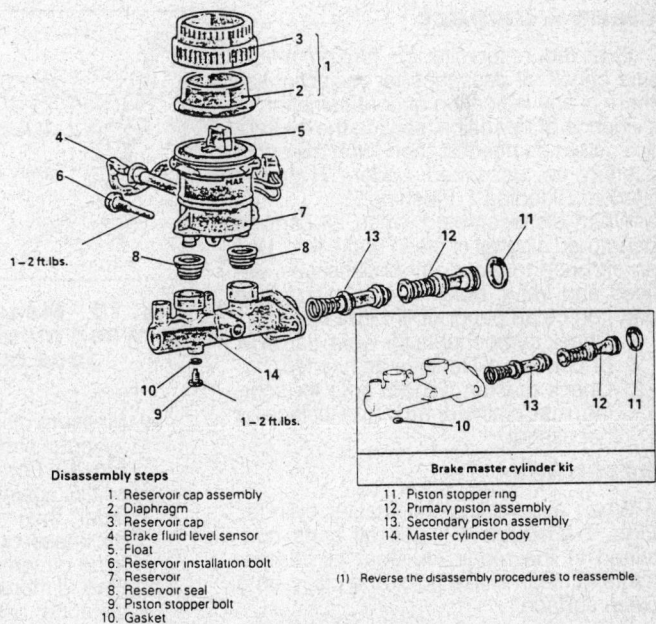

**Disassembly steps**

1. Reservoir cap assembly
2. Diaphragm
3. Reservoir cap
4. Brake fluid level sensor
5. Float
6. Reservoir installation bolt
7. Reservoir
8. Reservoir seal
9. Piston stopper bolt
10. Gasket
11. Piston stopper ring
12. Primary piston assembly
13. Secondary piston assembly
14. Master cylinder body

(1) Reverse the disassembly procedures to reassemble.

**Fig. 10 Type 7, composite master cylinder. Colt & Summit**

## MASTER CYLINDER OVERHAUL

When performing overhaul procedures, refer to **Figs. 7 through 12,**

### Disassembly

**When disassembling the master cylinder, note the position of all parts as they are removed for proper installation.**

1. Use a wooden stick or dowel to depress primary piston into cylinder bore.
2. With pushrod depressed, remove piston stopper bolt, then piston stopper ring.
3. Release pushrod, then remove piston assemblies. If secondary piston assembly is stuck in the bore, apply a light amount of compressed air to the secondary outlet port until piston assembly works free.

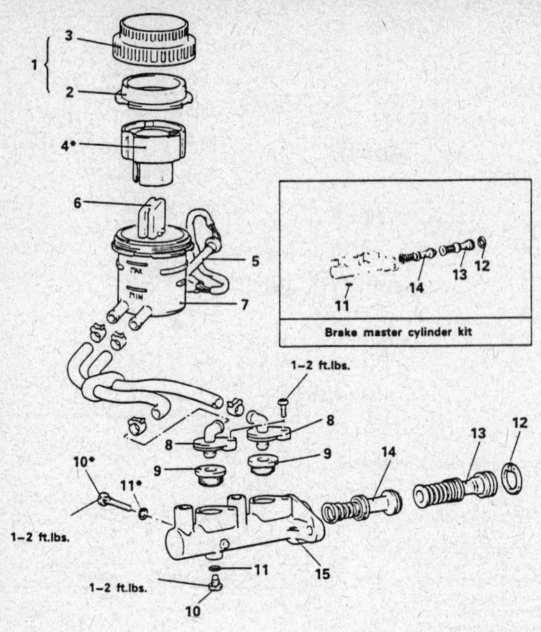


Disassembly steps

1. Reservoir cap assembly
2. Diaphragm
3. Reservoir cap
4. Filter
5. Brake fluid level sensor
6. Float
7. Reservoir
8. Nipple
9. Reservoir seal
10. Piston stopper bolt
11. Gasket
12. Piston stopper ring
13. Primary piston assembly
14. Secondary piston assembly
15. Master cylinder body

(1) Reverse the disassembly procedures to reassemble.

: Vehicles with ABS

**Fig. 11 Type 8, composite master cylinder. Laser & Talon**

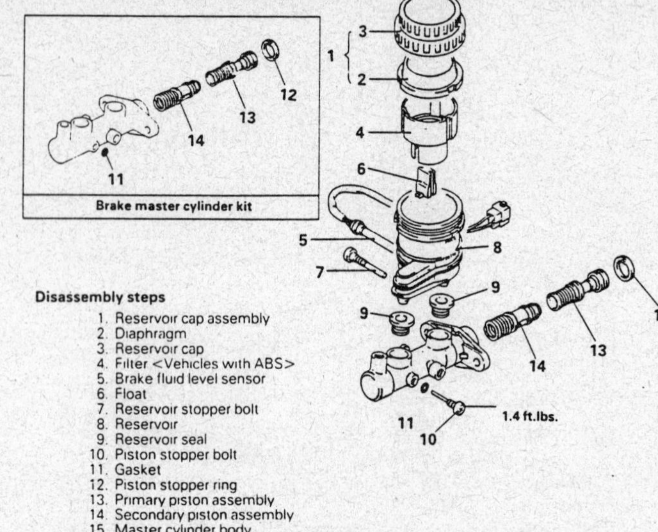


**Fig. 12 Type 9, composite master cylinder. Stealth**

## Clean & Inspect

Examine reservoirs for foreign matter and check all passages for restrictions. If there is any indication of contamination or evidence of corrosion, service the hydraulic system as needed, then flush the entire system as described under "Hydraulic System Bleeding & Flushing."

When disassembled, wash all parts in denatured alcohol or clean brake fluid. Use an air hose to blow out all passages, orifices and valve holes. Air dry and place parts on clean paper or lint-free cloth.

1. Check components for wear, damage, or corrosion. Replace as needed.
2. Check master cylinder bore for scoring, rust, pitting or etching. Replace as necessary.

## Assembly

When assembling the master cylinder, **Figs. 7 through 12,** use all parts contained in the repair kit. Coat all components in clean brake fluid, and place on a clean surface.

# ADJUSTMENTS

## Brake Booster Pushrod-To-Primary Piston Clearance

1. With master cylinder removed from vehicle, as described under "Master Cylinder Replace," proceed as follows:

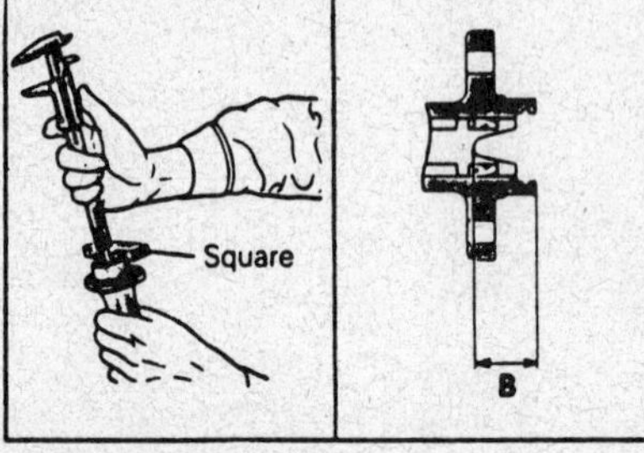


**Fig. 13 Measuring distance between master cylinder end face and piston**

a. Measure distance between master cylinder end face and the piston, **Fig. 13.** Position a square (straight scale) against edge of master cylinder, then measure and subtract thickness of the square to determine dimension B.
b. Find dimension C by measuring distance between brake booster mounting surface and the end face, **Fig. 14.**
c. Measure distance between master cylinder mounting surface and the pushrod end, **Fig. 15.** Find dimension D by subtracting the square's thickness from the measurement taken.
d. Find brake booster-to-primary piston clearance dimension A, **Fig. 16,** using the formula A = B–C–D. Refer to the "Hydraulic Brake System Specifications" chart for proper clearance specifications.
e. If dimension A is not as specified, adjust brake booster pushrod as shown **Fig. 17.**

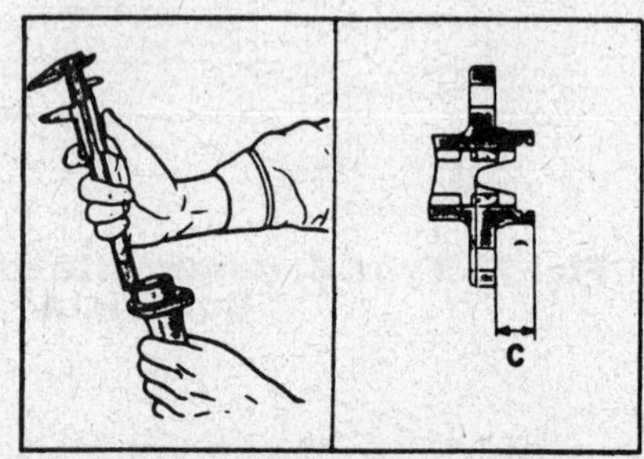


**Fig. 14 Measuring distance between brake booster mounting surface and end face**

## Brake Pedal Height

1. Measure brake pedal height dimension "A," as shown in **Fig. 18.**
2. Standard height is 6.2-6.4 inches on Colt Wagon, 6.6-6.7 inches on Colt and Summit, 6.9-7.1 inches on Laser and Talon, and 7.0-7.2 inches on Stealth.
3. If pedal height is not within standard, adjust as follows:
   a. Disconnect stop light switch electrical connector, then loosen locknut and move stop light switch to a position were it does not contact brake pedal arm.
   b. Adjust brake pedal height by turning operating rod with pliers, **Fig. 19,** until correct brake pedal height is obtained.
   c. **On Colt and Summit models,** remove clevis pin that connects master cylinder push rod and clutch pedal, then the nuts that secure clutch master cylinder, and

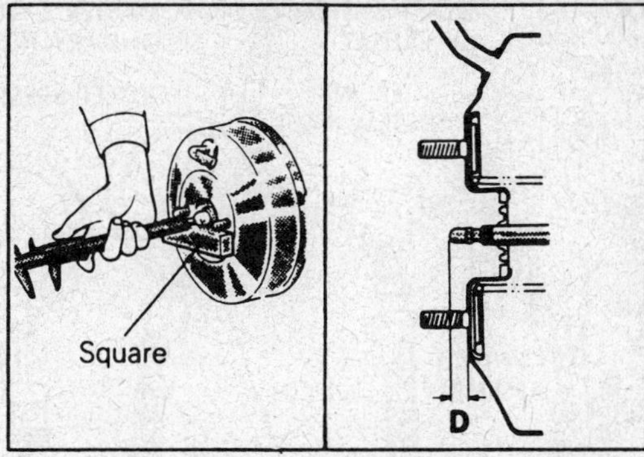


Fig. 15 Measuring distance between master cylinder mounting surface and pushrod end

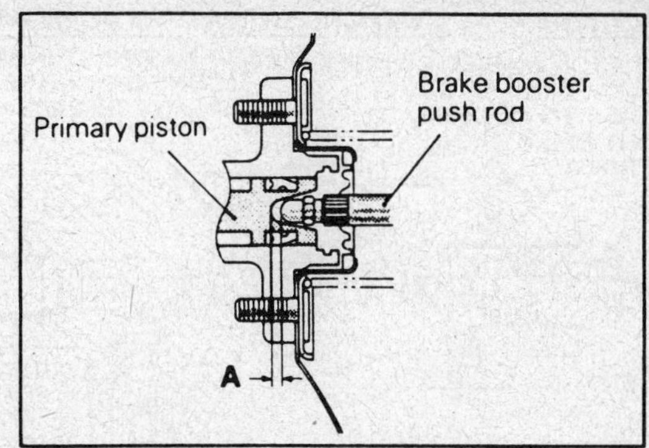


Fig. 16 Brake booster-to-primary piston clearance dimension A

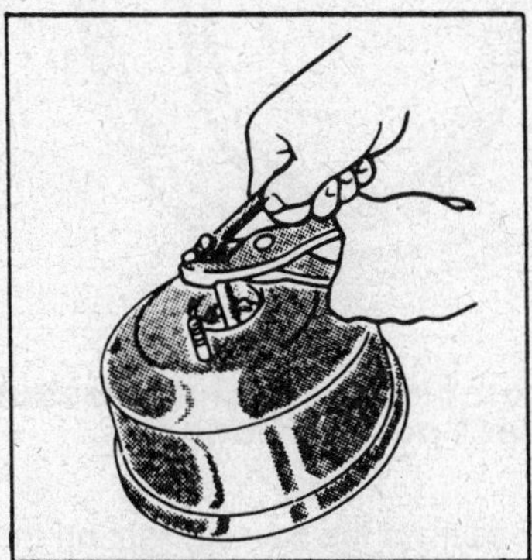

Fig. 17 Adjusting brake booster pushrod

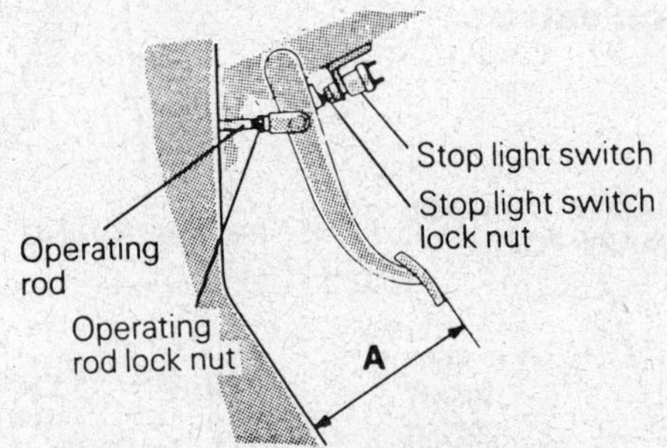


Fig. 18 Measuring brake pedal height dimension "A"

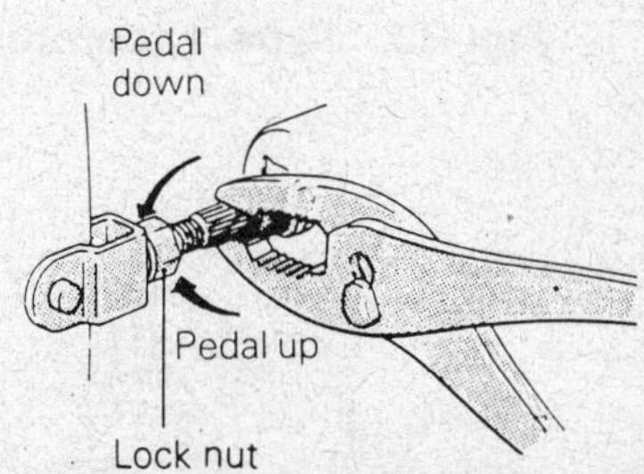


Fig. 19 Adjusting brake pedal height

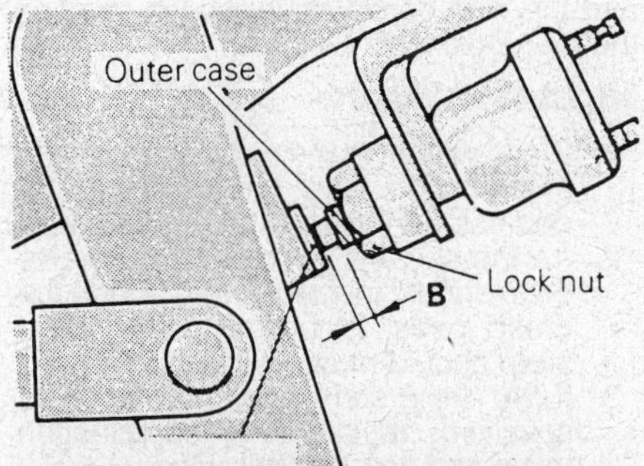


Fig. 20 Measuring stop light switch reference dimension "B"

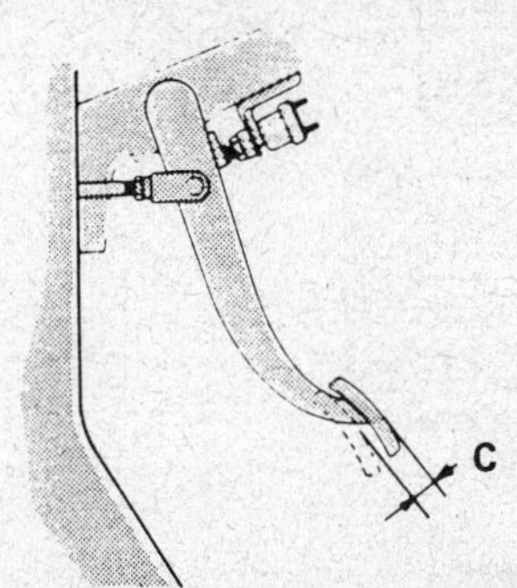


Fig. 21 Measuring brake pedal free play dimension "C"

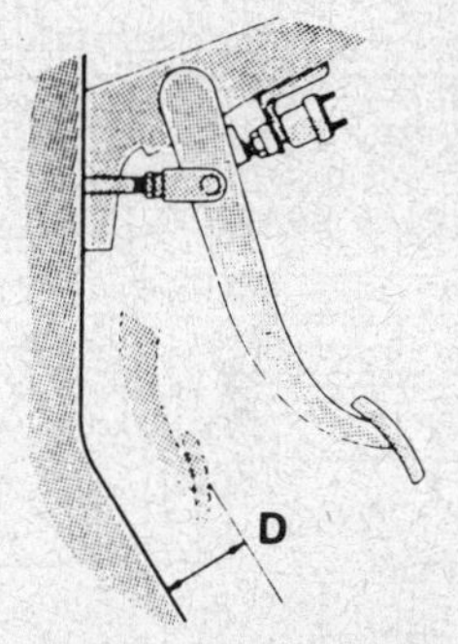


Fig. 22 Measuring clearance between brake pedal & floor board dimension "D"

pull master cylinder slightly toward engine compartment.

d. **On all models,** screw in stop light switch until it contacts brake pedal stopper, ensure that brake pedal does not move, then return stop light switch 1/2-1 turn and secure by tightening locknut.

e. Connect stop light switch electrical connector and ensure that stop light is not illuminated with brake pedal unpressed, then check reference dimension "B" as shown in **Fig. 20,** should be 0.02-0.04 inch.

f. **On 1991 models with shift lock mechanism,** check adjustment of shift lock after brake pedal height has been adjusted, refer to "Automatic Transaxles" section and adjust if necessary.

g. **On all models,** with engine stopped, depress brake pedal two or three times to eliminate vacuum in power brake booster, then press pedal down by hand and confirm that amount of free play, dimension "C," **Fig. 21,** before resistance is felt is within 0.1-0.3 inch on all models except Colt Wagon or 0.4-0.6 inch on Colt Wagon.

h. If free play is less than 0.1 inch, ensure that clearance between stop light switch and brake pedal is within specifications.

i. If free play is greater than 0.4 inch, it is probably due to excessive play between clevis pin and brake pedal arm. Check for excessive clearance and replace defective components as necessary.

j. Start engine, then depress brake pedal with approximately 110 lbs. of force and measure clearance dimension "D" between brake pedal and floorboard, **Fig. 22.** Clearance should be 3.1 inch or more.

k. If clearance is less than 3.1 inch, check for air trapped in brake lines, fluid leaks, excessive brake shoe clearance due to faulty self-adjusters and repair or replace defective components as necessary.

# HYDRAULIC BRAKE SYSTEM CONTROLS

## TYPE 1—COMBINATION VALVE

### DESCRIPTION

This valve assembly **Fig. 23,** is comprised of a warning switch, proportioning valve, and a hold-off valve.

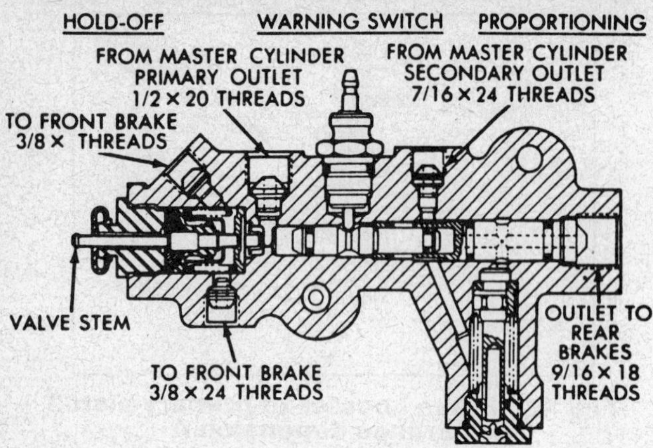


Fig. 23 Type 1, combination valve

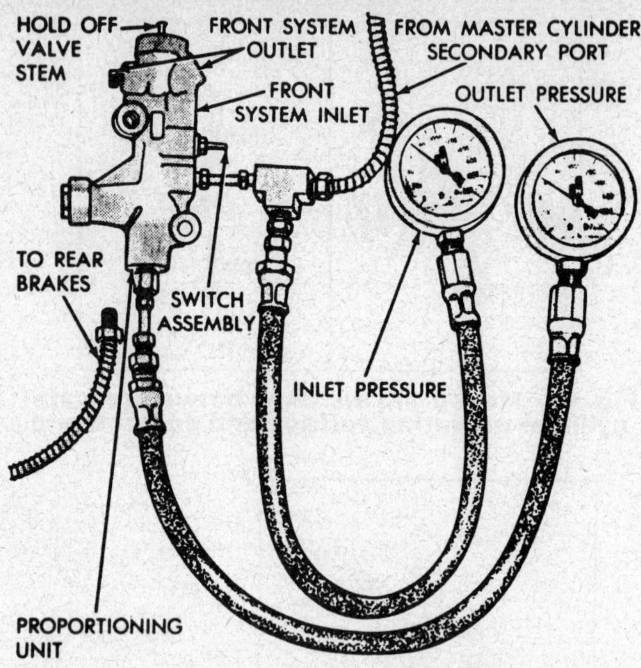


Fig. 24 Type 1, combination valve pressure gauge test connections

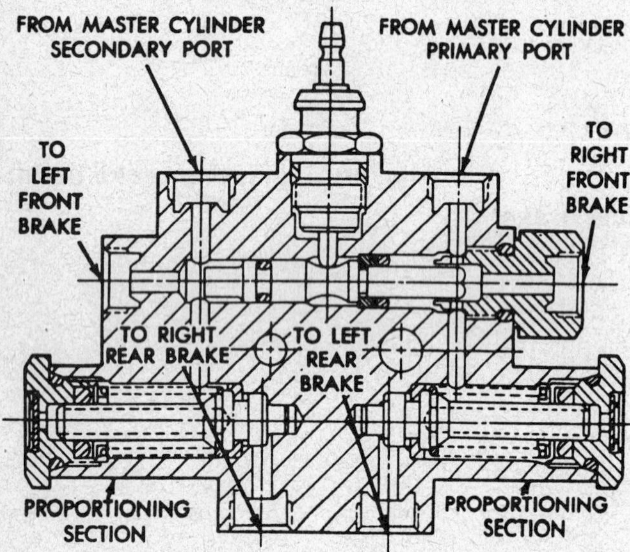


Fig. 25 Type 2, combination valve

The warning switch detects system failure when a pressure difference occurs between the front and rear brake systems. In such a case, the valve piston shuttles toward the side with the low pressure, forcing the switch plunger upward over the piston's tapered shoulder. This movement closes the switch contacts causing the brake warning lamp to illuminate. Upon restoration of equalized hydraulic system pressure the brake warning switch will reset.

The proportioning valve transfers full braking force to the rear brakes until a preset ratio called the split point is achieved. At this point the pressure increase is routed away from the rear brake system to prevent rear wheel lock-up.

The hold-off valve prevents front disc brake activation until the rear brake shoes can overcome return spring force, and achieve shoe to drum contact. The hold-off valve will not effect front brake pressure during hard stops, but will prevent front brake lock-up during light pedal application and on slippery road surfaces. This is achieved by keeping a low output pressure supplied to the front brakes until a preset hold-off pressure is achieved, wherein full output pressure is returned to the front brakes.

## TESTING

### Warning Light System

If the parking brake light is connected into the service brake warning light system, the brake warning light will flash only when the parking brake is applied with the ignition turned on. The same light will also glow should one of the two service brake systems fail when the brake pedal is applied.

To test the system, turn the ignition on and apply the parking brake. If the lamp fails to light, inspect for a burned out bulb, disconnected socket, a broken or disconnected wire at the switch.

To test the brake warning system, raise the car and open a wheel bleeder valve while a helper depresses the brake pedal and observes the warning light on the instrument panel. If the bulb fails to light, inspect for a burned out bulb, disconnected socket, or a broken or disconnected wire at the switch. If the bulb is not burned out, and the wire continuity is proven, replace the brake warning switch.

### Hold-Off Valve

1. While watching the valve stem on the combination valve, have an assistant depress and release the brake pedal.
2. As the pedal is depressed, the valve stem should move outward. When the brake pedal is released, the valve stem should move inward.
3. If the valve stem does not move as specified, replace the combination valve and note the following:
   a. After installing a new combination valve, bleed the hydraulic brake system as described under "Hydraulic Brake System Bleeding & Flushing."
   b. Upon completion of bleeding the hydraulic brake system, reset the brake warning switch by depressing the brake pedal with moderate force. The brake warning lamp will turn off when the switch is reset.

### Proportioning Valve

1. Install gauge set with T-fitting No. C-4007A, as shown in **Fig. 24.** Special adapter tubes may be fabricated from a short piece of brake tube, a 9/16 X 18 tube nut, and a 3/8 X 24 tube nut.
2. Bleed the hose and gauge set.
3. While watching pressure gauges, have an assistant depress the brake pedal. Note gauge readings, then refer to "Hydraulic Brake Controls Specifications" chart.

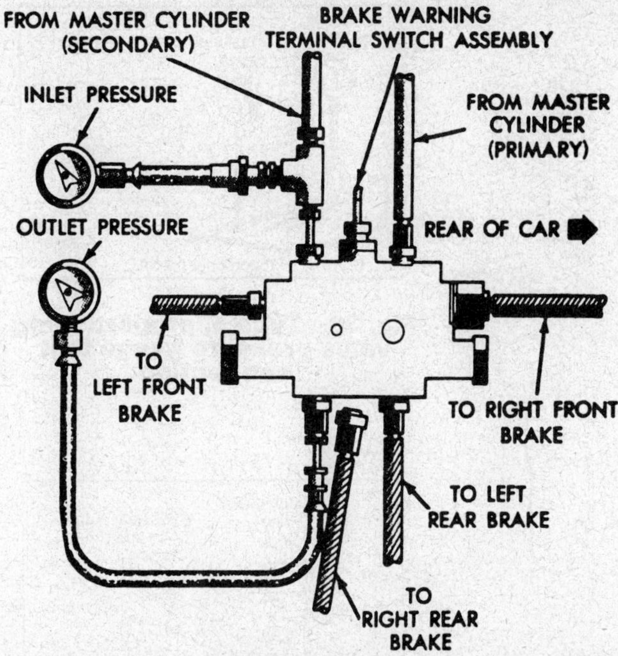


**Fig. 26 Type 2, combination valve pressure gauge test connections. Right wheel malfunction**

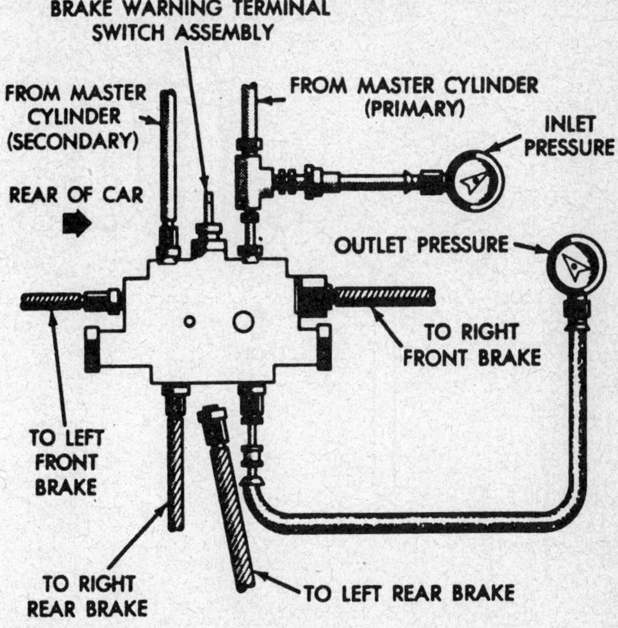


**Fig. 27 Type 2, combination valve pressure gauge test connections. Left wheel malfunction**

4. If pressure readings are not as specified, replace the combination valve and note the following:
   a. After installing a new combination valve, bleed the hydraulic brake system as described under "Hydraulic Brake System Bleeding & Flushing."
   b. Upon completion of bleeding the hydraulic brake system, reset the brake warning switch by depressing the brake pedal with moderate force. The brake warning lamp will turn off when the switch is reset.

## TYPE 2—COMBINATION VALVE

### DESCRIPTION

This valve assembly **Fig. 25,** is comprised of a warning switch, and a dual proportioning valve.

The warning switch detects system failure when a pressure difference occurs between the diagonally split systems. In such a case, the valve piston shuttles toward the side with the low pressure forcing the switch plunger upward over the piston's tapered shoulder. This movement closes the switch contacts causing the brake warning lamp to illuminate. Upon restoration of equalized system pressure the brake warning switch will reset.

The proportioning valve transfers full braking force to the rear brakes until a preset ratio called the split point is achieved. At this point the pressure increase is routed away from the rear brake system to prevent rear wheel lock-up.

### TESTING

#### Warning Light System

Refer to "Type 1—Combination Valve" for test procedure.

#### Proportioning Valve

**On vehicles with Bosch ABS-3, Bendix Anti-Lock 6 or Bendix Anti-Lock 10, refer to "Anti-Lock Brakes" section for "Testing" procedures.**

If premature rear wheel skid occurs on hard brake application, it could be an indication of a malfunctioning proportioning valve unit.

The proportioning valve is designed with two separate systems. One half controls the right rear brake, and the other half controls the left rear brake. A road test to determine which rear brake slides first must be performed.

1. To test proportioning valve when right rear wheel slides first, leave front brakes connected to valve, then proceed as follows:
   a. Install gauge set No. C-4007A, as shown in **Fig. 26.** A special adapter may be fabricated from a short piece of brake tube and two 3/8 X 24 tube nuts.
   b. Bleed the hose and gauge set.
   c. While watching pressure gauges, have an assistant depress the brake pedal. Note gauge readings, then refer to "Hydraulic Brake Controls Specifications" chart.
2. To test proportioning valve when left rear wheel slides first, leave front brakes connected to valve, then proceed as follows:
   a. Install gauge set No. C-4007A, as shown in **Fig. 27.** A special adapter may be fabricated from a 7/16 X 24 tube nut, a short piece of brake tube and a 3/8 X 24 tube nut.
   b. Bleed hose and gauge set.
   c. While watching pressure gauges, have an assistant depress the brake pedal. Note gauge readings, then refer to "Hydraulic Brake Controls Specifications" chart.
3. If pressure readings are not as specified for left or right rear wheel, replace the combination valve noting the following:
   a. After installing a new combination valve, bleed hydraulic brake system as described under "Hydraulic Brake System Bleeding & Flushing."
   b. Upon completion of bleeding hydraulic brake system, reset brake warning switch by depressing brake pedal with moderate force. Brake warning lamp will turn off when switch is reset.

## TYPE 3—COMPENSATOR LIMITER VALVE

### Description

This system utilizes a compensator limiter valve with a diagonally split hydraulic system. The compensator limiter valve is incorporated into the hydraulic system to control braking force to the rear brakes. The valve is body mounted, and connected to the rear axle by a control rod and link.

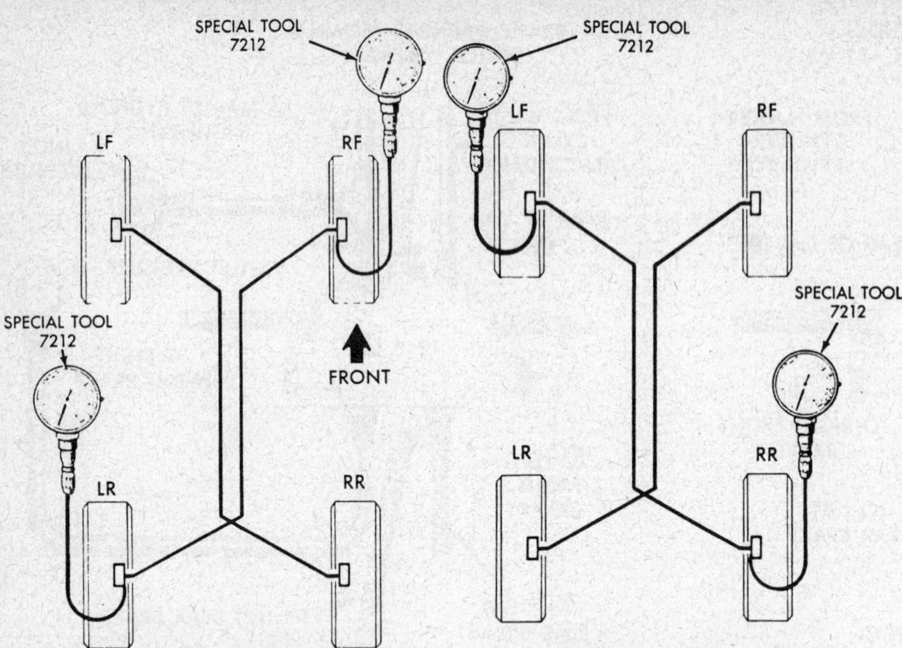


**Fig. 28 Type 3, compensator-limiter valve & Type 4, proportioning valve pressure gauge test connections. Right front & left rear**

**Fig. 29 Type 3, compensator-limiter valve & Type 4, proportioning valve pressure gauge test connections. Left front & right rear**

### Testing

1. Ensure that vehicle is unloaded, weight is on tires, one person is on board and fuel tank is full, also rear brake adjustment should be within specifications.
2. Remove bleed screws from right front caliper and left rear wheel cylinder or caliper.
3. Install pressure gauge 7212 or equivalent in each caliper or wheel cylinder in place of bleed screws as shown in **Fig. 28.**
4. Bleed air out through gauge bleed valves, then start engine and observe gauge readings while a helper applies brake pedal, refer to "Hydraulic Brake Controls Specifications" chart.
5. Stop engine, then remove pressure gauges and install bleed screws. Bleed right front caliper and left rear wheel cylinder or caliper prior to continuing, refer to "Hydraulic Brake System Bleeding & Flushing."
6. Remove bleed screws from left front caliper and right rear wheel cylinder or caliper.
7. Install pressure gauge 7212 or equivalent in each caliper or wheel cylinder in place of bleed screws as shown in **Fig. 29.**
8. Repeat steps 4 and 5, then if gauge readings are within specifications valve is operating properly, if not, replace valve.

## TYPE 4—PROPORTIONING VALVE

### Description

This system utilizes a proportioning valve with a diagonally split hydraulic system. The proportioning valve is incorporated into the hydraulic system to control braking force to the rear brakes.

### Testing

**On models with Bendix Anti-Lock 10, refer to "Anti-Lock Brakes" section for "Testing" procedures.**

Refer to "Type 3—Compensator Limiter Valve" for test procedure.

## TYPE 5—PROPORTIONING VALVE

### Testing

1. Install suitable pressure gauges, one each on input side and output side of proportioning valve as shown in **Fig. 30.**
2. Bleed brake line and pressure gauge, then gradually depress brake pedal and observe gauge readings. Refer to "Hydraulic Brake Controls Specifications" chart.
3. Observe left and right output pressures, pressure difference between left and right should not be greater than 57 psi.
4. If gauge readings are not within specifications, replace proportioning valve.

## TYPE 6—LOAD SENSING PROPORTIONING VALVE

Prior to performing the following test procedures, park vehicle on a level surface, ensure vehicle is unloaded and at normal curb height.

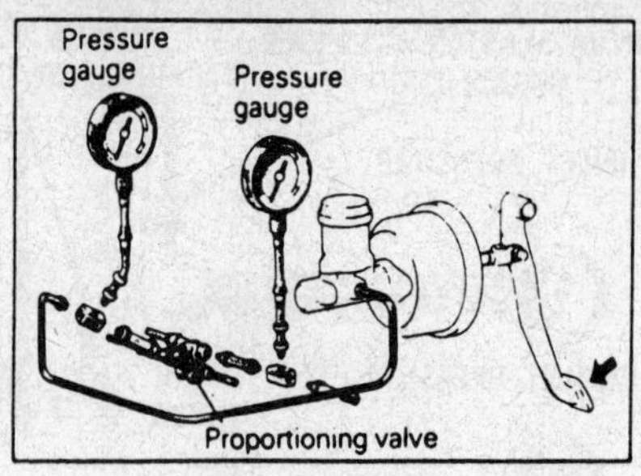


**Fig. 30 Type 5, proportioning valve pressure gauge test connection**

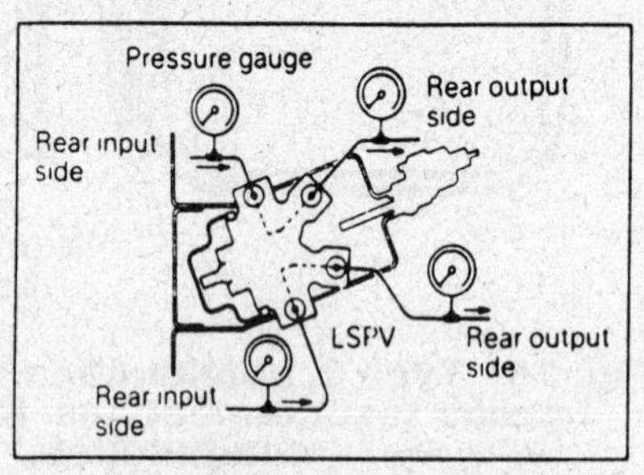


**Fig. 31 Type 6, load sensing proportioning valve pressure gauge test connection**

### TESTING

### Colt Vista

1. Install suitable gauge set as shown in **Fig. 31.**
2. Bleed hose and gauge set.
3. Loosen load sensing unit adjusting nuts, **Fig. 32.**
4. While watching pressure gauges, have an assistant depress the brake pedal.
5. Gauge pressure reading should be as follows:
   a. When input pressure is 740 psi, output pressure should read 307-377 psi.
   b. When input pressure is 1991 psi, output pressure should read 660-774 psi.
   c. Output pressure side to side difference should not exceed 57 psi.
6. If pressure readings are as specified proceed to step 7. If pressure readings are not as specified, replace the proportioning valve and bleed the hydraulic brake system as described under "Hydraulic Brake System Bleeding & Flushing."
7. Adjust load sensing spring distance L to 4.07 inch, **Fig. 32.**
8. While watching pressure gauges, have an assistant depress the brake pedal.
9. Gauge pressure reading should be as follows:
   a. When input pressure is 1991 psi, output pressure should read 1228-1580.

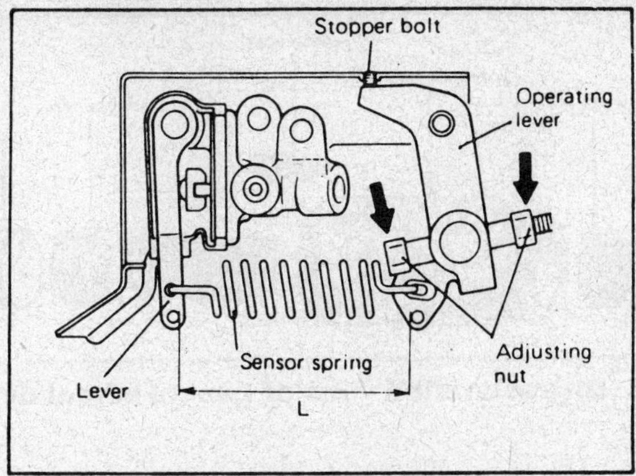

Fig. 32 Type 5, load sensing proportioning valve sensor spring. Colt Vista

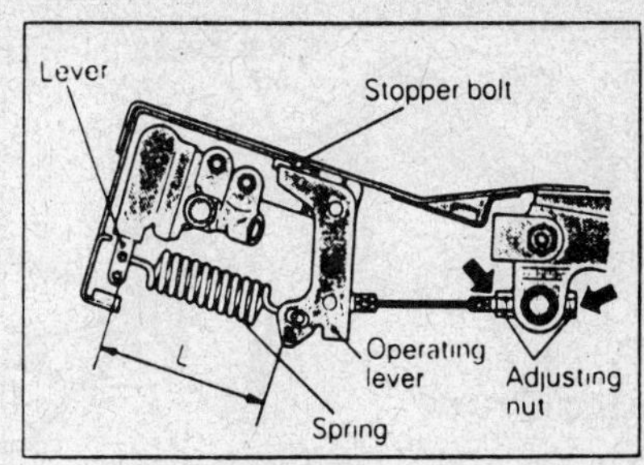

Fig. 33 Type 5, load sensing proportioning valve sensor spring. Colt Wagon 2WD

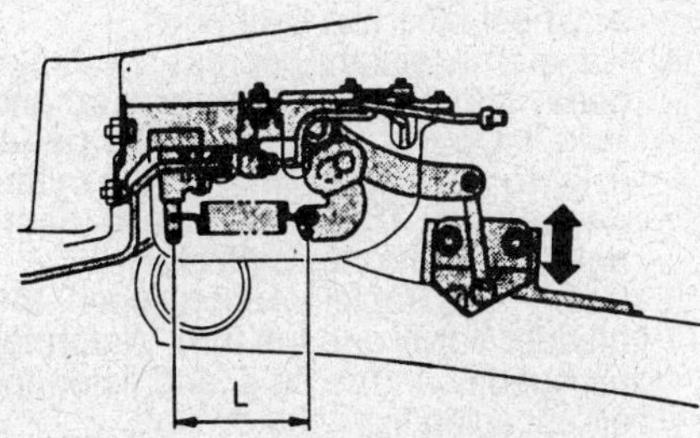

Fig. 34 Type 5, load sensing proportioning valve sensor spring. Colt Wagon 4WD

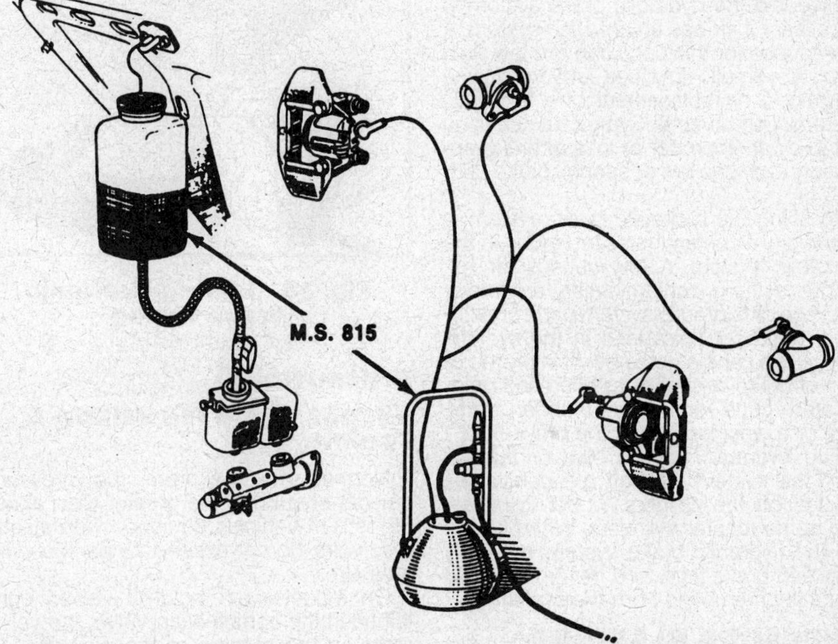

Fig. 35 Power bleeding brakes. Eagle Medallion & Premier

b. Output pressure side to side difference should not exceed 121 psi.

10. If pressure readings are as specified, proceed to step 11. If pressure readings are not as specified, replace the proportioning valve and bleed the hydraulic brake system as described under "Hydraulic Brake System Bleeding & Flushing."
11. Adjust load sensing spring distance L to 3.42-3.50 inch, **Fig. 32.**

## Colt Wagon

1. Install suitable gauge set as shown in **Fig. 31.**
2. Bleed the hose and gauge set.
3. **On 2WD models,** loosen load sensing unit adjusting nuts, **Fig. 33.**
4. **On 4WD models,** loosen mounting brackets to free operating lever, **Fig 34.**
5. **On all models,** while watching pressure gauges, have an assistant depress the brake pedal.
6. Gauge pressure reading should be as follows:
   a. When input pressure is 889 psi, output pressure should read 455-526 psi.
   b. When input pressure is 1991 psi, output pressure should read 765-879 psi.
   c. Output pressure side to side difference should not exceed 57 psi.
7. If pressure readings are as specified proceed to steps 9 or 10 as applicable.
8. If pressure readings are not as specified, replace the proportioning valve and bleed the hydraulic brake system as described under "Hydraulic Brake System Bleeding & Flushing."
9. **On 2WD models,** adjust load sensing spring distance L to 4.10 inch, **Fig. 33.**
10. **On 4WD models,** adjust load sensing spring distance L to 3.97 inch, **Fig. 34.**
11. **On all models,** while watching pressure gauges, have an assistant depress the brake pedal.
12. **On 2WD models,** gauge pressure reading should be as follows:
    a. When input pressure is 1991 psi, output pressure should read 1254-1496 psi.
    b. Output pressure side to side difference should not exceed 121 psi.
13. **On 4WD models,** gauge pressure reading should be as follows:
    a. When input pressure is 1991 psi, output pressure should read 1249-1491 psi.
    b. Output pressure side to side difference should not exceed 121 psi.
14. **On all models,** if pressure readings are as specified, proceed to steps 16 or 17 as applicable.
15. If pressure readings are not as specified, replace the proportioning valve and bleed the hydraulic brake system as described under "Hydraulic Brake System Bleeding & Flushing."
16. **On 2WD models,** adjust load sensing spring distance L to 3.51-3.59 inch, **Fig. 33.**
17. **On 4WD models,** Adjust load sensing spring distance L to 3.47-3.55 inch, **Fig. 34.**

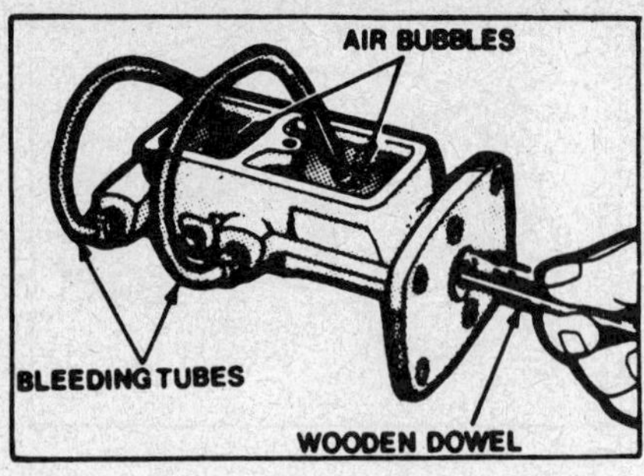


**Fig. 36 Common means of bench bleeding a master cylinder**

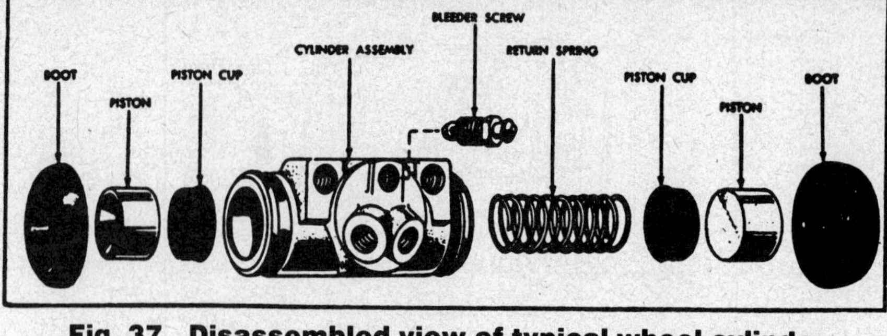


**Fig. 37 Disassembled view of typical wheel cylinder**

# HYDRAULIC SYSTEM BLEEDING & FLUSHING

## DESCRIPTION

Bleeding the hydraulic brake system is necessary if air has entered the system. A few causes for this condition are low fluid level, a hydraulic fluid leak, a hydraulic line is opened, or replacement of a hydraulic system component. Symptoms can be noted by an improper or loss of brake operation, and/or a low or spongy brake pedal.

Flushing the hydraulic brake system is necessary if contaminates are found in the hydraulic system. A few causes for hydraulic system contamination are moisture, age of hydraulic system parts and fluid, or improper fluid used in the system. Symptoms can be noted by an improper or loss of brake operation, swollen and deteriorated cups and other rubber parts, and/or a discoloration of the brake fluid.

The hydraulic fluid is bled or flushed from the system through bleeder valves located on the calipers, wheel cylinders, and some master cylinders. When bleeding the hydraulic brake system, use only specified brake fluid, and never reuse old brake fluid removed from the system.

## PRESSURE BLEEDING

Pressure bleeding is recommended for all hydraulic brake systems. It is the fastest method because the master cylinder is automatically fed brake fluid from the pressure bleeder reservoir, and no pedal pumping is needed so only one person is required to perform the procedure. However, if pressure bleeding equipment is not available, the hydraulic system may be bled as described under "Manual Bleeding."

When pressure bleeding, to prevent air from getting into the hydraulic system, do not shake the pressure tank. Set the tank in the required location, bring the air hose to the tank, and do not move it during the bleeding operation. The tank should be kept at least one-third full.

The bleeder valve should be opened at least one full turn, and intermittently closed at about four-second intervals. This gives a whirling action to fluid in the hydraulic system, and helps expel the air. Refer to "Hydraulic Brake System Specifications" chart for proper wheel bleeding sequence.

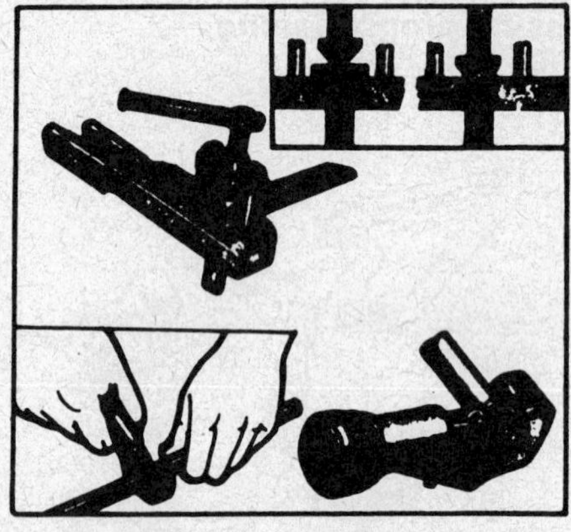

**Fig. 38 Flaring hydraulic brake tubing**

### Precautions

### Except Eagle Medallion & Premier

Normal pressure from the pressure bleeder should not be greater than about 35 psi. On vehicles equipped with plastic reservoirs, do not exceed 25 psi bleeding pressure.

On models with hold-off valves contained in the combination valve, the valve stem on the outside of the combination valve must be held in position during bleeding using valve holding tool No. C-4121 or equivalent.

### Eagle Medallion & Premier

Use brake bleeding apparatus M.S.815 as shown, **Fig. 35.** When bleeding the hydraulic brake system, always support rear wheels at their normal curb height, and never start the engine. Open fluid feed valve until reservoir is full, then turn on compressed air to a minimum pressure of 73 psi. Upon completion, fill reservoir as needed.

## MANUAL BLEEDING

On models with power brakes, if bleeding the hydraulic system without the engine running, first reduce vacuum in the power unit to zero by pumping the brake pedal several times with the engine off.

1. Ensure master cylinder reservoir is full. Add suitable brake fluid as needed, and securely reinstall the master cylinder cap.
2. Raise and support vehicle.
3. Position a drain pan under the wheel being bled. Refer to "Hydraulic Brake System Specifications" chart for proper wheel bleeding sequence.
4. Have an assistant depress the brake pedal with a slow even pressure and hold it. **Do not depress brake pedal fully to the end of the master cylinder stroke. This may cause damage to the master cylinder.**
5. Using a suitable wrench, open the bleeder valve one full turn. Watch for air bubbles in the fluid, and listen for air escaping from the system.
6. With the brake pedal still depressed, close the bleeder valve.
7. Have the assistant pump the brake pedal several times. **Do not depress brake pedal fully to the end of the master cylinder stroke, this may cause damage to the master cylinder.**
8. Repeat steps 4 through 7 following the wheel bleeding sequence specified in "Hydraulic Brake System Specifications" chart. Ensure all air is removed from the hydraulic system. **While bleeding the system, recheck brake fluid supply in the master cylinder often so as not to allow the master cylinder to run dry.**
9. Upon completion of hydraulic system bleeding proceed as follows:
   a. Ensure the master cylinder reservoir is full. Add suitable brake fluid as needed, and securely reinstall the master cylinder cap.
   b. Lower the vehicle. Ensure brake pedal is firm and braking operation is proper.

# BLEEDING MASTER CYLINDER

Refer to "Bench Bleeding" procedure first if the master cylinder has been removed from the vehicle for service or replacement.

## ON-VEHICLE SERVICE

Master cylinders may be bled manually or by pressure bleeding. It is recommended that the master cylinder be bled before bleeding the wheel cylinders and calipers.

### Pressure Bleeding

1. Ensure master cylinder reservoir is full. Add suitable brake fluid as needed.
2. Install pressure bleeder according to manufacturer specifications.
3. Position a drain pan under the master cylinder.
4. Loosen brake lines, or bleeder valves if equipped, at the master cylinder. Watch for air bubbles in the fluid and listen for air escaping from the system.
5. Retighten brake lines or bleeder valves.
6. Bleed the master cylinder until all air is removed. Upon completion of bleeding, proceed as follows:
   a. Ensure the master cylinder reservoir is full. Add suitable brake fluid as needed, and securely reinstall the master cylinder cap.
   b. Ensure brake pedal is firm, and braking operation is proper.

### Manual Bleeding

1. Ensure master cylinder reservoir is full. Add suitable brake fluid as needed, and securely reinstall the master cylinder cap.
2. Position a drain pan under the master cylinder.
3. Have an assistant depress the brake pedal with a slow even pressure and hold it. **Do not depress brake pedal fully to the end of the master cylinder stroke. This may cause damage to the master cylinder.**
4. Loosen the brake lines, or bleeder valves if equipped, at the master cylinder. Watch for air bubbles in the fluid and listen for air escaping from the system. **While bleeding the system, recheck brake fluid supply in the master cylinder often so as not to allow the master cylinder to run dry.**
5. With brake pedal still depressed, tighten the brake lines or bleeder valves.
6. Bleed the master cylinder until all air is removed. Upon completion of bleeding, proceed as follows:
   a. Ensure the master cylinder reservoir is full. Add suitable brake fluid as needed, and securely reinstall the master cylinder cap.
   b. Ensure brake pedal is firm, and braking operation is proper.

### BENCH BLEEDING

**When replacing or overhauling a master cylinder it is advisable to bleed it before installing it on the car.**

1. Properly support master cylinder assembly and attach special bleeding tubes as shown in, **Fig. 36.**
2. Fill reservoir with approved brake fluid.
3. Using a wooden stick or dowel (cars with power brakes) depress pushrod slowly and allow the pistons to return under pressure of the springs. Do this several times until all air bubbles are expelled.
4. Remove bleeding tubes from cylinder and install cover and gasket.
5. Install master cylinder onto vehicle as described under "Master Cylinder, Replace."
6. Bleed the entire hydraulic system as described previously.

### Precautions

**Combination valves containing brake warning or pressure differential type valves** are self-centering. They will reset after hydraulic system pressure is equalized, and by doing the following: Upon completion of bleeding the hydraulic system, depress the brake pedal with moderate force. The brake warning lamp will turn off when the switch is recentered.

## WHEEL CYLINDERS SERVICE

### REMOVAL

1. Remove wheel, drum and brake shoes.
2. Loosen brake line fitting at wheel cylinder. Do not pull metal line away from cylinder.
3. Remove screws holding cylinder to backing plate.
4. Separate wheel cylinder from brake line and backing plate by pulling the cylinder outward and away from backing plate.

### OVERHAUL

Note position of all parts as they are removed for proper installation.

#### Disassembly

1. Refer to **Fig. 37,** then remove boots, pistons, cups and spring from wheel cylinder.
2. Wipe cylinder walls with denatured alcohol or clean brake fluid.
3. Examine cylinder bore. A scored bore may be honed providing the bore diameter is not increased more than .005 inch. Replace as necessary.
4. Check pistons for wear or damage. Replace as necessary.

#### Assembly

1. Before assembling, wash hands with soap and water so as not to contaminate rubber parts.
2. Use all parts contained in repair kit. Lubricate cylinder wall and rubber cups with brake fluid.
3. Properly install spring, cups, pistons and boots in housing.

### INSTALLATION

1. Wipe end of hydraulic line to remove any foreign matter.
2. Position wheel cylinder to backing plate. Install brake line to cylinder and start connecting fitting.
3. Secure wheel cylinder to backing plate, then complete tightening of brake line fitting.
4. Install brake shoes, drum and wheel.
5. Bleed system as outlined previously, and adjust brakes.

## HYDRAULIC TUBING SERVICE

**Never use copper tubing as a replacement for steel tubing. Copper tubing is subject to fatigue cracking and corrosion which could result in brake system failure.**

Steel tubing is used to transfer hydraulic pressure to the brakes. All fittings, tubing and hose should be inspected for rust, damage or defective flared seats. The tubing is equipped with a double flare/inverted seat or I.S.O. flare to insure more positive seating in the fitting.

### DOUBLE FLARE/INVERTED SEAT

1. Using the tool shown in **Fig. 38** or equivalent, cut off the damaged seat or damaged tubing.
2. Ream out any burrs or rough edges showing on inside edges of tubing. This will make the ends of the tubing square and insure better seating on the flared end. Before flaring tubing, place a compression nut on tubing.
3. Open handles of flaring tool and rotate jaws of tool until mating jaws of tubing size are centered in the area between vertical posts.
4. Slowly close handles with tubing inserted in jaws but do not apply heavy pressure to handle as this will lock tubing in place.
5. Referring to **Fig. 38,** place gauge on edge over end of tubing and push tubing through jaws until end of tubing contacts recessed notch of gauge matching size of tubing.
6. Squeeze handles of flaring tool and lock tubing in place.
7. Place proper size plug of gauge down in end of tubing. Swing compression disc over gauge and center tapered flaring screw in recess in disc.
8. Lubricate taper of flaring or screw and screw in until plug gauge has seated in jaws of flaring tool. This action has started to invert the extended end of tubing.
9. Remove gauge and apply lubricant to tapered end of flaring screw and continue to screw down until tool is firmly seated in tubing.
10. Remove tubing from flaring tool and inspect the seat. If seat is cracked, cut off cracked end and repeat flaring operation.

# HYDRAULIC BRAKE SYSTEM SPECIFICATIONS

| Year | Model | Master Cylinder Bore Dia. Inch | Booster to Primary Piston Clearance Inch | Wheel Bleeding Sequence |
|---|---|---|---|---|
| 1989 | Chrysler RWD | 1.031 | — | RR,LR,RF,LF |
| | Conquest | .940 | .028-.043 | RR,LR,Modulator,RF,LF |
| | Eagle Medallion | .810 | .878 | — |
| | Eagle Premier | .944 | — | RR,LR,RF,LF |
| 1989-90 | Chrysler FWD | .826 | — | — |
| | Colt & Eagle Summit | ① | ② | LR,RF,RR,LF |
| | Colt Wagon | .870 | .004-.020 | LR,RF,RR,LF |
| 1989-91 | Colt Vista | .875 | ③ | LR,RF,RR,LF |
| 1990 | Laser & Eagle Talon | ④ | ⑤ | RR,LF,LR,RF |
| 1990-91 | Monaco & Eagle Premier | .944 | — | RR,LR,RF,LF |
| 1991 | Chrysler FWD | ⑥ | — | — |
| | Colt & Eagle Summit Hatchback | .8125 | .020-.028 | LR,RF,RR,LF |
| | Eagle Summit Sedan | .8750 | .024-.031 | LR,RF,RR,LF |
| | Eagle Talon AWD⑦ | 1.00 | .020-.028 | RR,LF,LR,RF |
| | Laser & Eagle Talon FWD⑦ | .9375 | .020-.028 | RR,LF,LR,RF |
| | Laser & Eagle Talon FWD⑧ | .8750 | .031-.039 | RR,LF,LR,RF |
| | Stealth AWD | 1.0625 | .026-.033 | RR,LF,LR,RF |
| | Stealth FWD | 1.00 | .022-.030 | RR,LF,LR,RF |

①—Models w/1.5L engine, .8125 inch; models w/1.6L engine, .8750 inch.

②—Models w/7 inch booster, .020–.028 inch; models w/8 inch booster, .024–.031 inch.

③—At 0 psi, .016–.031 inch; at 10 psi, .004–.020 inch.

④—Non turbo models, .8750 inch; turbo models, .9375 inch.

⑤—Non turbo models, .031–.039 inch; turbo models, .020–.028 inch.

⑥—.826, .875 & .944 inch.

⑦—Turbo models.

⑧—Non turbo models.

## HYDRAULIC BRAKE CONTROLS SPECIFICATIONS

| Year | Model | Valve Identification | Valve Tag Color ① | Split Point psi/Slope | Hold-Off Cut-In psi | Inlet Pressure psi From Master Cylinder | Outlet Pressure psi To Rear Brakes |
|---|---|---|---|---|---|---|---|
| 1989 | Aries & Reliant | ② | Tan | 600/.43 | — | 1000 | 725-825 |
| | Chrysler RWD | ③ | Black | 300/.27 | 117 | 1000 | 430-550 |
| | Colt | ④ | — | 420-491 | — | 1024 | 590-661 |
| | Conquest | ④ | — | 519-619 | — | 996 | 696-795 |
| | Eagle Medallion Sedan | ⑤ | — | — | — | 1450 | 566-624 |
| | Eagle Medallion Wagon | ⑤ | — | — | — | 1450 | 638-696 |
| | Eagle Premier | ④ | — | — | — | 1200 | 557-677 |
| | Lancer & Lebaron GTS | ② | White | 750/.43 | — | 1000 | 800-900 |
| | New Yorker | ② | Black | 800/.59 | — | 1000 | 875-950 |
| 1989–90 | Colt Wagon | ⑥ | — | 320 | — | — | ⑦ |
| | Colt Wagon 4WD | ⑥ | — | 320 | — | — | ⑧ |
| | Daytona ⑨ | ② | Tan | 600/.43 | — | 1000 | 725-825 |
| | Daytona ⑩ | ② | Yellow | 400/.43 | — | 1000 | 600-700 |
| | Dynasty & New Yorker Landau | ② | Black | 800/.59 | — | 1000 | 875-950 |
| | Horizon & Omni | ② | Gray | 500/.27 | — | 1000 | 575-700 |
| | Lebaron Except GTS ⑨ | ② | Gray | 600/.43 | — | 1000 | 725-825 |
| | Lebaron Except GTS ⑩ | ② | Yellow | 400/.43 | — | 1000 | 600-70 0 |
| | Shadow & Sundance | ② | Gray | 500/.27 | — | 1000 | 575-700 |
| | Shadow & Sundance | ② | Tan | 600/.43 | — | 1000 | 725-825 |
| 1989–91 | Colt Vista | ⑥ | — | — | — | — | ⑪ |
| | Colt Vista 4WD | ④ | — | 562-632 | — | 1166 | 733-803 |
| | Eagle Summit Sedan | ④ | — | 420-491 | — | 1024 | 590-661 |
| 1990 | Acclaim, LeBaron Landau & Spirit | ② | Tan | 600/.43 | — | 1000 | 725-825 |
| | Eagle Talon AWD | ④ | — | 562-633 | — | 1163 | 789-860 |
| | New Yorker Salon | ② | Black | 800/.59 | — | 1000 | 875-950 |
| 1990–91 | Colt | ④ | — | 348-420 | — | 953 | 519-590 |
| | Laser & Eagle Talon FWD | ④ | — | 562-633 | — | 1163 | 732-804 |
| | Monaco Except LE & Eagle Premier ⑫ | ④ | — | 300/.37 | — | 2000 | 710-810 |
| | Monaco LE ⑬ | ④ | — | 430/.37 | — | 2000 | 950-1070 |
| 1991 | Acclaim, LeBaron Landau & Spirit ⑭ | ② | Tan | 300/.43 | — | — | — |
| | Acclaim, LeBaron Landau & Spirit ⑮ | ② | Yellow | 400/.43 | — | 1000 | 600-700 |
| | Daytona | ② | Yellow | 400/.43 | — | 1000 | 600-700 |
| | Dynasty & New Yorker/Salon | ② | Black | 500/.59 | — | 1000 | 725-850 |
| | Eagle Summit Hatchback | ④ | — | 348-420 | — | 953 | 519-590 |
| | Eagle Talon AWD | ④ | — | 491-561 | — | 1095 | 661-732 |
| | Fifth Avenue & Imperial | ② | Black | 500/.59 | — | 1000 | 725-850 |
| | Lebaron Except Landau | ② | Yellow | 400/.43 | — | 1000 | 600-700 |
| | Shadow & Sundance | ② | Yellow | 400/.43 | — | 1000 | 600-700 |
| | Stealth AWD | ④ | — | 533-604 | — | 1138 | 744-815 |
| | Stealth FWD | ④ | — | 533-604 | — | 1138 | 744-815 |

① —Color tag located under boot of valve stem.
② —Differential-Proportioning Valve.
③ —Brake Warning, Proportioning & Hold-Off Valve assembly.
④ —Proportioning Valve.
⑤ —Compensator-Limiter Valve.
⑥ —Load Sensing Proportioning Valve.
⑦ —455–526 psi with sensor spring free and input pressure of 889 psi; 765–879 psi with sensor spring free and input pressure of 1991 psi; 1254–1496 psi with sensor spring length of 4.10 inch and input pressure of 1991 psi.
⑧ —455–526 psi with sensor spring free and input pressure of 889 psi; 765–879 psi with sensor spring free and input pressure of 1991 psi; 1249–1491 psi with sensor spring length of 4.10 inch and input pressure of 1991 psi.
⑨ —With 14 inch disc.
⑩ —With 15 inch disc.
⑪ —305.8–376.9 psi with sensor spring free and input pressure of 740 psi; 660.0–773.7 psi with sensor spring free and input pressure of 1991 psi; 1338.4–1580.2 psi with sensor spring length of 4.07 inch and input pressure of 1991 psi.
⑫ —With 10.43 inch disc-disc.
⑬ —With 10.43 inch disc-drum.
⑭ —With 14 inch disc-disc.
⑮ —With 14 inch disc-drum.

# POWER BRAKE UNITS

INDEX



## GENERAL SERVICE

In order to properly service and repair available brake systems, a thorough understanding of the power assist systems is necessary. The vacuum assist diaphragm assembly multiplies the force exerted on the master cylinder piston in order to increase the hydraulic pressure delivered to the wheel cylinders or calipers while decreasing the effort necessary to obtain acceptable stopping performance.

Vacuum assist units get their energy by opposing engine vacuum to atmospheric pressure. A piston, cylinder and flexible diaphragm utilize this energy to provide brake assistance. The diaphragm is balanced with engine vacuum until the brake pedal is depressed, allowing atmospheric pressure to unbalance the unit and apply force to the brake system.

Brakes will operate even if the power unit fails. This means the conventional brake system and the power assist system are completely separate. Troubleshooting conventional and power assist systems are exactly the same until the power unit is reached. As with conventional hydraulic brakes, a spongy pedal still means air is trapped in the hydraulic system. Power brakes give higher line pressure, making leaks more critical.

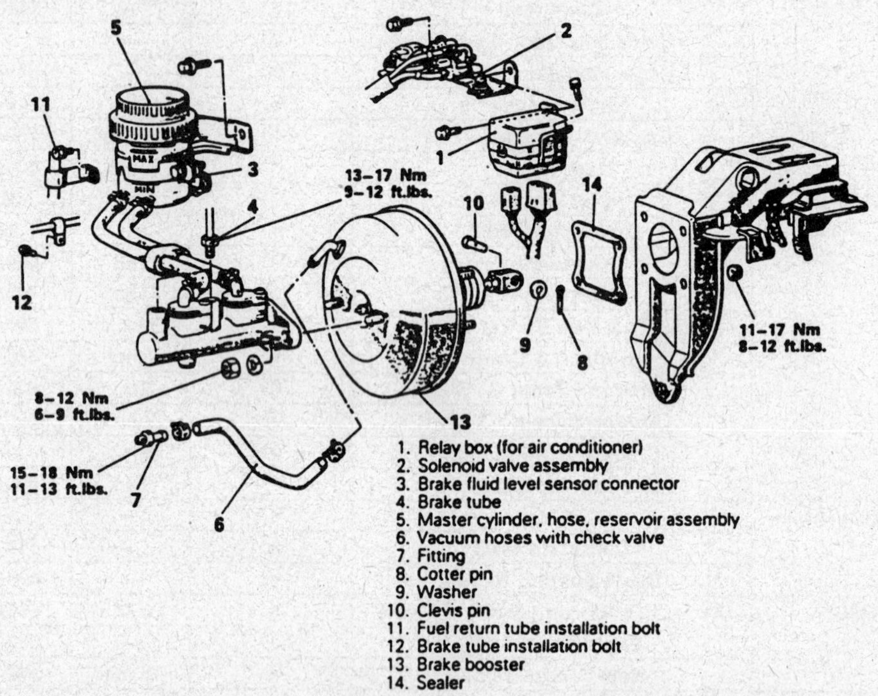


**Fig. 1 Replacing power brake unit. Laser & Eagle Talon**

## CHECKING COMPLAINTS

Complaints about power brake operation should be handled as if two separate systems exist. Check for faults in the hydraulic system first. If it is satisfactory, start inspecting the power brake circuit. For a quick check of proper power unit operation, press the brake pedal firmly and then start the engine. The pedal should fall away slightly and less pressure should be needed to maintain the pedal in any position.

Another check begins with installation of a suitable pressure gauge in the brake hydraulic system. Take a reading with the engine off and the power unit not operating. Maintaining the same pedal height, start the engine and take another reading. There should be a substantial pressure increase in the second reading.

Pedal free travel and total travel are critical on cars equipped with power brakes. Pedal travel should be kept strictly to specifications.

Take a manifold vacuum reading if the power unit isn't giving enough assistance. Remember, though, currently produced emission controlled engines, manifold vacuum readings may be less than 15 inches Hg at idle. If manifold vacuum is abnormally low, tune the engine and then try the power brakes again. Naturally, loose vacuum lines and clogged air intake filters will cut down brake efficiency. Most units have a check valve that retains some vacuum in the system when the engine is off. A vacuum gauge check of this valve will tell you when it is restricted or stuck open or closed.

Failure of the brakes to release in most instances is caused by a tight or misaligned connection between the power unit and the brake linkage. If this connection is free, look for a broken piston, diaphragm or bellows and return spring.

A simple check of the hydraulic system should be made before proceeding. Loosen the connection between the master cylinder and the brake booster. If the brakes release, the trouble is in the power unit; if the brakes still will not release, look for a restricted brake line or similar difficulties in the hydraulic circuit.

A residual pressure check valve is usually included immediately under the brake line connection on hydraulic assist power brakes. This valve maintains a slight hydraulic pressure within the brake lines and wheel cylinders or caliper to give better pedal response. If it is sticking, the brakes may not release.

Power brakes that have a hard pedal are usually suffering from a milder form of the same ills that cause complete power unit failure. Collapsed or leaking vacuum lines or insufficient manifold vacuum, as well as punctured diaphragms or bellows and leaky piston seals, all lead to weak power unit operation. A steady hiss when the brake is held down means a vacuum leak that will cause poor power unit operation.

Do not immediately condemn the power unit if the brakes grab. First look for all the usual causes, such as greasy linings, scored rotors or drums. Then investigate the power unit. When the trouble has been traced to the power unit, check for a damaged reaction control. The reaction control is usually made up of a diaphragm, spring and valves that tends to resist pedal action. It is put in the system to give the pedal "feel."

## TROUBLESHOOTING

### Decreasing Brake Pedal Travel

If a decreasing brake pedal is encountered, the power brake unit may be binding internally. To test the power brake unit for this condition proceed as follows:

1. Place transmission shift lever into Neutral and start engine.
2. Increase engine speed to approximately 1500 RPM, close throttle and

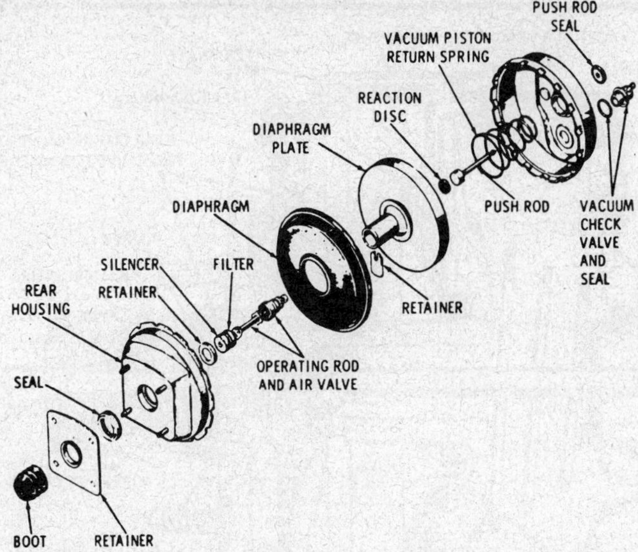


**Fig. 2 Bendix single diaphragm power brake unit**

completely depress brake pedal.
3. Slowly release brake pedal and stop engine.
4. Remove vacuum check valve and hose from power brake unit. Observe for backward movement of brake pedal.
5. If brake pedal moves backward, power brake unit has internal binding.
6. Replace power brake unit.

### Hard Brake Pedal

An internal bind or a failed vacuum check valve would cause this condition. Refer to Decreasing Brake Pedal Travel to test power brake unit for an internal bind. To check for a failed vacuum check valve proceed as follows:

1. Start engine and increase engine speed to approximately 1500 RPM, then close throttle and stop engine.
2. Wait 90 seconds, then try brake action.
3. If brakes are not vacuum assisted for two or more applications, replace check valve.

### Dragging Brakes

If slow or incomplete release of brakes (dragging brakes) is encountered the power brake unit has an internal bind condition. Test for an internal bind condition as described previously.

## POWER BOOSTER, REPLACE

### Chrysler Rear Wheel Drive Except Conquest

1. Remove master cylinder retaining nuts, then carefully slide out master cylinder from power brake and allow it to rest on fender shield. **Ensure brake lines do not bend or twist.**
2. Disconnect vacuum hose from check valve. **Do not remove check valve from booster.**
3. From under instrument panel, install a suitable screwdriver between center tang on retainer clip and brake pedal pin. Rotate screwdriver so retainer center tang will pass over brake pedal pin. Pull retainer clip from pin.
4. Remove lower pivot retaining bolt and nut, then the four booster retaining nuts.
5. Rotate linkage as necessary and remove power brake unit from vehicle.
6. Remove pivot bushings and sleeve for reuse.
7. Reverse procedure to install noting the following:
   a. Coat bearing surface of pedal pin, pivot bushings and sleeve with lubriplate or a suitable equivalent.
   b. Check stoplight operation and readjust if necessary.

### Chrysler Front Wheel Drive Models Except Colt, Colt Vista, Colt Wagon, Laser, Monaco & Stealth

1. Remove master cylinder attaching nuts, disconnect brake tubes between master cylinder and valve assembly, then remove master cylinder.
2. Remove clutch cable mounting bracket, if equipped.
3. Disconnect vacuum hose from check valve on power brake unit. **Do not remove check valve from booster.**
4. Pull wiring harness away from and up shock tower. If more slack is required, disconnect wiring harness from bulkhead connector.
5. From under instrument panel, install a suitable screwdriver between center tang on retainer clip and brake pedal pin. Rotate screwdriver so retainer center tang will pass over brake pedal pin. Pull retainer clip from pin.
6. Remove power brake unit attaching nuts and power brake unit from vehicle.
7. Reverse procedure to install. Bleed brake system.

### Monaco & Eagle Premier

1. Disconnect battery ground cable.
2. Remove vacuum supply hose from check valve.
3. Remove throttle cable attaching clip and position cable aside.
4. Remove intake hose at air cleaner and throttle body, then position hose aside.
5. Remove master cylinder as outlined in "Master Cylinder, Replace" under "Type 2—Recessed Cartridge Master Cylinder."
6. Remove retaining clip attaching booster push rod to brake pedal and discard.
7. Remove power brake unit attaching nuts and the unit.
8. Reverse procedure to install.

### Eagle Medallion

1. Disconnect battery ground cable.
2. Remove master cylinder as described in "Master Cylinder, Replace" under "Type 3—Composite Master Cylinder."
3. Disconnect vacuum hose from power brake unit.
4. Remove power brake unit to brake pedal clevis pin.
5. Remove nuts attaching power brake unit to dash panel, then remove power brake unit.
6. Reverse procedure to install.

### Laser & Eagle Talon

Remove power brake unit in numbered sequence, **Fig. 1,** noting the following:

1. Check valve is integral with vacuum line. If valve is defective, replace as an assembly.
2. When installing vacuum hose fitting, apply semi-drying sealant to threaded portion.
3. Reverse procedure to install.

### Colt, Colt Vista, Colt Wagon, Conquest, Stealth & Summit

1. Remove master cylinder as described in "Master Cylinder, Replace" under "Type 4, 5, 6, 7, 8 & 9—Composite Master Cylinders."
2. Disconnect vacuum hose from power brake unit.
3. Remove pin connecting power brake rod with brake pedal.
4. Remove power brake unit attaching nuts and the power brake unit.
5. Reverse procedure to install.

## PUSHROD ADJUSTMENT

In some cases adjustment of the brake booster pushrod is necessary to ensure proper operation of the power brake system. A pushrod that is too long will cause the master cylinder piston to close off the compensating port, preventing hydraulic pressure from being released and resulting in brake drag. A pushrod that is too short will cause excessive brake pedal travel and cause groaning noises to come from the booster when the brakes are applied. A properly adjusted pushrod that remains assembled to the booster with which is was matched during production should not require service adjustment. However, if the booster, master cylinder or pushrod are serviced, the pushrod may require adjustment.

### Eagle Medallion

Refer to "Master Cylinder Replace" as described under "Type 3—Composite Master Cylinder," in the "Hydraulic Brake System" chapter for pushrod adjustment procedure.

### Colt, Colt Vista, Conquest, Laser, Eagle Summit & Talon

Refer to "Adjustments" as described under "Types 4, 5, 6, 7, 8 & 9—Composite Master Cylinders" in the "Hydraulic Brake System" chapter for pushrod adjustment procedure.

## BENDIX DIAPHRAGM TYPES

These units are of the vacuum suspended type. Some units are of the single diaphragm type, **Fig. 2,** while others are of the tandem diaphragm type, **Fig. 3.** Both single piston and double piston or split system type master cylinders are used.

The vacuum suspended diaphragm type units utilize engine manifold vacuum and atmospheric pressure for its power. It consists of three basic elements combined into a single power unit. The three basic elements of the single diaphragm type are:

1. A vacuum power section which includes a front and rear shell, a power diaphragm, a return spring and a push rod.
2. A control valve, built integral with the power diaphragm and connected through a valve rod to the brake pedal, controls the degree of brake application or release in accordance with the pressure applied to the brake pedal.
3. A hydraulic master cylinder, attached to the vacuum power section which contains all the elements of the conventional brake master cylinder except for the pushrod, supplies fluid under pressure to the wheel brakes in proportion to the pressure applied to the brake pedal.

## OPERATION

Upon application of the brakes, the valve rod and plunger move to the left in the power diaphragm to close the vacuum port and open the atmospheric port to admit air through the air cleaner and valve at the rear diaphragm chamber. With vacuum present in the rear chamber, a force is developed to move the power diaphragm, hydraulic pushrod and hydraulic piston or pistons to close the compensating port or ports and force fluid under pressure through the residual check valve or valves and lines into the front and rear wheel cylinders to actuate the brakes.

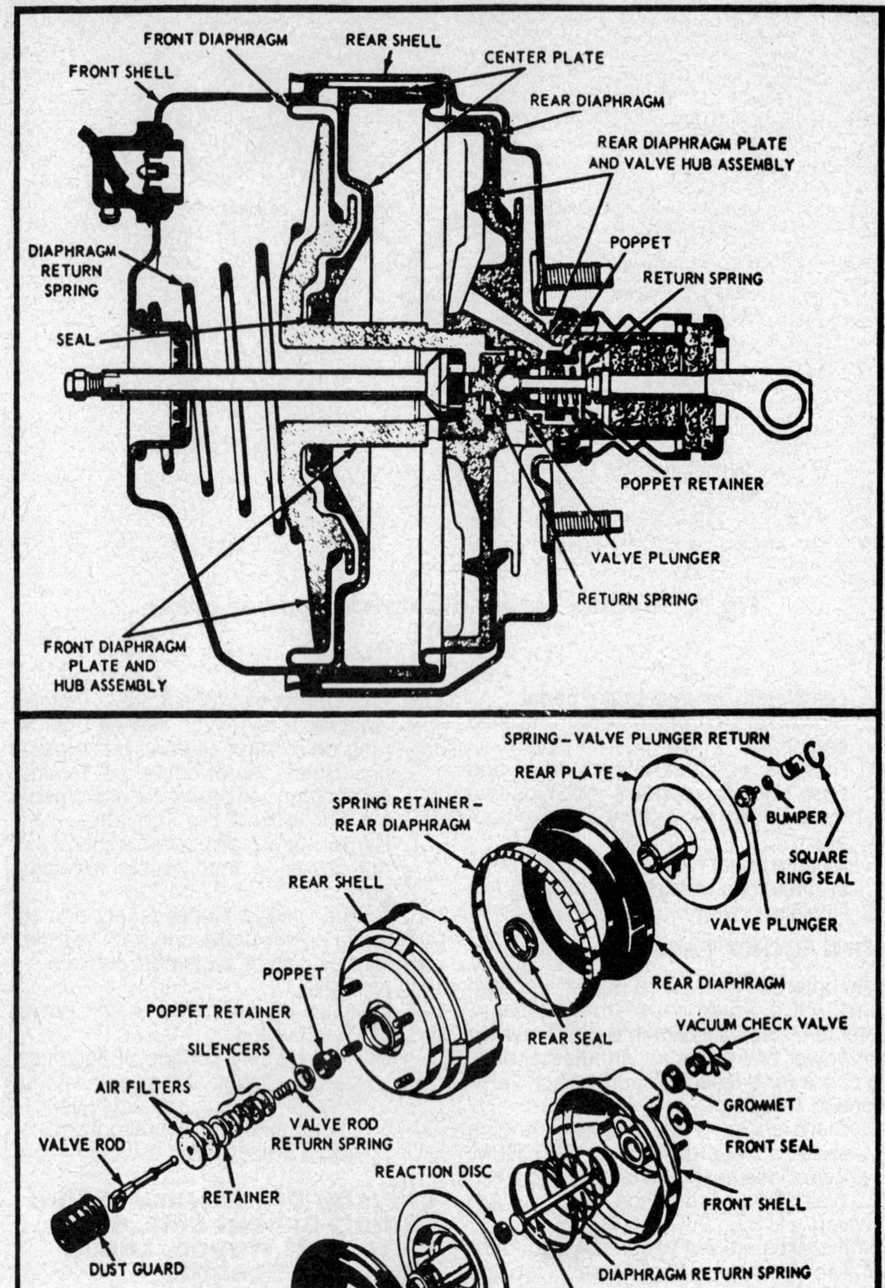


**Fig. 3 Bendix tandem diaphragm power brake**

As pressure is developed within the master cylinder a counter force acting through the hydraulic pushrod and reaction disc against the vacuum power diaphragm and valve plunger sets up a reaction force opposing the force applied to the valve rod and plunger. This reaction force tends to close the atmospheric port and reopen the vacuum port. Since this force is in opposition to the force applied to the brake pedal by the driver it gives the driver a "feel" of the amount of brake applied. The proportion of reactive force applied to the valve plunger through the reaction disc is designed into the Master-Vac to assure maximum power consistent with maintaining pedal feel. The reaction force is in direct proportion to the hydraulic pressure developed within the brake system.

# ANTI-LOCK BRAKES

## TABLE OF CONTENTS



# Application Chart

| Year | Model | Body Code | System |
|---|---|---|---|
| 1989 | Conquest | — | Type 2 |
| | Dynasty | AC | Type 1 |
| | New Yorker | AC | Type 1 |
| | New Yorker Landau | AC | Type 1 |
| 1990 | Dynasty | AC | ① |
| | Imperial | AY | ① |
| | New Yorker Landau | AC | ① |
| | New Yorker Salon | AC | ① |
| | New Yorker Fifth Avenue | AY | ① |
| 1991 | Acclaim | AA | Type 3 |
| | Daytona | AG | Type 3 |
| | Daytona Shelby | AG | Type 3 |
| | Dynasty | AC | Type 4 |
| | Fifth Avenue | AY | Type 4 |
| | Imperial | AY | Type 4 |
| | Laser | — | Type 5 |
| | LeBaron | AJ | Type 3 |
| | LeBaron Landau | AA | Type 3 |
| | New Yorker | AC | Type 4 |
| | New Yorker Salon | AC | Type 4 |
| | Premier | BB | Type 4 |
| | Spirit | AA | Type 3 |
| | Stealth | — | Type 5 |
| | Talon | — | Type 5 |

①—Early production models, Type 1; late production models, Type 4.

# Type 1—Bosch ABS-3 Anti-Lock Braking System

**NOTE:** Wire Code Identification and Symbol Identification located in the front of this manual can be used as an aid when using wiring circuits found in this section.

## INDEX



## DESCRIPTION

The Anti-Lock Braking System (ABS) prevents the wheels from locking up when braking, regardless of the surface conditions. This allows the car to stop in a shorter distance, and allows the driver to maintain directional control of the vehicle during heavy braking.

During normal braking conditions, the ABS operates like a conventional diagonally split, hydraulic power assist system. During heavy braking, however, each wheel's braking pressure is modulated according to its speed. To maintain vehicle stability, both rear wheels receive the same signal.

There are four major components, **Fig. 1**, in the ABS which act in unison to control brake operation.

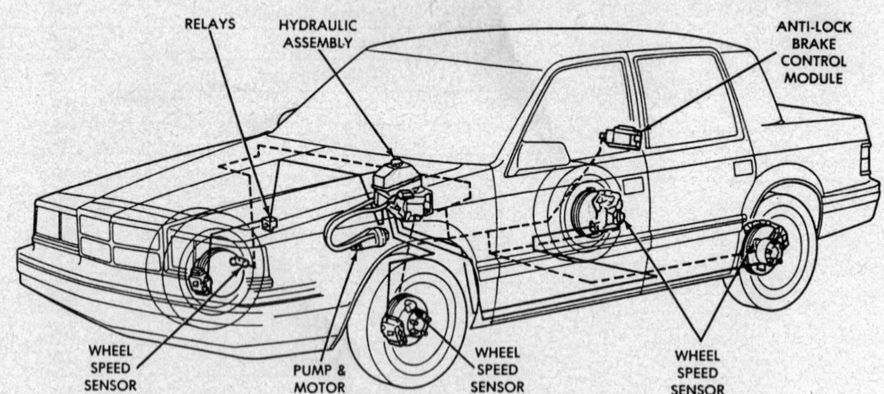


**Fig. 1 Anti-Lock Brake System (ABS) major components**

### HYDRAULIC ASSEMBLY

The hydraulic assembly acts as an integral master cylinder and hydraulic booster and contains the wheel circuit valves for brake pressure modulation.

### WHEEL SPEED SENSOR (WSS)

Each wheel is equipped with a wheel speed sensor to transmit speed information to the control module during ABS operation.

### ANTI-LOCK BRAKE CONTROL MODULE (ABCM)

The ABCM receives wheel speed information, controls anti-lock operation and monitors system performance.

### PUMP/MOTOR ASSEMBLY

The pump/motor assembly is an electric pump that takes low pressure fluid from the hydraulic assembly and stores it under pressure in an accumulator for power assist and ABS operation.

## DIAGNOSIS

The ABS system has a self-diagnostic mode which helps isolate fault codes which are displayed by the flashing red brake warning lamp on the instrument panel. One fault code is stored at a time, and is erased when ignition is turned off.

| ITEM | INSPECT FOR | CORRECTIVE ACTION |
|---|---|---|
| Brake Fluid Reservoir | Low fluid Level | Add fluid as required. Determine cause of fluid loss and repair. |
| ABCM | Proper connector engagement. External Damage | Repair as required Verify defect and repair as required. |
| Hydraulic Assembly | Proper Connector Engagement External Leaks Damaged wiring/connectors Control Pressure Switch Fluid Level Sensor Defect | Repair as required Repair Leaks as required Repair as required Repair as required Repair as required |
| Pump/Motor Assembly and Hoses | Proper assembly Damaged/Leaking Hoses Damaged wiring/connector | Install components properly Repair hoses as required Repair as required |
| Parking Brake | Full release<br><br>Park Brake Switch | Operate manual release lever to verify operation. Adjust cable or repair release mechanism as required Verify correct operation. Repair as required |
| Front & Rear Wheel Speed Sensors | Proper connector engagement Broken or damaged wires | Repair as required Go to appropriate ABS Code chart and verify fault. Correct as required |
| OVPR & Pump/Motor Relays | Proper connector engagement Loose wires or terminals | Repair as required Repair as required |
| Pump/Motor Ground | Corroded, broken or loose eyelets | Repair as required |

**Fig. 2 Visual inspection chart**

| SYMPTOM | REFER TO |
|---|---|
| No power assist (with or without BRAKE warning lamp on) High pedal effort (with or without BRAKE warning lamp on) Pump does not run Pumps runs for extended periods of time Pump runs every brake apply BRAKE warning lamp stays on for more than 20 seconds after key-on BRAKE warning lamp comes on while braking BRAKE warning lamp on continuously Brake boost system will not hold pressure (excessive pressure leakdown) | Chart C |
| BRAKE warning lamp inoperative | Chart D |
| LOW BRAKE FLUID message displayed and BRAKE warning lamp on continuously (EVID equipped cars only) | Chart E |
| BRAKE warning lamp on and power assist available | Chart F |
| No system power | Chart G |
| ANTI-LOCK warning lamp on (BRAKE warning lamp off) and no Fault Codes set | Chart H |
| Low or spongy pedal | Chart J |

**Fig. 3 Symptom diagnosis table**

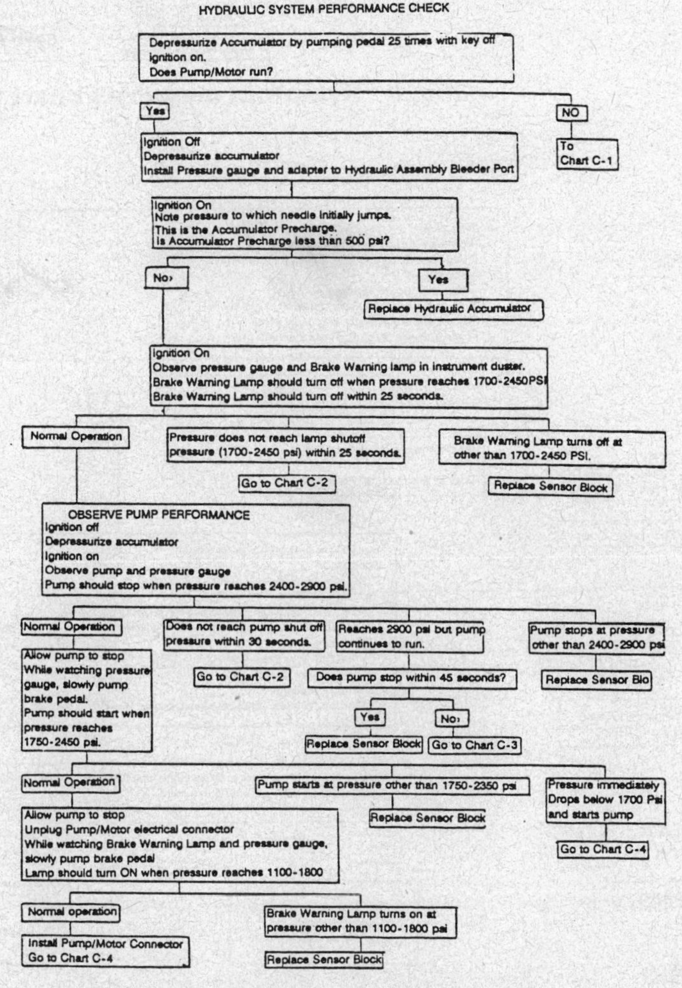


**Fig. 4 Symptom diagnosis chart C**

## VISUAL INSPECTION

A visual inspection is the first step in the diagnostic procedure. All components must be checked for proper operation or condition as listed in **Fig. 2.**

## SELF-DIAGNOSIS

Before using the self-diagnostic procedure, or symptom diagnosis charts, a visual inspection of system components should be made to verify that they are in good working order **Fig. 2.**

1. With ignition on, ensure the parking brake is fully released so that it is not causing brake warning lamp to light.
2. Check that brake warning or anti-lock warning lamp is illuminated, indicating a fault has been detected.
3. When a fault is detected, with ignition on, depress brake pedal firmly. After about five seconds if a fault code is present the brake warning light will begin to flash. The number of times the lamp flashes is the number of the code. **If ignition is turned off, fault code will be erased.** If brake pedal is held while lamp is flashing trouble code, the code will repeat after a ten second delay. Releasing the brake pedal stops code from repeating.
4. If lamp does not come on at all, crank the engine and perform a brake warning lamp bulb check and repair as necessary. If the lamp does light and no fault codes are present, the complaint should be verified and diagnosed with appropriate symptom diagnosis charts, **Figs. 3 through 14.**
5. To exit from diagnostic mode, release the brake pedal.

**SERVICE BULLETIN:** Symptom diagnosis charts "C" and "C-4," **Figs. 4 and 8,** have been revised by a Technical Service Bulletin.

## FUNCTIONAL CHECK

The functional check, **Fig. 15,** is done to determine the nature of system troubles. The process will isolate the proper system diagnosis procedure, **Figs. 3 through 14,** or trouble code diagnostic procedure, **Figs. 16 through 21,** to be followed.

## INTERMITTENT FAULT CODES

Most intermittent faults are due to faulty electrical connections or wiring. Check for poorly seated connectors, damaged connectors or wiring, or any other connector/wiring defects.

Intermittent illumination of the brake and/or anti-lock warning lamps can be caused by the following conditions:

1. Low system voltage, which will illuminate the anti-lock warning lamp until voltage returns to normal.
2. Low brake fluid, which will illuminate the brake warning lamp.
3. Low accumulator pressure, which will illuminate both anti-lock and brake warning lamps.

*Continued on page 16-9*

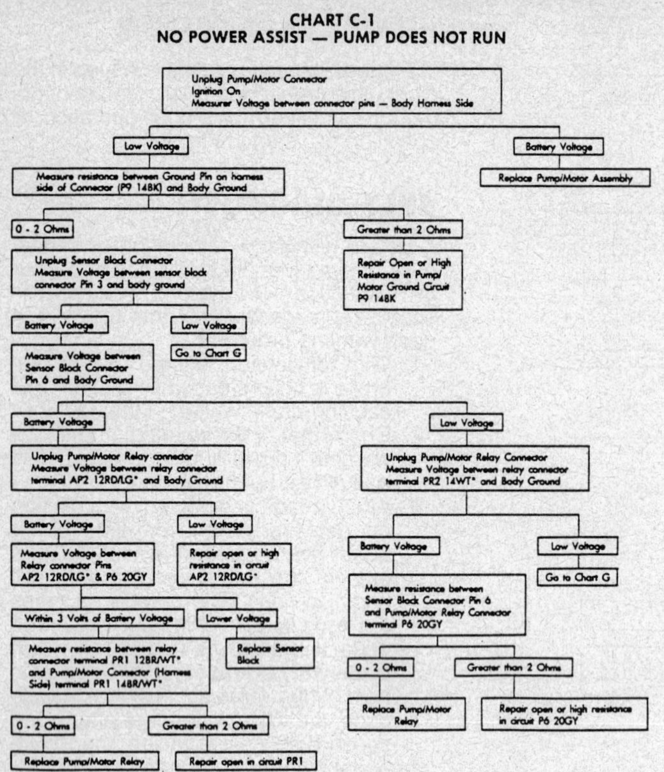


**Fig. 5 Symptom diagnosis chart C-1**

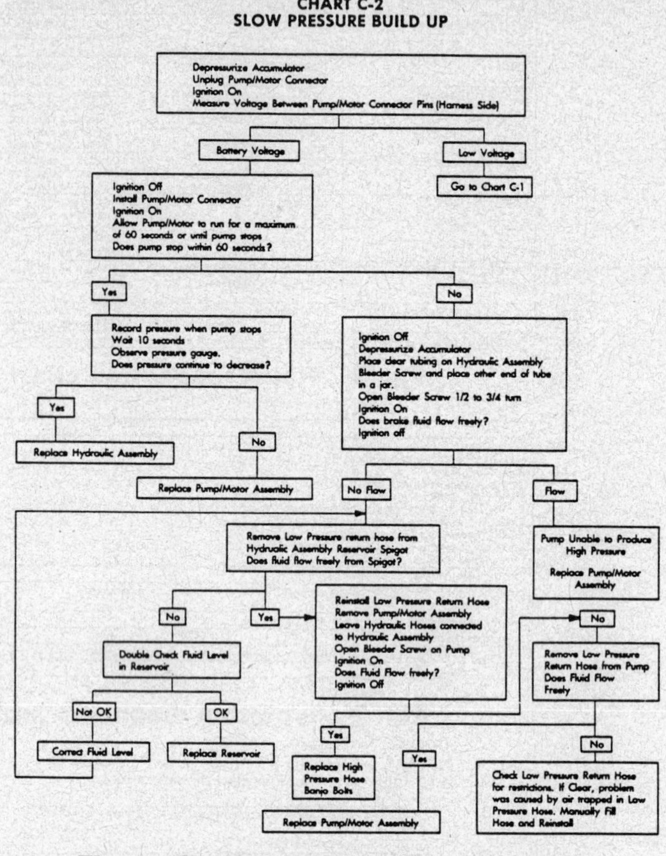


**Fig. 6 Symptom diagnosis chart C-2**

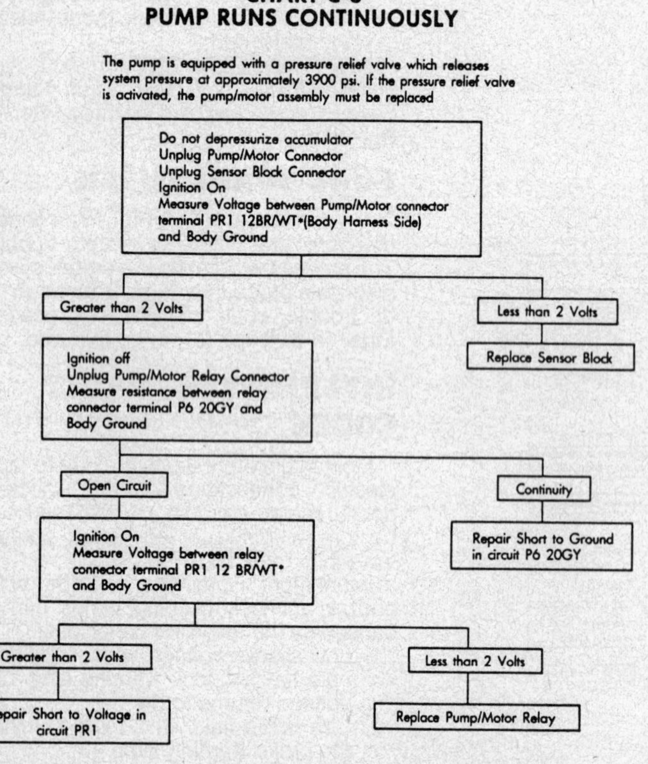


**Fig. 7 Symptom diagnosis chart C-3**

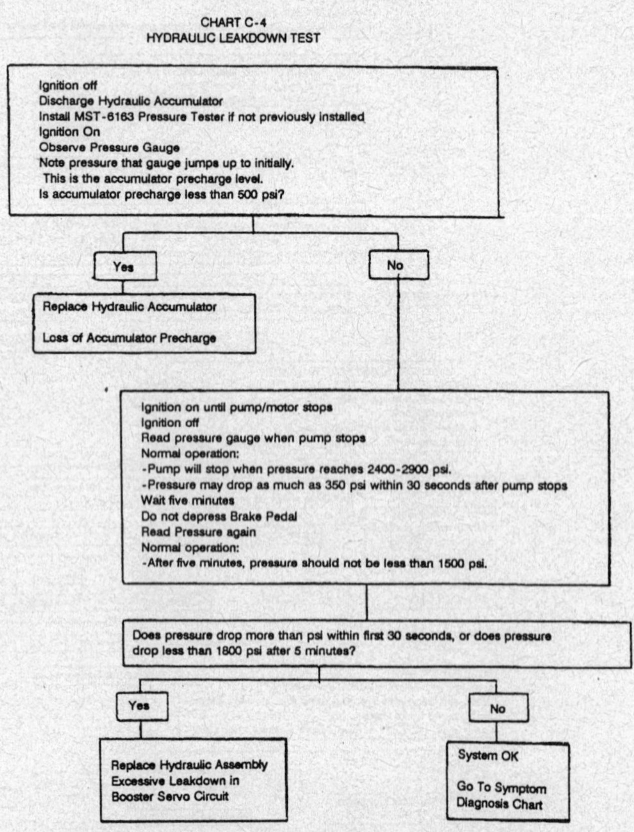


**Fig. 8 Symptom diagnosis chart C-4**

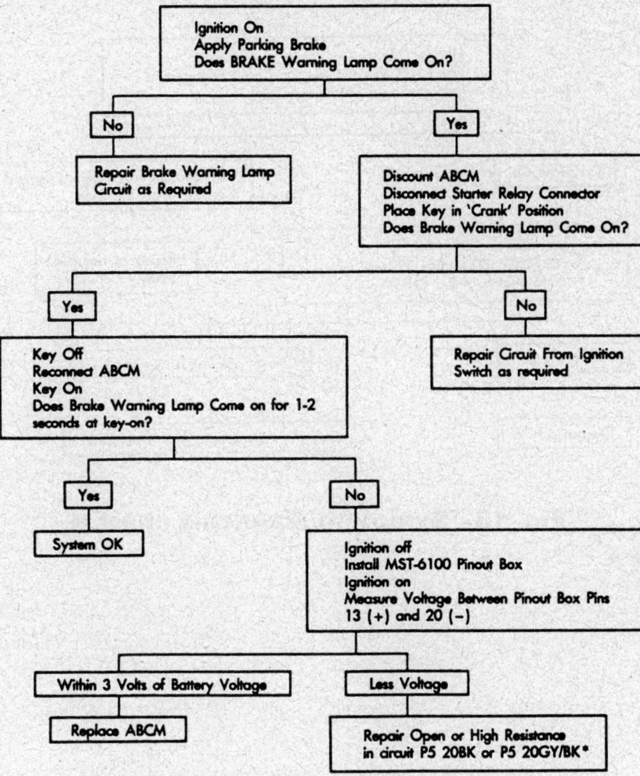


**Fig. 9 Symptom diagnosis chart D**

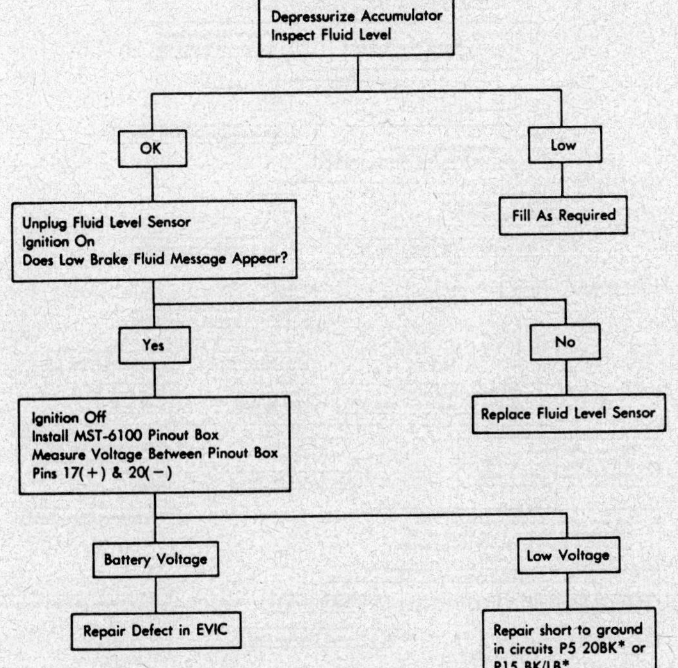


**Fig. 10 Symptom diagnosis chart E**

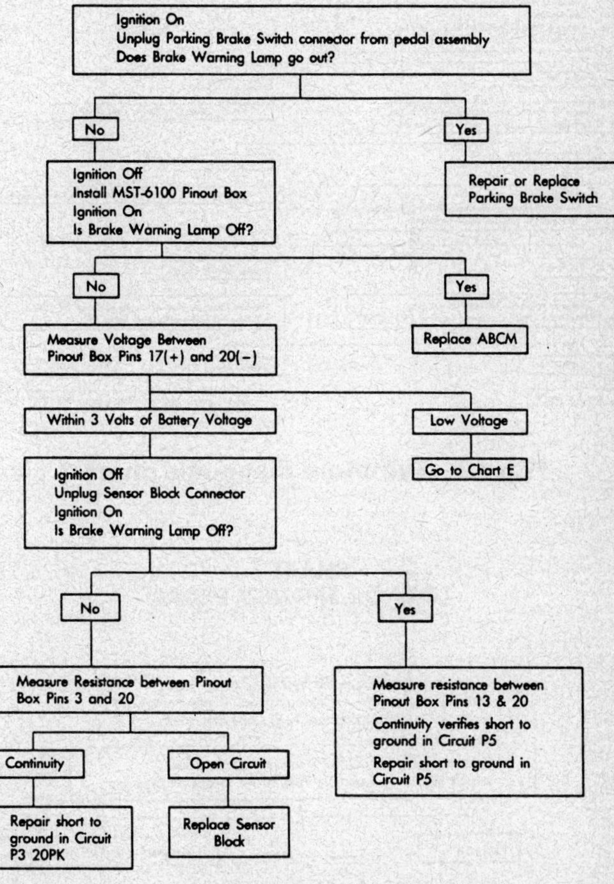


**Fig. 11 Symptom diagnosis chart F**

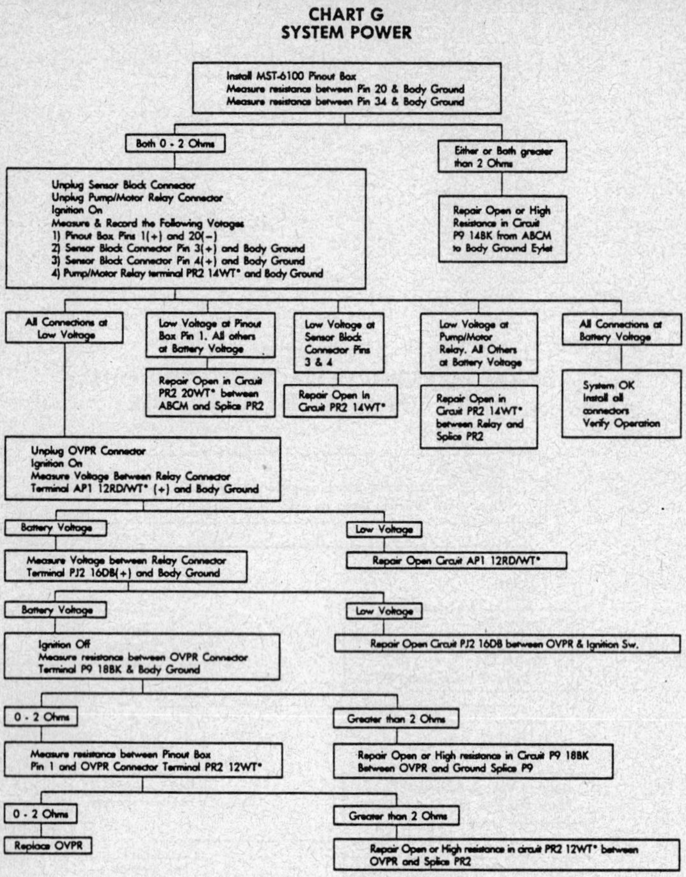

CHART G
SYSTEM POWER
Install MST-6100 Pinout Box
Measure resistance between Pin 20 & Body Ground
Measure resistance between Pin 34 & Body Ground
Both 0 - 2 Ohms
Either or Both greater than 2 Ohms
Repair Open or High Resistance in Circuit P9 14BK from ABCM to Body Ground Eylet
Unplug Sensor Block Connector
Unplug Pump/Motor Relay Connector
Ignition On
Measure & Record the Following Votages
1) Pinout Box Pins 1(+) and 20(−)
2) Sensor Block Connector Pin 3(+) and Body Ground
3) Sensor Block Connector Pin 4(+) and Body Ground
4) Pump/Motor Relay terminal PR2 14WT* and Body Ground
All Connections at Low Voltage
Low Voltage at Pinout Box Pin 1. All others at Battery Voltage
Repair Open in Circuit PR2 20WT* between ABCM and Splice PR2
Low Voltage at Sensor Block Connector Pins 3 & 4
Repair Open In Circuit PR2 14WT*
Low Voltage at Pump/Motor Relay. All Others at Battery Voltage
Repair Open in Circuit PR2 14WT* between Relay and Splice PR2
All Connections at Battery Voltage
System OK
Install all connectors
Verify Operation
Unplug OVPR Connector
Ignition On
Measure Voltage Between Relay Connector Terminal AP1 12RD/WT* (+) and Body Ground
Battery Voltage
Low Voltage
Repair Open Circuit AP1 12RD/WT*
Measure Voltage between Relay Connector Terminal PJ2 16DB(+) and Body Ground
Battery Voltage
Low Voltage
Repair Open Circuit PJ2 16DB between OVPR & Ignition Sw.
Ignition Off
Measure resistance between OVPR Connector Terminal P9 18BK & Body Ground
0 - 2 Ohms
Greater than 2 Ohms
Repair Open or High resistance in Circuit P9 18BK Between OVPR and Ground Splice P9
Measure resistance between Pinout Box Pin 1 and OVPR Connector Terminal PR2 12WT*
0 - 2 Ohms
Replace OVPR
Greater than 2 Ohms
Repair Open or High resistance in circuit PR2 12WT* between OVPR and Splice PR2

**Fig. 12 Symptom diagnosis chart G**

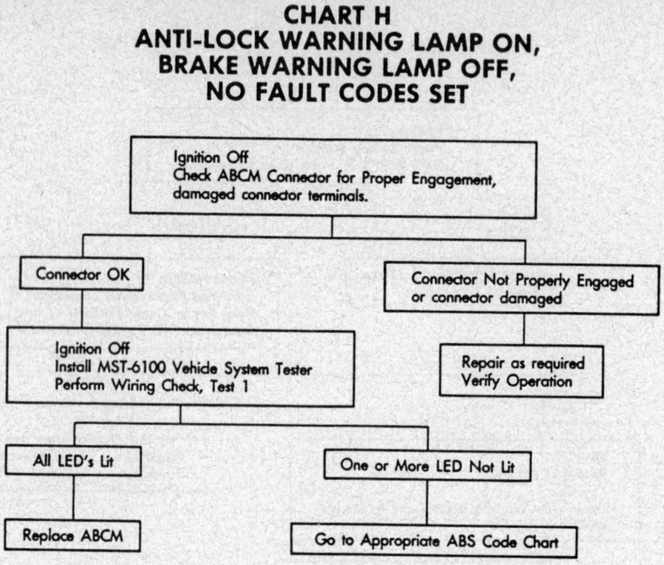

CHART H
ANTI-LOCK WARNING LAMP ON,
BRAKE WARNING LAMP OFF,
NO FAULT CODES SET
Ignition Off
Check ABCM Connector for Proper Engagement, damaged connector terminals.
Connector OK
Connector Not Properly Engaged or connector damaged
Repair as required
Verify Operation
Ignition Off
Install MST-6100 Vehicle System Tester
Perform Wiring Check, Test 1
All LED's Lit
One or More LED Not Lit
Replace ABCM
Go to Appropriate ABS Code Chart

**Fig. 13 Symptom diagnosis chart H**

CHART J
LOW OR SPONGY PEDAL
Slight amounts of air in the hydraulic brake system will not normally cause a low or spongy pedal. If any Fault Code is set, go to the appropriate Fault Code Chart first
Remove Underdash Driver's sound insulator panel
Inspect Hydraulic Assembly Pushrod for proper engagement
Pushrod OK
Pushrod mounted incorrectly
Repair as required
Inspect Hydraulic Assembly mounting on dash panel
Mounting OK
Incorrect of Loose Mounting
Repair as Required
Inspect Front & Rear Calipers, tubes & hoses
Components OK
Components Improper
Repair as Required
Bleed Brake System
If condition is not corrected by bleeding, replace Hydraulic Assembly

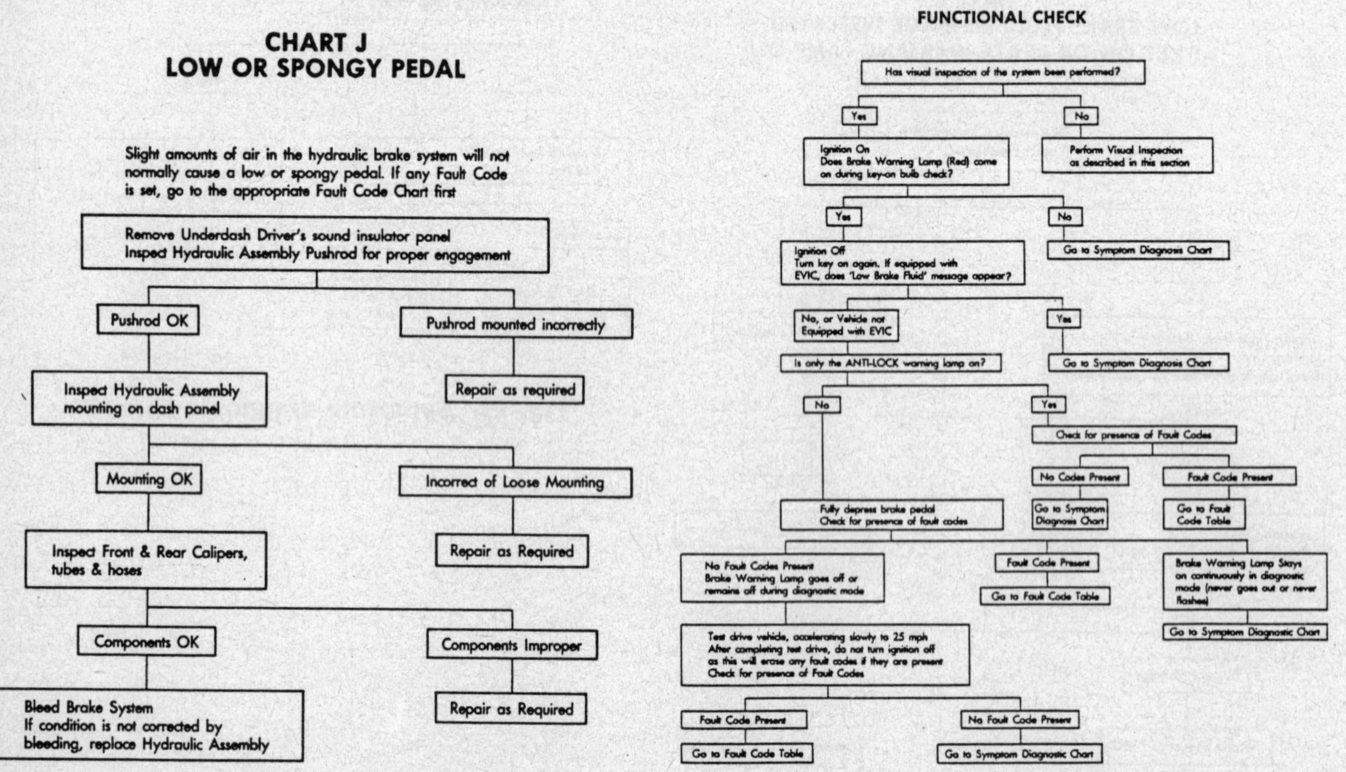

**Fig. 14 Symptom diagnosis chart J**

FUNCTIONAL CHECK
Has visual inspection of the system been performed?
Yes
No
Perform Visual Inspection as described in this section
Ignition On
Does Brake Warning Lamp (Red) come on during key-on bulb check?
Yes
No
Go to Symptom Diagnosis Chart
Ignition Off
Turn key on again. If equipped with EVIC, does 'Low Brake Fluid' message appear?
No, or Vehicle not Equipped with EVIC
Yes
Go to Symptom Diagnosis Chart
Is only the ANTI-LOCK warning lamp on?
No
Yes
Check for presence of Fault Codes
No Codes Present
Fault Code Present
Go to Symptom Diagnosis Chart
Go to Fault Code Table
Fully depress brake pedal
Check for presence of fault codes
No Fault Codes Present
Brake Warning Lamp goes off or remains off during diagnostic mode
Fault Code Present
Go to Fault Code Table
Brake Warning Lamp Stays on continuously in diagnostic mode (never goes out or never flashes)
Go to Symptom Diagnostic Chart
Test drive vehicle, accelerating slowly to 25 mph
After completing test drive, do not turn ignition off as this will erase any fault codes if they are present
Check for presence of Fault Codes
Fault Code Present
Go to Fault Code Table
No Fault Code Present
Go to Symptom Diagnostic Chart

**Fig. 15 Functional check chart**

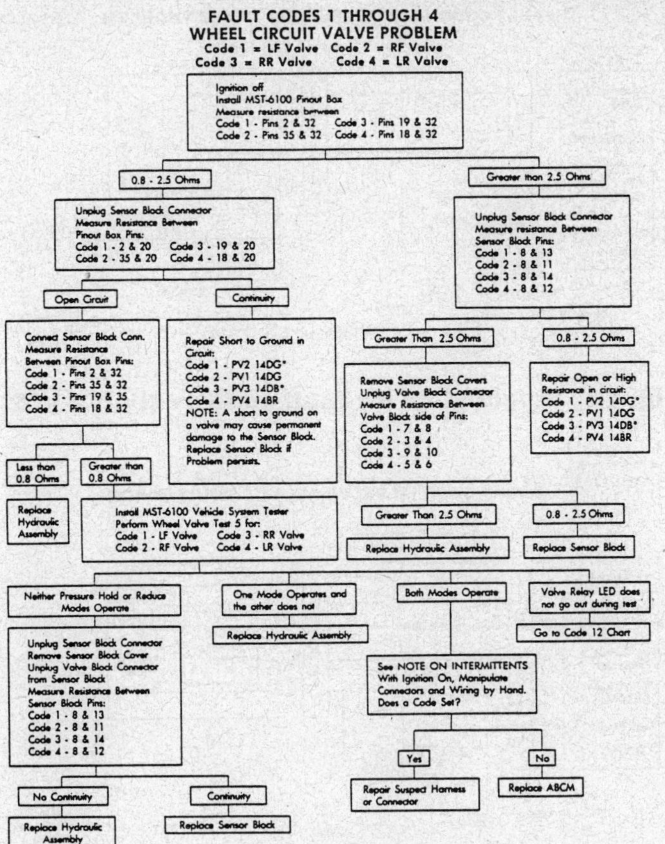


**Fig. 16 Diagnostics for fault codes 1 through 4 (Part 1 of 2)**

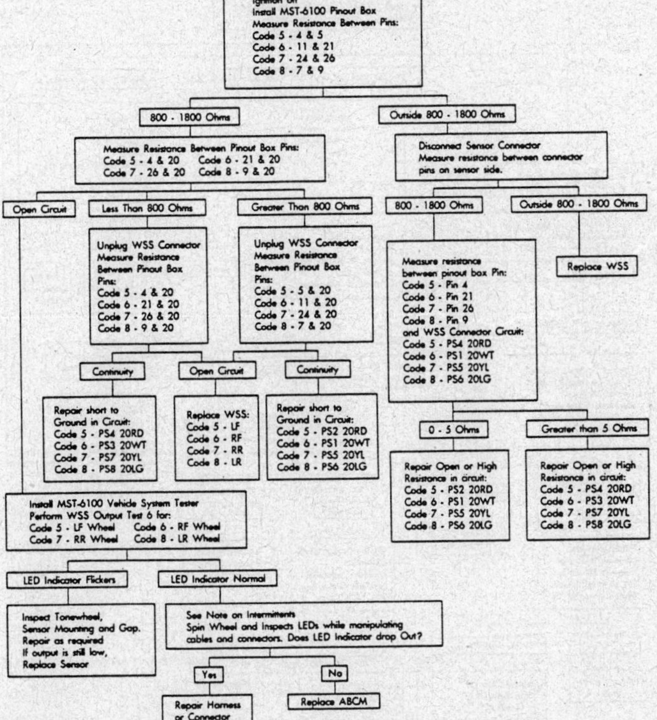


**Fig. 17 Diagnostics for fault codes 5 through 8 (Part 1 of 3)**

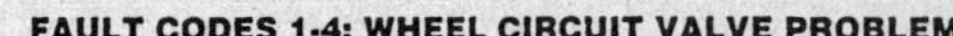


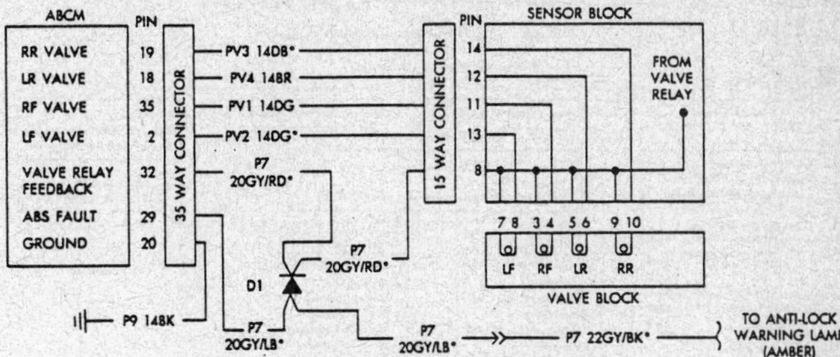


**Fig. 16 Diagnostics for fault codes 1 through 4 (Part 2 of 2)**

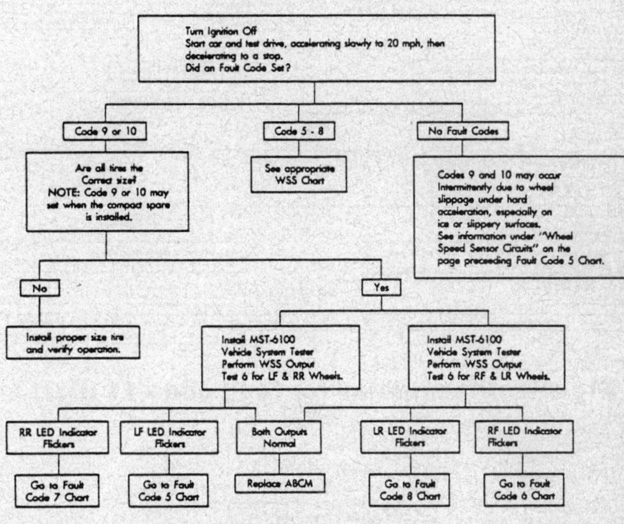


**Fig. 17 Diagnostics for fault codes 9 & 10 (Part 2 of 3)**

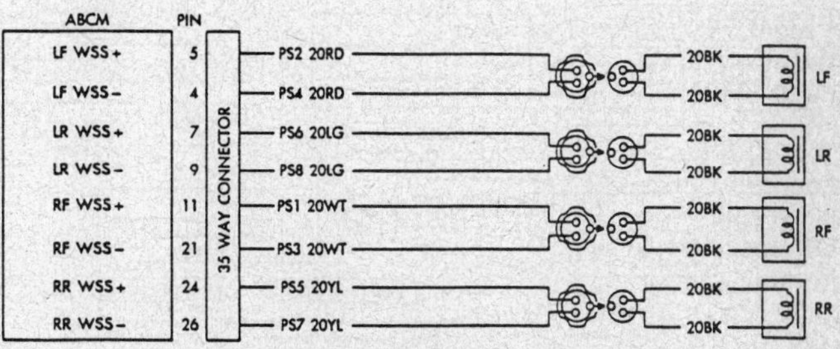


**Fig. 17 Diagnostics for fault codes 5 through 10 (Part 3 of 3)**

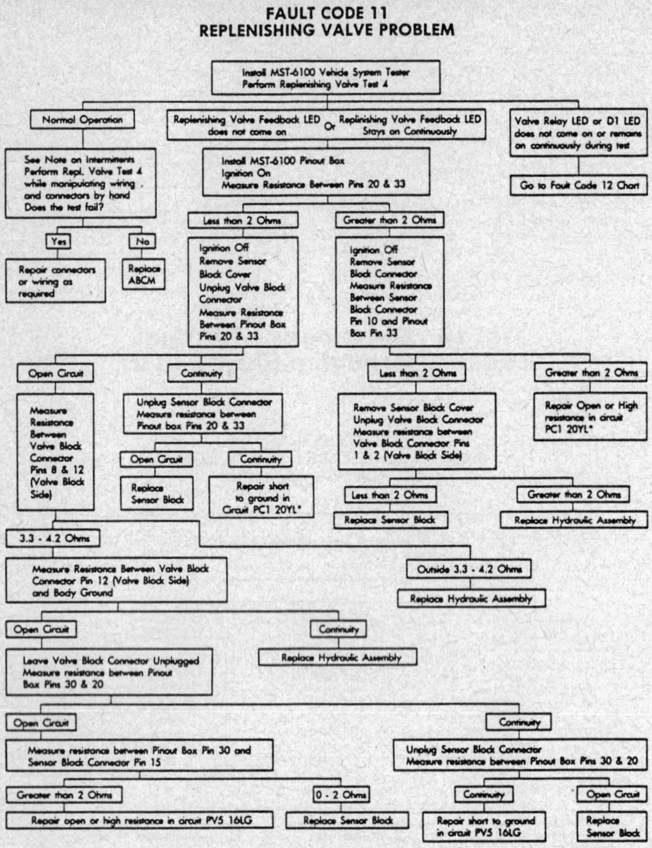

FAULT CODE 11
REPLENISHING VALVE PROBLEM

Install MST-6100 Vehicle System Tester
Perform Replenishing Valve Test 4

Normal Operation

See Note on Intermittents
Perform Repl. Valve Test 4
while manipulating wiring
and connectors by hand
Does the test fail?

Yes — Repair connectors or wiring as required

No — Replace ABCM

Replenishing Valve Feedback LED does not come on Or Replenishing Valve Feedback LED Stays on Continuously

Install MST-6100 Pinout Box
Ignition On
Measure Resistance Between Pins 20 & 33

Less than 2 Ohms

Ignition Off
Remove Sensor Block Cover
Unplug Valve Block Connector
Measure Resistance Between Pinout Box Pins 20 & 33

Greater than 2 Ohms

Ignition Off
Remove Sensor Block Connector
Measure Resistance Between Sensor Block Connector Pin 10 and Pinout Box Pin 33

Valve Relay LED or D1 LED does not come on or remains on continuously during test

Go to Fault Code 12 Chart

Open Circuit

Measure Resistance Between Valve Block Connector Pins 8 & 12 (Valve Block Side)

Continuity

Unplug Sensor Block Connector
Measure resistance between Pinout box Pins 20 & 33

Open Circuit — Replace Sensor Block

Continuity — Repair short to ground in Circuit PC1 20YL*

Less than 2 Ohms

Remove Sensor Block Cover
Unplug Valve Block Connector
Measure resistance between Valve Block Connector Pins 1 & 2 (Valve Block Side)

Less than 2 Ohms — Replace Sensor Block

Greater than 2 Ohms — Replace Hydraulic Assembly

Greater than 2 Ohms

Repair Open or High resistance in circuit PC1 20YL*

3.3 - 4.2 Ohms

Measure Resistance Between Valve Block Connector Pin 12 (Valve Block Side) and Body Ground

Outside 3.3 - 4.2 Ohms — Replace Hydraulic Assembly

Open Circuit

Leave Valve Block Connector Unplugged
Measure resistance between Pinout Box Pins 30 & 20

Continuity — Replace Hydraulic Assembly

Open Circuit

Measure resistance between Pinout Box Pin 30 and Sensor Block Connector Pin 15

Greater than 2 Ohms — Repair open or high resistance in circuit PV5 16LG

0 - 2 Ohms — Replace Sensor Block

Continuity

Unplug Sensor Block Connector
Measure resistance between Pinout Box Pins 30 & 20

Continuity — Repair short to ground in circuit PV5 16LG

Open Circuit — Replace Sensor Block

**Fig. 18 Diagnostics for fault code 11 (Part 1 of 2)**

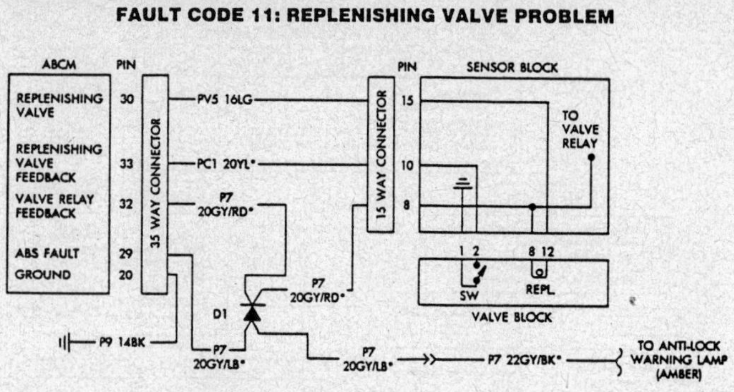

FAULT CODE 11: REPLENISHING VALVE PROBLEM

ABCM | PIN | 35 WAY CONNECTOR | 15 WAY CONNECTOR | PIN | SENSOR BLOCK

REPLENISHING VALVE — 30 — PV5 16LG — 15

REPLENISHING VALVE FEEDBACK — 33 — PC1 20YL* — 10

VALVE RELAY FEEDBACK — 32 — P7 20GY/RD* — 8

ABS FAULT — 29

GROUND — 20

TO VALVE RELAY

1 2 SW — 8 12 REPL.

VALVE BLOCK

D1

P9 14BK

P7 20GY/RD*

P7 20GY/LB*

P7 20GY/LB* — P7 22GY/BK* — TO ANTI-LOCK WARNING LAMP (AMBER)

**Fig. 18 Diagnostics for fault code 11 (Part 2 of 2)**

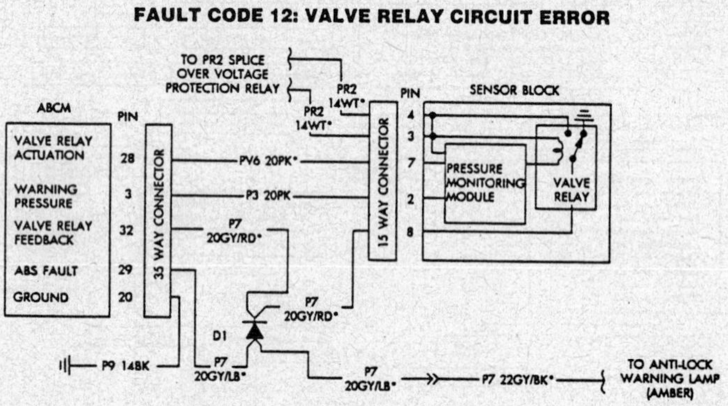

FAULT CODE 12: VALVE RELAY CIRCUIT ERROR

TO PR2 SPLICE OVER VOLTAGE PROTECTION RELAY

PR2 14WT*

PR2 14WT*

ABCM | PIN | 35 WAY CONNECTOR | 15 WAY CONNECTOR | PIN | SENSOR BLOCK

VALVE RELAY ACTUATION — 28 — PV6 20PK* — 7

WARNING PRESSURE — 3 — P3 20PK — 2

VALVE RELAY FEEDBACK — 32 — P7 20GY/RD* — 8

ABS FAULT — 29

GROUND — 20

4, 3

PRESSURE MONITORING MODULE

VALVE RELAY

D1

P9 14BK

P7 20GY/RD*

P7 20GY/LB*

P7 20GY/LB* — P7 22GY/BK* — TO ANTI-LOCK WARNING LAMP (AMBER)

**Fig. 19 Diagnostics for fault code 12 (Part 2 of 2)**

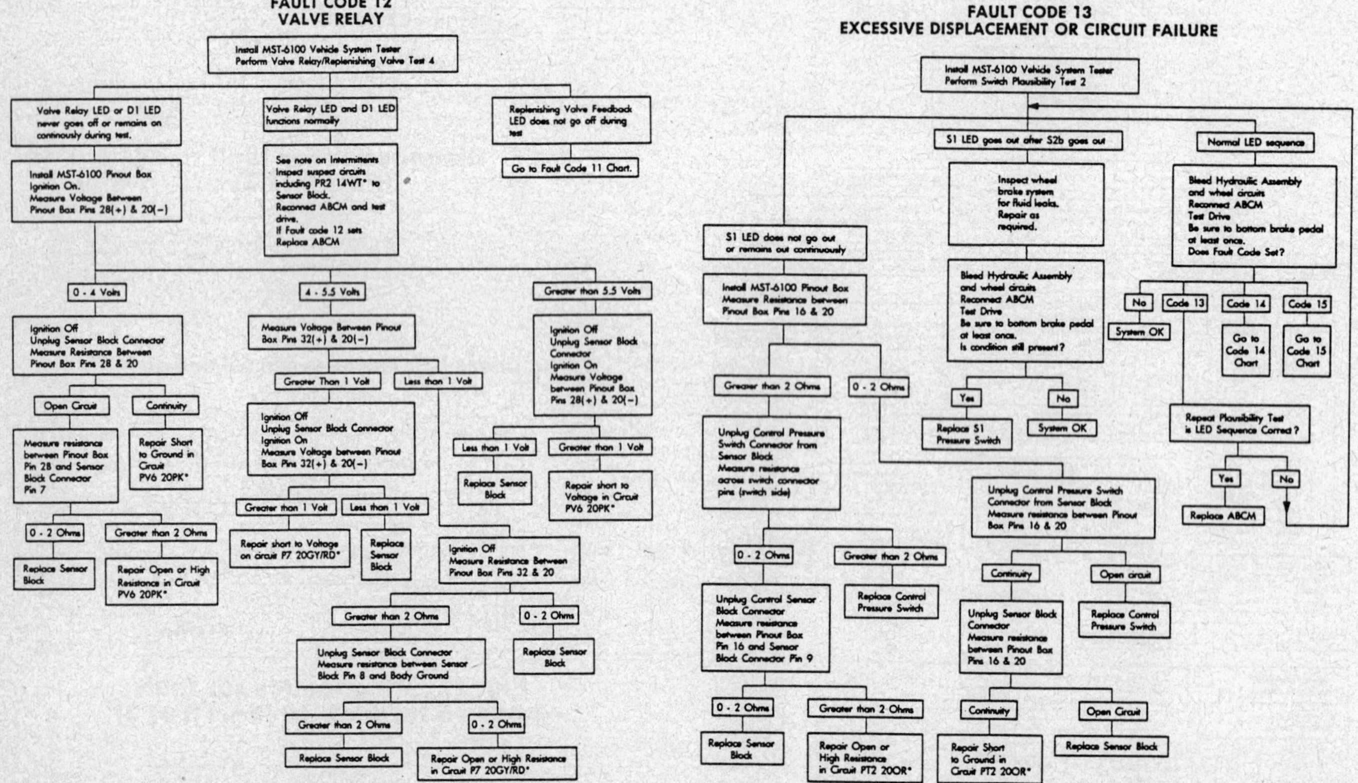


**Fig. 19 Diagnostics for fault code 12 (Part 1 of 2)**

**Fig. 20 Diagnostics for fault code 13 (Part 1 of 4)**

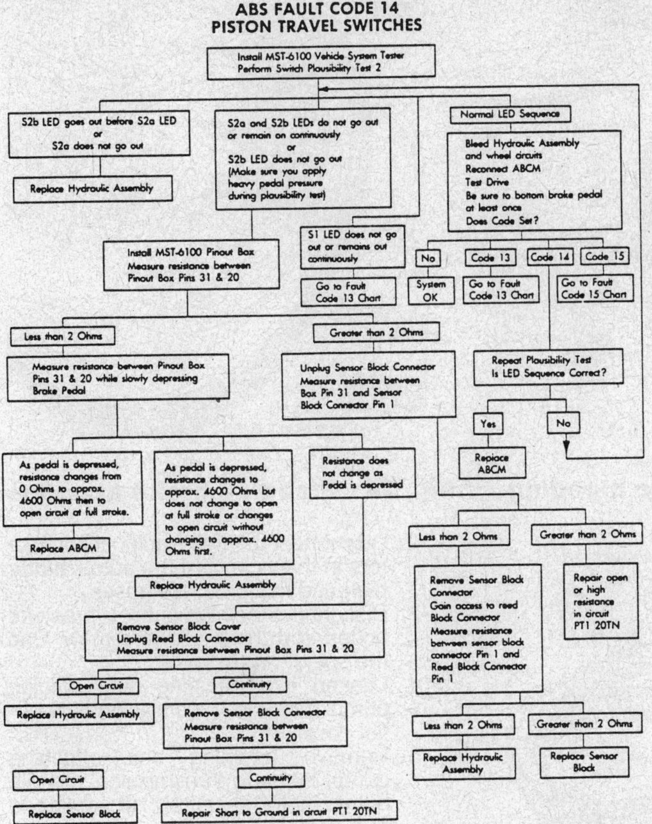


**Fig. 20 Diagnostics for fault code 14 (Part 2 of 4)**

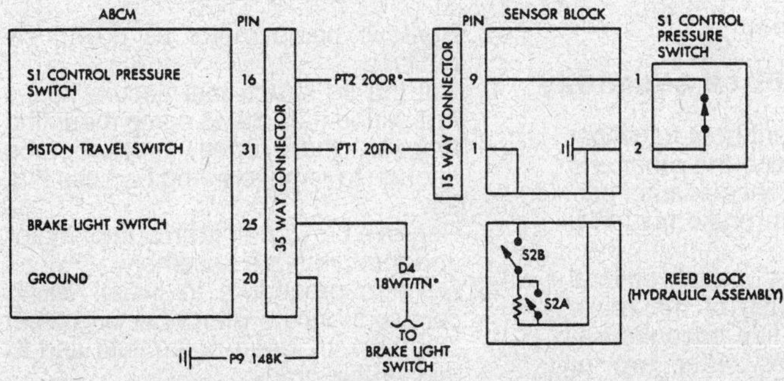


**Fig. 20 Diagnostics for fault codes 13 through 15 (Part 4 of 4)**

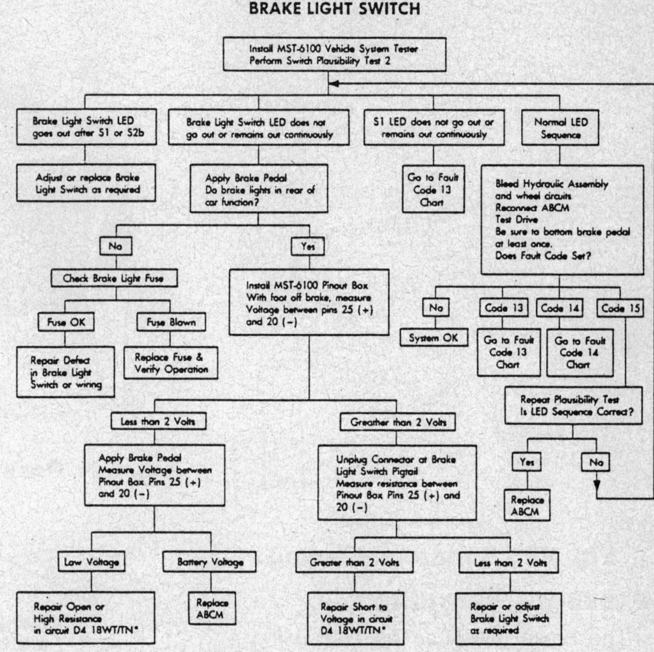


**Fig. 20 Diagnostics for fault code 15 (Part 3 of 4)**

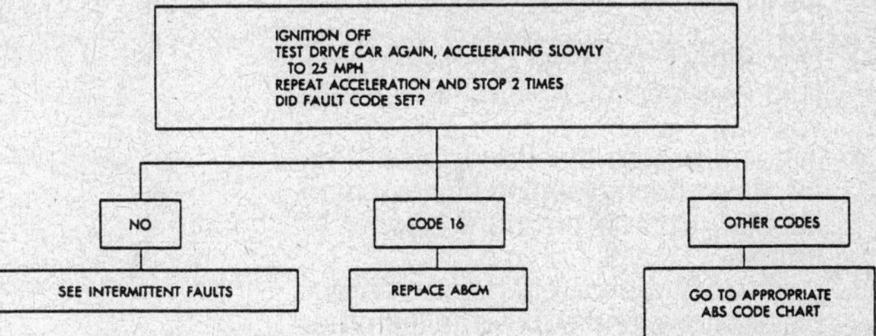


**Fig. 21 Diagnostics for fault code 16**

# SYSTEM SERVICING

## BRAKE BLEEDING

Any time air is allowed to enter the brake system, due to damage or service, the system must be bled. Air in the system will not cause a spongy pedal, but instead may cause a trouble code to appear.

When bleeding brakes, maintain an appropriate level of DOT 3 brake fluid, and do not allow the pump/motor assembly to run continuously for more than 60 seconds. If it becomes necessary to run the pump for more than 60 seconds, allow it to cool for several minutes before running it again.

### Booster Bleeding

1. Depressurize hydraulic accumulator as follows:
   a. Disconnect battery ground cable, and ensure ignition is in the Off position.
   b. Pump the brake pedal at least 25 times with about 50 lbs. of force. A noticeable change in pedal feel should be evident.
   c. When a definite increase in pedal effort is felt, pump pedal a few more times to remove hydraulic pressure from lines.
2. Connect battery negative cable.
3. Check that all brake lines and hoses are tight, and fill fluid reservoir.
4. Connect a transparent hose to the bleeder screw, **Fig. 22,** and place the other end into a clear container to hold brake fluid.
5. Open bleeder screw 1/2 –3/4 of a turn.
6. Turn on the ignition switch to force fluid out the open bleeder. When the fluid flowing from the tube is free of air bubbles, turn off ignition. **If fluid does not flow when ignition is turned on, the pump may need to be primed. First try shaking the pump return hose, with the ignition still on to break up air bubbles. If necessary, turn off ignition, remove pump return hose at one end, fill with brake fluid and reconnect. Attempt bleeding operation again.**
7. Remove bleeder hose, and **torque** bleeder screw to 7.5 ft. lbs. **Do not over torque.**
8. Top off reservoir to correct level, then turn on ignition to allow pump to charge the accumulator. The pump should stop after about 30 seconds.

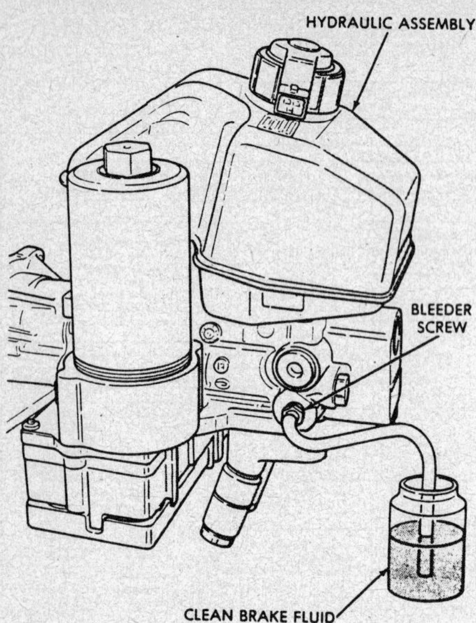


**Fig. 22 Booster bleeding**

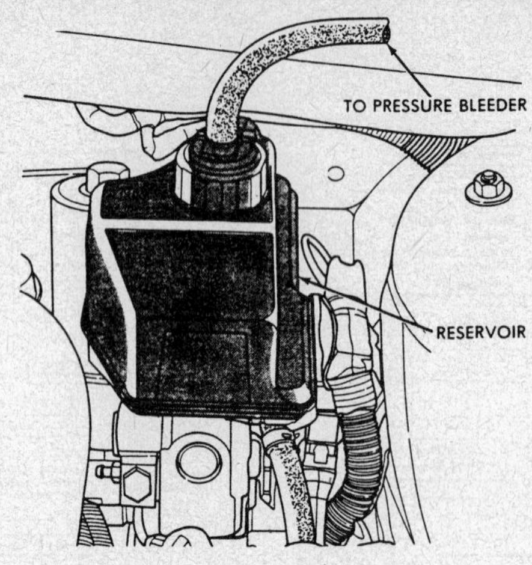


**Fig. 23 Pressure bleeding**

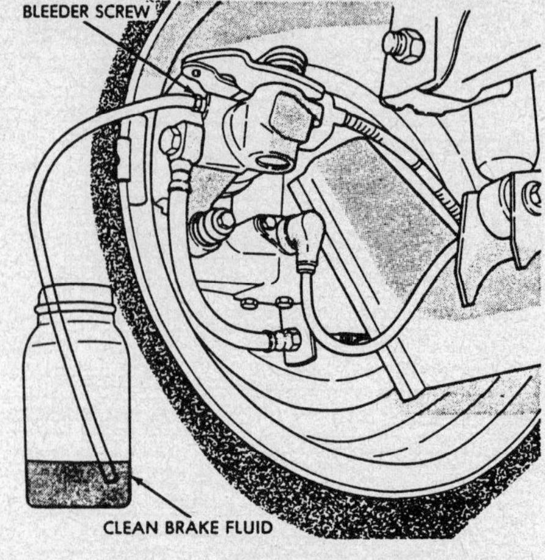


**Fig. 24 Bleeding brake at caliper**

### Pressure Bleeding

The brake lines can be bled using a standard diaphragm type pressure bleeding system. Use only a diaphragm type system to prevent contaminants from entering the system.

1. Ensure ignition remains off for the entire procedure.
2. Depressurize the hydraulic accumulator as outlined under "Booster Bleeding."
3. Disconnect electrical connector from fluid level sensor, then remove reservoir cap.
4. Install pressure bleeder adapter, **Fig. 23,** then attach bleeding equipment to adapter. Charge pressure bleeder to 20 psi.
5. Connect a transparent hose to caliper bleed screw, and submerge the other end in a clear container, partially filled with clean brake fluid **Fig. 24.**
6. Turn pressure bleeder on, then open caliper bleed screw 1/2-3/4 turn allowing fluid to escape until no more air bubbles are present. If reservoir has been drained, or hydraulic assembly removed prior to bleeding, pump the brake pedal slowly one or two times with bleed screw open to purge air from hydraulic assembly.
7. Repeat step 6 for each caliper in the following order: LR-RR-LF-RF.
8. After bleeding all calipers, close the pressure bleeder valve and **torque** to 7.5 ft. lbs., then slowly unscrew the bleeder adapter from the hydraulic assembly reservoir.
9. Use a syringe or other method to remove excess fluid from reservoir and adjust to the full mark.
10. Install reservoir cap, connect the fluid level sensor connector, and turn on ignition to allow pump to charge the accumulator.

### Manual Bleeding

1. Depressurize the hydraulic accumulator as outlined under "Booster Bleeding."

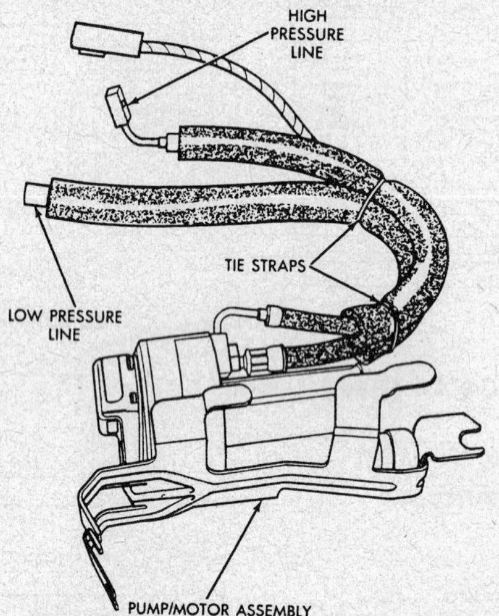


**Fig. 25 Pressure hose assembly**

2. Connect a transparent host to caliper bleed screw, and place the other end of hose in a transparent container partially filled with clean brake fluid **Fig. 24.**
3. Slowly pump brake pedal several times with full strokes of the brake pedal. Allow about five seconds between pedal strokes. After two or three strokes, continue holding pedal under pressure at the bottom of its travel.
4. Open the bleed screw 1/2-3/4 turn. Keep screw open until fluid no longer comes out from bleeder, then tighten bleeder screw and release brake pedal.
5. Repeat this procedure until air bubbles are no longer present in fluid coming from bleeder hose.
6. Repeat for all wheels in the following order: LR-RR-LF-RF.

## PUMP/MOTOR, REPLACE

1. Depressurize hydraulic accumulator as outlined under "Booster Bleeding," then remove the two fresh air intake ducts from engine induction system.
2. Disconnect the five electrical connectors in the vicinity of the pump/motor high and low pressure hoses.
3. Disconnect the high and low pressure hoses from hydraulic assembly. Cap the spigot on reservoir.
4. Loosen two retaining nuts holding pump/motor to transmission differential cover.
5. Remove retaining bolt attaching pump/motor to transmission, then lift pump/motor assembly off studs and out of vehicle.
6. Remove heat shield from pump/motor and discard.
7. Reverse procedure to install, installing a new heat shield and adjusting gearshift linkage as necessary.

## PRESSURE & RETURN HOSES, REPLACE

1. Remove pump/motor as previously outlined.
2. Cut the tie straps that secure hoses and wiring harness to pump mounting bracket, then open bracket tabs enough to remove wiring harness **Fig. 25.**
3. Remove banjo bolt from pump/motor and remove hose assembly.
4. Reverse procedure to install taking care to lubricate all rubber and steel O-rings with clean brake fluid and to replace tie straps.

## HYDRAULIC ASSEMBLY, REPLACE

1. Depressurize hydraulic accumulator as outlined under "Booster Bleeding," then remove fresh air ducts from vehicle.
2. Disconnect electrical connectors from hydraulic assembly, then remove as much fluid as possible from reservoir on hydraulic assembly.
3. Remove pressure hose banjo bolt from hydraulic assembly taking care not to drop the two washers.
4. Disconnect return hose from reservoir nipple and cap spigot on reservoir.
5. Disconnect all brake lines from hydraulic assembly **Fig. 26.**

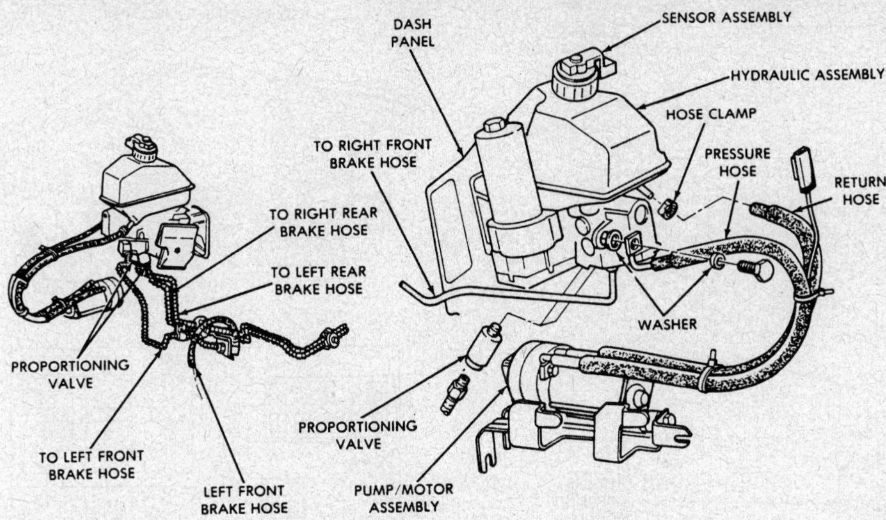


**Fig. 26 Hydraulic assembly**

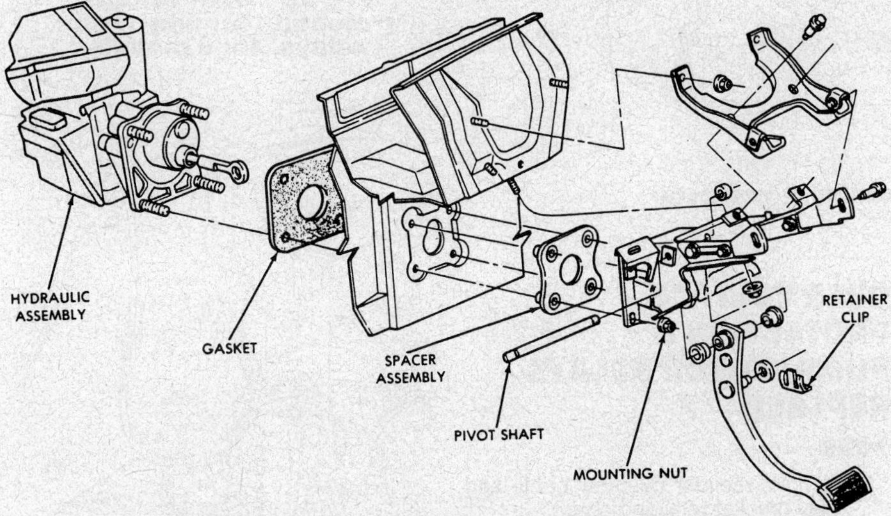


**Fig. 27 Hydraulic assembly & brake pedal assembly**

6. Use a screwdriver to remove the retaining clip from the brake pedal pin under the instrument panel **Fig. 27.**
7. Remove driver's side insulator panel, then remove four hydraulic assembly mounting nuts and hydraulic assembly.
8. Reverse procedure to install, noting the following:
   a. **Torque** hydraulic assembly nuts to 250 inch. lbs.
   b. Use Lubriplate or equivalent lubricant to coat pedal pin bearing surface, then install a new retaining clip.
   c. Ensure brake tubes are correctly installed. The longer tube goes on the inboard proportioning valve, **Fig. 26.**
   d. **Torque** banjo bolt to 160 inch lbs.
   e. Bleed entire brake system.

## RESERVOIR, REPLACE

1. Depressurize hydraulic accumulator as outlined under "Booster Bleeding," then disconnect fluid level sensor.
2. Remove as much brake fluid as possible from reservoir, then disconnect return hose from reservoir nipple.
3. Remove reservoir by gently prying between it and hydraulic assembly, then remove grommets from hydraulic assembly, **Fig. 28.**
4. Reverse procedure to install, noting the following:
   a. Lubricate new grommets with clean brake fluid.
   b. Install reservoir by hand using a slight rocking motion.

## FLUID LEVEL SENSOR, REPLACE

The fluid level sensor, **Fig. 28,** is part of the reservoir cap which must be replaced as an assembly.

## PROPORTIONING VALVES, REPLACE

**Proportioning valves should never be disassembled.**

1. Remove brake tube and fitting from proportioning valve, then remove valve from hydraulic assembly, **Fig. 28.**
2. Install new proportioning valve. **Torque** valve to 20 ft. lbs. and brake tube to 11 ft. lbs.
3. Bleed the affected brake line as outlined under "Brake Bleeding."

## CONTROL PRESSURE SWITCH, REPLACE

1. Depressurize hydraulic accumulator as outlined under "Booster Bleeding," then remove electrical connector from hydraulic assembly, **Fig. 28.**
2. Unscrew pressure switch from hydraulic assembly.
3. Reverse procedure to install. Lubricate O-ring with clean brake fluid before installation.

## SENSOR BLOCK, REPLACE

### Removal

1. Depressurize the hydraulic accumulator as outlined under "Booster Bleeding," then disconnect electrical connectors from hydraulic assembly.
2. Using a screwdriver, remove the retaining clip at the brake pedal pin under the instrument panel **Fig. 27.**
3. Remove driver's side sound insulator panel, then the four hydraulic assembly mounting nuts.
4. From under the hood, remove hydraulic assembly enough to gain access to sensor block, **Fig. 28. Do not remove or deform brake lines.**
5. Remove sensor block cover taking care not to damage gasket.
6. Disconnect the 12 pin valve block connector from sensor block.
7. Pull outward on the reed block connector (marked Push) to disengage it. The connector retaining clip will only move approximately 1/2 inch.
8. Remove three sensor block retaining bolts, then disengage sensor block pressure port from hydraulic and sensor block from car.
9. Inspect O-rings and sensor block for any damage.

### Installation

1. Pull reed block connector to disengaged position.
2. Lubricate pressure port O-ring with clean brake fluid, then insert pressure port into hydraulic assembly orifice without damaging O-ring.
3. Position sensor block, then install mounting bolts and **torque** to 11 ft. lbs.
4. Engage reed block connector by pressing orange connector marked Push.
5. Connect 12 pin valve block connector to sensor block, sensor block cover, gasket and mounting bolt.

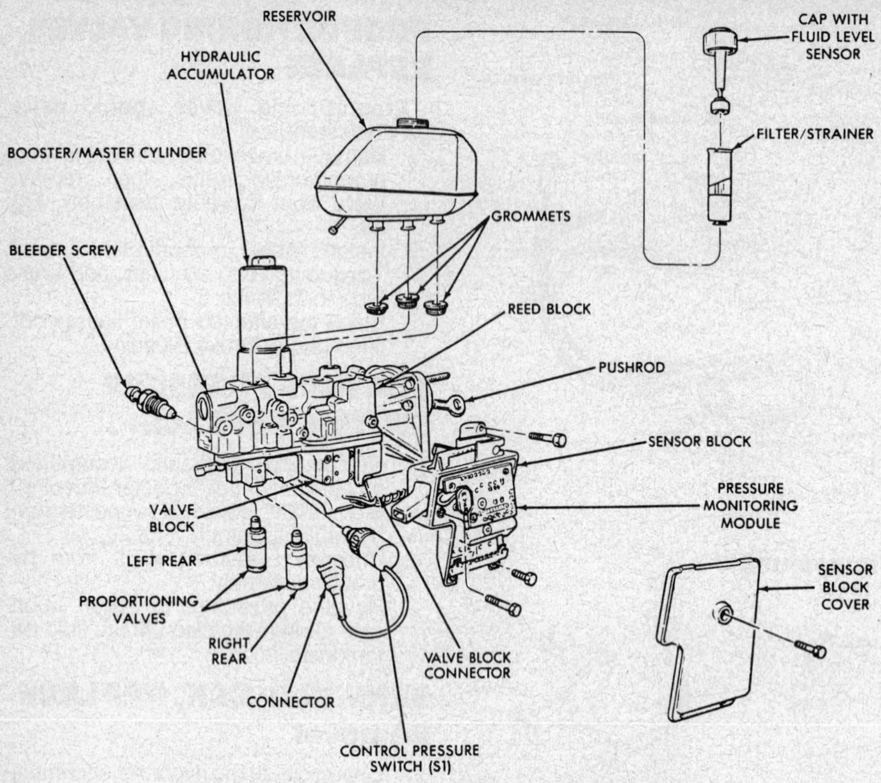


**Fig. 28 Hydraulic assembly & reservoir**

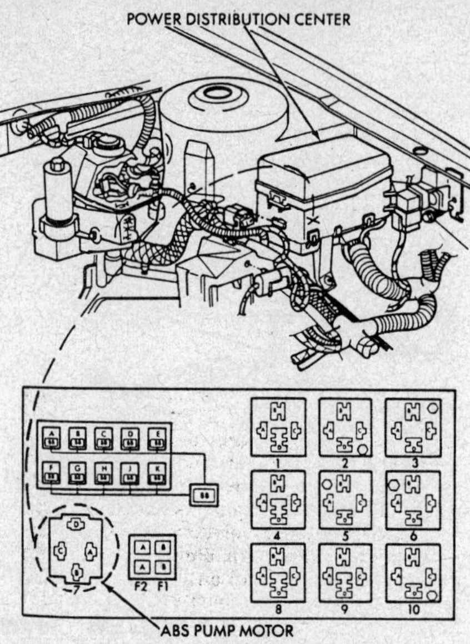


**Fig. 29 Over voltage protection & pump motor relays. 1990 models**

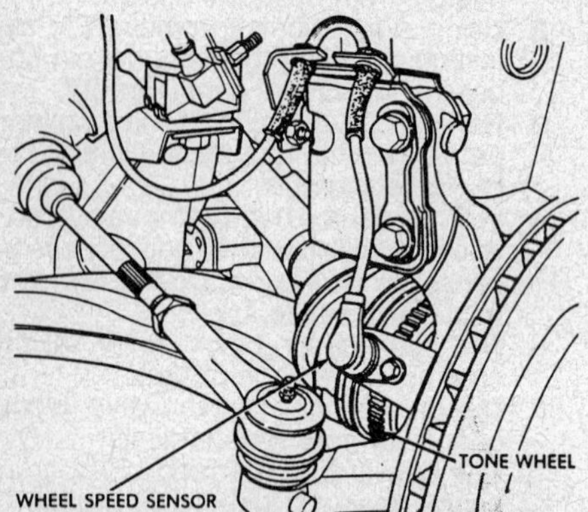


**Fig. 30 Front wheel speed sensor & tonewheel assembly**

6. Connect sensor block and control pressure switch connectors, then reinstall hydraulic assembly.

## ANTI-LOCK BRAKE CONTROL MODULE (ABCM), REPLACE

1. Remove rear seat bulkhead trim panel from trunk.
2. Pull back the lock plate and rotate connector away from ABCM, then remove retaining screws and ABCM.
3. Reverse procedure to install. **Install ground terminal securely.**

## OVER VOLTAGE PROTECTION & PUMP/MOTOR RELAYS, REPLACE

### 1989

1. Remove radiator overflow bottle and relay bracket retaining screw.
2. Disconnect relay from connector.
3. Reverse procedure to install.

### 1990

1. Open Power Distribution Center cover, **Fig. 29.**
2. Remove component by pulling upward.
3. Reverse procedure to install.

## WHEEL SPEED SENSOR (WSS), REPLACE

The wheel speed sensor generates a small AC voltage by magnetic induction as a tonewheel rotates. The front tonewheel is an integral part of the outer CV joint and must be replaced as an assembly with the outer CV joint **Fig. 30.** The rear tonewheel is an integral part of the hub assembly and must be replaced as an assembly with hub assembly.

Inspect tonewheel for missing or damaged teeth which can cause erratic operation. There should not be any contact with wheel speed sensor. Runout of the tonewheel should not exceed .010 inch. Replace assembly if runout exceeds specifications.

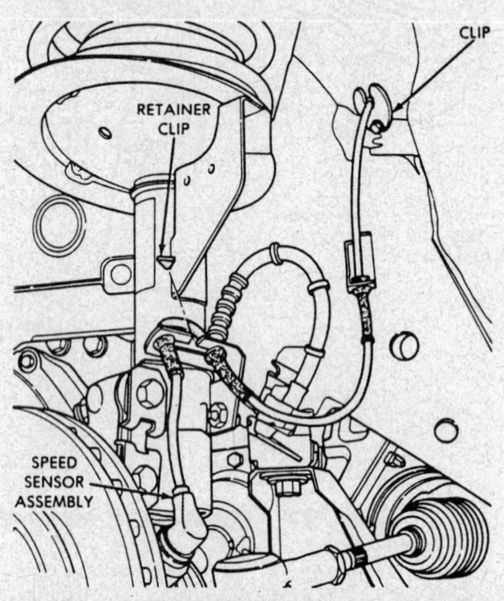


**Fig. 31 Front wheel speed sensor assembly**

## FRONT WHEEL SPEED SENSOR

### Removal

1. Raise and support vehicle.
2. Remove wheel and tire assembly, then the retaining screw and clip from fender shield **Fig. 31.**
3. Carefully remove sensor assembly grommet from fender shield, then remove sensor connector lock and disconnect sensor.
4. Remove strut damper bracket retaining clip.
5. Remove three assembly grommets, then the sensor head screw.
6. Remove sensor head from steering knuckle. If difficult to remove, use a hammer and punch to tap the sensor gently back and forth until free. **Do not use pliers on sensor head.**

### Installation

1. Before installing, coat sensor with suitable high temperature grease. **Torque** to 60 inch lbs.
2. Connect sensor connector to harness, then install connector lock, assembly grommet, clip and screw.
3. Install sensor grommets in brackets, and retainer clip on retainer at strut damper, **Fig. 31.** Proper installation of wheel speed sensor cable is critical to continued system operation. Reinstall as shown in **Fig. 31.**

### REAR WHEEL SPEED SENSOR

1. Raise and support vehicle.
2. Remove wheel and tire assembly, then the sensor assembly grommet and pull harness through hole.
3. Remove connector lock and unplug from harness.
4. Remove spool grommet clip retaining screw from hose bracket just in front of trailing arm bushing
5. Remove assembly clip located at the inboard side of trailing arm, then remove outboard sensor assembly retainer nut.
6. Remove sensor head nut and carefully remove sensor head from adapter. If sensor is difficult to remove, use a hammer and punch to gently tap sensor back and forth until free. **Do not use pliers on sensor head.**
7. Reverse procedure to install being sure to coat sensor with suitable high temperature grease. **Torque** screw to 60 inch lbs.

# SERVICE BULLETINS

## WHEEL SPEED SENSOR CONNECTOR REPLACEMENT

### 1989 NEW YORKER, 1989–90 DYNASTY & NEW YORKER LANDAU & 1990 IMPERIAL, NEW YORKER FIFTH AVENUE & NEW YORKER SALON

### Symptom/Condition

The amber "ANTILOCK" warning lamp is illuminated and a wheel speed sensor fault code (codes 5 through 10) is stored. The fault may be intermittent and replacement of the wheel speed sensor does not correct the problem.

Some vehicles have been found with a cold solder joint on the vehicle harness side of the wheel speed sensor connector. Since this is a molded connector, diagnosis may be difficult.

### Diagnosis

Refer to "Self-Diagnosis" for obtaining fault codes.

Confirm presence of a wheel speed sensor fault to identify the suspect sensor. If a code 9 or 10 is present, test drive the vehicle again, accelerating at a very slow rate until a code 5 through 8 is obtained.

1. Upon illumination of "ANTILOCK" lamp, stop vehicle, but do not turn Off

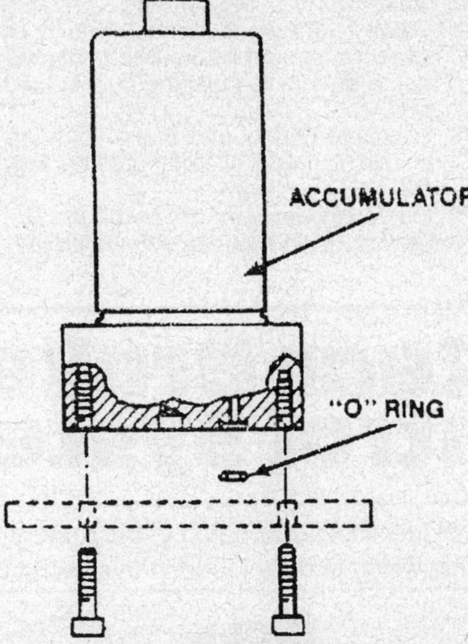


**Fig. 32 Installing accumulator O-ring**

ignition. Apply brakes firmly for 10-15 seconds.
2. Count number of times red "BRAKE" warning lamp flashes. This is the fault code.
3. Fault codes are as follows:
   a. Code 5-Left Front Wheel Speed Sensor.
   b. Code 6-Right Front Wheel Speed Sensor.
   c. Code 7-Right Rear Wheel Speed Sensor.
   d. Code 8-Left Rear Wheel Speed Sensor.
4. Once suspect sensor is identified, install ABS tester MST6100 or equivalent to 35-way connector in trunk and plug cable into pin-out box. Plug leads of an ohmmeter or suitable continuity tester into terminals for suspect wheel speed sensor as follows:
   a. Right front wheel speed sensor, terminals 11 and 21.
   b. Left front wheel speed sensor, terminals 4 and 5.
   c. Right rear wheel speed sensor, terminals 24 and 26.
   d. Left rear wheel speed sensor, terminals 7 and 9.
5. Gain access to suspected wheel speed sensor connector (rear sensor connectors are accessed under vehicle by pulling grommet from body, front sensor connectors are accessed by removing sensor grommet retainer in front wheel well and pulling grommet from body). Gently bend and twist connector while observing ohmmeter for continuity. If continuity is lost at any time, connector should be replaced.

### Connector, Replace

1. Disconnect wheel speed sensor at connector.
2. Trim new connector pigtail wire to a length of approximately four inches.
3. Remove approximately three inches of outer jacket being careful not to damage wire insulators. **Cut one wire back two inches to stagger repair splice.**
4. Prepare harness on vehicle in same manner by cutting off old connector and removing last three inches of outer jacket. **Cut one wire back two inches to stagger repair splice.**
5. Strip ends of wires exposing about $1/2$-$3/4$ inch of bare wire, then slip a piece of shrink tube approximately $1\,1/2$ inches long on each wire.
6. Twist short end of repair connector wire to long end of harness wire, then long end of repair connector to short end of harness. **This will keep splices staggered.**
7. Heat each splice with a suitable high temperature soldering gun, apply rosin core solder until it flows freely, then remove soldering gun and allow to cool. **Do not use acid core solder.**
8. Cover soldered splice with shrink tubing and apply heat using a suitable heat gun.
9. Tape repaired area using friction or suitable electrical tape, then reconnect connector and verify correct operation of antilock brake system.

## HYDRAULIC ASSEMBLY ACCUMULATOR REPLACEMENT

### 1989 DYNASTY, NEW YORKER & NEW YORKER LANDAU

### Symptom/Condition

Vehicle must exhibit all of the following symptoms:

1. BRAKE and ANTI-LOCK warning lamp illuminates during brake pedal application and extinguishes a few seconds later. If vehicle is in motion as the warning lights extinguish, a series of clicks can be heard as the system goes through its self check.
2. ABS Pump/Motor cycles for 1-2 seconds on every brake pedal application.
3. No fault codes are stored.

### Diagnosis

1. Confirm all symptoms above.
2. Turn ignition Off and discharge hydraulic accumulator by pumping brake pedal 25 times minimum.
3. Install hydraulic pressure tester MST-6163 or equivalent per manufacturers instructions.
4. Turn ignition On and observe initial pressure reading. This is accumulator precharge pressure.
5. If accumulator precharge pressure is below 500 psi, replacement of accumulator is necessary.
6. **Before removing pressure tester, turn ignition Off and discharge hydraulic accumulator by pumping brake pedal 25 times minimum.**

### Accumulator, Replace

Replacement of hydraulic accumulator requires removal of the hydraulic assembly from the vehicle. **Do not attempt to replace accumulator with hydraulic assembly installed in vehicle.**

1. Remove hydraulic assembly as described under "Hydraulic Assembly, Replace."
2. Using a No. 30 torx bit, carefully remove accumulator from hydraulic assembly by removing two torx head screws underneath base of accumulator.
3. Clean hydraulic assembly in area of base of accumulator, being careful not to get dirt or cleaning fluid in fluid port.
4. Lubricate O-ring with brake fluid and install on base of accumulator, **Fig. 32.**
5. Install accumulator to hydraulic assembly using new M6 screws provided in repair kit and **torque** to 5-6 ft. lbs., then tighten both screws and additional 90° (1/4 turn).
6. Install hydraulic assembly as described under "Hydraulic Assembly, Replace."
7. Bleed brake system as described under "Brake Bleeding," then inspect for leaks and verify proper operation.
8. Ensure brake fluid is at proper level.

# Type 2—Rear Brake Lock-Up Control System

**NOTE:** Wire Code Identification and Symbol Identification located in the front of this manual can be used as an aid when using wiring circuits found in this section.

## INDEX



## DESCRIPTION

**On Conquest models,** the rear brake lock-up control system is an automatic brake control system and is designed for maximum braking efficiency on wet or icy road surfaces, and to reduce the possibility of the vehicle skidding. The rear brake lock-up control system automatically maintains optimum control of braking according to road conditions. However, this system is designed for rear wheel control only. If the front wheels become locked, the front brakes will not be automatically controlled.

The rear brake lock-up control system is designed to control the relationship between the tires and the road surface (friction factor between tires, road surface and slip rate of tires). By maintaining the maximum friction factor, braking distance can be reduced and lateral stability can be maintained.

There are four major components, **Fig. 1**, in the rear brake lock-up control system which act together to control rear brake operation.

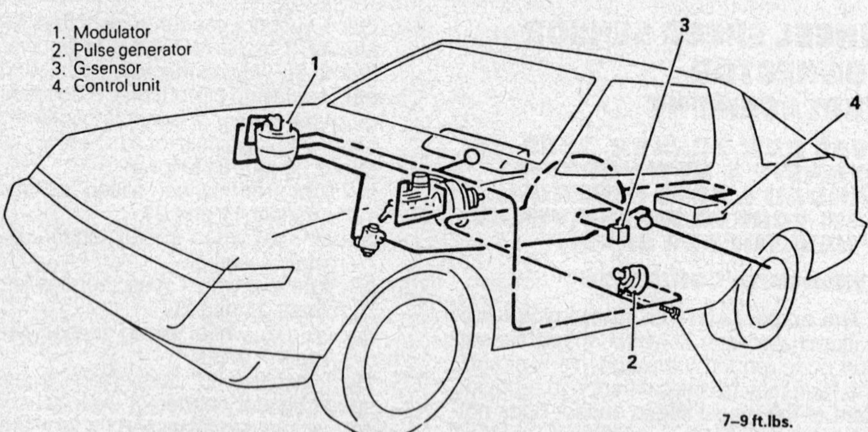


**Fig. 1 Rear Brake Lock-Up Control System major components**

The electronic control unit (ECU) determines the ideal vehicle speed reduction rate using input signals from the G-sensor and pulse generator. The ECU compares the ideal vehicle speed reduction rate and the actual speed reduction rate of the rear wheels. If the actual speed reduction rate of the rear wheels is greater (rotation speed of the wheels is decreasing too rapidly), brake fluid pressure for the rear brakes is decreased, and the ideal rate of vehicle speed reduction is restored. If the actual speed reduction rate of the rear wheels is smaller (rotation speed of the wheels is decreasing too slowly), brake fluid pressure for the rear brakes is increased, and the ideal rate of vehicle speed reduction is restored. In this manner, the rear wheels are controlled to maintain the ideal rate of speed reduction.

In the event of a malfunction in the rear brake lock-up control system, a signal from the ECU causes the warning lamp on the dashboard to illuminate and system operation is interrupted. Normal brake system operation (no rear lock-up control) continues. In addition, the warning light will illuminate for approximately three seconds when the ignition is turned to the On position. If the light does not illuminate, there is a malfunction of the light or the light circuit. If the light remains on, there is a malfunction in the rear brake lock-up control sys-

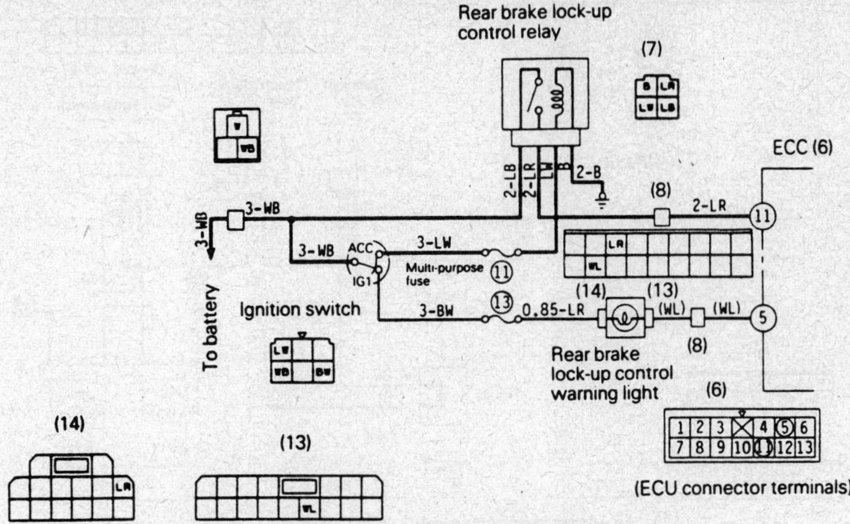

Fig. 2 Power supply circuit diagram

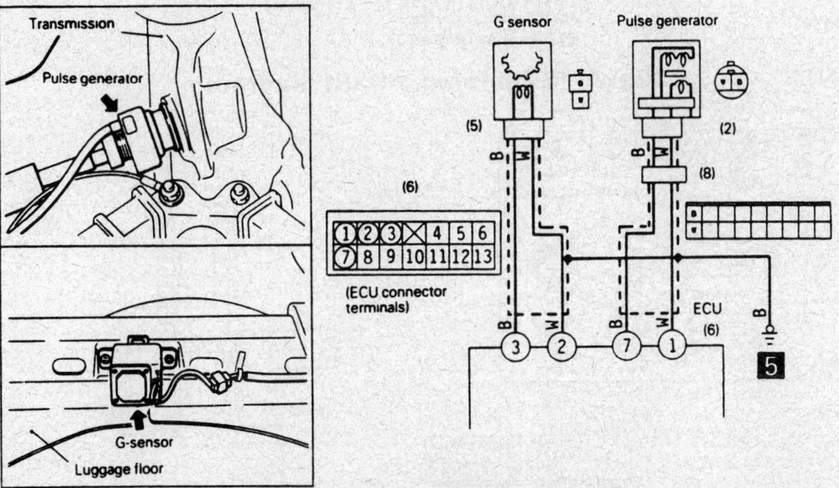

Fig. 3 Sensor circuit diagram

tem. Refer to procedures outlined under "Troubleshooting" and "Component Testing."

## PULSE GENERATOR

The pulse generator is located on the speedometer exit port of the transmission and is used for detection of rear wheel speed. The pulse generator consists of a permanent magnet, coil and rotor. The rotor is turned by the speedometer drive gear. The magnetic flux generated from the permanent magnet varies according to rotation of the rotor, and AC voltage is generated in the coil.

The voltage generated is proportional to the rotating speed of the rotor, and the frequency varies. The speed of the rear wheels is detected by using the frequency variations of the voltage generated by the pulse generator. The frequency of the generated voltage is the average value of the speeds of the left rear and right rear wheels.

## G-SENSOR

The G-sensor is located on the floor of the luggage compartment and is used to detect reduction of vehicle speed. The G-sensor consists of a differential transformer and a control circuit (printed circuit board). The core within the differential transformer is normally stationary at the center of the coil. When a reduction of speed occurs, the core moves and a voltage proportional to the amount of core displacement is generated. This voltage is used to detect the extent of reduction in vehicle speed.

## ELECTRONIC CONTROL UNIT (ECU)

The electronic control unit (ECU) is located inside the luggage compartment and receives signals from the pulse generator, G-sensor and the stop lamp switch. The ECU transmits a brake fluid pressure control signal to the modulator.

The signal to lower the brake fluid pressure of the rear brakes causes the modulator release valve to operate when the amount of slippage of the tires on the road surface is greater than the specified value. The specified value is calculated according to to the relationship between the speed reduction of the wheels and the vehicle. **There is no lock-up control of the rear wheels when the vehicle speed is approximately five mph. or less.**

## MODULATOR

The modulator is a vacuum servo type brake fluid pressure control device located on the righthand side of the engine compartment. Using the control signal (voltage) from the ECU, the modulator controls brake fluid pressure to the rear brakes.

The modulator consists of a brake fluid pressure control section (to control brake fluid pressure for the rear brakes), a vacuum pressure drive section (to drive the brake fluid control section), and a solenoid valve (to control the vacuum pressure of the vacuum pressure drive section).

## TROUBLESHOOTING

If a malfunction occurs in the rear brake lock-up control system, follow the troubleshooting procedures to check system operation. Check all circuits and components (including wiring) except the ECU. If no malfunctions are found in circuits or components, replace ECU.

## HYDRAULIC SYSTEM

1. Brakes lock and vehicle skids: Restriction in modulator hydraulic circuit (clogged orifice). Check fluid pressure as outlined under "Component Testing, Modulator."
2. Brakes lock and vehicle skids: Faulty release solenoid valve in modulator. Check modulator as outlined under "Component Testing, Modulator."
3. Low braking force and efficiency: Restriction in modulator hydraulic circuit (clogged orifice). Check fluid pressure as outlined under "Component Testing, Modulator."
4. Low braking force and efficiency: Faulty build-up solenoid valve in modulator. Check modulator as outlined under "Component Testing, Modulator."

## POWER SUPPLY CIRCUIT

Power is supplied to the ECU through the rear brake lock-up control relay, **Fig. 2.** The rear brake lock-up relay is switched on with the ignition switch in the Accessory or On positions. Supply voltage to the ECU is interrupted with the ignition switch in the Start position.

If there is an open circuit in the power supply circuit (indicated by solid lines on the rear brake lock-up control relay), the warning lamp illuminates when the ignition switch is turned on.

If the supply voltage drops below 10.5 volts, the rear brake lock-up control warning lamp illuminates and the system operation is interrupted. When the supply voltage returns to 10.5 volts, the system operation resumes.

1. Check supply voltage to terminal No. 11 (ECU power supply) of ECU connector as follows:
   a. Disconnect ECU electrical connector.
   b. Connect a suitable multimeter between terminal No. 11 of disconnected ECU connector and ground, **Fig. 2.**

c. With ignition switch in Accessory or On position, voltage indicated should be approximately battery voltage (12 volts).
d. With ignition switch in Off position, voltage indicated should be approximately 0 volts.
e. With ignition switch in Start position, voltage indicated should be approximately 0 volts.

## SENSOR CIRCUIT

Refer to **Fig. 3,** when troubleshooting the sensor circuit.

1. Rear brake lock-up control warning light illuminates, and system operation is interrupted: Sensor signals are not input to the ECU, open circuit in G-sensor, pulse sensor or wiring. Check G-sensor and/or pulse generator as outlined under "Component Testing."
2. Rear brake lock-up control warning light illuminates, and system operation is interrupted: Abnormal sensor signal output (rotor deformation). Check G-sensor and/or pulse generator as outlined under "Component Testing."
3. Rear brake lock-up control warning light illuminates, and system operation is interrupted: Noise (interference) is easily picked up, and speed sensor may generate abnormal signals, damaged or disconnected ground of the shielded line. Check ground connection of the shielded line.

## STOP LIGHT CIRCUIT

When the brake pedal is depressed (stop light switch on), input voltage (12 volts) is applied through the diode to ECU connector terminal No. 8 **Fig. 4,** through circuit indicated by solid lines, and the system operates.

If there is an open in the circuit from the stop light switch to the ECU, or if all the stop light bulbs are burned out, the current flows to the circuit with a resistor (indicated by broken lines). This resistor causes input voltage to ECU connector terminal No. 8 to decrease to approximately 7.5-8.5 volts. This interrupts system operation and the warning lamp will illuminate. Normal brake system operation (no rear lock-up control) continues.

1. Check supply voltage to terminal No. 8 (stop light switch) of ECU connector as follows:
   a. Disconnect ECU electrical connector.
   b. Connect a suitable multimeter between terminal No. 8 of disconnected ECU connector and ground, **Fig. 4.**
   c. With brake pedal depressed, voltage indicated should be approximately 0 volts.
   d. With brake pedal depressed, voltage indicated should be approximately battery voltage (12 volts).

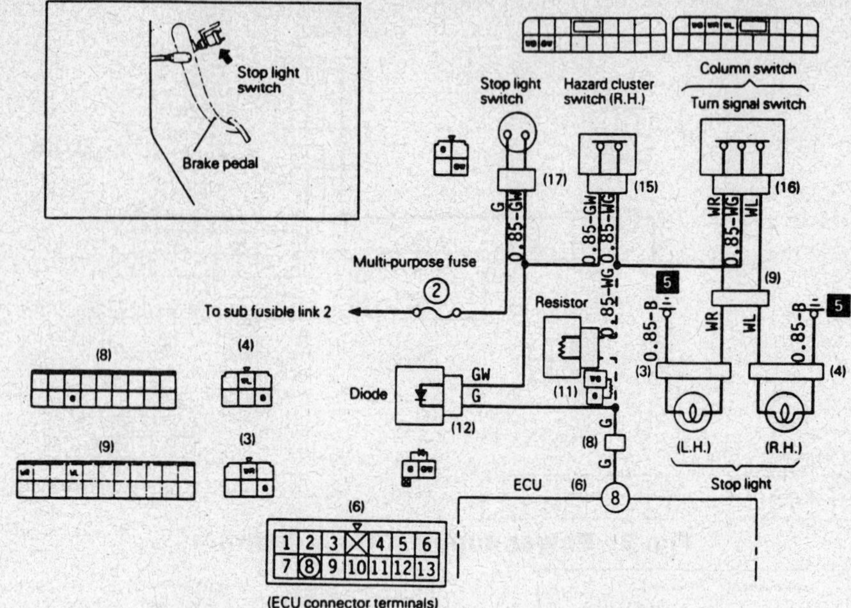


**Fig. 4 Stop lamp circuit diagram**

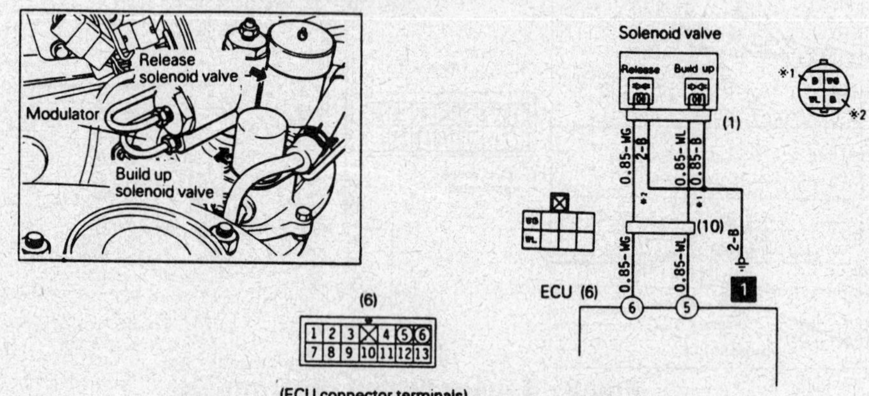


**Fig. 5 Solenoid valve circuit diagram**

## SOLENOID VALVE CIRCUIT

If an open circuit is present in the release solenoid valve, build-up solenoid valve or wiring harness **Fig. 5,** the warning lamp will illuminate and system operation will be interrupted.

If the output transistor for ECU connector terminal Nos. 5 and/or 6 is shorted, the warning lamp will illuminate and system operation will be interrupted.

If the release solenoid valve and/or build-up solenoid valve has continue d to operate for more than five seconds, the warning lamp will illuminate and system operation will be interrupted.

1. Check supply voltage to terminal No. 5 (build-up solenoid valve drive) of ECU connector as follows:
   a. Disconnect ECU electrical connector.
   b. Connect a suitable multimeter between terminal No. 5 of disconnected ECU connector and ground, **Fig. 5.**
   c. With ignition switch in Accessory or On position, voltage indicated should be approximately battery voltage (12 volts).
   d. With ignition switch in Off position, voltage indicated should be approximately 0 volts.
2. Check supply voltage to terminal No. 6 (release solenoid valve drive) of ECU connector as follows:
   a. Disconnect ECU electrical connector.
   b. Connect a suitable multimeter between terminal No. 6 of disconnected ECU connector and ground, **Fig. 5.**
   c. With ignition switch in Accessory or On position, voltage indicated should be approximately battery voltage (12 volts).
   d. With ignition switch in Off position, voltage indicated should be approximately 0 volts.

# DIAGNOSIS & TESTING

## SYSTEM TESTS

### SELF-DIAGNOSIS CHECK

Self-diagnosis system is checked by causing the release solenoid valve to operate.

1. Start and run engine for at least five seconds with vehicle not moving, turn

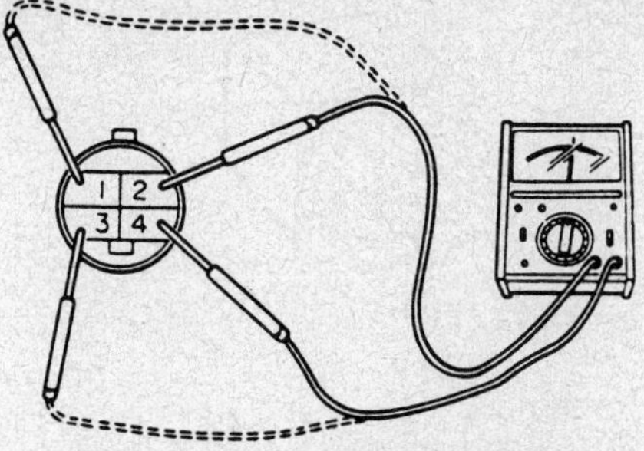


**Fig. 6 Modulator connector terminal identification**

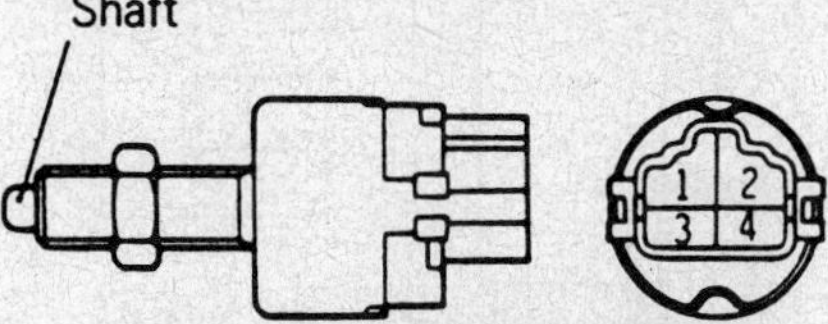


**Fig. 8 Stop light switch connector terminal identification**

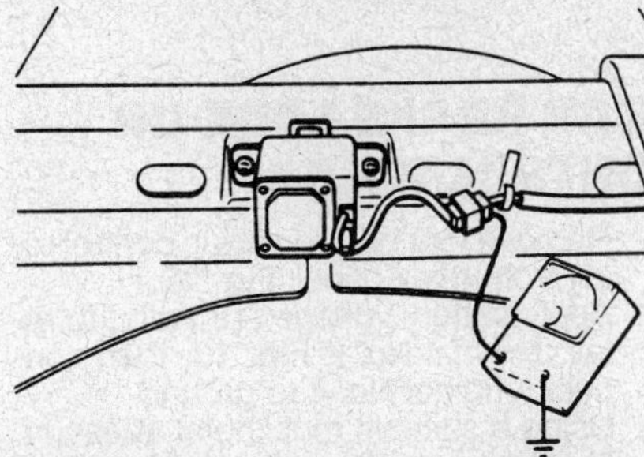

**Fig. 10 Testing G-sensor**

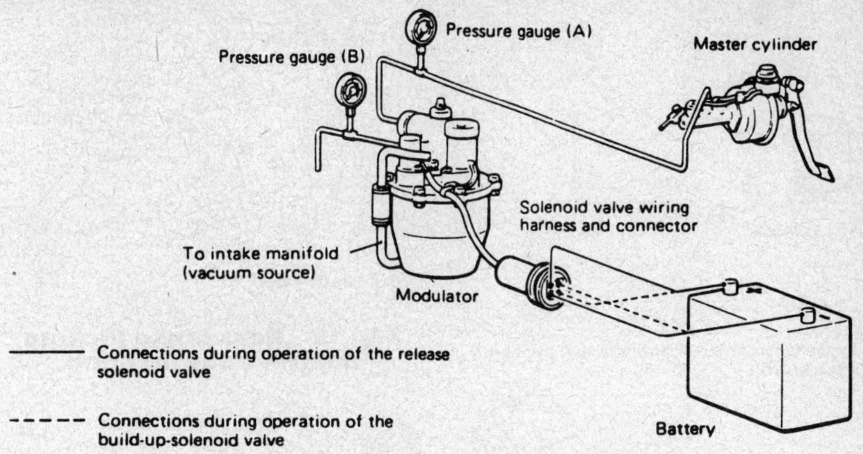


**Fig. 7 Connecting pressure gauge**

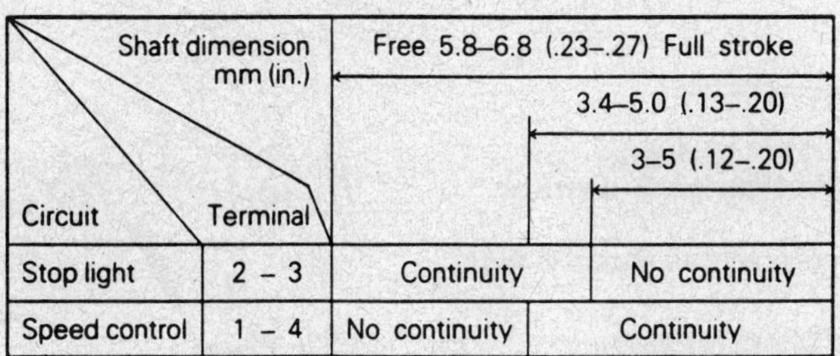

| Circuit | Terminal | Shaft dimension mm (in.): Free 5.8–6.8 (.23–.27) Full stroke | 3.4–5.0 (.13–.20) | 3–5 (.12–.20) |
|---|---|---|---|---|
| Stop light | 2 – 3 | Continuity | | No continuity |
| Speed control | 1 – 4 | No continuity | Continuity | |

**Fig. 9 Stop light switch resistance test**

ignition to Lock position, then depress brake pedal.

2. With brake pedal still depressed, turn ignition from Lock to On position, and ensure the modulator audibly operates.
3. A dull clicking sound indicates the solenoid valve is operating correctly.

### Function Check

1. Raise and support vehicle, ensure rear wheels are completely off the ground, then block front wheels.
2. With engine at normal operating temperature, place shift lever in 2nd gear and accelerate until speedometer indicates approximately 19 mph.
3. While maintaining accelerator pedal position (approximately 19 mph.), suddenly depress brake pedal.
4. The brakes will attempt to stop the rotation of the rear wheels. As the rear brake lock-up control system begins to operate, brake fluid pressure will be reduced, and rotation of the rear wheels will continue. This process should repeat as long as brake pedal is depressed.

# COMPONENT TESTING

## MODULATOR

### ELECTRICAL TEST

1. Disconnect modulator electrical connector.
2. Connect a suitable multimeter between terminals Nos. 1 and 3 (release solenoid valve) of modulator connector **Fig. 6,** and measure resistance.
3. Resistance indicated should be 3.8-4.8 ohms.
4. If resistance indicated is not as specified, replace release solenoid valve.
5. Measure resistance between modulator connector terminals Nos. 2 and 4 (build-up solenoid valve).
6. Resistance indicated should be 4.5-5.5 ohms.
7. If resistance indicated is not as specified, replace build-up solenoid valve.

### Pressure Test

1. Connect suitable pressure gauges (A) and (B) with ranges of 0-2100 psi. or more, as shown in **Fig. 7.** Connect one pressure gauge to the rear brake exit point of modulator (B), and the other gauge between master cylinder and modulator (A).
2. Start engine and allow to run at idle.
3. Depress brake pedal far enough to obtain a pressure reading of approximately 711 psi. on pressure gauge (B), connected to rear brake exit port of modulator.
4. While observing pressure gauge (B), operate release solenoid valve as follows:
   a. Disconnect modulator electrical connector.
   b. Connect 12 volts to terminal No. 1 of modulator connector **Figs. 6 and 7,** then connect terminal No. 3 to ground. **Do not apply 12 volts for more than one minute.**
5. Pressure indicated on pressure gauge (B) should drop to approximately 0 psi. when release solenoid valve is operated.
6. With release solenoid valve still connected, operate build-up solenoid as follows:
   a. Connect 12 volts to terminal No. 2 of modulator connector **Figs. 6 and 7,** then connect terminal No. 4 to ground. **Do not apply to 12 volts for more than one minute.**
7. Disconnect release solenoid valve while observing pressure gauge (B).
8. Pressure indicated should increase to approximately 711 psi. when release solenoid is disconnected.
9. Connect release solenoid valve, then disconnect build-up solenoid valve.
10. While observing pressure gauge (B), disconnect release solenoid valve.
11. Pressure indicated should increase to approximately 710 psi. within one second.
12. With both solenoid valves disconnected, increase fluid pressure of the master cylinder (A), and check the relationship with rear brake fluid pressure (B).
13. Ensure pressure gauge (B) indicates 1,422 psi. with brake pedal depressed until pressure gauge (A) indicates 1,707 psi.
14. If specified values cannot be obtained, replace modulator.

## STOP LIGHT SWITCH

Disconnect stop light switch electrical connector, then operate stop lamp switch

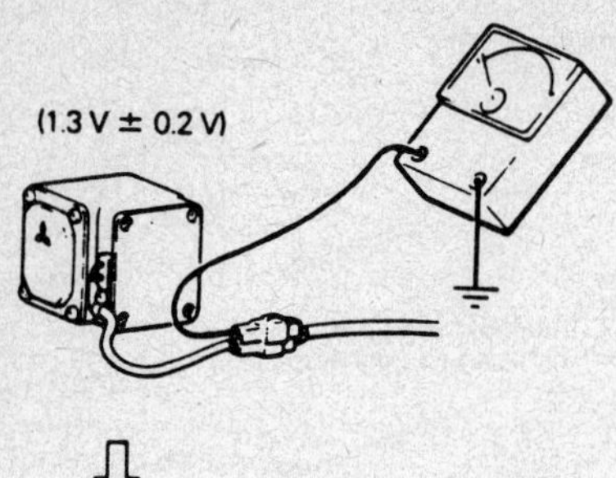


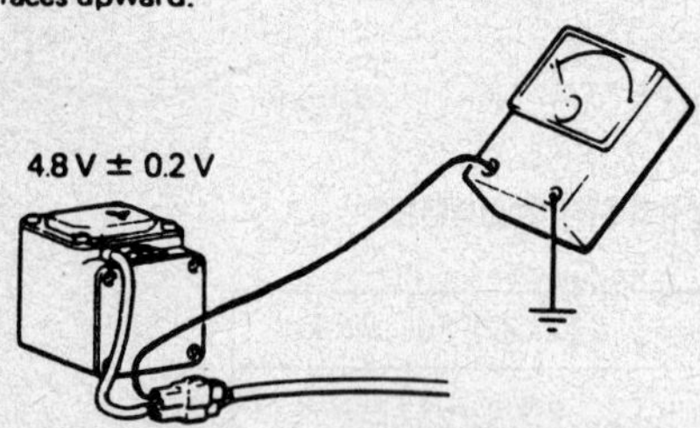


**Fig. 11 Voltage characteristics of G-sensor**

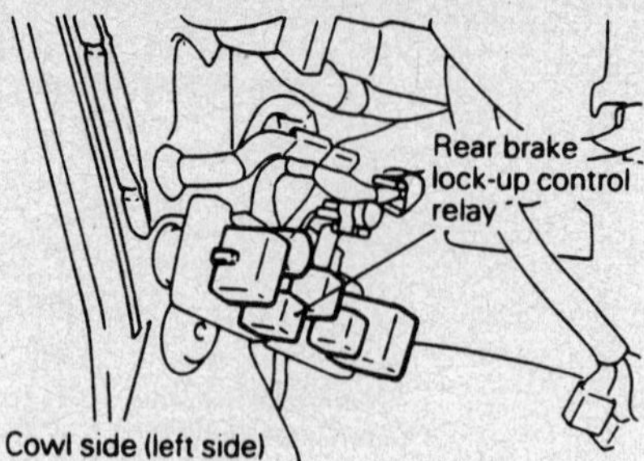


**Fig. 12 Rear brake lock-up control relay location**

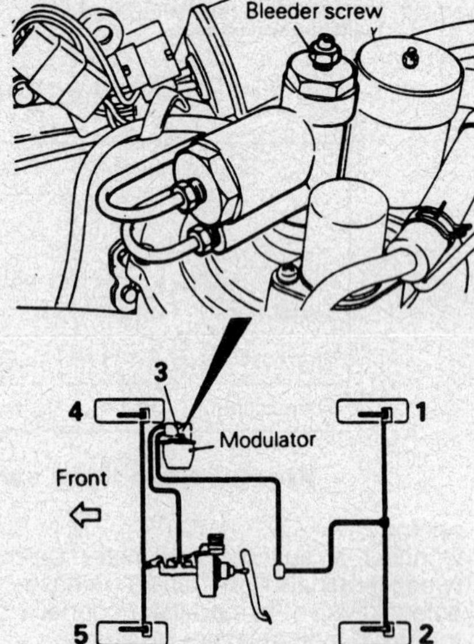


**Fig. 14 Brake system bleeding sequence**

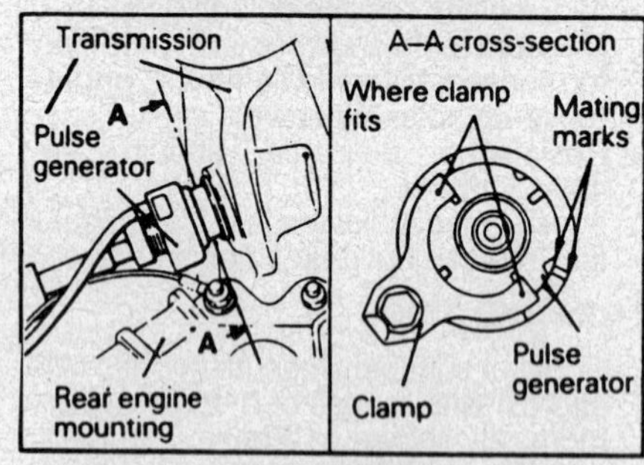


**Fig. 15 Installing pulse generator**

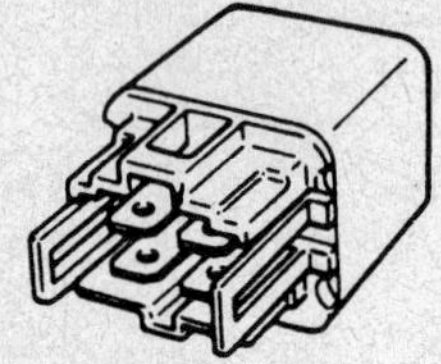

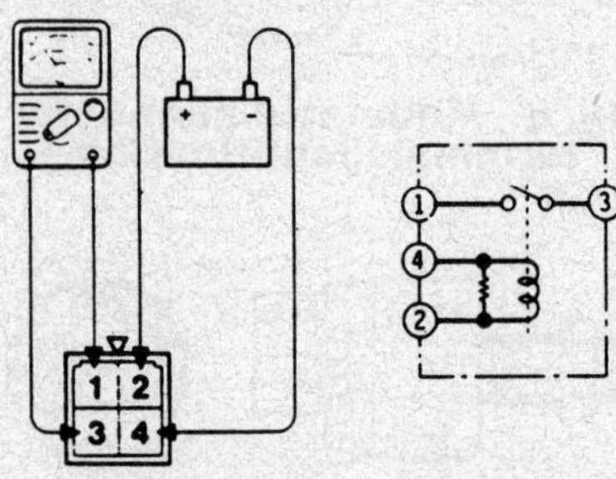

**Fig. 13 Testing rear brake lock-up control relay**

and check for continuity as shown in **Figs. 8 and 9.**

## PULSE GENERATOR

1. Disconnect pulse generator electrical connector.
2. Using a suitable multimeter, measure resistance between pulse generator terminals.
3. Resistance indicated should be 600-800 ohms.
4. If resistance indicated is not as specified, replace pulse generator.
5. Measure resistance between pulse generator terminals and pulse generator case.
6. Infinite ohms should be indicated.
7. If continuity is indicated, replace pulse generator.

## G-SENSOR

1. Ensure G-sensor is correctly mounted as follows:
   a. Position the vehicle, unloaded, on a level surface.
   b. Using a suitable level, ensure G-sensor is within 1° of level in both lateral and longitudinal directions.
   c. Adjust if necessary by installing a suitable shim to bring within 1° of level
2. Ensure no oil leakage is present. If any leaks exist, replace G-sensor.
3. Using a suitable multimeter, measure voltage across red wire of G-sensor and ground, **Fig. 10. Ensure multimeter is set to voltage measurement range before connecting to protect the ECU from possible damage.**
4. Voltage indicated should be 7.0-7.5 volts.
5. If voltage indicated is not as specified, ECU is faulty. Replace ECU.
6. Remove G-sensor, leaving harness connected, then connect G-sensor to ground with a suitable wire.
7. With G-sensor mark positioned as shown in **Fig. 11,** measure voltage across green wire of G-sensor and ground.
8. Voltage indicated should be 1.1-1.5 volts.
9. Turn G-sensor with mark upward, **Fig. 11,** then measure voltage across green wire of G-sensor and ground.
10. Voltage indicated should be 4.6-5.0 volts.
11. If specified voltages are not obtained, replace G-sensor.
12. Install G-sensor, ensuring it is level.

## REAR BRAKE LOCK-UP CONTROL RELAY

1. Remove rear brake lock-up control relay from relay panel, **Fig. 12.**
2. Apply battery voltage (12 volts) to relay terminal No. 2 **Fig. 13,** then connect terminal No. 4 to ground.
3. Using a suitable multimeter, measure resistance between relay terminals Nos. 1 and 3.
4. Continuity should be indicated.
5. Disconnect voltage supply from relay terminal No. 2, then measure resistance between relay terminals Nos. 1 and 3.
6. Infinite ohms should be indicated.
7. With voltage supply disconnected, measure resistance between relay terminals Nos. 2 and 4.
8. Continuity should be indicated.
9. If specified resistance values are not obtained, replace rear brake lock-up control relay.

# SYSTEM SERVICING

## BRAKE BLEEDING

The brake hydraulic system should be bled any time air is allowed to enter the brake system due to damage or service, or if the brake pedal feels spongy when depressed. Bleed the brake system in the sequence shown in **Fig. 14. Bleed modulator prior to bleeding front brakes.**

## MODULATOR, REPLACE

1. Remove two attaching bolts, then the heat protector.
2. Disconnect vacuum hose, brake tube, and solenoid valve connector from modulator.
3. Remove modulator bracket from toeboard, then remove modulator.
4. Reverse procedure to install. Bleed brake system as necessary.

## G-SENSOR, REPLACE

1. Disconnect G-sensor electrical connector.
2. Remove two G-sensor attaching screws, then the G-sensor. **Do not subject G-sensor to any impact or violent shaking.**
3. Reverse procedure to install, noting the following:
   a. Position the vehicle, unloaded, on a level surface.
   b. Using a suitable level, ensure G-sensor is within 1° of level in both lateral and longitudinal directions.
   c. Adjust if necessary by installing a suitable shim to bring within 1° of level.

## PULSE GENERATOR, REPLACE

1. Disconnect speedometer cable at pulse generator side.
2. Remove clamp attaching bolt, then the pulse generator.
3. Reverse procedure to install, noting the following:
   a. Align mating marks of pulse generator and transmission as shown in **Fig. 15.**
   b. Securely fit clamp in grooves in pulse generator body, **Fig. 15.**
   c. **Torque** clamp attaching bolt to 7-9 ft. lbs.

## ELECTRONIC CONTROL UNIT (ECU), REPLACE

1. Disconnect ECU electrical connector.
2. Remove four attaching screws (located under the high floor side panel on the right side of luggage compartment), then remove control unit.
3. Reverse procedure to install.

# Type 3—Bendix Anti-Lock 6 Anti-Lock Braking System

INDEX



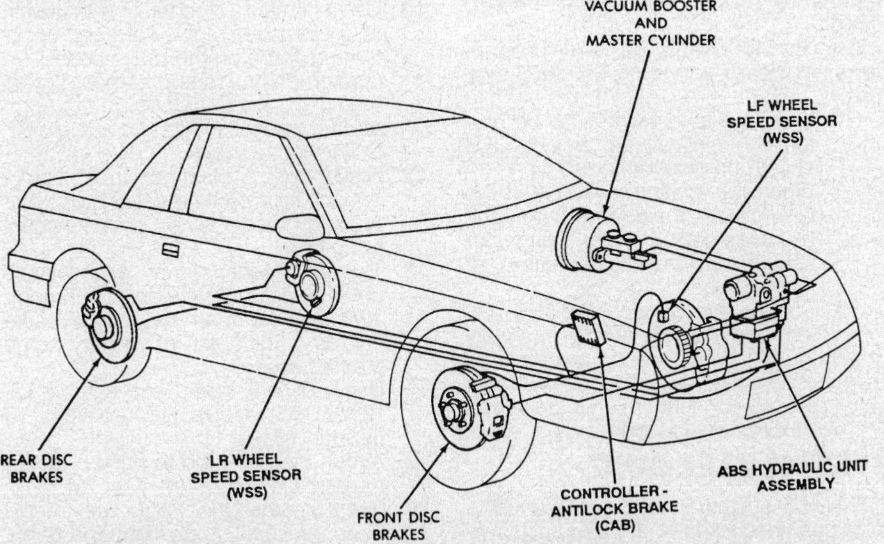


**Fig. 1 Bendix Anti-Lock 6 braking system components**

## DESCRIPTION

The Anti-Lock Braking System (ABS) prevents the wheels from locking up when braking, regardless of the surface conditions. This allows the car to stop in a shorter distance, and allows the driver to maintain directional control of the vehicle during heavy braking.

During normal braking conditions, the ABS operates like a conventional diagonally split, hydraulic power assist system. During heavy braking, however, each wheel's braking pressure is modulated according to its speed. To maintain vehicle stability, both rear wheels receive the same signal.

There are four major components, **Fig. 1**, in the ABS which act in unison to control brake operation.

## SYSTEM COMPONENTS

### MASTER CYLINDER & BRAKE BOOSTER

This system uses the vehicles standard master cylinder and power brake booster. The master cylinder primary and secondary outputs are connected directly to the modulator assembly.

### MODULATOR & PUMP MOTOR ASSEMBLY

This assembly contains the wheel circuit valves used for brake pressure modulation and the pump motor.

The pump motor pumps brake fluid at a low pressure into the ABS accumulator during a stop that requires the ABS system to become operational.

### WHEEL SPEED SENSORS (WSS)

These sensors located at each wheel transmit information to the Controller Anti-Lock Brake (CAB).

### CONTROLLER-ANTILOCK BRAKE (CAB)

This control computer using signals from the wheel speed sensors, controls the Anti-Lock operation and monitors system operation.

## DIAGNOSIS & TESTING

The Bendix Anti-Lock 6 Braking System has self diagnosis capability. The self diagnosis cycle begins when the ignition switch is in the ON position. An electrical check is completed on the ABS components such as wheel speed sensors continuity, system continuity and other relay continuity. During this check the Anti-Lock

Light will be on for approximately one to two seconds.

Once the vehicle is set into motion the solenoid valves and pump motor are activated briefly to verify proper operation. The voltage output of the speed sensors is verified to be within the correct operating range.

If the vehicle is not set into motion within three minutes from the time the ignition is set to the ON position. The solenoid test is bypassed but the pump motor will be activated briefly to verify proper operation.

## ABS WARNING LIGHT

The Anti-Lock warning light will normally come on for approximately one to two seconds when the ignition switch is first turned to the ON position.

Anytime the Controller-AntiLock Brake (CAB) detects a condition which results in a shutdown of the ABS function other than when the ignition switch is first turned on it will activate the ABS warning lamp. When the light is on only the Anti-Lock function of the brake system is affected. The standard brake system and ability to stop the vehicle will not be affected.

## SYSTEM SELF DIAGNOSIS

This ABS system has a self-diagnosis connector located under the fuse panel access cover. The access cover is located on the lower section of the instrument panel to the left of the steering column. The ABS diagnostic connector is a blue 6-way connector which can be connected to a DRB II diagnostic readout box.

Any fault codes present in the CAB memory will be displayed on the DRB II. There are 16 fault codes which may be stored and displayed. These fault codes will remain in the CAB memory even after the ignition is turned off.

Some fault codes detected by the CAB are latching, and ABS is disabled until the ignition switch is reset, even if the original fault has disappeared.

Other faults are non-latching, any warning lights that are illuminated are only illuminated as long as the fault exists. As soon as the fault goes away, the light(s) are extinguished, although a fault code will be set in most cases.

### Visual Inspection

Visually inspect system components and their connectors as described below prior to performing diagnostic tests.

1. Inspect brake fluid level, and ensure that fluid is not contaminated.
2. Inspect brake lines and master cylinder for leaks and/or damage.
3. Inspect ABS hydraulic unit for leaks, and ensure that hydraulic unit 10-way and differential pressure switch (Delta P) electrical connectors are not damaged or disconnected.
4. Inspect CAB for a secure mounting, and ensure that its electrical connector is not damaged or loose.
5. Inspect pump/motor, warning lamp and system relay connectors for any terminal corrosion, damage or improper connections.
6. Inspect all wheel speed sensors (WSS) and their connectors for damage or disconnection.

### Diagnostic Tests

Refer to wiring diagram and connector identification, **Figs. 2 and 3,** when performing testing procedures.

Refer to **Figs. 4 through 38** for diagnostic test procedures, noting the following:

1. Connect Diagnostic Readout Box (DRB II) following manufacturers instructions. **All diagnostic test procedures assume DRB II is being used, and have been designed specifically for the DRB II.**
2. After completion of diagnosis and repair of the system, perform verification test 20A.

## CLEARING FAULT CODES

Fault codes can be cleared by using the DRB II diagnostics tester, or they will be automatically cleared after 50 ignition switch ON/OFF cycles.

# SYSTEM SERVICE

**Certain components of the ABS system are not intended to be serviced individually. Attempting to remove or disconnect certain system components, may result in personal injury and/or improper system operation. Only the components with removal and installation procedures should be serviced.**

**Use the following general precautions whenever servicing the ABS system:**

1. If any welding work is to be performed using an arc welder, CAB should be disconnected.
2. When the ignition switch is in the ON position, the CAB and modulator assembly 10-way connector should not be disconnected or connected.
3. Some components of the ABS system are not serviced separately and must be serviced as complete assemblies. Do not disassemble any component which is designated as non-serviceable.

## SYSTEM BLEEDING

The ABS system must be bled anytime air is permitted to enter the hydraulic system. If the modulator assembly is removed from the vehicle. Both the hydraulic and ABS systems will have to be bled. The ABS system must be bled separately from the hydraulic portion of the braking system, using a DRB II tester.

During bleeding procedures, ensure that the brake fluid level remains close to the full level in the reservoir. Check the fluid periodically during the bleeding procedure.

**When bleeding the modulator assembly wear safety glasses. A bleed tube should be attached to the bleeder screws, to direct flow of brake fluid away from the painted surfaces of the vehicle. Brake fluid at high pressure may come out of the bleeder screws when they are opened.**

The modulator assembly must be bled in the following sequence; No. 1 secondary sump, No. 2 primary sump, No. 3 primary accumulator and No. 4 secondary accumulator. To ensure proper operation of the ABS system.

1. Remove battery to gain access to modulator assembly No. 4 bleeder screws, then connect a battery to the vehicle using jumper cables.
2. Connect DRB II to diagnostic connector and ensure that CAB has no fault codes stored in its memory.
3. Attach bleeder tube to secondary sump bleeder screw, **Fig. 39.**
4. Use a pressure bleeder, or with the aid of an assistant, apply light and constant pressure on the brake pedal.
5. Loosen secondary sump bleeder screw, then using the DRB II select the Actuate Valves test mode and actuate LF Build/Decay Valve.
6. Bleed until a clear air free flow of brake fluid is coming out of the secondary sump bleeder screw, or brake pedal bottoms.
7. Tighten bleeder screw and release brake pedal, repeat steps 4 through 6 until a clean air free flow of brake fluid is coming out of secondary sump bleeder screw.
8. Using DRB II, select and actuate RR Build/Decay Valve. Repeat steps 4 through 7.
9. Attach bleeder tube to primary sump bleeder screw, **Fig. 39.**
10. Use a pressure bleeder, or with the aid of an assistant, apply light and constant pressure on the brake pedal.
11. Loosen primary sump bleeder screw, then using the DRB II select the Actuate Valves test mode and actuate RF Build/Decay Valve.
12. Bleed until a clear air free flow of brake fluid is coming out of the primary sump bleeder screw, or brake pedal bottoms.
13. Tighten bleeder screw and release brake pedal, repeat steps 10 through 12 until a clean air free flow of brake fluid is coming out of primary sump bleeder screw.
14. Using DRB II, select and actuate LR Build/Decay Valve. Repeat steps 10 through 13.
15. Attach bleeder tube to primary accumulator bleeder screw, **Fig. 39.**
16. Use a pressure bleeder, or with the aid of an assistant, apply light and constant pressure on the brake pedal.
17. Loosen primary accumulator bleeder screw, then using the DRB II select the Actuate Valves test mode and actuate RF/LR Isolation Valve.
18. Bleed until a clear air free flow of brake fluid is coming out of the primary accumulator bleeder screw, or brake pedal bottoms.
19. Tighten bleeder screw and release brake pedal, repeat steps 16 through 18 until a clean air free flow of brake fluid is coming out of primary accumulator bleeder screw.
20. Using DRB II, select and actuate RF Build/Decay Valve. Repeat steps 16 through 19.
21. Attach bleeder tube to secondary ac-

*Continued on page 16-35*

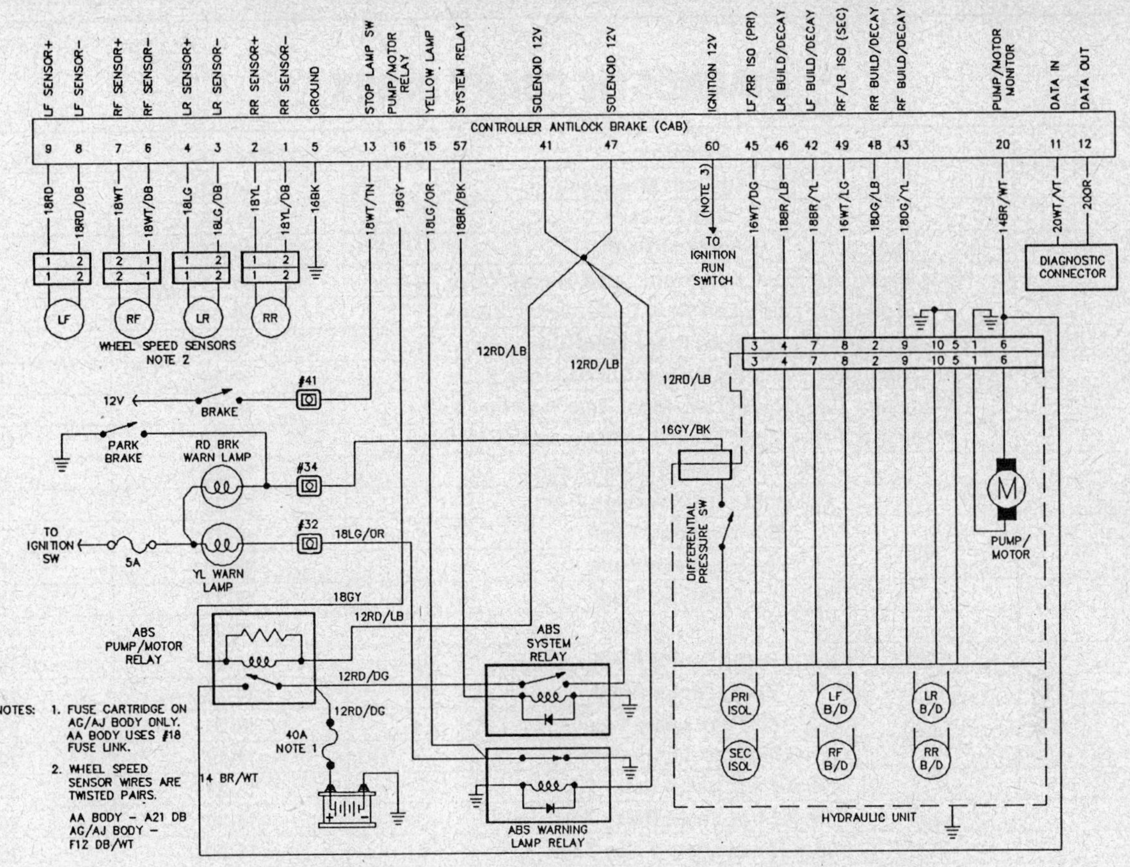


**Fig. 2 Bendix Anti-Lock 6 braking system wiring diagram**

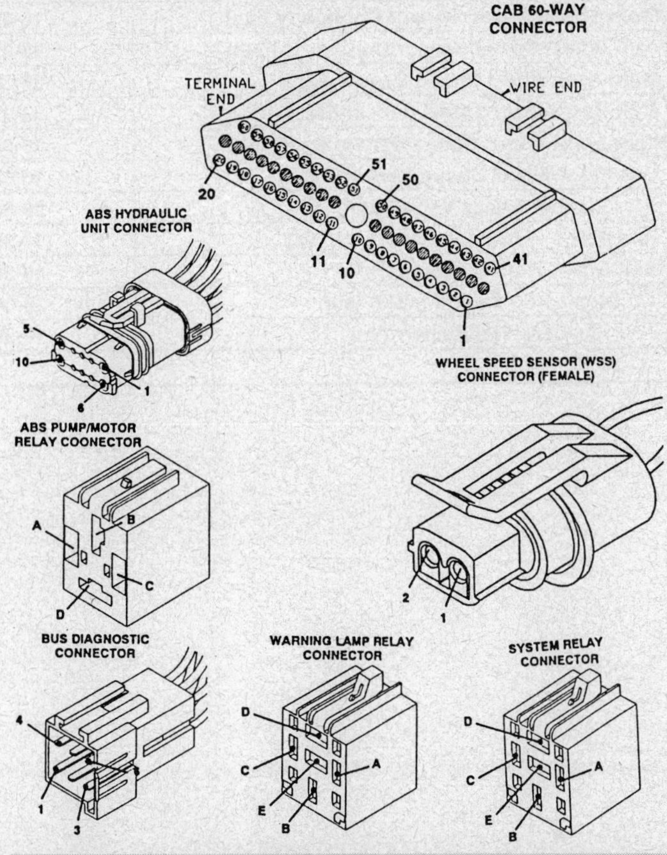


**Fig. 3 Bendix Anti-Lock 6 braking system connector identification**

## DIAGNOSTIC CHART INDEX

| Test No. | Symptom | Page No. | Fig. No. |
|---|---|---|---|
| 1A | Reading Fault Messages | 16-23 | 4 |
| 2A | Cab Fault | 16-23 | 5 |
| 3A | Modulator Fault | 16-23 | 6 |
| 3B | Modulator Fault, Left Front Build/Decay Valve | 16-24 | 7 |
| 3C | Modulator Fault, Left Rear Build/Decay Valve | 16-24 | 8 |
| 3D | Modulator Fault, Right Front Build/Decay Valve | 16-25 | 9 |
| 3E | Modulator Fault, Right Rear Build/Decay Valve | 16-25 | 10 |
| 3F | Modulator Fault, Left Front/Right Rear Isolation Valve | 16-25 | 11 |
| 3G | Modulator Fault, Right Front/Left Rear Isolation Valve | 16-25 | 12 |
| 4A | Solenoid Under Voltage Fault | 16-26 | 13 |
| 4B | Solenoid Under Voltage Fault | 16-26 | 14 |
| 5A | System Relay Fault | 16-27 | 15 |
| 5B | System Relay Fault | 16-28 | 16 |
| 6A | Pump/Motor Fault | 16-28 | 17 |
| 6B | Pump/Motor Fault | 16-28 | 18 |
| 6C | Pump/Motor Fault | 16-28 | 19 |
| 6D | Pump/Motor Fault | 16-29 | 20 |
| 7A | Anti-Lock Lamp Fault | 16-29 | 21 |
| 7B | Anti-Lock Lamp Fault | 16-29 | 22 |
| 8A | Anti-Lock Lamp Relay Fault | 16-29 | 23 |
| 8B | Anti-Lock Lamp Relay Fault | 16-30 | 24 |
| 8C | Anti-Lock Lamp Relay Fault | 16-30 | 25 |
| 9A | Right Rear Wheel Speed Sensor Continuity Fault | 16-31 | 26 |
| 10A | Left Rear Wheel Speed Sensor Continuity Fault | 16-31 | 27 |
| 11A | Right Front Wheel Speed Sensor Continuity Fault | 16-32 | 28 |
| 12A | Left Front Wheel Speed Sensor Continuity Fault | 16-32 | 29 |
| 13A | Right Rear Wheel Speed Sensor Fault | 16-33 | 30 |
| 14A | Left Rear Wheel Speed Sensor Fault | 16-33 | 31 |
| 15A | Right Front Wheel Speed Sensor Fault | 16-33 | 32 |
| 16A | Left Front Wheel Speed Sensor Fault | 16-33 | 33 |
| 17A | Excess Decay Valve Fault | 16-34 | 34 |
| 18A | Red Brake Warning Lamp Input Test | 16-34 | 35 |
| 18B | Red Brake Warning Lamp Input Test | 16-34 | 36 |
| 19A | Stop Lamp Switch Input Test | 16-34 | 37 |
| 20A | System Verification Test | 16-38 | 38 |

Read faults. If there are no fault messages present, perform TEST 19A.

In some instances the cause of one fault message may trigger the setting of an additional fault message. If multiple fault messages appear on the DRBII when reading faults, fault repairs must be performed in the order in which they are displayed in the chart below. If only one fault has occurred, perform the indicated test for that fault message.

**NOTE:** If a fault has occurred more than 2 key cycles ago, perform the Verification Test procedure (TEST 20A) before any attempt is made to diagnose that particular fault message.

| | |
|---|---|
| CAB FAULT | PERFORM TEST 2A |
| MODULATOR FAULT | PERFORM TEST 3A |
| SOLENOID UNDERVOLTAGE FAULT | PERFORM TEST 4A |
| SYSTEM RELAY FAULT | PERFORM TEST 5A |
| PUMP/MOTOR FAULT | PERFORM TEST 6A |
| ANTILOCK LAMP FAULT | PERFORM TEST 7A |
| ANTILOCK LAMP RELAY FAULT | PERFORM TEST 8A |
| RR WHEEL SPEED SENS CONTINUITY FAULT | PERFORM TEST 9A |
| LR WHEEL SPEED SENS CONTINUITY FAULT | PERFORM TEST 10A |
| RF WHEEL SPEED SENS CONTINUITY FAULT | PERFORM TEST 11A |
| LF WHEEL SPEED SENS CONTINUITY FAULT | PERFORM TEST 12A |
| RIGHT REAR WHEEL SPEED SENSOR FAULT | PERFORM TEST 13A |
| LEFT REAR WHEEL SPEED SENSOR FAULT | PERFORM TEST 14A |
| RIGHT FRONT WHEEL SPEED SENSOR FAULT | PERFORM TEST 15A |
| LEFT FRONT WHEEL SPEED SENSOR FAULT | PERFORM TEST 16A |
| EXCESS DECAY FAULT | PERFORM TEST 17A |

**Fig. 4 Test 1A—Reading Fault Messages**

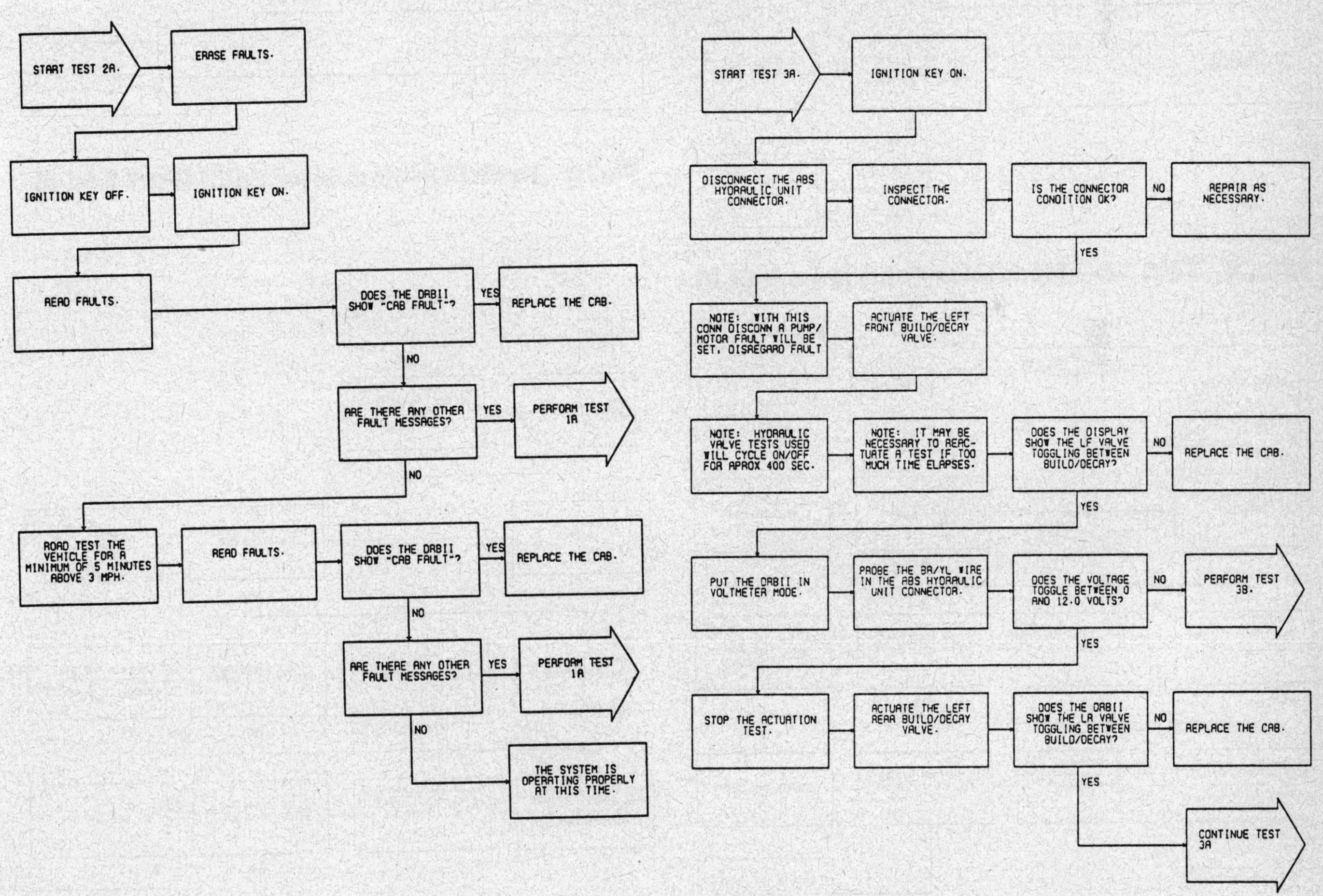


**Fig. 5 Test 2A—Cab Fault**

**Fig. 6 Test 3A—Modulator Fault (Part 1 Of 3)**

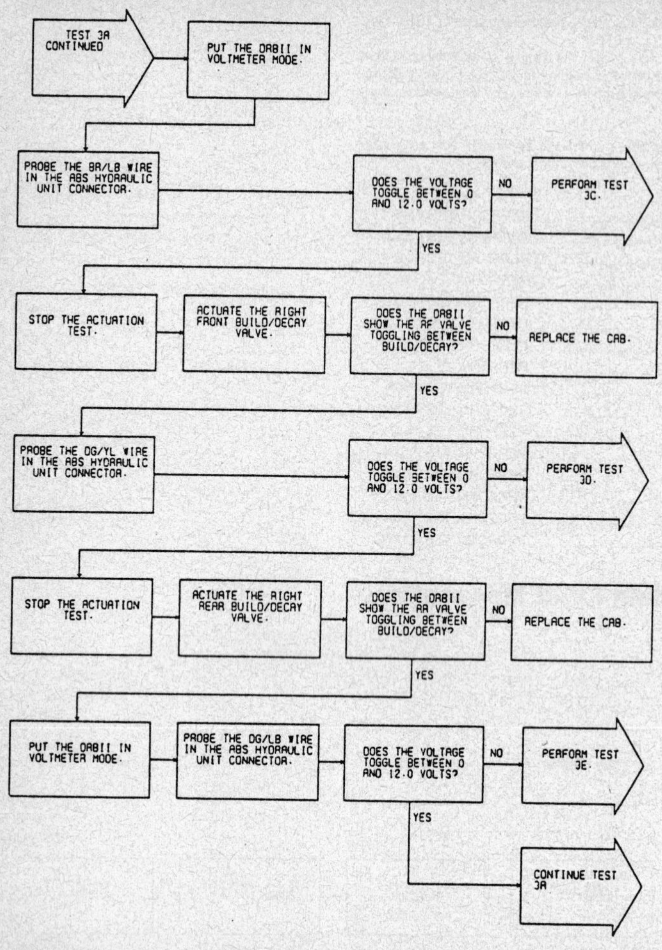

TEST 3A CONTINUED
PUT THE DRBII IN VOLTMETER MODE.
PROBE THE BR/LB WIRE IN THE ABS HYDRAULIC UNIT CONNECTOR.
DOES THE VOLTAGE TOGGLE BETWEEN 0 AND 12.0 VOLTS?
NO
PERFORM TEST 3C.
YES
STOP THE ACTUATION TEST.
ACTUATE THE RIGHT FRONT BUILD/DECAY VALVE.
DOES THE DRBII SHOW THE RF VALVE TOGGLING BETWEEN BUILD/DECAY?
NO
REPLACE THE CAB.
YES
PROBE THE DG/YL WIRE IN THE ABS HYDRAULIC UNIT CONNECTOR.
DOES THE VOLTAGE TOGGLE BETWEEN 0 AND 12.0 VOLTS?
NO
PERFORM TEST 3D.
YES
STOP THE ACTUATION TEST.
ACTUATE THE RIGHT REAR BUILD/DECAY VALVE.
DOES THE DRBII SHOW THE RR VALVE TOGGLING BETWEEN BUILD/DECAY?
NO
REPLACE THE CAB.
YES
PUT THE DRBII IN VOLTMETER MODE.
PROBE THE DG/LB WIRE IN THE ABS HYDRAULIC UNIT CONNECTOR.
DOES THE VOLTAGE TOGGLE BETWEEN 0 AND 12.0 VOLTS?
NO
PERFORM TEST 3E.
YES
CONTINUE TEST 3A

**Fig. 6 Test 3A—Modulator Fault (Part 2 Of 3)**

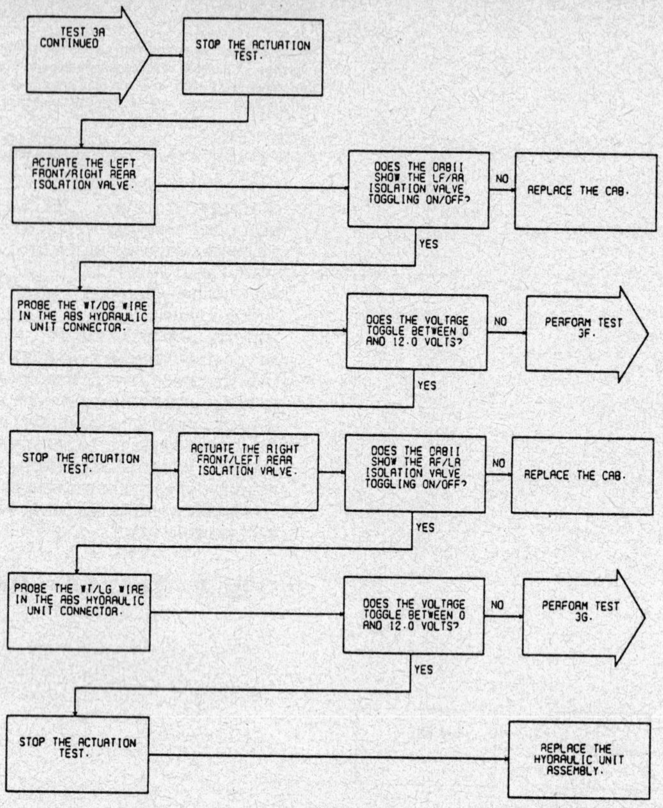

TEST 3A CONTINUED
STOP THE ACTUATION TEST.
ACTUATE THE LEFT FRONT/RIGHT REAR ISOLATION VALVE.
DOES THE DRBII SHOW THE LF/RR ISOLATION VALVE TOGGLING ON/OFF?
NO
REPLACE THE CAB.
YES
PROBE THE WT/DG WIRE IN THE ABS HYDRAULIC UNIT CONNECTOR.
DOES THE VOLTAGE TOGGLE BETWEEN 0 AND 12.0 VOLTS?
NO
PERFORM TEST 3F.
YES
STOP THE ACTUATION TEST.
ACTUATE THE RIGHT FRONT/LEFT REAR ISOLATION VALVE.
DOES THE DRBII SHOW THE RF/LR ISOLATION VALVE TOGGLING ON/OFF?
NO
REPLACE THE CAB.
YES
PROBE THE WT/LG WIRE IN THE ABS HYDRAULIC UNIT CONNECTOR.
DOES THE VOLTAGE TOGGLE BETWEEN 0 AND 12.0 VOLTS?
NO
PERFORM TEST 3G.
YES
STOP THE ACTUATION TEST.
REPLACE THE HYDRAULIC UNIT ASSEMBLY.

**Fig. 6 Test 3A—Modulator Fault (Part 3 Of 3)**

START TEST 3B.
DISCONNECT THE CAB 60-WAY CONNECTOR.
INSPECT THE CONNECTOR.
IS THE CONNECTOR CONDITION OK?
NO
REPAIR AS NECESSARY.
YES
PUT THE DRBII IN OHMMETER MODE.
PROBE THE BR/YL WIRE IN THE ABS HYDRAULIC UNIT CONNECTOR.
IS THE RESISTANCE BELOW 10.0 OHMS?
YES
REPAIR THE B142 BR/YL WIRE FOR A SHORT TO GROUND.
NO
CONNECT A JUMPER WIRE BETWEEN CAVITY 42 IN THE CAB CONNECTOR AND GRD.
PROBE THE BR/YL WIRE IN THE ABS HYDRAULIC UNIT CONNECTOR.
IS THE RESISTANCE BELOW 10.0 OHMS?
YES
REPLACE THE CAB.
NO
REPAIR THE OPEN B142 BR/YL WIRE.

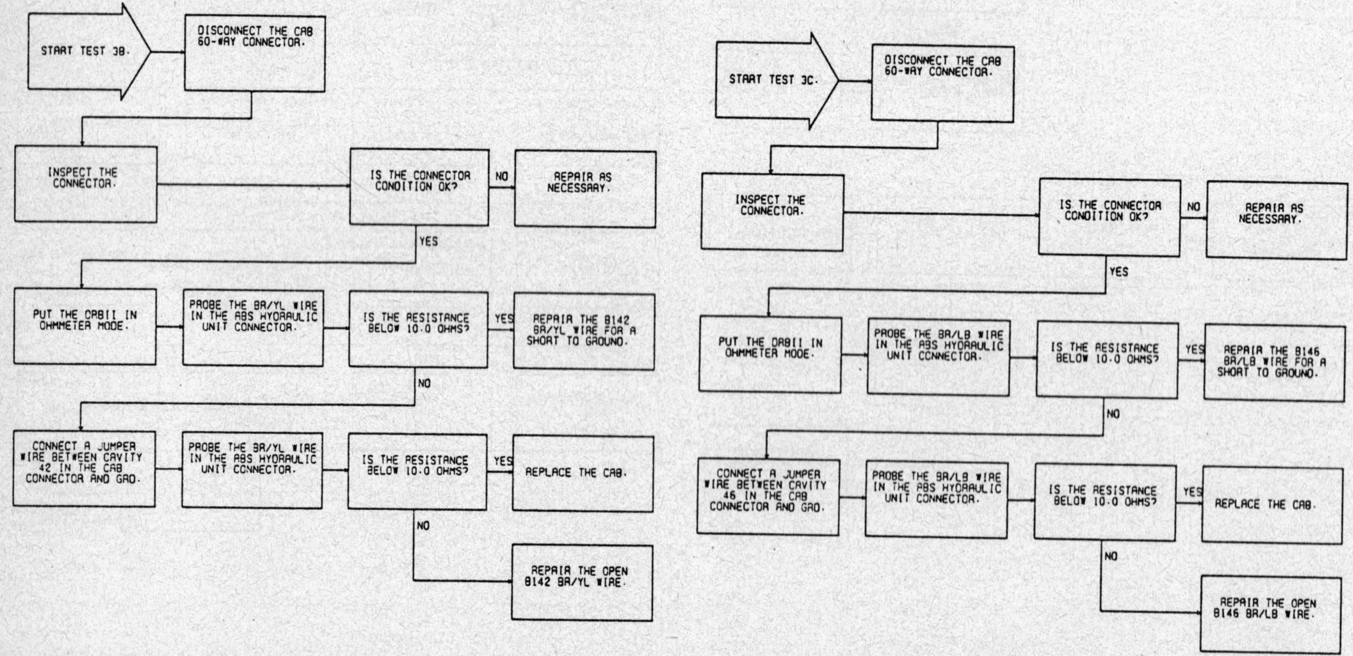

**Fig. 7 Test 3B—Modulator Fault, Left Front Build/Decay Valve**

START TEST 3C.
DISCONNECT THE CAB 60-WAY CONNECTOR.
INSPECT THE CONNECTOR.
IS THE CONNECTOR CONDITION OK?
NO
REPAIR AS NECESSARY.
YES
PUT THE DRBII IN OHMMETER MODE.
PROBE THE BR/LB WIRE IN THE ABS HYDRAULIC UNIT CONNECTOR.
IS THE RESISTANCE BELOW 10.0 OHMS?
YES
REPAIR THE B146 BR/LB WIRE FOR A SHORT TO GROUND.
NO
CONNECT A JUMPER WIRE BETWEEN CAVITY 46 IN THE CAB CONNECTOR AND GRD.
PROBE THE BR/LB WIRE IN THE ABS HYDRAULIC UNIT CONNECTOR.
IS THE RESISTANCE BELOW 10.0 OHMS?
YES
REPLACE THE CAB.
NO
REPAIR THE OPEN B146 BR/LB WIRE.

**Fig. 8 Test 3C—Modulator Fault, Left Rear Build/Decay Valve**

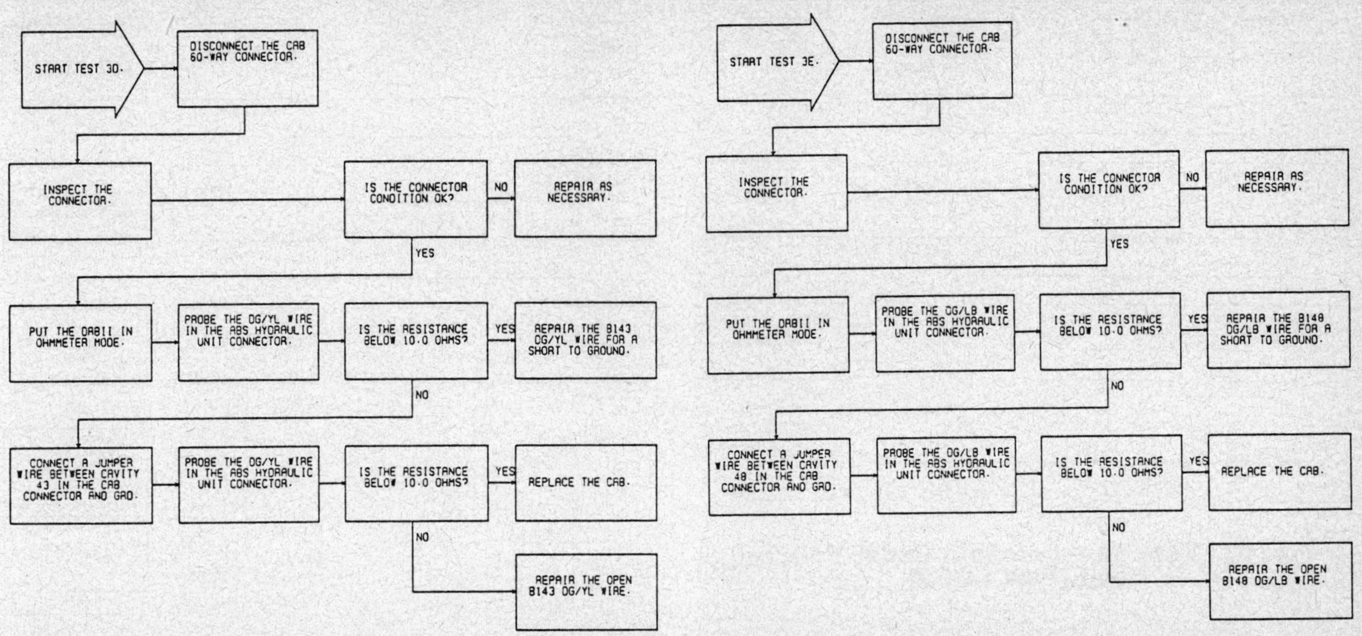


**Fig. 9 Test 3D—Modulator Fault, Right Front Build/Decay Valve**

**Fig. 10 Test 3E—Modulator Fault, Right Rear Build/Decay Valve**

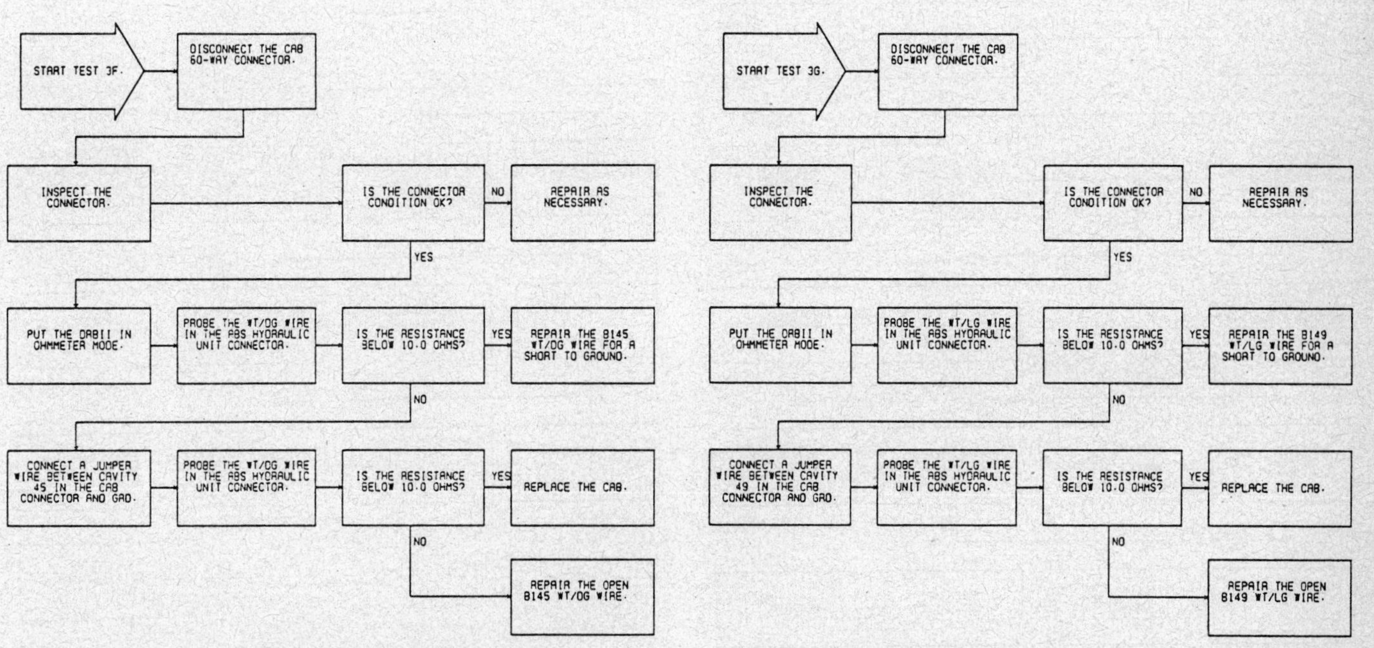


**Fig. 11 Test 3F—Modulator Fault, Left Front/Right Rear Isolation Valve**

**Fig. 12 Test 3G—Modulator Fault, Right Front/Left Rear Isolation Valve**

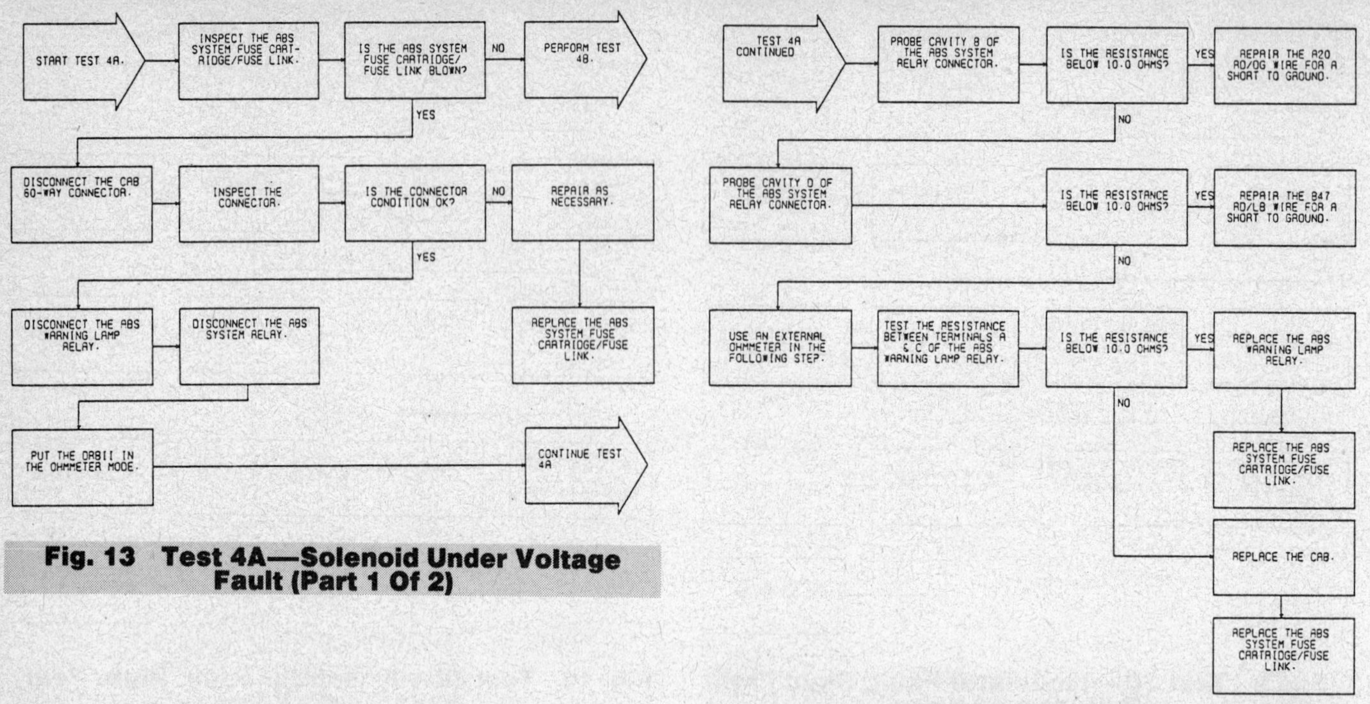

START TEST 4A.
INSPECT THE ABS SYSTEM FUSE CARTRIDGE/FUSE LINK.
IS THE ABS SYSTEM FUSE CARTRIDGE/FUSE LINK BLOWN?
NO
PERFORM TEST 4B.
YES
DISCONNECT THE CAB 60-WAY CONNECTOR.
INSPECT THE CONNECTOR.
IS THE CONNECTOR CONDITION OK?
NO
REPAIR AS NECESSARY.
YES
DISCONNECT THE ABS WARNING LAMP RELAY.
DISCONNECT THE ABS SYSTEM RELAY.
REPLACE THE ABS SYSTEM FUSE CARTRIDGE/FUSE LINK.
PUT THE DRBII IN THE OHMMETER MODE.
CONTINUE TEST 4A

**Fig. 13 Test 4A—Solenoid Under Voltage Fault (Part 1 Of 2)**

TEST 4A CONTINUED
PROBE CAVITY B OF THE ABS SYSTEM RELAY CONNECTOR.
IS THE RESISTANCE BELOW 10.0 OHMS?
YES
REPAIR THE A20 RD/OG WIRE FOR A SHORT TO GROUND.
NO
PROBE CAVITY D OF THE ABS SYSTEM RELAY CONNECTOR.
IS THE RESISTANCE BELOW 10.0 OHMS?
YES
REPAIR THE B47 RD/LB WIRE FOR A SHORT TO GROUND.
NO
USE AN EXTERNAL OHMMETER IN THE FOLLOWING STEP.
TEST THE RESISTANCE BETWEEN TERMINALS A & C OF THE ABS WARNING LAMP RELAY.
IS THE RESISTANCE BELOW 10.0 OHMS?
YES
REPLACE THE ABS WARNING LAMP RELAY.
NO
REPLACE THE ABS SYSTEM FUSE CARTRIDGE/FUSE LINK.
REPLACE THE CAB.
REPLACE THE ABS SYSTEM FUSE CARTRIDGE/FUSE LINK.

**Fig. 13 Test 4A—Solenoid Under Voltage Fault (Part 2 Of 2)**

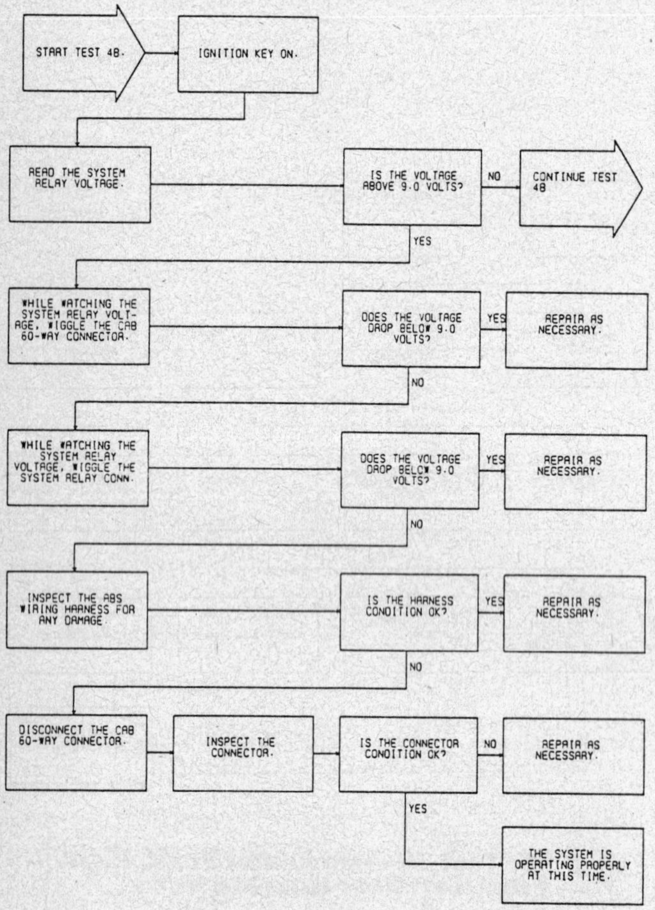

START TEST 4B.
IGNITION KEY ON.
READ THE SYSTEM RELAY VOLTAGE.
IS THE VOLTAGE ABOVE 9.0 VOLTS?
NO
CONTINUE TEST 4B
YES
WHILE WATCHING THE SYSTEM RELAY VOLTAGE, WIGGLE THE CAB 60-WAY CONNECTOR.
DOES THE VOLTAGE DROP BELOW 9.0 VOLTS?
YES
REPAIR AS NECESSARY.
NO
WHILE WATCHING THE SYSTEM RELAY VOLTAGE, WIGGLE THE SYSTEM RELAY CONN.
DOES THE VOLTAGE DROP BELOW 9.0 VOLTS?
YES
REPAIR AS NECESSARY.
NO
INSPECT THE ABS WIRING HARNESS FOR ANY DAMAGE.
IS THE HARNESS CONDITION OK?
YES
REPAIR AS NECESSARY.
NO
DISCONNECT THE CAB 60-WAY CONNECTOR.
INSPECT THE CONNECTOR.
IS THE CONNECTOR CONDITION OK?
NO
REPAIR AS NECESSARY.
YES
THE SYSTEM IS OPERATING PROPERLY AT THIS TIME.

**Fig. 14 Test 4B—Solenoid Under Voltage Fault (Part 1 Of 5)**

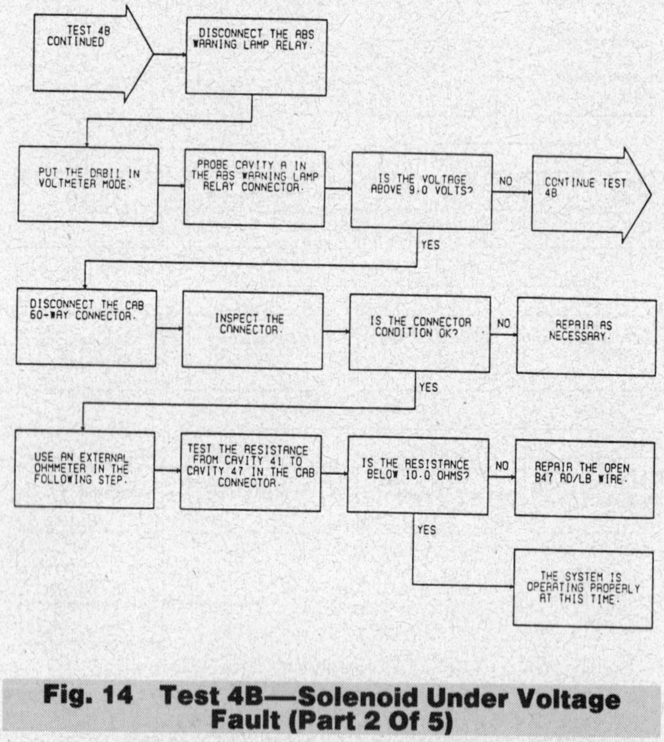

TEST 4B CONTINUED
DISCONNECT THE ABS WARNING LAMP RELAY.
PUT THE DRBII IN VOLTMETER MODE.
PROBE CAVITY A IN THE ABS WARNING LAMP RELAY CONNECTOR.
IS THE VOLTAGE ABOVE 9.0 VOLTS?
NO
CONTINUE TEST 4B
YES
DISCONNECT THE CAB 60-WAY CONNECTOR.
INSPECT THE CONNECTOR.
IS THE CONNECTOR CONDITION OK?
NO
REPAIR AS NECESSARY.
YES
USE AN EXTERNAL OHMMETER IN THE FOLLOWING STEP.
TEST THE RESISTANCE FROM CAVITY 41 TO CAVITY 47 IN THE CAB CONNECTOR.
IS THE RESISTANCE BELOW 10.0 OHMS?
NO
REPAIR THE OPEN B47 RD/LB WIRE.
YES
THE SYSTEM IS OPERATING PROPERLY AT THIS TIME.

**Fig. 14 Test 4B—Solenoid Under Voltage Fault (Part 2 Of 5)**

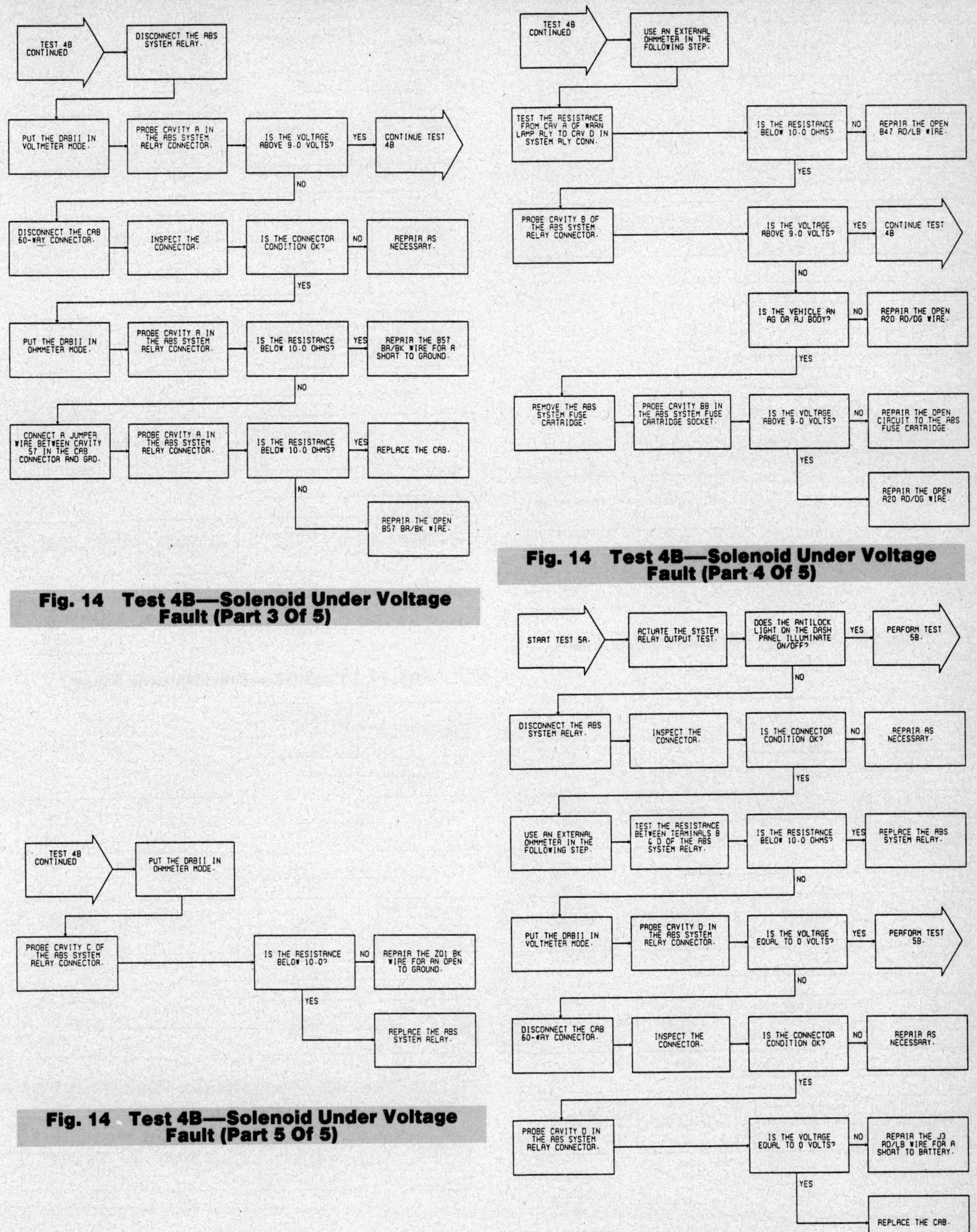


**Fig. 14 Test 4B—Solenoid Under Voltage Fault (Part 3 Of 5)**

**Fig. 14 Test 4B—Solenoid Under Voltage Fault (Part 4 Of 5)**

**Fig. 14 Test 4B—Solenoid Under Voltage Fault (Part 5 Of 5)**

**Fig. 15 Test 5A—System Relay Fault**

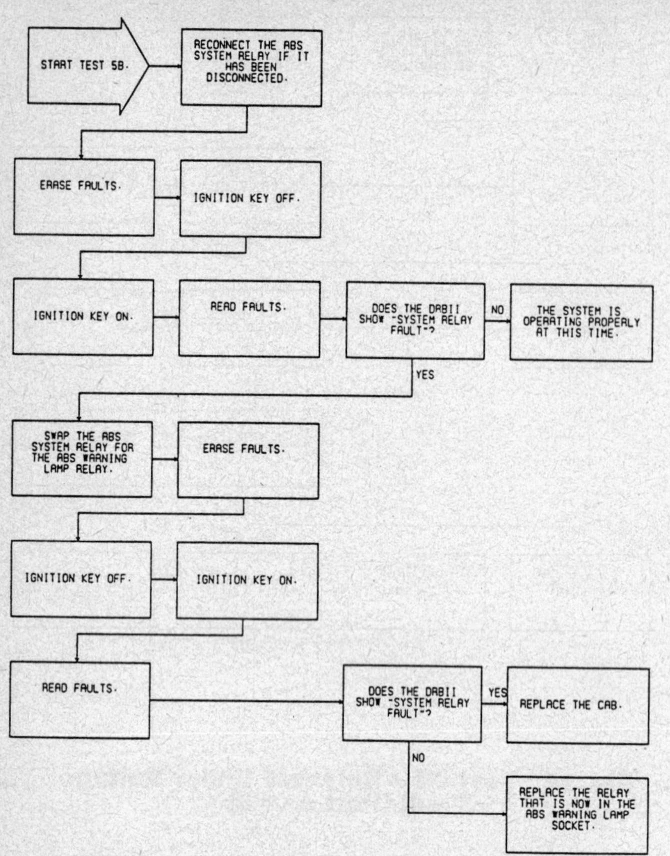


**Fig. 16 Test 5B—System Relay Fault**

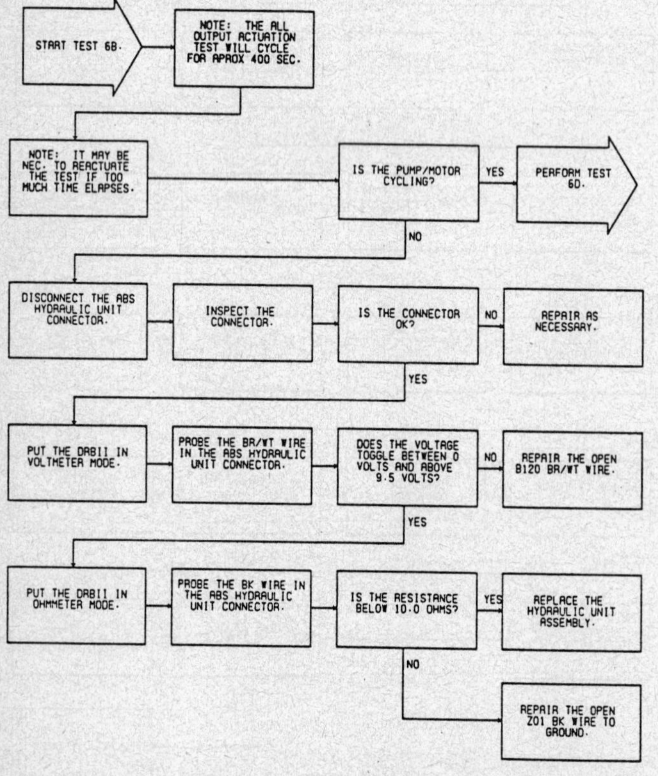


**Fig. 18 Test 6B—Pump/Motor Fault**

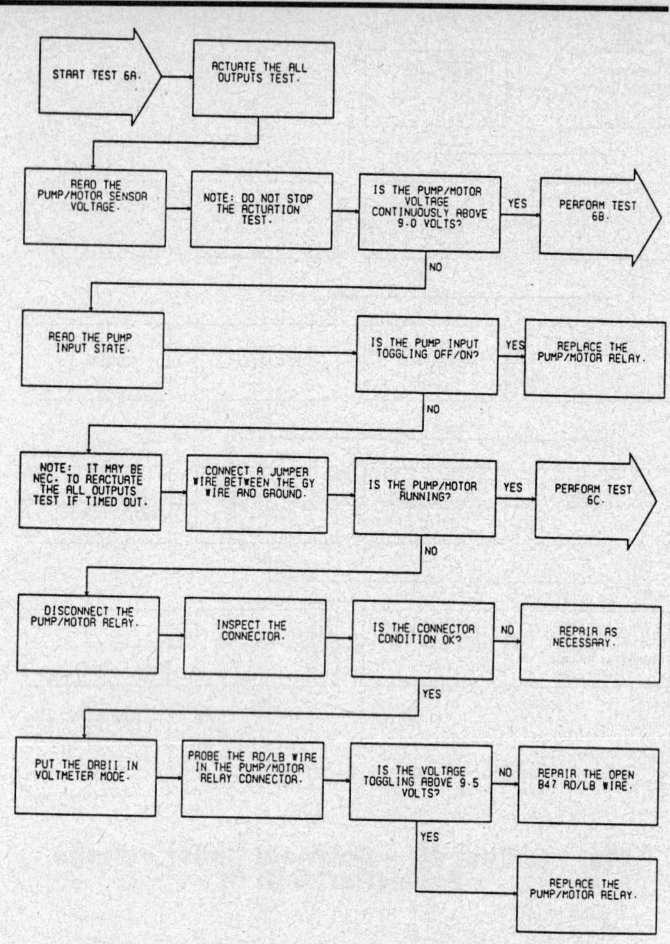


**Fig. 17 Test 6A—Pump/Motor Fault**

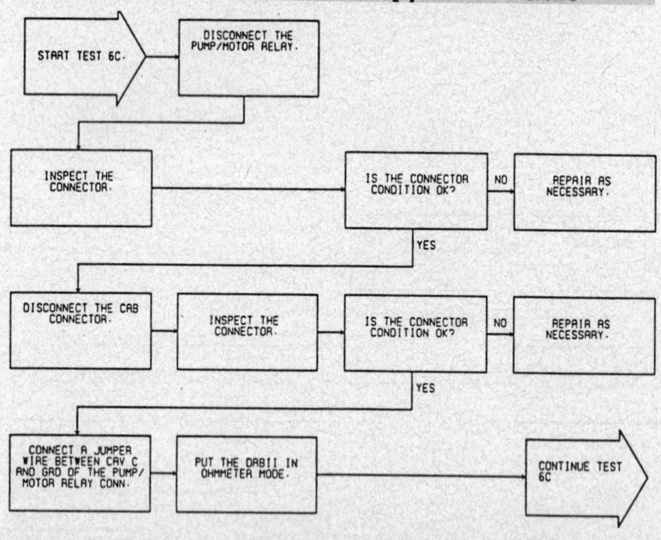


**Fig. 19 Test 6C—Pump/Motor Fault (Part 1 Of 2)**

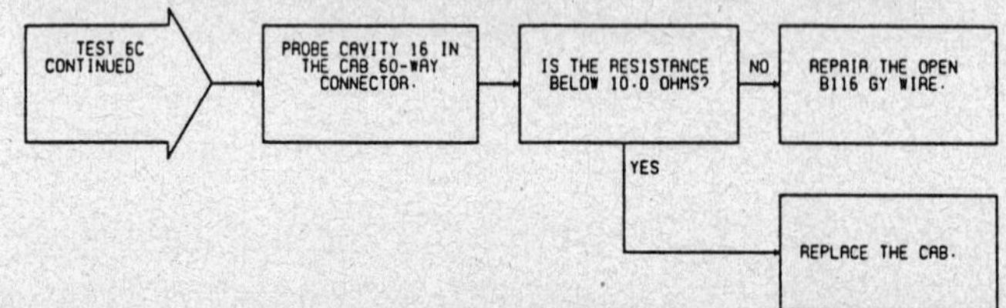


**Fig. 19 Test 6C—Pump/Motor Fault (Part 2 Of 2)**

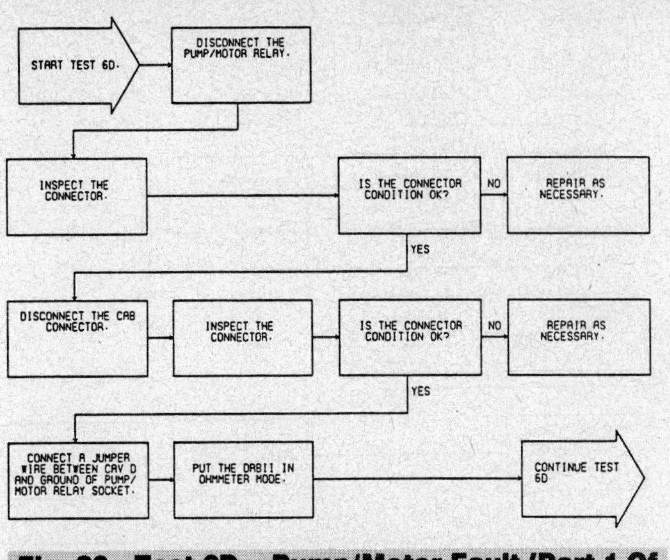


**Fig. 20 Test 6D—Pump/Motor Fault (Part 1 Of 2)**

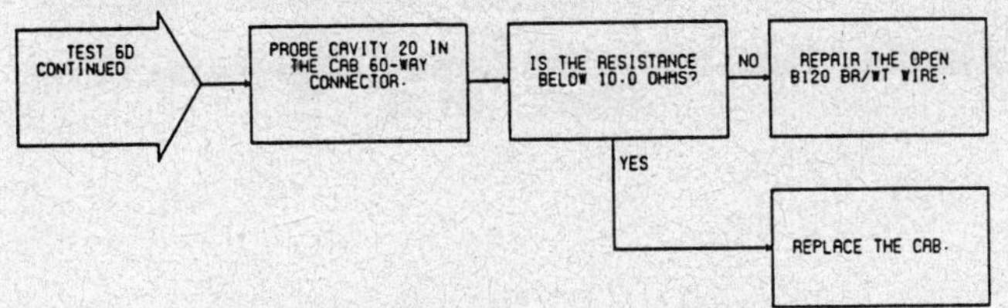


**Fig. 20 Test 6D—Pump/Motor Fault (Part 2 Of 2)**

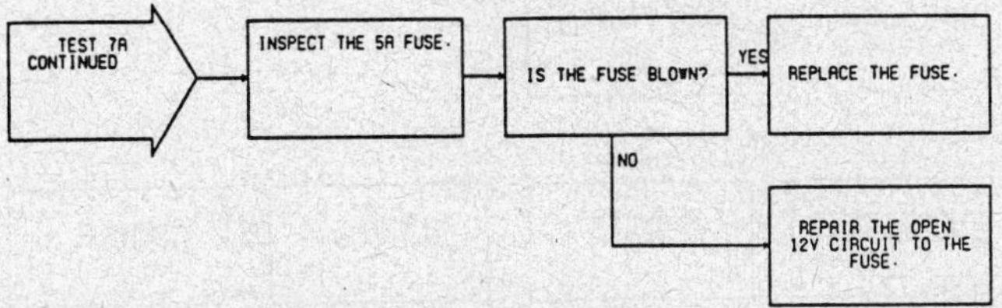


**Fig. 21 Test 7A—Anti-Lock Lamp Fault (Part 2 Of 2)**

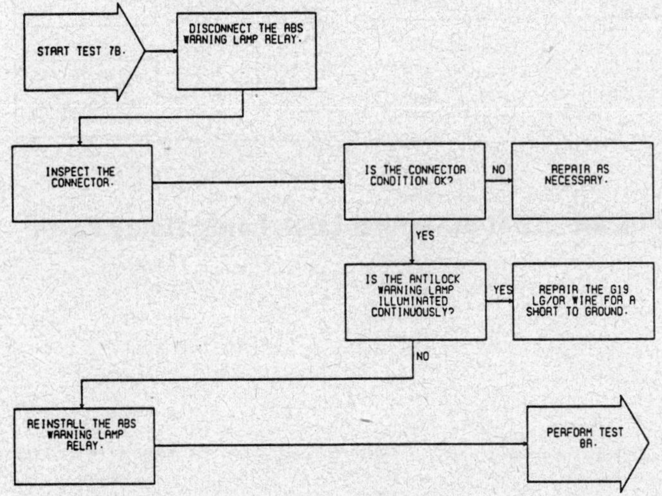


**Fig. 22 Test 7B—Anti-Lock Lamp Fault**

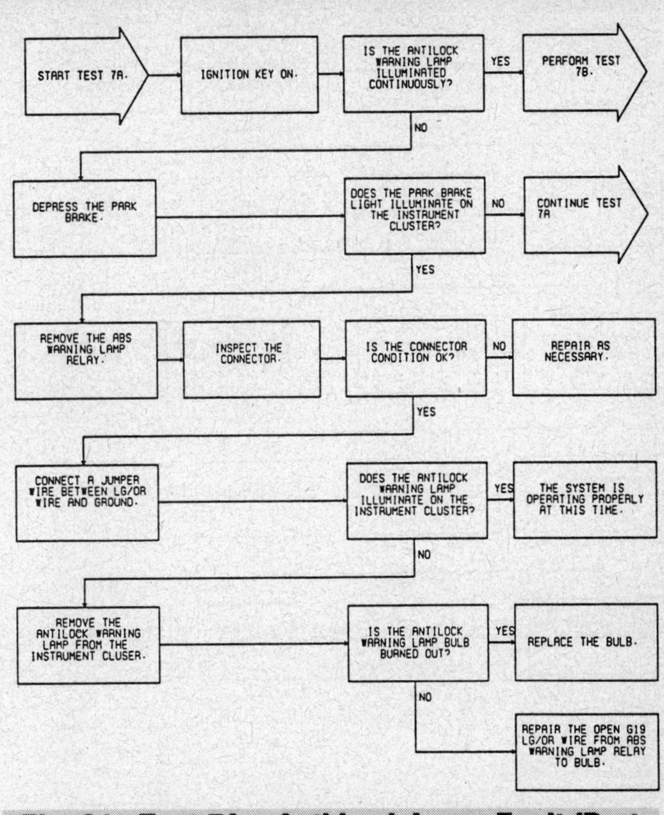


**Fig. 21 Test 7A—Anti-Lock Lamp Fault (Part 1 Of 2)**

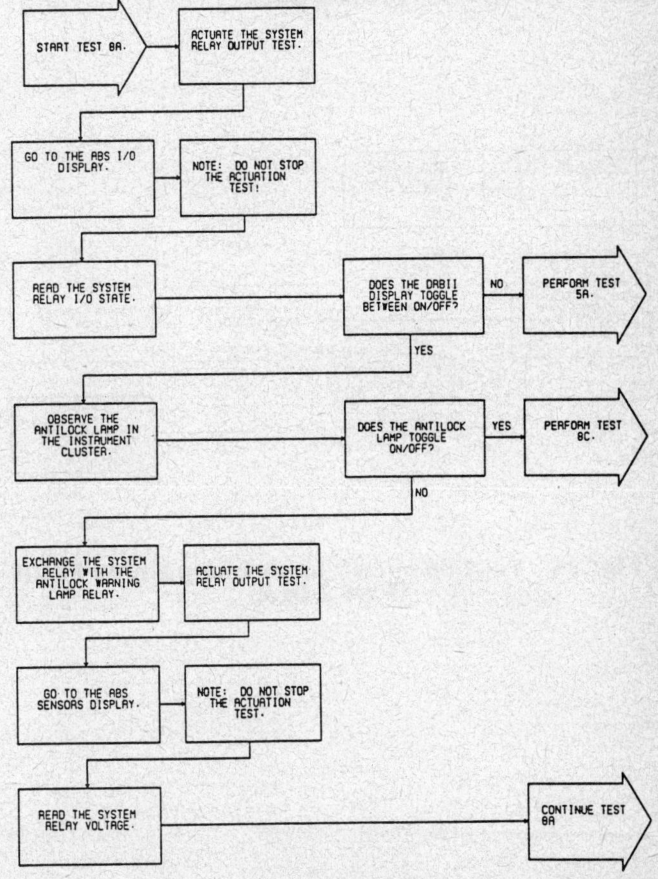


**Fig. 23 Test 8A—Anti-Lock Lamp Relay Fault (Part 1 Of 2)**

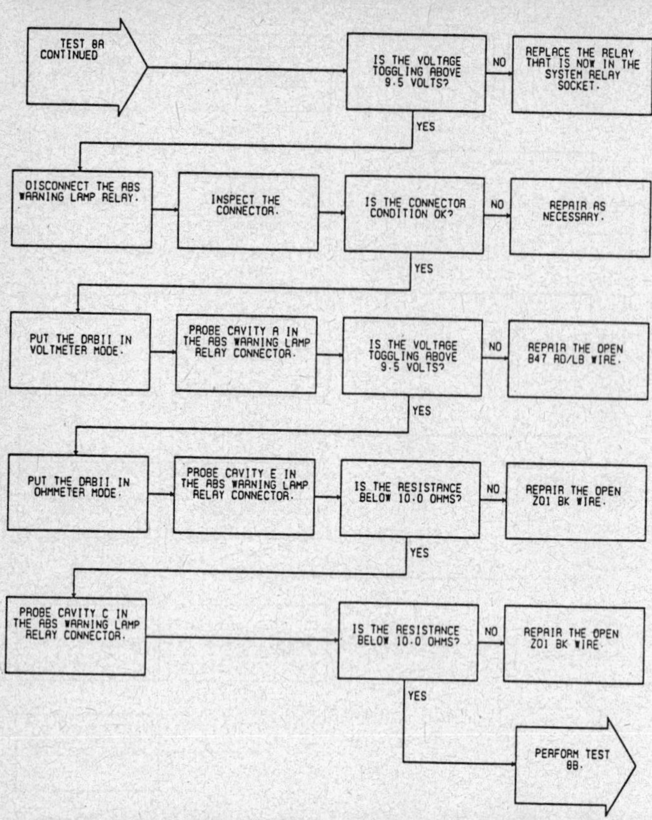


**Fig. 23 Test 8A—Anti-Lock Lamp Relay Fault (Part 2 Of 2)**

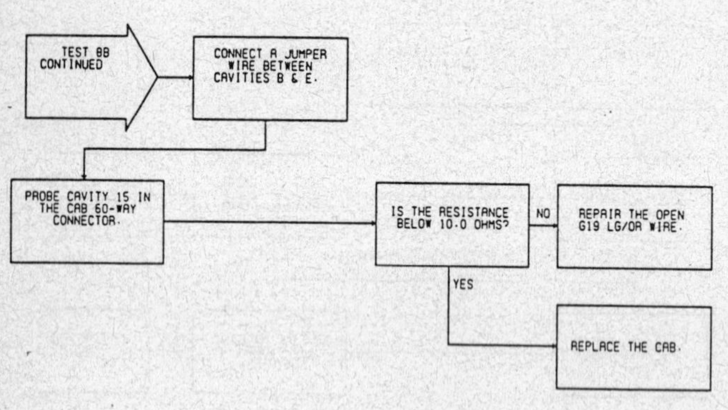


**Fig. 24 Test 8B—Anti-Lock Lamp Relay Fault (Part 2 Of 2)**

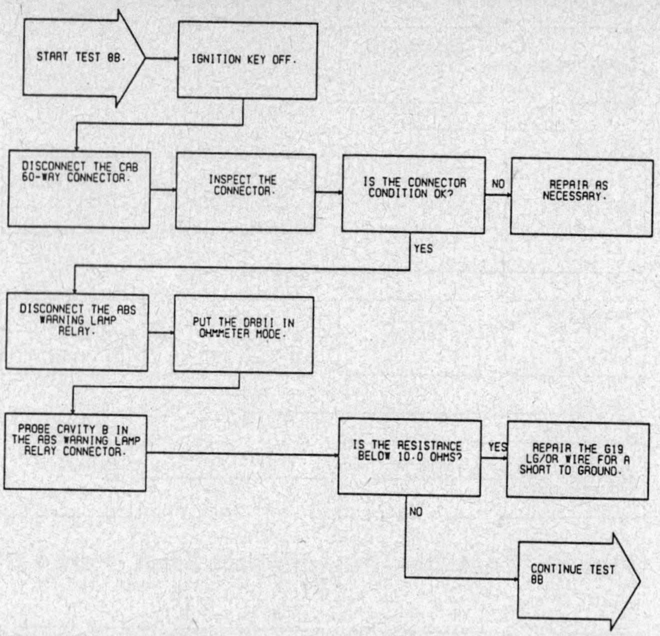

START TEST 8B.
IGNITION KEY OFF.
DISCONNECT THE CAB 60-WAY CONNECTOR.
INSPECT THE CONNECTOR.
IS THE CONNECTOR CONDITION OK?
NO
REPAIR AS NECESSARY.
YES
DISCONNECT THE ABS WARNING LAMP RELAY.
PUT THE DRBII IN OHMMETER MODE.
PROBE CAVITY B IN THE ABS WARNING LAMP RELAY CONNECTOR.
IS THE RESISTANCE BELOW 10.0 OHMS?
YES
REPAIR THE G19 LG/OR WIRE FOR A SHORT TO GROUND.
NO
CONTINUE TEST 8B

**Fig. 24 Test 8B—Anti-Lock Lamp Relay Fault (Part 1 Of 2)**

START TEST 8C.
DISCONNECT THE ABS WARNING LAMP RELAY.
DISCONNECT THE CAB 60-WAY CONNECTOR.
INSPECT THE CONNECTOR.
IS THE CONNECTOR CONDITION OK?
NO
REPAIR AS NECESSARY.
YES
CONNECT A JUMPER WIRE BETWEEN CAVITY 15 AND GROUND
OBSERVE THE ANTILOCK LAMP IN THE INSTRUMENT CLUSTER
IS THE ANTILOCK WARNING LAMP ILLUMINATED
YES
REPLACE THE CAB.
NO
REPAIR THE OPEN G19 LG/OR WIRE BETWEEN CAB AND WARN LAMP RELAY

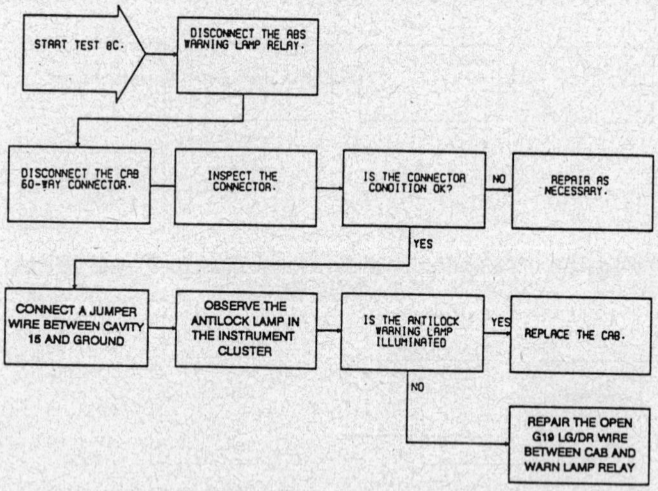

**Fig. 25 Test 8C—Anti-Lock Lamp Relay Fault**

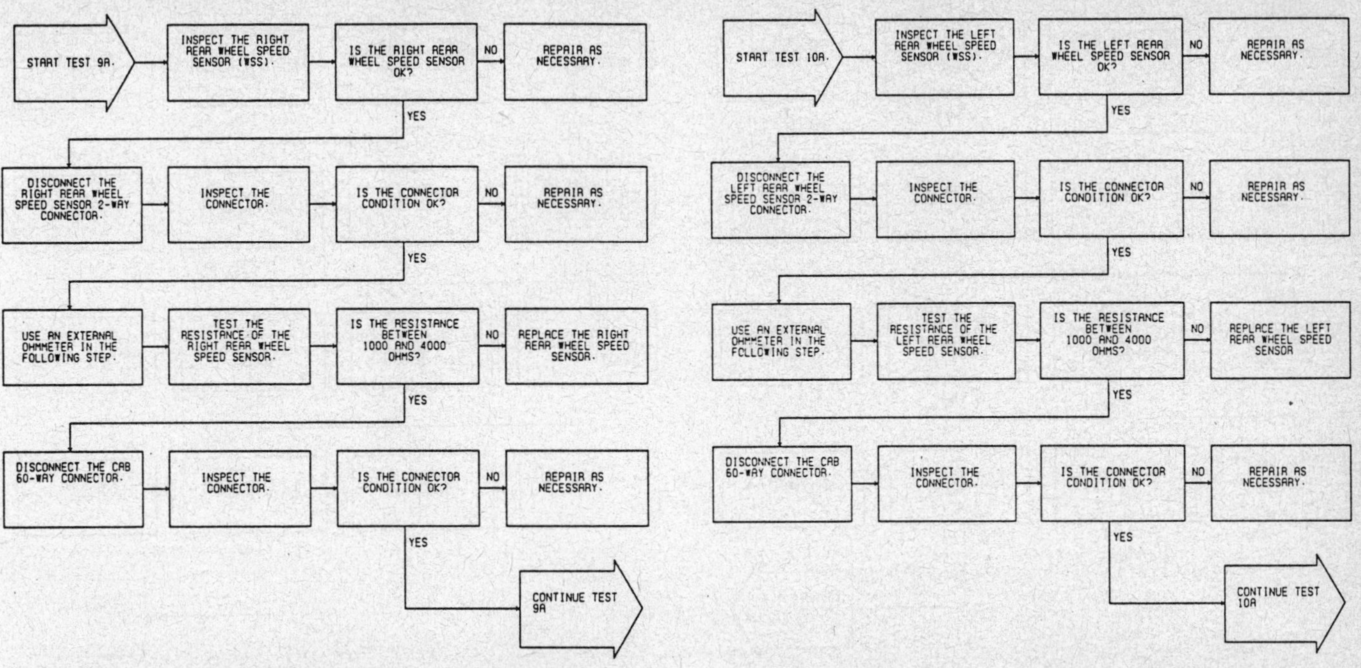


**Fig. 26 Test 9A—Right Rear Wheel Speed Sensor Continuity Fault (Part 1 Of 2)**

**Fig. 27 Test 10A—Left Rear Wheel Speed Sensor Continuity Fault (Part 1 Of 2)**

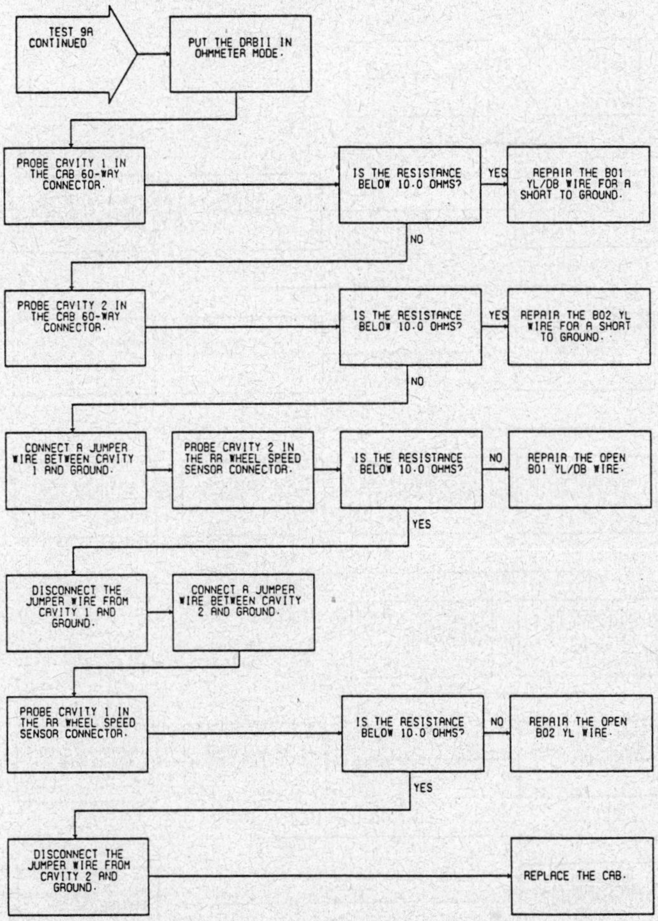

TEST 9A CONTINUED
PUT THE DRBII IN OHMMETER MODE.
PROBE CAVITY 1 IN THE CAB 60-WAY CONNECTOR.
IS THE RESISTANCE BELOW 10.0 OHMS?
YES
REPAIR THE B01 YL/DB WIRE FOR A SHORT TO GROUND.
NO
PROBE CAVITY 2 IN THE CAB 60-WAY CONNECTOR.
IS THE RESISTANCE BELOW 10.0 OHMS?
YES
REPAIR THE B02 YL WIRE FOR A SHORT TO GROUND.
NO
CONNECT A JUMPER WIRE BETWEEN CAVITY 1 AND GROUND.
PROBE CAVITY 2 IN THE RR WHEEL SPEED SENSOR CONNECTOR.
IS THE RESISTANCE BELOW 10.0 OHMS?
NO
REPAIR THE OPEN B01 YL/DB WIRE.
YES
DISCONNECT THE JUMPER WIRE FROM CAVITY 1 AND GROUND.
CONNECT A JUMPER WIRE BETWEEN CAVITY 2 AND GROUND.
PROBE CAVITY 1 IN THE RR WHEEL SPEED SENSOR CONNECTOR.
IS THE RESISTANCE BELOW 10.0 OHMS?
NO
REPAIR THE OPEN B02 YL WIRE.
YES
DISCONNECT THE JUMPER WIRE FROM CAVITY 2 AND GROUND.
REPLACE THE CAB.

**Fig. 26 Test 9A—Right Rear Wheel Speed Sensor Continuity Fault (Part 2 Of 2)**

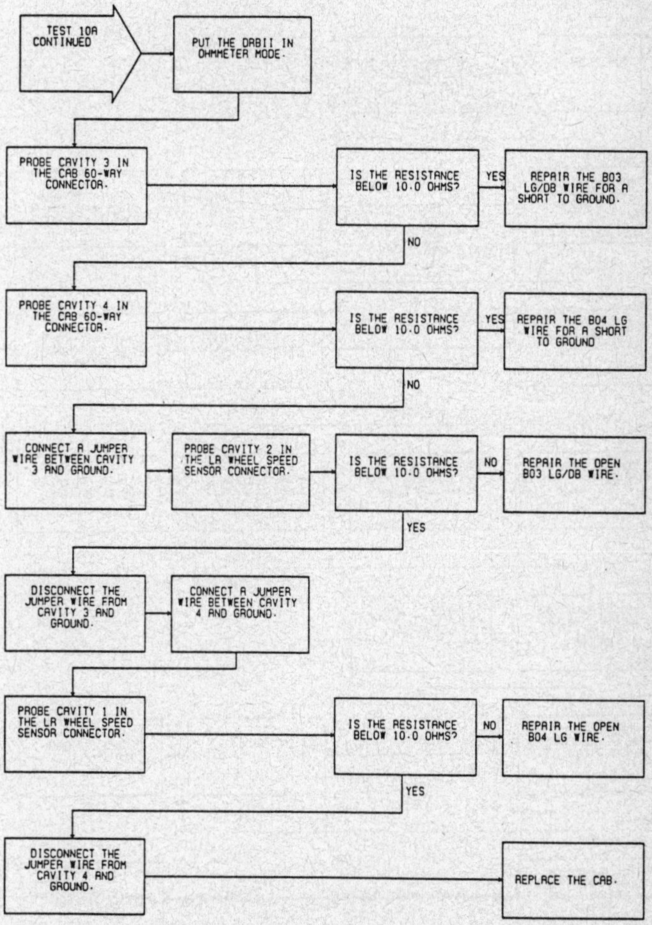

TEST 10A CONTINUED
PUT THE DRBII IN OHMMETER MODE.
PROBE CAVITY 3 IN THE CAB 60-WAY CONNECTOR.
IS THE RESISTANCE BELOW 10.0 OHMS?
YES
REPAIR THE B03 LG/DB WIRE FOR A SHORT TO GROUND.
NO
PROBE CAVITY 4 IN THE CAB 60-WAY CONNECTOR.
IS THE RESISTANCE BELOW 10.0 OHMS?
YES
REPAIR THE B04 LG WIRE FOR A SHORT TO GROUND
NO
CONNECT A JUMPER WIRE BETWEEN CAVITY 3 AND GROUND.
PROBE CAVITY 2 IN THE LR WHEEL SPEED SENSOR CONNECTOR.
IS THE RESISTANCE BELOW 10.0 OHMS?
NO
REPAIR THE OPEN B03 LG/DB WIRE.
YES
DISCONNECT THE JUMPER WIRE FROM CAVITY 3 AND GROUND.
CONNECT A JUMPER WIRE BETWEEN CAVITY 4 AND GROUND.
PROBE CAVITY 1 IN THE LR WHEEL SPEED SENSOR CONNECTOR.
IS THE RESISTANCE BELOW 10.0 OHMS?
NO
REPAIR THE OPEN B04 LG WIRE.
YES
DISCONNECT THE JUMPER WIRE FROM CAVITY 4 AND GROUND.
REPLACE THE CAB.

**Fig. 27 Test 10A—Left Rear Wheel Speed Sensor Continuity Fault (Part 2 Of 2)**

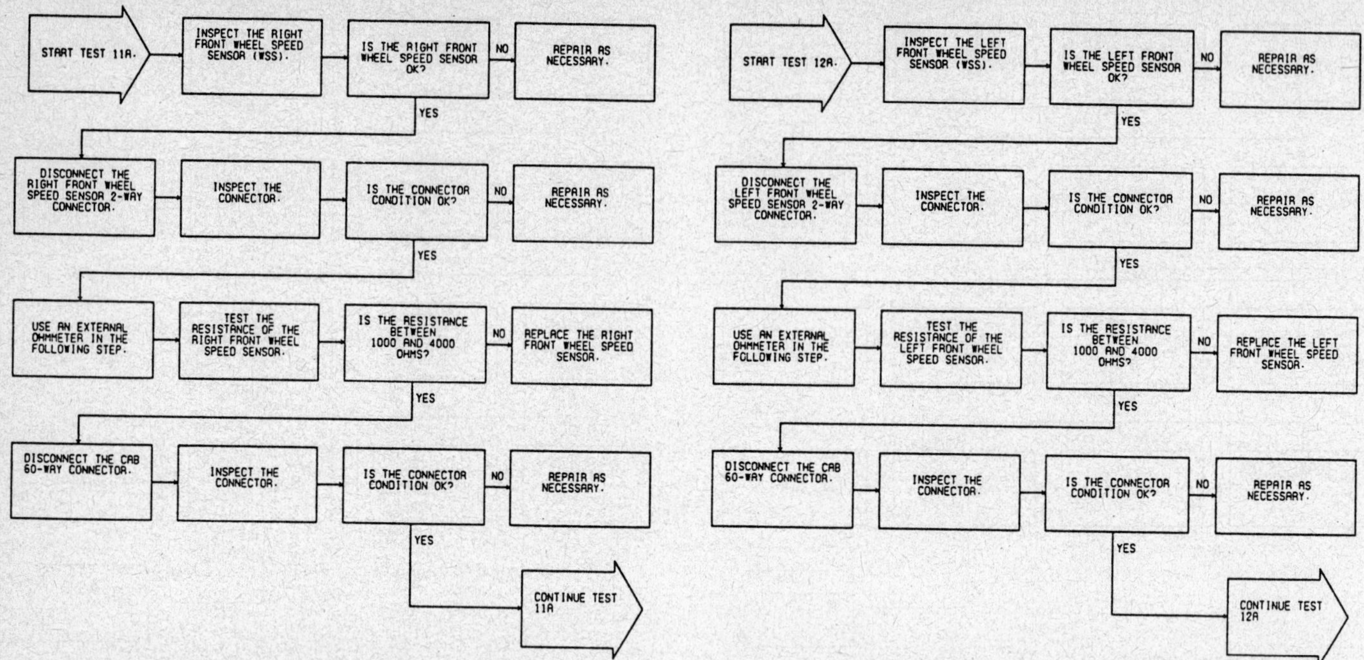


**Fig. 28 Test 11A—Right Front Wheel Speed Sensor Continuity Fault (Part 1 Of 2)**

**Fig. 29 Test 12A—Left Front Wheel Speed Sensor Continuity Fault (Part 1 Of 2)**

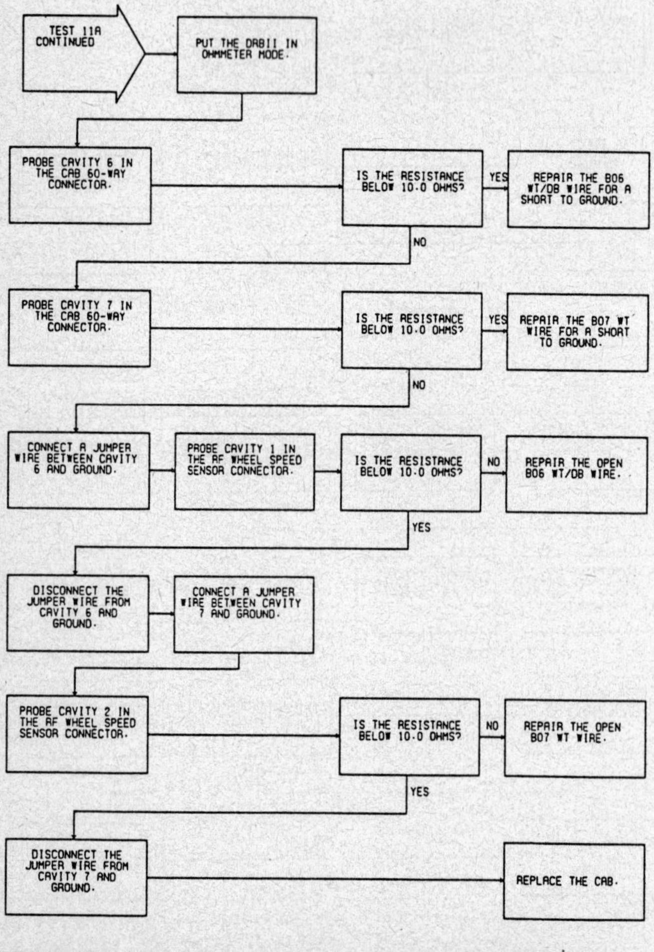

TEST 11A CONTINUED
PUT THE DRBII IN OHMMETER MODE.
PROBE CAVITY 6 IN THE CAB 60-WAY CONNECTOR.
IS THE RESISTANCE BELOW 10.0 OHMS?
YES
REPAIR THE B06 WT/DB WIRE FOR A SHORT TO GROUND.
NO
PROBE CAVITY 7 IN THE CAB 60-WAY CONNECTOR.
IS THE RESISTANCE BELOW 10.0 OHMS?
YES
REPAIR THE B07 WT WIRE FOR A SHORT TO GROUND.
NO
CONNECT A JUMPER WIRE BETWEEN CAVITY 6 AND GROUND.
PROBE CAVITY 1 IN THE RF WHEEL SPEED SENSOR CONNECTOR.
IS THE RESISTANCE BELOW 10.0 OHMS?
NO
REPAIR THE OPEN B06 WT/DB WIRE.
YES
DISCONNECT THE JUMPER WIRE FROM CAVITY 6 AND GROUND.
CONNECT A JUMPER WIRE BETWEEN CAVITY 7 AND GROUND.
PROBE CAVITY 2 IN THE RF WHEEL SPEED SENSOR CONNECTOR.
IS THE RESISTANCE BELOW 10.0 OHMS?
NO
REPAIR THE OPEN B07 WT WIRE.
YES
DISCONNECT THE JUMPER WIRE FROM CAVITY 7 AND GROUND.
REPLACE THE CAB.

**Fig. 28 Test 11A—Right Front Wheel Speed Sensor Continuity Fault (Part 2 Of 2)**

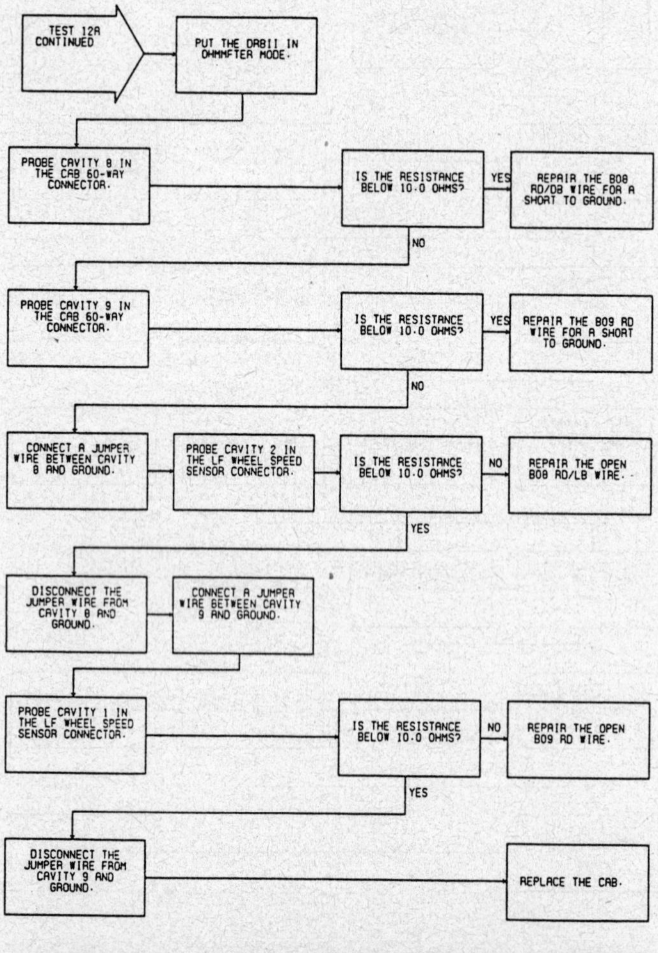

TEST 12A CONTINUED
PUT THE DRBII IN OHMMETER MODE.
PROBE CAVITY 8 IN THE CAB 60-WAY CONNECTOR.
IS THE RESISTANCE BELOW 10.0 OHMS?
YES
REPAIR THE B08 RD/DB WIRE FOR A SHORT TO GROUND.
NO
PROBE CAVITY 9 IN THE CAB 60-WAY CONNECTOR.
IS THE RESISTANCE BELOW 10.0 OHMS?
YES
REPAIR THE B09 RD WIRE FOR A SHORT TO GROUND.
NO
CONNECT A JUMPER WIRE BETWEEN CAVITY 8 AND GROUND.
PROBE CAVITY 2 IN THE LF WHEEL SPEED SENSOR CONNECTOR.
IS THE RESISTANCE BELOW 10.0 OHMS?
NO
REPAIR THE OPEN B08 RD/LB WIRE.
YES
DISCONNECT THE JUMPER WIRE FROM CAVITY 8 AND GROUND.
CONNECT A JUMPER WIRE BETWEEN CAVITY 9 AND GROUND.
PROBE CAVITY 1 IN THE LF WHEEL SPEED SENSOR CONNECTOR.
IS THE RESISTANCE BELOW 10.0 OHMS?
NO
REPAIR THE OPEN B09 RD WIRE.
YES
DISCONNECT THE JUMPER WIRE FROM CAVITY 9 AND GROUND.
REPLACE THE CAB.

**Fig. 29 Test 12A—Left Front Wheel Speed Sensor Continuity Fault (Part 2 Of 2)**

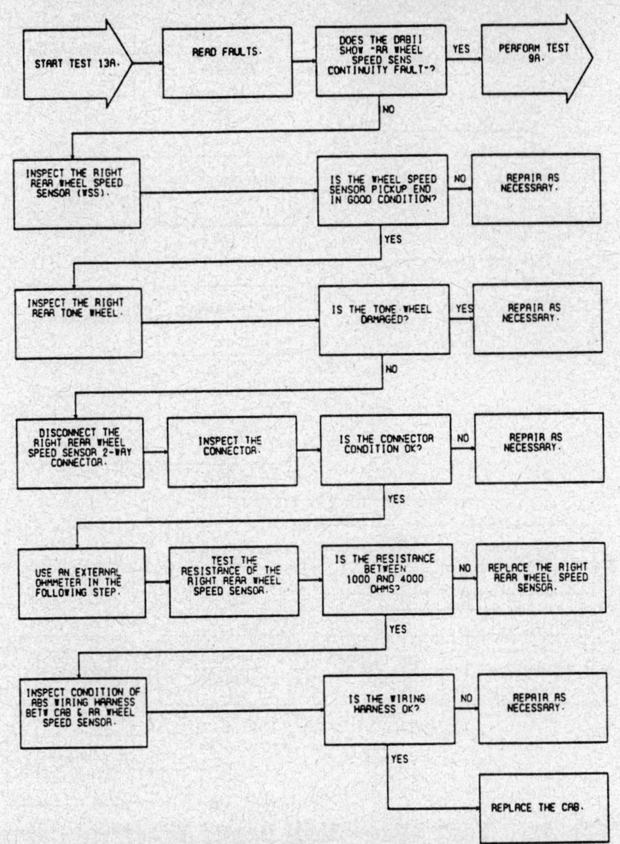


**Fig. 30 Test 13A—Right Rear Wheel Speed Sensor Fault**

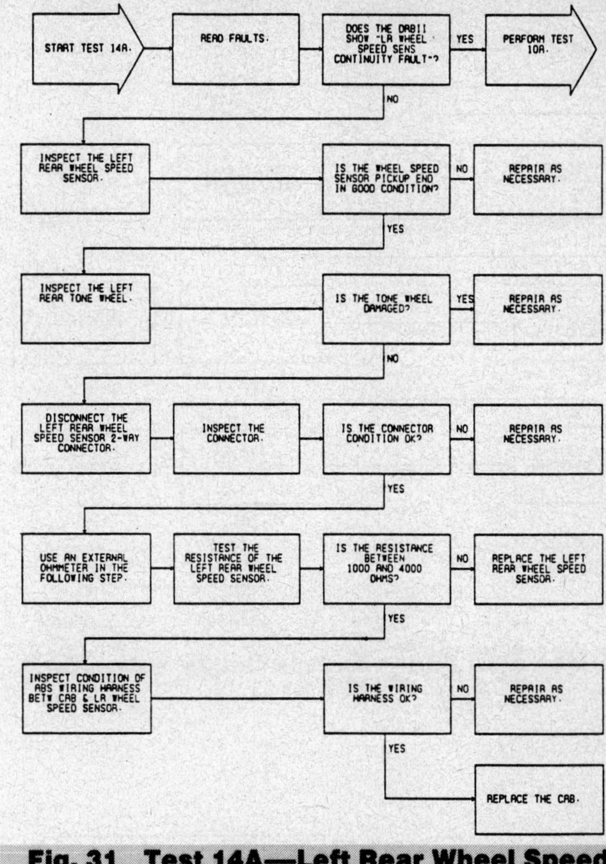


**Fig. 31 Test 14A—Left Rear Wheel Speed Sensor Fault**

START TEST 15A.
READ FAULTS.
DOES THE DRBII SHOW "RF WHEEL SPEED SENS CONTINUITY FAULT"?
YES
PERFORM TEST 11A.
NO
INSPECT THE RIGHT FRONT WHEEL SPEED SENSOR.
IS THE WHEEL SPEED SENSOR PICKUP END IN GOOD CONDITION?
NO
REPAIR AS NECESSARY.
YES
INSPECT THE RIGHT FRONT TONE WHEEL.
IS THE TONE WHEEL DAMAGED?
YES
REPAIR AS NECESSARY.
NO
DISCONNECT THE RIGHT FRONT WHEEL SPEED SENSOR 2-WAY CONNECTOR.
INSPECT THE CONNECTOR.
IS THE CONNECTOR CONDITION OK?
NO
REPAIR AS NECESSARY.
YES
USE AN EXTERNAL OHMMETER IN THE FOLLOWING STEP.
TEST THE RESISTANCE OF THE RIGHT FRONT WHEEL SPEED SENSOR.
IS THE RESISTANCE BETWEEN 1000 AND 4000 OHMS?
NO
REPLACE THE RIGHT REAR WHEEL SPEED SENSOR.
YES
INSPECT CONDITION OF ABS WIRING HARNESS BETW CAB & RF WHEEL SPEED SENSOR.
IS THE WIRING HARNESS OK?
NO
REPAIR AS NECESSARY.
YES
REPLACE THE CAB.

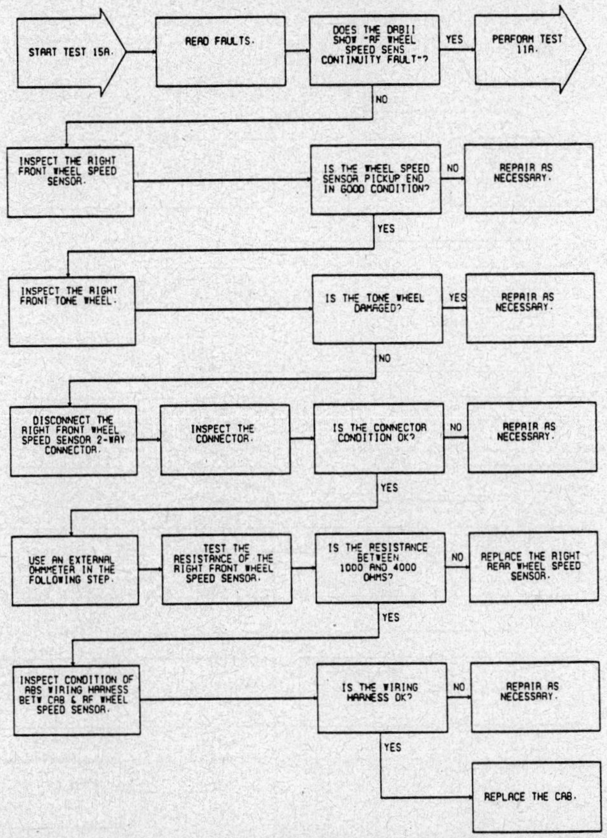

**Fig. 32 Test 15A—Right Front Wheel Speed Sensor Fault**

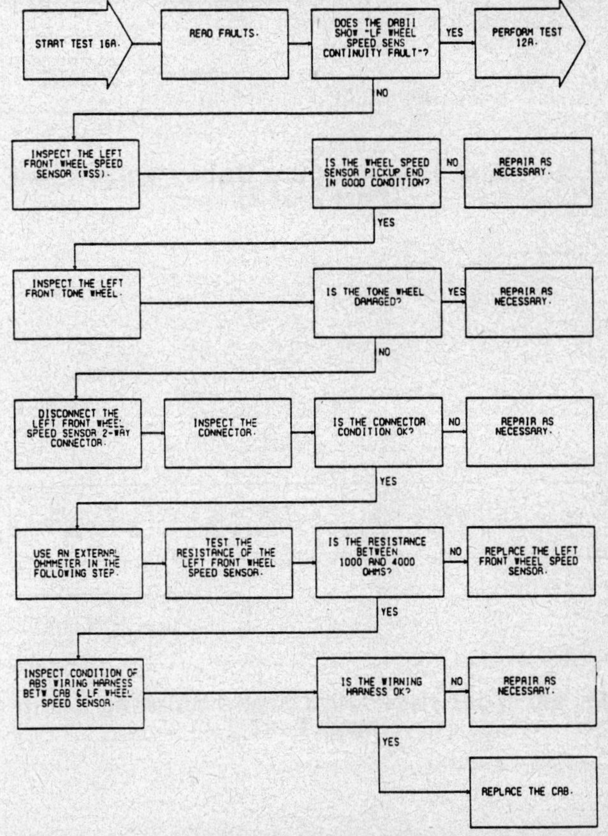


**Fig. 33 Test 16A—Left Front Wheel Speed Sensor Fault**

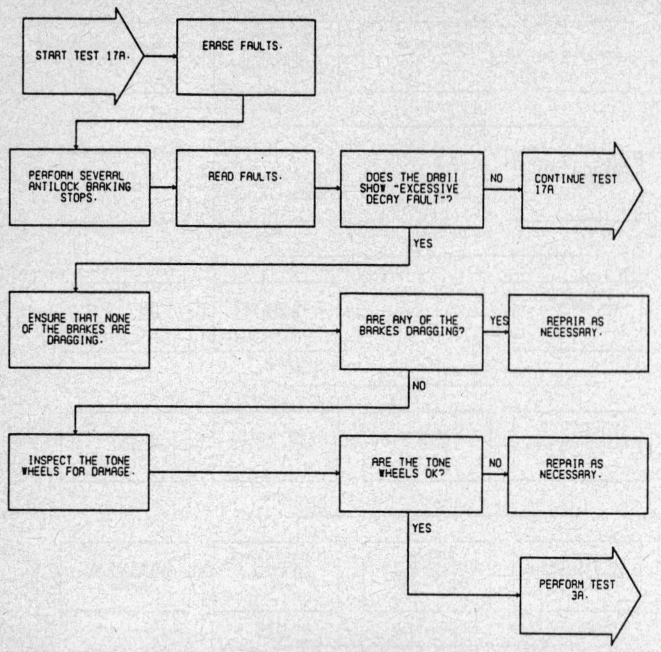


**Fig. 34 Test 17A—Excess Decay Valve Fault (Part 1 Of 2)**

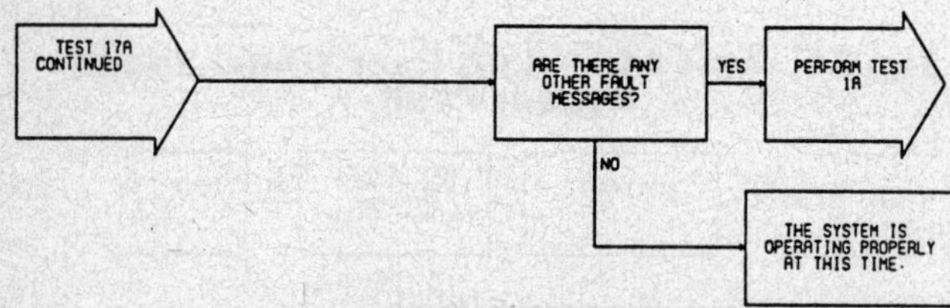


**Fig. 34 Test 17A—Excess Decay Valve Fault (Part 2 Of 2)**

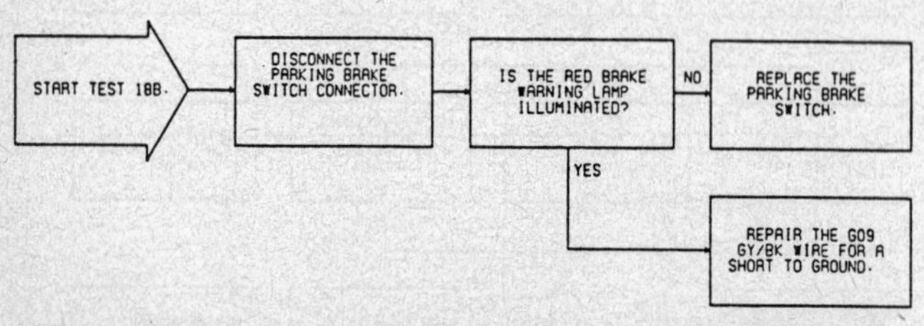


**Fig. 36 Test 18B—Red Brake Warning Lamp Input Test**

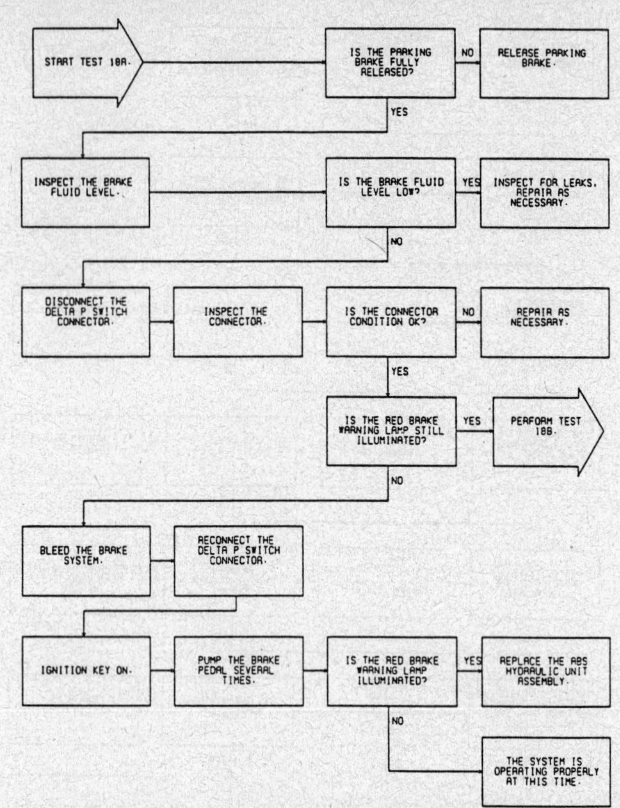


**Fig. 35 Test 18A—Red Brake Warning Lamp Input Test**

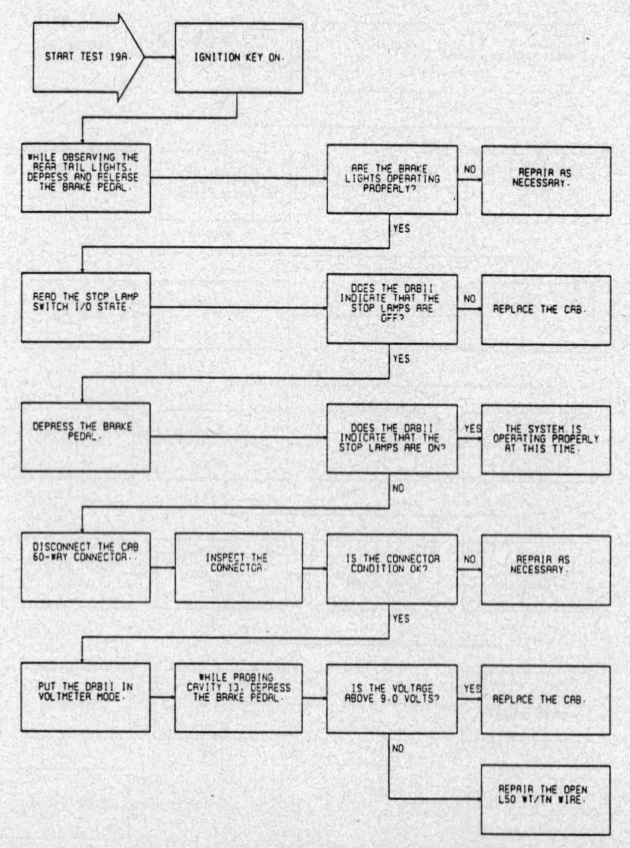


**Fig. 37 Test 19A—Stop Lamp Switch Input Test**

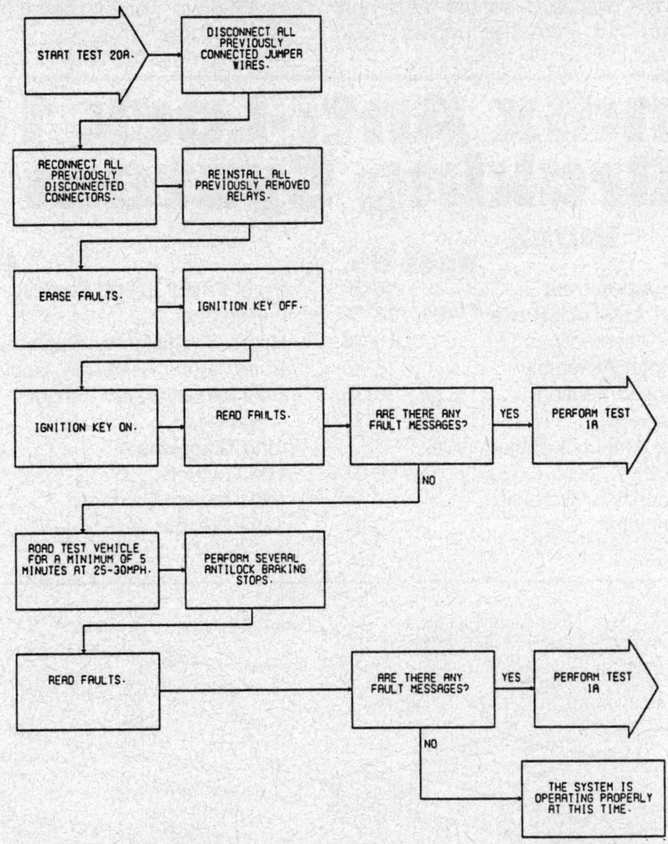


**Fig. 38 Test 20A—System Verification Test**

cumulator bleeder screw, **Fig. 39.**

22. Use a pressure bleeder, or with the aid of an assistant, apply light and constant pressure on the brake pedal.
23. Loosen secondary accumulator bleeder screw, then using the DRB II select the Actuate Valves test mode and actuate LF/RR Isolation Valve.
24. Bleed until a clear air free flow of brake fluid is coming out of the secondary accumulator bleeder screw, or brake pedal bottoms.
25. Tighten bleeder screw and release brake pedal, repeat steps 21 through 24 until a clean air free flow of brake fluid is coming out of secondary accumulator bleeder screw.
26. Using DRB II, select and actuate LF Build/Decay Valve. Repeat steps 21 through 25.

## MODULATOR ASSEMBLY, REPLACE

### Removal

1. Disconnect and remove battery, battery tray and acid shield that covers the modulator assembly.
2. Disconnect delta switch electrical connector from modulator assembly.
3. Remove top modulator assembly bracket to fender shield mounting bolt.
4. Disconnect two master cylinder supply tubes at modulator assembly, then loosen the tubes at the master cylinder so tubes can be swung out of the way without kinking them.
5. Raise and support vehicle.
6. Disconnect modulator assembly 10-way connector, then remove remaining hydraulic brake lines from modulator.
7. Remove modulator assembly bracket mounting bolt that is nearest the junction block.
8. Loosen but do not remove mounting bracket bolt that is nearest the radiator.
9. Lower vehicle, then remove modulator and bracket assembly.

### Installation

1. Install modulator assembly into vehicle, using protruding tab on modulator to locate and hold assembly in place. Ensure bracket is held by front mounting bolt.
2. Install but do not tighten modulator bracket to fender shield mounting bolt.
3. Raise and support vehicle, then install mounting bracket bolt located nearest to the junction block. **Torque** both lower mounting bolts to 21 ft. lbs.
4. Attach four hydraulic fluid lines to modulator assembly and **torque** fittings to 12 ft. lbs.
5. Connect modulator assembly 10-way electrical connector.
6. Lower vehicle, then install two master cylinder supply tubes and **torque** fittings at modulator and master cylinder to 12 ft. lbs.

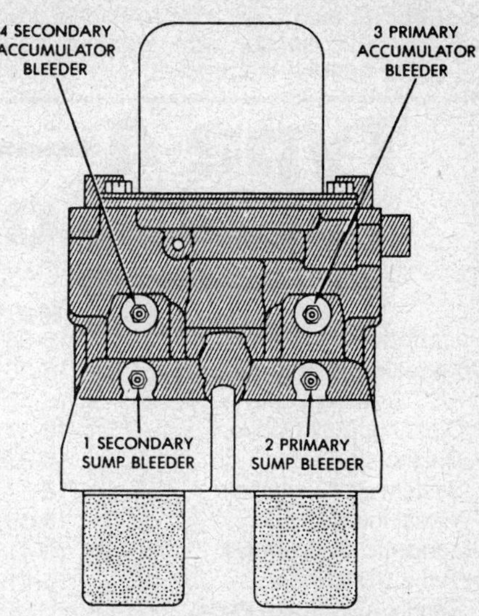


**Fig. 39 Bleeding ABS modulator assembly**

7. **Torque** modulator assembly to fender shield mounting bolt to 21 ft. lbs.
8. Bleed brake system, then install acid shield, battery tray and battery.

## CONTROLLER ANTI-LOCK BRAKE (CAB), REPLACE

1. Turn ignition off, then disconnect CAB and wiring harness 60-way connector. **Ensure ignition is in the OFF position.**
2. Remove CAB module bracket to frame mounting bolts.
3. Remove CAB module from vehicle.
4. Reverse procedure to install.

## FRONT WHEEL SPEED SENSORS, REPLACE

1. Raise and support vehicle, then remove tire and wheel assembly.
2. Remove grommet retainer clip that holds grommet in to fender shield.
3. Remove two sensor routing tube to frame rail attaching screws.
4. Carefully pull sensor assembly grommet from fender shield.
5. Unplug connector from harness, then remove triangular retainer clip from bracket on strut damper.
6. Remove sensor head screw, then the sensor head from steering knuckle.
7. Reverse procedure to install.

## REAR WHEEL SPEED SENSORS, REPLACE

1. Raise and support vehicle, then remove tire and wheel assemblies.
2. Remove sensor assembly grommet from underbody and pull harness through hole in underbody.
3. Unplug connector from harness, then remove sensor assembly grommets from bracket which is screwed into the body hose bracket, just forward of trailing arm bushing.
4. Remove sensor and brake tube assembly clip, located on inboard side of

trailing arm.
5. Remove sensor wire fastener from rear brake hose bracket.
6. Remove outboard sensor assembly retainer nut, then the sensor head screw.
7. Remove sensor head from adapter assembly.
8. Reverse procedure to install.

# Type 4—Bendix Anti-Lock 10 Anti-Lock Braking System

## INDEX



## DESCRIPTION

The Anti-Lock Braking System (ABS) prevents the wheels from locking up when braking, regardless of the surface conditions. This allows the car to stop in a shorter distance, and allows the driver to maintain directional control of the vehicle during heavy braking.

During normal braking conditions, the ABS operates like a conventional diagonally split, hydraulic power assist system. During heavy braking, however, each wheel's braking pressure is modulated according to its speed. To maintain vehicle stability, both rear wheels receive the same signal.

There are four major components, **Fig. 1**, in this ABS system that act in unison to control brake operation.

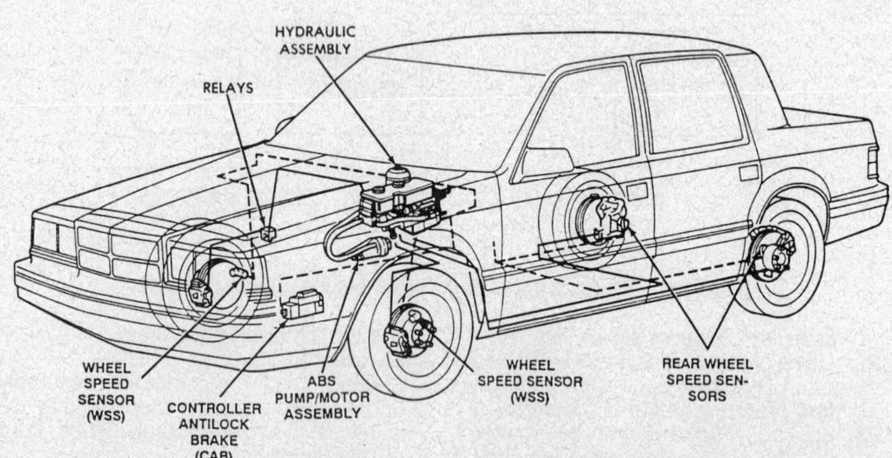


**Fig. 1 Bendix Anti-Lock 10 braking system components**

## SYSTEM COMPONENTS

### HYDRAULIC ASSEMBLY

This ABS system uses an integral hydraulic assembly which contains the wheel circuit valves used for brake pressure modulation.

### WHEEL SPEED SENSORS

The wheel speed sensors are located at each wheel and transmit wheel speed information to the Controller Anti-Lock Brake.

### CONTROLLER ANTI-LOCK BRAKE (CAB)

The Controller Anti-Lock Brake (CAB) is located on the front lefthand side of the engine compartment. The CAB uses the wheel speed information from the wheel speed sensors to control the ABS system function. The CAB also monitors ABS operation and detects system faults.

### PUMP/MOTOR ASSEMBLY

The Pump/Motor assembly is located under the hydraulic assembly at the rear lefthand side of the engine compartment. This pump is electrically driven and takes low pressure brake fluid from the hydraulic assembly reservoir and pressurizes it for storage in two accumulators for power assist and anti-lock braking.

## DIAGNOSIS & TESTING

The Bendix Anti-Lock 10 Brake System has self diagnosis capability. The self diagnosis cycle begins when the ignition switch is in the ON position. An electrical check is completed on the ABS components such as wheel speed sensors continuity, system continuity and other relay continuity. During this check the Anti-Lock Light will be on for approximately one to two seconds.

The ABS system is constantly monitored by the CAB. If the CAB detects a fault, it can disable the brake system anti-lock function. Depending on the fault the CAB will light either one or both brake system warning lamps.

The CAB contains a Self-Diagnostic Program which activates the indicator lights when a system fault is detected. Faults are stored in a diagnostic program memory. There are 19 fault codes which may be stored in the CAB and displayed through the DRB II. These fault codes will remain in the memory even after the ignition switch is turned off.

### VISUAL INSPECTION

Visually inspect system components and their connectors as described below prior to performing diagnostic tests.

1. Inspect brake fluid level, and ensure that fluid is not contaminated. **To establish proper fluid level, fully depress brake pedal 40 times prior to inspection.**
2. Inspect brake lines and master cylinder for leaks and/or damage.
3. Inspect ABS hydraulic unit for leaks, and ensure that electrical connectors are not damaged or disconnected.
4. Inspect Power Distribution Center (PDC) and ensure that all ABS relays are properly installed.
5. Inspect CAB for a secure mounting, and ensure that its electrical connec-

tor is not damaged or loose.

6. Inspect all wheel speed sensors (WSS) and their connectors for damage or improper connections.

## DIAGNOSTIC TESTS

Refer to wiring diagrams and connector identifications, **Figs. 2 through 7,** when performing testing procedures.

Refer to **Figs. 8 through 129** for diagnostic test procedures, noting the following:

1. Connect Diagnostic Readout Box (DRB II) following manufacturers instructions. **All diagnostic test procedures assume DRB II is being used, and have been designed specifically for the DRB II.**
2. After completion of diagnosis and repair of the system, perform verification test 20A.

## ABS WARNING LAMP

The Anti-Lock warning light will normally come on for approximately one to two seconds when the ignition switch is first turned to the ON position.

Anytime the Controller Anti-Lock Brake (CAB) detects a condition which results in a shutdown of the ABS function other than when the ignition switch is first turned on it will activate the ABS warning lamp. When the light is on only the Anti-Lock function of the brake system is affected. The standard brake system and ability to stop the vehicle will not be affected.

## CLEARING FAULT CODES

Fault codes can be cleared by using the DRB II diagnostics tester, or they will be automatically cleared after 50 ignition switch ON/OFF cycles.

## SYSTEM SELF DIAGNOSIS

This ABS system has a self diagnostic connector located under the lefthand side of the instrument panel, left of the steering column. The diagnostic connector is a blue 6-way connector which can be connected to a DRB II readout box.

# SYSTEM SERVICE

**Certain components of the ABS system are not intended to be serviced individually. Attempting to remove or disconnect certain system components, may result in personal injury and/or improper system operation. Only the components with removal and installation procedures should be serviced.**

**Use the following general precautions whenever servicing the ABS system:**

1. If any welding work is to be performed using an arc welder, CAB should be disconnected.
2. When the ignition switch is in the ON position, the CAB electrical connector should not be disconnected or connected.
3. Some components of the ABS system are not serviced separately and must be serviced as complete assemblies. Do not disassemble any component which is designated as non-serviceable.

## DE-PRESSURIZING HYDRAULIC ACCUMULATOR

The ABS pump/motor assembly will keep the hydraulic accumulator charged to a pressure between 1600-2000 psi anytime the ignition is in the ON position. The pump/motor cannot run if the ignition is off or either battery cable is disconnected.

**The hydraulic accumulator should be depressurized before disassembling any portion of the hydraulic system.**

1. Turn ignition switch to the OFF position, or disconnect battery ground cable.
2. Pump brake pedal a minimum of 40 times using approximately 50 pounds of pedal force. Pedal feel should change noticeably when accumulator is discharged.
3. After a definite increase in pedal effort is felt, pump pedal a few additional times. This will remove all hydraulic pressure from the system.

## PUMP/MOTOR ASSEMBLY, REPLACE

1. De-pressurize hydraulic accumulator as described in "De-Pressurizing Hydraulic Accumulator." **Failure to de-pressurize the hydraulic accumulator, may result in personal injury, or damage to painted surfaces.**
2. Remove fresh air intake ducts from engine induction system.
3. Disconnect electrical connectors from the pump/motor assembly and any additional connectors in area close to pump/motor assembly.
4. Disconnect high and low pressure hoses from hydraulic assembly, then cap spigot on reservoir.
5. Disconnect pump/motor electrical connector from engine mount, then remove pump heat shield attaching bolt from front of pump bracket.
6. Remove front heat shield, then lift pump/motor assembly out of vehicle.
7. Reverse procedure to install, lubricate O-rings on high and low pressure hose connections to pump/motor assembly with brake fluid prior to installation.

## HYDRAULIC ASSEMBLY, REPLACE

1. De-pressurize hydraulic accumulator as described in "De-Pressurizing Hydraulic Accumulator." **Failure to de-pressurize the hydraulic accumulator, may result in personal injury, or damage to painted surfaces.**
2. Remove fresh air intake ducts from engine induction system.
3. Disconnect all electrical connectors from hydraulic assembly.
4. Remove as much fluid as possible from the reservoir on hydraulic assembly.
5. Remove high pressure hose fitting from assembly.
6. Disconnect pump return hose from filter nipple, then cap spigot on filter.
7. Disconnect all brake tubes from hydraulic assembly.
8. Working under the instrument panel, position a small screwdriver between center tang on retainer clip and pin in brake pedal. Rotate screwdriver enough to allow retainer clip center tang to pass over end of brake pedal pin.
9. Remove four hydraulic assembly mounting nuts, then the hydraulic assembly from vehicle.
10. Reverse procedure to install.

## CONTROLLER ANTI-LOCK BRAKE (CAB), REPLACE

1. Turn ignition switch to the OFF position, then raise and support vehicle.
2. Remove transmission oil cooler line routing clip, then disconnect CAB 60-way connector. **Verify that ignition switch is in the OFF position before disconnecting connector.**
3. Remove CAB mounting bolts, the the CAB from the vehicle.
4. Reverse procedure to install.

## FRONT WHEEL SPEED SENSORS, REPLACE

1. Raise and support vehicle, then remove wheel and tire assembly.
2. Remove screw from clip that attaches sensor assembly to fender shield.
3. Pull sensor assembly grommet from fender shield, then unplug sensor connector from harness.
4. Remove retainer clip from bracket on strut damper, then the three sensor assembly grommets from retainer brackets.
5. Remove sensor head screw, then remove sensor head from steering knuckle. **If sensor has seized, due to corrosion. Do not use pliers on sensor head. Use a hammer and a punch and tap edge of sensor ear, rocking sensor side to side until free.**
6. Reverse procedure to install, coat speed sensor with High Temperature Multi-Purpose grease before installing into steering knuckle. **Proper installation of wheel speed sensor cables is critical for continued system operation. Failure to install cables in retainers, may result in contact with moving parts, resulting in an open circuit.**

## REAR WHEEL SPEED SENSORS, REPLACE

1. Raise and support vehicle, then remove wheel and tire assembly.
2. Remove sensor assembly grommet from underbody and pull harness

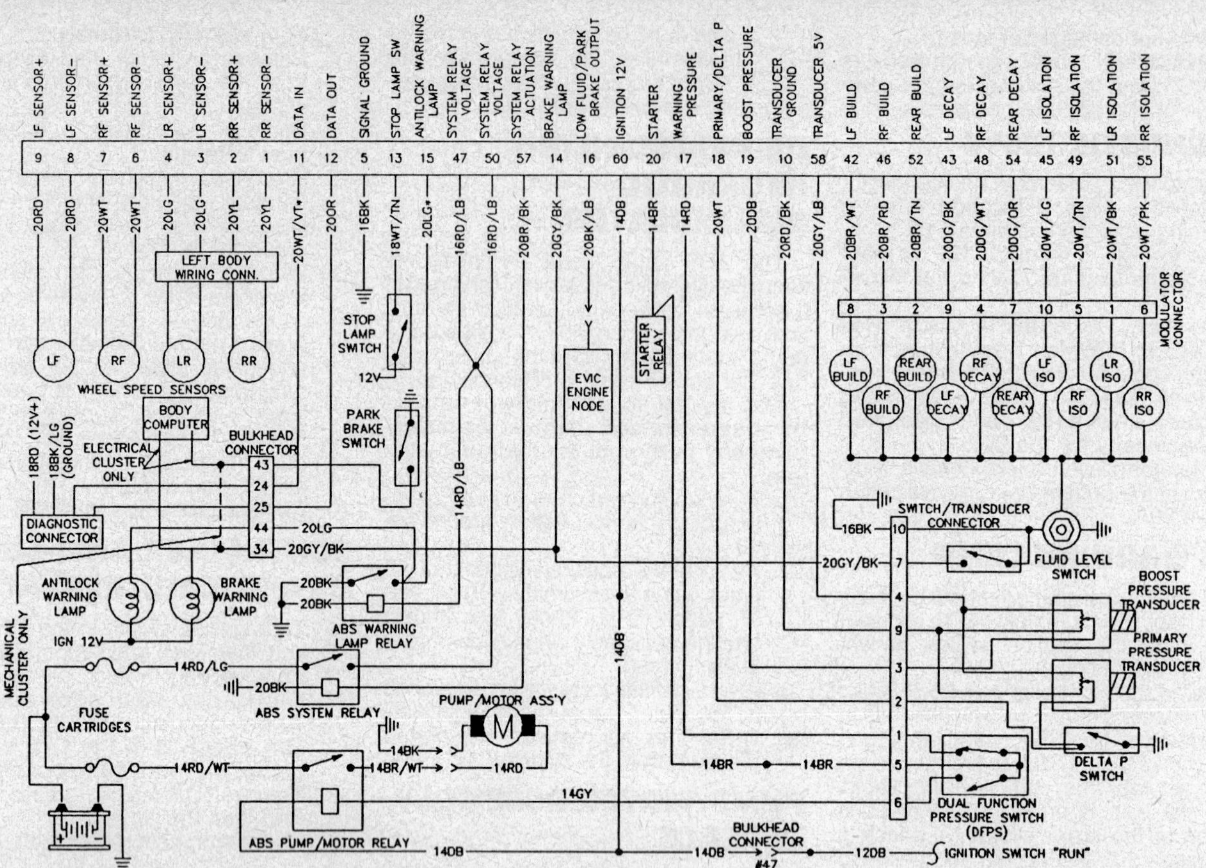

Fig. 2 Bendix Anti-Lock 10 braking system wiring diagram. 1990 Models

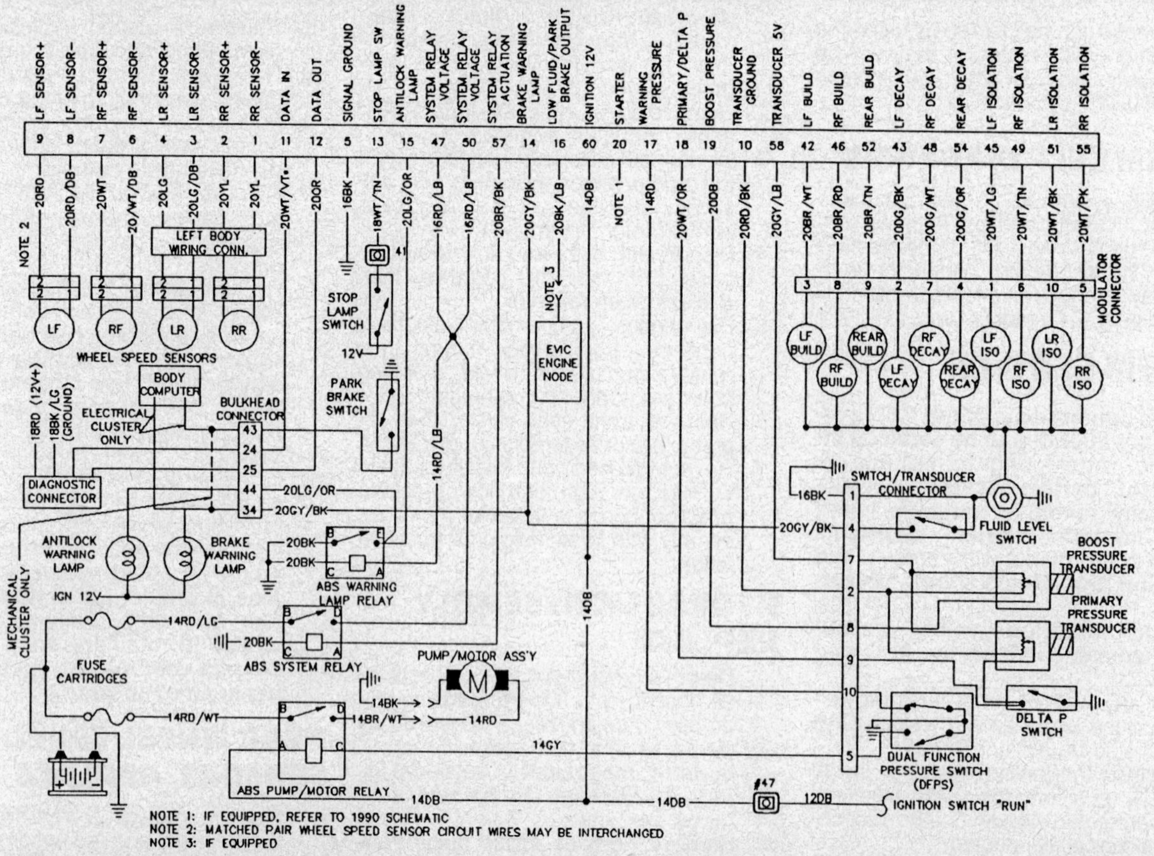
NOTE 1: IF EQUIPPED, REFER TO 1990 SCHEMATIC
NOTE 2: MATCHED PAIR WHEEL SPEED SENSOR CIRCUIT WIRES MAY BE INTERCHANGED
NOTE 3: IF EQUIPPED

Fig. 3 Bendix Anti-Lock 10 braking system wiring diagram. 1991 Except Premier

LF SENSOR+
LF SENSOR–
RF SENSOR+
RF SENSOR–
LR SENSOR+
LR SENSOR–
RR SENSOR+
RR SENSOR–
DATA IN
DATA OUT
SIGNAL GROUND
STOP LAMP SW
ANTILOCK WARNING LAMP
SYSTEM RELAY VOLTAGE
SYSTEM RELAY VOLTAGE
SYSTEM RELAY ACTUATION
BRAKE WARNING LAMP
IGNITION 12V
WARNING PRESSURE
PRIMARY/DELTA P
BOOST PRESSURE
TRANSDUCER GROUND
TRANSDUCER 5V
LF BUILD
RF BUILD
REAR BUILD
LF DECAY
RF DECAY
REAR DECAY
LF ISOLATION
RF ISOLATION
LR ISOLATION
RR ISOLATION
WHEEL SPEED SENSORS
STOP LAMP SWITCH
PARK BRAKE SWITCH
BULKHEAD CONNECTOR
DIAGNOSTIC CONNECTOR
10-WAY CONNECTOR
ANTILOCK WARNING LAMP
BRAKE WARNING LAMP
ABS WARNING LAMP RELAY
ABS SYSTEM RELAY
PUMP/MOTOR ASS'Y
ABS PUMP/MOTOR RELAY
MODULATOR CONNECTOR
SWITCH/TRANSDUCER CONNECTOR
FLUID LEVEL SWITCH
BOOST PRESSURE TRANSDUCER
PRIMARY PRESSURE TRANSDUCER
DELTA P SWITCH
STARTER MOTOR RELAY
DUAL FUNCTION PRESSURE SWITCH (DFPS)
IGNITION SWITCH "RUN"


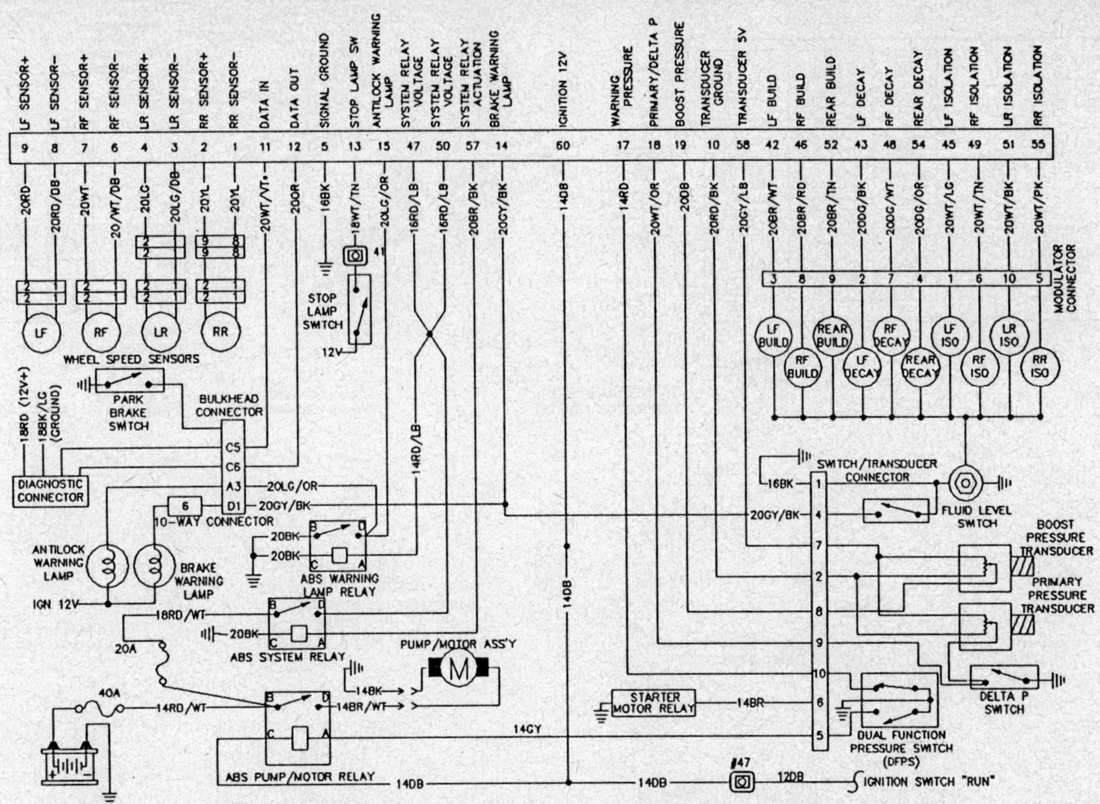

**Fig. 4 Bendix Anti-Lock 10 braking system wiring diagram. 1991 Premier**

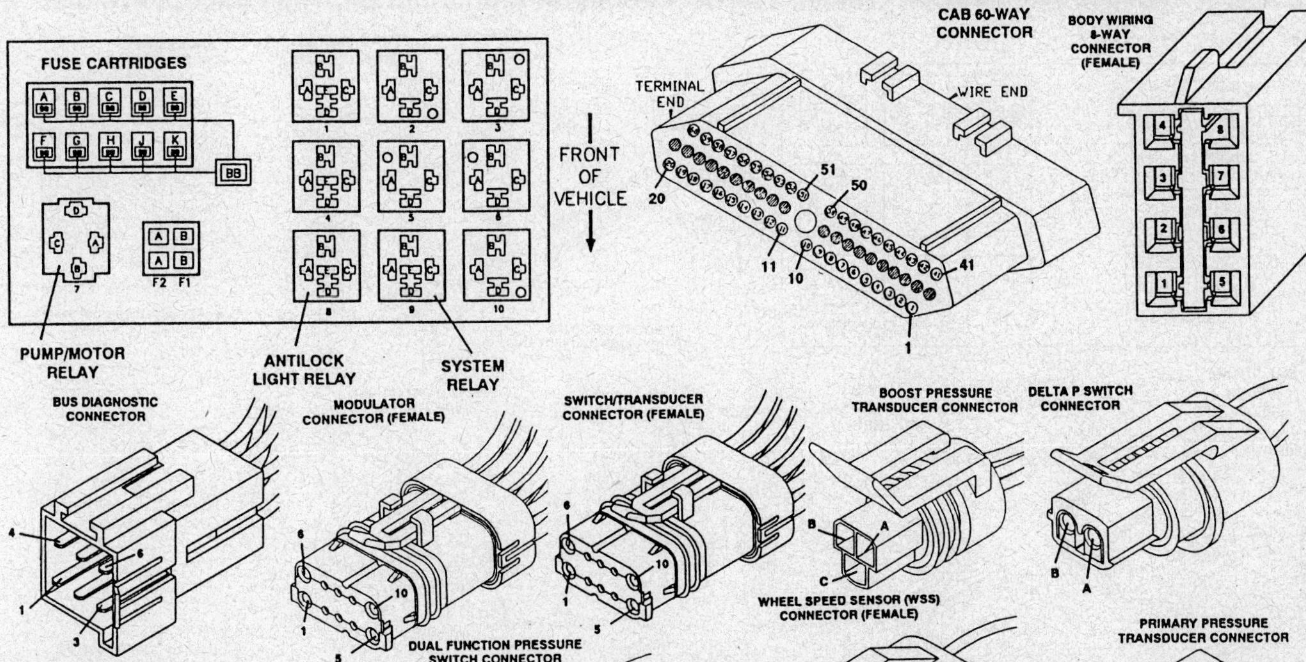

FUSE CARTRIDGES
FRONT OF VEHICLE
PUMP/MOTOR RELAY
ANTILOCK LIGHT RELAY
SYSTEM RELAY
CAB 60-WAY CONNECTOR
TERMINAL END
WIRE END
BODY WIRING 8-WAY CONNECTOR (FEMALE)
BUS DIAGNOSTIC CONNECTOR
MODULATOR CONNECTOR (FEMALE)
SWITCH/TRANSDUCER CONNECTOR (FEMALE)
BOOST PRESSURE TRANSDUCER CONNECTOR
DELTA P SWITCH CONNECTOR
WHEEL SPEED SENSOR (WSS) CONNECTOR (FEMALE)
PRIMARY PRESSURE TRANSDUCER CONNECTOR
DUAL FUNCTION PRESSURE SWITCH CONNECTOR
PUMP/MOTOR CONNECTOR


**Fig. 5 Bendix Anti-Lock 10 braking system connector identification. 1990 Models**

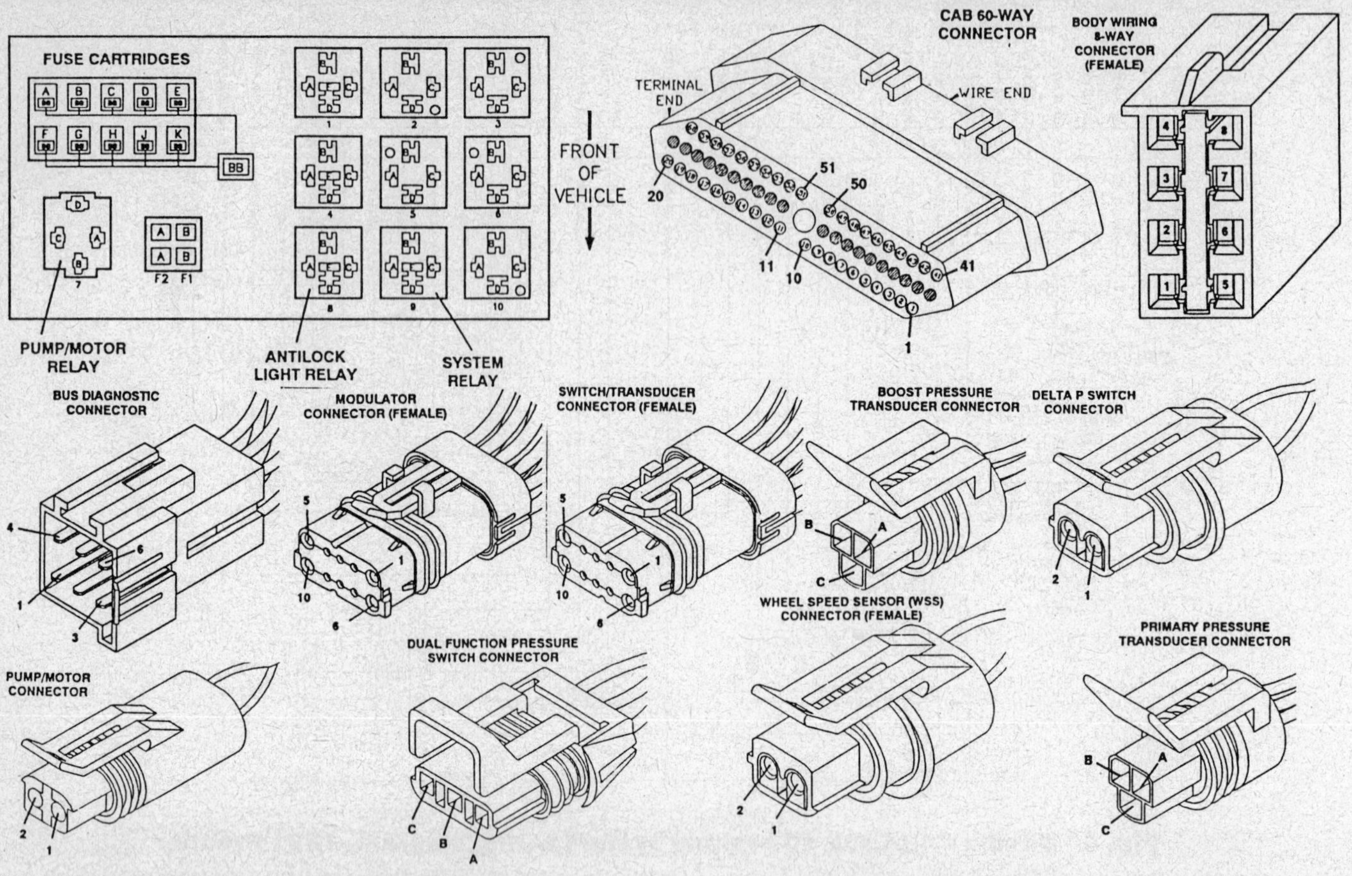

FUSE CARTRIDGES
A B C D E
F G H J K
BB
F2 F1
PUMP/MOTOR RELAY
ANTILOCK LIGHT RELAY
SYSTEM RELAY
FRONT OF VEHICLE
CAB 60-WAY CONNECTOR
TERMINAL END
WIRE END
BODY WIRING 8-WAY CONNECTOR (FEMALE)
BUS DIAGNOSTIC CONNECTOR
MODULATOR CONNECTOR (FEMALE)
SWITCH/TRANSDUCER CONNECTOR (FEMALE)
BOOST PRESSURE TRANSDUCER CONNECTOR
DELTA P SWITCH CONNECTOR
WHEEL SPEED SENSOR (WSS) CONNECTOR (FEMALE)
PRIMARY PRESSURE TRANSDUCER CONNECTOR
PUMP/MOTOR CONNECTOR
DUAL FUNCTION PRESSURE SWITCH CONNECTOR

**Fig. 6 Bendix Anti-Lock 10 braking system connector identification. 1991 Except Premier**

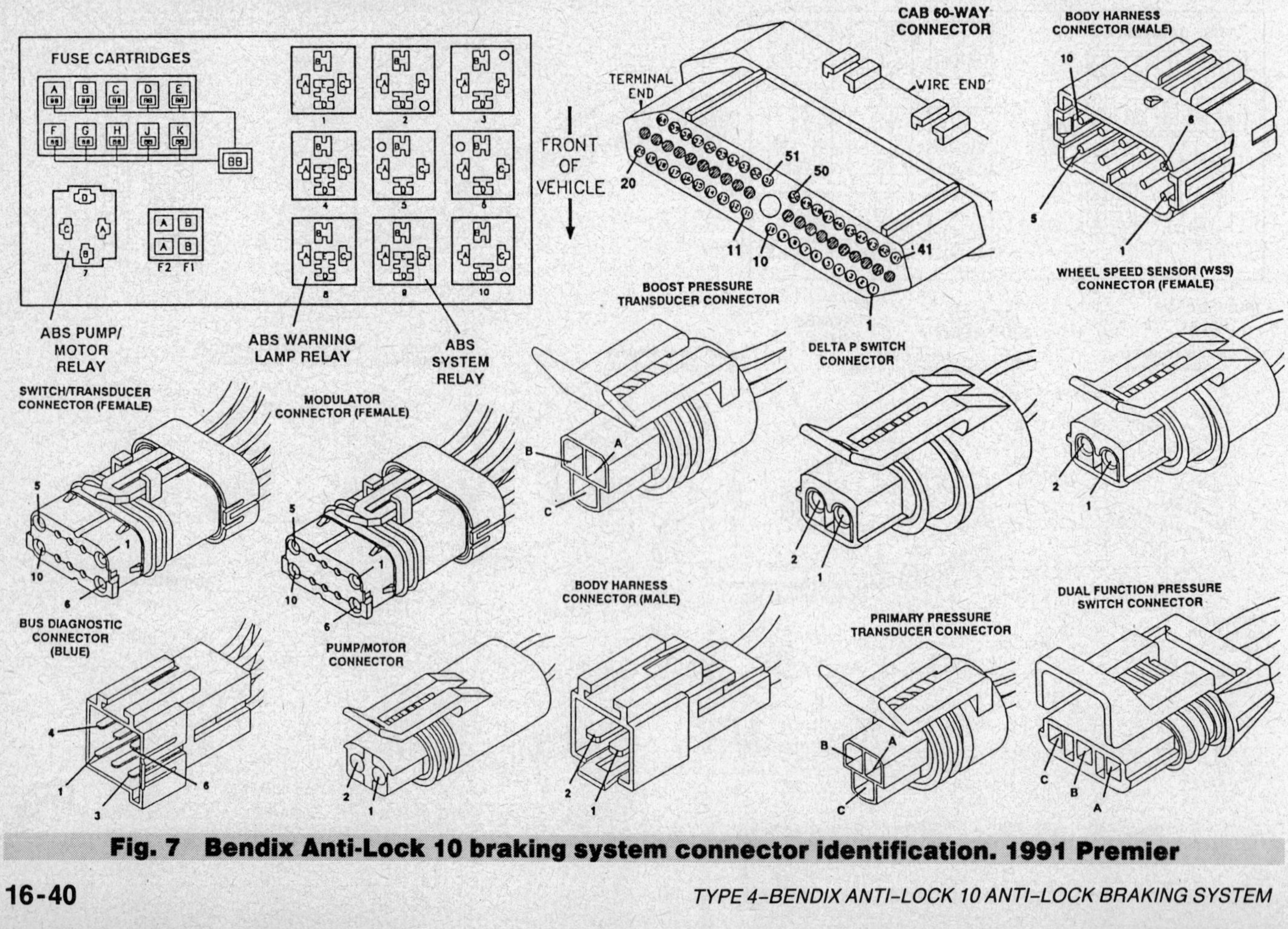

FUSE CARTRIDGES
A B C D E
F G H J K
BB
F2 F1
ABS PUMP/ MOTOR RELAY
ABS WARNING LAMP RELAY
ABS SYSTEM RELAY
FRONT OF VEHICLE
CAB 60-WAY CONNECTOR
TERMINAL END
WIRE END
BODY HARNESS CONNECTOR (MALE)
WHEEL SPEED SENSOR (WSS) CONNECTOR (FEMALE)
BOOST PRESSURE TRANSDUCER CONNECTOR
DELTA P SWITCH CONNECTOR
SWITCH/TRANSDUCER CONNECTOR (FEMALE)
MODULATOR CONNECTOR (FEMALE)
BUS DIAGNOSTIC CONNECTOR (BLUE)
PUMP/MOTOR CONNECTOR
BODY HARNESS CONNECTOR (MALE)
PRIMARY PRESSURE TRANSDUCER CONNECTOR
DUAL FUNCTION PRESSURE SWITCH CONNECTOR

**Fig. 7 Bendix Anti-Lock 10 braking system connector identification. 1991 Premier**

through hole in underbody.
3. Unplug connector from harness, then remove sensor grommet bracket screw from body hose bracket, just forward of trailing arm bushing.
4. Remove sensor assembly clip, located on inboard side of trailing arm.
5. Remove rear sensor wire fastener from rear brake hose bracket, then the outboard sensor assembly retainer nut.
6. Remove sensor head screw, then remove sensor head from adapter assembly. **If sensor has seized, due to corrosion. Do not use pliers on sensor head. Use a hammer and a punch and tap edge of sensor ear, rocking sensor side to side until free.**
7. Reverse procedure to install, coat speed sensor with High Temperature Multi-Purpose grease before installing into steering knuckle and **torque** screw to 5 ft. lbs.

## SERVICE BULLETINS

### BENDIX ABS BRAKE PEDAL RETURNABILITY

### 1990 NEW YORKER FIFTH AVENUE & NEW YORKER LANDAU, 1990–91 DYNASTY, IMPERIAL & NEW YORKER SALON & 1991 FIFTH AVENUE & NEW YORKER

#### Symptom/Condition

Some 1990 and early production 1991 models with Bendix Anti-Lock 10 braking system serial No. 3CA010200 and earlier, may exhibit a condition where the brake pedal may not return to its fully released position. As a result, the rear brake lights may remain illuminated when the brake pedal is released or the cruise control may be inoperative.

#### Diagnosis

1. Verify that the stop lamp switch is properly adjusted.
2. Pump up hydraulic unit by stroking brake pedal and then slowly releasing brake pedal and verifying by hand that pedal is at its fully released position.
3. If brake pedal does not return to fully released position, replace ABS hydraulic assembly.

## DIAGNOSTIC CHART INDEX



*Continued*

## DIAGNOSTIC CHART INDEX —Continued



*Continued*

## DIAGNOSTIC CHART INDEX—Continued

| Test No. | Symptom | Page No. | Fig. No. |
|---|---|---|---|
| **1991 Models** | | | |
| 8C | Boost Pressure Fault | 16-62 | 58 |
| 8D | Boost Pressure Fault | 16-63 | 60 |
| 9A | Right Rear Wheel Speed Sensor Continuity Fault | 16-63 | 62 |
| 9B | Right Rear Wheel Speed Sensor Continuity Fault | 16-64 | 64 |
| 9C | Right Rear Wheel Speed Sensor Continuity Fault | 16-64 | 66 |
| 9D | Right Rear Wheel Speed Sensor Continuity Fault | 16-65 | 68 |
| 9E | Right Rear Wheel Speed Sensor Continuity Fault | 16-65 | 69 |
| 9F | Right Rear Wheel Speed Sensor Continuity Fault | 16-65 | 70 |
| 9G | Right Rear Wheel Speed Sensor Continuity Fault | 16-65 | 71 |
| 9H | Right Rear Wheel Speed Sensor Continuity Fault | 16-65 | 72 |
| 9J | Right Rear Wheel Speed Sensor Continuity Fault | 16-66 | 73 |
| 9K | Right Rear Wheel Speed Sensor Continuity Fault | 16-66 | 74 |
| 9L | Right Rear Wheel Speed Sensor Continuity Fault | 16-66 | 75 |
| 9M | Right Rear Wheel Speed Sensor Continuity Fault | 16-66 | 76 |
| 9N | Right Rear Wheel Speed Sensor Continuity Fault | 16-66 | 77 |
| 10A | Left Rear Wheel Speed Sensor Continuity Fault | 16-67 | 79 |
| 10B | Left Rear Wheel Speed Sensor Continuity Fault | 16-67 | 81 |
| 10C | Left Rear Wheel Speed Sensor Continuity Fault | 16-68 | 83 |
| 10D | Left Rear Wheel Speed Sensor Continuity Fault | 16-68 | 85 |
| 10E | Left Rear Wheel Speed Sensor Continuity Fault | 16-68 | 86 |
| 10F | Left Rear Wheel Speed Sensor Continuity Fault | 16-68 | 87 |
| 10G | Left Rear Wheel Speed Sensor Continuity Fault | 16-69 | 88 |
| 10H | Left Rear Wheel Speed Sensor Continuity Fault | 16-69 | 89 |
| 10J | Left Rear Wheel Speed Sensor Continuity Fault | 16-69 | 90 |
| 10K | Left Rear Wheel Speed Sensor Continuity Fault | 16-69 | 91 |
| 10L | Left Rear Wheel Speed Sensor Continuity Fault | 16-69 | 92 |
| 10M | Left Rear Wheel Speed Sensor Continuity Fault | 16-69 | 93 |
| 10N | Left Rear Wheel Speed Sensor Continuity Fault | 16-69 | 94 |
| 11A | Right Front Wheel Speed Sensor Continuity Fault | 16-70 | 96 |
| 12A | Left Front Wheel Speed Sensor Continuity Fault | 16-71 | 98 |
| 13A | Right Rear Wheel Speed Sensor Fault | 16-72 | 99 |
| 14A | Left Rear Wheel Speed Sensor Fault | 16-72 | 100 |
| 15A | Right Front Wheel Speed Sensor Fault | 16-72 | 101 |
| 16A | Left Front Wheel Speed Sensor Fault | 16-72 | 102 |
| 17A | Primary Pressure/Delta P Fault | 16-73 | 103 |
| 17B | Primary Pressure/Delta P Fault | 16-74 | 104 |
| 17C | Primary Pressure/Delta P Fault | 16-74 | 106 |
| 17D | Primary Pressure/Delta P Fault | 16-74 | 107 |
| 17E | Primary Pressure/Delta P Fault | 16-75 | 108 |
| 18A | Anti-Lock Lamp Fault | 16-75 | 110 |
| 18B | Anti-Lock Lamp Fault | 16-76 | 112 |
| 19A | Anti-Lock Lamp Relay Fault | 16-77 | 114 |
| 19B | Anti-Lock Lamp Relay Fault | 16-77 | 116 |
| 20A | Excess Decay Fault | 16-78 | 117 |
| 21A | Hydraulic Pump/Motor Circuit Test | 16-79 | 119 |
| 21B | Hydraulic Pump/Motor Circuit Test | 16-79 | 120 |
| 21C | Hydraulic Pump/Motor Circuit Test | 16-80 | 122 |
| 21D | Hydraulic Pump/Motor Circuit Test | 16-81 | 124 |
| 21E | Hydraulic Pump/Motor Circuit Test | 16-82 | 125 |
| 22A | Hydraulic Pressure Performance Test | 16-82 | 126 |
| 22B | Hydraulic Pressure Performance Test | 16-82 | 127 |
| 23A | Stop Lamp Switch Input Test | 16-83 | 128 |
| 24A | System Verification Test | 16-83 | 129 |

*Continued*

## DIAGNOSTIC CHART INDEX—Continued

| Test No. | Symptom | Page No. | Fig. No. |
|---|---|---|---|
| **1991 Models** | | | |
| 25A | DRB II Error Messages | 16-83 | 130 |
| 25B | DRB II Error Messages | 16-83 | 131 |
| 25C | DRB II Error Messages | 16-84 | 132 |

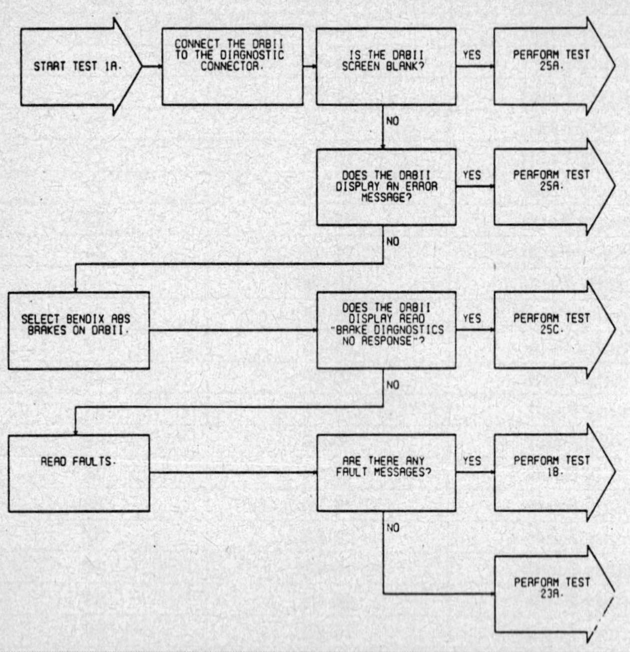


Fig. 8 Test 1A—Read Fault Message

**FAULT MESSAGES**

| | |
|---|---|
| CAB FAULT | Perform TEST 2A |
| MODULATOR FAULT | Perform TEST 3A |
| SOLENOID UNDERVOLT | Perform TEST 4A |
| LOW FLUID/PARK BRAKE | Perform TEST 5A |
| SYSTEM RELAY | Perform TEST 6A |
| LOW ACCUMULATOR | Perform TEST 7A |
| PRIMARY PRESS/DELTA P | Perform TEST 17A |
| BOOST PRESSURE | Perform TEST 8A |
| RIGHT REAR CONTIN | Perform TEST 9A |
| LEFT REAR CONTIN | Perform TEST 10A |
| RIGHT FRONT CONTIN | Perform TEST 11A |
| LEFT FRONT CONTIN | Perform TEST 12A |
| RIGHT REAR SENSOR | Perform TEST 13A |
| LEFT REAR SENSOR | Perform TEST 14A |
| RIGHT FRONT SENSOR | Perform TEST 15A |
| LEFT FRONT SENSOR | Perform TEST 16A |
| ANTILOCK LIGHT | Perform TEST 18A |
| ANTILOCK LIGHT RELAY | Perform TEST 19A |
| EXCESS DECAY FAULT | Perform TEST 20A |

Fig. 9 Test 1B—Read Fault Message

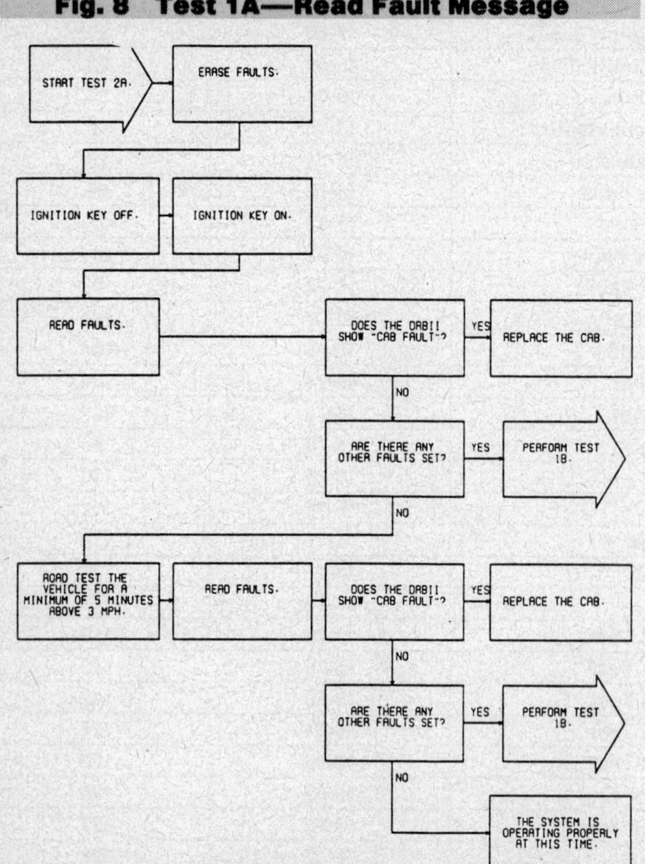


Fig. 10 Test 2A—Cab Fault. 1990 Models

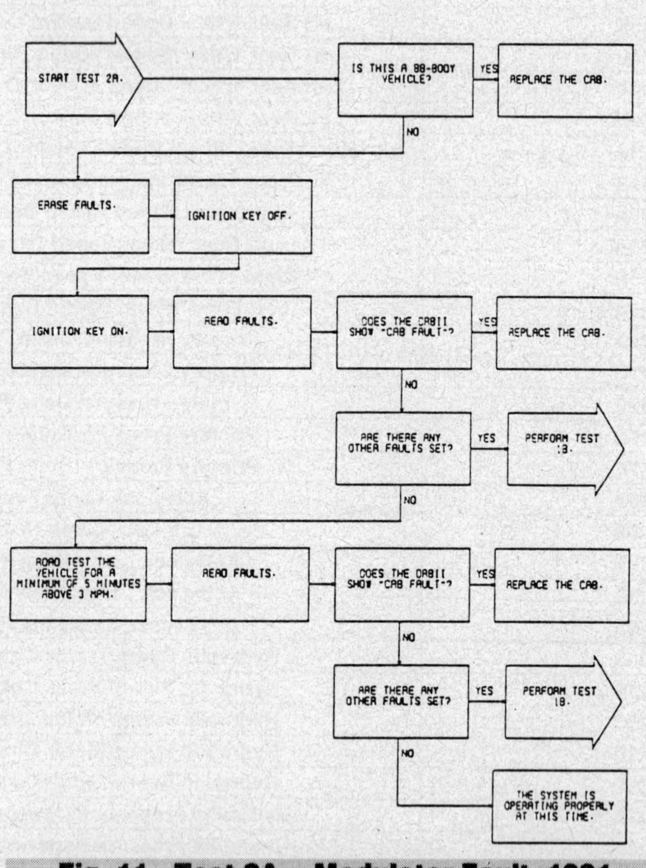


Fig. 11 Test 2A—Modulator Fault. 1991 Models

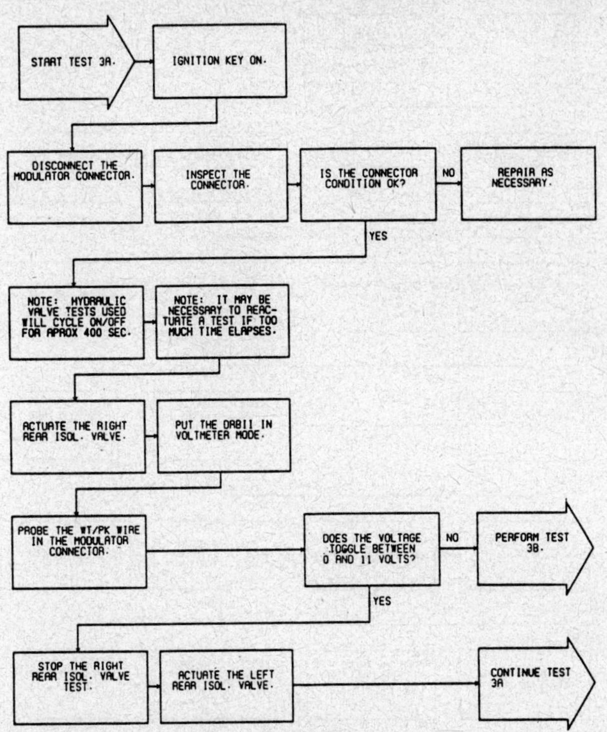


Fig. 12 Test 3A—Modulator Fault Message (Part 1 Of 4). 1990 Models

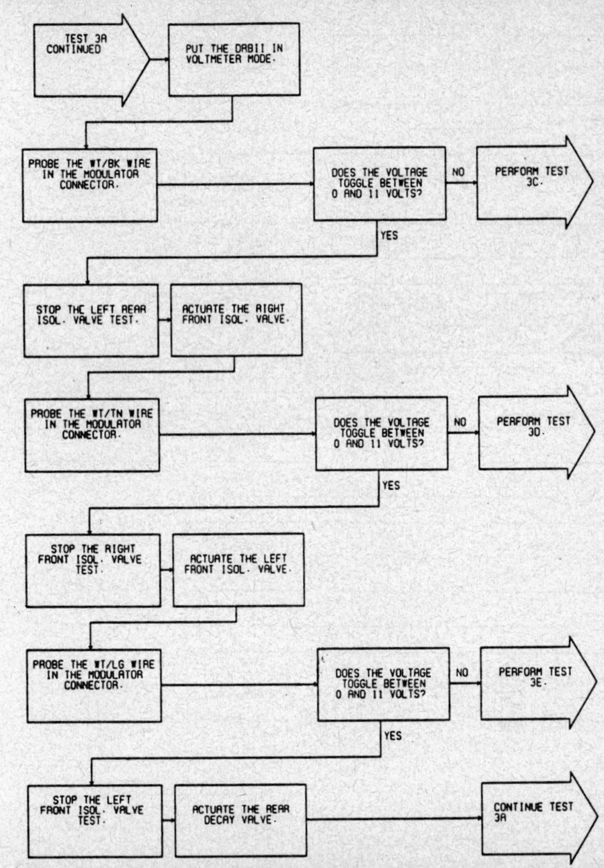


Fig. 12 Test 3A—Modulator Fault Message (Part 2 Of 4). 1990 Models

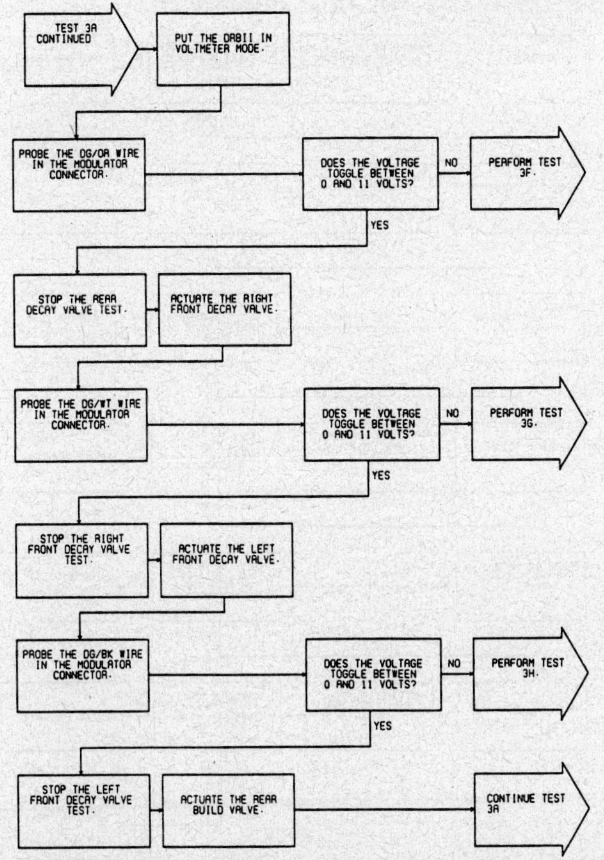


Fig. 12 Test 3A—Modulator Fault Message (Part 3 Of 4). 1990 Models

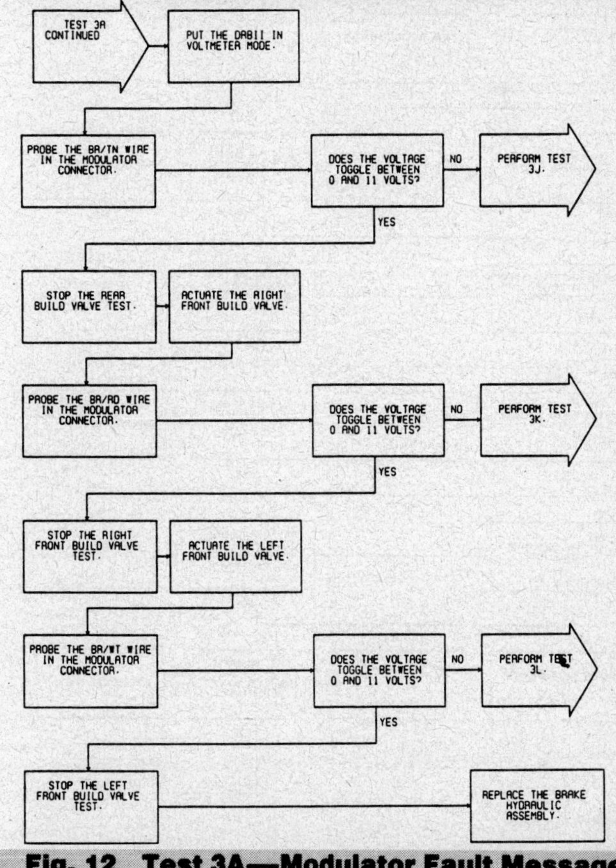


Fig. 12 Test 3A—Modulator Fault Message (Part 4 Of 4). 1990 Models

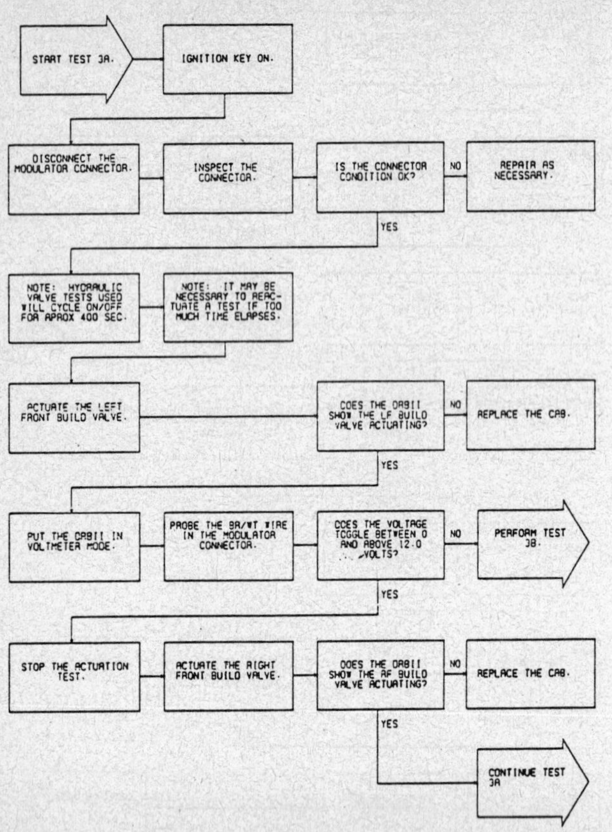


**Fig. 13 Test 3A—Modulator Fault (Part 1 Of 5). 1991 Models**

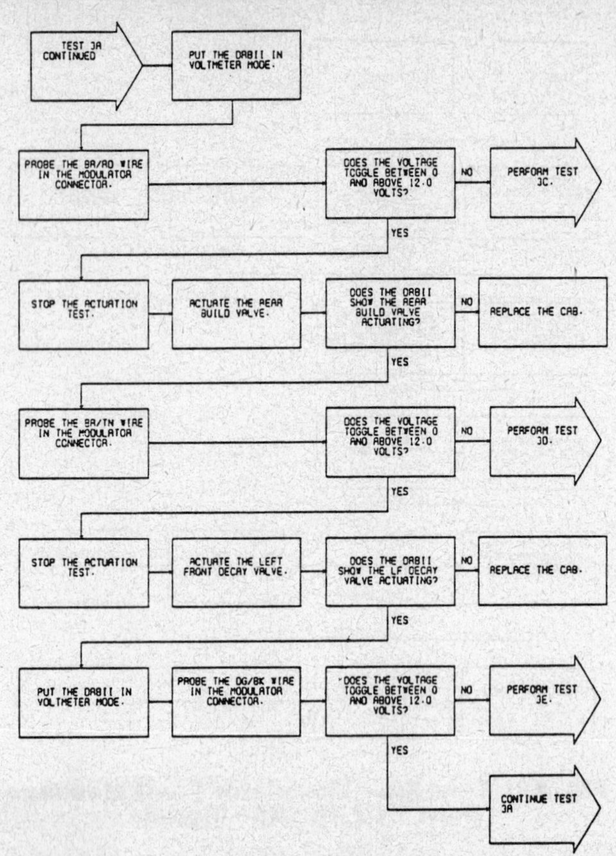


**Fig. 13 Test 3A—Modulator Fault (Part 2 Of 5). 1991 Models**

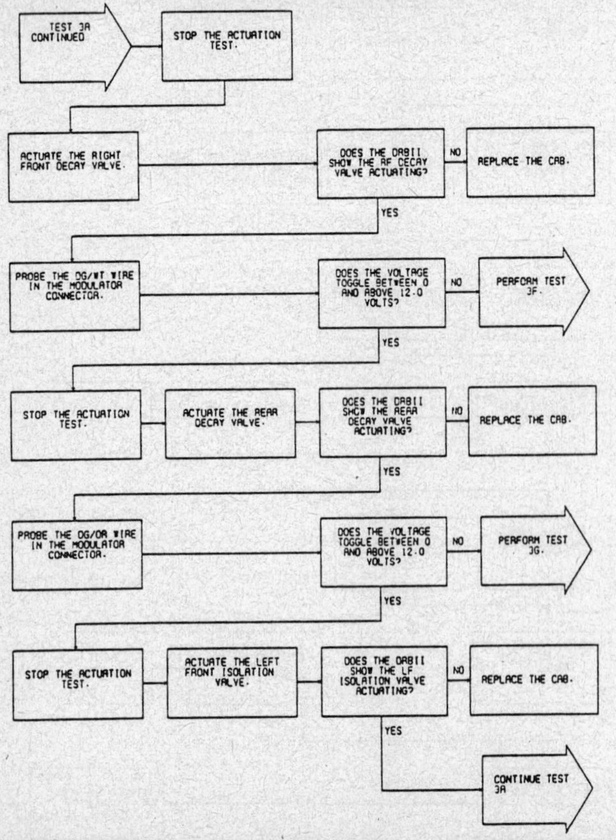


**Fig. 13 Test 3A—Modulator Fault (Part 3 Of 5). 1991 Models**

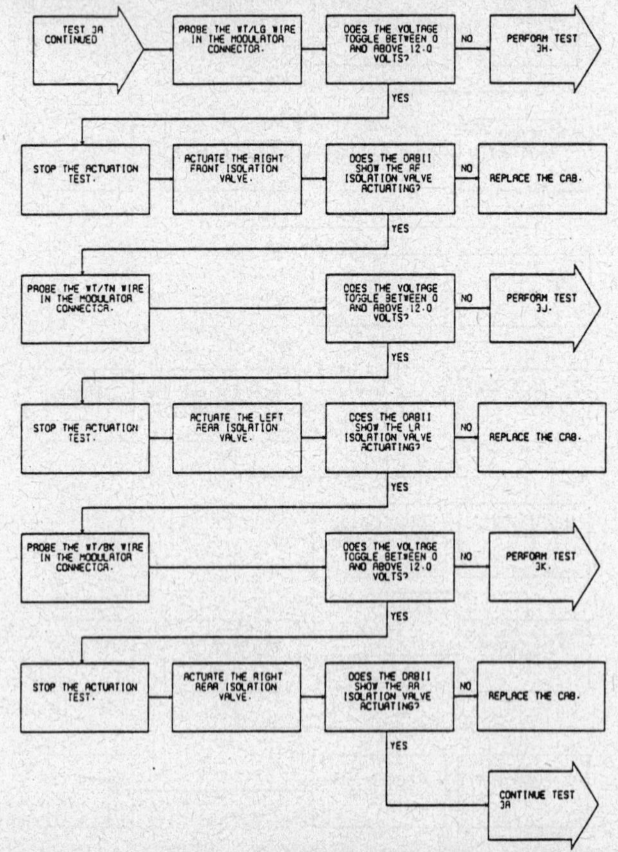


**Fig. 13 Test 3A—Modulator Fault (Part 4 Of 5). 1991 Models**

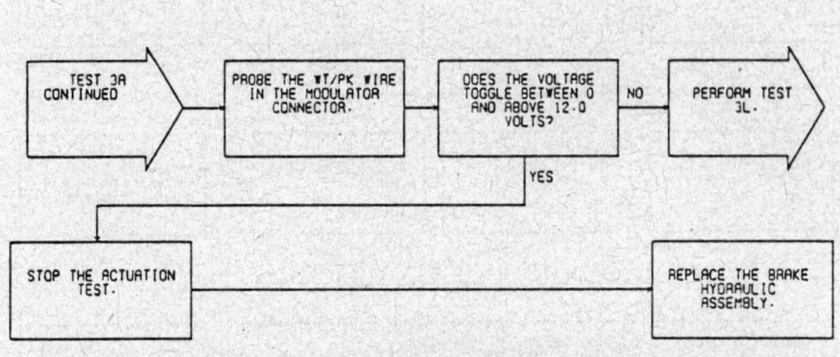


**Fig. 13 Test 3A—Modulator Fault (Part 5 Of 5). 1991 Models**

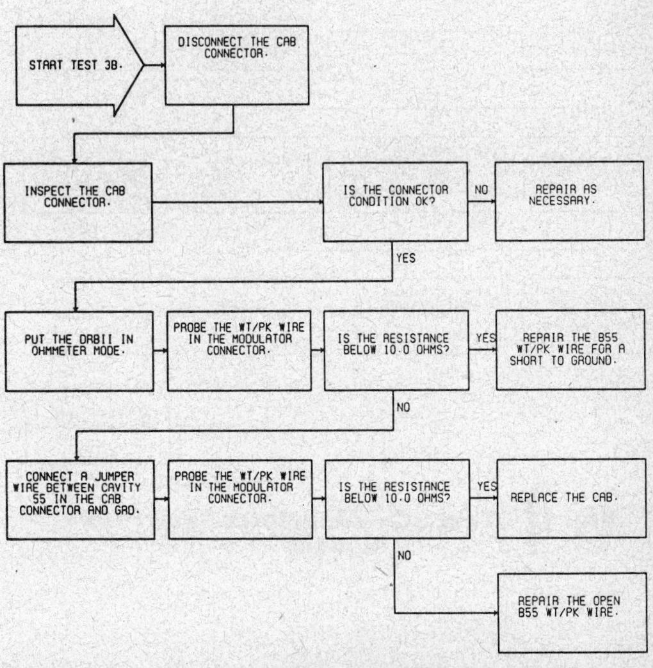


**Fig. 14 Test 3B—Right Rear Isolation Valve. 1990 Models**

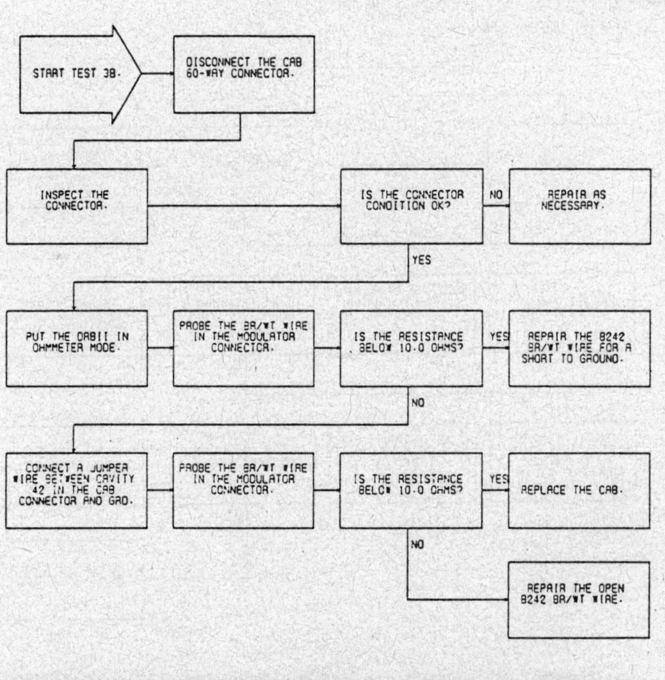


**Fig. 15 Test 3B—Modulator Fault. 1991 Models**

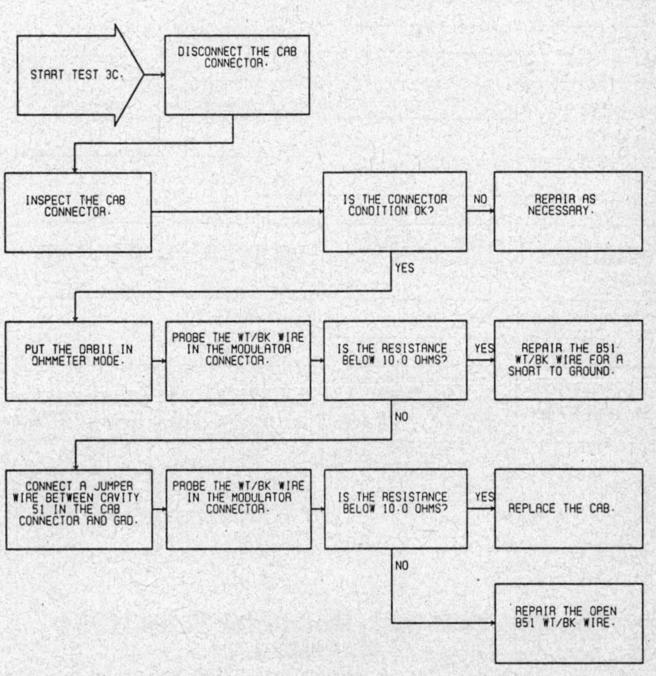


**Fig. 16 Test 3C—Left Rear Isolation Valve. 1990 Models**

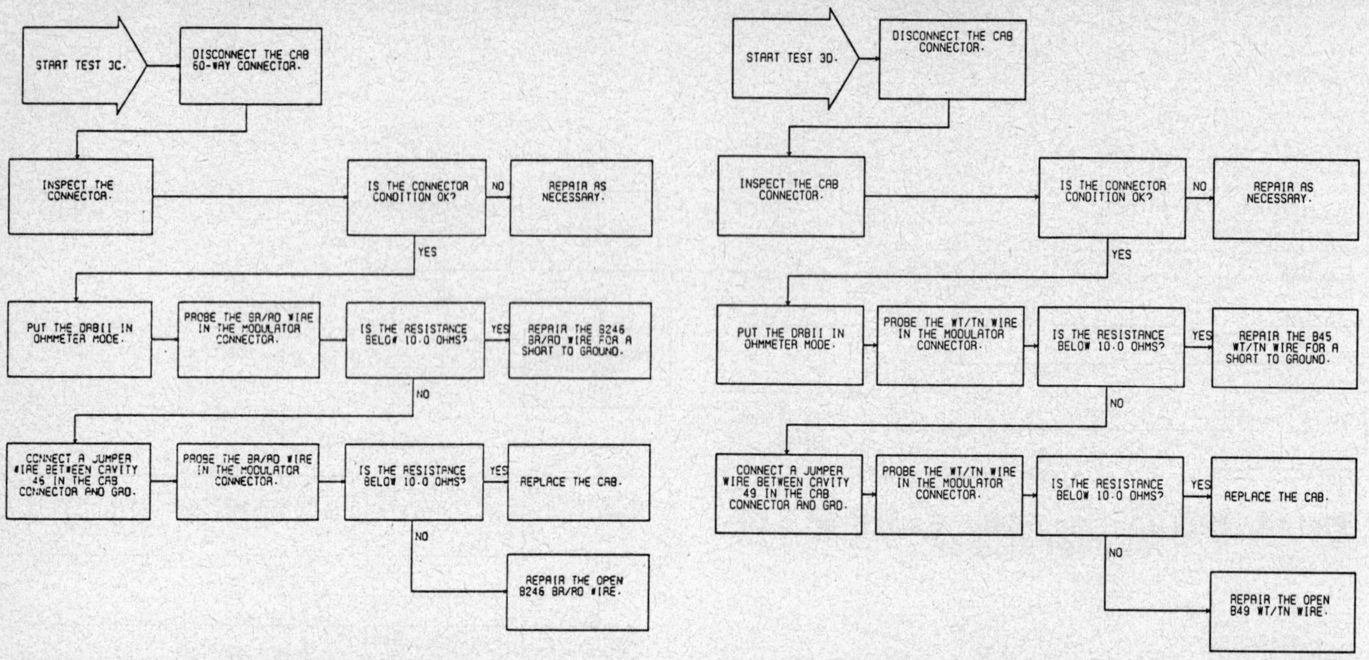


**Fig. 17 Test 3C—Modulator Fault. 1991 Models**

**Fig. 18 Test 3D—Right Front Isolation Valve. 1990 Models**

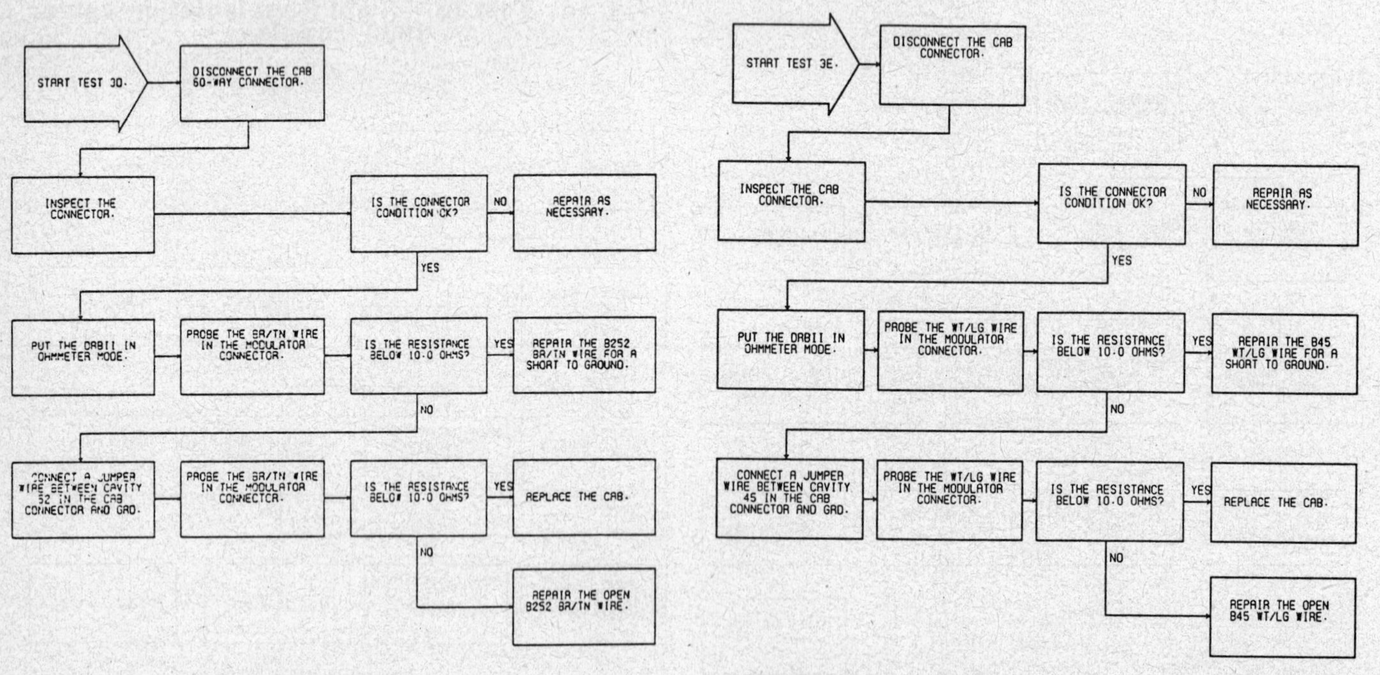


**Fig. 19 Test 3D—Modulator Fault. 1991 Models**

**Fig. 20 Test 3E—Left Front Isolation Valve. 1990 Models**

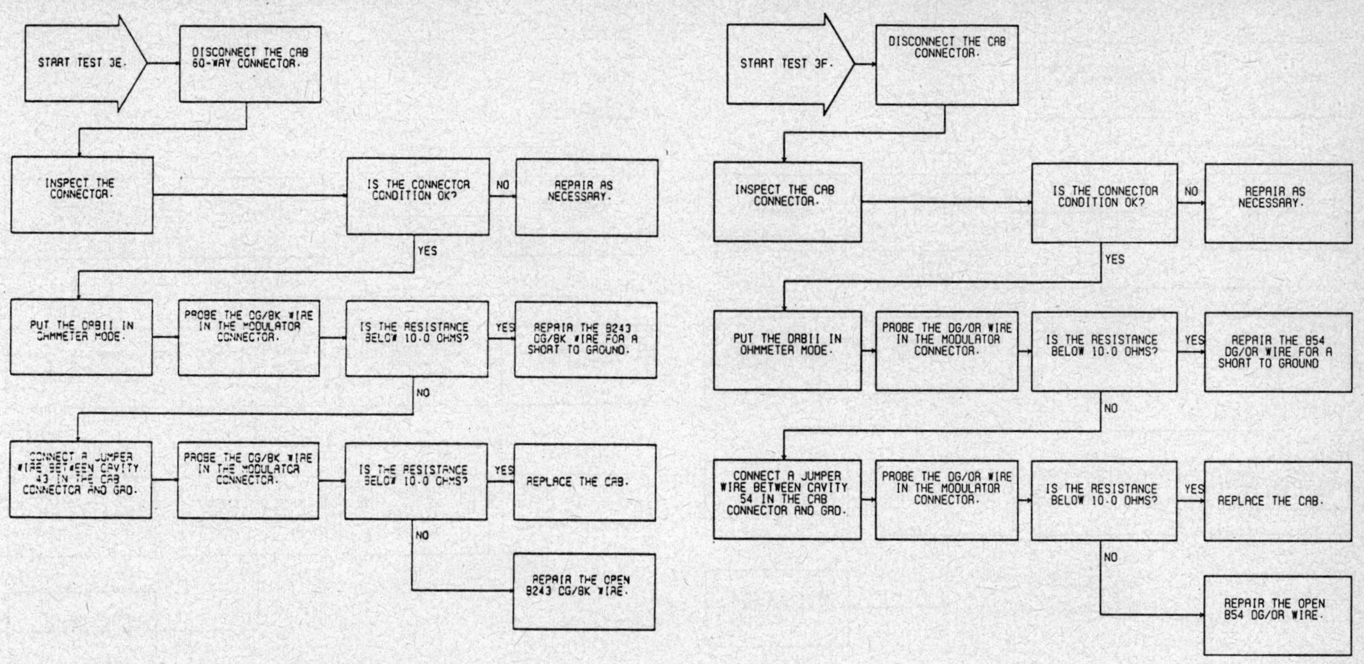


**Fig. 21 Test 3E—Modulator Fault. 1991 Models**

**Fig. 22 Test 3F—Rear Decay Valve. 1990 Models**

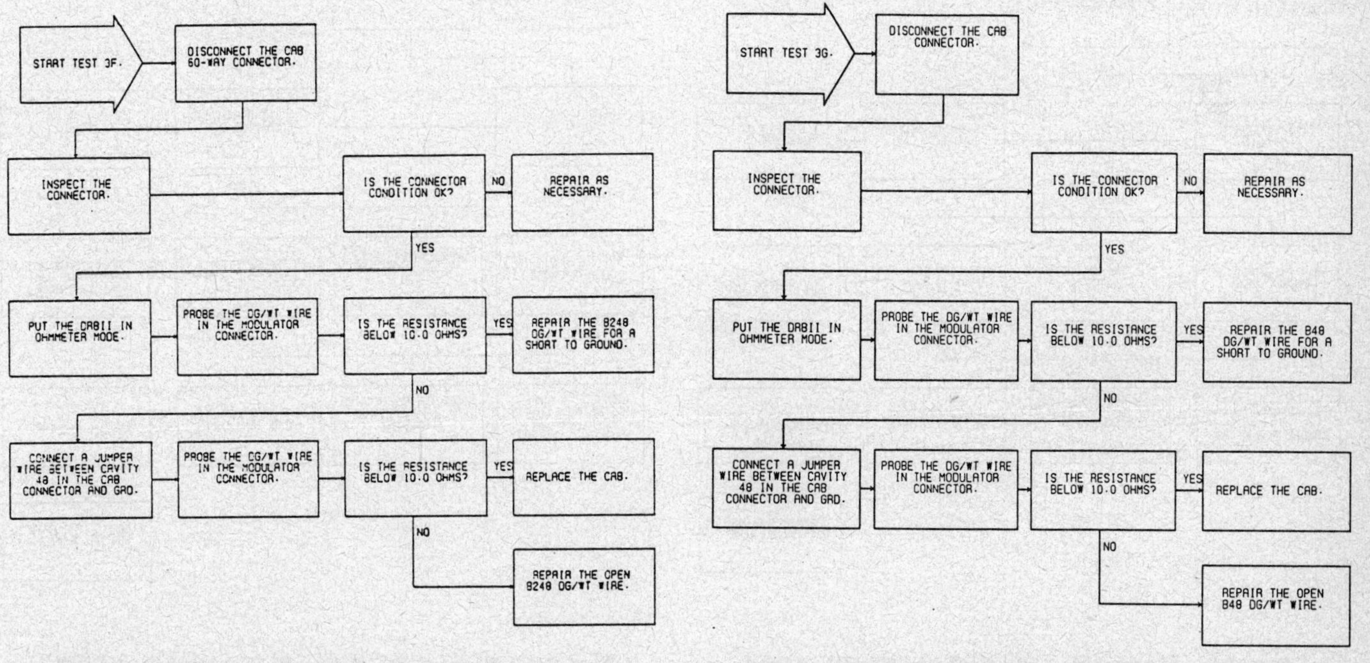


**Fig. 23 Test 3F—Modulator Fault. 1991 Models**

**Fig. 24 Test 3G—Right Front Decay Valve. 1990 Models**

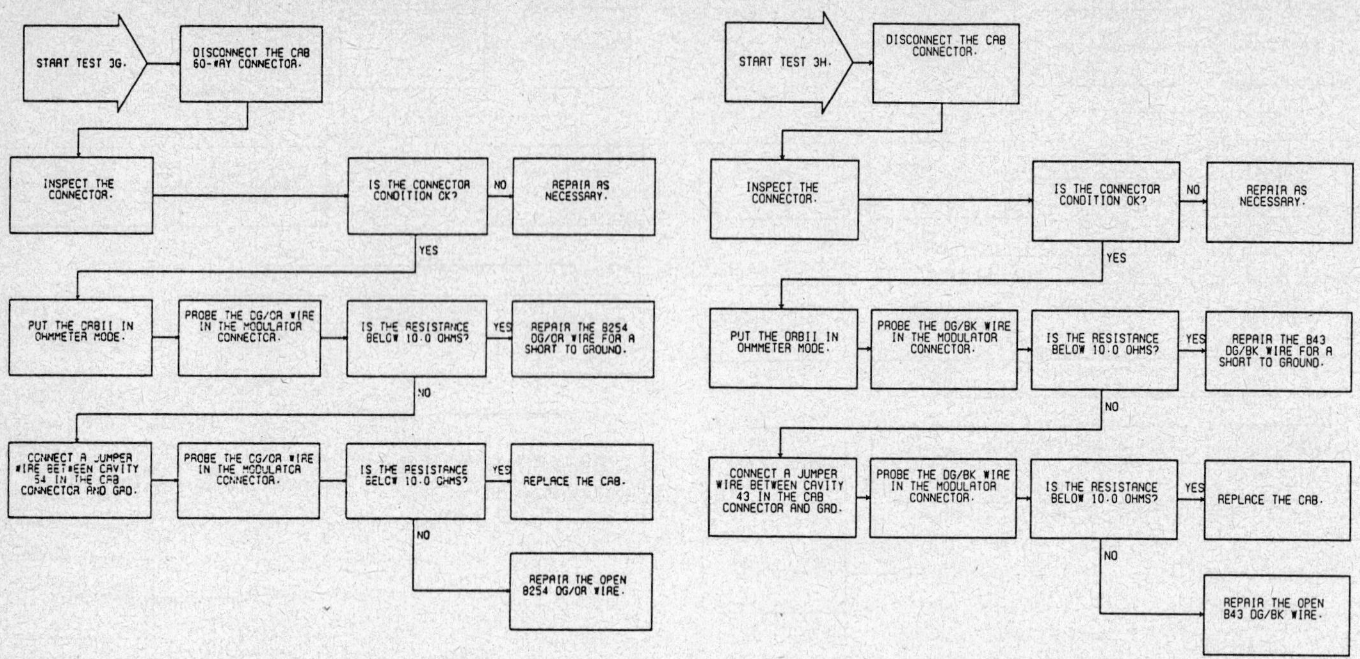


**Fig. 25 Test 3G—Modulator Fault. 1991 Models**

**Fig. 26 Test 3H—Left Front Decay Valve. 1990 Models**

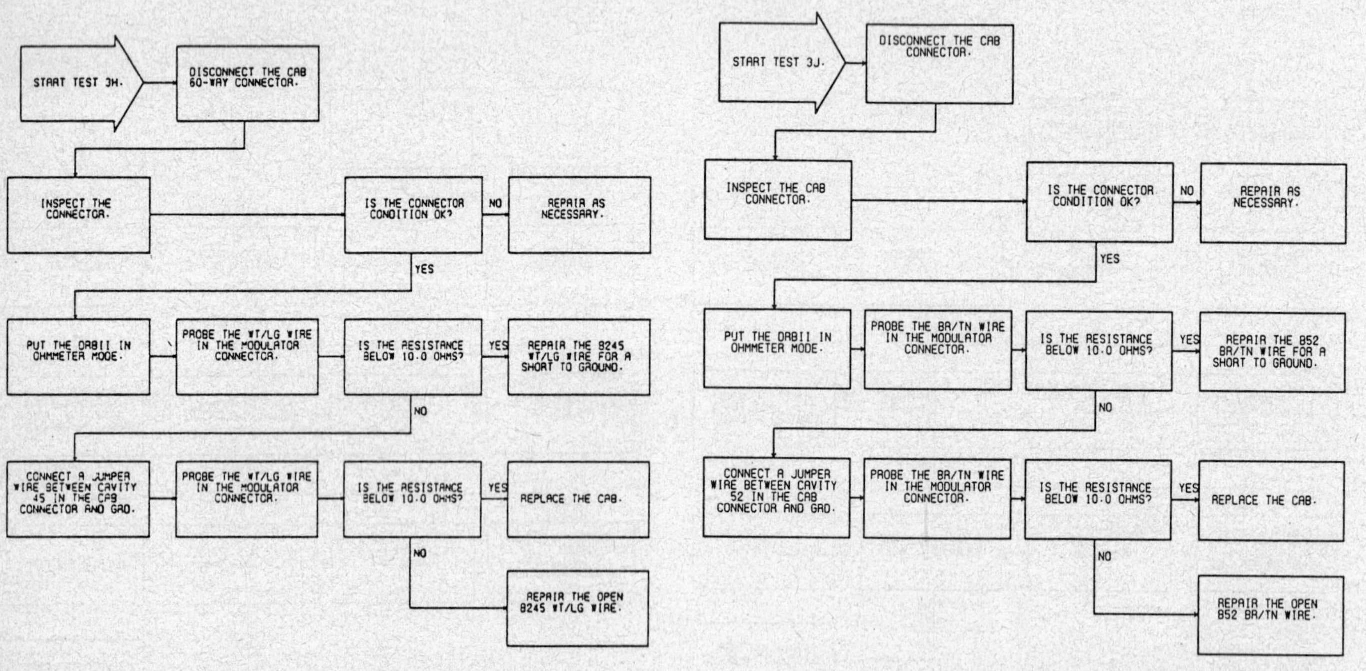


**Fig. 27 Test 3H—Modulator Fault. 1991 Models**

**Fig. 28 Test 3J—Rear Build Valve. 1990 Models**

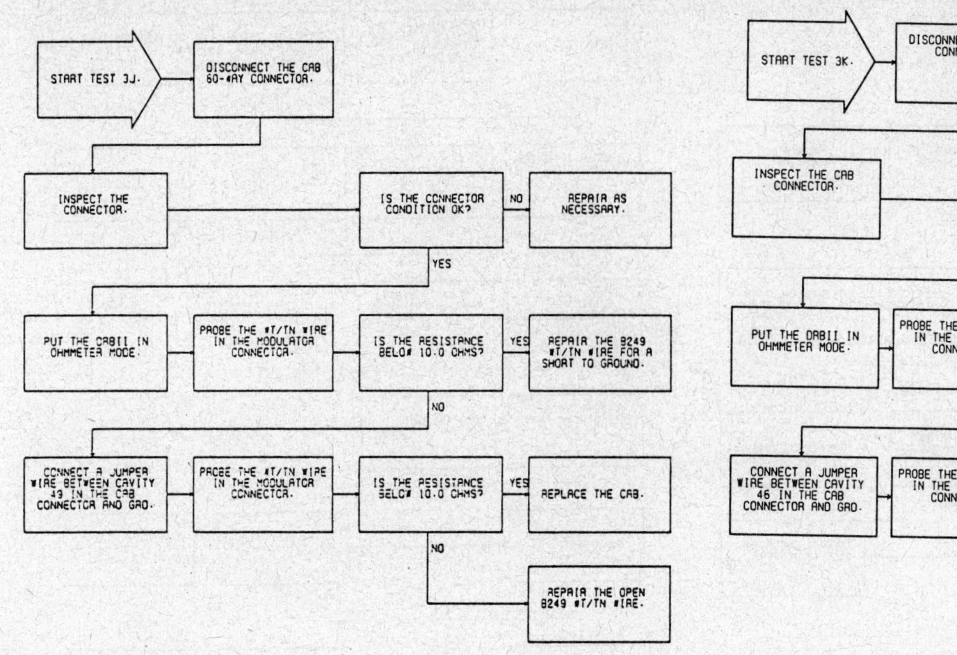


**Fig. 29 Test 3J—Modulator Fault. 1991 Models**

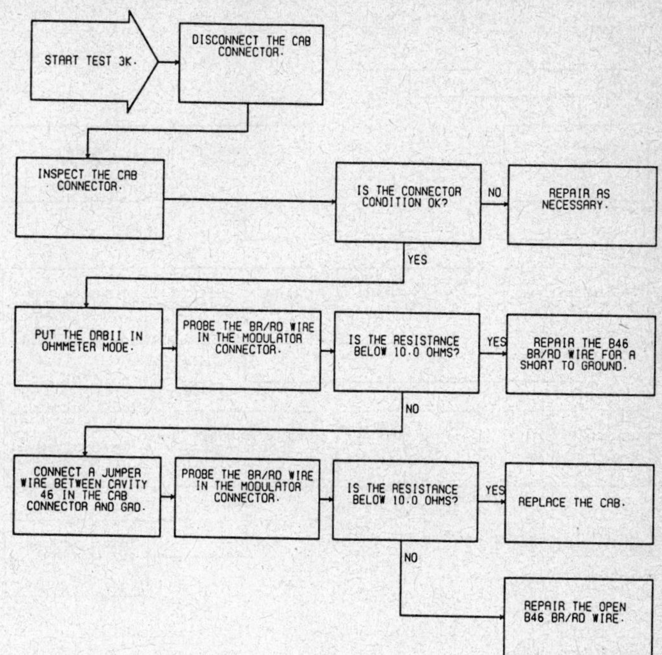


**Fig. 30 Test 3K—Right Front Build Valve. 1990 Models**

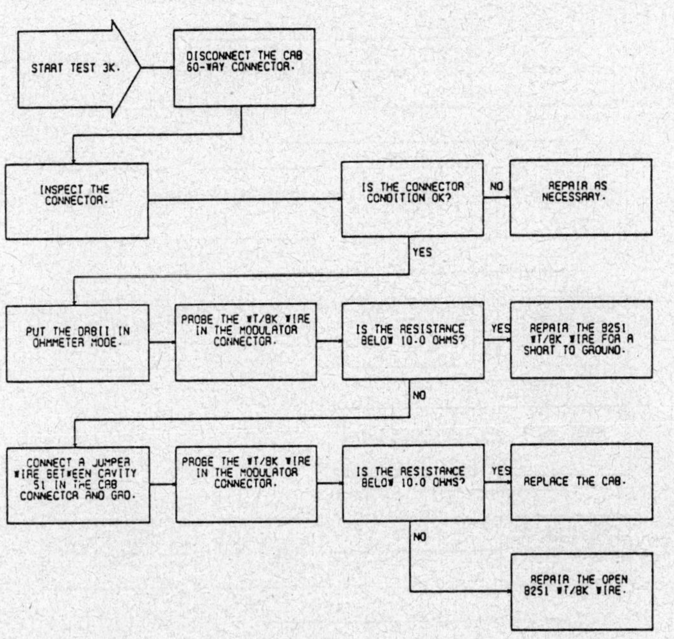


**Fig. 31 Test 3K—Modulator Fault. 1991 Models**

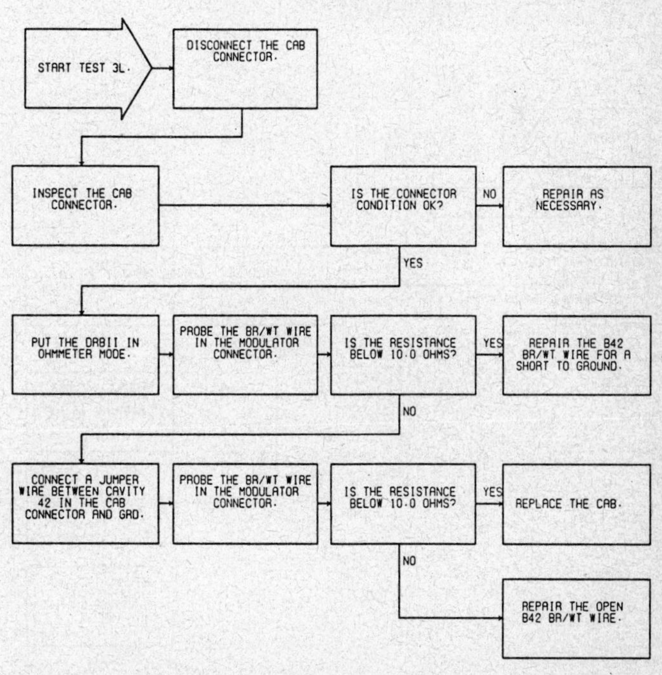


**Fig. 32 Test 3L—Left Front Build Valve. 1990 Models**

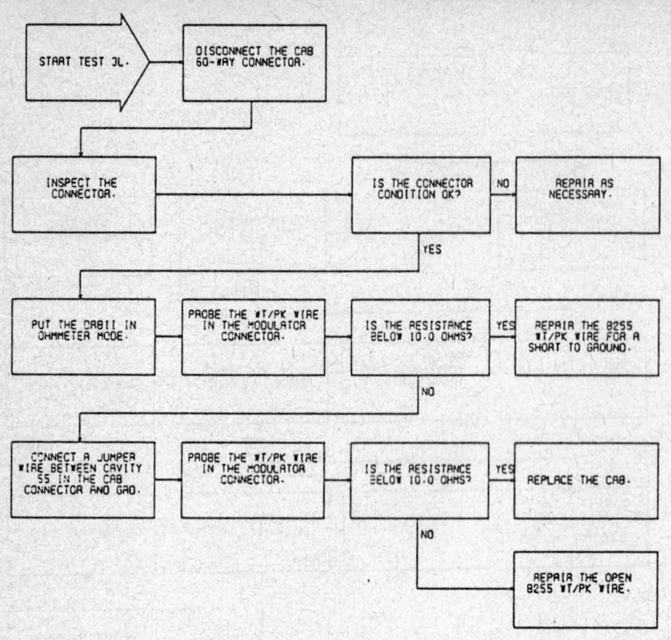


**Fig. 33 Test 3L—Modulator Fault. 1991 Models**

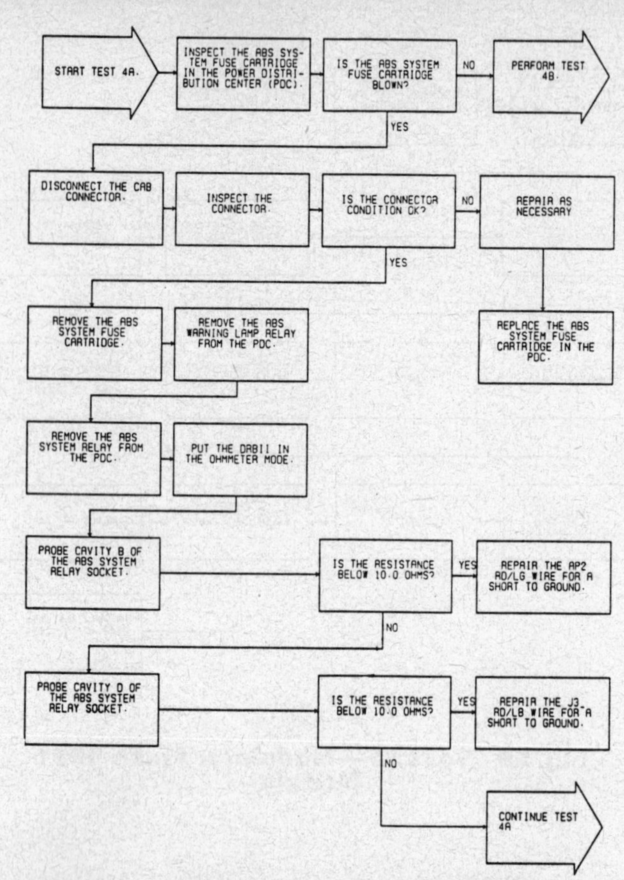


**Fig. 34 Test 4A—Solenoid Undervoltage Message (Part 1 Of 2). 1990 Models**

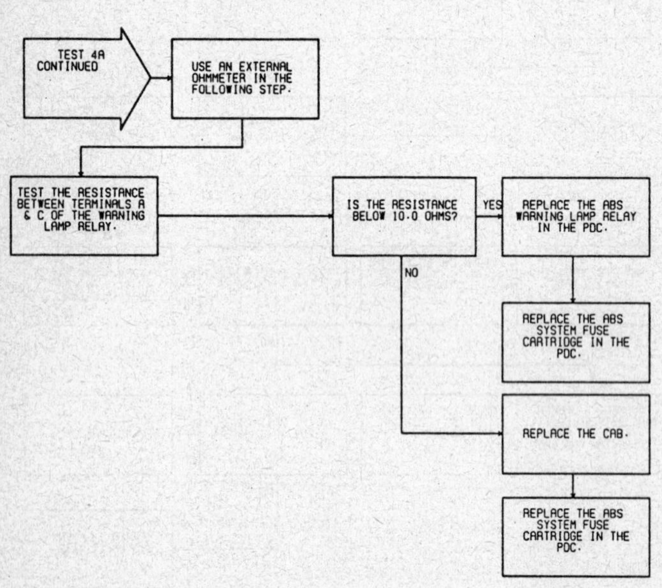


**Fig. 34 Test 4A—Solenoid Undervoltage Message (Part 2 Of 2). 1990 Models**

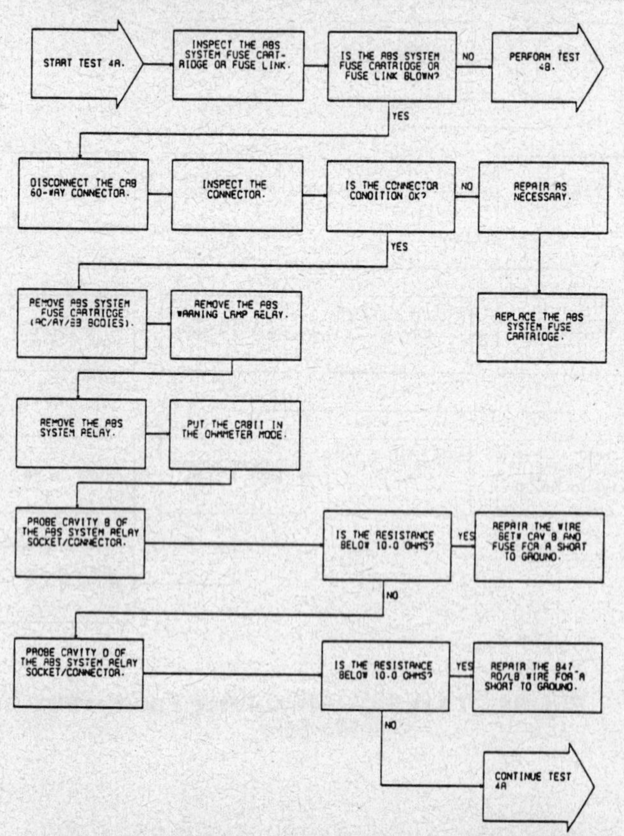


**Fig. 35 Test 4A—Solenoid Undervoltage Fault (Part 1 Of 2). 1991 Models**

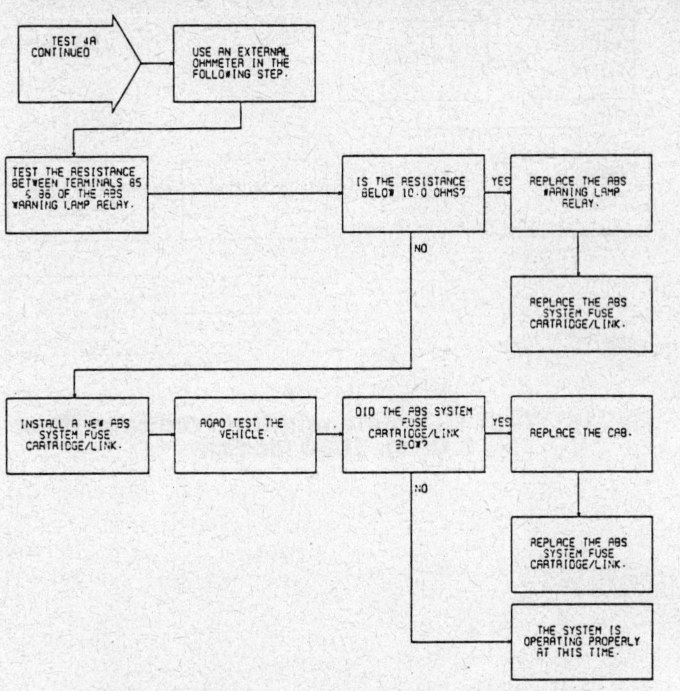


**Fig. 35 Test 4A—Solenoid Undervoltage Fault (Part 2 Of 2). 1991 Models**

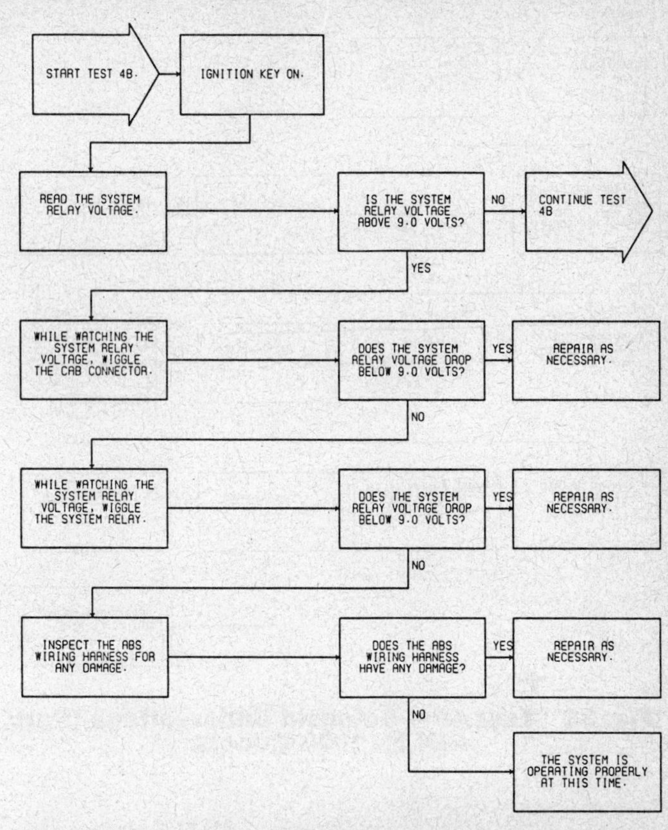


**Fig. 36 Test 4B—Solenoid Undervoltage (Part 1 Of 5). 1990 Models**

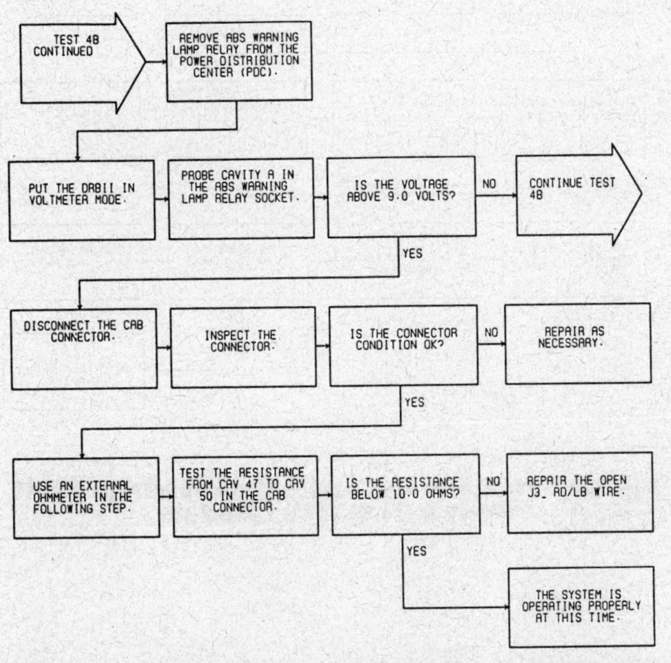


**Fig. 36 Test 4B—Solenoid Undervoltage (Part 2 Of 5). 1990 Models**

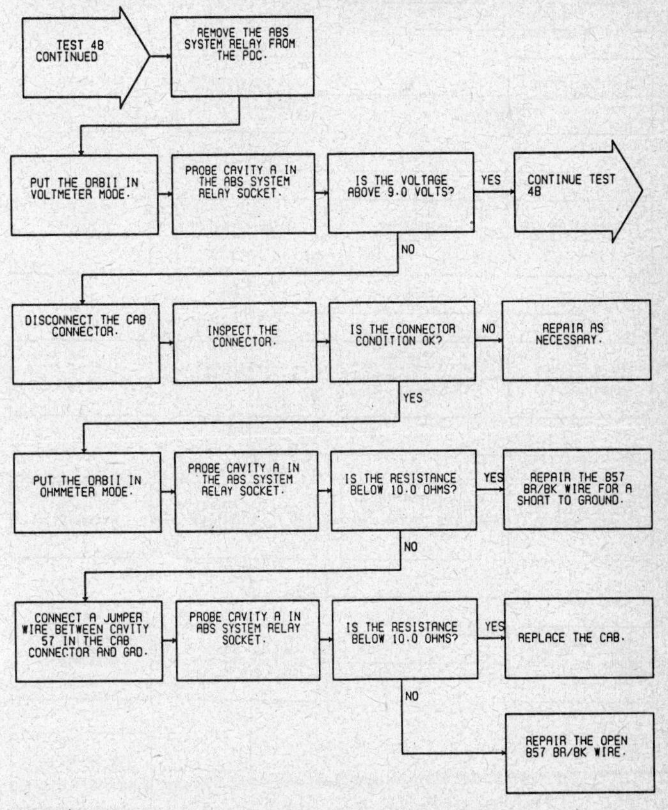


**Fig. 36 Test 4B—Solenoid Undervoltage (Part 3 Of 5). 1990 Models**

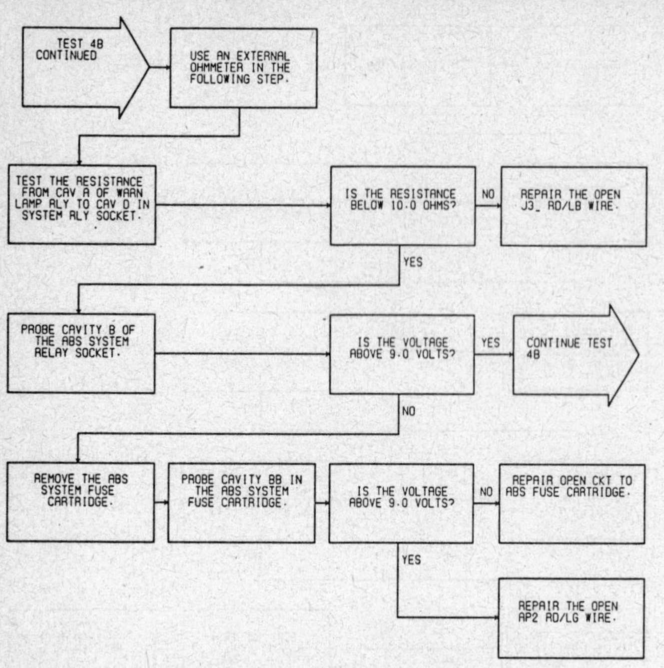


**Fig. 36 Test 4B—Solenoid Undervoltage (Part 4 Of 5). 1990 Models**

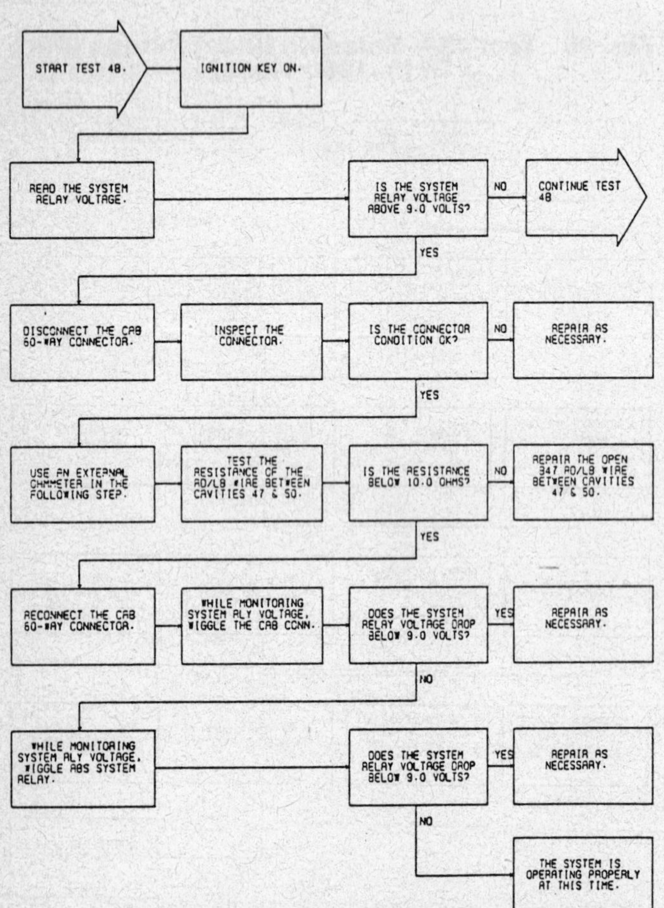


**Fig. 37 Test 4B—Solenoid Undervoltage Fault (Part 1 Of 6). 1991 Models**

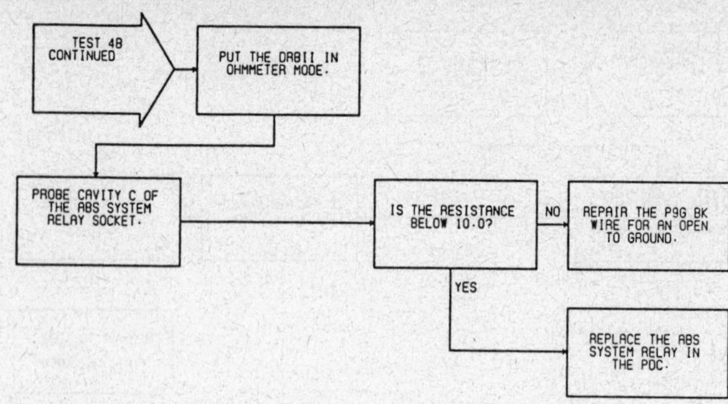


**Fig. 36 Test 4B—Solenoid Undervoltage (Part 5 Of 5). 1990 Models**

TEST 4B CONTINUED
REMOVE THE ABS WARNING LAMP RELAY.
PUT THE DRBII IN VOLTMETER MODE.
PROBE CAVITY A IN THE ABS WARNING LAMP RELAY SOCKET/CONN.
IS THE VOLTAGE ABOVE 9.0 VOLTS?
NO
CONTINUE TEST 4B
YES
DISCONNECT THE CAB 60-WAY CONNECTOR.
INSPECT THE CONNECTOR.
IS THE CONNECTOR CONDITION OK?
NO
REPAIR AS NECESSARY.
YES
USE AN EXTERNAL OHMMETER IN THE FOLLOWING STEP.
TEST THE RESISTANCE FROM CAV 47 TO CAV 50 IN THE CAB 60-WAY CONNECTOR.
IS THE RESISTANCE BELOW 10.0 OHMS?
NO
REPAIR THE OPEN B47_ RD/LB WIRE.
YES
THE SYSTEM IS OPERATING PROPERLY AT THIS TIME.

**Fig. 37 Test 4B—Solenoid Undervoltage Fault (Part 2 Of 6). 1991 Models**

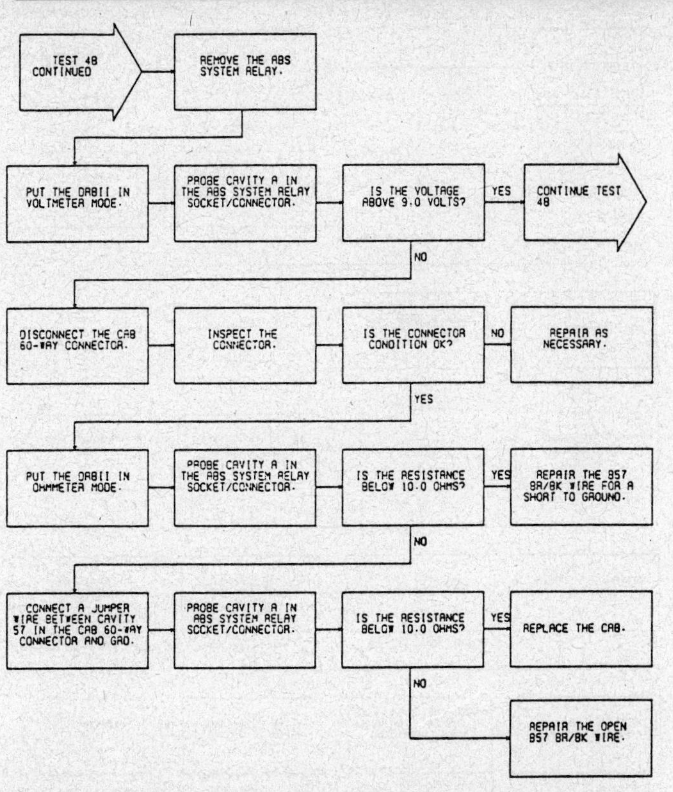


**Fig. 37 Test 4B—Solenoid Undervoltage Fault (Part 3 Of 6). 1991 Models**

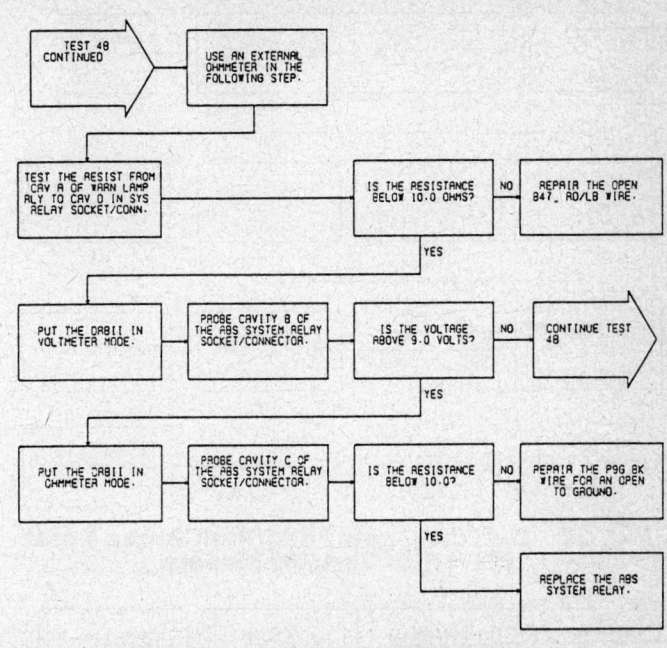

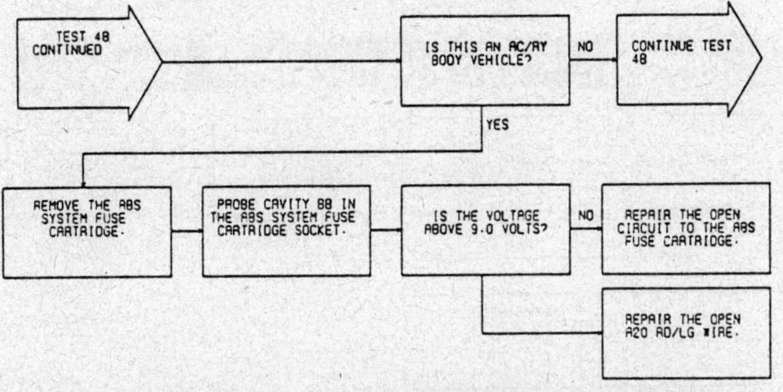


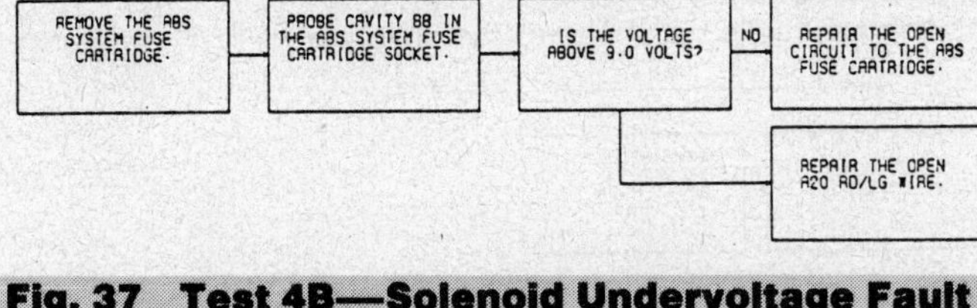

**Fig. 37 Test 4B—Solenoid Undervoltage Fault (Part 5 Of 6). 1991 Models**

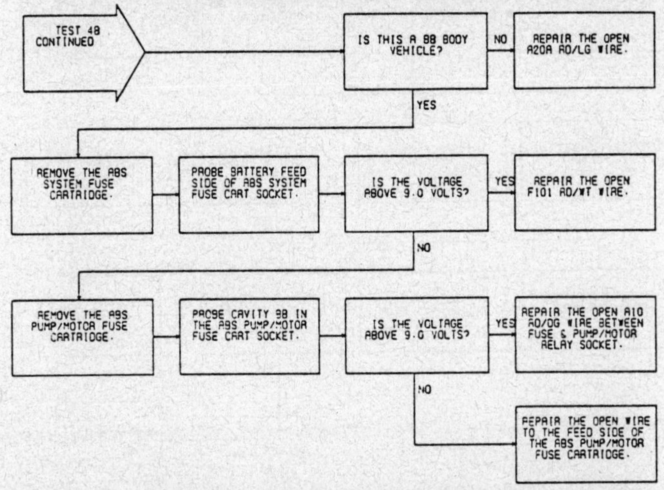


**Fig. 37 Test 4B—Solenoid Undervoltage Fault (Part 6 Of 6). 1991 Models**

TEST 4B CONTINUED
USE AN EXTERNAL OHMMETER IN THE FOLLOWING STEP.
TEST THE RESIST FROM CAV A OF WARN LAMP RLY TO CAV D IN SYS RELAY SOCKET/CONN.
IS THE RESISTANCE BELOW 10.0 OHMS?
NO
REPAIR THE OPEN B47_ RD/LB WIRE.
YES
PUT THE DRBII IN VOLTMETER MODE.
PROBE CAVITY B OF THE ABS SYSTEM RELAY SOCKET/CONNECTOR.
IS THE VOLTAGE ABOVE 9.0 VOLTS?
NO
CONTINUE TEST 4B
YES
PUT THE DRBII IN OHMMETER MODE.
PROBE CAVITY C OF THE ABS SYSTEM RELAY SOCKET/CONNECTOR.
IS THE RESISTANCE BELOW 10.0?
NO
REPAIR THE P9G BK WIRE FOR AN OPEN TO GROUND.
YES
REPLACE THE ABS SYSTEM RELAY.

**Fig. 37 Test 4B—Solenoid Undervoltage Fault (Part 4 Of 6). 1991 Models**

START TEST 5A.
IS THE VEHICLE EQUIPPED WITH AN ELECTRONIC CLUSTER?
NO
PERFORM TEST 5B.
YES
IGNITION KEY OFF.
COMPLETELY DEPRESS AND RELEASE THE BRAKE PEDAL 40 TIMES.
CHECK THE BRAKE FLUID LEVEL.
IS THE BRAKE FLUID LEVEL LOW?
YES
PERFORM TEST 5C.
NO
DISCONNECT THE SWITCH/TRANSDUCER CONNECTOR.
INSPECT THE CONNECTOR.
IS THE CONNECTOR CONDITION OK?
NO
REPAIR AS NECESSARY.
YES
PUT THE DRBII IN OHMMETER MODE.
PROBE THE GY/BK WIRE IN THE SWITCH/MODULATOR CONNECTOR.
IS THE RESISTANCE BELOW 10.0 OHMS?
YES
PERFORM TEST 5D.
NO
CONTINUE TEST 5A

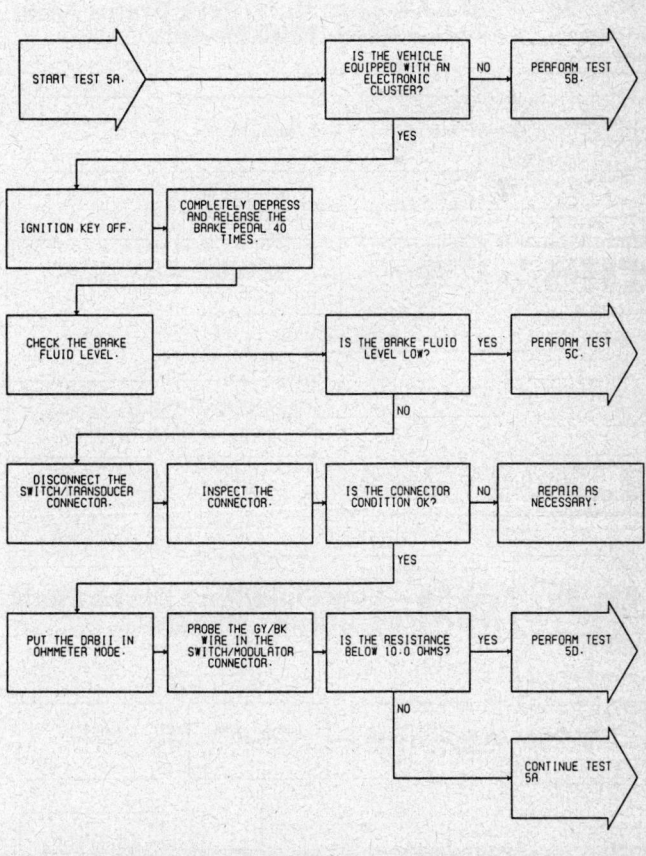

**Fig. 38 Test 5A—Low Fluid/Park Brake Fault (Part 1 Of 3). 1990 Models**

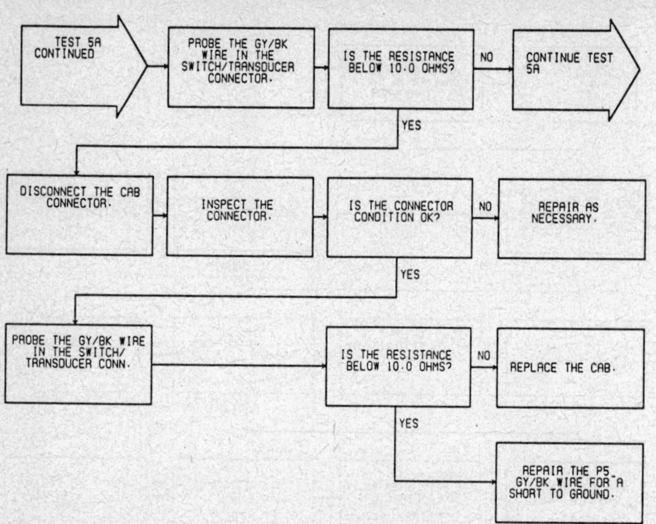


**Fig. 38 Test 5A—Low Fluid/Park Brake Fault (Part 2 Of 3). 1990 Models**

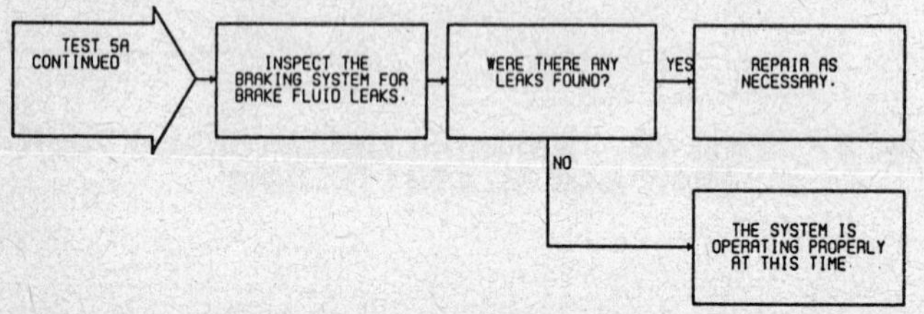


**Fig. 38 Test 5A—Low Fluid/Park Brake Fault (Part 3 Of 3). 1990 Models**

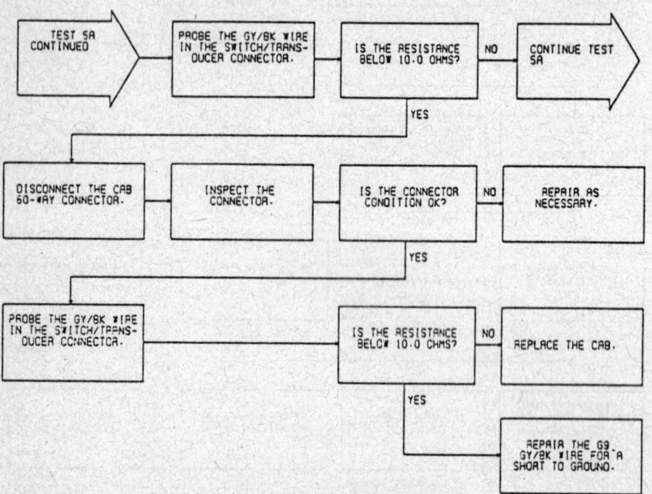


**Fig. 39 Test 5A—Low Fluid/Park Brake Fault (Part 2 Of 3). 1991 Models**

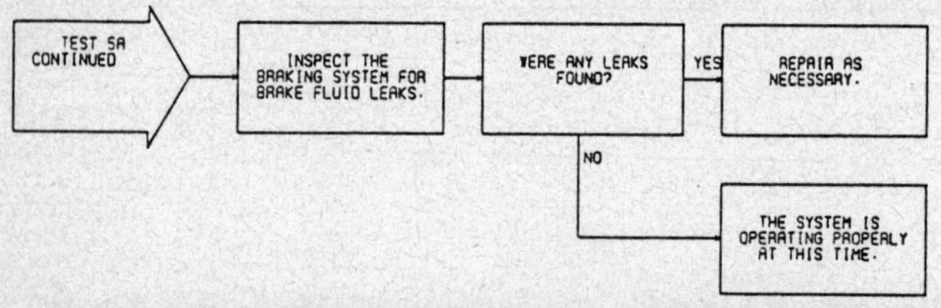


**Fig. 39 Test 5A—Low Fluid/Park Brake Fault (Part 3 Of 3). 1991 Models**

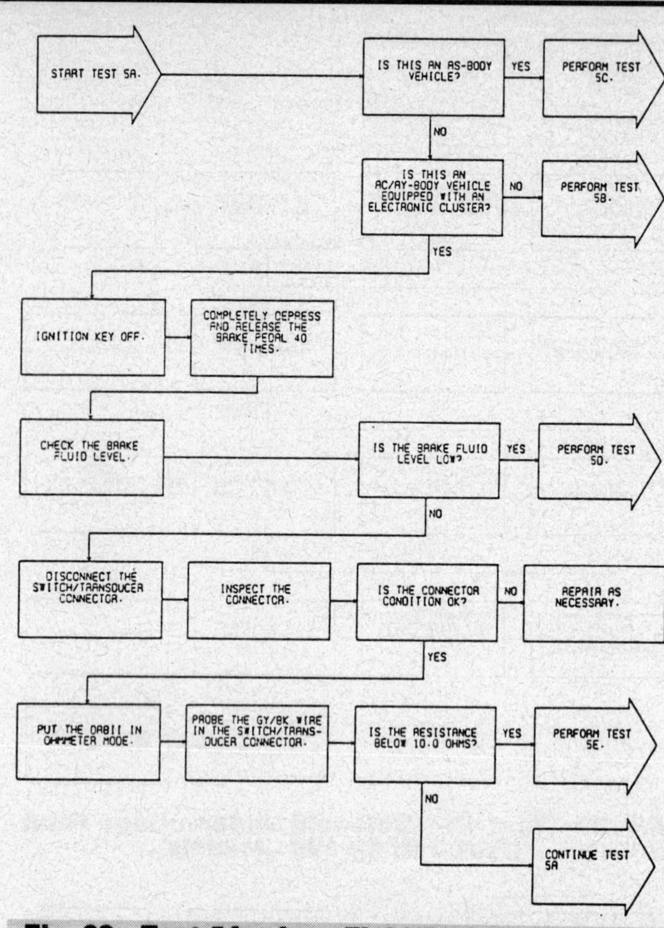


**Fig. 39 Test 5A—Low Fluid/Park Brake Fault (Part 1 Of 3). 1991 Models**

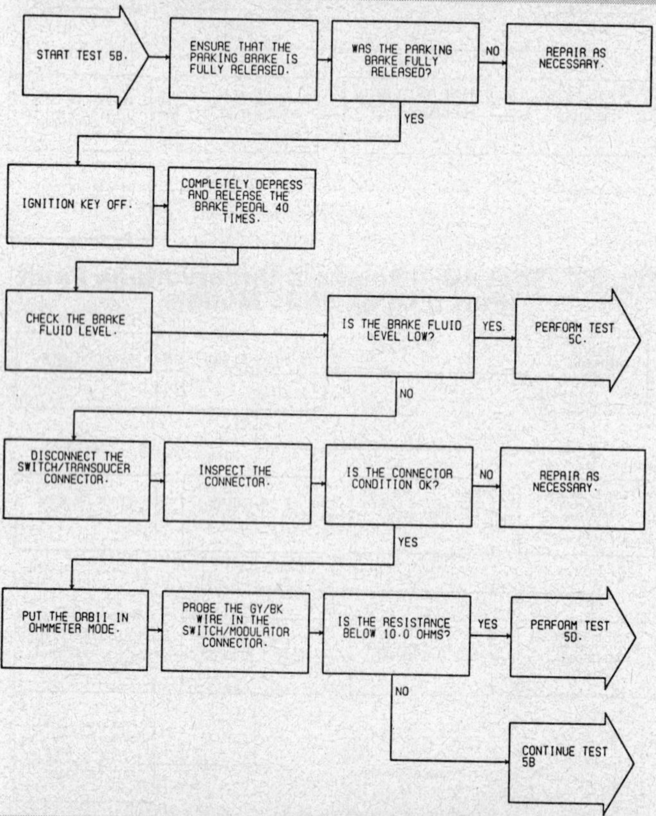


**Fig. 40 Test 5B—Low Fluid/Park Brake Fault (Part 1 Of 3). 1990 Models**

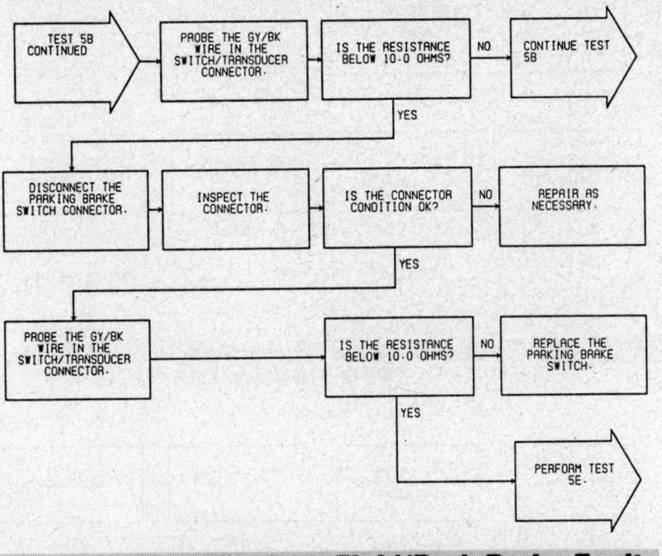


**Fig. 40 Test 5B—Low Fluid/Park Brake Fault (Part 2 Of 3). 1990 Models**

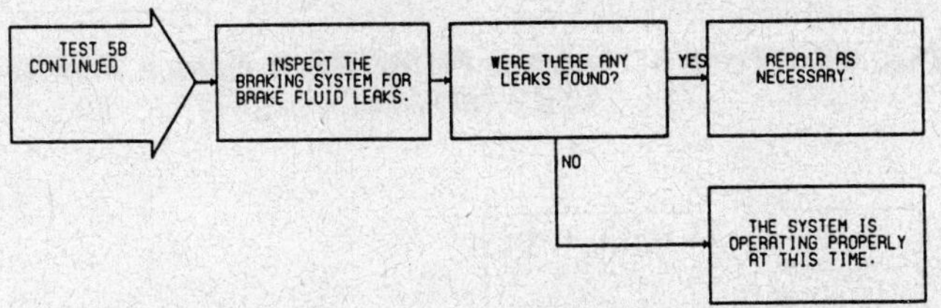


**Fig. 40 Test 5B—Low Fluid/Park Brake Fault (Part 3 Of 3). 1990 Models**

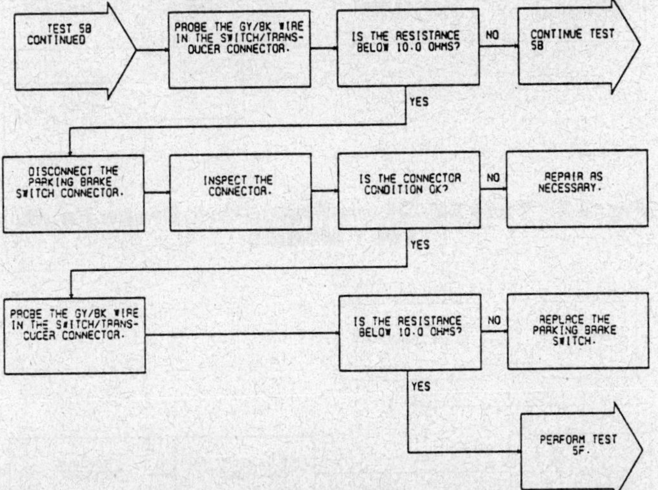


**Fig. 41 Test 5B—Low Fluid/Park Brake Fault (Part 2 Of 3). 1991 Models**

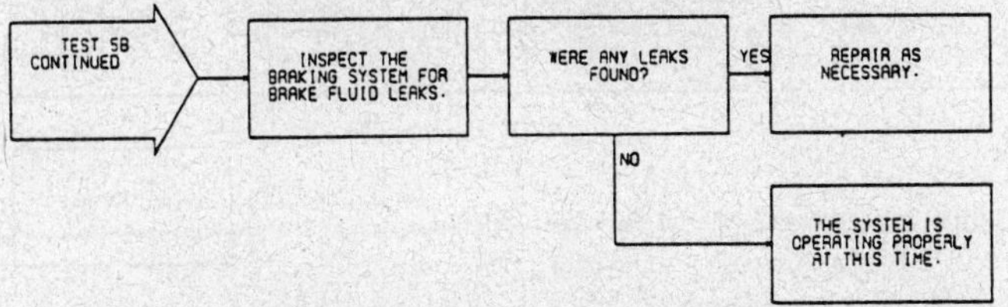


**Fig. 41 Test 5B—Low Fluid/Park Brake Fault (Part 3 Of 3). 1991 Models**

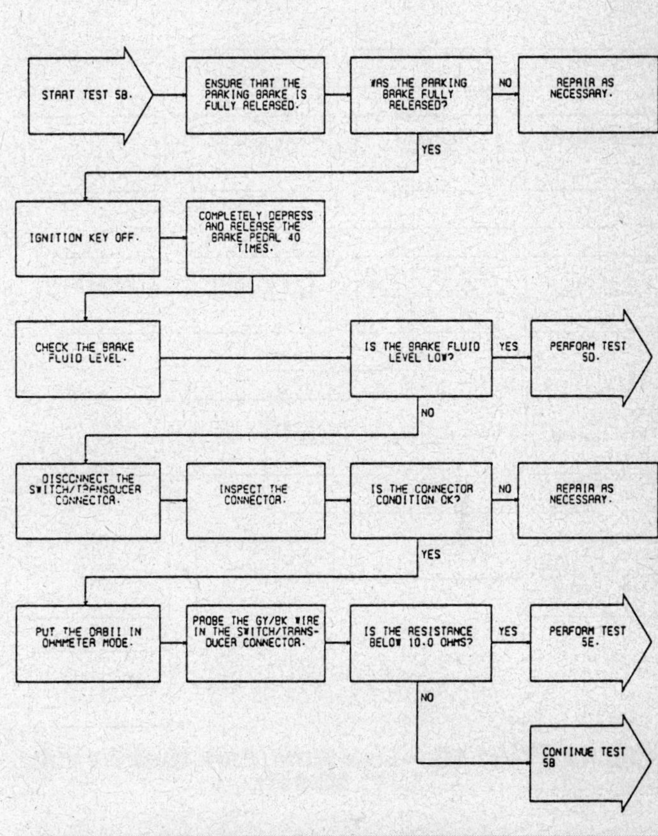


**Fig. 41 Test 5B—Low Fluid/Park Brake Fault (Part 1 Of 3). 1991 Models**

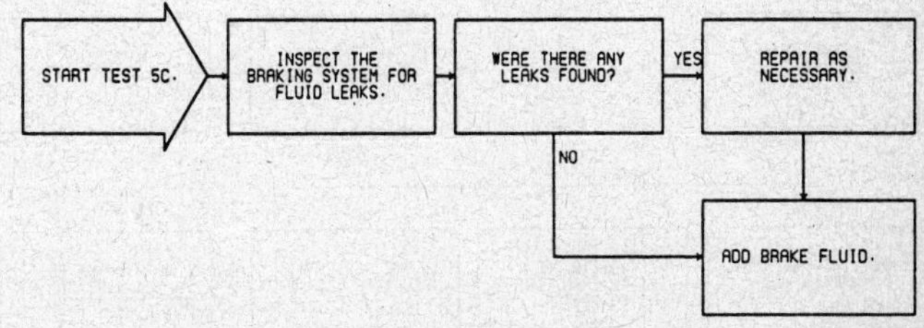


**Fig. 42 Test 5C—Low Fluid/Park Brake Fault. 1990 Models**

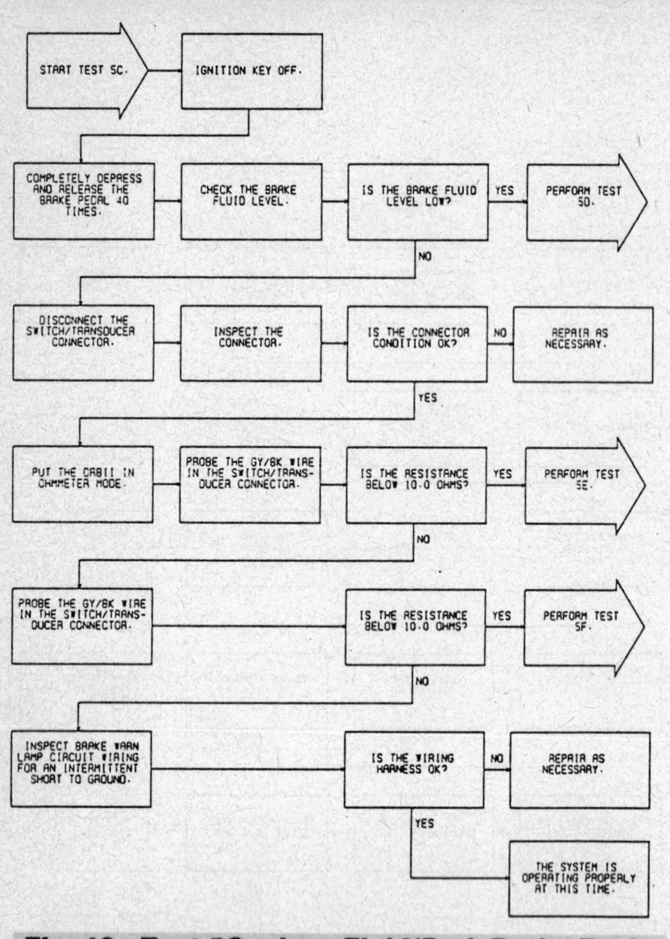


**Fig. 43 Test 5C—Low Fluid/Park Brake Fault. 1991 Models**

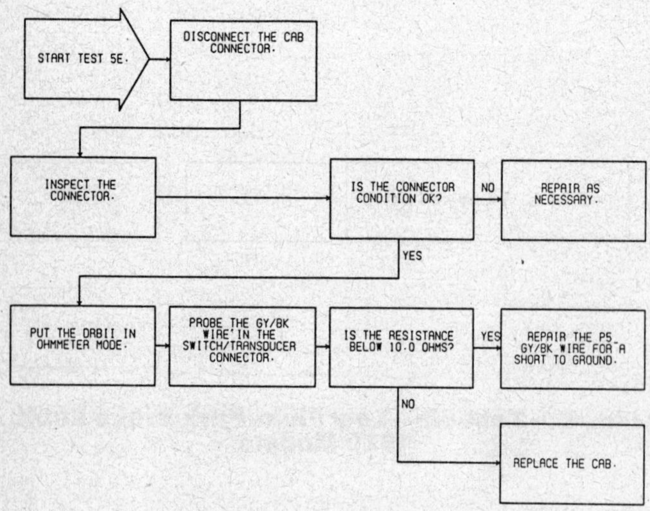


**Fig. 46 Test 5E—Low Fluid/Park Brake Fault. 1990 Models**

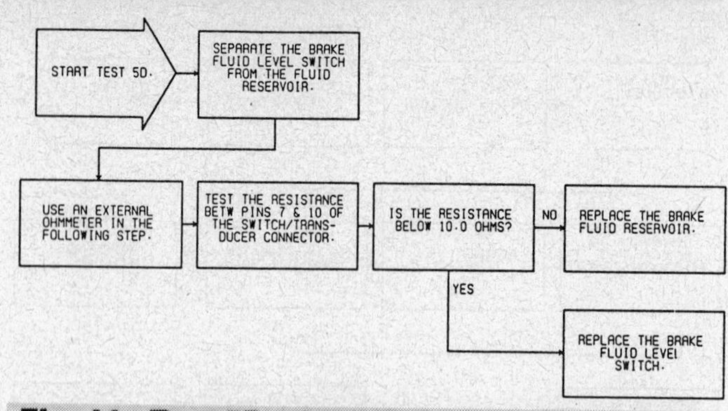


**Fig. 44 Test 5D—Low Fluid/Park Brake Fault. 1990 Models**

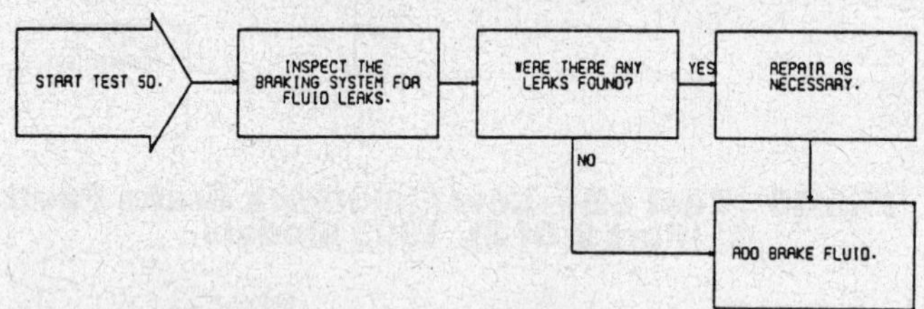


**Fig. 45 Test 5D—Low Fluid/Park Brake Fault. 1991 Models**

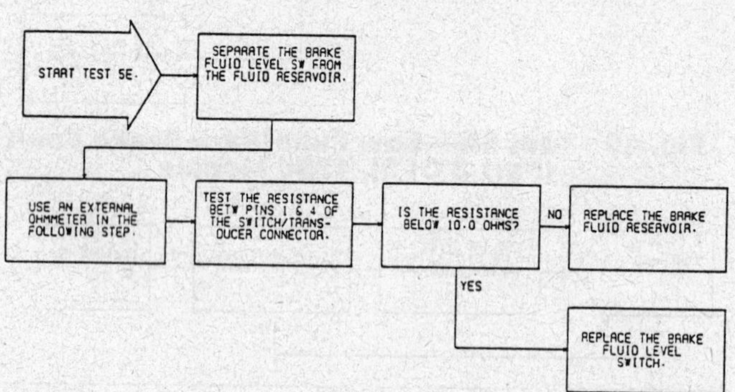


**Fig. 47 Test 5E—Low Fluid/Park Brake Fault. 1991 Models**

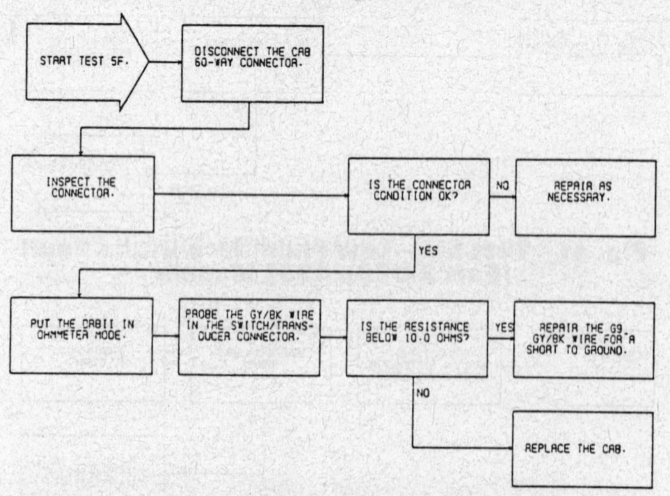


**Fig. 48 Test 5F—Low Fluid/Park Brake Fault. 1991 Models**

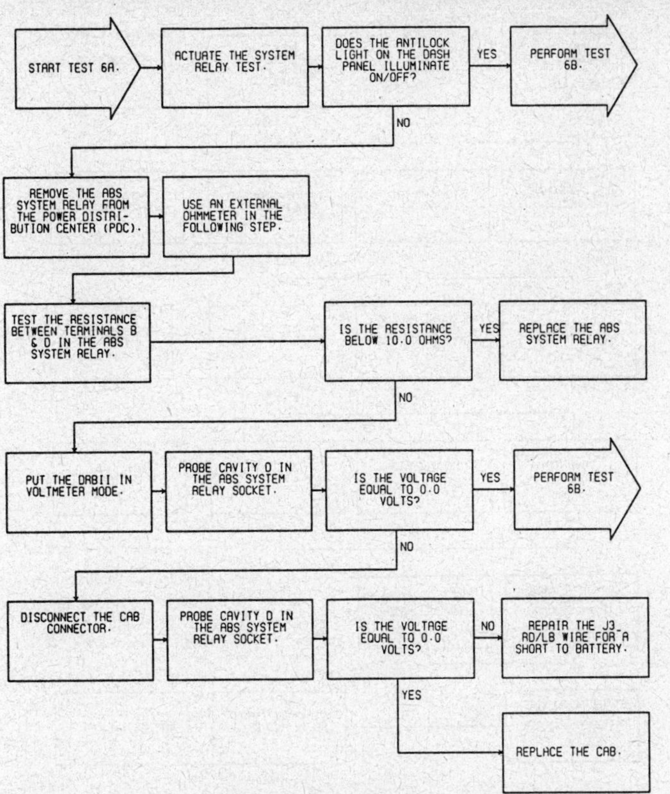


**Fig. 49 Test 6A—System Relay Fault. 1990 Models**

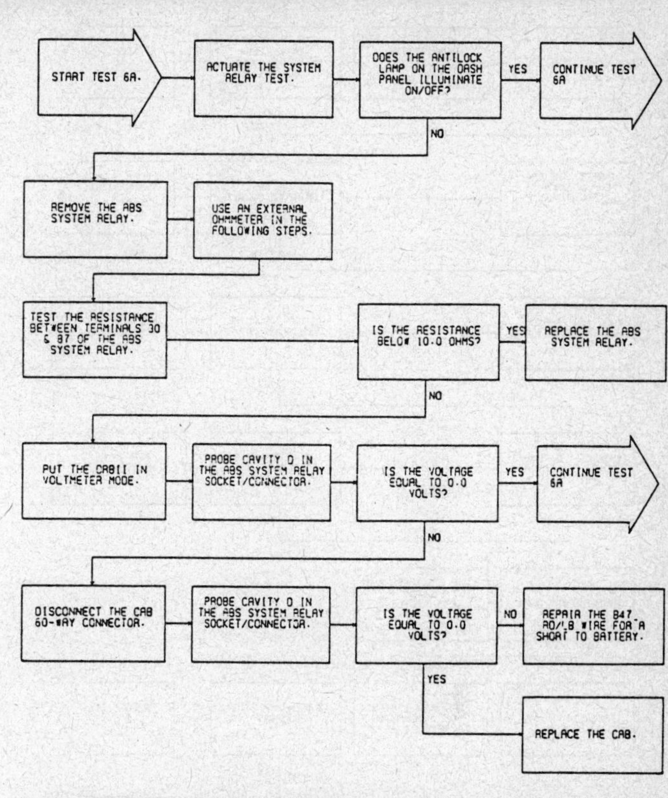


**Fig. 50 Test 6A—System Relay Fault (Part 1 Of 2). 1991 Models**

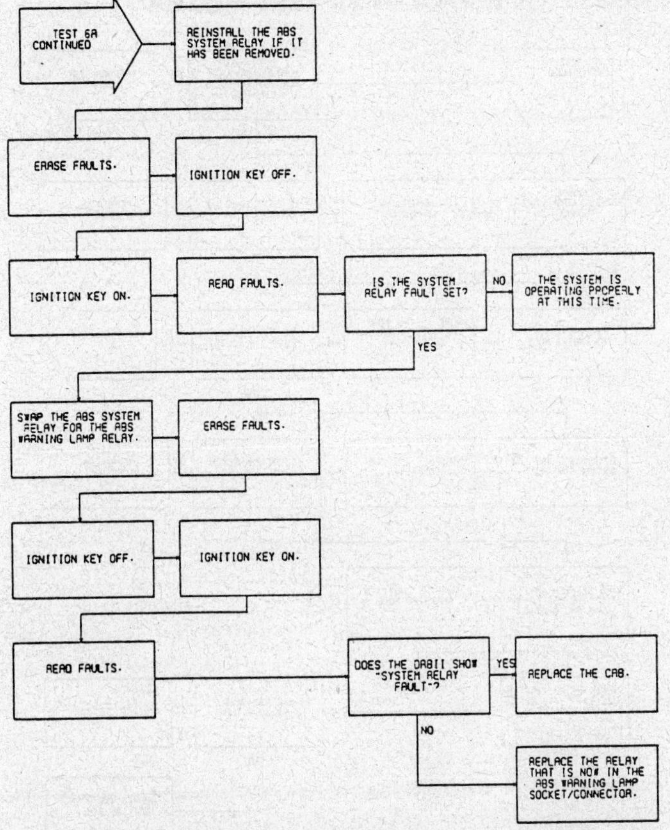


**Fig. 50 Test 6A—System Relay Fault (Part 2 Of 2). 1991 Models**

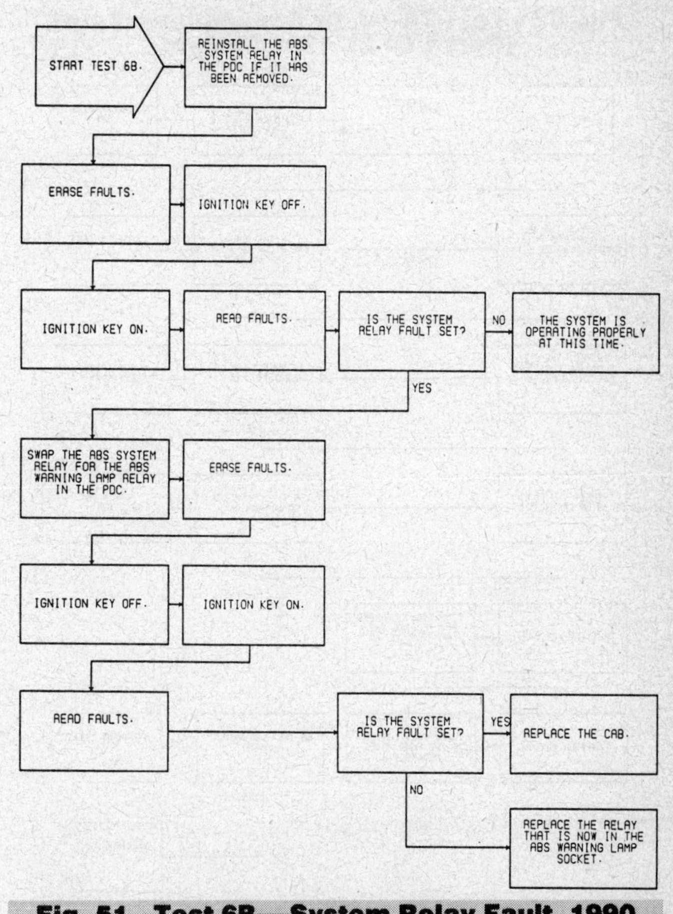


**Fig. 51 Test 6B—System Relay Fault. 1990 Models**

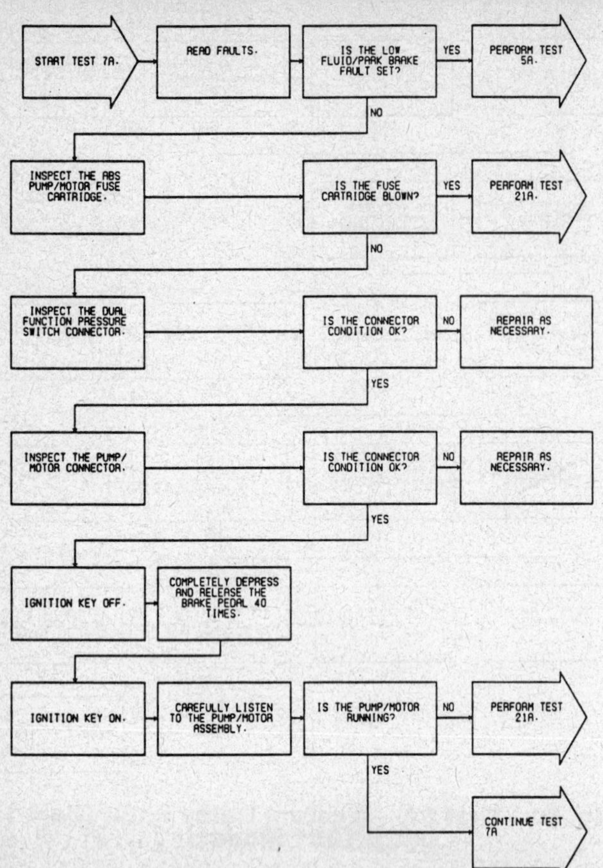


**Fig. 52 Test 7A—Low Accumulator Fault (Part 1 Of 2). 1990 Models**

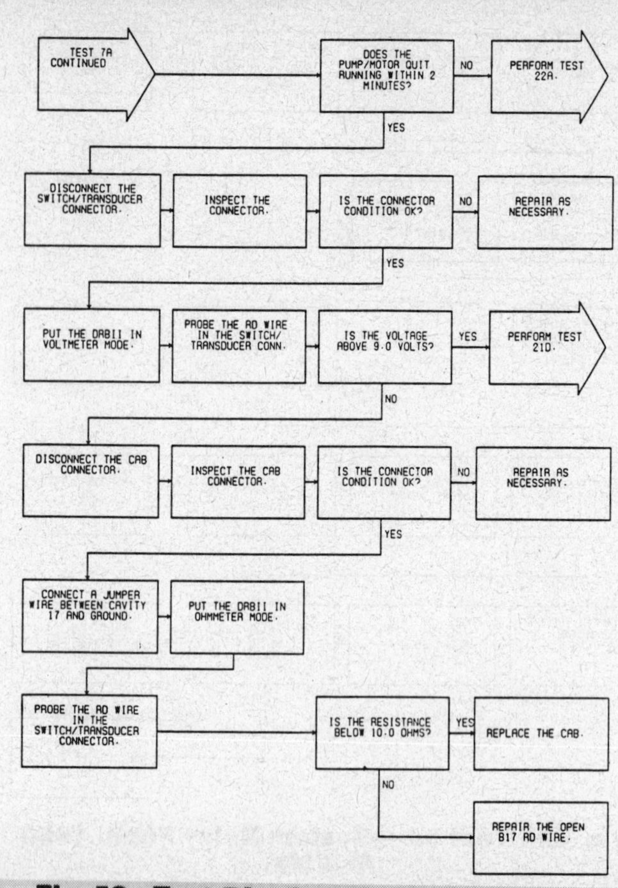


**Fig. 52 Test 7A—Low Accumulator Fault (Part 2 Of 2). 1990 Models**

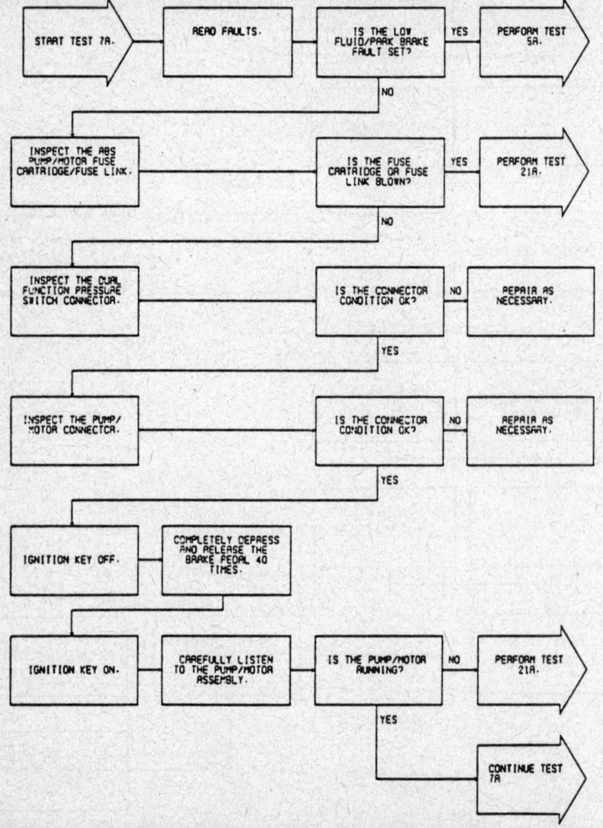


**Fig. 53 Test 7A—Low Accumulator Fault (Part 1 Of 2). 1991 Models**

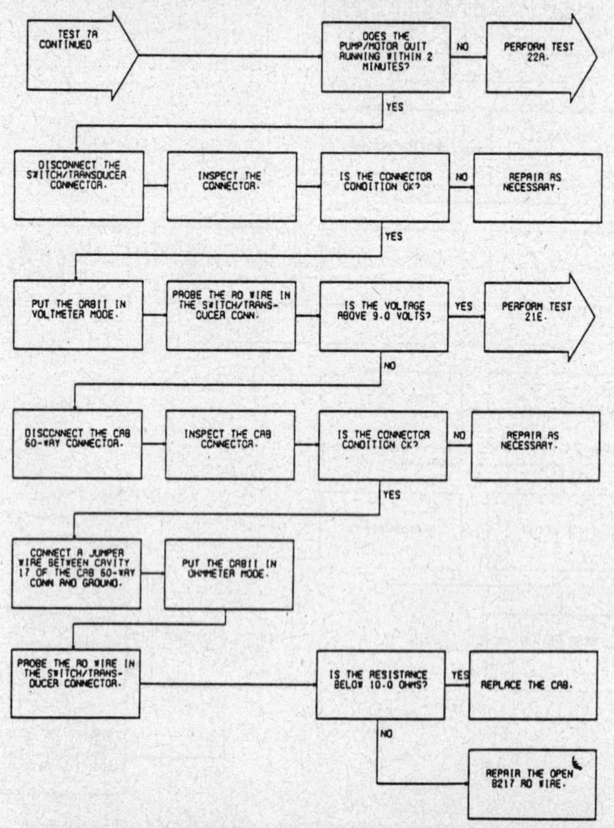


**Fig. 53 Test 7A—Low Accumulator Fault (Part 2 Of 2). 1991 Models**

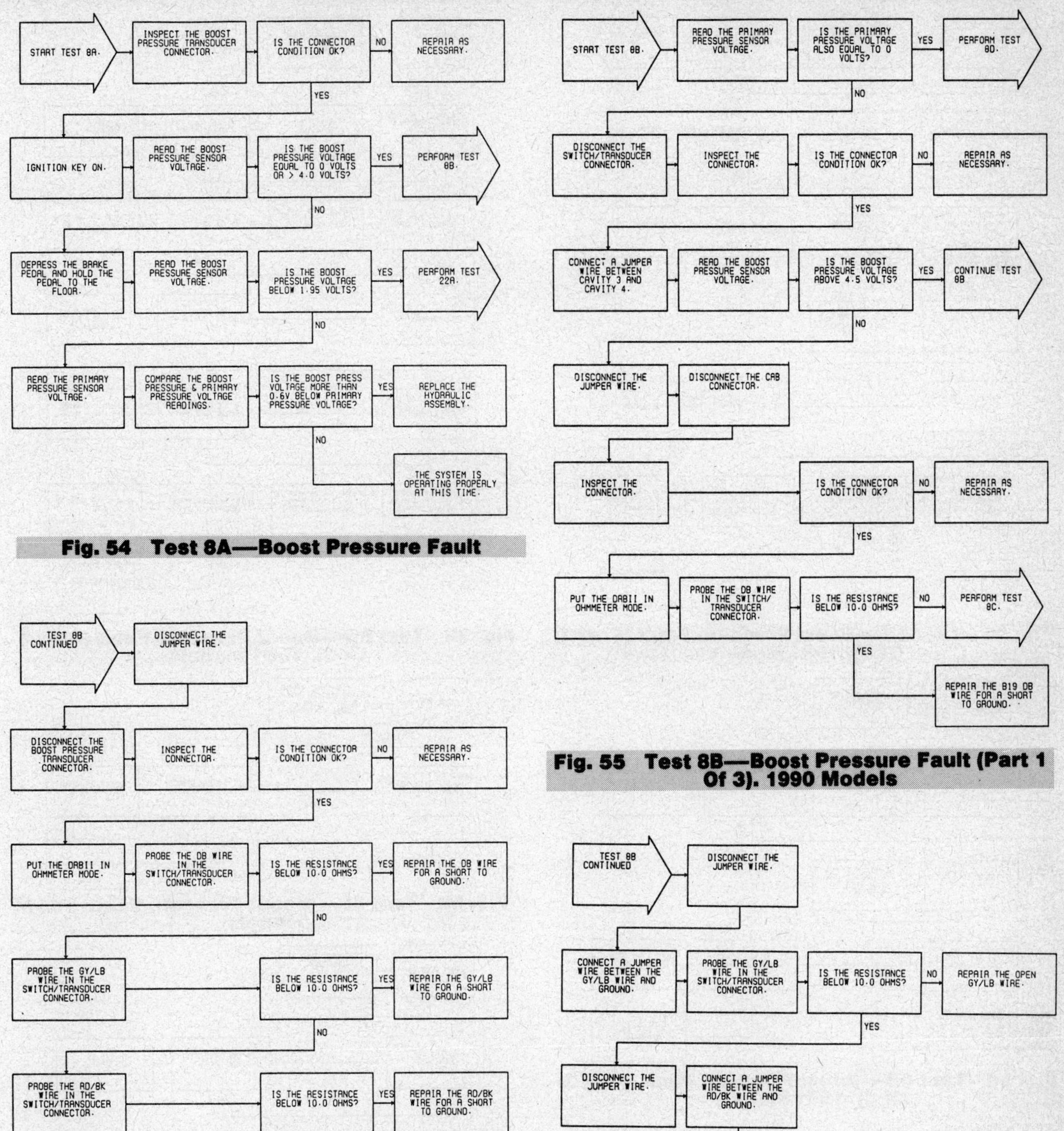


**Fig. 54 Test 8A—Boost Pressure Fault**

**Fig. 55 Test 8B—Boost Pressure Fault (Part 1 Of 3). 1990 Models**

**Fig. 55 Test 8B—Boost Pressure Fault (Part 2 Of 3). 1990 Models**

**Fig. 55 Test 8B—Boost Pressure Fault (Part 3 Of 3). 1990 Models**

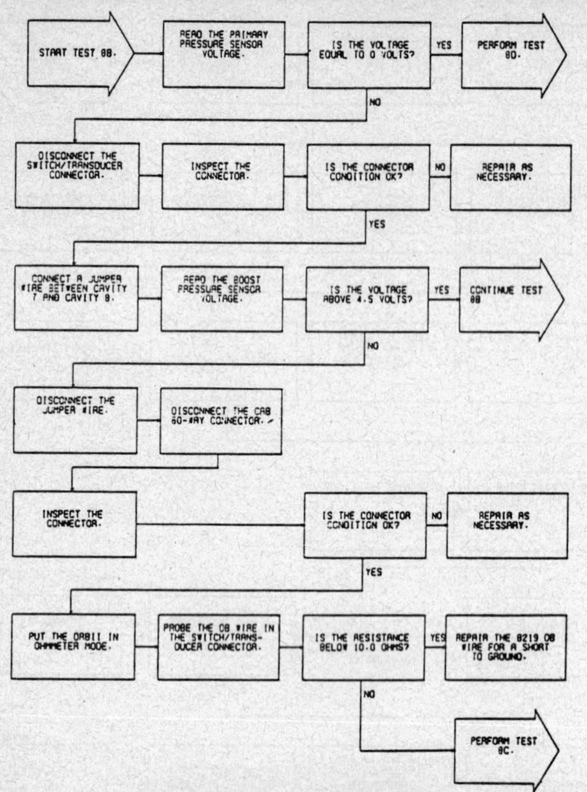


**Fig. 56 Test 8B—Boost Pressure Fault (Part 1 Of 3). 1991 Models**

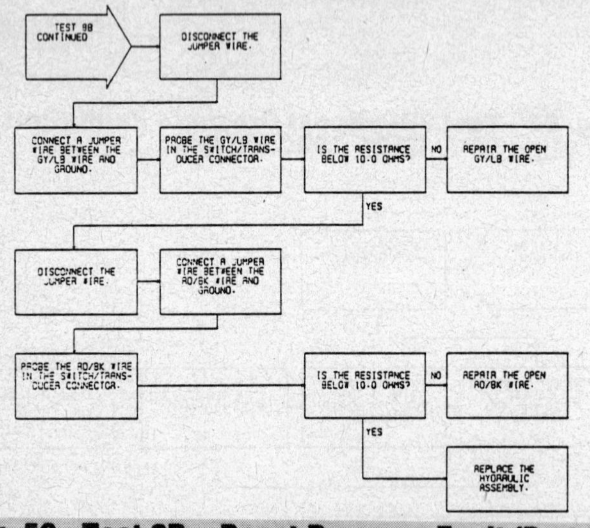


**Fig. 56 Test 8B—Boost Pressure Fault (Part 3 Of 3). 1991 Models**

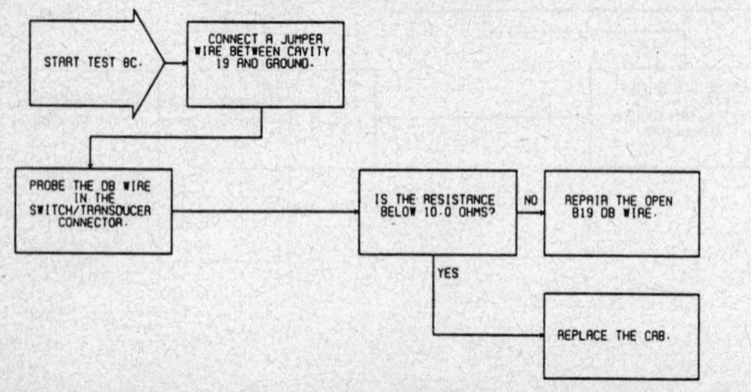


**Fig. 57 Test 8C—Boost Pressure Fault. 1990 Models**

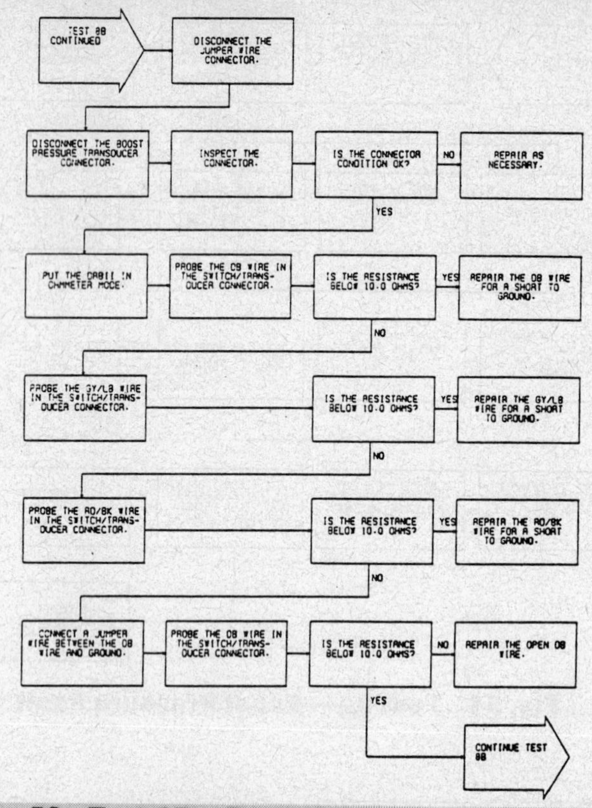


**Fig. 56 Test 8B—Boost Pressure Fault (Part 2 Of 3). 1991 Models**

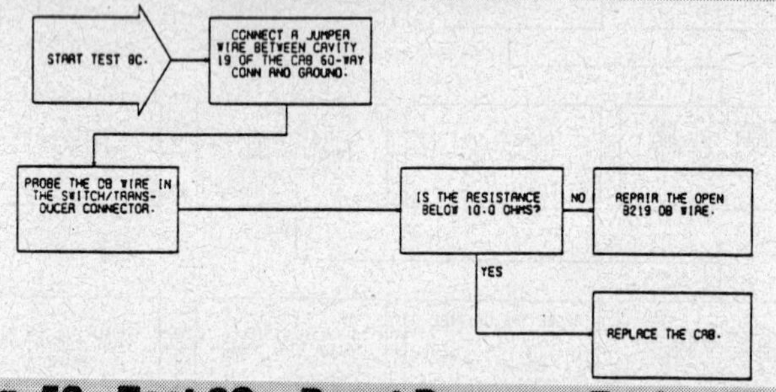


**Fig. 58 Test 8C—Boost Pressure Fault. 1991 Models**

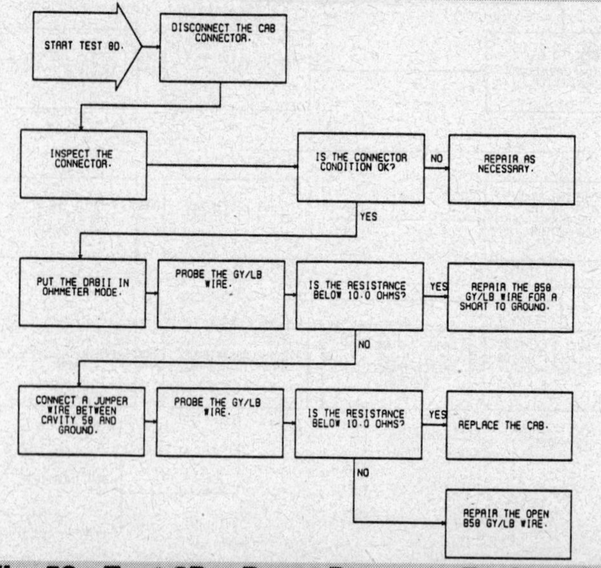


**Fig. 59 Test 8D—Boost Pressure Fault. 1990 Models**

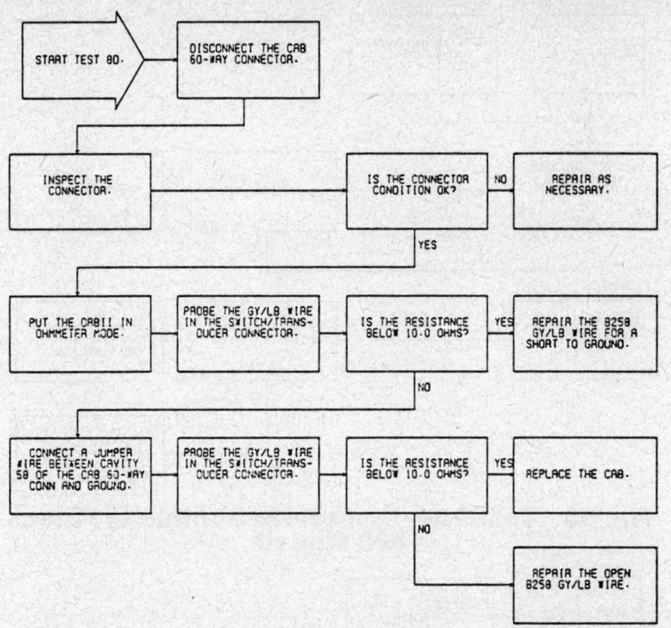


**Fig. 60 Test 8D—Boost Pressure Fault. 1991 Models**

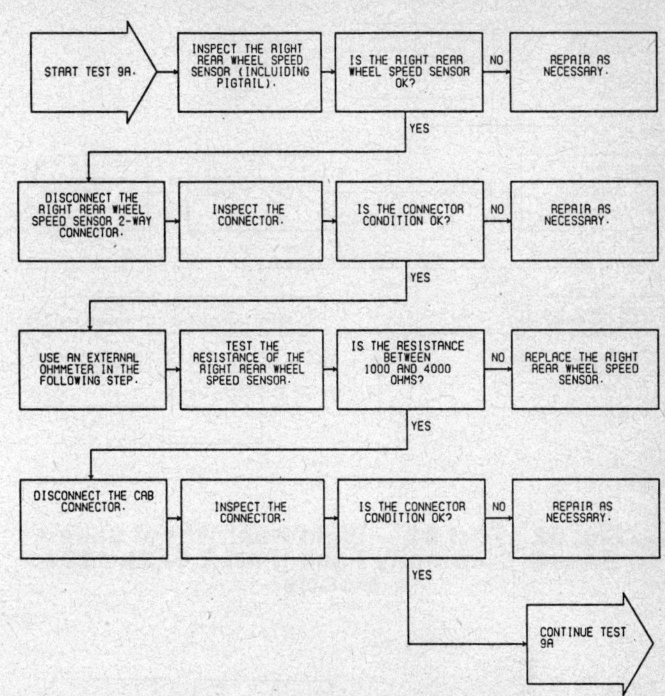


**Fig. 61 Test 9A—Right Rear Continuity Fault (Part 1 Of 2). 1990 Models**

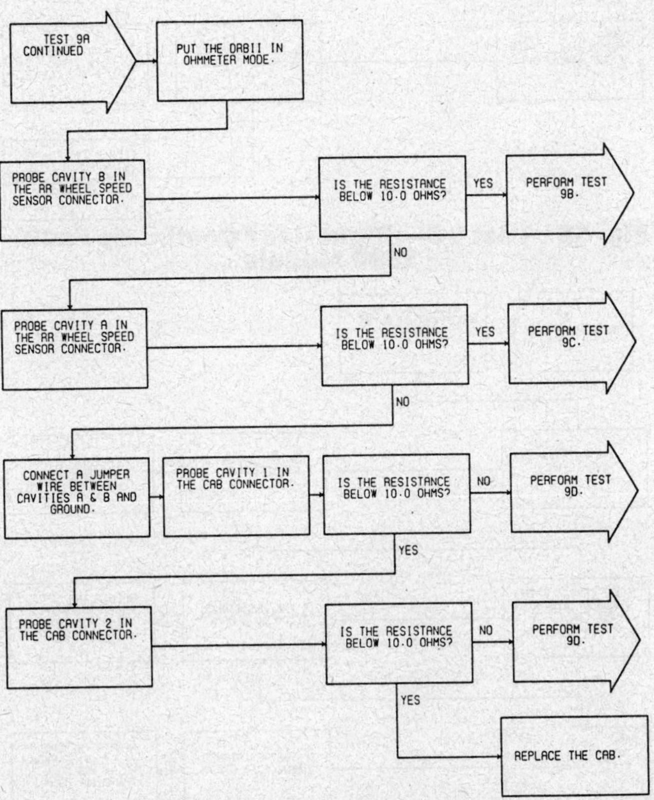


**Fig. 61 Test 9A—Right Rear Continuity Fault (Part 2 Of 2). 1990 Models**

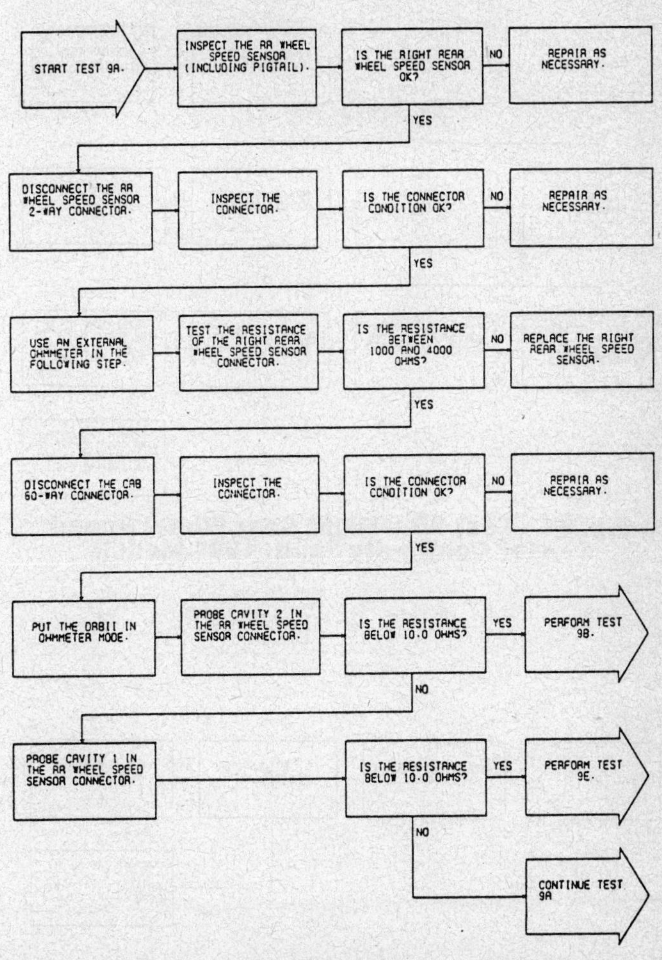


**Fig. 62 Test 9A—Right Rear Wheel Speed Sensor Continuity Fault (Part 1 Of 2). 1991 Models**

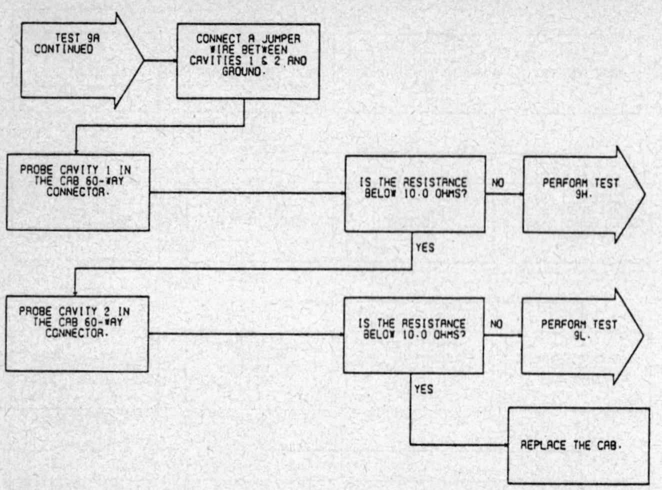


**Fig. 62 Test 9A—Right Rear Wheel Speed Sensor Continuity Fault (Part 2 Of 2). 1991 Models**

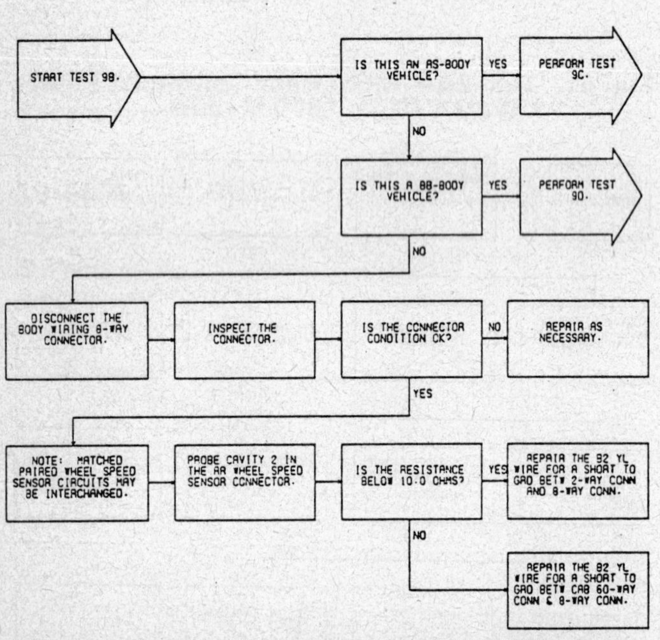


**Fig. 64 Test 9B—Right Rear Wheel Speed Sensor Continuity Fault. 1991 Models**

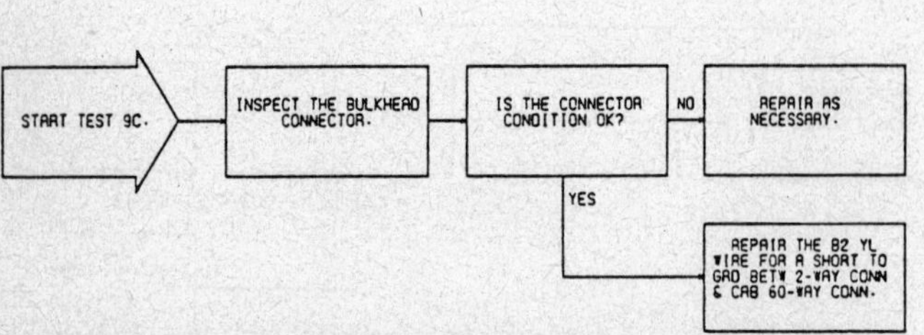


**Fig. 66 Test 9C—Right Rear Wheel Speed Sensor Continuity Fault. 1991 Models**

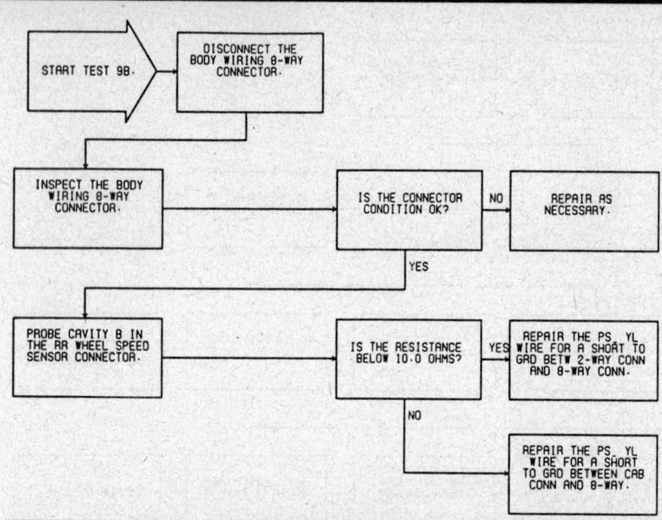


**Fig. 63 Test 9B—Right Rear Continuity Fault. 1990 Models**

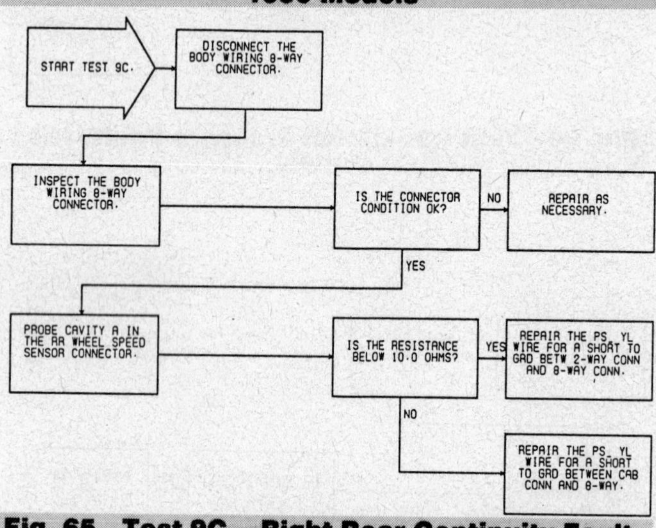


**Fig. 65 Test 9C—Right Rear Continuity Fault. 1990 Models**

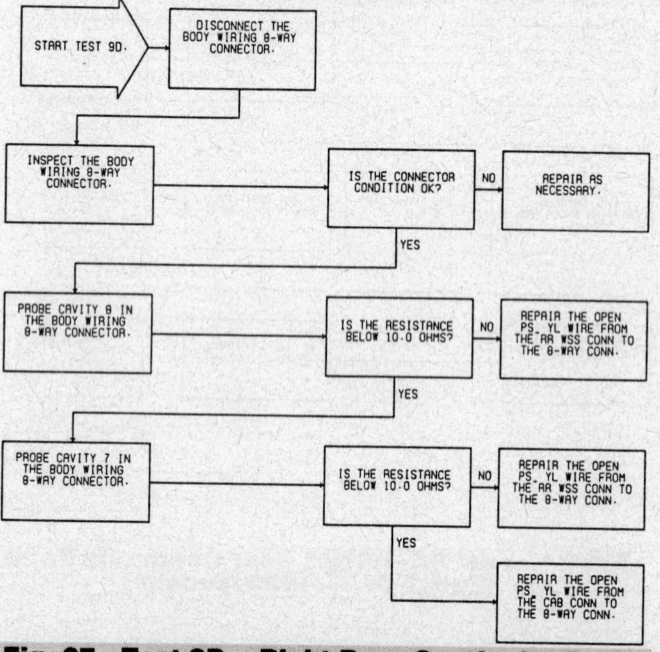


**Fig. 67 Test 9D—Right Rear Continuity Fault. 1990 Models**

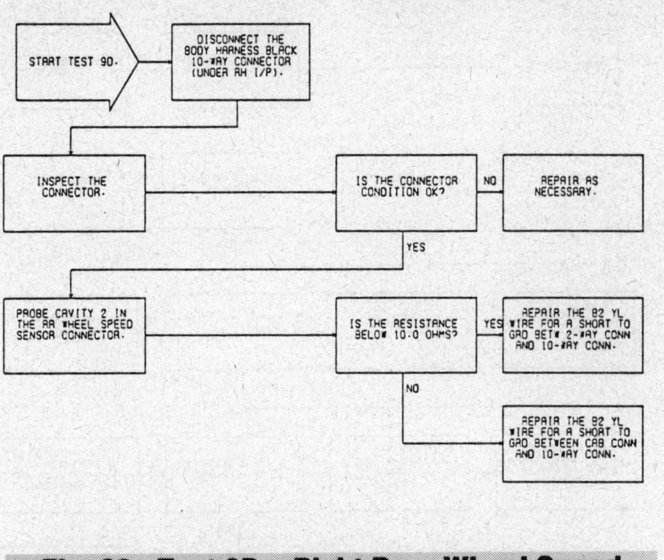


**Fig. 68 Test 9D—Right Rear Wheel Speed Sensor Continuity Fault. 1991 Models**

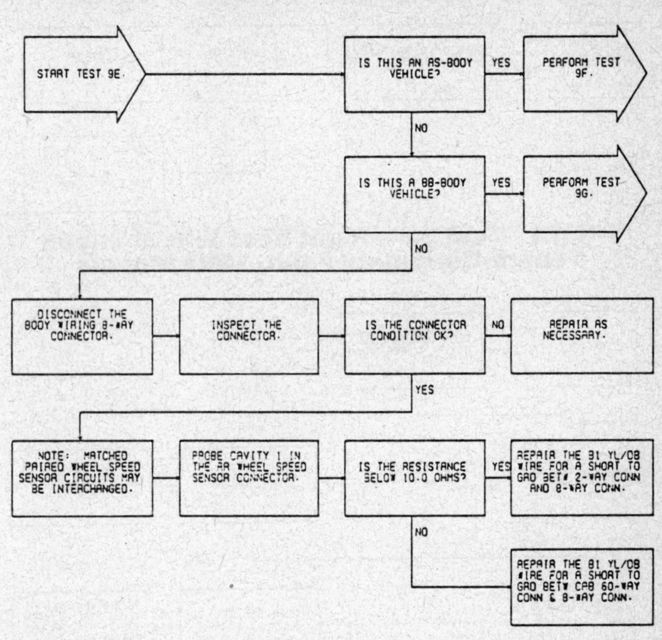


**Fig. 69 Test 9E—Right Rear Wheel Speed Sensor Continuity Fault. 1991 Models**

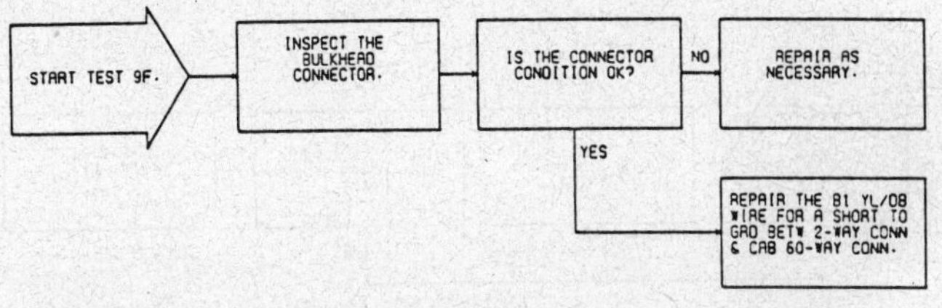


**Fig. 70 Test 9F—Right Rear Wheel Speed Sensor Continuity Fault. 1991 Models**

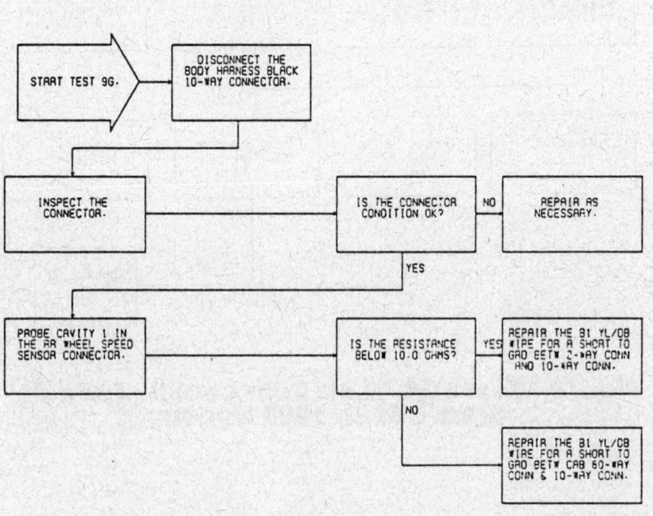


**Fig. 71 Test 9G—Right Rear Wheel Speed Sensor Continuity Fault. 1991 Models**

START TEST 9H.
IS THIS AN AS-BODY VEHICLE?
YES
PERFORM TEST 9J.
NO
IS THIS A BB-BODY VEHICLE?
YES
PERFORM TEST 9K.
NO
DISCONNECT THE BODY WIRING 8-WAY CONNECTOR.
INSPECT THE CONNECTOR.
IS THE CONNECTOR CONDITION OK?
NO
REPAIR AS NECESSARY.
YES
NOTE: MATCHED PAIRED WHEEL SPEED CIRCUITS MAY BE INTERCHANGED.
PROBE CAVITY 8 IN THE BODY WIRING 8-WAY CONNECTOR.
IS THE RESISTANCE BELOW 10.0 OHMS?
NO
REPAIR THE OPEN B1 YL/DB WIRE BETWEEN THE 2-WAY CONN AND THE 8-WAY CONN.
YES
REPAIR THE OPEN B1 YL/DB WIRE BETWEEN THE CAB 60-WAY CONN & 8-WAY CONN.

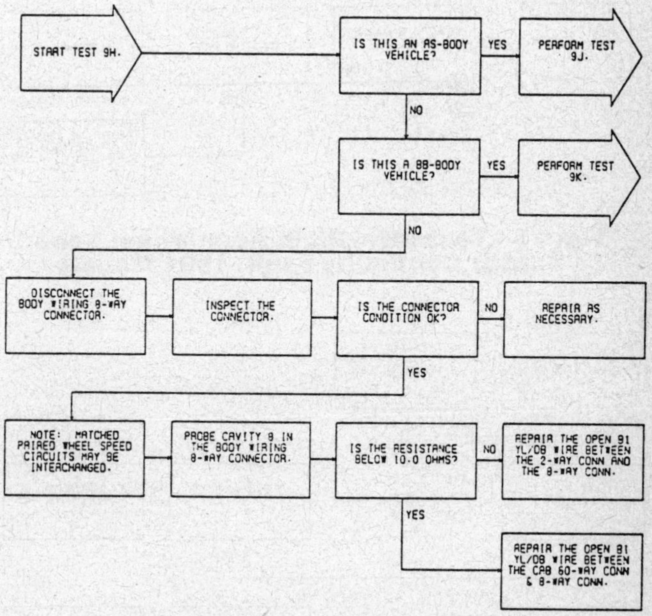

**Fig. 72 Test 9H—Right Rear Wheel Speed Sensor Continuity Fault. 1991 Models**

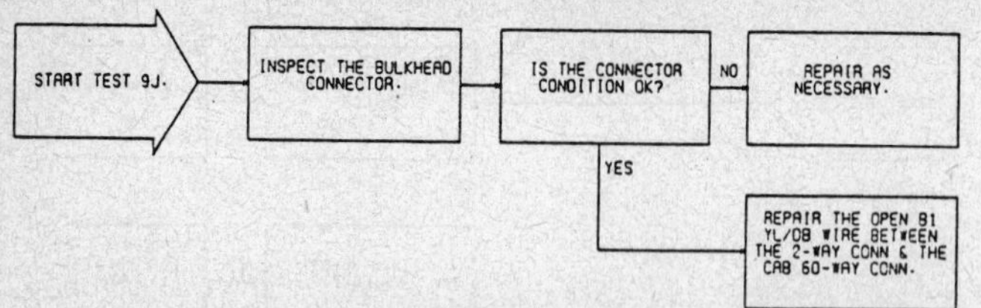


**Fig. 73 Test 9J—Right Rear Wheel Speed Sensor Continuity Fault. 1991 Models**

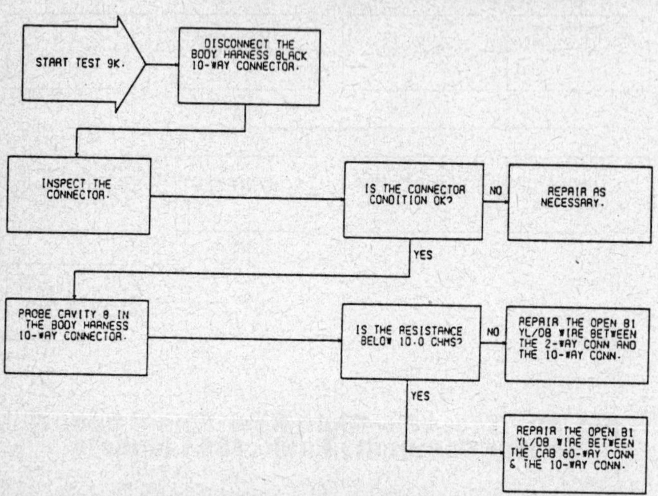


**Fig. 74 Test 9K—Right Rear Wheel Speed Sensor Continuity Fault. 1991 Models**

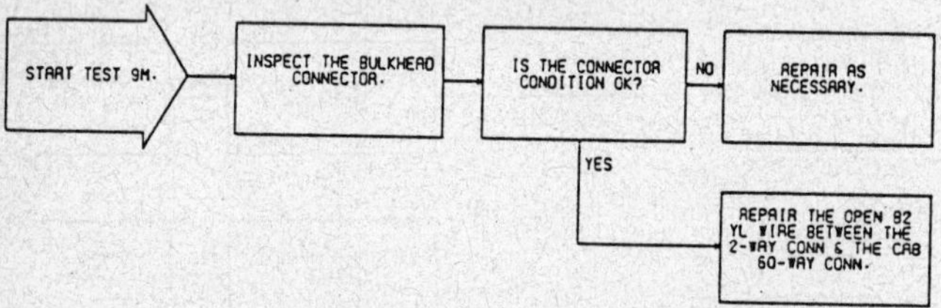


**Fig. 76 Test 9M—Right Rear Wheel Speed Sensor Continuity Fault. 1991 Models**

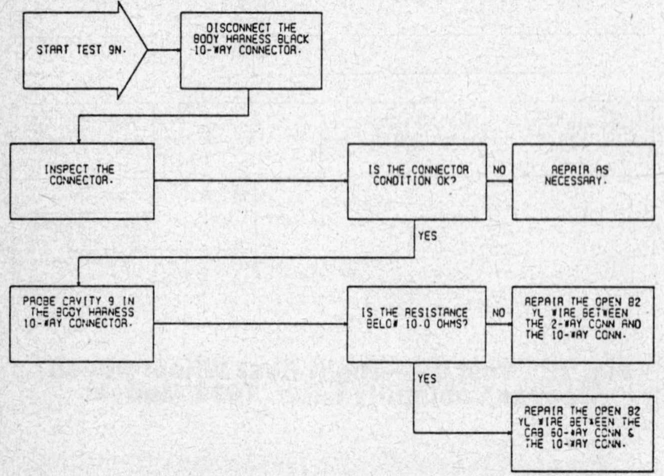


**Fig. 77 Test 9N—Right Rear Wheel Speed Sensor Continuity Fault. 1991 Models**

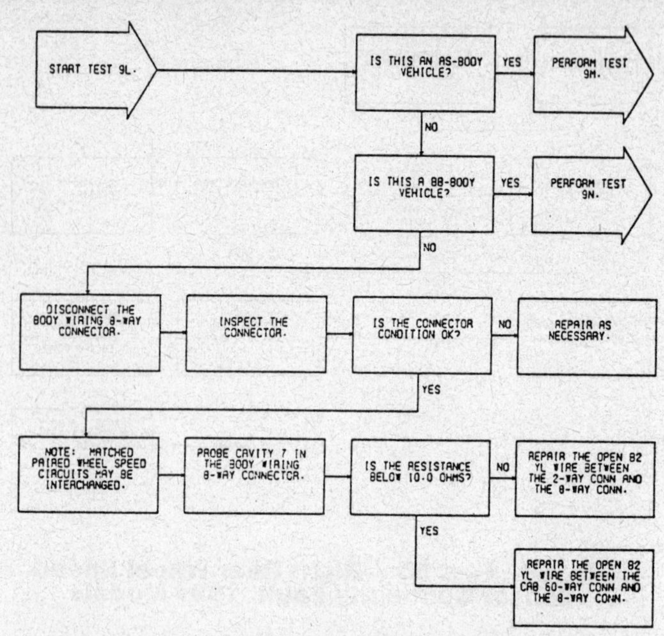


**Fig. 75 Test 9L—Right Rear Wheel Speed Sensor Continuity Fault. 1991 Models**

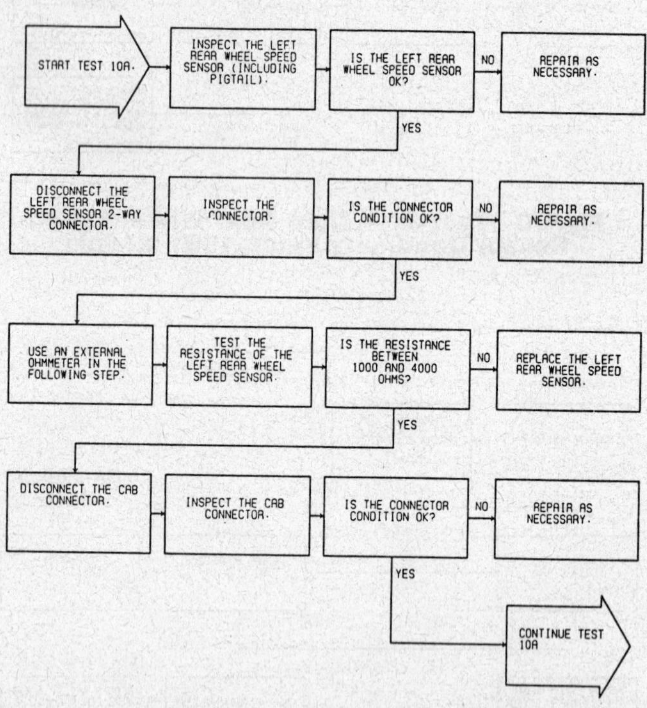


**Fig. 78 Test 10A—Left Rear Continuity Fault (Part 1 Of 2). 1990 Models**

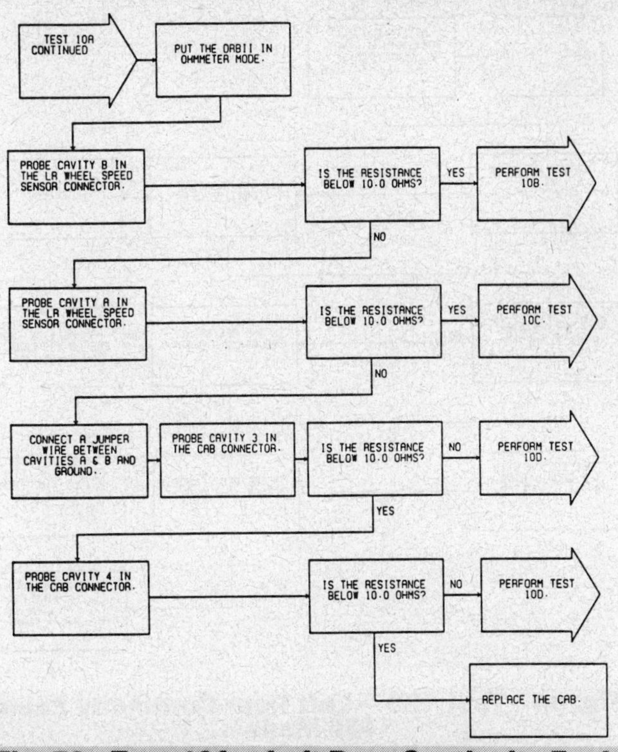


**Fig. 78 Test 10A—Left Rear Continuity Fault (Part 2 Of 2). 1990 Models**

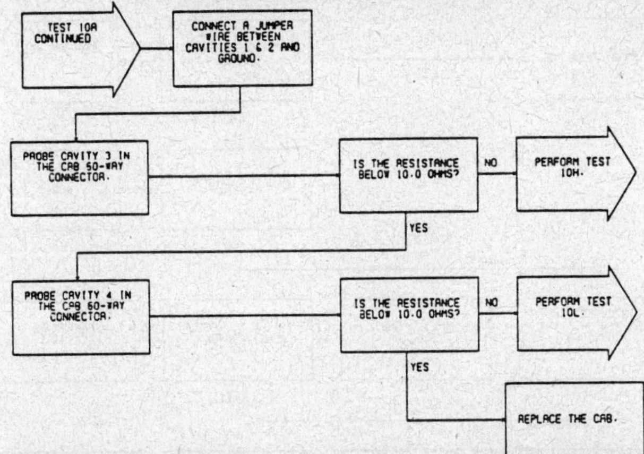


**Fig. 79 Test 10A—Left Rear Wheel Speed Sensor Continuity Fault (Part 2 Of 2). 1991 Models**

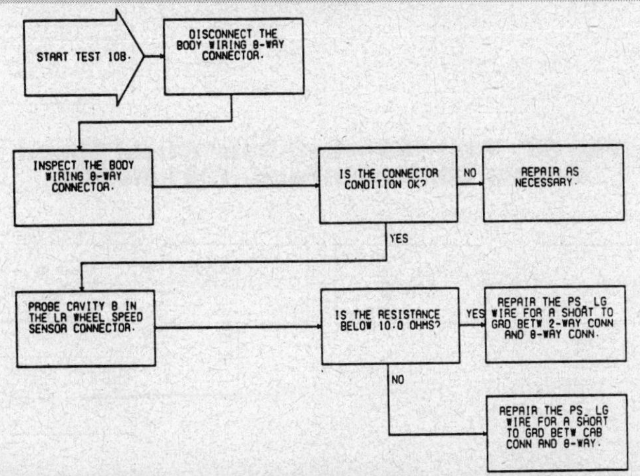


**Fig. 80 Test 10B—Left Rear Continuity Fault. 1990 Models**

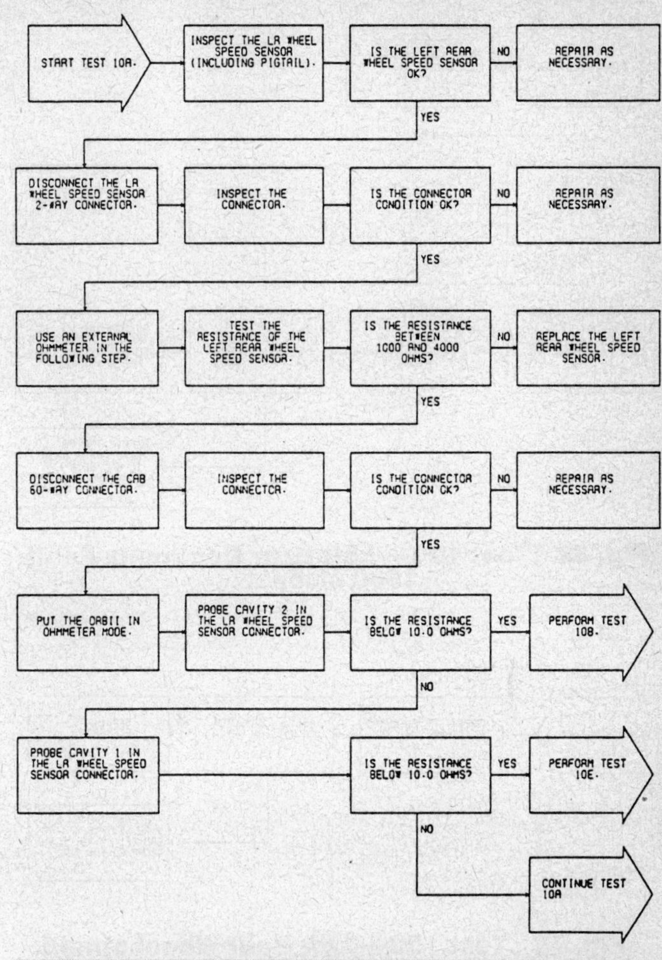


**Fig. 79 Test 10A—Left Rear Wheel Speed Sensor Continuity Fault (Part 1 Of 2). 1991 Models**

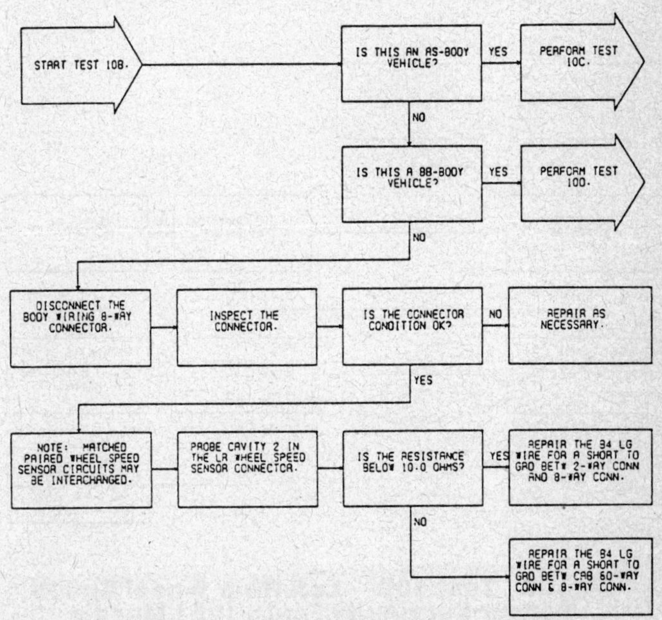


**Fig. 81 Test 10B—Left Rear Wheel Speed Sensor Continuity Fault. 1991 Models**

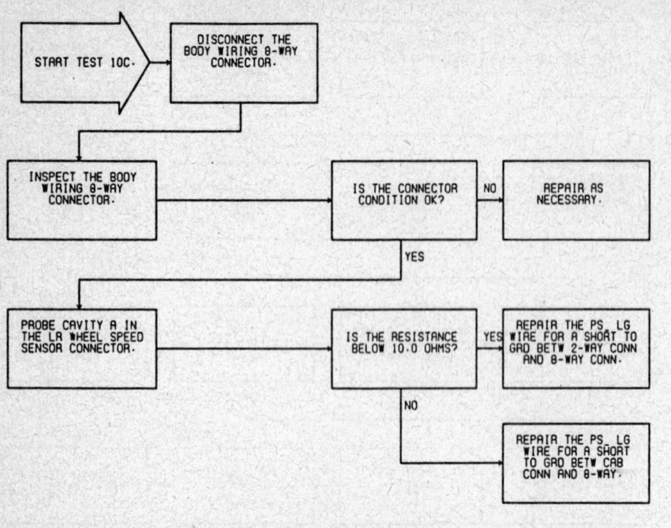


**Fig. 82 Test 10C—Left Rear Continuity Fault. 1990 Models**

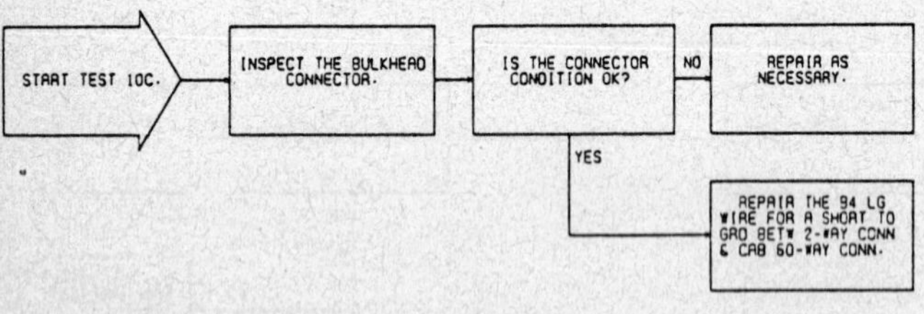


**Fig. 83 Test 10C—Left Rear Wheel Speed Sensor Continuity Fault. 1991 Models**

START TEST 10D.
DISCONNECT THE CROSS BODY BLACK 2-WAY CONNECTOR.
INSPECT THE CONNECTOR.
IS THE CONNECTOR CONDITION OK?
NO
REPAIR AS NECESSARY.
YES
PROBE CAVITY 2 IN THE LR WHEEL SPEED SENSOR CONNECTOR.
IS THE RESISTANCE BELOW 10.0 OHMS?
YES
REPAIR THE 94 LG WIRE FOR A SHORT TO GROUND BETWEEN THE 2-WAY CONNECTORS.
NO
REPAIR THE 94 LG WIRE FOR A SHORT TO GRD BETWEEN CAB CONN AND 2-WAY CONN.

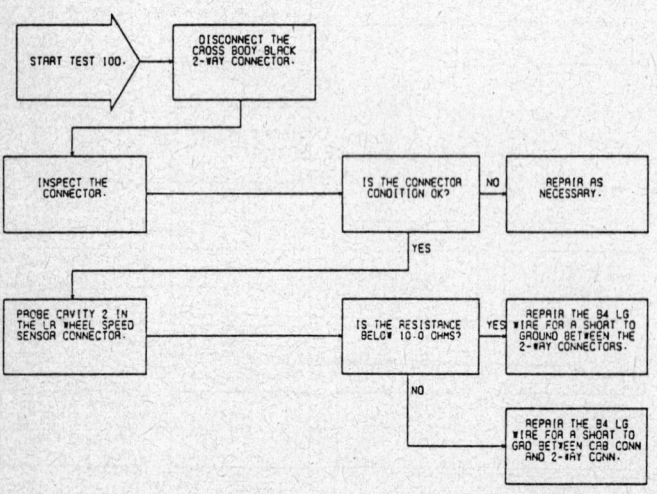

**Fig. 85 Test 10D—Left Rear Wheel Speed Sensor Continuity Fault. 1991 Models**

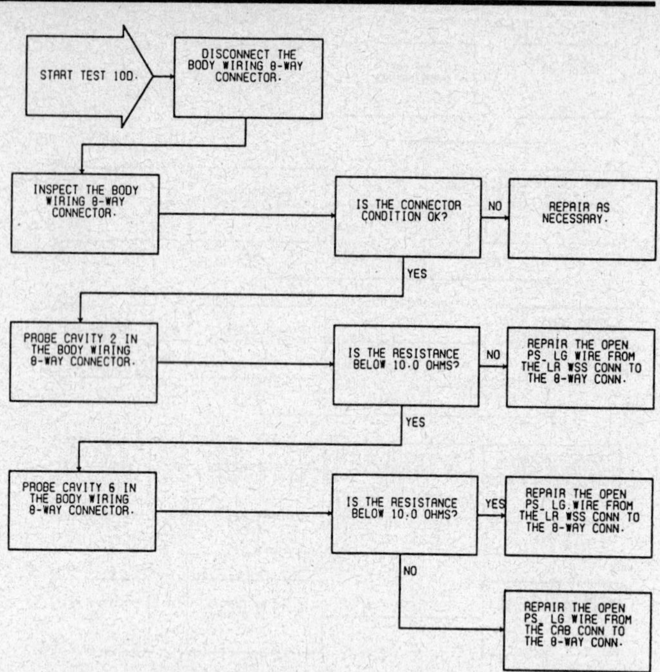


**Fig. 84 Test 10D—Left Rear Continuity Fault. 1990 Models**

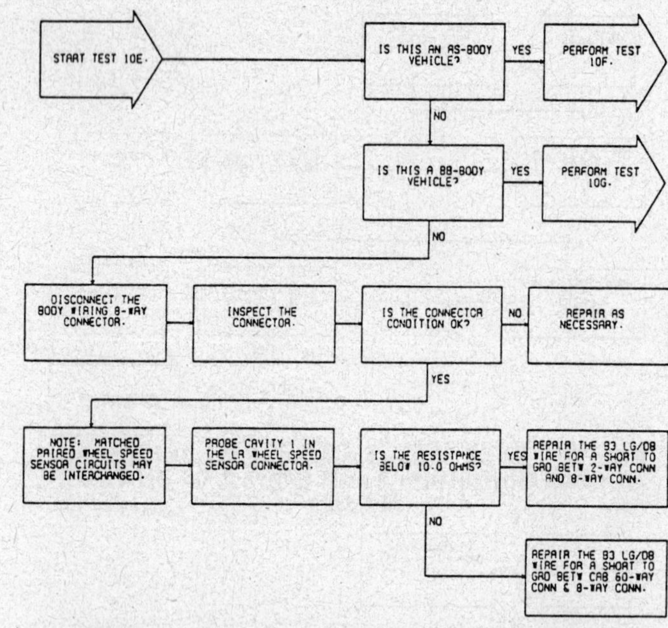


**Fig. 86 Test 10E—Left Rear Wheel Speed Sensor Continuity Fault. 1991 Models**

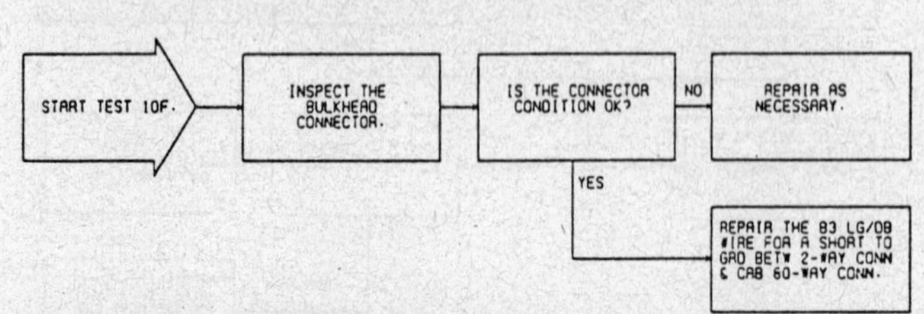


**Fig. 87 Test 10F—Left Rear Wheel Speed Sensor Continuity Fault. 1991 Models**

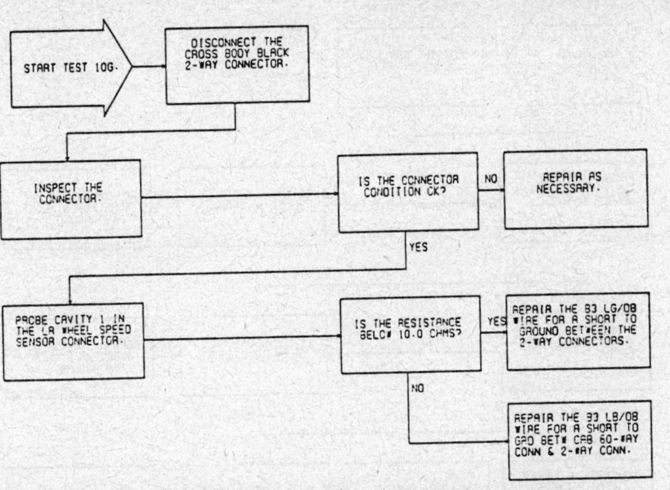


**Fig. 88 Test 10G—Left Rear Wheel Speed Sensor Continuity Fault. 1991 Models**

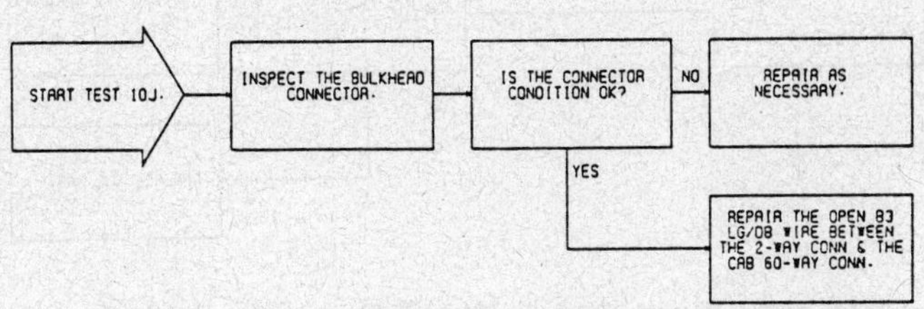


**Fig. 90 Test 10J—Left Rear Wheel Speed Sensor Continuity Fault. 1991 Models**

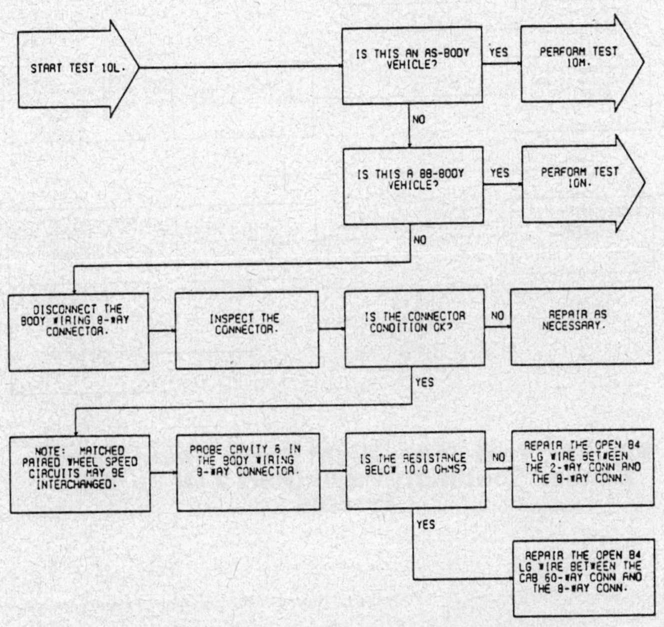


**Fig. 92 Test 10L—Left Rear Wheel Speed Sensor Continuity Fault. 1991 Models**

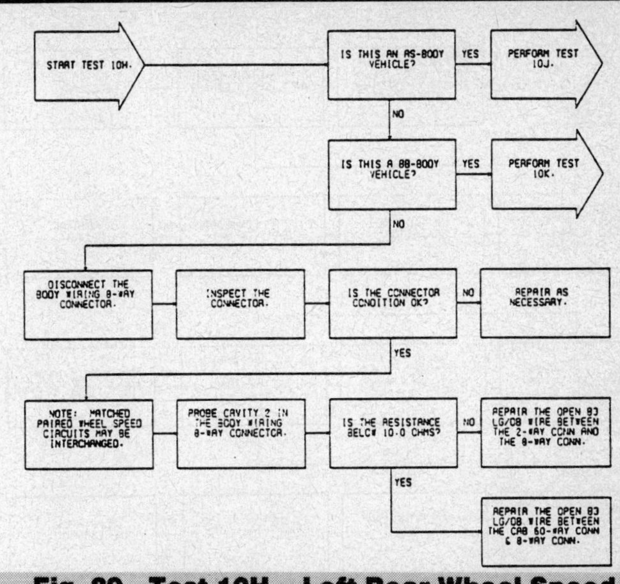


**Fig. 89 Test 10H—Left Rear Wheel Speed Sensor Continuity Fault. 1991 Models**

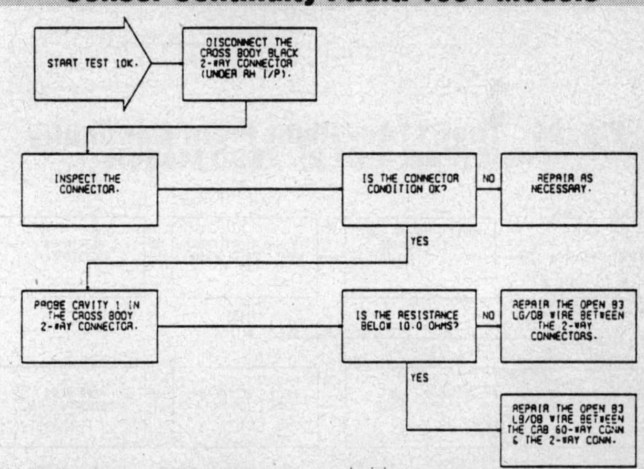


**Fig. 91 Test 10K—Left Rear Wheel Speed Sensor Continuity Fault. 1991 Models**

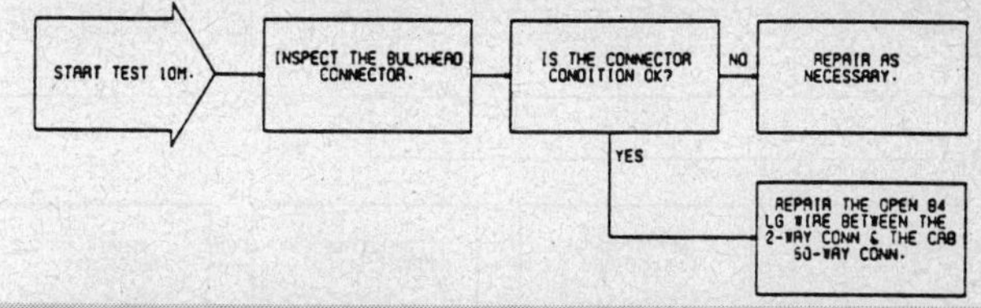


**Fig. 93 Test 10M—Left Rear Wheel Speed Sensor Continuity Fault. 1991 Models**

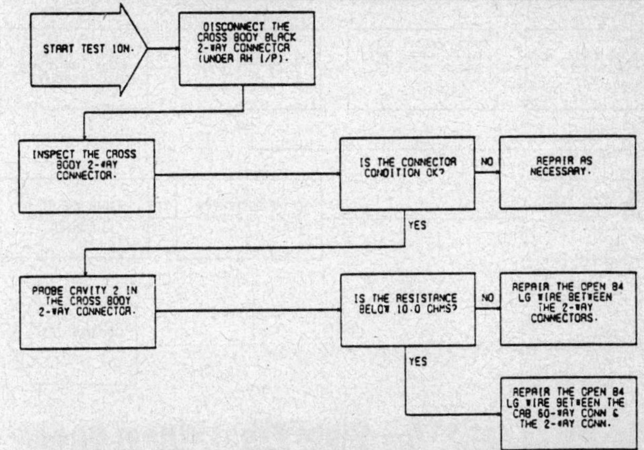


**Fig. 94 Test 10N—Left Rear Wheel Speed Sensor Continuity Fault. 1991 Models**

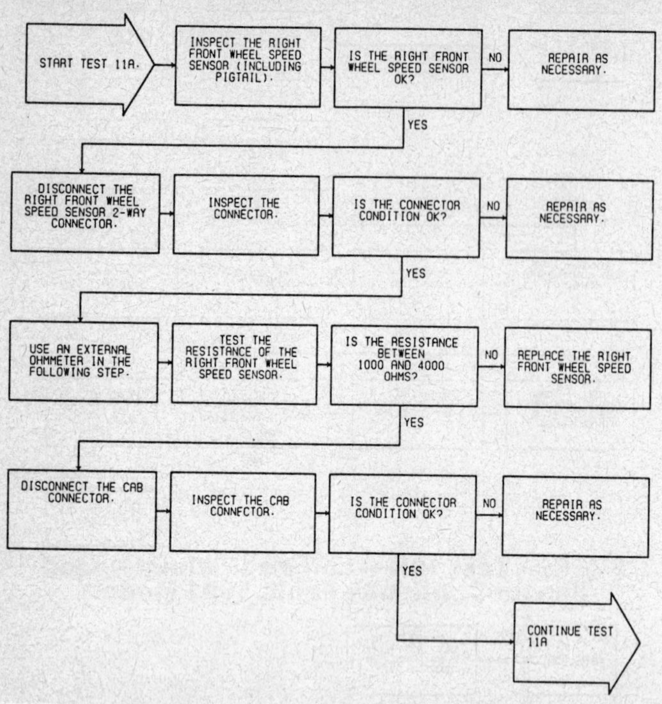


**Fig. 95 Test 11A—Right Front Continuity Fault (Part 1 Of 2). 1990 Models**

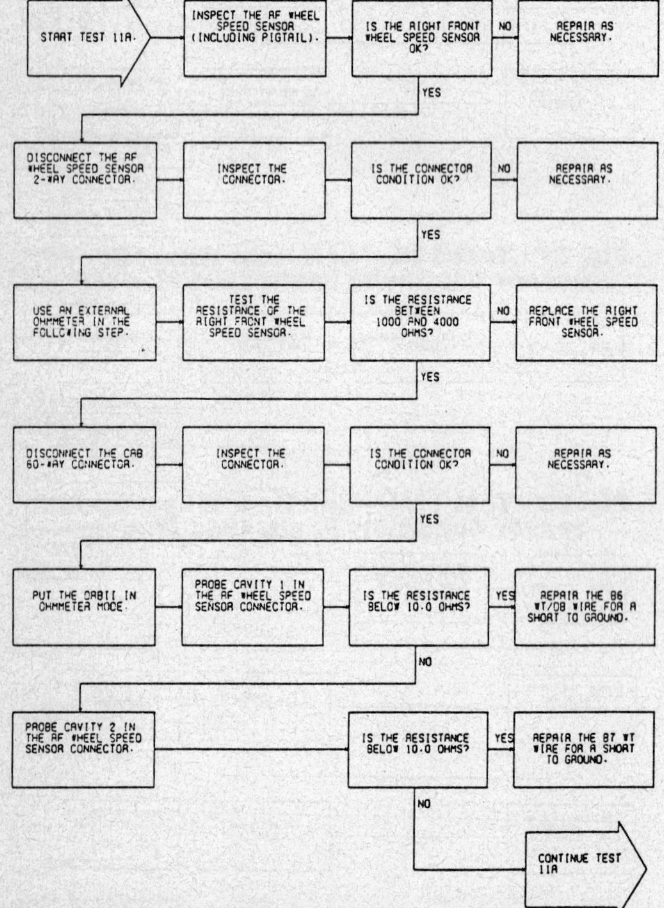


**Fig. 96 Test 11A—Right Front Wheel Speed Sensor Continuity Fault (Part 1 Of 2). 1991 Models**

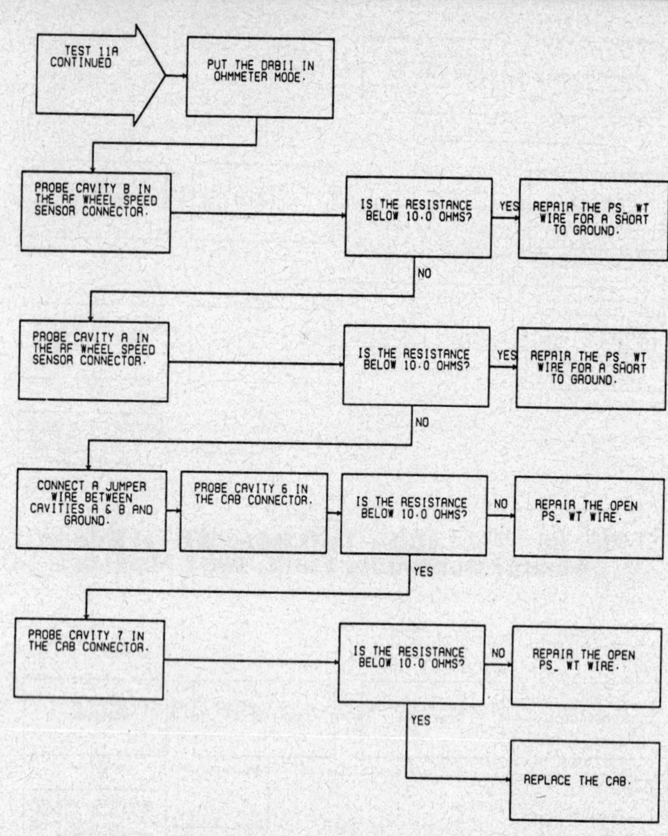


**Fig. 95 Test 11A—Right Front Continuity Fault (Part 2 Of 2). 1990 Models**

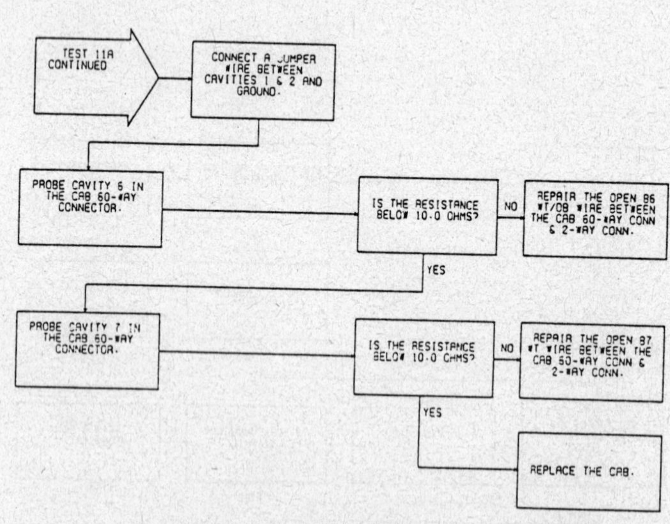


**Fig. 96 Test 11A—Right Front Wheel Speed Sensor Continuity Fault (Part 2 Of 2). 1991 Models**

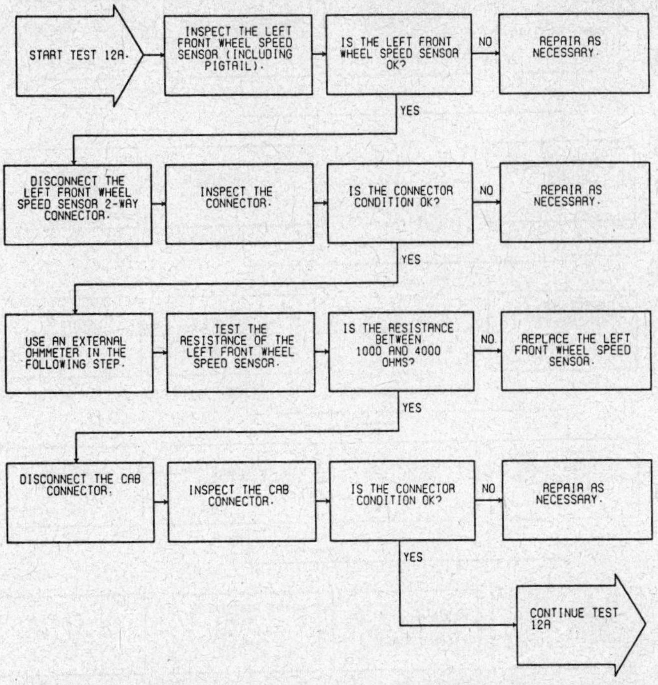

START TEST 12A.
INSPECT THE LEFT FRONT WHEEL SPEED SENSOR (INCLUDING PIGTAIL).
IS THE LEFT FRONT WHEEL SPEED SENSOR OK?
NO
REPAIR AS NECESSARY.
YES
DISCONNECT THE LEFT FRONT WHEEL SPEED SENSOR 2-WAY CONNECTOR.
INSPECT THE CONNECTOR.
IS THE CONNECTOR CONDITION OK?
NO
REPAIR AS NECESSARY.
YES
USE AN EXTERNAL OHMMETER IN THE FOLLOWING STEP.
TEST THE RESISTANCE OF THE LEFT FRONT WHEEL SPEED SENSOR.
IS THE RESISTANCE BETWEEN 1000 AND 4000 OHMS?
NO
REPLACE THE LEFT FRONT WHEEL SPEED SENSOR.
YES
DISCONNECT THE CAB CONNECTOR.
INSPECT THE CAB CONNECTOR.
IS THE CONNECTOR CONDITION OK?
NO
REPAIR AS NECESSARY.
YES
CONTINUE TEST 12A

**Fig. 97 Test 12A—Left Front Continuity Fault (Part 1 Of 2). 1990 Models**

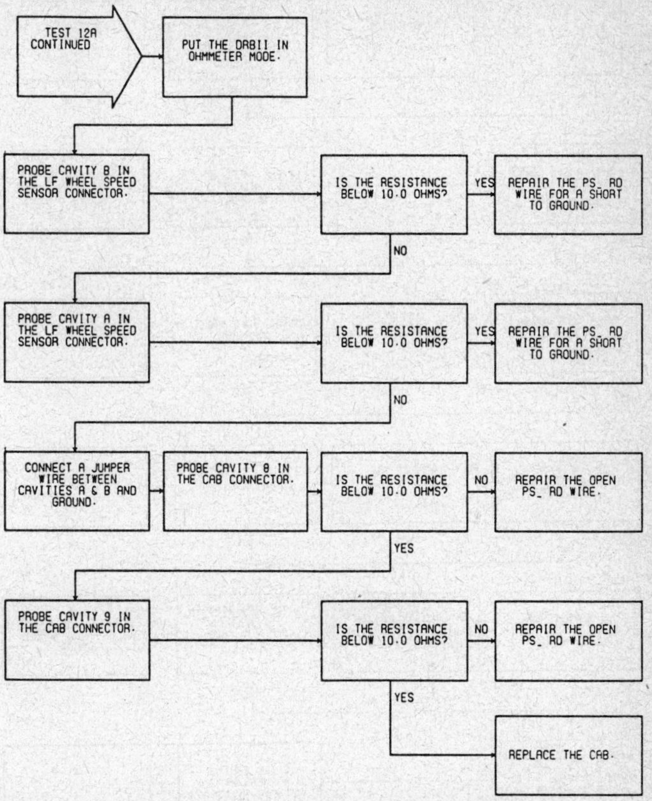

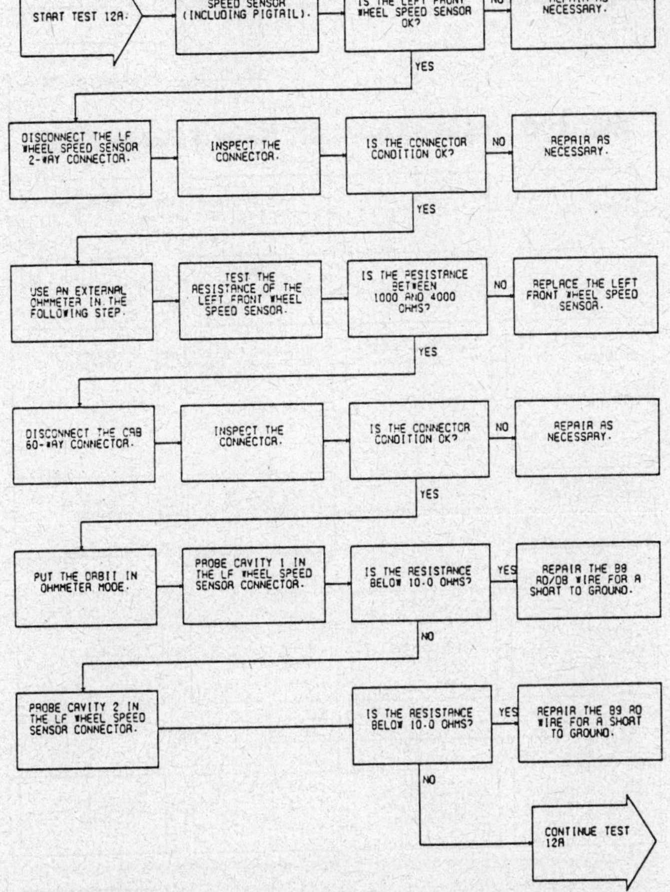


**Fig. 98 Test 12A—Left Front Wheel Speed Sensor Continuity Fault (Part 1 Of 2). 1991 Models**

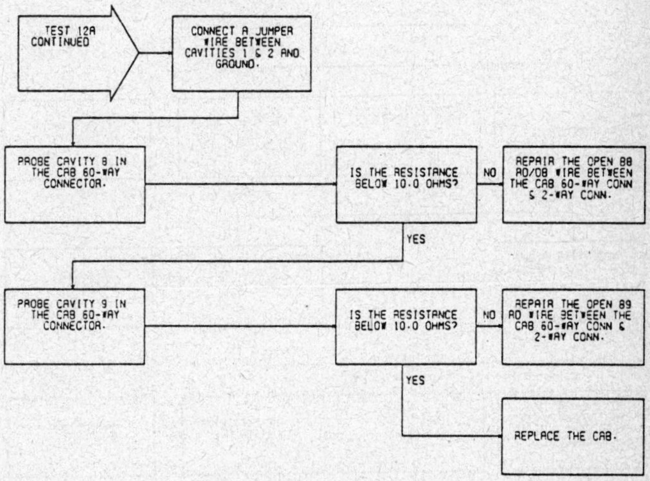

TEST 12A CONTINUED
PUT THE DRBII IN OHMMETER MODE.
PROBE CAVITY 8 IN THE LF WHEEL SPEED SENSOR CONNECTOR.
IS THE RESISTANCE BELOW 10.0 OHMS?
YES
REPAIR THE PS. RD WIRE FOR A SHORT TO GROUND.
NO
PROBE CAVITY A IN THE LF WHEEL SPEED SENSOR CONNECTOR.
IS THE RESISTANCE BELOW 10.0 OHMS?
YES
REPAIR THE PS. RD WIRE FOR A SHORT TO GROUND.
NO
CONNECT A JUMPER WIRE BETWEEN CAVITIES A & B AND GROUND.
PROBE CAVITY 8 IN THE CAB CONNECTOR.
IS THE RESISTANCE BELOW 10.0 OHMS?
NO
REPAIR THE OPEN PS. RD WIRE.
YES
PROBE CAVITY 9 IN THE CAB CONNECTOR.
IS THE RESISTANCE BELOW 10.0 OHMS?
NO
REPAIR THE OPEN PS. RD WIRE.
YES
REPLACE THE CAB.

**Fig. 97 Test 12A—Left Front Continuity Fault (Part 2 Of 2). 1990 Models**

TEST 12A CONTINUED
CONNECT A JUMPER WIRE BETWEEN CAVITIES 1 & 2 AND GROUND.
PROBE CAVITY 8 IN THE CAB 60-WAY CONNECTOR.
IS THE RESISTANCE BELOW 10.0 OHMS?
NO
REPAIR THE OPEN B8 RD/DB WIRE BETWEEN THE CAB 60-WAY CONN & 2-WAY CONN.
YES
PROBE CAVITY 9 IN THE CAB 60-WAY CONNECTOR.
IS THE RESISTANCE BELOW 10.0 OHMS?
NO
REPAIR THE OPEN 89 RD WIRE BETWEEN THE CAB 60-WAY CONN & 2-WAY CONN.
YES
REPLACE THE CAB.

**Fig. 98 Test 12A—Left Front Wheel Speed Sensor Continuity Fault (Part 2 Of 2). 1991 Models**

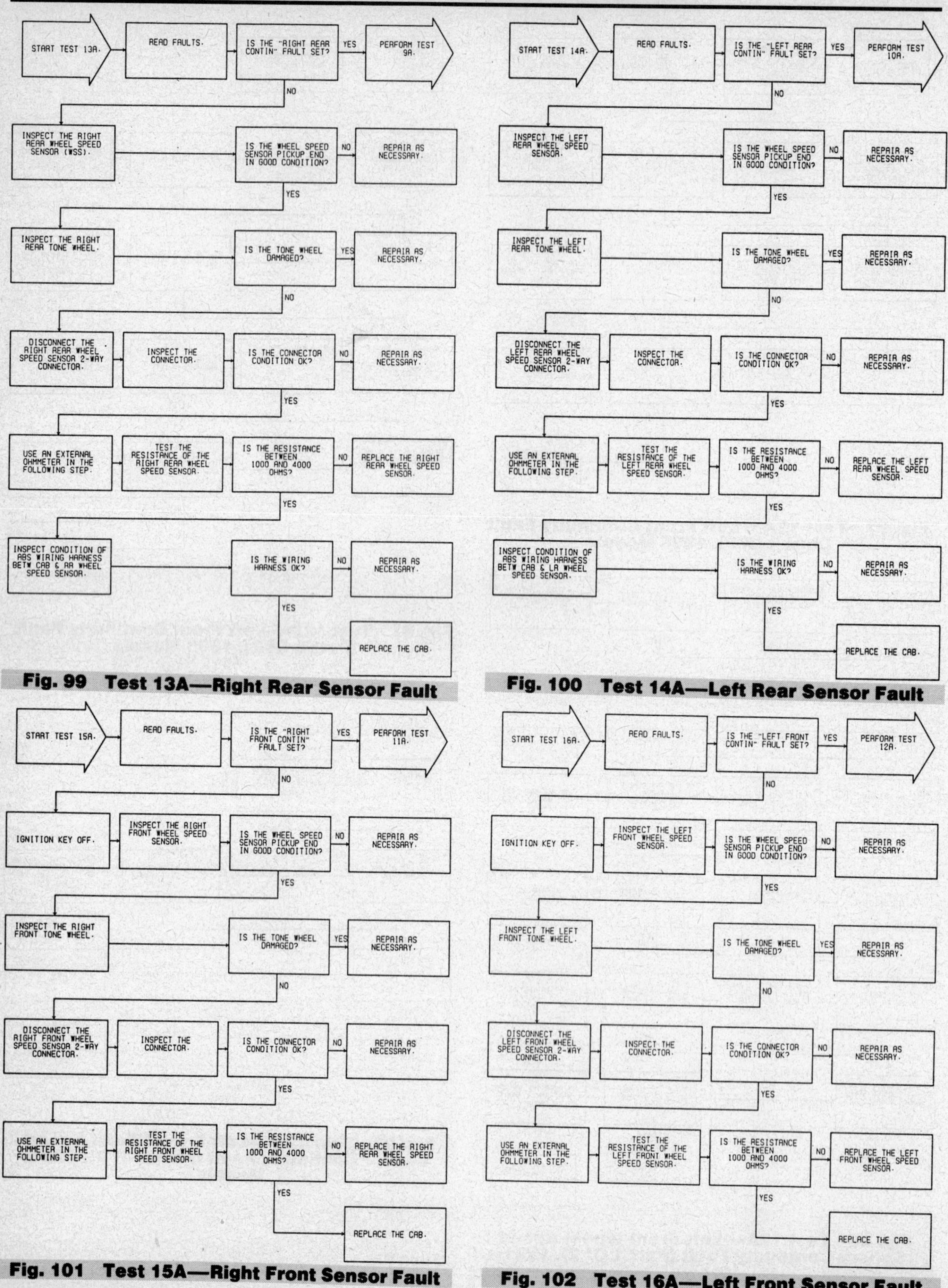


**Fig. 99 Test 13A—Right Rear Sensor Fault**

**Fig. 100 Test 14A—Left Rear Sensor Fault**

**Fig. 101 Test 15A—Right Front Sensor Fault**

**Fig. 102 Test 16A—Left Front Sensor Fault**

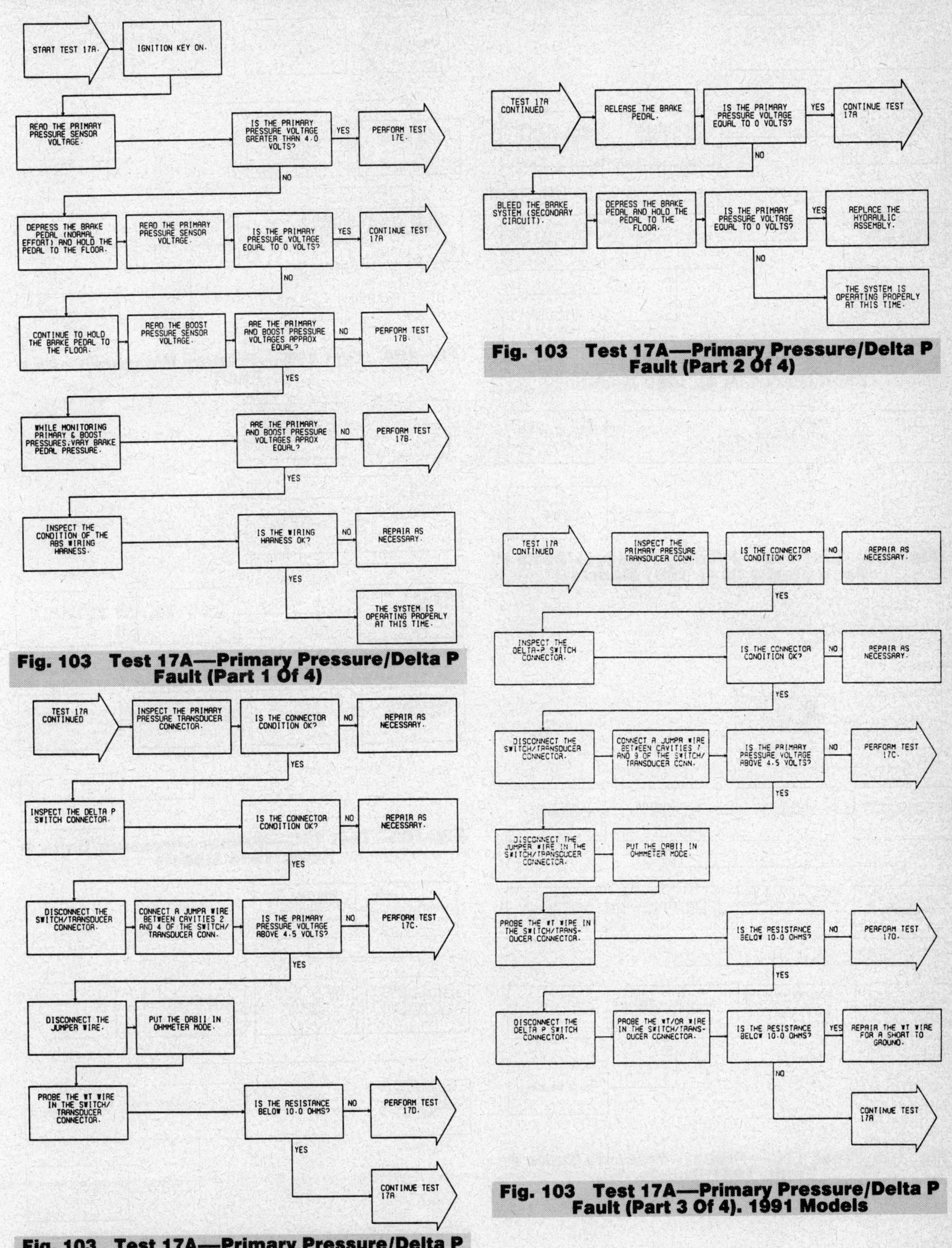
START TEST 17A.
IGNITION KEY ON.
READ THE PRIMARY PRESSURE SENSOR VOLTAGE.
IS THE PRIMARY PRESSURE VOLTAGE GREATER THAN 4.0 VOLTS?
YES
PERFORM TEST 17E.
NO
DEPRESS THE BRAKE PEDAL (NORMAL EFFORT) AND HOLD THE PEDAL TO THE FLOOR.
READ THE PRIMARY PRESSURE SENSOR VOLTAGE.
IS THE PRIMARY PRESSURE VOLTAGE EQUAL TO 0 VOLTS?
YES
CONTINUE TEST 17A
NO
CONTINUE TO HOLD THE BRAKE PEDAL TO THE FLOOR.
READ THE BOOST PRESSURE SENSOR VOLTAGE.
ARE THE PRIMARY AND BOOST PRESSURE VOLTAGES APPROX EQUAL?
NO
PERFORM TEST 17B.
YES
WHILE MONITORING PRIMARY & BOOST PRESSURES; VARY BRAKE PEDAL PRESSURE.
ARE THE PRIMARY AND BOOST PRESSURE VOLTAGES APPROX EQUAL?
NO
PERFORM TEST 17B.
YES
INSPECT THE CONDITION OF THE ABS WIRING HARNESS.
IS THE WIRING HARNESS OK?
NO
REPAIR AS NECESSARY.
YES
THE SYSTEM IS OPERATING PROPERLY AT THIS TIME.
Fig. 103 Test 17A—Primary Pressure/Delta P Fault (Part 1 Of 4)
TEST 17A CONTINUED
INSPECT THE PRIMARY PRESSURE TRANSDUCER CONNECTOR.
IS THE CONNECTOR CONDITION OK?
NO
REPAIR AS NECESSARY.
YES
INSPECT THE DELTA P SWITCH CONNECTOR.
IS THE CONNECTOR CONDITION OK?
NO
REPAIR AS NECESSARY.
YES
DISCONNECT THE SWITCH/TRANSDUCER CONNECTOR.
CONNECT A JUMPR WIRE BETWEEN CAVITIES 2 AND 4 OF THE SWITCH/TRANSDUCER CONN.
IS THE PRIMARY PRESSURE VOLTAGE ABOVE 4.5 VOLTS?
NO
PERFORM TEST 17C.
YES
DISCONNECT THE JUMPER WIRE.
PUT THE DRBII IN OHMMETER MODE.
PROBE THE WT WIRE IN THE SWITCH/TRANSDUCER CONNECTOR.
IS THE RESISTANCE BELOW 10.0 OHMS?
NO
PERFORM TEST 17D.
YES
CONTINUE TEST 17A
Fig. 103 Test 17A—Primary Pressure/Delta P Fault (Part 3 Of 4). 1990 Models
TEST 17A CONTINUED
RELEASE THE BRAKE PEDAL.
IS THE PRIMARY PRESSURE VOLTAGE EQUAL TO 0 VOLTS?
YES
CONTINUE TEST 17A
NO
BLEED THE BRAKE SYSTEM (SECONDARY CIRCUIT).
DEPRESS THE BRAKE PEDAL AND HOLD THE PEDAL TO THE FLOOR.
IS THE PRIMARY PRESSURE VOLTAGE EQUAL TO 0 VOLTS?
YES
REPLACE THE HYDRAULIC ASSEMBLY.
NO
THE SYSTEM IS OPERATING PROPERLY AT THIS TIME.
Fig. 103 Test 17A—Primary Pressure/Delta P Fault (Part 2 Of 4)
TEST 17A CONTINUED
INSPECT THE PRIMARY PRESSURE TRANSDUCER CONN.
IS THE CONNECTOR CONDITION OK?
NO
REPAIR AS NECESSARY.
YES
INSPECT THE DELTA-P SWITCH CONNECTOR.
IS THE CONNECTOR CONDITION OK?
NO
REPAIR AS NECESSARY.
YES
DISCONNECT THE SWITCH/TRANSDUCER CONNECTOR.
CONNECT A JUMPA WIRE BETWEEN CAVITIES 7 AND 3 OF THE SWITCH/TRANSDUCER CONN.
IS THE PRIMARY PRESSURE VOLTAGE ABOVE 4.5 VOLTS?
NO
PERFORM TEST 17C.
YES
DISCONNECT THE JUMPER WIRE IN THE SWITCH/TRANSDUCER CONNECTOR.
PUT THE DRBII IN OHMMETER MODE.
PROBE THE WT WIRE IN THE SWITCH/TRANSDUCER CONNECTOR.
IS THE RESISTANCE BELOW 10.0 OHMS?
NO
PERFORM TEST 17D.
YES
DISCONNECT THE DELTA P SWITCH CONNECTOR.
PROBE THE WT/OR WIRE IN THE SWITCH/TRANSDUCER CONNECTOR.
IS THE RESISTANCE BELOW 10.0 OHMS?
YES
REPAIR THE WT WIRE FOR A SHORT TO GROUND.
NO
CONTINUE TEST 17A
Fig. 103 Test 17A—Primary Pressure/Delta P Fault (Part 3 Of 4). 1991 Models

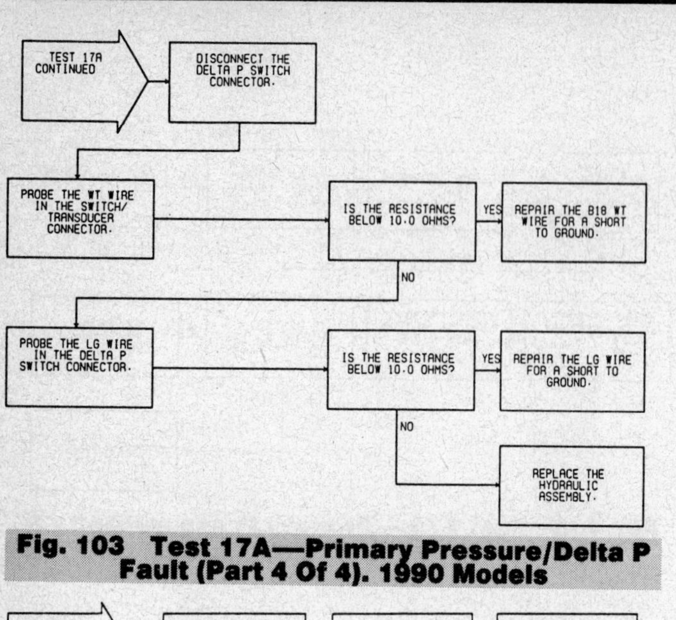


**Fig. 103 Test 17A—Primary Pressure/Delta P Fault (Part 4 Of 4). 1990 Models**

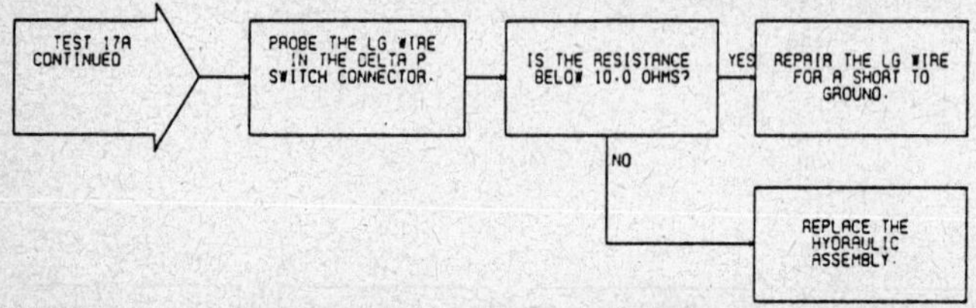


**Fig. 103 Test 17A—Primary Pressure/Delta P Fault (Part 4 Of 4). 1991 Models**

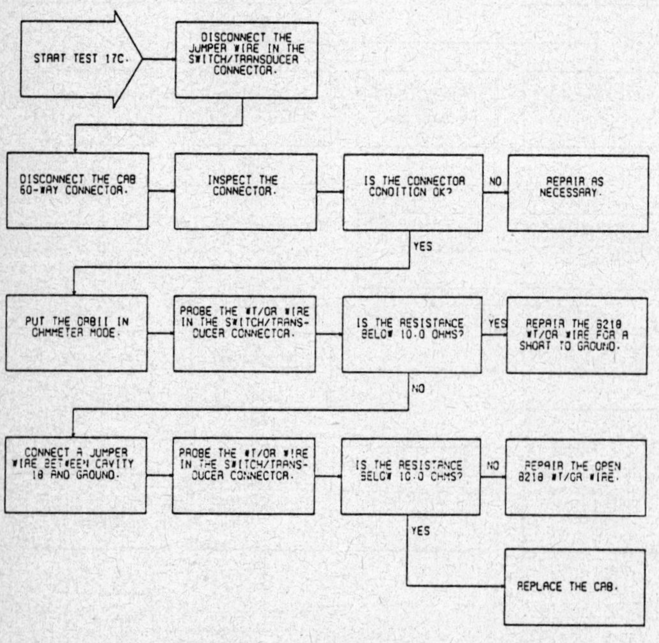


**Fig. 106 Test 17C—Primary Pressure/Delta P Fault. 1991 Models**

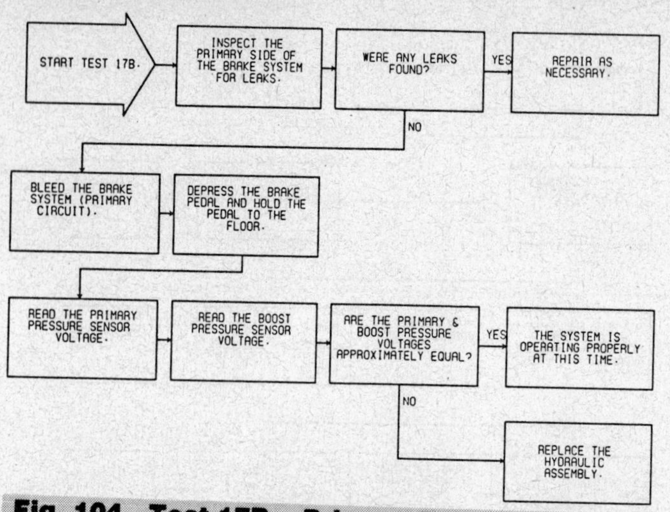


**Fig. 104 Test 17B—Primary Pressure/Delta P Fault**

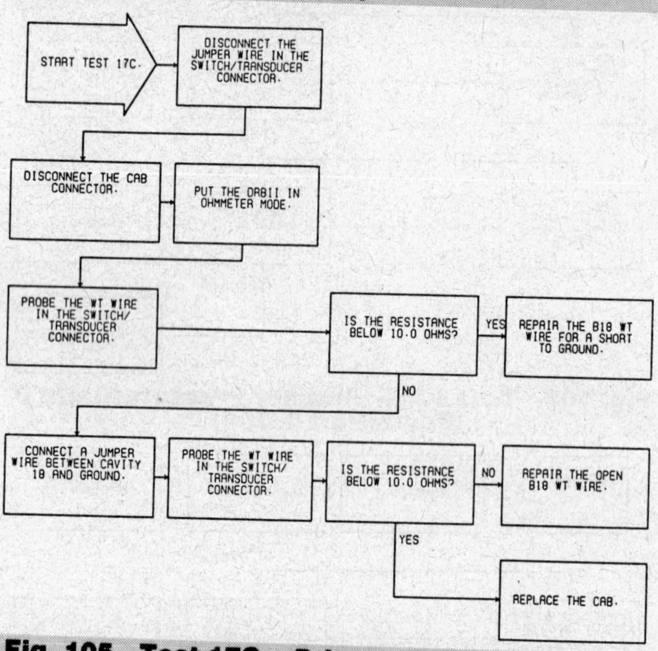


**Fig. 105 Test 17C—Primary Pressure/Delta P Fault. 1990 Models**

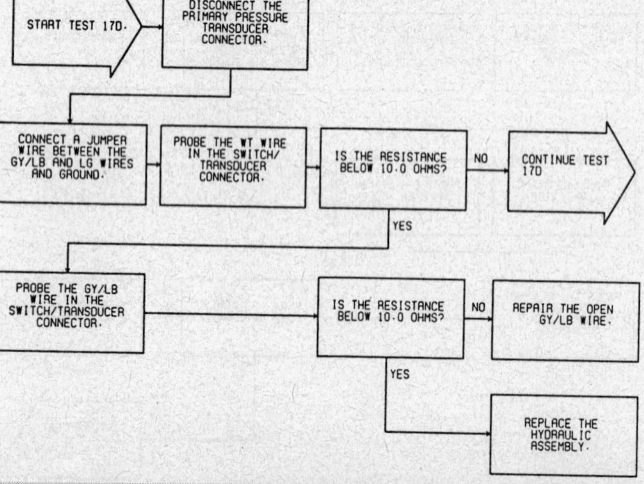


**Fig. 107 Test 17D—Primary Pressure/Delta P Fault (Part 1 Of 2)**

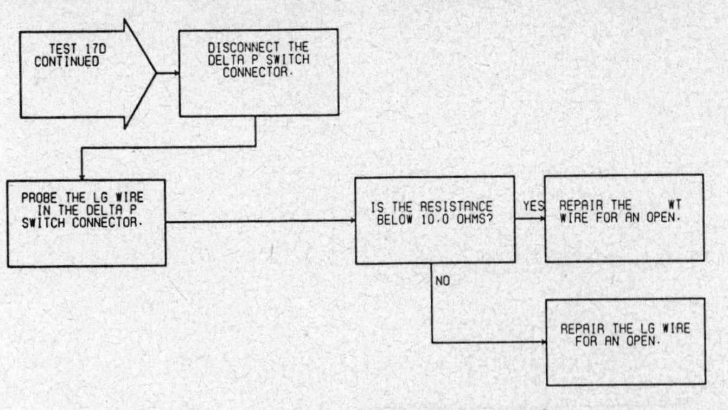


**Fig. 107 Test 17D—Primary Pressure/Delta P Fault (Part 2 Of 2)**

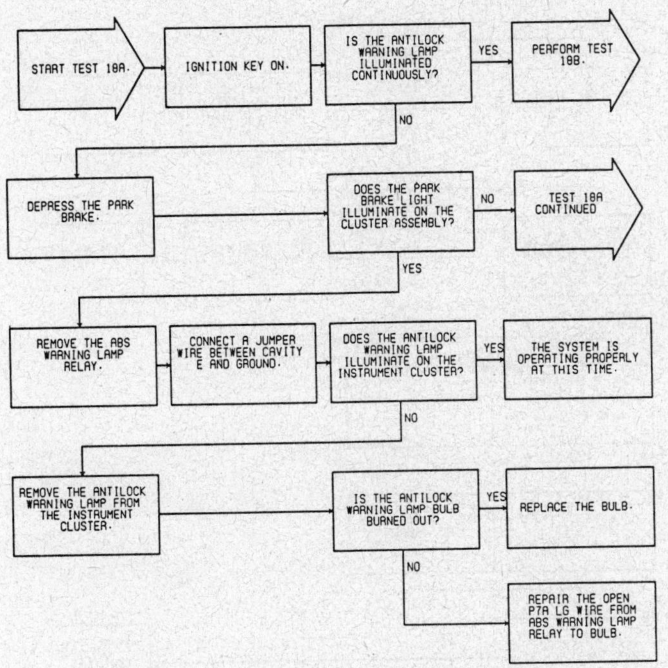


**Fig. 109 Test 18A—Anti-Lock Lamp Fault (Part 1 Of 2). 1990 Models**

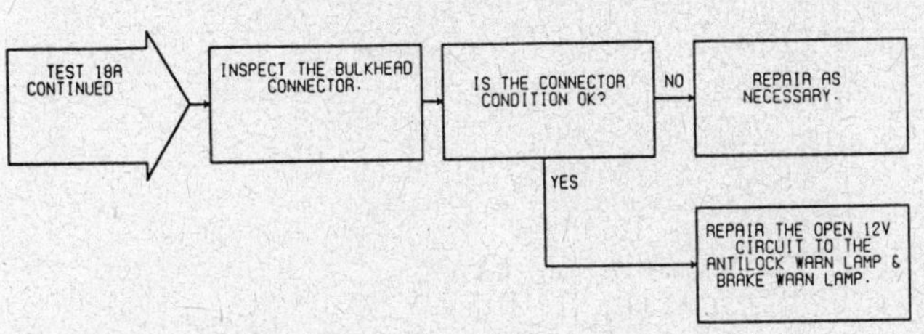


**Fig. 109 Test 18A—Anti-Lock Lamp Fault (Part 2 Of 2). 1990 Models**

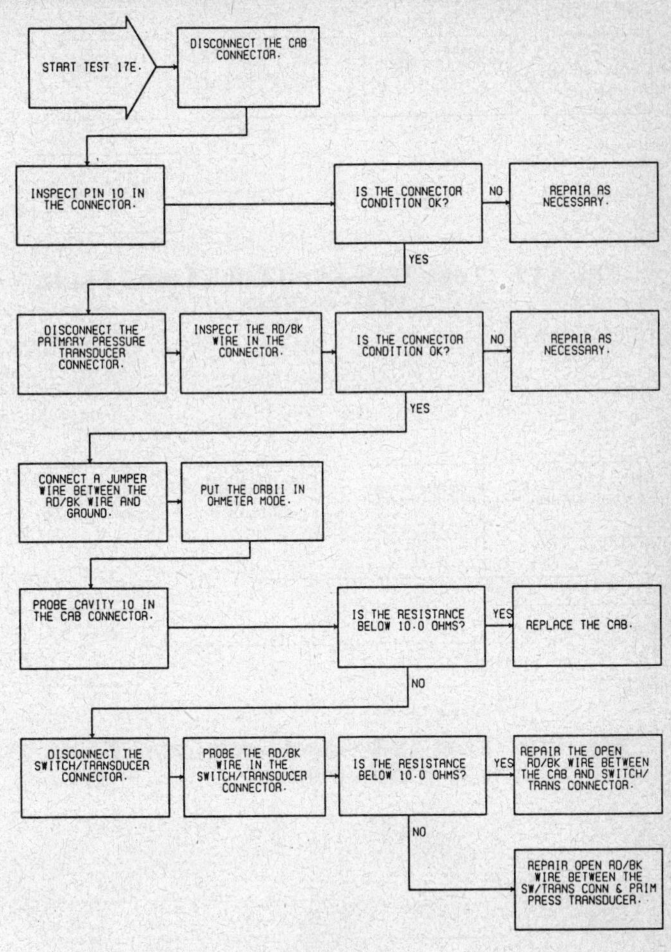


**Fig. 108 Test 17E—Primary Pressure/Delta P Fault.**

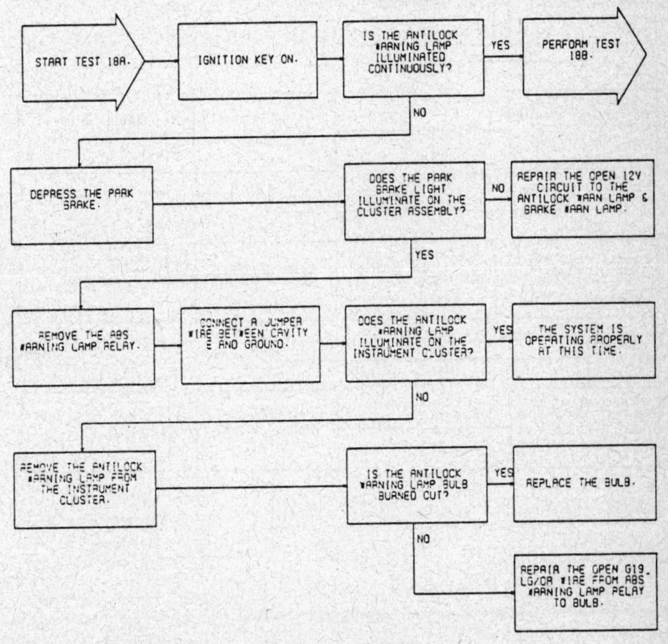


**Fig. 110 Test 18A—Anti-Lock Lamp Fault. 1991 Models**

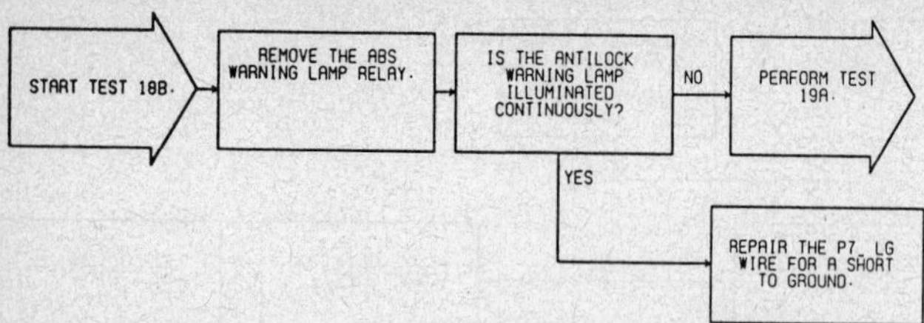


**Fig. 111 Test 18B—Anti-Lock Lamp Fault. 1990 Models**

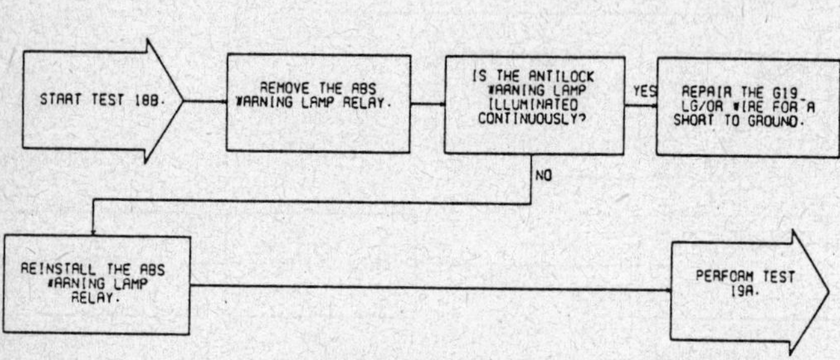


**Fig. 112 Test 18B—Anti-Lock Lamp Fault. 1991 Models**

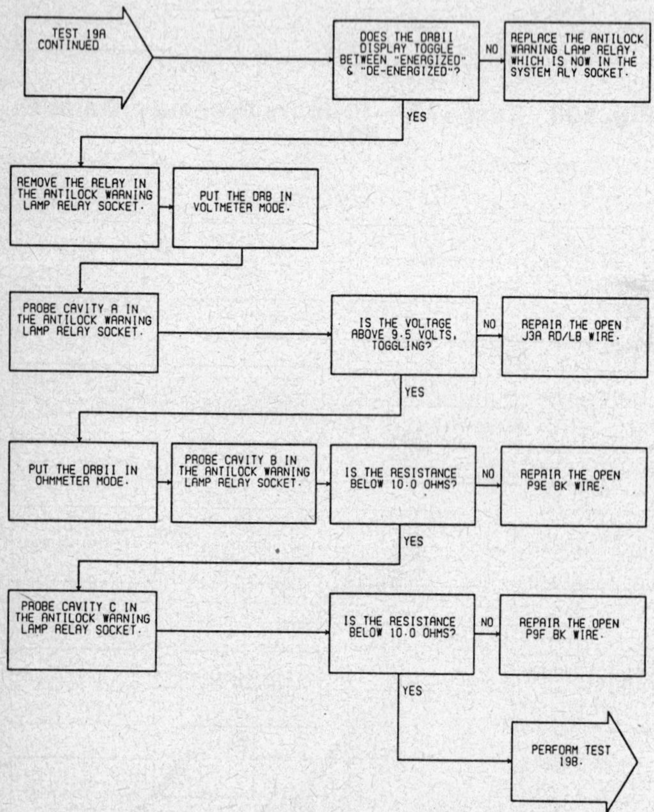


**Fig. 113 Test 19A—Anti-Lock Lamp Relay Fault (Part 2 Of 2). 1990 Models**

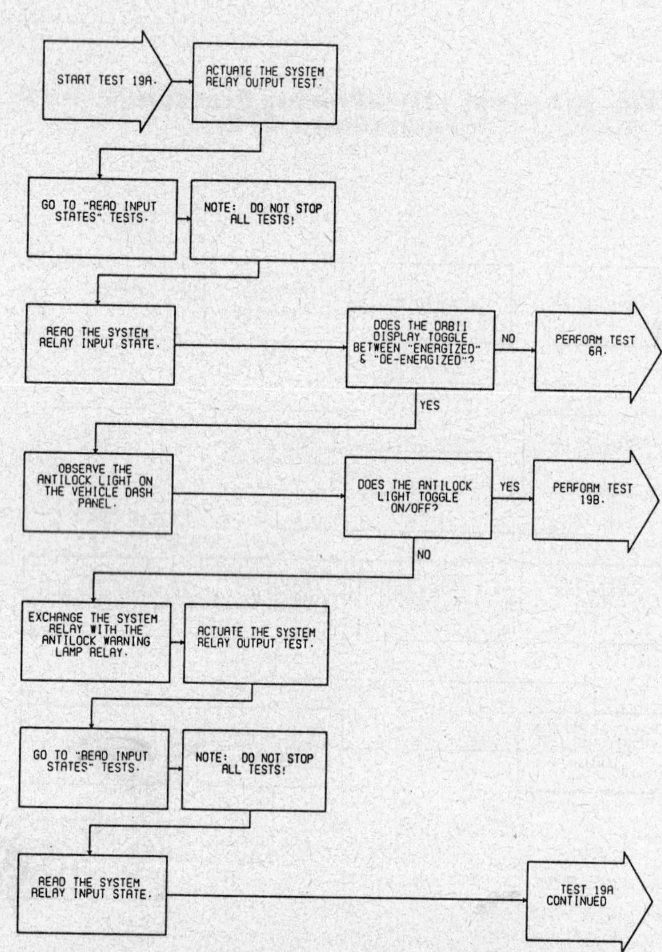


**Fig. 113 Test 19A—Anti-Lock Lamp Relay Fault (Part 1 Of 2). 1990 Models**

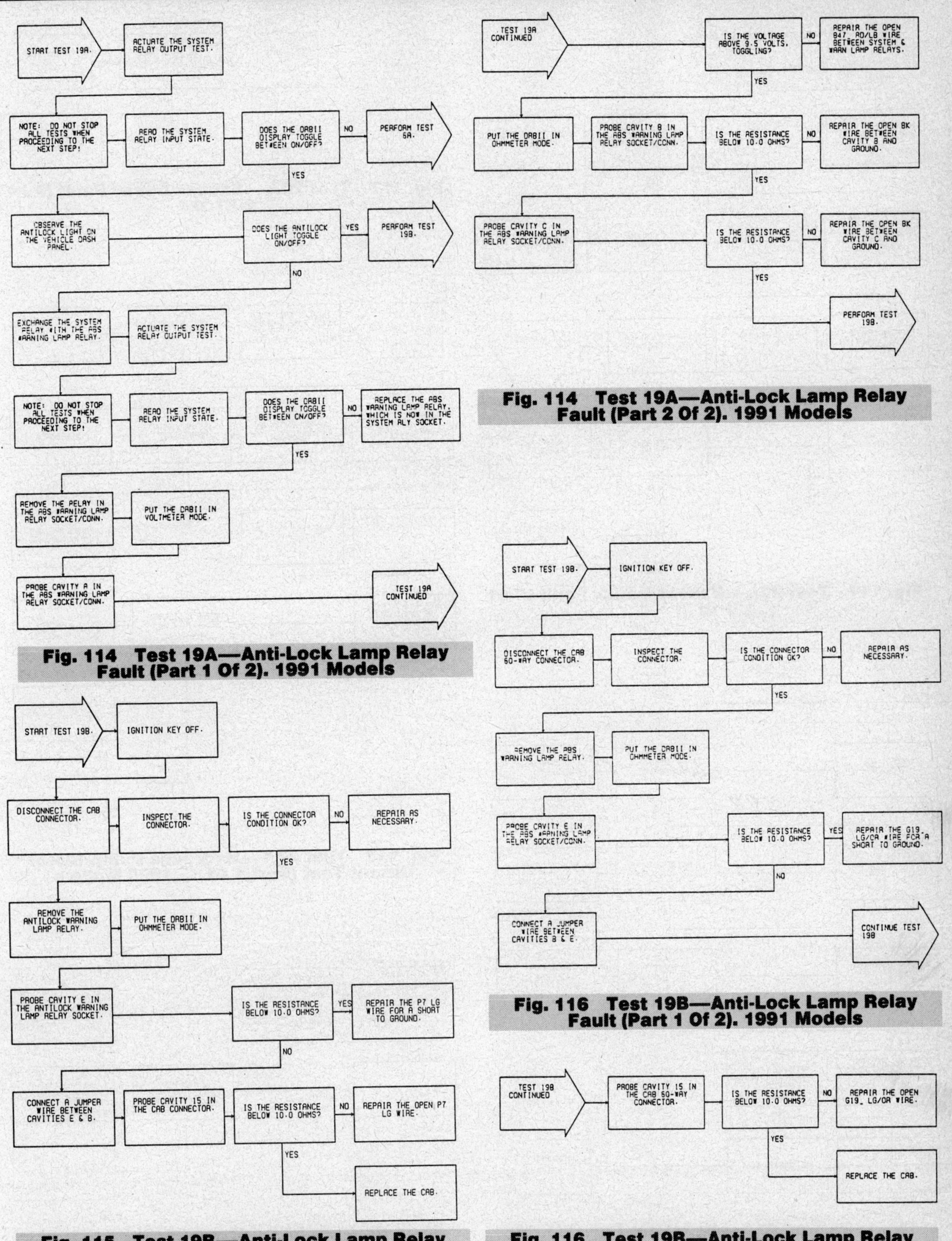


Fig. 114 Test 19A—Anti-Lock Lamp Relay Fault (Part 1 Of 2). 1991 Models



Fig. 114 Test 19A—Anti-Lock Lamp Relay Fault (Part 2 Of 2). 1991 Models



Fig. 115 Test 19B—Anti-Lock Lamp Relay Fault. 1990 Models



Fig. 116 Test 19B—Anti-Lock Lamp Relay Fault (Part 1 Of 2). 1991 Models



Fig. 116 Test 19B—Anti-Lock Lamp Relay Fault (Part 2 Of 2). 1991 Models

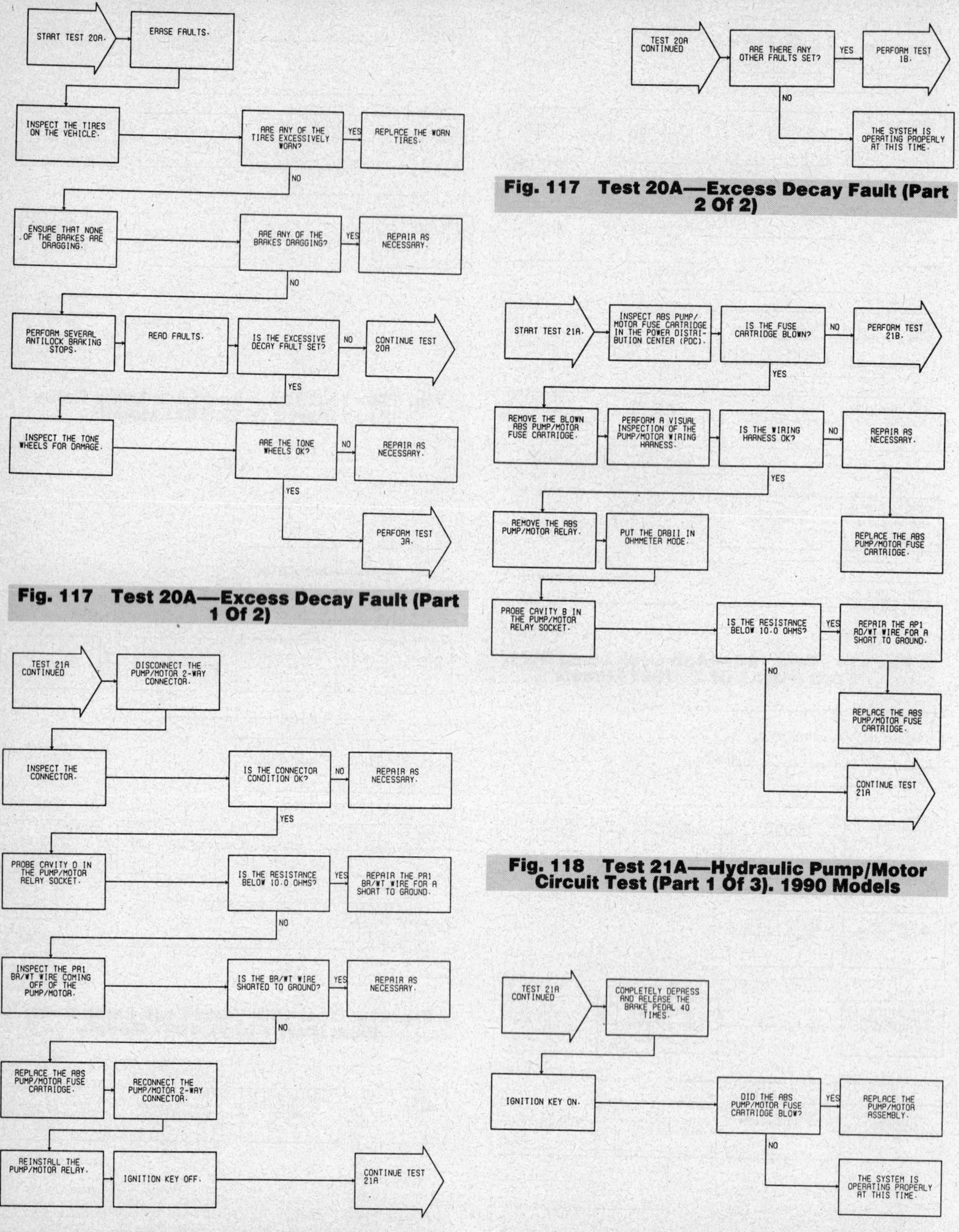


**Fig. 117 Test 20A—Excess Decay Fault (Part 1 Of 2)**

**Fig. 117 Test 20A—Excess Decay Fault (Part 2 Of 2)**

**Fig. 118 Test 21A—Hydraulic Pump/Motor Circuit Test (Part 1 Of 3). 1990 Models**

**Fig. 118 Test 21A—Hydraulic Pump/Motor Circuit Test (Part 2 Of 3). 1990 Models**

**Fig. 118 Test 21A—Hydraulic Pump/Motor Circuit Test (Part 3 Of 3). 1990 Models**

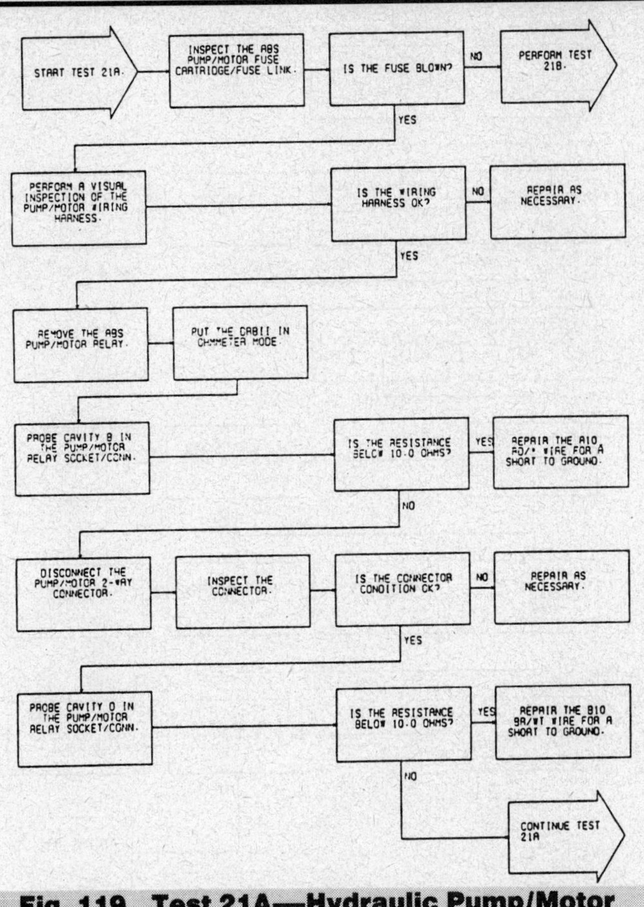


**Fig. 119 Test 21A—Hydraulic Pump/Motor Circuit Test (Part 1 Of 2). 1991 Models**

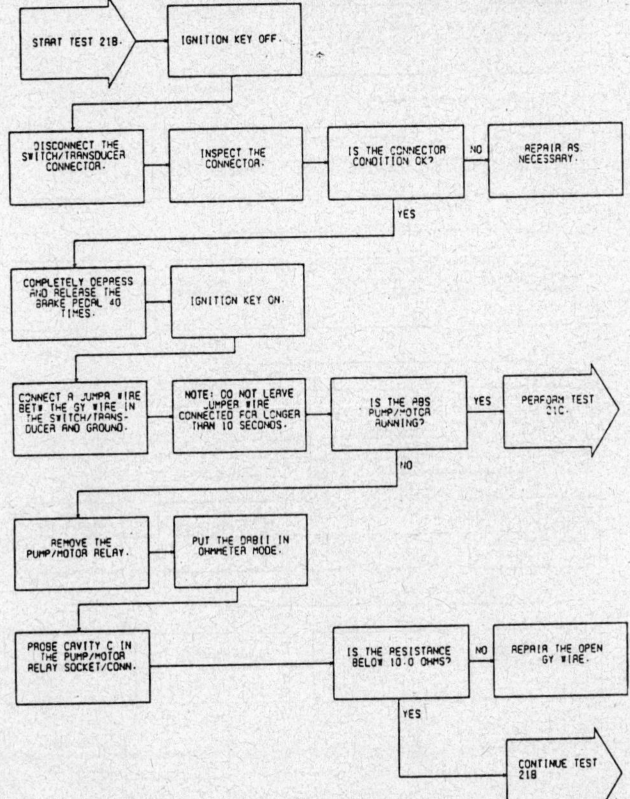


**Fig. 120 Test 21B—Hydraulic Pump/Motor Circuit Test (Part 1 Of 3)**

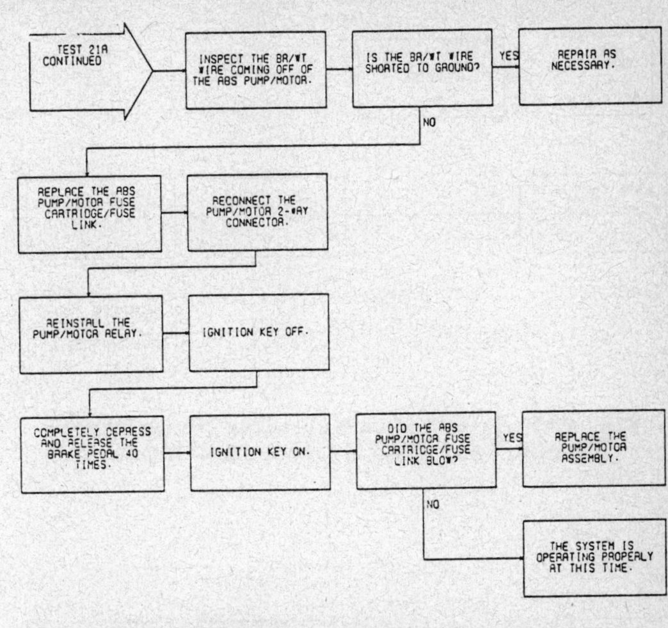


**Fig. 119 Test 21A—Hydraulic Pump/Motor Circuit Test (Part 2 Of 2). 1991 Models**

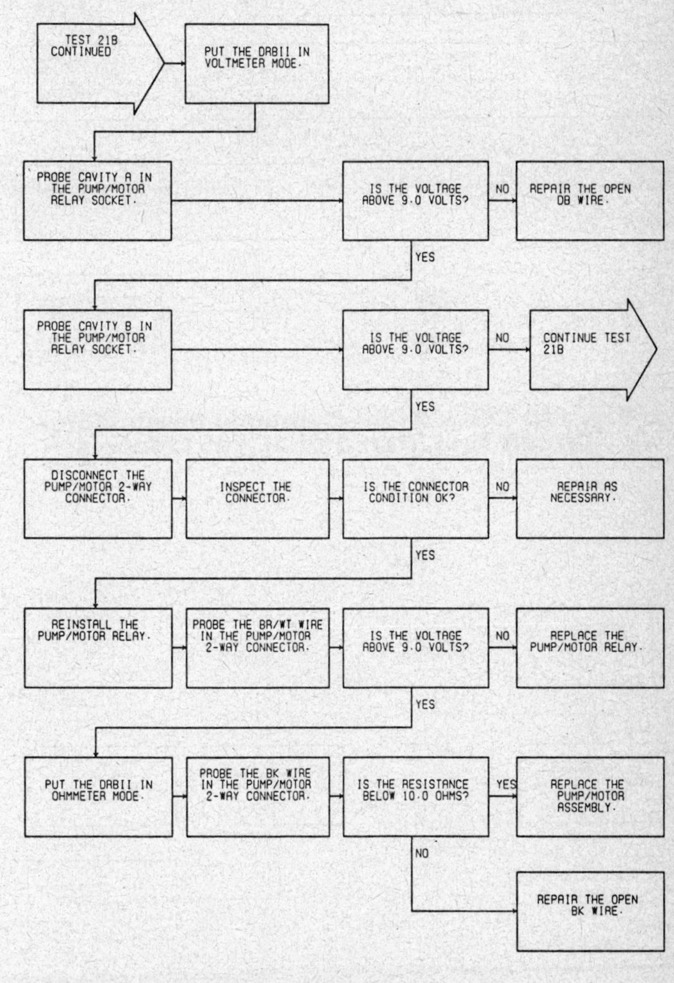


**Fig. 120 Test 21B—Hydraulic Pump/Motor Circuit Test (Part 2 Of 3)**

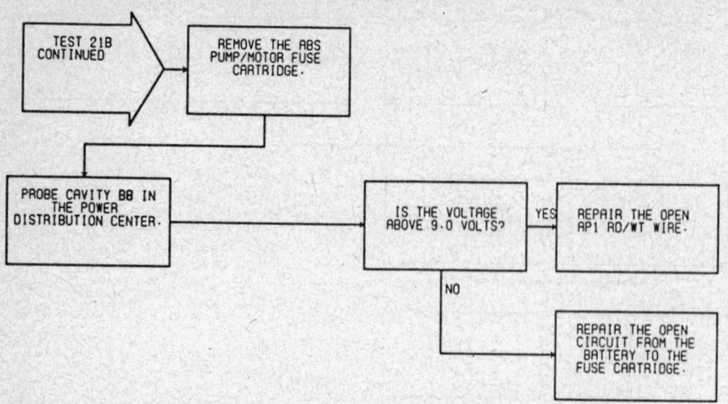


**Fig. 120 Test 21B—Hydraulic Pump/Motor Circuit Test (Part 3 Of 3). 1990 Models**

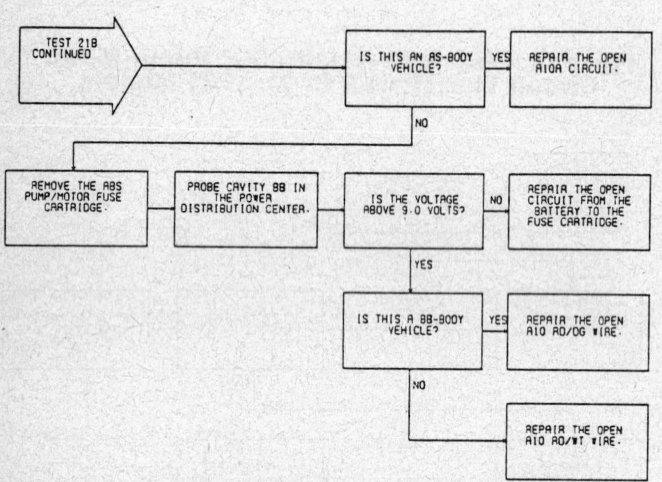


**Fig. 120 Test 21B—Hydraulic Pump/Motor Circuit Test (Part 3 Of 3). 1991 Models**

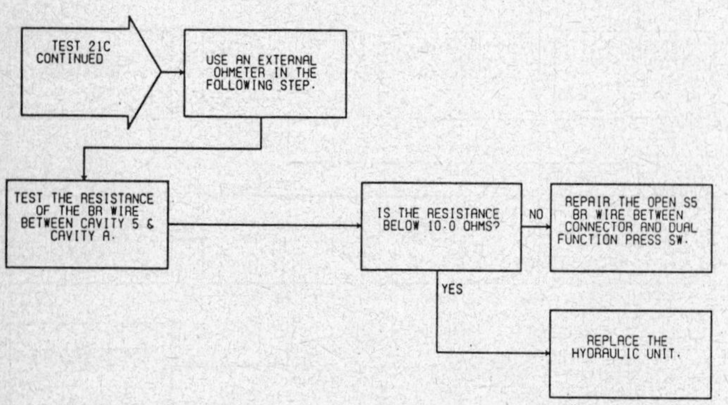


**Fig. 121 Test 21C—Hydraulic Pump/Motor Circuit Test (Part 2 Of 2). 1990 Models**

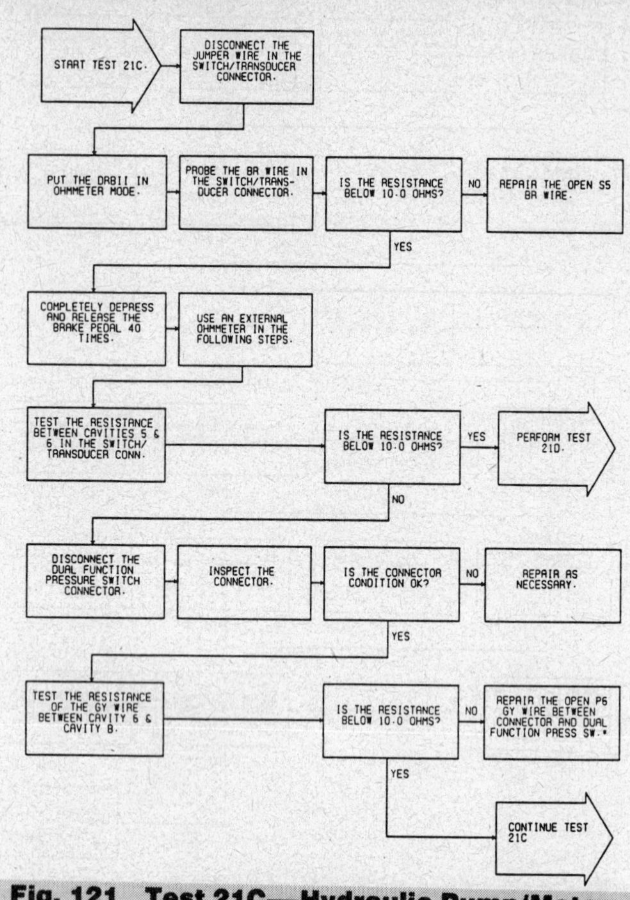


**Fig. 121 Test 21C—Hydraulic Pump/Motor Circuit Test (Part 1 Of 2). 1990 Models**

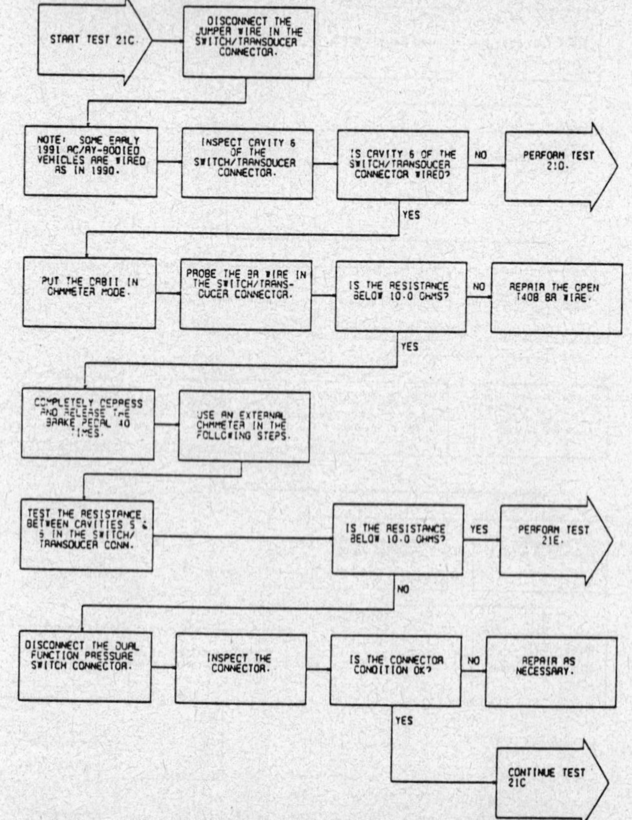


**Fig. 122 Test 21C—Hydraulic Pump/Motor Circuit Test (Part 1 Of 2). 1991 Models**

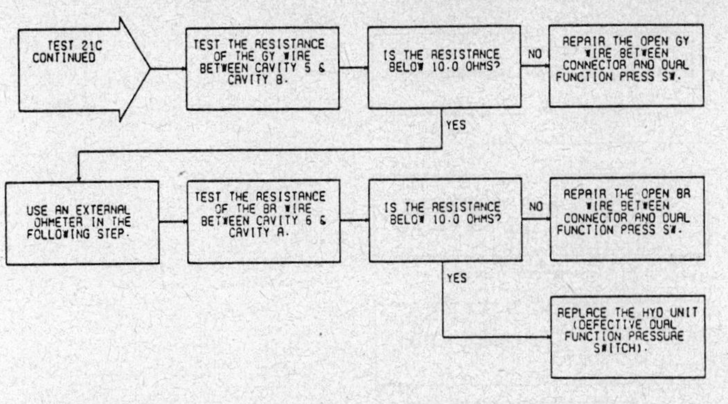


**Fig. 122 Test 21C—Hydraulic Pump/Motor Circuit Test (Part 2 Of 2). 1991 Models**

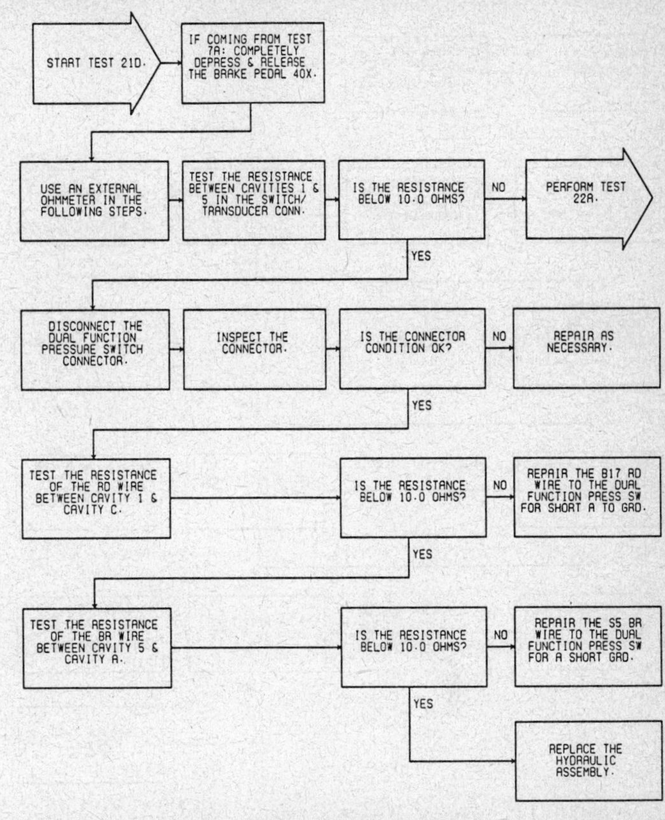


**Fig. 123 Test 21D—Hydraulic Pump/Motor Circuit Test. 1990 Models**

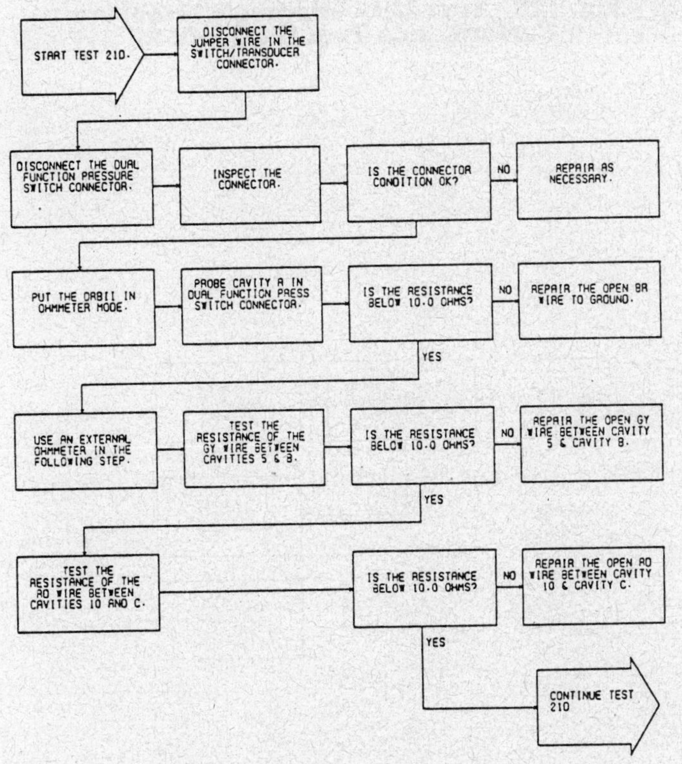


**Fig. 124 Test 21D—Hydraulic Pump/Motor Circuit Test (Part 1 Of 2). 1991 Models**

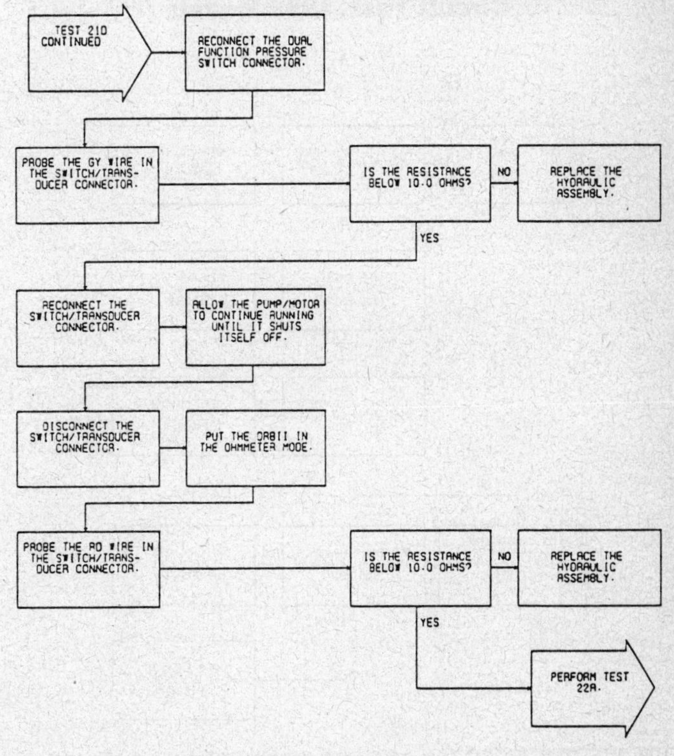


**Fig. 124 Test 21D—Hydraulic Pump/Motor Circuit Test (Part 2 Of 2). 1991 Models**

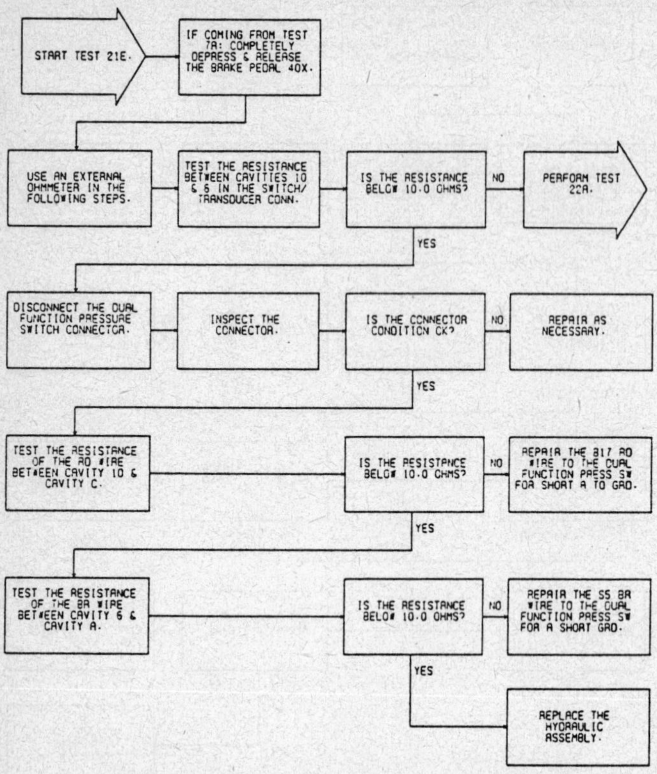

START TEST 21E.
IF COMING FROM TEST 7A: COMPLETELY DEPRESS & RELEASE THE BRAKE PEDAL 40X.
USE AN EXTERNAL OHMMETER IN THE FOLLOWING STEPS.
TEST THE RESISTANCE BETWEEN CAVITIES 10 & 6 IN THE SWITCH/ TRANSDUCER CONN.
IS THE RESISTANCE BELOW 10.0 OHMS?
NO
PERFORM TEST 22A.
YES
DISCONNECT THE DUAL FUNCTION PRESSURE SWITCH CONNECTOR.
INSPECT THE CONNECTOR.
IS THE CONNECTOR CONDITION OK?
NO
REPAIR AS NECESSARY.
YES
TEST THE RESISTANCE OF THE RD WIRE BETWEEN CAVITY 10 & CAVITY C.
IS THE RESISTANCE BELOW 10.0 OHMS?
NO
REPAIR THE 817 RD WIRE TO THE DUAL FUNCTION PRESS SW FOR SHORT A TO GRD.
YES
TEST THE RESISTANCE OF THE BR WIRE BETWEEN CAVITY 6 & CAVITY A.
IS THE RESISTANCE BELOW 10.0 OHMS?
NO
REPAIR THE S5 BR WIRE TO THE DUAL FUNCTION PRESS SW FOR A SHORT GRD.
YES
REPLACE THE HYDRAULIC ASSEMBLY.

**Fig. 125 Test 21E—Hydraulic Pump/Motor Circuit Test. 1991 Models**

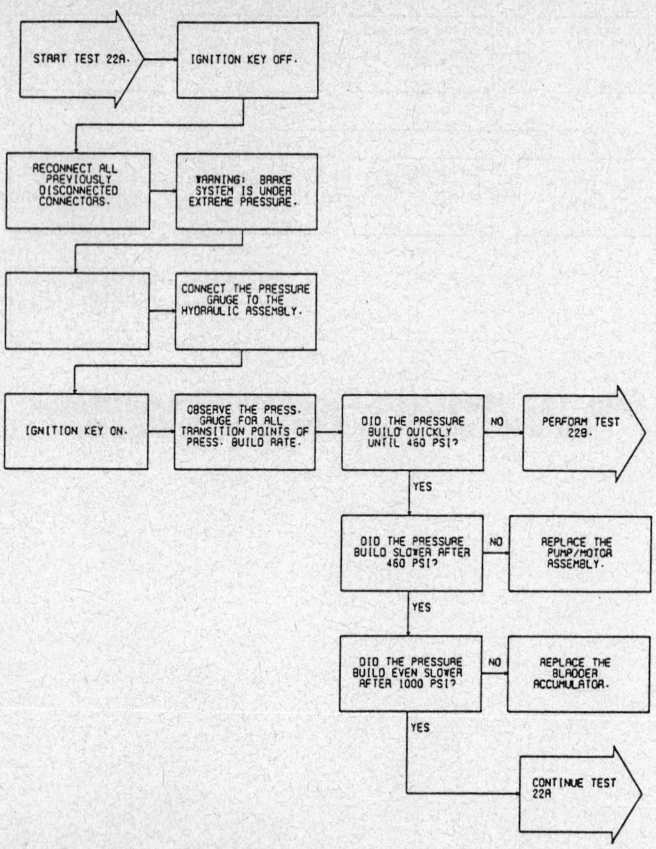

START TEST 22A.
IGNITION KEY OFF.
RECONNECT ALL PREVIOUSLY DISCONNECTED CONNECTORS.
WARNING: BRAKE SYSTEM IS UNDER EXTREME PRESSURE.
CONNECT THE PRESSURE GAUGE TO THE HYDRAULIC ASSEMBLY.
IGNITION KEY ON.
OBSERVE THE PRESS. GAUGE FOR ALL TRANSITION POINTS OF PRESS. BUILD RATE.
DID THE PRESSURE BUILD QUICKLY UNTIL 460 PSI?
NO
PERFORM TEST 22B.
YES
DID THE PRESSURE BUILD SLOWER AFTER 460 PSI?
NO
REPLACE THE PUMP/MOTOR ASSEMBLY.
YES
DID THE PRESSURE BUILD EVEN SLOWER AFTER 1000 PSI?
NO
REPLACE THE BLADDER ACCUMULATOR.
YES
CONTINUE TEST 22A

**Fig. 126 Test 22A—Hydraulic Pressure Performance Test (Part 1 Of 2)**

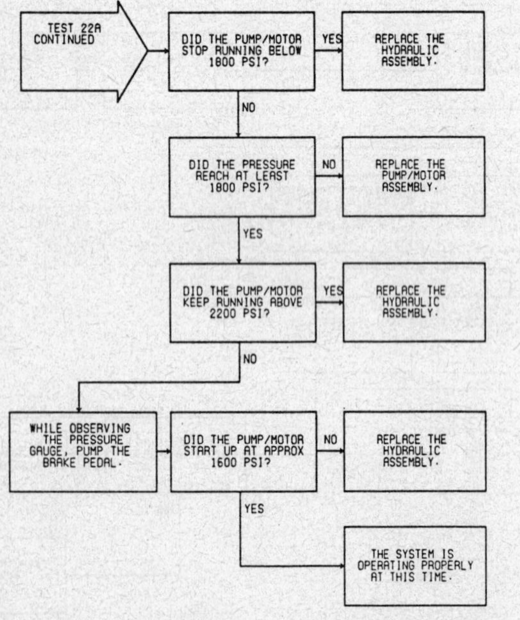

TEST 22A CONTINUED
DID THE PUMP/MOTOR STOP RUNNING BELOW 1800 PSI?
YES
REPLACE THE HYDRAULIC ASSEMBLY.
NO
DID THE PRESSURE REACH AT LEAST 1800 PSI?
NO
REPLACE THE PUMP/MOTOR ASSEMBLY.
YES
DID THE PUMP/MOTOR KEEP RUNNING ABOVE 2200 PSI?
YES
REPLACE THE HYDRAULIC ASSEMBLY.
NO
WHILE OBSERVING THE PRESSURE GAUGE, PUMP THE BRAKE PEDAL.
DID THE PUMP/MOTOR START UP AT APPROX 1600 PSI?
NO
REPLACE THE HYDRAULIC ASSEMBLY.
YES
THE SYSTEM IS OPERATING PROPERLY AT THIS TIME.

**Fig. 126 Test 22A—Hydraulic Pressure Performance Test (Part 2 Of 2)**

START TEST 22B.
DID THE PRESSURE BUILD RATE CHANGE AT 1000 PSI?
YES
REPLACE THE PUMP/MOTOR ASSEMBLY.
NO
REPLACE THE BLADDER ACCUMULATOR.
REPLACE THE PUMP/MOTOR ASSEMBLY.

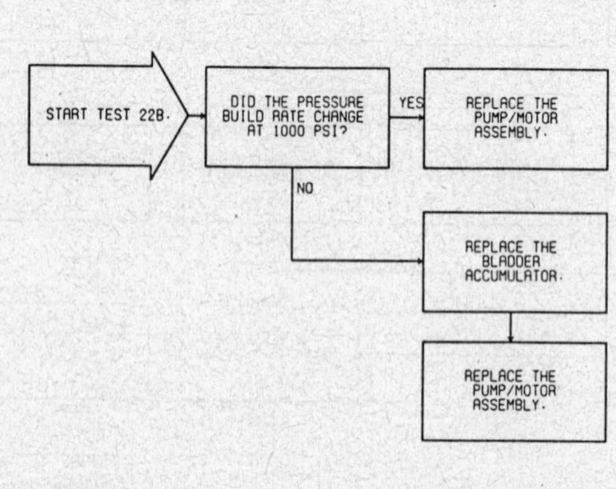

**Fig. 127 Test 22B—Hydraulic Pressure Performance Test**

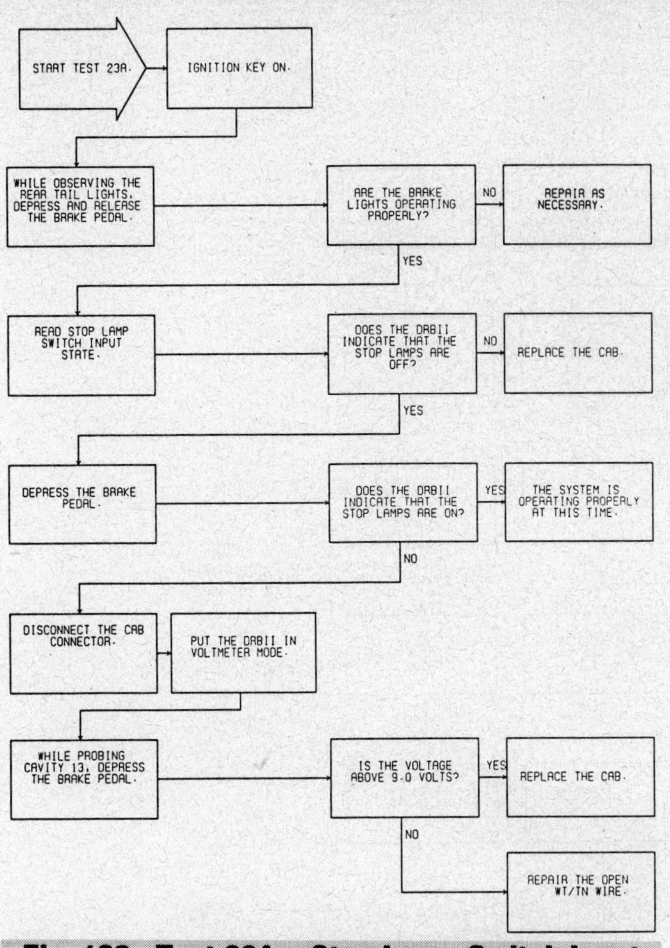


**Fig. 128 Test 23A—Stop Lamp Switch Input Test**

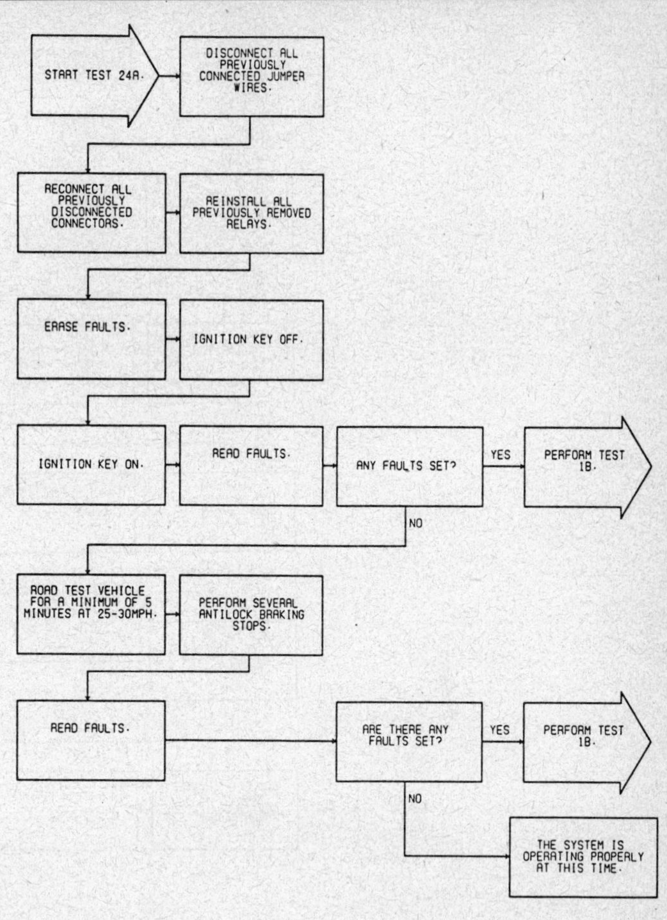


**Fig. 129 Test 24A—System Verification Test**

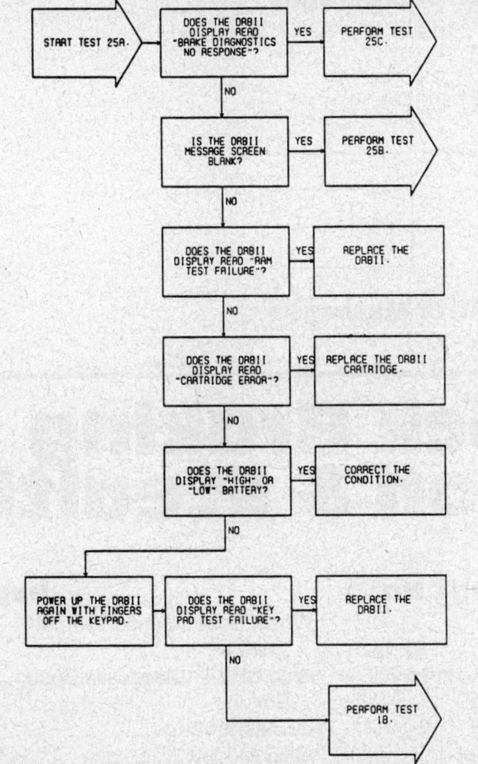


**Fig. 130 Test 25A—DRB II Error Messages**

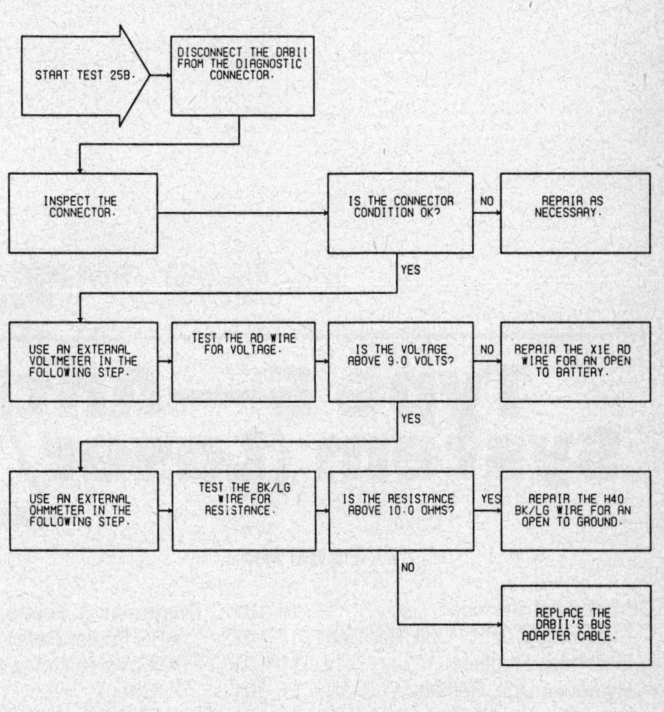


**Fig. 131 Test 25B—DRB II Error Messages**

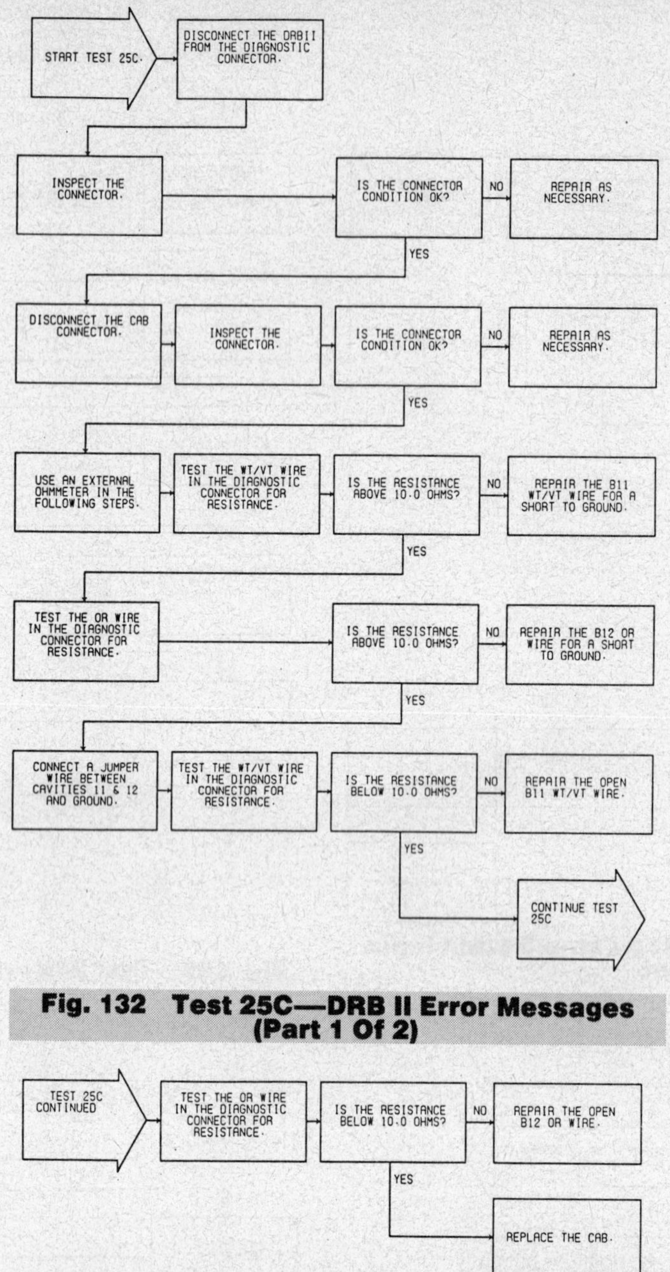


**Fig. 132 Test 25C—DRB II Error Messages (Part 1 Of 2)**

**Fig. 132 Test 25C—DRB II Error Messages (Part 2 Of 2)**

# Type 5—Anti-Lock Braking System (Laser/Talon & Stealth)

## INDEX

# DESCRIPTION

The Anti-Lock Braking System (ABS) prevents the wheels from locking up when braking, regardless of the surface conditions. This allows the car to stop in a shorter distance, and allows the driver to maintain directional control of the vehicle during heavy braking.

During normal braking conditions, the ABS operates like a conventional diagonally split, hydraulic power assist system. During heavy braking, however, each wheel's braking pressure is modulated according to its speed. To maintain vehicle stability, both rear wheels receive the same signal.

# TROUBLESHOOTING

## FWD MODELS

Refer to **Figs. 1 and 2** when troubleshooting the ABS system on FWD models.

## AWD MODELS

Refer to **Figs. 3 and 4** when troubleshooting the ABS system on AWD models.

# DIAGNOSIS & TESTING

## WITH DRB II(DIAGNOSTIC READOUT BOX II)

### FWD Models

1. Connect Diagnostic Readout Box (DRB II) per manufacturers instructions.
2. After DRB II has been connected, DRB II will now display fault code(s).
3. After fault code(s) have been displayed, refer to the following for ABS Chart number relating to fault code displayed:
   a. Fault codes 11–Right Front Wheel Speed Sensor Error, 12–Left Front Wheel Speed Sensor Error, 13–Right Rear Wheel Speed Sensor Error and 14–Left Rear Wheel Speed Sensor Error, refer to ABS Chart E1, **Fig. 5.**
   b. Fault code 15–Vehicle Velocity Error, refer to ABS Chart E2, **Figs. 6 and 7.**
   c. Fault code 22–Brake Switch Error, refer to ABS Chart E3, **Figs. 8 and 9.**
   d. Fault codes 41–Left Front Wheel Valve Error, 42–Right Front Wheel Valve Error and 43–Rear Wheel Valve Error, refer to ABS Chart E4, **Figs. 10 and 11.**
   e. Fault code 51–Valve Relay Error, refer to ABS Chart E5, **Figs. 12 and 13.**
   f. Fault code 52–Motor Relay or Motor Error, refer to ABS Chart E6, **Figs. 14 and 15.**
   g. Fault code 55–ECU Error, refer to appropriate ABS Chart A, B, C or D **Figs. 16 through 23.**

### AWD Models

1. Connect Diagnostic Readout Box (DRB II) per manufacturers instructions.
2. After DRB II has been connected, DRB II will now display fault code(s).
3. After fault code(s) have been displayed, refer to the following for ABS Chart number relating to fault code displayed:
   a. Fault codes 11–Right Front Wheel Speed Sensor Error, 12–Left Front Wheel Speed Sensor Error, 13–Right Rear Wheel Speed Sensor Error and 14–Left Rear Wheel Speed Sensor Error, refer to ABS Chart E1, **Fig. 24.**
   b. Fault code 15–Vehicle Velocity Error, refer to ABS Chart E2, **Figs. 25 and 26.**
   c. Fault code 21–G Sensor Error, refer to ABS Chart E3, **Figs. 27 and 28.**
   d. Fault code 22–Brake Switch Error, refer to ABS Chart E4, **Figs. 29 and 30.**
   e. Fault codes 41–Left Front/Right Rear Wheel Valve Error and 42–Right Front/Left Rear Wheel Valve Error, refer to ABS Chart E5, **Figs. 31 and 32.**
   f. Fault code 43–Valve Drift Error, refer to ABS Chart E5, **Figs. 31 and 32.**
   g. Fault code 51–Valve Relay Error, refer to ABS Chart E6, **Figs. 33 and 34.**
   h. Fault code 52–Motor Relay or Motor Error, refer to ABS Chart E7, **Figs. 35 and 36.**
   i. Fault code 55–ECU Error, refer to appropriate ABS Chart A, B, C or D **Figs. 37 through 44.**

## LESS DRB II(DIAGNOSTIC READOUT BOX II)

### FWD Models

Refer to **Figs. 5 through 23** when diagnosing the ABS system on FWD models.

### AWD Models

Refer to **Figs. 24 through 44** when diagnosing the ABS system on AWD models.

## WHEEL SPEED SENSOR OUTPUT VOLTAGE

### Laser & Talon

1. Raise and support vehicle, then release parking brake.
2. Disconnect Electronic Control Unit (ECU) electrical connector, then measure speed sensor output voltage at vehicle side harness connector.
3. Put shift lever in 1st position on models with manual transmission or L position on models with automatic transmission and proceed as follows:
   a. Rotate wheels and observe wave shape for each wheel and compare to **Fig. 45.**
   b. If output voltage is to low or there is no voltage output, check each wheel speed sensor. On FWD vehicles, check sensor gap.
   c. If there is variation in wave shape, check axle hub.
   d. If there is noise in wave shape or distortion, check for a broken or disconnected speed sensor wire, faulty wheel speed sensor, or missing teeth.

### Stealth

1. Raise and support vehicle, then release parking brake.
2. Disconnect Electronic Control Unit (ECU) electrical connector, then measure speed sensor output voltage with adapter harness MB991356 or equivalent connected to harness side connector. **Never insert a probe into connector as it may result in poor contact later. Do not connect connector marked "" except when recording wave form on a driving test. If necessary, connect connector to ECU.**
3. Manually turn wheel to be measured by 1/2-1 turn per second, then measure output voltage with a circuit tester or oscilloscope, **Figs. 46 and 47.**
4. Output voltage when measured with a circuit tester should be 70 milivolts (mV) or more.
5. Output voltage when measured with a oscilloscope (maximum voltage) should be 100 mV or more.
6. Probable causes of low output voltage are: speed sensor pole piece to rotor clearance to great, or faulty speed sensor.
7. **On AWD models,** in order to observe output state of wheel speed sensors, shift into low gear and drive wheels.
8. **On FWD models,** in order to observe output state of wheel speed sensors on front wheels, shift into low gear and drive wheels. On rear wheels turn manually at a constant speed.
9. **On all models,** observe output voltage wave form of each wheel speed sensor with an oscilloscope, output voltage is low when wheel speed is low and increases as wheel speed increases.
10. Refer to chart in **Fig. 48** to diagnose waveform measurement.

## ABS POWER RELAY CHECK

### Laser & Talon

1. Remove ABS power relay from ABS control unit bracket.
2. Connect terminal 2 of the power relay to battery voltage, then check continuity between terminals as shown in **Figs. 49 and 50** with terminal 4 grounded.
3. If continuity is not as specified, replace power relay.

### Stealth

1. Remove relay box cover in engine compartment, then the power relay.
2. Apply battery voltage to terminal 1 and check for continuity between ter-

Does the ABS warning light illuminate as described below up to the time the engine starts?
(1) When the ignition key is turned to the "ON" position, the ABS warning light illuminates for approximately 1 second due to the ABS ECU (as a self check of the valve relays is performed), then it blinks twice and goes out and stays out.
(2) With the ignition key in the "START" position, power to the ABS ECU is interrupted and the ABS warning light remains lit because the valve relay is OFF.
(3) When the ignition key is turned from the "START" position to the "ON" position, the ABS warning light illuminates for approximately 1 second (during this time a recheck of the valve relays is performed), then it blinks twice and then goes out and stays out.

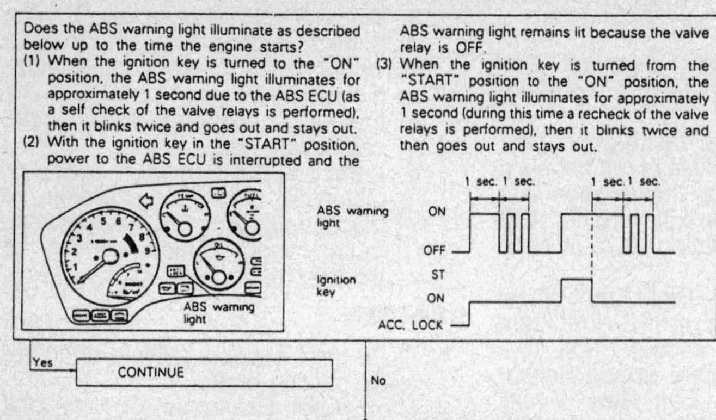


Yes → CONTINUE

No ↓

| No. | Trouble condition | Major causes | Remedy |
|---|---|---|---|
| 1 | ABS warning light does not light up at all. | • ABS warning light bulb is burnt out. • Open in ABS warning light electrical circuit (check for blown fuse) | Check, using flow chart A |
| 2 | When the ignition key is turned to the "ON" position, it remains lighted. | • Fail safe is functioning due to ECU self diagnosis • Short in ECU warning light drive circuit • Malfunction of ECU | Check, using flow chart B |
| 3 | Does not illuminate when ignition key is in "START" position. | • Malfunction of valve relay • Break in harness between ABS warning light and HU • Break in harness between HU and body ground | Check, using flow chart C |

**Fig. 1 Anti-Lock brake system troubleshooting (Part 1 of 2). Laser & Talon FWD models**

Does the ABS warning light illuminate as described below up to the time the engine starts?
(1) When the ignition key is turned to the "ON" position, the ABS ECU causes the ABS warning light to flash twice in about one second (during which the valve relay self check is made) and then causes it to go out.
(2) With the ignition key in the "START" position, power to the ABS ECU is interrupted and the ABS warning light remains lit because the valve relay is OFF.
(3) When the ignition key is returned from the "START" position to "ON" position, the ABS warning light flashes twice in about a second (during which the valve relay self check is made again) and then goes out.

Yes → CONTINUE

No ↓

| No. | Trouble condition | Major causes | Remedy |
|---|---|---|---|
| 1 | ABS warning light does not light up at all. | • ABS warning light bulb is burnt out. • Open in ABS warning light electrical circuit (check for blown fuse) | Check, using flow chart A |
| 2 | When the ignition key is turned to the "ON" position, it remains lighted. | • Fail safe is functioning due to ECU self diagnosis. • Short in ECU warning light drive circuit • Malfunction of ECU | Check, using flow chart B |
| 3 | Does not illuminate when ignition key is in "START" position. | • Malfunction of valve relay • Break in harness between ABS warning light and HU • Break in harness between HU and body ground | Check, using flow chart C |

**Fig. 2 Anti-Lock brake system troubleshooting (Part 1 of 2). Stealth FWD models**

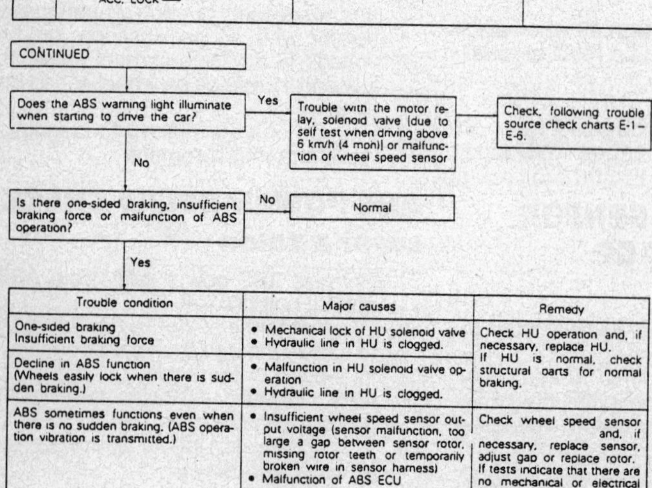

| No. | Trouble condition | Major causes | Remedy |
|---|---|---|---|
| 4 | After the ignition key is turned to the "ON" position, it blinks once and then illuminates when it is turned to the "START" position. When the key is returned to the "ON" position, the light blinks again. (Blinking with the ignition key in the "ON" position is synchronized with operation noise of the valve relay.) | • Break in harness for ECU warning light drive circuit • Malfunction of ECU | Check, using flow chart D |

CONTINUED

Does the ABS warning light illuminate when starting to drive the car?
- Yes → Trouble with the motor relay, solenoid valve (due to self test when driving above 6 km/h (4 mph)) or malfunction of wheel speed sensor → Check, following trouble source check charts E-1 – E-6.
- No ↓

Is there one-sided braking, insufficient braking force or malfunction of ABS operation?
- No → Normal
- Yes ↓

| Trouble condition | Major causes | Remedy |
|---|---|---|
| One-sided braking Insufficient braking force | • Mechanical lock of HU solenoid valve • Hydraulic line in HU is clogged. | Check HU operation and, if necessary, replace HU. If HU is normal, check structural parts for normal braking. |
| Decline in ABS function (Wheels easily lock when there is sudden braking.) | • Malfunction in HU solenoid valve operation • Hydraulic line in HU is clogged. | |
| ABS sometimes functions even when there is no sudden braking. (ABS operation vibration is transmitted.) | • Insufficient wheel speed sensor output voltage (sensor malfunction, too large a gap between sensor rotor, missing rotor teeth or temporarily broken wire in sensor harness) • Malfunction of ABS ECU | Check wheel speed sensor and, if necessary, replace sensor, adjust gap or replace rotor. If tests indicate that there are no mechanical or electrical failures, replace the ECU. |

**Fig. 1 Anti-Lock brake system troubleshooting (Part 2 of 2). Laser & Talon FWD models**

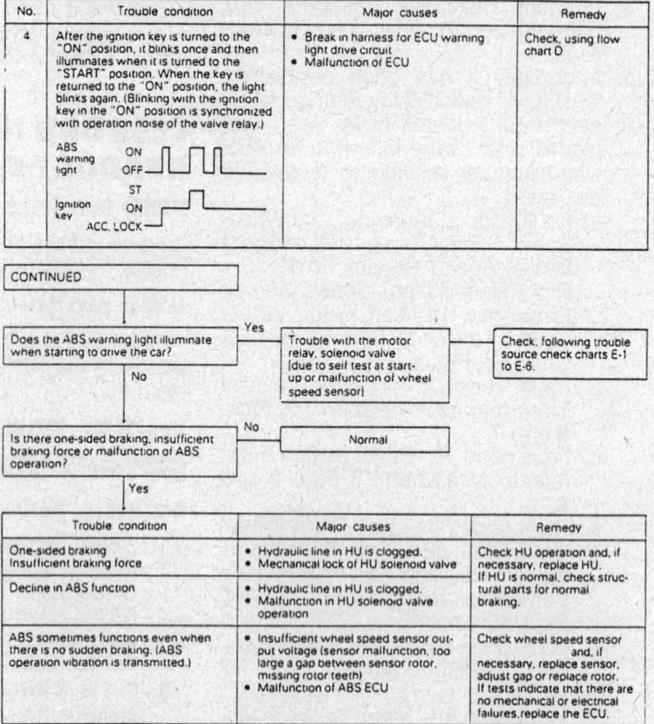

| No. | Trouble condition | Major causes | Remedy |
|---|---|---|---|
| 4 | After the ignition key is turned to the "ON" position, it blinks once and then illuminates when it is turned to the "START" position. When the key is returned to the "ON" position, the light blinks again. (Blinking with the ignition key in the "ON" position is synchronized with operation noise of the valve relay.) | • Break in harness for ECU warning light drive circuit • Malfunction of ECU | Check, using flow chart D |

CONTINUED

Does the ABS warning light illuminate when starting to drive the car?
- Yes → Trouble with the motor relay, solenoid valve (due to self test at start-up or malfunction of wheel speed sensor) → Check, following trouble source check charts E-1 to E-6.
- No ↓

Is there one-sided braking, insufficient braking force or malfunction of ABS operation?
- No → Normal
- Yes ↓

| Trouble condition | Major causes | Remedy |
|---|---|---|
| One-sided braking Insufficient braking force | • Hydraulic line in HU is clogged. • Mechanical lock of HU solenoid valve | Check HU operation and, if necessary, replace HU. If HU is normal, check structural parts for normal braking. |
| Decline in ABS function | • Hydraulic line in HU is clogged. • Malfunction in HU solenoid valve operation | |
| ABS sometimes functions even when there is no sudden braking. (ABS operation vibration is transmitted.) | • Insufficient wheel speed sensor output voltage (sensor malfunction, too large a gap between sensor rotor, missing rotor teeth) • Malfunction of ABS ECU | Check wheel speed sensor and, if necessary, replace sensor, adjust gap or replace rotor. If tests indicate that there are no mechanical or electrical failures, replace the ECU. |

**Fig. 2 Anti-Lock brake system troubleshooting (Part 2 of 2). Stealth FWD models**

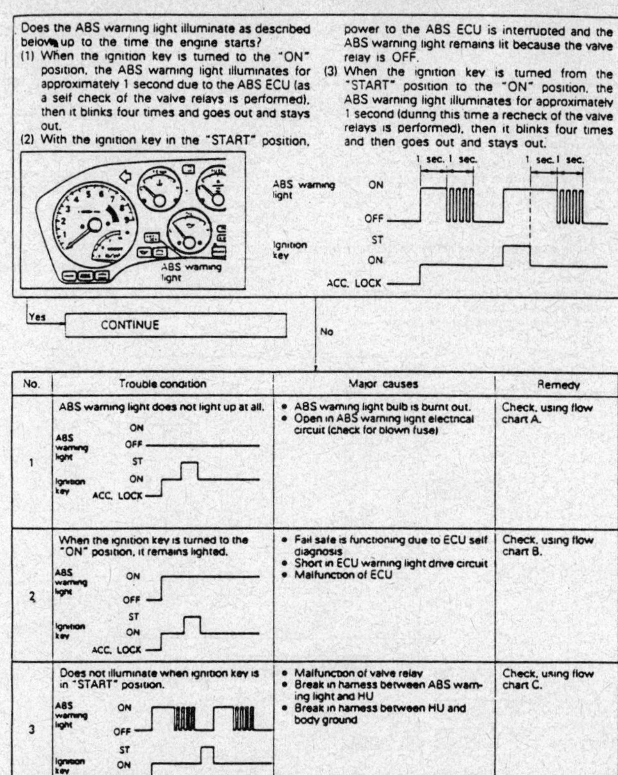

Does the ABS warning light illuminate as described below up to the time the engine starts?
(1) When the ignition key is turned to the "ON" position, the ABS warning light illuminates for approximately 1 second due to the ABS ECU (as a self check of the valve relays is performed), then it blinks four times and goes out and stays out.
(2) With the ignition key in the "START" position, power to the ABS ECU is interrupted and the ABS warning light remains lit because the valve relay is OFF.
(3) When the ignition key is turned from the "START" position to the "ON" position, the ABS warning light illuminates for approximately 1 second (during this time a recheck of the valve relays is performed), then it blinks four times and then goes out and stays out.



Yes → CONTINUE

No ↓

| No. | Trouble condition | Major causes | Remedy |
|---|---|---|---|
| 1 | ABS warning light does not light up at all. | • ABS warning light bulb is burnt out.<br>• Open in ABS warning light electrical circuit (check for blown fuse) | Check, using flow chart A. |
| 2 | When the ignition key is turned to the "ON" position, it remains lighted. | • Fail safe is functioning due to ECU self diagnosis<br>• Short in ECU warning light drive circuit<br>• Malfunction of ECU | Check, using flow chart B. |
| 3 | Does not illuminate when ignition key is in "START" position. | • Malfunction of valve relay<br>• Break in harness between ABS warning light and HU<br>• Break in harness between HU and body ground | Check, using flow chart C. |

Fig. 3 Anti-Lock brake system troubleshooting (Part 1 of 2). Laser & Talon AWD models

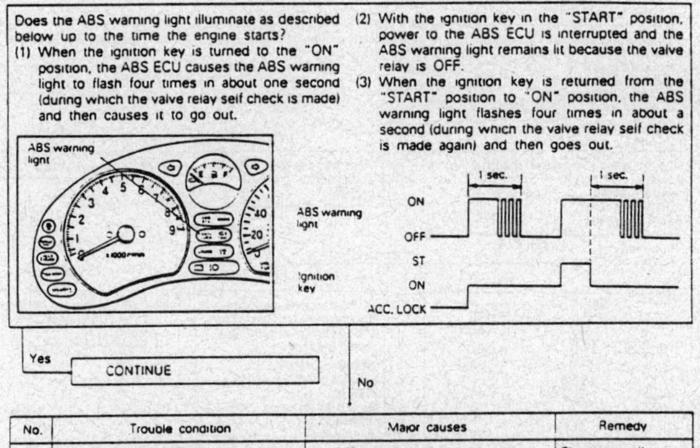

Does the ABS warning light illuminate as described below up to the time the engine starts?
(1) When the ignition key is turned to the "ON" position, the ABS ECU causes the ABS warning light to flash four times in about one second (during which the valve relay self check is made) and then causes it to go out.
(2) With the ignition key in the "START" position, power to the ABS ECU is interrupted and the ABS warning light remains lit because the valve relay is OFF.
(3) When the ignition key is returned from the "START" position to "ON" position, the ABS warning light flashes four times in about a second (during which the valve relay self check is made again) and then goes out.



Yes → CONTINUE

No ↓

| No. | Trouble condition | Major causes | Remedy |
|---|---|---|---|
| 1 | ABS warning light does not light up at all. | • ABS warning light bulb is burnt out.<br>• Open in ABS warning light electrical circuit (check for blown fuse) | Check, using flow chart A |
| 2 | When the ignition key is turned to the "ON" position, it remains lighted. | • Fail safe is functioning due to ECU self diagnosis.<br>• Short in ECU warning light drive circuit<br>• Malfunction of ECU | Check, using flow chart B |
| 3 | Does not illuminate when ignition key is in "START" position. | • Malfunction of valve relay<br>• Break in harness between ABS warning light and HU<br>• Break in harness between HU and body ground | Check, using flow chart C |

Fig. 4 Anti-Lock brake system troubleshooting (Part 1 of 2). Stealth AWD models

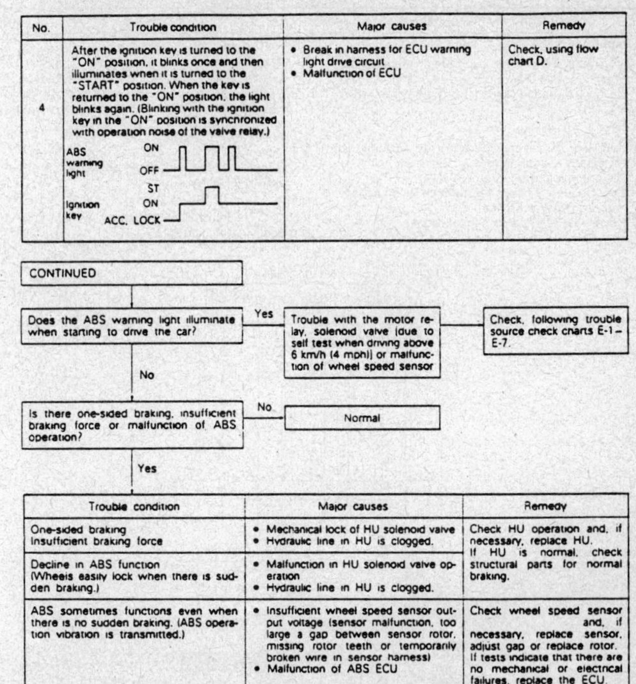

| No. | Trouble condition | Major causes | Remedy |
|---|---|---|---|
| 4 | After the ignition key is turned to the "ON" position, it blinks once and then illuminates when it is turned to the "START" position. When the key is returned to the "ON" position, the light blinks again. (Blinking with the ignition key in the "ON" position is synchronized with operation noise of the valve relay.) | • Break in harness for ECU warning light drive circuit<br>• Malfunction of ECU | Check, using flow chart D. |

CONTINUED

Does the ABS warning light illuminate when starting to drive the car? — Yes → Trouble with the motor relay, solenoid valve (due to self test when driving above 6 km/h (4 mph)) or malfunction of wheel speed sensor → Check, following trouble source check charts E-1 – E-7.

No ↓

Is there one-sided braking, insufficient braking force or malfunction of ABS operation? — No → Normal

Yes ↓

| Trouble condition | Major causes | Remedy |
|---|---|---|
| One-sided braking<br>Insufficient braking force | • Mechanical lock of HU solenoid valve<br>• Hydraulic line in HU is clogged. | Check HU operation and, if necessary, replace HU. If HU is normal, check structural parts for normal braking. |
| Decline in ABS function (Wheels easily lock when there is sudden braking.) | • Malfunction in HU solenoid valve operation<br>• Hydraulic line in HU is clogged. | |
| ABS sometimes functions even when there is no sudden braking. (ABS operation vibration is transmitted.) | • Insufficient wheel speed sensor output voltage (sensor malfunction, too large a gap between sensor rotor, missing rotor teeth or temporarily broken wire in sensor harness)<br>• Malfunction of ABS ECU | Check wheel speed sensor and, if necessary, replace sensor, adjust gap or replace rotor. If tests indicate that there are no mechanical or electrical failures, replace the ECU. |

Fig. 3 Anti-Lock brake system troubleshooting (Part 2 of 2). Laser & Talon AWD models

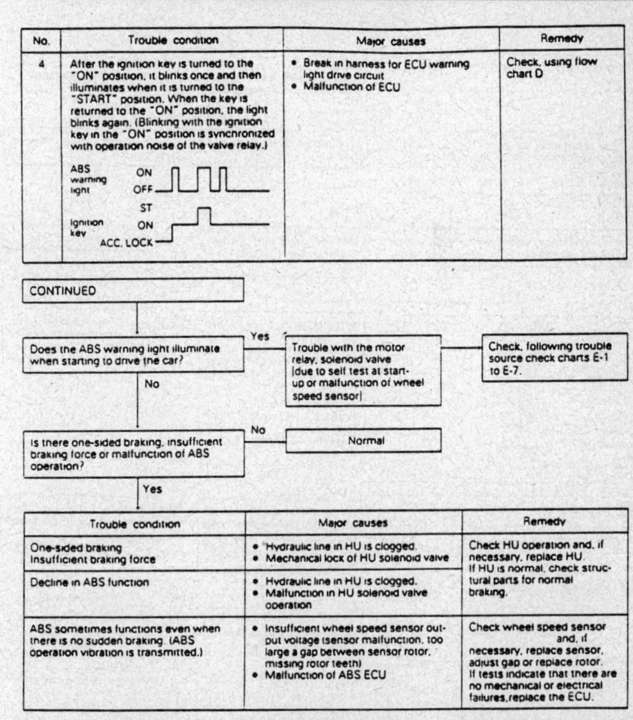

| No. | Trouble condition | Major causes | Remedy |
|---|---|---|---|
| 4 | After the ignition key is turned to the "ON" position, it blinks once and then illuminates when it is turned to the "START" position. When the key is returned to the "ON" position, the light blinks again. (Blinking with the ignition key in the "ON" position is synchronized with operation noise of the valve relay.) | • Break in harness for ECU warning light drive circuit<br>• Malfunction of ECU | Check, using flow chart D |

CONTINUED

Does the ABS warning light illuminate when starting to drive the car? — Yes → Trouble with the motor relay, solenoid valve (due to self test at start-up or malfunction of wheel speed sensor) → Check, following trouble source check charts E-1 to E-7.

No ↓

Is there one-sided braking, insufficient braking force or malfunction of ABS operation? — No → Normal

Yes ↓

| Trouble condition | Major causes | Remedy |
|---|---|---|
| One-sided braking<br>Insufficient braking force | • Hydraulic line in HU is clogged.<br>• Mechanical lock of HU solenoid valve | Check HU operation and, if necessary, replace HU. If HU is normal, check structural parts for normal braking. |
| Decline in ABS function | • Hydraulic line in HU is clogged.<br>• Malfunction in HU solenoid valve operation | |
| ABS sometimes functions even when there is no sudden braking. (ABS operation vibration is transmitted.) | • Insufficient wheel speed sensor output voltage (sensor malfunction, too large a gap between sensor rotor, missing rotor teeth)<br>• Malfunction of ABS ECU | Check wheel speed sensor and, if necessary, replace sensor, adjust gap or replace rotor. If tests indicate that there are no mechanical or electrical failures, replace the ECU. |

Fig. 4 Anti-Lock brake system troubleshooting (Part 2 of 2). Stealth AWD models

| E-1 | Input abnormality of wheel speed sensor |
|---|---|

**[Explanation]**
The ABS ECU detects breaks in the wheel speed sensor wire. The warning light lights up if the wheel speed sensor signal is not input (or short circuited) or if its output is low when starting to drive or while driving.

**[Hint]**
In addition to a broken wire/short circuit in the wheel speed sensor, also check whether the sensor gap is too large, rotor teeth are missing, sensor harness wire is temporarily broken, or sensor harness and body connector are not properly inserted.

Fig. 5 ABS Chart E1—Input abnormality of wheel speed sensor. FWD models

| E-2 | Output abnormality of wheel speed sensor |
|---|---|

**[Explanation]**

The warning light lights up when there is an abnormality (other than broken wire or short circuit) in the wheel speed sensor output signal while driving.

**[Hint]**

The following can be considered as the cause of the wheel speed sensor output abnormality.

- Distortion of rotor, teeth missing
- Low frequency noise interference when sensor harness wire is broken
- Noise interference in sensor signal
- When the sensor output signal is below the standard value or when amplitude modulation is over the standard value, using an oscilloscope to measure the wave shape of the wheel speed sensor output signal is very effective.
- Loose wheel bearing
- Temporarily broken wire in sensor harness
- Sensor harness and body connector are not properly inserted.

NOTE
If contact is poor, check the sensor cable by bending and lightly stretching it.

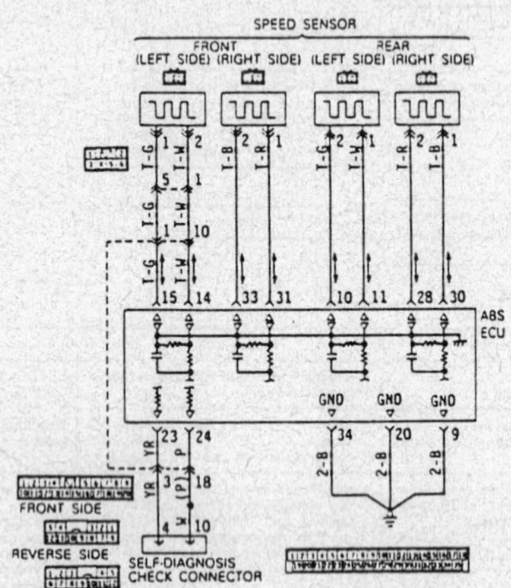


**Fig. 6 ABS Chart E-2—Output abnormality of wheel speed sensor (Part 1 of 2). Laser & Talon FWD models**

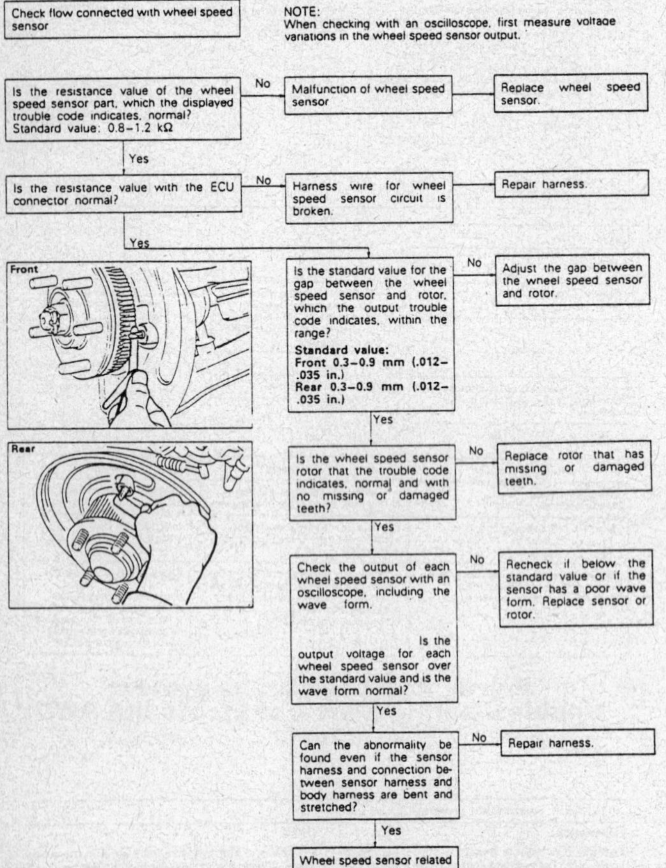


**Fig. 6 ABS Chart E-2—Output abnormality of wheel speed sensor (Part 2 of 2). Laser & Talon FWD models**

| E-2 | Output abnormality of wheel speed sensor |
|---|---|

**[Explanation]**

The warning light lights up when there is an abnormality (other than broken wire or short circuit) in any of the wheel speed sensor output signals while driving.

**[Hint]**

The following can be considered as the cause of the wheel speed sensor output abnormality.

- Distortion of rotor, teeth missing
- Low frequency noise interference when sensor harness wire is broken
- Noise interference in sensor signal
- The sensor output signal is below the standard value or amplitude modulation is over the standard value. Using an oscilloscope to measure the wave shape of the wheel speed sensor output signal is very effective.
- Broken sensor harness
- Poor connection of connector

NOTE
If contact is poor, check the sensor cable by bending and lightly stretching it.

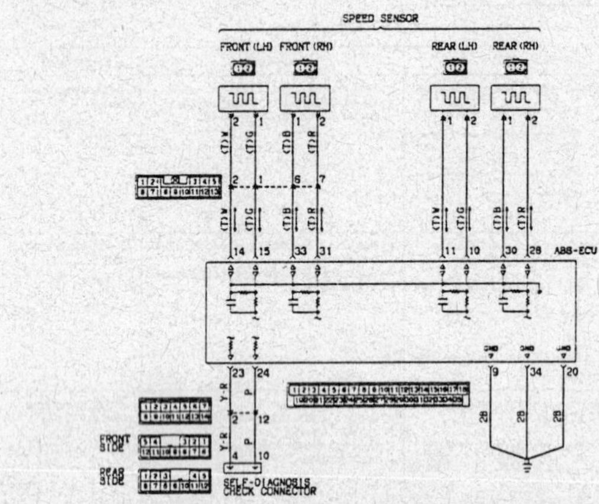


**Fig. 7 ABS Chart E-2—Output abnormality of wheel speed sensor (Part 1 of 2). Stealth FWD models**

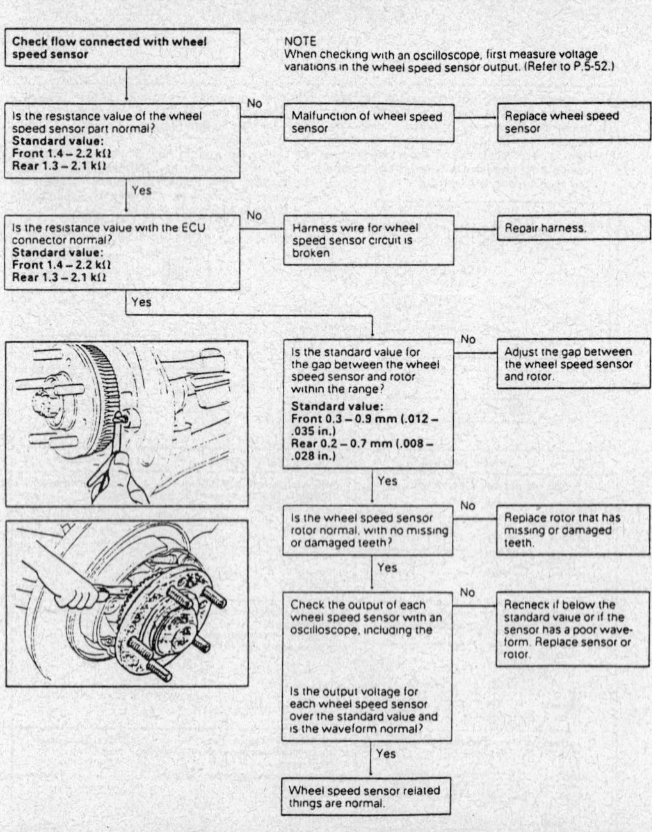


**Fig. 7 ABS Chart E-2—Output abnormality of wheel speed sensor (Part 2 of 2). Stealth FWD models**

| E-3 | Abnormality of stop light switch circuit |
|---|---|

**[Explanation]**

The ABS ECU turns on the warning light in the following cases.

- Stop light switch may remain on for more than 15 minutes without the ABS functions.
- The harness wire for the stop light switch may be open.

**[Hint]**

If the stop light operates normal, the ABS harness wire for the stop light switch input circuit to the ECU is broken or there is a malfunction in the ABS ECU.

Do the stop lights light up and go out normally? — No → Check the stop light related circuit and repair problem spots.

Yes ↓

Disconnect the ABS ECU connector and inspect at the harness side connector.

↓

When the brake pedal is pressed forcefully, does the voltage between connector terminal No. 29 and ground indicate battery voltage? — No → Harness wire between stop light switch and ABS ECU is broken. → Repair harness.

Yes ↓

Stop light switch circuit is normal.

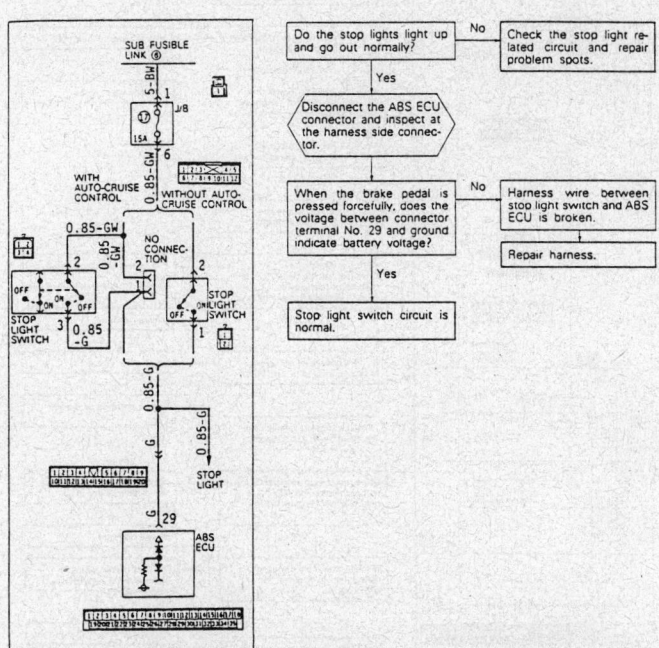

**Fig. 8 ABS Chart E-3—Abnormality of stop light switch circuit. Laser & Talon FWD models**

| E-3 | Abnormality of stop light switch circuit |
|---|---|

**[Explanation]**

The ABS ECU turns on the warning light in the following cases.

- Stop light switch may remain on for more than 15 minutes without ABS operation.
- The harness wire for the stop light switch may be open.

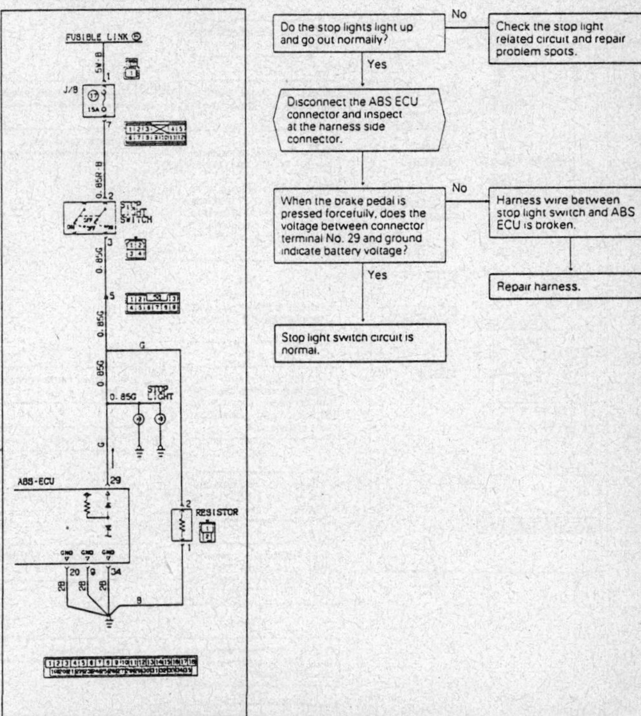


**Fig. 9 ABS Chart E-3—Abnormality of stop light switch circuit. Stealth FWD models**

| E-4 | Abnormality of solenoid valve drive circuit |
|---|---|

**[Explanation]**

The ABS ECU normally monitors the solenoid valve drive circuit.

If no current flows in the solenoid even if the ECU turns the solenoid ON or if it continues to flow even when turned OFF, the ECU determines the solenoid coil wire is broken/short circuited or the harness is broken short circuited and then warning light lights up.

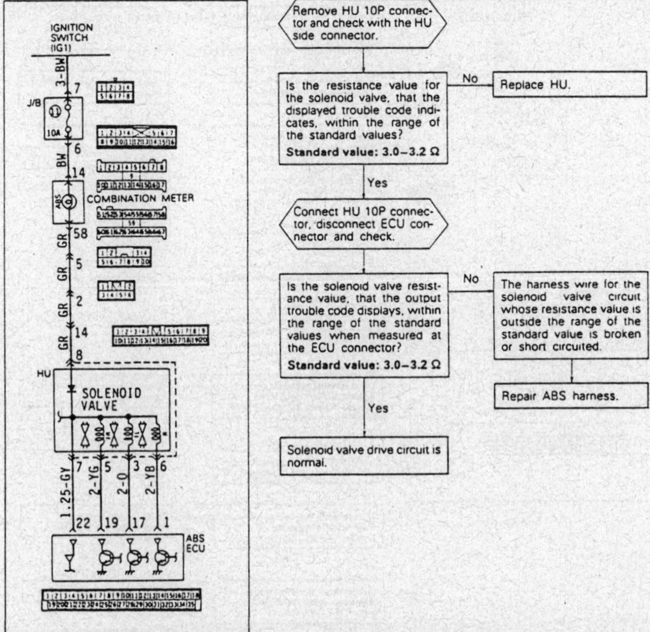


**Fig. 10 ABS Chart E-4—Abnormality of solenoid valve drive circuit. Laser & Talon FWD models**

| E-4 | Abnormality of solenoid valve drive circuit |
|---|---|

**[Explanation]**

The ABS ECU normally monitors the solenoid valve drive circuit.

If no current flows in the solenoid even if the ECU turns the solenoid ON or if it continues to flow even when turned OFF, the ECU determines the solenoid coil wire is broken/short-circuited or the harness is broken/short-circuited, and then warning light lights up.

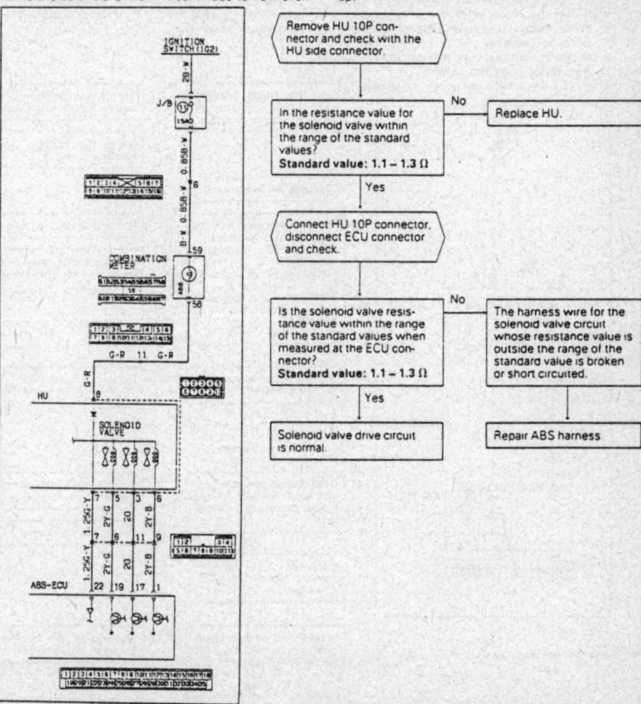


**Fig. 11 ABS Chart E-4—Abnormality of solenoid valve drive circuit. Stealth FWD models**

| E-5 | Abnormality of valve relay drive circuit |
|---|---|

**[Explanation]**

When the ignition switch is turned ON, the ABS ECU switches the valve relay OFF and ON for an initial check, compares the voltage of the signal to the valve relay and valve power monitor line voltage to check whether the valve relay operation is normal. In addition, normally it monitors whether or not there is power in the valve power monitor line since the valve relay is normally ON. Then, if the supply of power to the valve power monitor line is interrupted, the warning light illuminates.

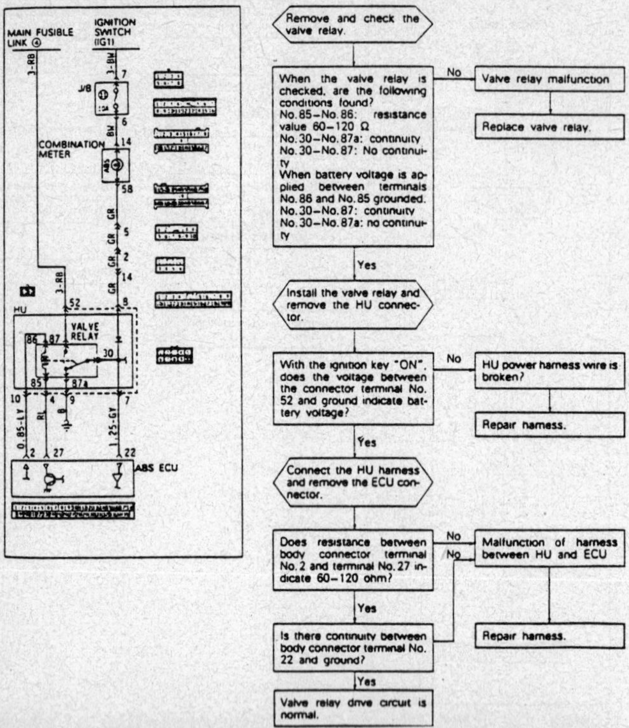


**Fig. 12 ABS Chart E-5—Abnormality of valve relay drive circuit. Laser & Talon FWD models**

| E-5 | Abnormality of valve relay drive circuit |
|---|---|

**[Explanation]**

When the ignition switch is turned ON, the ABS ECU switches the valve relay OFF and ON for an initial check, compares the voltage of the signal to the valve relay and valve power monitor line voltage to check whether the valve relay operation is normal. In addition, normally it monitors whether or not there is power in the valve power monitor line since the valve relay is normally ON. Then, if the supply of power to the valve power monitor line is interrupted, the warning light illuminates.

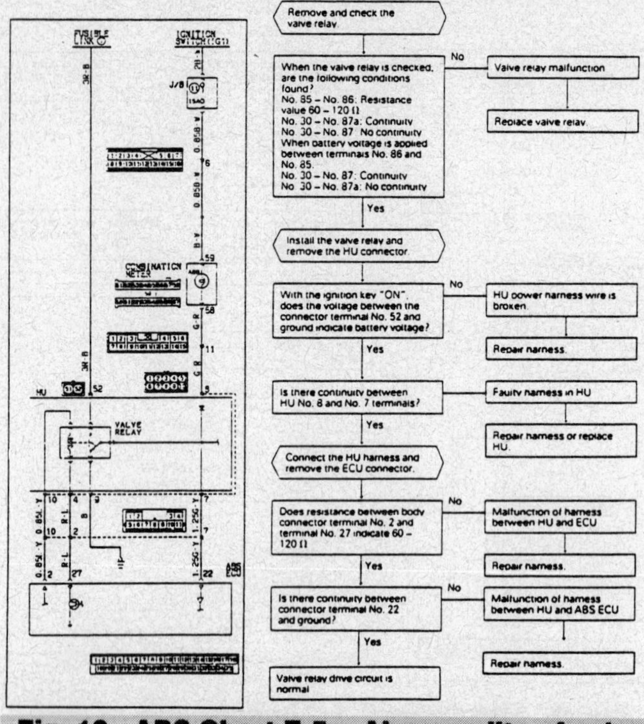


**Fig. 13 ABS Chart E-5—Abnormality of valve relay drive circuit. Stealth FWD models**

| E-6 | Abnormality of motor drive circuit |
|---|---|

**[Explanation]**

The ABS ECU illuminates the warning light for the motor relay and motor in the following cases.

- When the motor relay does not function
- When there is trouble with the motor itself and it does not revolve
- When the motor ground line is disconnected and the motor does not revolve
- When the motor continues to revolve

**[Hint]**

If there is motor operation noise when wheel speed exceeds 6km/h (4mph) when starting up after the engine is started, there is a broken or short circuited motor monitor wire.

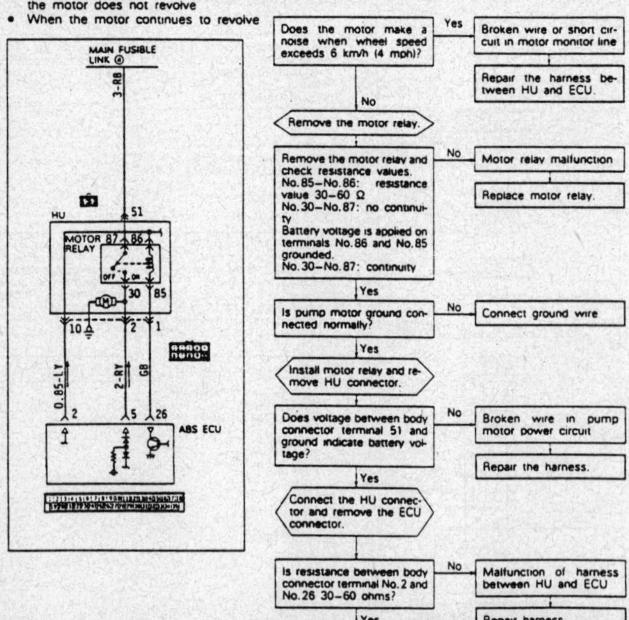


**Fig. 14 ABS Chart E-6—Abnormality of motor drive circuit. Laser & Talon FWD models**

| E-6 | Abnormality of motor drive circuit |
|---|---|

**[Explanation]**

The ABS ECU illuminates the warning light for the motor relay and motor in the following cases.

- When the motor relay does not function
- When there is trouble with the motor itself and it does not revolve
- When the motor ground line is disconnected and the motor does not revolve
- When the motor continues to revolve

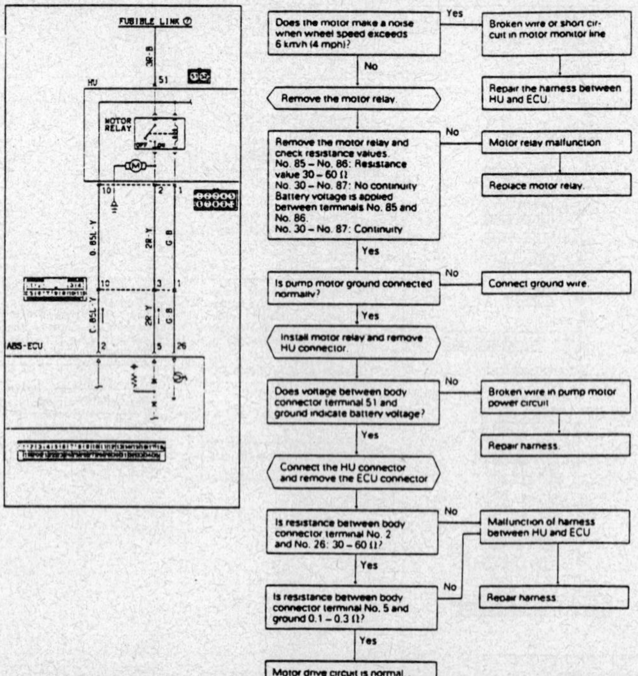


**Fig. 15 ABS Chart E-6—Abnormality of motor drive circuit. Stealth FWD models**

| A | ABS warning light does not light at all. |
|---|---|

**[Explanation]**

When it does not light up at all, there is a strong possibility that there is trouble with ABS warning light or with power to the light.

**[Hint]**

If other warning lights do not light up either, fuse is probably blown.

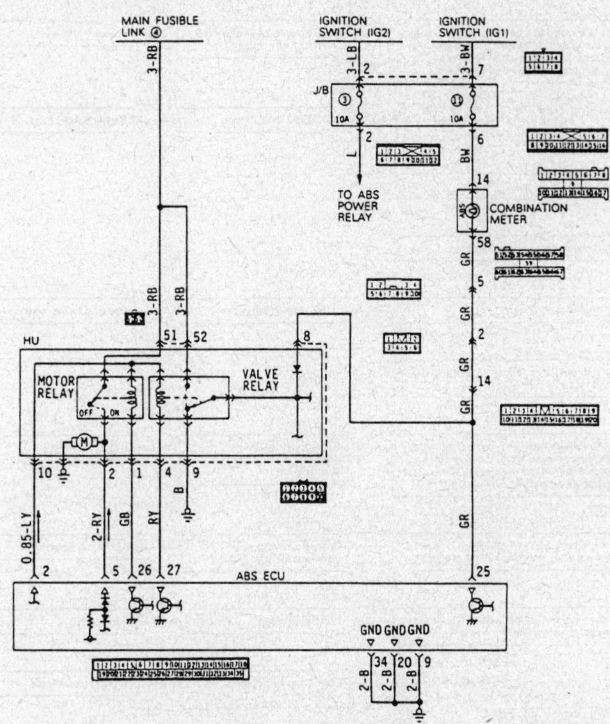


Fig. 16 ABS Chart A—ABS warning light does not light at all (Part 1 of 3). Laser & Talon FWD models

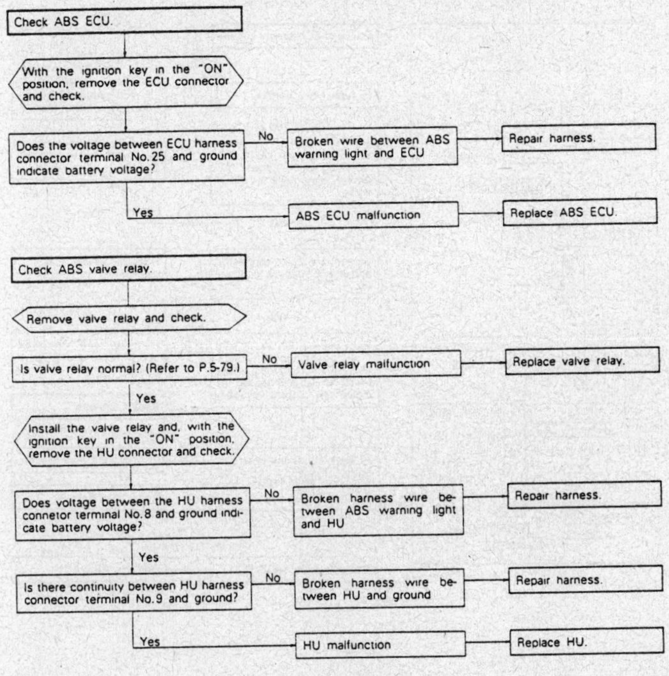


Fig. 16 ABS Chart A—ABS warning light does not light at all (Part 3 of 3). Laser & Talon FWD models

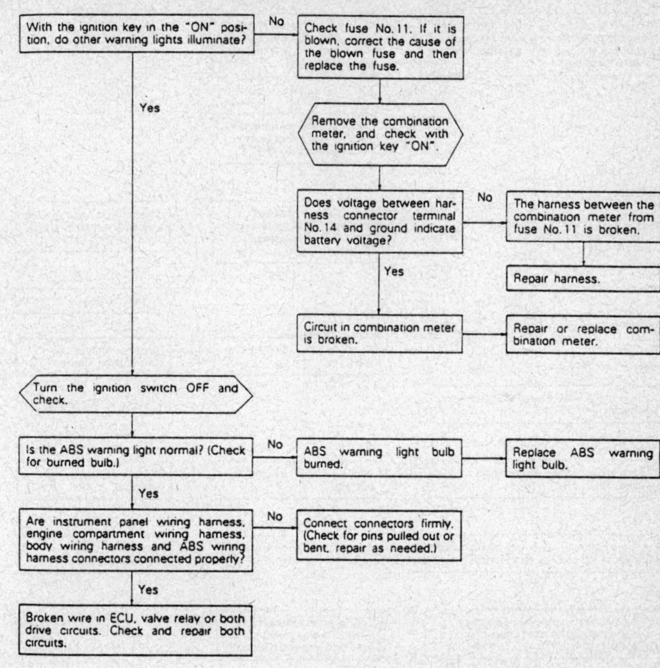


Fig. 16 ABS Chart A—ABS warning light does not light at all (Part 2 of 3). Laser & Talon FWD models

| A | ABS warning light does not light at all. |
|---|---|

**[Explanation]**

When it does not light up at all, there is a strong possibility that there is trouble with ABS warning light or with power to the light.

**[Hint]**

If other warning lights do not light up either, fuse is probably blown.

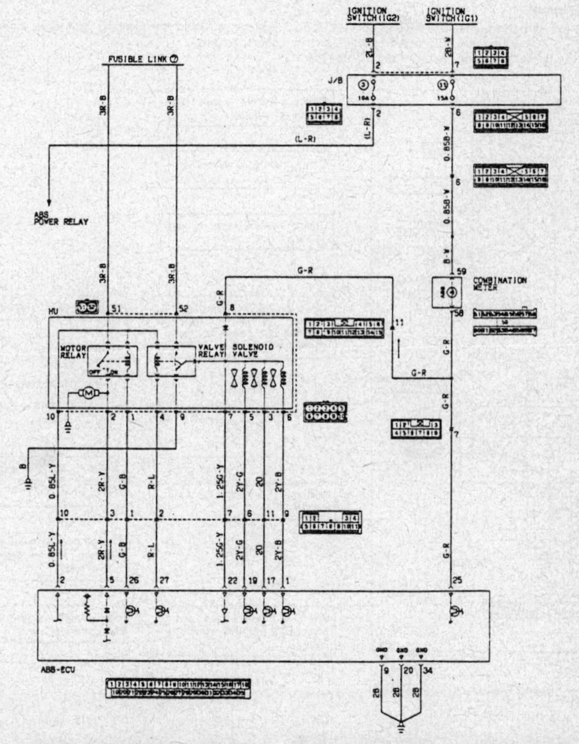


Fig. 17 ABS Chart A—ABS warning light does not light at all (Part 1 of 3). Stealth FWD models

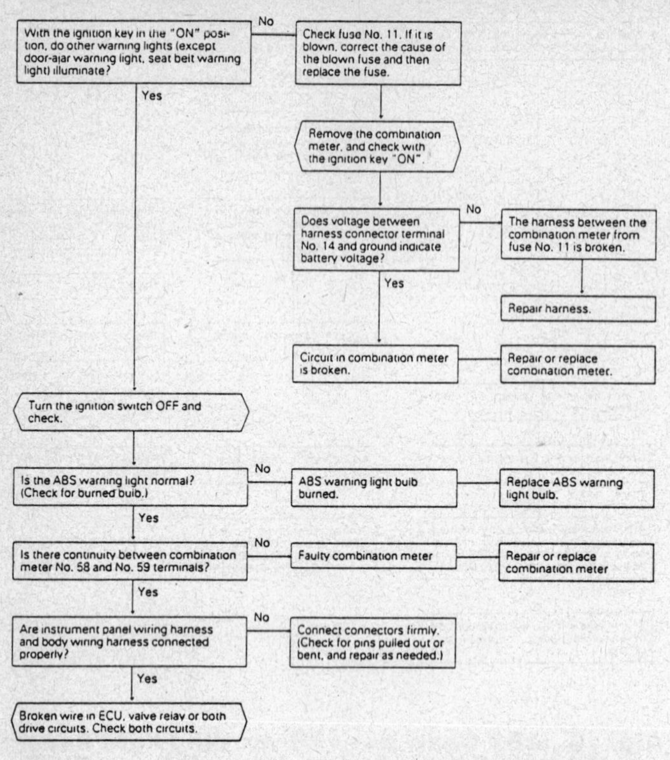


Fig. 17 ABS Chart A—ABS warning light does not light at all (Part 2 of 3). Stealth FWD models

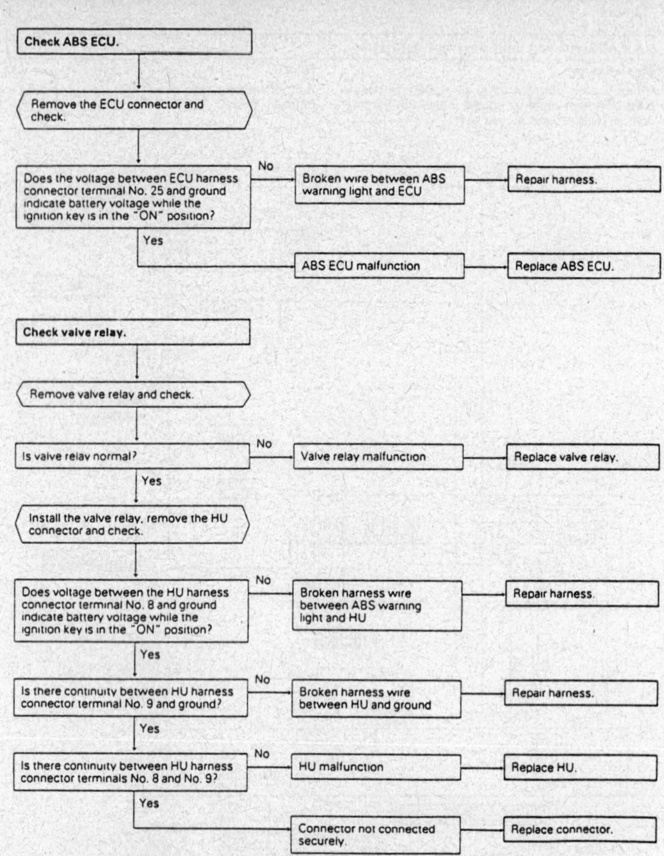


Fig. 17 ABS Chart A—ABS warning light does not light at all (Part 3 of 3). Stealth FWD models

| B | ABS warning light illuminated after the engine is started and remains on. |
|---|---|

**[Explanation]**

This is the symptom when the ABS ECU does not power up due to broken ECU power circuit, etc., when the fail safe function operates and isolates the system or when the warning light drive circuit is short circuited.

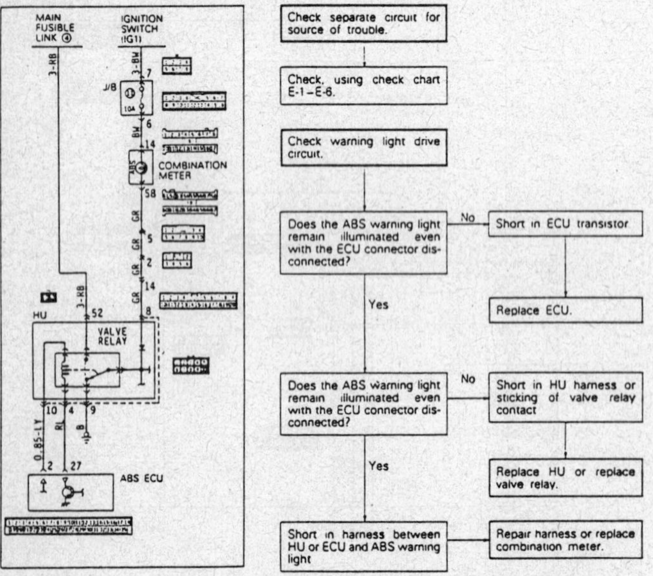


Fig. 18 ABS Chart B—ABS warning light illuminated after engine is started & remains on (Part 1 of 2). Laser & Talon FWD models

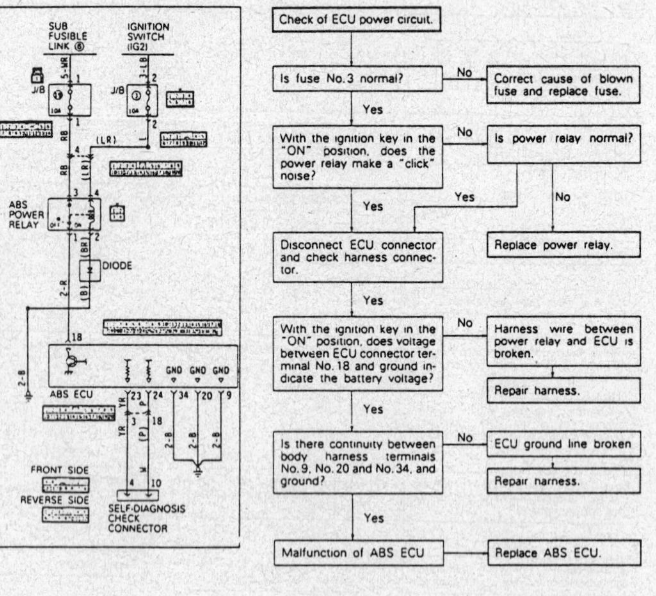


Fig. 18 ABS Chart B—ABS warning light illuminated after engine is started & remains on (Part 2 of 2). Laser & Talon FWD models

| B | ABS warning light stays on when the ignition key in the "ON" position. |
|---|---|

**[Explanation]**

This is the symptom when the ABS ECU does not power up due to broken ECU power circuit, etc., when the fail safe function operates and isolates the system or when the warning light drive circuit is short circuited.

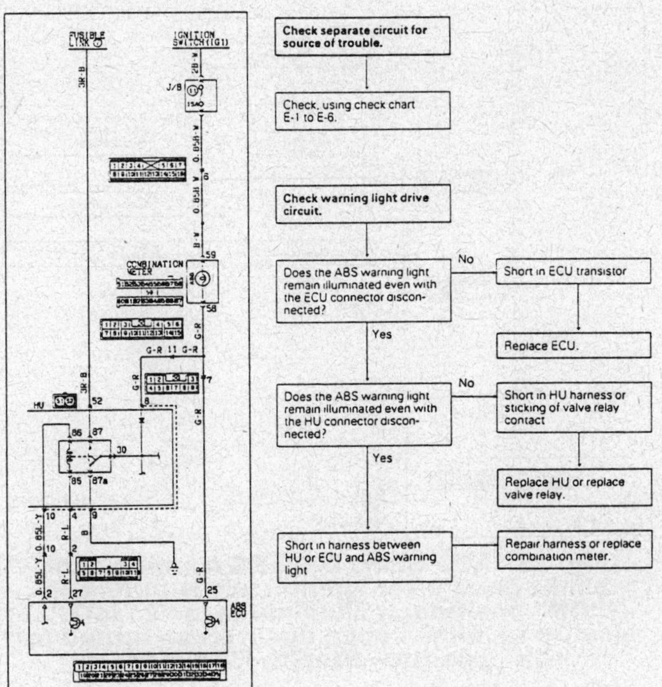


**Fig. 19 ABS Chart B—ABS warning light Stays on when ignition key is in "ON" position (Part 1 of 2). Stealth FWD models**

| C | ABS warning light does not illuminate when ignition key is in "START" position. |
|---|---|

**[Explanation]**

The ABS ECU uses the IG2 power source which is turned off in the "START" position. The ABS warning light uses the IG1 power source which is not turned off even in the "START" position. Consequently, in the "START" position, power is off and the ECU turns the valve relay OFF. If the warning light does not illuminate at this time, there is trouble in the warning light circuit on the valve relay side.

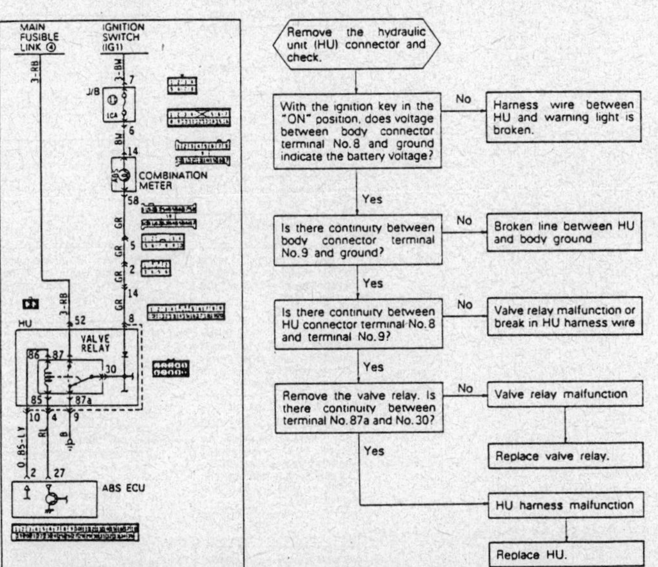


**Fig. 20 ABS Chart C—ABS warning light does not illuminate when ignition key is in "START" position. Laser & Talon FWD models**

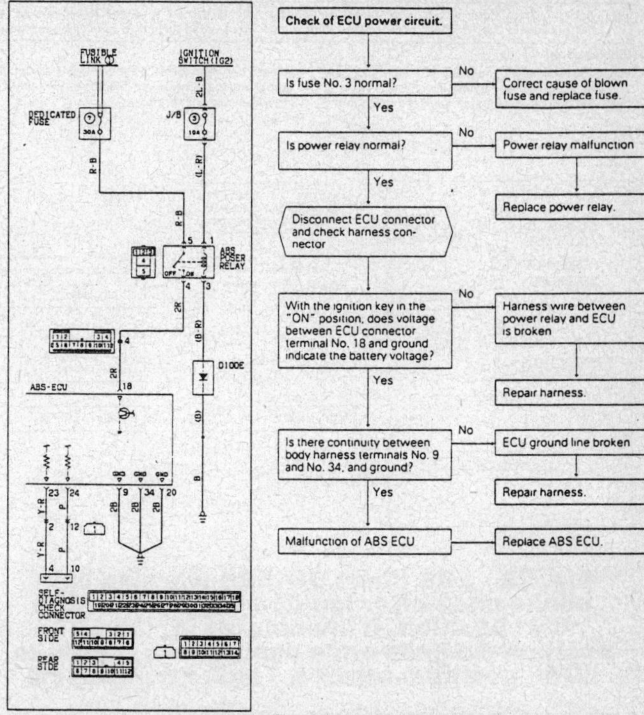


**Fig. 19 ABS Chart B—ABS warning light Stays on when ignition key is in "ON" position (Part 2 of 2). Stealth FWD models**

| C | ABS warning light does not illuminate when ignition key is in "START" position. |
|---|---|

**[Explanation]**

The ABS ECU uses the $IG_2$ power source which is turned off in the "START" position. The ABS warning light uses the $IG_1$ power source which is not turned off even in the "START" position. Consequently, in the "START" position, power is off and the ECU turns the valve relay OFF. If the warning light does not illuminate at this time, there is trouble in the warning light circuit on the valve relay side.

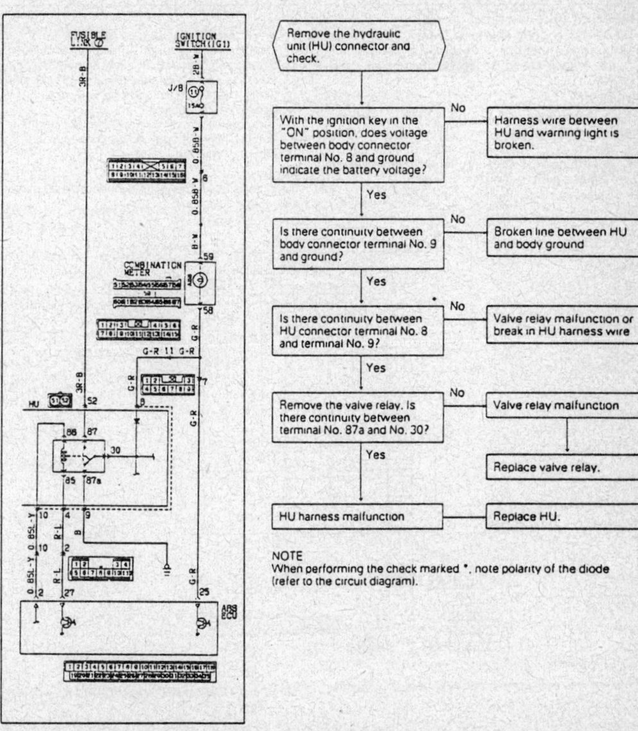


**Fig. 21 ABS Chart C—ABS warning light does not illuminate when ignition key is in "START" position. Stealth FWD models**

| D | ABS warning light blinks once after the ignition key is turned to the "ON" position. It illuminates in the "START" position and blinks once again when turned to the "ON" position. |
|---|---|

[Explanation]

When power flows, the ABS ECU turns on the warning light for approximately 1 sec. while it performs a valve relay test. If there is a break in the harness between the ECU and the warning light, the light illuminates only when the valve relay is off in the valve relay test, etc.

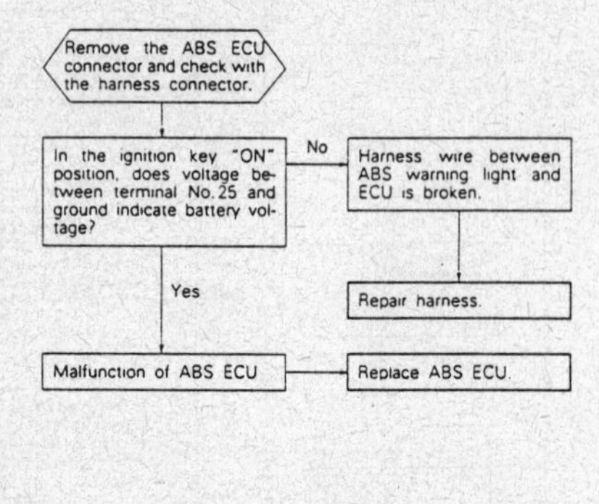


**Fig. 22 ABS Chart D—ABS warning light blinks once after ignition key is turned to "ON" position. It illuminates in "START" position & blinks once again when turned to "ON" position. Laser & Talon FWD models**



| D | ABS warning light blinks once after the ignition key is turned to the "ON" position. It illuminates in the "START" position and blinks once again when turned to the "ON" position. |
|---|---|

[Explanation]

When power flows, the ABS ECU turns on the warning light for approximately 1 sec. while it performs a valve relay test. If there is a break in the harness between the ECU and the warning light, the light illuminates only when the valve relay is off in the valve relay test, etc.



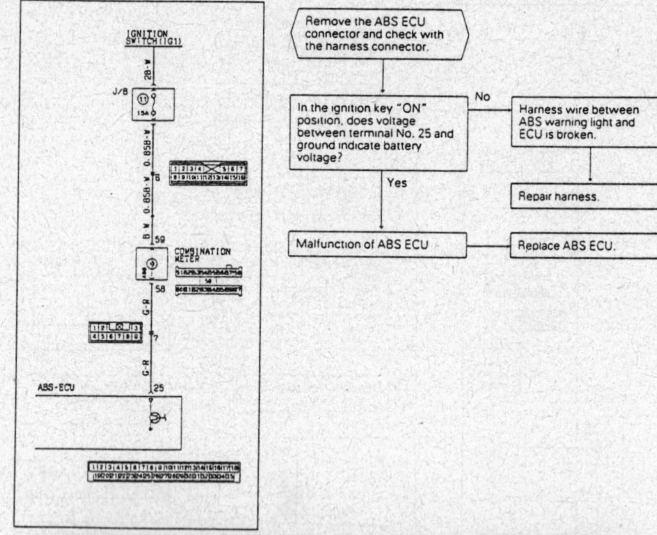


**Fig. 23 ABS Chart D—ABS warning light blinks once after ignition key is turned to "ON" position. It illuminates in "START" position & blinks once again when turned to "ON" position. Stealth FWD models**

| E-1 | Input abnormality of wheel speed sensor |
|---|---|

[Explanation]

The ABS ECU detects breaks in the wheel speed sensor wire. The warning light lights up if the wheel speed sensor signal is not input (or short circuited) or if its output is low when starting to drive or while driving.

[Hint]

In addition to a broken wire/short circuit in the wheel speed sensor, also check whether the sensor gap is too large, rotor teeth are missing, sensor harness wire is temporarily broken, or sensor harness and body connector are not properly inserted.

**Fig. 24 ABS Chart E1—Input abnormality of wheel speed sensor. AWD models**

| E-2 | Output abnormality of wheel speed sensor |
|---|---|

[Explanation]

The warning light lights up when there is an abnormality (other than broken wire or short circuit) in the wheel speed sensor output signal while driving.

[Hint]

The following can be considered as the cause of the wheel speed sensor output abnormality.

- Distortion of rotor, teeth missing
- Low frequency noise interference when sensor harness wire is broken
- Noise interference in sensor signal
- When the sensor output signal is below the standard value or when amplitude modulation is over the standard value, using an oscilloscope to measure the wave shape of the wheel speed sensor output signal is very effective.
- Loose wheel bearing
- Temporarily broken wire in sensor harness
- Sensor harness and body connector are not properly inserted.

NOTE

If contact is poor, check the sensor cable by bending and lightly stretching it.

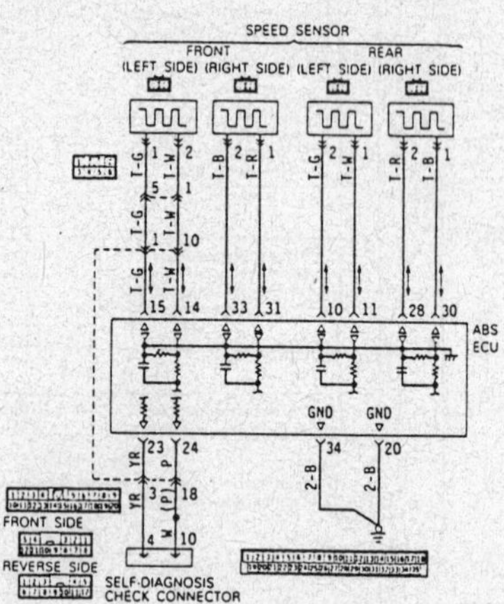


**Fig. 25 ABS Chart E-2—Output abnormality of wheel speed sensor (Part 1 of 2). Laser & Talon AWD models**

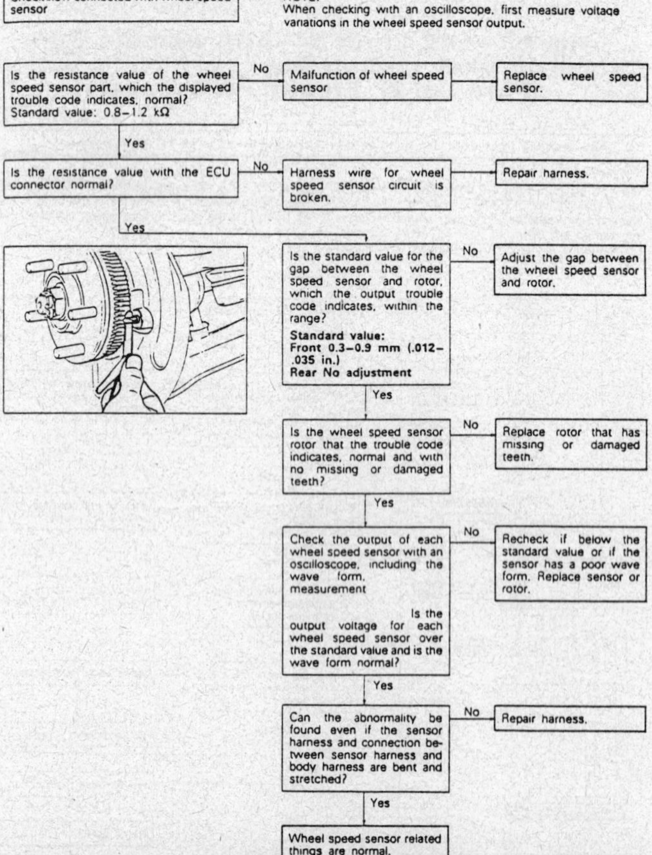


**Fig. 25 ABS Chart E-2—Output abnormality of wheel speed sensor (Part 2 of 2). Laser & Talon AWD models**

| E-2 | Output abnormality of wheel speed sensor |
|---|---|

**[Explanation]**

The warning light lights up when there is an abnormality (other than broken wire or short circuit) in any of the wheel speed sensor output signals while driving.

**[Hint]**

The following can be considered as the cause of the wheel speed sensor output abnormality.

- Distortion of rotor, teeth missing
- Low frequency noise interference when sensor harness wire is broken
- Noise interference in sensor signal
- The sensor output signal is below the standard value or amplitude modulation is over the standard value. Using an oscilloscope to measure the wave shape of the wheel speed sensor output signal is very effective.
- Broken sensor harness
- Poor connection of connector

NOTE
If contact is poor, check the sensor cable by bending and lightly stretching it.

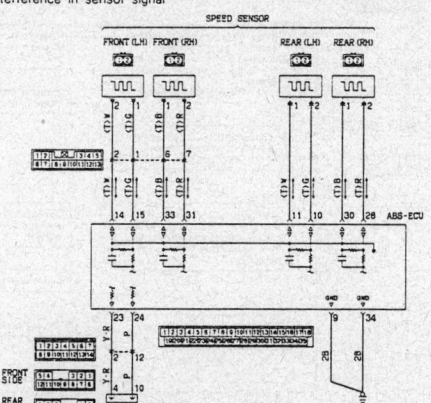

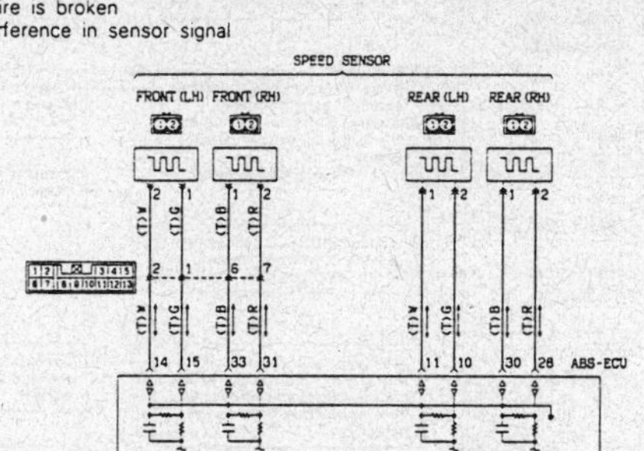


**Fig. 26 ABS Chart E-2—Output abnormality of wheel speed sensor (Part 1 of 2). Stealth AWD models**

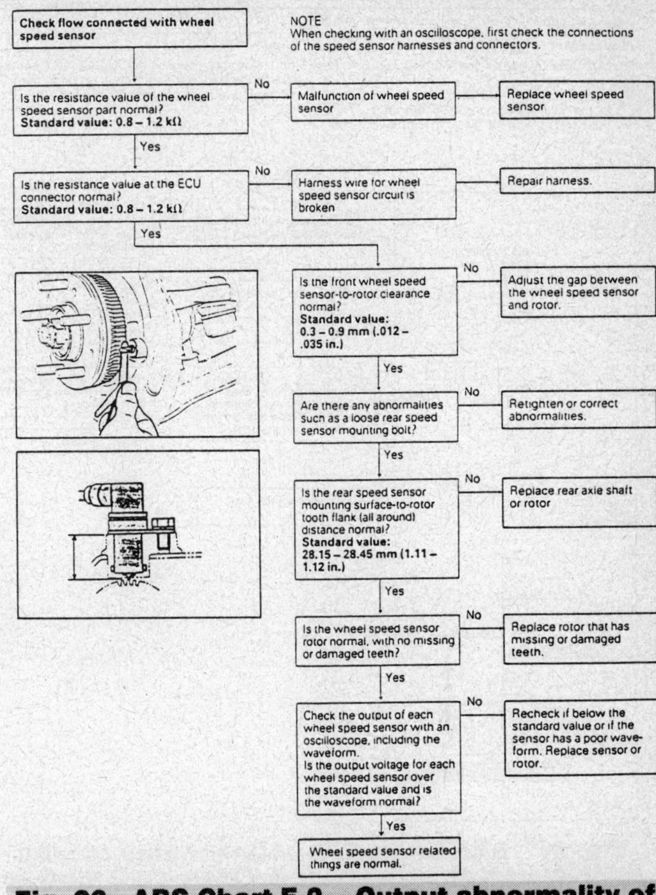


**Fig. 26 ABS Chart E-2—Output abnormality of wheel speed sensor (Part 2 of 2). Stealth AWD models**

| E-3 | Abnormality of G sensor circuit |
|---|---|

**[Explanation]**

The ABS ECU turns on the warning light in the following cases.

- OFF trouble turning G sensor OFF (It is judged that the G sensor continues to be OFF for more than approximately 13 seconds except when the
- When there is a broken wire or short circuit in the harness for the G sensor system.

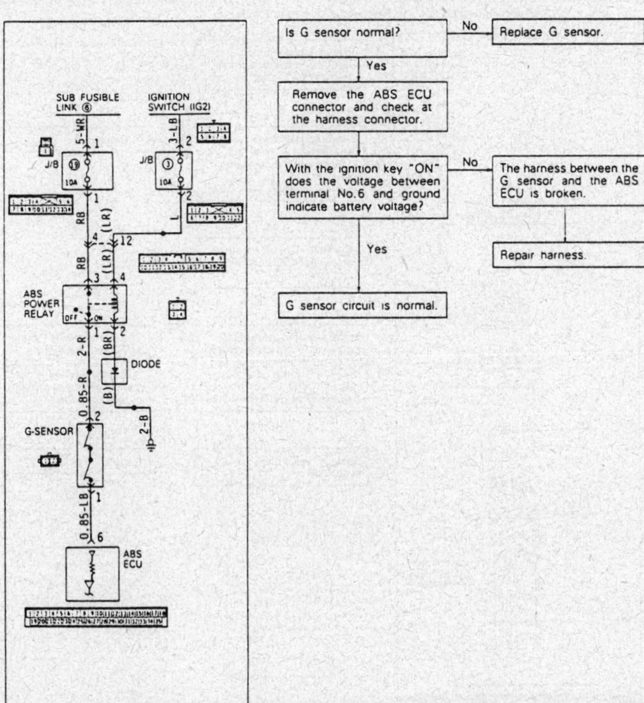


**Fig. 27 ABS Chart E-3—Abnormality of G sensor circuit. Laser & Talon AWD models**

| E-3 | Abnormality of G sensor circuit |
|---|---|

**[Explanation]**

The ABS ECU turns on the warning light in the following cases.

- G sensor OFF trouble (It is judged that the G sensor continues to be OFF for more than approximately 13 seconds except when the vehicle is stopped or when there is stop light switch input.
- When there is a broken wire or short circuit in the harness for the G sensor system.

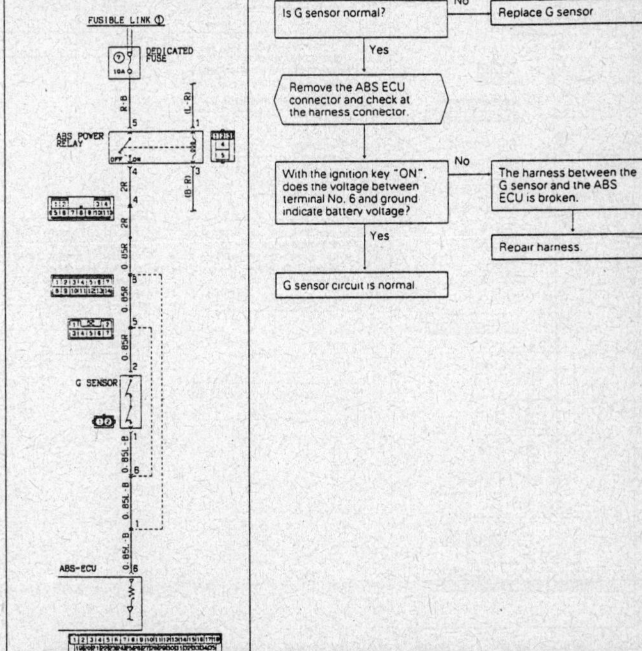


**Fig. 28 ABS Chart E-3—Abnormality of G sensor circuit. Stealth AWD models**

| E-4 | Abnormality of stop light switch circuit |
|---|---|

**[Explanation]**

The ABS ECU turns on the warning light in the following cases.

- Stop light switch may remain on for more than 15 minutes without the ABS functions.
- The harness wire for the stop light switch may be open.

**[Hint]**

If the stop light operates normal, the ABS harness wire for the stop light switch input circuit to the ECU is broken or there is a malfunction in the ABS ECU.

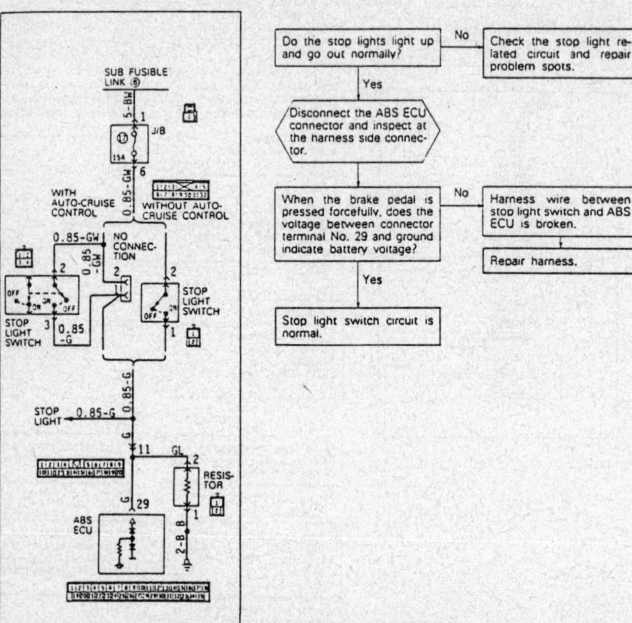


**Fig. 29 ABS Chart E-4—Abnormality of stop light switch circuit. Laser & Talon AWD models**

| E-4 | Abnormality of stop light switch circuit |
|---|---|

**[Explanation]**

The ABS ECU turns on the warning light in the following cases.

- Stop light switch may remain on for more than 15 minutes without ABS operation.

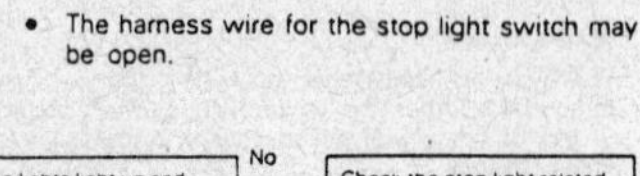

- The harness wire for the stop light switch may be open.

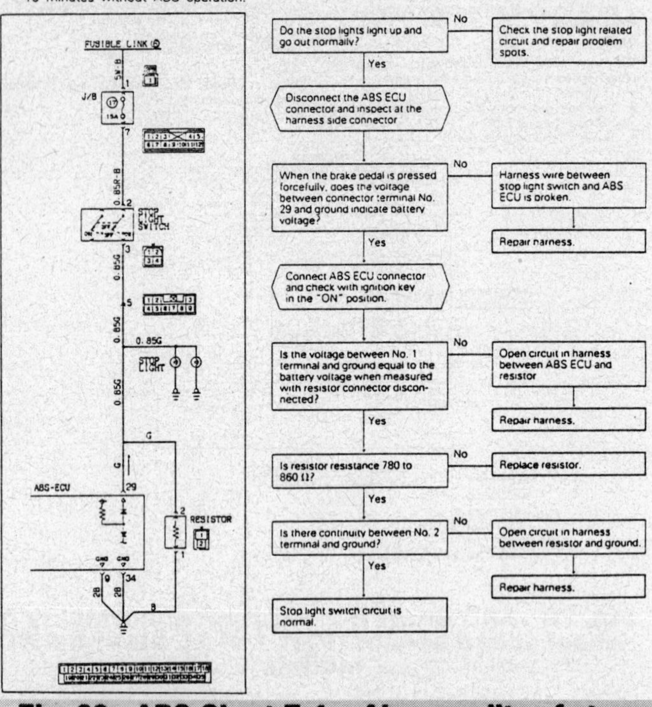


**Fig. 30 ABS Chart E-4—Abnormality of stop light switch circuit. Stealth AWD models**

| E-5 | Abnormality of solenoid valve drive circuit |
|---|---|

**[Explanation]**

The ABS ECU normally monitors the solenoid valve drive circuit.

If no current flows in the solenoid even if the ECU turns the solenoid ON or if it continues to flow even when turned OFF, the ECU determines the solenoid coil wire is broken/short circuited or the harness is broken/short circuited and then the warning light lights up.

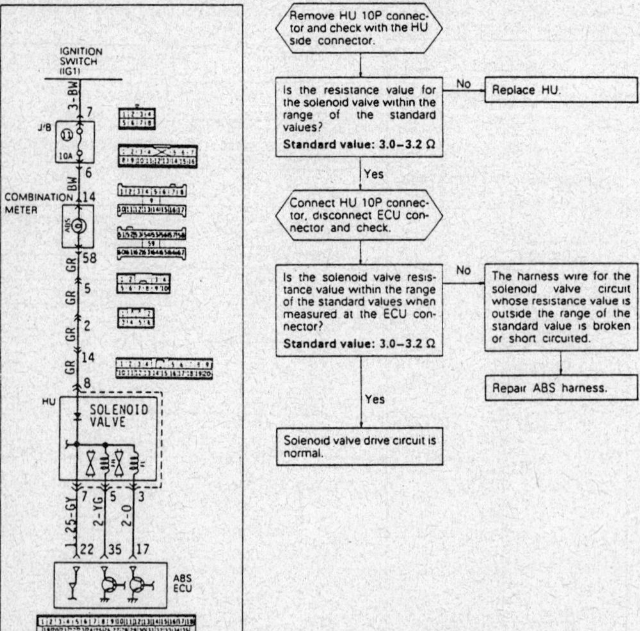


**Fig. 31 ABS Chart E-5—Abnormality of solenoid valve drive circuit. Laser & Talon AWD models**

| E-5 | Abnormality of solenoid valve drive circuit |
|---|---|

**[Explanation]**

The ABS ECU normally monitors the solenoid valve drive circuit.

If no current flows in the solenoid even if the ECU turns the solenoid ON or if it continues to flow even when turned OFF, the ECU determines the solenoid coil wire is broken/short-circuited or the harness is broken/short-circuited, and then warning light lights up. ABS ECU controls the solenoid valve current and if the current value of the solenoid valves differs from each other in the same mode, solenoid valve drift error is produced and the ABS ECU stops functioning.

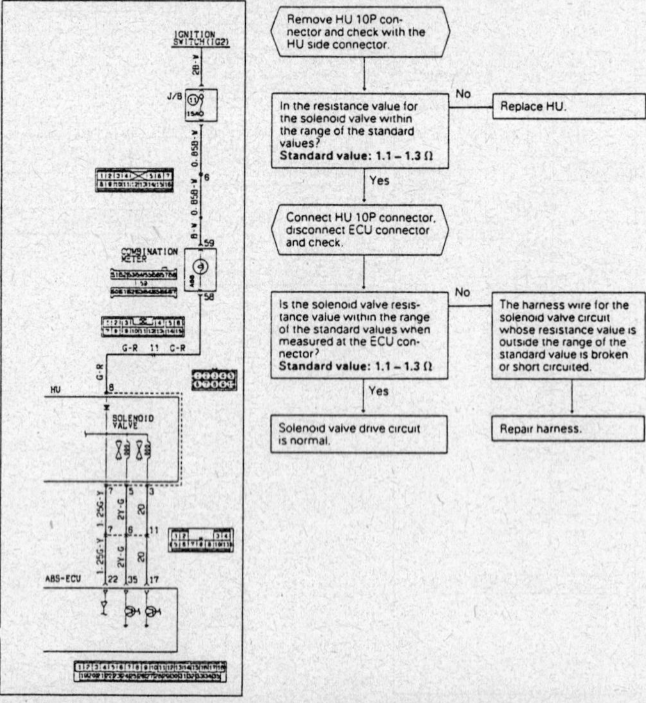


**Fig. 32 ABS Chart E-5—Abnormality of solenoid valve drive circuit. Stealth AWD models**

| E-6 | Abnormality of valve relay drive circuit |
|---|---|

**[Explanation]**

When the ignition switch is turned ON, the ABS ECU switches the valve relay OFF and ON for an initial check, compares the voltage of the signal to the valve relay and valve power monitor line voltage to check whether the valve relay operation is normal. In addition, normally it monitors whether or not there is power in the valve power monitor line since the valve relay is normally ON. Then, if the supply of power to the valve power monitor line is interrupted, the warning light illuminates.

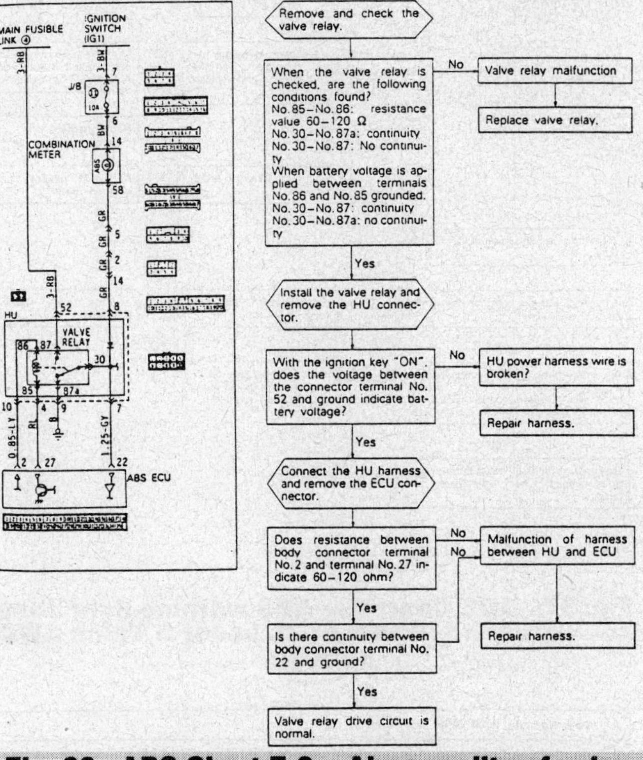


**Fig. 33 ABS Chart E-6—Abnormality of valve relay drive circuit. Laser & Talon AWD models**

| E-7 | Abnormality of motor drive circuit |
|---|---|

**[Explanation]**

The ABS ECU illuminates the warning light for the motor relay and motor in the following cases.

- When the motor relay does not function
- When there is trouble with the motor itself and it does not revolve
- When the motor ground line is disconnected and the motor does not revolve
- When the motor continues to revolve

**[Hint]**

If there is motor operation noise when wheel speed exceeds 6km/h (4mph) when starting up after the engine is started, there is a broken or short circuited motor monitor wire.

Does the motor make a noise when wheel speed exceeds 6 km/h (4 mph)?
- Yes: Broken wire or short circuit in motor monitor line → Repair the harness between HU and ECU.
- No: Remove the motor relay.

Remove the motor relay and check resistance values.
No. 85 – No. 86: resistance value 30 – 60 Ω
No. 30 – No. 87: no continuity
Battery voltage is applied on terminals No. 86 and No. 85 grounded
No. 30 – No. 87: continuity
- No: Motor relay malfunction → Replace motor relay.
- Yes: Is pump motor ground connected normally?
  - No: Connect ground wire.
  - Yes: Install motor relay and remove HU connector.

Does voltage between body connector terminal 51 and ground indicate battery voltage?
- No: Broken wire in pump motor power circuit → Repair the harness.
- Yes: Connect the HU connector and remove the ECU connector.

Is resistance between body connector terminal No. 2 and No. 26 30 – 60 ohms?
- No: Malfunction of harness between HU and ECU → Repair harness.
- Yes: Motor drive circuit is normal.

MAIN FUSIBLE LINK ④ — HU — MOTOR RELAY — ABS ECU

**Fig. 35 ABS Chart E-7—Abnormality of motor drive circuit. Laser & Talon AWD models**

| E-6 | Abnormality of valve relay drive circuit |
|---|---|

**[Explanation]**

When the ignition switch is turned ON, the ABS ECU switches the valve relay OFF and ON for an initial check, compares the voltage of the signal to the valve relay and valve power monitor line voltage to check whether the valve relay operation is normal. In addition, normally it monitors whether or not there is power in the valve power monitor line since the valve relay is normally ON. Then, if the supply of power to the valve power monitor line is interrupted, the warning light illuminates.

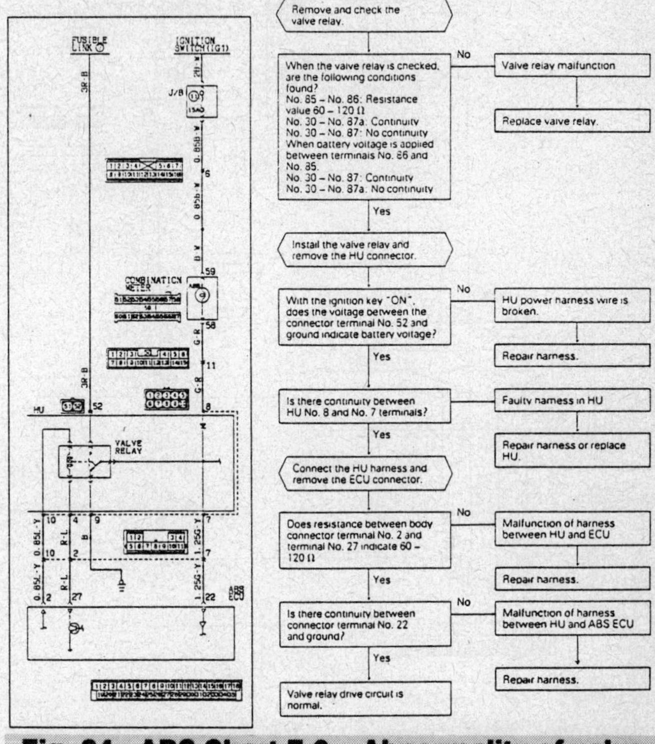


**Fig. 34 ABS Chart E-6—Abnormality of valve relay drive circuit. Stealth AWD models**

| E-7 | Abnormality of motor drive circuit |
|---|---|

**[Explanation]**

The ABS ECU illuminates the warning light for the motor relay and motor in the following cases.

- When the motor relay does not function
- When there is trouble with the motor itself and it does not revolve
- When the motor ground line is disconnected and the motor does not revolve
- When the motor continues to revolve

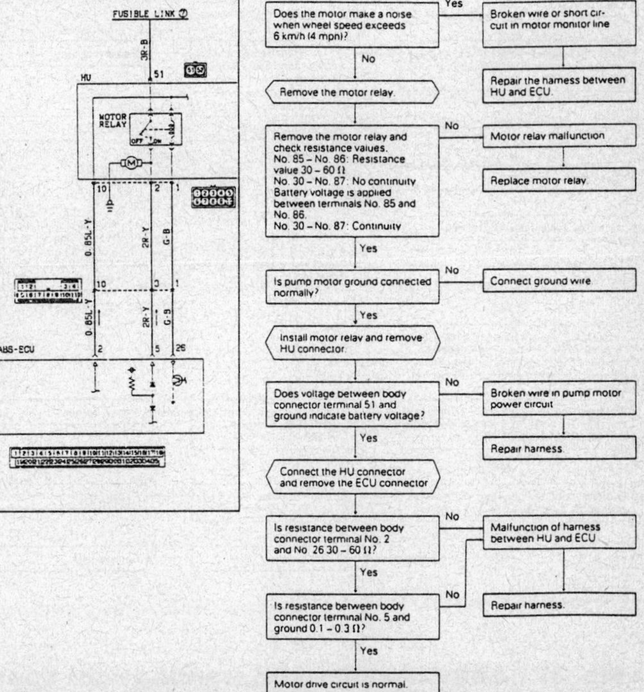


**Fig. 36 ABS Chart E-7—Abnormality of motor drive circuit. Stealth AWD models**

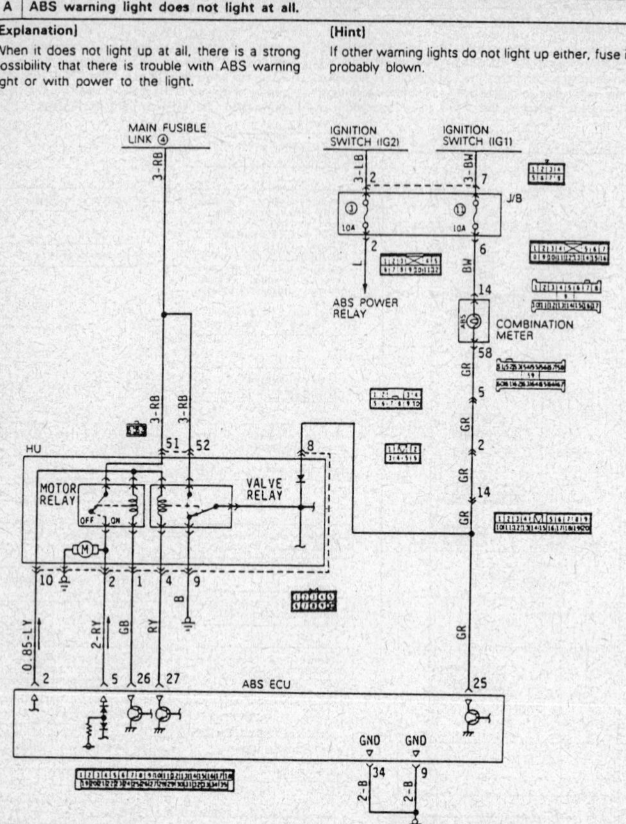


Fig. 37 ABS Chart A—ABS warning light does not light at all (Part 1 of 3). Laser & Talon AWD models

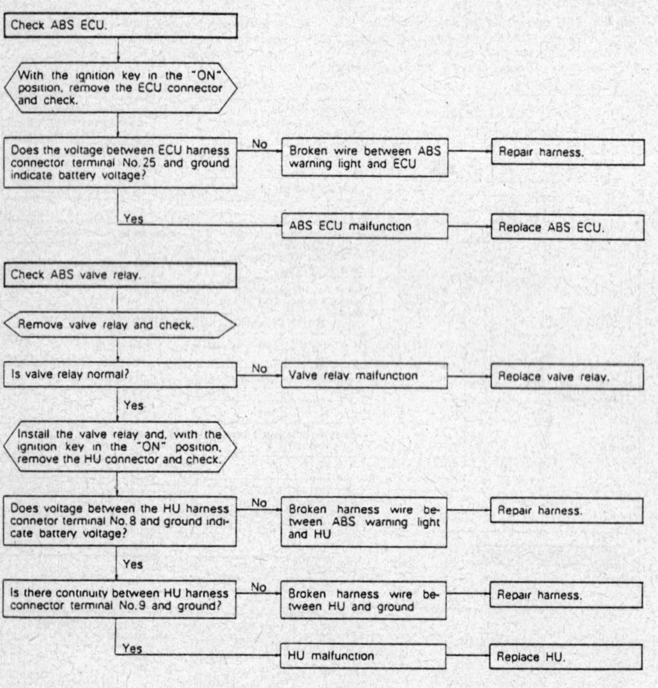


Fig. 37 ABS Chart A—ABS warning light does not light at all (Part 3 of 3). Laser & Talon AWD models

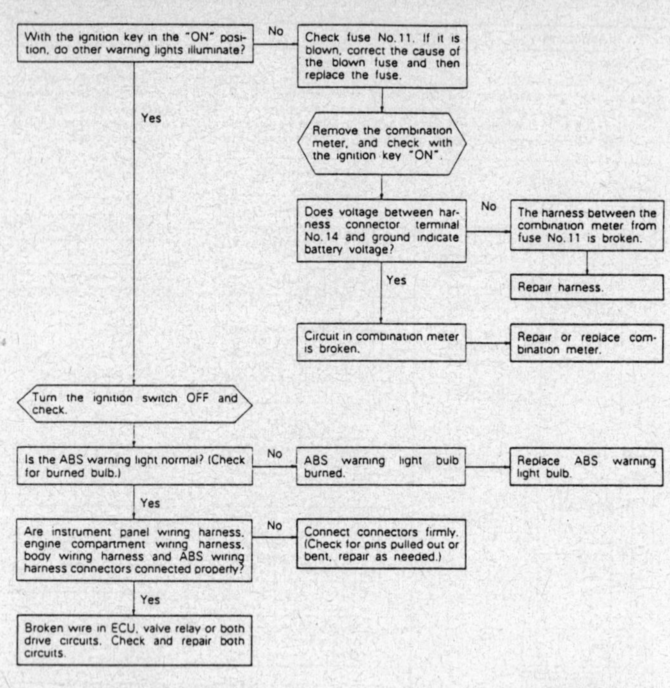


Fig. 37 ABS Chart A—ABS warning light does not light at all (Part 2 of 3). Laser & Talon AWD models

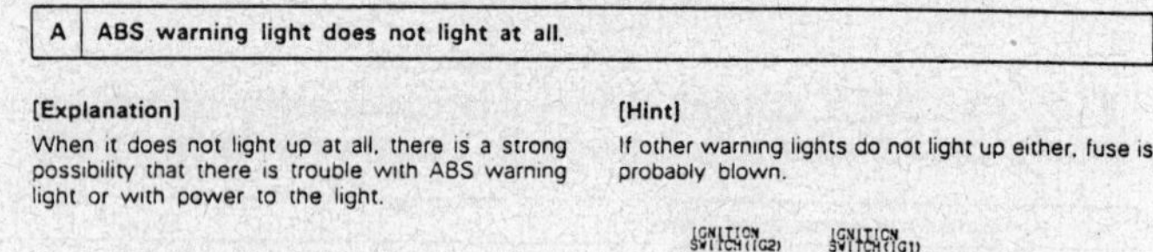


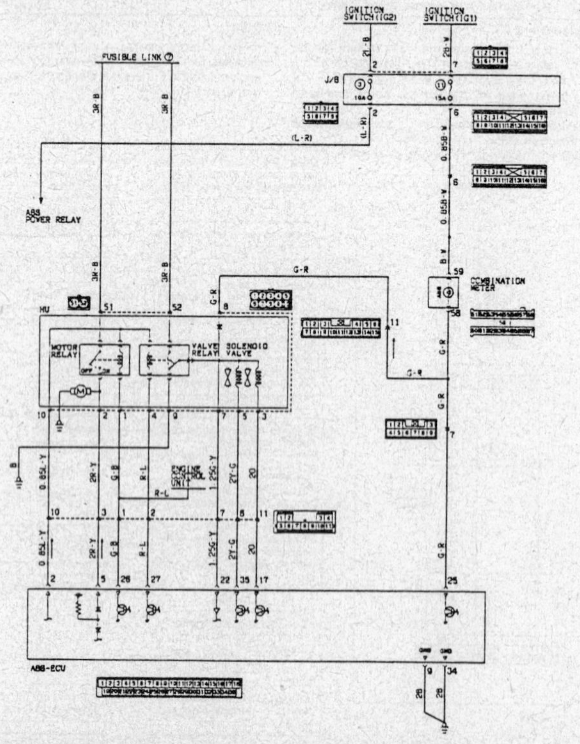


Fig. 38 ABS Chart A—ABS warning light does not light at all (Part 1 of 3). Stealth AWD models

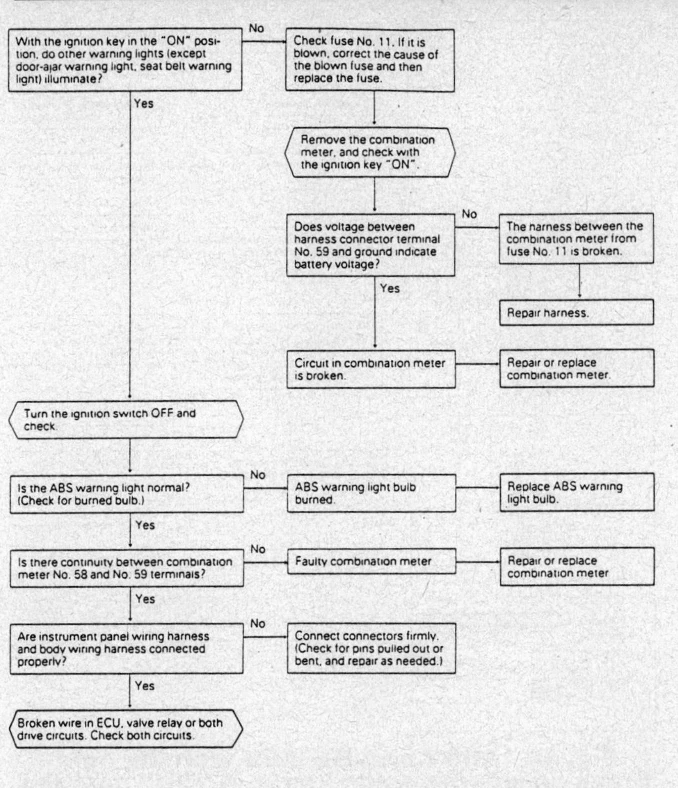


**Fig. 38 ABS Chart A—ABS warning light does not light at all (Part 2 of 3). Stealth AWD models**

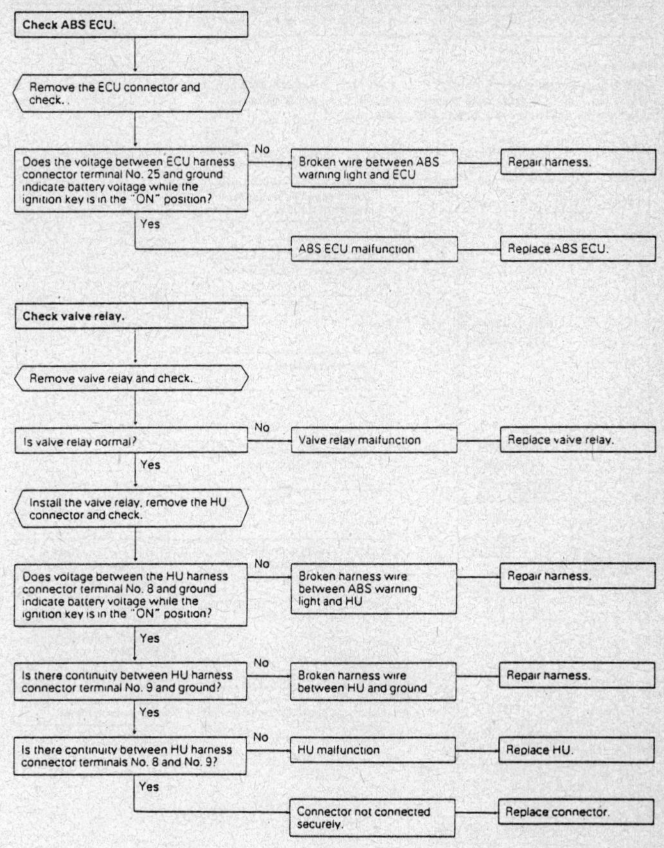


**Fig. 38 ABS Chart A—ABS warning light does not light at all (Part 3 of 3). Stealth AWD models**

| B | ABS warning light illuminated after the engine is started and remains on. |
|---|---|

**[Explanation]**

This is the symptom when the ABS ECU does not power up due to broken ECU power circuit, etc., when the fail safe function operates and isolates the system or when the warning light drive circuit is short circuited.

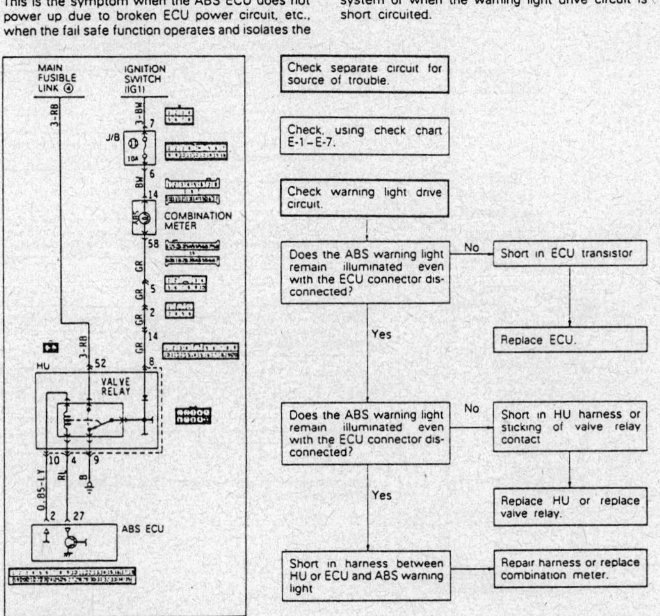


**Fig. 39 ABS Chart B—ABS warning light illuminated after engine is started & remains on (Part 1 of 2). Laser & Talon AWD models**

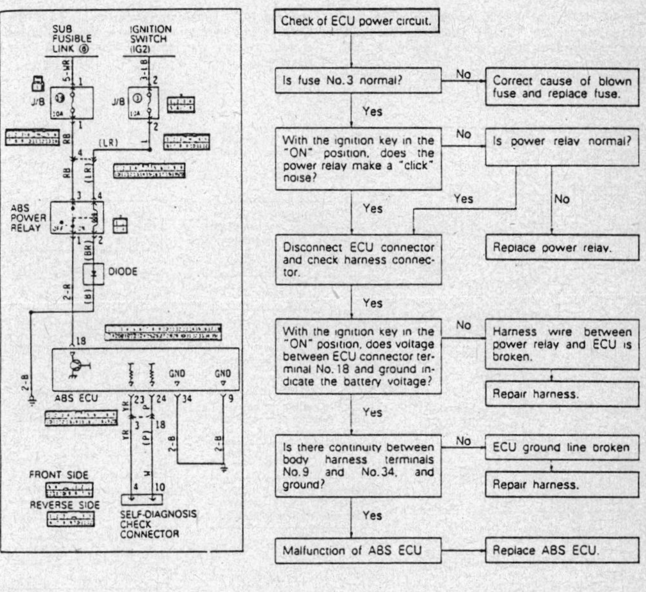


**Fig. 39 ABS Chart B—ABS warning light illuminated after engine is started & remains on (Part 2 of 2). Laser & Talon AWD models**

| B | ABS warning light stays on when the ignition key in the "ON" position. |
|---|---|

**[Explanation]**

This is the symptom when the ABS ECU does not power up due to broken ECU power circuit, etc., when the fail safe function operates and isolates the system or when the warning light drive circuit is short circuited.

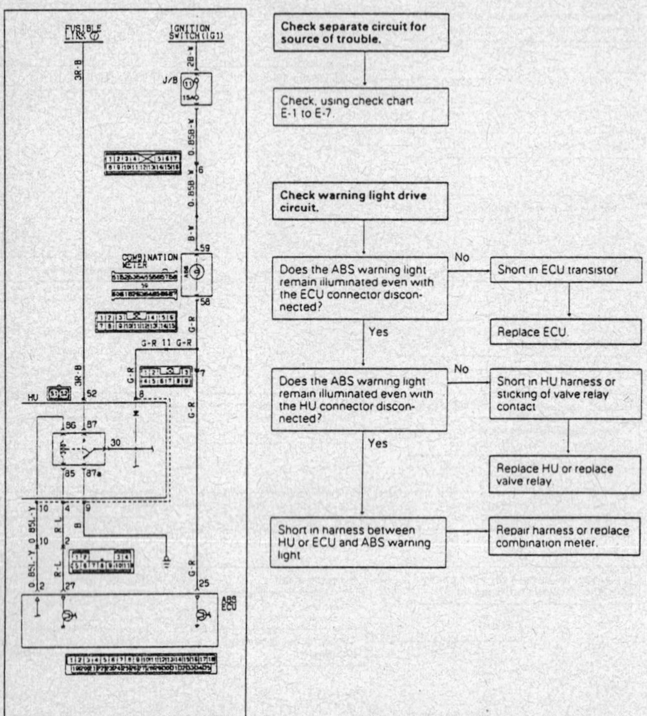


**Fig. 40 ABS Chart B—ABS warning light Stays on when ignition key is in "ON" position (Part 1 of 2). Stealth AWD models**

| C | ABS warning light does not illuminate when ignition key is in "START" position. |
|---|---|

**[Explanation]**

The ABS ECU uses the IG2 power source which is turned off in the "START" position. The ABS warning light uses the IG1 power source which is not turned off even in the "START" position. Consequently, in the "START" position, power is off and the ECU turns the valve relay OFF. If the warning light does not illuminate at this time, there is trouble in the warning light circuit on the valve relay side.

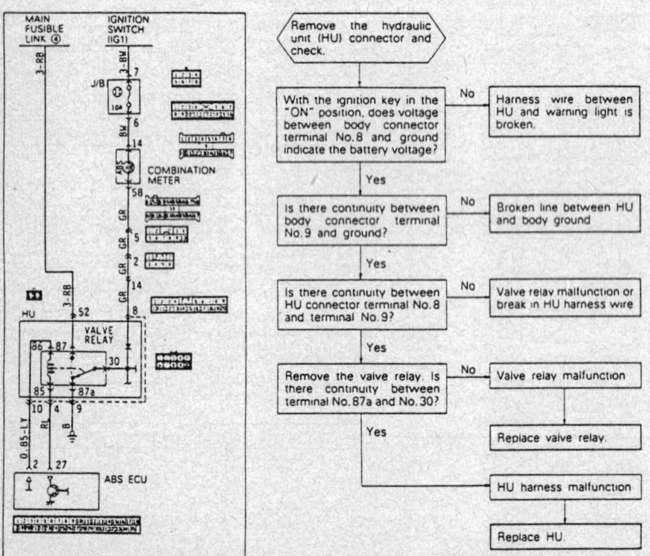


**Fig. 41 ABS Chart C—ABS warning light does not illuminate when ignition key is in "START" position. Laser & Talon AWD models**

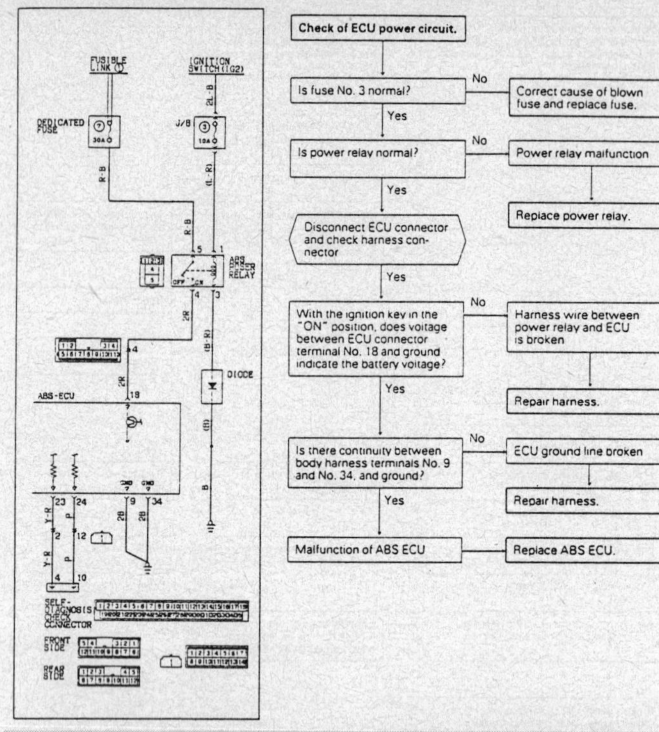


**Fig. 40 ABS Chart B—ABS warning light Stays on when ignition key is in "ON" position (Part 2 of 2). Stealth AWD models**

| C | ABS warning light does not illuminate when ignition key is in "START" position. |
|---|---|

**[Explanation]**

The ABS ECU uses the $IG_2$ power source which is turned off in the "START" position. The ABS warning light uses the $IG_1$ power source which is not turned off even in the "START" position. Consequently, in the "START" position, power is off and the ECU turns the valve relay OFF. If the warning light does not illuminate at this time, there is trouble in the warning light circuit on the valve relay side.

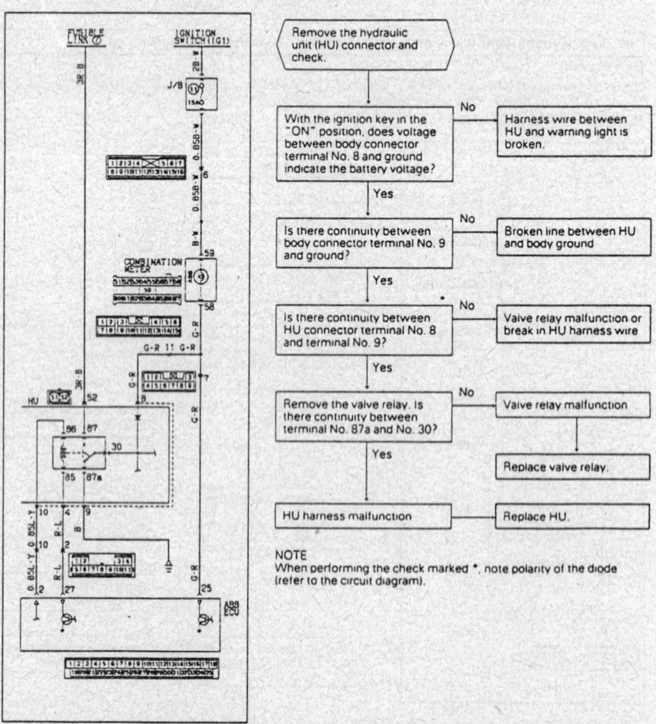


**Fig. 42 ABS Chart C—ABS warning light does not illuminate when ignition key is in "START" position. Stealth AWD models**

| D | ABS warning light blinks once after the ignition key is turned to the "ON" position. It illuminates in the "START" position and blinks once again when turned to the "ON" position. |
|---|---|

**[Explanation]**

When power flows, the ABS ECU turns on the warning light for approximately 1 sec. while it performs a valve relay test. If there is a break in the harness between the ECU and the warning light, the light illuminates only when the valve relay is off in the valve relay test, etc.

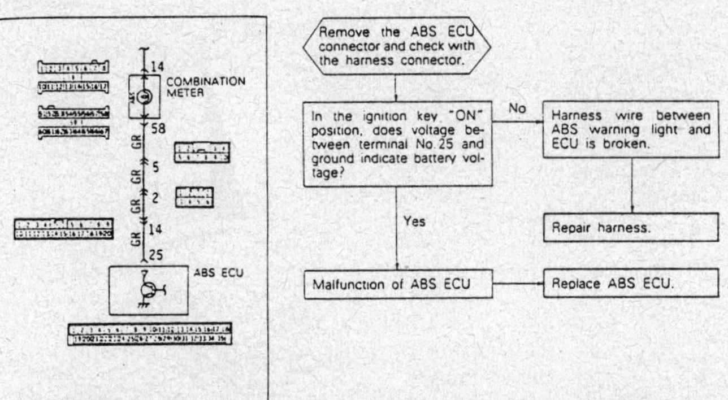


Fig. 43 ABS Chart D—ABS warning light blinks once after ignition key is turned to "ON" position. It illuminates in "START" position & blinks once again when turned to "ON" position. Laser & Talon AWD models

| D | ABS warning light blinks once after the ignition key is turned to the "ON" position. It illuminates in the "START" position and blinks once again when turned to the "ON" position. |
|---|---|

**[Explanation]**

When power flows, the ABS ECU turns on the warning light for approximately 1 sec. while it performs a valve relay test. If there is a break in the harness between the ECU and the warning light, the light illuminates only when the valve relay is off in the valve relay test, etc.

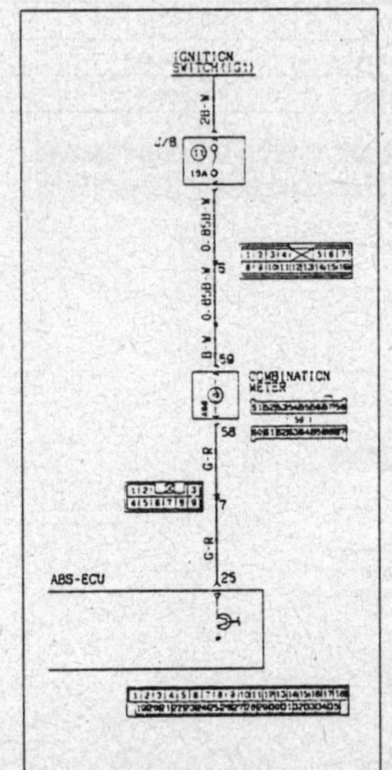


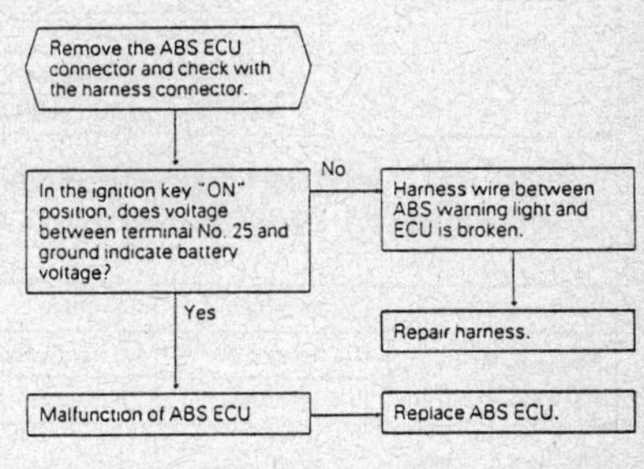


Fig. 44 ABS Chart D—ABS warning light blinks once after ignition key is turned to "ON" position. It illuminates in "START" position & blinks once again when turned to "ON" position. Stealth AWD models

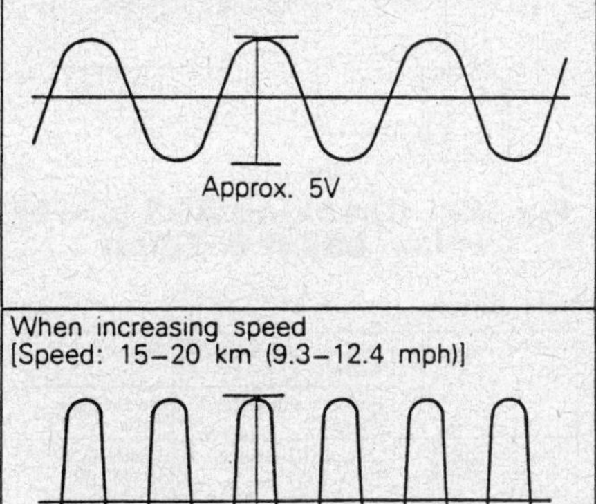


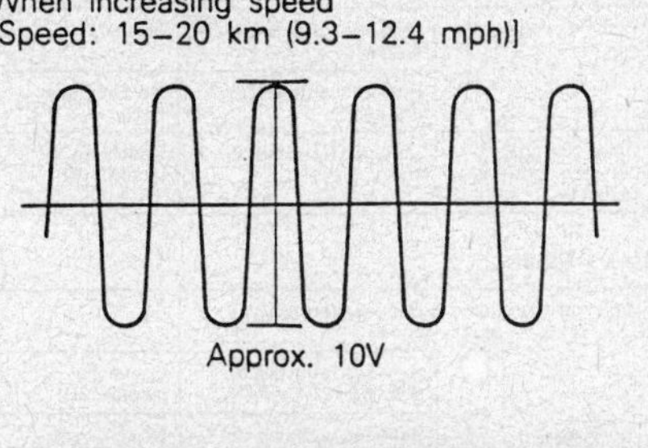


Fig. 45 Wheel speed sensor output voltage wave shape monitoring points. Laser & Talon

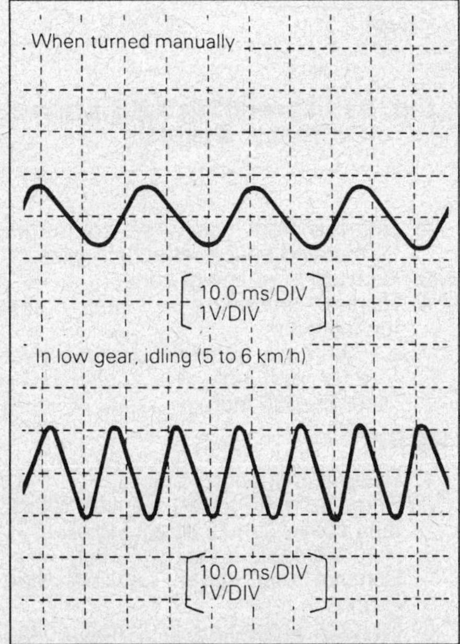


Fig. 46 Wheel speed sensor output voltage wave shape monitoring points. Stealth

| Terminal No. (same for AWD and FWD) | | | |
|---|---|---|---|
| FL | RR | FR | RL |
| 4 | 24 | 21 | 8 |
| 5 | 26 | 23 | 9 |

Fig. 47 Wheel speed sensor terminal output voltages. Stealth

minals as shown in **Figs. 51 and 52** with terminal 3 short-circuited to ground.

3. If continuity is not as specified, replace power relay.

## ABS VALVE RELAY & MOTOR RELAY CHECK

1. Remove right front splash shield, then the relay box cover by inserting a screwdriver between hydraulic unit and cover to pry off lock.
2. Remove relays, large one is motor relay and small one is valve relay.
3. Check continuity of relays both when energized and de-energized as shown in **Figs. 53 and 54.**
4. If continuity is not as specified, replace valve or motor relay.

# COMPONENT SERVICE

## HYDRAULIC UNIT, REPLACE

1. Remove splash shield, relay box, and air duct, if necessary.
2. Disconnect brake tube connections, then harness connections.
3. Remove bracket bolts.
4. Remove hydraulic unit bolts, then hydraulic unit.
5. Remove ground wire.
6. This unit cannot be disassembled. Do not drop or turn upside down.
7. Reverse procedure to install.

## WHEEL SPEED SENSOR, REPLACE

### FWD MODELS

#### Front

1. Raise and support vehicle.
2. Remove front speed sensor rotors, then speed sensor attaching clips.
3. Remove front speed sensor and bracket.
4. Reverse procedure to install, noting

| Symptom | Probable causes | Remedy |
|---|---|---|
| Too small or zero waveform amplitude | Faulty wheel speed sensor | Replace sensor |
| | Incorrect pole piece-to-rotor clearance | Adjust clearance |
| Waveform amplitude fluctuates excessively (this is no problem if the minimum amplitude is 100 mV or more) | Axle hub eccentric or with large runout | Replace hub |
| Noisy or disturbed waveform | Open circuit in sensor | Replace sensor |
| | Open circuit in harness | Correct harness |
| | Incorrectly mounted wheel speed sensor | Mount correctly |
| | Rotor with missing or damaged teeth | Replace rotor |

**Fig. 48 Wheel speed sensor output voltage waveform measurement diagnosis. Stealth**

| Power is supplied | 1–3 terminals | Continuity |
|---|---|---|
| Power is not supplied | 1–3 terminals | No continuity |
| | 2–4 terminals | Continuity |

**Fig. 50 ABS power relay continuity chart. Laser & Talon**

| When energized | Between terminals 4 and 5 | Continuity |
|---|---|---|
| When de-energized | Between terminals 4 and 5 | No continuity |
| | Between terminals 1 and 3 | Continuity |

**Fig. 52 ABS power relay continuity chart. Stealth**

Motor Relay

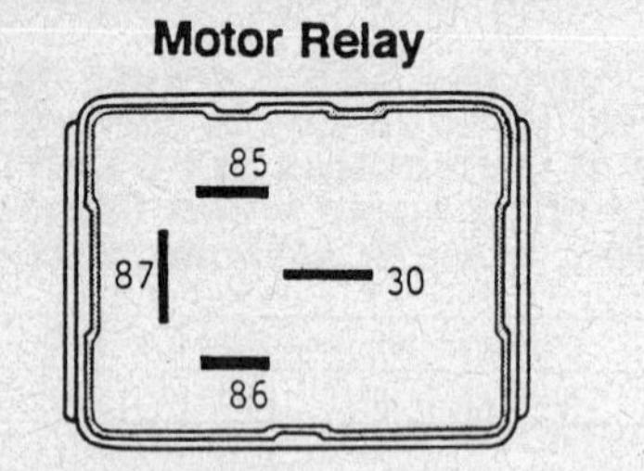


Valve Relay

**Fig. 53 ABS motor & valve relay terminal identification**

the following:
   a. Clearance between speed sensor rotor and pole piece should be .012–.035 inch.

**Rear**

1. Raise and support vehicle.
2. Remove rear speed sensor rotors, then speed sensor attaching clips.
3. Remove rear speed sensors.
4. Reverse procedure to install, noting the following:
   a. Clearance between speed sensor rotor and pole piece should be .008–.028 inch.

## AWD MODELS

### Front

1. Raise and support vehicle.

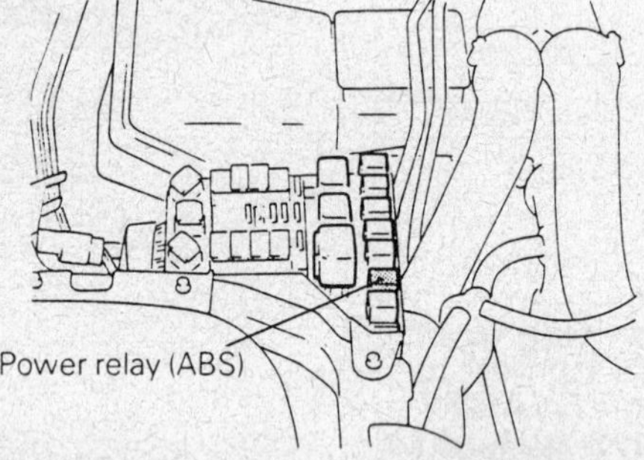


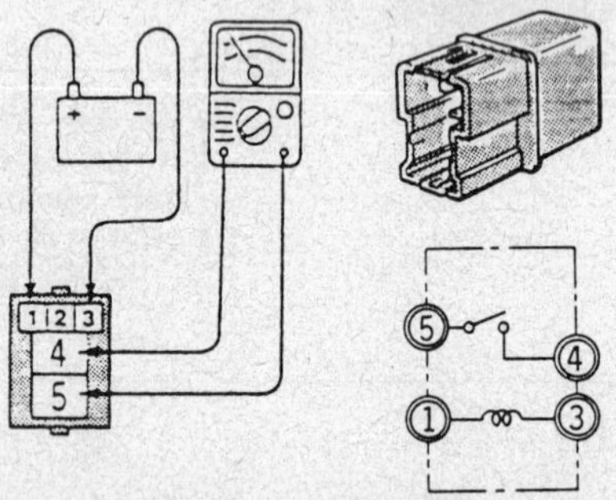


**Fig. 51 Checking ABS power relay. Stealth**

2. Remove front speed sensor rotors, then speed sensor attaching clips.
3. Remove front speed sensors.
4. Reverse procedure to install, noting the following:
   a. Clearance between speed sensor rotor and pole piece should be .012–.035 inch.

**Rear**

1. Raise and support vehicle.
2. Remove rear speed sensor rotors, then speed sensor attaching clips.
3. Remove cable band.
4. Remove rear speed sensors, then O-rings.
5. Reverse procedure to install, noting the following:
   a. The rear speed sensor pole piece to rotor tooth surface clearance is not adjustable. Measure the sensor surface to rotor tooth surface clearance, it should be between 1.11–1.12 inch.

## G SENSOR, REPLACE

### AWD Models

1. Remove front and rear console assemblies.

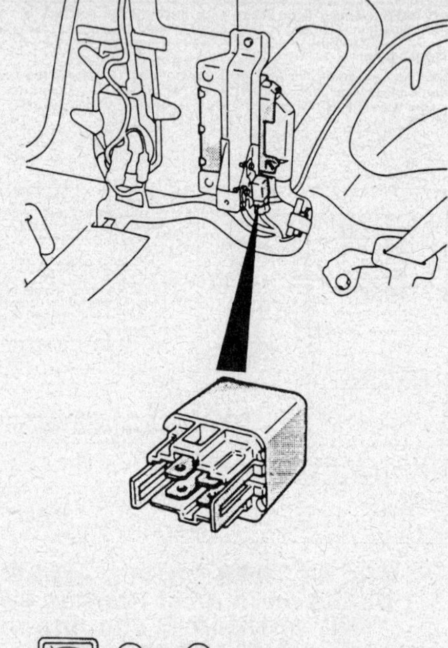

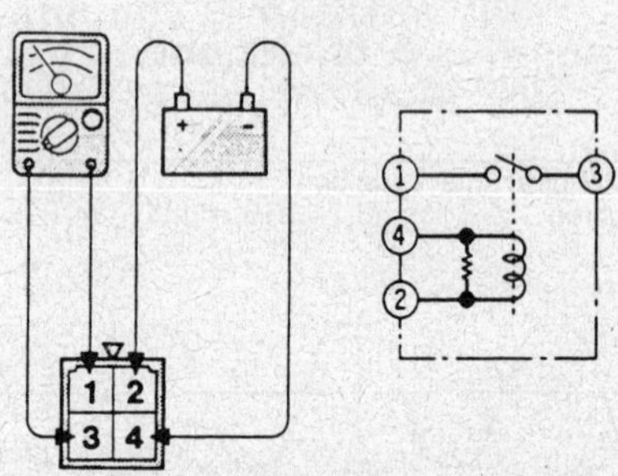


**Fig. 49 Checking ABS power relay. Laser & Talon**

Motor Relay

| When de-energized | Between terminals 85 and 86 | 30 – 60Ω |
|---|---|---|
| | Between terminals 30 and 87 | No continuity (∞Ω) |
| When energized between terminals 85 and 86 | Between terminals 30 and 87 | Continuity (approx. 0Ω) |

Valve Relay

| When de-energized | Between terminals 85 and 86 | 60 – 120 Ω |
|---|---|---|
| | Between terminals 30 and 87a | Continuity (approx. 0Ω) |
| | Between terminals 30 and 87 | No continuity (∞Ω) |
| When energized between terminals 85 and 86 | Between terminals 30 and 87a | No continuity (∞Ω) |
| | Between terminals 30 and 87 | Continuity (approx. 0Ω) |

**Fig. 54 ABS motor and valve relay continuity charts.**

2. Disconnect electrical connector.
3. Remove G sensor and bracket.
4. Reverse procedure to install.

## ELECTRONIC CONTROL UNIT, REPLACE

1. Remove rear seat cushion, then rear seat back.
2. Remove right rear quarter panel trim.
3. Disconnect electrical connector.
4. Remove ECU attaching bolts, then remove ECU.
5. Reverse procedure to install.

# REAR DRIVE AXLES

## INDEX



## DRIVE AXLE IDENTIFICATION

| Year | Model | Axle Code | Gear Ratio |
|---|---|---|---|
| 1989 | Chrysler Except Conquest | 7¼① | 2.26 |
| | | 8¼① | ② |
| | Conquest | — | 3.545 |

**①—Ring gear diameter**
**②—2.24 or 2.94, Stamped on differential housing tag.**

## TROUBLESHOOTING

Refer to **Figs. 1 and 2,** when troubleshooting rear axle assembly.

## REMOVAL

### DIFFERENTIAL CASE ASSEMBLY

#### Chrysler Except Conquest

1. Block brake pedal in the up position using suitable wooden block.
2. Raise and support rear of vehicle, then remove rear axles. Refer to "Axle Shaft, Replace" for procedure.
3. If not done previously, loosen axle housing cover bolts and allow lubricant to drain, then remove bolts and cover.
4. Remove propeller shaft. Refer to "Propeller Shaft, Replace" in the Chrysler "Rear Wheel Drive" chapter for procedure.
5. Using suitable cleaning solvent, clean inside axle housing and differential case.
6. Using a suitable pry bar or screwdriver positioned between left side of axle housing and differential case flange, check for differential side play by attempting to move differential with a prying motion. No side play should be present. **If side play is evident and is the result of the bearing cones becoming loose from the differential case hubs, the case must be replaced. If side play is the result of any other cause, adjust side play using threaded adjuster so next step can be performed.**
7. Mount suitable dial indicator on axle housing with stylus against left side of ring gear. Rotate differential case while observing dial indicator. Mark ring gear and differential case at point of maximum runout for later use. If runout exceeds .005 inch, the case may be damaged. Refer to "Differential Case" disassembly procedure for further service.
8. Using suitable tool, mark bearing caps and axle housing to be used as reference marks during reassembly.
9. Remove adjuster locks from each cap, then loosen, but do not remove bearing cap bolts.
10. Insert hex adjuster tool No. C-4164, **Fig. 3,** through axle tube on each side and loosen hex adjuster.
11. While holding differential assembly in place with one hand, remove bearing cap bolts, then very carefully remove bearing caps, adjusters and differential assembly. Differential bearing cups must remain with their respective bearing cones. **On 8¼ inch axles, the threaded adjusters must also be kept with their respective bearings. On 7¼ and 9¼ inch axles, the threaded adjusters will remain in the axle housing.**
12. Mount differential assembly in vise equipped with soft jaws.

#### Conquest

1. Drain oil from differential gear housing.
2. Remove both right and left side axle shafts.
3. Remove driveshaft, then the torque tube using the following procedure:
   a. Apply parking brake, then loosen torque tube companion flange attaching nut. Do not remove nut at this time.
   b. Remove torque tube to differential carrier attaching bolts, then the torque tube to front support attaching bolts.
   c. Using suitable puller, disconnect extension shaft spline from spline coupling.
   d. Remove puller assembly, then remove torque tube assembly from out rear of vehicle.
4. Remove rear support insulator to crossmember and rear support to rear support insulator attaching bolts.
5. Raise differential carrier with a suitable jack and disconnect differential from rear support insulators, then remove assembly from vehicle.
6. Remove rear supports, cover and gaskets.

### DRIVE PINION

#### Chrysler Except Conquest

1. Using suitable inch lbs. torque wrench, measure pinion bearing preload and record. Remove drive pinion nut, washer and flange.
2. Using suitable screwdriver and hammer, remove front oil seal.
3. Using suitable hammer, drive pinion shaft rearward to remove drive pinion and front bearing cone. **After drive pinion removal, both bearings and cones will be damaged and must**

| Condition | Possible Cause | Correction |
|---|---|---|
| REAR WHEEL NOISE | (a) Wheel loose. | (a) Tighten loose nuts. |
| | (b) Faulty, brinelled wheel bearing. | (b) Faulty or brinelled bearings must be replaced. |
| REAR AXLE DRIVE SHAFT NOISE | (a) Misaligned axle housing. | (a) Inspect rear axle housing, alignment. Correct as necessary. |
| | (b) Bent or sprung axle shaft. | (b) Replace bent or sprung axle shaft. |
| | (c) End play in drive pinion bearings. | (c) Refer to Pinion Bearing Pre-Load. |
| | (d) Excessive gear lash between ring gear and pinion. | (d) Check adjustment of ring gear and pinion. Correct as necessary. |
| | (e) Improper adjustment of drive pinion shaft bearings. | (e) Adjust pinion bearings. |
| | (f) Loose drive pinion companion flange nut. | (f) Tighten drive pinion flange nut to torque specified |
| | (g) Improper wheel bearing adjustment. | (g) Readjust as necessary. |
| | (h) Scuffed gear tooth contact surfaces. | (h) If necessary, replace scuffed gears. |
| REAR AXLE DRIVE SHAFT BREAKAGE | (a) Misaligned axle housing. | (a) Replace broken shaft after correcting rear axle housing alignment. |
| | (b) Vehicle overloaded. | (b) Replace broken shaft. Avoid excessive weight on vehicle. |
| | (c) Abnormal clutch operation. | (c) Replace broken shaft, after checking for other possible causes. Avoid erratic use of clutch. |
| | (d) Grabbing clutch. | (d) Replace broken shaft. Inspect clutch and make necessary repairs or adjustments. |
| DIFFERENTIAL CASE BREAKAGE | (a) Improper adjustment of differential bearings. | (a) Replace broken case; examine gears and bearings for possible damage. At reassembly, adjust differential bearings. |
| | (b) Excessive ring gear clearance. | (b) Replace broken case; examine gears and bearings for possible damage. At reassembly, adjust ring gear and pinion backlash. |
| | (c) Vehicle overloaded. | (c) Replace broken case; examine gears and bearings for possible damage. Avoid excessive weight on vehicle. |
| | (d) Erratic clutch operation. | (d) Replace broken case. After checking for other possible causes, examine gears and bearings for possible damage. Avoid erratic use of clutch. |
| SCORING OF DIFFERENTIAL GEARS | (a) Insufficient lubrication. | (a) Replace scored gears. Scoring marks on the pressure face of gear teeth or in the bore are caused by instantaneous fusing of the mating surfaces. Scored gears should be replaced. Fill rear axle to required capacity with proper lubricant. |
| | (b) Improper grade of lubricant. | (b) Replace scored gears. Inspect all gears and bearings for possible damage. Clean out and refill axle to required capacity with proper lubricant. |
| | (c) Excessive spinning of one wheel. | (c) Replace scored gears. Inspect all gears, pinion bores and shaft for scoring, or bearings for possible damage. Service as necessary. |

**Fig. 1 Troubleshooting chart (Part 1 of 2). Chrysler Except Conquest**

| Condition | Possible Cause | Correction |
|---|---|---|
| LOSS OF LUBRICANT | (a) Lubricant level too high. | (a) Drain excess lubricant by removing filler plug and allow lubricant to level at lower edge of filler plug hole. |
| | (b) Worn axle shaft oil seals. | (b) Replace worn oil seals with new ones. Prepare new seals before replacement. |
| | (c) Cracked rear axle housing. | (c) Repair or replace housing as required. |
| | (d) Worn drive pinion oil seal. | (d) Replace worn drive pinion oil seal with a new one. |
| | (e) Scored and worn companion flange. | (e) Replace worn or scored companion flange and oil seal. |
| | (f) Axle cover not properly sealed. | (f) Remove cover and clean flange and reseal. |
| OVERHEATING OF UNIT | (a) Lubricant level too low. | (a) Refill rear axle. |
| | (b) Incorrect grade of lubricant. | (b) Drain, flush and refill rear axle with correct amount of the proper lubricant. |
| | (c) Bearings adjusted too tightly. | (c) Readjust bearings. |
| | (d) Excessive wear in gears. | (d) Check gears for excessive wear or scoring. Replace as necessary. |
| | (e) Insufficient ring gear to pinion clearance. | (e) Readjust ring gear and pinion backlash and check gears for possible scoring. |
| TOOTH BREAKAGE (RING GEAR AND PINION) | (a) Overloading. | (a) Replace gears. Examine other gears and bearings for possible damage. Replace parts as needed. Avoid overloading of vehicle. |
| | (b) Erratic clutch operation. | (b) Replace gears, and examine remaining parts for possible damage. Avoid erratic clutch operation. |
| | (c) Ice-spotted pavements. | (c) Replace gears. Examine remaining parts for possible damage. Replace parts as required. |
| | (d) Improper adjustment. | (d) Replace gears. Examine other parts for possible damage. Make sure ring gear and pinion backlash is correct. |
| REAR AXLE NOISE | (a) Insufficient lubricant. | (a) Refill rear axle with correct amount of the proper lubricant. Also check for leaks and correct as necessary. |
| | (b) Improper ring gear and pinion adjustment. | (b) Check ring gear and pinion tooth contact. |
| | (c) Unmatched ring gear and pinion. | (c) Remove unmatched ring gear and pinion. Replace with a new matched gear and pinion set. |
| | (d) Worn teeth on ring gear or pinion. | (d) Check teeth on ring gear and pinion for contact. If necessary, replace with new matched set. |
| | (e) Loose drive pinion bearings. | (e) Adjust drive pinion bearings. |
| | (f) Loose differential gear bearings. | (f) Adjust differential gear bearings. |
| | (g) Misaligned or sprung ring gear. | (g) Check ring gear for runout. |
| | (h) Loose carrier cap screws. | (h) Tighten to specifications. |

**Fig. 1 Troubleshooting chart (Part 2 of 2). Chrysler Except Conquest**

| Symptom | Probable cause | Remedy |
|---|---|---|
| AXLE SHAFT, AXLE HOUSING<br>Noise while wheels are rotating | Brake drag<br>Bent axle shaft<br>Worn or scarred axle shaft bearing | Replace |
| Grease leakage | Worn or damaged oil seal<br>Malfunction of bearing seal | Replace |
| DRIVE SHAFT<br>Noise | Wear, play or seizure of ball joint<br>Excessive drive shaft spline looseness | Replace |
| TORQUE TUBE<br>Noise | Wear, play or seizure of bearing | Replace |
| DIFFERENTIAL<br>Abnormal noise during driving or gear changing | Excessive final drive gear backlash<br>Insufficient drive pinion preload | Adjust |
| | Excessive differential gear backlash | Adjust or replace |
| | Worn spline of a side gear | Replace |
| | Loose spline coupling self-locking nut | Retighten or replace |
| NOTE<br>In addition to a malfunction of the differential carrier components, abnormal noise can also be caused by the universal joint of the propeller shaft, the axle shafts, the wheel bearings, etc. Before disassembling any parts, take all possibilities into consideration and confirm the source of the noise. | | |
| Abnormal noise when cornering | Damaged differential gears<br>Damaged pinion shaft<br>Nicked and/or abnormal wear of inner and outer clutch plates<br>Contaminated gear oil | Replace |
| | Insufficient gear oil quantity | Refill |
| Gear noise | Improper final drive gear tooth contact adjustment | Adjust or replace |
| | Incorrect final drive gear backlash<br>Improper drive pinion preload adjustment | Adjust |
| | Damaged, broken, and/or seized tooth surfaces of the drive gear and drive pinion<br>Damaged, broken, and/or seized drive pinion bearings<br>Damaged, broken, and/or seized side bearings<br>Damaged differential case<br>Contaminated gear oil | Replace |
| | Insufficient gear oil quantity | Refill |
| NOTE<br>Noise from the engine, muffler vibration, transmission, propeller shaft, wheel bearings, tires, body, etc., is easily mistaken as being caused by malfunctions in the differential carrier components. Be extremely careful and attentive when performing the driving test, etc.<br>Test methods to confirm the source of the abnormal noise include: coasting, acceleration, constant speed driving, raising the rear wheels on a jack, etc. Use the method most appropriate to the circumstances. | | |

**Fig. 2 Troubleshooting chart (Part 1 of 2). Conquest**

| Symptom | Probable cause | Remedy |
|---|---|---|
| Gear oil leakage | Worn or damaged front oil seal, or an improperly installed oil seal<br>Damaged gasket | Replace |
| | Loose spline coupling self-locking nut | Retighten or replace |
| | Loose filler or drain plug | Retighten or apply adhesive |
| | Clogged or damaged vent plug | Clean or replace |
| Seizure | Improper final drive gear backlash<br>Excessive drive pinion preload<br>Excessive side bearing preload<br>Improper differential gear backlash<br>Excessive clutch plate preload | Adjust |
| | Contaminated gear oil | Replace |
| | Insufficient gear oil quantity | Refill |
| NOTE<br>In the event of seizure, disassemble and replace the parts involved, and also be sure to check all components for any irregularities and repair or replace as necessary. | | |
| Breakdown | Incorrect final drive gear backlash<br>Incorrect drive pinion preload<br>Incorrect side bearing preload<br>Excessive differential gear backlash<br>Insufficient clutch plate preload | Adjust |
| | Loose drive gear clamping bolts | Retighten |
| | Operational malfunction due to overloaded clutch | Avoid excessively rough operation |
| NOTE<br>In addition to disassembling and replacing the failed parts, be sure to check all components for irregularities and repair or replace as necessary. | | |
| The limited slip differential does not function (on snow, mud, ice, etc.) | The limited slip device is damaged | Disassemble, check the functioning, and replace the damaged parts |

**Fig. 2 Troubleshooting chart (Part 2 of 2). Conquest**

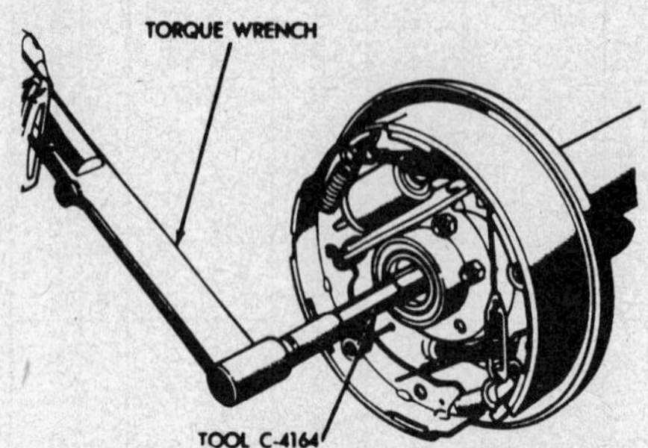


**Fig. 3 Hex adjuster tool installation**

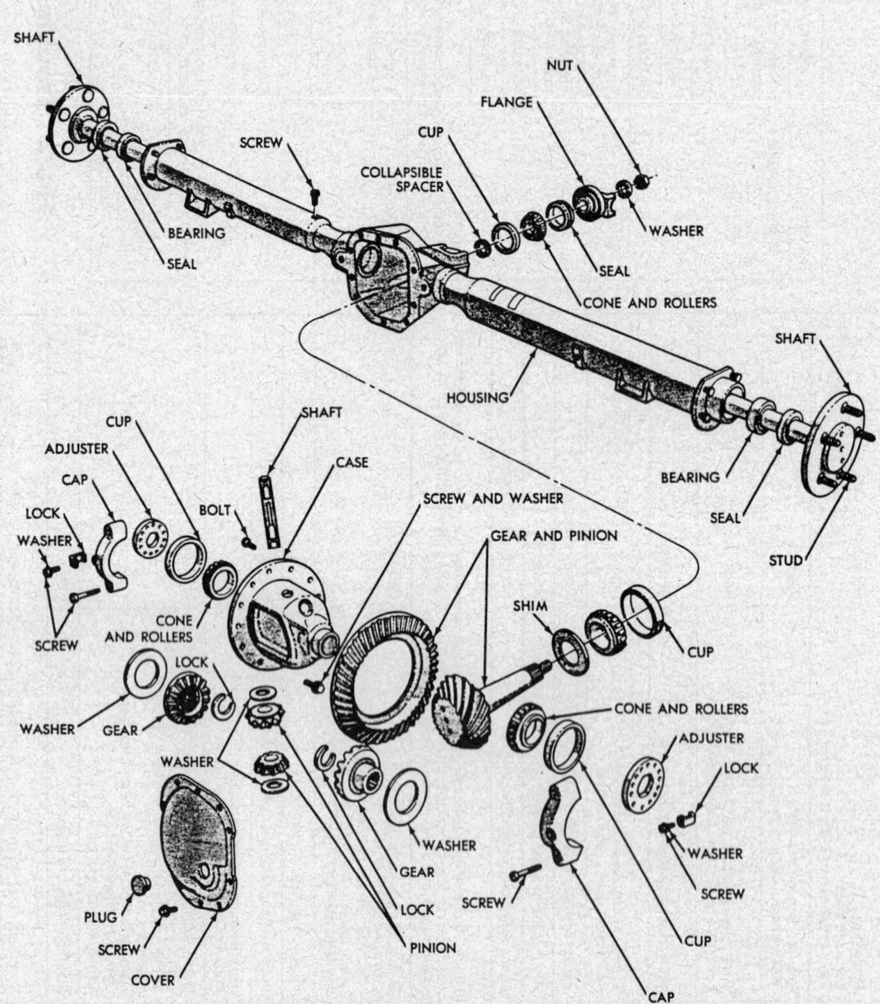


**Fig. 4 Exploded view of rear axle assembly (7¼ axle). Chrysler except Conquest**

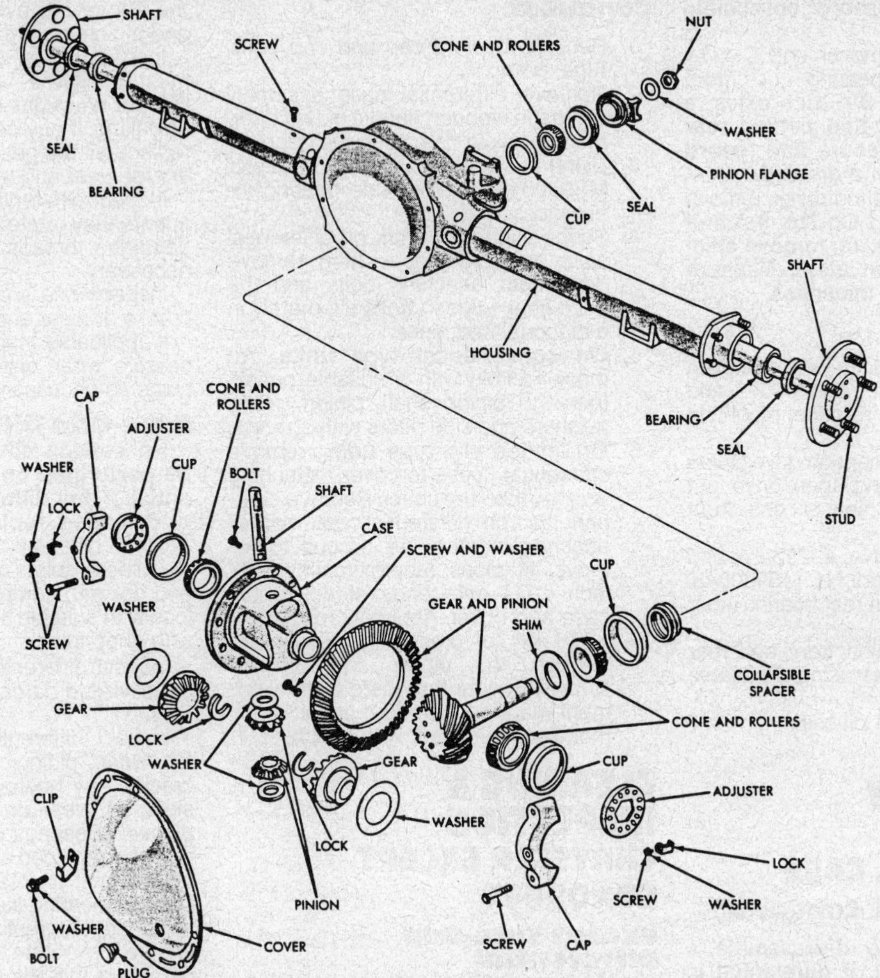


**Fig. 5 Exploded view of rear axle assembly (8¼ & 9¼ axles). Chrysler except Conquest**

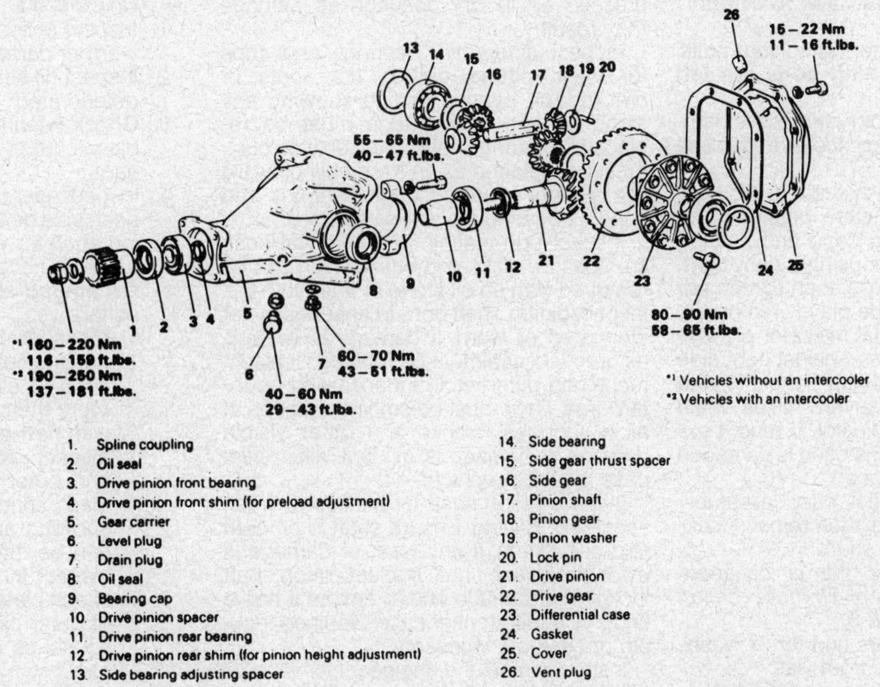


**Fig. 6 Exploded view of standard differential. Conquest**

**be replaced. Discard collapsible spacer.**

4. Using C-4306 remover and C-4171 handle, remove bearing cups from axle housing. **On 8¼ inch axles, a shim will be located behind rear bearing cup. Measure and record shim thickness and discard.**
5. Using suitable bearing puller, remove rear pinion bearing. **On 7¼, 9¼ and some 8¼ inch axles, remove shim from drive pinion stem. Measure and record shim thickness.**

### Conquest

1. Hold spline coupling with Coupling holder tool No. MB990907 and MB9900850 and remove mounting nut.
2. Scribe alignment mark on drive pinion and spline coupling, then drive out front pinion with spacer and front shims.
3. Using puller tool No. C-293-PA and bearing remover tool No. MB990648, remove drive pinion rear bearing inner race from shaft.
4. Remove drive pinion front and rear bearing outer races using a suitable drift.
5. Remove driveshaft oil seal.

# DISASSEMBLY

## DIFFERENTIAL CASE

### Chrysler Except Conquest

**Do not attempt to disassemble a Sure-Grip differential. If differential is defective, replace it as a unit only.**

**Do not remove ring gear from case unless gear set or case are to be replaced or ring gear runout measured in step 7 of "Differential Case Assembly" exceeds .005 inch.**

1. Remove ring gear attaching bolts. **Ring gear attaching bolts are left hand thread.**
2. Using brass drift or non-metallic hammer, tap drive gear loose from case and remove.
3. If ring gear runout exceeded .005 inch, install differential case, bearing cups, adjusters, bearing caps and bearing cap bolts in axle housing. Lightly tighten bearing cap bolts, then tighten adjusters until all side play is removed.
4. Mount suitable dial indicator on axle housing with stylus against right side of ring gear mounting flange. Rotate differential case several times while observing dial indicator. If runout exceeds .003 inch, the case is damaged and must be replaced.
5. Remove differential case assembly from axle housing, then remove lockscrew and pinion shaft.
6. Rotate side gears until pinion gears appear at opening. Remove pinion gears, **Figs. 4 and 5.**
7. Remove side gears and thrust washers, then the case from vise.
8. Using suitable puller, remove differential case bearings.

### Conquest

1. Remove bearing cap and cap bolts, **Figs. 6 and 7.**
2. Remove differential case assembly using the wooden handle of two hammers to avoid damaging the gears.
3. Using puller MB990810 and adapter MB990811, remove side bearing inner races.
4. Scribe alignment mark on differential case and drive gear, then remove drive gear attaching bolts and the drive gear. Loosen bolts alternately in a diagonal sequence.
5. **On conventional type units,** remove lockpin with a suitable punch, then the pinion shaft, pinion gears, washers and side gears with spacers.
6. **On limited slip type units,** remove differential case-to-cover attaching screws, then the cover. Remove components from differential case. If cover attaching screws are difficult to remove, fit pipes (approximately 1.97 inch O.D.) over ends of differential case and cover. Apply approximately 1,760 lbs. of pressure to assembly, through the pipes, and remove screws. Ensure that there is an alignment mark on case and cover. If not, make suitable mark with punch.

# CLEANING & INSPECTION

## CHRYSLER EXCEPT CONQUEST

### Except Sure-Grip Differential

Clean all parts in suitable solvent. Dry all parts except bearings with compressed air or shop towels. Allow bearings to air dry or dry with shop towels. Do not use compressed air to dry bearings as damage may result.

Inspect differential bearings and cups for wear, pitting, galling, flat spots or cracks. Any bearing or cup showing any signs of wear or damage must be replaced. Bearings and respective cups must be replaced as an assembly only. Do not attempt to interchange bearings and cups as bearing life will be affected.

Inspect non-machined differential case surfaces for nicks and burrs which can be removed with an oil stone or fine tooth file. Inspect pinion shaft bore to ensure it is not elongated or worn. If damage is evident, differential case must be replaced. Inspect machined differential surfaces and counterbores. They must be smooth and free of nicks, gouges, cracks and other visible damage. If damage is evident, differential case must be replaced.

Inspect pinion shaft for excessive wear, scoring or galling. Ensure shaft is smooth and concentric. If any wear or damage is evident, replace shaft. Inspect pinion shaft lockpin for damage and to ensure it has a snug fit in differential case. Replace lockpin or case as necessary.

Inspect pinion and ring gears for worn or chipped teeth, cracks, damaged bearing journals or attaching bolt threads. If any of the above are evident, replace ring gear and pinion as a matched set.

Inspect pinion and side gears. Gears must exhibit a uniform contact pattern without any signs of cracks, wear, scoring or galling. If any of the above are evident, replace all the gears. Inspect thrust washers for wear and replace as necessary.

Inspect differential bearing adjusters to ensure they rotate freely. If they bind, repair damaged threads or replace adjuster as necessary.

Inspect axle shaft C-locks for signs of cracks or wear and replace as necessary.

If applicable, inspect thrust block for excessive wear, distortion and cracks. Replace as necessary.

### Sure-Grip Differential

**No service other than cleaning can be performed on the Sure-Grip differential. If any differential parts are worn or damaged, replace unit.**

Clean differential parts in fast evaporating mineral spirits or a dry cleaning solvent and dry with compressed air. Clean bearings with suitable solvent and air dry or dry with shop towels.

Inspect differential case for cracks and other visible damage. Replace as necessary.

Inspect differential bearings and cups for wear, pitting, galling, flat spots or cracks. Any bearing or cup showing any signs of wear or damage must be replaced. Bearings and respective cups must be replaced as an assembly only. Do not attempt to interchange bearings and cups as bearing life will be affected.

Inspect differential bearing adjusters to ensure they rotate freely. If they bind, repair damaged threads or replace adjuster as necessary.

Inspect axle shaft C-locks for signs of cracks or wear and replace as necessary.

## CONQUEST

1. Inspect spline coupling and replace if worn or damaged.
2. Inspect oil seal and replace if worn or deteriorated.
3. Check bearings for wear, damage or discoloration and replace as necessary.
4. Inspect gear carrier, drive pinion, drive gear, side gears, pinion gears and pinion shaft for wear or damage and replace as necessary.
5. **On limited slip type units,** proceed as follows:
   a. Measure the thickness of both inner and outer clutch plates. If difference in clutch plate thickness is more than .004 inch, replace them with new parts.
   b. Inspect friction surfaces of inner and outer clutch plates and preload spring and replace parts showing any signs of severe friction, seizure or heat discoloration.
   c. Inspect inner projections of inner clutch plates and outer projections of outer clutch plates for nicks or scratches and replace as necessary.
   d. Inspect friction and sliding surfaces between pressure ring and

inner clutch plate for wear or damage and replace as necessary.
e. Carefully inspect all mating and sliding surfaces of the pressure ring and replace components as necessary.

# ASSEMBLY & ADJUSTMENT

## CHRYSLER EXCEPT CONQUEST

1. Lubricate all components with rear axle lubricant, then install thrust washers on side gears and position gears in counterbores of differential.
2. Install thrust washers on pinion gears, then mesh pinion gears with side gears exactly 180° apart.
3. Rotate side gears to align pinion gears and thrust washers with pinion shaft holes in case, then install pinion shaft and lock screw. **Torque** lock screw to 90 inch lbs.
4. If ring gear was removed, relieve sharp edge of chamfer on the inside diameter of ring gear with an Arkansas stone. This is to prevent removing metal from case during ring gear installation that may become embedded under the ring gear.
5. Install three pilot studs in case, then heat ring gear with heat lamp or by immersing the gear in hot oil. The temperature should not exceed 300°F. **Do not use a torch to heat ring gear.**
6. Insert new ring gear attaching bolts through case flange and into ring gear, then alternately tighten bolts to 70 ft. lbs.
7. Using arbor press and suitable adapters, install bearings on differential case.
8. Position both bearing cups in axle housing bore ensuring they are not cocked, then select and install rear axle pinion setting gauge as follows:
   a. **On 7¼ inch axles,** assemble pinion locating spacer SP-3244 over main body of tool No. SP-5385 followed by rear bearing cone. Position tool in axle housing and install shaft locating sleeve SP-3245, front bearing cone, compression sleeve SP-3194-B, centralizing washer SP-534 and compression nut SP-3193.
   b. **On 8¼ inch axles,** assemble pinion locating spacer SP-6030 over main body of tool No. SP-5385 followed by rear bearing cone. Position tool in axle housing and install shaft locating sleeve SP-5382, front bearing cone, SP-6022 washer followed by compression sleeve SP-3194-B, centralizing washer SP-534 and compression nut SP-3193.
   c. **On 9¼ inch axles,** assemble pinion locating spacer SP-6017 over main body of tool No. SP-526 followed by rear bearing cone. Position tool in axle housing and install front pinion bearing cone, shaft locating sleeve SP-1730, washer SP-6022, compression sleeve SP-535-A, centralizing washer SP-534 and compression nut SP-533.
9. **On all models,** while holding compression sleeve with tool No. C-3281, tighten compression nut to draw pinion bearing cups into axle housing cup bores. Allow tool to turn several revolutions during tightening operation to prevent brinnelling of bearing cups or cones.
10. Loosen compression nut, then lubricate front and rear pinion bearings with axle lubricant. Tighten compression nut until to produce 15-25 inch lbs. of rotating torque. Rotate pinion several turns to seat bearing rollers.
11. To determine pinion height, assemble tools as follows:
    a. **On 7¼ inch axles,** install gauge block SP-3250 on end of main body SP-5385, then install cap screw SP-536 and tighten securely with SP-531 wrench.
    b. **On 8¼ inch axles,** install gauge block SP-5383 on end of main body SP-5385, then install cap screw SP-536 and tighten securely with SP-531 wrench.
    c. **On 9¼ inch axles,** install gauge block SP-6020 on end of main body SP-526, then install cap screw SP-536 and tighten securely with SP-531 wrench.
12. **On all models,** position crossbore arbor in axle housing differential bearing seats. Tool numbers are as follows:
    a. **On 7¼ inch axles,** use tool No. SP-3243.
    b. **On 8¼ inch axles,** use tool No. SP-6029.
    c. **On 9¼ inch axles,** use tool No. SP-6018.
13. **On all models,** center arbor installed above, so that an approximate equal distance is maintained at both ends. Position a piece of .002 inch shim stock on arbor where bearing cap seats, then install bearing cap and bolts. **Torque** bolts to 10 ft. lbs.
14. Select pinion bearing mounting shim which will fit snugly between crossbore arbor and gauge block. Shims are available in .001 inch increments from .020 inch to .038 inch.
15. Read numbers on pinion shaft head. When number is preceded by a minus sign, add that amount to shim selected in step 14. When number is preceded by a plus sign, subtract that amount from shim selected in step 14.
16. Remove tools from axle housing, then install shim selected above. Refer to **Figs. 4 and 6,** for shim location.
17. Lubricate front and rear pinion bearings with suitable rear axle lubricant, then insert drive pinion and bearing assembly through axle housing. Install new collapsible spacer. Position front bearing cone over pinion stem then the companion flange and pinion nut.
18. **On 7¼ inch and 8¼ axles,** use companion flange holding tool No. C-3281 and installer C-3718 to install front pinion bearing cone on pinion stem. **On 9¼ inch axle,** use companion flange holding tool No. C-3281 and installer C-496 to install front pinion bearing cone on pinion stem. **Use caution during front pinion bearing cone installation not to collapse spacer.**
19. Remove tools used in step 18, then using suitable seal installer, install drive pinion oil seal. Seal is properly installed when seal flange contacts housing housing flange face.
20. While supporting pinion in carrier, install companion flange using tools outlined in step 18, then remove tools and install washer (convex side out) and pinion nut. Do not tighten at this time.
21. **On all models,** hold companion flange with holding tool No. C-3281, then while occasionally rotating pinion shaft to seat bearings, tighten pinion nut just enough to remove pinion endplay.
22. Remove holding tool, then rotate pinion several complete revolutions in either direction and **torque** pinion nut to 210 ft. lbs. Using a suitable torque wrench, measure torque required to rotate pinion and compare to specifications. If not within specifications, tighten pinion nut in small increments until proper preload is obtained. **Do not back off the pinion nut for any reason. If pinion nut is backed off for any reason, a new collapsible spacer must be installed and pinion nut tightened until proper preload is obtained.**
23. Apply suitable axle lubricant to differential bearings and adjusters, then position differential assembly in axle housing. Install bearing caps using marks made during disassembly for reference. Install cap bolts. Tighten top bolt to 10 ft. lbs. while tightening lower bolts finger tight.
24. Using tool No. C-4164, **Fig. 3,** tighten bearing adjusters until bearing freeplay is eliminated, but with some drive gear back lash remaining. Seat bearings by rotating differential assembly. **When rotating bearing adjusters, the bearing cups do not always move directly with them. To ensure accurate adjustment, always rotate differential assembly ½ turn in either direction five to ten times each time an adjustment is made.**
25. Mount suitable dial indicator to housing case with stylus positioned against drive side of gear tooth. Find point of minimum backlash by checking backlash at four points approximately 90° apart around ring gear. Rotate ring gear to position of least backlash. Mark index so all backlash readings will be taken with the same teeth in mesh.
26. Loosen right adjuster and tighten left adjuster until backlash is .003-.004 inch with each adjuster tightened to 10 ft. lbs. Seat bearings as outlined above.

27. **Torque** bearing cap bolts to 45 ft. lbs on 7¼ inch axles, or 100 ft. lbs. on other axles.
28. Using tool No. C-4164, **Fig. 3,** tighten right side adjuster to 70 ft. lbs. on 7¼ inch and 8¼ inch axles, or 75 ft. lbs. on 9¼ inch axles. Seat bearings as outlined above.
29. Continue to tighten right side adjuster and seat bearings until **torque** remains constant at 70 ft. lbs. on 7¼ inch and 8¼ inch axles, or 75 ft. lbs. on 9¼ inch axles.
30. Measure backlash and compare to specifications. If not within specifications, continue to increase tightening torque on right side adjuster and seat bearings until backlash is within specifications.
31. Using tool No. C-4164, **Fig. 3,** tighten left side adjuster to 70 ft. lbs. on 7¼ inch and 8¼ inch axles, or 75 ft. lbs. on 9¼ inch axles. Seat bearings as outlined above.
32. Continue to tighten left side adjuster and seat bearings until **torque** remains constant at 70 ft. lbs. on 7¼ inch and 8¼ inch axles, or 75 ft. lbs. on 9¼ inch axles. If above steps were performed properly, initial torque reading should be 70 ft. lbs. on 7¼ inch and 8¼ inch axles, or 75 ft. lbs. on 9¼ inch axles. If torque reading is substantially less, entire procedure must be repeated.
33. Install adjuster lock screws. **Torque** screws to 90 inch lbs.
34. Apply thin coat of hydrated ferric oxide (yellow oxide of iron) to ring gear teeth, then with load applied at companion flange, rotate ring gear one complete revolution in both directions. This action will leave a distinct contact pattern on the ring gear teeth.
35. Observe tooth contact pattern and compare to **Figs. 8 through 10.** If contact pattern resembles **Fig. 8,** pinion mesh of depth and backlash are set properly and no further adjustments are necessary.
36. If contact pattern resembles **Fig. 9,** the drive pinion is too far away from ring gear center line. To correct this condition, a thicker pinion height shim is required.
37. If contact pattern resembles **Fig. 10,** the drive pinion is too close to the ring gear centerline. To correct this condition, a thinner pinion height shim is required.
38. When correct tooth contact pattern is established, install propeller shaft and axle shafts. Refer to "Propeller Shaft, Replace" and "Axle Shafts, Replace" in the Chrysler "Rear Wheel Drive" chapter for procedures.
39. Remove axle filler plug, then using capacities listed below, fill rear axle with Multi-Purpose Axle Gear Lubricant. On axles equipped with Sure-Grip differential, 4 ounces of MOPAR Hypoid Gear Oil Additive Friction Modifier, part No. 4057100 must be included with every refill.
    a. **On 7¼ inch axles,** 2.5 pints.
    b. **On 8¼ inch axles,** 4.4 pints.
    c. **On 9¼ inch axles,** 4.5 pints.
40. **On all models,** lower vehicle and road test.

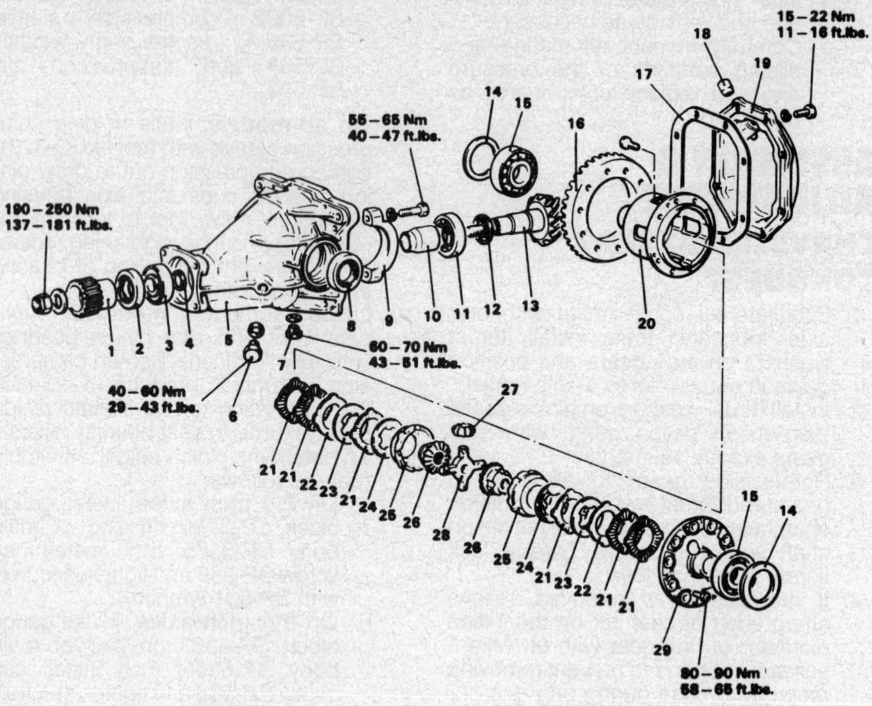

1. Spline coupling
2. Oil seal
3. Drive pinion front bearing
4. Drive pinion front shim (for preload adjustment)
5. Gear carrier
6. Level plug
7. Drain plug
8. Oil seal
9. Bearing cap
10. Drive pinion spacer
11. Drive pinion rear bearing
12. Drive pinion rear shim (for pinion height adjustment)
13. Drive pinion
14. Side bearing adjusting spacer
15. Side bearing
16. Drive gear
17. Gasket
18. Vent plug
19. Cover
20. Differential case (B)
21. Friction plate
22. Spring plate
23. Spring disc
24. Friction disc
25. Pressure ring
26. Side gear
27. Pinion gear
28. Pinion shaft
29. Differential case (A)

**Fig. 7 Exploded view of limited slip differential. Conquest**

## CONQUEST

### Drive Pinion

1. Press drive pinion front and rear bearing outer races into gear carrier, **Fig. 11.**
2. Adjust drive pinion height as follows:
    a. Install tool No. C-462b and drive pinion front and rear bearing into the gear carrier. Apply a thin coat of suitable grease to face of washer on tool.
    b. Tighten nut on tool and measure drive pinion preload, which should be within specifications without oil seal installed. Loosen or tighten nut as necessary to bring preload within specifications.
    c. Position cylinder of gage tool No. MB990552 in side bearing seat of gear carrier, **Fig. 12.**
    d. Using a feeler gauge, measure clearance between the two tools and select drive pinion rear shim(s) corresponding to this measurement.
    e. Install shim(s) to drive pinion, then press rear bearings onto pinion.
3. Adjust drive pinion preload as follows:
    a. Install drive pinion front shim(s) between drive pinion spacer and front bearing inner race.
    b. **Torque** spline coupling retaining nut to specifications, **Figs. 6 and 7,** then measure drive pinion preload, without oil seal, as described in step 2.
    c. Adjust preload, as necessary, by replacing drive pinion front shim(s) or spacer.
4. Remove spline coupling and drive pinion, then drive seal into place using suitable seal installer.
5. Install spline coupling and drive pinion assembly with reference marks

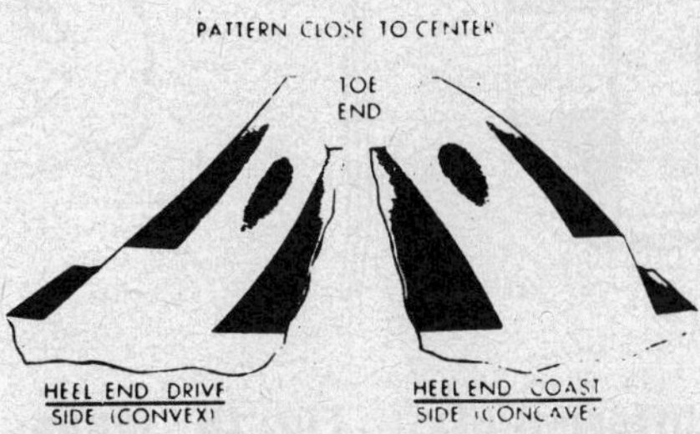


**Fig. 8 Proper tooth contact. Chrysler except Conquest**

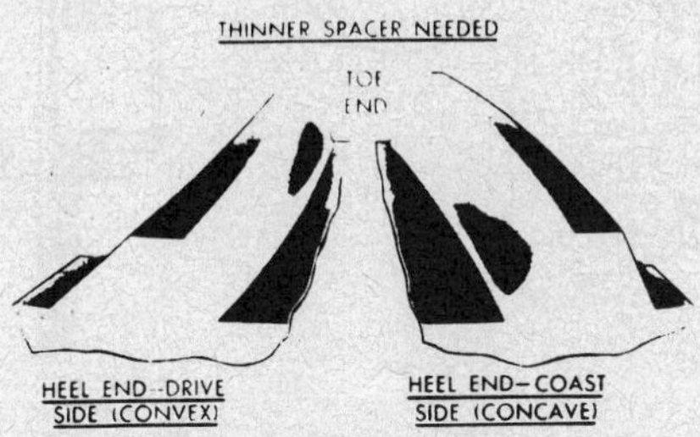


**Fig. 9 Improper tooth contact requiring thinner pinion height shim. Chrysler except Conquest**

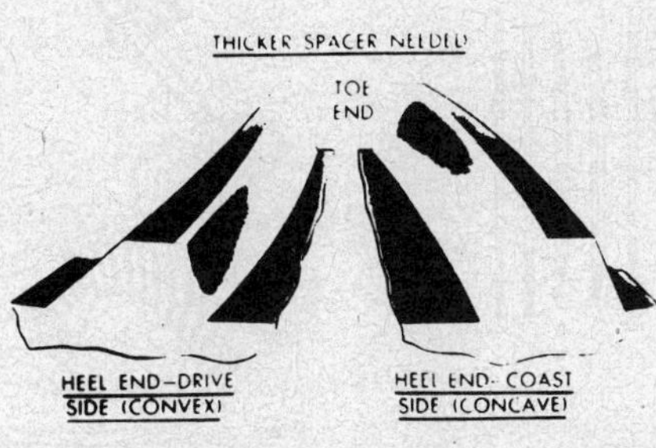


**Fig. 10 Improper tooth contact requiring thicker pinion height shim. Chrysler except Conquest**

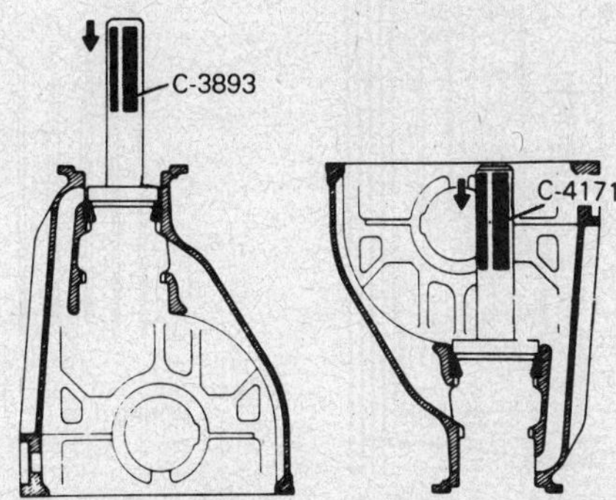


**Fig. 11 Drive pinion bearing race installation. Conquest**

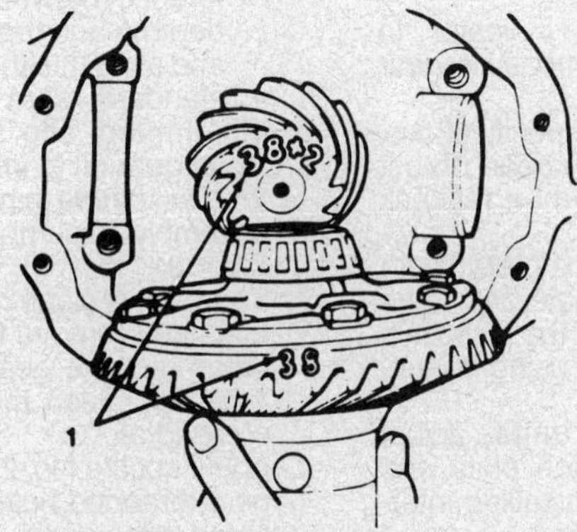


**Fig. 12 Measuring drive pinion height. Conquest**

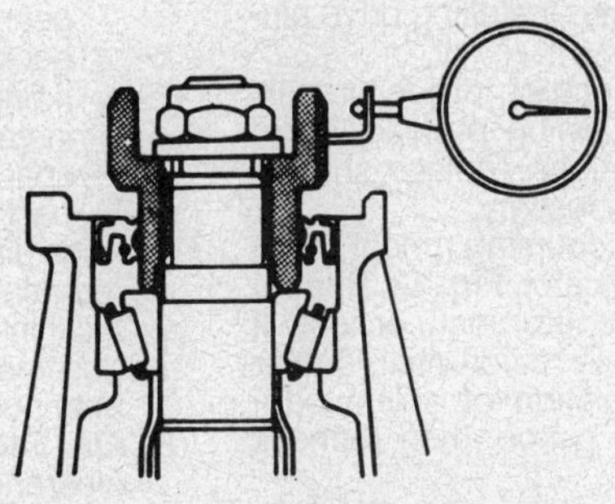

**Fig. 13 Measuring spline coupling runout. Conquest**

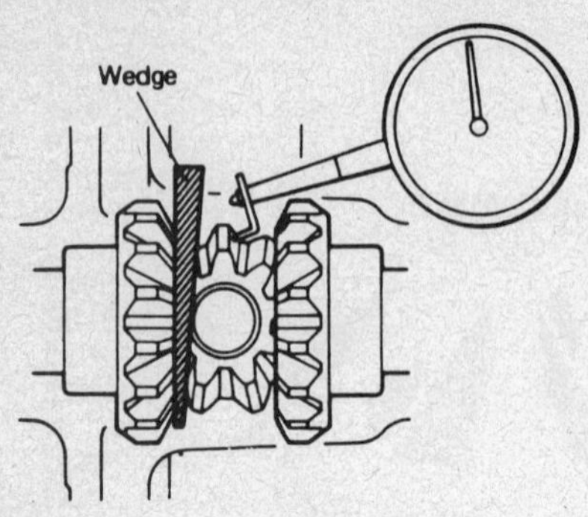


**Fig. 14 Measuring differential gear backlash. Conquest**

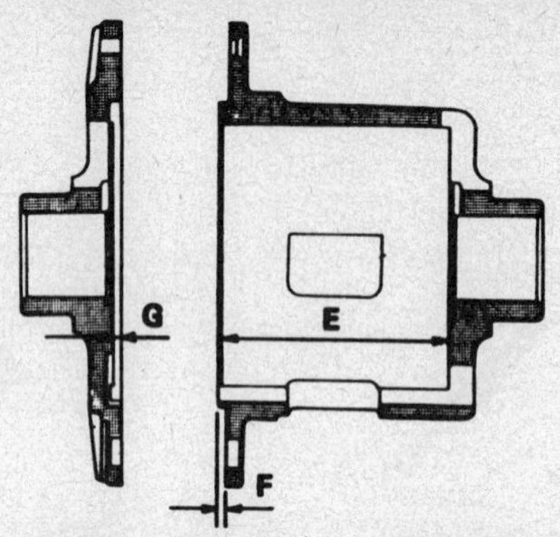


**Fig. 15 Measuring differential case depth. Conquest**

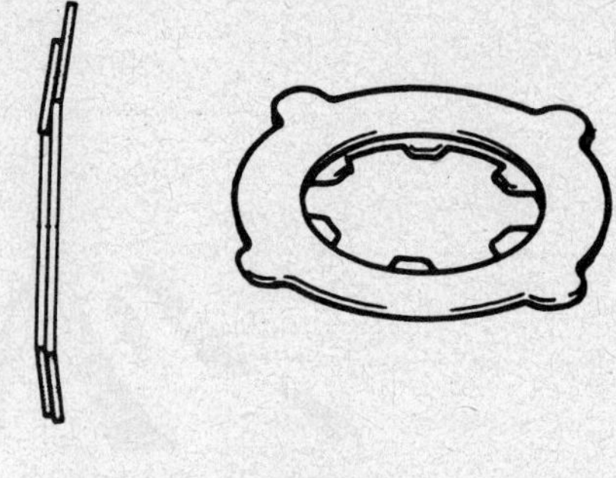

**Fig. 16 Measuring preload spring thickness. Conquest**

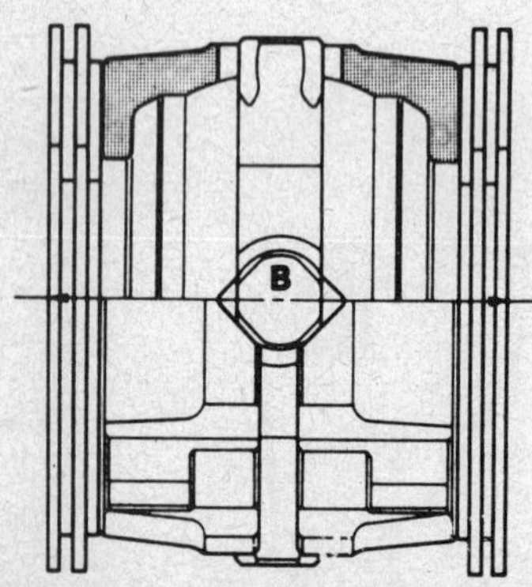


**Fig. 17 Measuring pinion shaft & clutch plate assembly width. Conquest w/limited slip**

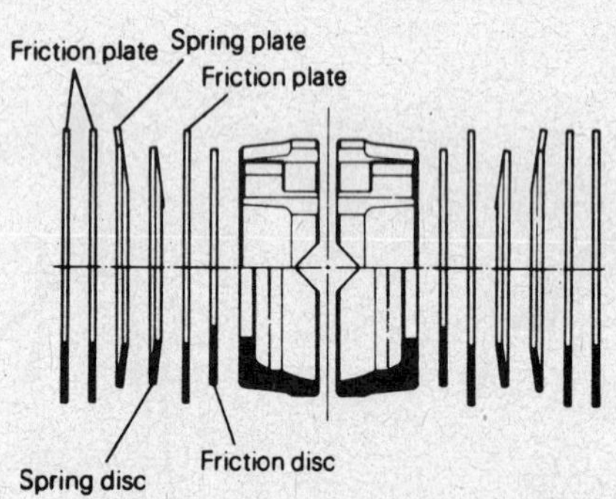


**Fig. 18 Clutch assembly. Conquest w/limited slip**

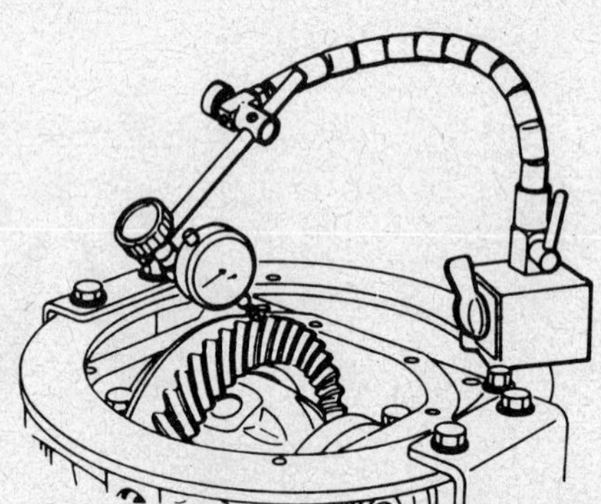

**Fig. 19 Measuring drive gear backlash. Conquest**

aligned. **Torque** spline coupling retaining nut to specifications, **Figs. 6 and 7.** Apply a thin coat of suitable grease to spline coupling washer mating surface before installing drive pinion assembly.

6. Using suitable inch lb. torque wrench, measure drive pinion preload. If not within specifications, replace shim(s) or spacer as necessary.
7. Measure spline coupling runout using suitable dial indicator, **Fig. 13.** Runout should measure .004 inch, or less. If not, disassemble differential carrier and change position of spline coupling and drive pinion, then recheck runout.

## Differential Case Assembly

1. **On conventional type units,** install side gears and thrust spacers, and pinion gears and washers into differential case. Install side gear thrust washers with oil grooves facing side gears.
2. **On all models,** install pinion shaft. Do not install lockpin at this time.
3. Adjust differential gear backlash as follows:
   a. Insert a wedge between side gear and pinion shaft to prevent side gear from turning.
   b. Install suitable dial indicator to gear, **Fig. 14,** and measure gear backlash.
   c. If backlash exceeds specifications, install thicker side gear thrust spacers as needed, then recheck backlash.
4. Align pinion shaft lockpin hole with differential case lockpin hole and drive lockpin into place. Stake the lockpin in position in two places, using a suitable punch.
5. **On limited slip type units,** adjust clearance between clutch plate and differential case when installing internal components as follows:
   a. A = E − F + G, **Fig. 15.**
   b. Measure thickness of preload spring, **Fig. 16.** The total thickness of both springs will be considered as value L.
   c. Assemble pinion shaft holder, pinion shafts, pressure rings and inner and outer clutch plates, and measure the total width, **Fig. 17.** This measurement will be considered as value B.
   d. Select shims and adjust so that difference between differential case depth A and the sum of values L, B and shim thickness C becomes the standard value.
6. **On limited slip type units,** apply clean gear oil to internal components, then assemble in reverse order of disassembly. Assemble clutch as shown, **Fig. 18.**
7. Thoroughly clean drive gear attaching bolts and remove tape from threaded holes of drive gear using an M10 X 1.25 tap. Clean the holes with compressed air.
8. Apply Loctite No. 270, or 271, to drive gear threaded holes, then install gear onto case with reference marks aligned. **Torque** attaching bolts alternately, in a diagonal sequence, to 58-65 ft. lbs.
9. Press side bearings into differential case using bearing installer tool No. MB990802.
10. Adjust drive gear backlash as follows:
    a. Install side bearing adjusting spacers, thinner than those removed, to the side gear bearings,

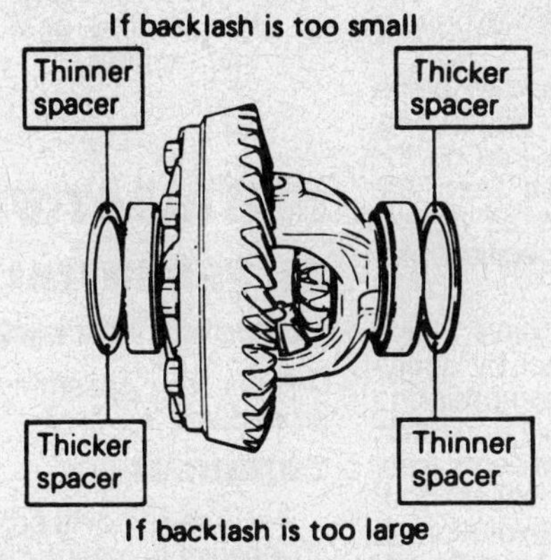
If backlash is too small
Thinner spacer
Thicker spacer
Thicker spacer
Thinner spacer
If backlash is too large

**Fig. 20 Adjusting drive gear backlash. Conquest**

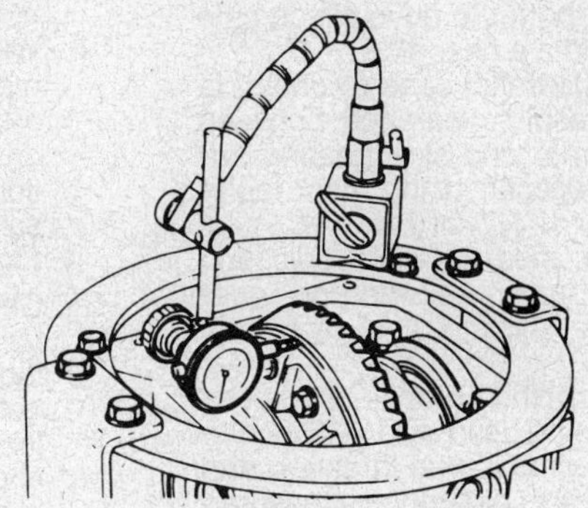

**Fig. 22 Measuring drive gear runout. Conquest**

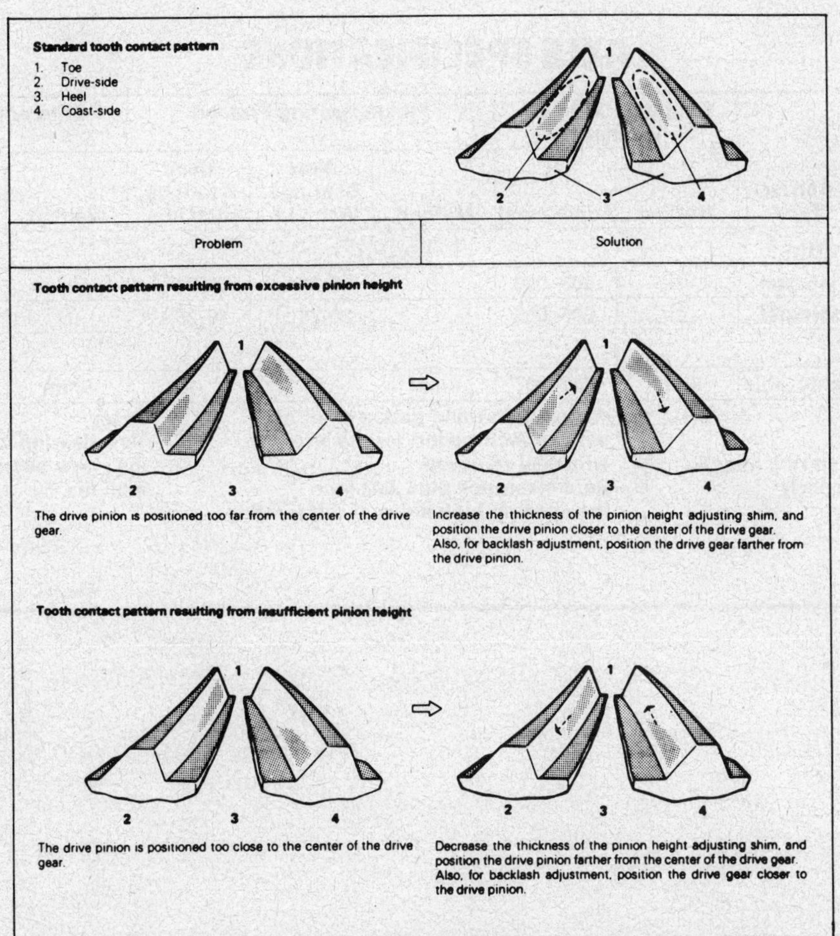
Standard tooth contact pattern
1. Toe
2. Drive-side
3. Heel
4. Coast-side
1
2
3
4
Problem
Solution
Tooth contact pattern resulting from excessive pinion height
The drive pinion is positioned too far from the center of the drive gear.
Increase the thickness of the pinion height adjusting shim, and position the drive pinion closer to the center of the drive gear.
Also, for backlash adjustment, position the drive gear farther from the drive pinion.
Tooth contact pattern resulting from insufficient pinion height
The drive pinion is positioned too close to the center of the drive gear.
Decrease the thickness of the pinion height adjusting shim, and position the drive pinion farther from the center of the drive gear.
Also, for backlash adjustment, position the drive gear closer to the drive pinion.

**Fig. 21 Gear tooth contact pattern check. Conquest**

then install differential case assembly into gear carrier. Select adjusting spacers of the same thickness for both the drive pinion side and the drive gear side.

b. Push differential case to one side and measure clearance between gear carrier and side bearing adjusting spacer using two feeler gauges.
c. Remove side bearing adjusting spacers from one side and measure the thickness of adjusting spacers.
d. To determine proper thickness spacer to be used, add .002 inch to thickness measured in step c and one-half the clearance measured in step b.
e. Install one pair of the correct spacers each to the drive pinion side and drive gear side.
f. Install differential case assembly, with side bearing adjusting spacers, into gear carrier. Gently tap spacers with a brass drift to seat them on bearing outer race.
g. Install bearing cap with reference marks aligned. **Torque** cap bolts to 40-47 ft. lbs.
h. With drive pinion locked in place, measure drive gear backlash, **Fig. 19,** at four different points on the drive gear. If not within specifications, replace spacers as necessary to bring within specifications, **Fig. 20.**
i. Check drive gear and drive pinion for proper tooth contact by applying suitable marking compound to both surfaces of drive gear teeth. Insert a brass rod between carrier and case and rotate spline coupling by hand one revolution in each direction. **Fig. 21,** while applying a load of approximately 2 ft. lbs. to the drive pinion. Adjust pinion height and backlash as needed until tooth contact pattern resembles standard pattern, **Fig. 21.**

11. Measure drive gear runout using a suitable dial indicator, **Fig. 22.** If runout exceeds .002 inch, change position of drive gear in differential case and recheck.

# INSTALLATION

## DIFFERENTIAL CASE

### Chrysler Except Conquest

Refer To "Assembly And Adjustment" procedure.

### Conquest

Reverse removal procedure. Apply suitable sealer to mating surfaces of vent plug, cover, rear cover and gasket.

## DRIVE PINION

### Chrysler Except Conquest

Refer To "Assembly And Adjustment" procedure.

# AXLE SPECIFICATIONS

| Year | Model | Carrier Type | Ring Gear & Pinion Backlash | | Pinion Bearing Preload | | | Differential Bearing Preload | | |
|---|---|---|---|---|---|---|---|---|---|---|
| | | | Method | Adjustment | Method | New Bearings, Inch Lbs. | Used Bearings, Inch Lbs. | Method | New Bearings, Inch Lbs. | Used Bearings, Inch Lbs. |
| **Chrysler Except Conquest** | | | | | | | | | | |
| 1989 | 7¼" | Integral | ② | .003-.006 | ① | 15-30④ | 10-25④ | ② | ③ | ③ |
| | 8¼" | Integral | ② | .005-.008 | ① | 20-35④ | 10-25④ | ② | ③ | ③ |
| **Conquest** | | | | | | | | | | |
| 1989 | — | Removable | Shim | .005-.007 | Shim | ⑥ | — | Shim | ⑤ | ⑤ |

①—Collapsible spacer.
②—Threaded adjusters.
③—Preload is correct when ring gear & pinion backlash is properly adjusted.
④—Adjust by turning pinion shaft nut with an inch-pound torque wrench with seal removed.
⑤—Zero clearance plus .002 inch installed on both sides of differential case.
⑥—New bearing with seal, 3.5–4.3 inch lbs.; New bearing less seal, 1.3–2.2 inch lbs.

# MANUAL STEERING GEARS

## INDEX



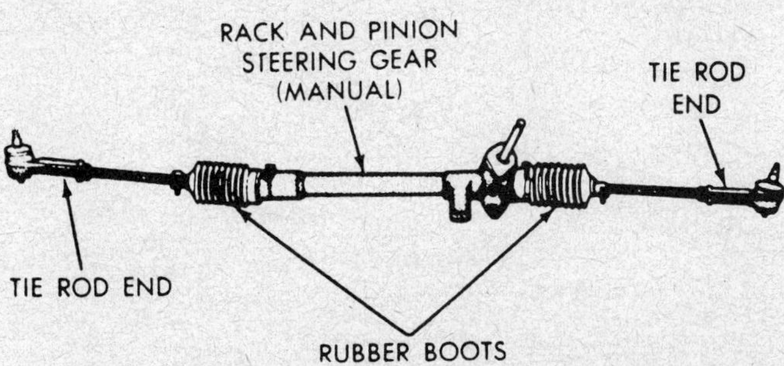


**Fig. 1 Manual rack & pinion steering gear. Chrysler Domestic Front Wheel Drive Vehicles**

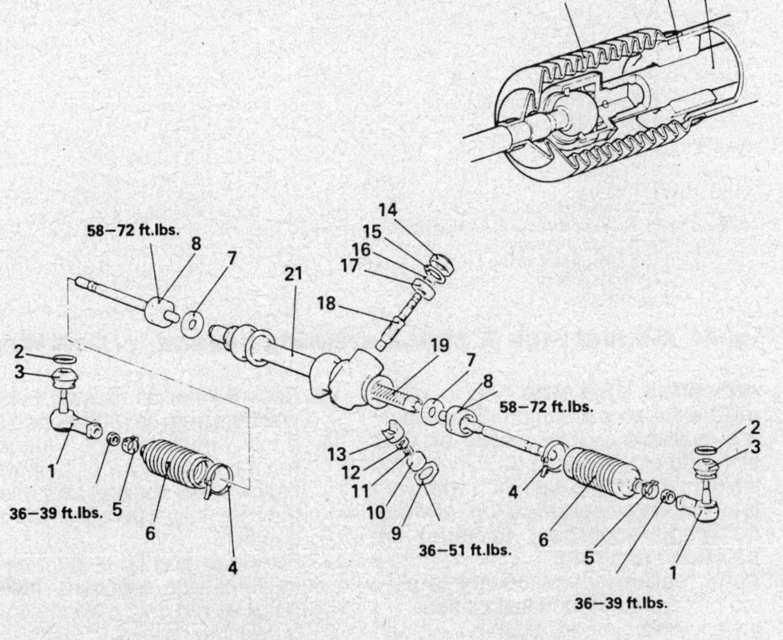


1. Tie rod end
2. Clip ring
3. Dust cover
4. Band
5. Clip
6. Bellows
7. Tab washer
8. Tie rod
9. Locking nut
10. Rack support cover
11. Rack support spring
12. Cushion rubber
13. Rack support
14. Oil seal
15. Snap ring
16. Snap ring
17. Bearing
18. Pinion
19. Rack
20. Rack bushing
21. Gear housing

**Fig. 2 Manual rack & pinion steering assembly. Colt Vista**

# CHRYSLER DOMESTIC FRONT WHEEL DRIVE VEHICLES

## DESCRIPTION

The steering gear assembly used on Chrysler Corp. front wheel drive vehicles, consists of a housing which contains a toothed rack, a pinion, rack slipper and rack slipper spring, **Fig. 1.** The steering gear rack and pinion assembly converts rotational movement of the pinion assembly into transverse movement of the rack. Tie rods and tie rod ends transmit this movement to the steering arms and wheels while accommodating suspension movement at the same time. The tie rods are coupled to the ends of the rack. This connection is protected by a bellows type oil seal which retains steering gear lubricant. The pinion runs on straddle-mounted ball bearings. The lower bearing is incorporated in the pinion housing. The upper bearing is swagged to the pinion shaft. Lock stops are built into the steering gear.

## STEERING SERVICE

**The steering gear cannot be adjusted or repaired. If a malfunction occurs, the entire rack and pinion assembly must be replaced. If bellows seal is leaking or damaged, remove gear from vehicle. Drain, clean and lube gear with 1/4 pt. of MS-5644 (90 weight) hypoid oil. Replace damaged or leaking bellows.**

# EAGLE MEDALLION

## DESCRIPTION

The Manual Steering Gear is not serviceable and should only be replaced as an assembly.

## GEAR PRELOAD, ADJUST

**The manual steering gear should not be replaced until preload has been checked and adjusted. Incorrect preload can cause steering gear play, roughness or steering wander. The preload adjustment procedure is performed with the gear installed in the vehicle. Adjust preload as follows:**

1. Unlock tabs on the adjusting nut.
2. Pry tabs upward and out of the notches in the gear housing.

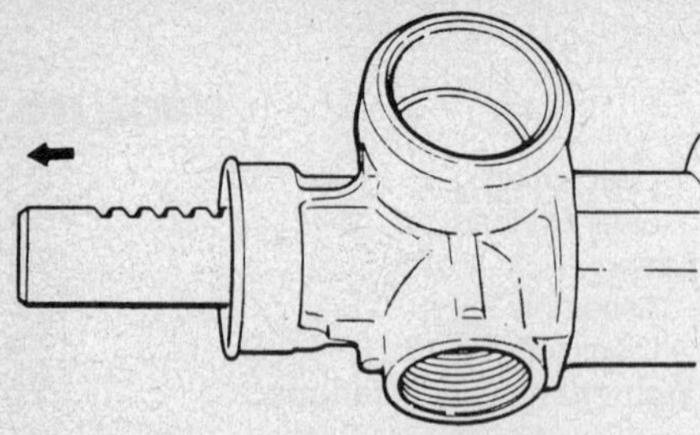

**Fig. 3 Rack removal direction. Colt, Colt Vista, Colt Wagon, Laser & Eagle Summit.**

3. Tighten adjusting nut until gear turning effort increases.
4. Back off adjuster nut one notch.
5. Secure adjusting nut by seating nut tabs into the corresponding housing notches.

## COLT VISTA

Refer to **Fig. 2** when performing the following procedure.

### DISASSEMBLY

1. Place steering gear assembly in a suitable soft-jawed vise.
2. Remove outer tie rod ends, clip rings, dust covers, bands, clips and bellows.
3. Separate tab washers from inner tie rods using a chisel, then remove inner tie rods and tab washers.
4. Remove rack support cover lock nut, then the rack support cover using torque wrench socket MB990607-A or equivalent.
5. Remove rack support spring, cushion rubber and rack support.
6. Remove pinion oil seal and snap rings, then the pinion and bearing assembly.
7. Remove pinion bearing from pinion using a suitable press and steering/pinion gear remover/installer MB990783 or equivalent.
8. Remove rack from gear housing by pulling in direction shown in **Fig. 3. If rack is pulled from housing in wrong direction, rack bushing in gear housing may be damaged by rack threads.**
9. Inspect rack support for uneven wear or damage, rack support spring for deterioration, rack pinion tooth surfaces for wear or damage, pinion bearing for noise, uneven rotation or damage and rack bushing for damage. Replace as necessary.

### ASSEMBLY

1. Apply Mopar multi-mileage lubricant 2525035 or equivalent to rack tooth surfaces, rack bushing and pinion needle bearing in rack housing.
2. Install rack into gear housing opposite of removal.
3. Press pinion bearing onto pinion using steering/pinion gear remover/installer MB990783 or equivalent, then install small snap ring.
4. Install pinion and bearing assembly into housing, then select and install appropriate large snap ring to minimize axial play of pinion. Snap rings are available in thicknesses of .062 inch with blue marking, .065 inch with white marking and .068 inch with yellow marking. **Identification should be made according to color of paint on snap ring.**
5. Apply multi-mileage lubricant to pinion oil seal lip, then install oil seal.
6. Install rack support, cushion rubber and rack support spring.
7. Apply multi-mileage lubricant to inside of rack support cover, and a semi-drying sealant to threaded part of locknut.
8. With rack placed in center position, attach rack support cover to gear housing, then torque cover to specifications using torque wrench socket MB990607-A or equivalent. Back off cover approximately 30-60°, then install and torque locking nut to specifications.
9. Install tab washers and inner tie rods, then torque inner tie rods to specifications.
10. Secure inner tie rods by bending tab washers onto tie rod stepped portions.
11. Apply multi-mileage lubricant to mounting surfaces of bellows, install bellows into position and ensure that they are not twisted, then the clips and bands.
12. Fill inside and lip of dust cover with multi-mileage lubricant, install onto outer tie rod end, then fit clip ring securely into groove.
13. Install outer tie rod end locknuts, then the tie rod ends.
14. Adjust so that length between outer lip of bellows and inner side of locknut is 6.7-6.8 inches, then torque locknuts to specifications and recheck length.
15. Check steering gear for total pinion starting torque as follows:
    a. Rotate pinion gear at a rate of one revolution every 4 to 6 seconds using preload socket CT-1108 and a suitable torque wrench. Starting torque should be 6-11 inch lbs. **Measure starting torque through whole stroke of rack.**

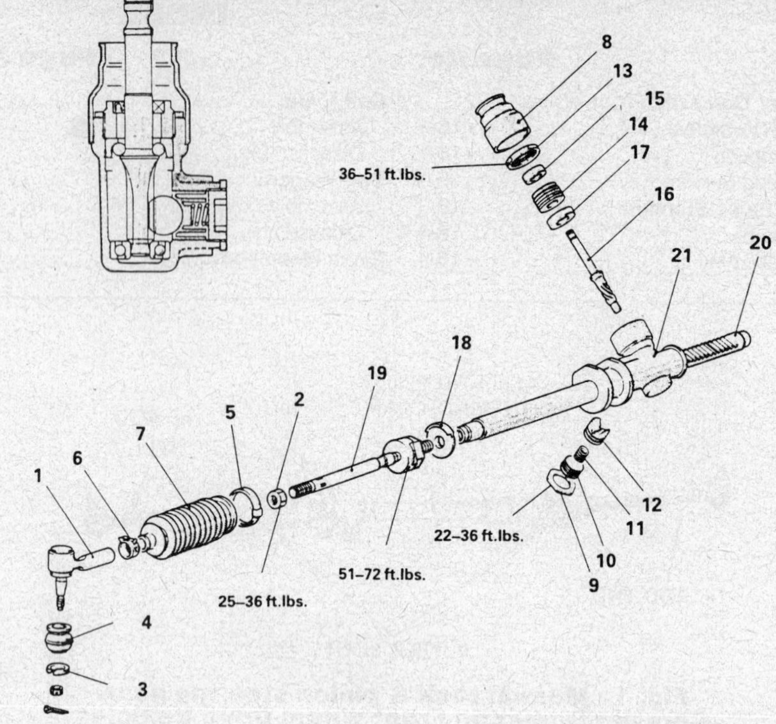


1. Tie rod end
2. Tie rod end locking nut
3. Snap ring
4. Dust cover
5. Band
6. Clip
7. Bellows
8. Joint cover
9. Rack support cover locking nut
10. Rack support cover
11. Rack support spring
12. Rack support
13. Lock nut
14. Top cover
15. Oil seal
16. Pinion
17. Bearing
18. Tab washer
19. Tie rod
20. Rack
21. Gear housing

**Fig. 4 Manual rack & pinion steering assembly. Colt Wagon**

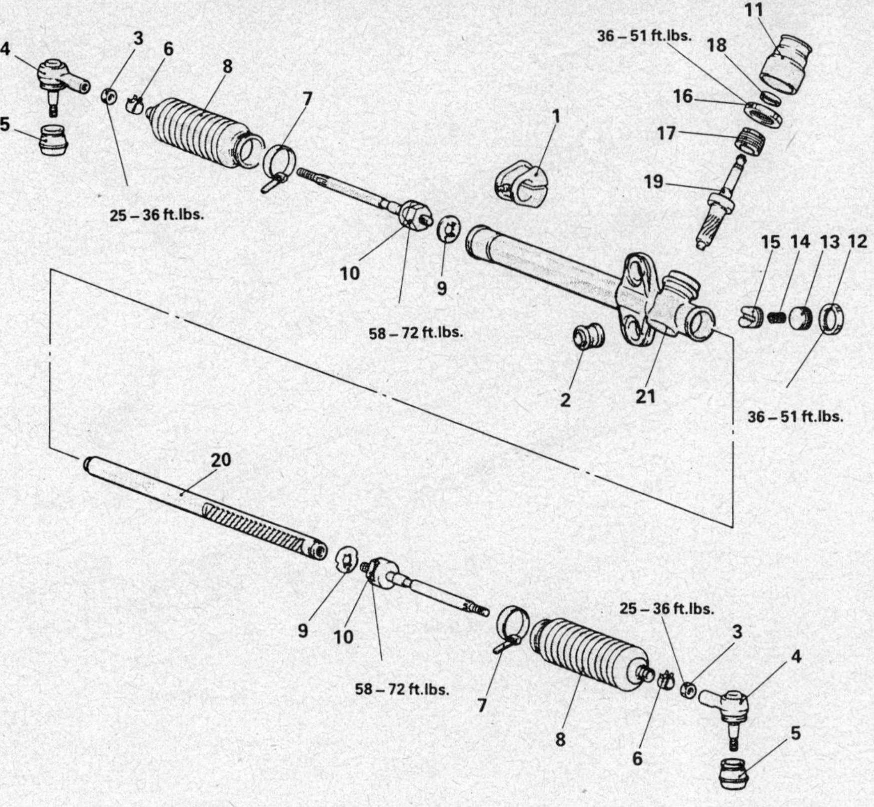


1. Mounting rubber
2. Mounting bush
3. Tie rod end locking nuts
4. Tie rod end
5. Dust covers
6. Bellows clips
7. Bellows bands
8. Bellows
9. Tab washers
10. Tie rod
11. Joint cover
    Adjustment of total pinion torque
12. Locking nut
13. Rack support cover
14. Rack support spring
15. Rack support
16. Locking nut
17. Top cover
18. Oil seal
19. Pinion
20. Rack
21. Rack housing

**Fig. 5 Manual rack & pinion steering assembly. Colt & Eagle Summit**

   b. If measured values are not within specifications, readjust rack support cover, then recheck.
   c. If still not within specifications, check rack support cover, rack support spring and rack support and replace parts as necessary.

## COLT WAGON

Refer to **Fig. 4** when performing the following procedure.

### DISASSEMBLY

1. Place steering gear assembly in a suitable soft-jawed vise.
2. Remove outer tie rod ends, locking nuts, snap rings, dust covers, bands, clips and bellows.
3. Remove joint cover, rack support cover locknut, then the rack support cover using torque wrench socket MB990607-A or equivalent.
4. Hold top cover with a suitable wrench, then loosen locknut using housing locking nut spanner MB990913 or equivalent.
5. Remove locknut and top cover, pry oil seal out of top cover using a suitable screwdriver, then remove pinion bearing.
6. Separate tab washers from inner tie rods using a chisel, then remove inner tie rods and tab washers using care not to twist rack in gear housing.
7. Remove rack from gear housing by pulling in direction shown in **Fig. 3. If rack is pulled from housing in wrong direction, rack bushing in gear housing may be damaged by rack threads.**
8. Inspect rack support for uneven wear or damage, rack support spring for deterioration, rack pinion tooth surfaces for wear or damage, pinion bearing for noise, uneven rotation or damage and rack bushing for damage. Replace as necessary.

### ASSEMBLY

1. Apply Mopar multi-mileage lubricant 2525035 or equivalent to rack tooth surfaces, rack bushing and pinion needle bearing in rack housing.
2. Install rack into gear housing opposite of removal and stop rack when portion of rack where teeth have been removed is aligned with pinion housing.
3. Install pinion and bearing into housing and ensure that pinion rotates freely in this position.
4. Install tab washers and inner tie rods, then torque inner tie rods to specifications.
5. Secure inner tie rods by bending tab washers onto tie rod stepped portions.
6. Apply multi-mileage lubricant to inner surface of pinion oil seal, then install oil seal into top cover.
7. Install top cover to pinion and tighten so that a rotating torque of 0.9-2.6 inch lbs. is achieved. **Check rotating torque using a suitable torque wrench and preload socket CT-1108 or equivalent.**
8. Install top cover locknut, hold top cover with a suitable wrench and torque locknut to specifications using housing locking nut spanner, then recheck rotating torque.
9. Install rack support, rack support spring and rack support cover, place rack in a neutral position and torque rack support cover to specifications using torque wrench socket, then back off 20-25°.
10. Rotate pinion gear at a rate of one revolution every 4 to 6 seconds using preload socket CT-1108 and a suitable torque wrench. Total rotating torque should be 6-11 inch lbs. **Measure total rotating torque through whole stroke of rack.**
11. Back off rack support cover in increments of approximately 5° until total rotating torque of pinion is adjusted to specifications.
12. While holding rack support cover with a suitable wrench, torque locking nut to specifications.
13. Install bellows into position and ensure that they are not twisted, then the clips and bands.
14. Fill inside and lip of dust cover with multi-mileage lubricant, install onto outer tie rod end, then fit clip ring securely into groove.
15. Install outer tie rod end locknuts, then the tie rod ends.
16. Adjust so that length between outer lip of bellows and inner side of locknut is 6.3 inches, then torque locknuts to specifications and recheck length.
17. Recheck total rotating torque of pinion. If not within specifications, readjust rack support cover.

## COLT & EAGLE SUMMIT

Refer to **Fig. 5** when performing the following procedure.

## DISASSEMBLY

1. Place steering gear assembly in a suitable soft-jawed vise.
2. Remove mounting rubber and bushings, outer tie rod ends, locking nuts, dust covers, bands, clips and bellows.
3. Separate tab washers from inner tie rods using a chisel, then remove inner tie rods and tab washers.
4. Remove joint cover, locking nut, then the rack support cover using torque wrench socket MB990607-A or equivalent.
5. Remove rack support spring and rack support.
6. Remove pinion locking nut, top cover, oil seal, then the pinion.
7. Remove rack from gear housing by pulling in direction shown in **Fig. 3. If rack is pulled from housing in wrong direction, rack bushing in gear housing may be damaged by rack threads.**
8. Inspect rack support for uneven wear or damage, rack support spring for deterioration, rack pinion tooth surfaces for wear or damage, pinion bearing for noise, uneven rotation or damage and rack bushing for damage. Replace as necessary.

## ASSEMBLY

1. Apply Mopar multi-mileage lubricant 2525035 or equivalent to rack tooth surfaces and rack bushing. **Ensure that grease does not obstruct air passage of rack bushing.**
2. Install rack into gear housing opposite of removal.
3. Apply multi-mileage lubricant to toothed surface of pinion, then install into rack housing.
4. Press oil seal into top cover, then apply semi-drying sealant to threaded portion of top cover.
5. Install top cover and locking nut, then torque locking nut to specifications.
6. Apply a coating of multi-mileage lubricant to surface of rack support that contacts rack, then install rack support.
7. Fill inner side of rack support spring with multi-mileage lubricant, then install rack support spring.
8. Apply a coating of semi-drying sealant to threaded part of rack support cover, then install rack support cover.
9. With rack placed in center position, torque cover to specifications using torque wrench socket.
10. In neutral position, rotate pinion shaft at a rate of one revolution every 4 to 6 seconds using preload socket CT-1108 and a suitable torque wrench. Back off cover approximately 30-60° and adjust torque to 3-12 inch lbs. **When adjusting, set torque at its highest end, ensure that there is no ratcheting or catching when operating rack towards shaft direction. Measure total rotating torque through whole stroke of rack.**
11. Install and torque locking nut to specifications.
12. Install joint cover, tab washers and inner tie rods, then torque inner tie rods to specifications.
13. Secure inner tie rods by bending tab washers onto tie rod stepped portions.
14. Apply multi-mileage lubricant to mounting surfaces of bellows, install bellows into position and ensure that they are not twisted, then the clips and bands.
15. Fill inside and lip of dust cover with multi-mileage lubricant, install onto outer tie rod end.
16. Install outer tie rod end locknuts, then the tie rod ends.
17. Adjust so that length between outer lip of bellows and inner side of locknut is 7.2 inches, then torque locknuts to specifications and recheck length.
18. Install mounting rubber and bushings.

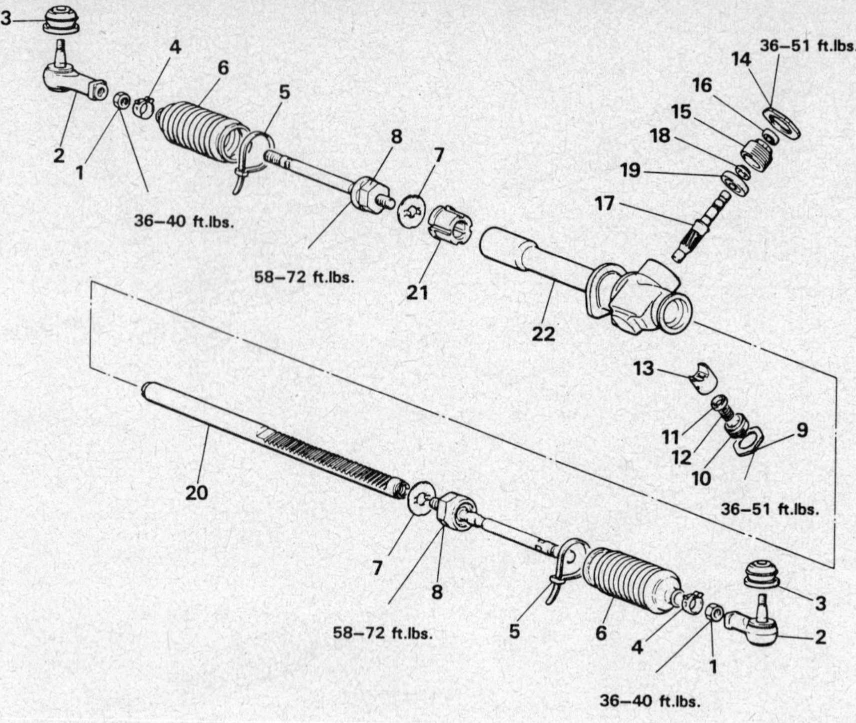


1. Tie-rod end locking nuts
2. Tie-rod end
3. Dust covers
4. Bellows clips
5. Bellows bands
6. Bellows
7. Tab washers
8. Tie-rod
Adjustment of total pinion torque
9. Locking nut
10. Rack support cover
11. Cushion rubber
12. Rack support spring
13. Rack support
14. Locking nut
15. Top plug
16. Oil seal
17. Pinion
18. Pinion collar
19. Ball bearing
20. Rack
21. Rack bushing
22. Rack housing

**Fig. 6 Manual rack & pinion steering assembly. Laser**

## LASER

Refer to **Fig. 6** when performing the following procedure.

## DISASSEMBLY

1. Place steering gear assembly in a suitable soft-jawed vise.
2. Remove outer tie rod ends and locking nuts, then place tie rod ends in a suitable soft-jawed vise and remove dust covers using a hammer and screwdriver.
3. Remove bellows clips, bands, and bellows.
4. Separate tab washers from inner tie rods using a chisel, then remove inner tie rods and tab washers.
5. Remove rack support cover lock nut, rack support cover, rack support spring, cushion rubber and rack support.
6. Remove top plug lock nut, top plug, pinion oil seal, pinion collar, then the pinion and bearing assembly.
7. Remove pinion bearing from pinion using a suitable press and steering/pinion gear remover/installer MB990783 or equivalent.
8. Remove rack from gear housing by pulling in direction shown in **Fig. 3. If rack is pulled from housing in wrong direction, rack bushing in gear housing may be damaged by rack threads.**

9. Remove rack bushing from rack housing.
10. Inspect rack support for uneven wear or damage, rack support spring for deterioration, rack pinion tooth surfaces for wear or damage, pinion bearing for noise, uneven rotation or damage and rack bushing for damage. Replace as necessary.

## ASSEMBLY

1. Apply Mopar multi-mileage lubricant 2525035 or equivalent to rack tooth surfaces, rack bushing and pinion needle bearing in rack housing.
2. Install rack bushing, then the rack into gear housing opposite of removal.
3. Press pinion bearing onto pinion using steering/pinion gear remover/installer MB990783 or equivalent.
4. Apply multi-mileage lubricant to toothed surface of pinion, install pinion and bearing assembly into housing, then the pinion collar.
5. Press oil seal into top plug, apply semi-drying sealant to threaded portion of top plug, install top plug, then the top plug locking nut and torque to specifications.
6. Apply multi-mileage lubricant to surface of rack support that contacts rack, then install rack support to rack housing.
7. Apply multi-mileage lubricant to inner side of rack support spring, then install rack support spring to rack housing.
8. Install rubber cushion to rack support cover, apply a coating of semi-drying sealant to threaded part of rack support cover, install rack support cover to rack housing, then the lock nut.
9. With rack placed in center position, torque cover to specifications.
10. In a neutral position, rotate pinion shaft at a rate of one revolution every 4 to 6 seconds using preload socket CT-1108 and a suitable torque wrench. Return rack support cover 30-60° and adjust torque as follows:
    a. From 0-90°, torque should be 5-11 inch lbs., from 90-650°, torque should be 2-9 inch lbs.
11. When adjusting, set at highest value, ensure that there is no ratcheting or catching when operating rack towards shaft direction.
12. If specified values cannot be obtained, check rack support cover components and replace as necessary.
13. Install and torque locking nut to specifications.
14. Install tab washers and inner tie rods, then torque inner tie rods to specifications.
15. Secure inner tie rods by bending tab washers onto tie rod stepped portions.
16. Pack tie rod bellows lock groove with suitable silicone grease, install bellows into position and ensure that they are not twisted, then the clips and bands.
17. Fill inside and lip of dust covers with multi-mileage lubricant, apply semi-drying sealant to dust covers, then press dust covers onto tie rod ends using front axle base MB990776-A or equivalent.
18. Install outer tie rod end locknuts, then the tie rod ends.
19. Adjust so that length between outer lip of bellows and inner side of tie rod end is 7.68-7.76 inches, then torque locknuts to specifications and recheck length.

## TIGHTENING SPECIFICATIONS

| Model | Component | Torque/Ft. Lbs. |
|---|---|---|
| Colt & Summit | Inner Tie Rod End | 58–72 |
| | Outer Tie Rod End Locknut | 25–36 |
| | Rack Support Cover | 11 |
| | Rack Support Cover Locknut | 36–51 |
| | Top Cover Locknut | 36–51 |
| Colt Vista | Inner Tie Rod End | 58–72 |
| | Outer Tie Rod End Locknut | 36–39 |
| | Rack Support Cover | 5–7 |
| | Rack Support Cover Locknut | 36–51 |
| | Top Cover Locknut | 36–51 |
| Colt Wagon | Inner Tie Rod End | 51–72 |
| | Outer Tie Rod End Locknut | 25–36 |
| | Rack Support Cover | 2–5 |
| | Rack Support Cover Locknut | 22–36 |
| | Top Cover Locknut | 36–51 |
| Laser | Inner Tie Rod End | 58–72 |
| | Outer Tie Rod End Locknut | 36–40 |
| | Rack Support Cover | 11 |
| | Rack Support Cover Locknut | 36–51 |
| | Top Cover Locknut | 36–51 |

# POWER STEERING

## TABLE OF CONTENTS



# Application Chart

## POWER STEERING PUMPS

| Year | Model | Type | Page No. |
|---|---|---|---|
| Front | | | |
| 1989 | Chrysler Conquest | Type 5 | 18-23 |
| | Chrysler Domestic Front Wheel Drive Vehicles | ① | — |
| | Chrysler Rear Wheel Drive Except Conquest | Type 1 | 18-15 |
| | Eagle Medallion | Type 4 | 18-21 |
| | Colt | Type 6 | 18-23 |
| | Colt Wagon | Type 6 | 18-23 |
| | Colt Vista | Type 7 | 18-23 |
| | Eagle Premier | ② | — |
| | Eagle Summit | ③ | — |
| 1990 | Chrysler Domestic Front Wheel Drive Vehicles | ① | — |
| | Colt | Type 6 | 18-23 |
| | Colt Wagon | Type 6 | 18-23 |
| | Colt Vista | Type 7 | 18-23 |
| | Eagle Premier | ② | — |
| | Eagle Summit | ③ | — |
| | Eagle Talon | Type 7 | 18-23 |
| | Laser | Type 7 | 18-23 |
| | Monaco | ② | — |

*Continued*

## POWER STEERING PUMPS—Continued

| Year | Model | Type | Page No. |
|---|---|---|---|
| **Front** | | | |
| 1991 | Chrysler Domestic Front Wheel Drive Vehicles | ① | — |
| | Colt Vista | Type 7 | 18-23 |
| | Colt | Type 8 | 18-23 |
| | Eagle Premier | Type 4 | 18-21 |
| | Eagle Summit | Type 8 | 18-23 |
| | Eagle Talon | Type 9 | 18-23 |
| | Laser | Type 9 | 18-23 |
| | Monaco | Type 4 | 18-21 |
| | Stealth | Type 10 | 18-27 |
| **Rear** | | | |
| 1991 | Stealth | Type 11④ | 18-28 |

①—Vehicles may be equipped with either Type 1-Saginaw or Type 2-ZF vane type pump.

②—2.5L engine, Type 3-TC-Series vane type pump; 3.0L engine, Type 4-N-Series vane type pump.

③—1.5L engine, Type 6-vane type pump; 1.6L engine, Type 8-vane type pump.

④—AWD models.

## POWER STEERING GEARS

| Year | Model | Type | Page No. |
|---|---|---|---|
| **Front** | | | |
| 1989 | Chrysler Conquest | Type 10 | 18-27 |
| | Chrysler Domestic Front Wheel Drive Vehicles | Type 2 | 18-31 |
| | Chrysler Rear Wheel Drive Except Conquest | Type 1 | 18-28 |
| | Colt | Type 5 | 18-37 |
| | Colt Wagon | Type 4 | 18-37 |
| | Colt Vista 2WD | Type 6 | 18-37 |
| | Colt Vista 4WD | Type 7 | 18-37 |
| | Eagle Medallion | Type 11 | 18-44 |
| | Eagle Premier | Type 3 | 18-32 |
| | Eagle Summit | Type 5 | 18-37 |
| 1990 | Chrysler Domestic Front Wheel Drive Vehicles | Type 2 | 18-31 |
| | Colt | Type 5 | 18-37 |
| | Colt Wagon | Type 4 | 18-37 |
| | Colt Vista 2WD | Type 6 | 18-37 |
| | Colt Vista 4WD | Type 7 | 18-37 |
| | Eagle Summit | Type 5 | 18-37 |
| | Eagle Premier | Type 2 | 18-31 |
| | Eagle Talon | Type 8 | 18-37 |
| | Laser | Type 8 | 18-37 |
| | Monaco | Type 2 | 18-31 |
| 1991 | Chrysler Domestic Front Wheel Drive Vehicles | Type 2 | 18-31 |
| | Colt | Type 5 | 18-37 |
| | Colt Vista 2WD | Type 6 | 18-37 |
| | Colt Vista 4WD | Type 7 | 18-37 |
| | Eagle Summit | Type 5 | 18-37 |
| | Eagle Premier | Type 2 | 18-31 |
| | Eagle Talon | Type 8 | 18-37 |
| | Laser | Type 8 | 18-37 |
| | Monaco | Type 2 | 18-31 |
| | Stealth | Type 8 | 18-37 |
| **Rear** | | | |
| 1991 | Stealth① | Type 9 | 18-42 |

①—AWD models.

# Power Steering Pressure Specifications

| Year | Model | Initial Pressure, Psi | Maximum Pressure, Psi | Relief Pressure, Psi |
|---|---|---|---|---|
| **Front** | | | | |
| 1989 | Conquest | ① | ② | — |
| | Chrysler Rear Wheel Drive Except Conquest | — | 1200-1300 | — |
| | Eagle Medallion | 1145-1247 | — | — |
| | Chrysler Domestic Front Wheel Drive Vehicles | 30-50 | — | — |
| | Colt Wagon | ③ | ④ | — |
| | Colt | ⑤ | ⑥ | 1138 |
| | Colt Vista 2WD | ③ | ⑦ | — |
| | Colt Vista 4WD | ⑧ | ⑦ | — |
| | Eagle Premier | ⑨ | 1100-1200 | — |
| | Eagle Summit | ⑤ | ⑥ | 1138 |
| 1990 | Chrysler Domestic Front Wheel Drive Vehicles | 30-50 | — | — |
| | Colt Wagon | ③ | ④ | — |
| | Colt | ⑤ | ⑥ | 1138 |
| | Colt Vista 2WD | ③ | ⑦ | — |
| | Colt Vista 4WD | ⑧ | ⑦ | — |
| | Eagle Premier | ⑨ | 1100-1200 | — |
| | Eagle Summit | ⑤ | ⑥ | 1138 |
| | Eagle Talon | ⑩ | ⑥ | 1138 |
| | Laser | ⑩ | ⑥ | 1138 |
| | Monaco | ⑨ | 1100-1200 | — |
| 1991 | Chrysler Domestic Front Wheel Drive Vehicles | 30-50 | — | 1175-1225 |
| | Colt | ⑤ | ⑥ | 1138 |
| | Colt Vista 2WD | ③ | ⑦ | — |
| | Colt Vista 4WD | ⑧ | ⑦ | — |
| | Eagle Premier | ⑨ | 1100-1200 | — |
| | Eagle Summit | ⑤ | ⑥ | 1138 |
| | Eagle Talon | ⑩ | ⑥ | 1138 |
| | Laser | ⑩ | ⑥ | 1138 |
| | Monaco | ⑨ | 1100-1200 | — |
| | Stealth | ⑩ | ⑥ | 1138 |

① —Pressure gauge valve open, 142 psi or less; pressure gauge valve closed, 1067–1166 psi.
② —Pressure gauge valve closed, 218 psi.
③ —Pressure gauge valve open, 142 psi or less; pressure gauge valve closed, 780–880 psi.
④ —Pressure gauge valve closed, 1110 psi.
⑤ —Pressure gauge valve open, 114–142 psi; pressure gauge valve closed, 782–881 psi.
⑥ —Pressure gauge valve opened, 213 psi.
⑦ —Pressure gauge valve opened, 142 psi.
⑧ —Pressure gauge valve open, 142 psi or less; pressure gauge valve closed, 920–1000 psi.
⑨ —Less than 150 psi.
⑩ —Pressure gauge valve open, 114–142 psi; pressure gauge valve closed, 1067–1166 psi.

# Troubleshooting

**NOTE:** This section covers general troubleshooting procedures for power steering pumps, power steering gears and rack and pinion power steering systems. Refer to Figs. 1 through 4 for these procedures.

**PUMP NOISE**

There is some noise in all power steering systems. One of the most common is a hissing sound evident at standstill parking. Hiss is a high frequency noise similar to that experienced while slowly closing a water tap. The noise is present in every valve and results from high velocity fluid passing valve orifice edges. There is no relationship between this noise and performance of the steering. Hiss may be expected when steering wheel is at end of travel or when slowly turning at standstill.

| CONDITION | POSSIBLE CAUSE | CORRECTION |
|---|---|---|
| OBJECTIONAL HISS OR WHISTLE | 1. Noisy valve in gear | 1. Check for proper seal between steering column coupling and dash seal.<br>Ensure steering column lower coupling has no metal-to-metal contact within the coupling by performing an electrical continuity check. (Remove coupling for check.)<br>If hiss is still extremely objectionable, replace steering gear. |
| RATTLE OR CLUNK | 1. Gear loose on front crossmember | 1. Check gear-to-crossmember mounting bolts. Tighten to specification. |
| | 2. Crossmember-to-frame bolts or studs loose | 2. Torque bolts and studs to specifications. |
| | 3. Tie rod looseness (outer or inner) | 3. Check tie rod pivot points for wear. Replace if necessary. |
| | 4. Pressure hose touching other parts of vehicle | 4. Adjust hose to proper position by loosening, repositioning, and retightening fitting. Do not bend tubing. |
| | 5. Noise internal to gear | 5. Replace gear. |
| CHIRP OR SQUEAL (IN THE AREA OF PUMP) PARTICULARLY NOTICEABLE AT FULL WHEEL TRAVEL AND DURING STANDSTILL PARKING | 1. Loose belt | 1. Adjust belt tension to specification. |

**Fig. 1 Power steering system troubleshooting (Part 1 Of 6). Chrysler domestic front wheel drive vehicles**

**PUMP GROWL**

Pump growl results from the development of high pressure fluid flow. Normally this noise should not be high enough to be objectionable. Abnormal situations, such as a low oil level causing aeration or hoses touching the vehicle body, can create a noise level that could bring complaints.

| CONDITION | POSSIBLE CAUSE | CORRECTION |
|---|---|---|
| WHINE OR GROWL (PUMP NOISE) | 1. Low fluid level<br>2. Hose touching vehicle body or frame<br>3. Extreme wear of pump internal parts | 1. Fill to proper level and perform leakage diagnosis. (Recheck after system is free of aeration.)<br>2. Reposition hose. Replace hose if tube ends are bent.<br>3. Replace pump and flush system. |
| SUCKING AIR SOUND | 1. Loose return line clamp<br>2. Missing O-ring on hose connection<br>3. Low fluid level<br>4. Air leak between reservoir and pump | 1. Tighten or replace clamp.<br>2. Inspect connection and replace o-ring as required.<br>3. Fill to proper level and perform leakage diagnosis.<br>4. Inspect and replace reservoir as required. |
| SQUEAK OR RUB SOUND | 1. Sound from steering column<br>2. Sound internal to steering gear | 1. Check for squeak in steering column. Inspect for contact between shroud intermediate shaft, column, and wheel. (Realign if necessary.)<br>2. Replace gear. |
| SCRUBBING/KNOCKING | 1. Incorrect tire size<br>2. Check clearance between tires and other vehicle components, through full travel<br>3. Check for interference between steering gear and other components<br>4. Incorrect gear supplied | 1. Verify tire size is the same as originally supplied.<br>2. Correct as necessary.<br>3. Correct as necessary.<br>4. Replace gear. |

**Fig. 1 Power steering system troubleshooting (Part 2 of 6). Chrysler domestic front wheel drive vehicles**

**BINDS STICKS SEIZED**

| CONDITION | POSSIBLE CAUSE | CORRECTION |
|---|---|---|
| CATCHES, STICKS IN CERTAIN POSITIONS OR DIFFICULT TO TURN | 1. Low fluid level<br>2. Tires not properly inflated<br>3. Lack of lube in ball joints<br>4. Lack of lube in outer tie rod ends<br>5. Loose pump belt<br>6. Faulty pump flow control (Verify cause using Pump Test Procedure)<br>7. Excessive friction in steering column or intermediate shaft<br>8. Steering column coupling binding<br>9. Excessive friction in gear | 1. Fill to proper level and perform leakage diagnosis.<br>2. Inflate tires to proper pressure.<br>3. Lubricate where possible.<br>4. Lubricate where possible.<br>5. Tighten or replace belt.<br>6. Replace pump.<br>7. Correct condition.<br>8. Realign as necessary.<br>9. Replace gear. |

**SHAKE SHUDDER VIBRATION**

| CONDITION | POSSIBLE CAUSE | CORRECTION |
|---|---|---|
| VIBRATION OF THE STEERING WHEEL AND/OR DASH DURING DRY PARK OR LOW SPEED STEERING MANEUVERS | 1. Air in the power steering system<br>2. Tires not properly inflated<br>3. Excessive engine vibration<br>4. Faulty accessory drive belt tensioner. (Poly-V belt systems only)<br>5. Overcharged air conditioner | 1. Steering shudder can be expected in new vehicles and vehicles with recent steering system repairs. Shudder should improve after the vehicle has been driven several weeks.<br>2. Inflate tires to proper pressure.<br>3. Make sure that engine is running properly.<br>4. Check dynamic belt tensioner for abnormal vibration.<br>5. Check air conditioning pump head pressure. |

**Fig. 1 Power steering system troubleshooting (Part 3 Of 6). Chrysler domestic front wheel drive vehicles**

**LOW ASSIST, NO ASSIST, OR HARD STEERING**

| CONDITION | POSSIBLE CAUSE | CORRECTION |
|---|---|---|
| STIFF, HARD TO TURN, SURGES, MOMENTARY INCREASE IN EFFORT WHEN TURNING | 1. Tires not properly inflated | 1. Inflate tires to proper pressure. |
| | 2. Low fluid level | 2. Add power steering fluid as required and perform leakage diagnosis. |
| | 3. Loose belt | 3. Tighten or replace belt. |
| | 4. Lack of ball joint lubrication | 4. Lubricate or replace as required. |
| | 5. Low pressure pump (Verify using Pump Test Procedure) | 5. Verify cause using Pump Test Procedure. Replace pump if necessary. |
| | 6. High internal leak gear | 6. Check steering system using test procedure. If steering gear is at fault, replace steering gear. |

**POOR RETURN TO CENTER**

| CONDITION | POSSIBLE CAUSE | CORRECTION |
|---|---|---|
| STEERING WHEEL DOES NOT WANT TO RETURN TO CENTER POSITION | 1. Tires not properly inflated | 1. Inflate tires to proper pressure. |
| | 2. Improper front wheel alignment | 2. Check and adjust as necessary. |
| | 3. Lack of lubrication in ball joint | 3. Replace as required or lubricate. |
| | 4. Steering column U-joints misaligned | 4. Realign steering column U-joints. |
| | 5. Mispositioned dash cover | 5. Reposition dash cover. |
| | | To evaluate items 6 and 7, disconnect the intermediate steering shaft. Turn the steering wheel and listen for internal rubbing in column. |
| | 6. Steering wheel rubbing | 6. Adjust covers. |
| | 7. Tight steering shaft bearings | 7. Replace bearings. |
| | 8. Excessive friction coupling universal joint | 8. Replace U-joints. |
| | 9. High friction in the steering gear | 9. Replace steering gear. |

**Fig. 1 Power steering system troubleshooting (Part 4 Of 6). Chrysler domestic front wheel drive vehicles**

**LOOSE STEERING**

| CONDITION | POSSIBLE CAUSE | CORRECTION |
|---|---|---|
| EXCESSIVE WHEEL KICKBACK OR TOO MUCH STEERING WHEEL PLAY | 1. Air in system | 1. Add fluid. |
| | 2. Gear loose on crossmember | 2. Check gear to crossmember mounting bolts. Tighten to specification. |
| | 3. Worn/broken intermediate shaft | 3. Check for worn universal joint and broken isolator. Replace intermediate shaft if worn. |
| | 4. Free play in steering column | 4. Check and replace as required. |
| | 5. Loose ball joints | 5. Check and replace as required. |
| | 6. Front wheel bearings loose or worn | 6. Tighten hub nut or replace with new parts as necessary. |
| | 7. Loose outer tie rod ends | 7. Check and replace as required. |
| | 8. Loose inner tie rod ends | 8. Replace gear. |
| | 9. Defective steering gear rotary valve | 9. Replace gear. |

**VEHICLE LEADS TO THE SIDE**

| CONDITION | POSSIBLE CAUSE | CORRECTION |
|---|---|---|
| WHEEL DOES NOT WANT TO RETURN TO CENTER POSITION | 1. Radial tire lead | 1. Rotate tires as recommended in Tire Service. |
| | 2. Front end misaligned | 2. Align front end as recommended in Wheel Alignment Service Procedure. |
| | 3. Wheel braking | 3. Check for dragging brakes as directed in Brake Service Procedure. |
| | 4. Unbalanced steering gear valve. (If this is the cause, the steering efforts will be very light in direction of lead and heavier in the opposite direction) | 4. Checking for pull with outer tie rod end disconnected. If verified, replace gear. |

**Fig. 1 Power steering system troubleshooting (Part 5 Of 6). Chrysler domestic front wheel drive vehicles**

| FLUID LEAK | | |
|---|---|---|
| **CONDITION** | **POSSIBLE CAUSE** | **CORRECTION** |
| LOW FLUID LEVEL WITH:<br>• NO VISIBLE SIGNS OF LEAKS ON THE STEERING GEAR, PUMP, ON FLOOR, OR ANYWHERE ELSE | 1. Overfilled reservoir<br>2. Hose connections at pump or gear | 1. Adjust fill level.<br>2. Check for loose fittings and tighten to specifications. If fittings are tight, examine for damaged or missing O-ring and replace as required. |
| LOW FLUID LEVEL WITH:<br>• VISIBLE LEAK ON STEERING GEAR, PUMP, FLOOR, OR ANYWHERE ELSE | 3. Pump or gear leak | 3. Identify location of leak and repair or replace as indicated in Power Steering Pump and/or Gear sections of this service manual. |

| FOAMY OR MILKY FLUID | | |
|---|---|---|
| **CONDITION** | **POSSIBLE CAUSE** | **CORRECTION** |
| AERATION AND OVERFLOW OF FLUID | 1. Air leaks | 1. Check for air leak as described under sucking air and correct. |
| | 2. Low fluid level | 2. Extremely cold temperatures may cause system aeration if the oil level is low. Add fluid as required. |
| | 3. Cracked pump housing | 3. Remove pump from vehicle and separate reservoir from housing. Check expansion plug and housing for cracks. Replace pump as required. |
| | 4. Water contamination | 4. Drain and refill fluid if there is evidence of contamination. |

**Fig. 1 Power steering system troubleshooting (Part 6 Of 6). Chrysler domestic front wheel drive vehicles**

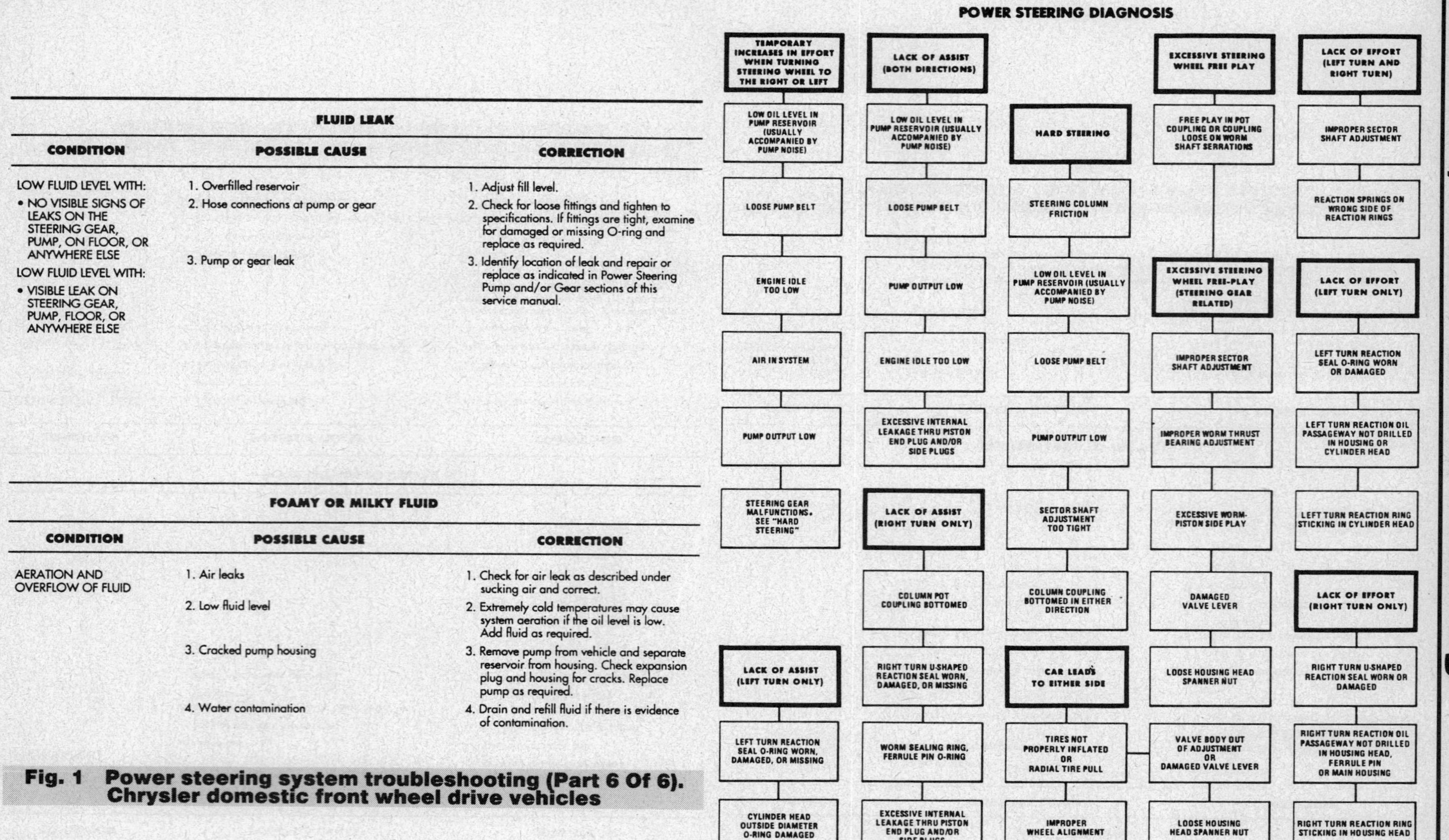


**Fig. 2 Power steering system troubleshooting (Part 1 Of 2). Chrysler domestic rear wheel drive vehicles**

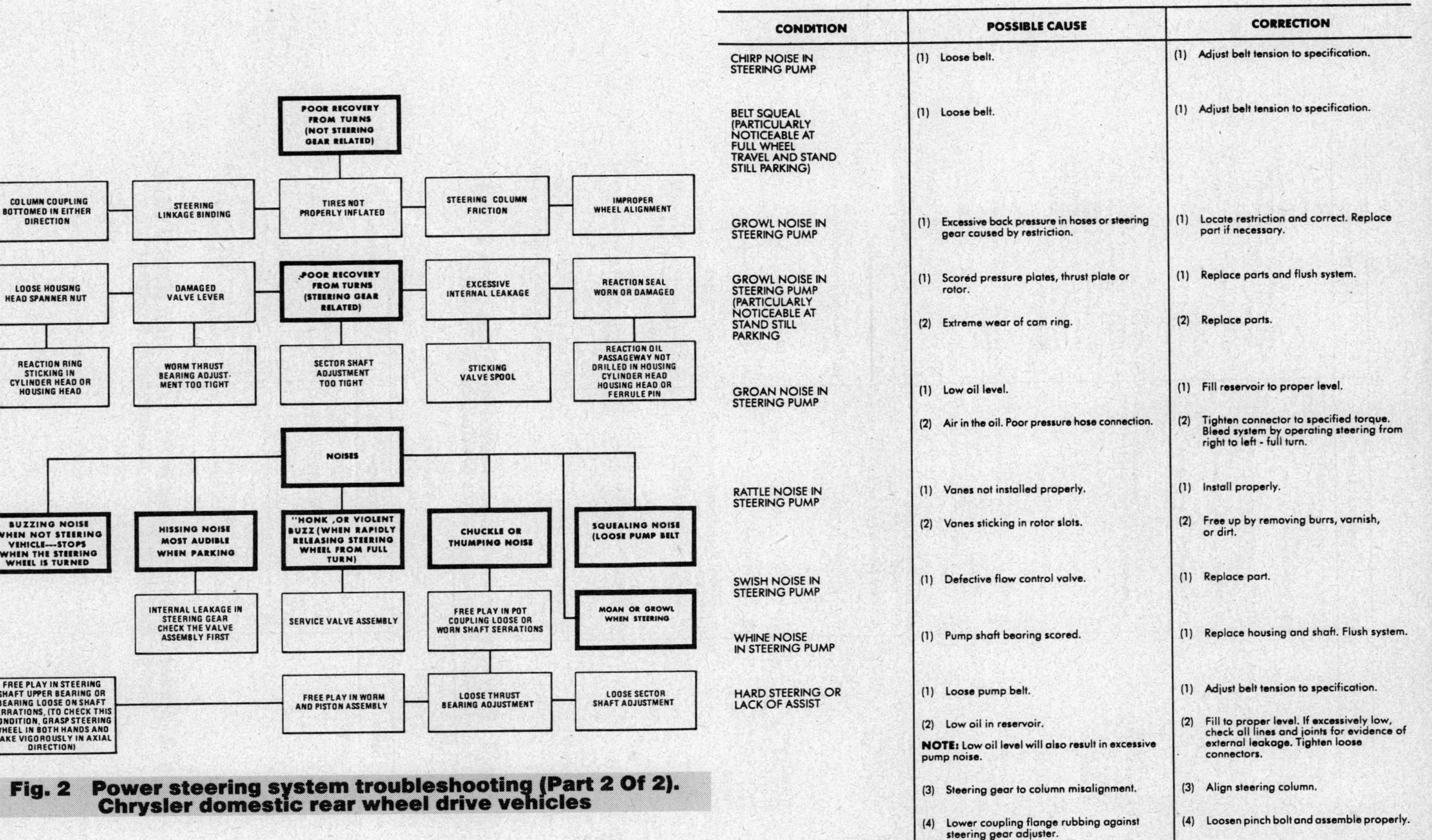


**Fig. 2 Power steering system troubleshooting (Part 2 Of 2). Chrysler domestic rear wheel drive vehicles**

| CONDITION | POSSIBLE CAUSE | CORRECTION |
|---|---|---|
| CHIRP NOISE IN STEERING PUMP | (1) Loose belt. | (1) Adjust belt tension to specification. |
| BELT SQUEAL (PARTICULARLY NOTICEABLE AT FULL WHEEL TRAVEL AND STAND STILL PARKING) | (1) Loose belt. | (1) Adjust belt tension to specification. |
| GROWL NOISE IN STEERING PUMP | (1) Excessive back pressure in hoses or steering gear caused by restriction. | (1) Locate restriction and correct. Replace part if necessary. |
| GROWL NOISE IN STEERING PUMP (PARTICULARLY NOTICEABLE AT STAND STILL PARKING | (1) Scored pressure plates, thrust plate or rotor. | (1) Replace parts and flush system. |
| | (2) Extreme wear of cam ring. | (2) Replace parts. |
| GROAN NOISE IN STEERING PUMP | (1) Low oil level. | (1) Fill reservoir to proper level. |
| | (2) Air in the oil. Poor pressure hose connection. | (2) Tighten connector to specified torque. Bleed system by operating steering from right to left - full turn. |
| RATTLE NOISE IN STEERING PUMP | (1) Vanes not installed properly. | (1) Install properly. |
| | (2) Vanes sticking in rotor slots. | (2) Free up by removing burrs, varnish, or dirt. |
| SWISH NOISE IN STEERING PUMP | (1) Defective flow control valve. | (1) Replace part. |
| WHINE NOISE IN STEERING PUMP | (1) Pump shaft bearing scored. | (1) Replace housing and shaft. Flush system. |
| HARD STEERING OR LACK OF ASSIST | (1) Loose pump belt. | (1) Adjust belt tension to specification. |
| | (2) Low oil in reservoir. **NOTE:** Low oil level will also result in excessive pump noise. | (2) Fill to proper level. If excessively low, check all lines and joints for evidence of external leakage. Tighten loose connectors. |
| | (3) Steering gear to column misalignment. | (3) Align steering column. |
| | (4) Lower coupling flange rubbing against steering gear adjuster. | (4) Loosen pinch bolt and assemble properly. |
| | (5) Tires not properly inflated. | (5) Inflate to recommended pressure. |

**Fig. 3 Power steering pump troubleshooting (Part 1 Of 3). Dodge Monaco & Eagle Medallion & Premier**

| CONDITION | POSSIBLE CAUSE | CORRECTION |
|---|---|---|
| | Further possible causes could be: | |
| | (6) Sticking flow control valve. | In order to diagnose conditions such as listed in (6), (7), (8), (9) a pressure test of the entire power steering system is required. |
| | (7) Insufficient pump pressure output. | |
| | (8) Excessive internal pump leakage. | |
| | (9) Excessive internal gear leakage. | |
| FOAMING MILKY POWER STEERING FLUID, LOW FLUID LEVEL AND POSSIBLE LOW PRESSURE | (1) Air in the fluid, and loss of fluid due to internal pump leakage causing overflow. | (1) Check for leaks and correct. Bleed system. Extremely cold temperatures will cause system aeriation should the oil level be low. If oil level is correct and pump still foams, remove pump from vehicle and separate reservoir from body. Check welsh plug and body for cracks. If plug is loose or body is cracked, replace body. |
| LOW PUMP PRESSURE | (1) Flow control valve stuck or inoperative. | (1) Remove burrs or dirt or replace. Flush system. |
| | (2) Pressure plate not flat against cam ring. | (2) Correct. |
| MOMENTARY INCREASE IN EFFORT WHEN TURNING WHEEL FAST TO RIGHT OR LEFT | (1) Low oil level in pump. | (1) Add power steering fluid as required. |
| | (2) Pump belt slipping. | (2) Tighten or replace belt. |
| | (3) High internal leakage. | (3) Check pump pressure. (See pressure test.) |
| STEERING WHEEL SURGES OR JERKS WHEN TURNING WITH ENGINE RUNNING ESPECIALLY DURING PARKING | (1) Low oil level. | (1) Fill as required. |
| | (2) Loose pump belt. | (2) Adjust tension to specification. |
| | (3) Steering linkage hitting engine oil pan at full turn. | (3) Correct clearance. |
| | (4) Insufficient pump pressure. | (4) Check pump pressure. (See pressure test.) Replace flow control valve if defective. |
| | (5) Sticking flow control valve. | (5) Inspect for varnish or damage, replace if necessary. |
| EXCESSIVE WHEEL KICKBACK OR LOOSE STEERING | (1) Air in system. | (1) Add oil to pump reservoir and bleed by operating steering. Check hose connectors for proper torque and adjust as required. |

**Fig. 3 Power steering pump troubleshooting (Part 2 Of 3). Dodge Monaco, Eagle Medallion & Premier**

| CONDITION | POSSIBLE CAUSE | CORRECTION |
|---|---|---|
| LOW PUMP PRESSURE | (1) Flow control valve stuck or inoperative. | (1) Remove burrs or dirt. Replace valve if damaged. |
| | (2) Pump pressure plate not seating (flat) against cam ring. | (2) Disassemble pump and correct. |
| | (3) Extreme wear of cam ring. | (3) Replace parts. Flush system. |
| | (4) Scored pressure plate, thrust plate, or rotor. | (4) Replace parts. Flush system. |
| | (5) Vanes not installed properly. | (5) Install properly. |
| | (6) Vanes sticking in rotor slots. | (6) Freeup by removing burrs, varnish, or dirt. |
| | (7) Cracked or broken thrust or pressure plate. | (7) Replace part. |

**Fig. 3 Power steering pump troubleshooting (Part 3 Of 3). Dodge Monaco, Eagle Medallion & Premier**

| Symptom | Probable cause | Remedy |
|---|---|---|
| Excessive play of steering wheel | Loose rack support cover | Retighten |
| | Loose steering gear mounting bolts | Retighten |
| | Loose or worn stud of tie-rod end | Retighten or replace as necessary |
| Steering wheel operation is hard (Improper power assist) | V-belt slippage | Check |
| | Damaged V-belt | Replace |
| | Low fluid level | Refill |
| | Air in the fluid | Bleed |
| | Twisted or damaged hoses | Correct the routing or replace |
| | Improper oil pump pressure | Repair or replace oil pump |
| | Sticky flow control valve | Replace |
| | Excessive internal oil pump leakage | Replace damaged parts |
| | Excessive oil leaks from rack & pinion in gear box | Replace damaged parts |
| | Bent or damaged gear box or valve body seal ring | Replace |
| Steering wheel does not return properly | Excessive turning resistance of tie-rod ball joint | Replacee |
| | Excessively tightened rack support cover | Adjust |
| | Rough turning of inner tie-rod and/or ball joint | Replace |
| | Worn steering shaft joint and/or body grommet | Correct or replace |
| | Bent rack | Replace |
| | Damaged pinion bearing | Replace |
| | Twisted or damaged hoses | Reroute or replace |
| | Damaged oil pressure control valve | Replace |
| | Damaged oil pump input shaft bearing | Replace |
| Noise | **Hissing Noise in Steering Gear** There is some noise in all power steering systems. One of the most common is a hissing sound when the steering wheel is turned and the car is not moving. This noise will be most evident when turning the wheel while the brakes are applied. There is no relationship between this noise and steering performance. Do not replace the valve unless the "hissing" noise is extremely objectionable. A replacement valve will also have a slight noise, and is not always a cure for the condition. | |
| Rattling or chucking noise in rack & pinion | Pressure hose touching other parts of vehicle | Reroute |
| | Loose gear box bracket | Retighten |
| | Loose tie-rod end ball joint | Retighten |
| | Worn tie-rod end ball joint | Replace |
| Groaning noise in oil pump | Low fluid level | Refill |
| | Air in the fluid | Bleed |
| | Loose pump mounting bolts | Retighten |

**Fig. 4 Power steering system troubleshooting. Colt, Colt Vista, Colt Wagon, Conquest, Laser, Stealth, Summit & Talon**

# Type 1—Saginaw Vane Type Power Steering Pumps

## INDEX



## CHRYSLER FRONT WHEEL DRIVE VEHICLES

Because of unique shaft bearings, flow control levels or pump displacements, These pumps may not be interchanged with pumps from other vehicles. Because of different flow control levels, pumps used with quick-ratio steering gears are not interchangeable with pumps used with standard-ratio steering gears.

### PUMP PRESSURE TEST

1. Ensure fluid level and drive belt tension are correct, disconnect pressure hose and cap, then connect a spare pressure hose to pump fitting.
2. Connect spare pressure hose to gauge side of tool C-3309-E or equivalent, then the pressure hose from gear valve to valve side of tool L-4601 and C-3309-E or their equivalents. **New fittings will be required on tool C-3309-E to adapt to new O-ring type hose tube ends.**

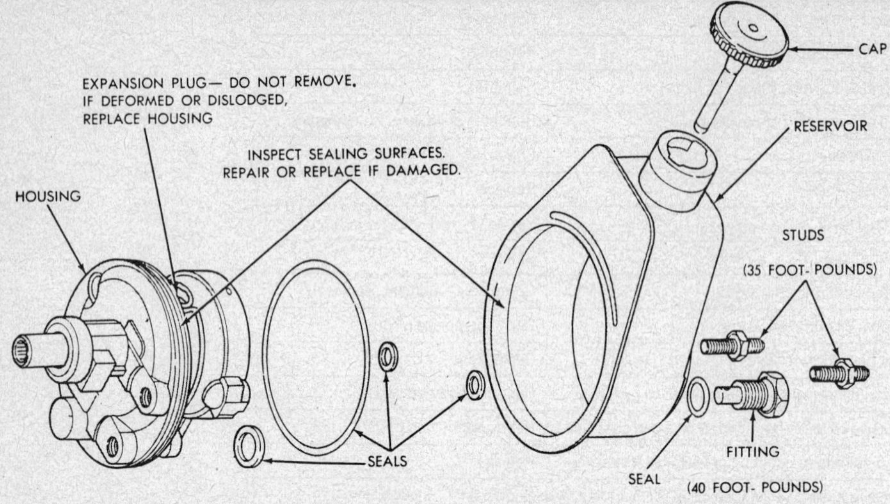


**Fig. 1 Saginaw pump & reservoir assembly. Chrysler front wheel drive vehicles**

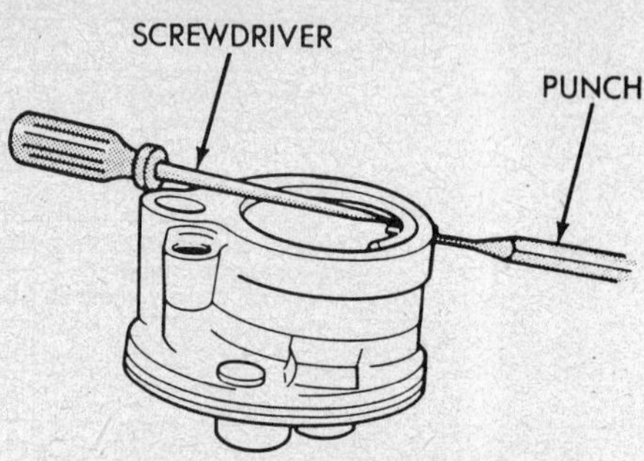


**Fig. 2 Removing end plate retaining ring. Chrysler front wheel drive vehicles**

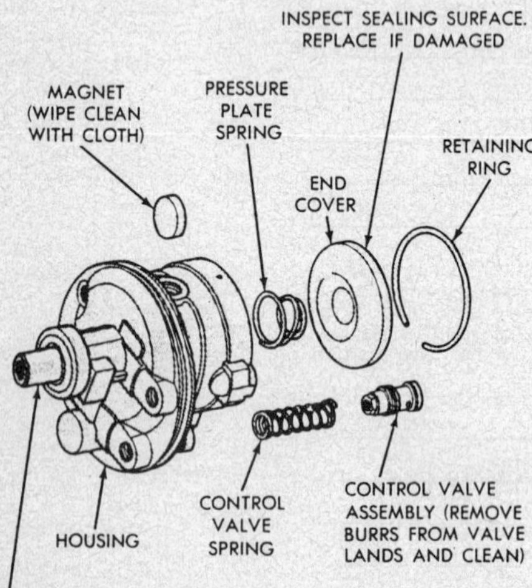


**Fig. 3 End cover, pressure plate spring & control valve and spring assembly. Chrysler front wheel drive vehicles**

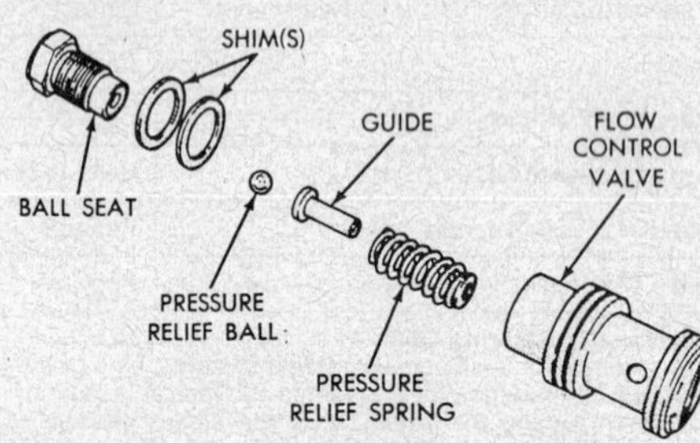


**Fig. 4 Flow control valve assembly. Chrysler front wheel drive vehicles**

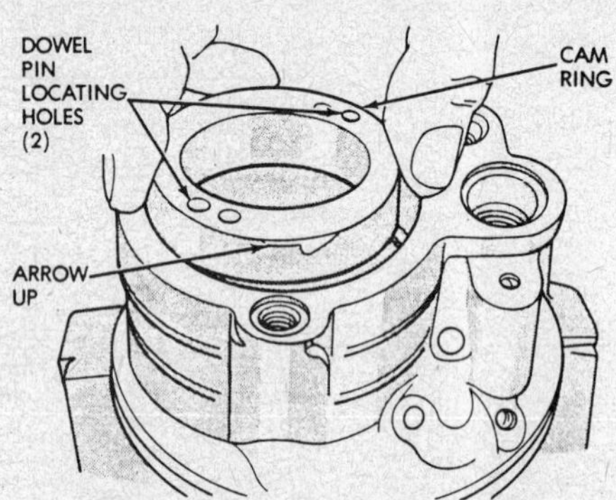


**Fig. 5 Installing cam ring. Chrysler front wheel drive vehicles**

3. Open hand valve on C-3309-E, insert a thermometer into fluid reservoir, start engine and allow fluid to reach a temperature between 150 and 170°F. Turn wheels from stop to stop to aid in warming fluid. **Do not hold wheels against stop for an extended period. Internal pump overheating may result.**
4. With engine at idle speed and gauge valve open, check initial pressure, should be within specifications. Refer to "Power Steering Pressure Specifications."
5. If pressure is in excess of 100 psi, check hoses for restrictions and/or crimped oil lines.
6. Close gauge valve completely three times and record highest pressure attained each time. **Do not leave valve closed for more than 5 seconds, pump could be damaged.**
7. If recorded pressures are within specifications and range of readings are within 50 psi, pump is operating properly.
8. If recorded pressures are high, but do not repeat within 50 psi, flow control valve in pump is sticking. Remove valve, clean and remove any burrs with crocus cloth. If system contains some dirt, it must be thoroughly flushed. If it is exceptionally dirty, both pump and gear must be removed, completely disassembled, cleaned and reassembled before further usage.
9. If recorded pressures are constant, but less than minimum specification, clean or replace pressure relief valve assembly. If pressures are still low, repair or replace pump.
10. If pump is within specifications, leave gauge valve open and turn steering wheel from stop to stop with engine idling. Record highest pressures attained at each wheel stop and compare with maximum pump pressure recorded previously. If this pressure cannot be obtained in either side of gear, gear is leaking internally and must be disassembled and repaired.
11. Shut engine Off, remove tool C-3309-E, reconnect pressure hose, then perform repairs if necessary.

## PUMP SERVICE

### Disassembly

1. Remove filler cap and drain oil from reservoir.
2. Remove pulley using puller C-4068 and block C-4068-1 or their equivalents.
3. Remove reservoir parts as shown in **Fig. 1.** Rock reservoir by hand or tap with a soft-faced mallet to remove.
4. Remove retaining ring from housing as shown in **Fig. 2,** then the end cover and pressure plate spring, **Fig. 3.**
5. Remove control valve assembly and control valve spring.
6. Clamp land end of control valve assembly into a suitable soft-jawed vise, then remove ball seat, **Fig. 4.**
7. Remove parts as shown in **Fig. 4,** inspect ball and ball seat and replace if worn or damaged.
8. Using a suitable plastic hammer, tap drive shaft end lightly until pressure plate is free, then remove shaft. **Prior to removal of shaft, inspect and if corroded, clean with crocus cloth. This will prevent damage to shaft bushing.**
9. Remove drive shaft seal using a suitable screwdriver. **Use caution not to damage housing.**
10. Disassemble parts as shown in **Fig. 5,** inspect all wear surfaces, and if any part shows signs of excessive wear, replace pump.

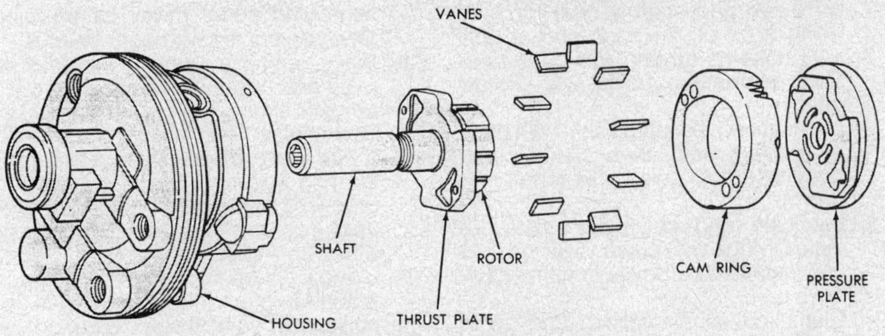


**Fig. 6 Shaft, thrust plate & rotor assembly. Chrysler front wheel drive vehicles**

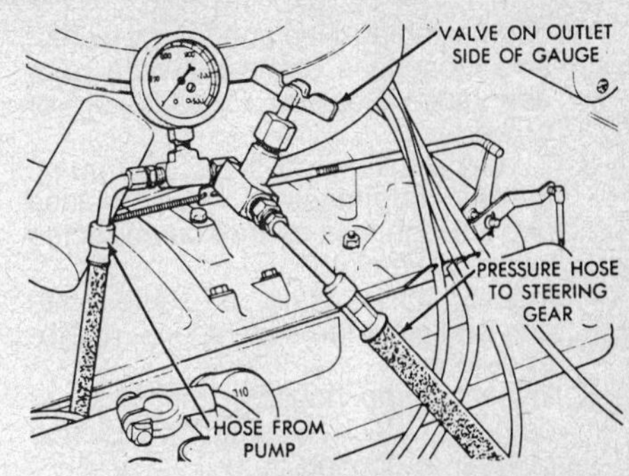


**Fig. 7 Installing C-3309-E gauge. Chrysler rear wheel drive vehicles**

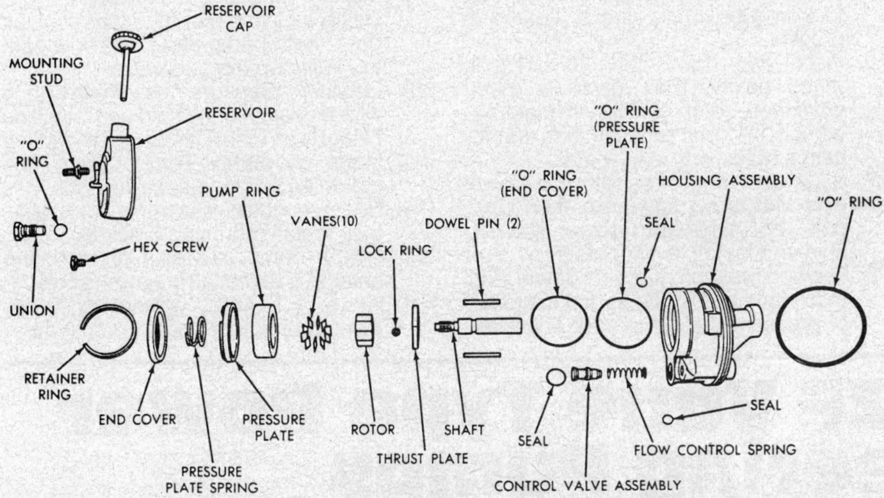


**Fig. 8 Type 1—Saginaw pump assembly. Chrysler rear wheel drive vehicles**

### Assembly

1. Clean all parts in a suitable solvent, then install drive shaft seal into housing using a hammer and suitable size socket. **Use caution, excessive force will distort seal.**
2. Lubricate new O-rings and seals with power steering fluid, then install.
3. Install thrust plate, shaft and rotor assembly, then the cam ring as shown in **Fig. 6.**
4. Install vanes into rotor and lubricate all parts with power steering fluid.
5. Install and seat pressure plate using a suitable socket and thumb pressure.
6. Install pressure plate spring and end cover lubricated with power steering fluid, then the retaining ring.
7. Reassemble control valve, then install control valve and spring into housing.
8. Install reservoir components as shown in **Fig. 1.**

# CHRYSLER REAR WHEEL DRIVE VEHICLES

## PUMP PRESSURE TEST

1. Ensure fluid level and drive belt tension are correct, disconnect high pressure hose at steering gear and connect free end of hose to gauge side of gauge C-3309-E or equivalent.
2. Connect a second pressure hose from valve side of C-3309-E to steering gear. Valve must be installed on outlet side of gauge, **Fig. 7.**
3. Insert a thermometer into fluid reservoir, start engine and allow fluid to reach a temperature between 150 and 170°F. Turn wheels from stop to stop to aid in warming fluid. **Do not hold wheels against stop for an extended period. Internal pump overheating may result.**
4. With engine at idle speed and gauge valve open, note pressure while turning wheel to one stop momentarily.
5. If pressure is less than specified, momentarily close shut-off valve and note pressure. If pressure is less than specified, pump is faulty.
6. If pressure is low in step 4 and satisfactory in step 5, steering gear is defective.
7. Shut engine Off, remove tool C-3309-E, reconnect pressure hose, then perform repairs if necessary.

## PUMP SERVICE

### Disassembly

1. Clamp pump securely into vise at mounting bracket, then using puller C-4068-A or equivalent, remove pump pulley. **Ensure that puller screw is perfectly aligned with shaft end to prevent cocking.**
2. Remove brackets from pump, then clamp pump (shaft end down) in a suitable soft-jawed vise between square boss and shaft housing.
3. Remove two mounting studs and pressure hose fitting, **Fig. 8,** then gently tap reservoir filler tube back and forth with a plastic hammer to loosen.
4. Work reservoir off body, then using a suitable punch, tap end cover retaining ring around until one end of ring is near hole in pump body.
5. Insert punch into hole far enough to disengage ring from groove in pump bore and pry ring out of pump body.
6. Tap end cover with a plastic hammer to loosen, then remove end cover and spring.
7. Remove pump body from vise and place in inverted position on a flat surface and tap end of driveshaft with a plastic hammer to loosen pressure plate, rotor and thrust plate assembly from body.
8. Lift pump body off of rotor assembly. Flow control valve and spring should slide out of bore.
9. Place pump body on a flat surface and pry driveshaft oil seal out with a screwdriver.
10. If necessary, disassemble flow control valve for cleaning. Refer to **Fig. 4.**
11. Lift pressure plate and cam ring from rotor, then remove ten vanes from slots in rotor.
12. Clamp driveshaft in soft-jawed vise with rotor and thrust plate facing up, remove rotor lock ring, then slide rotor and thrust plate off shaft and remove from shaft from vise.

### Inspection

1. Clean all parts except the driveshaft oil seal in cleaning fluid. The seal will be damaged if immersed in cleaning fluid.
2. Check fit of vanes in slots of rotor for tightness or excessive looseness. Vanes must fit snugly but slide freely in slots in rotor. Tight fit of vanes in rotor can usually be corrected by thor-

ough cleaning. Replace rotor if excessive looseness exists between rotor and vanes. Replace vanes if worn or scored.

3. Examine machined surface of pump ring for roughness or wear. Replace ring if roughness cannot be corrected with crocus cloth.
4. Inspect thrust plate, pressure plate and end plate for wear, scores or other damage.
5. Inspect pump housing for cracks or damage. Check housing for evidence of wear or scoring.
6. Check all springs for free length, distortion or collapsed coils.
7. Inspect locating dowel pins for distortion.
8. Examine outer diameter of flow control valve for scoring or roughness. Slight damage may be cleaned up with crocus cloth. Check valve assembly for freedom of movement in bore of pump housing.
9. Check all oil passages in pump parts for obstruction. Use a piece of tag wire to clean holes.
10. Check bushing in pump housing for wear or damage.

### Assembly

1. Place pump body on a flat surface and drive new driveshaft oil seal into bore using a 7/8 or 15/16 inch socket until seal bottoms on shoulder. **Use caution, excessive force will distort seal.**
2. Lubricate driveshaft oil seal with power steering fluid, then clamp pump body in a soft-jawed vise (shaft end down).
3. Lubricate end cover and pressure plate O-rings with power steering fluid and install into grooves in pump cavity.
4. Clamp driveshaft splined end up in soft-jawed vise, then install thrust plate on driveshaft (ported side up).
5. Slide rotor over splines with counterbore of rotor facing down, then using tool C-4090 or equivalent, install rotor lock ring ensuring ring is seated in groove.
6. Install two dowel pins in holes in pump cavity, then carefully insert driveshaft, rotor and thrust plate assembly into pump cavity indexing locating holes with dowel pins.
7. Slide cam ring over rotor on dowel pins with arrow facing up, then lubricate ten vanes with power steering fluid and install in rotor slots.
8. Position pressure plate on dowel pins, then place a 1 1/4 inch socket in groove of pressure plate and seat entire assembly in pump cavity by pressing down on socket with both thumbs.
9. Place spring in groove in pressure plate and position end cover lip edge up over spring, then press end cover down below retaining ring groove with a vise or arbor press and install retaining ring ensuring that it is seated in groove. **Care should be used to prevent cocking end cover in bore or distorting assembly.**
10. Using a punch, tap retaining ring ends around in groove until opening is opposite flow control valve bore.
11. Lubricate new reservoir, mounting stud and flow control valve O-rings with power steering fluid, then carefully position reservoir on pump body aligning mounting stud holes.
12. Using a plastic hammer, tap reservoir down onto pump and insert flow control valve spring and valve.
13. Lubricate pressure hose fitting O-ring with power steering fluid and install on fitting, then install fitting and mounting studs on pump. Torque fitting and mounting studs to specifications.
14. Remove pump assembly from vise, then install mounting brackets.
15. Clamp pump into vise at mounting bracket, then install pulley on shaft using tool C-4063 without adapters. Tighten until tool bottoms on shaft.

# Type 2—ZF Vane Type Power Steering Pumps

INDEX

**Page No.**



## DESCRIPTION

The ZF power steering pump is not repairable. If the pump, reservoir or cap fails or leaks, it should be replaced. **Do not attempt to repair pump or reservoir, replace only.**

## PUMP PRESSURE TEST

1. Ensure fluid level and drive belt tension are correct, disconnect pressure hose and cap, then connect a spare pressure hose to pump fitting.
2. Connect spare pressure hose to gauge side of tool C-3309-E or equivalent, then the pressure hose from gear valve to valve side of tool L-4601 and C-3309-E or their equivalents. **New fittings will be required on tool C-3309-E to adapt to new O-ring type hose tube ends.**
3. Open hand valve on C-3309-E, insert a thermometer into fluid reservoir, start engine and allow fluid to reach a temperature between 150 and 170°F. Turn wheels from stop to stop to aid in warming fluid. **Do not hold wheels against stop for an extended period. Internal pump overheating may result.**
4. With engine at idle speed and gauge valve open, check initial pressure, should be within specifications. Refer to "Power Steering Pressure Specifications."
5. If pressure is in excess of 100 psi, check hoses for restrictions and/or crimped oil lines.
6. Close gauge valve completely three times and record highest pressure attained each time. **Do not leave valve closed for more than 5 seconds, pump could be damaged.**
7. If recorded pressures are within specifications and range of readings are within 50 psi, pump is operating properly.
8. If recorded pressures are high, but do not repeat within 50 psi, flow control valve in pump is sticking. Replace pump.
9. If recorded pressures are constant, but less than minimum specification,

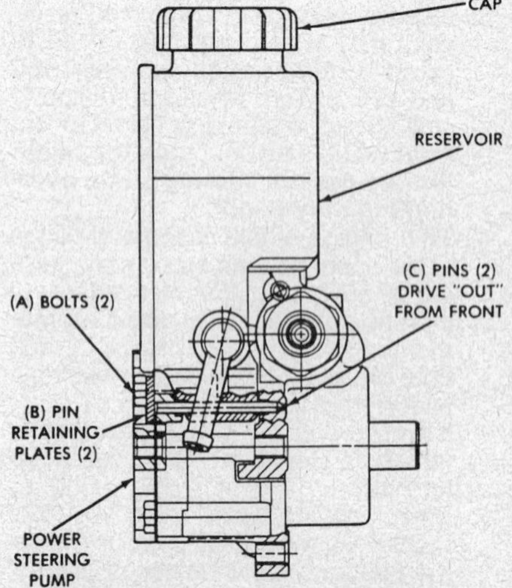


**Fig. 1 Type 2—ZF power steering pump assembly**

replace pump.

10. If pump is within specifications, leave gauge valve open and turn steering wheel from stop to stop with engine idling. Record highest pressures attained at each wheel stop and compare with maximum pump pressure recorded previously. If this pressure cannot be obtained in either side of gear, gear is leaking internally and must be disassembled and repaired.
11. Shut engine Off, remove tool C-3309-E, reconnect pressure hose, then perform repairs if necessary.

## RESERVOIR REPLACE

1. Remove pulley using puller C-4068 and block C-4068-1 or their equivalents.
2. Remove two bolts and retaining plates, **Fig. 1,** then drive pins out from front of pump. **Do not enlarge front access holes.**
3. Lift reservoir off power steering pump, then inspect pump inlet. Replace pump if inlet is damaged or worn.
4. Lubricate O-rings with power steering fluid and install , then carefully snap reservoir in place on power steering pump.
5. Install new pins from rear, push in until flush with back plate.
6. Install pin retaining plates and bolts and torque to specifications.

# Type 3—TC-Series Vane Type Power Steering Pumps

## INDEX



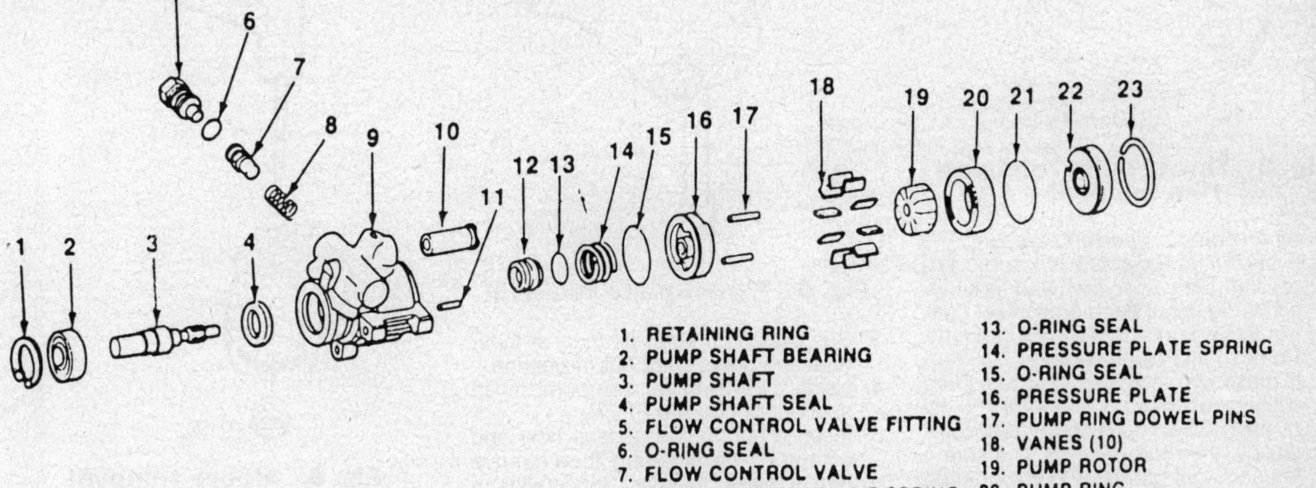


**Fig. 1 Type 3—TC series pump exploded view**

## DESCRIPTION

The TC series pump, **Fig. 1,** is a vane type pump, and is used on the Eagle Premier and Dodge Monaco when equipped with the 2.5L/4-150 cylinder engine. It utilizes a remote fluid reservoir located at the left inner fender panel.

## PUMP PRESSURE TEST

1. Ensure drive belt tension is correct, then place a drip pan under engine and disconnect pump high pressure hose at steering gear. Hold hose end raised above reservoir to prevent fluid loss.
2. Connect one side of a suitable pressure test gauge to pump high pressure hose with an adapter, then the other side of gauge to power steering pump with an adapter hose as shown in **Fig. 2. Ensure that test gauge is connected in fluid high pressure circuit between pump and steering gear.**
3. Open test valve completely, fill fluid reservoir with power steering fluid as necessary, then start engine and allow fluid to reach normal operating temperature of approximately 170°F.
4. Observe pressure test gauge, pressure should be within specifications. Refer to "Power Steering Pressure Specifications."
5. If pressure is greater than specified, check hoses for restrictions and repair as necessary.
6. Close test valve completely for 2-4 seconds, then immediately open. Repeat this procedure three times and record maximum pressure indicated on pressure test gauge each time test valve is closed. **Do not leave valve closed for more than 5 seconds, pump could be damaged.**
7. Compare maximum indicated pressures. If pressures are within specifications and variance of three indicated pressures are within 50 psi of each

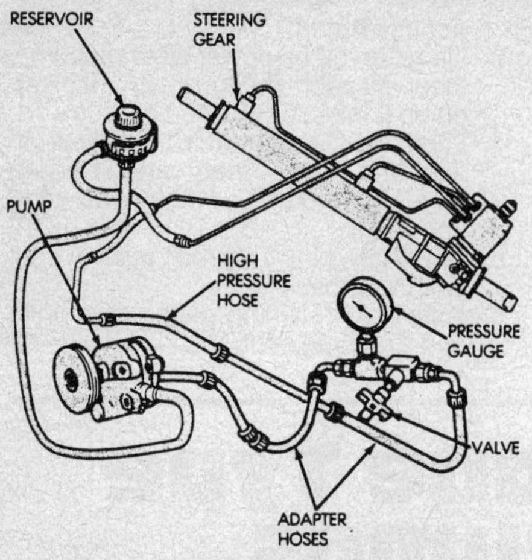


**Fig. 2 Connecting pump pressure test equipment**

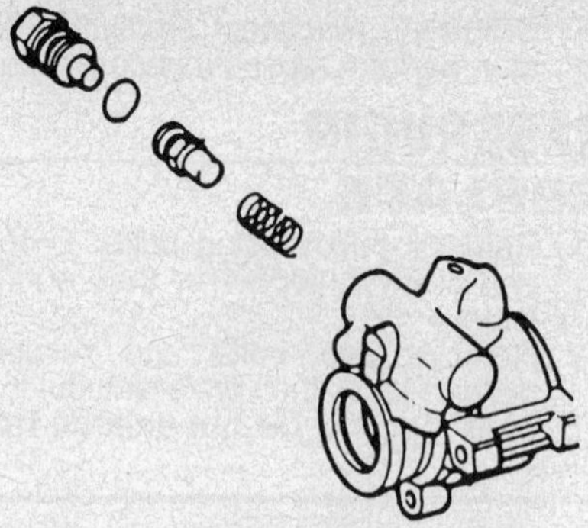

**Fig. 3 Flow control valve removal**

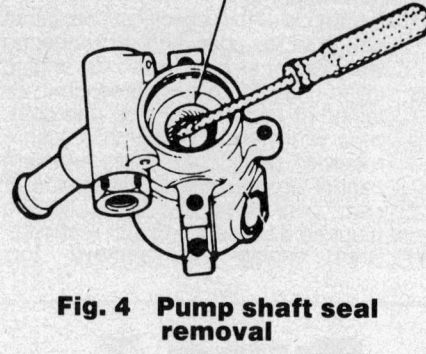

**Fig. 4 Pump shaft seal removal**

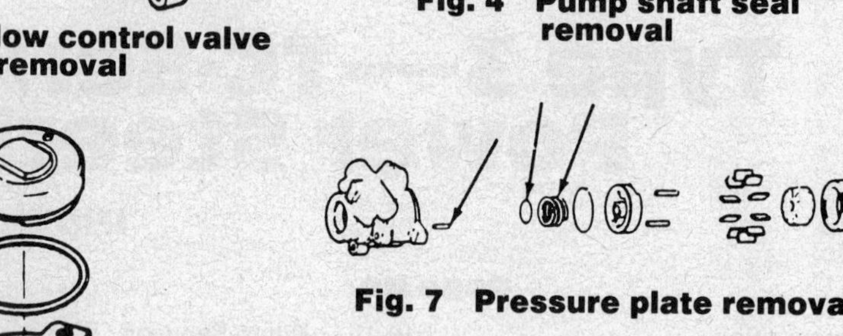

**Fig. 7 Pressure plate removal**

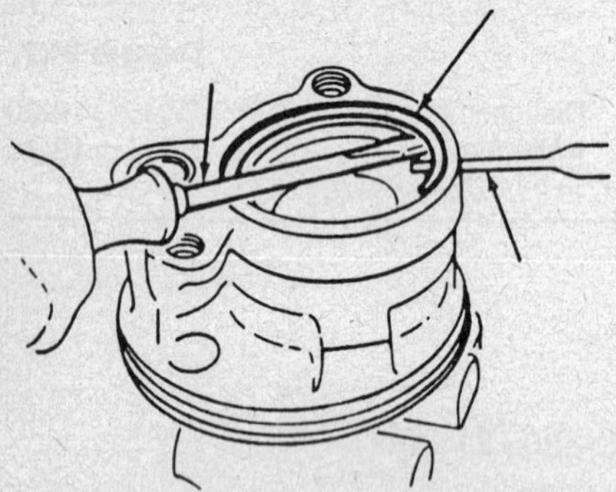

**Fig. 5 Thrust plate retaining ring removal**

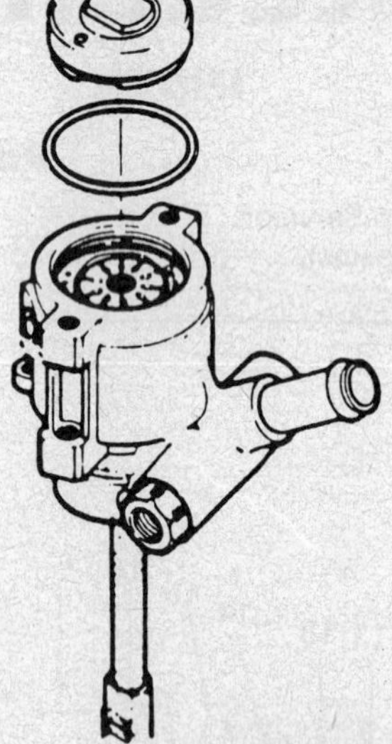

**Fig. 6 Thrust plate removal**

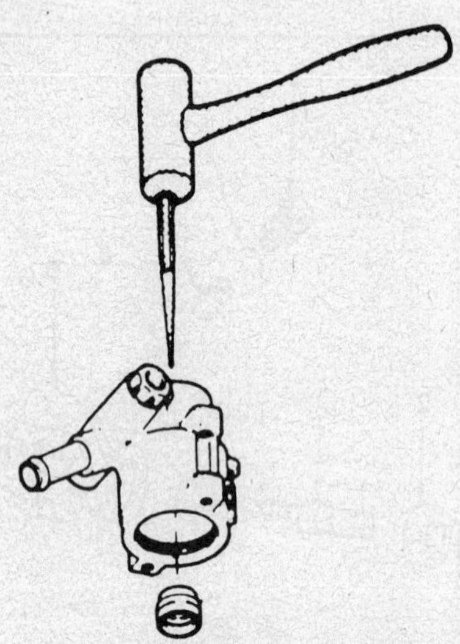

**Fig. 8 Sleeve removal**

other, pump is operating properly.

8. If maximum indicated pressures are greater than specified and are not within 50 psi of each other, flow control valve is not functioning properly. Remove and clean valve.
9. If maximum indicated pressures are within specifications and within 50 psi of each other, open test valve completely, then turn wheels to extreme left and right positions to force pump to operate against steering "stops."
10. Record pressure at each extreme position, then compare extreme left and right pressures with previously recorded maximum pressures. If pump maximum output pressure are not repeated when pump is forced to operate against either "stop," steering gear is leaking internally and must be disassembled and repaired.
11. Shut engine Off, remove test equipment, reconnect pressure hose, then perform repairs if necessary.

# PUMP SERVICE

## DISASSEMBLY

1. Remove pump from engine, remove pulley, flow control valve fitting, O-ring and flow control valve and spring, **Fig. 3.**
2. Remove pump shaft retaining ring, pump shaft and bearing assembly.
3. Support pump shaft bearing at inner race and press shaft out of bearing.
4. Using a screwdriver, pry pump shaft seal out of housing **Fig. 4.**
5. Insert a punch into access hole and compress retaining ring, then remove thrust plate retaining ring with a screwdriver **Fig. 5.**
6. Press out thrust plate with a 5/8 inch brass drift, **Fig. 6,** then remove and discard thrust plate O-ring.
7. Remove pump ring, rotor, vanes, dowel pins and pressure plate. It may be necessary to use a press to remove pressure plate. Remove and discard pressure plate O-ring.
8. Remove pressure plate spring, dowel pin and sleeve assembly O-ring **Fig. 7.**
9. From pump shaft side of housing, using a punch and hammer, remove sleeve assembly **Fig. 8.**

## INSPECTION

Clean all components with mineral spirits and dry them with compressed air. Replace all O-rings.

1. Inspect flow control valve for nicks and scratches. Remove minor imperfections with crocus cloth. Valve should move freely in bore. If valve sticks inspect valve and housing bore. Replace housing or valve if damaged.
2. Inspect pressure and thrust plates for flatness, and replace if scored, worn, or surfaces are not flat.
3. Inspect pump ring for any wear or damage. A polished appearance is normal. Replace if damaged in any way.
4. Inspect thrust plate dowels, pressure plate spring, rotor and rotor vanes. Replace if worn, cracked or distorted.
5. Inspect pump shaft and splines, and replace shaft retaining ring. Replace shaft if worn, cracked or damaged.
6. Inspect pump housing and bores checking for distortion, cracks and porosity. Inspect pump fitting for any damage. Inspect end plate for wear. Replace parts if damage is found. If the end plate retaining ring is distorted in any way, it must be replaced.
7. Inspect sleeve assembly and shaft bearing. Replace if worn or damaged.

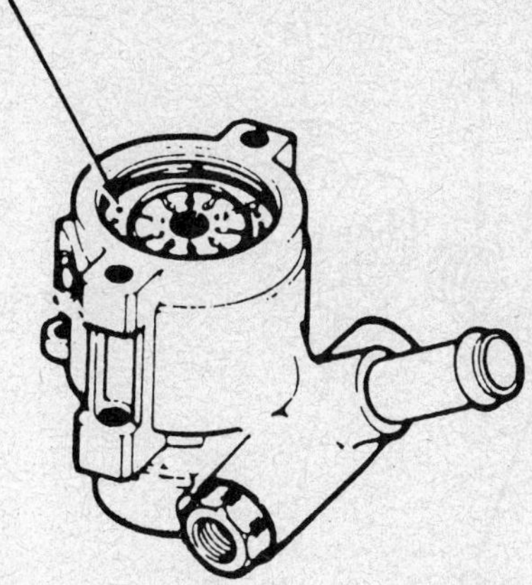

Fig. 9 Pump ring installation

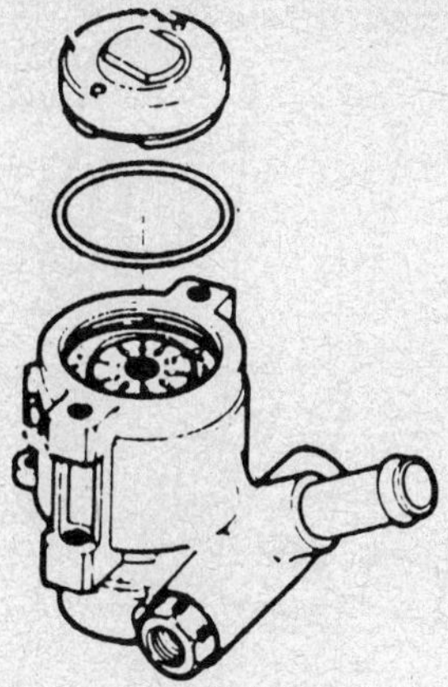

Fig. 10 Thrust plate installation

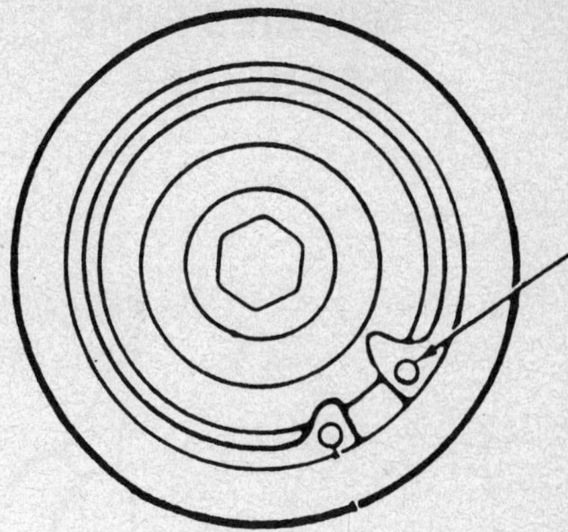

Fig. 11 Bearing retaining ring installation

## ASSEMBLY

Be sure all parts are clean and well lubricated with power steering fluid only. Dirt in the assembly will cause noise, leaks, and premature wear.

1. Press sleeve assembly with a socket into housing. Make sure sleeve is fully seated. **Do not over press sleeve as this could damage O-ring seat.**
2. Install O-ring on sleeve assembly. Install short dowel pin in pump housing, then install the pressure plate spring over sleeve assembly into housing.
3. Install O-ring on pressure plate. Place a reference mark on the pressure plate directly over the dowel pin hole in the plate. This mark will help align short dowel pin and hole when installing pressure plate.
4. Install pressure plate in housing, taking care to fully seat short dowel in pressure plate pin hole, then install two pump ring dowel pins in pressure plate.
5. Install pump ring on the dowel pins. Ensure pump ring identification marks are facing upward. **The identification marks are two shallow dots located next to the dowel pin hole, Fig. 9.**
6. Install pump rotor with counterbore toward pump shaft end or housing, then install rotor vanes with rounded edges facing outward.
7. Install thrust plate O-ring, and thrust plate, **Fig. 10,** ensuring thrust plate engages pump ring dowel pins.
8. Press thrust plate into pump housing, then install thrust plate retaining ring.
9. Install new shaft seal by pressing into housing with a suitable size socket, ensuring seal is fully seated.
10. Install pump shaft bearing onto pump shaft, taking care to support bearing inner race when pressing into position.
11. Install shaft in pump housing, rotating until splines engage with rotor. Ensure shaft is bottomed in the housing, then install bearing retaining ring. **Install retaining ring so large lug of ring is to the right of the small lug Fig. 11.**
12. Install pump pulley, then the pump in vehicle.

# Type 4—N-Series Vane Type Power Steering Pumps

INDEX



## DESCRIPTION

The N series, pump **Fig. 1,** which is used on the Eagle Medallion models and Eagle Premier and Dodge Monaco equipped with 3.0L/V6-180 engines is a vane type pump, and utilizes a remote fluid reservoir located near the front of the left cylinder head.

## PUMP PRESSURE TEST

Refer to "Type 3—TC-Series Vane Type Power Steering Pumps" for procedure.

## PUMP SERVICE

### DISASSEMBLY

1. Remove pump, pump mounting brackets and pump pulley.
2. Remove pump end plate retaining ring as follows:
   a. Position a socket (1) on the pump shaft and end plate **Fig. 2.**
   b. Mount pump and sockets in a vise as shown in **Fig. 2.**
   c. Tighten fixture slightly to compress spring under end plate. **End plate is under spring pressure. Use caution when removing retaining ring to avoid personal injury.**
   d. Insert a punch (2), **Fig. 2,** into access hole in pump and push ring outward.
   e. Remove retaining ring (3), **Fig. 2,** with a screwdriver, release vise jaws and remove pump and sockets from vise.
3. Place pump into vise with wood blocks between shaft end of pump housing and vise jaws **Fig. 3.**
4. Remove end plate by gently rocking back and forth, or tapping with a soft mallet.
5. Remove high pressure fitting and O-ring from housing, then remove flow control valve and spring noting position for assembly **Fig. 4.**
6. Remove pressure plate spring and pressure plate.
7. Tap pump shaft from housing, then remove shaft retaining ring, pump ring, rotor and vanes and thrust plate from the shaft **Fig. 5.**
8. Remove thrust plate and dowel pins **Fig. 5.**
9. Remove pressure plate and end plate O-rings, and shaft seal from pump housing **Fig. 6.**

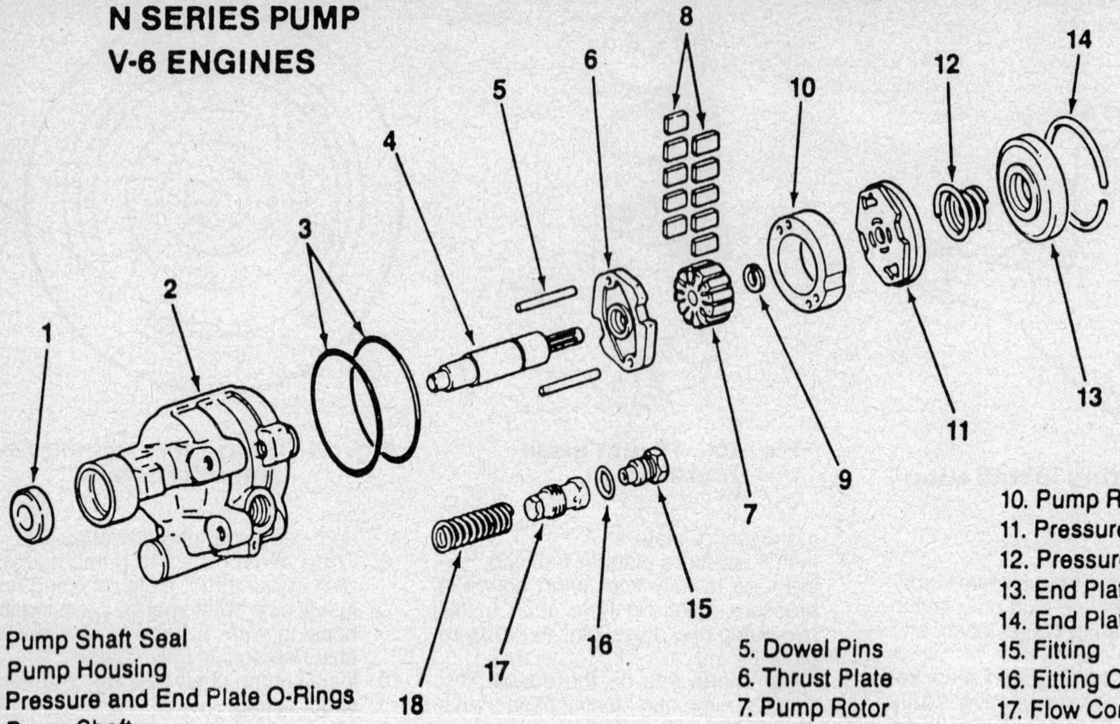

N SERIES PUMP
V-6 ENGINES

1. Pump Shaft Seal
2. Pump Housing
3. Pressure and End Plate O-Rings
4. Pump Shaft
5. Dowel Pins
6. Thrust Plate
7. Pump Rotor
8. Pump Vanes (10)
9. Shaft Retaining Ring
10. Pump Ring
11. Pressure Plate
12. Pressure Plate Spring
13. End Plate
14. End Plate Retaining Ring
15. Fitting
16. Fitting O-Ring Seal
17. Flow Control Valve
18. Flow Control Valve Spring

**Fig. 1 Type 4—N series pump exploded view**

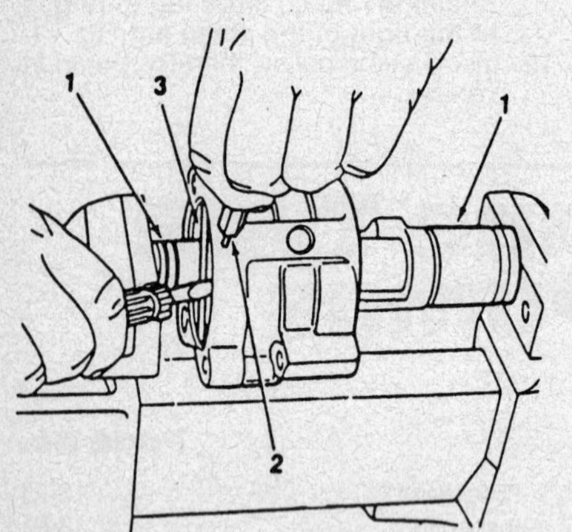


**Fig. 2 End plate retaining ring removal**

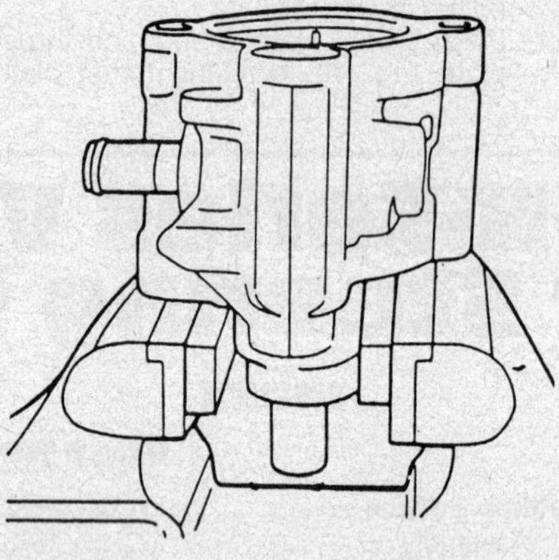

**Fig. 3 End plate removal**

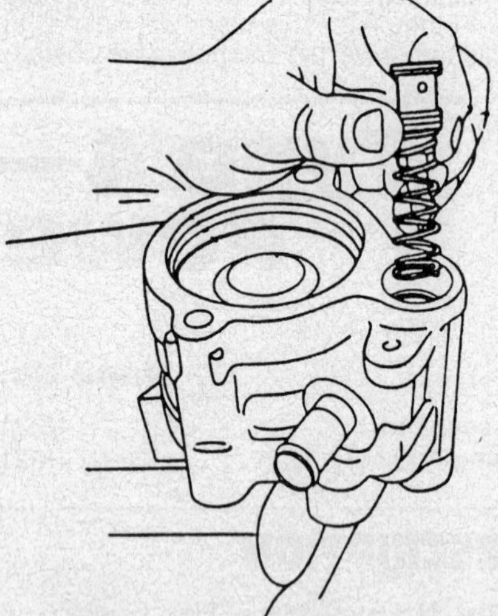

**Fig. 4 Flow control valve removal**

## INSPECTION

1. Clean all parts with solvent and blow dry with compressed air.
2. Inspect flow control valve for nicks, scratches and burrs. Clean up minor surface marks with crocus cloth. Replace valve as an assembly if damaged.
3. Check pressure and thrust plates for flatness and replace if worn or scored.
4. Inspect pump ring and replace if damaged in any way.
5. Inspect thrust plate dowels, pressure plate spring, rotor, splines and surfaces for distortion or any other damage. Replace as needed.

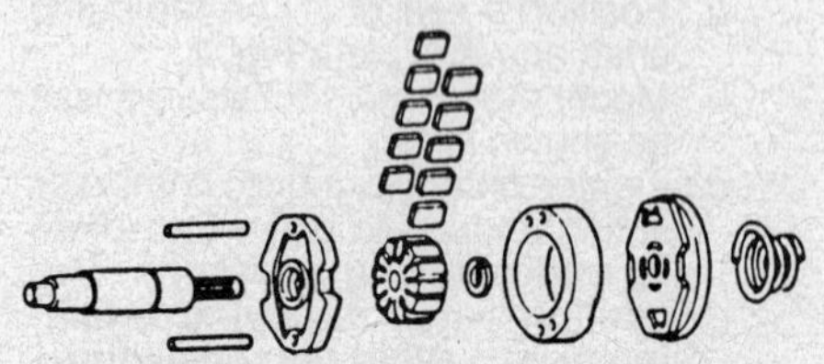

**Fig. 5 Pump ring, rotor & rotor vanes removal**

6. Inspect pump shaft and splines and replace if scored or damaged. Replace shaft retaining ring.
7. Inspect pump housing and bores, and pump fittings for wear and porosity. Replace as necessary.
8. Inspect end plate and end plate retaining ring. Replace if damaged or distorted in any way.

## ASSEMBLY

**Ensure all parts are clean and lubricated with clean power steering fluid. Dirt will cause noise, leaks, and accelerated wear.**

1. Install pump shaft seal with installer tool No. J-7728 or equivalent.

Fig. 6 Pump shaft seal removal

2. Install pressure plate and end plate O-rings in housing, then install thrust plate dowels in housing.
3. Install thrust plate and rotor on pump shaft. Be sure rotor is installed with counterbore facing thrust plate, then secure rotor to shaft with retaining ring.
4. Align thrust plate to dowels and install shaft, rotor, and plate in pump.
5. Align pump ring to dowels and install over rotor. Ensure directional arrows are facing up **Fig. 7.**
6. Install rotor vanes with rounded edges facing outward.
7. Install pressure plate with spring groove facing upward, then install spring in groove.
8. Install end plate then end plate retaining ring as follows:
   a. Position sockets on pump shaft and end plate, then position pump and sockets in a vise.
   b. Tighten the vise slightly to compress spring under end plate, then install end plate retaining ring.
   c. Remove pump and sockets from vise.
9. Install flow control valve and spring with hex nut side of valve toward bore.
10. Install O-ring and fitting in the flow control valve bore and torque to specifications, then position pulley on pump.
11. Install pump and fill reservoir to specified level.

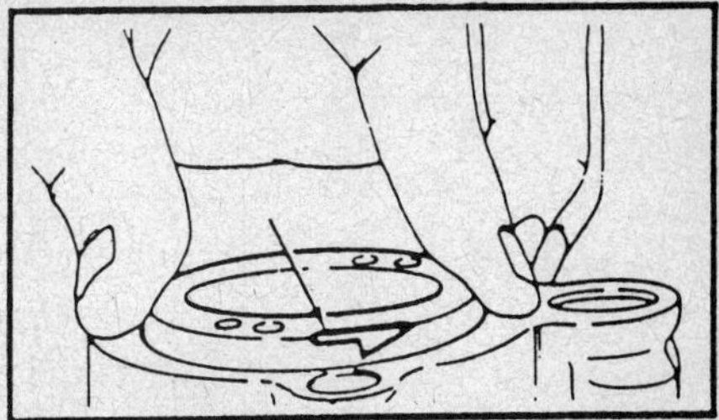

Fig. 7 Pump ring installation

# Types 5, 6, 7, 8 & 9—Vane Type Power Steering Pumps

## INDEX



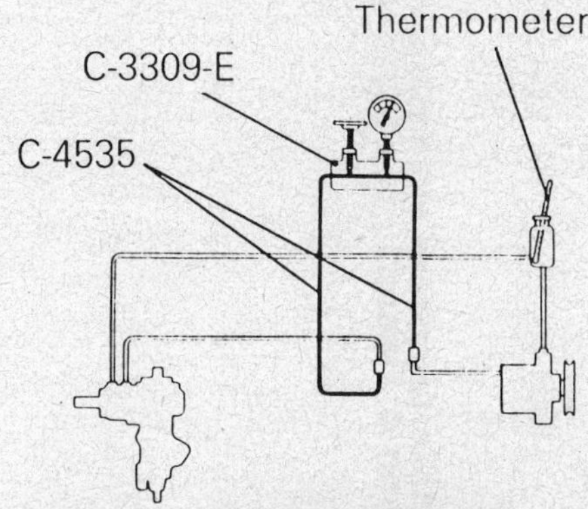


Fig. 1 Connecting pump pressure test equipment

## PUMP PRESSURE TEST

1. Disconnect pressure hose from pump and install gauge and shut-off valve C-3309-E and hoses C-4535 or their equivalents as shown in **Fig. 1. Use an adapter to connect hoses to pump.**
2. Bleed power steering system, then start engine and allow fluid to reach a temperature of approximately 131°F.
3. Set engine speed to 1000 RPM, then completely close shut-off valve. **Do not close shut-off valve for more than 3 seconds, damage to pump may occur.**
4. If pressure is not within minimum

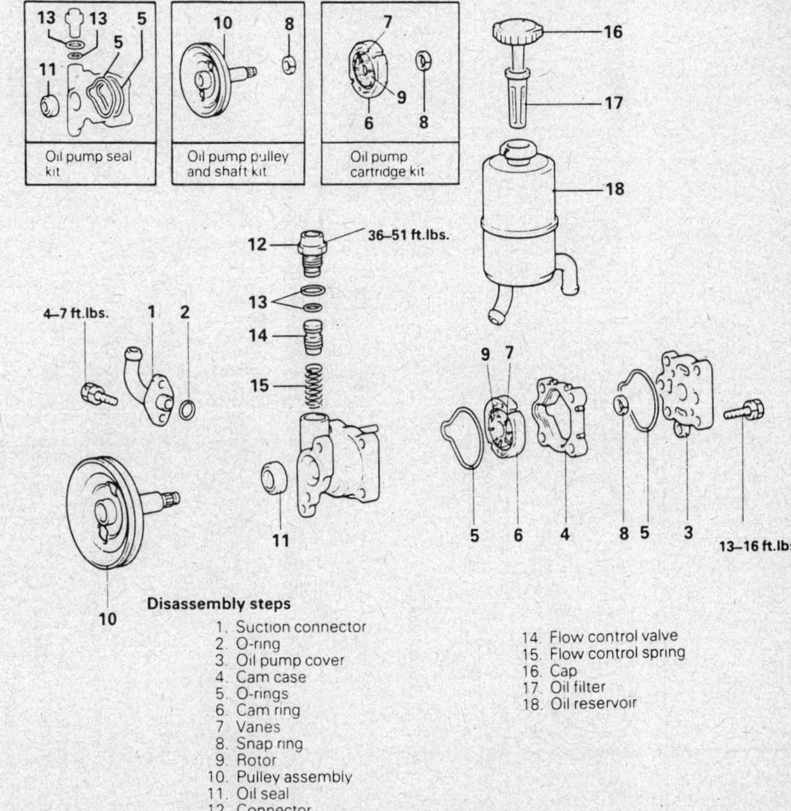


Fig. 2 Type 5—Vane type power steering pump assembly. Conquest

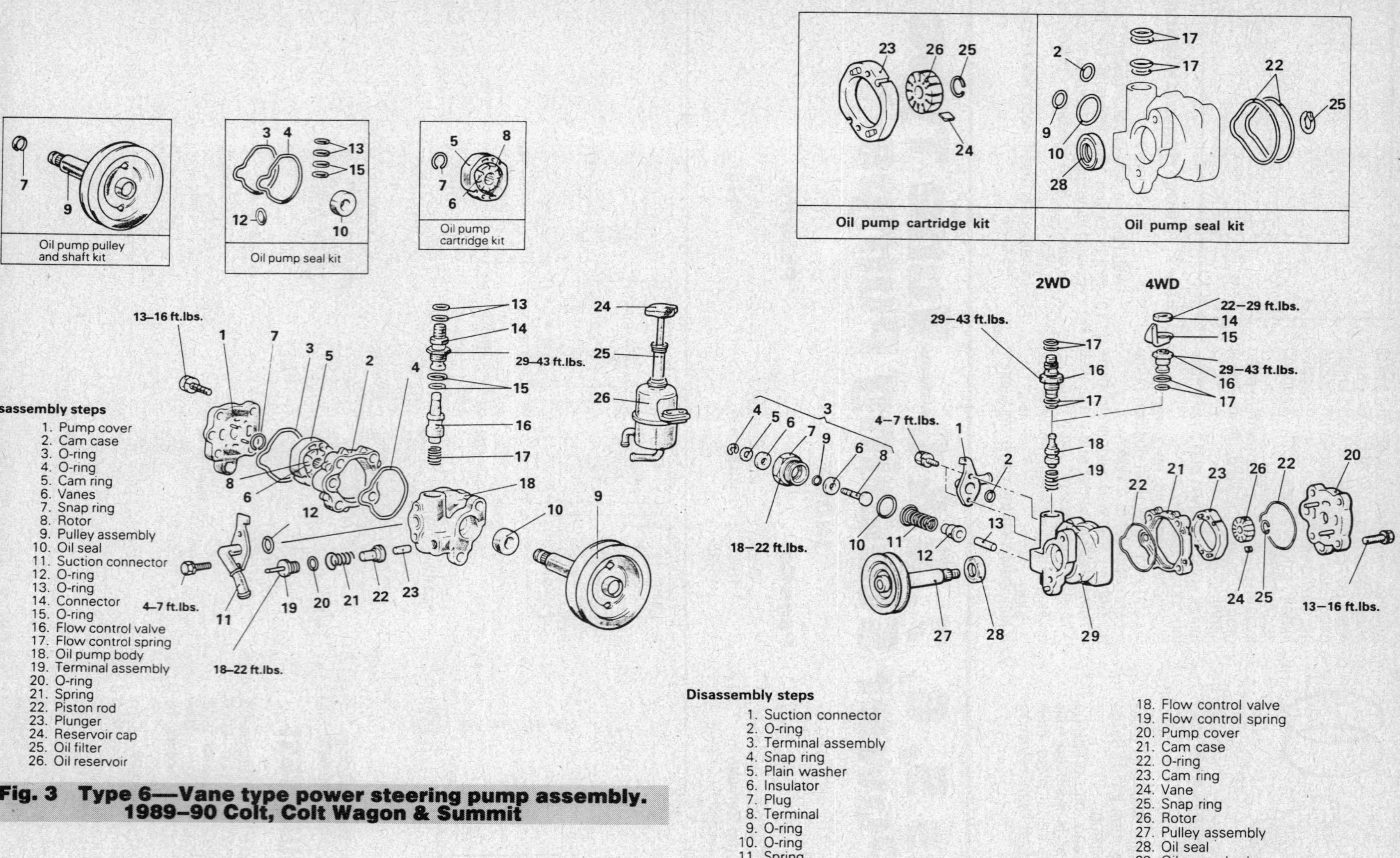


**Disassembly steps**

1. Pump cover
2. Cam case
3. O-ring
4. O-ring
5. Cam ring
6. Vanes
7. Snap ring
8. Rotor
9. Pulley assembly
10. Oil seal
11. Suction connector
12. O-ring
13. O-ring
14. Connector
15. O-ring
16. Flow control valve
17. Flow control spring
18. Oil pump body
19. Terminal assembly
20. O-ring
21. Spring
22. Piston rod
23. Plunger
24. Reservoir cap
25. Oil filter
26. Oil reservoir

**Fig. 3 Type 6—Vane type power steering pump assembly. 1989–90 Colt, Colt Wagon & Summit**

**Disassembly steps**

1. Suction connector
2. O-ring
3. Terminal assembly
4. Snap ring
5. Plain washer
6. Insulator
7. Plug
8. Terminal
9. O-ring
10. O-ring
11. Spring
12. Piston rod
13. Plunger
14. Locking nut (for 4 WD)
15. Guide bracket (for 4 WD)
16. Connector
17. O-ring
18. Flow control valve
19. Flow control spring
20. Pump cover
21. Cam case
22. O-ring
23. Cam ring
24. Vane
25. Snap ring
26. Rotor
27. Pulley assembly
28. Oil seal
29. Oil pump body

**Fig. 4 Type 7—Vane type power steering pump assembly. 1989–91 Colt Vista & 1990 Laser & Talon**

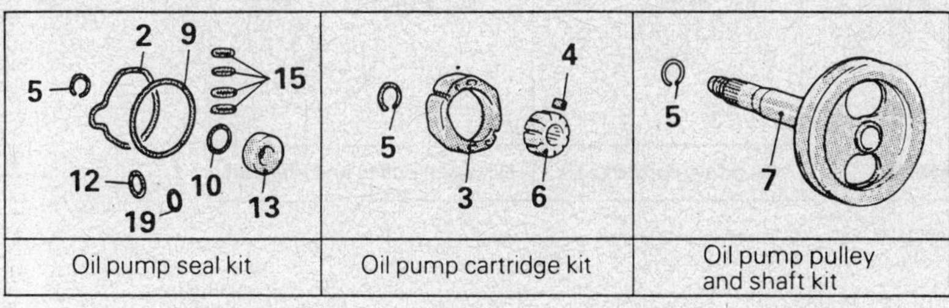


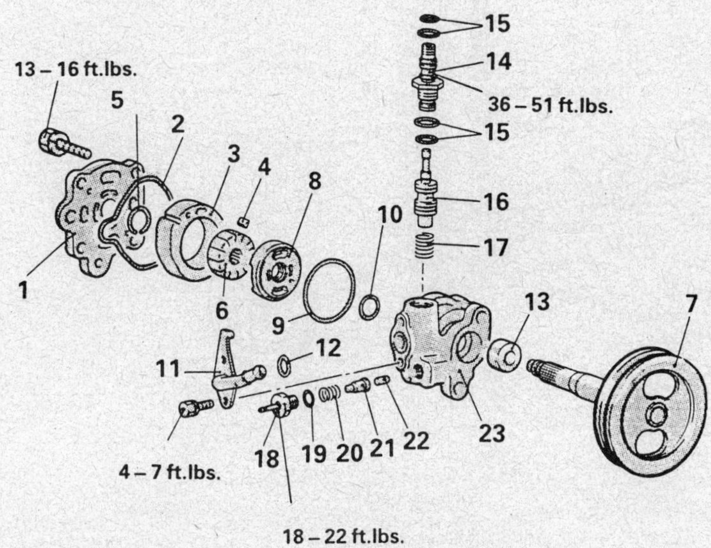


**Disassembly steps**

1. Pump cover
2. O-ring
3. Cam ring
4. Vanes
5. Snap ring
6. Rotor
7. Pulley assembly
8. Side plate
9. O-ring
10. O-ring
11. Suction connector
12. O-ring
13. Oil seal
14. Connector
15. O-ring
16. Flow control valve
17. Flow control spring
18. Terminal assembly
19. O-ring
20. Spring
21. Plunger
22. Piston rod
23. Oil pump body

**Fig. 5 Type 8—Vane type power steering pump assembly. 1991 Colt & Summit**

specifications, repair or replace pump. Refer to "Power Steering Pressure Specifications."

5. Completely open shut-off valve. If pressure is not within minimum specifications, check for clogged or collapsed oil line, or clogged oil line inside gear box and repair as necessary.
6. With shut-off valve completely open, turn wheels completely right or left. If pressure is not within minimum specifications, valve of gear box is faulty, replace gear box.

## PUMP SERVICE

### DISASSEMBLY

Disassemble pump in numbered sequence shown in **Figs. 2 through 6,** noting the following:

1. Tap rotor side of pulley assembly slightly with a plastic hammer, then remove from pump housing.
2. **Do not disassemble flow control valve.**

### INSPECTION

1. Clean all parts in a suitable cleaning fluid.
2. Check fit of vanes in slots of rotor for tightness or excessive looseness. Vanes must fit snugly but slide freely in slots in rotor. Replace rotor if excessive looseness exists between rotor and vanes. Replace vanes if worn or scored.
3. Inspect pump housing for cracks or damage. Check housing for evidence of wear or scoring.
4. Check all springs for free length, distortion or collapsed coils.
5. Inspect locating dowel pins for distortion.
6. Examine outer diameter of flow control valve for scoring or roughness. Slight damage may be cleaned up with crocus cloth. Check valve assembly for freedom of movement in bore of pump housing.
7. Check all oil passages in pump parts for obstruction.
8. Check bushing in pump housing for wear or damage.

### ASSEMBLY

Reassemble pump in reverse order of numbered sequence shown in **Figs. 2 through 6,** noting the following:

1. Apply power steering fluid to all O-rings prior to installation.
2. Install rotor with countersunk part facing pump cover.
3. Ensure that rotor snap ring is secured in countersunk part of rotor.
4. Install cam ring with punched mark facing pump body and dowel pin holes aligned with dowel pins on pump body.

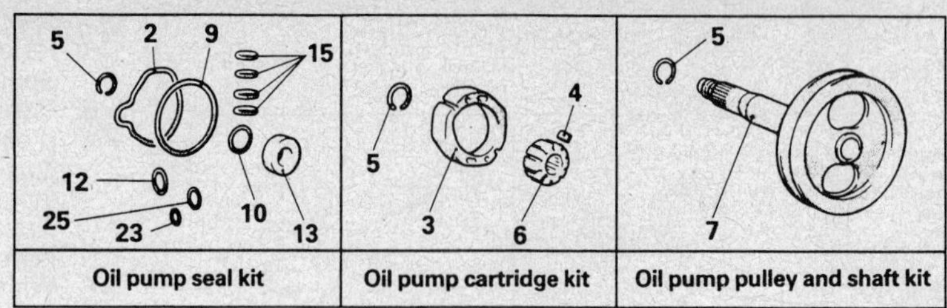


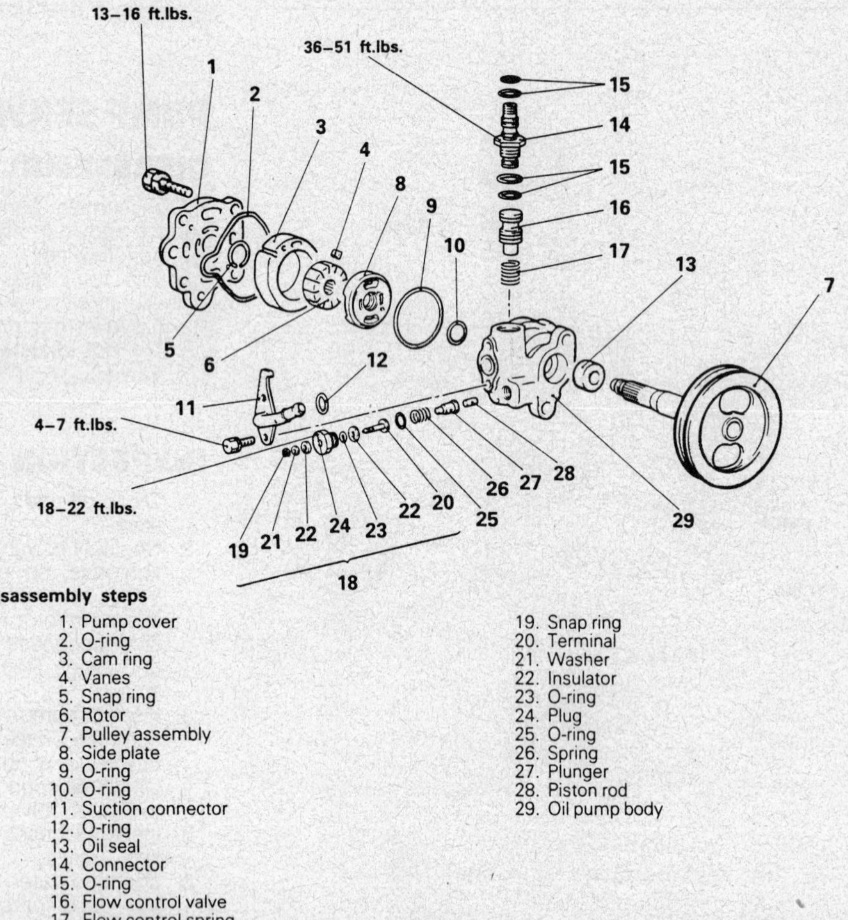


**Disassembly steps**

1. Pump cover
2. O-ring
3. Cam ring
4. Vanes
5. Snap ring
6. Rotor
7. Pulley assembly
8. Side plate
9. O-ring
10. O-ring
11. Suction connector
12. O-ring
13. Oil seal
14. Connector
15. O-ring
16. Flow control valve
17. Flow control spring
18. Terminal assembly
19. Snap ring
20. Terminal
21. Washer
22. Insulator
23. O-ring
24. Plug
25. O-ring
26. Spring
27. Plunger
28. Piston rod
29. Oil pump body

**Fig. 6 Type 9—Vane type power steering pump assembly. 1991 Laser & Talon**

# Type 10—Vane Type Power Steering Pumps

INDEX



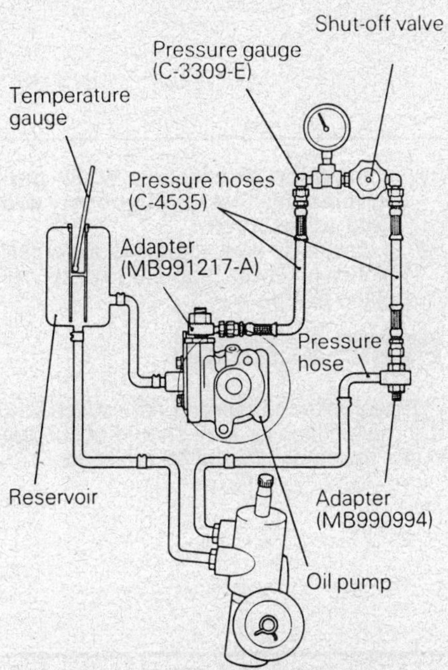


**Fig. 1 Connecting pump pressure test equipment**

## PUMP PRESSURE TEST

1. Disconnect pressure hose from pump and install gauge and shut-off valve C-3309-E and pressure hoses C-4535 using adapters MB990994 and MB991217-A or their equivalents as shown in **Fig. 1.**
2. Bleed power steering system, then start engine and turn steering wheel several times so that fluid temperature rises to approximately 122-140°F.
3. Allow engine to idle at 900-1100 RPM, then completely close shut-off valve. **Do not close shut-off valve for more than 10 seconds, damage to pump may occur.**
4. If pressure is not within minimum specifications, repair or replace pump. Refer to "Power Steering Pressure Specifications."
5. Completely open shut-off valve. If pressure is not within minimum specifications, check for clogged or collapsed oil line, or faulty gear box and repair as necessary.
6. With shut-off valve completely open and closed, turn wheels completely right or left. If pressure is not within minimum specifications, valve of gear box is faulty, repair or replace gear box.

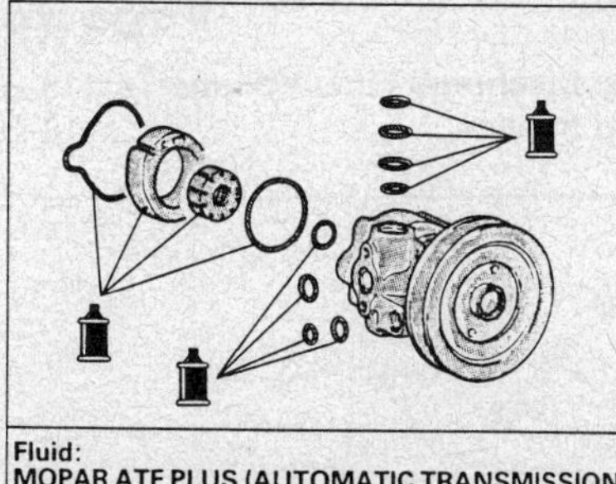

Fluid:
MOPAR ATF PLUS (AUTOMATIC TRANSMISSION FLUID TYPE 7176) or DEXRON II


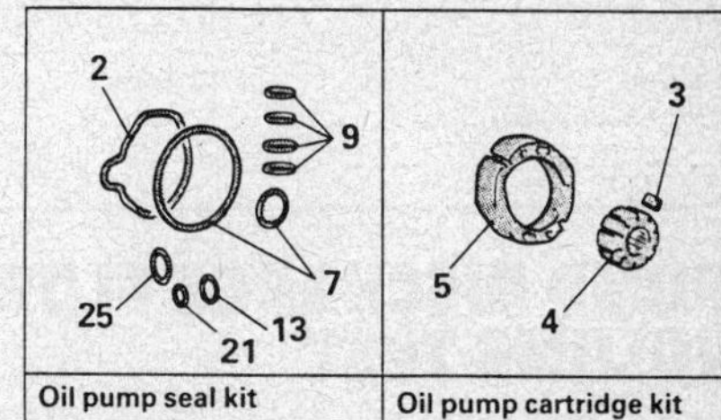


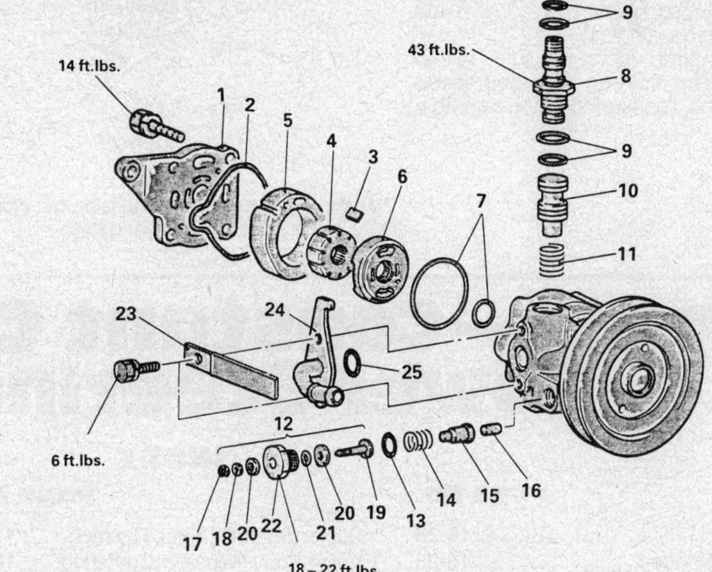


Disassembly steps

1. Pump cover
2. O-ring
3. Vanes
4. Rotor
5. Cam ring
6. Side plate
7. O-ring
8. Connector
9. O-ring
10. Flow control valve
11. Flow control spring
12. Terminal assembly
13. O-ring
14. Spring
15. Plunger
16. Piston rod
17. Snap ring
18. Terminal
19. Washer
20. Insulator
21. O-ring
22. Plug
23. Clip
24. Suction connector
25. O-ring
26. Oil pump body and Pulley assembly

Caution
Do not disassemble the flow control valve.

**Fig. 2 Type 10—Vane type power steering pump assembly. Stealth**

## PUMP SERVICE

### DISASSEMBLY

Disassemble pump in numbered sequence shown in **Fig. 2.**

### INSPECTION

Refer to "Types 5, 6, 7, 8 & 9—Vane Type Power Steering Pumps" for procedures.

### ASSEMBLY

Reassemble pump in reverse order of

numbered sequence shown in **Fig. 2**, noting the following:

1. Apply power steering fluid to all O-rings prior to installation.
2. Fit spring to pump body with large diameter end facing terminal assembly side.
3. Align dowel pin hole of side plate with dowel pin of pump body when installing side plate.
4. Install cam ring with punched mark facing side plate.

# Type 11—Vane Type Power Steering Pumps

## INDEX



## PUMP DISCHARGE FLOW VOLUME TEST

1. Disconnect pressure hose from pump and install adapter MB991217-A or equivalent with a suitable hose, then place hose in a container which permits measurement of flow rate (graduated cylinder).
2. Start engine, increase idle speed slowly, then hold an indicated speed of 31 mph, measuring discharge flow volume for 30 seconds. **While performing this test, continuously add fluid to reservoir.**
3. If discharge flow volume is extremely higher or lower than 1.06 quarts, replace pump.

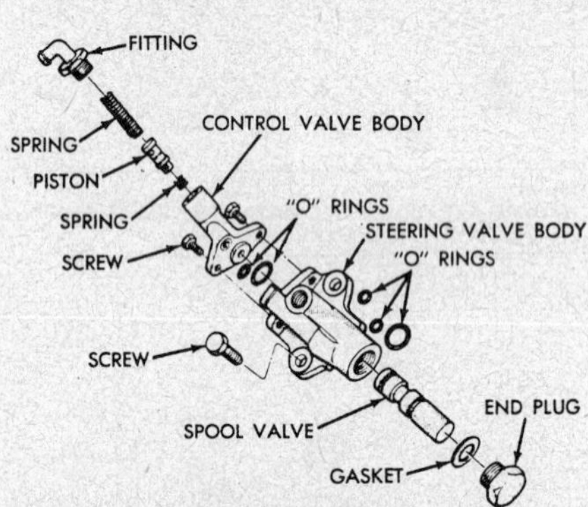


**Fig. 1 Exploded view of valve body assembly**

## PUMP SERVICE

Power steering pump is not serviceable. If a malfunction or leak should occur, the pump assembly should be replaced.

# Type 1—Constant Control Type Power Steering Gear

## INDEX



## DESCRIPTION

The constant control full time power steering gear consists of a gear housing containing a sector shaft with sector gear, a power piston with gear teeth broached into side of piston which is in constant mesh with sector shaft teeth, and a wormshaft connecting steering wheel to power piston through a pot type coupling. The wormshaft is geared to piston through recirculating ball contact. The steering valve mounted on top steering gear, directs flow of fluid in system.

## IN-VEHICLE SERVICE

### SECTOR SHAFT, ADJUST

1. Disconnect center link from steering gear arm, then start engine and run at idle.
2. Turn steering wheel gently from one stop to the other, counting number of turns, then turn wheel back exactly half way to center position.
3. Loosen sector shaft adjusting screw until there is backlash in steering gear arm. **Feel backlash by holding end of steering gear arm between thumb and forefinger with a light grip.**
4. Tighten adjusting nut until backlash just disappears, then continue to tighten 3/8-1/2 turn from this position and torque locknut to specifications.

## VALVE BODY REPAIR & CENTERING

The valve body assembly consists of two sub-assemblies, **Fig. 1,** back pressure control valve assembly and steering valve body assembly. The back pressure control valve assembly is serviceable without removing or recentering the steering valve assembly. The following procedure applies to both sub-assemblies.

1. Disconnect high pressure and return hoses and secure ends above reservoir fluid level.
2. Remove two screws attaching valve body to main gear housing, then lift valve body up ward to disengage from valve lever.
3. Remove two screws attaching control valve body to steering valve body and separate two bodies.
4. Remove outlet fitting, spring and valve piston, then carefully shake out spool valve and inspect for nicks, burrs and scores. **Do not remove valve body**

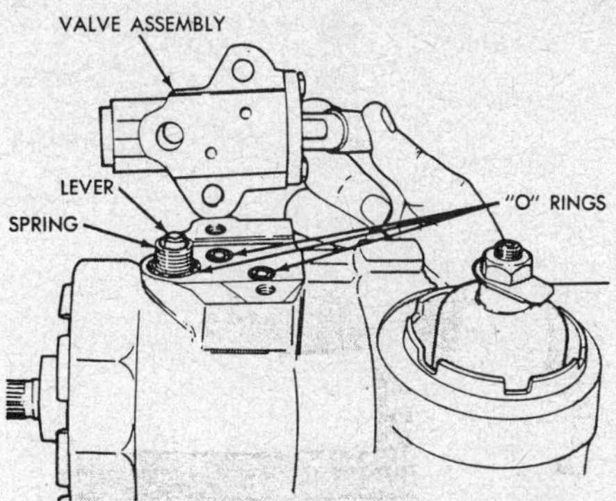


**Fig. 2 Removing valve body assembly**

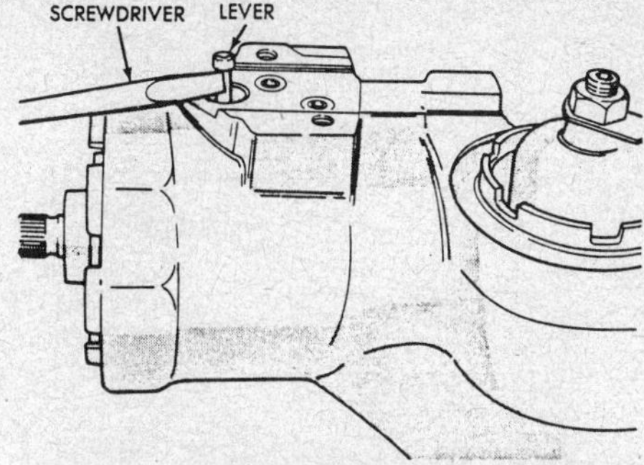


**Fig. 3 Removing valve lever and spring**

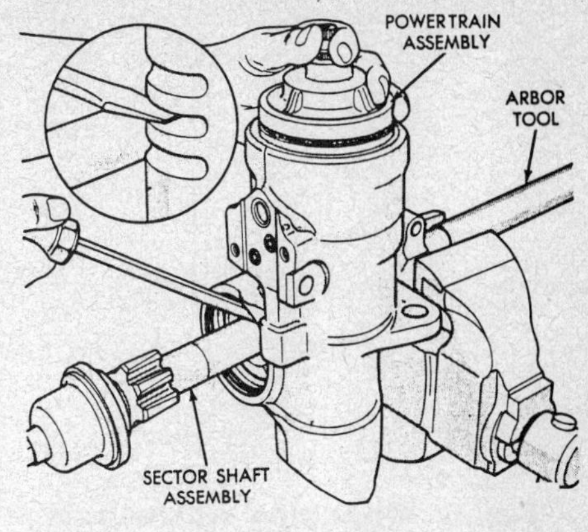


**Fig. 4 Removing power train**

**end plug unless inspection indicates a leak at gasket. If spool valve or valve body is damaged, replace valve and body assembly. Small burrs and nicks may be removed with crocus cloth if extreme care is used not to round off sharp edge of valve.**

5. Clean valve bodies, valve piston and spool valve thoroughly in a suitable solvent, blow out all passages with compressed air, then lubricate piston, spool valve and bores with power steering fluid.
6. Install steering spool valve in valve body so valve lever hole is aligned with lever opening in valve body. **Valve must be free in valve body without sticking or binding.**
7. If end plug was removed, install a new gasket on end plug and torque to specifications.
8. Install piston and springs into control valve body, then the fitting and torque to specifications.
9. Install new O-rings onto control valve body and assemble to steering valve body. Torque attaching screws to specifications.
10. Align lever hole in spool valve with lever opening in valve body, then install on gear housing ensuring that valve lever enters hole in spool valve and key section on bottom of valve body meshes with keyway in housing. **These parts should go together easily, use of force may damage lever. If not, lift off valve assembly, realign spool valve with lever opening and reinstall valve body.**
11. Install two screws and torque to specifications to prohibit leakage during valve centering operation.
12. Connect high pressure and return hoses to valve body, then start engine.
13. If unit is steering itself, tap valve body up or down as necessary to correct.
14. Turn steering wheel from stop to stop several times to expel air from system, then refill reservoir as necessary. **Do not turn hard against ends of travel, this will generate high pressure and may blow out O-rings since valve body screws have not been finally torqued.**
15. With steering wheel in straight ahead, centered position, start and stop engine several times, tapping valve body up or down as necessary until there is no movement of steering wheel when engine is started or stopped.
16. Valve is now centered, torque screws attaching valve body to housing to specifications.

## SECTOR SHAFT OIL SEAL, REPLACE

1. Remove steering arm nut and disconnect from sector shaft using puller C-4150 or equivalent. **Puller C-4150 or a suitable equivalent must be used to avoid damage to "T" slot ears on sector shaft.**
2. Slide threaded adapter SP-3056 of tool C-3350-A or equivalent over end of sector shaft and thread tool nut on sector shaft. **Maintain pressure on threaded adapter with tool nut while screwing adapter far enough to engage metal portion of grease retainer.**
3. Place two half rings SP-3056 or equivalent and tool retainer ring over both portions of tool, then turn tool nut counterclockwise to withdraw grease retainer from housing.
4. Remove oil seal snap ring with suitable pliers, then the seal back-up washer.
5. Use tool C-3350-A in same manner as in steps 2 and 3 to remove inner seal.
6. Place new seal on flat surface, lip down, lubricate inside diameter with power steering fluid and insert seal protector sleeve SP-1601 or equivalent.
7. Position seal with protector over sector shaft with lip of seal toward housing, then place tool adapter SP-5148 or equivalent with long step of adapter against new seal.
8. Install tool nut on sector shaft and tighten until shoulder of adapter contacts gear housing.
9. Remove tool nut, adapter and protector, install seal back-up washer and oil seal snap ring with sharp edge out. **Snap ring must be installed with sharp edge and identification stamp to outside of gear assembly.**
10. Fill housing cavity outside of retainer and snap ring with multi-purpose chassis grease 4318062 or equivalent, then position new grease retainer in housing bore with metal side outboard.
11. Place tool adapter so that short step of adapter is against retainer, then install tool nut on sector shaft and tighten until shoulder of adapter contacts gear housing.
12. Remove nut and adapter, place steering gear and front wheels in straight ahead position and install steering gear arm and nut, then torque steering gear arm nut to specifications.

## WORMSHAFT OIL SEAL, REPLACE

1. Remove steering column as described under "Steering Column, Replace" in "Steering Column" section.
2. Remove oil seal using tool C-3638 or equivalent, then drive new seal in place with lip towards housing using tool C-3650 or equivalent.
3. Install and align steering column as described under "Steering Column, Replace" in "Steering Column" section.

## STEERING GEAR SERVICE

1. Clean gear assembly thoroughly in a suitable solvent, then secure in a soft-jawed vise.
2. Drain steering gear through pressure and return connections by rotating wormshaft from stop to stop.
3. Remove valve body and three O-rings, **Fig. 2.**
4. Remove valve lever by prying under spherical head, **Fig. 3.** Use care not to collapse slotted end of valve lever as this will destroy bearing tolerances of head.
5. Loosen sector shaft adjusting screw locknut, then remove sector shaft cover spanner nut using tool C-3988 or equivalent.
6. Rotate wormshaft to position sector shaft teeth at center of piston travel, then loosen powertrain retaining nut using tool C-3988 or equivalent.
7. Rotate wormshaft to full left turn position to compress powertrain components, then remove powertrain retain-

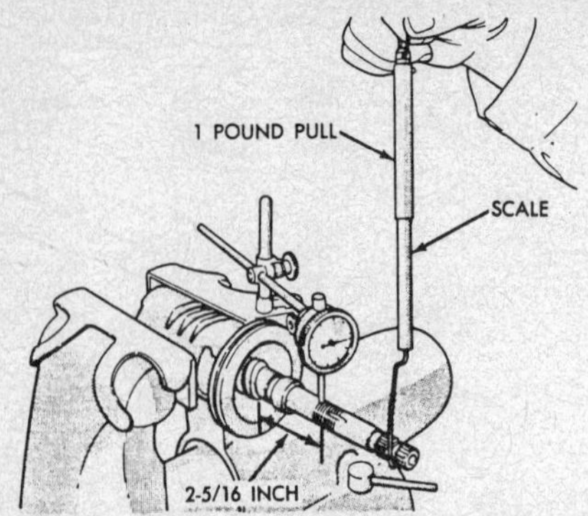


**Fig. 5 Checking wormshaft side play**

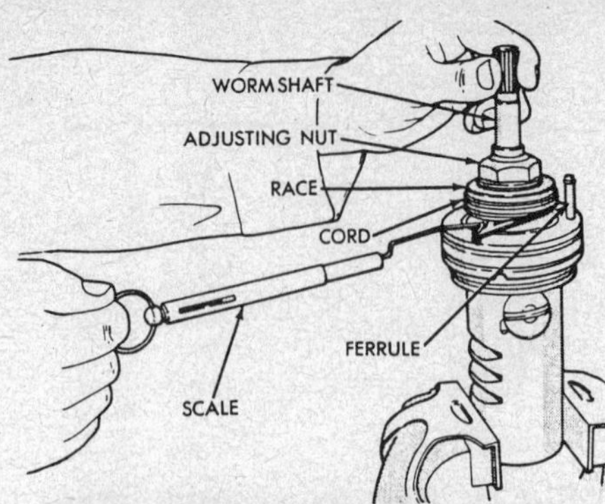


**Fig. 6 Checking center bearing preload**

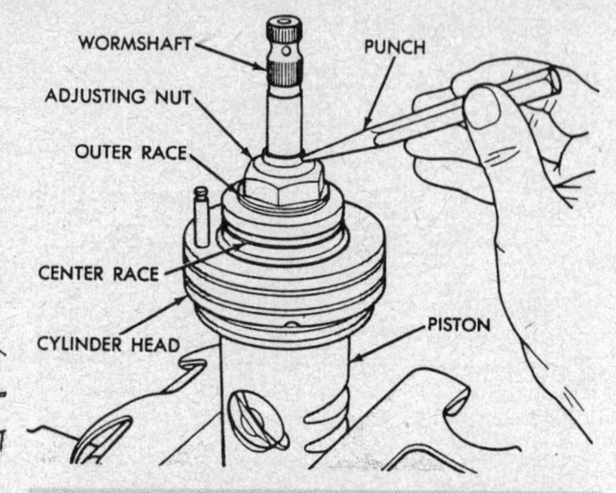


**Fig. 7 Staking adjusting nut**

ing nut using tool C-3989 or equivalent.

8. While holding powertrain firmly compressed, pry on piston teeth using sector shaft as a fulcrum and remove complete power train, **Fig. 4. Cylinder head, center race, spacer assembly and the housing head must be kept in close contact with each other to eliminate possibility of reaction rings becoming disengaged from grooves in cylinder head and housing head. It will also prevent center spacer from becoming separated from center race and jamming in the housing, making it impossible to remove powertrain without damaging spacer or housing.**
9. **If it is necessary to replace wormshaft oil seal, perform operation with housing head assembled in steering gear housing. Refer to "In-Vehicle Service" for procedure.**
10. Raise housing head until wormshaft oil seal just clears top of wormshaft, then position arbor tool C-3929 or equivalent on top of wormshaft and into oil seal.
11. With arbor in position, pull up on housing head until arbor is positioned in bearing, then remove housing head and arbor. **Worm bearing needle rollers (33) will fall out when housing head is removed from wormshaft if arbor is not used. If rollers should become dislodged during removal, reinstall rollers using wheel bearing lubricant to retain rollers in cage.**
12. Remove large O-ring from groove in housing head, then the reaction seal from groove in face of housing head using air pressure directed into ferrule chamber.
13. Inspect all grooves for burrs and ensure that passage from ferrule chamber to upper reaction chamber is not obstructed.
14. Remove reaction spring, reaction ring, worm balancing ring and spacer.
15. Hold wormshaft from turning, then turn nut with sufficient force to release from knurled section and remove nut. **Use a wire brush to remove chips from knurled sections, then blow out nut and wormshaft using compressed air to remove any metal particles.**
16. Remove upper thrust bearing race (thin) and upper thrust bearing, center bearing race, lower thrust bearing and lower thrust bearing race (thick), lower reaction ring and reaction spring, then the cylinder head assembly.
17. Remove two O-rings in two outer grooves of cylinder head, then the reaction O-ring from groove in face of cylinder head using air pressure directed into oil hole located between two O-ring outer grooves.
18. Remove snap ring and seal, then test operation of wormshaft as follows:
    a. Torque required to rotate wormshaft throughout its travel in or out of piston should not exceed 1½ inch lbs.
    b. **Worm and piston assembly is serviced as complete assembly and should not be disassembled.**
    c. Test for excessive side play with piston held firmly in a soft-jawed vise with rack teeth pointing up and worm in its approximate center of travel, **Fig. 5.** Vertical side play measured at a point 2⁵⁄₁₆ inches from piston flange should not exceed .008 inch when end of worm is lifted with a force of 1 pound.
19. Inspect teflon piston ring for cuts, nicks and gaps, if necessary, replace as follows:
    a. Remove old teflon ring and rectangular ring, then install new rectangular ring ensuring that it does not twist.
    b. Using only as much stretching as is necessary, first put one side of teflon ring into piston flange groove, then thumb around flange until full circle drops into groove without twisting.
    c. It will be necessary to resize stretched teflon ring in order to reassemble into gear housing without damaging. Using a suitable engine piston ring compressor, tighten down to flange size for a few seconds, then release. Teflon will have sufficient "memory" to return to and retain a useable size.
20. Place piston assembly in a vertical position (wormshaft up) in a soft-jawed vise.
21. Inspect wormshaft teflon seal for nicks and gaps, if necessary, replace as follows:
    a. Cut and remove continuous ring from groove in wormshaft.
    b. Replacement seal is noncontinuous and is cut at right angle, install using multi-purpose grease 4318062 or equivalent to hold seal centered on shaft. **Ensure that end gap is closed to avoid damaging seal when cylinder head is installed.**
22. Inspect cylinder head ferrule oil passage for obstructions and lands for burrs, then lubricate two large O-rings and install them in cylinder head grooves.
23. Install lower reaction O-ring in cylinder head groove, then slide cylinder head assembly (ferrule up) on wormshaft. **Ensure that wormshaft seal ring gap is closed to avoid damaging ring as cylinder head moves against piston flange.**
24. Lubricate with power steering fluid, then install lower thrust bearing race (thick), lower thrust bearing, lower reaction spring (with small hole over ferrule), lower reaction ring (flange up so ring protrudes through reaction spring and contacts reaction O-ring in cylinder head), center bearing race, upper thrust bearing and upper thrust bearing race (thin).
25. Start new wormshaft thrust bearing adjusting nut, but do not tighten.
26. Turn wormshaft clockwise ½ turn, hold wormshaft in this position using splined nut tool C-3637 or equivalent and socket wrench during steps 27 through 29d, then torque adjusting nut to specifications to prestretch threads.
27. Loosen adjusting nut, then place several rounds of cord around center bearing, make a loop in one end of cord and hook a spring scale in cord loop, **Fig. 6.**
28. Retighten worm bearing adjusting nut while pulling on cord with scale to adjust preload. When adjusting nut is tightened properly (preload adjustment), reading on scale should be 16-24 ounces (20 ounces preferred) while race is turning.
29. Stake upper part of wormshaft adjusting nut as follows:
    a. Hold a ¼ inch flat end punch on

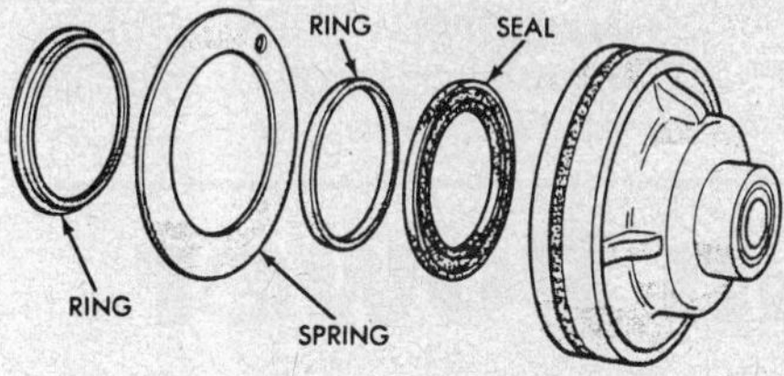


**Fig. 8 Reaction components & housing head**

center line of wormshaft end at a slight angle to nut flange, **Fig. 7.**

b. Strike punch a sharp blow with a hammer, then retest preload. **If adjusting nut moved during staking operation, it can be corrected by striking nut a glancing blow in direction required to regain proper preload.**

c. After retesting preload, stake nut at three more locations 90° apart around upper part of nut.

d. Test total staking by applying 20 ft. lbs of torque in each direction. If nut does not move, staking is satisfactory, retest preload to ensure that adjustment remained constant after nut was securely locked.

30. Position spacer assembly over center race, engaging dowel pin of spacer in slot of race, and slot of spacer entered over cylinder head ferrule. This will align valve lever hole in center bearing spacer assembly.
31. Install upper reaction ring on center race and spacer with flange down against spacer, upper reaction spring over reaction ring with cylinder head ferrule through hole in reaction spring, then the worm balancing ring (without flange) inside upper reaction ring.
32. Lubricate ferrule O-ring and install in groove on cylinder head ferrule, then the reaction seal in groove in face of housing with flat side of seal out, **Figs. 8 and 9.**
33. Install O-ring in groove on housing head, then slide housing over wormshaft carefully engaging cylinder head ferrule and O-ring, powertrain is now ready for installation in housing. **Ensure reaction rings enter circular groove in housing head.**
34. It is generally not necessary to remove sector shaft cover. If necessary, remove locknut and combination aluminum gasket and date tag, then turn adjusting screw clockwise while holding cover until shaft becomes disengaged from cover. Adjusting screw will now slide out of "T" slot in end of shaft.
35. If necessary, replace sector shaft seal. Refer to "In-Vehicle Service" for procedure.
36. Insert gear shaft and adjusting screw into cover, turn screw counterclockwise to pull shaft completely into cover. Install combination aluminum gasket and date tag and adjusting screw locknut, but do not tighten at this time.
37. Install sector shaft cover O-ring on under-cut shelf of cover, then lubricate power train bore of housing with power steering fluid and carefully install power train assembly. **Keep worm turned fully counterclockwise to keep reaction rings from coming out of their grooves. Piston teeth must be facing to right and valve lever hole in center race and spacer must be in "Up" position. Ensure cylinder head is bottomed against housing shoulder.**
38. Align valve lever hole in center bearing race and spacer with valve lever hole in gear housing, install valve lever (double bearing end first) into center race and spacer through hole in steering gear housing so that slots in valve lever are parallel to wormshaft, then lightly tap on end of valve lever with wooden end of hammer handle or handle of plastic screwdriver to seat lower pivot point in center race.
39. Center lever in hole in housing by turning housing. Tap on a reinforcing rib with a hammer and drift.

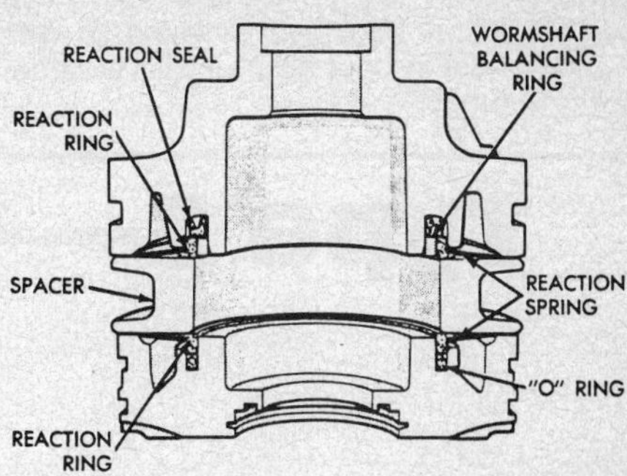


**Fig. 9 Reaction rings installed**

40. Install housing head tang washer aligned with groove in housing, then the spanner nut and torque to specifications. **Factory assembled gears do not have a tang washer under spanner nut. When reassembling power gear, a tang washer should be used. Ensure valve lever remains centered in housing hole by rotating wormshaft until piston bottoms in both directions and observe valve lever action. The valve lever must be in center of hole and return to the center position when wormshaft torque is relieved.**
41. Install valve lever spring (small end first), position power piston at center of travel and install sector shaft and cover assembly, indexing sector teeth with piston rack teeth. Ensure sector shaft cover O-ring is installed properly.
42. Install and torque cover nut to specifications using tool C-3988 or equivalent.
43. Install valve body onto housing with valve lever entering hole in valve spool. Ensure O-rings are installed properly, then install and torque valve retaining screws to specifications.

# Type 2—TRW Rack & Pinion Power Steering

## INDEX



## DESCRIPTION

The TRW rack and pinion power steering gear used on Chrysler domestic front wheel drive vehicles, Monaco and 1990-91 Eagle Premier should not be serviced or adjusted. If a malfunction or oil leak should occur, the complete steering gear should be replaced.

## OUTER TIE ROD & BOOT REPLACE

### CHRYSLER DOMESTIC FRONT WHEEL DRIVE VEHICLES

1. Loosen jam nut, then disconnect tie rod from steering knuckle.
2. Remove outer tie rod and jam nut, then the outer boot clamp.
3. Use pliers to expand boot snorkel clamp, then slide clamp onto breather tube.
4. Remove inner boot clamp, then mark breather tube location and remove boot.
5. Reverse procedure to install, noting the following:
   a. Line up mark and breather tube location.

b. Install boot over housing lip with hole in boot aligned with breather tube.

c. Lubricate outer boot groove with silicone prior to installing outer boot clamp and ensure boot is not twisted.

d. Torque tie rod jam nut to specifications.

# Type 3—Rack & Pinion Power Steering

INDEX



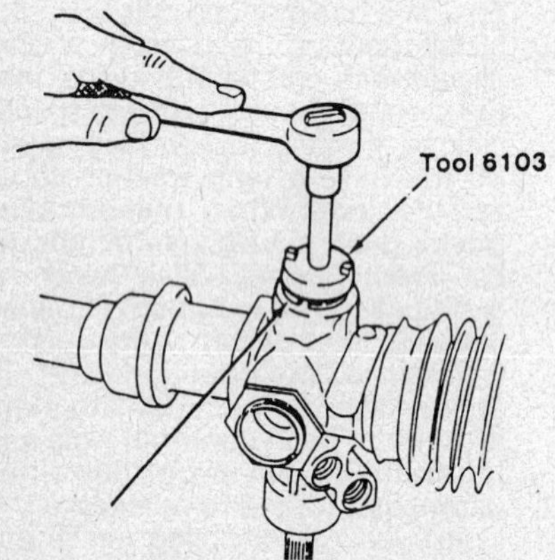

Fig. 1 End plug removal

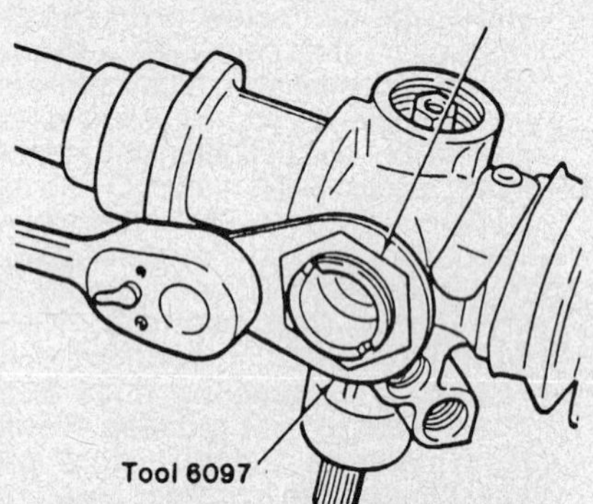

Fig. 2 Preload adjustment cap locknut removal

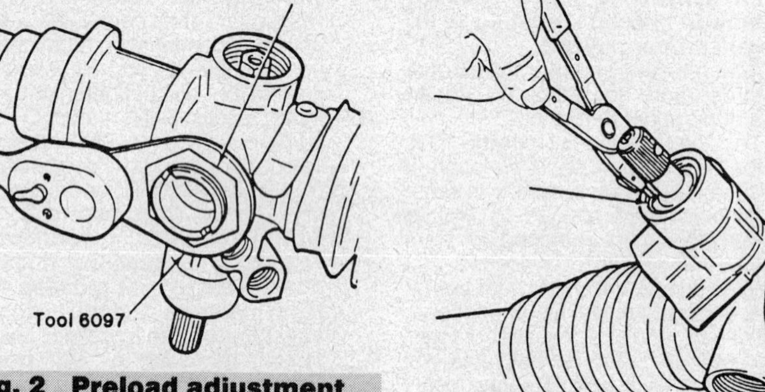
Fig. 3 Steering gear shaft snap ring removal

## RACK & PINION SERVICE

### DISASSEMBLY

All special service tools required to service steering gear are available in overhaul tool kit 6118.

1. Mount rack in a vise with jaws clamped on cast housing only.
2. Remove end plug from gear shaft bore using plug remover/installer 6103 or equivalent, **Fig. 1.**
3. Remove preload adjustment cap locknut using locknut remover/installer tool No. 6097 or equivalent, **Fig. 2.**
4. Remove preload adjustment cap from gear housing bore using plug remover/installer, then the thrust bearing from gear housing bore using a suitable pair of pliers.
5. Remove gear shaft retaining ring from gear shaft bore using snap ring pliers, **Fig. 3,** then loosen nut using shaft holder SP-3616 or equivalent, and combination wrench. Remove nut with socket and handle, **Fig. 4.**
6. Press gear shaft out of housing using pinion gear remover 6095 or equivalent, **Fig. 5,** then remove outer seal and bearing from shaft.
7. Remove seal rings from shaft by cutting with a knife, then the inner bearing from gear shaft bore using a hammer and brass drift, **Fig. 6.**
8. Remove gear shaft inner seal from gear shaft bore, **Fig. 7,** with seal remover C-4694 or equivalent as follows:
   a. Insert tool with threaded rod through gear shaft bore and through inner seal, then install and tighten tool lower nut to expand tool inside inner seal.
   b. Position cup over tool over threaded rod and against gear housing, **Fig. 8.**
   c. Install and tighten upper nut to draw inner seal out of gear housing.
9. Remove gear tube end cap retaining wire using end cap remover/installer 6101 or equivalent by rotating end cap clockwise or counterclockwise to force retaining wire out of tube, **Fig. 9.**
10. Disconnect fluid line outer fitting from gear tube, **Fig. 10. Do not disconnect any other lines at this time.**
11. Remove tube end cap using compressed air through fluid line outer fitting, then the O-ring from end cap.
12. Remove attaching bolts, tie rods and spacer washers from steering rack shaft spacer block, then cut and remove clamps that attach dust boot to cast metal housing.
13. Remove all remaining steering gear fluid lines.
14. Remove steering gear bracket and rubber isolators. **Before removing bracket, take a reference measurement from bracket to end of tube to aid in proper steering gear assembly, Fig. 11.**
15. Install protective caps 6116 or equivalent on fluid line fitting bosses of steering gear tube to prevent damage to dust boot when removed, then squeeze boot into an oval shape and slide over protective caps to remove.
16. Temporarily secure spacer block to steering rack shaft with one tie rod bolt to keep steering rack from rotating, then remove the rivet from tube with a hammer and chisel, **Fig. 12.**
17. Remove piston retaining nut at end of steering rack shaft with a socket and ratchet.
18. Remove tie rod bolt and spacer block, then relocate steering rack shaft plastic bushing/guide as follows:
   a. Insert a screwdriver into one tie rod bolt hole in steering rack shaft to prevent rack from turning, then use a second screwdriver to rotate bushing/guide around roll pin in direction shown in **Fig. 13.**
   b. Rotate bushing/guide on shaft until separation is aligned with roll pin, then slide bushing/guide approximately 2 inches along rack shaft in direction shown in, **Fig. 14.**
19. Install slide hammer adapter 6099 or equivalent on the end of a slide hammer and thread tool onto end of steering rack shaft, **Fig. 15.**
20. Remove steering rack shaft, bushing and piston as an assembly from gear

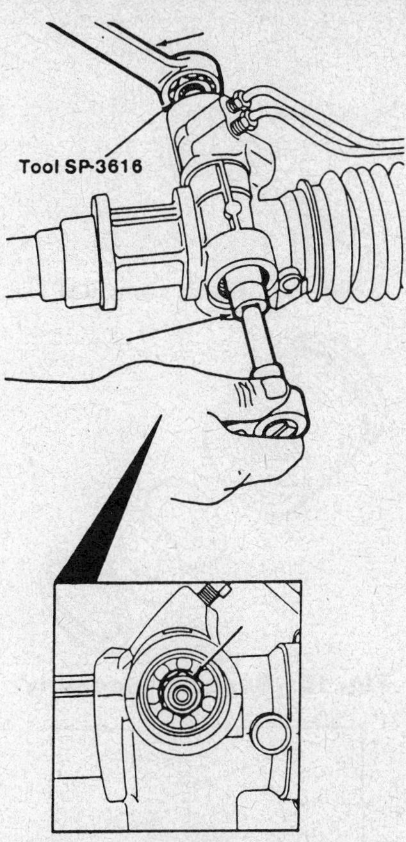


Fig. 4 Steering gear shaft retaining nut removal

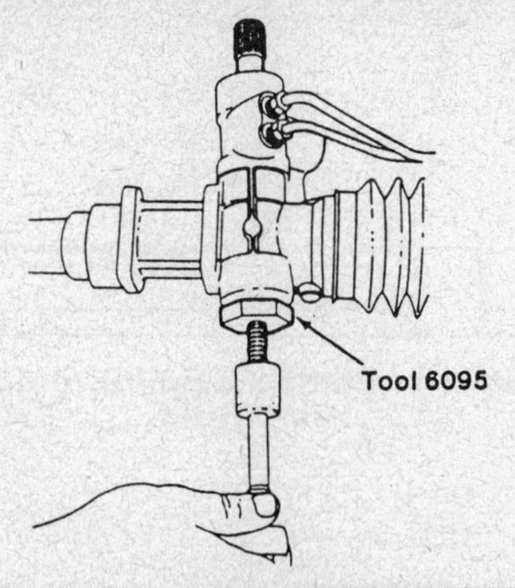


Fig. 5 Steering gear shaft removal

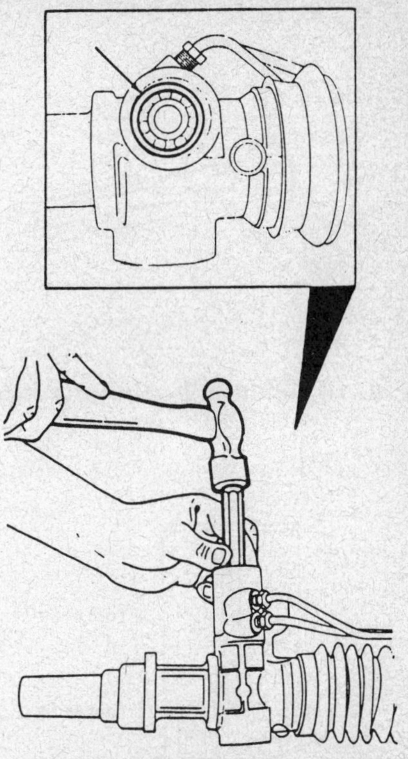

Fig. 6 Steering gear shaft inner bearing removal

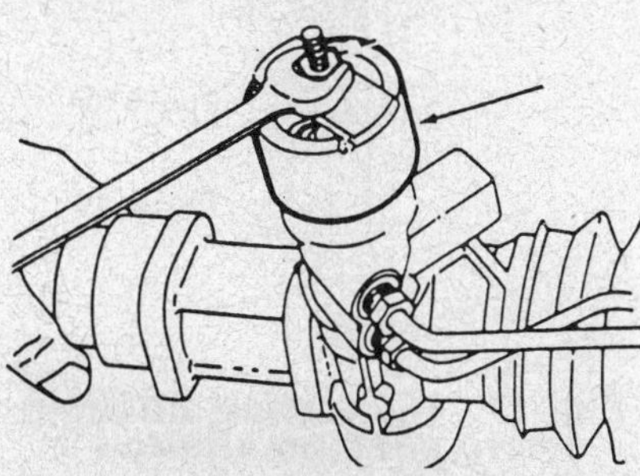

Fig. 8 Steering gear shaft inner seal removal

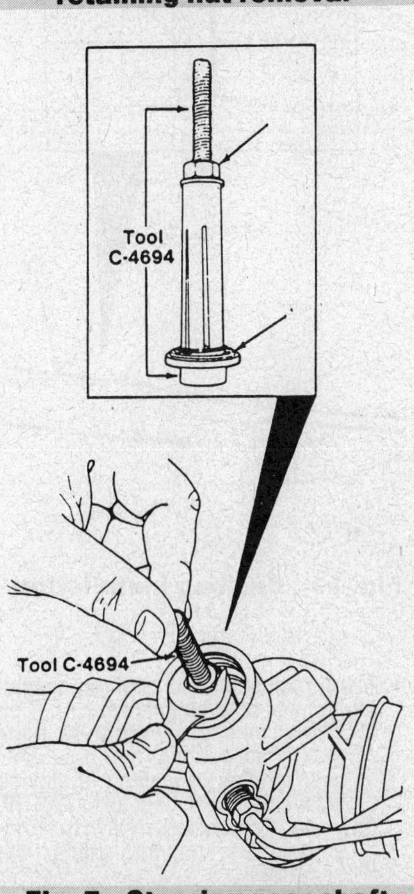


Fig. 7 Steering gear shaft inner seal removal

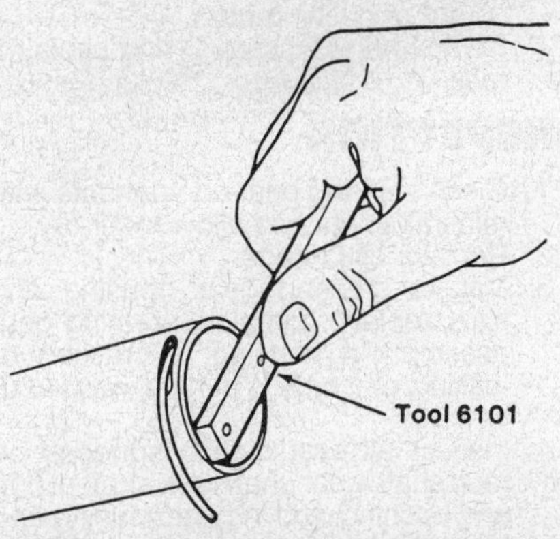


Fig. 9 Steering gear tube end cap retaining wire removal

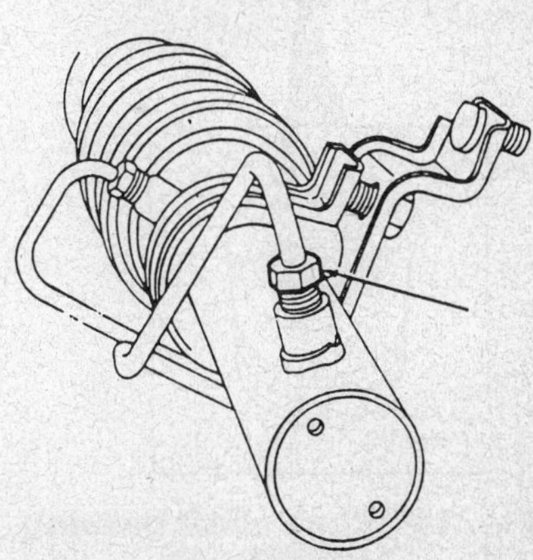

Fig. 10 Fluid line outer fitting removal

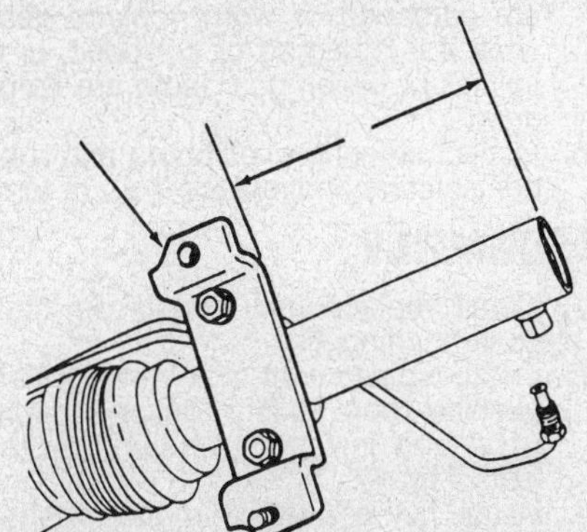

Fig. 11 Steering gear bracket reference distance measurement

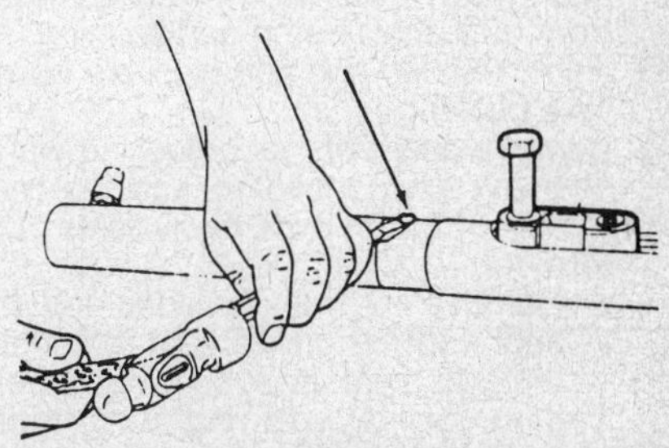

Fig. 12 Steering gear tube rivet removal

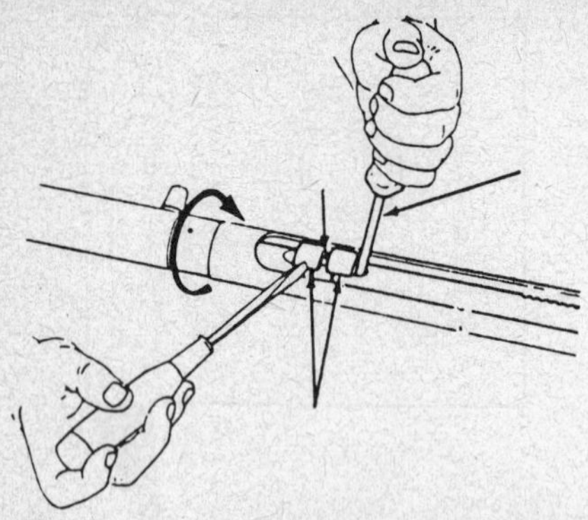

Fig. 13 Plastic bushing/guide rotation

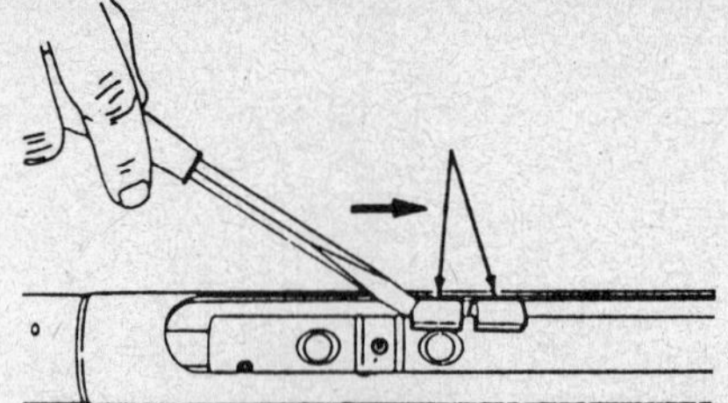

Fig. 14 Plastic bushing/guide relocation

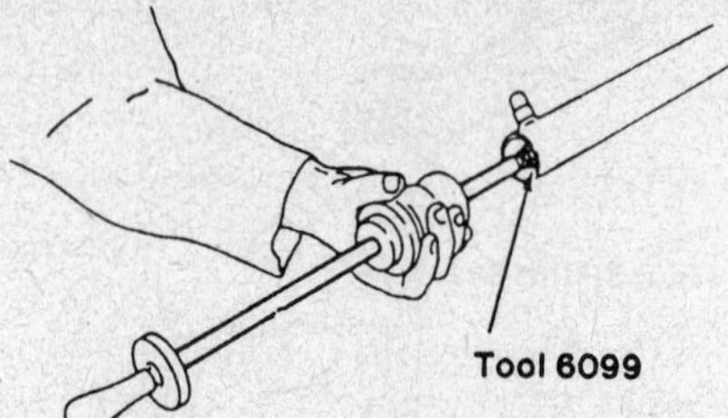


Fig. 15 Rack removal

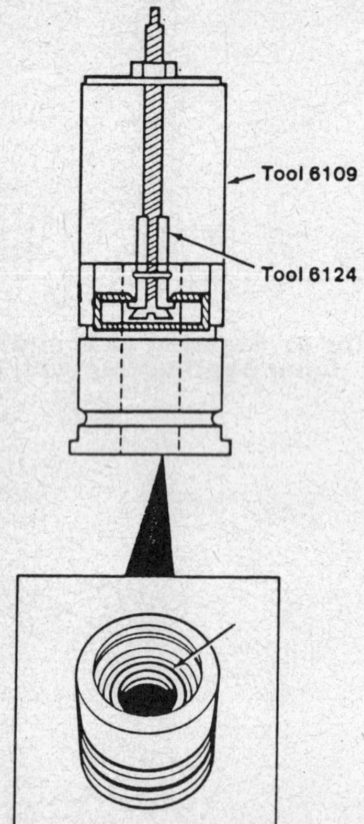


Fig. 16 Rack shaft bushing seal removal

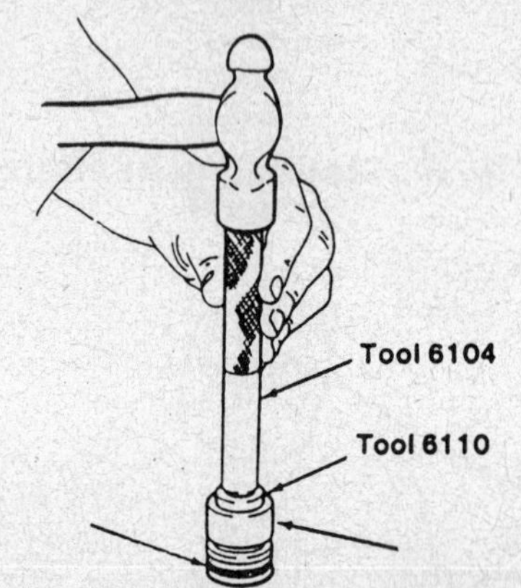


Fig. 17 Rack shaft bushing bore seal installation

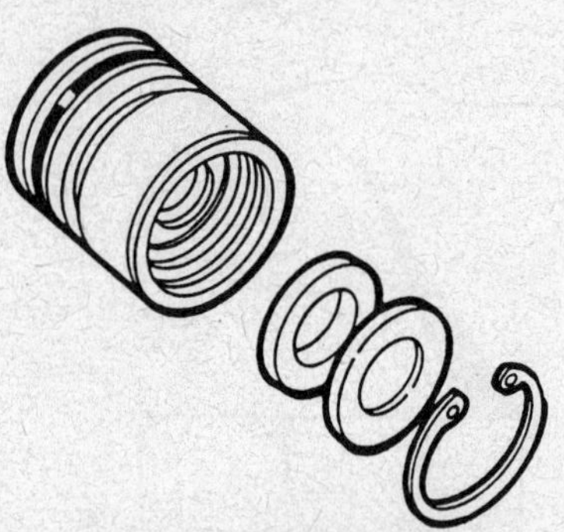

Fig. 18 Bushing assembly

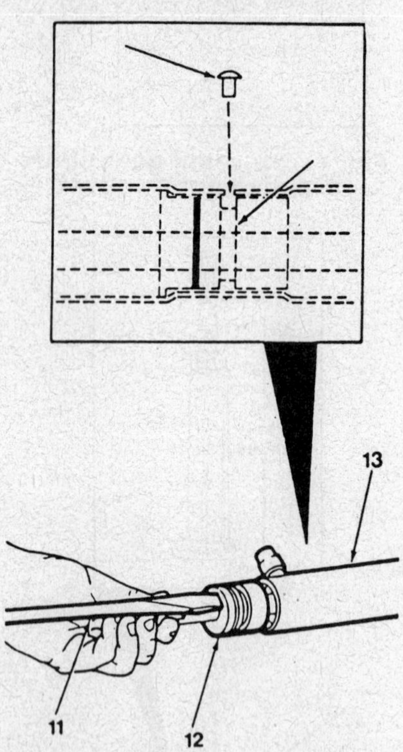


Fig. 19 Bushing installation

tube, then remove tool from rack shaft.

21. Remove piston and slide bushing off rack shaft, remove and discard ring seals from rack shaft, then cut O-rings from rack shaft piston and bushing.
22. Remove snap ring and washers from rack bushing.
23. Remove seal from rack bushing with seal ring sizing tool 6109 and seal remover 6124 or their equivalents as follows:
    a. Remove nut from threaded end of seal remover, insert seal remover through seal and bushing bore, then position seal ring sizing tool on top of bushing.
    b. Install nut on threaded end of seal remover, then retain end of seal remover and tighten nut to force seal out of bushing bore.
24. Remove and discard O-ring seals on rack.

## INSPECTION

1. Clean steering gear components with mineral spirits and allow to air dry.
2. Replace all O-rings.
3. Inspect steering gear housing and tube, replace complete steering gear assembly if housing is cracked or leaking, or if tube is dented, warped or cracked.
4. Inspect all seal mating surfaces on rack shaft, gear shaft rack shaft piston and bushing, and in gear housing and tube. Replace any component showing excessive wear or damage.
5. Inspect condition of rack shaft and rack gear, replace rack shaft if teeth are damaged or worn, replace gear shaft if it is scored or corroded, or if splines or pinion gear teeth are damaged.
6. Inspect steering gear boots and rubber isolators and replace if cut or torn.

## ASSEMBLY

1. Install replacement O-ring on rack shaft bushing, **Fig. 16.**
2. Install replacement seal in rack shaft bushing bore using driver handle 6104 and installer 6110 or equivalents, **Fig. 17.**
3. Install nylon washer, metal washer and snap ring in that order in the bushing, **Fig. 18.**
4. Install new O-ring seals on rack shaft, then slide bushing onto rack shaft.
5. Insert rack shaft and bushing assembly in gear tube as follows:
    a. Use a long screwdriver to force rack shaft bushing into tube until rivet groove in bushing is aligned with rivet hole in gear tube, **Fig. 19.**
    b. Install replacement rivet in tube rivet hole and tap into place with hammer.
6. Install rack piston with seal ring sizing tool 6111 as follows:

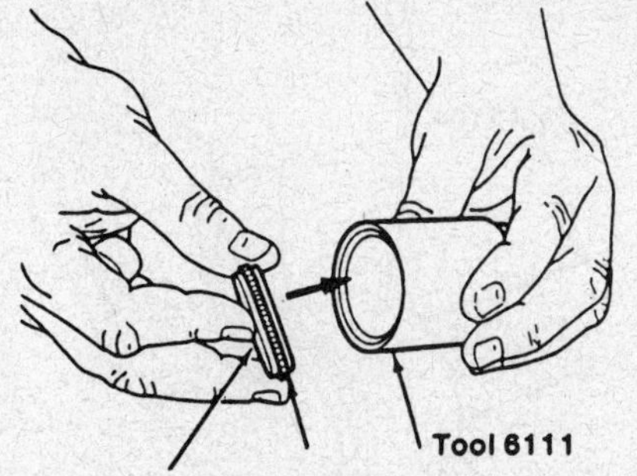


Fig. 20 Piston installation tool

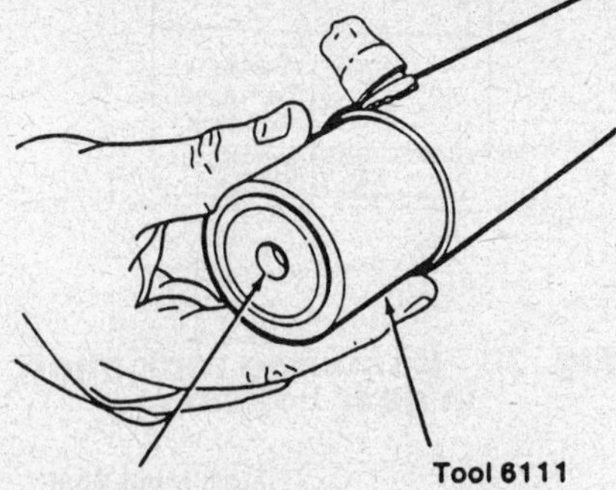


Fig. 21 Piston installation

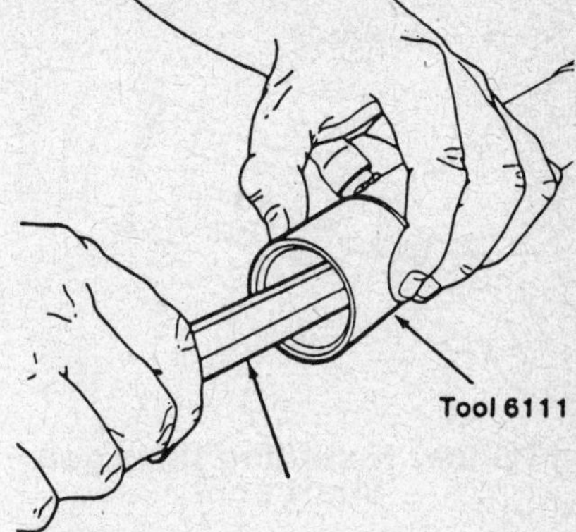


Fig. 22 Seating the piston

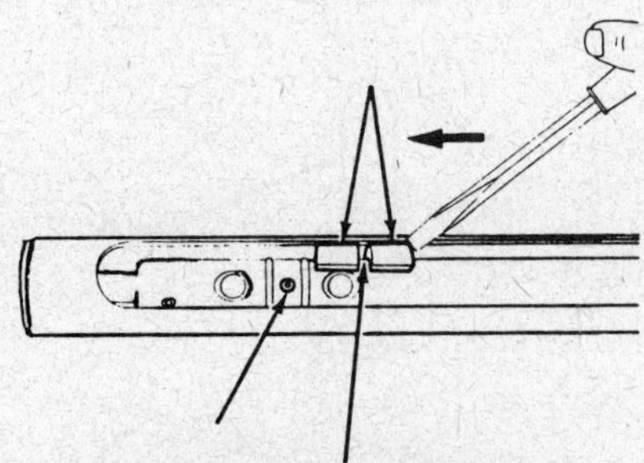

Fig. 23 Aligning bushing/guide with roll pin

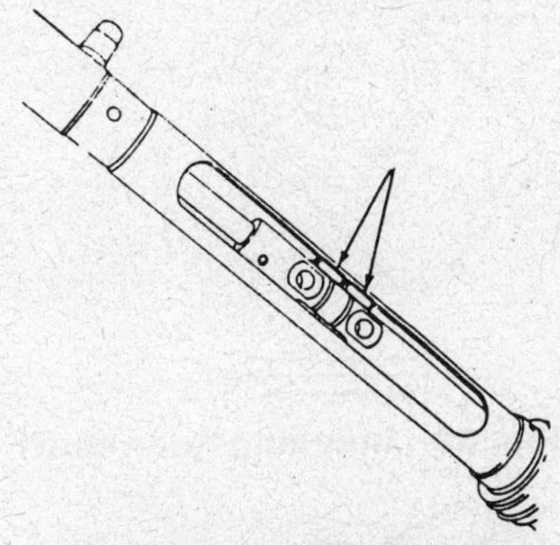

Fig. 24 Bushing/guide relocating

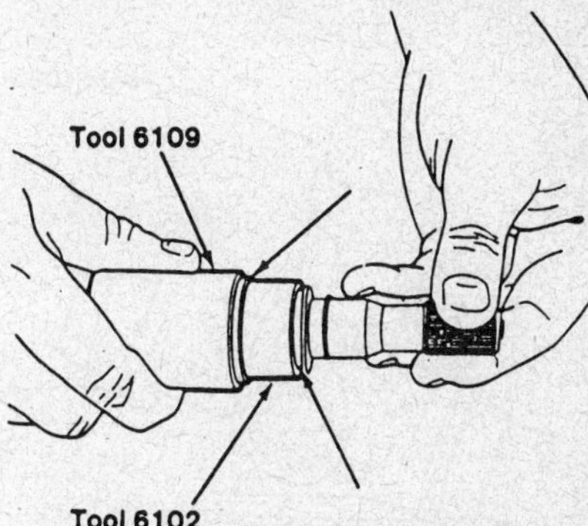


Fig. 25 Installing first gear shaft seal

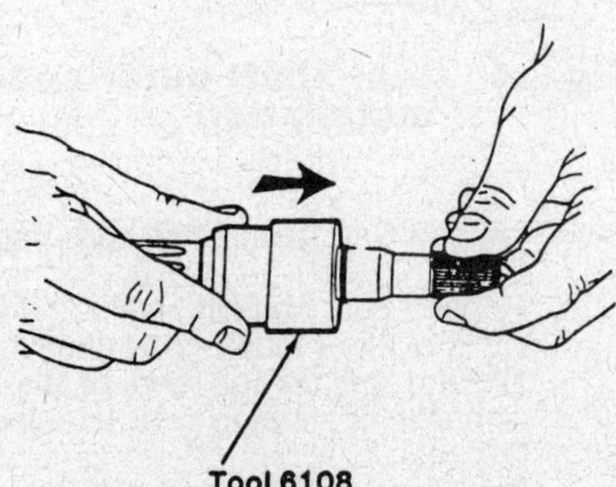


Fig. 26 Compressing gear shaft seals

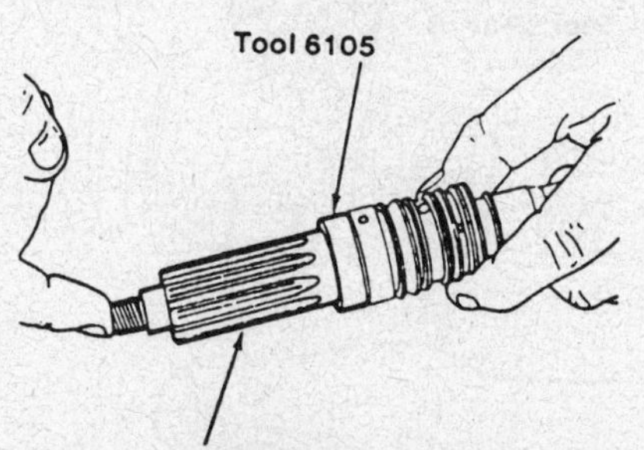
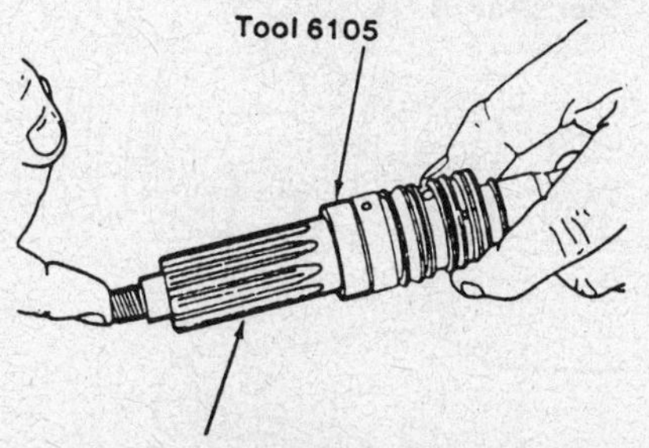


Fig. 27 Installing second gear shaft seal

Tool 6102

Tool 6109

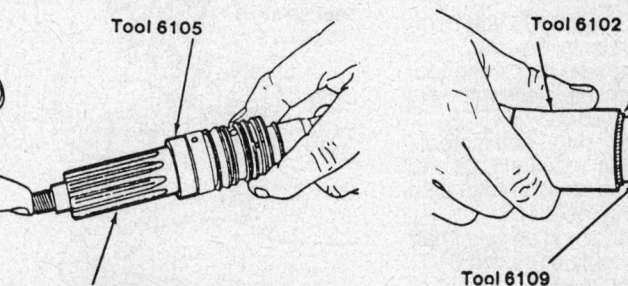

Fig. 28 Seating second gear shaft seal

a. Install replacement seal ring on piston and insert assembled seal ring and piston in seal ring sizing tool, **Fig. 20.**
b. Position tool into end of gear tube ensuring tool is aligned with tube bore, **Fig 21.**
c. Use a brass drift to carefully push piston through tool and into end of gear tube until it mates with end of rack shaft, **Fig. 22.**
d. Remove drift and tool.

7. Install piston retaining nut on end of rack shaft, but do not tighten at this time.
8. Temporarily install spacer block on rack shaft and secure with a tie rod bolt.
9. Tighten rack shaft piston retaining nut securely after spacer block and tie rod bolt are installed. The spacer block must be installed to prevent rack from turning while tightening piston nut.
10. Remove bolt and spacer block from rack shaft.
11. Position separation in plastic bushing/guide so that it is aligned with roll pin in rack shaft, **Fig. 23**, then slide bushing/guide toward roll pin until slot is aligned with roll pin.
12. Rotate bushing/guide slot toward roll pin until end of slot contacts roll pin.
13. Rotate rack shaft 180° to position roll pin at opposite side of gear tubes as shown in **Fig. 24.**
14. Install four seal rings on gear shaft as follows:
    a. Install first seal on gear shaft using seal ring sizing tool 6102 or equivalent on shaft. The tool will automatically align with first seal ring groove.
    b. Slide seal onto tool and push seal using seal ring sizing tool 6109 or equivalent into ring groove, **Fig. 25.**
    c. Compress seal to proper size using seal ring sizing tool 6108 or equivalent by sliding tool with large inside diameter forward over shaft and seal to compress it, **Fig. 26. Be sure tool is centered on seal before compressing.**
    d. Install second seal ring on gear shaft using spacer sizing tool adapter 6105 or equivalent on gear shaft, **Fig. 27.**
    e. Install seal ring sizing tool 6109 on shaft. The tools will align for installation at second ring groove.
    f. Install second seal on seal ring sizing tool 6109, then push seal into groove with seal ring sizing tool 6102, **Fig. 28.**
    g. Compress second seal ring to size with seal ring sizing tool 6108 ensuring tool is centered before sizing.
    h. Install third seal ring on gear shaft

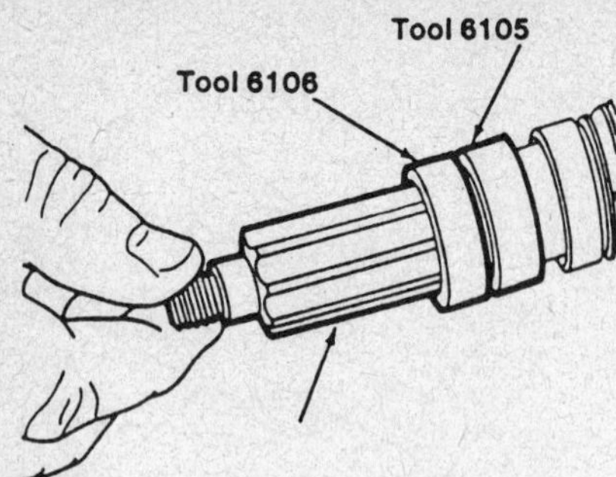


**Fig. 29 Installing third gear shaft seal**

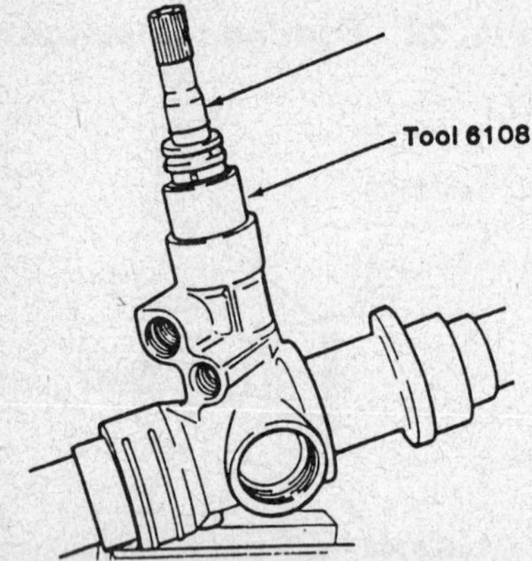


**Fig. 32 Gear shaft installation**

using spacer tools 6105 and 6106 or their equivalents, **Fig. 29.**

i. Install seal on seal ring sizing tool 6109 and push into place with seal ring sizing tool 6102.

j. Remove seal ring sizing tools 6102, 6109 and spacers 6105 and 6106, then compress seal with seal ring sizing tool 6108.

k. Install fourth seal ring on gear shaft using spacer tools 6105 and 6107 on gear shaft.

l. Place fourth seal on seal ring sizing tool 6109 and press into place with seal ring sizing tool 6102. Compress with seal ring sizing tool 6108.

15. Center rack shaft in gear housing and tube, then measure length of elongated oval opening in gear tube, **Fig. 30.** Divide dimension by 2 and center rack shaft as shown in **Fig. 30.** Use center point between two rack shaft ring seals as center of rack shaft.
16. Temporarily install spacer block on rack shaft and secure with a tie rod bolt.
17. Assemble driver handle 6104 and seal installer 6098 or equivalents.
18. Position gear housing inner seal on driver handle and seat against seal installer, **Fig. 31.**
19. Install inner seal in gear housing by tapping inward until bottomed against machined shoulder in bore.
20. Install gear shaft inner bearing with driver handle 6104 and installer 6115 or their equivalents.

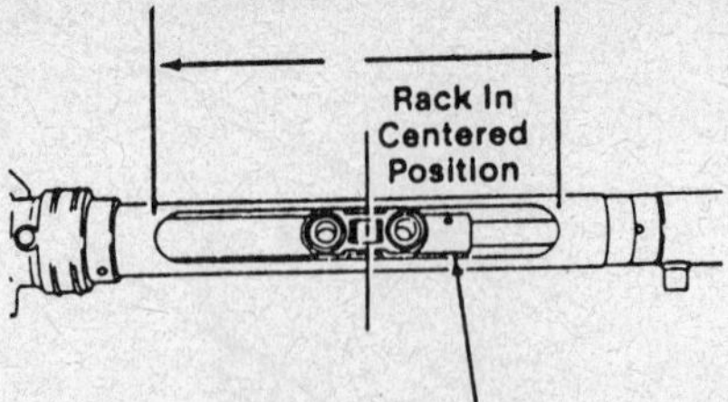


**Fig. 30 Centering rack shaft in gear housing**

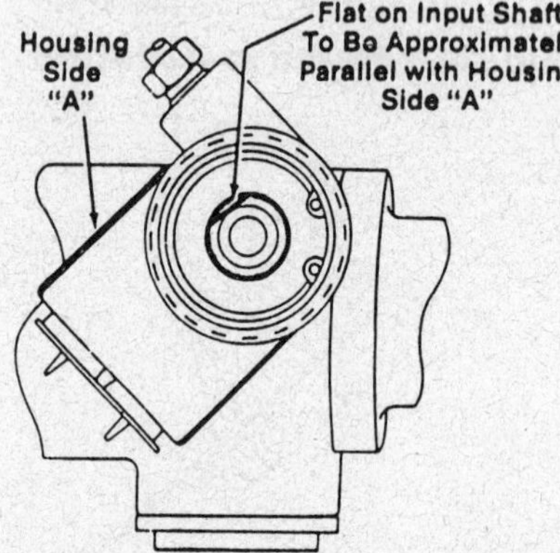


**Fig. 33 Indexing gear shaft**

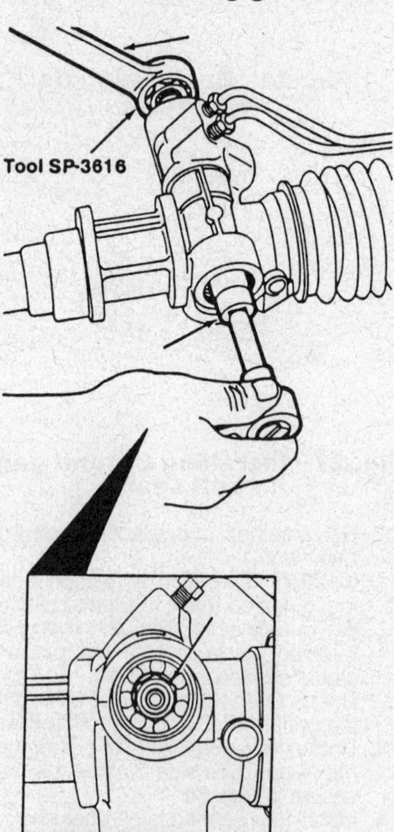


**Fig. 35 Spacer block installation**

21. Install gear shaft as follows:
    a. Ensure rack shaft is centered in housing and tube, then insert small diameter end of seal ring sizing

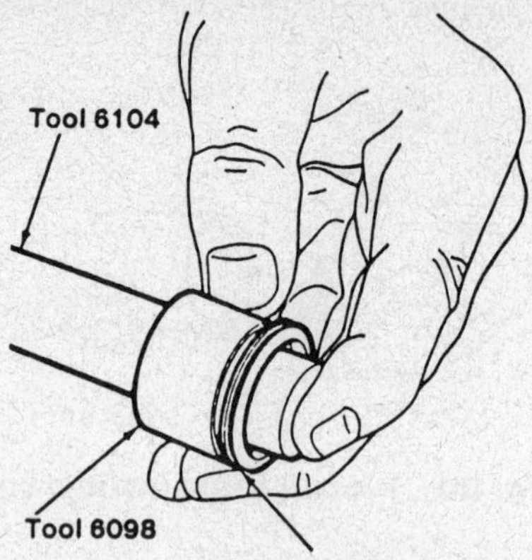


**Fig. 31 Gear housing inner seal installation**

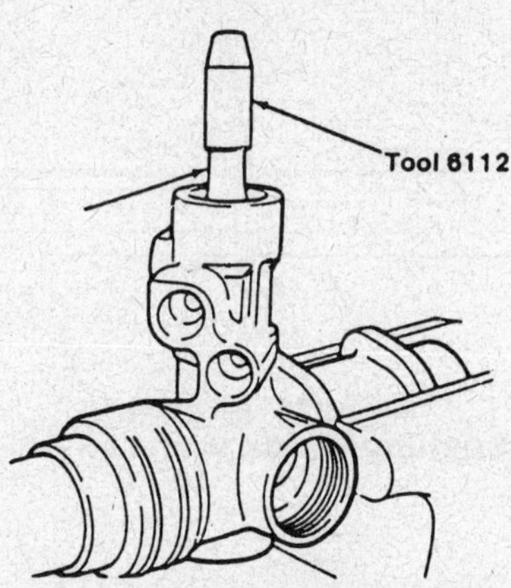


**Fig. 34 Gear shaft outer seal installation**

tool 6108 in gear shaft bore, **Fig. 32.**

b. Position gear shaft in seal ring sizing tool, then index gear shaft by aligning flat on the end of shaft with side of steering gear housing, **Fig. 33.**

c. Push gear shaft inward through seal ring sizing tool and into shaft bore, then remove tool when shaft is seated.

22. Install gear shaft nut. Use shaft holder tool SP-3616 or equivalent, and a combination wrench to hold shaft when tightening nut with a socket, **Fig. 4.**
23. Install outer bearing over gear shaft and into shaft bore.
24. Install seal protector 6112 or equivalent over end of gear shaft, then slip shaft outer seal over seal protector and slide down until it is flush with outer edge of shaft bore, **Fig. 34.**
25. Seat shaft outer seal in shaft bore using seal installer 6096 or equivalent.
26. Install gear shaft retaining ring using suitable snap ring pliers.
27. Install gear shaft end plug using plug remover/installer 6103 or equivalent and torque to specifications.
28. Install thrust bearing and thrust spring, then the gear housing preload adjustment cap using plug remover/installer 6103. Torque plug to

specifications, then back off 45-50°.
29. Secure preload adjustment cap with locknut and use locknut wrench 6097 or equivalent to secure locknut. **Do not allow adjustment cap to turn when tightening locknut.**
30. Install replacement O-ring on end cap.
31. Align wire clip hole in end cap with slot in tube, then press end cap into tube.
32. Install new end cap wire clip into retaining hole in end cap, then rotate end cap clockwise with end cap remover/installer 6101 or equivalent to draw wire completely into tube.
33. Install spacer block on rack shaft, **Fig. 35,** then install dust boot.
34. Align bolt holes in dust boot with bolt holes in spacer block, then snap spacer washers into dust boot.
35. Align and install lock tab plate on tie rods, then position tie rods on the steering gear.
36. Install tie rod bolts, tighten finger tight then loosen two turns to allow movement as needed during installation of gear.
37. Install the rubber ring with recess on ring positioned over rivet head in tube, **Fig. 36.**
38. Install and tighten replacement dust boot clamp with plier tool J-22610 or equivalent, then install rubber isolator and clamp over isolator.

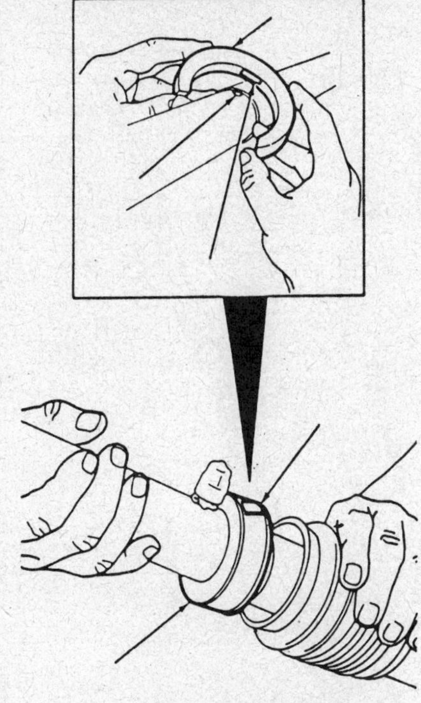

**Fig. 36 Rubber ring installation**

39. Position mounting clamp at reference mark made during disassembly and torque nuts to specifications.
40. Install replacement seal rings on steering gear fluid lines as follows:
    a. Remove seal ring with a twisting motion, then discard old ring. **Do not cut ring.**
    b. Stretch replacement seal ring using O-ring sizing tool 6181 or equivalent, then push ring one-third of the way onto tapered shank of tool.
    c. With other half of tool, press ring all way onto shank to stretch it.
    d. Carefully remove ring from tool and install on fluid line and compress back into original size with opposite side of O-ring sizing tool.
    e. Insert fluid line into tapered bore in O-ring sizing tool until bottomed, then push seal ring downward into tool bore 1/8 inch.
    f. Use fluid line fitting as driver tool and push seal ring into O-ring sizing tool. Press fitting downward and tool upward at the same time to help compress ring back to size.
    g. Carefully remove fitting, seal ring and line from tool.
    h. Examine condition of ring and replace if damaged.
41. Connect fluid lines to steering gear and torque to specifications.

# Types 4, 5, 6, 7, & 8—Rack & Pinion Power Steering

INDEX



## RACK & PINION SERVICE

### DISASSEMBLY

Disassemble rack and pinion in numbered sequence shown in **Figs. 1 through 5,** noting the following.

#### Type 4

1. Separate tab washers from inner tie rods using a chisel, then remove inner tie rods and tab washers.
2. Remove rack support cover lock nut, then the rack support cover using torque wrench socket MB990607-A or equivalent.
3. Remove rack stopper circlip by turning rack stopper clockwise until end of circlip comes out of slot in gear housing, then when end of circlip comes out of notched hole of housing, turn rack stopper counterclockwise and remove circlip.
4. Use a suitable brass drift to remove pinion lower bearing, oil seal and needle bearing.
5. Use a suitable pipe to remove to remove back-up washer and oil seal from housing.

#### Types 5 & 8

1. Separate tab washers from inner tie rods using a chisel, then remove inner tie rods and tab washers.
2. Remove rack support cover lock nut, then the rack support cover using torque wrench socket MB990607-A or equivalent.
3. Using a plastic hammer, gently tap pinion to remove.
4. Remove oil seal and ball bearing simultaneously from valve housing using a suitable socket to drive out.
5. Remove rack stopper circlip by turning rack stopper clockwise until end of circlip comes out of slot in gear housing, then when end of circlip comes out of notched hole of housing, turn rack stopper counterclockwise and remove circlip.
6. Pull rack out slowly while simultaneously removing rack stopper and bushing.
7. Use a suitable brass drift to remove pinion lower bearing, oil seal and needle bearing.
8. Use a suitable pipe to remove to remove back-up washer and oil seal from housing.

#### Type 6

1. Separate tab washers from inner tie rods using a chisel, then remove inner tie rods and tab washers.
2. Remove rack support cover lock nut, then the rack support cover using torque wrench socket MB990607-A or equivalent.
3. Remove oil seal and ball bearing simultaneously from valve housing using a suitable tool to drive out.
4. Use a suitable screwdriver to undo crimped part of pinion housing assembly locknut, then loosen locknut and separate pinion housing assembly and cylinder assembly. **When separating two assemblies, ensure that grooved pin in pinion housing assembly does not fall and damage to O-ring does not occur.**
5. Use a suitable brass drift to remove pinion lower bearing, oil seal and needle bearing.

#### Type 7

1. Separate tab washers from inner tie rods using a chisel, then remove inner tie rods and tab washers.

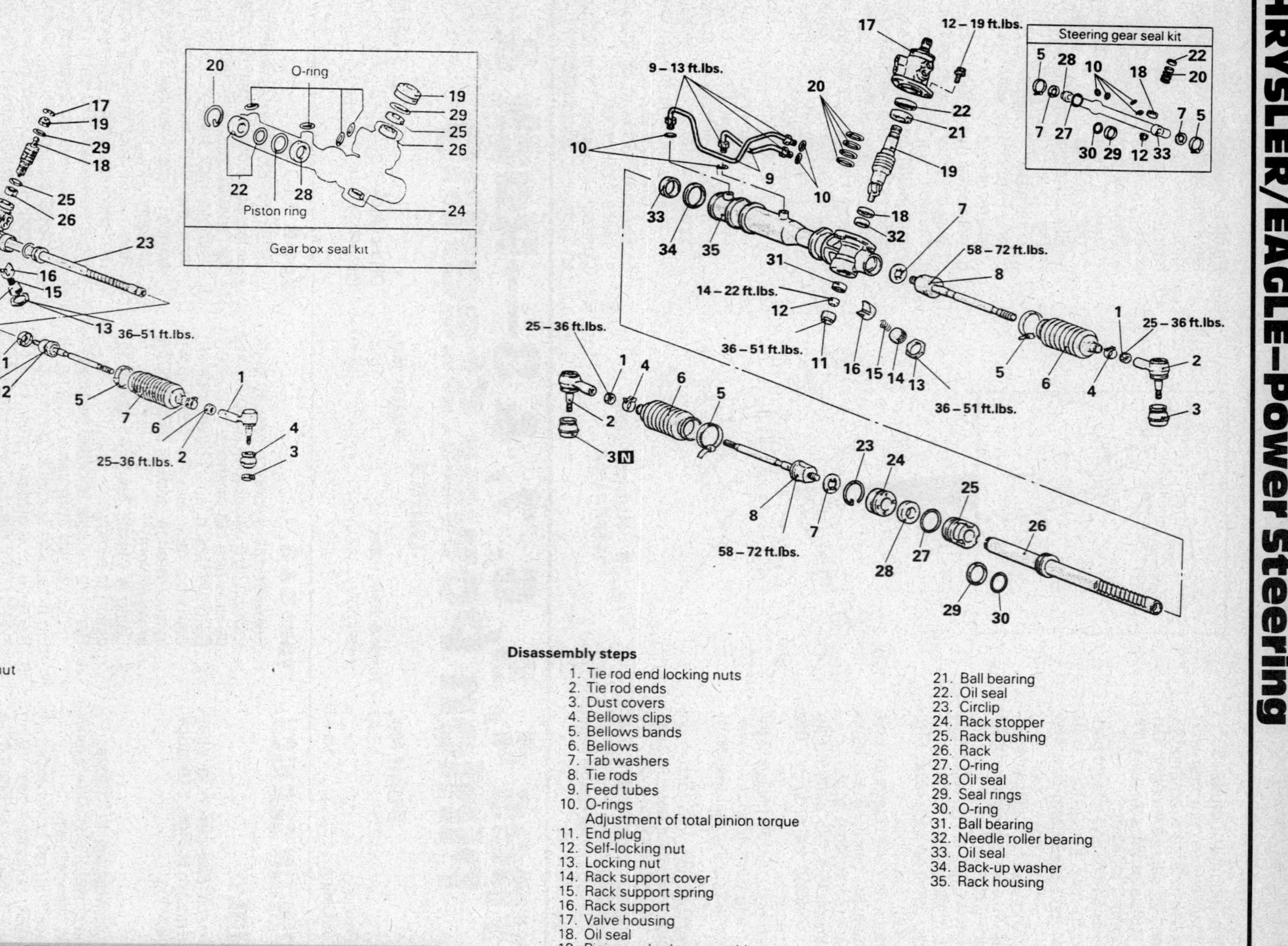


Disassembly steps

1. Tie rod end
2. Tie rod end locking nut
3. Snap ring
4. Dust cover
5. Band
6. Clip
7. Bellows
8. Feed tube
9. End plug
10. Self-locking nut
11. Tab washer
12. Tie rod
13. Rack support cover locking nut
14. Rack support cover
15. Rack support spring
16. Rack support
17. Snap ring
18. Pinion and valve assembly
19. Oil seal
20. Circlip
21. Rack stopper
22. Rack bushing assembly
23. Rack
24. Ball bearing
25. Oil seal
26. Needle bearing
27. Oil seal
28. Back-up washer
29. Seal ring
30. Gear housing

**Fig. 1 Exploded view of Type 4—Rack & Pinion. Colt Wagon**

Disassembly steps

1. Tie rod end locking nuts
2. Tie rod ends
3. Dust covers
4. Bellows clips
5. Bellows bands
6. Bellows
7. Tab washers
8. Tie rods
9. Feed tubes
10. O-rings
    Adjustment of total pinion torque
11. End plug
12. Self-locking nut
13. Locking nut
14. Rack support cover
15. Rack support spring
16. Rack support
17. Valve housing
18. Oil seal
19. Pinion and valve assembly
20. Seal rings
21. Ball bearing
22. Oil seal
23. Circlip
24. Rack stopper
25. Rack bushing
26. Rack
27. O-ring
28. Oil seal
29. Seal rings
30. O-ring
31. Ball bearing
32. Needle roller bearing
33. Oil seal
34. Back-up washer
35. Rack housing

**Fig. 2 Exploded view of Type 5—Rack & Pinion. Colt & Summit**

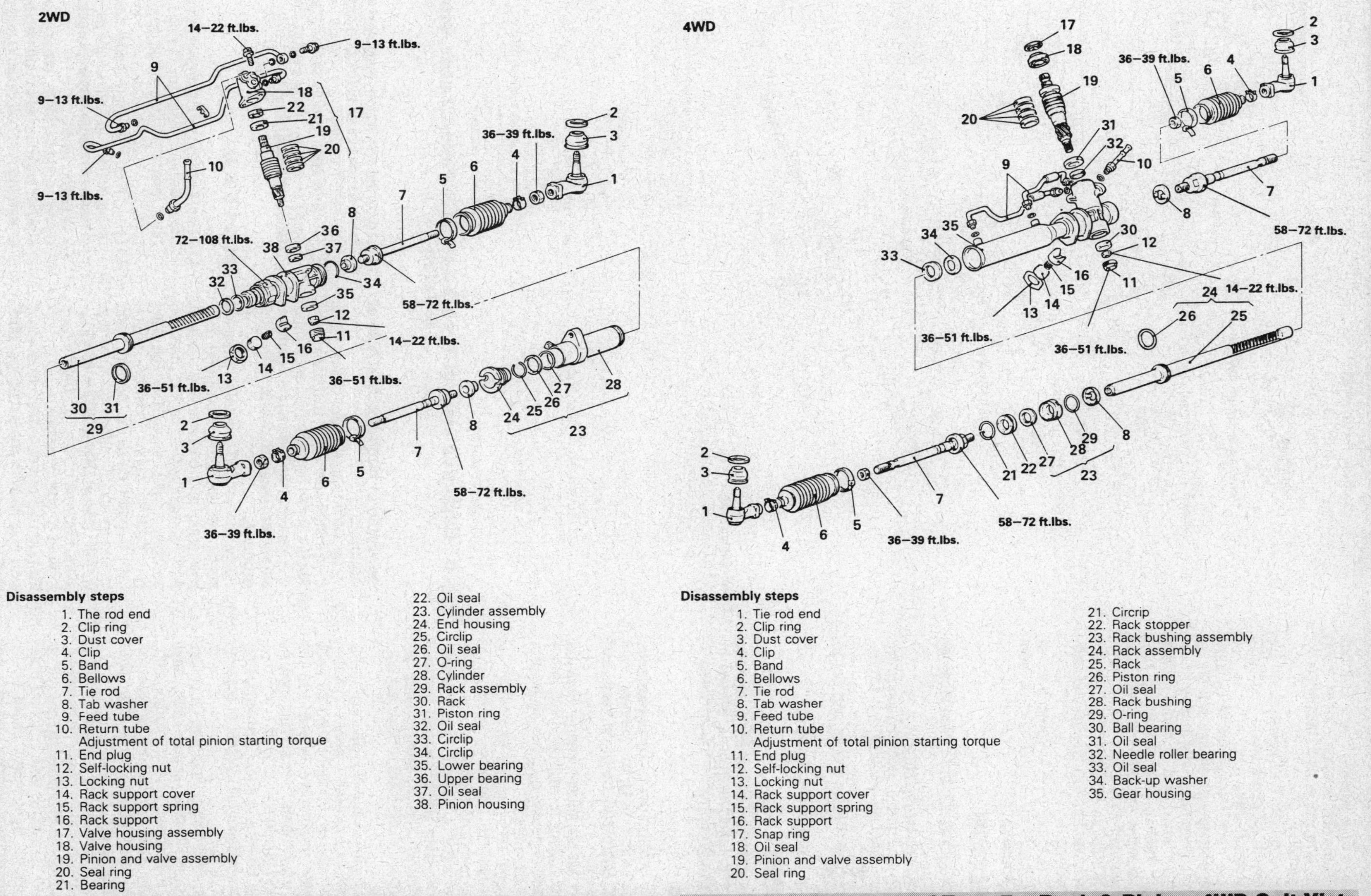


**Disassembly steps**

1. The rod end
2. Clip ring
3. Dust cover
4. Clip
5. Band
6. Bellows
7. Tie rod
8. Tab washer
9. Feed tube
10. Return tube
    Adjustment of total pinion starting torque
11. End plug
12. Self-locking nut
13. Locking nut
14. Rack support cover
15. Rack support spring
16. Rack support
17. Valve housing assembly
18. Valve housing
19. Pinion and valve assembly
20. Seal ring
21. Bearing
22. Oil seal
23. Cylinder assembly
24. End housing
25. Circlip
26. Oil seal
27. O-ring
28. Cylinder
29. Rack assembly
30. Rack
31. Piston ring
32. Oil seal
33. Circlip
34. Circlip
35. Lower bearing
36. Upper bearing
37. Oil seal
38. Pinion housing

**Fig. 3 Exploded view of Type 6—Rack & Pinion. 2WD Colt Vista**

**Disassembly steps**

1. Tie rod end
2. Clip ring
3. Dust cover
4. Clip
5. Band
6. Bellows
7. Tie rod
8. Tab washer
9. Feed tube
10. Return tube
    Adjustment of total pinion starting torque
11. End plug
12. Self-locking nut
13. Locking nut
14. Rack support cover
15. Rack support spring
16. Rack support
17. Snap ring
18. Oil seal
19. Pinion and valve assembly
20. Seal ring
21. Circrip
22. Rack stopper
23. Rack bushing assembly
24. Rack assembly
25. Rack
26. Piston ring
27. Oil seal
28. Rack bushing
29. O-ring
30. Ball bearing
31. Oil seal
32. Needle roller bearing
33. Oil seal
34. Back-up washer
35. Gear housing

**Fig. 4 Exploded view of Type 7—Rack & Pinion. 4WD Colt Vista**

2. Remove rack support cover lock nut, then the rack support cover using torque wrench socket MB990607-A or equivalent.
3. Remove pinion and valve assembly along with oil seals using a suitable brass drift to drive out.
4. Remove rack stopper circlip by turning rack stopper clockwise until end of circlip comes out of slot in gear housing, then when end of circlip comes out of notched hole of housing, turn rack stopper counterclockwise and remove circlip.
5. Use a suitable brass drift to remove pinion lower bearing, oil seal and needle bearing.
6. Use a suitable pipe to remove to remove back-up washer and oil seal from housing.

## INSPECTION

1. Check rack teeth and pinion teeth for wear.
2. Check rack for distortion.
3. Check ball and needle bearings for seizure, uneven rotation and excessive play.
4. Check bellows for cracks and deformation.
5. Check gear housing for rust.

## ASSEMBLY

Reassemble rack and pinion in reverse order of numbered sequence shown in **Figs. 2 through 6,** noting the following.

### Type 4

1. Apply Dextron or Dextron II automatic transmission fluid to O-rings, seal rings, entire surface of oil seals and rack.
2. Apply Mopar multi-mileage lubricant or equivalent to ball bearings, entire surface of needle bearings, rack teeth and pinion teeth.
3. Use seal ring installer MB991317 or equivalent to compress pinion seal rings during installation.
4. Install back-up washer and oil seal into housing using oil seal installer MB991097 and oil seal installer attachment MB991098 or their equivalents.
5. Install pinion needle bearing using bearing and oil seal installer MB991100 and bearing and oil seal installer attachment MB991102 or their equivalents. Set scribed side of bearing in installer.
6. Install oil seal to rack bushing using oil seal installer MB991097 or equivalent.
7. Cover rack with a vinyl bag (supplied in repair kit) and secure with vinyl tape, then insert slowly into housing. **Ensure that vinyl bag is free of wrinkles and that bag is not damaged after installation.**
8. Wrap vinyl tape around end of rack, then install rack bushing and stopper. Push stopper in until circlip groove of stopper is aligned with notched hole of housing, then install circlip while turning stopper. **Circlip end should be visible through notched hole of housing.**
9. Wrap vinyl tape around pinion teeth, then install seal using a suitable pipe.
10. Secure inner tie rods by bending tab washers onto tie rod stepped portions. **Align tab washer pawls with rack grooves.**
11. Apply semi-drying sealant to threaded section of end plug, install end plug, then stake at two points with a punch.
12. Apply semi-drying sealant to threaded section of rack support cover, then with rack in center position, attach rack support cover to housing and torque to specifications using torque wrench socket MB990607-A or equivalent. Back-off cover 10°, then torque locknut to specifications.
13. Fill outer tie rod end dust cover inner side and lip with multi-mileage lubricant.
14. Adjust tie rod length between end of bellows and inner side of tie rod locknut to 6.1 inches.
15. Confirm total pinion preload as described under "Total Pinion Preload, Checking/Adjusting."

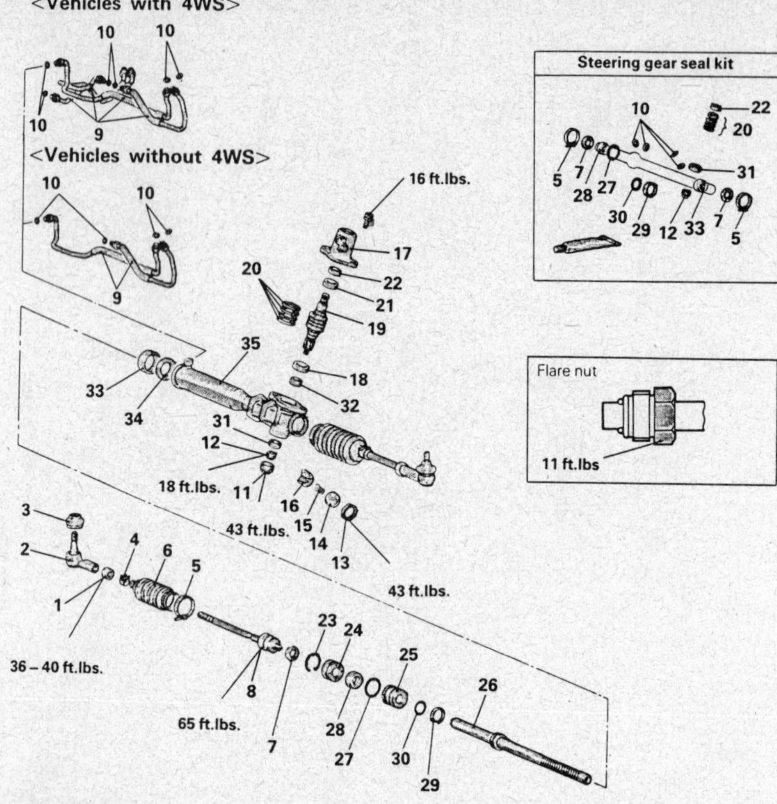


Disassembly steps

1. Tie rod end locking nuts
2. Tie rod ends
3. Dust shield
4. Bellows clips
5. Bellows bands
6. Bellows
7. Tab washers
8. Tie rods
9. Feed tubes
10. O-rings
    Adjustment of total pinion torque
11. End plug
12. Self-locking nut
13. Locking nut
14. Rack support cover
15. Rack support spring
16. Rack support
17. Valve housing
18. Oil seal
19. Pinion and valve assembly
20. Seal rings
21. Ball bearing
22. Oil seal
23. Circlip
24. Rack stopper
25. Rack bushing
26. Rack
27. O-ring
28. Oil seal
29. Seal rings
30. O-ring
31. Ball bearing
32. Needle roller bearing
33. Oil seal
34. Back-up washer
35. Rack housing

**Fig. 5 Exploded view of Type 8—Rack & Pinion. Laser, Stealth & Talon**

### Types 5 & 8

1. Apply Dextron or Dextron II automatic transmission fluid to O-rings, seal rings, entire surface of oil seals and rack.
2. Apply Mopar multi-mileage lubricant or equivalent to ball bearings, entire surface of needle bearings, rack teeth and pinion teeth.
3. Using suitable tools, press back-up washer and oil seal, pinion needle roller bearing and ball bearing and housing oil seals into housing.

4. Cover rack teeth with rack installer MB991212 or equivalent, apply Dextron or Dextron II to installer, then match oil seal center with rack to prevent retainer spring from slipping and slowly insert rack from power cylinder side.
5. Wrap vinyl tape around end of rack, then install rack bushing and stopper. Push stopper in until circlip groove of stopper is aligned with notched hole of housing, then install circlip while turning stopper. **Circlip end should be visible through notched hole of housing.**
6. Using suitable tools, press oil seal and ball bearing into valve housing.
7. Use seal ring installer MB991317 or equivalent to compress pinion seal rings during installation.
8. Wrap vinyl tape around pinion teeth, then install seal using a suitable pipe.
9. Secure inner tie rods by bending tab washers onto tie rod stepped portions.
10. Apply semi-drying sealant to threaded section of rack support cover, then secure temporarily with locknut.
11. Apply semi-drying sealant to threaded section of end plug, install end plug, then stake at two points with a punch.
12. Fill outer tie rod end dust cover inner side and lip with multi-mileage lubricant.
13. Adjust tie rod length between end of bellows and inner side of tie rod locknut to 7.1 inches.
14. Adjust total pinion preload as described under "Total Pinion Preload, Checking/Adjusting."

### Type 6

1. Apply Dextron or Dextron II automatic transmission fluid to O-rings, seal rings, entire surface of oil seals and rack.
2. Apply Mopar multi-mileage lubricant or equivalent to ball bearings, entire surface of needle bearings, rack teeth and pinion teeth.
3. Using suitable tools, press oil seal and upper and lower bearings into pinion housing.
4. Cover rack with a vinyl bag (supplied in repair kit) and secure with vinyl tape, then insert slowly into housing. **Ensure that vinyl bag is free of wrinkles and that bag is not damaged after installation.**
5. Crimp end of cylinder assembly after installation.
6. Align positions of grooved pins in pinion housing assembly and cylinder assembly, torque locknut to specifications, then crimp locknut.
7. Using suitable tools, press oil seal and bearing into valve housing.
8. Use seal ring installer MB991317 or equivalent to compress pinion seal rings during installation.
9. Wrap vinyl tape around pinion teeth, then install seal using a suitable pipe.
10. Apply semi-drying sealant to threaded section of rack support cover, then install and temporarily tighten locknut.
11. Apply semi-drying sealant to threaded section of end plug, install end plug, then stake at two points with a punch.
12. Adjust total pinion preload as described under "Total Pinion Preload, Checking/Adjusting."
13. Secure inner tie rods by bending tab washers onto tie rod stepped portions.
14. Fill outer tie rod end dust cover inner side and lip with multi-mileage lubricant.
15. Adjust tie rod length between end of bellows and inner side of tie rod locknut to 6.6-6.7 inches.

### Type 7

1. Apply Dextron or Dextron II automatic transmission fluid to O-rings, seal rings, entire surface of oil seals and rack.
2. Apply Mopar multi-mileage lubricant or equivalent to ball bearings, entire surface of needle bearings, rack teeth and pinion teeth.
3. Install back-up washer and oil seal into housing using oil seal installer MB991097 and oil seal installer attachment MB991098 or their equivalents.
4. Install pinion needle bearing using bearing and oil seal installer MB991100 and bearing and oil seal installer attachment MB991102 or their equivalents. Set scribed side of bearing in installer.
5. Using suitable tools, press oil seal and bearing into pinion housing.
6. Using suitable tools, press oil seal into rack housing.
7. Cover rack with a vinyl bag (supplied in repair kit) and secure with vinyl tape, then insert slowly into housing. **Ensure that vinyl bag is free of wrinkles and that bag is not damaged after installation.**
8. Wrap vinyl tape around end of rack, then install rack bushing and stopper. Push stopper in until circlip groove of stopper is aligned with notched hole of housing, then install circlip while turning stopper. **Circlip end should be visible through notched hole of housing.**
9. Wrap vinyl tape around pinion teeth, then install seal using a suitable pipe.
10. Apply semi-drying sealant to threaded section of rack support cover, then install and temporarily tighten locknut.
11. Apply semi-drying sealant to threaded section of end plug, install end plug, then stake at two points with a punch.
12. Adjust total pinion preload as described under "Total Pinion Preload, Checking/Adjusting."
13. Secure inner tie rods by bending tab washers onto tie rod stepped portions.
14. Fill outer tie rod end dust cover inner side and lip with multi-mileage lubricant.
15. Adjust tie rod length between end of bellows and inner side of tie rod locknut to 7.1-7.2 inches.

# ADJUSTMENTS

## TOTAL PINION PRELOAD, CHECKING/ADJUSTING

### Type 4

1. With rack placed in center position, attach rack support cover to gear housing, then torque cover to specifications using torque wrench socket MB990607-A or equivalent. Back off cover approximately 10°, then install and torque locking nut to specifications.
2. Rotate pinion gear at a rate of one revolution every 4 to 6 seconds using preload socket CT-1108 and a suitable torque wrench. Total pinion preload should be 5-11 inch lbs. **Measure starting torque through whole stroke of rack.**
3. If measured values are not within specifications, readjust rack support cover, then recheck.
4. If still not within specifications, check rack support cover, rack support spring and rack support and replace parts as necessary.

### Type 5, 6, 7 & 8

1. With rack placed in center position, attach rack support cover to gear housing, then torque cover to specifications using torque wrench socket MB990607-A or equivalent. Back off cover approximately 30-60°, then install and torque locking nut to specifications.
2. In neutral position, rotate pinion shaft clockwise at a rate of one revolution every 4 to 6 seconds using preload socket CT-1108 and a suitable torque wrench. Return rack support cover 30-60° and adjust torque to specifications. Total pinion preload should be 5-11 inch lbs. **Measure starting torque through whole stroke of rack.**
3. If measured values are not within specifications, readjust rack support cover, then recheck.
4. If still not within specifications, check rack support cover, rack support spring and rack support and replace parts as necessary.

# Type 9—Rack & Pinion Power Cylinder

INDEX



## RACK & PINION POWER CYLINDER SERVICE

Outer tie rod ends are the only serviceable components on the power cylinder. When reinstalling tie rod ends, adjust length between end of boot and center of tie rod end ball joint to 2.82 inches.

# Type 10—Ball & Nut Torsion Bar Type Power Steering Gear

INDEX



## DISASSEMBLY

1. Remove adjusting locknut, then side cover bolts and turn in adjusting bolt 2 or 3 turns, **Fig. 1.**
2. With gear in neutral (center) position, tap bottom of cross shaft with plastic hammer to remove shaft.
3. Remove valve housing nut using housing locking nut spanner wrench tool No. MB990667 for large gear and No. MB990852 for small gear, then valve housing bolts. While holding rack piston to avoid rotation, remove valve housing and rack piston.
4. Secure valve housing in vise with dial indicator as shown in **Fig. 2,** then move rack and piston up and down to check backlash between groove of rack piston and the balls. Backlash should be .0039 inch for large gear and .080 inch for small gear maximum. Measure backlash with piston fully tightened and loosened 2 turns. If backlash exceeds limit, replace ball screw unit and rack piston as an assembly.
5. Remove rack piston from valve housing by turning counterclockwise. **Do not lose any of the 26 balls.**
6. Remove top cover of valve housing using top cover remover tool No. MB990853 for small gear or special spanner wrench as shown in **Fig. 3.**
7. Remove circulator holder, circulator, seal ring and O-ring from rack piston, **Fig. 4.**
8. Remove thrust unit, thrust needle roller bearing, seal rings and O-rings from input worm unit.

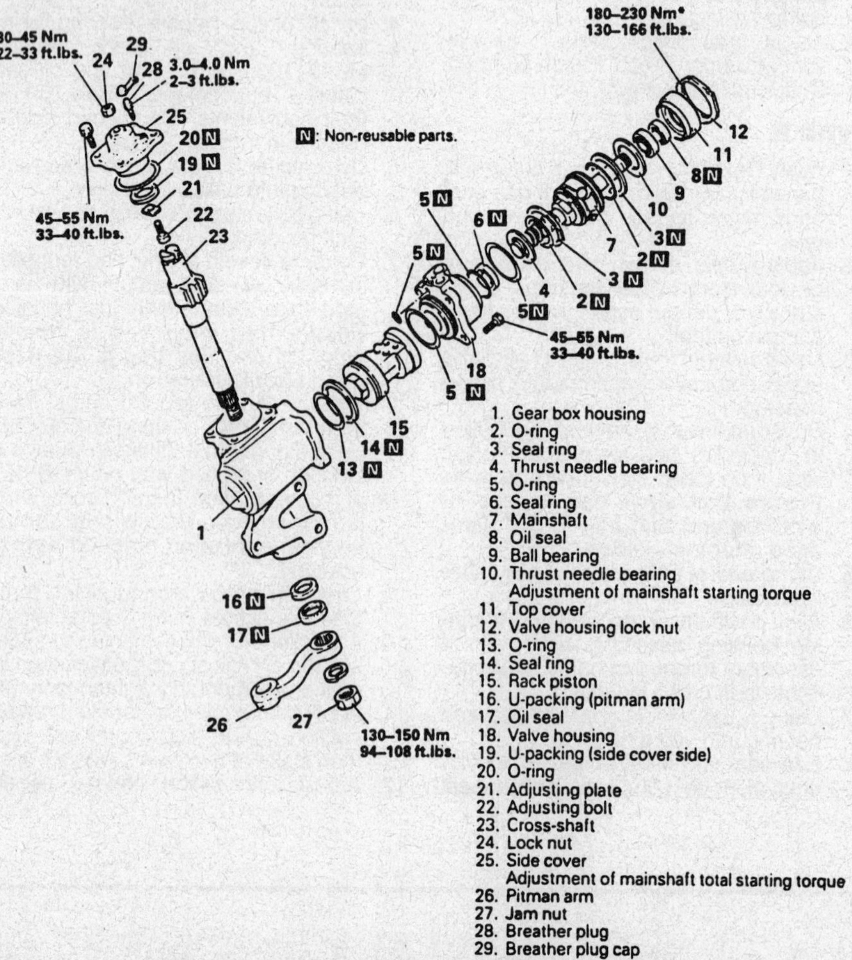


**Fig. 1 Exploded view of steering gear**

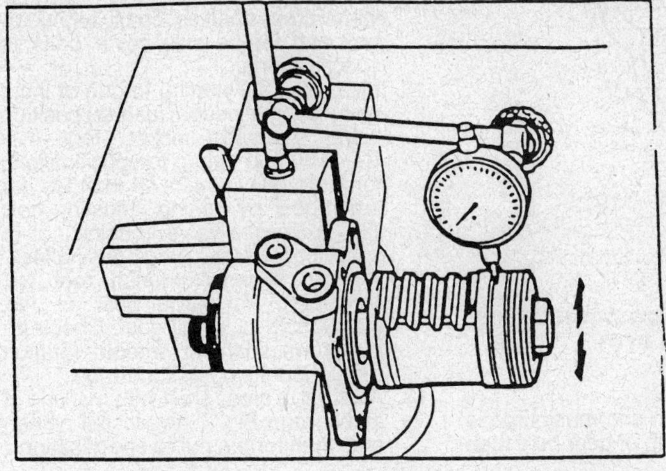

**Fig. 2 Measurement of rack piston backlash**

**Fig. 3 Removal of top cover**

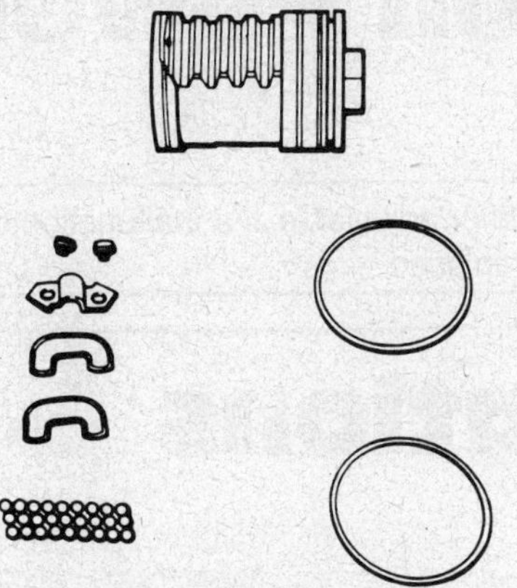

**Fig. 4 Components of rack piston**

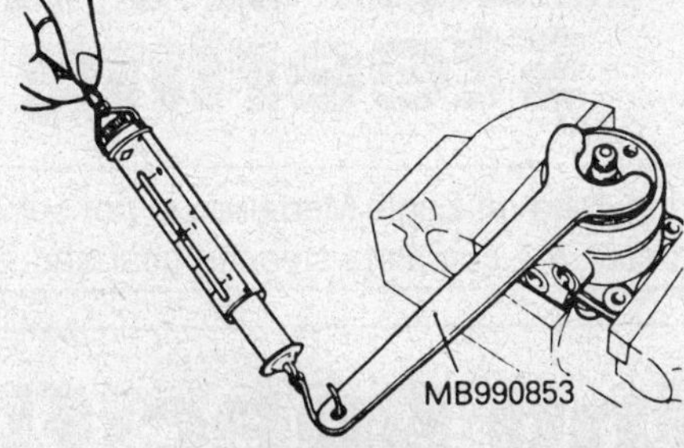


**Fig. 5 Tightening of top cover**

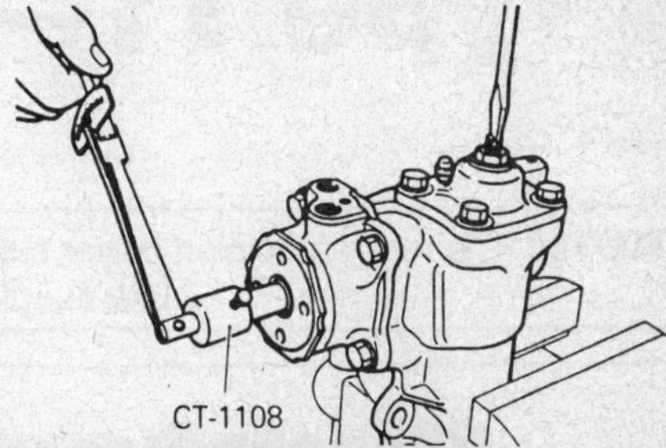


**Fig. 6 Measurement of total starting torque**

9. To disassemble subassembly components, proceed as follows:
   a. Turn in adjusting bolt at tip of cross shaft and remove side cover. **Do not lose any needle bearing rollers.**
   b. Remove adjusting bolt and plate, O-ring and needle bearing from side cover. Do not remove O-ring and sealing at rear of needle bearing if no oil leaks from thread of adjusting bolt. Also, do not remove bleeder plug unless necessary.
   c. Remove seal ring and O-ring from valve housing.
   d. Remove ball bearing and oil seal from top cover.
   e. Remove snap ring at bottom of gearbox, then back-up ring and oil seal. Pull out seal housing.
   f. Remove seal ring and O-rings from seal housing.
10. To assemble subassembly components, proceed as follows. Replace O-rings, seal rings and oil seals whenever disassembled.
   a. Apply thin coat of multi-purpose grease to bearing surface of needle bearing and install rollers into side cover, then apply grease to bottom of side cover.
   b. Insert adjusting bolt and plate into "T" slot on top of cross shaft, and adjust play to 0-.002 inch by selecting proper adjusting plate. When installing adjusting plate, place chamfered portion of plate to contact surface of cross shaft.
   c. Install O-ring into side cover.
   d. Align cross shaft with side cover and tighten with adjusting bolt, then tighten lock bolt temporarily.
   e. Apply thin coat of multipurpose grease to lip of oil seal and press into top cover, then press fit ball bearing.
   f. Apply thin coat of ATF to O-ring and seal ring, then insert into seal housing. Install seal housing straight into gear box with O-ring side positioned near mainshaft.
   g. Apply thin coat of multipurpose grease to lip of oil seal, then press into gear box using seal installer tool No. CT-1008. Install back-up ring and snap ring.

## ASSEMBLY

1. Apply thin coat of ATF to input worm unit O-rings and install O-rings and seal rings alternately onto worm unit. **Do not apply excessive force.**
2. Install thrust plate, thrust needle bearing and thrust plate to both ends of worm unit in that order, then apply thin coat of ATF to each.
3. Install O-ring and seal ring into groove of valve housing and apply thin coat of ATF to each.
4. Install input worm unit into valve housing, then O-ring into top cover and top cover with bearing and oil seal onto valve housing. While turning worm unit, tighten by using spring scale and special spanner wrench as in **Fig. 5.** Rotate worm unit to check for uniform movement.
5. Install valve housing nut and tighten temporarily using housing locking nut spanner wrench tool No. MB990667 for large gear and No. MB990852 for small gear. Do not allow top cover to rotate. The final tightening will occur during total starting torque measurement later in assembly procedure.
6. Measure starting torque by using preload socket tool No. CT-1108 and torque wrench while turning input worm unit, ensure preload is 3.5-6.9 inch lbs. If necessary, readjust by loosening valve housing nut as in steps 4-5.
7. Install O-ring and seal ring to rack piston and apply thin coat of ATF to each.
8. Install rack piston into worm shaft until piston contacts worm shaft end, then insert 19 balls into groove through 2 openings on top of piston. Do not rotate worm unit and piston while inserting balls. Do not allow hole to offset or turn during insertion of balls so balls will not fall into wrong groove. After insertion of all balls, ensure balls reach approximately .080 inch for large gear,

or .5 inch for small gear below end of piston. Excessive clearance is an indication that a ball has fallen into wrong groove. If so, remove rack piston and reinsert balls.

9. Insert 7 balls into rack piston circulator. Apply multipurpose grease to balls to prevent them from falling from circulator. Install circulator and holder into rack piston.
10. Secure gear box in vise, then install valve housing and rack piston assembly into gear box and torque bolts to specifications. After installation, rotate assembly to move rack piston to neutral (center) position. **Do not force rack piston into gearbox as seal ring may be damaged.**
11. Apply thin coat of ATF to teeth and shaft of rack piston and multipurpose grease to oil seal lip of gear box, then install cross shaft assembly into gearbox and torque side cover bolts to specifications.
12. Measure total starting torque of input worm shaft at neutral (center) position using preload socket tool No. CT-1108 and torque to specifications for large gear or 4.3-7.8 inch lbs. for small gear by turning adjusting bolt, **Fig. 6.** Torque valve housing nut to specifications lbs. using housing locking nut spanner wrench tool No. MB990667 for large gear or No. MB990852 for small gear. Check input worm shaft for smooth rotation throughout its operation range.
13. Align slit of cross shaft with marking of pitman arm **Fig. 7** and install pitman arm, then torque nut to specifications.

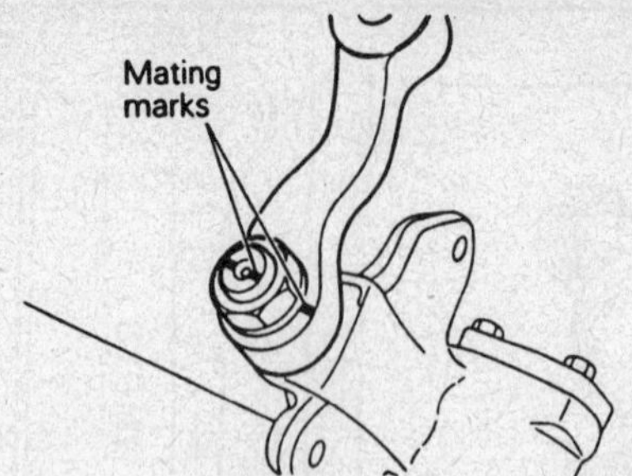


**Fig 7 Installation position of pitman arm**

# Type 11—Rack & Pinion Power Steering

**NOTE:** The rack and pinion power steering used on Eagle Medallion is not serviceable or adjustable. If a malfunction or oil leak should occur, the complete steering gear should be replaced.

# Tightening Specifications

## POWER STEERING PUMPS

| Pump Type | Component | Torque/Ft. Lbs. |
|---|---|---|
| Type 1 | Flow Control Valve Plug | 50① |
| | Pressure Hose Fitting | 35 |
| | Rear Mounting Studs | 30 |
| Type 2 | Pin Retaining Plate Bolts | 90① |
| Type 5 | Oil Pump Cover Bolts | 13–16 |
| | Pressure Hose Connector | 36–51 |
| | Suction Connector Bolts | 4–7 |
| Type 6 | Oil Pump Cover Bolts | 13–16 |
| | Pressure Hose Connector | 29–43 |
| | Suction Connector Bolts | 4–7 |
| | Terminal Plug | 18–22 |
| Type 7 | Oil Pump Cover Bolts | 13–16 |
| | Pressure Hose Connector | 29–43 |
| | Pressure Hose Connector Locknut | 22–29 |
| | Suction Connector Bolts | 4–7 |
| | Terminal Plug | 18–22 |
| Type 8 | Oil Pump Cover Bolts | 13–16 |
| | Pressure Hose Connector | 36–51 |
| | Suction Connector Bolts | 4–7 |
| | Terminal Assembly | 18–22 |
| Type 9 | Oil Pump Cover Bolts | 13–16 |
| | Pressure Hose Connector | 36–51 |
| | Suction Connector Bolts | 4–7 |
| | Terminal Assembly Plug | 18–22 |

# TIGHTENING SPECIFICATIONS—Continued

## POWER STEERING PUMPS

| Pump Type | Component | Torque/Ft. Lbs. |
|---|---|---|
| Type 10 | Oil Pump Cover Bolts | 14 |
| | Pressure Hose Connector | 43 |
| | Suction Connector Bolts | 6 |
| | Terminal Assembly Plug | 18–22 |

①—Inch Lbs.

## POWER STEERING GEARS

| Type | Component | Torque/Ft. Lbs. |
|---|---|---|
| Type 1 | Control Valve To Steering Valve Body Mounting Screws | 95① |
| | Powertrain Spanner Nut | 150–250 |
| | Sector Shaft Cover Spanner Nut | 150 |
| | Sector Shaft Locknut | 28 |
| | Steering Gear Arm Nut | 175 |
| | Valve Body End Plug | 25 |
| | Valve Body End Plug | 25 |
| | Valve Body Fitting | 20 |
| | Valve Body To Gear Housing | 15–20 |
| | Wormshaft Adjusting Nut | 50 |
| Type 2 | Outer Tie Rod End Locknut | 55 |
| Type 3 | Attaching Bracket Clamp Nuts | 41 |
| | Steering Gear Housing Preload Adjustment Cap | 45–50① |
| | Steering Gear Shaft End Plug | 45 |
| | Tie Rod To Steering Gear Spacer Block | 50–60 |
| | Tubing Fittings | 15–20 |
| Type 4 | Inner Tie Rod End | 58–72 |
| | Outer Tie Rod End Locknut | 25–36 |
| | Pinion Housing End Plug | 36–51 |
| | Pinion Shaft Self-Locking Nut | 14–22 |
| | Rack Support Cover | 14–18 |
| | Rack Support Cover Locknut | 36–51 |
| Type 5 | Inner Tie Rod End | 58–72 |
| | Outer Tie Rod End Locknut | 25–36 |
| | Pinion Housing End Plug | 36–51 |
| | Pinion Shaft Self-Locking Nut | 14–22 |
| | Rack Support Cover | 11 |
| | Rack Support Cover Locknut | 36–51 |
| | Valve Housing Mounting Bolt | 12–19 |
| Type 6 | Inner Tie Rod End | 58–72 |
| | Outer Tie Rod End Locknut | 36–39 |
| | Pinion Housing End Plug | 36–51 |
| | Pinion Housing Locknut | 72–108 |
| | Pinion Shaft Self-Locking Nut | 14–22 |
| | Rack Support Cover | 14–18 |
| | Rack Support Cover Locknut | 36–51 |
| | Valve Housing Mounting Bolt | 14–22 |
| Type 7 | Inner Tie Rod End | 58–72 |
| | Outer Tie Rod End Locknut | 36–39 |
| | Pinion Housing End Plug | 36–51 |
| | Pinion Shaft Self-Locking Nut | 14–22 |
| | Rack Support Cover | 14–18 |
| | Rack Support Cover Locknut | 36–51 |

## POWER STEERING GEARS—Continued

| Type | Component | Torque/Ft. Lbs. |
|---|---|---|
| Type 8 | Inner Tie Rod End | 65 |
| | Outer Tie Rod End Locknut | 36–40 |
| | Pinion Housing End Plug | 43 |
| | Pinion Shaft Self-Locking Nut | 18 |
| | Rack Support Cover | 11 |
| | Rack Support Cover Locknut | 43 |
| | Valve Housing Mounting Bolt | 16 |
| Type 9 | Outer Tie Rod End Locknut | 30 |
| | Power Cylinder Bleeder Screws | 5 |
| Type 10 | Cross Shaft Adjusting Bolt Locknut | 22–33 |
| | Pittman Arm Mounting Nut | 94–108 |
| | Side Cover Breather Plug | 2–3 |
| | Side Cover Mounting Bolts | 33–40 |
| | Valve Housing Top Cover Locknut | 130–166 |
| | Valve Housing To Gear Housing Mounting Bolt | 33–40 |

①—Inch Lbs.

# DASH PANEL SERVICE

## INDEX



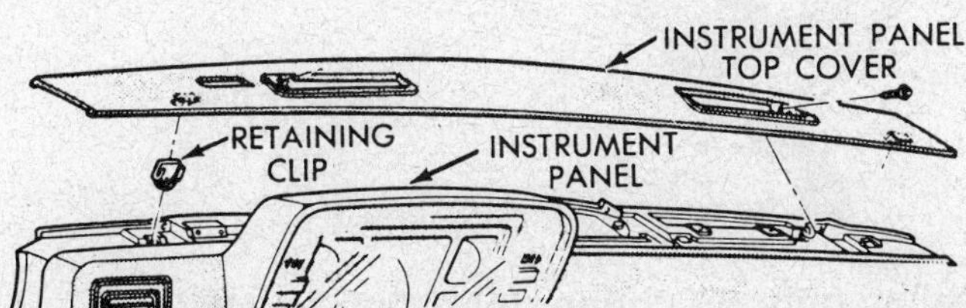


**Fig. 1 Instrument panel top cover. Omni & Horizon**

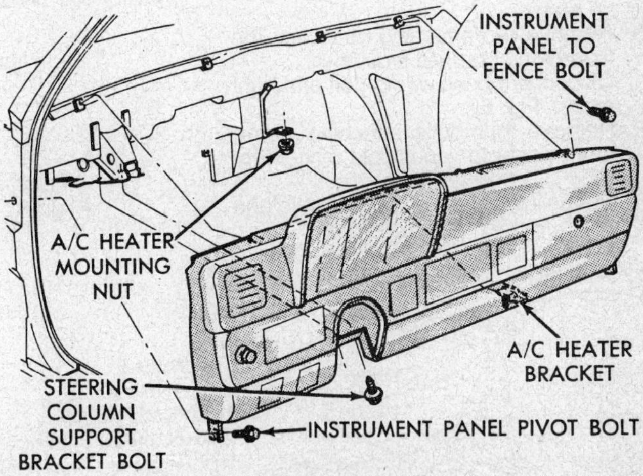

INSTRUMENT PANEL TO FENCE BOLT
A/C HEATER MOUNTING NUT
A/C HEATER BRACKET
STEERING COLUMN SUPPORT BRACKET BOLT
INSTRUMENT PANEL PIVOT BOLT

**Fig. 2 Instrument panel mounting bolts. Omni & Horizon**

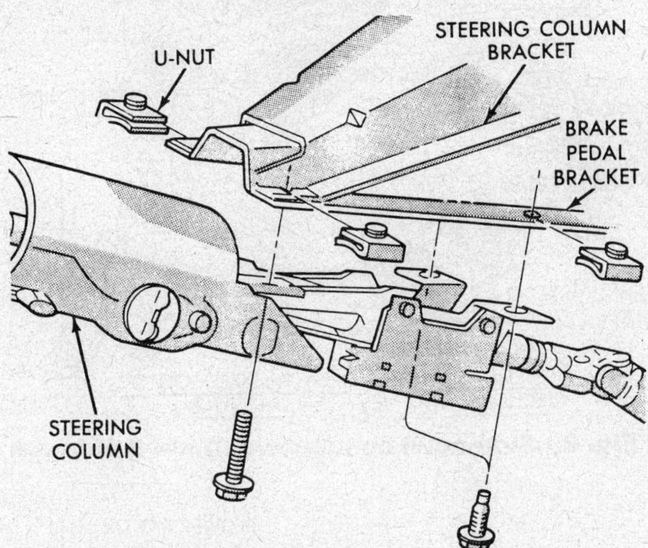


**Fig. 3 Steering column mounting bolts. Omni & Horizon**

## AIRBAG SYSTEM DISARMING

1. Place ignition switch in lock position.
2. Disconnect and tape battery ground cable connector.
3. **Wait at least 1 minute** after disconnecting battery ground cable before doing any further work on vehicle. The SRS system is designed to retain enough voltage to deploy airbag for a short time even after battery has been disconnected.
4. After repairs are complete, reconnect battery ground cable.
5. From passenger side of vehicle, turn ignition switch to On position.
6. SRS warning light should illuminate for 6 to 8 seconds, then gof and remain off for at least 45 seconds if SRS system is functioning correctly.
7. If SRS indicator does not perform as described refer to appropriate section in "Passive Restraints."

## OMNI & HORIZON

1. Disarm airbag as described under "Airbag System Disarming.".
2. Remove instrument panel top cover as follows:
   a. Remove two screws from outer edge of defroster openings, **Fig. 1.**
   b. Pry rear edge of cover up, then disengage cover-to-panel retaining clips.
   c. Remove cover by lifting up and pulling to rear.
3. Remove side cowl trim panels (left and right) as follows:
   a. Remove two trim panel attaching screws.
   b. Remove forward-most scuff plate attaching screw.
   c. Remove panels by rotating lower edge inward and forward.
4. Loosen instrument panel pivot bolts (left and right side), **Fig. 2.**
5. Remove one nut attaching instrument panel to A/C heater unit bracket, located on lower left side of glove box under instrument panel, **Fig. 2.**
6. Remove instrument cluster assembly as follows:
   a. Remove four cluster bezel attaching screws, then the bezel.
   b. Remove four screws attaching cluster to base panel.
   c. Pull cluster rearward, then disconnect speedometer cable and wiring connectors.
7. Move driver's seat to full rearward position.
8. Lower steering column as follows:
   a. Remove four bolts attaching steering column to brake pedal bracket, **Fig. 3.**

   b. Lower steering column, then allow steering wheel to rest on driver's seat.
9. Remove two bolts attaching steering column support bracket to brake pedal bracket.
10. Disconnect steering column wiring connectors, **Fig. 4.**
11. Disconnect stop lamp switch connector.
12. Remove bulkhead disconnect as follows:
   a. From engine compartment side, loosen bolt joining bulkhead disconnect, **Fig. 5.**
   b. From under instrument panel, depress holding tabs on bulkhead disconnect, then pull free of plenum.
13. Remove two attaching nuts, then the fuse block from left side cowl.
14. Disconnect cowl wiring (left and right sides), **Fig. 6.**
15. Remove four bolts attaching instrument panel to windshield fence, **Fig. 2.**
16. Rotate instrument panel rearward and down, **Fig. 7.**

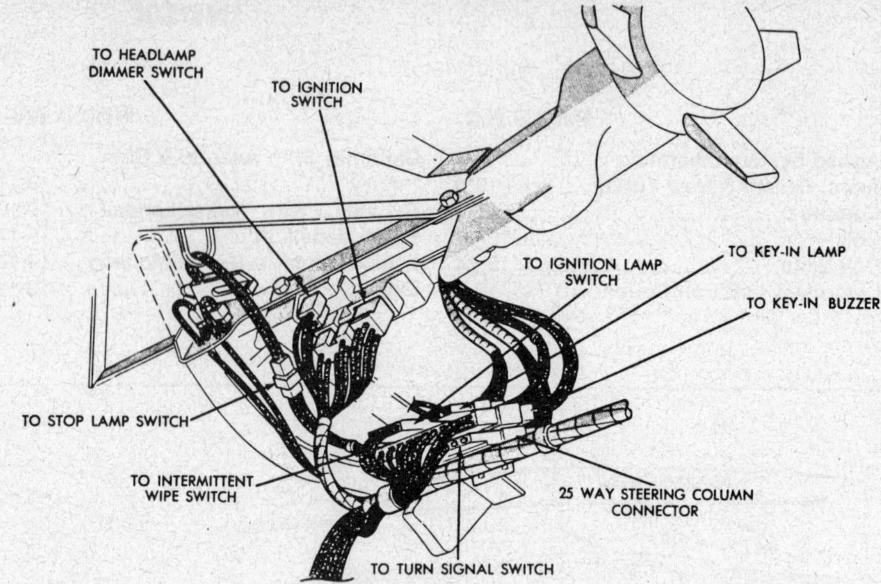


**Fig. 4 Steering column connectors. Omni & Horizon**

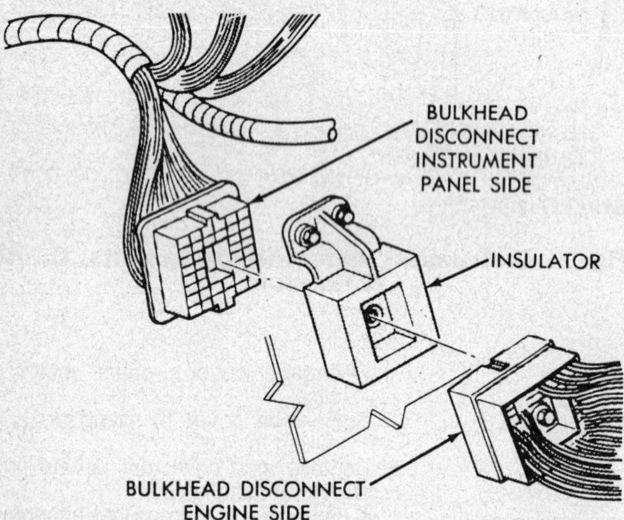


**Fig. 5 Exploded view of bulkhead disconnect. Omni & Horizon**

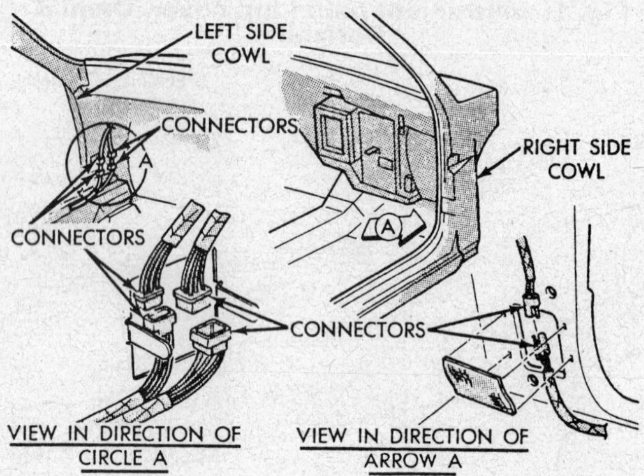


**Fig. 6 Side cowl connectors. Omni & Horizon**

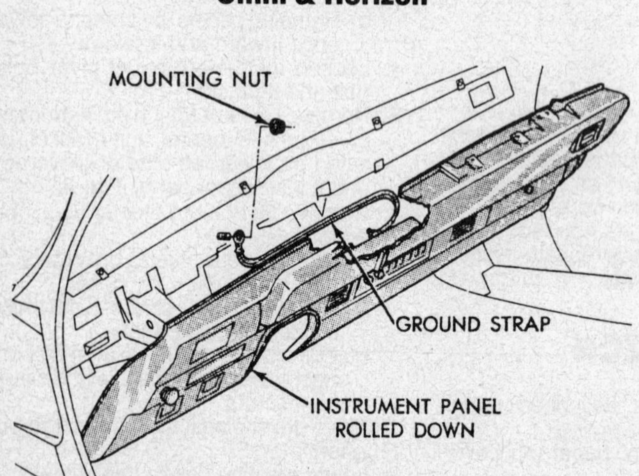


**Fig. 7 Rotating instrument panel down. Omni & Horizon**

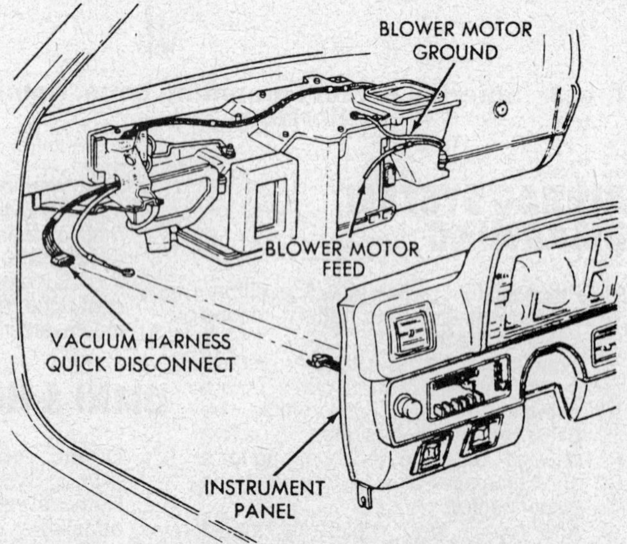


**Fig. 8 A/C heater unit vacuum & electrical connections. Omni & Horizon**

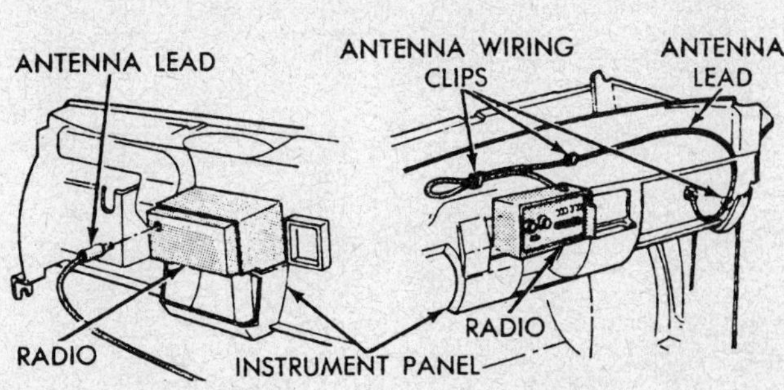


**Fig. 9 Antenna connections. Omni & Horizon**

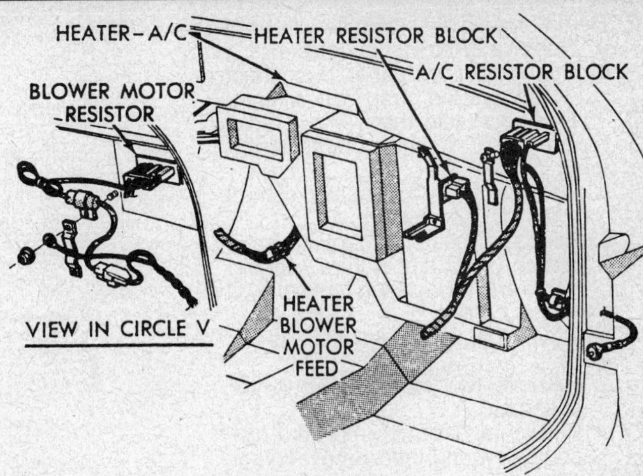


**Fig. 10 Blower motor & resistor block wiring. Omni & Horizon**

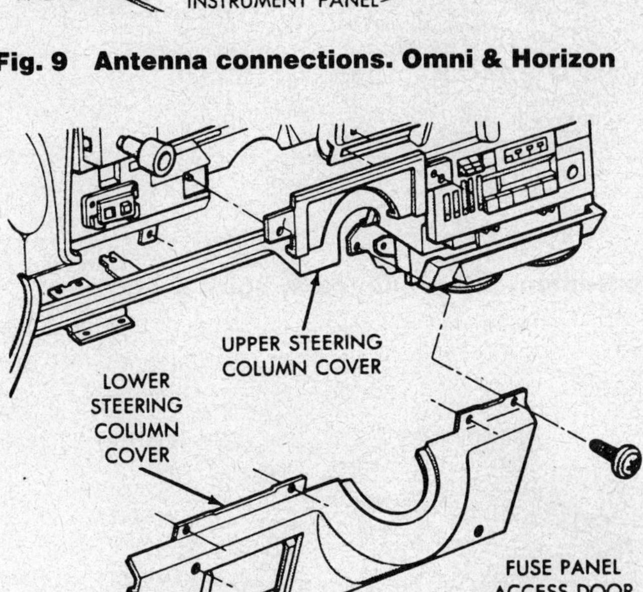


**Fig. 11 Lower steering column cover. Spirit & Acclaim**

17. Disconnect A/C heater unit vacuum harness, **Fig. 8.**
18. Disconnect A/C heater unit control cable.
19. Disconnect radio antenna from radio, then remove cable from instrument panel wiring clips, **Fig. 9.**
20. Remove one attaching nut, then disconnect radio ground strap from plenum, **Fig. 7.**
21. Disconnect blower motor wiring, then disconnect resistor block wiring, **Fig. 10.**
22. Lift instrument panel clear of side pivot bolts, then remove from vehicle.
23. Reverse procedure to install.
24. Refer to "Airbag System Disarming" procedure to reactivate airbag.

## SPIRIT & ACCLAIM

1. Refer to "Airbag System Disarming" procedure.
2. Remove left and right side A-pillar trim by disengaging retaining clips.
3. Remove left and right cowl side trim panels as follows:
   a. Remove four scuff plate/cowl panel assembly attaching screws, then the cowl side trim panels.
4. Remove glove box assembly as follows:
   a. Open glove box door, then disconnect check strap.
   b. Remove glove box switch and light by pulling rearward, then disconnecting wiring connectors.
   c. Remove six attaching screws, then the glove box assembly.
5. Remove four relays located above glove box assembly.
6. Reach through glove box opening, then disconnect A/C heater control vacuum lines, radio noise suppressor wires and blower motor/cycling switch wires.
7. Remove hood release handle.
8. Remove lower steering column cover as follows:
   a. Disconnect parking brake release rod from parking brake.
   b. Remove fuse panel access door, then remove one screw from lower column cover, **Fig. 11.**
   c. Remove six screws from lower cover, four across top of panel and two on bottom, then remove lower steering column cover.
9. Remove lower left instrument panel silencer and reinforcement as follows:
   a. Remove two screws from front of silencer, **Fig. 12.**
   b. Remove one push nut, then disconnect courtesy lamp and remove silencer.
10. Remove instrument panel center bezel by pulling straight back, disengaging five clips.
11. Remove floor console as follows:
    a. Place transaxle shifter in N position.
    b. Remove both side carpet panels from front console.
    c. Remove two screw cover plates from rear console, **Fig. 13.**
    d. Remove coin holder, then the two rear console-to-front console attaching screws.
    e. Remove two rear console-to-mounting bracket screws, then the rear console assembly.
    f. **On models equipped with automatic transaxle,** remove shift lever bezel as follows: (1) Remove two screws, then pull up to remove automatic transaxle shift knob; (2) Lift shift lever bezel from front to unsnap from console, then disconnect wiring harness and remove shift lever bezel.
    g. **On models equipped with manual transaxle,** remove shift lever bezel as follows: (1) Unscrew shifter knob from shifter; (2) Remove nut, then lift ring from shaft; (3) Lift shift lever bezel from front to unsnap from console, then remove shift lever bezel.
    h. **On all models,** remove two console-to-mounting bracket screws.
    i. Remove six console-to-instrument panel screws.
    j. Slide console assembly rearward to unlatch console from instrument panel, then remove console assembly.

12. Remove radio assembly as follows:
    a. Remove radio mounting screws.
    b. Pull radio from panel, disconnect wiring, ground strap and antenna lead from radio, then remove radio.
13. Remove A/C heater control as follows:
    a. Remove two A/C heater control mounting screws, **Fig. 14.**
    b. Slide A/C heater control rearward, disconnect temperature control cable and wiring, then remove A/C heater control.
14. Remove cigar lighter assembly as follows:
    a. Remove two screws from lighter assembly.
    b. Pull lighter assembly rearward, disconnect wiring, then remove lighter assembly.
15. Remove message center/traveler as follows:
    a. Remove four attaching screws.
    b. Pull unit rearward, disconnect wiring, then remove message center/traveler.
16. Disconnect demister hoses.
17. Remove instrument panel top cover as follows:
    a. Lift up rear edge of instrument panel top panel up, **Fig. 15.**
    b. Remove panel by pulling rearward.
18. Remove nuts attaching steering column bracket to instrument panel support and lower bracket support, then lower steering column.
19. Loosen instrument panel pivot bolts, **Fig. 15.**
20. Remove screws attaching instrument panel to cowl panel.
21. Allow instrument panel to roll down slightly, then disconnect remaining electrical connections.
22. With the aid of a helper, remove panel pivot bolts, then the instrument panel from vehicle.
23. Reverse procedure to install.
24. Refer to "Airbag System Disarming" procedure to reactivate airbag.

## ARIES, RELIANT & NEW YORKER

1. Refer to "Airbag System Disarming" procedure.
2. Remove instrument panel upper pad as follows:
    a. Remove three screws from defroster trough.
    b. Remove four screws under brow, **Fig. 16.**
    c. Remove three screws from lower edge of pad above glove box.
    d. Slide pad rearward to remove.
3. Remove both side A-pillar trim covers as follows:
    a. Loosen end attaching screws on windshield header upper garnish moulding and roof rail garnish mouldings.
    b. Remove one A-pillar trim cover attaching screw, then the trim cover.
4. **On Reliant 4-door models,** remove right side lower trim panel from under glove box as follows:
    a. Remove three trim panel attaching screws below glove box, **Fig. 17.**

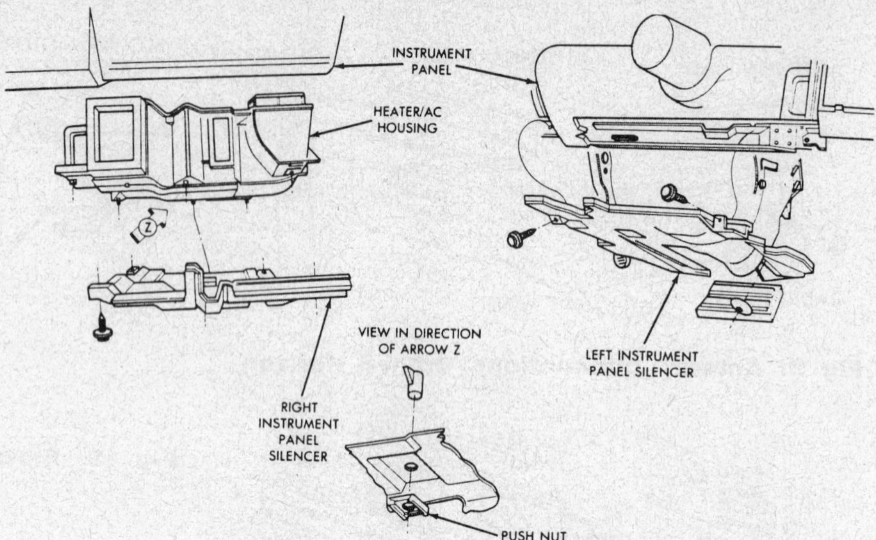


**Fig. 12 Instrument panel silencers. Spirit & Acclaim**

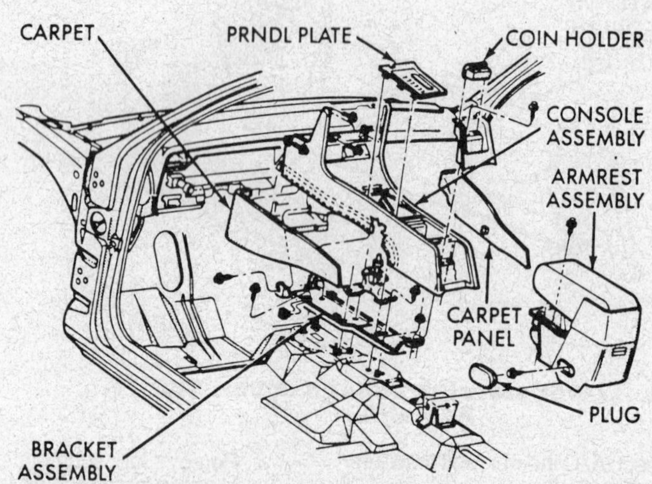


**Fig. 13 Exploded view of console assembly . Spirit & Acclaim**

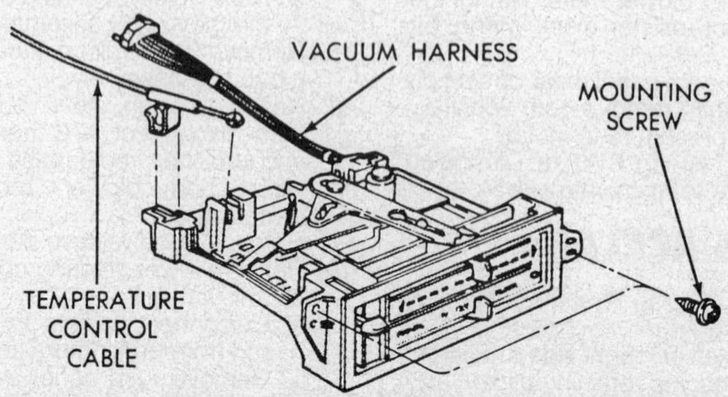


**Fig. 14 A/C heater control. Spirit & Acclaim**

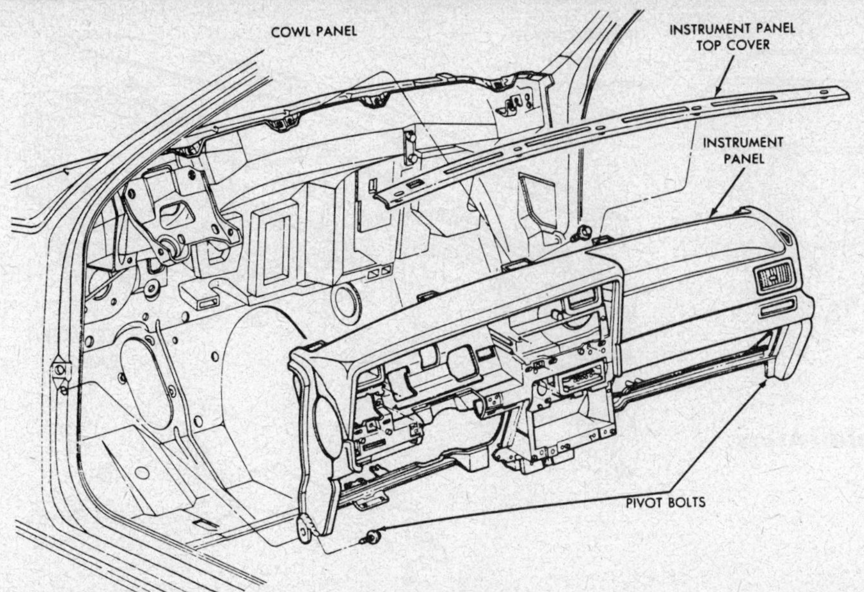


**Fig. 15 Instrument panel, top cover & mounting bolts. Spirit & Acclaim**

b. Remove console attaching clip by pushing forward on left end of trim panel.
c. Rotate panel downward, then slide side cowl attaching bracket over side cowl attaching button head.

5. **On all models,** remove both side cowl trim covers as follows:
   a. Remove four front scuff plate attaching screws, then the front scuff plates.
   b. Remove two cowl side trim panel attaching screws.
   c. Pull panel out from bottom, then remove from vehicle.
6. Remove lower steering column cover, **Fig. 18.**
7. Disconnect parking brake release rod from parking brake mechanism.
8. **On column shift models equipped with automatic transaxle,** disconnect shift indicator wire.
9. **On all models,** remove column wiring harness from clip on lower column bracket.

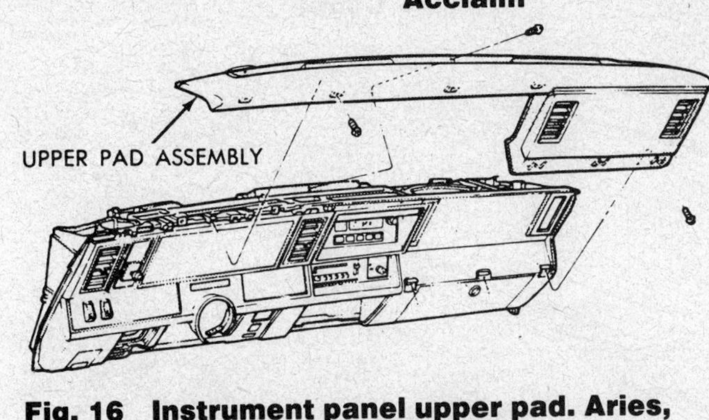


**Fig. 16 Instrument panel upper pad. Aries, Reliant & New Yorker**

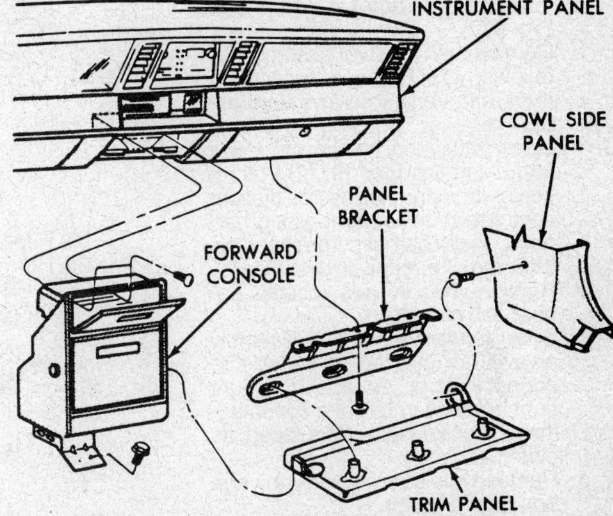


**Fig. 17 Right side lower trim panel & forward console. Reliant 4-door**

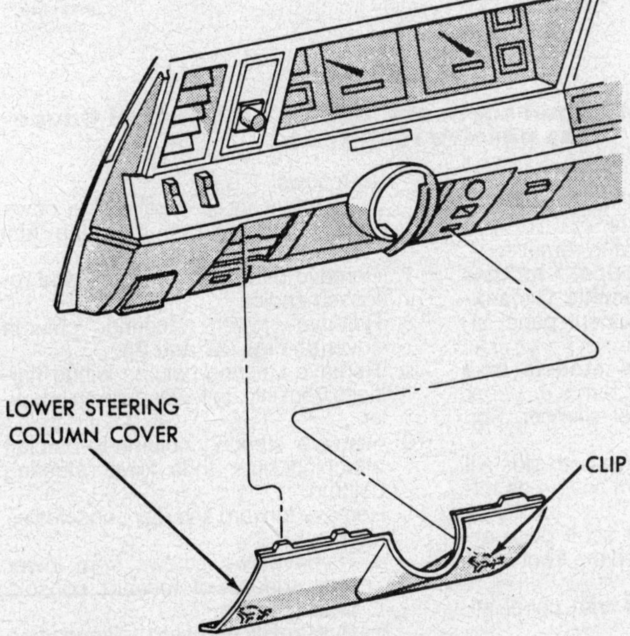


**Fig. 18 Lower steering column cover. Aries, Reliant & New Yorker**

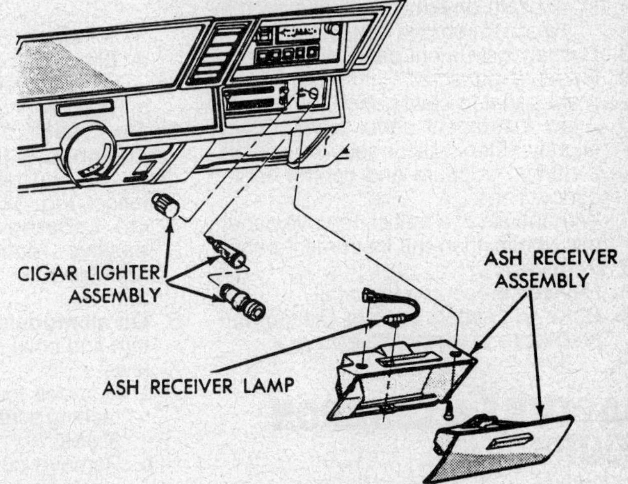


**Fig. 19 Ash receiver assembly. Aries, Reliant & New Yorker**

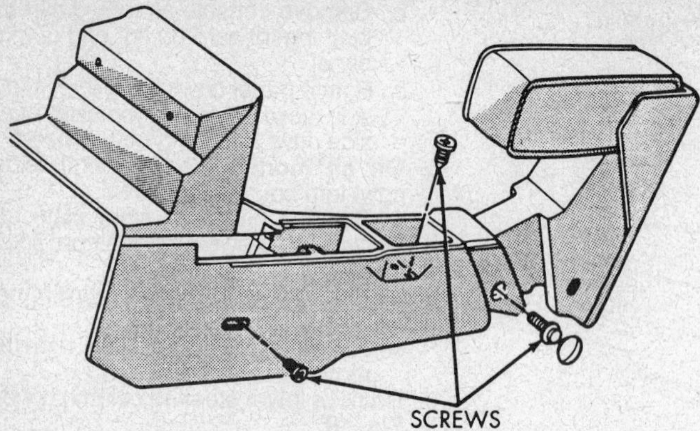


**Fig. 20 Rear console attaching bolts. Aries, Reliant & New Yorker**

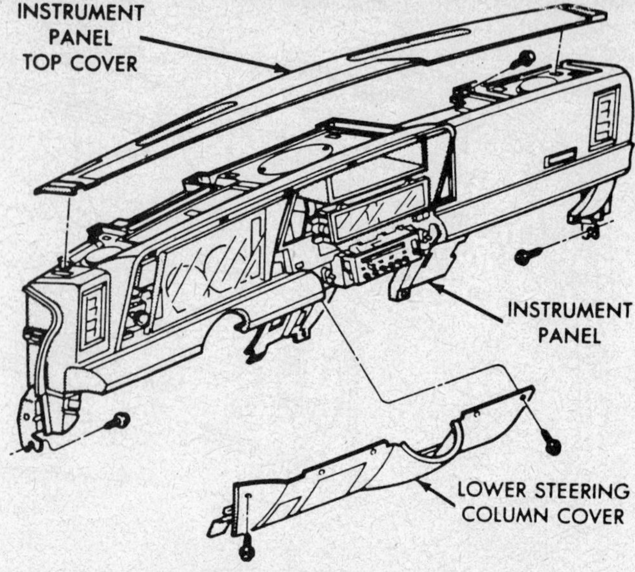


**Fig. 21 Instrument panel, top cover & lower steering column cover. Daytona & LeBaron Coupe**

10. Remove three nuts from lower portion of column and two nuts from upper portion, then lower steering column.
11. Remove forward console, if equipped, as follows:
    a. Remove two screws from from lower console bracket to floor pan, **Fig. 17.**
    b. Remove ash receiver assembly as follows: (1) Remove receptacle, then remove two screws from upper receiver housing and one screw attaching housing to lower reinforcement, **Fig. 19;** (2) Pull receiver housing rearward, disconnect ash receiver light wiring harness, unclip harness from housing, then remove receiver housing.
    c. Remove two screws located behind ash receiver.
    d. Slide forward console assembly away from instrument panel, disconnect lower storage box light connector, then remove console.
12. Remove rear console, if equipped, as follows:
    a. Remove two screws from stowage box floor, **Fig. 20.**
    b. Remove two screws from sides of console near the bottom.
    c. Remove two screws from rear of console on either side of stowage bin, then remove console.
13. Loosen instrument panel pivot bolts.
14. Remove four screws attaching instrument panel to cowl panel.
15. Allow instrument panel to roll down slightly, then disconnect remaining electrical, vacuum and control cable connections.
16. With the aid of a helper, remove panel pivot bolts, then the instrument panel from vehicle.
17. Reverse procedure to install.
18. Refer to "Airbag System Disarming" procedure to reactivate airbag.

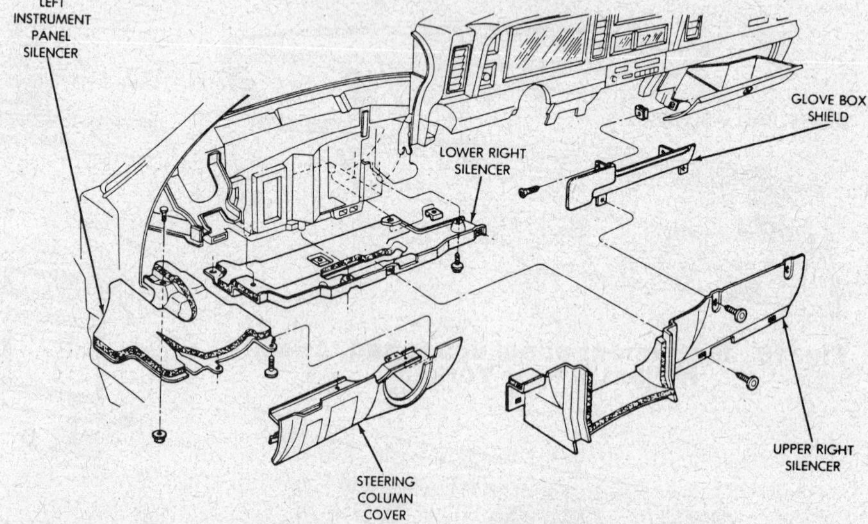


**Fig. 22 Instrument panel silencers. Daytona & LeBaron Coupe less passive restraints**

## DAYTONA & LEBARON COUPE

1. Refer to "Airbag System Disarming" procedure.
2. Remove instrument panel top cover as follows:
    a. Lift up rear edge of instrument panel top cover, **Fig. 21.**
    b. Pull panel rearward to remove.
3. **On LeBaron coupe models equipped with automatic transaxle,** remove left instrument panel silencer, **Fig. 22.**
4. **On LeBaron coupe models less passive restraints,** remove upper right instrument panel silencer, **Fig. 22.**
5. **On all models,** remove both side sill trim and cowl side trim covers as follows:
    a. Remove four front scuff plate attaching screws, then the front scuff plates.
    b. Remove cowl side trim panel attaching screws.
    c. Pull panel out from bottom, then remove from vehicle.
6. Remove both side A-pillar trim covers as follows:
    a. Remove three A-pillar trim cover attaching screws, then the trim covers.
7. Remove parking brake and hood release handles.
8. Remove lower steering column cover(s), **Figs. 22 and 23.**
9. Remove steering column wiring harness from clip on lower column bracket.
10. Remove steering column-to-bracket attaching nuts, then lower steering column.
11. Remove forward and rear consoles as follows:
    a. Remove two screws from lower rear surface of forward console bezel, **Fig. 24.**
    b. Pull bezel rearward, disengaging upper clips to remove.
    c. Set parking brake, then place shift lever in N position.

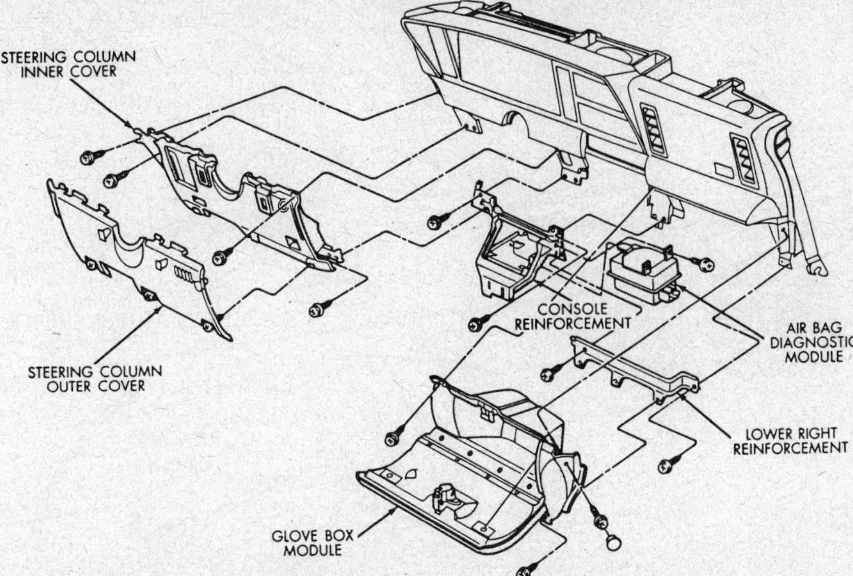


**Fig. 23 Instrument panel components. Daytona & LeBaron Coupe w/passive restraints**

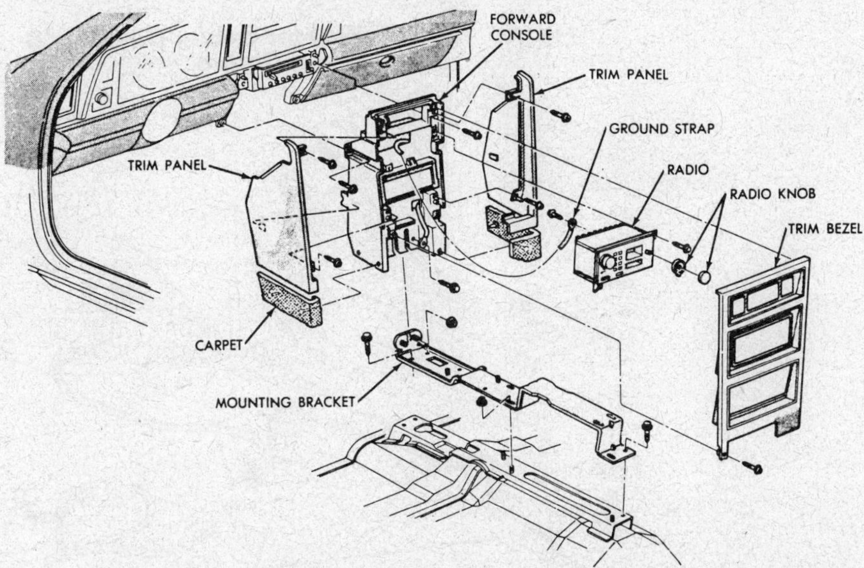


**Fig. 24 Exploded view of forward console assembly. Daytona & LeBaron Coupe**

d. Remove both side carpet panels from rear console by grasping each carpet panel along lower edge with pliers and firmly pulling straight down.
e. Remove two screws attaching rear console to front console, **Fig. 25.**
f. Remove shift knob as follows: (1) On models equipped with automatic transaxle, remove one 5 mm setscrew, then pull up and remove shifter knob; (2) Loosen hex head screw on right side of shifter mechanism base, then disconnect nylon shift indicator cable from shifter bracket, **Fig. 26;** (3) On models equipped with manual transaxle, unscrew shift knob from shift lever. Do not attempt to remove lift ring. Shift boot must be stretched over lift ring when console is removed.
g. **On all models,** remove two bolts, one from each side of rear console, then remove two screws from inside of armrest stowage area, **Fig. 25.**
h. Disconnect all wiring to rear console, **Fig. 27,** then remove rear console.
i. Remove forward console trim panels, **Fig. 24.**
j. Remove two nuts attaching lower portion of forward console to mounting bracket.
k. Remove four screws attaching forward console to base panel.
l. Reach behind forward console, then disconnect antenna, wiring and ground strap from radio.
m. Pull forward console rearward to remove.

12. **On models equipped with passive restraints,** remove glove box module, **Fig. 23,** as follows:
    a. Remove glove box light by pulling out of module, then disconnect wiring.
    b. Remove glove box seven retaining screws, then remove glove box module.
13. **On models equipped with passive restraints,** remove lower right reinforcement, then the center instrument panel-to-floor console reinforcement, **Fig. 23.**
14. **On all models,** loosen instrument panel pivot bolts, **Fig. 21.**
15. Remove screws attaching instrument panel to cowl panel, **Fig. 21.**
16. Allow instrument panel to roll down slightly, then disconnect remaining electrical, vacuum and control cable connections.
17. With the aid of a helper, remove panel pivot bolts, then the instrument panel from vehicle.
18. Reverse procedure to install, adjusting shift indicator cable in P position, **Fig. 26.**
19. Refer to "Airbag System Disarming" procedure to reactivate airbag.

## LANCER & LEBARON GTS

1. Refer to "Airbag System Disarming" procedure.
2. Remove front and rear consoles as follows:
    a. Place shift lever in N position.
    b. Remove both side carpet panels from front console, **Fig. 28.**
    c. Remove two screw cover plates from rear console.
    d. Remove cubby box, navigator or cassette tape storage unit, as equipped.
    e. Remove cubby box as follows: (1) Open cubby box door; (2) Remove four attaching screws, then the cubby box.
    f. Remove navigator as follows: (1) Remove two Torx head attaching screws; (2) Pull navigator straight out, then disconnect harness connector.
    g. Pull cassette tape storage unit straight out to remove.
    h. **On models equipped with automatic transaxle,** remove shift lever bezel as follows: (1) Remove two screws, then pull up up on shift knob to remove; (2) Loosen hex head screw on right side of shifter, slide gear selector off bracket, then remove cable; (3) Remove two shift lever bezel attaching screws, lift shift lever bezel from front and disconnect wiring harness, then remove shift lever bezel.
    i. **On models equipped with manual transaxle,** remove shift lever

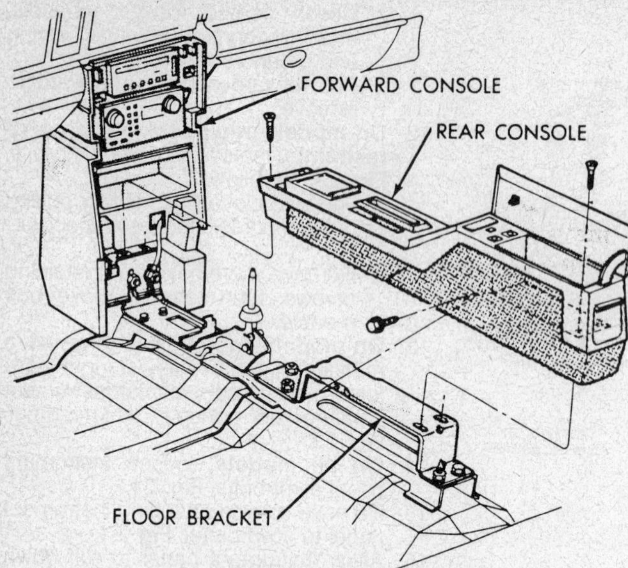


**Fig. 25 Rear console attaching screws & bolts. Daytona & LeBaron Coupe**

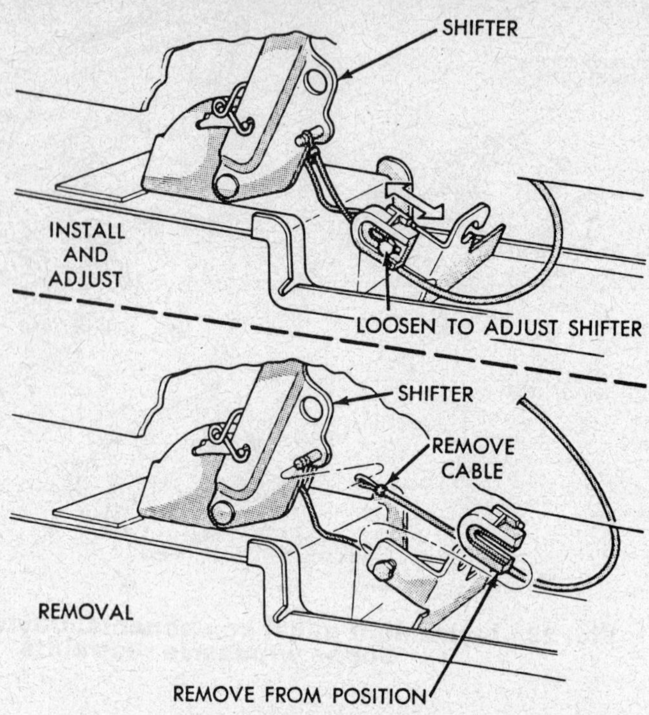


**Fig. 26 Shift indicator cable. Daytona & LeBaron Coupe**

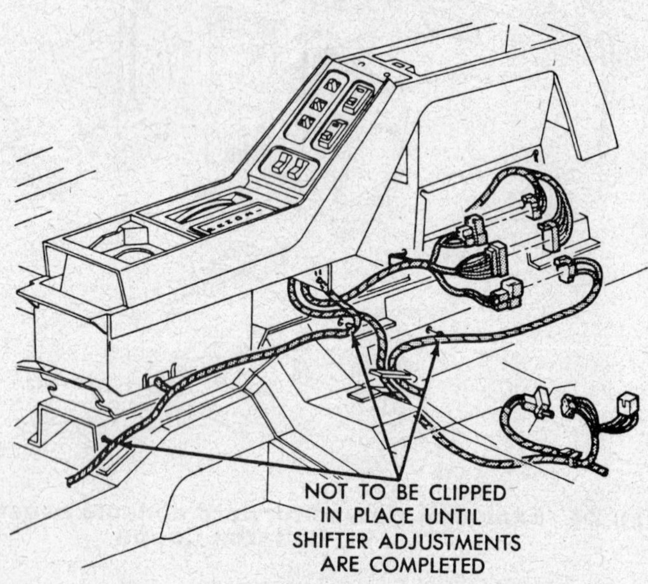


**Fig. 27 Rear console wiring. Daytona & LeBaron Coupe**

bezel as follows: (1) Unscrew shifter knob from shifter shaft; (2) Remove nut and lift ring from shaft; (3) Remove two shift lever bezel attaching screws, lift shift lever bezel from front and disconnect wiring harness, then remove shift lever bezel.

j. **On all models,** disconnect rear console wiring harness.
k. Remove four front console mounting screws (two per side).
l. Remove two front console-to-instrument panel screws.
m. Slide console assembly rearward to unlatch console from instrument panel, then remove console assembly.

3. Remove right and left cowl side and scuff plate trim mouldings by removing five attaching screws per side.
4. Remove right and left A-pillar trim mouldings by removing two push-pin fasteners per side and disengaging from clip on B-pillar trim.
5. Remove instrument panel top cover by pushing forward and prying up, using a straightedge to aid in removal, **Fig. 29.**
6. Disconnect bulkhead connector from brace under instrument panel.
7. Remove hood and parking brake release module as follows:
   a. Disconnect parking brake release cable from parking brake mechanism, **Fig. 30.**
   b. Disconnect hood release cable from hood latch.
   c. Pull parking brake release handle, then remove two module attaching screws.
   d. Pull hood release handle, then remove two remaining module attaching screws.
   e. Pull module and cable assembly rearward to remove.
8. Remove lower steering column cover by pulling straight out.
9. Lower steering column by removing five attaching nuts (six on models equipped with cruise control).
10. Disconnect wiring from steering column, cruise control switch, if equipped, stop lamp switch, parking brake switch and ignition switch.
11. Remove two steering column upper studs, then loosen side cowl tie-down bolts.
12. Remove one nut attaching A/C heater control unit to instrument panel, then remove five screws attaching instrument panel to cowl panel, **Fig. 29.**
13. Roll instrument down, attach a hook to hold in place, then remove four screws and the defroster duct.
14. Disconnect body wiring from both side 25-way connectors.
15. Disconnect A/C heater control cable, wiring connectors and vacuum harness.
16. Disconnect antenna, wiring and radio ground strap.

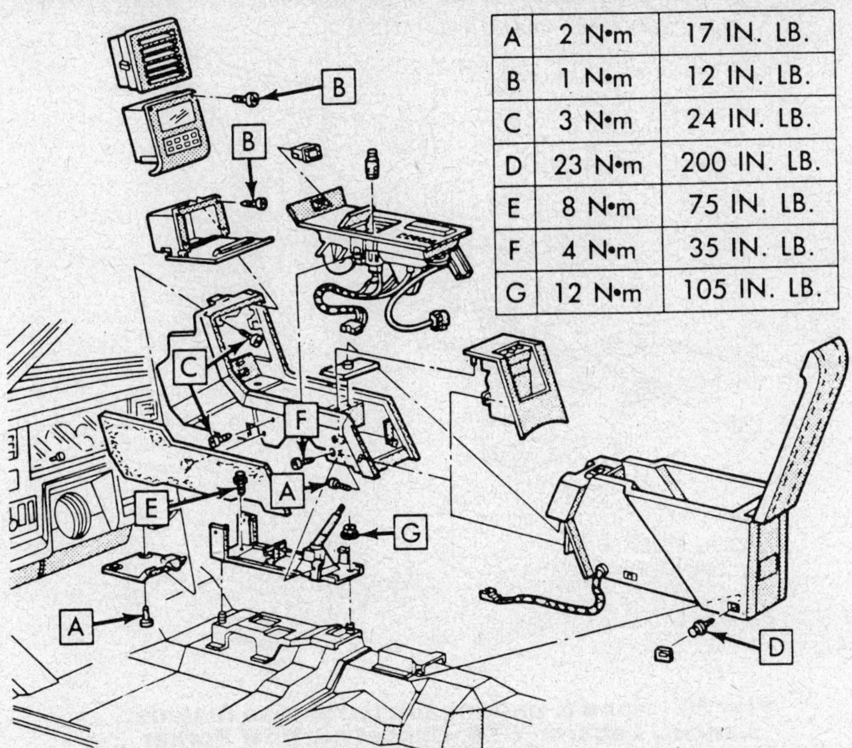

| | | |
|---|---|---|
| A | 2 N•m | 17 IN. LB. |
| B | 1 N•m | 12 IN. LB. |
| C | 3 N•m | 24 IN. LB. |
| D | 23 N•m | 200 IN. LB. |
| E | 8 N•m | 75 IN. LB. |
| F | 4 N•m | 35 IN. LB. |
| G | 12 N•m | 105 IN. LB. |

**Fig. 28 Exploded view of front & rear console assembly. Lancer & LeBaron GTS**

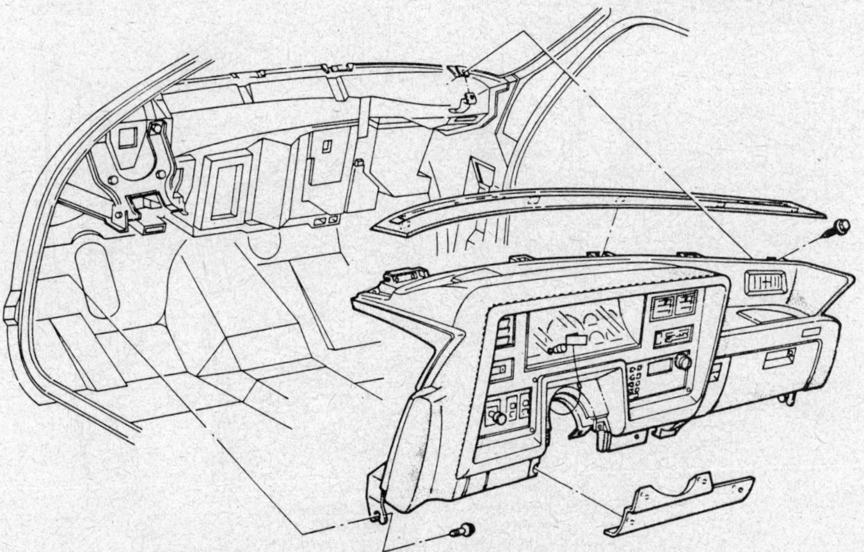

**Fig. 29 Instrument panel, top cover & lower steering column cover. Lancer & LeBaron GTS**

17. Disconnect remaining electrical connections.
18. Remove both side front door weatherstrips in area of roll-up points.
19. Remove instrument panel pivot bolts, then the instrument panel assembly, **Fig. 29.**
20. Reverse procedure to install.
21. Refer to "Airbag System Disarming" procedure to reactivate airbag.

## SHADOW & SUNDANCE

1. Refer to "Airbag System Disarming" procedure.
2. **On 1989 models**, proceed as follows:
   a. Remove windshield wiper arms.
   b. Remove windshield washer fluid reservoir.
   c. Pull connector loose from A/C heater resistor block, then push wiring and grommet through bulkhead and into passenger compartment.
3. **On all models,** remove consolette assembly, if equipped, as follows:
   a. Remove shifter handle.
   b. Unsnap shift indicator bezel or shift boot bezel from consolette, disconnect wiring, then remove bezel assembly.
   c. **On 1989 models,** open armrest lid and remove three screws attaching armrest to console retractor bracket.
   d. **On all models,** remove four caps which cover attaching screws, then remove four attaching screws.
   e. Lift consolette up and over shift mechanism to remove.
4. Remove front and center console assemblies, if equipped as follows:
   a. Remove shifter handle.
   b. Unsnap shift indicator bezel or shift boot bezel from console assembly, disconnect wiring, then remove bezel assembly, **Fig. 31.**
   c. Unsnap power mirror/window switch bezel, if equipped, then disconnect switch wiring.
   d. Open armrest lid and remove three screws attaching armrest to console retractor bracket.
   e. Remove armrest and center console section as a unit by lifting and unsnapping from front console section.
   f. Remove center module bezel.
   g. Remove front console and sidewalls as a unit by removing six screws attaching sidewall to instrument panel and console bracket.
   h. Slide front console assembly rearward, then lift to remove.
5. **On 1989 models,** proceed as follows:
   a. Disconnect passive restraint seat belt logic control module wiring connector.
   b. Remove six attaching nuts securing instrument panel to console support brace.
   c. Remove instrument-to-console support brace with passive restraint seat belt logic control module attached.
6. **On all models,** remove right and left cowl side and scuff plate trim mouldings as follows:
   a. Remove three scuff plate trim moulding attaching screws.
   b. Remove cowl side trim attaching screw and lower most push-pin from A-pillar trim mouldings.
   c. Remove side cowl and scuff plate trim mouldings.
7. Remove right and left A-pillar trim mouldings by removing remaining push-pins.
8. Remove instrument panel top cover as follows:
   a. Insert suitable trim stick tool in groove between instrument panel top cover and instrument panel pad surface, **Fig. 32.**

b. Pry cover up and forward until cover is released from instrument panel pad.
c. Lift top cover up and rearward to remove.

9. Remove lower steering column cover as follows:
   a. **On 1989 models,** disconnect parking brake release rod from parking brake handle.
   b. Remove two screws attaching hood release handle, then the handle.
   c. Remove fuse access door, then remove lower steering column cover attaching screw located directly above fuse block, **Fig. 33.**
   d. Remove six attaching screws around outside of steering column cover, then the cover.
10. **On all models,** disconnect steering column wiring from 25-way connector.
11. Disconnect parking brake, stop lamp and cruise control wiring, if equipped.
12. Remove five steering column support nuts, lower steering column, then remove two column attaching studs.
13. **On all models,** disconnect engine wiring harness from 18-way and 16-way connectors located on left side panel support bracket.
14. **On models with floor brace located under center of instrument panel,** remove nuts attaching intermediate bracket to upper and lower brackets.
15. **On 1989 models,** remove glove box module as follows:
   a. Open glove box door, then remove check strap attaching screws to allow full downward movement of glove box door.
   b. Remove six screws attaching glove box module to instrument panel, **Fig. 34.**
   c. Pull glove box module rearward, disconnect wiring from glove box lamp and switch, then remove glove box module.
16. **On all models,** loosen instrument panel pivot bolts, **Fig. 32.**
17. **On 1989 models,** remove defroster duct adapter from defroster duct.
18. **On all models,** remove screws attaching instrument panel to cowl panel.
19. Roll instrument panel down, attach heavy wire to hold in position, then remove defroster duct retaining screws.
20. Disconnect body wiring from right side 18-way connector and left side 25-way connector.
21. Disconnect temperature mode cable from control unit, vacuum line from in-line connector and resistor block and blower motor wiring connections.
22. Disconnect speedometer and antenna cables.
23. Disconnect left and right demister hoses from demister outlets on panel.
24. Disconnect remaining electrical connections and radio ground strap.
25. Remove instrument panel pivot bolts, then the instrument panel.
26. Reverse procedure to install.

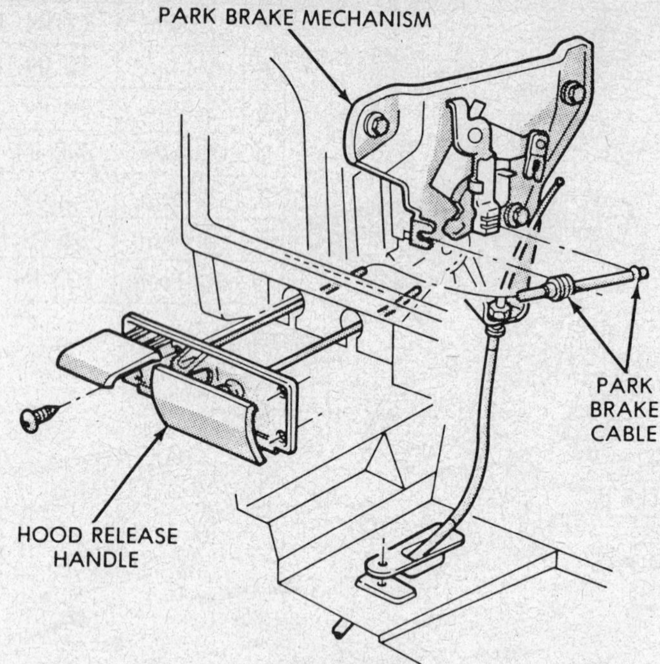


**Fig. 30 Hood & parking brake release module. Lancer, Lebaron GTS, Dynasty & New Yorker Landau**

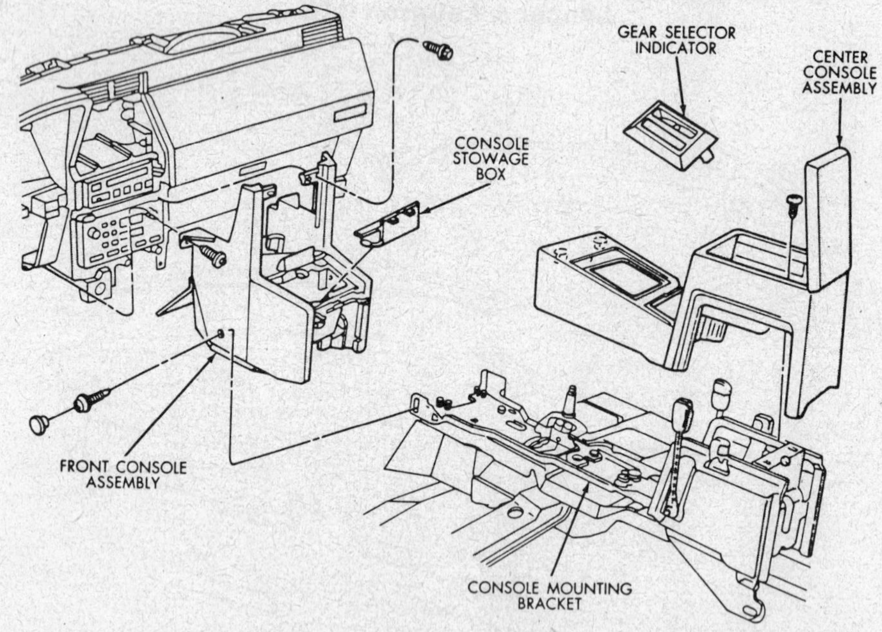


**Fig. 31 Front & center console assembly. Shadow & Sundance**

27. Refer to "Airbag System Disarming" procedure to reactivate airbag.

## DYNASTY & NEW YORKER LANDAU

1. Refer to "Airbag System Disarming" procedure.
2. Remove upper right and left instrument panel silencers, **Fig. 35.**
3. Remove right and left cowl side and scuff plate trim mouldings by removing five attaching screws per side.
4. Remove right and left A-pillar trim mouldings by removing two push-pin fasteners per side and disengaging from clip on B-pillar trim.
5. Remove instrument panel top cover by pushing forward and prying up, using a straightedge to aid in removal, **Fig. 36.**
6. Disconnect bulkhead connector from brace under left side of instrument panel.
7. Remove hood and parking brake release module as follows:

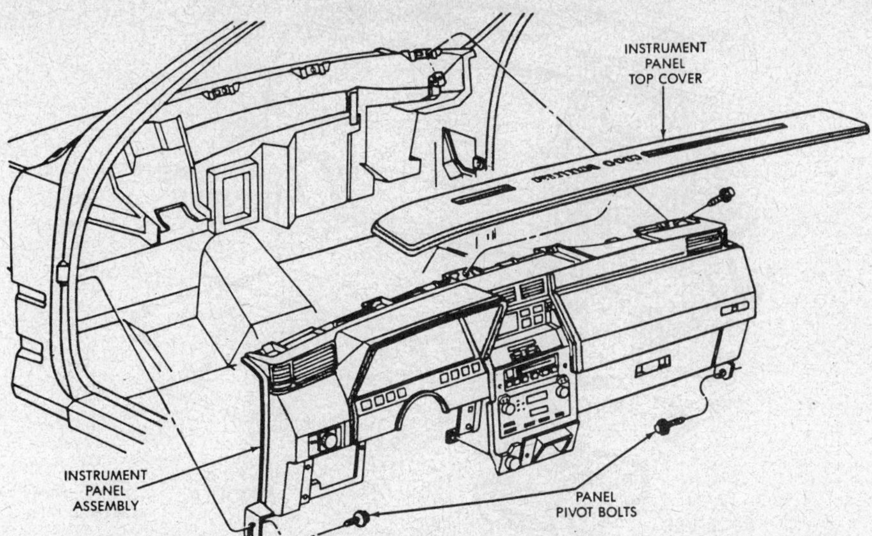


**Fig. 32 Instrument panel & top cover. Shadow & Sundance**

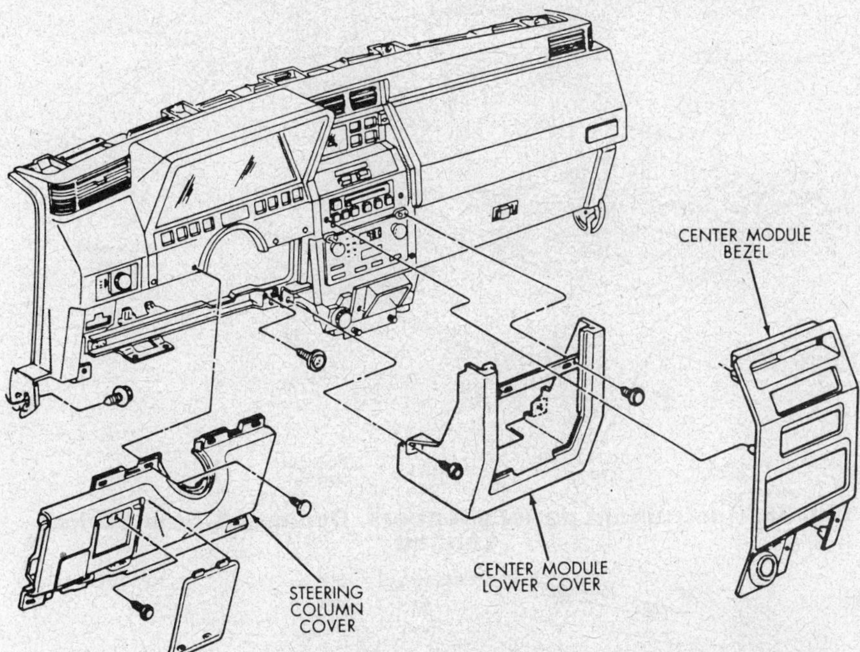


**Fig. 33 Lower instrument panel components. Shadow & Sundance**

a. Disconnect parking brake release cable from parking brake mechanism, **Fig. 30.**
b. Disconnect hood release cable from hood latch.
c. Pull parking brake release handle, then remove two module attaching screws.
d. Pull hood release handle, then remove two remaining module attaching screws.
e. Pull module and cable assembly rearward to remove.

8. Remove lower steering column cover by pulling straight out, then lower steering column by removing five attaching nuts (six on models equipped with cruise control).
9. Disconnect wiring from steering column, stop lamp switch, parking brake switch, ignition switch and cruise control switch, if equipped.
10. Remove two steering column upper studs, then loosen side cowl tie-down bolts.
11. Remove one nut attaching A/C heater unit to panel, then remove five screws attaching instrument panel to cowl panel, **Fig. 36.**
12. Loosen instrument panel pivot bolts, roll instrument panel down, attach a hook to hold panel in position, then remove four screws to remove defroster duct.
13. Disconnect body wiring from right and left 25-way connectors.
14. Disconnect wiring for resister block and blower motor, then the right demister hose.
15. Disconnect A/C heater unit control cable, wiring connectors and vacuum harness.
16. Disconnect radio wiring, ground strap and antenna lead.
17. Remove right side instrument panel ground wire, then disconnect body computer wiring.
18. Disconnect remaining electrical and cable connections.
19. Remove instrument panel pivot bolts, then the instrument panel.
20. Reverse procedure to install.
21. Refer to "Airbag System Disarming" procedure to reactivate airbag.

## DIPLOMAT, FIFTH AVENUE & GRAN FURY

1. Refer to "Airbag System Disarming" procedure.
2. Remove cluster bezel as follows:
   a. Remove four attaching screws located along upper edge of bezel, **Fig. 37.**
   b. Place gearshift indicator in L (1) position.
   c. Remove bezel by pulling rearward and releasing four lower fastener clips.
3. Remove 12 cowl top cover and trim panel assembly attaching screws located as follows:
   a. Three from lower right of trim pad, **Fig. 37.**
   b. One from lower right side of instrument cluster.
   c. One from lower left side of instrument cluster.
   d. Three from trim pad brow above cluster.
   e. Four from cowl top in defroster openings.
4. Disconnect wiring for glove box light and trunk lid release switch, if equipped, **Fig. 38.**
5. Remove cowl top cover and trim panel assembly from instrument panel.
6. Remove steering column cover as follows:
   a. Remove left vent control, if equipped, from bottom of cover and allow to hang down.
   b. Remove hood release handle from bottom of cover.
   c. Remove six attaching screws, then the cover.
7. Remove floor brace cover by spreading end flanges, then pulling cover rearward **Fig. 39.**
8. Pull carpet away from instrument panel floor brace, remove four attaching nuts, then the brace.
9. Remove left lower reinforcement attaching screws from left side cowl.
10. Remove two attaching nuts from center support.
11. Disconnect wiring from chime module and intermittent wiper module, if equipped.

12. Slide fuse box off of mounting bracket, then remove flasher from reinforcement.
13. Remove lower left reinforcement, **Fig. 39.**
14. Remove upper panel assembly retaining screws.
15. Remove right side lower kick panel, then loosen lower instrument panel pivot bolt.
16. Remove one nut attaching center support to lower instrument panel assembly.
17. Roll panel down and disconnect electrical connectors.
18. Remove pivot bolt, then the lower instrument panel assembly.
19. Reverse procedure to install, positioning steering column cover into place and indexing to lower instrument panel, **Fig. 37. Torque** steering column cover mounting screws to 170-230 inch lbs.
20. Refer to "Airbag System Disarming" procedure to reactivate airbag.

## CONQUEST

Disarm airbag as described under "Airbag System Disarming." Remove components in order as they appear in **Fig. 40,** noting the following:

1. Remove steering wheel (1) as follows:
   a. Remove horn pad, then disconnect horn contact connector.
   b. Remove steering wheel using steering wheel puller tool No. DT-1001-A or equivalent. Do not hammer on steering wheel to remove. The collapsible mechanism may be damaged.
2. Remove knee protector (4) as follows:
   a. Remove hole cover.
   b. Remove four knee protector attaching screws (A) **Fig. 41,** then the knee protector.
3. Remove lower and upper steering column covers (5 and 6) as follows:
   a. Remove four steering column cover attaching screws (B) **Fig. 42,** then the column covers.
4. Remove column switch (7) as follows:
   a. Remove two column switch attaching screws (C) **Fig. 43.**
   b. Disconnect column switch harness connectors, then remove column switch.
5. Remove meter hood (8) as follows:
   a. Remove four meter hood mounting screws (D) **Fig. 44.**
   b. Pull bottom edge of hood forward, then pull hood up and out.
   c. Disconnect cluster switch connectors from both sides of hood, then remove meter hood.
6. Remove combination meter (9) as follows:
   a. Remove two attaching screws (E) from bottom of meter case, **Fig. 45.**
   b. Remove two mounting nuts (B) from top of meter case, **Fig. 45.**
   c. Pull bottom edge of meter case up and out to remove.
7. Remove side console covers (10) as follows:

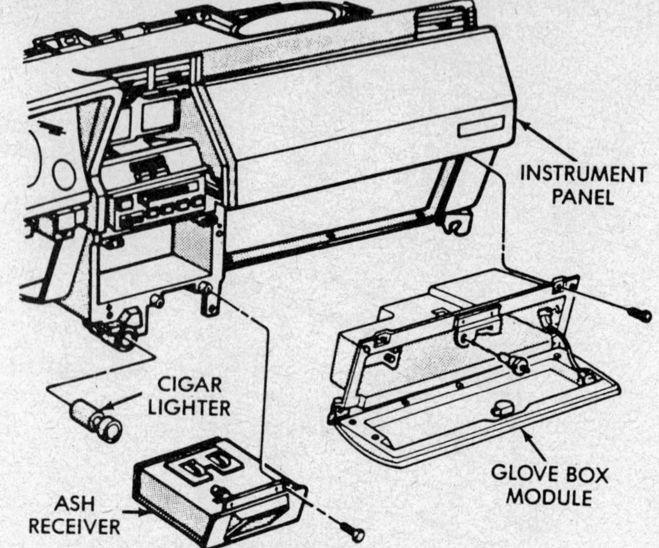


**Fig. 34 Glove box module. Shadow & Sundance**

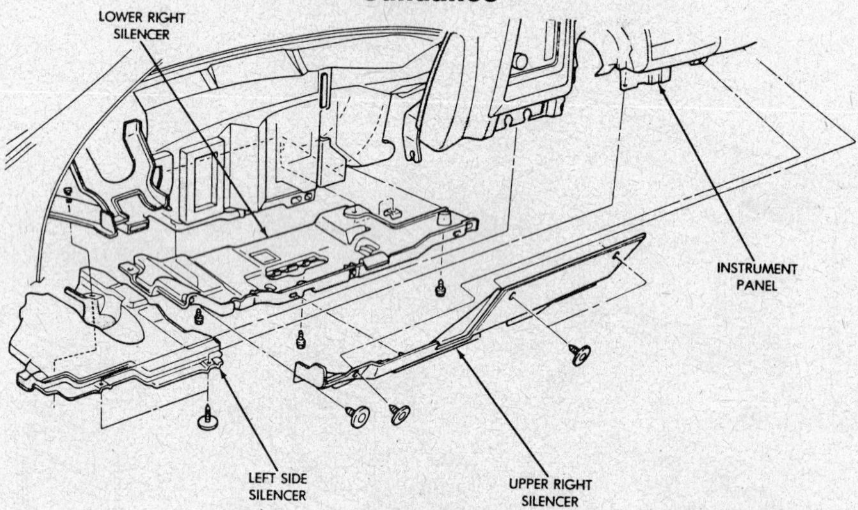


**Fig. 35 Instrument panel silencers. Dynasty & New Yorker Landau**

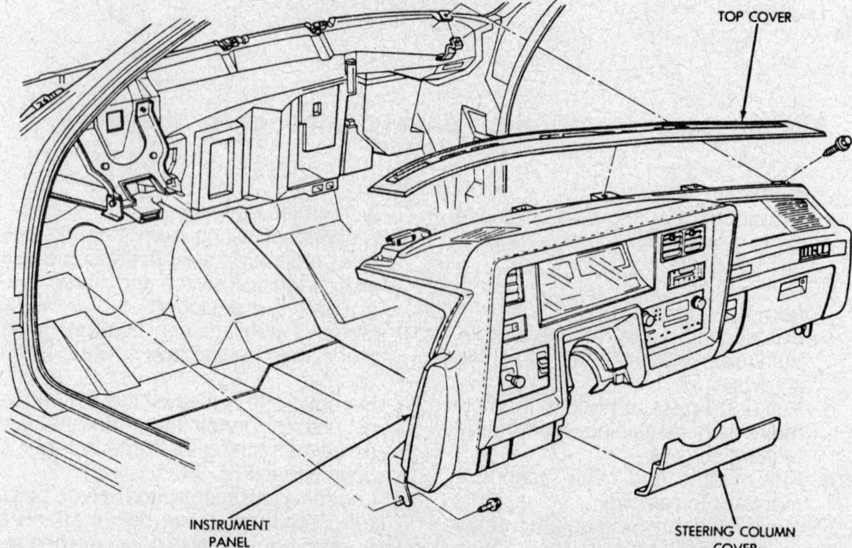


**Fig. 36 Instrument panel, top cover & steering column cover. Dynasty & New Yorker Landau**

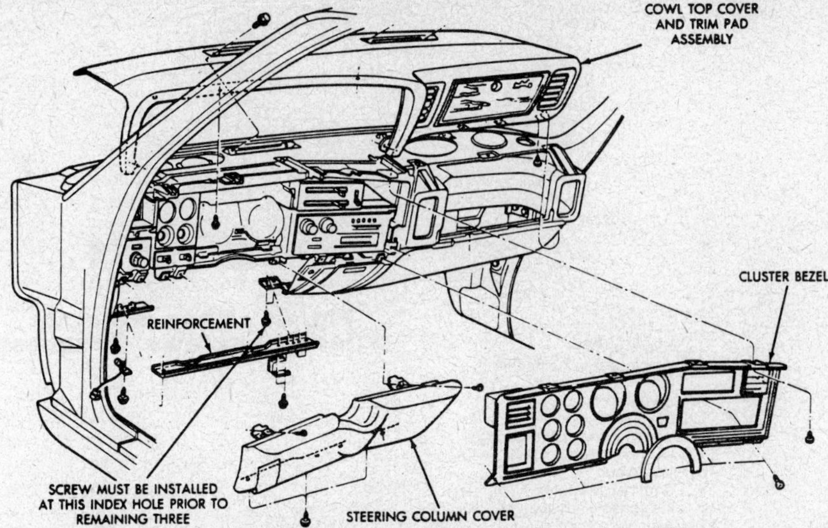


**Fig. 37 Exploded view of instrument panel. Diplomat, Fifth Avenue & Gran Fury**

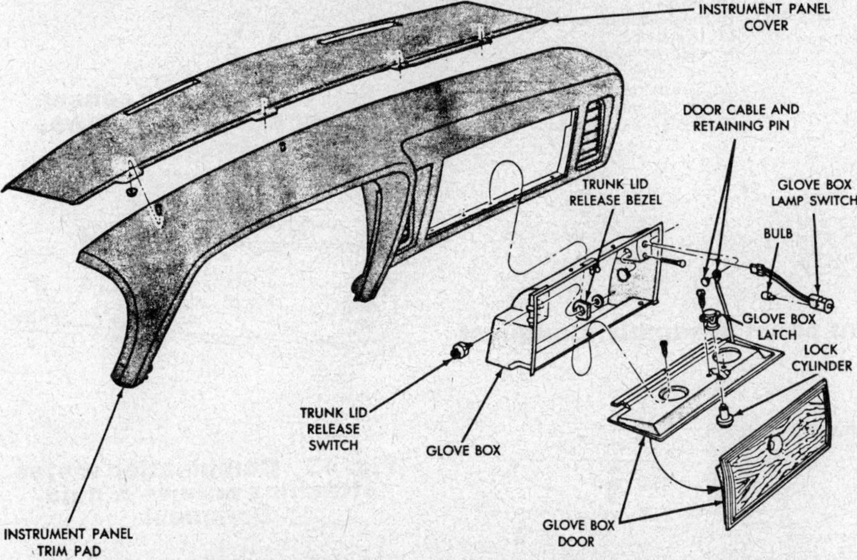


**Fig. 38 Instrument panel trim pad & glove box assembly. Diplomat, Fifth Avenue & Gran Fury**

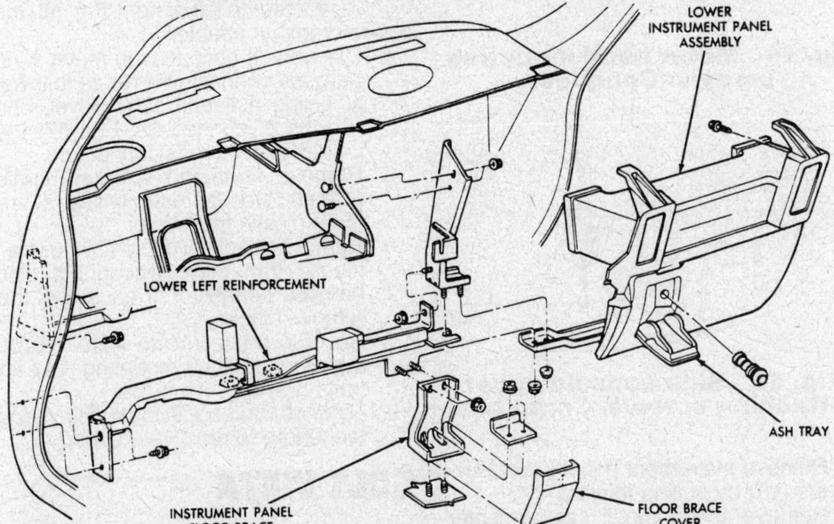


**Fig. 39 Exploded view of lower instrument panel assembly. Diplomat, Fifth Avenue & Gran Fury**

   a. Remove two side console cover attaching screws (D) **Fig. 46.**
   b. Pull cover down while pushing slightly forward to remove.
8. Remove components of rear and front console boxes (11 and 12) **Fig. 40,** in order as they appear in **Fig. 47,** noting the following:
   a. Remove four rear console box attaching screws (D) **Fig. 48,** then the bezel.
   b. Remove radio mounting screws from center reinforcement, **Fig. 49.**
   c. Position transmission shift lever in 4th gear.
   d. Pull front console box slightly to rear.
   e. Disconnect radio wiring connector and antenna lead from radio.
   f. Pull front console box out toward passenger seat.
9. Remove glove box (14) as follows:
   a. Open glove box door.
   b. Pull glove box forward while pressing both sides of glove box in.
   c. Remove three glove box retaining screws, then the glove box.
10. Remove heater control panel (16) as follows:
   a. Remove heater control knobs by pulling straight off.
   b. Insert tool shown in **Fig. 50** into lever hole of heater control panel, then pull tool to remove panel.
   c. Disconnect control panel light connector, then remove heater control panel.
11. Remove side defroster upper grilles (18) as follows:
   a. Insert a screwdriver from door glass side.
   b. Twist and pry side defroster grille forward to remove.
12. Remove instrument pad side covers (19) as follows:
   a. Insert tip of suitable trim stick between instrument panel and pad side cover.
   b. Twist trim stick to remove instrument pad side covers.
13. Remove instrument panel (21) as follows:
   a. Remove attaching screws and bolts (A, E, F, G and H) from locations shown in **Fig. 51.**
   b. Disconnect front and glove box wiring harnesses.
   c. Pull instrument panel outward to remove.
14. Remove center reinforcement (22), if necessary, as follows:
   a. Remove four center reinforcement attaching bolts (H) **Fig. 52.**
   b. Loosen clamp for main wiring harness, then remove panel.
   c. Remove center reinforcement.
15. Reverse procedure to install, noting the following:
   a. Position instrument panel so that guide pin contacts upper portion of heater unit body, **Fig. 53.**
   b. Ensure ventilation ducts and wiring harnesses are correctly installed.
   c. When installing glove box, temporarily tighten attaching screws, ensure glove box door is centered in

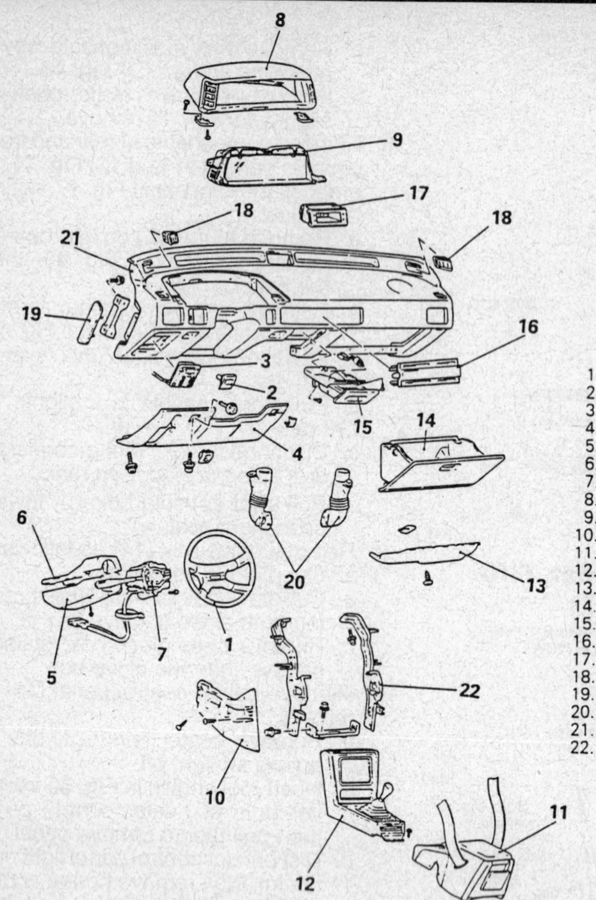


1. Steering wheel
2. Hood lock release handle
3. Fuse block
4. Knee protector
5. Lower steering column cover
6. Upper steering column cover
7. Column switch
8. Meter hood
9. Combination meter
10. Side console cover
11. Rear console box
12. Front console box
13. Under cover
14. Glove box
15. Ashtray
16. Heater control panel
17. Digital clock
18. Side defroster upper grille
19. Instrument pad side cover
20. Side defroster duct
21. Instrument panel
22. Center reinforcement

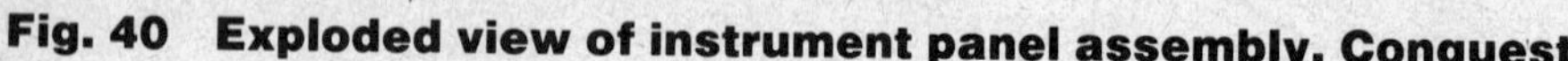

**Fig. 40 Exploded view of instrument panel assembly. Conquest**

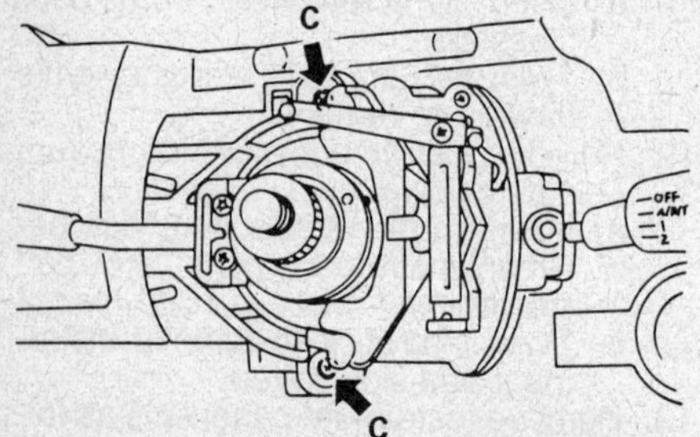


**Fig. 43 Column switch attaching screws. Conquest**

instrument panel when closed, then tighten attaching screws completely.

d. When installing bezels on rear console box, ensure bezels are correctly installed as shown, **Fig. 54. If bezels are incorrectly installed, seat belt will twist in console box.**

e. Refer to "Airbag System Disarming" procedure to reactivate airbag.

## COLT

Disarm airbag as described under "Airbag System Disarming." Remove both side cowl trim panels. Remove components in order as they appear in **Fig. 55,** noting the following:

1. Remove sunglass pocket (3) using a plastic trim stick.

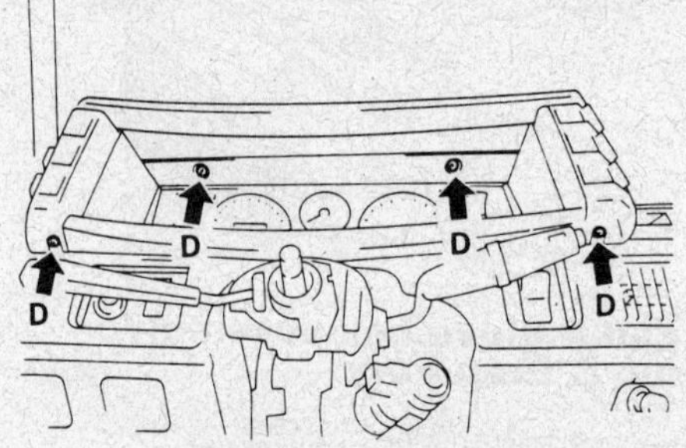


**Fig. 44 Meter hood mounting screws. Conquest**

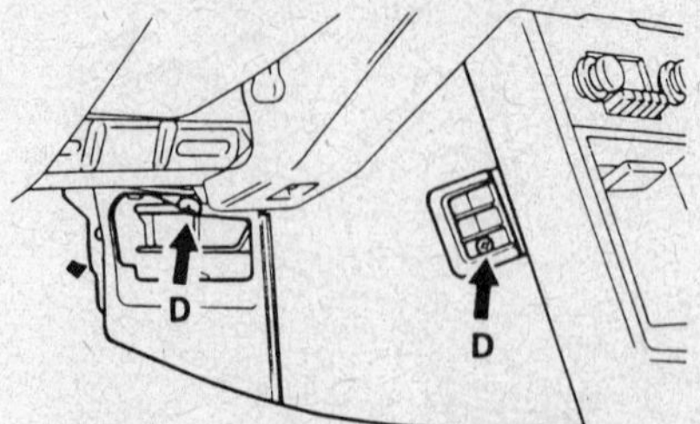


**Fig. 46 Side console cover attaching screws. Conquest**

2. Remove instrument panel lower covers (13) by pulling forward.
3. Remove speedometer cable adapter (17) as follows:
   a. Disconnect speedometer cable from transaxle end of cable.

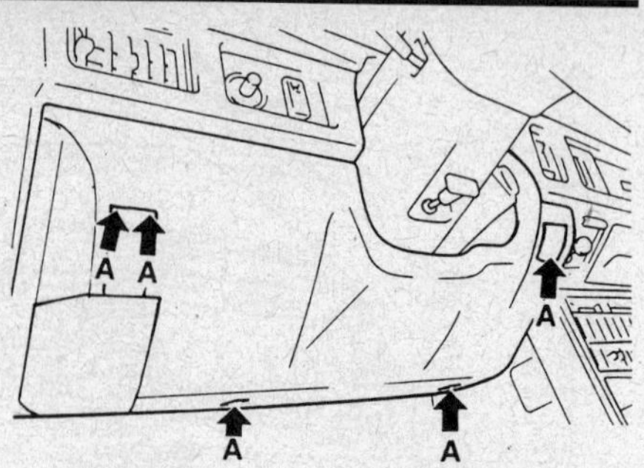


**Fig. 41 Knee protector attaching screws. Conquest**

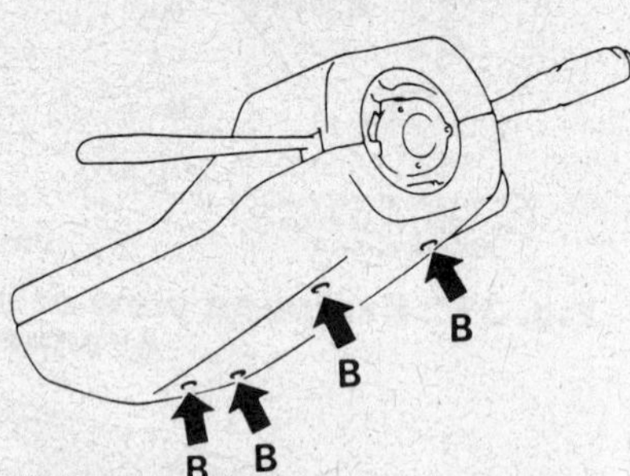


**Fig. 42 Steering column cover attaching screws. Conquest**

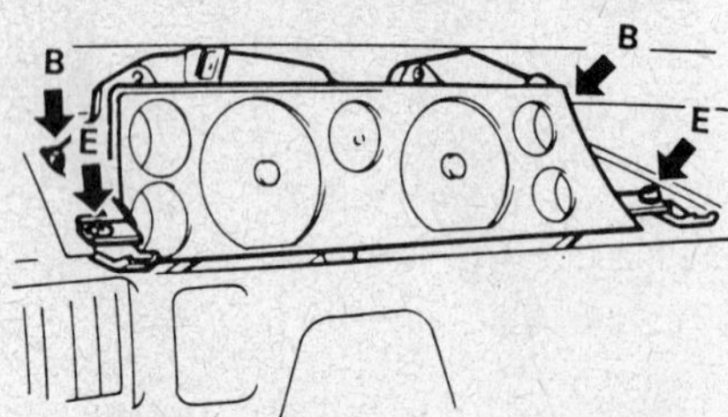


**Fig. 45 Combination meter attaching screws & nuts. Conquest**

   b. Pull speedometer cable slightly toward vehicle interior, release lock by turning speedometer cable adapter to left or right, **Fig. 56,** then remove adapter.
4. Disconnect combination meter wiring harness connectors (18) as follows:
   a. Using a flat-tip screwdriver, open tabs of connectors, **Fig. 57,** then remove harness connectors.
5. Remove righthand speaker garnish (19) and side defroster grilles (21) using a plastic trim stick.
6. Remove clock or plug (22) using a plastic trim stick, disconnect clock harness connector, if equipped, then remove clock.
7. Reverse procedure to install, **torquing** steering shaft mounting nuts and bolts (23) to 7-10 ft. lbs.
8. Refer to "Airbag System Disarming" procedure to reactivate airbag.

## COLT VISTA

Disarm airbag as described under "Airbag System Disarming." Remove steering column as outlined under applicable sec-

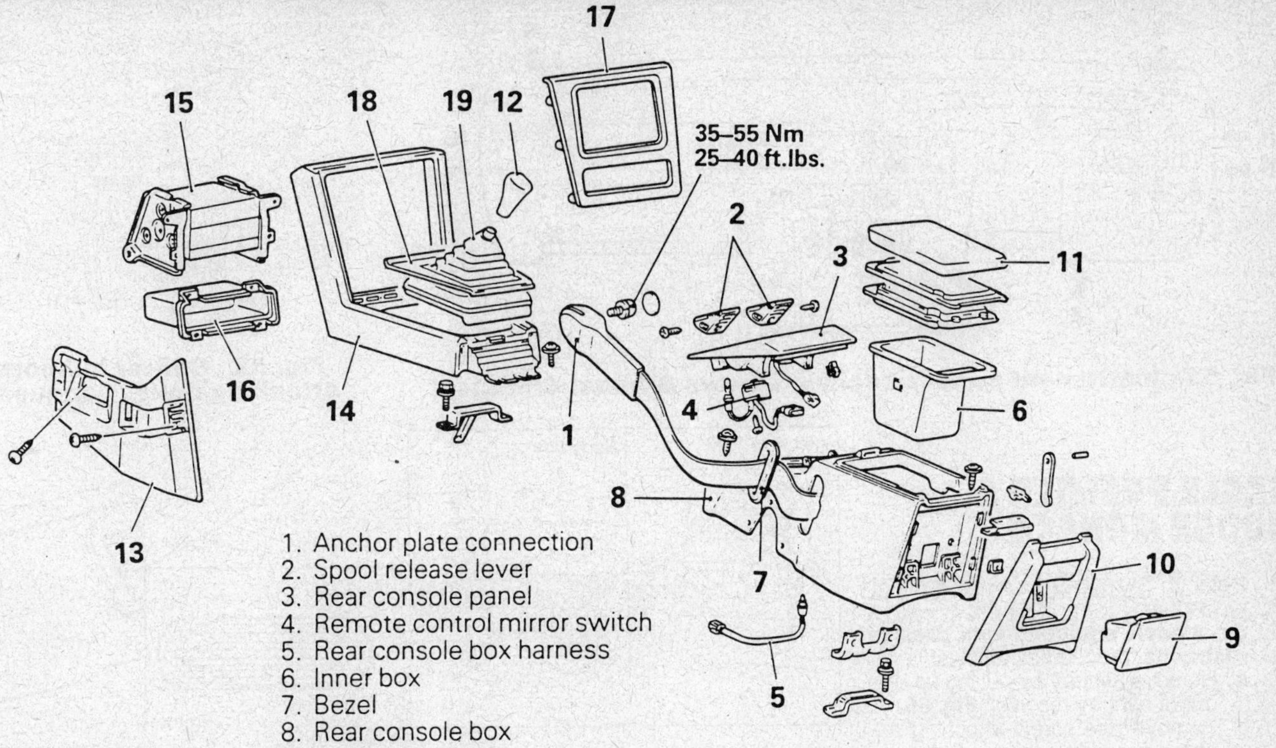

35–55 Nm
25–40 ft.lbs.

1. Anchor plate connection
2. Spool release lever
3. Rear console panel
4. Remote control mirror switch
5. Rear console box harness
6. Inner box
7. Bezel
8. Rear console box
9. Ashtray
10. Accessory panel
11. Accessory box lid
12. Shift lever knob
13. Side console cover
14. Front console box
15. Radio
16. Parcel box
17. Radio panel
18. M/T garnish
19. Shift lever cover

**Fig. 47 Exploded view of front & rear console assembly. Conquest**

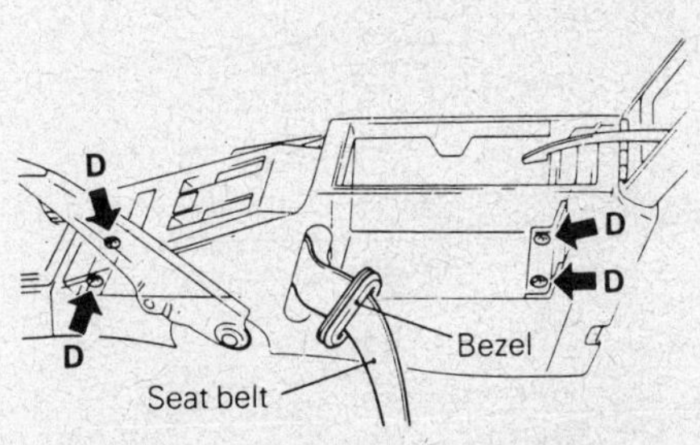


**Fig. 48 Rear console box attaching screws. Conquest**

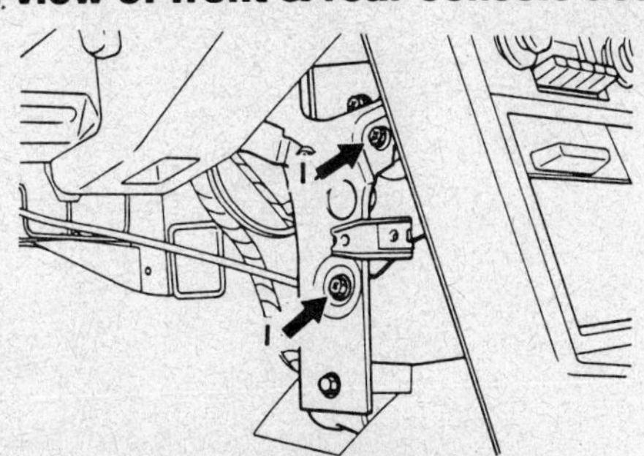


**Fig. 49 Radio mounting screws. Conquest**

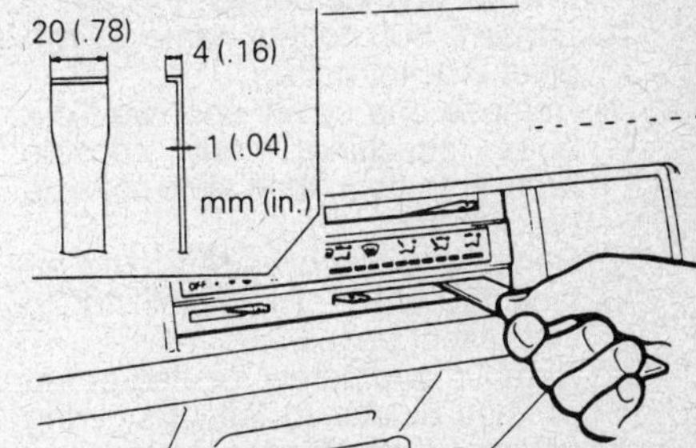


**Fig. 50 Removing heater control panel. Conquest**

tion of " Steering Column" chapter. Remove components in order as they appear in **Fig. 58,** noting the following:

1. Remove lower and upper glove box (1 and 2) as follows:
   a. Remove two lower glove box attaching screws (A) **Fig. 59,** then the lower glove box. Remove two upper glove box attaching screws (B) **Fig. 60,** then the upper glove box.
2. Remove lap heater duct (3) as follows:
   a. Remove two attaching screws (C) **Fig. 61,** then the lap heater duct.
3. Remove meter hood (10) as follows:
   a. Remove meter hood cover (9) using a suitable trim stick.
   b. Remove four meter hood attaching screws (D and E) **Fig. 62,** then pull meter hood slightly forward.
   c. Disconnect all connectors attached to meter hood, then remove meter hood.
4. Remove meter case (12) as follows:
   a. Remove four meter case attaching screws (D) **Fig. 63.**
   b. Disconnect speedometer cable (11) and all electrical connectors from meter case, then remove meter case.
5. Remove trim panels B and A (16 and 17) as follows:
   a. Remove trim panel attaching clips shown in **Fig. 64,** then remove trim panels B and A.
6. Remove instrument panel (19) as follows:
   a. Remove 15 instrument panel attaching fasteners (C, F, G and H) **Fig. 65,** then the instrument panel.
7. Reverse procedure to install.
8. Refer to "Airbag System Disarming" procedure to reactivate airbag.

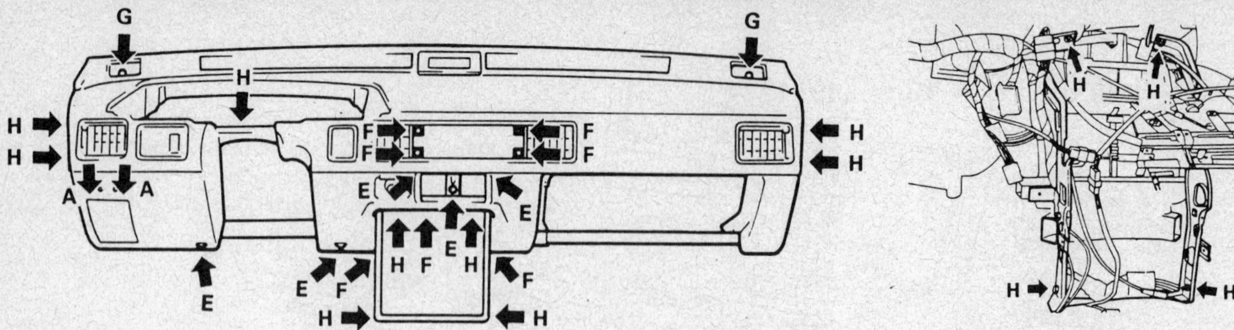


Fig. 51 Instrument panel attaching screws & bolts. Conquest

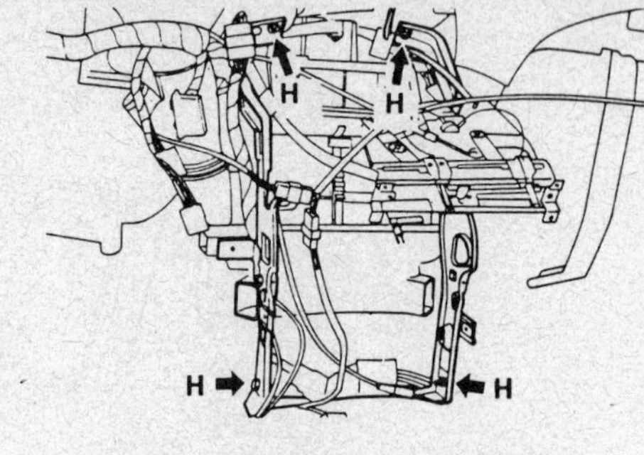


Fig. 52 Center support attaching bolts. Conquest

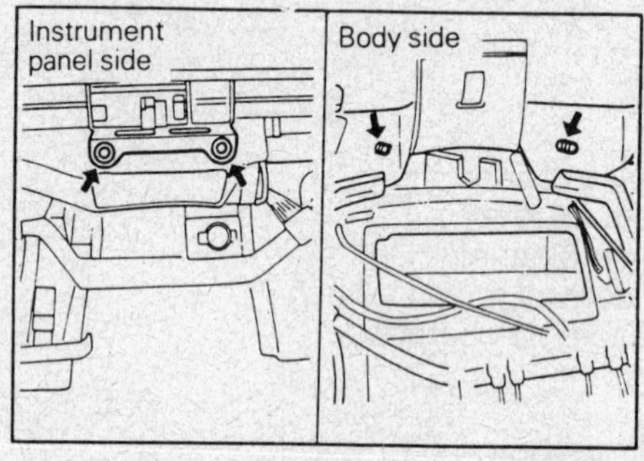


Fig. 53 Aligning instrument panel guide pin. Conquest

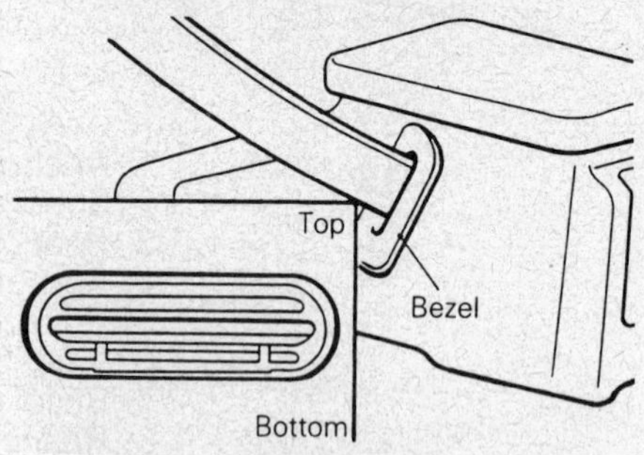


Fig. 54 Installing seat belt bezels. Conquest

## EAGLE PREMIER & DODGE MONACO

1. Refer to "Airbag System Disarming" procedure.
2. **On models equipped with passive restraints,** proceed as follows:
   a. Remove ashtray by pulling up and out of ashtray receiver, **Fig. 66.**
   b. Remove one screw attaching ashtray receiver, disconnect wire from cigar lighter, then remove receiver.
   c. Remove two screws attaching front of console to bracket.
   d. Remove three screws attaching armrest assembly to console, then remove armrest by pulling up and out of console.
   e. Remove two screws attaching rear of console to bracket.
   f. Reach inside console and push out seat belt guides, then remove console.
   g. Remove two bolts attaching pivot bracket to knee bolster, **Fig. 67.**
   h. Loosen, but do not remove, two pivot bracket bolts.
   i. Remove one screw and two Torx bolts attaching front console bracket to floor, then slide console bracket back.
   j. Remove two screws attaching attaching center of knee bolster to instrument panel.
   k. Remove one screw located at top of knee bolster to left of steering column, then remove one screw attaching air duct to knee bolster.
   l. Remove both knee bolster end caps.
   m. Remove one screw attaching bottom of garnish moulding to instrument panel.
   n. Remove four nuts attaching ends of knee bolster to instrument panel.
   o. Move knee bolster rearward far enough to gain access to parking brake release handle screws, remove two parking brake handle attaching screws, then the knee bolster.
3. **On models less passive restraints,** remove three attaching screws, then the instrument panel lower cover, **Fig. 68.**

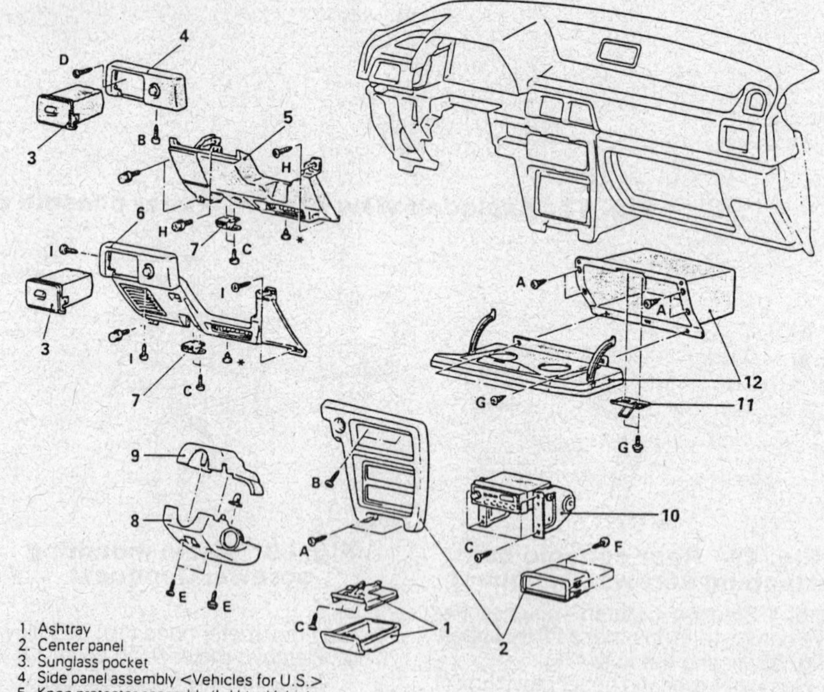


Fig. 55 Exploded view of instrument panel assembly (Part 1 of 2). Colt

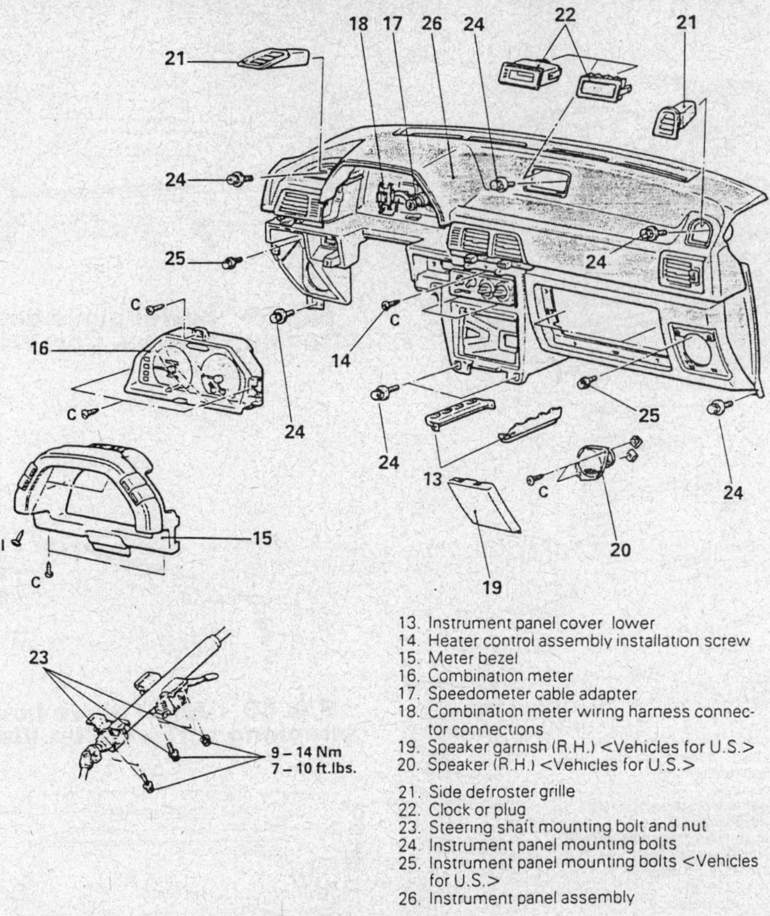


**Fig. 55 Exploded view of instrument panel assembly (Part 2 of 2). Colt**

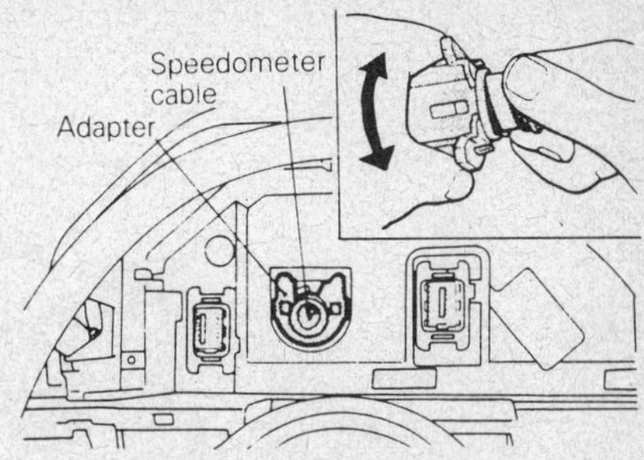


**Fig. 56 Removing speedometer cable adapter. Colt**

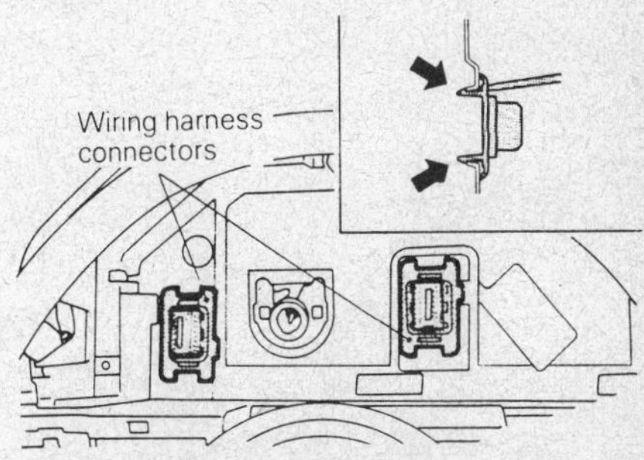


**Fig. 57 Disconnecting combination meter wiring connectors. Colt**

4. **On all models,** remove steering column as outlined under applicable section of "Steering Column" chapter.
5. Remove defroster grille, **Fig. 69,** then the four upper instrument panel attaching bolts, **Fig. 70.**
6. **Loosen, but do not remove,** one nut located near parking brake release handle, **Fig. 71** and one nut located on passenger side kick panel, **Fig. 72.**
7. **On models less passive restraints,** proceed as follows:
   a. Remove two parking brake release handle attaching screws, the lower the parking brake release handle assembly.
   b. Remove ashtray by releasing tab, then ashtray pulling forward and out of instrument panel.
   c. Disconnect cigar lighter connectors, then remove one screw from ashtray cavity, **Fig. 73.**
8. **On all models,** remove one bolt from brake sled, **Fig. 74.**
9. Disconnect all electrical connectors shown in **Fig. 75.**
10. **On models less passive restraints,** remove two bolts attaching instrument panel to center floor bracket, **Fig. 76.**
11. **On all models,** open glove box door, remove six glove box liner attaching screws, then the glove box liner, **Fig. 77.**
12. Reach through glove box opening and remove plastic fastener attaching interior temperature sensor, **Fig. 78.**
13. Disconnect interior temperature sensor by pressing tabs together, **Fig. 79** and pressing pressing air temperature sensor hose rearward.
14. Carefully lift instrument panel up and rearward to disengage, then remove the instrument panel.
15. Reverse procedure to install, noting the following:
   a. When installing instrument panel, position instrument panel ensuring instrument panel mounting brackets engage studs on kick panels.
   b. Ensure wire harness is routed behind center mounting bracket.
   c. Connect all electrical connections and interior temperature sensor.
   d. **Torque** nuts and bolts attaching steering column to instrument panel to 35 ft. lbs.
   e. Refer to "Airbag System Disarming" procedure to reactivate airbag.

## EAGLE MEDALLION

1. Refer to "Airbag System Disarming" procedure.
2. Remove both side rocker trim panels.
3. Disconnect instrument panel wiring from both side A-pillars.
4. Disconnect ground cables from both side rocker sills.
5. Disconnect fuse panel and door buzzer.
6. Remove seven lower instrument panel cover attaching screws, **Fig. 80,** then the cover.
7. Disconnect speedometer cable from speedometer.
8. Remove six console retaining screws (A) **Fig. 81.**
9. Open glove box door, then pull edge of console out to free it from instrument panel.
10. **On models equipped with manual transaxle,** pry off shift boot cover using a screwdriver.
11. **On models equipped with automatic transaxle,** proceed as follows:
   a. Loosen shift indicator plate by prying up at edge using a screwdriver.
   b. Remove shift lever knob by pulling straight off.
   c. Remove shift indicator plate.
12. **On all models,** remove two screws (C) attaching console to support, **Fig. 82.**
13. Pull lower section of console straight back and lift up to remove.
14. Pull upper section of console down and out of instrument panel.
15. Remove four radio bezel attaching screws (A) **Fig. 83.**
16. Drill out six radio retaining rivets (B), then remove radio bracket (D) **Fig. 84.**
17. Remove retaining screw (E) from heater control, **Fig. 85.**
18. Remove heater control knobs, then lower heater control panel and disconnect two control cables and all electrical connections, **Fig. 86.**

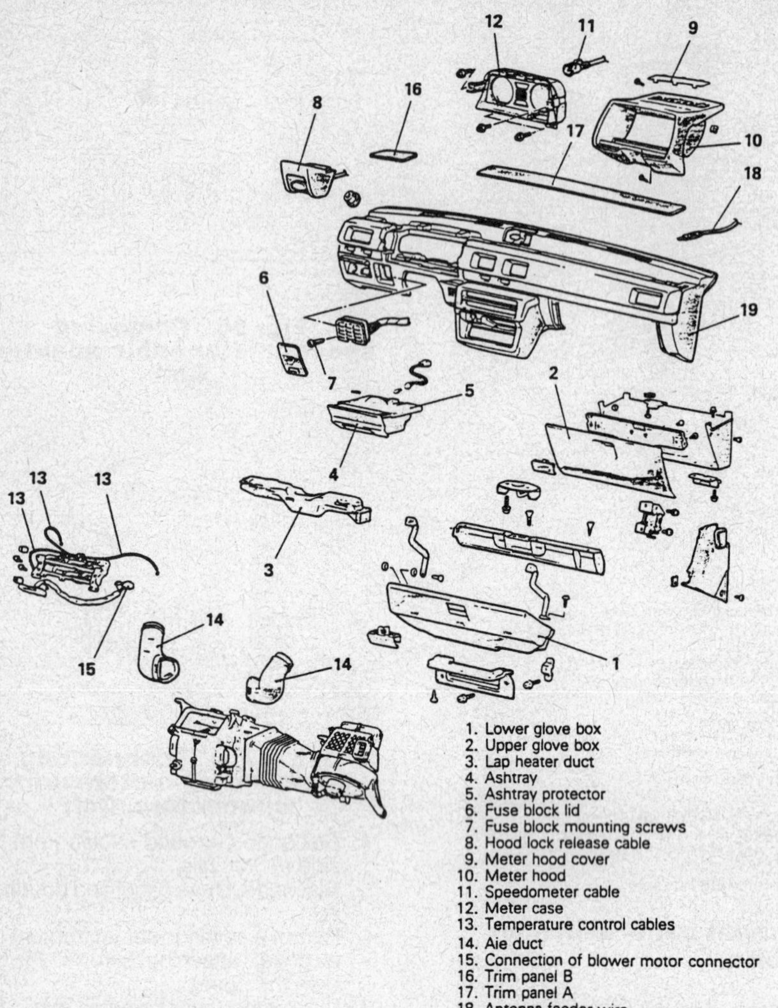


**Fig. 58 Exploded view of instrument panel assembly. Colt Vista**

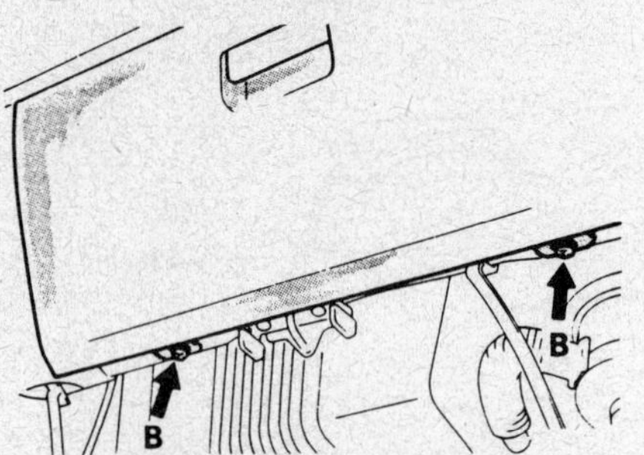


**Fig. 59 Lower glove box attaching screws. Colt Vista**

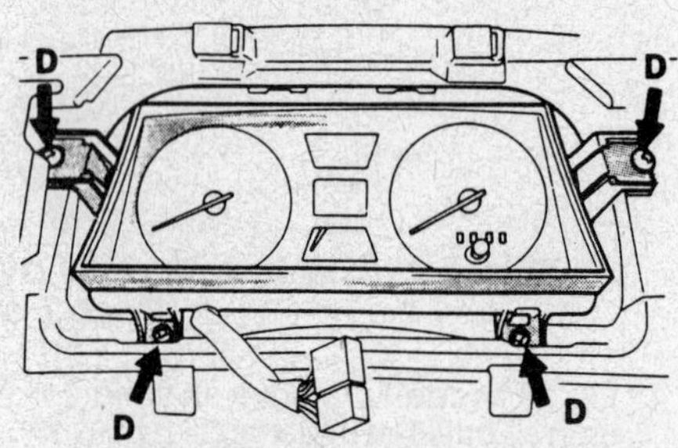


**Fig. 60 Upper glove box attaching screws. Colt Vista**

**Fig. 63 Meter case attaching screws. Colt Vista**

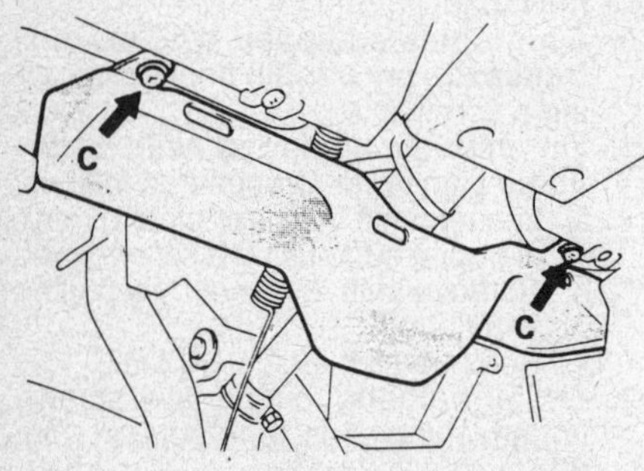


**Fig. 61 Lap heater duct attaching screws. Colt Vista**

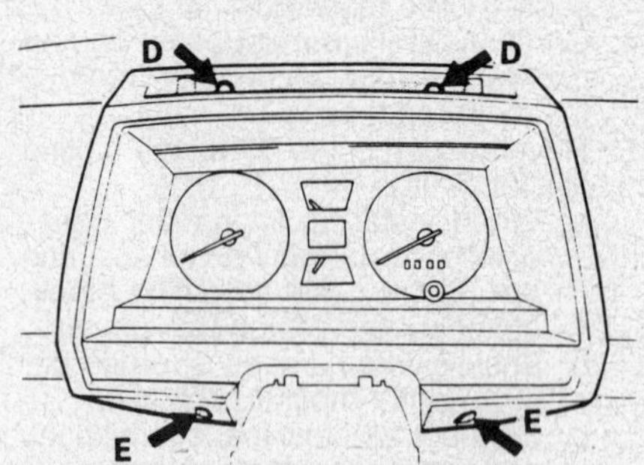


**Fig. 62 Meter hood attaching screws. Colt Vista**

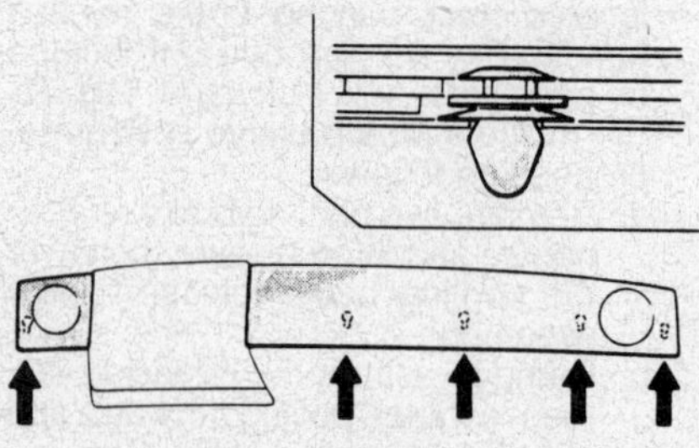

**Fig. 64 Trim panel attaching clips. Colt Vista**

19. Remove steering column as outlined under applicable section of "Steering Column" chapter.
20. Remove speaker covers (A) from upper corners of dash, **Fig. 87.**
21. Remove attaching bolts (B) from each corner of dash, **Fig. 87.**
22. Disconnect all electrical connections, then remove instrument panel.
23. Reverse procedure to install, noting the following:
    a. Position instrument panel on centering device (A) **Fig. 88.**
    b. Connect ground cables to both side rocker sills as shown, **Fig. 89.**
    c. Refer to "Airbag System Disarming" procedure to reactivate airbag.

## EAGLE TALON & PLYMOUTH LASER

Disarm airbag as described under "Airbag System Disarming." Remove components in order they appear in **Fig. 90,** noting the following:

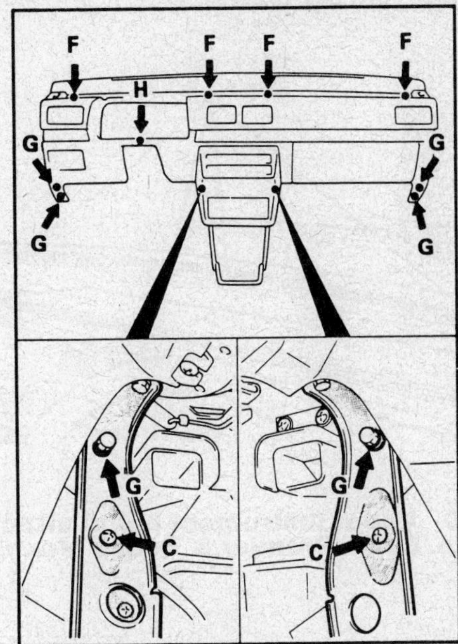


Fig. 65 Instrument panel attaching fasteners. Colt Vista

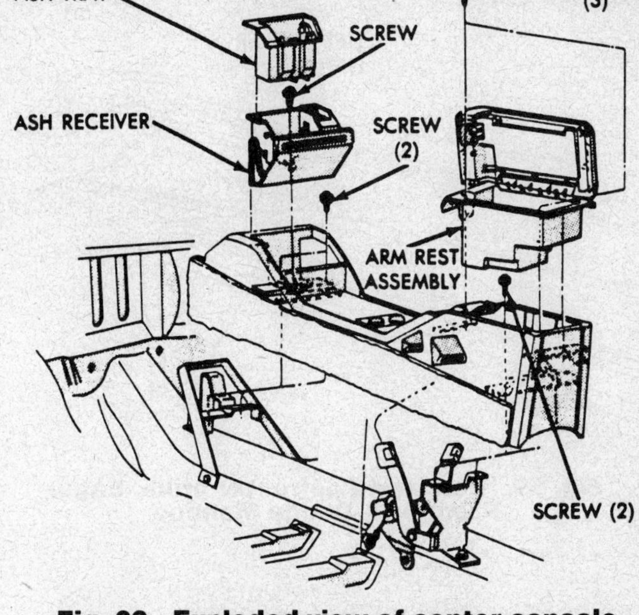


Fig. 66 Exploded view of center console assembly. Eagle Premier & Dodge Monaco w/passive restraints

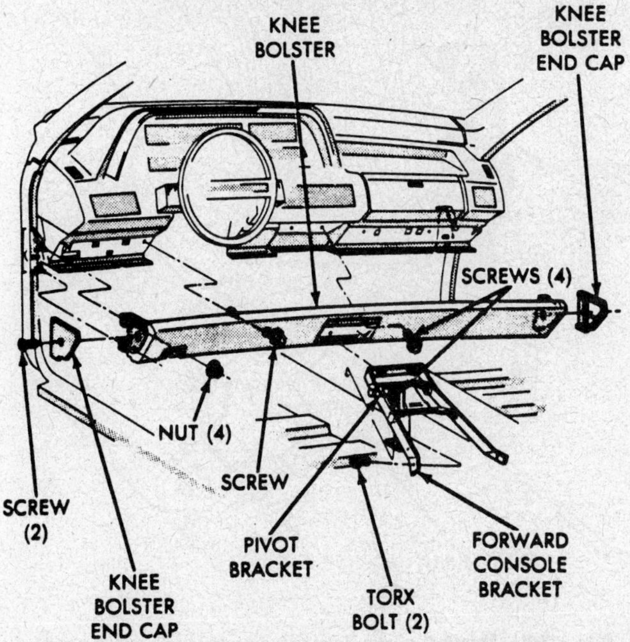


Fig. 67 Knee bolster. Eagle Premier & Dodge Monaco w/passive restraints

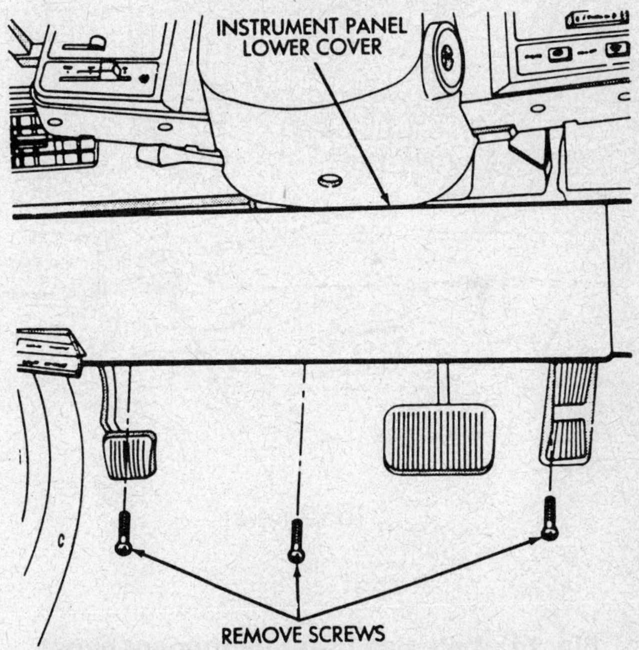


Fig. 68 Lower instrument panel. Eagle Premier & Dodge Monaco less passive restraints

1. Remove floor console & components in order they appear in **Fig. 91.**
2. Use a suitable plastic trim tool when removing dash plug and radio panel No. 1 and No. 8 in **Fig. 90,** so as not to damage instrument panel.
3. Use a suitable screwdriver to pry back retaining pawls of center air outlet assembly, **Fig. 92,** then remove using a plastic trim tool.
4. When removing speedometer cable adapter, disconnect cable from the transaxle and pull the cable slightly toward the vehicle interior. Release the lock by turning the adapter to the left or right, then remove adapter, **Fig. 93.**
5. Remove bolts, then lower steering column to allow clearance for removal of instrument panel.
6. Remove cluster panels, knee protector, glove box and instrument panel in order they appear in **Fig. 94.**
7. Remove instrument panel and related parts in order as they appear in **Fig. 95.**
8. Using a suitable screwdriver, open tabs on the connectors of the combination meter wiring harness, then disconnect connectors, **Fig. 96.**
9. Reverse procedure to install, ensuring all connectors are securely connected and wiring harnesses are not pinched.
10. Refer to "Airbag System Disarming" procedure to reactivate airbag.

## EAGLE SUMMIT

Refer to procedure outlined under "Colt."

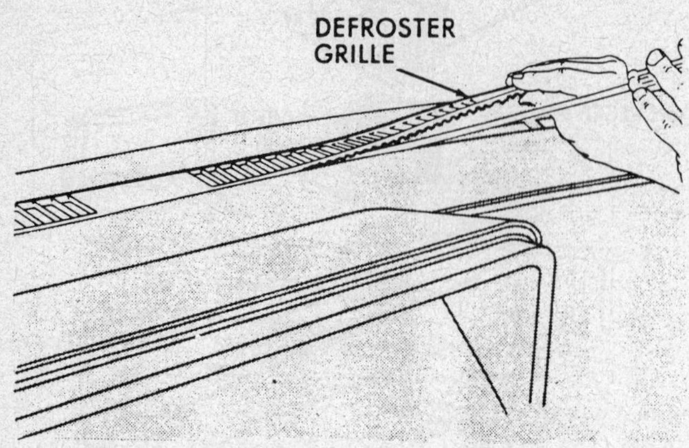


**Fig. 69 Removing defroster grille. Eagle Premier & Dodge Monaco**

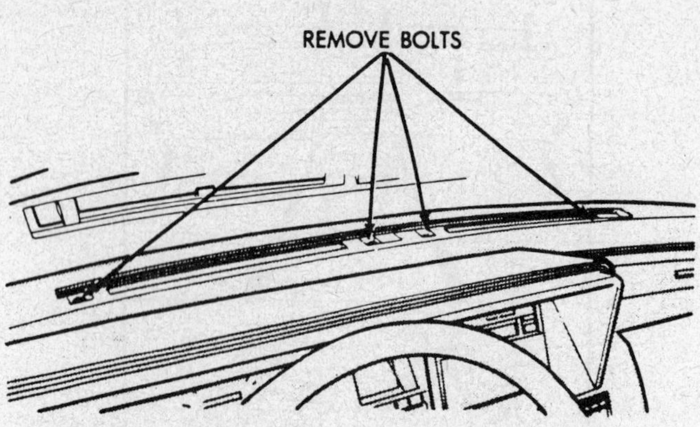


**Fig. 70 Upper instrument panel attaching bolts. Eagle Premier & Dodge Monaco**

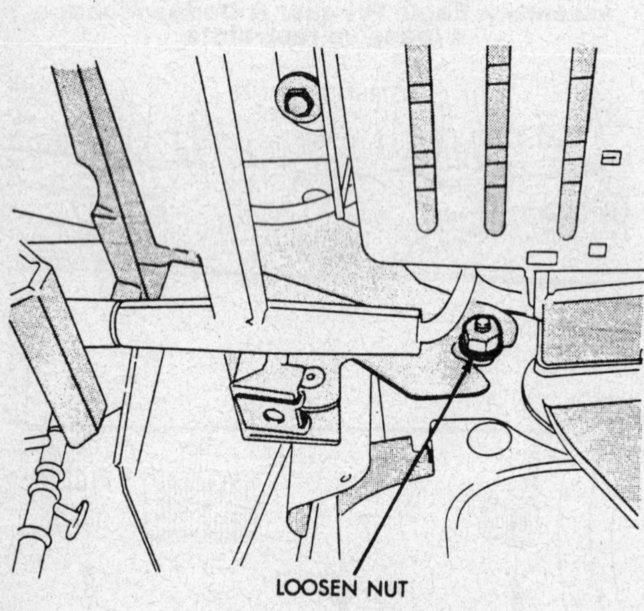


**Fig. 71 Left side lower instrument panel bracket nut. Eagle Premier & Dodge Monaco**

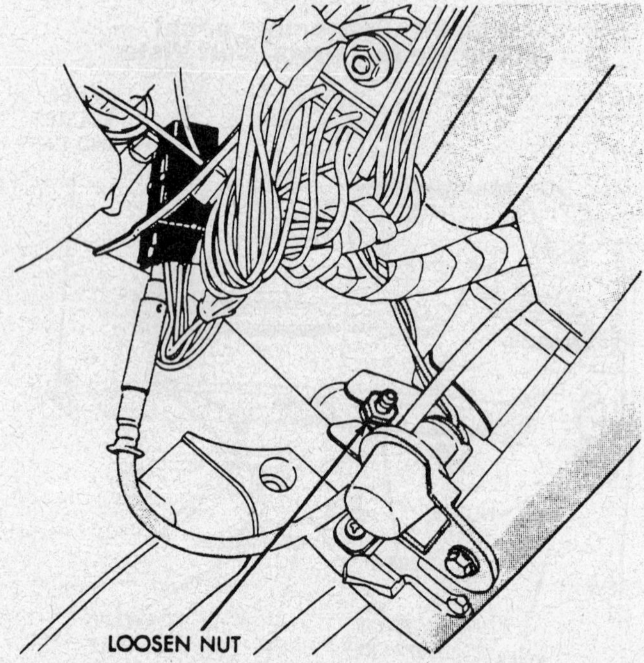


**Fig. 72 Right side lower instrument panel bracket nut. Eagle Premier & Dodge Monaco**

# STEALTH

1. Refer to "Airbag System Disarming" procedure.
2. Remove console assembly as follows:
   a. Remove cup holder and console plug, **Fig. 97.**
   b. Remove rear console assembly.
   c. Remove radio panel and radio.
   d. Remove switch trim panel C and console side cover.
   e. Remove front console trim panel.
   f. **On models with manual transaxle,** remove shift lever knob.
   g. **On all models,** remove front console assembly.
3. Remove hood release handle and rheostat, **Fig. 98.**
4. Remove switch trim panel B and knee protector assembly.
5. Remove steering column cover.
6. Remove glove box striker, glove box and cross pipe cover.
7. Using a flat tip screwdriver, remove center air outlet assembly.
8. Remove heater control assembly retaining screws.
9. Remove meter bezel.
10. Remove combination meter.
11. **On all models w/mechanical speedometer,** disconnect speedometer at transaxle, then remove adapter locks from instrument panel.
12. Pull lightly on speedometer cable toward passenger compartment and remove adapter.
13. **On all models,** remove speaker or instrument panel top covers.
14. Remove steering column retaining bolts.
15. Remove instrument panel assembly.
16. Reverse procedure to install.
17. Refer to "Airbag System Disarming" procedure to reactivate airbag.

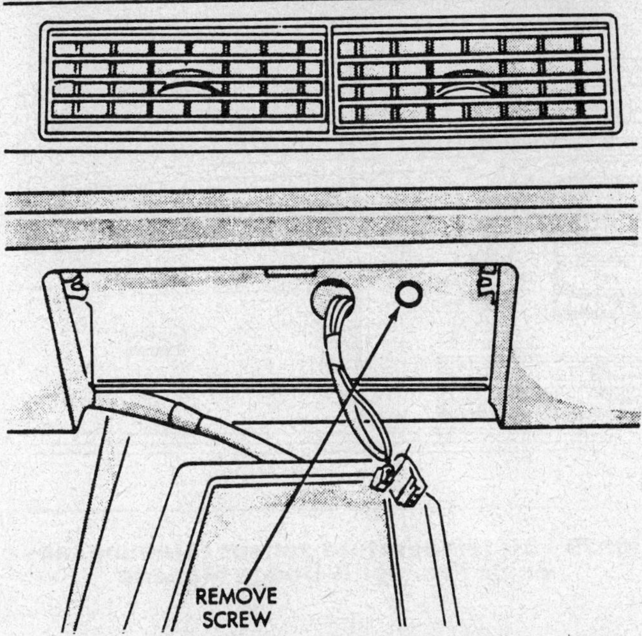


**Fig. 73 Instrument panel attaching screw. Eagle Premier & Dodge Monaco**

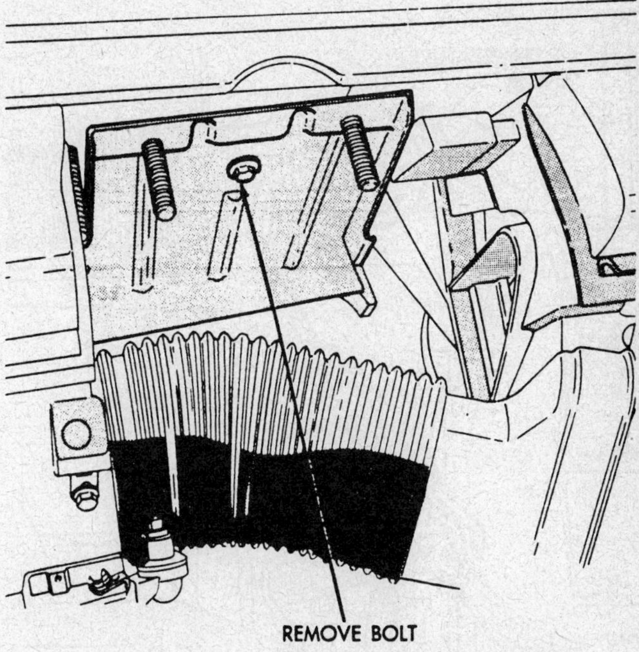


**Fig. 74 Brake sled bolt. Eagle Premier & Dodge Monaco**

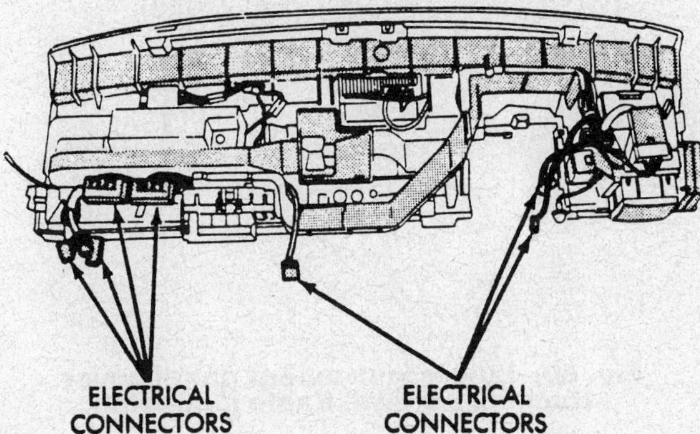


**Fig. 75 Instrument panel electrical connectors. Eagle Premier & Dodge Monaco**

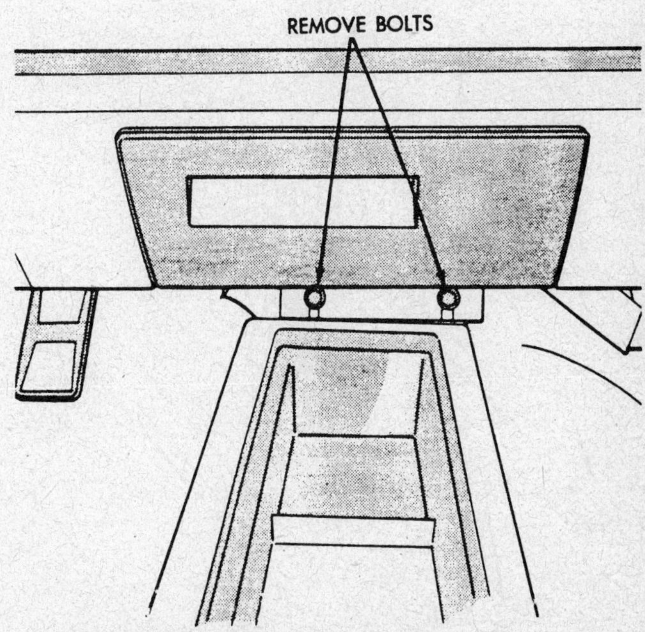


**Fig. 76 Instrument panel to center floor bracket attaching bolts. Eagle Premier & Dodge Monaco less passive restraints**

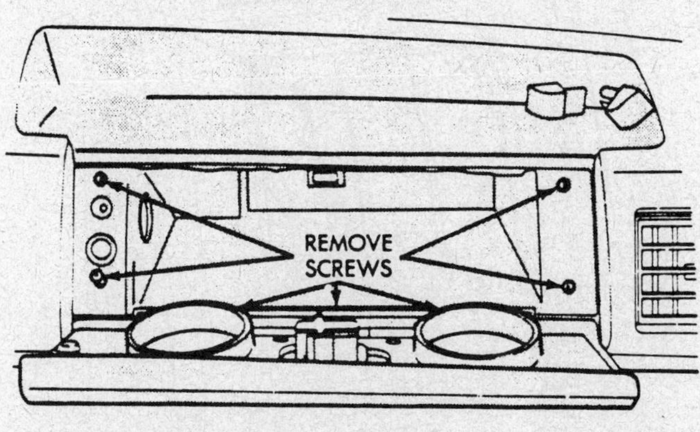


**Fig. 77 Glove box liner attaching screws. Eagle Premier & Dodge Monaco**

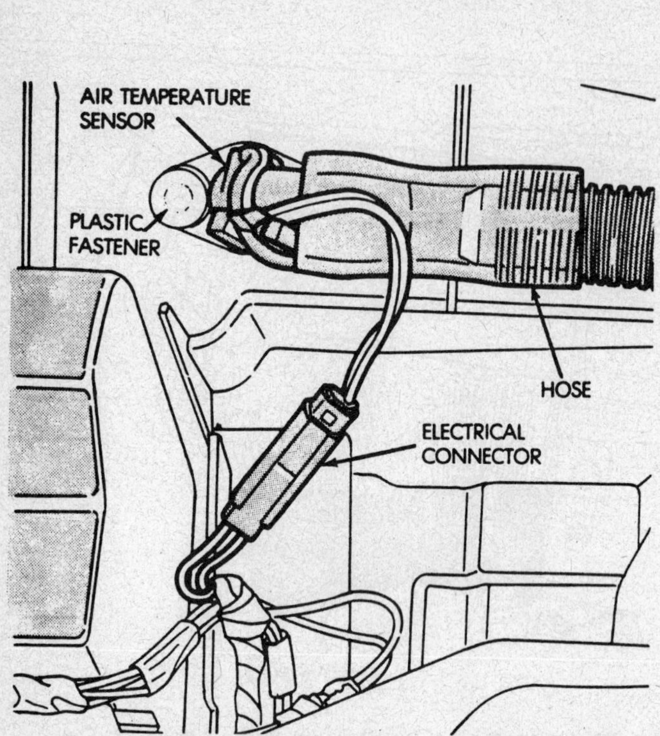


**Fig. 78 Air temperature sensor fastener. Eagle Premier & Dodge Monaco**

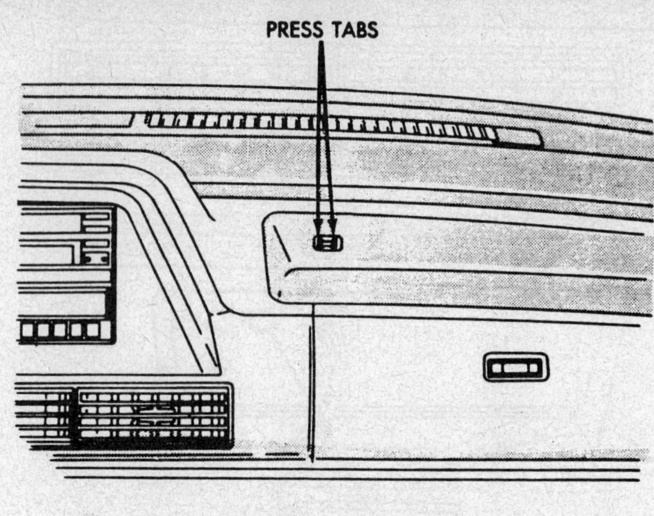


**Fig. 79 Air temperature sensor retaining tabs. Eagle Premier & Dodge Monaco**

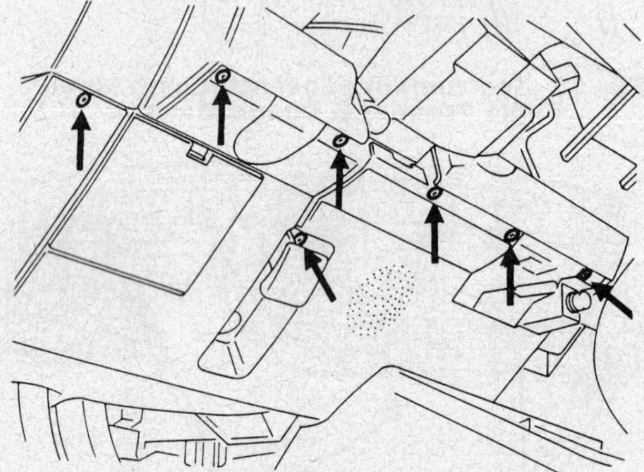

**Fig. 80 Lower instrument panel cover attaching screws. Eagle Medallion**

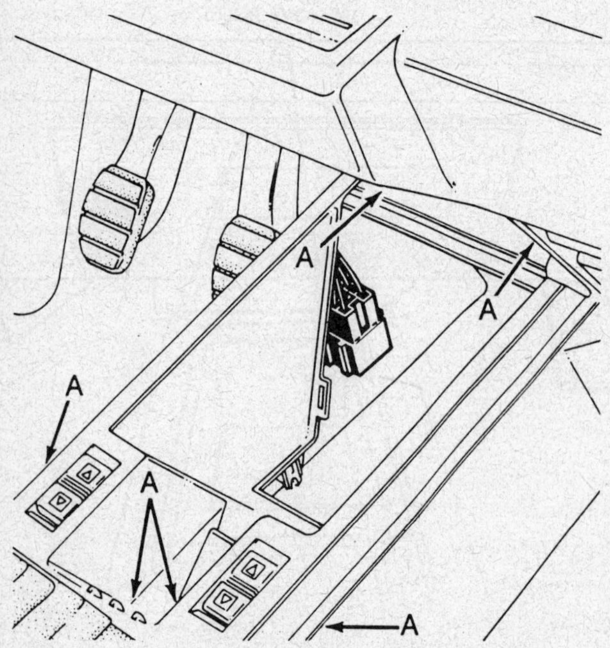


**Fig. 81 Console retaining screws. Eagle Medallion**

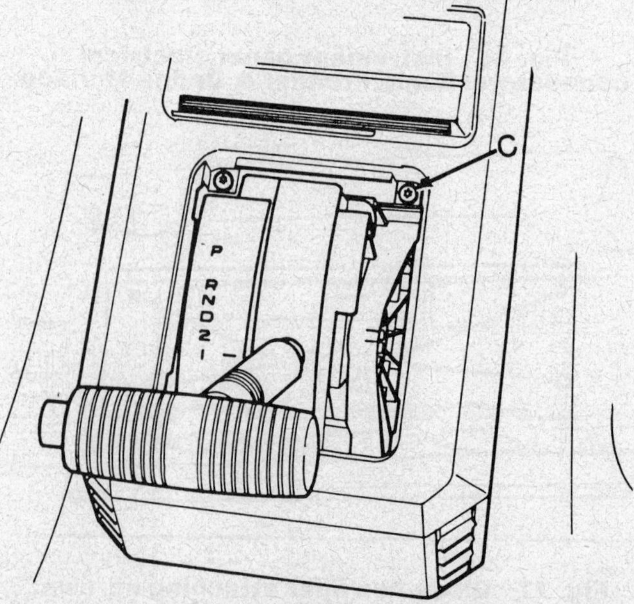


**Fig. 82 Console to support attaching screws. Eagle Medallion**

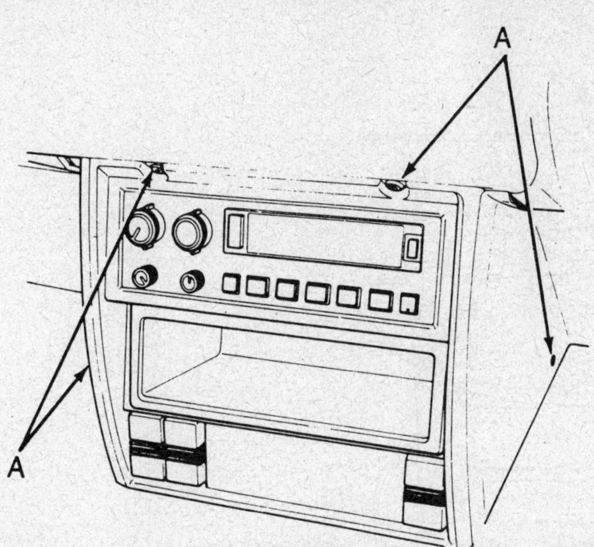


**Fig. 83 Radio bezel attaching screws. Eagle Medallion**

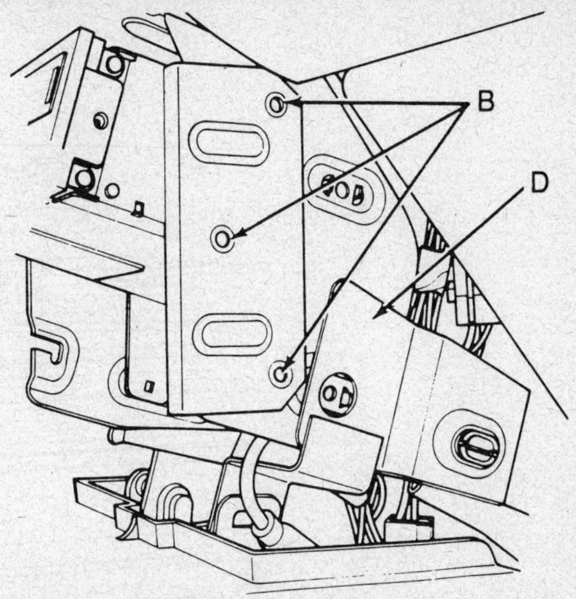


**Fig. 84 Radio retaining rivets & bracket. Eagle Medallion**

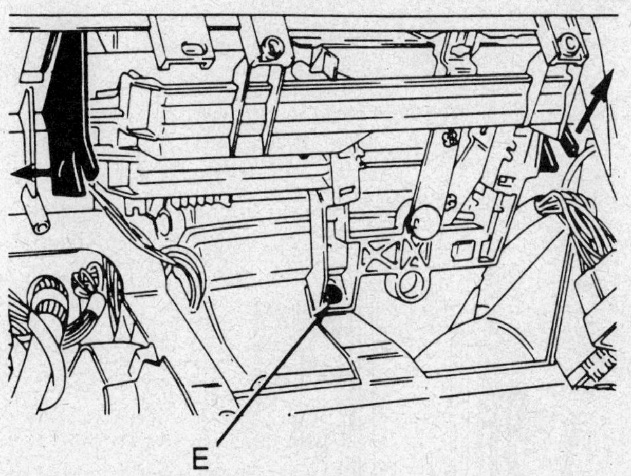


**Fig. 85 Heater control retaining screw. Eagle Medallion**

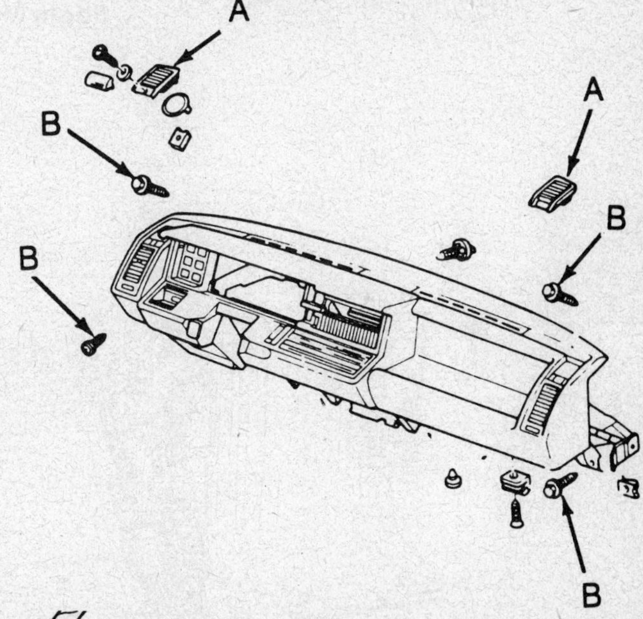


**Fig. 87 Instrument panel. Eagle Medallion**

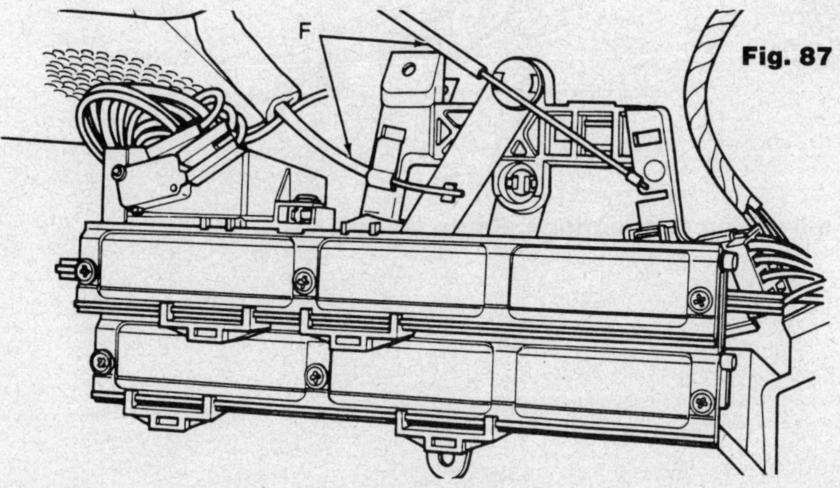


**Fig. 86 Heater control cables & electrical connections. Eagle Medallion**

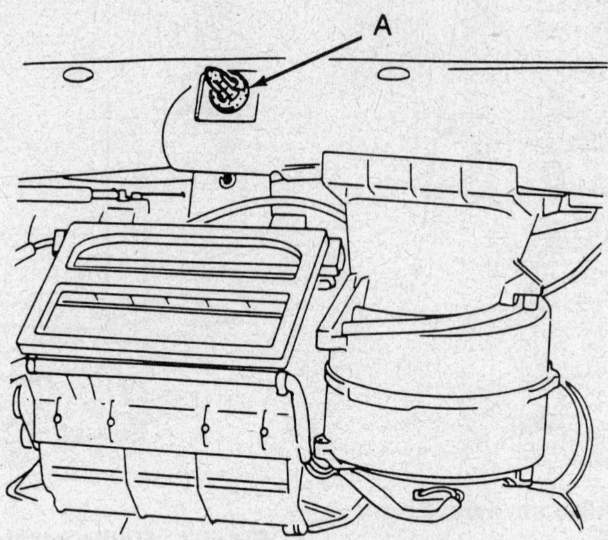


**Fig. 88 Instrument panel centering device. Eagle Medallion**

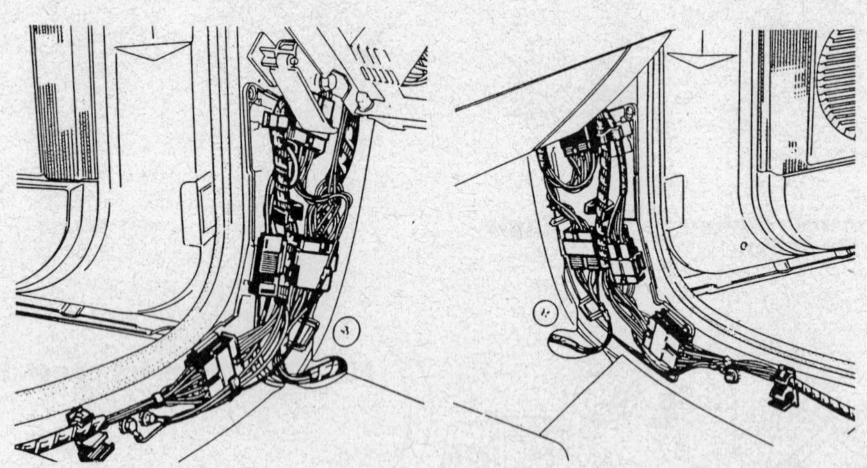

**Fig. 89 Rocker sill wiring connections. Eagle Medallion**

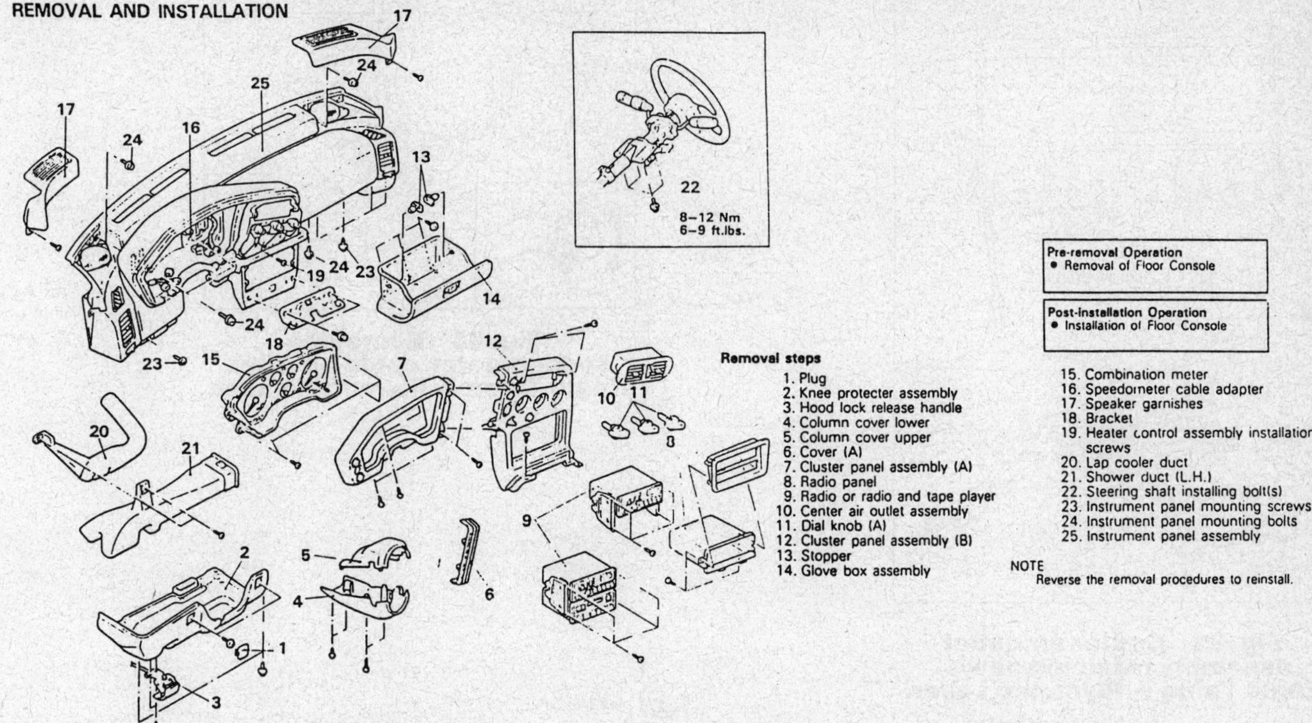


**Fig. 90 Exploded view of instrument panel. Eagle Talon & Plymouth Laser**

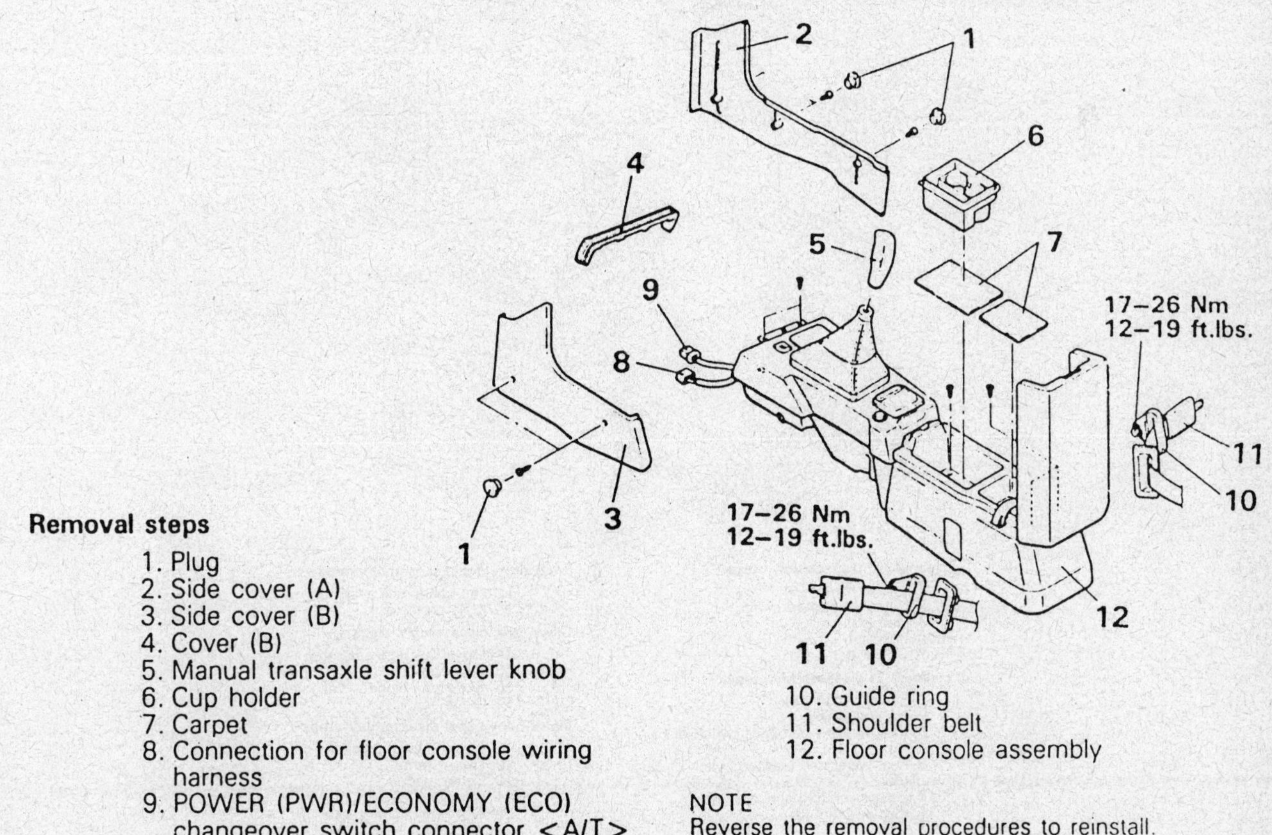


**Fig. 91 Exploded view of floor console. Eagle Talon & Plymouth Laser**

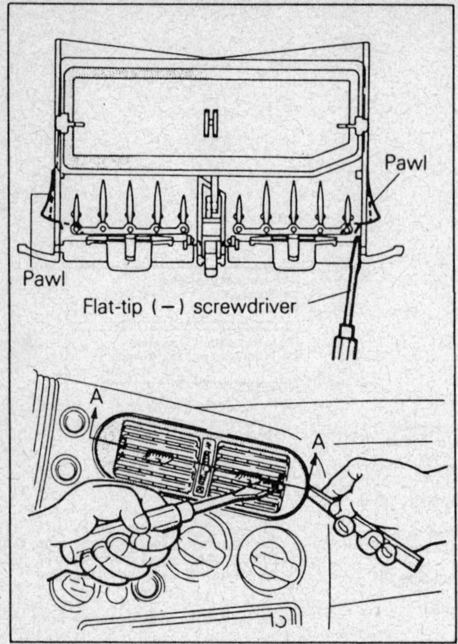


**Fig. 92 Center air outlet assembly retaining pawls. Eagle Talon & Plymouth Laser.**

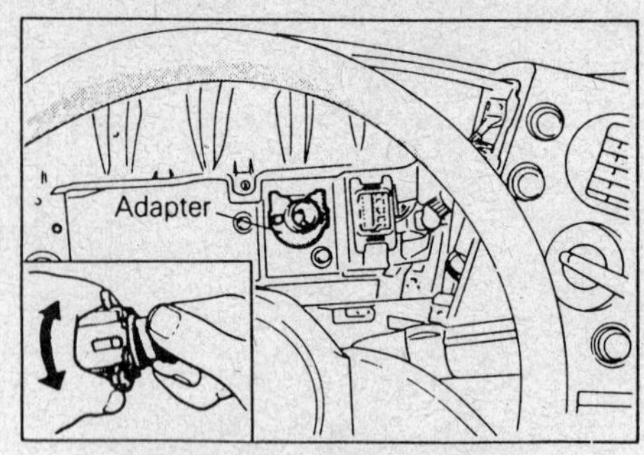


**Fig. 93 Removing speedometer cable adapter. Eagle Talon & Plymouth Laser.**

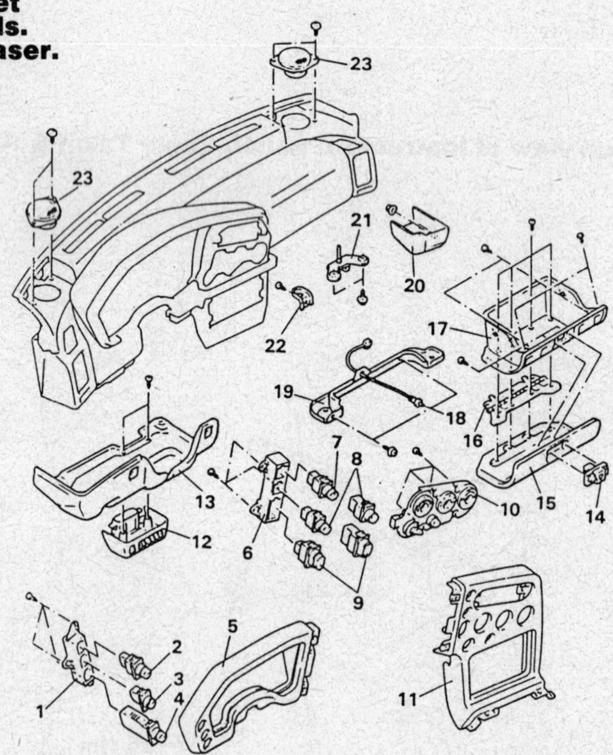

**panel (A) disassembly steps**

1. Switch holder (A)
2. Headlight pop-up switch
3. Plug (A)
4. Rheostat
5. Cluster panel (A)

**panel (B) disassembly steps**

6. Switch holder (B)
7. Hazard switch
8. Rear window defogger switch or plug (A)
9. Rear wiper and washer switch or plug (B)
10. Heater control panel assembly
11. Cluster panel (B)

**Knee protector disassembly steps**

12. Lap cooler grill assembly
13. Knee protector

**Glove box disassembly steps**

14. Glove box lock assembly
15. Glove box pad
16. Glove box hinge
17. Glove box

**Instrument panel disassembly steps**

18. Glove box light switch
19. Lower frame
20. Corner pad
21. Glove box striker
22. Glove box light bracket
23. Speakers

**Fig. 94 Exploded view of instrument panel. Eagle Talon & Plymouth Laser.**

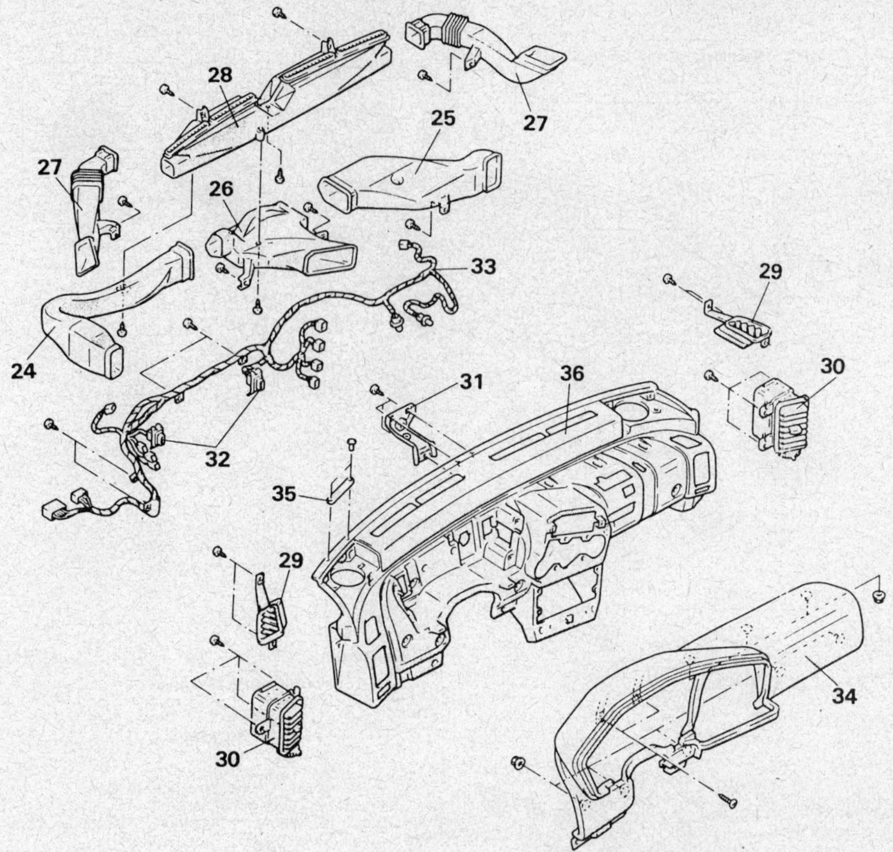


24. Air duct (A)
25. Air duct (B)
26. Distribution duct
27. Side defroster hoses
28. Defroster nozzle assembly
29. Side defroster grilles
30. Side air outlet assembly
31. Bracket
32. Combination meter wiring harness connector connections
33. Instrument panel wiring harness
34. Instrument panel pad
35. Vin plate
36. Instrument panel

NOTE
(1) Reverse the disassembly procedures to reassemble.

**Fig. 95 Exploded view of instrument panel. Eagle Talon & Plymouth Laser.**

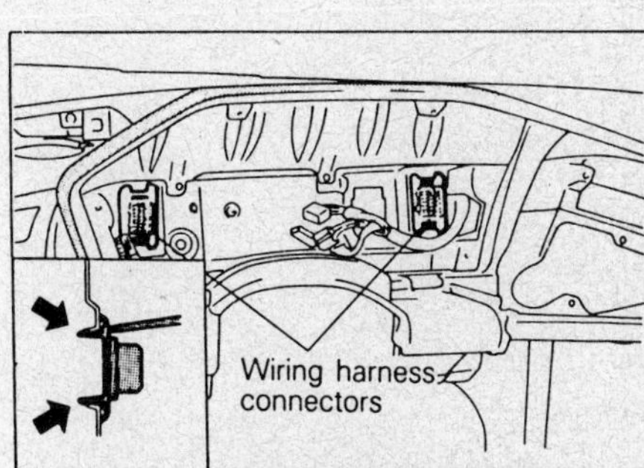


**Fig. 96 Disconnecting combination meter wiring connectors. Eagle Talon & Plymouth Laser.**

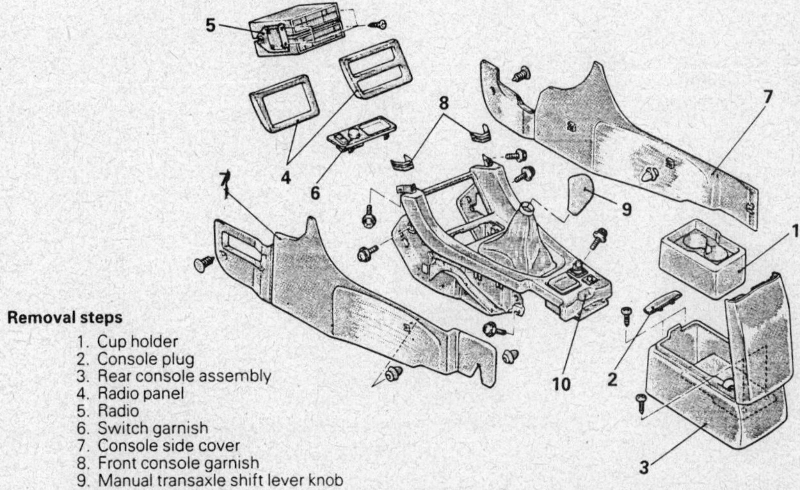


**Removal steps**

1. Cup holder
2. Console plug
3. Rear console assembly
4. Radio panel
5. Radio
6. Switch garnish
7. Console side cover
8. Front console garnish
9. Manual transaxle shift lever knob
10. Front console assembly

**Fig. 97 Console assembly. Stealth**

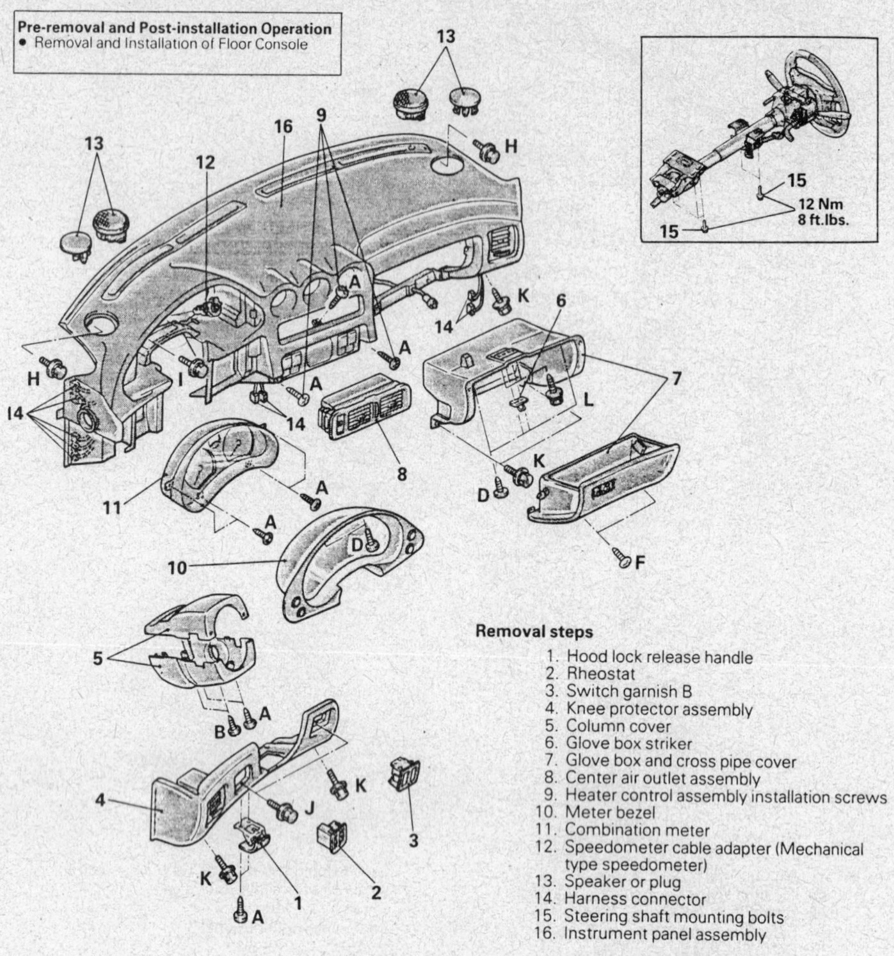
Pre-removal and Post-installation Operation
• Removal and Installation of Floor Console
12 Nm
8 ft.lbs.
Removal steps
1. Hood lock release handle
2. Rheostat
3. Switch garnish B
4. Knee protector assembly
5. Column cover
6. Glove box striker
7. Glove box and cross pipe cover
8. Center air outlet assembly
9. Heater control assembly installation screws
10. Meter bezel
11. Combination meter
12. Speedometer cable adapter (Mechanical type speedometer)
13. Speaker or plug
14. Harness connector
15. Steering shaft mounting bolts
16. Instrument panel assembly

**Fig. 98 Dash panel assembly. Stealth**

# STEERING COLUMNS

## INDEX



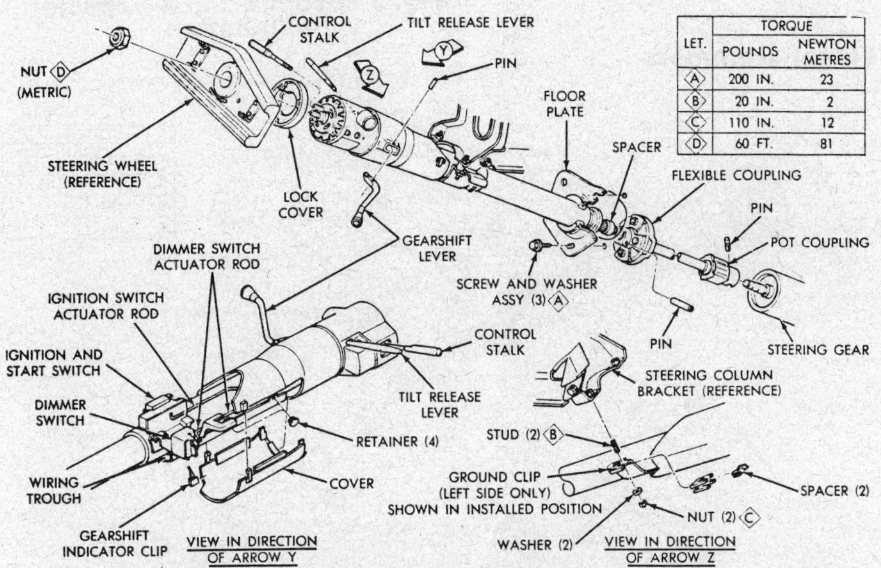


**Fig. 1 Steering column installation. Chrysler RWD models except imports**

## AIRBAG SYSTEM DISARMING

1. Place ignition switch in lock position.
2. Disconnect and tape battery ground cable connector.
3. **Wait at least 1 minute after disconnecting battery ground cable before doing any further work on vehicle. The SRS system is designed to retain enough voltage to deploy airbag for a short time even after battery has been disconnected.**
4. After repairs are complete, reconnect battery ground cable.
5. From passenger side of vehicle, turn ignition switch to On position.
6. SRS warning light should illuminate for 6 to 8 seconds, then remain off for at least 45 seconds to indicate if SRS system is functioning correctly.
7. If SRS indicator does not perform as described refer to the "Passive Restraint Systems" section.

## SERVICE PRECAUTIONS

**Whenever service procedures are required on or near the steering wheel and/or instrument panel, disabling of the airbag system is required to prevent accidental deployment.**

When servicing collapsible steering columns, care should be exercised since they are extremely susceptible to damage. Dropping of or leaning on column or striking sharp blows on end of steering shaft or shift levers could loosen or shear plastic fasteners which maintain column rigidity.

It is important that only the specified screws, bolts and nuts be used during the mandatory reassembly sequence and torque to specifications to insure proper breakaway action of column under impact. Avoid using excessively long bolts, as they may prevent a portion of the steering column from collapsing under impact.

When removing or installing steering wheel, ignition switch or lock, turn signal switch, adjusting transmission linkage, or installing and adjusting neutral-start or back-up light switch, refer to appropriate car chapter.

If a shift tube shows a sheared plastic injection, a new shift tube must be installed. **On Chrysler vehicles,** if a steering shaft shows a sheared plastic, but it is not bent, it can be repaired by using a Service Steering Shaft Repair Kit part number 3514996.The kit contains instructions and dimensions for all steering columns. **On some models,** the attaching brackets will shear under impact and must also be replaced.

## STEERING COLUMN REPLACE

**On Chrysler models equipped with the Driver Airbag Restraint System, it is necessary to follow special procedures when servicing steering column components. These procedures are necessary to avoid accidental deployment of airbag which may cause damage or personal injury.**

### CHRYSLER EXCEPT COLT, COLT VISTA, CONQUEST, LASER, MONACO & STEALTH

#### RWD MODELS

##### Removal

1. Disconnect battery ground cable.
2. **On column shift vehicles,** disconnect link rod(s) by prying out of grommet in shift lever(s).
3. **On all models,** remove steering shaft lower coupling to wormshaft roll pin, **Fig. 1.**
4. Disconnect wiring connectors at steering column jacket.
5. Remove steering wheel center pad assembly.
6. Disconnect horn wires and remove horn switch.
7. Remove steering wheel and turn signal lever.
8. Remove floor plate to floor pan retaining screws, then expose steering column bracket by removing the cluster bezel and panel lower reinforcement, or the panel lower skirt.
9. Disconnect shift indicator pointer from shift housing.
10. Remove nuts retaining steering column bracket to instrument panel support.
11. Carefully remove lower coupling from steering gear wormshaft, then remove column assembly out through passenger compartment using care to avoid damaging the paint or trim.
12. Cut plastic grommet(s) from shift lever(s) and install new grommet(s) from rod side of lever(s) using pliers and a back-up washer to snap

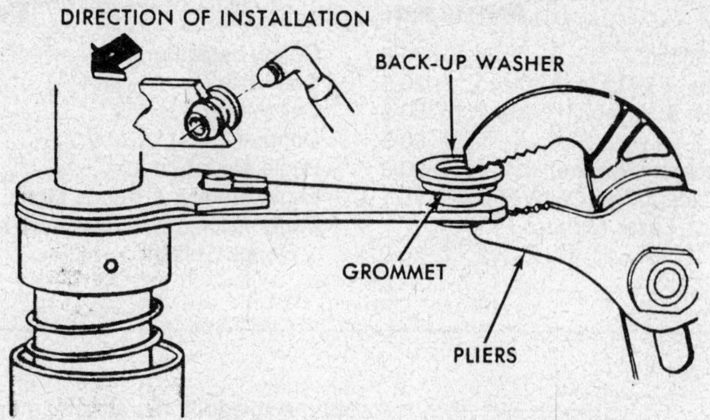


**Fig. 2 Installing shift lever grommets**

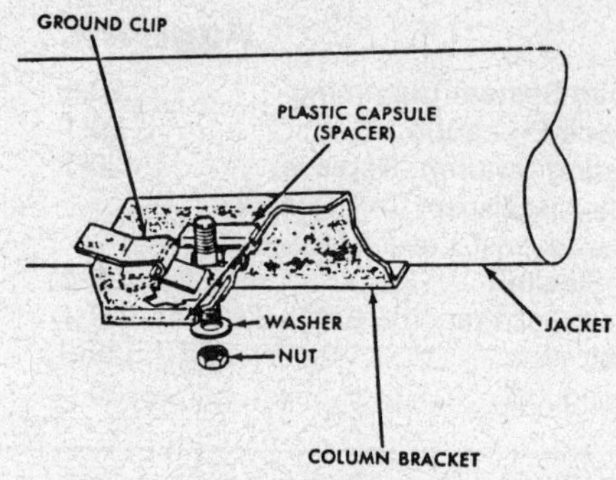


**Fig. 3 Ground clip & capsule installation**

grommet(s) into place, **Fig. 2.** Use grease to aid installation of grommet(s). **New grommet(s) must be installed whenever rod is disconnected from lever(s).**

## Installation

1. With plastic capsules pre-assembled in bracket slots, install ground clip on left capsule slot, **Fig. 3.** Install column through floor pan opening using care to avoid damaging paint or trim.
2. With front wheels in a straight ahead position and master splines on wormshaft and coupling aligned, engage coupling with wormshaft and install roll pin. **Do not apply end loads to steering shaft.**
3. While holding column assembly with bracket slots on mounting studs, install but do not tighten the two upper bracket washers and nuts.
4. Making sure that both capsules are fully seated in their slots in the column support bracket, and that the washer makes contact with the ground clip in the left capsule slot, torque upper bracket retaining nuts to specifications, **Fig. 1.**
5. Place floor plate over floor pan opening, then center it around the column and install the retaining bolts.
6. Connect wiring connectors to steering column jacket, then connect battery ground cable and check operation of lights and horn.
7. Connect link rods to shift levers by snapping rod into grommet with pliers. Use grease to ease installation. Readjust linkage. **Grommet must be installed into lever before rod is inserted into grommet.**
8. Connect gearshift indicator pointer in approximate original location, then slowly move gearshift lever from 1 (L) to P position while pausing briefly at each selector position. The indicator pointer must align with each selector position. If not, loosen the Allen head screw and readjust to align pointer correctly.
9. Reinstall panel lower reinforcement and cluster bezel or panel lower skirt.

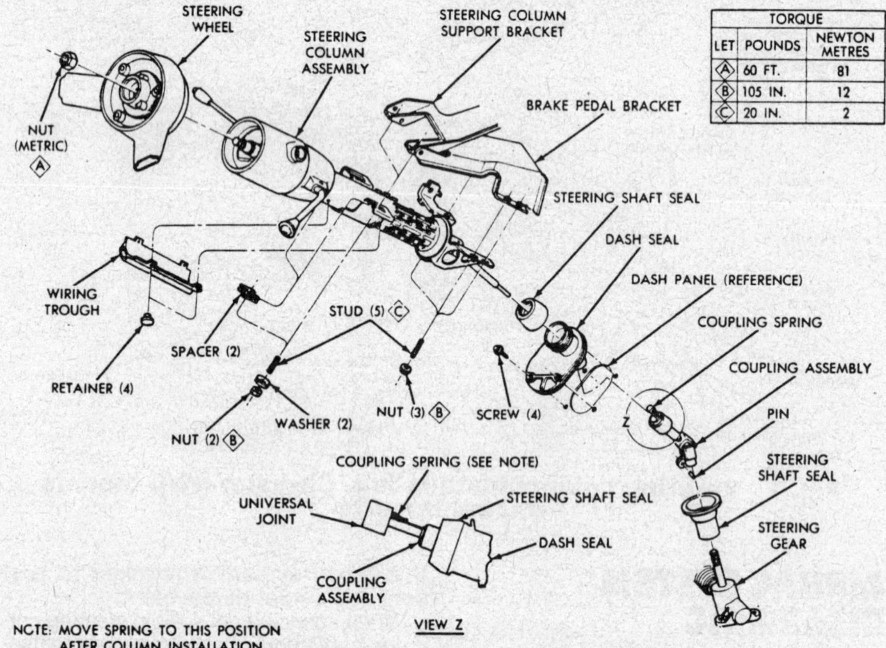


| TORQUE | | |
|---|---|---|
| LET | POUNDS | NEWTON METRES |
| A | 60 FT. | 81 |
| B | 105 IN. | 12 |
| C | 20 IN. | 2 |

**Fig. 4 Steering column installation. 1989–90 FWD w/standard column except Horizon & Omni**

## 1989–90 FWD MODELS W/STANDARD STEERING COLUMN EXCEPT HORIZON & OMNI

### Removal

1. Disable airbag system as outlined under "Airbag System Disarming." **This is extremely important when servicing a vehicle that is equipped with an airbag restraint system.**
2. **On column shift vehicles,** disconnect cable rod by prying rod out of grommet in shift lever.
3. **On all models,** disconnect all wiring connectors at steering column jacket and remove steering wheel center pad, **Fig. 4.**
4. **On vehicles equipped with airbag restraint system,** proceed as follows:
   a. Use special socket tool No. 6239 or equivalent to remove tamper proof hold-down nuts.
   b. Lift module a few inches and remove clockspring connecting wire, then remove airbag module.
   c. Remove clockspring setscrew ,**Fig. 5,** and place it in the clockspring to ensure clockspring positioning. Do not remove plastic tether.
5. **On all models,** disconnect horn wires and horn switch.
6. Remove steering wheel.
7. Expose steering column bracket, remove instrument panel steering column cover and lower reinforcement. Remove bezel.
8. Remove indicator setscrew and shaft indicator pointer from shift housing.
9. Remove nuts attaching steering column bracket to instrument panel support, then lower the bracket support to the floor. **Do not remove roll pin to remove steering column assembly.**
10. Pull steering column rearward, and disconnect lower shaft from coupling.

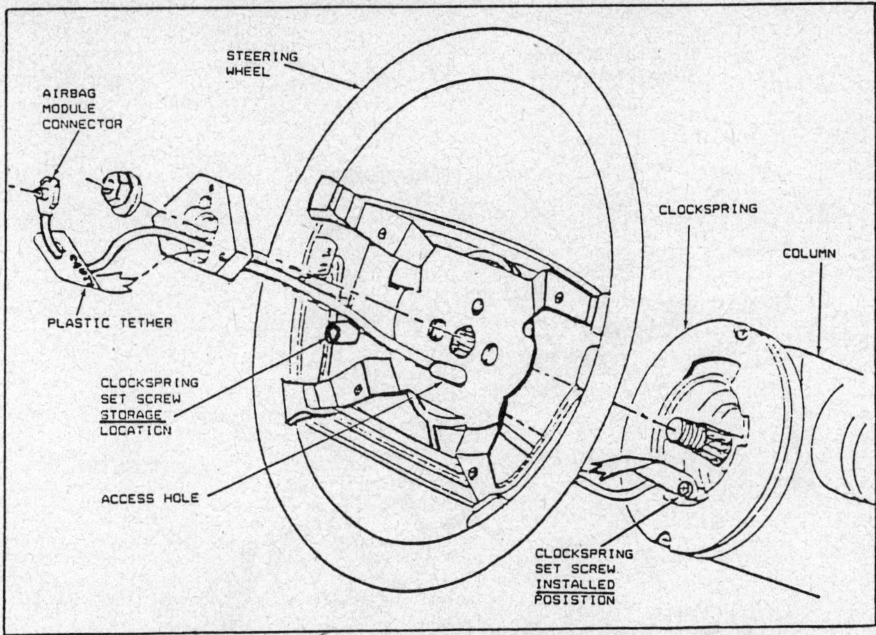


**Fig. 5 Airbag module & steering wheel assembly**

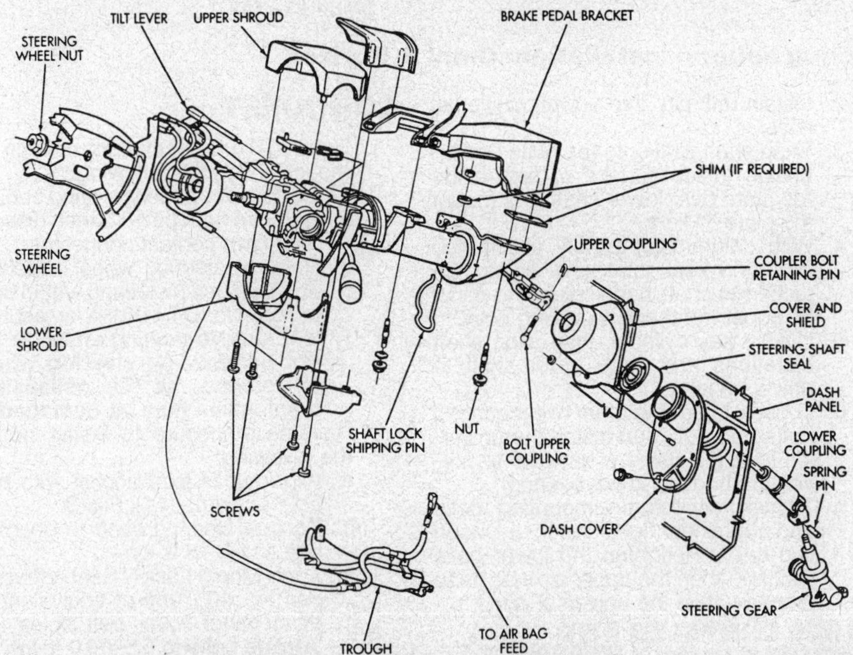


**Fig. 6 Acustar steering column assembly. 1990 Chrysler FWD models w/Acustar tilt steering column**

11. Reinstall anti-rattle clip into lower coupling tube slot, **Fig. 4.**
12. Remove column assembly out through passenger compartment being careful not to damage paint or trim.
13. **Cut plastic grommets from shift levers and install new grommets from rod side of lever using pliers and a back-up washer, Fig. 2.** Apply grease to grommets. When storing a steering column with an airbag module attached, never stand it on the steering wheel. If airbag is deployed the column will become a projectile and may cause damage or personal injury.

## Installation

1. Align and insert lower stub shaft into coupling, raise column into position and loosely install bracket nuts. Pull column assembly rearward and **torque** nuts to 105 inch lbs.
2. With needle nose pliers, pull coupling spring upward until it touches the universal joint flange. **Fig. 4.**
3. Snap gearshift rods into grommets.
4. Readjust gearshift linkage, as necessary.
5. **On airbag equipped models,** remove clockspring setscrew, attach wiring lead to airbag module and install module in steering wheel. Replace clockspring setscrew securely in it's storage location **Fig. 5.**
6. **On all models,** install steering wheel and **torque** nut to 45 ft. lbs.
7. Install horn switch and horn switch wire.
8. Connect all wiring connectors at steering column jacket and install steering wheel pad.
9. Connect battery ground cable and test operation of lights and horn.
10. **On column shift vehicles,** connect gearshift indicator pointer to its approximate original location. Slowly move gearshift lever from 1 (L) to P position, pausing briefly at each position. The indicator pointer must align with each selector position. If necessary, loosen and readjust pointer correctly.
11. **On all models,** install instrument panel steering column cover.

## 1991 FWD MODELS W/STANDARD STEERING COLUMN

The Acustar steering column has been designed to be serviced as an assembly less wiring, switches, shrouds & steering wheel. Also most steering column components can be serviced without removing the column from the vehicle, **Fig. 6.**

1. Disarm airbag system as outlined under "Airbag System Disarming'."
2. Ensure wheels are in a straight ahead position.
3. Disconnect battery ground cable.
4. **On models with column shift,** disconnect link rod by prying it out of grommet in shift lever.
5. **On models less airbag,** remove steering wheel center pad.
6. **On models with airbag,** remove airbag as outlined under "Passive Restraint Systems."
7. **On all models,** disconnect electrical components.
8. Remove steering wheel nut and steering wheel using puller tool No. C-3228-B or equivalent. **Do not bump or hammer on steering column shaft to remove wheel.**
9. Remove upper coupling retaining pin.
10. Remove nut and bolt from upper coupling then separate the upper coupling from the lower coupling.
11. **On models with column shift,** place shift lever in Low 1 position and remove PRNDL driver cable. Place shift lever in Park position.
12. **On models with tilt steering,** remove tilt lever.
13. **On all models,** remove upper and lower lock housing shrouds.
14. Remove lower fixed shroud Torx head screws and shroud.
15. Remove turn signal multi-function switch.
16. remove electrical connections from key-in light, main ignition switch, horn and/or airbag clock spring. On models with airbag, remove clock spring

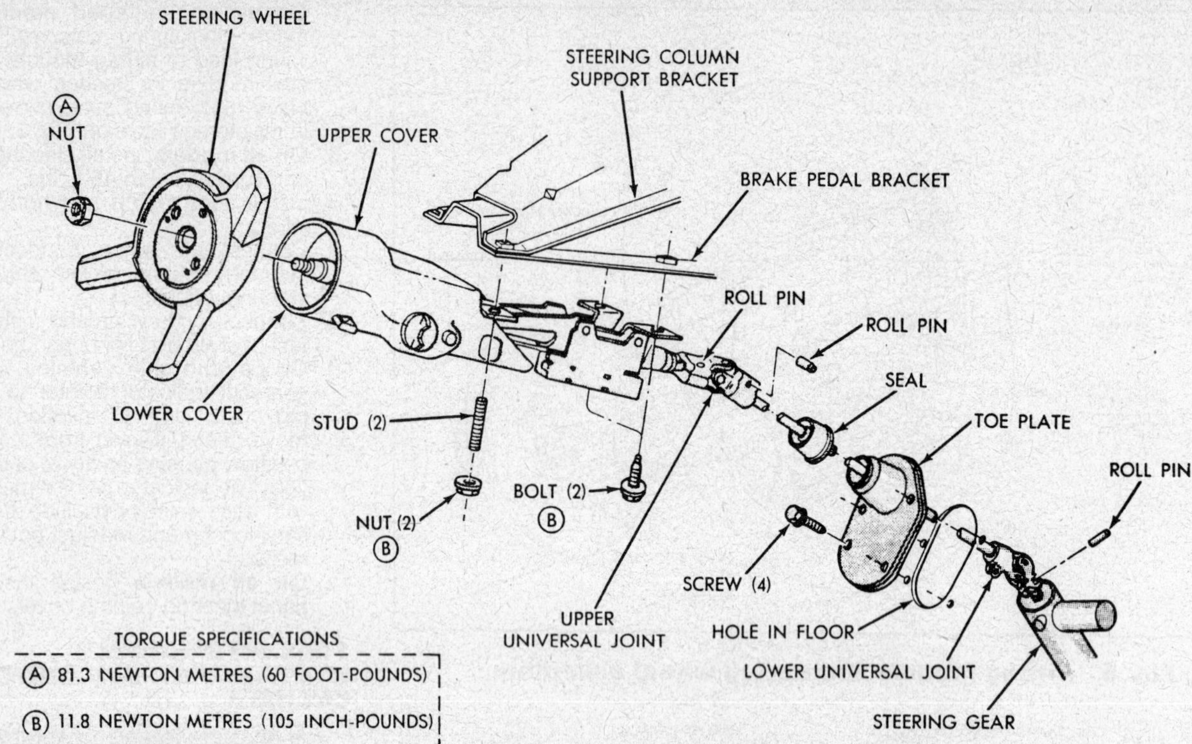


**Fig. 7 Steering column installation. Omni & Horizon**

electrical connections as outlined under "Passive Restraint Systems."

17. Loosen upper support bracket nuts then remove upper fixed shroud.
18. Remove wiring harness by prying out plastic retainer buttons.
19. Remove lower dash panel and support bracket standoff fasteners.
20. Remove column through passenger compartment.
21. Reverse procedure to install, noting the following:
    a. **On models with column shift,** replace shift rod grommet.
    b. **On all models,** ensure ground clip on left capsule slot in in place.
    c. Ensure to install upper coupling bolt retainer pin.
    d. Ensure breakaway capsules are fully seated in slots in column bracket then **torque** bracket nuts to 105 inch lbs.
    e. **Torque** steering wheel nut to 45 ft. lbs. **Do not force steering wheel on column shaft by driving wheel with a heavy object. Use retaining nut.**

## HORIZON & OMNI

### Removal

1. Disconnect battery ground cable.
2. Disconnect all column wiring connectors.
3. Remove lower roll pin from upper universal joint, **Fig. 7.**
4. Remove the four retaining bolts and remove column from vehicle.

### Installation

1. Align master serrations, then install lower shaft assembly onto steering gear input shaft.
2. Install roll pin into lower universal joint.
3. Snap shaft seal onto toe plate and lubricate inside surface of seal. Slide toe plate over lower shaft and mount toe plate to floor.
4. With column completely assembled and universal joint and spring attached to shaft, hang column to panel by upper righthand mounting point.
5. Unlock key cylinder, then align shaft serrations and mate lower shaft to universal joint.
6. Loosely install the other two mounting bolts and nut, then install the universal joint pin using a back-up to prevent damage to lower bearing.
7. Tighten all column mounting bolts and nuts finger tight, and then loosen two turns. Retighten the lower bolts first, and then the upper nuts so as to properly align the universal joints.

## 1989 CHRYSLER FWD MODELS W/TILT STEERING COLUMN

Refer to "FWD Models Except Laser & Horizon & Omni" for removal and installation of steering column assembly.

## 1990–91 CHRYSLER FWD MODELS W/TILT STEERING COLUMN

The Acustar steering column has been designed to be serviced as an assembly less wiring, switches, shrouds & steering wheel. Also most steering column components can be serviced without removing the column from the vehicle, **Fig. 6.**

Refer to "1991 FWD Models w/Standard Steering Column" for removal and installation of steering column assembly.

## CONQUEST

1. Refer to **Fig. 8,** for steering column removal, noting the following:
    a. Disconnect battery ground cable.
    b. Remove horn pad (1), then disconnect horn contact connector.
    c. Remove steering wheel attaching nut, then using steering wheel puller tool No. DT-1001-A or equivalent, remove steering wheel (2). **Do not hammer on steering wheel to remove, as the collapsible mechanism may be damaged.**
2. Reverse procedure to install, noting the following:
    a. Align cut of joint socket with bolt hole of clamp (11), **Fig. 9.**
    b. **Torque** steering shaft to gearbox bolt to 14-18 ft. lbs.
    c. Apply Mopar Lock N'Seal Adhesive part No. 4057989 or equivalent to dash panel cover bolt holes (9). **Torque** bolts to 6.5-10.0 ft. lbs.
    d. When installing steering wheel (2), ensure front wheels are in the straight ahead position, align the three cancel pins with holes in steering wheel, then **torque** steering wheel locknut to 25-33 ft. lbs. **Ensure turn signal lever cancels when steering wheel is turned in both directions.**

## COLT, COLT WAGON & EAGLE SUMMIT

1. Refer to **Figs. 10 and 11,** for steering column removal, noting the following:
    a. Disconnect battery ground cable.
    b. **On 1989-90 models,** remove trim clip (2) **Fig. 11,** by lightly pushing pin at center of clip with a Phillips

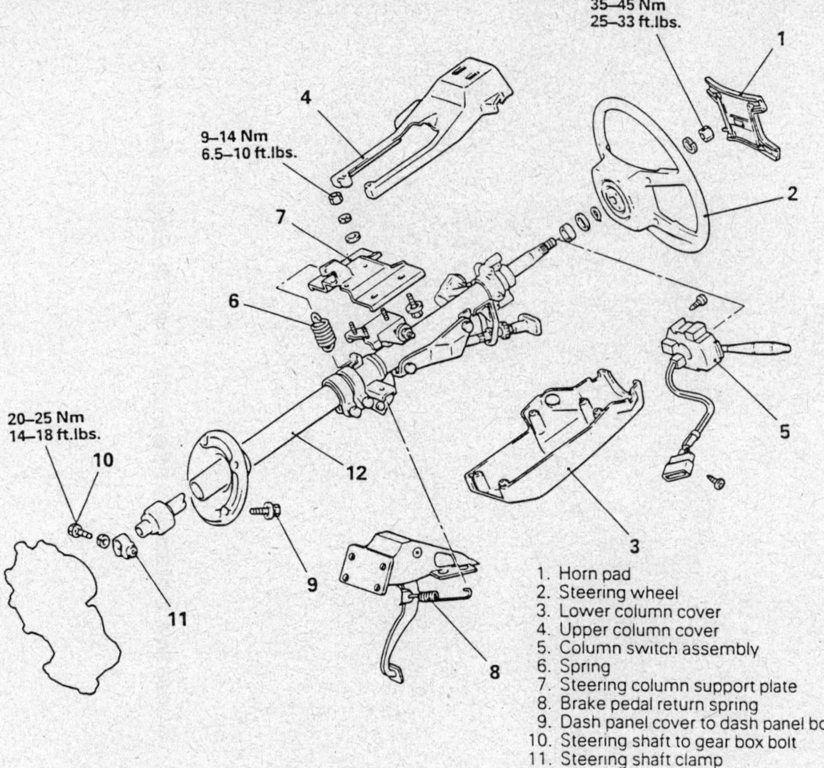


**Fig. 8 Steering column assembly. Conquest**

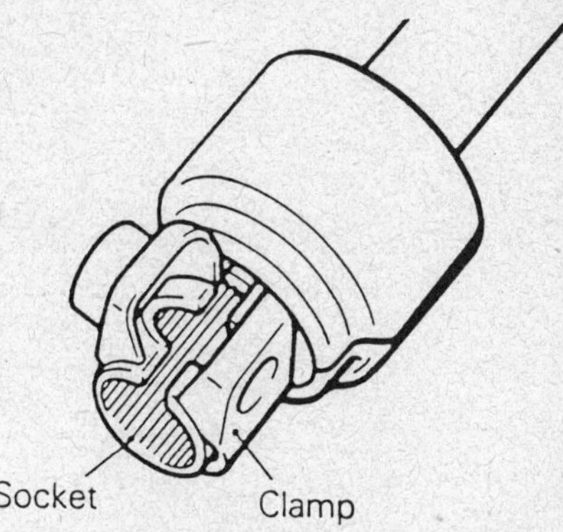


**Fig. 9 Installing steering shaft clamp**

screwdriver, then pull out clip. **Do not push pin in any further than necessary.**

c. **On all models,** remove steering wheel using a suitable puller. **Do not hammer on steering wheel to remove, as the collapsible mechanism may be damaged.**

d. **On Colt Wagon models,** straighten claws of column switch (13) **Fig. 10,** remove two attaching screws, then the column switch.

e. **On all models,** reverse procedure to install.

## COLT VISTA

1. Refer to **Fig. 12,** for steering column removal, noting the following:
   a. Disconnect battery ground cable.
   b. Remove steering wheel attaching nut, then using steering wheel puller tool No. DT-1001-A or equivalent, remove steering wheel. **Do not hammer on steering wheel to remove, as the collapsible mechanism may be damaged.**
   c. Reverse procedure to install.

## EAGLE PREMIER & DODGE MONACO

### Removal

1. Disconnect battery ground cable, then remove instrument panel lower trim cover.
2. Remove instrument panel support rod **Fig. 13.**
3. Disconnect column electrical connector, and remove screw holding steering column wiring harness bulkhead connector **Fig. 14.**
4. Disconnect automatic transaxle shift cable with a screwdriver **Fig. 15.**
5. Disconnect shift cable from steering column. Compress cable retainer tangs with pliers, then slide out of column bracket **Fig. 16.**
6. Remove shift indicator bracket mounting screw, and lift indicator wire off the pin.
7. Unsnap the steering column boot and slide down the steering column.
8. Scribe reference marks on steering column shaft and intermediate shaft U-joint for assembly reference.
9. Remove hold-down bolt from intermediate steering shaft, **Fig. 17,** then remove bolts and nuts holding steering column to instrument panel.
10. Carefully lower steering assembly and separate steering column shaft from intermediate shaft, then remove from vehicle.

### Installation

1. Align and insert steering column shaft in intermediate steering shaft U-joint using the marks made during disassembly, then install but do not torque U-joint bolt.
2. Position column and install nuts and bolts attaching column to instrument panel and **torque** to 35 ft. lbs.
3. Tighten intermediate shaft U-joint bolt.
4. Loop shift indicator wire on mounting pin, then install bracket attaching screw.
5. Snap shift cable into steering column bracket, then snap shift cable head onto mounting ball in shift arm.
6. Move gearshift lever into N position and check that shift pointer is aligned correctly. Adjust by loosening indicator bracket screw, and moving into position as needed.
7. Install bulkhead connector and attaching screw, then connect column connector.
8. Install instrument panel support rod and tighten screws securely.
9. Align the two halves of steering shaft boot with the "X" mark of lower half is centered in the oval mark on the upper half. Alignment mark on metal boot flange should be at the 6 o'clock position **Fig. 18.**
10. Install instrument panel lower trim cover, then the battery ground cable.

## EAGLE TALON & PLYMOUTH LASER

Refer to **Figs. 19 and 20,** for removal and installation of steering column assembly.

## EAGLE MEDALLION

Refer to "Steering Column Service" section for steering column replacement procedure.

## STEALTH

1. Disarm airbag system as outlined under "Airbag System Disarming."
2. Remove airbag module as outlined under "Passive Restraint Systems."
3. Replace the steering column in numbered sequence shown in **Fig. 21.**

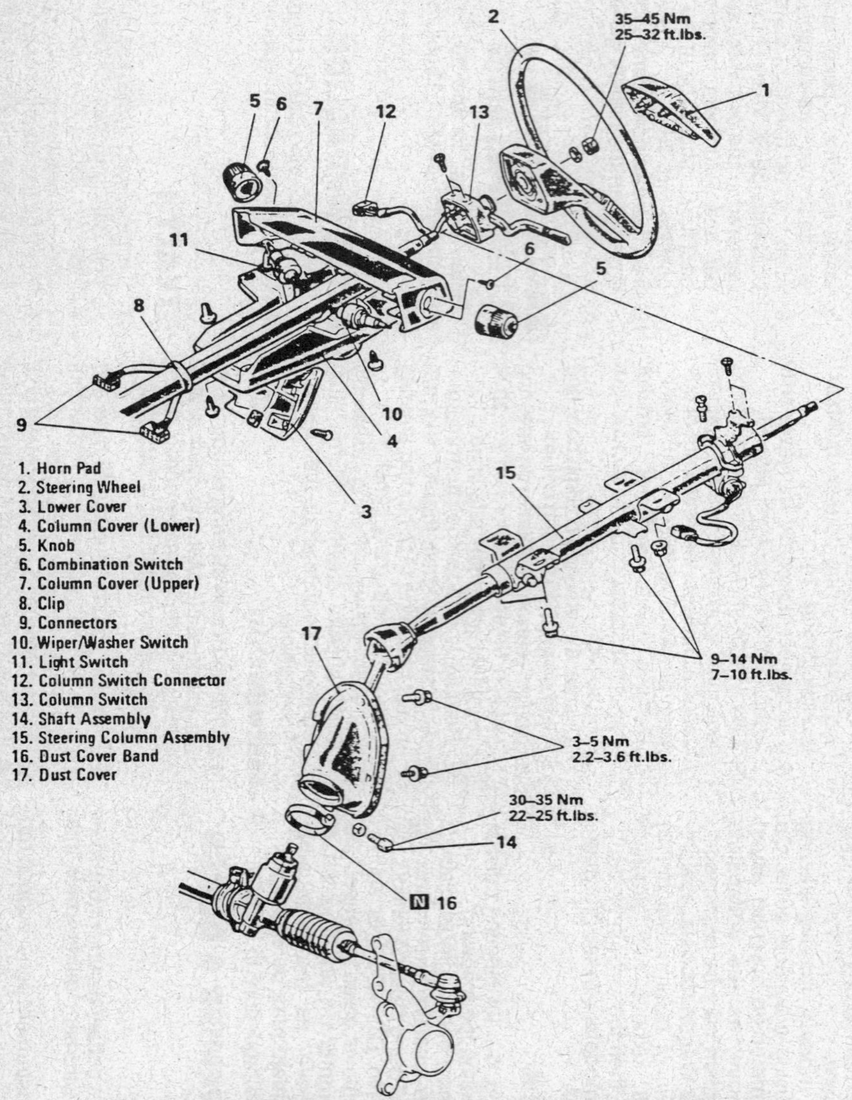

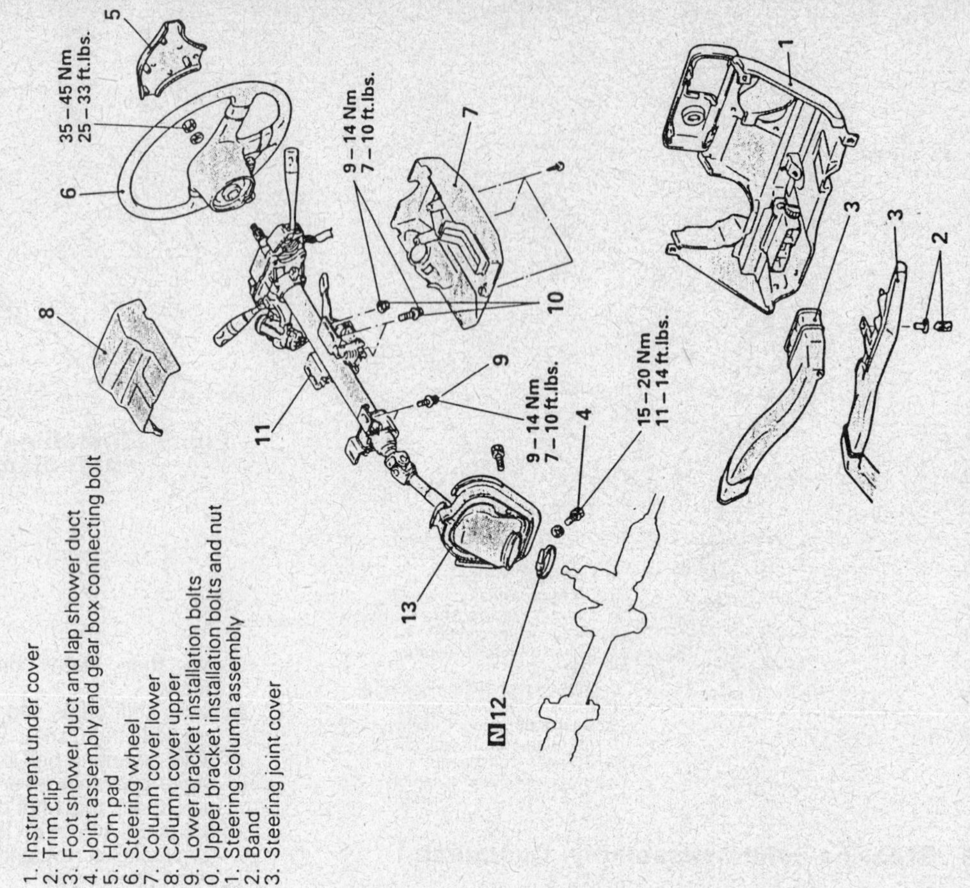


**Fig. 11 Steering column assembly. Colt & Eagle Summit**

35–45 Nm
25–32 ft.lbs.

9–14 Nm
7–10 ft.lbs.

3–5 Nm
2.2–3.6 ft.lbs.

30–35 Nm
22–25 ft.lbs.

1. Horn Pad
2. Steering Wheel
3. Lower Cover
4. Column Cover (Lower)
5. Knob
6. Combination Switch
7. Column Cover (Upper)
8. Clip
9. Connectors
10. Wiper/Washer Switch
11. Light Switch
12. Column Switch Connector
13. Column Switch
14. Shaft Assembly
15. Steering Column Assembly
16. Dust Cover Band
17. Dust Cover

**Fig. 10 Steering column assembly. Colt Wagon**

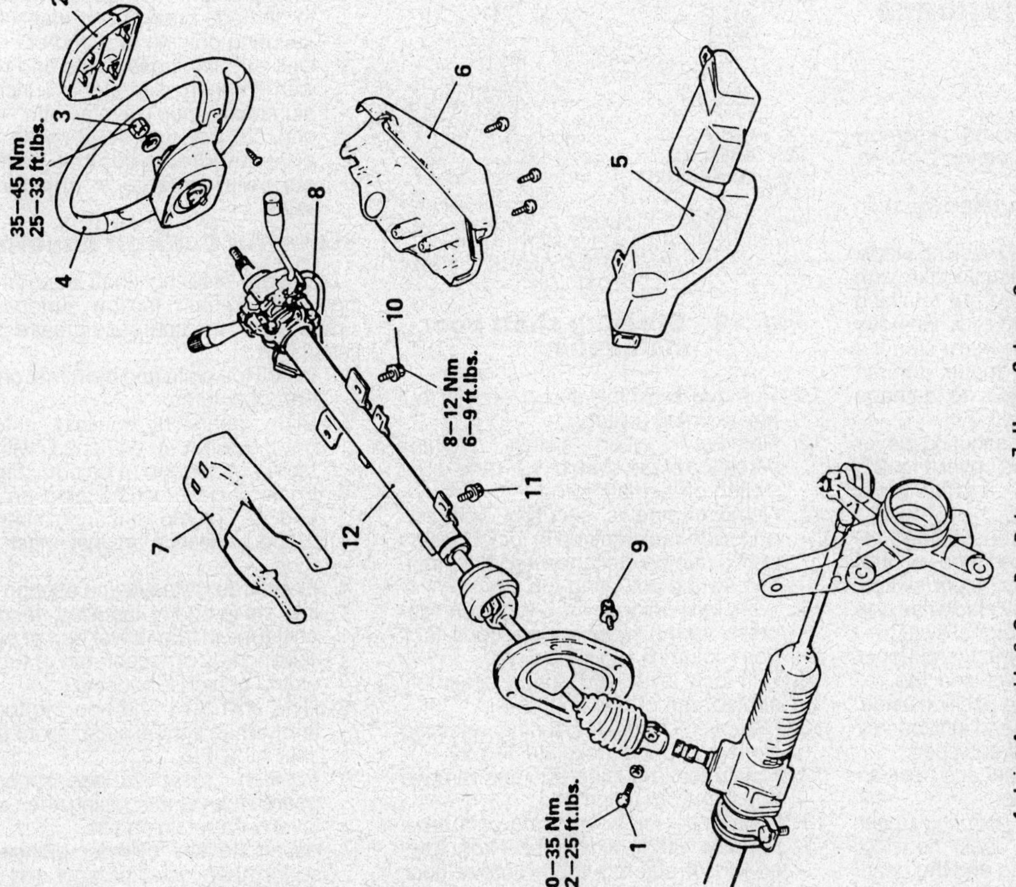


1. Joint Assembly & Gear Box Bolt
2. Horn Pad
3. Steering Wheel Mount Bolt
4. Steering Wheel
5. Lap Heater Duct
6. Lower Column Cover
7. Upper Column Cover
8. Column Switch Connectors
9. Cover Mounting Bolt
10. Upper Bracket Bolt
11. Lower Bracket Bolt
12. Steering Column & Shaft

**Fig. 12 Steering column assembly. Colt Vista**

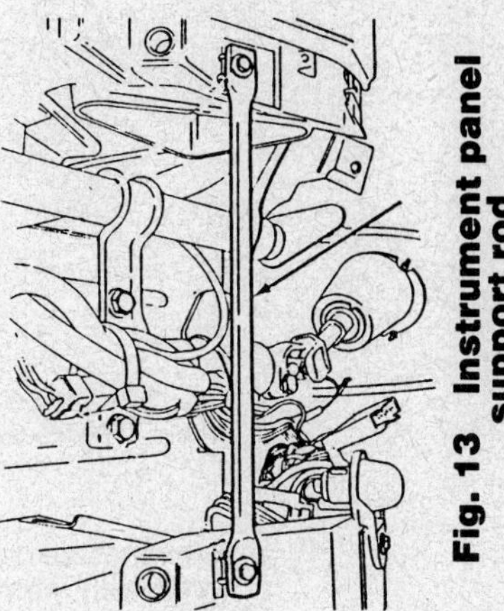

**Fig. 13 Instrument panel support rod**

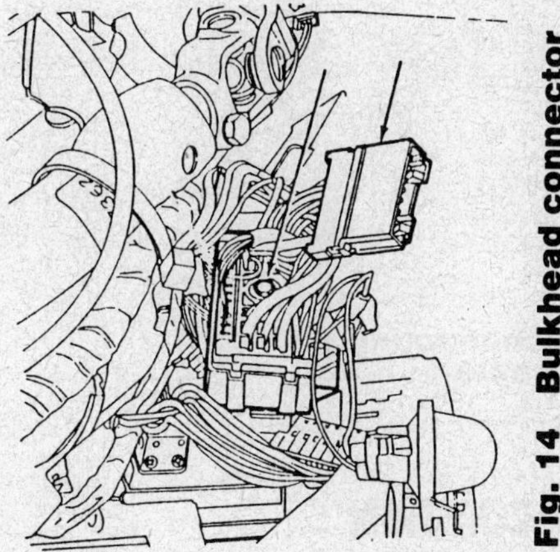

**Fig. 14 Bulkhead connector**

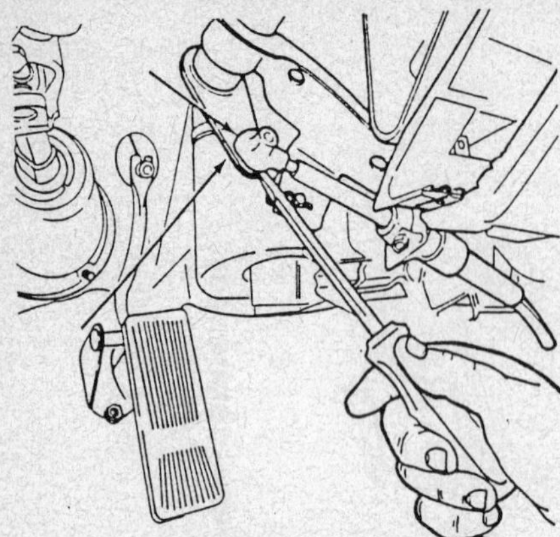

Fig. 15 Disconnecting shift cable

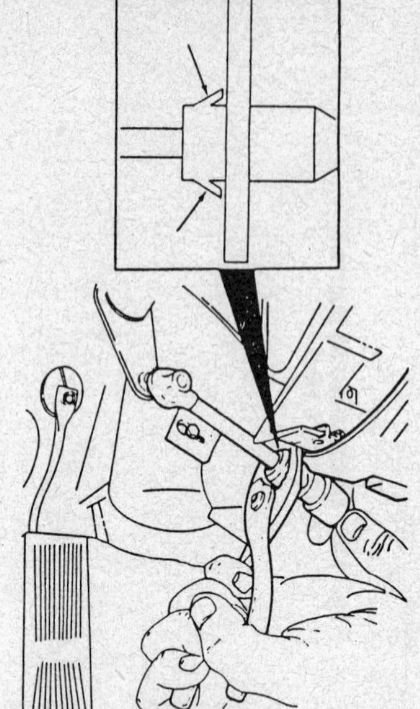

Fig. 16 Disconnecting cable retainer

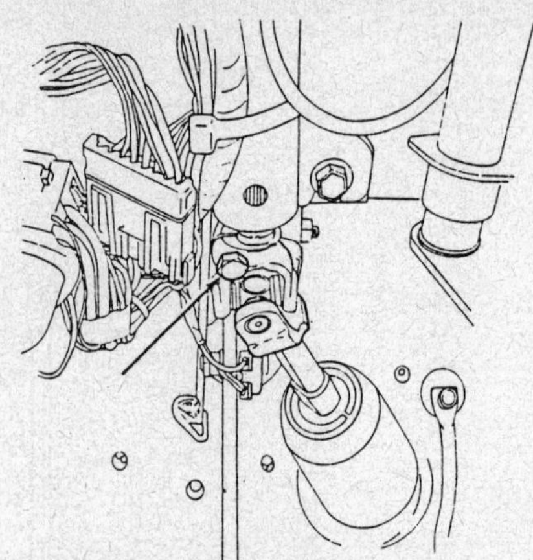

Fig. 17 Intermediate shaft hold-down bolt

# STEERING COLUMN SERVICE

## CHRYSLER EXCEPT COLT, COLT VISTA, CONQUEST, LASER, MONACO & STEALTH

### RWD MODELS w/STANDARD STEERING COLUMN

#### Steering Column Disassembly

1. Remove steering column assembly as outlined under "Steering Column, Replace."
2. Pry out wiring trough retainers, then remove trough.
3. Protect paint using masking tape, back-up shift lever retaining pin with deep socket, then drive out retaining pin and remove shift lever. Remove breakaway capsules from steering column bracket, then mount column in vise, taking care not to damage bracket.
4. Remove two screws securing cover to lock housing and the cover, **Fig. 22.**
5. Remove windshield washer/wiper switch.
6. Pull hider up on control stalk and remove two screws securing control stalk sleeve to washer/wiper switch, rotate control stalk fully clockwise and pull control from turn signal switch.
7. Remove turn signal switch and upper bearing retainer screws and the retainer, lift switch up and position aside, then disconnect horn and ignition key lamp ground wires, as equipped.
8. Remove retaining screw and position ignition key lamp aside.
9. Remove four screws securing upper bearing housing to lock housing, steering shaft snap ring and the bearing housing.
10. Remove spring and steering lockplate, **Fig. 22,** then withdraw steering shaft from lower end of column.

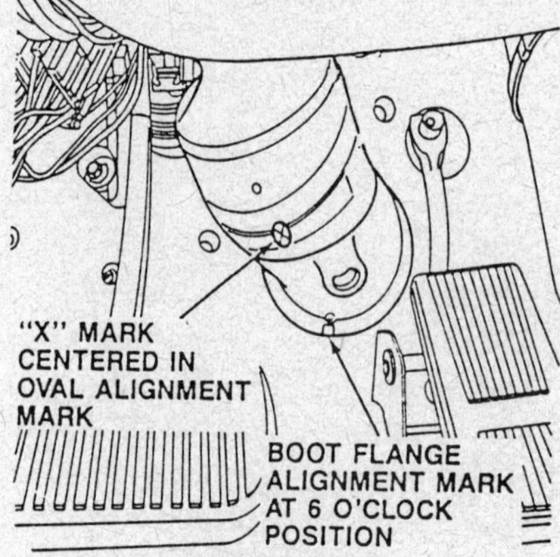


Fig. 18 Steering shaft boot installation

11. Remove retaining screw and lift out key warning switch.
12. Remove ignition switch retaining screws, rotate switch 90° and slide switch off actuating rod.
13. Remove screws securing bellcrank and slide bellcrank up in lock housing until it can be disconnected from ignition switch actuating rod.
14. With ignition lock in L position, depress spring retainers and pull lock from column.
15. Pull lock lever and spring assembly straight out of housing.
16. Remove four lock housing retaining screws and the lockplate, **Fig 22.**
17. Rotate lock housing 90° and remove housing from column.
18. Loosen setscrew securing shift tube, **Fig. 23,** withdraw shift tube from lower end of column, then remove floor plate and grommet.

#### Inspection

1. Inspect all components and replace any that are damaged, distorted or excessively worn.
2. Inspect switches and related harnesses, replacing assemblies that are worn, damaged or distorted.
3. Inspect steering shaft support bearings and replace if they are worn or fail to operate smoothly.
4. If shift tube is to be reused, inspect seal and support bushing and replace as needed.
5. Clamp column in vise taking care not to damage bracket and inspect rivets securing column to mandrel.
6. Drill out any loose rivets and replace with 1/8 inch diameter, 1/4 inch long aluminum "pop" rivets, with 1/8 inch grip. **Do not use steel rivets to secure mandrel to column, as the rivets must be able to shear on impact.**

#### Steering Column Assembly

Lubricate steering shaft support bearings and column friction surfaces with Grade 2 E.P. multipurpose grease prior to assembly.

1. Install toe plate and grommet on lower end of column.
2. Slide gearshift housing extension onto column, if equipped, with tabs facing upper end of column, **Fig. 22.**
3. Position gearshift housing on upper end of column, ensuring support is properly seated against mast jacket tabs.
4. Ensure dust sleeve and support bushing are properly installed, then slide shift tube in from lower end of column, guiding key on upper end of tube into slot in gearshift housing.
5. Hold shift tube and housing together firmly, then tighten setscrew to secure shift tube, **Fig. 23.**
6. Position crossover load spring and gearshift lever in housing, then secure lever with retaining pin.
7. Assemble key cylinder plunger and spring, then install plunger and spring assembly and shift gate on lock housing, **Fig. 22.**
8. Insert ignition switch rod through shift housing.

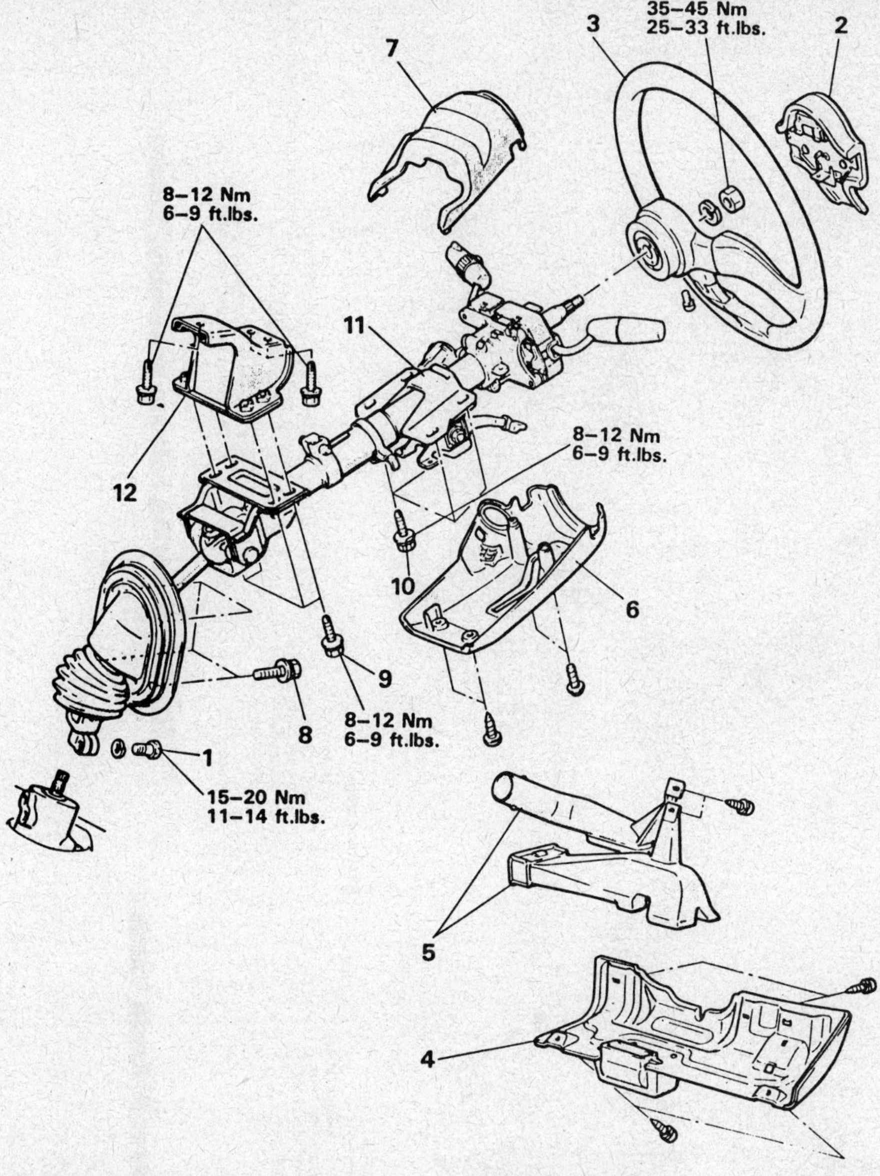


1. Joint assembly and gear box connecting bolt
2. Horn pad
3. Steering wheel
4. Instrument under cover
5. Foot shower duct and lap shower duct
6. Column cover lower
7. Column cover upper
8. Cover attaching bolts
9. Lower bracket installation bolts
10. Tilt bracket installation bolts
11. Steering column assembly
12. Column support

**Fig. 19 Steering column assembly. 1990 Laser & Eagle Talon**

9. Place shift lever in mid-position and position lock housing assembly on mast jacket, guiding ignition switch rod through oval shaped hole and indexing keyway in housing with slot in jacket.
10. Insert four lock housing retaining screws and tighten screws alternately and evenly, **torquing** screws to 90 inch lbs. in several steps.
11. Lubricate and assemble lock lever and spring assembly, **Fig. 24,** then install assembly in lock, seating pin firmly in bottom of slots and ensuring spring leg is in place in lock casting notch.
12. Place gearshift lever in P position, position bellcrank assembly into lock housing and insert ignition switch actuating rod into bellcrank while pulling actuator rod down column, then install bellcrank into mounting surface, **Fig. 22.**
13. Install ignition switch onto actuator rod and rotate switch 90° to lock actuating rod position.
14. Rotate ignition lock to L position and remove key. Insert lock cylinder into bore until it contacts switch actuator, then insert key and rotate cylinder while pressing inward until components align and cylinder snaps into place.
15. Feed key warning switch harness behind post and down through channel between housing and mast jacket, then remove ignition key and secure switch.
16. Lubricate inside of steering shaft lockplate, then install lockplate and spring.
17. Ensure bearing is properly seated in upper bearing housing, then install upper bearing housing and retaining screws and torque screws to specifications, **Fig. 22.**
18. Press steering shaft into column to compress springs and install upper bearing snap ring.
19. Reverse remaining procedure to complete assembly, noting the following:
    a. Install dimmer switch actuator rod up through housing into pocket of washer/wiper switch, then compress switch and install .093 inch rod into adjusting hole, **Fig. 25.** Mount switch and apply slightly upward pressure against actuator rod, then tighten retaining screws and remove rod from hole.
    b. Ensure switch harnesses are properly aligned, then install wiring trough. Secure trough with new retainers.

## RWD MODELS W/TILT STEERING COLUMN

### Steering Column Disassembly

1. Remove steering column assembly as outlined under "Steering Column, Replace."
2. Remove four bolts attaching bracket assembly to column jacket, **Fig. 26.**
3. Remove wiring protector from column jacket.
4. Attach column holding fixture tool No. C-4132 or equivalent to jacket, then mount column in vise with holding fixture.
5. Remove tilt lever, push hazard warning knob in, then unscrew to remove.
6. Remove ignition key lamp assembly, then pull knob off wiper/washer switch assembly.
7. Pull hider up on control stalk and remove two screws attaching sleeve to wiper/washer switch, then remove sleeve.
8. Rotate shaft in wiper switch to full clockwise position, then remove shaft by pulling straight out of wiper/washer switch.
9. Remove plastic cover from lockplate, then depress lockplate with lockplate depressing tool No. C-4156 or equivalent and pry retaining ring out of groove, **Fig. 27. Do not relieve full load of upper bearing spring as retaining ring will rotate making removal difficult.**
10. Remove lockplate depressing tool, then lockplate, canceling cam, and upper bearing spring. **The lockplate is under considerable spring pressure. Do not attempt to remove it without using the compressor tool.**
11. Remove switch actuator screw and arm.
12. Remove three turn signal switch at-

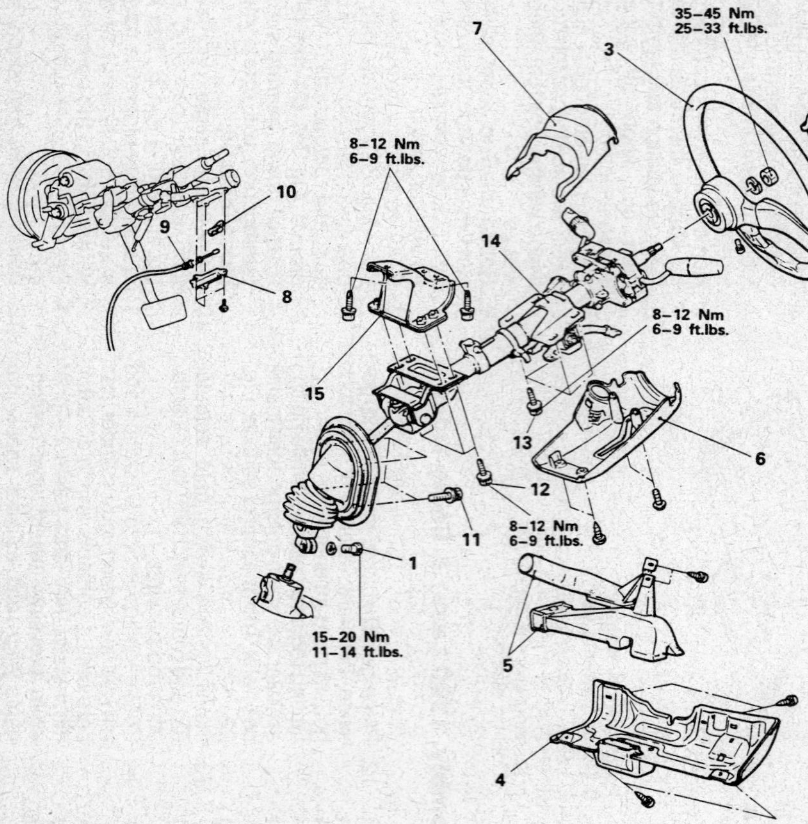

**Removal steps**

1. Joint assembly and gear box connecting bolt
2. Horn pad
3. Steering wheel
4. Instrument under cover
5. Foot shower duct and lap shower duct
6. Column cover lower
7. Column cover upper
8. Cover <A/T>
9. Key interlock cable (steering lock assembly side) <A/T>
10. Slide lever <A/T>
11. Cover attaching bolts
12. Lower bracket installation bolts
13. Tilt bracket installation bolts
14. Steering column assembly
15. Column support

**Fig. 20 Steering column assembly. 1991 Laser & Eagle Talon**

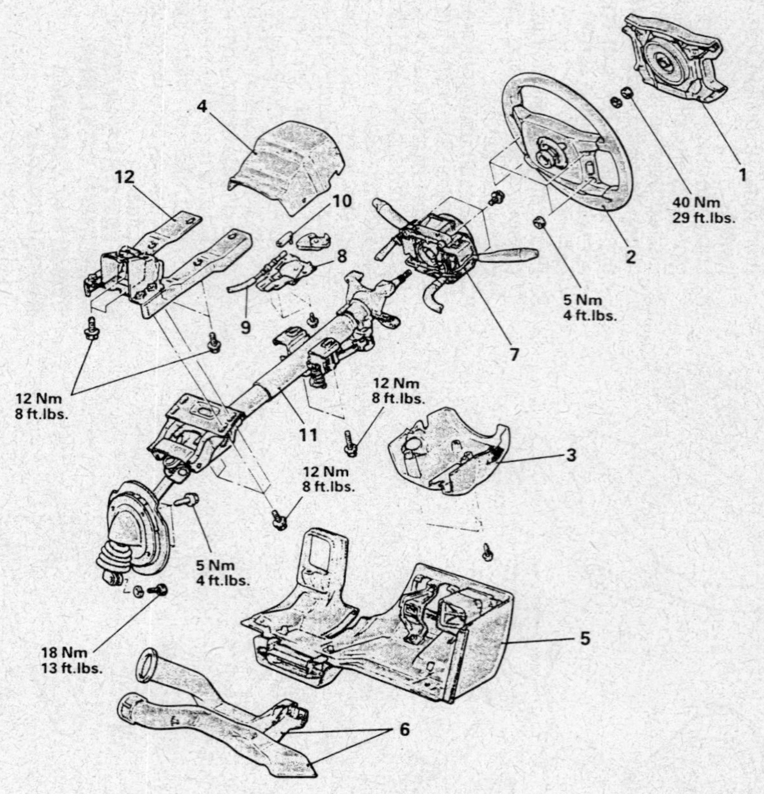


**Removal steps**

1. Air bag module
2. Steering wheel
3. Lower column cover
4. Upper column cover
5. Knee protector
6. Lap cooler duct and foot shower duct
7. Column switch assembly
8. Cover } <Automatic transaxle vehicles>
9. Key interlock cable }
10. Slide lever }
11. Steering column assembly
12. Column support assembly

**Fig. 21 Steering column assembly. Stealth**

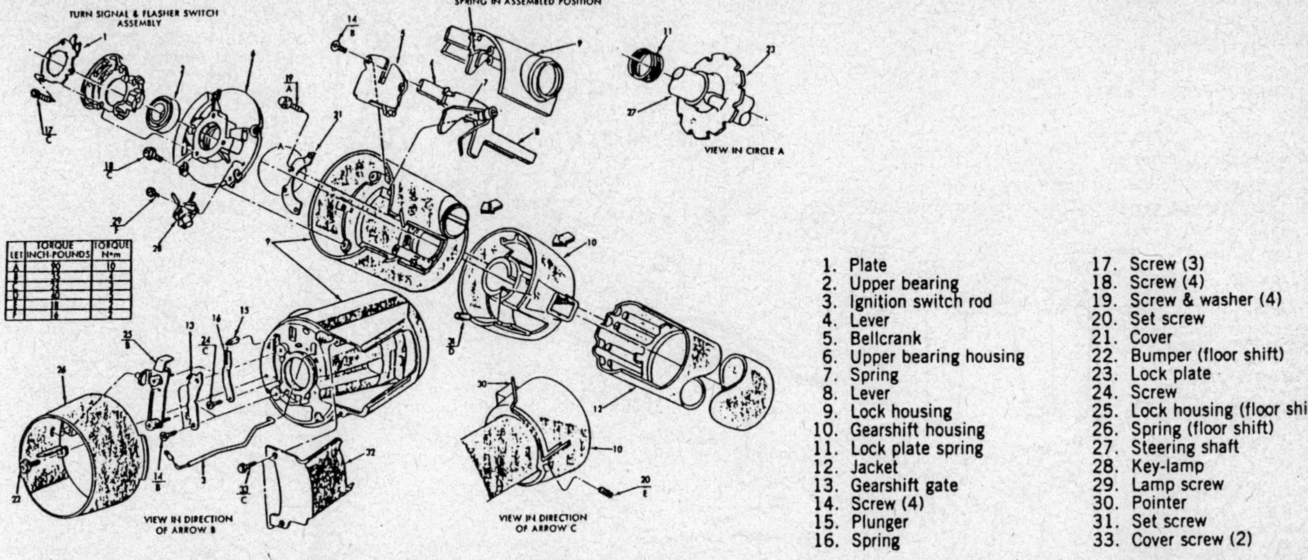


**Fig. 22 Exploded view of upper steering column. RWD models w/standard steering column**

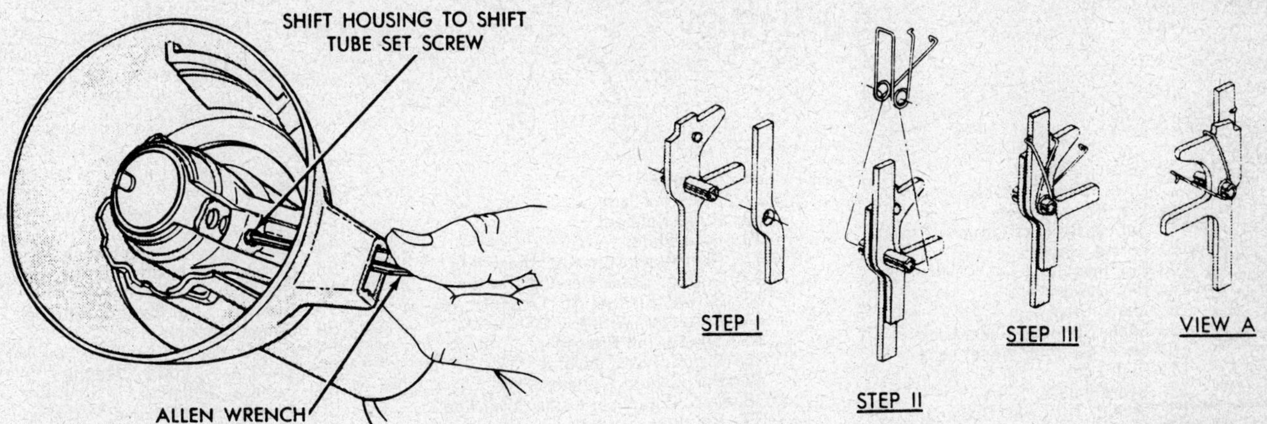


**Fig. 23 Shift tube setscrew location**

**Fig. 24 Lock lever & spring assembly**

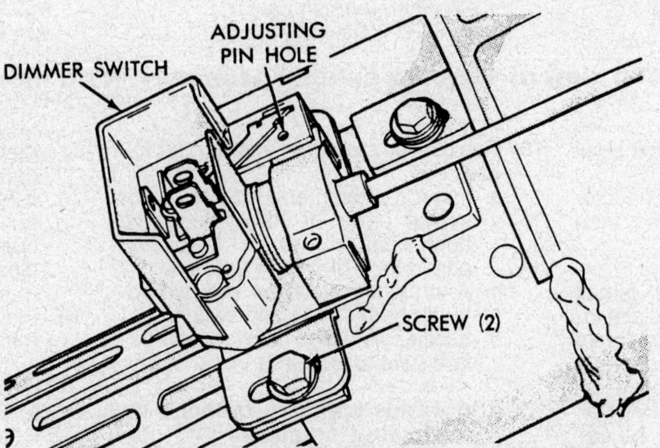


**Fig. 25 Column mounted dimmer switch installation. Models w/standard steering column**

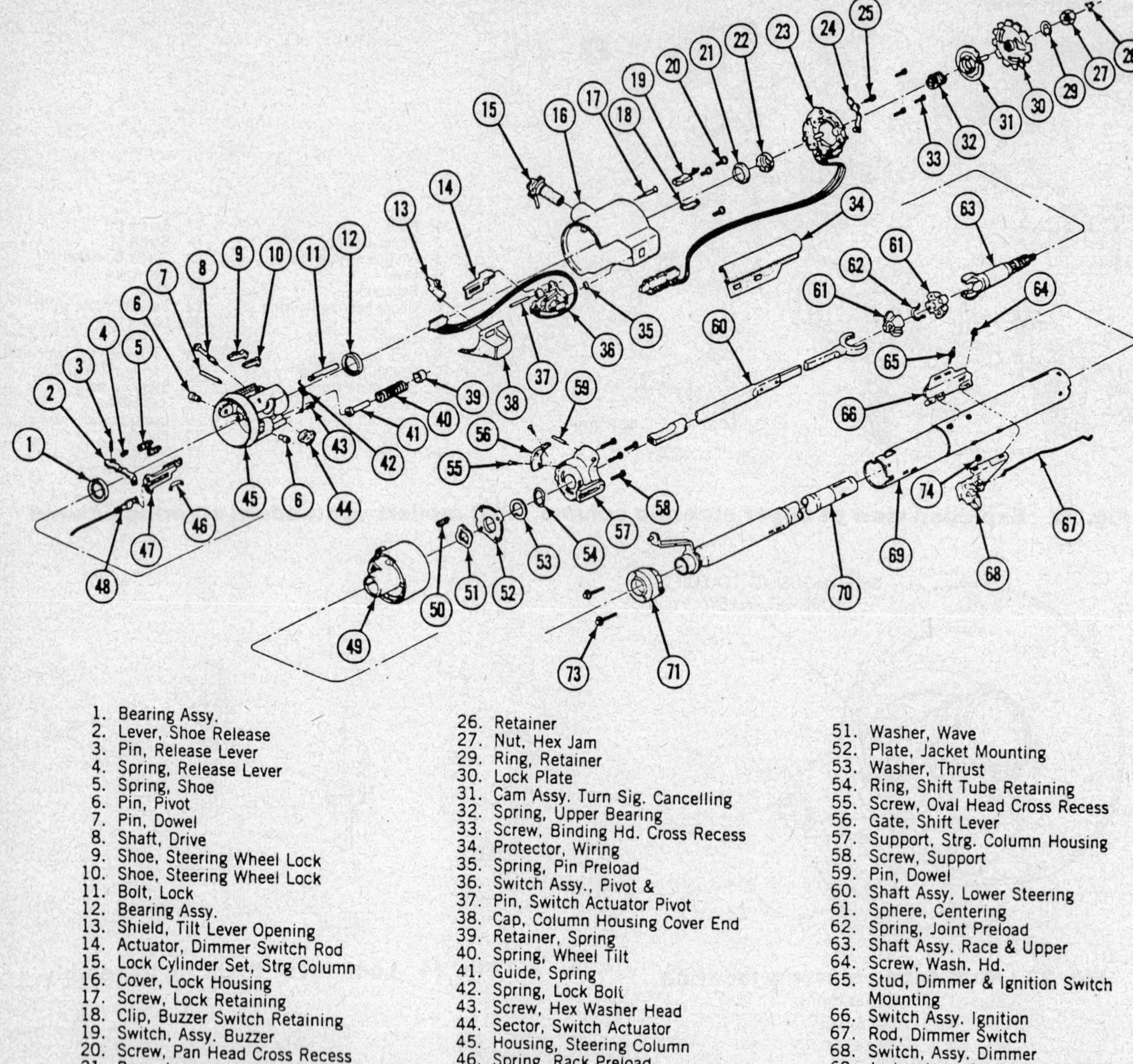

1. Bearing Assy.
2. Lever, Shoe Release
3. Pin, Release Lever
4. Spring, Release Lever
5. Spring, Shoe
6. Pin, Pivot
7. Pin, Dowel
8. Shaft, Drive
9. Shoe, Steering Wheel Lock
10. Shoe, Steering Wheel Lock
11. Bolt, Lock
12. Bearing Assy.
13. Shield, Tilt Lever Opening
14. Actuator, Dimmer Switch Rod
15. Lock Cylinder Set, Strg Column
16. Cover, Lock Housing
17. Screw, Lock Retaining
18. Clip, Buzzer Switch Retaining
19. Switch, Assy. Buzzer
20. Screw, Pan Head Cross Recess
21. Race, Inner
22. Seat, Upper Bearing Inner Race
23. Switch Assy. Turn Signal
24. Arm Assy. Signal Switch
25. Screw, Round Washer Head
26. Retainer
27. Nut, Hex Jam
29. Ring, Retainer
30. Lock Plate
31. Cam Assy. Turn Sig. Cancelling
32. Spring, Upper Bearing
33. Screw, Binding Hd. Cross Recess
34. Protector, Wiring
35. Spring, Pin Preload
36. Switch Assy., Pivot &
37. Pin, Switch Actuator Pivot
38. Cap, Column Housing Cover End
39. Retainer, Spring
40. Spring, Wheel Tilt
41. Guide, Spring
42. Spring, Lock Bolt
43. Screw, Hex Washer Head
44. Sector, Switch Actuator
45. Housing, Steering Column
46. Spring, Rack Preload
47. Rack, Switch Actuator
48. Actuator Assy. Ignition Switch
49. Bowl, Gearshift Lever
50. Spring, Shift Lever
51. Washer, Wave
52. Plate, Jacket Mounting
53. Washer, Thrust
54. Ring, Shift Tube Retaining
55. Screw, Oval Head Cross Recess
56. Gate, Shift Lever
57. Support, Strg. Column Housing
58. Screw, Support
59. Pin, Dowel
60. Shaft Assy. Lower Steering
61. Sphere, Centering
62. Spring, Joint Preload
63. Shaft Assy. Race & Upper
64. Screw, Wash. Hd.
65. Stud, Dimmer & Ignition Switch Mounting
66. Switch Assy. Ignition
67. Rod, Dimmer Switch
68. Switch, Assy. Dimmer
69. Jacket Assy. Steering Column
70. Tube Assy. Shift
71. Bearing Assy., Adapter &
73. Screw, Hex. Washer Head Tapping
74. Nut, Hex.

**Fig. 26 Exploded view of steering column assembly. RWD models w/tilt column**

taching screws, then place shift bowl in Low (1) position.

13. Tape turn signal switch connector and wires to prevent snagging, then remove switch and wiring.
14. Remove key lamp.
15. Insert a suitable thin tool (small screwdriver or shim stock) into slot located next to switch mounting screw boss (righthand slot), and depress spring latch at bottom of slot to release lock, then remove lock cylinder, **Fig. 28. Lock cylinder can be removed in any position from Accessory to On. Lock position is recommended because of it's positive location.**
16. Remove buzzer/chime switch as follows:
    a. Insert a straightened paper clip or similar piece of stiff wire with a hook bent on one end in the exposed loop of wedge spring.
    b. A straight pull of the wire will remove both spring and switch.
    c. If lock cylinder is not removed before switch, it must be in the On position.
    d. **If wedge spring is dropped on removal, it could fall into column, requiring complete disassembly to retrieve spring.**
17. Remove three housing cover screws, then housing cover. With housing cover removed, wiper/washer switch can be removed.
18. If required, pivot pin can be pressed out using a suitable punch. Also, if required, tilt lever opening shield and dimmer switch actuator rod can be removed from cap.
19. Place column in full Up position, then remove tilt spring retainer as follows:
    a. Insert a large Phillips screwdriver in opening, **Fig. 29.**
    b. Press in approximately $3/16$ inch, then turn approximately $1/8$ turn counterclockwise until ears align with grooves in housing.
    c. Remove spring and guide.
20. Remove dimmer switch mounting

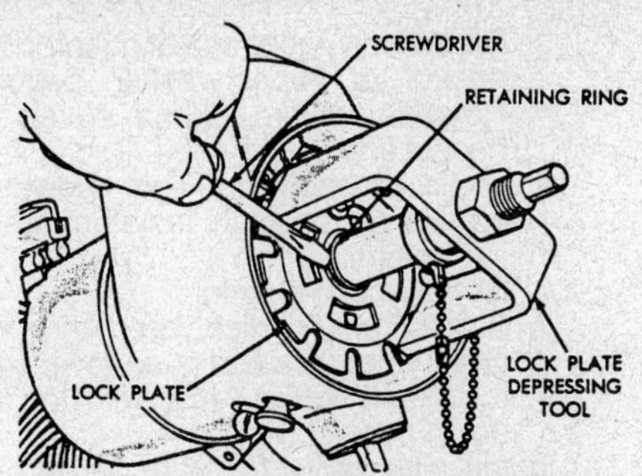

**Fig. 27 Removing lockplate retaining ring. RWD models w/tilt column**

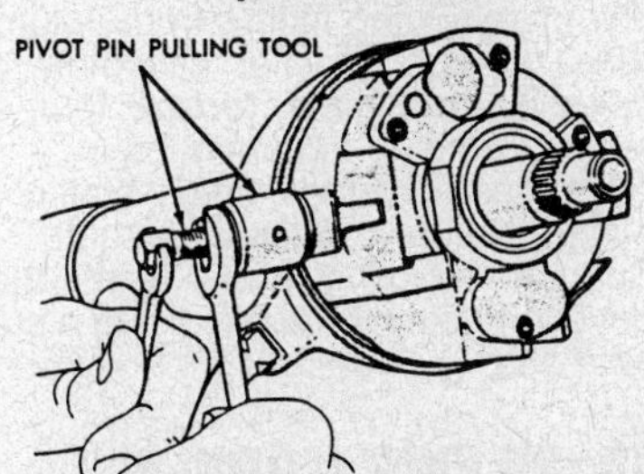

**Fig. 30 Removing pivot pin. RWD models w/tilt column**

screws, then the dimmer switch. Separate dimmer switch from rod by pulling.

21. Push upper steering shaft in enough to remove steering shaft inner race seat and inner race.
22. With ignition switch in Accessory position, remove ignition switch mounting screws, then ignition switch.
23. Install pivot pin removal tool No. C-4016 or equivalent over pivot pin, then thread small portion of screw firmly into pin.
24. Hold screw with wrench to prevent it from turning, then using a second wrench, turn nut clockwise to remove pivot pin from support, **Fig. 30.**
25. Repeat procedure to remove pivot pin on opposite side of column.
26. Use tilt release lever to disengage lock shoes.
27. Remove bearing housing assembly by pulling upward to extend rack fully. Move housing assembly to the left to disengage rack from actuator.
28. Rotate bearing housing clockwise to free dimmer switch actuator rod, then remove actuator assembly.
29. Remove coupling from lower end of steering shaft. **Double coupling is retained to shaft with roll pin.**
30. Remove steering shaft assembly from upper end. **Do not bump or drop steering shaft. Plastic pins may shear off.**
31. Disassemble steering shaft assembly by removing centering spheres and anti-lash springs as shown in **Figs. 31 and 32.**
32. Remove four bolts attaching support to lockplate, then remove support from end of column jacket. Remove two attaching screws and shift gate from support, if necessary. **Dimmer switch actuator rod is removed with support.**

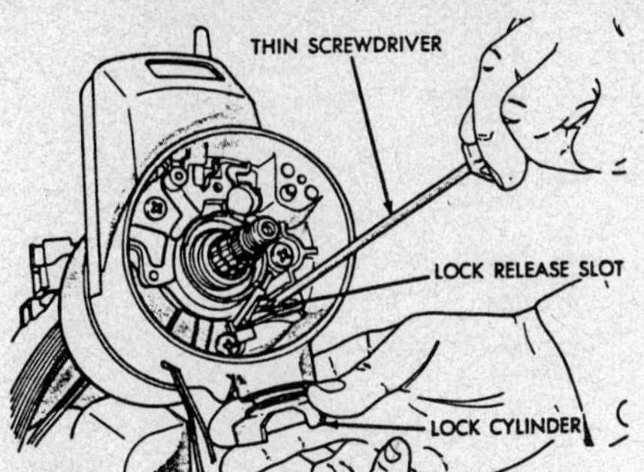

**Fig. 28 Removing lock cylinder. RWD models w/tilt column**

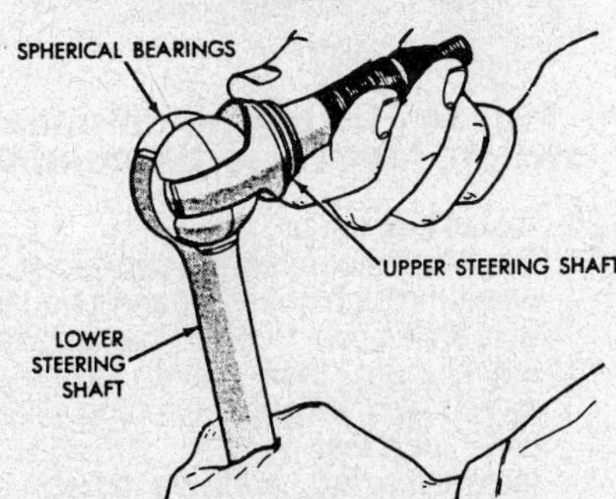

**Fig. 31 Disassembling steering shafts**

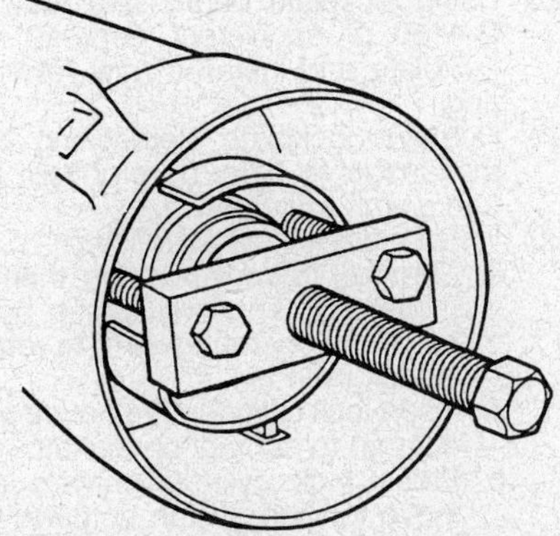
**Fig. 33 Removing shift tube**

33. Using a screwdriver, remove shift tube retaining ring, then the thrust washer.
34. Using a small screwdriver, carefully disengage plastic shift tube support from lower end of column jacket.
35. Remove shift tube from bowl using shift tube removal tool No. C-4120 or equivalent, **Fig. 33.** Insert bushing on end of tool in shift tube, then push tube out of bowl. **Do not hammer or pull on lower or upper shift tubes. Plastic joint may be sheared off.**
36. Remove shift tube from jacket from lower end.
37. Remove jacket mounting plate by sliding mounting plate out of jacket notches, tipping down toward bowl hub at 12 o'clock position and under jacket opening, then remove wave washer.
38. Remove bowl from jacket, then remove shift lever spring from bowl by turning spring with pliers and pulling out.

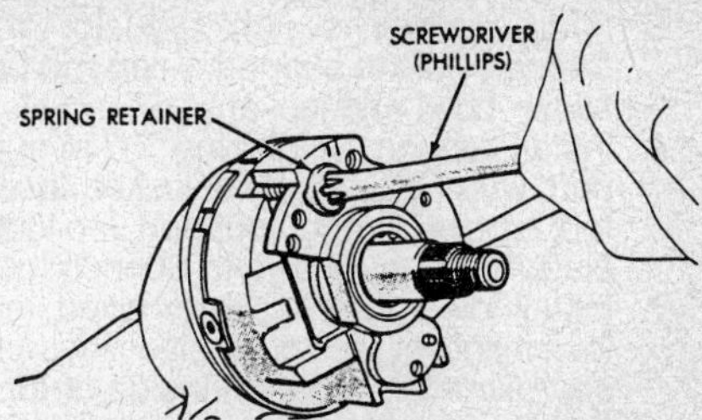

**Fig. 29 Removing tilt spring retainer. RWD models w/tilt column**

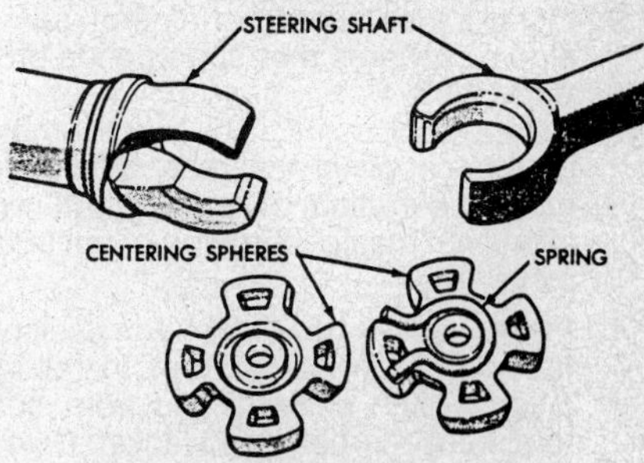

**Fig. 32 Steering shaft centering spheres**

## Inspection

1. Inspect all bearings and race seats for damage and/or wear.
2. Inspect centering sphere for nicks, damage or wear. If damage is found, check shaft coupling for nicks, burrs or rough spots.
3. Inspect actuator housing, shift lever bowl and support for cracks and damage.
4. Inspect switches and related harnesses, replacing assemblies that are worn, damaged or distorted.
5. Inspect steering shaft and gearshift tube for loose and/or broken plastic shear joints.

## Steering Column Assembly

Lubricate steering shaft support bearings and column friction surfaces with Grade 2 E.P. multipurpose grease prior to assembly.

1. Install shift lever spring in bowl by turning with pliers and pushing in. Slide bowl into jacket.
2. Install wave washer and position jacket mounting plate in place. Install jacket mounting plate into notches in jacket as follows:
   a. Tip jacket mounting plate toward bowl hub at 12 o'clock position and under jacket opening.
   b. Slide jacket mounting plate into notches in jacket.
3. Carefully install shift tube in lower end of jacket. Align key in tube with keyway in bowl, then using shift tube installer tool No. C-4119 or equivalent, pull shift tube into bowl. **Do not push or tap on end of shift tube.**
4. Install thrust washer and retaining ring by pulling bowl up to compress wave washer.

5. Slide dimmer switch actuator rod through hole in support. Feed rod between bowl and jacket.
6. Install support by aligning "U" in support with "U" notch in jacket. Insert four screws through support into lockplate. **Torque** screws to 60 inch lbs.
7. Install lower bearing, if removed, into lower end of jacket. Position bearing approximately 3/16 inch inside of tube (use soap solution or suitable rubber lubricant to ease installation).
8. Install centering spheres and anti-lash spring in upper steering shaft, **Fig. 32.**
9. Install lower steering shaft from same side of spheres that spring ends protrude from.
10. Temporarily assemble double-coupling assembly to ensure master serration of upper shaft will align with master serration of pot coupling.
11. Place shift bowl in P position (counterclockwise to stop). Install ignition switch actuator rod from bottom, between bowl and jacket. Guide back of coupling into support slot.
12. Install bearing housing assembly over steering shaft, then engage rack over end of end of ignition switch actuator rod.
13. Position access hole of bearing housing over end of dimmer switch actuator rod. Rotate housing counterclockwise to assemble.
14. Holding lock shoes in disengaged position, position bearing housing over steering steering shaft until pivot holes align with holes in support.
15. Install pivot pins. Install as far as possible, using palm pressure to prevent broaching of support pivot hole. Once pivot pins are started, tap in fully using a small hammer and punch.
16. Install wiper/washer pivot assembly, then press pivot pin in cover, if removed. **Ensure pivot assembly moves freely. If pivot assembly binds, tap other end of pin back for necessary clearance.**
17. Install wiper/washer switch.
18. Install tilt lever opening shield in cover, if removed. Position cap over dimmer switch actuator rod. Guide end of actuator rod into pivot slot during assembly. Position cap so cover will slide over it.
19. Place housing in full Up position, then install guide after ensuring there is suitable lubricant between guide and peg on support, tilt spring, and tilt spring retainer.
20. Using a Phillips screwdriver in retainer slot, **Fig. 29,** turn retainer clockwise to engage.
21. Install bearing inner race and seat.
22. Install lock housing cover and **torque** three attaching screws to 100 inch lbs.
23. Install buzzer/chime switch to spring clip with formed end of clip under end of switch and spring bowed away from switch on side opposite contact. Push switch and spring into hole in lock housing cover with contacts facing lock cylinder hole.

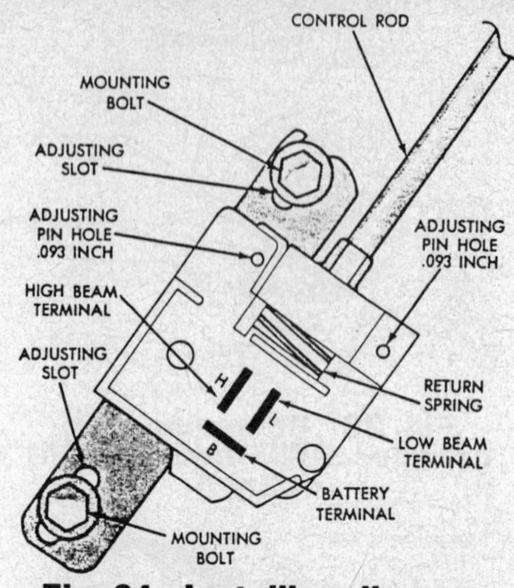


**Fig. 34 Installing dimmer switch. Models w/tilt column**

24. Install key lamp.
25. Feed turn signal switch connector and wires through cover, bearing housing, and shift bowl. Push in hazard warning plunger, then install turn signal switch and **torque** attaching screws to 25 inch lbs.
26. Install hazard warning knob and screw, then pull knob out.
27. Install cancelling cam spring, cancelling cam (carrier assembly) and lockplate.
28. Using lockplate depressing tool No. C-4156 or equivalent, depress shift lockplate and install a new retaining ring.
29. Remove lockplate depressing tool, then install tilt lever (if removed) and turn signal switch lever.
30. Install ignition lock as follows:
    a. Turn key to Lock position, then remove key. This will cause buzzer/chime operating lever to retract in lock cylinder.
    b. Insert lock cylinder into housing far enough to contact driveshaft.
    c. Press lock cylinder inward and move ignition switch actuator rod up and down to align parts.
    d. When parts align, lock cylinder will move inward and a spring loaded retainer will snap into place, locking cylinder into housing.
    e. If ignition switch is replaced, position key cylinder in Lock detent and remove key, then place ignition switch in Lock position (second detent from bottom).
31. Install ignition switch actuator rod into slider hole and loosely attach to column using two screws.
32. Push ignition switch lightly toward lock housing, to take up lash in actuator rod, then tighten mounting screws. **Torque** mounting screws to 35 inch lbs. **Use caution not to move switch out of detent. Use only the correct length screws.**
33. Install dimmer switch as follows:
    a. Firmly seat pushrod into dimmer switch.
    b. Compress switch until two .093 inch drill shanks can be inserted into alignment holes, **Fig. 34.**
    c. Reposition upper end of pushrod in pocket of wiper/washer switch. Remove lower column cover, if necessary.
    d. While maintaining light upward pressure on switch, install mounting bolts.
    e. Remove drill shanks.
    f. Switch should click when lever is lifted; and click again, as lever returns, just before it reaches stop in down position.
34. Install wire protector over wires on column jacket. **Use caution not to pinch any wires.**
35. Remove column from vise.
36. Remove holding fixture from column, then position bracket assembly on column. Install and **torque** four attaching bolts to 120 inch lbs.
37. Align master splines, then install coupling assembly on steering shaft.
38. Support coupling under joint, then drive in retaining roll pin, using a suitable drift.

## 1989–90 FWD MODELS W/STANDARD COLUMN EXCEPT HORIZON & OMNI

### Disassembly

1. Remove wiring cover retainers and the wiring cover.
2. Remove shift lever by driving retaining roll pin out with a suitable punch.
3. Remove breakaway capsules and secure steering column in vise. **On vehicles equipped with intermittent wipe or intermittent wipe with speed control,** remove turn signal lever from lock housing.
4. Remove wiper/washer switch assembly. Pull cover up control stalk and unscrew control stalk sleeve from wiper/washer switch.
5. Move control stalk shaft to full clockwise position, then by pulling straight out, separate shaft from switch.
6. Remove upper bearing and turn signal switch retaining screws, **Fig. 35.** Remove retainer and move switch to side.
7. Disconnect horn and key light ground wires and unscrew ignition key lamp retaining screw. Move ignition key lamp assembly to side.
8. Remove bearing housing to lock housing screws. Remove snap ring from upper end of steering shaft, then remove bearing housing. **Do not allow steering shaft to slide out of jacket.**
9. Remove lockplate spring and lockplate from shaft and remove shaft through lower end of column.
10. Remove ignition key. Remove screw and lift out buzzer/chime switch.
11. Remove ignition switch to column jacket screws, rotate switch 90° on rod and lift off rod.
12. Remove dimmer switch retaining screws and switch from actuator rod.
13. Remove bellcrank mounting screws and slide bellcrank up until it can be disconnected from ignition switch actuator rod.

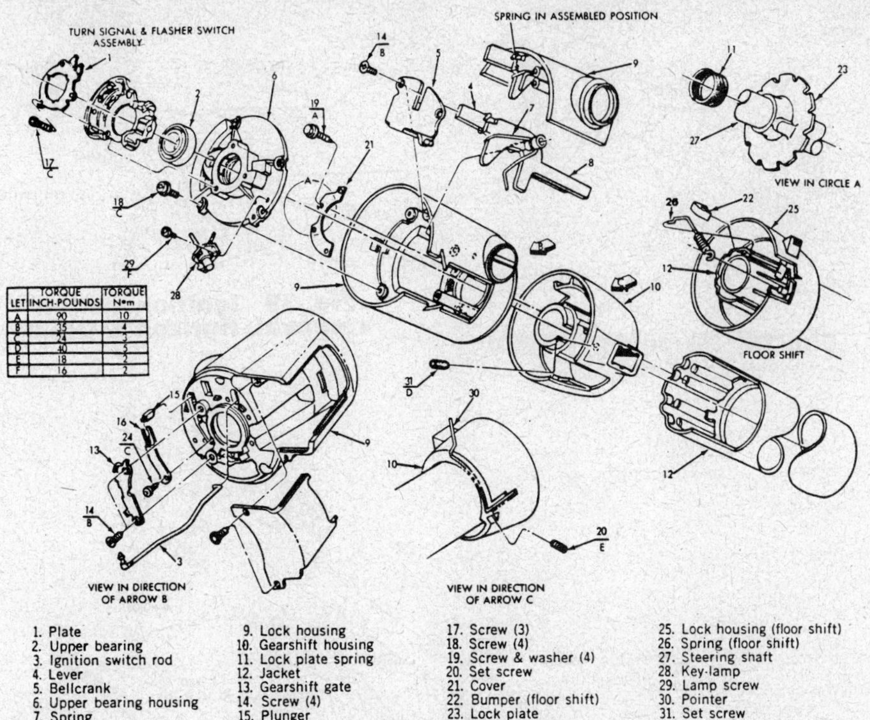


| LET | TORQUE INCH-POUNDS | TORQUE N•m |
|---|---|---|
| A | 90 | 10 |
| B | 35 | 4 |
| C | 24 | 3 |
| D | 40 | 5 |
| E | 18 | 2 |
| F | 16 | 2 |

1. Plate
2. Upper bearing
3. Ignition switch rod
4. Lever
5. Bellcrank
6. Upper bearing housing
7. Spring
8. Lever
9. Lock housing
10. Gearshift housing
11. Lock plate spring
12. Jacket
13. Gearshift gate
14. Screw (4)
15. Plunger
16. Spring
17. Screw (3)
18. Screw (4)
19. Screw & washer (4)
20. Set screw
21. Cover
22. Bumper (floor shift)
23. Lock plate
24. Screw
25. Lock housing (floor shift)
26. Spring (floor shift)
27. Steering shaft
28. Key-lamp
29. Lamp screw
30. Pointer
31. Set screw

**Fig. 35 Exploded view of upper steering column. 1989–90 FWD models w/standard column except Horizon & Omni**

14. Place lock cylinder in Lock position and remove key. Install small diameter screwdriver in lock cylinder release holes and push in to release lock retainers while pulling lock cylinder out of bore.
15. Pull lock lever and spring assembly from housing. Remove lock housing retaining screws and the lock housing plate and housing from jacket.
16. **On column shift automatic models,** loosen shift tube setscrew in shift housing and remove shift tube through lower end of jacket.
17. **On models with floor shift,** remove spring securing shift housing to mast jacket, rubber bumper and the shift housing, **Fig. 36.**

## Assembly

Apply a thin coat of multi-purpose grease to all friction surfaces during assembly.

1. Clamp column in vise and check column tube to mandrel rivets for tightness. Use aluminum pop rivets (1/8 inch grip) for replacement. **Do not use steel rivets. Rivets at this joint must shear upon impact.**
2. Install shift tube and/or gearshift housing as follows:
   a. Apply coat of multipurpose grease to shift housing seat in mast jacket.
   b. **On models with floor shift,** install rubber bumper and spring securing housing to mast jacket, **Fig. 36.**
   c. **On column shift models,** insert shift tube from lower end of column, ensuring key on tube engages slot in housing, hold assembly together and tighten setscrew to secure assembly.
3. **On all models,** place crossover load spring and gearshift lever into housing and tap pivot pin into place.
4. Assemble key cylinder plunger and spring and install in lock housing, **Fig. 35.**
5. Install shift lever gate on lock housing.
6. Move shift lever to mid-position, then with keyway in housing indexed with slot in jacket, seat lock housing in jacket. Insert screws and **torque** alternately to 90 inch lbs.
7. Position dimmer switch pushrod into switch. Compress switch until two .093 inch drills can be inserted into alignment holes, **Fig. 25.** Place upper end of pushrod into washer/wiper switch. With slight rearward pressure on switch, install screws and remove drills. **Switch should click when lever is lifted and when lever returns, just before stop in down position.**
8. Assemble lock levers, lock lever springs and pin, **Fig. 24.** Install assembly into housing with lock lever spring leg firmly seated in lock casting notch.
9. Place gearshift lever in Park position. Install ignition switch actuator rod from bottom through oblong hole in lock housing and attach to bellcrank. Position bellcrank onto mounting surface while pulling ignition switch rod down column.
10. Install ignition switch onto ignition switch actuator rod. Rotate 90° to lock rod into position.
11. Insert key into lock cylinder, turn to Lock position and remove key. Insert cylinder into housing so that it contacts switch actuator. Insert key, press inward and rotate cylinder until cylinder locks into housing.
12. Place key cylinder and ignition switch in Lock position (second detent from top) and tighten ignition switch mounting screws.
13. Remove ignition key. Install buzzer/chime switch wires behind wiring post and down through space between jacket and housing. Position switch in housing, then install and tighten mounting screws.
14. Install lower bearing support, bearing and spring on steering shaft. Install O-ring in lower groove on upper end of shaft. Insert shaft into column assembly.
15. Press upper bearing into upper bearing housing, ensuring bearing is fully bottomed in housing.
16. Install lockplate, upper bearing spring, upper bearing housing and upper bearing housing retaining screws, press steering shaft into column to compress springs, then install upper bearing snap ring, ensuring snap ring is fully seated in shaft groove and bearing housing recess.
17. Install ignition key lamp assembly and turn signal switch on bearing housing. Install bearing retainer plate and **torque** screws to 24 inch lbs. **Position ground wires toward ground clips before torquing.**
18. Install ground clips for ignition key lamp and turn signal switch onto bearing retaining plate.
19. Assemble wiper switch, shaft and cover or speed control switch, cover and knob. Install washer/wiper switch assembly into lock housing and fasten to turn signal switch.
20. Install turn signal lever cover, breakaway capsules and wiring cover over wires and retainers.

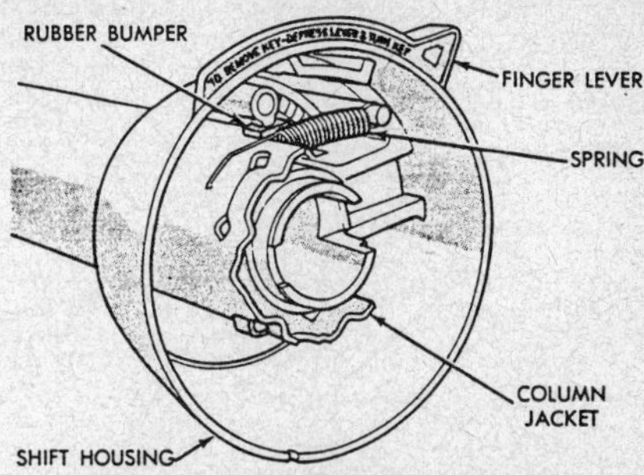


**Fig. 36 Shift housing installation. Models w/floor shifter except Horizon & Omni**

## 1991 FWD MODELS W/STANDARD COLUMN

The Acustar steering column has been designed to be serviced as an assembly less wiring, switches, shrouds & steering wheel. Also most steering column components can be serviced without removing the column from the vehicle, **Fig. 6.**

The only other serviceable components are as follows:

1. **On models with column shift,** the gear shift lever assembly. Use a drift

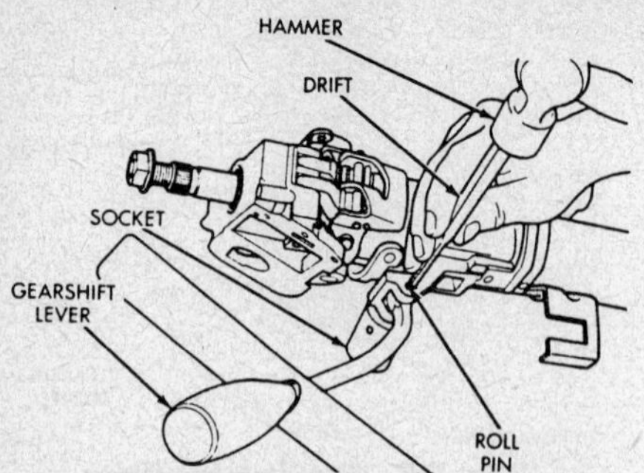

Fig. 37 Removing Gear Shift Lever

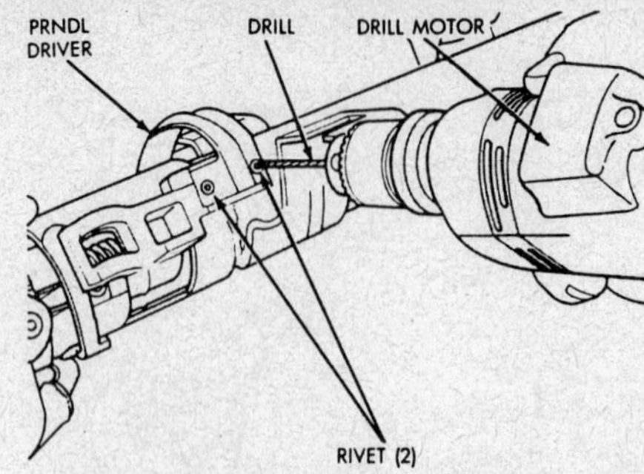

Fig. 38 Removing PRNDL driver

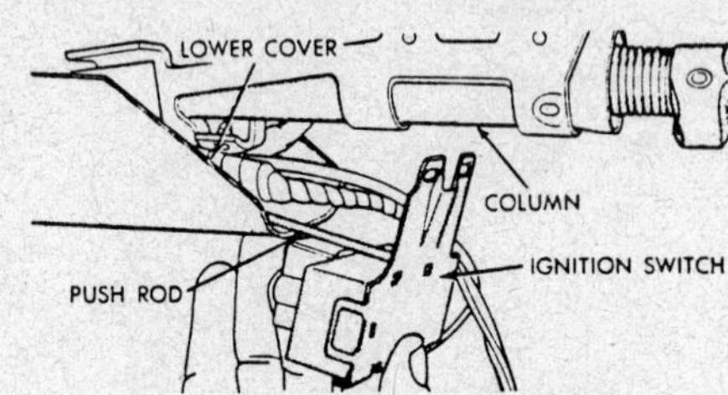

Fig. 39 Ignition switch removal. Horizon & Omni

and a suitable size socket to drive out lever retaining pin, **Fig. 37.**

2. The PRNDL driver can be removed by drilling out rivets, **Fig. 38. Use care to prevent bending when installing new driver and use only correct replacement rivets.**

## HORIZON & OMNI

### Disassembly

1. Disconnect battery ground cable.
2. Remove steering wheel and column covers, **Fig. 7,** key lamp, ignition switch, **Fig. 39,** and dimmer switch, key buzzer switch, washer/wiper switch, key cylinder and turn signal switch.
3. Unlock key cylinder and carefully remove upper snap ring and steering shaft out through lower end of jacket.
4. To service lower bearing and spring, remove the universal joint.
5. To service upper bearing, remove turn signal switch and gently pry bearing from housing using a flat screwdriver.
6. The inhibitor lever can be removed by removing its retaining screw.
7. The ignition switch pushrod can be removed by unhooking it from ignition switch.
8. The housing assembly is serviced as a unit and should not be removed unless it is to be replaced. The housing assembly can be removed by driving it off or by splitting it with a hacksaw. If removed, a new housing is required.
9. To remove toe plate, seal and lower shaft assembly, pull back carpeting from toe plate and remove the four screws. Slide toe plate and seal off shaft. The seal can be removed from plate.
10. Remove lower universal joint retainer (roll pin), to disassemble lower shaft assembly from steering gear.

### Assembly

1. If housing assembly has been removed, install a new housing. Align keyway in jacket with key in housing, the position lock mechanisms so that lock bolt is withdrawn into housing. Press housing onto jacket until it bottoms. Check to assure that lock mechanism operates smoothly and that lock bolt extends and withdraws freely.
2. Place upper bearing in place, then mount turn signal switch and retainer plate on housing.
3. Install lower bearing, shaft spring and upper universal joint on lower end of steering shaft, then place lower snap ring in its groove and slide shaft into lower end of jacket. Compress lower bearing spring and carefully install upper snap ring into groove. Check to make sure that snap ring is fully seated, and check for proper lock mechanism operation.
4. Install inhibitor lever and spring, ignition switch pushrod, ignition switch, dimmer switch, washer/wiper switch, key lamp, key buzzer switch, key cylinder, column covers and steering wheel.

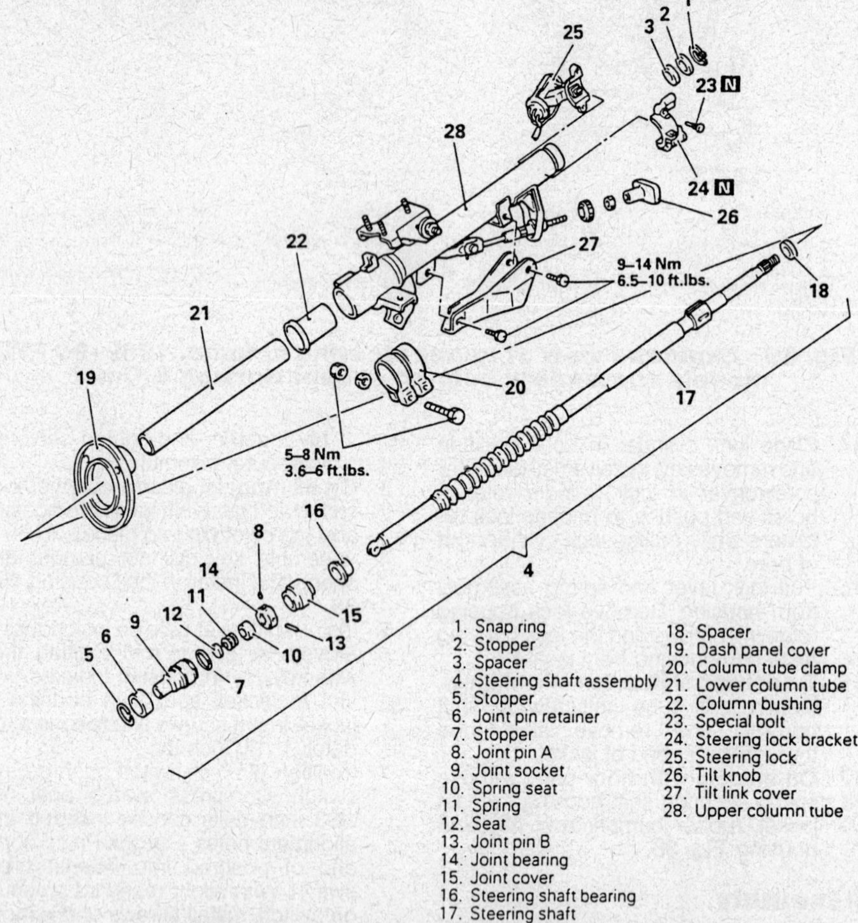

Fig. 40 Exploded view of steering column assembly. Conquest

## 1989 FWD MODELS w/TILT STEERING COLUMN

For service procedures refer to "RWD Models w/Tilt Steering Column" section.

## 1990–91 FWD MODELS w/TILT STEERING COLUMN

For available service procedures, refer to "1991 FWD Models w/Standard Column."

## CONQUEST

### Disassembly

Remove steering column as outlined under "Steering Column, Replace." Remove components in order as they appear

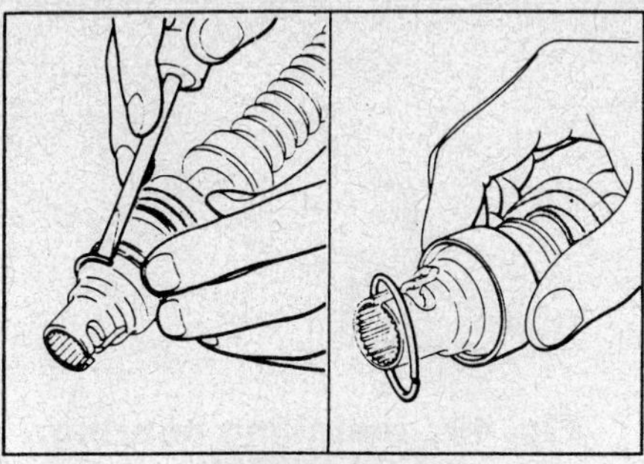

Fig. 41 **Removing joint pin retainer**

Fig. 42 **Removing joint pin A**

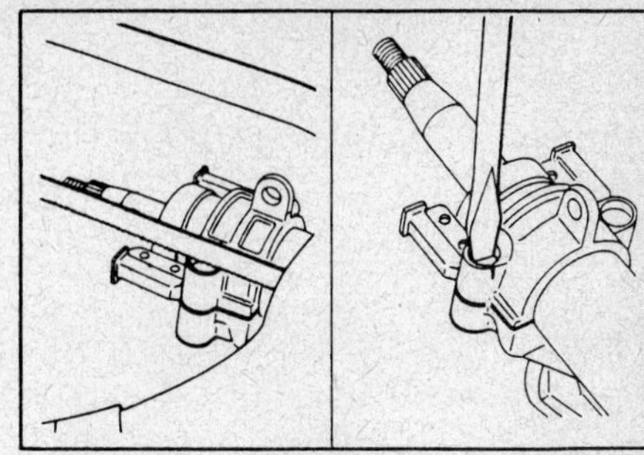

Fig. 43 **Removing steering lock**

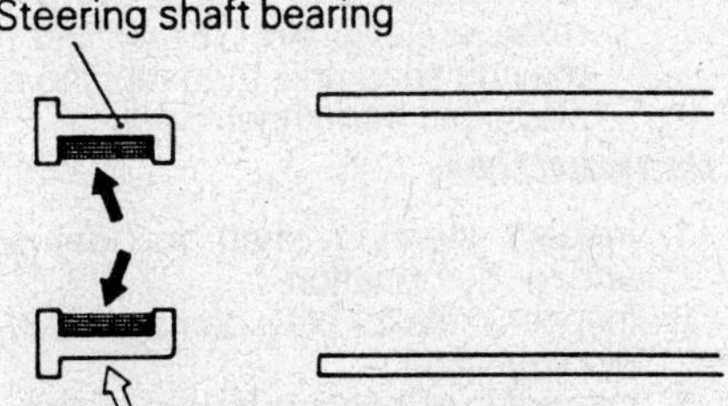


Fig. 44 **Installing steering shaft bearing**

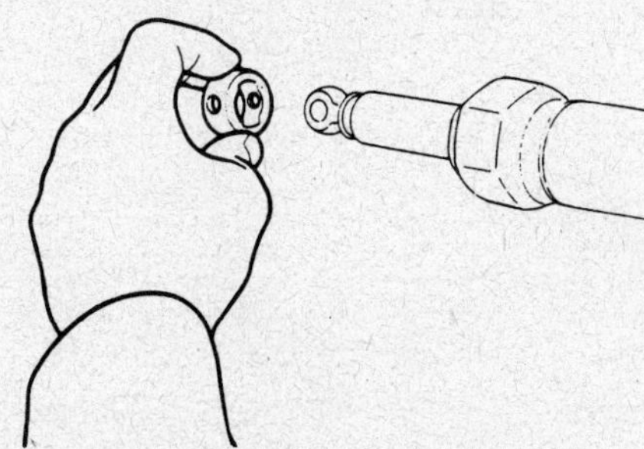

Fig. 45 **Installing joint bearing**

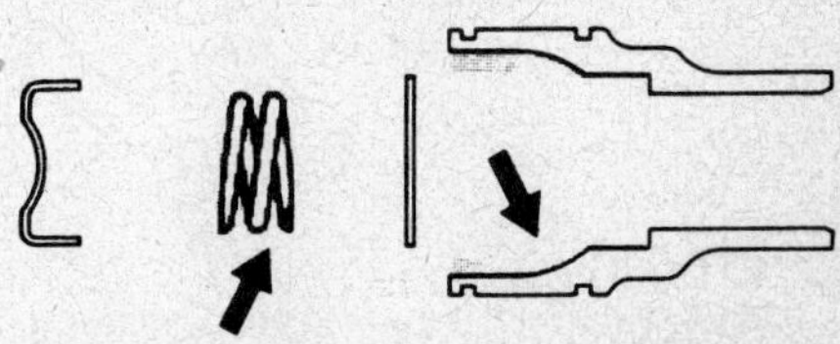

Fig. 46 **Installing joint socket**

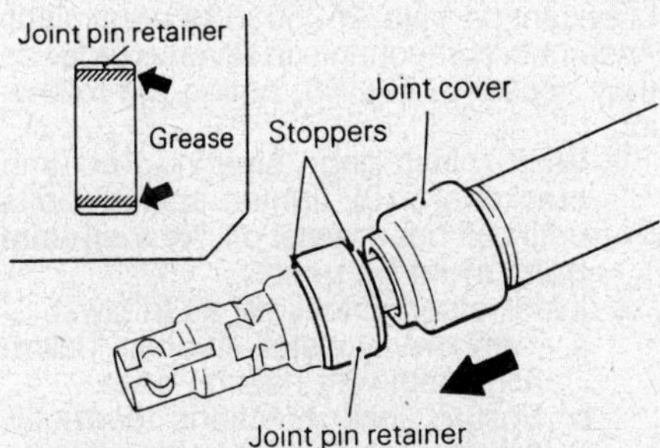


Fig. 47 **Installing joint pin retainer**

in **Fig. 40,** noting the following:

1. Remove steering shaft assembly (4) as follows:
   a. Remove steering shaft bearing from lower column tube.
   b. Remove snap ring of upper column shaft using snap ring pliers.
   c. Remove steering shaft from tube.
2. Remove joint pin retainer (6) as follows:
   a. Slide off joint cover from socket assembly.
   b. Remove stoppers, then pull out joint pin retainer, **Fig. 41.**
3. Remove joint pin A (8) as follows:
   a. With steering shaft in upright position, pull out joint pin A on both sides of socket, using a magnet, while holding shaft downward, **Fig. 42. Remove joint pin A only by using a magnet. Striking pin with a hammer will make it unremovable.**
   b. Remove joint socket (9).
4. Remove joint pin B (13) as follows:
   a. Press out joint pin B from steering shaft, then remove joint bearing (14).
   b. Remove joint cover (15), then the steering shaft bearing (16).
5. If removal of steering lock (25) is necessary, proceed as follows:
   a. Cut a groove in head of special bolt using a hacksaw, **Fig. 43.**
   b. Remove steering lock using a screwdriver. **Upper steering lock bracket and special bolts must be replaced with new ones when installing steering lock.**

## Inspection

1. Inspect tilt bracket for cracks and/or damage.
2. Inspect column bushing for damage.
3. Inspect steering shaft bearing for wear.
4. Inspect steering shaft for damage and/or deformation. Steering shaft length should be 26.62 inches (727 mm).
5. Inspect joint cover for wear.
6. Inspect joint bearing for damage and/or wear.

## Assembly

Apply lubricant to surfaces as indicated. Specified lubricant is Mopar Multi-mileage Lubricant part No. 2525035 or equivalent. Assemble components in reverse order as they appear in **Fig. 40,** noting the following:

1. Install steering lock as follows:
   a. Temporarily install steering lock in alignment with column boss.
   b. Ensure lock functions correctly, then tighten special bolts until bolt heads twist off. **Upper steering lock bracket and special bolts must be replaced with new ones when installing steering lock.**
2. Install column tube clamp (20) as follows:
   a. Attach column bushing to upper and lower column tubes.
   b. Secure upper tube with clamp.
   c. Install clamp so that bolt tightening portion of clamp is at the bottom.
   d. **Torque** clamp bolt to 3.6-6.0 ft. lbs.
3. Install steering shaft bearing (16) as follows:
   a. Apply specified lubricant to inner surface of steering shaft bearing, **Fig. 44,** then insert steering shaft into bearing.
   b. Apply suitable adhesive to surface where steering shaft and column tube contact, **Fig. 44.**
   c. Apply specified lubricant to inner surface of upper bearing.
   d. Install steering shaft with steering shaft bearing in column tube.
4. Install joint bearing (14) as follows:
   a. Install joint bearing with flanged surface facing upward on steering shaft lower end, **Fig. 45.**
   b. Align joint bearing hole and steering shaft hole.
   c. Apply specified lubricant to joint pin B (13), then insert in joint bearing. **Ensure joint pin B does not project over bearing surface.**
5. Install joint socket as follows:
   a. Fill socket with specified lubricant, then insert seat, spring and spring seat, **Fig. 46.**
6. Install joint pin A (8) as follows:
   a. Apply specified lubricant to joint pin A.
   b. Insert steering shaft lower end into socket, then while holding shaft down, install joint pin A by hand.
7. Install joint pin retainer (6) as follows:

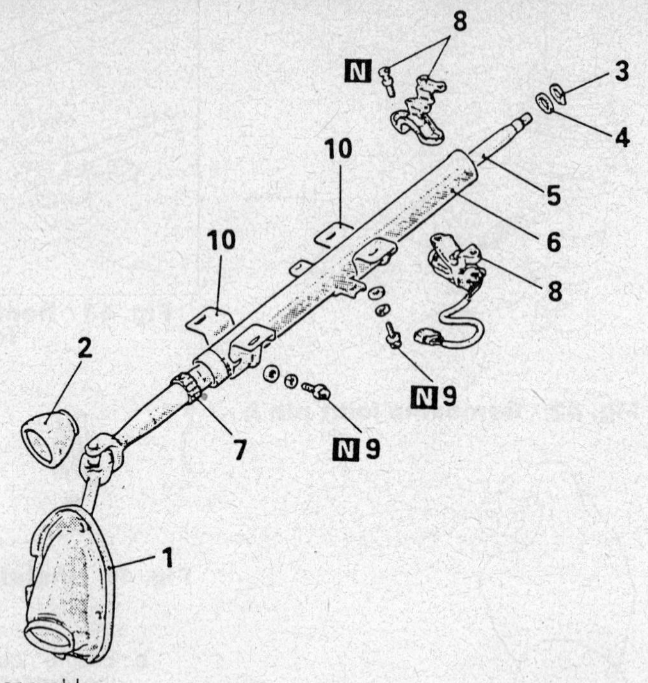


1. Dust cover
2. Boot
3. Snap ring
4. Spacer
5. Steering shaft
6. Column tube
7. Lower bearing
8. Steering lock assembly
9. Column bracket attaching special screws
10. Steering column bracket

**Fig. 48 Exploded view of steering column assembly. Colt Wagon**

a. Apply specified lubricant to inner surface of joint pin retainer, **Fig. 43.**
b. Attach joint pin retainer, securing with stoppers.
c. Cover joint pin retainer with joint pin cover.

## COLT WAGON

### Disassembly

1. Remove steering column as outlined under "Steering Column, Replace."
2. Remove components in order as they appear in **Fig. 48,** noting the following:
   a. Remove snap ring (3), then remove steering shaft (5) downward.
   b. If removal of steering lock assembly (8) is necessary, use a hacksaw to cut a groove in head of special bolts, then use a screwdriver to remove steering lock.
   c. If removal of steering column bracket(s) (10) is necessary, use a hacksaw to cut a groove in head of special bolts, then use a screwdriver to remove steering column bracket(s).

### Inspection

1. Inspect steering shaft for bends and/or deformation.
2. Inspect steering shaft spline for breakage and/or damage.
3. Inspect steering shaft joints for play and/or binding.
4. Inspect all rubber parts for cracks and/or breakage.

### Assembly

Apply lubricant to surfaces as indicated. Specified lubricant is Mopar Multi-mileage Lubricant part No. 2525035 or equivalent. Assemble components in reverse order as they appear in **Fig. 48,** noting the following:

1. When installing steering column bracket(s) (10), tighten special bolts until bolt heads twist off. **New special bolts must be used.**
2. Install steering lock (8) as follows:
   a. Temporarily install steering lock in alignment with column boss.
   b. Ensure lock functions correctly, then tighten special bolts until bolt heads twist off. **Steering lock bracket and special bolts must be replaced with new ones when installing steering lock.**
3. Install bearing (7) as follows:
   a. Apply specified lubricant to lower bearing before installing in lower portion of steering column.
   b. Ensure projections on bearing are fitted to holes in steering column, **Fig. 49.**

## COLT & EAGLE SUMMIT

### Disassembly

1. Remove steering column as outlined under Steering Column, Replace."
2. Remove components in order as they appear in **Fig 48,** noting the following:
   a. If removal of steering lock (4) is necessary, use a hacksaw to cut special bolts at steering lock bracket side.
   b. Remove snap ring (5), then remove steering shaft (6) downward.
   c. If removal of steering column bracket(s) is necessary, use a hacksaw to cut a groove in head of special bolts, then use a screwdriver to remove steering column bracket(s).
   d. **On models with Type 2 columns** remove clevis pin (15) by first removing snap ring, then tapping out clevis pin from inner side.

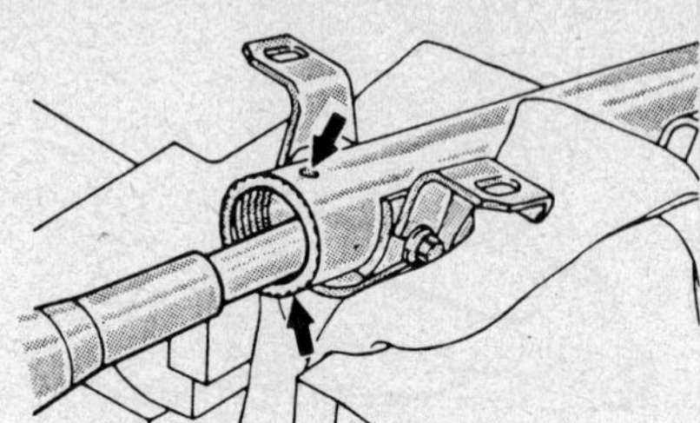

**Fig. 49 Installing bearing. Colt Wagon**

### Inspection

1. Inspect steering shaft for damage and/or deformation.
2. Inspect joints for play, damage and/or binding.
3. Inspect joint bearing for wear and/or damage.
4. Inspect bushing for wear and/or damage.

### Assembly

Apply lubricant to surfaces as indicated. Specified lubricant is Mopar Multi-mileage Lubricant part No. 2525035 or equivalent. Assemble components in reverse order as they appear in **Fig. 50,** noting the following:

1. When installing steering column bracket(s), tighten special bolts until bolt heads twist off. **New special bolts must be used.**
2. Apply suitable drying adhesive to outer circumference of bearing (11), **Fig. 51,** before installing in column tube.
3. Apply a coating of specified lubricant to sliding portion of bearing, **Fig. 51.**
4. Install steering lock (8) as follows:
   a. Temporarily install steering lock in alignment with column boss.
   b. Ensure lock functions correctly, then tighten special bolts until bolt heads twist off. **Steering lock bracket and special bolts must be replaced with new ones when installing steering lock.**

## COLT VISTA

### Disassembly

1. Remove steering column as outlined under "Steering Column, Replace."
2. Remove components in order as they appear in **Fig. 52,** noting the following:
   a. If removal of steering wheel lock assembly (3) is necessary, use a hacksaw to cut a groove in head of special bolts, then use a screwdriver to remove steering lock.
   b. If removal of steering column bracket(s) is necessary, use a hacksaw to cut a groove in head of special bolts, then use a screwdriver to remove steering column bracket(s).

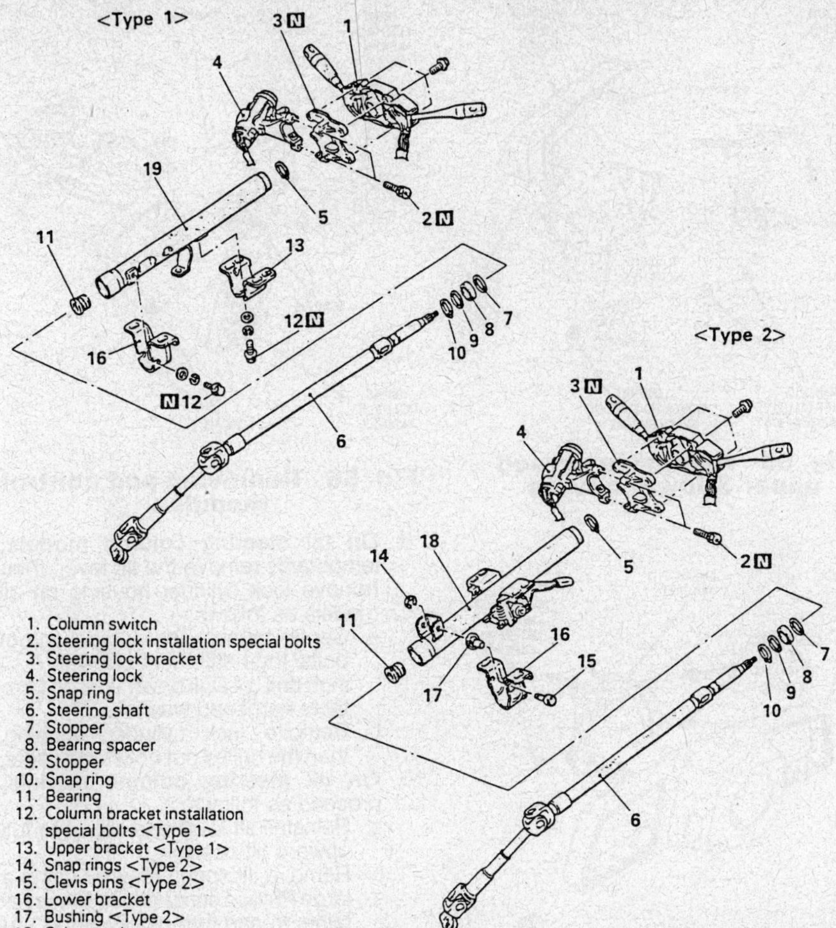


**Fig. 50 Exploded view of steering column assembly. 1989 Colt & Eagle Summit**

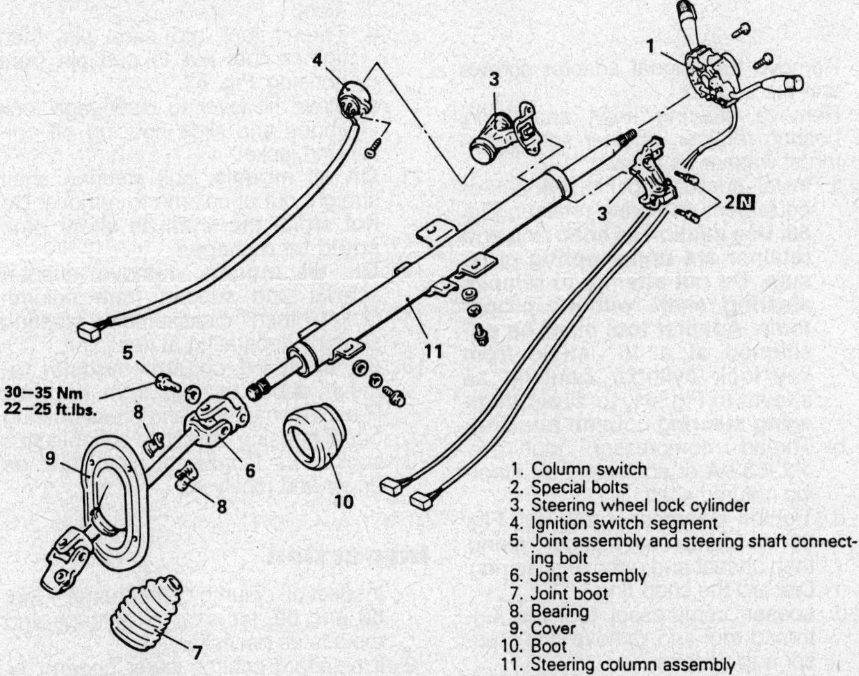


**Fig. 52 Exploded view of steering column assembly. Colt Vista**

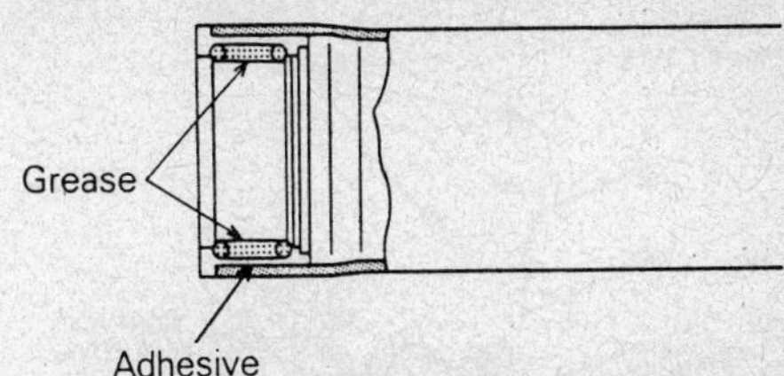


**Fig. 51 Installing bearing. 1989–90 Colt & Eagle Summit**

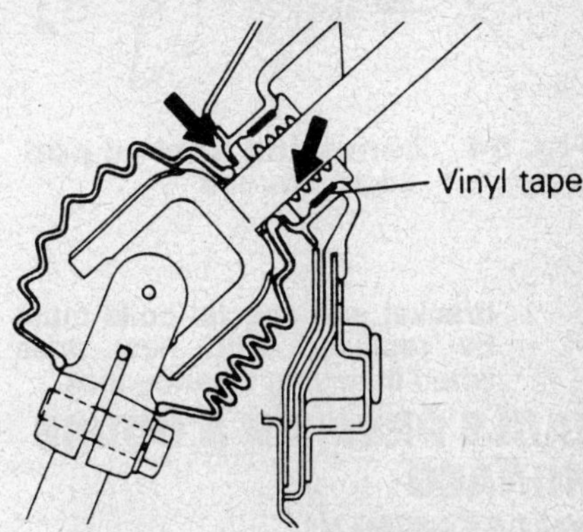


**Fig. 53 Installing cover, bearing & joint assembly. Colt Vista**

## Inspection

1. Inspect steering shaft for bends and/or deformation.
2. Inspect steering shaft spline for breakage.
3. Inspect steering shaft joints for play, damage and/or binding.
4. Inspect rubber parts for cracks and/or breakage.

## Assembly

Apply lubricant to surfaces as indicated. Specified lubricant is Mopar Multi-mileage Lubricant part No. 2525035 or equivalent. Assemble components in reverse order as they appear in **Fig. 52,** noting the following:

1. When installing steering column bracket(s), tighten special bolts until bolt heads twist off. **New special bolts must be used.**
2. Install cover (9), bearing (8) and joint assembly (6) as follows:
   a. Install cover on joint assembly.
   b. Fill inside of bearing with specified lubricant.
   c. Install bearings to shaft of joint assembly.
   d. Wrap vinyl tape approximately 1 1/2 times around concave circumference of bearing, then press bearing into cover, **Fig. 53.**
   e. Apply specified lubricant to mating surfaces of joint and cover assemblies.
3. Install steering wheel lock assembly (3) as follows:
   a. Temporarily install steering lock in alignment with column boss.
   b. Ensure lock functions correctly, then tighten special bolts until bolt heads twist off. **Steering lock**

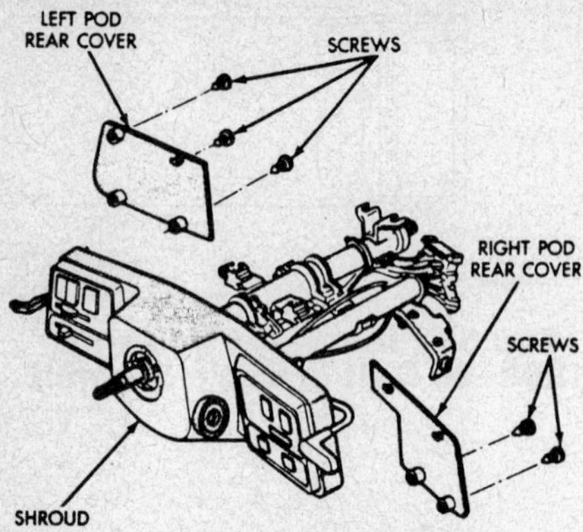


**Fig. 54 Removing shroud pod rear covers**

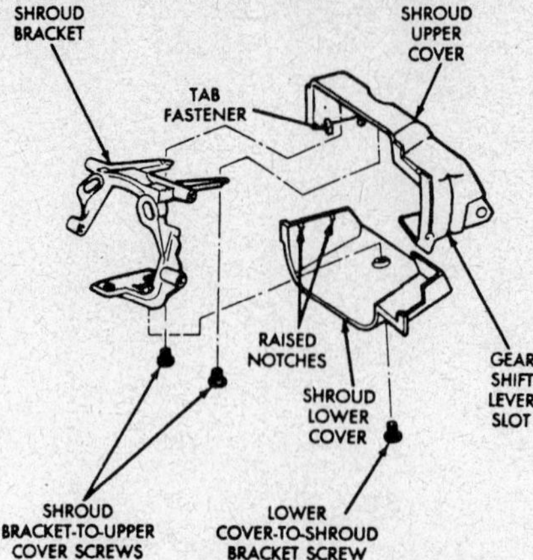


**Fig. 55 Removing shroud upper & lower covers**

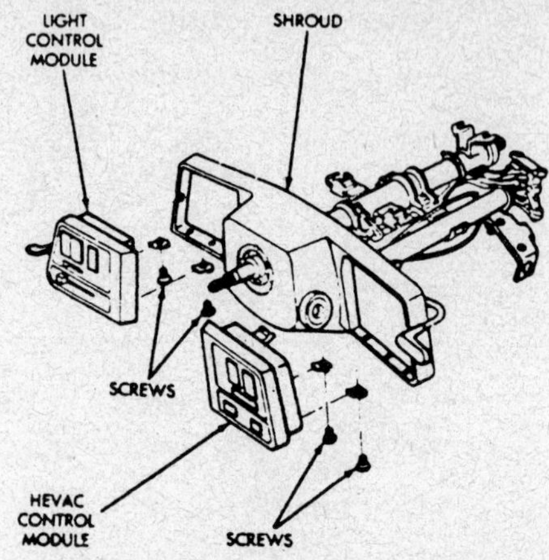


**Fig. 56 Removing pod control modules**

**bracket and special bolts must be replaced with new ones when installing steering lock.**

# EAGLE PREMIER & DODGE MONACO

## DISASSEMBLY

1. Disconnect battery ground cable.
2. Remove steering wheel and column as outlined under "Steering Column, Replace."
3. Remove steering column shroud as follows:
   a. Remove three screws attaching rear cover to left shroud pod, **Fig. 54.**
   b. Remove two screws attaching rear cover to right shroud pod, **Fig. 54.**
   c. Remove rear covers from both shroud pods.
   d. Remove lower cover to shroud bracket screw, then carefully separate lower cover from upper cover by detaching upper cover tab fasteners from lower cover notches, **Fig. 55.**
   e. Remove two shroud bracket to upper cover screws, then the upper shroud cover. Slide shroud upper cover off gearshift lever.
   f. Remove shroud to control module screws, then remove both control modules from pods, **Fig. 56.** This will provide access to four shroud to bracket internal screws.
   g. Remove key/lock cylinder bezel from shroud.
   h. Cover tilt lever stalk with a shop towel and remove by unthreading from tilt lever using locking pliers. **Use caution not to damage stalk with plier teeth.**
   i. Remove four shroud to bracket internal screws, then the shroud from bracket, **Fig. 57.**
4. Remove cancelling cam, wave washer and turn signal switch, **Figs. 58 and 59.**
5. Remove shroud bracket, then the two ignition switch retaining screws and switch from key/lock cylinder housing. Turn ignition key to unmarked position, push the cylinder lock tab inward and remove.

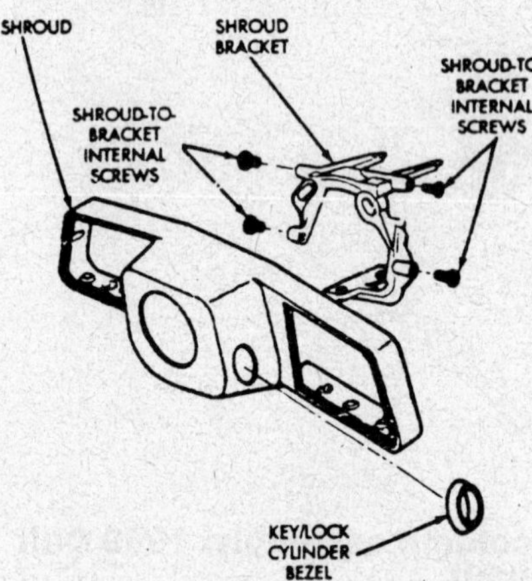


**Fig. 57 Removing shroud**

6. Remove turn signal adapter screws and the adapter.
7. Remove steering shaft snap ring, bearing retainer, retainer spring and thrust washer as follows:
   a. Install adapter tool No. J-35899 or equivalent on spring retainer, **Fig. 60. Use caution as snap ring and retainer are under spring pressure. Do not attempt to remove steering shaft without proper tools. Adapter tool must be positioned at a 45° angle from key/lock cylinder housing as shown in Fig. 61, to avoid damaging steering column housing.**
   b. Thread compressor tool No. J-23653-A or equivalent on steering column shaft.
   c. Tighten compressor tool nut, **Fig. 60,** to compress retainer spring, then unseat and remove snap ring. Discard the snap ring.
   d. Loosen compressor tool nut, unthread tool and remove compressor and adapter.
   e. Remove spring, washer and retainer.
8. Remove shift cable from housing by pressing the retaining tab.
9. **On tilt steering column models,** temporarily remove the tilt lever, then remove lock cylinder housing on all models as follows:
   a. Center punch the tamper proof bolts, then drill them out with a 1/4 inch drill bit. Drill down until bit contacts hardened washer.
   b. Remove lock cylinder housing, then the drilled out bolts with pliers.
10. **On tilt steering column models,** proceed as follows:
    a. Reinstall tilt lever and adjust to full upward tilt position.
    b. Remove tilt spring retainer using a large Phillips screwdriver. Press retainer in and turn clockwise to unlock, **Fig. 62,** then remove retainer and spring.
    c. Place column in center position and remove pivot pins using pin removal tool No. J-21854-1 or equivalent.
    d. Thread tool into each pin, then tighten tool nut to pull pin from housing, **Fig. 63.**
    e. Move tilt lever to disengage lock shoes and slide housing off column jacket.
11. **On all models,** pull steering shaft straight out of column to remove. **Do not strike the shaft as shear pins could be damaged.**
12. **On tilt models,** remove support screws and support from column jacket, then disassemble steering shaft by separating at flex joint.
13. **On standard column models,** remove upper bearing from housing. Remove snap ring, and press bearing out of housing using two suitable size sockets or lengths of steel tube as driver and receiver.

## Inspection

1. Inspect all column components, **Figs. 58 and 59,** for wear or damage and replace as necessary.
2. If standard column lower bearing, or either upper or lower tilt column bearing needs replacement, the entire column jacket assembly must be replaced.

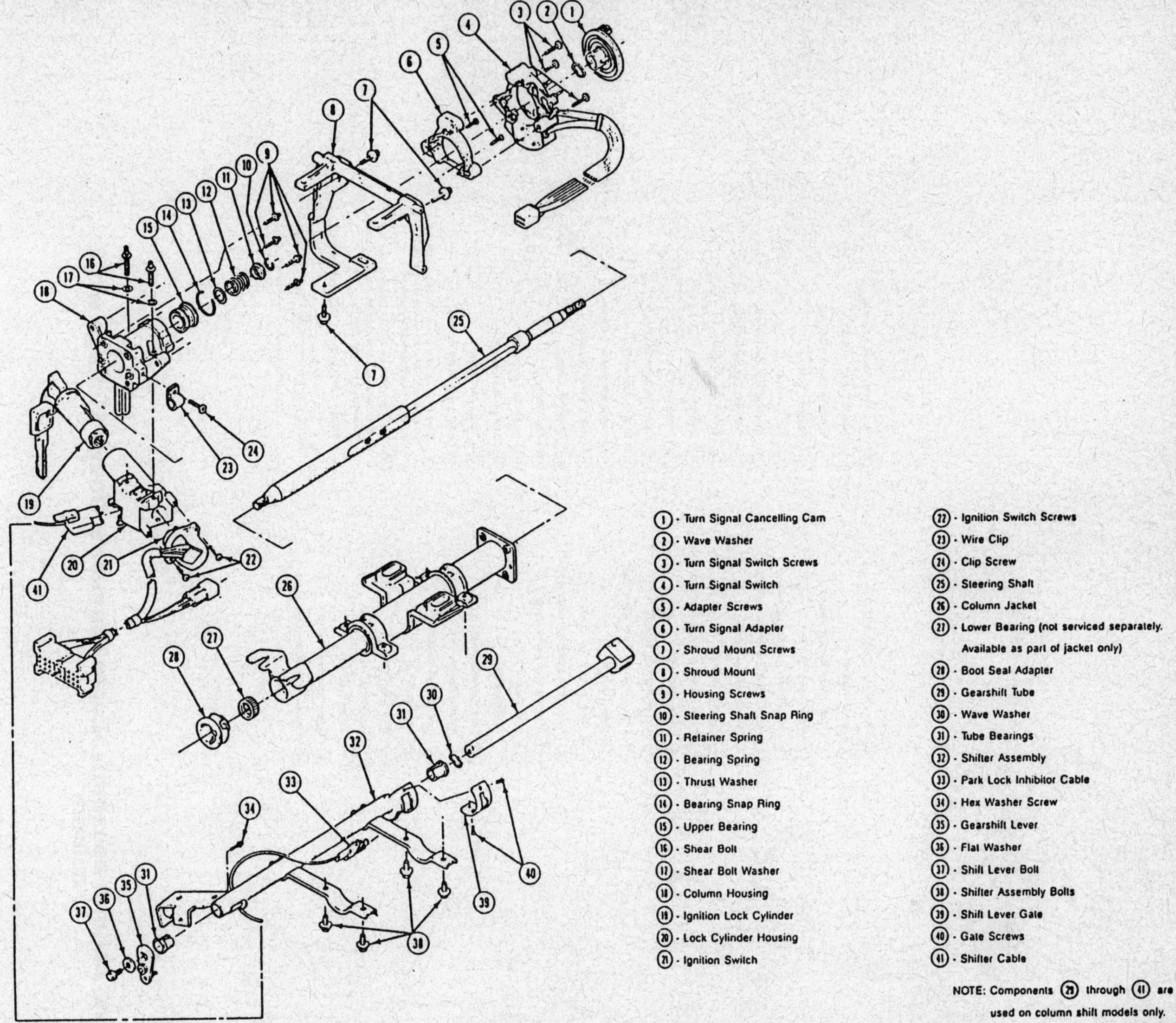


**Fig. 58 Exploded view of steering column assembly. Eagle Premier & Dodge Monaco w/standard column**

## Assembly

1. Press upper bearing into housing using two suitable size sockets as press tool and support.
2. **On tilt column models,** proceed as follows:
   a. Install support and assemble steering shafts.
   b. Insert steering shaft into support and column jacket, then install housing over steering shaft onto support.
   c. Align pivot pin and support holes. Housing lock shoes must be retracted with lever, **Fig. 64,** in order to align holes.
   d. Insert and seat pivot pins with a punch and hammer, then stake each pin in two places.
   e. Install tilt spring in column and position retainer on spring.
   f. Using a large Phillips screwdriver, push retainer in and turn counterclockwise to lock.
3. **On standard column models,** lubricate column bearings with chassis grease, then insert steering shaft into column jacket and secure with four Torx bolts.
4. **On all models,** position lock cylinder housing on column housing and secure with replacement tamper proof bolts and torque until bolt head shears off.
5. Press tab and install shift cable on housing.
6. Position washer, spring and retainer for standard columns, or race, seat and spring for tilt columns, on steering shaft.
7. **On all models,** position a new snap ring, then using adapter tool No. J-35899 and compressor tool No. J-23653-A or equivalents, compress retainer spring as outlined under "Disassembly."
8. Seat snap ring in the bottom groove of steering shaft and remove tools and adapter.
9. Install ignition switch, then the shroud mount on column.
10. Install turn signal switch adapter and turn signal switch.
11. Install wave washer, cancelling cam and ignition lock cylinder in housing.
12. Reverse disassembly procedure to install remaining components.

# EAGLE MEDALLION

## STEERING COLUMN REMOVAL & DISASSEMBLY

### Upper Steering Shaft & Bushing

1. Remove instrument panel lower trim cover.
2. **On models with cruise control,** grasp wire located on lower cover. Pull wire downward to release spring loaded commutator brush. **If wire is not readily accessible, loosen trim cover attaching screws enough to reach the wire.**
3. Remove screws attaching trim cover to column, then the cover.

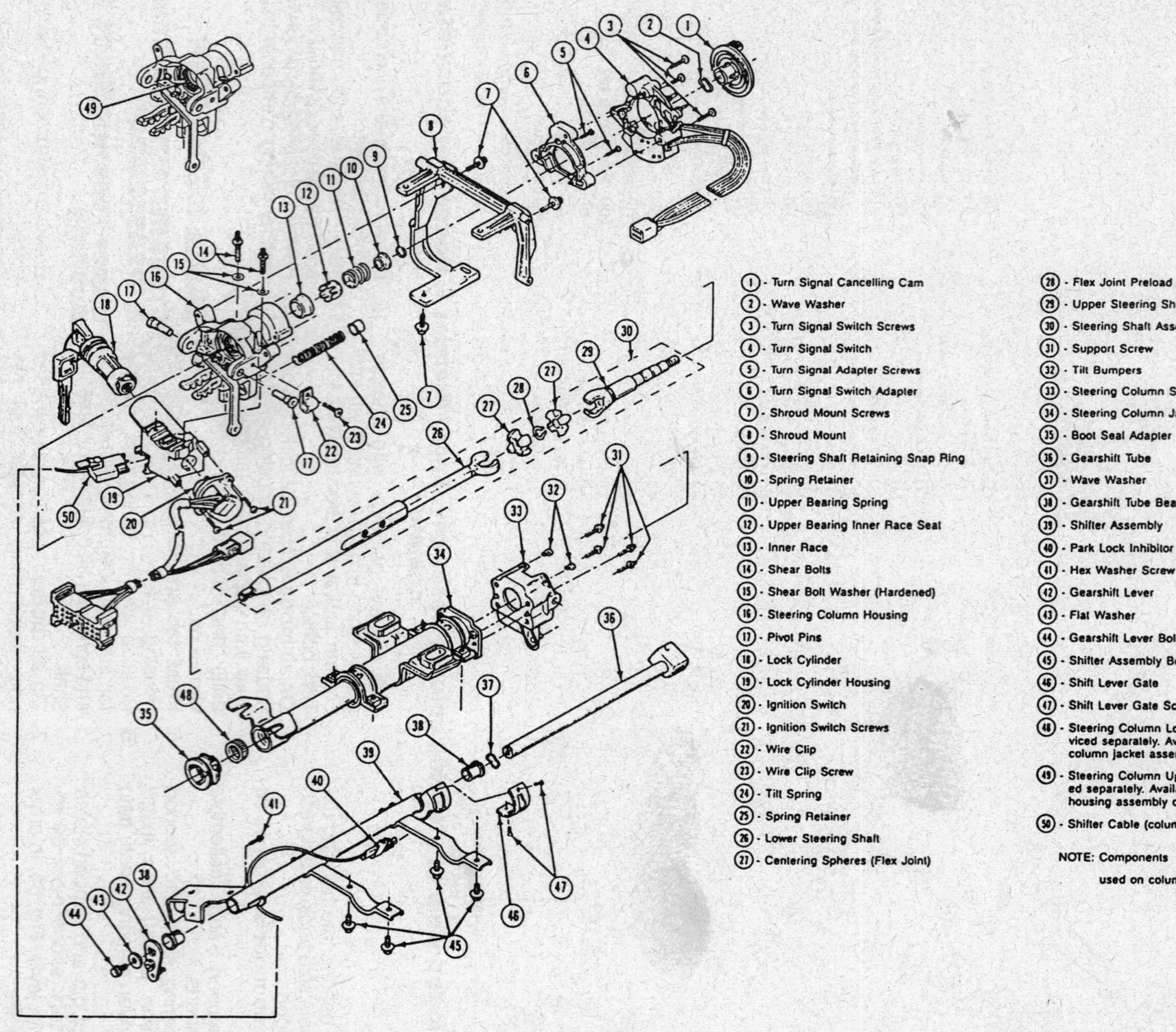


**Fig. 59 Exploded view of steering column assembly. Eagle Premier & Dodge Monaco w/tilt column**

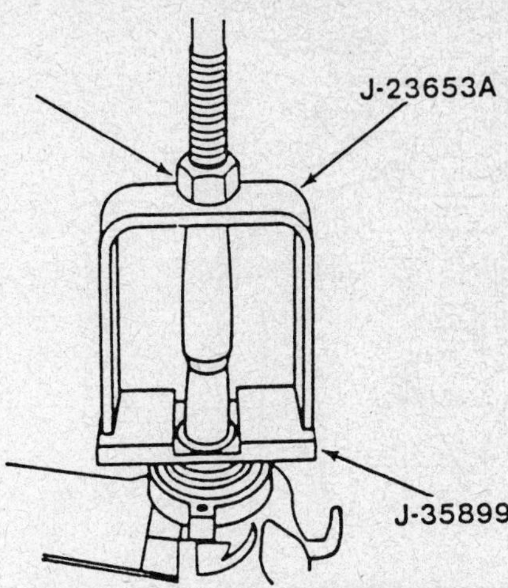


Fig. 60 Steering shaft spring compressor. Eagle Premier & Dodge Monaco

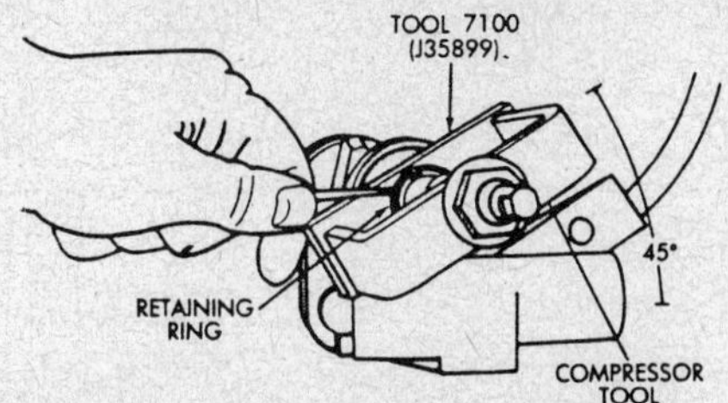


Fig. 61 Positioning adapter tool

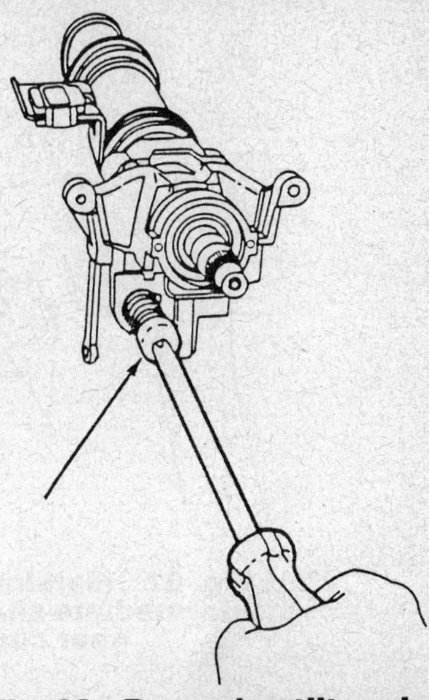

Fig. 62 Removing tilt spring retainer. Eagle Premier & Dodge Monaco

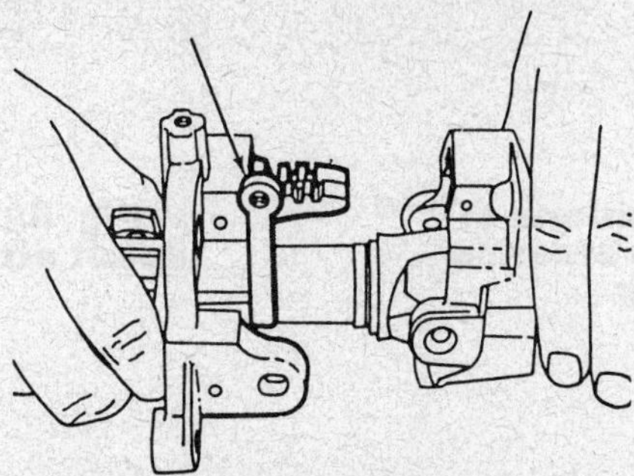

Fig. 64 Lock shoe retracting lever

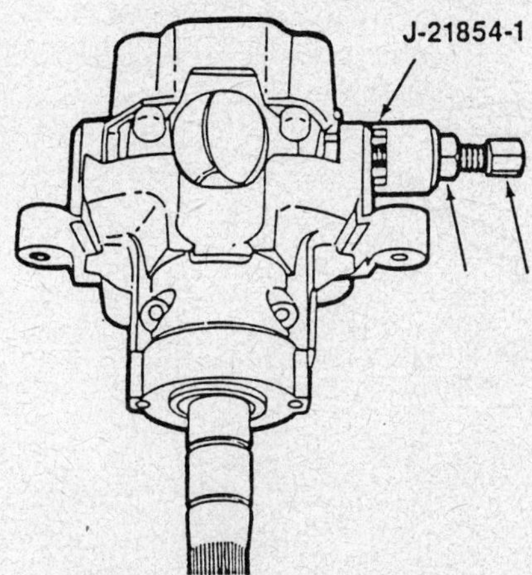


Fig. 63 Removing pivot pin. Eagle Premier & Dodge Monaco

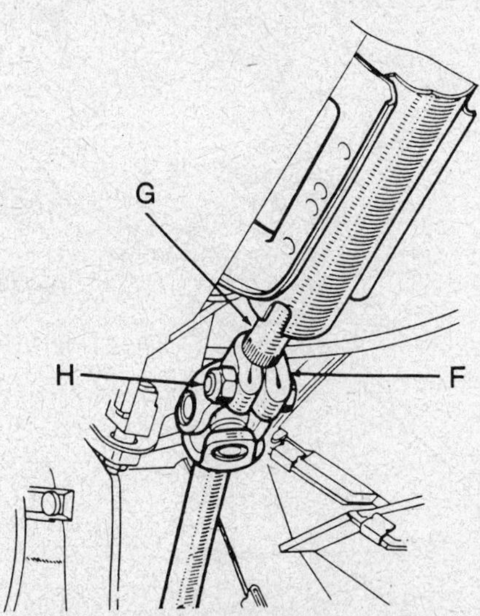


Fig. 65 Steering coupling, steering shaft and pinch bolt assembly

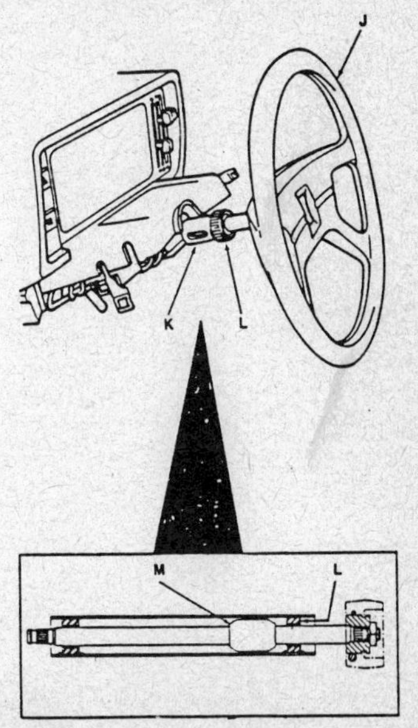


Fig. 66 Temporarily installing steering wheel

4. Remove trim cover from steering wheel.
5. Mark position of steering wheel and column shaft for assembly.
6. Remove steering wheel nut, then pull steering wheel off of shaft.
7. Remove attaching screw securing electrical switches to column assembly.
8. Mark position of coupling (F) and upper steering shaft (G) for assembly, then remove coupling pinch bolt (H), **Fig. 65.**
9. Remove ignition switch.
10. Remove upper steering shaft and shaft bushing as follows:
    a. Temporarily mount steering wheel (J) and wheel nut onto shaft, **Fig. 66.**
    b. Pull upward on shaft (K) until top bushing (L) comes out of column jacket. **Shaft guide (M) will push top bushing out of column as steering wheel and shaft are pulled upward.**
11. Remove steering wheel, top bushing and upper steering shaft from column jacket as an assembly.
12. Remove steering wheel from shaft, then remove top bushing.

### Intermediate Steering Shaft Removal

1. Remove upper steering shaft and top bushing.
2. Move toeboard boot away from intermediate shaft coupling.
3. Mark position of intermediate shaft to steering gear coupling (N) for assembly, **Fig. 67.** Mark both coupling and shaft on steering gear.
4. Remove coupling pinch bolt (P), then remove intermediate steering shaft (Q) and toe board boot, **Fig. 67.**

### Steering Column Jacket Removal

1. Remove bolt (R) attaching column jacket (S) to instrument panel, **Fig. 68.**
2. Remove nuts and bolts (T) attaching column jacket to cowl panel.
3. Remove column jacket (S).
4. If necessary, remove bottom bushing from column jacket.

## STEERING COLUMN ASSEMBLY & INSTALLATION

### Steering Shaft Bottom Bushing

1. If removed, coat steering shaft bottom bushing with clean chassis grease.

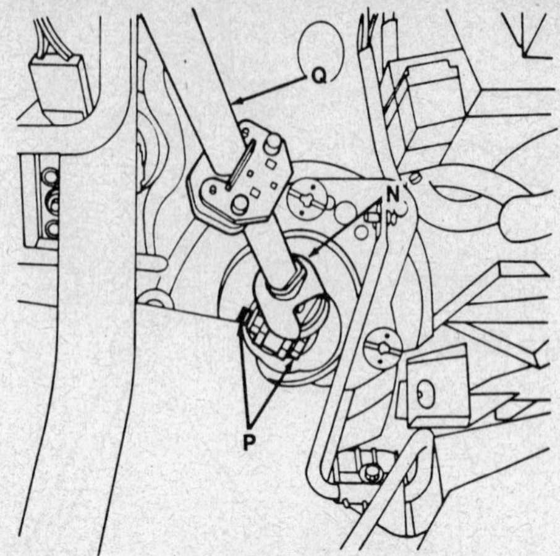

Fig. 67 Marking positions of intermediate shaft to steering gear coupling

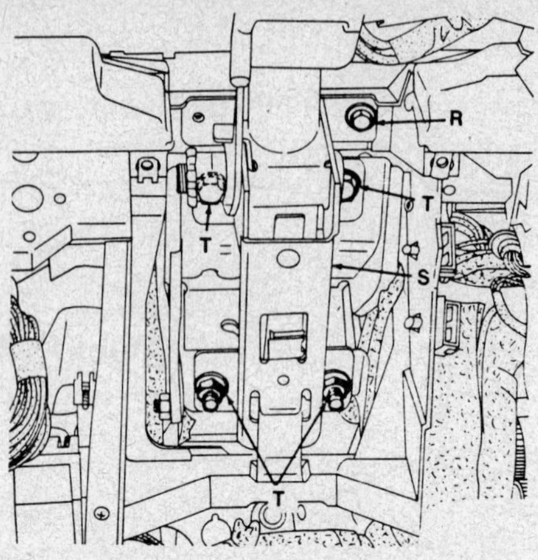

Fig. 68 Steering column jacket attaching bolt locations

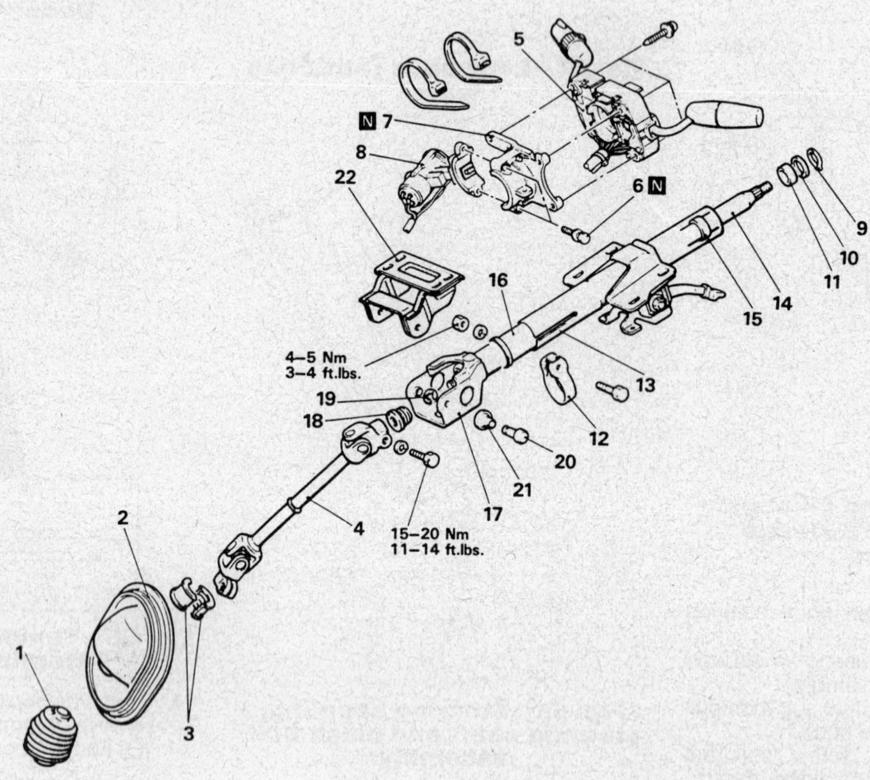


**Disassembly steps**

1. Boot
2. Cover assembly
3. Bearing
4. Joint assembly
5. Column switch
6. Steering lock installation special bolt
7. Steering lock bracket
8. Steering lock
9. Snap ring
10. Stopper
11. Bearing spacer
12. Column tube clamp
13. Column tube upper
14. Steering shaft
15. Bearing spacer
16. Column bushing
17. Column tube lower
18. Bearing
19. Snap ring
20. Clevis pin
21. Bushing
22. Lower bracket

N : Non-reusable parts

Fig. 69 Exploded view of steering column assembly. Eagle Talon & Plymouth Laser

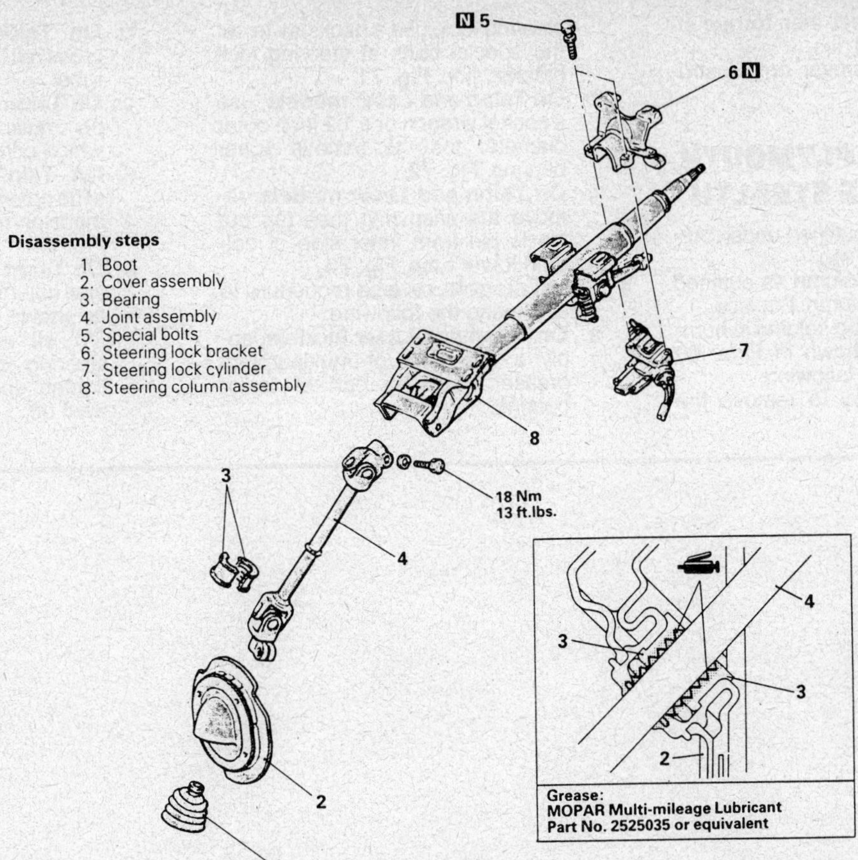


**Fig. 70 Exploded view of steering column assembly. Stealth**

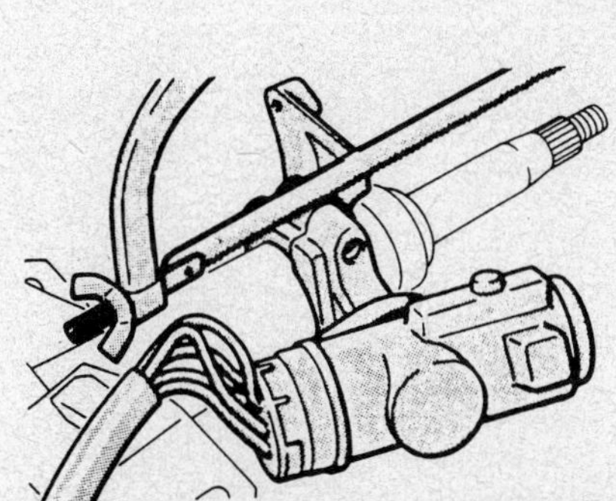

**Fig. 71 Steering lock removal**

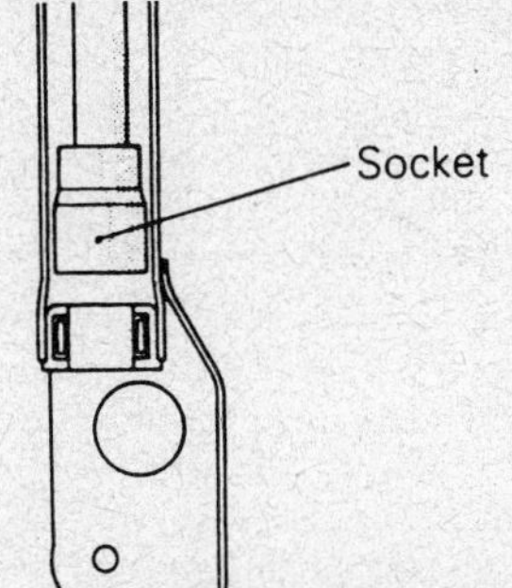


**Fig. 72 Removing lower bearing. Eagle Talon & Plymouth Laser**

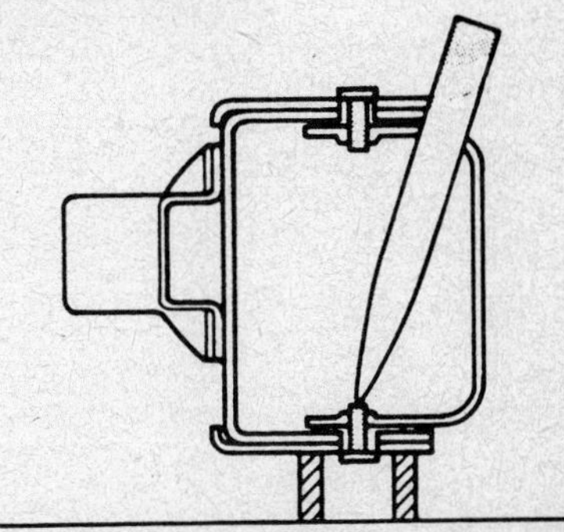

**Fig. 73 Removal of clevis pin. Eagle Talon & Plymouth Laser**

2. Install bottom bushing into steering column jacket using a suitable length of tubing. Tap bushing into column jacket until bushing seats against locating tabs in jacket.

## Intermediate Shaft & Steering Column

1. Install ignition switch onto column.
2. Position toeboard boot onto intermediate shaft.
3. Align and install intermediate shaft onto steering gear shaft.
4. Insert upper steering shaft into column jacket and through bottom bushing.
5. Coat top bushing with clean chassis grease, then install onto shaft.
6. Tap top bushing onto shaft and into column jacket using a suitable length of tubing. Tap bushing into column jacket until bushing seats against locating tabs in jacket.
7. Secure toeboard boot.
8. Install and tighten intermediate shaft coupling pinch bolt and nut.
9. Install steering column assembly as follows:
   a. Align intermediate shaft coupling and upper steering shaft.
   b. Insert upper shaft into intermediate shaft coupling, then install coupling pinch bolt and nut.
10. Position assembled steering column into instrument panel.
11. Install and tighten attaching bolts and nuts securing column to instrument and cowl panels.
12. Position electrical switches onto column and install attaching bolt.
13. Install trim covers onto column assembly.

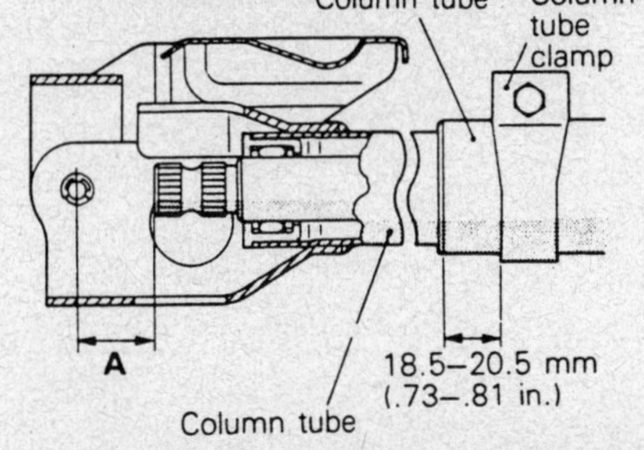


**Fig. 74 Installation of column tube clamp. Eagle Talon & Plymouth Laser**

14. Install steering wheel, then **torque** attaching nut to 30 ft. lbs.
15. install lower trim cover onto instrument panel.

## EAGLE TALON, PLYMOUTH LASER & DODGE STEALTH

1. Disable airbag as outlined under "Airbag System Disarming."
2. Remove steering column as outlined under "Steering Column, Replace."
3. Disassemble steering column in numbered sequence shown in **Figs. 69 and 70**, noting the following:
   a. If it is necessary to remove the steering lock, use a hacksaw to cut the special bolts at steering lock bracket side, **Fig. 71.**
   b. **On Talon and Laser models,** use a socket wrench or a 1.2 inch outer diameter tool, to remove lower bearing, **Fig. 72.**
   c. **On Talon and Laser models,** remove the snap ring then tap out clevis pin from inner side of column lower tube, **Fig. 73.**
4. **On all models,** reverse procedure to install, noting the following:
   a. **On Talon and Laser models,** apply a thin coat of multipurpose grease to sliding part of lower bearing.
   b. **On Talon and Laser models,** press oil seal into lower column tube.
   c. **On Talon and Laser models,** apply multipurpose bearing grease which contacts steering shaft.
   d. **On Talon and Laser models,** slide column tube and adjust so dimension marked A is .98-.99 inch, **Fig. 74.**
   e. **On Talon and Laser models,** install column tube clamp at position as shown in **Fig. 74.**
   f. **On all models,** after ensuring steering lock operates correctly, tighten special bolts until heads twist off.

# PASSIVE RESTRAINT SYSTEMS (Supplemental Restraint System)

## TABLE OF CONTENTS



# Airbag System

## INDEX



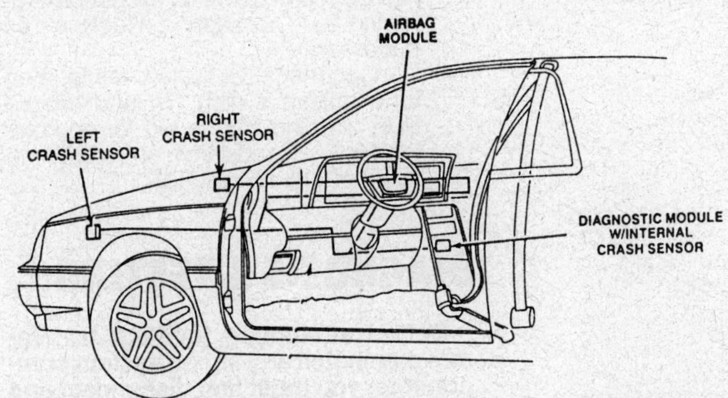


**Fig. 1 Airbag restraint system. Except Stealth**

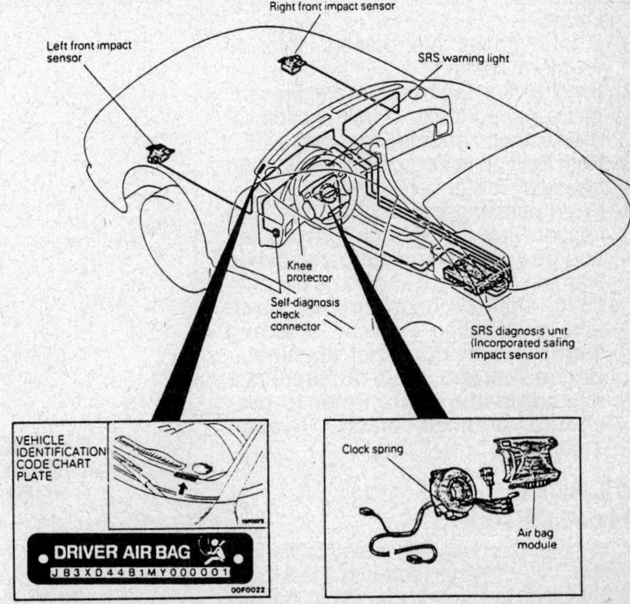


**Fig. 2 Airbag restraint system. 1991 Stealth**

## AIRBAG SYSTEM DISARMING

**This system is a complex, electro-mechanical unit. Before attempting to diagnose, remove or install any airbag system components, you must first disconnect and isolate the battery ground cable unless otherwise noted. Wait a minimum of 30 seconds before working on vehicle. Failure to do so could result in accidental deployment and possible personal injury.**

## DESCRIPTION

This airbag system has five major components, **Figs. 1 and 2;** the airbag module, unique steering column, clockspring switch, front impact sensors and Airbag System Diagnostic Module (ASDM). If any of these parts should fail, they must be replaced, as they cannot be repaired.

**The fasteners, screws and bolts used for airbag components have special coatings and are specifically designed for the airbag system. They must not be replaced with substitutes. If fastener replacement is required, use the correct fasteners provided in the service package.**

## SYSTEM CHECK

### EXCEPT STEALTH

**Before attempting to diagnose, remove or install any airbag system components, you must first disconnect and isolate the battery ground cable. Failure to do so could result in accidental deployment and possible personal injury.**

1. Disconnect and isolate battery ground cable.
2. Connect DRBII readout tool to ASDM diagnostic connector, following manufacturer's instructions. The module is located behind the center console on all models except Fifth Avenue. Fifth Avenue models have a DRBII connector located in the right kick panel.

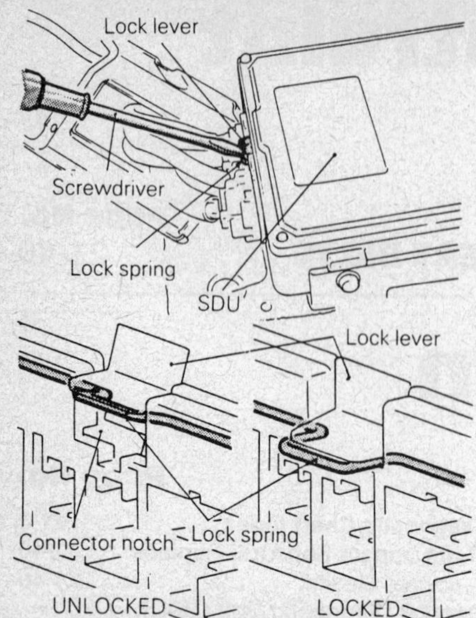


**Fig. 3 Disconnecting diagnostic unit connector. 1991 Stealth**

3. From passenger side of vehicle, turn ignition to On position. Exit vehicle with DRBII.
4. Ensure no one is inside of vehicle, then connect battery ground cable.
5. Read and record any stored fault codes.
6. If fault codes are present, refer to "System Testing."
7. If no active fault codes are present, erase stored faults. If malfunction remains, fault codes will not erase.
8. With ignition in On position, ensure no one is inside of vehicle.
9. From passenger side of vehicle, turn ignition key to Off then On position and observe instrument panel airbag warning light. Light should go out after six to eight seconds, indicating system is operating correctly. **If airbag warning light does not illuminate, or goes on and stays on, there is a system malfunction. Refer to procedure outlined under "System Testing."**

## STEALTH

### Visual Check

1. With ignition key ON or engine started, the "SRS"(Supplemental Restraint System) warning lamp will illuminate for about 7 seconds, then turn off. This indicates the system is functioning.
2. Turn ignition to Lock position.
3. **Disconnect and isolate the battery ground cable. Failure to do so could result in accidental deployment and possible personal injury.**
4. Remove rear console system assembly.
5. Disconnect SRS from SDU (Supplemental Diagnostic Unit), using screwdriver to push in lock spring of lock lever, **Fig. 3.** A double-lock connector is used, ensure not to damage connector with the use of excessive force.
6. Disconnect the red 14-pin connector from SRS diagnosis unit while pressing down the lock of connector.
7. Check SDU case, brackets and connectors for deformities.
8. Remove airbag module from steering wheel, refer to "Clockspring, Replace" for removal procedure.
9. Check pad, hooks, and connectors for cracks, deformities or damage.
10. Check airbag inflator case for damage or deformities.
11. Check steering wheel harness and connectors for damage or deformities.
12. Remove steering wheel using suitable steering wheel puller.
13. Remove steering column covers.
14. Remove clockspring, refer to "Clockspring, Replace"
15. Check clockspring, connectors, case and gear for damage. If clockspring or any other components, including connectors are damaged, replace as necessary.
16. Check SRS body wiring and connectors for damage or poor connections, replace as necessary, **Fig. 4.**
17. Reverse procedure to assemble, referring to "Clockspring, Replace" as necessary.
18. Connect negative battery cable, then turn ignition switch On and ensure SRS warning light is On for approximately 7 seconds, then stays Off for a minimum of 45 seconds.

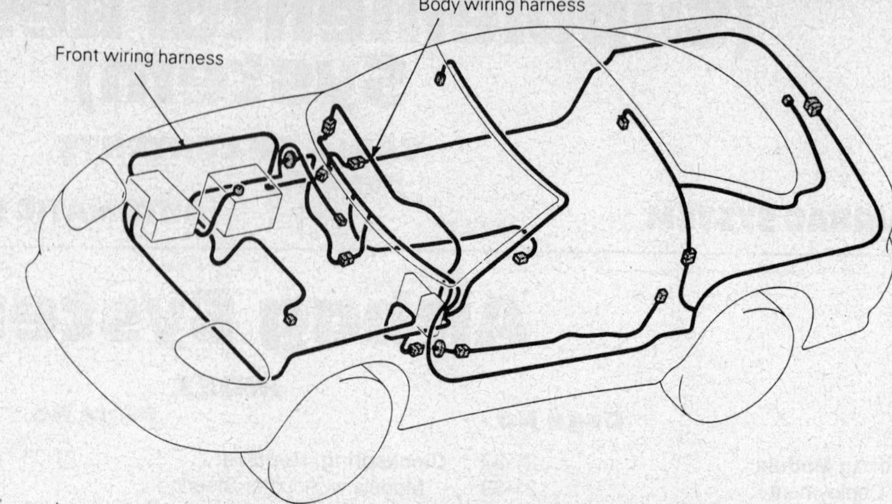


**Fig. 4 SRS wiring harness. 1991 Stealth**

1. RIGHT FRONT SENSOR R48 TN
2. LEFT FRONT SENSOR R49 LB
3. LAMP R41 BK/TN
4. IGNITION (RUN) B1 WT
5. IGNITION (RUN/START) G5 DB/*
6. RIGHT FRONT SENSOR R46 BR/LB
7. LEFT FRONT SENSOR R47 DB/LB
8. GROUND H40 BK/PK
9. SPARE
10. BATTERY X1 RD

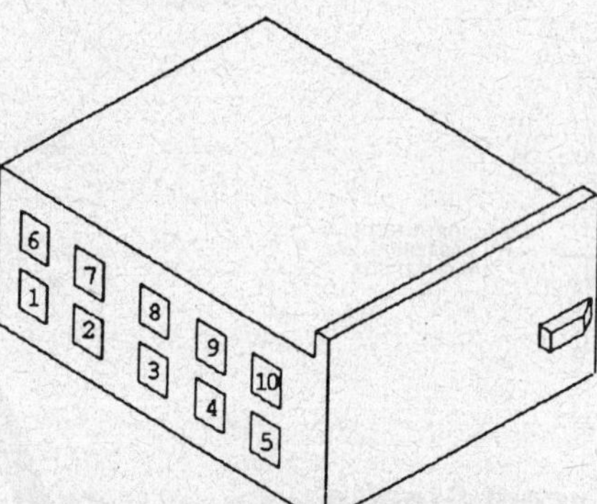


**Fig. 5 ASDM connector terminal identification. Except Stealth**

## DIAGNOSIS & TESTING

**Before attempting to diagnose, remove or install any airbag system components, you must first disconnect and isolate the battery ground cable. Failure to do so could result in accidental deployment and possible personal injury.**

To diagnose and test the airbag system, the DRBII readout tool must be co nnected to the ASDM, following manufacturer's instructions. The module is located behind the center console on all models except Fifth Avenue. Fifth Avenue models have a DRBII connector located in the right kick panel.

## SYSTEM TESTING

### Except Stealth

**Before attempting to diagnose, remove or install any airbag system components, you must first disconnect and isolate the battery ground cable. Failure to do so could result in accidental deployment and possible personal injury.**

Refer to **Fig. 5,** for ASDM module connector terminal identification and **Figs. 6 through 50,** to diagnose and test the airbag system.

## DIAGNOSTIC CHART INDEX

| Test No. | Symptom | Page No. | Fig. No. |
|---|---|---|---|
| **1989** | | | |
| 1 | System Function | 21-5 | 6 |
| 2 | No Response Message On DRBII | 21-6 | 9 |
| 3 | Fault Messages | 21-7 | 13 |
| 4 | Safing Sensor Open Fault | 21-8 | 16 |
| 5 | Two Front Sensors Open Fault | 21-9 | 17 |
| 6 | Squib (Initiator) Open Fault | 21-11 | 21 |
| 7 | Squib (Initiator) Short Fault | 21-12 | 23 |
| 8 | Safing Sensor Short Fault | 21-13 | 25 |
| 9 | Front Sensor Short Fault | 21-14 | 26 |
| 10 | One Front Sensor Open Fault | 21-16 | 31 |
| 11 | Low Stored Energy Fault | 21-18 | 34 |
| 12 | Ignition 2 (Run Only) Low Fault | 21-19 | 37 |
| 13 | Chassis Ground Open Fault | 21-21 | 40 |
| 14 | Warning Lamp Open Fault | 21-22 | 43 |
| 15 | Ignition 1 (Run/Start) Low Fault | 21-22 | 45 |
| **1990** | | | |
| 1 | System Function | 21-5 | 6 |
| 2 | No Response Message On DRBII | 21-6 | 10 |
| 3 | Fault Messages | 21-8 | 14 |
| 4 | Safing Sensor Open Fault | 21-8 | 16 |
| 5 | Two Front Sensors Open Fault | 21-9 | 18 |
| 6 | Squib (Initiator) Open Fault | 21-11 | 21 |
| 7 | Squib (Initiator) Short Fault | 21-12 | 23 |
| 8 | Safing Sensor Short Fault | 21-13 | 25 |
| 9 | Front Sensor Short Fault | 21-14 | 27 |
| 10 | One Front Sensor Open Fault | 21-17 | 32 |
| 11 | Low Stored Energy Fault | 21-18 | 34 |
| 12 | Ignition 2 (Run Only) Low Fault | 21-19 | 37 |
| 13 | Warning Lamp Short Fault | 21-21 | 41 |
| 14 | Warning Lamp Open Fault | 21-22 | 43 |
| 15 | Ignition 1 (Run/Start) Low Fault | 21-22 | 45 |
| **1991 Except Stealth** | | | |
| 1A | System Function | 21-5 | 7 |
| 1B | System Function | 21-6 | 8 |
| 2A | No Response Message On DRBII | 21-7 | 11 |
| 2B | No Response Message On DRBII | 21-7 | 12 |
| 3A | Fault Messages | 21-8 | 15 |
| 5A | Testing For Two Front Sensors Open Code | 21-10 | 19 |
| 5B | Testing For Two Front Sensors Open Code | 21-10 | 20 |
| 6A | Testing For "Squib (Initiator) Open" Code | 21-12 | 22 |
| 7A | Squib (Initiator) Short Code | 21-13 | 24 |
| 9A | Testing For "Front Sensor Short" Code | 21-15 | 28 |
| 9B | Testing For "Front Sensor Short" Code | 21-16 | 29 |
| 9C | Testing For "Front Sensor Short" Code | 21-16 | 30 |
| 10A | One Front Sensor Open Code | 21-17 | 33 |
| 11A | Testing For "Low Stored Energy" Code | 21-19 | 35 |
| 11B | Testing For "Low Stored Energy" Code | 21-19 | 36 |
| 12A | Testing For "Ignition 2 (Run) Low" Code | 21-20 | 38 |
| 12B | Testing For "Low Stored Energy Code" Code | 21-20 | 39 |
| 13A | Testing For "Warning Lamp Open" Code | 21-21 | 42 |
| 14A | Testing For "Warning Lamp Short" Code | 21-22 | 44 |

*Continued*

## DIAGNOSTIC CHART INDEX—Continued



### Stealth

**Before attempting to diagnose, remove or install any airbag system components, you must first disconnect and isolate the battery ground cable. Failure to do so could result in accidental deployment and possible personal injury.**

Refer to **Figs. 51 through 84**, to diagnose and test the airbag system.

## COMPONENT TESTING

### STEALTH

### Clockspring

1. Remove airbag module. Refer to removal procedure.
2. Using suitable volt/ohmmeter check for continuity between No. 1 connector of clock spring and connectors No. 3, 4, 5 and 6, **Fig. 85 and 86.**
3. Connect No. 2 connector (airbag module side) and No. 7 connector of clock spring to connector No. 4 and connector No. 3 of SRS check harness part No. MB991349, **Fig. 87.**
4. Check for continuity between terminal 1 and terminal 21, then terminal 2 and 22 of check connector of SRS check harness using suitable volt/ohmmeter.
5. Reading should be than 0.4 ohms. If not as specified, replace clock spring.

### Front Impact Sensor

1. **Remove and isolate battery ground cable and wait at least 30 seconds before working on vehicle. Failure to do so could result in accidental deployment and possible personal injury.**
2. Remove front splash shield extensions, then ensure arrow marks face front of vehicle, **Fig. 88.**
3. Check front upper frame lowers and sensor brackets for deformities or rust.
4. Check connectors and wiring for proper connections.
5. Remove impact sensors.
6. Using suitable volt/ohmmeter measure resistance between terminals. Resistance should be 1,960-2,040 ohms. If not as specified replace sensor.
7. Install sensors, ensuring connectors are properly fastened.
8. Connect battery ground cable, then turn ignition switch on and ensure SRS warning light is on for approximately 7 seconds and then stays off for a minimum of 45 seconds.

*Continued on page 21-35*

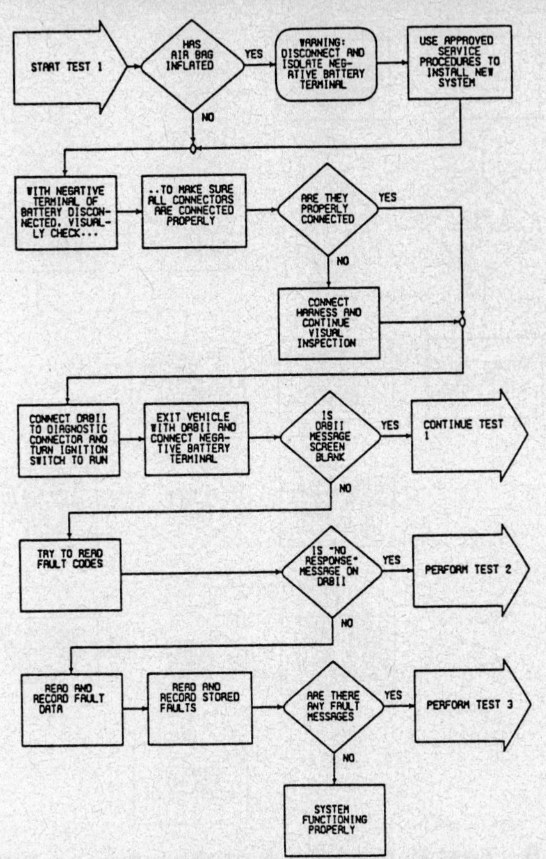


**Fig. 6 Test 1, System function (Part 1 of 2). 1989–90 models**

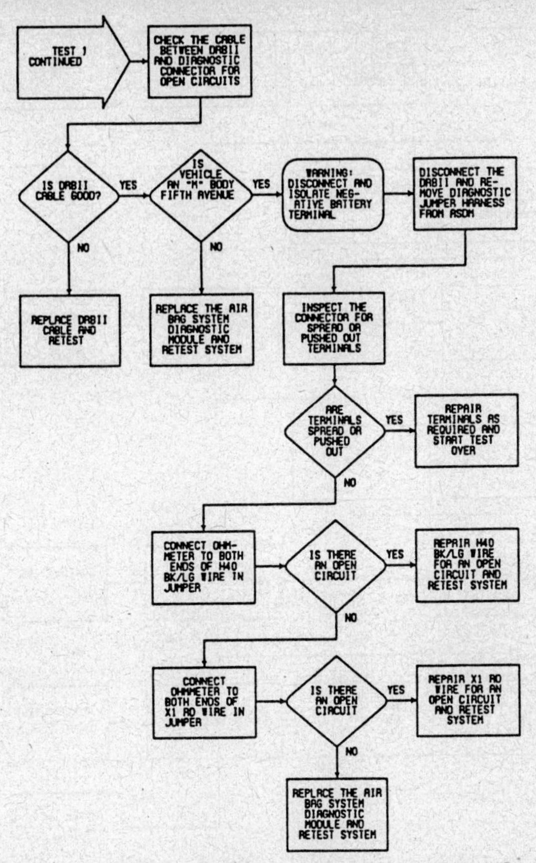


**Fig. 6 Test 1, System function (Part 2 of 2). 1989 models**

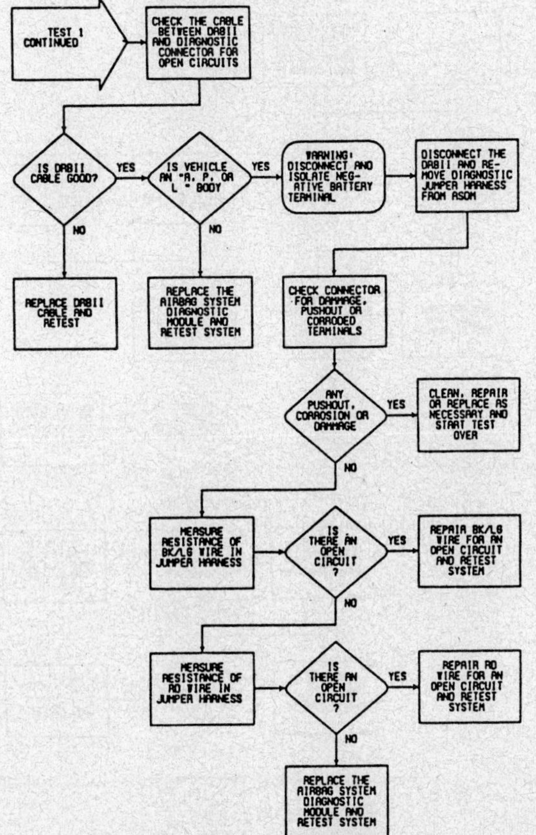


**Fig. 6 Test 1, System function (Part 2 of 2). 1990 models**

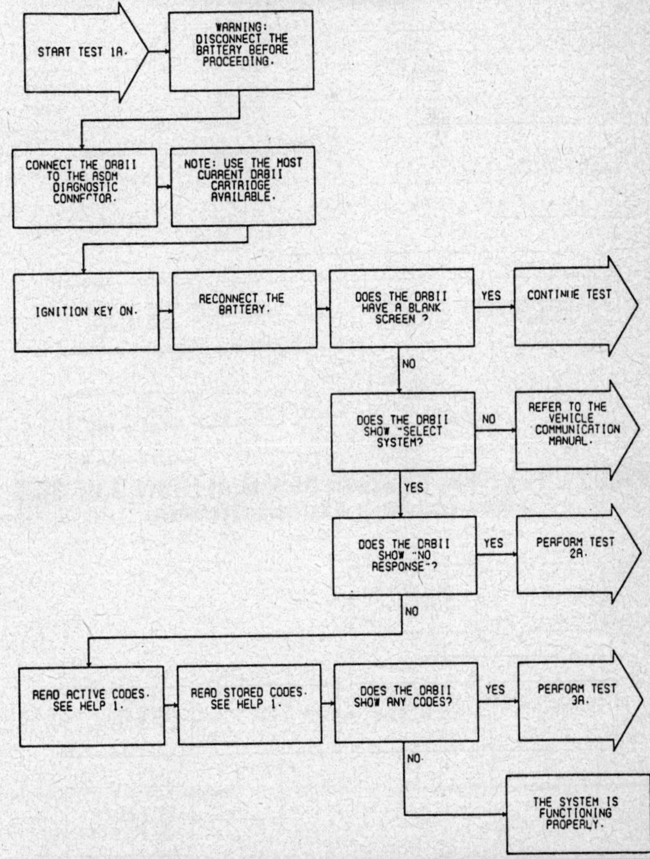


**Fig. 7 Test 1A, System function (Part 1 of 3). 1991 models except Stealth**

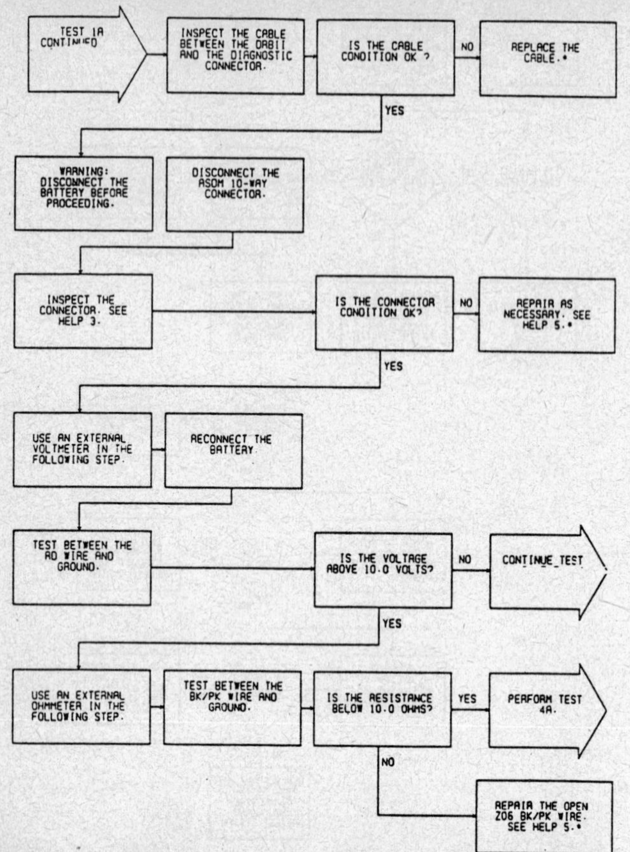


**Fig. 7 Test 1A, System function (Part 2 of 3). 1991 models except Stealth**

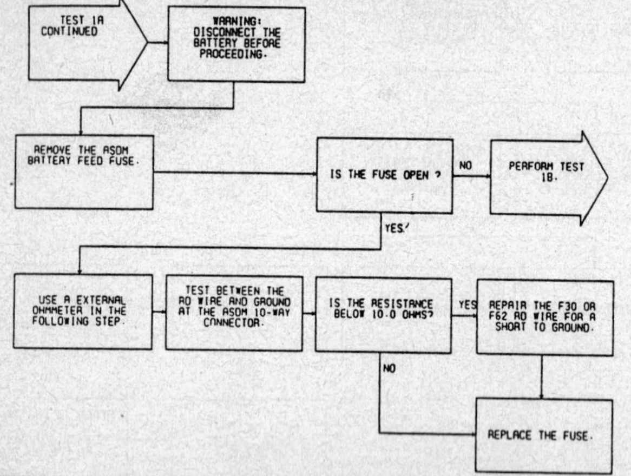


**Fig. 7 Test 1A, System function (Part 3 of 3). 1991 models except Stealth**

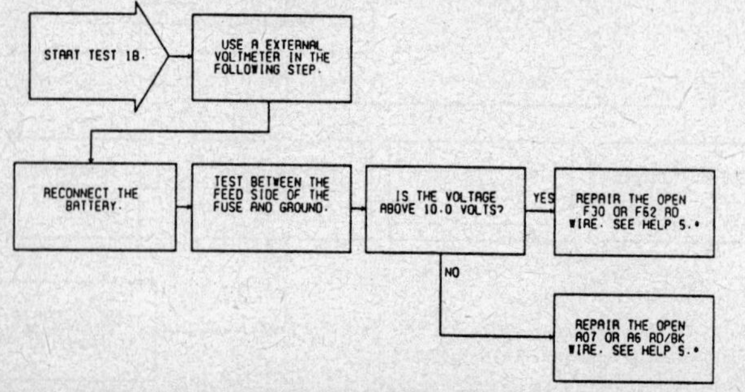


**Fig. 8 Test 1B, System function. 1991 models except Stealth**

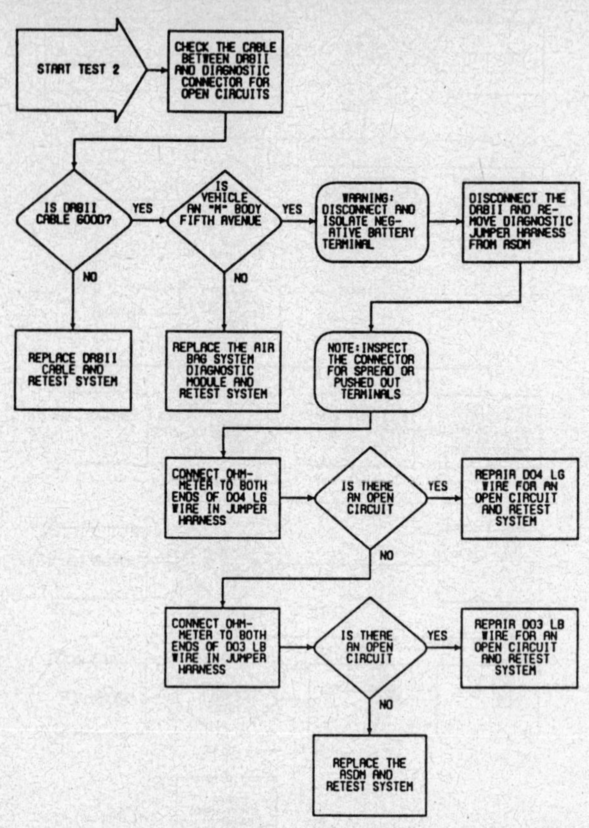


**Fig. 9 Test 2, No response message on DRBII. 1989 models**

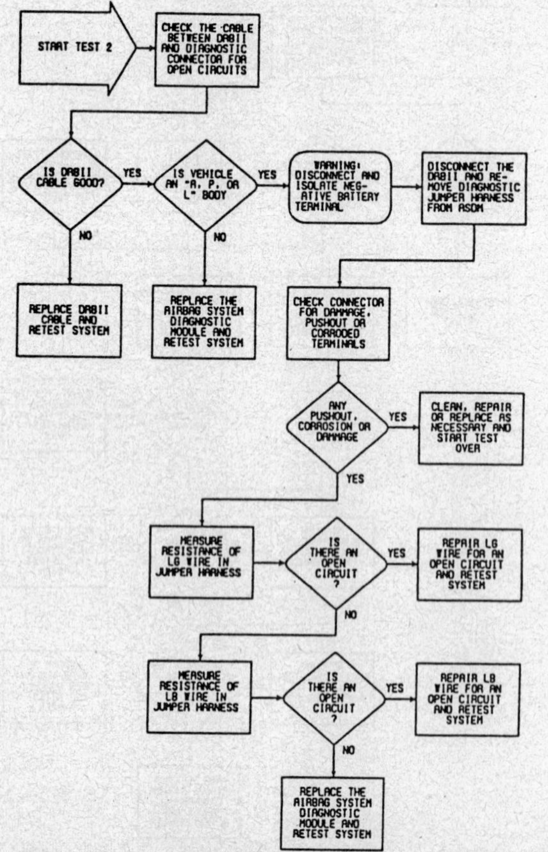


**Fig. 10 Test 2, No response message on DRBII. 1990 models**

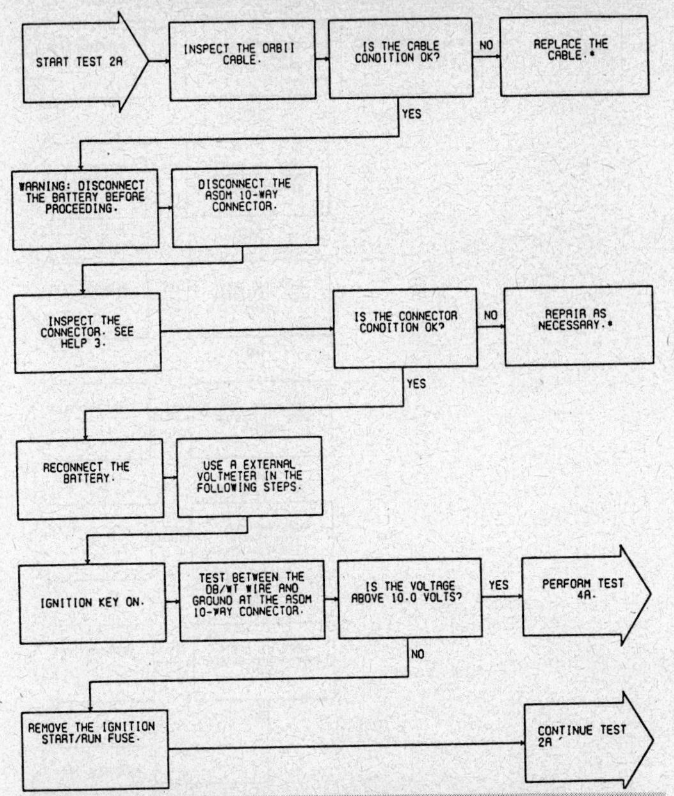


Fig. 11 Test 2A, No response message on DRBII (Part 1 of 2). 1991 models except Stealth

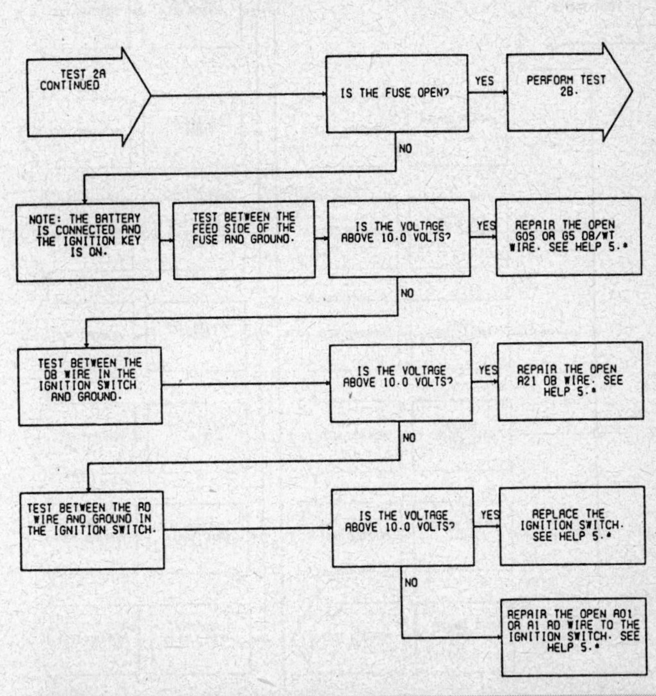


Fig. 11 Test 2A, No response message on DRBII (Part 2 of 2). 1991 models except Stealth

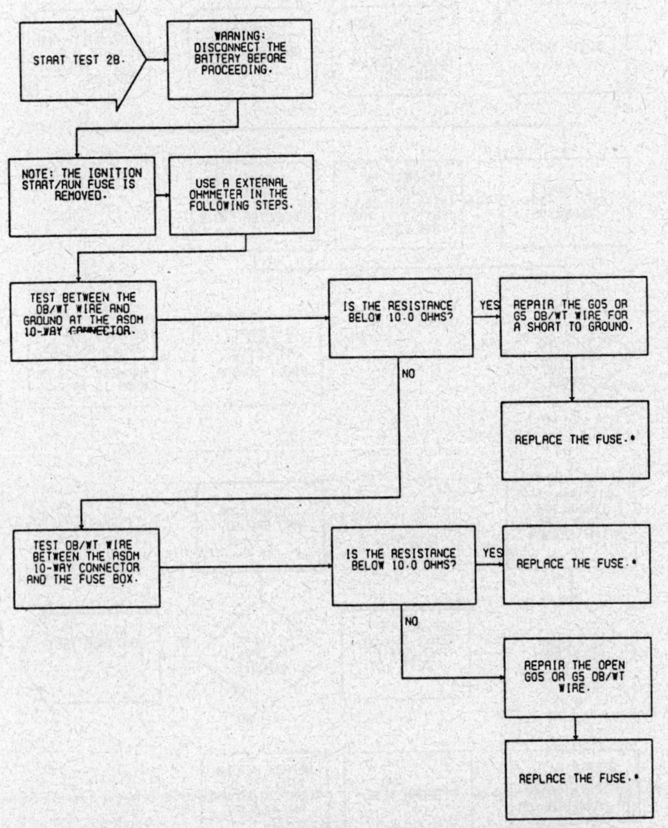


Fig. 12 Test 2B, No response message on DRBII. 1991 models except Stealth

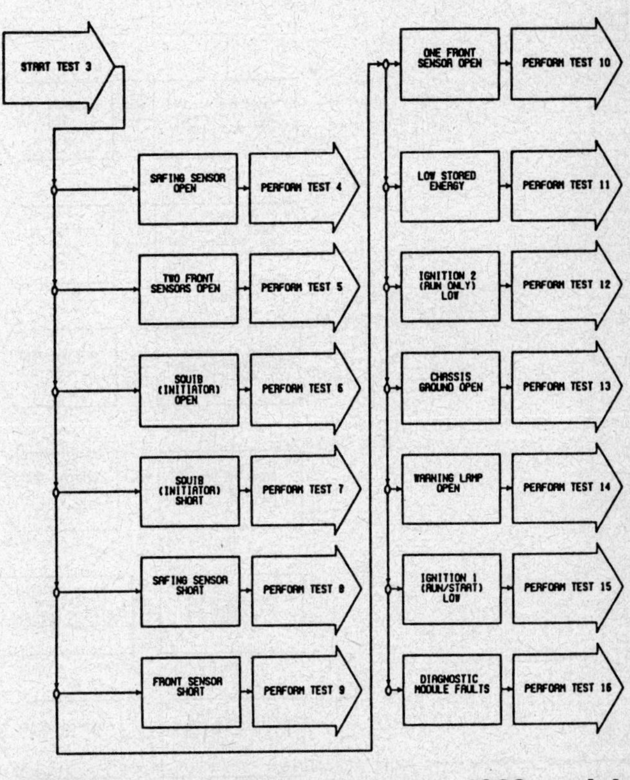


Fig. 13 Test 3, Fault messages. 1989 models

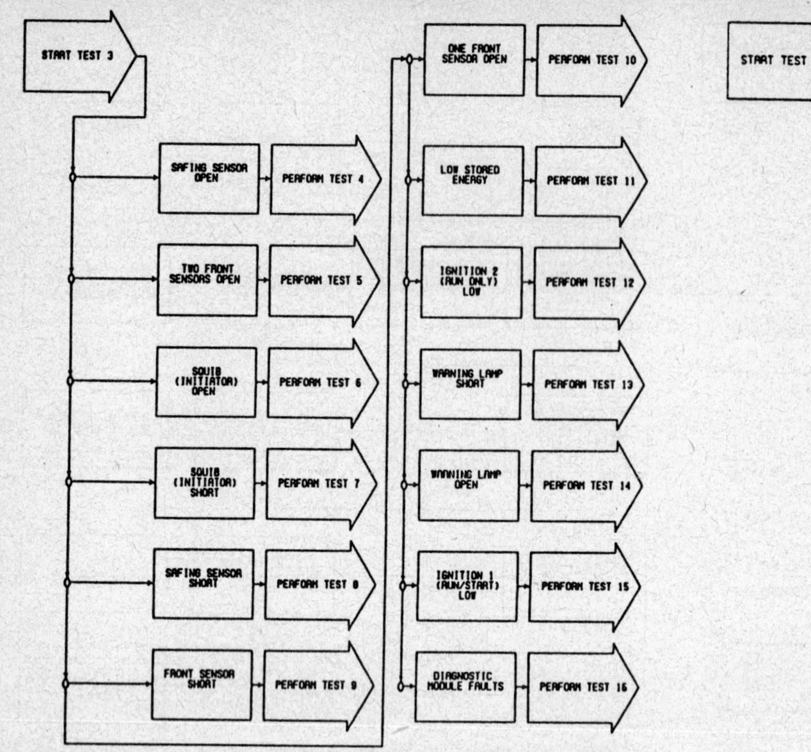


**Fig. 14 Test 3, Fault messages. 1990 models**

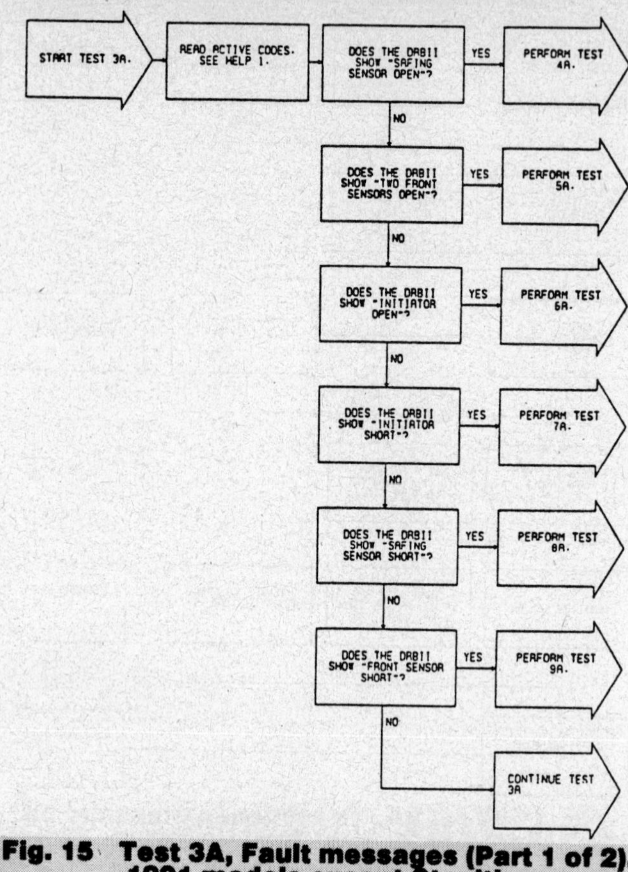


**Fig. 15 Test 3A, Fault messages (Part 1 of 2). 1991 models except Stealth**

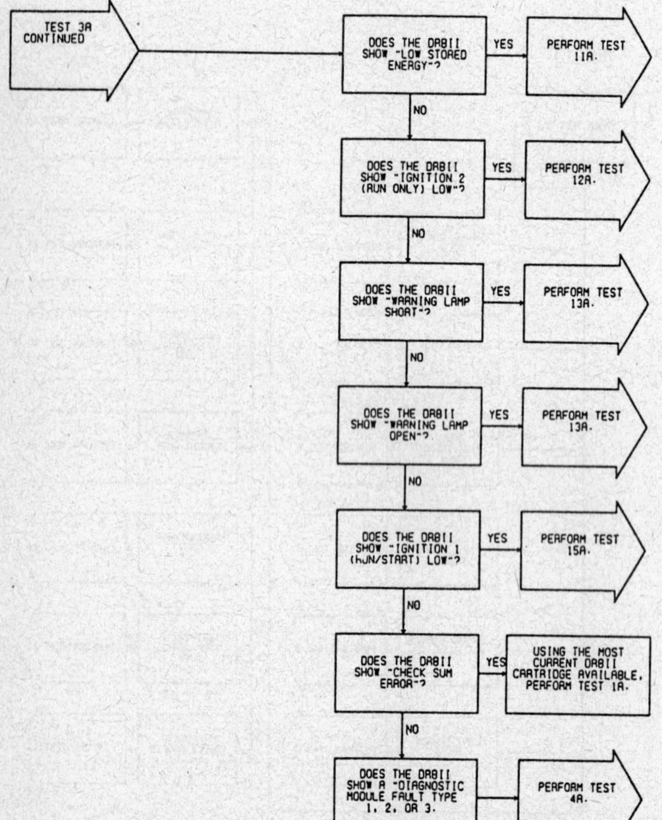


**Fig. 15 Test 3A, Fault messages (Part 2 of 2). 1991 models except Stealth**

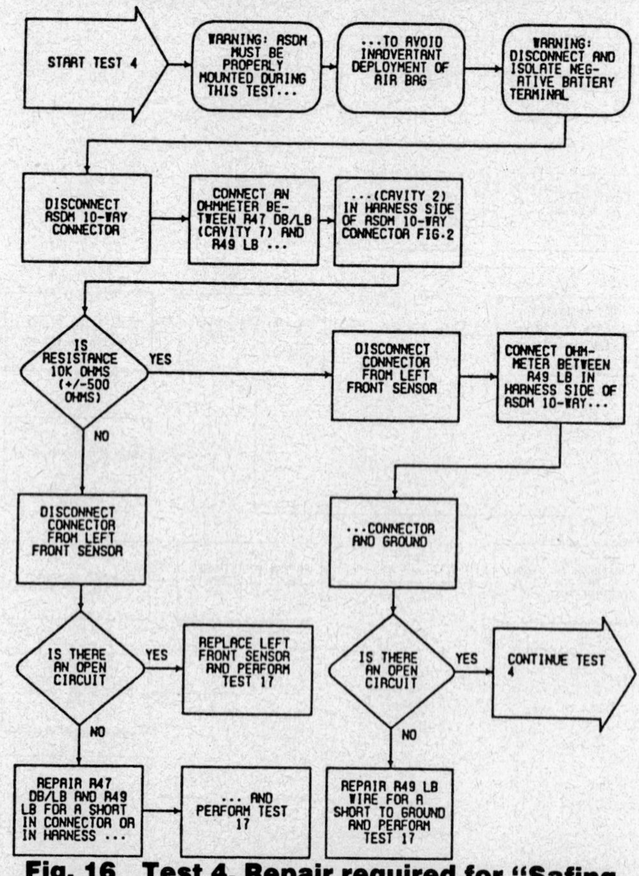


**Fig. 16 Test 4, Repair required for "Safing Sensor Open" fault (Part 1 of 2). 1989–90 models**

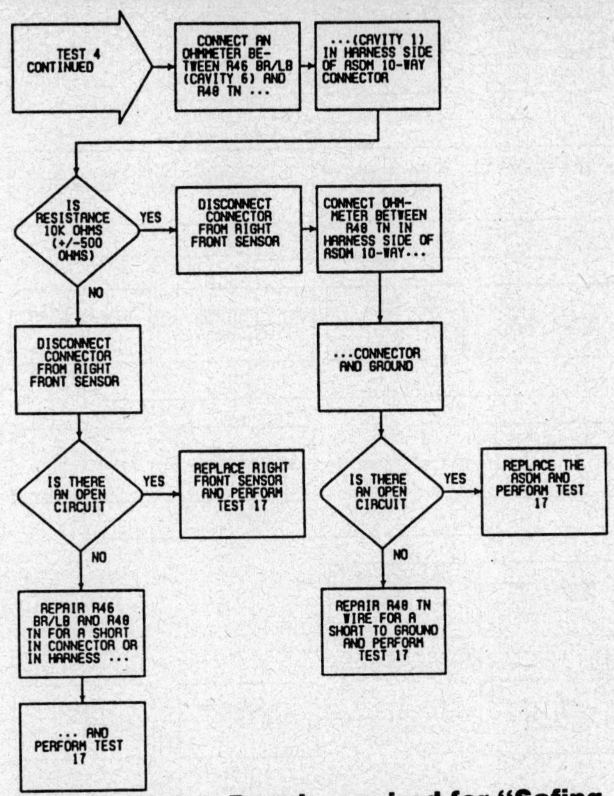


**Fig. 16 Test 4, Repair required for "Safing Sensor Open" fault (Part 2 of 2). 1989–90 models**

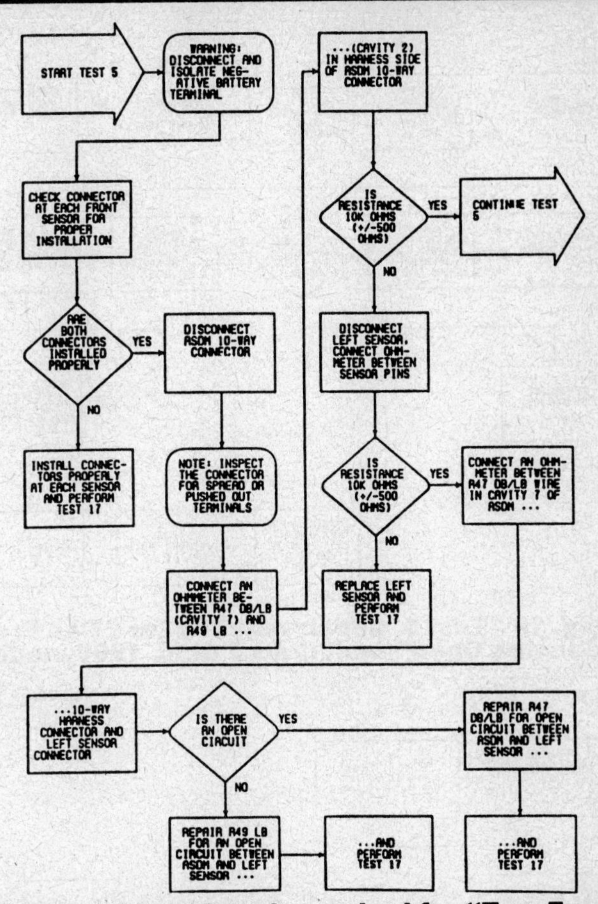


**Fig. 17 Test 5, Repair required for "Two Front Sensors Open" fault (Part 1 of 2). 1989 models**

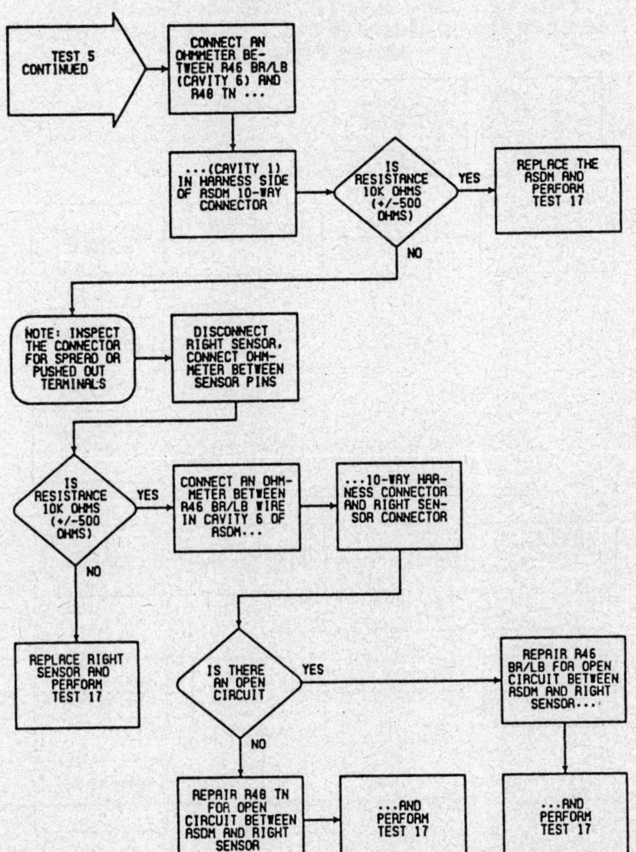


**Fig. 17 Test 5, Repair required for "Two Front Sensors Open" fault (Part 2 of 2). 1989 models**

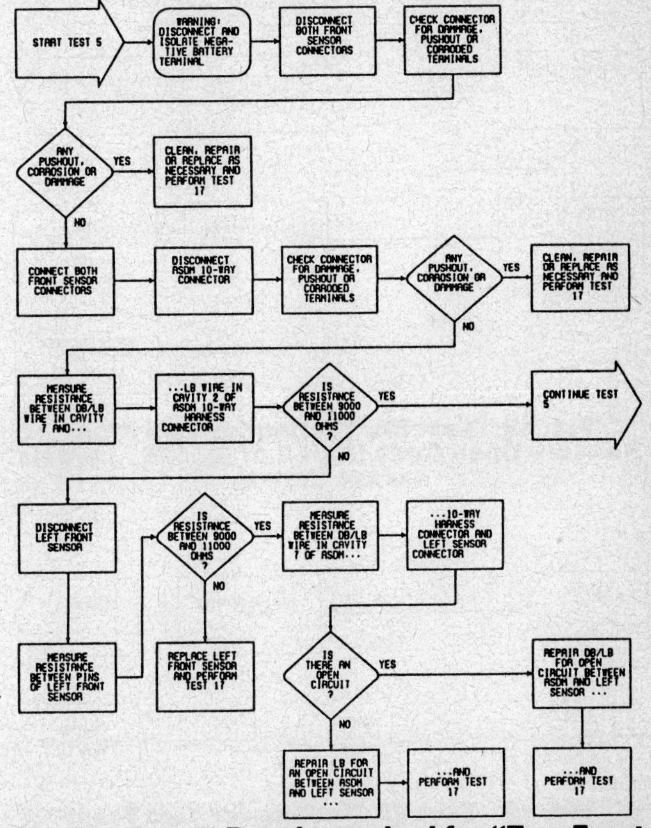


**Fig. 18 Test 5, Repair required for "Two Front Sensors Open" fault (Part 1 of 2). 1990 models**

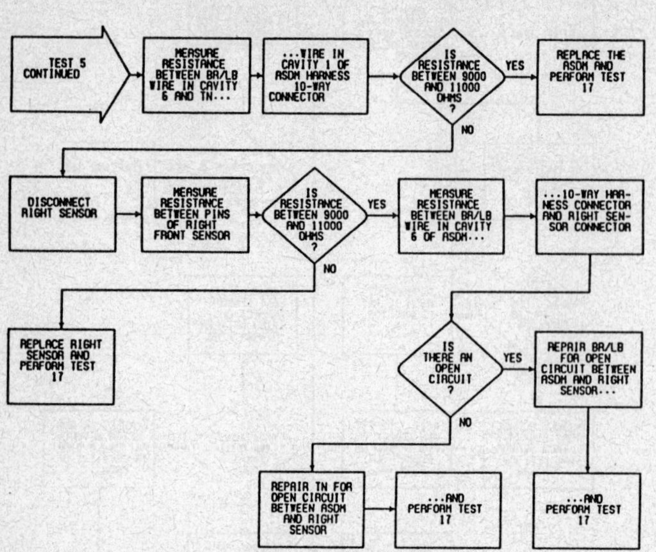


**Fig. 18 Test 5, Repair required for "Two Front Sensors Open" fault (Part 2 of 2). 1990 models**

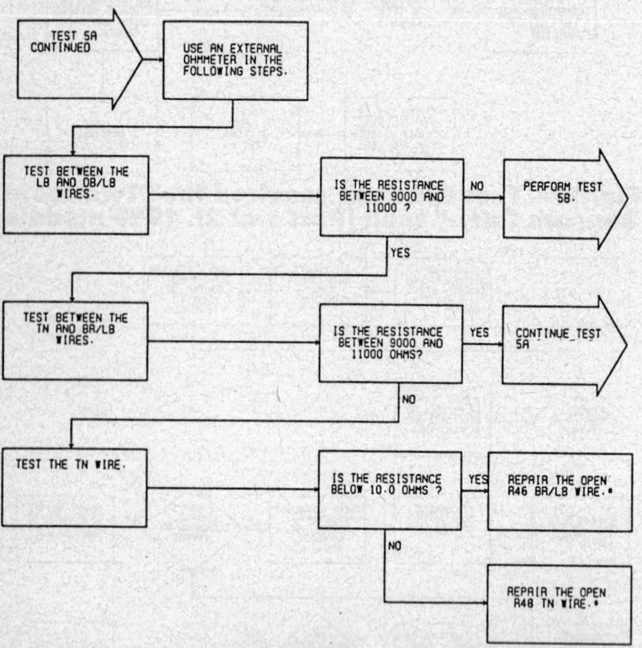


**Fig. 19 Test 5A, Testing for Two Front Sensors Open Code (Part 2 of 3). 1991 models except Stealth**

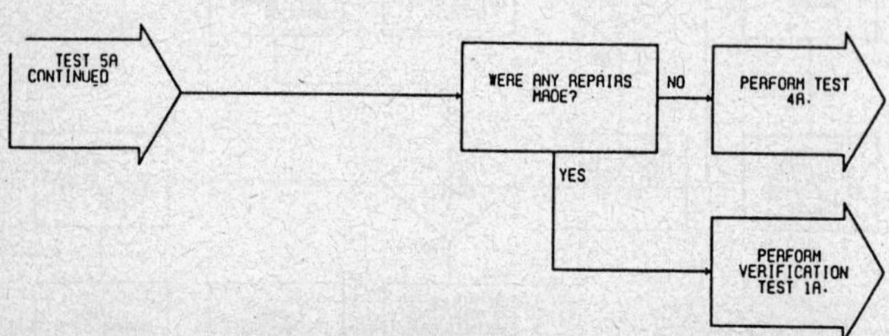


**Fig. 19 Test 5A, Testing for Two Front Sensors Open Code (Part 3 of 3). 1991 models except Stealth**

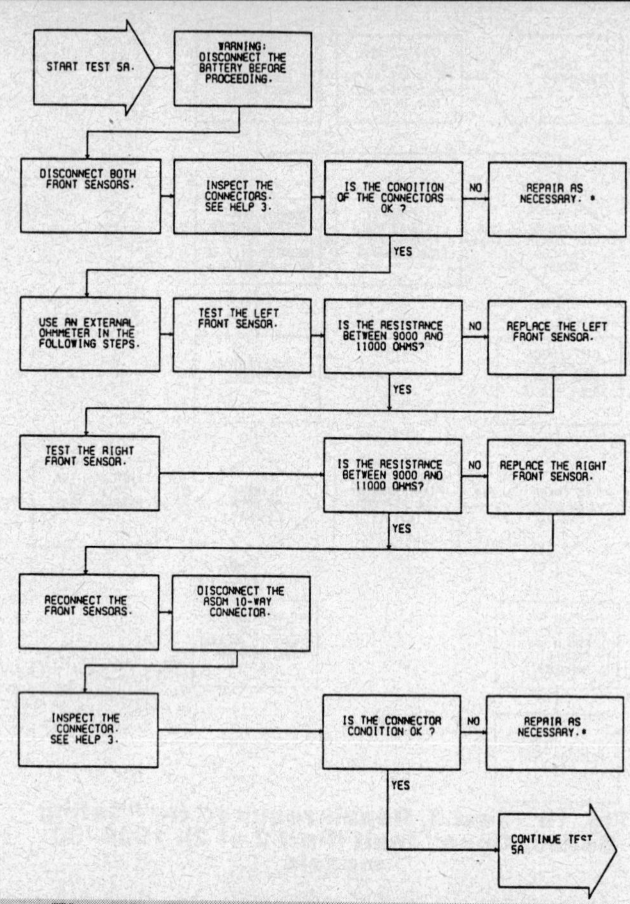


**Fig. 19 Test 5A, Testing for Two Front Sensors Open Code (Part 1 of 3). 1991 models except Stealth**

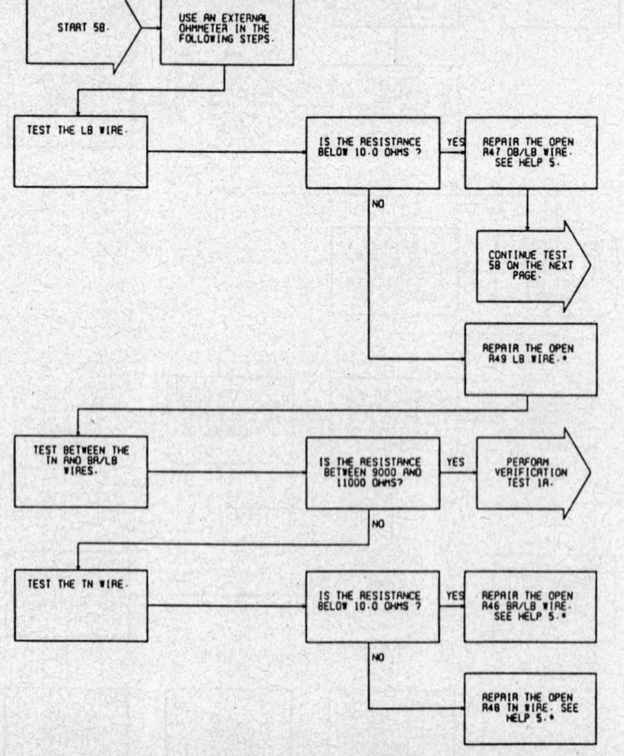


**Fig. 20 Test 5B, Testing for Two Front Sensors Open Code (Part 1 of 2). 1991 models except Stealth**

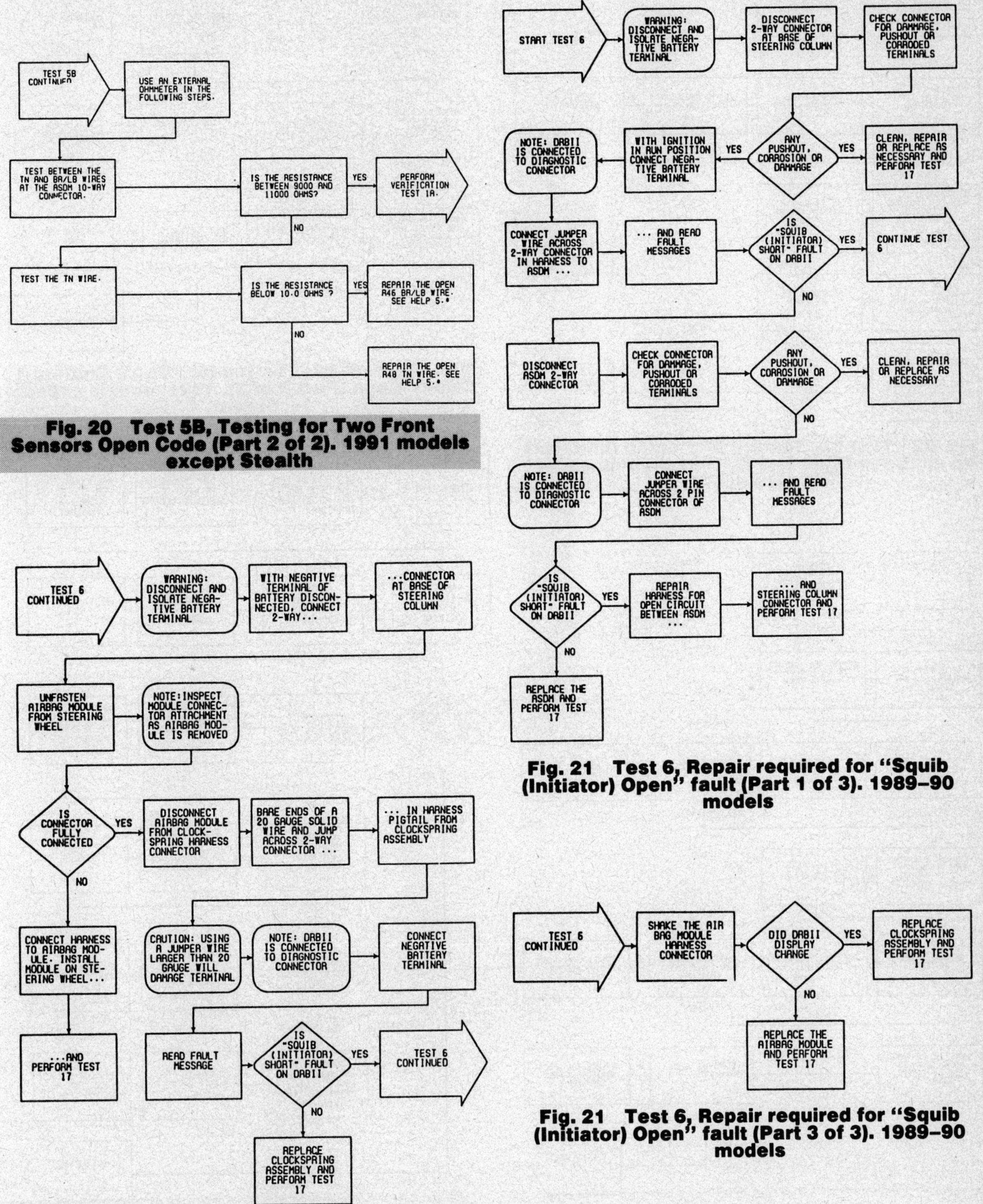


**Fig. 20 Test 5B, Testing for Two Front Sensors Open Code (Part 2 of 2). 1991 models except Stealth**

**Fig. 21 Test 6, Repair required for "Squib (Initiator) Open" fault (Part 2 of 3). 1989–90 models**

**Fig. 21 Test 6, Repair required for "Squib (Initiator) Open" fault (Part 1 of 3). 1989–90 models**

**Fig. 21 Test 6, Repair required for "Squib (Initiator) Open" fault (Part 3 of 3). 1989–90 models**

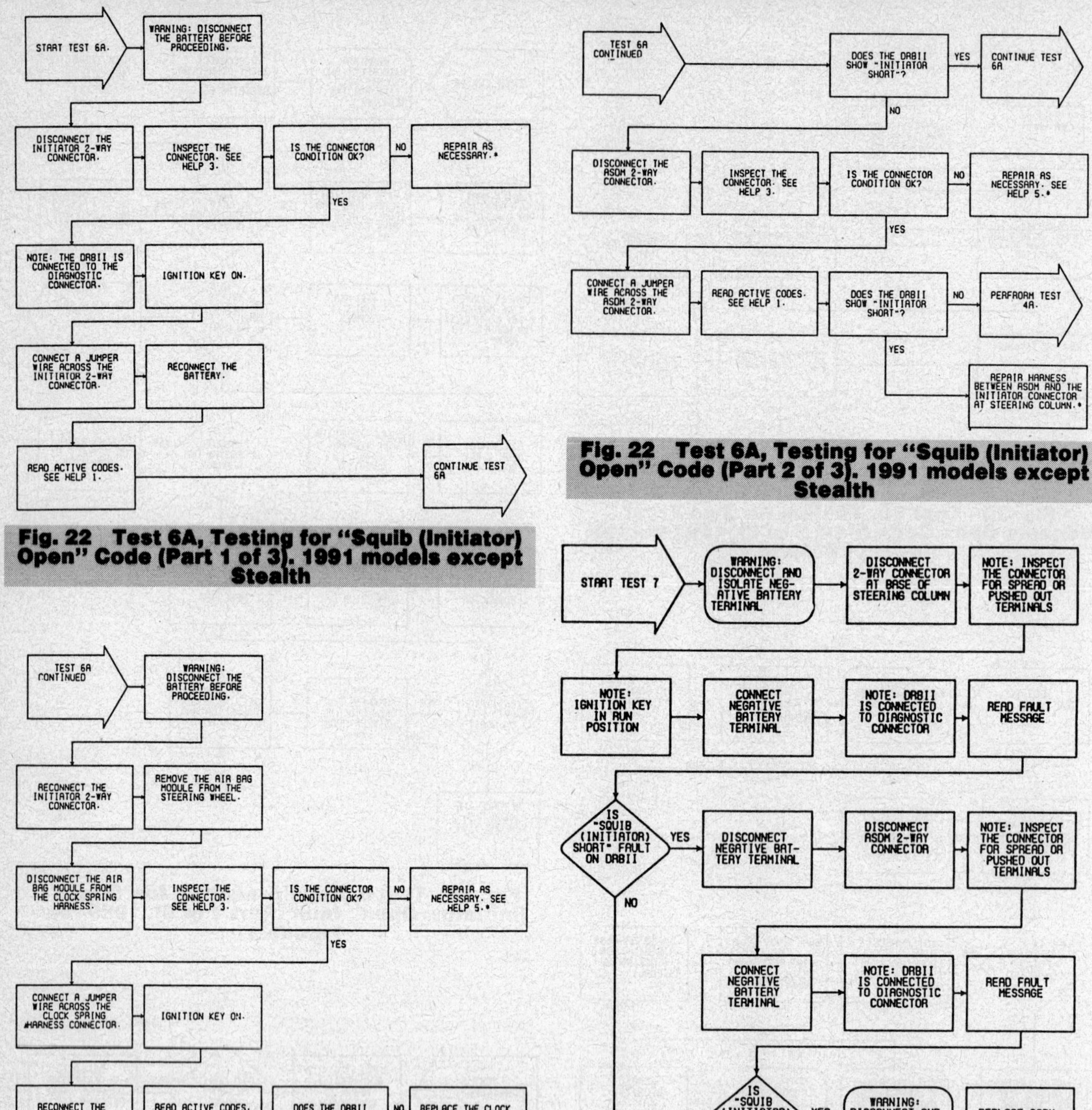


Fig. 22 Test 6A, Testing for "Squib (Initiator) Open" Code (Part 1 of 3). 1991 models except Stealth



Fig. 22 Test 6A, Testing for "Squib (Initiator) Open" Code (Part 2 of 3). 1991 models except Stealth



Fig. 22 Test 6A, Testing for "Squib (Initiator) Open" Code (Part 3 of 3). 1991 models except Stealth

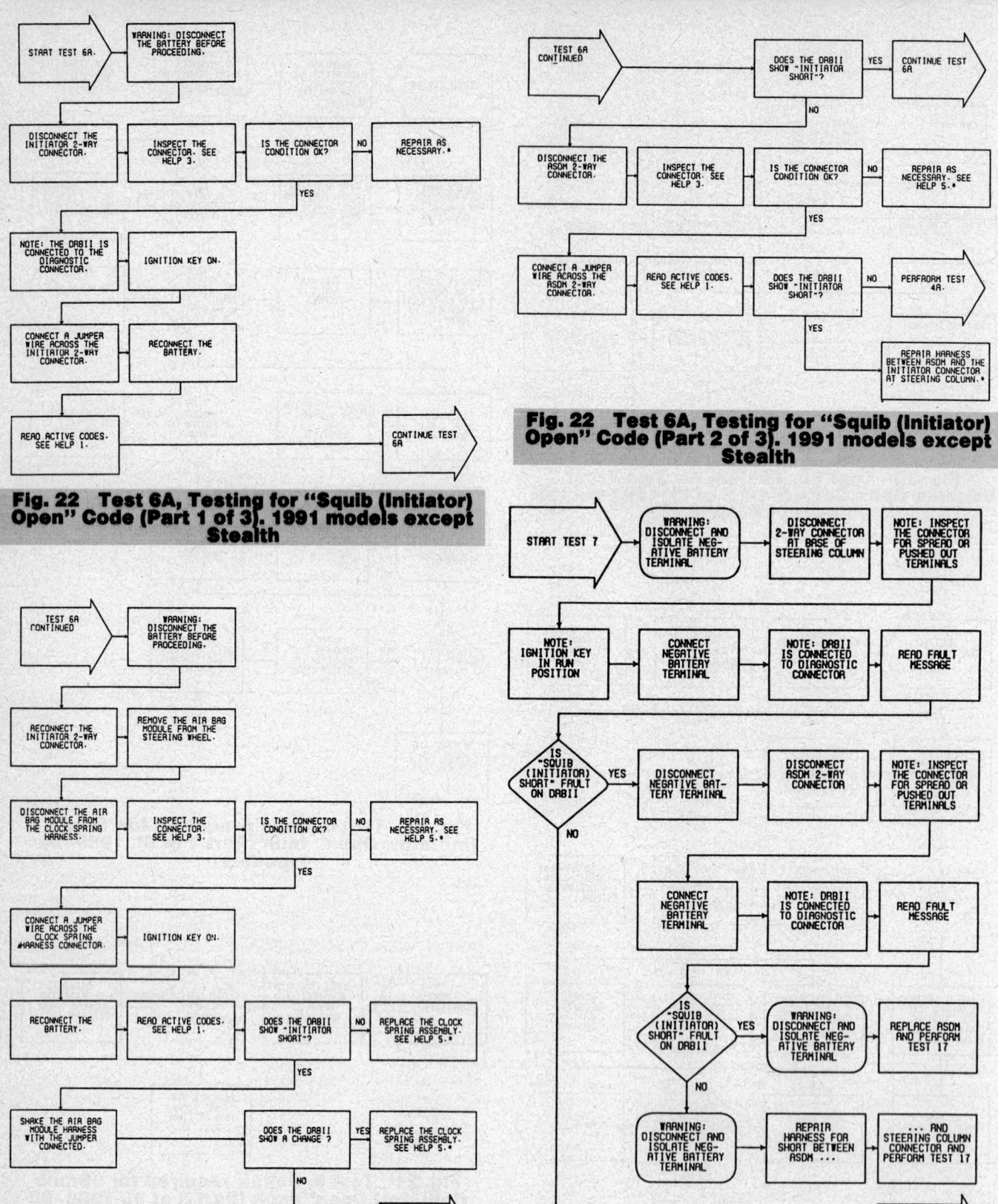

Fig. 23 Test 7, Repair required for "Squib (Initiator) Short" fault (Part 1 of 2). 1989–90 models

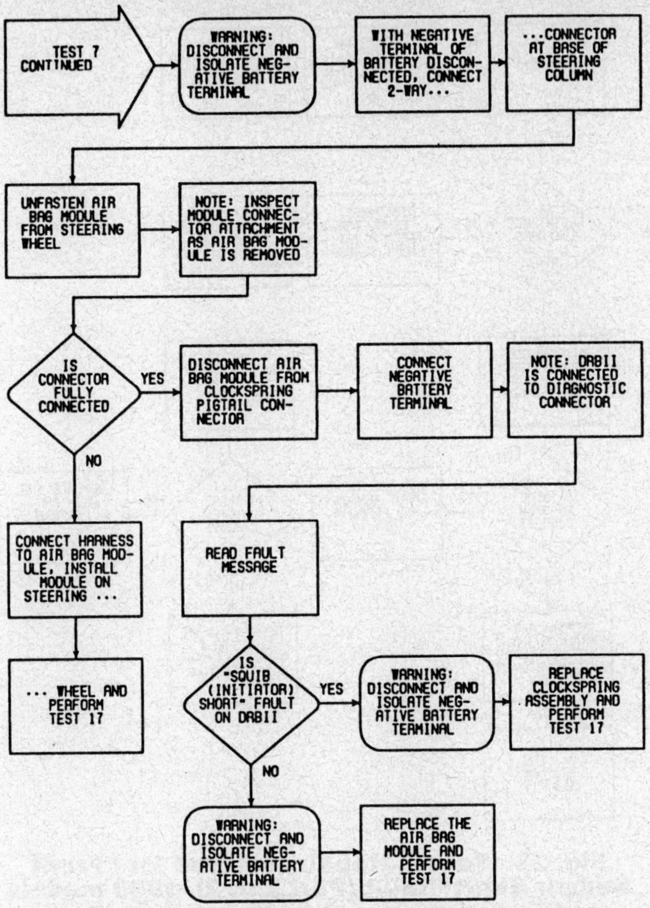

TEST 7 CONTINUED
WARNING: DISCONNECT AND ISOLATE NEGATIVE BATTERY TERMINAL
WITH NEGATIVE TERMINAL OF BATTERY DISCONNECTED, CONNECT 2-WAY...
...CONNECTOR AT BASE OF STEERING COLUMN
UNFASTEN AIR BAG MODULE FROM STEERING WHEEL
NOTE: INSPECT MODULE CONNECTOR ATTACHMENT AS AIR BAG MODULE IS REMOVED
IS CONNECTOR FULLY CONNECTED
YES
DISCONNECT AIR BAG MODULE FROM CLOCKSPRING PIGTAIL CONNECTOR
CONNECT NEGATIVE BATTERY TERMINAL
NOTE: DRBII IS CONNECTED TO DIAGNOSTIC CONNECTOR
NO
CONNECT HARNESS TO AIR BAG MODULE, INSTALL MODULE ON STEERING ...
... WHEEL AND PERFORM TEST 17
READ FAULT MESSAGE
IS "SQUIB (INITIATOR) SHORT" FAULT ON DRBII
YES
WARNING: DISCONNECT AND ISOLATE NEGATIVE BATTERY TERMINAL
REPLACE CLOCKSPRING ASSEMBLY AND PERFORM TEST 17
NO
WARNING: DISCONNECT AND ISOLATE NEGATIVE BATTERY TERMINAL
REPLACE THE AIR BAG MODULE AND PERFORM TEST 17

**Fig. 23 Test 7, Repair required for "Squib (Initiator) Short" fault (Part 2 of 2). 1989–90 models**

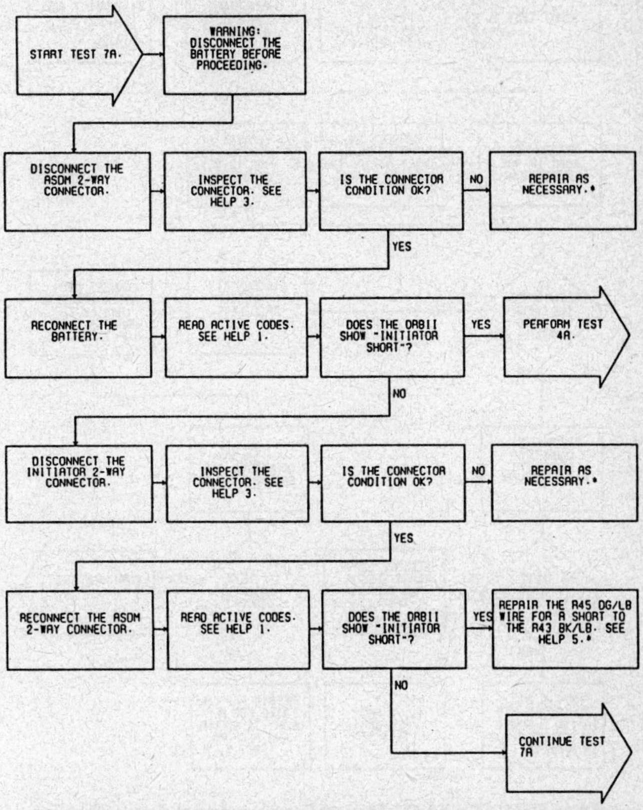

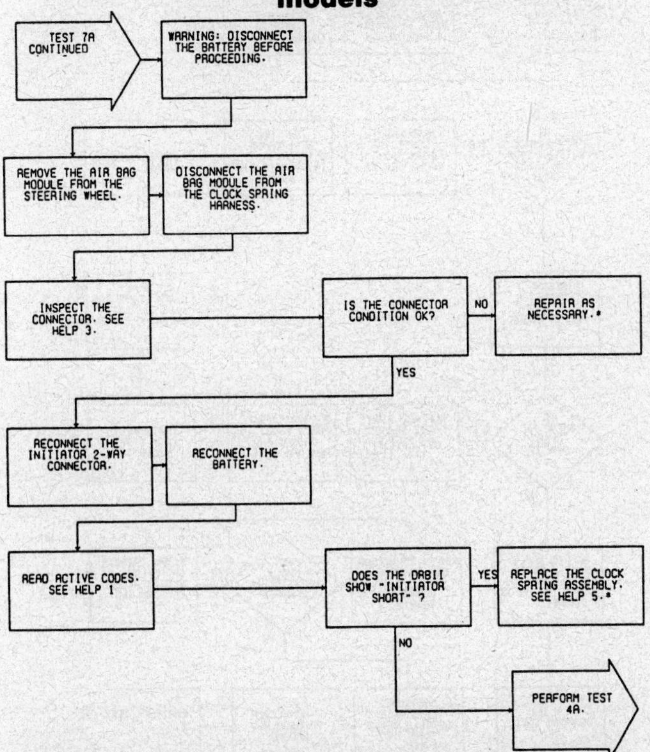

START TEST 7A.
WARNING: DISCONNECT THE BATTERY BEFORE PROCEEDING.
DISCONNECT THE ASDM 2-WAY CONNECTOR.
INSPECT THE CONNECTOR. SEE HELP 3.
IS THE CONNECTOR CONDITION OK?
NO
REPAIR AS NECESSARY.*
YES
RECONNECT THE BATTERY.
READ ACTIVE CODES. SEE HELP 1.
DOES THE DRBII SHOW "INITIATOR SHORT"?
YES
PERFORM TEST 4A.
NO
DISCONNECT THE INITIATOR 2-WAY CONNECTOR.
INSPECT THE CONNECTOR. SEE HELP 3.
IS THE CONNECTOR CONDITION OK?
NO
REPAIR AS NECESSARY.*
YES
RECONNECT THE ASDM 2-WAY CONNECTOR.
READ ACTIVE CODES. SEE HELP 1.
DOES THE DRBII SHOW "INITIATOR SHORT"?
YES
REPAIR THE R45 DG/LB WIRE FOR A SHORT TO THE R43 BK/LB. SEE HELP 5.*
NO
CONTINUE TEST 7A

**Fig. 24 Test 7A, Repair required for "Squib (Initiator) Short" code (Part 1 of 2). 1991 models except Stealth**

TEST 7A CONTINUED
WARNING: DISCONNECT THE BATTERY BEFORE PROCEEDING.
REMOVE THE AIR BAG MODULE FROM THE STEERING WHEEL.
DISCONNECT THE AIR BAG MODULE FROM THE CLOCK SPRING HARNESS.
INSPECT THE CONNECTOR. SEE HELP 3.
IS THE CONNECTOR CONDITION OK?
NO
REPAIR AS NECESSARY.*
YES
RECONNECT THE INITIATOR 2-WAY CONNECTOR.
RECONNECT THE BATTERY.
READ ACTIVE CODES. SEE HELP 1
DOES THE DRBII SHOW "INITIATOR SHORT" ?
YES
REPLACE THE CLOCK SPRING ASSEMBLY. SEE HELP 5.*
NO
PERFORM TEST 4A.

**Fig. 24 Test 7A, Repair required for "Squib (Initiator) Short" code (Part 2 of 2). 1991 models except Stealth**

START TEST 8
WARNING: DISCONNECT AND ISOLATE NEGATIVE BATTERY TERMINAL
REPLACE ASDM AND PERFORM TEST 17

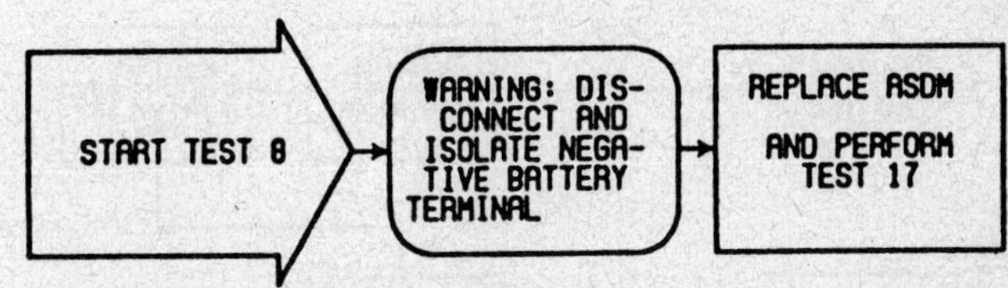

**Fig. 25 Test 8. Repair required for "Safing Sensor Short" fault. 1989–90 models**

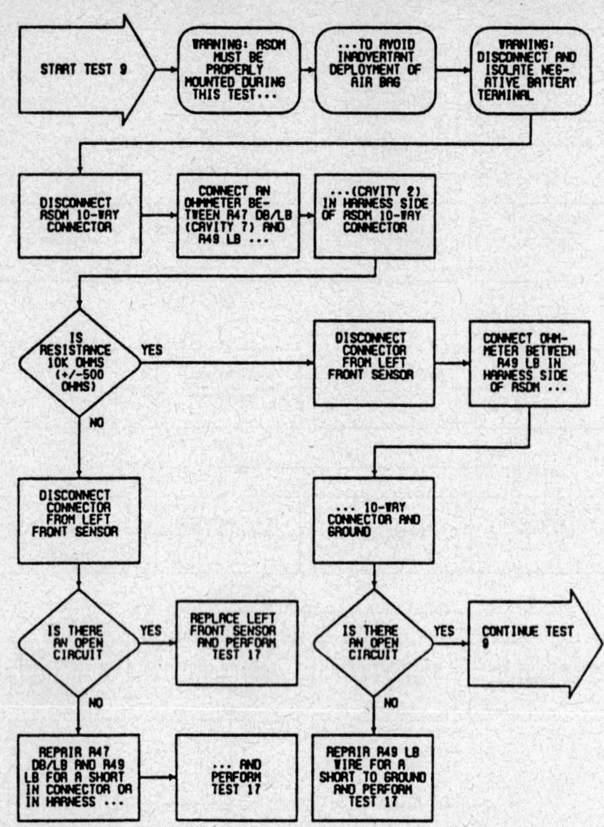


**Fig. 26 Test 9, Repair required for "Front Sensor Short" fault (Part 1 of 2). 1989 models**

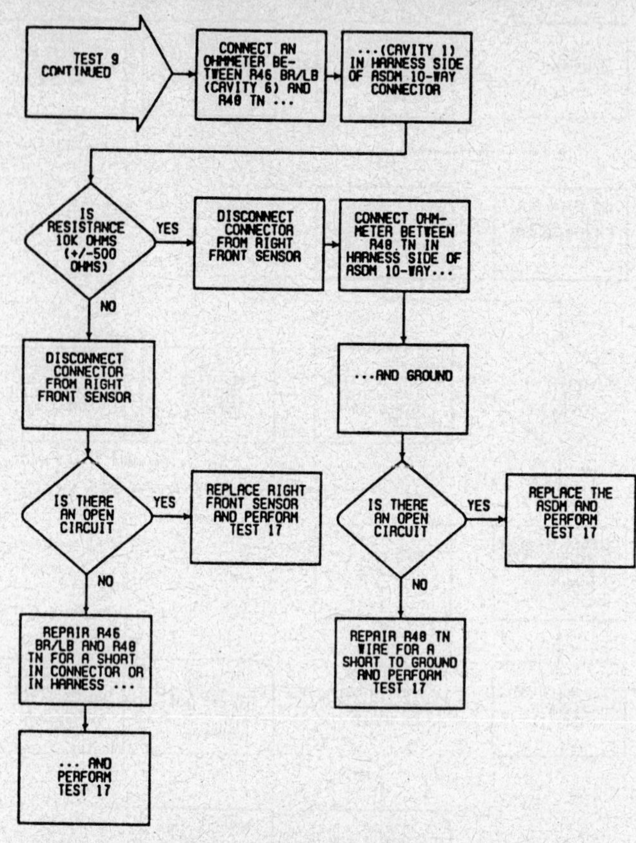


**Fig. 26 Test 9, Repair required for "Front Sensor Short" fault (Part 2 of 2). 1989 models**

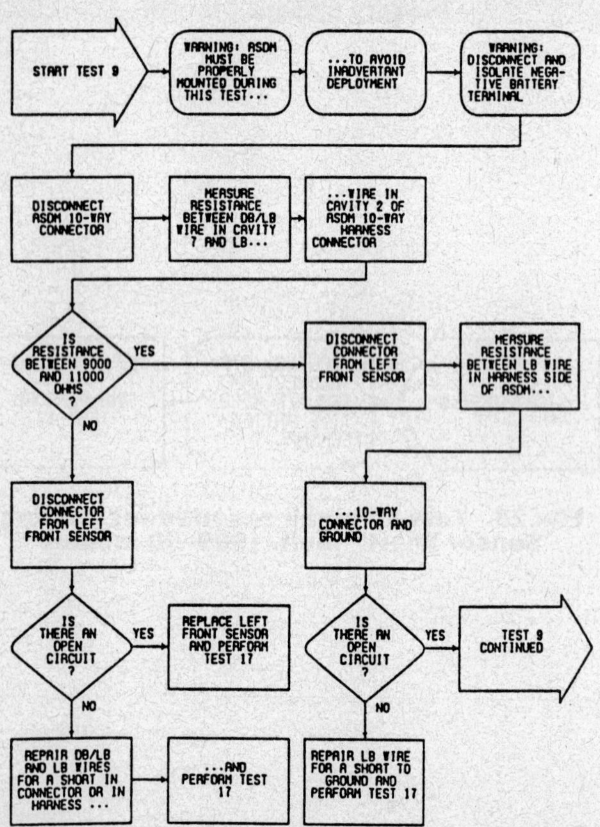


**Fig. 27 Test 9, Repair required for "Front Sensor Short" fault (Part 1 of 3). 1990 models**

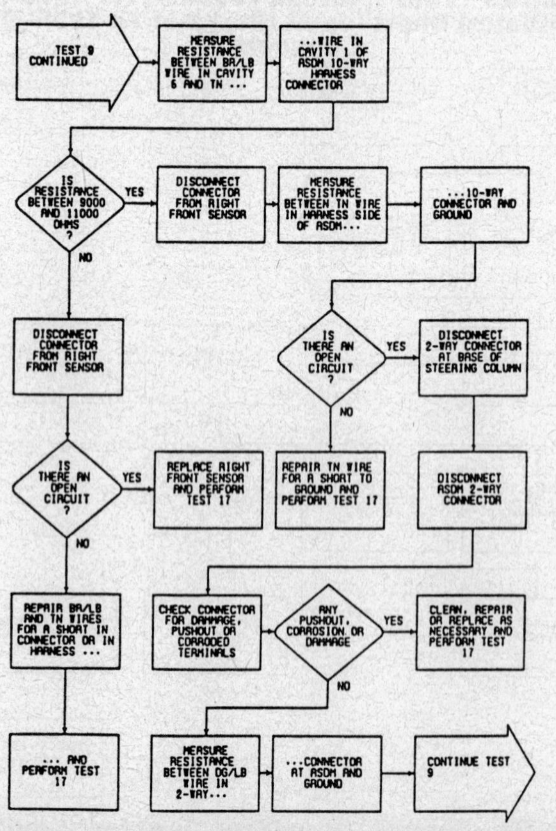


**Fig. 27 Test 9, Repair required for "Front Sensor Short" fault (Part 2 of 3). 1990 models**

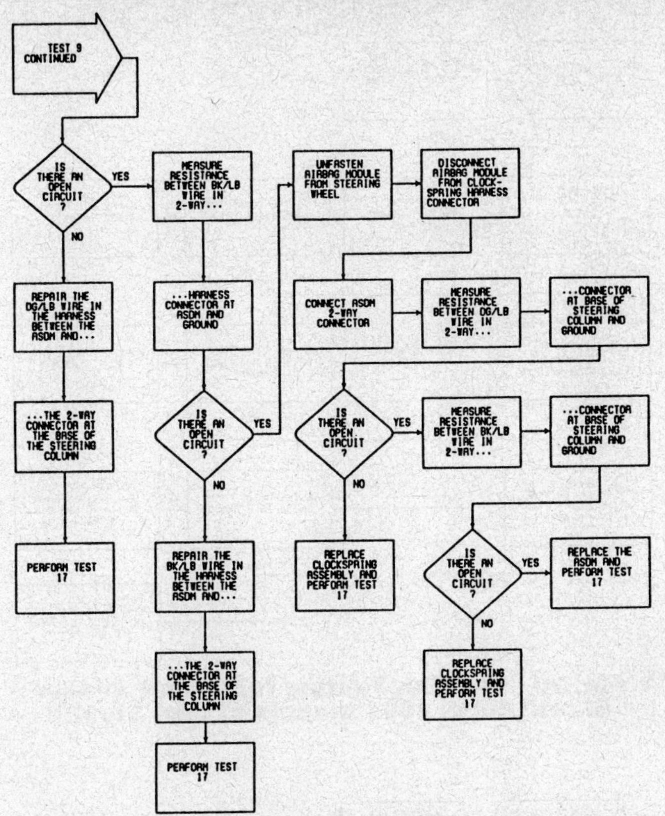


**Fig. 27 Test 9, Repair required for "Front Sensor Short" fault (Part 3 of 3). 1990 models**

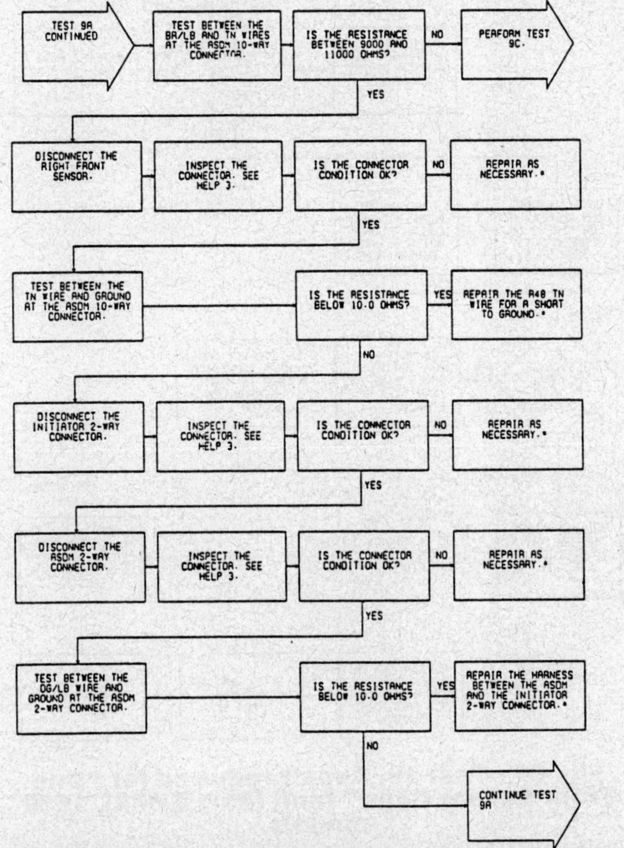


**Fig. 28 Test 9A, Testing for "Front Sensor Short" code (Part 2 of 3). 1991 models except Stealth**

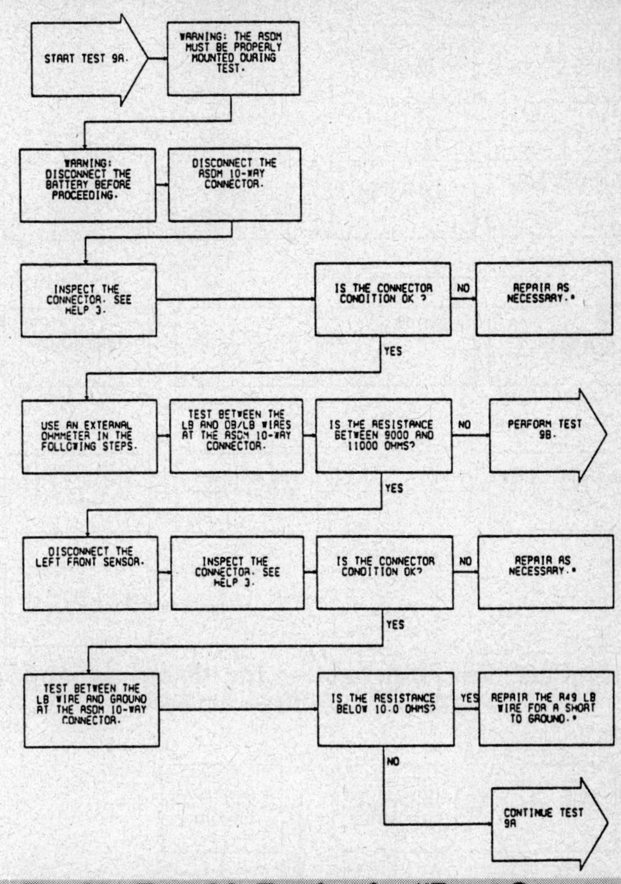


**Fig. 28 Test 9A, Testing for "Front Sensor Short" code (Part 1 of 3). 1991 models except Stealth**

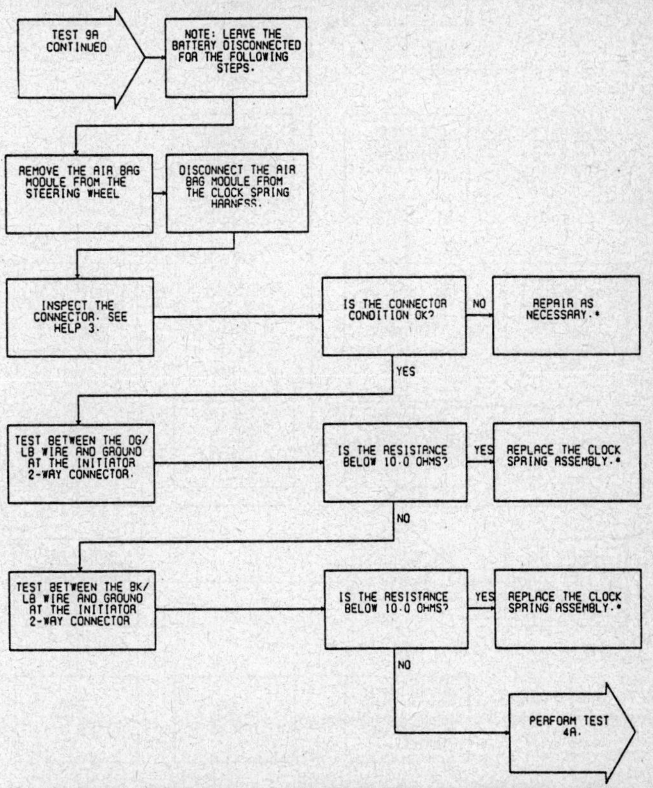


**Fig. 28 Test 9A, Testing for "Front Sensor Short" code (Part 3 of 3). 1991 models except Stealth**

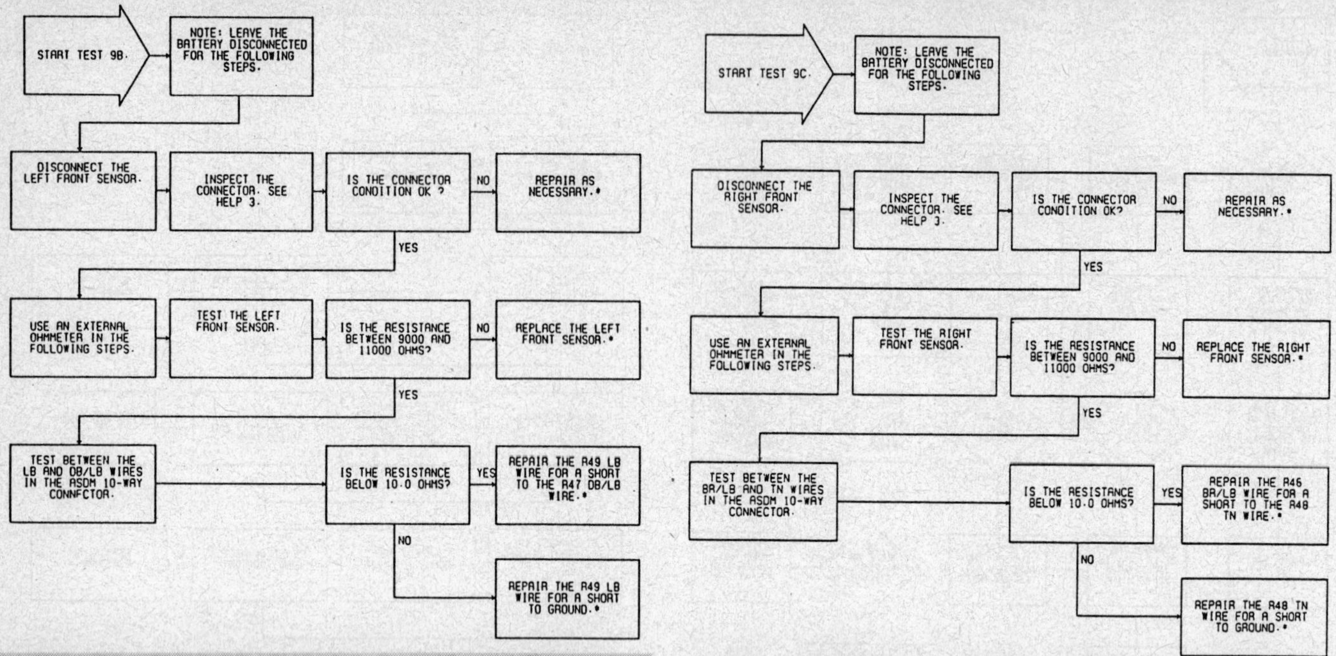


**Fig. 29 Test 9B, Testing for "Front Sensor Short" code. 1991 models except Stealth**

**Fig. 30 Test 9C, Testing for "Front Sensor Short" code. 1991 models except Stealth**

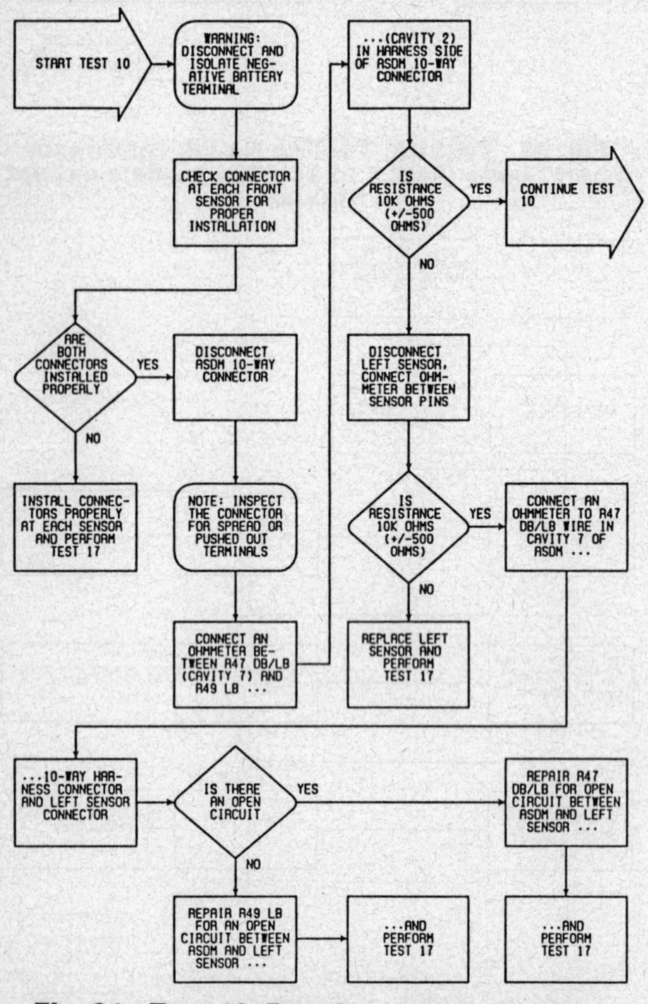


**Fig. 31 Test 10, Repair required for "One Front Sensor Open" fault (Part 1 of 2). 1989 models**

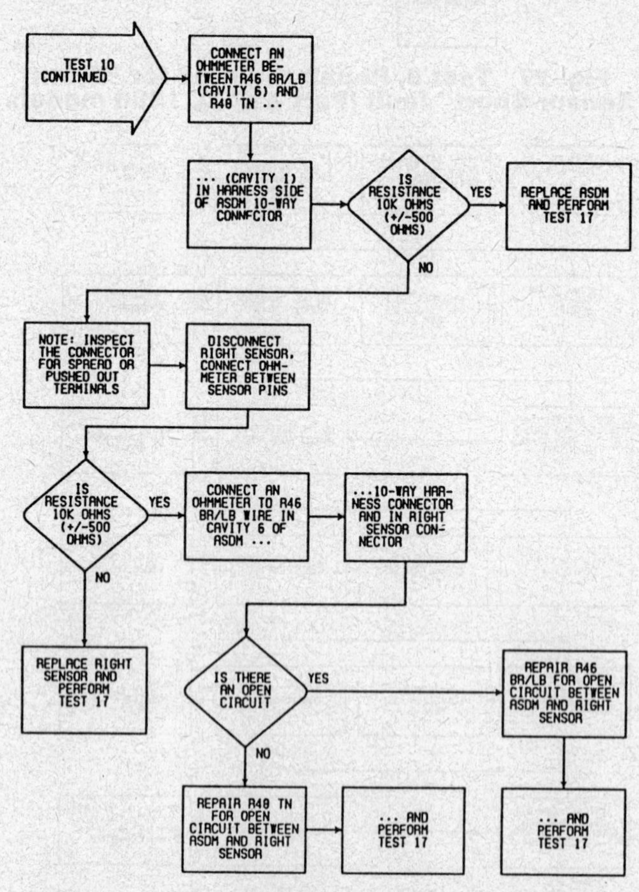


**Fig. 31 Test 10, Repair required for "One Front Sensor Open" fault (Part 2 of 2). 1989 models**

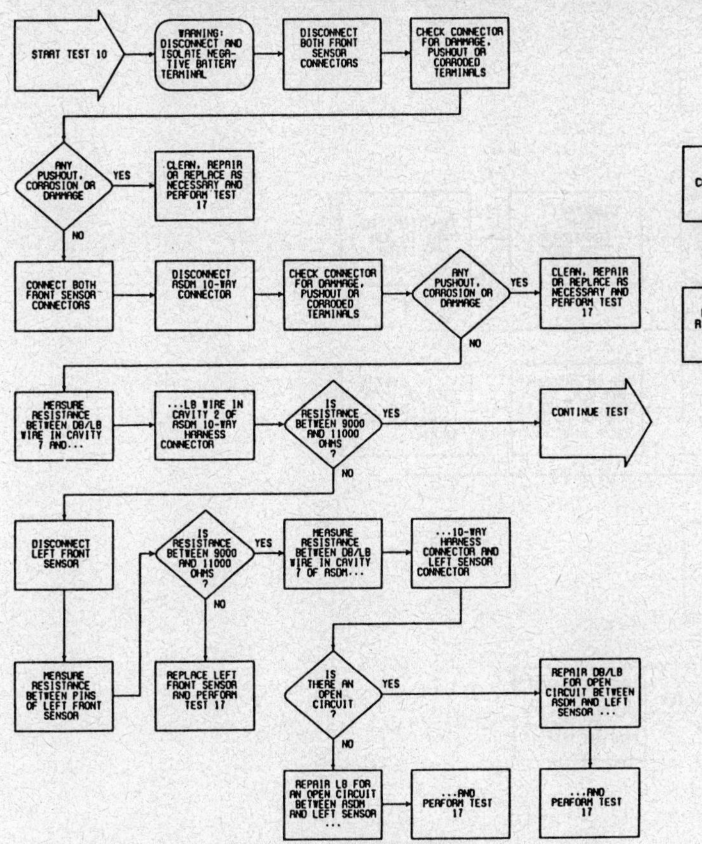


Fig. 32 Test 10, Repair required for "One Front Sensor Open" fault (Part 1 of 2). 1990 models

TEST 10 CONTINUED
MEASURE RESISTANCE BETWEEN BR/LB WIRE IN CAVITY 6 AND TN...
...WIRE IN CAVITY 1 OF ASDM HARNESS 10-WAY CONNECTOR
IS RESISTANCE BETWEEN 9000 AND 11000 OHMS ?
YES
REPLACE THE ASDM AND PERFORM TEST 17
NO
DISCONNECT RIGHT SENSOR
MEASURE RESISTANCE BETWEEN PINS OF RIGHT FRONT SENSOR
IS RESISTANCE BETWEEN 9000 AND 11000 OHMS ?
YES
MEASURE RESISTANCE BETWEEN BR/LB WIRE IN CAVITY 6 OF ASDM...
...10-WAY HARNESS CONNECTOR AND RIGHT SENSOR CONNECTOR
NO
REPLACE RIGHT SENSOR AND PERFORM TEST 17
IS THERE AN OPEN CIRCUIT ?
YES
REPAIR BR/LB WIRE FOR OPEN CIRCUIT BETWEEN ASDM AND RIGHT SENSOR...
...AND PERFORM TEST 17
NO
REPAIR TN WIRE FOR OPEN CIRCUIT BETWEEN ASDM AND RIGHT SENSOR
...AND PERFORM TEST 17

Fig. 32 Test 10, Repair required for "One Front Sensor Open" fault (Part 2 of 2). 1990 models

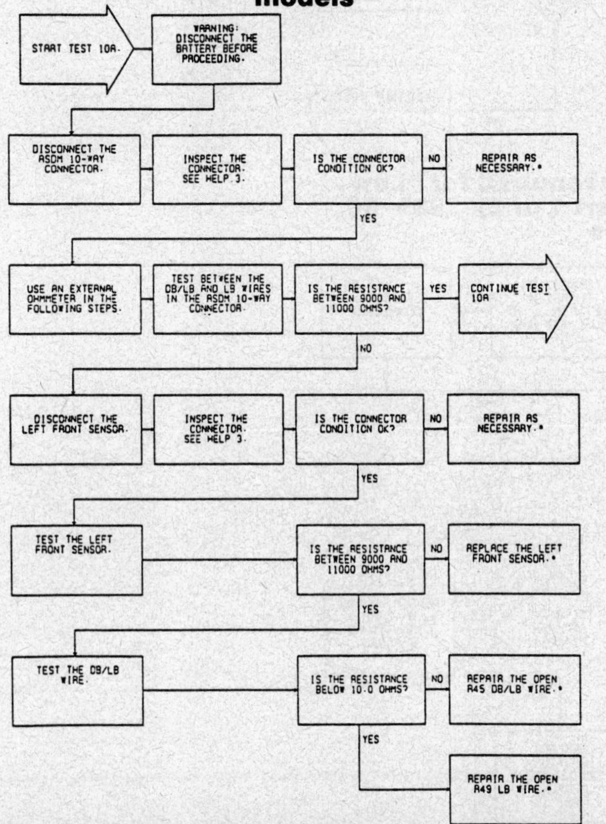


Fig. 33 Test 10A, Repair required for "One Front Sensor Open" code (Part 1 of 2). 1991 models except Stealth

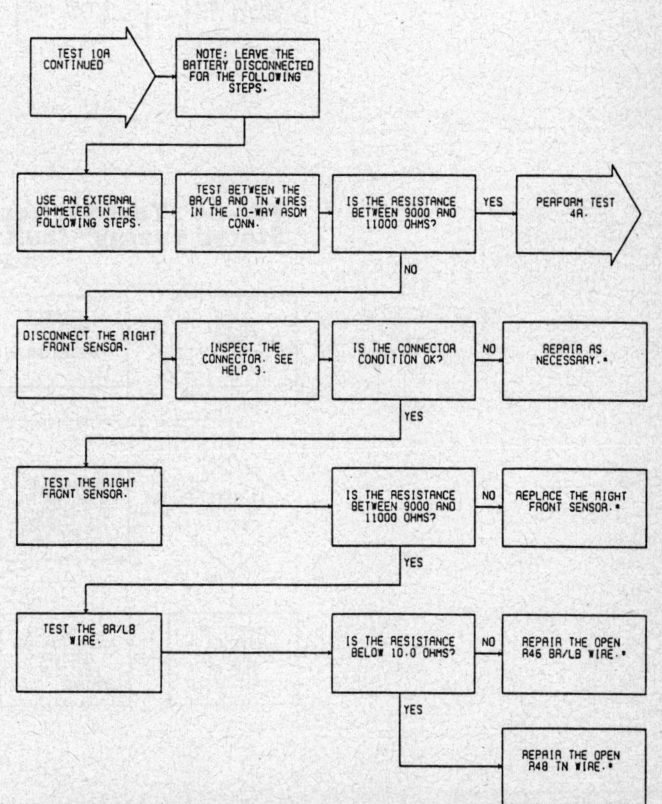


Fig. 33 Test 10A, Repair required for "One Front Sensor Open" code (Part 2 of 2). 1991 models except Stealth

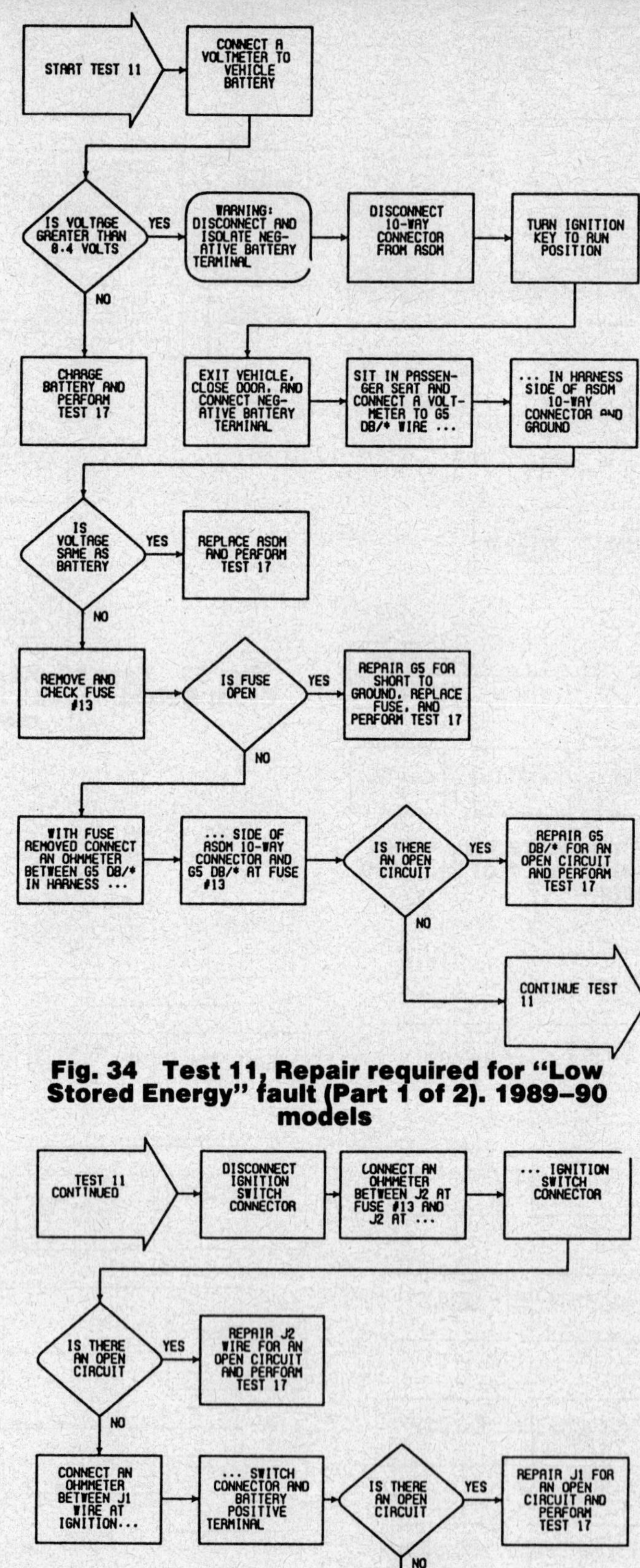


**Fig. 34 Test 11, Repair required for "Low Stored Energy" fault (Part 1 of 2). 1989–90 models**

**Fig. 34 Test 11, Repair required for "Low Stored Energy" fault (Part 2 of 2). 1989–90 models**

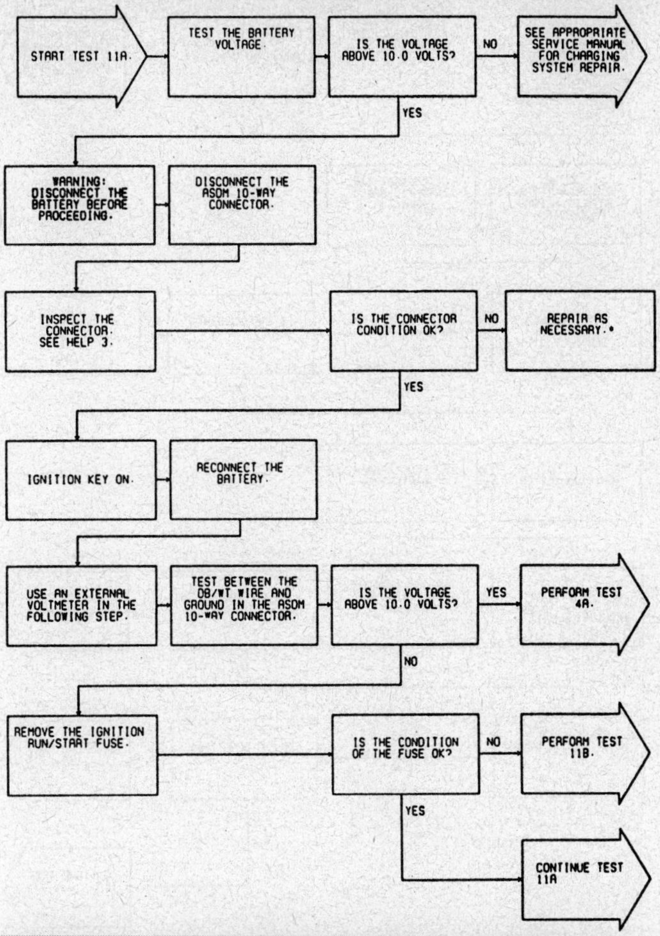

START TEST 11A.
TEST THE BATTERY VOLTAGE.
IS THE VOLTAGE ABOVE 10.0 VOLTS?
NO
SEE APPROPRIATE SERVICE MANUAL FOR CHARGING SYSTEM REPAIR.
YES
WARNING: DISCONNECT THE BATTERY BEFORE PROCEEDING.
DISCONNECT THE ASDM 10-WAY CONNECTOR.
INSPECT THE CONNECTOR. SEE HELP 3.
IS THE CONNECTOR CONDITION OK?
NO
REPAIR AS NECESSARY.*
YES
IGNITION KEY ON.
RECONNECT THE BATTERY.
USE AN EXTERNAL VOLTMETER IN THE FOLLOWING STEP.
TEST BETWEEN THE DB/WT WIRE AND GROUND IN THE ASDM 10-WAY CONNECTOR.
IS THE VOLTAGE ABOVE 10.0 VOLTS?
YES
PERFORM TEST 4A.
NO
REMOVE THE IGNITION RUN/START FUSE.
IS THE CONDITION OF THE FUSE OK?
NO
PERFORM TEST 11B.
YES
CONTINUE TEST 11A

**Fig. 35 Test 11A, Testing for "Low Stored Energy" code (Part 1 of 2). 1991 models except Stealth**

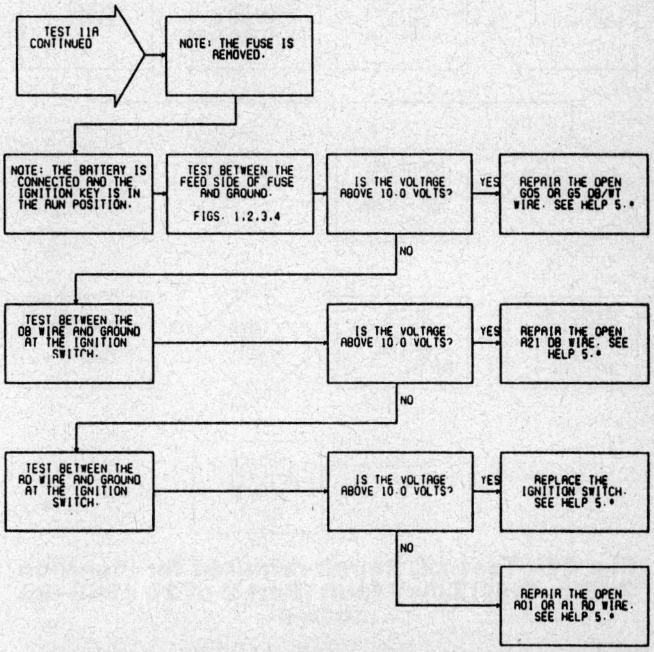

TEST 11A CONTINUED
NOTE: THE FUSE IS REMOVED.
NOTE: THE BATTERY IS CONNECTED AND THE IGNITION KEY IS IN THE RUN POSITION.
TEST BETWEEN THE FEED SIDE OF FUSE AND GROUND.
FIGS. 1,2,3,4
IS THE VOLTAGE ABOVE 10.0 VOLTS?
YES
REPAIR THE OPEN G05 OR G5 DB/WT WIRE. SEE HELP 5.*
NO
TEST BETWEEN THE DB WIRE AND GROUND AT THE IGNITION SWITCH.
IS THE VOLTAGE ABOVE 10.0 VOLTS?
YES
REPAIR THE OPEN A21 DB WIRE. SEE HELP 5.*
NO
TEST BETWEEN THE RD WIRE AND GROUND AT THE IGNITION SWITCH.
IS THE VOLTAGE ABOVE 10.0 VOLTS?
YES
REPLACE THE IGNITION SWITCH. SEE HELP 5.*
NO
REPAIR THE OPEN A01 OR A1 RD WIRE. SEE HELP 5.*

**Fig. 35 Test 11A, Testing for "Low Stored Energy" code (Part 2 of 2). 1991 models except Stealth**

START TEST 11B.
WARNING: DISCONNECT THE BATTERY BEFORE PROCEEDING.
USE A EXTERNAL OHMMETER IN THE FOLLOWING STEPS.
TEST BETWEEN THE DB/WT WIRE AND GROUND AT THE ASDM 10-WAY CONNECTOR.
IS THE RESISTANCE BELOW 10.0 OHMS?
YES
REPAIR THE G05 OR G5 DB/WT WIRE FOR A SHORT TO GROUND.
REPLACE THE FUSE.*
NO
TEST THE DB/WT WIRE BETWEEN THE ASDM 10-WAY CONNECTOR AND THE FUSE BOX. FIGS. 2,3,4,5
IS THE RESISTANCE BELOW 10.0 OHMS?
NO
REPAIR THE OPEN G05 OR G5 DB/WT WIRE.
YES
REPLACE THE FUSE.*

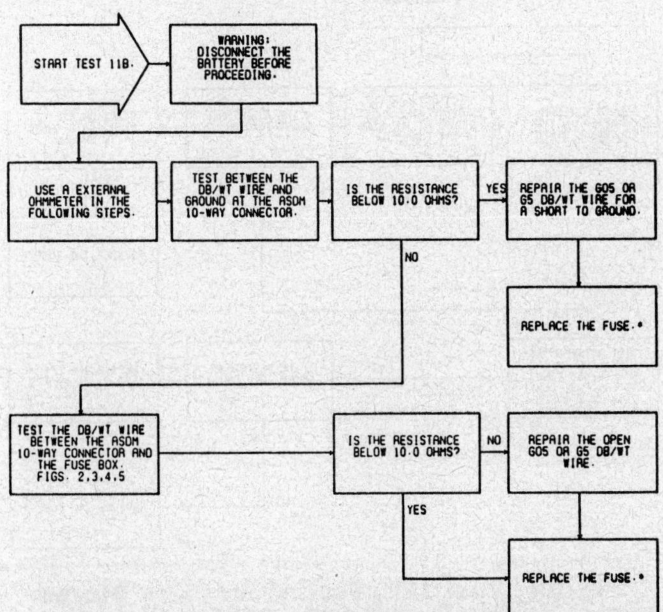

**Fig. 36 Test 11B, Testing for "Low Stored Energy" code. 1991 models except Stealth**

START TEST 12
CONNECT A VOLTMETER TO VEHICLE BATTERY
IS VOLTAGE GREATER THAN 8.4 VOLTS
YES
WARNING: DISCONNECT AND ISOLATE NEGATIVE BATTERY TERMINAL
DISCONNECT 10-WAY CONNECTOR FROM ASDM
TURN IGNITION KEY TO RUN POSITION
NO
CHARGE BATTERY AND PERFORM TEST 17
EXIT VEHICLE, CLOSE DOOR, AND CONNECT NEGATIVE BATTERY TERMINAL
SIT IN PASSENGER SEAT AND CONNECT A VOLTMETER TO B1 WT WIRE ...
... IN HARNESS SIDE OF ASDM 10-WAY CONNECTOR AND GROUND
IS VOLTAGE SAME AS BATTERY
YES
REPLACE ASDM AND PERFORM TEST 17
NO
VISUALLY CHECK FUSE #2
IS FUSE OPEN
YES
REPAIR B1 FOR SHORT TO GROUND, REPLACE FUSE, AND PERFORM TEST 17
NO
CONNECT AN OHMMETER BETWEEN B1 WT WIRE IN HARNESS SIDE OF ASDM 10-WAY ...
... CONNECTOR AND B1 WT WIRE AT FUSE #2
IS THERE AN OPEN CIRCUIT
YES
REPAIR B1 WT WIRE FOR AN OPEN CIRCUIT AND PERFORM TEST 17
NO
CONTINUE TEST 12

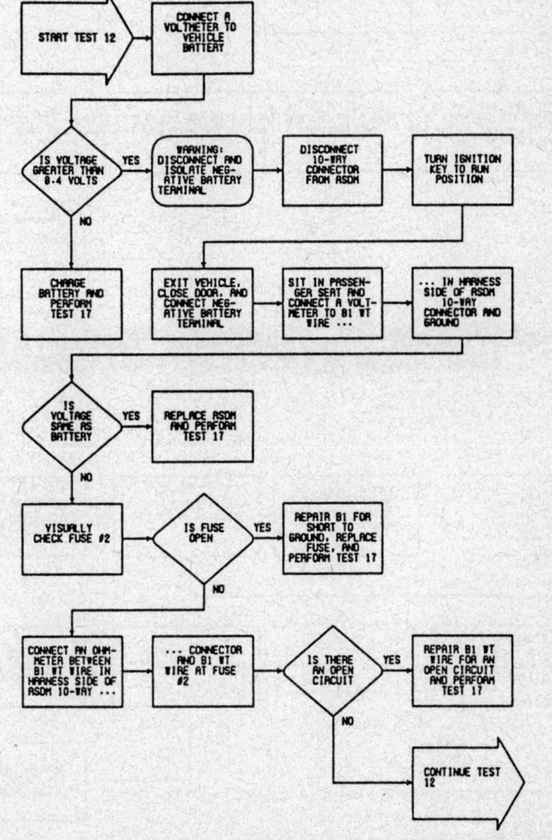

**Fig. 37 Test 12, Repair required for "Ignition 2 (Run Only) Low" fault (Part 1 of 2). 1989–90 models**

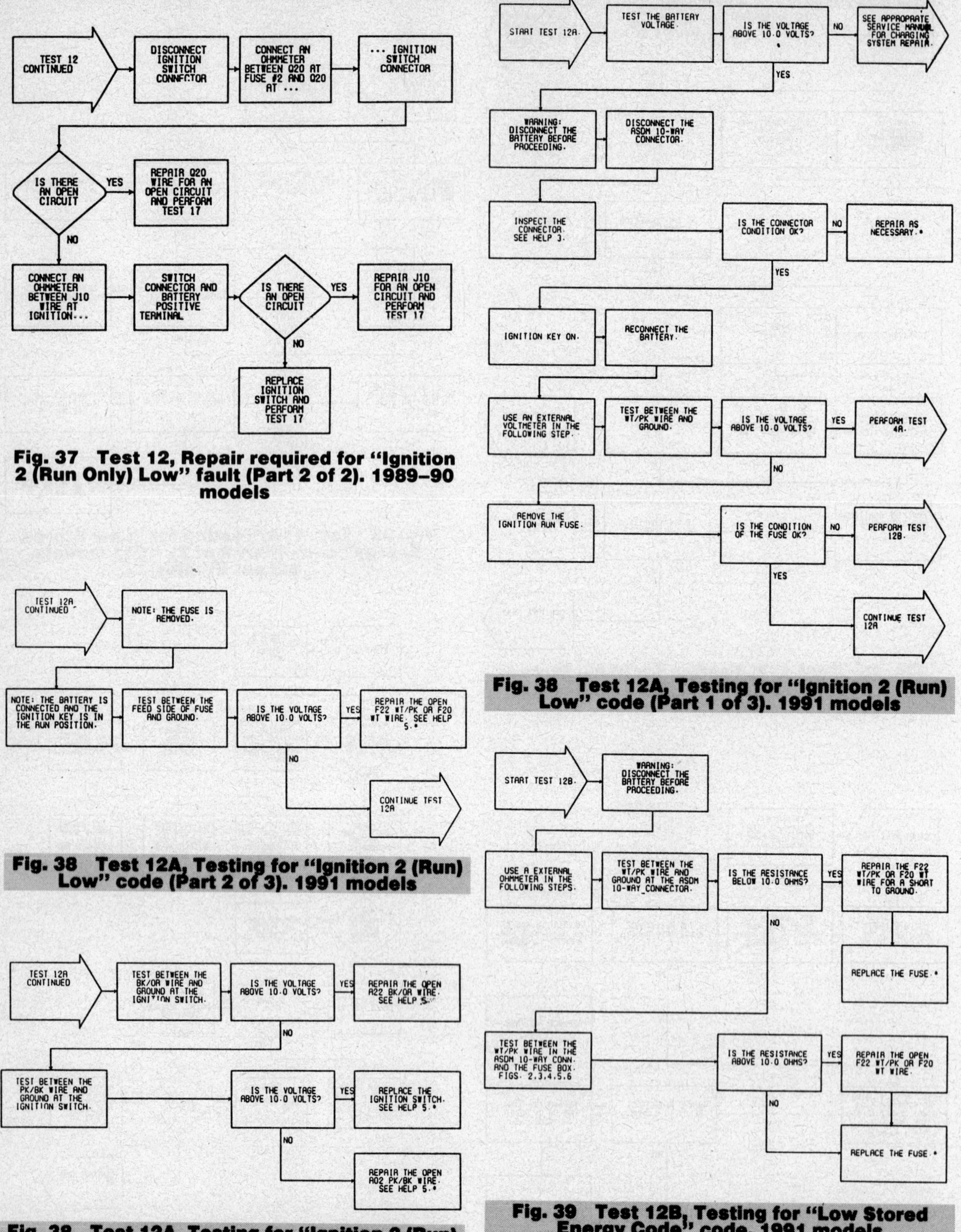


**Fig. 37 Test 12, Repair required for "Ignition 2 (Run Only) Low" fault (Part 2 of 2). 1989–90 models**

**Fig. 38 Test 12A, Testing for "Ignition 2 (Run) Low" code (Part 1 of 3). 1991 models**

**Fig. 38 Test 12A, Testing for "Ignition 2 (Run) Low" code (Part 2 of 3). 1991 models**

**Fig. 38 Test 12A, Testing for "Ignition 2 (Run) Low" code (Part 3 of 3). 1991 models**

**Fig. 39 Test 12B, Testing for "Low Stored Energy Code" code. 1991 models**

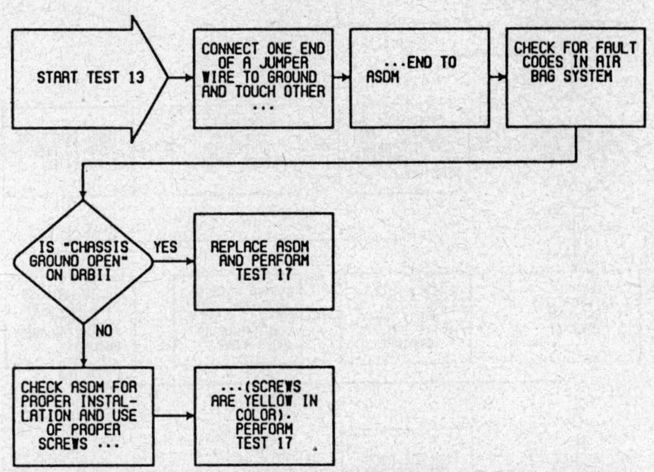


Fig. 40 Test 13, Repair required for "Chassis Ground Open" fault. 1989 models

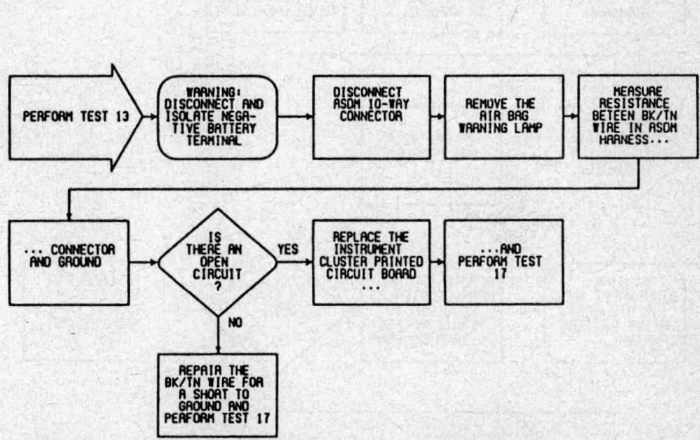


Fig. 41 Test 13, Repair required for "Warning Lamp Short" fault. 1990 models

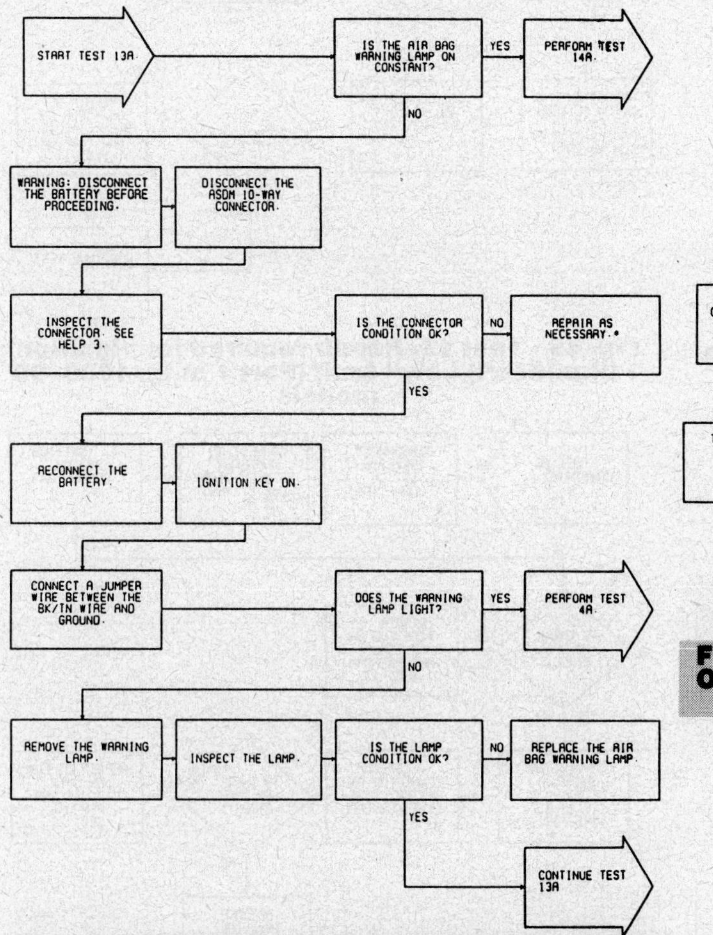


Fig. 42 Test 13A, Testing for "Warning Lamp Open" code (Part 1 of 2). 1991 models except Stealth

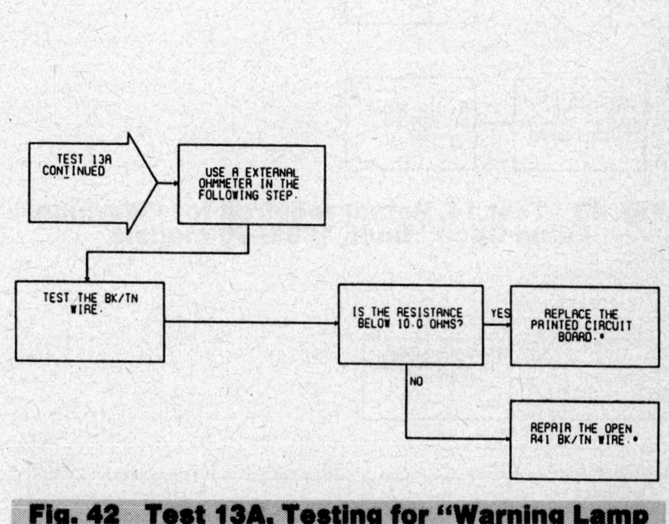


Fig. 42 Test 13A, Testing for "Warning Lamp Open" code (Part 2 of 2). 1991 models except Stealth

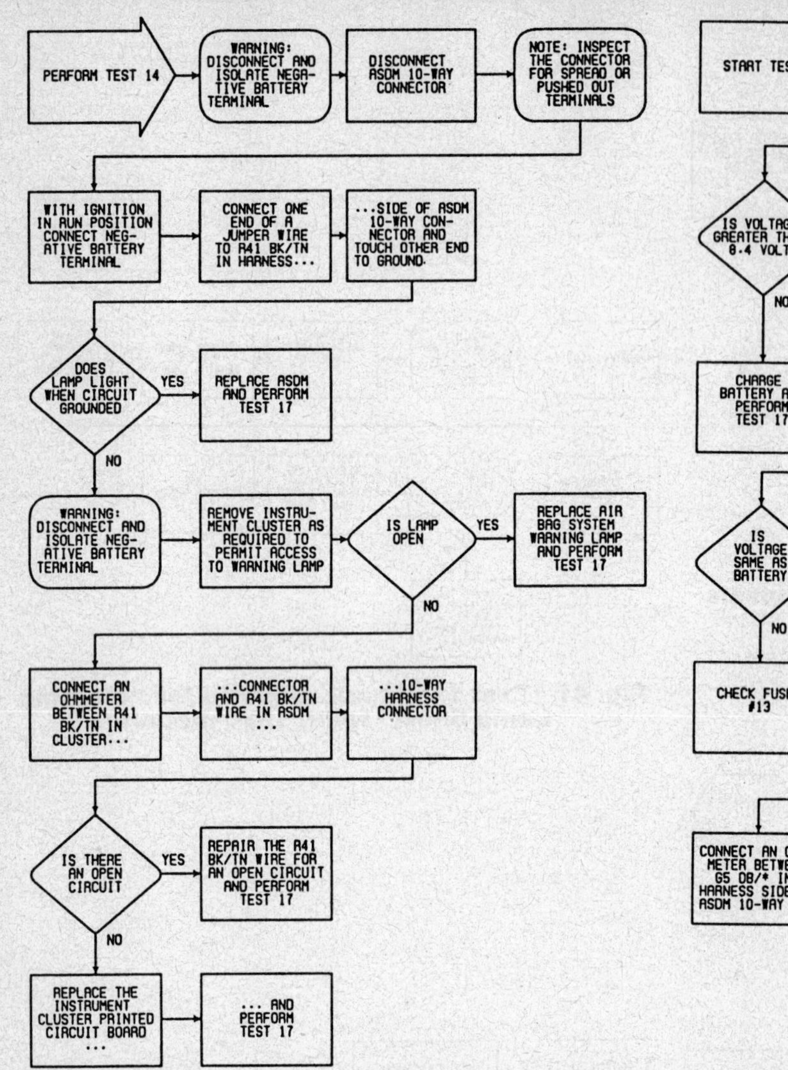


**Fig. 43 Test 14, Repair required for "Warning Lamp Open" fault. 1989–90 models**

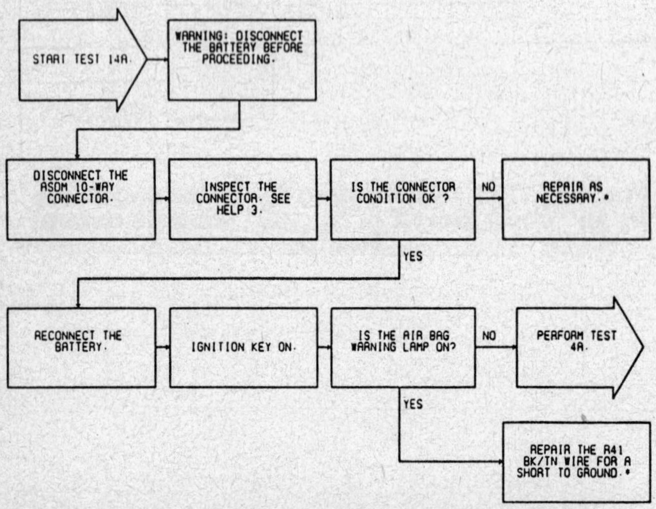


**Fig. 44 Test 14A, Testing for "Warning Lamp Short" code. 1991 models except Stealth**

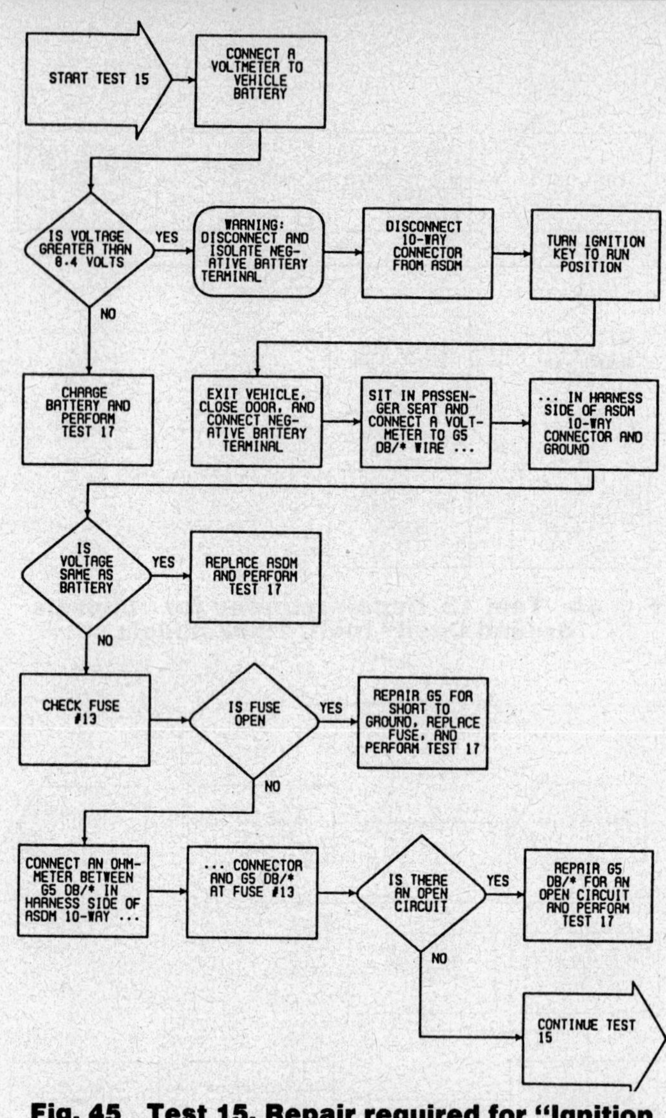


**Fig. 45 Test 15, Repair required for "Ignition 1 (Run/Start) Low" fault (Part 1 of 2). 1989–90 models**

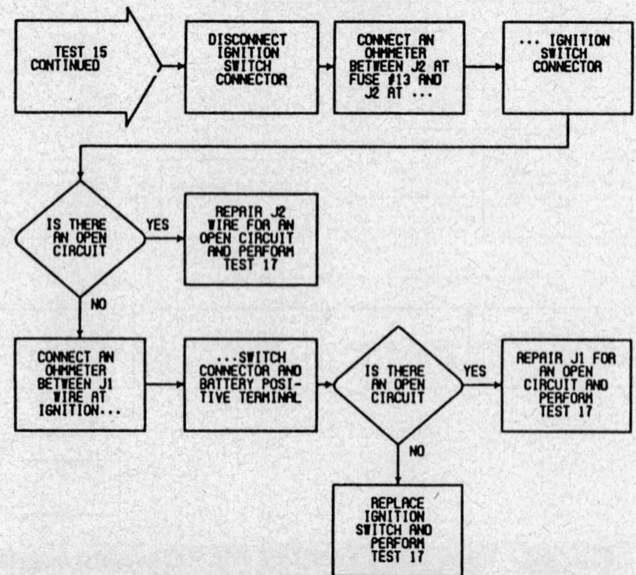


**Fig. 45 Test 15, Repair required for "Ignition 1 (Run/Start) Low" fault (Part 2 of 2). 1989–90 models**

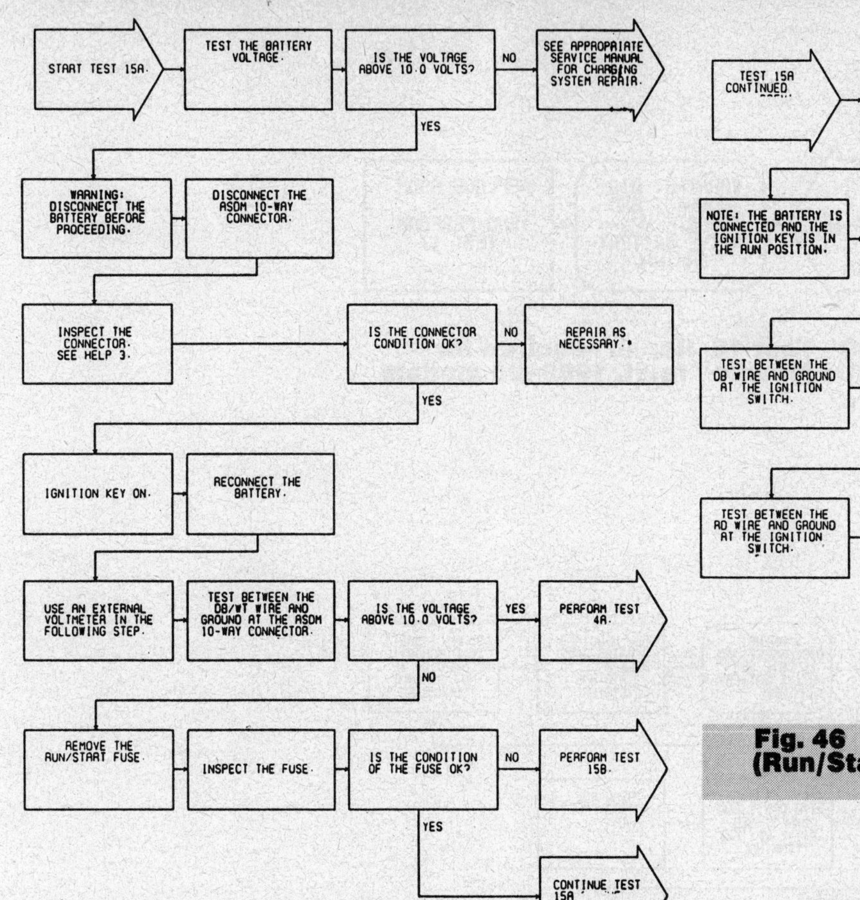


Fig. 46 Test 15A, Testing for "Ignition 1 (Run/Start) Low" code (Part 1 of 2). 1991 models except Stealth

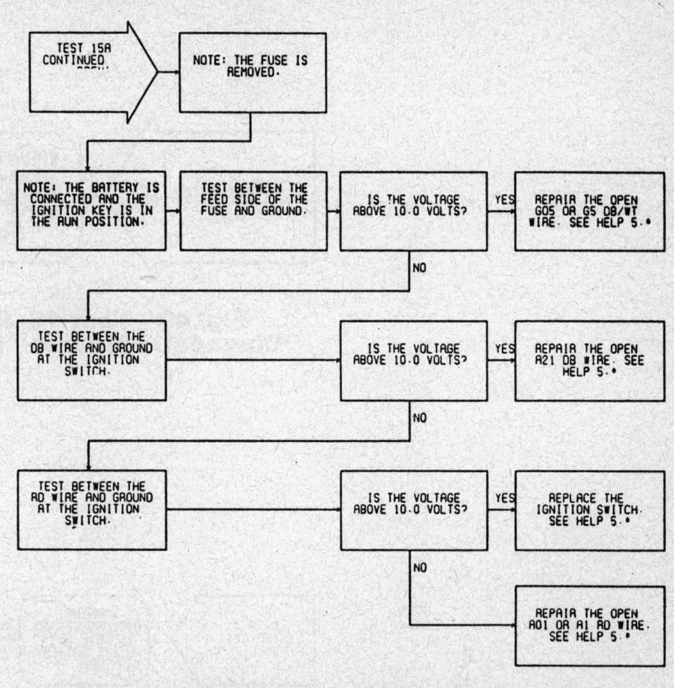


Fig. 46 Test 15A, Testing for "Ignition 1 (Run/Start) Low" code (Part 2 of 2). 1991 models except Stealth

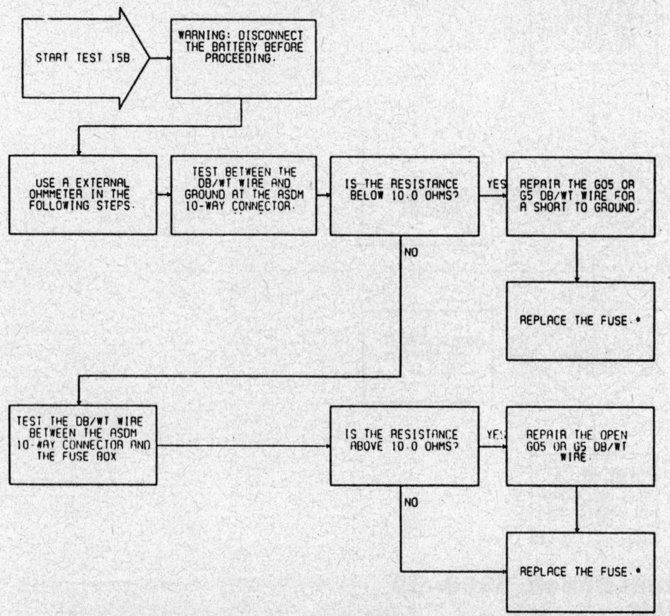


Fig. 47 Test 15B, Testing for "Ignition 1 (Run/Start) Low" code. 1991 models except Stealth

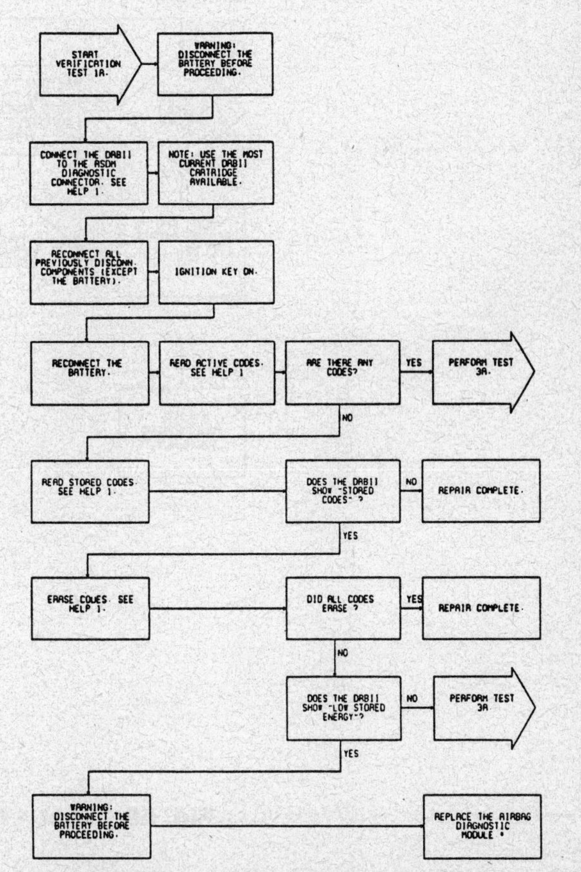


Fig. 48 Test 1A, 'Verification Test." 1991 models except Stealth

**Fig. 49 Test 16, Repair required for "Diagnostic Module" fault. 1989–90 models**

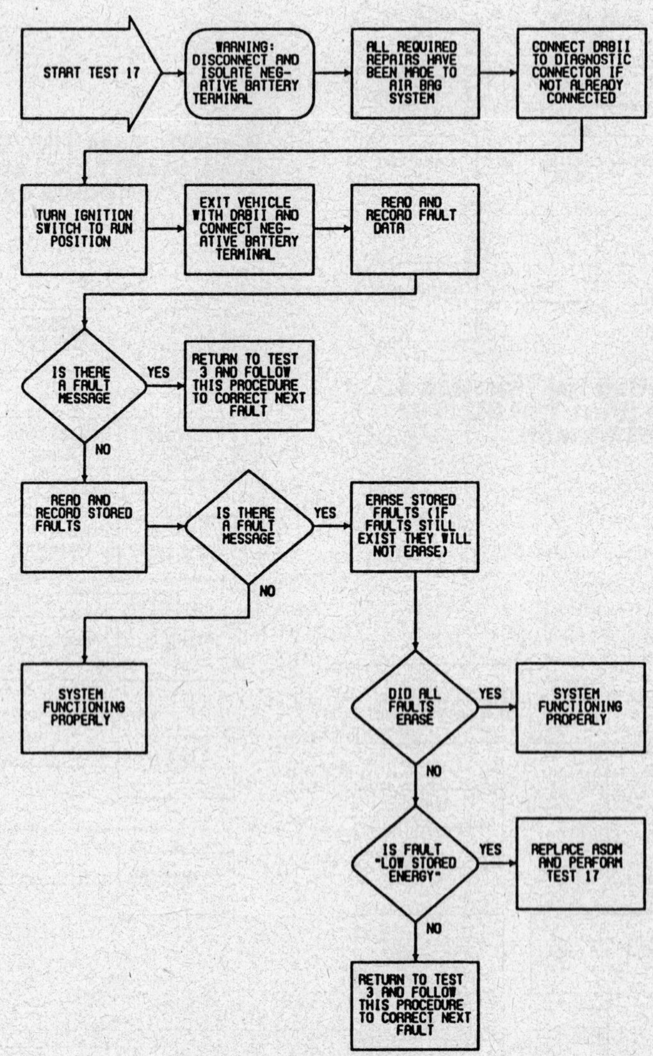


**Fig. 50 Test 17, System Check. 1989–90 models**

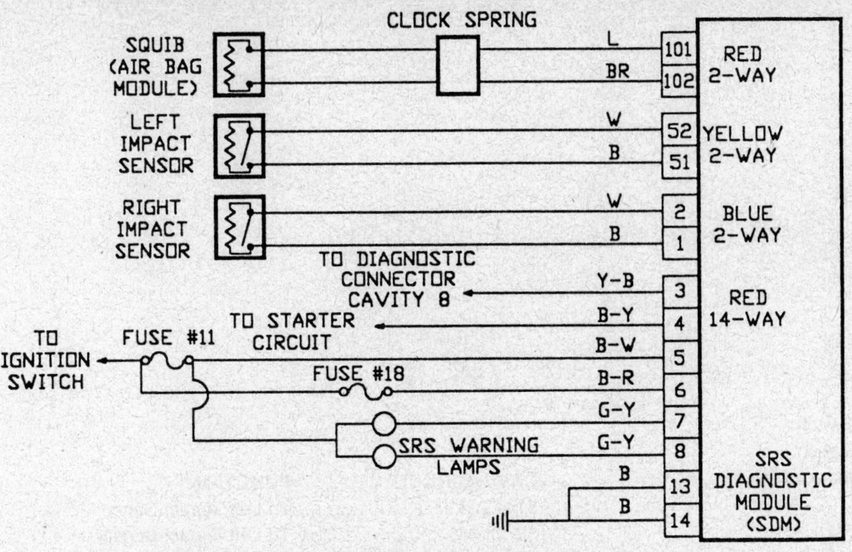


Fig. 51 ABS wiring schematic. Stealth

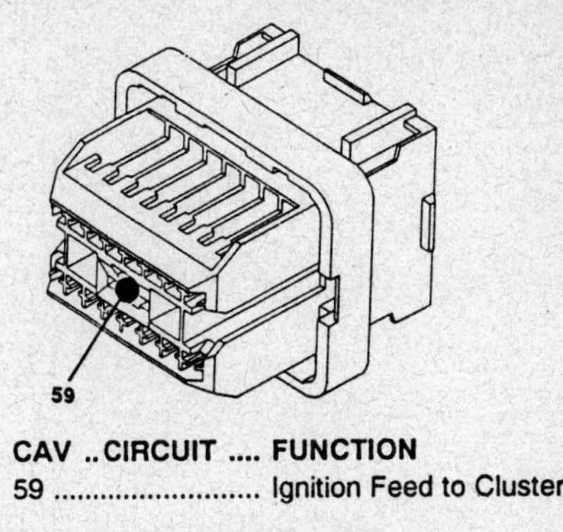


CAV ..CIRCUIT .... FUNCTION
59 .......................... Ignition Feed to Cluster

Fig. 52 D-04 cluster connector. Stealth

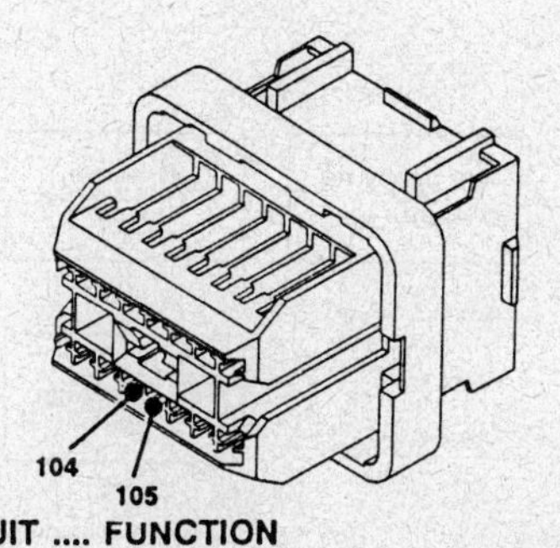


CAV ..CIRCUIT .... FUNCTION
104 .... G-Y ............ To SRS Diagnostic Module-Warning Lamp
105 .... G-Y ............ To SRS Diagnostic Module-Warning Lamp

Fig. 53 D-05 cluster connector. Stealth

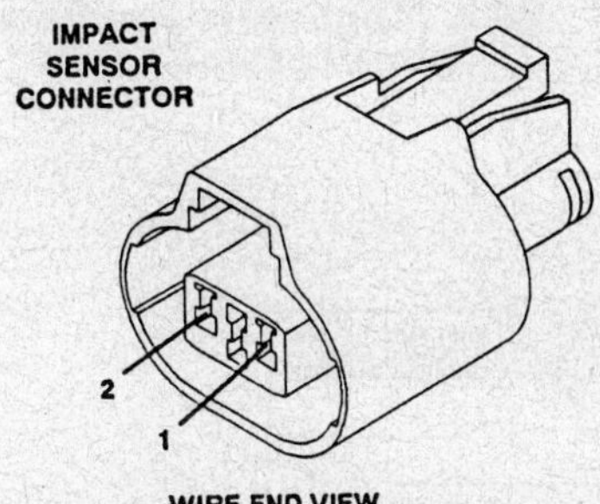


CAV ..CIRCUIT .... FUNCTION
1 ........ B ................ To SRS Diagnostic Module
2 ........ W .............. To SRS Diagnostic Module

Fig. 54 Front impact sensor connector. Stealth

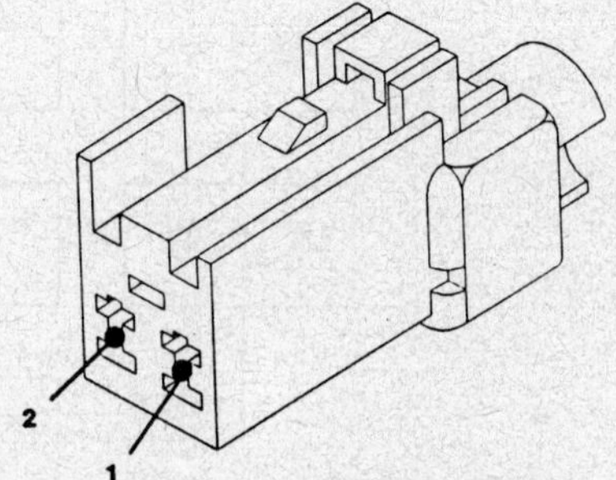


CAV CIRCUIT .... FUNCTION
1 ...... B ................ To Right Impact Sensor Circuit
2 ...... W................ To Right Impact Sensor Circuit

Fig. 55 SRS diagnostic module blue 2-way connector. Stealth

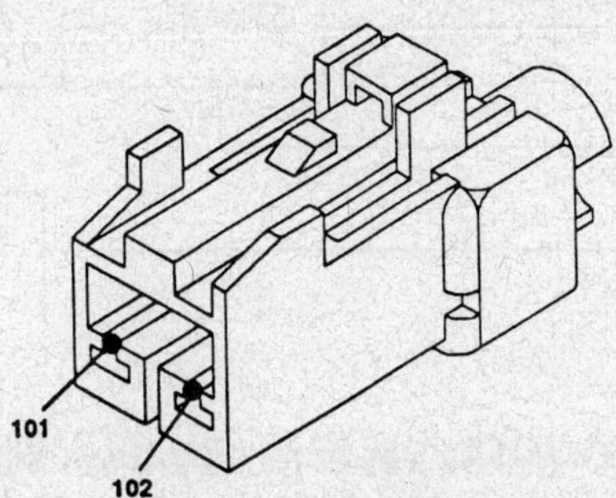


CAV CIRCUIT .... FUNCTION
101 .. BR .............. To Clock Spring (Air Bag Module)
102 .. L ................ To Clock Spring (Air Bag Module)

Fig. 56 SRS diagnostic module red 2-way connector. Stealth

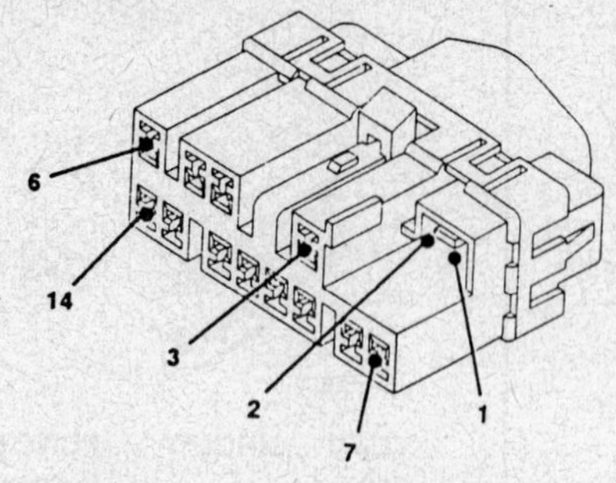


| CAV | CIRCUIT .... | FUNCTION |
|---|---|---|
| 1 ............................ | | Connector Lock Switch |
| 2 ............................ | | Connector Lock Switch |
| 3 ...... | Y-B ........... | To Diagnostic Connector Pin #8 |
| 4 ...... | B-Y ........... | To Starter Circuit |
| 5 ...... | B-W ........... | Ignition 2 (Fuse #11) |
| 6 ...... | B-R ........... | Ignition 1 (Fuse #18) |
| 7 ...... | G-Y ........... | SRS Warning Lamp (Pin 105) |
| 8 ...... | G-Y ........... | SRS Warning Lamp (Pin 104) |
| 9-12........................ | | Not Used |
| 13 .... | B ............... | Module Ground |
| 14 .... | B ............... | Module Ground |

**Fig. 57 SRS diagnostic module red 14-way connector. Stealth**

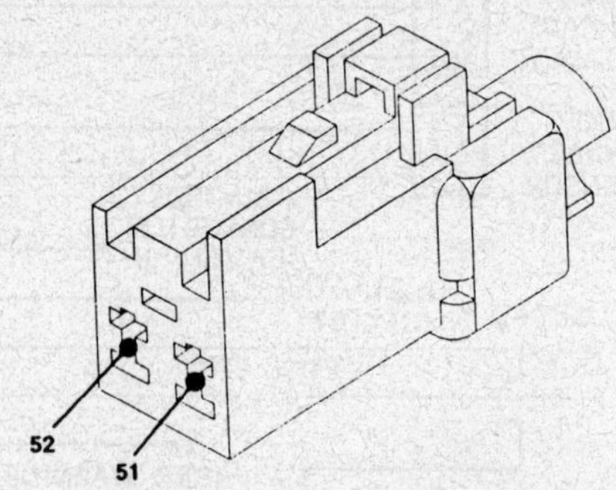


| CAV | CIRCUIT ............. | FUNCTION |
|---|---|---|
| 51 .... | B .......................... | To Left Impact Sensor |
| 52 .... | W.......................... | To Left Impact Sensor |

**Fig. 58 SRS diagnostic module yellow 2-way connector. Stealth**

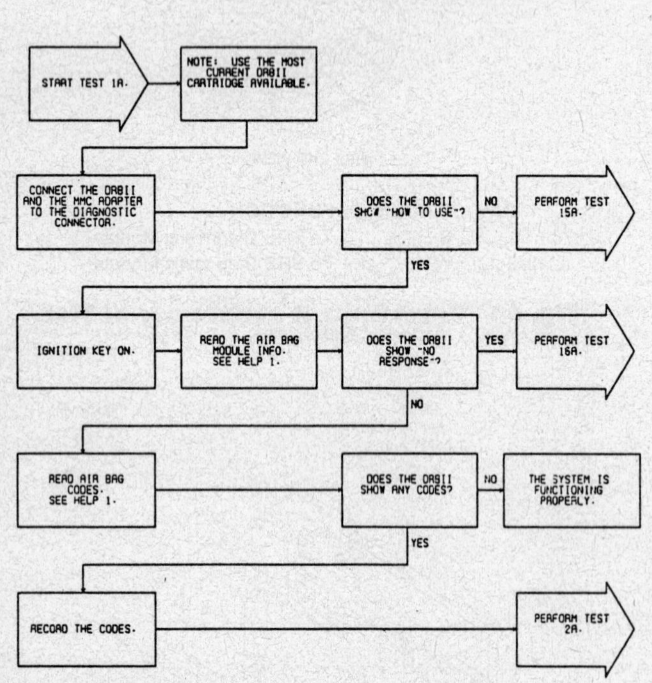


**Fig. 59 Test 1A, System function. Stealth**

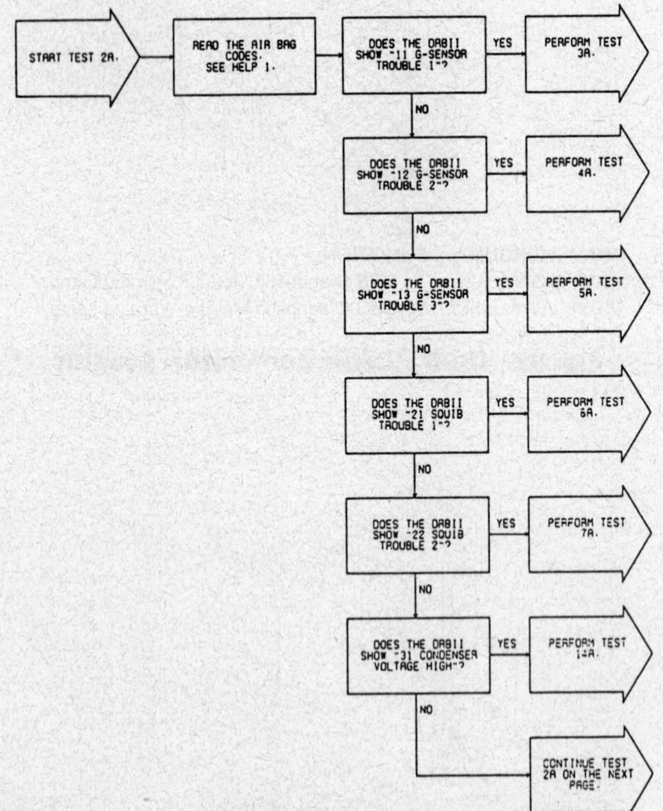


**Fig. 60 Test 2A, SRS airbag codes (Part 1 of 3). Stealth**

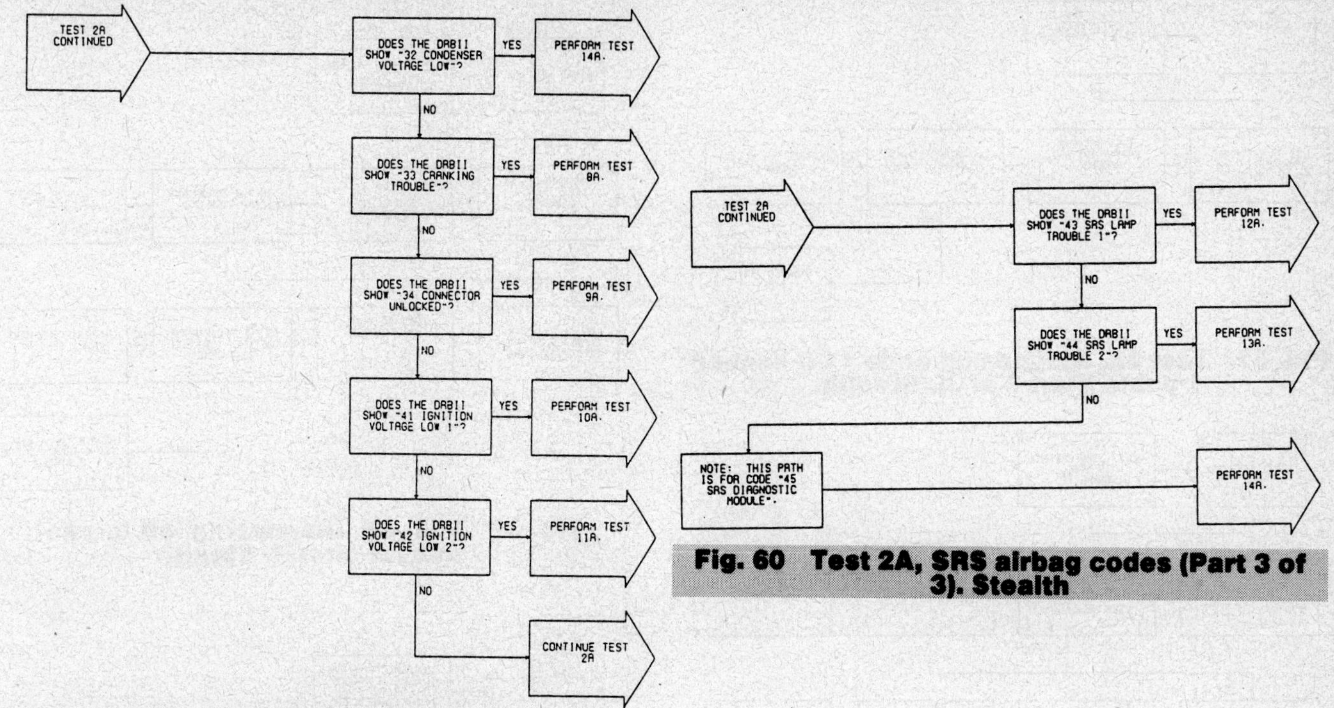


**Fig. 60 Test 2A, SRS airbag codes (Part 2 of 3). Stealth**

**Fig. 60 Test 2A, SRS airbag codes (Part 3 of 3). Stealth**

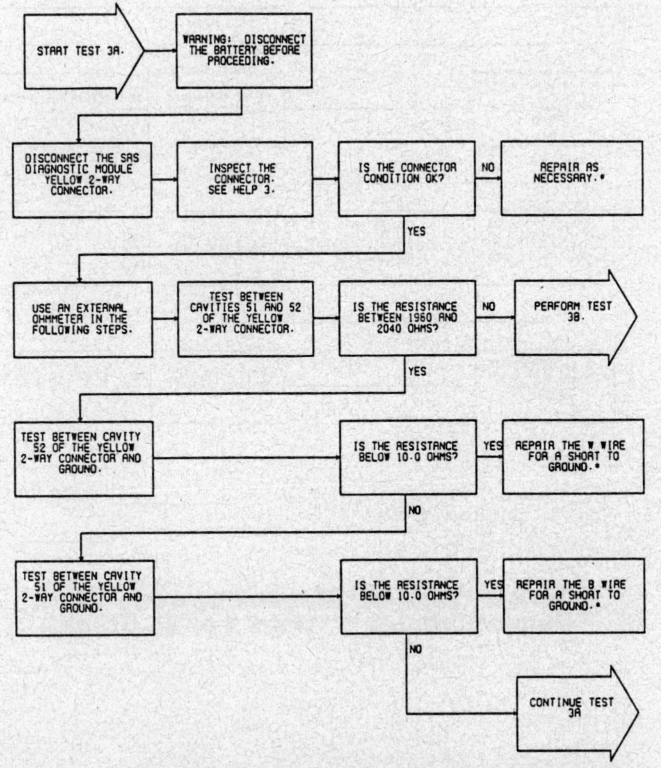


**Fig. 61 Test 3A, Diagnosing code 11 G sensor trouble (Part 1 of 3). Stealth**

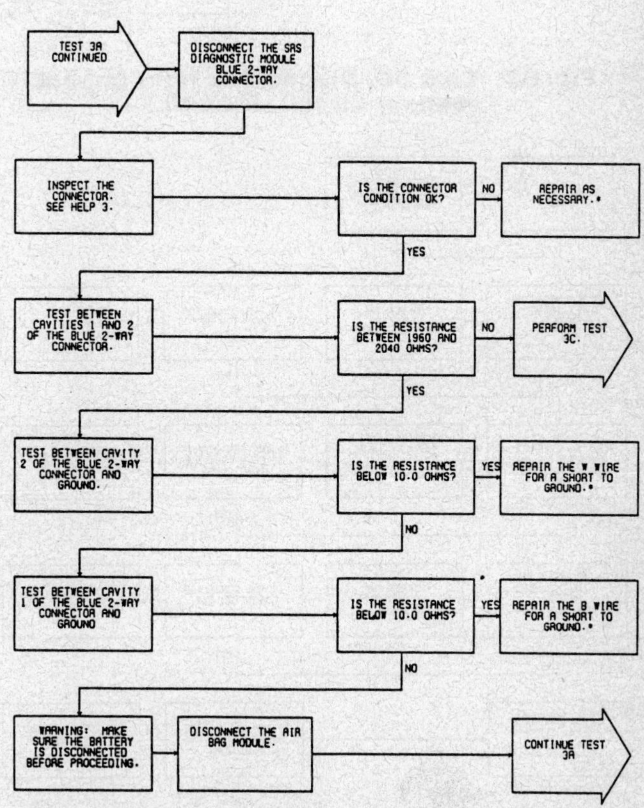


**Fig. 61 Test 3A, Diagnosing code 11 G sensor trouble (Part 2 of 3). Stealth**

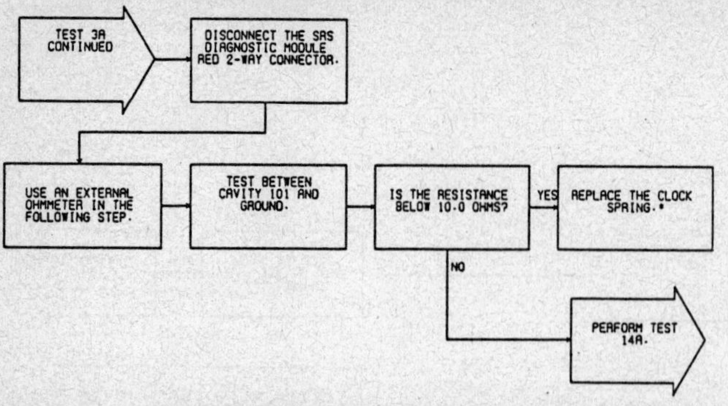


**Fig. 61 Test 3A, Diagnosing code 11 G sensor trouble (Part 3 of 3). Stealth**

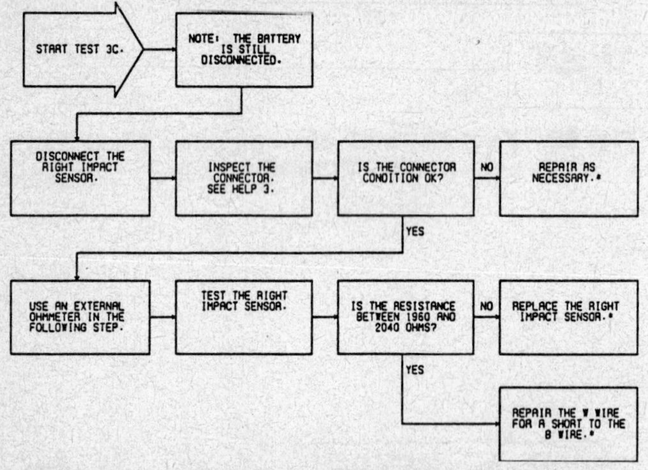


**Fig. 63 Test 3C, Diagnosing right impact sensor circuit. Stealth**

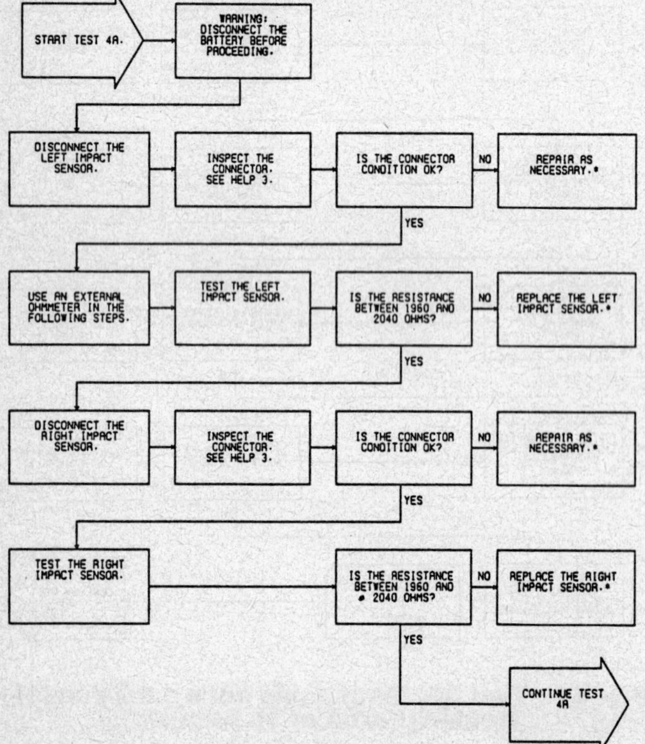


**Fig. 64 Test 4A, Diagnosing code 12 "G Sensor Trouble 2" (Part 1 of 2). Stealth**

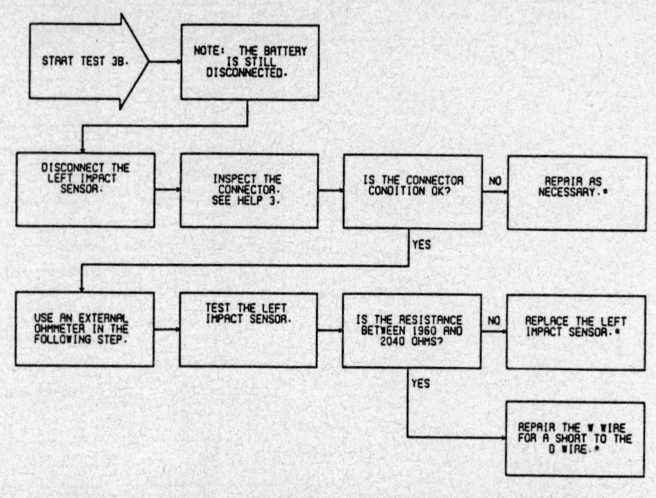


**Fig. 62 Test 3B, Diagnosing left impact sensor circuit. Stealth**

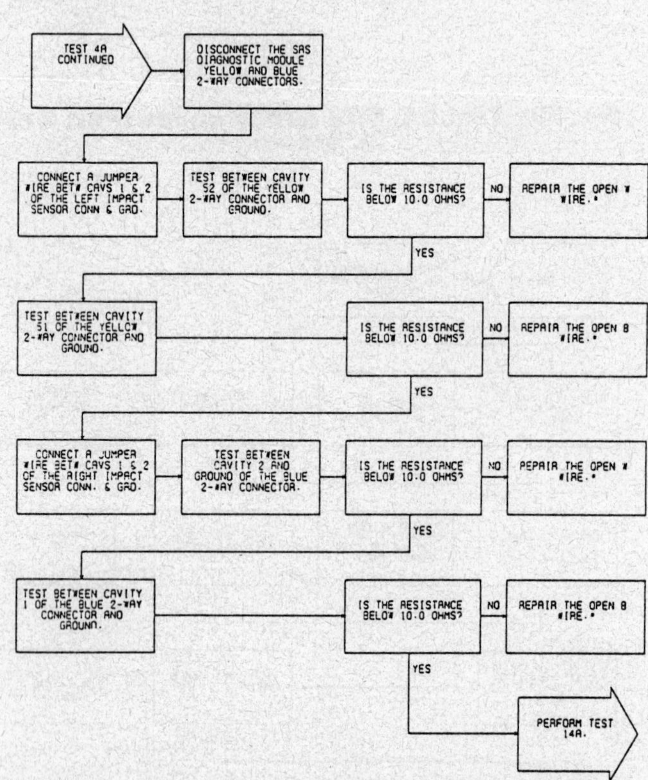


**Fig. 64 Test 4A, Diagnosing code 12 "G Sensor Trouble 2" (Part 2 of 2). Stealth**

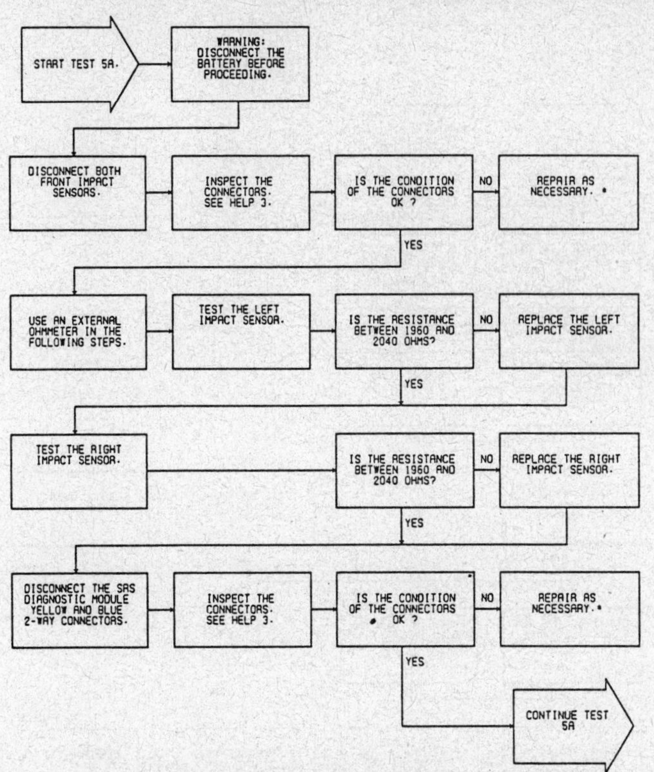


Fig. 65 Test 5A, Diagnosing code 13 "G Sensor Trouble 3" (Part 1 of 3). Stealth

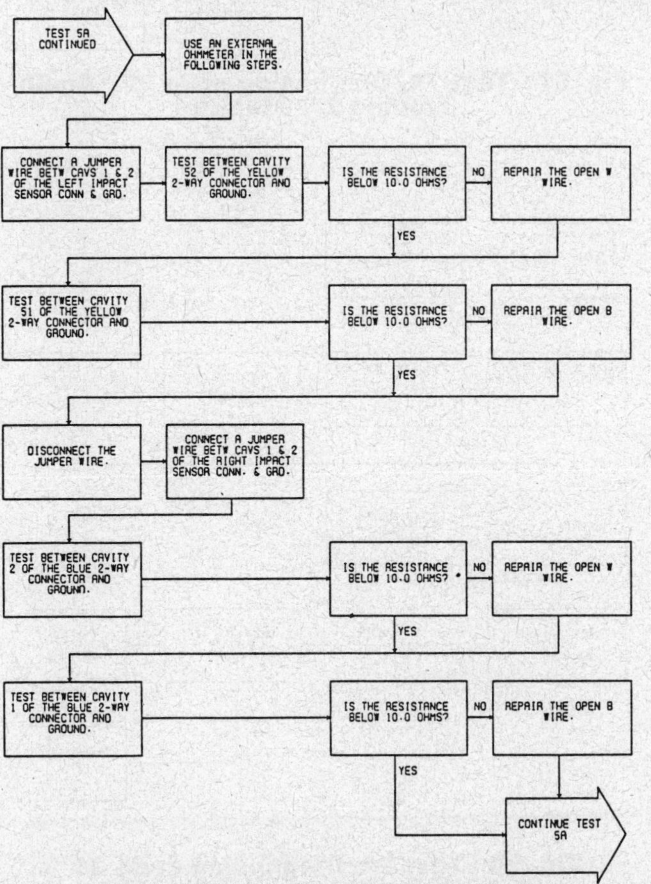


Fig. 65 Test 5A, Diagnosing code 13 "G Sensor Trouble 3" (Part 2 of 3). Stealth

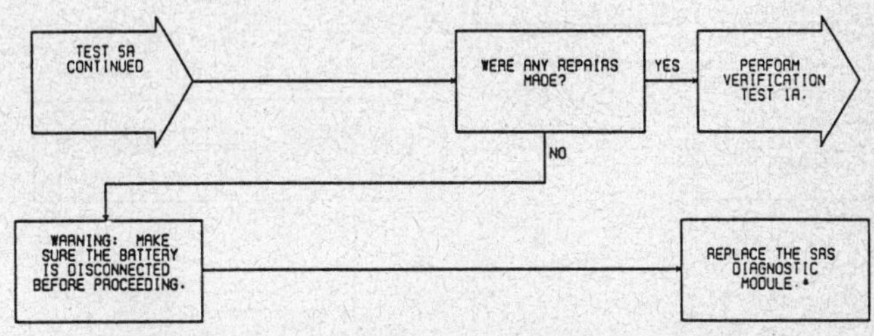


Fig. 65 Test 5A, Diagnosing code 13 "G Sensor Trouble 3" (Part 3 of 3). Stealth

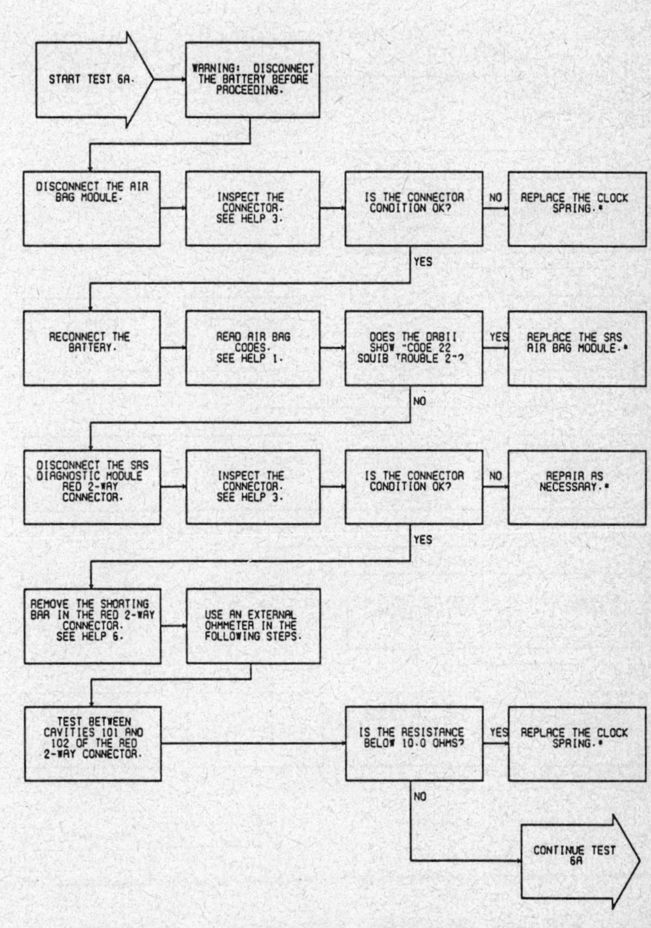


Fig. 66 Test 6A, Diagnosing code 21 "Squib Trouble 1" (Part 1 of 2). Stealth

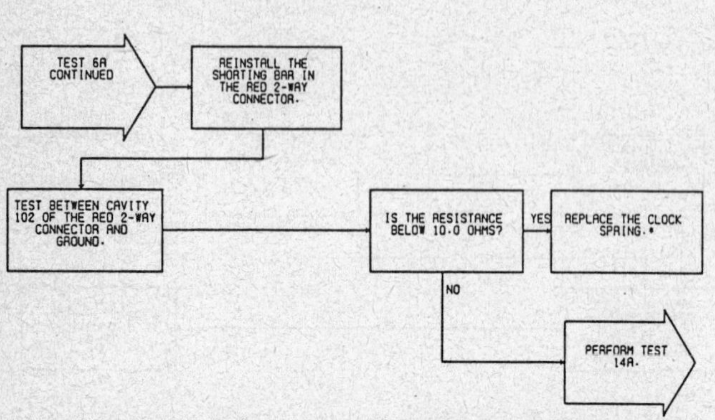


Fig. 66 Test 6A, Diagnosing code 21 "Squib Trouble 1" (Part 2 of 2). Stealth

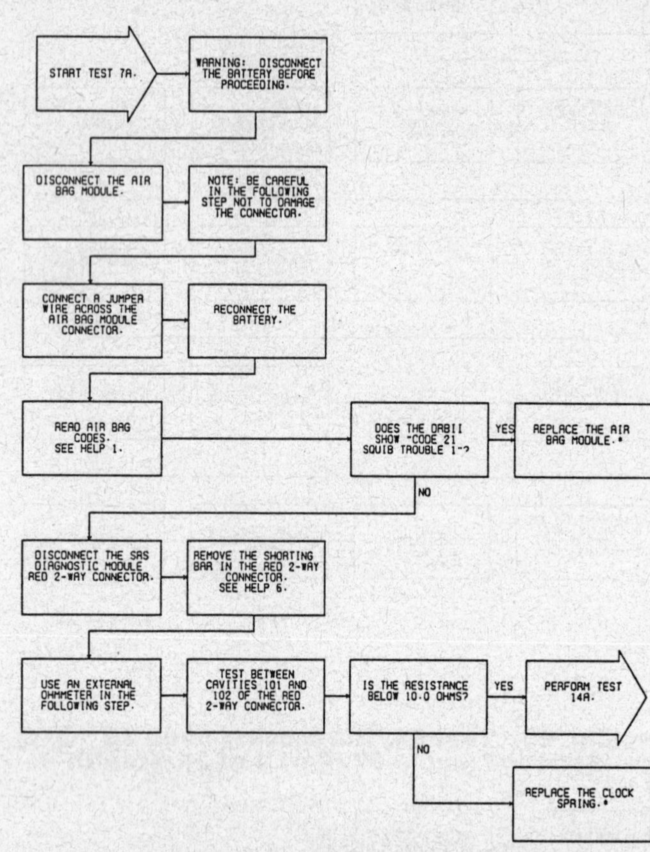


Fig. 67 Test 7A, Diagnosing code 22 "Squib Trouble 2." Stealth

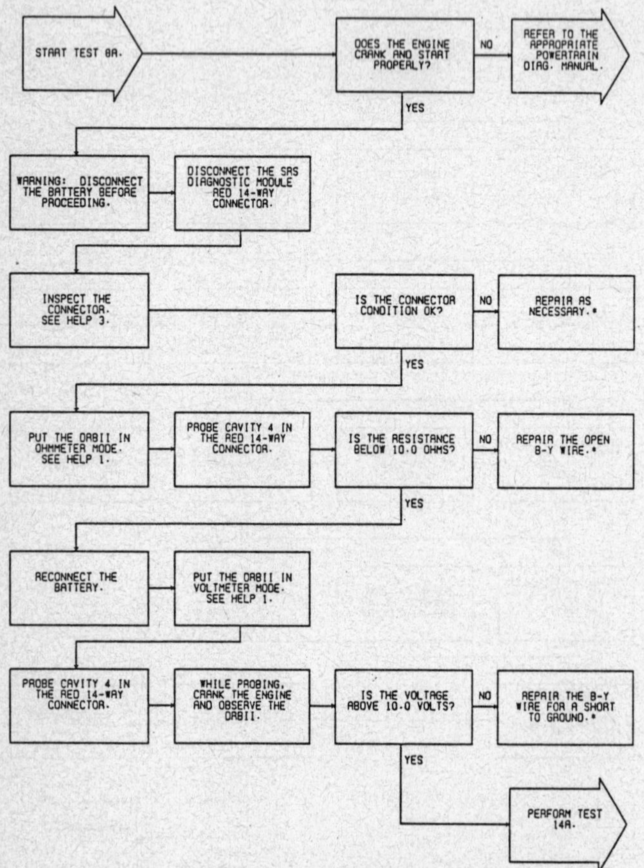


Fig. 68 Test 8A, Diagnosing code 33 "Cranking Trouble." Stealth

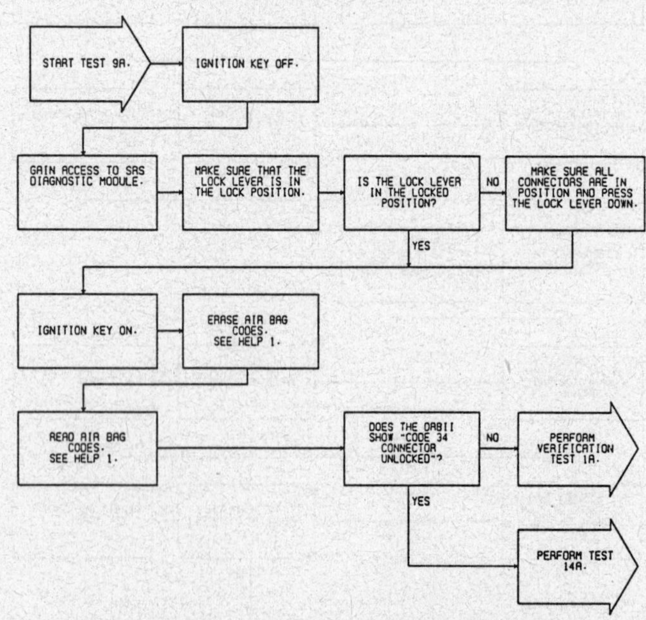


Fig. 69 Test 9A, Diagnosing code 34 "Connector Unlocked." Stealth

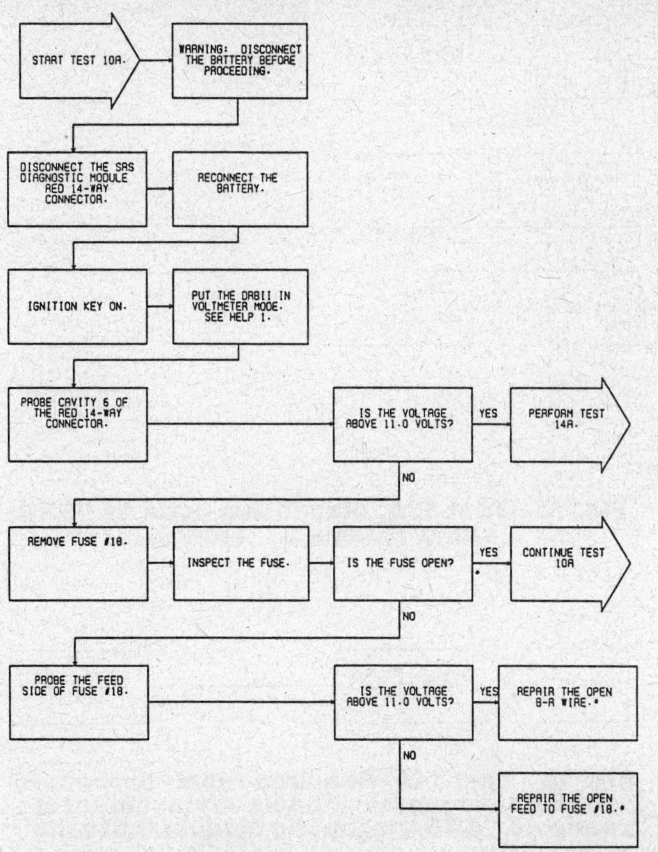


Fig. 70 Test 10A, Diagnosing code 41 "Ignition Voltage Low 1" (Part 1 of 2). Stealth

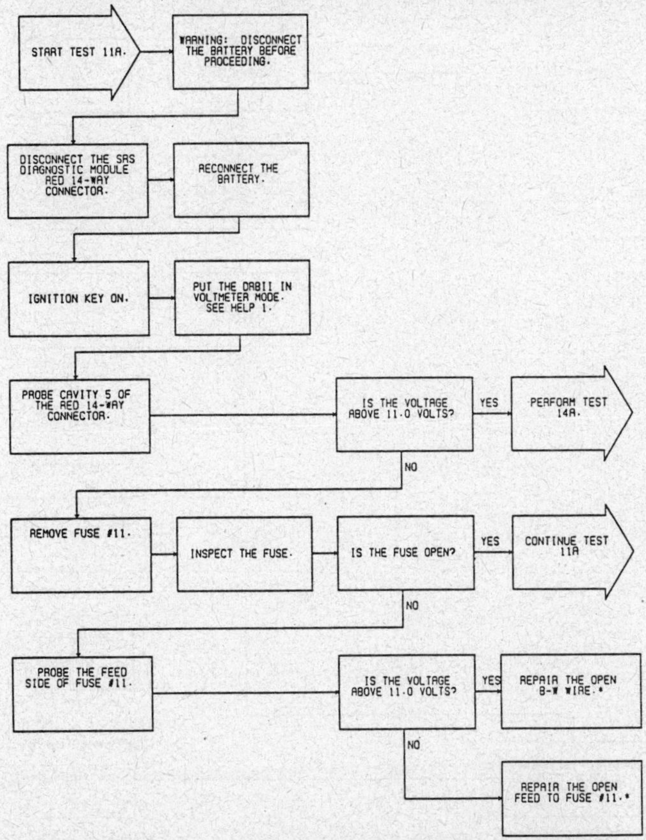


Fig. 71 Test 11A, Diagnosing code 42 "Ignition Voltage Low 2" (Part 1 of 2). Stealth

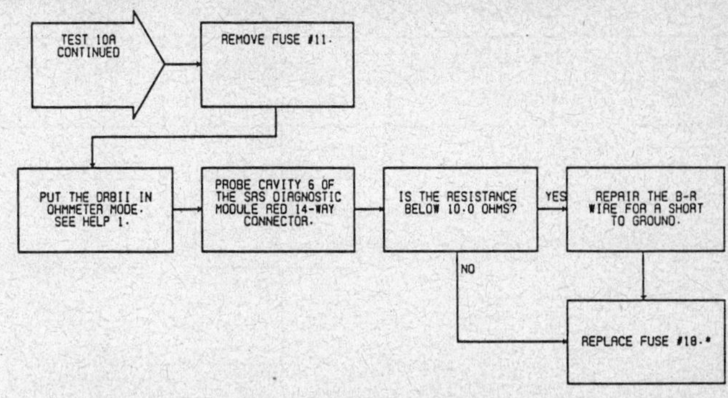


Fig. 70 Test 10A, Diagnosing code 41 "Ignition Voltage Low 1" (Part 2 of 2). Stealth

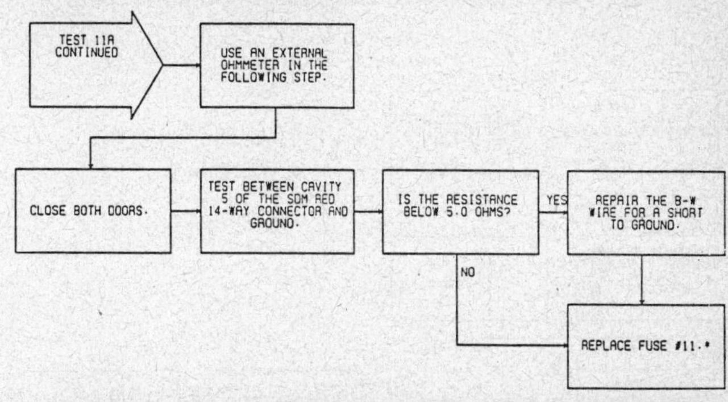


Fig. 71 Test 11A, Diagnosing code 42 "Ignition Voltage Low 2" (Part 2 of 2). Stealth

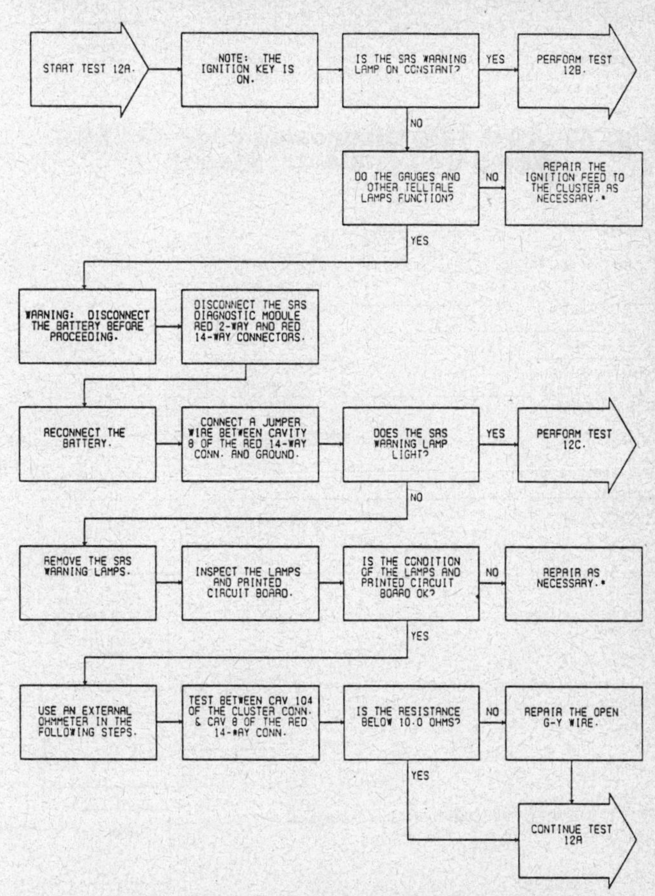


Fig. 72 Test 12A, Diagnosing code 43 "SRS Lamp Trouble 1" (Part 1 of 2). Stealth

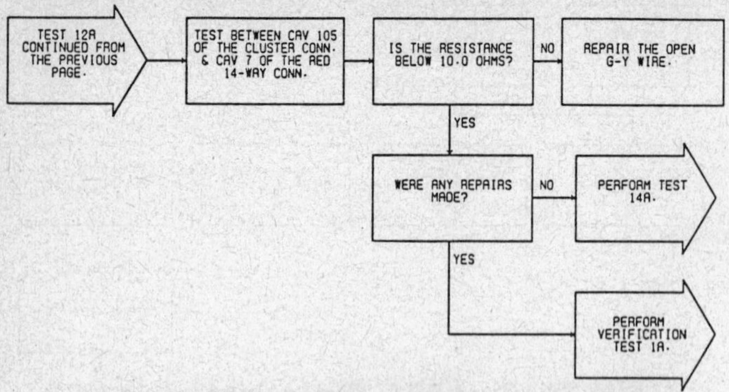


Fig. 72 Test 12A, Diagnosing code 43 "SRS Lamp Trouble 1" (Part 2 of 2). Stealth

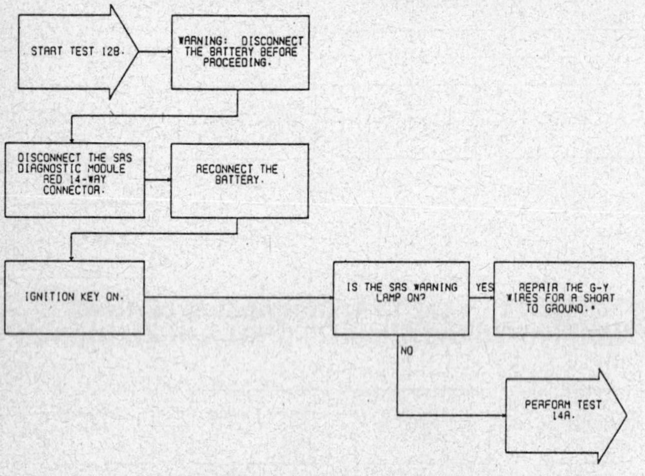


Fig. 73 Test 12B, Diagnosing code 43 "SRS Lamp On Constant." Stealth

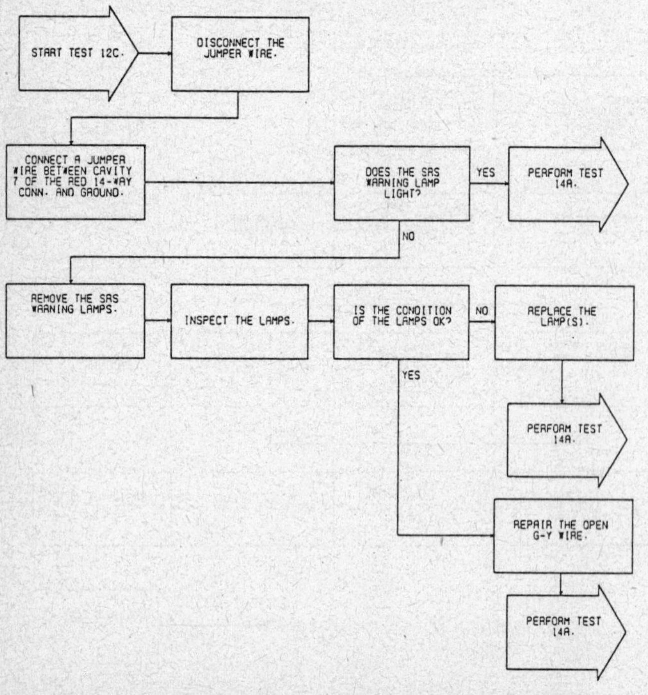


Fig. 74 Test 12C, Testing backup SRS warning lamp circuit. Stealth

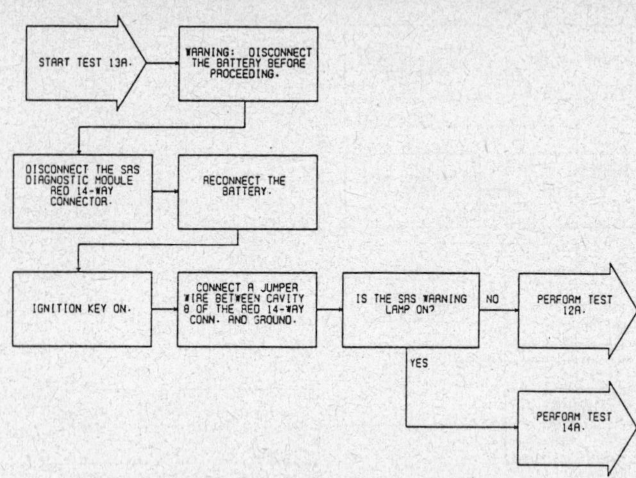


Fig. 75 Test 13A, Diagnosing code 44 "SRS Lamp Trouble 2." Stealth

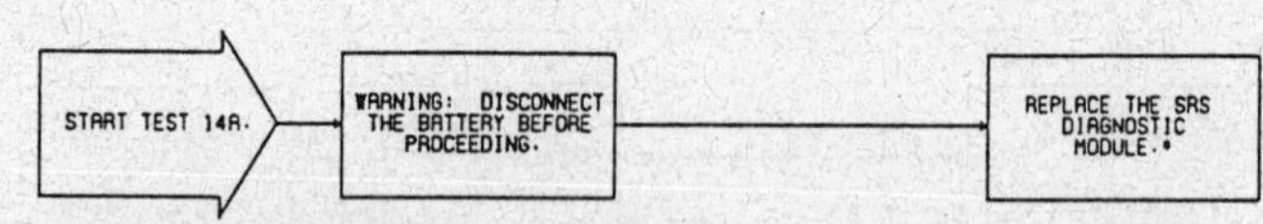


Fig. 76 Test 14A, Required repair procedure for SRS diagnostic module replacement & code 45 "SRS Diagnostic Module." Stealth

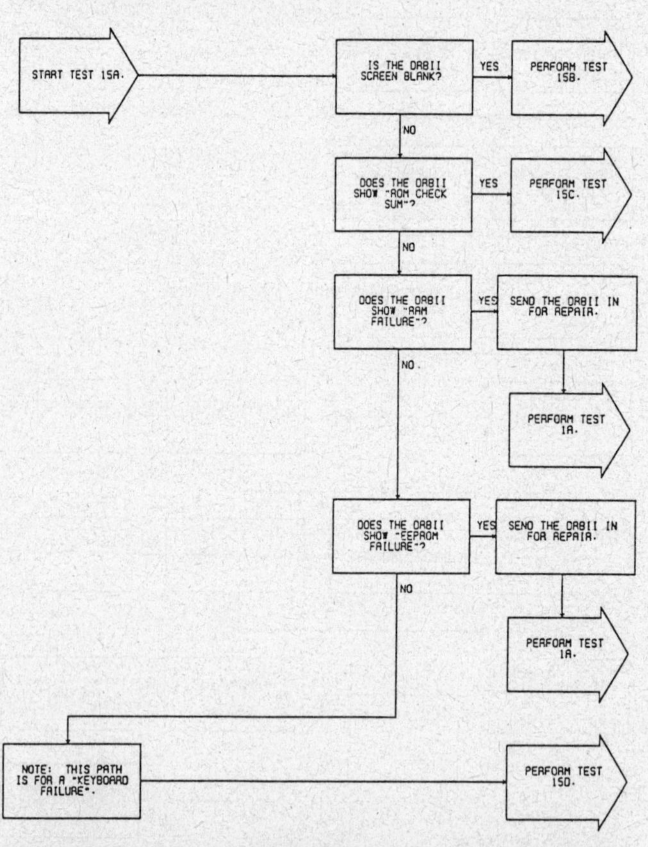


Fig. 77 Test 15A, Diagnosing DRBII function. Stealth

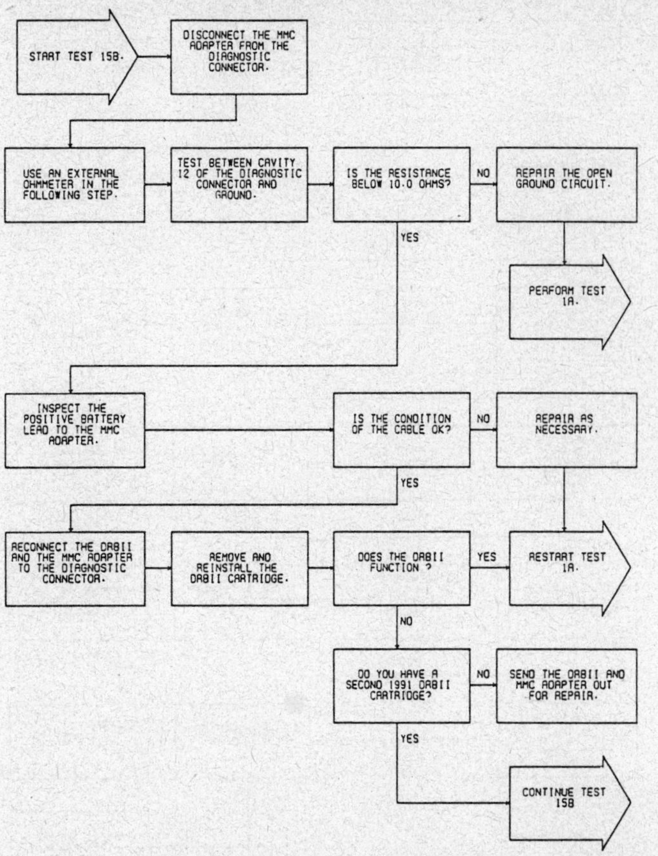


**Fig. 78 Test 15B, Diagnosing blank screen on DRBII (Part 1 of 2). Stealth**

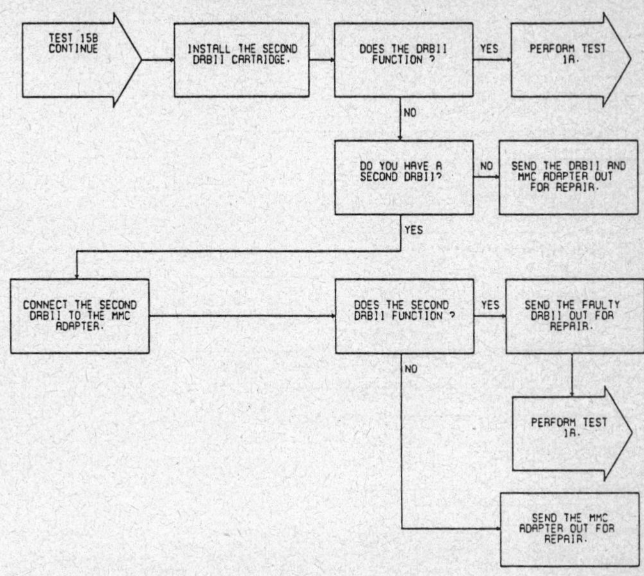


**Fig. 78 Test 15B, Diagnosing blank screen on DRBII (Part 2 of 2). Stealth**

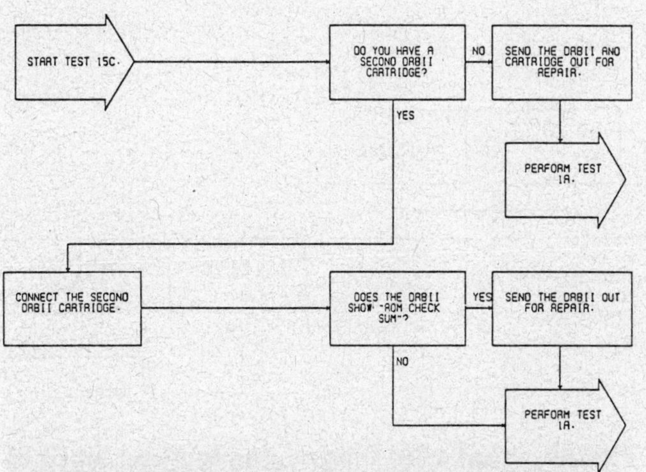


**Fig. 79 Test 15C, Diagnosing DRBII "ROM Check Sum" error message. Stealth**

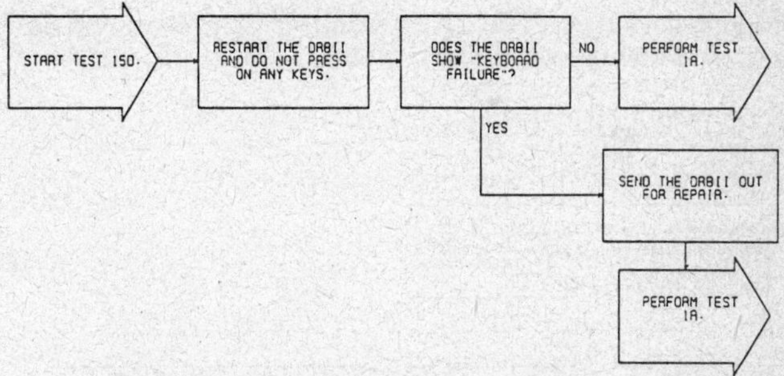


**Fig. 80 Test 15D, Diagnosing DRBII "Keyboard Failure" error message. Stealth**

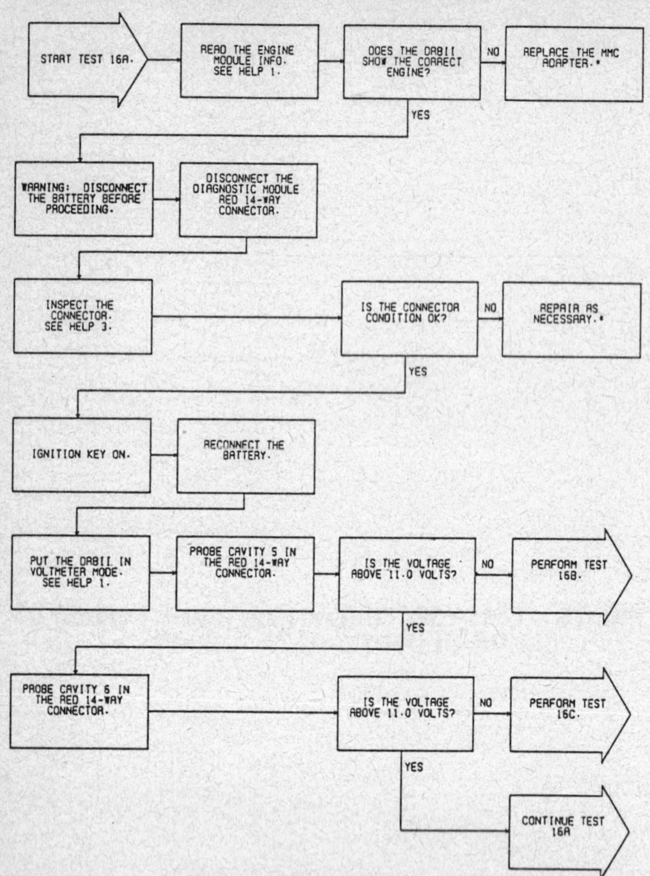


**Fig. 81 Test 16A, Diagnosing "No Response" message on DRBII (Part 1 of 2). Stealth**

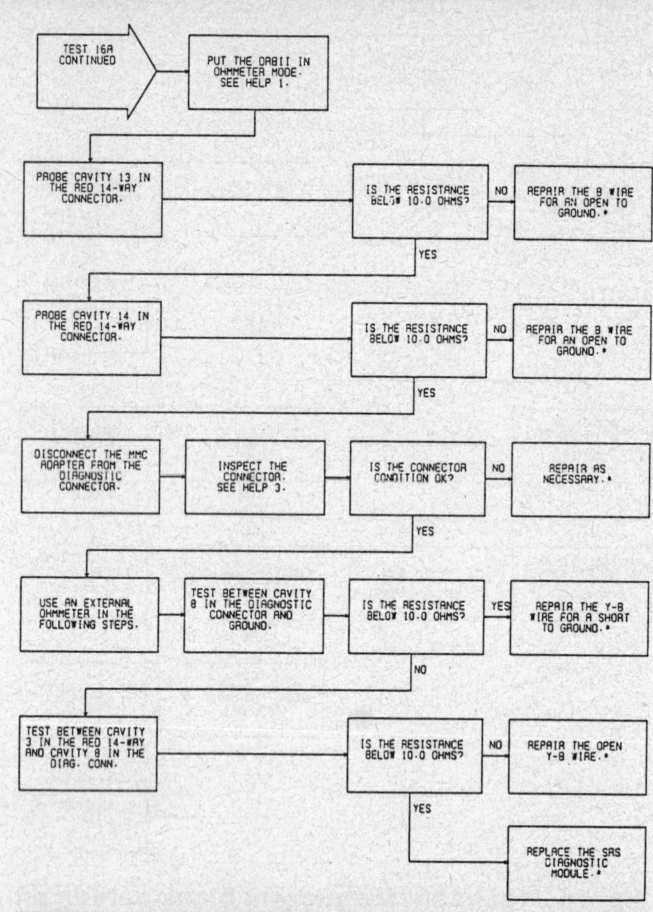


**Fig. 81 Test 16A, Diagnosing "No Response" message on DRBII (Part 2 of 2). Stealth**

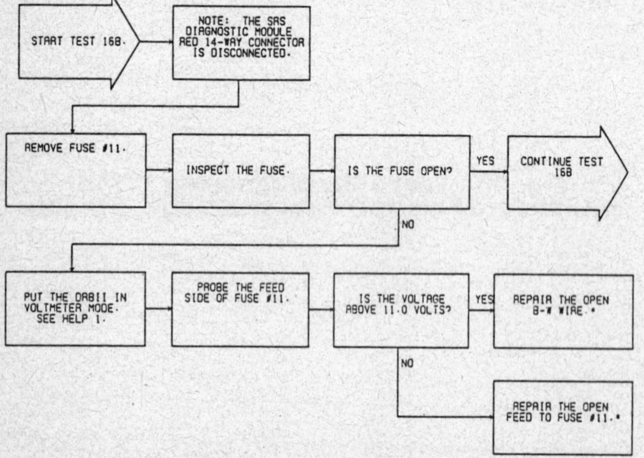


**Fig. 82 Test 16B, Diagnosing ignition input to SRS diagnostic module (Part 1 of 2). Stealth**

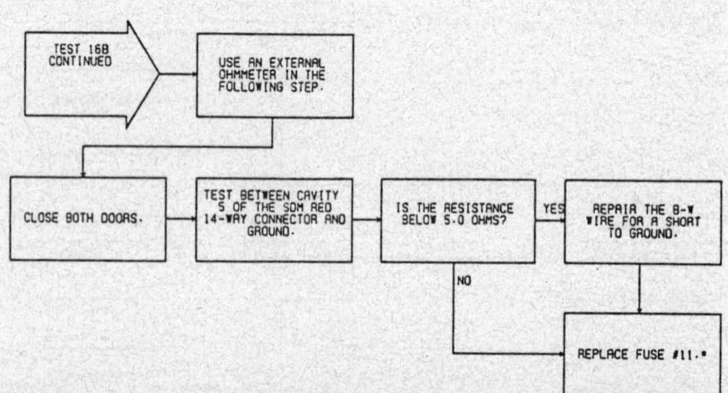


**Fig. 82 Test 16B, Diagnosing ignition input to SRS diagnostic module (Part 2 of 2). Stealth**

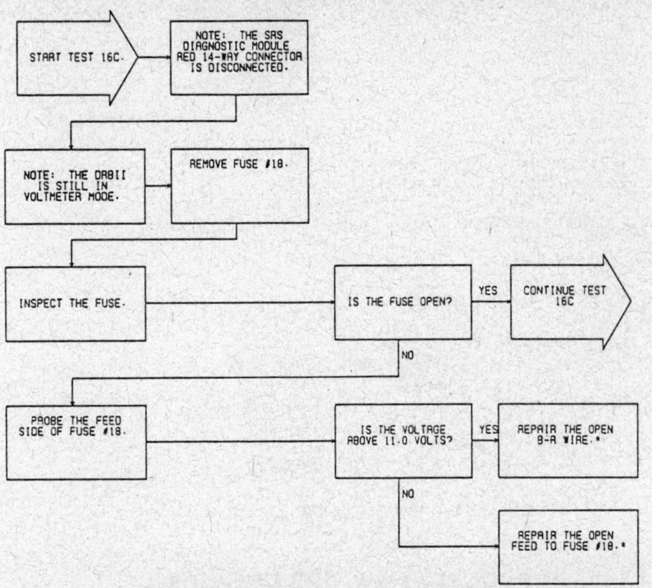


Fig. 83 Test 16C, Diagnosing ignition 1 input to SRS diagnostic module (Part 1 of 2). Stealth

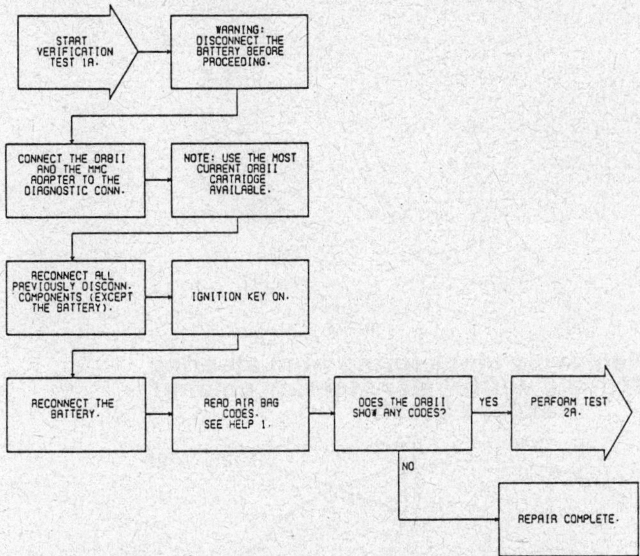


Fig. 84 Verification test 1. Stealth

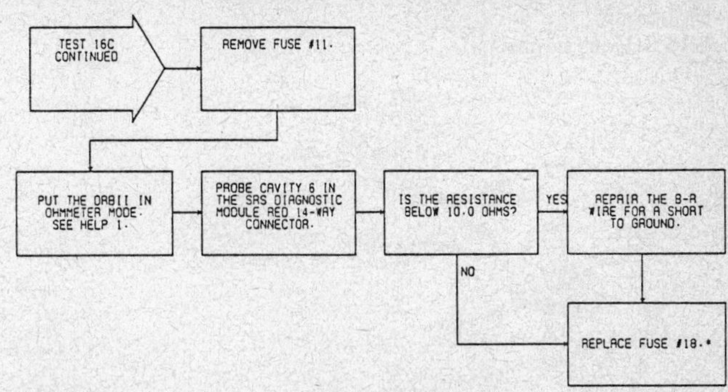


Fig. 83 Test 16C, Diagnosing ignition 1 input to SRS diagnostic module (Part 2 of 2). Stealth

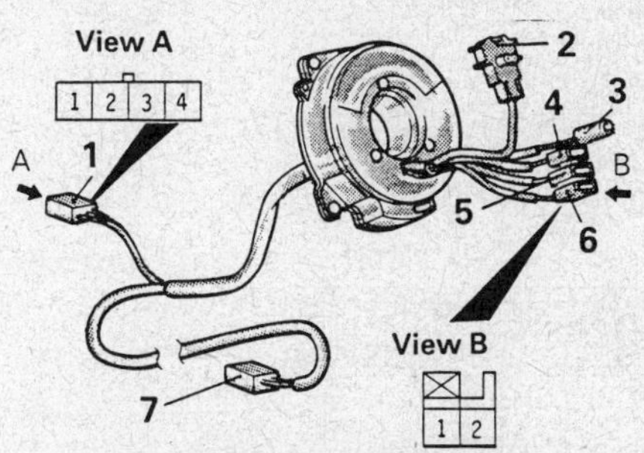


Fig. 85 Airbag module harness. 1991 Stealth

| No. 1 connector | | | | No. 3 connector | No. 4 connector | No. 5 connector | No. 6 connector | |
|---|---|---|---|---|---|---|---|---|
| Terminal 1 | Terminal 2 | Terminal 3 | Terminal 4 | | | | Terminal 1 | Terminal 2 |
| O | | | | | | | | O |
| | O | | | | | | O | |
| | O | | | | O | | | |
| | | O | | O | | | | |
| | | | O | | | O | | |
| To cruise control unit | To ACC power | To horn relay | To radio | To horn switch | To steering remote control switch | | To cruise control switch | |

NOTE
O–O indicates that there is continuity between the terminal.

Fig. 86 Airbag module harness continuity testing. 1991 Stealth

## CLOCKSPRING REPLACE

**Before attempting to diagnose, remove or install any airbag system components, unless otherwise noted, you must first disconnect and isolate battery ground cable. Failure to do so could result in accidental deployment and possible personal injury.**

Two different types of clocksprings are used, one with a setscrew, Chrysler steering columns (1989 & 1990), the other with a automatic lock, Acustar column (1990 & 1991), which engages when the steering wheel is removed. Automatic locking clocksprings can be identified by the lack of a setscrew and tether strap.

## MODELS w/CHRYSLER STEERING COLUMN

### Removal

When the steering column is separated from the steering gear for any reason, the steering column must be locked to prevent any damage to the airbag slip ring.

1. Disconnect and isolate battery ground cable.
2. Remove airbag module from steering wheel.
3. Remove clockspring setscrew from its resting place on steering wheel and place it in clockspring to ensure clockspring positioning, if equipped. **Screw is on a tether which must not be removed, Fig. 89.**
4. Remove steering wheel retaining nut.
5. **On Daytona and LeBaron models with automatic transmission,** remove damper assembly.
6. **On all models,** with a suitable tool, remove steering wheel.
7. Disconnect two-way connector between clockspring and instrument panel wiring harness at base of column.
8. Loosen two mounting screws at clockspring assembly.
9. Remove connector at base of steering column and tape another piece of wire approximately 12 inches long to clockspring wire lead.
10. Pull wire up through column and untape two wires to remove clockspring, making sure to leave second piece of wire in column.

MB991349
SRS CHeck Harness

(3)
2
No. 7 connector of clock spring
1
(4)
A
(5)
Hollow portion
No. 2 connector of clock spring
White paint
21 22

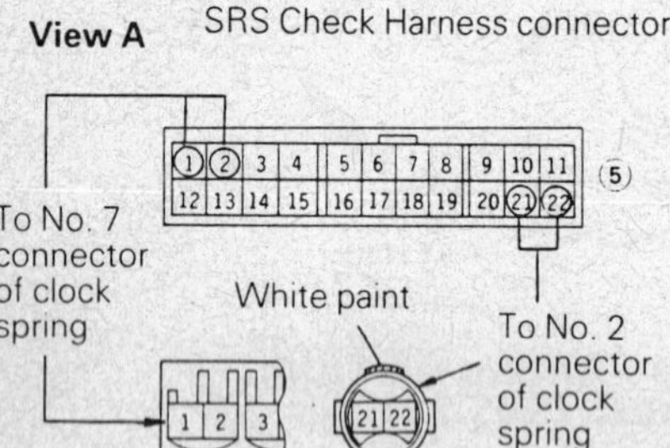


**Fig. 87 Airbag module check harness connection. 1991 Stealth**

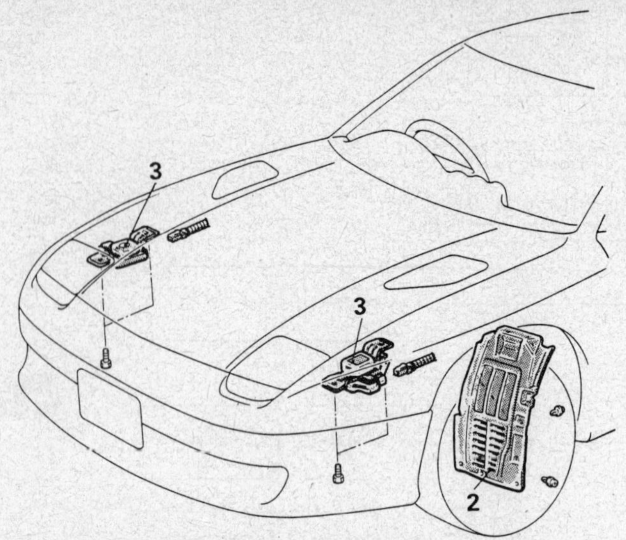


**Fig. 88 Front impact sensors. 1991 Stealth**

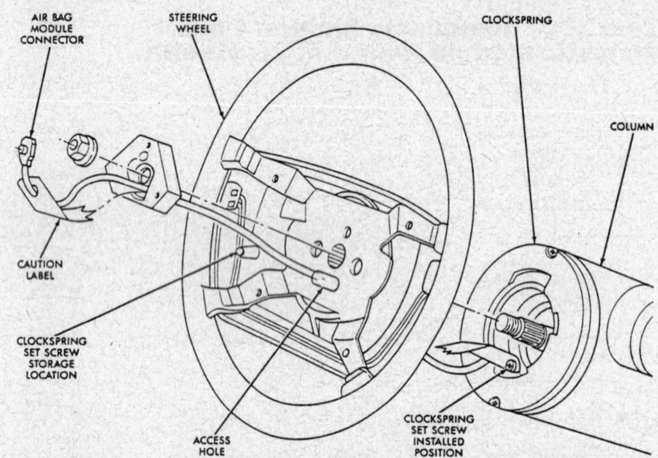


**Fig. 89 Removing clockspring from steering column. Models w/Chrysler steering column except Stealth**

## Centering

If the rotating part of the clockspring is not properly positioned with the steering column and front wheels, the clockspring may fail during use. The following procedure must be used if the clockspring is not known to be properly positioned.

Two different types of clocksprings are used, one with a setscrew, the other with a automatic lock, which engages when the steering wheel is removed. Automatic locking clocksprings can be identified by the lack of a setscrew and tether strap.

1. Place front wheels in straight ahead position.
2. Rotate clockspring rotor **counter-clockwise** to the end of its travel.
3. From this position, rotate clockspring rotor clockwise two full turns.
4. **On models equipped with non-auto-locking type clock-spring,** continue to turn rotor clockwise until setscrew mounting boss is aligned with recessed flat on clock-spring housing, **Fig. 90. Do not rotate more than 1/2 turn to align.**

## Installation

Obtain new clockspring assembly service kit containing clockspring assembly and lower two way connector. Ensure all parts are with this kit.

1. Tape new clockspring wire lead to wire that was fed into steering column.

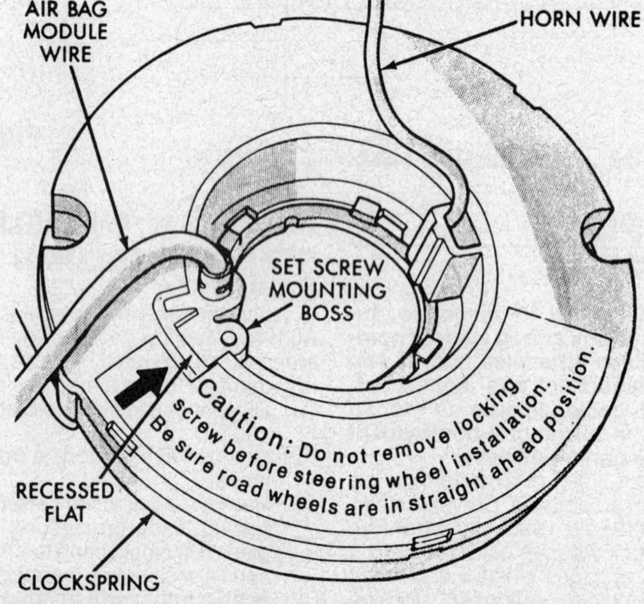


**Fig. 90 Non-auto-locking type clockspring**

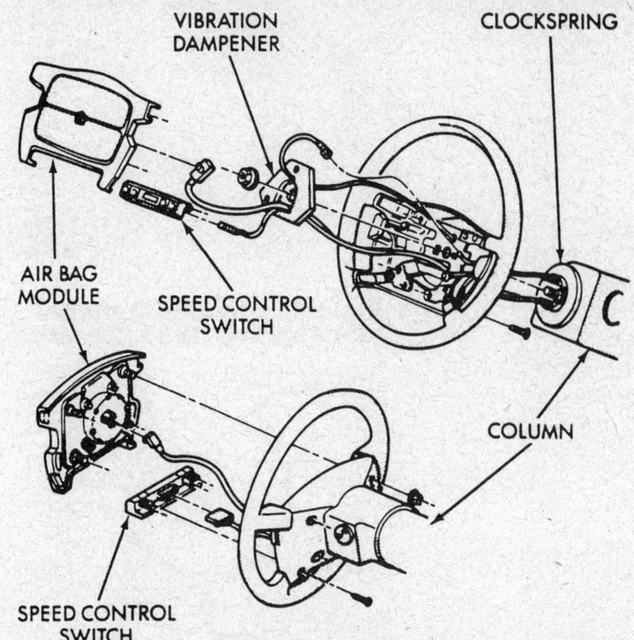


**Fig. 91 Removing clockspring from steering column. Models w/ Acustar steering column except Stealth**

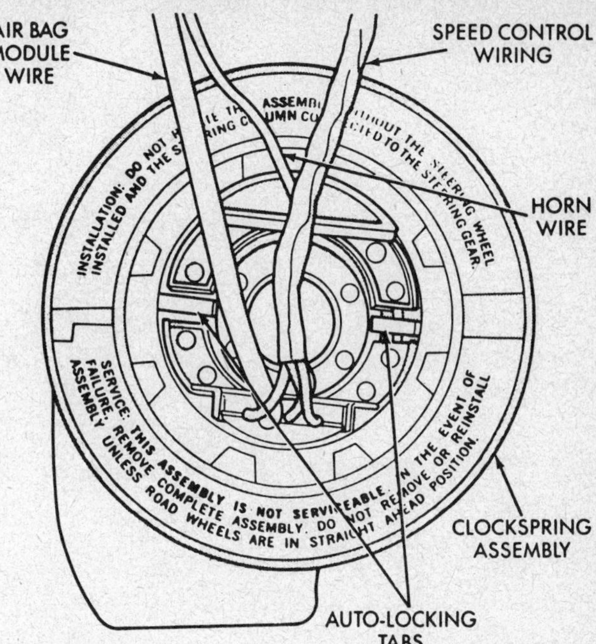


**Fig. 92 Auto-locking type clockspring**

2. Pull new clockspring wire lead down through column using wire that it was taped to.
3. Once clockspring lead is through column, untape two wires, then insert clockspring lead terminals into connector.
4. Install locking wedge and reconnect clockspring assembly to instrument panel wiring harness.
5. Mount clockspring assembly to turn signal switch using two screws, then **torque** to 10-20 inch lbs. If clockspring is not properly positioned, follow procedure outlined under "Centering" prior to installing steering wheel.
6. Install steering wheel and vibration damper (if so equipped), making sure to pull horn lead through upper smaller hole and clockspring lead through bottom larger hole.
7. Index flats on hub of steering wheel with formations on inside of clockspring.
8. Remove clockspring assembly locking screw and insert screw into steering wheel where it was stored, if equipped, then **torque** to 4 inch lbs.
9. Connect horn lead wire and then clockspring lead wire to airbag module.
10. Using a 10 mm thinwall socket, install airbag module and **torque** nuts to 80-100 inch lbs.
11. **Do not connect battery ground cable. Refer to "System Check" for proper procedure.**

## MODELS w/ACUSTAR STEERING COLUMN

### Removal

1. Ensure front wheels are in straight ahead position.
2. Disconnect and isolate battery ground cable, wait minimum of 30 seconds before working on vehicle.
3. Remove airbag module, **Fig. 91.**
4. Remove speed control switch and connector, if equipped.
5. Remove steering wheel and vibration dampner, if equipped.
6. Disconnect horn terminals.
7. Remove upper and lower steering column shrouds, then disconnect the 2-way connector between clockspring and instrument panel wiring harness at base of steering column.
8. Remove clockspring by lifting locating tabs as necessary, **Fig. 92.**

### Centering

1. Place front wheels in straight ahead position.
2. Depress two plastic locking pins or spread apart two metal locking tabs in center of clockspring.
3. At the same time, rotate clockspring rotor **clockwise** to the end of its travel.
4. From this position, rotate clockspring rotor counterclockwise 2 1/2 turns. The horn wire should be at the top and the squib wire at the bottom. While turning the rotor, visually inspect flat cable for bends or kinks. If clockspring is bent or kinked, replace clockspring assembly.

### Installation

1. Snap clockspring onto steering column. Ensure clockspring is centered, if not follow clockspring centering procedure.
2. Connect clockspring assembly to instrument panel wiring harness, ensure wiring locator clips are properly seated on outside of wiring trough and locking tabs are engaged.
3. Install steering column shrouds, ensure wire is inside shroud.
4. Ensure front wheels are in straight ahead position. Install steering wheel and vibration dampner, if equipped. **Torque** to 45 ft. lbs. Fit flats on hub of steering wheel with formations on inside of clockspring.
5. Ensure to pull horn lead through upper smaller hole and clockspring lead through bottom larger hole.
6. Connect horn lead wire, then airbag lead wire to airbag module. To assure complete connections, latching arms must be visible on top of connector housing.
7. Install airbag module, **torque** nuts to 80 to 100 inch lbs.
8. Do not connect negative battery cable. Refer to "System Check" for proper procedure.

## AIRBAG MODULE

**Before attempting to diagnose, remove or install any airbag system components, you must first disconnect and isolate the battery ground cable. Failure to do so could result in accidental deployment and possible personal injury.**

## STORAGE

The airbag module must be stored in its original special container until it is used. It must be stored in a clean, dry place, away from heat, sparks and sources of electricity. Always place or store the module on a surface with the trim cover facing up.

## HANDLING

**At no time should any source of electricity be permitted near the inflator on the back of the module. When handling**

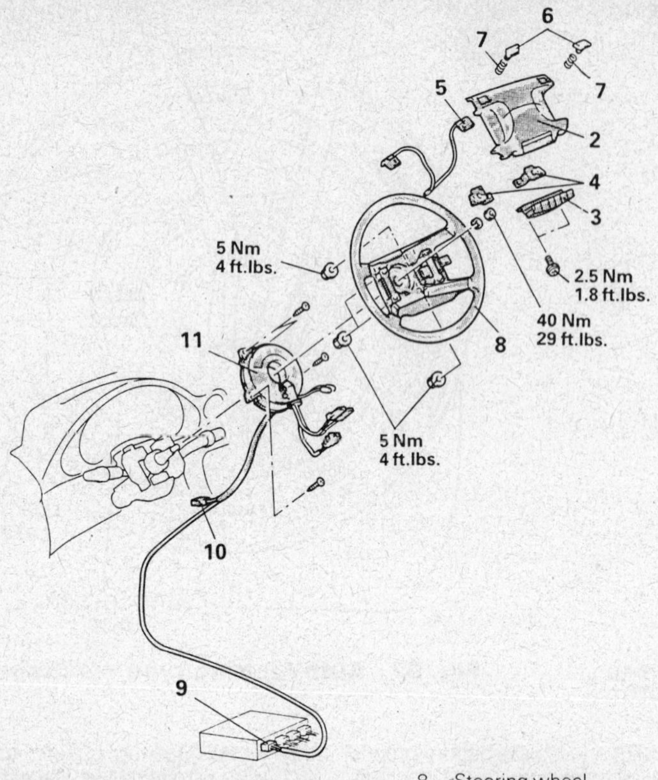


2. Air bag module
3. Radio remote control assembly
4. Horn contact plate
5. Horn contact plate and wire
6. Horn button
7. Spring
8. Steering wheel
   Knee protector
   Column cover
9. Clock spring and SRS diagnosis unit connection
10. Clock spring and body wiring harness connection
11. Clock spring

**Fig. 93 Airbag & clockspring assembly. 1991 Stealth**

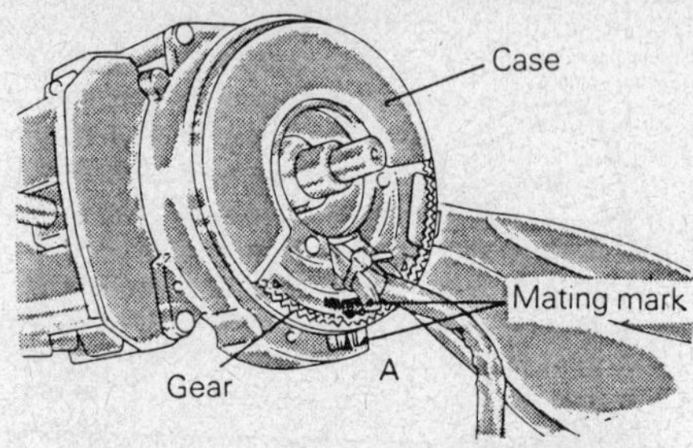


**Fig. 94 Alignment marks clockspring. 1991 Stealth**

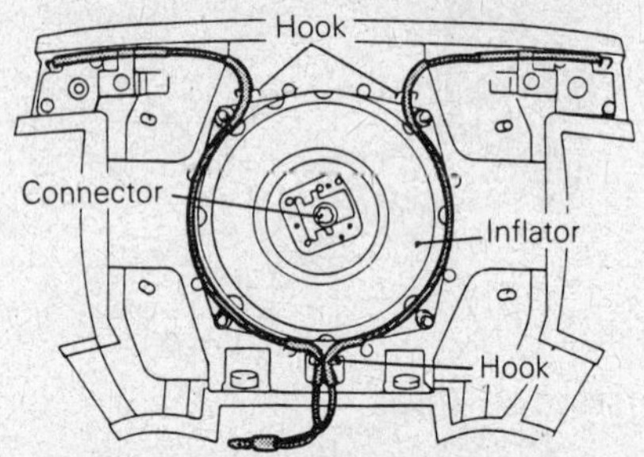


**Fig. 95 Airbag module steering column wiring. 1991 Stealth**

**a live module, the trim cover should be pointed away from the body to minimize injury in the event of accidental deployment. Always place or store the module on a surface with the trim cover facing up.**

## REPLACEMENT

**If replacing a deployed module, wear gloves and eye protection. There will be deposits on and around the airbag that could cause skin and eye irritation. If material does come into contact with the body, flush with plenty of cold water. Refer to "Disposal" for proper disposal procedure of a deployed airbag.**

### EXCEPT STEALTH

1. Disconnect and isolate battery ground cable.
2. Using a 10 mm thinwall, remove four holding airbag module in place on steering wheel, **Fig. 89 and 91.**
3. Lift module high enough to remove clockspring connecting wire and remove airbag module.
4. If replacing a deployed module, clockspring must also be replaced. Refer to procedure outlined under ""Clockspring, Replace."
5. Reverse procedure to install and **torque** nuts to 80-100 inch lbs.
6. **Do not connect battery ground cable. Refer to "System Check" for proper procedure.**

### STEALTH

#### Removal

1. Ensure front wheels are in straight ahead position.
2. Remove airbag module as follows:
   a. Remove airbag module mounting nut using a socket wrench from rear, **Fig. 93.**
   b. Disconnect connector of clockspring from airbag module by pressing airbag lock toward outer side spreading it open, then gently pry connector out.
   c. Airbag module should be stored in a clean, dry place with pad cover facing up. If airbag module is to be terminated, refer to "Deployment."
3. Remove steering wheel using appropriate steering wheel puller.
4. Disconnect the SDU (SRS Diagnostic Unit) as follows:
   a. Remove rear console assembly.
   b. Disconnect SRS from SDU (Supplemental Diagnostic Unit), using screwdriver to push in lock spring of lock lever, **Fig. 3.** A double-lock connector is used, ensure care is taken as not to damage connector.
   c. Remove the 2 pin red connector of clockspring SDU while pressing down the lock of the clockspring connector.

#### Installation

1. Prior to installation, check clockspring, airbag module, connectors, case and gear for damage. If clockspring or any other components, including connectors are damaged, replace as necessary.
2. Prior to installing clockspring, check resistance between No. 2 and No. 7 connectors using SRS check harness No. MB991349 and suitable digital volt/ohmmeter, refer to "Component Testing" for procedure. Resistance must be less than 0.4 ohms. If not, replace clockspring.
3. Ensure front wheels are straight ahead, then align mating mark and Neutral position indicator of clockspring, **Fig. 94.**
4. Connect clockspring and SDU connectors, ensure connectors are snug and locked.
5. Install steering wheel, ensure that front wheels are straight and mating marks and Neutral position indicator of clockspring are aligned. **Torque** nut to 29 ft. lbs.
6. After installation of steering wheel, turn wheels totally in both directions to ensure proper operation.
7. Ensure wiring is correctly installed, **Fig. 95,** then install airbag module.
8. After connecting battery ground cable, turn ignition switch on and ensure

SRS warning light is on for approximately 7 seconds and then stays off for a minimum of 45 seconds.

## DEPLOYMENT

### IN-VEHICLE

#### Except Stealth

1. Disconnect battery ground cable.
2. Remove knee blocker.
3. Disconnect clockspring lead from base of steering column at instrument panel harness.
4. Cut connector off clockspring lead and strip one inch of insulation from end.
5. Make a harness consisting of two wires at least 20 ft. long.
6. Connect two wires at lower end of clockspring lead to new harness.
7. Making sure that no one is within 20 ft. of the vehicle, touch two new harness wire leads to terminals of a 12 volt car battery. **When deployment is achieved, there will be a loud bang and airbag will inflate. Wait at least 20 minutes before approaching vehicle. Let airbag cool off and dust settle.**

#### Stealth

1. Open windows and doors of vehicle if possible.
2. **Remove battery, wait at least 30 seconds before working on vehicle.**
3. Remove rear console assembly.
4. Disconnect SRS from SDU (Supplemental Diagnostic Unit), using screwdriver to push in lock spring of of lock lever, **Fig. 3.** A double-lock connector is used, ensure care is taken as not to damage connector.
5. Disconnect the red 14-pin connector from SRS diagnosis unit while pressing down the lock of connector.
6. Connect two wires, each 20 feet long to the two leads of the SRS airbag adapter harness A part No. MB686560.
7. Connect the SRS airbag adapter harness to clockspring connector.
8. Run the other end of leads as far away as possible from vehicle.
9. Ensure deployment area is clear of personnel, then connect end leads of harness to battery terminals to trigger airbag explosion.
10. **Inflator will be hot after deployment. Wait 30 minutes before attempting to handle inflator.**
11. Refer to "Disposal" for proper disposal of inflator.

### OUT OF VEHICLE

#### Except Stealth

1. Disconnect battery ground cable.
2. Remove airbag module from steering wheel.
3. Cut wiring harness that goes from clockspring to airbag as close to clockspring as possible.
4. Place other end of harness back into airbag module.
5. Strip one inch of insulation from cut end of harness and connect two 20 ft. wires.
6. Place airbag module face up and move at least 20 ft. away.
7. Touch two ends of 20 ft. long wires to terminals of a 12 volt battery. **When deployment is achieved, there will be a loud bang and airbag will inflate. Wait at least 20 minutes before approaching, let airbag cool off and dust settle.**

#### Stealth

1. Remove battery, wait at least 30 seconds before working on vehicle.
2. Remove airbag module from vehicle.
3. Connect two wires, each 20 feet long to the two leads of the SRS airbag adapter harness B part No. MB628919.
4. Place airbag module with pad cover face up in a flat, clear area, then connect adapter harness to connector on back of module.
5. Clear a minimum 20 foot radius deployment operations area of personnel.
6. Run other lead as far away as possible from deployment operations area.
7. Connect end leads of harness to battery terminals to trigger airbag explosion.
8. Inflator will be hot after deployment. **Wait 30 minutes before attempting to handle inflator.**
9. Refer to "Disposal" for proper disposal of inflator.

## DISPOSAL

**Whenever handling a deployed airbag, gloves and eye protection should be worn. There will be deposits on and around the airbag that could cause skin and eye irritation. If material does come into contact with the body, flush with plenty of cold water.**

The deployed airbag module should be placed in a plastic bag before it is disposed of.

## AIRBAG SYSTEM DIAGNOSTIC MODULE (ASDM)

### REPLACE

### EXCEPT STEALTH

**Before attempting to diagnose, remove or install any airbag system components, you must first disconnect and isolate the battery ground cable. Failure to do so could result in accidental deployment and possible personal injury.**

The ASDM contains one of the impact sensors which enables the system to a ctivate the airbag. To avoid accidental deployment, never connect ASDM electrically to system unless it is bolted to vehicle.

#### Removal

1. Disconnect and isolate battery ground cable.
2. Remove floor console, vertical console trim bezel, vertical console carrier and radio as necessary.
3. Remove glove box, and the left side fasteners on instrument panel reinforcement, if necessary.
4. Disconnect electrical connectors and remove ASDM.

#### Installation

1. Install ASDM (arrow pointing forward) in instrument panel support bracket, or on console reinforcement, as applicable, ensuring insert tab on ASDM is in slot on support bracket.
2. Attach ASDM to support bracket and **torque** to 15-20 inch lbs.
3. Remount instrument panel center support bracket to left and right instrument panel reinforcements.
4. Connect ASDM electrical connectors.
5. Install vertical console carrier and floor console.
6. **Do not connect battery ground cable. Refer to "System Check" for proper procedure.**

## SERVICE DIAGNOSTIC UNIT (SDU)

### REPLACE

### STEALTH

1. Note the following before servicing the SDU:
   a. After airbag deployment, replace SDU.
   b. The SDU is not serviceable, if faulty replace.
   c. Do not expose unit to vibration or drop.
   d. Do not use volt/ohmmeter on or near SDU. Use only specified equipment.
2. **Disconnect battery ground cable, then wait 30 seconds before working on vehicle.**
3. Disconnect SRS from SDU

(Supplemental Diagnostic Unit), using screwdriver to push in lock spring of of lock lever, **Fig. 3.** A double-lock connector is used, ensure care is taken not damage connector.
4. Disconnect the red 14-pin connector from SRS diagnosis unit while pressing down the lock of connector.
5. Check SDU case, brackets and connectors for deformities.
6. Reverse procedure to install. Ensure connectors are properly connected.

## FRONT IMPACT SENSORS

### REPLACE

#### EXCEPT STEALTH

**Before attempting to diagnose, remove or install any airbag system components, you must first disconnect and isolate the battery ground cable. Failure to do so could result in accidental deployment and possible personal injury.**

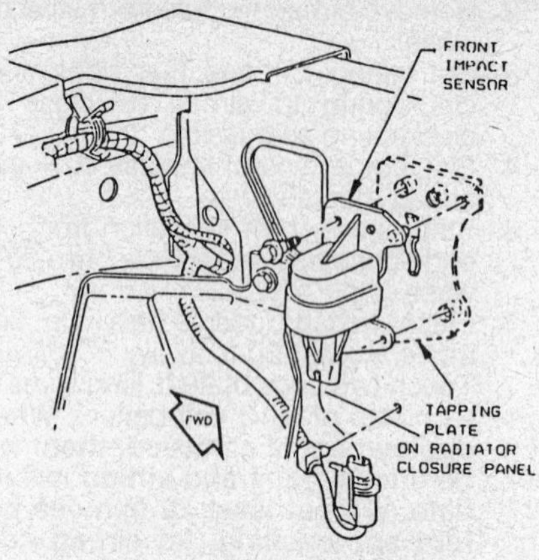


**Fig. 96 Left front impact sensor. Except Stealth**

#### LEFT SENSOR

1. Disconnect battery ground cable.
2. Disconnect speed control servo from battery tray.
3. Remove battery, battery tray and coolant bottle.
4. Disconnect sensor electrical connector.
5. Remove three screws holding sensor to radiator closure panel and remove sensor, **Fig. 96.**
6. Reverse procedure to install. **Torque** mounting screws to 100 inch lbs.
7. **Do not connect battery ground cable. Refer to "System Check" for proper procedure.**

#### RIGHT SENSOR

1. Disconnect and isolate battery ground cable.
2. Disconnect sensor electrical connector.
3. Remove three screws holding sensor to engine side of closure panel and remove right sensor.
4. Reverse procedure to install. **Torque** mounting screws to 100 inch lbs.
5. **Do not connect battery ground cable. Refer to "System Check" for proper procedure.**

# Automatic Seat Belts

## INDEX



## DESCRIPTION

The automatic seat belt system incorporates the use of both mechanical and electronic components. The system operates mechanically by the use of track and drive assemblies, lap belt retractor assemblies and a console mounted retractor. Electronically, the system uses a passive belt control module which controls motors, tension eliminators and the system warning lamp. Inputs from the ignition switch, retractor and limit switches and distance sensor are used by the control module to operate the outputs to the motors and warning lamp.

## TROUBLESHOOTING

### COLT, COLT VISTA, LASER, TALON & SUMMIT

Refer to **Fig. 1** when troubleshooting these systems.

| Trouble symptom | Cause |
|---|---|
| Driver's and/or front passenger's system does not function | Fuse blown or disconnected |
| | Open harness wire or disconnected connector |
| | Defective switch |
| | Defective motor |
| | Defective relay |
| | Defective control unit |
| Warning light does not illuminate or flash | Fuse blown or disconnected |
| | Open harness wire or disconnected connector |
| | Defective switch |
| | Warning light bulb blown or in poor contact |
| | Defective control unit |
| Buzzer does not sound | Fuse blown or disconnected |
| | Defective buzzer |
| | Open harness wire of disconnected connector |
| | Defective control unit |
| The slide anchor does not move from the "fasten" range into "release" range, or from the "release" range into the "fasten" range | Defective driving device, or problem in electrical circuit |
| Slide anchor moves too slowly | Defective control unit |
| | Foreign matter in guide rail |
| Slide anchor stops halfway | Defective retractor (remains in locked state) |
| | Defective driving device or problem in electrical circuit |

**Fig. 1 Troubleshooting chart. Colt, Colt Vista, Eagle Talon, Plymouth Laser & Summit**

| Trouble symptom | Cause |
|---|---|
| The "fasten seat belt" indicator light and spool release indicator light neither go on nor blink, and the buzzer does not sound when the ignition switch is turned from "LOCK" or "ACC" to "ON" while the spool release lever remains in its "release" position (spool release switch is turned off). | Damaged or disconnected wiring of spool release indicator light and spool release lever switch circuit |
| | Damaged or disconnected wiring of ignition switch input circuit |
| | Damaged or disconnected wiring of ECU power supply and ground circuit |
| | Malfunction of ECU |
| The buzzer does not sound when the L.H. door is opened even with the key inserted in the cylinder (key-reminder switch is turned on). | Damaged or disconnected wiring of key-reminder switch input circuit |
| | Damaged or disconnected wiring of L.H. door lock switch input circuit |
| | Damaged or disconnected wiring of buzzer circuit |
| | Damaged or disconnected wiring of ECU power supply and ground circuit. |
| | Malfunction of ECU |
| Either the L.H. or R.H. system does not operate. | Damaged or disconnected wiring of door lock switch input circuit |
| | Damaged or disconnected wiring of motor drive input circuit |
| | Malfunction of ECU |
| | Foreign matter caught in slide rail<br>Foreign matter in tape guide |
| | Tape guide locally deformed |

**Fig. 2 Troubleshooting chart (Part 1 of 2). Conquest**

## CONQUEST

Refer to **Fig. 2** when troubleshooting this system.

## 1991 MONACO & PREMIER

### SHOULDER BELT DOES NOT OPERATE

With control module connectors disconnected, ignition switch in run position, both shoulder belts buckled and doors closed, proceed as follows:

1. Measure resistance from terminals 1, 21 and 27 with shoulder belt in forward position, **Fig. 3.**
2. Resistance should be 0 ohms. If not as specified, check for open ground.
3. Measure resistance from terminals 4 and 28 with shoulder belt in rearward position.
4. Resistance should be 0 ohms. If not as specified, check for open ground.
5. Measure resistance from terminals 12, 35, 5 and 6.
6. Resistance should be zero. If not as specified, repair short.
7. Measure voltage at terminals 8 and 30.
8. Voltage should be approximately 12 volts. If not as specified, check fuses and/or repair short to fuse block.
9. Disconnect speed sensor module, then check for continuity.
10. If continuity exists, replace seat belt control module. If no continuity is present check for open wire.

### SEAT BELT INDICATOR &/OR CHIME MODULE DOES NOT OPERATE

With ignition switch in run position and shoulder belts buckled, proceed as follows:

1. Check for approximately 12 volts at terminal 34, **Fig. 3.**
2. If not as specified, replace shoulder belt control module.

### SHOULDER BELTS FAIL TO MOVE IN FORWARD DIRECTION

#### Testing Motor Relay Connector

With ignition in run position, shoulder belts buckled, doors open, LH or RH front motor relay disconnected, shoulder belt control module disconnected and terminals 8 and 36 RH side or 8 and 25 LH side jumpered, **Fig. 4,** proceed as follows:

1. Voltage between terminals 4 and 5 should be approximately 12 volts.
2. If not as specified, check for short in wiring.
3. Measure resistance to ground from terminals 2 and 3. Resistance should be 0 ohms.
4. If not as specified, check for short to ground.
5. Voltage at terminal 1 should be approximately 12 volts.
6. If not as specified, replace relay.

#### Testing Motor Connector

With LH side or RH seat belt motor disconnected, shoulder belt control module disconnected, terminals 8 and 25 RH side or 8 and 36 LH side jumpered, proceed as follows:

1. Voltage at terminal C should be approximately 12 volts.
2. If not as specified, check wire(s) from front motor relay.
3. Measure resistance from ground to terminal D. If resistance is 0 ohms, replace seat belt motor.
4. If resistance is not 0 ohms, check wiring for short, if wiring is good replace control module.

## SHOULDER BELTS FAIL TO MOVE IN REARWARD DIRECTION

### Testing Motor Relay

With ignition in run position, shoulder belts buckled, doors closed, LH side or RH side back motor relay disconnected, shoulder belt control module disconnected, terminals 8 and 23 RH side or 8 and 24 LH side jumpered, proceed as follows:

1. Voltage between terminals 4 and 5 should be approximately 12 volts.
2. If not as specified, check wire from front relay.
3. Measure resistance between ground and terminals 2 and 3. Resistance should read 0 ohms. If correct replace seat belt motor.
4. If not as specified, check ground wire.
5. Measure voltage at terminal 1. Voltage should be approximately 12 volts.
6. If not as specified, replace relay.

### Testing Motor Connector

With LH side or RH side seat belt motor disconnected, seat belt control module disconnected and terminals 8 and 25 RH side or 8 and 36 LH side jumpered, proceed as follows:

1. Voltage at terminal D should be approximately 12 volts.
2. If not as specified, check front motor relay wire.
3. Measure resistance from ground to terminal C. Resistance should read 0 ohms.
4. If as specified replace seat belt motor, if not check for open wire.
5. If open wire not at fault replace control module.

## SHOULDER BELT INDICATOR LAMP DOES NOT LIGHT

1. With belt not buckled and using suitable volt/ohmmeter, check control module terminal 30 for voltage. Voltage should read approximately 12 volts.
2. If not as specified, check for open circuit.
3. Check control module terminal 1 for resistance. Resistance should be 0 ohms.
4. If not as specified, check for open circuit.
5. Check control module terminal 33 for test voltage. Voltage should be approximately 12 volts.
6. If not as specified, replace lamp and/or check terminal 6 and 5 for closed circuit and if OK, replace module.

| Trouble symptom | Cause |
|---|---|
| The system performs fastening operations but not unfastening operations, or vice-versa. | Damaged or disconnected wiring of door lock switch input circuit |
| | Damaged or disconnected wiring of motor drive input circuit |
| | Malfunction of ECU |
| Even after turning the ignition switch from "LOCK" or "ACC" to "ON" without fastening the L.H. seat lap belt, neither the "fasten seat belt" indicator light goes on nor does the buzzer sound. | Damaged or disconnected wiring of "fasten seat belt" indicator light and buckle switch input circuit |
| | Damaged or disconnected wiring of buzzer circuit |
| | Damaged or disconnected wiring of ECU power supply and ground circuit |
| | Malfunction of ECU |
| The "fasten seat belt" indicator and the spool release indicator light neither go on nor blink, and the buzzer does not sound when the ignition switch is turned from "LOCK" or "ACC" to "ON" while the spool release lever remains in its "release" position (spool release switch is turned off). | Damaged or disconnected wiring of "fasten seat belt" indicator light and buckle switch input circuit |
| | Damaged or disconnected wiring of buzzer circuit |

**Fig. 2 Troubleshooting chart (Part 2 of 2). Conquest**

## SHOULDER BELT INDICATOR DOES NOT GO OFF

1. With belt buckled and using suitable volt/ohmmeter check terminals 5 and 6 for resistance. Resistance should be 0 ohms.
2. If not as specified, check for short and if not fault, replace switch.
3. Check for resistance between terminals 27 and 28. Resistance should be 0 ohms.
4. If not as specified, check for short and if not fault, replace switch.

# COMPONENT TESTING

## COLT, COLT VISTA, CONQUEST, LASER, TALON & SUMMIT

### Motor

1. Disconnect the automatic seat belt motor relay connector.
2. Connect the terminals of the automatic seat belt wiring harness connector to the battery as shown in **Fig. 4.** Ensure motor operates smoothly.
3. Reverse the polarity and ensure motor operates smoothly in reverse position.

### Release Switch

1. Remove the release switch.
2. Using a suitable ohmmeter, check for continuity between switch terminals, **Fig. 5.**
3. Continuity should be present with switch knob released and no continuity should be present with the knob pushed in.

### Fasten Switch

1. Remove the fasten switch.
2. Using a suitable ohmmeter, check for continuity between switch terminals, **Fig. 6.**
3. Continuity should be present with switch knob released and no continuity should be present with the knob pushed in.

### Seat Belt Motor Relay

1. Remove the relay.

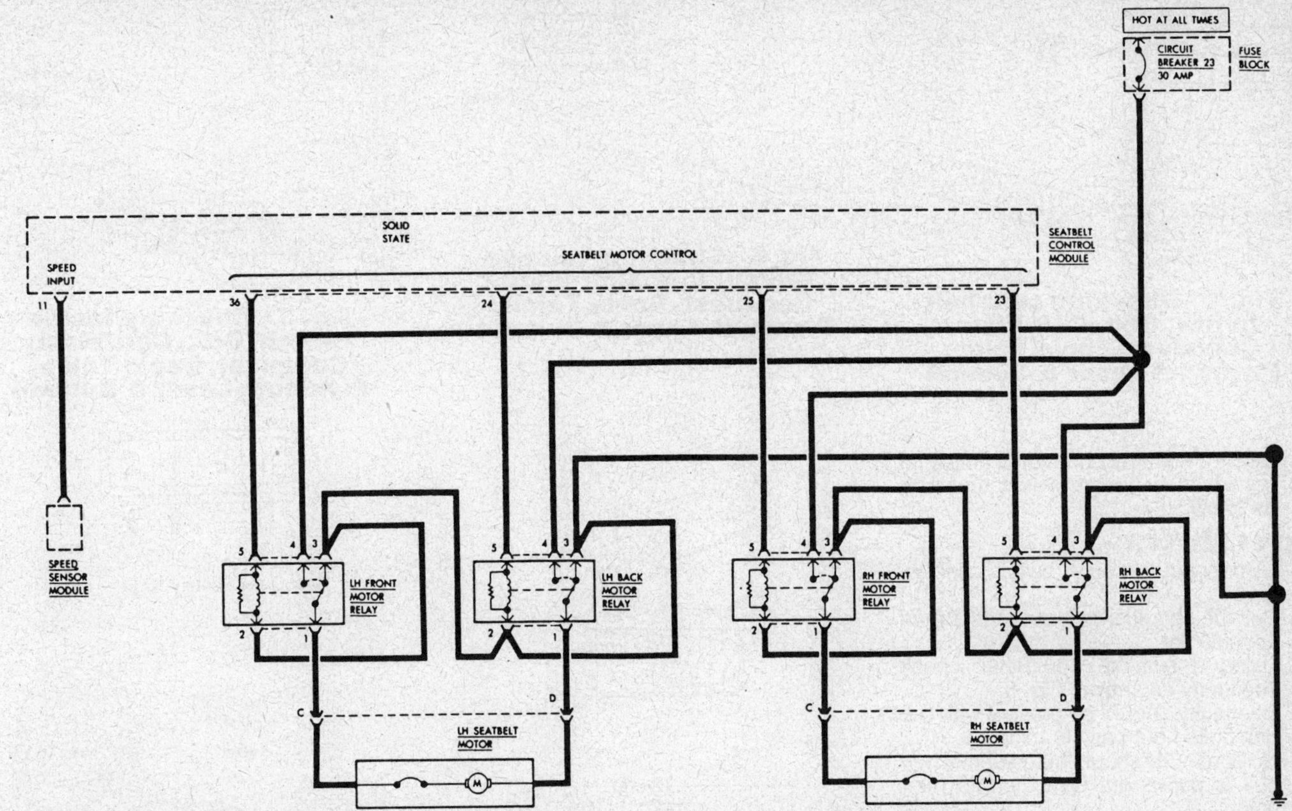

HOT AT ALL TIMES
CIRCUIT BREAKER 23 30 AMP
FUSE BLOCK
SOLID STATE
SEATBELT MOTOR CONTROL
SEATBELT CONTROL MODULE
SPEED INPUT
SPEED SENSOR MODULE
LH FRONT MOTOR RELAY
LH BACK MOTOR RELAY
RH FRONT MOTOR RELAY
RH BACK MOTOR RELAY
LH SEATBELT MOTOR
RH SEATBELT MOTOR

**Fig. 3 Automatic seat belt wiring circuit. Inputs (Part 1 of 2). 1991 Monaco & Premier**

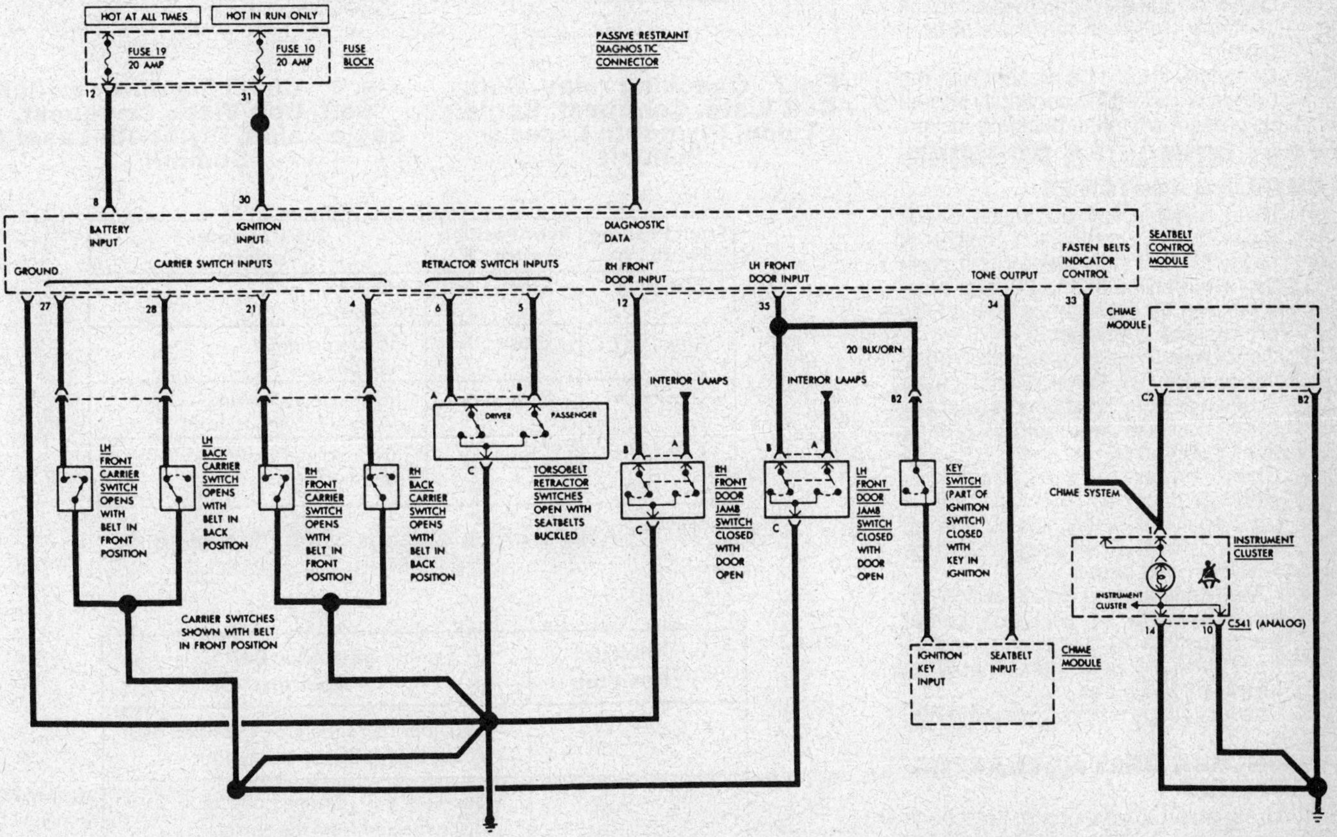

HOT AT ALL TIMES
HOT IN RUN ONLY
FUSE 19 20 AMP
FUSE 10 20 AMP
FUSE BLOCK
PASSIVE RESTRAINT DIAGNOSTIC CONNECTOR
BATTERY INPUT
IGNITION INPUT
DIAGNOSTIC DATA
SEATBELT CONTROL MODULE
GROUND
CARRIER SWITCH INPUTS
RETRACTOR SWITCH INPUTS
RH FRONT DOOR INPUT
LH FRONT DOOR INPUT
TONE OUTPUT
FASTEN BELTS INDICATOR CONTROL
CHIME MODULE
20 BLK/ORN
INTERIOR LAMPS
DRIVER
PASSENGER
LH FRONT CARRIER SWITCH OPENS WITH BELT IN FRONT POSITION
LH BACK CARRIER SWITCH OPENS WITH BELT IN BACK POSITION
RH FRONT CARRIER SWITCH OPENS WITH BELT IN FRONT POSITION
RH BACK CARRIER SWITCH OPENS WITH BELT IN BACK POSITION
TORSOBELT RETRACTOR SWITCHES OPEN WITH SEATBELTS BUCKLED
RH FRONT DOOR JAMB SWITCH CLOSED WITH DOOR OPEN
LH FRONT DOOR JAMB SWITCH CLOSED WITH DOOR OPEN
KEY SWITCH (PART OF IGNITION SWITCH) CLOSED WITH KEY IN IGNITION
CHIME SYSTEM
INSTRUMENT CLUSTER
C541 (ANALOG)
CARRIER SWITCHES SHOWN WITH BELT IN FRONT POSITION
IGNITION KEY INPUT
SEATBELT INPUT
CHIME MODULE

**Fig. 3 Automatic seat belt wiring circuit. Outputs (Part 2 of 2). 1991 Monaco & Premier**

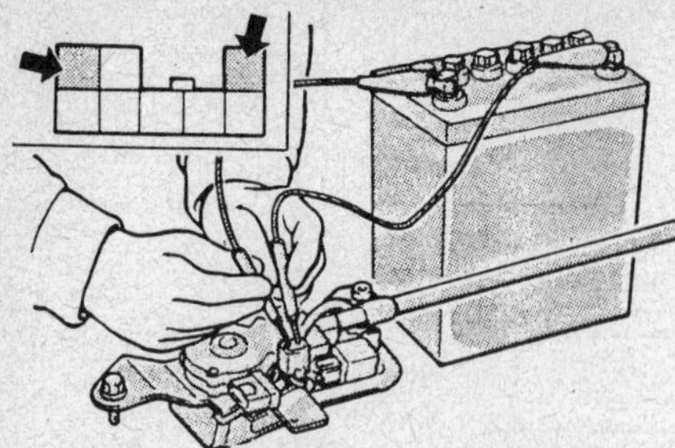

Fig. 4 Checking seat belt motor. Colt, Colt Vista, Conquest, Eagle Talon, Plymouth Laser & Summit

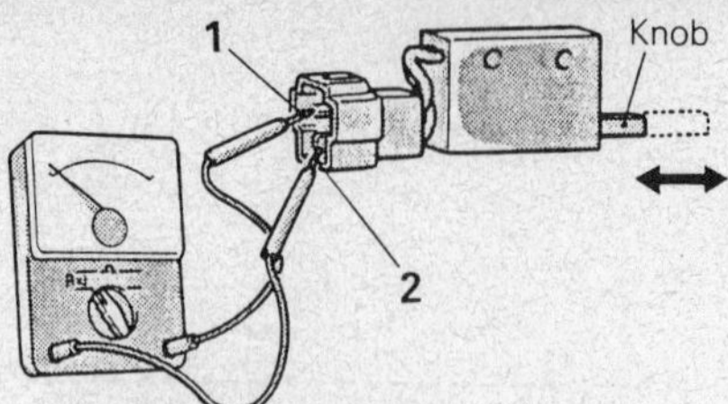


Fig. 5 Checking release switch. Colt, Colt Vista, Conquest, Eagle Talon, Plymouth Laser & Summit

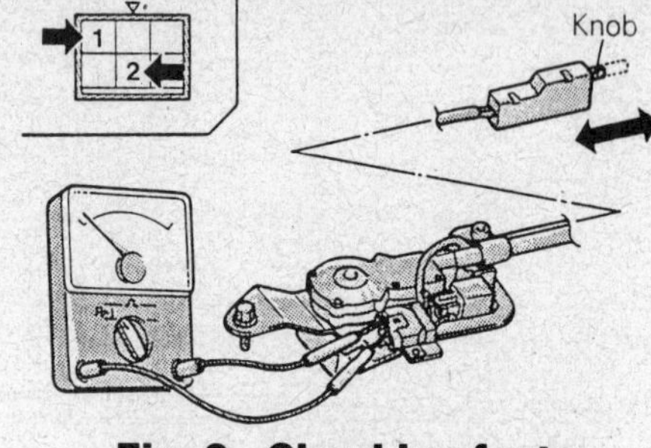


Fig. 6 Checking fasten switch. Colt, Colt Vista, Conquest, Eagle Talon, Plymouth Laser & Summit

2. Using a suitable ohmmeter, check for continuity between switch terminals as shown, **Fig. 7.**

### Outer Switch

1. Disconnect the outer switch connector.
2. Pull the shoulder belt out farther than its midpoint.
3. Using a suitable ohmmeter, check continuity as shown, **Fig. 8.**
4. Continuity should be present with the belt pulled out past its midpoint.
5. No continuity should be present when belt is pulled out less then its midpoint.

### Buckle Switch

1. Disconnect the buckle switch connector.
2. Using a suitable ohmmeter, check continuity between terminals of connector.
3. Continuity should be present with the buckle unlocked, no continuity should be present when the buckle is locked.

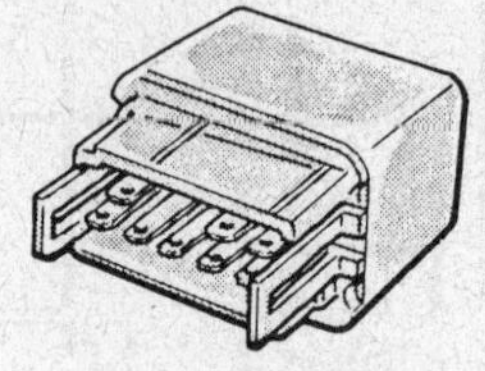

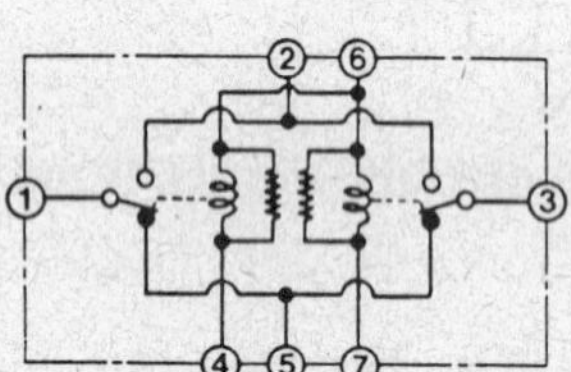


Fig.7 Checking relay. Colt, Colt Vista, Conquest, Eagle Talon, Plymouth Laser & Summit

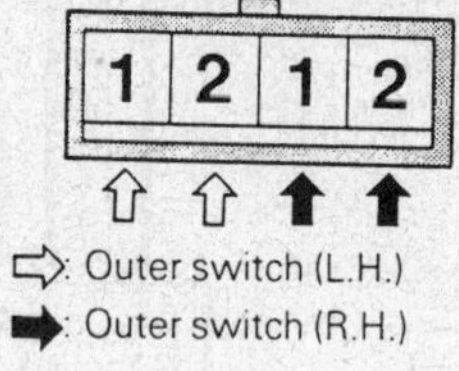


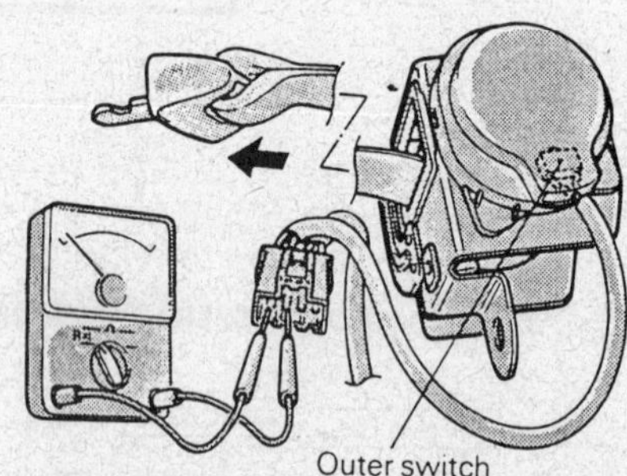


Fig. 8 Checking outer switch. Colt, Colt Vista, Conquest, Eagle Talon, Plymouth Laser & Summit

## 1991 MONACO & PREMIER

### CARRIER SWITCHES

1. Using suitable volt/ohmmeter, check resistance at open switch position at cavity 27 (LH side, carrier front position switch circuit), and 28 (rear position), **Fig 3.** Resistance should be greater than 3,000 ohms.
2. Check resistance at open switch position at cavity 21 (RH side, carrier front position switch circuit), and 4 (rear position). Resistance should be greater than 3,000 ohms.
3. Check resistance at closed switch position at cavity 27 (RH side, carrier front position switch circuit), and 28 (rear position). Resistance should be less than 100 ohms.
4. Check resistance at closed switch position at cavity 21 (RH side, carrier front position switch circuit), and 4 (rear position). Resistance should be less than 100 ohms.
5. Ensure voltage is concurrent with **Fig. 9.**

### SHOULDER BELT RETRACTOR SWITCHES

1. Using suitable volt/ohmmeter, check resistance in open switch of RH switch at cavity 6 and LH switch at cavity 5, **Fig. 3.** Resistance should be more than 3,000 ohms.

| Front Position Switch "A" | Rear Position Switch "B" | Tab Or Carrier Position |
|---|---|---|
| Closed 0v | Open 12v | Tab or carrier in rear position |
| Open 12v | Closed 0v | Tab or carrier in front position |
| Closed 0v | Closed 0v | Tab or carrier leaving rear and moving to front |
| Closed 0v | Closed 0v | Tab or carrier leaving front and moving to rear |

Fig. 9 Carrier switch voltage. 1991 Monaco & Premier

| Switch Position | Shoulder Belt Position |
|---|---|
| Open 12v | Shoulder belt should be extended and connected to the carrier or tab |
| Closed 0v | Shoulder belt retracted and/or disconnected from the carrier |

Fig. 10 Shoulder belt retractor switch voltage. 1991 Monaco & Premier

| 10 | 9 | 8 | 7 | | □ | | 4 | 3 | 2 | 1 |
|---|---|---|---|---|---|---|---|---|---|---|
| 21 | 20 | 19 | 18 | 17 | 16 | 15 | 14 | 13 | 12 | 11 |

**Fig. 11 Control module connector terminal identification. Conquest**

| Name | Terminal No. | Voltage level |
|---|---|---|
| Battery (+B) | 21 | H |
| Automatic seat belt motor (+B) | 11 | H |
| GROUND (GND) | 16 | L |

**Fig. 12 Power supply & ground circuit test. Conquest**

| Input name | Terminal No. | Switch operation and condition | | Voltage level | Input signal waveform |
|---|---|---|---|---|---|
| Key-reminder switch | 12 | Ignition key is inserted | ON | H | ON / OFF |
| | | Ignition key is removed | OFF | L | |
| Release switch (driver's side, front) | 8 | Driver's door is open and shoulder belt is going off | ON | L | OFF / ON |
| | | Driver's door is closed or shoulder belt is released completely | OFF | H | |
| Fasten switch (driver's side, rear) | 9 | Driver's door is closed or shoulder belt is not fastened | ON | L | OFF / ON |
| | | Driver's door is open or shoulder belt is fastened completely | OFF | H | |
| Door lock switch (driver's side) | 13 | Driver's door is closed | ON (lock) | L | ON (unlock) / ON (lock) |
| | | Driver's door is open and key in | ON (unlock) | H | |
| Release switch (passenger's side, front) | 3 | Passenger's door is open and shoulder belt is going off | ON | L | OFF / ON |
| | | Passenger's door is closed or shoulder belt is released completely | OFF | H | |
| Fasten switch (passenger's side, rear) | 2 | Passenger's door is closed or shoulder belt is not fastened | ON | L | OFF / ON |
| | | Passenger's door is open or shoulder belt is fastened completely | OFF | H | |

**Fig. 13 Input signal test (Part 1 of 2). Conquest**

| Input name | Terminal No. | Switch operation and condition | | Voltage level | Input signal waveform |
|---|---|---|---|---|---|
| IG₁ | 18 | Ignition switch | ON | H | ON / ACC or LOCK |
| | | | ACC or LOCK | L | |
| Spool release lever switch | 15 | Lever is not operated | ON | L | OFF / ON |
| | | Lever is pulled up | OFF | H | |
| Buckle switch (driver's seat) | 17 | Lap belt is fastened | OFF | H | OFF / ON |
| | | Lap belt is not fastened | ON | L | |

**Fig. 13 Input signal test (Part 2 of 2). Conquest**

2. Check resistance in closed switch of RH switch at cavity 6 and LH switch at cavity 5, **Fig. 3.** Resistance should be less than 40 ohms.
3. Ensure voltage is concurrent with Fig. 10.

# SYSTEM TESTING

## CONQUEST

Refer to **Fig. 11,** for automatic seat belt control unit terminal identification when testing system. **Voltage levels H and L indicated in charts are represented as follows:** H, battery voltage; L, .8 volts or less.

### Power Supply & Ground Circuit

Refer to **Fig. 12,** for power and ground circuit testing.

### Input Signals

Refer to **Fig. 13,** for input signal testing. **Note that ignition switch should be in the On position during input signal testing.**

### Output signals

Refer to **Figs. 14 through 18** for testing of output signals.

## EAGLE MEDALLION

Refer **Fig. 19** for wiring circuit, when performing diagnosis and testing.

### Using M.S.1700 Tester

Refer to **Figs. 20 through 35,** for diagnosis and testing of automatic seat belt system using M.S. 1700 tester per manufacturer's instructions.

### Manual Testing

Refer to **Figs. 36 through 51,** for diagnosis and testing of automatic seat belt system.

### Seat Belt Control Module Checkout Procedure

1. Disconnect battery ground cable.
2. Disconnect passive restraint module from wiring harness connector.
3. Inspect harness connector and passive restraint control module for foreign material on connector pins, repair as necessary.
4. Inspect passive restraint control module harness connector for bent or missing pins, broken wires, missing wires, improper or missing insulation and repair as necessary.
5. Reconnect passive restraint module to harness connector and retest the system using the M.S. 1700 tester.
6. If the vehicle does not pass the test, and fails with the same fault code as earlier, replace the passive restraint module.

## 1989–90 EAGLE PREMIER & 1990 DODGE MONACO

To properly perform testing of the automatic seat belt system, the use of a DRBII readout box or equivalent is required to obtain system fault codes. Follow tool manufacturer's instructions for installation and operation of readout box.

Refer to **Figs. 52 through 72,** for system fault code diagnosis and testing.

## 1991 DODGE MONACO & EAGLE PREMIER

To properly perform testing of the automatic seat belt system, the use of a DRBII readout box or equivalent is required to obtain system fault codes. Follow tool manufacturer's instructions for installation and operation of readout box.

Refer to **Figs. 73 through 102,** for system fault code diagnosis and testing.

| Condition at input side | | | Output signal waveform and its operation | |
|---|---|---|---|---|
| | | | Output signal | Buzzer |
| Buckle switch at ON (not fastened) | Ignition switch | LOCK or ACC | H L 0.7 sec 6 sec | OFF |
| | | ON | | ON |
| Ignition switch at LOCK and ACC and key-in | Door lock switch (close side) | ON | H L Door closed Door open | OFF |
| | | OFF | | ON |
| Spool release lever pulled up | Ignition switch | LOCK or ACC | H L 0.7 sec. | OFF |
| | | ON | | ON |
| Door open and shoulder belt going off | Belt anchor and shoulder belt | FREE | H L 0.7 sec. 1.7 sec | OFF |
| | | An impact or sudden pull force is applied | | ON |

**Fig. 14 Output signal test (Buzzer drive, terminal No. 14). Conquest**

## SHADOW & SUNDANCE

When testing operation of system, ensure care is taken not to damage connectors, terminals or seals. Damage to terminals and connectors may result in system malfunction or failure.

### With DRBII Readout Box

When testing system using DRBII, follow manufacturers instructions for installation of DRBII readout box.

Refer to **Figs. 103 through 120**, for diagnosis and testing of automatic seat belt system using the DRBII.

### Without DRBII Readout Box

Use suitable volt and ohmmeters when performing the following tests.

### Belts Do Not Move With Carriers In Any Position

1. Check battery voltage to module for motors as follows:
   a. Check for battery voltage at red wire of module 10-way connector.
   b. Check system circuit breaker in fuse block.
   c. Check for proper connection of the right side 25-way connector.
2. Check for ground at module for motors as follows:
   a. Check black wire of module 10-way connector for continuity to ground.
   b. If circuit shows no continuity, repair open in circuit.
3. Check ignition input to the module as follows:
   a. Disconnect module 21-way connector, then place ignition in On position.
   b. Check for battery voltage at dark blue/white wire of 21-way connector.
   c. If no voltage is present, check fuse, right side 25-way connector and ignition switch.
   d. If voltage is present, Check all wiring connectors and terminals, then replace control module if system fails to operate properly.

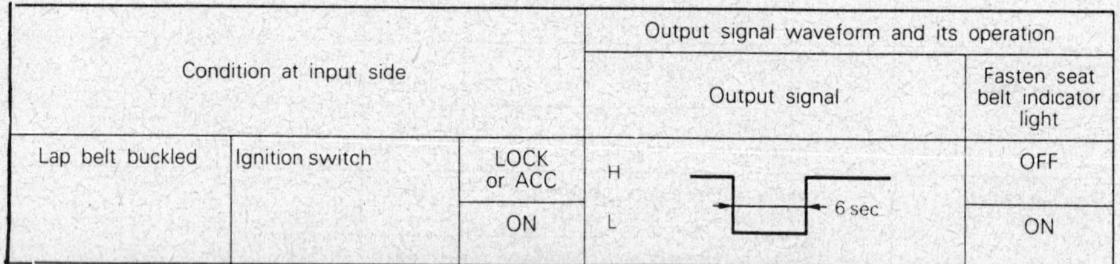

| Condition at input side | | | Output signal waveform and its operation | |
|---|---|---|---|---|
| | | | Output signal | Fasten seat belt indicator light |
| Lap belt buckled | Ignition switch | LOCK or ACC | H L 6 sec | OFF |
| | | ON | | ON |

**Fig. 15 Output signal test (Fasten seat belt indicator drive, terminal No. 20, Part 1 of 2). Conquest**

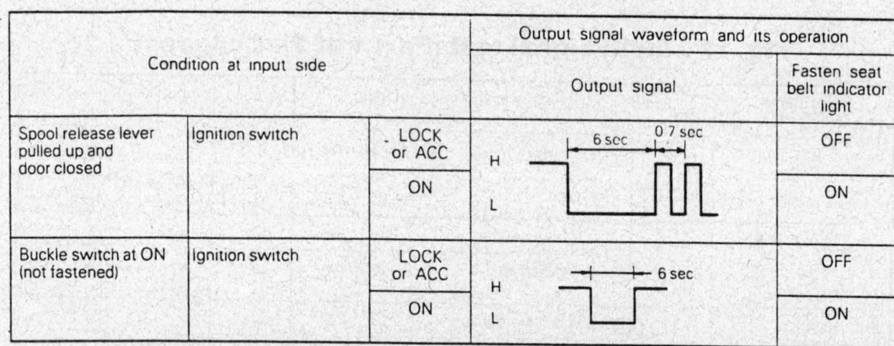

| Condition at input side | | | Output signal waveform and its operation | |
|---|---|---|---|---|
| | | | Output signal | Fasten seat belt indicator light |
| Spool release lever pulled up and door closed | Ignition switch | LOCK or ACC | H L 6 sec 0.7 sec | OFF |
| | | ON | | ON |
| Buckle switch at ON (not fastened) | Ignition switch | LOCK or ACC | H L 6 sec | OFF |
| | | ON | | ON |

**Fig. 15 Output signal test (Fasten seat belt indicator drive, terminal No. 20, Part 2 of 2). Conquest**

| Condition at input side | | | Output signal waveform and its operation | |
|---|---|---|---|---|
| | | | Output signal | Spool release indicator light |
| | Ignition switch | LOCK or ACC | H L 1.5 sec | OFF |
| | | ON | | ON |
| Spool release lever pulled up | Ignition switch | LOCK or ACC | H L 1.5 sec | OFF |
| | | ON | | ON |

**Fig. 16 Output signal test (Spool release indicator light drive, terminal No. 19). Conquest**

| Condition at input side | | | Output signal waveform and its operation | |
|---|---|---|---|---|
| | | | Output signal | Motor |
| Door open | Ignition switch | ON | H | Operate |
| | | LOCK or ACC | L | Stop |

**Fig. 17 Output signal test (Shoulder belt release side: driver side terminal No. 7; passenger side, terminal No. 4). Conquest**

| Condition at input side | | | Output signal waveform and its operation | |
|---|---|---|---|---|
| | | | Output signal | Motor |
| Door closed | Ignition switch | ON | H | Operate |
| | | LOCK or ACC | L | Stop |

**Fig. 18 Output signal test (Shoulder belt fasten side: driver side terminal No. 10; passenger side, terminal No. 1). Conquest**

### Belt Will Not Move From B-Pillar Position

1. Check console limit switches as follows:
   a. Disconnect torso belt and allow it to retract, then check brown wire of 21-way connector for left side or brown/white wire for right side, for continuity to ground.
   b. If circuit shows continuity, pull torso belt out and ensure circuit goes open.
   c. If no continuity is present, check ground circuit, then replace torso belt assembly if system still fails.
2. Check A-limit switch as follow:
   a. Disconnect module 21-way connector, then check light blue wire of 21-way connector for left side or light blue/white wire for right side, for continuity to ground.
   b. If no continuity is present, check ground circuit for opens and/or poor connections. If circuit checks are satisfactory, replace track and motor as an assembly.
3. Check 5 volt module output to limit switch as follows:
   a. Disconnect motor connectors, then place key in the On position and check for five volts at the light blue wires of the module 21-way connector.
   b. If no voltage is present, check connections and wiring, then replace module if system still fails to operate properly.
4. Check motor circuit continuity as follows:
   a. Reconnect motor connectors, then check for continuity between dark green and dark blue wires of module 10-way connector for left side motor or between dark green and dark blue/white wires for right side motor.
   b. If no continuity is present, check wiring and connections for opens. If circuit is found to be satisfactory, replace motor and track assembly.
5. Check door jamb switches for complete circuit to ground with doors open as follows:
   a. Disconnect module 21-way connector, then check black/light blue wire for continuity to ground for left side or violet/yellow wire to ground for right side.
   b. If no continuity is present, check for a poor connection, defective switch or open ground.
6. Check for mechanical problems as follows:
   a. Check anti-rollover latch for freeness.
   b. Check cable for binding.
   c. Check for a stuck carrier
7. Check module forward relay contacts as follows:
   a. Connect a test light between dark blue and dark green wires of harness side motor connector. Turn ignition Off, then On.
   b. If test light illuminates, replace motor and track assembly.
   c. If test light does not light, check for open or bad wire connection. If wires and connections are satisfactory, replace module.

### Belt Will Not Move From A-Pillar Position

1. Check for an open B-limit switch as follows:
   a. Disconnect module 21-way connector, then check tan wire of 21-way connector for left side or tan/white wire for right side, for continuity to ground.
   b. If no continuity is present, check for open between control module and motor. If circuit checks are satisfactory, replace track and motor as an assembly.
2. Check 5 volt module output to limit switch as follows:
   a. Disconnect motor connectors, then place key in the On position and check for five volts at the tan wires of the module 21-way connector.
   b. If no voltage is present, check connections and wiring, then replace module if system still fails to operate properly.
3. Check motor circuit continuity as follows:
   a. Reconnect motor connectors, then check for continuity between dark green and dark blue wires of module 10-way connector for left side motor or between dark green and dark blue/white wires for right side motor.
   b. If no continuity is present, check wiring and connections for opens. If circuit is found to be satisfactory, replace motor and track assembly.
4. Check door jamb switches for complete circuit to ground with doors open as follows:
   a. Disconnect module 21-way connector, then check black/light blue wire for continuity to ground for left side or violet/yellow wire to ground for right side.
   b. If no continuity is present, check for poor connection, defective switch or open ground.
5. Check for mechanical problems as follows:
   a. Check antirollover latch for freeness.
   b. Check cable for binding.
   c. Check for a stuck carrier
6. Check module rearward relay contacts as follows:
   a. Connect a test light between dark blue and dark green wires of harness side motor connector. Turn ignition Off, then On.
   b. If test light illuminates, replace motor and track assembly.
   c. If test light does not light, check for open or bad wire connection. If wires and connections are satisfactory, replace module.

*Continued on page 21-93*

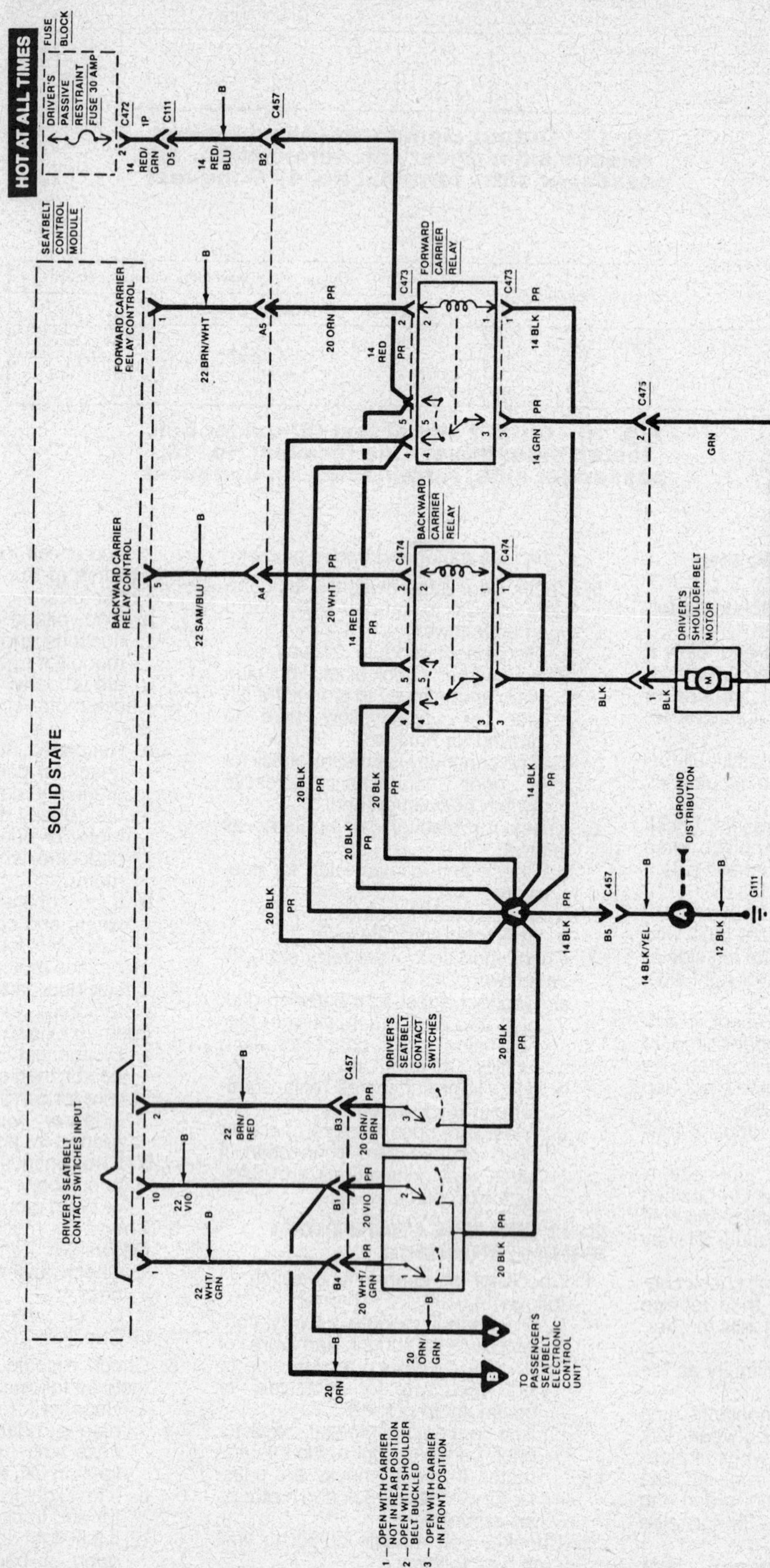


**Fig. 19 Automatic seat belt wiring circuit (Part 1 of 3). Eagle Medallion**

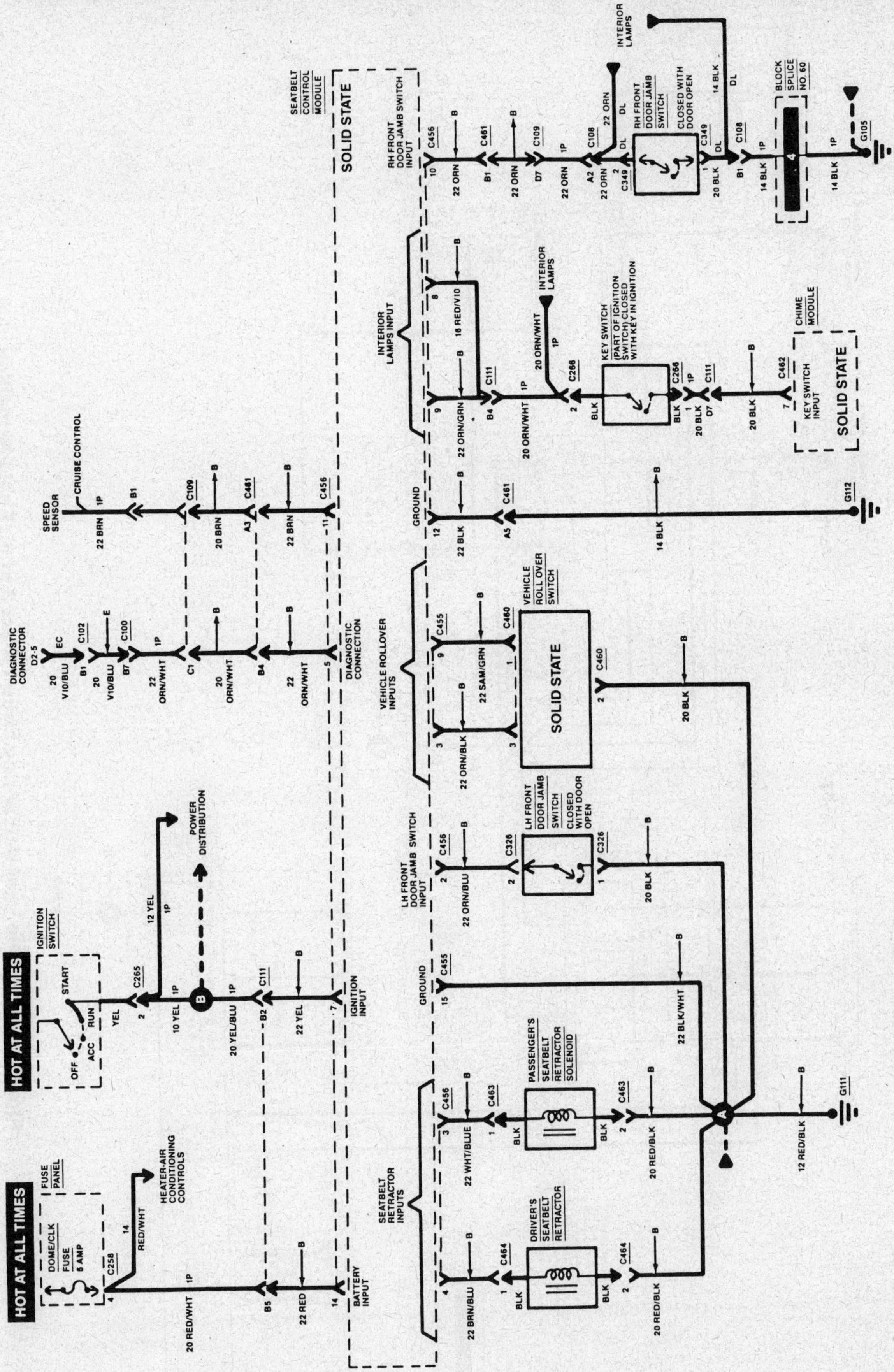

Fig. 19 Automatic seat belt wiring circuit (Part 2 of 3). Eagle Medallion

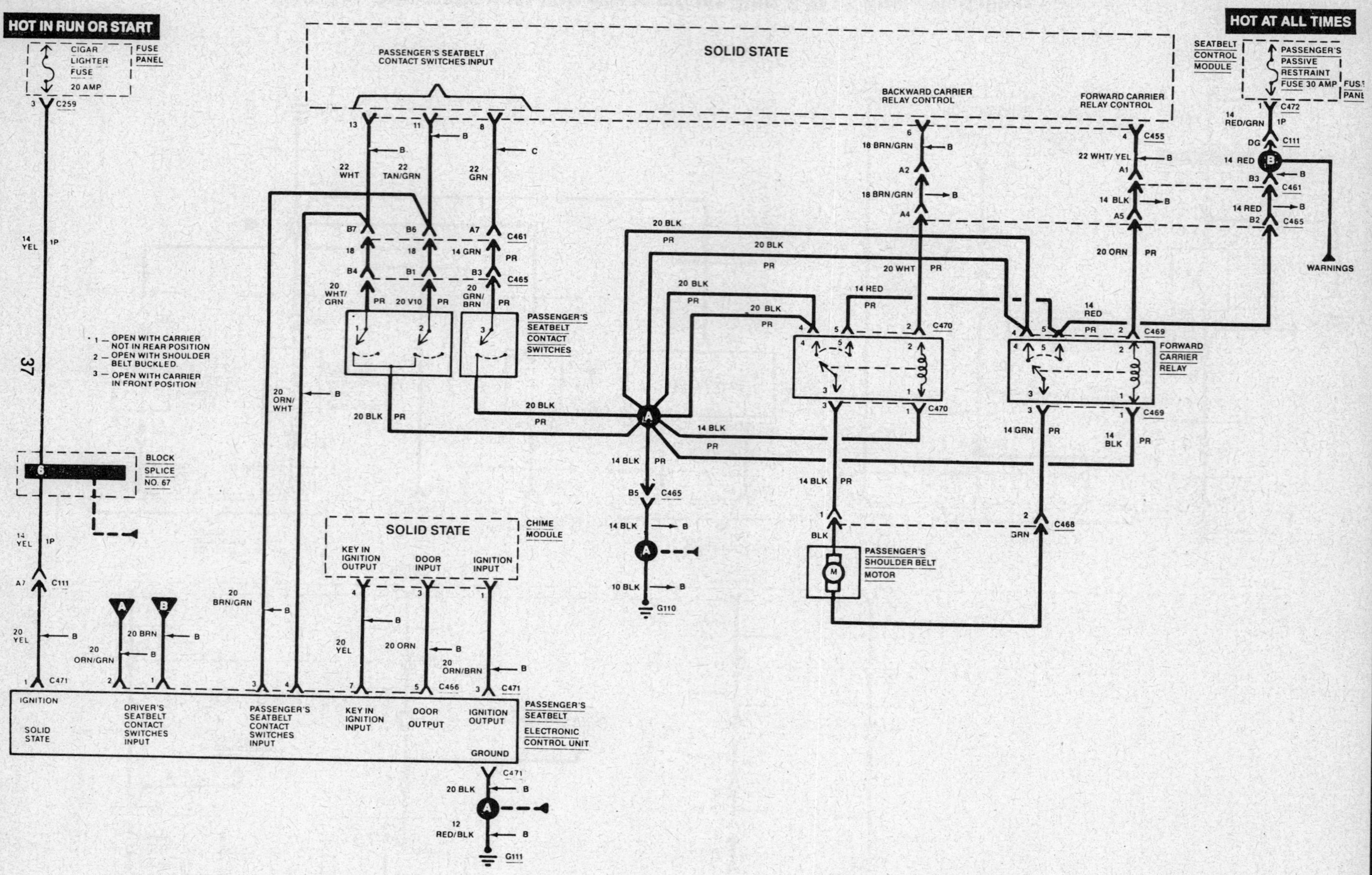


Fig. 19 Automatic seat belt wiring circuit (Part 3 of 3). Eagle Medallion

## DIAGNOSTIC CHART INDEX



*Continued*

## DIAGNOSTIC CHART INDEX—Continued

| Fault No. | Symptom | Page No. | Fig. No. |
|---|---|---|---|
| 1989–90 Eagle Premier & 1990 Dodge Monaco -Cont. | | | |
| 413 | Passenger Door Switch Closed | 21-79 | 93 |
| 414 | Passenger Door Switch Open | 21-79 | 94 |
| 415 | Passenger Forward Station Seen | 21-79 | 95 |
| 416 | Passenger Forward Station Not Seen | 21-81 | 98 |
| 417 | Passenger Rear Station Seen | 21-81 | 99 |
| 418 | Passenger Rear Station Not Seen | 21-82 | 102 |
| Shadow & Sundance | | | |
| 1 | Checking For Fault Codes | 21-83 | 103 |
| 2 | Checking RX & TX Wires For Open Circuit | 21-84 | 104 |
| 3 | Motorized Seat Belt Fault Messages | 21-84 | 105 |
| 4 | Checking R02 & R12 Wires For Open Circuits | 21-85 | 106 |
| 5 | Checking R01 & R11 Wires For Open Circuits | 21-85 | 107 |
| 6 | Checking R32 & R34 Wires For Open Circuits | 21-85 | 108 |
| 7 | Checking R31 & R33 Wires For Open Circuits | 21-86 | 109 |
| 8 | Checking R20 Wire For Open Circuit | 21-86 | 110 |
| 9 | Checking R19 Wire For Open Circuit | 21-86 | 111 |
| 10 | Checking G11 & G5 Wires For Open Circuits | 21-87 | 112 |
| 11 | Checking G7 Wire For Open Circuit | 21-88 | 113 |
| 12 | Checking M16 Wire For Open Circuit | 21-88 | 114 |
| 13 | Checking R32 & R34 Wires For Open Circuits | 21-89 | 115 |
| 14 | Checking R31 & R33 Wires For Open Circuits | 21-90 | 116 |
| 15 | Checking R19 & M1 Wires For Open Circuits | 21-90 | 117 |
| 16 | Checking R20 & M1 Wires For Open Circuits | 21-91 | 118 |
| 17 | Checking G7 Wire For Open Circuit | 21-91 | 119 |
| 18 | Checking G5 Wire For Open Circuit | 21-91 | 120 |

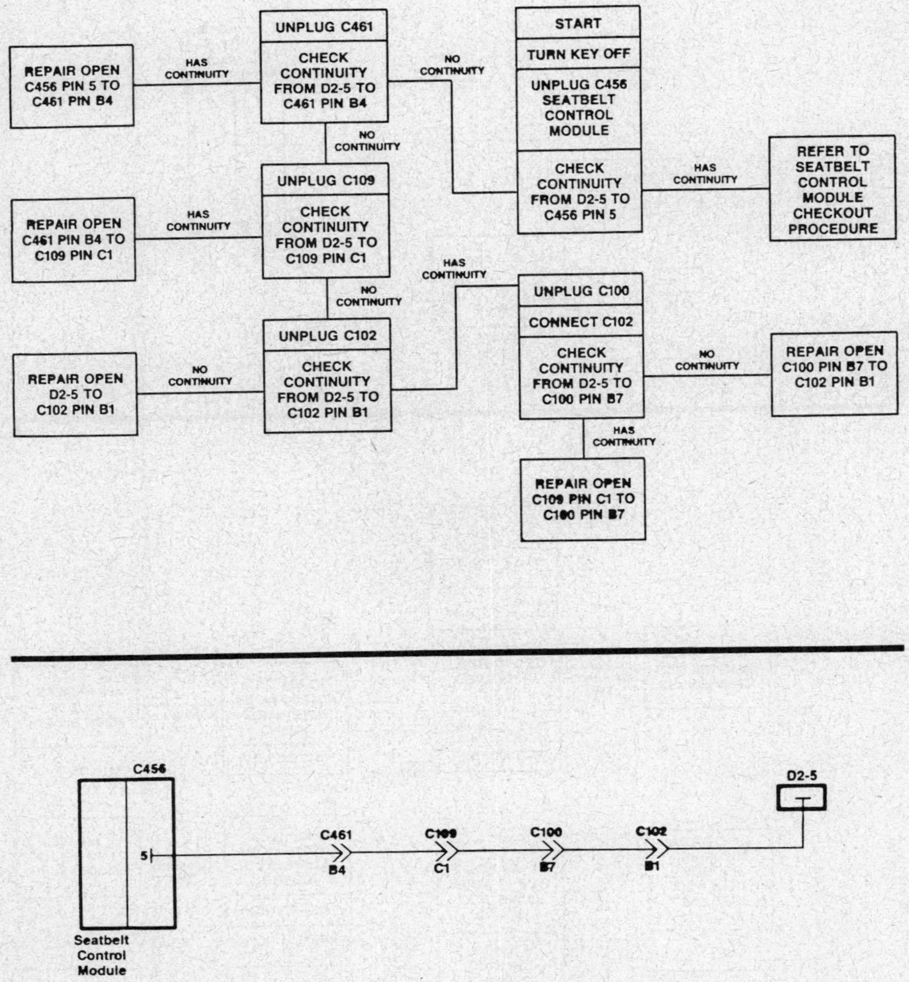

START
TURN KEY OFF
UNPLUG C456 SEATBELT CONTROL MODULE
CHECK CONTINUITY FROM D2-5 TO C456 PIN 5
HAS CONTINUITY
REFER TO SEATBELT CONTROL MODULE CHECKOUT PROCEDURE
NO CONTINUITY
UNPLUG C461
CHECK CONTINUITY FROM D2-5 TO C461 PIN B4
HAS CONTINUITY
REPAIR OPEN C456 PIN 5 TO C461 PIN B4
NO CONTINUITY
UNPLUG C109
CHECK CONTINUITY FROM D2-5 TO C109 PIN C1
HAS CONTINUITY
REPAIR OPEN C461 PIN B4 TO C109 PIN C1
NO CONTINUITY
UNPLUG C102
CHECK CONTINUITY FROM D2-5 TO C102 PIN B1
NO CONTINUITY
REPAIR OPEN D2-5 TO C102 PIN B1
HAS CONTINUITY
UNPLUG C100
CONNECT C102
CHECK CONTINUITY FROM D2-5 TO C100 PIN B7
NO CONTINUITY
REPAIR OPEN C100 PIN B7 TO C102 PIN B1
HAS CONTINUITY
REPAIR OPEN C109 PIN C1 TO C100 PIN B7
C456
5
Seatbelt Control Module
C461
B4
C109
C1
C100
B7
C102
B1
D2-5

Fig. 20 Fault 550 (No serial data from passive restraint module). Eagle Medallion

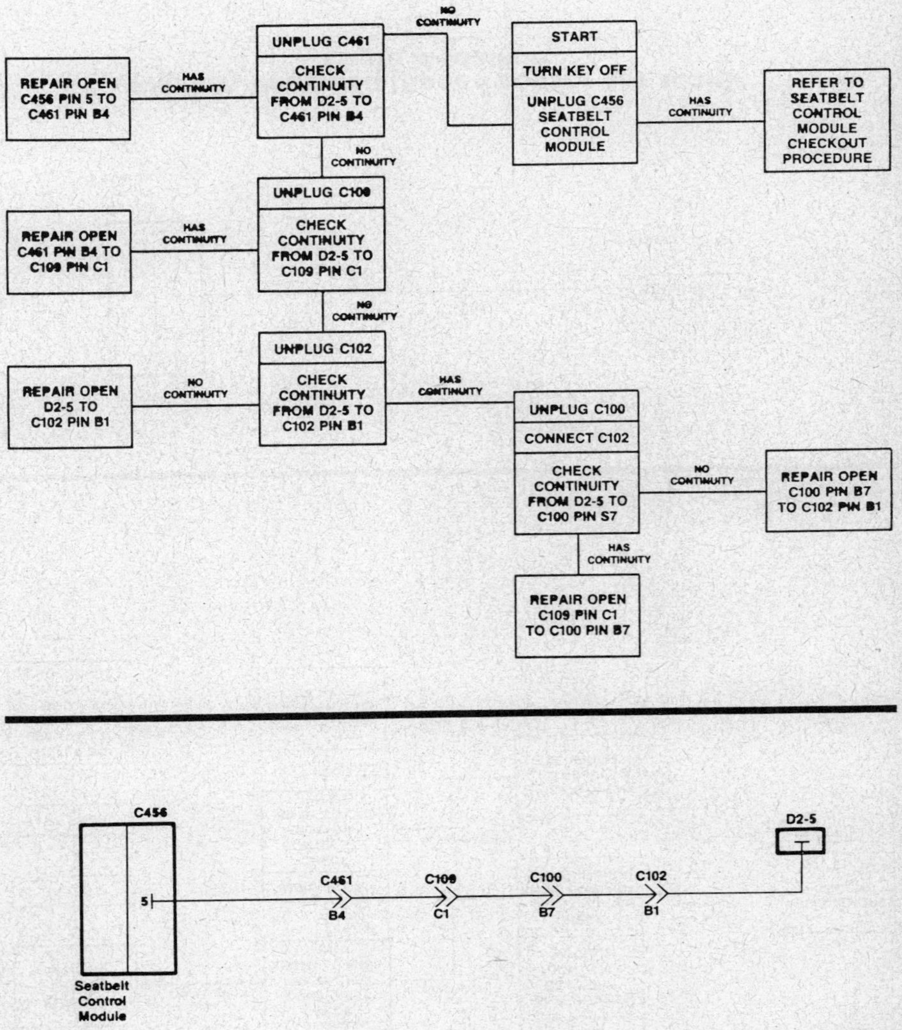

START
TURN KEY OFF
UNPLUG C456 SEATBELT CONTROL MODULE
HAS CONTINUITY
REFER TO SEATBELT CONTROL MODULE CHECKOUT PROCEDURE
NO CONTINUITY
UNPLUG C461
CHECK CONTINUITY FROM D2-5 TO C461 PIN B4
HAS CONTINUITY
REPAIR OPEN C456 PIN 5 TO C461 PIN B4
NO CONTINUITY
UNPLUG C109
CHECK CONTINUITY FROM D2-5 TO C109 PIN C1
HAS CONTINUITY
REPAIR OPEN C461 PIN B4 TO C109 PIN C1
NO CONTINUITY
UNPLUG C102
CHECK CONTINUITY FROM D2-5 TO C102 PIN B1
NO CONTINUITY
REPAIR OPEN D2-5 TO C102 PIN B1
HAS CONTINUITY
UNPLUG C100
CONNECT C102
CHECK CONTINUITY FROM D2-5 TO C100 PIN S7
NO CONTINUITY
REPAIR OPEN C100 PIN B7 TO C102 PIN B1
HAS CONTINUITY
REPAIR OPEN C109 PIN C1 TO C100 PIN B7
C456
5
Seatbelt Control Module
C461
B4
C109
C1
C100
B7
C102
B1
D2-5

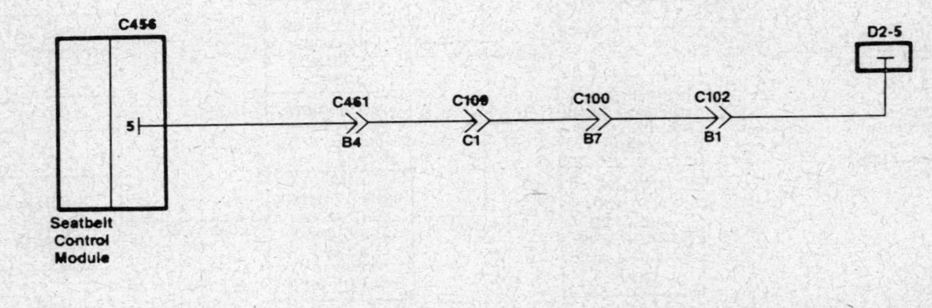

Fig. 21 Fault 551 (Error reading serial data). Eagle Medallion

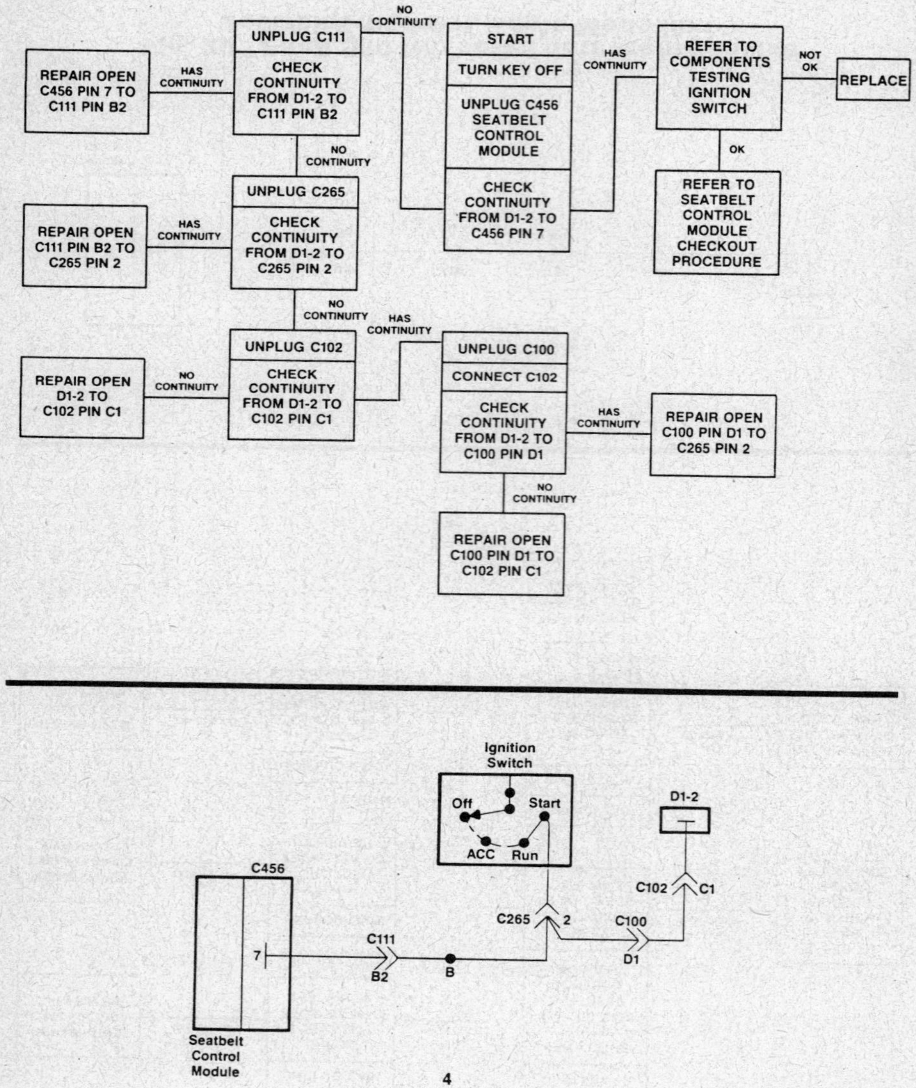

START
TURN KEY OFF
UNPLUG C456 SEATBELT CONTROL MODULE
CHECK CONTINUITY FROM D1-2 TO C456 PIN 7

- HAS CONTINUITY → REFER TO COMPONENTS TESTING IGNITION SWITCH
  - OK → REFER TO SEATBELT CONTROL MODULE CHECKOUT PROCEDURE
  - NOT OK → REPLACE
- NO CONTINUITY → UNPLUG C111; CHECK CONTINUITY FROM D1-2 TO C111 PIN B2
  - HAS CONTINUITY → REPAIR OPEN C456 PIN 7 TO C111 PIN B2
  - NO CONTINUITY → UNPLUG C265; CHECK CONTINUITY FROM D1-2 TO C265 PIN 2
    - HAS CONTINUITY → REPAIR OPEN C111 PIN B2 TO C265 PIN 2
    - NO CONTINUITY → UNPLUG C102; CHECK CONTINUITY FROM D1-2 TO C102 PIN C1
      - NO CONTINUITY → REPAIR OPEN D1-2 TO C102 PIN C1
      - HAS CONTINUITY → UNPLUG C100; CONNECT C102; CHECK CONTINUITY FROM D1-2 TO C100 PIN D1
        - HAS CONTINUITY → REPAIR OPEN C100 PIN D1 TO C265 PIN 2
        - NO CONTINUITY → REPAIR OPEN C100 PIN D1 TO C102 PIN C1

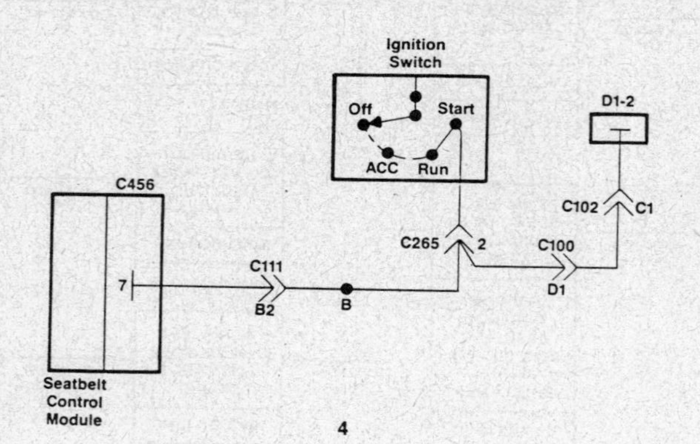


**Fig. 22 Fault 552 (Ignition switch not seen). Eagle Medallion**

START
UNPLUG C456 SEATBELT CONTROL MODULE
CHECK CONTINUITY FROM C456 PIN11 TO GROUND

- HAS CONTINUITY → REPAIR SHORT TO GROUND
- NO CONTINUITY → UNPLUG C106; CHECK CONTINUITY FROM C106 PIN B1 TO C456 PIN 11
  - HAS CONTINUITY → REPLACE SPEED SENSOR → RETEST → SAME FAULT? → REFER TO SEATBELT CONTROL MODULE CHECKOUT PROCEDURE
  - NO CONTINUITY → UNPLUG C461; CHECK CONTINUITY FROM C106 PIN B1 TO C461 PIN A3
    - HAS CONTINUITY → REPAIR OPEN C456 PIN11TO C461 PIN A3
    - NO CONTINUITY → REPAIR OPEN C106 PIN B1 TO C461 PIN A3

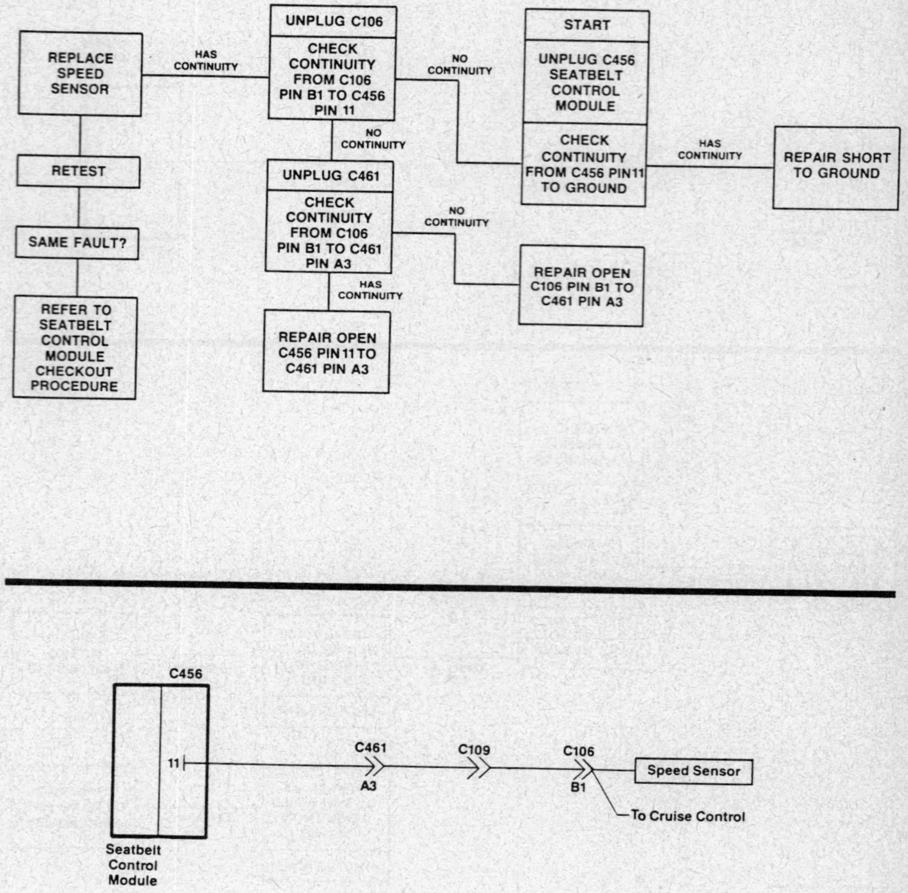

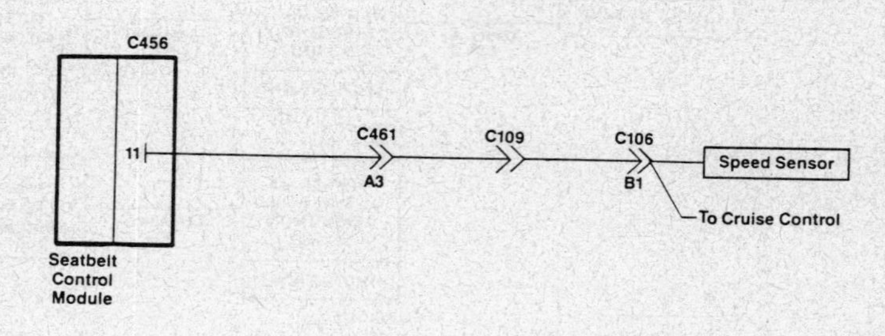


**Fig. 23 Fault 553 (Speed sensor not seen). Eagle Medallion**

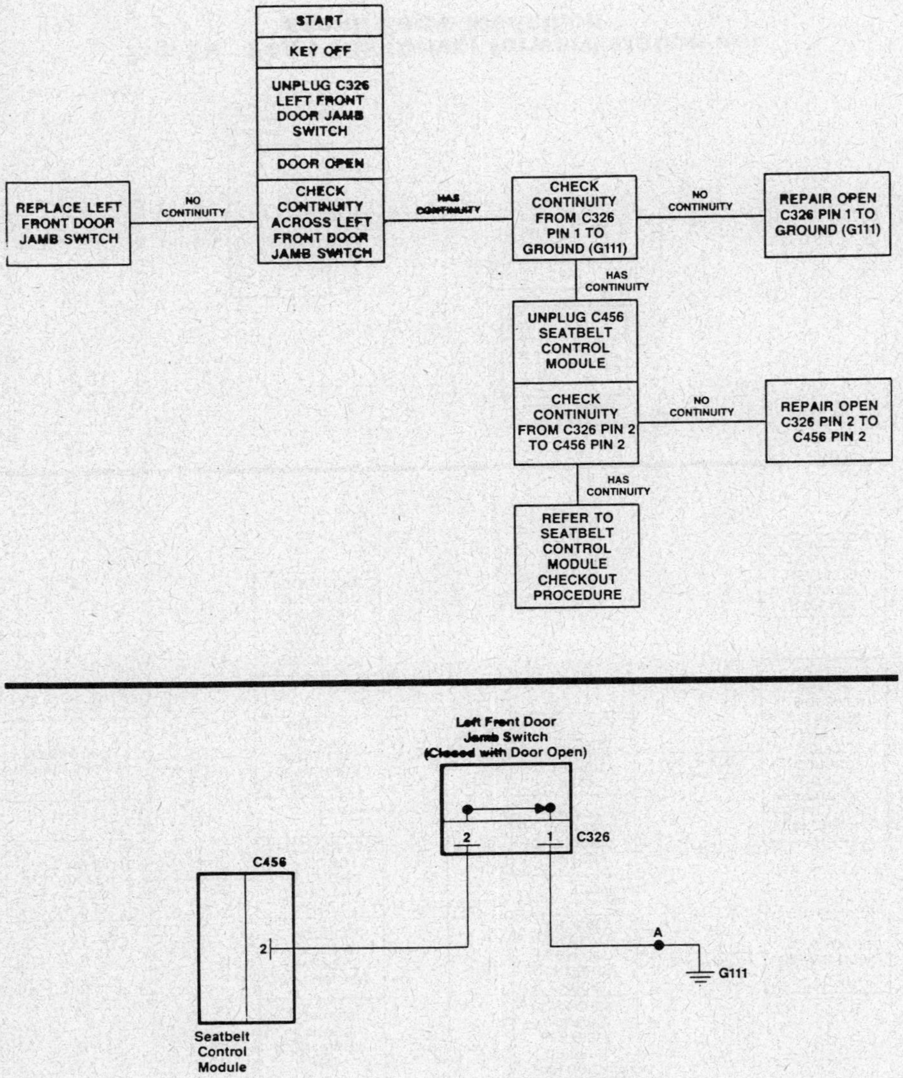

START

KEY OFF

UNPLUG C326 LEFT FRONT DOOR JAMB SWITCH

DOOR OPEN

CHECK CONTINUITY ACROSS LEFT FRONT DOOR JAMB SWITCH

- NO CONTINUITY → REPLACE LEFT FRONT DOOR JAMB SWITCH
- HAS CONTINUITY → CHECK CONTINUITY FROM C326 PIN 1 TO GROUND (G111)
  - NO CONTINUITY → REPAIR OPEN C326 PIN 1 TO GROUND (G111)
  - HAS CONTINUITY → UNPLUG C456 SEATBELT CONTROL MODULE; CHECK CONTINUITY FROM C326 PIN 2 TO C456 PIN 2
    - NO CONTINUITY → REPAIR OPEN C326 PIN 2 TO C456 PIN 2
    - HAS CONTINUITY → REFER TO SEATBELT CONTROL MODULE CHECKOUT PROCEDURE

Left Front Door Jamb Switch (Closed with Door Open)

2 1 C326

C456

2

A

G111

Seatbelt Control Module

**Fig. 24 Fault 554 (Driver door switch open). Eagle Medallion**

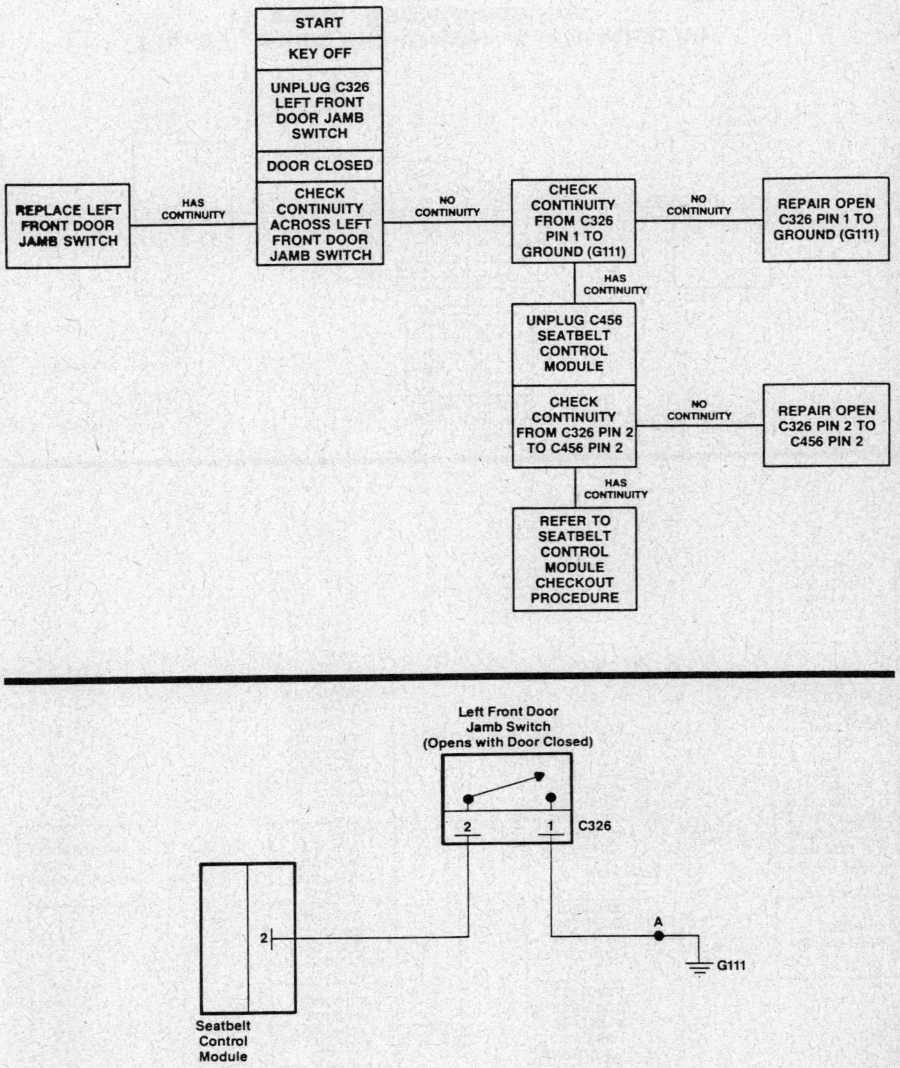

START

KEY OFF

UNPLUG C326 LEFT FRONT DOOR JAMB SWITCH

DOOR CLOSED

CHECK CONTINUITY ACROSS LEFT FRONT DOOR JAMB SWITCH

- HAS CONTINUITY → REPLACE LEFT FRONT DOOR JAMB SWITCH
- NO CONTINUITY → CHECK CONTINUITY FROM C326 PIN 1 TO GROUND (G111)
  - NO CONTINUITY → REPAIR OPEN C326 PIN 1 TO GROUND (G111)
  - HAS CONTINUITY → UNPLUG C456 SEATBELT CONTROL MODULE; CHECK CONTINUITY FROM C326 PIN 2 TO C456 PIN 2
    - NO CONTINUITY → REPAIR OPEN C326 PIN 2 TO C456 PIN 2
    - HAS CONTINUITY → REFER TO SEATBELT CONTROL MODULE CHECKOUT PROCEDURE

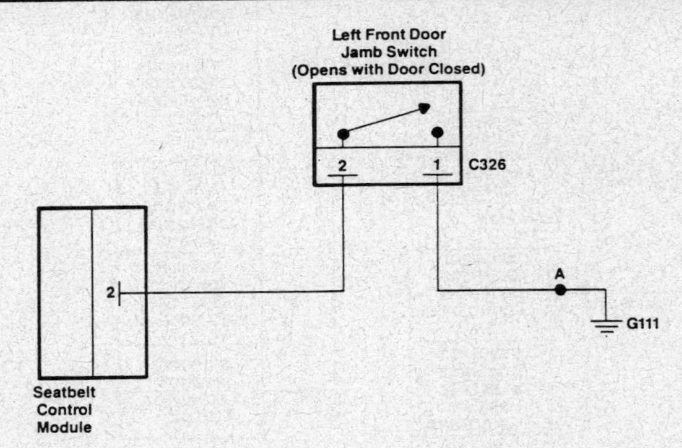


**Fig. 25 Fault 555 (Driver door switch closed). Eagle Medallion**

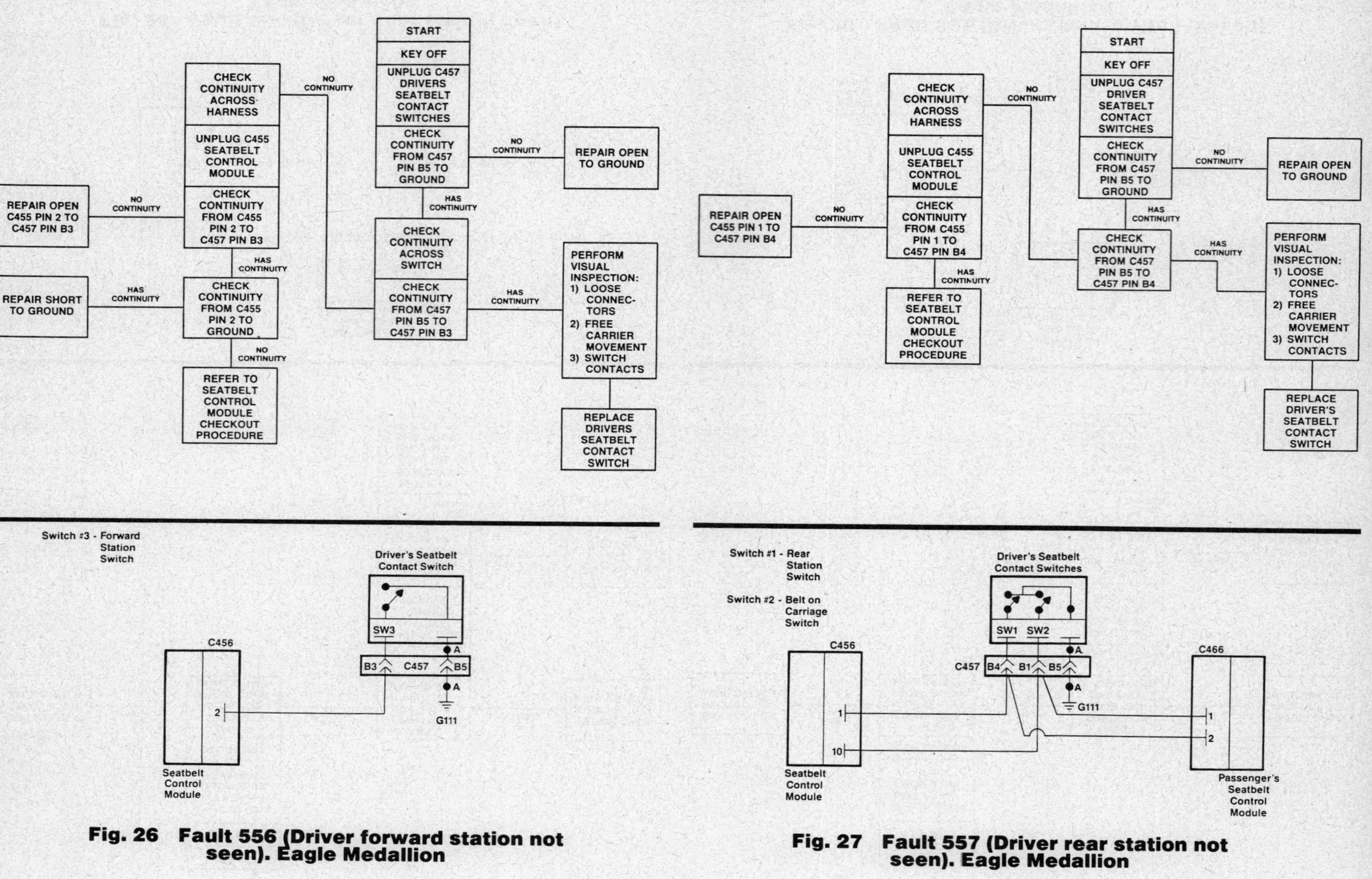


**Fig. 26 Fault 556 (Driver forward station not seen). Eagle Medallion**



**Fig. 27 Fault 557 (Driver rear station not seen). Eagle Medallion**

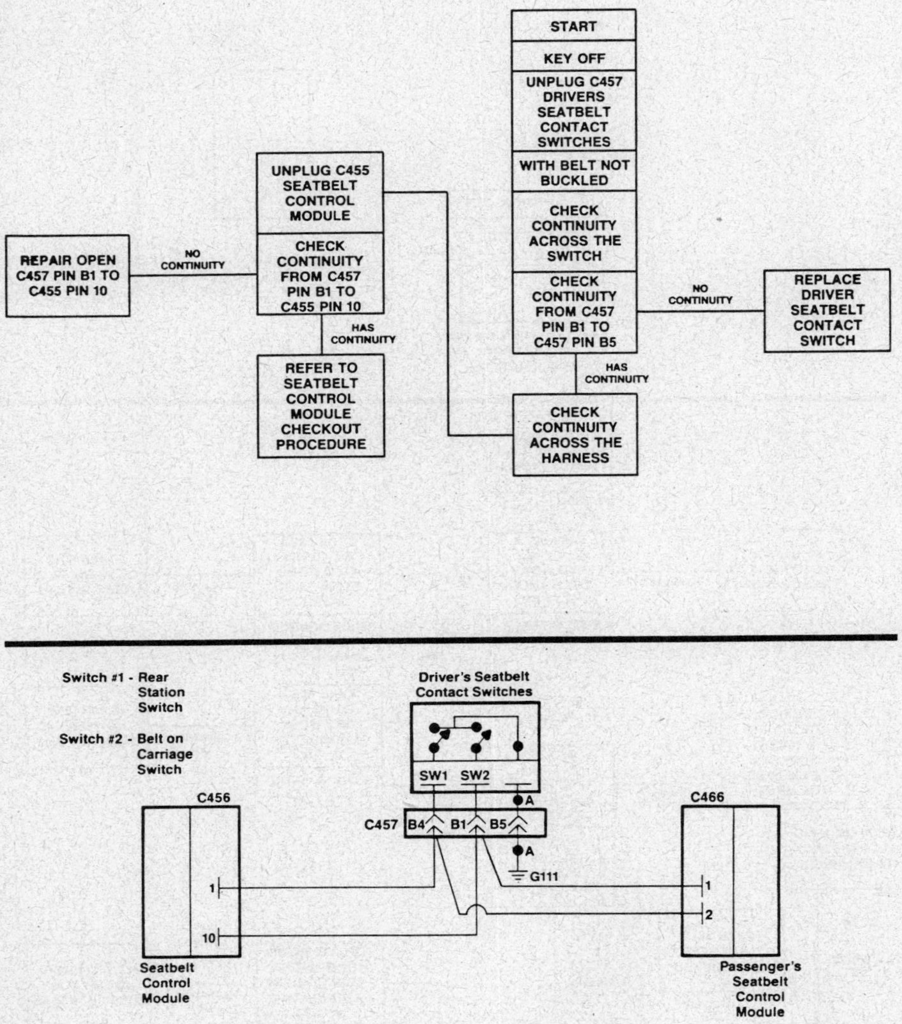

START

KEY OFF

UNPLUG C457 DRIVERS SEATBELT CONTACT SWITCHES

WITH BELT NOT BUCKLED

CHECK CONTINUITY ACROSS THE SWITCH

CHECK CONTINUITY FROM C457 PIN B1 TO C457 PIN B5

NO CONTINUITY → REPLACE DRIVER SEATBELT CONTACT SWITCH

HAS CONTINUITY → CHECK CONTINUITY ACROSS THE HARNESS

UNPLUG C455 SEATBELT CONTROL MODULE

CHECK CONTINUITY FROM C457 PIN B1 TO C455 PIN 10

NO CONTINUITY → REPAIR OPEN C457 PIN B1 TO C455 PIN 10

HAS CONTINUITY → REFER TO SEATBELT CONTROL MODULE CHECKOUT PROCEDURE

Switch #1 - Rear Station Switch

Switch #2 - Belt on Carriage Switch

Driver's Seatbelt Contact Switches

SW1 SW2

C456 C457 B4 B1 B5 A A G111 C466

1 10 1 2

Seatbelt Control Module

Passenger's Seatbelt Control Module

**Fig. 28 Fault 558 (Driver belt on carriage seen). Eagle Medallion**

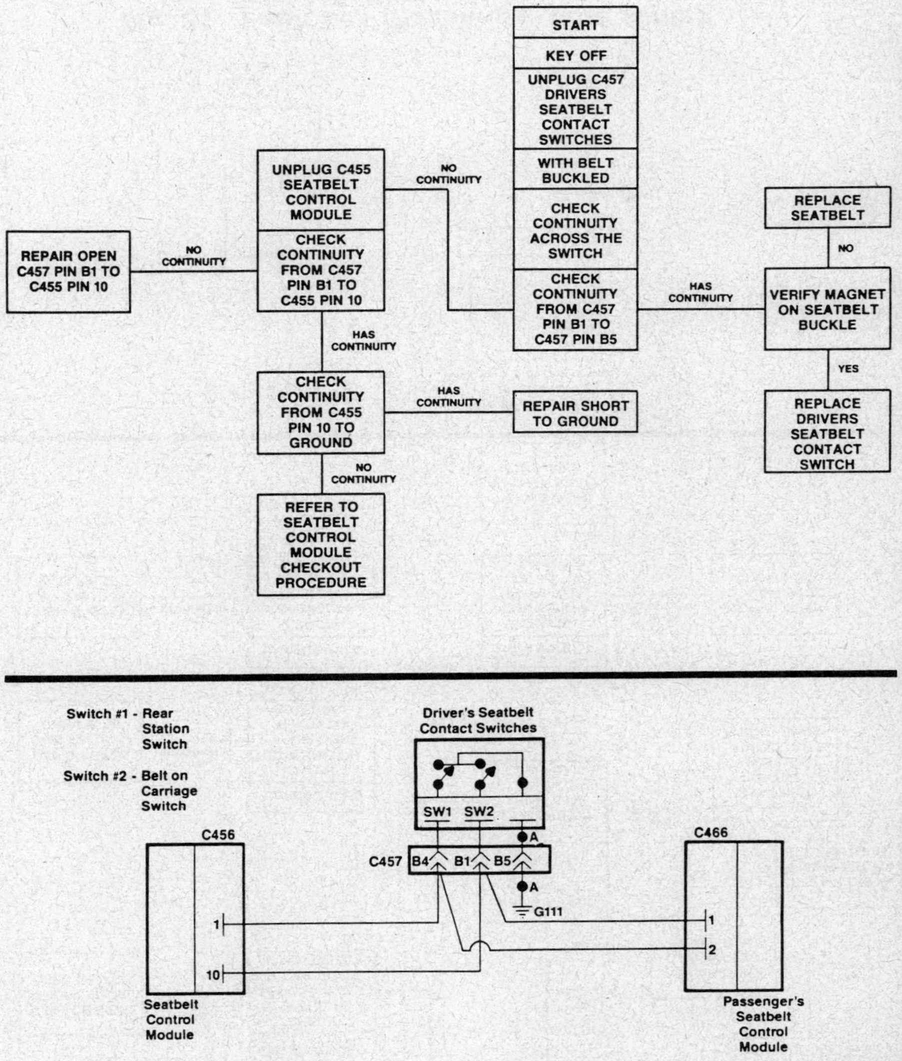

START

KEY OFF

UNPLUG C457 DRIVERS SEATBELT CONTACT SWITCHES

WITH BELT BUCKLED

CHECK CONTINUITY ACROSS THE SWITCH

CHECK CONTINUITY FROM C457 PIN B1 TO C457 PIN B5

HAS CONTINUITY → VERIFY MAGNET ON SEATBELT BUCKLE

NO → REPLACE SEATBELT

YES → REPLACE DRIVERS SEATBELT CONTACT SWITCH

NO CONTINUITY → UNPLUG C455 SEATBELT CONTROL MODULE

CHECK CONTINUITY FROM C457 PIN B1 TO C455 PIN 10

NO CONTINUITY → REPAIR OPEN C457 PIN B1 TO C455 PIN 10

HAS CONTINUITY → CHECK CONTINUITY FROM C455 PIN 10 TO GROUND

HAS CONTINUITY → REPAIR SHORT TO GROUND

NO CONTINUITY → REFER TO SEATBELT CONTROL MODULE CHECKOUT PROCEDURE

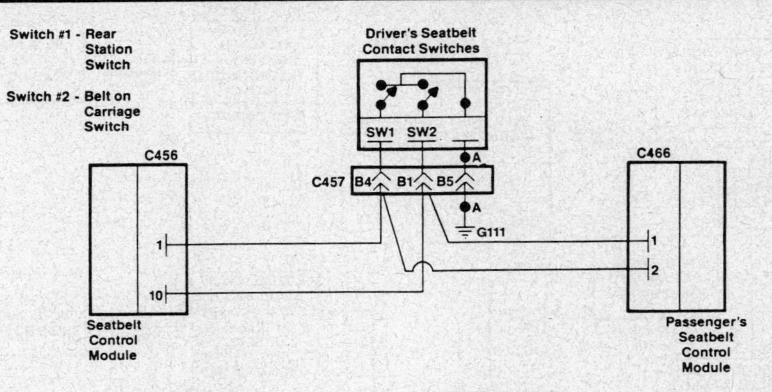


**Fig. 29 Fault 559 (Driver belt on carriage not seen). Eagle Medallion**

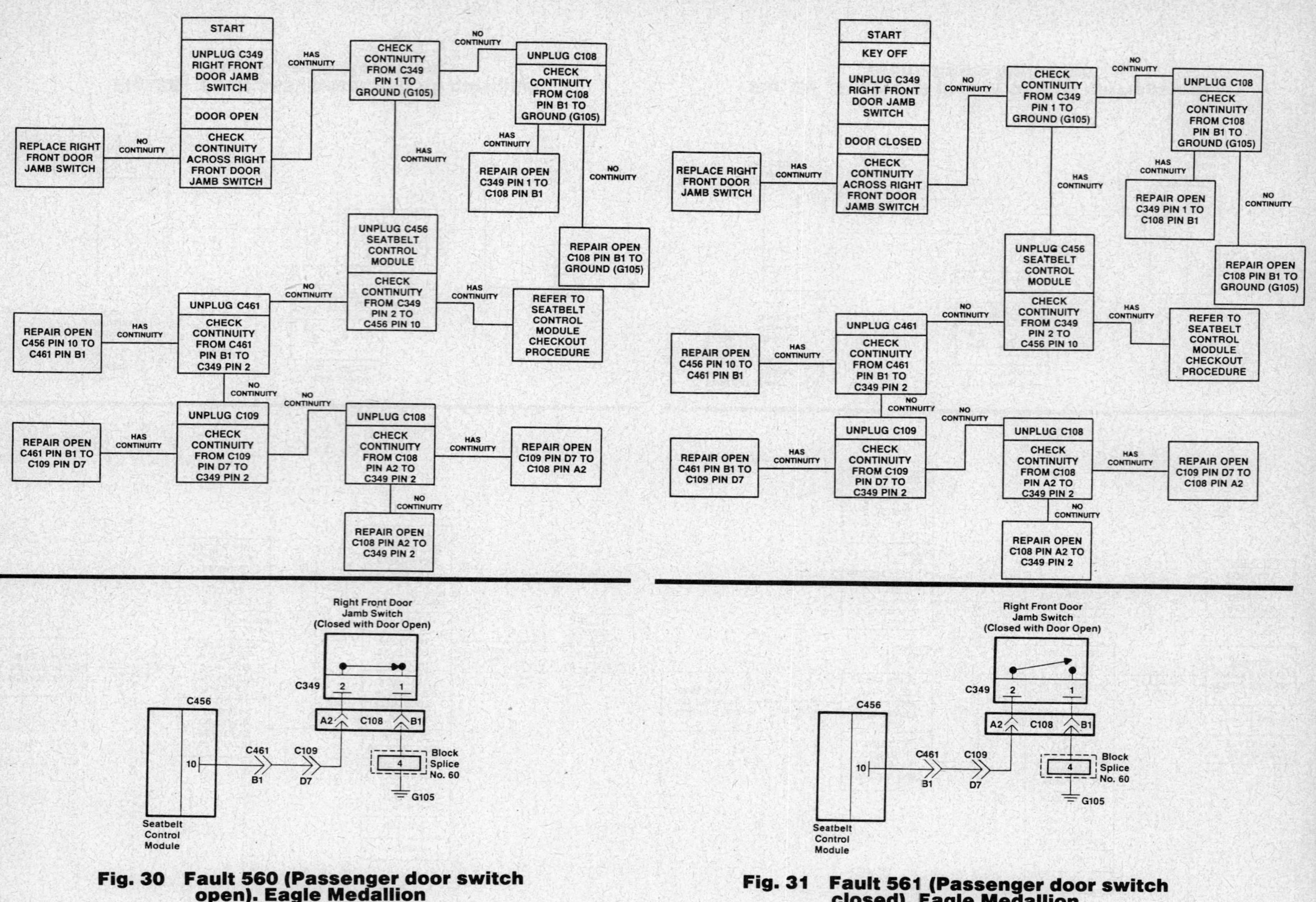


**Fig. 30 Fault 560 (Passenger door switch open). Eagle Medallion**

**Fig. 31 Fault 561 (Passenger door switch closed). Eagle Medallion**

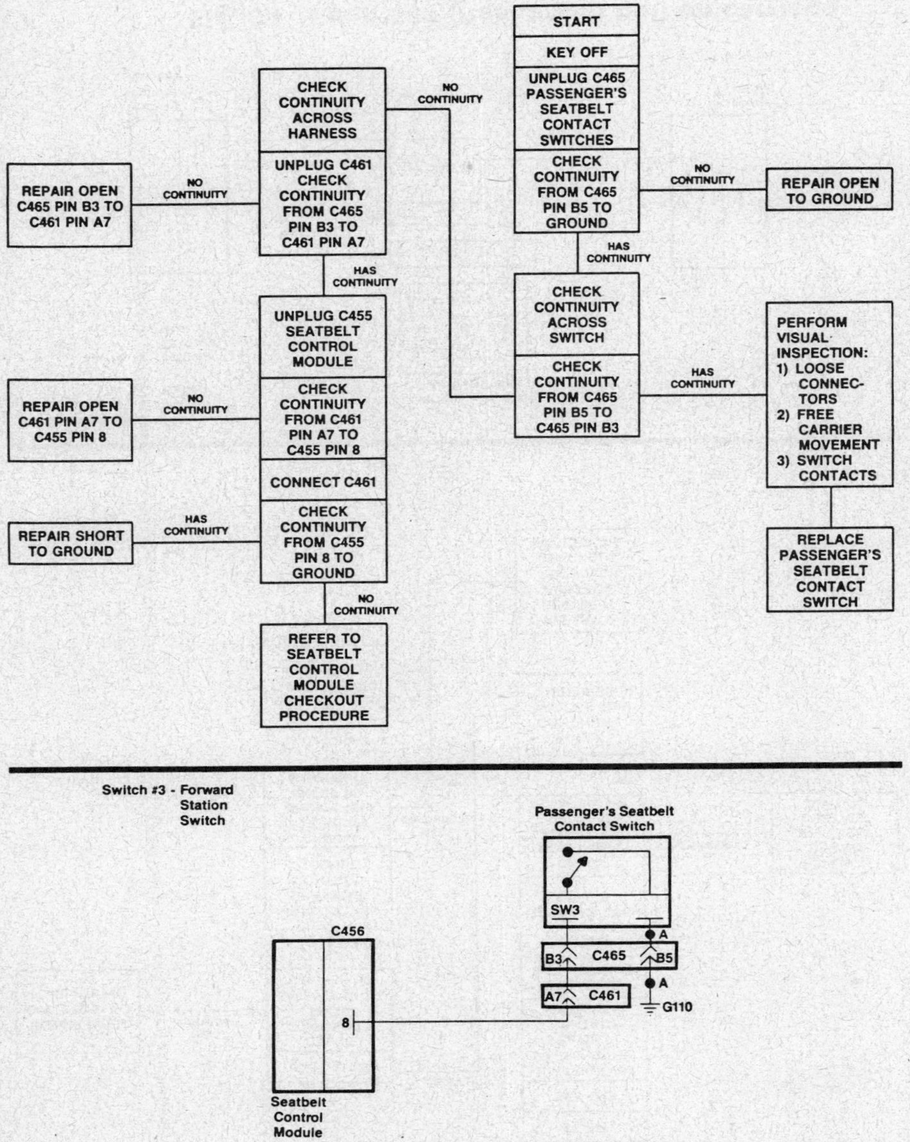

START

KEY OFF

UNPLUG C465 PASSENGER'S SEATBELT CONTACT SWITCHES

CHECK CONTINUITY FROM C465 PIN B5 TO GROUND

- NO CONTINUITY → REPAIR OPEN TO GROUND
- HAS CONTINUITY → CHECK CONTINUITY ACROSS SWITCH / CHECK CONTINUITY FROM C465 PIN B5 TO C465 PIN B3
  - HAS CONTINUITY → PERFORM VISUAL INSPECTION: 1) LOOSE CONNECTORS 2) FREE CARRIER MOVEMENT 3) SWITCH CONTACTS → REPLACE PASSENGER'S SEATBELT CONTACT SWITCH
  - NO CONTINUITY → CHECK CONTINUITY ACROSS HARNESS / UNPLUG C461 CHECK CONTINUITY FROM C465 PIN B3 TO C461 PIN A7
    - NO CONTINUITY → REPAIR OPEN C465 PIN B3 TO C461 PIN A7
    - HAS CONTINUITY → UNPLUG C455 SEATBELT CONTROL MODULE / CHECK CONTINUITY FROM C461 PIN A7 TO C455 PIN 8
      - NO CONTINUITY → REPAIR OPEN C461 PIN A7 TO C455 PIN 8
      - CONNECT C461 / CHECK CONTINUITY FROM C455 PIN 8 TO GROUND
        - HAS CONTINUITY → REPAIR SHORT TO GROUND
        - NO CONTINUITY → REFER TO SEATBELT CONTROL MODULE CHECKOUT PROCEDURE

Switch #3 - Forward Station Switch

Passenger's Seatbelt Contact Switch

SW3

B3 C465 B5

A

A7 C461

G110

C456

8

Seatbelt Control Module

**Fig. 32 Fault 562 (Passenger forward station not seen). Eagle Medallion**

START

KEY OFF

UNPLUG C465 PASSENGER'S SEATBELT CONTACT SWITCHES

CHECK CONTINUITY FROM C465 PIN B5 TO GROUND

- NO CONTINUITY → REPAIR OPEN TO GROUND
- HAS CONTINUITY → CHECK CONTINUITY FROM C465 PIN B5 TO C465 PIN B4
  - HAS CONTINUITY → PERFORM VISUAL INSPECTION: 1) LOOSE CONNECTORS 2) FREE CARRIER MOVEMENT 3) SWITCH CONTACT → REPLACE PASSENGER'S SEATBELT CONTACT SWITCH
  - NO CONTINUITY → CHECK CONTINUITY ACROSS HARNESS / UNPLUG C461 / CHECK CONTINUITY FROM C465 PIN B4 TO C461 PIN B7
    - NO CONTINUITY → REPAIR OPEN C465 PIN B4 TO C461 PIN B7
    - HAS CONTINUITY → UNPLUG C455 SEATBELT CONTROL MODULE / CHECK CONTINUITY FROM C455 PIN 13 TO C461 PIN B7
      - NO CONTINUITY → REPAIR OPEN C455 PIN 13 TO C461 PIN B7
      - HAS CONTINUITY → REFER TO SEATBELT CONTROL MODULE CHECKOUT PROCEDURE

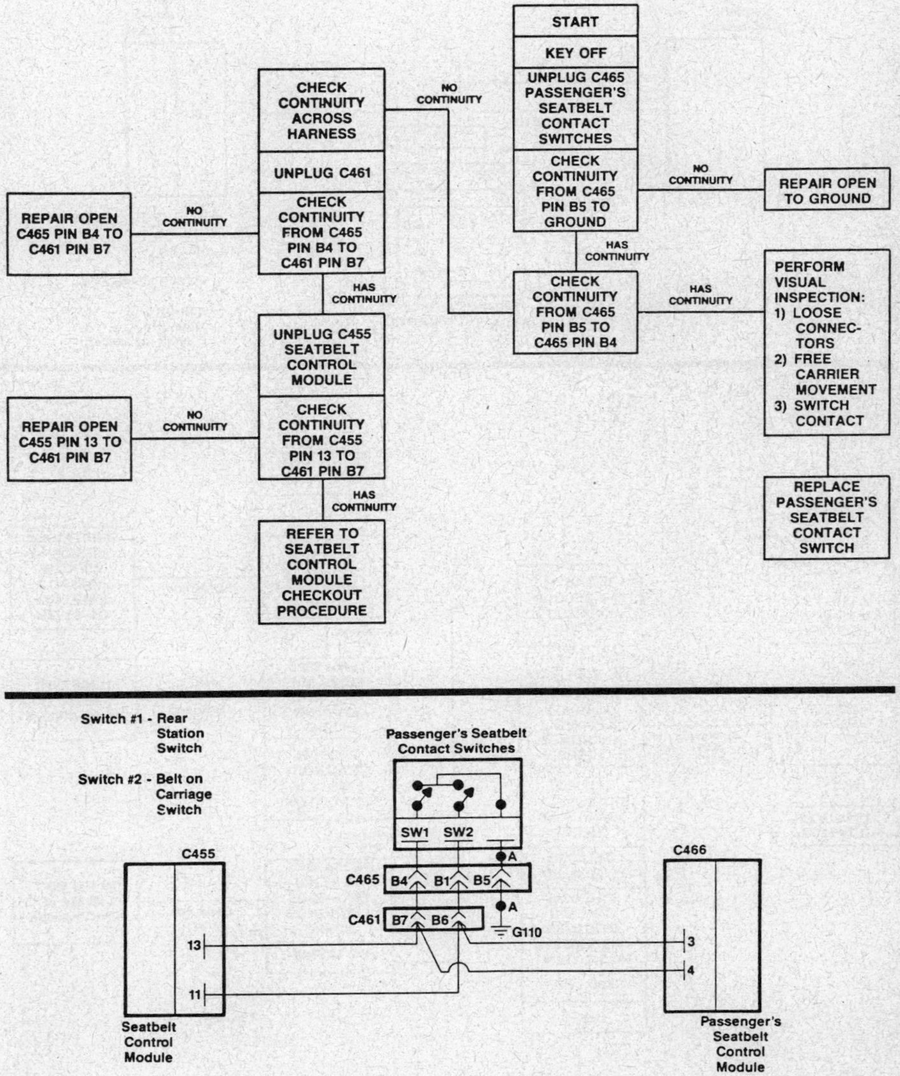

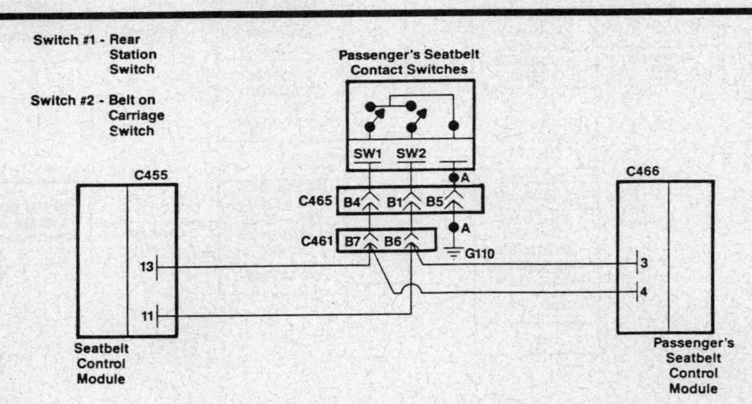


**Fig. 33 Fault 563 (Passenger rear station not seen). Eagle Medallion**

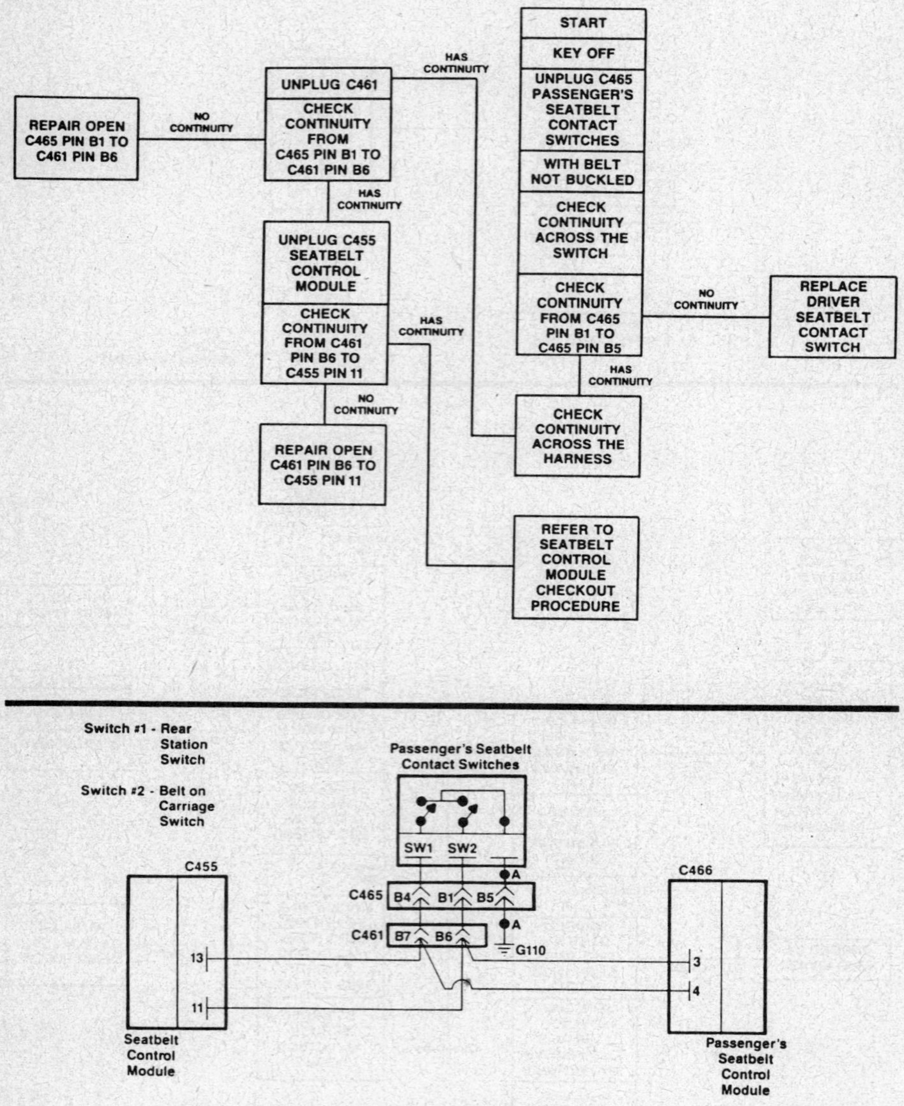

START
KEY OFF
UNPLUG C465 PASSENGER'S SEATBELT CONTACT SWITCHES
WITH BELT NOT BUCKLED
CHECK CONTINUITY ACROSS THE SWITCH
CHECK CONTINUITY FROM C465 PIN B1 TO C465 PIN B5

- NO CONTINUITY → REPLACE DRIVER SEATBELT CONTACT SWITCH
- HAS CONTINUITY → CHECK CONTINUITY ACROSS THE HARNESS
  - HAS CONTINUITY → UNPLUG C461 / CHECK CONTINUITY FROM C465 PIN B1 TO C461 PIN B6
    - NO CONTINUITY → REPAIR OPEN C465 PIN B1 TO C461 PIN B6
    - HAS CONTINUITY → UNPLUG C455 SEATBELT CONTROL MODULE / CHECK CONTINUITY FROM C461 PIN B6 TO C455 PIN 11
      - NO CONTINUITY → REPAIR OPEN C461 PIN B6 TO C455 PIN 11
      - HAS CONTINUITY → REFER TO SEATBELT CONTROL MODULE CHECKOUT PROCEDURE

Switch #1 - Rear Station Switch
Switch #2 - Belt on Carriage Switch

Passenger's Seatbelt Contact Switches
SW1 SW2
C465 B4 B1 B5 A
C461 B7 B6 A G110
C455 13 11 Seatbelt Control Module
C466 3 4 Passenger's Seatbelt Control Module

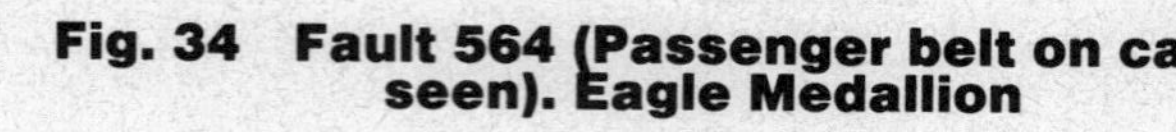

Fig. 34 Fault 564 (Passenger belt on carriage seen). Eagle Medallion

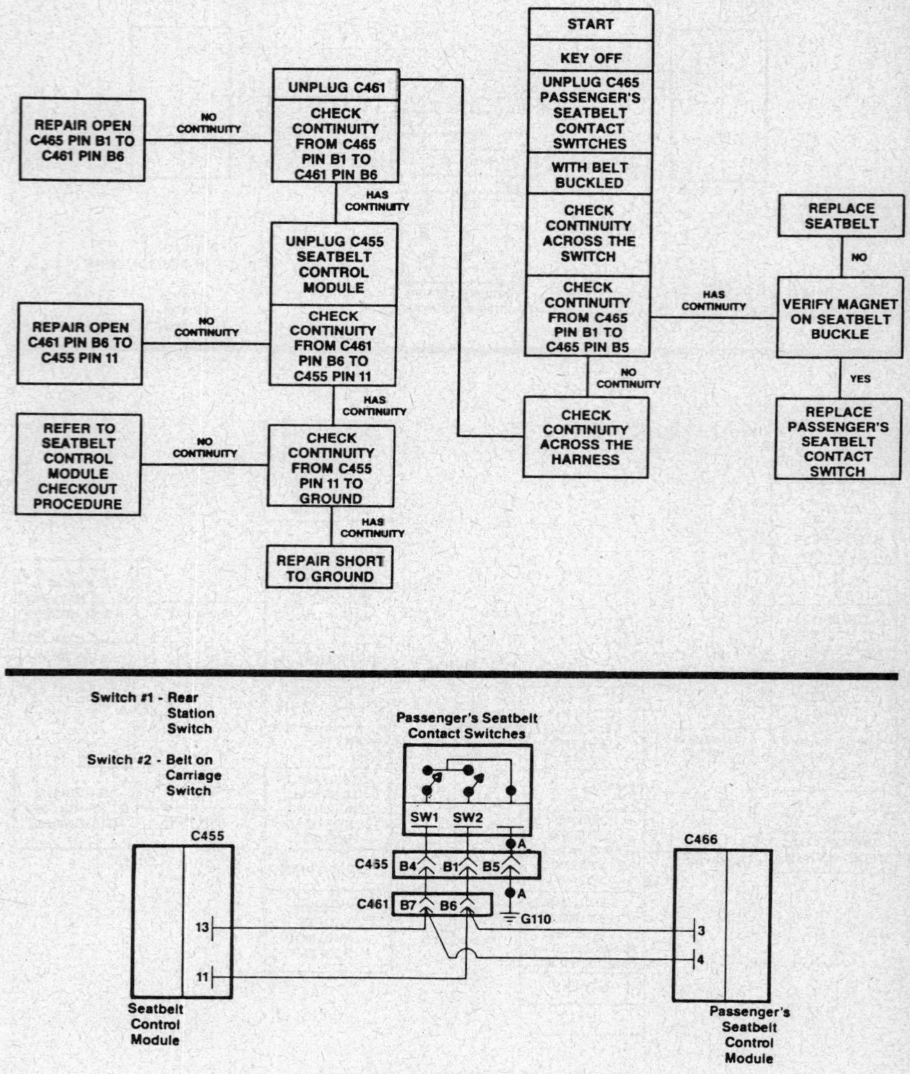

START
KEY OFF
UNPLUG C465 PASSENGER'S SEATBELT CONTACT SWITCHES
WITH BELT BUCKLED
CHECK CONTINUITY ACROSS THE SWITCH
CHECK CONTINUITY FROM C465 PIN B1 TO C465 PIN B5

- HAS CONTINUITY → VERIFY MAGNET ON SEATBELT BUCKLE
  - NO → REPLACE SEATBELT
  - YES → REPLACE PASSENGER'S SEATBELT CONTACT SWITCH
- NO CONTINUITY → CHECK CONTINUITY ACROSS THE HARNESS
  - UNPLUG C461 / CHECK CONTINUITY FROM C465 PIN B1 TO C461 PIN B6
    - NO CONTINUITY → REPAIR OPEN C465 PIN B1 TO C461 PIN B6
    - HAS CONTINUITY → UNPLUG C455 SEATBELT CONTROL MODULE / CHECK CONTINUITY FROM C461 PIN B6 TO C455 PIN 11
      - NO CONTINUITY → REPAIR OPEN C461 PIN B6 TO C455 PIN 11
      - HAS CONTINUITY → CHECK CONTINUITY FROM C455 PIN 11 TO GROUND
        - NO CONTINUITY → REFER TO SEATBELT CONTROL MODULE CHECKOUT PROCEDURE
        - HAS CONTINUITY → REPAIR SHORT TO GROUND

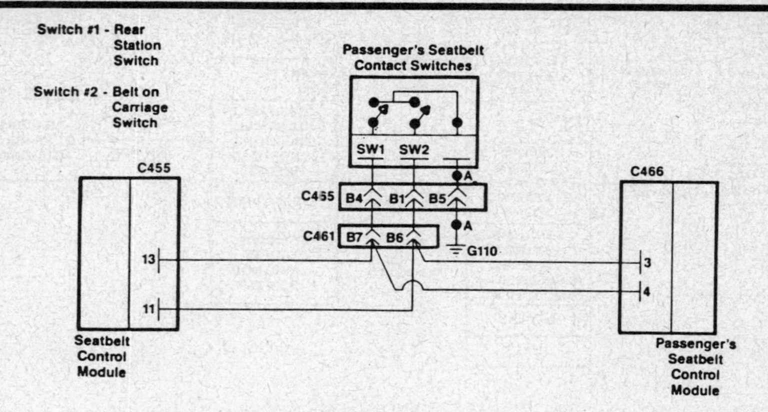


Fig. 35 Fault 565 (Passenger belt on carriage not seen). Eagle Medallion

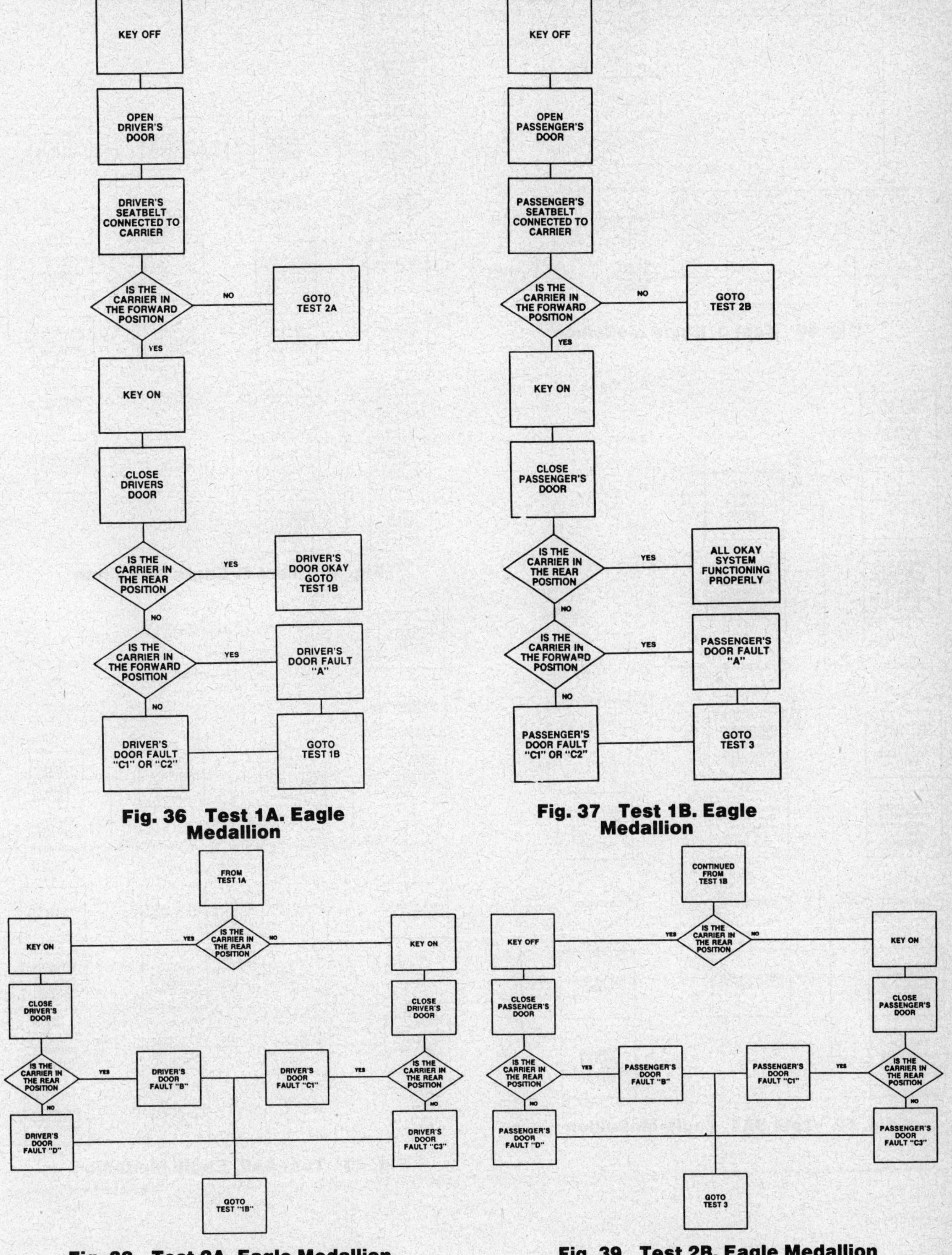


Fig. 36 Test 1A. Eagle Medallion

Fig. 37 Test 1B. Eagle Medallion



Fig. 38 Test 2A. Eagle Medallion

Fig. 39 Test 2B. Eagle Medallion

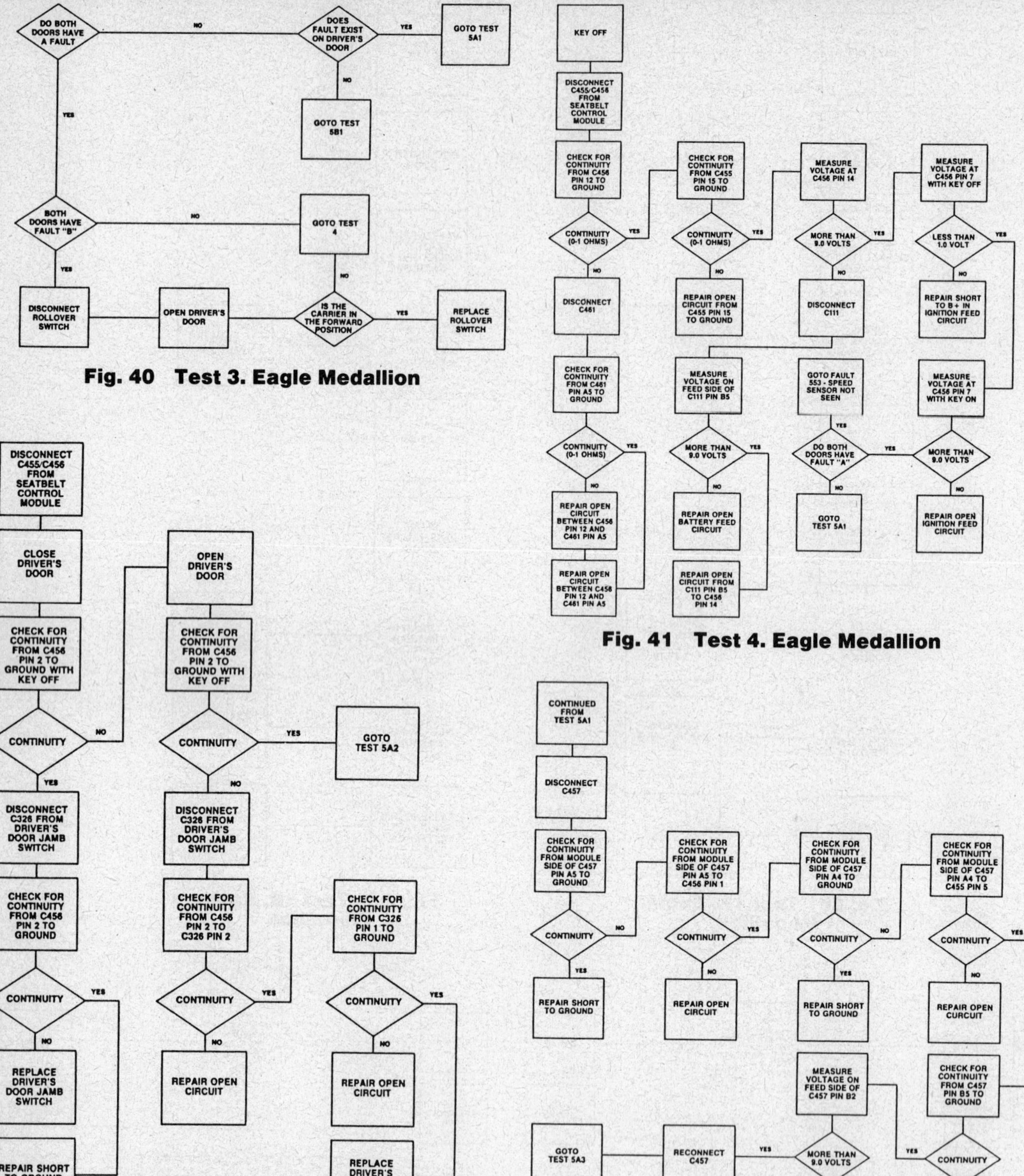


**Fig. 40 Test 3. Eagle Medallion**

**Fig. 41 Test 4. Eagle Medallion**

**Fig. 42 Test 5A1. Eagle Medallion**

**Fig. 43 Test 5A2. Eagle Medallion**

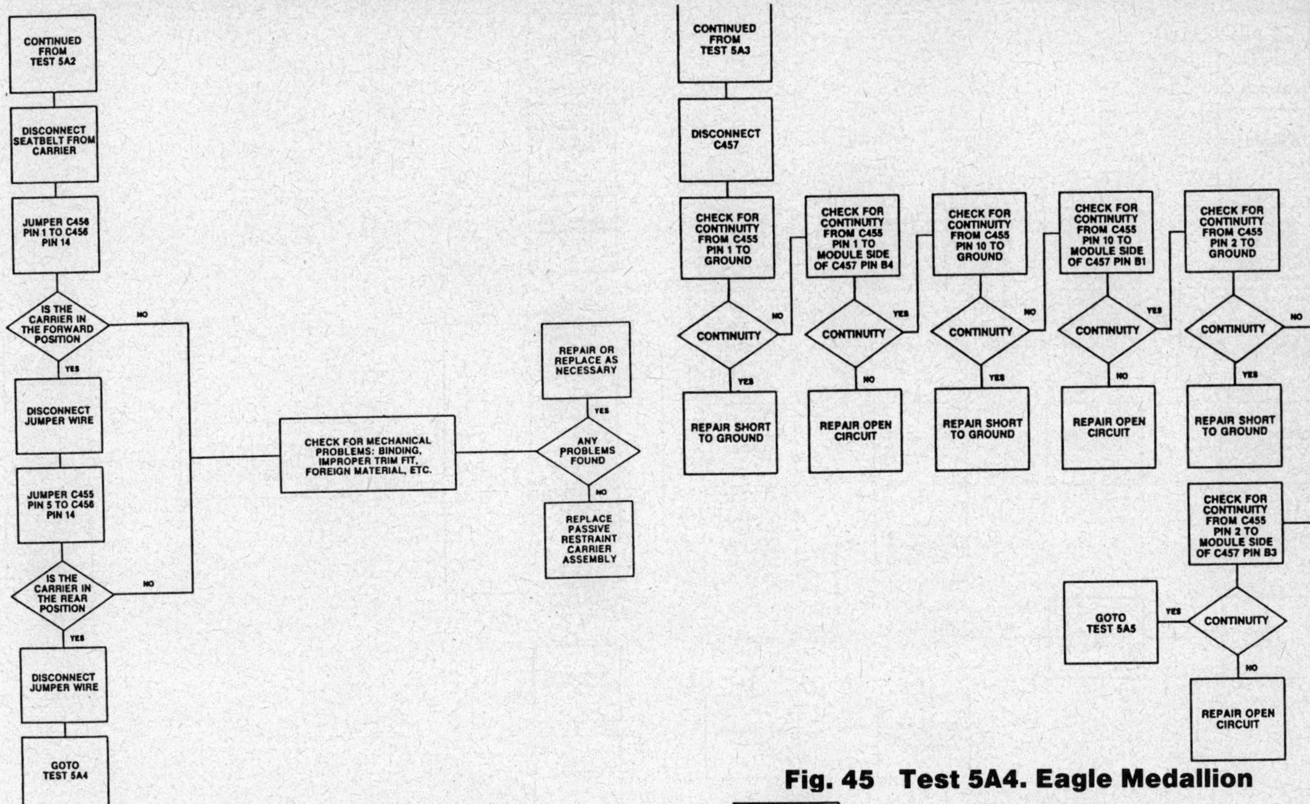


**Fig. 44 Test 5A3. Eagle Medallion**

**Fig. 45 Test 5A4. Eagle Medallion**

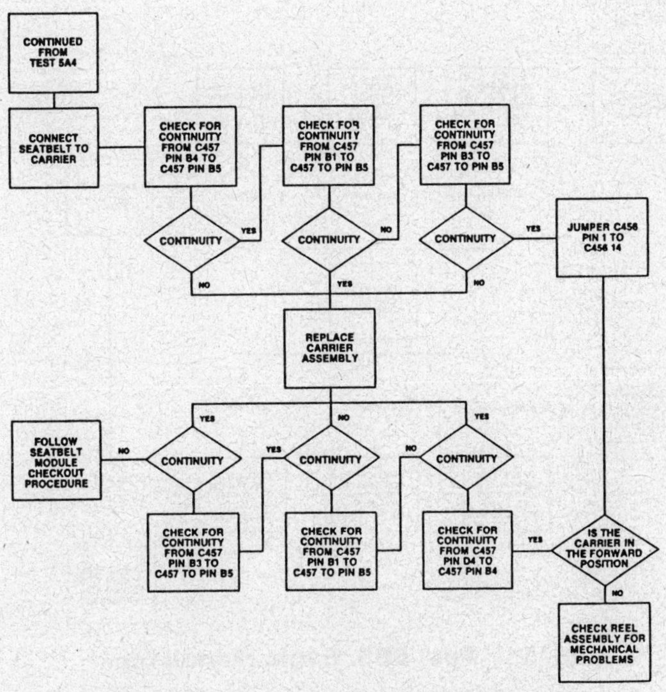


**Fig. 46 Test 5A5. Eagle Medallion**

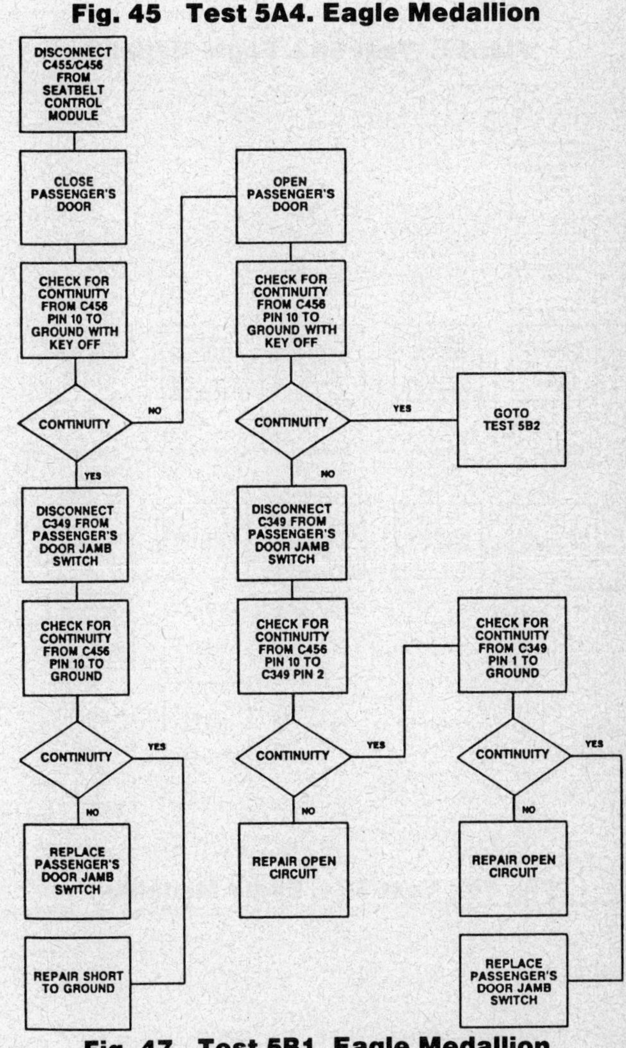


**Fig. 47 Test 5B1. Eagle Medallion**

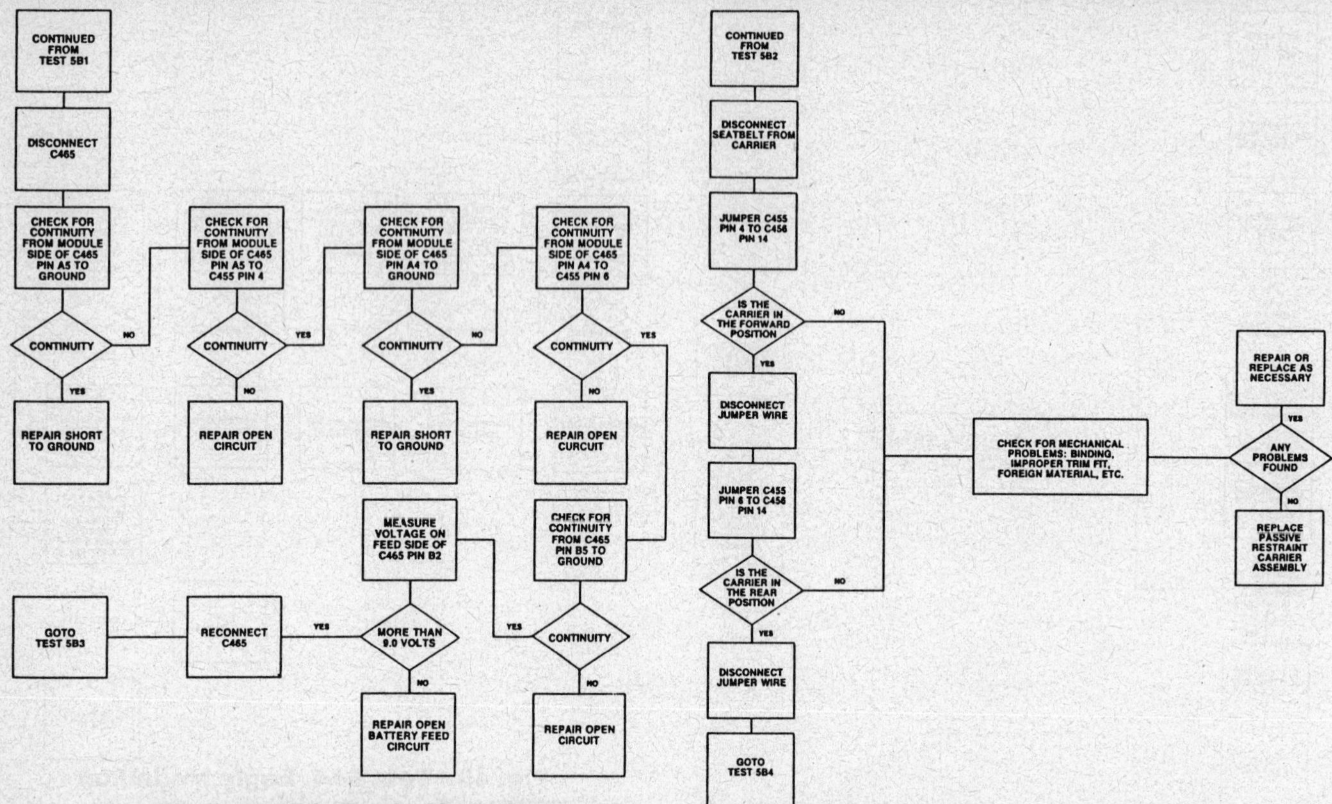


**Fig. 48 Test 5B2. Eagle Medallion**

**Fig. 49 Test 5B3. Eagle Medallion**

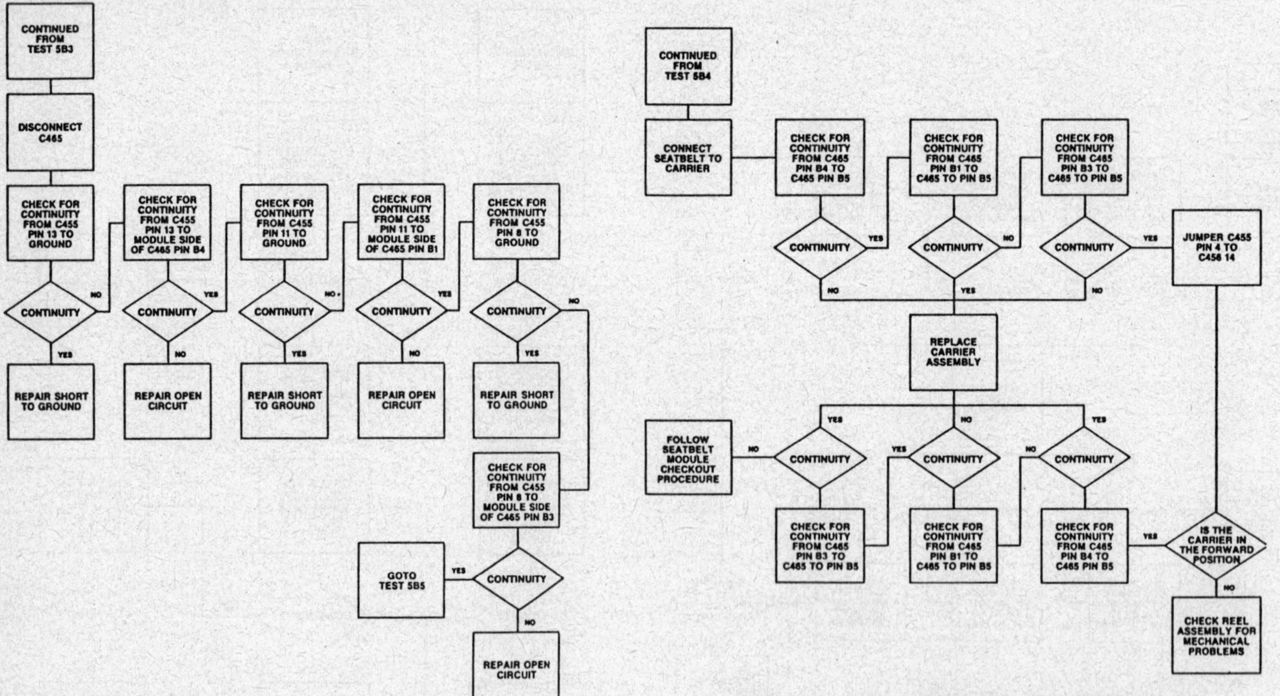


**Fig. 50 Test 5B4. Eagle Medallion**

**Fig. 51 Test 5B5. Eagle Medallion**

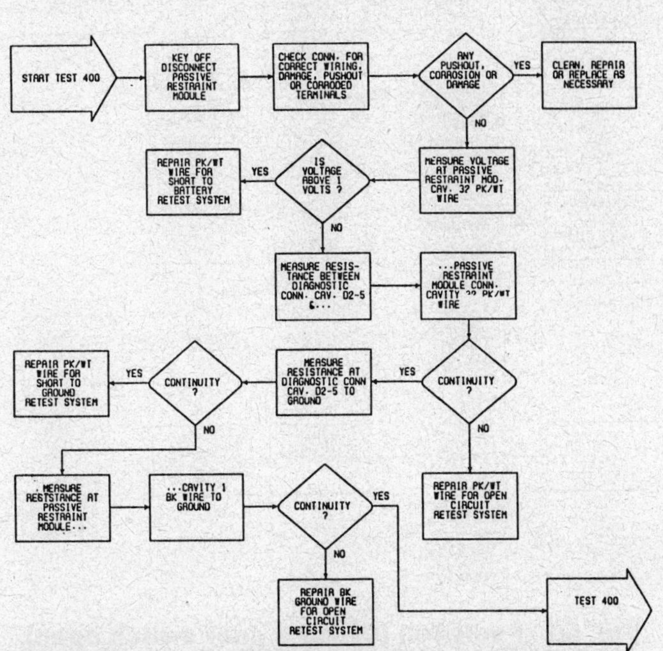


**Fig. 52 Fault 400 (No serial data from passive restraint module, Part 1 of 2). 1989–90 Eagle Premier & 1990 Dodge Monaco**

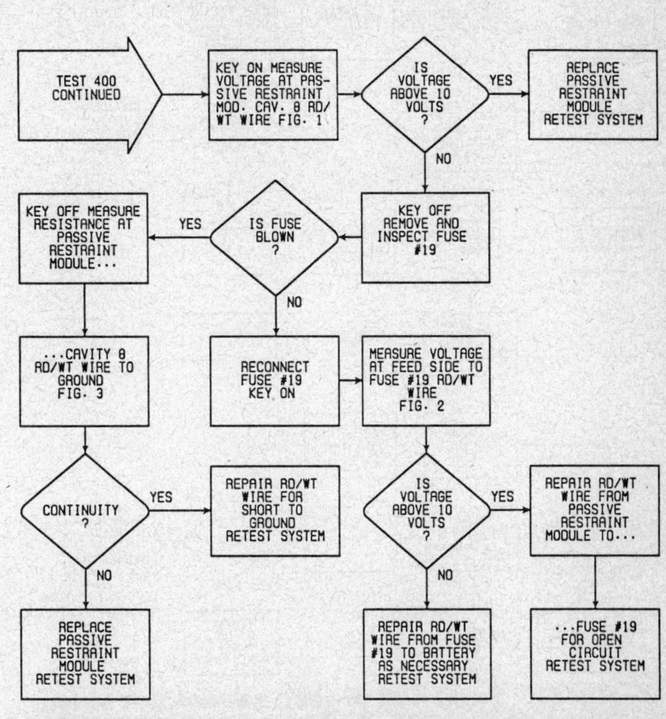


**Fig. 52 Fault 400 (No serial data from passive restraint module, Part 2 of 2). 1989–90 Eagle Premier & 1990 Dodge Monaco**

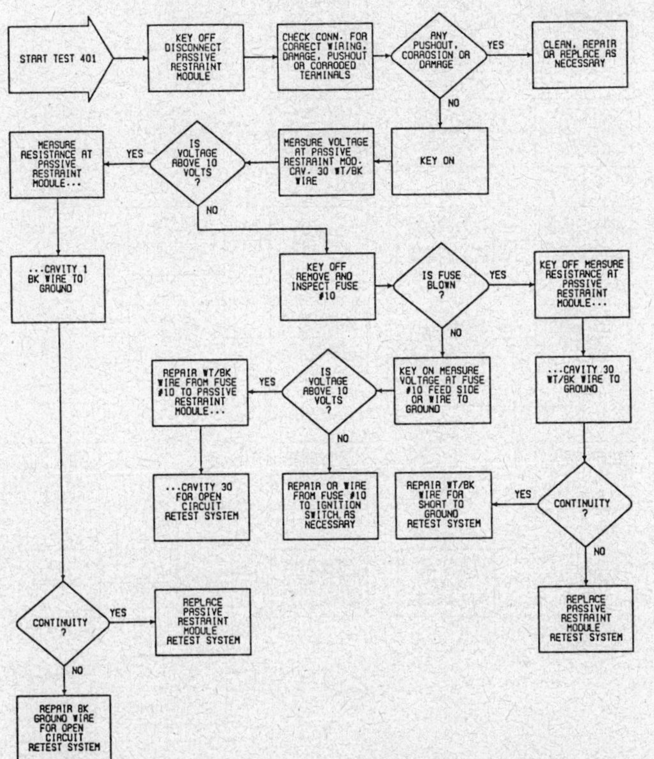


**Fig. 53 Fault 401 (Error reading serial data) 1989–90 Eagle Premier & 1990 Dodge Monaco**

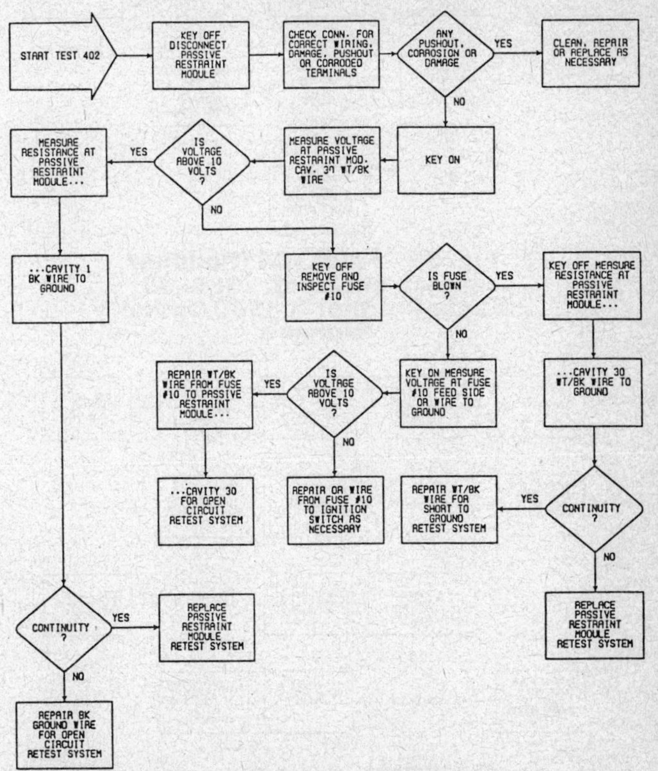


**Fig. 54 Fault 402 (Ignition switch not seen). 1989–90 Eagle Premier & 1990 Dodge Monaco**

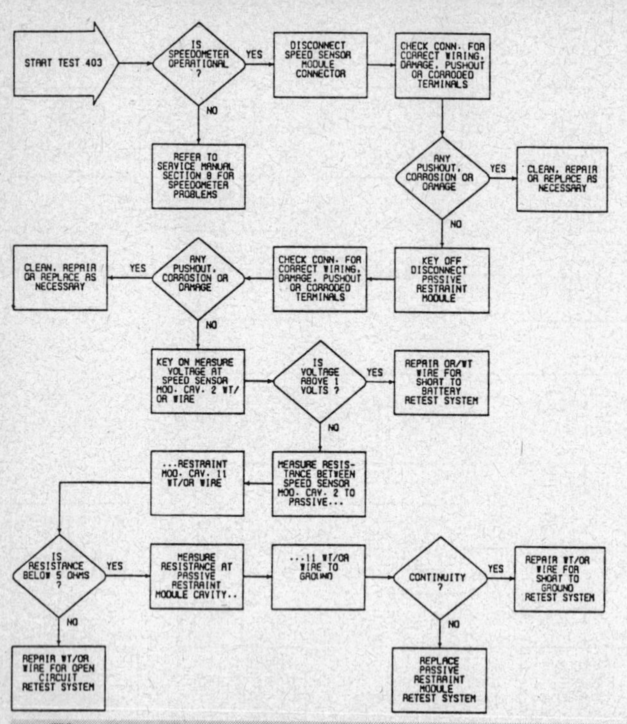


**Fig. 55 Fault 403 (Speed sensor not seen, Part 1 of 2). 1989–90 Eagle Premier & 1990 Dodge Monaco**

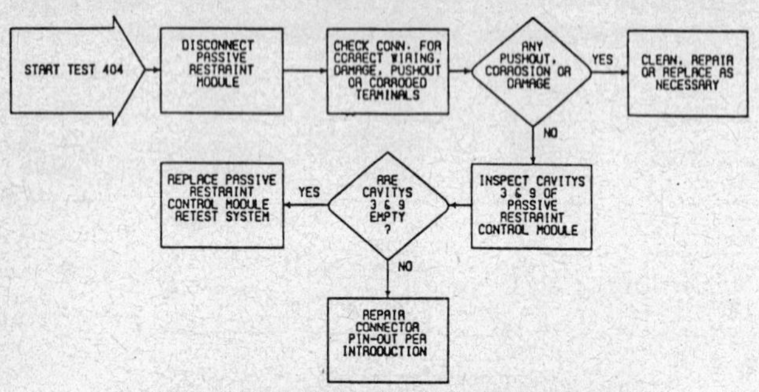


**Fig. 56 Fault 404 (Rollover switch shorted). 1989–90 Eagle Premier & 1990 Dodge Monaco**

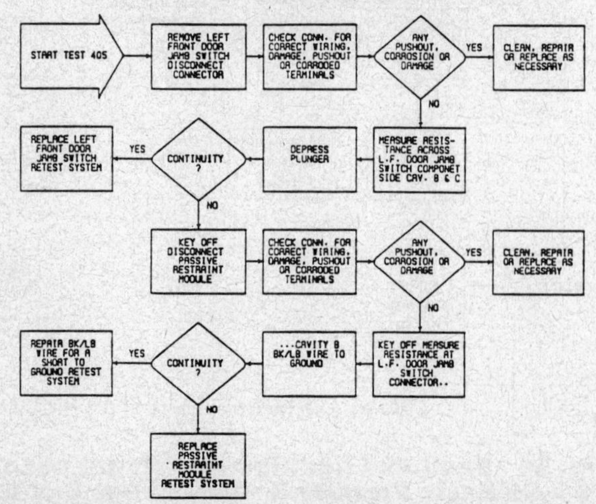


**Fig. 57 Fault 405 (Driver's door switch closed). 1989–90 Eagle Premier & 1990 Dodge Monaco**

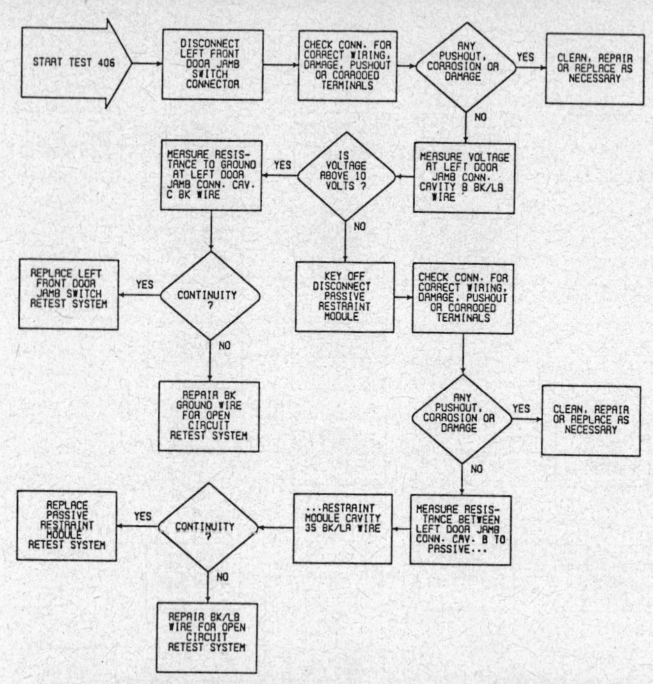


**Fig. 58 Fault 406 (Driver's door switch open). 1989–90 Eagle Premier & 1990 Dodge Monaco**

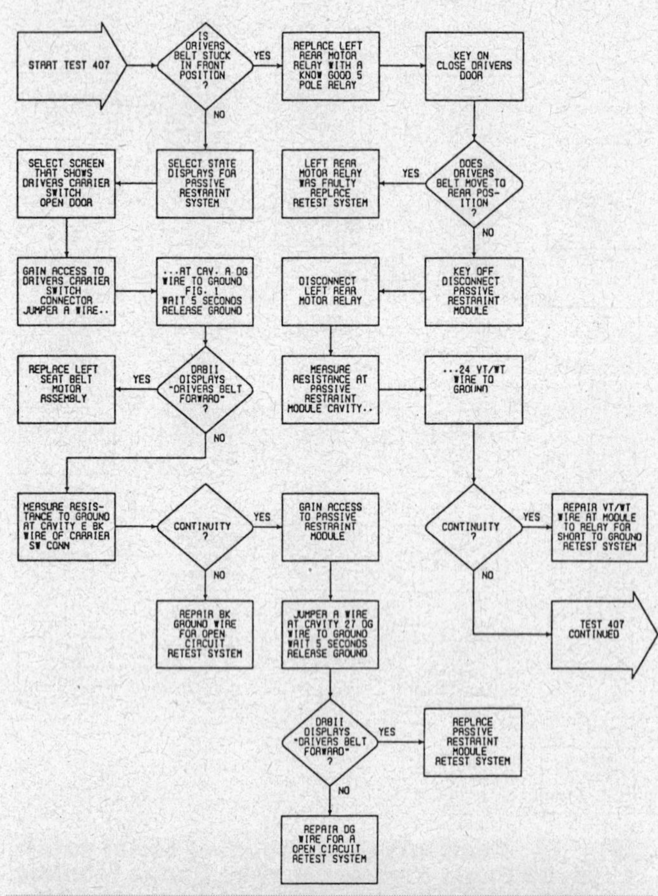


**Fig. 59 Fault 407 (Driver's forward station seen, Part 1 of 3). 1989–90 Eagle Premier & 1990 Dodge Monaco**

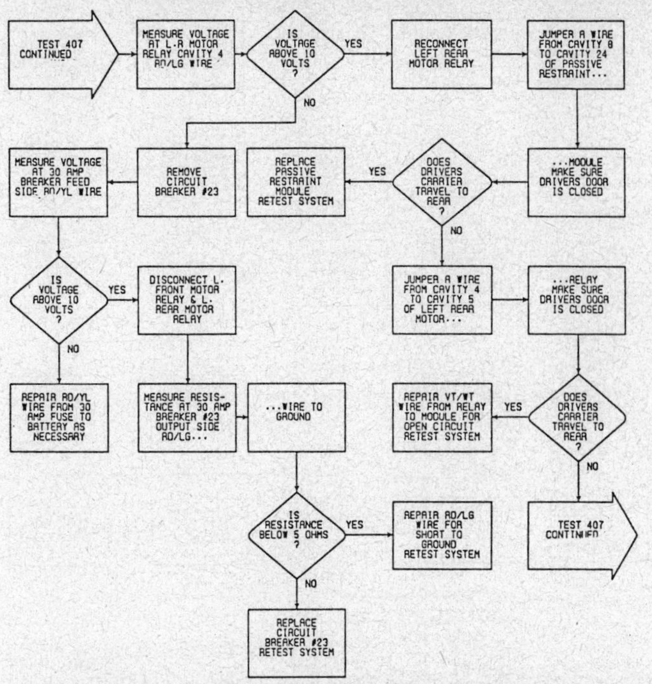


**Fig. 59 Fault 407 (Driver's forward station seen, Part 2 of 3). 1989–90 Eagle Premier & 1990 Dodge Monaco**

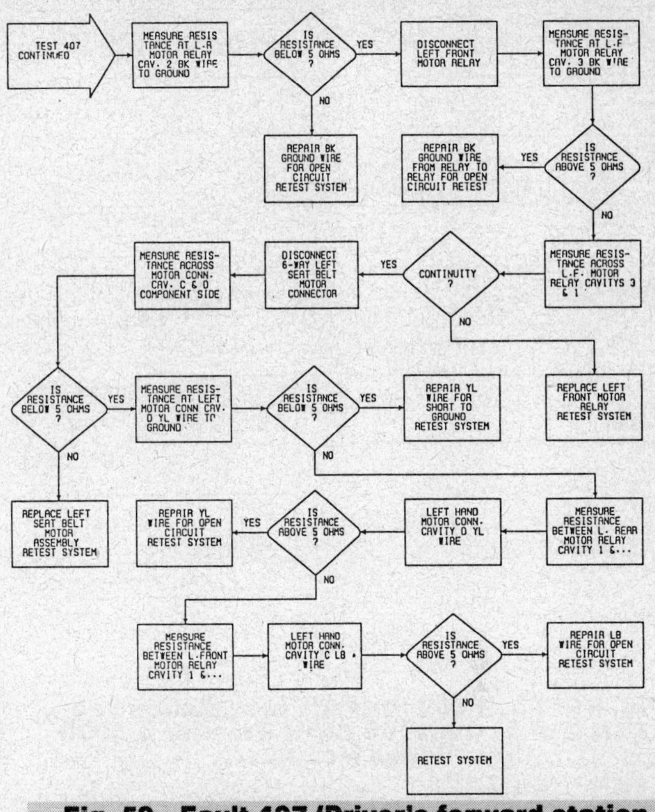


**Fig. 59 Fault 407 (Driver's forward station seen, Part 3 of 3). 1989–90 Eagle Premier & 1990 Dodge Monaco**

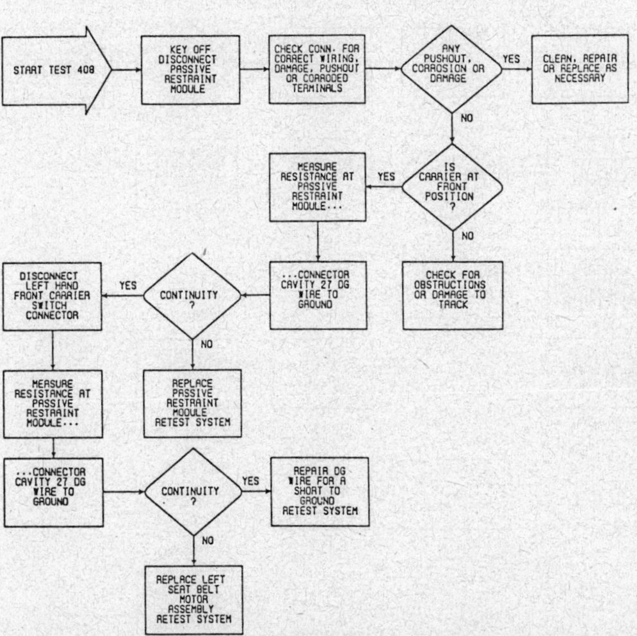


**Fig. 60 Fault 408 (Driver's forward station not seen). 1989–90 Eagle Premier & 1990 Dodge Monaco**

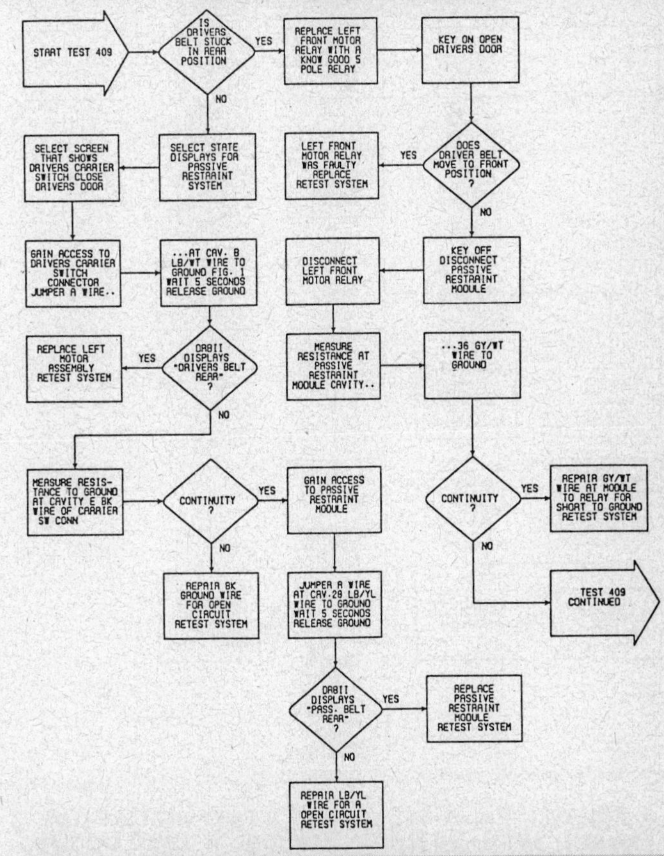


**Fig. 61 Fault 409 (Driver's rear station seen, Part 1 of 3). 1989–90 Eagle Premier & 1990 Dodge Monaco**

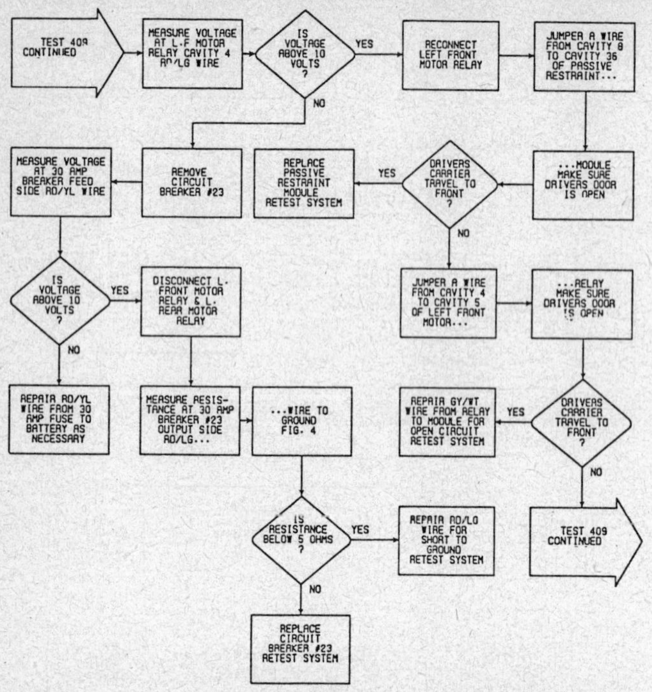


**Fig. 61 Fault 409 (Driver's rear station seen, Part 2 of 3). 1989–90 Eagle Premier & 1990 Dodge Monaco**

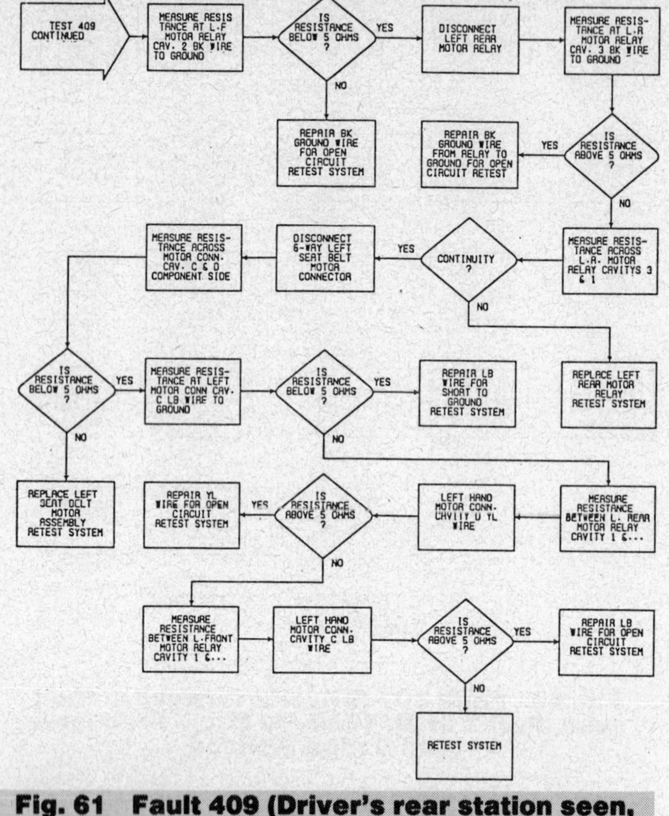


**Fig. 61 Fault 409 (Driver's rear station seen, Part 3 of 3). 1989–90 Eagle Premier & 1990 Dodge Monaco**

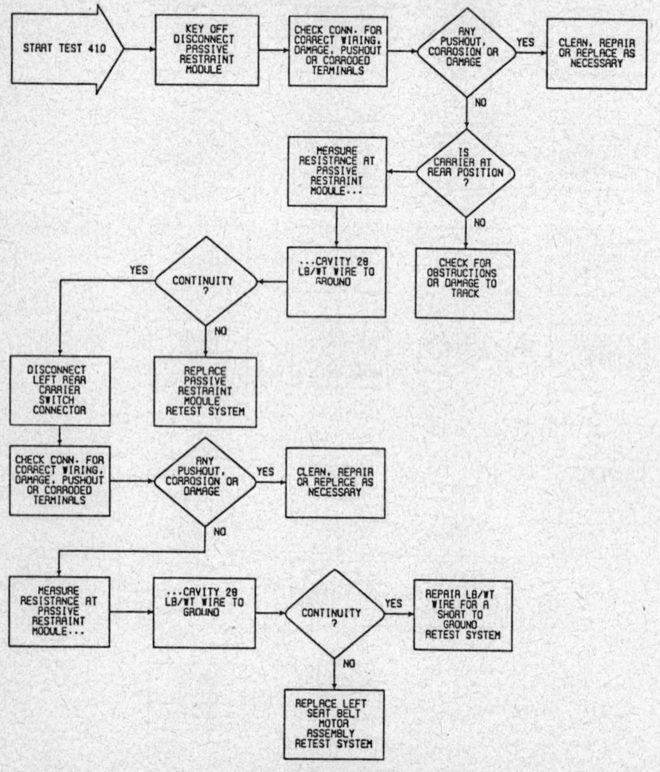


**Fig. 62 Fault 410 (Driver's rear station not seen). 1989–90 Eagle Premier & 1990 Dodge Monaco**

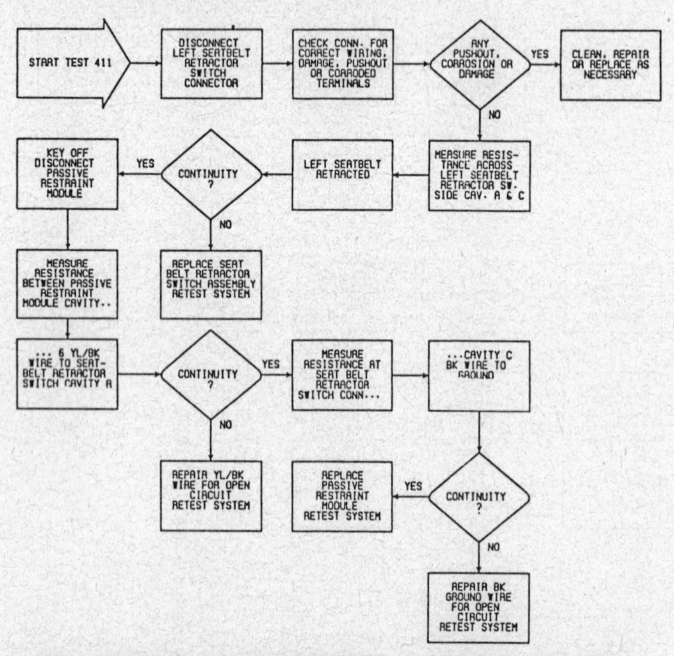


**Fig. 63 Fault 411 (Driver's belt on carriage seen). 1989–90 Eagle Premier & 1990 Dodge Monaco**

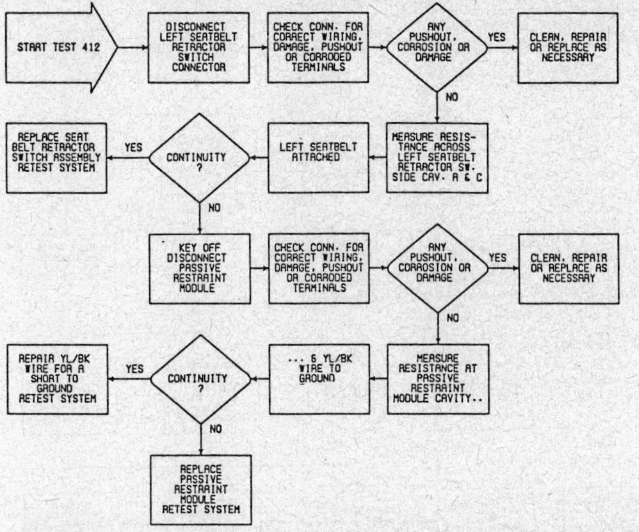


**Fig. 64 Fault 412 (Drivers belt on carriage not seen). 1989–90 Eagle Premier & 1990 Dodge Monaco**

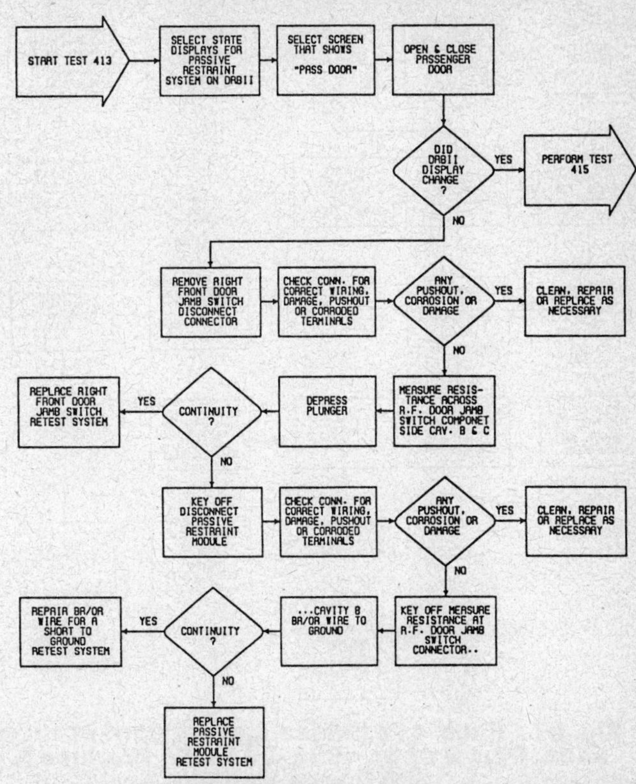


**Fig. 65 Fault 413 (Passenger door switch closed). 1989–90 Eagle Premier & 1990 Dodge Monaco**

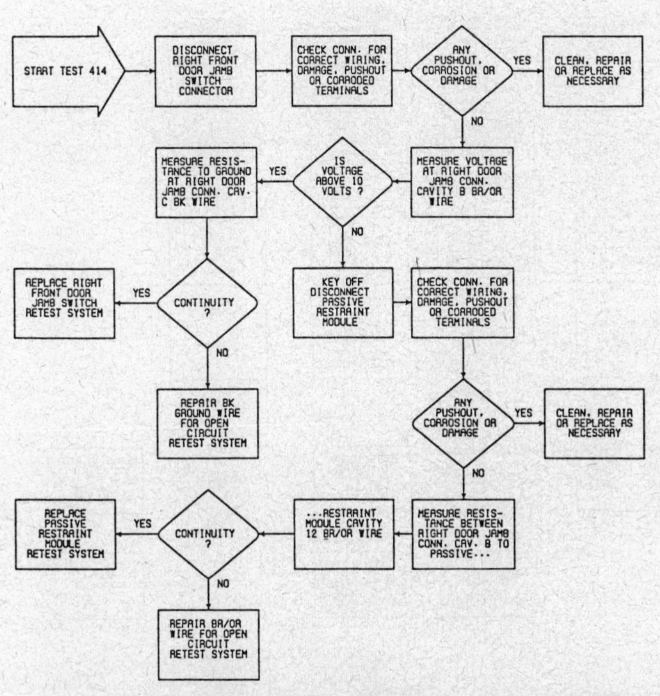


**Fig. 66 Fault 414 (Passenger door switch open). 1989–90 Eagle Premier & 1990 Dodge Monaco**

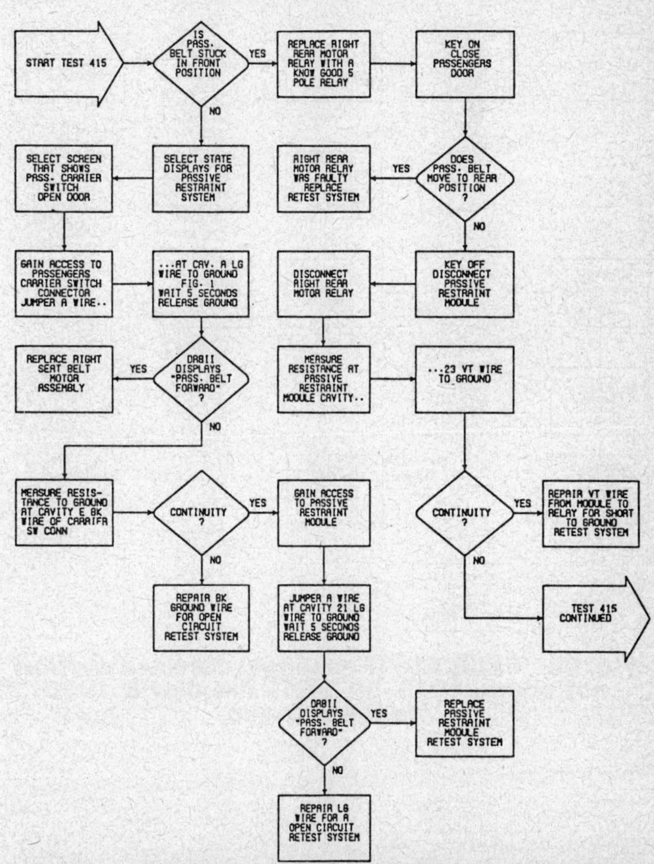


**Fig. 67 Fault 415 (Passenger forward station seen, Part 1 of 3). 1989–90 Eagle Premier & 1990 Dodge Monaco**

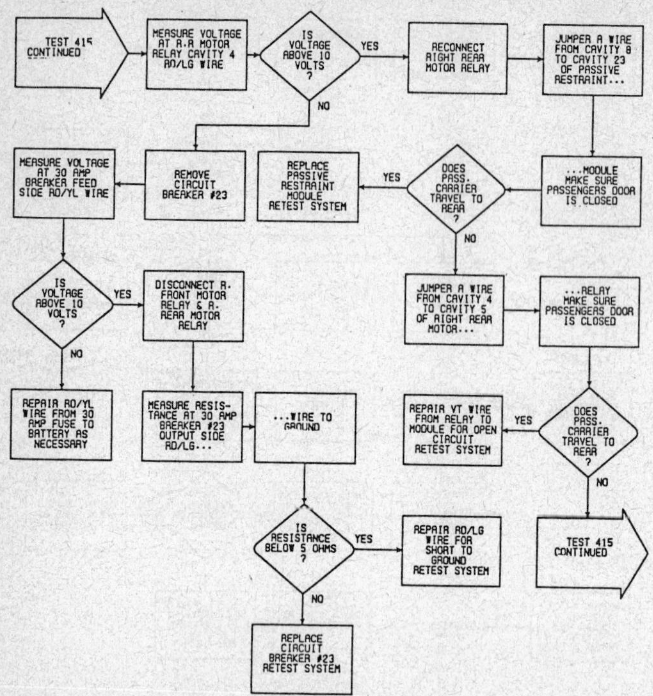


**Fig. 67 Fault 415 (Passenger forward station seen, Part 2 of 3). 1989–90 Eagle Premier & 1990 Dodge Monaco**

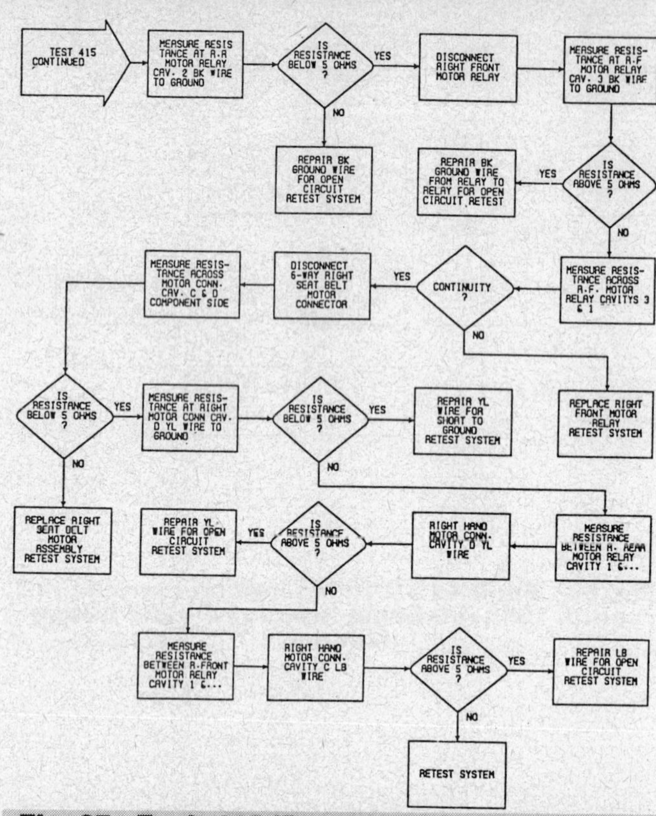


**Fig. 67 Fault 415 (Passenger forward station seen, Part 3 of 3). 1989–90 Eagle Premier & 1990 Dodge Monaco**

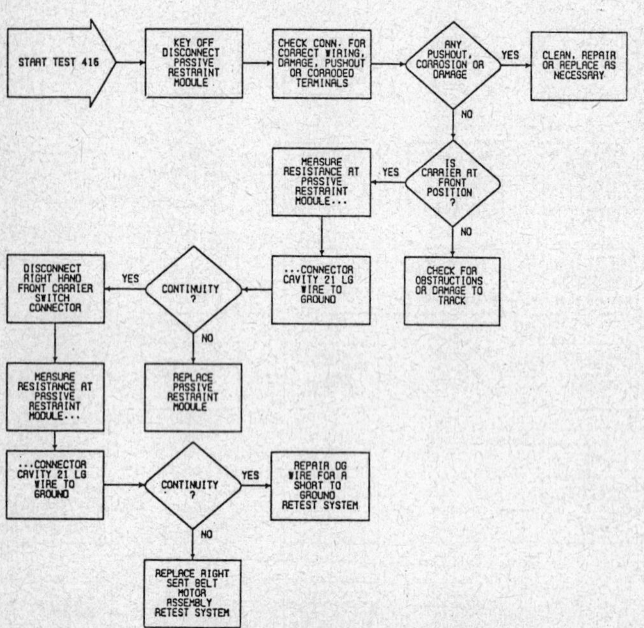


**Fig. 68 Fault 416 (Passenger forward station not seen). 1989–90 Eagle Premier & 1990 Dodge Monaco**

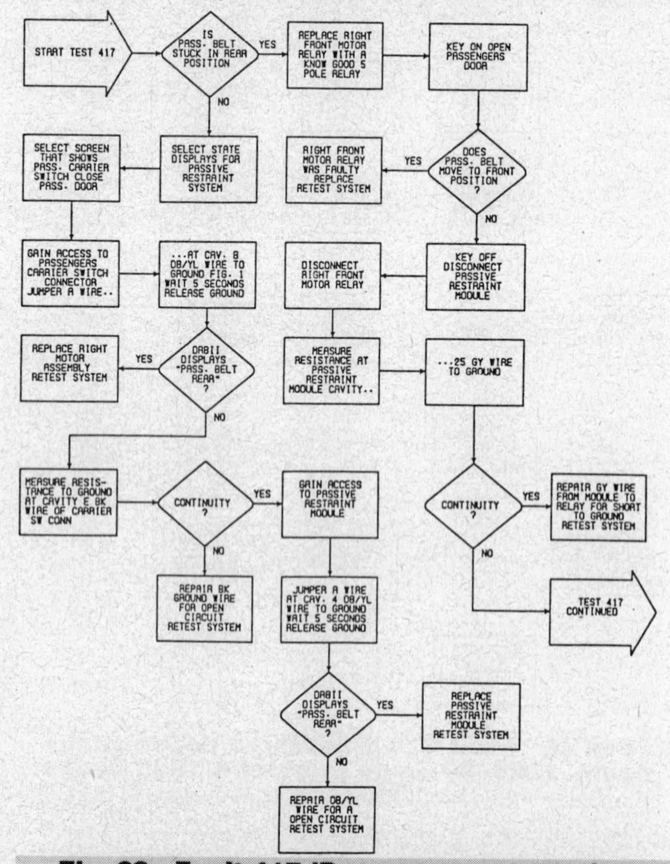


**Fig. 69 Fault 417 (Passenger rear station seen, Part 1 of 3). 1989–90 Eagle Premier & 1990 Dodge Monaco**

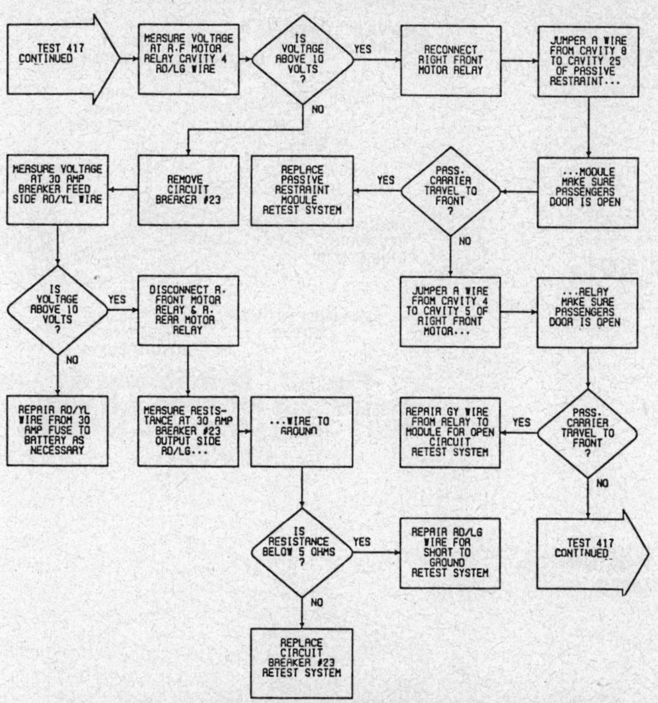


**Fig. 69 Fault 417 (Passenger rear station seen, Part 2 of 3). 1989–90 Eagle Premier & 1990 Dodge Monaco**

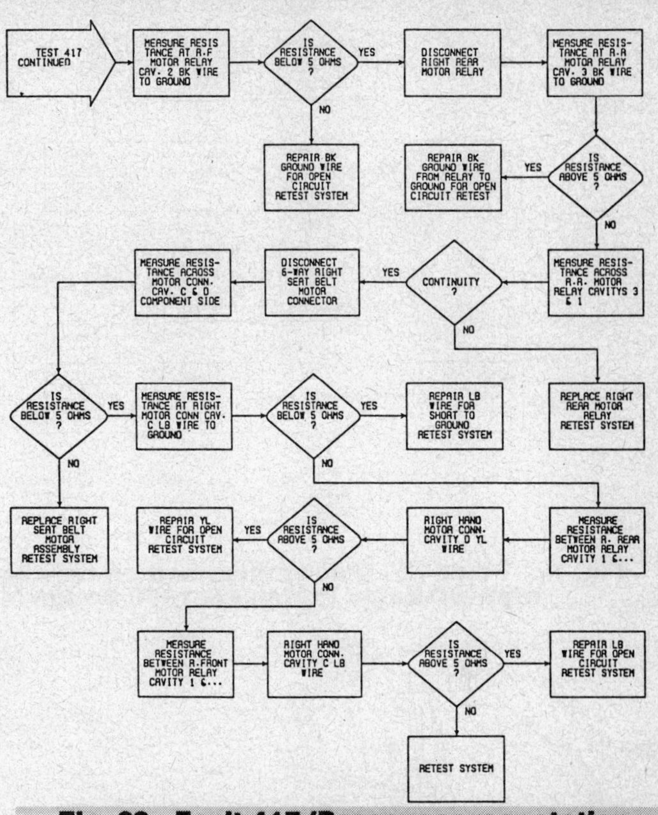


**Fig. 69 Fault 417 (Passenger rear station seen, Part 3 of 3). 1989–90 Eagle Premier & 1990 Dodge Monaco**

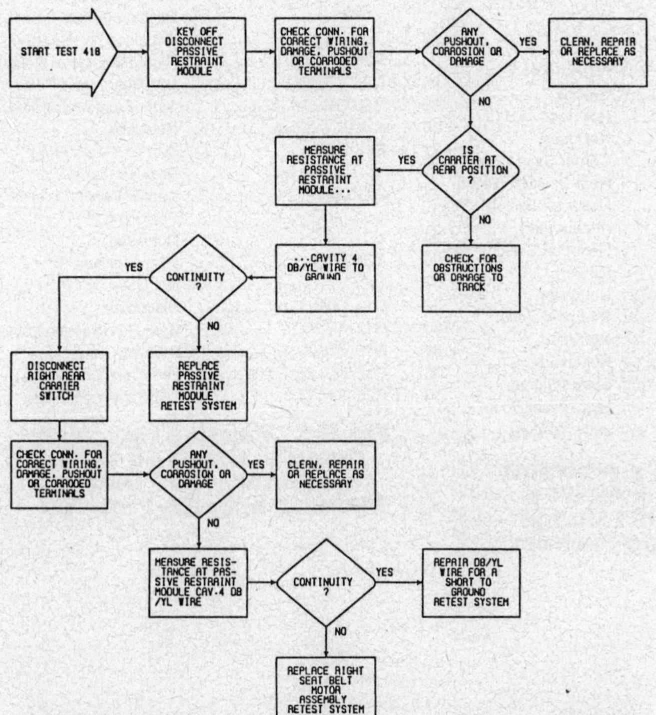


**Fig. 70 Fault 418 (Passenger rear station not seen) 1989–90 Eagle Premier & 1990 Dodge Monaco**

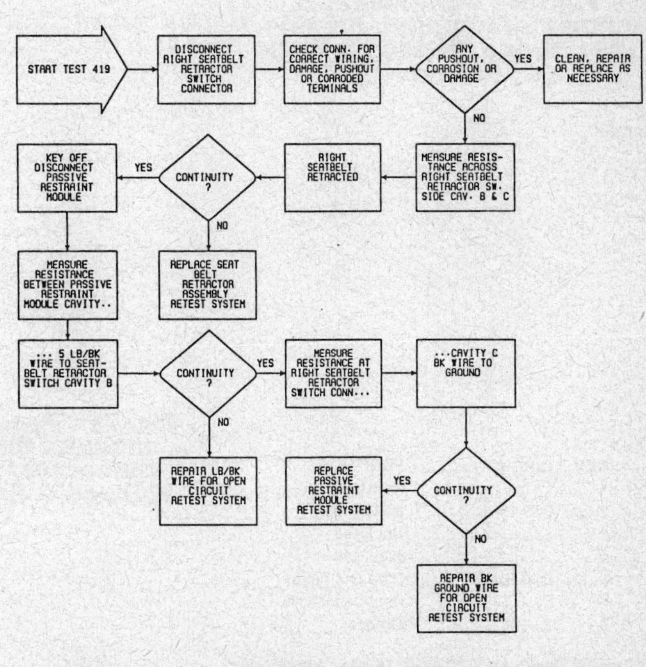


**Fig. 71 Fault 419 (Passengers belt on carriage seen). 1989–90 Eagle Premier & 1990 Dodge Monaco**

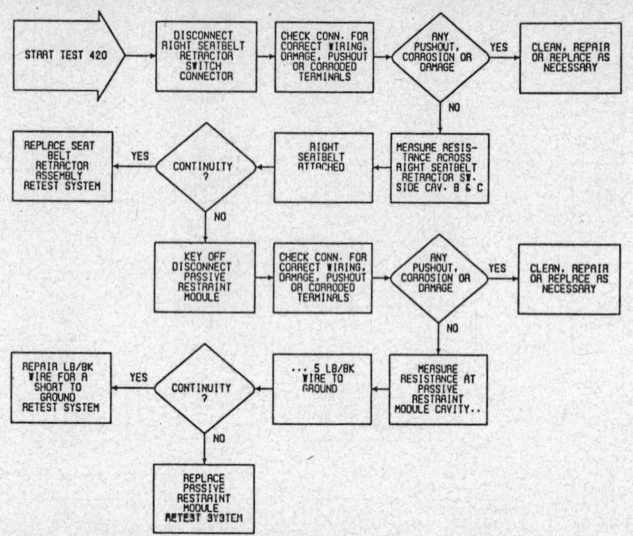


**Fig. 72 Fault 420 (Passengers belt on carriage not seen). 1989–90 Eagle Premier & 1990 Dodge Monaco**

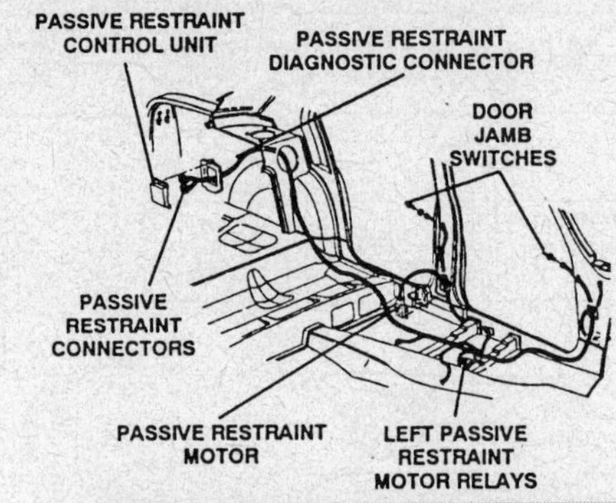


**Fig. 73 Component & connector location. LH side, 1991 Dodge Monaco & Eagle Premier**

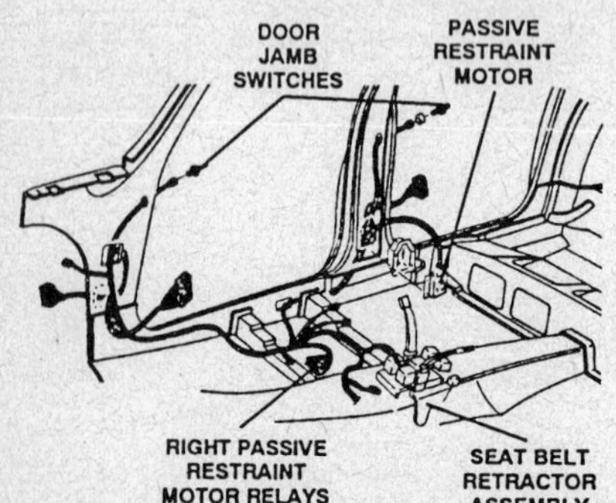


**Fig. 74 Component & connector location. RH side, 1991 Dodge Monaco & Eagle Premier**

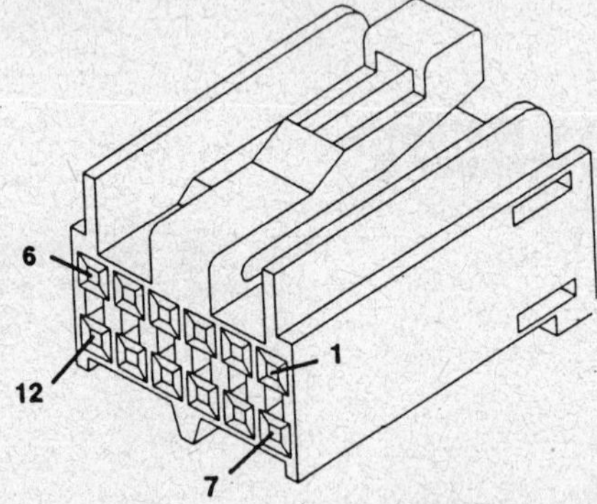


| CAV | CIRCUIT | FUNCTION |
|---|---|---|
| 1 | Z1 BK | Ground |
| 2 | | Not Used |
| 3 | | Not Used |
| 4 | R17 DB/YL | Carrier Switch Right Rear Position (Right) |
| 5 | R28 LB/BK | Retractor Switch (Passenger) |
| 6 | R27 YL/BK | Retractor Switch (Driver) |
| 7 | | Not Used |
| 8 | F30 RD | B+ For Module |
| 9 | | Not Used |
| 10 | | Not Used |
| 11 | G7 WT/OR | Speed Signal |
| 12 | R30 BR/OR | Right Front Door Jamb Switch |

**Fig. 75 Passive restraint module. Black 12 way connector, 1991 Dodge Monaco & Eagle Premier**

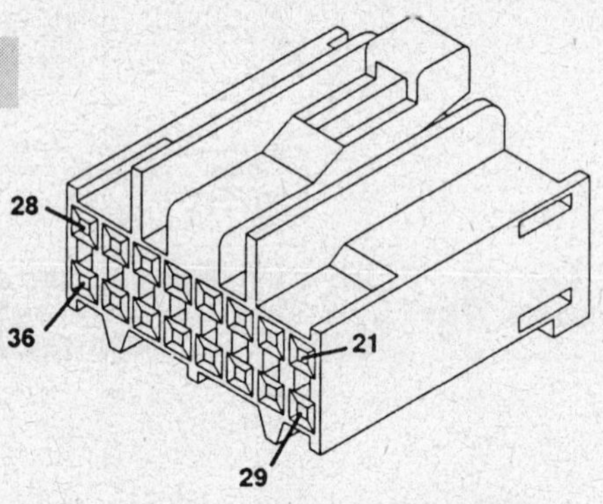


| CAV | CIRCUIT | FUNCTION |
|---|---|---|
| 21 | R16 LG | Carrier Switch Front Position (Right) |
| 22 | | Not Used |
| 23 | R24 VT | Right Rear Motor Relay |
| 24 | R26 VT/WT | Left Rear Motor Relay |
| 25 | R23 GY | Right Front Motor Relay |
| 26 | | Not Used |
| 27 | R18 DG | Carrier Switch Front Position (Left) |
| 28 | R19 LB/WT | Carrier Switch Right Rear Position (Left) |
| 29 | | Not Used |
| 30 | F20 WT | Fused Ignition "C" |
| 31 | | Not Used |
| 32 | D10 PK/WT | Diagnostic |
| 33 | G11 WT/YL | Seat Belt Warning Lamp |
| 34 | G80 VT/BK | Warning Tone |
| 35 | G16 BK/LB | Left Front Door Jamb |
| 36 | R25 GY/WT | Left Passenger Relay |

**Fig. 76 Passive restraint module. Black 16 way connector, 1991 Dodge Monaco & Eagle Premier**

| CAV | CIRCUIT | FUNCTION |
|---|---|---|
| 1 | | Not Used |
| 2 | F30 19RD | Battery 12V |
| 3 | | Not Used |
| 4 | | Not Used |
| 5 | D10 PK/WT | Data Out From Passive Module |
| 6 | Z1 BK | Ground |

**Fig. 77 Passive restraint module. Diagnostic connector, 1991 Dodge Monaco & Eagle Premier**

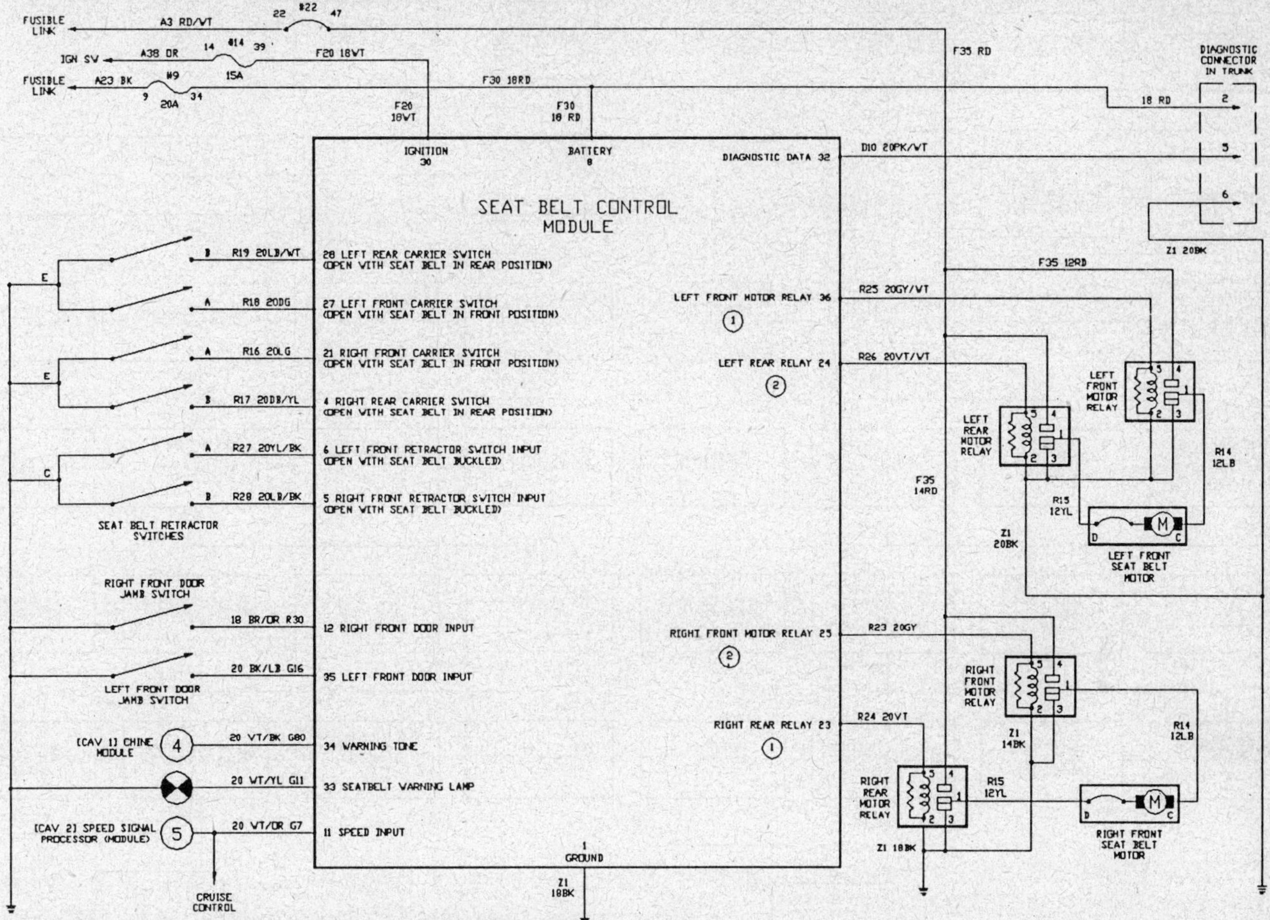


**Fig. 78 Passive restraint system schematic. 1991 Dodge Monaco & Eagle Premier**

1. Turn the ignition key to the on position.
2. Plug the DRBII in the diagnostic connector (left right side of trunk).
3. Select the system test and follow the DRBII instructions.

   If you are prompted by the DRBII to perform an instruction, do it. If the DRBII does not respond within 5 seconds or if the component is in the specified position, press and hold the ENTER key until the command is confirmed.

**NOTE:** Skip this note if any fault is detected on the DRBII. If no faults are detected and the belt does not travel to the far front when opening the door, replace the seat belt motor assembly.

Refer to the following table for fault identification:

| DRBII FAULT CODES | DIAGNOSTIC TEST |
|---|---|
| No Response | Refer to the vehicle communication manual. |
| Fault 403 | 2A |
| Fault 404 | Replace the passive restraint module. |
| Fault 405 | 3A |
| Fault 406 | 4A |
| Fault 407 | 5A |
| Fault 408 | 6A |
| Fault 409 | 7A |
| Fault 410 | 8A |
| Fault 411 | 9A |
| Fault 412 | 10A |
| Fault 413 | 11A |
| Fault 414 | 12A |
| Fault 415 | 13A |
| Fault 416 | 14A |
| Fault 417 | 15A |
| Fault 418 | 16A |
| Fault 419 | 17A |
| Fault 420 | 18A |

**Fig. 79 Test 1A (Passive restraint functional test). 1991 Dodge Monaco & Eagle Premier**

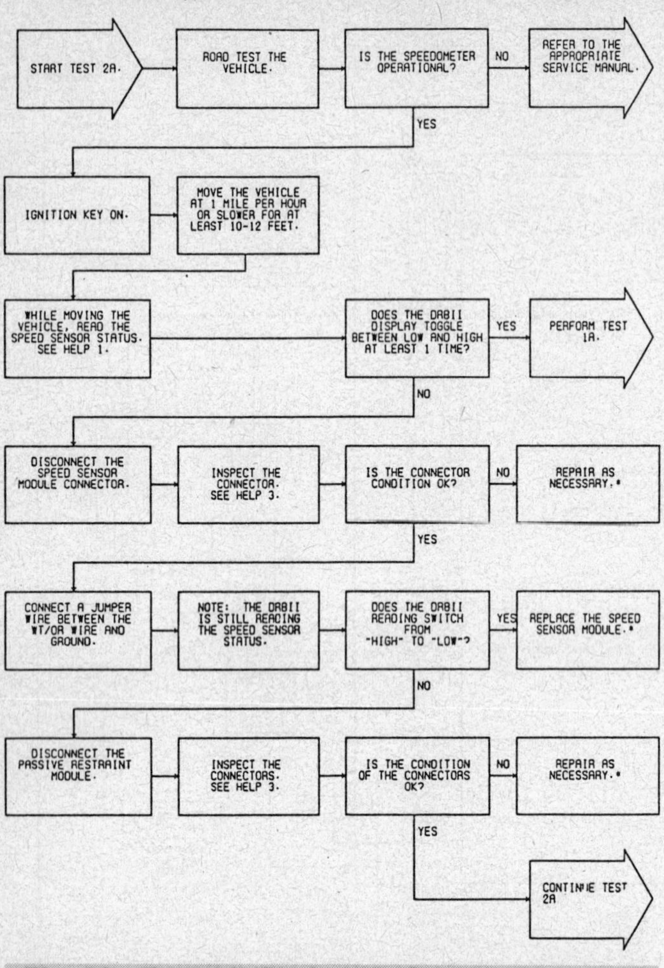

START TEST 2A.
ROAD TEST THE VEHICLE.
IS THE SPEEDOMETER OPERATIONAL?
NO
REFER TO THE APPROPRIATE SERVICE MANUAL.
YES
IGNITION KEY ON.
MOVE THE VEHICLE AT 1 MILE PER HOUR OR SLOWER FOR AT LEAST 10-12 FEET.
WHILE MOVING THE VEHICLE, READ THE SPEED SENSOR STATUS. SEE HELP 1.
DOES THE DRBII DISPLAY TOGGLE BETWEEN LOW AND HIGH AT LEAST 1 TIME?
YES
PERFORM TEST 1A.
NO
DISCONNECT THE SPEED SENSOR MODULE CONNECTOR.
INSPECT THE CONNECTOR. SEE HELP 3.
IS THE CONNECTOR CONDITION OK?
NO
REPAIR AS NECESSARY.*
YES
CONNECT A JUMPER WIRE BETWEEN THE WT/OR WIRE AND GROUND.
NOTE: THE DRBII IS STILL READING THE SPEED SENSOR STATUS.
DOES THE DRBII READING SWITCH FROM "HIGH" TO "LOW"?
YES
REPLACE THE SPEED SENSOR MODULE.*
NO
DISCONNECT THE PASSIVE RESTRAINT MODULE.
INSPECT THE CONNECTORS. SEE HELP 3.
IS THE CONDITION OF THE CONNECTORS OK?
NO
REPAIR AS NECESSARY.*
YES
CONTINUE TEST 2A

**Fig. 80 Test 2A, Fault 403 (Speed sensor not seen, Part 1 of 2). 1991 Dodge Monaco & Eagle Premier**

START TEST 3A.
OPEN THE LEFT FRONT DOOR.
VISUALLY INSPECT THE LEFT FRONT DOOR JAMB SWITCH.
IS THE SWITCH CONDITION OK?
NO
REPLACE THE LEFT FRONT DOOR JAMB SWITCH.*
YES
DISCONNECT THE LEFT FRONT DOOR JAMB SWITCH CONNECTOR. FIG. 1
INSPECT THE CONNECTOR. SEE HELP 3.
IS THE CONNECTOR CONDITION OK?
NO
REPAIR AS NECESSARY.*
YES
IGNITION KEY ON.
READ THE LEFT FRONT DOOR JAMB SWITCH STATUS. SEE HELP 1.
DOES THE DRBII SHOW "LF DOOR JAMB CLOSED"?
NO
REPLACE THE LEFT FRONT DOOR JAMB SWITCH.*
YES
DISCONNECT THE PASSIVE RESTRAINT MODULE.
INSPECT THE CONNECTORS. SEE HELP 3.
IS THE CONDITION OF THE CONNECTORS OK?
NO
REPAIR AS NECESSARY.*
YES
PUT THE DRBII IN OHMMETER MODE. SEE HELP 1.
PROBE THE BK/LB WIRE IN THE MODULE CONNECTOR.
IS THE RESISTANCE BELOW 10.0 OHMS?
NO
REPLACE THE PASSIVE RESTRAINT MODULE.*
YES
REPAIR THE G16 BK/LB WIRE FOR A SHORT TO GROUND.*

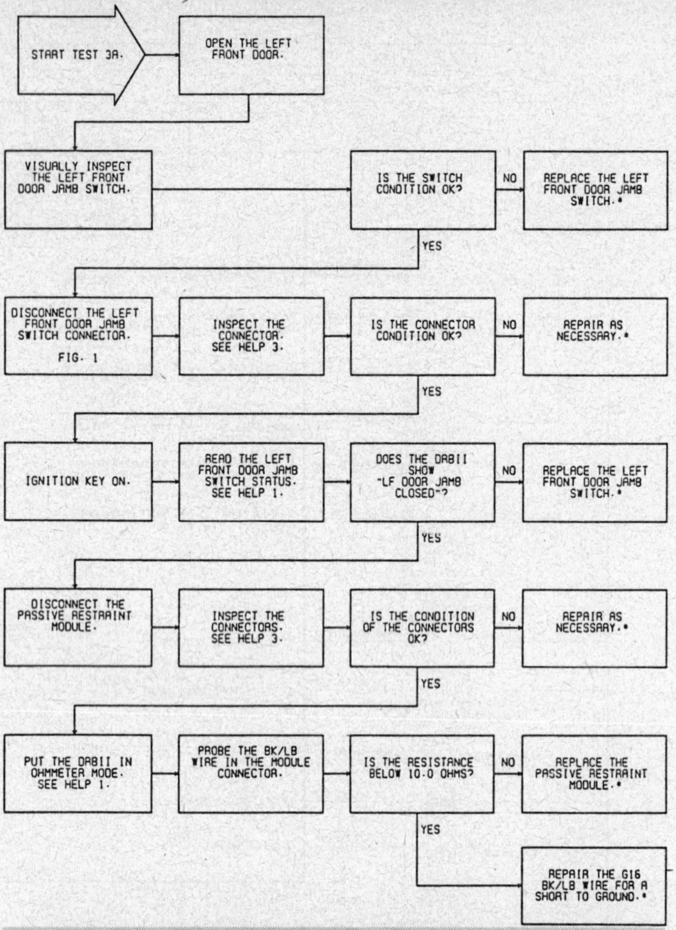

**Fig. 81 Test 3A, Fault 405 (Driver's door switch closed). 1991 Dodge Monaco & Eagle Premier**

TEST 2A CONTINUED
PROBE THE WT/OR WIRE IN THE SPEED SENSOR MODULE CONNECTOR.
IS THE VOLTAGE ABOVE 10.0 VOLTS?
YES
REPAIR THE G7 WT/OR WIRE FOR A SHORT TO BATTERY.*
NO
PUT THE DRBII IN OHMMETER MODE. SEE HELP 1.
PROBE THE WT/OR WIRE IN THE SPEED SENSOR MODULE CONNECTOR.
IS THE RESISTANCE BELOW 10.0 OHMS?
YES
REPAIR THE G7 WT/OR WIRE FOR A SHORT TO GROUND.*
NO
USE AN EXTERNAL OHMMETER IN THE FOLLOWING STEP.
TEST THE WT/OR WIRE FOR RESISTANCE.
IS THE RESISTANCE BELOW 10.0 OHMS?
NO
REPAIR THE OPEN G7 WT/OR WIRE.*
YES
REPLACE THE PASSIVE RESTRAINT MODULE.*

**Fig. 80 Test 2A, Fault 403 (Speed sensor not seen, Part 2 of 2). 1991 Dodge Monaco & Eagle Premier**

START TEST 4A.
IGNITION KEY ON.
DISCONNECT THE LEFT FRONT DOOR JAMB SWITCH.
VISUALLY INSPECT THE LEFT FRONT DOOR JAMB SWITCH.
IS THE SWITCH CONDITION OK?
NO
REPLACE THE LEFT FRONT DOOR JAMB SWITCH.*
YES
CONNECT A JUMPER WIRE BETWEEN THE BK/LB AND BK WIRES.
READ THE LEFT FRONT DOOR JAMB SWITCH STATUS. SEE HELP 1.
DOES THE DRBII SHOW "LF DOOR JAMB CLOSED"?
YES
REPLACE THE LEFT FRONT DOOR JAMB SWITCH.*
NO
DISCONNECT THE JUMPER WIRE.
CONNECT A JUMPER WIRE BETWEEN THE BK/LB WIRE AND GROUND.
DOES THE DRBII SHOW "LF DOOR JAMB CLOSED"?
YES
REPAIR THE Z1 BK WIRE FOR AN OPEN TO GROUND.*
NO
DISCONNECT THE JUMPER WIRE.
GAIN ACCESS TO THE PASSIVE RESTRAINT MODULE (LEFT REAR SIDE OF TRUNK).
CONNECT A JUMPER WIRE BETWEEN THE BK/LB WIRE AND GROUND.
NOTE: THE DRBII IS STILL READING THE LEFT FRONT DOOR JAMB SWITCH STATUS.
DOES THE DRBII SHOW "LF DOOR JAMB CLOSED"?
YES
REPAIR THE OPEN G16 BK/LB WIRE.*
NO
REPLACE THE PASSIVE RESTRAINT MODULE.*

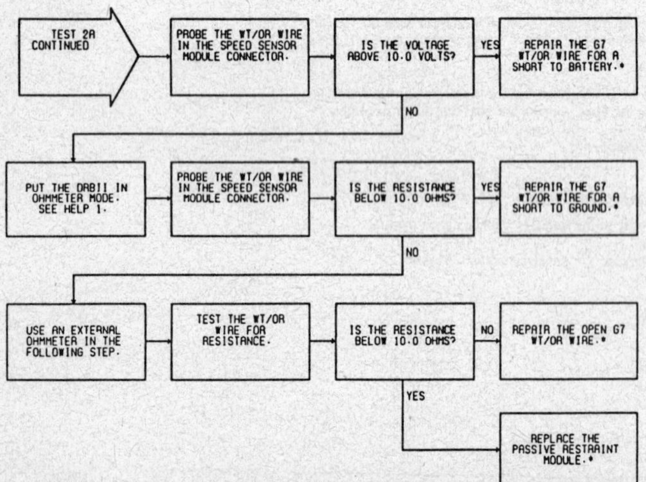

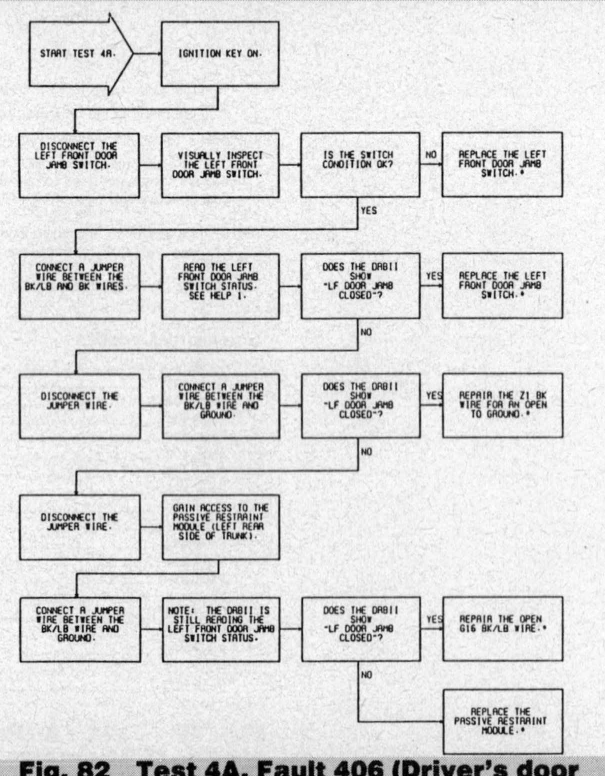

**Fig. 82 Test 4A, Fault 406 (Driver's door switch open). 1991 Dodge Monaco & Eagle Premier**

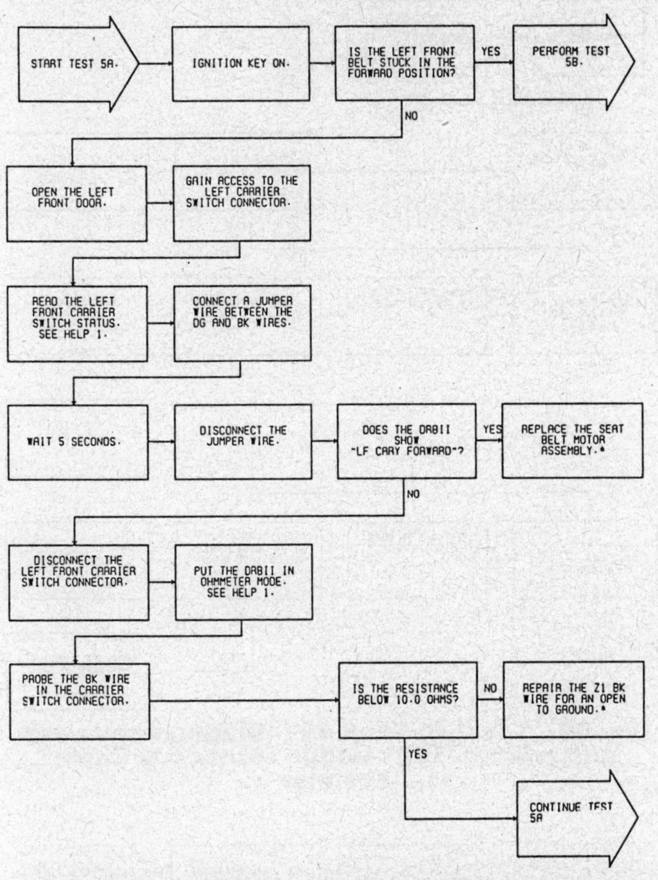


**Fig. 83 Test 5A, Fault 407 (Driver's forward station seen, Part 1 of 2). 1991 Dodge Monaco & Eagle Premier**

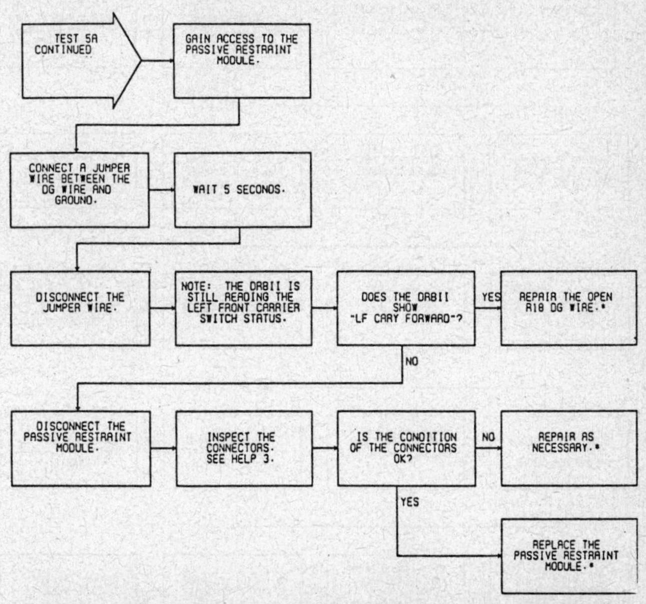


**Fig. 83 Test 5A, Fault 407 (Driver's forward station seen, Part 2 of 2). 1991 Dodge Monaco & Eagle Premier**

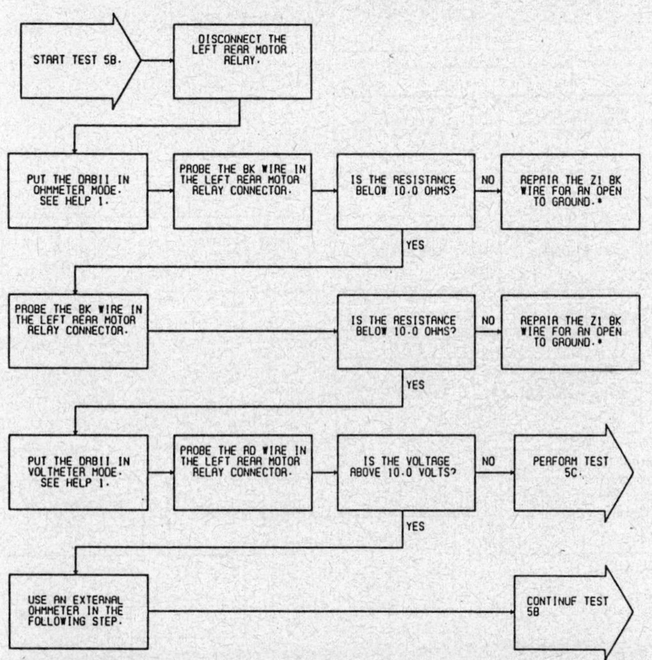


**Fig. 84 Test 5B, Fault 407 (Diagnosing relays and wiring, Part 1 of 3). 1991 Dodge Monaco & Eagle Premier**

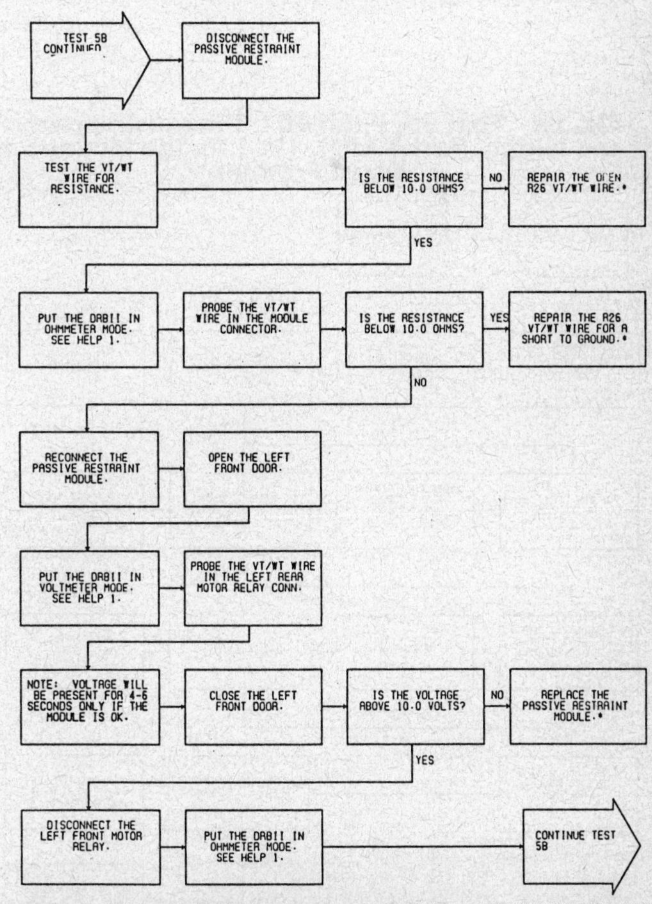


**Fig. 84 Test 5B, Fault 407 (Diagnosing relays and wiring, Part 2 of 3). 1991 Dodge Monaco & Eagle Premier**

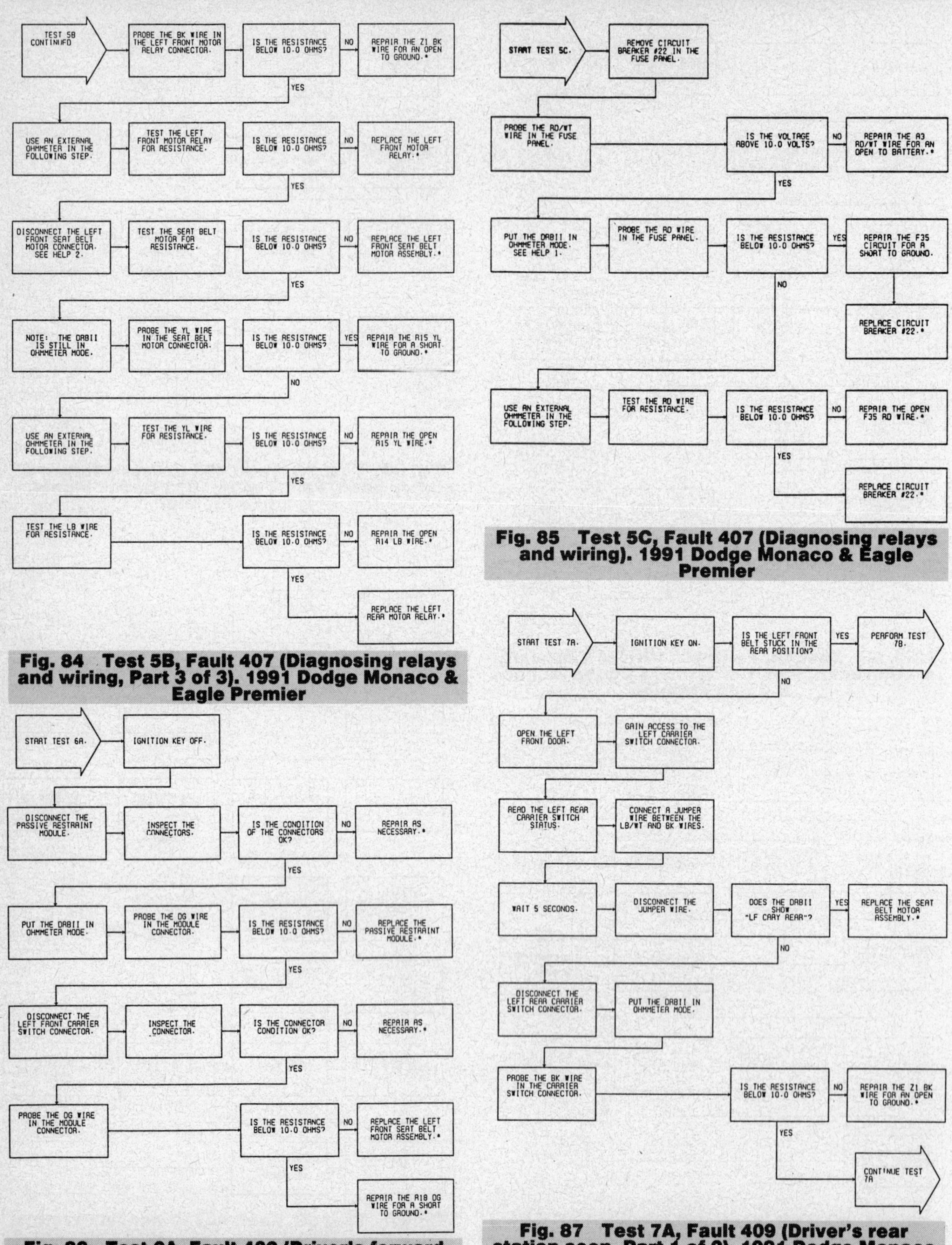


**Fig. 84 Test 5B, Fault 407 (Diagnosing relays and wiring, Part 3 of 3). 1991 Dodge Monaco & Eagle Premier**

**Fig. 85 Test 5C, Fault 407 (Diagnosing relays and wiring). 1991 Dodge Monaco & Eagle Premier**

**Fig. 86 Test 6A, Fault 408 (Driver's forward station not seen). 1991 Dodge Monaco & Eagle Premier**

**Fig. 87 Test 7A, Fault 409 (Driver's rear station seen, Part 1 of 2). 1991 Dodge Monaco & Eagle Premier**

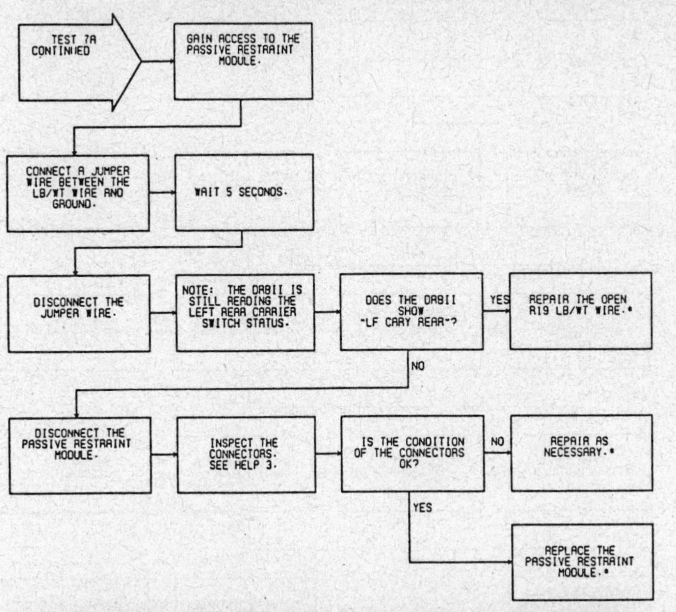


**Fig. 87 Test 7A, Fault 409 (Driver's rear station seen, Part 2 of 2). 1991 Dodge Monaco & Eagle Premier**

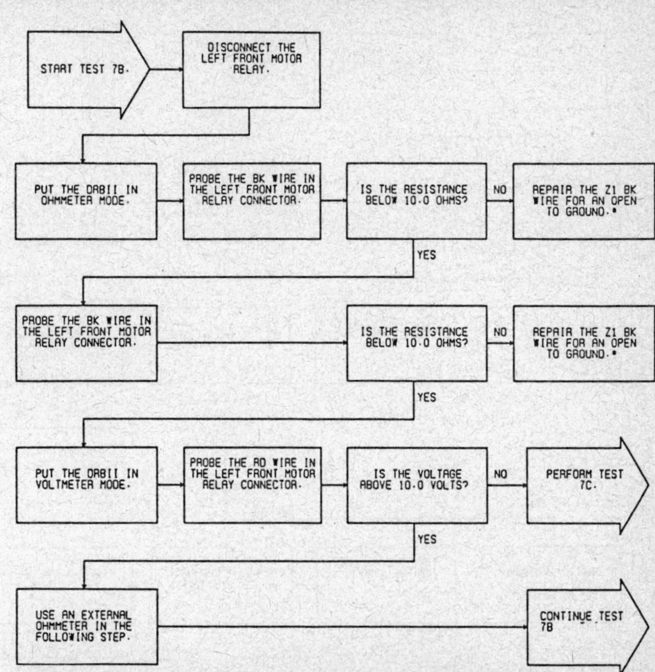


**Fig. 88 Test 7B, Fault 409 (Diagnosing relays and wiring, Part 1 of 3). 1991 Dodge Monaco & Eagle Premier**

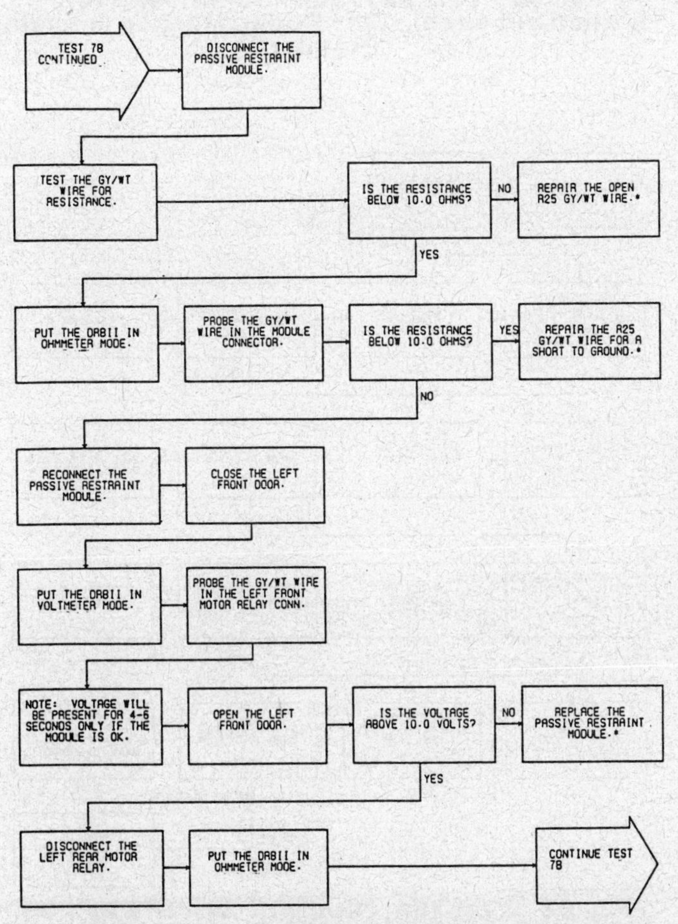


**Fig. 88 Test 7B, Fault 409 (Diagnosing relays and wiring, Part 2 of 3). 1991 Dodge Monaco & Eagle Premier**

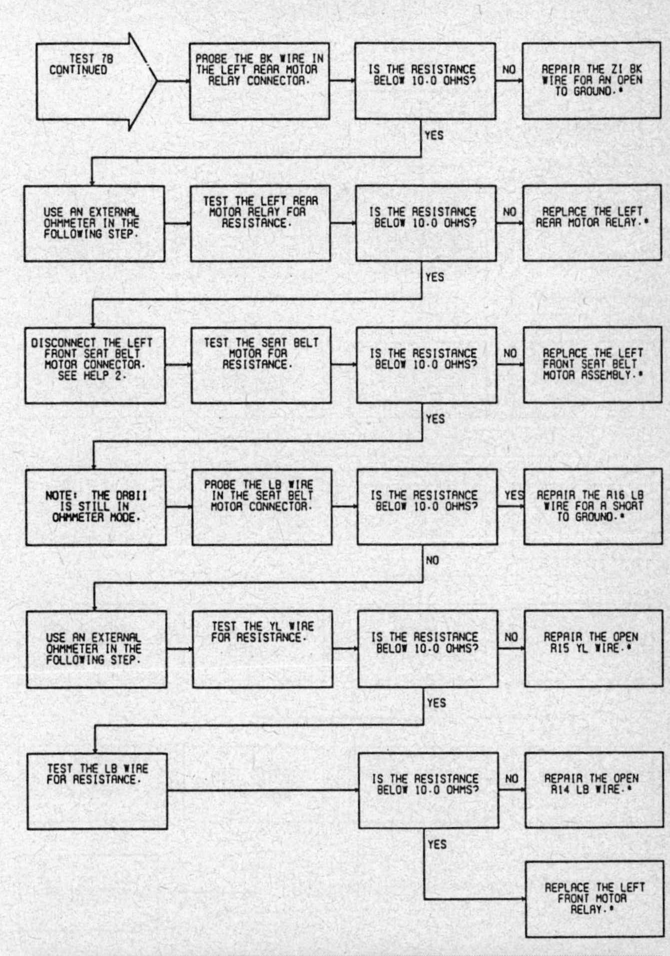


**Fig. 88 Test 7B, Fault 409 (Diagnosing relays and wiring, Part 3 of 3). 1991 Dodge Monaco & Eagle Premier**

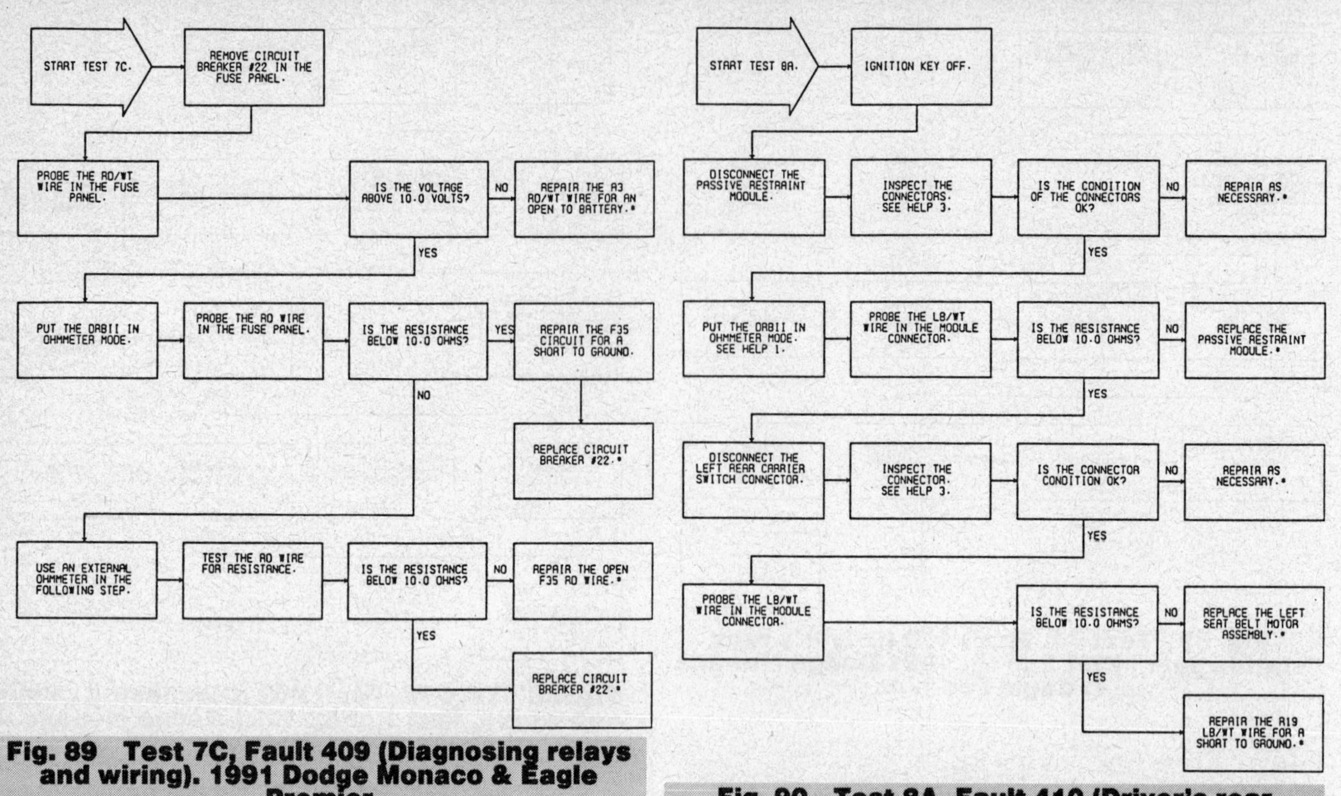


**Fig. 89 Test 7C, Fault 409 (Diagnosing relays and wiring). 1991 Dodge Monaco & Eagle Premier**

**Fig. 90 Test 8A, Fault 410 (Driver's rear station not seen). 1991 Dodge Monaco & Eagle Premier**

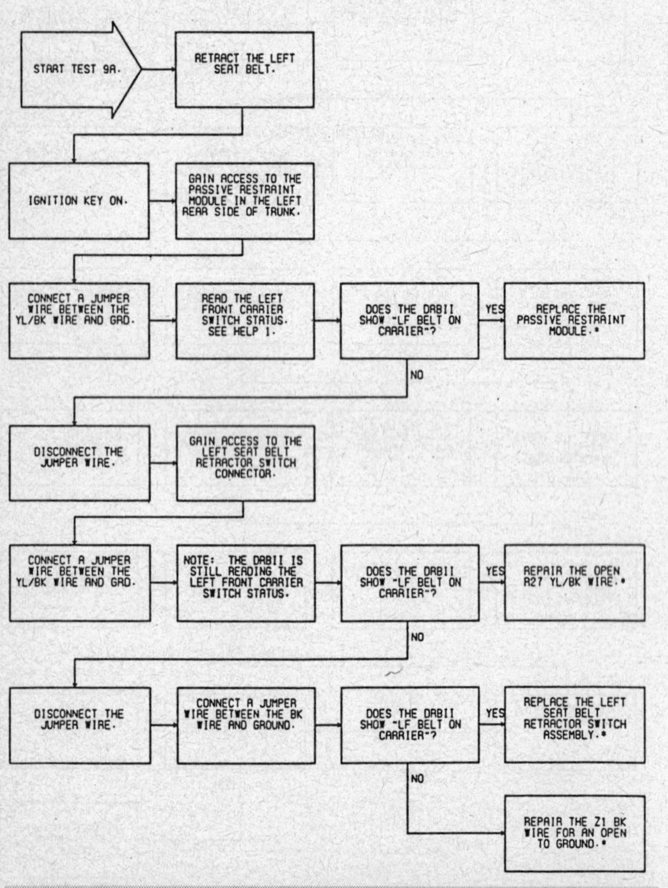


**Fig. 91 Test 9A, Fault 411 (Driver's belt on carriage seen). 1991 Dodge Monaco & Eagle Premier**

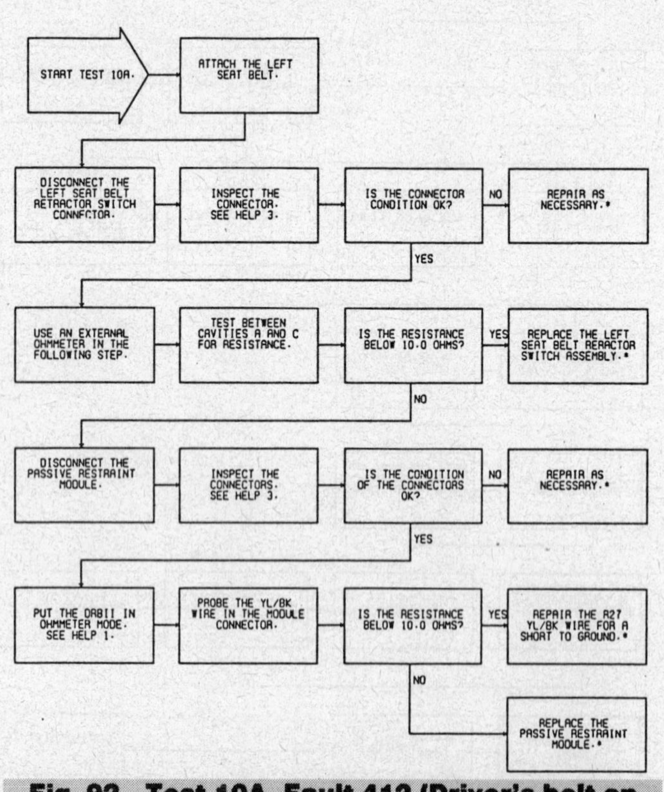


**Fig. 92 Test 10A, Fault 412 (Driver's belt on carriage not seen). 1991 Dodge Monaco & Eagle Premier**

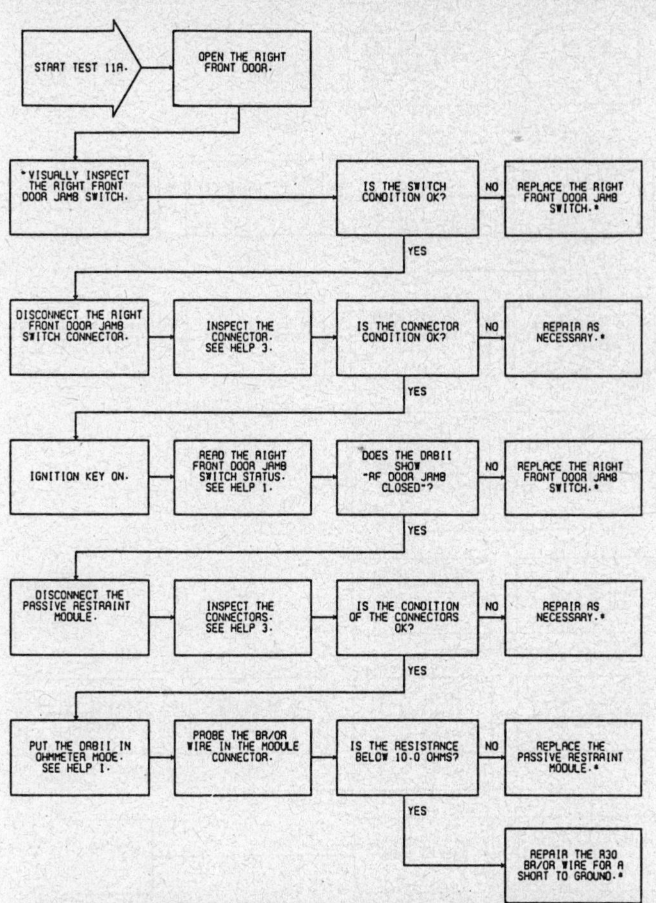


**Fig. 93 Test 11A, Fault 413 (Passenger door switch closed). 1991 Dodge Monaco & Eagle Premier**

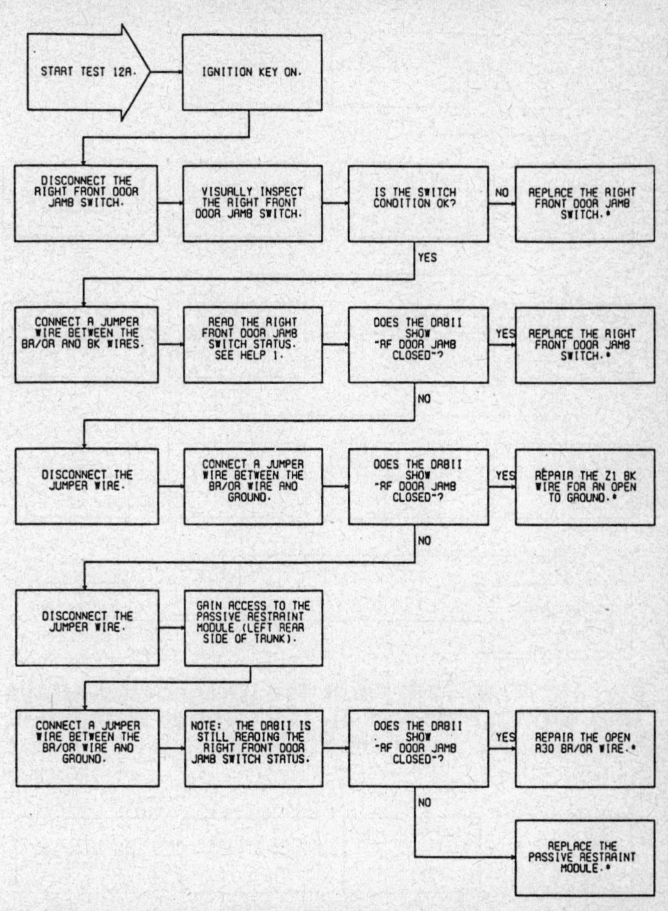


**Fig. 94 Test 12A, Fault 414 (Passenger door switch open). 1991 Dodge Monaco & Eagle Premier**

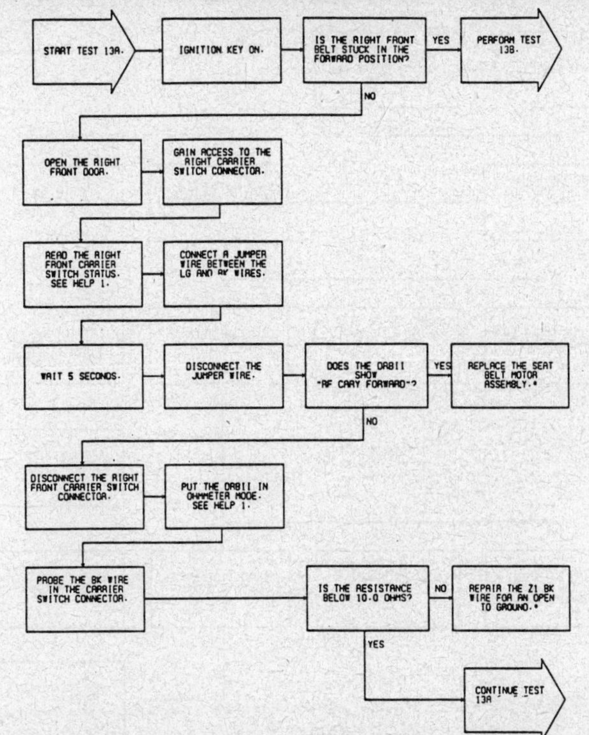


**Fig. 95 Test 13A, Fault 415 (Passenger forward station seen, Part 1 of 2). 1991 Dodge Monaco & Eagle Premier**

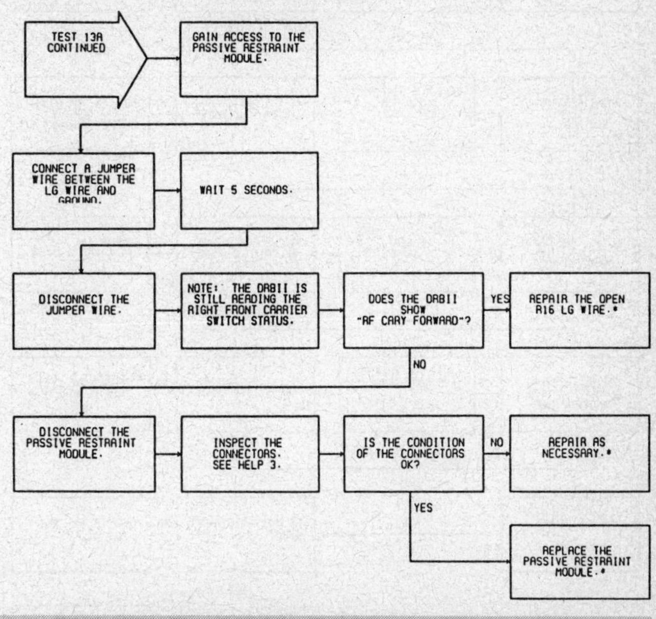


**Fig. 95 Test 13A, Fault 415 (Passenger forward station seen, Part 2 of 2). 1991 Dodge Monaco & Eagle Premier**

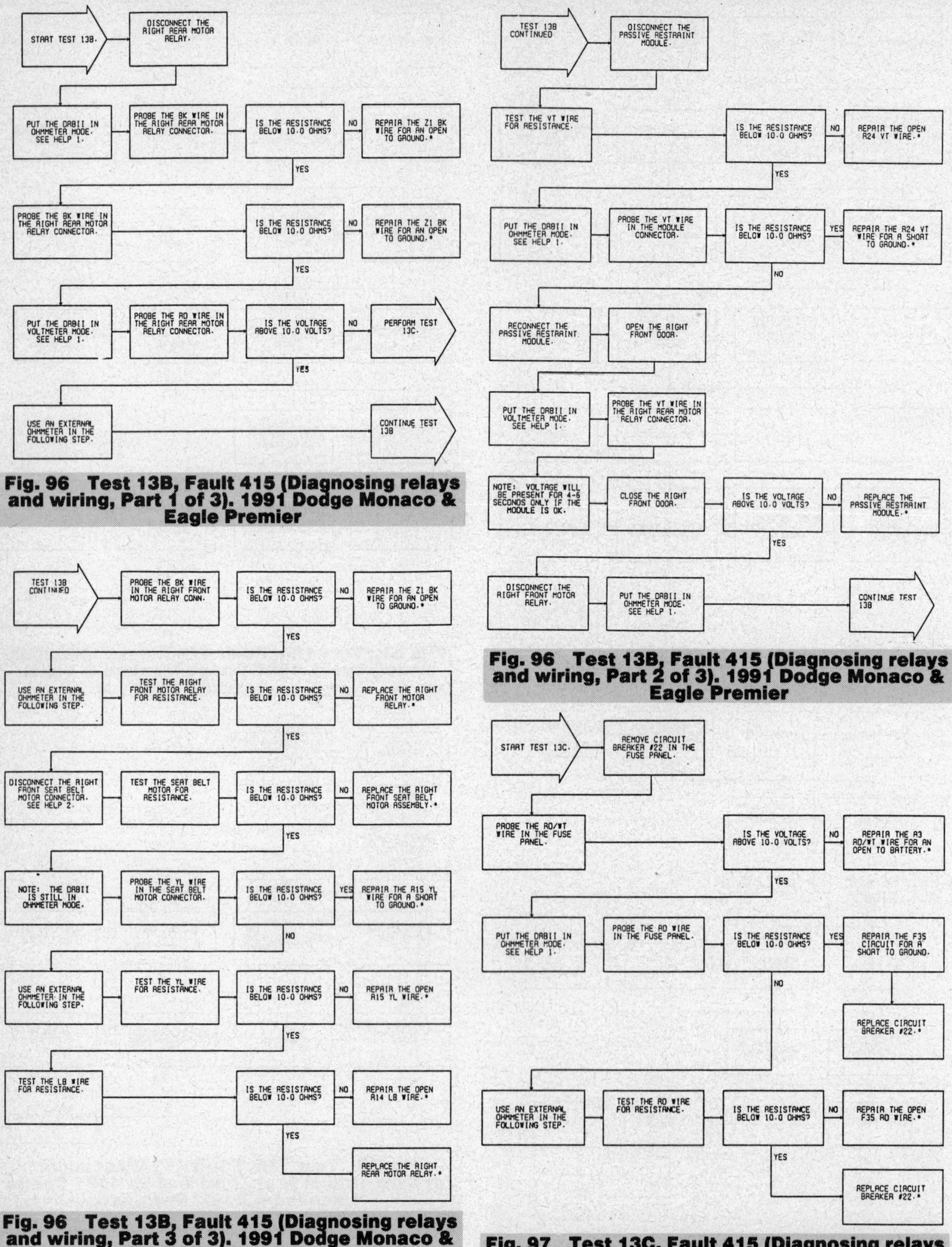


**Fig. 96 Test 13B, Fault 415 (Diagnosing relays and wiring, Part 1 of 3). 1991 Dodge Monaco & Eagle Premier**

**Fig. 96 Test 13B, Fault 415 (Diagnosing relays and wiring, Part 2 of 3). 1991 Dodge Monaco & Eagle Premier**

**Fig. 96 Test 13B, Fault 415 (Diagnosing relays and wiring, Part 3 of 3). 1991 Dodge Monaco & Eagle Premier**

**Fig. 97 Test 13C, Fault 415 (Diagnosing relays and wiring). 1991 Dodge Monaco & Eagle Premier**

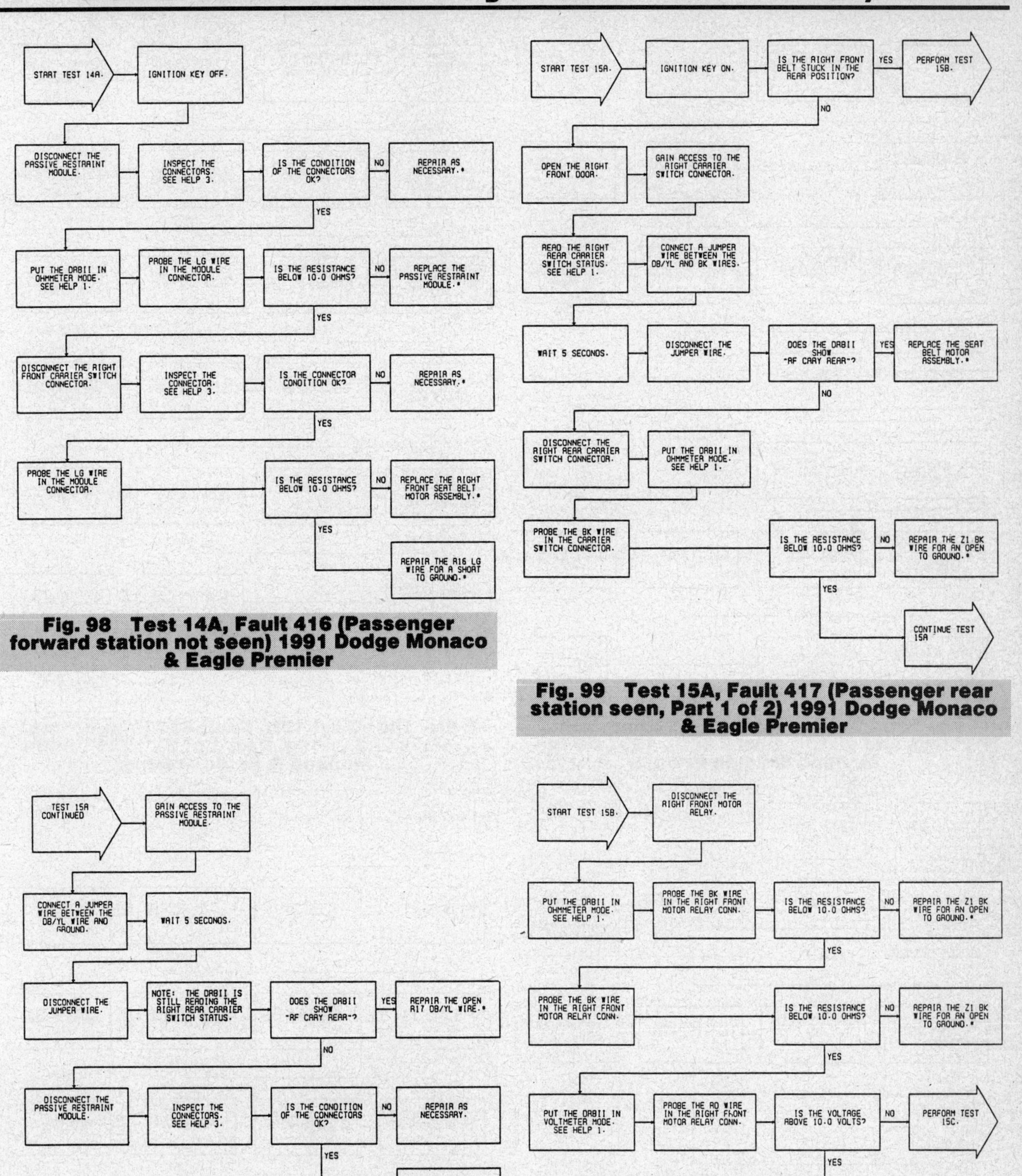


Fig. 98 Test 14A, Fault 416 (Passenger forward station not seen) 1991 Dodge Monaco & Eagle Premier



Fig. 99 Test 15A, Fault 417 (Passenger rear station seen, Part 1 of 2) 1991 Dodge Monaco & Eagle Premier



Fig. 99 Test 15A, Fault 417 (Passenger rear station seen, Part 2 of 2) 1991 Dodge Monaco & Eagle Premier



Fig. 100 Test 15B, Fault 417 (Diagnosing relays and wiring, Part 1 of 3). 1991 Dodge Monaco & Eagle Premier

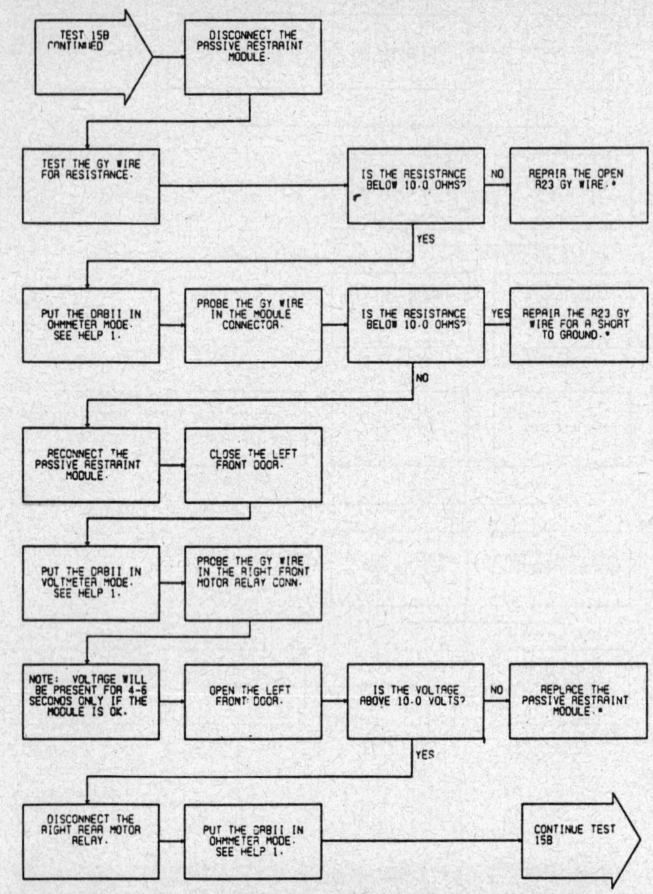

TEST 15B CONTINUED

DISCONNECT THE PASSIVE RESTRAINT MODULE.

TEST THE GY WIRE FOR RESISTANCE.

IS THE RESISTANCE BELOW 10.0 OHMS? — NO — REPAIR THE OPEN R23 GY WIRE.*

YES

PUT THE DRBII IN OHMMETER MODE. SEE HELP 1.

PROBE THE GY WIRE IN THE MODULE CONNECTOR.

IS THE RESISTANCE BELOW 10.0 OHMS? — YES — REPAIR THE R23 GY WIRE FOR A SHORT TO GROUND.*

NO

RECONNECT THE PASSIVE RESTRAINT MODULE.

CLOSE THE LEFT FRONT DOOR.

PUT THE DRBII IN VOLTMETER MODE. SEE HELP 1.

PROBE THE GY WIRE IN THE RIGHT FRONT MOTOR RELAY CONN.

NOTE: VOLTAGE WILL BE PRESENT FOR 4-6 SECONDS ONLY IF THE MODULE IS OK.

OPEN THE LEFT FRONT DOOR.

IS THE VOLTAGE ABOVE 10.0 VOLTS? — NO — REPLACE THE PASSIVE RESTRAINT MODULE.*

YES

DISCONNECT THE RIGHT REAR MOTOR RELAY.

PUT THE DRBII IN OHMMETER MODE. SEE HELP 1.

CONTINUE TEST 15B

**Fig. 100 Test 15B, Fault 417 (Diagnosing relays and wiring, Part 2 of 3). 1991 Dodge Monaco & Eagle Premier**

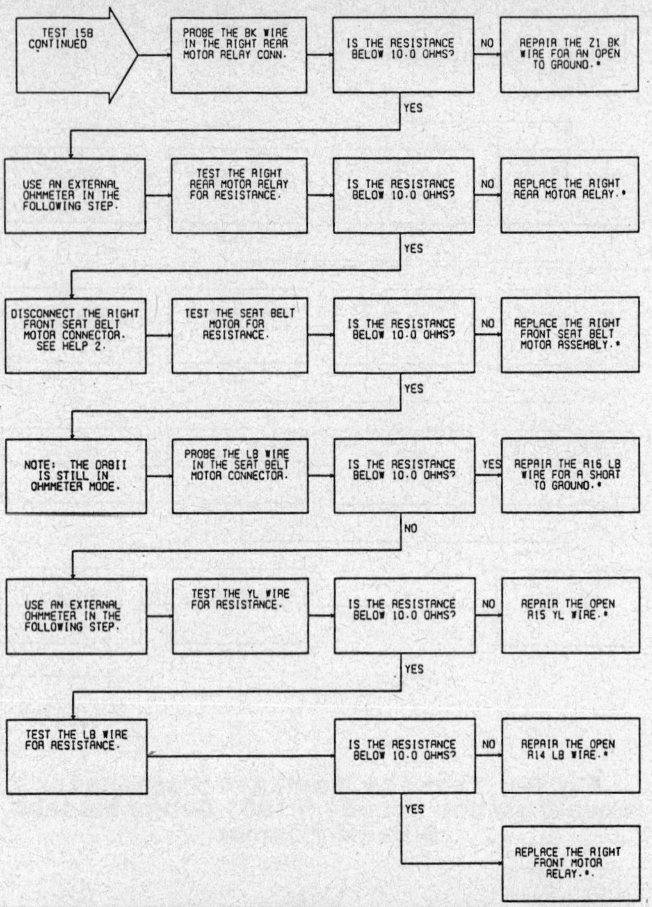

TEST 15B CONTINUED

PROBE THE BK WIRE IN THE RIGHT REAR MOTOR RELAY CONN.

IS THE RESISTANCE BELOW 10.0 OHMS? — NO — REPAIR THE Z1 BK WIRE FOR AN OPEN TO GROUND.*

YES

USE AN EXTERNAL OHMMETER IN THE FOLLOWING STEP.

TEST THE RIGHT REAR MOTOR RELAY FOR RESISTANCE.

IS THE RESISTANCE BELOW 10.0 OHMS? — NO — REPLACE THE RIGHT REAR MOTOR RELAY.*

YES

DISCONNECT THE RIGHT FRONT SEAT BELT MOTOR CONNECTOR. SEE HELP 2.

TEST THE SEAT BELT MOTOR FOR RESISTANCE.

IS THE RESISTANCE BELOW 10.0 OHMS? — NO — REPLACE THE RIGHT FRONT SEAT BELT MOTOR ASSEMBLY.*

YES

NOTE: THE DRBII IS STILL IN OHMMETER MODE.

PROBE THE LB WIRE IN THE SEAT BELT MOTOR CONNECTOR.

IS THE RESISTANCE BELOW 10.0 OHMS? — YES — REPAIR THE R16 LB WIRE FOR A SHORT TO GROUND.*

NO

USE AN EXTERNAL OHMMETER IN THE FOLLOWING STEP.

TEST THE YL WIRE FOR RESISTANCE.

IS THE RESISTANCE BELOW 10.0 OHMS? — NO — REPAIR THE OPEN R15 YL WIRE.*

YES

TEST THE LB WIRE FOR RESISTANCE.

IS THE RESISTANCE BELOW 10.0 OHMS? — NO — REPAIR THE OPEN R14 LB WIRE.*

YES

REPLACE THE RIGHT FRONT MOTOR RELAY.*.

**Fig. 100 Test 15B, Fault 417 (Diagnosing relays and wiring, Part 3 of 3). 1991 Dodge Monaco & Eagle Premier**

START TEST 15C.

REMOVE CIRCUIT BREAKER #22 IN THE FUSE PANEL.

PROBE THE RD/WT WIRE IN THE FUSE PANEL.

IS THE VOLTAGE ABOVE 10.0 VOLTS? — NO — REPAIR THE A3 RD/WT WIRE FOR AN OPEN TO BATTERY.*

YES

PUT THE DRBII IN OHMMETER MODE. SEE HELP 1.

PROBE THE RD WIRE IN THE FUSE PANEL.

IS THE RESISTANCE BELOW 10.0 OHMS? — YES — REPAIR THE F35 CIRCUIT FOR A SHORT TO GROUND. — REPLACE CIRCUIT BREAKER #22.*

NO

USE AN EXTERNAL OHMMETER IN THE FOLLOWING STEP.

TEST THE RD WIRE FOR RESISTANCE.

IS THE RESISTANCE BELOW 10.0 OHMS? — NO — REPAIR THE OPEN F35 RD WIRE.*

YES

REPLACE CIRCUIT BREAKER #22.*

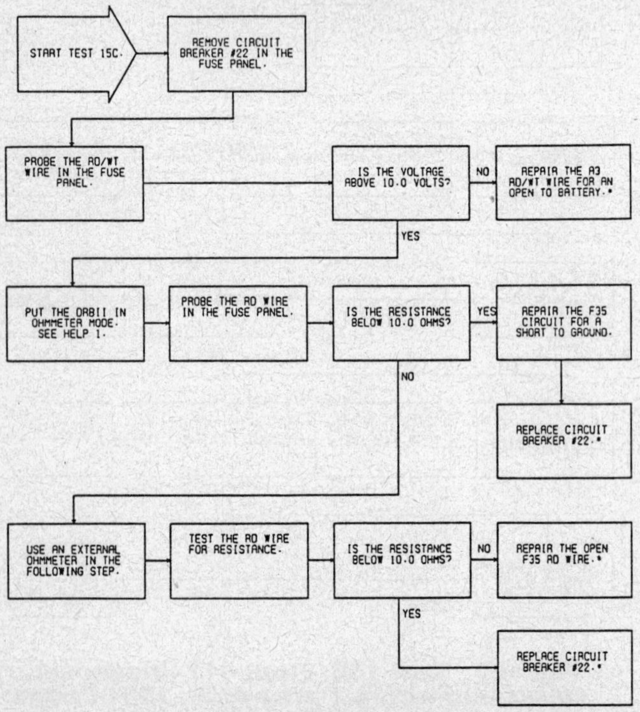

**Fig. 101 Test 15C, Fault 417 (Diagnosing relays and wiring). 1991 Dodge Monaco & Eagle Premier**

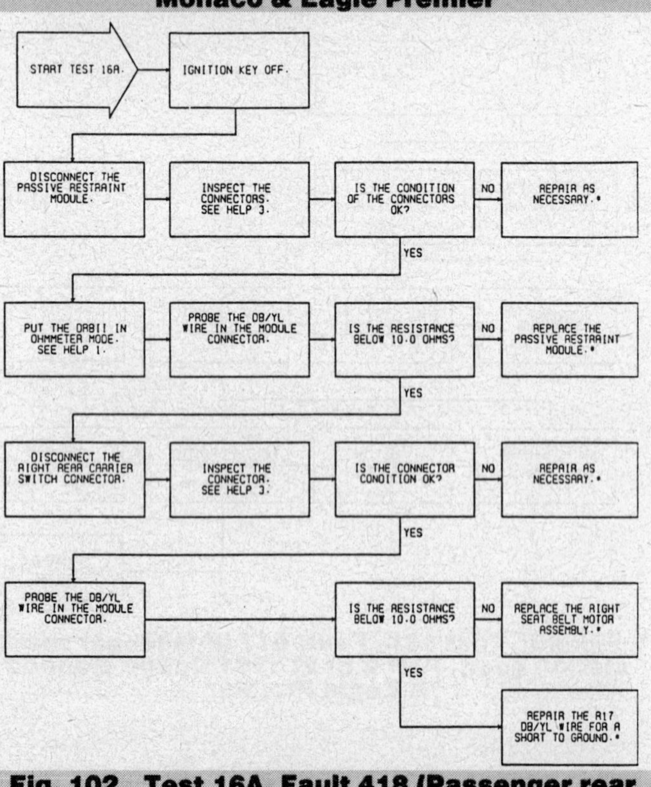


**Fig. 102 Test 16A, Fault 418 (Passenger rear station not seen) 1991 Dodge Monaco & Eagle Premier**

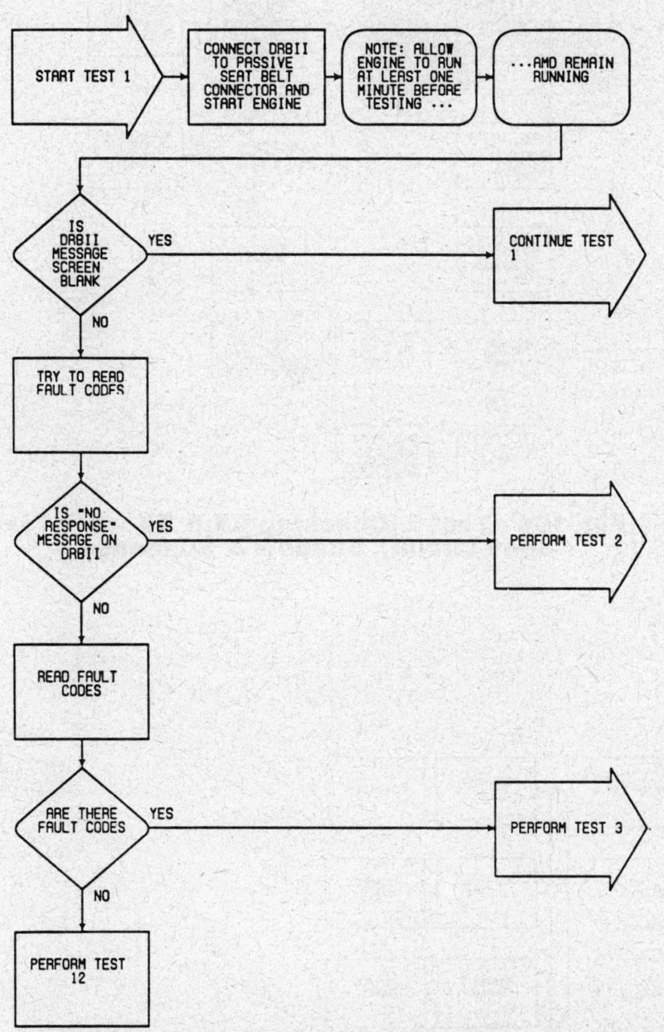


**Fig. 103 Test 1 (Checking for fault codes, Part 1 of 3). Shadow & Sundance**

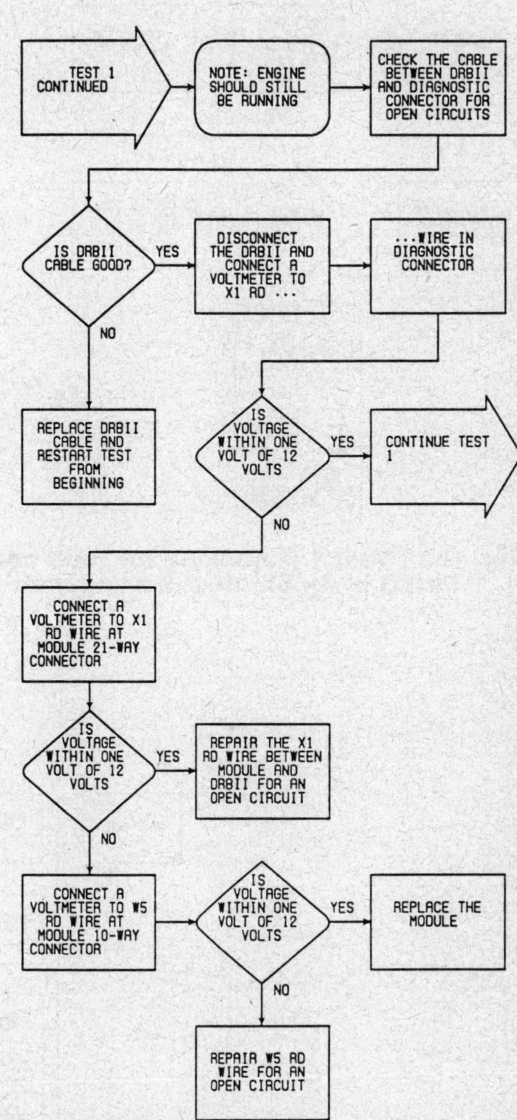


**Fig. 103 Test 1 (Checking for fault codes, Part 2 of 3). Shadow & Sundance**

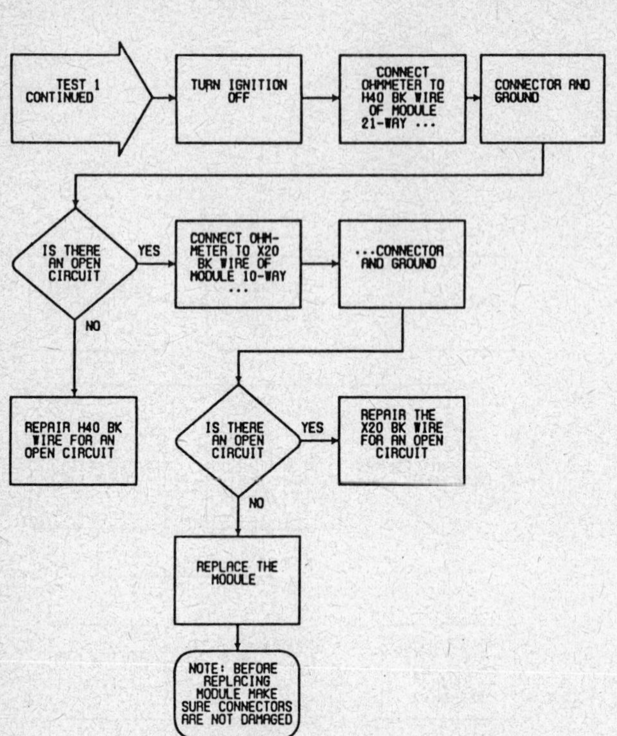


**Fig. 103 Test 1 (Checking for fault codes, Part 3 of 3). Shadow & Sundance**

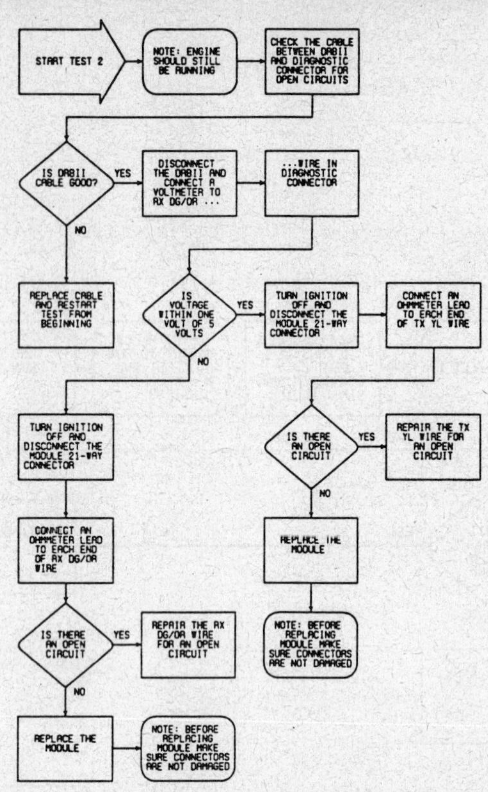


**Fig. 104 Test 2 (Checking RX & TX wires for open circuit). Shadow & Sundance**

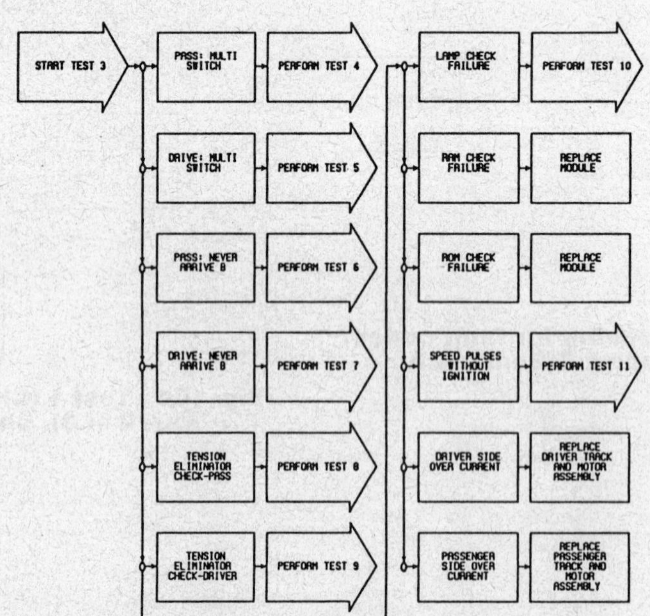


**Fig. 105 Test 3 (Motorized seat belt fault messages). Shadow & Sundance**

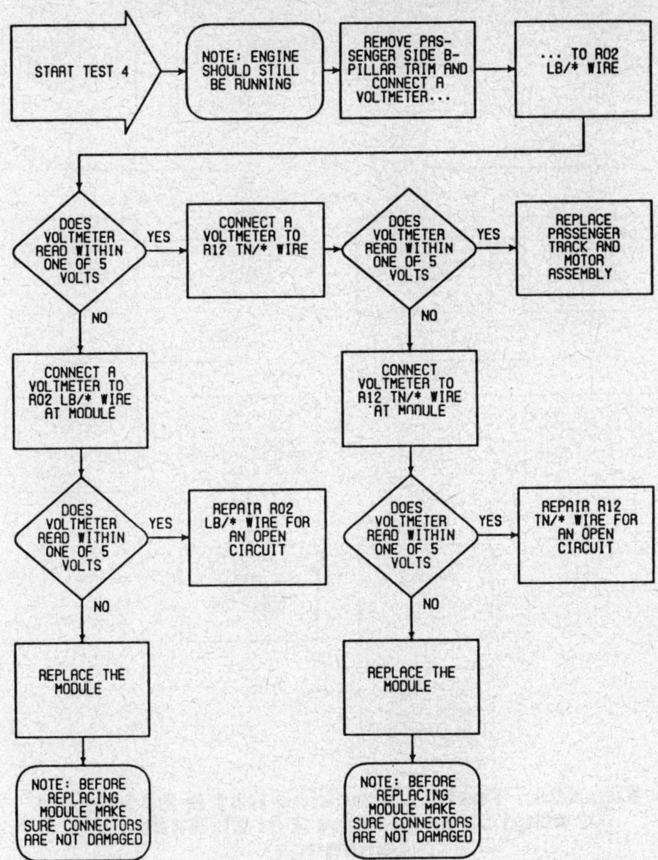


**Fig. 106 Test 4 (Checking R02 & R12 wires for open circuits). Shadow & Sundance**

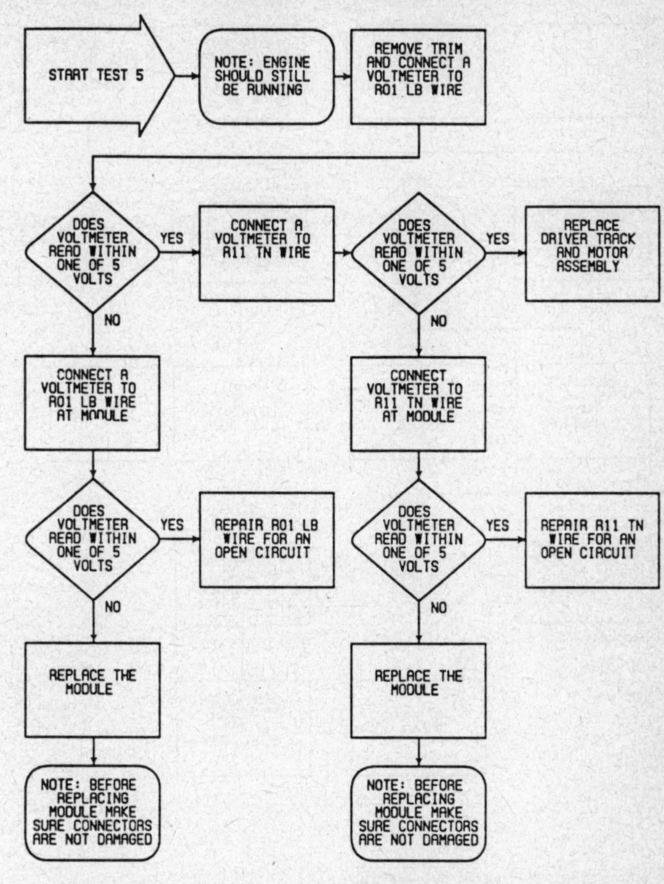


**Fig. 107 Test 5 (Checking R01 & R11 wires for open circuits). Shadow & Sundance**

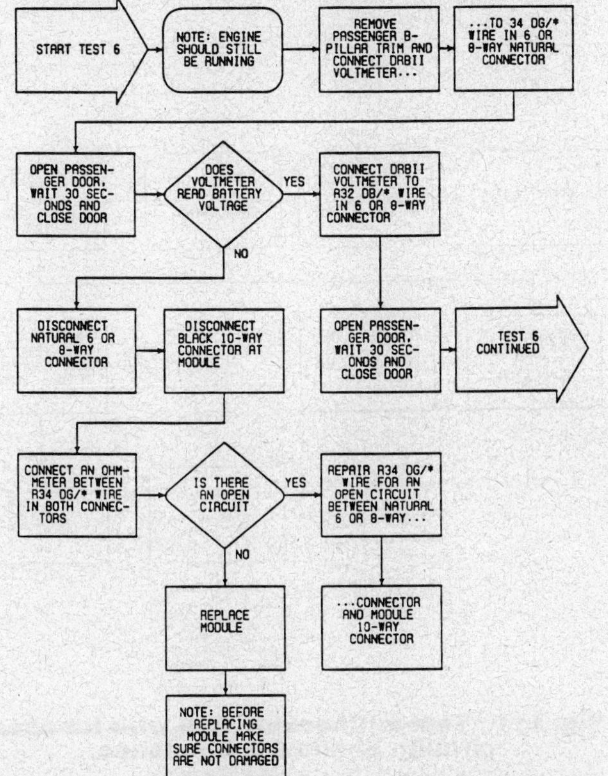


**Fig. 108 Test 6 (Checking R32 & R34 wires for open circuits, Part 1 of 2). Shadow & Sundance**

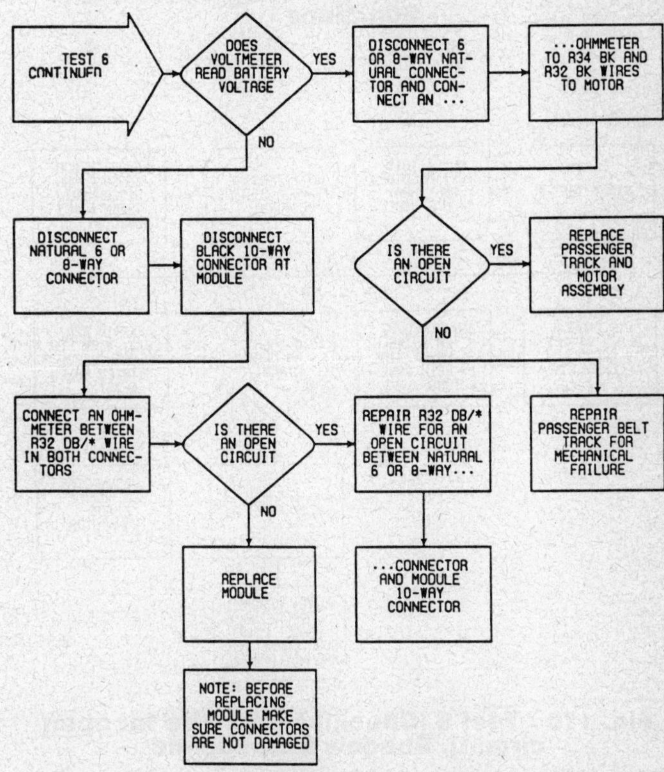


**Fig. 108 Test 6 (Checking R32 & R34 wires for open circuits, Part 2 of 2). Shadow & Sundance**

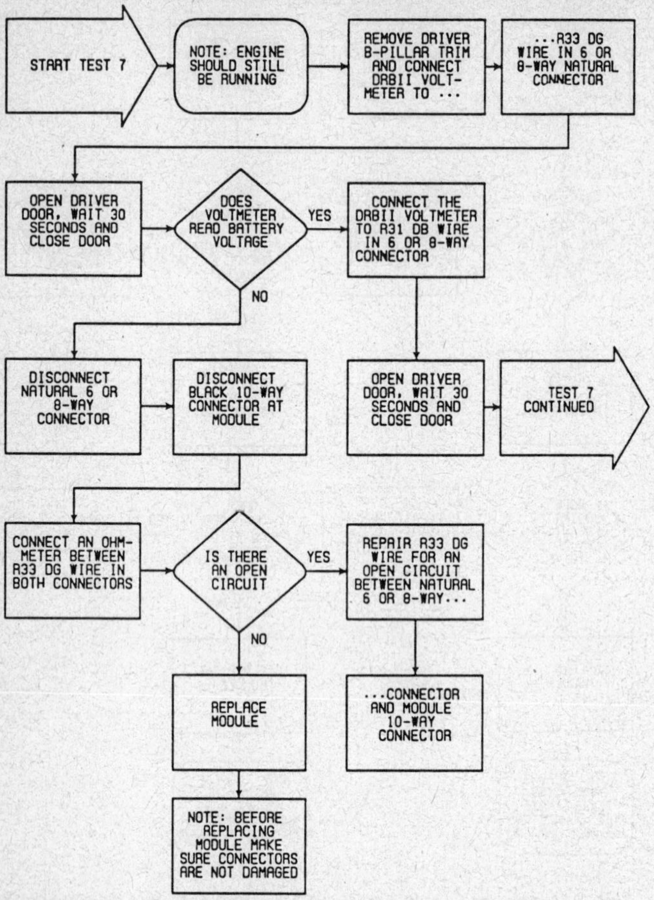

START TEST 7
NOTE: ENGINE SHOULD STILL BE RUNNING
REMOVE DRIVER B-PILLAR TRIM AND CONNECT DRBII VOLTMETER TO ...
...R33 DG WIRE IN 6 OR 8-WAY NATURAL CONNECTOR
OPEN DRIVER DOOR, WAIT 30 SECONDS AND CLOSE DOOR
DOES VOLTMETER READ BATTERY VOLTAGE
YES
NO
CONNECT THE DRBII VOLTMETER TO R31 DB WIRE IN 6 OR 8-WAY CONNECTOR
DISCONNECT NATURAL 6 OR 8-WAY CONNECTOR
DISCONNECT BLACK 10-WAY CONNECTOR AT MODULE
OPEN DRIVER DOOR, WAIT 30 SECONDS AND CLOSE DOOR
TEST 7 CONTINUED
CONNECT AN OHMMETER BETWEEN R33 DG WIRE IN BOTH CONNECTORS
IS THERE AN OPEN CIRCUIT
YES
REPAIR R33 DG WIRE FOR AN OPEN CIRCUIT BETWEEN NATURAL 6 OR 8-WAY...
NO
REPLACE MODULE
...CONNECTOR AND MODULE 10-WAY CONNECTOR
NOTE: BEFORE REPLACING MODULE MAKE SURE CONNECTORS ARE NOT DAMAGED

**Fig. 109 Test 7 (Checking R31 & R33 wires for open circuits, Part 1 of 2). Shadow & Sundance**

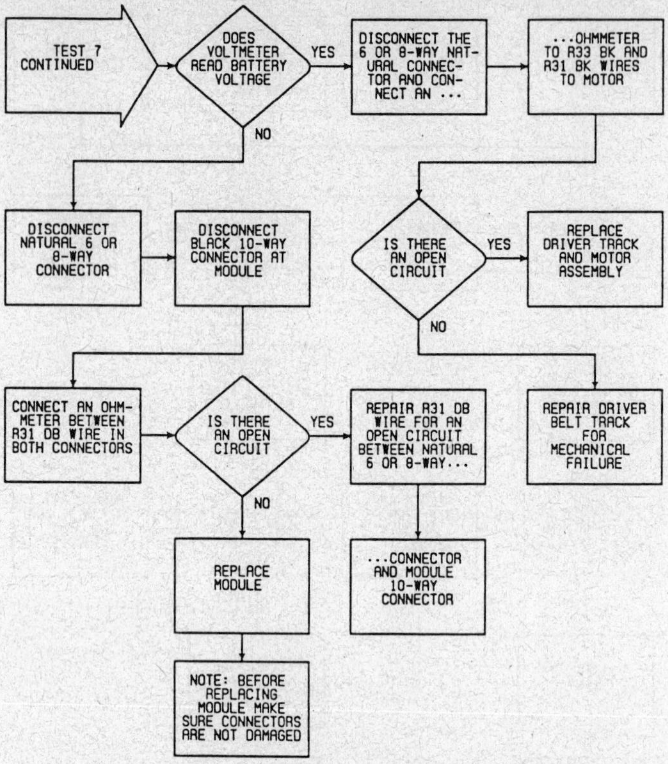

TEST 7 CONTINUED
DOES VOLTMETER READ BATTERY VOLTAGE
YES
NO
DISCONNECT THE 6 OR 8-WAY NATURAL CONNECTOR AND CONNECT AN ...
...OHMMETER TO R33 BK AND R31 BK WIRES TO MOTOR
DISCONNECT NATURAL 6 OR 8-WAY CONNECTOR
DISCONNECT BLACK 10-WAY CONNECTOR AT MODULE
IS THERE AN OPEN CIRCUIT
YES
REPLACE DRIVER TRACK AND MOTOR ASSEMBLY
NO
CONNECT AN OHMMETER BETWEEN R31 DB WIRE IN BOTH CONNECTORS
IS THERE AN OPEN CIRCUIT
YES
REPAIR R31 DB WIRE FOR AN OPEN CIRCUIT BETWEEN NATURAL 6 OR 8-WAY...
REPAIR DRIVER BELT TRACK FOR MECHANICAL FAILURE
NO
REPLACE MODULE
...CONNECTOR AND MODULE 10-WAY CONNECTOR
NOTE: BEFORE REPLACING MODULE MAKE SURE CONNECTORS ARE NOT DAMAGED

**Fig. 109 Test 7 (Checking R31 & R33 wires for open circuits, Part 2 of 2). Shadow & Sundance**

START TEST 8
NOTE: THIS TEST REQUIRED ONLY FOR 2-DOOR MODELS
NOTE: ENGINE SHOULD STILL BE RUNNING
REMOVE FLOOR CONSOLE AND DISCONNECT GREEN 6-WAY CONNECTOR
DISCONNECT BLACK 21-WAY MODULE CONNECTOR
CONNECT OHMMETER BETWEEN R20 LB/GY WIRE IN BOTH CONNECTORS
IS THERE AN OPEN CIRCUIT
YES
REPAIR R20 LB/GY WIRE FOR AN OPEN CIRCUIT BETWEEN GREEN 6-WAY ...
NO
REPLACE MODULE
...CONNECTOR AND MODULE 21-WAY CONNECTOR
NOTE: BEFORE REPLACING MODULE MAKE SURE CONNECTORS ARE NOT DAMAGED

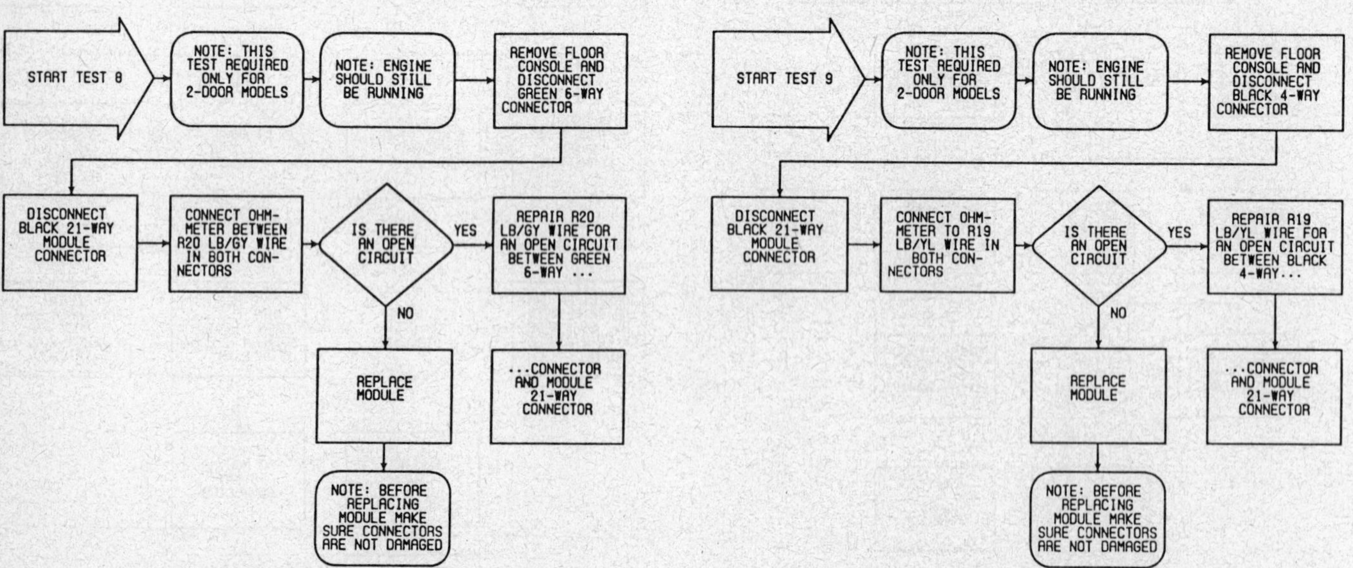

**Fig. 110 Test 8 (Checking R20 wire for open circuit). Shadow & Sundance**

START TEST 9
NOTE: THIS TEST REQUIRED ONLY FOR 2-DOOR MODELS
NOTE: ENGINE SHOULD STILL BE RUNNING
REMOVE FLOOR CONSOLE AND DISCONNECT BLACK 4-WAY CONNECTOR
DISCONNECT BLACK 21-WAY MODULE CONNECTOR
CONNECT OHMMETER TO R19 LB/YL WIRE IN BOTH CONNECTORS
IS THERE AN OPEN CIRCUIT
YES
REPAIR R19 LB/YL WIRE FOR AN OPEN CIRCUIT BETWEEN BLACK 4-WAY...
NO
REPLACE MODULE
...CONNECTOR AND MODULE 21-WAY CONNECTOR
NOTE: BEFORE REPLACING MODULE MAKE SURE CONNECTORS ARE NOT DAMAGED

**Fig. 111 Test 9 (Checking R19 wire for open circuit). Shadow & Sundance**

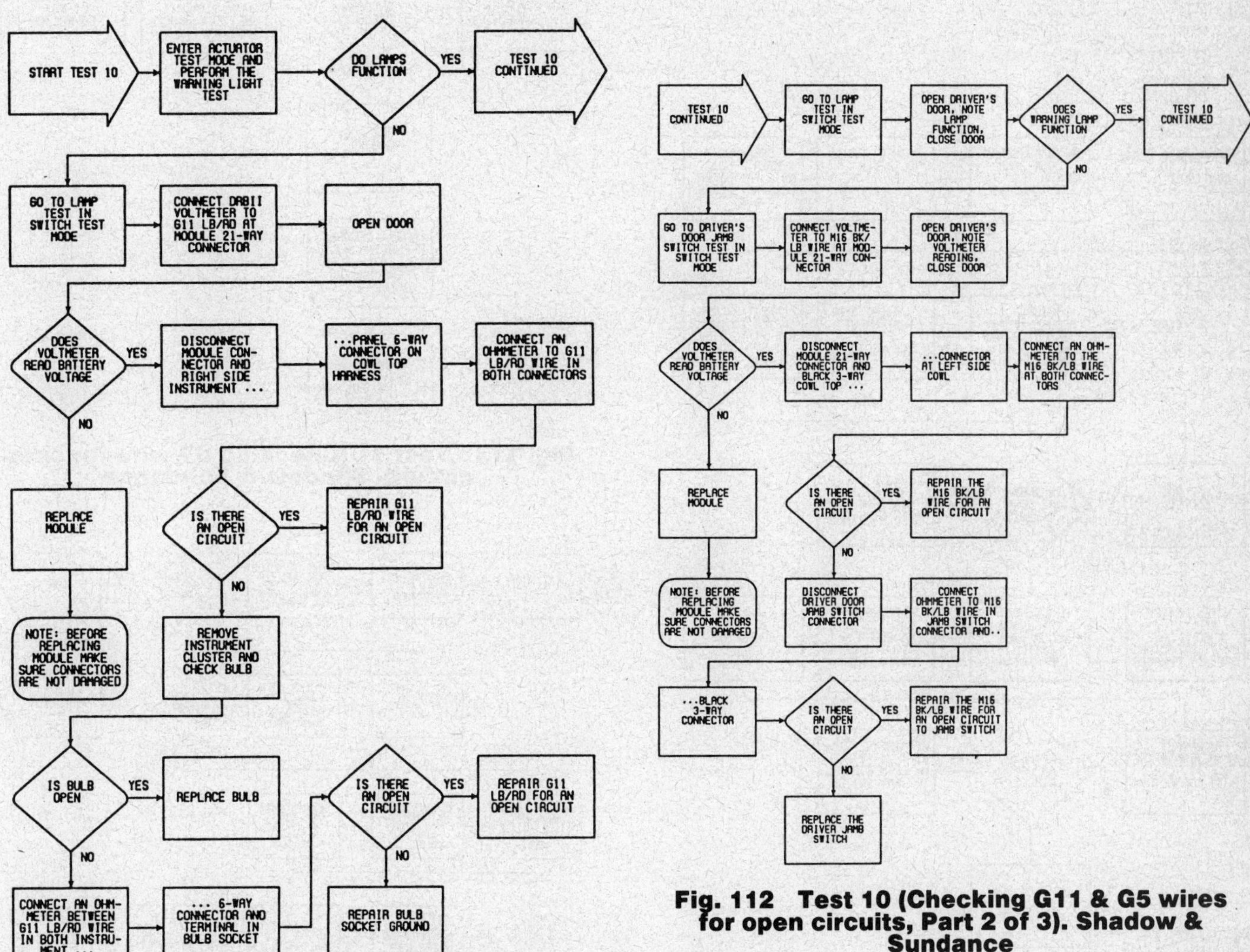


**Fig. 112 Test 10 (Checking G11 & G5 wires for open circuits, Part 1 of 3). Shadow & Sundance**

**Fig. 112 Test 10 (Checking G11 & G5 wires for open circuits, Part 2 of 3). Shadow & Sundance**

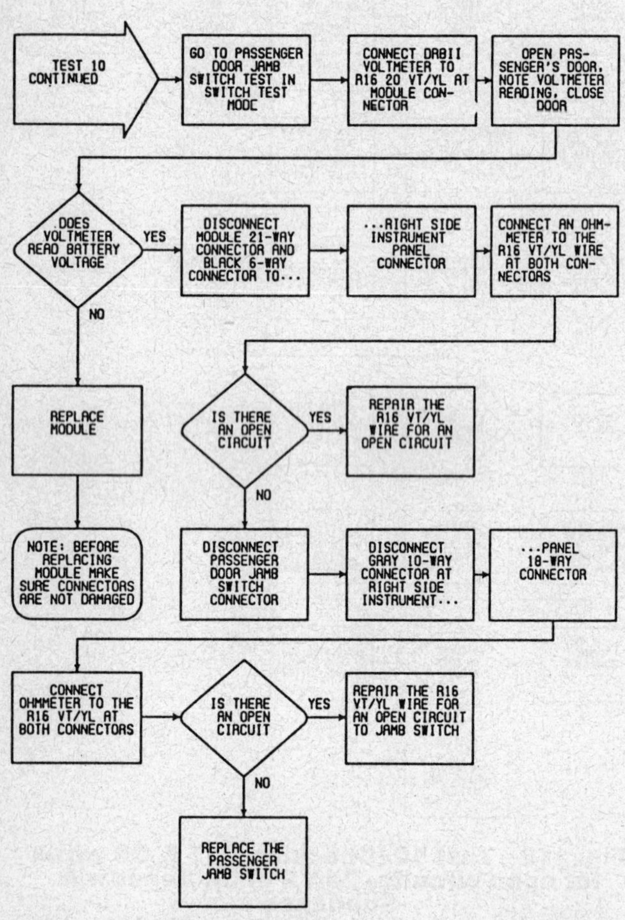


**Fig. 112 Test 10 (Checking G11 & G5 wires for open circuits, Part 3 of 3). Shadow & Sundance**

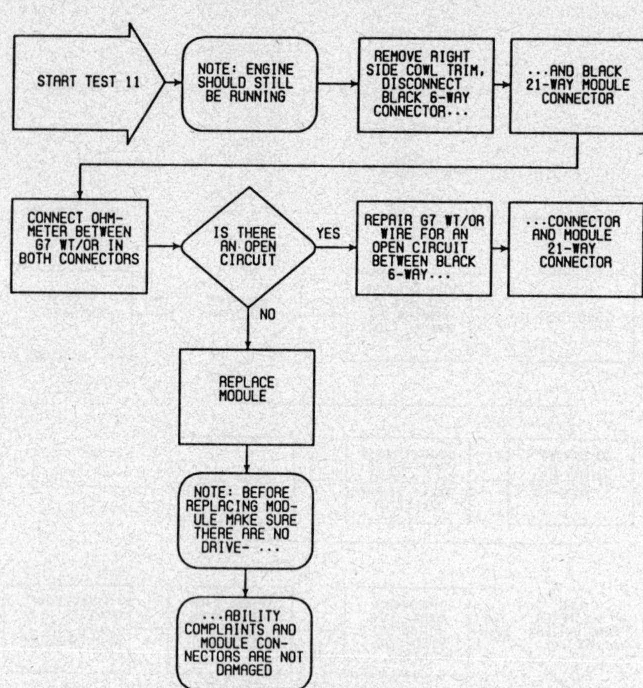


**Fig. 113 Test 11 (Checking G7 wire for open circuit). Shadow & Sundance**

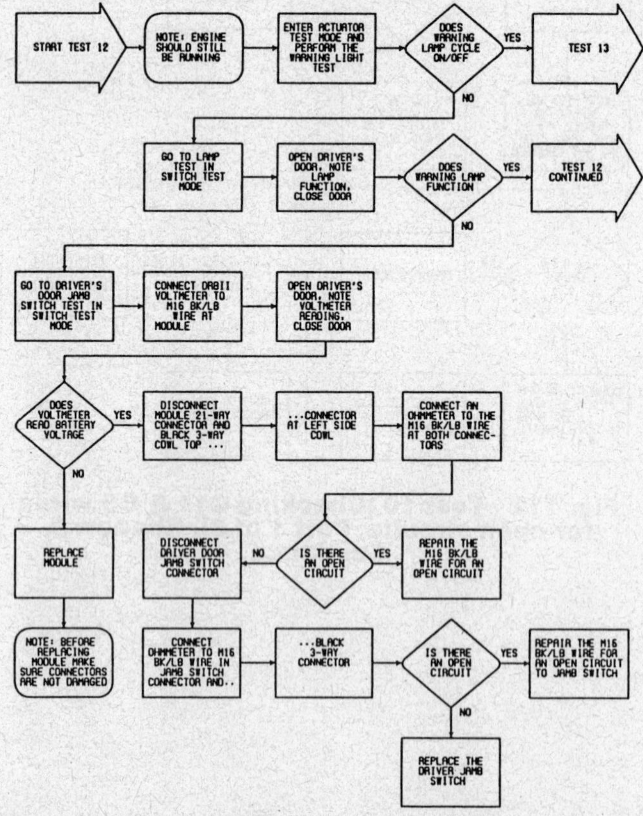


**Fig. 114 Test 12 (Checking M16 wire for open circuit, Part 1 of 2). Shadow & Sundance**

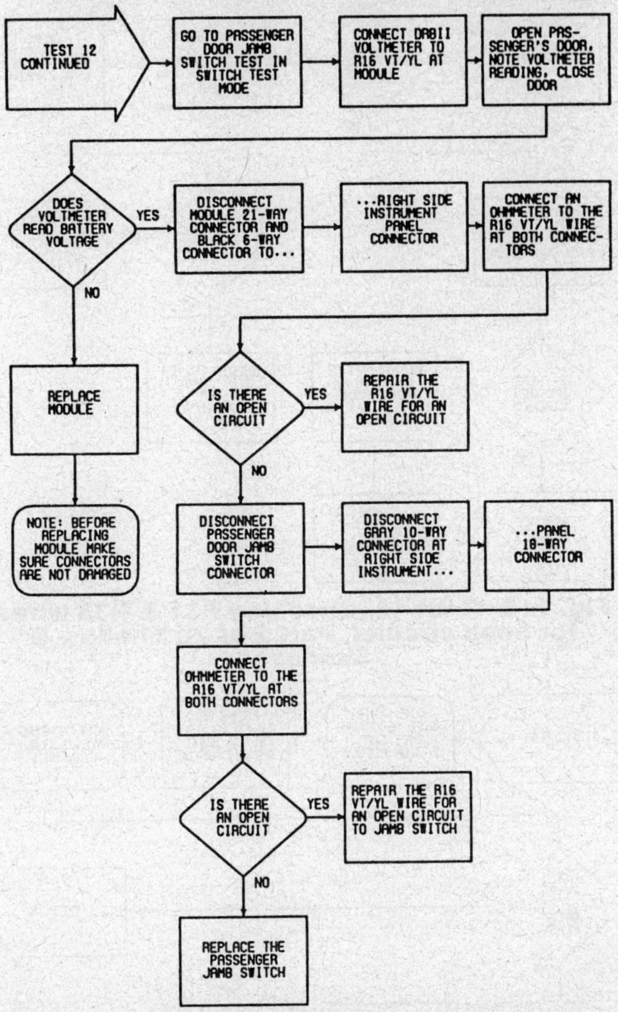

TEST 12 CONTINUED
GO TO PASSENGER DOOR JAMB SWITCH TEST IN SWITCH TEST MODE
CONNECT DRBII VOLTMETER TO R16 VT/YL AT MODULE
OPEN PASSENGER'S DOOR, NOTE VOLTMETER READING, CLOSE DOOR
DOES VOLTMETER READ BATTERY VOLTAGE
YES
DISCONNECT MODULE 21-WAY CONNECTOR AND BLACK 6-WAY CONNECTOR TO...
...RIGHT SIDE INSTRUMENT PANEL CONNECTOR
CONNECT AN OHMMETER TO THE R16 VT/YL WIRE AT BOTH CONNECTORS
NO
REPLACE MODULE
NOTE: BEFORE REPLACING MODULE MAKE SURE CONNECTORS ARE NOT DAMAGED
IS THERE AN OPEN CIRCUIT
YES
REPAIR THE R16 VT/YL WIRE FOR AN OPEN CIRCUIT
NO
DISCONNECT PASSENGER DOOR JAMB SWITCH CONNECTOR
DISCONNECT GRAY 10-WAY CONNECTOR AT RIGHT SIDE INSTRUMENT...
...PANEL 10-WAY CONNECTOR
CONNECT OHMMETER TO THE R16 VT/YL AT BOTH CONNECTORS
IS THERE AN OPEN CIRCUIT
YES
REPAIR THE R16 VT/YL WIRE FOR AN OPEN CIRCUIT TO JAMB SWITCH
NO
REPLACE THE PASSENGER JAMB SWITCH

**Fig. 114 Test 12 (Checking M16 wire for open circuit, Part 2 of 2). Shadow & Sundance**

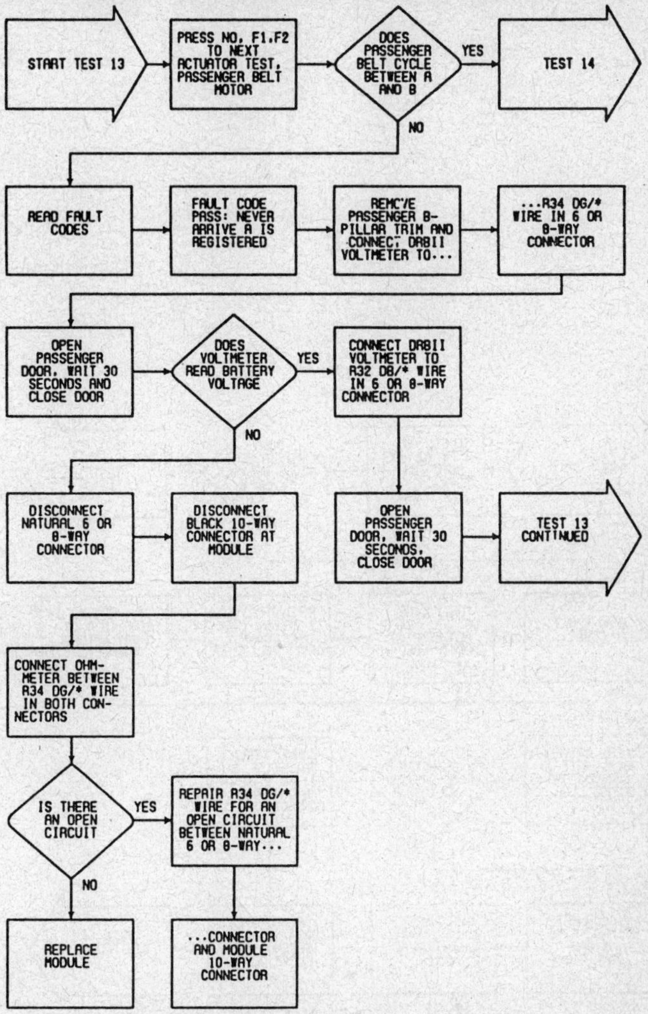

START TEST 13
PRESS NO, F1,F2 TO NEXT ACTUATOR TEST, PASSENGER BELT MOTOR
DOES PASSENGER BELT CYCLE BETWEEN A AND B
YES
TEST 14
NO
READ FAULT CODES
FAULT CODE PASS: NEVER ARRIVE A IS REGISTERED
REMOVE PASSENGER B-PILLAR TRIM AND CONNECT DRBII VOLTMETER TO...
...R34 DG/* WIRE IN 6 OR 8-WAY CONNECTOR
OPEN PASSENGER DOOR, WAIT 30 SECONDS AND CLOSE DOOR
DOES VOLTMETER READ BATTERY VOLTAGE
YES
CONNECT DRBII VOLTMETER TO R32 DB/* WIRE IN 6 OR 8-WAY CONNECTOR
NO
DISCONNECT NATURAL 6 OR 8-WAY CONNECTOR
DISCONNECT BLACK 10-WAY CONNECTOR AT MODULE
OPEN PASSENGER DOOR, WAIT 30 SECONDS, CLOSE DOOR
TEST 13 CONTINUED
CONNECT OHMMETER BETWEEN R34 DG/* WIRE IN BOTH CONNECTORS
IS THERE AN OPEN CIRCUIT
YES
REPAIR R34 DG/* WIRE FOR AN OPEN CIRCUIT BETWEEN NATURAL 6 OR 8-WAY...
NO
REPLACE MODULE
...CONNECTOR AND MODULE 10-WAY CONNECTOR

**Fig. 115 Test 13 (Checking R32 & R34 wires for open circuits, Part 1 of 2). Shadow & Sundance**

TEST 13 CONTINUED
DOES VOLTMETER READ BATTERY VOLTAGE
YES
DISCONNECT THE 6 OR 8-WAY NATURAL CONNECTOR AND CONNECT AN ...
...OHMMETER TO R34 BK AND R32 BK WIRES TO MOTOR
NO
CONNECT AN OHMMETER BETWEEN R32 DB/* WIRE IN BOTH CONNECTORS
IS THERE AN OPEN CIRCUIT
YES
REPLACE PASSENGER TRACK AND MOTOR ASSEMBLY
NO
REPAIR PASSENGER BELT TRACK FOR MECHANICAL FAILURE
IS THERE AN OPEN CIRCUIT
YES
REPAIR R32 DB/* WIRE FOR AN OPEN CIRCUIT BETWEEN NATURAL 6 OR 8-WAY...
NO
REPLACE MODULE
...CONNECTOR AND MODULE 10-WAY CONNECTOR

**Fig. 115 Test 13 (Checking R32 & R34 wires for open circuits, Part 2 of 2). Shadow & Sundance**

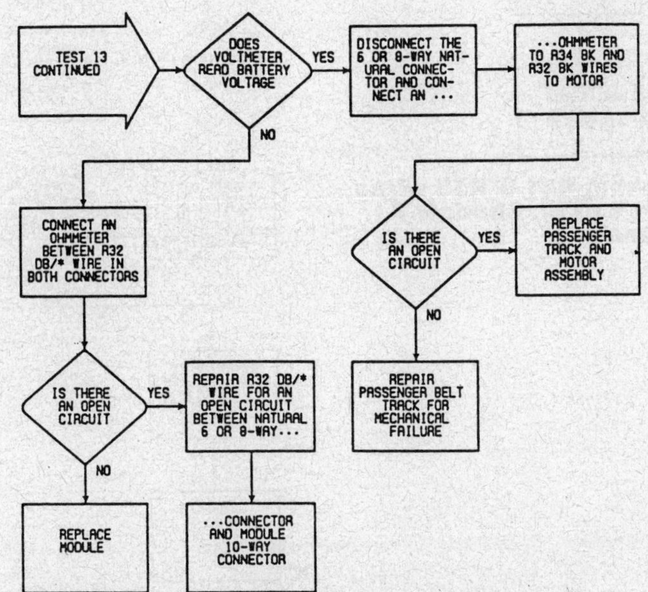

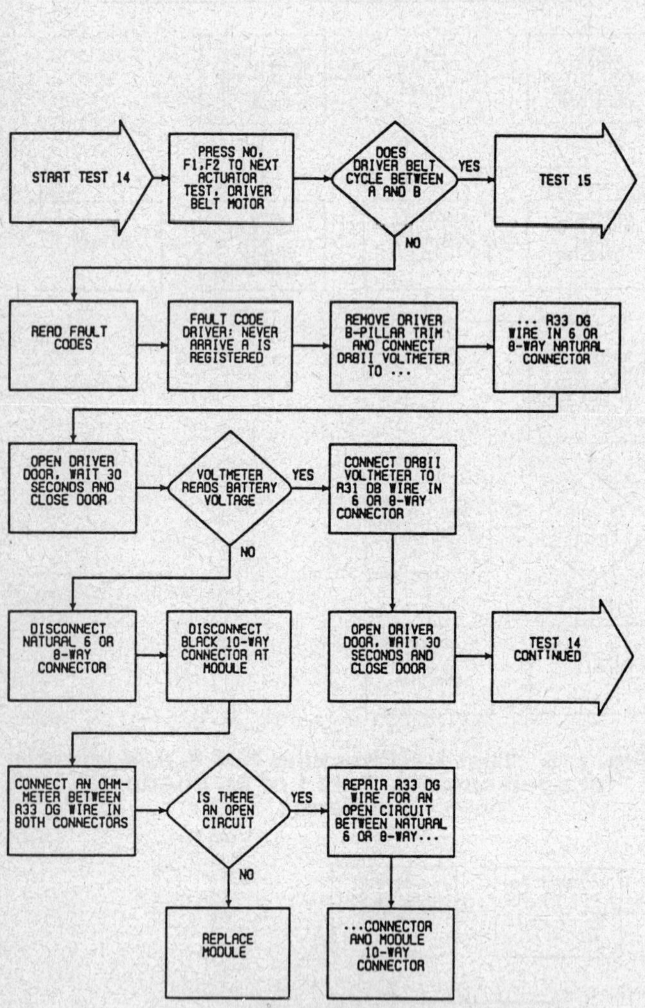


**Fig. 116 Test 14 (Checking R31 & R33 wires for open circuits, Part 1 of 2). Shadow & Sundance**

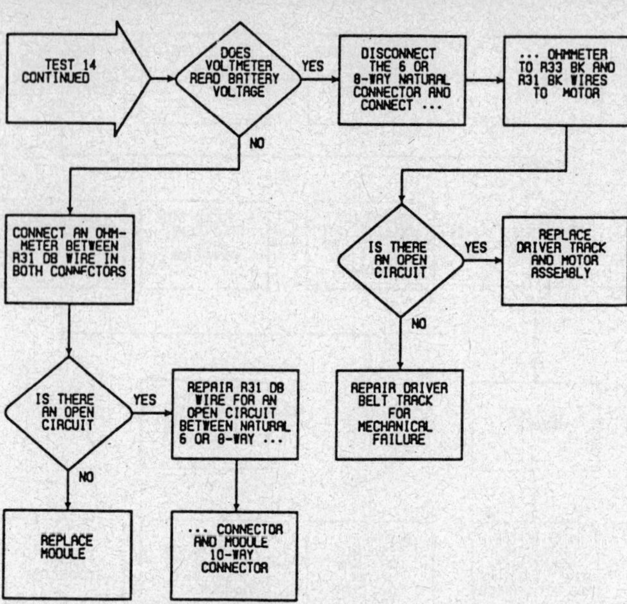


**Fig. 116 Test 14 (Checking R31 & R33 wires for open circuits, Part 2 of 2). Shadow & Sundance**

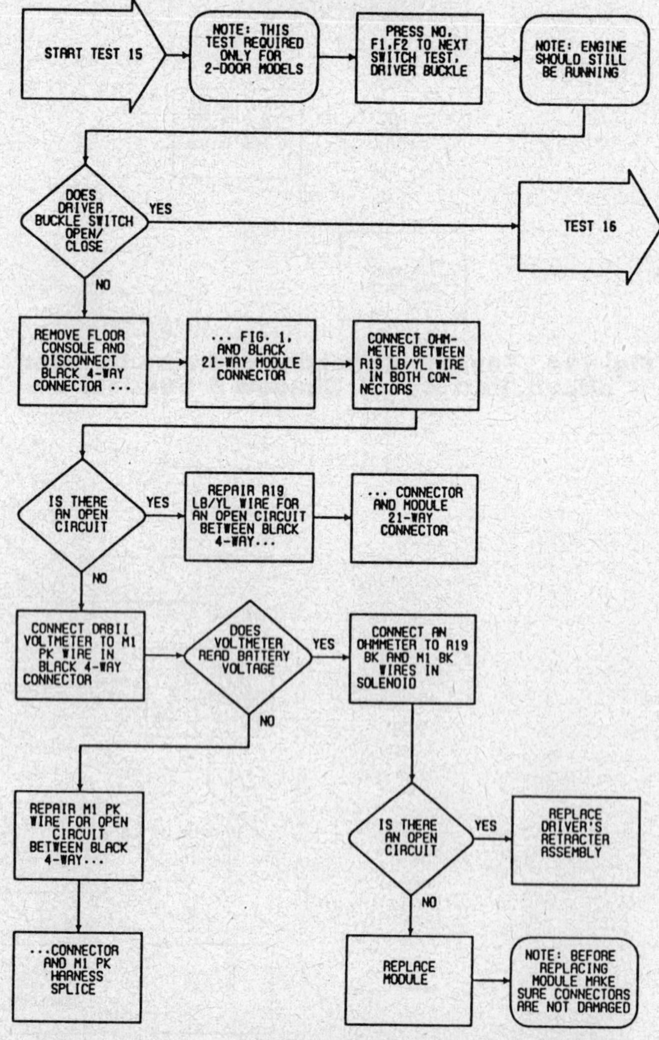


**Fig. 117 Test 15 (Checking R19 & M1 wires for open circuits). Shadow & Sundance**

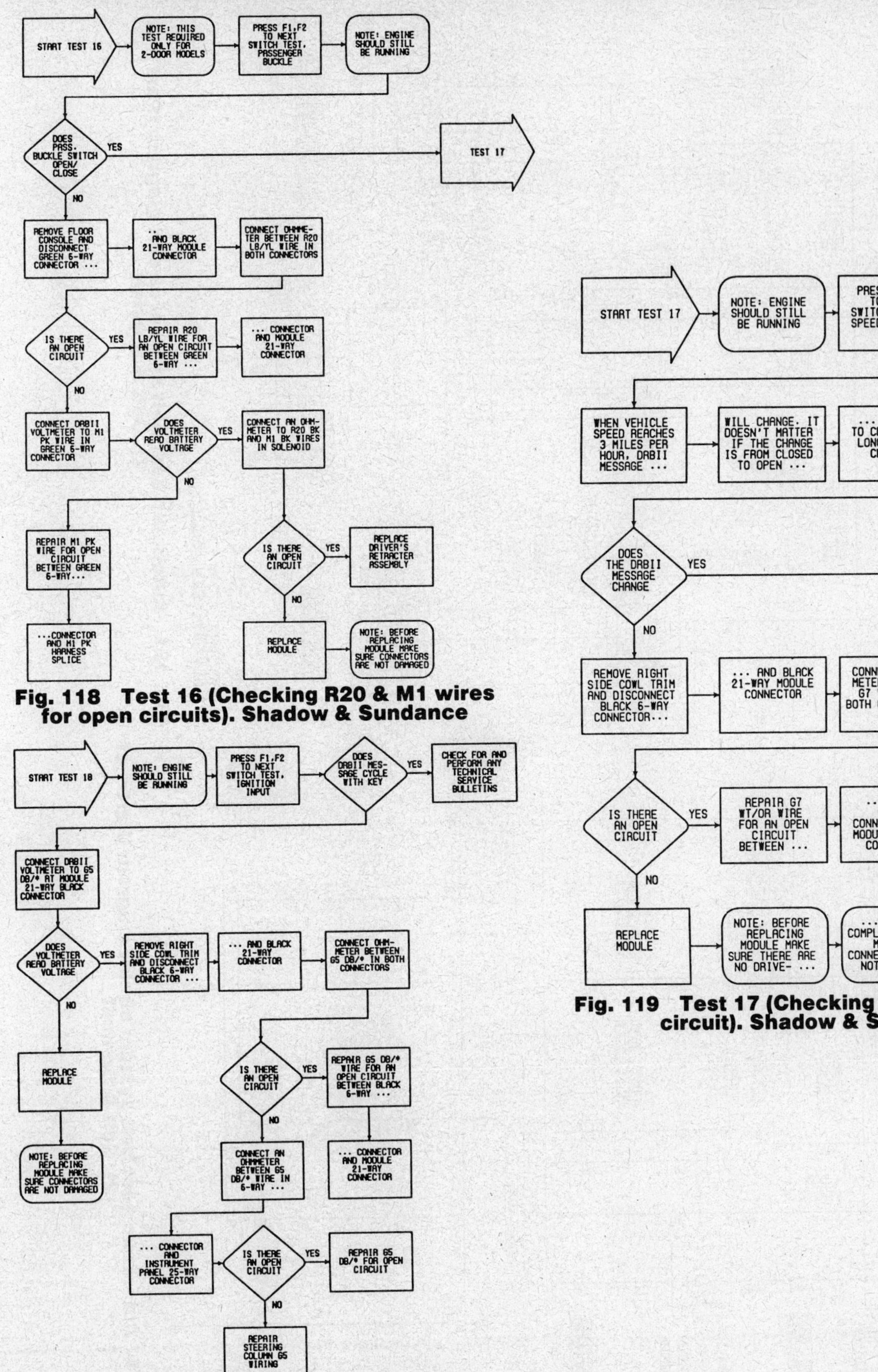


**Fig. 118 Test 16 (Checking R20 & M1 wires for open circuits). Shadow & Sundance**

**Fig. 119 Test 17 (Checking G7 wire for open circuit). Shadow & Sundance**

**Fig. 120 Test 18 (Checking G5 wire for open circuit). Shadow & Sundance**

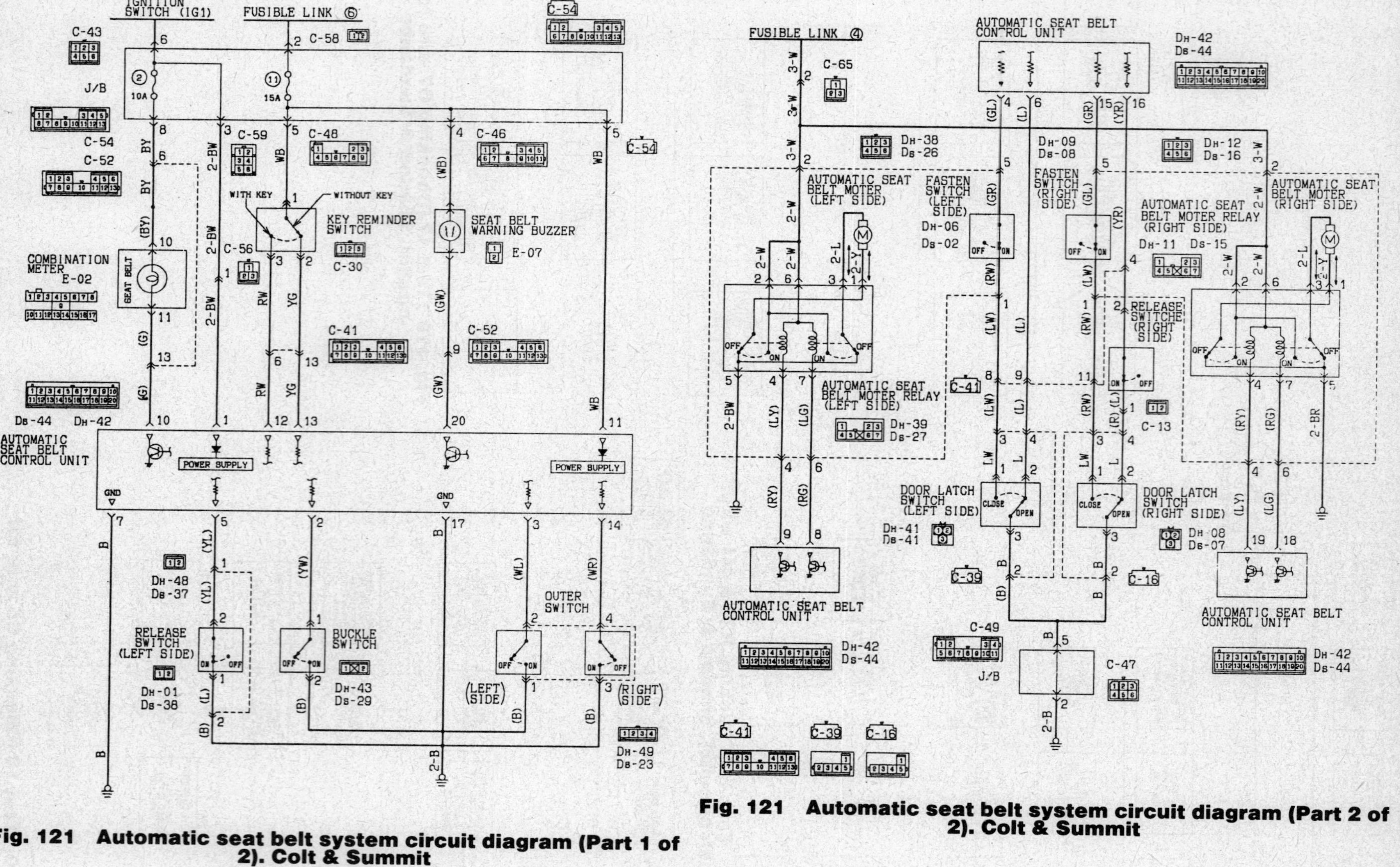


Fig. 121 Automatic seat belt system circuit diagram (Part 1 of 2). Colt & Summit

Fig. 121 Automatic seat belt system circuit diagram (Part 2 of 2). Colt & Summit

# CIRCUIT TESTING

## COLT & SUMMIT

Refer to **Fig. 121** for automatic seat belt system circuit diagram on Colt and Summit models.

### Control Unit Power Supply & Ground

Refer to **Fig. 122** when performing these tests.

1. Disconnect control unit harness connector.
2. Connect a suitable voltmeter between control unit connector terminal 11 and ground.
3. Voltage indicated should be approximately 12 volts.
4. If voltage indicated is as specified, circuit is satisfactory. Proceed to step 6.
5. If voltage indicated is not as specified, repair circuit as necessary.
6. Connect a suitable voltmeter between control unit connector terminal 1 and ground.
7. Turn ignition switch On.
8. Voltage indicated should be approximately 12 volts.
9. If voltage indicated is as specified, circuit is satisfactory. Proceed to step 11.
10. If voltage indicated is not as specified, repair circuit as necessary.
11. Connect a suitable ohmmeter between control unit connector terminal 7 and ground, then terminal 17 and ground.
12. Turn ignition switch Off.
13. Ohmmeter should indicate continuity.
14. If continuity is indicated, circuit is satisfactory.
15. If continuity is not indicated, repair circuit as necessary.

### Warning Light, Key Reminder Switch & Buzzer

Refer to **Fig. 123** when performing these tests.

1. Check warning light circuit as follows:
   a. Disconnect warning light harness connector.
   b. Connect a suitable voltmeter between warning light connector terminal 10 and ground.
   c. Turn ignition switch On.
   d. Voltage indicated should be approximately 12 volts.
   e. If voltage indicated is as specified, circuit is satisfactory. Proceed to step g.
   f. If voltage indicated is not as specified, repair circuit as necessary.
   g. Connect warning light harness connector.
   h. Disconnect control unit harness connector.
   i. Connect a suitable voltmeter between control unit connector terminal 10 and ground.
   j. Turn ignition switch On.
   k. Voltage indicated should be approximately 12 volts.
   l. If voltage indicated is as specified, circuit is satisfactory. Proceed to step 2.
   m. If voltage indicated is not as specified, repair circuit or replace warning light bulb as necessary.
2. Check key reminder switch circuit as follows:
   a. Disconnect key reminder switch harness connector.
   b. Connect a suitable voltmeter between key reminder switch connector terminal 1 and ground.
   c. Voltage indicated should be approximately 12 volts.
   d. If voltage indicated is as specified, circuit is satisfactory. Proceed to step f.
   e. If voltage indicated is not as specified, repair circuit as necessary.
   f. Connect key reminder switch harness connector.
   g. Disconnect control unit harness connector.
   h. Remove key from ignition switch.
   i. Connect a suitable voltmeter between control unit connector terminal 13 and ground.
   j. Voltage indicated should be approximately 12 volts.
   k. If voltage indicated is as specified, circuit is satisfactory. Proceed to step m.
   l. If voltage indicated is not as specified, repair circuit as necessary.
   m. Connect a suitable voltmeter between control unit connector terminal 12 and ground.
   n. Voltage indicated should be 0 volts.
   o. If voltage indicated is as specified, circuit is satisfactory. Proceed to step q.
   p. If voltage indicated is not as specified, replace key reminder switch.
   q. Insert ignition key.
   r. Connect a suitable voltmeter between control unit connector terminal 13 and ground.
   s. Voltage indicated should be 0 volts.
   t. If voltage indicated is as specified, circuit is satisfactory. Proceed to step v.
   u. If voltage indicated is not as specified, replace key reminder switch.
   v. Connect a suitable voltmeter between control unit connector terminal 12 and ground.
   w. Voltage indicated should be approximately 12 volts.
   x. If voltage indicated is as specified, circuit is satisfactory. Proceed to step 3.
   y. If voltage indicated is not as specified, repair harness as necessary.
3. Check buzzer circuit as follows:
   a. Disconnect buzzer harness connector.
   b. Connect a suitable voltmeter between buzzer connector terminal 1 and ground.
   c. Voltage indicated should be approximately 12 volts.
   d. If voltage indicated is as specified, circuit is satisfactory. Proceed to step f.
   e. If voltage indicated is not as specified, repair harness as necessary.
   f. Connect buzzer harness connector, then disconnect control unit harness connector.
   g. Connect a suitable voltmeter between control unit connector terminal 20 and ground.
   h. Voltage indicated should be approximately 12 volts.
   i. If voltage indicated is as specified, circuit is satisfactory.
   j. If voltage indicated is not as specified, repair harness as necessary.

### Motor Power Supply & Drive

Refer to **Fig. 124** when performing these tests.

1. Disconnect motor relay harness connector.
2. Connect a suitable ohmmeter between motor relay connector terminals 1 and 3 (motor relay side).
3. Ohmmeter should indicate continuity.
4. If continuity is indicated, circuit is satisfactory. Proceed to step 6.
5. If continuity is not indicated, replace motor and track assembly.
6. Connect ohmmeter between motor relay connector terminal 5 (harness side) and ground.
7. Ohmmeter should indicate continuity.
8. If continuity is indicated, circuit is satisfactory. Proceed to step 10.
9. If continuity is not indicated, repair harness as necessary.
10. Disconnect control unit harness connector.
11. Connect ohmmeter between motor relay connector terminal 1 (motor relay side) and ground, then between terminal 3 (motor relay side) and ground.
12. Ohmmeter should indicate continuity.
13. If continuity is indicated, circuit is satisfactory. Proceed to step 15.
14. If continuity is not indicated, replace motor and track assembly.
15. Connect a suitable voltmeter between motor relay connector terminal 2 (harness side) and ground, then between terminal 6 (harness side) and ground.
16. Voltage indicated should be approximately 12 volts.
17. If voltage indicated is as specified, circuit is satisfactory. Proceed to step 19.
18. If voltage indicated is not as specified, repair harness as necessary.
19. Connect motor relay harness connector.
20. Connect voltmeter between control unit connector terminals 8, 9 and ground (left side), then between terminals 18, 19 and ground (right side).
21. Voltage indicated should be approximately 12 volts.
22. If voltage indicated is as specified, circuit is satisfactory.
23. If voltage indicated is not as specified, repair harness or replace motor and track assembly as necessary.

### Release Switch (Driver's Side), Buckle Switch & Release Switch

Refer to **Fig. 125** when performing these tests.

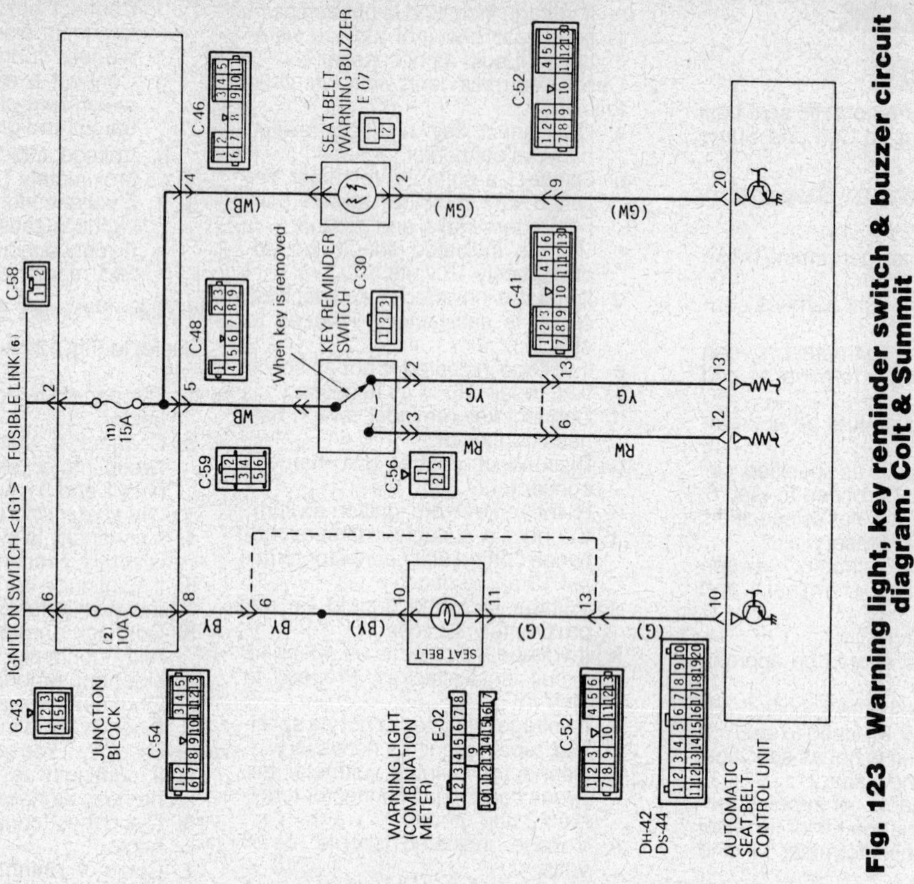


Fig. 123 Warning light, key reminder switch & buzzer circuit diagram. Colt & Summit

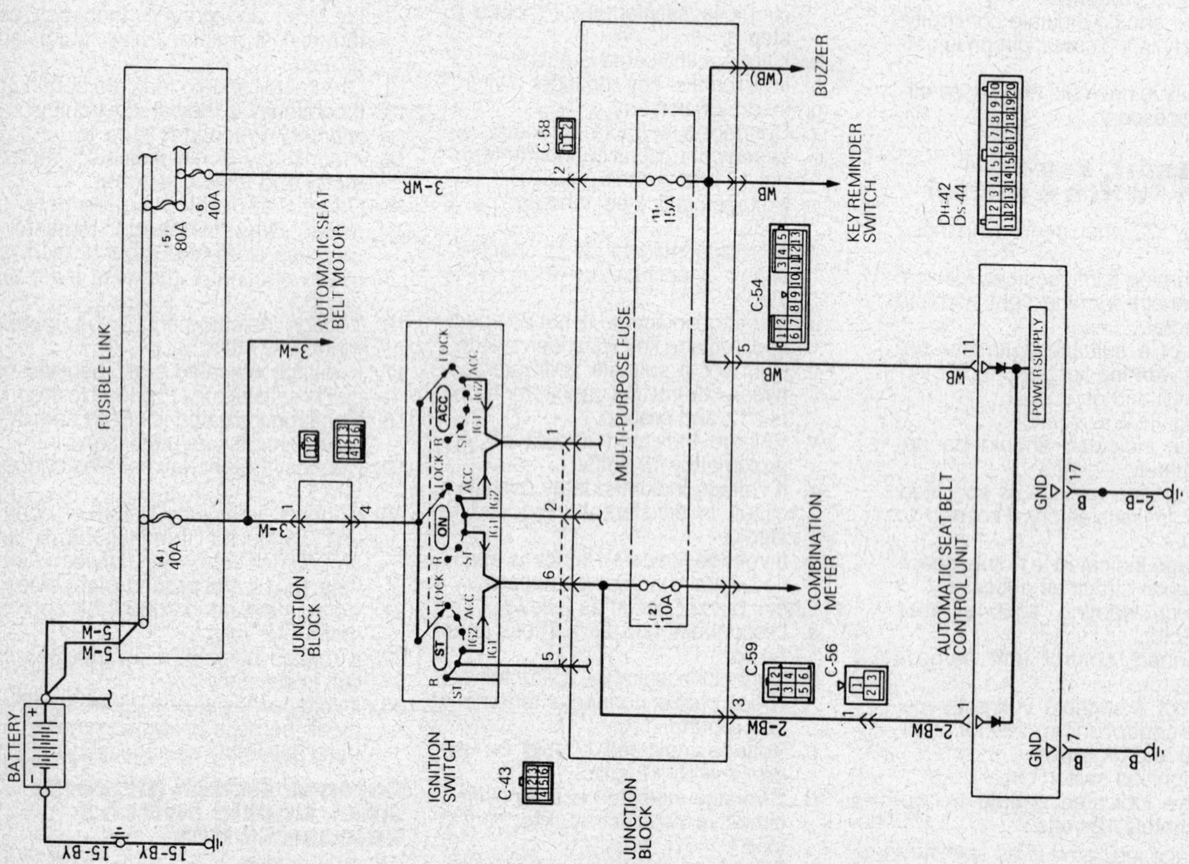


Fig. 122 Control unit power supply & ground circuit diagram. Colt & Summit

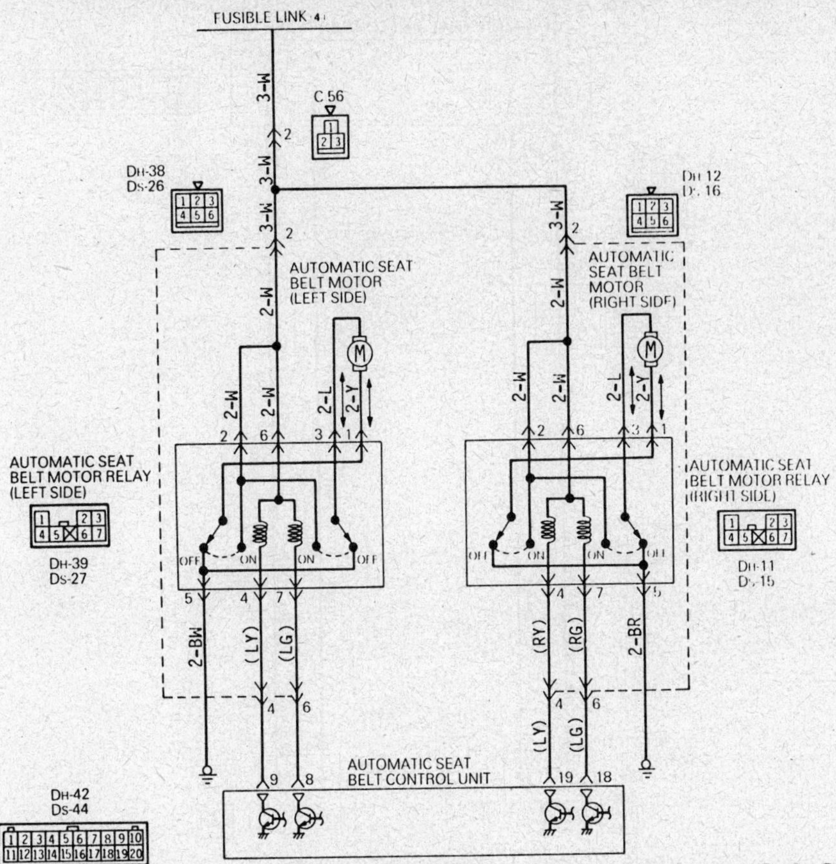


**Fig. 124 Motor power supply & drive circuit diagram. Colt & Summit**

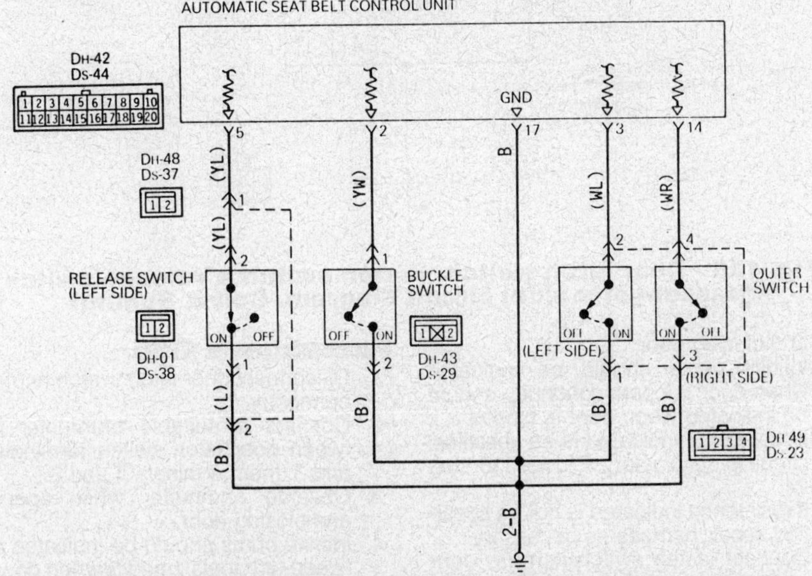


**Fig. 125 Release switch (driver's side), buckle switch & release switch circuit diagram. Colt & Summit**

1. Check release switch (driver's side) circuit as follows:
   a. Disconnect release switch harness connector.
   b. Connect a suitable ohmmeter between release switch connector terminal 1 and ground.
   c. Ohmmeter should indicate continuity.
   d. If continuity is indicated, circuit is satisfactory. Proceed to step f.
   e. If continuity is not indicated, repair harness as necessary.
   f. Connect release switch harness connector, then disconnect control unit harness connector.
   g. Connect ohmmeter between control unit connector terminal 5 and ground.
   h. Observe ohmmeter while moving slide anchor.
   i. Ohmmeter should indicate continuity when slide anchor is not in release (switch On) range.
   j. Ohmmeter indicate infinite ohms when slide anchor is in release (switch Off) range.
   k. If resistance indicated is as specified, circuit is satisfactory. Proceed to step 2.
   l. If resistance indicated is not as specified, repair harness or replace motor and track assembly as necessary.
2. Check buckle switch circuit as follows:
   a. Disconnect buckle switch harness connector.
   b. Connect a suitable ohmmeter between buckle switch connector terminal 2 and ground.
   c. Ohmmeter should indicate continuity.
   d. If continuity is indicated, circuit is satisfactory. Proceed to step f.
   e. If continuity is not indicated, repair harness as necessary.
   f. Connect buckle switch harness connector, then disconnect control unit harness connector. Ensure lap belt is unfastened (buckle switch On).
   g. Connect ohmmeter between control unit connector terminal 2 and ground.
   h. Ohmmeter should indicate continuity.
   i. If continuity is indicated, circuit is satisfactory. Proceed to step 3.
   j. If continuity is not indicated, repair harness or replace buckle as necessary.
3. Check outer switch circuit as follows:
   a. Disconnect outer switch harness connector.
   b. Connect ohmmeter between outer switch connector (harness side) terminal 1 and ground, then terminal 3 and ground.
   c. Ohmmeter should indicate continuity.
   d. If continuity is indicated, circuit is satisfactory. Proceed to step f.
   e. If continuity is not indicated, repair harness as necessary.
   f. Connect ohmmeter between outer switch connector (switch side) terminals 1 and 2 (left side), then between terminals 3 and 4 (right side).
   g. Observe ohmmeter while pulling out and retracting shoulder belt.
   h. With shoulder belt fully retracted to pulled out approximately half way (outer switch Off), infinite ohms should be indicated.
   i. With shoulder belt pulled half way out to fully pulled out position (outer switch On), continuity should be indicated.
   j. If resistance indicated is as specified, circuit is satisfactory. Proceed to step l.
   k. If resistance indicated is not as

specified, replace shoulder belt retractor assembly.

l. Connect shoulder belt to slide anchor (outer switch On). Connect outer switch harness connector, then disconnect control unit harness connector.
m. Connect ohmmeter between control unit connector terminal 3 and ground, then terminal 14 and ground.
n. Ohmmeter should indicate continuity.
o. If continuity is indicated, circuit is satisfactory.
p. If continuity is not indicated, repair harness as necessary.

## DOOR LATCH SWITCH, FASTEN SWITCH & RELEASE SWITCH (PASSENGER'S SIDE)

Refer to **Fig. 126** when performing these tests.

### Driver's Side

1. Disconnect door latch switch harness connector.
2. Connect a suitable ohmmeter between door latch switch terminals 1 and 3, then terminals 2 and 3.
3. Observe ohmmeter while opening and closing door.
4. Infinite ohms should be indicated between terminals 1 and 3 when door is open, continuity should be indicated between terminals 1 and 3 when door is closed.
5. Continuity should be indicated between terminals 2 and 3 when door is open, infinite ohms should be indicated between terminals 2 and 3 when door is closed.
6. If resistance indicated is as specified, circuit is satisfactory. Proceed to step 8.
7. If resistance indicated is not as specified, replace door latch switch.
8. Connect ohmmeter between door latch switch connector terminal 3 and ground.
9. Ohmmeter should indicate continuity.
10. If continuity is indicated, circuit is satisfactory. Proceed to step 12.
11. If continuity is not indicated, repair harness as necessary.
12. Connect door latch switch harness connector, then disconnect control unit harness connector.
13. Connect ohmmeter between control unit connector terminal 6 and ground.
14. Observe ohmmeter while opening and closing door.
15. Continuity should be indicated when door is open, infinite ohms should be indicated is closed.
16. If resistance indicated is as specified, circuit is satisfactory. Proceed to step 18.
17. If resistance indicated is not as specified, repair harness as necessary.
18. Disconnect fasten switch harness connector.
19. Connect ohmmeter between fasten switch connector terminal 1 and ground.
20. Observe ohmmeter while opening and closing door.
21. Infinite ohms should be indicated when door is open, continuity should be indicated when door is closed.
22. If resistance indicated is as specified, circuit is satisfactory. Proceed to step 24.
23. If resistance indicated is not as specified, repair harness as necessary.
24. Connect fasten switch harness connector.
25. Connect ohmmeter between control unit connector terminal 4 and ground.
26. Close door.
27. Infinite ohms should be indicated when slide anchor is in fasten range (fasten switch Off), continuity should be indicated when slide anchor is not in fasten range (fasten switch On).
28. If resistance indicated is as specified, circuit is satisfactory.
29. If resistance is not as specified, replace motor and track assembly.

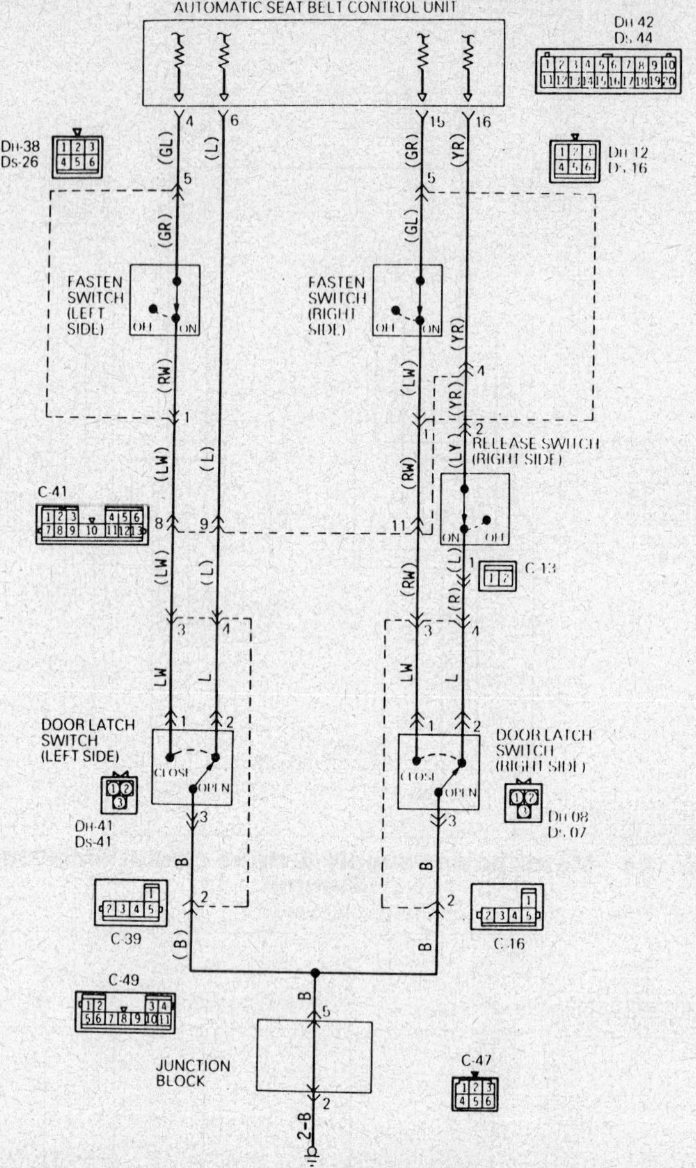


**Fig. 126 Door latch switch, fasten switch & release switch (passenger's side) circuit diagram. Colt & Summit**

### Passenger's Side

1. Disconnect door latch switch harness connector.
2. Connect a suitable ohmmeter between door latch switch terminals 1 and 3, then terminals 2 and 3.
3. Observe ohmmeter while opening and closing door.
4. Infinite ohms should be indicated between terminals 1 and 3 when door is open, continuity should be indicated between terminals 1 and 3 when door is closed.
5. Continuity should be indicated between terminals 2 and 3 when door is open, infinite ohms should be indicated between terminals 2 and 3 when door is closed.
6. If resistance indicated is as specified, circuit is satisfactory. Proceed to step 8.
7. If resistance indicated is not as specified, replace door latch switch.

8. Connect ohmmeter between door latch switch connector terminal 3 and ground.
9. Ohmmeter should indicate continuity.
10. If continuity is indicated, circuit is satisfactory. Proceed to step 12.
11. If continuity is not indicated, repair harness as necessary.
12. Connect door latch switch harness connector, then disconnect release switch harness connector.
13. Connect ohmmeter between release switch connector terminal 1 and ground.
14. Observe ohmmeter while opening and closing door.
15. Continuity should be indicated when door is open, infinite ohms should be indicated is closed.
16. If resistance indicated is as specified, circuit is satisfactory. Proceed to step 18.
17. If resistance indicated is not as specified, repair harness as necessary.
18. Connect release switch harness connector, then disconnect control unit harness connector.
19. Connect ohmmeter between control unit connector terminal 16 and ground.
20. Observe ohmmeter while opening and closing door.
21. Continuity should be indicated when door is open, infinite ohms should be indicated when door is closed.
22. If resistance indicated is as specified, circuit is satisfactory. Proceed to step 24.
23. If resistance indicated is not as specified, repair harness or replace motor and track assembly as necessary.
24. Disconnect fasten switch harness connector.
25. Connect ohmmeter between fasten switch connector terminal 1 and ground.
26. Observe ohmmeter while opening and closing door.
27. Infinite ohms should be indicated when door is open, continuity should be indicated when door is closed.
28. If resistance indicated is as specified, circuit is satisfactory. Proceed to step 30.
29. If resistance indicated is not as specified, repair harness as necessary.
30. Connect fasten switch harness connector.
31. Connect ohmmeter between control unit connector terminal 15 and ground.
32. Observe ohmmeter while opening and closing door.
33. Continuity should be indicated when door is open and slide anchor is not in fasten range (fasten switch On), infinite ohms should be indicated when door is closed and slide anchor is in fasten range (fasten switch Off).
34. If resistance indicated is as specified, circuit is satisfactory.
35. If resistance is not as specified, repair harness or replace motor and track assembly as necessary.

### COLT VISTA

Refer to **Fig. 127** for automatic seat belt system circuit diagram on Colt Vista models.

#### Control Unit Power Supply & Ground

Refer to **Fig. 128** when performing these tests.

1. Disconnect control unit harness connector.
2. Connect a suitable voltmeter between control unit connector terminal WB and ground.
3. Voltage indicated should be approximately 12 volts.
4. If voltage indicated is as specified, circuit is satisfactory. Proceed to step 6.
5. If voltage indicated is not as specified, repair circuit as necessary.
6. Connect a suitable voltmeter between control unit connector terminal BY and ground.
7. Turn ignition switch On.
8. Voltage indicated should be approximately 12 volts.
9. If voltage indicated is as specified, circuit is satisfactory. Proceed to step 11.
10. If voltage indicated is not as specified, repair circuit as necessary.
11. Connect a suitable ohmmeter between control unit connector terminal B5 and ground, then terminal B6 and ground.
12. Turn ignition switch Off.
13. Ohmmeter should indicate continuity.
14. If continuity is indicated, circuit is satisfactory.
15. If continuity is not indicated, repair circuit as necessary.

#### Warning Light, Key Reminder Switch & Buzzer

Refer to **Fig. 129** when performing these tests.

1. Check warning light circuit as follows:
   a. Disconnect warning light harness connector.
   b. Connect a suitable voltmeter between warning light connector terminal RB and ground.
   c. Turn ignition switch On.
   d. Voltage indicated should be approximately 12 volts.
   e. If voltage indicated is as specified, circuit is satisfactory. Proceed to step g.
   f. If voltage indicated is not as specified, repair circuit as necessary.
   g. Connect warning light harness connector.
   h. Disconnect control unit harness connector.
   i. Connect a suitable voltmeter between control unit connector terminal G and ground.
   j. Turn ignition switch On.
   k. Voltage indicated should be approximately 12 volts.
   l. If voltage indicated is as specified, circuit is satisfactory. Proceed to step 2.
   m. If voltage indicated is not as specified, repair circuit or replace warning light bulb as necessary.
2. Check key reminder switch circuit as follows:
   a. Disconnect key reminder switch harness connector.
   b. Connect a suitable voltmeter between key reminder switch connector terminal RB and ground.
   c. Voltage indicated should be approximately 12 volts.
   d. If voltage indicated is as specified, circuit is satisfactory. Proceed to step f.
   e. If voltage indicated is not as specified, repair circuit as necessary.
   f. Connect key reminder switch harness connector.
   g. Disconnect control unit harness connector.
   h. Remove key from ignition switch.
   i. Connect a suitable voltmeter between control unit connector terminal RW and ground.
   j. Voltage indicated should be approximately 12 volts.
   k. If voltage indicated is as specified, circuit is satisfactory. Proceed to step m.
   l. If voltage indicated is not as specified, repair circuit as necessary.
   m. Connect a suitable voltmeter between control unit connector terminal YG and ground.
   n. Voltage indicated should be 0 volts.
   o. If voltage indicated is as specified, circuit is satisfactory. Proceed to step q.
   p. If voltage indicated is not as specified, replace key reminder switch.
   q. Insert ignition key.
   r. Connect a suitable voltmeter between control unit connector terminal RW and ground.
   s. Voltage indicated should be 0 volts.
   t. If voltage indicated is as specified, circuit is satisfactory. Proceed to step v.
   u. If voltage indicated is not as specified, replace key reminder switch.
   v. Connect a suitable voltmeter between control unit connector terminal YG and ground.
   w. Voltage indicated should be approximately 12 volts.
   x. If voltage indicated is as specified, circuit is satisfactory. Proceed to step 3.
   y. If voltage indicated is not as specified, repair harness as necessary.
3. Check buzzer circuit as follows:
   a. Disconnect buzzer harness connector.
   b. Connect a suitable voltmeter between buzzer connector terminal RB and ground.
   c. Voltage indicated should be approximately 12 volts.
   d. If voltage indicated is as specified, circuit is satisfactory. Proceed to step f.
   e. If voltage indicated is not as specified, repair harness as necessary.
   f. Connect buzzer harness connector, then disconnect control unit harness connector.
   g. Connect a suitable voltmeter be-

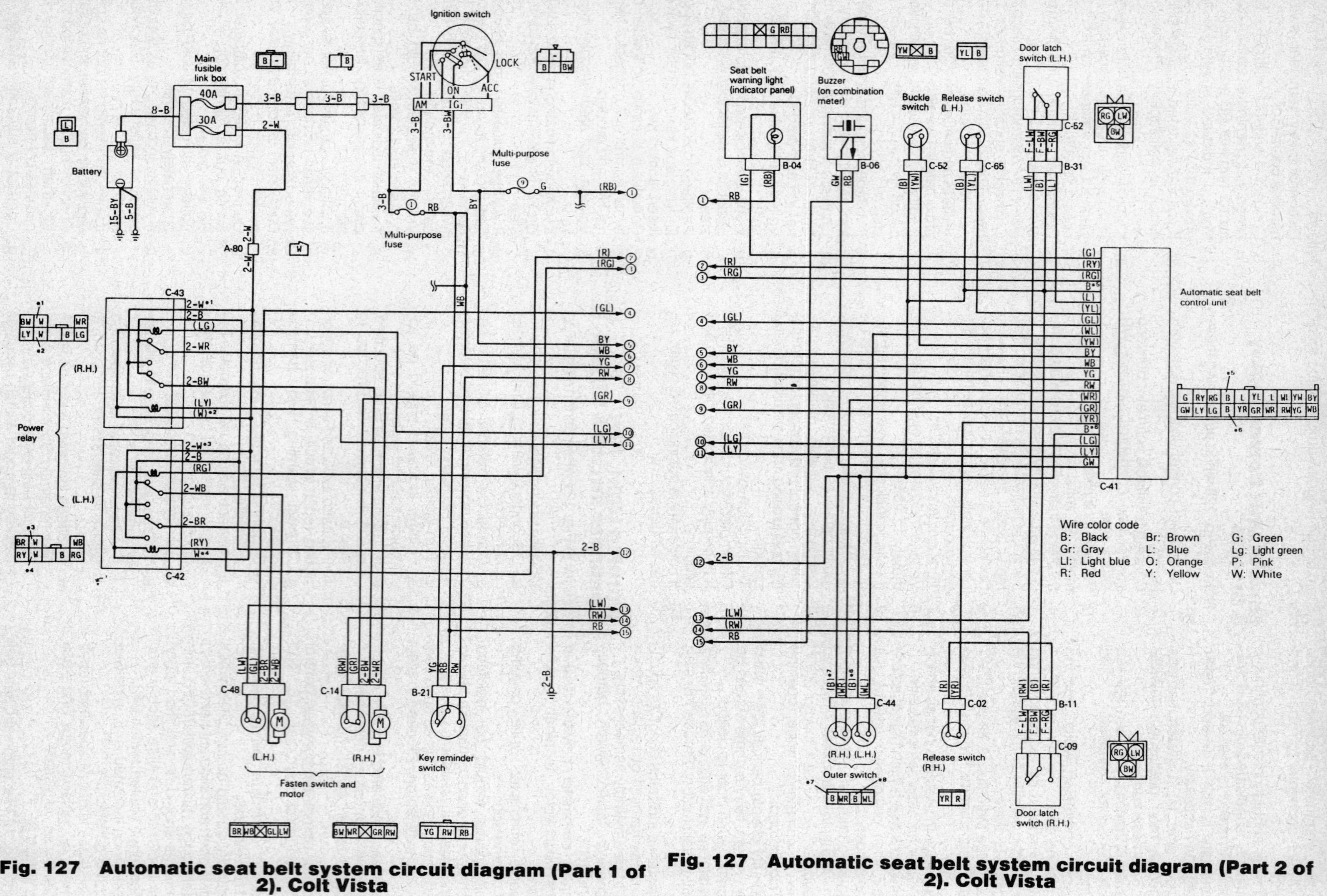


Fig. 127 Automatic seat belt system circuit diagram (Part 1 of 2). Colt Vista

Fig. 127 Automatic seat belt system circuit diagram (Part 2 of 2). Colt Vista

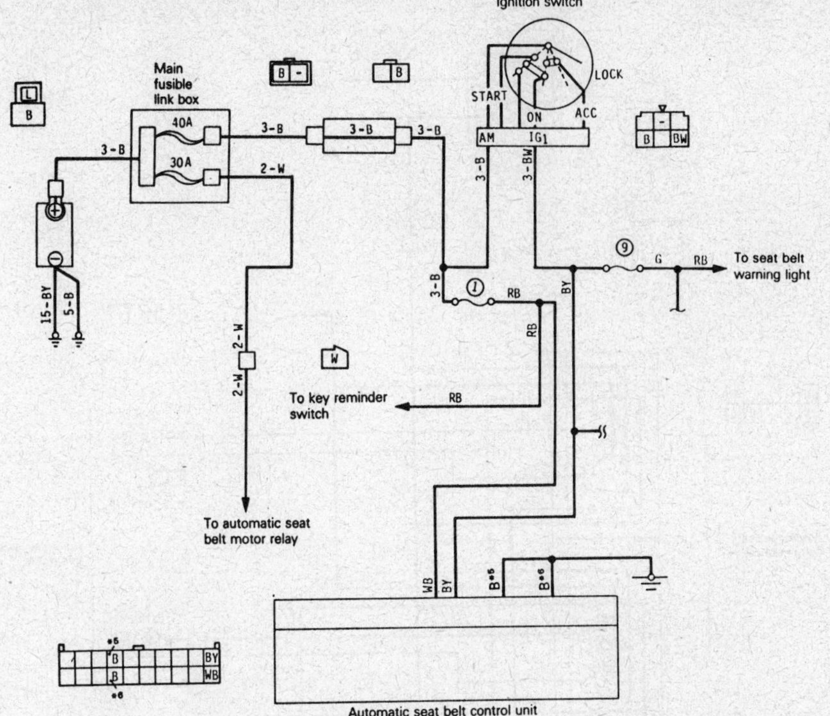


**Fig. 128 Control unit power supply & ground circuit diagram. Colt & Vista**

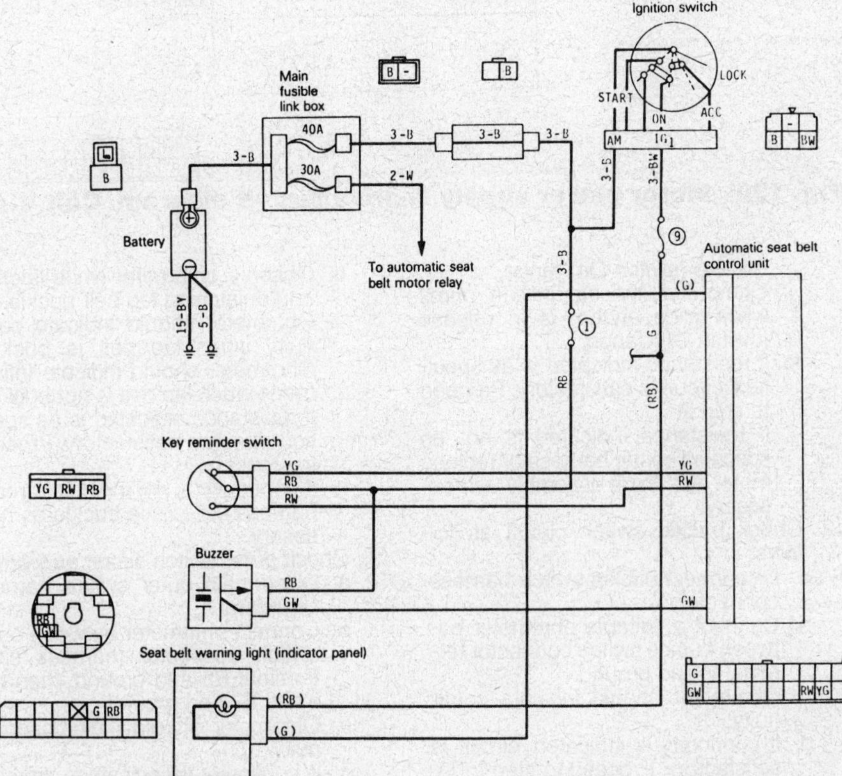


**Fig. 129 Warning light, key reminder switch & buzzer circuit diagram. Colt Vista**

tween control unit connector terminal GW and ground.

h. Voltage indicated should be approximately 12 volts.

i. If voltage indicated is as specified, circuit is satisfactory.

j. If voltage indicated is not as specified, repair harness as necessary.

## Motor Power Supply & Drive

Refer to **Fig. 130** when performing these tests.

1. Disconnect motor relay harness connector.
2. Connect a suitable ohmmeter between motor relay connector terminal B (relay side) and ground.
3. Ohmmeter should indicate continuity.
4. If continuity is indicated, circuit is satisfactory. Proceed to step 6.
5. If continuity is not indicated, repair harness as necessary.
6. Connect motor relay harness connector, then disconnect automatic seat belt motor harness connector.
7. Connect ohmmeter between motor connector terminal BR (motor side) and ground, terminal WB and ground, terminal BW and ground, then terminal WR and ground.
8. Ohmmeter should indicate continuity.
9. If continuity is indicated, circuit is satisfactory. Proceed to step 11.
10. If continuity is not indicated, repair harness or replace motor relay as necessary.
11. Connect automatic seat belt motor harness connector, then disconnect motor relay harness connector.
12. Apply battery voltage to motor relay connector terminals (harness side) as follows:
    a. Terminal WB (left side); positive side of power source.
    b. Terminal BR (left side); negative side of power source.
    c. Terminal WR (right side); positive side of power source.
    d. Terminal BW (right side); negative side of power source.
13. With voltage applied, slide anchor should move from Release position to Fasten position.
14. If slide anchor responds as specified, circuit is satisfactory. Proceed to step 16.
15. If slide anchor does not respond as specified, replace motor and track assembly.
16. Apply battery voltage to motor relay connector terminals (harness side) as follows:
    a. Terminal BR (left side); positive side of power source.
    b. Terminal WB (left side); negative side of power source.
    c. Terminal BW (right side); positive side of power source.
    d. Terminal WR (right side); negative side of power source.
17. With voltage applied, slide anchor should move from Fasten position to Release position.
18. If slide anchor responds as specified, circuit is satisfactory. Proceed to step 20.
19. If slide anchor does not respond as specified, replace motor and track assembly.
20. Connect a suitable voltmeter between motor relay connector terminal W3 and ground, terminal W4 and ground, terminal W1 and ground, then terminal W2 and ground.

21. Voltage indicated should be approximately 12 volts.
22. If voltage indicated is as specified, circuit is satisfactory. Proceed to step 24.
23. If voltage indicated is not as specified, repair harness as necessary.
24. Connect motor relay harness connector, then disconnect control unit harness connector.
25. Connect voltmeter between control unit connector terminal RY ground, terminal RG and ground, terminal LY and ground, then between terminal LG and ground.
26. Voltage indicated should be approximately 12 volts.
27. If voltage indicated is as specified, circuit is satisfactory. Proceed to step 29.
28. If voltage indicated is not as specified, repair harness or replace motor and track assembly as necessary.
29. Ground control unit connector terminal RG.
30. Left slide anchor should move from Release position to Fasten position.
31. Ground control unit connector terminal RY.
32. Left slide anchor should move from Fasten position to Release position.
33. If slide anchor responds as indicated, circuit is satisfactory. Proceed to step 35.
34. If slide anchor does not respond as indicated, replace lefthand motor relay.
35. Ground control unit connector terminal LG.
36. Right slide anchor should move from Release position to Fasten position.
37. Ground control unit connector terminal LY.
38. Right slide anchor should move from Fasten position to Release position.
39. If slide anchor responds as indicated, circuit is satisfactory.
40. If slide anchor does not respond as indicated, replace righthand motor relay.

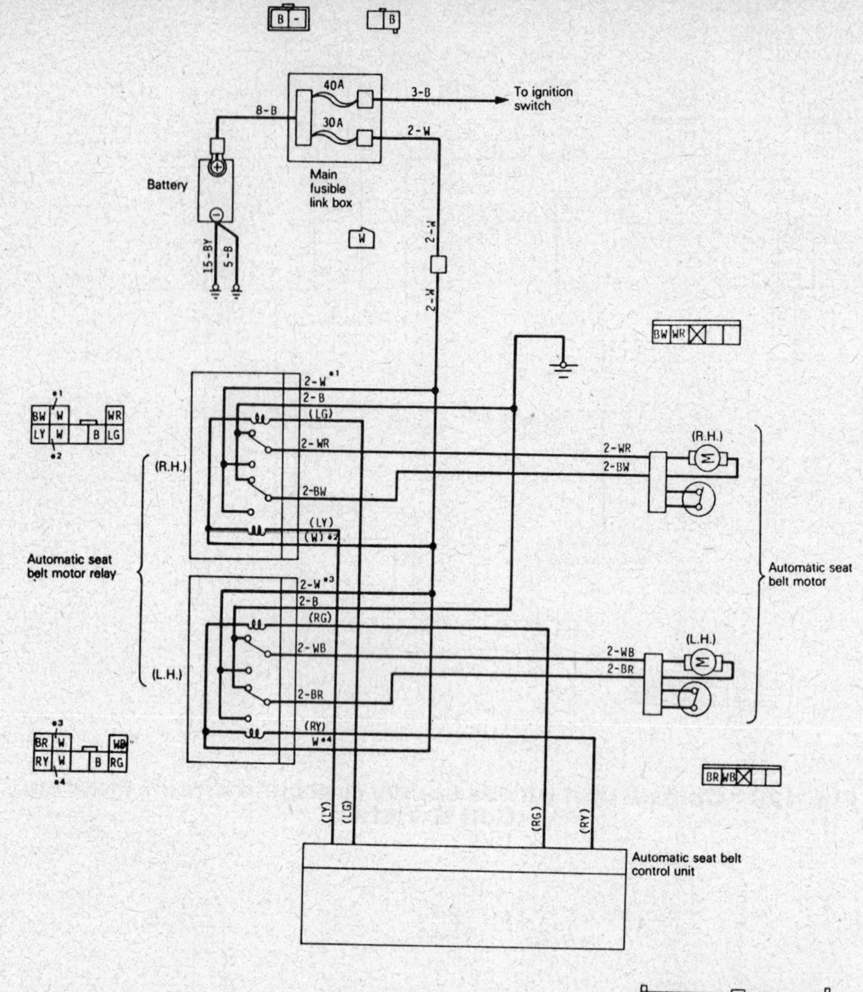


**Fig. 130 Motor power supply & drive circuit diagram. Colt Vista**

## Release Switch (Driver's Side), Buckle Switch & Release Switch

Refer to **Fig. 131** when performing these tests.

1. Check release switch (driver's side) circuit as follows:
   a. Disconnect release switch harness connector.
   b. Connect a suitable ohmmeter between release switch connector terminal B and ground.
   c. Ohmmeter should indicate continuity.
   d. If continuity is indicated, circuit is satisfactory. Proceed to step f.
   e. If continuity is not indicated, repair harness as necessary.
   f. Connect release switch harness connector, then disconnect control unit harness connector.
   g. Connect ohmmeter between control unit connector terminal YL and ground.
   h. Observe ohmmeter while manually moving slide anchor.
   i. Ohmmeter should indicate continuity when slide anchor is not in release (switch On) range.
   j. Ohmmeter indicate infinite ohms when slide anchor is in release (switch Off) range.
   k. If resistance indicated is as specified, circuit is satisfactory. Proceed to step 2.
   l. If resistance indicated is not as specified, repair harness or replace motor and track assembly as necessary.
2. Check buckle switch circuit as follows:
   a. Disconnect buckle switch harness connector.
   b. Connect a suitable ohmmeter between buckle switch connector terminal B and ground.
   c. Ohmmeter should indicate continuity.
   d. If continuity is indicated, circuit is satisfactory. Proceed to step f.
   e. If continuity is not indicated, repair harness as necessary.
   f. Connect buckle switch harness connector, then disconnect control unit harness connector.
   g. Connect ohmmeter between control unit connector terminal YW and ground.
   h. Observe ohmmeter while latching and unlatching lap belt buckle.
   i. Ohmmeter should indicate continuity when lap belt is buckled. Ohmmeter should indicate infinite ohms when lap belt is not buckled.
   j. If resistance indicated is as specified, circuit is satisfactory. Proceed to step 3.
   k. If continuity is not indicated, repair harness or replace buckle as necessary.
3. Check outer switch circuit as follows:
   a. Disconnect outer switch harness connector.
   b. Connect ohmmeter between outer switch connector (harness side) terminal B8 and ground, then terminal B7 and ground.
   c. Ohmmeter should indicate continuity.
   d. If continuity is indicated, circuit is satisfactory. Proceed to step f.
   e. If continuity is not indicated, repair harness as necessary.
   f. Connect ohmmeter between outer switch connector (switch side) terminals B8 and WL (left side), then between terminals B7 and WR (right side).

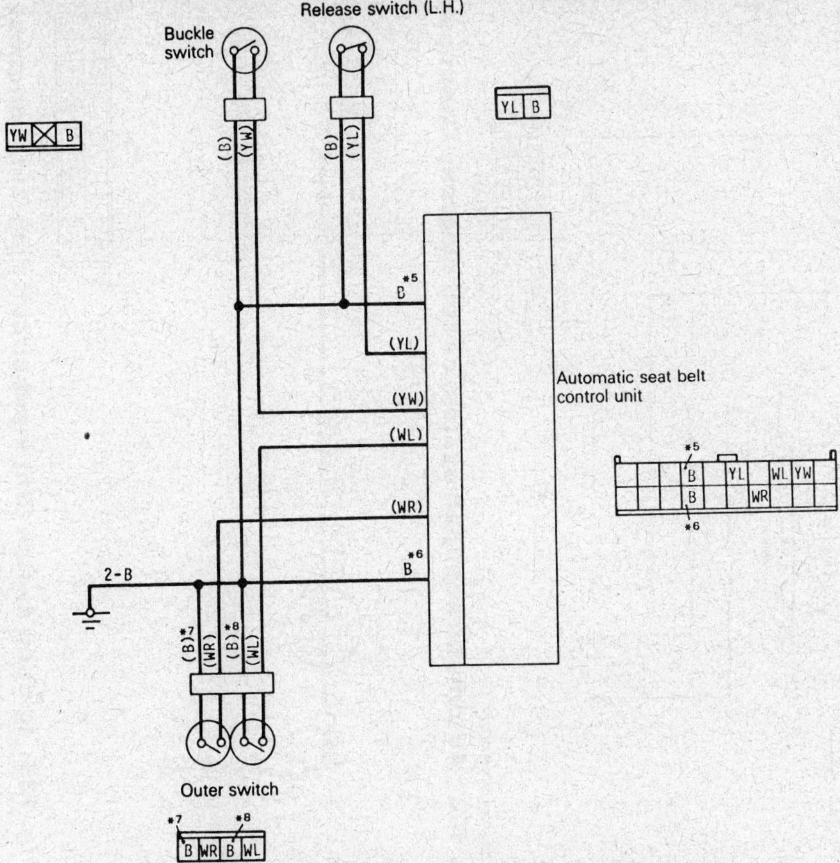


**Fig. 131 Release switch (driver's side), buckle switch & release switch circuit diagram. Colt Vista**

g. Observe ohmmeter while pulling out and retracting shoulder belt.
h. With shoulder belt fully retracted to pulled out approximately half way (outer switch Off), infinite ohms should be indicated.
i. With shoulder belt pulled half way out to fully pulled out position (outer switch On), continuity should be indicated.
j. If resistance indicated is as specified, circuit is satisfactory. Proceed to step l.
k. If resistance indicated is not as specified, replace shoulder belt retractor assembly.
l. Connect shoulder belt to slide anchor (outer switch On). Connect outer switch harness connector, then disconnect control unit harness connector.
m. Connect ohmmeter between control unit connector terminal WL and ground, then terminal WR and ground.
n. Ohmmeter should indicate continuity.
o. If continuity is indicated, circuit is satisfactory.
p. If continuity is not indicated, repair harness as necessary.

## DOOR LATCH SWITCH, FASTEN SWITCH & RELEASE SWITCH (PASSENGER'S SIDE)

Refer to **Fig. 132** when performing these tests.

### Driver's Side

1. Disconnect door latch switch harness connector.
2. Connect a suitable ohmmeter between door latch switch terminals RG and BW, then terminals LW and BW.
3. Observe ohmmeter while opening and closing door.
4. Infinite ohms should be indicated between terminals LW and BW when door is open, continuity should be indicated between terminals LW and BW when door is closed.
5. Continuity should be indicated between terminals RG and BW when door is open, infinite ohms should be indicated between terminals RG and BW when door is closed.
6. If resistance indicated is as specified, circuit is satisfactory. Proceed to step 8.
7. If resistance indicated is not as specified, replace door latch switch.
8. Connect ohmmeter between door latch switch connector terminal BW and ground.
9. Ohmmeter should indicate continuity.
10. If continuity is indicated, circuit is satisfactory. Proceed to step 12.
11. If continuity is not indicated, repair harness as necessary.
12. Connect door latch switch harness connector, then disconnect control unit harness connector.
13. Connect ohmmeter between control unit connector terminal L and ground.
14. Observe ohmmeter while opening and closing door.
15. Continuity should be indicated when door is open, infinite ohms should be indicated is closed.
16. If resistance indicated is as specified, circuit is satisfactory. Proceed to step 18.
17. If resistance indicated is not as specified, repair harness as necessary.
18. Disconnect fasten switch harness connector.
19. Connect ohmmeter between fasten switch connector terminal LW and ground.
20. Observe ohmmeter while opening and closing door.
21. Infinite ohms should be indicated when door is open, continuity should be indicated when door is closed.
22. If resistance indicated is as specified, circuit is satisfactory. Proceed to step 24.
23. If resistance indicated is not as specified, repair harness as necessary.
24. Connect fasten switch harness connector.
25. Connect ohmmeter between control unit connector terminal GL and ground.
26. Close door, then manually move slide anchor.
27. Infinite ohms should be indicated when slide anchor is in fasten range (fasten switch Off), continuity should be indicated when slide anchor is not in fasten range (fasten switch On).
28. If resistance indicated is as specified, circuit is satisfactory.
29. If resistance is not as specified, replace motor and track assembly.

### Passenger's Side

1. Disconnect door latch switch harness connector.
2. Connect a suitable ohmmeter between door latch switch terminals RG and BW, then terminals LW and BW.
3. Observe ohmmeter while opening and closing door.
4. Infinite ohms should be indicated between terminals LW and BW when door is open, continuity should be indicated between terminals LW and BW when door is closed.
5. Continuity should be indicated between terminals RG and BW when door is open, infinite ohms should be indicated between terminals RG and BW when door is closed.
6. If resistance indicated is as specified, circuit is satisfactory. Proceed to step 8.
7. If resistance indicated is not as specified, replace door latch switch.
8. Connect ohmmeter between door latch switch connector terminal BW and ground.
9. Ohmmeter should indicate continuity.
10. If continuity is indicated, circuit is satisfactory. Proceed to step 12.
11. If continuity is not indicated, repair harness as necessary.
12. Connect door latch switch harness connector, then disconnect release switch harness connector.

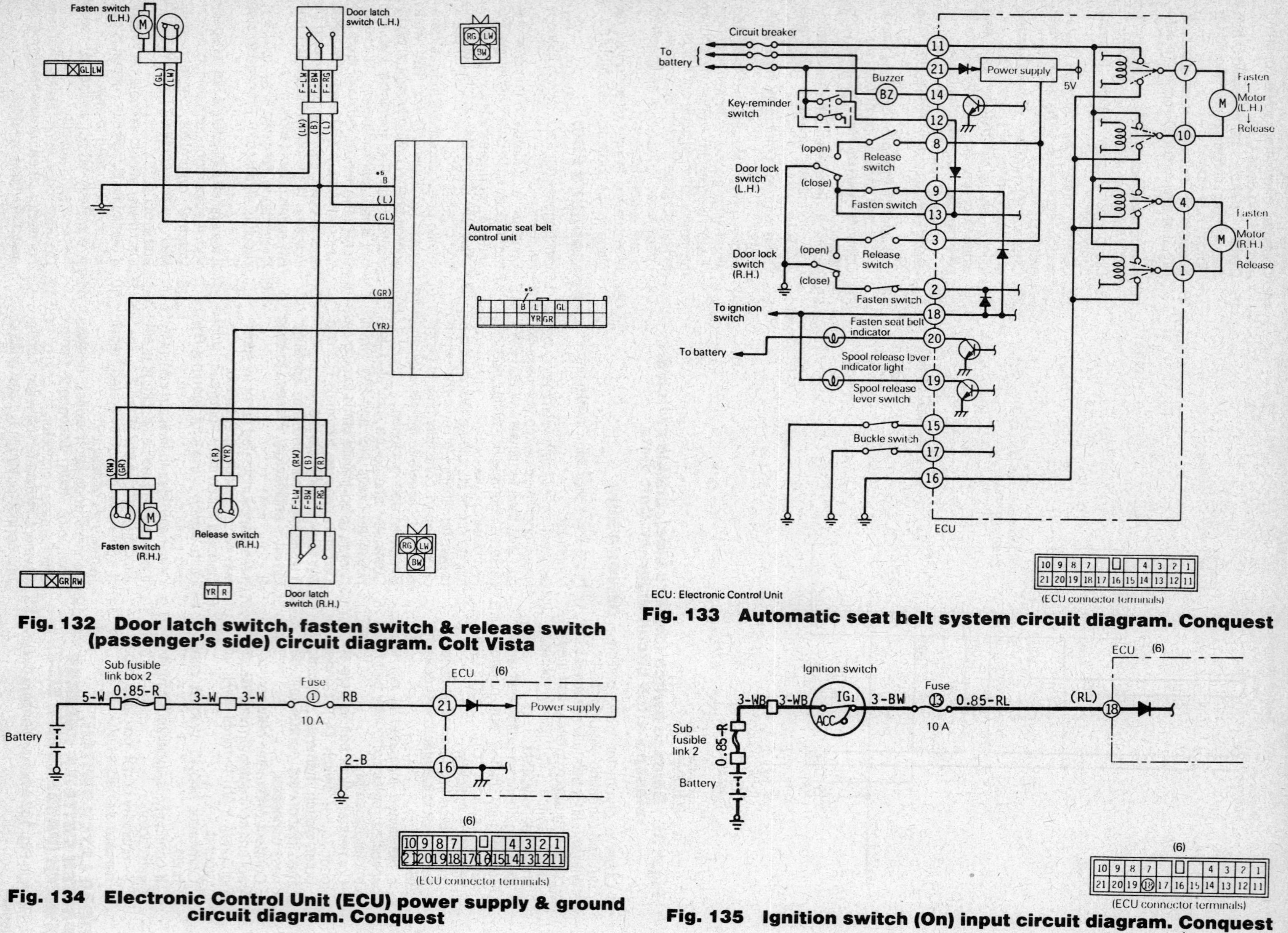


Fig. 132 Door latch switch, fasten switch & release switch (passenger's side) circuit diagram. Colt Vista

Fig. 133 Automatic seat belt system circuit diagram. Conquest



Fig. 134 Electronic Control Unit (ECU) power supply & ground circuit diagram. Conquest

Fig. 135 Ignition switch (On) input circuit diagram. Conquest

13. Connect ohmmeter between release switch connector terminal R and ground.
14. Observe ohmmeter while opening and closing door.
15. Continuity should be indicated when door is open, infinite ohms should be indicated is closed.
16. If resistance indicated is as specified, circuit is satisfactory. Proceed to step 18.
17. If resistance indicated is not as specified, repair harness as necessary.
18. Connect release switch harness connector, then disconnect control unit harness connector.
19. Connect ohmmeter between control unit connector terminal YR and ground.
20. Observe ohmmeter while opening and closing door. Manually move slide anchor.
21. Continuity should be indicated when door is open and slide anchor is not in Release position (release switch On), infinite ohms should be indicated when door is closed and slide anchor is in Release position (release switch Off).
22. If resistance indicated is as specified, circuit is satisfactory. Proceed to step 24.
23. If resistance indicated is not as specified, repair harness or replace motor and track assembly as necessary.
24. Disconnect fasten switch harness connector.
25. Connect ohmmeter between fasten switch connector terminal RW and ground.
26. Observe ohmmeter while opening and closing door.
27. Infinite ohms should be indicated when door is open, continuity should be indicated when door is closed.
28. If resistance indicated is as specified, circuit is satisfactory. Proceed to step 30.
29. If resistance indicated is not as specified, repair harness as necessary.
30. Connect fasten switch harness connector.
31. Connect ohmmeter between control unit connector terminal GR and ground.
32. Observe ohmmeter while opening and closing door. Manually move slide anchor.
33. Continuity should be indicated when door is open and slide anchor is not in fasten range (fasten switch On), infinite ohms should be indicated when door is closed and slide anchor is in fasten range (fasten switch Off).
34. If resistance indicated is as specified, circuit is satisfactory.
35. If resistance is not as specified, repair harness or replace motor and track assembly as necessary.

## CONQUEST

Refer to **Fig. 133** for automatic seat belt system circuit diagram on Conquest models.

### Electronic Control Unit (ECU) Power Supply & Ground

Refer to **Fig. 134** when performing these tests.

1. Connect a suitable voltmeter between ECU terminal 21 and ground.
2. Voltage indicated should be approximately 12 volts.
3. If voltage indicated is as specified, circuit is satisfactory. Proceed to step 5.
4. If voltage indicated is not as specified, replace fuse No. 1 or repair harness as necessary.
5. Disconnect ECU harness connector.
6. Connect a suitable ohmmeter between ECU connector terminal 16 and ground.
7. Ohmmeter should indicated continuity.
8. If continuity is indicated, circuit is satisfactory.
9. If continuity is not indicated, repair harness as necessary.

### Ignition Switch (On) Input

Refer to **Fig. 135** when performing these tests.

1. Connect a suitable voltmeter between ECU terminal 18 and ground.
2. Turn ignition switch On.
3. Voltage indicated should be approximately 12 volts.
4. If voltage indicated is as specified, circuit is satisfactory.
5. If voltage indicated is not as specified, replace fuse No. 13 or repair harness as necessary.

### Door Lock Switch, Fasten & Release Switch Input

Refer to **Fig. 136** when performing these tests.

1. Disconnect door lock switch harness connectors.
2. Connect a suitable ohmmeter between door lock switch connector terminals B and G, then terminals B and R.
3. Observe ohmmeter while operating door lock switches.
4. Ohmmeter should indicate continuity with switch in Close position and indicate infinite ohms with switch in Open position.
5. If resistance indicated is as specified, circuit is satisfactory. Proceed to step 7.
6. If resistance indicated is not as specified, replace appropriate door lock switch.
7. Disconnect fasten switch harness connectors.
8. Connect ohmmeter between lefthand fasten switch connector terminals GL and GB, then righthand fasten switch terminals YB and G.
9. Observe ohmmeter while operating fasten switches.
10. Ohmmeter should indicate continuity with switch in On position and indicate infinite ohms with switch in Off position.
11. If resistance indicated is as specified, circuit is satisfactory. Proceed to step 13.
12. If resistance indicated is not as specified, replace appropriate fasten switch.
13. Disconnect release switch harness connectors.
14. Connect ohmmeter between lefthand release switch connector terminals RL and GW, then righthand fasten switch terminals R and YW.
15. Observe ohmmeter while operating release switches.
16. Ohmmeter should indicate continuity with switch in On position and indicate infinite ohms with switch in Off position.
17. If resistance indicated is as specified, circuit is satisfactory. Proceed to step 19.
18. If resistance indicated is not as specified, replace appropriate release switch.
19. Connect door lock switch and fasten switch harness connectors, then disconnect ECU harness connector.
20. Connect ohmmeter between ECU connector terminal 9 and ground, then terminal 2 and ground.
21. Ohmmeter should indicate continuity.
22. If continuity is indicated, circuit is satisfactory. Proceed to step 24.
23. If continuity is not indicated, repair harness as necessary.
24. Connect release switch harness connectors. Ensure door lock switches are in Open position.
25. Connect ohmmeter between ECU connector terminal 8 and ground, then terminal 3 and ground.
26. Observe ohmmeter while operating release switch.
27. Continuity should be indicated with release switch in On position, infinite ohms should be indicated with release switch in Off position.
28. If resistance indicated is as specified, circuit is satisfactory.
29. If resistance indicated is not as specified, repair harness as necessary.

### Motor Supply & Drive

Refer to **Fig. 137** when performing these tests.

1. Disconnect motor harness connectors.
2. Connect a suitable ohmmeter between motor connector terminals LW and RW (motor side), then terminals LY and RY (motor side).
3. Ohmmeter should indicate continuity.
4. If continuity is indicated, circuit is satisfactory. Proceed to step 6.
5. If continuity is not indicated, replace motor assembly.
6. Connect motor harness connectors, then disconnect ECU harness connector.
7. Connect ohmmeter between ECU connector terminals 7 and 10, then terminals 4 and 1.
8. Ohmmeter should indicate continuity.
9. If continuity is indicated, circuit is satisfactory. Proceed to step 11.
10. If continuity is not indicated, repair harness as necessary.

11. Connect a suitable between ECU connector terminal 11 and ground.
12. Voltage indicated should be approximately 12 volts.
13. If voltage indicated is as specified, circuit is satisfactory. Proceed to step 15.
14. If voltage indicated is not as specified, reset/replace circuit breaker or repair harness as necessary.
15. Connect ohmmeter between ECU connector terminal 6 and ground.
16. Ohmmeter should indicate continuity.
17. If continuity is indicated, circuit is satisfactory..
18. If continuity is not indicated, repair harness as necessary.

## Spool Release Lever Switch & Indicator Light

Refer to **Fig. 138** when performing these tests.

1. Disconnect spool release lever switch harness connector.
2. Connect a suitable ohmmeter between spool release lever switch connector terminals LB and B.
3. Observe ohmmeter while operating right door lock switch.
4. Continuity should be indicated with lock switch in closed position, infinite ohms should be indicated with lock switch in Open position.
5. If resistance indicated is as specified, circuit is satisfactory. Proceed to step 7.
6. If resistance indicated is not as specified, replace spool release lever switch.
7. Disconnect spool release lever indicator light harness connector.
8. Connect a suitable ohmmeter between spool release lever indicator light connector terminals LR and LO.
9. Ohmmeter should indicate continuity.
10. If continuity is indicated, circuit is satisfactory. Proceed to step 12.
11. If continuity is not indicated, replace spool release lever light indicator.
12. Connect spool release lever switch harness connector, then disconnect ECU harness connector.
13. Connect ohmmeter between ECU connector terminal 15 and ground.
14. Observe ohmmeter while operating spool release switch.
15. Continuity should be indicated with spool release switch in On position, infinite ohms should be indicated with spool release switch in Off position.
16. If resistance indicated is as specified, circuit is satisfactory. Proceed to step 18.
17. If resistance indicated is not as specified, repair harness as necessary.
18. Connect spool release lever indicator light harness connector.
19. Connect a suitable voltmeter between ECU connector terminal 19 and ground.
20. Turn ignition switch On.
21. Voltage indicated should be approximately 12 volts.
22. If voltage indicated is as specified, circuit is satisfactory.
23. If voltage indicated is not as specified, replace fuse No. 13 or repair harness as necessary.

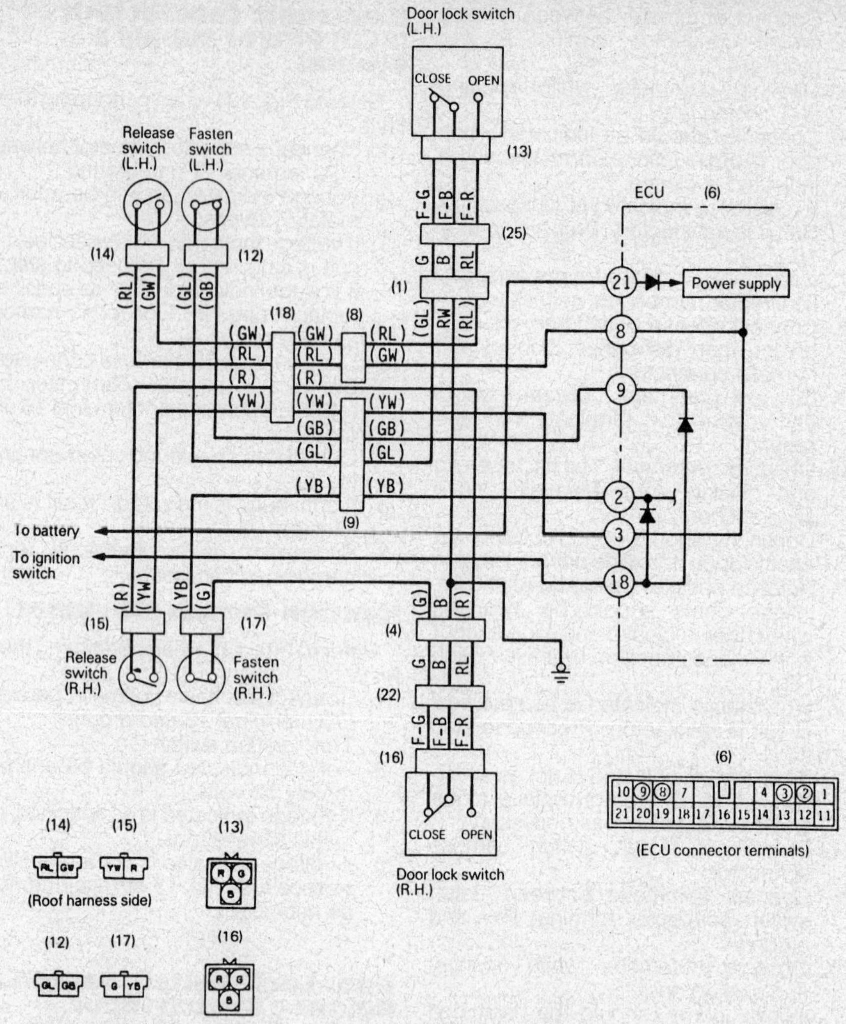


**Fig. 136 Door latch switch, fasten & release switch circuit diagram. Conquest**

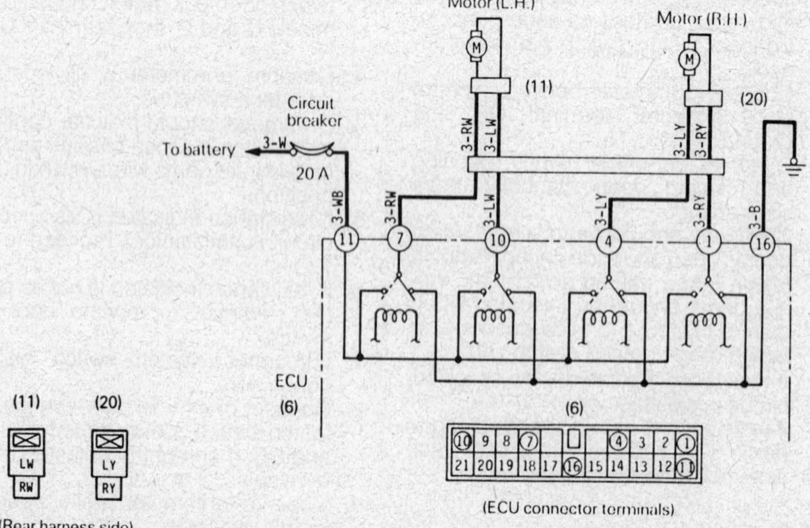


**Fig. 137 Motor power supply & drive circuit diagram. Conquest**

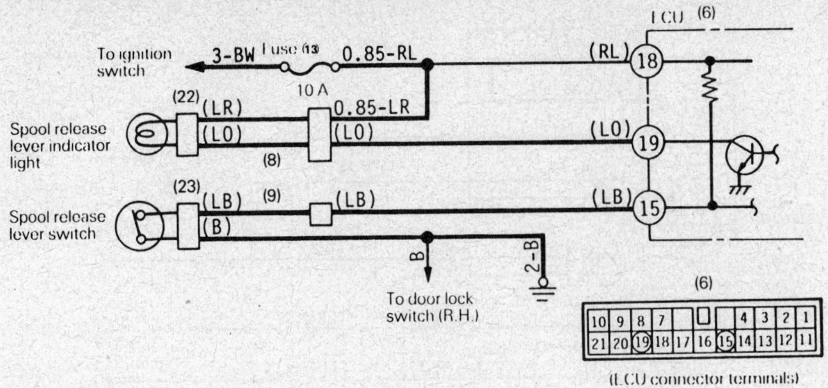


**Fig. 138 Spool release lever switch & indicator light circuit diagram. Conquest**

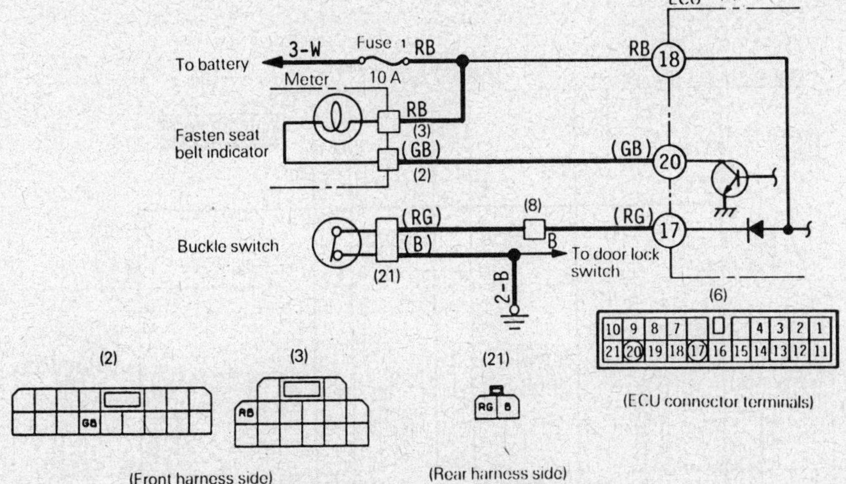


**Fig. 139 Buckle switch & fasten seat belt indicator light circuit diagram. Conquest**

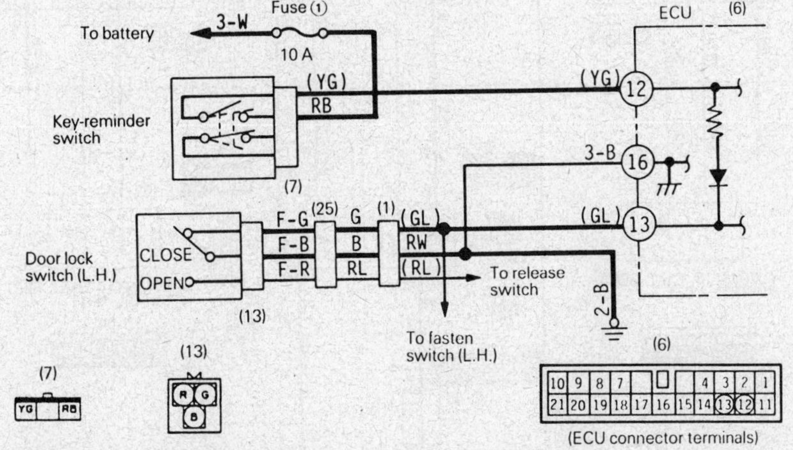


**Fig. 140 Key reminder input circuit diagram. Conquest**

## Buckle Switch & Fasten Seat Belt Indicator Light

Refer to **Fig. 139** when performing these tests.

1. Disconnect buckle switch harness connector.
2. Connect a suitable ohmmeter between buckle switch connector terminals RG and B (switch side).
3. Observe ohmmeter while operating buckle switch.
4. Continuity should be indicated with buckle switch in On position, infinite ohms should be indicated with buckle switch in Off position.
5. If resistance indicated is as specified, circuit is satisfactory. Proceed to step 7.
6. If resistance indicated is not as specified, replace buckle switch.
7. Disconnect fasten seat belt indicator harness connectors.
8. Connect ohmmeter between fasten seat belt indicator terminals RB and GB (indicator side).
9. Ohmmeter should indicate continuity.
10. If continuity is indicated, circuit is satisfactory. Proceed to step 12.
11. If continuity is not indicated, replace fasten seat belt indicator light.
12. Connect buckle switch harness connector, then disconnect ECU harness connector.
13. Connect ohmmeter between ECU connector terminal 17 and ground.
14. Observe ohmmeter while operating buckle switch.
15. Continuity should be indicated with buckle switch in On position, infinite ohms should be indicated with buckle switch in Off position.
16. If resistance indicated is as specified, circuit is satisfactory. Proceed to step 18.
17. If resistance indicated is not as specified, repair harness as necessary.
18. Connect fasten seat belt indicator connectors.
19. Connect a suitable voltmeter between ECU connector terminal 20 and ground.
20. Turn ignition switch On.
21. Voltage indicated should be approximately 12 volts.
22. If voltage indicated is as specified, circuit is satisfactory.
23. If voltage indicated is not as specified, replace fuse No. 1 or repair harness as necessary.

## Key Reminder Switch Input

Refer to **Fig. 140** when performing these tests.

1. Disconnect key reminder switch harness connector.
2. Connect a suitable ohmmeter between key reminder switch terminals YG and RB.
3. Observe ohmmeter while inserting and removing ignition key.
4. Continuity should be indicated with ignition switch inserted (switch On), infinite ohms should be indicated with ignition key removed (switch Off).
5. If resistance indicated is as specified, circuit is satisfactory. Proceed to step 7.

6. If resistance indicated is not as specified, replace key reminder switch.
7. Disconnect lefthand door lock switch harness connector.
8. Connect ohmmeter between door lock switch terminals G and B, then terminals B and R.
9. Observe ohmmeter while operating door lock switch.
10. Continuity should be indicated with door lock switch in Close position, infinite ohms should be indicated with door lock switch in Open position.
11. If resistance indicated is as specified, circuit is satisfactory. Proceed to step 13.
12. If resistance indicated is not as specified, replace door lock switch.
13. Connect key reminder switch harness connector, then disconnect ECU harness connector.
14. Connect a suitable voltmeter between ECU connector terminal 12 and ground.
15. Turn ignition switch On.
16. Voltage indicated should be approximately 12 volts.
17. If voltage indicated is as specified, circuit is satisfactory. Proceed to step 19.
18. If voltage indicated is not as specified, replace fuse No. 1 or repair harness as necessary.
19. Connect lefthand door lock switch harness connector.
20. Connect ohmmeter between ECU connector terminal 13 and ground.
21. Observe ohmmeter while operating door lock switch.
22. Continuity should be indicated with door lock switch in Close position, infinite ohms should be indicated with door lock switch in Open position.
23. If resistance indicated is as specified, circuit is satisfactory.
24. If resistance indicated is not as specified, repair harness as necessary.

## Buzzer

Refer to **Fig. 141** when performing these tests.

1. Disconnect buzzer harness connector.
2. Connect a suitable voltmeter between connector terminal LO and ground.
3. Voltage indicated should be approximately 12 volts.
4. If voltage indicated is as specified, circuit is satisfactory. Proceed to step 6.
5. If voltage indicated is not as specified, replace fuse No. 8 or repair harness as necessary.
6. Connect buzzer harness connector, then disconnect ECU harness connector.
7. Connect voltmeter between ECU connector terminal 14 and ground.
8. Voltage indicated should be approximately 12 volts.
9. If voltage indicated is as specified, circuit is satisfactory.
10. If voltage indicated is not as specified, replace buzzer or repair harness as necessary.

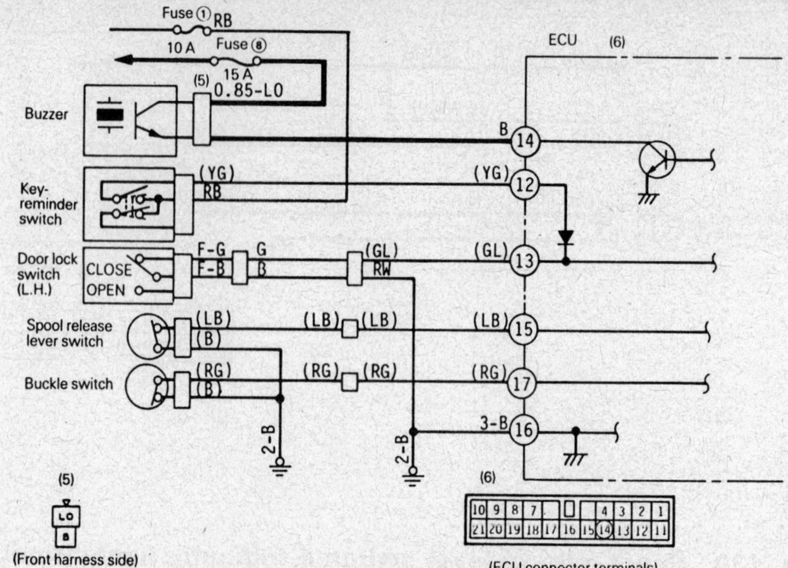


**Fig. 141 Buzzer circuit diagram. Conquest**

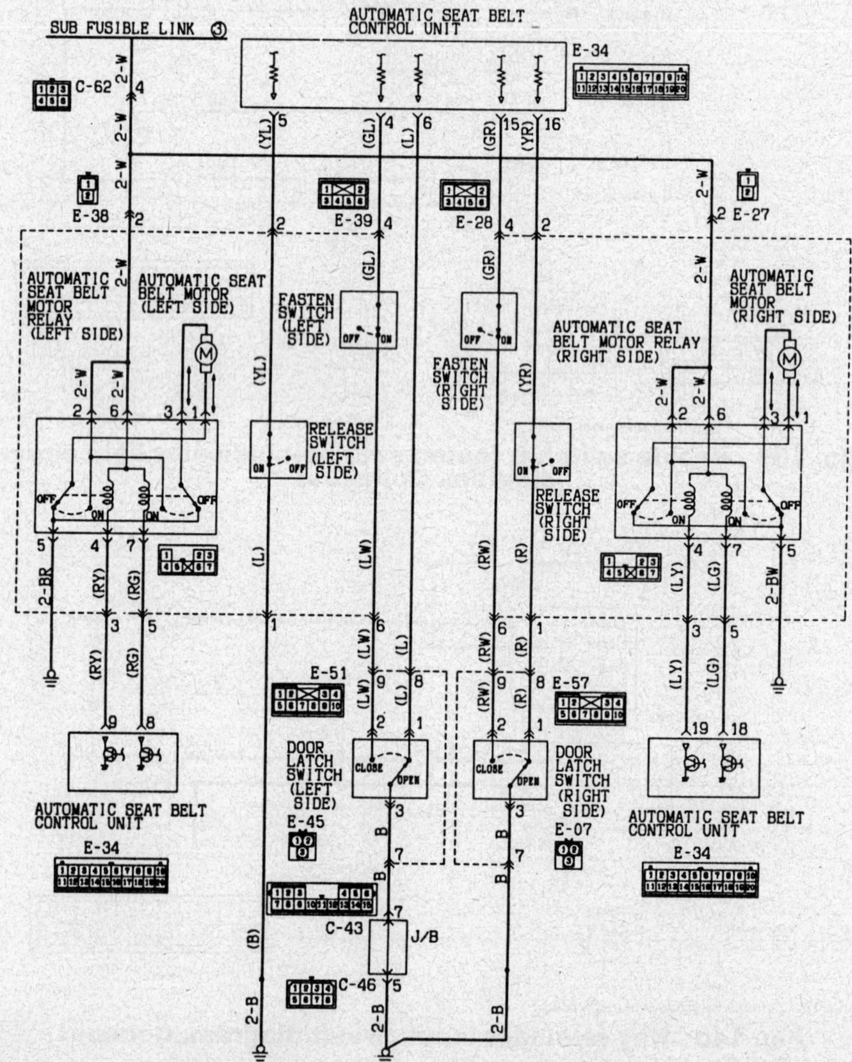


**Fig. 142 Automatic seat belt system circuit diagram (Part 1 of 2). Eagle Talon & Plymouth Laser**

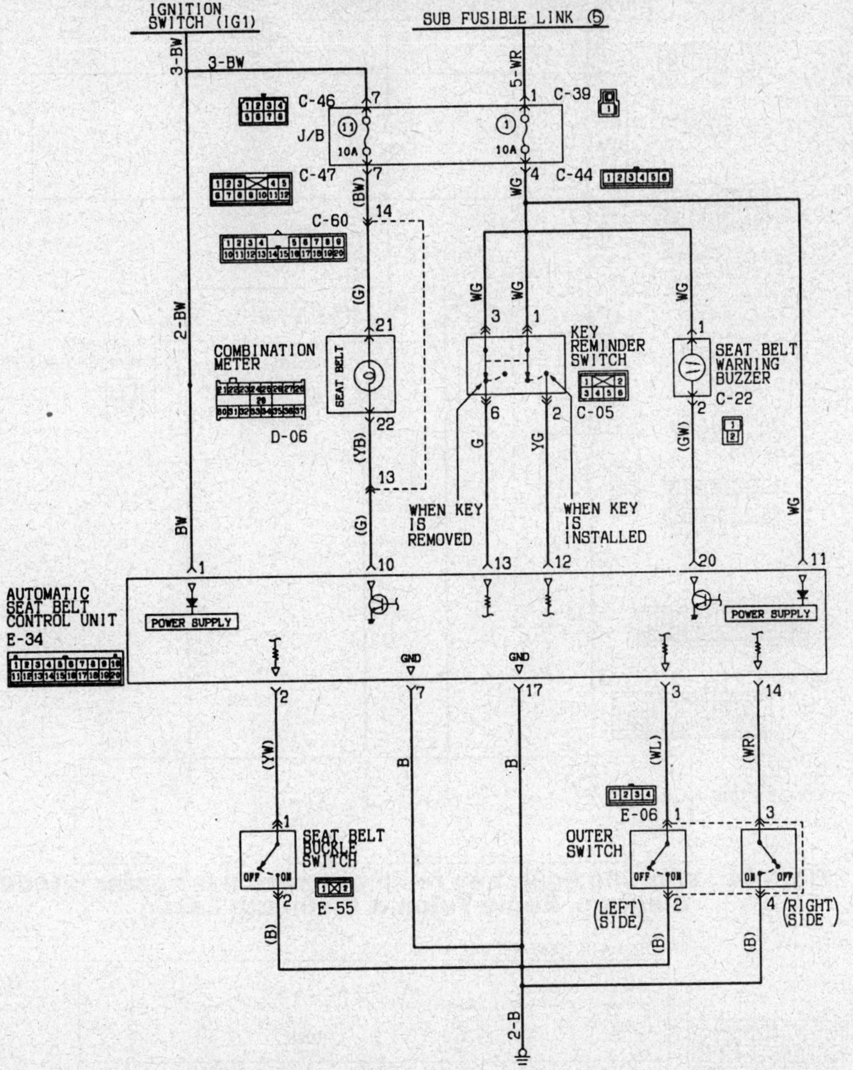


**Fig. 142 Automatic seat belt system circuit diagram (Part 2 of 2). Eagle Talon & Plymouth Laser**

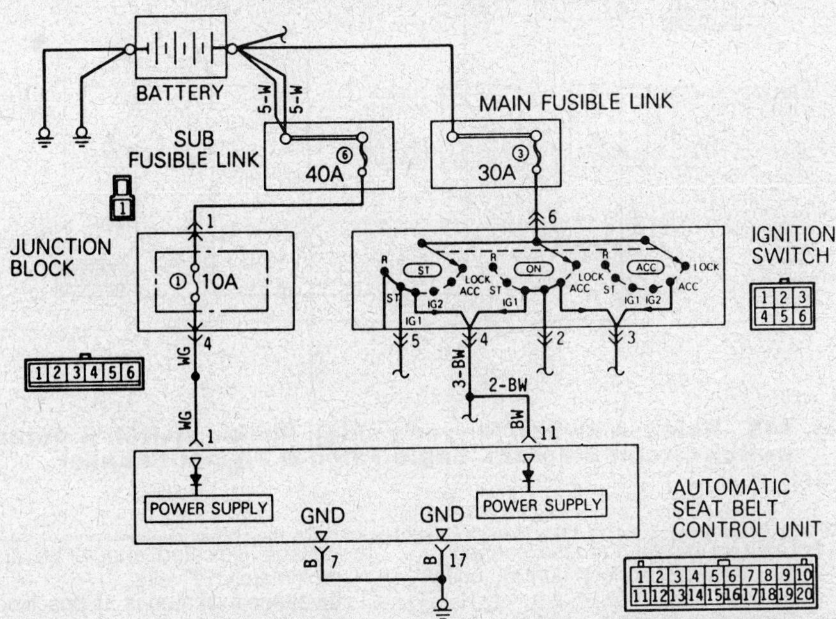


**Fig. 143 Control unit power supply & ground circuit diagram. Eagle Talon & Plymouth Laser**

## EAGLE TALON & PLYMOUTH LASER

Refer to **Fig. 142** for automatic seat belt system circuit diagram on Eagle Talon and Plymouth Laser models.

### Control Unit Power Supply & Ground

Refer to **Fig. 143** when performing these tests.

1. Disconnect control unit harness connector.
2. Connect a suitable voltmeter between control unit connector terminal 11 and ground.
3. Voltage indicated should be approximately 12 volts.
4. If voltage indicated is as specified, circuit is satisfactory. Proceed to step 6.
5. If voltage indicated is not as specified, repair circuit as necessary.
6. Connect a suitable voltmeter between control unit connector terminal 1 and ground.
7. Turn ignition switch On.
8. Voltage indicated should be approximately 12 volts.
9. If voltage indicated is as specified, circuit is satisfactory. Proceed to step 11.
10. If voltage indicated is not as specified, repair circuit as necessary.
11. Connect a suitable ohmmeter between control unit connector terminal 7 and ground, then terminal 17 and ground.
12. Turn ignition switch Off.
13. Ohmmeter should indicate continuity.
14. If continuity is indicated, circuit is satisfactory.
15. If continuity is not indicated, repair circuit as necessary.

### Warning Light, Key Reminder Switch & Buzzer

Refer to **Fig. 144** when performing these tests.

1. Check warning light circuit as follows:
   a. Disconnect warning light harness connector.
   b. Connect a suitable voltmeter between warning light connector terminal 1 and ground.
   c. Turn ignition switch On.
   d. Voltage indicated should be approximately 12 volts.
   e. If voltage indicated is as specified, circuit is satisfactory. Proceed to step g.
   f. If voltage indicated is not as specified, repair circuit as necessary.
   g. Connect warning light harness connector.
   h. Disconnect control unit harness connector.
   i. Connect a suitable voltmeter between control unit connector terminal 1 and ground.
   j. Turn ignition switch On.
   k. Voltage indicated should be approximately 12 volts.
   l. If voltage indicated is as specified, circuit is satisfactory. Proceed to step 2.

m. If voltage indicated is not as specified, repair circuit or replace warning light bulb as necessary.

2. Check key reminder switch circuit as follows:
   a. Disconnect key reminder switch harness connector.
   b. Connect a suitable voltmeter between key reminder switch connector terminal 1 and ground, then terminal 3 and ground.
   c. Voltage indicated should be approximately 12 volts.
   d. If voltage indicated is as specified, circuit is satisfactory. Proceed to step f.
   e. If voltage indicated is not as specified, repair circuit as necessary.
   f. Connect key reminder switch harness connector.
   g. Disconnect control unit harness connector.
   h. Remove key from ignition switch.
   i. Connect a suitable voltmeter between control unit connector terminal 13 and ground.
   j. Voltage indicated should be approximately 12 volts.
   k. If voltage indicated is as specified, circuit is satisfactory. Proceed to step m.
   l. If voltage indicated is not as specified, repair circuit as necessary.
   m. Connect a suitable voltmeter between control unit connector terminal 12 and ground.
   n. Voltage indicated should be 0 volts.
   o. If voltage indicated is as specified, circuit is satisfactory. Proceed to step q.
   p. If voltage indicated is not as specified, replace key reminder switch.
   q. Insert ignition key.
   r. Connect a suitable voltmeter between control unit connector terminal 13 and ground.
   s. Voltage indicated should be 0 volts.
   t. If voltage indicated is as specified, circuit is satisfactory. Proceed to step v.
   u. If voltage indicated is not as specified, replace key reminder switch.
   v. Connect a suitable voltmeter between control unit connector terminal 12 and ground.
   w. Voltage indicated should be approximately 12 volts.
   x. If voltage indicated is as specified, circuit is satisfactory. Proceed to step 3.
   y. If voltage indicated is not as specified, repair harness as necessary.

3. Check buzzer circuit as follows:
   a. Disconnect buzzer harness connector.
   b. Connect a suitable voltmeter between buzzer connector terminal 1 and ground.
   c. Voltage indicated should be approximately 12 volts.
   d. If voltage indicated is as specified, circuit is satisfactory. Proceed to step f.
   e. If voltage indicated is not as specified, repair harness as necessary.
   f. Connect buzzer harness connector, then disconnect control unit harness connector.
   g. Connect a suitable voltmeter between control unit connector terminal 20 and ground.
   h. Voltage indicated should be approximately 12 volts.
   i. If voltage indicated is as specified, circuit is satisfactory.
   j. If voltage indicated is not as specified, repair harness as necessary.

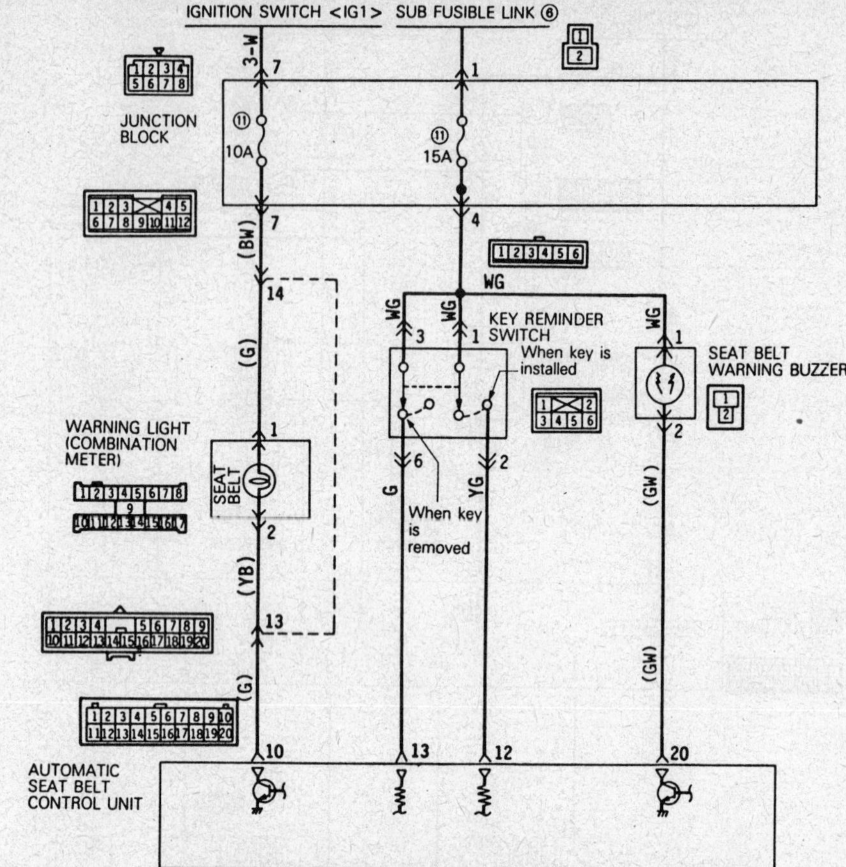


**Fig. 144 Warning light, key reminder switch & buzzer circuit diagram. Eagle Talon & Plymouth Laser**

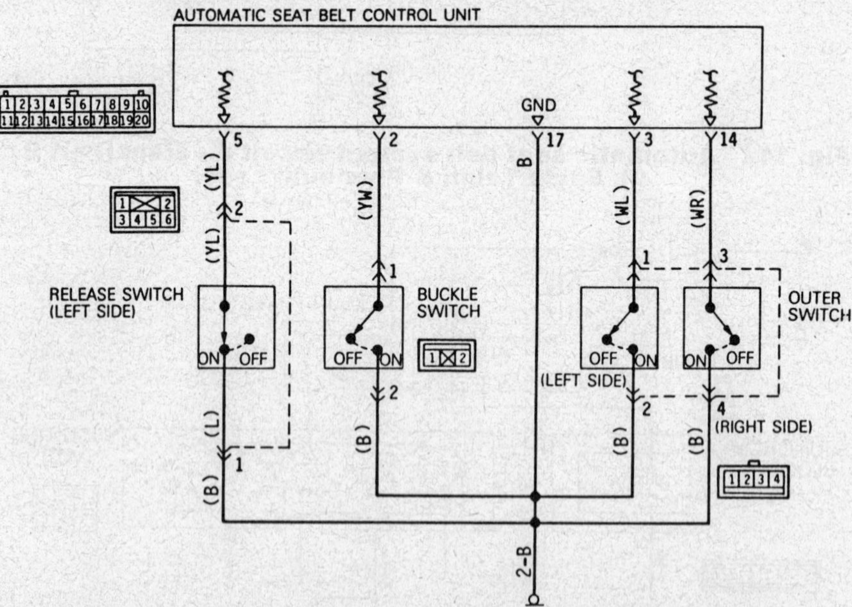


**Fig. 145 Release switch (driver's side), buckle switch & outer switch circuit diagram. Eagle Talon & Plymouth Laser**

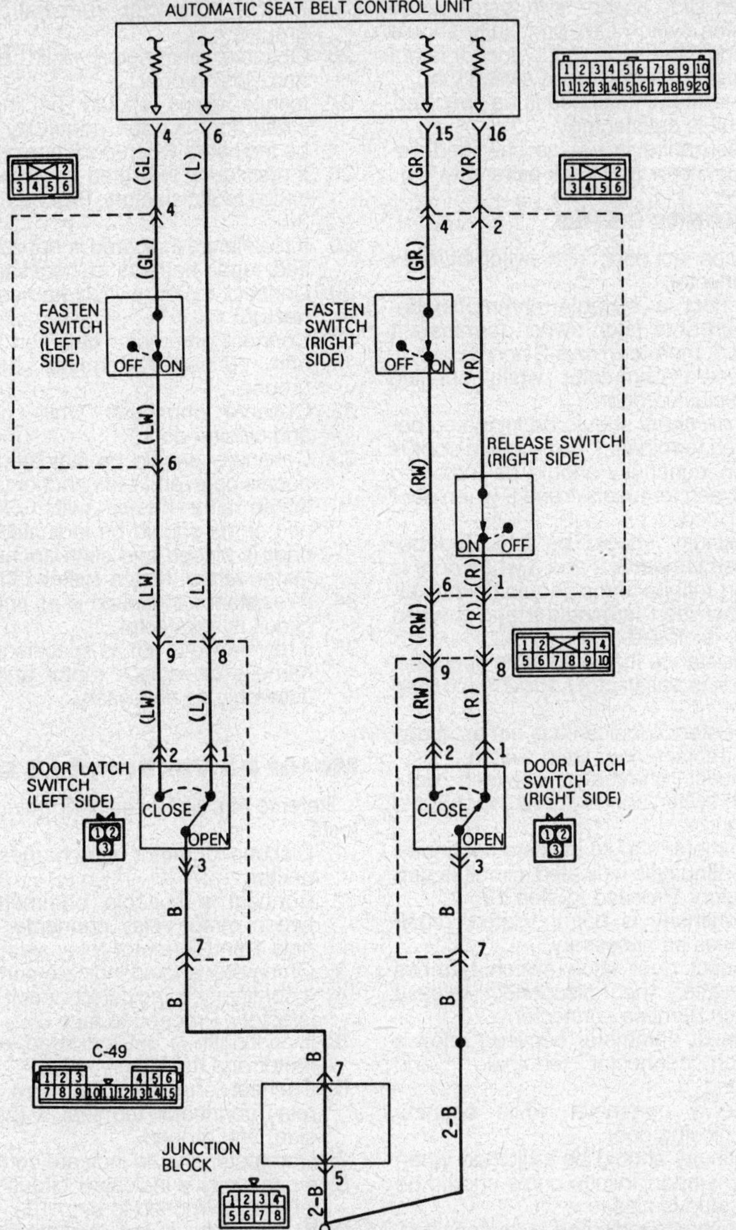


**Fig. 146 Door latch switch, fasten switch & release switch (passenger's side) circuit diagram. Eagle Talon & Plymouth Laser**

## Release Switch (Driver's Side), Buckle Switch & Release Switch

Refer to **Fig. 145** when performing these tests.

1. Check release switch (driver's side) circuit as follows:
   a. Disconnect release switch harness connector.
   b. Connect a suitable ohmmeter between release switch connector terminal 1 and ground.
   c. Ohmmeter should indicate continuity.
   d. If continuity is indicated, circuit is satisfactory. Proceed to step f.
   e. If continuity is not indicated, repair harness as necessary.
   f. Connect release switch harness connector, then disconnect control unit harness connector.
   g. Connect ohmmeter between control unit connector terminal 5 and ground.
   h. Observe ohmmeter while manually moving slide anchor.
   i. Ohmmeter should indicate continuity when slide anchor is not in release (switch On) range.
   j. Ohmmeter indicate infinite ohms when slide anchor is in release (switch Off) range.
   k. If resistance indicated is as specified, circuit is satisfactory. Proceed to step 2.
   l. If resistance indicated is not as specified, repair harness or replace motor and track assembly as necessary.
2. Check buckle switch circuit as follows:
   a. Disconnect buckle switch harness connector.
   b. Connect a suitable ohmmeter between buckle switch connector terminal 2 and ground.
   c. Ohmmeter should indicate continuity.
   d. If continuity is indicated, circuit is satisfactory. Proceed to step f.
   e. If continuity is not indicated, repair harness as necessary.
   f. Connect buckle switch harness connector, then disconnect control unit harness connector.
   g. Connect ohmmeter between control unit connector terminal 2 and ground.
   h. Ensure lap belt is not fastened.
   i. Ohmmeter should indicate continuity.
   j. If continuity is indicated, circuit is satisfactory. Proceed to step 3.
   k. If continuity is not indicated, repair harness or replace buckle as necessary.
3. Check outer switch circuit as follows:
   a. Disconnect outer switch harness connector.
   b. Connect ohmmeter between outer switch connector (harness side) terminal 2 and ground, then terminal 4 and ground.
   c. Ohmmeter should indicate continuity.
   d. If continuity is indicated, circuit is satisfactory. Proceed to step f.
   e. If continuity is not indicated, repair harness as necessary.
   f. Connect ohmmeter between outer switch connector (switch side) terminals 1 and 2 (left side), then between terminals 3 and 4 (right side).
   g. Observe ohmmeter while pulling out and retracting shoulder belt.
   h. With shoulder belt fully retracted to pulled out approximately half way (outer switch Off), infinite ohms should be indicated.
   i. With shoulder belt pulled half way out to fully pulled out position (outer switch On), continuity should be indicated.
   j. If resistance indicated is as specified, circuit is satisfactory. Proceed to step l.
   k. If resistance indicated is not as specified, replace shoulder belt retractor assembly.
   l. Connect shoulder belt to slide anchor (outer switch On). Connect outer switch harness connector, then disconnect control unit harness connector.
   m. Connect ohmmeter between control unit connector terminal 3 and ground, then terminal 14 and ground.
   n. Ohmmeter should indicate continuity.
   o. If continuity is indicated, circuit is satisfactory.

p. If continuity is not indicated, repair harness as necessary.

### DOOR LATCH SWITCH, FASTEN SWITCH & RELEASE SWITCH (PASSENGER'S SIDE)

Refer to **Fig. 146** when performing these tests.

#### Driver's Side

1. Disconnect door latch switch harness connector.
2. Connect a suitable ohmmeter between door latch switch terminals 1 and 3, then terminals 2 and 3.
3. Observe ohmmeter while opening and closing door.
4. Infinite ohms should be indicated between terminals 1 and 3 when door is open, continuity should be indicated between terminals 1 and 3 when door is closed.
5. Continuity should be indicated between terminals 2 and 3 when door is open, infinite ohms should be indicated between terminals 2 and 3 when door is closed.
6. If resistance indicated is as specified, circuit is satisfactory. Proceed to step 8.
7. If resistance indicated is not as specified, replace door latch switch.
8. Connect ohmmeter between door latch switch connector terminal 3 and ground.
9. Ohmmeter should indicate continuity.
10. If continuity is indicated, circuit is satisfactory. Proceed to step 12.
11. If continuity is not indicated, repair harness as necessary.
12. Connect door latch switch harness connector, then disconnect control unit harness connector.
13. Connect ohmmeter between control unit connector terminal 6 and ground.
14. Observe ohmmeter while opening and closing door.
15. Continuity should be indicated when door is open, infinite ohms should be indicated is closed.
16. If resistance indicated is as specified, circuit is satisfactory. Proceed to step 18.
17. If resistance indicated is not as specified, repair harness as necessary.
18. Disconnect fasten switch harness connector.
19. Connect ohmmeter between fasten switch connector terminal 6 and ground.
20. Observe ohmmeter while opening and closing door.
21. Infinite ohms should be indicated when door is open, continuity should be indicated when door is closed.
22. If resistance indicated is as specified, circuit is satisfactory. Proceed to step 24.
23. If resistance indicated is not as specified, repair harness as necessary.
24. Connect fasten switch harness connector.
25. Connect ohmmeter between control unit connector terminal 4 and ground.
26. Close door.
27. Infinite ohms should be indicated when slide anchor is in fasten range (fasten switch Off), continuity should be indicated when slide anchor is not in fasten range (fasten switch On).
28. If resistance indicated is as specified, circuit is satisfactory.
29. If resistance is not as specified, replace motor and track assembly.

#### Passenger's Side

1. Disconnect door latch switch harness connector.
2. Connect a suitable ohmmeter between door latch switch terminals 1 and 3, then terminals 2 and 3.
3. Observe ohmmeter while opening and closing door.
4. Infinite ohms should be indicated between terminals 1 and 3 when door is open, continuity should be indicated between terminals 1 and 3 when door is closed.
5. Continuity should be indicated between terminals 2 and 3 when door is open, infinite ohms should be indicated between terminals 2 and 3 when door is closed.
6. If resistance indicated is as specified, circuit is satisfactory. Proceed to step 8.
7. If resistance indicated is not as specified, replace door latch switch.
8. Connect ohmmeter between door latch switch connector terminal 3 and ground.
9. Ohmmeter should indicate continuity.
10. If continuity is indicated, circuit is satisfactory. Proceed to step 12.
11. If continuity is not indicated, repair harness as necessary.
12. Connect door latch switch harness connector, then disconnect release switch harness connector.
13. Connect ohmmeter between release switch connector terminal 1 and ground.
14. Observe ohmmeter while opening and closing door.
15. Continuity should be indicated when door is open, infinite ohms should be indicated is closed.
16. If resistance indicated is as specified, circuit is satisfactory. Proceed to step 18.
17. If resistance indicated is not as specified, repair harness as necessary.
18. Connect release switch harness connector, then disconnect control unit harness connector.
19. Connect ohmmeter between control unit connector terminal 16 and ground.
20. Observe ohmmeter while opening and closing door.
21. Continuity should be indicated when door is open, infinite ohms should be indicated when door is closed.
22. If resistance indicated is as specified, circuit is satisfactory. Proceed to step 24.
23. If resistance indicated is not as specified, repair harness or replace motor and track assembly as necessary.
24. Disconnect fasten switch harness connector.
25. Connect ohmmeter between fasten switch connector terminal 6 and ground.
26. Observe ohmmeter while opening and closing door.
27. Infinite ohms should be indicated when door is open, continuity should be indicated when door is closed.
28. If resistance indicated is as specified, circuit is satisfactory. Proceed to step 30.
29. If resistance indicated is not as specified, repair harness as necessary.
30. Connect fasten switch harness connector.
31. Connect ohmmeter between control unit connector terminal 15 and ground.
32. Observe ohmmeter while opening and closing door.
33. Continuity should be indicated when door is open and slide anchor is not in fasten range (fasten switch On), infinite ohms should be indicated when door is closed and slide anchor is in fasten range (fasten switch Off).
34. If resistance indicated is as specified, circuit is satisfactory.
35. If resistance is not as specified, repair harness or replace motor and track assembly as necessary.

#### Motor Power Supply & Drive

Refer to **Fig. 147** when performing these tests.

1. Disconnect motor relay harness connector.
2. Connect a suitable ohmmeter between motor relay connector terminals 1 and 3 (motor relay side).
3. Ohmmeter should indicate continuity.
4. If continuity is indicated, circuit is satisfactory. Proceed to step 6.
5. If continuity is not indicated, replace motor and track assembly.
6. Connect ohmmeter between motor relay connector terminal 5 (harness side) and ground.
7. Ohmmeter should indicate continuity.
8. If continuity is indicated, circuit is satisfactory. Proceed to step 10.
9. If continuity is not indicated, repair harness as necessary.
10. Disconnect control unit harness connector.
11. Connect ohmmeter between motor relay connector terminal 2 (motor relay side) and ground, then between terminal 6 (motor relay side) and ground.
12. Ohmmeter should indicate continuity.
13. If continuity is indicated, circuit is satisfactory. Proceed to step 15.
14. If continuity is not indicated, replace motor and track assembly.
15. Connect a suitable voltmeter between motor relay connector terminal 2 (harness side) and ground, then between terminal 6 (harness side) and ground.
16. Voltage indicated should be approximately 12 volts.
17. If voltage indicated is as specified, circuit is satisfactory. Proceed to step 19.
18. If voltage indicated is not as specified, repair harness as necessary.

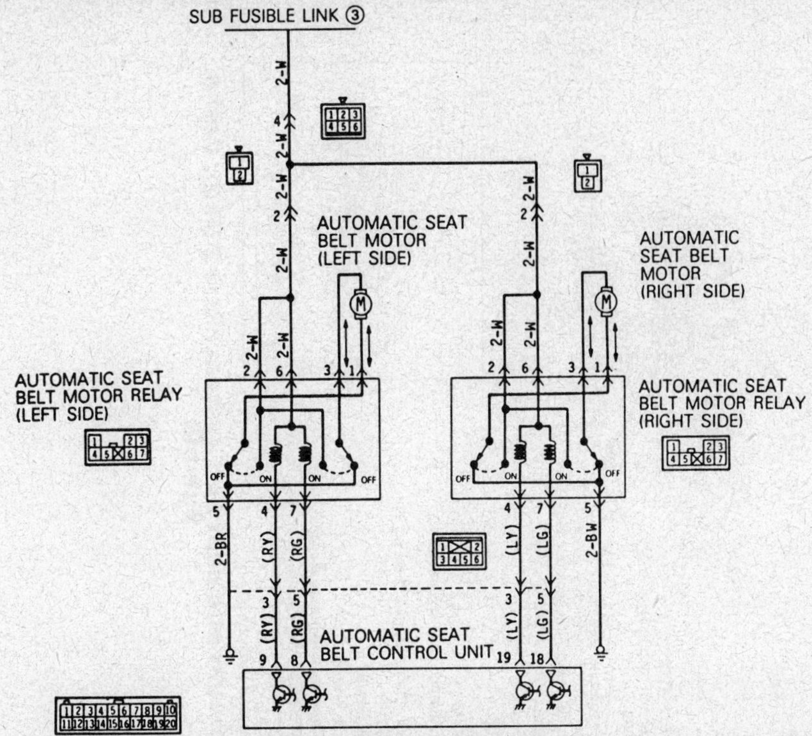


**Fig. 147 Motor power supply & drive circuit diagram. Eagle Talon & Plymouth Laser**

19. Connect motor relay harness connector.
20. Connect voltmeter between control unit connector terminals 8, 9 and ground (left side), then between terminals 18, 19 and ground (right side).
21. Voltage indicated should be approximately 12 volts.
22. If voltage indicated is as specified, circuit is satisfactory.
23. If voltage indicated is not as specified, repair harness or replace motor and track assembly as necessary.

# SYSTEM SERVICE

## MOTOR & TRACK ASSEMBLY, REPLACE

### COLT & SUMMIT

Refer to **Fig. 148,** when performing the following procedure.

1. **On hatchback models,** proceed as follows:
   a. Remove scuff plate, then upper and lower quarter trim.
   b. Remove front pillar trim, then the front belt rail trim.
   c. Remove headlining.
2. **On sedan models,** proceed as follows:
   a. Remove front and rear scuff plates.
   b. Remove center pillar upper and lower trim panels.
   c. Remove front pillar trim panel, then the front belt rail trim.
   d. Remove headlining.
3. **On all models,** remove shoulder belt tongue plate.
4. Disconnect release switch connector.
5. Disconnect seat belt wiring harness connector.
6. Remove outer casing mounting bolts.
7. Remove motor mounting bolts.
8. Remove guide rail mounting bolts, then the track and motor assembly.
9. Reverse procedure to install.

### COLT VISTA

Refer to **Fig. 149,** when performing the following procedure.

1. Remove front and rear scuff plates.
2. Remove center pillar corner garnish.
3. Remove center pillar upper and lower trim panels.
4. Remove front pillar trim panel, then the flange trim trim.
5. Remove shoulder belt tongue plate.
6. Disconnect release switch connector.
7. Disconnect seat belt wiring harness connector.
8. Remove outer casing mounting bolts.
9. Remove motor mounting bolts.
10. Remove guide rail mounting bolts, then the track and motor assembly.
11. Reverse procedure to install.

### CONQUEST

Refer to **Fig. 150,** when performing the following procedure.

1. Remove headlining, front pillar and roof side trim.
2. Remove upper quarter, wrap around and quarter trim panels.
3. Remove door sill scuff plate.
4. Remove buckle, then the front seat.
5. Disconnect buckle switch and anchor plate electrical connectors.
6. Remove lap belt retractor, then the outer casing (B), tape guide, outer casing (A) and rail guide.
7. Disconnect release and fasten switch electrical connector.
8. Remove drive motor.
9. Reverse procedure to install.

### EAGLE TALON & PLYMOUTH LASER

Refer to **Fig. 151,** when performing the following procedure.

1. Remove scuff plates, quarter trim, center and front pillar trim.
2. Disconnect seat belt wiring harness connector.
3. Remove outer casing mounting bolts.
4. Remove motor mounting bolts.
5. Remove guide rail mounting bolts, then the track and motor assembly.
6. Reverse procedure to install.

### SHADOW & SUNDANCE

#### Removal

1. Remove necessary trim panels to access track and motor.
2. Disconnect electrical connector.
3. Remove drive motor attaching nut, then the cable retaining screws, **Fig. 152.**
4. Remove track attaching screws, **Fig. 153.**
5. Remove lock box attaching screws, then motor and track assembly.

#### Installation

1. Install motor and track assembly, then align rail holes with body holes and install a Christmas tree fastener at the mid point of the rail.
2. Install the motor assembly to the body.
3. Install the drive motor nut and **torque** to 10 ft. lbs.
4. Connect electrical connectors, then install and finger tighten the two lock box screws.
5. Install the rearward rail attaching screw and **torque** to 35 inch lbs.
6. **Torque** lock box screws to 12 ft. lbs.
7. Install the forward track screws and **torque** to 35 inch lbs.
8. Install the remaining two track screws and **torque** to 35 inch lbs.
9. Install drive cable retaining clips.
10. Install trim panels.

### MONACO & PREMIER

1. Remove front door garnish molding, then B-pillar trim, **Fig. 154.**
2. Remove lower door opening trim, then move trim back to gain access to motor mounting bolts.
3. Disconnect electrical connector at motor.
4. Remove track and motor assembly.
5. Reverse procedure to install. **Torque,** motor mounting bolts to 3.7 ft. lbs., lock box mounting bolt to 24 ft. lbs, and track mounting bolts to 1 ft. lb.

## SHOULDER BELT, REPLACE

### Colt, Colt Vista, Eagle Talon, Plymouth Laser & Summit

1. Remove shoulder belt tongue plate, then the guide ring.

*Continued on page 21-116*

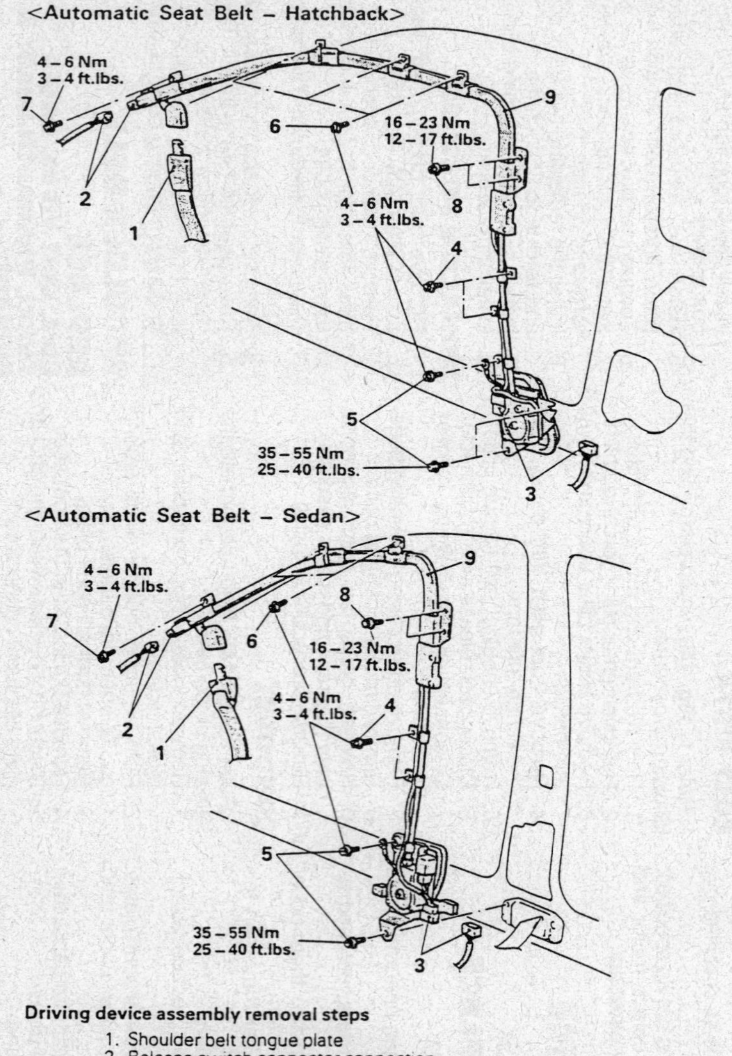


**Driving device assembly removal steps**

1. Shoulder belt tongue plate
2. Release switch connector connection
3. Automatic seat belt wiring harness connector connection
4. Outer casing mounting bolts
5. Motor mounting bolts
6. Guide rail mounting bolts (A)
7. Guide rail mounting bolts (B)
8. Guide rail mounting bolts (C)
9. Driving device assembly

**Fig. 148 Automatic seat belt system (Part 1 Of 2). Colt & Summit**

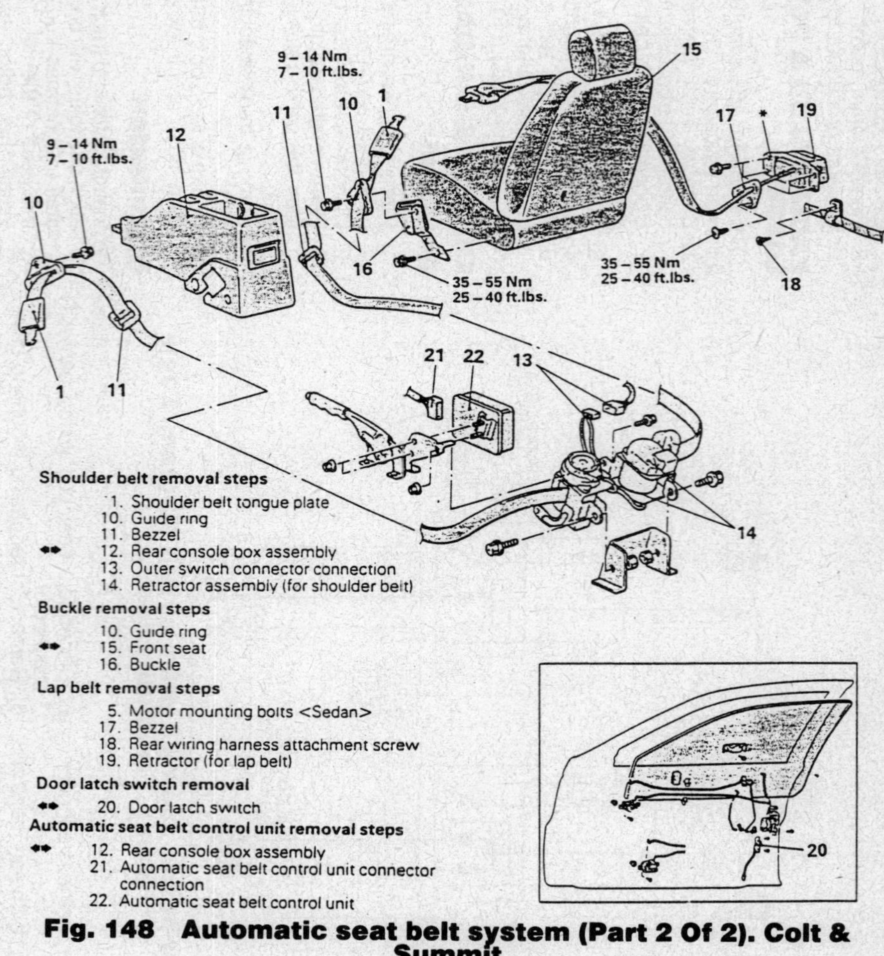


**Shoulder belt removal steps**

1. Shoulder belt tongue plate
10. Guide ring
11. Bezzel
◆◆ 12. Rear console box assembly
13. Outer switch connector connection
14. Retractor assembly (for shoulder belt)

**Buckle removal steps**

10. Guide ring
◆◆ 15. Front seat
16. Buckle

**Lap belt removal steps**

5. Motor mounting bolts <Sedan>
17. Bezzel
18. Rear wiring harness attachment screw
19. Retractor (for lap belt)

**Door latch switch removal**

◆◆ 20. Door latch switch

**Automatic seat belt control unit removal steps**

◆◆ 12. Rear console box assembly
21. Automatic seat belt control unit connector connection
22. Automatic seat belt control unit

**Fig. 148 Automatic seat belt system (Part 2 Of 2). Colt & Summit**

**Driving device assembly removal steps**

1. Shoulder belt tongue plate
2. Release switch connector connection
3. Automatic seat belt wiring harness connector connection
4. Outer casing mounting bolts
5. Motor mounting bolts
6. Guide rail mounting bolts (A)
7. Guide rail mounting bolts (B)
8. Guide rail mounting bolts (C)
9. Driving device assembly
10. Roof side bracket

**Door latch switch removal**

11. Door latch switch

**Fig. 149 Automatic seat belt system (Part 1 Of 2). Colt Vista**

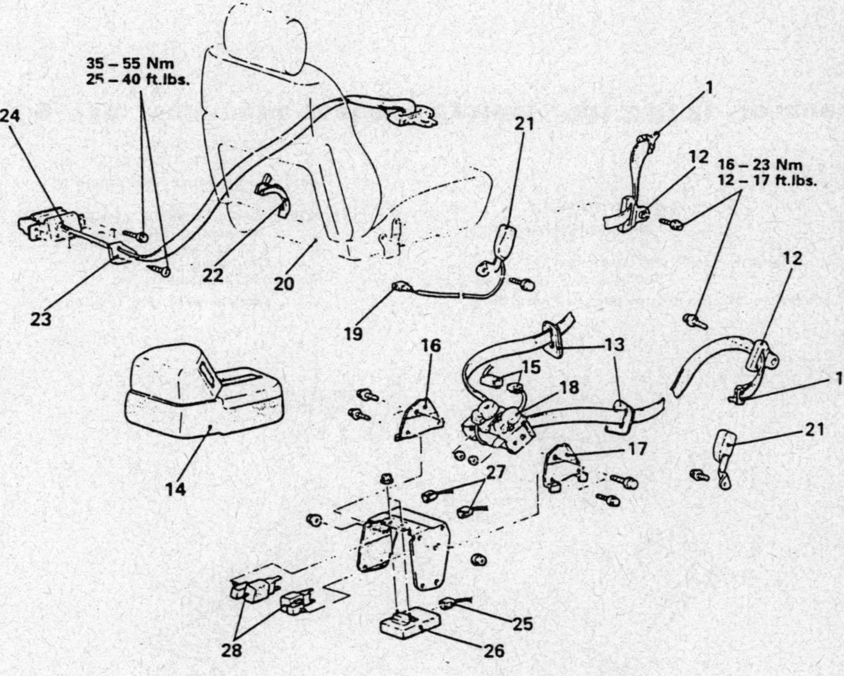


**Shoulder belt removal steps**

1. Shoulder belt tongue plate
12. Guide ring
13. Bezzel
14. Rear console box assembly
15. Outer switch connector connection
16. Retractor bracket (L.H)
17. Retractor bracket (R.H.)
18. Retractor assembly (for shoulder belt)

**Buckle removal steps**

12. Guide ring
19. Buckle switch connector connection
20. Front seat
21. Buckle

**Lap belt removal steps**

22. Removal of lap belt from belt holder
23. Bezzel
24. Retractor (for lap belt)

**Automatic seat belt control unit removal steps**

14. Rear console box assembly
25. Automatic seat belt control unit connector connection
26. Automatic seat belt control unit

**Automatic seat belt motor relay removal steps**

14. Rear console box assembly
27. Automatic seat belt motor relay connector connection
28. Automatic seat belt motor relay

**Fig. 149 Automatic seat belt system (Part 2 Of 2). Colt Vista**

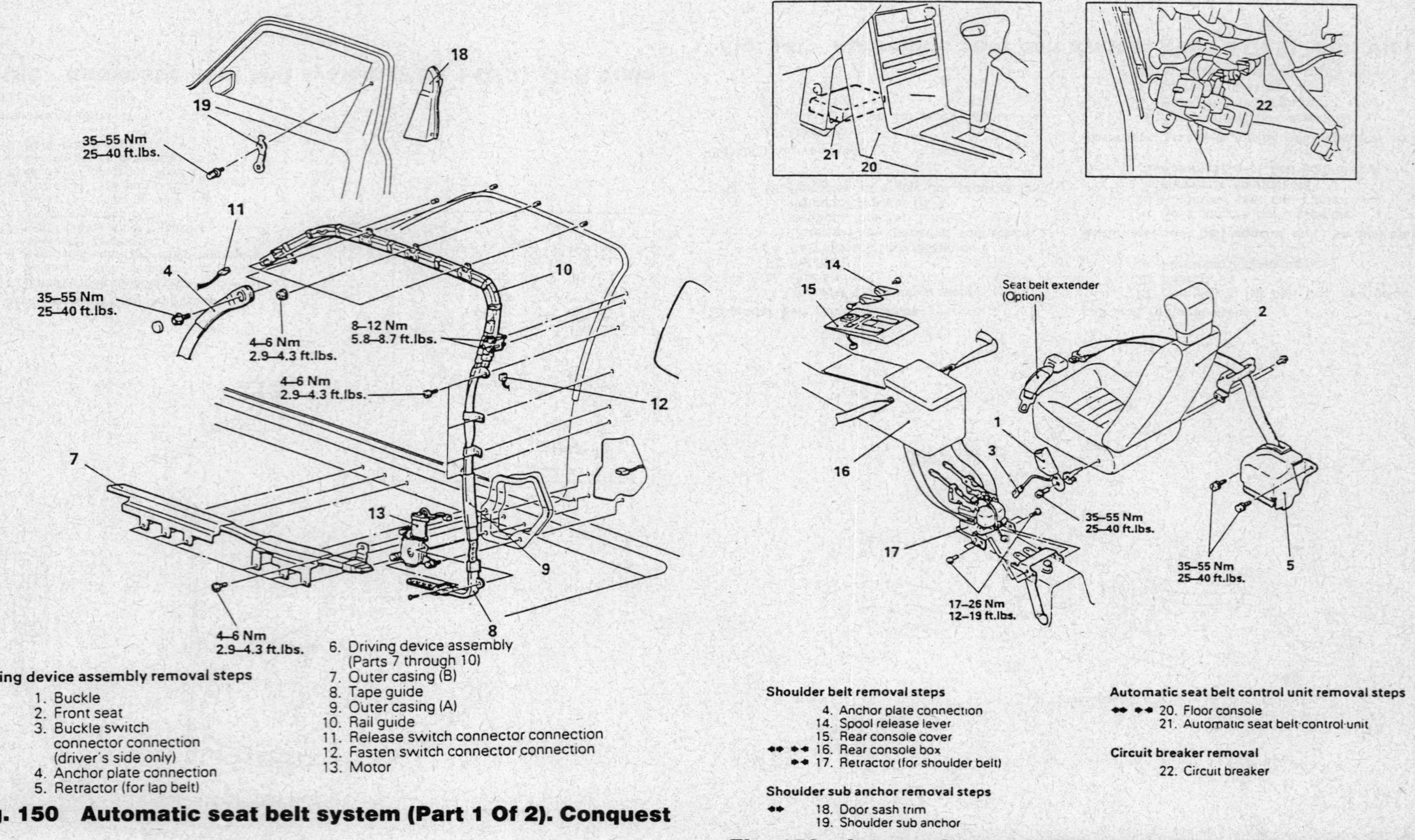


**Driving device assembly removal steps**

1. Buckle
2. Front seat
3. Buckle switch connector connection (driver's side only)
4. Anchor plate connection
5. Retractor (for lap belt)
6. Driving device assembly (Parts 7 through 10)
7. Outer casing (B)
8. Tape guide
9. Outer casing (A)
10. Rail guide
11. Release switch connector connection
12. Fasten switch connector connection
13. Motor

**Fig. 150 Automatic seat belt system (Part 1 Of 2). Conquest**

**Shoulder belt removal steps**

4. Anchor plate connection
14. Spool release lever
15. Rear console cover
16. ◆◆ ◆◆ Rear console box
17. ◆◆ Retractor (for shoulder belt)

**Shoulder sub anchor removal steps**

18. ◆◆ Door sash trim
19. Shoulder sub anchor

**Automatic seat belt control unit removal steps**

20. ◆◆ ◆◆ Floor console
21. Automatic seat belt control unit

**Circuit breaker removal**

22. Circuit breaker

**Fig. 150 Automatic seat belt system (Part 2 Of 2). Conquest**

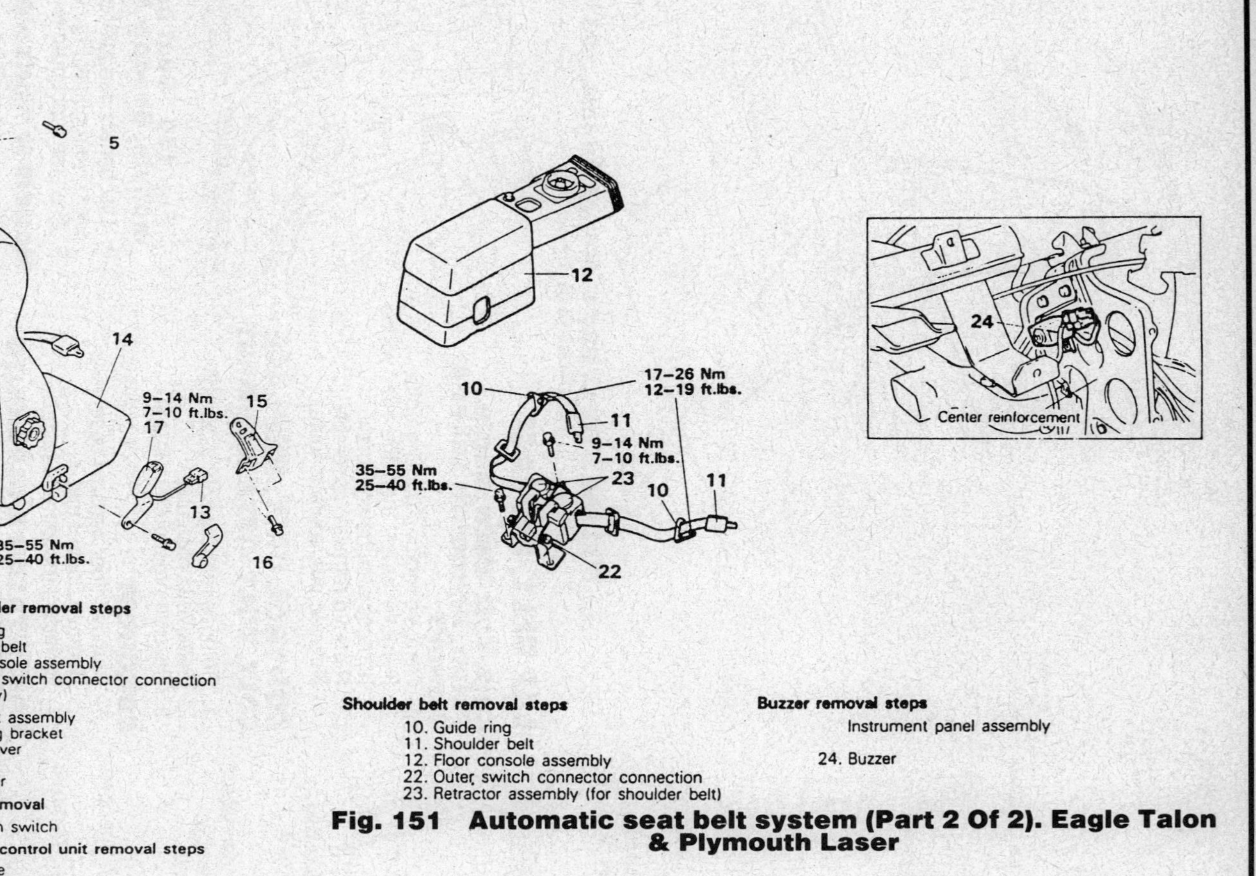


**Driving device assembly removal steps**

Scuff plate
Quarter trim
Center pillar trim
Front pillar trim
1. Automatic seat belt wiring harness connector connection
2. Outer casing mounting screws
3. Motor mounting bolts
4. Guide rail mounting bolts (A)
5. Guide rail mounting bolt (B)
6. Guide rail mounting bolts (C)
7. Driving device assembly

**Lap belt removal steps**

Scuff plate
Quarter trim
8. Bezzel
9. Retractor (for lap belt)

**Buckle and belt holder removal steps**

10. Guide ring
11. Shoulder belt
12. Floor console assembly
13. Seat belt switch connector connection (L.H. only)
14. Front seat assembly
15. Guide ring bracket
16. Buckle cover
17. Buckle
18. Belt holder

**Door latch switch removal**

19. Door latch switch

**Automatic seat belt control unit removal steps**

Scuff plate
Quarter trim
20. Automatic seat belt control unit connector connection
21. Automatic seat belt control unit

**Fig. 151 Automatic seat belt system (Part 1 Of 2). Eagle Talon & Plymouth Laser**

**Shoulder belt removal steps**

10. Guide ring
11. Shoulder belt
12. Floor console assembly
22. Outer switch connector connection
23. Retractor assembly (for shoulder belt)

**Buzzer removal steps**

Instrument panel assembly

24. Buzzer

**Fig. 151 Automatic seat belt system (Part 2 Of 2). Eagle Talon & Plymouth Laser**

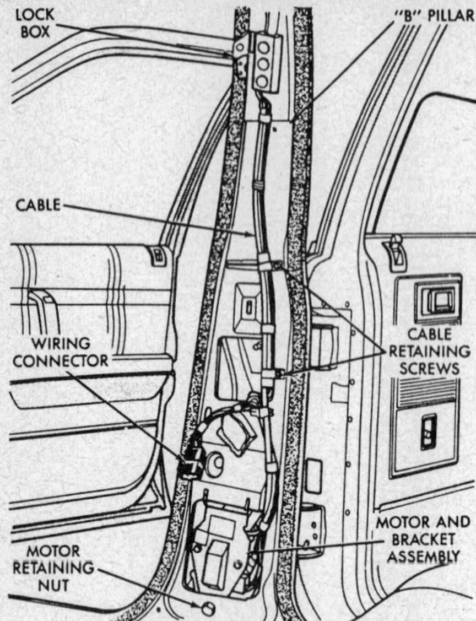


**Fig. 152 Motor & cable assembly. Shadow & Sundance**

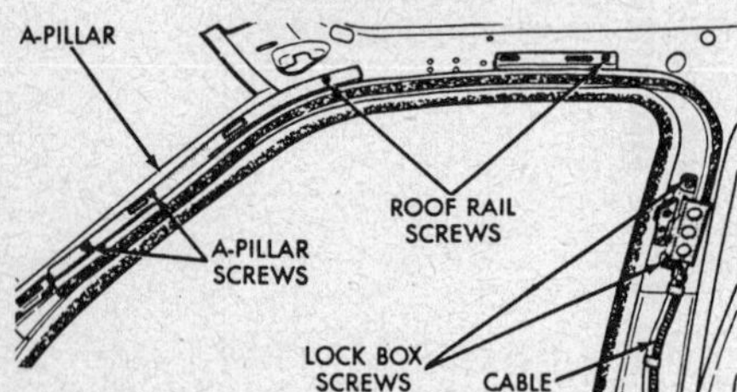


**Fig. 153 Track assembly. Shadow & Sundance**

2. Remove rear console box.
3. Disconnect outer switch connector, then remove retractor assembly.
4. Reverse procedure to install.

### Conquest

1. Remove anchor plate, then spool release lever.
2. Remove rear console cover, then rear console box.
3. Remove retractor assembly.
4. Reverse procedure to install.

## RETRACTOR, REPLACE

### Monaco & Premier

1. Remove center console as follows:
   a. Remove ash tray and ash tray receiver, the disconnect connector from cigar lighter.
   b. Remove armrest, then console.
2. From inside of vehicle, remove retractor assembly.
3. Reverse procedure to install. **Torque,** retractor bolts to 27 ft. lbs. and seat belt anchor brace to 26 ft. lbs.

## BUCKLE, REPLACE

### Colt, Colt Vista, Eagle Talon, Plymouth Laser & Summit

1. Remove guide ring, then the front seat.
2. Remove buckle.
3. Reverse procedure to install.

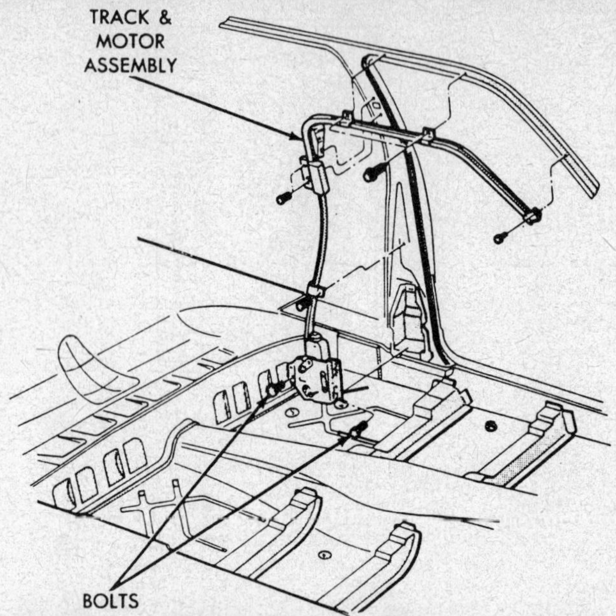


**Fig. 154 Track and motor assembly. 1991 Monaco & Premier**

## LAP BELT, REPLACE

### Colt, Colt Vista, Eagle Talon, Plymouth Laser & Summit

1. Remove motor mounting bolts.
2. Remove bezel, then the rear wiring harness attachment screw.
3. Remove retractor assembly.
4. Reverse procedure to install.

## CONTROL UNIT, REPLACE

### COLT, COLT VISTA & SUMMIT

1. Remove rear console assembly.
2. Remove control unit.
3. Reverse procedure to install.

### CONQUEST

1. Remove floor console assembly.
2. Remove control unit.
3. Reverse procedure to install.

### EAGLE TALON & PLYMOUTH LASER

1. Remove scuff plate and quarter trim
2. Disconnect control unit harness connector.
3. Remove control unit.
4. Reverse procedure to install.

### SHADOW & SUNDANCE Models w/Floor Console

1. Remove shifter handle.
2. Unsnap shifter bezel, then disconnect electrical connectors and remove bezel.
3. Remove power mirror switch and disconnect electrical connector, if equipped.
4. Remove armrest attaching screws from center console retractor bracket.
5. Remove armrest and center console section as an assembly by unsnapping from front console section.
6. Remove center module bezel.
7. Remove sidewall attaching screws, then the module-to-bracket attaching screws.

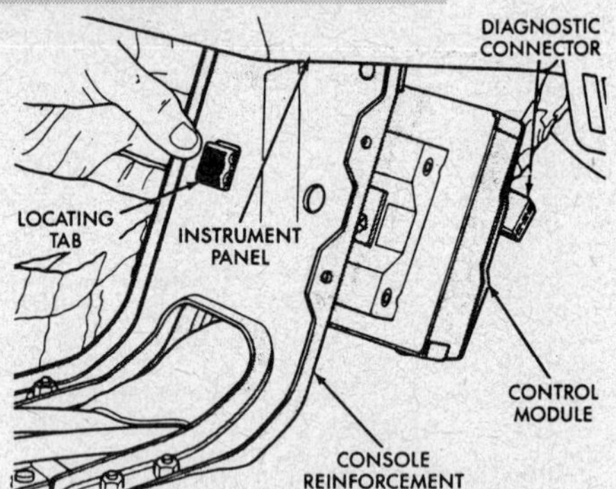


**Fig. 155 Seat belt control module. Shadow & Sundance**

8. Disconnect module connectors and remove module, **Fig. 155.**
9. Reverse procedure to install.

### Models w/Consolette

1. Remove trim caps and screws from consolette.
2. **On models with manual transmissions,** remove shifter knob. On models with automatic transmission, remove shifter knob and gear selector indicator.
3. **On all models,** remove consolette to retractor and lap belt assembly attaching screws.
4. Remove consolette.
5. Remove module-to-console attaching screws.
6. Disconnect electrical connectors and remove module.
7. Reverse procedure to install.

## MOTOR RELAY, REPLACE

### Colt Vista

1. Remove rear console assembly.
2. Disconnect motor relay harness connector.
3. Remove motor relay.
4. Reverse procedure to install.

# ACTIVE SUSPENSIONS

TABLE OF CONTENTS



# Automatic Level Control

INDEX



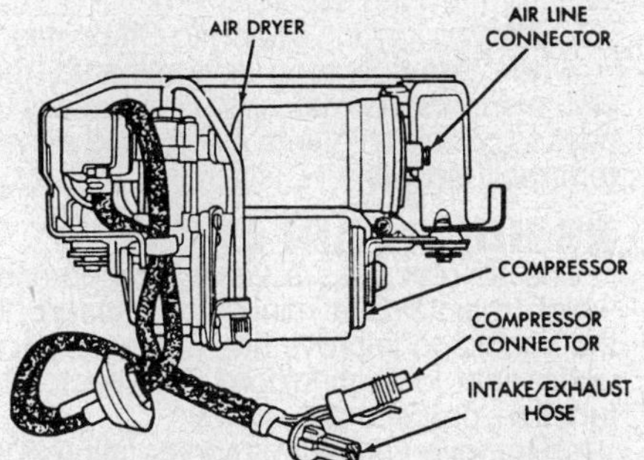


**Fig. 1 Compressor assembly**

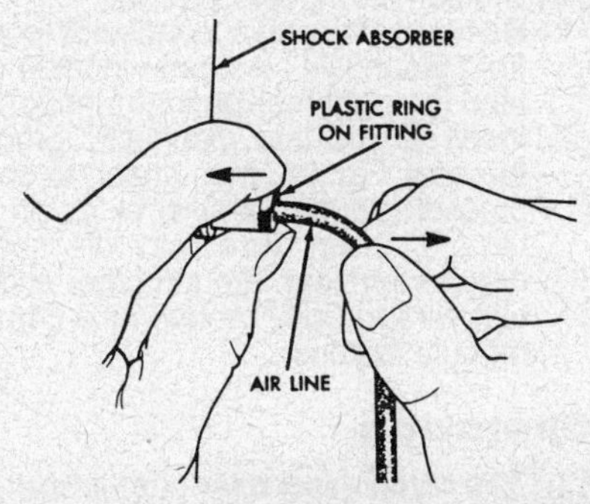


**Fig. 2 Removing air lines**

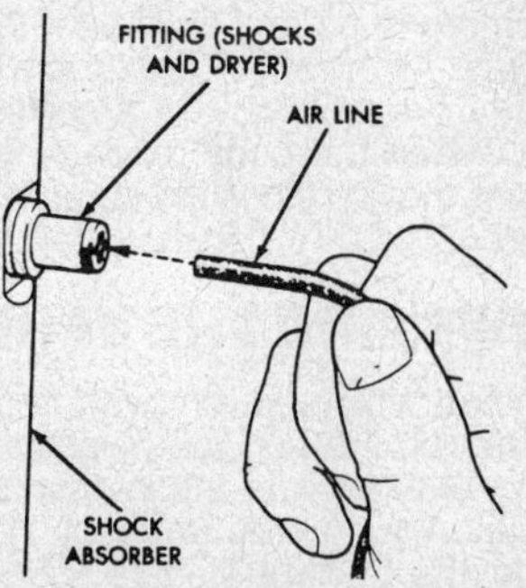


**Fig. 3 Installing air lines**

## DESCRIPTION

The Automatic Load Leveling System (ALLS) performs the function of adjusting the carrying height of the vehicle when weight is added too or removed from the vehicle. The ALLS system consists of the following components: air compressor, air adjustable shock absorbers, electronic height sensor, compressor relay, manual switch, exhaust solenoid, air dryer and the necessary wiring and tubing.

## SYSTEM COMPONENTS

### AIR COMPRESSOR

The Air Compressor assembly is located under rear of vehicle, **Fig. 1.** It supplies between 170-220 psi to the rear shocks, with an exhaust valve located in the compressor head assembly. To prevent excessive cycling between the compressor and exhaust solenoid during a normal drive, there is a 12-18 second delay programed into the microprocessor.

### CONTROL MODULE (CM)

The Control Module (CM) is a device that controls the ground circuits for the compressor relay and the exhaust valve solenoid. A microprocessor within the CM limits the compressor pump operation time to 140 to 160 seconds to prevent damage to compressor motor.

In addition, there is an air regeneration cycle that is controlled by the CM, if the height sensor signal is the neutral or high position. When the ignition switch in turned to the On position, after a 22 to 28 second delay the compressor will run from 2 to 6 seconds.

To prevent excessive cycling, a 12 to 18 second delay is incorporated in the microprocessor.

### HEIGHT SENSOR

This sensor switch is located in the RH rear shock absorber and monitors the height at rear of vehicle. The sensor sends signals to the control module as to the status of the height, low, trim or high.

### AIR LINES & FITTINGS

To release an air line from its fitting, pull back on plastic ring and pull air line from fitting, **Fig. 2.** The fitting has a unique push in feature. A brass type collet locks the air line in place. One rubber O-ring seals the air line. To attach air line, push line into fitting, **Fig. 3.**

## COMPRESSOR RELAY

The compressor relay completes the circuit to the compressor when energized by the height sensor. The relay is located either next to the compressor, in relay panel under instrument panel or in wiring harness above steering column.

## AIR ADJUSTABLE SHOCKS ABSORBERS

Air shock absorbers are essentially hydraulic shock absorbers with a neoprene bladder sealing the upper and lower sections together, forming an air cylinder.

## AIR DRYER

The air dryer, **Fig. 1,** is attached externally to the air compressor output and performs two functions. First, the air dryer absorbs moisture from the air before is delivered into the system. Second, the air dryer contains a valve arrangement that maintains minimum air pressure in the air adjustable shock absorbers.

# SYSTEM OPERATION

## RAISING THE VEHICLE

When weight is added to the rear suspension lowering the height sensor, this action will activate the internal time delay circuit. After a time delay of 12—18 seconds, the Control Module (CM) activates the ground circuit to the compressor relay.

With the relay grounded, the compressor motor runs and air is sent through the system. As the shock absorbers inflate, the body moves upward to a corrected position. When the body reaches the correct height, the CM stops the compressor operation.

## LOWERING THE VEHICLE

When weight is removed from the rear suspension raising the height sensor, this action will activate the internal time delay circuit. After a time delay of 12—18 seconds, the Control Module (CM) activates the ground circuit to the exhaust valve solenoid. Air is exhausted from the shock absorbers through the air dryer and exhaust solenoid into the atmosphere.

As the shock absorbers deflate, the body moves downward to its original position. When the body reaches the original height, the CM opens the exhaust solenoid valve circuit.

# TROUBLESHOOTING

Refer to **Figs. 4 and 5,** for troubleshooting of auto level control system.

# DIAGNOSIS & TESTING

Prior to performing diagnosis tests, check and ensure that all fuses and fuse links are in good condition. Check all connectors that link the system to the main body wiring harness. These include the compressor, height sensor, control module, relay and underbody to trunk and load leveling harness to main harness. Check all air lines, connectors and other components for correct installation.

Refer to **Figs. 6 and 7,** for system wiring circuits when performing diagnosis of system.

To properly perform the following diagnosis and testing the use of a DRBII readout tool or equivalent is required, follow tool manufacturers instructions for proper installation of the tool prior to testing speed control system.

Refer to **Figs. 8 through 16,** on 1989-90 models or **Figs. 17 through 25,** on 1991 models, for diagnosis and testing of automatic load leveling system. **On 1991 models,** after system testing has been completed, perform verification test shown in **Fig. 18.**

## SYSTEM TESTING

Refer to **Figs. 6 and 7,** for system wiring circuits when performing testing of system.

## SYSTEM OPERATIONAL TEST

A test weight of 275-300 lbs. must be added before starting diagnosis tests.

### Preparation

The following system test operation is started only by connecting the diagnostic ground terminal to ground after the ignition switch is turned to the On position. A monitor lamp must be connected between the Test lamp ground terminal, **Fig. 26,** to display the control module status.

1. Remove protective connector cover from diagnosis connector located behind the right rear quarter trim panel.
2. Insert a wire into diagnostic ground terminal, **Fig. 26,** then attach to compressor ground terminal or as an alternate, insert wire into diagnostic ground terminal. Ground other end of test wire to body ground or a control module fastener.

### Operation

1. The compressor relay output, from the Control Module (CM), is activated until the vehicle is in the high position. The maximum relay output operation time is 140-160 seconds. If the expected position is not obtained, the CM ceases test and any further operation. The monitor lamp output is continuously activated until the ignition is cycled from Off to On or 1 hour has passed after the ignition switch was turned to the Off position.
2. The monitor lamp output should flash to indicate the position of the height sensor. The sensor should be in the high position. A continuously lighted monitor lamp will indicate a failure.
3. Next the exhaust solenoid output is activated until the vehicle is in the low position. The maximum exhaust solenoid operation time is 110-130 seconds. If the expected position is not obtained, the CM ceases test and any further operation. The monitor lamp output is lighted continuously until the ignition is cycled from Off to On or 1 hour has passed after the ignition switch was turned to the Off position.
4. The monitor lamp should flash to indicate the height sensor in the low position. A continuously lighted monitor lamp will indicate a failure.
5. The compressor relay output is activated to return the vehicle to the level position. The maximum operation time of the relay is 140-160 seconds. If the expected position is not obtained, the CM ceases test and any further operation. The monitor lamp is continuously lighted until the ignition is cycled from Off to On or 1 hour has passed after the ignition switch was turned to the Off position.
6. Completion of test is when test successfully completed, the CM resumes normal operation. The test is now complete. throughout the testing, the vehicle load must be maintained, no loads are allow to be added or removed to or from the vehicle once the test have been started.
7. If any of the tests fail, refer to the charts shown under "Troubleshooting."

### Verification Test

To verify system operation test, disconnect test ground wire then reconnect and perform test again.

### Termination Of Test

The test operation is terminated when any of the following takes place:

1. Disconnecting the diagnostic input from ground circuit.
2. Turning ignition switch to Off position.

When test operation is terminated, the CM resumes normal operation unless it ceases operation due to it detecting a system malfunction.

## RESIDUAL AIR CHECK

The air dryer has a valve arrangement which maintains a minimum pressure in the shocks to improve ride characteristics under light load conditions. To check this function, proceed as follows:

1. Remove air line from dryer fitting and right shock absorber. Install inline a 0-300 psi inline as shown in, **Fig. 27.**
2. Cycle ignition switch from Off to On.
3. Apply a load to rear suspension of 275-300 lbs. to run compressor and raise vehicle.
4. Remove load and allow the system to exhaust and lower.
5. When no more air can be exhausted, the gage should indicate 10-22 psi.
6. Remove pressure gage then repeat steps 2 through 4 to ensure that system air pressure on in the shocks.

## LEAK CHECKS

1. Repeat steps 1 through 3 under "Residual Air Check." Allow system to fill until gage reads 70-90 psi. **If the compressor is permitted to run until it reaches its maximum output pressure, the vent solenoid valve will function as a relief valve resulting in a leak when compressor shuts Off.**

*Continued on page 22-18*

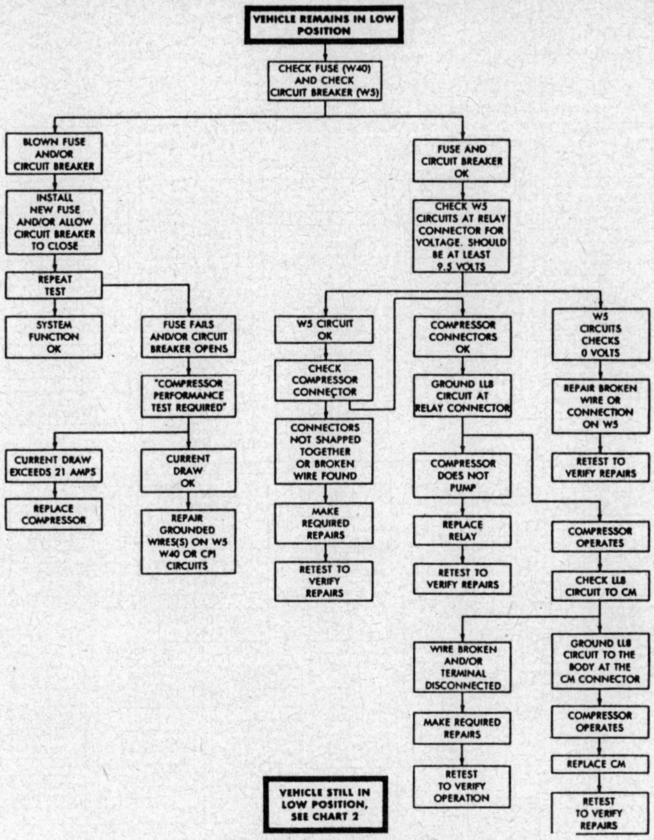

VEHICLE REMAINS IN LOW POSITION

CHECK FUSE (W40) AND CHECK CIRCUIT BREAKER (W5)

BLOWN FUSE AND/OR CIRCUIT BREAKER

INSTALL NEW FUSE AND/OR ALLOW CIRCUIT BREAKER TO CLOSE

REPEAT TEST

SYSTEM FUNCTION OK

FUSE FAILS AND/OR CIRCUIT BREAKER OPENS

"COMPRESSOR PERFORMANCE TEST REQUIRED"

CURRENT DRAW EXCEEDS 21 AMPS

REPLACE COMPRESSOR

CURRENT DRAW OK

REPAIR GROUNDED WIRES(S) ON W5 W40 OR CPI CIRCUITS

FUSE AND CIRCUIT BREAKER OK

CHECK W5 CIRCUITS AT RELAY CONNECTOR FOR VOLTAGE. SHOULD BE AT LEAST 9.5 VOLTS

W5 CIRCUIT OK

CHECK COMPRESSOR CONNECTOR

CONNECTORS NOT SNAPPED TOGETHER OR BROKEN WIRE FOUND

MAKE REQUIRED REPAIRS

RETEST TO VERIFY REPAIRS

COMPRESSOR CONNECTORS OK

GROUND LL8 CIRCUIT AT RELAY CONNECTOR

COMPRESSOR DOES NOT PUMP

REPLACE RELAY

RETEST TO VERIFY REPAIRS

W5 CIRCUITS CHECKS 0 VOLTS

REPAIR BROKEN WIRE OR CONNECTION ON W5

RETEST TO VERIFY REPAIRS

COMPRESSOR OPERATES

CHECK LL8 CIRCUIT TO CM

WIRE BROKEN AND/OR TERMINAL DISCONNECTED

MAKE REQUIRED REPAIRS

RETEST TO VERIFY OPERATION

GROUND LL8 CIRCUIT TO THE BODY AT THE CM CONNECTOR

COMPRESSOR OPERATES

REPLACE CM

RETEST TO VERIFY REPAIRS

VEHICLE STILL IN LOW POSITION, SEE CHART 2

**Fig. 4 Troubleshooting (Part 1 of 5). 1989–90 Models**

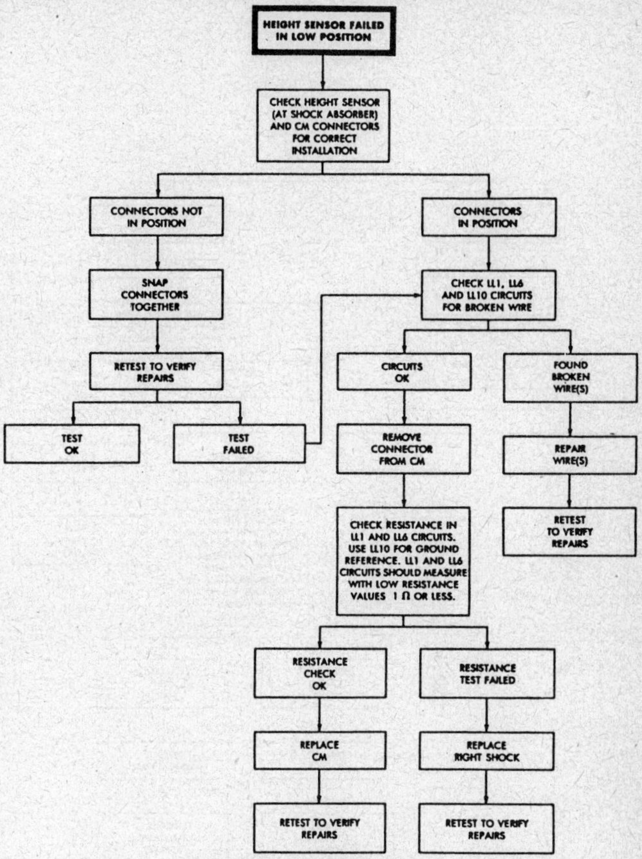

HEIGHT SENSOR FAILED IN LOW POSITION

CHECK HEIGHT SENSOR (AT SHOCK ABSORBER) AND CM CONNECTORS FOR CORRECT INSTALLATION

CONNECTORS NOT IN POSITION

SNAP CONNECTORS TOGETHER

RETEST TO VERIFY REPAIRS

TEST OK

TEST FAILED

CONNECTORS IN POSITION

CHECK LL1, LL6 AND LL10 CIRCUITS FOR BROKEN WIRE

CIRCUITS OK

REMOVE CONNECTOR FROM CM

CHECK RESISTANCE IN LL1 AND LL6 CIRCUITS. USE LL10 FOR GROUND REFERENCE. LL1 AND LL6 CIRCUITS SHOULD MEASURE WITH LOW RESISTANCE VALUES 1 Ω OR LESS.

RESISTANCE CHECK OK

REPLACE CM

RETEST TO VERIFY REPAIRS

RESISTANCE TEST FAILED

REPLACE RIGHT SHOCK

RETEST TO VERIFY REPAIRS

FOUND BROKEN WIRE(S)

REPAIR WIRE(S)

RETEST TO VERIFY REPAIRS

**Fig. 4 Troubleshooting (Part 2 of 5). 1989–90 Models**

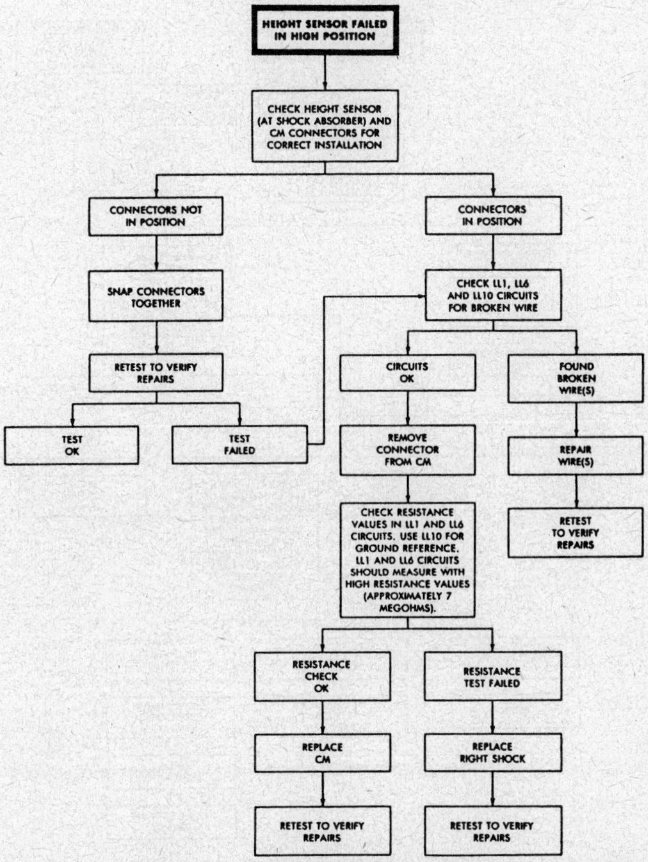

HEIGHT SENSOR FAILED IN HIGH POSITION

CHECK HEIGHT SENSOR (AT SHOCK ABSORBER) AND CM CONNECTORS FOR CORRECT INSTALLATION

CONNECTORS NOT IN POSITION

SNAP CONNECTORS TOGETHER

RETEST TO VERIFY REPAIRS

TEST OK

TEST FAILED

CONNECTORS IN POSITION

CHECK LL1, LL6 AND LL10 CIRCUITS FOR BROKEN WIRE

CIRCUITS OK

REMOVE CONNECTOR FROM CM

CHECK RESISTANCE VALUES IN LL1 AND LL6 CIRCUITS. USE LL10 FOR GROUND REFERENCE. LL1 AND LL6 CIRCUITS SHOULD MEASURE WITH HIGH RESISTANCE VALUES (APPROXIMATELY 7 MEGOHMS).

RESISTANCE CHECK OK

REPLACE CM

RETEST TO VERIFY REPAIRS

RESISTANCE TEST FAILED

REPLACE RIGHT SHOCK

RETEST TO VERIFY REPAIRS

FOUND BROKEN WIRE(S)

REPAIR WIRE(S)

RETEST TO VERIFY REPAIRS

**Fig. 4 Troubleshooting (Part 3 of 5). 1989–90 Models**

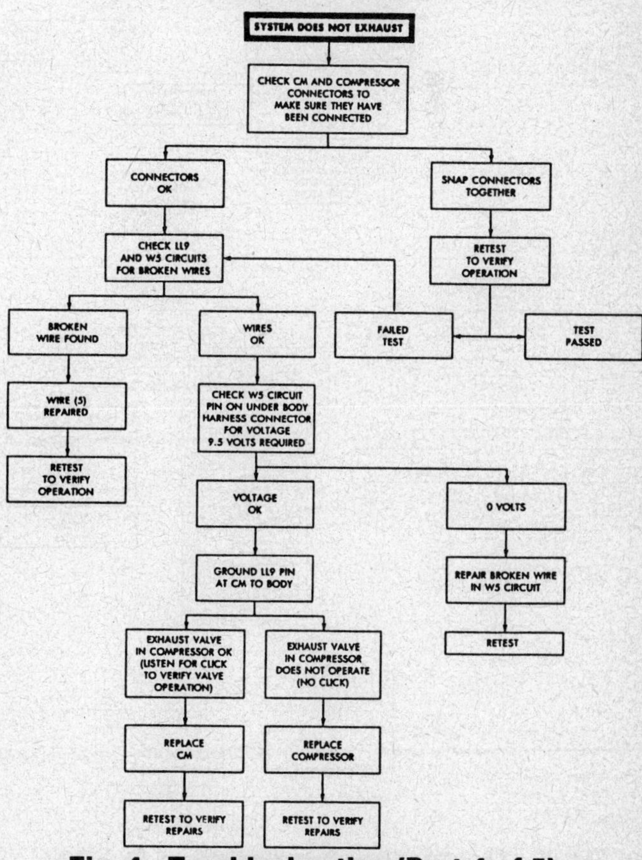


**Fig. 4 Troubleshooting (Part 4 of 5). 1989–90 Models**

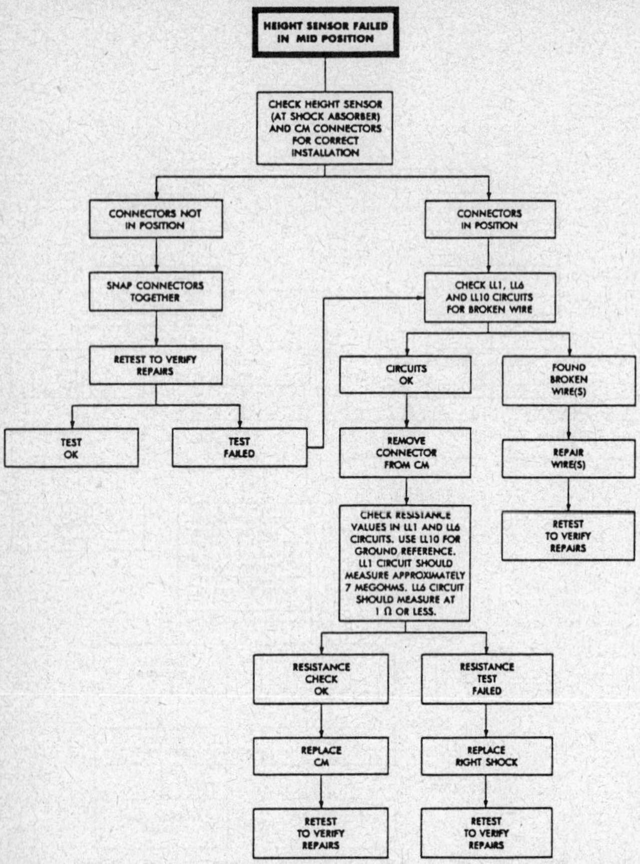

HEIGHT SENSOR FAILED IN MID POSITION

CHECK HEIGHT SENSOR (AT SHOCK ABSORBER) AND CM CONNECTORS FOR CORRECT INSTALLATION

CONNECTORS NOT IN POSITION

SNAP CONNECTORS TOGETHER

RETEST TO VERIFY REPAIRS

TEST OK

TEST FAILED

CONNECTORS IN POSITION

CHECK LL1, LL6 AND LL10 CIRCUITS FOR BROKEN WIRE

CIRCUITS OK

REMOVE CONNECTOR FROM CM

CHECK RESISTANCE VALUES IN LL1 AND LL6 CIRCUITS. USE LL10 FOR GROUND REFERENCE. LL1 CIRCUIT SHOULD MEASURE APPROXIMATELY 7 MEGOHMS. LL6 CIRCUIT SHOULD MEASURE AT 1 Ω OR LESS.

RESISTANCE CHECK OK

REPLACE CM

RETEST TO VERIFY REPAIRS

RESISTANCE TEST FAILED

REPLACE RIGHT SHOCK

RETEST TO VERIFY REPAIRS

FOUND BROKEN WIRE(S)

REPAIR WIRE(S)

RETEST TO VERIFY REPAIRS

**Fig. 4 Troubleshooting (Part 5 of 5). 1989-90 Models**

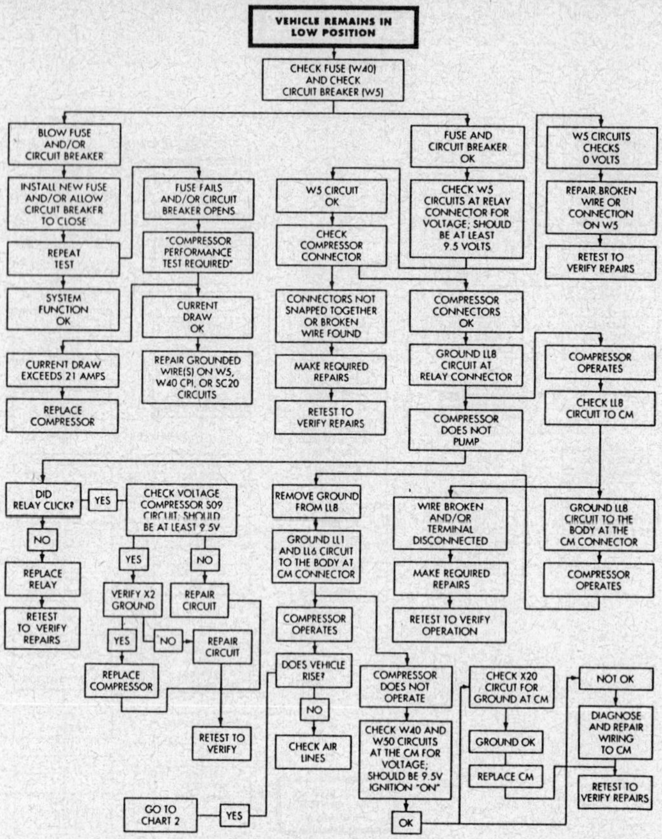

VEHICLE REMAINS IN LOW POSITION

CHECK FUSE (W40) AND CHECK CIRCUIT BREAKER (W5)

BLOW FUSE AND/OR CIRCUIT BREAKER

INSTALL NEW FUSE AND/OR ALLOW CIRCUIT BREAKER TO CLOSE

REPEAT TEST

SYSTEM FUNCTION OK

CURRENT DRAW EXCEEDS 21 AMPS

REPLACE COMPRESSOR

FUSE FAILS AND/OR CIRCUIT BREAKER OPENS

"COMPRESSOR PERFORMANCE TEST REQUIRED"

CURRENT DRAW OK

REPAIR GROUNDED WIRE(S) ON W5, W40 CPI, OR SC20 CIRCUITS

W5 CIRCUIT OK

CHECK COMPRESSOR CONNECTOR

CONNECTORS NOT SNAPPED TOGETHER OR BROKEN WIRE FOUND

MAKE REQUIRED REPAIRS

RETEST TO VERIFY REPAIRS

FUSE AND CIRCUIT BREAKER OK

CHECK W5 CIRCUITS AT RELAY CONNECTOR FOR VOLTAGE; SHOULD BE AT LEAST 9.5 VOLTS

COMPRESSOR CONNECTORS OK

GROUND LL8 CIRCUIT AT RELAY CONNECTOR

COMPRESSOR DOES NOT PUMP

W5 CIRCUITS CHECKS 0 VOLTS

REPAIR BROKEN WIRE OR CONNECTION ON W5

RETEST TO VERIFY REPAIRS

COMPRESSOR OPERATES

CHECK LL8 CIRCUIT TO CM

GROUND LL8 CIRCUIT TO THE BODY AT THE CM CONNECTOR

COMPRESSOR OPERATES

DID RELAY CLICK? — YES / NO

NO: REPLACE RELAY — RETEST TO VERIFY REPAIRS

YES: CHECK VOLTAGE COMPRESSOR S09 CIRCUIT: SHOULD BE AT LEAST 9.5V

YES: VERIFY X2 GROUND — YES: REPLACE COMPRESSOR; NO: REPAIR CIRCUIT

NO: REPAIR CIRCUIT

RETEST TO VERIFY

REMOVE GROUND FROM LL8

GROUND LL1 AND LL6 CIRCUIT TO THE BODY AT CM CONNECTOR

COMPRESSOR OPERATES

DOES VEHICLE RISE?

NO: CHECK AIR LINES

YES: GO TO CHART 2

COMPRESSOR DOES NOT OPERATE

CHECK W40 AND W50 CIRCUITS AT THE CM FOR VOLTAGE; SHOULD BE 9.5V IGNITION "ON"

OK

WIRE BROKEN AND/OR TERMINAL DISCONNECTED

MAKE REQUIRED REPAIRS

RETEST TO VERIFY OPERATION

CHECK X20 CIRCUIT FOR GROUND AT CM

GROUND OK

REPLACE CM

NOT OK

DIAGNOSE AND REPAIR WIRING TO CM

RETEST TO VERIFY REPAIRS

**Fig. 5 Troubleshooting (Part 1 of 5). 1991 models**

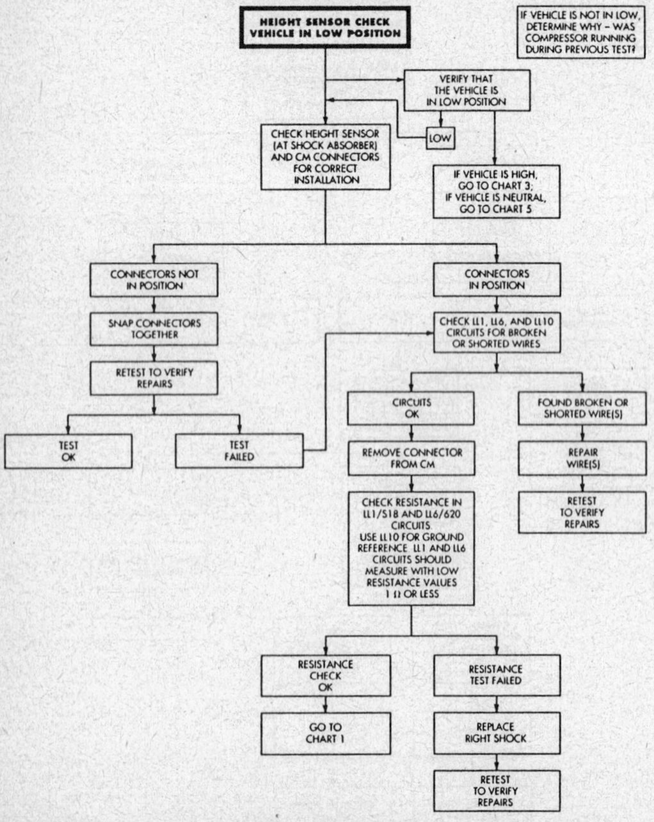

HEIGHT SENSOR CHECK VEHICLE IN LOW POSITION

IF VEHICLE IS NOT IN LOW, DETERMINE WHY – WAS COMPRESSOR RUNNING DURING PREVIOUS TEST?

VERIFY THAT THE VEHICLE IS IN LOW POSITION

LOW

IF VEHICLE IS HIGH, GO TO CHART 3; IF VEHICLE IS NEUTRAL, GO TO CHART 5

CHECK HEIGHT SENSOR (AT SHOCK ABSORBER) AND CM CONNECTORS FOR CORRECT INSTALLATION

CONNECTORS NOT IN POSITION

SNAP CONNECTORS TOGETHER

RETEST TO VERIFY REPAIRS

TEST OK

TEST FAILED

CONNECTORS IN POSITION

CHECK LL1, LL6, AND LL10 CIRCUITS FOR BROKEN OR SHORTED WIRES

CIRCUITS OK

REMOVE CONNECTOR FROM CM

CHECK RESISTANCE IN LL1/S18 AND LL6/620 CIRCUITS USE LL10 FOR GROUND REFERENCE. LL1 AND LL6 CIRCUITS SHOULD MEASURE WITH LOW RESISTANCE VALUES 1 Ω OR LESS

RESISTANCE CHECK OK

GO TO CHART 1

RESISTANCE TEST FAILED

REPLACE RIGHT SHOCK

RETEST TO VERIFY REPAIRS

FOUND BROKEN OR SHORTED WIRE(S)

REPAIR WIRE(S)

RETEST TO VERIFY REPAIRS

**Fig. 5 Troubleshooting (Part 2 of 5). 1991 models**

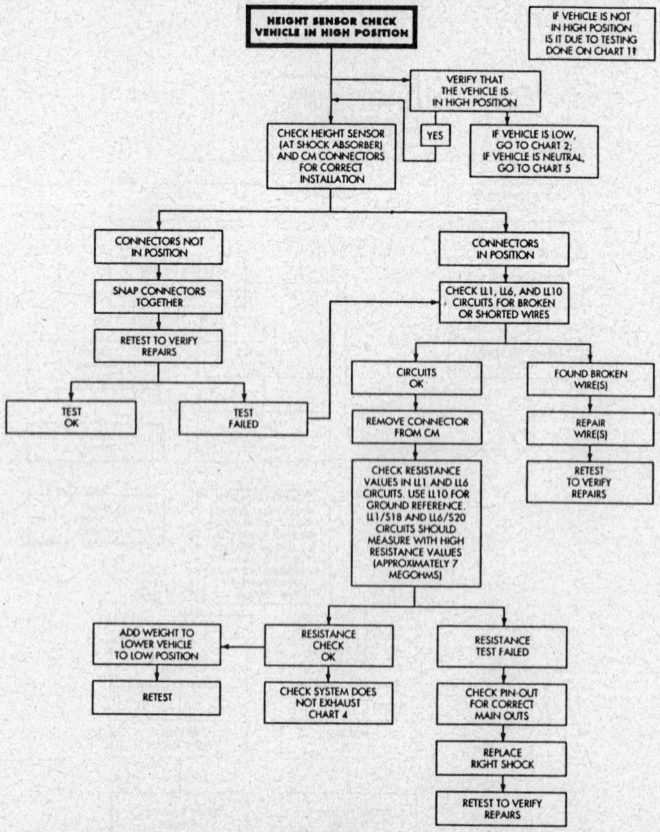

HEIGHT SENSOR CHECK VEHICLE IN HIGH POSITION

IF VEHICLE IS NOT IN HIGH POSITION IS IT DUE TO TESTING DONE ON CHART 1?

VERIFY THAT THE VEHICLE IS IN HIGH POSITION

YES

IF VEHICLE IS LOW, GO TO CHART 2; IF VEHICLE IS NEUTRAL, GO TO CHART 5

CHECK HEIGHT SENSOR (AT SHOCK ABSORBER) AND CM CONNECTORS FOR CORRECT INSTALLATION

CONNECTORS NOT IN POSITION

SNAP CONNECTORS TOGETHER

RETEST TO VERIFY REPAIRS

TEST OK

TEST FAILED

CONNECTORS IN POSITION

CHECK LL1, LL6, AND LL10 CIRCUITS FOR BROKEN OR SHORTED WIRES

CIRCUITS OK

REMOVE CONNECTOR FROM CM

CHECK RESISTANCE VALUES IN LL1 AND LL6 CIRCUITS. USE LL10 FOR GROUND REFERENCE. LL1/S18 AND LL6/S20 CIRCUITS SHOULD MEASURE WITH HIGH RESISTANCE VALUES (APPROXIMATELY 7 MEGOHMS)

RESISTANCE CHECK OK

ADD WEIGHT TO LOWER VEHICLE TO LOW POSITION

RETEST

CHECK SYSTEM DOES NOT EXHAUST CHART 4

RESISTANCE TEST FAILED

CHECK PIN-OUT FOR CORRECT MAIN OUTS

REPLACE RIGHT SHOCK

RETEST TO VERIFY REPAIRS

FOUND BROKEN WIRE(S)

REPAIR WIRE(S)

RETEST TO VERIFY REPAIRS

**Fig. 5 Troubleshooting (Part 3 of 5). 1991 models**

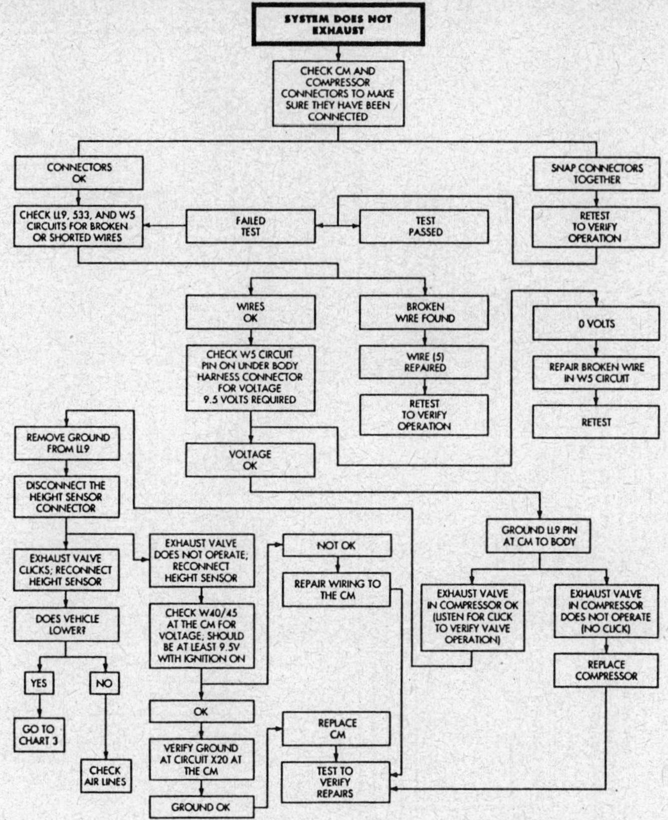


**Fig. 5 Troubleshooting (Part 4 of 5). 1991 models**

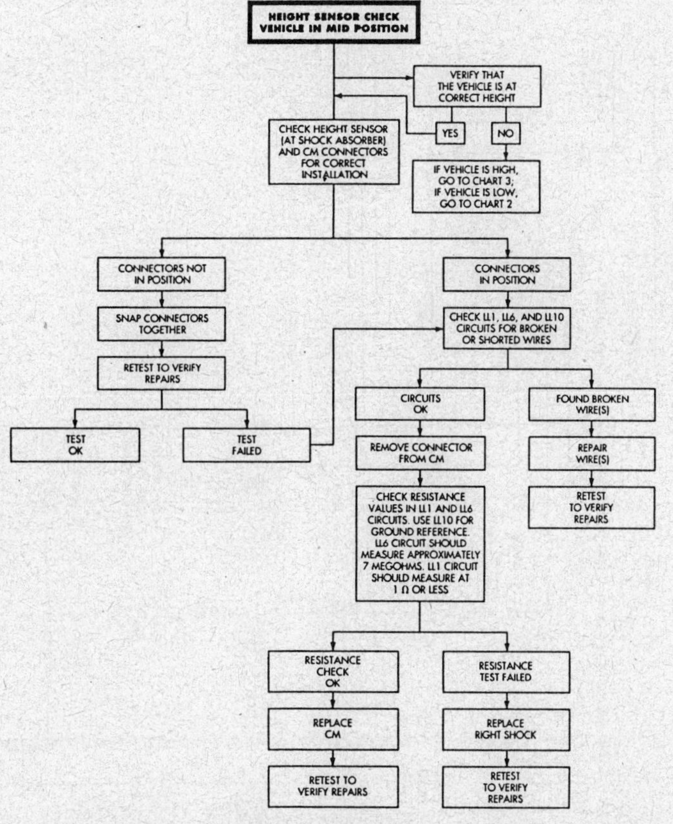


**Fig. 5 Troubleshooting (Part 5 of 5). 1991 models**

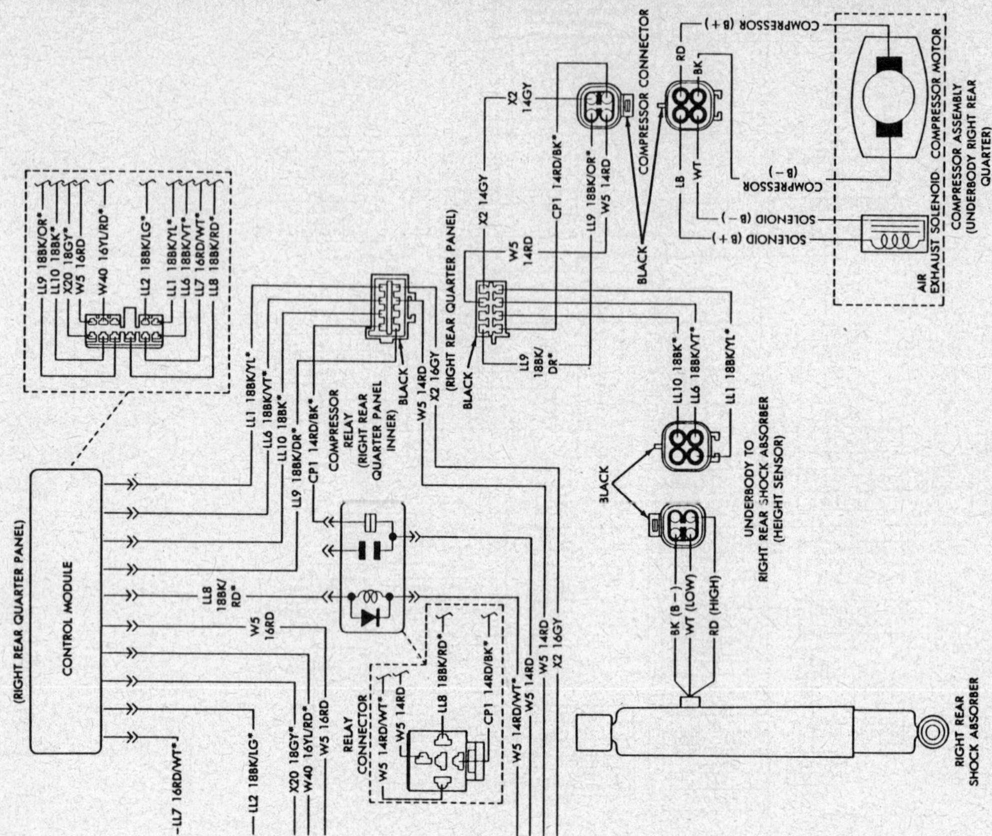

**Fig. 6 System wiring circuit (Part 2 of 2). 1989–90 models**

**Fig. 6 System wiring circuit (Part 1 of 2). 1989–90 models**

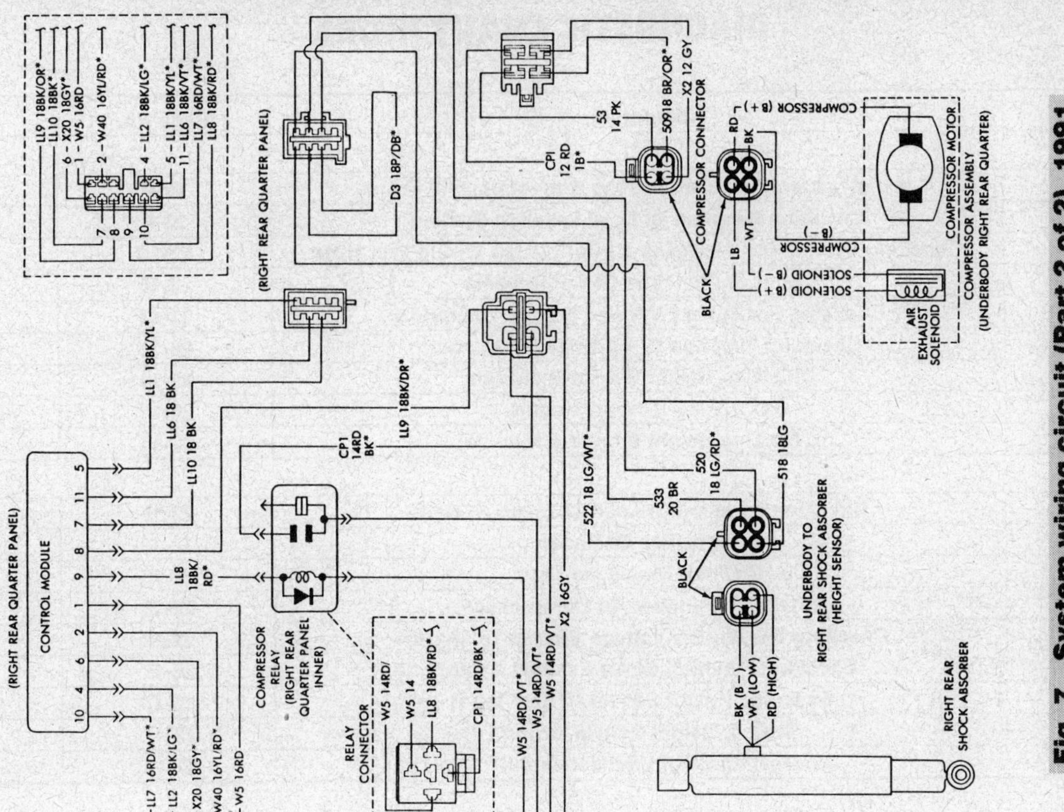

Fig. 7 System wiring circuit (Part 2 of 2). 1991 models

Fig. 7 System wiring circuit (Part 1 of 2). 1991 models

## DIAGNOSTIC CHART INDEX

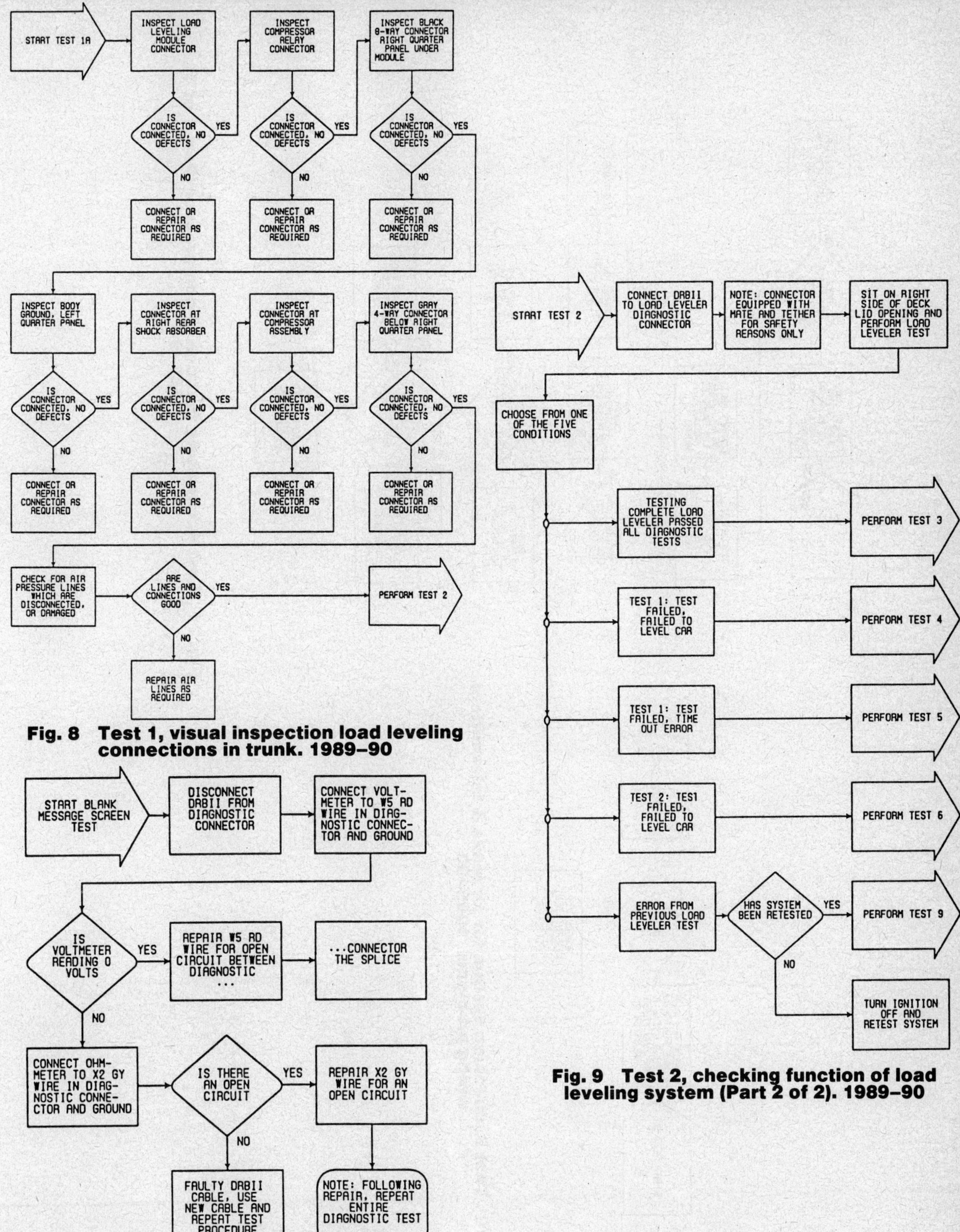


**Fig. 8 Test 1, visual inspection load leveling connections in trunk. 1989–90**



**Fig. 9 Test 2, checking function of load leveling system (Part 1 of 2). 1989–90**



**Fig. 9 Test 2, checking function of load leveling system (Part 2 of 2). 1989–90**

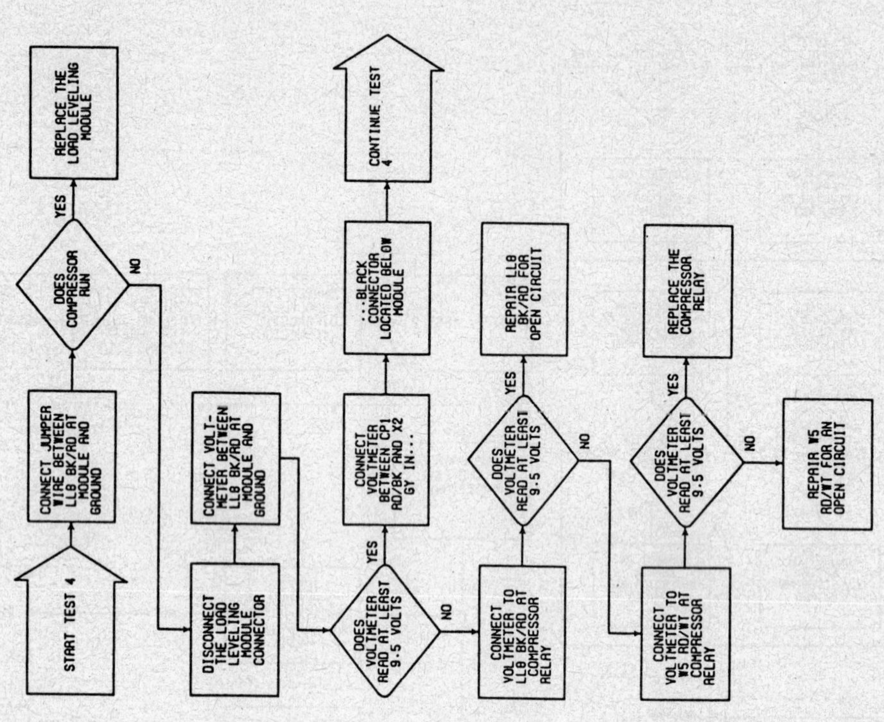


**Fig. 11 Test 4, checking function of compressor (Part 1 of 3). 1989–90**

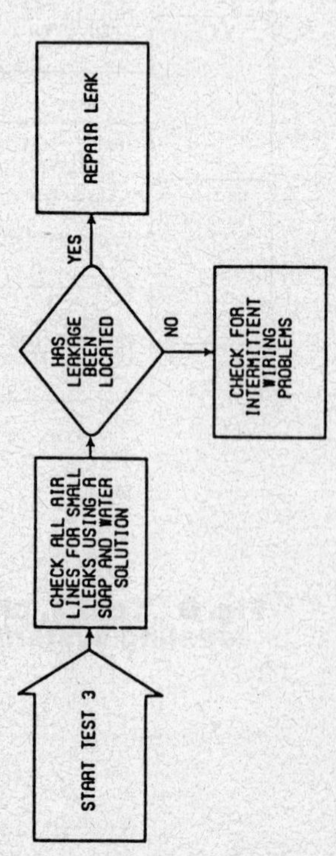


**Fig. 10 Test 3, checking system for air leaks & intermittent wiring problems. 1989–90**

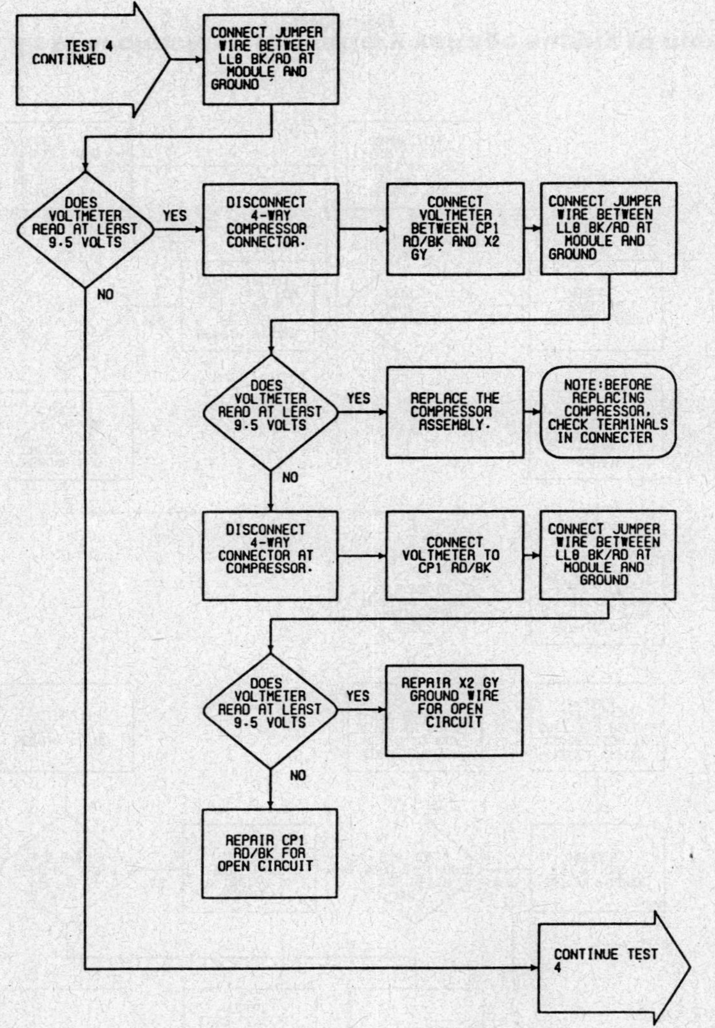


**Fig. 11 Test 4, checking function of compressor (Part 2 of 3). 1989–90**

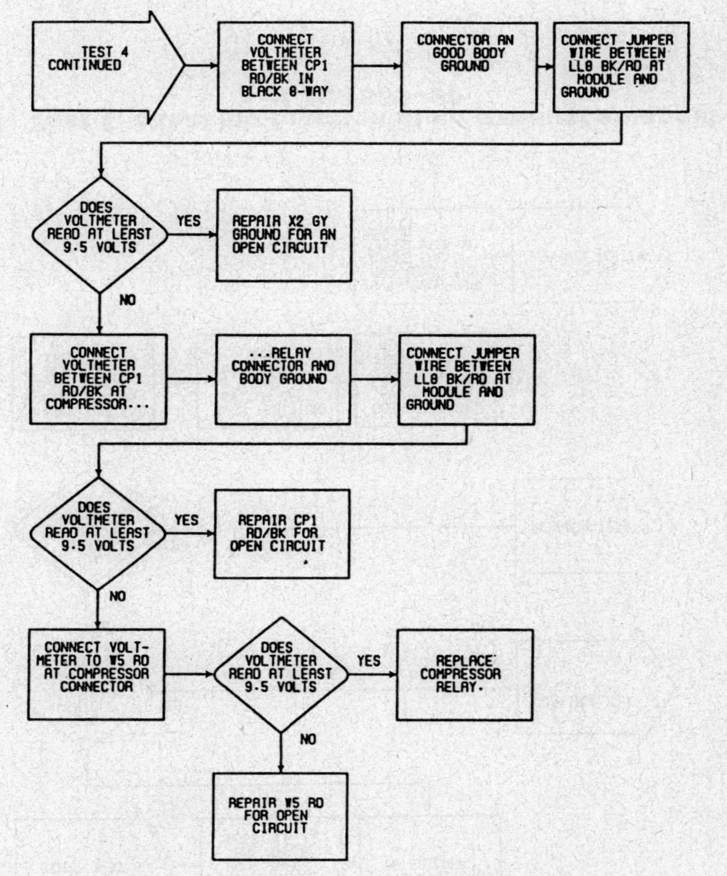


**Fig. 11 Test 4, checking function of compressor (Part 3 of 3). 1989–90**

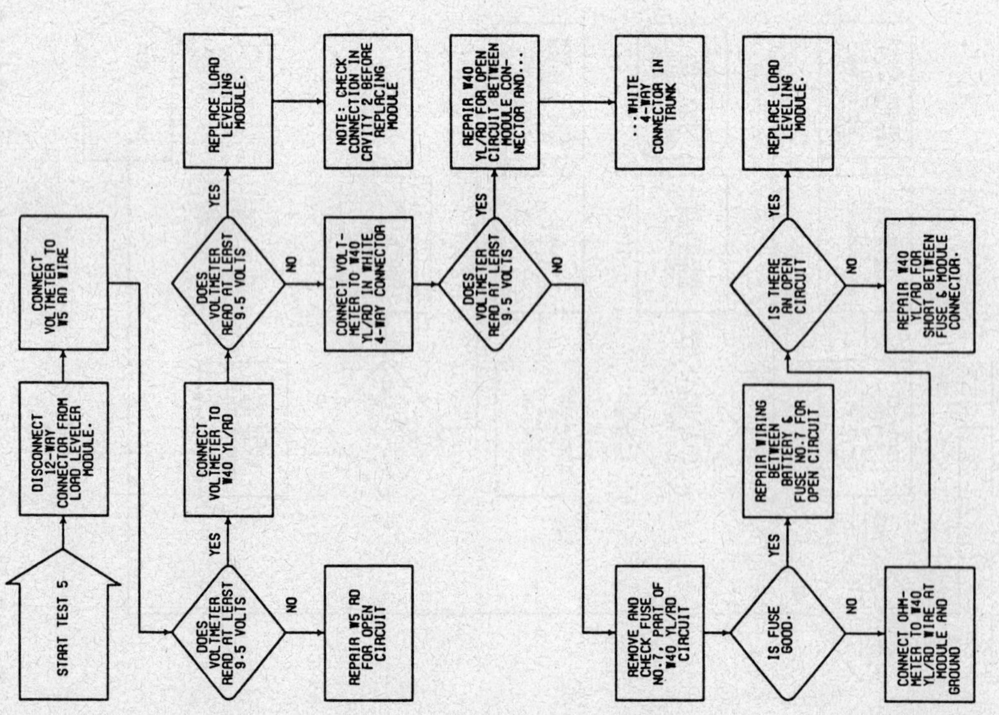


**Fig. 12 Test 5, checking for battery voltage supply to module. 1989–90**

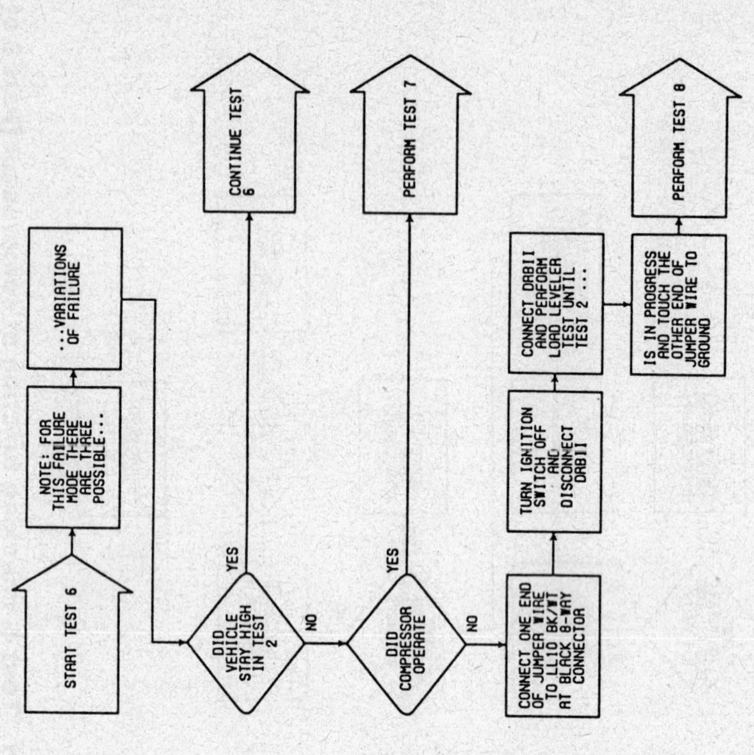


**Fig. 13 Test 6, checking function of air exhaust solenoid (Part 1 of 3). 1989–90**

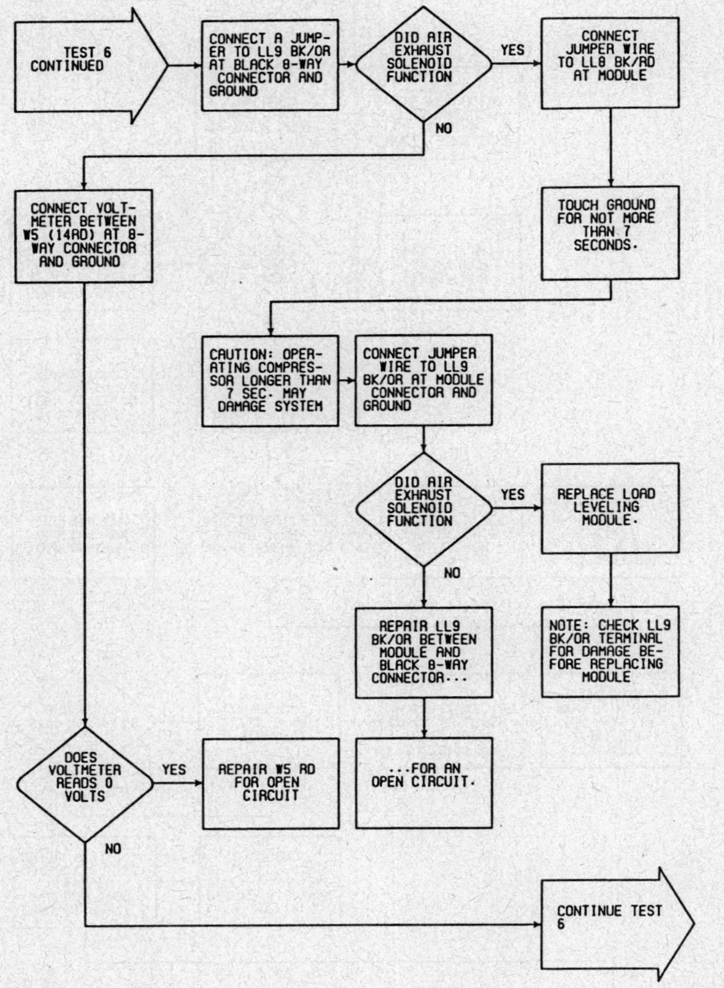


**Fig. 13 Test 6, checking function of air exhaust solenoid (Part 2 of 3). 1989–90**

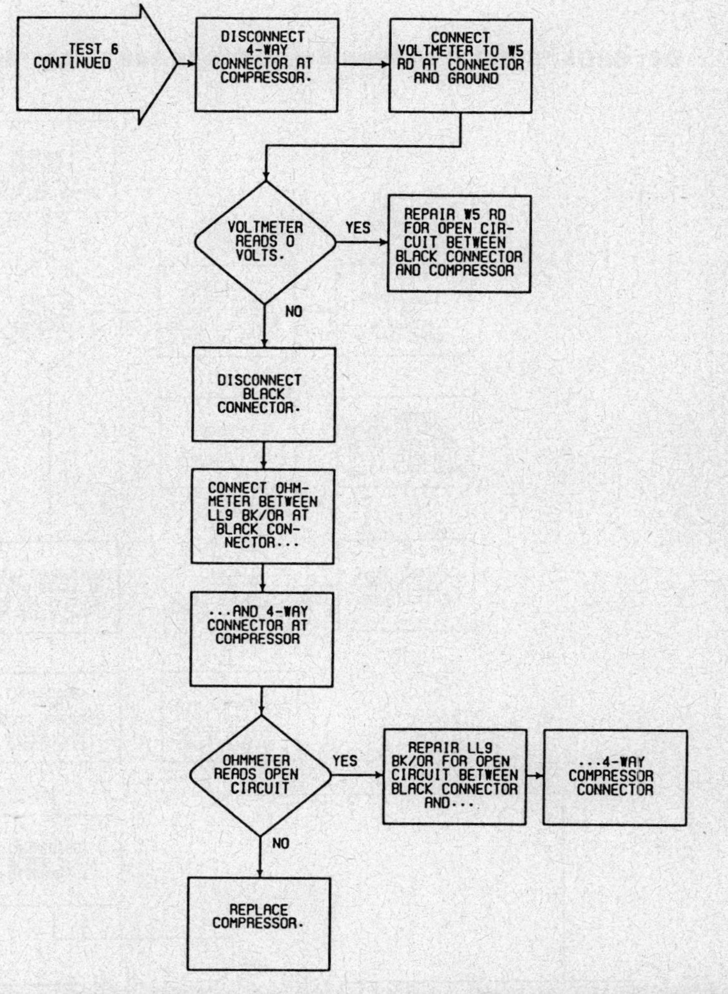


**Fig. 13 Test 6, checking function of air exhaust solenoid (Part 3 of 3). 1989–90**

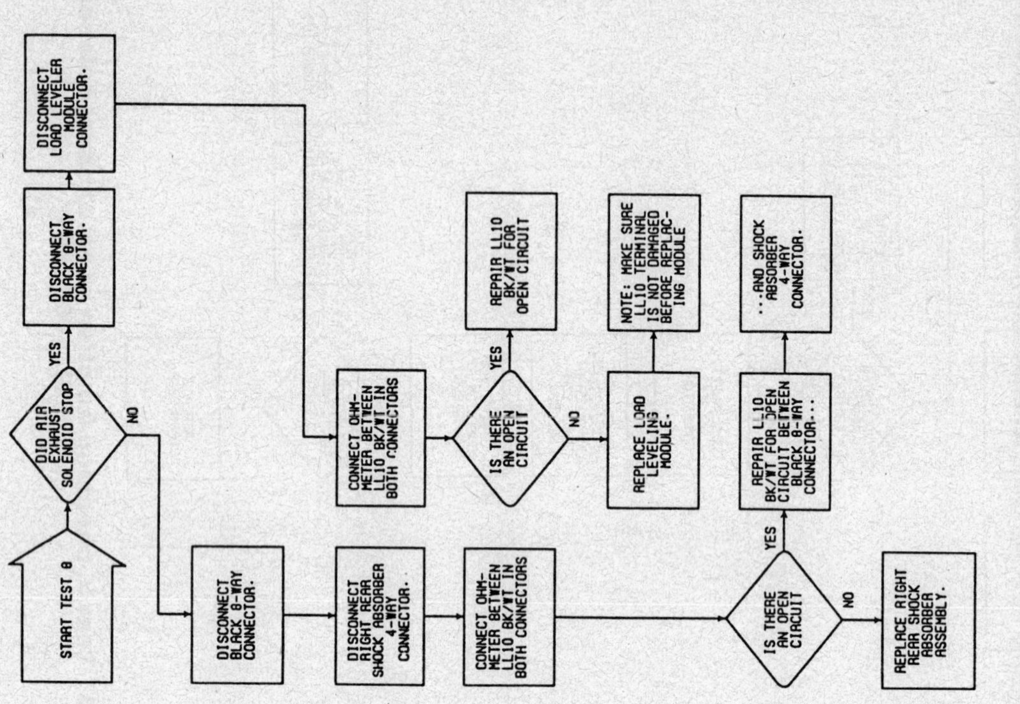


**Fig. 15 Test 8, checking sensor ground. 1989–90**

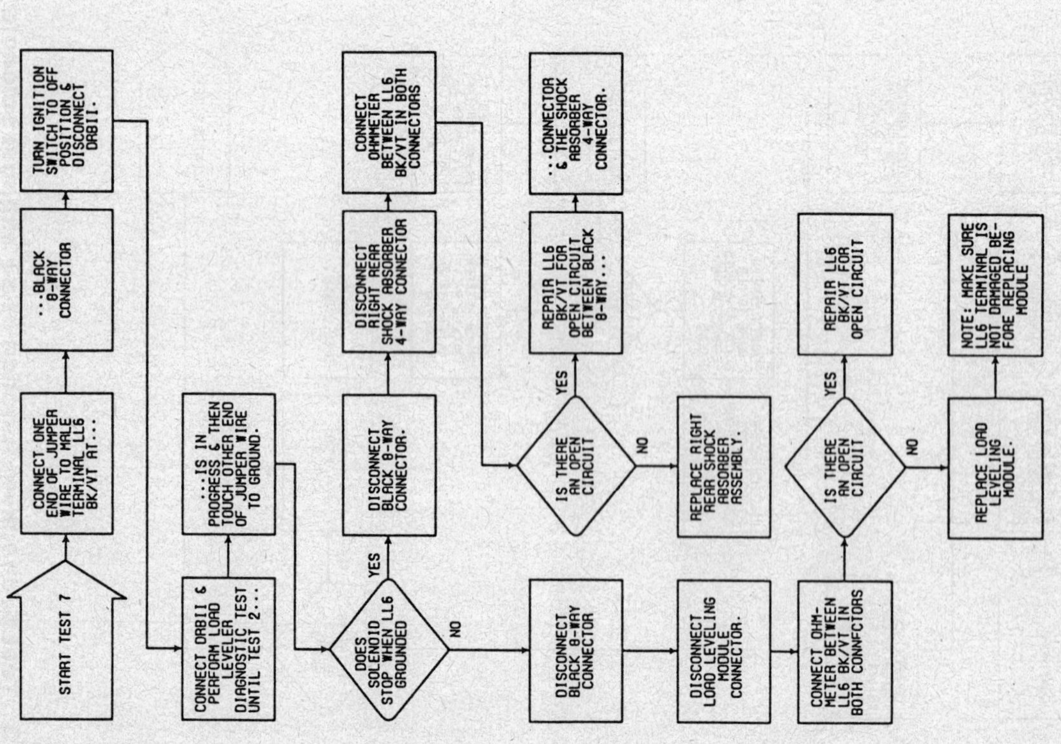


**Fig. 14 Test 7, checking height sensor & module. 1989–90**

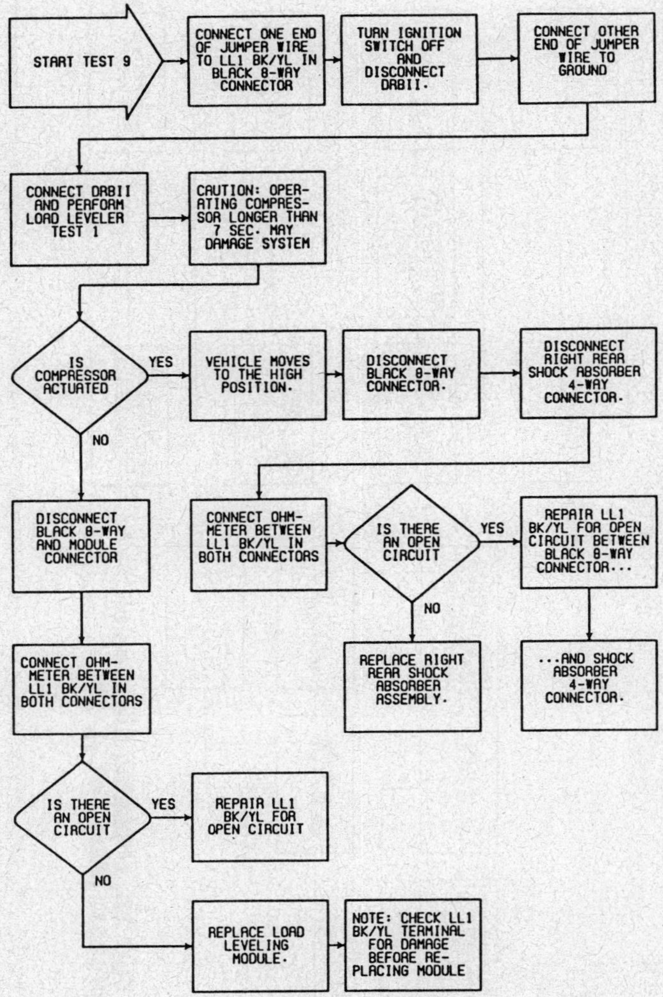

START TEST 9

CONNECT ONE END OF JUMPER WIRE TO LL1 BK/YL IN BLACK 8-WAY CONNECTOR

TURN IGNITION SWITCH OFF AND DISCONNECT DRBII.

CONNECT OTHER END OF JUMPER WIRE TO GROUND

CONNECT DRBII AND PERFORM LOAD LEVELER TEST 1

CAUTION: OPERATING COMPRESSOR LONGER THAN 7 SEC. MAY DAMAGE SYSTEM

IS COMPRESSOR ACTUATED

YES

VEHICLE MOVES TO THE HIGH POSITION.

DISCONNECT BLACK 8-WAY CONNECTOR.

DISCONNECT RIGHT REAR SHOCK ABSORBER 4-WAY CONNECTOR.

NO

DISCONNECT BLACK 8-WAY AND MODULE CONNECTOR

CONNECT OHMMETER BETWEEN LL1 BK/YL IN BOTH CONNECTORS

IS THERE AN OPEN CIRCUIT

YES

REPAIR LL1 BK/YL FOR OPEN CIRCUIT BETWEEN BLACK 8-WAY CONNECTOR...

...AND SHOCK ABSORBER 4-WAY CONNECTOR.

NO

REPLACE RIGHT REAR SHOCK ABSORBER ASSEMBLY.

CONNECT OHMMETER BETWEEN LL1 BK/YL IN BOTH CONNECTORS

IS THERE AN OPEN CIRCUIT

YES

REPAIR LL1 BK/YL FOR OPEN CIRCUIT

NO

REPLACE LOAD LEVELING MODULE.

NOTE: CHECK LL1 BK/YL TERMINAL FOR DAMAGE BEFORE REPLACING MODULE

**Fig. 16 Test 9, checking height sensor & module. 1989–90**

1. Perform a visual inspection.
2. Connect the DRBII to the load leveling diagnostic connector located near the LLCM.
3. Turn the ignition key on.
4. Using the DRBII, actuate the load leveler system test.
   >> **Do not** turn the ignition key off during the test.
   >> Sit on the trunk lid opening throughout the test. This must be done to force the vehicle to the the "low" position. Only 150 pounds are necessary, and more weight may cause the test to "time out."
5. Refer to the following message list for the correct diagnostic test to perform for each message that is displayed on the DRBII.

"TESTING COMPLETE LOAD LEVELER PASSED ALL DIAGNOSTIC TESTS" .......... Test 2B

"TEST 1: TEST FAILED, FAILED TO LEVEL CAR" .......... Test 3A

"TEST 1: TEST FAILED, TIME OUT ERROR" .......... Test 4A

"TEST 2: TEST FAILED, FAILED TO LEVEL CAR" .......... Test 5A

"TEST 3: TEST FAILED, FAILED TO LEVEL CAR" .......... Test 3A

"ERROR FROM PREVIOUS LOAD LEVELER TEST"
Turn the ignition off and retest system. If the message reappears, go to .... Test 8A

**Fig. 17 Test 1A, checking function of load leveling system. 1991**

1. Reconnect all connectors that were disconnected during your repair.
2. Use the DRBII to re-perform the system test.
3. If any further fault messages appear, perform TEST 1A again.
4. Replace all covers and trim, and return vehicle to owner.

**Fig. 18 Test 2A, verification of repair. 1991**

1. Make sure that no leaks are present in the load leveling system. To do this, use a soap and water spray bottle to check and pinpoint any leaks.
2. If the owner's complaint is that the load leveling system does not level the vehicle, a compressor output test should be done.
3. Return the vehicle to the owner.

**Fig. 19 Test 2B, no fault messages test. 1991**

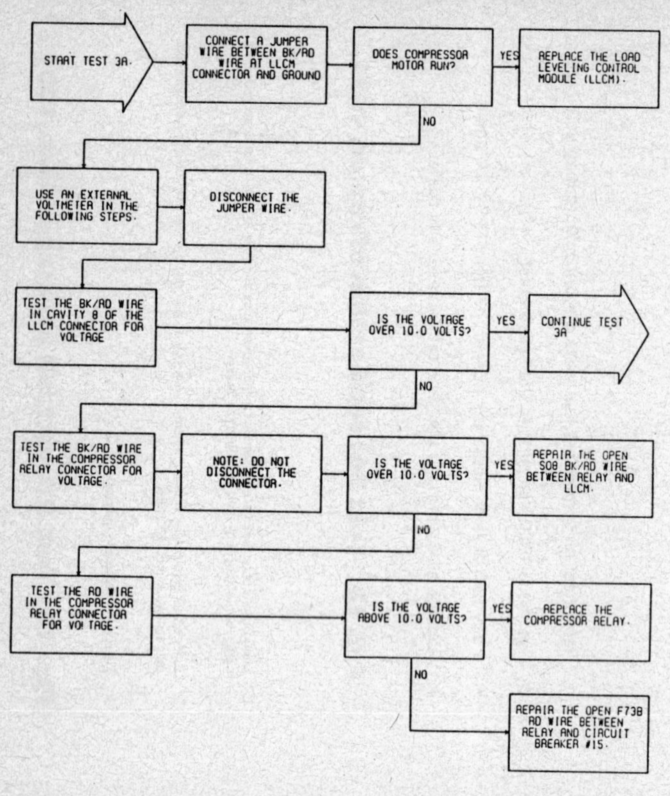

**Fig. 20 Test 3A, checking function of compressor (Part 1 of 3). 1991**

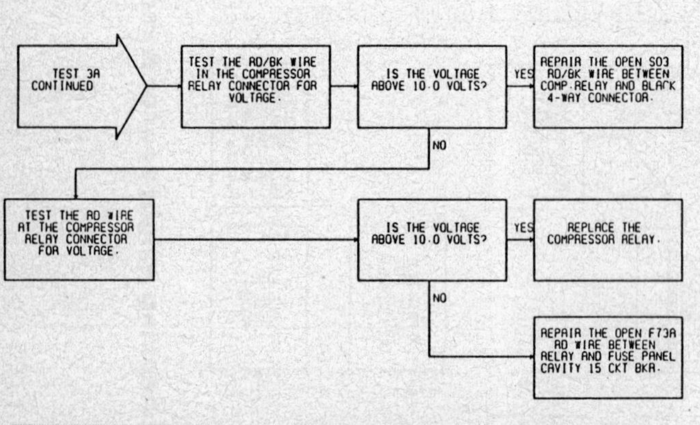


**Fig. 20 Test 3A, checking function of compressor (Part 3 of 3). 1991**

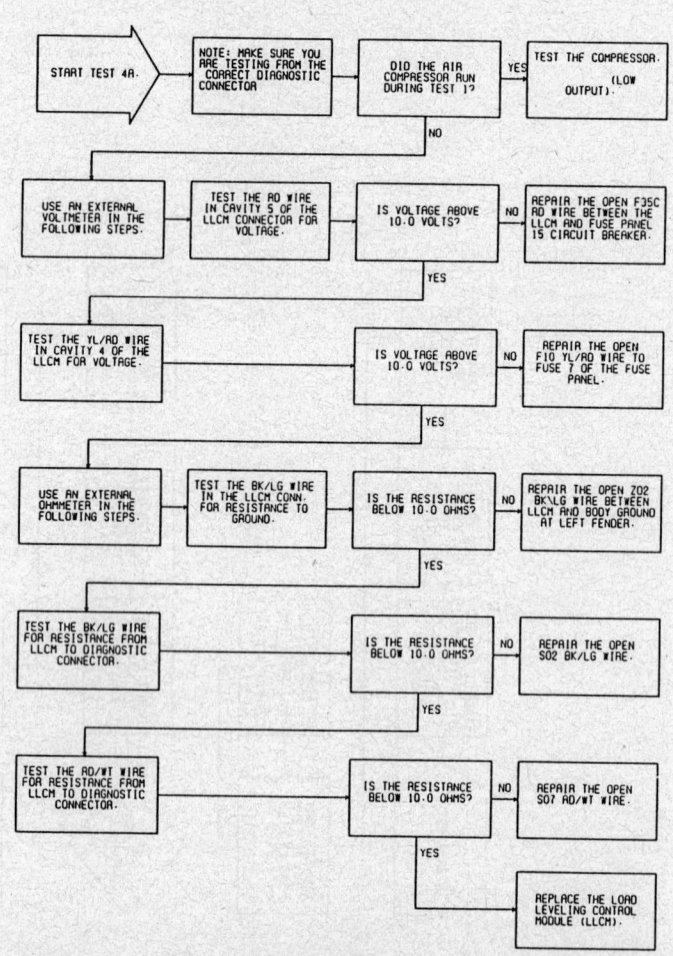

TEST 3A CONTINUED
RECONNECT JUMPER WIRE BETWEEN BK/RD AT LLCM CONNECTOR CAVITY 8 AND GROUND.
USE AN EXTERNAL VOLTMETER IN THE FOLLOWING STEPS.
TEST THE RD/BK WIRE IN THE BLACK 4-WAY CONNECTOR FOR VOLTAGE.
IS THE VOLTAGE ABOVE 10.0 VOLTS?
NO
CONTINUE TEST 3A
YES
DISCONNECT THE 4-WAY CONNECTOR AT THE COMPRESSOR.
TEST THE RD/BK WIRE IN THE 4-WAY COMPRESSOR CONNECTOR FOR VOLTAGE.
IS THE VOLTAGE ABOVE 10.0 VOLTS?
NO
REPAIR THE OPEN S03 RD/BK WIRE BETWEEN THE COMPRESSOR AND 4-WAY CONNECTORS.
YES
USE AN EXTERNAL OHMMETER IN THE FOLLOWING STEPS.
TEST THE BK WIRE IN THE COMPRESSOR CONN. FOR RESISTANCE TO GROUND.
IS THE RESISTANCE LESS THAN 10.0 OHMS?
NO
REPAIR THE OPEN Z01 BK WIRE TO GROUND.
YES
REPLACE THE COMPRESSOR ASSEMBLY.

**Fig. 20 Test 3A, checking function of compressor (Part 2 of 3). 1991**

START TEST 4A.
NOTE: MAKE SURE YOU ARE TESTING FROM THE CORRECT DIAGNOSTIC CONNECTOR
DID THE AIR COMPRESSOR RUN DURING TEST 1?
YES
TEST THE COMPRESSOR. (LOW OUTPUT).
NO
USE AN EXTERNAL VOLTMETER IN THE FOLLOWING STEPS.
TEST THE RD WIRE IN CAVITY 5 OF THE LLCM CONNECTOR FOR VOLTAGE.
IS VOLTAGE ABOVE 10.0 VOLTS?
NO
REPAIR THE OPEN F35C RD WIRE BETWEEN THE LLCM AND FUSE PANEL 15 CIRCUIT BREAKER.
YES
TEST THE YL/RD WIRE IN CAVITY 4 OF THE LLCM FOR VOLTAGE.
IS VOLTAGE ABOVE 10.0 VOLTS?
NO
REPAIR THE OPEN F10 YL/RD WIRE TO FUSE 7 OF THE FUSE PANEL.
YES
USE AN EXTERNAL OHMMETER IN THE FOLLOWING STEPS.
TEST THE BK/LG WIRE IN THE LLCM CONN. FOR RESISTANCE TO GROUND.
IS THE RESISTANCE BELOW 10.0 OHMS?
NO
REPAIR THE OPEN Z02 BK\LG WIRE BETWEEN LLCM AND BODY GROUND AT LEFT FENDER.
YES
TEST THE BK/LG WIRE FOR RESISTANCE FROM LLCM TO DIAGNOSTIC CONNECTOR.
IS THE RESISTANCE BELOW 10.0 OHMS?
NO
REPAIR THE OPEN S02 BK/LG WIRE.
YES
TEST THE RD/WT WIRE FOR RESISTANCE FROM LLCM TO DIAGNOSTIC CONNECTOR.
IS THE RESISTANCE BELOW 10.0 OHMS?
NO
REPAIR THE OPEN S07 RD/WT WIRE.
YES
REPLACE THE LOAD LEVELING CONTROL MODULE (LLCM).

**Fig. 21 Test 4A, checking for battery voltage supply to module. 1991**

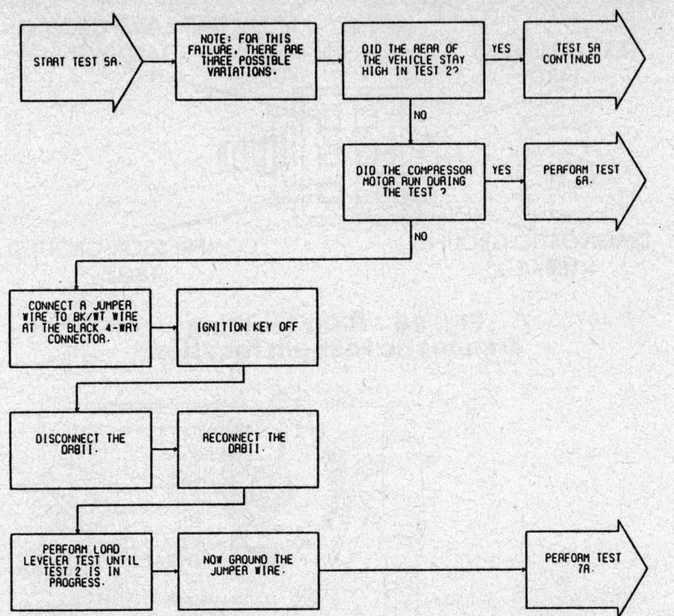


**Fig. 22 Test 5A, checking function of air exhaust system (Part 1 of 2). 1991**

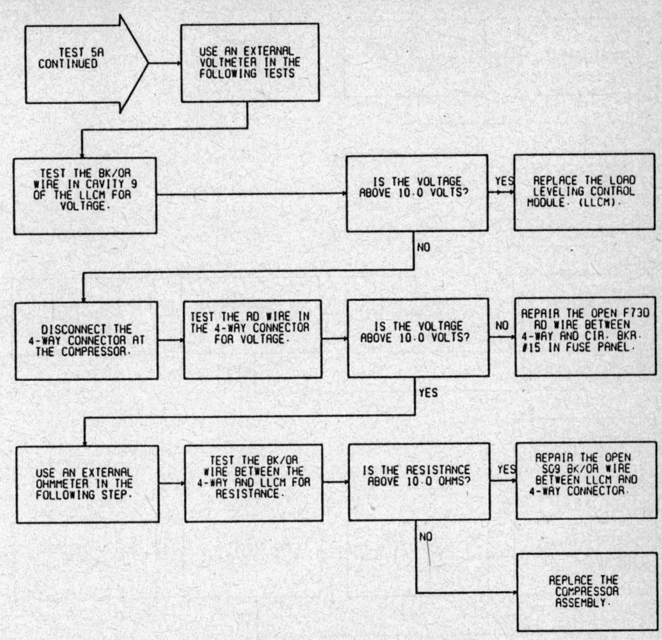


**Fig. 22 Test 5A, checking function of air exhaust system (Part 2 of 2). 1991**

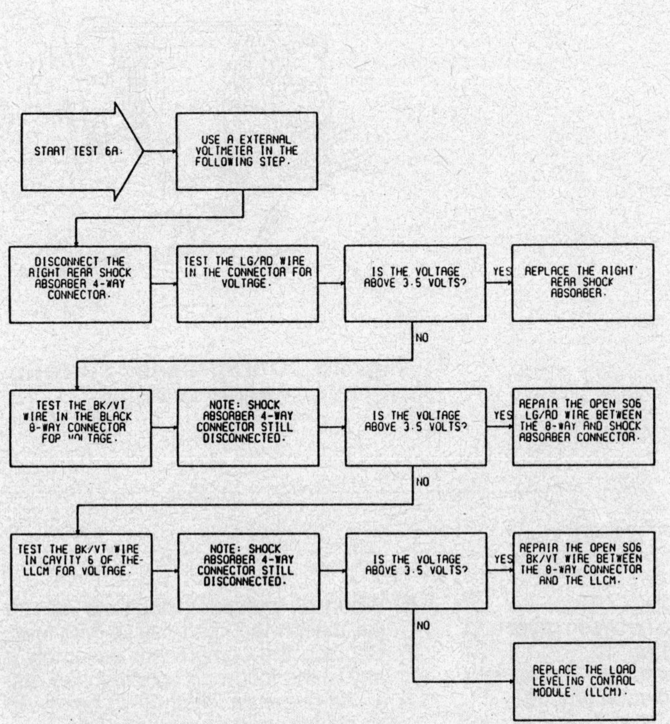


**Fig. 23 Test 6A, checking height sensor "Trim" input. 1991**

START TEST 7A.

DID THE EXHAUST SOLENOID STOP CLICKING WHEN THE JUMPER WIRE WAS GROUNDED?

YES

REPLACE THE RIGHT REAR SHOCK ABSORBER.

NO

DISCONNECT THE RIGHT REAR SHOCK ABSORBER 4-WAY CONNECTOR.

DISCONNECT THE BLACK 8-WAY CONNECTOR.

USE AN EXTERNAL OHMMETER IN THE FOLLOWING STEP.

TEST THE BR WIRE BETWEEN THE BLACK 8-WAY CONNECTOR AND 4 WAY CONN.

IS THE RESISTANCE ABOVE 10.0 OHMS?

YES

REPAIR THE S10 BR WIRE FOR AN OPEN CIRCUIT.

NO

TEST THE BK/WT WIRE FOR RESISTENCE FROM THE 8-WAY CONNECTOR TO THE LLCM.

IS THE RESISTANCE ABOVE 10.0 OHMS?

YES

REPAIR THE S10 BK/WT WIRE FOR AN OPEN CIRCUIT.

NO

REPLACE THE LOAD LEVELING CONTROL MODULE.

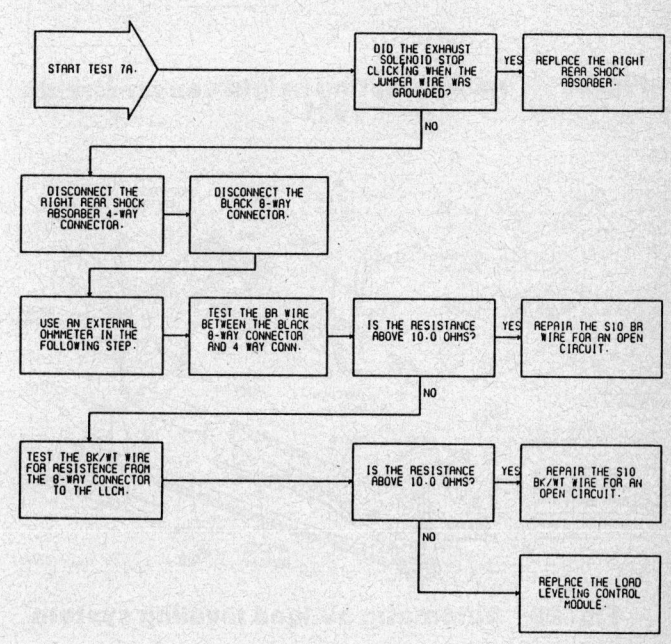

**Fig. 24 Test 7A, testing height sensor ground. 1991**

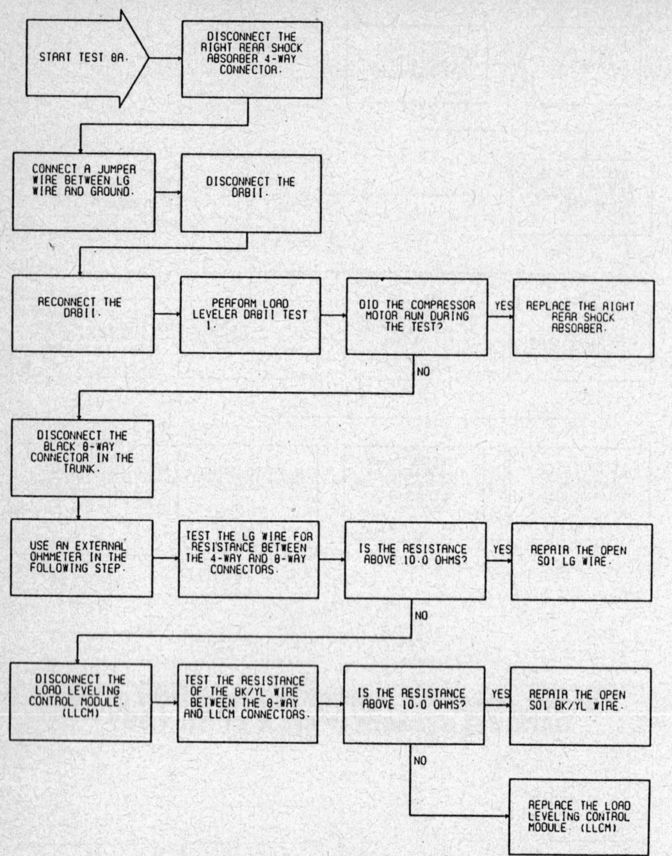


**Fig. 25 Test 8A, testing height sensor circuit. 1991**

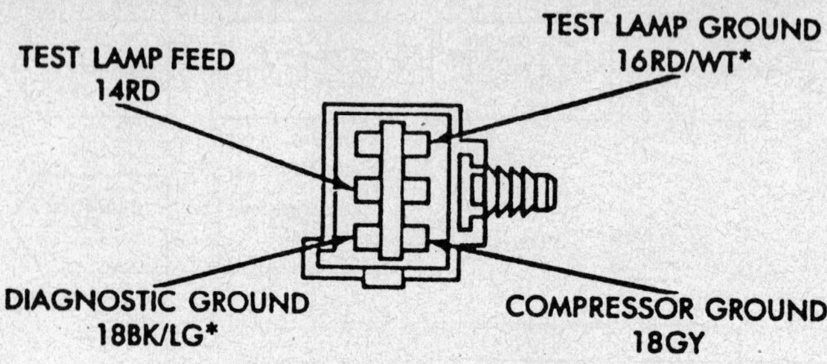


**Fig. 26 Rear leveling diagnostic test pin location**

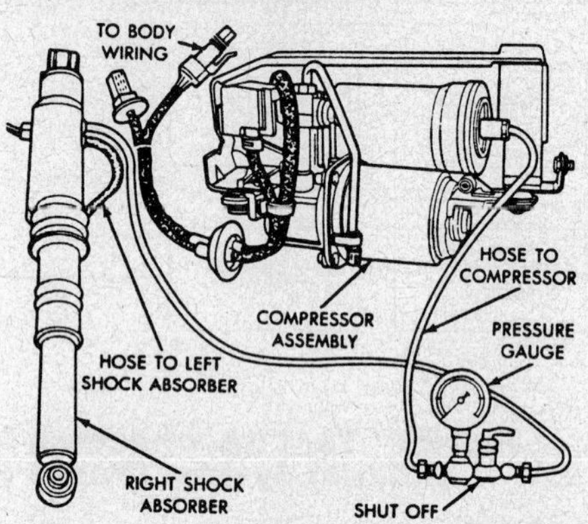


**Fig. 27 Installing pressure gage**

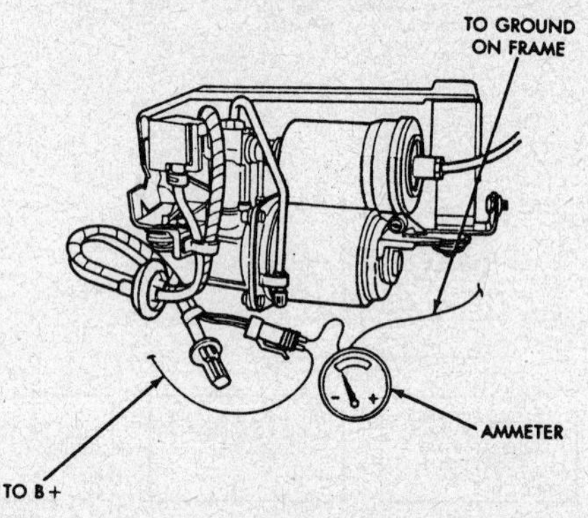


**Fig. 28 Compressor current draw test**

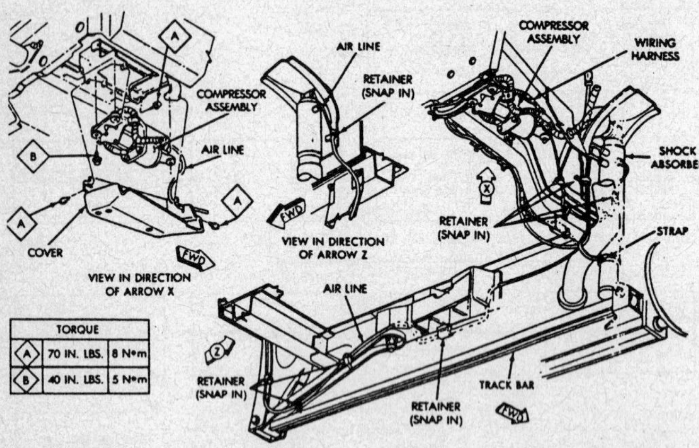


**Fig. 29 Automatic air load leveling system**

2. With load still applied, disconnect Control Module (CM) wiring harness connector, then remove applied load. Vehicle should rise.
3. Turn ignition switch to Off position.
4. Observe if pressure leaks down or holds steady after 15 minutes.
5. If system will not inflate beyond 50 psi, a severe leak may be indicated. Check for pinched pressure line between compressor and shocks.

## COMPRESSOR PERFORMANCE TEST

1. Disconnect compressor motor wiring harness connector.
2. Disconnect air line between dryer and right shock absorber.
3. Connect an air pressure gauge into the system as shown in **Fig. 28.**
4. Connect an ammeter in series between the red wire terminal in compressor connector and a 12 volt power source. Connect a ground wire from the black wire terminal on the compressor connector to a good ground on frame, **Fig. 28.**
5. If current draw to motor exceeds 21 amperes, replace compressor assembly.
6. When air pressure stabilizes at 120 psi, disconnect the positive wire lead.
7. Replace the compressor assembly if any of the following conditions exists:
   a. Air pressure leaks down below 90 psi before it remains steady.
   b. Output pressure builds up to less than 110 psi when stabilizes.
8. If the compressor is allow to run during this test until it reaches its maximum output pressure of 220 psi, the solenoid exhaust valve will act as a pressure relief valve. the resulting leak down, after the compressor is shutoff will indicate a false leak.

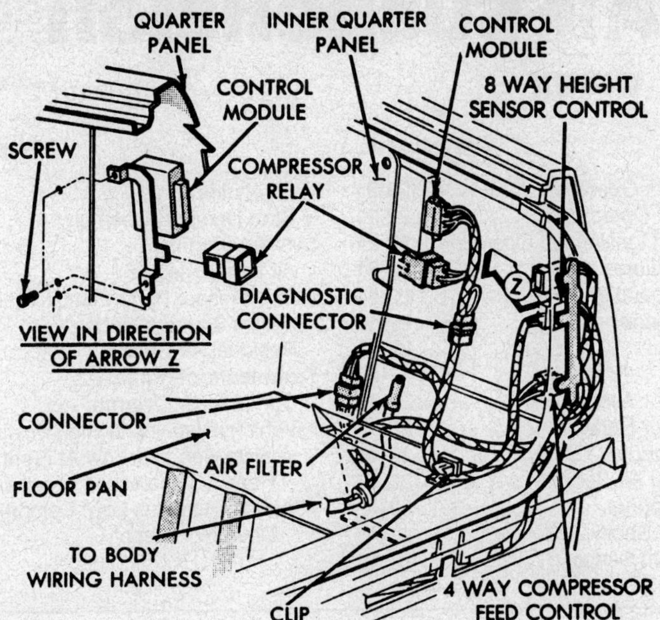


**Fig. 30 Control module & compressor relay wiring.**

# COMPONENT REPLACEMENT

## COMPRESSOR ASSEMBLY

### REMOVAL

1. Disconnect battery negative cable and raise vehicle.
2. Remove compressor cover, air hose and electrical connectors, **Fig. 29.**
3. Remove compressor mounting bracket screws, then lower assembly from vehicle.
4. Remove mounting bracket screws, then mounting bracket from compressor.

### INSTALLATION

1. Reverse procedures to install, **torquing** all screws to 70 inch lbs.
2. Refer to """System Diagnosis" while checking operation if necessary to make adjustments.

## CONTROL MODULE

### REMOVAL

1. Disconnect battery negative cable, then remove trim panel from RH side of trunk.
2. Disconnect electrical connector and relay from control module, **Fig. 30.**
3. Remove control module mounting screws, then the assembly.

### INSTALLATION

1. Install relay on control module bracket, then place control module on bracket and install screws. **Torque screws to 19-29 inch lbs.**
2. Connect relay and module electrical connectors, then replace trim panel.

## COMPRESSOR RELAY

Refer to "Control Module" and **Fig. 30** for compressor relay replacement procedure.

## RIGHT SHOCK ABSORBER W/HEIGHT SENSOR

### REMOVAL

1. Disconnect battery negative cable and raise vehicle, then remove tire assembly.
2. Disconnect height sensor connector, located on RH frame rail, then remove air lines connected to Shock Absorber.
3. To remove Shock Absorber, refer to "Shock Absorber Removal" to replace Shocks.
4. Reverse procedure to install.

# Automatic Air Suspension

## INDEX



## DESCRIPTION

The Automatic Air Suspension (AAS) system, **Fig. 1,** provides automatic height control and low spring rates to improve suspension performance and automatically level the front and rear of the vehicle. It also maintains optimum vehicle attitude regardless of load conditions.

The AAS system consists of the following components: Air compressor/dryer assembly, compressor relay, front struts, rear springs and shocks absorbers, control module, air lines, rear height sensor and compressor cover.

Front springs and height sensors are integral with the strut assemblies while rear air springs replace conventional steel units. Rear height is controlled by a height sensor contained in the right rear shock absorber. Solenoids which are integral with each air spring control air pressure and volume requirements. Pressurized air is distributed from the air compressor/dryer assembly and is routed to each air spring by four separate air lines. The AAS system is monitored and controlled by the control module.

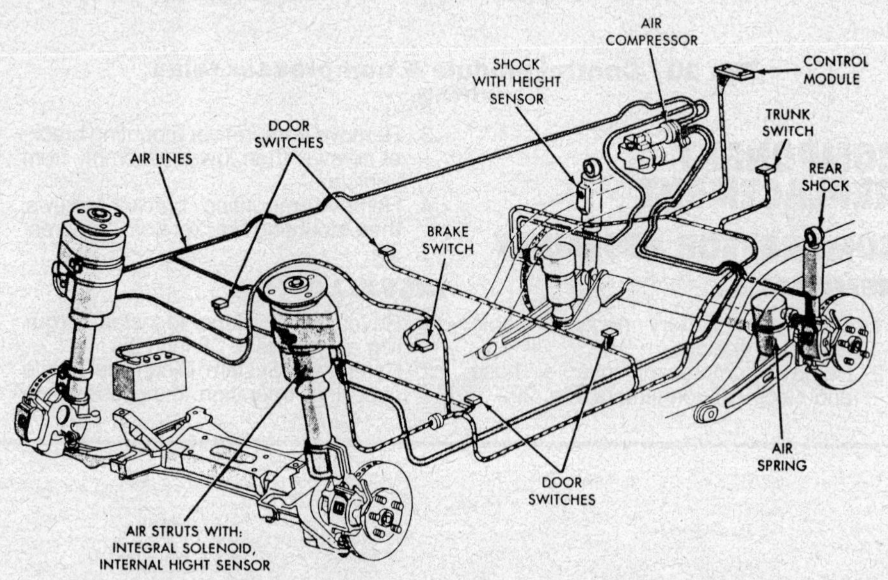


**Fig. 1 Automatic Air Suspension (AAS) system**

## SYSTEM COMPONENTS

### AIR SPRINGS

The front and rear air springs, **Fig. 2,** are pneumatic cylinders that replace steel coil springs. The air springs allow suspension height to be adjusted for all load conditions. The air springs allow the reduction of spring rates to improve ride characteristics.

### SPRING SOLENOIDS

The front and rear spring solenoids control air flow in and out of the front and rear air springs. The Air Suspension Control Module (ASCM) opens the solenoids when the system requires air to be added to or exhausted from the air springs. The solenoids operate at a current draw range of 0.6-1.5 amps.

### HEIGHT SENSORS

The height sensor is a magnetic switch type sensor, located in the right rear shock absorber, left and right front struts, **Fig. 2,** which monitors vehicle height. The sensors transmit signals to the ASCM relating to vehicle status (low, trim, medium and high).

### CONTROL MODULE

The Air Suspension Control Module (ASCM) is a device that controls the ground circuits for the compressor relay, compressor exhaust solenoid valve, front and rear solenoid valves. A microprocessor with in the ASCM controls compressor pump operation from 170-190 seconds. This prevents damage to the AAS system.

To prevent excessive cycling between the compressor and the exhaust solenoid circuits during normal ride conditions, a 12-18 second delay is incorporated in the microprocessor logic.

System operation is inhibited when a door(s) are opened, the trunk is opened, the service brakes are applied or the throttle position sensor is 65-100%. System operation is also inhibited during high speed cornering. The control module is on the CCD bus system.

### AIR COMPRESSOR/DRYER ASSEMBLY

#### Compressor Assembly

The compressor assembly, **Fig. 3,** is driven by an electric motor and supplies air pressure of 135-180 psi. A solenoid operated exhaust valve, located in the compressor head assembly, releases air when energized. A heat actuated circuit breaker,

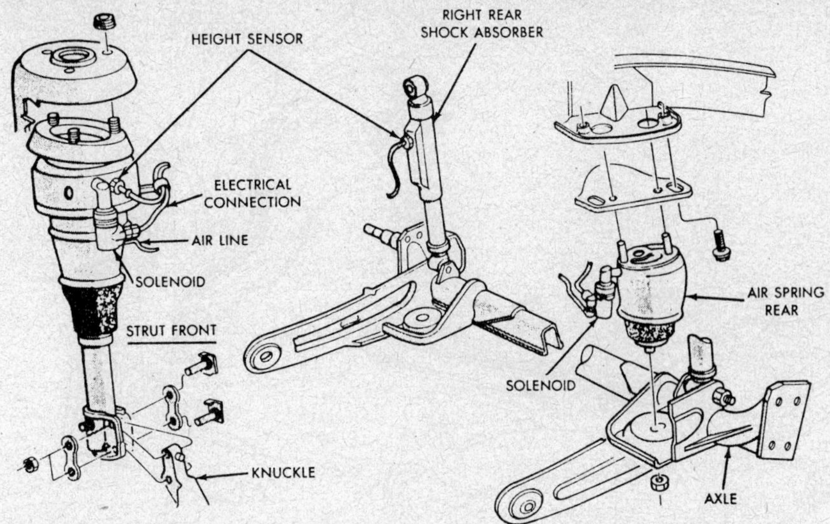


**Fig. 2 Front & rear air springs**

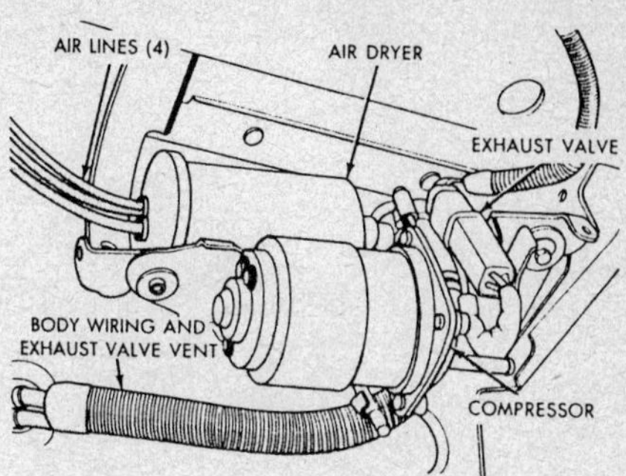


**Fig. 3 Air compressor/dryer assembly**

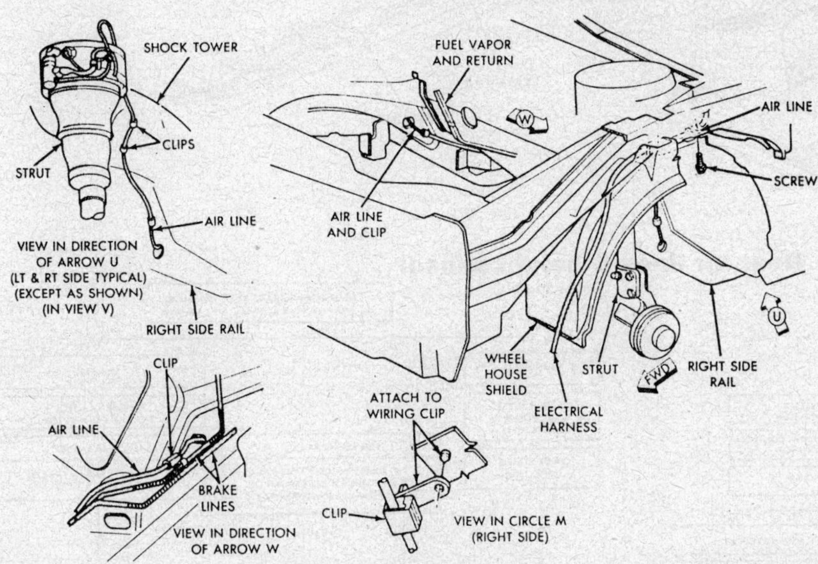


**Fig. 4 Front air lines**

located inside the compressor motor housing, is used to prevent damage to the compressor motor in the event of control module failure.

### Compressor Air Dryer

The air dryer is attached to the compressor. The air dryer has two functions; it absorbs moisture from the atmosphere before it enters the system, and with internal valveing, maintains a residual pressure of 25-40 psi.

## AIR LINES

Four nylon air lines, **Figs. 4 and 5,** are routed from the compressor air dryer to each strut/spring assembly. Right side strut and air spring air lines are routed with the fuel line. Left side strut and air spring air lines are routed across the vehicle in front of the fuel tank and forward with the fuel line.

# SYSTEM OPERATION

## ENGINE RUN OPERATION

The AAS system will compensate for load addition or removal after; the trunk and all doors are closed, engine speed exceeds 600 RPM and a 15 second time delay.

## ENGINE OFF OPERATION

After passengers and/or load are removed from the vehicle, the AAS system will correct the vehicle attitude after; the trunk and all doors are closed, ignition switch is in the Off position and the 15 second delay is completed. **Opening a door or the trunk activates the body computer and the ASCM. The AAS is now capable of leveling if required.**

## LONG TERM IGNITION OFF OPERATION

The AAS system is capable of one additional leveling cycle after two hours of continuous of ignition key Off and no door open or trunk open conditions. This feature is intended to eliminate possible ice freeze-up between the tire and the inner fender shield.

## SYSTEM OPERATION INHIBITORS

The AAS system system operation is inhibited when; the trunk is open, a door(s) are open, the service brakes are applied, the throttle is in the wide open position or the charging system fails. **The maximum compressor pump or exhaust time is three minutes.**

## SYSTEM FAILURES

Models equipped with air suspension and overhead console will alert the driver if an AAS system malfunction has occurred. The overhead console will display a "Check Air Suspension" warning when a malfunction has occurred.

# TROUBLESHOOTING

Refer to **Figs. 6 through 9,** when troubleshooting this system.

# DIAGNOSIS

Refer to **Fig. 10,** for ASCM connector terminal identification and **Fig. 11,** for system wiring circuit diagram when diagnosing this system.

## INITIAL DIAGNOSTIC CHECK

**All doors and trunk must be closed for the system to function.**

1. Check for blown or missing fuses.
2. Ensure all connector terminals are correctly installed.
3. Check pin 21 for a minimum o volts.
4. Check pin 20 for a minir volts with ignition key in

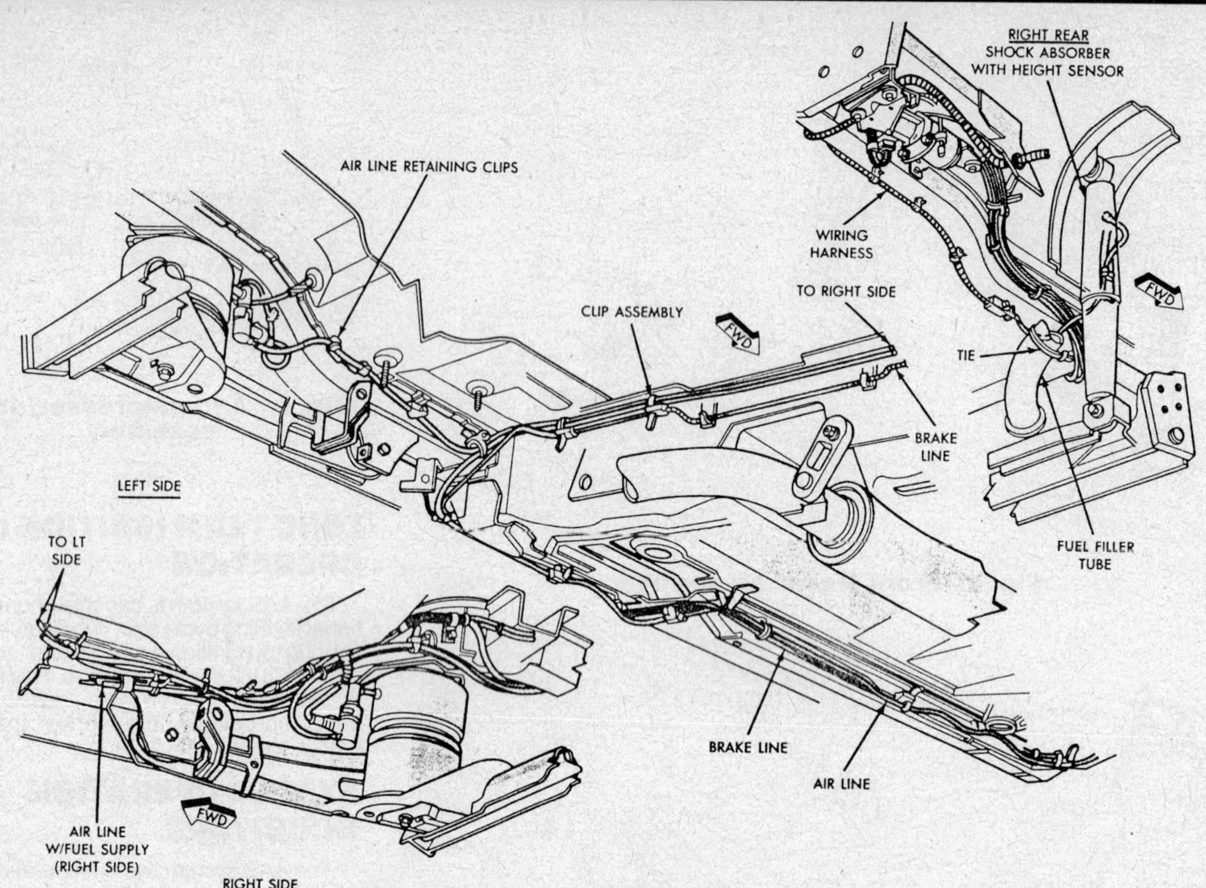


**Fig. 5 Rear air lines & height sensor**

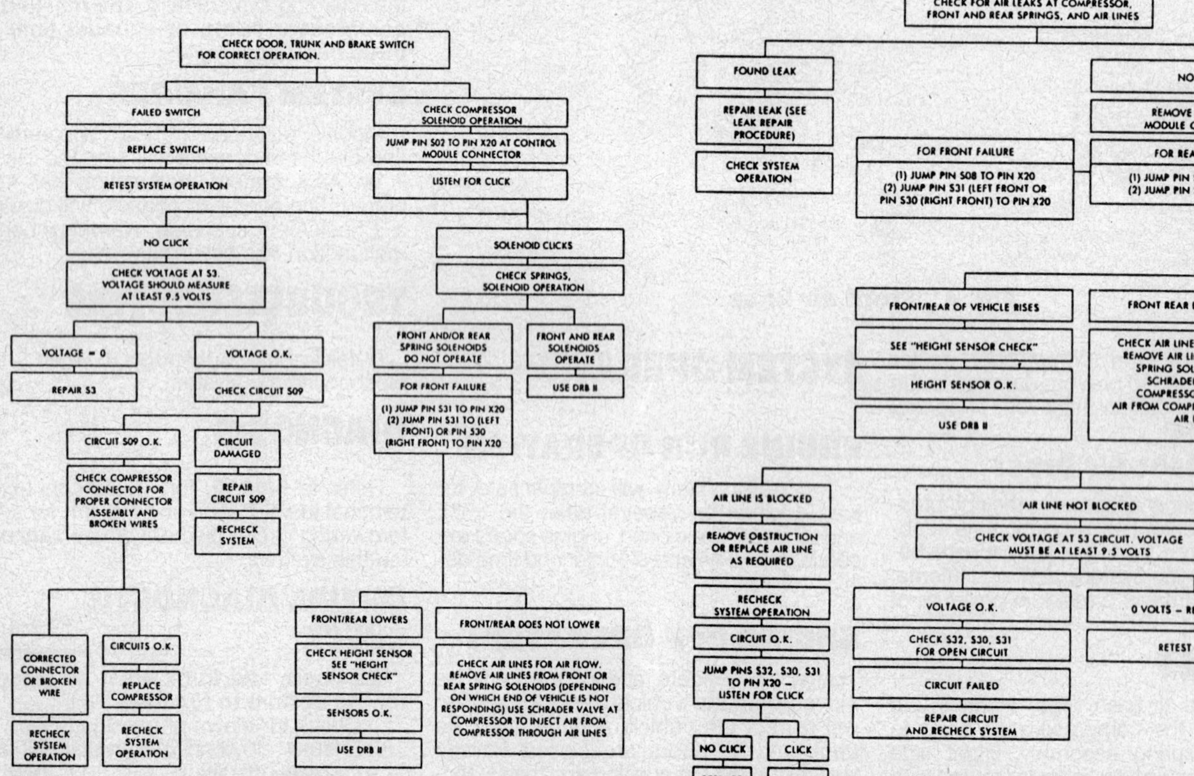


**Fig. 6 Troubleshooting. Vehicle remains in high position**



**Fig. 7 Troubleshooting. Vehicle remains low at front or rear, compressor operates**

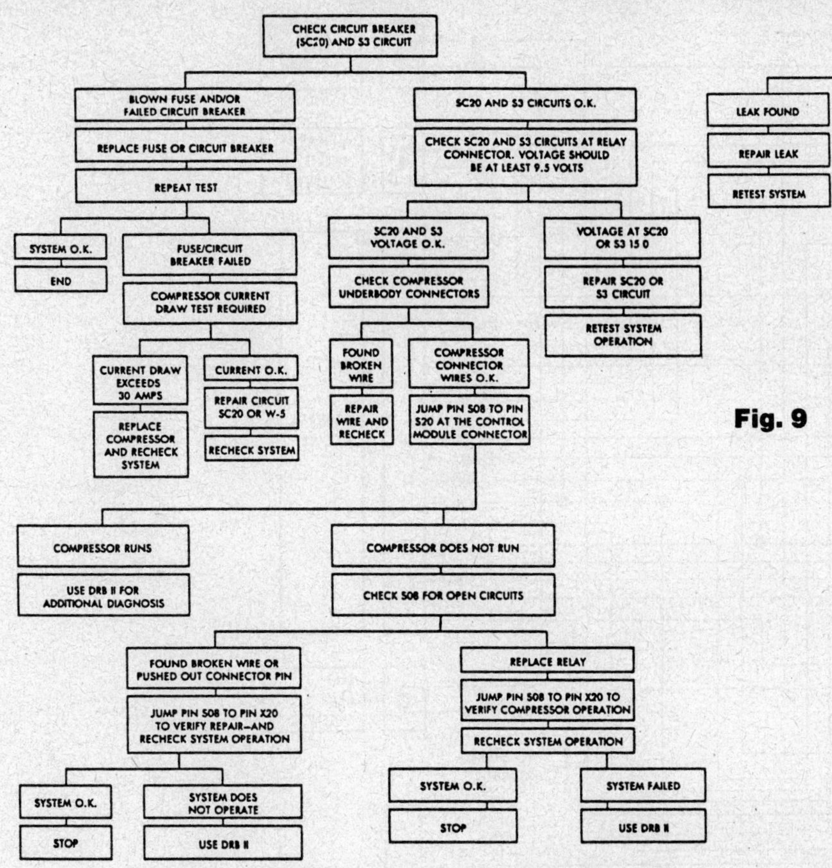


**Fig. 8 Troubleshooting. Vehicle remains low, compressor does not pump**

CHECK SYSTEM FOR AIR LEAKS
LEAK FOUND
REPAIR LEAK
RETEST SYSTEM
NO LEAK FOUND
CHECK COMPRESSOR RELAY FOR WELDED CONTACTS
RELAY O.K.
CHECK FOR SHORTED WIRES AT S08 CIRCUIT
CIRCUIT O.K.
USE DRB II
FOUND SHORTED CIRCUIT
REPAIR CIRCUIT
RECHECK OPERATION
RELAY FAILED. CONTACTS WELDED TOGETHER
REPLACE RELAY
RECHECK SYSTEM OPERATION

**Fig. 9 Troubleshooting. Compressor overrun**

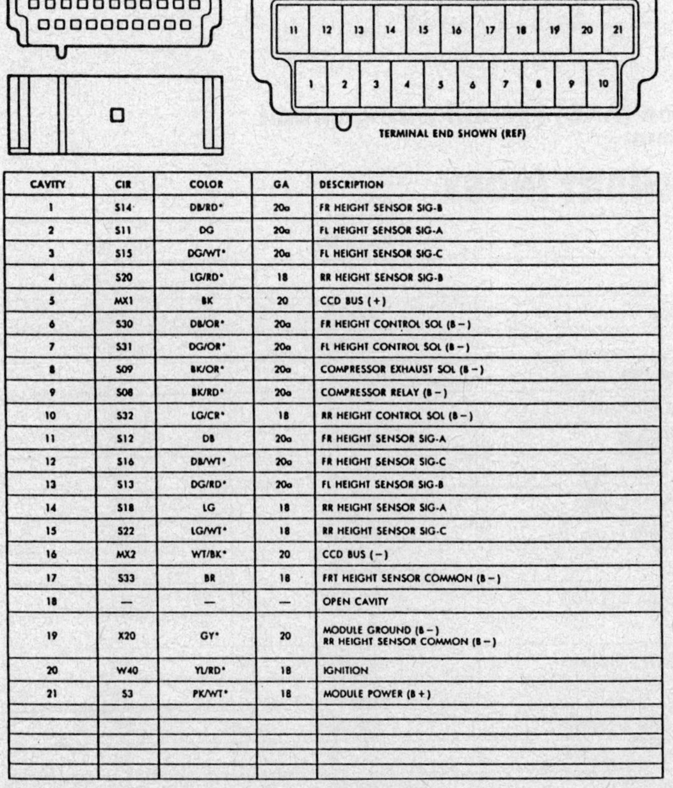


| CAVITY | CIR | COLOR | GA | DESCRIPTION |
|---|---|---|---|---|
| 1 | S14 | DB/RD* | 20a | FR HEIGHT SENSOR SIG-B |
| 2 | S11 | DG | 20a | FL HEIGHT SENSOR SIG-A |
| 3 | S15 | DG/WT* | 20a | FL HEIGHT SENSOR SIG-C |
| 4 | S20 | LG/RD* | 18 | RR HEIGHT SENSOR SIG-B |
| 5 | MX1 | BK | 20 | CCD BUS (+) |
| 6 | S30 | DB/OR* | 20a | FR HEIGHT CONTROL SOL (B−) |
| 7 | S31 | DG/OR* | 20a | FL HEIGHT CONTROL SOL (B−) |
| 8 | S09 | BK/OR* | 20a | COMPRESSOR EXHAUST SOL (B−) |
| 9 | S08 | BK/RD* | 20a | COMPRESSOR RELAY (B−) |
| 10 | S32 | LG/CR* | 18 | RR HEIGHT CONTROL SOL (B−) |
| 11 | S12 | DB | 20a | FR HEIGHT SENSOR SIG-A |
| 12 | S16 | DB/WT* | 20a | FR HEIGHT SENSOR SIG-C |
| 13 | S13 | DG/RD* | 20a | FL HEIGHT SENSOR SIG-B |
| 14 | S18 | LG | 18 | RR HEIGHT SENSOR SIG-A |
| 15 | S22 | LG/WT* | 18 | RR HEIGHT SENSOR SIG-C |
| 16 | MX2 | WT/BK* | 20 | CCD BUS (−) |
| 17 | S33 | BR | 18 | FRT HEIGHT SENSOR COMMON (B−) |
| 18 | — | — | — | OPEN CAVITY |
| 19 | X20 | GY* | 20 | MODULE GROUND (B−)<br>RR HEIGHT SENSOR COMMON (B−) |
| 20 | W40 | YL/RD* | 18 | IGNITION |
| 21 | S3 | PK/WT* | 18 | MODULE POWER (B+) |

**Fig. 10 Control module (ASCM) connector terminal identification**

5. Check voltage at pins 5 and 16. Voltage indicated should exceed 0 volts.
6. Check pin 19 for continuity.
7. Ensure engine idle speed is above 680 RPM.

## DIAGNOSTIC PROCEDURE

Diagnosis of the AAS system requires use of the DRB II diagnostic read out tool and air suspension cartridge or equivalents. Follow manufacture's instructions for use of the tool.

1. Use DRB II tester and air suspension cartridge to begin diagnostic procedure.
2. Use DRB mating connector under drivers's side dash panel to connect DRB II test connector.
3. The tester will conduct a complete check of the AAS system status.
4. The tester will list the steps to access and diagnose the failure.
5. A volt/ohmmeter can be used for some diagnostic testing.
6. Perform diagnostic procedures as shown in **Figs. 12 through 27** on 1990 models or in **Figs. 28 through 43** on 1991 models.
7. After procedure is completed, verify test as shown in **Fig. 13,** for 1990 models or **Fig. 29** for 1991 models.

# SYSTEM TESTING

Refer to **Fig. 10,** for ASCM connector terminal identification and **Fig. 11,** for system wiring circuit diagram when performing system testing procedures.

## RESIDUAL AIR CHECK

The air dryer has a valve arrangement which maintains a minimum pressure of 25-40 psi. To check this function, proceed as follows:

1. Remove air line from dryer fitting and strut or spring. Attach a piece of bulk nylon tubing to one side of a suitable 0-300 psi pressure gauge and to the strut or spring solenoid, **Fig. 44.**
2. Attach another piece of nylon tubing from dryer to the other side of the pressure gauge. A compression ball sleeve nut and sleeve for 3/16 inch tubing with ball sleeve connector and internal pipe T-fitting can be used to attach the tubing to the gauge.

Continued

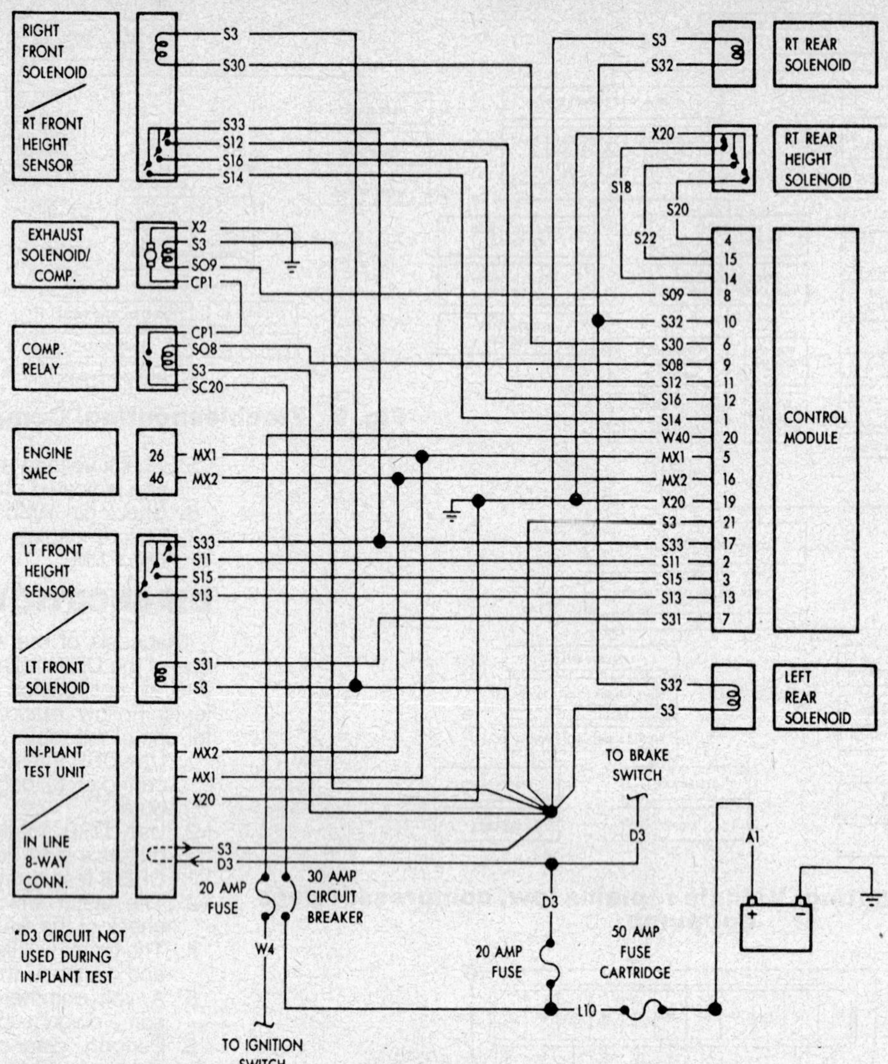


**Fig. 11 Automatic Air Suspension (AAS) system wiring circuit diagram**

# DIAGNOSTIC CHART INDEX

## DIAGNOSTIC CHART INDEX—CONTINUED



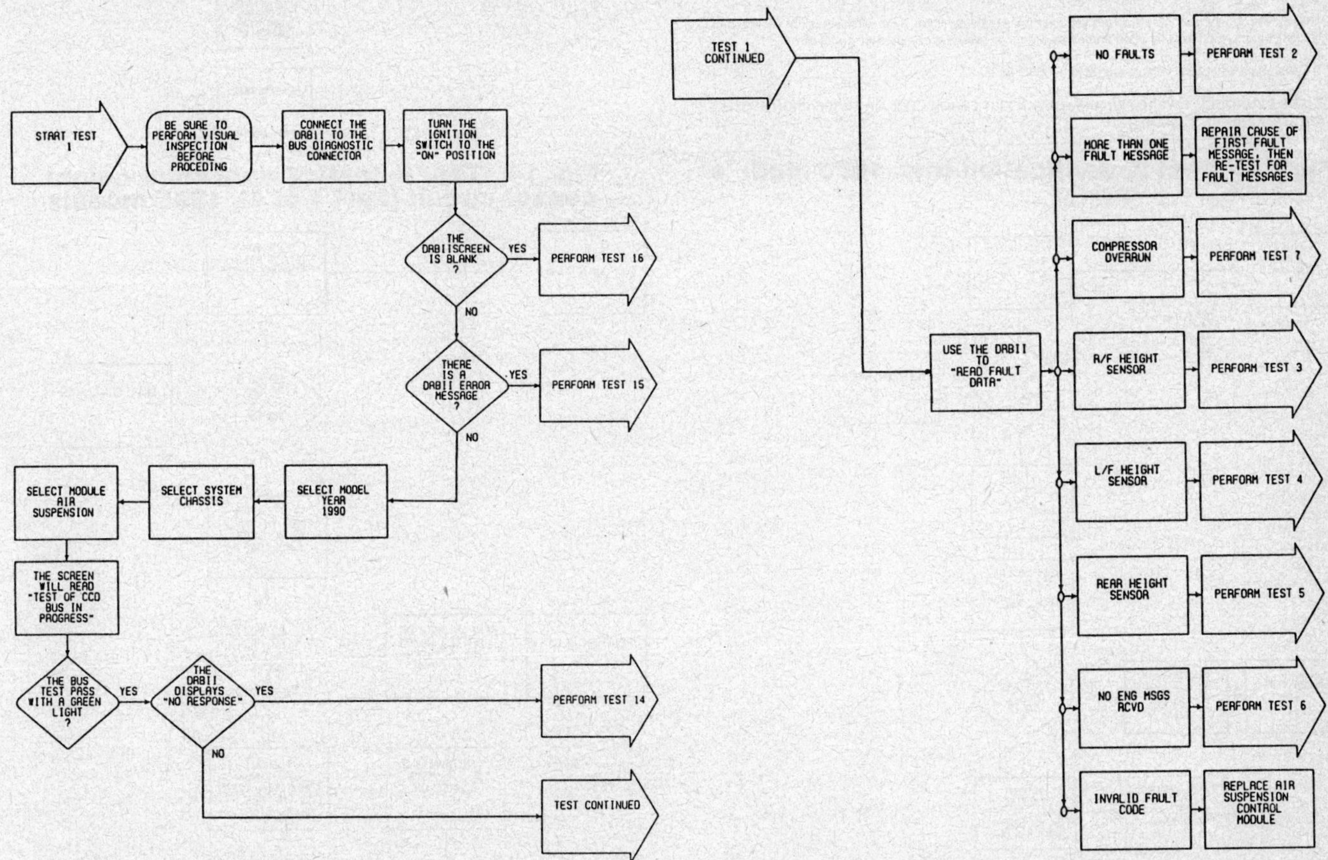


**Fig. 12 Test 1, DRB II hook-up/bus testing (Part 1 of 2). 1990 models**

**Fig. 12 Test 1, DRB II hook-up/bus testing (Part 2 of 2). 1990 models**

**ALWAYS PERFORM THIS TEST AFTER A REPAIR HAS BEEN COMPLETED**

- Perform these steps using the DRBII Diagnostic Tester in the "SYSTEM ACTUATORS" mode.

**NOTE:** The Vehicle must have a **FULLY CHARGED BATTERY** during these tests.

- **VEHICLE MUST NOT BE HOISTED DURING THIS TEST.**
- Step numbers **MUST BE PERFORMED IN ORDER.**
- All steps must be accomplished without error before the vehicle is returned to the owner.
- If you have problems performing a step, use the description found below to locate the correct test procedure.

1. Use the DRBII to raise the right front of vehicle until the sensor display indicates "HIGH".
   If the compressor won't run, go to .......... TEST 9
   If the compressor runs but right front won't raise, go to .......... TEST 10
   If the right front raises but the sensor display indicates "ILL" go to .......... TEST 3
2. Use the DRBII to lower the right front of vehicle until the sensor display indicates "LOW".
   If the right front won't lower, go to .......... TEST 11
   If the right front lowers but sensor display indicates "ILL", go to .......... TEST 3
3. Use the DRBII to raise the left front of vehicle until the sensor display indicates "HIGH".
   If the left front won't raise, go to .......... TEST 12
   If the left front raises but sensor display indicates "ILL", go to .......... TEST 4
4. Use the DRBII to lower the left front of vehicle until the sensor display indicates "LOW".
   If the left front lowers but sensor display indicates "ILL", go to .......... TEST 4
5. Use the DRBII to raise the rear of vehicle until the sensor display indicates "HIGH".
   If the rear won't raise, go to .......... TEST 14
   If the rear raises but sensor display indicates "ILL", go to .......... TEST 5
6. Use the DRBII to lower the rear of vehicle until the sensor display indicates "LOW".
   If the rear lowers but sensor display indicates "ILL", go to .......... TEST 5
7. Turn key off and with all doors and deck lid closed, allow the system to adjust the vehicle until the right front, left front, and rear sensor DRBII displays read "CUST".

   **NOTE:** The compressor may stop running after three minutes or so. If the vehicle has not yet reached "CUST" height, momentarily open and close a door to reset the compressor run cycle.

   If system fails to correct vehicle height to "CUST", go to .......... TEST 8

**IF STEPS 1 THROUGH 7 WERE PERFORMED WITHOUT ERROR - THE AIR SUSPENSION SYSTEM IS FUNCTIONING AS DESIGNED.**

**Fig. 13 Test 2, verification test. 1990 models**

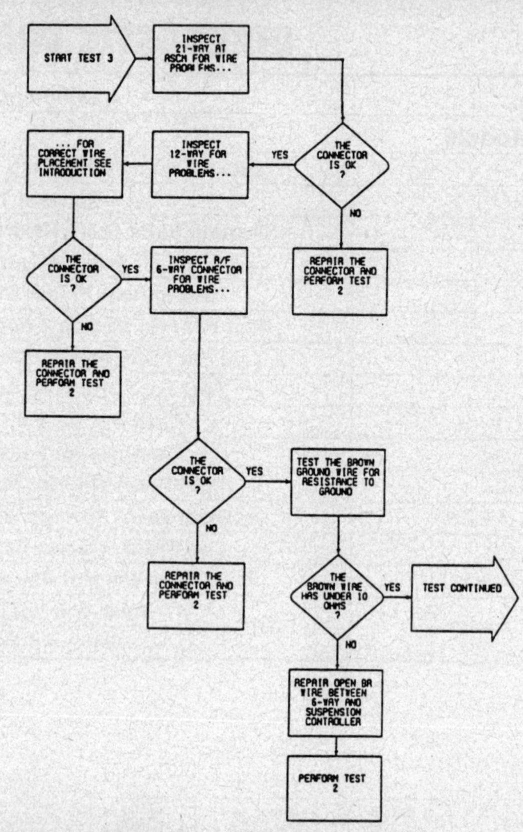


**Fig. 14 Test 3, testing right front height sensor circuit (Part 1 of 4). 1990 models**

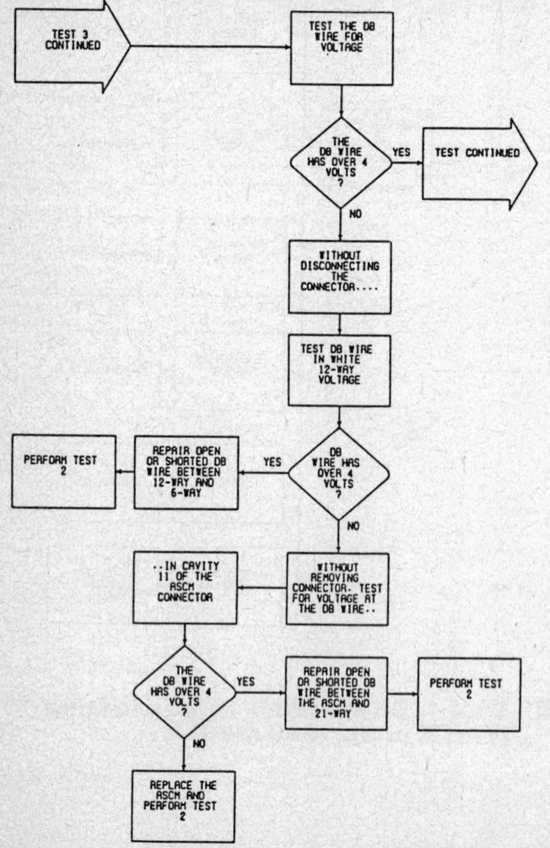


**Fig. 14 Test 3, testing right front height sensor circuit (Part 2 of 4). 1990 models**

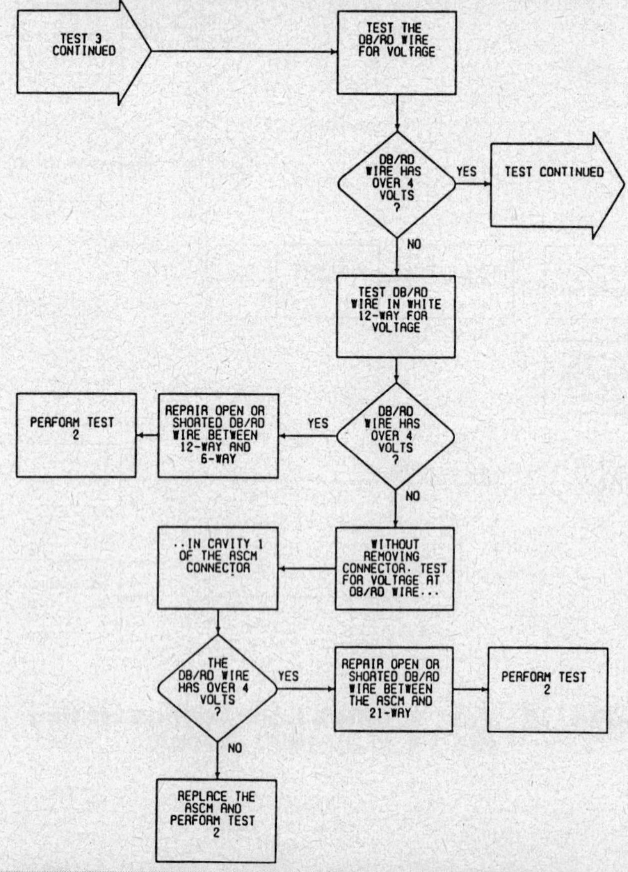


**Fig. 14 Test 3, testing right front height sensor circuit (Part 3 of 4). 1990 models**

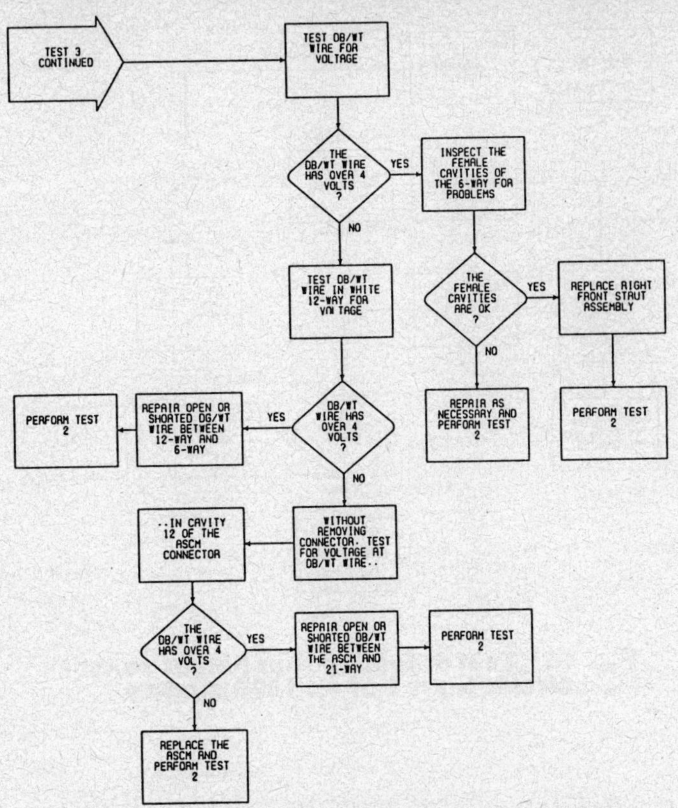


**Fig. 14 Test 3, testing right front height sensor circuit (Part 4 of 4). 1990 models**

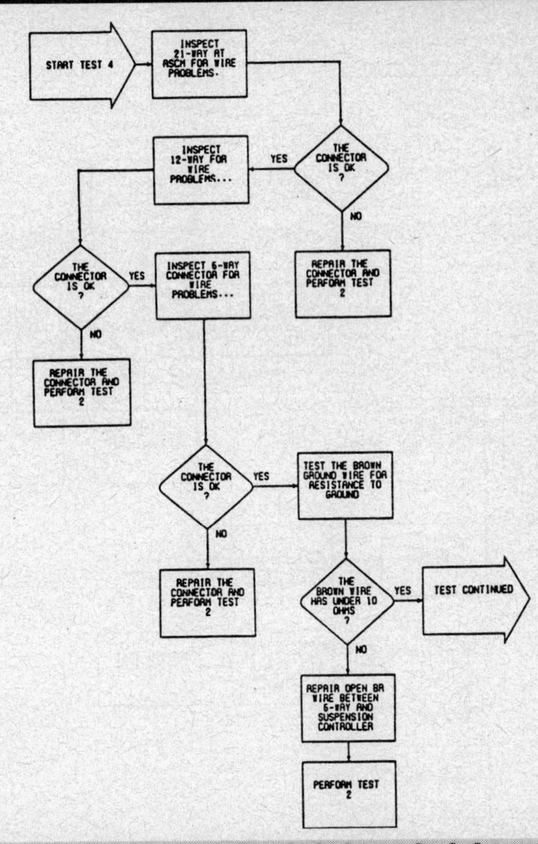


**Fig. 15 Test 4, testing left front height sensor circuit (Part 1 of 4). 1990 models**

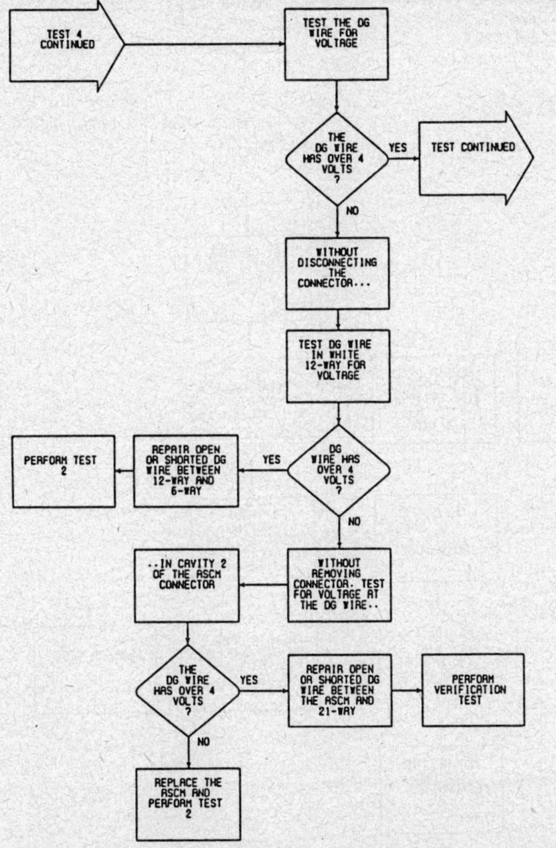


**Fig. 15 Test 4, testing left front height sensor circuit (Part 2 of 4). 1990 models**

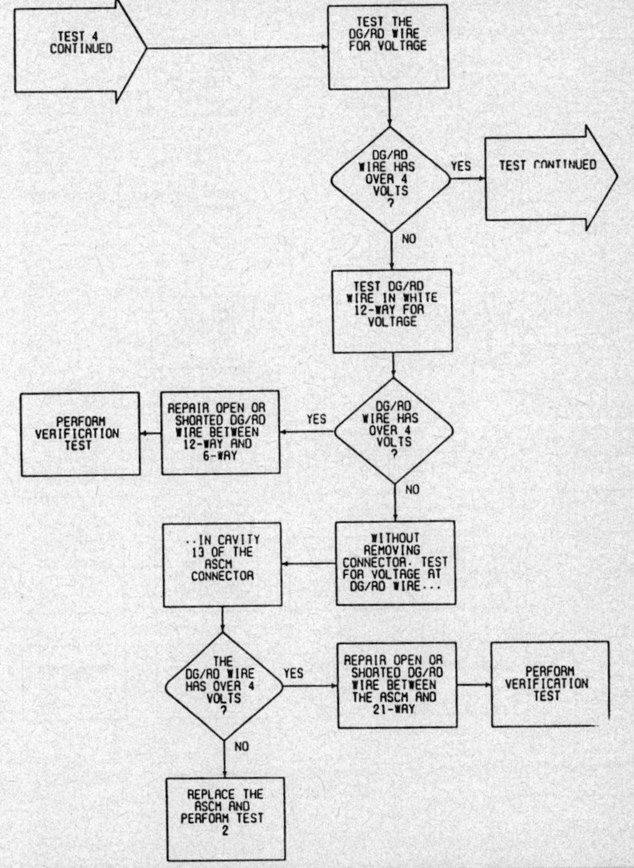


**Fig. 15 Test 4, testing left front height sensor circuit (Part 3 of 4). 1990 models**

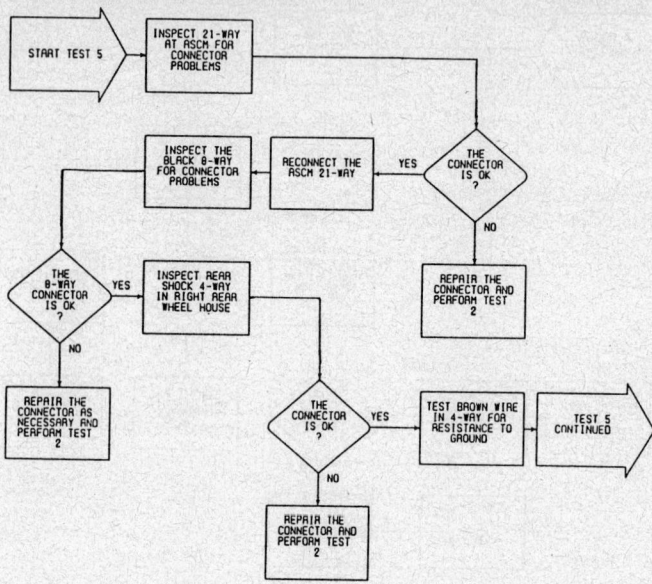

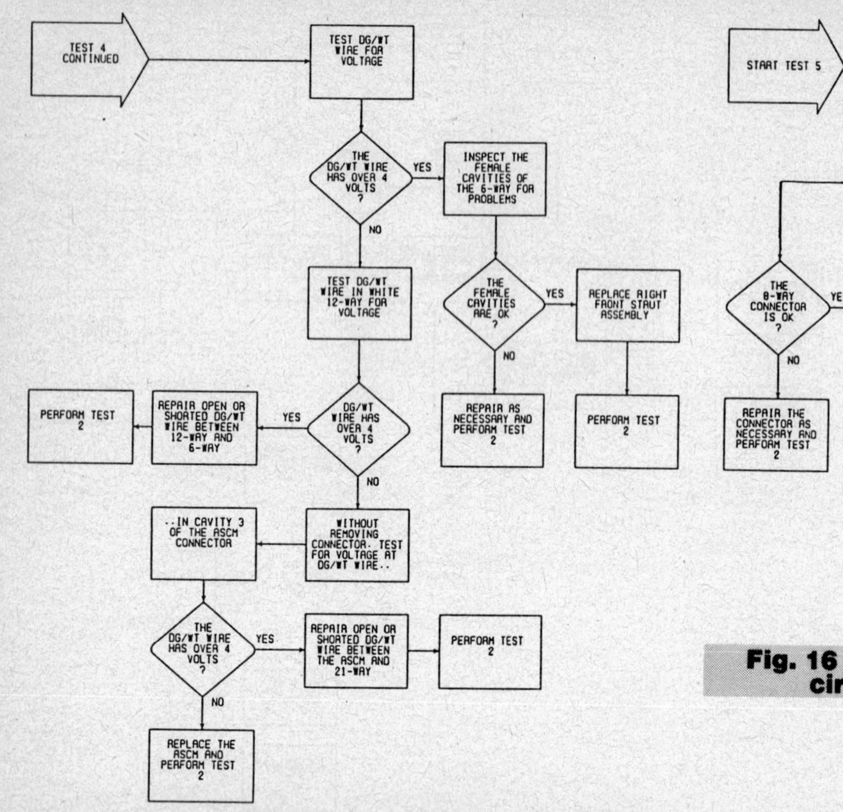


**Fig. 15 Test 4, testing left front height sensor circuit (Part 4 of 4). 1990 models**

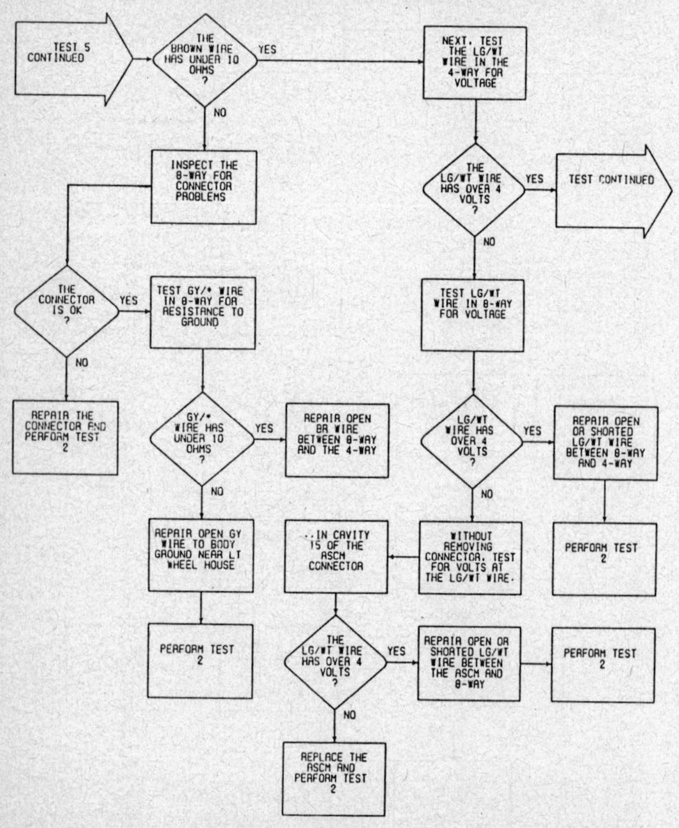


**Fig. 16 Test 5, testing rear height sensor circuit (Part 2 of 4). 1990 models**

START TEST 5 flowchart:



**Fig. 16 Test 5, testing rear height sensor circuit (Part 1 of 4). 1990 models**

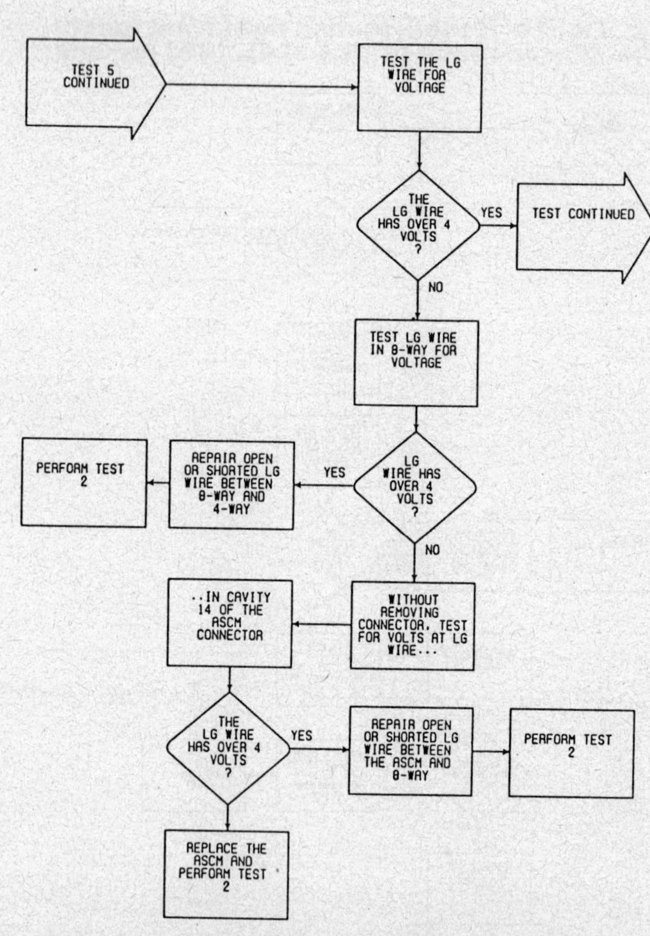


**Fig. 16 Test 5, testing rear height sensor circuit (Part 3 of 4). 1990 models**

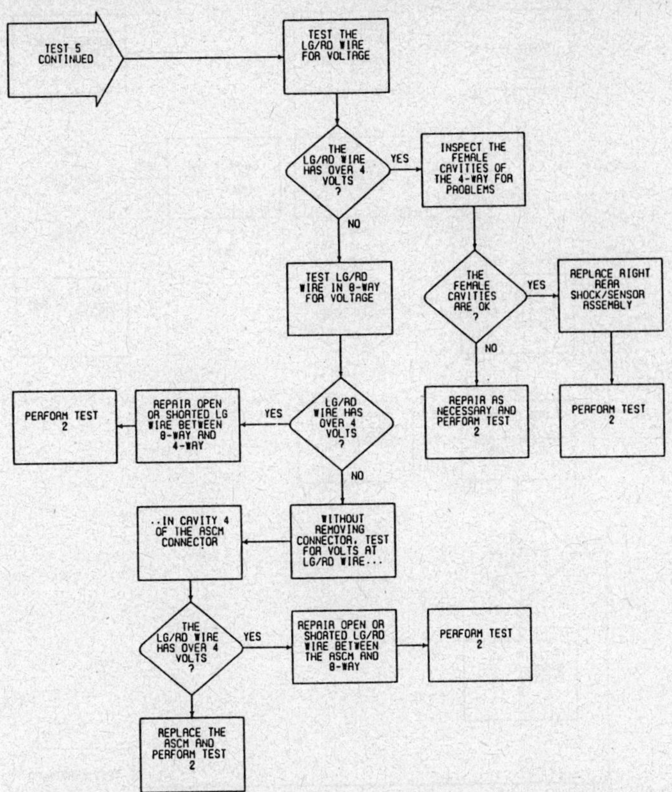


**Fig. 16 Test 5, testing rear height sensor circuit (Part 4 of 4). 1990 models**

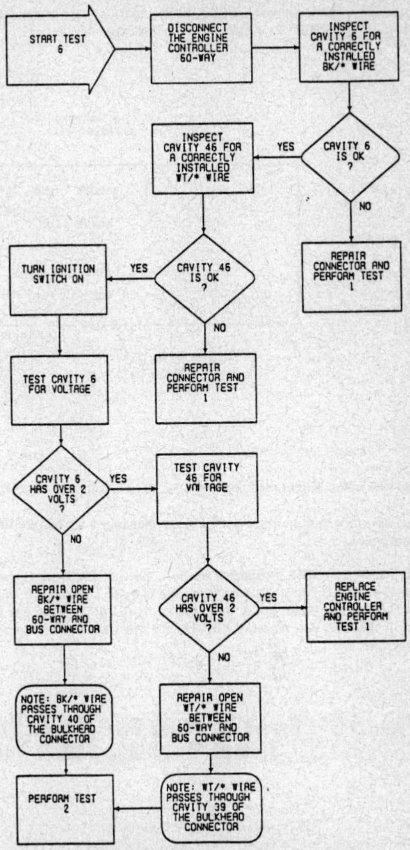

START TEST 6

DISCONNECT THE ENGINE CONTROLLER 60-WAY

INSPECT CAVITY 6 FOR A CORRECTLY INSTALLED BK/* WIRE

CAVITY 6 IS OK ? — YES: INSPECT CAVITY 46 FOR A CORRECTLY INSTALLED WT/* WIRE — NO: REPAIR CONNECTOR AND PERFORM TEST 1

CAVITY 46 IS OK ? — YES: TURN IGNITION SWITCH ON — NO: REPAIR CONNECTOR AND PERFORM TEST 1

TEST CAVITY 6 FOR VOLTAGE

CAVITY 6 HAS OVER 2 VOLTS ? — YES: TEST CAVITY 46 FOR VOLTAGE — NO: REPAIR OPEN BK/* WIRE BETWEEN 60-WAY AND BUS CONNECTOR

NOTE: BK/* WIRE PASSES THROUGH CAVITY 40 OF THE BULKHEAD CONNECTOR

PERFORM TEST 2

CAVITY 46 HAS OVER 2 VOLTS ? — YES: REPLACE ENGINE CONTROLLER AND PERFORM TEST 1 — NO: REPAIR OPEN WT/* WIRE BETWEEN 60-WAY AND BUS CONNECTOR

NOTE: WT/* WIRE PASSES THROUGH CAVITY 39 OF THE BULKHEAD CONNECTOR

PERFORM TEST 2

**Fig. 17 Test 6, test for "No Message Received" message. 1990 models**

The fault message "COMPRESSOR OVERRUN" is generated by the ASCM when the compressor has run for longer than 180 seconds (three minutes).

Since the memory that the ASCM uses to hold fault messages is volatile - fault messages are lost when the key is switched off - Air Suspension fault messages can only be seen while the fault is actually occuring.

Knowing this, the actual symptom that causes this fault message should be easy to hear. If the compressor **is not** running for unusual durations - more than three minutes - when this code is set, you will have to suspect a faulty controller.

However, if the compressor **is** running for unusally long periods, consider the following suggestions:

- stuck relay contacts
- shorted relay coil driver
- possible air leak
- defective ASCM

**Fig. 18 Test 7, test for "Compressor Overrun" message. 1990 models**

After successfully completing Step 6 of TEST 2, the vehicle should be low at all four corners. Step 7 of TEST 2 requires the Air Suspension System to raise and level the vehicle to "CUST" height. Closed doors and deck lid are prerequisites. Failure of the system to level the vehicle during this last step is likely due to a disabling message on the CCD bus.

To view current bus messages available to the ASCM, use the DRBII to enter Air Suspension Diagnostics and select Test "BUS MSG MONITOR".

The figure below shows a normal DRBII display for a vehicle sitting in a flat stall with:

- doors and deck lid closed
- engine off
- throttle closed
- key on (key on keeps the bus alive and makes engine messages available)

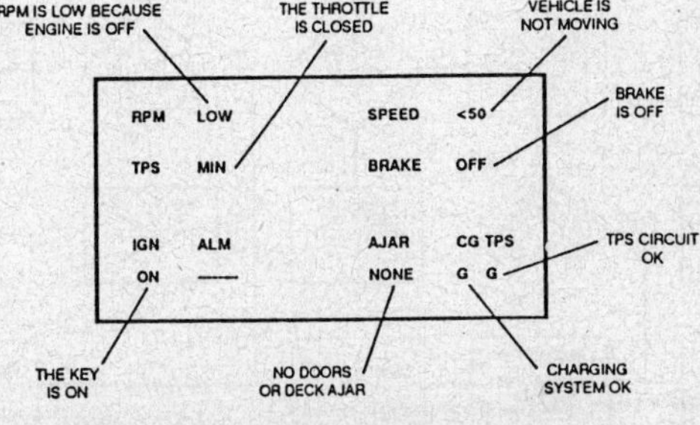


**Fig. 19 Test 8, test for disabling bus message (Part 1 of 2). 1990 models**

The figure below shows a DRBII display that contains some bus messages that will cause the Air Suspension System to suspend normal leveling activities.

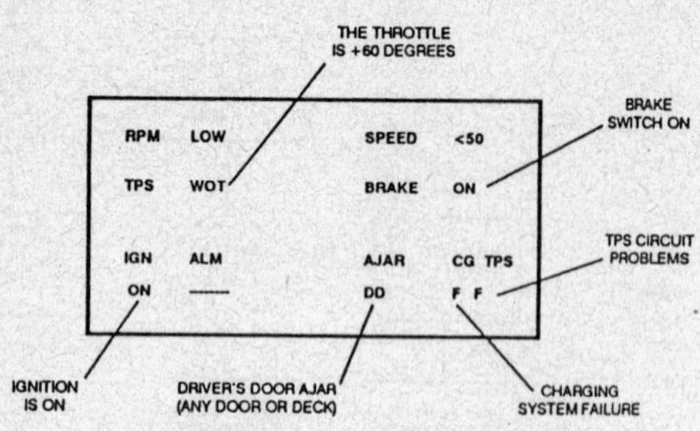


Only one of the above messages is needed to interrupt air suspension activities.

**It is important to note that none of these messages are related to the failure of any air suspension component.**

The "AJAR" and "IGN" messages are from the vehicle's Body Computer. These messages represent what the Body Computer "thinks" the state of these switches are. If the brake message says "ON" and you are sure the brake pedal is not being depressed, or if the ajar message says the "RR" (right rear) door is ajar and you are sure it is not, see the 1990 Body Diagnostics Manual for the correct repair procedure.

**Fig. 19 Test 8, test for disabling bus message (Part 2 of 2). 1990 models**

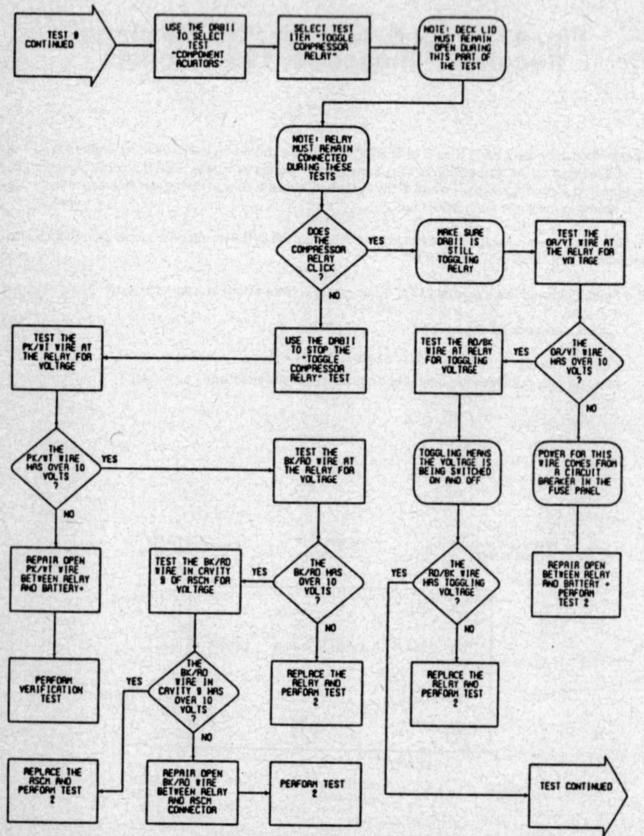


**Fig. 20 Test 9, compressor fails to run (Part 2 of 3). 1990 models**

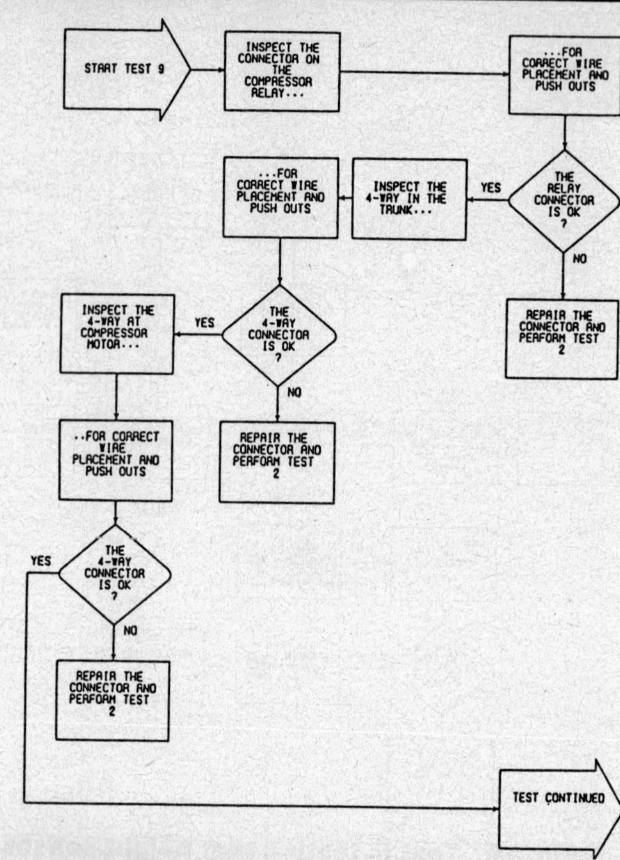


**Fig. 20 Test 9, compressor fails to run (Part 1 of 3). 1990 models**

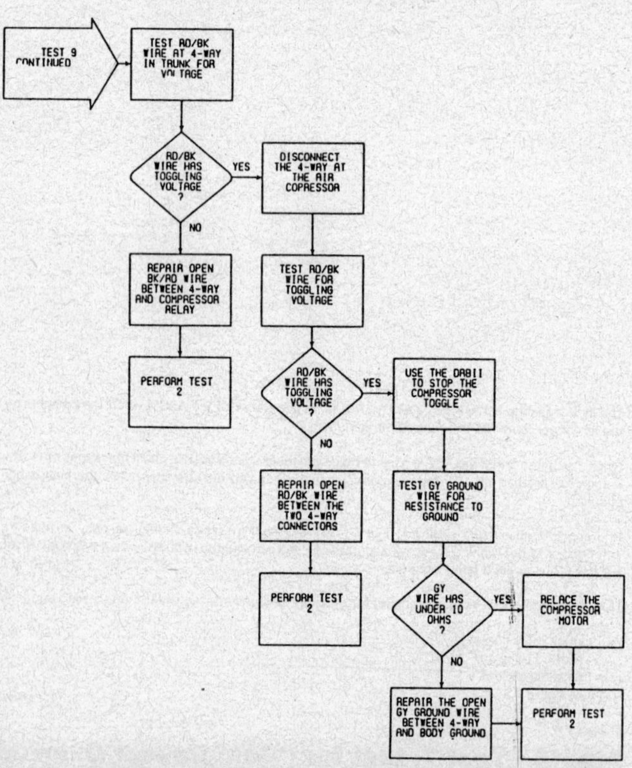


**Fig. 20 Test 9, compressor fails to run (Part 3 of 3). 1990 models**

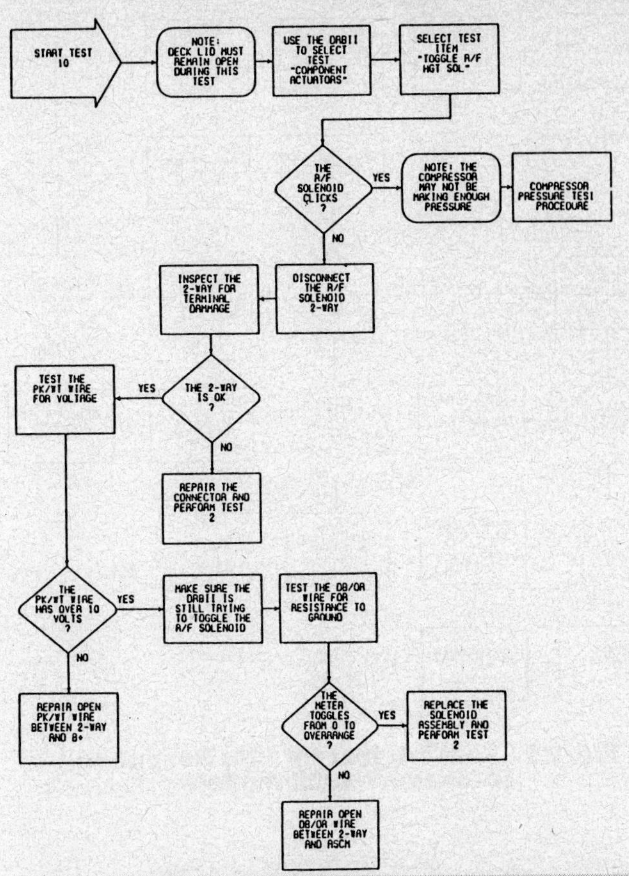


**Fig. 21 Test 10, compressor runs but right front won't raise. 1990 models**

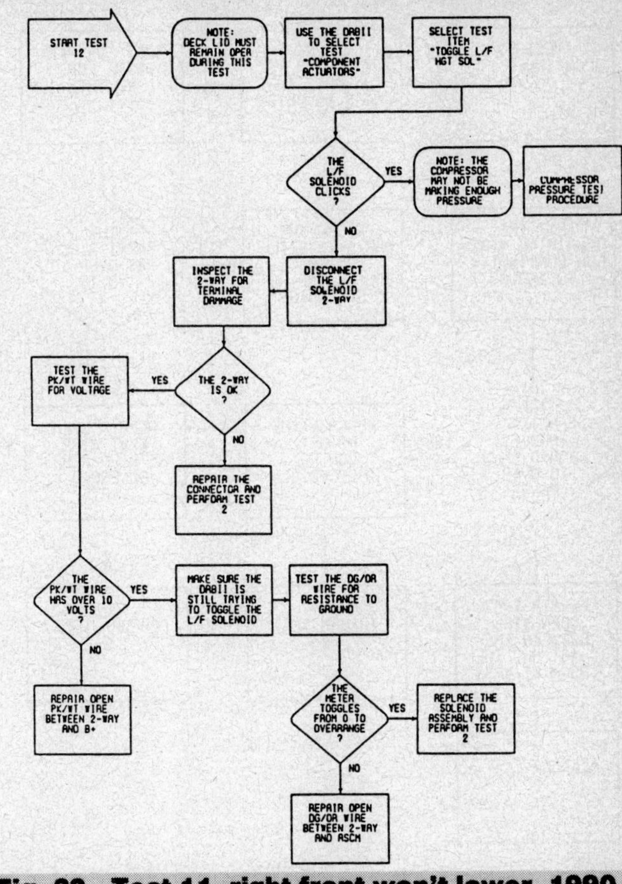


**Fig. 22 Test 11, right front won't lower. 1990 models**

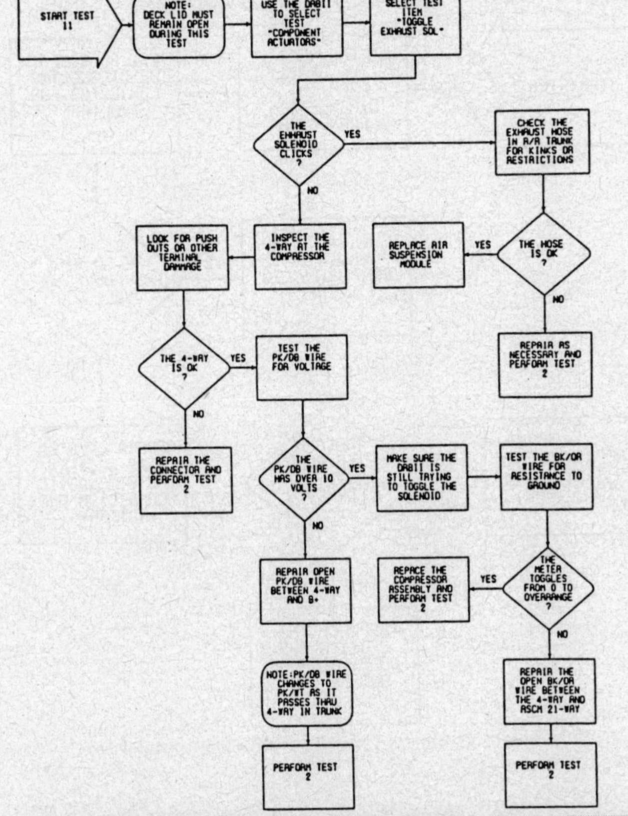


**Fig. 23 Test 12, compressor runs but left front won't raise. 1990 models**

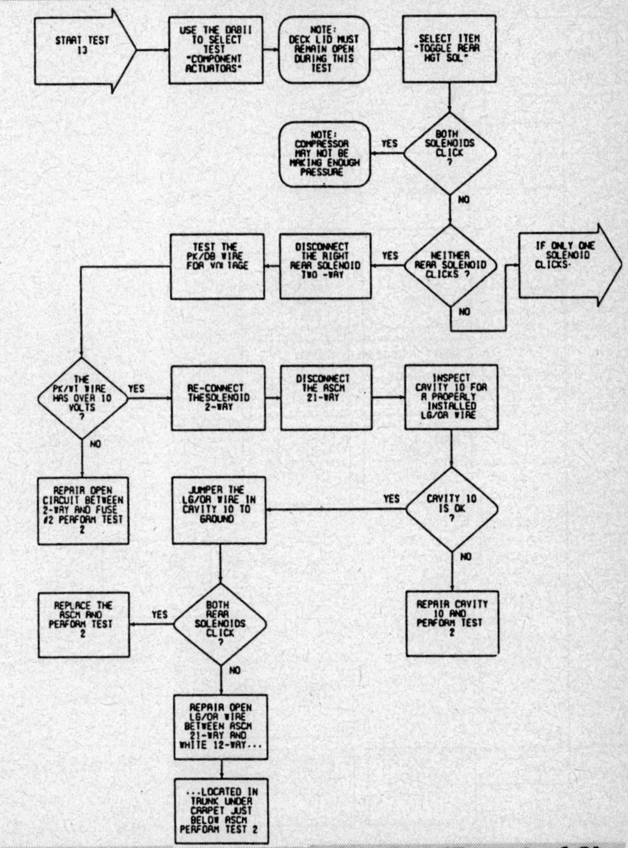


**Fig. 24 Test 13, rear won't raise (Part 1 of 2). 1990 models**

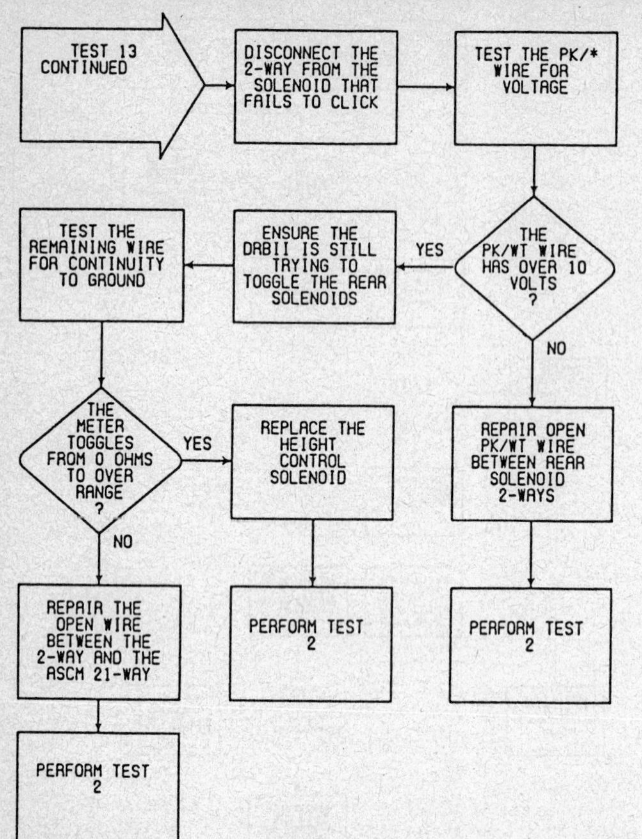


**Fig. 24 Test 13, rear won't raise (Part 2 of 2). 1990 models**

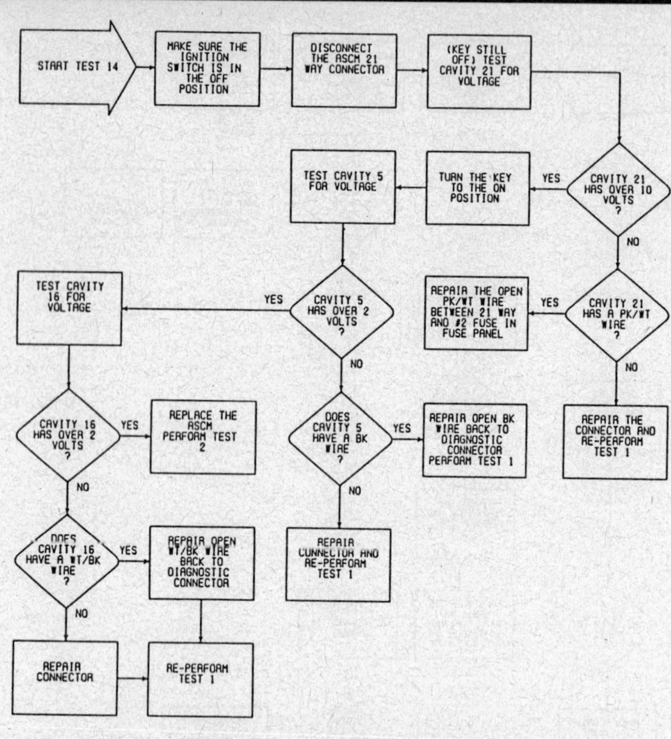


**Fig. 25 Test 14, test for "No Response Message." 1990 models**

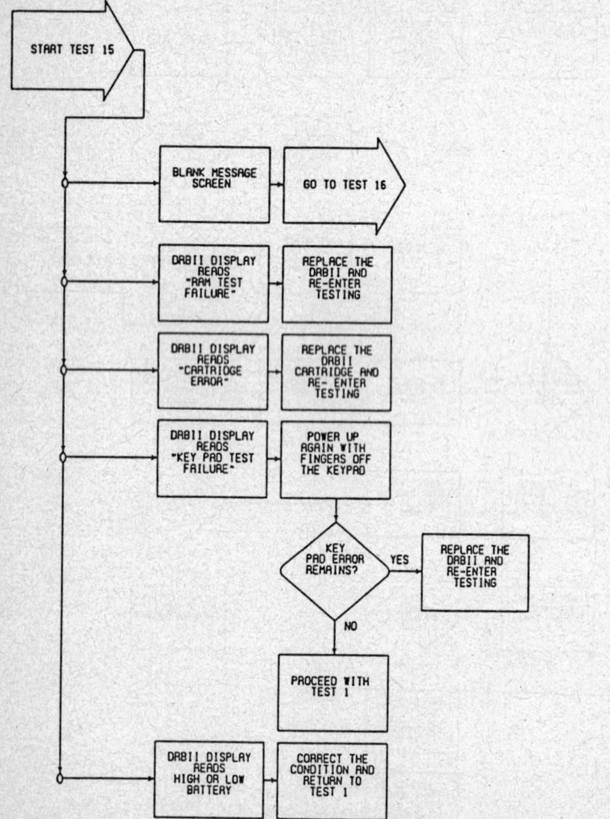


**Fig. 26 Test 15, DRB II error message tests. 1990 models**

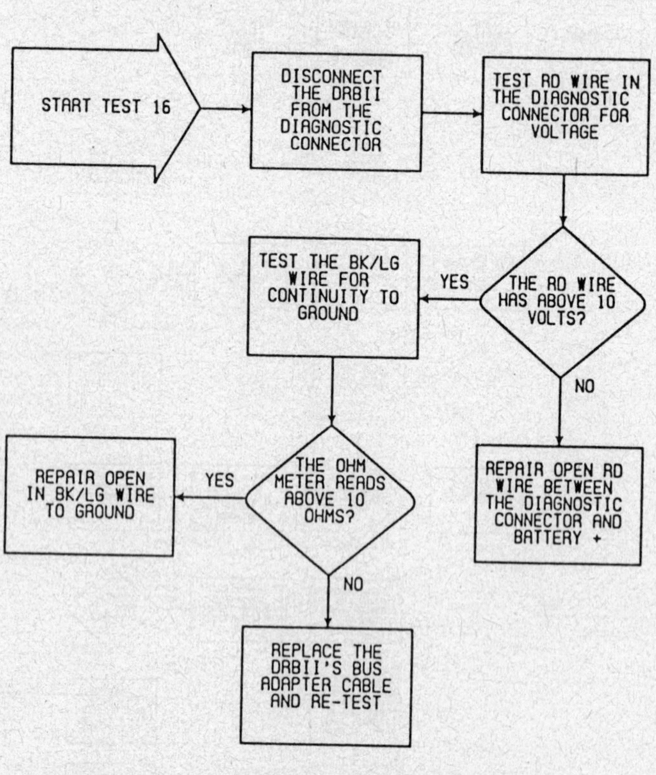


**Fig. 27 Test 16, blank message screen test. 1990 models**

This test gives instructions for using the DRBII to read the air suspension system faults that have been recorded in the memory of the Air Suspension Control Module (ASCM). It then gives directions about what diagnostic test(s) must be performed.

1. Perform a visual inspection.

2. Connect the DRBII to the bus diagnostic connector.

3. Turn the ignition key on.

   If the DRBII screen is blank, displays an error message, fails the bus test ("BUS TEST FAILS"), or displays "NO RESPONSE", there is a DRBII or bus failure.

   **NOTE:** DRBII or bus problems must be corrected before proceeding with fault diagnosis testing.

4. Read faults with the DRBII and write them down.

5. Refer to the following list for the correct diagnostic test to perform for each fault that is displayed on the DRBII.

   **NOTE:** Repairing one fault may sometimes correct other faults. If more than one fault is read, repair the faults in the order shown below. After the first fault is repaired, read faults again.

   If no faults are read, go to .......... Test 2A
   COMPRESSOR OVERRUN .......... Test 7A
   R/F HEIGHT SENSOR .......... Test 3A
   L/F HEIGHT SENSOR .......... Test 4A
   REAR HEIGHT SENSOR .......... Test 5A
   NO ENG MSGS RCVD .......... Test 6A

**Fig. 28 Test 1A, DRB II hook-up/reading fault messages. 1991 models**

This test verifies the correct operation of the air suspension system. It must be performed after reading faults with the DRBII and finding none, or after a vehicle repair has been made.

A. Reconnect all previously disconnected connectors.

B. As diagnostic tests are performed, watch the DRBII display. The term "ILL" may be displayed briefly or steadily. In either case, go to the test indicated in the procedure below for the "ILL" message.

C. The battery must be charged and at a rated capacity before performing any of these air suspension tests.

D. The vehicle must be on a flat surface during these tests.

E. The step numbers below must be followed in order.

F. The vehicle must be in "CUST" (customer) height mode, not in "SHIP" mode.

G. The deck lid or a door must be open to perform these tests.

H. Turn the ignition key to the ON position.

**NOTE:** Use the DRBII to raise and lower the vehicle as instructed in the following steps. During the tests, use the DRBII to read the state of the height sensors.

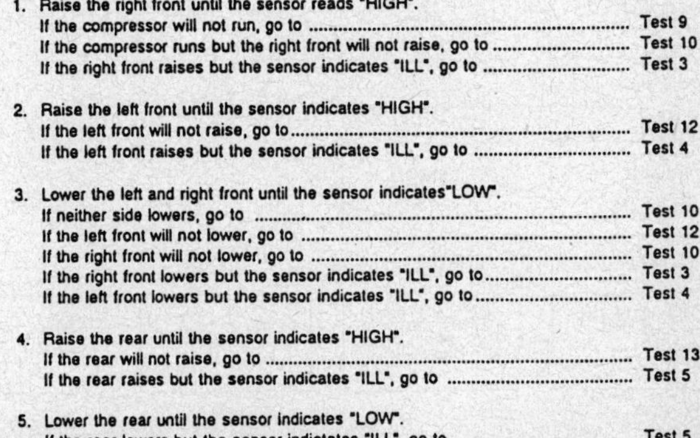

1. Raise the right front until the sensor reads "HIGH".
   If the compressor will not run, go to .......... Test 9
   If the compressor runs but the right front will not raise, go to .......... Test 10
   If the right front raises but the sensor indicates "ILL", go to .......... Test 3

2. Raise the left front until the sensor indicates "HIGH".
   If the left front will not raise, go to .......... Test 12
   If the left front raises but the sensor indicates "ILL", go to .......... Test 4

3. Lower the left and right front until the sensor indicates"LOW".
   If neither side lowers, go to .......... Test 10
   If the left front will not lower, go to .......... Test 12
   If the right front will not lower, go to .......... Test 10
   If the right front lowers but the sensor indicates "ILL", go to .......... Test 3
   If the left front lowers but the sensor indicates "ILL", go to .......... Test 4

4. Raise the rear until the sensor indicates "HIGH".
   If the rear will not raise, go to .......... Test 13
   If the rear raises but the sensor indicates "ILL", go to .......... Test 5

5. Lower the rear until the sensor indicates "LOW".
   If the rear lowers but the sensor indictates "ILL", go to .......... Test 5

**Fig. 29 Test 2A, verification test (Part 1 of 2). 1991 models**

6. Turn the ignition key to the OFF position. Close all doors and the deck lid.

7. Allow the system to adjust the vehicle height until all sensors indicate "CUST" height.

   **NOTE:** You will have to change the DRBII to "SENSOR STATE" to read "CUST" height.

   **NOTE:** The compressor may stop running after 3 minutes. If the vehicle has not yet reached "CUST" height, open and close a door to reset the compressor.

   If the system fails to adjust the vehicle height to "CUST" height, go to .......... Test 8

If Steps 1 through 7 were performed without error, the air suspension system is working normally.

**Fig. 29 Test 2A, verification test (Part 2 of 2). 1991 models**

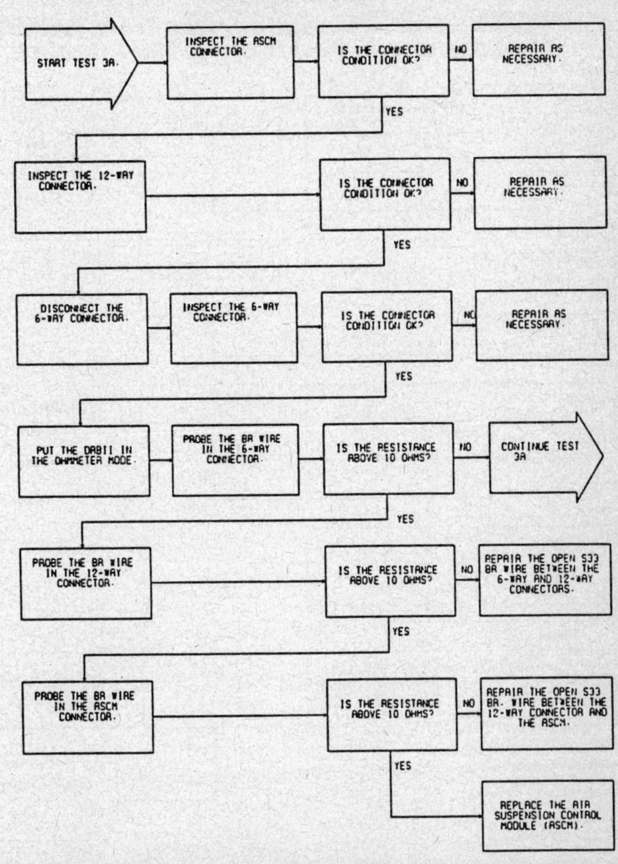


**Fig. 30 Test 3A, testing right front height sensor circuit (Part 1 of 4). 1991 models**

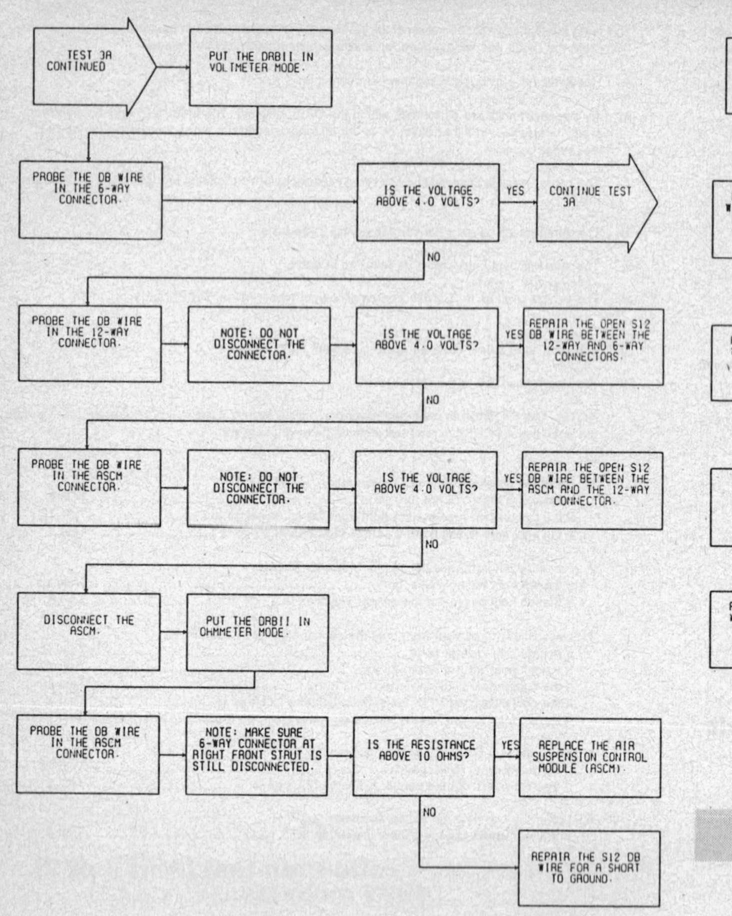


**Fig. 30 Test 3A, testing right front height sensor circuit (Part 2 of 4). 1991 models**

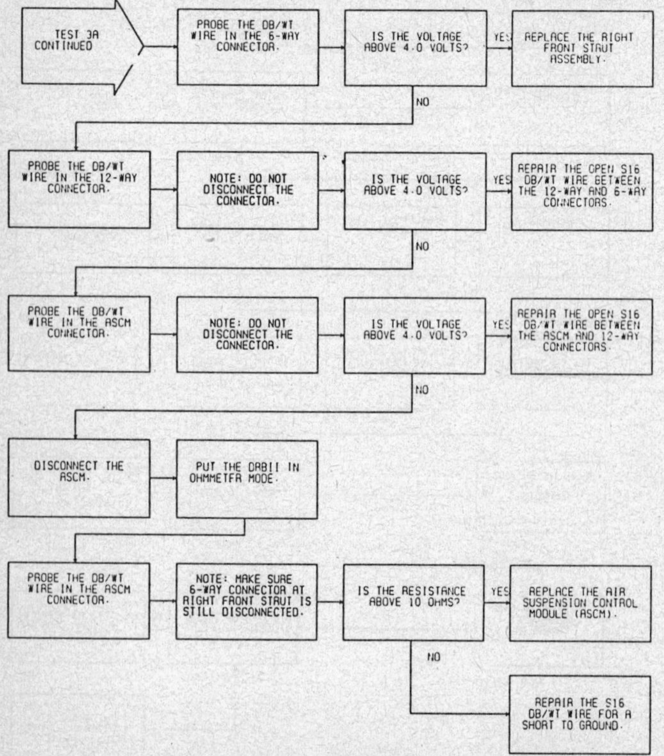


**Fig. 30 Test 3A, testing right front height sensor circuit (Part 4 of 4). 1991 models**

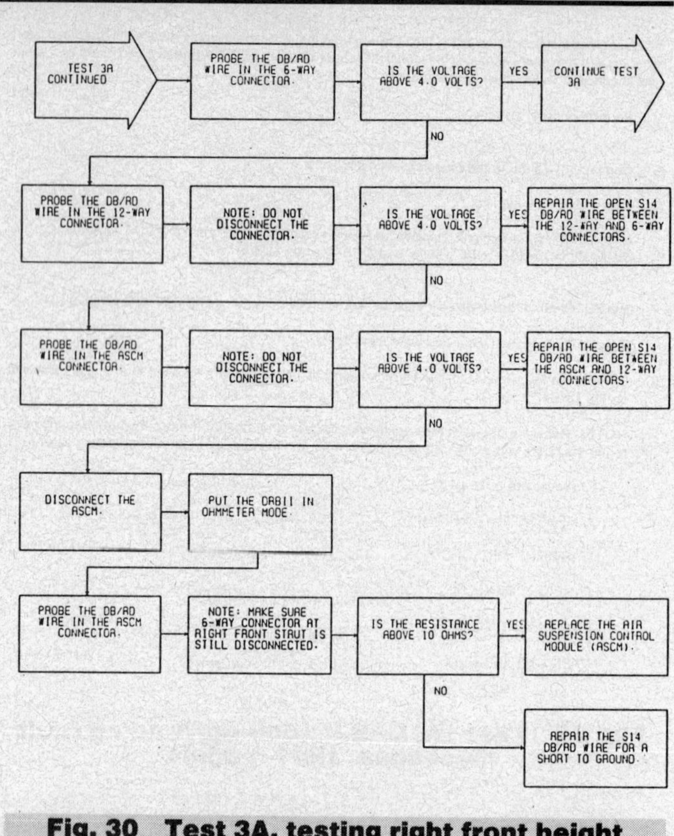


**Fig. 30 Test 3A, testing right front height sensor circuit (Part 3 of 4). 1991 models**

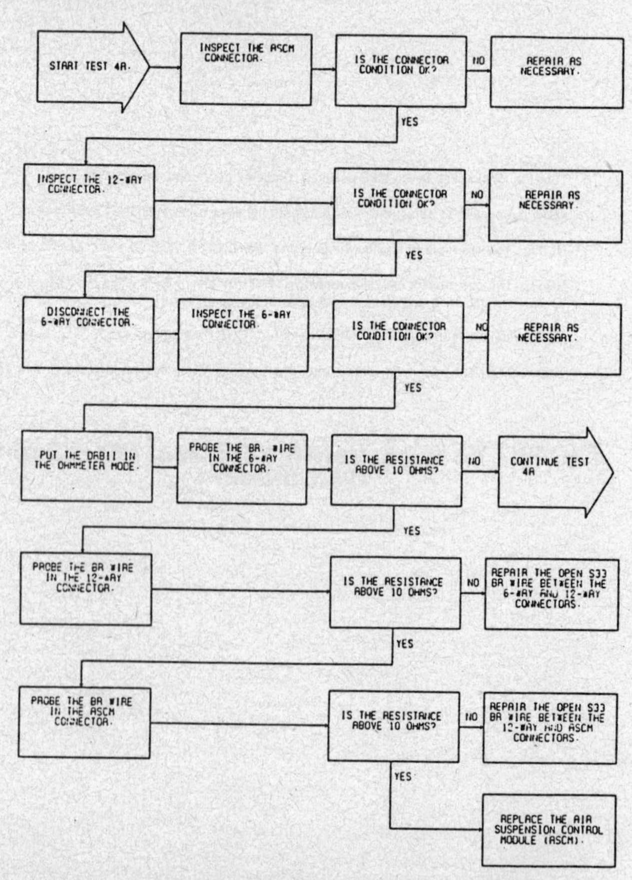


**Fig. 31 Test 4A, testing left front height sensor circuit (Part 1 of 4). 1991 models**

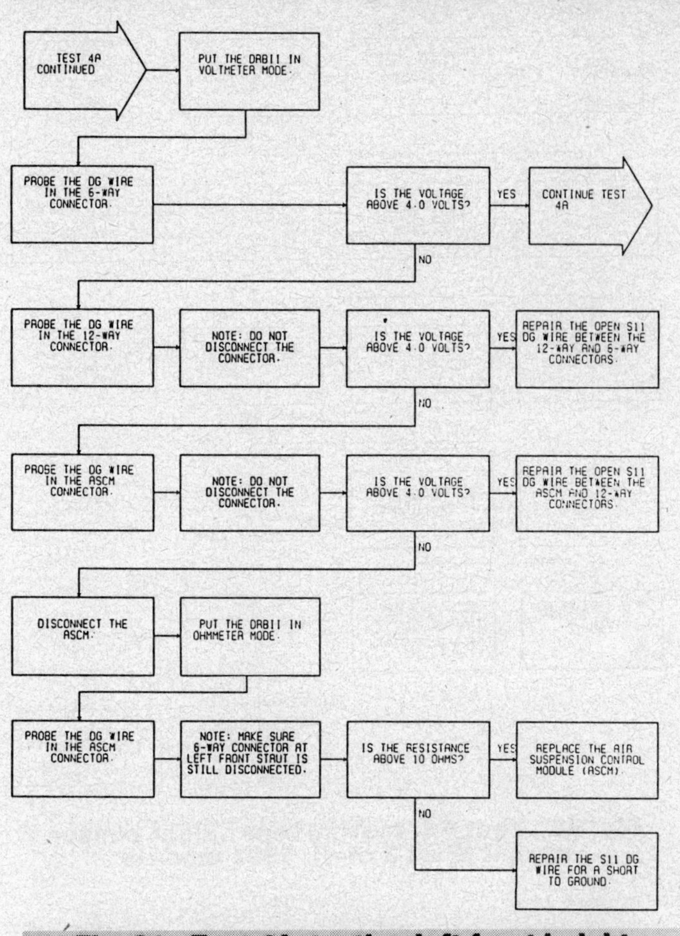


**Fig. 31 Test 4A, testing left front height sensor circuit (Part 2 of 4). 1991 models**

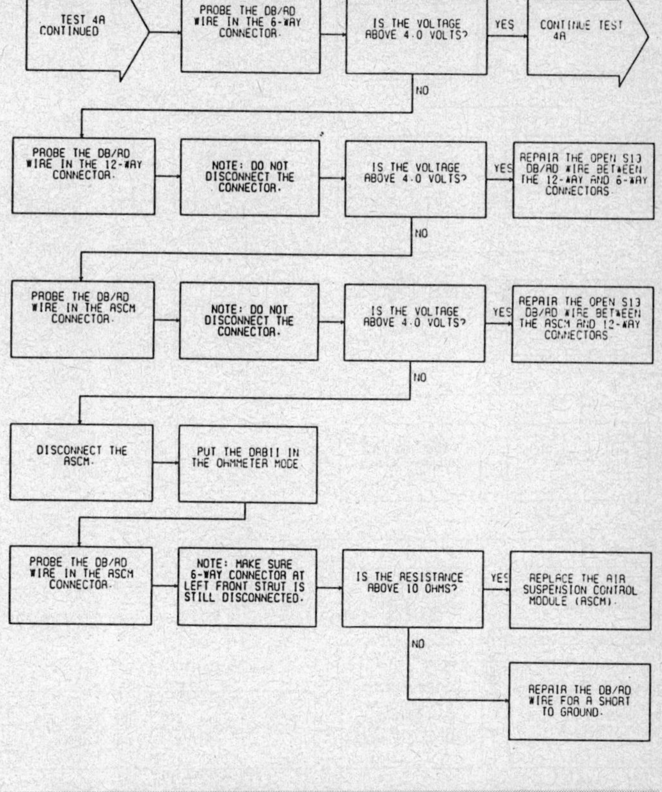


**Fig. 31 Test 4A, testing left front height sensor circuit (Part 3 of 4). 1991 models**

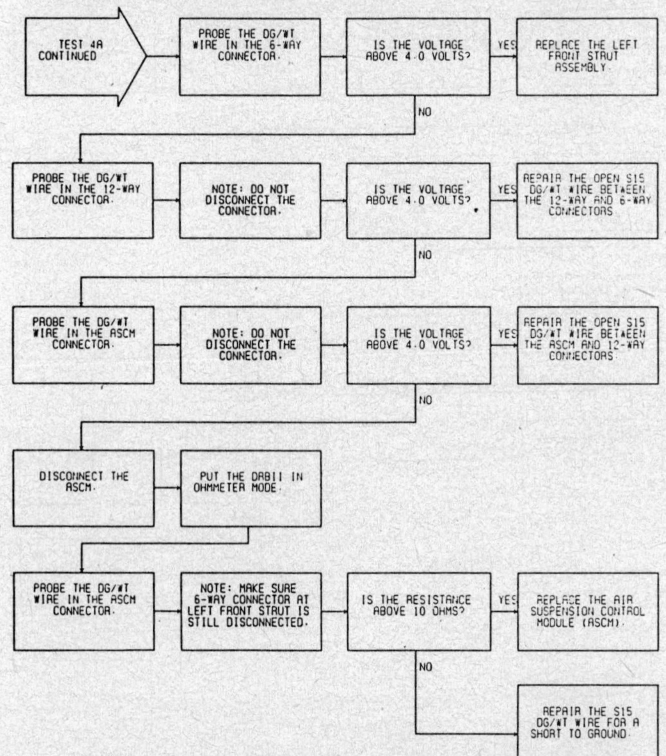


**Fig. 31 Test 4A, testing left front height sensor circuit (Part 4 of 4). 1991 models**

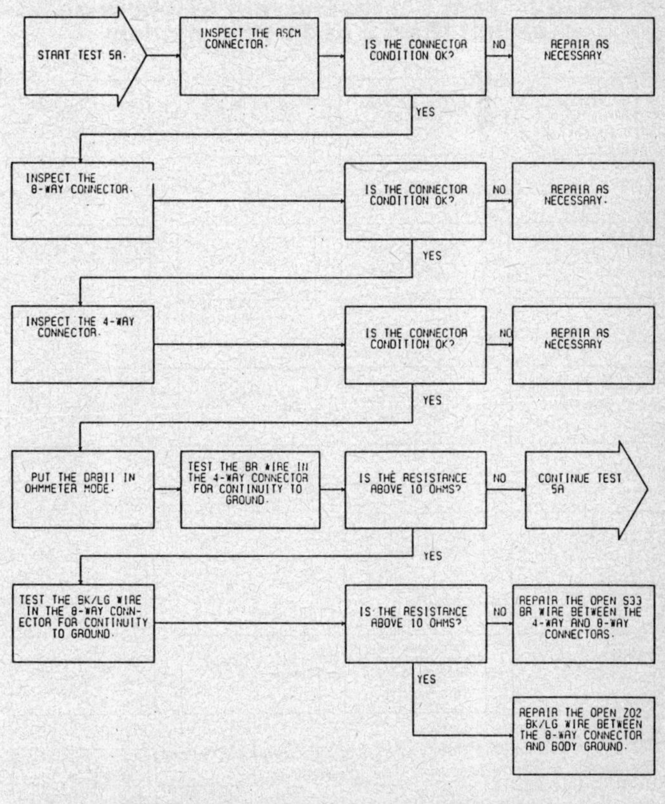


**Fig. 32 Test 5A, testing rear height sensor circuit (Part 1 of 4). 1991 models**

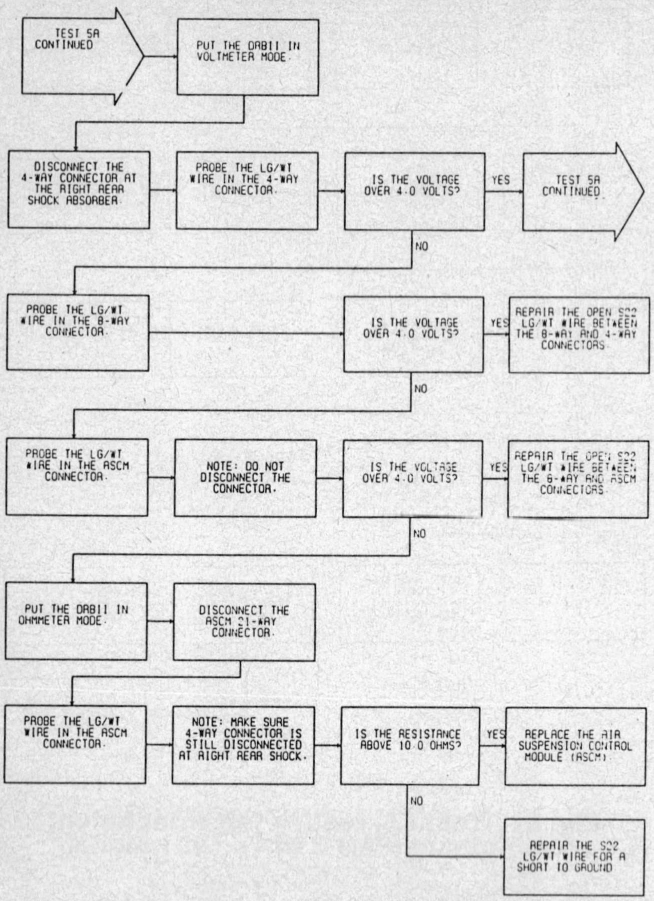

TEST 5A CONTINUED
PUT THE DRBII IN VOLTMETER MODE.
DISCONNECT THE 4-WAY CONNECTOR AT THE RIGHT REAR SHOCK ABSORBER.
PROBE THE LG/WT WIRE IN THE 4-WAY CONNECTOR.
IS THE VOLTAGE OVER 4.0 VOLTS?
YES
TEST 5A CONTINUED
NO
PROBE THE LG/WT WIRE IN THE 8-WAY CONNECTOR.
IS THE VOLTAGE OVER 4.0 VOLTS?
YES
REPAIR THE OPEN S22 LG/WT WIRE BETWEEN THE 8-WAY AND 4-WAY CONNECTORS.
NO
PROBE THE LG/WT WIRE IN THE ASCM CONNECTOR.
NOTE: DO NOT DISCONNECT THE CONNECTOR.
IS THE VOLTAGE OVER 4.0 VOLTS?
YES
REPAIR THE OPEN S22 LG/WT WIRE BETWEEN THE 8-WAY AND ASCM CONNECTORS.
NO
PUT THE DRBII IN OHMMETER MODE.
DISCONNECT THE ASCM 21-WAY CONNECTOR.
PROBE THE LG/WT WIRE IN THE ASCM CONNECTOR.
NOTE: MAKE SURE 4-WAY CONNECTOR IS STILL DISCONNECTED AT RIGHT REAR SHOCK.
IS THE RESISTANCE ABOVE 10.0 OHMS?
YES
REPLACE THE AIR SUSPENSION CONTROL MODULE (ASCM).
NO
REPAIR THE S22 LG/WT WIRE FOR A SHORT TO GROUND

**Fig. 32 Test 5A, testing rear height sensor circuit (Part 2 of 4). 1991 models**

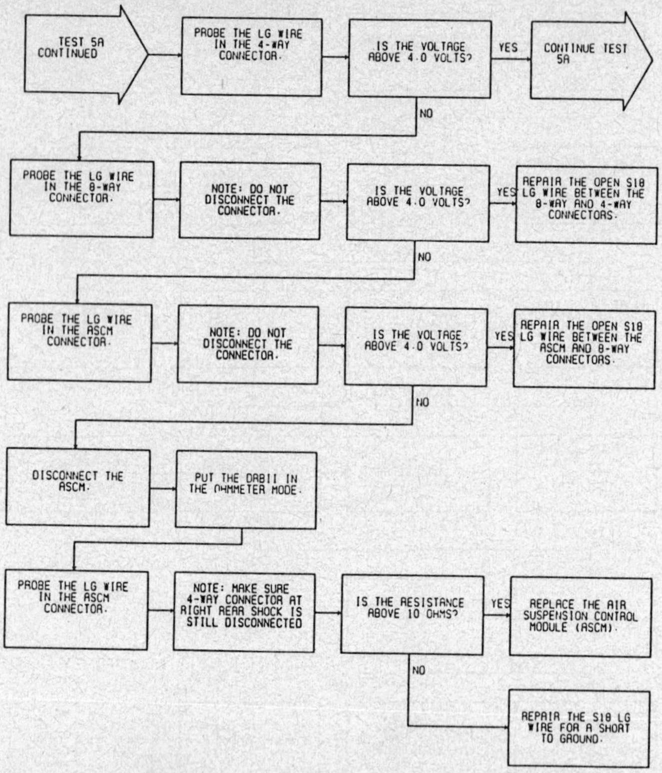

TEST 5A CONTINUED
PROBE THE LG WIRE IN THE 4-WAY CONNECTOR.
IS THE VOLTAGE ABOVE 4.0 VOLTS?
YES
CONTINUE TEST 5A
NO
PROBE THE LG WIRE IN THE 8-WAY CONNECTOR.
NOTE: DO NOT DISCONNECT THE CONNECTOR.
IS THE VOLTAGE ABOVE 4.0 VOLTS?
YES
REPAIR THE OPEN S18 LG WIRE BETWEEN THE 8-WAY AND 4-WAY CONNECTORS.
NO
PROBE THE LG WIRE IN THE ASCM CONNECTOR.
NOTE: DO NOT DISCONNECT THE CONNECTOR.
IS THE VOLTAGE ABOVE 4.0 VOLTS?
YES
REPAIR THE OPEN S18 LG WIRE BETWEEN THE ASCM AND 8-WAY CONNECTORS.
NO
DISCONNECT THE ASCM.
PUT THE DRBII IN THE OHMMETER MODE.
PROBE THE LG WIRE IN THE ASCM CONNECTOR.
NOTE: MAKE SURE 4-WAY CONNECTOR AT RIGHT REAR SHOCK IS STILL DISCONNECTED
IS THE RESISTANCE ABOVE 10 OHMS?
YES
REPLACE THE AIR SUSPENSION CONTROL MODULE (ASCM).
NO
REPAIR THE S18 LG WIRE FOR A SHORT TO GROUND.

**Fig. 32 Test 5A, testing rear height sensor circuit (Part 3 of 4). 1991 models**

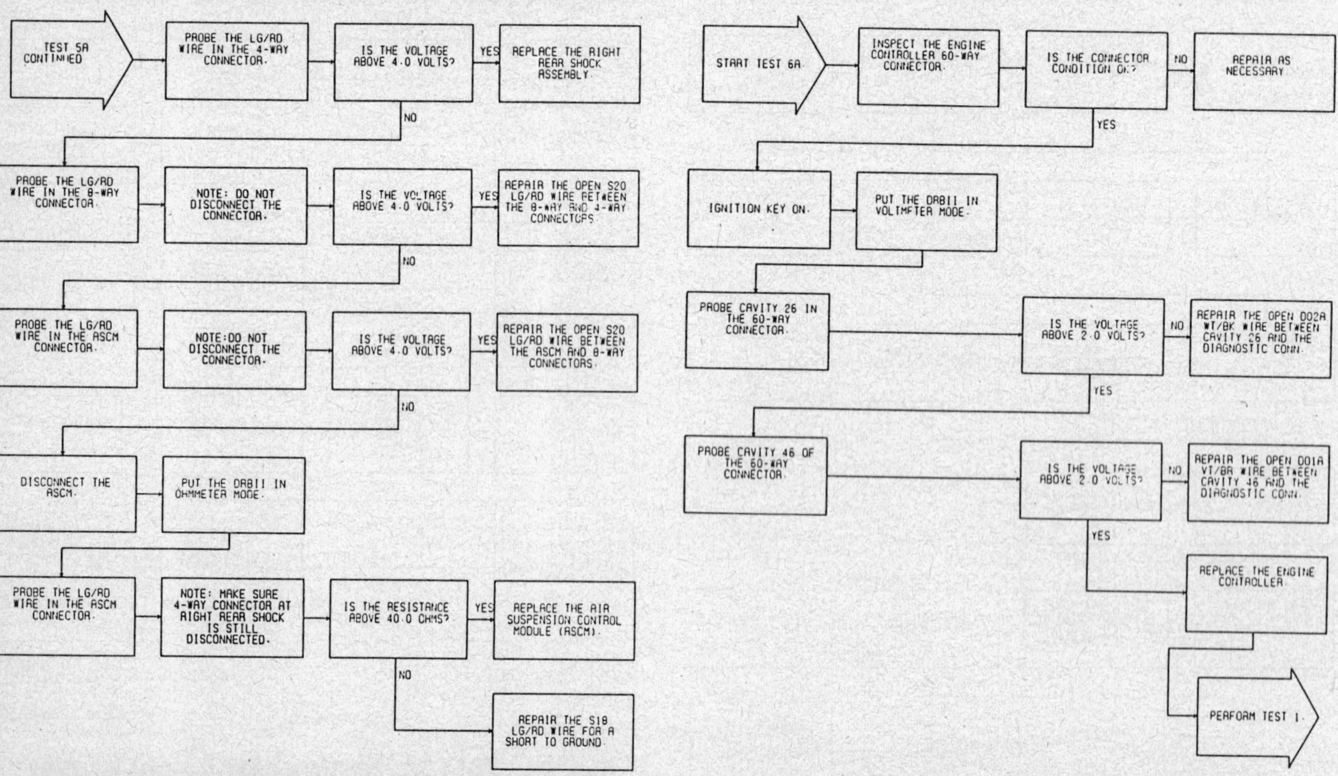

TEST 5A CONTINUED
PROBE THE LG/RD WIRE IN THE 4-WAY CONNECTOR.
IS THE VOLTAGE ABOVE 4.0 VOLTS?
YES
REPLACE THE RIGHT REAR SHOCK ASSEMBLY.
NO
PROBE THE LG/RD WIRE IN THE 8-WAY CONNECTOR.
NOTE: DO NOT DISCONNECT THE CONNECTOR.
IS THE VOLTAGE ABOVE 4.0 VOLTS?
YES
REPAIR THE OPEN S20 LG/RD WIRE BETWEEN THE 8-WAY AND 4-WAY CONNECTORS
NO
PROBE THE LG/RD WIRE IN THE ASCM CONNECTOR.
NOTE: DO NOT DISCONNECT THE CONNECTOR.
IS THE VOLTAGE ABOVE 4.0 VOLTS?
YES
REPAIR THE OPEN S20 LG/RD WIRE BETWEEN THE ASCM AND 8-WAY CONNECTORS.
NO
DISCONNECT THE ASCM.
PUT THE DRBII IN OHMMETER MODE.
PROBE THE LG/RD WIRE IN THE ASCM CONNECTOR.
NOTE: MAKE SURE 4-WAY CONNECTOR AT RIGHT REAR SHOCK IS STILL DISCONNECTED.
IS THE RESISTANCE ABOVE 40.0 OHMS?
YES
REPLACE THE AIR SUSPENSION CONTROL MODULE (ASCM).
NO
REPAIR THE S18 LG/RD WIRE FOR A SHORT TO GROUND.

**Fig. 32 Test 5A, testing rear height sensor circuit (Part 4 of 4). 1991 models**

START TEST 6A.
INSPECT THE ENGINE CONTROLLER 60-WAY CONNECTOR.
IS THE CONNECTOR CONDITION OK?
NO
REPAIR AS NECESSARY
YES
IGNITION KEY ON.
PUT THE DRBII IN VOLTMETER MODE.
PROBE CAVITY 26 IN THE 60-WAY CONNECTOR.
IS THE VOLTAGE ABOVE 2.0 VOLTS?
NO
REPAIR THE OPEN D02A WT/BK WIRE BETWEEN CAVITY 26 AND THE DIAGNOSTIC CONN.
YES
PROBE CAVITY 46 OF THE 60-WAY CONNECTOR.
IS THE VOLTAGE ABOVE 2.0 VOLTS?
NO
REPAIR THE OPEN D01A VT/BR WIRE BETWEEN CAVITY 46 AND THE DIAGNOSTIC CONN.
YES
REPLACE THE ENGINE CONTROLLER.
PERFORM TEST 1.

**Fig. 33 Test 6A, test for "No Message Received" message. 1991 models**

The fault message "COMPRESSOR OVERRUN" is generated by the Air Suspension Control Module (ASCM) when the compressor has run for longer than 180 seconds (three minutes).

The memory that the ASCM uses to hold fault messages is volatile. This means that the fault messages are lost when the key is turned off. Because of this, air suspension fault messages can only be seen while the fault is actually occurring.

However, the problem that causes the "COMPRESSOR OVERRUN" fault message can be easily detected by listening to the compressor run.

If the compressor does not run for an unusual length of time (more than three minutes) when this fault is set, the ASCM is probably defective.

If the compressor does run for an unusual length of time, the following problems may be the cause of the fault:

- stuck relay contacts
- shorted relay coil driver within the ASCM
- possible air leak
- defective ASCM
- restricted air compressor intake
- low air compressor capacity

**Fig. 34 Test 7A, test for "Compressor Overrun" message. 1991 models**

After successfully completing Step 6 of Test 2, the vehicle should be low at all four corners.

Step 7 of Test 2 asks the air suspension system to raise and level the vehicle to "CUST" (customer) height. **NOTE:** The doors and deck lid must be closed for the system to do this.

Failure of the system to level the vehicle to "CUST" height during Step 7 is likely because of a "disabling" message on the CCD bus. (The CCD bus is the information link between the on-board vehicle computers.)

To view the bus messages the Air Suspension Control Module (ASCM) is currently receiving, use the DRBII to select the "CCD Bus Monitor" test.

The figure below shows a normal DRBII display for a vehicle sitting in a flat stall with:

- doors and deck lid closed
- engine idling
- throttle closed
- key on (keeps the bus on and makes engine messages available)

**NORMAL MESSAGES**

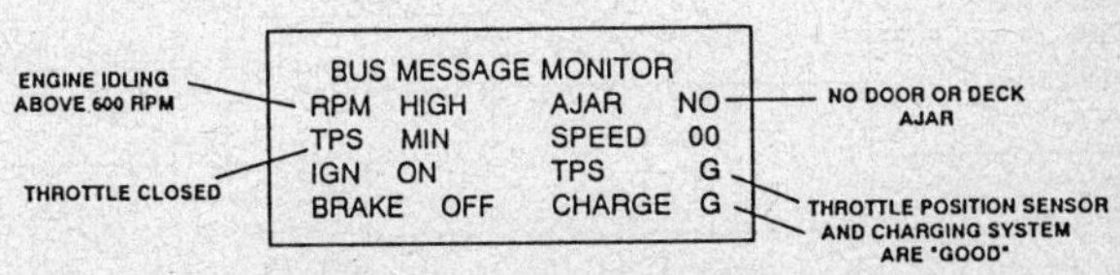


**Fig. 35 Test 8A, test for "Disabling Bus Message" (Part 1 of 2). 1991 models**

The figure below shows a DRBII display containing some bus messages that will cause the air suspension system to stop operating normally.

**DISABLING MESSAGES**

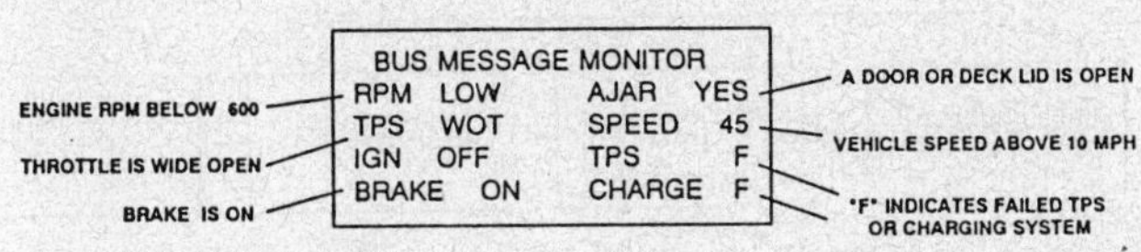


During any of the above conditions, the ASCM will decide to stop height correction. This is the normal program of the ASCM.

**NOTE: None of these messages indicates a failure of any air suspension component.**

The "AJAR" and "IGN" messages are from the vehicle's Body Controller. These messages represent what the Body Controller "thinks" the state of these switches is. For example, the brake message may say "ON" even though you are sure the brake pedal is not being depressed; or, the door ajar message may say "RR" (right rear door is ajar) even though you are sure it is not.

**NOTE: Disabling messages on the bus must be corrected before proceeding with fault diagnosis testing.**

**Fig. 35 Test 8A, test for "Disabling Bus Message" (Part 2 of 2). 1991 models**

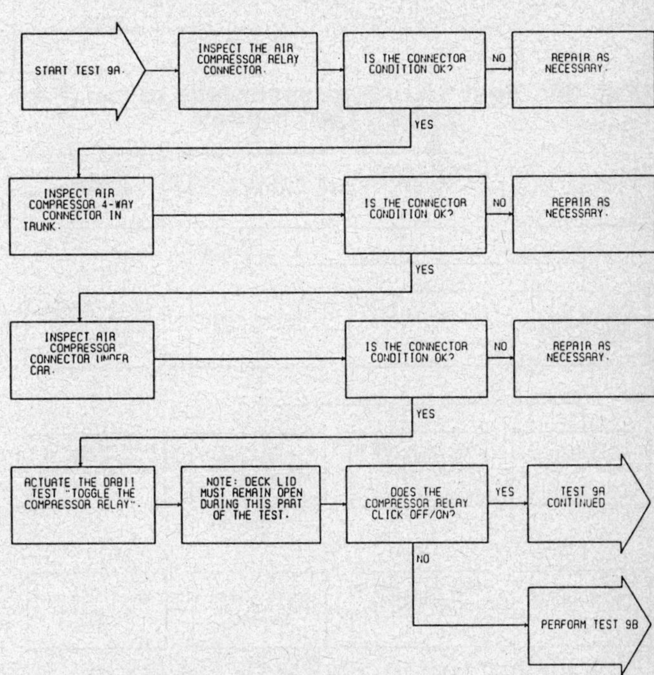


**Fig. 36 Test 9A, compressor fails to run (Part 1 of 2). 1991 models**

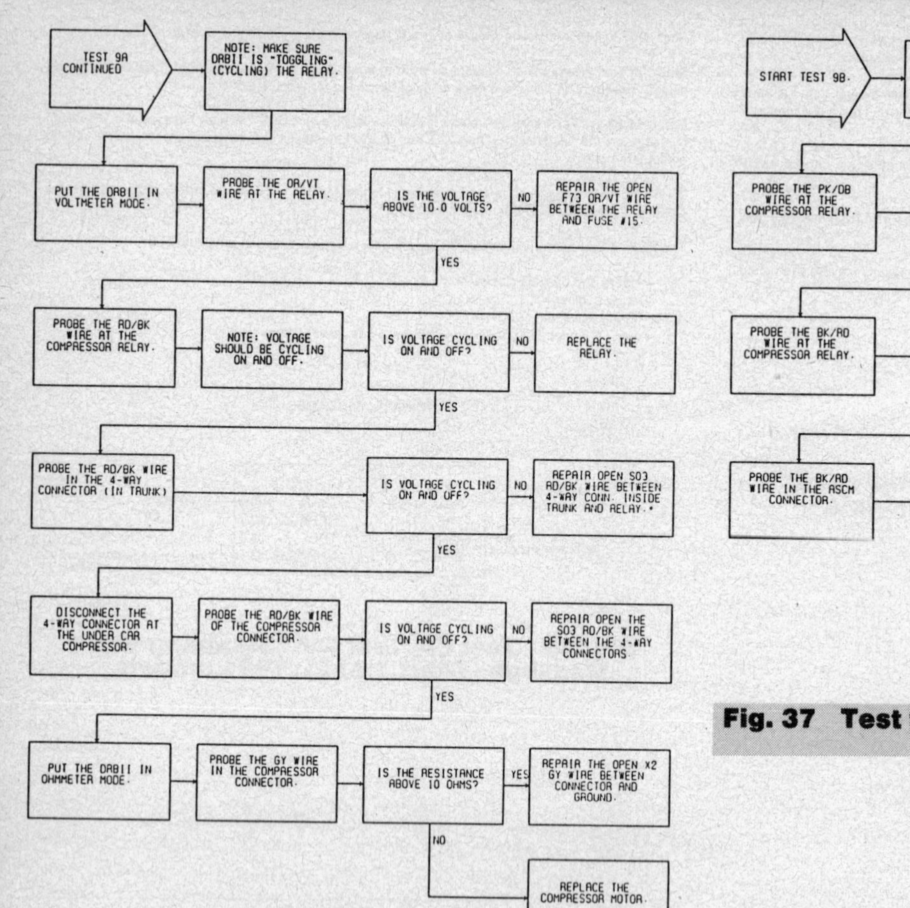


**Fig. 36 Test 9A, compressor fails to run (Part 2 of 2). 1991 models**

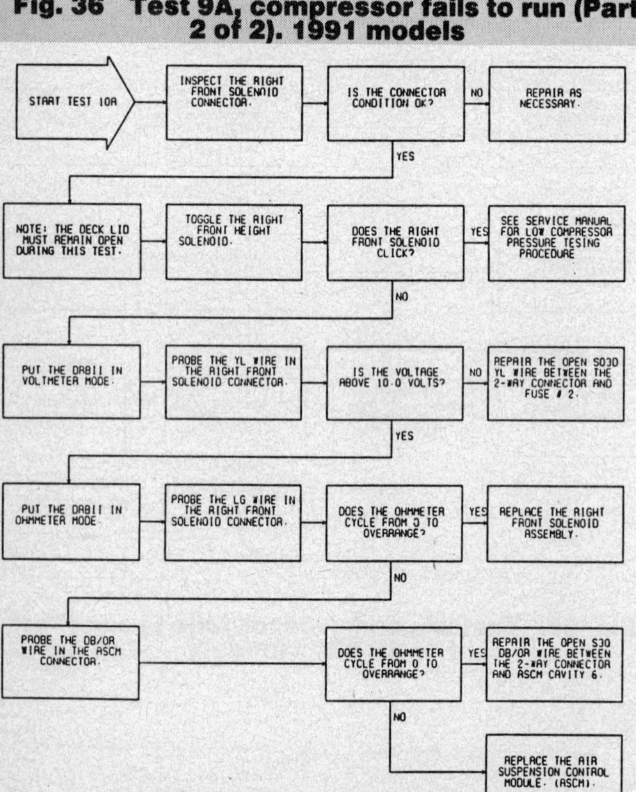


**Fig. 38 Test 10A, right front will not raise or lower. 1991 models**

START TEST 9B.
PUT THE DRBII IN VOLTMETER MODE.
PROBE THE PK/DB WIRE AT THE COMPRESSOR RELAY.
IS THE VOLTAGE ABOVE 10 VOLTS?
NO
REPAIR THE OPEN S03C PK/DB WIRE BETWEEN THE RELAY AND FUSE #2.
YES
PROBE THE BK/RD WIRE AT THE COMPRESSOR RELAY.
IS THE VOLTAGE ABOVE 10 VOLTS?
NO
REPLACE THE COMPRESSOR RELAY.
YES
PROBE THE BK/RD WIRE IN THE ASCM CONNECTOR.
IS THE VOLTAGE ABOVE 10 VOLTS?
NO
REPAIR THE OPEN S08 BK/RD WIRE BETWEEN THE RELAY AND ASCM CONNECTORS.
YES
REPLACE THE AIR SUSPENSION CONTROL MODULE (ASCM).

**Fig. 37 Test 9B, compressor fails to run. 1991 models**

START TEST 11A.
INSPECT THE AIR COMPRESSOR CONNECTOR UNDER CAR .
IS THE CONNECTOR CONDITION OK?
NO
REPAIR AS NECESSARY.
YES
NOTE: THE DECK LID MUST REMAIN OPEN DURING THIS TEST.
TOGGLE THE EXHAUST SOLENOID.
DOES THE EXHAUST SOLENOID CLICK?
YES
REPLACE THE AIR COMPRESSOR ASSEMBLY.
NO
PUT THE DRBII IN VOLTMETER MODE.
PROBE THE PK/DB WIRE IN THE 4-WAY CONNECTOR.
IS THE VOLTAGE ABOVE 10.0 VOLTS?
NO
REPAIR THE OPEN S03D PK/DB WIRE BETWEEN THE 4-WAY CONNECTOR AND FUSE # 2.
YES
PUT THE DRBII IN OHMMETER MODE.
PROBE THE BK/OR WIRE IN THE 4-WAY CONNECTOR.
DOES THE OHMMETER CYCLE FROM 0 TO OVERRANGE?
YES
REPLACE THE AIR COMPRESSOR ASSEMBLY.
NO
PROBE THE BK/OR WIRE IN THE ASCM CONNECTOR.
DOES THE OHMMETER CYCLE FROM 0 TO OVERRANGE?
YES
REPAIR THE OPEN S09 BK/OR WIRE BETWEEN THE 4-WAY CONNECTOR AND ASCM CAVITY 8.
NO
REPLACE THE AIR SUSPENSION CONTROL MODULE. (ASCM).

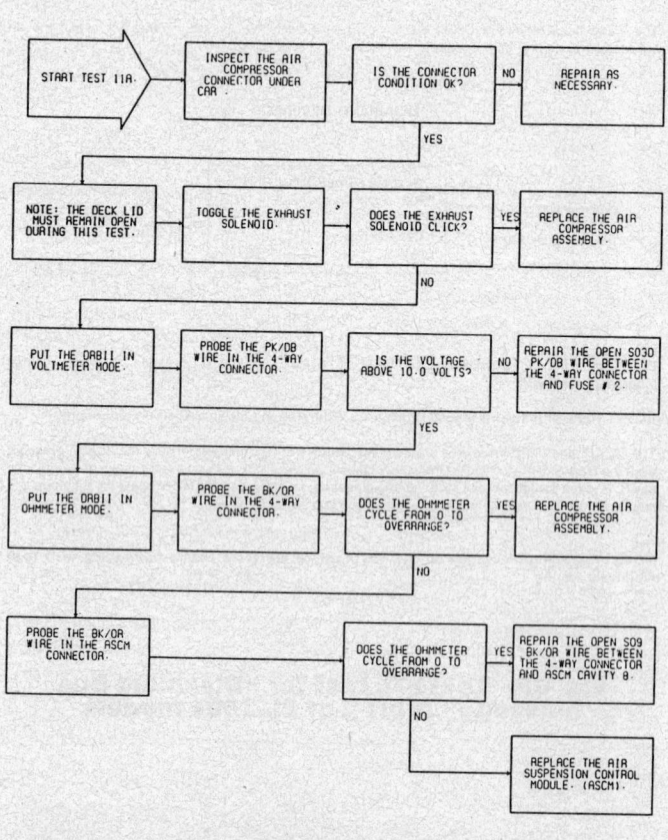

**Fig. 39 Test 11A, both front springs will not lower. 1991 models**

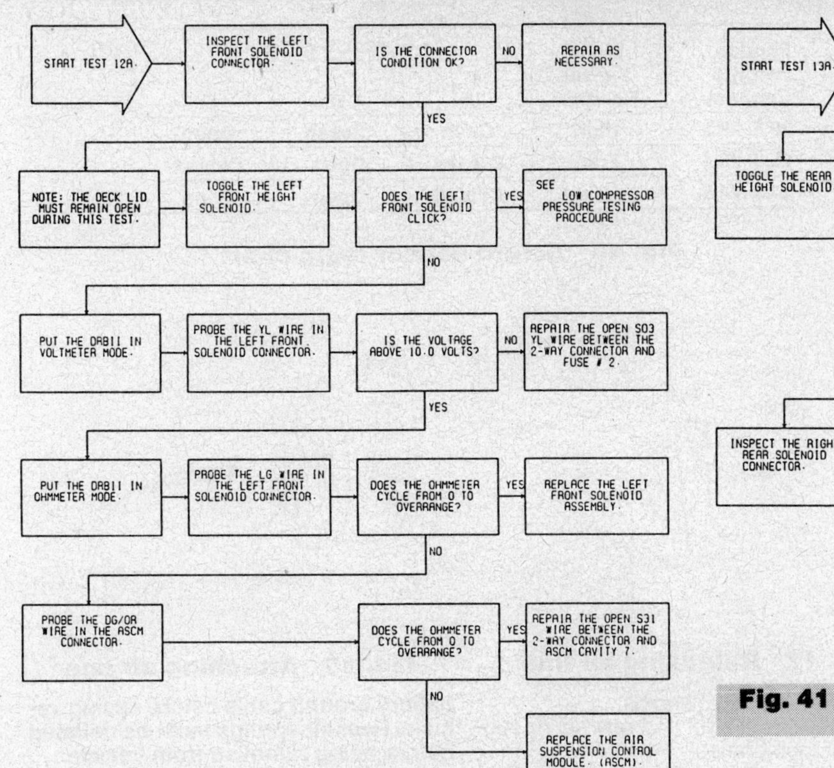


**Fig. 40 Test 12A, left front will not raise or lower. 1991 models**

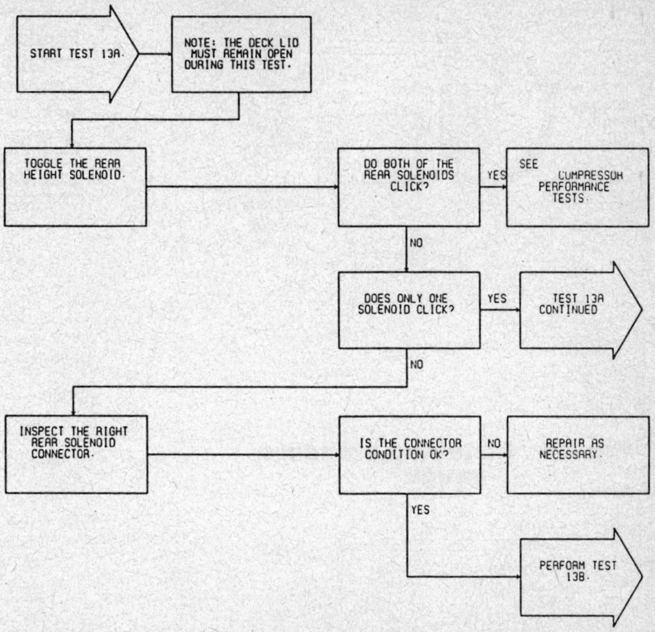

START TEST 13A.

NOTE: THE DECK LID MUST REMAIN OPEN DURING THIS TEST.

TOGGLE THE REAR HEIGHT SOLENOID.

DO BOTH OF THE REAR SOLENOIDS CLICK? — YES — SEE COMPRESSOR PERFORMANCE TESTS.

NO

DOES ONLY ONE SOLENOID CLICK? — YES — TEST 13A CONTINUED

NO

INSPECT THE RIGHT REAR SOLENOID CONNECTOR.

IS THE CONNECTOR CONDITION OK? — NO — REPAIR AS NECESSARY.

YES

PERFORM TEST 13B.

**Fig. 41 Test 13A, rear will not raise or lower (Part 1 of 2). 1991 models**

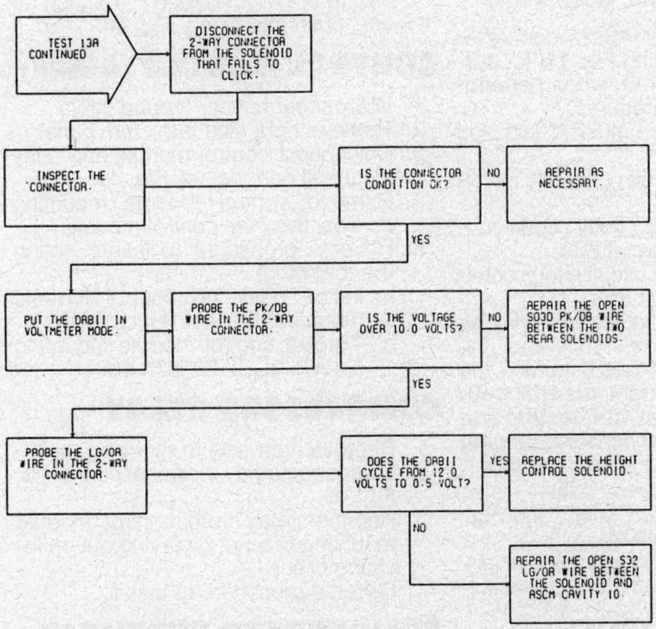

TEST 13A CONTINUED

DISCONNECT THE 2-WAY CONNECTOR FROM THE SOLENOID THAT FAILS TO CLICK.

INSPECT THE CONNECTOR.

IS THE CONNECTOR CONDITION OK? — NO — REPAIR AS NECESSARY.

YES

PUT THE DRBII IN VOLTMETER MODE.

PROBE THE PK/DB WIRE IN THE 2-WAY CONNECTOR.

IS THE VOLTAGE OVER 10.0 VOLTS? — NO — REPAIR THE OPEN S03D PK/DB WIRE BETWEEN THE TWO REAR SOLENOIDS.

YES

PROBE THE LG/OR WIRE IN THE 2-WAY CONNECTOR.

DOES THE DRBII CYCLE FROM 12.0 VOLTS TO 0.5 VOLT? — YES — REPLACE THE HEIGHT CONTROL SOLENOID.

NO

REPAIR THE OPEN S32 LG/OR WIRE BETWEEN THE SOLENOID AND ASCM CAVITY 10.

**Fig. 41 Test 13A, rear will not raise or lower (Part 2 of 2). 1991 models**

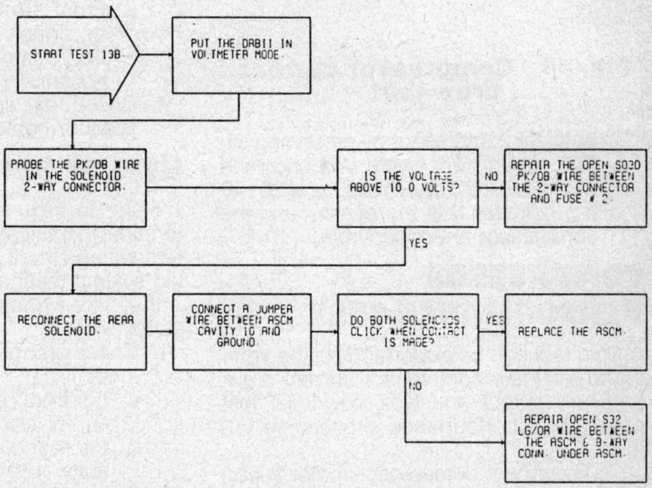

START TEST 13B.

PUT THE DRBII IN VOLTMETER MODE.

PROBE THE PK/DB WIRE IN THE SOLENOID 2-WAY CONNECTOR.

IS THE VOLTAGE ABOVE 10.0 VOLTS? — NO — REPAIR THE OPEN S03D PK/DB WIRE BETWEEN THE 2-WAY CONNECTOR AND FUSE # 2.

YES

RECONNECT THE REAR SOLENOID.

CONNECT A JUMPER WIRE BETWEEN ASCM CAVITY 10 AND GROUND.

DO BOTH SOLENOIDS CLICK WHEN CONTACT IS MADE? — YES — REPLACE THE ASCM.

NO

REPAIR OPEN S32 LG/OR WIRE BETWEEN THE ASCM & 8-WAY CONN. UNDER ASCM.

**Fig. 42 Test 13B, rear will not raise. 1991 models**

In Test 2, when you tried to raise either the front or rear of the car, the opposite end of the car also raised. This is a fault condition caused by one or both of the front solenoids allowing pressurized air to enter the air springs when they should be closed.

The solenoids may be stuck open by frozen water, dirt, or other foreign matter, or they may be held open electrically by the solenoid control wire shorted to ground.

Knowing this, do the following:

- Visually inspect the solenoids for foreign matter or seizure
- Inspect the solenoid control wires.

**Fig. 43 Test 14A, solenoid test. 1991 models**

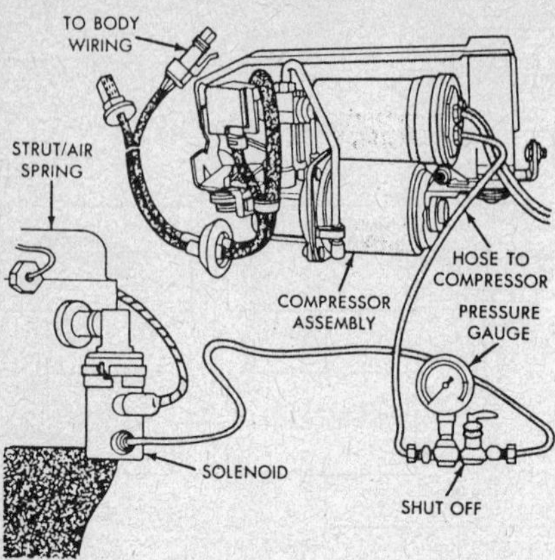


**Fig. 44 Installing pressure gauge**

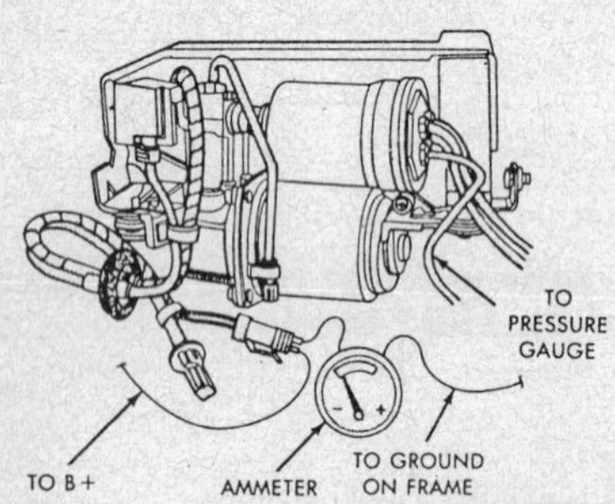


**Fig. 45 Compressor current draw test**

3. Activate compressor by grounding pin S08 to pin X20. Cycle unit and read actual air pressure. Pressure of 25-40 psi indicates that the system and the compressor are acceptable.

## COMPRESSOR PERFORMANCE TEST

This test can be performed on the vehicle to evaluate compressor current draw, pressure output and leak down. To test compressor performance, proceed as follows:

1. Disconnect compressor motor wiring harness.
2. Disconnect air line between dryer and strut or spring solenoid.
3. Connect a suitable air pressure gauge into the AAS system. Refer to "Residual Air Check."
4. Connect a suitable ampere meter in series between compressor connector red wire terminal and a 12 volt power source. Also connect a ground wire from compressor connector black terminal to an known good ground on frame, **Fig. 45.**
5. If compressor motor current draw exceeds 30 amps, replace compressor assembly.

## AIR LEAK CHECK

Use a soap and water solution or a liquid designed for leak detection.

1. Check all air line to connector joints:
   a. Air line to compressor connectors.
   b. Air line to solenoids.
2. Check front strut and rear spring rubber membranes.
3. Check solenoid to volume canister joint:
   a. Front strut to solenoid valve connections.
   b. Rear spring to solenoid valve connections.
4. Check air lines for ruptures, cuts, splits or heat damage.

| Fender Heights (Inches) | Mode Sensor Position | Sensor Signals | | |
|---|---|---|---|---|
| | | A | B | C |
| 28.5–29.9 | High | Open | Closed | Open |
| 25.9–26.5 | Trim | Closed | Open | Closed |
| 24.0–24.5 | Low | Closed | Open | Open |

**Fig. 46 Height sensor logic chart**

## HEIGHT SENSOR CHECK

Refer to **Fig. 10,** for ASCM connector terminal identification and **Fig. 11,** for system wiring circuit diagram when performing system testing procedures.

If sensor signal(s) are missing, proceed as follows:

1. Check ground circuit continuity as follows:
   a. For front ground circuit circuit continuity, check circuit S33.
   b. For rear ground circuit circuit continuity, X20 circuit S33.
2. If a open circuit is indicated, repair as necessary.
3. If continuity is indicated, replace the applicable strut or right rear shock absorber. **Complete circuit testing and check connectors before replacing a strut or right rear shock absorber.**
4. To measure resistance values, refer to "Initial Diagnostic Check" and **Fig. 46,** noting the following:
   a. Height sensor signals must be verified using a ohmmeter to measure resistance.
   b. Refer to **Fig. 46,** for sensor signal information.
   c. Measure resistance values by completing the circuit between the appropriate sensor pin and the appropriate ground pin.

## SYSTEM SERVICE

**Open trunk, door(s) or disconnect battery ground cable before raising vehicle. Rear air springs must be deflated before being removed from vehicle.**

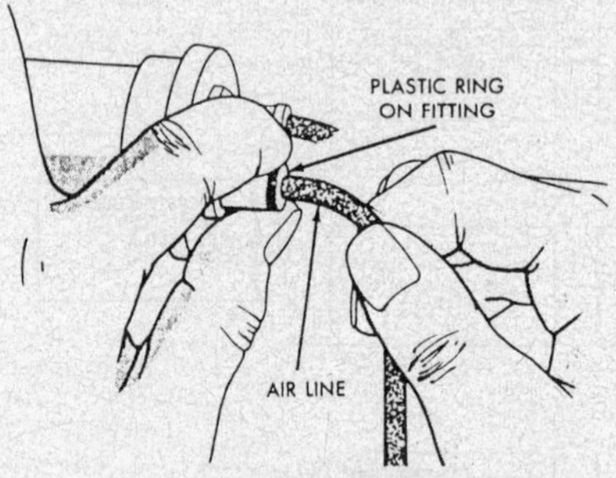


**Fig. 47 Releasing air line**

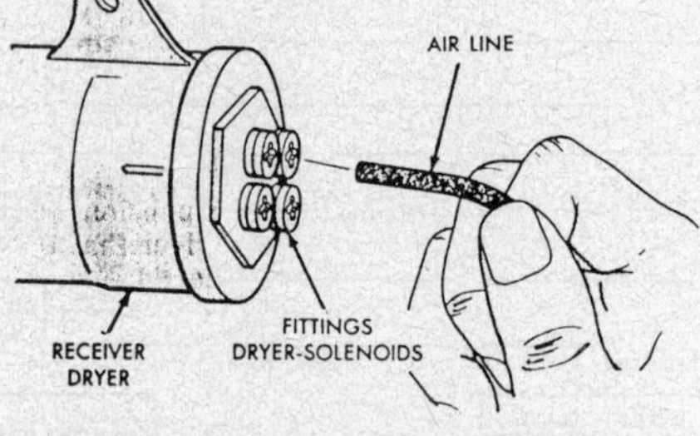


**Fig. 48 Attaching air line**

## AIR LINES

1. To release an air line from fitting, pull back on plastic ring, then remove line from fitting, **Fig. 47.**
2. Air line fittings have a push-in feature. A brass type collet locks the air line in place. One rubber O-ring seals the air line to prevent leakage. To attach air line, push into fitting, **Fig. 48.**

## CONTROL MODULE (ASCM)

1. Disconnect battery ground cable.
2. Remove right side trunk trim panel.
3. Disconnect control module and relay electrical connectors, **Fig. 49.**
4. Remove control module mounting screws, then the control module.
5. Reverse procedure to install, noting the following:
   a. Install relay on control module mounting bracket, if required.
   b. **Torque** control module mounting screws to 19-29 inch lbs.

## COMPRESSOR RELAY

1. Remove right side trunk trim panel.
2. Disconnect relay electrical connector, **Fig. 49.**
3. Remove relay from control module mounting bracket by prying out on locating clip.
4. Reverse procedure to install.

## COMPRESSOR ASSEMBLY

1. Disconnect battery ground cable.
2. Raise and support vehicle.
3. Remove cover from compressor assembly.
4. Disconnect air lines and electrical connectors. Refer to procedure outlined under "Air Lines" and **Fig. 50.**
5. Remove compressor assembly

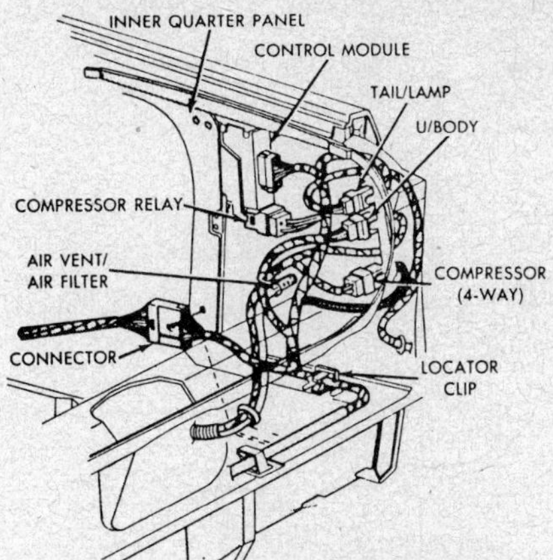


**Fig. 49 Removing control module (ASCM) & relay**

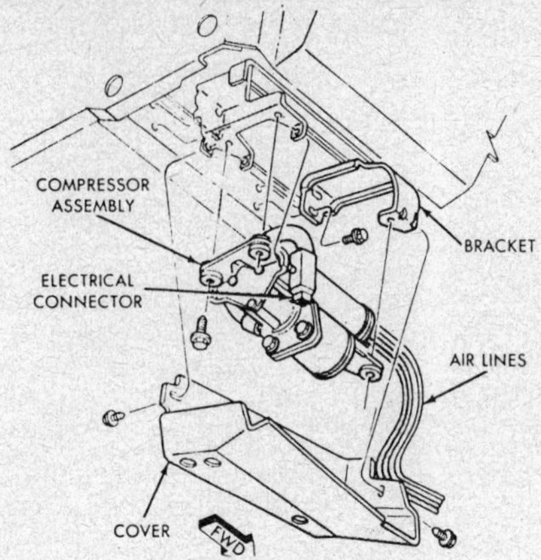


**Fig. 50 Removing compressor assembly**

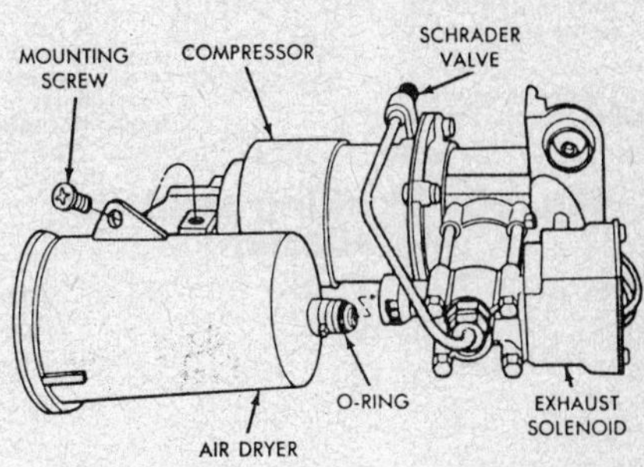


**Fig. 51 Removing & installing air dryer**

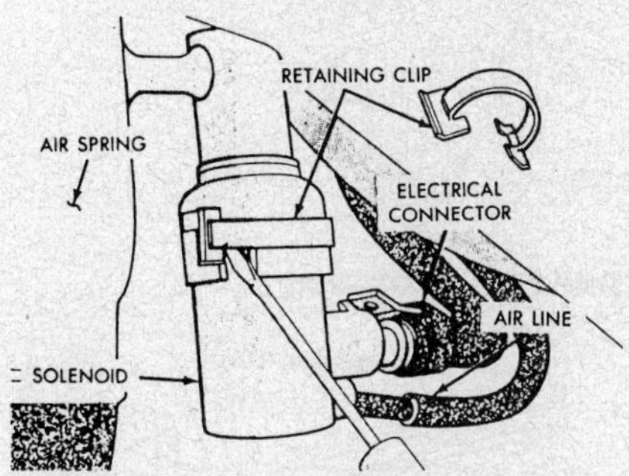


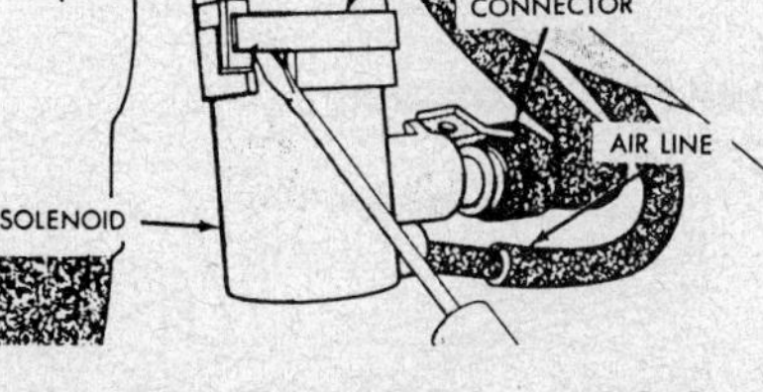

**Fig. 52 Removing retaining clips**

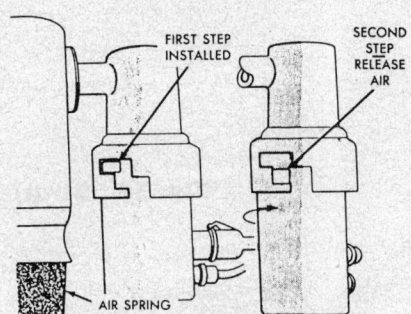

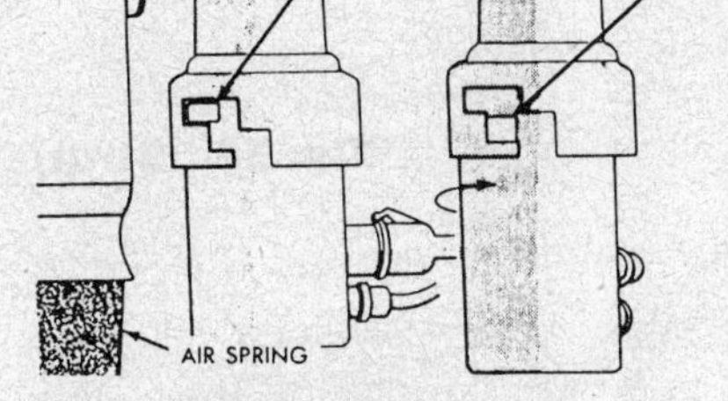


**Fig. 53 Releasing air pressure**

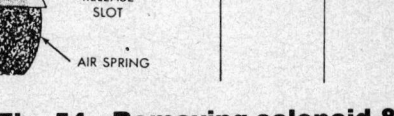

**Fig. 54 Removing solenoid & inspecting O-ring**

mounting screws, then the compressor assembly.

6. Remove mounting bracket screws, then slide mounting bracket away from compressor.
7. Reverse procedure to install, noting the following:
   a. **Torque** compressor mounting bracket screws to 70 inch lbs.
   b. **Torque** compressor assembly mounting screws to 70 inch lbs.
   c. **Torque** compressor cover mounting screws to 40 inch lbs.
   d. Check system operation.

## AIR DRYER

1. Remove compressor assembly. Refer to procedure outlined under "Compressor Assembly."
2. Remove air dryer mounting screw.
3. Rotate air dryer assembly 90° to release retaining tangs from exhaust solenoid housing, then remove air dryer assembly, **Fig. 51.**
4. Reverse procedure to install, noting the following:
   a. Inspect O-ring for damage and location on air dryer.
   b. Insert and index air dryer locking tangs into exhaust solenoid outlet.
   c. Rotate air dryer assembly to lock into position.

## SOLENOIDS

**Do not attempt to remove or install solenoids while the AAS system is supporting the vehicle.**

1. Disconnect battery ground cable.
2. Raise and support vehicle, then remove wheel and tire.
3. Disconnect solenoid electrical connector.
4. Disconnect air line. Refer to procedure outlined under "Air Lines." Solenoids have molded square tangs that fit into stepped notches of the air spring housing. The notches provide an air relief position and a retaining position. The retaining position is locked with a retaining clip.
5. Remove retaining clip, **Fig. 52.**
6. Rotate solenoid to second step in housing to allow air pressure to vent, **Fig. 53.**
7. Rotate solenoid to release slot, then remove solenoid, **Fig 54.**
8. Reverse procedure to install, noting the following:
   a. Inspect O-ring condition and position. O-ring can become dislodged during removal, **Fig. 54.**
   b. Install solenoid with tangs to top ledge of housing, then install retaining clip.

## STRUT DAMPER ASSEMBLY

### Removal

1. Disconnect battery ground cable.
2. Raise and support vehicle, then remove wheel and tire.
3. Disconnect air line. Refer to procedure outlined under "Air Lines."
4. Disconnect solenoid and height sensor electrical connectors.
5. Relieve air pressure, then remove solenoid. Refer to procedure outlined under "Solenoids."
6. Remove strut damper assembly as follows:
   a. Mark position of camber adjusting cam for proper alignment during installation, **Fig. 55.**
   b. Mark outline of strut on knuckle for proper alignment during installation, **Fig. 55.**
   c. Remove cam bolt, knuckle bolt or bolts, washer plate or plates and brake hose to damper bracket attaching screw, **Fig. 56.**
   d. **On all models,** remove strut damper to fender shield attaching nut and washer assemblies.
   e. Remove strut damper from vehicle.

### Disassembly & Assembly

Disassembly is limited to upper mount and bearing housing. The strut shock absorber, air spring with internal height sensor, solenoid and wiring harness are serviced as an assembly.

1. Using a suitable tool, hold retaining plate locking washer in place, then remove strut rod nut.
2. Remove locking washer retainer plate, spacer, flat washer and mount/bearing housing assembly, **Fig. 57.**
3. Reverse procedure to assemble. Using a suitable tool, hold retaining plate locking washer in place, then **torque** strut rod nut to 55 ft. lbs.

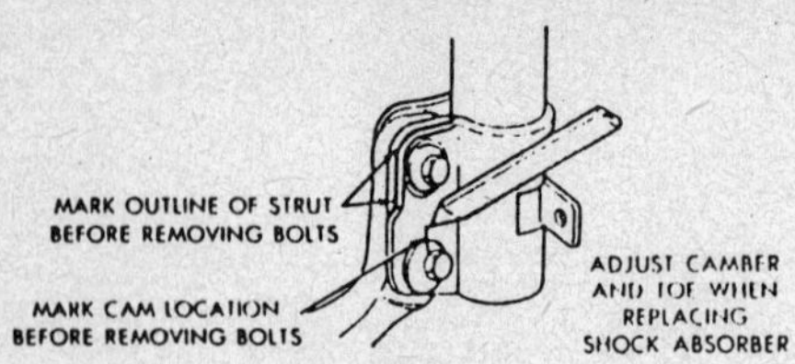


**Fig. 55 Marking strut for installation**

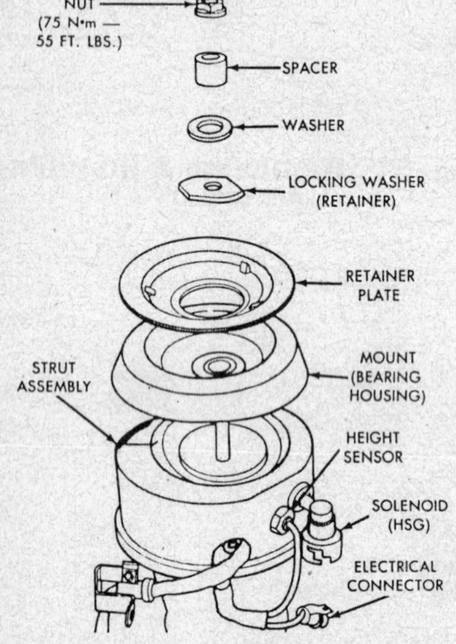


**Fig. 57 Air strut upper mount assembly**

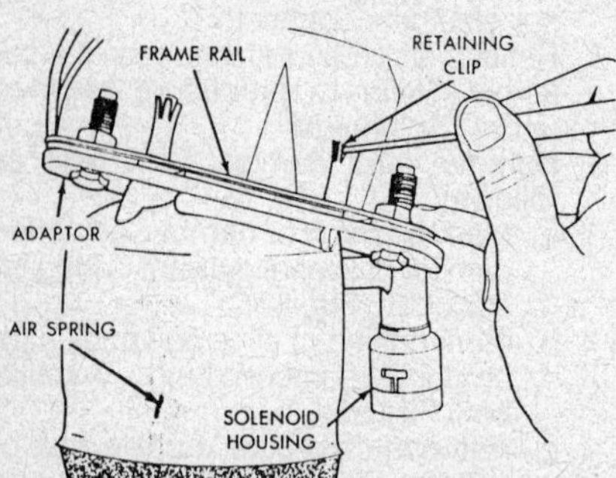


**Fig. 58 Releasing retaining clips**

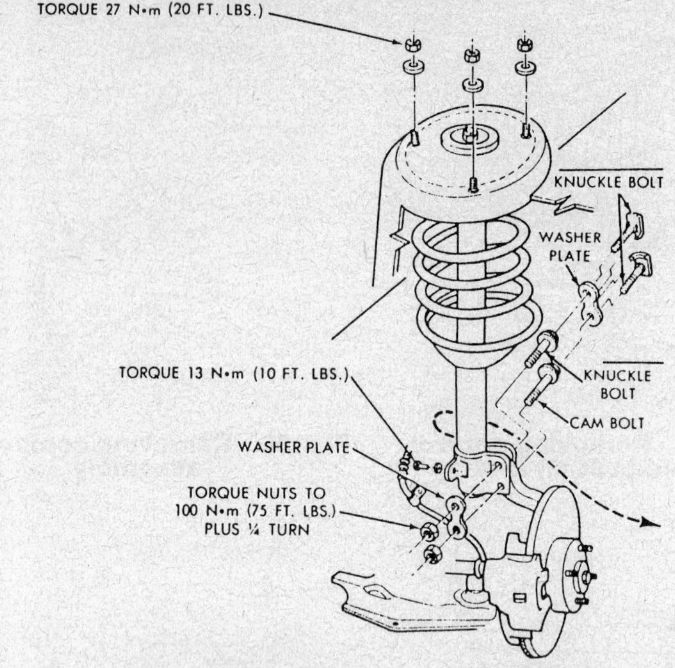


**Fig. 56 Strut/damper replacement**

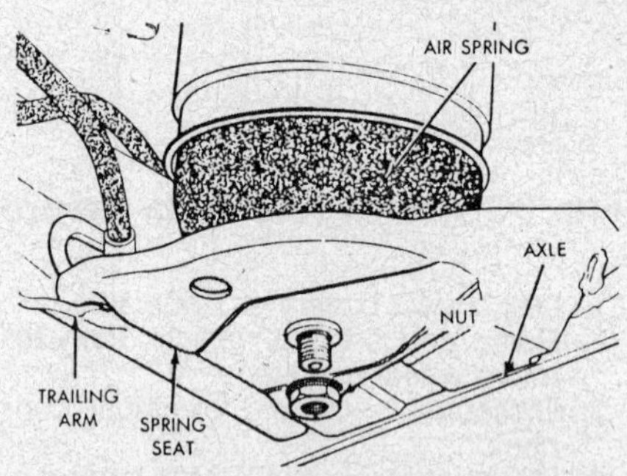


**Fig. 59 Removing & installing lower spring to axle nut**

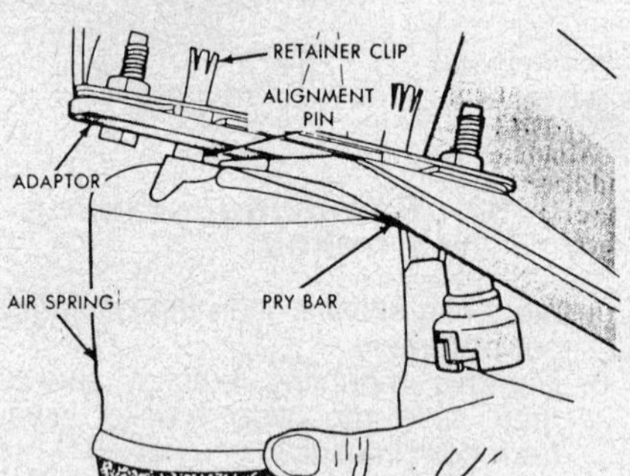


**Fig. 60 Removing rear air spring assembly**

### Installation

1. Install strut damper assembly as follows:
   a. Position strut assembly into fender reinforcement, then install retaining nuts and washers and **torque** to 20 ft. lbs.
   b. Position steering knuckle and washer plate to strut, then install cam and through bolts.
   c. Install brake hose retainer on damper, then index alignment marks made during removal.
   d. Position a four inch or larger C-clamp on steering knuckle and strut, then tighten clamp just enough to eliminate any looseness between strut and knuckle. Check alignment of marks made during removal. **Torque** cam bolt nuts to 75 ft. lbs, then advance nuts an additional 1/4 turn. Remove C-clamp.
2. Install solenoid. Refer to procedure outlined under "Solenoids."
3. Connect solenoid and height sensor connectors.
4. Charge (inflate) air spring. Refer to procedure outlined under "Recharging Air Springs" to activate spring solenoid and air compressor. Add air for 60 seconds.

## RECHARGING AIR SPRINGS

1. To activate compressor, ground pin S08 to pin X20.
2. To activate left front spring solenoid, ground pin S31 to pin X20.
3. To activate right front spring solenoid, ground pin S30 to pin X20.
4. To activate right rear spring solenoid, ground pin S32 to pin X20.

## REAR AIR SPRINGS

### Removal

1. Disconnect battery ground cable.
2. Raise and support vehicle, then remove wheel and tire assembly.
3. Disconnect solenoid electrical connector and air line. Refer to procedure outlined under "Air Lines."
4. Relieve air pressure, then remove solenoid. Refer to procedure outlined under "Solenoids."
5. Release upper air spring alignment/retaining clips, **Fig. 58.**
6. Remove lower spring to axle nut, **Fig. 59.**
7. Pry assembly down and pull alignment studs through retaining clips, **Fig. 60,** then remove rear air spring assembly.

### Installation

1. Position rear air spring assembly lower stud into axle seat and upper alignment pins through frame rail adapter.
2. Install upper retaining clips.
3. Install lower spring to axle nut. Do not torque nut.

4. Install solenoid, then connect air line and electrical connector.
5. Charge (inflate) air spring. Refer to procedure outlined under ""Recharging Air Springs." Add air for 60 seconds.
6. After inflating air spring, **torque** lower spring to axle nut to 50 ft. lbs.
7. Install wheel and tire, lower vehicle and connect battery ground cable.

## RIGHT REAR SHOCK ABSORBER (W/HEIGHT SENSOR)

1. Disconnect battery ground cable.
2. Raise and support vehicle, then remove wheel and tire.
3. Disconnect height sensor electrical connector located on right rear frame rail.
4. Remove shock absorber as follows:
   a. Support rear axle.
   b. Remove upper and lower shock absorber fasteners, then the shock absorber.
5. Reverse procedure to install, noting the following:
   a. **Torque** upper shock absorber fasteners to 45 ft. lbs.
   b. Route height sensor wire through retaining clips, then secure to fuel filler tub e with a tie strap.
   c. With suspension supporting vehicle, **torque** lower shock absorber fastener to 40 ft. lbs.

# Variable Damping Suspension

## INDEX



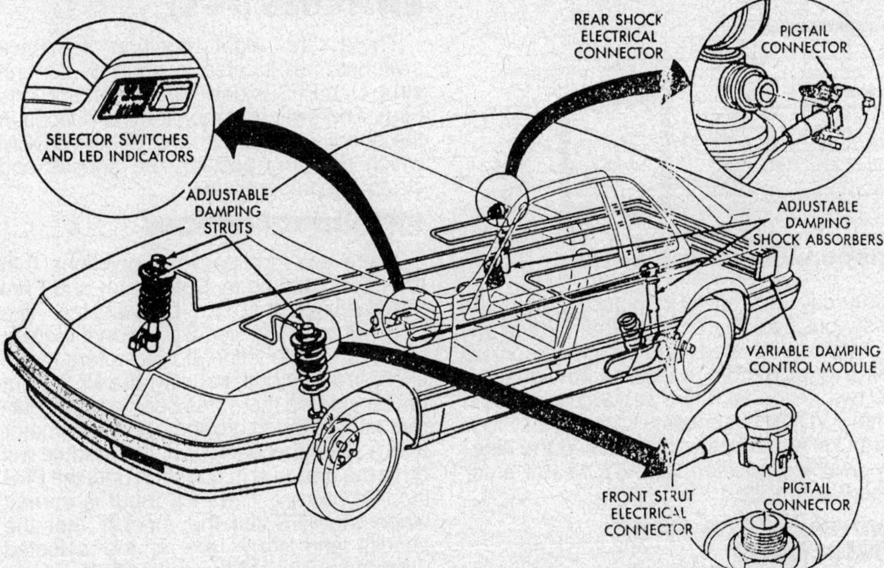


**Fig. 1 Variable damping suspension components**

## DESCRIPTION

The Variable Damping Suspension (VDS) system, **Fig. 1,** allows the driver to select between three different suspension calibrations; Firm, Normal or Soft, whenever the ignition switch is On.

Suspension control is provided by an electric motor driven valve in each strut and shock absorber that can change the fluid bypass orifices in each unit. The size of the fluid orifices are varied to obtain the three suspension calibrations. The VDS system only controls vehicle ride and does not control vehicle height.

The VAS system consists of variable damping struts and shock absorbers, a Variable Damping Control Module (VDCM) and selector switches.

## SYSTEM COMPONENTS

### VARIABLE DAMPING CONTROL MODULE (VDCM)

The VDCM is used to monitor and control the VDS system. The VDCM has one 25-way connector and is attached to a bracket in the lefthand side of the trunk. The diagnostic connector is also located in the trunk. The VDCM uses a 6-way connector to access DRB II diagnostics. The VDS system, including the VDCM, is grounded at the left rear quarter panel inside the trunk (circuit Z02A), **Fig. 2.**.

#### VDCM Inputs

The VDCM receives power from the battery through the ignition switch (circuit F20A).

The VDCM receives information from two selector switches located on the center console. The position of these switches tell the module which damping position has been selected.

The VDCM also monitors and receives information from eight Position Feedback Switches (PFS). Two PFS are located in each shock/strut. These switches indicate the present damping position of the shocks/struts.

#### VDCM Outputs

The VDCM controls four small electric motors. One motor is located in each shock/strut. These motors vary the sizes of the fluid orifices in the shock/struts to achieve the different damping positions.

The VDCM also controls three LEDs on the switch bezel in the center console which indicate the present setting of the VDS system. The VDCM dims the LEDs when the headlamps are On and brightens the LEDs when the headlamps are Off. The VDCM uses the park lamp dim input (pin 14) to determine is the headlamps are On or Off. The LEDs are also used to inform if a system fault occurs.

#### VDCM Reset

The VDCM has a volatile memory and will reset whenever the ignition is turned On. When the VDCM is reset it will: Clear the VDCM memory of any faults; Read selector switch inputs; Attempt to drive the

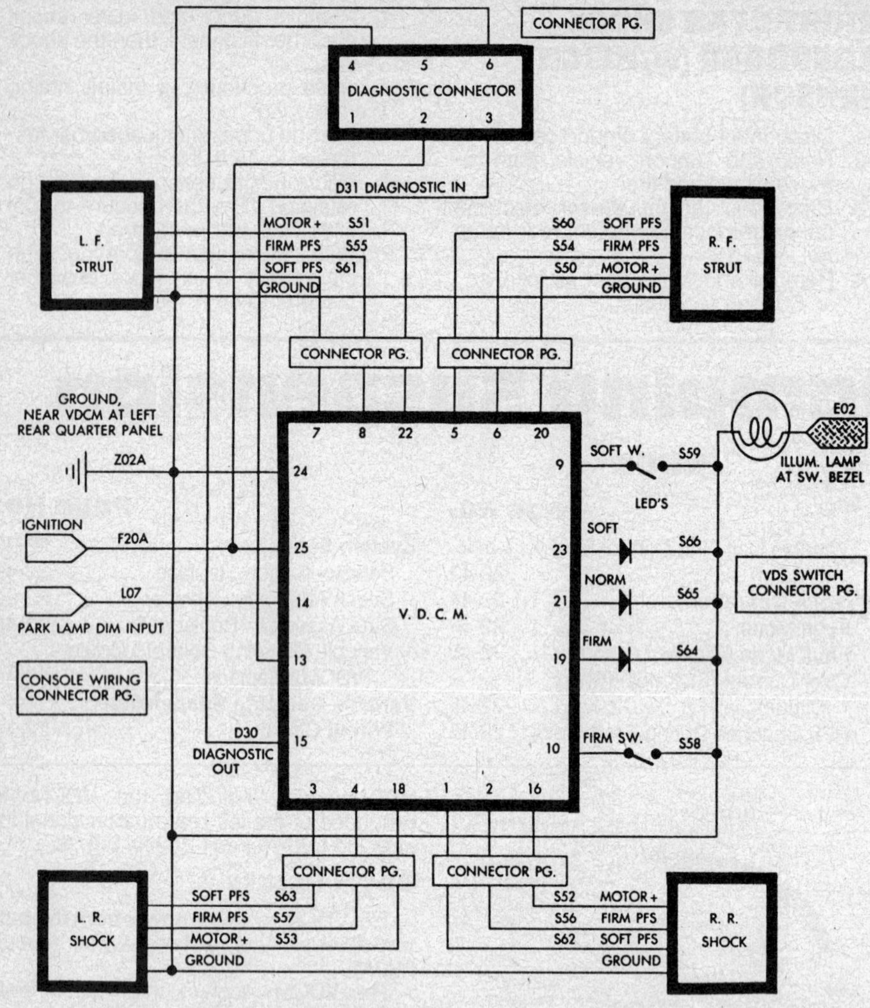


**Fig. 2 Variable damping suspension wiring circuit**

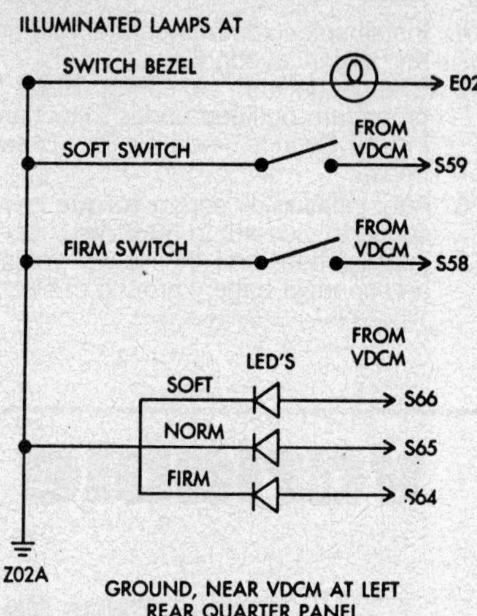


**Fig. 3 Selector switch wiring circuit**

motors in the shocks/struts to the selected damping position if they are not already in the selected position.

The VDCM can be reset two additional ways. First, by grounding the diagnostic input pin (pin 13) for three seconds, then ungrounding the pin and allowing the voltage to return to normal (5 volts). Second, by exiting the DRB II VDS diagnostic routine.

## SELECTOR SWITCHES

There are two selector switches located on the center console. On Soft and one Firm switch. When the VDCM senses that neither switch is activated (pins 9 and 10 both reading 5 volts) it will automatically choose the Norm setting. Vehicle ride behavior is selected with the appropriate switch; soft button down for Soft, both buttons up for Norm, firm button down for Firm. An LED illuminates to indicate the selected position.

### Selector Switch Input Changes

If the selector switch input changes and no faults are present, the VDCM will illuminate the LED for the new selection. The VDCM will then attempt to drive all four motors (inside the shocks/struts) to the new position. If the system is functioning correctly and all four motors obtain the new position, the LED for that setting will remain illuminated. The typical response time for all motors to reach a new position is two seconds. If two seconds pass and the VDCM senses that the four shocks/struts have not obtained the newly selected position, the VDCM will enter the Fault mode.

### Norm, Soft & Firm Selections

If neither the Soft or Firm switch is closed, the module will illuminate the Norm LED and drive the motors to the Norm setting. The LED illuminating means a damping selection was received by the module. The brightness of the switch bezel display is controlled by circuit E02 from the headlamp switch, **Fig. 3.**

## SHOCKS & STRUTS

Internally, each shock and strut, **Fig. 4,** has a Soft position feedback switch, a Firm position feedback switch, a motor and fluid bypass orifices. The position feedback switches monitor the position of the motor. The switches then supply this information to the VDCM. The motor varies the size of the fluid orifices in the shocks and struts to achieve the three different damping settings. At the top of each shock and strut is a connector which electrically connects it to the VDCM.

## POSITION FEEDBACK SWITCHES (PFS)

There are eight position feedback switches, two located in each shock and strut. One PFS is designated Soft and one Firm. The switches monitor the orifices in the shocks and struts and tell the VDCM which damping position the shocks and struts are presently in.

### PFS Input Changes

There are four possible positions that the PFS could be in. Soft, Norm and Firm are positions that can be selected. The PFS will be in the Illegal position if there is a system malfunction. If the motors in the shocks/struts drift, causing the PFS input to change and there has been no over current fault (short to ground or internal motor short) since the last Reset, the module will drive the motor(s) in question until the PFS input is correct. The PFS input is correct when the PFS tell the module that the shocks and struts are in the selected damping position. If two seconds pass and PFS input is still incorrect, the module will enter the Fault mode.

Refer to **Fig. 5,** for voltages of the PFS circuits when the shocks/struts are in the various positions. The pin numbers refer to the pins at the VDCM 25-way connector, **Fig. 6.**

## SYSTEM OPERATION

The VDS system is controlled by the VDCM which operates on battery voltage supplied through the ignition switch. This system uses stand alone diagnostics which can be accessed using the DRB II diagnostic tester.

The vehicle's ride setting is selected by operating one of two switches on the center console. When a new damping position

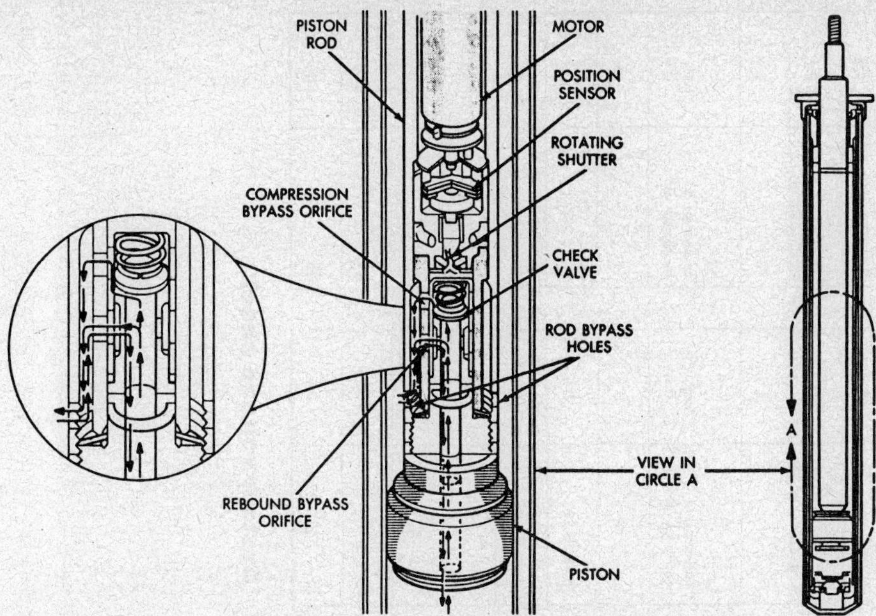


Fig. 4 Shock/strut assembly

| Shock/Strut Setting | Position Feedback Switch Circuits | |
|---|---|---|
| | Soft - Pins 1-RR, 3-LR 5-RF and 7-LF | Firm - Pins 2-RR, 4-LR, 6-RF and 8-LF |
| Soft | 0 volts | 5 volts |
| Norm | 0 volts | 0 volts |
| Firm | 5 volts | 0 volts |
| ILLEGAL | 5 volts | 5 volts |

**Fig. 5 PFS system voltages**

(Soft) is selected, the VDCM will:

1. Sense that the Soft selector switch circuit is grounded.
2. Illuminate the Soft LED.
3. Check the settings of the shocks and struts, via the PFS.
4. Drive the motors (inside the shocks and struts) that are not in the selected position to the selected position.
5. Keep the LED illuminated when all four shocks/struts reach the selected position.
6. Continue to monitor selector switch inputs and PFS inputs for changes.

If a system failure occurs, the Norm LED will flash for approximately one minute and then go out. The system will then enter the Fault mode. The vehicle can be driven with the VDS system inoperative.

## FAULT MODE

In the Fault mode the VDCM will turn Off whichever LED was illuminated and attempt to drive all four motors to the Default position. **The Norm position is used as the Default position.** The module will then flash the Norm LED for approximately one minute, then no LED will be illuminated. During the LED flashing, the VDCM attempts to drive any motor which is not in the Default position to the Default position.

## FAULT MODE CHANGE LOCKOUT

During the Fault mode, whenever the selector switch input changes, the LED for that selector will not illuminate. The Norm LED will flash for approximately one minute, then go out. During the LED flashing, the VDCM attempts to drive any motor which is not in the Default position to the Default position. All changes are locked out during the fault mode until the next module Reset. **Changes are not locked out while in the diagnostic mode.**

## OVER CURRENT SHUTDOWN (SHORT CIRCUIT)

An over current shutdown will occur if there is a short circuit in a motor or a short to ground. Over current shutdown is put into effect if any over current condition is detected by the VDCM. There are three differences between the Fault mode and over current shutdown. During an over current shutdown condition the VDCM will:

1. Immediately stop driving all motors.
2. The module will not attempt to drive the motors to the Default (Norm) position.
3. The Norm LED will not flash.

The VDCM never attempts to drive the motors during an over current condition and all changes are locked out until the next module Reset.

## PFS CHANGES DURING FAULT MODE

If, while in the Fault mode, the VDCM detects a drift or change of PFS input, the VDCM will attempt to drive the motors which are not in the Default position to the Default position. The VDCM will stop driving the motors when they all reach the Default position or when the Norm LED has stopped flashing (approximately one minute).

## DIAGNOSIS

Refer to **Figs. 2, 6, 7 and 8,** during VDS system diagnosis.

## W/DRB II

The DRB II can only detect the faults for the damper setting that the VDS system is currently in. In order to properly test the system, the selector switches must be used to put the system in each of the three damping settings.

Connect the DRB II to diagnostic connector located in the vehicles trunk, **Figs. 9 and 10.** Follow manufacture's instructions for use of the tool.

### Change Of Selected Position While In Diagnostics

If the selector switches are changed to a new position while in diagnostics, the system will try to go to the new position and will report faults only for the new position. System changes are not locked out during diagnostics. Any previous faults are cleared and only faults for the current damping position selected are reported.

The following example illustrates the diagnostic output with Firm being the selected damping position and the right front strut and left rear shock not operating correctly. The right front strut is stuck in the Soft position and the left rear shock gives Illegal sensor output. The same diagnostic output continues until a change occurs in the system. The change could come from the fault being repaired, selector switch position changing or a PFS drifting out of position. When a change occurs, the diagnostic output will show only the current status of the system.

1. Firm is the selected position (Firm switch grounded).
2. Left front and right rear PFS indicate Firm.
3. Right front PFS indicates Soft.
4. Left rear PFS indicates Illegal.

By pressing the Soft selector switch, the left front and right rear will go to the Soft position (if they are working correctly). The right front is still in the Soft position, but will not be detected as a fault because Soft is the selected position. The left rear continues to indicate an Illegal condition. The diagnostic output changes as the system changes. The DRB II now indicates that the left rear is the only **present** failure.

### Special Over current Shutdown Diagnostic Routine

If an over current condition is detected as a short in one of the shock/strut motor(s) circuit(s), the VDCM will report the shock/strut(s) which has the over current. It will be necessary to repair any over currents and Reset the VDCM before the module can diagnose any other faults. **An over current shutdown condition takes precedence over the normal diagnostic routine.** The VDCM will return to the nor-

1 2 3 4 5 6 7 8 9 10 11 12 13 14 15 16 17 18 19 20 21 22 23 24 25

VIEW FROM WIRE END

| Cav | Circuit | Gauge | Color | Function |
|---|---|---|---|---|
| 1 | S62 | 20 | TN | Soft PFS - RR |
| 2 | S56 | 20 | YL/BK* | Firm PFS - RR |
| 3 | S63 | 20 | LG | Soft PFS - LR |
| 4 | S57 | 20 | YL | Firm PFS - LR |
| 5 | S60 | 20 | DB | Soft PFS - RF |
| 6 | S54 | 20 | BR | Firm PFS - RF |
| 7 | S61 | 20 | BK | Soft PFS - LF |
| 8 | S55 | 20 | DB/YL* | Firm PFS - LF |
| 9 | S59 | 20 | PK/BK* | Soft Selector Switch |
| 10 | S58 | 20 | PK | Firm Selector Switch |
| 11 | - | - | - | Not Used |
| 12 | - | - | - | Not Used |
| 13 | D31 | 20 | TN/BK* | Diagnostic Input Pin |
| 14 | L07 | 18 | BK/YL* | Park Lamp Dim Input |
| 15 | D30 | 20 | LG/BK* | Diagnostic Output Pin |
| 16 | S52 | 20 | RD | Shock Motor - RR |
| 17 | - | - | - | Not Used |
| 18 | S53 | 20 | WT/BK* | Shock Motor - LR |
| 19 | S64 | 20 | DG | Firm LED |
| 20 | S50 | 20 | LB | Strut Motor - RF |
| 21 | S65 | 20 | VT | Normal LED |
| 22 | S51 | 20 | LB/BK* | Strut Motor - LF |
| 23 | S66 | 20 | VT/WT* | Soft LED |
| 24 | Z02A | 18 | BK/LG* | Ground |
| 25 | F20A | 18 | WT | Ignition |

**Fig. 6 Control module connector identification**

| NORM | | SOFT | | FIRM | |
|---|---|---|---|---|---|
| Pin(s) | Voltage | Pin(s) | Voltage | Pin(s) | Voltage |
| 1,3,5,7 | 0 v | 1,3,5,7 | 0 v | 1,3,5,7 | 5 v |
| 2,4,6,8 | 0 v | 2,4,6,8 | 5 v | 2,4,6,8 | 0 v |
| 9 | 5 v | 9 | 0 v | 9 | 5 v |
| 10 | 5 v | 10 | 5 v | 10 | 0 v |
| 13 | 5 v | 13 | 5 v | 13 | 5 v |
| 14<br>headlamps on<br>headlamps off | <br>batt. v<br>0 v | 14<br>headlamps on<br>headlamps off | <br>batt. v<br>0 v | 14<br>headlamps on<br>headlamps off | <br>batt. v<br>0 v |
| 15 | 5 v | 15 | 5 v | 15 | 5 v |
| 16,18,20,22 | 0 v | 16,18,20,22 | 0 v | 16,18,20,22 | 0 v |
| 19 | 0 v | 19 | 0 v | 19 | 2 v |
| 21 | 2 v | 21 | 0 v | 21 | 0 v |
| 23 | 0 v | 23 | 2 v | 23 | 0 v |
| 24 | batt. v | 24 | batt. v | 24 | batt. v |
| 25 | 0 v | 25 | 0 v | 25 | 0 v |

**Fig. 7 System voltage checks**

DIAGNOSTIC CONNECTOR - blue

Location:

G-body, in trunk under scuff plate.
J-body, in trunk near V.D.C.M.

| Cavity | Circuit | Gauge | Color | Function |
|---|---|---|---|---|
| 1 | — | — | — | Not Used |
| 2 | F20B | 18 | WT | Ignition |
| 3 | D31 | 20 | TN/BK* | Diagnostic Input Pin |
| 4 | D30 | 20 | LG/BK* | Diagnostic Output Pin |
| 5 | — | — | — | Not Used |
| 6 | Z20B | 20 | BK/LG* | Ground |

SHOCK TO BODY HARNESS CONNECTORS (4)

Location: In trunk on right side.

black   grey

RIGHT

| Cavity | Circuit | Gauge | Color | Function |
|---|---|---|---|---|
| 1 | Z02C | 20 | BK/LG* | Shock Motor Ground, left rear |
| 2 | S53 | 20 | WT/BK* | Shock Motor +, left rear |
| 3 | S57 | 20 | YL | Firm PFS, left rear |
| 4 | S63 | 20 | LG | Soft PFS, left rear |

Location: In trunk on left side.

black   grey

LEFT

| Cavity | Circuit | Gauge | Color | Function |
|---|---|---|---|---|
| 1 | Z02E | 20 | BK/LG* | Shock Motor Ground, right rear |
| 2 | S52 | 20 | RD | Shock Motor +, right rear |
| 3 | S56 | 20 | YL/BK* | Firm PFS, right rear |
| 4 | S62 | 20 | TN | Soft PFS, right rear |

STRUT - TWO 4-WAY CONNECTORS - black
Locations: 1 left side strut tower.
1 right side strut tower.

LEFT 6 5 2 1-A   RIGHT 4 8 7 1-B

8-WAY CONNECTOR TO ENGINE WIRING black

Location: Right side kick panel near body controller

The wiring is routed from the struts to their respective 4-ways and then combined at the 8-way.

| Cavity | Circuit | Gauge | Color | Function |
|---|---|---|---|---|
| 1 | Z02F | 20 | BK/LG* | Ground |
| 1-B | Z02B | 20 | BK/LG* | Ground |
| 1-A | Z02A | 20 | BK/LG* | Ground |
| 2 | S61 | 20 | BK | Soft PFS, left front |
| 3 | — | — | — | Not Used |
| 4 | S50 | 20 | LB | Strut Motor, right front |
| 5 | S55 | 20 | DB/YL* | Firm PFS, left front |
| 6 | S51 | 20 | LB/BK* | Strut Motor, left front |
| 7 | S54 | 20 | DB | Soft PFS, right front |
| 8 | S60 | 20 | BR | Firm PFS, right front |

**Fig. 8 System connector identification (Part 1 of 2)**

CONSOLE WIRING CONNECTOR - black

Location: On floor under driver's seat.

| Cavity | Circuit | Gauge | Color | Function |
|---|---|---|---|---|
| 1 | F20 | 18 | WT | Ignition |
| 2 | E02 | 20 | OR | Illuminated Lamp at Switch Bezel |
| 3 | L07 | 18 | BK/YL* | Park Lamp Dim Input |

VARIABLE DAMPING SUSPENSION SWITCH CONNECTOR - black
Location: Under center console.

| Cavity | Circuit | Gauge | Color | Function |
|---|---|---|---|---|
| 1 | S59 | 20 | PK/BK* | Soft Selector Switch |
| 2 | Z02D | 20 | BK/LG* | Ground |
| 3 | S58 | 20 | PK | Firm Selector Switch |
| 4 | E02 | 20 | OR | Illuminated Lamp at Switch Bezel |
| 5 | S66 | 20 | VT/WT* | Soft LED |
| 6 | S65 | 20 | VT | Norm LED |
| 7 | S64 | 20 | DG | Firm LED |

**Fig. 8 System connector identification (Part 2 of 2)**

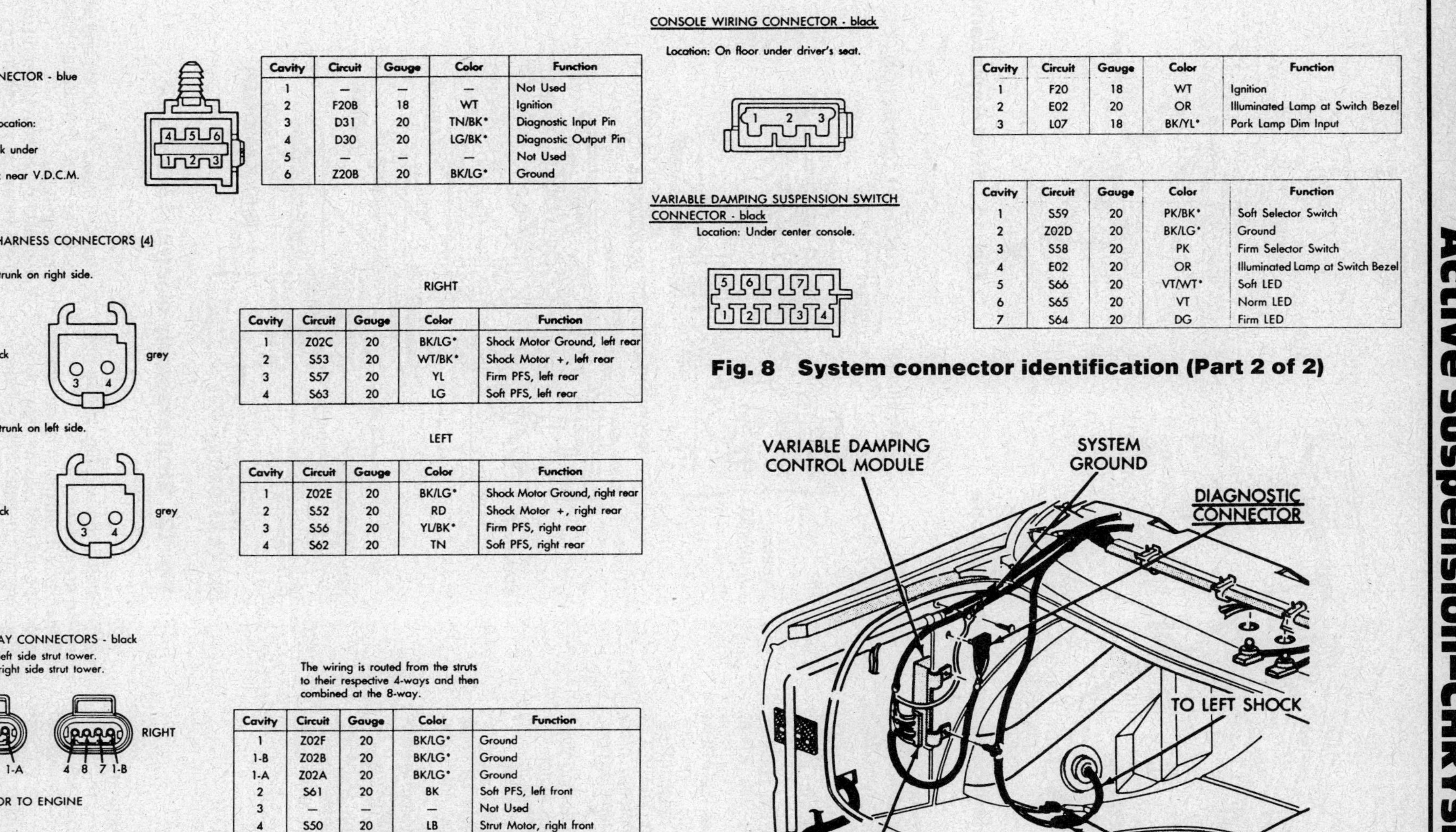


**Fig. 9 Diagnostic connector. LeBaron**

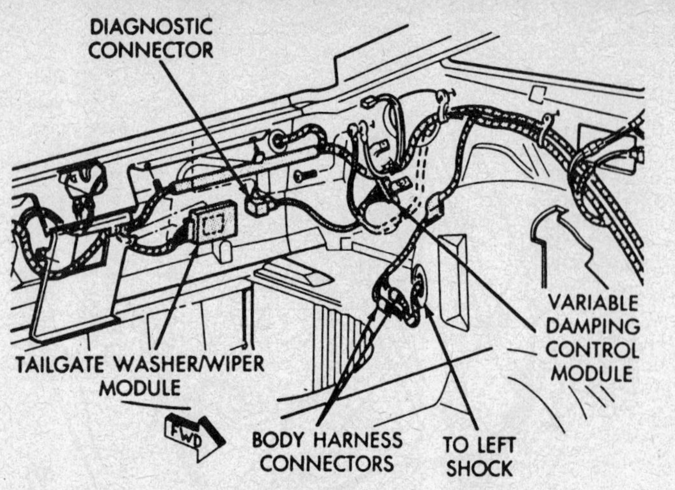


**Fig. 10 Diagnostic connector. Daytona**

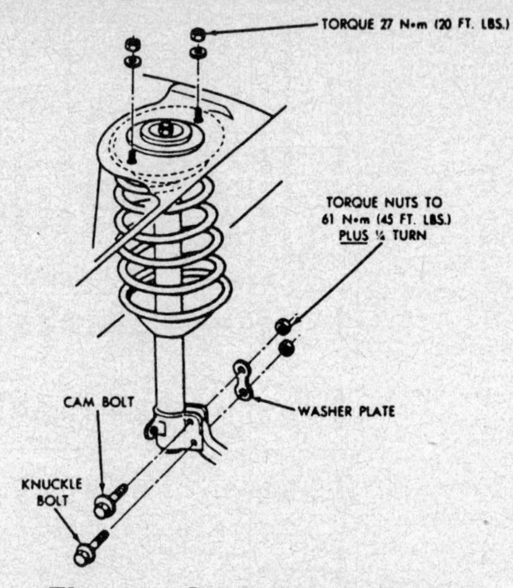


**Fig. 11 Strut Replacement**

mal diagnostic routine whenever the over current shutdown condition is repaired.

## LESS DRB II

If a DRB II is not available, the following procedure can be performed with a suitable volt/ohmmeter:

1. With ignition switch in On position, ground diagnostic input pin 21 at VDCM.
2. Grounding pin 21 causes the ADCM to run the motor(s) in the shocks/struts until they reach the selected damping position. The VDCM will stop driving the motor(s) once they reach the selected damping position.
3. Check voltages at the following pins:
   a. Pin 16, right rear shock motor.
   b. Pin 18, left rear shock motor.
   c. Pin 20, right front strut motor.
   d. Pin 22, left front strut motor.
4. Whichever pin(s) indicates 12 volts, that is the shock/strut(s) not in the correct position.
5. Repeat step 3 with the system in each of the three damping settings.
6. To check the complete system, select each position (Soft, Norm and Firm) while observing the selector switch, LEDs and PFS circuits using the DRB II or a volt/ohmmeter.

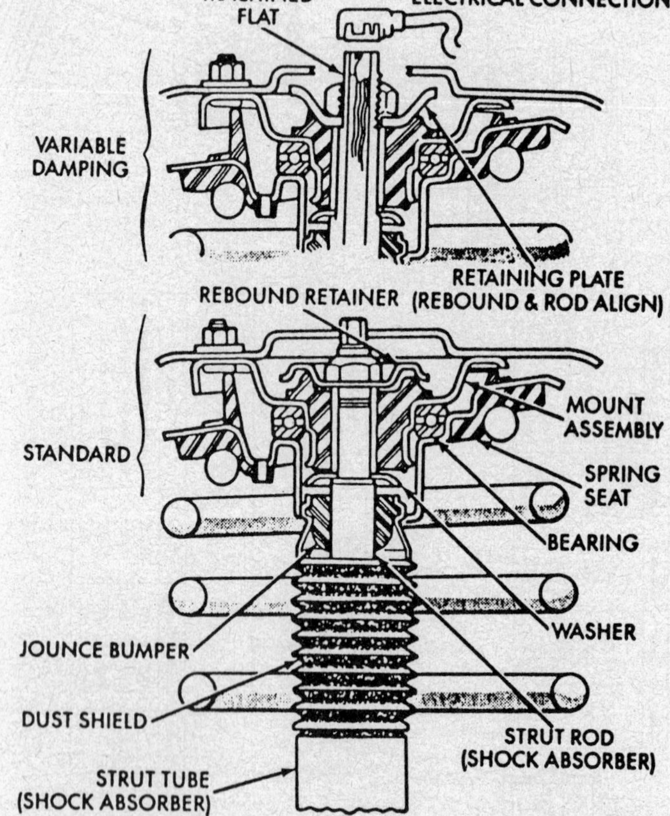


**Fig. 12 Strut assembly electrical connector**

# SYSTEM SERVICE

## STRUT ASSEMBLY, REPLACE

### Removal

1. Raise and support vehicle, then remove front wheels.
2. Mark position of camber adjusting cam for proper alignment during installation.
3. Remove cam bolt, knuckle bolt or bolts, washer plate or plates and brake hose to damper bracket attaching screw, **Fig. 11.**
4. Disconnect electrical connector from upper strut rod by pinching the two latching arms, then pulling connector straight off of rod end, **Fig. 12. Do not rotate connector.**
5. Remove strut damper to fender shield attaching nut and washer assemblies.
6. Remove strut damper from vehicle.

### Installation

1. Position strut assembly into fender reinforcement, then install retaining nuts and washers and torque to specification.
2. Position steering knuckle and washer plate to strut, then install cam and through bolts.
3. Install brake hose retainer on damper, then index alignment marks made during removal.
4. Position a four inch or larger C-clamp on steering knuckle and strut, then tighten clamp just enough to eliminate any looseness between strut and knuckle. Check alignment of marks

made during removal. Torque cam bolt nuts to specifications, then advance nuts an additional 1/4 turn.
5. Remove C-clamp, then install wheel and tire assembly. Torque wheel nuts to specification.
6. Connect electrical connector to top of strut rod, using caution to align key-way (wire should point toward vehicle center line), **Fig. 12.** Connector is correctly installed when both latching fingers engage in strut stem.

## SHOCK ABSORBER, REPLACE

1. Raise and support vehicle.
2. Support axle assembly, then remove wheel and tire assemblies.
3. Disconnect electrical connector from upper strut rod by pinching the two latching arms, then pulling connector straight off of rod end. **Do not rotate connector.**
4. Remove mounting bolts, then the shock absorber.
5. Reverse procedure to install.

## VARIABLE DAMPING CONTROL MODULE (VDCM), REPLACE

1. Turn ignition Off.
2. **On Daytona models,** remove left lower quarter trim panel as follows:
   a. Disconnect battery ground cable.
   b. Remove lower liftgate trim panel.
   c. Remove door sill scuff plate and rear seat latch cover.
   d. Remove lower quarter trim panel fasteners, then the lower quarter trim panel.
3. **On LeBaron models,** remove quarter trim panel as follows:
   a. Fold down 40-seat back, then remove the three fasteners retaining carpet to floor pan.
   b. Fold back seat back carpeting, then remove outboard pivot bracket screws.
   c. Remove 40-seat back.
   d. Remove four carpeting to floor pan fasteners on 60-seat back side.
   e. Remove outboard pivot brackets.
   f. Remove seat cushion, then the seat back.
   g. Remove cowl and scuff plate rear trim screw.
   h. Remove quarter trim lower extension panel, then pull out rear A-pillar fastening clips from roof rail.
   i. Remove front seat belt turning loop and cover.
   j. Remove rear reading lamp from trim panel.
   k. Remove two retaining screws, then the quarter trim panel.
4. **On all models,** disconnect 25-pin connector from module.
5. Remove two bracket attaching screws.
6. Remove module and bracket.
7. Reverse procedure to install.

## SELECTOR SWITCH, REPLACE

1. Turn ignition Off.
2. Using a plastic screwdriver, pry selector switch from center armrest console.
3. Disconnect electrical connector.
4. Remove switch.
5. Reverse procedure to install.

# Electronic Control Suspension (ECS)

INDEX



## AIRBAG SYSTEM DISARMING

1. Place ignition switch in lock position.
2. Disconnect and tape battery ground cable connector.
3. **Wait at least 1 minute after disconnecting battery ground cable before doing any further work on vehicle. The SRS system is designed to retain enough voltage to deploy airbag for a short time even after battery has been disconnected.**
4. After repairs are complete, reconnect battery ground cable.
5. From passenger side of vehicle, turn ignition switch to On position.
6. SRS warning light should illuminate for 6 to 8 seconds, then remain off for at least 45 seconds to indicate if SRS system is functioning correctly.
7. If SRS indicator does not perform as described refer to the "Passive Restraint Systems" section.

## ON VEHICLE INSPECTION

If a problem associated with the following items occurs, the ESC indicator light (Tour Sport) in the combination light flashes at intervals of .5 seconds. At the same time, the self diagnosis code associated with the problem is output to the diagnosis connector. Warning indication items are G sensor, Steering angular velocity sensor, Vehicle speed sensor and Damping force changeover actuator (including position detection switch).

## DIAGNOSIS & TESTING

Refer to **Fig. 1** for system wiring diagram when diagnosing the ECS system.

## OBTAINING FAULT (TROUBLE) CODES

1. Set ignition switch to Off position.
2. Connect the positive lead of a voltmeter to No. 3 terminal of diagnosis connector and the negative lead to terminal No. 12, **Fig. 2.** The diagnosis connector is located beside the junction block.
3. Turn ignition switch to On position.
4. Read self diagnosis code on basis of deflection of pointer on voltmeter, **Fig. 3.**
5. Based on self diagnosis code, repair the associated defective portion, **Fig. 4.**
6. Turn ignition switch to Off position.
7. After repairs have been made, disconnect battery cables from battery then reconnect them after 10 seconds or more.
8. Turn ignition switch to On position with voltmeter installed, then verify that a code zero is displayed. If code zero is not displayed, repeat steps 5 through 8 until code zero is displayed.

## SYSTEM INSPECTION

### Actuator Operating Sound

1. Turn ignition switch to On position.
2. Check for actuator operating sound at

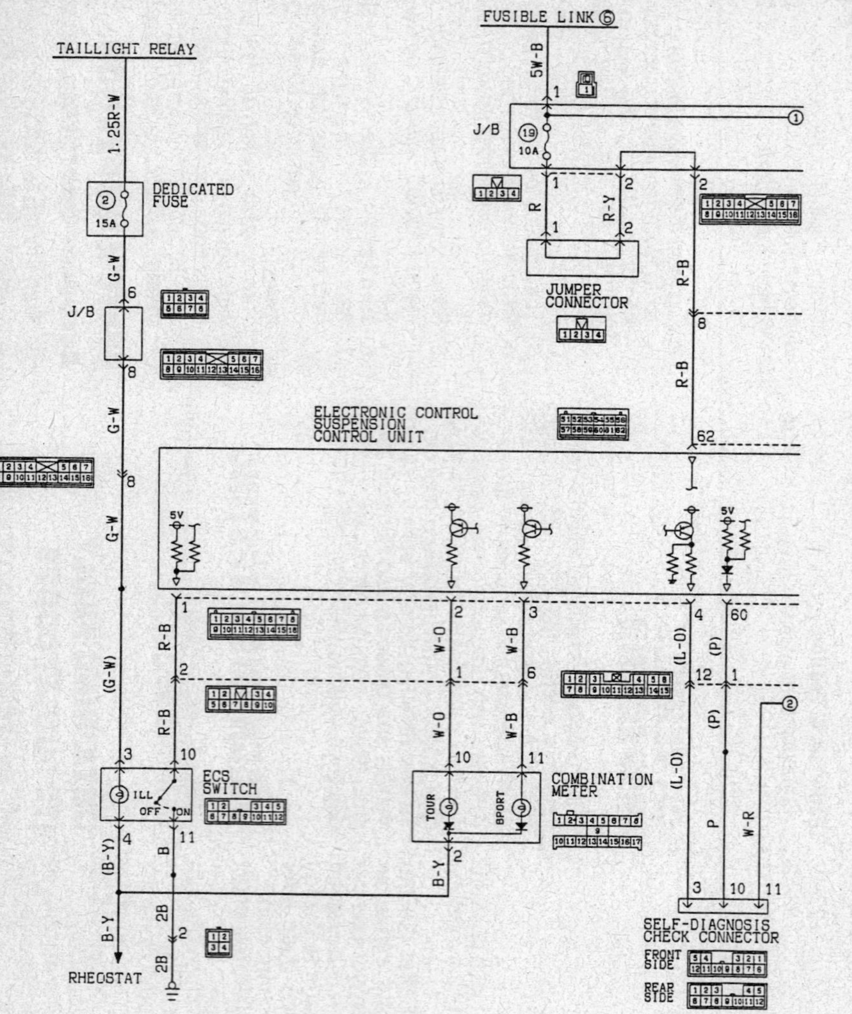



**Fig. 1 Electronic Controlled Suspension (ECS) wiring diagram (Part 1 of 3)**

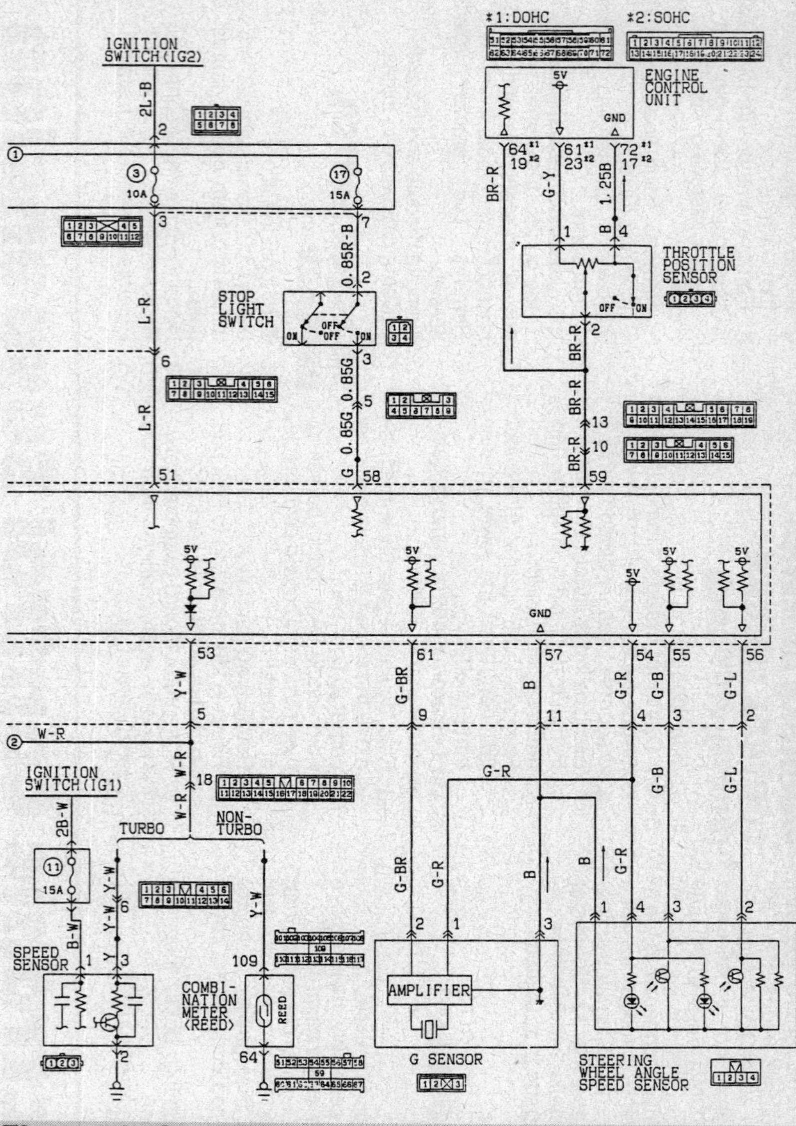



**Fig. 1 Electronic Controlled Suspension (ECS) wiring diagram (Part 2 of 3)**

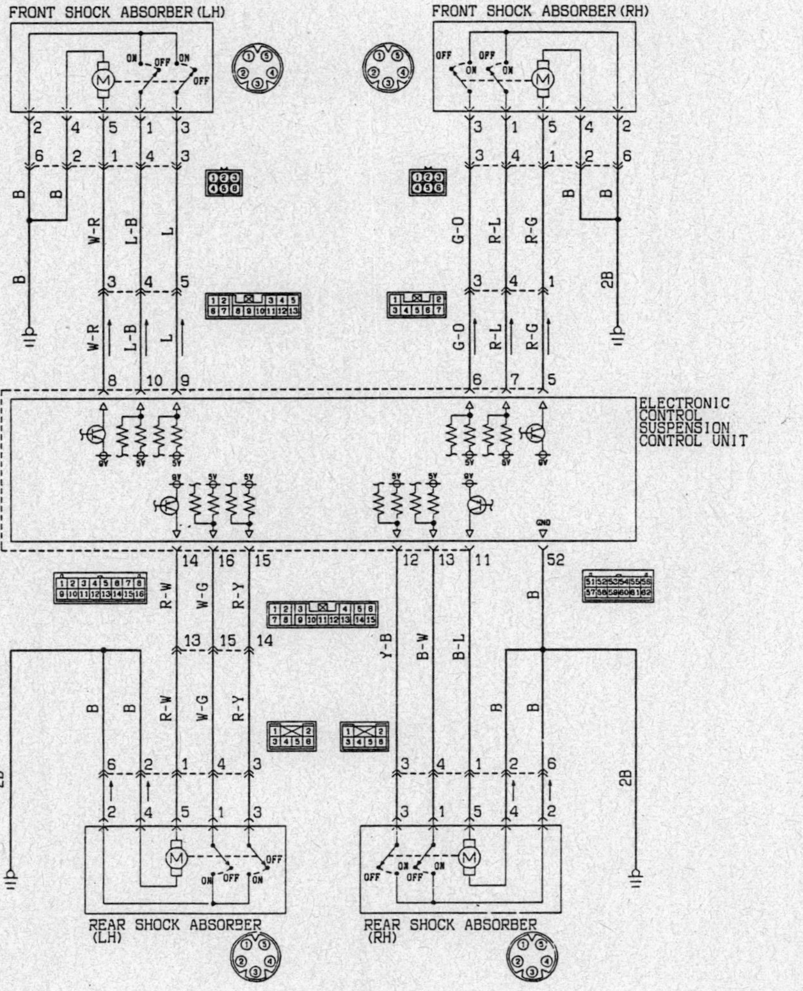


**Fig. 1 Electronic Controlled Suspension (ECS) wiring diagram (Part 3 of 3)**

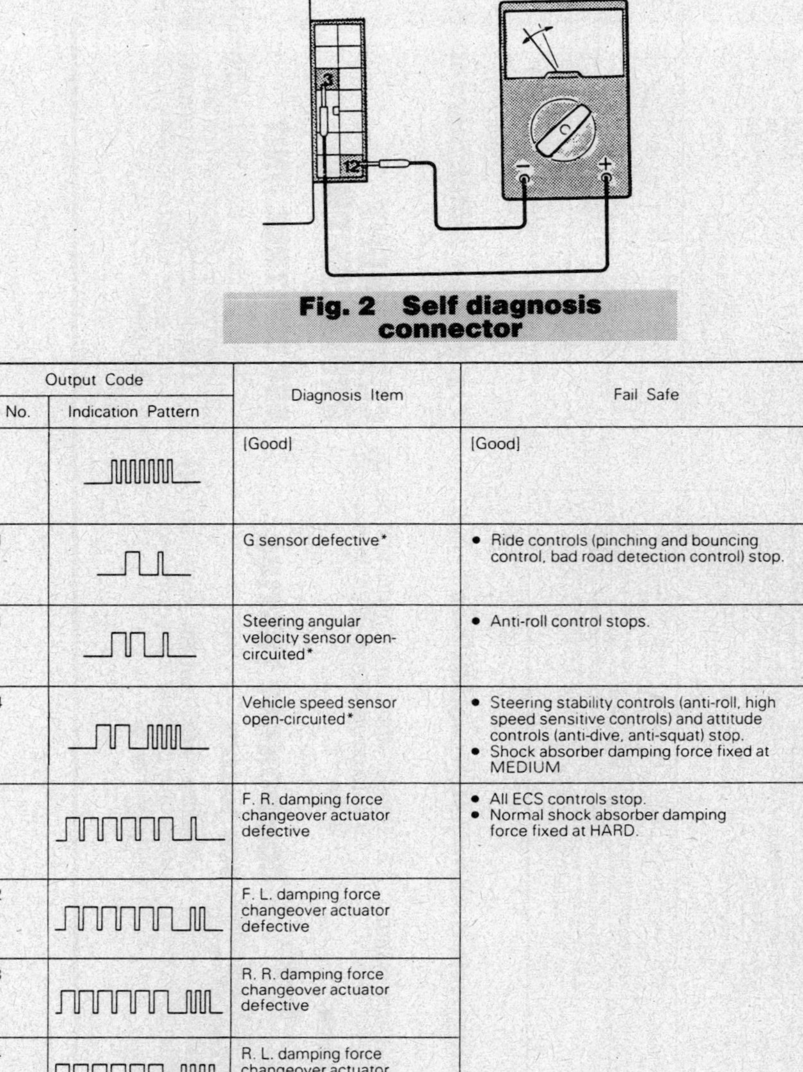


**Fig. 2 Self diagnosis connector**

| Output Code | | Diagnosis Item | Fail Safe |
|---|---|---|---|
| Code No. | Indication Pattern | | |
| 0 | | [Good] | [Good] |
| 11 | | G sensor defective* | • Ride controls (pinching and bouncing control, bad road detection control) stop. |
| 21 | | Steering angular velocity sensor open-circuited* | • Anti-roll control stops. |
| 24 | | Vehicle speed sensor open-circuited* | • Steering stability controls (anti-roll, high speed sensitive controls) and attitude controls (anti-dive, anti-squat) stop. • Shock absorber damping force fixed at MEDIUM |
| 61 | | F. R. damping force changeover actuator defective | • All ECS controls stop. • Normal shock absorber damping force fixed at HARD. |
| 62 | | F. L. damping force changeover actuator defective | |
| 63 | | R. R. damping force changeover actuator defective | |
| 64 | | R. L. damping force changeover actuator defective | |

NOTE
(1) Control stop, warning indication and fixed damping force return to normal when the ignition switch is set to OFF. When any of the problems marked* occurs, if no subsequent problem occurs (for example, when the problem is transient), normal operation will be restored even if the ignition switch is not set to OFF.
(2) Even if control stop, warning indication and fixed damping force return to normal as described above, the self-diagnosis code is stored in the memory in the ECS control unit.
(3) The self-diagnosis code can be cleared by stopping the power supply to the ECS control unit. In addition, it is automatically cleared if the ON/OFF control of the ignition switch is repeated 60 times after the self-diagnosis code has been output, provided that no new self-diagnosis code is output during the period.

**Fig. 3 Self diagnosis coded**

| Code No. | What is defective | Self-diagnosis determination conditions |
|---|---|---|
| 11 | G sensor defective | When sensor input of 0.5 or less or 4.5 V or more lasts for more than 10 seconds. |
| 21 | Steering angular velocity sensor open-circuited | Open circuit detected on the basis of difference in voltage level of sensor signal. |
| 24 | Vehicle speed sensor defective | When throttle opening of 30% (1.5 V) or more lasts for more than 60 seconds with the ignition switch at ON and if there is no input from the vehicle speed sensor during the period, it is regarded as a problem. |
| 61 – 64 | Damping force changeover actuator defective | If no damping force changeover is made in a second after actuator drive signal has been output (position detection switch output pattern does not change to that of target damping force), it is regarded as a problem. |

**Fig. 4 Self diagnosis determination conditions**

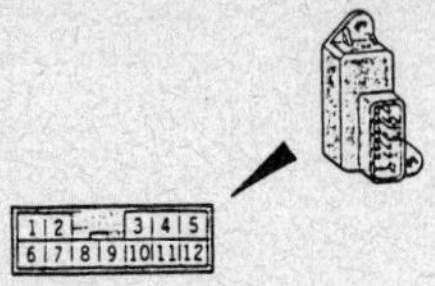

| Switch position \ Terminal | | 3 | 4 | 10 | 11 |
|---|---|---|---|---|---|
| ECS switch | ON | ○ | ○ | ○ | ○ |
| | OFF | ○ | ○ | | |

NOTE
○–○ indicates that there is continuity between the terminals.

**Fig. 5 ECS switch inspection**

top of shock tower each time control modes are changed.

### Damping Force Check

1. Turn ignition switch to On position.
2. Set ESC indicator on Tour.
3. Check damping force Soft state by shaking top mounting points of shock absorbers up and down.
4. Press ESC switch to change mode to Sport.
5. Repeat step 3 and ensure that damping force is harder than in the Soft state.

## COMPONENT TESTING

### ECS Switch

Remove ESC switch then operate switch and ensure continuity exists as shown in **Fig. 5.**

## COMPONENT REPLACEMENT

### ESC CONTROL UNIT

1. Remove cargo floor righthand box.
2. Remove ECS control unit lid.
3. Disconnect ECS control unit electrical connector, then remove the ECS control unit.

# WIPER SYSTEMS

## INDEX



## PRECAUTIONS

**Whenever service procedures are required on or near the steering wheel and/or instrument panel, disabling of the airbag system is required to prevent accidental deployment.**

## AIRBAG SYSTEM DISARMING

1. Place ignition switch in lock position.
2. Disconnect and tape battery ground cable connector.
3. **Wait at least 1 minute after disconnecting battery ground cable before doing any further work on vehicle.** The SRS system is designed to retain enough voltage to deploy airbag for a short time even after battery has been disconnected.
4. After repairs are complete, reconnect battery ground cable.
5. From passenger side of vehicle, turn ignition switch to On position.
6. SRS warning light should illuminate for 6 to 8 seconds, then remain off for at least 45 seconds to indicate if SRS system is functioning correctly.
7. If SRS indicator does not perform as described refer to the "Passive Restraint Systems" section.

## 1989–90 CHRYSLER EXCEPT COLT, COLT VISTA, CONQUEST, LASER, MONACO & STEALTH

Windshield wiper operation is controlled by a dash or column mounted switch. Wiper motors have permanent magnet fields, and high and low speeds are determined by current flow to the appropriate set of brushes. Delay operation on intermittent systems is controlled by a variable resistor in the wiper switch, a dwell switch in the wiper motor and a control unit/relay assembly.

Wiper arms on both systems return to a park position when the system is switched off with ignition in on position. Depending upon application, wipers either park on the glass at their lowest point of travel, or "depress park" in a concealed position. Standard two speed systems complete the wipe cycle and stop in park position, while intermittent systems complete a full wipe cycle before parking.

To park wipers in the concealed position, motor direction is reversed when wipers reach their lowest point of travel. A parking cam assembly rotates 180°, changing the length of the motor output arm and parks wipers in the concealed position. Normal operation returns the output arm/parking cam assembly to the run position.

### TROUBLESHOOTING

#### Wiper Fails To Operate

1. Binding linkage.
2. Faulty instrument panel switch.
3. Linkage disconnected.

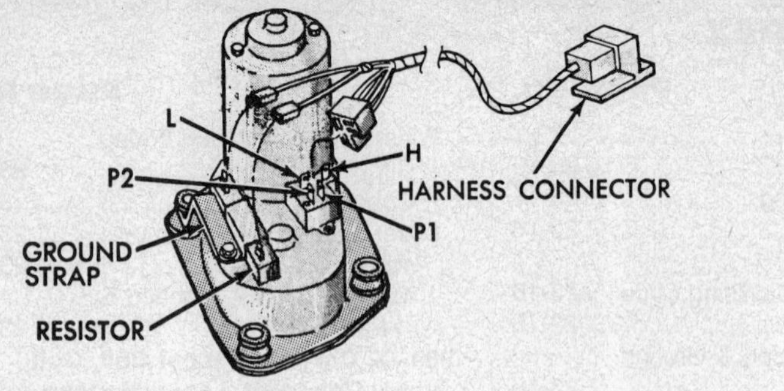


**Fig. 1 Two speed motor terminal locations**

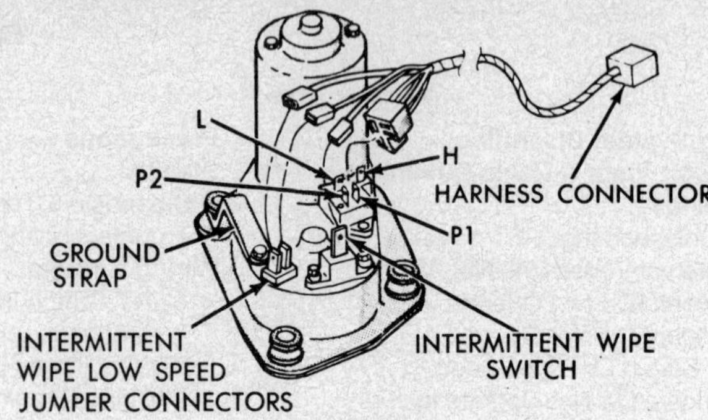


**Fig. 2 Intermittent wiper motor terminal locations**

4. Faulty motor.
5. Open or grounded wiring.
6. Motor not grounded.
7. Faulty circuit breaker.
8. Shorted park switch.
9. Jammed or faulty gearbox mechanism.
10. Motor overheated.

## Motor Runs But Output Crank Does Not Turn

1. Stripped intermediate gear.
2. Stripped output gear.
3. Output gear slips on output shaft.
4. Crank not fastened properly to output gear shaft.
5. Broken latch slips on output shaft.

## Motor Draws Excessive Current

1. Shorted or burned armature.
2. Seized armature bearing.
3. Bearings loose in housing.
4. Loose or chipped magnets and loose clips or chips interfering with armature.
5. Broken brush holder.
6. Binding linkage.
7. Jammed gearbox mechanism.

## No Speed Control (Motor Runs At One Speed Only)

1. Open circuit in red or brown wiring.
2. Defective control switch.
3. Brush sticking in holder.
4. No brush spring.
5. Broken brush holder.
6. Low speed torque limiting resistor open.

## Motor Will Not Stop When Instrument Panel Switch Is Turned "Off"

1. Broken island on gear.
2. Motor housing not grounded (two speed with concealed wipers).
3. Defective armature brake switch.
4. Broken brush holder.
5. Defective motor park switch.

## Motor Stops In Any Position When Instrument Panel Switch Is Turned "Off"

1. Motor park switch failure.
2. Open parking circuit.
3. Open field circuit.

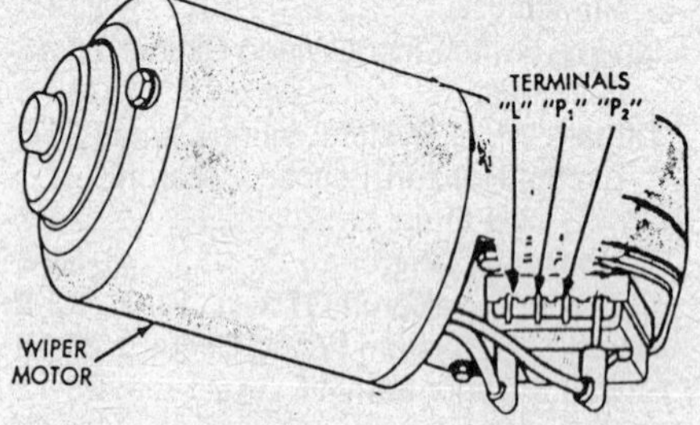


**Fig. 3 Wiper motor terminal location**

## Wiper Blades Not Parking Properly

1. Arm set at incorrect position.
2. Motor park switch timing incorrect.
3. Loose clutch spring on crank (two speed concealed).

## Blades Stop Against Windshield Moldings

1. Improperly adjusted wiper arm.
2. Looseness of the motor crank or other drive parts.

## Blades Chatter

1. Twisted arm holds blade at wrong angle to glass.
2. Bent or damaged blades.
3. Foreign substances such as body polish on glass.

# DIAGNOSIS & TESTING

## TWO SPEED WIPER SYSTEM

### Motor Will Not Operate In Any Switch Position

Prior to performing diagnostic procedures, check for blown fuse in fuse block. If fuse is good, proceed to step 1. If fuse is defective, replace and check for motor operation in all switch positions. If motor is still inoperative, and fuse does not blow, proceed to step 1. If replacement fuse blows, disconnect motor wiring connector, then replace fuse. If fuse does not blow, motor is defective. If fuse blows, faulty switch or wiring is indicated.

1. Place wiper switch in low position and listen to hear if motor is running.
2. If motor is running, but output shaft is not rotating, replace gearbox assembly. If driveshaft is turning, check drive link to output shaft or linkage for proper connection.
3. Check wiper system fuse on FWD models, and replace if necessary. If fuse blows again, proceed to step 8. If fuse does not blow, continue with next step.
4. Connect voltmeter between wiper motor terminal L and ground, **Figs. 1, 2 and 3** leaving electrical connector in place.
5. If meter indicates approximately 12 volts, check motor ground as follows:
   a. **On models less concealed wipers**, ensure ground strap is properly connected and free of corrosion.
   b. **On models with concealed wipers,** connect jumper wire between motor terminal $P_2$ and ground, **Figs. 1, 2 and 3.** If motor runs, check continuity of wiring between motor and switch, switch continuity and ensure switch is grounded.
6. If motor ground is satisfactory in step 5, check wiper motor brushes and armature, and repair as needed.
7. If voltmeter indicates no voltage at motor terminal L, and fuse or circuit breaker is satisfactory, check continuity of wiper system wiring and wiper switch. Repair wiring or replace switch as needed.
8. If wiper system fuse is blown on front wheel drive models or if circuit breaker is cycling on all other models, disconnect electrical connector to wiper motor. On FWD models install a suitable test circuit breaker across wiper system fuse terminals.
9. Check voltage at terminal L in electrical connector to wiper motor.
10. If circuit breaker continues to cycle, check for short circuit in wiper system wiring or defective switch.
11. If meter indicates approximately 12 volts in step 9, and circuit breaker does not cycle, check motor as follows:
   a. Remove wiper arm assemblies.
   b. Connect positive lead of ammeter to battery positive post, and connect negative lead to motor terminal L. On models with concealed

wipers, connect jumper wire between motor terminal $P_2$ and ground.
- c. If motor operates and draws less than 6 amps, motor is satisfactory. Recheck switch, wiring and circuit breaker.
- d. If motor does not operate, or operates but draws more than 6 amps, disconnect ammeter and remove crank arm retainer and arm from motor.
- e. Repeat step b. If motor operates and draws 3 amps or less, repair wiper linkage. If motor does not operate, or operates but draws more than 3 amps, repair or replace motor.

## Motor Runs Slowly At All Speeds

1. Disconnect electrical connector from motor, then remove wiper arms and blades.
2. Connect an ammeter from motor "L" terminal to battery **Figs. 1, 2 and 3.**
3. If motor operates and ammeter reads more than 6 amps, proceed to step 4. If ammeter reads less than 6 amps, proceed to step 5.
4. Check for wiper linkage binding, then disconnect drive link from motor. If motor now draws less than 3 amps, repair linkage. If motor draws more than 3 amps, replace motor.
5. Check for shorts between high and low speed wires at harness as follows:
   - a. Install one lead of a voltmeter or test lamp at motor ground strap and set wiper switch to Low position, then connect the other lead to the "H" terminal of wiring harness.
   - b. If voltage is indicated, repair wiring or wiper switch.
   - c. If zero voltage is indicated, set switch to High position and move voltmeter lead from "H" terminal to "L" terminal.
   - d. If voltage is indicated, repair short in wiring or wiper switch.

## Motor Operates At Either High Or Low Speed Only

1. If motor operates at low speed, place wiper switch in high position and connect test lamp between motor terminal H and ground, **Figs. 1, 2 and 3.** If motor operates at high speed, place wiper switch in low position and connect test lamp between motor terminal L and ground, **Figs. 1, 2 and 3.** Leave electrical connector connected to motor.
2. If test lamp does not light at motor terminal, there is an open circuit in wiper switch or wiring. If test lamp lights at motor terminal, brush is not making good contact with commutator.

## Wiper Motor Will Continue To Operate With Switch In Off Position

1. **On models with non-concealed wipers,** remove wire connector and connect jumper wire from motor terminal L to terminal $P_2$, **Figs. 1, 2 and 3.** Connect a second jumper wire from terminal $P_1$ to battery. If motor runs to park position and stops, wiper switch is defective. If motor continues to operate and does not park, replace gearbox assembly.
2. **On models with concealed wipers,** disconnect wire connector and connect a jumper wire from terminal $P_1$ to battery. Connect a second jumper wire from terminal L to ground. If motor runs to park position and stops, wiper switch is defective. If motor continues to operate, replace gearbox assembly.

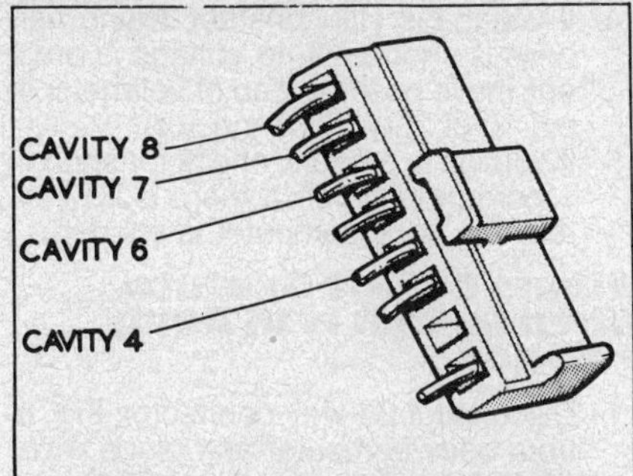


**Fig. 4 Intermittent wiper control 8 cavity connector**

## Wipers Do Not Return To Park Position

1. Remove wiper motor wire connector and clean terminals.
2. Place wiper switch in park position.
3. Connect a voltmeter between terminals $P_1$ and L, **Figs. 1, 2 and 3.** If a reading of 12 volts is obtained at terminal $P_1$, check voltage at terminal $P_2$. If voltage at terminal $P_2$ is zero, park switch is defective and gearbox assembly must be replaced. If there is 12 volts at terminal $P_2$, there is an open circuit in wiper switch or wiring.

# INTERMITTENT WIPER SYSTEM, EXCEPT DYNASTY & NEW YORKER

To diagnose system malfunctions that do not involve the delay function, refer to "Two-Speed Wiper System."

## Wipers Run Without Delay With Switch In Delay Position

1. **On models with concealed wipers,** proceed as follows:
   - a. Place wiper switch in low position and disconnect electrical connector to dwell switch, **Figs. 2 and 3.**
   - b. Connect ohmmeter between dwell switch terminal and ground. Meter should indicate continuity once per wipe cycle.
   - c. If meter does not indicate continuity as specified, repair or replace dwell switch and recheck system. **If meter indicates constant continuity, bend dwell switch contacts outward; if meter indicates no continuity, bend contacts inward.**
   - d. If meter indicates continuity as specified, disconnect 8 cavity connector at control unit and check for battery voltage at cavity 5 in connector, **Fig. 4.**
   - e. If voltage is present, replace control unit. If there is no voltage, check wiring and switch and repair as needed.
2. **On models equipped with non-concealed wiper system,** proceed as follows:
   - a. Verify that motor will return to park position when control switch is turned off.
   - b. Turn control switch to low position, then disconnect 8 wire connector from intermittent wipe control unit and inspect contacts for damage, **Fig. 4.**
   - c. Connect test lamp between cavities 1 and 3 of connector. Lamp should light once during each wipe cycle.
   - d. If lamp lights intermittently, replace control unit. If lamp does not light, connect test lamp between motor terminals P1 and P2, **Figs. 2 and 3.**
   - e. If lamp lights intermittently, check motor wiring.

## Wipers Do Not Operate When Switch Is In Delay Position

1. Disconnect wire connector from intermittent wiper control unit.
2. Place wiper switch in maximum delay position.
3. Connect volt meter between cavity 4 and cavity 6 on wire connector, **Fig. 4.**
4. If volt meter reading is zero, check wiper switch and wiring.
5. If volt meter reading is 10 to 15 volts, place column switch in low position and connect voltmeter between cavity 3 and 4. If voltmeter reads 10-15 volts, control unit is faulty and should be replaced. If no voltage, check wiring.

## Wipers Immediately Give First Wipe, But Do Not Operate With Switch In Delay Mode

1. Disconnect wire connect from intermittent control unit and check for bent contacts.
2. Place panel wiper switch in maximum delay position.
3. Connect a volt meter between cavity 4 and cavity 8 on wire connector, **Fig. 4.**
4. If volt meter reading is zero, check wiper switch and wiring.
5. If volt meter reading is 10 to 15 volts, control unit is faulty and should be replaced.

## Excessive Delay Or Inadequate Variation In Delay

1. Variations in delay should be as follows:
   - a. Minimum delay: delay control to extreme right position before first detent, one half to two seconds.

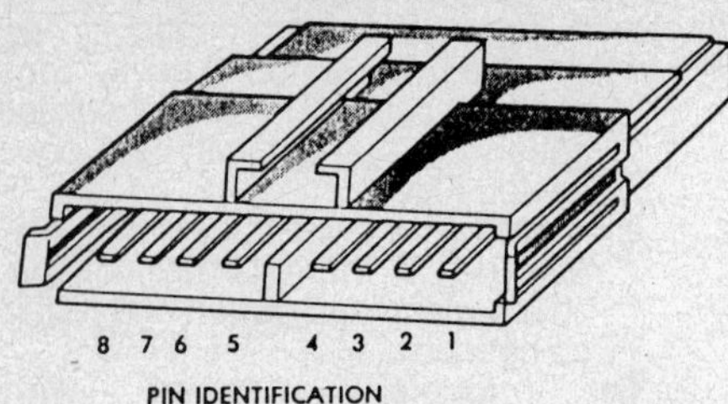


**Fig. 5 Wiper switch 8-way connector. 1989 Dynasty & New Yorker**

   b. Maximum delay: delay control to extreme left position before off detent, ten to thirty seconds.
2. If there is excessive delay or no variations in delay, replace wiper switch.

### Wipers Do Not Run Continually When Washer Control Is Operated During Delay Mode

1. Disconnect wire connector from intermittent control unit.
2. Connect a voltmeter between cavity 4 and cavity 7 on wire connector, **Fig. 4.**
3. Depress washer switch, if voltmeter reading is zero, check switch and wiring.
4. If voltage reading is 10 to 15 volts, control unit is faulty and should be replaced.

### Wipers Continually Run When Washer Is Operated But Do Not Provide An Extra Wipe When Washer Control Is Released

1. If this condition is encountered, replace the control unit.

### Wipers Start Erratically When In Delay Mode

1. Verify good ground at instrument panel, motor ground strap and intermittent control unit.
2. If grounds are satisfactory and condition persists, replace control unit.

## INTERMITTENT WIPER SYSTEM, DYNASTY & NEW YORKER

To diagnose system malfunctions that do not involve the delay function, refer to "Two-Speed Wiper System."

### Wipers Do Not Delay When In Delay Position

1. Verify that the motor will park when switch is turned off.
2. Disconnect 8-way wiper connector in steering column, **Fig. 5,** and connect jumper wire from pin 8 to pin 5, then connect another jumper from pin 5 to pin 1.
3. Connect a voltmeter or test lamp between pin 2 and a good ground. Voltage should be present, pulsing at 2 second intervals for a duration of 1 second. If voltage is constant, remove 25-way connector **Fig. 6,** from body computer.
4. If voltage is still constant, wiring harness is shorted. If no voltage is present, move positive lead of voltmeter to pin 10 of 25-way connector.
5. If voltage is present, check for short in wiper pump circuit. If there is no voltage, the body computer is shorted.

### Wipers Do Not Operate When Switch Is In Delay Position

1. Disconnect 25-way connector, **Fig. 6,** from body computer and place wiper control in maximum delay position.
2. Connect positive lead of voltmeter to pin 9 and negative lead to metal case of body computer.
3. If voltmeter indicates zero voltage, check control switch and wiring for open circuit. If 10-15 volts is indicated, connect positive lead of voltmeter to pin 22.
4. If voltmeter indicates zero voltage, check control switch and wiring for open circuit. If 10-15 volts is indicated, connect positive lead of voltmeter to pin 24.
5. Disconnect wiring harness from wiper motor and set control switch to Low position.
6. If voltmeter indicates zero voltage, check wiring harness to body computer for open circuit. If 10-15 volts is indicated, replace body computer.

### Wipers Do Not Return To Park

1. Verify that motor will park when switch is off.
2. Set wiper control on maximum delay, then between wipes when blades are at rest, disconnect 25-way connector, **Fig. 6,** from body computer.
3. Connect positive voltmeter lead to pin 20 and negative lead to metal case of body computer.
4. If voltmeter indicates zero voltage, check for open in wiring. If 10-15 volts is indicated, check for continuity between pins 20 and 24 using an ohmmeter.
5. Reverse leads of ohmmeter between pins 20 and 24 and check continuity again. If there is no continuity in either direction, replace body computer.

### Excessive Delay Or Inadequate Variation Of Delay

1. Normal operating range of the delay switch are 1/2 second to 30 seconds. If delay is outside these parameters, remove wiper motor wiring harness while motor is parked in the Off position
2. Remove 25-way connector, **Fig. 6,** from body computer, and set wiper control to maximum delay position.
3. With ignition on, measure voltage between pin 9 and metal case of body computer.
4. If voltmeter indicators zero volts, go to step 6. If 10-15 volts remove wiper motor circuit fuse and using an ohmmeter, measure resistance between pins 9 and 22 of body computer with wiper control first set at minimum, then at maximum delay.
5. If resistance at minimum setting is 0-15 ohms, and 240K-330K ohms at maximum delay setting, replace body computer. If resistances are not as listed, replace wiper control switch.
6. Set wiper control switch to minimum delay setting and measure voltage between pin 9 and metal case of body computer. Zero volts indicates open in intermittent wipe wiring circuit. If 10-15 volts are present, replace wiper control switch.

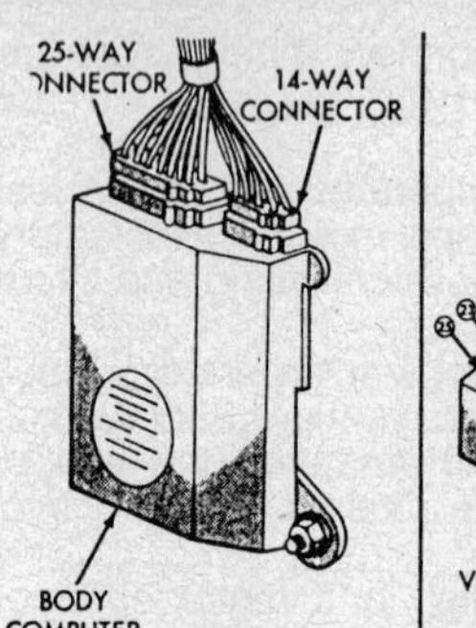


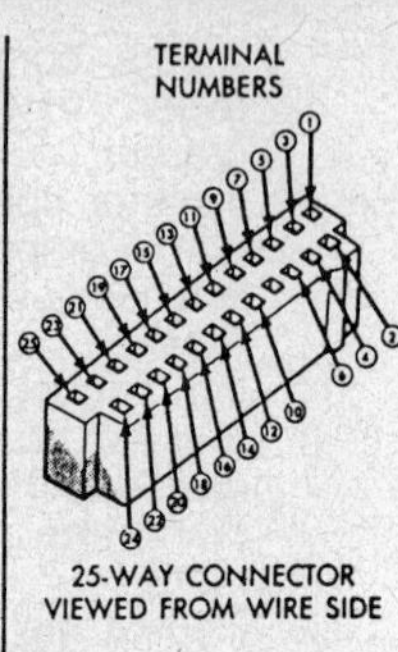


**Fig. 6 Body computer 25-way connector. 1989 Dynasty & New Yorker**

### Wipers Fail To Run When Wash Control Is Operated During Delay Mode

1. Disconnect 25-way connector **Fig. 6,** from body computer, then connect voltmeter positive lead to pin 10, and negative lead to metal case of body computer.
2. Set wiper control to delay position and depress wash switch.
3. If voltmeter indicates zero voltage, check switch and wiring. If voltage measures 10-15 volts, the body computer is defective.

### Wipers Do Not Provide An Extra Wipe When Wash Control Is Released

Replace body computer.

### Wipers Start Erratically During Delay Mode

1. Verify good ground at instrument panel and motor ground strap.
2. Verify good wiring connections at body computer, wiper motor and wiper switch.
3. If condition persists, replace body computer.

## INTERMITTENT WIPER SWITCH TESTING

### Except 1990 New Yorker, Daytona, Dynasty, Imperial & LeBaron

1. **On models with an instrument panel switch,** remove switch to gain access to terminals.
2. **On models with a column mounted switch,** disconnect electrical connector to switch at body wiring harness connector.

| INTERMITTENT WIPE SWITCH CONTINUITY CHART | |
|---|---|
| SWITCH POSITION | CONTINUITY BETWEEN |
| OFF | Pin 2 & Pin 4 |
| DELAY | Pin 5 & Pin 8<br>Pin 4 & Pin 7<br>Pin 5 & Pin 1* |
| LOW | Pin 2 & Pin 5 |
| HIGH | Pin 3 & Pin 5 |

*Resistance at maximum delay position should be between 270,000 ohms and 330,000 ohms.
*Resistance at minimum delay position should be zero with ohmmeter set on high ohm scale.

**Fig. 7 Wiper switch continuity chart. 1989 Dynasty & New Yorker**

| INTERMITTENT WIPE SWITCH CONTINUITY CHART | |
|---|---|
| SWITCH POSITION | CONTINUITY BETWEEN |
| OFF | L and $P_2$ |
| DELAY | $P_1$ and $I_1$<br>R and $I_1$*<br>$I_2$ and G |
| LOW | $P_1$ and L |
| HIGH | $P_1$ and H |

*Resistance at maximum delay position should be between 270,000 ohms and 330,000 ohms.
*Resistance at minimum delay position should be zero with ohmmeter set on the high ohm scale.

**Fig. 8 Wiper switch continuity chart. 1989 Except Dynasty & New Yorker**

INTERMITTENT WIPE SWITCH CONTINUITY CHART
NON-TILT

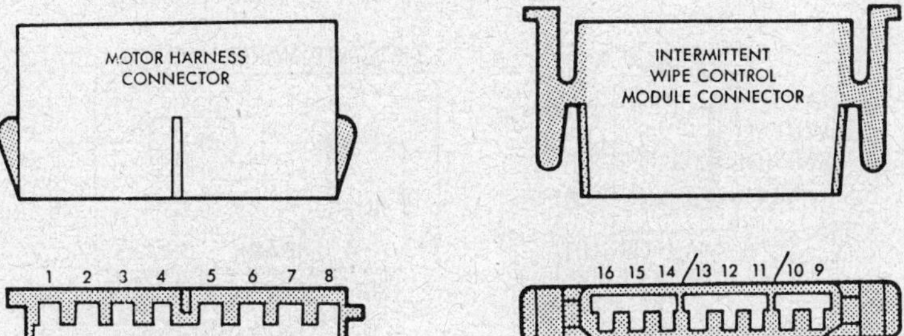


VIEW FROM TERMINAL SIDE

| SWITCH POSITION | CONTINUITY BETWEEN |
|---|---|
| OFF | PIN 1-13, PIN 3-10, PIN 4-11, PIN 5-12 |
| DELAY | PIN 1-13, PIN 3-10, PIN 4-16, PIN 4-11, PIN 4-9, PIN 5-12, PIN 8-15, PIN 9-16, PIN 11-16, PIN 9-11 |
| LOW | PIN 1-13, PIN 3-10, PIN 4-7, PIN 4-11, PIN 5-12, PIN 7-11 |
| HIGH | PIN 1-13, PIN 3-10, PIN 4-6, PIN 4-11, PIN 5-12, PIN 6-11 |

**Fig. 9 Intermittent wiper switch continuity chart w/non-tilt column. 1990 New Yorker, Dynasty & Imperial**

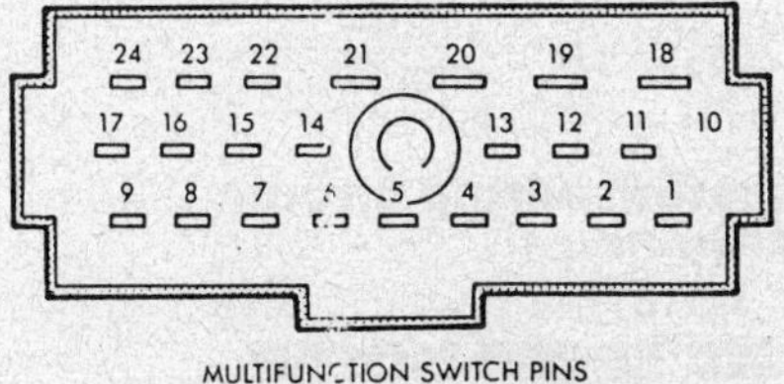


MULTIFUNCTION SWITCH PINS

| INTERMITTENT WIPE SWITCH CONTINUITY CHART | |
|---|---|
| SWITCH POSITION | CONTINUITY BETWEEN |
| OFF | PIN 6 & PIN 7 |
| DELAY | PIN 8 & PIN 9<br>PIN 2 & PIN 4<br>PIN 1 & PIN 2 |
| LOW | PIN 4 & PIN 6 |
| HIGH | PIN 4 & PIN 5 |

*RESISTANCE AT MAXIMUM DELAY POSITION SHOULD BE BETWEEN 270,000 OHMS AND 300,000 OHMS.
*RESISTANCE AT MINIMUM DELAY POSITION SHOULD BE ZERO WITH OHMMETER SET ON HIGH OHM SCALE.

**Fig. 10 Intermittent wiper switch continuity chart w/tilt column. 1990 New Yorker, Dynasty & Imperial**

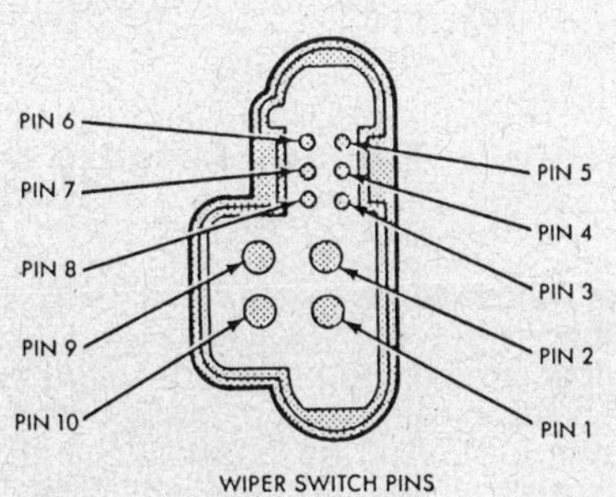


| SWITCH POSITION | CONTINUITY BETWEEN |
|---|---|
| OFF | PIN 9 AND PIN 10 |
| DELAY | PIN 1 AND PIN 5 |
| LOW | PIN 1 AND PIN 10 |
| HIGH | PIN 1 AND PIN 2 |

**Fig. 11 Front wiper continuity chart. 1990 Daytona & LeBaron**

3. **On all models,** operate switch in all positions, and check continuity between terminals with an ohmmeter. On instrument panel mounted switches, ground is the switch body.
4. If continuity is not as specified in charts, **Figs. 7 and 8,** replace switch.

### 1990 New Yorker, Dynasty & Imperial, Non-Tilt Column Models

1. Disconnect switch wires from body wiring in steering column.
2. Test for continuity, using a suitable ohmmeter, as indicated in **Fig. 9.**

### 1990 New Yorker, Dynasty & Imperial, Tilt Column Models

1. Disconnect switch wires from body wiring in steering column.
2. Test for continuity, using a suitable ohmmeter, as indicated in **Fig. 10.**

### 1990 Daytona & LeBaron

Remove switch pod from instrument panel, then using a suitable ohmmeter, test for continuity between terminals as indicated in **Fig. 11.**

## INTERMITTENT WIPER SWITCH SERVICE

On all models equipped with Driver Airbag Restraint System, it is necessary to remove and isolate negative (-) battery cable from vehicle battery. This procedure is necessary to avoid accidental deployment of airbag which may cause damage or personal injury.

### 1990 New Yorker, Dynasty & Imperial

The wiper switch is part of the multi-function switch assembly. With wiper switch failure, refer to "Steering Column" section for the removal of steering wheel and switch.

### 1990 Daytona & LeBaron

1. Remove switch assembly from instrument panel, then remove 5 screws holding the inner switch pod.
2. Disconnect switch linkage from buttons, then remove mounting screws and the switch.
3. When installing the new switch, place linkage in the up position, then insert the switch and install 5 mounting screws.
4. Install linkage on push buttons and operate switch modes for correct operation.
5. Install inner switch pod panel, then install complete switch back in instrument panel.

## WIPER MOTOR SERVICE

### Endplay Adjustment

Most windshield wiper motors have a provision to adjust the armature shaft endplay by turning the adjustment screw in until it bottoms and backing off 1/16 turn, **Fig. 12.** This adjustment can be made without removing the wiper motor from the vehicle.

## LIFTGATE WIPER MOTOR

### DIAGNOSIS & TESTING

#### Horizon & Omni

1. Remove wiper motor plastic cover from liftgate, then disconnect feed wire connector from wiper motor, **Fig. 13.**
2. Place ignition switch in the On position and check for battery voltage at blue wire.
3. With ignition switch and wiper switch in the On position, check for battery voltage at blue and brown wires.
4. If battery voltage is not obtained in steps 2 and 3, check circuit breaker, wiper switch and wiring, **Fig. 14.**
5. If battery voltage is obtained in steps 2 and 3, apply 12 volts to terminal on switch plate without wire, **Fig. 15.** If motor operates and driveshaft rotates, replace switch plate. If motor does not operate, replace motor assembly.
6. If motor operates but driveshaft does not rotate, remove wiper motor cover and inspect drive gear, driveshaft and drive link and repair as necessary.

#### Except Horizon, Lancer, Lebaron GTS & Omni

1. Remove liftgate trim panel.
2. Ensure link, pivot or motor parts are not disconnected.
3. Disconnect wiper motor feed connector.
4. With ignition on and wiper switch off, check for battery voltage at brown wire.
5. With ignition switch on and wiper switch on, check for battery voltage at positive wire. If battery voltage is not obtained in steps 4 and 5, inspect circuit breaker, liftgate wiper switch and wiring, **Fig. 16.**
6. If battery voltage is obtained in steps 4 and 5 but wiper motor does not operate, remove motor and linkage assembly from vehicle and apply 12 volts to blue wire terminal of motor connector. If motor operates, inspect pivot for binding and replace if necessary. If motor does not operate, replace motor.

#### Lancer & Lebaron GTS

Refer to **Fig. 17,** for liftgate wiper system wiring schematic.

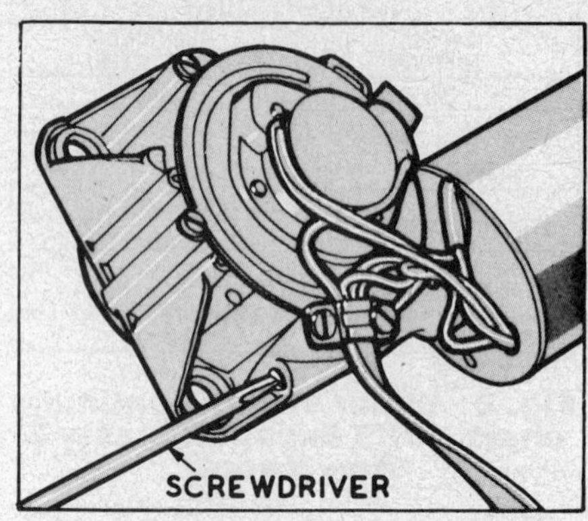


**Fig. 12 Endplay adjustment**

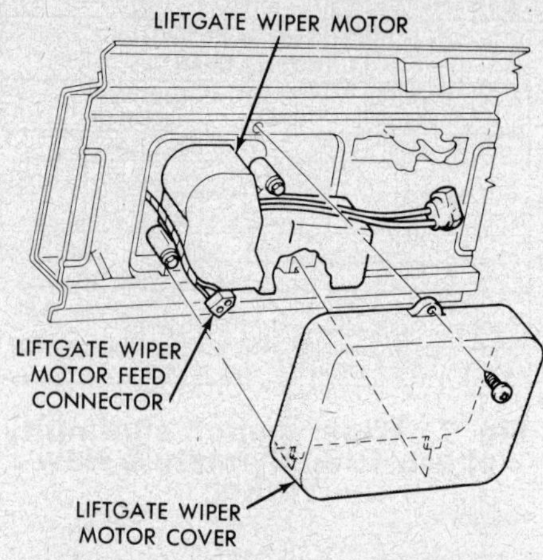


**Fig. 13 Removing liftgate wiper motor cover. Horizon & Omni**

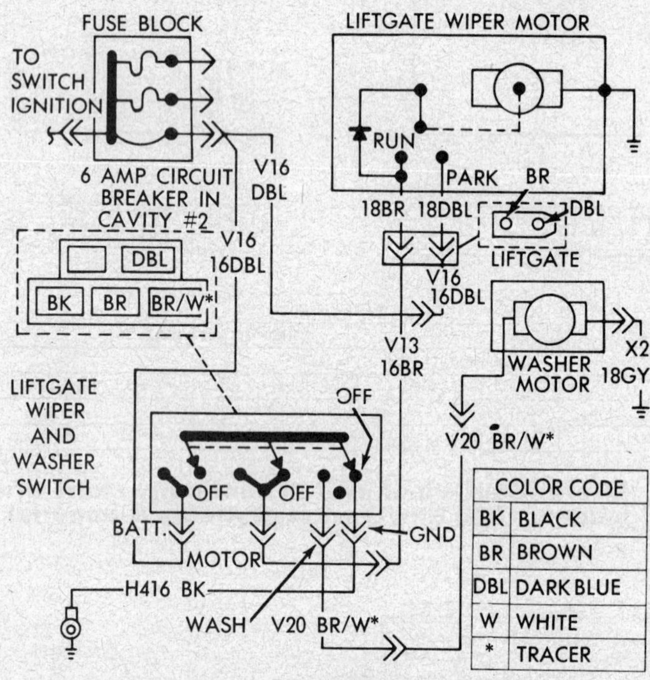


| COLOR CODE | |
|---|---|
| BK | BLACK |
| BR | BROWN |
| DBL | DARK BLUE |
| W | WHITE |
| * | TRACER |

**Fig. 14 Liftgate wiper system wiring circuit. Horizon & Omni**

# 1991 CHRYSLER EXCEPT COLT, COLT VISTA, CONQUEST, LASER, MONACO & STEALTH

Windshield wiper operation is controlled by a dash or column mounted switch. Wiper motors have permanent magnet fields, and high and low speeds are determined by current flow to the appropriate set of brushes. Delay operation on intermittent systems is controlled by a variable resistor in the wiper switch, a dwell switch in the wiper motor and a control unit/relay assembly.

Wiper arms on both systems return to a park position when the system is switched off with ignition in on position. Standard two speed systems complete the wipe cycle and stop in park position, while intermittent systems complete a full wipe cycle before parking.

## TROUBLESHOOTING

Refer to **Figs. 18 and 19,** for troubleshooting the wiper/washer system.

## DIAGNOSIS & TESTING

Whenever a wiper motor malfunction occurs, first ensure that wiper motor wire harness is properly connected before starting with normal diagnosis and repair procedures.

### TWO SPEED MOTOR FUNCTION TESTS

#### Motor Will Not Run In Any Switch Position

1. Check for blown fuse.
2. If fuse is not defective proceed to step 6.
3. If fuse is defective, replace and recheck motor operation in all switch positions.
4. If motor is still inoperative and fuse does not blow, proceed to step 6.
5. If replacement fuse blows, proceed to step 15.
6. Place switch in Low speed position.
7. Listen for motor operation sound. If motor sound is not heard, proceed to step 10.
8. If motor sound is heard, check motor

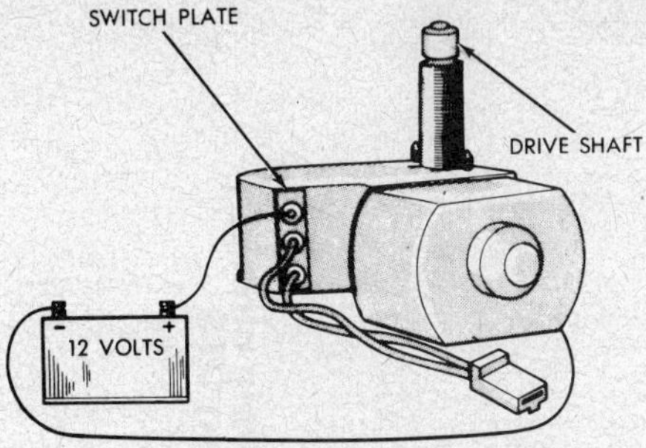


**Fig. 15 Testing liftgate wiper motor. Horizon & Omni**

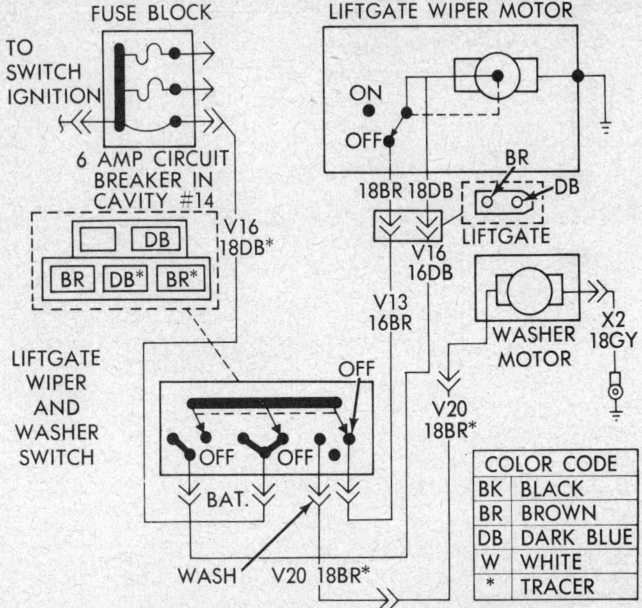


| COLOR CODE | |
|---|---|
| BK | BLACK |
| BR | BROWN |
| DB | DARK BLUE |
| W | WHITE |
| * | TRACER |

**Fig. 16 Liftgate wiper system wiring circuit. Except Horizon, Lancer, LeBaron GTS & Omni**

output shaft.

9. If shaft is not turning, replace motor assembly. If motor shaft is turning, check for proper connection of drive link or linkage.
10. Connect a voltmeter between motor terminal 3 and ground, **Fig. 20.**
11. If no or little voltage is present, move negative test lead to battery ground terminal.
12. If an increase in voltage is noticed, problem is a bad ground circuit. Ensure motor mounting is free of paint and all attaching bolts are tight.
13. If there is still no indication of voltage, problem is an open circuit in wiring harness or wiper switch.
14. If no more than 3 volt increase in voltage is observed, problem is a faulty motor assembly.
15. Disconnect motor wiring connector and replace fuse.
16. If fuse does not blow, motor is defective.
17. If fuse blows, switch or wiring is at fault.

### Motor Runs Slowly At All Speeds

1. Disconnect wiring harness connector at motor.
2. Remove wiper arms and blades.
3. Connect an ohmmeter between battery positive terminal and terminal 3 on motor.
4. If motor runs and average ammeter reading is more than 6 amps, proceed to step 6.
5. If motor runs and average ammeter reading is less than 6 amps, proceed to step 9.
6. Check wiper linkage or pivots for binding. Disconnect drive link from motor.
7. If motor now runs and draws less than 3 amps, repair linkage system.
8. If motor continues to draw more than 3 amps, replace motor assembly.
9. Check motor wiring harness for shorting between high and low speed wires as follows:
   a. Connect a voltmeter or test lamp to motor ground strap.
   b. Set wiper switch on Low position.
   c. Connect other lead to terminal 4 of wiring harness.
   d. If voltage is present, there is a short in the wiring or wiper switch. If no voltage is present, proceed to step e.
   e. Set switch to high position.
   f. Move voltmeter lead from terminal 4 to terminal 3.
   g. If voltage is present, there is a short in the wiring or wiper switch.

### Motor Will Not Run At High Speed, But Not At Low Speed; Motor Will Run At Low Speed, But Not At High Speed

1. If motor will not run at high speed, place switch in High position and connect a test lamp between motor terminal 4 and ground.
2. If motor will not run on low speed, place switch in Low position and connect a test lamp to motor terminal 3 and ground.
3. If test lamp does not light at motor terminal, there is an open in wiring or switch.
4. If test lamp lights, replace motor assembly.

### Motor Keeps Running With Switch In Off Position

Remove wiring harness. Connect a jumper wire between terminals 1 and 3 on motor. Connect a second jumper wire from terminal 2 to battery positive terminal. If motor runs to park position and stops, wiper switch is faulty. If motor continues to operate, replace motor assembly.

### Motor Will Stop Wherever It Is When Switch Is Placed In Off Position; Wipers Do Not Continue Running To Park Position

1. Disconnect motor wiring harness connector and clean terminals. Reconnect connector and test motor.
2. If condition persists, set wiper switch to Off position. Disconnect motor wiring connector. Connect a voltmeter to motor ground strap and other lead to terminal 2 on harness connector.
3. If voltage is not present, check for an open circuit in wiring harness or wiper control switch.
4. If voltage is present, connect an ohmmeter between terminals 3 and 1.
5. If continuity exists, problem is a defective motor.
6. If no continuity exists, problem is an open circuit in wiper control switch or wiring harness.

## REAR WIPER MOTOR TEST

### Daytona

1. Remove lower cover on liftgate.
2. Disconnect feed connector from wiper motor.
3. With ignition switch in On position, check for voltage at blue wire.
4. With both ignition and wiper switches in On position, check for voltage at blue and brown wires.
5. If battery voltage is not present in steps 3 and 4, check fuse, liftgate wiper switch and wiring.
6. With ignition switch in On position and wiper switch in Off position, check for battery voltage between blue and brown wires.
7. If no voltage is present, check ground wire to liftgate switch.
8. If battery voltage is present in steps 3 and 4, replace motor.

## INTERMITTENT WIPER MOTOR SYSTEM TEST

On models with intermittent wipers, the intermittent wipe function is controlled by

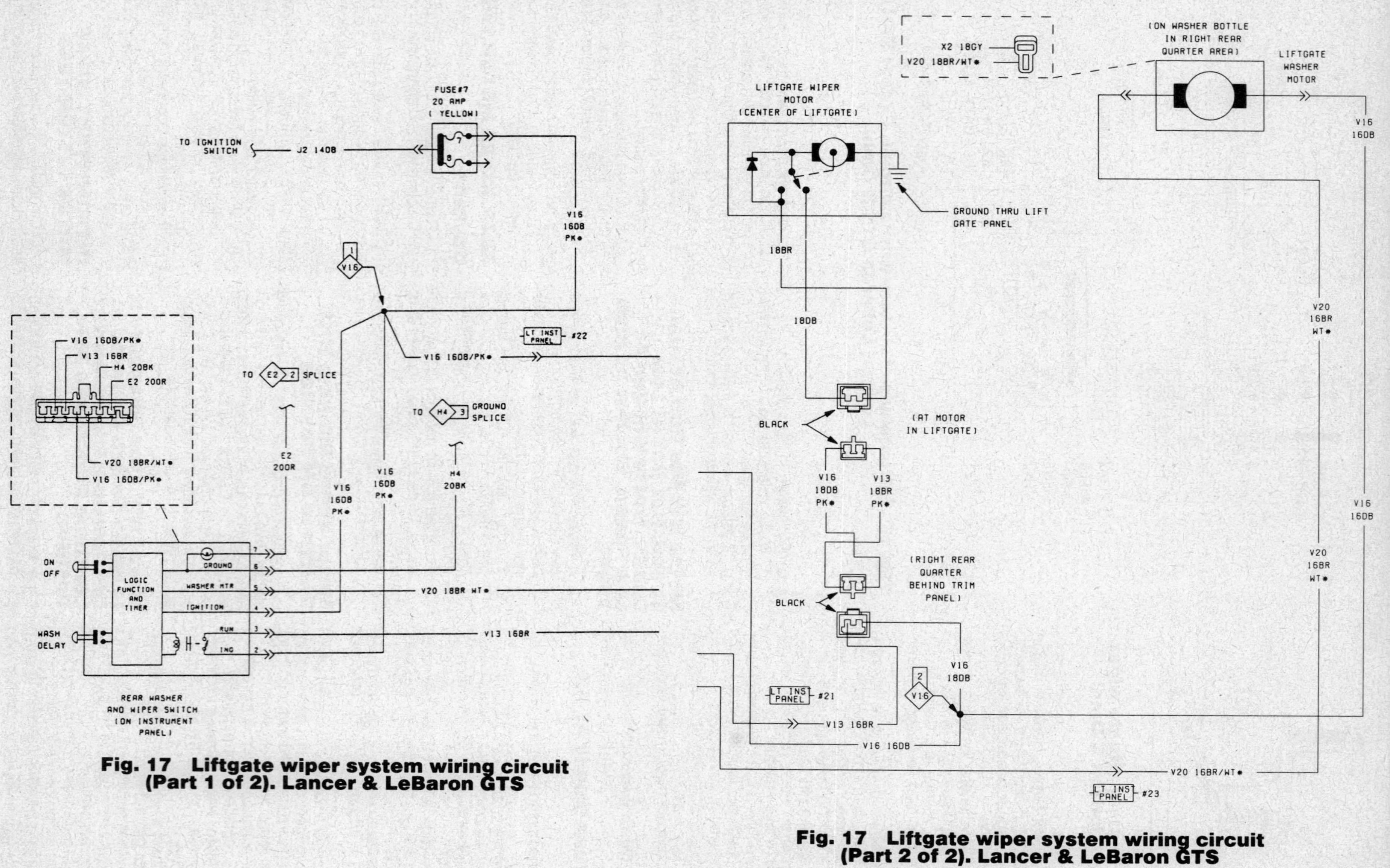


**Fig. 17 Liftgate wiper system wiring circuit (Part 1 of 2). Lancer & LeBaron GTS**

**Fig. 17 Liftgate wiper system wiring circuit (Part 2 of 2). Lancer & LeBaron GTS**

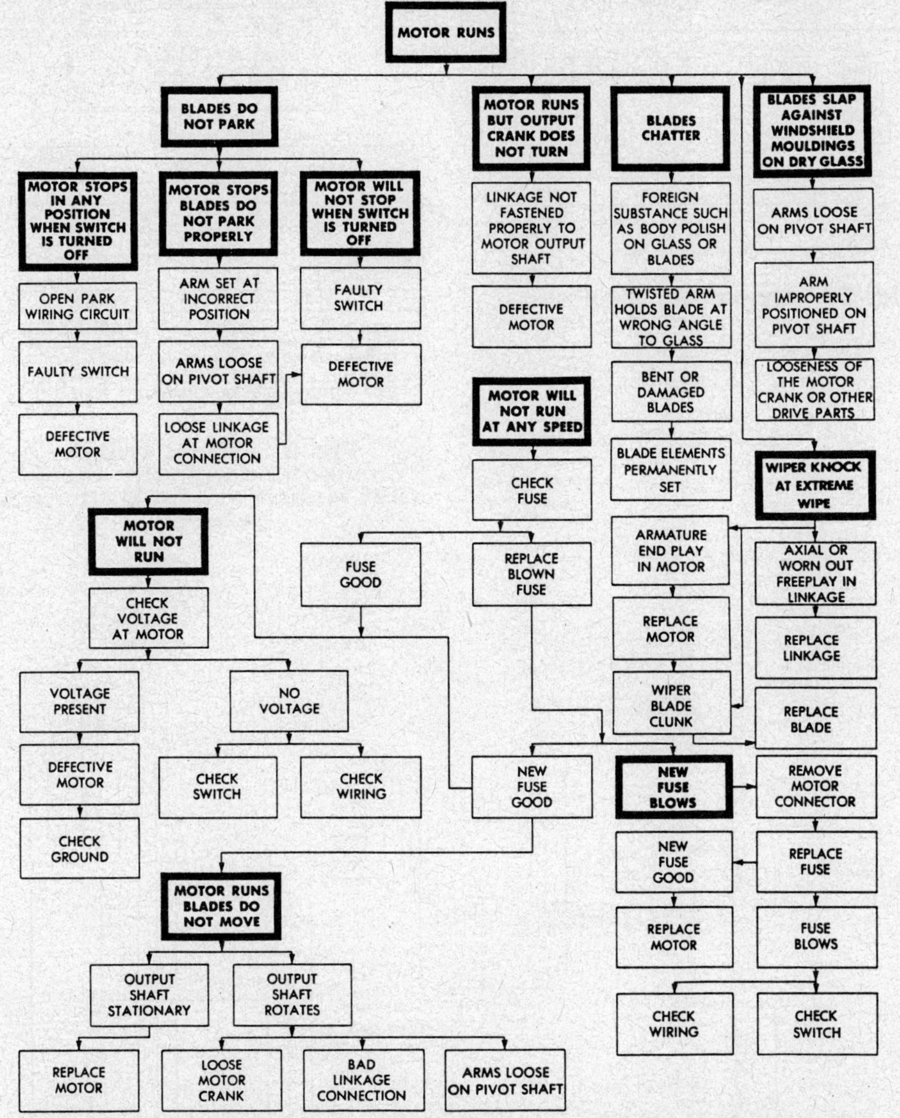


**Fig. 18 Wiper system troubleshooting chart. 1991 Chrysler except Colt, Colt Vista, Conquest, Laser, Monaco & Stealth**

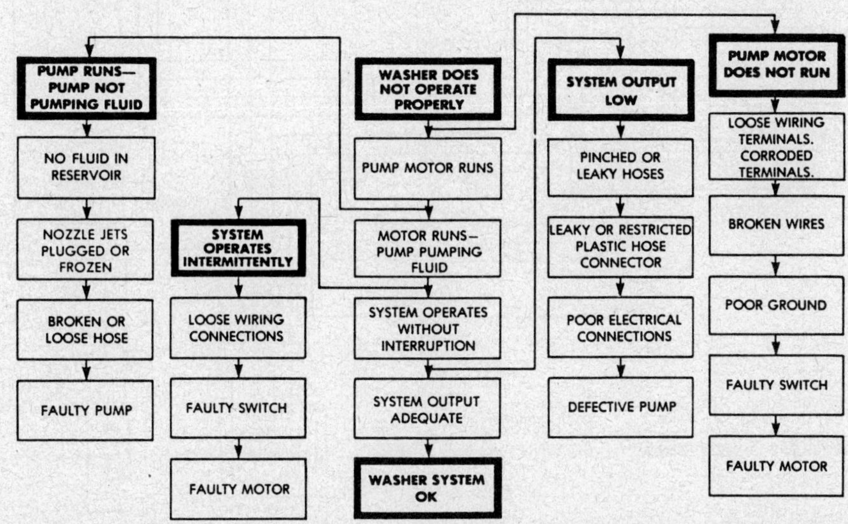


**Fig. 19 Washer system troubleshooting chart. 1991 Chrysler except Colt, Colt Vista, Conquest, Laser, Monaco & Stealth**

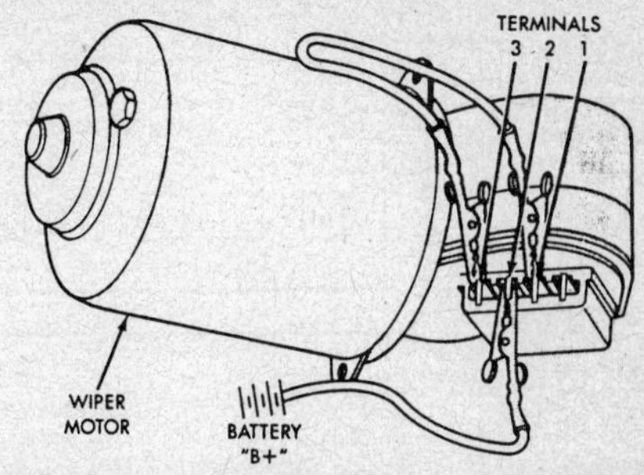


**Fig. 20 Wiper motor terminal location**

the body controller, located in the passenger compartment behind the right side kick panel.

**To diagnose system malfunctions that do not involve the delay function, refer to "Two-Speed Motor Function Test."**

## Wipers Do Not Come On When Switch Is In Delay Position

1. Disconnect the 25-way (black) connector from the body controller.
2. Place wiper control switch in maximum delay position.
3. Connect positive lead of voltmeter to pin 9 of black connector and negative lead to metal case of body controller, **Fig. 21.**
4. If no voltage is present, check switch and wiring for an open circuit.
5. If voltage is present, connect positive lead of voltmeter to pin 22 black connector and negative to a good ground.
6. If no voltage is present, check fuses and wiring for an open circuit.
7. If voltage is present, reconnect body controller.
8. Connect positive lead of voltmeter to pin 24 and negative lead to metal case of body controller.
9. Disconnect wiring harness from wiper motor. set control switch to minimum delay mode.
10. If no voltage is present, check wiring from intermittent wipe switch to body controller for an open circuit.
11. If voltage is present, connect voltmeter to pin L of intermittent wiper switch. Place intermittent wiper switch in maximum delay position.
12. If no voltage is present, replace intermittent wiper switch.
13. If voltage is present, check wiring between intermittent wiper switch and wiper motor for an open circuit.
14. If all tests have been perform and problem was not found, replace body controller.

## Wipers Start To Wipe But Stop Before one Complete Cycle & Do Not Return To Park Position

1. Verify that motor will park when switch is in Off position.
2. Set wiper control switch to maximum delay and allow motor to run until it stops during a wipe cycle then discon-

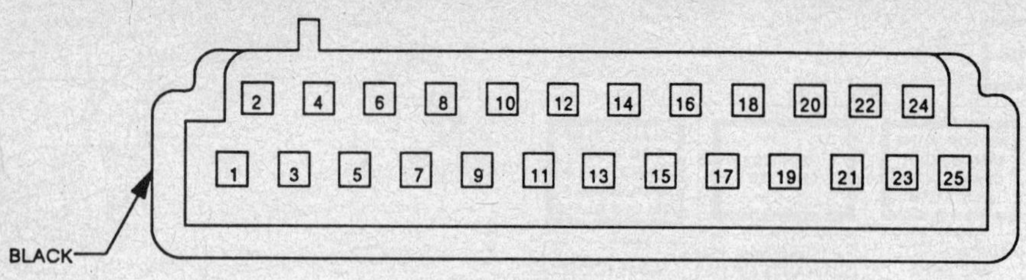


CONNECTOR VIEWED FROM WIRE END

**Fig. 21 Body controller 25-way connector**

MULTIFUNCTION SWITCH PINS

| SWITCH POSITION | CONTINUITY BETWEEN |
|---|---|
| OFF | PIN 6 AND PIN 7 |
| DELAY | PIN 8 AND PIN 9<br>PIN 2 AND PIN 4<br>PIN 1 AND PIN 2<br>PIN 1 AND PIN 4 |
| LOW | PIN 4 AND PIN 6 |
| HIGH | PIN 4 AND PIN 5 |
| WASH | PIN 3 AND PIN 4 |

*RESISTANCE AT MAXIMUM DELAY POSITION SHOULD BE BETWEEN 270,000 OHMS AND 330,000 OHMS.

*RESISTANCE AT MINIMUM DELAY POSITION SHOULD BE ZERO WITH OHMMETER SET ON HIGH OHM SCALE.

**Fig. 22 Wiper switch connecter continuity check. 1991 Models except Daytona & LeBaron**

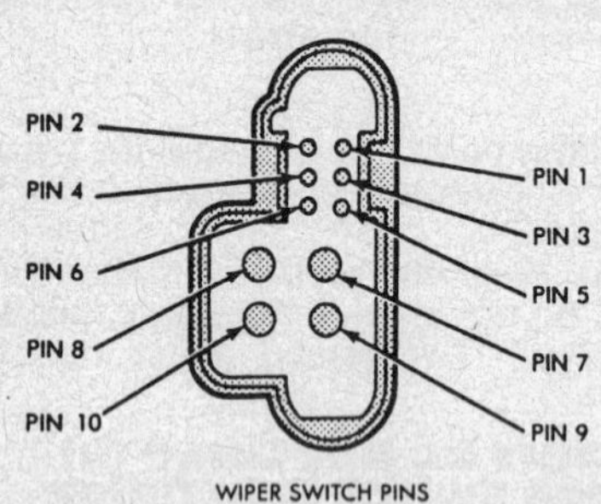


WIPER SWITCH PINS

| SWITCH POSITION | CONTINUITY BETWEEN |
|---|---|
| OFF | PIN 8 AND PIN 10 |
| DELAY | PIN 1 AND PIN 9 |
| LOW | PIN 9 AND PIN 10 |
| HIGH | PIN 9 AND PIN 7 |

**Fig. 23 Wiper switch connecter continuity check. 1991 Daytona & LeBaron**

nect 25-way (black) connector from body controller.

3. Connect positive lead of a voltmeter to pin 20 of black connector and negative lead to metal case of body controller, **Fig. 21.**
4. If no voltage is present, check wiring for an open circuit.
5. If voltage is present, check for continuity between the following terminals of the body controller connector:
   a. Between terminals 20 and 24.
   b. Reverse ohmmeter leads then check between terminals 20 and 24.
6. If continuity does not exist between terminals 20 and 24 in both directions, replace body controller.

## Excessive Delay Of More Than 30 Seconds Or Inadequate Variation In Delay

1. Verify delay as follows:
   a. Minimum delay is 1/2 to 2 seconds.
   b. Maximum delay is 15 to 25 seconds.
2. If there is excessive delay or no variations in delay, remove wiper motor wiring harness while motor is parked in Off position.
3. Remove 25-way (Black) body controller connector, **Fig. 21.**

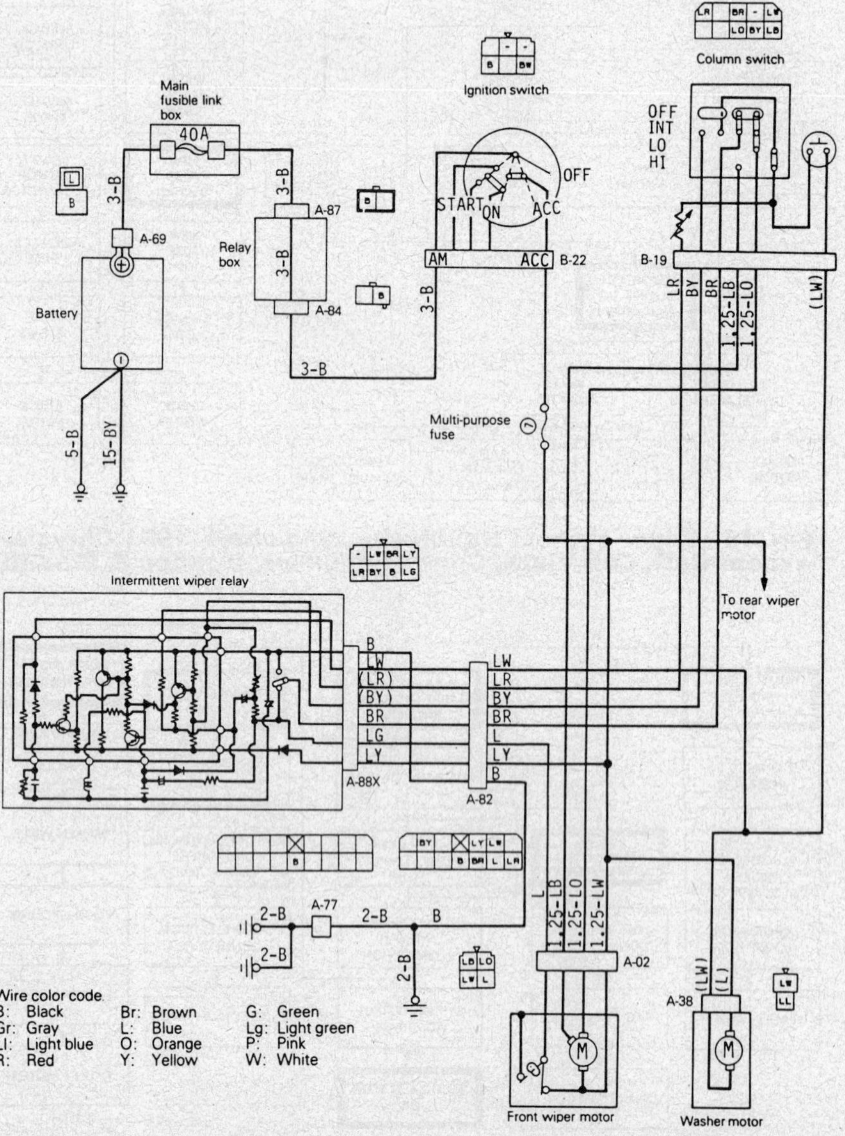


**Fig. 24 Front wiper system wiring diagram. Colt Vista**

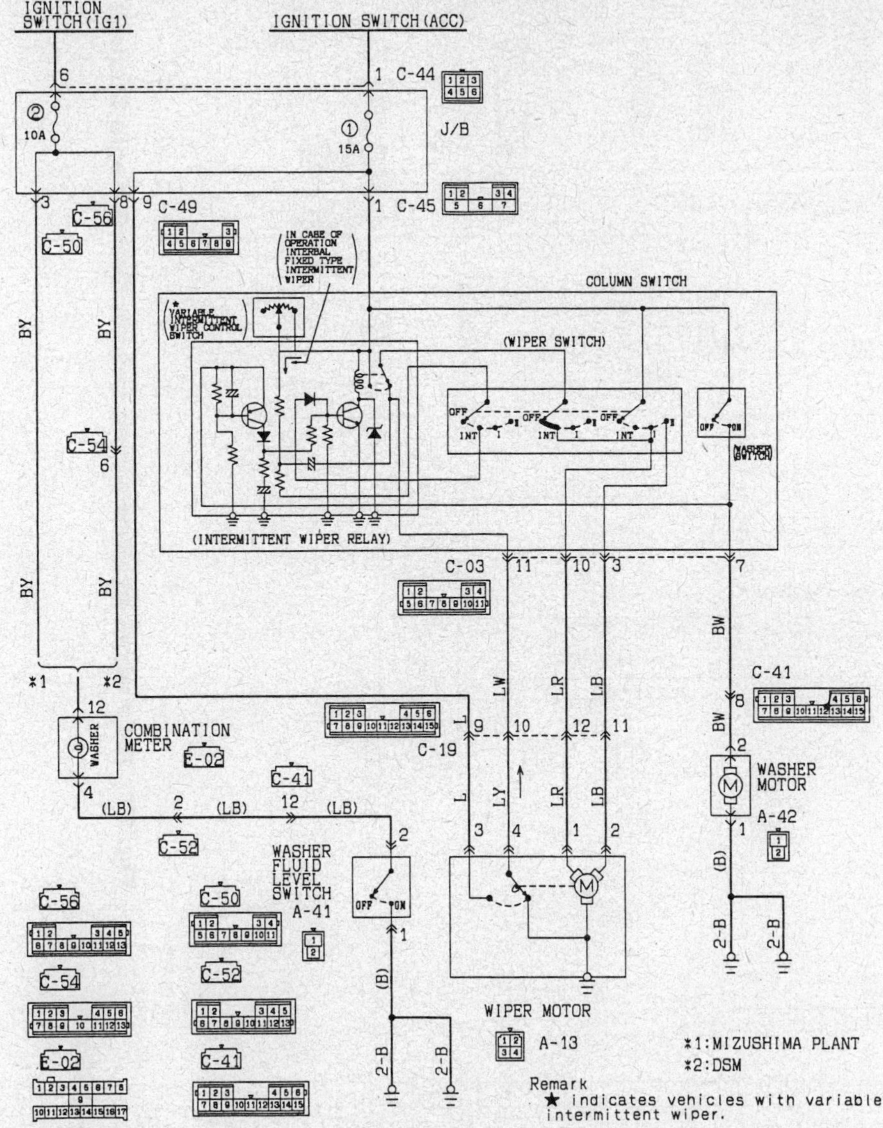


**Fig. 25 Front wiper system wiring diagram. Colt & Eagle Summit**

4. Set wiper control to maximum delay position.
5. With ignition switch in On position, measure voltage between terminal 9 and body ground.
6. If voltage is present, proceed to step 9.
7. If no voltage is present, set wiper control switch to minimum delay position and measure voltage between terminal 9 and body ground.
8. If no voltage is present, check for an open circuit in the intermittent wipe wiring harness.
9. Remove wiper motor circuit fuse.
10. Using an ohmmeter, measure resistance between pins 9 and 22 of the black connector with wiper control first set to minimum delay and then maximum delay.
11. If resistance at minimum delay is between 0 and 15 ohms and resistance at maximum delay is between 240,000 ans 330,000 ohms, replace body controller.
12. If resistance is not as specified in step 11, replace wiper control switch.

### Wipers Do Not Run Continually When Wash Control Is Operated During Delay

1. Disconnect 25-way (black) body controller connector, **Fig. 21.**
2. Using a voltmeter, connect positive lead to pin 10 and negative lead to body controller metal case.
3. Set wiper control switch to Delay position.
4. Depress wash switch.
5. If no voltage is present, check switch relay and wiring.
6. If voltage is present, replace body controller.

### In Delay Mode, Wipers Run Continually When Wash Is Operated But Do Not Provide Four Extra Wipes When Wash Control Is Released

Replace body controller.

### Wipers Start Erratically During Delay Mode

1. Verify that ground connections at instrument panel and motor mounting bolts are tight.
2. Verify motor ground strap is making good contact.
3. Verify that wiring connections to body controller, wiper motor and wiper motor switch are tight and free of corrosion.
4. If condition is not corrected, replace body controller.

## INTERMITTENT WIPER FUNCTION TESTS

### Excessive Delay Of More Than 30 Seconds Or Inadequate Variation In Delay

1. Verify delay as follows:
   a. Minimum delay is ½ to 2 seconds.
   b. Maximum delay is 15 to 25 seconds.
2. If there is excessive delay or no variations in delay, proceed to "Intermittent Wipe Switch Test."

### In Delay Mode Wipers Run Continually When Wash Is Operated But Do Not Provide An Extra Wipe When Wash Control Is Released

Replace intermittent control unit.

### Wipers Start Erratically During Delay Mode

1. Ensure that ground connections at instrument panel is making good contact and are tight.
2. Ensure that motor ground strap is making good contact and that motor bolts are tight.
3. Ensure that wiring ground connections for intermittent wipe control unit and wiper switch are tight.
4. If condition is not corrected, replace intermittent control unit.

## INTERMITTENT WIPE SWITCH TEST

Disconnect wipe switch from body wiring harness in steering column. Test for continuity between terminals as shown in **Figs. 22 and 23.**

# COLT, COLT VISTA & EAGLE SUMMIT

## TROUBLESHOOTING

### Wipers Do Not Operate

1. Blown fuse No. 7.
2. Defective wiper switch.
3. Defective wiper motor.

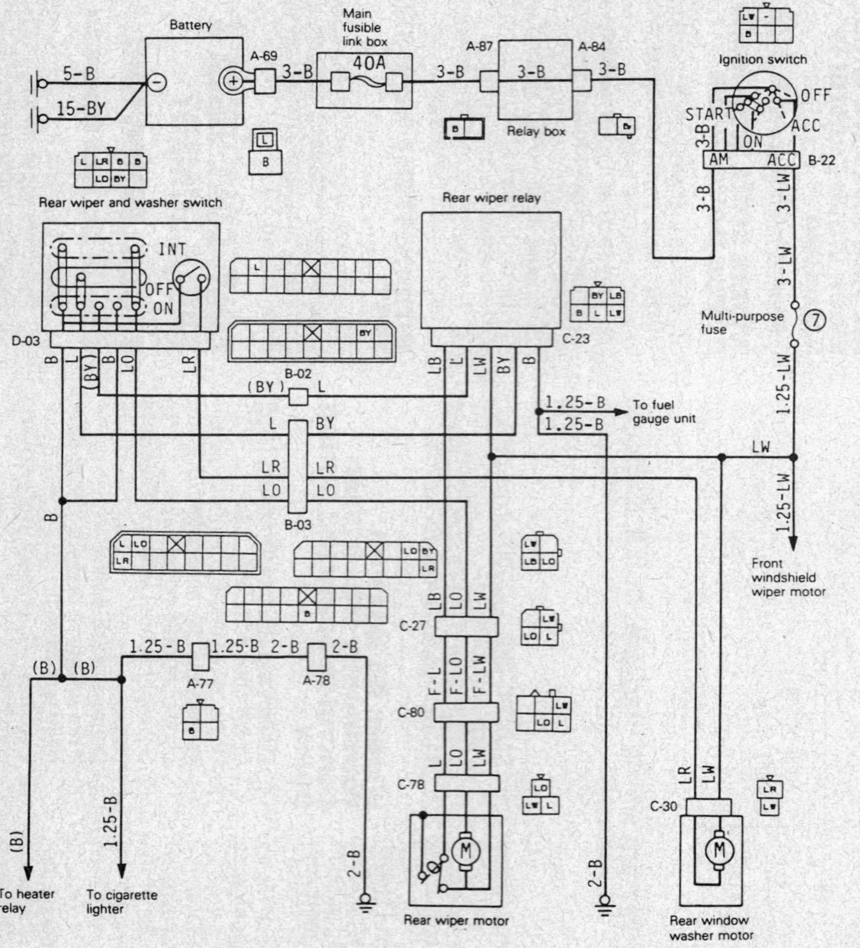


Fig. 26 Rear wiper system wiring circuit. Colt Vista

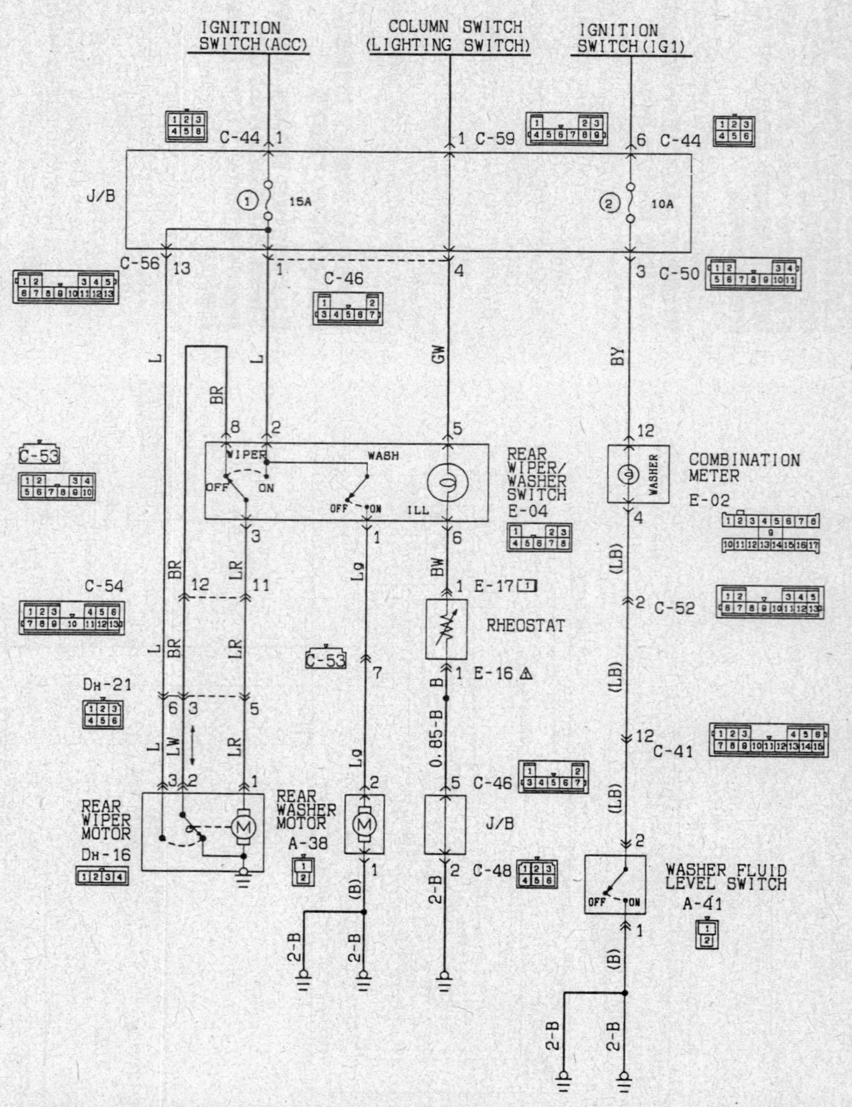


Fig. 27 Rear wiper system wiring circuit. Colt & Eagle Summit

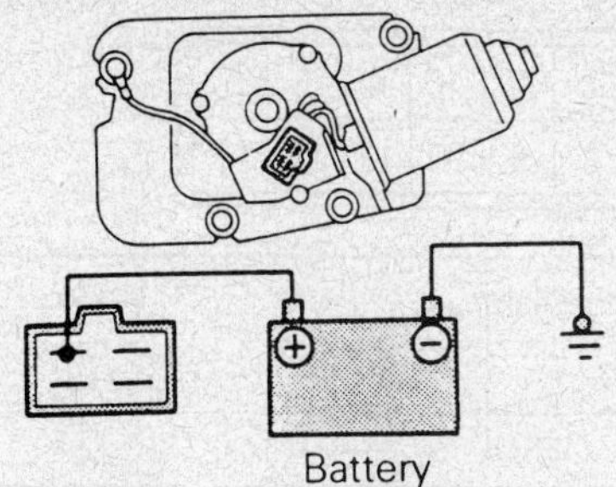


Fig. 28 Wiper motor low speed test. Colt & Eagle Summit

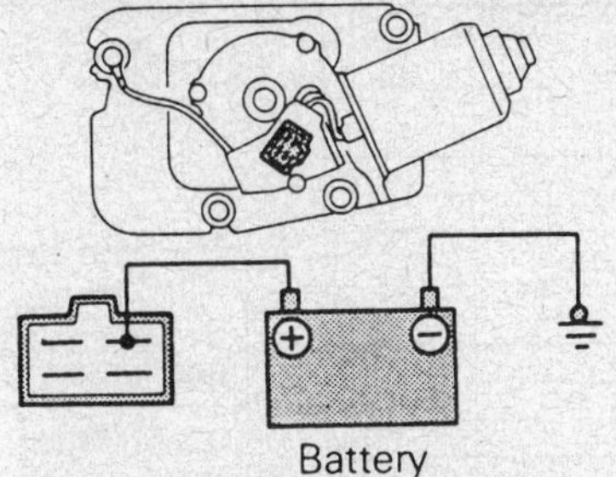


Fig. 29 Wiper motor high speed test. Colt & Eagle Summit

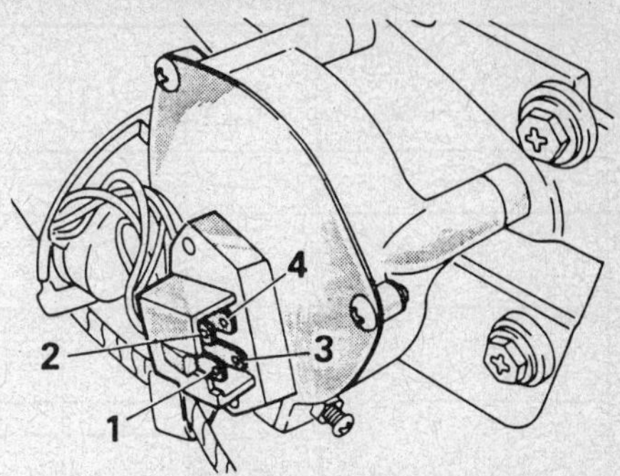


Fig. 30 Wiper motor terminal locations. Colt Vista

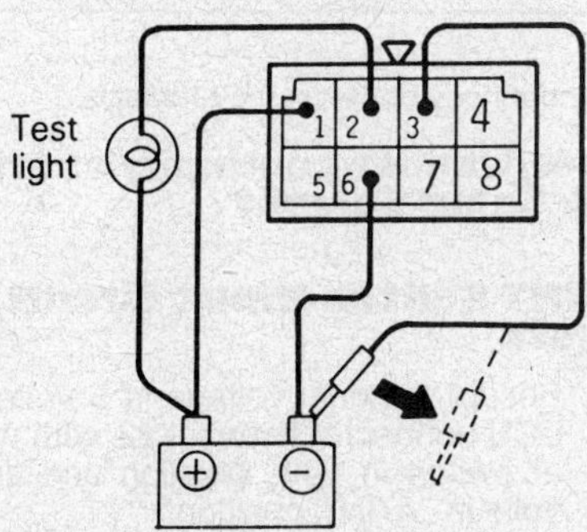


Fig. 31 Intermittent terminal locations. Colt Vista

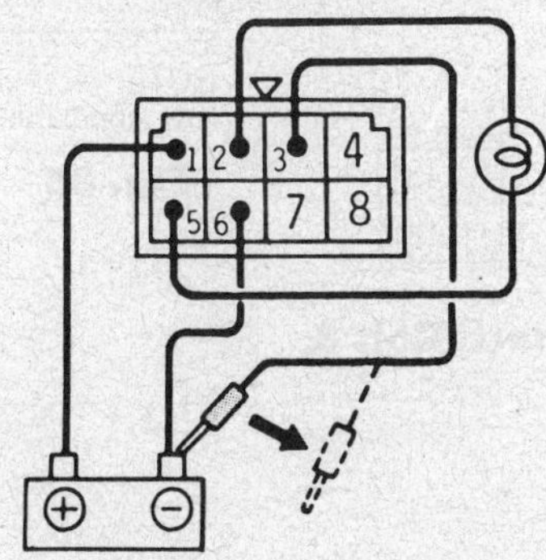


Fig. 32 Washer terminal locations. Colt Vista

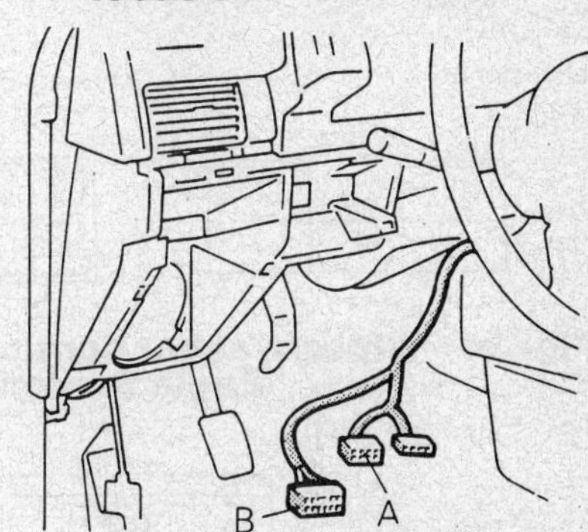


Fig. 33 Removing wiper/washer switch. Colt & Eagle Summit

4. Check ground connection.
5. Check wiper linkage.

### Wipers Do Not Operate At Low Speed Or High Speed

1. Defective wiper switch.
2. Defective wiper motor.
3. Check wiring harness connection.

### Wipers Do Not Operate In Intermittent Mode

1. Check intermittent wiper relay terminal voltage with relay energized.
2. Connect a voltmeter between terminal No. 3 and ground.
3. If voltmeter indicates zero voltage, check wiper switch.
4. If voltmeter indicates 12 volts, check intermittent wiper relay.
5. If voltmeter changes between zero volts and 12 volts repeatedly, system is operating satisfactory.

### Wipers Fail To Stop

1. Check wiper motor.

### Interval Period Will Not Adjust

1. Check interval adjustment switch.
2. Check intermittent wiper relay.

### Washer Is Inoperative

1. Check washer motor.
2. Check washer switch.

### Wiper Operation Not Coordinated With Washer

1. Check intermittent wiper relay.

## TESTING

Refer to **Figs. 24 through 27** for wiring circuits when testing the wiper system.

### WIPER MOTOR

#### Colt & Eagle Summit

1. Connect battery to wiper motor, **Fig. 28,** and ensure motor operation at low speed.
2. Connect battery to wiper motor, **Fig. 29,** and ensure motor operates at high speed.

#### Colt Vista

1. Disconnect wiring connector from wiper, then connect battery to wiper motor connector and ensure wiper motor runs.
2. Connect battery positive lead to terminal 3 and negative lead to terminal 1, and ensure motor runs at low speed, **Fig. 30.**
3. Connect battery positive lead to terminal 4 and negative lead to terminal 2, and ensure motor runs at high speed.

### INTERMITTENT OPERATION TEST

#### Colt Vista

1. Connect battery and suitable test lamp to control unit, **Fig. 31.**
2. With terminal 3 connected to battery negative post, light will illuminate when wipers pulse.
3. If light stops illumination condition is satisfactory.

### WASHER INTERLOCKING TEST

1. Connect battery and suitable test lamp to control unit, **Fig. 32.**
2. With terminal 3 connected to battery negative post, light will illuminate for approximately 0.8 seconds.
3. If light stops illumination after three seconds condition is satisfactory.

### WIPER & WASHER SWITCH

#### Colt & Eagle Summit

1. Remove lower panel assembly and the column cover, **Fig. 33.**
2. Disconnect column switch electrical connector, then check continuity between terminals for each switch, **Fig. 34.**
3. If continuity is not as specified, replace switch, **Fig. 33.**

### REAR WIPER & WASHER SWITCH

#### Colt & Eagle Summit

1. Disconnect wiper/washer switch electrical connector.
2. Check continuity between terminals, **Fig. 35**
3. If continuity is not as specified, replace switch.

#### Colt Vista

1. Remove rear wiper/washer switch from instrument panel.
2. Check continuity between terminals, **Fig. 36.**
3. If continuity is not as specified, replace switch.

| Switch position \ Terminal | 10 | 17 | 18 | 4 | 14 |
|---|---|---|---|---|---|
| OFF | | ○— | —○ | ○- - - | - - -○ |
| *INT | | ○—<br>○— | <br>—○ | —○<br>○- - - | <br>- - -○ |
| 1 | | ○— | | —○<br>○- - - | <br>- - -○ |
| 2 | ○— | | | —○<br>○- - - | <br>- - -○ |

Connector A

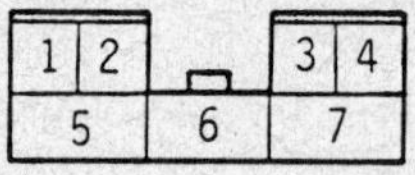

| 1 | 2 | | 3 | 4 |
|---|---|---|---|---|
| 5 | | 6 | | 7 |

Connector B

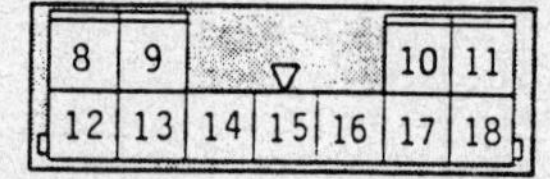


**Fig. 34 Wiper/washer continuity chart. Colt & Eagle Summit**

| Switch Position \ Terminal | 2 | 4 | 6 | 1 | 7 | 3 |
|---|---|---|---|---|---|---|
| Wiper OFF | | ○— | — | — | —○ | |
| Wiper ON | ○— | — | — | — | —○ | |
| INT | | ○— | ○—<br>— | —○<br>— | <br>—○ | |
| Washer ON | ○— | — | — | — | — | —○ |

NOTE
○–○ indicates that there is continuity between the terminals.

**Fig. 36 Rear wiper/washer continuity chart. Colt Vista**

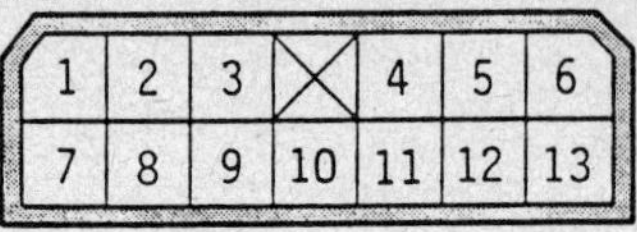


| Switch position | Terminal | 8 | 9 | 7 | 10 |
|---|---|---|---|---|---|
| Wiper switch | OFF | ○— | —○ | | |
| | ON | ○— | — | — | —○ |
| Washer switch | OFF | | | | |
| | ON | | | ○— | —○ |

NOTE
○–○ indicates that there is continuity between the terminals.

**Fig. 35 Rear wiper/washer continuity chart. Colt & Eagle Summit**

### A/INT Switch Input Circuit Tests

1. Ensure terminal voltage is 5 volts at ECU connector terminal 22, with wiper switch in "Off" position and zero volts in "A/INT position."
2. Ensure no continuity exists between ECU connector terminal 22 and ground, with wiper switch in "Off" position.
3. Ensure continuity exists between ECU connector terminal 22 and ground, with wiper switch in "A/INT" position, **Fig. 41**.

### Slow, Fast Switch Input Circuit Tests

1. Ensure terminal voltage is 0-5 volts at ECU connector terminal 5, with slow switch On.
2. Ensure terminal voltage is 0-5 volts at ECU connector terminal 6, with fast switch On.
3. Ensure continuity exists between ECU connector terminal 5 and ground, with slow switch On.
4. Ensure continuity exists between ECU connector terminal 6 and ground, with fast switch On, **Fig. 42**.

### Vehicle-Speed Sensor Input Circuit Tests

1. Ensure terminal voltage is zero volts at ECU connector terminal 17 to ground, with vehicle speed sensor On.
2. Ensure terminal voltage is 5 volts at ECU connector terminal 17 to ground, with vehicle speed sensor Off, **Fig. 43**.
3. Connect ohmmeter between ECU connector terminal 17 and ground, then check condition as follows:
   a. Raise front end of vehicle.
   b. Rotate tires in forward direction.
   c. Continuity should exist as wheels are rotating.

### Wiper Relay Activation Circuit Test

1. Ensure terminal voltage is zero volts at ECU connector terminal 23, with wiper and ignition switch Off.

# CONQUEST

## TROUBLESHOOTING

Refer to **Fig. 37**, when troubleshooting wiper system.

## DIAGNOSIS & TESTING

### CHECKING INPUT

With glove compartment open, connect a voltmeter between terminal for Electronic Time and Alarm Control System (ETACS) and ground, **Fig. 37**, or a multi-use tester to diagnosis connector. Ensure voltage output is present with ignition key off and door switch on for each sensor. If there is no output of a voltage pattern, check for malfunction of switch or damaged or disconnected wiring.

### CIRCUIT TESTS

### Power Supply & Ground Circuit Test

1. Ensure battery voltage is present at ECU connector terminal 2 at all times.
2. Ensure continuity exists between ECU connector terminal 15 and ground at all times, **Fig. 39**.

### Ignition Switch Input Circuit Test

1. Ensure terminal voltage is zero volts at ECU connector terminal 14, with ignition switch in "Off" position and battery voltage is present in "Accessory" position.
2. Ensure battery voltage is present at ECU connector terminal 18, with ignition switch in "On" position, **Fig. 40**.

VEHICLE-SPEED-RESPONSE TYPE INTERMITTENT WIPERS

| Problem | Probable cause(s) | Checking procedure | Remedy |
|---|---|---|---|
| The wipers don't operate when the wiper switch is set to the "A/INT" position. [The wipers do operate, however, when the wiper switch is set to the "1" (low speed) position.] | Damage or disconnection of the wiring of the wiper switch ("A/INT") input circuit. | If a malfunction is discovered as a result of the checking of the input conduct check of the individual part and circuit. | Repair the wiring harness, or replace the column switch. |
| | Damage or disconnection of the wiring of the wiper switch ("A/INT"). | | |
| | Damage or disconnection of the wiring of the ignition switch input circuit. | If a malfunction is discovered as a result of the checking of the input conduct check of the individual part and circuit. | Repair the wiring harness. |
| | Damage or disconnection of the wiring of the wiper relay activation circuit. | Conduct check of the individual part and circuit. | Repair the wiring harness, or replace the wiper relay. |
| | Malfunction of the wiper relay. | | |
| | Malfunction of the electronic control unit. | – | Replace the electronic control unit. |
| The wipers don't stop when the wiper switch is switched OFF. (This problem occurs at the low speed of the wipers.) NOTE If the wipers continue operating (without stopping) at the "2" position (high speed) of the wiper switch, there is a short-circuit in the circuit at the wiper motor high-speed side. | Short-circuit in the wiper switch ("A/INT") input circuit. | If a malfunction is discovered as a result of the checking of the input conduct check of the individual part and circuit. | Repair the wiring harness, or replace the column switch. |
| | Short-circuit in the wiper switch ("A/INT"). | | |
| | Short-circuit in the wiper relay activation circuit. | Conduct check of the individual part and circuit. | Repair the wiring harness. |
| | Malfunction of the electronic control unit. | – | Replace the electronic control unit. |
| When the wiper switch is set to the "A/INT" position, the wipers operate continuously at low speed, not intermittent operation. (The wipers stop, however, when the wiper switch is set to "OFF".) | Short-circuit in the wiper switch ("A/INT") input circuit. | If a malfunction is discovered as a result of the checking of the input conduct check of the individual part and circuit. | Repair the wiring harness, or replace the column switch. |
| | Short-circuit in the wiper switch ("A/INT"). | | |
| | Malfunction of the electronic control unit. | – | Replace the electronic control unit. |

**Fig. 37 Wiper system troubleshooting chart (Part 1 of 2). Conquest**

| Problem | Probable cause(s) | Checking procedure | Remedy |
|---|---|---|---|
| The intermittent time does not change when the intermittent variable volume switch setting is changed. (The vehicle speed is a constant speed.) | Damage or disconnection of the wiring of the intermittent variable volume switch input circuit. | If a malfunction is discovered as a result of the checking of the input conduct check of the individual part and circuit. | Repair the wiring harness, or replace the column switch. |
| | Damage or disconnection of the wiring of the intermittent variable volume switch. | | |
| | Malfunction of the electronic control unit. | – | Replace the electronic control unit. |
| The wipers' intermittent time does not change according to changes in the vehicle speed. (The intermittent variable volume switch setting is fixed.) | Damage or disconnection of the wiring of the vehicle-speed sensor input circuit, or a short-circuit. | If a malfunction is discovered as a result of the checking of the input conduct check of the individual part and circuit. | Repair the wiring harness, or replace the vehicle-speed sensor. |
| | Malfunction of the vehicle-speed sensor. | | |
| | Malfunction of the electronic control unit. | – | Replace the electronic control unit. |

MIST WIPERS/WASHER-INTERLOCKED WIPERS

| Problem | Probable cause(s) | Checking procedure | Remedy |
|---|---|---|---|
| The wipers do not function when the washer switch is switched ON for 0.6 second or longer. (With the wiper switch at the "A/INT" position, however, intermittent operation of the wipers is normal, and the washer function is normal.) | Damage or disconnection of the wiring of the washer switch input circuit. | If a malfunction is discovered as a result of the checking of the input conduct check of the individual part and circuit. | Repair the wiring harness, or replace the washer switch. |
| | Damage or disconnection of the wiring of the washer switch. | | |
| | Malfunction of the electronic control unit. | – | Replace the electronic control unit. |
| The wipers do not function when the washer switch is switched ON for less than 0.6 second. (The wipers and washer do function, however, when the washer switch is switched ON for 0.6 second or longer.) | Malfunction of the electronic control unit. | – | Replace the electronic control unit. |

**Fig. 37 Wiper system troubleshooting chart (Part 2 of 2). Conquest**

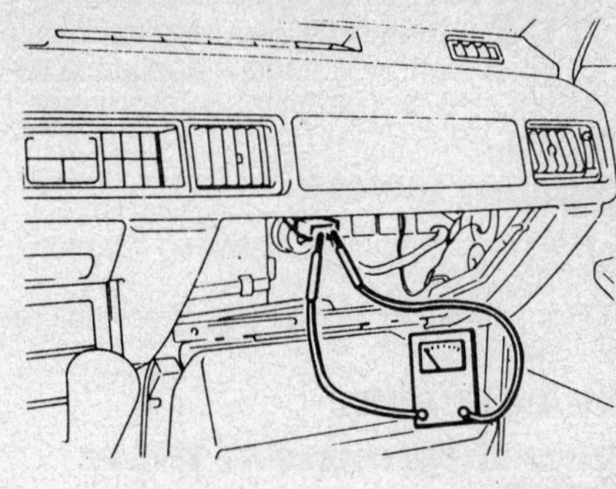

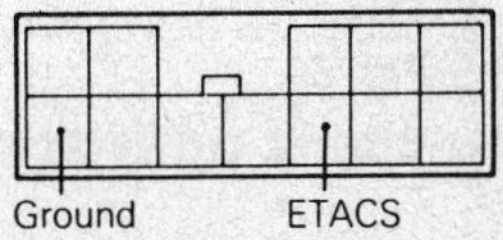


**Fig. 38 ETACS diagnosis connector. Conquest**

2. Ensure battery voltage is present at ECU connector terminal 23, with wiper switch "Off" and ignition in "Accessory" position, **Fig. 44.**

### Washer Switch Input Circuit Test

1. Ensure terminal voltage is zero volts at ECU connector terminal 4, with washer switch Off.
2. Ensure battery voltage is present at ECU connector terminal 4, with washer switch On, **Fig. 45.**

## COMPONENT TESTING

### Ignition Switch

1. Remove knee protector, then disconnect ignition switch connector.
2. Check continuity between terminals, **Fig. 46.**
3. If continuity is not as specified, replace switch.

### Wiper Switch

1. Check continuity between terminals, **Fig. 47.**
2. If continuity is not as specified, replace switch.

### Slow, Fast Switch

1. Check continuity between terminals, **Fig. 47.**
2. If continuity is not as specified, replace switch.

### Vehicle Speed Sensor

Using an ohmmeter, check continuity between terminals 1 and 2, continuity should be present four times every rotation of shaft at speedometer cable connection, **Fig. 48.**

### Wiper Relay Switch

1. Remove wiper relay.

2. Check continuity between terminals when battery voltage is applied to terminal 2 and terminal 5 is grounded, **Fig. 49.**

### Washer Switch

1. Check continuity between terminals, **Fig. 47.**
2. If continuity is not as specified, replace switch.

## REAR WIPER

### Rear Intermittent Wiper Relay

1. Remove rear intermittent wiper relay from rear end panel.
2. Check continuity between terminals 1 and 5, **Fig. 50.**

### Intermittent Operation Check

1. Connect battery and test light to relay, **Fig. 50.**
2. If light illuminates when battery negative lead is connected to terminal 5, condition is satisfactory.

# STEALTH

## TROUBLESHOOTING

Refer to **Fig. 51,** when troubleshooting wiper system.

## DIAGNOSIS & TESTING

### CHECKING INPUT

Connect a voltmeter between terminal for Electronic Time and Alarm Control System (ETACS) and ground, **Fig. 52,** or a multi-use tester to diagnosis connector. Ensure voltage output is present when each of the following sensors are activated.

1. Ignition switch.
2. Wiper Switch (INT).
3. Intermittent variable-volume switch.
4. Washer switch.

If there is no output of a voltage pattern, check for malfunction of switch or damaged or disconnected wiring.

### CIRCUIT TESTS

Refer to **Figs. 53 and 54** when testing circuits.

### Check No. 1, Power Supply & Ground Circuit Test

1. Ensure battery voltage is present at ECU connector terminal 53 when ignition switch in turned to On or ACC position.

### Check No. 2, INT Switch Input Circuit Tests

1. Ensure terminal voltage is 5 volts at ECU connector terminal 9, on models without theft alarm, or terminal 11, on models with theft alarm, with wiper switch in "Off" position and zero volts in "INT" position.
2. Ensure no continuity exists between ECU connector terminal 9 and ground, on models without theft

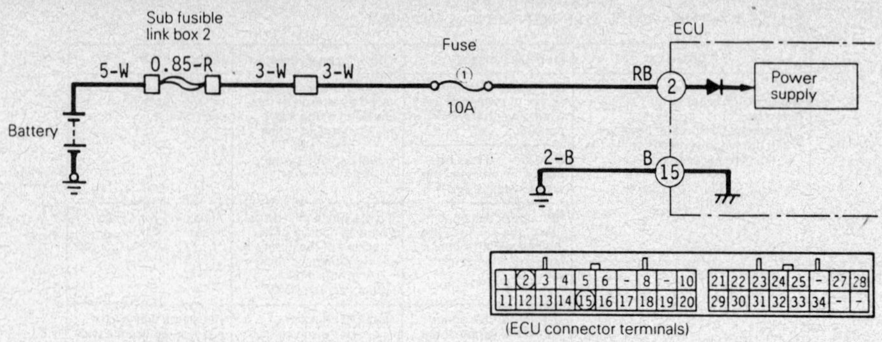


**Fig. 39 ETACS power supply & ground wiring circuit. Conquest**

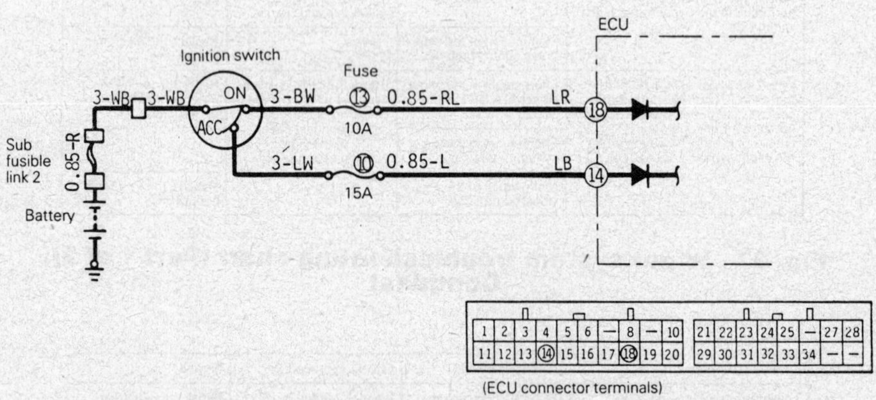


**Fig. 40 Ignition switch input wiring circuit. Conquest**

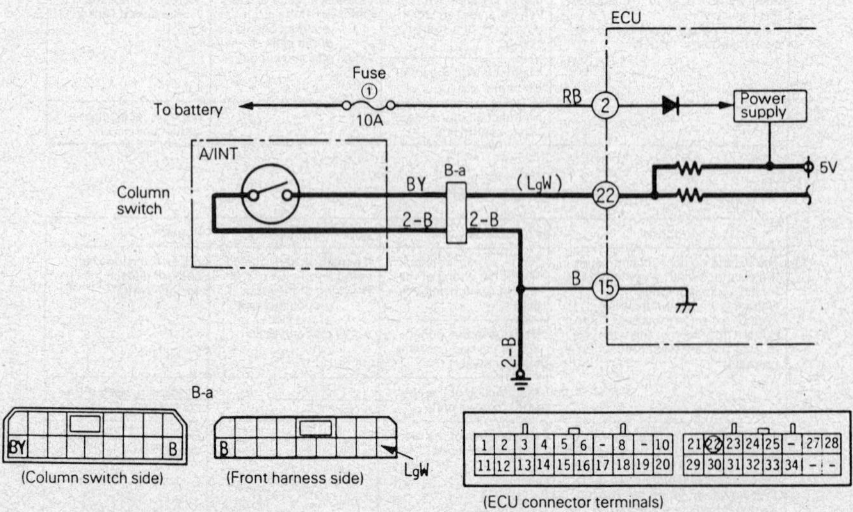


NOTE
The "ECU" (electronic control unit) indicates the ETACS control unit.

**Fig. 41 A/INT switch input wiring circuit. Conquest**

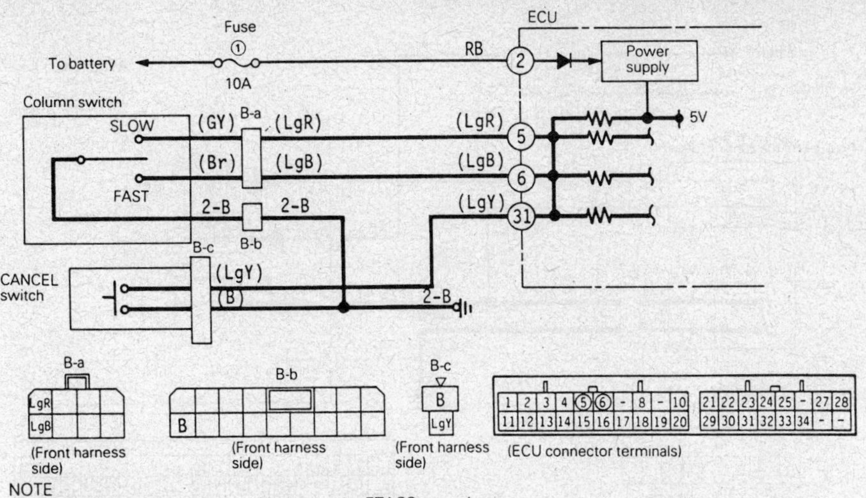

NOTE
The "ECU" (electronic control unit) indicates the ETACS control unit.

**Fig. 42 Slow, fast switch input wiring circuit. Conquest**

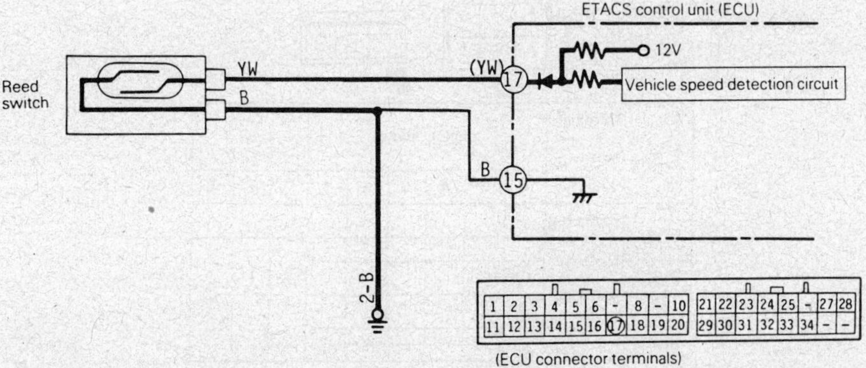


**Fig. 43 Vehicle speed sensor input wiring circuit. Conquest**

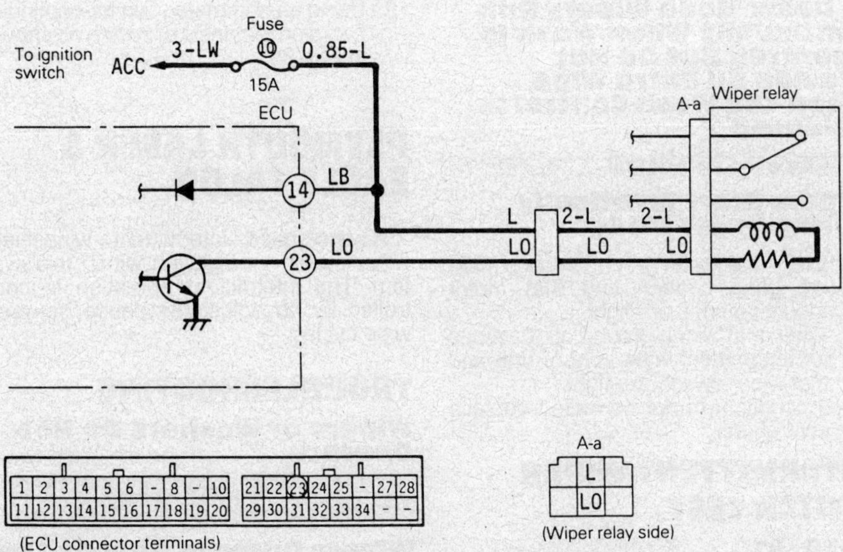


**Fig. 44 Wiper relay activation wiring circuit. Conquest**

alarm, or terminal 11 and ground, on models with theft alarm, with wiper switch in "Off" position.

3. Ensure continuity exists between ECU connector terminal 9 and ground, on models without theft alarm, or terminal 11 and ground, on models with theft alarm, with wiper switch in "INT" position.

### Check No. 3, Intermittent Variable Volume Switch Input Circuit Tests

1. Ensure terminal voltage is 0-2.5 volts at ECU connector terminal 13, on models without theft alarm, or terminal 15, on models with theft alarm, with intermittent variable volume switch turned from Fast to Slow.
2. Ensure continuity is 0 to 1000 ohms between ECU connector terminal 13 and ground, on models without theft alarm, or terminal 15 and ground, on models with theft alarm, intermittent variable volume switch turned from Fast to Slow.

### Check No. 4, Wiper Relay Activation Circuit Test

1. Ensure terminal voltage is zero volts at ECU connector terminal 4, on models without theft alarm, or terminal 6, on models with theft alarm, with wiper and ignition switch Off.
2. Ensure battery voltage is present at ECU connector terminal 4, on models without theft alarm, or terminal 6, on models with theft alarm, with wiper switch "Off" and ignition in "Accessory" position.

### Check No. 5, Washer Switch Input Circuit Test

1. Ensure terminal voltage is zero volts at ECU connector terminal 58, on models without theft alarm, or terminal 60, on models with theft alarm, with ignition switch in ACC position and washer switch Off.
2. Ensure battery voltage is present at ECU connector terminal 58, on models without theft alarm, or terminal 60, on models with theft alarm, with ignition switch in ACC position and washer switch On.

## COMPONENT TESTING

### Front Wiper Motor

Connect battery voltage to wiper motor as shown in **Fig. 55**, and ensure that it operates at slow and high speeds.

### Front Wiper Motor Stop Position

1. Operate wiper motor at low speed and intermediately disconnect battery to allow wiper motor to stop.
2. Connect terminals as well as battery as shown in **Fig. 55**, and ensure wiper motor stops at automatically stopped position following low speed operation.

### Front Wiper Switch

1. Check continuity between terminals, **Fig. 56.**

2. If continuity is not as specified, replace switch.

### Front Wiper Relay

1. Ensure that continuity exists between terminals 5 and 11 and between terminals 6 and 10 and no continuity exists between terminals 6 and 11, **Fig. 57.**
2. Connect positive terminal of battery voltage to terminal 5 and negative terminal to terminal 11 to ensure that battery voltage is available at terminal 6.

### Rear Wiper Motor

Connect battery voltage as shown in **Fig. 58**, and ensure motor operates.

### Rear Wiper Motor Stop Position

1. Operate wiper motor and intermediately disconnect battery to allow wiper motor to stop.
2. Connect terminals as well as battery as shown in **Fig. 58**, and ensure wiper motor stops at automatically stopped position following low speed operation.

### Rear Intermittent Wiper Relay

1. Remove quarter trim panel.
2. With relay connected and wipers operating at intermittent mode, ensure that battery voltage exists at terminal 2, **Fig. 59.**

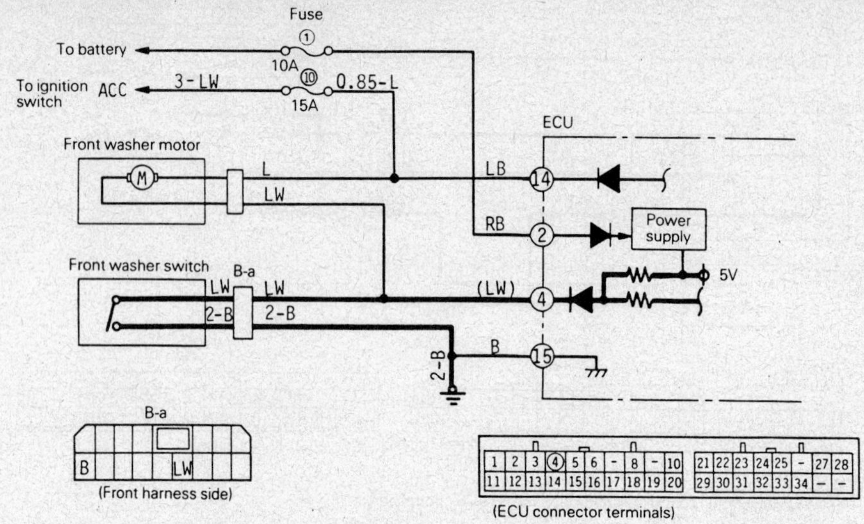


**Fig. 45 Washer switch input wiring circuit. Conquest**

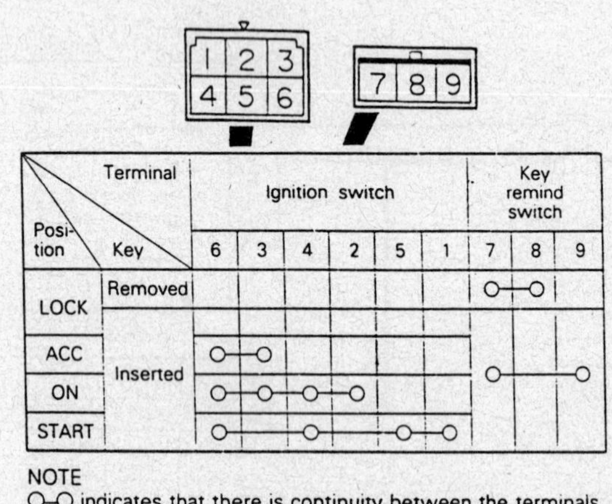

| Position | Key | Ignition switch 6 | 3 | 4 | 2 | 5 | 1 | Key remind switch 7 | 8 | 9 |
|---|---|---|---|---|---|---|---|---|---|---|
| LOCK | Removed | | | | | | | O | O | |
| ACC | Inserted | O | O | | | | | O | | O |
| ON | Inserted | O | O | O | O | | | O | | O |
| START | Inserted | O | | O | | O | O | O | | O |

NOTE
O—O indicates that there is continuity between the terminals.

**Fig. 46 Ignition switch continuity chart. Conquest**

# DODGE MONACO, EAGLE MEDALLION & PREMIER

A two-speed intermittent windshield wiper motor is employed within this system. The intermittent operation is controlled by an adjustable pause between wipe cycles. The controls are located in a pod, attached to LH side of steering column.

## TROUBLESHOOTING

Refer to **Figs. 60 and 61** for system wiring diagrams and **Figs. 62 through 64** for troubleshooting these models.

## INTERMITTENT WIPER FUNCTION TEST

### 1990–91

### Excessive Delay Of More Than 30 Seconds or Inadequate Variation In Delay

1. Verify wiper delay as follows:
   a. Minimum delay should be at intervals of 1.5 to 2 seconds.
   b. Maximum delay should be at intervals of 10 to 30 seconds.
2. If wiper verification is not as specified, perform "Intermittent Wiper Switch Test."

### In Delay Mode Wipers Run Continually When Wash Is Operated But Do Not Provide An Extra Wipe When The Wash Control Is Released

Replace the control unit.

### Wipers Start Erratically During Delay Mode

1. Verify that motor ground strap is making good contact and that motor mounting bolts are tight.
2. Verify that wiring ground connections for intermittent wipe control unit and that wiper switch are tight.
3. If condition in not corrected, replace control unit.

## INTERMITTENT WIPER SWITCH TEST

### 1990–91

1. Disconnect wiper switch wires from switch body in steering column.
2. Using an ohmmeter, test for continuity between terminals of switch as shown in **Fig. 65.**

# PLYMOUTH LASER & EAGLE TALON

A two-speed intermittent windshield wiper motor is employed within this system. The intermittent operation is controlled by an adjustable pause between wipe cycles.

## TROUBLESHOOTING

### Wipers Or Washers Do Not Operate

1. Check multi-purpose fuse No. 9.
2. Check ground.

### Wipers Operate Only At Low Or High Speed

1. Check Wiper Switch.

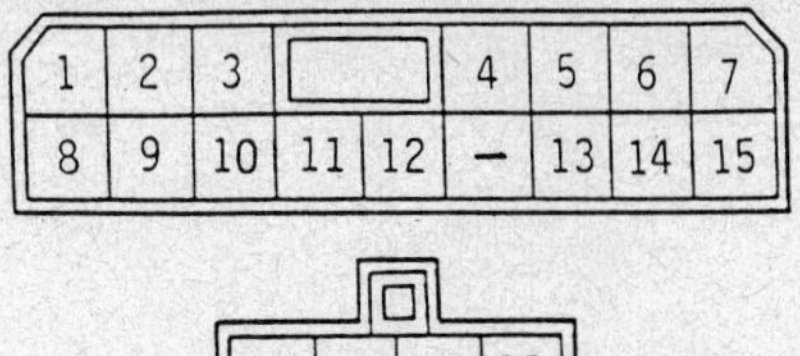


| Switch position | | 8 | 17 | 9 | 10 | 14 | 11 | 23 | 19 |
|---|---|---|---|---|---|---|---|---|---|
| Wiper switch | OFF | | | O | | O | | | |
| | A/INT | O | O | O | | O | | | |
| | 1 | | O | O | | | | | |
| | 2 | | O | | O | | | | |
| Washer switch | OFF | | | | | | | | |
| | ON | | O | | | | O | | |
| FAST | OFF | | | | | | | | |
| | ON | | O | | | | | O | |
| SLOW | OFF | | | | | | | | |
| | ON | | O | | | | | | O |

**Fig. 47 Wiper/washer & fast, slow switch continuity chart. Conquest**

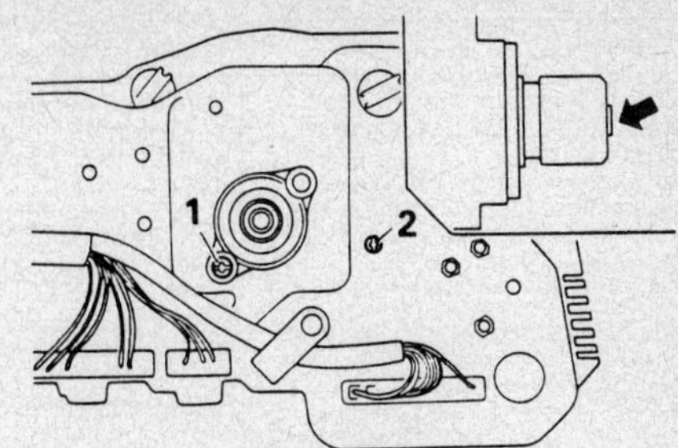


**Fig. 48 Vehicle speed sensor. Conquest**

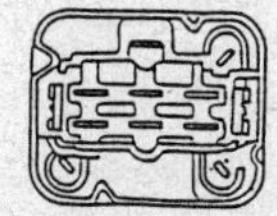

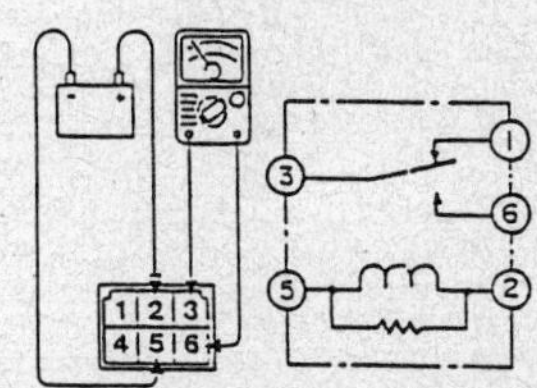


| Voltage applied | Terminals 3 – 6 | Conductive |
|---|---|---|
| Voltage not applied | Terminals 3 – 6 | Non-conductive |
| | Terminals 1 – 3 | Conductive |
| | Terminals 2 – 5 | |

**Fig. 49 Wiper relay continuity chart. Conquest**

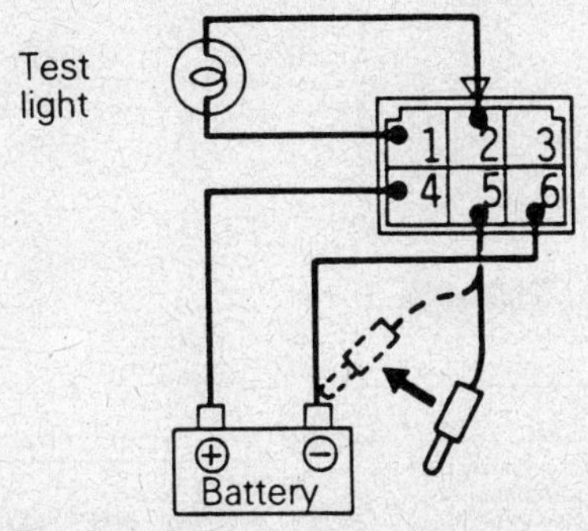


**Fig. 50 Testing intermittent. Conquest**

### Wipers Do Not Stop

1. Check wiper motor.
2. Check intermittent wiper relay.
3. Check wiper switch.

### Wipers Do Not Operate On Intermittent Wipe

1. Check terminal voltage at steering column switch connector terminal 3.
2. If voltage is 0 volts, check intermittent wiper relay or wiper switch.
3. If voltage is 12 volts, Check intermittent wiper relay.
4. If voltage alternates from 0 to 12 volts, system is operating normally.

### Length Of Pause For Intermittent Operation Cannot Be Varied

1. Check variable intermittent wiper control switch.
2. Check intermittent wiper relay.

### Washer Only Is Inoperative

1. Check washer motor.

### Washer-Wiper Operation Is Inoperative

1. Check intermittent relay.

## COMPONENT TESTING

Refer to **Figs. 67 and 68**, for wiring diagrams when testing components.

### Front Wiper Motor

Connect a battery as shown in **Fig. 69**, to check wiper motor low and high speed operation.

### Front Wiper/Washer Switch & Intermittent Wiper Relay

Disconnect wiper switch connector and check for continuity as shown in **Fig. 69.**

### Rear Wiper Motor

Connect a battery as shown in **Fig. 70**, to check wiper motor operation.

### Rear Wiper/Washer Switch

Disconnect wiper switch connector and check for continuity as shown in **Fig. 71.**

### Rear Intermittent Wiper Relay

With relay connector connected, ensure no voltage is present at terminal 2 when rear wiper stops and 12 volts when rear wiper operates, **Fig. 72.**

| Problem | Probable cause (s) | Checking procedure | Remedy |
|---|---|---|---|
| The wipers don't operate when the wiper switch is set to the "INT" position. (The wipers do operate, however, when the wiper switch is set to the "1" (low speed) position.) | Damage or disconnection of the wiring of the wiper switch ("INT") input circuit. | If a malfunction is discovered as a result of the checking of the input conduct check No. 2, of the individual part and circuit. | Repair the wiring harness, or replace the column switch. |
| | Damage or disconnection of the wiring of the wiper switch ("INT"). | | |
| | Damage or disconnection of the wiring of the ignition switch input circuit. | If a malfunction is discovered as a result of the checking of the input conduct check No. 1 of the individual part and circuit. | Repair the wiring harness. |
| | Damage or disconnection of the wiring of the wiper relay activation circuit. | Conduct check No. 4 of the individual part and circuit. | Repair the wiring harness, or replace the column switch. |
| | Malfunction of the wiper relay. | | |
| | Malfunction of the electronic control unit. | – | Replace the electronic control unit. |
| The wipers don't stop when the wiper switch is OFF. (This problem occurs at the low speed of the wipers.) NOTE If the wipers continue operating (without stopping) at the "2" position (high speed) of the wiper switch, there is a short-circuit in the circuit at the wiper motor high-speed side. | Short-circuit in the wiper switch ("INT") input circuit. | If a malfunction is discovered as a result of the checking of the input , conduct check No. 2 of the individual part and circuit. | Repair the wiring harness, or replace the column switch. |
| | Short-circuit in the wiper switch ("INT"). | | |
| | Short-circuit in the wiper relay activation circuit. | Conduct check No. 4 of the individual part and circuit. | Repair the wiring harness. |
| | Malfunction of the electronic control unit. | – | Replace the electronic control unit. |
| When the wiper switch is set to the "INT" position, the wipers operate continuously at low speed, not intermittent operation. (The wipers stop, however, when the wiper switch is set to "OFF".) | Short-circuit in the wiper switch ("INT") input circuit. | If a malfunction is discovered as a result of the checking of the input , conduct check No. 2 of the individual part and circuit. | Repair the wiring harness, or replace the column switch. |
| | Short-circuit in the wiper switch ("INT"). | | |
| | Malfunction of the electronic control unit. | – | Replace the electronic control unit. |
| The intermittent time does not change when the intermittent variable volume switch setting is changed. | Damage or disconnection of the wiring of the intermittent variable volume switch input circuit. | If a malfunction is discovered as a result of the checking of the input , conduct check No. 3 of the individual part and circuit. | Repair the wiring harness, or replace the column switch. |
| | Damage or disconnection of the wiring of the intermittent variable volume switch. | | |
| | Malfunction of the electronic control unit. | – | Replace the electronic control unit. |

**Fig. 51 Wiper system troubleshooting (Part 1 of 2). Stealth**

| Problem | Probable cause (s) | Checking procedure | Remedy |
|---|---|---|---|
| The wipers do not function when the washer switch is switched ON for 0.6 second or longer. (With the wiper switch at the "INT" position, however, intermittent operation of the wipers is normal, and the washer function is normal.) | Damage or disconnection of the wiring of the washer switch input circuit. | If a malfunction is discovered as a result of the checking of the input , conduct check No. 5 of the individual part and circuit. | Repair the wiring harness, or replace the column switch. |
| | Damage or disconnection of the wiring of the washer switch. | | |
| | Malfunction of the electronic control unit. | – | Replace the electronic control unit. |
| The wipers do not function when the washer switch is switched ON for less than 0.6 second. (The wipers and washer do function, however, when the washer switch is switched ON for 0.6 second or longer.) | Malfunction of the electronic control unit. | – | Replace the electronic control unit. |

NOTE
"ECU" (electronic control unit) indicates the ETACS unit.

**Fig. 51 Wiper system troubleshooting (Part 2 of 2). Stealth**

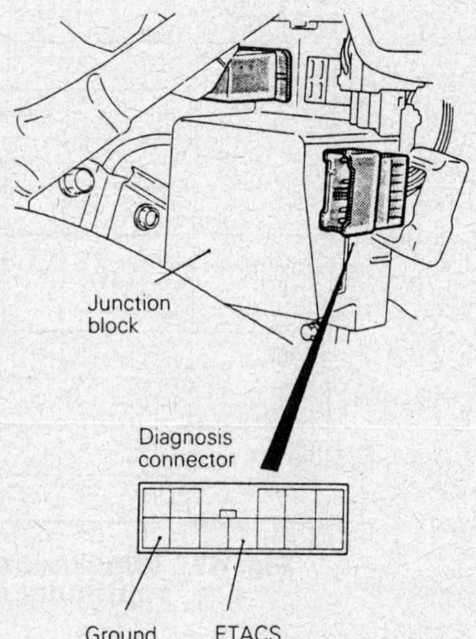


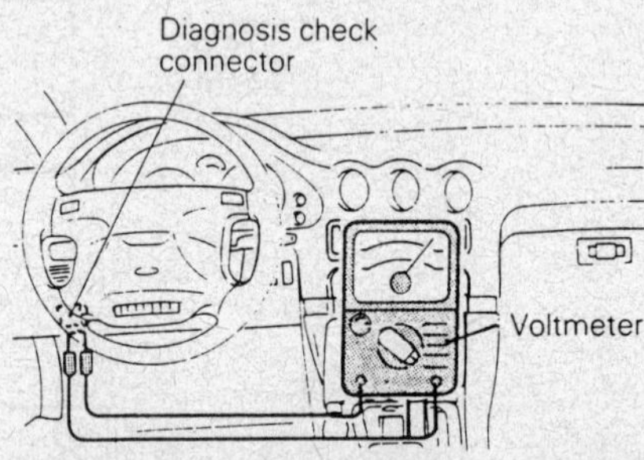


**Fig. 52 Diagnosis check connector location. Stealth**

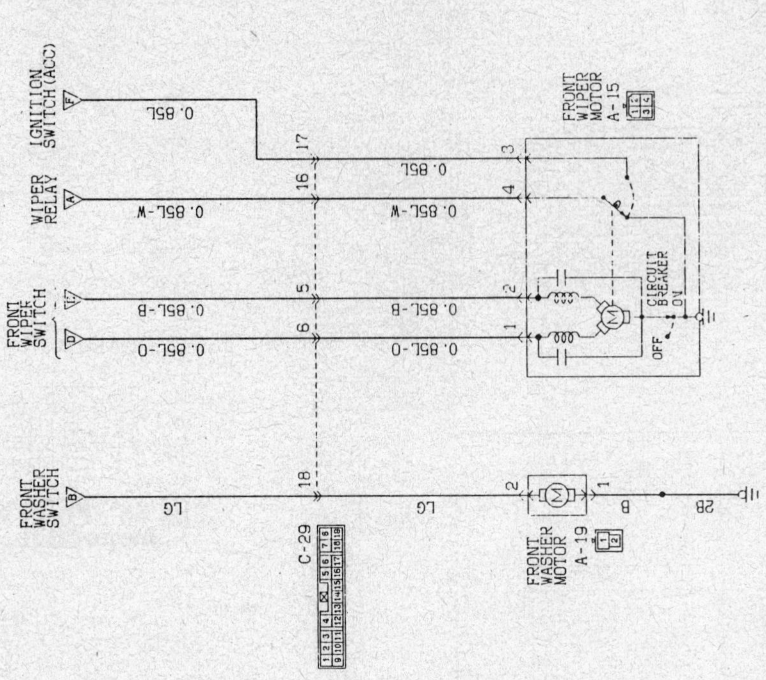


Fig. 53 Front wiper system wiring circuit (Part 2 of 2). Stealth

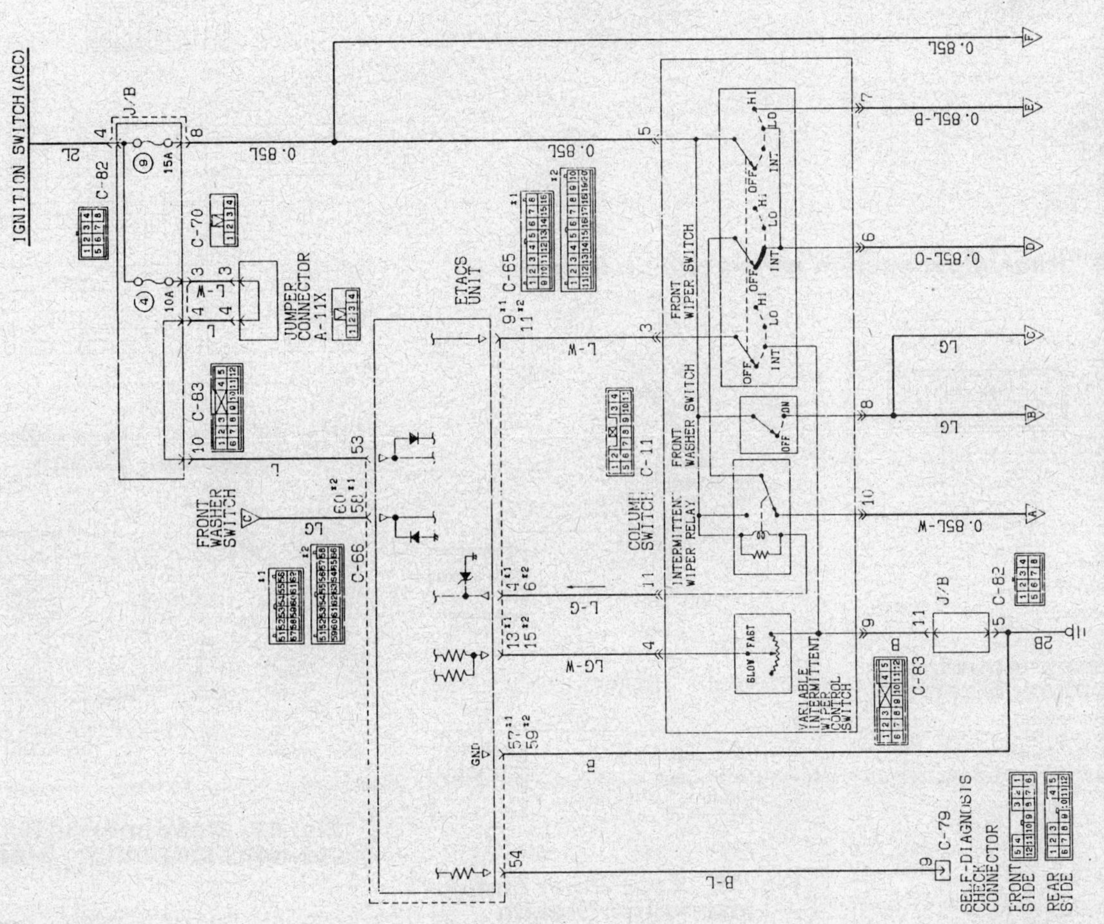


Fig. 53 Front wiper system wiring circuit (Part 1 of 2). Stealth

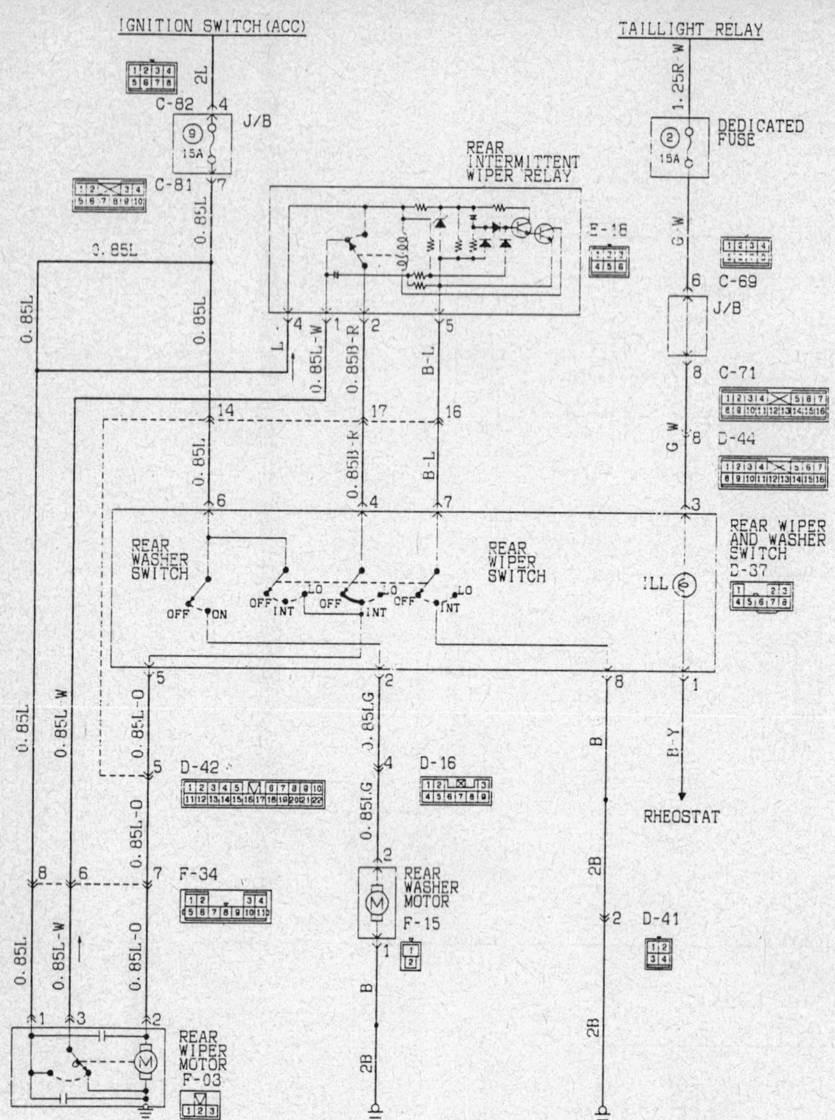


Fig. 54 Rear wiper system wiring circuit. Stealth

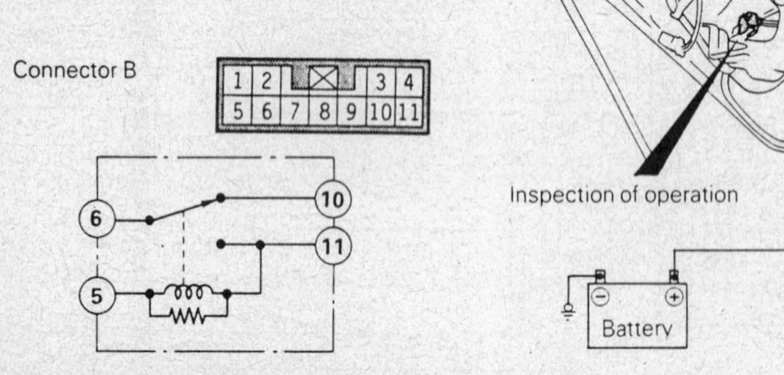


Fig. 57 Intermittent wiper relay inspection. Stealth

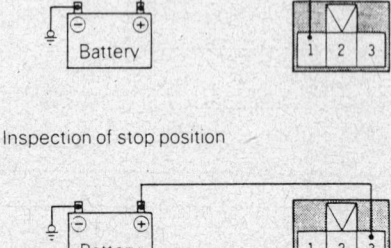

Inspection of operation

Battery

1 2 3

Inspection of stop position

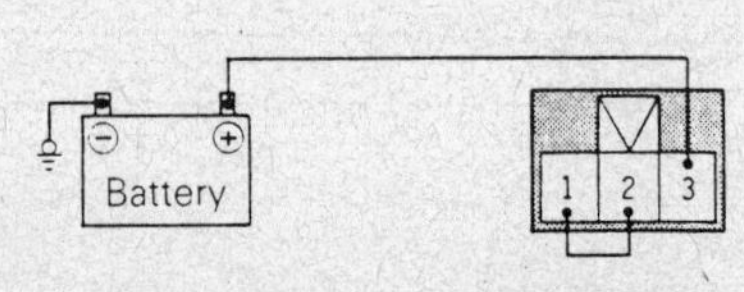


Fig. 58 Rear wiper motor inspection. Stealth

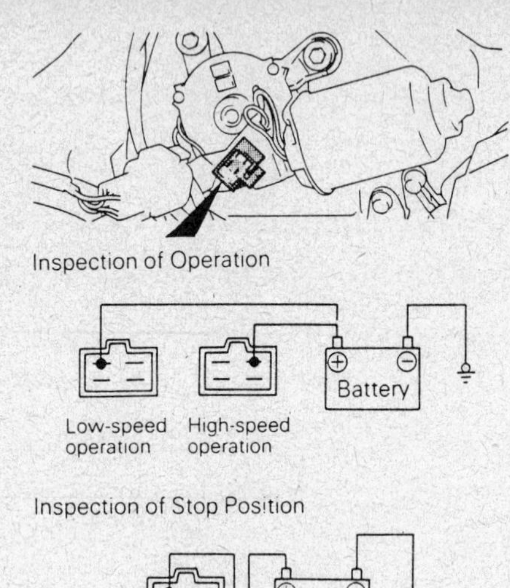


Fig. 55 Front wiper motor inspection. Stealth

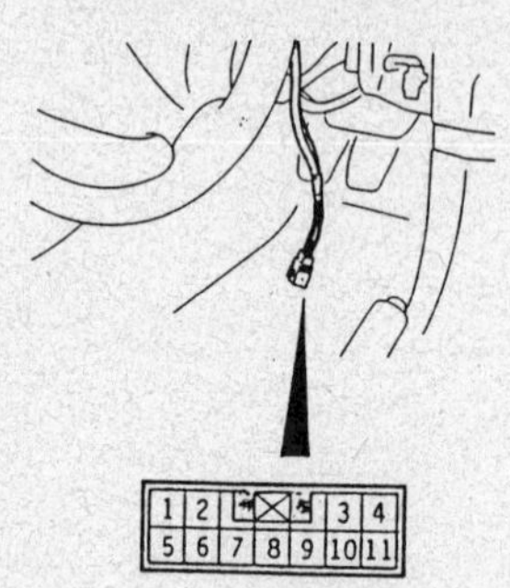


| Switch position \ Terminal No. | | 3 | 4 | 5 | 6 | 7 | 8 | 9 | 10 |
|---|---|---|---|---|---|---|---|---|---|
| Wiper switch | OFF | | | | O | — | — | — | O |
| | INT | O | — | — | — | — | — | O | |
| | | | | | O | — | — | — | O |
| | LO | | | O | O | | | | |
| | HI | | | O | — | O | | | |
| Variable intermittent wiper control switch | | | O | — | — | — | — | O | |
| Washer switch | | | | O | — | — | O | | |

NOTE
O–O denotes that there is continuity between the terminals.

Fig. 56 Front wiper switch inspection. Stealth

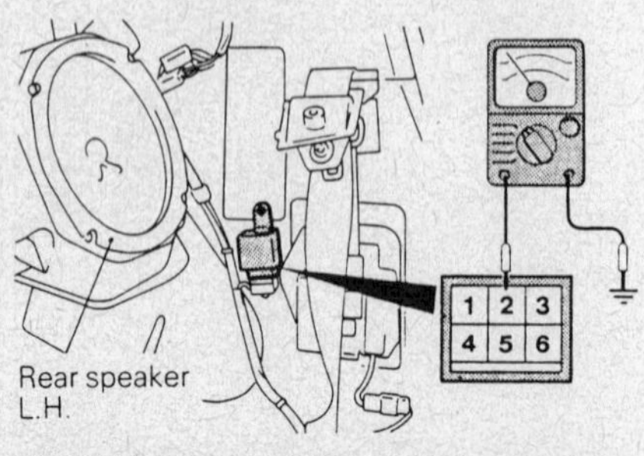


Fig. 59 Rear intermittent wiper relay inspection. Stealth

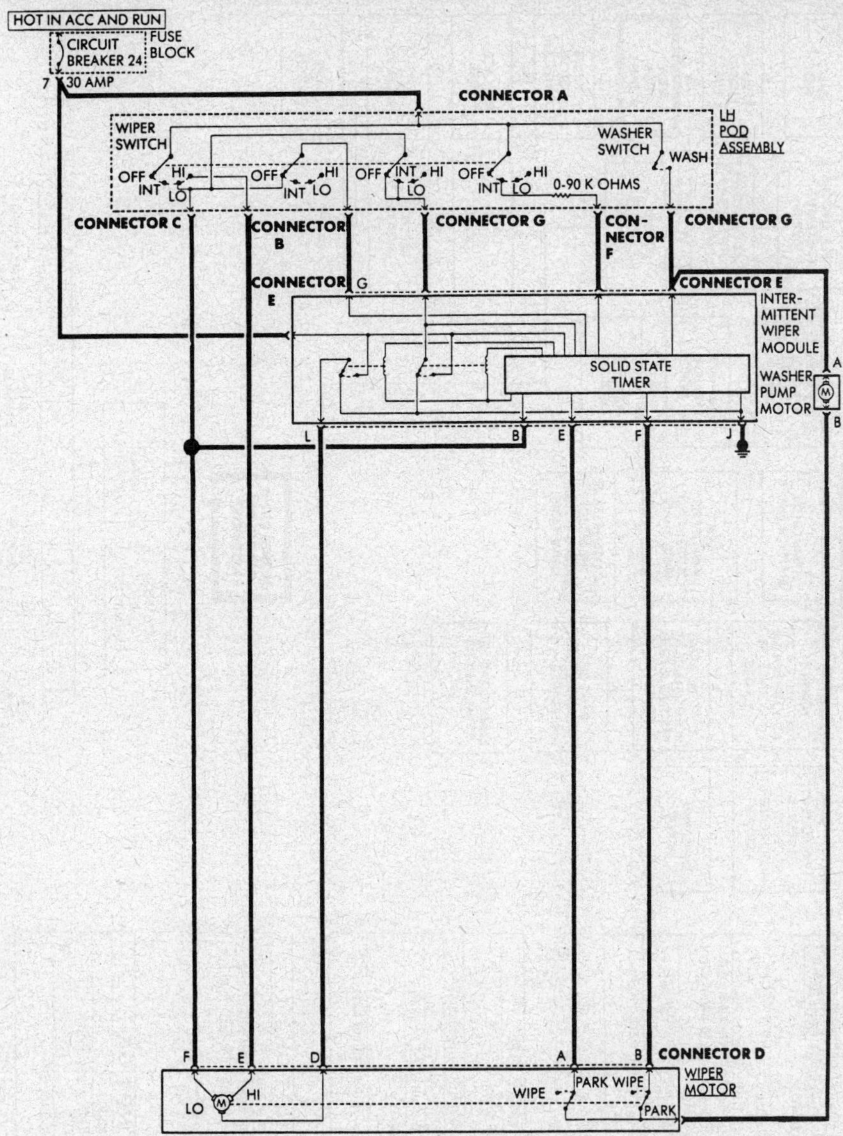


**Fig. 60 Wiper system wiring circuit. 1989 Eagle Premier**

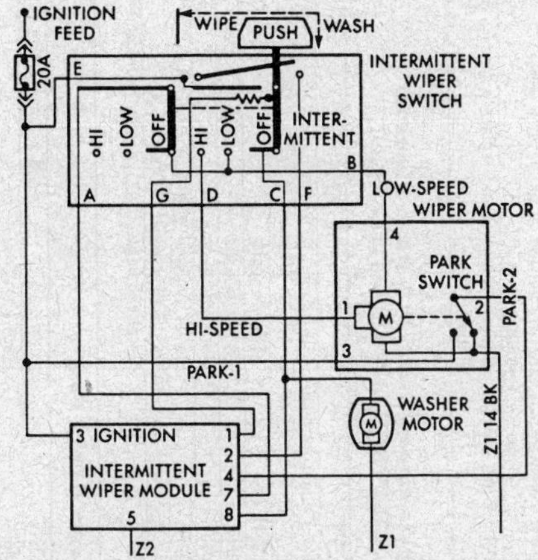


**Fig. 61 Wiper system wiring circuit. 1990–91 Dodge Monaco & Eagle Premier**

TROUBLESHOOTING CHART INDEX

| Chart No. | SYMPTOM |
|---|---|
| 1 | Windshield Wipers Inoperative |
| 2 | Windshield Wipers Inoperative in INT, ok in LO and HI |
| 3 | Windshield Wipers Do Not Park |
| 4 | Windshield Washers Inoperative |
| 5 | Windshield Wipers Inoperative During Washer Operation |

***1.Windshield Wipers Inoperative***

IGNITION SWITCH IN RUN, WIPER SWITCH IN LO OR HI POSITION

| TEST | OK | NOT OK |
|---|---|---|
| Inspect Circuit Breaker 24 | Not blown | Replace Circuit Breaker 24 |
| Battery side of circuit breaker | Battery voltage | Repair open from ignition switch. |
| Connector A - Terminal S | Battery voltage | Repair open from Circuit Breaker 24 |
| Connector B - Terminal S Wiper Switch In HI | Battery voltage | Replace LH module |
| Connector C - Terminal S Wiper Switch In LO | Battery voltage | Replace LH module |
| Connector D - Terminal D to ground | Wiper motor does not run. Go to next step | Wiper motor runs. Check circuit for an open. If circuit is good go to intermittent wiper module test |
| Connector D - Terminal E Wiper Switch In HI | Battery voltage. If ok, replace wiper motor | Repair open from wiper switch in LH module |
| Connector D - Terminal F Wiper Switch in LO | Battery voltage. If ok, replace wiper motor | Repair open from wiper switch in LH module |

***2.Windshield Wipers Inoperative In INT, OK In HI and LO***

IGNITION SWITCH IN RUN, WIPER SWITCH IN INT.

| TEST | OK | NOT OK |
|---|---|---|
| Connector E - Terminal J Wiper module disconnected | Zero ohms | Repair open to ground |
| Connector E - Terminal H | Battery voltage | Repair open from Circuit Breaker 24 |
| Connector E - Terminal D | Battery voltage | Go to wiper switch test |
| Connector E - Terminal C | Battery voltage | Replace intermittent wiper module |
| Connector F - Terminal S | Battery voltage. If ok; repair open to intermittent wiper module | Replace LH module |
| Connector G - Terminal S | Battery voltage. If ok, replace LH module | Repair open from intermittent wiper module |

***3.Windshield Wipers Do Not Park***

| TEST | OK | NOT OK |
|---|---|---|
| Connector D - Terminal C | Zero ohms | Repair open to ground |
| Connector E - Terminal J | Zero ohms. Replace intermittent wiper module | Repair open between wiper motor and Intermittent wiper module. If ok, replace wiper motor |

***4.Windshield Washers Inoperative***

IGNITION IN RUN, WIPER SWITCH IN WASH

| TEST | OK | NOT OK |
|---|---|---|
| Connector G - Terminal S | Battery voltage | Replace LH module |
| Washer Pump Motor connector - Terminal A | Battery voltage | Repair open from wiper switch |
| Washer Pump Motor connector - Terminal B Washer switch OFF | Zero ohms. If zero ohms, replace washer pump motor | Repair open to ground |

***5.Windshield Wipers Inoperative During Washer Operation***

IGNITION IN RUN, WIPER SWITCH IN WASH

| TEST | OK | NOT OK |
|---|---|---|
| Connector E - Terminal K | Battery voltage. If ok, replace intermittent wiper module | Repair open from LH module |

**Fig. 62 Troubleshooting charts. 1989 Eagle Medallion & Premier**

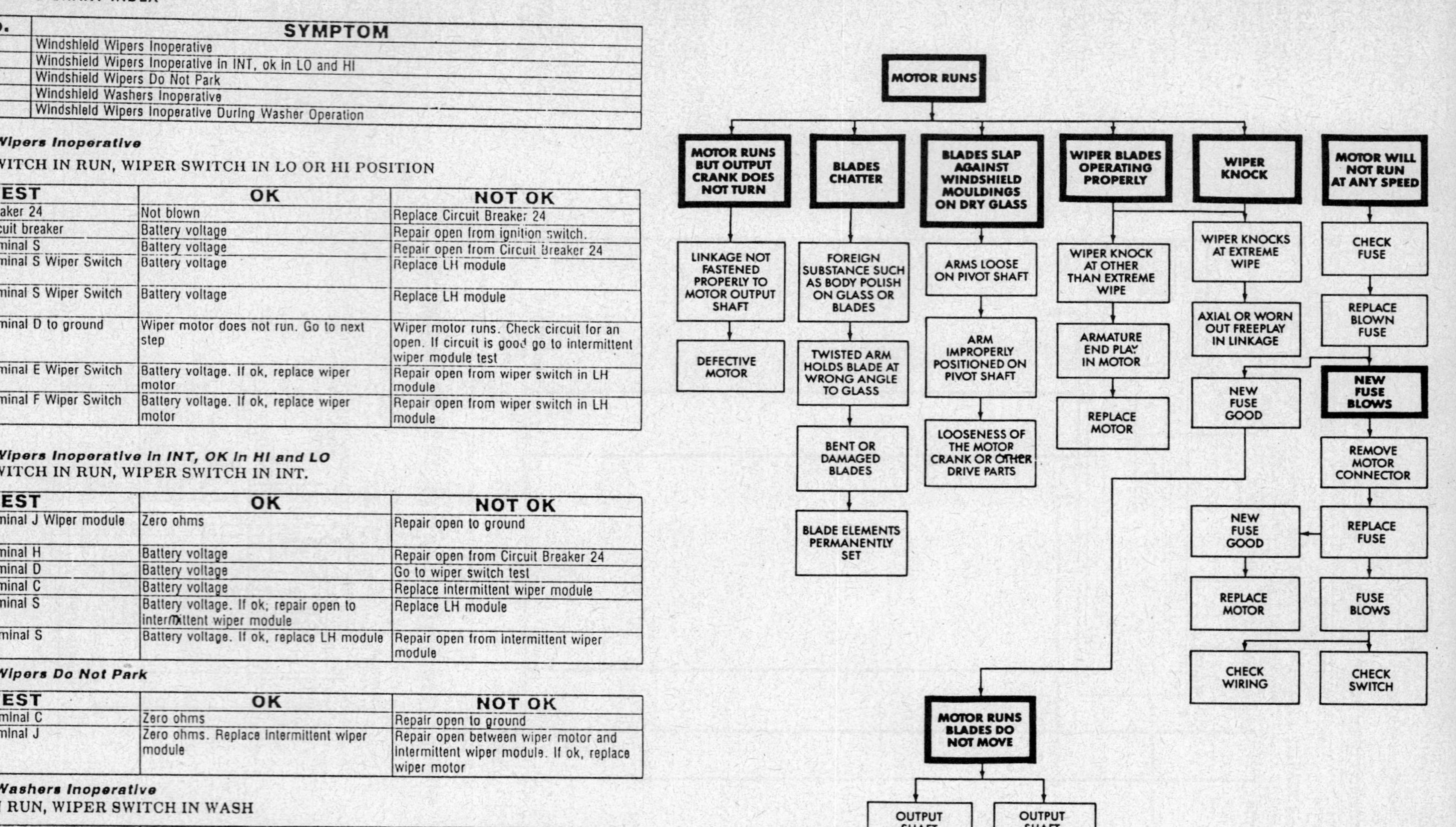


**Fig. 63 Wiper system troubleshooting charts (Part 1 of 2). 1990–91 Dodge Monaco & Eagle Premier**

**Windshield Wipers Inoperative**—Ignition Switch in RUN, Wiper Switch in LO or HI Position

| TEST | OK | NOT OK |
|---|---|---|
| Inspect fuse | Not blown | Replace 20 A fuse |
| Battery side of fuse | Battery voltage | Repair open from ignition S |
| Ground on wiper motor frame | Ground | Repair open ground |
| Connector 4 on motor switch on LO | Battery voltage | Repair lead from switch or check switch |
| Connector 1 on motor switch on HI | Battery voltage | Repair lead from switch or check switch |

**Windshield Wipers Inoperative in Intermittent Mode, OK in HI and LO**—Ignition Switch in RUN, Wiper Switch in Intermittent Mode—See Intermittent Wiper Module

**Windshield Wipers do Not Park**

| TEST | OK | NOT OK |
|---|---|---|
| Turn motor to OFF | Blades at bottom of wipe pattern | Loose linkage at motor crank or next test |
| Connector 3 on motor | Battery voltage | Repair lead from 20 A fuse |
| Connector 2 on motor | 0 voltage when connected to wiring. If OK replace motor | Repair lead to I wipe modul or check I wipe module or wiper switch |

**Windshield Wipers Inoperative During Washer Operation**—Ignition in RUN, Wiper Switch in Wash-Replace Switch

**Windshield Washer Inoperative**—Ignition in RUN, Wiper Switch in Wash

| TEST | OK | NOT OK |
|---|---|---|
| Washer pump motor Terminal A | Battery voltage | Repair open from wiper switch |
| Washer pump motor Terminal B | Zero ohms. If zero ohms replace pump motor | Repair open to ground |

**Fig. 63 Wiper system troubleshooting charts (Part 2 of 2). 1990–91 Dodge Monaco & Eagle Premier**

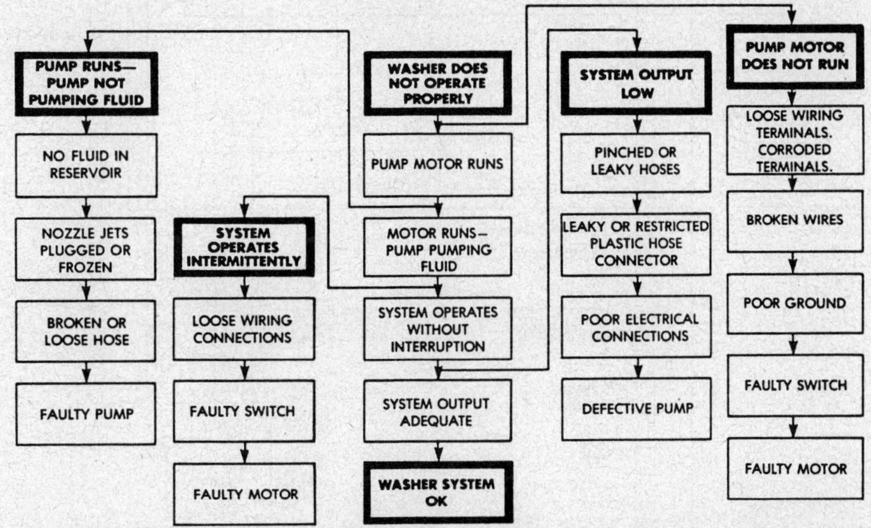


**Fig. 64 Washer system troubleshooting chart. 1990–91 Dodge Monaco & Eagle Premier**

H G F E D C B A

BLACK

INTERMITTENT WIPER SWITCH CONNECTOR

| SWITCH POSITION | CONTINUITY BETWEEN |
|---|---|
| Off | Pin A and Pin B |
| Delay | Pin E and Pin C<br>Pin E and Pin G<br>Pin A and Pin B |
| Low | Pin E and Pin B |
| High | Pin E and Pin D |
| Wash (Button pushed in) | Pin E and Pin F |

**Fig. 65 Intermittent wiper switch test. 1990–91 Dodge Monaco & Eagle Premier**

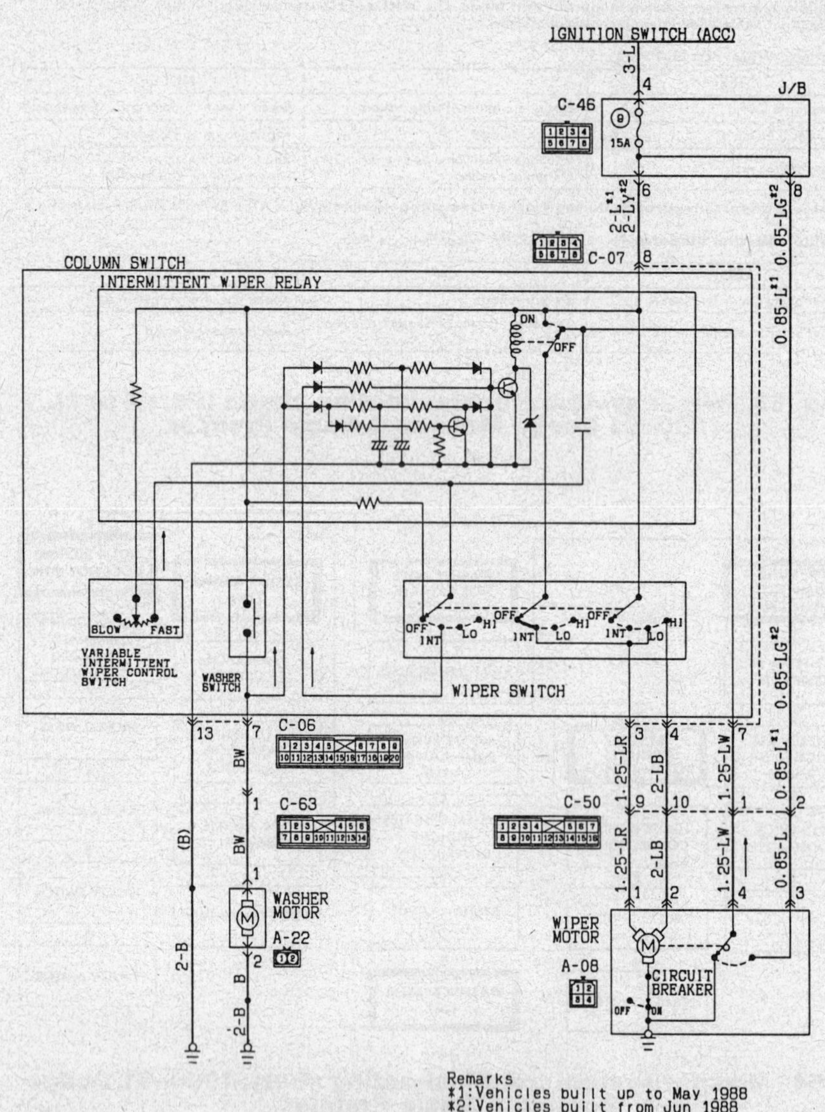


**Fig. 66 Front wiper system wiring diagram. Plymouth Laser & Eagle Talon**

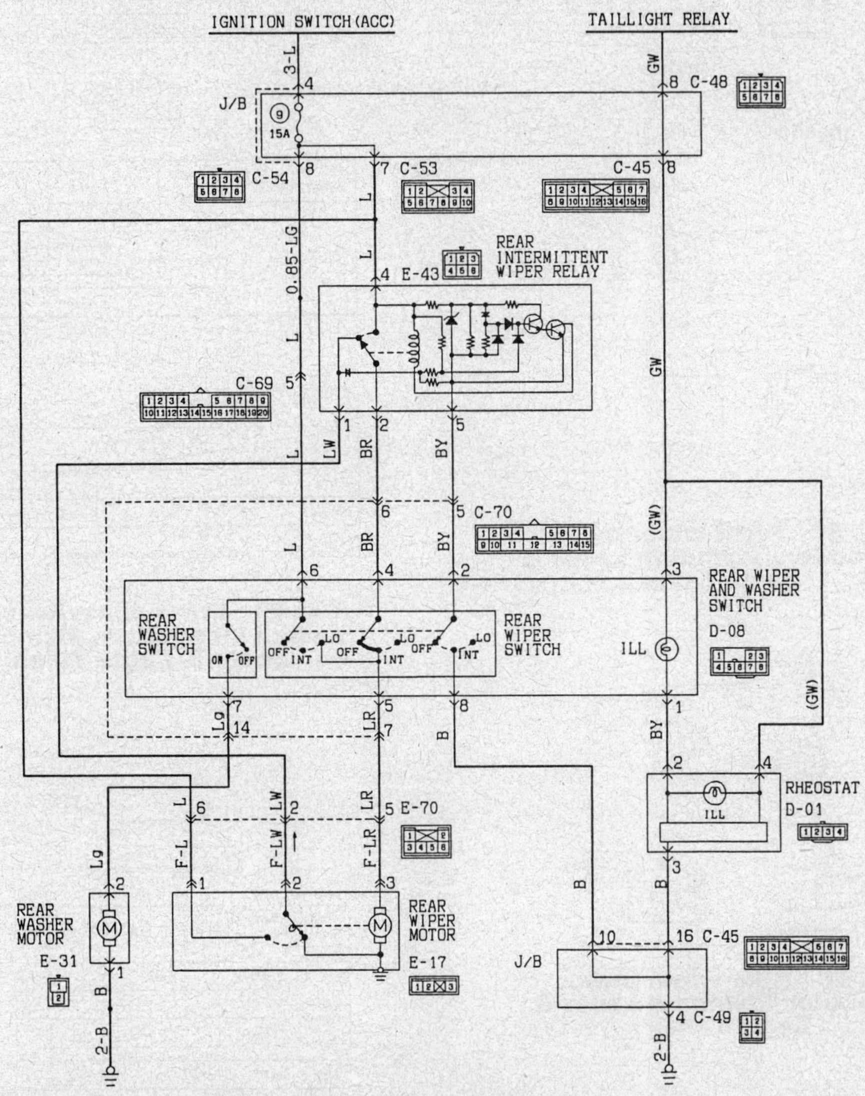


Fig. 67 Rear wiper system wiring diagram. Plymouth Laser & Eagle Talon

<Low speed>

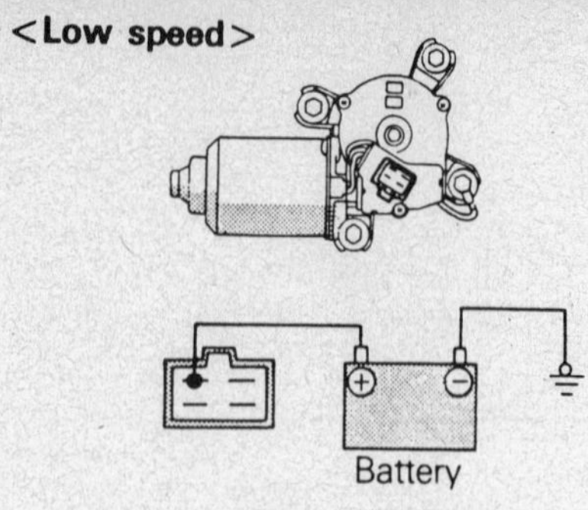


<High speed>

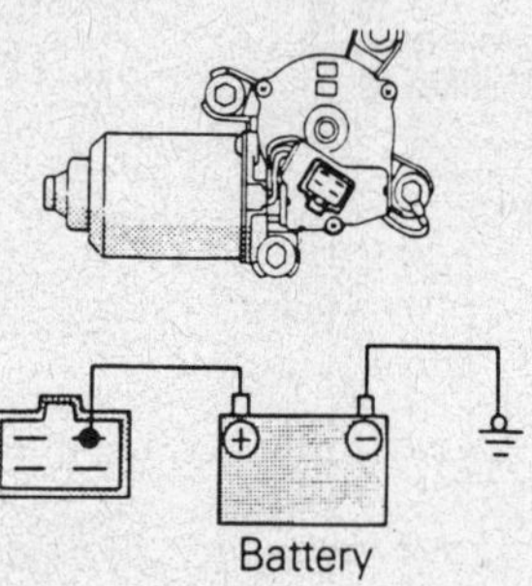


**Fig. 68 Front wiper motor inspection. Plymouth Laser & Eagle Talon**

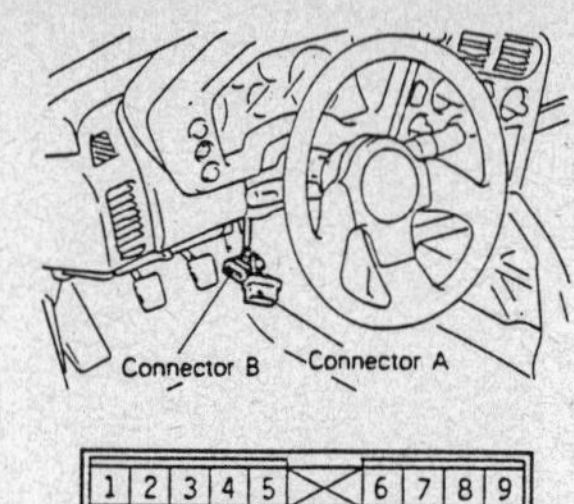


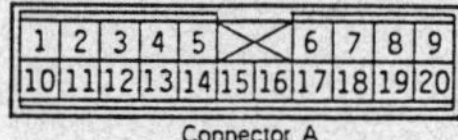


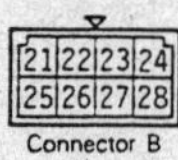


| Switch position \ Terminal | | 23 | 24 | 27 | 28 |
|---|---|---|---|---|---|
| Wiper switch | OFF | O | — | O | |
| | INT | O | — | O | |
| | LO | O | — | — | O |
| | HI | | O | — | O |

| Switch position \ Terminal | 7 | 28 |
|---|---|---|
| OFF | | |
| ON | O | O |

NOTE
O—O indicates that there is continuity between the terminals.

**Fig. 69 Front wiper/washer switch inspection. Plymouth Laser & Eagle Talon**

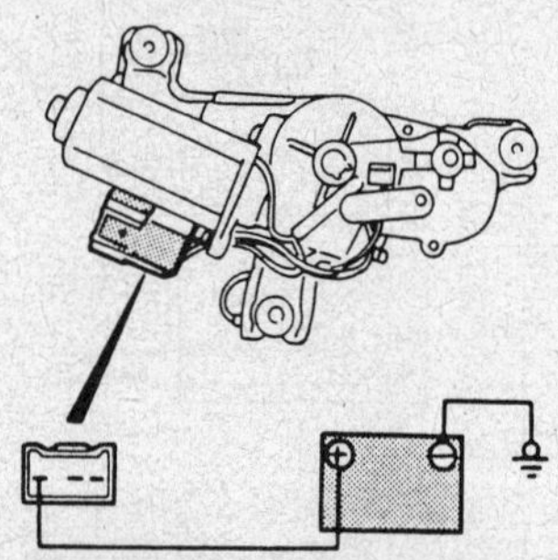

**Fig. 70 Rear wiper motor inspection. Plymouth Laser & Eagle Talon**

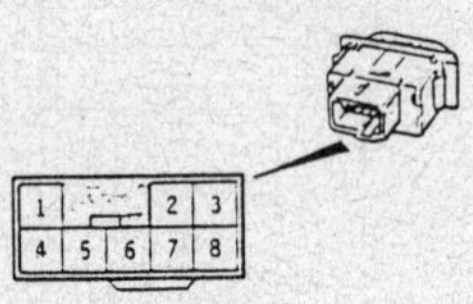


| Switch position \ Terminal | | 2 | 4 | 5 | 6 | 7 | 8 | 3 | 1 |
|---|---|---|---|---|---|---|---|---|---|
| Wiper switch | OFF | | O | O | | | | | |
| | ON | | | O | O | | | | |
| | INT | O | O | O | — | — | O | | |
| Washer switch | | | | | O | O | | Illumination light | |

NOTE
O—O indicates that there is continuity between the terminals.

**Fig. 71 Rear wiper/washer switch inspection. Plymouth Laser & Eagle Talon**

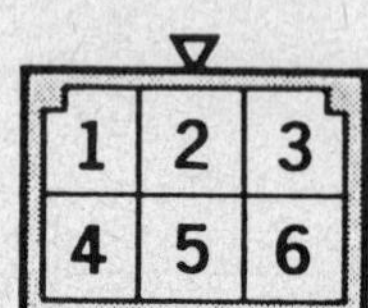


**Fig. 72 Rear intermittent wiper relay inspection. Plymouth Laser & Eagle Talon**

# SPEED CONTROL SYSTEMS

## TABLE OF CONTENTS



# Application Chart

| Year | Model | Type |
|---|---|---|
| 1989 | Acclaim | 1 |
| | Aries | 1 |
| | Colt | 2 |
| | Colt Vista | 2 |
| | Conquest | 2 |
| | Daytona | 1 |
| | Diplomat | 1 |
| | Dynasty | 1 |
| | Fifth Avenue | 1 |
| | Horizon | 1 |
| | Lancer | 1 |
| | LeBaron 2 Door | 1 |
| | LeBaron Convertible | 1 |
| | LeBaron GTS | 1 |
| | Medallion | 4 |
| | New Yorker | 1 |
| | New Yorker Landau | 1 |
| | Omni | 1 |
| | Premier | 3 |
| | Reliant | 1 |
| | Shadow | 1 |
| | Spirit | 1 |
| | Summit | 2 |
| | Sundance | 1 |
| 1990 | Acclaim | 1 |
| | Colt | 2 |
| | Colt Vista | 2 |
| | Colt Wagon | 2 |
| | Daytona | 1 |
| | Dynasty | 1 |
| | Fifth Avenue | 1 |
| | Horizon | 1 |
| | Imperial | 1 |
| | Laser | 2 |

| Year | Model | Type |
|---|---|---|
| | LeBaron Convertible | 1 |
| | LeBaron Coupe | 1 |
| | LeBaron Landau | 1 |
| | Monaco | 3 |
| | New Yorker Landau | 1 |
| | New Yorker Salon | 1 |
| | Omni | 1 |
| | Premier | 3 |
| | Shadow | 1 |
| | Spirit | 1 |
| | Summit | 2 |
| | Sundance | 1 |
| | Talon | 2 |
| 1991 | Acclaim | 1 |
| | Colt | 2 |
| | Colt Vista | 2 |
| | Daytona | 1 |
| | Dynasty | 1 |
| | Fifth Avenue | 1 |
| | Imperial | 1 |
| | Laser | 2 |
| | LeBaron Convertible | 1 |
| | LeBaron Coupe | 1 |
| | LeBaron Sedan | 1 |
| | Monaco | 1 |
| | New Yorker Salon | 1 |
| | Premier | 1 |
| | Shadow | 1 |
| | Shadow Convertible | 1 |
| | Spirit | 1 |
| | Stealth | 2 |
| | Summit | 2 |
| | Sundance | 1 |
| | Talon | 2 |

# Type 1

## INDEX

**NOTE:** Wire Code Identification And Symbol Identification Located In The Front Of This Manual Can Be Used As An Aid When Using Wiring Circuits Found In This Section.



## AIRBAG SYSTEM DISARMING

1. Place ignition switch in lock position.
2. Disconnect and tape battery ground cable connector.
3. **Wait at least 1 minute after disconnecting battery ground cable before doing any further work on vehicle. The SRS system is designed to retain enough voltage to deploy airbag for a short time even after battery has been disconnected.**
4. After repairs are complete, reconnect battery ground cable.
5. From passenger side of vehicle, turn ignition switch to On position.
6. SRS warning light should illuminate for 6 to 8 seconds, then remain off for at least 45 seconds to indicate if SRS system is functioning correctly.
7. If SRS indicator does not perform as described refer to the "Passive Restraint Systems" section.

## DESCRIPTION & OPERATION

This Speed Control System is electrically actuated and vacuum operated. The control lever on the steering column incorporates a slide switch which has three positions, "Off," "On" and "Resume." The "Set" button is located at the end of the three position slide switch. The system is designed to operate at speeds exceeding 30 mph.

To engage the speed control when desired speed is achieved, depress and release the "Set" button to engage the system. Speed will be maintained at this level. By moving the slide switch from "Off" to "On" while vehicle is in motion establishes memory without system engagement.

To disengage speed control, a normal brake application or soft tap on the brake pedal will disengage system without erasing speed memory. Moving the slide switch to "Off" also disengages the system and also erases the speed memory.

## TROUBLESHOOTING

Refer to **Fig. 1** when troubleshooting the speed control system.

## DIAGNOSIS & TESTING

### ROAD TEST

Road test vehicle to verify reports of speed control system malfunction. The road test should include attention to the speedometer. Speedometer operation should be smooth and without flutter at all speeds or surging may be caused in the speed control system.

### INOPERATIVE SYSTEM

If road test verifies an inoperative system check and verify the following:

1. Inspect system electrical connections for loose, corrosion or bent terminals.
2. Verify correct installation and condition of vacuum hoses.
3. Check for correct installation of vacuum check valve. End marked VAC must point toward vacuum source.

### CHECKING FOR FAULT (TROUBLE) CODES

When trying to verify a speed control system electronic malfunction, one of two methods may be used and are described as follows:

#### USING DIAGNOSTIC TOOL

If a DRB II Diagnostic Tool is available, plug tool into diagnostic connector and verify that either a fault (trouble) codes 15 or 34 on except 1991 Dodge Monaco & Eagle Premier is indicated or fault (trouble) codes 15, 34 or 77 on 1991 Dodge Monaco & Eagle Premier is indicated, then refer to the appropriate diagnostic chart shown in **Figs. 2 through 13** for 1989 models, **Figs. 14 through 25** for 1990 models and **Figs. 26 through 55** for 1991 models. Follow tool manufacturers instructions for proper installation of the tool prior to testing speed control system.

If no problems were found, replace engine controller.

#### USING VOLTMETER

If a DRB II Diagnostic tool is not available, check for fault (trouble) codes as follows:

1. Cycle ignition switch to On position three times. On third cycle, leave switch in On position.
2. Observe Check Engine indicator on instrument cluster. If a fault (trouble) code is present, indicator lamp will flash (blink) in a series which will show which fault (trouble) code is the problem.
3. If fault (trouble) code 34 is observed, determine source of problem by performing tests described under "Speed Control System Tests." Refer to **Figs. 56 through 71** for speed control system wiring diagrams.
4. If fault (trouble) code 15 is present, testing of the distance sensor is required. **Testing of the distance sensor requires the use of the DRB II diagnostic tool.**
5. **On 1991 Dodge Monaco & Eagle Premier,** if fault (trouble) code 77 is present, perform "Speed Control Relay Test" under "Speed Control System Test."
6. **On all models,,** if no problems were found, replace engine controller.

*Continued on page 24-36*

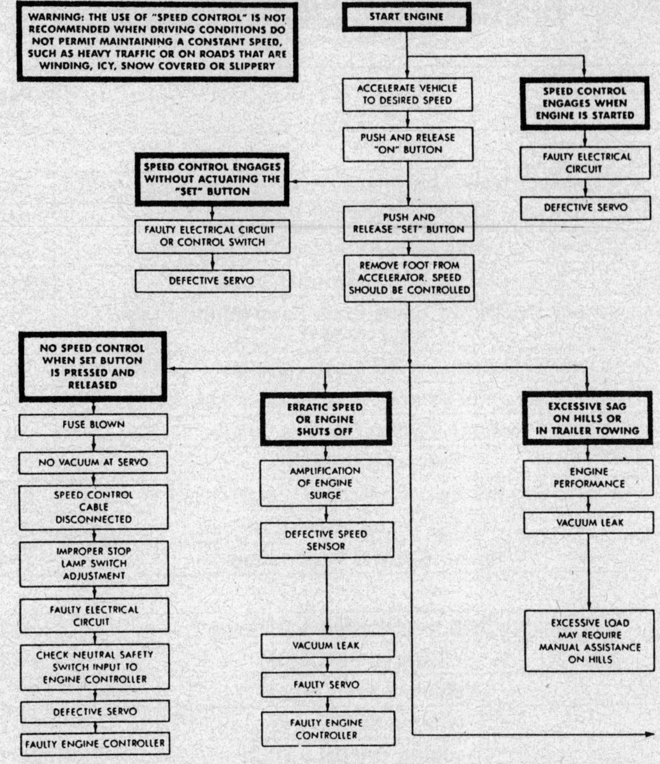


**Fig. 1 Cruise control system troubleshooting (Part 1 of 2)**

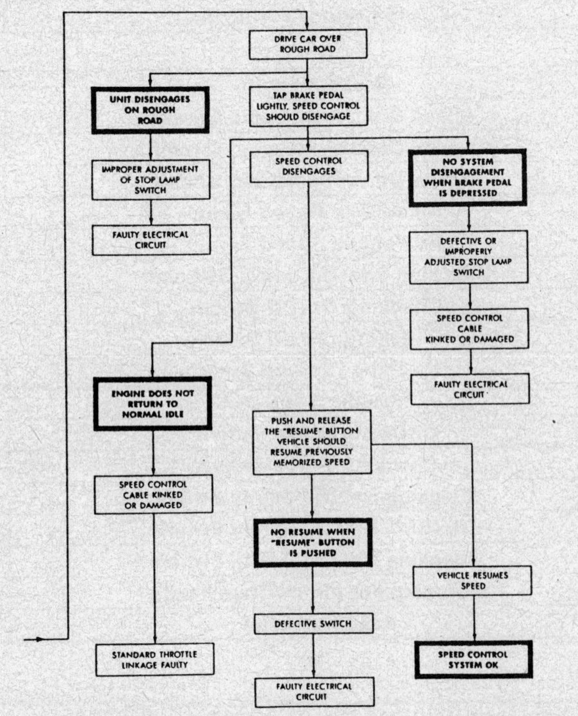


**Fig. 1 Cruise control system troubleshooting (Part 2 of 2)**

# DIAGNOSTIC CHART INDEX



*Continued*

## DIAGNOSTIC CHART INDEX-Continued



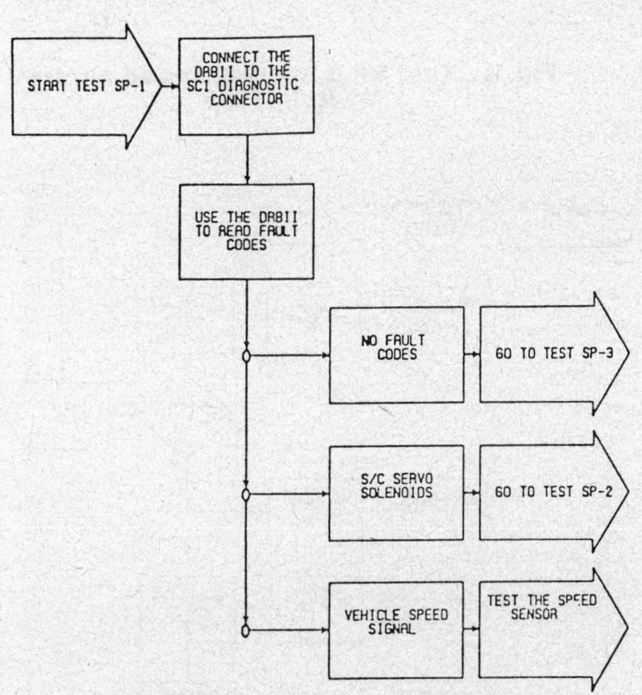


**Fig. 2 Test SP-1, checking speed control system for fault codes. 1989**

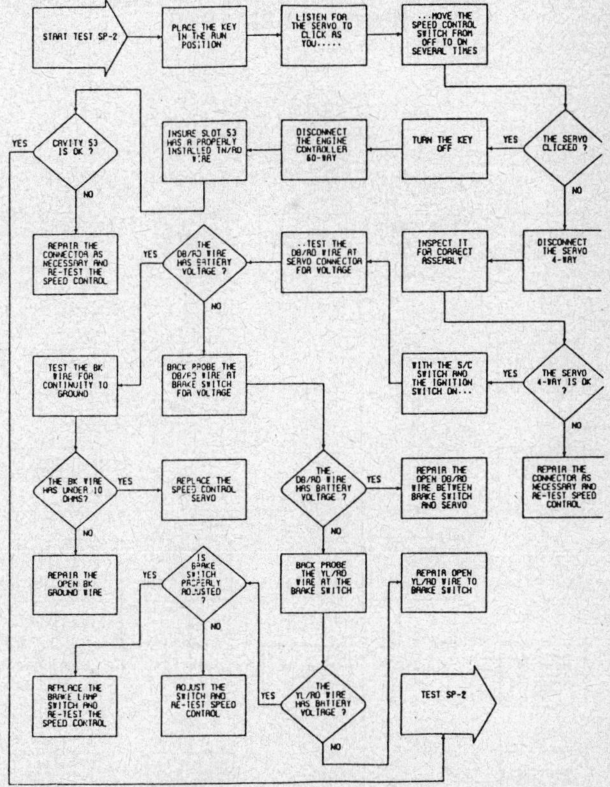


**Fig. 3 Test SP-2, checking for fault code 34 (Part 1 of 2). 1989**

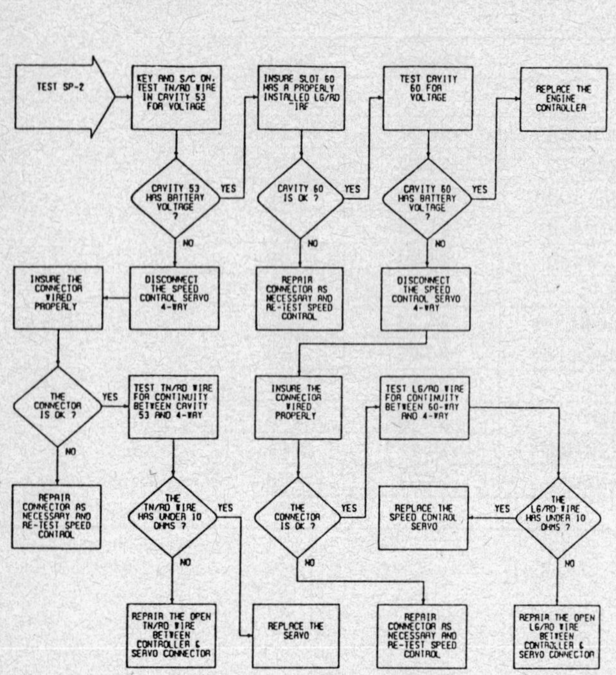


**Fig. 3 Test SP-2, checking for fault code 34 (Part 2 of 2). 1989**

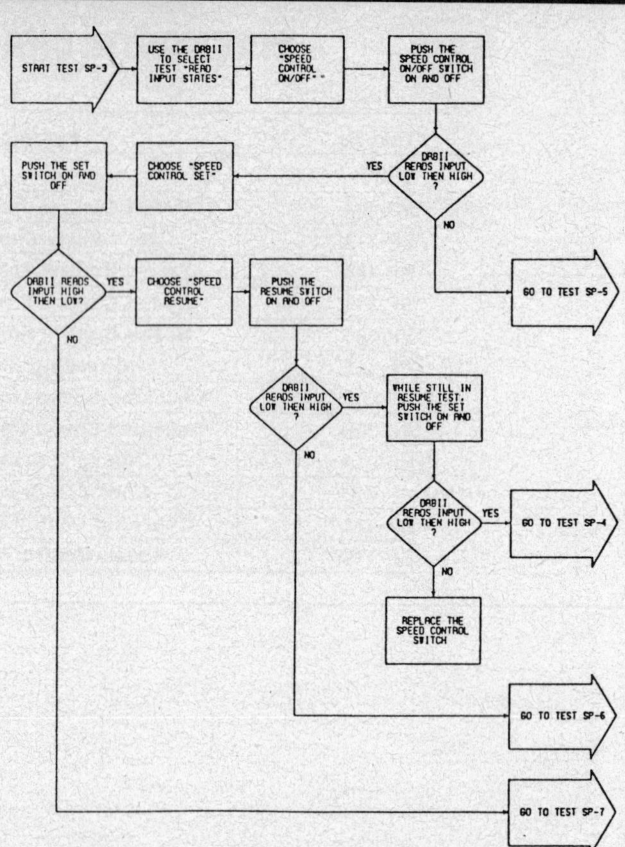


**Fig. 4 Test SP-3, testing speed control switch. 1989**

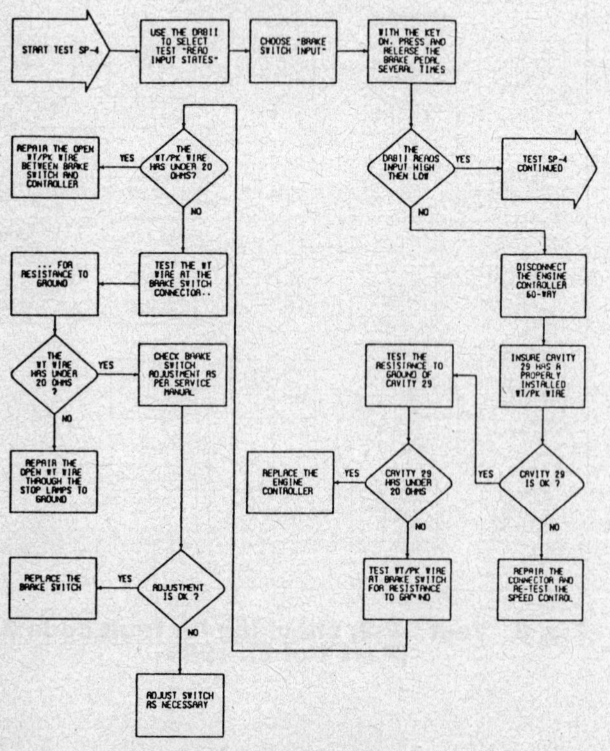


**Fig. 5 Test SP-4, testing brake switch circuit (Part 1 of 4). 1989**

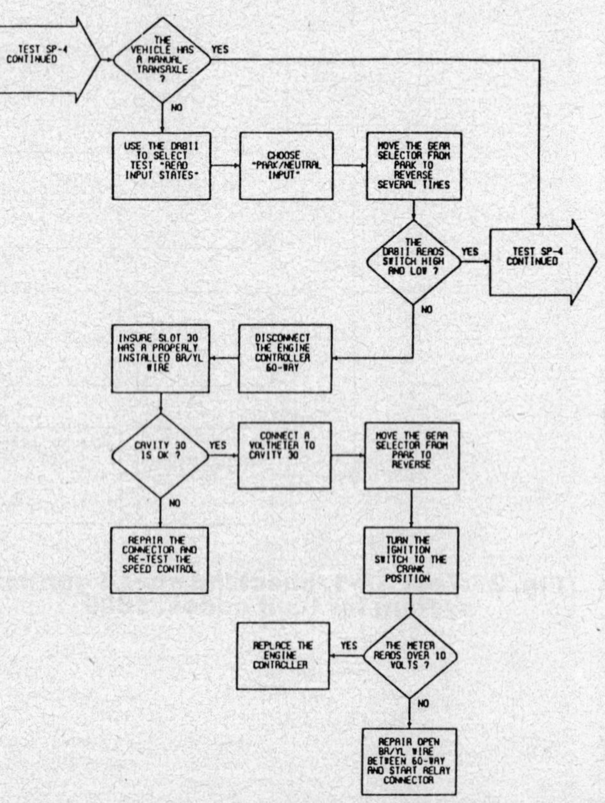


**Fig. 5 Test SP-4, testing brake switch circuit (Part 2 of 4). 1989**

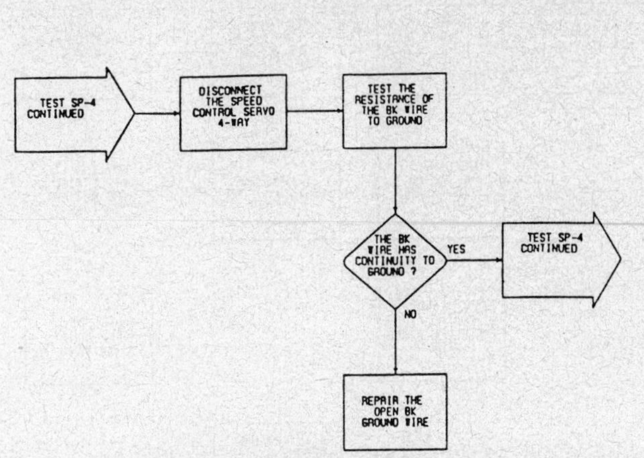


**Fig. 5 Test SP-4, testing brake switch circuit (Part 3 of 4). 1989**

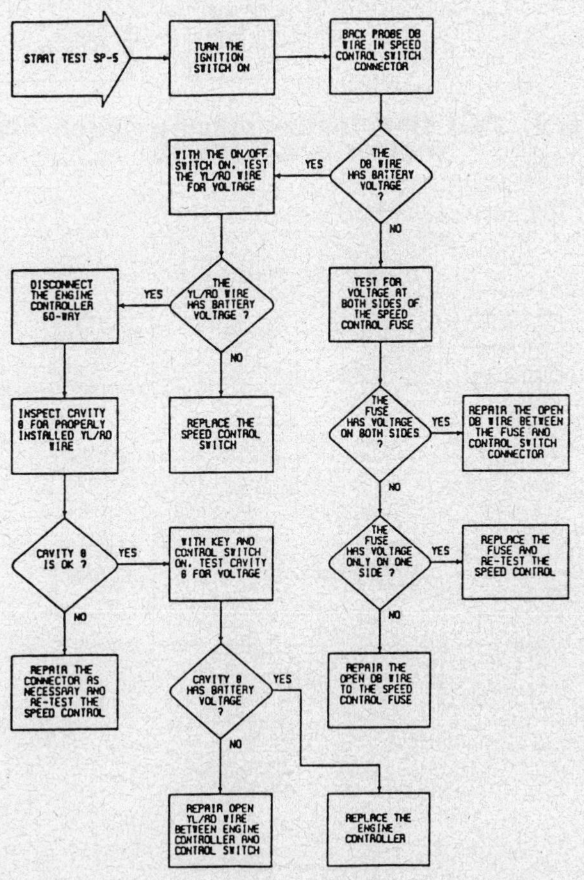


**Fig. 6 Test SP-5, check On/Off switch & stalk feed. 1989 models less 3.0L/V6-181**

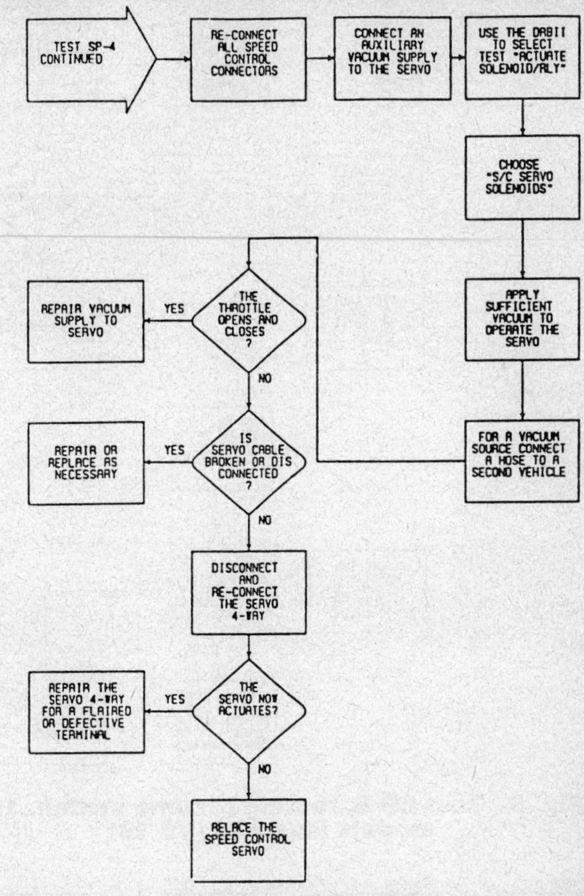


**Fig. 5 Test SP-4, testing brake switch circuit (Part 4 of 4). 1989**

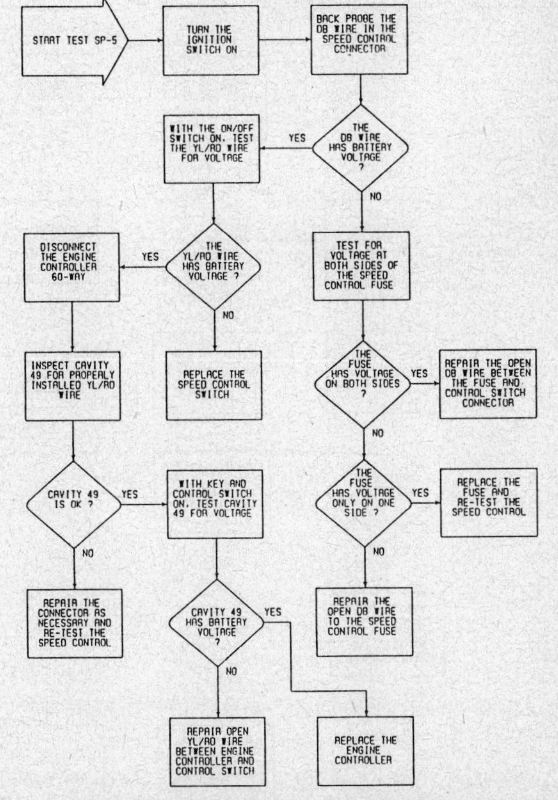


**Fig. 7 Test SP-5, check On/Off switch & stalk feed. 1989 models w/3.0L/V6-181**

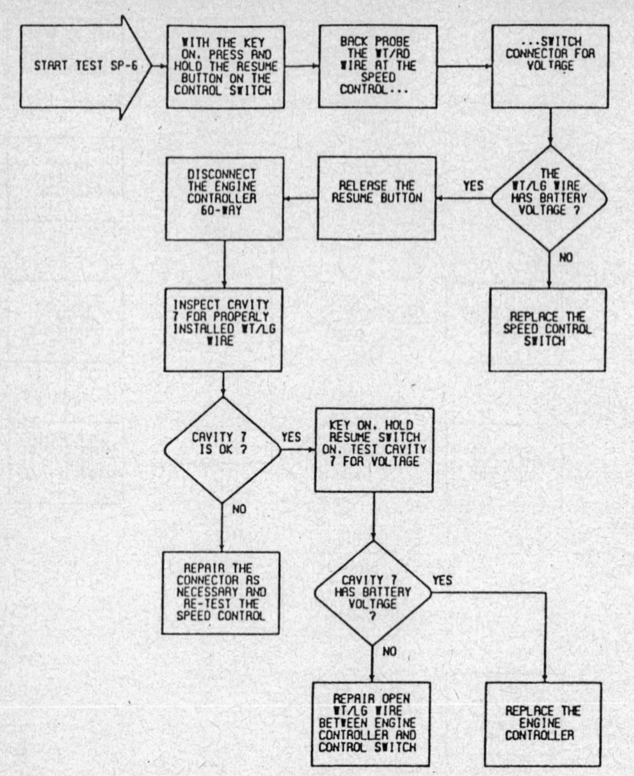


**Fig. 8 Test SP-6, testing resume switch. 1989 models less 3.0L/V6-181**

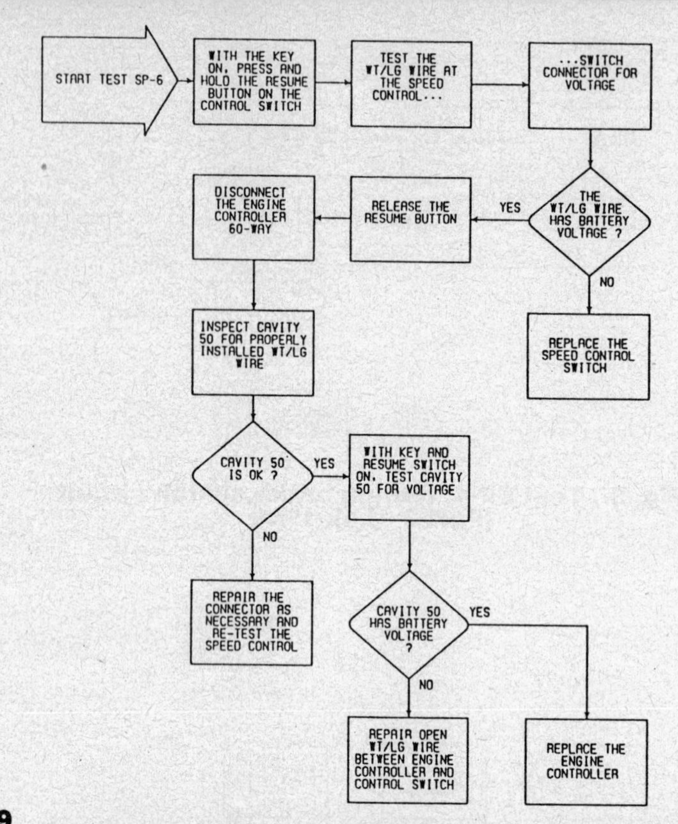


**Fig. 9 Test SP-6, testing resume switch. 1989 models w/3.0L/V6-181**

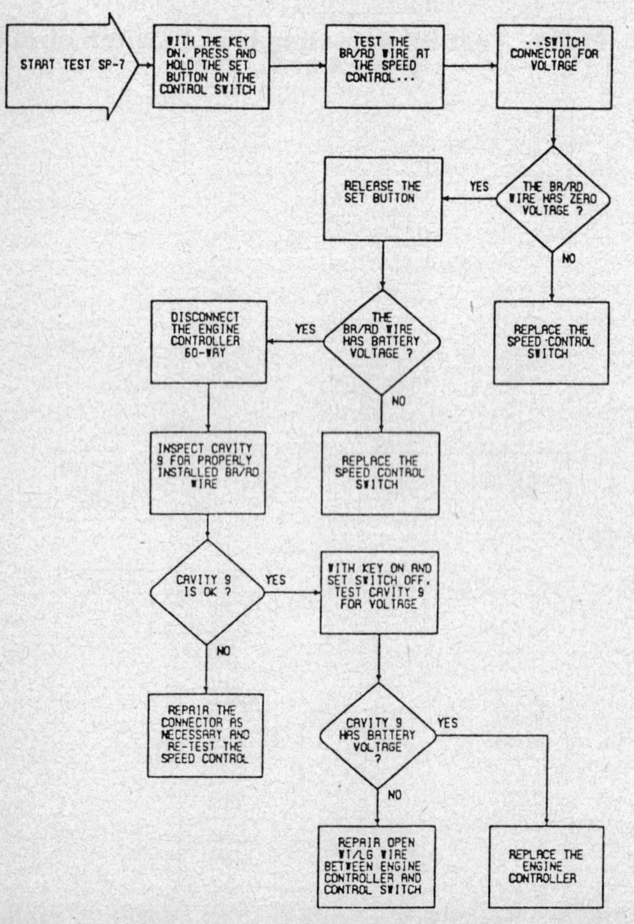


**Fig. 10 Test SP-7, testing set switch. 1989**

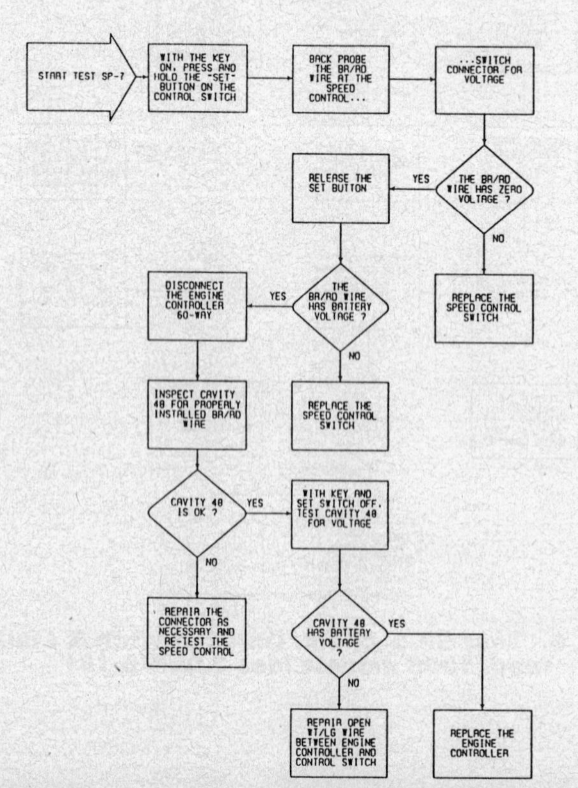


**Fig. 11 Test SP-7, testing set switch. 1989 models w/3.0L/V6-181**

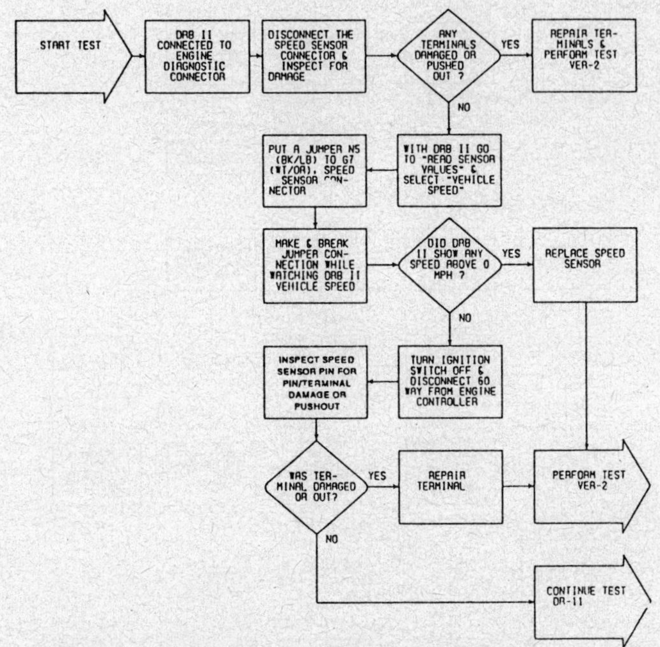


Fig. 12 Test SP-8, checking vehicle speed signal (Part 1 of 2). 1989

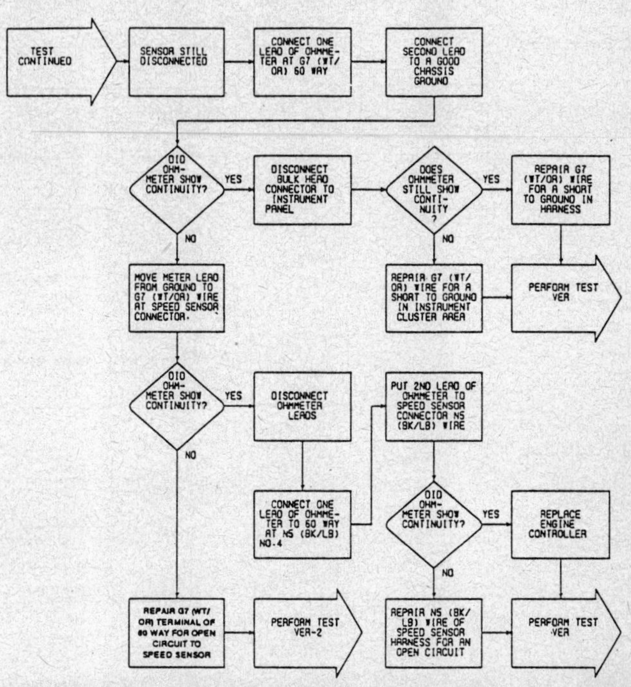


Fig. 12 Test SP-8, checking vehicle speed signal (Part 2 of 2). 1989

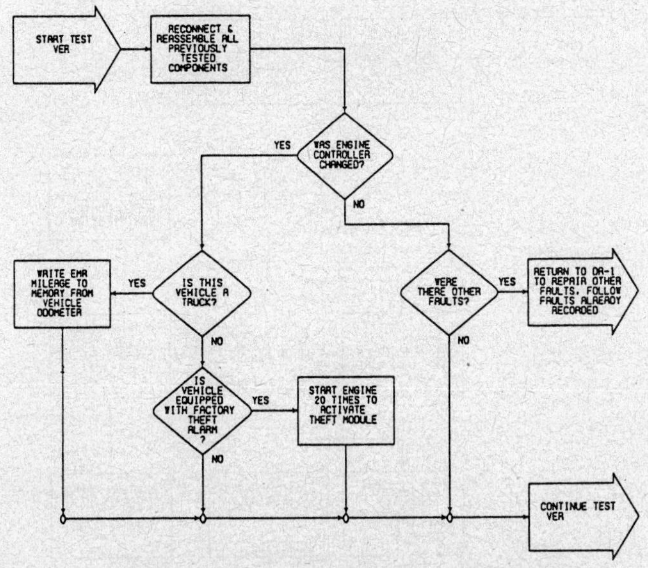


Fig. 13 Test SP-VER, speed control verification (Part 1 of 2). 1989

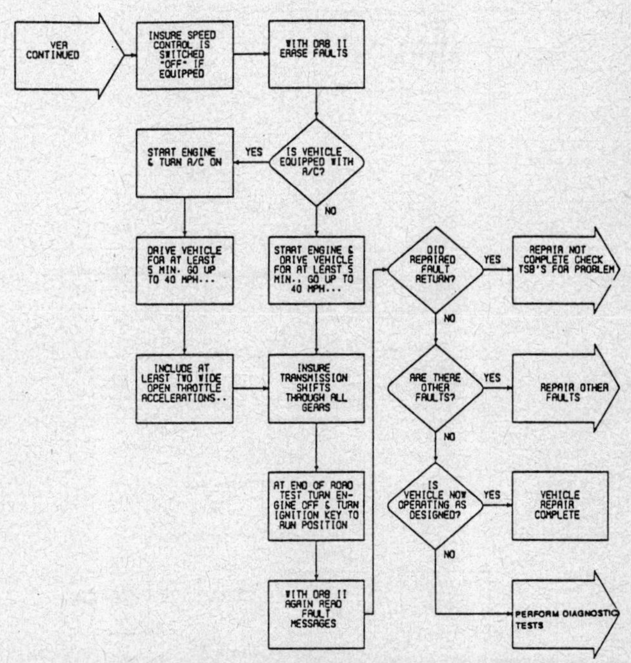


Fig. 13 Test SP-VER, speed control verification (Part 2 of 2). 1989

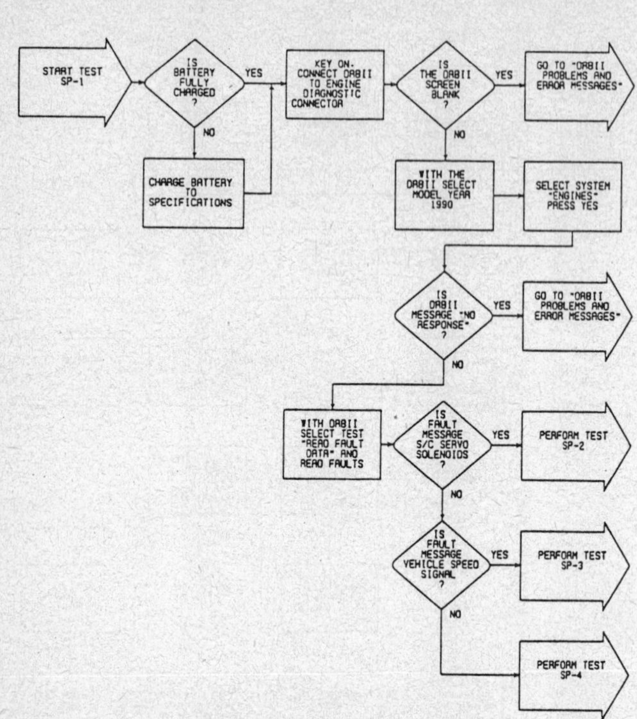


**Fig. 14 Test SP-1, checking DRB II operation & reading faults**

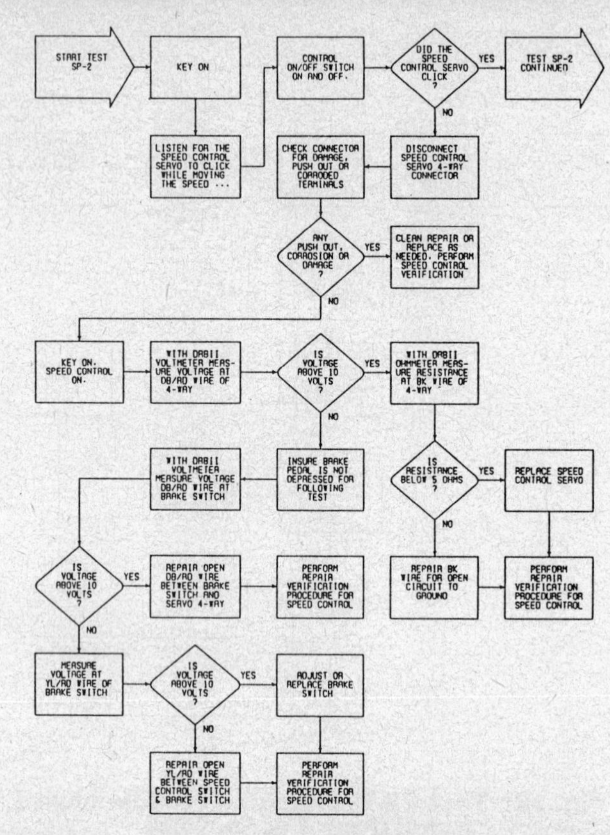


**Fig. 15 Test SP-2, S/C servo solenoids (Part 1 of 3). 1990**

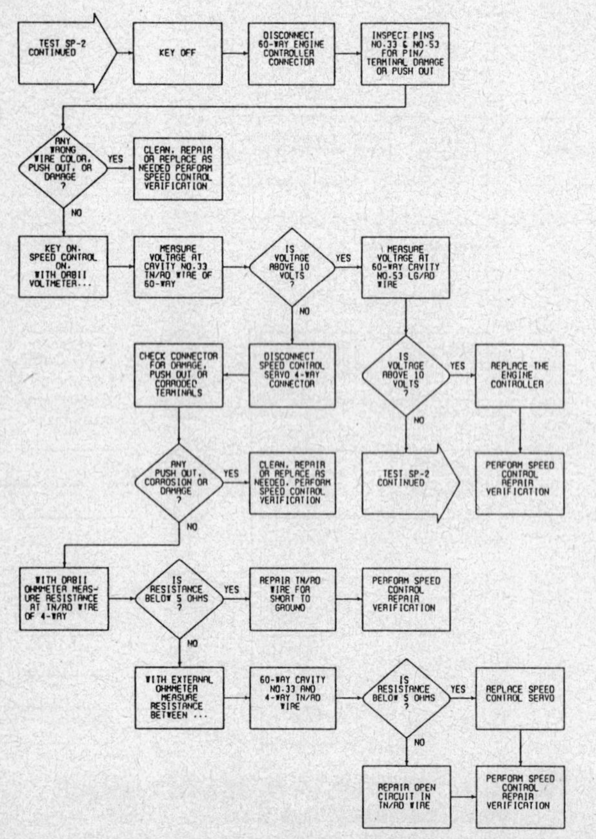


**Fig. 15 Test SP-2, S/C servo solenoids (Part 2 of 3). 1990**

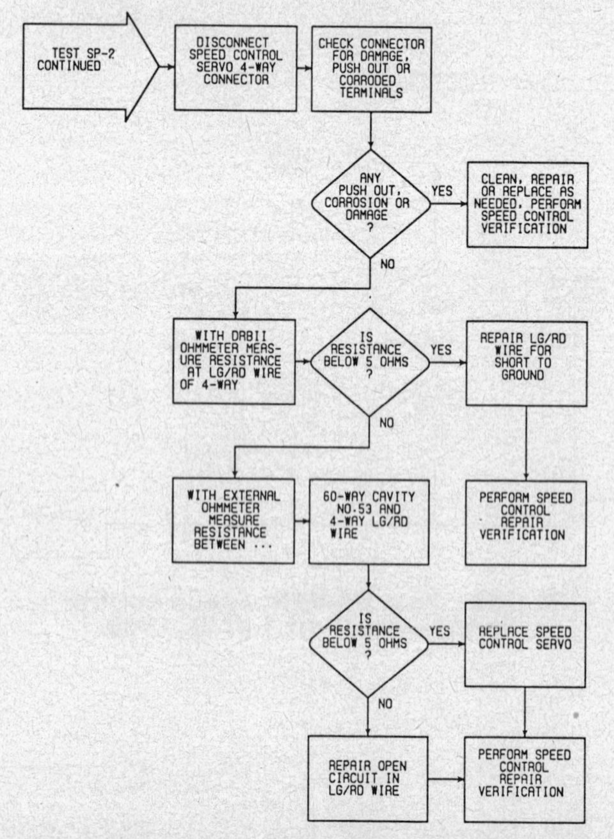


**Fig. 15 Test SP-2, S/C servo solenoids (Part 3 of 3). 1990**

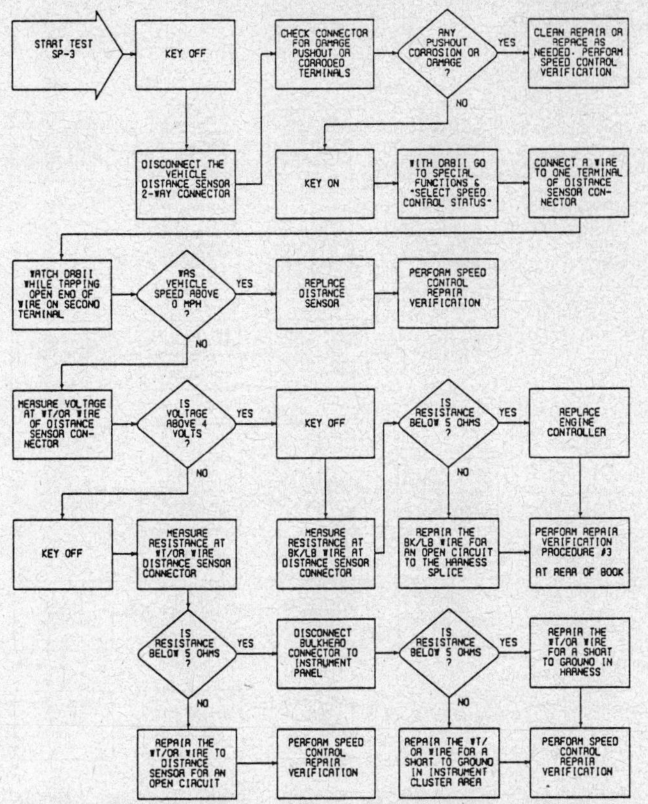

Fig. 16 Test SP-3, vehicle speed signal. 1990

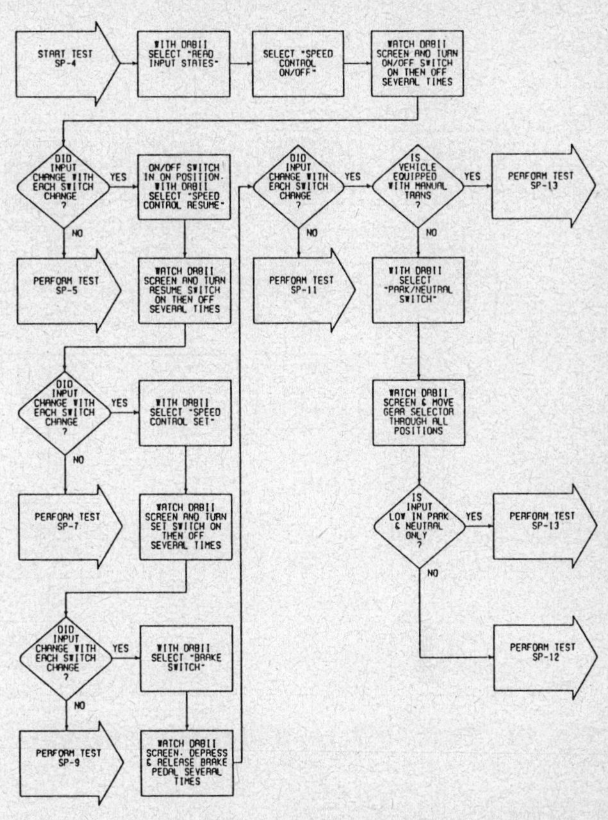

Fig. 17 Test SP-4, checking switch input. 1990

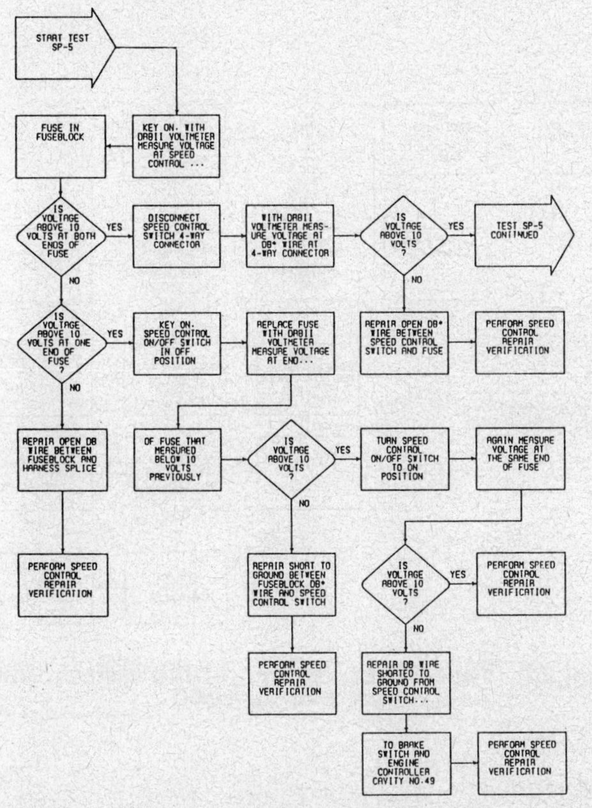

Fig. 18 Test SP-5, checking On/Off switch (Part 1 of 2). 1990

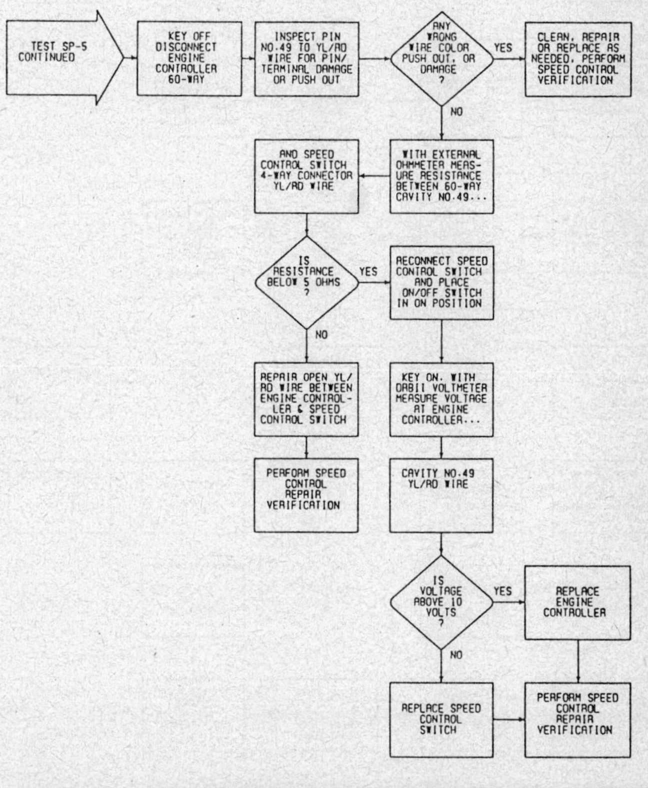

Fig. 18 Test SP-5, checking On/Off switch (Part 2 of 2). 1990

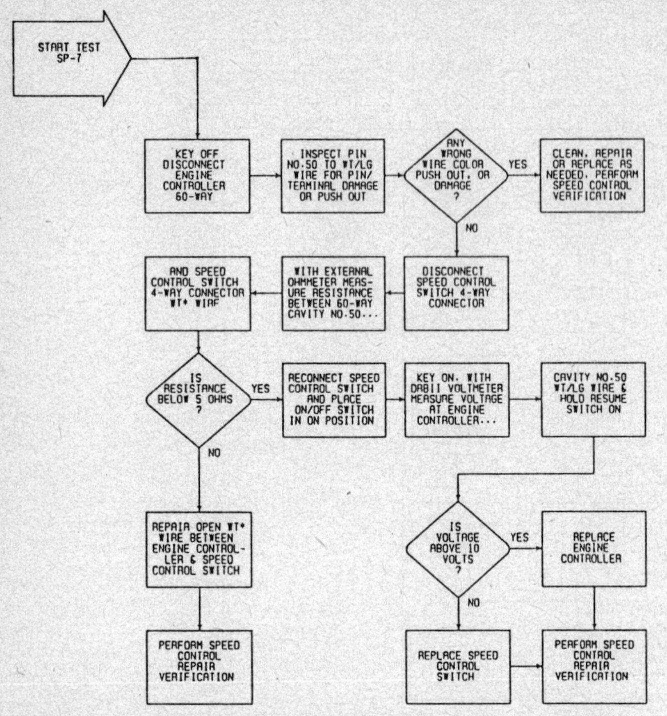


**Fig. 19 Test SP-7, testing resume switch. 1990**

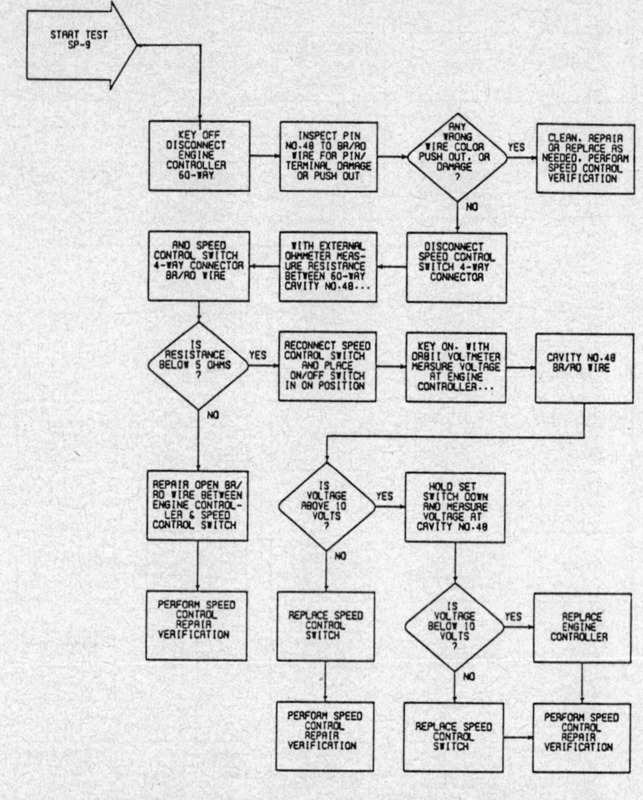


**Fig. 20 Test SP-9, testing set switch. 1990**

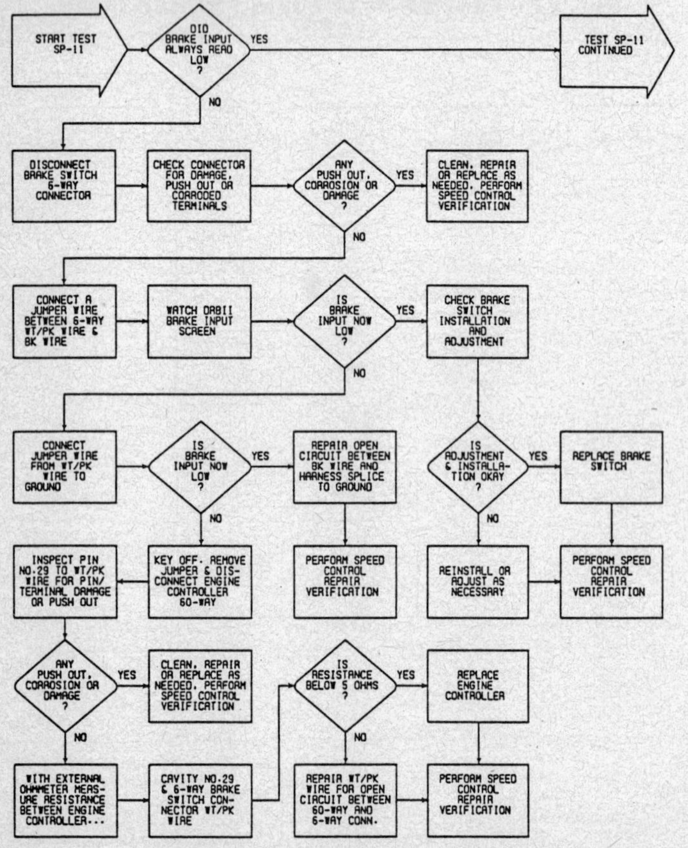


**Fig. 21 Test SP-11, testing brake switch input (Part 1 of 2). 1990**

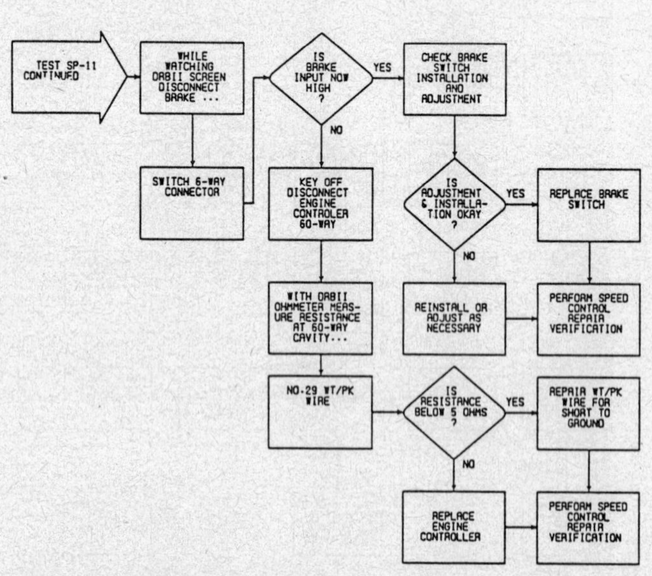


**Fig. 21 Test SP-11, testing brake switch input (Part 2 of 2). 1990**

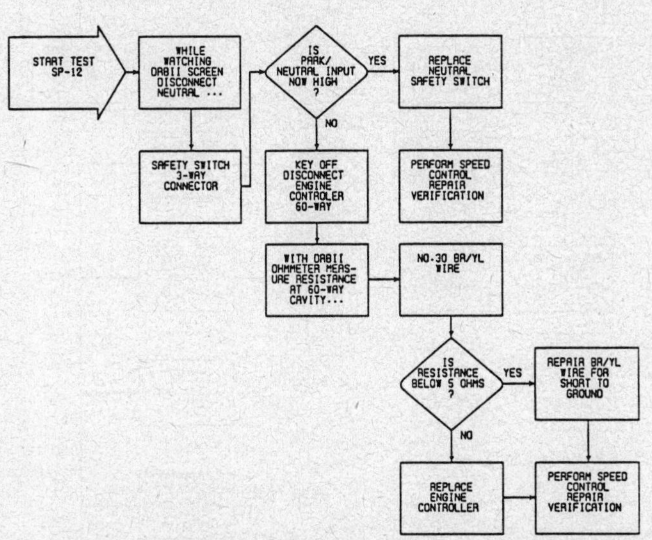


Fig. 22 Test SP-12, testing park/neutral switch input. 1990

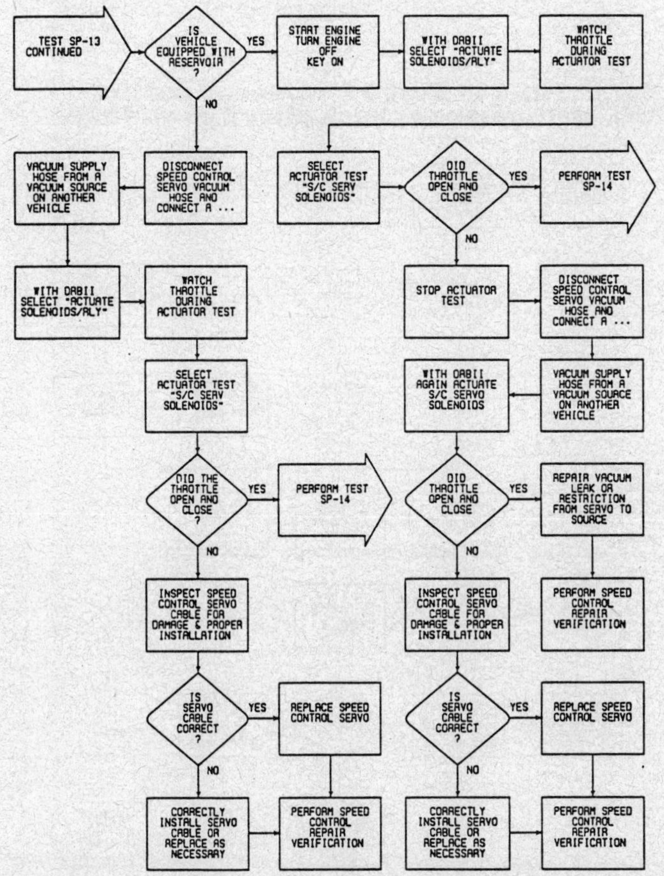


Fig. 23 Test SP-13, checking servo power & ground circuits (Part 2 of 2). 1990

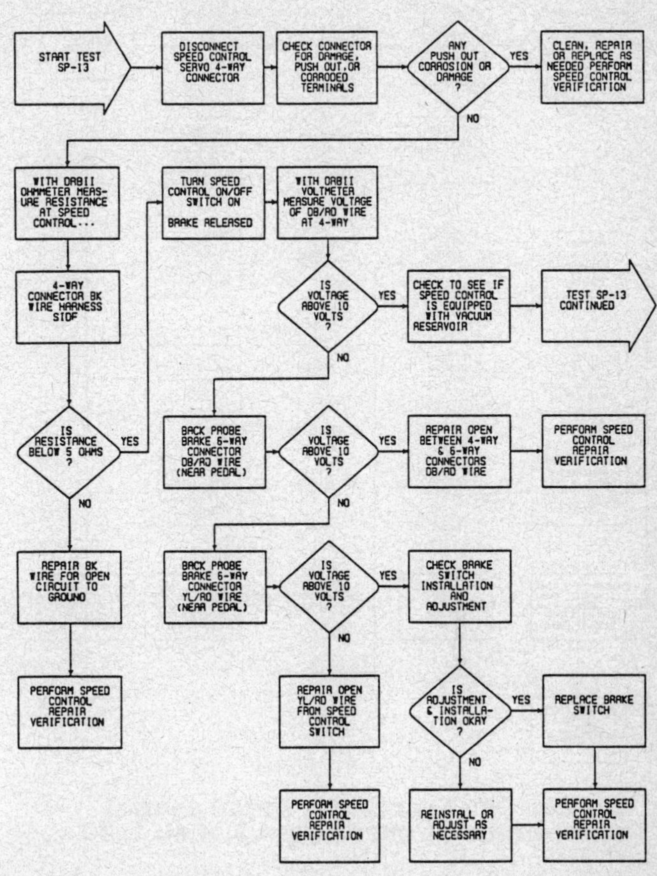


Fig. 23 Test SP-13, checking servo power & ground circuits (Part 1 of 2). 1990

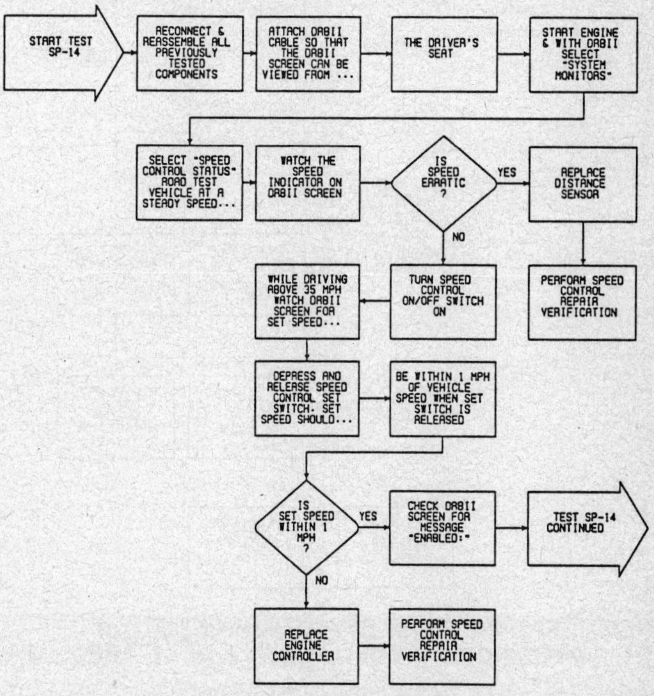


Fig. 24 Test SP-14, speed control performance check (Part 1 of 4). 1990

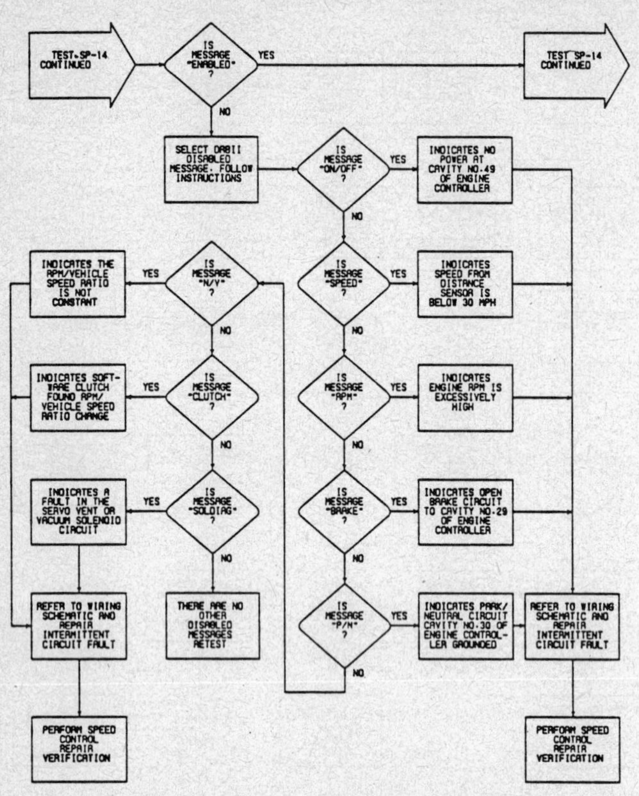


**Fig. 24 Test SP-14, speed control performance check (Part 2 of 4). 1990**

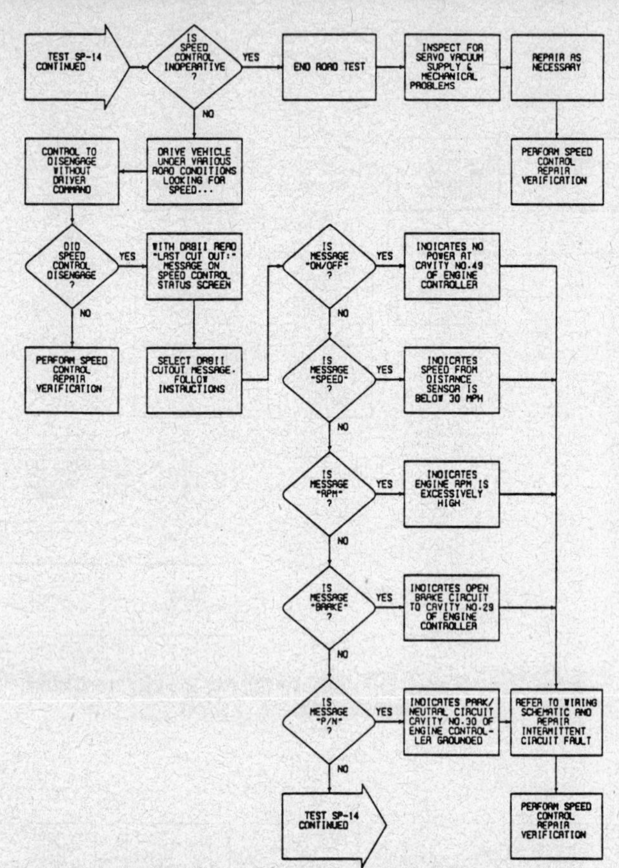


**Fig. 24 Test SP-14, speed control performance check (Part 3 of 4). 1990**

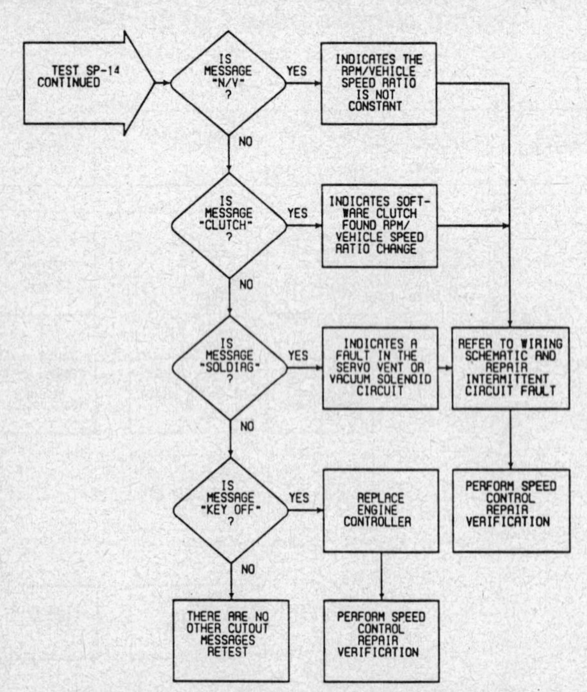


**Fig. 24 Test SP-14, speed control performance check (Part 4 of 4). 1990**

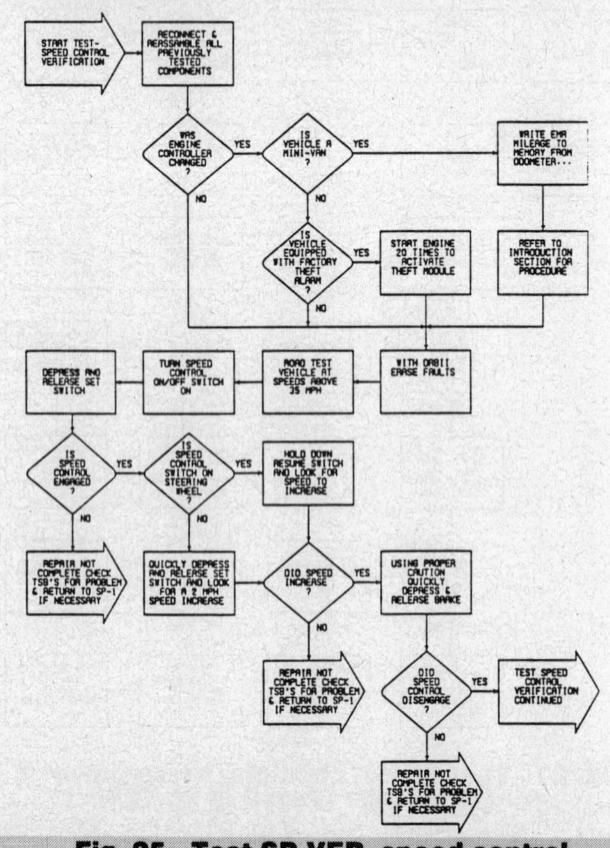


**Fig. 25 Test SP-VER, speed control verification (Part 1 of 2). 1990**

TEST SPEED CONTROL VERIFICATION CONTINUED
ASSURE SPEED IS ABOVE 35 MPH AND SWITCH ON RESUME
DID SPEED CONTROL RETURN TO SET SPEED ?
YES
HOLD DOWN SET SWITCH AND LOOK FOR DEACCELERATION
NO
REPAIR NOT COMPLETE CHECK TSB'S FOR PROBLEM & RETURN TO SP-1 IF NECESSARY
DID VEHICLE DEACCELERATE ?
YES
ASSURE SPEED IS ABOVE 35 MPH AND RELEASE SET SWITCH
NO
REPAIR NOT COMPLETE CHECK TSB'S FOR PROBLEM & RETURN TO SP-1 IF NECESSARY
DID SPEED CONTROL SET AT NEW SPEED ?
YES
TURN SPEED CONTROL ON/OFF SWITCH OFF
NO
REPAIR NOT COMPLETE CHECK TSB'S FOR PROBLEM & RETURN TO SP-1 IF NECESSARY
DID SPEED CONTROL DISENGAGE ?
YES
REPAIR COMPLETE
NO
REPAIR NOT COMPLETE CHECK TSB'S FOR PROBLEM & RETURN TO SP-1 IF NECESSARY

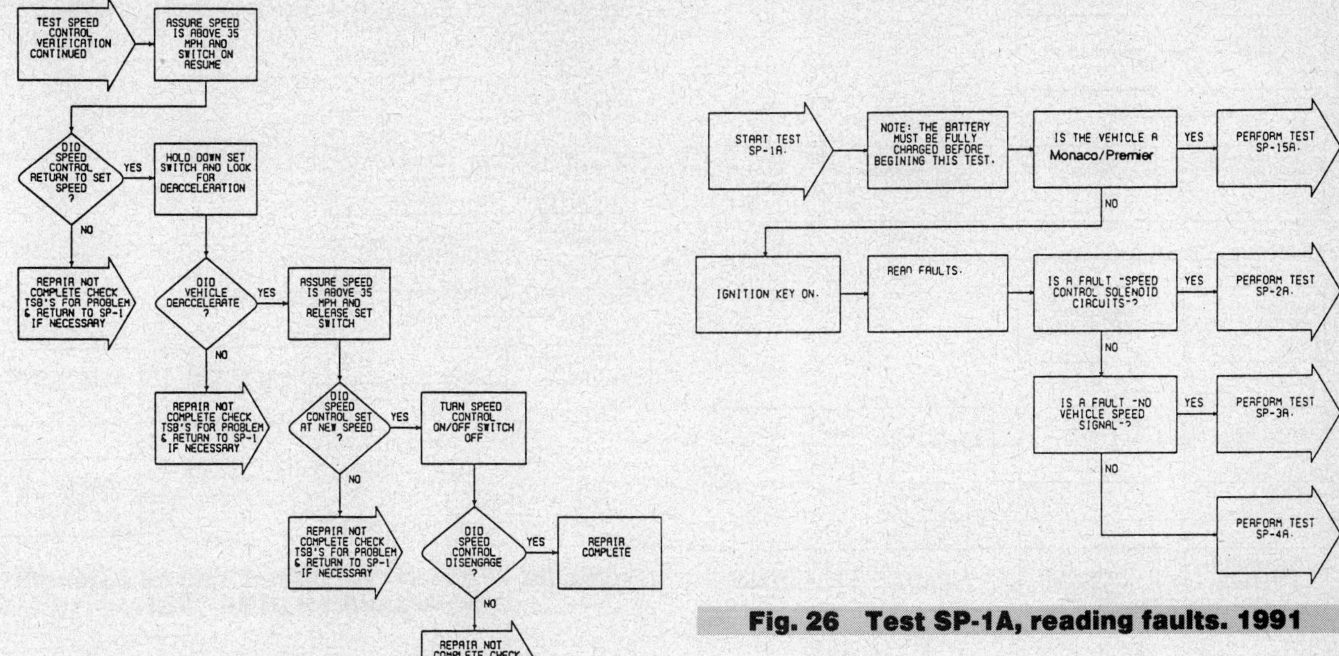

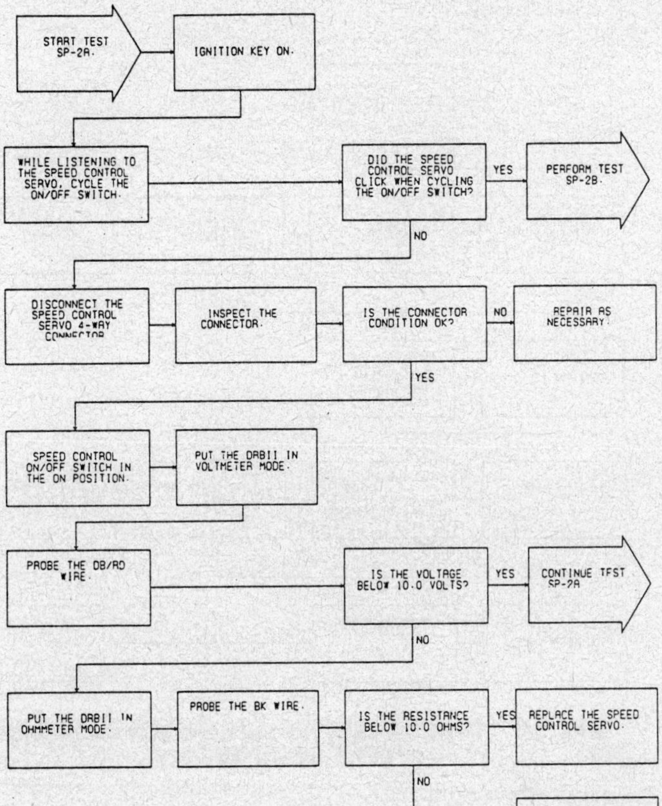

**Fig. 25 Test SP-VER, speed control verification (Part 2 of 2). 1990**

START TEST SP-1A.
NOTE: THE BATTERY MUST BE FULLY CHARGED BEFORE BEGINING THIS TEST.
IS THE VEHICLE A Monaco/Premier
YES
PERFORM TEST SP-15A.
NO
IGNITION KEY ON.
READ FAULTS.
IS A FAULT "SPEED CONTROL SOLENOID CIRCUITS"?
YES
PERFORM TEST SP-2A.
NO
IS A FAULT "NO VEHICLE SPEED SIGNAL"?
YES
PERFORM TEST SP-3A.
NO
PERFORM TEST SP-4A.

**Fig. 26 Test SP-1A, reading faults. 1991**

START TEST SP-2A.
IGNITION KEY ON.
WHILE LISTENING TO THE SPEED CONTROL SERVO, CYCLE THE ON/OFF SWITCH.
DID THE SPEED CONTROL SERVO CLICK WHEN CYCLING THE ON/OFF SWITCH?
YES
PERFORM TEST SP-2B.
NO
DISCONNECT THE SPEED CONTROL SERVO 4-WAY CONNECTOR
INSPECT THE CONNECTOR.
IS THE CONNECTOR CONDITION OK?
NO
REPAIR AS NECESSARY.
YES
SPEED CONTROL ON/OFF SWITCH IN THE ON POSITION.
PUT THE DRBII IN VOLTMETER MODE.
PROBE THE DB/RD WIRE.
IS THE VOLTAGE BELOW 10.0 VOLTS?
YES
CONTINUE TEST SP-2A
NO
PUT THE DRBII IN OHMMETER MODE.
PROBE THE BK WIRE.
IS THE RESISTANCE BELOW 10.0 OHMS?
YES
REPLACE THE SPEED CONTROL SERVO.
NO
REPAIR THE Z1 BK WIRE FOR AN OPEN TO GROUND.

**Fig. 27 Test SP-2A, speed control solenoid circuit (Part 1 of 2). 1991**

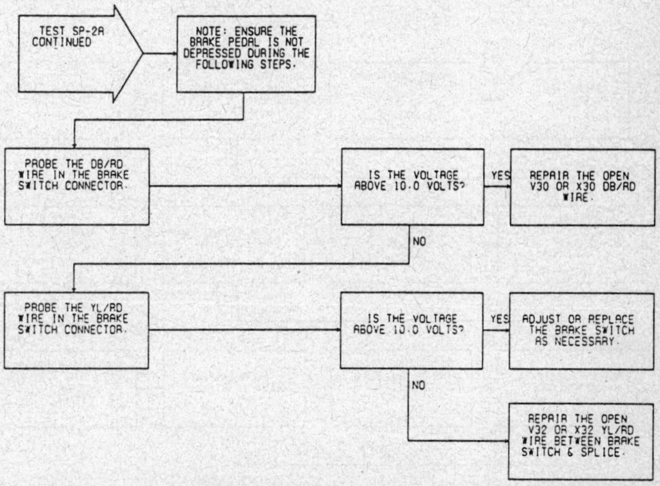

TEST SP-2A CONTINUED
NOTE: ENSURE THE BRAKE PEDAL IS NOT DEPRESSED DURING THE FOLLOWING STEPS.
PROBE THE DB/RD WIRE IN THE BRAKE SWITCH CONNECTOR.
IS THE VOLTAGE ABOVE 10.0 VOLTS?
YES
REPAIR THE OPEN V30 OR X30 DB/RD WIRE.
NO
PROBE THE YL/RD WIRE IN THE BRAKE SWITCH CONNECTOR.
IS THE VOLTAGE ABOVE 10.0 VOLTS?
YES
ADJUST OR REPLACE THE BRAKE SWITCH AS NECESSARY.
NO
REPAIR THE OPEN V32 OR X32 YL/RD WIRE BETWEEN BRAKE SWITCH & SPLICE.

**Fig. 27 Test SP-2A, speed control solenoid circuit (Part 2 of 2). 1991**

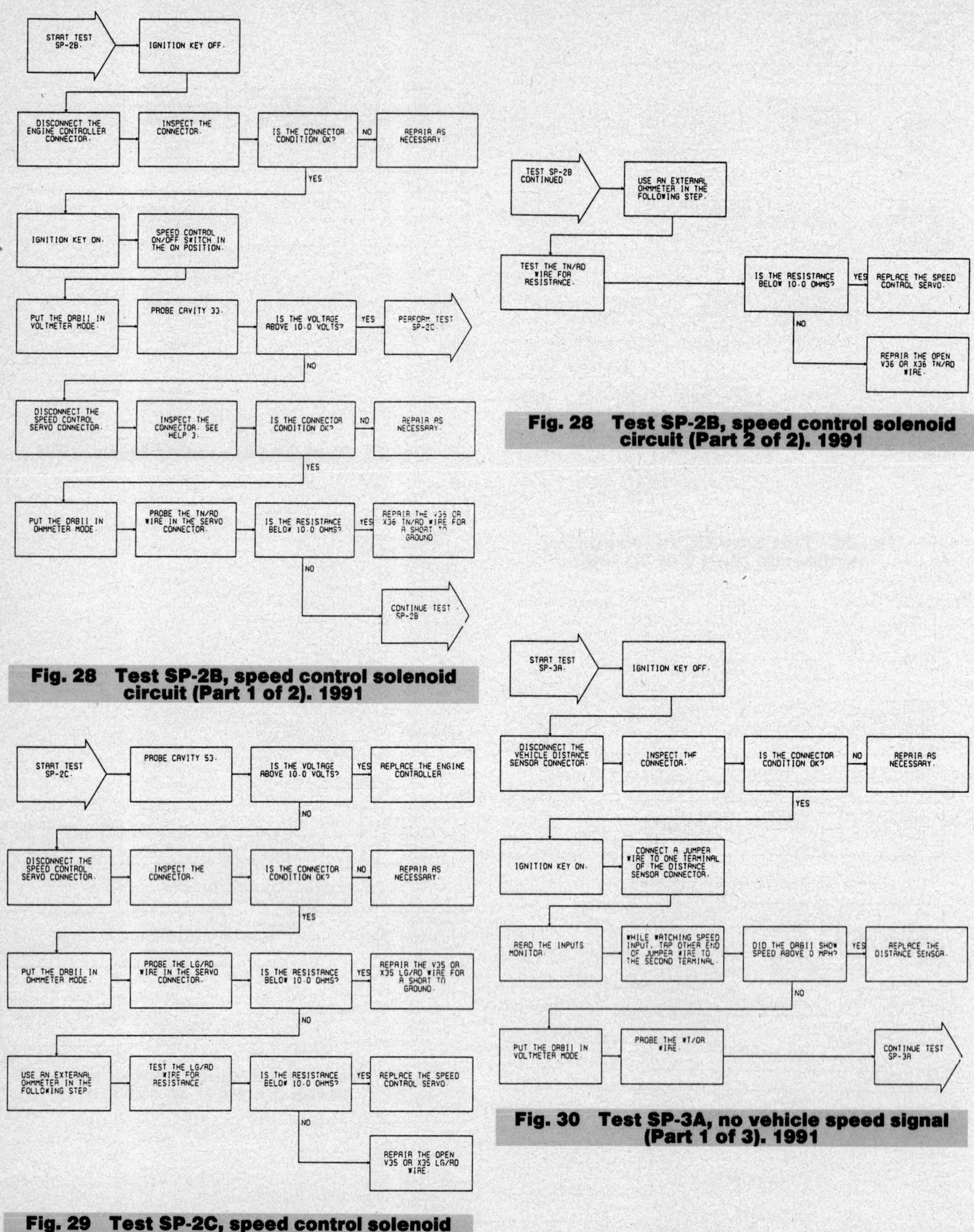


**Fig. 28 Test SP-2B, speed control solenoid circuit (Part 1 of 2). 1991**

**Fig. 28 Test SP-2B, speed control solenoid circuit (Part 2 of 2). 1991**

**Fig. 29 Test SP-2C, speed control solenoid circuit. 1991**

**Fig. 30 Test SP-3A, no vehicle speed signal (Part 1 of 3). 1991**

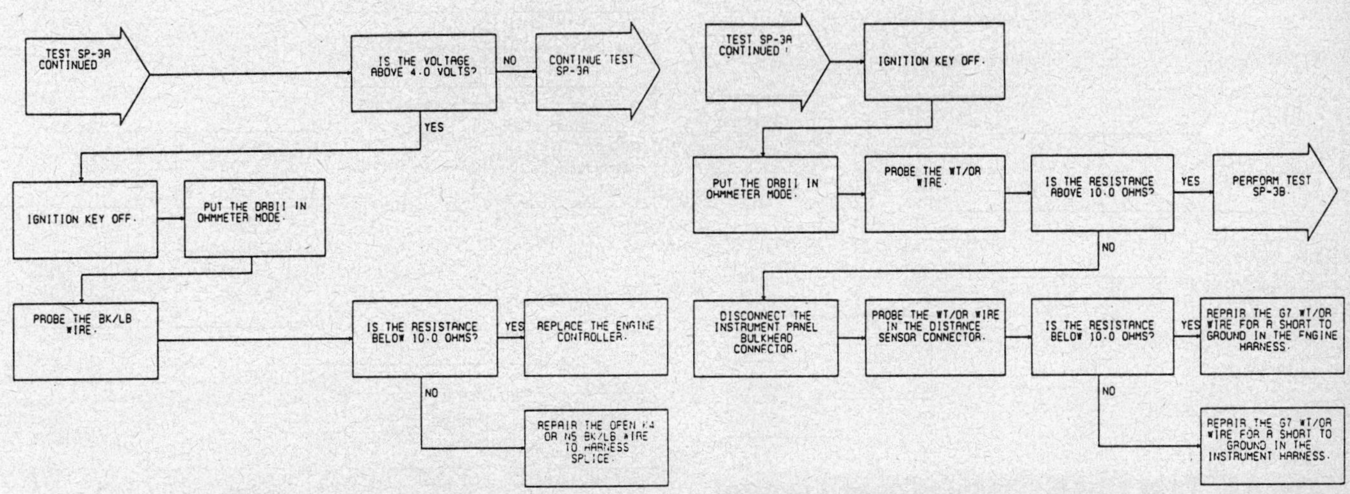

TEST SP-3A CONTINUED
IS THE VOLTAGE ABOVE 4.0 VOLTS?
NO
CONTINUE TEST SP-3A
YES
IGNITION KEY OFF.
PUT THE DRBII IN OHMMETER MODE.
PROBE THE BK/LB WIRE.
IS THE RESISTANCE BELOW 10.0 OHMS?
YES
REPLACE THE ENGINE CONTROLLER.
NO
SPLICE.

Fig. 30 Test SP-3A, no vehicle speed signal (Part 2 of 3). 1991

TEST SP-3A CONTINUED
IGNITION KEY OFF.
PUT THE DRBII IN OHMMETER MODE.
PROBE THE WT/OR WIRE.
IS THE RESISTANCE ABOVE 10.0 OHMS?
YES
PERFORM TEST SP-3B.
NO
DISCONNECT THE INSTRUMENT PANEL BULKHEAD CONNECTOR.
PROBE THE WT/OR WIRE IN THE DISTANCE SENSOR CONNECTOR.
IS THE RESISTANCE BELOW 10.0 OHMS?
YES
REPAIR THE G7 WT/OR WIRE FOR A SHORT TO GROUND IN THE ENGINE HARNESS.
NO
REPAIR THE G7 WT/OR WIRE FOR A SHORT TO GROUND IN THE INSTRUMENT HARNESS.

Fig. 30 Test SP-3A, no vehicle speed signal (Part 3 of 3). 1991

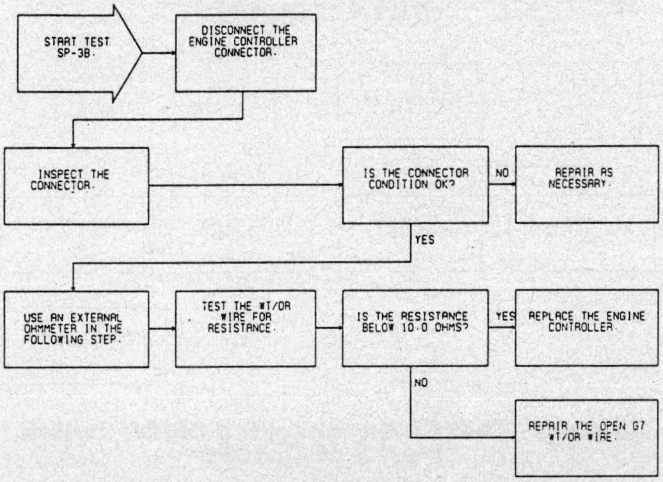

START TEST SP-3B.
DISCONNECT THE ENGINE CONTROLLER CONNECTOR.
INSPECT THE CONNECTOR.
IS THE CONNECTOR CONDITION OK?
NO
REPAIR AS NECESSARY.
YES
USE AN EXTERNAL OHMMETER IN THE FOLLOWING STEP.
TEST THE WT/OR WIRE FOR RESISTANCE.
IS THE RESISTANCE BELOW 10.0 OHMS?
YES
REPLACE THE ENGINE CONTROLLER.
NO
REPAIR THE OPEN G7 WT/OR WIRE.

Fig. 31 Test SP-3B, no vehicle speed signal. 1991

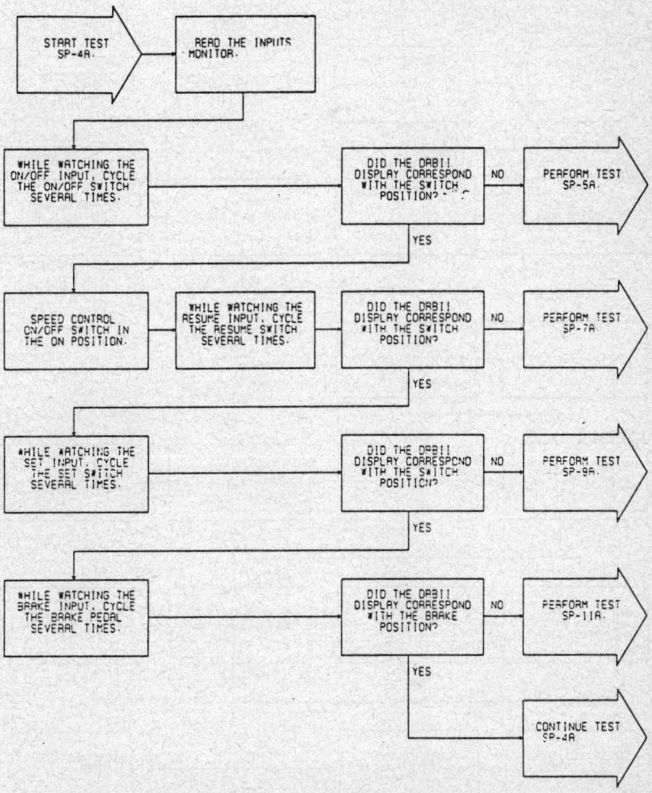

START TEST SP-4A.
READ THE INPUTS MONITOR.
WHILE WATCHING THE ON/OFF INPUT, CYCLE THE ON/OFF SWITCH SEVERAL TIMES.
DID THE DRBII DISPLAY CORRESPOND WITH THE SWITCH POSITION?
NO
PERFORM TEST SP-5A.
YES
SPEED CONTROL ON/OFF SWITCH IN THE ON POSITION.
WHILE WATCHING THE RESUME INPUT, CYCLE THE RESUME SWITCH SEVERAL TIMES.
DID THE DRBII DISPLAY CORRESPOND WITH THE SWITCH POSITION?
NO
PERFORM TEST SP-7A.
YES
WHILE WATCHING THE SET INPUT, CYCLE THE SET SWITCH SEVERAL TIMES.
DID THE DRBII DISPLAY CORRESPOND WITH THE SWITCH POSITION?
NO
PERFORM TEST SP-9A.
YES
WHILE WATCHING THE BRAKE INPUT, CYCLE THE BRAKE PEDAL SEVERAL TIMES.
DID THE DRBII DISPLAY CORRESPOND WITH THE BRAKE POSITION?
NO
PERFORM TEST SP-11A.
YES
CONTINUE TEST SP-4A

Fig. 32 Test SP-4A, checking speed control switches (Part 1 of 2). 1991

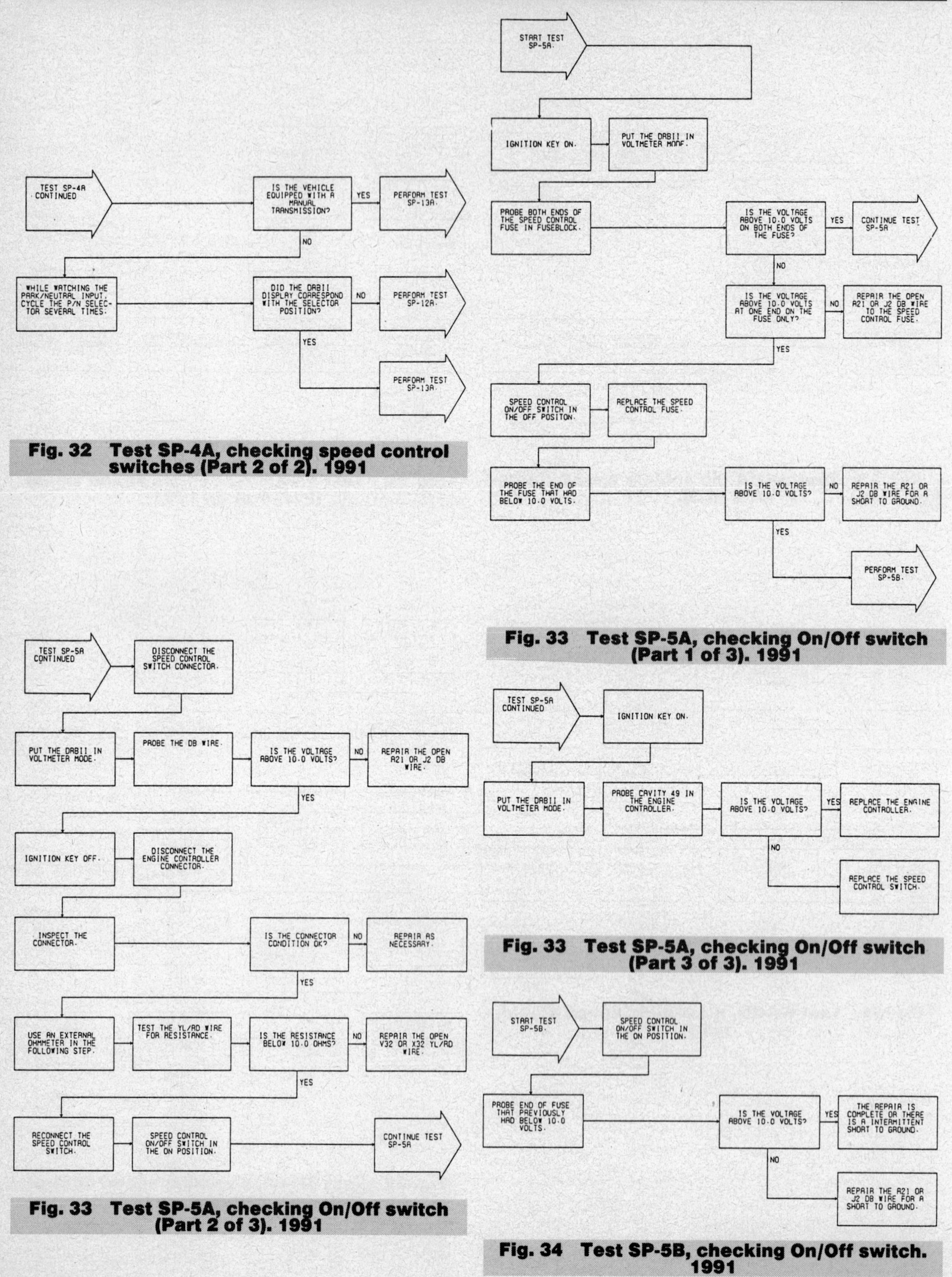


Fig. 32 Test SP-4A, checking speed control switches (Part 2 of 2). 1991

Fig. 33 Test SP-5A, checking On/Off switch (Part 1 of 3). 1991



Fig. 33 Test SP-5A, checking On/Off switch (Part 3 of 3). 1991



Fig. 33 Test SP-5A, checking On/Off switch (Part 2 of 3). 1991

Fig. 34 Test SP-5B, checking On/Off switch. 1991

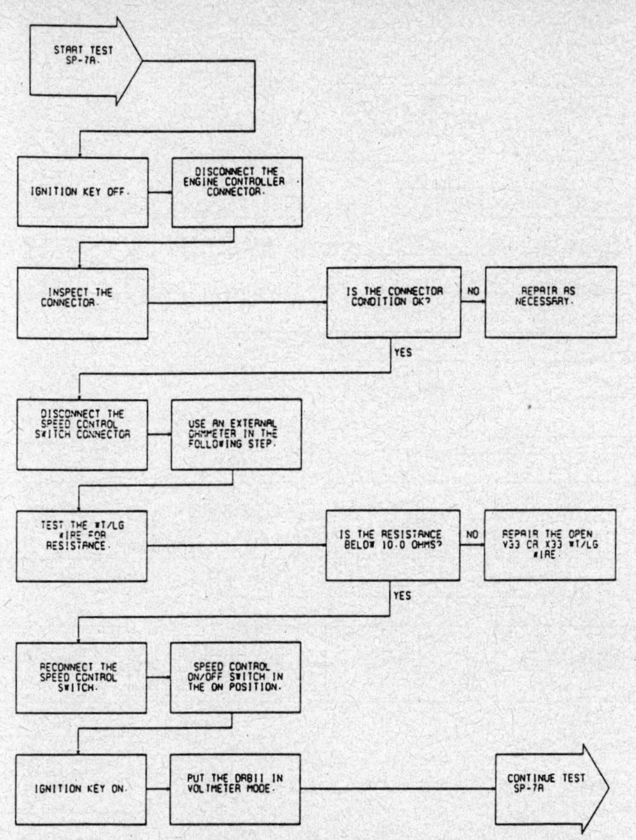


Fig. 35 Test SP-7A, checking resume switch (Part 1 of 2). 1991

TEST SP-7A CONTINUED
PROBE CAVITY 50 IN THE ENGINE CONTROLLER.
WHILE HOLDING DOWN THE RESUME SWITCH, READ THE VOLTAGE.
IS THE VOLTAGE ABOVE 10.0 VOLTS?
YES
REPLACE THE ENGINE CONTROLLER.
NO
REPLACE THE SPEED CONTROL SWITCH.

Fig. 35 Test SP-7A, checking resume switch (Part 2 of 2). 1991

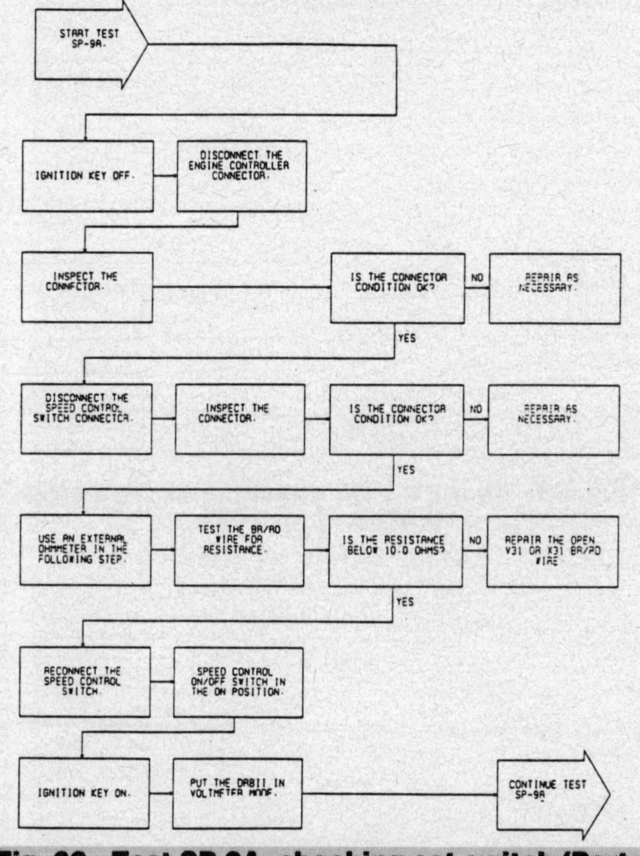


Fig. 36 Test SP-9A, checking set switch (Part 1 of 2). 1991

TEST SP-9A CONTINUED
PROBE CAVITY 48 IN THE ENGINE CONTROLLER.
IS THE VOLTAGE ABOVE 10.0 VOLTS?
NO
REPLACE THE SPEED CONTROL SWITCH.
YES
WHILE HOLDING DOWN THE SET SWITCH, PROBE CAVITY 48.
IS THE VOLTAGE BELOW 10.0 VOLTS?
YES
REPLACE THE ENGINE CONTROLLER.
NO
REPLACE THE SPEED CONTROL SWITCH.

Fig. 36 Test SP-9A, checking set switch (Part 2 of 2). 1991

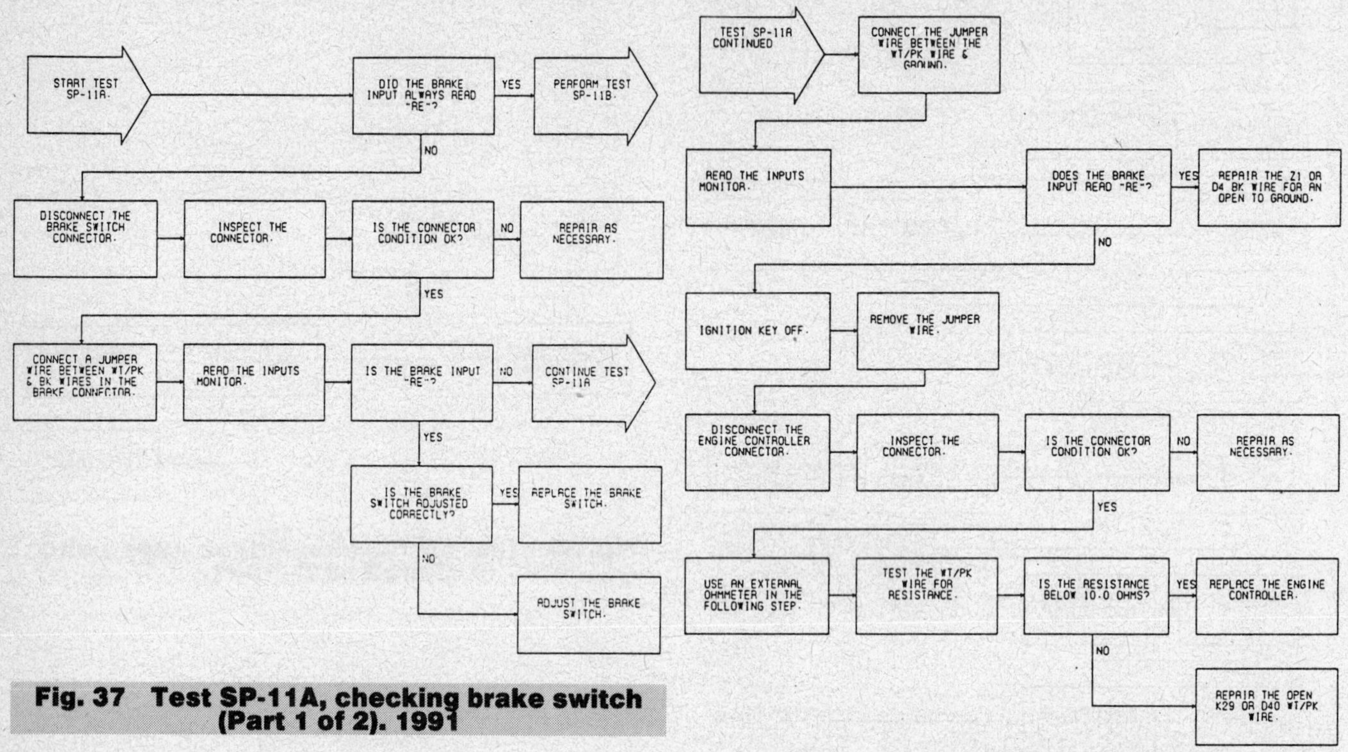


**Fig. 37 Test SP-11A, checking brake switch (Part 1 of 2). 1991**

**Fig. 37 Test SP-11A, checking brake switch (Part 2 of 2). 1991**

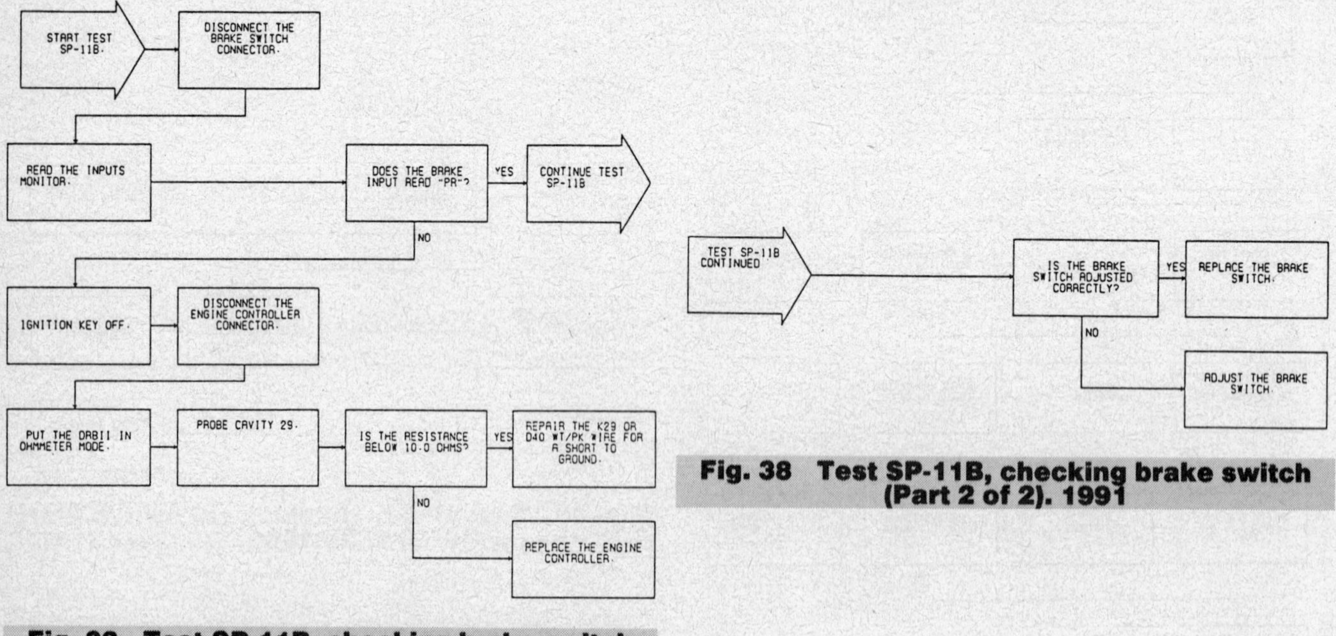


**Fig. 38 Test SP-11B, checking brake switch (Part 1 of 2). 1991**

**Fig. 38 Test SP-11B, checking brake switch (Part 2 of 2). 1991**

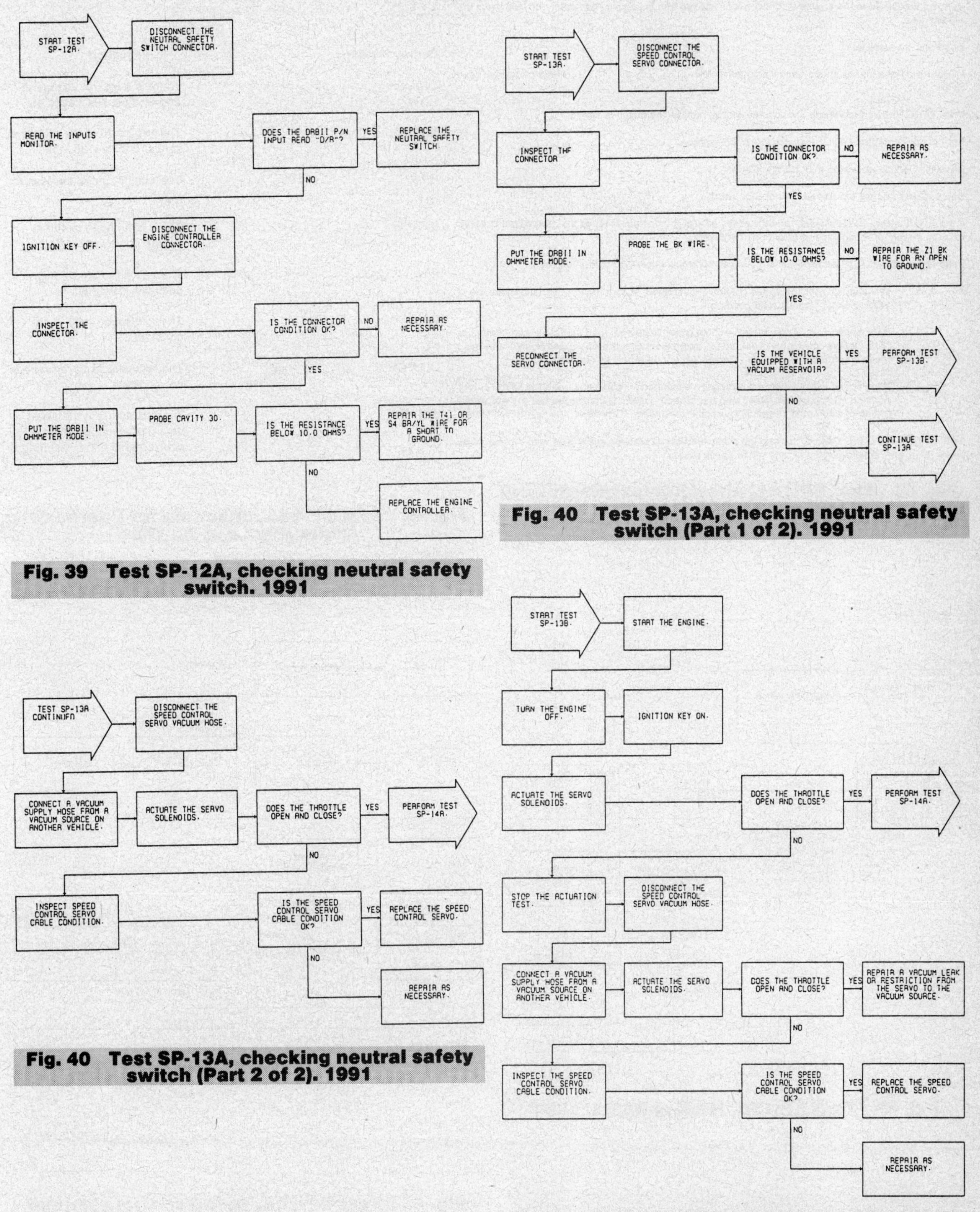


**Fig. 39 Test SP-12A, checking neutral safety switch. 1991**

**Fig. 40 Test SP-13A, checking neutral safety switch (Part 1 of 2). 1991**

**Fig. 40 Test SP-13A, checking neutral safety switch (Part 2 of 2). 1991**

**Fig. 41 Test SP-13B, checking neutral safety switch. 1991**

Reconnect and reassemble all previously tested components.

Connect the DRBII to the engine diagnostic connector so that the display can safely be seen from the driver's seat.

Road test the vehicle.

While driving at a steady speed, read the cutout monitor. Have passenger read DRBII.

If the DRBII shows the vehicle speed to be erratic, replace the distance sensor.

Put the speed control ON/OFF switch in the ON position.

Drive the vehicle above 35 mph for the following steps.

Depress and release the speed control SET switch.

If the DRBII shows "S/C Allowed," and the speed control is inoperative, repair the speed control servo vacuum supply or mechanical problems as necessary.

If the DRBII shows "S/C Allowed," and the speed control is operative, do the following:

1. While looking for the speed control to disengage without driver command, drive the vehicle under various road conditions.
2. If the speed control disengages without driver command, read the DRBII cutout monitor "S/C Denied" message. Look up the intermittent circuit problem associated with this message in the chart on the following page, and repair as necessary.
3. If the speed control does not disengage without driver command, read the DRBII cutout monitor. Compare the "Goal" with the "Speed" value. If the two valves are not within 2 mph of each other, replace the engine controller. Otherwise, the test is complete.

If the DRBII shows "S/C Denied," look up the intermittent circuit problem associated with this message in the chart on the following page, and repair as necessary.

**Fig. 42 Test SP-14A, checking for intermittent faults (Part 1 of 2). 1991**

| Denied Message | Indication |
|---|---|
| ON/OFF | There is a lack of voltage at engine controller cavity 49. |
| SPEED | The vehicle from the distance sensor is below 35 mph. |
| RPM | The engine rpm is excessively high. |
| BRAKE | There is an open circuit at engine controller cavity 29. |
| P/N | There is a ground at engine controller cavity 30. |
| RPM/SPD | The rpm/speed ratio is not constant. |
| CLUTCH | The rpm/vehicle speed ratio is not constant. |
| SOL FLT | There is a fault in the servo vent or vacuum solenoid circuit that is either maturing or set. |

**Fig. 42 Test SP-14A, checking for intermittent faults (Part 2 of 2). 1991**

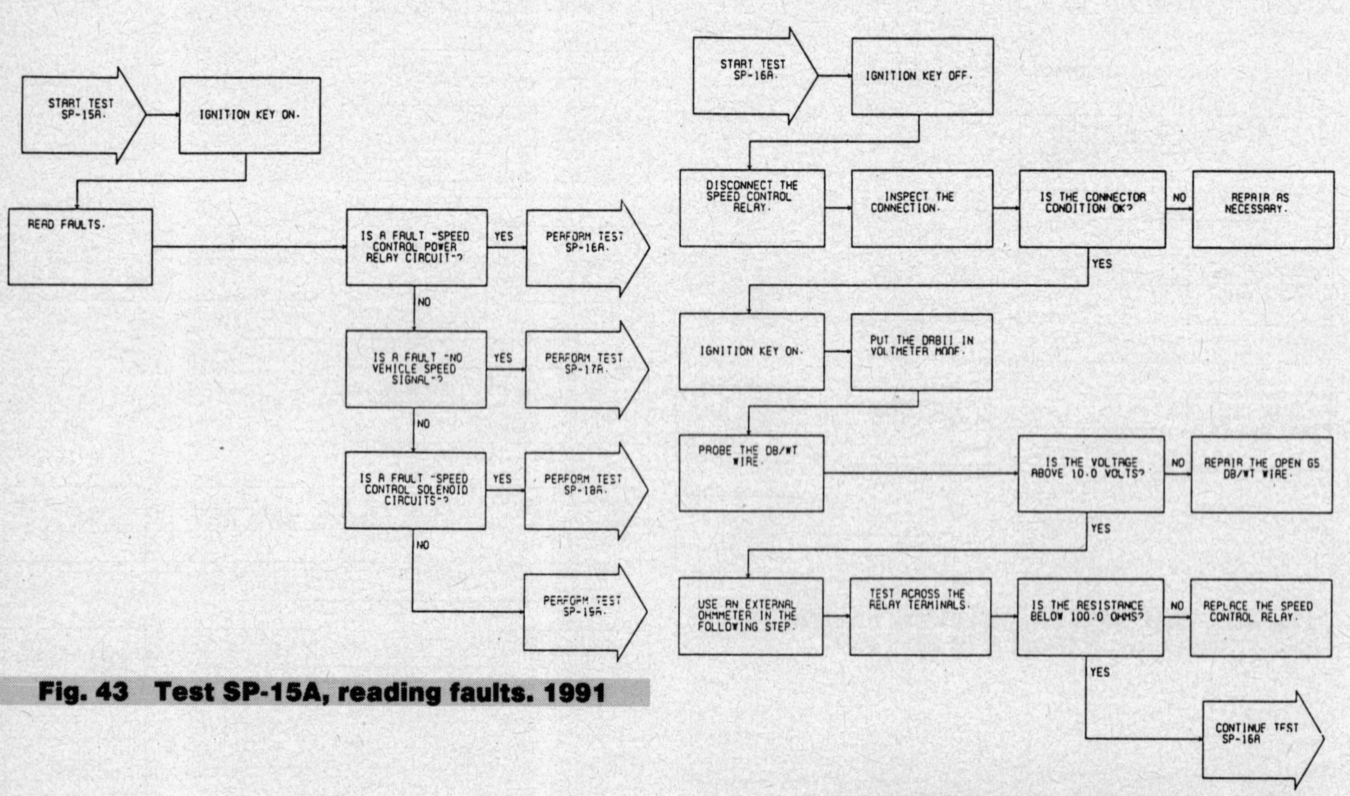


**Fig. 43 Test SP-15A, reading faults. 1991**

**Fig. 44 Test SP-16A, speed control solenoid circuit (Part 1 of 2). 1991**

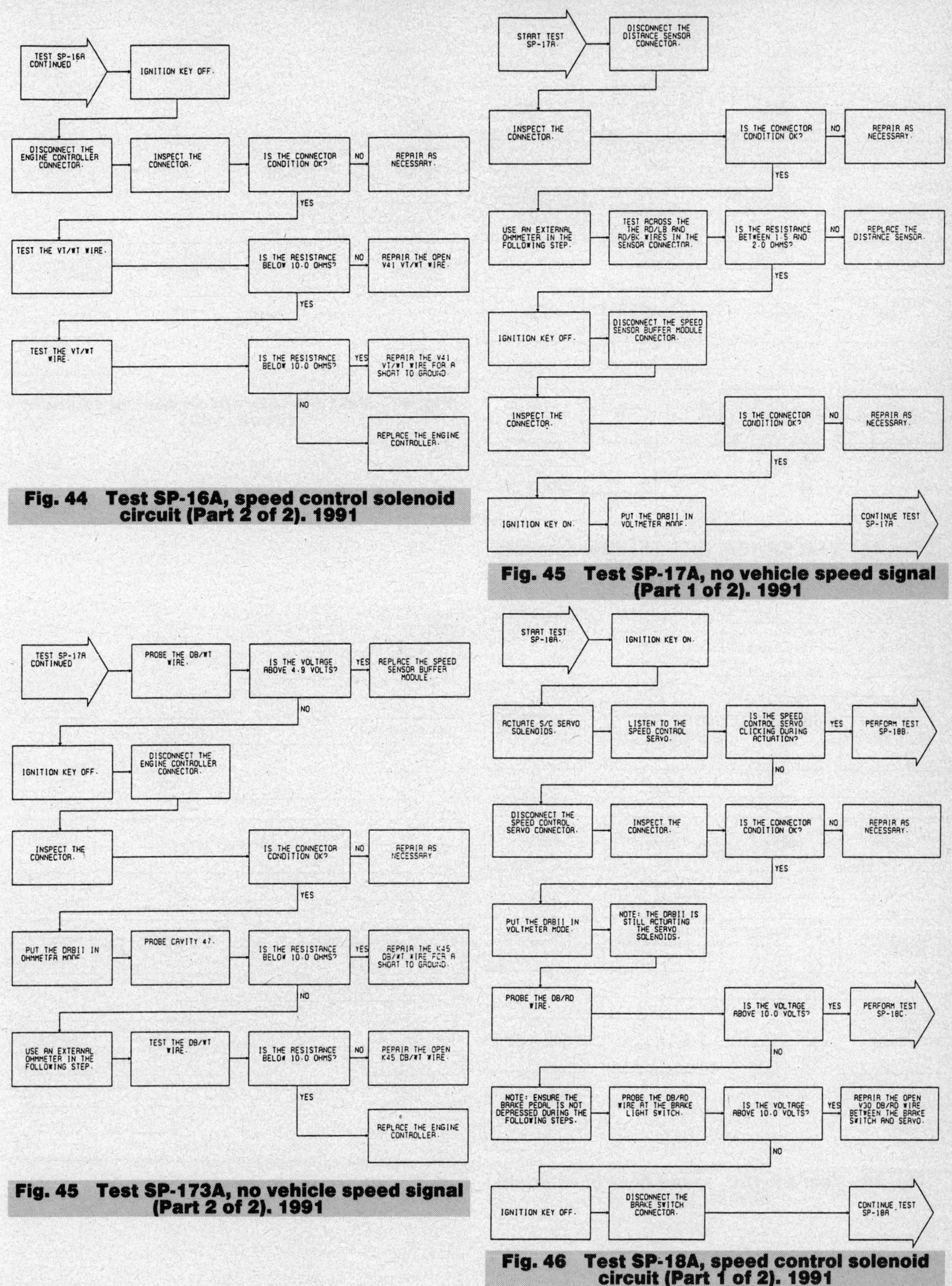


**Fig. 44 Test SP-16A, speed control solenoid circuit (Part 2 of 2). 1991**

**Fig. 45 Test SP-17A, no vehicle speed signal (Part 1 of 2). 1991**



**Fig. 45 Test SP-173A, no vehicle speed signal (Part 2 of 2). 1991**

**Fig. 46 Test SP-18A, speed control solenoid circuit (Part 1 of 2). 1991**

TEST SP-18A CONTINUED
INSPECT THE CONNECTOR.
IS THE CONNECTOR CONDITION OK?
NO
REPAIR AS NECESSARY.
YES
USE AN EXTERNAL OHMMETER IN THE FOLLOWING STEP.
WITH THE BRAKE PEDAL RELEASED, TEST ACROSS THE BRAKE SWITCH TERMINALS.
IS THE RESISTANCE ABOVE 10.0 OHMS?
YES
ADJUST OR REPLACE THE BRAKE LIGHT SWITCH AS NECESSARY.
NO
DISCONNECT THE SPEED CONTROL RELAY.
INSPECT THE CONNECTOR.
IS THE CONNECTOR CONDITION OK?
NO
REPAIR AS NECESSARY.
YES
USE AN EXTERNAL OHMMETER IN THE FOLLOWING STEP.
TEST THE TN WIRE FOR RESISTANCE.
IS THE RESISTANCE BELOW 10.0 OHMS?
NO
REPAIR THE OPEN V42 TN WIRE
YES
REPLACE THE SPEED CONTROL RELAY.

**Fig. 46 Test SP-18A, speed control solenoid circuit (Part 2 of 2). 1991**

START TEST SP-18B.
WIGGLE THE SPEED CONTROL HARNESS.
LISTEN FOR THE ACTUATION CLICKING PATTERN TO BE INTERRUPTED.
WAS THE CLICKING PATTERN INTERRUPTED WHEN THE HARNESS WAS WIGGLED?
YES
REPAIR THE HARNESS WHERE WIGGLING INTERRUPTED THE CLICKING PATTERN.
NO
REPLACE THE ENGINE CONTROLLER.

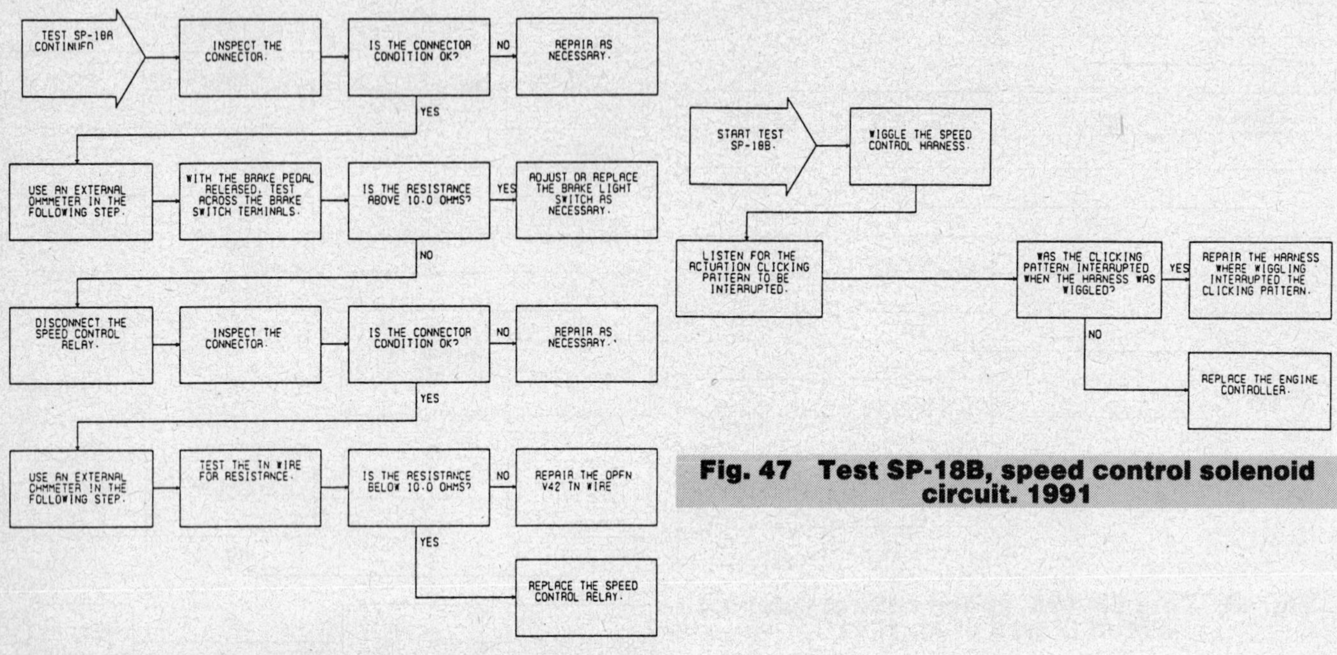

**Fig. 47 Test SP-18B, speed control solenoid circuit. 1991**

START TEST SP-18C.
IGNITION KEY OFF.
PUT THE DRBII IN OHMMETER MODE.
PROBE THE BK WIRE.
IS THE RESISTANCE BELOW 10.0 OHMS?
NO
REPAIR THE OPEN Z1 BK WIRE BETWEEN THE SERVO CONNECTOR & SPLICE.
YES
DISCONNECT THE ENGINE CONTROLLER CONNECTOR.
INSPECT THE CONNECTOR.
IS THE CONNECTOR CONDITION OK?
NO
REPAIR AS NECESSARY.
YES
USE AN EXTERNAL OHMMETER IN THE FOLLOWING STEP.
TEST THE TN/RD WIRE FOR RESISTANCE.
IS THE RESISTANCE BELOW 10.0 OHMS?
NO
REPAIR THE OPEN V36 TN/RD WIRE.
YES
TEST THE LG/RD WIRE FOR RESISTANCE.
IS THE RESISTANCE BELOW 10.0 OHMS?
NO
REPAIR THE OPEN V35 LG/RD WIRE.
YES
REPLACE THE ENGINE CONTROLLER.

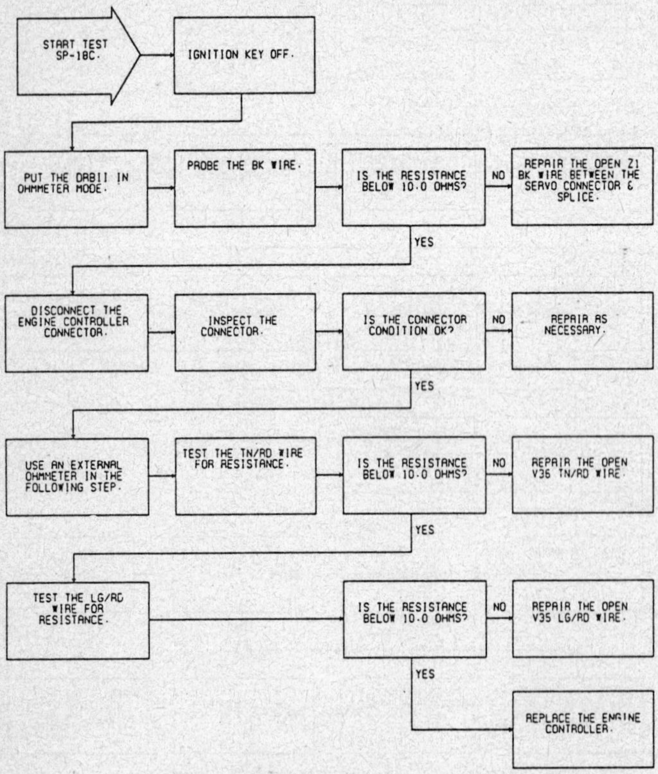

**Fig. 48 Test SP-18C, speed control solenoid circuit. 1991**

START TEST SP-19A.
READ THE INPUTS MONITOR.
WHILE WATCHING THE ON/OFF INPUT, CYCLE THE ON/OFF SWITCH SEVERAL TIMES.
DID THE DRBII DISPLAY CORRESPOND WITH THE SWITCH POSITION?
NO
PERFORM TEST SP-20A.
YES
SPEED CONTROL ON/OFF SWITCH IN THE ON POSITION.
WHILE WATCHING THE RESUME INPUT, CYCLE THE RESUME SWITCH SEVERAL TIMES.
DID THE DRBII DISPLAY CORRESPOND WITH THE SWITCH POSITION?
NO
PERFORM TEST SP-20A.
YES
WHILE WATCHING THE SET INPUT, CYCLE THE SET SWITCH SEVERAL TIMES.
DID THE DRBII DISPLAY CORRESPOND WITH THE SWITCH POSITION?
NO
PERFORM TEST SP-20A.
YES
WHILE WATCHING THE BRAKE INPUT, CYCLE THE BRAKE PEDAL SEVERAL TIMES.
DID THE DRBII DISPLAY CORRESPOND WITH THE BRAKE POSITION?
NO
PERFORM TEST SP-21A.
YES
CONTINUE TEST SP-19A

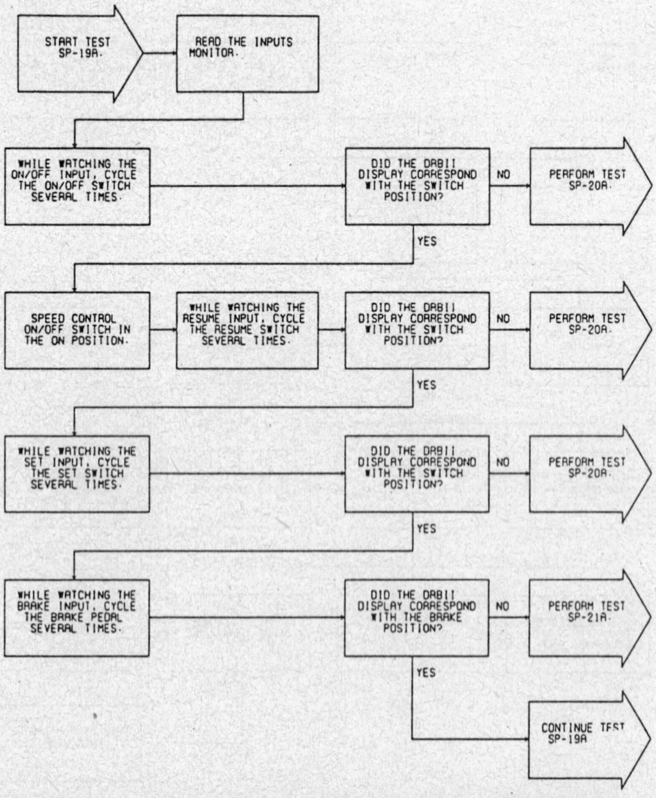

**Fig. 49 Test SP-19A, checking switches (Part 1 of 2). 1991**

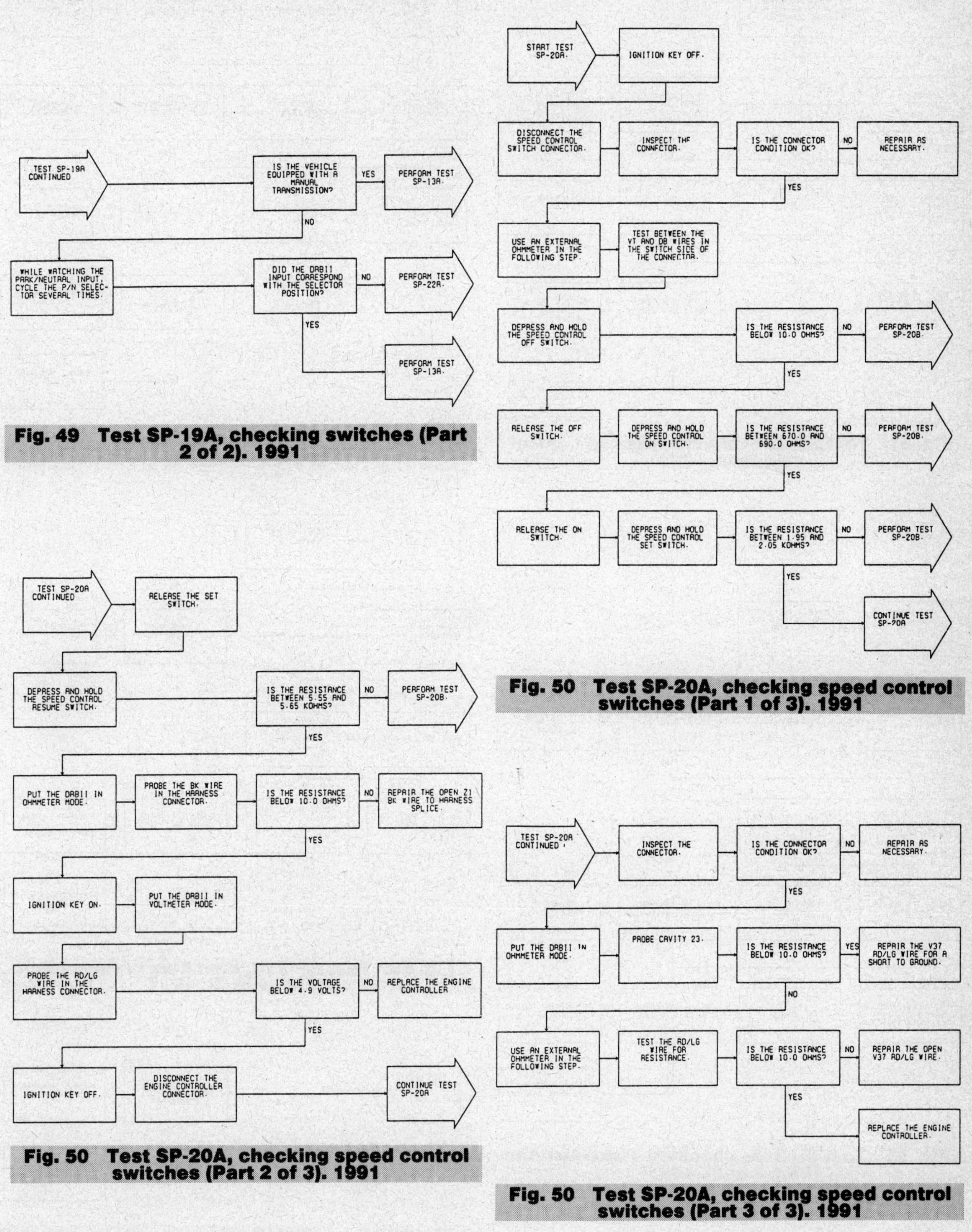


**Fig. 49 Test SP-19A, checking switches (Part 2 of 2). 1991**

**Fig. 50 Test SP-20A, checking speed control switches (Part 1 of 3). 1991**

**Fig. 50 Test SP-20A, checking speed control switches (Part 2 of 3). 1991**

**Fig. 50 Test SP-20A, checking speed control switches (Part 3 of 3). 1991**

START TEST SP-20B.
DISCONNECT THE SPEED CONTROL SWITCH AT THE SLIP RING CONNECTOR.
INSPECT THE CONNECTOR.
IS THE CONNECTOR CONDITION OK?
NO
REPAIR AS NECESSARY.
YES
USE AN EXTERNAL OHMMETER IN THE FOLLOWING STEP.
TEST THE RD/LG WIRE FOR RESISTANCE.
IS THE RESISTANCE BELOW 10.0 OHMS?
NO
REPLACE THE SLIP RINGS.
YES
TEST THE BK WIRE FOR RESISTANCE.
IS THE RESISTANCE BELOW 10.0 OHMS?
NO
REPLACE THE SLIP RINGS.
YES
REPLACE THE SPEED CONTROL SWITCH ASSEMBLY.

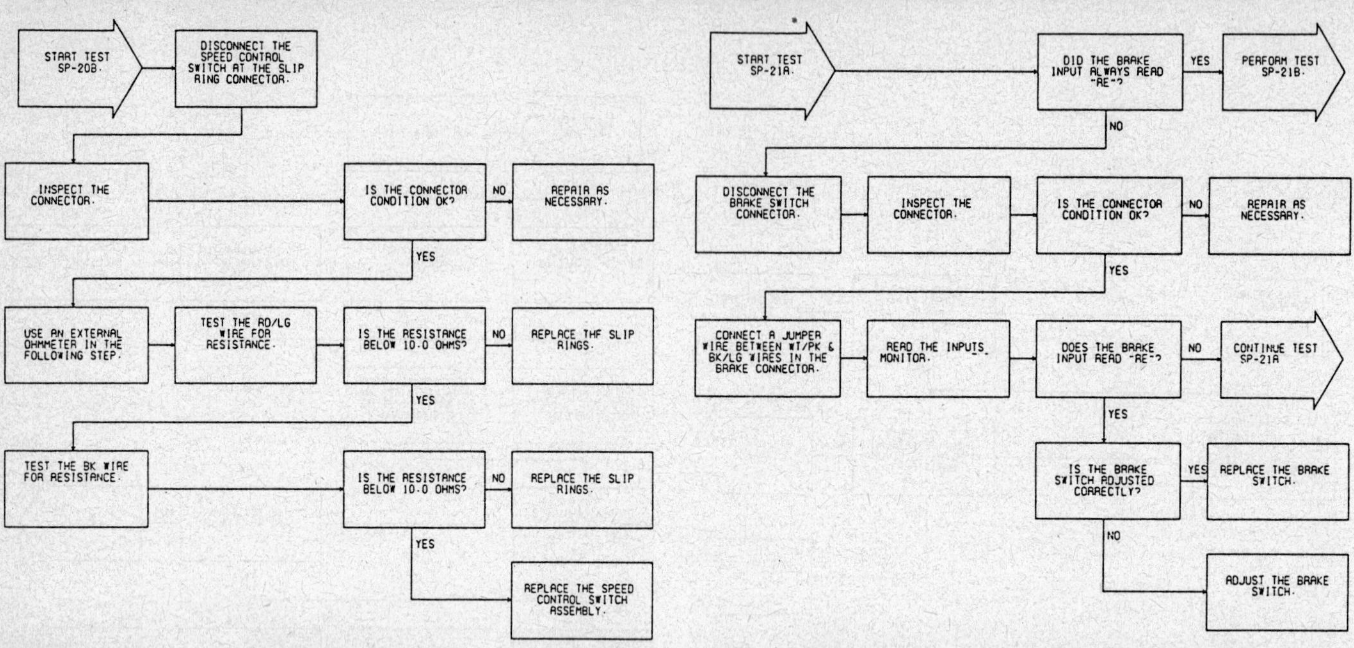

**Fig. 51 Test SP-20B, checking speed control switches. 1991**

START TEST SP-21A.
DID THE BRAKE INPUT ALWAYS READ "RE"?
YES
PERFORM TEST SP-21B.
NO
DISCONNECT THE BRAKE SWITCH CONNECTOR.
INSPECT THE CONNECTOR.
IS THE CONNECTOR CONDITION OK?
NO
REPAIR AS NECESSARY.
YES
CONNECT A JUMPER WIRE BETWEEN WT/PK & BK/LG WIRES IN THE BRAKE CONNECTOR.
READ THE INPUTS MONITOR.
DOES THE BRAKE INPUT READ "RE"?
NO
CONTINUE TEST SP-21A
YES
IS THE BRAKE SWITCH ADJUSTED CORRECTLY?
YES
REPLACE THE BRAKE SWITCH.
NO
ADJUST THE BRAKE SWITCH.

**Fig. 52 Test SP-21A, checking brake switch (Part 1 of 2). 1991**

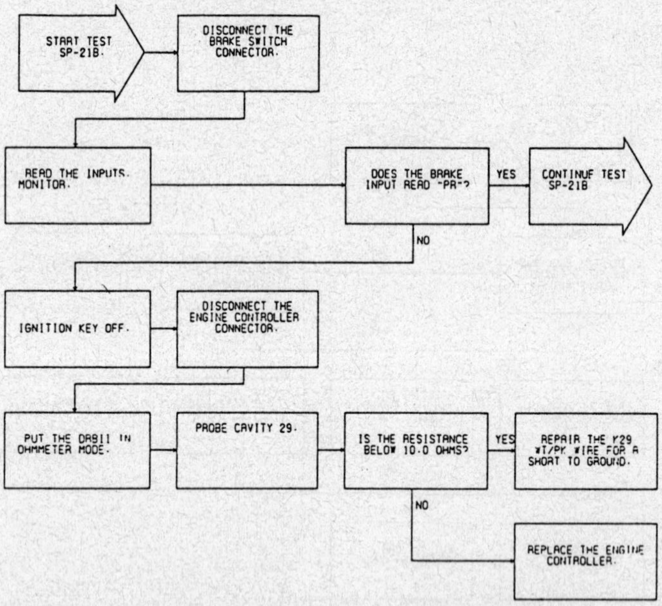

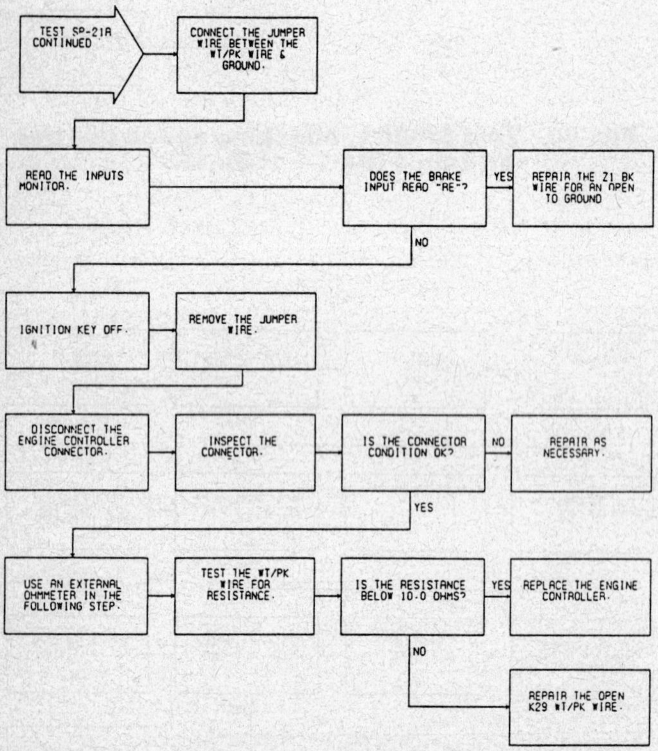

TEST SP-21A CONTINUED
CONNECT THE JUMPER WIRE BETWEEN THE WT/PK WIRE & GROUND.
READ THE INPUTS MONITOR.
DOES THE BRAKE INPUT READ "RE"?
YES
REPAIR THE Z1 BK WIRE FOR AN OPEN TO GROUND
NO
IGNITION KEY OFF.
REMOVE THE JUMPER WIRE.
DISCONNECT THE ENGINE CONTROLLER CONNECTOR.
INSPECT THE CONNECTOR.
IS THE CONNECTOR CONDITION OK?
NO
REPAIR AS NECESSARY.
YES
USE AN EXTERNAL OHMMETER IN THE FOLLOWING STEP.
TEST THE WT/PK WIRE FOR RESISTANCE.
IS THE RESISTANCE BELOW 10.0 OHMS?
YES
REPLACE THE ENGINE CONTROLLER.
NO
REPAIR THE OPEN K29 WT/PK WIRE.

**Fig. 52 Test SP-21A, checking brake switch (Part 2 of 2). 1991**

START TEST SP-21B.
DISCONNECT THE BRAKE SWITCH CONNECTOR.
READ THE INPUTS MONITOR.
DOES THE BRAKE INPUT READ "PR"?
YES
CONTINUE TEST SP-21B
NO
IGNITION KEY OFF.
DISCONNECT THE ENGINE CONTROLLER CONNECTOR.
PUT THE DRBII IN OHMMETER MODE.
PROBE CAVITY 29.
IS THE RESISTANCE BELOW 10.0 OHMS?
YES
REPAIR THE K29 WT/PK WIRE FOR A SHORT TO GROUND.
NO
REPLACE THE ENGINE CONTROLLER.

**Fig. 53 Test SP-21B, checking brake switch (Part 1 of 2). 1991**

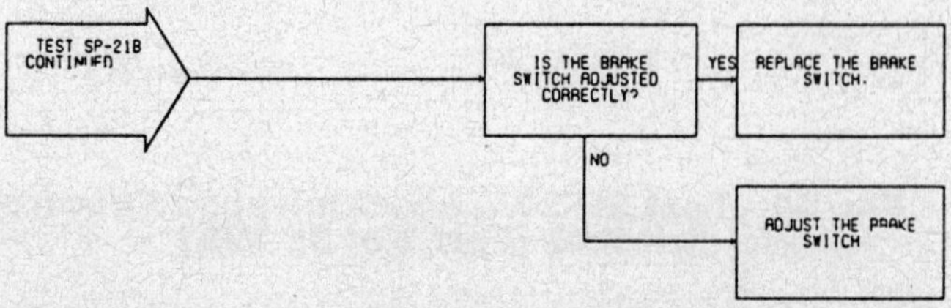

TEST SP-21B CONTINUED
IS THE BRAKE SWITCH ADJUSTED CORRECTLY?
YES
REPLACE THE BRAKE SWITCH.
NO
ADJUST THE BRAKE SWITCH

**Fig. 53 Test SP-21B, checking brake switch (Part 2 of 2). 1991**

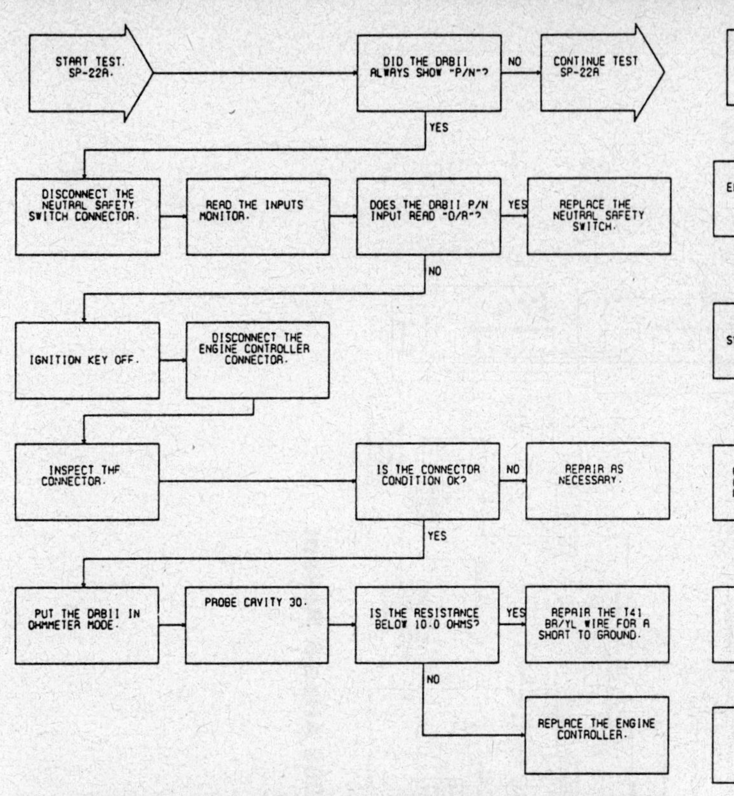


**Fig. 54 Test SP-22A, checking neutral safety switch (Part 1 of 2). 1991**

Inspect the vehicle to ensure that all engine components are connected. Reassemble and reconnect components as necessary.

If the engine controller has been changed, do the following:

1. If the vehicle is equipped with a factory theft alarm, start the vehicle at least 20 times so that the alarm system may be activated when desired.
2. If the vehicle is a minivan or truck body, write the EMR mileage into the new engine controller.

Connect the DRBII to the engine diagnostic connector and erase faults.

Ensure no other speed control problem remains by doing the following:

1. Road test the vehicle at speeds above 35 mph.
2. Turn the speed control ON/OFF switch to the on position.
3. Depress and release the SET switch.

   If the speed control did not engage, the repair is not complete.
4. For vehicles that have the speed control switches on the stalk, quickly depress and release the SET switch.

   For vehicles that have the speed control switches on the steering wheel, quickly depress and release the RESUME/ACCEL switch.

If the vehicle did not increase by 2 mph, the repair is not complete.

5. Using proper caution, depress and release the brake.

   If the speed control did not disengage, the repair is not complete.
6. Bring the vehicle speed back up to 35 mph.
7. Depress the RESUME/ACCEL switch.

   If the speed control did not resume the previously set speed, the repair is not complete.
8. Hold down the SET switch.

   If the vehicle did not decelerate, the repair is not complete.

**Fig. 55 Test SP-VER, speed control verification (Part 1 of 2). 1991**

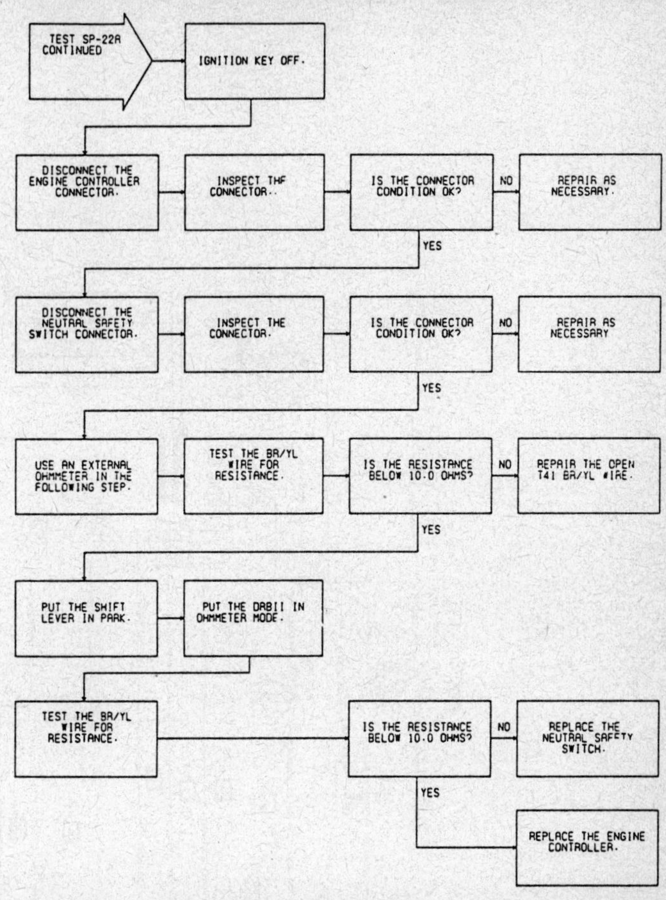


**Fig. 54 Test SP-22A, checking neutral safety switch (Part 2 of 2). 1991**

9. Ensure the vehicle speed is greater than 35 mph and release the SET switch.

   If the vehicle did not adjust and set at the new vehicle speed, the repair is not complete
10. Turn the ON/OFF switch to the off position.

    If the speed control did not disengage, the repair is not complete.

If the vehicle successfully passed all of the previous tests, the speed control system is now functioning as designed. The repair is now complete.

Check for Technical Service Bulletins that pertain to this speed control problem and then, if necessary, return to TEST SP-1A.

**Fig. 55 Test SP-VER, speed control verification (Part 2 of 2). 1991**

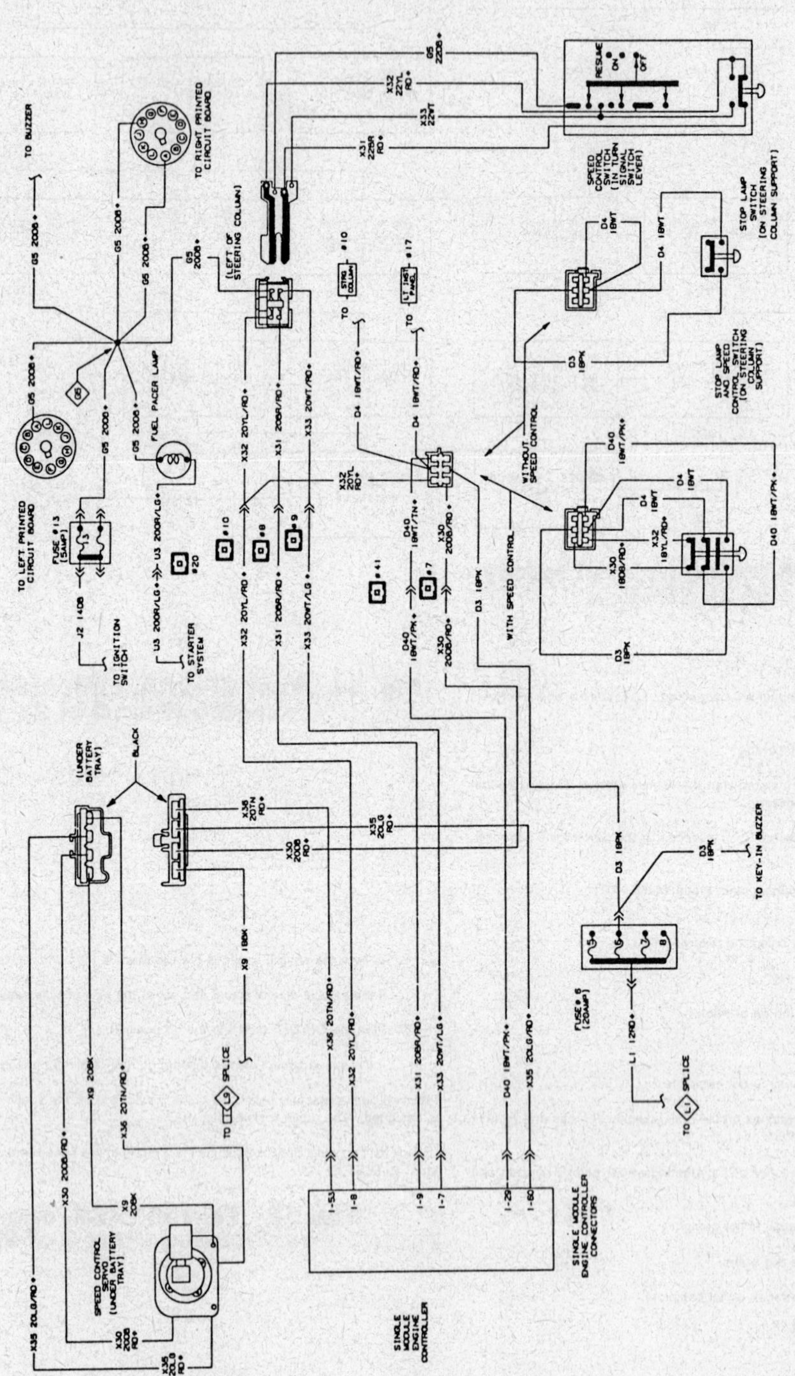

**Fig. 56 Speed control wiring diagram. 1989 Aries & Reliant**

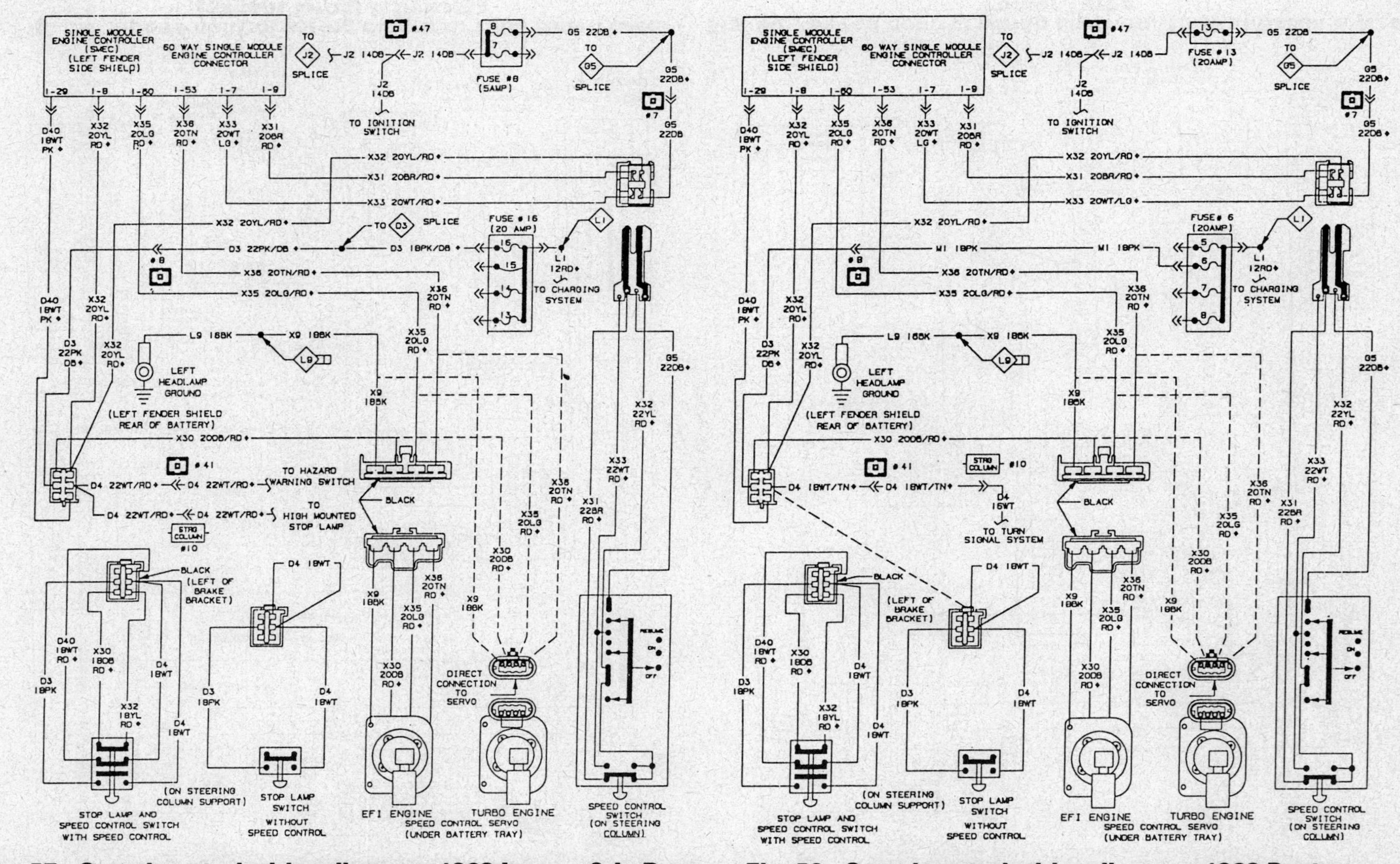


Fig. 57 Speed control wiring diagram. 1989 Lancer & LeBaron GTS

Fig. 58 Speed control wiring diagram. 1989 Daytona

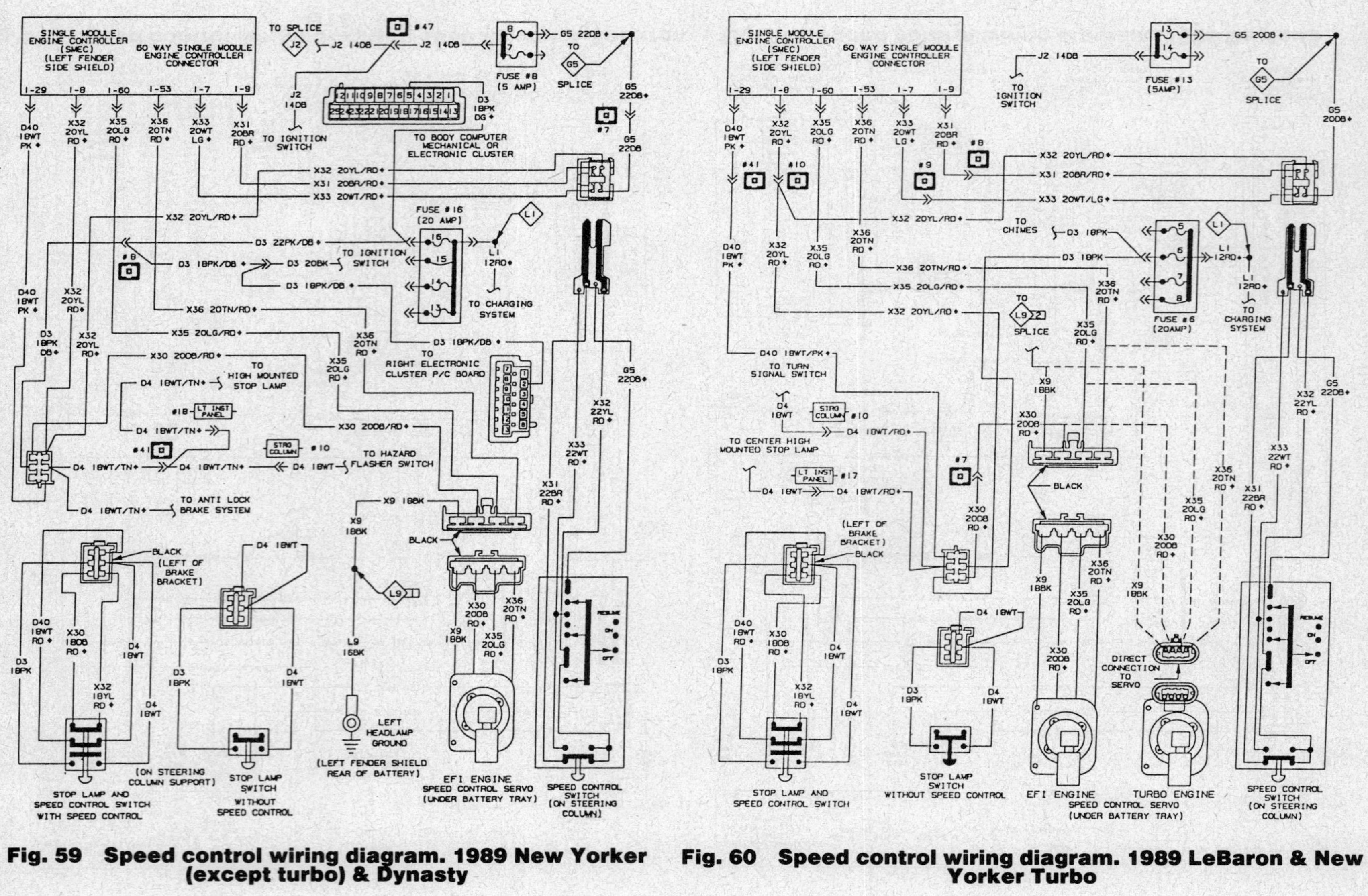


**Fig. 59 Speed control wiring diagram. 1989 New Yorker (except turbo) & Dynasty**

**Fig. 60 Speed control wiring diagram. 1989 LeBaron & New Yorker Turbo**

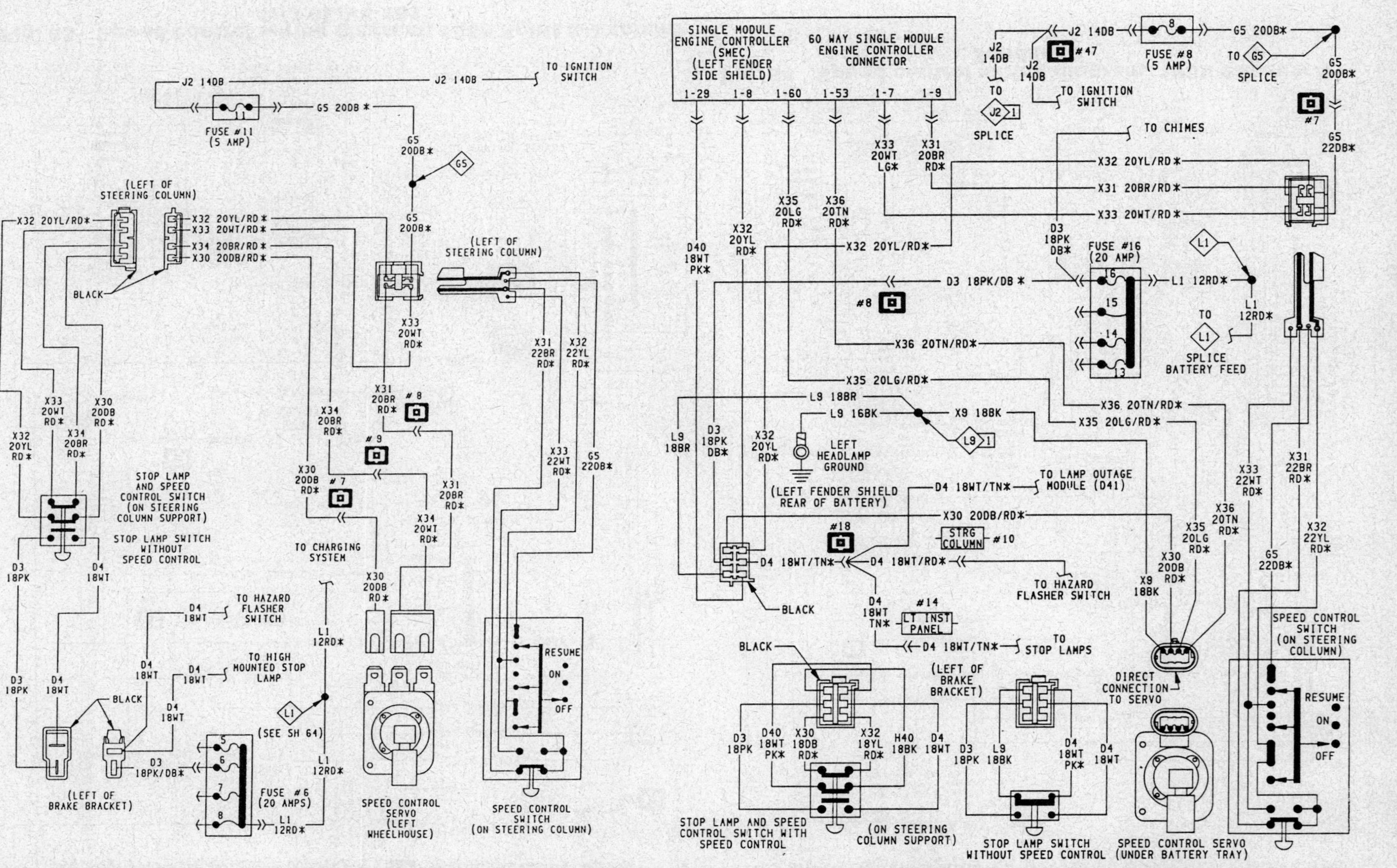


Fig. 61 Speed control wiring diagram. 1989 Diplomat, Fifth Avenue & Gran Fury

Fig. 62 Speed control wiring diagram. 1989 Spirit & Acclaim w/2.5L/4-153

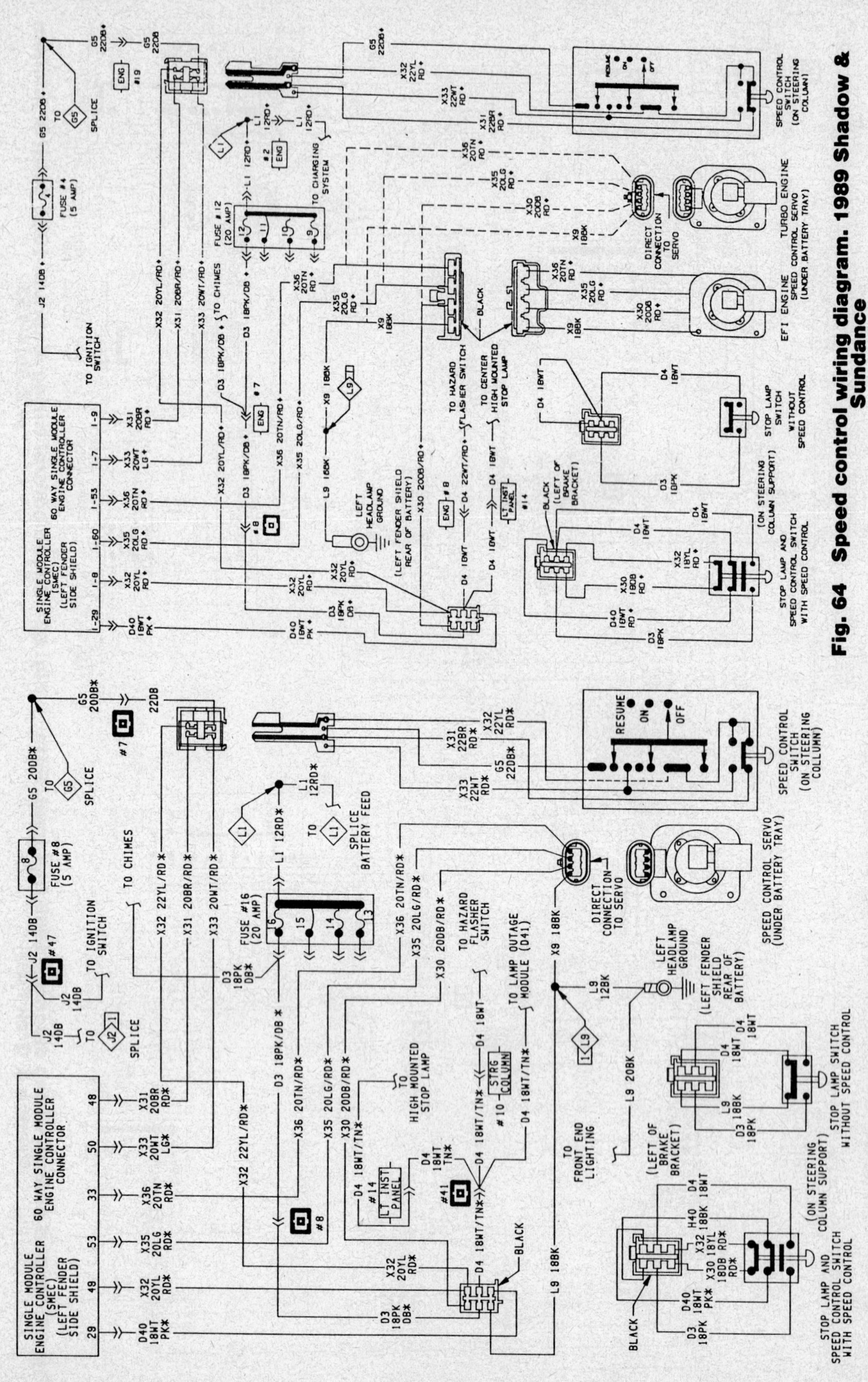


**Fig. 64 Speed control wiring diagram. 1989 Shadow & Sundance**

**Fig. 63 Speed control wiring diagram. 1989 Spirit & Acclaim w/3.0L/V6-181**

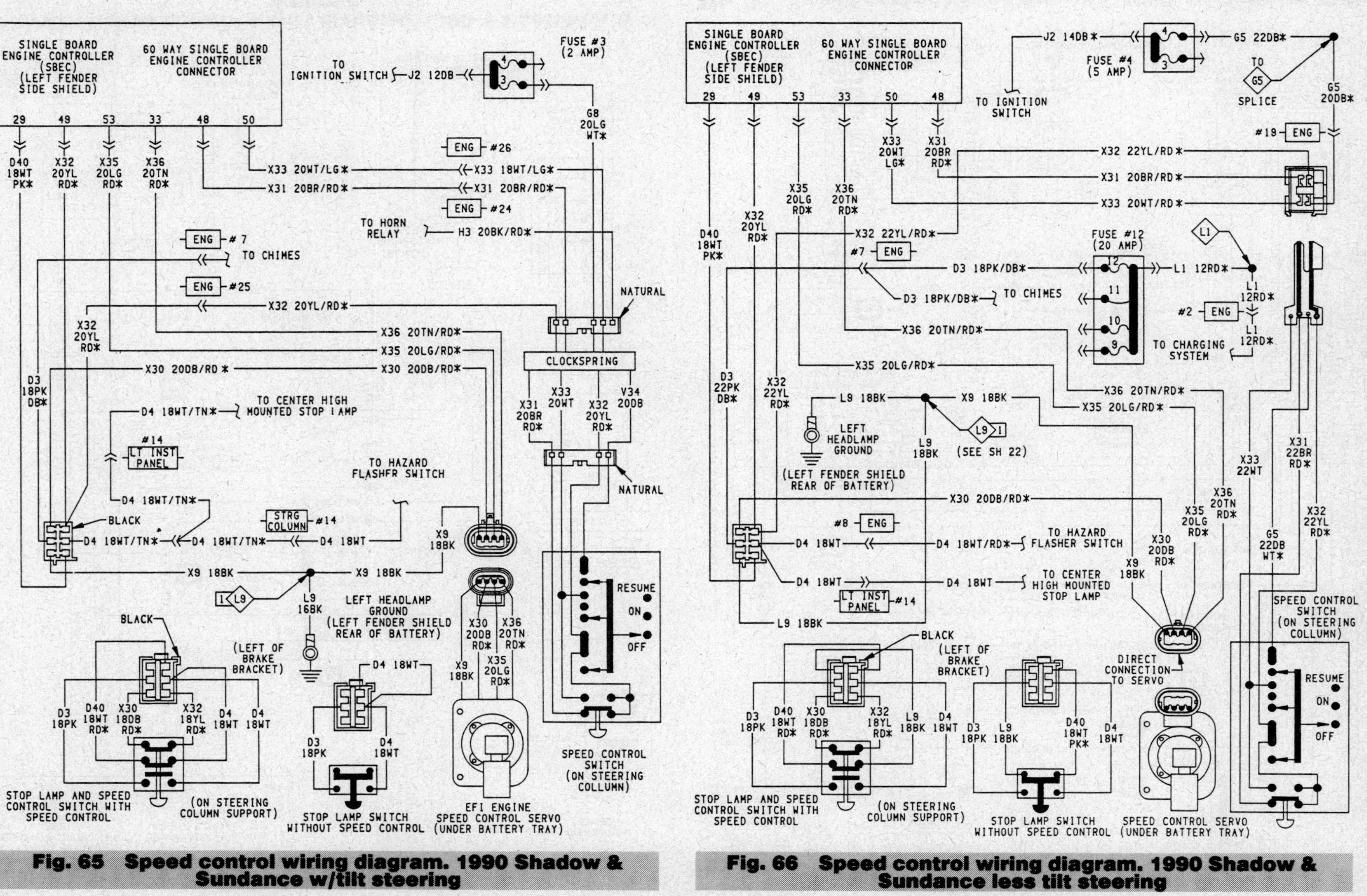


Fig. 65 Speed control wiring diagram. 1990 Shadow & Sundance w/tilt steering

Fig. 66 Speed control wiring diagram. 1990 Shadow & Sundance less tilt steering

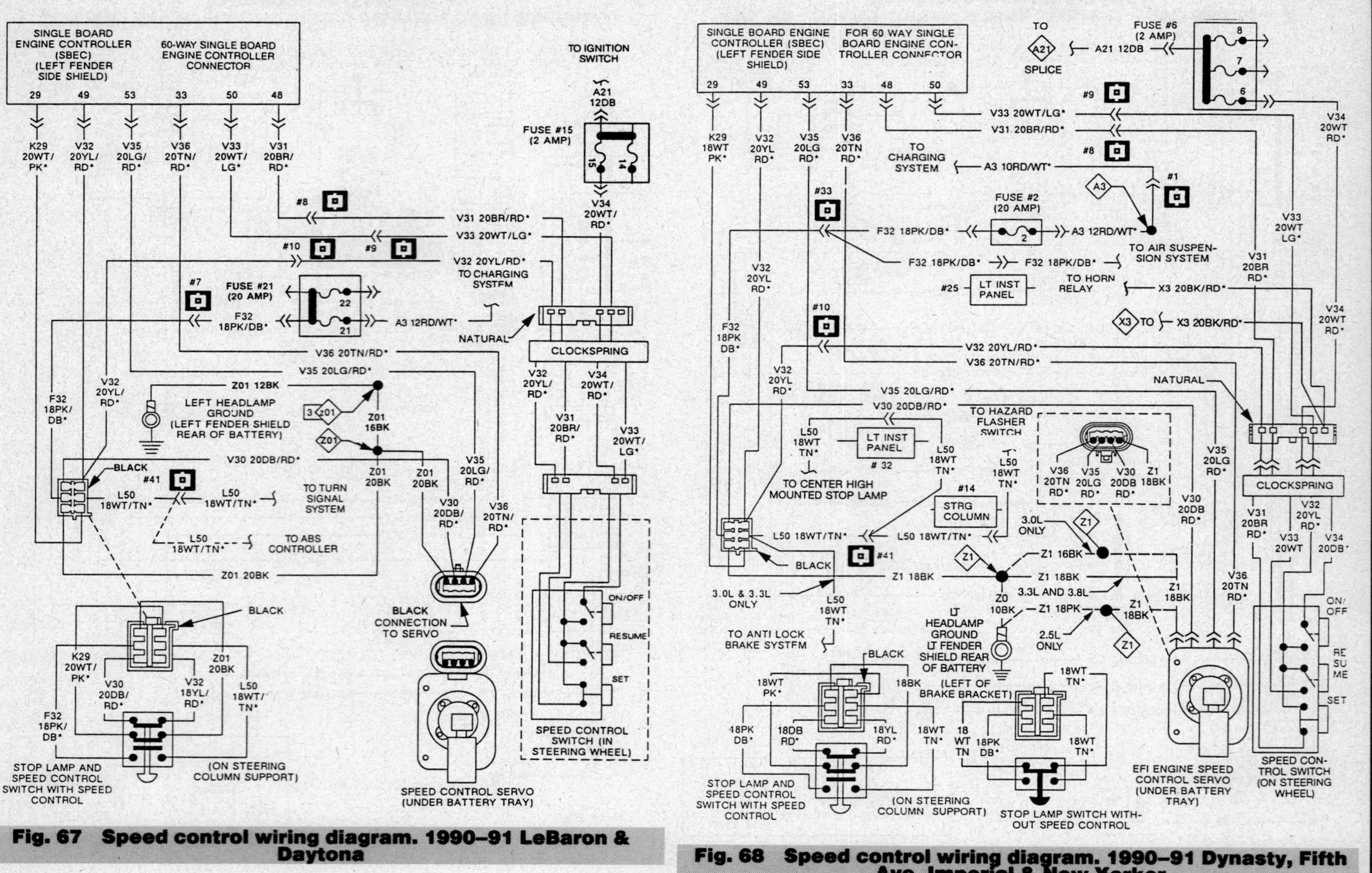


**Fig. 67** Speed control wiring diagram. 1990–91 LeBaron & Daytona

**Fig. 68** Speed control wiring diagram. 1990–91 Dynasty, Fifth Ave, Imperial & New Yorker

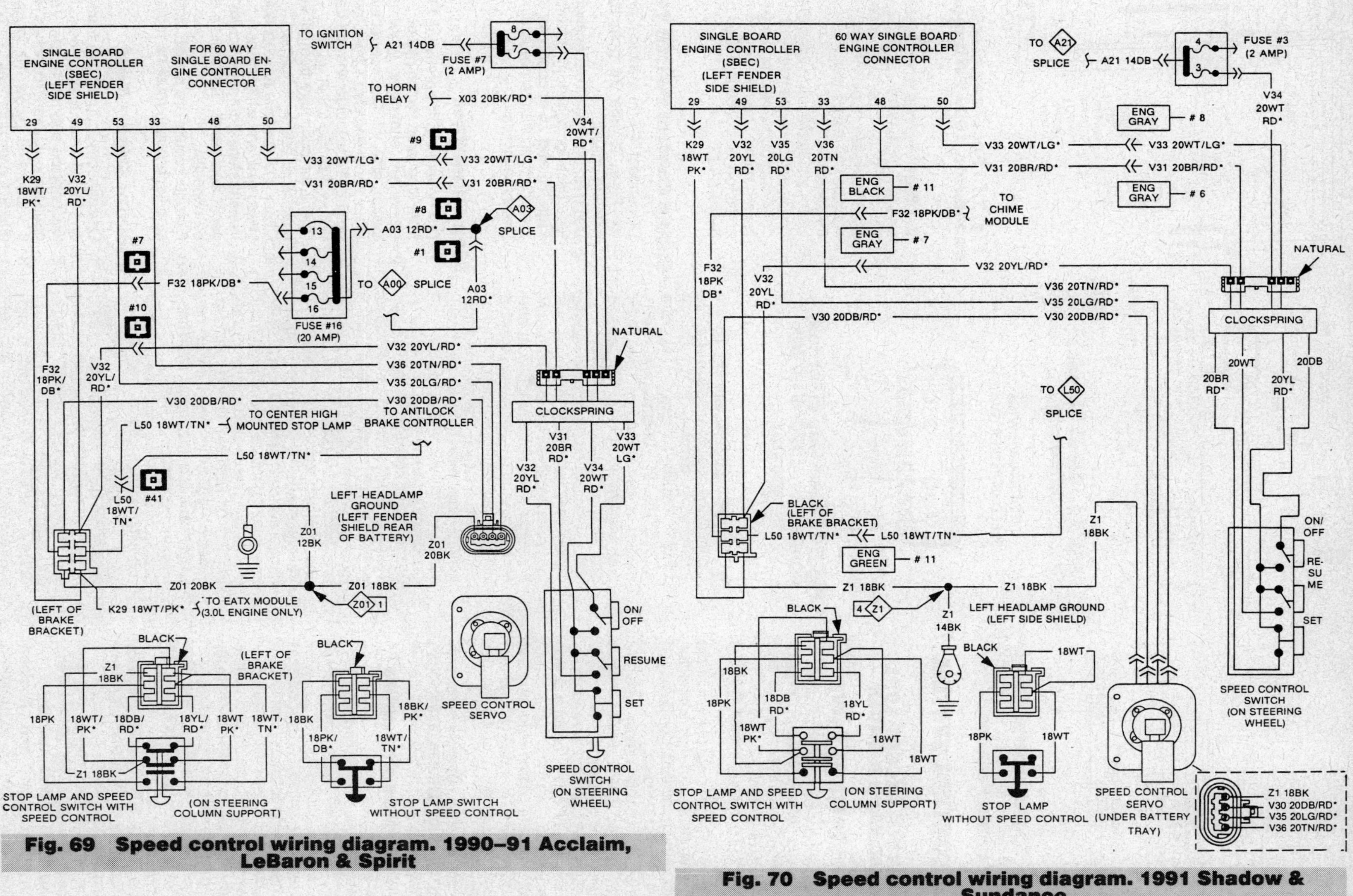


Fig. 69 Speed control wiring diagram. 1990–91 Acclaim, LeBaron & Spirit

Fig. 70 Speed control wiring diagram. 1991 Shadow & Sundance

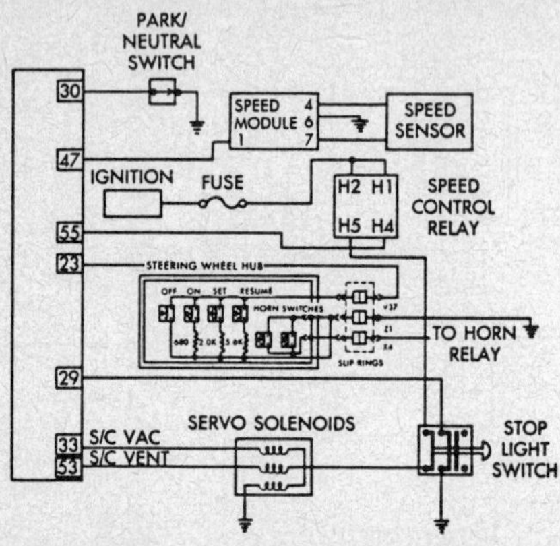


Fig. 71 Speed control wiring diagram. 1991 Dodge Monaco & Eagle Premier

## SPEED CONTROL SYSTEM TESTS

### FWD MODELS EXCEPT 1991 DODGE MONACO & EAGLE PREMIER

#### Electrical Tests At Servo

1. Turn ignition switch to On position.
2. With speed control switch in On position, connect voltmeter negative lead to a chassis ground.
3. Disconnect 4-way connector at servo, **Fig. 72.**
4. If battery voltage is not present at pin 2 of main harness 4-way connector, check and repair loose or damaged connectors or harness.
5. Connect a suitable jumper wire between pin No. 2 of 4-way connector and pin No. 2 of speed control servo.
6. In battery voltage is not present at remaining pin at servo, replace speed control servo.
7. Using suitable ohmmeter, connect negative lead to chassis ground and positive lead to pin 1 of 4-way connector.
8. If continuity does not exist, check and repair loose or damaged connectors or harness.

#### Electrical Tests At Engine Controller

1. Unplug 60-way engine controller harness connector, then turn ignition switch to On position.
2. Connect the positive lead of a suitable voltmeter to the following terminals. If voltage is not 0 volts with speed control switch in Off position and battery voltage with switch in On position, repair main harness as necessary.
   a. **On except 1989 Spirit and Acclaim models w/3.0L/V6-181 engine,** terminal 53.
   b. **On 1989 Spirit and Acclaim models w/3.0L/V6-181 engine,** terminal 33.
   c. **On except 1989 Spirit and Acclaim w/3.0L/V6-181 engine and 1991 models,** terminal 60.
   d. **On 1989 Spirit and Acclaim models w/3.0L/V6-181 engine,** terminal 53.

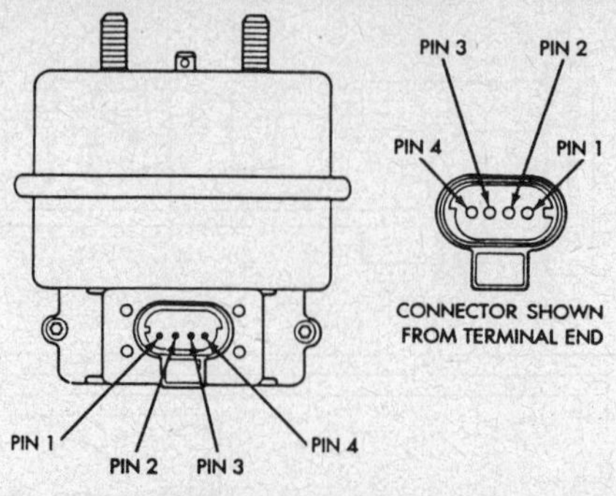


Fig. 72 Servo harness connector

BOTTOM VIEW OF SPEED CONTROL SWITCH

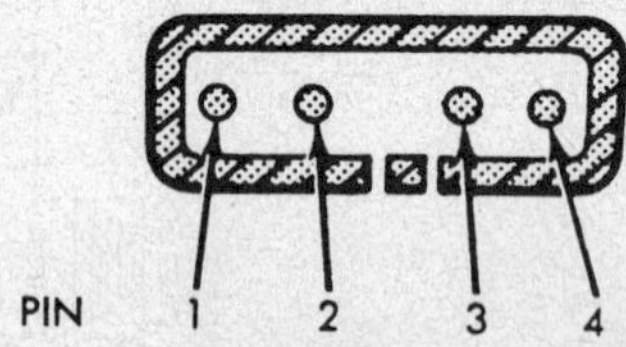


Fig. 74 Four-way electrical connector. 1990–91 FWD models

   e. **On 1991 models,** terminal 33.
3. Connect the positive lead of a suitable voltmeter to terminal 9 on except 1989 Spirit and Acclaim w/3.0L/V6-181 engine and 1991 models or terminal 48 on 1989 Spirit and Acclaim w/3.0L/V6-181 engine and 1991 models.
4. Voltage should be 0 volts with speed control switch in Off position and battery voltage with switch in On position. If voltage does not change from battery voltage to 0 volts when pressing Set button, perform speed control switch test. If switch operation is satisfactory, repair main harness as necessary.
5. Connect the positive lead of a suitable voltmeter to terminal 7 on except 1989 Spirit and Acclaim w/3.0L/V6-181 engine and 1991 models or terminal 50 on 1989 Spirit and Acclaim w/3.0L/V6-181 engine and 1991 models.
6. Voltage should be 0 volts with speed control switch in either On or Off position. If voltage does not change from 0 volts to battery voltage when pressing Set or Resume button, perform speed control switch test. If switch operation is satisfactory, repair main harness as necessary.
7. Connect the positive lead of a suitable voltmeter to terminal 8 on except 1989 Spirit and Acclaim w/3.0L/V6-181 engine and 1991 models or terminal 49 on 1989 Spirit and Acclaim w/3.0L/V6-181 engine and 1991 models.
8. Voltage should be 0 volts with speed control switch in Off position and battery voltage with switch in On position.

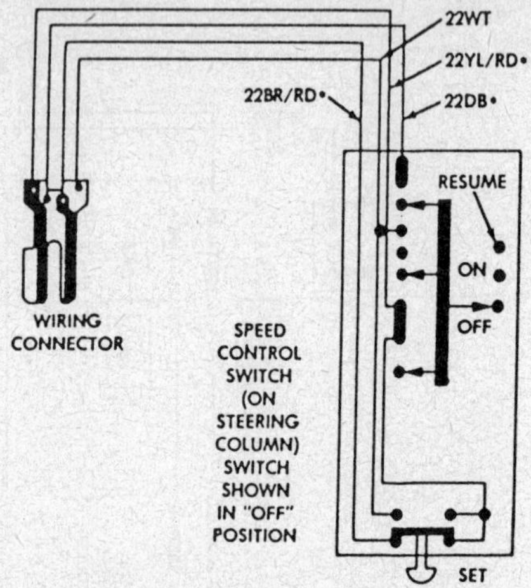


Fig. 73 Four-way electrical connector. 1989 FWD models

If voltage changes from battery voltage to 0 volts when pressing Set or Resume button, perform speed control switch test. If switch operation is satisfactory, repair main harness as necessary.
9. Using a suitable ohmmeter, check for continuity between terminal 29 and chassis ground. With brake pedal released meter should show continuity and show no continuity when pedal is depressed.

#### Speed Control Switch Test

1. Disconnect 4-way electrical connector, **Figs. 73 and 74** from base of steering column
2. Using an ohmmeter or continuity tester, check for continuity according to **Figs. 75 and 76** at connector wires.
3. If correct results are not attained, replace the switch.

#### Stop Lamp Test

1. Disconnect 6-way connector, **Fig. 77,** from stop lamp switch pigtail.
2. Using an ohmmeter work at the switch side of the connector with brake pedal released. Check for continuity from dark blue and red tracer to yellow with red tracer wires.
3. Check for continuity from white with pink tracer and white wires.
4. Check that there is no continuity between pink and white wires.
5. Repeat steps 2 through 4 with brake pedal depressed. The results should be opposite.
6. If proper results are not obtained, the stop lamp switch must be replaced.

#### Vacuum Supply Test

1. Disconnect vacuum hose from servo and install a vacuum gauge in hose.
2. Start engine and run at idle. Vacuum gauge should read 10 inches Hg.
3. If vacuum is below 10 inches Hg, check for vacuum leaks or poor engine performance.

| SPEED CONTROL SWITCH CONTINUITY CHART | |
|---|---|
| SWITCH POSITION | CONTINUITY BETWEEN |
| OFF | BR/RD and YL/RD |
| ON | BR/RD and YL/RD<br>BR/RD and DB/WT<br>YL/RD and DB/WT |
| SET | YL/RD and WT<br>DB/WT and WT<br>YL/RD and DB/WT |
| RESUME | DB/WT and WT<br>DB/WT and YL/RD<br>BR/RD and YL/RD<br>BR/RD and DB/WT<br>BR/RD and WT |

**Fig. 75 Continuity chart. 1989 FWD models**

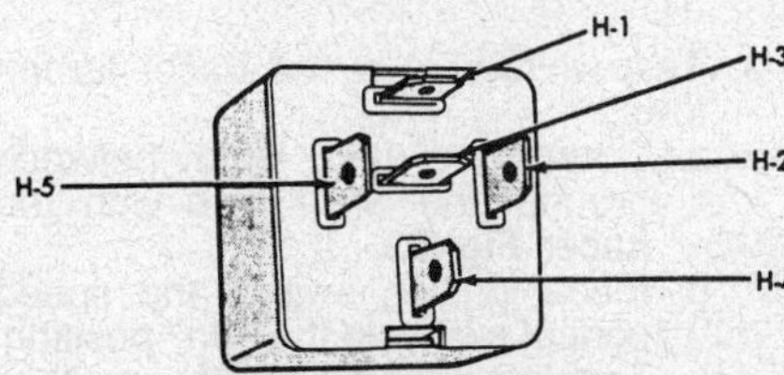


**Fig. 78 Speed control relay. 1991 Dodge Monaco & Eagle Premier**

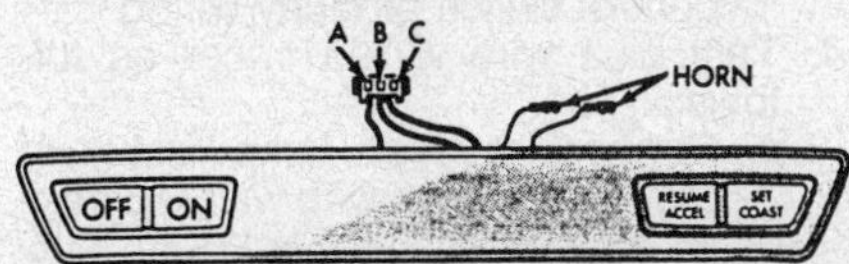


**Fig. 81 Speed control switch pod. 1991 Dodge Monaco & Eagle Premier**

## 1991 DODGE MONACO & EAGLE PREMIER

### Speed Control Relay Test

1. With ignition switch in Off position, remove speed control power relay located in the instrument panel relay bank, **Fig. 78.**
2. With ignition switch in On position, measure voltage at pin 4 of the relay connector.
3. If voltage is less than 10 volts, check fuse or repair open wire between relay and fuse panel or between ignition and fuse panel.
4. Remove speed control relay from relay bank and measure resistance between terminals H2 and H5. If resistance is greater than 100 ohms, replace the relay.
5. With ignition switch in Off position, disconnect engine controller. Measure resistance between engine controller connector terminal 55 and relay connector terminal H4, **Fig. 79.**
6. If resistance is greater than 10 ohms, repair open circuit.
7. With ignition in Off position, measure resistance between engine controller connector terminal 55 and ground. If resistance is less than 10 ohms, repair

| SPEED CONTROL SWITCH CONTINUITY CHART | |
|---|---|
| SWITCH POSITION | CONTINUITY BETWEEN |
| OFF | PIN 1 AND PIN 4 |
| ON | PIN 1 AND PIN 4<br>PIN 1 AND PIN 2<br>PIN 2 AND PIN 4 |
| ON + SET | PIN 1 AND PIN 2 |
| ON + RESUME | PIN 1 AND PIN 3 |

**Fig. 76 continuity chart. 1990–91 FWD models**

**Fig. 79 Engine controller connector. 1991 Dodge Monaco & Eagle Premier**

wire for a short to ground.

8. If resistance is above 10 ohms, replace the engine controller.

### Electrical Test At Servo

1. Turn ignition switch to On position
2. Press speed control switch On, immediately after the speed control relay becomes energized. Test for battery voltage.
3. Disconnect 4-way connector from speed control servo, **Fig. 80.** Using a voltmeter, test pin 2 on connector. If voltage is 12 volts, proceed to step 5.
4. If voltage is less than 12 volts, disconnect 6-way connector on stop lamp switch. Measure voltage at dash harness circuit No. 42 at brake lamp switch. If voltage is 12 volts, perform tests under "Stop Lamp Switch Test."
5. Measure voltage at speed control relay connector H4, **Fig. 81.** If battery voltage is present, repair circuit between relay and brake switch.
6. If no voltage is present, re-check for fault code 77. If fault code 77 is found, perform tests under "Speed Control Relay Test."
7. If code 77 is not present, perform tests under "Speed Control Switch Test."

### Speed Control Switch Test

1. Remove speed control switch as outlined under "Speed Control Switch" under "Component Replacement."
2. Measure resistance at terminals B and C of speed control switch with switches pressed, **Fig. 81.** resistance should be as follows:
   a. With switch in Off position, 0-5 ohms.
   b. With switch in On position, 645-715 ohms.
   c. With switch Resume/Accel switch pressed, 1900-2100 ohms.
   d. With switch Set/Coast switch pressed, 5370-5925 ohms.
3. If resistance is not as specified, replace the speed control switch bar.

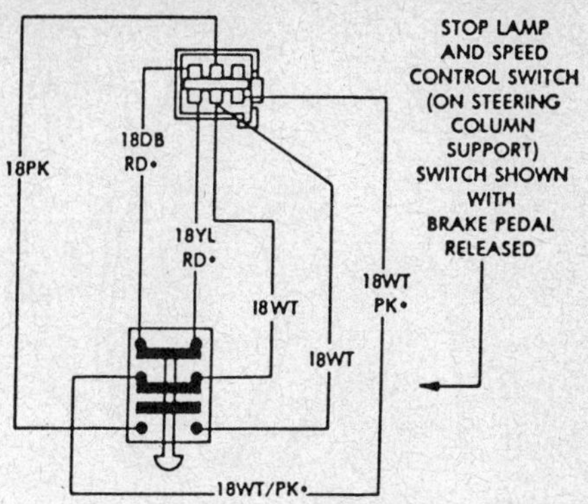


**Fig. 77 Six-way connector. FWD models**

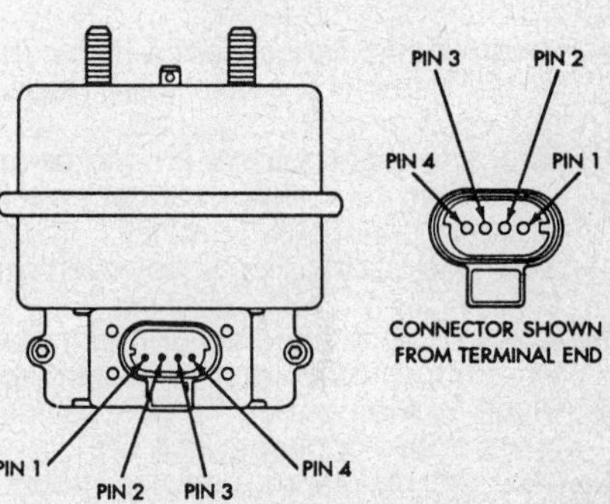


**Fig. 80 Speed control servo. 1991 Dodge Monaco & Eagle Premier**

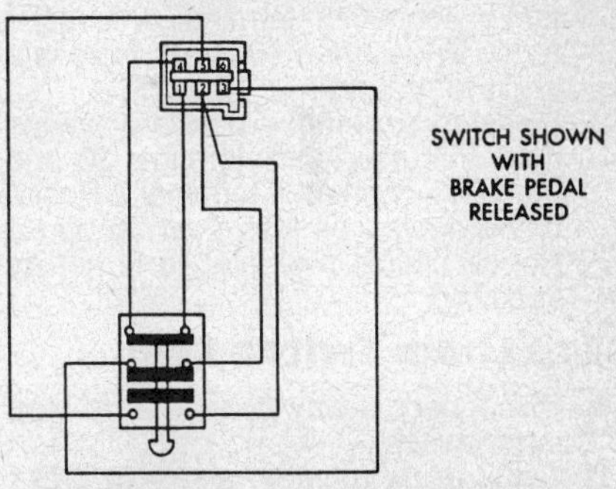


**Fig. 82 Stop lamp switch circuit. 1991 Dodge Monaco & Eagle Premier**

4. Disconnect turn signal cancel switch 8-way connector located in the lower steering column.
5. Install a suitable jumper wire between speed control switch terminal C to terminal E (white wire) and between speed control switch terminal B to terminal F (blue wire). With jumpers in place, press speed control On switch. Speed control relay should now be energized and battery voltage should be at servo terminal 2, **Fig. 80.**
6. If battery voltage is present at servo, repair open or replace turn signal cancel cam and switch.
7. If voltage is not present at servo, disconnect engine controller and test for continuity from connector terminal 23

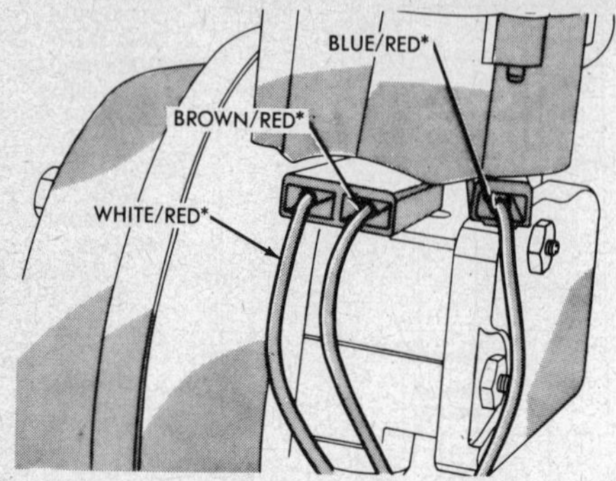

**Fig. 83 Servo terminal electrical connections**

to turn signal cancel cam switch connector terminal E (white wire). Repair any open or short to ground.
8. Check for continuity to ground or an open from turn signal cancel switch harness connector terminal F (blue wire) and ground. Repair any open circuit.
9. Connect negative lead of ohmmeter to ground near engine controller. Place ignition switch in Off position, press speed control switch Off.
10. Measure resistance between ground and engine controller connector terminal 53 then between ground and servo connector terminal 3. Repair any short to ground.
11. Measure resistance between engine controller connector terminal 53 and servo connector terminal 3. If resistance is less than 10 ohms there is a short to ground.
12. Measure resistance between engine controller connector terminal 33 and the servo connector terminal 2. Resistance should be less than 10 ohms. Repair circuit if resistance is not as specified.

## Stop Lamp Switch Test

1. Disconnect 6-way connector at stop lamp switch.
2. Using an ohmmeter, and with brake pedal released, continuity should be present between switch terminals, **Fig. 82**, as follows:
   a. Between terminals 1 and 4.
   b. Between terminals 3 and 6.
3. No continuity should exists between switch terminals 2 and 5 with brake pedal released.
4. With brake pedal depressed, continuity should not be present between switch terminals as follows:
   a. Between terminals 1 and 4.
   b. Between terminals 3 and 6.
5. Continuity should exists with brake pedal depressed between switch terminals 2 and 5.
6. If continuity tests are not as specified, replace stop lamp switch.

## Vacuum Supply Test

1. Disconnect vacuum hose from servo and install a vacuum gauge in hose.
2. Start engine and run at idle. Vacuum gauge should read 10 inches Hg.

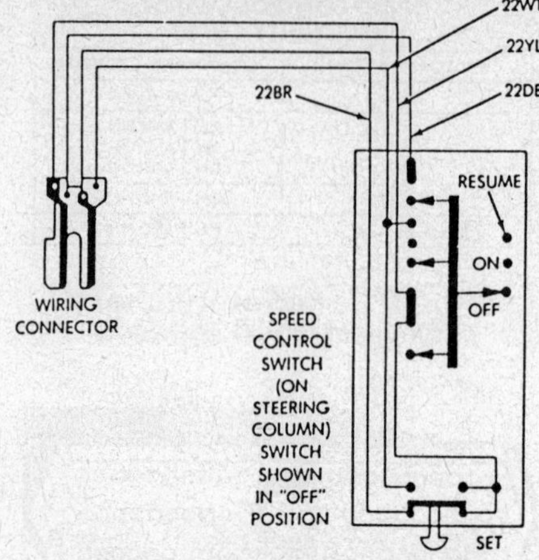

**Fig. 84 Four-way electrical connector. 1989 RWD models**

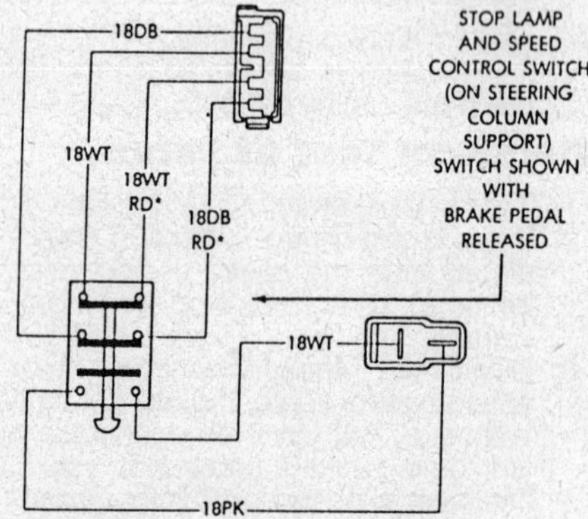

**Fig. 86 Two & four-way connectors. 1989 RWD models**

3. If vacuum is below 10 inches Hg, check for vacuum leaks or poor engine performance.

## RWD MODELS

## Electrical Servo Test

1. Before servo test is performed, check servo for proper ground.
2. Test brown wire w/red tracer as follows:
   a. Connect a test lamp between ground and brown wire with red tracer, **Fig. 83.**
   b. Place ignition switch and speed control switch in the "On" position. Test lamp should go on.
   c. Push in "set" button. Test lamp should go out and a click should be heard at the servo.
   d. Release "set" button. Test lamp should go on and another click should be heard at the servo.
   e. If test lamp does not light as specified, check for a blown fuse, faulty wiring or defective speed control switch. If clicks are not heard at servo, servo is defective.

| SPEED CONTROL SWITCH CONTINUITY CHART | |
|---|---|
| SWITCH POSITION | CONTINUITY BETWEEN |
| OFF | BR and YL |
| ON | BR and YL<br>BR and DB<br>YL and DB |
| SET | YL and WT<br>DB and WT<br>YL and DB/WT |
| RESUME | DB and WT<br>DB and YL<br>BR and YL<br>BR and DB<br>BR and WT |

**Fig. 85 Continuity chart. 1989 RWD models**

3. Test white wire w/red tracer as follows:
   a. Connect a test lamp between ground and white wire with red tracer, **Fig. 83.**
   b. Place ignition switch and speed control switch in the "On" position. Test lamp should be off.
   c. Push in "set" button. Test lamp should be on while set button is depressed.
   d. If test lamp does not light as specified, check for defective speed control switch or faulty wiring.
4. Test blue wire w/red tracer as follows:
   a. Connect a test lamp between ground and blue wire with red tracer, **Fig. 83.**
   b. Place ignition switch and speed control switch in the "On" position. Test lamp should go on.
   c. If test lamp does not light as specified, check for faulty wiring, brake switch, clutch switch or speed control switch.

## Speed Control Switch Test

1. Disconnect 4-way electrical connector, **Fig. 84** from base of steering column
2. Using an ohmmeter or continuity tester, check for continuity according to **Fig. 85** at connector wires.
3. If correct results are not attained, replace the switch.

## Stop Lamp Test

1. Disconnect 2 and 4-way connectors, **Fig. 86,** from the stop lamp switch.
2. Using an ohmmeter, work from the switch side of the connector with brake pedal released. Check for continuity from dark blue and red tracer, and dark blue wires.
3. Check for continuity from white with red tracer to white wires.
4. Check that there is no continuity between pink and white wires.
5. With brake pedal depressed, repeat steps 2 through 4. The results should be opposite.
6. If proper results are not obtained, the stop lamp switch must be replaced.

## Vacuum Supply Test

1. Disconnect vacuum hose from servo

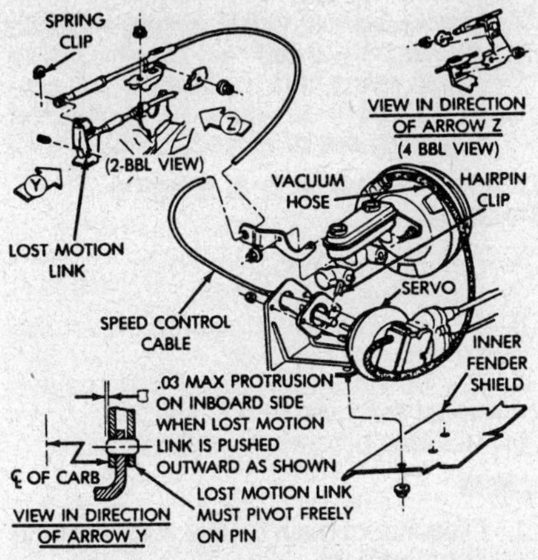


**Fig. 87 Speed control system. FWD models**

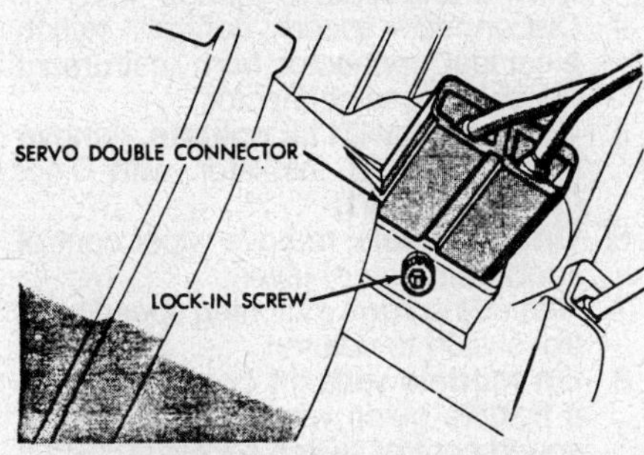


**Fig. 90 Lock in screw adjustment. RWD models**

and install a vacuum gauge in hose.

2. Start engine and run at idle. Vacuum gauge should read 10 inches Hg.
3. If vacuum is below 10 inches Hg, check for vacuum leaks or poor engine performance.

# ADJUSTMENTS

## SPEED CONTROL CABLE, ADJUST

### RWD MODELS

The speed control cable is attached to a cable support bracket by a clip located seven inches from stud on lost motion link, **Fig. 87.**

1. Raise engine temperature to normal operating temperature.
2. Carburetor should be at curb idle and with choke Off.
3. Remove spring clip from lost motion link stud. Clearance between stud and cable clevis should be 1/16 inch.
4. Insert a gauge pin between cable clevis and stud then loosen clip at cable support bracket.
5. Pull all slack out of cable. **Do not pull throttle away from curb idle position.**
6. **Torque** clip at support bracket to 45 inch lbs.
7. Remove gauge pin and install spring clip on stud.

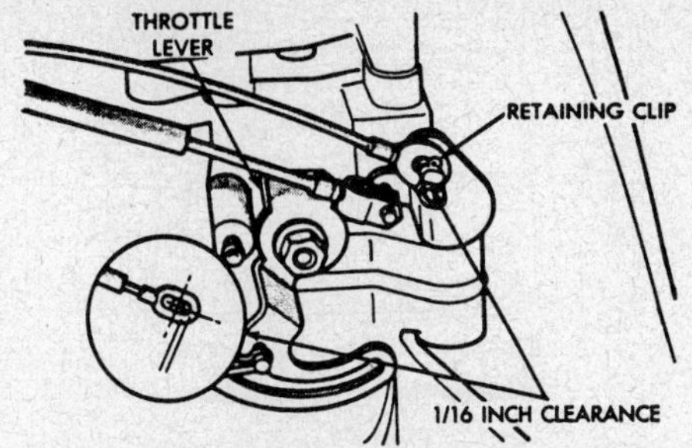


**Fig. 88 Speed control cable adjustment. FWD models**

### FWD MODELS

### 2.2L/4-135 & 2.5L/4-153

1. Clearance between throttle stud and cable clevis should be 1/16 inch, **Fig. 88.**
2. Adjust cable by removing cable retaining clip at throttle bracket, **Fig. 89. Do not pull throttle away from curb idle.**
3. Reinstall cable retaining clip.

## SERVO LOCK IN SCREW, ADJUST

### RWD Models

The lock in screw adjustment, **Fig. 90,** controls the accuracy of the speed control unit. When the Set button is depressed and released at speeds above 30 mph, the speed control system locks in and should hold vehicle at same speed at which it is traveling. Lock in accuracy will be affected by the following:

1. Poor engine performance.
2. Power to weight ratio (as in pulling a trailer).
3. Improper slack in throttle control cable.

Need for adjustment can be determined only after accurate diagnosis of the speed control system operation.

If speed drops more than 2 to 3 mph, the lock in adjusting screw should be turned counterclockwise to correct. **Turning the lock in adjusting screw 1/4 turn adjust the lock in accuracy about 1 mph.** If speed increases more than 2 to 3 mph, the lock in adjusting screw should be turned clockwise to correct.

If the lock in adjusting screw is loose replace the servo. **This adjustment must not exceed two turns in either direction or damage to unit may occur.**

# COMPONENT REPLACEMENT

## SPEED CONTROL SERVO

### 1989 RWD

1. Disconnect speedometer cables, vacuum hose and electrical connectors from servo.
2. Remove nuts attaching servo and throttle cable to servo bracket.
3. Pull servo away from cable to expose cable retaining clip. Remove clip attaching cable to servo diaphragm pin,

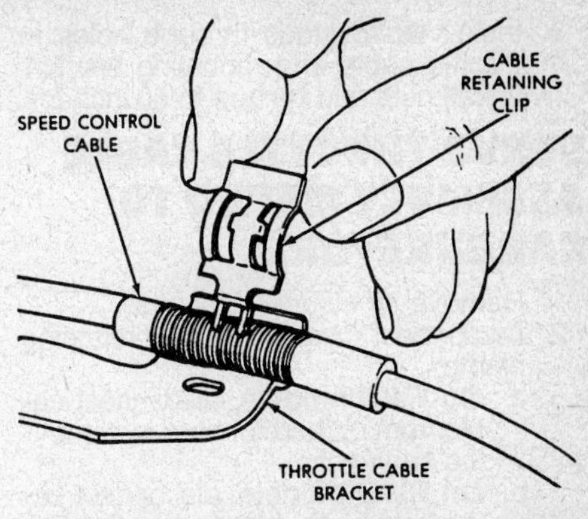


**Fig. 89 Cable retaining clip. FWD models**

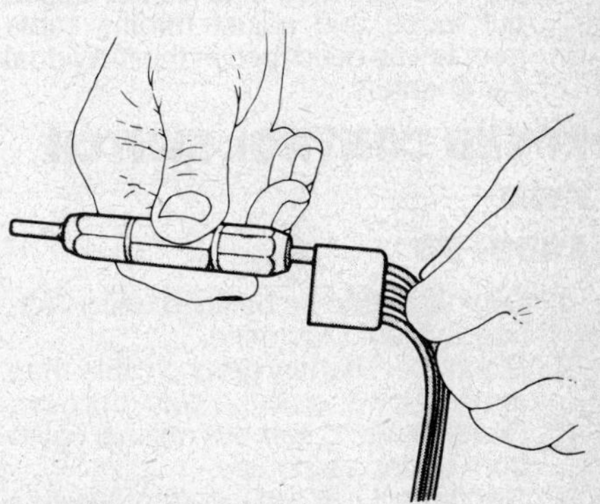

**Fig. 91 Removing wiring terminals**

then the servo.

4. To install, position throttle in full open position, then align hole in throttle cable with hole in servo pin and install retaining clip.
5. Reconnect throttle cable to servo bracket and install attaching nuts to servo.
6. Reconnect speedometer cables, vacuum hose and electrical connectors to servo.

### FWD

1. Remove throttle cable attaching nuts and mounting bracket to servo.
2. Remove two screws attaching servo mounting bracket to battery tray, then the servo mounting bracket.
3. Disconnect vacuum hoses and electrical connectors, then speedometer cable from servo.
4. Pull servo away from cable to expose cable retaining clip, then remove clip attaching cable to servo.
5. To install, position throttle in full open position, then align hole in throttle cable with hole in servo pin and install retaining clip.
6. Connect vacuum hose to servo, speedometer cable and electrical connectors.
7. Place mounting bracket in position, then install two screws attaching bracket to battery tray. **Torque** to 105 inch lbs.

8. Install servo studs through holes in throttle cable and mounting bracket. Install nuts and **torque** to 80 inch lbs.

## SERVO THROTTLE CABLE ASSEMBLY (SERVO TO CARBURETOR)

1. Remove air cleaner assembly.
2. Disconnect cable from retaining clamp:
   a. **On FWD models,** disconnect cable from carburetor stud by removing spring clip.
   b. **On RWD models,** disconnect cable from carburetor lost motion link by removing spring clip.
3. Disconnect cable from servo, then remove cable assembly.
4. Reverse procedure to install. Leave nut loose and adjust throttle cable freeplay as described in the individual car chapters.

## SPEED CONTROL SWITCH

### FWD

### 1989–90

1. Disable airbag as outlined under "Airbag System Disarming."
2. Disconnect battery ground cable, then remove lower steering column cover.
3. Remove wiring harness retainer cover from under dashboard.
4. Disconnect speed control switch electrical connector from harness connector.
5. **On models with tilt column,** remove terminals from insulator using tool No. C-4135 or equivalent, **Fig. 91.**
6. **On all models,** remove wiper control knob from end of lever.
7. Remove speed control switch to column attaching screws.
8. **On models with tilt column,** attach a flexible guide wire to lower end of speed control switch harness.
9. **On models with standard column,** remove upper steering column lock cover attaching screws, then the cover.

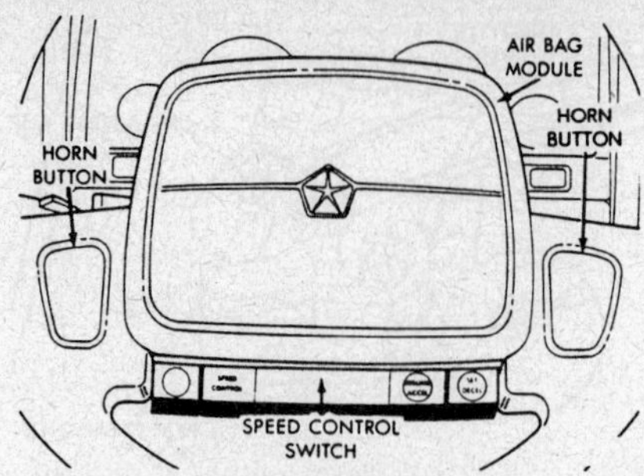


**Fig. 92 Speed control switch location. 1991 models**

10. **On all models,** remove switch and harness from steering column.
11. **On models with tilt column,** pull wires through lock housing between lock plate and side of housing.
12. **On all models,** reverse procedure to install.

### 1991 Except Dodge Monaco & Eagle Premier

The speed control switch is mounted in the steering wheel and wired through the clock spring device under the steering wheel hub, **Fig. 92.**

1. Disable airbag as outlined under "Airbag System Disarming."
2. Remove airbag module as described under "Airbag Module" in the "Passive Restraint Systems" section.
3. Turn ignition switch to Off position.
4. Remove two screws from back side of steering wheel.
5. Rock switch away from airbag or horn pad while lifting switch out of steering wheel. **Do not point airbag module toward yourself or others when performing this operation to prevent injury in case of accidental deployment of airbag module.**
6. Disconnect 4-way electrical connector.
7. Reverse procedure to install, sliding the forward edge of switch under airbag or horn pad. Line up locating pins on switch with holes in steering wheel frame. **Do not point airbag module toward yourself or others when performing this operation to prevent injury in case of accidental deployment of airbag module.**

### Dodge Monaco & Eagle Premier

1. Pull rearward on horn cover.
2. Disconnect horn wires.
3. Disconnect speed control electrical connector.
4. Pry up on switch panel and remove panel from steering wheel.
5. Reverse procedure to install.

### RWD

1. Disconnect main fusible link in engine compartment.
2. Remove lower instrument panel bezel from steering column.
3. **On standard column,** unsnap retainer clips and remove wiring.
4. Disconnect speed control switch electrical connector from instrument panel harness connector.
5. **On models with tilt column,** remove terminals from insulator with Tool C-4135, **Fig. 91.**
6. **On all models,** remove wiper control knob from end of lever.
7. Remove screws attaching speed control switch to column.
8. **On models with tilt column,** attach a flexible guide wire to lower end of speed control switch harness.
9. **On models with standard column,** remove upper steering column lock cover which is retained by two screws.
10. Remove switch and harness from steering column.
11. Reverse procedure to install, noting the following:
    a. **On standard steering column,** insert harness connector through turn signal lever opening in column and pull down and out lower end.
    b. **On tilt column,** insert harness wires through turn signal lever opening in column and pull upward through upper housing.

# Type 2

## INDEX

**NOTE:** Wire Code Identification And Symbol Identification Located In The Front Of This Manual Can Be Used As An Aid When Using Wiring Circuits Found In This Section.



## AIRBAG SYSTEM DISARMING

1. Place ignition switch in lock position.
2. Disconnect and tape battery ground cable connector.
3. **Wait at least 1 minute after disconnecting battery ground cable before doing any further work on vehicle. The SRS system is designed to retain enough voltage to deploy airbag for a short time even after battery has been disconnected.**
4. After repairs are complete, reconnect battery ground cable.
5. From passenger side of vehicle, turn ignition switch to On position.
6. SRS warning light should illuminate for 6 to 8 seconds, then remain off for at least 45 seconds to indicate if SRS system is functioning correctly.
7. If SRS indicator does not perform as described refer to the "Passive Restraint Systems" section.

## DESCRIPTION

The speed control system, performs control functions for setting or cancellation of fixed-speed driving speed based upon data provided by input signals. When the speed control system is cancelled, the cause is memorized in a separate circuit by the ECU whether the condition is normal or abnormal. This provides the ECU with a self-diagnosis function by monitoring certain fixed patterns and is able to check whether the ECU input switch or sensor is normal. When using these functions time required for checking and repair can be shortened.

## DIAGNOSIS & TESTING

Refer to **Figs. 1 through 14** for wiring circuits when diagnosing and testing the speed control system.

### SELF DIAGNOSIS

**Ensure (ECU) power supply is left on until checking is completed.**

1. Connect a voltmeter between ground and auto-cruise control terminal of diagnosis harness connector, located on lower left side of instrument panel, **Fig. 15.**
2. There are up to six diagnosis codes, including one for normal condition. Check voltmeter readings with display patterns shown in **Figs. 16 through 18,** then refer to the appropriate circuit check chart indicated. On except Laser and Talon, refer to **Figs. 19 through 67,** on Laser Talon, refer to text shown under "Circuit Tests." Fault codes indicated by an asterisk can be caused by an intermittent condition. Check related connectors and wiring circuits.

### SYMPTOM DIAGNOSIS

Refer to **Figs. 68 through 72** for symptom diagnosing the speed control system, then refer to the appropriate circuit check chart indicated. On except Laser and Talon, refer to **Figs. 19 through 67,** on Laser and Talon, refer to text shown under "Circuit Tests."

### INPUT TEST

Input test should be performed when the speed control system cannot be set, but necessary to check if the signals are normal when system malfunctions.

#### Colt Vista, Conquest & 1989 Colt & Eagle Summit

1. Connect a voltmeter between ground and auto-cruise control terminal of diagnosis harness connector, located on lower left side of instrument panel, **Fig. 15.**
2. Turn ignition key to On position, then check No. 1 and 3 of input check table, **Fig. 73.**
3. Start engine, check table No. 4 and 5 of the input check table.
4. Turn the Set switch to On position while holding Resume switch On. This procedure enables the display of the input check results.
5. Perform each input operation according to input check table then read codes. **Each code will be displayed in order of priority, beginning with check No. 1. If there is no display, a possible malfunction of the ECU power supply. Check using circuit tests.**

#### Laser, Stealth, Eagle Talon & 1990–91 Colt & Summit

1. Connect a voltmeter between ground and auto-cruise control terminal of diagnosis harness connector, located on lower left side of instrument panel, **Fig. 15.**

*Continued on page 24-78*

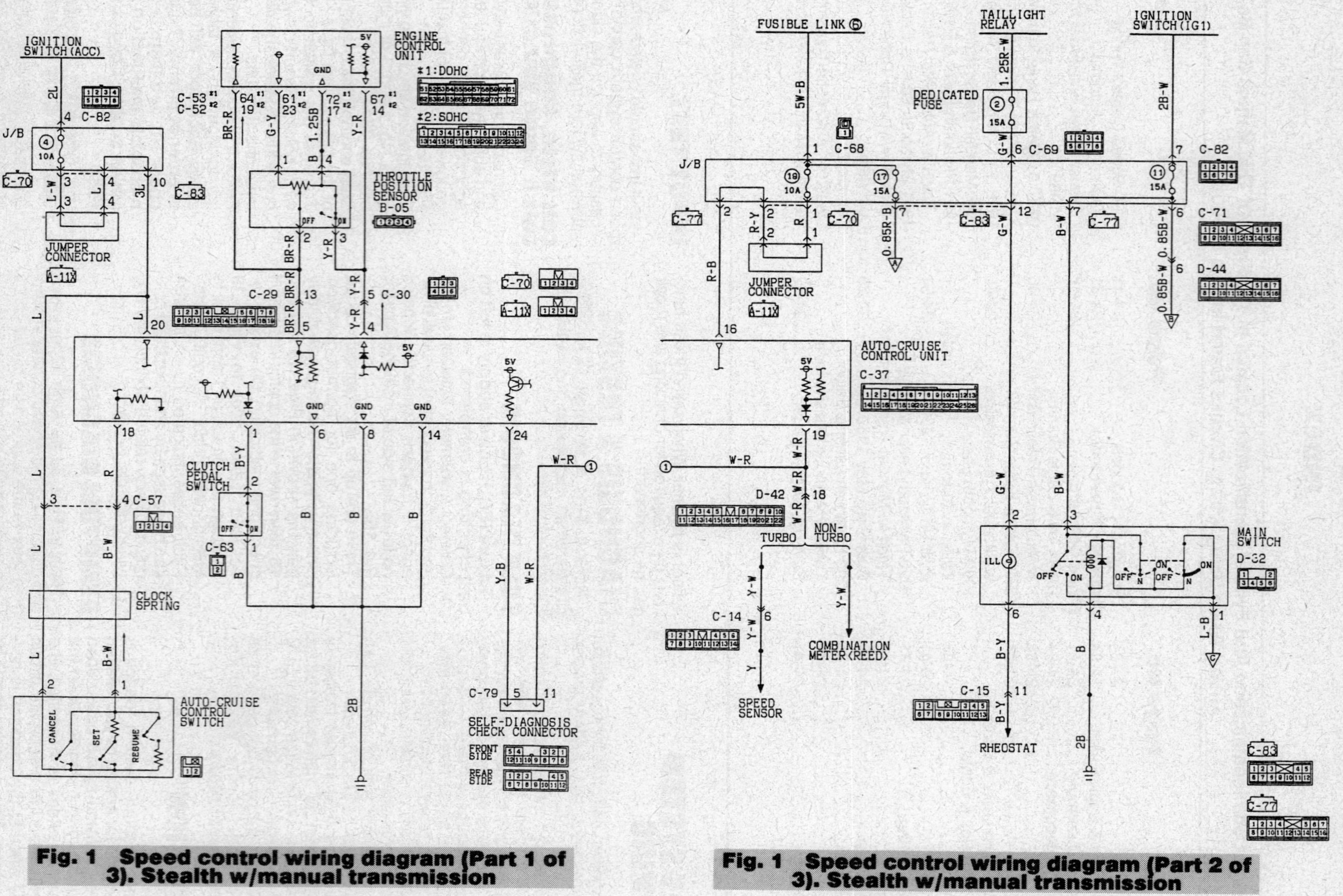


Fig. 1 Speed control wiring diagram (Part 1 of 3). Stealth w/manual transmission

Fig. 1 Speed control wiring diagram (Part 2 of 3). Stealth w/manual transmission

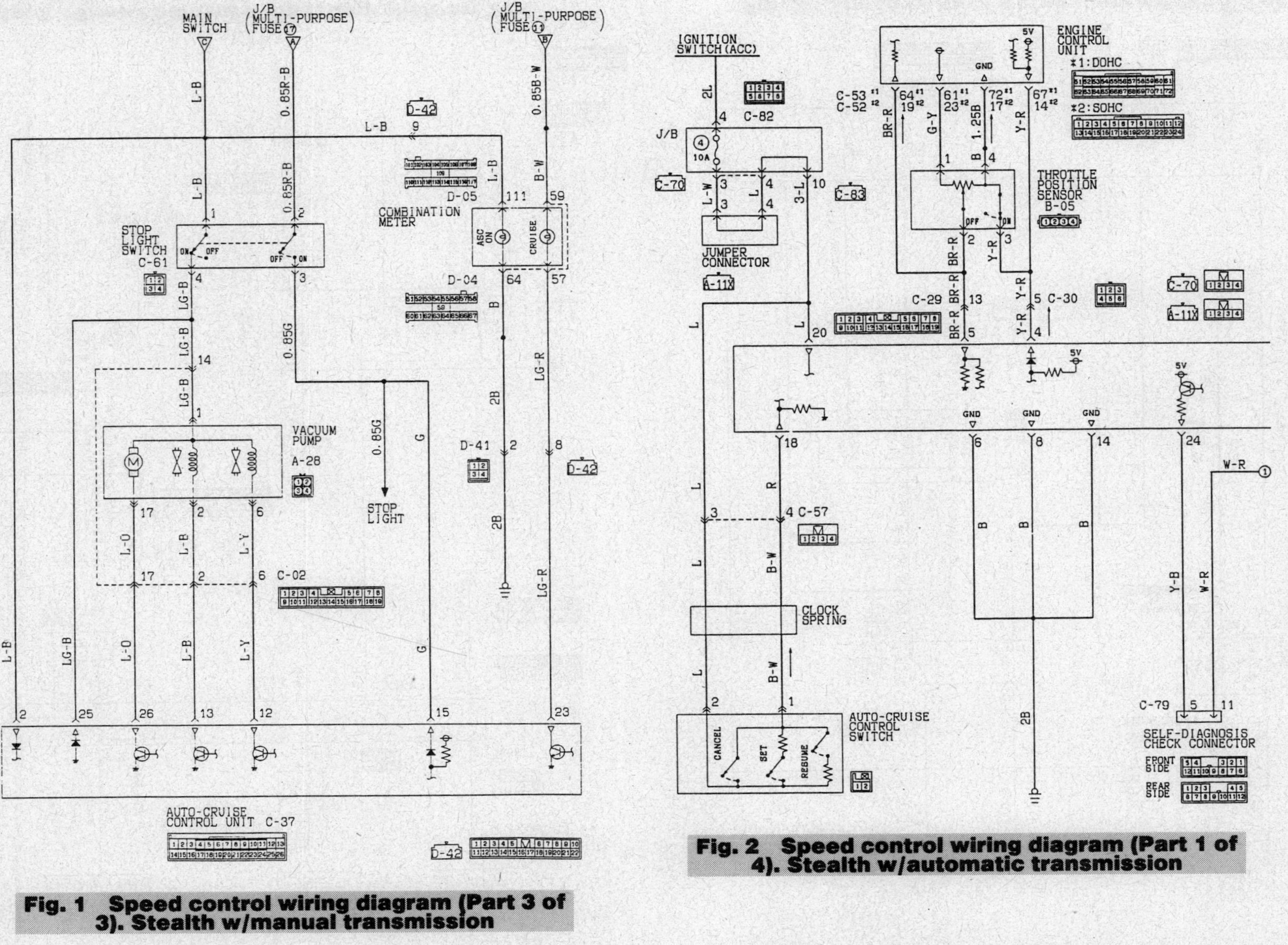


Fig. 1 Speed control wiring diagram (Part 3 of 3). Stealth w/manual transmission

Fig. 2 Speed control wiring diagram (Part 1 of 4). Stealth w/automatic transmission

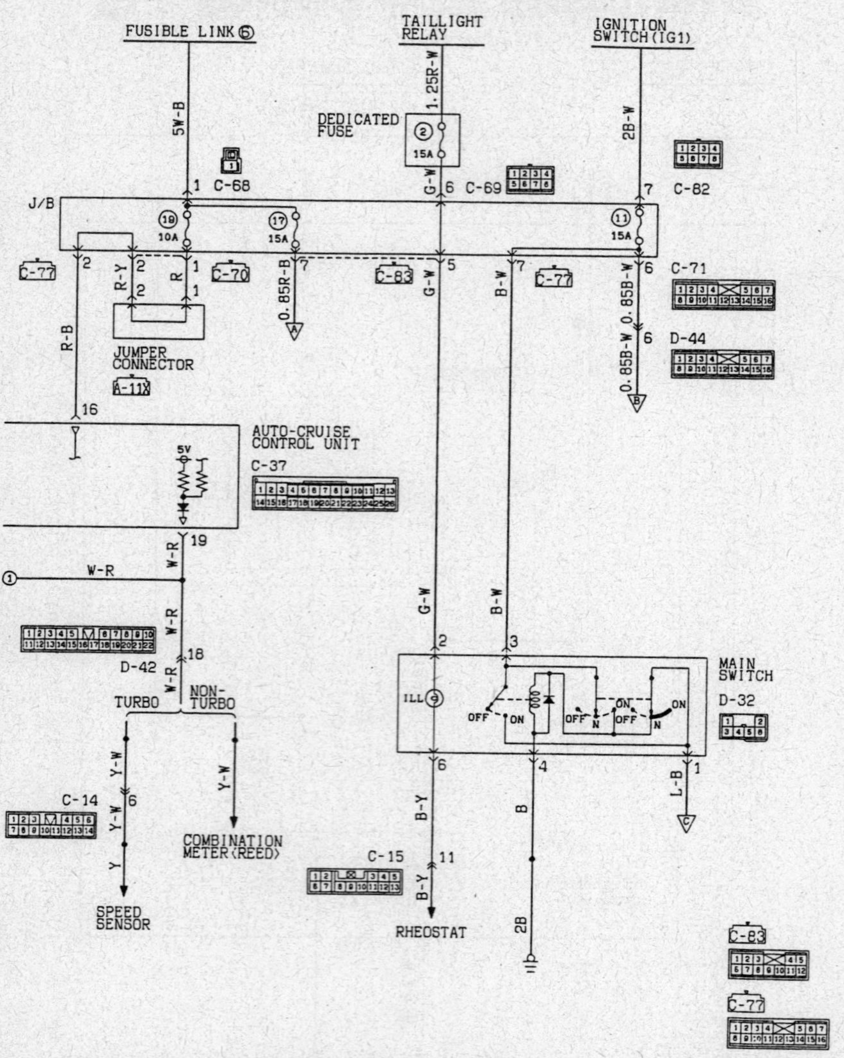


Fig. 2 Speed control wiring diagram (Part 2 of 4). Stealth w/automatic transmission

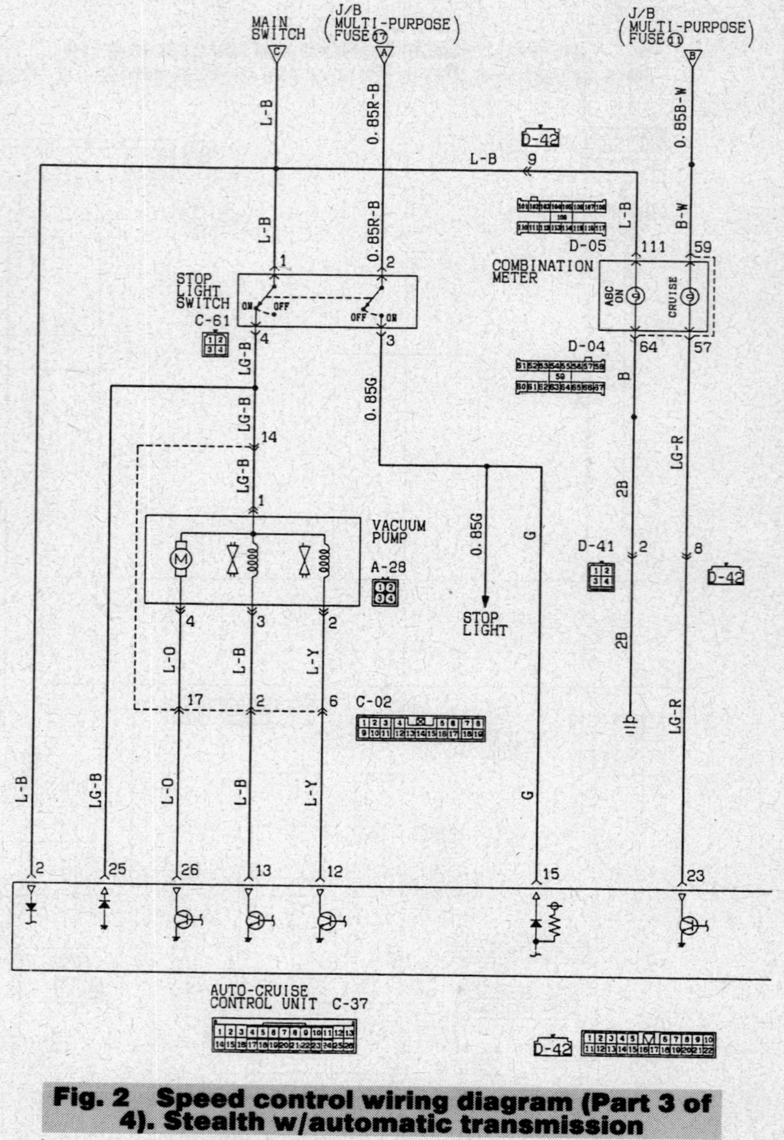


Fig. 2 Speed control wiring diagram (Part 3 of 4). Stealth w/automatic transmission

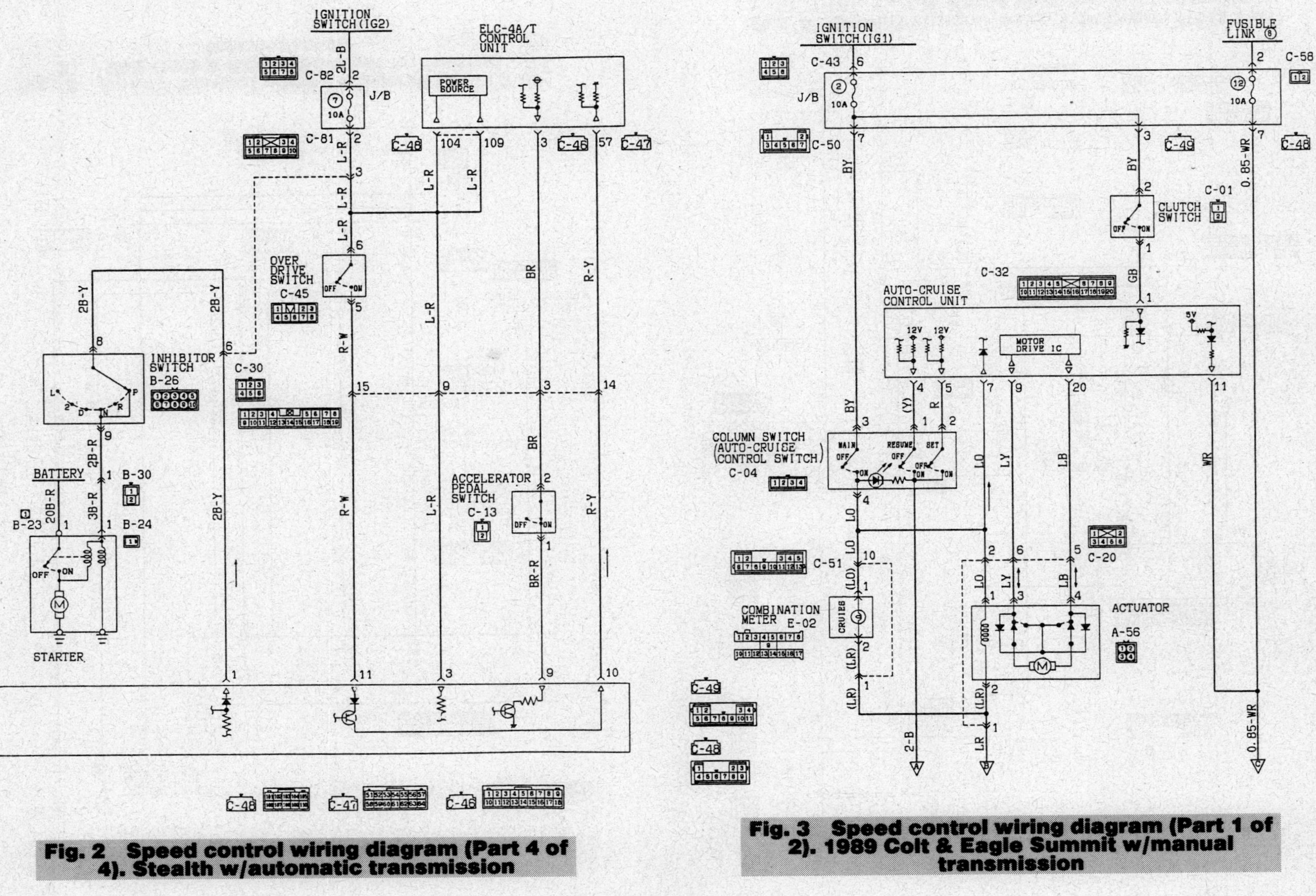


**Fig. 2 Speed control wiring diagram (Part 4 of 4). Stealth w/automatic transmission**

**Fig. 3 Speed control wiring diagram (Part 1 of 2). 1989 Colt & Eagle Summit w/manual transmission**

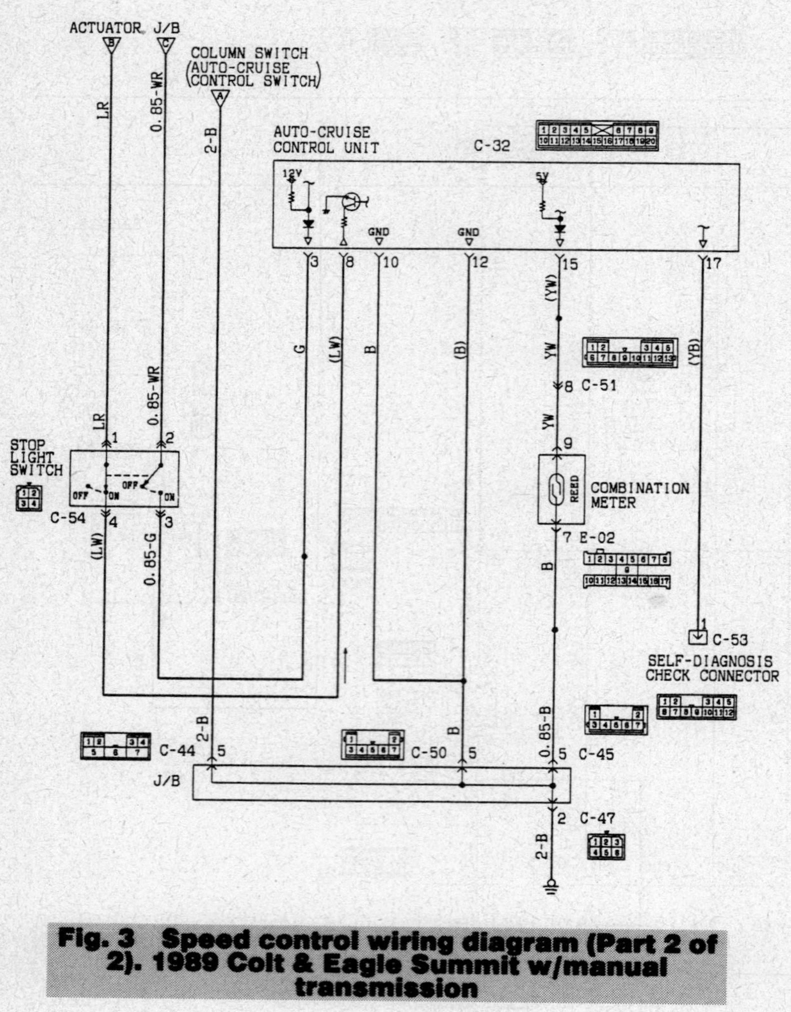


**Fig. 3 Speed control wiring diagram (Part 2 of 2). 1989 Colt & Eagle Summit w/manual transmission**

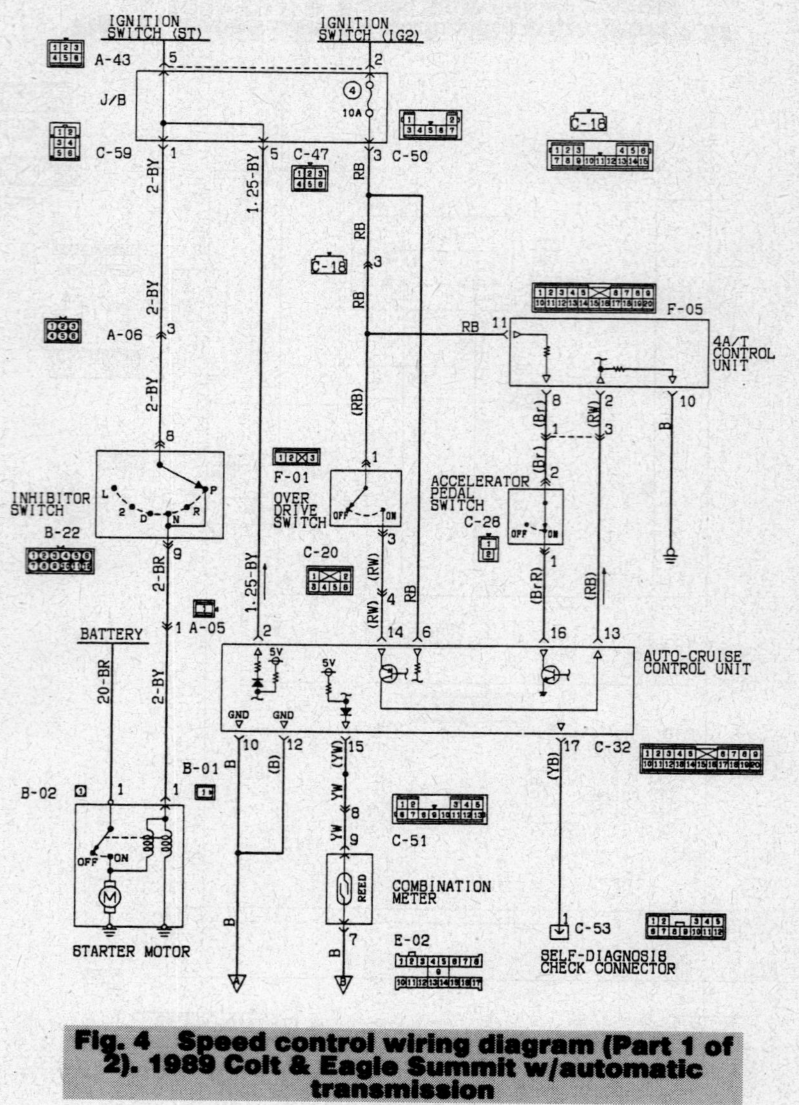


**Fig. 4 Speed control wiring diagram (Part 1 of 2). 1989 Colt & Eagle Summit w/automatic transmission**

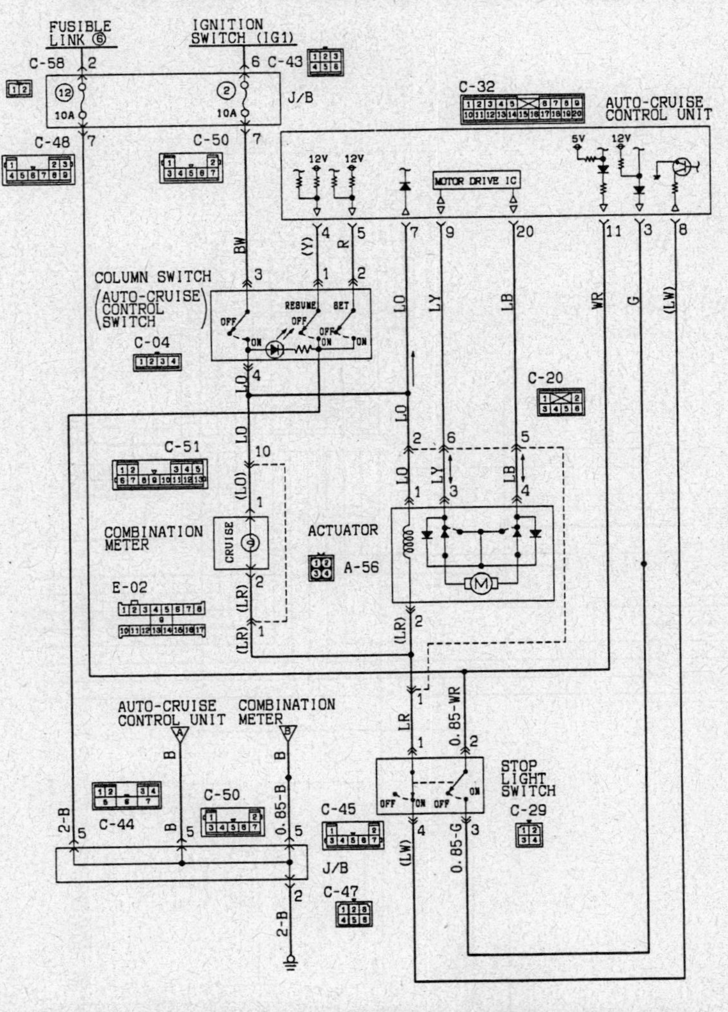



**Fig. 4 Speed control wiring diagram (Part 2 of 2). 1989 Colt & Eagle Summit w/automatic transmission**

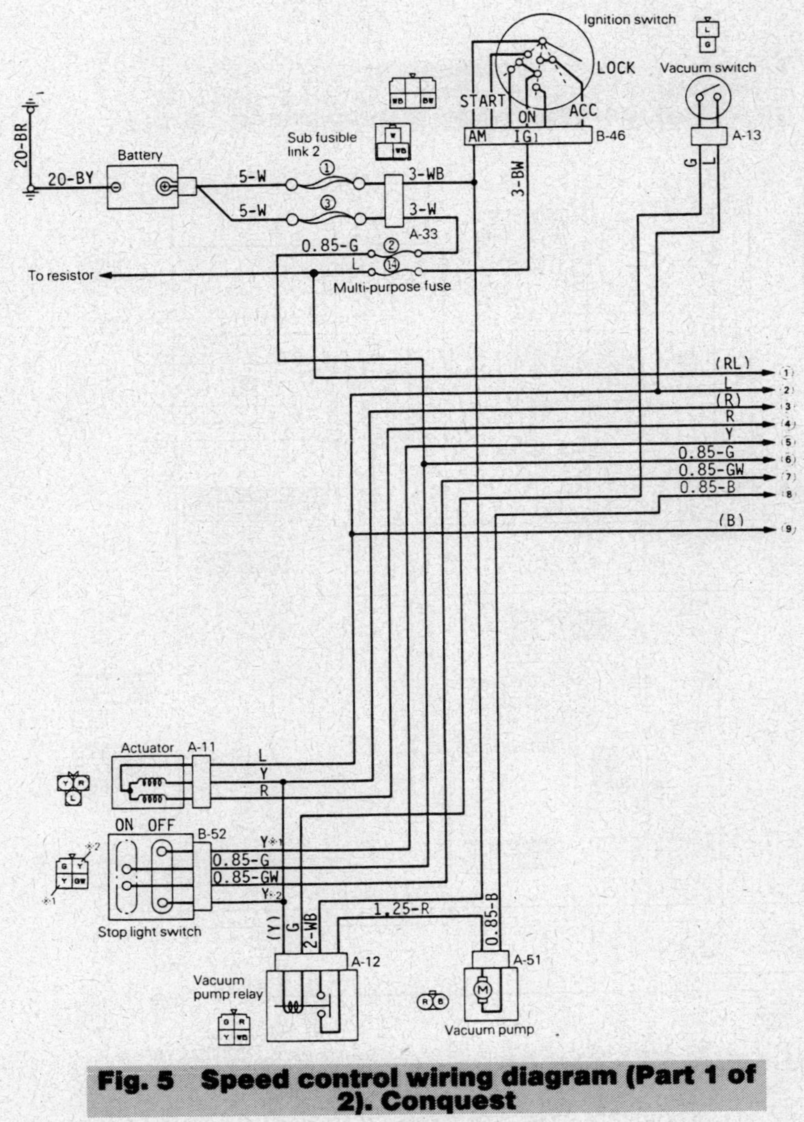



**Fig. 5 Speed control wiring diagram (Part 1 of 2). Conquest**

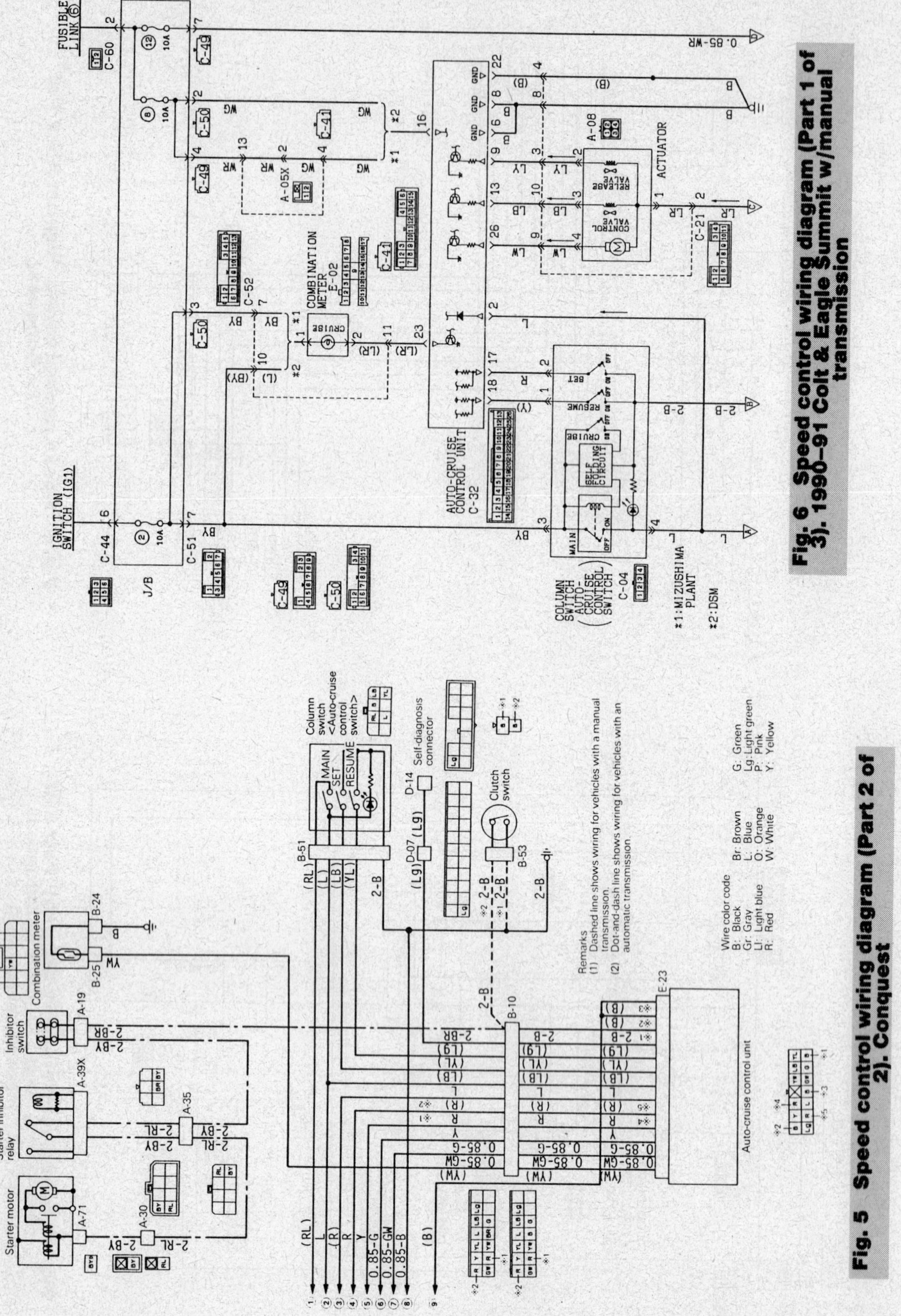

Fig. 6 Speed control wiring diagram (Part 1 of 3). 1990–91 Colt & Eagle Summit w/manual transmission

Fig. 5 Speed control wiring diagram (Part 2 of 2). Conquest

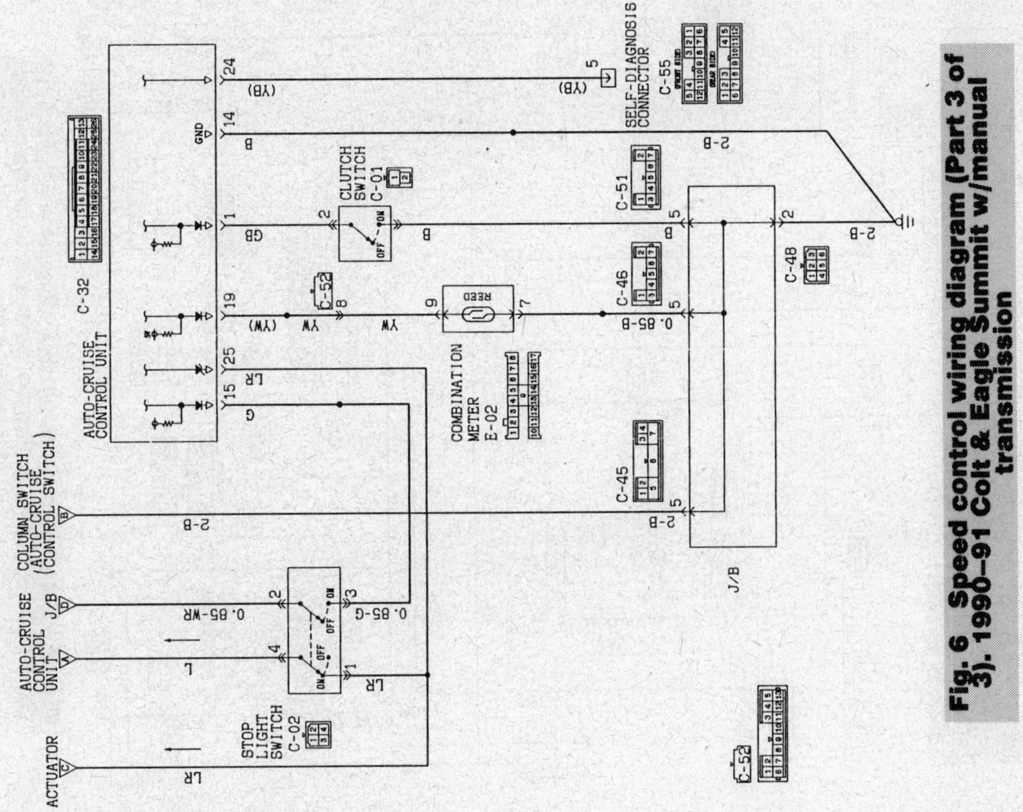


**Fig. 6 Speed control wiring diagram (Part 3 of 3). 1990–91 Colt & Eagle Summit w/manual transmission**

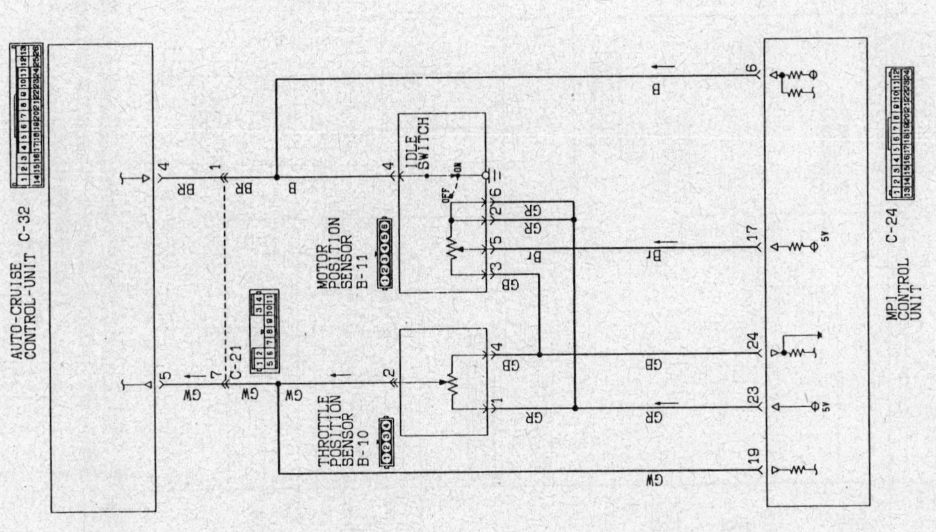


**Fig. 6 Speed control wiring diagram (Part 2 of 3). 1990–91 Colt & Eagle Summit w/manual transmission**

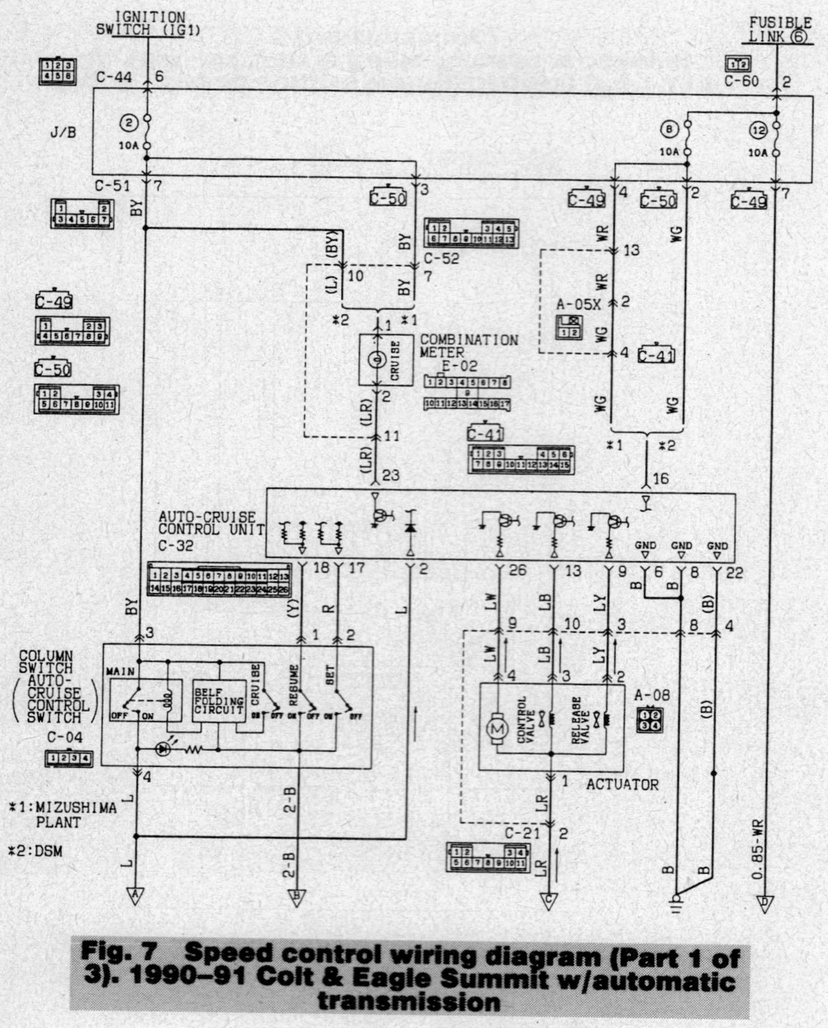


**Fig. 7 Speed control wiring diagram (Part 1 of 3). 1990–91 Colt & Eagle Summit w/automatic transmission**

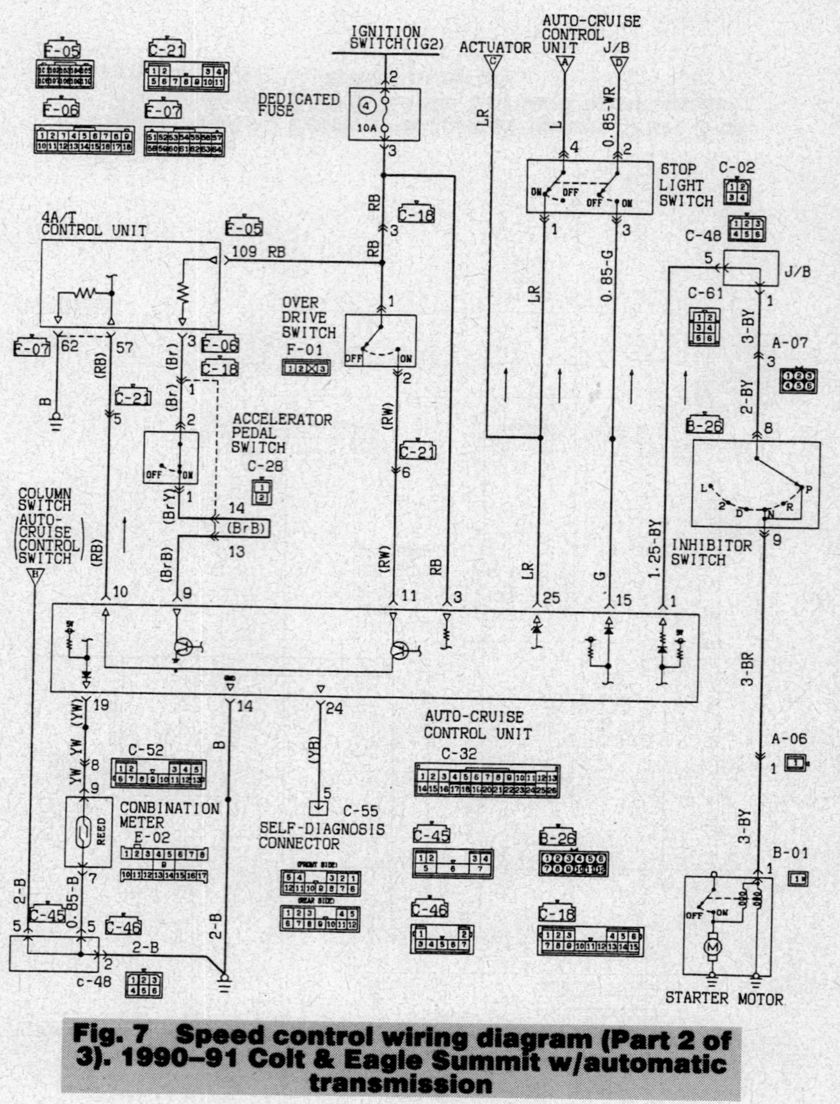


**Fig. 7 Speed control wiring diagram (Part 2 of 3). 1990–91 Colt & Eagle Summit w/automatic transmission**

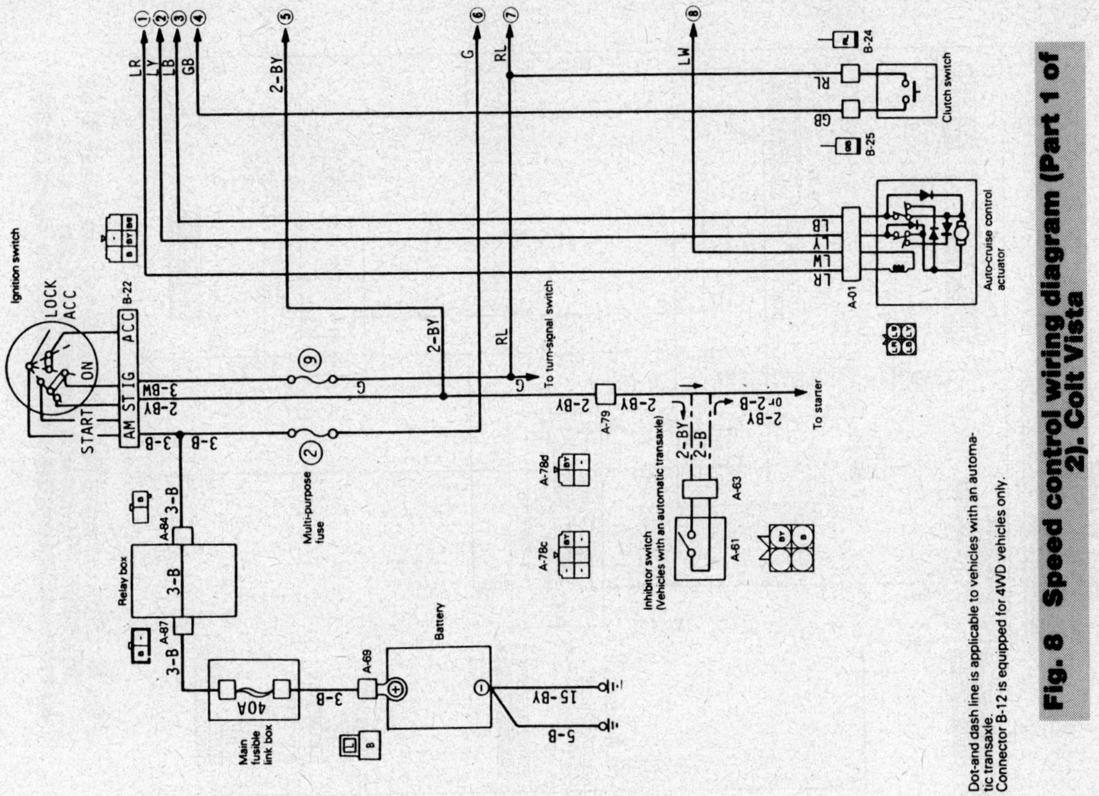


(3) Dot-and dash line is applicable to vehicles with an automatic transaxle.
(4) Connector B-12 is equipped for 4WD vehicles only.

**Fig. 8 Speed control wiring diagram (Part 1 of 2). Colt Vista**

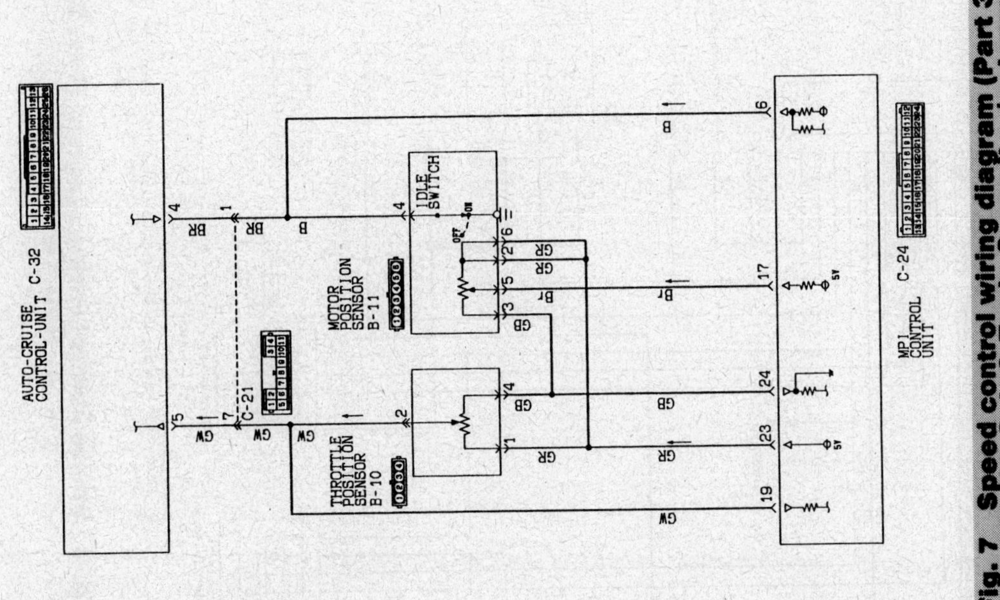


**Fig. 7 Speed control wiring diagram (Part 3 of 3). 1990–91 Colt & Eagle Summit w/automatic transmission**

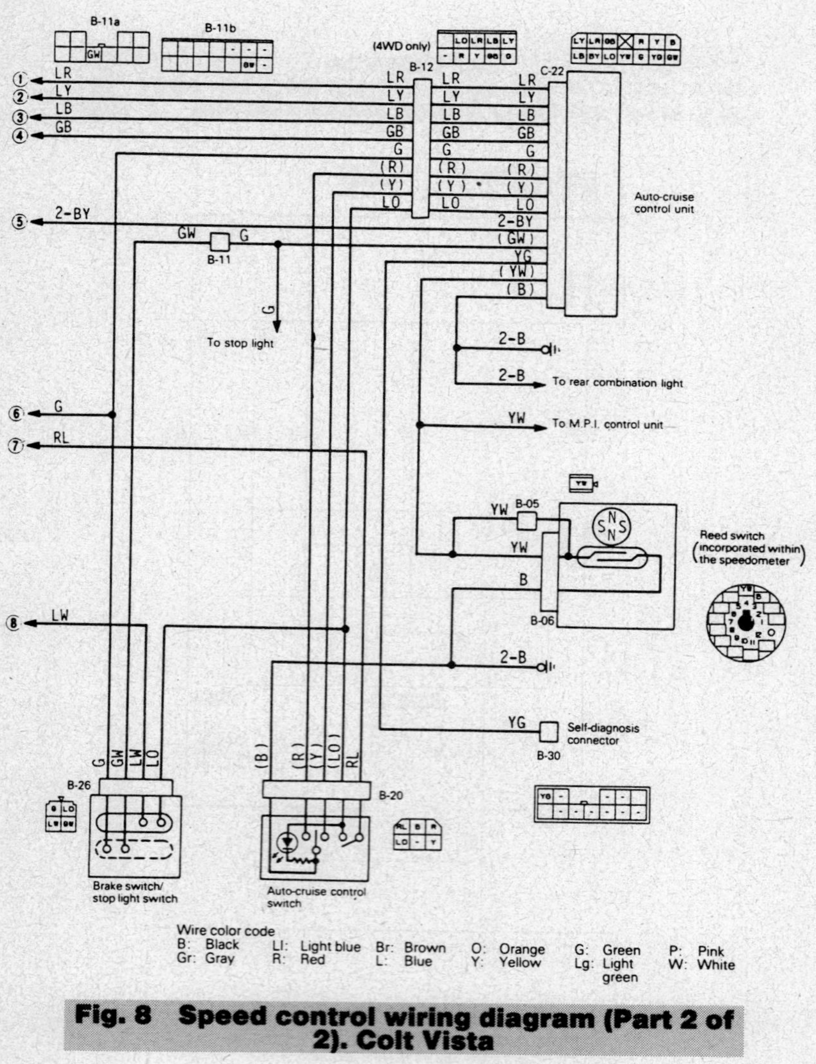


**Fig. 8 Speed control wiring diagram (Part 2 of 2). Colt Vista**

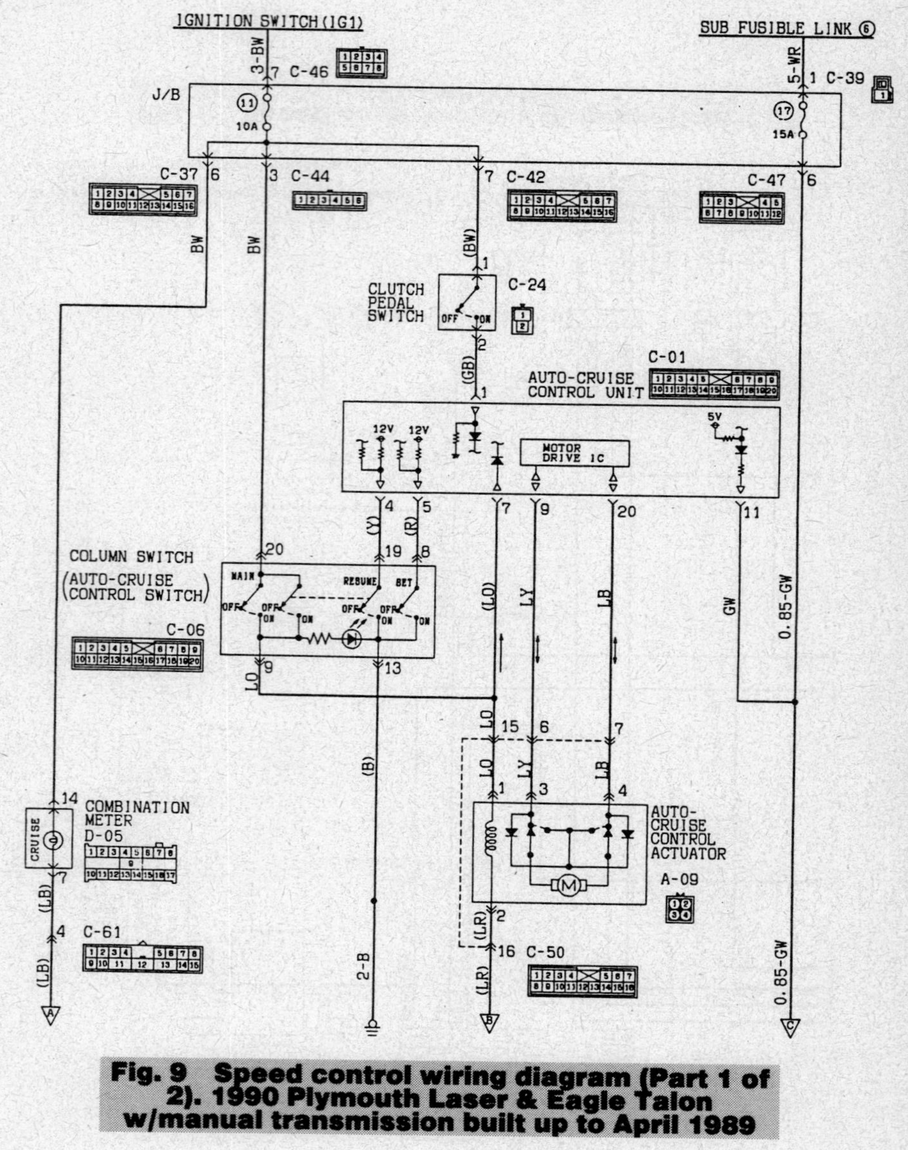


**Fig. 9 Speed control wiring diagram (Part 1 of 2). 1990 Plymouth Laser & Eagle Talon w/manual transmission built up to April 1989**

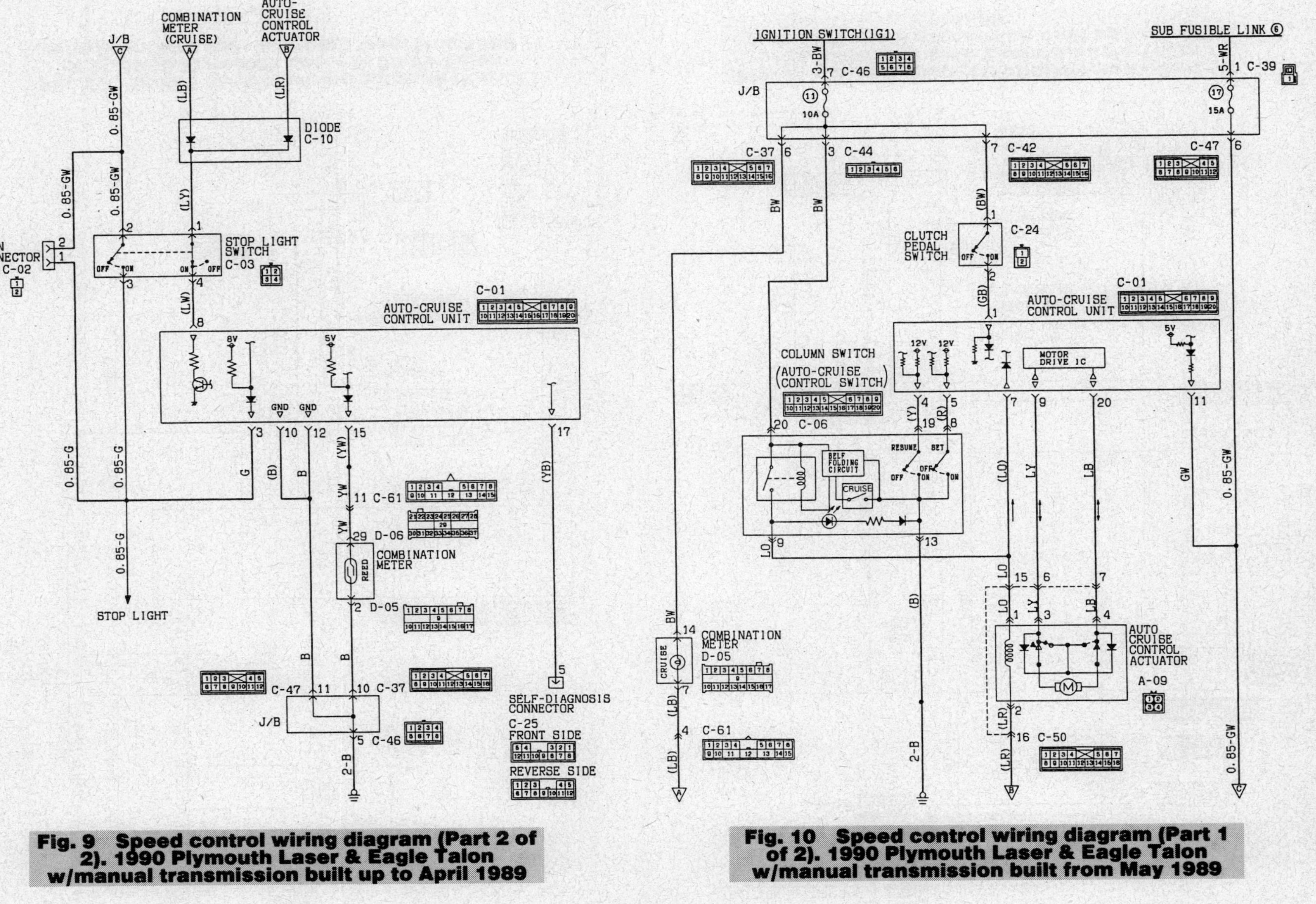


**Fig. 9 Speed control wiring diagram (Part 2 of 2). 1990 Plymouth Laser & Eagle Talon w/manual transmission built up to April 1989**

**Fig. 10 Speed control wiring diagram (Part 1 of 2). 1990 Plymouth Laser & Eagle Talon w/manual transmission built from May 1989**

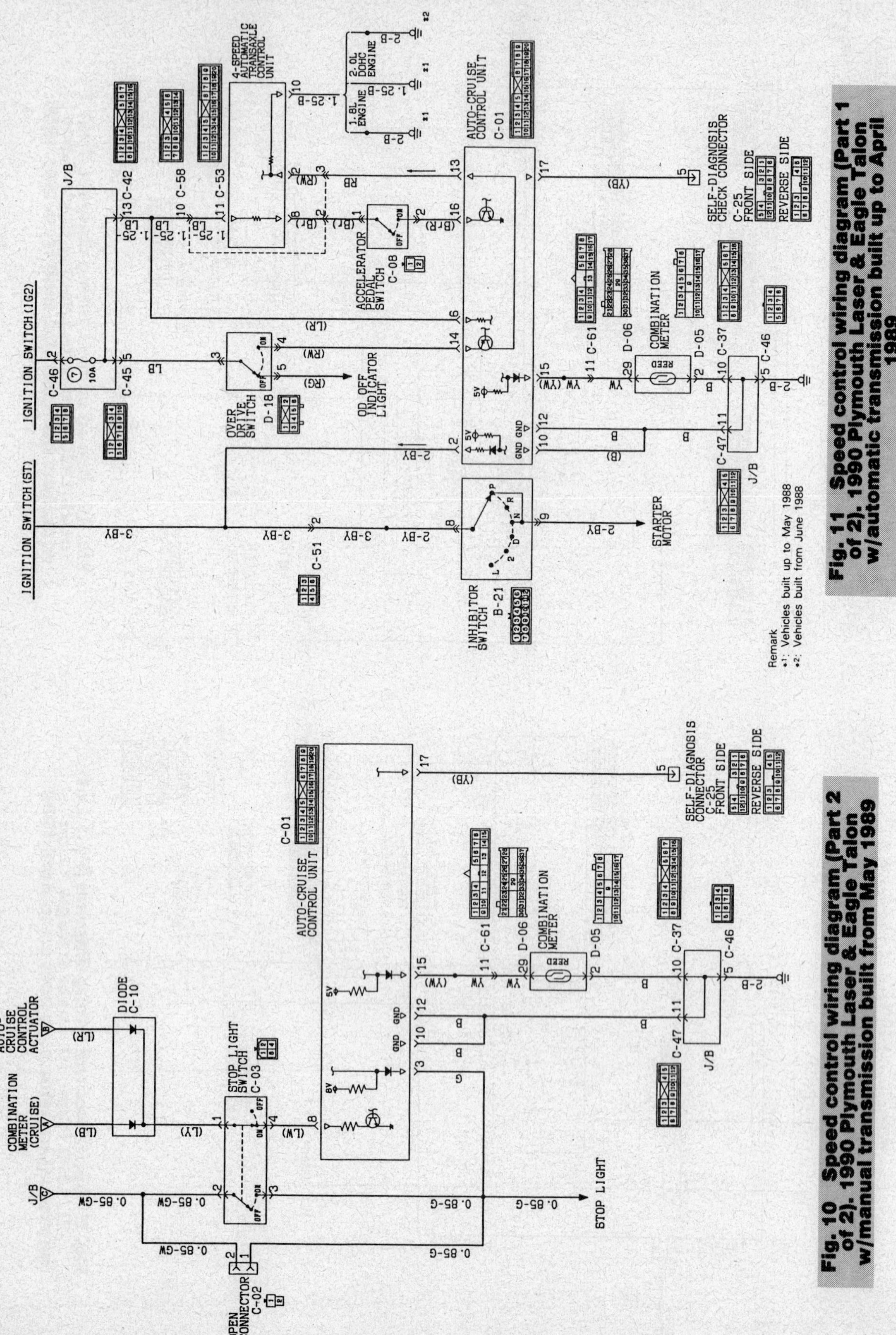


**Fig. 11 Speed control wiring diagram (Part 1 of 2). 1990 Plymouth Laser & Eagle Talon w/automatic transmission built up to April 1989**

**Fig. 10 Speed control wiring diagram (Part 2 of 2). 1990 Plymouth Laser & Eagle Talon w/manual transmission built from May 1989**

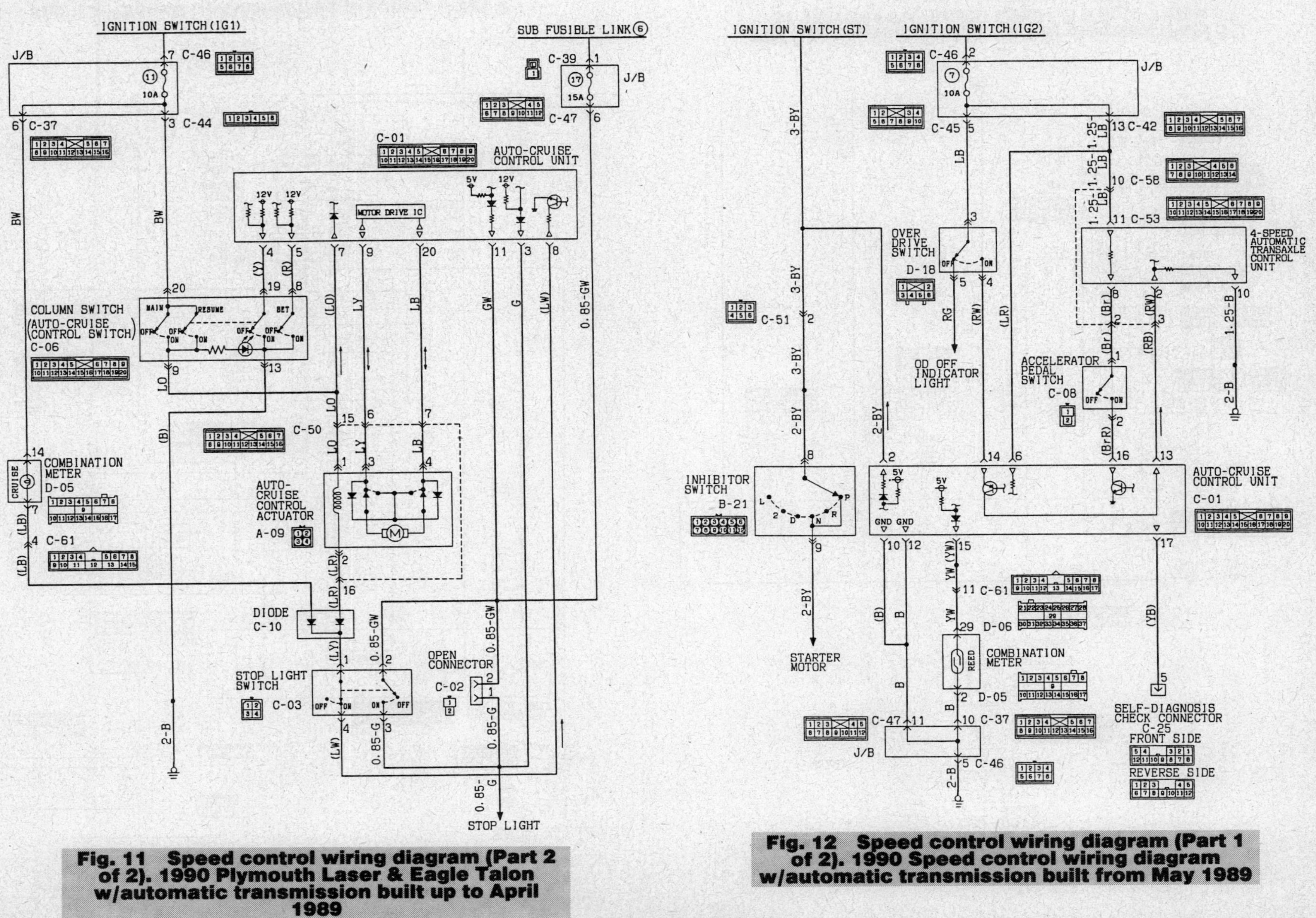


**Fig. 11 Speed control wiring diagram (Part 2 of 2). 1990 Plymouth Laser & Eagle Talon w/automatic transmission built up to April 1989**

**Fig. 12 Speed control wiring diagram (Part 1 of 2). 1990 Speed control wiring diagram w/automatic transmission built from May 1989**

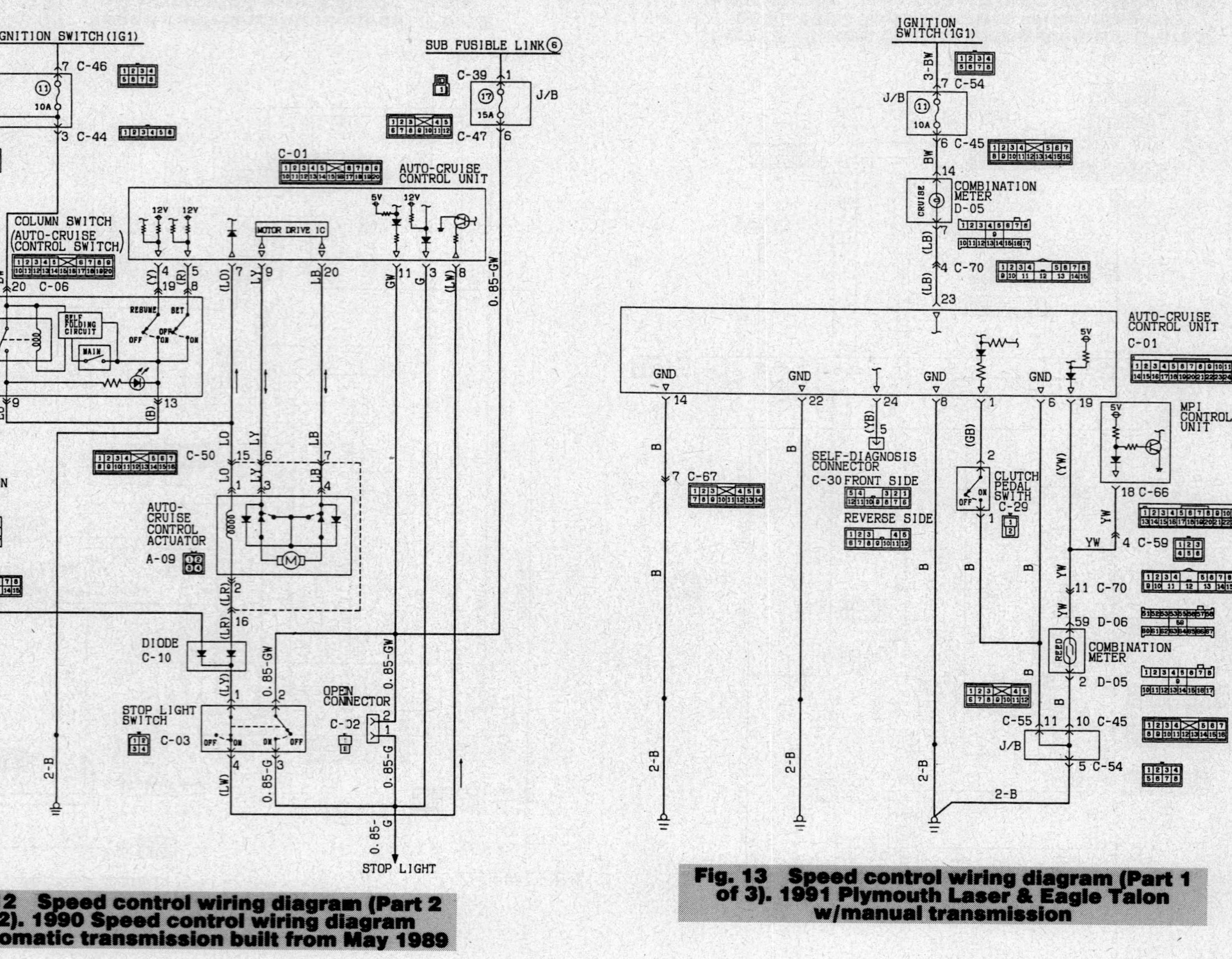


**Fig. 12 Speed control wiring diagram (Part 2 of 2). 1990 Speed control wiring diagram w/automatic transmission built from May 1989**

**Fig. 13 Speed control wiring diagram (Part 1 of 3). 1991 Plymouth Laser & Eagle Talon w/manual transmission**

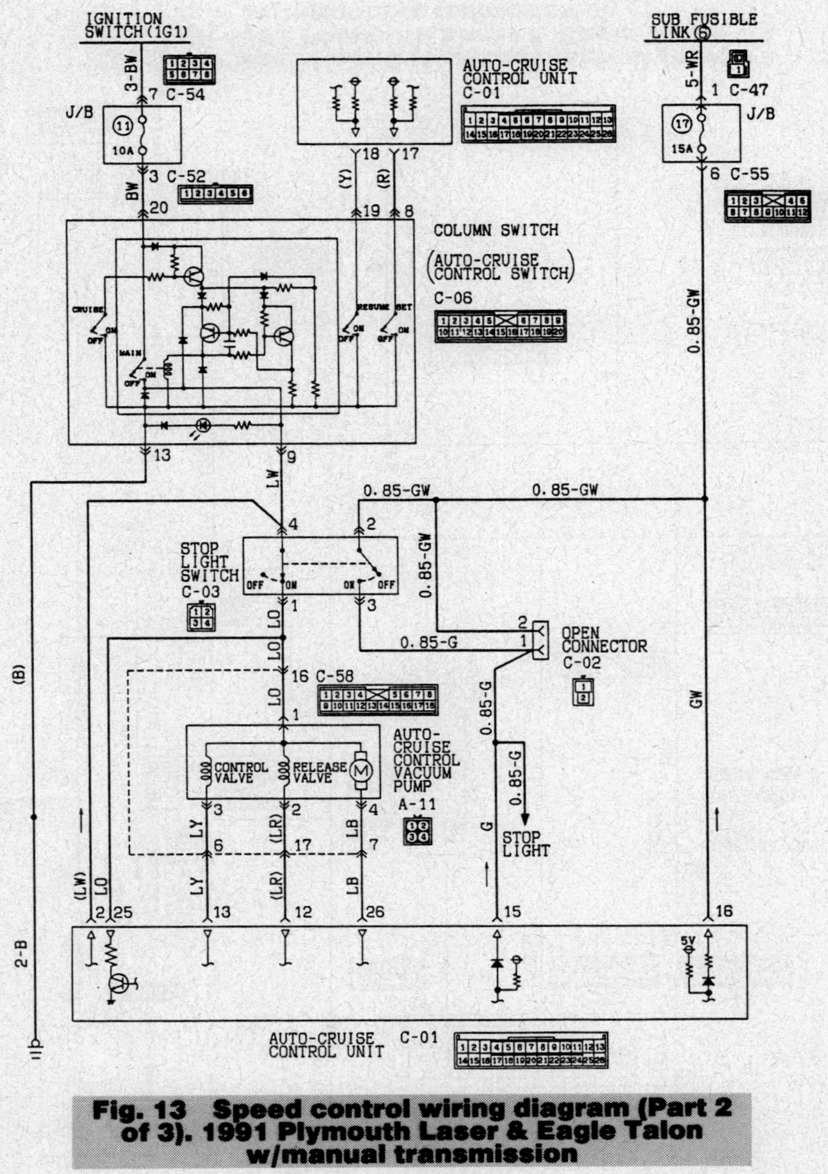


Fig. 13 Speed control wiring diagram (Part 2 of 3). 1991 Plymouth Laser & Eagle Talon w/manual transmission

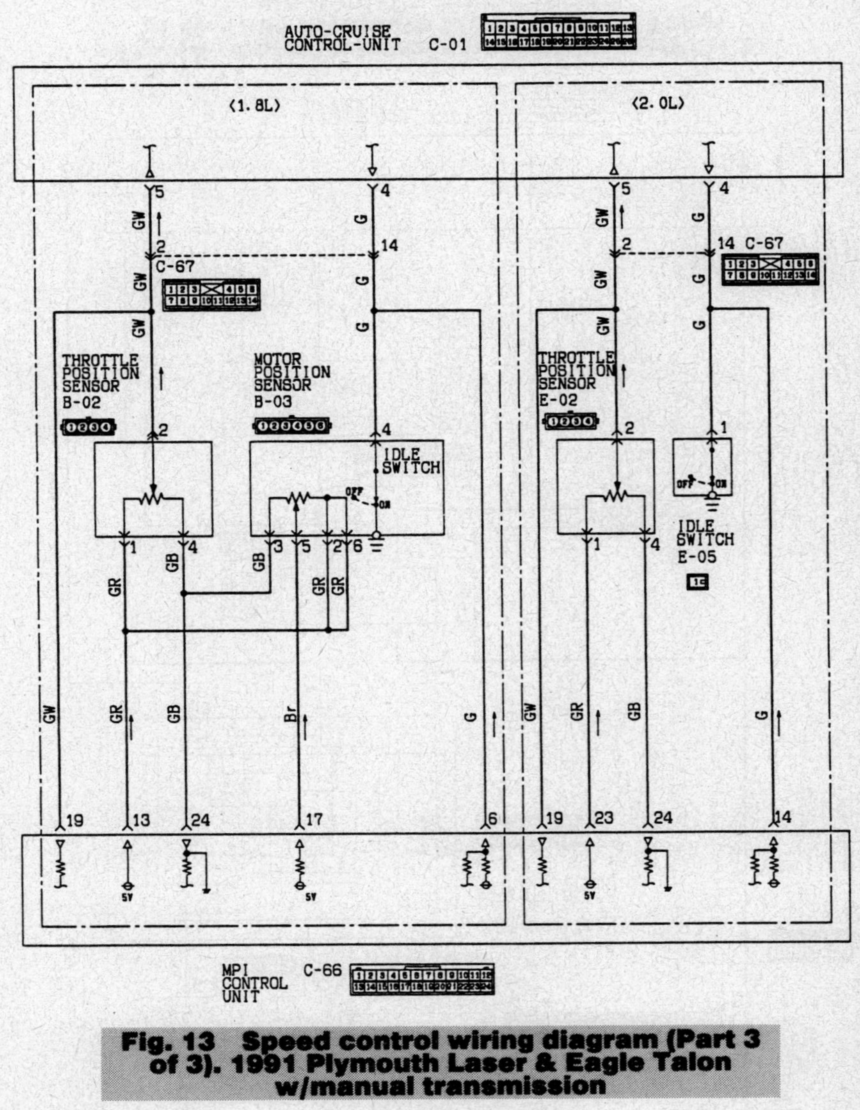


Fig. 13 Speed control wiring diagram (Part 3 of 3). 1991 Plymouth Laser & Eagle Talon w/manual transmission

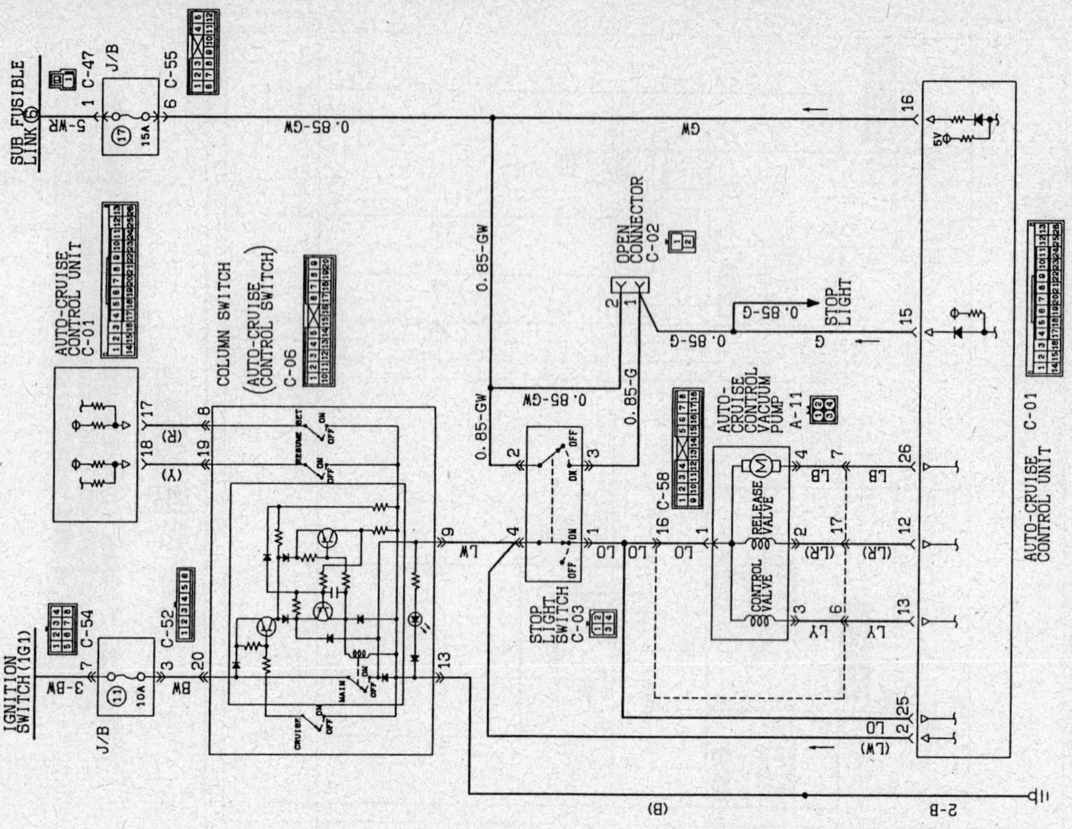

Fig. 14 Speed control wiring diagram (Part 2 of 4). 1991 Plymouth Laser & Eagle Talon w/automatic transmission

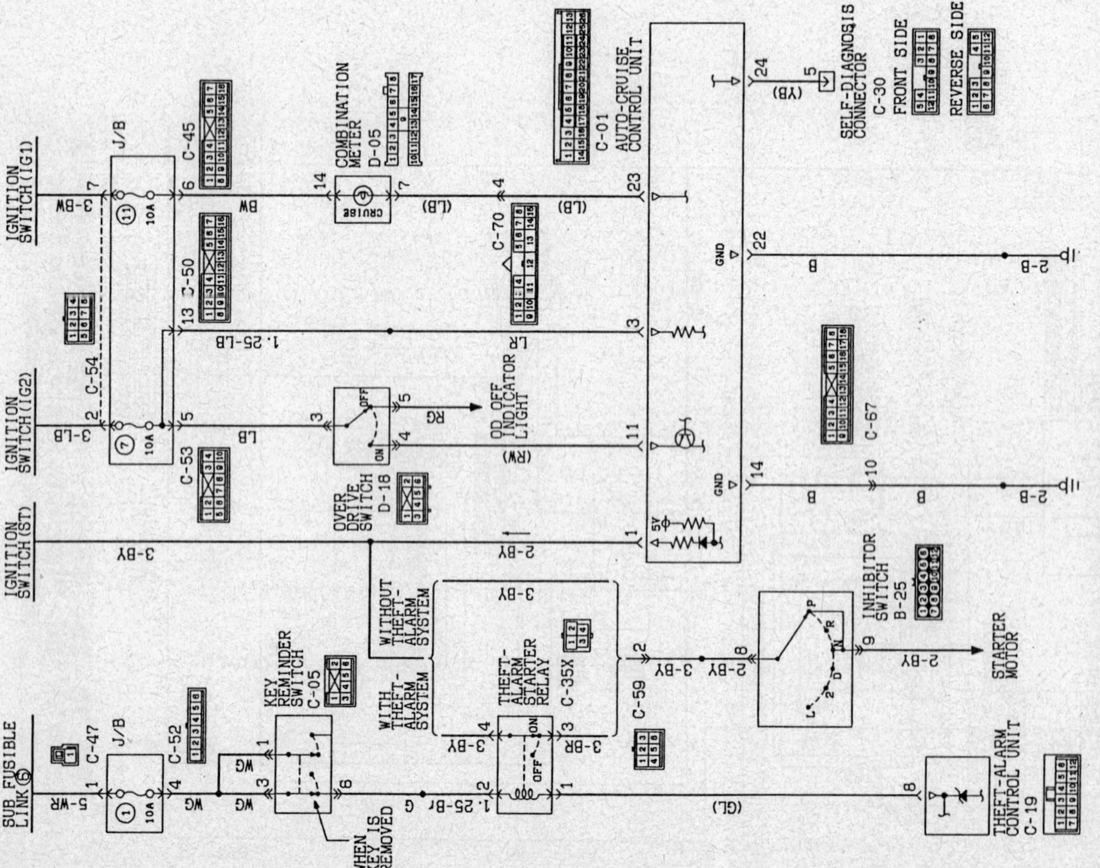

Fig. 14 Speed control wiring diagram (Part 1 of 4). 1991 Plymouth Laser & Eagle Talon w/automatic transmission

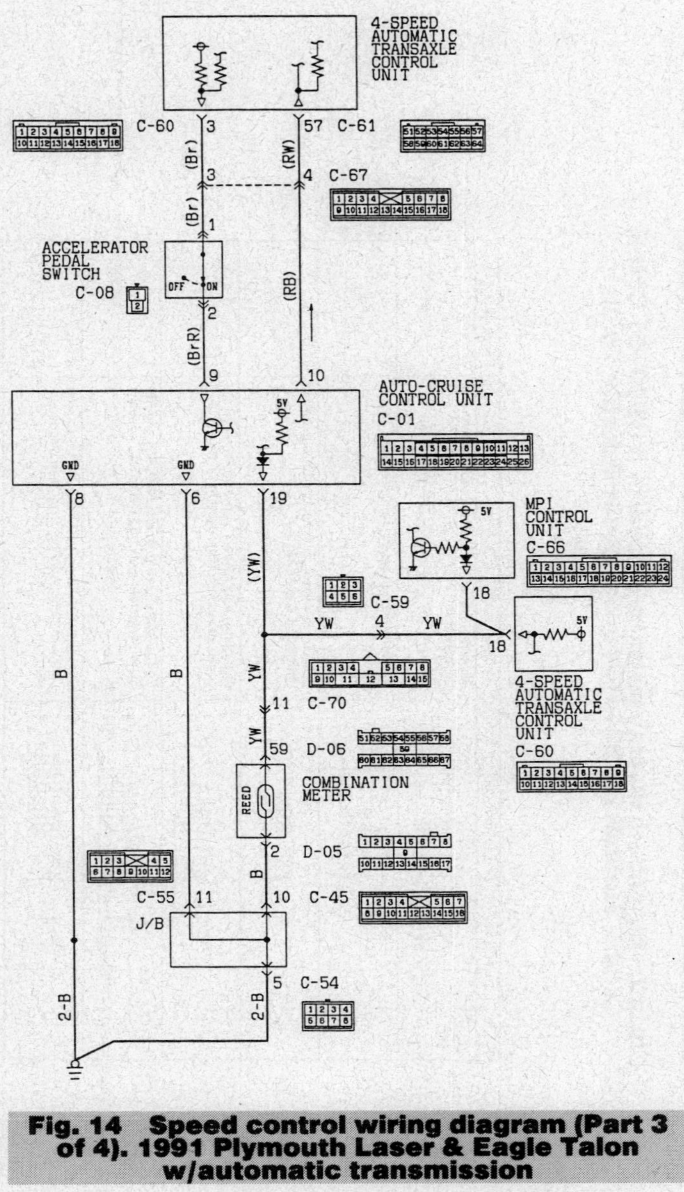


Fig. 14 Speed control wiring diagram (Part 3 of 4). 1991 Plymouth Laser & Eagle Talon w/automatic transmission

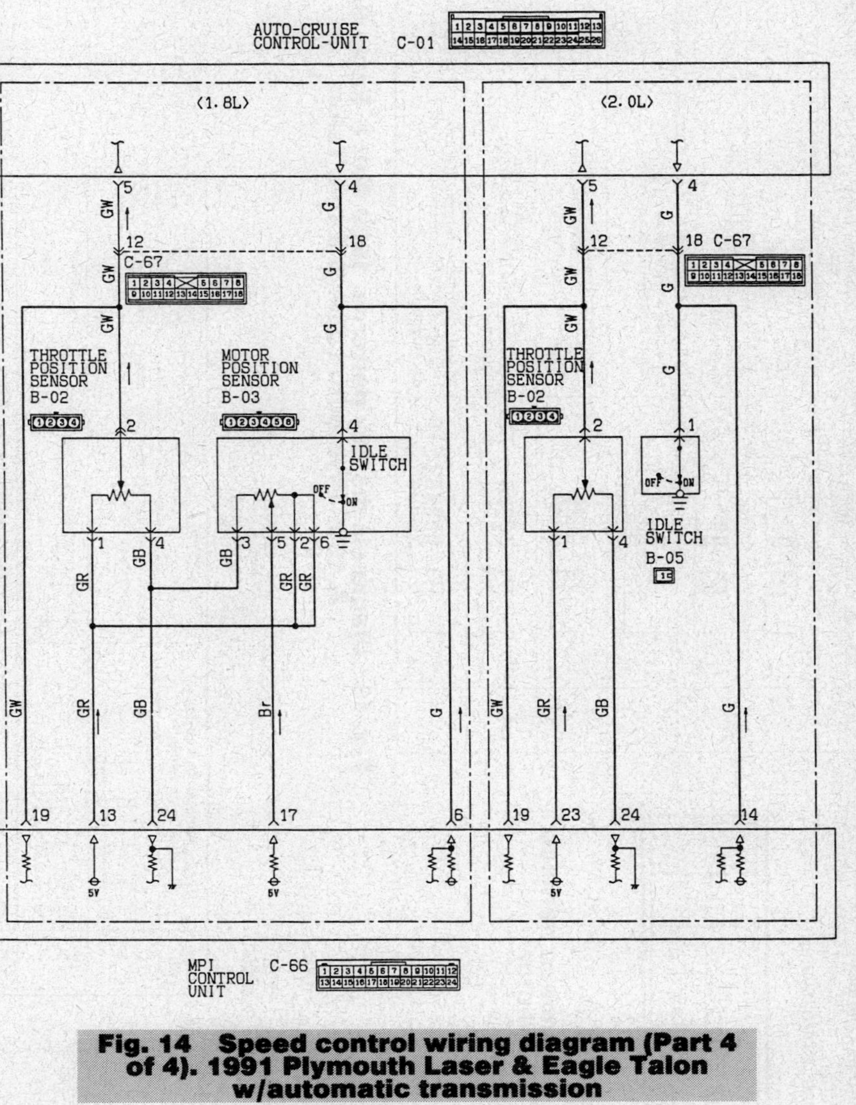


Fig. 14 Speed control wiring diagram (Part 4 of 4). 1991 Plymouth Laser & Eagle Talon w/automatic transmission

Diagnosis harness connector

Auto-cruise control system

Ground

**Fig. 15 Diagnostic harness connector**

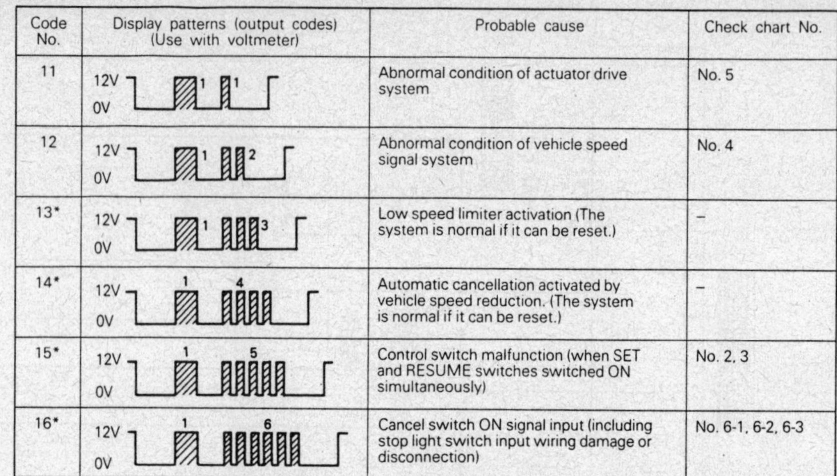

| Code No. | Display patterns (output codes) (Use with voltmeter) | Probable cause | Check chart No. |
|---|---|---|---|
| 11 | 12V 0V 1 1 | Abnormal condition of actuator drive system | No. 5 |
| 12 | 12V 0V 1 2 | Abnormal condition of vehicle speed signal system | No. 4 |
| 13* | 12V 0V 1 3 | Low speed limiter activation (The system is normal if it can be reset.) | – |
| 14* | 12V 0V 1 4 | Automatic cancellation activated by vehicle speed reduction. (The system is normal if it can be reset.) | – |
| 15* | 12V 0V 1 5 | Control switch malfunction (when SET and RESUME switches switched ON simultaneously) | No. 2, 3 |
| 16* | 12V 0V 1 6 | Cancel switch ON signal input (including stop light switch input wiring damage or disconnection) | No. 6-1, 6-2, 6-3 |

**Fig. 16 Diagnosis display patterns. 1989 Colt & Eagle Summit & 1990 Plymouth Laser & Eagle Talon**

| Code No. | Display patterns (output codes) (Use with voltmeter) | Probable cause | Check chart No. |
|---|---|---|---|
| 11 | 12V 0V | Abnormal condition of auto-cruise vacuum pump drive system | No. 6 |
| 12 | 12V 0V | Abnormal condition of vehicle speed signal system | No. 5 |
| 15* | 12V 0V | Control switch malfunction (when SET and RESUME switches switched ON simultaneously for more than 25 seconds) | No. 2, 3 |
| 16* | 12V 0V | Abnormal condition of auto-cruise control unit | – |
| 17 | 12V 0V | Defective throttle position sensor<br>Defective idle switch | No. 10 |

**Fig. 17 Diagnosis display patterns. Stealth & 1990–91 Colt & Eagle Summit & 1991 Plymouth Laser & Eagle Talon**

| Code No. | Display patterns (output codes) | Probable cause | Check chart No. |
|---|---|---|---|
| 11 | 12V 0V 1 1 | Abnormal condition of actuator clutch coil drive system | 4 |
| 12 | 12V 0V 1 2 | Abnormal condition of vehicle-speed signal system | 3 |
| 13* | 12V 0V 1 3 | Low-speed limiter activation (The system is normal if it can be reset.) | – |
| 14* | 12V 0V 1 4 | Automatic cancelation activated by vehicle speed reduction. (The system is normal if it can be reset.) | – |
| 15* | 12V 0V 1 5 | Control switch malfunction (when SET and RESUME switches switched ON simultaneously) | 1<br>2 |
| 16* | 12V 0V 1 6 | Cancel switch ON signal input (including stop light switch input wiring damage or disconnection) | 5-1<br>5-2<br>5-3 |

**Fig. 18 Diagnosis display patterns. Conquest & Colt Vista**

## DIAGNOSTIC CHART INDEX

| Check Chart No. | Symptom | Page No. | Fig. No. |
|---|---|---|---|
| **Colt Vista** | | | |
| — | Symptom Diagnosis Chart | 24-70 | 68 |
| 0 | ECU Power Supply Wiring Circuit | 24-64 | 29 |
| 1 | Set Switch Wiring Circuit | 24-64 | 30 |
| 2 | Resume Switch Wiring Circuit | 24-64 | 31 |
| 3 | Vehicle Speed Sensor Wiring Circuit | 24-64 | 32 |
| 4 | Actuator Wiring Circuit | 24-65 | 33 |
| 5-1 | Stop Lamp Switch Wiring Circuit | 24-65 | 34 |
| 5-2 | Clutch Switch Wiring Circuit M/T | 24-65 | 35 |
| 5-3 | Inhibitor Switch Wiring Circuit A/T | 24-65 | 36 |
| **Conquest** | | | |
| — | Symptom Diagnosis Chart | 24-70 | 68 |
| 0 | Check Chart | 24-65 | 37 |
| 1 | Set Switch Wiring Circuit | 24-66 | 38 |
| 2 | Resume Switch Wiring Circuit | 24-66 | 39 |
| 3 | Vehicle Speed Sensor Wiring Circuit | 24-66 | 40 |
| 4 | Actuator Wiring Circuit | 24-66 | 41 |
| 5-1 | Stop Light Switch Wiring Circuit | 24-66 | 42 |
| 5-2 | Clutch Switch Wiring Circuit | 24-66 | 43 |
| 5-3 | Inhibitor Switch Wiring Circuit | 24-66 | 44 |
| **Plymouth Laser & Eagle Talon** | | | |
| — | Symptom Diagnosis Chart (1990 Models) | 24-74 | 71 |
| — | Symptom Diagnosis Chart (1991 Models) | 24-76 | 72 |
| 1 | Control Unit Power Supply | 24-78 | — |
| 2 | Set Switch | 24-78 | — |
| 3 | Resume Switch | 24-78 | — |
| 4 | Vehicle Speed Sensor | 24-78 | — |
| 5 | Vehicle Speed Sensor (1990 Models) | 24-78 | — |
| 5 | Cruise Control Vacuum Pump (1991 Models) | 24-79 | — |
| 6-1 | Stop Light Switch | 24-79 | — |
| 6-2 | Inhibitor Switch | 24-79 | — |
| 6-3 | Clutch Circuit Switch | 24-79 | — |
| 7 | Accelerator Switch Off Function | 24-79 | — |
| 8 | Overdrive Cancellation Function | 24-79 | — |
| **Stealth** | | | |
| — | Symptom Diagnosis Chart | 24-72 | 70 |
| 1 | Control Unit Power Supply Circuit | 24-68 | 57 |
| 2 | Control Switch Wiring Circuit | 24-68 | 58 |
| 3 | Indicator Light Wiring Circuit | 24-68 | 59 |
| 4 | Vehicle Speed Sensor Wiring Circuit | 24-68 | 60 |
| 5 | Vacuum Pump Drive Wiring Circuit | 24-69 | 61 |
| 6 | Stop Light Switch Wiring Circuit | 24-69 | 62 |
| 7 | Clutch Switch Wiring Circuit M/T | 24-69 | 63 |
| 8 | Inhibitor Switch Wiring Circuit A/T | 24-69 | 64 |
| 9 | Throttle Position Sensor & Idle Switch Wiring Circuit | 24-69 | 65 |
| 10 | Accelerator Switch Off Function Related Circuits | 24-70 | 66 |
| 11 | Overdrive Cancellation Function Related Circuits | 24-70 | 67 |

*Continued*

## DIAGNOSTIC CHART INDEX-Continued



| Terminal No. | Signal | Conditions | Terminal voltage |
|---|---|---|---|
| 7 | Control unit power supply | When the auto-cruise control switch ("MAIN") is switched ON | 12V |
| 10 | Control unit ground | At all times | 0V |

**Fig. 19 Check Chart No. 1, control unit power supply circuit. 1989 Colt & Eagle Summit**

| Terminal No. | Signal | Conditions | Terminal voltage |
|---|---|---|---|
| 5 | SET switch | When the SET switch is switched ON | 0V |
| | | When the SET switch is switched OFF | 12V |

**Fig. 20 Check Chart No. 2, set switch wiring circuit. 1989 Colt & Eagle Summit**

| Terminal No. | Signal | Conditions | Terminal voltage |
|---|---|---|---|
| 4 | RESUME switch | When the RESUME switch is switched ON | 0V |
| | | When the RESUME switch is switched OFF | 12V |

**Fig. 21 Check Chart No. 3, resume switch wiring circuit. 1989 Colt & Eagle Summit**

| Terminal No. | Signal | Conditions | Terminal voltage |
|---|---|---|---|
| 15 | Vehicle speed sensor | Move the vehicle forward slowly. | 0V – 0.6V ↕ Flashing 2V or higher |

**Fig. 22 Check Chart No. 4, vehicle speed sensor wiring circuit. 1989 Colt & Eagle Summit**

| Terminal No. | Signal | Conditions | Terminal voltage |
|---|---|---|---|
| 3 | Stop light switch (load side) | When the brake pedal is depressed | 12V |
| | | When the brake pedal is not depressed | 0V |
| 11 | Stop light switch (power supply side) | At all times | 12V |

**Fig. 24 Check Chart No. 6-1, stop light switch wiring circuit. 1989 Colt & Eagle Summit**

| Terminal No. | Signal | Conditions | Terminal voltage |
|---|---|---|---|
| 1 | Clutch switch | When the clutch pedal is depressed | 12V |
| | | When the clutch pedal is not depressed | 0V |

**Fig. 26 Check Chart No. 6-3, clutch switch wiring circuit M/T. 1989 Colt & Eagle Summit**

| Terminal No. | Signal | Conditions | Terminal voltage |
|---|---|---|---|
| 13 | 4-A/T control unit | When the overdrive switch is switched ON | 12V |
| 14 | Overdrive switch | When the overdrive switch is switched ON | 12V |

**Fig. 28 Check Chart No. 8, overdrive cancellation function wiring circuit A/T. 1989 Colt & Eagle Summit**

| Terminal No. | Signal | Conditions | Terminal voltage |
|---|---|---|---|
| 8 | Transistor for electromagnetic clutch coil | When the auto-cruise control switch (MAIN) is switched ON | 0V |
| 9 | DC motor drive ("PULL" side) | During acceleration by RESUME switch | 0V |
| | DC motor drive ("REL." side) | During speed reduction (coasting) by SET switch | 12V |
| 20 | DC motor drive ("PULL" side) | During acceleration by RESUME switch | 12V |
| | DC motor drive ("REL." side) | During speed reduction (coasting) by SET switch | 0V |

**Fig. 23 Check Chart No. 5, actuator wiring circuit. 1989 Colt & Eagle Summit**

| Terminal No. | Signal | Conditions | Terminal voltage |
|---|---|---|---|
| 2 | Inhibitor switch | At all times | 12V |

**Fig. 25 Check Chart No. 6-2, inhibitor switch wiring circuit A/T. 1989 Colt & Eagle Summit**

| Terminal No. | Signal | Conditions | Terminal voltage |
|---|---|---|---|
| 6 | Control unit power supply (IG2) | At all times | 12V |
| 16 | Accelerator switch | When the accelerator pedal is depressed | 0V |
| | | When the accelerator pedal is not depressed | 12V |

**Fig. 27 Check Chart No. 7, accelerator switch wiring circuit A/T. 1989 Colt & Eagle Summit**

| Step | Check method | | Judgment | | Cause | Remedy |
|---|---|---|---|---|---|---|
| | Condition | Check object | Normal | Malfunction | | |
| 1 | Ignition switch : ON | Connector Ⓐ terminal voltage [RL–Ground] | Battery voltage | 0V | Fuse ⑨ damaged or disconnected | Replace the fuse |
| | | | | | Harness damaged or disconnected | Repair the harness |
| 2 | Ignition switch : ON Main switch : ON ⟷ OFF | Connector Ⓐ terminal voltage (LO–Ground) | Battery voltage ⟷ 0V | Remains battery voltage; Remains 0V | Main switch or harness damaged or disconnected, or short-circuit | Replace the part or repair the harness. |
| 3 | Ignition switch : ON Main switch : ON | ECU terminal voltage (6–Ground) | Battery voltage | 0V | Harness damaged or disconnected | Repair the harness |
| 4 | Ignition switch : OFF Disconnect the ECU's harness connector. | Continuity of ECU ground circuit (12–Ground) | Continuity | ∞ Ω | Harness damaged or disconnected | Repair the harness |

NOTE
1. If confirmation of the diagnosis code or the input check code is possible, the ECU power-supply circuit can be considered to be normal, and therefore there is no need to check this chart.
2. When measuring terminal voltage or checking for continuity, do so by using an extra-thin probe for checking, and take care not to measure at the wrong terminal position.
3. If the results of the above checks are normal, the ECU power-supply circuit is normal.

**Fig. 29 Check Chart No. 0, ECU power supply wiring circuit. Colt Vista**

| Step | Check method | | Judgment | | Cause | Remedy |
|---|---|---|---|---|---|---|
| | Condition | Check object | Normal | Malfunction | | |
| 1 | Ignition switch : OFF Connector Ⓐ: separation RESUME switch : ON ⟷ OFF | Continuity between connector Ⓐ terminals (Y–B) | 0 Ω ⟷ ∞ Ω | Remains ∞ Ω; Remains 0 Ω | SET switch or harness damaged or disconnected, or short-circuit | Replace the part or repair the harness. |
| 2 | Ignition switch : OFF Connector Ⓐ: connection ECU connector : separation RESUME switch : ON ⟷ OFF | Continuity between ECU terminal and ground (10–Ground) | 0 Ω ⟷ ∞ Ω | Remains ∞ Ω | Damaged or disconnected wiring of B line, or of Y line between ECU and Ⓐ | Repair the harness |
| | | | | Remains 0 Ω | Short-circuit of Y line between ECU and Ⓐ | Repair the harness |

NOTE
1. When measuring terminal voltage or checking for continuity, do so by using the extra-thin probe for checking, and take care not to measure at the wrong terminal position.
2. If the results of the above checks are normal, the RESUME switch circuit is normal.

**Fig. 31 Check Chart No. 2, resume switch wiring circuit. Colt Vista**

| Step | Check method | | Judgment | | Cause | Remedy |
|---|---|---|---|---|---|---|
| | Condition | Check object | Normal | Malfunction | | |
| 1 | Ignition switch : OFF Connector Ⓐ: separation SET switch : ON ⟷ OFF | Continuity between connector Ⓐ terminals (R–B) | 0 Ω ⟷ ∞ Ω | Remains ∞ Ω; Remains 0 Ω | SET switch or harness damaged or disconnected, or short-circuit | Replace the part or repair the harness. |
| 2 | Ignition switch: OFF Connector Ⓐ: connection ECU connector: separation SET switch: ON ⟷ OFF | Continuity between ECU terminal and ground (8–Ground) | 0 Ω ⟷ ∞ Ω | Remains ∞ Ω | Damaged or disconnected wiring of B line, or of R line between ECU and Ⓐ | Repair the harness |
| | | | | Remains 0 Ω | Short-circuit of R line between ECU and Ⓐ | Repair the harness |

NOTE
1. When measuring terminal voltage or checking for continuity, do so by using an extra-thin probe for checking, and take care not to measure at the wrong terminal position.
2. If the results of the above checks are normal, the SET switch circuit is normal.

**Fig. 30 Check Chart No. 1, set switch wiring circuit. Colt Vista**

| Step | Check method | | Judgment | | Cause | Remedy |
|---|---|---|---|---|---|---|
| | Condition | Check object | Normal | Malfunction | | |
| 1 | Speed control main switch : OFF Manual driving | Speedometer indication error | During travel at 40 km/h (25 mph) $^{+4}_{0}$ km/h (±1.5 mph) | Exceeds allowable error range. Or, pointer oscillation is excessive. | Speedometer cable improperly arranged, or oil has entered. | Correct the speedometer cable layout, or replace the cable. |
| | | | | | Malfunction of the speedometer gear | Replace the speedometer gear. |
| 2 | Disconnect the transaxle installation part for the speedometer cable. Ignition switch : ON Speed control main switch : ON | ECU terminal voltage when inner cable of speedometer cable is turned slowly (7–Ground) | 3.5V or more ⟷ 0V (4 changes/inner cable rotation) | Remains 3.5V or more | Damaged or disconnected wiring of reed switch or of harness | Replace the part or repair the harness. |
| | | | | Remains 0V. | Short-circuit of reed switch or of harness | |
| | | | | Voltage changes are unstable. | Poor contact of connector terminal. | Check, and repair if necessary, the connector terminal contact pressure. |

NOTE
1. When measuring ECU terminal voltage, do so by using an extra-thin probe for checking, and take care not to measure at the wrong terminal position.
2. If the results of the above tests are all normal, the vehicle-speed sensor circuit is normal.

**Caution**
**When speedometer indication error is checked with a speedometer tester, apply chocks to the driven wheels to prevent the vehicle from running away.**

**Fig. 32 Check Chart No. 3, vehicle speed sensor wiring circuit. Colt Vista**

| Step | Check method | | Judgment | | Cause | Remedy |
|---|---|---|---|---|---|---|
| | Condition | Check object | Normal | Malfunction | | |
| 1 | Separate the ECU's harness connectors. Ignition switch : ON Speed control main switch : ON | Connector Ⓑ (harness side) terminal voltage when brake switch ON → OFF (LW–Ground) | Battery voltage ←→ 0V | Remains battery voltage. | Brake switch ON malfunction | Check the brake switch and replace it if defective. |
| | | | | Remains 0V | Damaged or disconnected wiring of brake switch | |
| | | | | | Harness damaged or disconnected or short-circuit | Repair the harness. |
| 2 | Ignition switch : OFF Separate the Ⓑ connector. | Resistance (clutch coil) between connector Ⓑ (actuator side) terminals (1-3) | Approx. 21.5Ω | ∞Ω | Damaged or disconnected wiring of clutch coil | Replace the actuator assembly. |
| | | | | Resistance value extremely low | Short-circuit of clutch coil | |
| 3 | Connect connector Ⓑ Connect the ECU's harness connectors. Ignition switch : ON Speed control switch: ON | ECU terminal voltage (3-Ground) | Battery voltage | Voltage extremely low | Short-circuit of ECU clutch drive transistor | Replace the ECU. |
| 4 | Ignition switch : OFF Separate the ECU's harness connectors. | Resistance (D.C. motor) between ECU harness side terminals (1→2*) | Approx. 12Ω | ∞Ω | Damaged or disconnected wiring of D.C. motor or of harness | Replace the actuator assembly or repair the harness. |
| | | | | Resistance value extremely low | Short-circuit of D.C motor coil | |

**Fig. 33 Check Chart No. 4, actuator wiring circuit. Colt Vista**

| Step | Check method | | Judgment | | Cause | Remedy |
|---|---|---|---|---|---|---|
| | Condition | Check object | Normal | Malfunction | | |
| 1 | Separate the ECU's harness connectors. Ignition switch : ON | Clutch switch connector terminal voltage (RL–Ground) | Battery voltage | 0V | Fuse damaged or disconnected | Replace the fuse. |
| | | | | | Damaged or disconnected wiring of the harness between ignition switch and clutch switch | Repair the harness. |
| 2 | Separate the ECU's harness connectors. Ignition switch : ON | ECU harness side connector terminal voltage when clutch switch is switched. ON → OFF (5–Ground) | Battery voltage ←→ 0V | Remains battery voltage. | Clutch switch ON malfunction | Replace the clutch switch. |
| | | | | Remains 0V. | Damaged or disconnected wiring of the clutch switch, or incorrect installation. | Replace the clutch switch, or correct the installation. |
| | | | | | Damaged or disconnected wiring of harness (GB line) | Repair the harness. |

NOTE
1. When measuring terminal voltage, do so by using an extra-thin probe for checking, and take care not to measure at the wrong terminal position.
2. If the results of the above checks are normal, the clutch switch circuit is normal.

**Fig. 35 Check chart No. 5-2, clutch switch wiring circuit M/T. Colt Vista**

| Step | Check method | | Judgment | | Cause | Remedy |
|---|---|---|---|---|---|---|
| | Condition | Check object | Normal | Malfunction | | |
| 1 | Separate the ECU's harness connectors. | ECU harness side connector terminal voltage (9–Ground) | Battery voltage | 0V | Damaged or disconnected wiring of the harness between fuse ② and ECU No. 9 terminal | Repair the harness. |
| | | | | | Fuse damaged or disconnected. | Replace the fuse. |
| 2 | Separate the ECU's harness connectors. Stop light switch : ON ←→ OFF | ECU harness side connector terminal voltage (13–Ground) | Battery voltage ←→ 0V | Remains battery voltage. | Stop light switch ON malfunction. | Replace the stop light switch. |
| | | | | Remains 0V | Damaged or disconnected wiring of the stop light switch, or incorrect installation. | Replace the stop light switch, or correct the installation. |
| | | | | | Harness damaged or disconnected. | Repair the harness. |

NOTE
1. When measuring ECU terminal voltage, do so by using an extra-thin probe for checking, and take care not to measure at the wrong terminal position.
2. If the results of the above tests are all normal, the stop light switch circuit is normal. (The stop lights should, however, illuminate also.)

**Fig. 34 Check chart No. 5-1, stop lamp switch wiring circuit. Colt Vista**

| Step | Check method | | Judgment | | Cause | Remedy |
|---|---|---|---|---|---|---|
| | Condition | Check object | Normal | Malfunction | | |
| 1 | Selector lever position: P or N | Does the starter turn over when the ignition key is turned to the START position? | Turns over | Doesn't turn over | Malfunction of the starter circuit | Starting System. |
| 2 | Selector lever position: D,2 or L | Does the starter turn over when the ignition key is turned to the START position? | Doesn't turn over | Turns over | Improper adjustment of inhibitor switch | Automatic Transaxle. |
| 3 | Separate the ECU's harness connectors. Selector lever position : P or N | Continuity between the ECU harness side connector terminal and ground (4-Ground) | Continuity | No continuity (∞Ω) | Damaged or disconnected wiring of harness (2-BY line) between ECU and inhibitor switch) | Repair the harness. |

NOTE
If the results of the above checks are normal, the inhibitor switch circuit is normal.

**Fig. 36 Check chart No. 5-3, inhibitor switch wiring circuit A/T. Colt Vista**

| Terminal No. | Signal | Conditions | Terminal voltage |
|---|---|---|---|
| 11 | Control unit power supply | When the cruise-control switch ("MAIN") is switched ON | VB |
| 10 | Control unit ground | At all times | 0V |

VB: Battery Voltage

**Fig. 37 Check Chart No. 0, check chart. Conquest**

| Terminal No. | Signal | Conditions | Terminal voltage |
|---|---|---|---|
| 2 | SET switch | When the SET switch is switched ON | 0V |
| | | When the SET switch is switched OFF | VB |

VB: Battery Voltage

**Fig. 38 Check Chart No. 1, set switch wiring circuit. Conquest**

| Terminal No. | Signal | Conditions | Terminal voltage |
|---|---|---|---|
| 1 | RESUME switch | When the RESUME switch is switched ON | 0V |
| | | When the RESUME switch is switched OFF | VB |

VB: Battery Voltage

**Fig. 39 Check Chart No. 2, resume switch wiring circuit. Conquest**

| Terminal No. | Signal | Conditions | Terminal voltage |
|---|---|---|---|
| 3 | Vehicle-speed sensor | Set the select lever to the "D" range or "1" range, and move the vehicle forward slowly. | 0V – 0.6 V ↑ Flashing ↓ 2V or higher |

**Fig. 40 Check Chart No. 3, vehicle speed sensor wiring circuit. Conquest**

| Terminal No. | Signal | Conditions | Terminal voltage |
|---|---|---|---|
| 4 | Actuator (control valve) | Auto-cruise control MAIN switch ON | VB |
| 12 | Actuator (release valve) | Auto-cruise control MAIN switch ON | VB |

VB: Battery Voltage

**Fig. 41 Check Chart No. 4, actuator wiring circuit. Conquest**

| Terminal No. | Signal | Conditions | Terminal voltage |
|---|---|---|---|
| 8 | Stop light switch (power supply side) | At all times | VB |
| 9 | Stop light switch (load side) | When the brake pedal is depressed | VB |
| | | When the brake pedal is not depressed | 0V |
| 5 | Stop light switch (load side) | When the brake pedal is depressed (MAIN switch ON) | 0V |
| | | When the brake pedal is not depressed (MAIN switch ON) | VB |

VB: Battery Voltage

**Fig. 42 Check Chart No. 5-1, stop light switch wiring circuit. Conquest**

| Terminal No. | Signal | Conditions | Terminal voltage |
|---|---|---|---|
| 7 | Clutch switch | When the clutch pedal is depressed | VB |
| | | When the clutch pedal is not depressed | 0V |

VB: Battery Voltage

**Fig. 43 Check Chart No. 5-2, clutch switch wiring circuit. Conquest**

| Terminal No. | Signal | Conditions | Terminal voltage |
|---|---|---|---|
| 7 | Inhibitor switch | At all times | VB |

VB: Battery Voltage

**Fig. 44 Check Chart No. 5-3, inhibitor switch wiring circuit. Conquest**

| Terminal No. | Signal | Conditions | Terminal voltage |
|---|---|---|---|
| 2 | Control unit power supply | When the auto-cruise control switch (CRUISE) is switched ON | System voltage |
| 8, 14 | Control unit ground | At all times | 0V |
| 16 | Control unit backup power supply | At all times | System voltage |

**Fig. 45 Check Chart No. 1, control unit power supply circuit. 1990–91 Colt & Eagle Summit**

| Terminal No. | Signal | Conditions | Terminal voltage |
|---|---|---|---|
| 17 | SET switch | When the SET switch is switched ON | 0V |
| | | When the SET switch is switched OFF | System voltage |

**Fig. 46 Check Chart No. 2, set switch wiring circuit. 1990–91 Colt & Eagle Summit**

| Terminal No. | Signal | Conditions | Terminal voltage |
|---|---|---|---|
| 23 | Auto-cruise control (CRUISE) indicator light | When auto-cruise control is active | System voltage |
| | | When auto-cruise control is inactive | 0V |

**Fig. 48 Check Chart No. 4, indicator light wiring circuit. 1990–91 Colt & Eagle Summit**

| Terminal No. | Signal | Conditions | Terminal voltage |
|---|---|---|---|
| 9 | Release valve drive signal | When release valve is ON | 0V |
| | | When release valve is OFF | System voltage |
| 13 | Control valve drive signal | When control valve is ON | 0V |
| | | When control valve is OFF | System voltage |
| 26 | DC motor drive signal | When DC motor is driven | 0V |
| | | When DC motor is stopped | System voltage |
| 25 | Surge absorption circuit terminal | When control switch is ON | System voltage |

**Fig. 50 Check Chart No. 6, vacuum pump drive wiring circuit. 1990–91 Colt & Eagle Summit**

| Terminal No. | Signal | Conditions | Terminal voltage |
|---|---|---|---|
| 18 | RESUME switch | When the RESUME switch is switched ON | 0V |
| | | When the RESUME switch is switched OFF | System voltage |

**Fig. 47 Check Chart No. 3, resume switch wiring circuit. 1990–91 Colt & Eagle Summit**

| Terminal No. | Signal | Conditions | Terminal voltage |
|---|---|---|---|
| 19 | Vehicle speed sensor | Move the vehicle forward slowly. | 0V – 0.6V ↕ Flashing 2V or higher |

**Fig. 49 Check Chart No. 5, vehicle speed sensor wiring circuit. 1990–91 Colt & Eagle Summit**

| Terminal No. | Signal | Conditions | Terminal voltage |
|---|---|---|---|
| 15 | Stop light switch | When brake pedal is depressed | System voltage |
| | | When brake pedal is not depressed | 0V |

NOTE
(1) NC: Indicates ON at all times.
(2) NO: Indicates OFF at all times.

**Fig. 51 Check Chart No. 7, stop light switch wiring circuit. 1990–91 Colt & Eagle Summit**

| Terminal No. | Signal | Conditions | Terminal voltage |
|---|---|---|---|
| 1 | Clutch switch | When clutch pedal is depressed | 0V |
| | | When clutch pedal is not depressed | System voltage |

**Fig. 52 Check Chart No. 8, clutch switch wiring circuit M/T. 1990–91 Colt & Eagle Summit**

| Terminal No. | Signal | Conditions | Terminal voltage |
|---|---|---|---|
| 1 | Inhibitor switch | Inhibitor switch is at "N" or "P" position | 0V |
| | | Inhibitor switch is at "D", "2", "L" or "R" position | System voltage |

**Fig. 53 Check Chart No. 9, inhibitor switch wiring circuit A/T. 1990–91 Colt & Eagle Summit**

| Terminal No. | Signal | Conditions | Terminal voltage |
|---|---|---|---|
| 4 | Idle switch | When accelerator pedal is depressed | System voltage |
| | | When accelerator pedal is not depressed | 0V |
| 5 | Throttle position sensor | When accelerator is in idling position | 0.45 to 0.55V |
| | | When accelerator is in fully opened position | 4.5 to 5.5V |

**Fig. 54 Check Chart No. 10, throttle position sensor & idle switch wiring circuit. 1990–91 Colt & Eagle Summit**

| Terminal No. | Signal | Conditions | Terminal voltage |
|---|---|---|---|
| 3 | Accelerator pedal switch control power supply | When ignition switch is switched ON | System voltage |
| 9 | Accelerator pedal switch | When accelerator pedal is depressed | 0V |
| | | When accelerator pedal is not depressed | System voltage |

**Fig. 55 Check Chart No. 11, accelerator switch Off function related circuits. 1990–91 Colt & Eagle Summit**

| Terminal No. | Signal | Conditions | Terminal voltage |
|---|---|---|---|
| 3 | Overdrive signal control power supply | When ignition switch is switched ON | System voltage |
| 10 | 4 A/T control unit | When overdrive is ON | System voltage |
| | | When overdrive is OFF | 0V |
| 11 | Overdrive switch | When overdrive switch is ON | System voltage |
| | | When overdrive switch is OFF | 0V |

**Fig. 56 Check Chart No. 12, overdrive cancellation function related circuits. 1990–91 Colt & Eagle Summit**

| Terminal No. | Signal name | Condition | Terminal voltage |
|---|---|---|---|
| 2 | Control unit power supply | Main switch ON and neutral position thereafter | System voltage |
| | | Main switch OFF and neutral position thereafter | 0V |
| 8, 14 | Control unit ground | At all times | 0V |
| 16 | Control unit back up power supply | At all times | System voltage |

**Fig. 57 Check Chart No. 1, control unit power supply circuit. 1991 Stealth**

| Terminal No. | Signal name | Condition | Terminal voltage |
|---|---|---|---|
| 18 | Control switch | When all switches are OFF | 0V |
| | | When SET switch is ON | 3V |
| | | When RESUME switch is ON | 6V |
| | | When CANCEL switch is ON | System voltage |

**Fig. 58 Check Chart No. 2, control switch wiring circuit. 1991 Stealth**

| Terminal No. | Signal name | Condition | Terminal voltage |
|---|---|---|---|
| 23 | Cruise control (CRUISE) indicator light | When cruise control is active | System voltage |
| | | When cruise control is inactive | 0V |

**Fig. 59 Check Chart No. 3, indicator light wiring circuit. 1991 Stealth**

| Terminal No. | Signal name | Condition | Terminal voltage |
|---|---|---|---|
| 19 | Vehicle speed sensor | Slowly drive forward with SELECT lever at "D" or "1st Speed" | 0 to 0.6V ↕ Flashing 2V or more |

**Fig. 60 Check Chart No. 4, vehicle speed sensor wiring circuit. 1991 Stealth**

| Terminal No. | Signal name | Condition | Terminal voltage |
|---|---|---|---|
| 12 | Relief valve drive signal | When relief valve is ON | 0V |
| | | When relief valve is OFF | System voltage |
| 13 | Control valve drive signal | When control valve is ON | 0V |
| | | When control valve is OFF | System voltage |
| 26 | DC motor drive signal | When DC motor is running | 0V |
| | | When DC motor is stationary | System voltage |
| 25 | Surge absorption circuit terminal | When main switch is ON | System voltage |

**Fig. 61 Check Chart No. 5, vacuum pump drive wiring circuit. 1991 Stealth**

| Terminal No. | Signal name | Condition | Terminal voltage |
|---|---|---|---|
| 1 | Inhibitor switch | Inhibitor switch in "N" or "P" position | 0V |
| | | Inhibitor switch in "D", "2", "L" or "R" position | System voltage |

**Fig. 64 Check Chart No. 8, inhibitor switch wiring circuit A/T. 1991 Stealth**

| Terminal No. | Signal name | Condition | Terminal voltage |
|---|---|---|---|
| 15 | Stop light switch | When brake pedal is depressed | System voltage |
| | | When brake pedal is not depressed | 0V |

**Fig. 62 Check Chart No. 6, stop light switch wiring circuit. 1991 Stealth**

| Terminal No. | Signal name | Condition | Terminal voltage |
|---|---|---|---|
| 1 | Clutch switch | When clutch pedal is depressed | 0V |
| | | When clutch pedal is not depressed | System voltage |

**Fig. 63 Check Chart No. 7, clutch switch wiring circuit M/T. 1991 Stealth**

| Terminal No. | Signal name | Condition | Terminal voltage |
|---|---|---|---|
| 4 | Idle switch | When accelerator pedal is depressed | 0V |
| | | When accelerator pedal is not depressed | 4.5 – 5.5V |
| 5 | Throttle position sensor | During idle | 0.48 – 0.72V |
| | | When fully opened | 4.0 – 5.5V |

**Fig. 65 Check Chart No. 9, throttle position sensor & idle switch wiring circuit. 1991 Stealth**

| Terminal No. | Signal name | Condition | Terminal voltage |
|---|---|---|---|
| 3 | Accelerator pedal switch control power supply | When ignition switch is placed at ON | System voltage |
| 9 | Accelerator pedal switch | When accelerator pedal is depressed | 0V |
| | | When accelerator pedal is not depressed | System voltage |

**Fig. 66 Check Chart No. 10, accelerator switch Off function related circuits. 1991 Stealth**

| Terminal No. | Signal name | Condition | Terminal voltage |
|---|---|---|---|
| 3 | OD signal control power supply | When ignition switch is ON | System voltage |
| 10 | ELC-4A/T control unit | When overdrive mode is active | System voltage |
| | | When overdrive mode is inactive | .0V |
| 11 | OD switch | When OD switch is ON | System voltage |
| | | When OD switch is OFF | 0V |

**Fig. 67 Check Chart No. 11, overdrive cancellation function related circuits. 1991 Stealth**

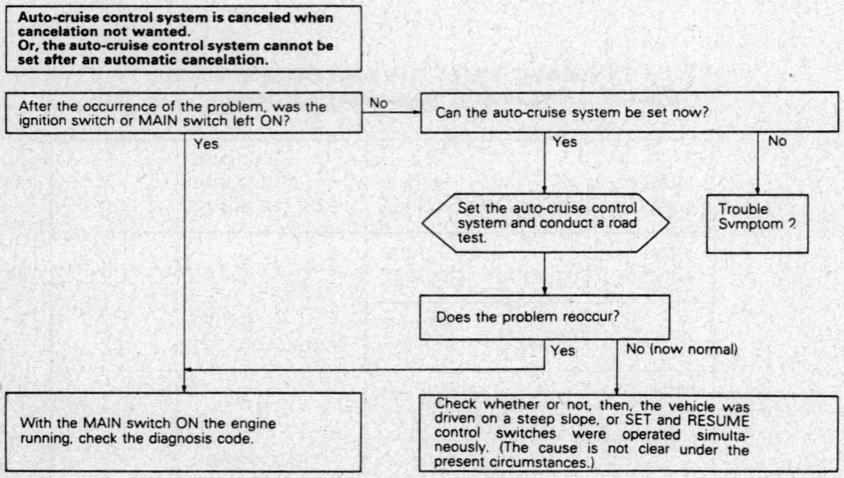

**Auto-cruise control system is canceled when cancelation not wanted.**
**Or, the auto-cruise control system cannot be set after an automatic cancelation.**

After the occurrence of the problem, was the ignition switch or MAIN switch left ON?

- Yes → With the MAIN switch ON the engine running, check the diagnosis code.
- No → Can the auto-cruise system be set now?
  - No → Trouble Symptom 2
  - Yes → Set the auto-cruise control system and conduct a road test. → Does the problem reoccur?
    - Yes → With the MAIN switch ON the engine running, check the diagnosis code.
    - No (now normal) → Check whether or not, then, the vehicle was driven on a steep slope, or SET and RESUME control switches were operated simultaneously. (The cause is not clear under the present circumstances.)

**Fig. 68 Symptom diagnosis chart (Part 1 of 4). Colt Vista, Conquest & 1989 Colt & Eagle Summit**

**Auto-cruise control system cannot be set.**

NOTE
If, after the occurrence of the problem, the ignition switch and the main switch have not been switched OFF, it is possible to determine (by checking the diagnosis output code) which circuit canceled the system's operation.
This chart is to be used, then, for troubleshooting if it is not possible to use the self-diagnosis for checking.

Prepare to conduct input check.

Were codes No. 21, 22 and 25 displayed when, with the vehicle stationary, the input check codes were recalled?

- No →
  - Damaged or disconnected wiring of the ECU power-supply circuit Go to check cahrt 0
  - Damaged or disconnected wiring of the SET or RESUME switch Go to check chart 1 and 2.
- Yes → Are the results of all input checks normal?
  - Yes → Check the actuator circuit. Go to check chart No. 4
  - No →

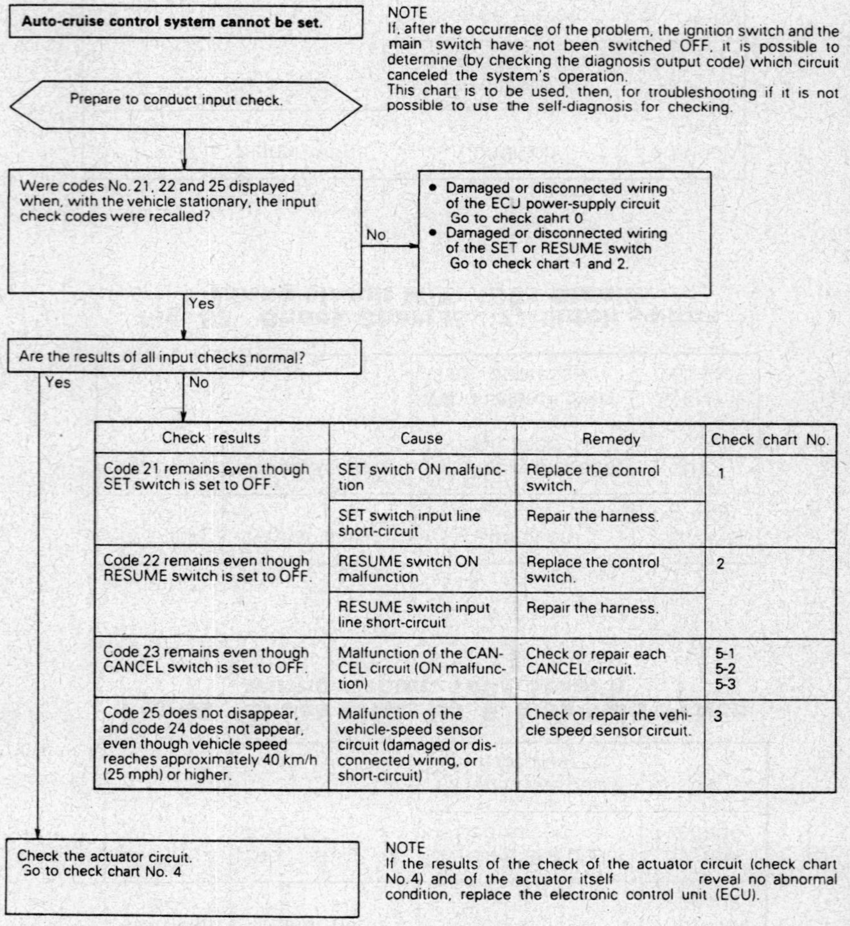

| Check results | Cause | Remedy | Check chart No. |
|---|---|---|---|
| Code 21 remains even though SET switch is set to OFF. | SET switch ON malfunction | Replace the control switch. | 1 |
| | SET switch input line short-circuit | Repair the harness. | |
| Code 22 remains even though RESUME switch is set to OFF. | RESUME switch ON malfunction | Replace the control switch. | 2 |
| | RESUME switch input line short-circuit | Repair the harness. | |
| Code 23 remains even though CANCEL switch is set to OFF. | Malfunction of the CANCEL circuit (ON malfunction) | Check or repair each CANCEL circuit. | 5-1<br>5-2<br>5-3 |
| Code 25 does not disappear, and code 24 does not appear, even though vehicle speed reaches approximately 40 km/h (25 mph) or higher. | Malfunction of the vehicle-speed sensor circuit (damaged or disconnected wiring, or short-circuit) | Check or repair the vehicle speed sensor circuit. | 3 |

Check the actuator circuit.
Go to check chart No. 4

NOTE
If the results of the check of the actuator circuit (check chart No. 4) and of the actuator itself reveal no abnormal condition, replace the electronic control unit (ECU).

**Fig. 68 Symptom diagnosis chart (Part 2 of 4). Colt Vista, Conquest & 1989 Colt & Eagle Summit**

| No. | Trouble symptom | Cause | Check method | Remedy |
|---|---|---|---|---|
| 3 | • The set vehicle speed varies greatly upward or downward.<br>• "Hunching" (repeated alternating acceleration and deceleration) occurs after setting is made. | Malfunction of the vehicle speed sensor circuit | Check by using check chart No.3 | Repair the vehicle-speed sensor system, or replace the part. |
| | | Malfunction of the speedometer cable or speedometer drive gear | | |
| | | Actuator circuit poor contact | Check by using check chart No.4 | Repair the actuator system, or replace the part. |
| | | Malfunction of the actuator | | |
| | | Malfunction of the ECU | – | Replace the ECU. |
| 4 | The auto-cruise control system is not canceled when the brake pedal is depressed. | Damaged or disconnected wiring of the stop light switch; brake switch (for auto-cruise control) ON malfunction (short-circuit) | If the input check code No.23 indicates a malfunction, check by using check chart No.5 – 1 | Repair the harness or replace the stop light switch. |
| | | Actuator clutch coil drive circuit short circuit | Check by using check chart No.4 | Repair the harness or replace the actuator. |
| | | Malfunction of the ECU | – | Replace the ECU. |
| 5 | The auto-cruise control system is not canceled when the clutch pedal is depressed. (Vehicles with a manual transaxle) (It is canceled, however, when the brake pedal is depressed.) | Damaged or disconnected wiring of clutch switch input circuit | If the input check code No.23 indicates a malfunction, check by using check chart No.5 – 2 | Repair the harness, or repair or replace the clutch switch. |
| | | Clutch switch installation malfunction (won't switch ON) | | |
| | | Malfunction of the ECU | – | Replace the ECU. |
| 6 | The auto-cruise control system is not canceled when the shift lever is moved to the "N" position. (Vehicles with an automatic transaxle) (It is canceled, however, when the brake pedal is depressed.) | Damaged or disconnected wiring of inhibitor switch input circuit | If the input check code No.23 indicates a malfunction, check by using check chart No.5 – 3 | Repair the harness, or repair or replace the inhibitor switch. |
| | | Improper adjustment of inhibitor switch | | |
| | | Malfunction of the ECU | – | Replace the ECU. |
| 7 | Cannot decelerate (coast) by using the SET switch. | Temporary damaged or disconnected wiring of SET switch input circuit | Check by using check chart No.1 | Repair the harness or replace the SET switch. |
| | | Actuator circuit poor contact | Check by using check chart No.4 | Repair the harness or replace the actuator. |
| | | Malfunction of the actuator | | |
| | | Malfunction of the ECU | – | Replace the ECU. |
| 8 | Cannot accelerate or resume speed by using the RESUME switch. | Damaged or disconnected wiring, or short-circuit, of RESUME switch input circuit | Check by using check chart No.2 | Repair the harness or replace the RESUME switch |
| | | Actuator circuit poor contact | Check by using check chart No.4 | Repair the harness or replace the actuator. |
| | | Malfunction of the actuator | | |
| | | Malfunction of the ECU | – | Replace the ECU |

**Fig. 68 Symptom diagnosis chart (Part 3 of 4). Colt Vista, Conquest & 1989 Colt & Eagle Summit**

| No. | Trouble symptom | Cause | Check method | Remedy |
|---|---|---|---|---|
| 9 | Auto-cruise control system can be set while traveling at a vehicle speed of less than 40 km/h (25 mph), or there is no automatic cancelation at that speed. | Malfunction of the vehicle-speed sensor circuit | Check by using check chart No.3 | Repair the vehicle-speed sensor system, or replace the part. |
| | | Malfunction of the speedometer cable or the speedometer drive gear | | |
| | | Malfunction of the ECU | – | Replace the ECU. |
| 10 | The control switch indicator light does not illuminate. (But auto-cruise control system is normal.) | Broken light-emitting diode of the control switch indicator | – | Raeplace the control switch. |

**Fig. 68 Symptom diagnosis chart (Part 4 of 4). Colt Vista, Conquest & 1989 Colt & Eagle Summit**

Auto-cruise control system is canceled when cancellation not wanted.
Or, the auto-cruise control system cannot be set after an automatic cancellation.

Check diagnosis output.
↓
Does diagnosis output check good? — No → Based on diagnosis output code, check circuit and individual parts.
↓ Yes
Can the auto-cruise control system be set now? — No → Refer to "Auto-cruise control system cannot be set".
↓ Yes
Set the auto-cruise control system and conduct a road test.
↓
Did the problem reoccur? — Yes → Check diagnosis output.
No (new normal) → AUTO CANCEL might have been activated by traveling on a steep slope, or temporary loose contact of connector might have occurred.

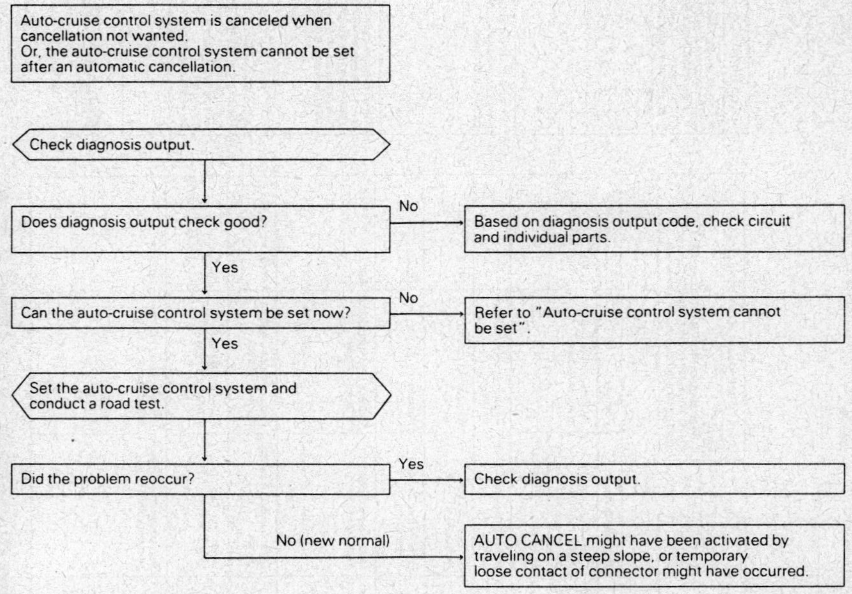

**Fig. 69 Symptom diagnosis chart (Part 1 of 4). 1990–91 Colt & Eagle Summit**

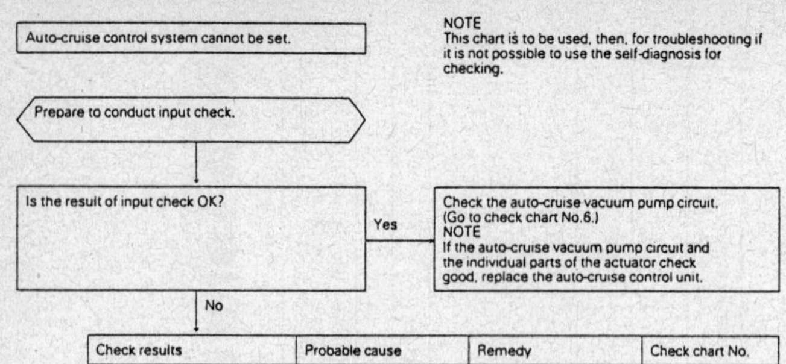
Auto-cruise control system cannot be set.
NOTE
This chart is to be used, then, for troubleshooting if it is not possible to use the self-diagnosis for checking.
Prepare to conduct input check.
Is the result of input check OK?
Yes
Check the auto-cruise vacuum pump circuit. (Go to check chart No.6.)
NOTE
If the auto-cruise vacuum pump circuit and the individual parts of the actuator check good, replace the auto-cruise control unit.
No

| Check results | Probable cause | Remedy | Check chart No. |
|---|---|---|---|
| Even if an attempt is made to enter data, no code appears. | Open circuit in auto-cruise control unit power supply circuit | Replace control switch or repair harness. | No. 1 |
| | Open circuit in control switch circuit | | |
| | Defective auto-cruise control unit | Replace auto-cruise control unit. | – |
| Code No. 21 remains even though SET switch is set to OFF. | SET switch ON malfunction | Replace the control switch. | No. 2 |
| Code No. 22 remains even though RESUME switch is set to OFF. | RESUME switch ON malfunction | Replace the control switch. | No. 3 |
| Code No. 23 does not appear when brake pedal is depressed. | Defective stop light switch circuit | Replace stop light switch or repair harness. | No. 7 |
| Code No. 23 does not disappear when brake pedal is released. | | | |
| Code No. 26 does not disappear when clutch pedal is released. <M/T> | Defective clutch switch circuit | Replace clutch switch or repair harness. | No. 8 |
| Code No. 26 does not disappear when SELECT lever is placed in a position other than "N" and "P". <A/T> | Defective inhibitor switch circuit | Replace inhibitor switch or repair harness. | No. 9 |
| Code No. 25 does not appear when vehicle is traveling at less than 40 km/h (25 mph). | Defective vehicle speed sensor circuit | Check or repair vehicle speed sensor circuit. | No. 5 |
| Code No. 25 does not disappear or code No. 24 does not appear when vehicle speed is increased to more than approximately 40 km/h (25 mph). | | | |

**Fig. 69 Symptom diagnosis chart (Part 2 of 4). 1990–91 Colt & Eagle Summit**

| Trouble symptom | Probable cause | Check chart No. | Remedy |
|---|---|---|---|
| Cannot decelerate by using the SET switch. | Temporary damaged or disconnected wiring of SET switch input circuit | No. 2 | Repair the harness or replace the SET switch. |
| | Auto-cruise vacuum pump circuit poor contact | No. 6 | Repair the harness or replace the auto-cruise vacuum pump and actuator. |
| | Malfunction of the auto-cruise vacuum pump and actuator (including blocking of negative pressure passage) | | |
| | Malfunction of the auto-cruise control unit | – | Replace the auto-cruise control unit. |
| Cannot accelerate or resume speed by using the RESUME switch. | Open or short circuit in RESUME switch circuit in control switch | No. 3 | Replace the control switch. |
| | Auto-cruise vacuum pump circuit poor contact | No. 6 | Repair the harness or replace the auto-cruise vacuum pump and actuator. |
| | Malfunction of the auto-cruise vacuum pump and actuator (including air leaks from negative pressure passage) | | |
| | Malfunction of the auto-cruise control unit | – | Replace the auto-cruise control unit. |
| Auto-cruise control system can be set while traveling at a vehicle speed of less than 40 km/h (25 mph), or there is no automatic cancellation at that speed. | Malfunction of the vehicle speed sensor circuit | No. 5 | Repair the vehicle speed sensor system, or replace the part. |
| | Malfunction of the speedometer cable or the speedometer drive gear | | |
| | Malfunction of the auto-cruise control unit | – | Replace the auto-cruise control unit. |
| The auto-cruise control switch indicator light does not illuminate. (But auto-cruise control system is normal.) | Damaged or disconnected bulb of auto-cruise control switch indicator | No. 4 | Repair the harness or replace the control switch. |
| | Harness damaged or disconnected | | |
| Malfunction of control function by ON/OFF switching of 4 A/T accelerator switch. (Non-operation of damper clutch, 2nd gear hold, etc.) | Malfunction of circuit related to accelerator switch OFF function | No. 11 | Repair the harness or replace the part. |
| | Malfunction of the auto-cruise control unit | | |
| Overdrive is not canceled during fixed speed driving. <A/T> | Malfunction of circuit related to overdrive cancellation, or malfunction of auto-cruise control unit | No. 12 | Repair the harness or replace the part. |
| No shift to overdrive during manual driving. <A/T> | | | |
| The auto-cruise control indicator light does not illuminate. (But auto-cruise control system is normal.) | Damaged or disconnected bulb of indicator light | No. 4 | Repair the harness or replace the bulb. |
| | Harness damaged or disconnected | | |

**Fig. 69 Symptom diagnosis chart (Part 4 of 4). 1990–91 Colt & Eagle Summit**

| Trouble symptom | Probable cause | Check chart No. | Remedy |
|---|---|---|---|
| • The set vehicle speed varies greatly upward or downward. • "Hunching" (repeated alternating acceleration and deceleration) occurs after setting is made. | Malfunction of the vehicle speed sensor circuit | No. 5 | Repair the vehicle speed sensor system, or replace the part. |
| | Malfunction of the speedometer cable or speedometer drive gear | | |
| | Auto-cruise vacuum pump circuit poor contact | No. 6 | Repair the auto-cruise vacuum pump system, or replace the part. |
| | Malfunction of the auto-cruise vacuum pump | | |
| | Malfunction of the auto-cruise control unit | – | Replace the auto-cruise control unit. |
| The auto-cruise control system is not canceled when the brake pedal is depressed. | Brake switch (for auto-cruise control) malfunction (short-circuit) | No. 7 | Repair the harness or replace the stop light switch. |
| | Auto-cruise vacuum pump drive circuit short-circuit | No. 6 | Repair the harness or replace the auto-cruise vacuum pump. |
| | Malfunction of the auto-cruise control unit | – | Replace the auto-cruise control unit. |
| The auto-cruise control system is not canceled when the clutch pedal is depressed. <M/T> (It is canceled, however, when the brake pedal is depressed.) | Damaged or disconnected wiring of clutch switch input circuit | If the input check code No. 26 indicates a malfunction. No. 8 | Repair the harness, or repair or replace the clutch switch. |
| | Clutch switch improper installation (won't switch ON) | | |
| | Malfunction of the auto-cruise control unit | – | Replace the auto-cruise control unit. |
| The auto-cruise control system is not canceled when the shift lever is moved to the "N" position. <A/T> (It is canceled, however, when the brake pedal is depressed.) | Damaged or disconnected wiring of inhibitor switch input circuit | If the input check code No. 26 indicates a malfunction. No. 9 | Repair the harness, or repair or replace the inhibitor switch. |
| | Improper adjustment of inhibitor switch | | |
| | Malfunction of the auto-cruise control unit | – | Replace the auto-cruise control unit. |

**Fig. 69 Symptom diagnosis chart (Part 3 of 4). 1990–91 Colt & Eagle Summit**

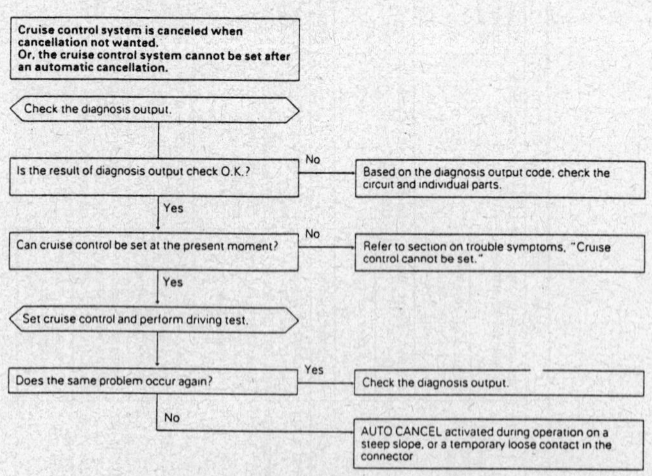
Cruise control system is canceled when cancellation not wanted.
Or, the cruise control system cannot be set after an automatic cancellation.
Check the diagnosis output.
Is the result of diagnosis output check O.K.?
No
Based on the diagnosis output code, check the circuit and individual parts.
Yes
Can cruise control be set at the present moment?
No
Refer to section on trouble symptoms, "Cruise control cannot be set."
Yes
Set cruise control and perform driving test.
Does the same problem occur again?
Yes
Check the diagnosis output.
No
AUTO CANCEL activated during operation on a steep slope, or a temporary loose contact in the connector

**Fig. 70 Symptom diagnosis chart (Part 1 of 4). 1991 Stealth**

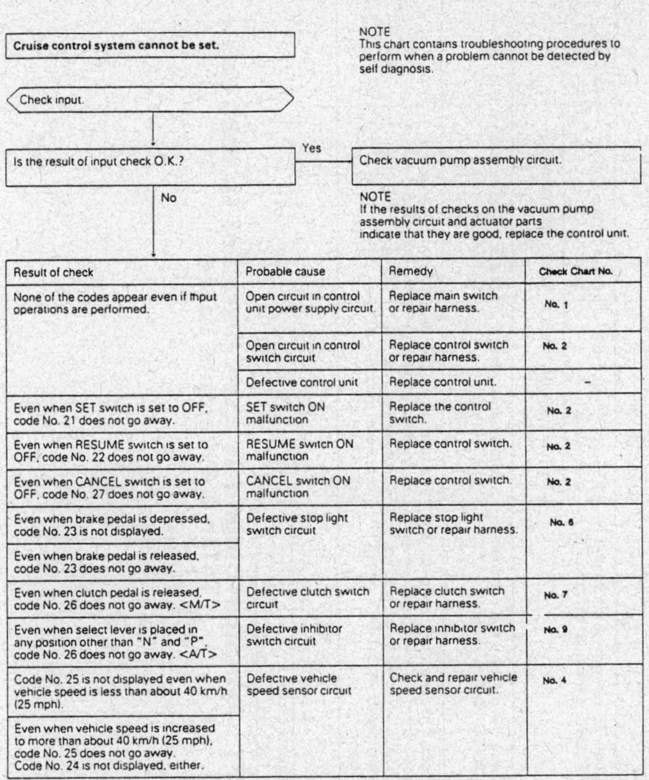

Cruise control system cannot be set.
NOTE
This chart contains troubleshooting procedures to perform when a problem cannot be detected by self diagnosis.
Check input.
Is the result of input check O.K.?
Yes
Check vacuum pump assembly circuit.
No
NOTE
If the results of checks on the vacuum pump assembly circuit and actuator parts indicate that they are good, replace the control unit.

| Result of check | Probable cause | Remedy | Check Chart No. |
|---|---|---|---|
| None of the codes appear even if input operations are performed. | Open circuit in control unit power supply circuit. | Replace main switch or repair harness. | No. 1 |
| | Open circuit in control switch circuit | Replace control switch or repair harness. | No. 2 |
| | Defective control unit | Replace control unit. | – |
| Even when SET switch is set to OFF, code No. 21 does not go away. | SET switch ON malfunction | Replace the control switch. | No. 2 |
| Even when RESUME switch is set to OFF, code No. 22 does not go away. | RESUME switch ON malfunction | Replace control switch. | No. 2 |
| Even when CANCEL switch is set to OFF, code No. 27 does not go away. | CANCEL switch ON malfunction | Replace control switch. | No. 2 |
| Even when brake pedal is depressed, code No. 23 is not displayed. | Defective stop light switch circuit | Replace stop light switch or repair harness. | No. 6 |
| Even when brake pedal is released, code No. 23 does not go away. | | | |
| Even when clutch pedal is released, code No. 26 does not go away. <M/T> | Defective clutch switch circuit | Replace clutch switch or repair harness. | No. 7 |
| Even when select lever is placed in any position other than "N" and "P", code No. 26 does not go away. <A/T> | Defective inhibitor switch circuit | Replace inhibitor switch or repair harness. | No. 9 |
| Code No. 25 is not displayed even when vehicle speed is less than about 40 km/h (25 mph). | Defective vehicle speed sensor circuit | Check and repair vehicle speed sensor circuit. | No. 4 |
| Even when vehicle speed is increased to more than about 40 km/h (25 mph), code No. 25 does not go away. Code No. 24 is not displayed, either. | | | |

**Fig. 70 Symptom diagnosis chart (Part 2 of 4). 1991 Stealth**

| Trouble symptom | Probable cause | Check chart No. | Remedy |
|---|---|---|---|
| • The set vehicle speed varies greatly upward or downward. • "Hunching" (repeated alternating acceleration and deceleration) occurs after setting is made. | Malfunction of the vehicle speed sensor circuit | No. 4 | Repair the vehicle speed sensor system, or replace the part. |
| | Malfunction of the speedometer cable or speedometer drive gear <Non turbo> | | |
| | Vacuum pump assembly circuit poor contact | No. 5 | Repair the actuator system, or replace the part. |
| | Malfunction of the vacuum pump assembly (including air leaks from negative pressure passage) | | |
| | Malfunction of the ECU | – | Replace the ECU. |
| The cruise control system is not canceled when the brake pedal is depressed. | Brake switch (for cruise control) malfunction (short-circuit) | No. 6 | Repair the harness or replace the stop light switch. |
| | Vacuum pump assembly drive circuit short-circuit | No. 5 | Repair the harness or replace the vacuum pump assembly. |
| | Malfunction of the ECU | – | Replace the ECU. |
| The cruise control system is not canceled when the clutch pedal is depressed. <M/T> (It is canceled, however, when the brake pedal is depressed.) | Damaged or disconnected wiring of clutch switch input circuit | If the input check code No. 26 indicates a malfunction. No. 7 | Repair the harness, or repair or replace the clutch switch. |
| | Clutch switch improper installation (won't switch ON) | | |
| | Malfunction of the ECU | – | Replace the ECU. |
| The cruise control system is not canceled when the shift lever is moved to the "N" position. <A/T> (It is canceled, however, when the brake pedal is depressed.) | Damaged or disconnected wiring of inhibitor switch input circuit | If the input check code No. 26 indicates a malfunction. No. 8 | Repair the harness, or repair or replace the inhibitor switch. |
| | Improper adjustment of inhibitor switch | | |
| | Malfunction of the ECU | – | Replace the ECU. |
| Cannot decelerate by using the SET switch. | Temporary damaged or disconnected wiring of control switch input circuit | No. 2 | Repair the harness or replace the control switch. |
| | Vacuum pump assembly circuit poor contact | No. 5 | Repair the harness or replace the vacuum pump assembly. |
| | Malfunction of the vacuum pump assembly | | |
| | Malfunction of the ECU | – | Replace the ECU. |

NOTE
ECU: Electronic control unit

**Fig. 70 Symptom diagnosis chart (Part 3 of 4). 1991 Stealth**

| Trouble symptom | Probable cause | Check chart No. | Remedy |
|---|---|---|---|
| Cannot accelerate or resume speed by using the RESUME switch. | Open or short circuit in RESUME switch circuit in control switch | No. 2 | Replace the control switch. |
| | Vacuum pump assembly circuit poor contact | No. 5 | Repair the harness or replace the vacuum pump assembly. |
| | Malfunction of the vacuum pump assembly (including air leaks from negative pressure passage) | | |
| | Malfunction of the ECU | – | Replace the ECU. |
| Even when CANCEL switch is set to ON, cruise control is not canceled (Cruise control, however, is canceled when brake pedal is depressed.) | Open or short circuit in CANCEL switch circuit in control switch | If the input check code No. 27 indicates a malfunction. No. 2 | Replace the control switch. |
| | Malfunction of the ECU | – | Replace the ECU |
| The cruise control system can be set while traveling at a vehicle speed of less than 40 km/h (25 mph), or there is no automatic cancellation at that speed. | Malfunction of the vehicle-speed sensor circuit | No. 4 | Repair the vehicle speed sensor system, or replace the part. |
| | Malfunction of the speedometer cable or the speedometer drive gear <Non turbo> | | |
| | Malfunction of the ECU | – | Replace the ECU. |
| The cruise control indicator light of the combination meter does not illuminate. (But cruise control system is normal) | Damaged or disconnected bulb of indicator light | No. 3 | Repair the harness or replace the light bulb. |
| | Harness damaged or disconnected | | |
| | Malfunction of the ECU | – | Replace the ECU. |
| Cruise control ON indicator light does not come on. (However, cruise control is functional.) | Burned-out indicator light bulb | No. 3 | Repair the harness or replace the main switch. |
| | Open or short circuit in harness | | |
| Malfunction of control function by ON/OFF switching of ELC 4 A/T accelerator switch. (Non-operation of damper clutch, 2nd gear hold, etc.) | Malfunction of circuit related to accelerator switch OFF function | No. 10 | Repair the harness or replace the part. |
| | Malfunction of the ECU | | |
| Overdrive is not canceled during fixed speed driving <A/T> | Malfunction of circuit related to overdrive cancellation, or malfunction of ECU | No. 11 | Repair the harness or replace the part. |
| No shift to overdrive during manual driving. <A/T> | | | |

**Fig. 70 Symptom diagnosis chart (Part 4 of 4). 1991 Stealth**

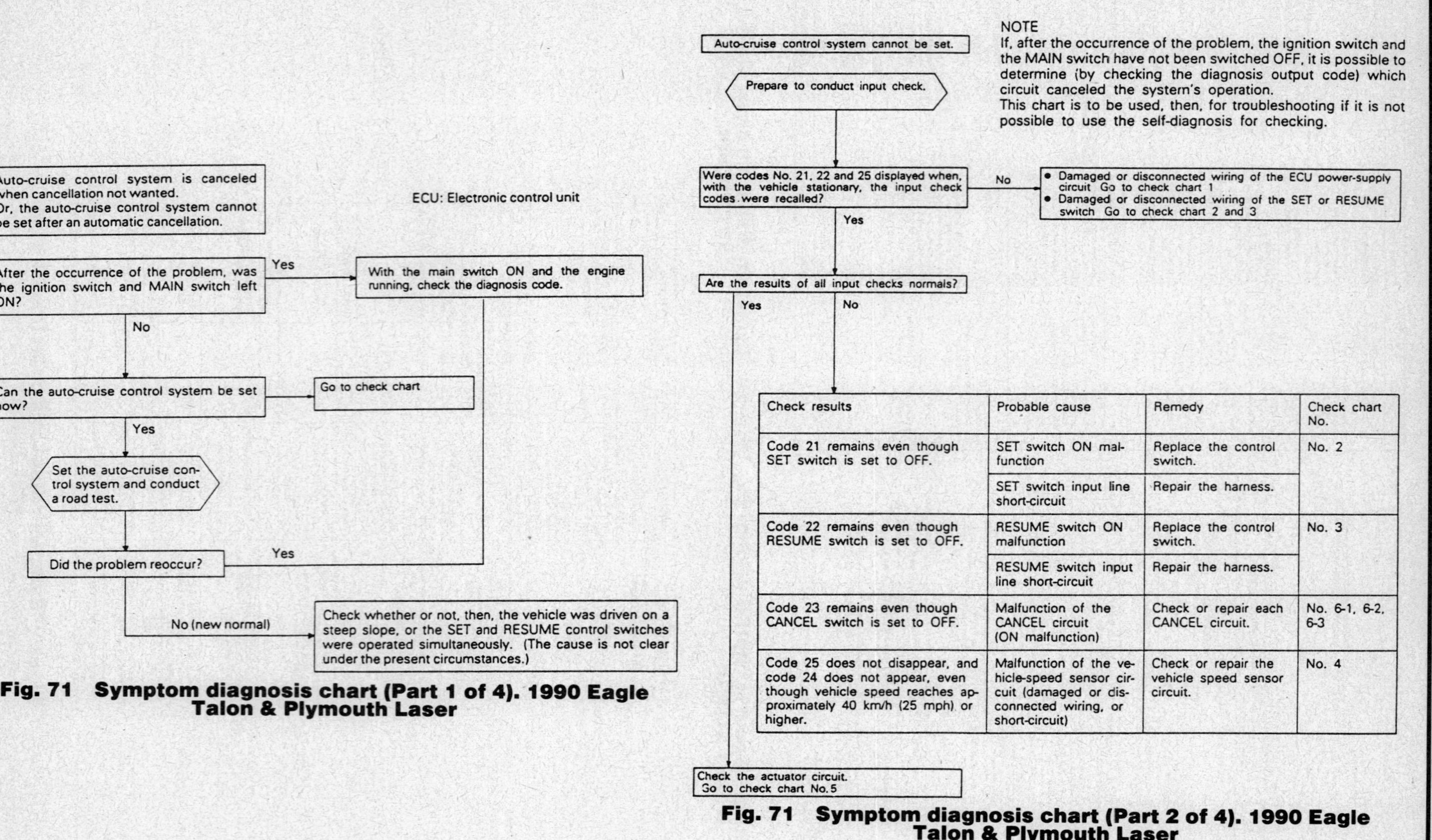
ECU: Electronic control unit
Auto-cruise control system is canceled when cancellation not wanted. Or, the auto-cruise control system cannot be set after an automatic cancellation.
After the occurrence of the problem, was the ignition switch and MAIN switch left ON?
Yes
With the main switch ON and the engine running, check the diagnosis code.
No
Can the auto-cruise control system be set now?
Go to check chart
Yes
Set the auto-cruise control system and conduct a road test.
Did the problem reoccur?
Yes
No (new normal)
Check whether or not, then, the vehicle was driven on a steep slope, or the SET and RESUME control switches were operated simultaneously. (The cause is not clear under the present circumstances.)

**Fig. 71 Symptom diagnosis chart (Part 1 of 4). 1990 Eagle Talon & Plymouth Laser**

Auto-cruise control system cannot be set.
Prepare to conduct input check.
Were codes No. 21, 22 and 25 displayed when, with the vehicle stationary, the input check codes were recalled?
No
• Damaged or disconnected wiring of the ECU power-supply circuit Go to check chart 1
• Damaged or disconnected wiring of the SET or RESUME switch Go to check chart 2 and 3
Yes
Are the results of all input checks normals?
Yes
No
Check the actuator circuit. Go to check chart No.5

NOTE
If, after the occurrence of the problem, the ignition switch and the MAIN switch have not been switched OFF, it is possible to determine (by checking the diagnosis output code) which circuit canceled the system's operation.
This chart is to be used, then, for troubleshooting if it is not possible to use the self-diagnosis for checking.

| Check results | Probable cause | Remedy | Check chart No. |
|---|---|---|---|
| Code 21 remains even though SET switch is set to OFF. | SET switch ON malfunction | Replace the control switch. | No. 2 |
| | SET switch input line short-circuit | Repair the harness. | |
| Code 22 remains even though RESUME switch is set to OFF. | RESUME switch ON malfunction | Replace the control switch. | No. 3 |
| | RESUME switch input line short-circuit | Repair the harness. | |
| Code 23 remains even though CANCEL switch is set to OFF. | Malfunction of the CANCEL circuit (ON malfunction) | Check or repair each CANCEL circuit. | No. 6-1, 6-2, 6-3 |
| Code 25 does not disappear, and code 24 does not appear, even though vehicle speed reaches approximately 40 km/h (25 mph) or higher. | Malfunction of the vehicle-speed sensor circuit (damaged or disconnected wiring, or short-circuit) | Check or repair the vehicle speed sensor circuit. | No. 4 |

**Fig. 71 Symptom diagnosis chart (Part 2 of 4). 1990 Eagle Talon & Plymouth Laser**

| Trouble symptom | Probable cause | Check chart No. | Remedy |
|---|---|---|---|
| • The set vehicle speed varies greatly upward or downward.<br>• "Hunching" (repeated alternating acceleration and deceleration) occurs after setting is made. | Malfunction of the vehicle speed sensor circuit | No. 4 | Repair the vehicle speed sensor system, or replace the part. |
| | Malfunction of the speedometer cable or speedometer drive gear | | |
| | Actuator circuit poor contact | No. 5 | Repair the actuator system, or replace the part. |
| | Malfunction of the actuator | | |
| | Malfunction of the ECU | – | Replace the ECU. |
| The auto-cruise control system is not canceled when the brake pedal is depressed. | Damaged or disconnected wiring of the stop light switch input circuit; brake switch (for auto-cruise control) malunction (short-circuit) | If the input check code No. 23 indicates a malfunction. No. 6–1 | Repair the harness or replace the stop light switch. |
| | Actuator drive circuit short-circuit | No. 5 | Repair the harness or replace the actuator. |
| | Malfunction of the ECU | – | Replace the ECU. |
| The auto-cruise control system is not canceled when the clutch pedal is depressed. (vehicles with a manual transaxle)<br>(It is canceled, however, when the brake pedal is depressed.) | Damaged or disconnected wiring of clutch switch input circuit | If the input check code No. 23 indicates a malfunction. No. 6–3 | Repair the harness, or repair or replace the clutch switch. |
| | Clutch switch improper installation (won't switch ON) | | |
| | Malfunction of the ECU | – | Replace the ECU. |
| The auto-cruise control system is not canceled when the shift lever is moved to the "N" position. (vehicles with an automatic transaxle)<br>(It is canceled, however, when the brake pedal is depressed.) | Damaged or disconnected wiring of inhibitor switch input circuit | If the input check code No. 23 indicates a malfunction. No. 6–2 | Repair the harness, or repair or replace the inhibitor switch. |
| | Improper adjustment of inhibitor switch | | |
| | Malfunction of the ECU | – | Replace the ECU. |
| Cannot decelerate by using the SET switch | Temporary damaged or disconnected wiring of SET switch input circuit | No. 2 | Repair the harness or replace the SET switch. |
| | Actuator circuit poor contact | No. 5 | Repair the harness or replace the actuator. |
| | Malfunction of the actuator | | |
| | Malfunction of the ECU | – | Replace the ECU. |

**Fig. 71 Symptom diagnosis chart (Part 3 of 4). 1990 Eagle Talon & Plymouth Laser**

| Trouble symptom | Probable cause | Check chart No. | Remedy |
|---|---|---|---|
| Cannot accelerate or resume speed by using the RESUME switch. | Damaged or disconnected wiring, or short-circuit, of RESUME switch input circuit | No. 3 | Repair the harness or replace the RESUME switch. |
| | Actuator circuit poor contact | No. 5 | Repair the harness or replace the actuator. |
| | Malfunction of the actuator | | |
| | Malfunction of the ECU | – | Replace the ECU. |
| Auto-cruise control system can be set while traveling at a vehicle speed of less than 40 km/h (25 mph), or there is no automatic cancellation at that speed. | Malfunction of the vehicle-speed sensor circuit | No. 4 | Repair the vehicle-speed sensor system, or replace the part. |
| | Malfunction of the speedometer cable or the speedometer drive gear | | |
| | Malfunction of the ECU | – | Replace the ECU. |
| The indicator light of combination meter does not illuminate.<br>(But auto-cruise control system is normal.) | Damaged or disconnected bulb of indicator light. | – | Repair the harness or replace the bulb. |
| | Harness damaged or disconnected | | |
| Malfunction of control function by ON/OFF switching of ELC 4 A/T accelerator switch<br>(Non-operation of damper clutch, 2nd gear hold, etc.) | Malfunction of circuit related to accelerator switch OFF function | No. 7 | Repair the harness or replace the part. |
| | Malfunction of the ECU | | |
| Overdrive is not canceled during fixed speed driving. <A/T> | Malfunction of circuit related to overdrive cancelation, or malfunction of ECU | No. 8 | Repair the harness or replace the part. |
| No shift to overdrive during manual driving. <A/T> | | | |

**Fig. 71 Symptom diagnosis chart (Part 4 of 4). 1990 Eagle Talon & Plymouth Laser**

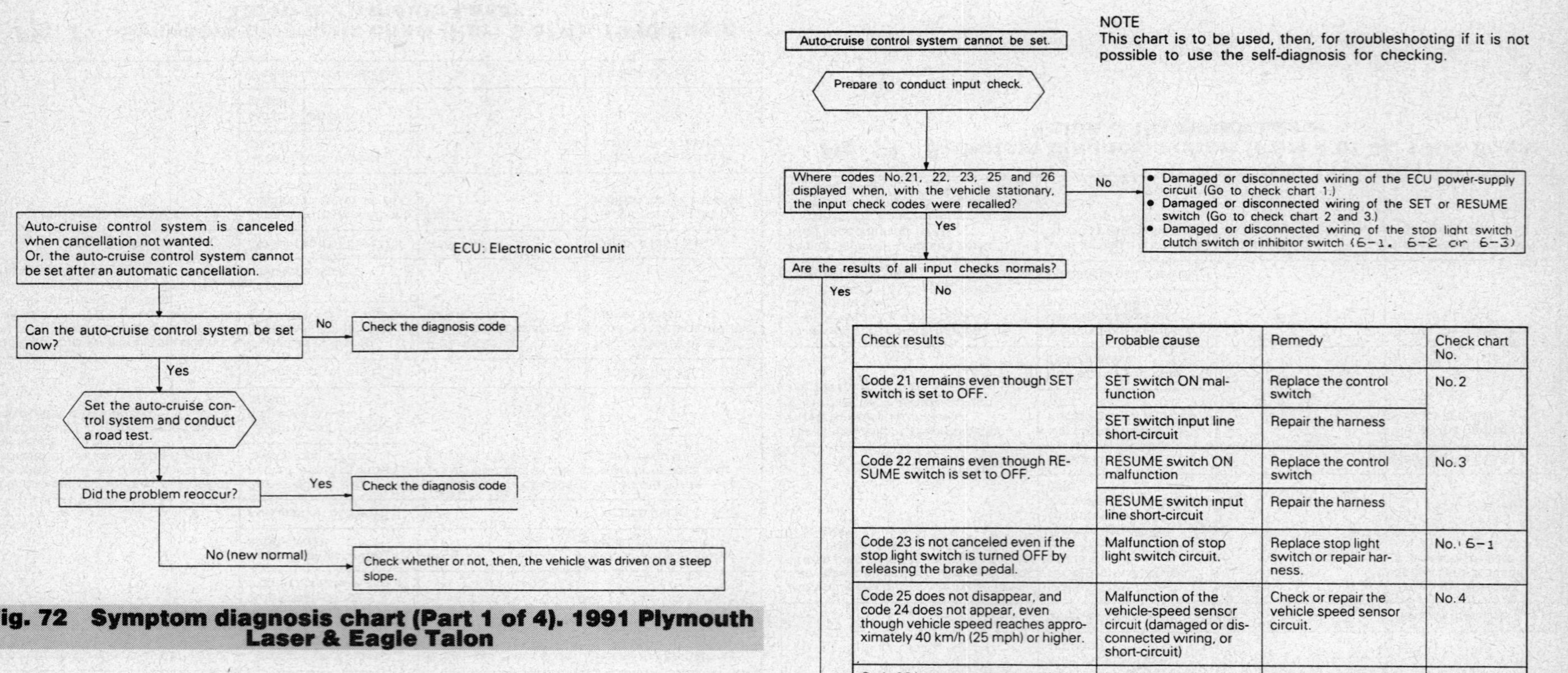
Auto-cruise control system is canceled when cancellation not wanted.
Or, the auto-cruise control system cannot be set after an automatic cancellation.
ECU: Electronic control unit
Can the auto-cruise control system be set now?
No
Check the diagnosis code
Yes
Set the auto-cruise control system and conduct a road test.
Did the problem reoccur?
Yes
Check the diagnosis code
No (new normal)
Check whether or not, then, the vehicle was driven on a steep slope.

**Fig. 72 Symptom diagnosis chart (Part 1 of 4). 1991 Plymouth Laser & Eagle Talon**

Auto-cruise control system cannot be set.
NOTE
This chart is to be used, then, for troubleshooting if it is not possible to use the self-diagnosis for checking.
Prepare to conduct input check.
Where codes No.21, 22, 23, 25 and 26 displayed when, with the vehicle stationary, the input check codes were recalled?
No
• Damaged or disconnected wiring of the ECU power-supply circuit (Go to check chart 1.)
• Damaged or disconnected wiring of the SET or RESUME switch (Go to check chart 2 and 3.)
• Damaged or disconnected wiring of the stop light switch clutch switch or inhibitor switch (6-1, 6-2 or 6-3)
Yes
Are the results of all input checks normals?
Yes
No

| Check results | Probable cause | Remedy | Check chart No. |
|---|---|---|---|
| Code 21 remains even though SET switch is set to OFF. | SET switch ON malfunction | Replace the control switch | No. 2 |
| | SET switch input line short-circuit | Repair the harness | |
| Code 22 remains even though RESUME switch is set to OFF. | RESUME switch ON malfunction | Replace the control switch | No. 3 |
| | RESUME switch input line short-circuit | Repair the harness | |
| Code 23 is not canceled even if the stop light switch is turned OFF by releasing the brake pedal. | Malfunction of stop light switch circuit. | Replace stop light switch or repair harness. | No. 6-1 |
| Code 25 does not disappear, and code 24 does not appear, even though vehicle speed reaches approximately 40 km/h (25 mph) or higher. | Malfunction of the vehicle-speed sensor circuit (damaged or disconnected wiring, or short-circuit) | Check or repair the vehicle speed sensor circuit. | No. 4 |
| Code 26 is not canceled even if the clutch switch is turned OFF by releasing the clutch pedal. | Malfunction of clutch switch circuit. | Replace clutch switch or repair harness. | No. 6-3 |
| Code 26 is not canceled even if the select lever is moved to anything but N, P <A/T>. | Malfunction of inhibitor switch circuit. | Replace inhibitor switch or repair harness. | No. 6-2 |

Check the auto-cruise vacuum pump circuit. (Go to check chart No.5.)

NOTE
If the results of the check of the auto-cruise vacuum pump circuit (check chart No. 5) and of the auto-cruise vacuum pump and actuator itself reveal no abnormal condition, replace the electronic control unit (ECU).

**Fig. 72 Symptom diagnosis chart (Part 2 of 4). 1991 Plymouth Laser & Eagle Talon**

| Trouble symptom | Probable cause | Check chart No. | Remedy |
|---|---|---|---|
| • The set vehicle speed varies greatly upward or downward.<br>• "Hunching" (repeated alternating acceleration and deceleration) occurs after setting is made. | Malfunction of the vehicle speed sensor circuit | No. 4 | Repair the vehicle speed sensor system, or replace the part. |
| | Malfunction of the speedometer cable or speedometer drive gear | | |
| | Auto-cruise vacuum pump circuit poor contact | No. 5 | Repair the auto-cruise vacuum pump, or replace the part. |
| | Malfunction of the auto-cruise vacuum pump | | |
| | Malfunction of the ECU | – | Replace the ECU. |
| The auto-cruise control system is not canceled when the brake pedal is depressed. | Damaged or disconnected wiring of the stop light switch input circuit; brake switch (for auto-cruise control) malfunction (short-circuit) | If the input check code No. 23 indicates a malfunction. No. 6–1 | Repair the harness or replace the stop light switch. |
| | Auto-cruise vacuum pump drive circuit short-circuit | No. 5 | Repair the harness or replace the auto-cruise vacuum pump. |
| | Malfunction of the ECU | – | Replace the ECU. |
| The auto-cruise control system is not canceled when the clutch pedal is depressed. (vehicles with a manual transaxle)<br>(It is canceled, however, when the brake pedal is depressed.) | Damaged or disconnected wiring of clutch switch input circuit | If the input check code No. 26 indicates a malfunction. No. 6–3 | Repair the harness, or repair or replace the clutch switch. |
| | Clutch switch improper installation (won't switch ON) | | |
| | Malfunction of the ECU | – | Replace the ECU. |
| The auto-cruise control system is not canceled when the shift lever is moved to the "N" position. (vehicles with an automatic transaxle)<br>(It is canceled, however, when the brake pedal is depressed.) | Damaged or disconnected wiring of inhibitor switch input circuit | If the input check code No. 26 indicates a malfunction. No. 6–2 | Repair the harness, or repair or replace the inhibitor switch. |
| | Improper adjustment of inhibitor switch | | |
| | Malfunction of the ECU | – | Replace the ECU. |
| Cannot decelerate by using the SET switch | Temporary damaged or disconnected wiring of SET switch input circuit | No. 2 | Repair the harness or replace the SET switch. |
| | Auto-cruise vacuum pump circuit poor contact | No. 5 | Repair the harness or replace the auto-cruise vacuum pump and actuator. |
| | Malfunction of the auto-cruise vacuum pump and actuator (including clogging of negative pressure passage) | | |
| | Malfunction of the ECU | – | Replace the ECU. |

**Fig. 72 Symptom diagnosis chart (Part 3 of 4). 1991 Plymouth Laser & Eagle Talon**

| Trouble symptom | Probable cause | Check chart No. | Remedy |
|---|---|---|---|
| Cannot accelerate or resume speed by using the RESUME switch. | Damaged or disconnected wiring, or short-circuit, of RESUME switch input circuit | No. 3 | Repair the harness or replace the RESUME switch. |
| | Auto-cruise vacuum pump circuit poor contact | No. 5 | Repair the harness or replace the auto-cruise vacuum pump and actuator. |
| | Malfunction of the auto-cruise vacuum pump and actuator (including air leak from negative pressure passage) | | |
| | Malfunction of the ECU | – | Replace the ECU. |
| Auto-cruise control system can be set while traveling at a vehicle speed of less than 40 km/h (25 mph), or there is no automatic cancellation at that speed. | Malfunction of the vehicle-speed sensor circuit | No. 4 | Repair the vehicle-speed sensor system, or replace the part. |
| | Malfunction of the speedometer cable or the speedometer drive gear | | |
| | Malfunction of the ECU | – | Replace the ECU. |
| The indicator light of combination meter does not illuminate.<br>(But auto-cruise control system is normal.) | Damaged or disconnected bulb of indicator light | – | Repair the harness or replace the bulb. |
| | Harness damaged or disconnected | | |
| Malfunction of control function by ON/OFF switching of ELC 4 A/T accelerator switch<br>(Non-operation of damper clutch, 2nd gear hold, etc.) | Malfunction of circuit related to accelerator switch OFF function | No. 7 | Repair the harness or replace the part. |
| | Malfunction of the ECU | | |
| Overdrive is not canceled during fixed speed driving. <A/T> | Malfunction of circuit related to overdrive cancellation, or malfunction of ECU | No. 8 | Repair the harness or replace the part. |
| No shift to overdrive during manual driving. <A/T> | | | |

**Fig. 72 Symptom diagnosis chart (Part 4 of 4). 1991 Plymouth Laser & Eagle Talon**

2. Turn ignition switch to On position and cruise control switch ot Off position.
3. Turn Set switch On, turn Cruise switch On then within one second, turn Resume switch to On position.
4. Perform each input operation according to input check chart, Fig. 74. **Each code will be displayed in order of priority, beginning with check No. 1. If there is no display, a possible malfunction of the ECU power supply. Check using circuit tests.**
5. If output code is not displayed after two cycles, either switch or sensor is defective.

| No. | Input operation | Code No. | Display patterns (output codes) | Check results |
|---|---|---|---|---|
| 1 | SET switch ON | 21 | 12V / 0V (2, 1) | SET switch circuit normal |
| 2 | RESUME switch ON | 22 | 12V / 0V (2, 2) | RESUME switch circuit normal |
| 3 | Each CANCEL switch ON<br>1 Stop light switch (brake pedal depressed)<br>2 Clutch switch *1 (clutch pedal depressed)<br>3 Inhibitor switch *2 (shift lever to "N" range) | 23 | 12V / 0V (2, 3) | Each CANCEL switch circuit normal |
| 4 | Driving at approximately 40 km/h (25 mph) or higher | 24 | 12V / 0V (2, 4) | When both No.4 and No.5 can be confirmed, vehicle-speed sensor circuit normal. |
| 5 | Driving at less than approximately 40 km/h (25 mph) or stopped | 25 | 12V / 0V (2, 5) | |

*1 : Vehicles with a manual transaxle *2 : Vehicles with an automatic transaxle

**Fig. 73 Input check table. Colt Vista, Conquest & 1989 Colt & Eagle Summit**

| Code No. | Display patterns (output codes) (use with voltmeter) | | Input operation | Check results |
|---|---|---|---|---|
| 21 | | | SET switch ON | SET switch circuit normal |
| 22 | | | RESUME switch ON | RESUME switch normal |
| 23 | | | Stop light switch ON (brake pedal depressed) | Stop light switch circuit normal |
| 24 | | | Vehicle speed more than approx. 40 km/h (25 mph) | Vehicle speed sensor circuit normal if code Nos. 24 and 25 are displayed |
| 25 | | | Vehicle speed less than approx. 40 km/h (25 mph) | |
| 26 | | M/T | Clutch switch ON (clutch pedal depressed) | Clutch switch circuit normal |
| | | A/T | Inhibitor switch ON (SELECT lever placed in "N" position) | Inhibitor switch circuit normal |
| 27 | | | CANCEL switch ON | CANCEL switch circuit normal |
| 28 | | | TPS output voltage 1.5 V or more (Accelerator pedal depressed more than half the way) | Throttle position sensor circuit normal |
| 29 | | | Idle switch OFF (Accelerator pedal depressed) | Idle switch circuit normal |

**Fig. 74 Input check table. Stealth & 1990–91 Colt, Laser & Eagle Summit & Talon**

## CIRCUIT TESTS

### EXCEPT PLYMOUTH LASER & EAGLE TALON

Refer to **Figs. 19 through 67**, for individual circuit tests.

### PLYMOUTH LASER & EAGLE TALON

#### Check 1, Control Unit Power Supply

When the ignition and main switches are in the On position current flows to the ignition switch, fuse 11 of the junction block, cruise control switch, control unit and to ground.

Check ECU terminal No. 7 on 1990 models or terminal No. 2 on 1991 models, control unit power supply. When the cruise control main switch is on. Voltage measured should be approximately 12 volts.

Check ECU terminal No. 10 on 1990 models or terminals No. 8 and 14 on 1991 models, control unit ground. No voltage should be present.

#### Check 2, Set Switch

When the ignition, cruise control and Set switches are in the On position, with the vehicle at the desired speed, vehicle speed should remain constant.

Constant speed can gradually be reduced when the Set switch is pressed and held while the vehicle is traveling at the previously set speed. The vehicle will coast to reduced speeds. When the desired speed is achieved, release the Set switch and the vehicle will remain at the new set speed.

Current flows to the control unit, cruise control Set switch and to ground.

Check ECU terminal No. 5 on 1990 models or terminal No. 17 on 1991 models, Set switch. With the Set switch in the On position, no voltage should be present. When the Set switch is in the Off position, voltage should measure approximately 12 volts.

#### Check 3, Resume Switch

The set speed prior to cancellation should resume when the resume switch is placed in the On position even if the constant speed control has been cancelled.

When the Resume switch is placed in the On position and held while the vehicle is traveling at the previously set constant speed, the vehicle speed will increase. When the switch is released, that speed will be the new set speed.

The set speed should not resume, even if the Resume switch remains in the On position, if the Main switch is turned off and vehicle speed falls below 25 mph.

Current flows to the control unit, Resume switch and to ground.

Check ECU terminal No. 4 on 1990 models or terminal No. 18 on 1991 models, Resume switch. No voltage should be present with the switch in the On position. Voltage should be approximately 12 volts with the switch in the Off position.

#### Check 4, Vehicle Speed Sensor

The vehicle speed sensor is installed within the speedometer and sends pulse signals to the control unit in proportion to vehicle speed. The vehicle speed sensor is a reed switch type of sensor, generating four pulse signals each rotation of the speedometer driven gear.

Check ECU terminal No. 15 on 1990 models or terminal No. 19 on 1991 models, vehicle speed sensor while moving the vehicle forward slowly. Terminal voltage should alternate between 0-0.7 volts to more than 3 volts.

#### 1990 Check 5, Vehicle Speed Sensor

With the main switch in the On position, turn the Set switch to the On position to set desired speed. The control unit sends current to the eleoctromagnetic clutch coil of the actuator. This attracts the clutch plate and also illuminates the Cruise indicator light. When the ring gear of the planetary pinion is secured, the control unit causes the DC motor to be switched On.

Rotation of the DC motor is transmitted to the worm gear, then the worm wheel, sun gear, then the planetary pinion. Because the ring gear is secured at this time, the planetary pinion rotates while revolving around the sun gear. Because the planetary pinion is installed into the carrier, the carrier and the selector driveshaft unified with it, as well as the selector, are caused to rotate.

The change in direction of rotation of the selector is accomplished by reversing the direction of current flow to the motor which is regulated by the control unit.

The current flow to the electromagnetic clutch is interrupted if the main switch is turned off, or if operation of the cruise control system is cancelled as a result of the input of a cancel signal to the control unit. This may be done by activation of the stop light switch, clutch switch, or the inhibitor switch.

As a result of this interruption, the clutch plate returns from the electromagnetic clutch side to the ring gear side by the force of the spring. The ring gear then becomes free.

When the ring gear becomes free, the planetary pinion releases from the sun gear, releasing the selector to its original position.

Measure voltage at terminal 8, testing the electromagnetic clutch coil transistor. Ensure the cruise control main switch is in the On position. Voltage should measure 0 volts.

Measure voltage at terminal 9, testing the DC motor drive (Pull side). Test during acceleration by use of the Resume switch. Voltage should measure 0 volts.

Measure voltage at terminal 9, testing the DC motor drive (Rel side). Test during speed reduction by use of the Set switch. Voltage should measure 12 volts.

Measure voltage at terminal 20, testing the DC motor drive (Pull side). Test during acceleration by use of the Resume switch. Voltage should measure 12 volts.

Measure voltage at terminal 20, testing the DC motor drive (Rel side). Test during speed reduction by use of the Set switch. Voltage should measure 0 volts.

### 1991 Check 5, Cruise Control Vacuum Pump

Hold Mode. When the Set switch is On and the Cruise switch is On, when a determined speed is reached the control unit receives a set signal and turns the cruise vacuum pump motor On. After constant speed is reached the motor, control valve and release valve are repeatedly turned On and Off according to driving conditions.

Acceleration Mode. When the Resume switch is pressed, the control unit receives a Resume signal and turns On the cruise vacuum pump motor, control valve and release valve.

Deceleration Mode. When the Set switch in held depressed, the control unit receives a set signal and turns the cruise vacuum pump and control valve Off and turns the release valve On.

Release Mode. When the Set switch is turned Off, the control unit receives a cancel signal and turns Off the cruise vacuum pump motor, control valve and release valve.

Measure voltage at terminal No. 26 then at terminal No. 13, vacuum pump drive and control valve open/close. Voltage should measure 12 volts or 0 volts during the Hold mode, 0 volts during the Acceleration mode and 12 volts during both the Deceleration and Release modes.

Measure voltage at terminal No. 12 release valve open/close. Voltage should measure 12 volts or 0 volts during the Hold mode, 0 volts during both the Acceleration and Deceleration modes and 12 volts during the Release mode.

### Check 6-1, Stop Light Switch

When the brake pedal is depressed during constant speed travel, the stop light switch contacts for the cruise control system open, creating an interruption in the signal to the actuator electromagnetic clutch, cancelling the constant speed travel.

The flow of current is from the battery to fuse No. 17 of the junction block, stop light switch, to the control unit.

Test terminal 3 on 1990 models or terminal No. 15 on 1991 models, stop light switch (load side), when the brake pedal is depressed. Voltage should measure 12 volts.

Test terminal 3 on 1990 models or terminal No. 15 on 1991 models, stop light switch (load side), when the brake pedal is not depressed. Voltage should measure 0 volts.

**On 1990 models,** test terminal 11, stop light switch (power supply side), with the brake pedal depressed and when not depressed. Voltage should measure 12 volts.

### Check 6-2, Inhibitor Switch

The inhibitor switch also functions as the switch for the starter. If the selector handle is moved to the N position during constant speed, a cancel signal is sent to the control unit, cancelling the constant speed travel.

Measure voltage at terminal 2 on 1990 models or terminal No. 1 on 1991 models, check inhibitor switch at all times. Voltage should measure 12 volts.

### Check 6-3, Clutch Circuit Switch

If the clutch pedal is depressed during constant speed travel, the contacts of the clutch switch close, sending a cancel signal to the control unit, cancelling the constant speed travel.

The flow of current is to the ignition switch, fuse No. 11 of the junction block, clutch switch, then the control unit.

Measure voltage at terminal No. 1, clutch switch. With the clutch pedal depressed, voltage should measure 12 volts. With the clutch pedal at rest, voltage should measure 0 volts.

Measure voltage at terminal No. 6 on 1990 models or terminal No. 3 on 1991 models, control unit power supply. Voltage should measure 12 volts at all times.

Measure voltage at terminal No. 16 on 1990 models or terminal No. 9 on 1991 models, accelerator switch. With the accelerator pedal depressed, voltage should measure 0 volts. With the accelerator pedal at rest, voltage should measure 12 volts.

### Check 7, Accelerator Switch Off Function

The accelerator switch detects the operational status of the accelerator pedal.

During constant speed driving, the accelerator pedal is not operational. The ground circuit of the accelerator switch if off during constant speed driving, as to not interfere with the function of the automatic transaxle.

### Check 8, Overdrive Cancellation Function

Overdrive is cancelled if the Resume switch is used, or if the vehicle speed drops 1 mph below the vehicle set speed. At this time, the signals to the control unit are cancelled. Drive will then be controlled in third gear.

Measure voltage at terminal No. 13 on 1990 models or terminal No. 10 on 1991 models, 4A/T control unit, with the overdrive switch in the On position. Voltage should measure 12 volts.

Measure voltage at terminal No. 14 on 1990 models or terminal No. 11 on 1991 models, overdrive switch, with the overdrive switch in the On position. Voltage should measure 12 volts.

## COMPONENT TESTING

### SPEED CONTROL SWITCH

#### Except Stealth

Gain access and disconnect connector to speed control main switch and check for continuity between terminals as shown in **Figs. 75 through 79**

#### Stealth

1. Remove main switch and garnish from console.
2. Remove switch from garnish.
3. Operate main switch and check for continuity across terminals as shown in **Fig. 80.**
4. Connect a positive lead from battery to terminal 3 and a negative lead to terminal 5. Check that battery voltage is available between terminals 4 and 5 when the switch is turned On and when the switch is turned Off.
5. Check that when turned to Off position thereafter, the battery voltage across terminal 4 and 5 is reduced to 0 volts.

**SERVICE BULLETIN: Speed control will not remain On when the main On/Off switch is depressed.**

This condition may be caused be improper wiring connection at the main switch. The wiring harness is too short and partially pulls the wiring off the back of the speed control switch. **Replacement of the main switch will not correct this condition.** Use the following procedure to correct this condition.

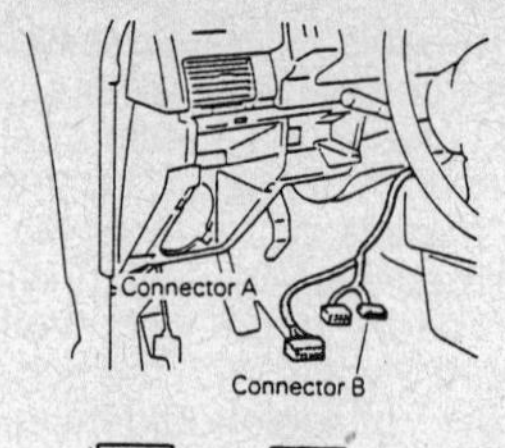


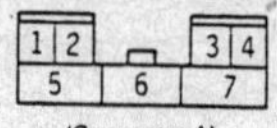


(Connector A)

8 9 10 11

(Connector B)

○–○: Continuity

| Switch position \ Terminal | 7 | 9 | 11 | 8 | 10 |
|---|---|---|---|---|---|
| OFF | | | | | |
| MAIN switch ON | | | ○— | — | —○ |
| SET switch ON | ○— | —○ | | | |
| RESUME switch ON | ○— | — | — | —○ | |
| | | | ○— | — | —○ |

**Fig. 75 Speed control main switch test. 1989 Colt & Eagle Summit**

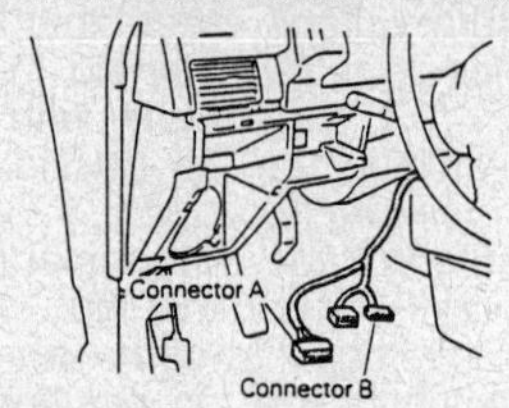


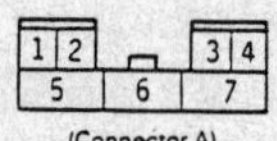


(Connector A)

(Connector B)

○–○: Continuity

| Switch position \ Terminal | 7 | 9 | 8 |
|---|---|---|---|
| OFF | | | |
| SET switch ON | ○— | —○ | |
| RESUME switch ON | ○— | — | —○ |

NOTE
If the continuity is other than shown, replace the column switch.

**Fig. 76 Speed control main switch test. 1990–91 Colt & Eagle Summit**

Disconnect the connection of the column switch connector, and check at the connector at the body side.

| Terminal | Connection or measured part | Measurement item | Tester connection | Check conditions | Standard |
|---|---|---|---|---|---|
| 1 | Power supply (IG) | Voltage | RL–Ground | IG S/W OFF → ON | 0V → Approx. 12V |
| 5 | Ground | Continuity | B–Ground | At all times | Continuity |

NOTE
If not within the standard, check the harness at the body side.

Disconnect the connection of the column switch connector, and check at the connector at the switch side.

| No. | Connection or measured part | Measurement item | Tester connection | Check conditions | Standard |
|---|---|---|---|---|---|
| 1 | Main switch | Continuity | W–L | Main switch OFF | No continuity |
| | | | | Main switch ON | Continuity |
| 2 | Indicator illumination (LED) | Continuity | L–B (→–)* | At all times | Continuity |
| | | | B–L (→–)* | At all times | No continuity |
| 3 | SET switch | Continuity | R–B | SET switch OFF | No continuity |
| | | | | SET switch ON | Continuity |
| 4 | RESUME switch | Continuity | Y–B | RESUME switch OFF | No continuity |
| | | | | RESUME switch ON | Continuity |

NOTE
(1) If not within the standard, disassemble the column switch assembly, and check each circuit.
(2) An asterisk (*) denotes tester polarity. To check the indicator light (LED) for open or short circuit, apply tester probes in such a manner that current flows in forward direction of the diode.

**Fig. 77 Speed control main switch test. Colt Vista**

Disconnect the column switch connectors and check at the vehicle body side connector.

| Terminal | Destination | Measuring item | Tester connection | Check conditions | Standard |
|---|---|---|---|---|---|
| 3 | Ignition switch (IG) | Voltage | 3 – Ground | Ignition switch: OFF → ON | 0 V → Battery voltage |
| 2 | Ground | Continuity | 2 – Ground | Normal | With continuity |

Disconnect the column switch connectors and check at the switch side connector.

| No. | Check item | Measuring item | Tester connection | Check conditions | Standard |
|---|---|---|---|---|---|
| 1 | MAIN switch | Continuity | 3 – 7 | MAIN switch OFF | Without continuity |
| | | | | MAIN switch ON | With continuity |
| 2 | Indication light | Continuity | 7 – 2 (→\|)* | Normal | With continuity |
| | | Continuity | 7 – 2 (\|←)* | Normal | Without continuity |
| 3 | SET switch | Continuity | 1 – 2 | SET switch OFF | Without continuity |
| | | | | SET switch ON | With continuity |
| 4 | RESUME switch | Continuity | 5 – 2 | RESUME switch OFF | Without continuity |
| | | | | RESUME switch ON | With continuity |

NOTE
1. Replace the switch if out of specification.
2. An asterisk (*) denotes tester polarity. To check for light (LED) open or short circuit, apply the circuit tester probes in such a manner that the current will flow in the forward direction of the diode symbol.

**Fig. 78 Speed control main switch test. Conquest**

1. Remove main switch and garnish.
2. Carefully pull on main speed control switch wiring harness to gain an additional 1/16–1/8 inch of wiring.
3. Install main speed control switch and garnish.

## STOP LIGHT/BRAKE SWITCH

1. Disconnect electrical connector from switch.
2. Check for continuity between terminal of switch, **Figs. 81 through 83.**

## CLUTCH SWITCH

1. Disconnect electrical connector from switch.
2. Check for continuity between terminal when clutch pedal is depressed.

## INHIBITOR SWITCH

1. Disconnect electrical connector from switch.
2. **On except Colt Vista & Conquest,** ensure there is continuity between connector terminals 8 and 9 when shift lever is moved to N range, **Fig. 84.**
3. **On Colt Vista models,** check for continuity between black/yellow terminals, **Fig. 85.**
4. **On Conquest models,** check for continuity in N, P and R ranges, **Fig. 86.**

## ACTUATOR

### Colt Vista; 1989 Colt, Conquest & Eagle Summit

1. Disconnect electrical connector.
2. **On Colt, Eagle Summit & Colt Vista models,** measure resistance value of clutch coil, between terminals 1 and 3. Standard value should read 20 ohms.
3. **On Conquest models,** measure resistance value of each coil. Standard value between terminals 1 and 2 should read 30 ohms and standard

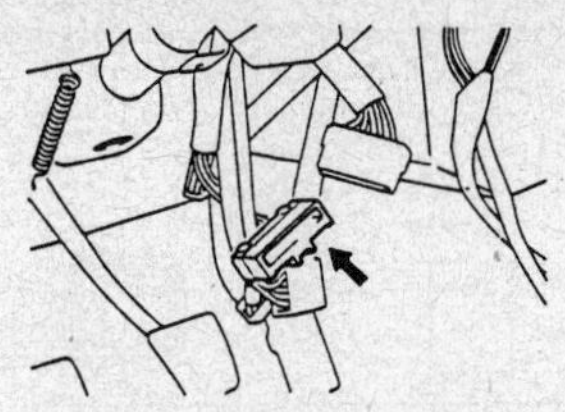

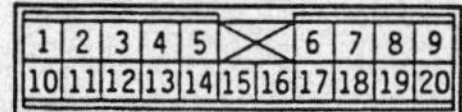


O—O: continuity

| Switch position \ Terminal | 13 | 8 | 9 | 19 | 20 |
|---|---|---|---|---|---|
| OFF | | | | | |
| SET switch ON | O— | —O | | | |
| Neutral | | | | | |
| RESUME switch ON | O— | — | — | —O | |

NOTE
If there is an abnormal condition (any condition not described in the table above), replace the column switch.

**Fig. 79 Speed control main switch test. Plymouth Laser & Eagle Talon**

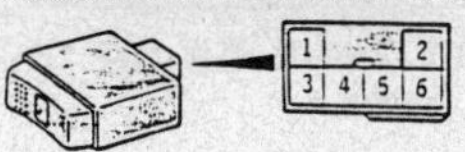


| Switch state \ Terminal No. | 1 | ILL | 2 | 3 | 4 | 5 |
|---|---|---|---|---|---|---|
| Press OFF. | O— | —⊙— | —O | | | |
| Neutral position | O— | —⊙— | —O | | O— | —O |
| Press ON. | O— | —⊙— | —O | O— | —O— | —O |

NOTE
(1) O—O denotes continuity across the terminals.
(2) ILL: Illumination light

**Fig. 80 Speed control main switch test. Stealth**

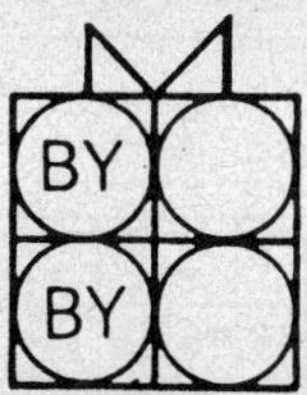


**Fig. 85 Inhibitor switch N & P position check. Colt Vista**

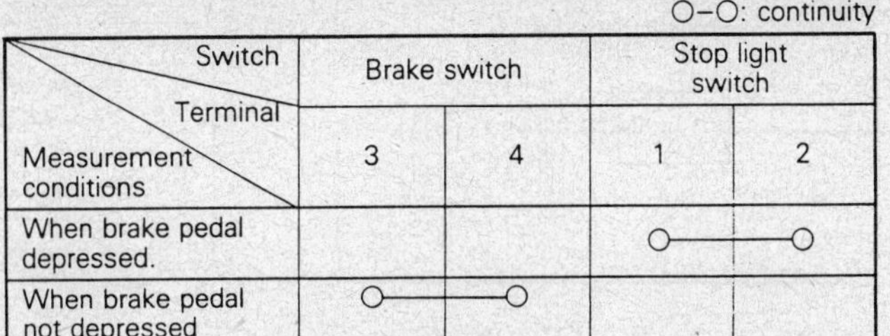

O—O: continuity

| Measurement conditions \ Switch / Terminal | Brake switch 3 | Brake switch 4 | Stop light switch 1 | Stop light switch 2 |
|---|---|---|---|---|
| When brake pedal depressed. | | | O— | —O |
| When brake pedal not depressed | O— | —O | | |

**Fig. 81 Stoplight/brake switch test. Except Conquest**

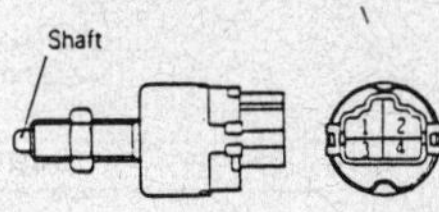


| Circuit | Terminal | Shaft dimension mm (in.): Free 5.8–6.8 (.23–.27) to 3.4–5.0 (.13–.20) | 3–5 (.12–.20) to Full stroke |
|---|---|---|---|
| Stop light | 2 – 3 | Continuity | No continuity |
| Speed control | 1 – 4 | No continuity | Continuity |

**Fig. 82 Stoplight/brake switch test. Conquest**

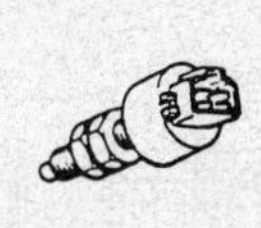

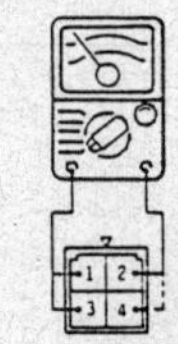

O—O :continuity

| Measurement conditions \ Switch / Terminal | Brake switch 1 | Brake switch 4 | Stop light siwtch 2 | Stop light siwtch 3 |
|---|---|---|---|---|
| When brake pedal depressed. | | | O— | —O |
| When brake pedal not depressed. | O— | —O | | |

**Fig. 83 Stoplight/brake switch test. Plymouth Laser & Eagle Talon**

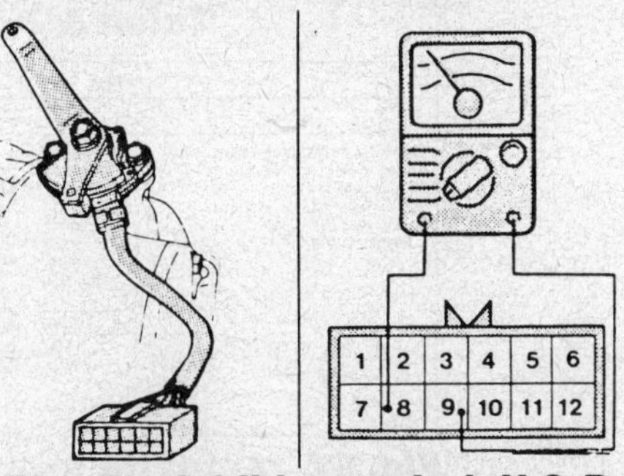


**Fig. 84 Inhibitor switch N & P position check. Stealth, Colt & Eagle Summit**

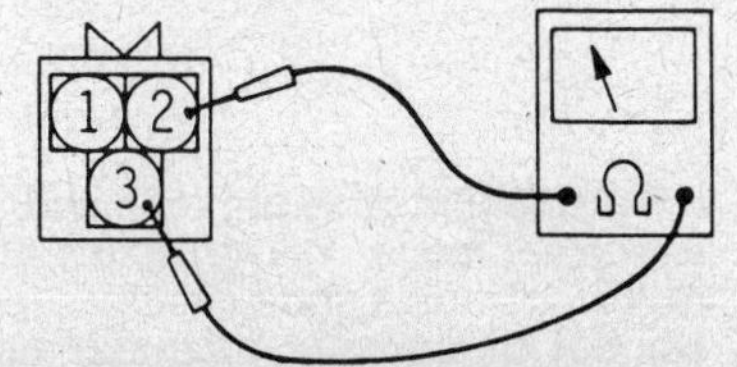


**Fig. 87 Actuator operation check. Conquest**

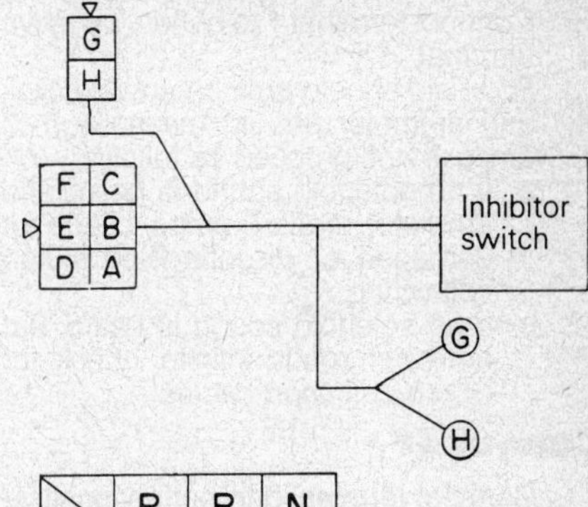


| | P | R | N |
|---|---|---|---|
| A | O | | O |
| B | O | | O |
| D | | O | |
| E | | O | |
| C | O | | |
| F | O | | |

**Fig. 86 Inhibitor switch N & P position check. Conquest**

value between terminals 1 and 3 should read 60 ohms, **Fig. 87.**

## Plymouth Laser & Eagle Talon

Measure resistance value of each clutch coil and ensure value is 20 ohms, on 1990 models or 50-60 ohms on 1991 models.

## Stealth; 1990–91 Colt & Eagle Summit; 1991 Plymouth Laser & Eagle Talon

1. Remove actuator.
2. Apply vacuum to actuator and ensure that holder moves more than 1.4 inches.
3. Ensure that no change in holder position as vacuum is maintained.

## ACTUATOR OPERATION CHECK

### Colt, Eagle Summit & Colt Vista

1. Connect terminal 3 of actuator through ammeter, to battery positive terminal, **Fig. 88.**

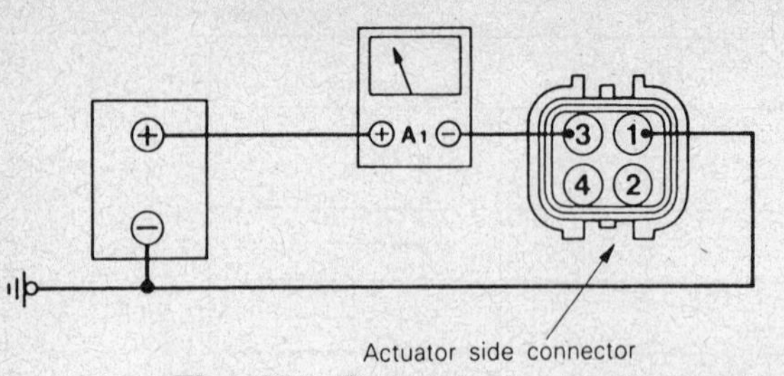


**Fig. 88 Actuator operation check. Colt Vista; 1989 Colt & Eagle Summit**

**Fig. 89 Actuator connector, single ammeter. Eagle Talon & Plymouth Laser**

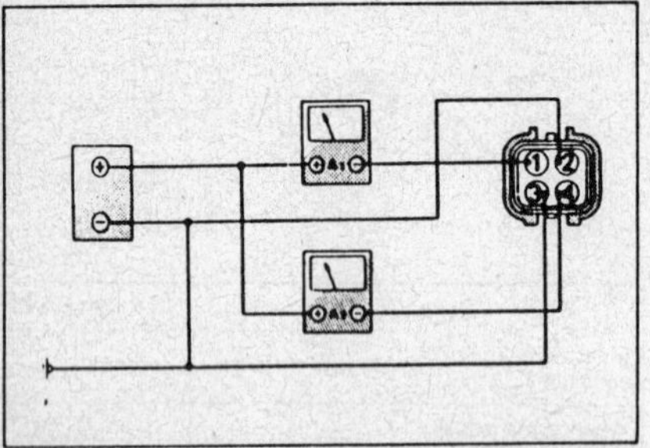

**Fig. 90 Actuator connector, dual ammeter. Eagle Talon & Plymouth Laser**

| Judgement | | Probable cause |
|---|---|---|
| Normal | Abnormal | |
| Current is cut off when selector is turned in PULL direction for full stroke (fully open). $A_1$: 0.5–0.7A $A_2$: less than 0.5A (when current ON) | Selector moves in PULL direction but $A_2$ equal or more than 1A $A_1$: 0.5–0.7A | • Improper backlash between gears • Imminent burning between shaft and metal • Insufficient thrust clearance |
| | Selector doesn't move. $A_2$ equal or more than 1A $A_1$: 0.5–0.7A | • Shaft burned • Foreign material caught between gears • Motor burned |
| | Selector doesn't move. $A_2$ = 0A $A_1$: 0.3–0.7A | • Damaged or disconnected internal lead wire • Damaged or disconnected motor wiring • Poor contact of limit switch • Open diode |
| With the selector stroke at the intermediate level, disconnect the connection to terminal (1) and cut the current flow to the clutch coil. | The selector doesn't return to the original position even if the current to the clutch coil is cut. | Malfunction of clutch operation (Clutch plate remains engaged with clutch) |

**Fig. 91 Actuator switch PULL test. Eagle Talon & Plymouth Laser**

| Judgement | | Probable cause |
|---|---|---|
| Normal | Abnormal | |
| Current is cut off when selector is turned in REL. direction for full stroke (fully closed). $A_1$: 0.5–0.7A $A_2$: less than 0.5A (when current ON) | Selector moves in REL. direction but $A_2$ equal or more than 1A $A_1$: 0.5–0.7A | • Improper backlash between gears • Imminent burning between shaft and metal • Insufficient thrust clearance |
| | Selector doesn't move. $A_2$ equal or more than 1A $A_1$: 0.5–0.7A | • Shaft burned • Foreign material caught between gears • Motor burned |
| | Selector doesn't move. $A_2$ = 0A $A_1$: 0.3–0.7A | • Damaged or disconnected internal lead wire • Damaged or disconnected motor wiring • Poor contact of limit switch • Open diode |

**Fig. 92 Actuator switch REL test. Eagle Talon & Plymouth Laser**

2. Connect terminal 1 to battery negative terminal.
3. Solenoid should emit an audible click and ammeter should measure .5-.7 amps. If not, proceed as follows:
   a. If no solenoid sound is heard and ammeter reads 0 amps, check for damaged or disconnected clutch coil wiring.
   b. If no solenoid sound is heard, but ammeter reads infinite, check for clutch coil short circuit.

### Conquest

1. Connect terminal 3 to battery positive terminal.
2. Connect terminal 1 and 2 to negative terminal.
3. Apply vacuum to port of actuator, then check accelerator cable is held in a drawn in position.
4. Disconnect terminal 2 from battery negative terminal, then check accelerator cable connecting point moves to initial position.
5. Repeat step 4 for terminal 1.

### 1990 Plymouth Laser & Eagle Talon

1. Disconnect actuator connector.
2. Connect an ammeter between terminal 1 of clutch coil solenoid and battery positive terminal. Connect ammeter between terminal 2 of clutch coil solenoid and battery negative terminal, **Fig. 89.**
3. An audible click should be heard and the ammeter should read 0.5-0.7 amps.
4. If the solenoid does not click and the ammeter reads 0.0 amps, the clutch coil or wiring is damaged or disconnected.
5. If the solenoid does not click and the ammeter reads infinite amps, the clutch coil has a short circuit.
6. **Do not disconnect ammeter connections from step 2.** Using a second ammeter, connect terminal 4 of the actuator through the ammeter, to the positive battery terminal. Connect terminal 3 of the actuator to the negative battery terminal, **Fig. 90.**
7. Refer to **Fig. 91,** for conditions and probable causes.
8. Reverse the connections in step 6, to terminals 3 and 4. Refer to **Fig. 92,** for conditions and probable causes.

### 1991 Plymouth Laser & Eagle Talon

1. Remove actuator.
2. Apply vacuum to actuator and ensure that holder moves more than 1.4 inches.
3. Ensure that no change in holder position as vacuum is maintained.

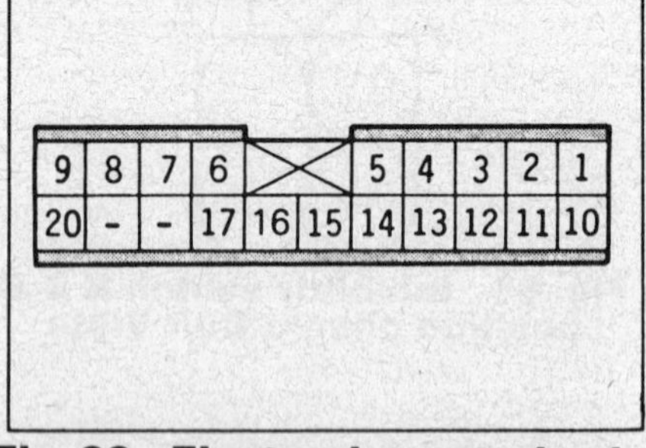


**Fig. 93 Electronic control unit terminal identification. Eagle Talon & Plymouth Laser**

## ELECTRONIC CONTROL UNIT SIGNAL CIRCUIT CHECK

### 1990 Plymouth Laser & Eagle Talon

1. Disconnect ECU connector, then check the connector half on the body side wiring harness referring to **Figs. 93 and 94.**

IG S/W: Ignition switch
MAIN S/W: MAIN switch
OD S/W: Overdrive switch

| Terminal | Connection or measured part | Measurement item | Tester connection | Check conditions | | Standard |
|---|---|---|---|---|---|---|
| 1 | Clutch switch | Voltage | 1–Ground | IG S/W ON | Clutch switch ON | Approx. 12V |
| | | | | | Clutch switch OFF | 0V |
| 2 | Inhibitor switch (P, N) | Continuity | 2–Ground | "P" or "N" range | | Continuity |
| | | | | Other than "P" or "N" range | | No continuity |
| 3 | Stop light switch load side | Voltage | 3–Ground | Press the brake pedal. | | Approx. 12V |
| 4 | RESUME switch | Continuity | 4–Ground | RESUME switch ON (Turn) | | Continuity |
| | | | | RESUME switch OFF (Release) | | No continuity |
| 5 | SET switch | Continuity | 5–Ground | SET switch ON (Press) | | Continuity |
| | | | | SET switch OFF (Release) | | No continuity |
| 6 | Power supply ($IG_2$) | Voltage | 6–Ground | IG switch ON | | Approx. 12V |
| 7 | Power supply (Main) | Voltage | 7–Ground | IG S/W ON; Main S/W ON | | Approx. 12V |

**Fig. 94 Electronic control unit test, (part 1 of 2). Eagle Talon & Plymouth Laser**

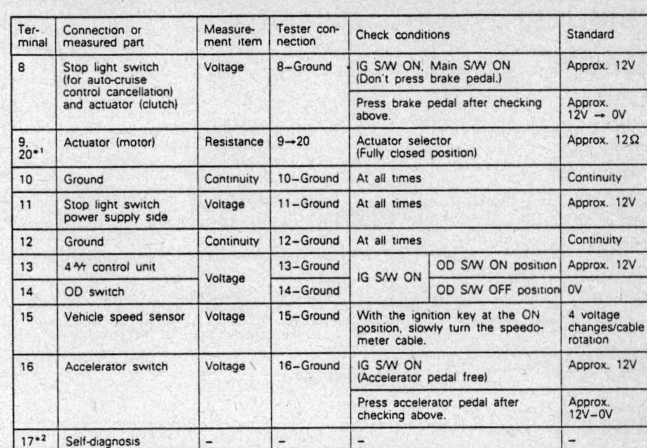

| Terminal | Connection or measured part | Measurement item | Tester connection | Check conditions | | Standard |
|---|---|---|---|---|---|---|
| 8 | Stop light switch (for auto-cruise control cancellation) and actuator (clutch) | Voltage | 8–Ground | IG S/W ON, Main S/W ON (Don't press brake pedal.) | | Approx. 12V |
| | | | | Press brake pedal after checking above. | | Approx. 12V → 0V |
| 9, 20*1 | Actuator (motor) | Resistance | 9→20 | Actuator selector (Fully closed position) | | Approx. 12Ω |
| 10 | Ground | Continuity | 10–Ground | At all times | | Continuity |
| 11 | Stop light switch power supply side | Voltage | 11–Ground | At all times | | Approx. 12V |
| 12 | Ground | Continuity | 12–Ground | At all times | | Continuity |
| 13 | 4 A/T control unit | Voltage | 13–Ground | IG S/W ON | OD S/W ON position | Approx. 12V |
| 14 | OD switch | | 14–Ground | | OD S/W OFF position | 0V |
| 15 | Vehicle speed sensor | Voltage | 15–Ground | With the ignition key at the ON position, slowly turn the speedometer cable. | | 4 voltage changes/cable rotation |
| 16 | Accelerator switch | Voltage | 16–Ground | IG S/W ON (Accelerator pedal free) | | Approx. 12V |
| | | | | Press accelerator pedal after checking above. | | Approx. 12V–0V |
| 17*2 | Self-diagnosis | – | – | – | | – |

**Fig. 94 Electronic control unit test, (part 2 of 2). Eagle Talon & Plymouth Laser**

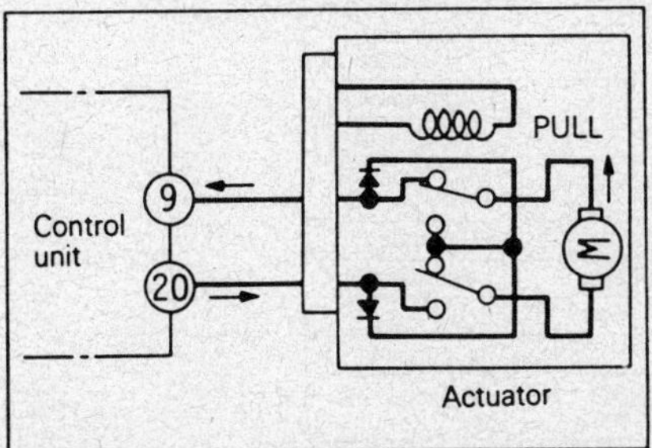


**Fig. 95 Actuator limit switch. Eagle Talon & Plymouth Laser**

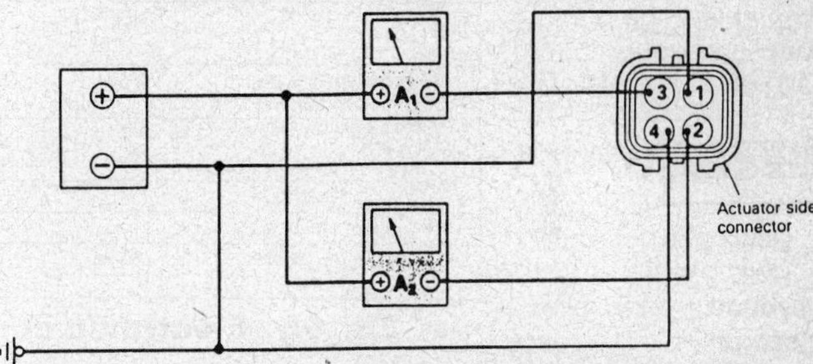


**Fig. 96 Motor pull direction & limit switch operation. Colt Vista; 1989 Colt & Eagle Summit**

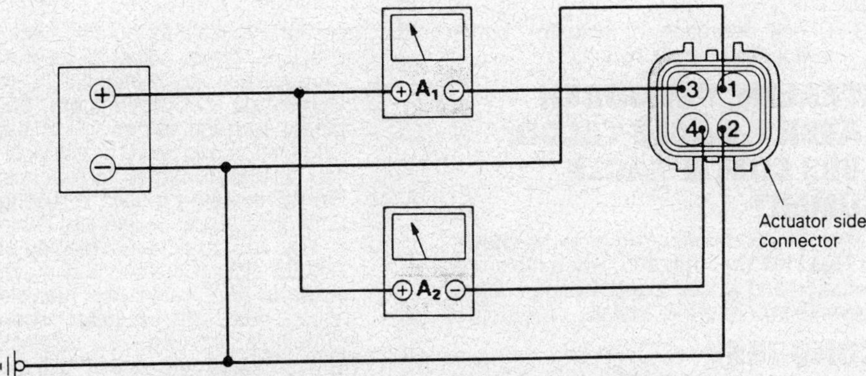


**Fig. 97 Motor release direction & limit switch operation. Colt Vista; 1989 Colt & Eagle Summit**

2. The indication of *1 shows the limit switch within the actuator becoming as shown in **Fig. 95.** The actuator selector is at the fully closed position when the resistance between terminals 9 and 20 is measured. For this reason, after checking polarity of the tester, the tester's probe should be connected so current flows from terminal 20 to terminal 9.
3. For terminals indicated by the *2, it is necessary to check individual terminal voltages with the ECU's harness connector connected and the ignition switch in the On position.

## MOTOR PULL DIRECTION & LIMIT SWITCH OPERATION

1. Connect ammeters to actuator side connector, **Fig. 96.**
2. Current should be cut off when selector is turned in Pull (fully open), direction for full stroke. Ammeter A1 should read .6-.7 amps. Ammeter A2 should read less tan .5 amps, when current is on.
3. If selector moves in Pull direction, ammeter reads .5-.7 amps but ammeter A2 reads 1 amp or more, check for improper gear backlash, burning between shaft and metal, or insufficient thrust clearance.
4. If selector does not move, ammeter A1 reads .5-.7 amps and ammeter A2 reads 1 amp or more, check the following:
   a. Burned shaft or motor, or foreign material caught between gears.
   b. If selector does not move, ammeter A1 reads .3-.7 amps and ammeter A2 reads .0 amps, proceed to step c.
   c. Check for damage to disconnected internal lead wire or motor wiring, poor connection of limit switch, or open diode.
5. With selector stroke in the intermediate level, disconnect connection to terminal 3, then cut the current flow to the clutch coil.
6. If selector does not return to original position, even if current is cut to the clutch coil, check for clutch plate remaining engaged with clutch.

## MOTOR RELEASE DIRECTION & LIMIT SWITCH OPERATION

1. Connect ammeters to actuator side connector, **Fig. 97.**
2. Turn selector in the Release (fully closed), direction. Current should be cut off, ammeter A1 should read .5-.7 amps and ammeter A2 should read less than .5 amps when current is On.
3. If selector moves in Release direction, ammeter A1 reads .5-.7 amps, but ammeter A2 reads 1 amp or more, check the following:
   a. Improper gear backlash, burning

ECU connector terminals

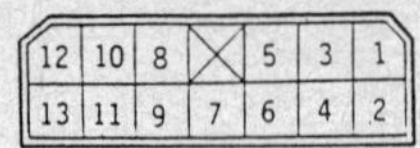


IG S/W: Ignition switch

| Terminal | Connection or measured part | Measurement item | Tester connection | Check conditions | Standard |
|---|---|---|---|---|---|
| 1 | Actuator (motor) | Resistance | 1→2*1 | Actuator lever (Fully closed position) | Approx. 12Ω |
| 2 | | | | | |
| 3 | Stop light switch (for automatic speed control cancellation) and actuator (clutch) | Voltage | 3-Ground | IG S/W ON, Main S/W ON (Don't press brake pedal.) | Approx. 12V |
| | | | | Press brake pedal after checking above. | Approx. 12V→0V |
| 4 | Inhibitor switch (P,N) | Continuity | 4-Ground | "P" or "N" range | Continuity |
| | | | | Other than "P" or "N" range | No continuity |
| 5 | Clutch switch | Voltage | 5-Ground | IG S/W ON — Clutch switch ON | Approx. 12V |
| | | | | IG S/W ON — Clutch switch OFF | 0V |
| 6 | Power supply | Voltage | 6-Ground | IG S/W ON, Main S/W ON | Approx. 12V |
| 7 | Vehicle-speed sensor | Continuity | 7-Ground | Slowly turn the speedometer cable. | 4 changes of continuity-non continuity/ cable rotation |
| 8 | SET swtich | Continuity | 8-Ground | SET switch ON (Press) | Continuity |
| | | | | SET swtich OFF (Release) | No continuity |
| 9 | Stop light switch power supply side | Voltage | 9-Ground | At all times | Approx. 12V |
| 10 | RESUME switch | Continuity | 10-Ground | RESUME switch ON (Turn) | Continuity |
| | | | | RESUME switch OFF (Release) | No continuity |
| 11*2 | Self-diagnosis | – | – | – | – |
| 12 | Ground | Continuity | 12-Ground | At all times | Continuity |
| 13 | Stop light switch load side | Voltage | 13-Ground | Press the brake pedal. | Approx. 12V |

**Fig. 98 Electronic control unit signal circuit. Colt Vista**

between shaft and metal, or insufficient thrust clearance.

4. If selector does not move, ammeter A1 reads .5-.7 amps, but ammeter A2 reads 1 amp or more, check the following:
   a. Burned shaft or motor, or foreign material caught between gears.
5. If selector does not move, ammeter A1 reads 0.3–0.7 amps and ammeter A2 reads 0 amps, check the following:
   a. Damaged or disconnected internal lead wire or motor wiring, poor limit switch contact, or open diode.

### CONTROL UNIT

Refer to **Figs. 98 and 99,** when checking control unit.

# COMPONENT REPLACEMENT

## COLT VISTA

Remove components in order as shown in **Fig. 100,** when replacing actuator cable. Reverse procedure to install, noting the following:

1. Check inner and outer cable for damage. Ensure cable is properly positioned without sharp bends.
2. Check connection of cable to end fitting.
3. Check operation of actuator, brake switch and clutch switch.

## STEALTH, PLYMOUTH LASER & EAGLE TALON; 1989 COLT & EAGLE SUMMIT

Remove components in order as shown in **Figs. 101 through 105,** when replacing actuator and speed control components. Reverse procedure to install.

## CONQUEST

Remove components in order as shown in **Fig. 106,** when replacing speed control components. Reverse procedure to install, noting the following:

1. Apply a drying sealant to accelerator arm bracket bolt.
2. Apply grease to clevis pin, spring and return spring.

# ADJUSTMENTS

## PLYMOUTH LASER & EAGLE TALON

### Accelerator Cables

1. Confirm there are no sharp bends in accelerator cables.
2. Check inner cables for correct slack.
3. If slack is incorrect, adjust as follows:
   a. Remove actuator protector.
   b. **On single overhead cam engines,** turn ignition switch to the On position and leave in this position for approximately 15 seconds.
   c. **On all models,** loosen adjusting bolts, then adjust accelerator cable B, **Fig. 107,** to achieve freeplay of .04-.08 inch. If there is too much slack in the cable, the vehicle speed drop will be great when climbing a slope. If there is no slack in the cable, idle speed will increase.
4. After adjusting accelerator cable B, ensure the throttle lever touches the idle switch.
5. Adjust accelerator cable A, by loosening the locknut, **Fig. 108.** Correct freeplay should measure 0.0-0.4 inch for manual transaxles and .08-.12 inch for automatic transaxles.
6. After making cable adjustments, ensure the throttle lever at the engine side is caused to move .04-.08 inch when the actuator link is turned, as shown in **Fig. 109.**
7. Install actuator protector, then ensure throttle valve opens and closes fully by use of the accelerator pedal.

Engine control unit connector terminals

| 19 | 17 | 15 | 13 | 11 | | | 7 | 5 | 3 | 1 |
|---|---|---|---|---|---|---|---|---|---|---|
| 20 | 18 | 16 | 14 | 12 | 10 | 9 | 8 | 6 | 4 | 2 |

| Terminal | Connection or measured part | Measurement item | Tester connection | Check conditions | Standard |
|---|---|---|---|---|---|
| 1 | Actuator (motor) | Resistance | 1 → *'2 | Actuator selector (Fully closed position) | Approx. 12 Ω |
| 2 | | | | | |
| 3 | Stop light switch (for auto-cruise control cancellation) and actuator (clutch) | Voltage | 3 – Ground | Ignition switch ON, MAIN switch ON (Don't press brake pedal.) | Approx. 12V |
| | | | | Press brake pedal after checking above. | Approx. 12V → 0V |
| 4 | None | – | – | – | – |
| 5 | Power supply (MAIN) | Voltage | 5 – Ground | Ignition switch ON, MAIN switch ON | Approx. 12V |
| 6 | None | – | – | – | – |
| 7 | Power supply ($IG_2$) | Voltage | 7 – Ground | Ignition switch ON | Approx. 12V |
| 8*[2] | Self-diagnosis | – | – | – | – |
| 9 | Accelerator pedal switch | Voltage | 9 – Ground | Ignition switch ON (Accelerator pedal free) | Approx. 12V |
| | | | | Press accelerator pedal after checking above. | Approx. 12V → 0V |
| 10 | Vehicle speed sensor | Voltage | 10 – Ground | With the ignition key at the ON position, slowly turn the speedometer cable. | 4 voltage changes/ cable rotation |
| 11 | SET switch | Continuity | 11 – Ground | SET switch ON (Press) | Continuity |
| | | | | SET switch OFF (Release) | No continuity |
| 12 | Overdrive switch | Voltage | 12 – Ground | Ignition switch ON / Overdrive switch ON | Approx. 12V |
| | | | | Overdrive switch OFF | 0V |
| 13 | RESUME switch | Continuity | 13 – Ground | RESUME switch ON (Turn) | Continuity |
| | | | | RESUME switch OFF (Release) | No continuity |

| Terminal | Connection or measured part | Measurement item | Tester connection | Check conditions | Standard |
|---|---|---|---|---|---|
| 14*[2] | 4-A/T control unit | – | – | – | – |
| 15 | Stop light switch load side | Voltage | 15 – Ground | Press the brake pedal. | Approx. 12V |
| 16 | Ground | Continuity | 16 – Ground | At all times | Continuity |
| 17 | Inhibitor switch (P, N) | Continuity | 17 – Ground | "P" or "N" range | Continuity |
| | | | | Other than "P" or "N" range | No continuity |
| 18 | Stop light switch power supply side | Voltage | 18 – Ground | At all times | Approx. 12V |
| 19 | Clutch switch | Voltage | 19 – Ground | Ignition switch ON / Clutch switch ON | Approx. 12V |
| | | | | Clutch switch OFF | 0V |
| 20 | Ground | Continuity | 20 – Ground | At all times | Continuity |

**Fig. 99 Electronic control unit signal circuit. 1989 Colt & Eagle Summit**

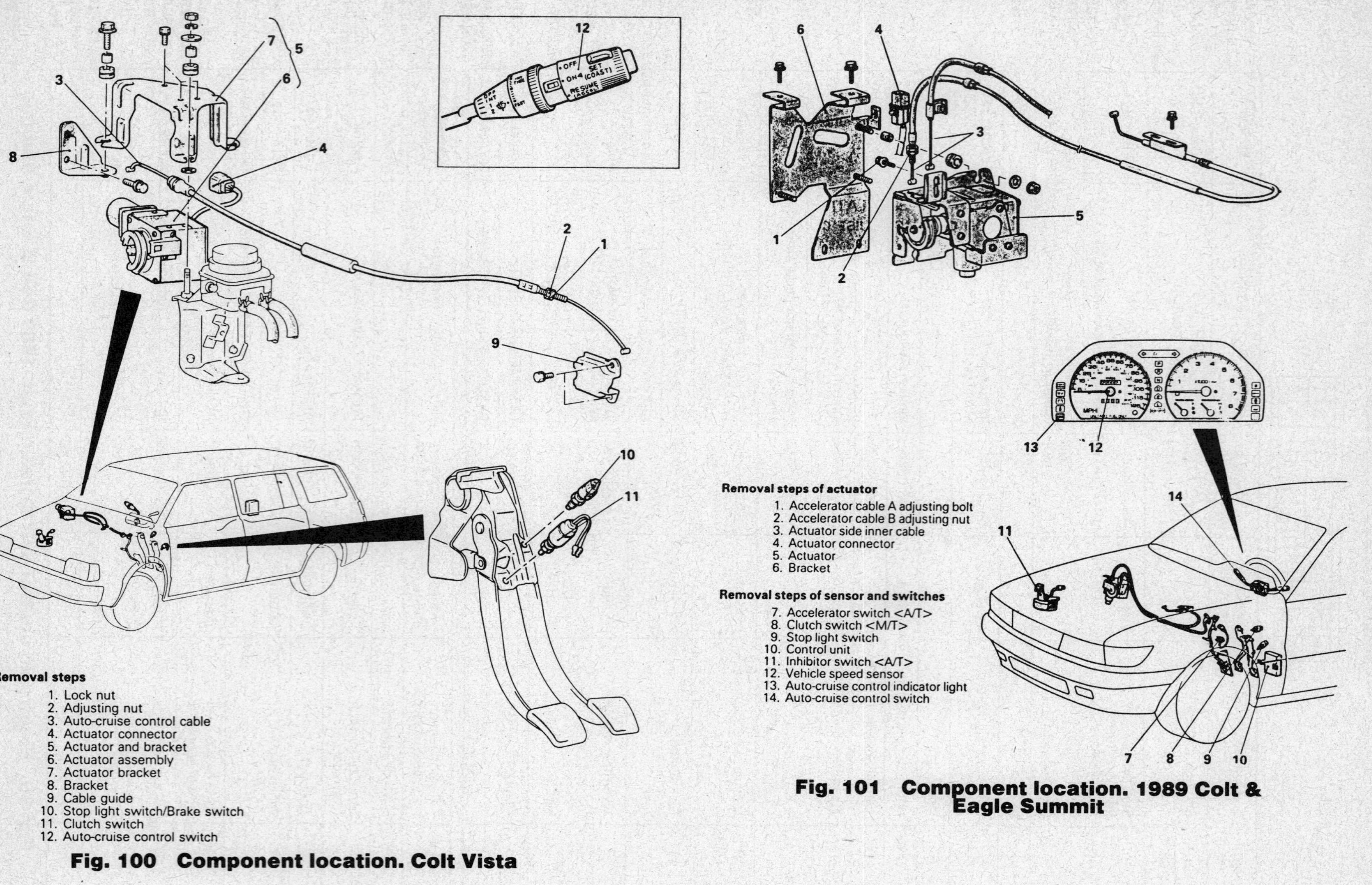


**Removal steps**

1. Lock nut
2. Adjusting nut
3. Auto-cruise control cable
4. Actuator connector
5. Actuator and bracket
6. Actuator assembly
7. Actuator bracket
8. Bracket
9. Cable guide
10. Stop light switch/Brake switch
11. Clutch switch
12. Auto-cruise control switch

**Fig. 100 Component location. Colt Vista**

**Removal steps of actuator**

1. Accelerator cable A adjusting bolt
2. Accelerator cable B adjusting nut
3. Actuator side inner cable
4. Actuator connector
5. Actuator
6. Bracket

**Removal steps of sensor and switches**

7. Accelerator switch <A/T>
8. Clutch switch <M/T>
9. Stop light switch
10. Control unit
11. Inhibitor switch <A/T>
12. Vehicle speed sensor
13. Auto-cruise control indicator light
14. Auto-cruise control switch

**Fig. 101 Component location. 1989 Colt & Eagle Summit**

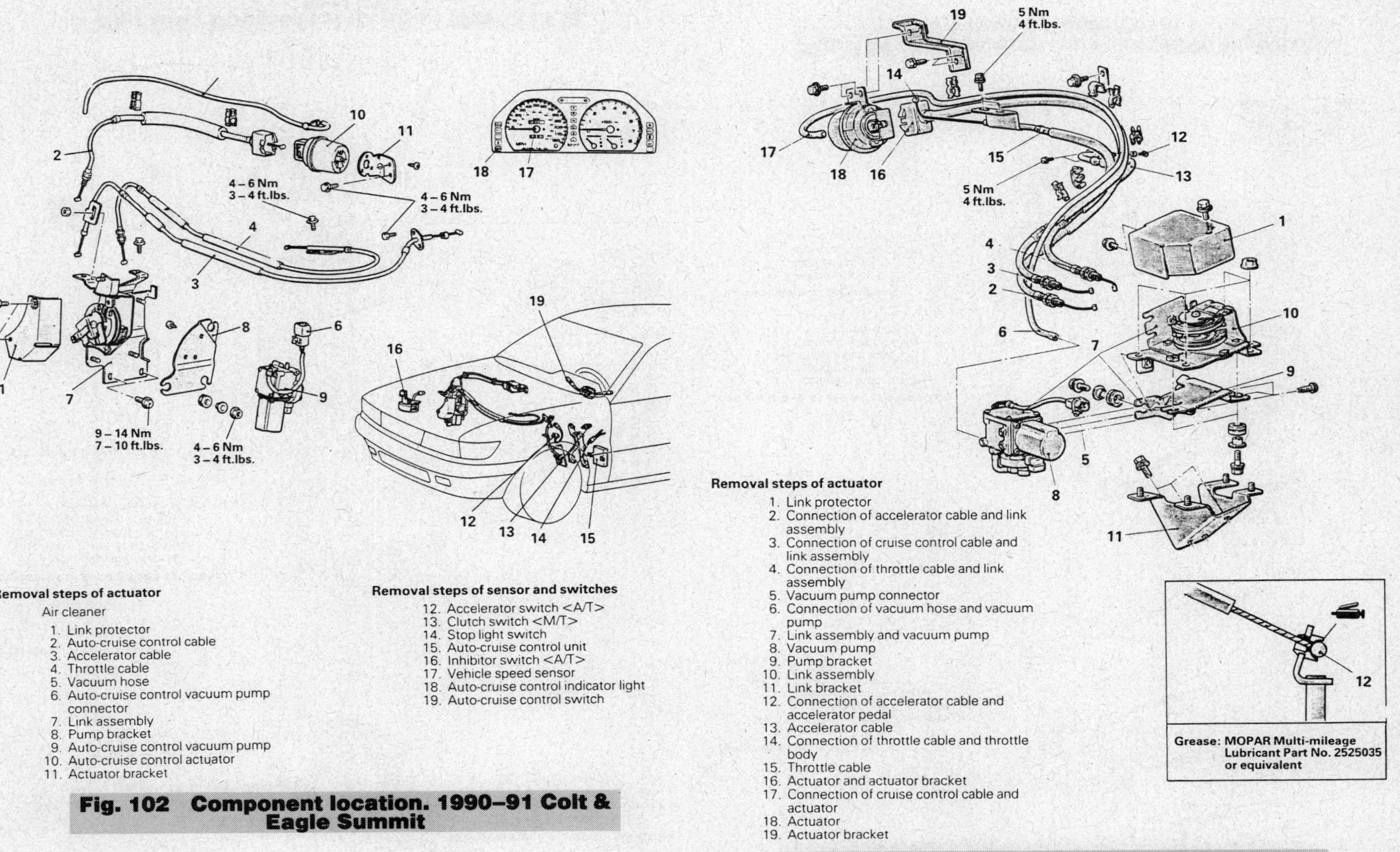


**Removal steps of actuator**

Air cleaner

1. Link protector
2. Auto-cruise control cable
3. Accelerator cable
4. Throttle cable
5. Vacuum hose
6. Auto-cruise control vacuum pump connector
7. Link assembly
8. Pump bracket
9. Auto-cruise control vacuum pump
10. Auto-cruise control actuator
11. Actuator bracket

**Removal steps of sensor and switches**

12. Accelerator switch <A/T>
13. Clutch switch <M/T>
14. Stop light switch
15. Auto-cruise control unit
16. Inhibitor switch <A/T>
17. Vehicle speed sensor
18. Auto-cruise control indicator light
19. Auto-cruise control switch

**Fig. 102 Component location. 1990–91 Colt & Eagle Summit**

**Removal steps of actuator**

1. Link protector
2. Connection of accelerator cable and link assembly
3. Connection of cruise control cable and link assembly
4. Connection of throttle cable and link assembly
5. Vacuum pump connector
6. Connection of vacuum hose and vacuum pump
7. Link assembly and vacuum pump
8. Vacuum pump
9. Pump bracket
10. Link assembly
11. Link bracket
12. Connection of accelerator cable and accelerator pedal
13. Accelerator cable
14. Connection of throttle cable and throttle body
15. Throttle cable
16. Actuator and actuator bracket
17. Connection of cruise control cable and actuator
18. Actuator
19. Actuator bracket

**Fig. 103 Component location (Part 1 of 2). Stealth**

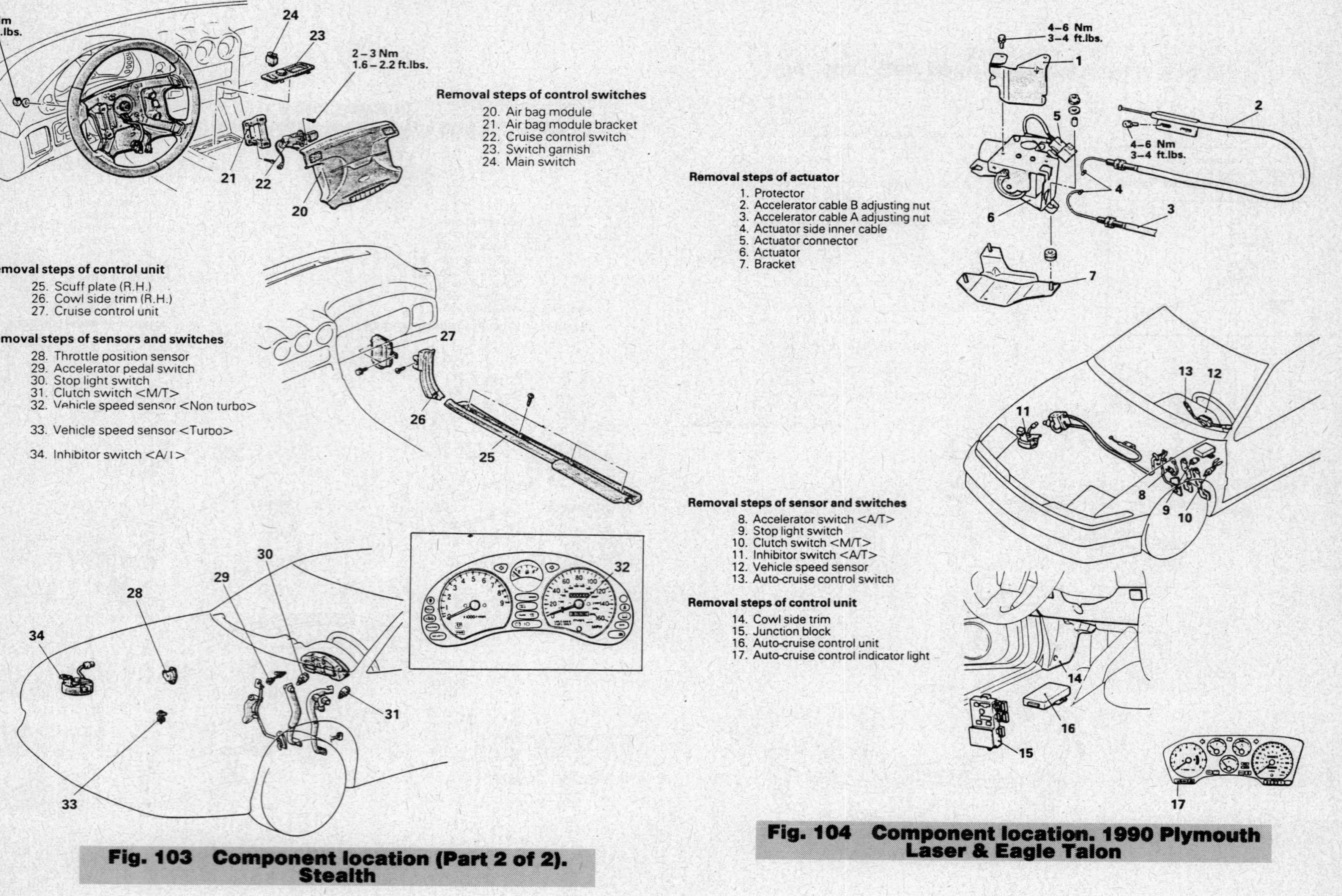


**Fig. 103 Component location (Part 2 of 2). Stealth**

**Fig. 104 Component location. 1990 Plymouth Laser & Eagle Talon**

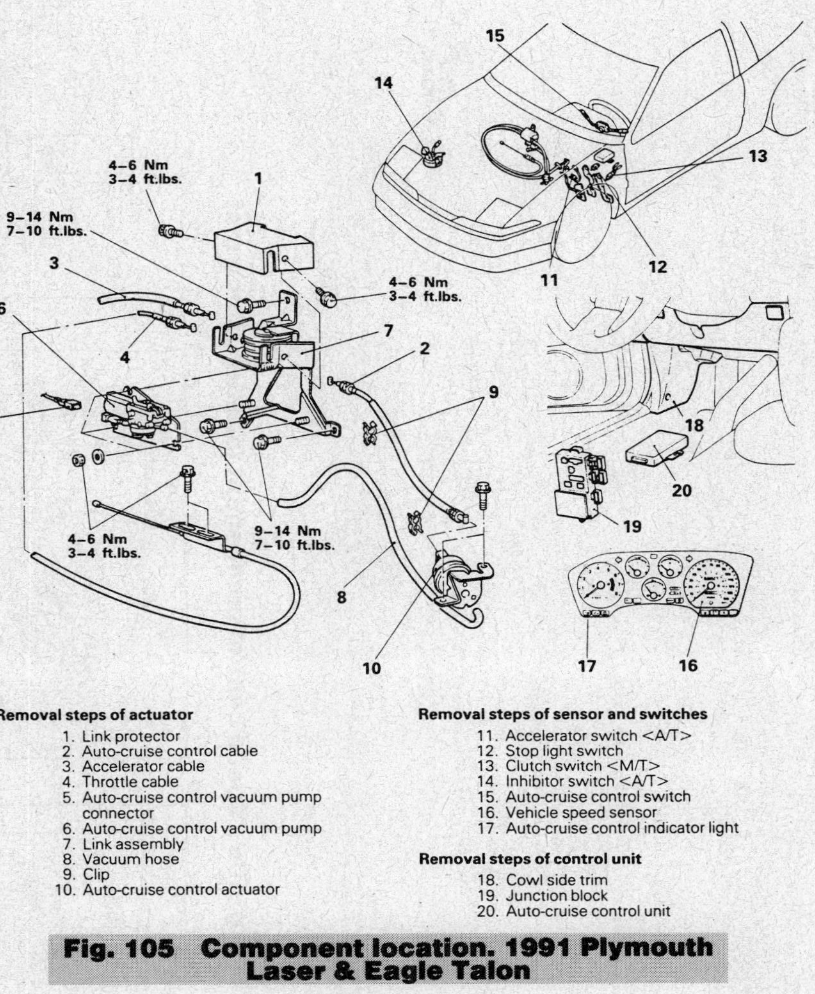


**Removal steps of actuator**

1. Link protector
2. Auto-cruise control cable
3. Accelerator cable
4. Throttle cable
5. Auto-cruise control vacuum pump connector
6. Auto-cruise control vacuum pump
7. Link assembly
8. Vacuum hose
9. Clip
10. Auto-cruise control actuator

**Removal steps of sensor and switches**

11. Accelerator switch <A/T>
12. Stop light switch
13. Clutch switch <M/T>
14. Inhibitor switch <A/T>
15. Auto-cruise control switch
16. Vehicle speed sensor
17. Auto-cruise control indicator light

**Removal steps of control unit**

18. Cowl side trim
19. Junction block
20. Auto-cruise control unit

**Fig. 105 Component location. 1991 Plymouth Laser & Eagle Talon**

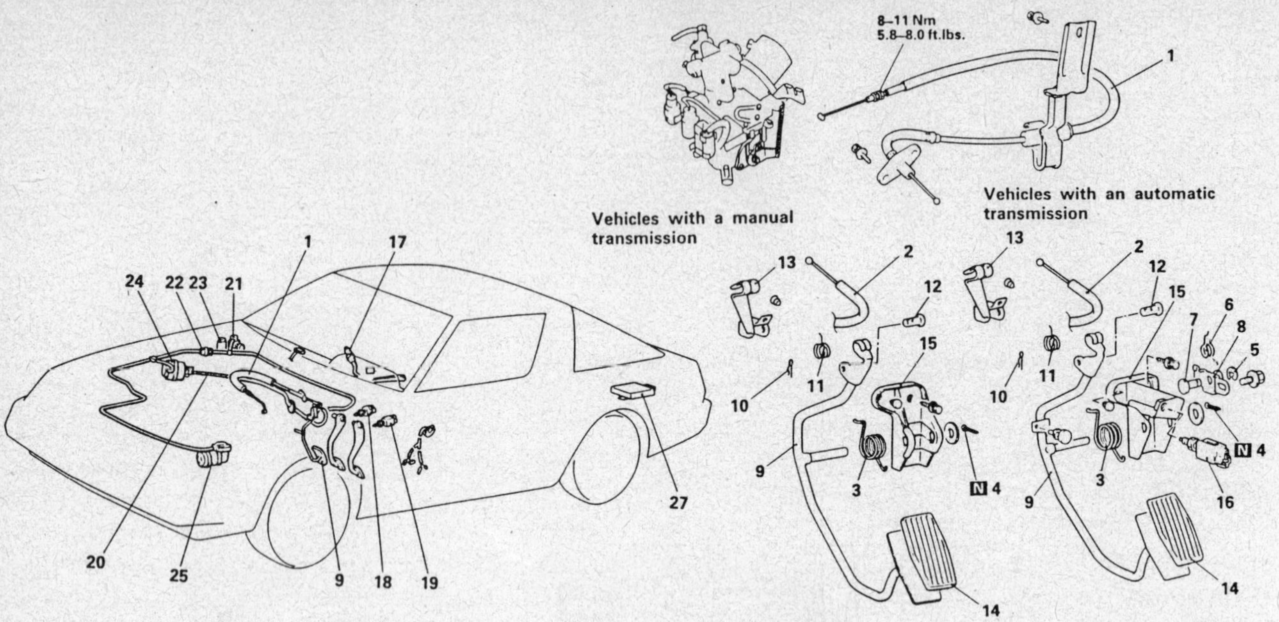

8–11 Nm
5.8–8.0 ft.lbs.

Vehicles with a manual transmission

Vehicles with an automatic transmission

1. Accelerator cable
2. Auto-cruise control cable connection
3. Return spring
4. Cotter pin
5. Snap ring
6. Spring
7. Clevis pin
8. Spring holder
9. Accelerator arm
10. Cotter pin
11. Spring
12. Clevis pin
13. Lever
14. Pedal pad
15. Accelerator arm bracket
16. Kickdown switch
17. Auto-cruise control switch
18. Brake switch
19. Clutch switch
20. Auto-cruise control cable
21. Vacuum switch
22. Vacuum check valve
23. Vacuum pump relay
24. Actuator
25. Vacuum pump
26. Vacuum hose
27. Electronic control unit (ECU)

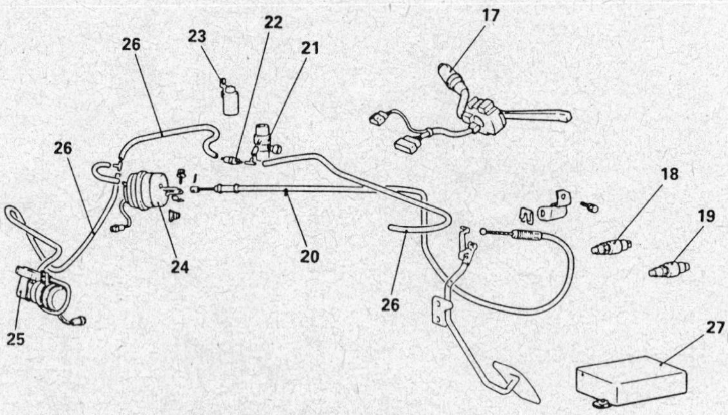

**Fig. 106 Speed control component location. Conquest**

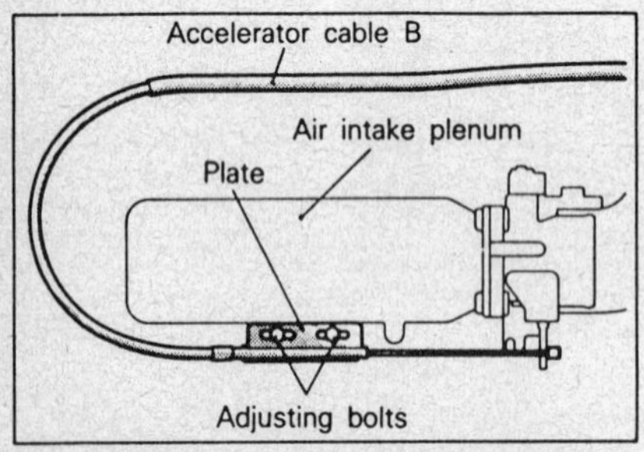


**Fig. 107 Accelerator cable adjustment. Eagle Talon & Plymouth Laser**

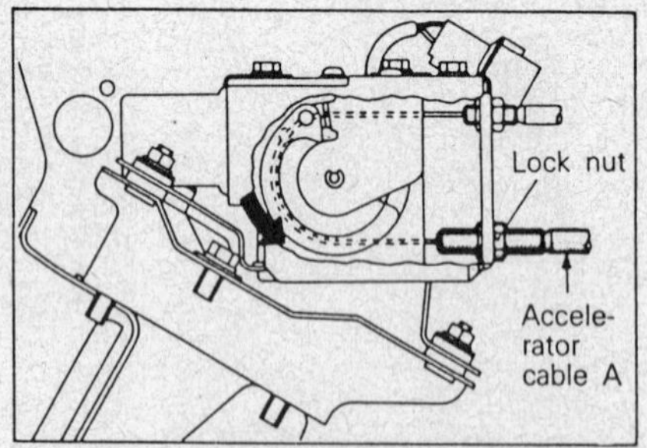


**Fig. 108 Accelerator cable A adjustment. Eagle Talon & Plymouth Laser**

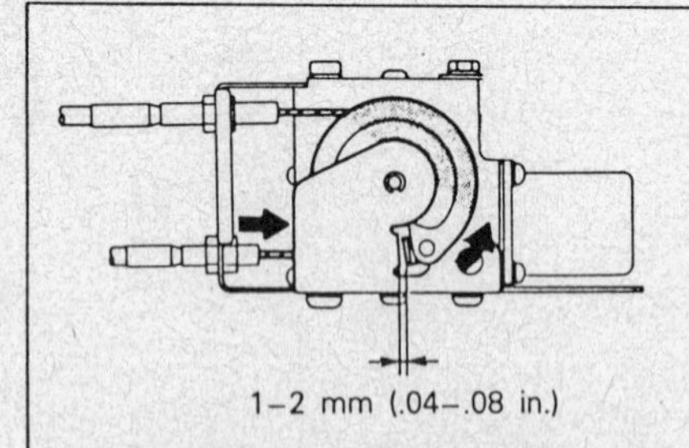

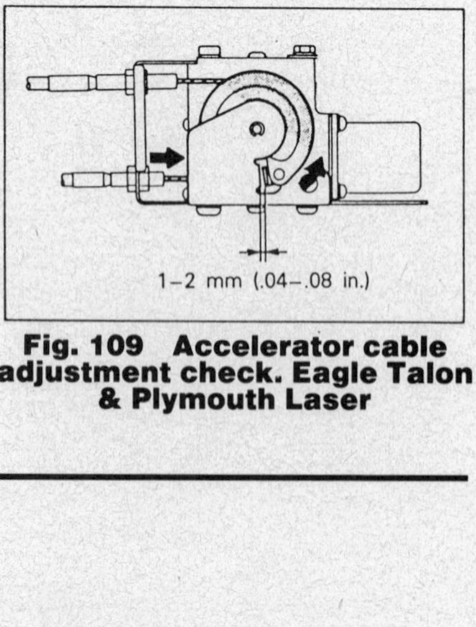

**Fig. 109 Accelerator cable adjustment check. Eagle Talon & Plymouth Laser**

# Type 3

## INDEX

**NOTE:** Wire Code Identification And Symbol Identification Located In The Front Of This Manual Can Be Used As An Aid When Using Wiring Circuits Found In This Section.



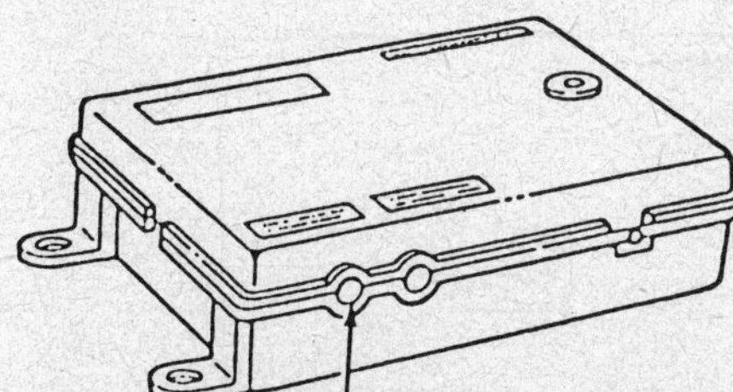

**Fig. 1 Centering adjustment. Dodge Monaco & Eagle Premier**

## DESCRIPTION

The Dodge Monaco and Eagle Premier cruise control system operates at any speed above 30 mph. The system may be disengaged by pushing the Off button, depressing the brake pedal, depressing the clutch, or turning the ignition off. If vehicle speed changes by more than 5 mph per second, the cruise control module will automatically disengage from cruise mode.

Road speed is maintained by a servo which controls throttle position according to module output. Vacuum to the servo is regulated by solenoid controlled manifold vacuum valves which balance the amount of vacuum charge and vent.

The major components of the Dodge Monaco and Eagle Premier cruise control system are; a cruise control module located behind the instrument panel, a servo which is mounted in the engine compartment and a speed sensor located in the transmission.

## ADJUSTMENT

If cruise control engages above or below the selected speed, adjustment is possible to correct the condition by turning the centering adjustment screw, **Fig. 1**, on the cruise control module.

1. If cruise control engages 2 mph or more above the selected speed, turn the centering adjustment screw counterclockwise.
2. If cruise control engages 2 mph or more below the selected speed, turn the centering adjustment screw clockwise.

## DIAGNOSIS & TESTING

When cruise control malfunction occurs, all vacuum lines and electrical connections should be checked first before any before any repairs are made.

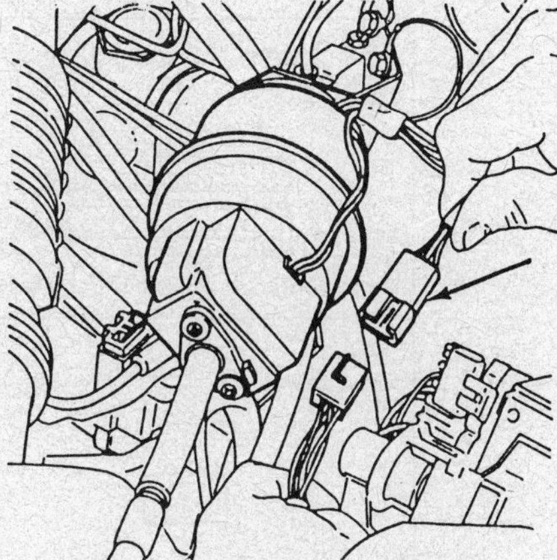

**Fig. 2 Servo electrical connector. Dodge Monaco & Eagle Premier**

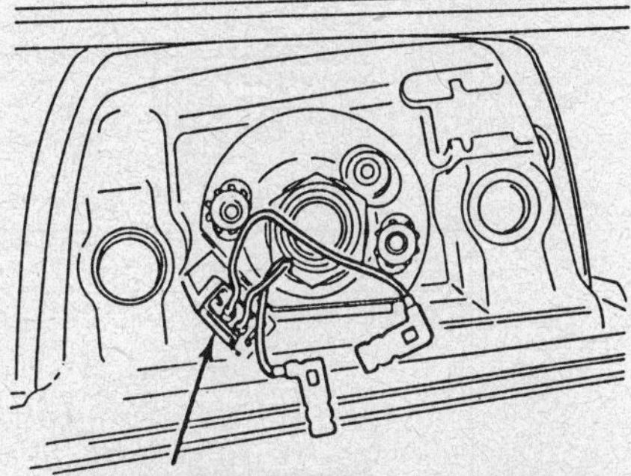

**Fig. 3 Servo vacuum line & mounting screws. Dodge Monaco & Eagle Premier**

### CONTROL MODULE

The Cruise Control Module calibration is preset by the manufacturer. If all vacuum lines, electrical connections and components are in good working order and system still does not function, it can be determined if the module is functioning using the following procedure.

1. Using a screwdriver, carefully turn the adjusting screw, **Fig. 1**, to the 10 O'clock position. **The adjuster has a turning limit of 3/4 turn. Do not press hard or turn adjuster hard against stops.**
2. If this adjustment has no effect on cruise control operation, replace the cruise control module.

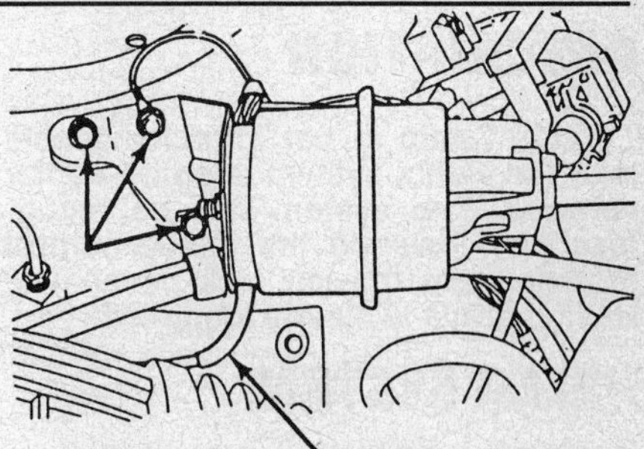

**Fig. 4 Horn wires. Dodge Monaco & Eagle Premier**

### SERVO

1. Check servo cable and vacuum hose for damage or binding.
2. Check vacuum can and hose connections.
3. If servo does not operate, replace servo.

## COMPONENT REPLACEMENT

### CRUISE CONTROL MODULE

1. Remove retaining screws.
2. Disconnect electrical connector, then remove module.
3. Reverse procedure to install.

### SERVO

1. Disconnect electrical connector, **Fig. 2,** then disconnect vacuum line from connector, **Fig. 3.**
2. Remove servo mounting screws, **Fig. 3,** then slide servo cable rearward and separate from from throttle body linkage.
3. Squeeze plastic tabs and remove cable from bracket, then the servo.
4. Reverse procedure to install.

### CRUISE SWITCH

1. Pull up to remove horn cover.
2. Disconnect horn wires and the electrical connector shown in **Fig. 4.**
3. Pry up to remove switch panel from steering wheel.
4. Reverse procedure to install.

# Type 4

## INDEX

**NOTE: Wire Code Identification And Symbol Identification Located In The Front Of This Manual Can Be Used As An Aid When Using Wiring Circuits Found In This Section.**



# DESCRIPTION

**This system in not interchangeable with the Renix system used on earlier vehicles. The system can be recognized by lowering the cruise control module from the left kick panel. The Hella module is clearly identified.**

# HELLA SYSTEM

## DESCRIPTION

The Hella Cruise Control system is composed of three control groups; the vacuum pump, venting safety solenoid and diaphragm which controls throttle linkage. The electronic control consists of the electronic cruise control module and engine overspeed relay. The safety control is composed of the master instrument panel switch, switches on the steering wheel and brake, clutch switches.

## DIAGNOSIS & TESTING

Refer to **Figs. 1 through 3,** when diagnosing speed control system.

## COMPONENT REPLACEMENT

### Servo Control (Regulator)

1. Press retaining clip (A) holding wiper/washer connector, then slide electrical connector out of bracket, **Fig. 4.**
2. Position tie strap (B) ensuring wiper/washer connector will separate. **Do not cut tie strap.**
3. Remove two retaining nuts (C) holding regulator housing to inner fender, **Fig. 5.**
4. Disconnect clip (D) holding vacuum line to housing, **Fig. 6.**
5. Remove Torx head screws (E), then slide regulator assembly from housing.
6. Disconnect safety solenoid electrical connector (F), then the vacuum control, **Fig. 7.**
7. Disconnect vacuum line (H), then remove regulator.
8. Reverse procedure to install.

### Safety Solenoid

1. Remove regulator as previously described.
2. Disconnect vacuum line (J), **Fig. 8.**
3. Remove two retaining bolts (K), then the solenoid.
4. Reverse procedure to install.

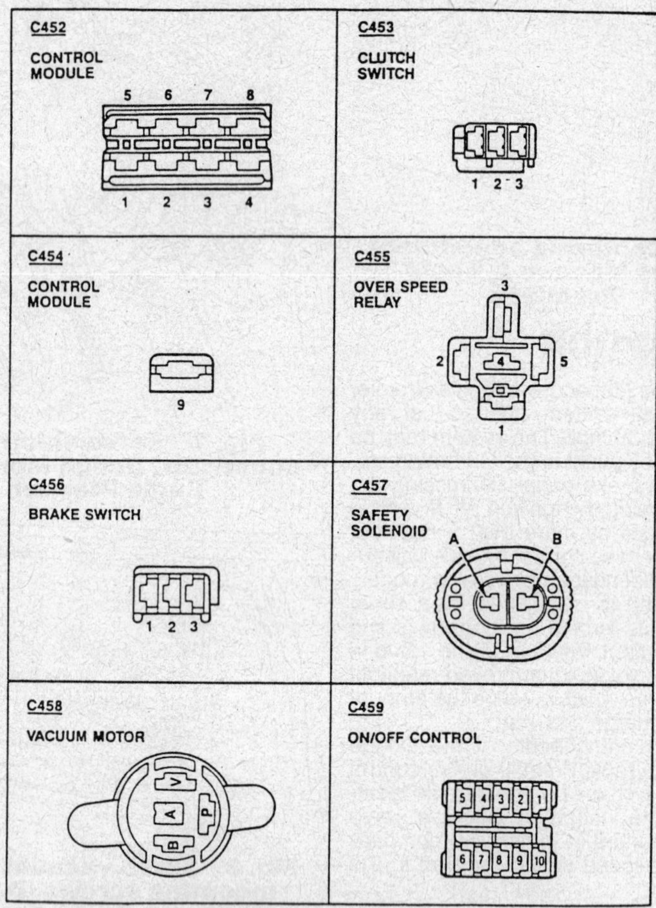


**Fig. 1 Connector identification. Eagle Medallion w/Hella system**

### Pneumatic Control

1. Remove regulator as previously described.
2. Disconnect vacuum line (L), **Fig. 9.**
3. Remove two retaining bolts, then the pneumatic control.
4. Reverse procedure to install.

### Engine Overspeed Relay

Refer to **Fig. 10** when replacing the engine overspeed relay.

# RENIX SYSTEM

## COMPONENT REPLACEMENT

### Servo Control

1. Remove two retaining nuts (A) securing assembly to inner fender, **Fig. 10.**
2. Remove screws securing plastic cover, then separate base and cover.
3. Disconnect vacuum hose (C) and electrical connector located on inner fender.
4. Reverse procedure to install.

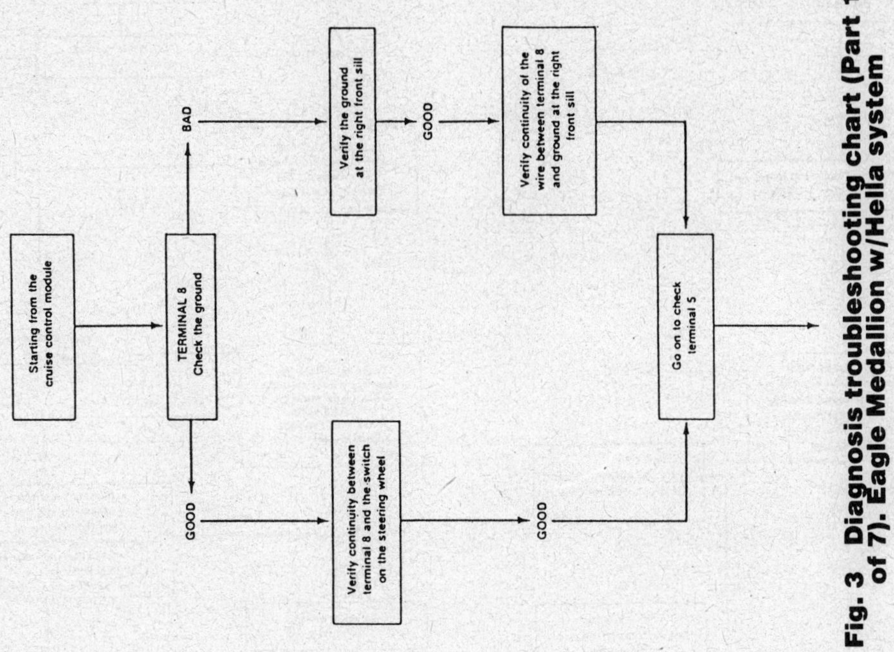


**Fig. 3 Diagnosis troubleshooting chart (Part 1 of 7). Eagle Medallion w/Hella system**

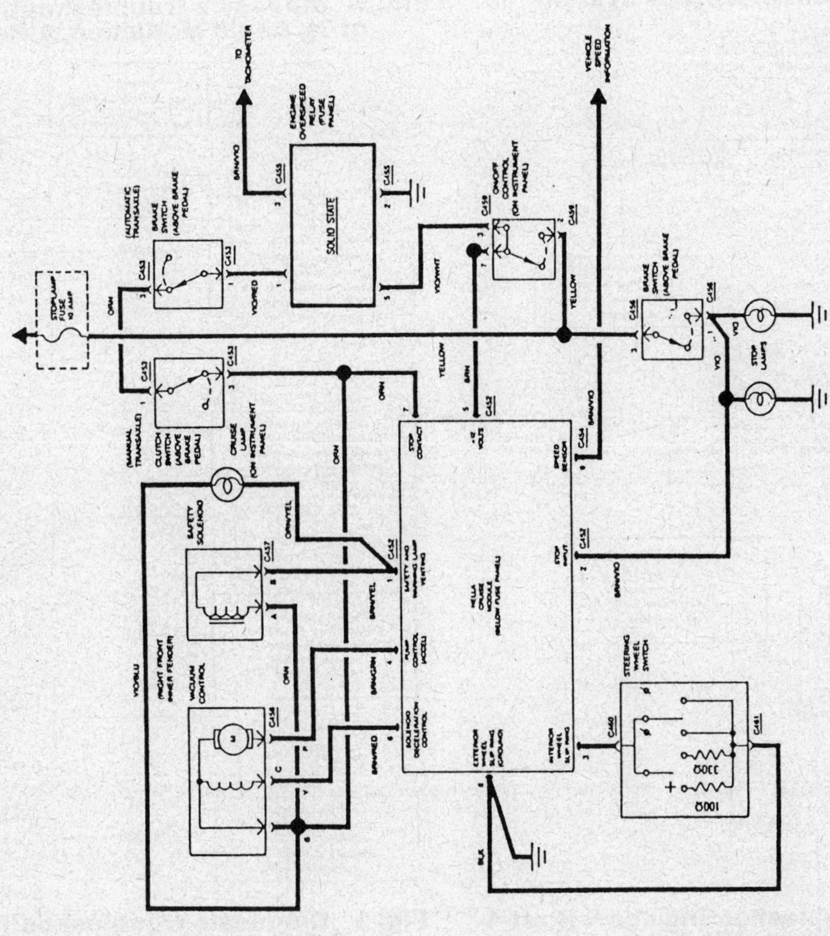


**Fig. 2 Speed control wiring diagram. Eagle Medallion w/Hella system**

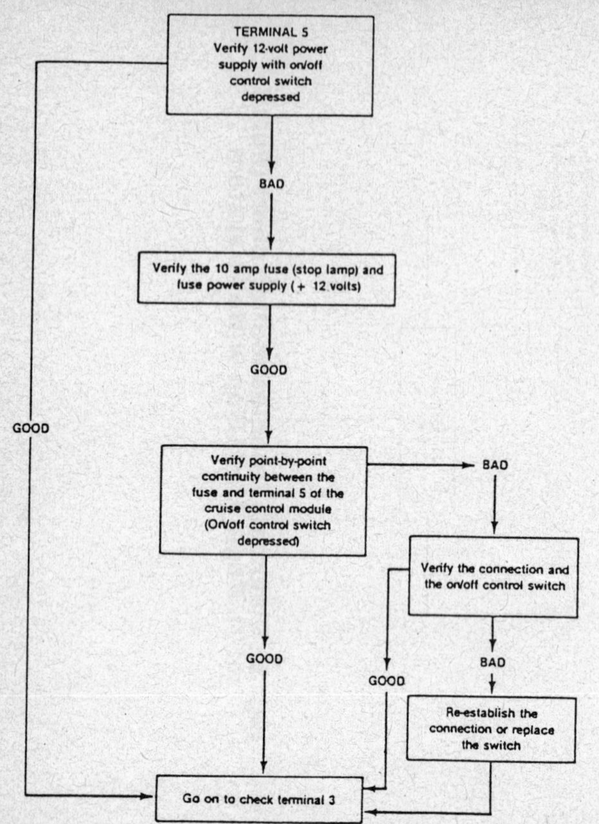


Fig. 3 Diagnosis troubleshooting chart (Part 2 of 7). Eagle Medallion w/Hella system

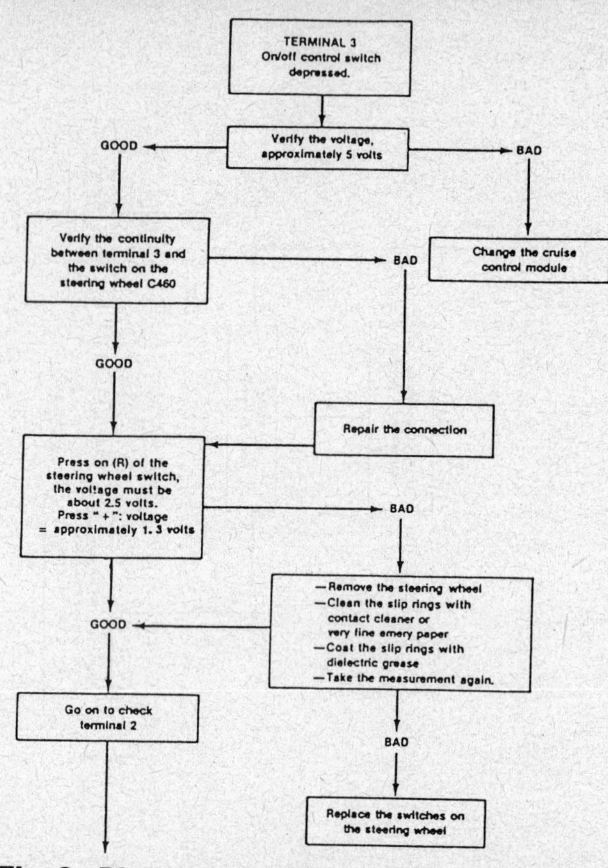


Fig. 3 Diagnosis troubleshooting chart (Part 3 of 7). Eagle Medallion w/Hella system

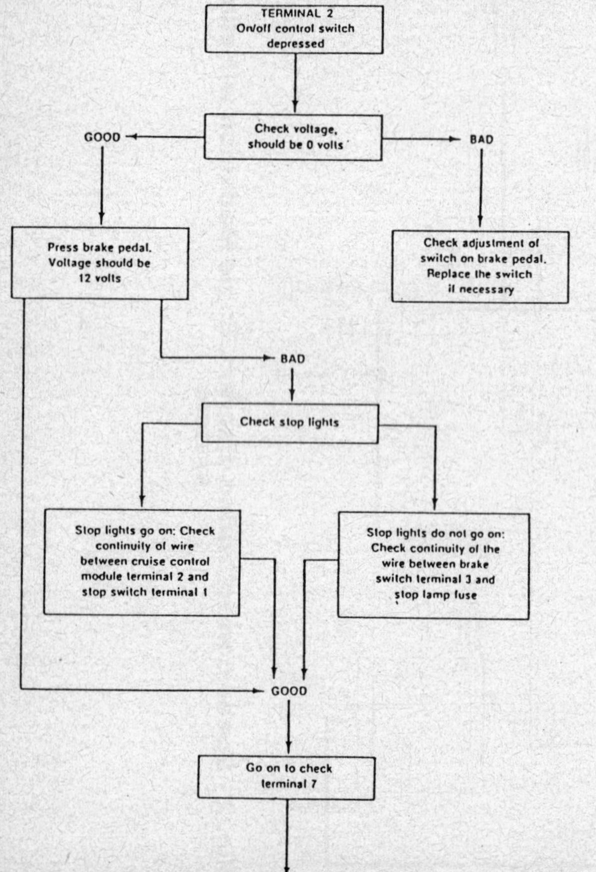


Fig. 3 Diagnosis troubleshooting chart (Part 4 of 7). Eagle Medallion w/Hella system

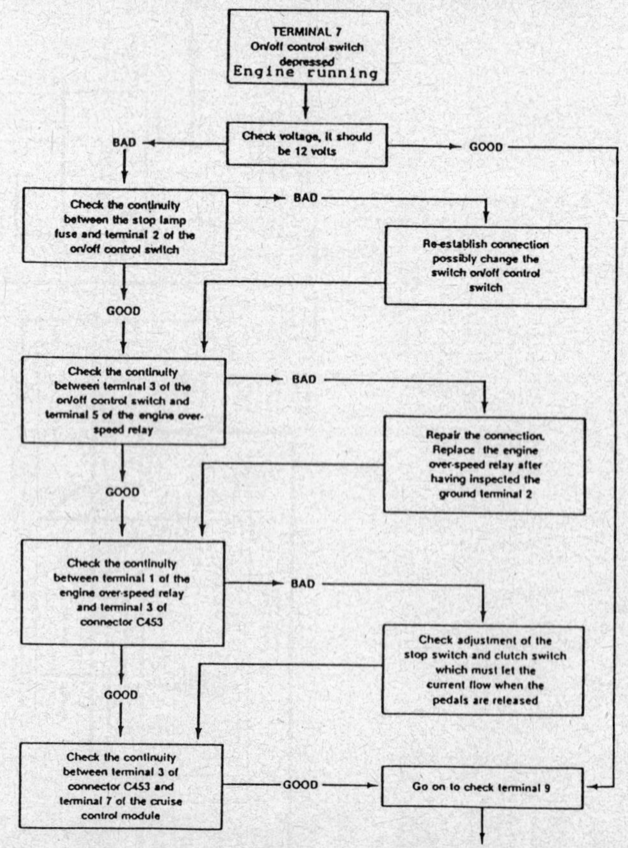


Fig. 3 Diagnosis troubleshooting chart (Part 5 of 7). Eagle Medallion w/Hella system

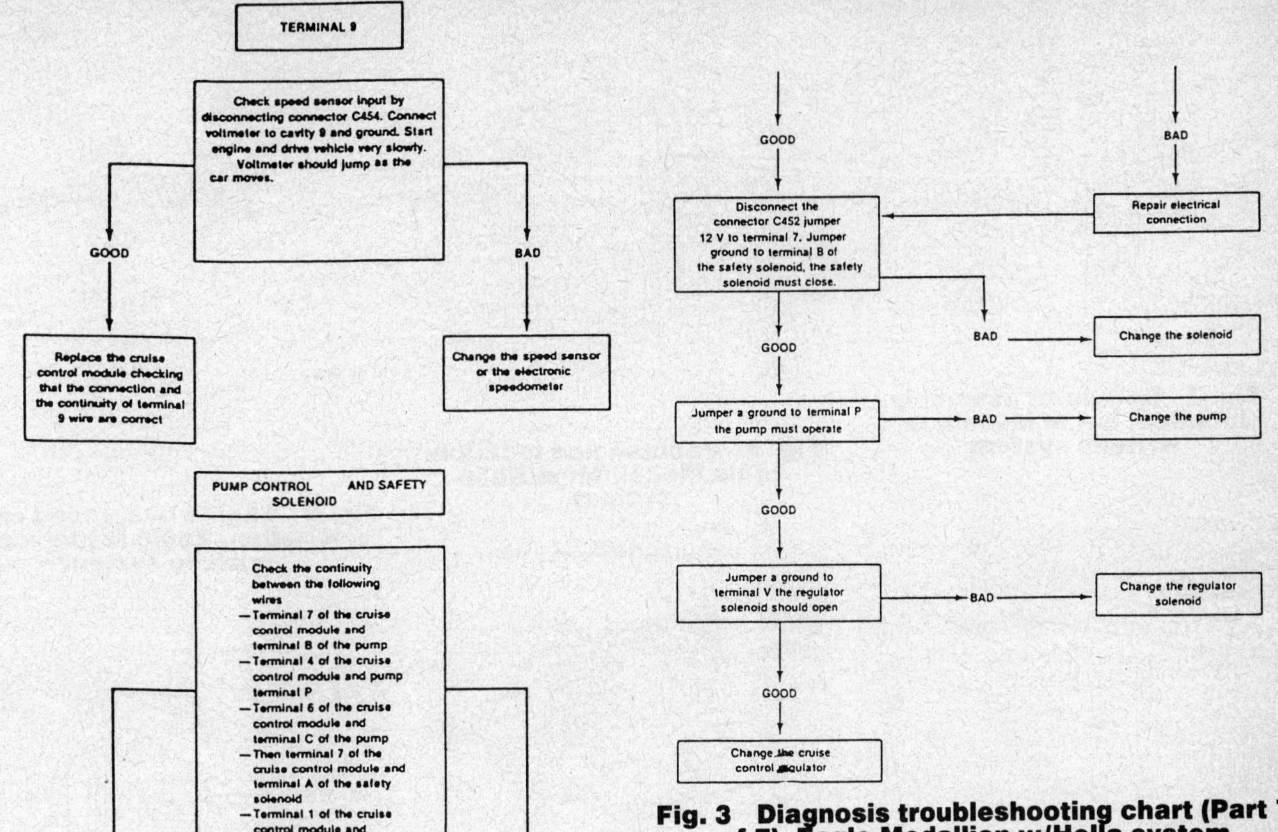
TERMINAL 9
Check speed sensor input by disconnecting connector C454. Connect voltmeter to cavity 9 and ground. Start engine and drive vehicle very slowly. Voltmeter should jump as the car moves.
GOOD
BAD
Replace the cruise control module checking that the connection and the continuity of terminal 9 wire are correct
Change the speed sensor or the electronic speedometer
PUMP CONTROL AND SAFETY SOLENOID
Check the continuity between the following wires
—Terminal 7 of the cruise control module and terminal B of the pump
—Terminal 4 of the cruise control module and pump terminal P
—Terminal 6 of the cruise control module and terminal C of the pump
—Then terminal 7 of the cruise control module and terminal A of the safety solenoid
—Terminal 1 of the cruise control module and terminal B of the safety solenoid
GOOD
BAD
Disconnect the connector C452 jumper 12 V to terminal 7. Jumper ground to terminal B of the safety solenoid, the safety solenoid must close.
Repair electrical connection
GOOD
BAD
Change the solenoid
Jumper a ground to terminal P the pump must operate
BAD
Change the pump
GOOD
Jumper a ground to terminal V the regulator solenoid should open
BAD
Change the regulator solenoid
GOOD
Change the cruise control regulator

**Fig. 3 Diagnosis troubleshooting chart (Part 7 of 7). Eagle Medallion w/Hella system**

**Fig. 3 Diagnosis troubleshooting chart (Part 6 of 7). Eagle Medallion w/Hella system**

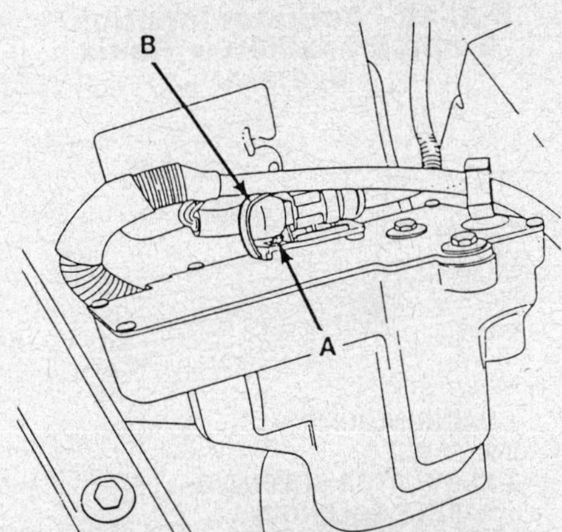
B
A

**Fig. 4 Wiper/washer electrical connector location. Eagle Medallion w/Hella system**

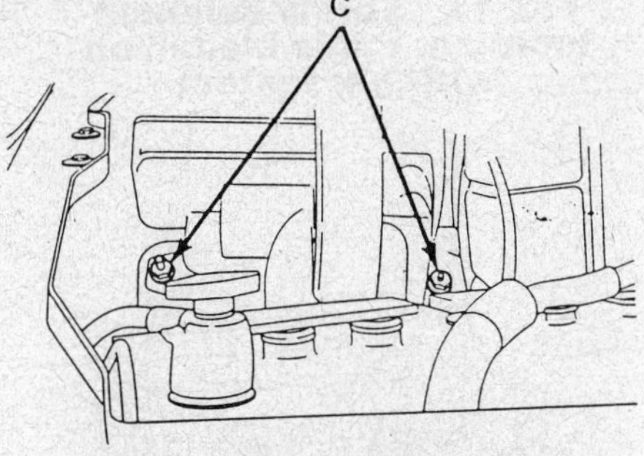
C

**Fig. 5 Regulator housing attaching nut location. Eagle Medallion w/Hella system**

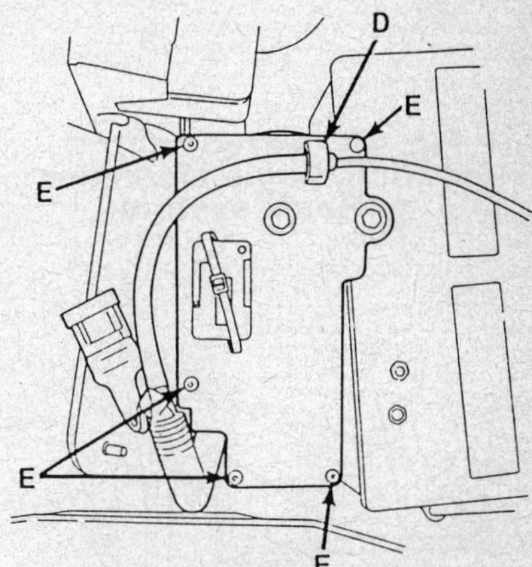
D
E
E
E
E

**Fig. 6 Torx head screws location. Eagle Medallion w/Hella system**

## Safety Solenoid

1. Remove servo control as previously described.
2. Disconnect vacuum hose and electrical connector and pull solenoid away from the servo unit, (D) **Fig. 11.**
3. Reverse procedure to install.

## Regulator Solenoid

1. Remove servo control as previously described.
2. Disconnect vacuum hose and electrical connector and pull solenoid away from the servo unit, (E) **Fig. 11.**
3. Reverse procedure to install.

## Vacuum Pump

1. Remove servo control as previously described.
2. Loosen retaining screws and pull vacuum pump away from the servo unit.
3. Reverse procedure to install.

## Actuator

1. Remove retaining nuts (B) and (C), **Fig. 12.**
2. Disconnect vacuum line hose, then remove the actuator.
3. Reverse procedure to install. Adjust as follows:
   a. Measure clearance between rod (Y) and arm (T), **Fig. 13.**
   b. Clearance should be 0.06 inch.
   c. If clearance is not as described, adjust by changing length of rod (Y).
   d. Loosen or tighten nut (C) on end of rod (Y).
   e. Connect vacuum hose to actuator.

## Cruise Control Module

The cruise control module is located behind dash panel, under carpet near left kick panel, **Fig. 14.**

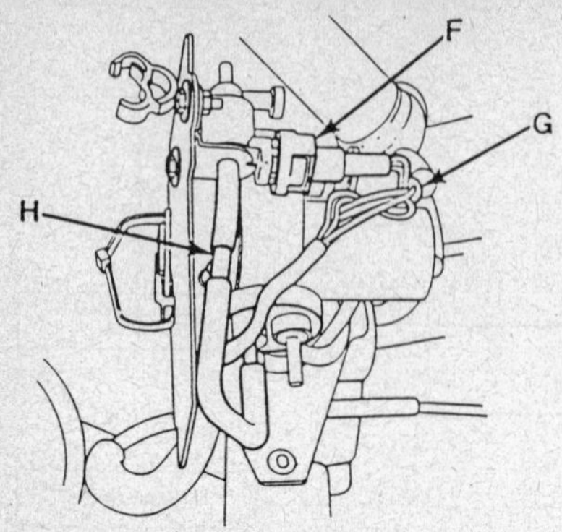


**Fig. 7 Regulator assembly location. Eagle Medallion w/Hella system**

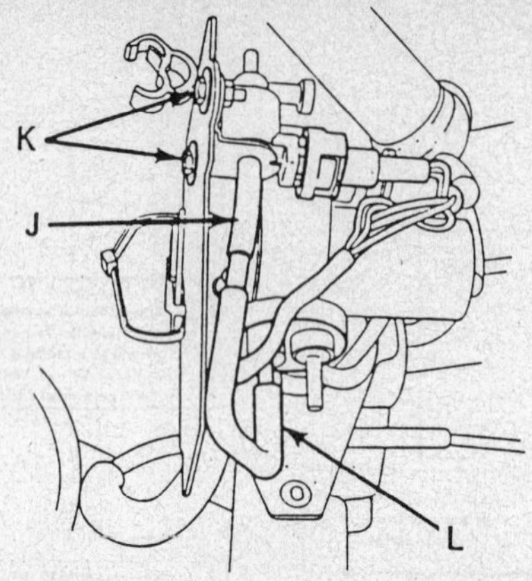


**Fig. 8 Vacuum line location. Eagle Medallion w/Hella system**

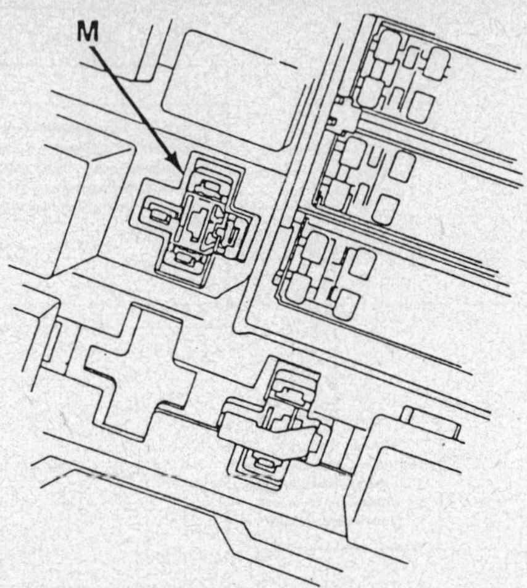


**Fig. 9 Engine overspeed relay location. Eagle Medallion w/Hella system**

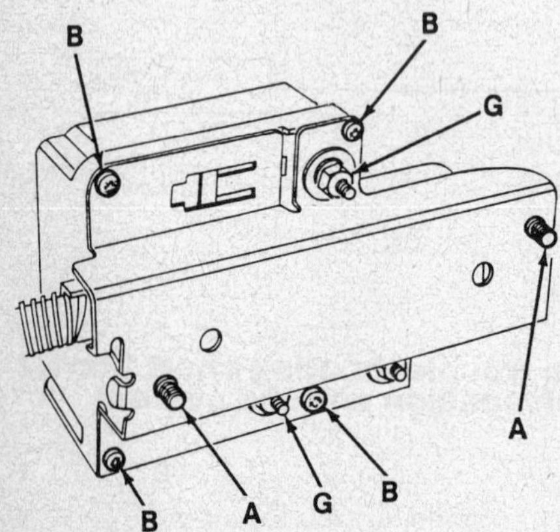


**Fig. 10 Servo control location. Eagle Medallion w/Renix system**

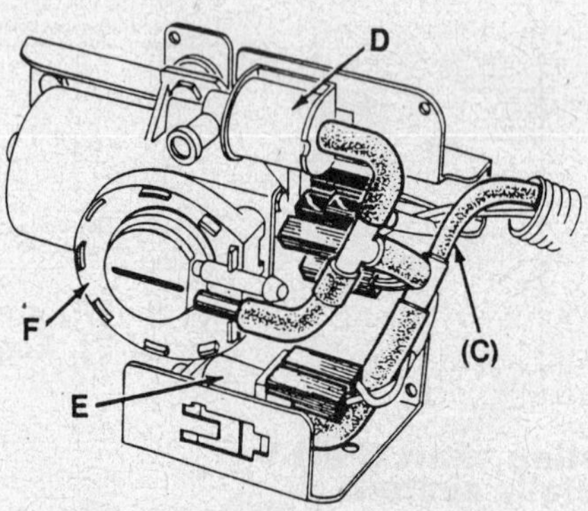


**Fig. 11 Safety solenoid location. Eagle Medallion w/Renix system**

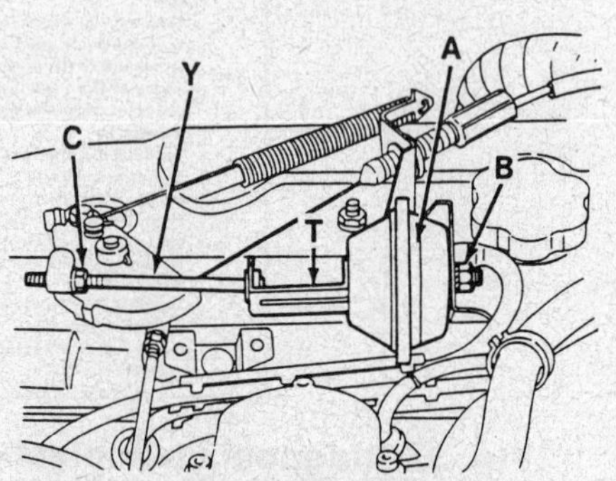


**Fig. 12 Actuator location. Eagle Medallion w/Renix system**

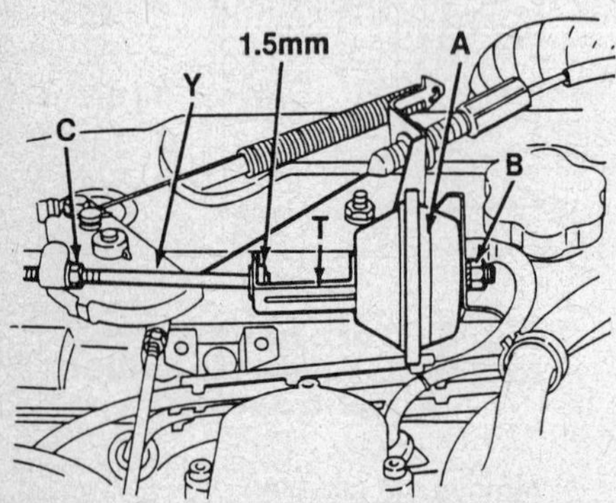


**Fig. 13 Actuator adjustment. Eagle Medallion w/Renix system**

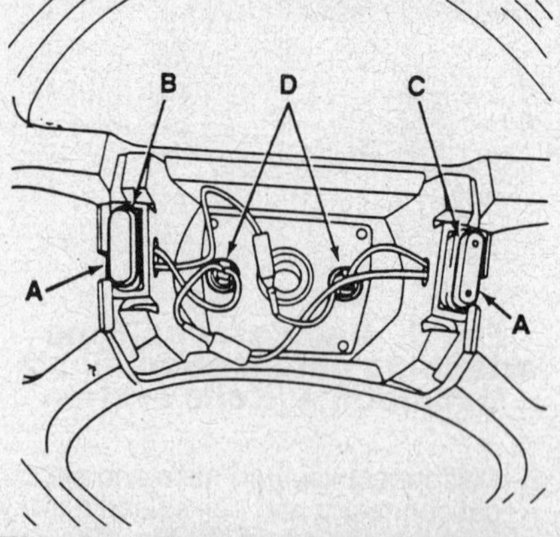


**Fig. 14 Cruise control module wiring connections. Eagle Medallion w/Renix system**

## Steering Wheel Switches

1. Remove retaining screws (A) on both sides of steering wheel cover, then the steering wheel cover, **Fig. 15.**
2. Mark steering wheel shaft for proper installation, then loosen steering wheel locknut. **Do not use a hammer to tap against end of steering column.**
3. Pull on steering wheel, then remove locknut and the steering wheel.
4. Unplug electrical connectors between On/Off switch (C), Res/Accel switch (B) and ring terminals (D).
5. With steering wheel removed, clean circular contacts. **Apply specified lubricant.**
6. If contacts are heavily contaminated, clean with fine emery paper.
7. Reverse procedure to install.

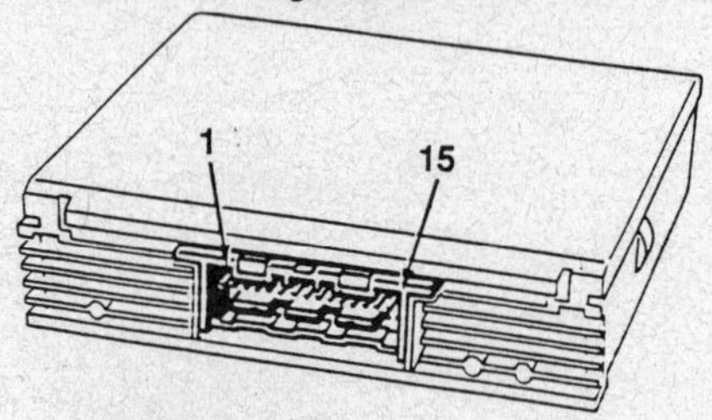


1-VACUUM PUMP
2-NOT USED
3-REGULATOR SOLENOID
4-SAFETY SOLENOID
5-INDICATOR LIGHT
6-SPEED SIGNAL LIGHT
7-CLUTCH AND BRAKE PEDAL SIGNAL
8-STEERING WHEEL INSIDE CIRCULAR CONTACT
9-STEERING WHEEL OUTSIDE CIRCULAR CONTACT
10-TACH SIGNAL
11-POWER TO VACUUM PUMP AND SOLENOIDS
12-IGNITION
13-GROUND
14-NOT USED
15-NOT USED

**Fig. 15 Steering wheel switches location. Eagle Medallion w/Renix system**

# TROUBLESHOOTING SUPPLEMENT

## TABLE OF CONTENTS



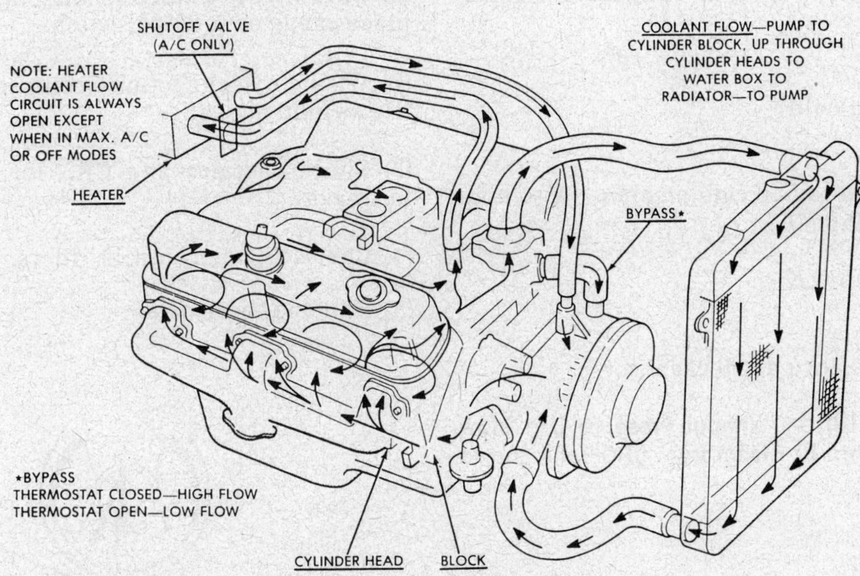


**Fig. 1 Cooling (Part 1 of 7)**

| Symptom | Action |
|---|---|
| **Blinking Engine Warning Light Or High Gage Indication—Without Coolant Loss** | Normal with temporary operation with heavy load, towing a light trailer, high outdoor temperatures, and/or on a steep grade. |
| **Coolant Loss** | Improper refilling procedures can result in trapped air in the system. Subsequent operation of the pressure cap and coolant recovery system will deaereate the cooling system. A low coolant level will then result in the Coolant Reserve Tank. Add coolant. |
| **Hot Vehicle (Not Engine)**<br>**Heat Damage**<br>**Hot Carpet, Seat, Trunk**<br>**Hot Catalytic Converter**<br>**Smoke, Burnt Odor** | Check heat shielding, exhaust system, emission controls, ignition timing—fuel/air ratio, misfiring. |
| **Hot Engine**<br>**Crackling Sounds**<br>**Hot Smell**<br>**Severe Local Hot Spots** | A moderate amount of sound of heating metal can be expected with any vehicle. However, a crackling sound from the thermostat housing, a hot smell and/or severe local hot spots on an engine can indicate blocked coolant passages. Inspect for plugged water passages, bad casting, core sand and plugging, a cracked block or head, or a blown head gasket. Usually accompanied with coolant loss. |
| **Coolant Color** | Coolant color is not necessarily an indication of adequate temperature or corrosion protection.<br>Some oily discoloration of the coolant recovery system bottle will occur due to the production use of soluble oil (also called water pump lubricant) which has been added for corrosion protection. |
| **Coolant Recovery Bottle —Level Changes** | Level changes are to be expected as coolant volume changes with engine temperature. If the level in the bottle is between the Maximum and Minimum marks at normal engine operating temperature, the level should return to within that range after operation at elevated temperatures. |
| **—Coolant NOT Returning** | Coolant will not return to the radiator if the radiator cap vent valve does not function, if an air leak destroys vacuum, or if the overflow passage is blocked or restricted.<br>Inspect all portions of the overflow passage, pressure cap, filler neck nipple, hose, and passages within the bottle for vacuum leak only. Coolant return failure will be evident by a low level in the radiator. Bottle level should increase during heat-up. |

**Fig. 1 Cooling (Part 2 of 7)**

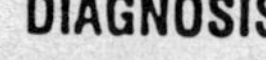

| CONDITION—AND CHECKS | DIAGNOSIS |
|---|---|
| **THERMAL 60° GAUGE READS LOW** | |

*Fig. 2—Normal Gauge Travel*

| CONDITION—AND CHECKS | DIAGNOSIS |
|---|---|
| (1) Varify gauge, (Fig. 2) Is temperature really low? | (1) Check temperature sending unit. Repair/Replace gauge or sending switch. |
| (2) Does it read cold? | (2) Wiring disconnect or wrong sending unit for lite switch, not gauge. |
| (3) Coolant level low in cold ambient. (Also poor heater performance) | (3) Check radiator and CRS for level—inspect for leaks. |
| (4) Coolant level O.K. | (4) Check heater controls, doors. |
| (5) Are above (1 thru 4) checks O.K.? | (5) Replace thermostat. |

**GAUGE READS HIGH—Without Pressure Cap Blow off without Coolant or Steam from CRS Tank and to Ground**

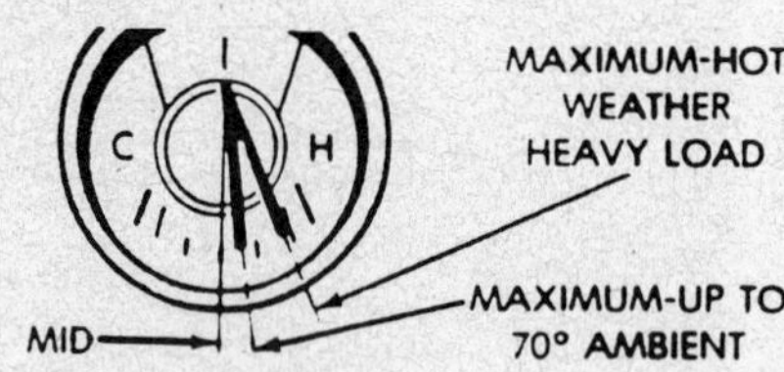


*Fig. 3—Gauge Reading—Hot Weather—Heavy Load*

| CONDITION—AND CHECKS | DIAGNOSIS |
|---|---|
| (1) Is it really reading high? | (1) See Figure 3. |
| (2) If at "H" without other signs of boiling. | (2) Look for Grounded gauge, sending unit or wire. |
| (3) Coolant Level low in Radiator and CRS | (3) a—Fill full.<br>b—Inspect for leaks, repair.<br>c—Assure Pressure Cap was shut tight and seals at top and bottom of neck are functioning properly. |
| (4) Coolant level low in Radiator but not in CRS. | (4) a—Fill full.<br>b—Inspect for leaks and repair.<br>c—Inspect for leaks in CRS to radiator connection.<br>d—Assure cap seals at top and bottom. |

**Fig. 1 Cooling (Part 3 of 7)**

| CONDITION—AND CHECKS | DIAGNOSIS |
|---|---|
| (5) Check freeze point | (5) a—Adjust to 50/50 Glyrol and water<br>b—If no reading or below –50°F, mixture is too rich clean system before refilling |
| (6) Assure Coolant Flow | (6) a—Look for flow through filler neck with some coolant removed and thermostat open<br>b—Repair water pump |
| (7) Other possible causes | (7) a—**High speed only**<br>—Radiator or Condensor air side plugged<br>—Radiator core tubes plugged<br>—Add on A/C without proper radiator<br>—Engine out of tune (specifications)<br>—Brakes dragging<br>—Bug screen<br>—Trailor towing or hill climbing<br>b—**High and Low Speed**<br>—Thermostat failed partially shut particularly if ambient temperature is below 70°F and vehicle has high mileage<br>—Condensor or radiator air side plugged.<br>—Add on A/C.<br>c—**Low Speed—NOT high speed**<br>—Check fan drive. |
| **TEMPERATURE GAUGE READS HOT, with Pressure Cap Blowoff and Steam and coolant to CRS and to Ground** | |
| (1) Coolant Level Low in Radiator and CRS | (1) a—Fill Cooling System Full and Air Vent.<br>b—Inspect for Leaks—repair.<br>c—Assure Pressure cap was shut and seals.<br>d—If low in radiator but not in CRS, also check connection to filler neck and pressure cap sealing. |
| (2) Check Coolant Freeze point | (2) Adjust to 50/50 Glycol and water, –35°F. Freeze Point. |
| (3) Assure Coolant Flow | (3) a—Look for flow through radiator filler neck with coolant lowered and thermostat open.<br>b—When accompanied with "metal cracking sound"—consider core sand and/or bad head casting. Look for plugged core tubes. |
| (4) Thermostat failed shut | (4) Especially in cold to medium ambient temperatures. |
| (5) Head Gasket Leak | (5) Use block leak checker |

**Fig. 1 Cooling (Part 4 of 7)**

| CONDITION—AND CHECKS | DIAGNOSIS |
|---|---|
| **TEMPERATURE GAUGE IS INCONSISTANT, Cycles—Irratic** | 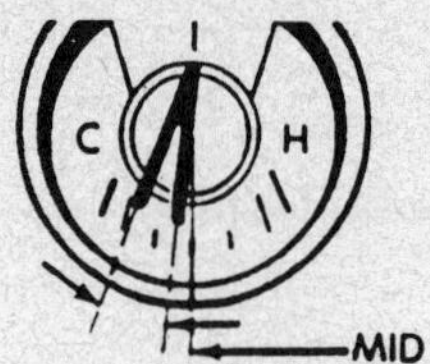*Fig. 4—Gauge Reaction to Thermostat* |
| (1) Is cycle normal? See figures 4 and 5. | —Normal Thermostat Cycle (Fig. 4).*Fig. 5—Gauge Reaction—Stop after Heavy Use*<br>—Hot water normal build up at stop after heavy use (Fig. 5). |
| (2) Is coolant level low in radiator (Low level can trap air in system which can put thermostat pellet in air and it opens late). | (2) Fill system and inspect for leaks. |
| (3) Is there a head gasket leak that puts exhaust gas in system? (This acts like trapped air with same effect as (2) above). | (3) Test with block leak checker and replace if necessary.<br>b—Coolant in engine oil.<br>c—White steam coming out of exhaust. |
| (4) Water pump impeller loose on shaft, slips sometimes. | (4) Replace. |
| (5) Air leak on suction side of water pump entraining Air; see 2 above. | (5) Find Leak and Repair. |
| **PRESSURE CAP BLOW OFF, with steam to CRS and coolant to ground without high reading. Temperature Gauge above normal** | |
| (1) Check pressure cap relief pressure | (1) Replace if lower than 14 psi. |
| **COOLANT LOSS TO GROUND without Pressure Cap Blow Off.** | |
| (1) Leaks | (1) a—Pressure test sysstem while shaking hoses<br>b—Water pump seal |

**Fig. 1 Cooling (Part 5 of 7)**

| CONDITION—AND CHECKS | DIAGNOSIS |
|---|---|
| **COOLANT LOSS PAST PRESSURE CAP TOP SEAL— Glycol seen on Filler Neck** | |
| (1) With normal gage reading | (1) a—Cap not on tight<br>b—Top seal leaking<br>c—Cap diaphragm "oil canned"<br>d—Filler neck damaged<br>e—Rubber seal out of position. |
| (2) With high gage reading or low gage reading on new vehicle. | (2) a—CRS Hose kinked.<br>b—CRS tank and plastic tube plugged.<br>c—Pressure Cap Rubber seal out of position. |
| **DETONATION OR PRE-IGNITION When Nothing to Cause It In Engine or Ignition** | |
| (1) Check coolant freeze point—If no reading on Vu-check or below −50°F. Freeze point **be aware that 100% Glycol makes engine metal run hotter even without a hot gage reading.** | (1) a—Adjust coolant to 50/50 Glycol and water (−35°F).<br>b—If 100% glycol has been found in the system. Clean and flush the system before replacing with 50/50 glycol and water. |
| **HOSES OBSERVED COLLAPSING ON COOL DOWN** | |
| (1) Check pressure cap Vent Valve | (1) a—Must have stroke. Gasket swell can. prevent valve from opening.<br>b—Replace cap. |
| (2) Check CRS hose for kinking or plugging. | (2) Repair as required. |
| (3) Inside of cap plugged with stop leak pellet, or green silica gel, or fiberglass. | (3) Clean cap. |
| **FAN NOISY** | |
| (1) Check for bent fan blades | (1) Repair as necessary |
| (2) Check for fan clearance to adjacent parts.<br>(3) Check for air obstructions on radiator or condensor<br>(4) Check for failed viscous fan drive. | |
| **INADEQUATE AIR CONDITIONING PERFORMANCE— Cooling System Suspected** | |
| (1) Check for plugged air side of condensor and radiator—front and rear | (1) Wash out with low velocity water. |
| (2) Check for missing air seals—recirculating air path<br>(3) Assure correct cooling system parts | |

**Fig. 1 Cooling (Part 6 of 7)**

| CONDITION—AND CHECKS | DIAGNOSIS |
|---|---|
| **HOT SMELL, Suspect Cooling System** | |
| (1) Was temperature gage high? | (1) a—Yes, See "Gauge Reads High".<br>b—No, See 2, 3, and 4. |
| (2) Heat shields all in place? | (2) a—Yes, See 3, 4 and 5.<br>b—No, Repair as required. |
| (3) Heat exchanger air side plugged? | (3) Clean as required. |
| (4) Catalytic Converter—Engine missing or running rich. | (4) Repair as required. |
| **POOR HEATER PERFORMANCE—Suspect Failed Open Thermostat?** | |
| (1) Does gage read low? | (1) a—See "Thermal 60° Gauge Reads Low" Condition 3. |
| (2) Check coolant level | (2) a—See "Thermal 60° Gauge Reads Low" Condition 4. |

**Fig. 1 Cooling (Part 7 of 7)**

## SERVICE DIAGNOSIS

| Condition | Possible Cause | Correction |
|---|---|---|
| EXCESSIVE EXHAUST NOISE | (a) Leaks at pipe joints.<br>(b) Burned or blown out muffler.<br>(c) Burned or rusted out exhaust pipe.<br>(d) Exhaust pipe leaking at manifold flange.<br>(e) Exhaust manifold cracked or broken.<br>(f) Leak between manifold and cylinder head.<br>(g) Restriction in muffler or tail pipe. | (a) Tighten clamps at leaking joints.<br>(b) Replace muffler assembly.<br>(c) Replace exhaust pipe.<br>(d) Tighten ball joint connection attaching bolts nuts to 24 ft. lb. (33 N·m), alternate tightening.<br>(e) Replace manifold.<br>(f) Tighten manifold to cylinder head stud nuts or bolts to specifications.<br>(g) Remove restriction, if possible, or replace as necessary. |
| LEAKING EXHAUST GASES | (a) Leaks at pipe joints.<br>(b) Damaged or improperly installed gaskets. | (a) Tighten U-bolt nuts at leaking joints to 150 in. lb. (17 N·m).<br>(b) Replace gaskets as necessary. |
| ENGINE HARD TO WARM UP OR WILL NOT RETURN TO NORMAL IDLE | (a) Heat control valve frozen in the open position.<br>(b) Blocked crossover passage in intake manifold. | (a) Free up manifold heat control valve using a suitable solvent.<br>(b) Remove restriction or replace intake manifold. |
| HEAT CONTROL VALVE NOISY | (a) Thermostat broken.<br>(b) Broken, weak or missing anti-rattle spring. | (a) Replace thermostat.<br>(b) Replace spring. |

**Fig. 2 Exhaust**

## ENGINE DIAGNOSIS

| Condition | Possible Cause | Correction |
|---|---|---|
| ENGINE WILL NOT START | (a) Weak battery. | (a) Test battery specific gravity. Recharge or replace as necessary. |
| | (b) Corroded or loose battery connections. | (b) Clean and tighten battery connections. Apply a coat of light mineral grease to terminals. |
| | (c) Faulty starter. | (c) |
| | (d) Moisture on ignition wires and distributor cap. | (d) Wipe wires and cap clean and dry. |
| | (e) Faulty ignition cables. | (e) Replace any cracked or shorted cables. |
| | (f) Faulty coil or control unit. | (f) Test and replace if necessary. |
| | (g) Incorrect spark plug gap. | (g) Set gap. |
| | (h) Incorrect ignition timing. | (h) |
| | (i) Dirt or water in fuel system. | (i) Clean system |
| | (j) Faulty fuel pump. | (j) Install new fuel pump. |
| ENGINE STALLS OR ROUGH IDLE | (a) Idle speed set too low. | (a) Electronic Fuel Injection. |
| | (b) Incorrect choke adjustment. | (b) Electronic Fuel Injection. |
| | (c) Idle mixture too lean or too rich. | (c) Electronic Fuel Injection. |
| | (d) Leak in intake manifold. | (d) Inspect intake manifold gasket and vacuum hoses replace if necessary. |
| | (e) Worn distributor rotor. | (e) Install new rotor. |
| | (f) Incorrect ignition wiring. | (f) Install correct wiring. |
| | (g) Faulty coil. | (g) Test and replace if necessary. |
| | (h) EGR valve leaking. | (h) Test and replace if necessary. |
| ENGINE LOSS OF POWER | (a) Incorrect ignition timing. | (a) |
| | (b) Worn distributor rotor. | (b) Install new rotor. |
| | (c) Worn distributor shaft. | (c) Remove and repair distributor. |
| | (d) Dirty or incorrectly gapped spark plugs. | (d) Clean plugs and set gap. |
| | (e) Dirt or water in fuel system.** | (e) Clean system. |
| | (f) Faulty fuel pump. | (f) Install new pump. |
| | (g) Incorrect valve timing. | (g) Check Valve Timing. |
| | (h) Blown cylinder head gasket. | (h) Install new head gasket. |
| | (i) Low compression. | (i) Test compression of each cylinder. |
| | (j) Burned, warped or pitted valves. | (j) Install new valves. |
| | (k) Plugged or restricted exhaust system. | (k) Install new parts as necessary. |
| | (l) Faulty ignition cables. | (l) Replace any cracked or shorted cables. |
| | (m) Faulty coil. | (m) Test and replace as necessary. |
| ENGINE MISSES ON ACCELERATION | (a) Dirty, or gap too wide in spark plugs. | (a) Clean spark plugs and set gap. |
| | (b) Incorrect ignition timing. | (b) |
| | (c) Dirt in fuel system. | (c) Clean fuel system. |
| | (d) Burned, warped or pitted valves. | (d) Install new valves. |
| | (e) Faulty coil. | (e) Test and replace if necessary. |
| ENGINE MISSES AT HIGH SPEED | (a) Dirty or gap set too wide in spark plug. | (a) Clean spark plugs and set gap. |
| | (b) Worn distributor shaft. | (b) Remove and repair distributor. |
| | (c) Worn distributor rotor. | (c) Install new rotor. |
| | (d) Faulty coil. | (d) Test and replace if necessary. |
| | (e) Incorrect ignition timing. | (e) |
| | (f) Dirt or water in fuel system or filter. | (f) Clean system and replace filter. |

**Fig. 3 Engine, Front Wheel Drive (Part 1 of 2)**

| Condition | Possible Cause | Correction |
|---|---|---|
| **NOISY VALVES** | (a) Thin or diluted oil-low pressure. | (a) Change oil. |
| | (b) Worn valve guides. | (b) Ream and install new valves with O/S Stems. |
| | (c) Excessive run-out of valve seats on valve faces. | (c) Grind valve seats and valves. |
| **CONNECTING ROD NOISE** | (a) Insufficient oil supply. | (a) Check engine oil level. |
| | (b) Low oil pressure. | (b) Check engine oil level. Inspect oil pump relief valve and spring. |
| | (c) Thin or diluted oil. | (c) Change oil to correct viscosity. |
| | (d) Excessive bearing clearance. | (d) Measure bearings for correct clearance. |
| | (e) Connecting rod journals out-of-round. | (e) Replace crankshaft or regrind journals. |
| | (f) Misaligned connecting rods. | (f) Replace bent connecting rods. |
| **MAIN BEARING NOISE** | (a) Insufficient oil supply. | (a) Check engine oil level. |
| | (b) Low oil pressure. | (b) Check engine oil level. Inspect oil pump relief valve and spring. |
| | (c) Thin or diluted oil. | (c) Change oil to correct viscosity. |
| | (d) Excessive bearing clearance. | (d) Measure bearings for correct clearances. |
| | (e) Excessive end play. | (e) Check No. 3 main bearing for wear on flanges. |
| | (f) Crankshaft journal out-of-round worn. | (f) Replace crankshaft or regrind journals. |
| | (g) Loose flywheel or torque converter. | (g) Tighten to correct torque. |
| **OIL CONSUMPTION OR SPARK PLUGS OIL FOULED** | (a) Worn, scuffed, or broken rings. | (a) Hone cylinder bores and install new rings. |
| | (b) Carbon in oil ring slot. | (b) Install new rings. |
| | (c) Rings fitted too tight in grooves. | (c) Remove the rings. Check grooves. If groove is not proper width, replace piston. |
| | (d) Worn valve guides. | (d) Ream guides and replace valves with oversize. |
| | (e) PCV system malfunction. | (e) Check system. |
| **OIL PRESSURE DROP** | (a) Low oil level. | (a) Check engine oil level. |
| | (b) Faulty oil pressure sending unit. | (b) Install new sending unit. |
| | (c) Clogged oil filter. | (c) Install new oil filter. |
| | (d) Worn parts in oil pump. | (d) Replace worn parts or pump. |
| | (e) Thin or diluted oil. | (e) Change oil to correct viscosity. |
| | (f) Excessive bearing clearance. | (f) Measure bearings for correct clearance. |
| | (g) Oil pump relief valve stuck. | (g) Remove valve and inspect, clean, and reinstall. |
| | (h) Oil pump cover bent or cracked. | (h) Install new oil pump. |

**Fig. 3 Engine, Front Wheel Drive (Part 2 of 2)**

| Condition | Possible Cause | Correction |
|---|---|---|
| OIL PRESSURE DROP | (a) Low oil level. | (a) Check engine oil level. |
| | (b) Faulty oil pressure sending unit. | (b) Check Oil Pressure or replace sending unit. |
| | (c) Clogged oil filter. | (c) Install new oil filter. |
| | (d) Worn parts in oil pump. | (d) Replace worn parts or pump. |
| | (e) Thin or diluted oil. | (e) Change oil to correct viscosity. |
| | (f) Excessive bearing clearance. | (f) Measure bearings for correct clearance. |
| | (g) Oil pump relief valve stuck. | (g) Remove valve and inspect, clean, and reinstall. |
| | (h) Oil pump suction tube loose, bent or cracked. | (h) Remove oil pan and install new tube if necessary. |
| | (i) Improperly installed or missing oil line plug. | (i) Check for correct installation in block. |
| OIL LEAKS | (a) Misaligned or deteriorated gaskets. Loose fastner, broken or porous metal part. | (a) Service Component |
| ENGINE MISSES AT HIGH SPEED | (a) Dirty or gap set too wide in spark plug. | (a) Clean spark plugs and set gap. |
| | (b) Worn distributor shaft. | (b) Remove and repair distributor. |
| | (c) Worn or burned distributor rotor. | (c) Install new rotor. |
| | (d) Faulty coil. | (d) Test and replace if necessary. |
| | (e) Incorrect ignition timing. | (e) |
| | (f) Dirty jets in carburetor. | (f) Clean jets. |
| | (g) Dirt or water in fuel line, carburetor or filter. | (g) Clean lines, carburetor and replace filter. |
| NOISY VALVES | (a) High or low oil level in crankcase. | (a) Check for correct oil level. |
| | (b) Thin or diluted oil. | (b) Change oil. |
| | (c) Low oil pressure. | (c) Check engine oil level. |
| | (d) Dirt in tappets. | (d) Clean tappets. |
| | (e) Bent push rods. | (e) Install new push rods. |
| | (f) Worn rocker arms. | (f) Inspect oil supply to rockers. |
| | (g) Worn tappets. | (g) Install new tappets. |
| | (h) Worn valve guides. | (h) Ream and install new valves with O/S Stems. |
| | (i) Excessive run-out of valve seats or valve faces. | (i) Grind valve seats and valves. |
| CONNECTING ROD NOISE | (a) Insufficient oil supply. | (a) Check engine oil level. |
| | (b) Low oil pressure. | (b) Check engine oil level. Inspect oil pump relief valve and spring. |
| | (c) Thin or diluted oil. | (c) Change oil to correct viscosity. |
| | (d) Excessive bearing clearance. | (d) Measure bearings for correct clearance. |
| | (e) Connecting rod journals out-of-round. | (e) Replace crankshaft or regrind journals. |
| | (f) Misaligned connecting rods. | (f) Replace bent connecting rods. |
| MAIN BEARING NOISE | (a) Insufficient oil supply. | (a) Check engine oil level. |
| | (b) Low oil pressure. | (b) Check engine oil level. Inspect oil pump relief valve and spring. |
| | (c) Thin or diluted oil. | (c) Change oil to correct viscosity. |
| | (d) Excessive bearing clearance. | (d) Measure bearings for correct clearances. |
| | (e) Excessive end play. | (e) Check No. 3 main bearing for wear on flanges. |
| | (f) Crankshaft journal out-of-round worn. | (f) Replace crankshaft or regrind journals. |
| | (g) Loose flywheel or torque converter. | (g) Tighten to correct torque. |
| OIL PUMPING AT RINGS (SPARK PLUGS FOULING) | (a) Worn, scuffed, or broken rings. | (a) Hone cylinder bores and install new rings. |
| | (b) Carbon in oil ring slot. | (b) Install new rings. |
| | (c) Rings fitted too tight in grooves. | (c) Remove the rings. Check grooves. If groove is not proper width, replace piston. |
| | (d) Worn valve guides. | (d) Ream guides and replace valves with oversize. |
| | (e) Leaking valve guide seals. | (e) Replace seals. |

**Fig. 4 Engine, Rear Wheel Drive (Part 1 of 2)**

## ENGINE DIAGNOSIS

| Condition | Possible Cause | Correction |
|---|---|---|
| ENGINE WILL NOT START | (a) Weak battery. | (a) Test battery specific gravity. Recharge or replace as necessary. |
| | (b) Corroded or loose battery connections. | (b) Clean and tighten battery connections. Apply a coat of light mineral grease to terminals. |
| | (c) Faulty starter. | (c) |
| | (d) Moisture on ignition wires and distributor cap. | (d) Wipe wires and cap clean and dry. |
| | (e) Faulty ignition cables. | (e) Replace any cracked or shorted cables. |
| | (f) Faulty coil or control unit. | (f) Test and replace if necessary. |
| | (g) Incorrect spark plug gap. | (g) Set gap. |
| | (h) Incorrect ignition timing. | (h) |
| | (i) Dirt or water in fuel line or carburetor. | (i) Clean lines and carburetor. |
| | (j) Carburetor flooded. | (j) Adjust float level—check seats. |
| | (k) Incorrect carburetor float setting. | (k) Adjust float level—check seats. |
| | (l) Faulty fuel pump. | (l) Install new fuel pump. |
| | (m) Carburetor percolating. No fuel in the carburetor. | (m) Measure float level. Adjust bowl vent. Inspect operation of manifold heat control valve. |
| ENGINE STALLS OR ROUGH IDLE | (a) Idle speed set too low. | (a) Adjust carburetor. |
| | (b) Incorrect choke adjustment. | (b) Adjust choke. |
| | (c) Idle mixture too lean or too rich. | (c) Adjust carburetor. |
| | (d) Incorrect carburetor float setting. | (d) Adjust float setting. |
| | (e) Leak in intake manifold. | (e) Inspect intake manifold gasket and replace if necessary. |
| | (f) Worn or burned distributor rotor. | (f) Install new rotor. |
| | (g) Incorrect ignition wiring. | (g) Install correct wiring. |
| | (h) Faulty coil. | (h) Test and replace if necessary. |
| | (i) EGR valve leaking. | (i) Test and replace if necessary. |
| ENGINE LOSS OF POWER | (a) Incorrect ignition timing. | (a) |
| | (b) Worn or burned distributor rotor. | (b) Install new rotor. |
| | (c) Worn distributor shaft. | (c) Remove and repair distributor. |
| | (d) Dirty or incorrectly gapped spark plugs. | (d) Clean plugs and set gap. |
| | (e) Dirt or water in fuel line, carburetor or filter. | (e) Clean lines, carburetor and replace filter. |
| | (f) Incorrect carburetor float setting | (f) Adjust float level. |
| | (g) Faulty fuel pump. | (g) Install new pump. |
| | (h) Incorrect valve timing. | (h) Check Valve Timing. |
| | (i) Blown cylinder head gasket. | (i) Install new head gasket. |
| | (j) Low compression. | (j) Test compression of each cylinder. |
| | (k) Burned, warped or pitted valves. | (k) Install new valves. |
| | (l) Plugged or restricted exhaust system. | (l) Install new parts as necessary. |
| | (m) Faulty ignition cables. | (m) Replace any cracked or shorted cables. |
| | (n) Faulty coil. | (n) Test and replace as necessary. |
| | (o) Amplifier defective. | (o) Test and replace as necessary. |
| ENGINE MISSES ON ACCELERATION | (a) Dirty, or gap too wide in spark plugs. | (a) Clean spark plugs and set gap. |
| | (b) Incorrect ignition timing. | (b) |
| | (c) Dirt in carburetor. | (c) Clean carburetor. |
| | (d) Acceleration pump in carburetor. | (d) Install new pump. |
| | (e) Burned, warped or pitted valves. | (e) Install new valves. |
| | (f) Faulty coil. | (f) Test and replace if necessary. |

**Fig. 4 Engine, Rear Wheel Drive (Part 2 of 2)**

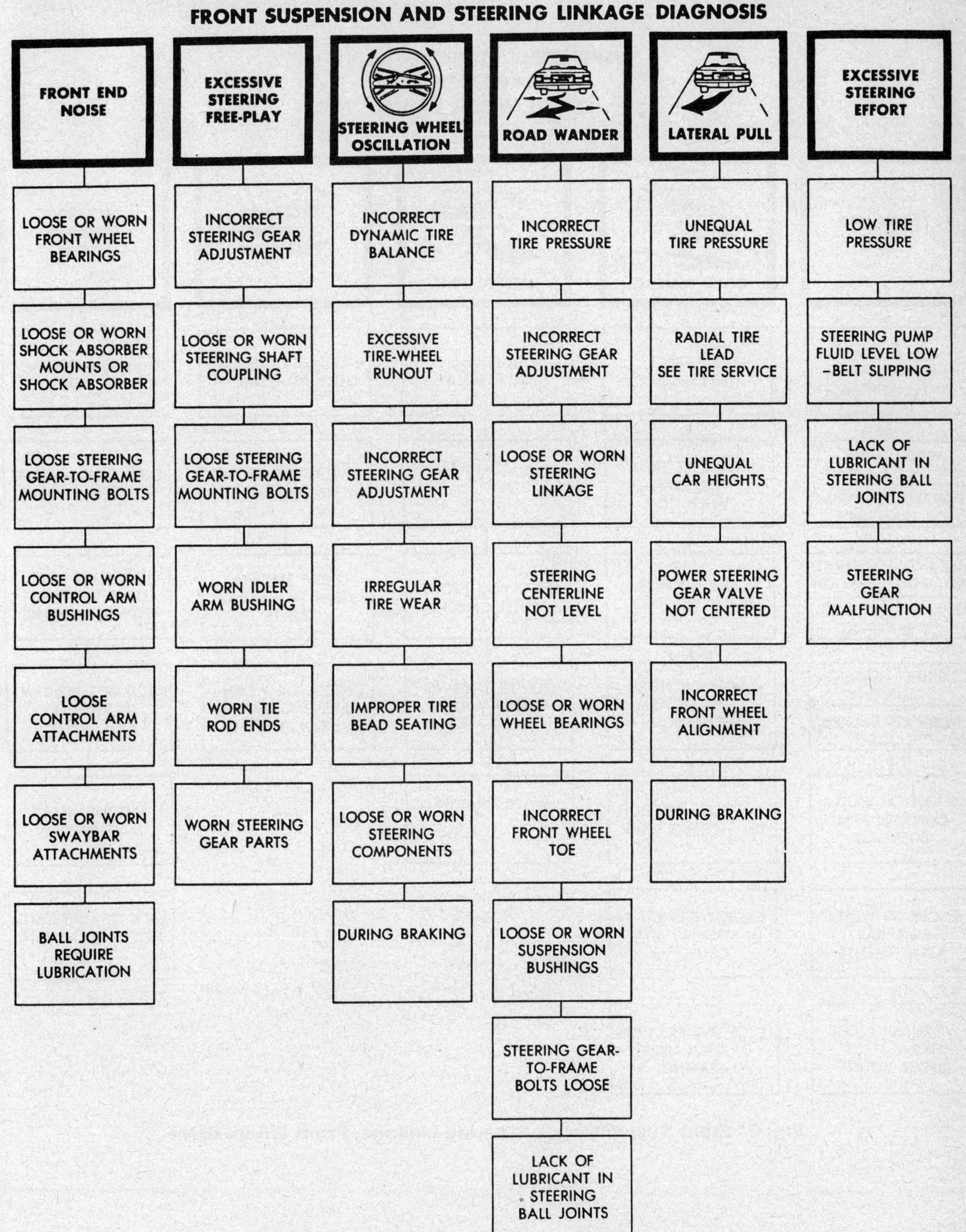
FRONT SUSPENSION AND STEERING LINKAGE DIAGNOSIS
FRONT END NOISE
LOOSE OR WORN FRONT WHEEL BEARINGS
LOOSE OR WORN SHOCK ABSORBER MOUNTS OR SHOCK ABSORBER
LOOSE STEERING GEAR-TO-FRAME MOUNTING BOLTS
LOOSE OR WORN CONTROL ARM BUSHINGS
LOOSE CONTROL ARM ATTACHMENTS
LOOSE OR WORN SWAYBAR ATTACHMENTS
BALL JOINTS REQUIRE LUBRICATION
EXCESSIVE STEERING FREE-PLAY
INCORRECT STEERING GEAR ADJUSTMENT
LOOSE OR WORN STEERING SHAFT COUPLING
LOOSE STEERING GEAR-TO-FRAME MOUNTING BOLTS
WORN IDLER ARM BUSHING
WORN TIE ROD ENDS
WORN STEERING GEAR PARTS
STEERING WHEEL OSCILLATION
INCORRECT DYNAMIC TIRE BALANCE
EXCESSIVE TIRE-WHEEL RUNOUT
INCORRECT STEERING GEAR ADJUSTMENT
IRREGULAR TIRE WEAR
IMPROPER TIRE BEAD SEATING
LOOSE OR WORN STEERING COMPONENTS
DURING BRAKING
ROAD WANDER
INCORRECT TIRE PRESSURE
INCORRECT STEERING GEAR ADJUSTMENT
LOOSE OR WORN STEERING LINKAGE
STEERING CENTERLINE NOT LEVEL
LOOSE OR WORN WHEEL BEARINGS
INCORRECT FRONT WHEEL TOE
LOOSE OR WORN SUSPENSION BUSHINGS
STEERING GEAR-TO-FRAME BOLTS LOOSE
LACK OF LUBRICANT IN STEERING BALL JOINTS
LATERAL PULL
UNEQUAL TIRE PRESSURE
RADIAL TIRE LEAD SEE TIRE SERVICE
UNEQUAL CAR HEIGHTS
POWER STEERING GEAR VALVE NOT CENTERED
INCORRECT FRONT WHEEL ALIGNMENT
DURING BRAKING
EXCESSIVE STEERING EFFORT
LOW TIRE PRESSURE
STEERING PUMP FLUID LEVEL LOW -BELT SLIPPING
LACK OF LUBRICANT IN STEERING BALL JOINTS
STEERING GEAR MALFUNCTION

**Fig. 5 Front Suspension & Steering Linkage, Rear Wheel Drive**

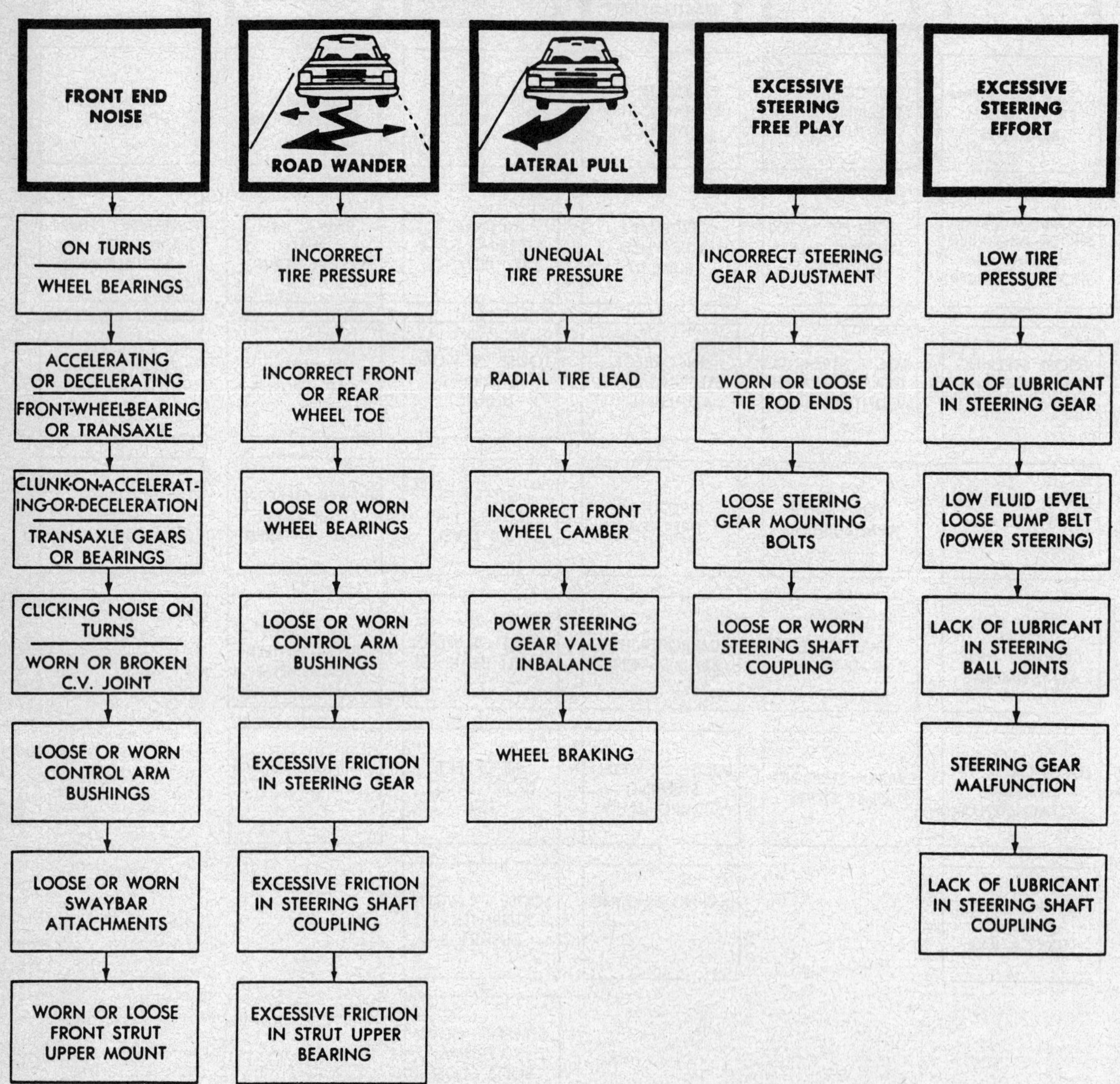
SUSPENSION/STEERING/DRIVE
DIAGNOSIS
(FRONT WHEEL DRIVE)
FRONT END NOISE
ON TURNS
WHEEL BEARINGS
ACCELERATING OR DECELERATING
FRONT-WHEEL-BEARING OR TRANSAXLE
CLUNK-ON-ACCELERATING-OR-DECELERATION
TRANSAXLE GEARS OR BEARINGS
CLICKING NOISE ON TURNS
WORN OR BROKEN C.V. JOINT
LOOSE OR WORN CONTROL ARM BUSHINGS
LOOSE OR WORN SWAYBAR ATTACHMENTS
WORN OR LOOSE FRONT STRUT UPPER MOUNT
ROAD WANDER
INCORRECT TIRE PRESSURE
INCORRECT FRONT OR REAR WHEEL TOE
LOOSE OR WORN WHEEL BEARINGS
LOOSE OR WORN CONTROL ARM BUSHINGS
EXCESSIVE FRICTION IN STEERING GEAR
EXCESSIVE FRICTION IN STEERING SHAFT COUPLING
EXCESSIVE FRICTION IN STRUT UPPER BEARING
LATERAL PULL
UNEQUAL TIRE PRESSURE
RADIAL TIRE LEAD
INCORRECT FRONT WHEEL CAMBER
POWER STEERING GEAR VALVE INBALANCE
WHEEL BRAKING
EXCESSIVE STEERING FREE PLAY
INCORRECT STEERING GEAR ADJUSTMENT
WORN OR LOOSE TIE ROD ENDS
LOOSE STEERING GEAR MOUNTING BOLTS
LOOSE OR WORN STEERING SHAFT COUPLING
EXCESSIVE STEERING EFFORT
LOW TIRE PRESSURE
LACK OF LUBRICANT IN STEERING GEAR
LOW FLUID LEVEL LOOSE PUMP BELT (POWER STEERING)
LACK OF LUBRICANT IN STEERING BALL JOINTS
STEERING GEAR MALFUNCTION
LACK OF LUBRICANT IN STEERING SHAFT COUPLING

**Fig. 6 Front Suspension & Steering Linkage, Front Wheel Drive**

## POWER STEERING DIAGNOSIS

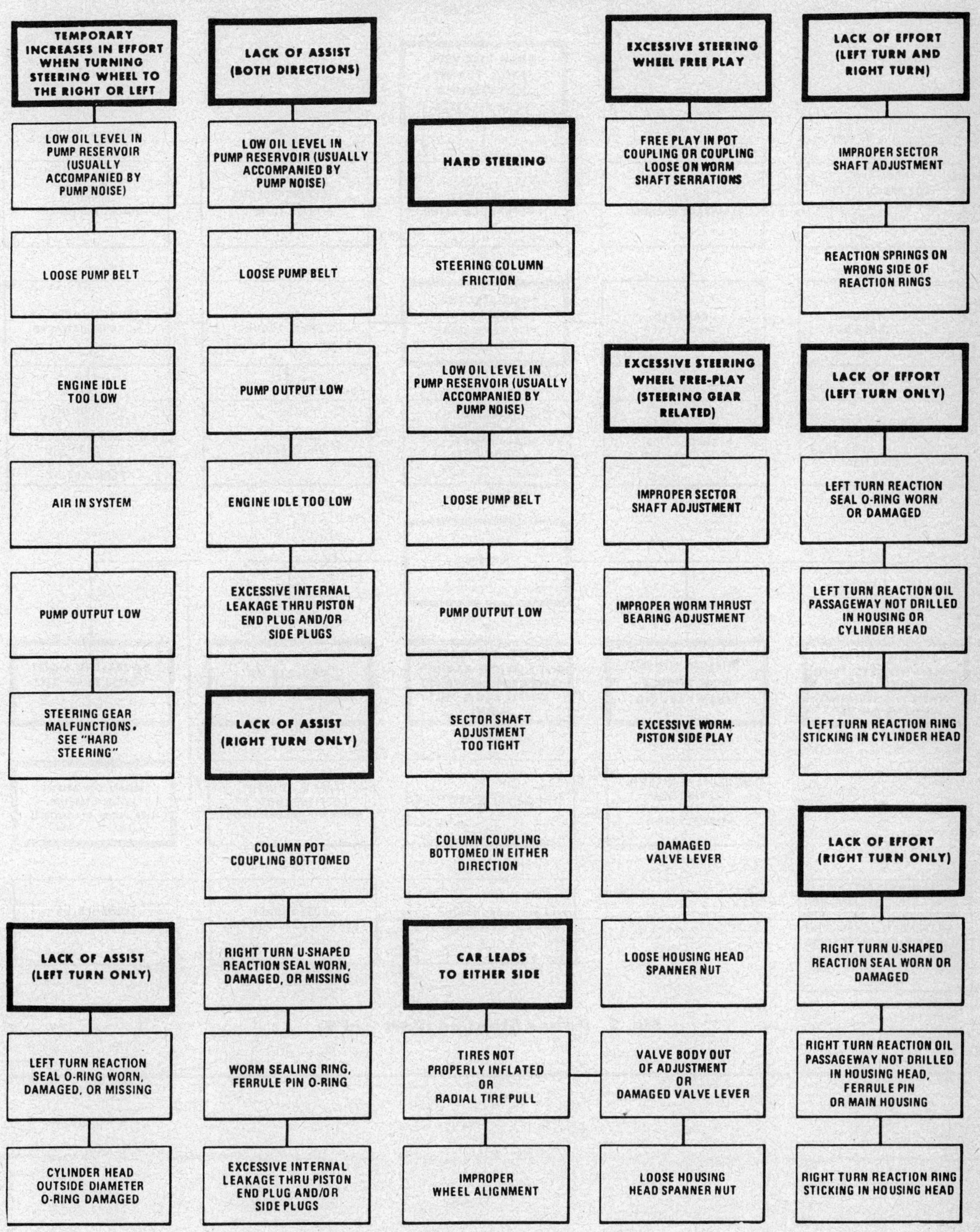


**Fig. 7 Power Steering (Part 1 of 2)**

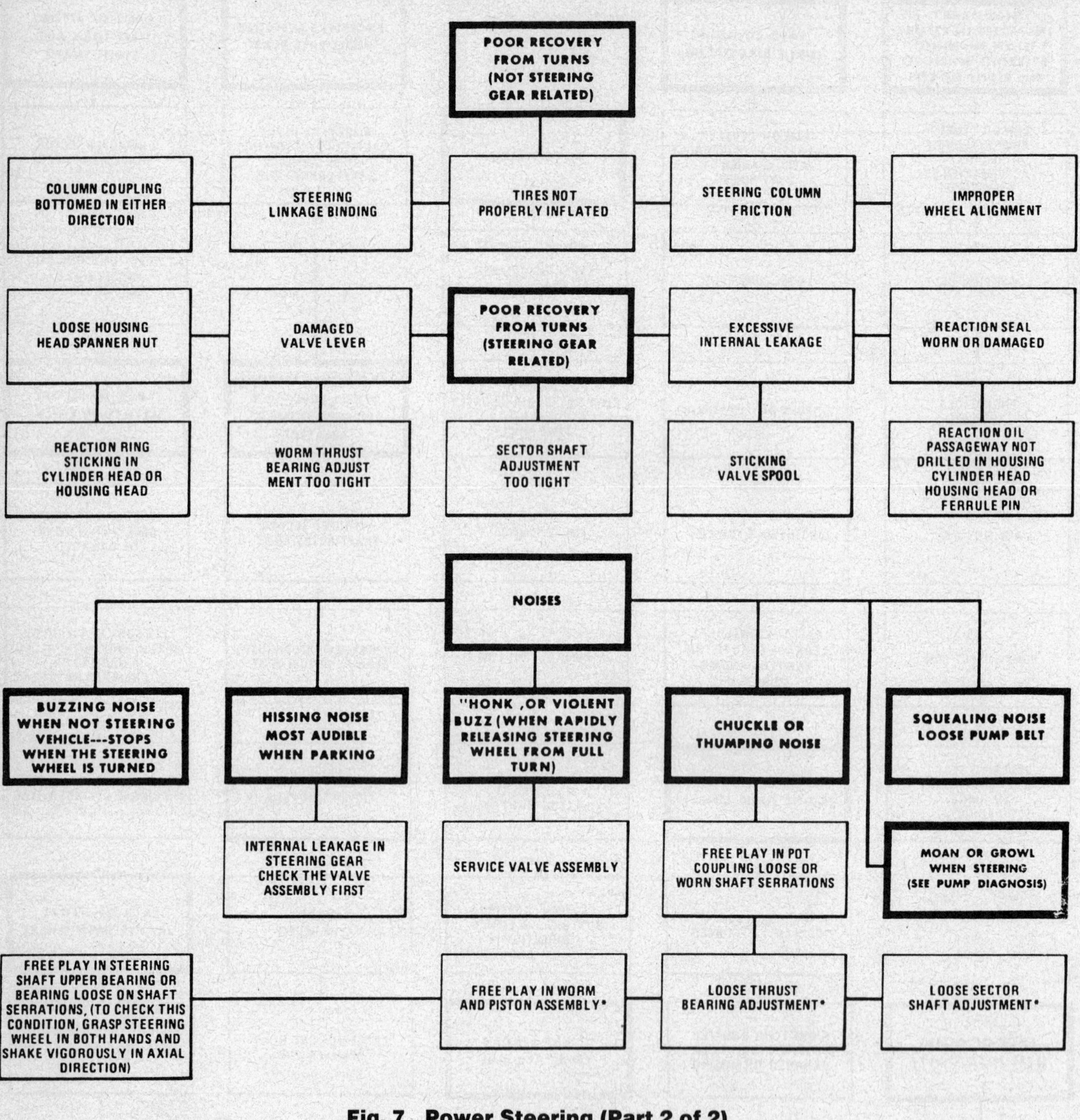


**Fig. 7 Power Steering (Part 2 of 2)**

# ENGINE REBUILDING SPECIFICATIONS

**All specifications given in inches unless otherwise noted.**

## TABLE OF CONTENTS



# Chrysler

## INDEX



## CYLINDER HEAD, VALVE GUIDES & VALVE SEATS

| Engine Liter/CID | Year | Cylinder Head Warpage Limit | Cylinder Head Overall Thickness | Valve Guides: Inside Diameter (Standard) | Valve Guides: Stem To Guide Clearance | Valve Seats: Seat Angle | Valve Seats: Seat Width Intake | Valve Seats: Seat Width Exhaust | Valve Seats: Run Out |
|---|---|---|---|---|---|---|---|---|---|
| 1.5L/4-89.6 | 1989-91 | .008 | 4.21⑦ | — | ⑤ | 44-44.5° | .035-.051 | .035-.051 | — |
| 1.6L/4-97 | 1989-90 | .008 | 5.193-5.201⑦ | — | ⑥ | 44-44.5° | .035-.051 | .035-.051 | — |
| 1.8L/4-107 | 1990-91 | .008 | 3.484⑦ | — | ② | 45-45.5° | .035-.051 | .035-.051 | — |
| 2.0L/4-122⑨ | 1989-91 | .008 | 3.54⑦ | — | ② | 45° | .035-.051 | .035-.051 | — |
| 2.0L/4-122⑩ | 1990-91 | .008 | 5.197⑦ | — | ⑥ | 45-45.5° | .035-.051 | .035-.051 | — |
| 2.2L/4-135 | 1989-91 | .004 | — | .3133-.3150 | ① | 45° | .069-.088 | .059-.078 | .002 |
| 2.5L/4-153 | 1989-91 | .004 | — | .3133-.3150 | ① | 45° | .069-.088 | .059-.078 | .002 |
| 2.6L/4-156 | 1989 | .008 | 3.543⑦ | — | ② | 45° | .028-.047 | .028-.047 | — |
| 3.0L/V6-181⑫ | 1989-91 | .002 | — | .314-.315 | ② | 45-45.5° | .035-.051 | .035-.051 | — |
| 3.0L/V6-181⑪ | 1990-91 | .002 | 4.363 | .315 | — | 45° | — | — | — |
| 3.0L/V6-181⑬⑨ | 1991 | .008 | 3.31⑦ | .314-.315 | ② | 45-45.5° | .035-.051 | .035-.051 | — |
| 3.0L/V6-181⑬⑩ | 1991 | .008 | 5.20⑦ | .260-.261 | ⑤ | 45-45.5° | .035-.051 | .035-.051 | — |
| 3.3L/V6-201 | 1990-91 | .008 | — | .313-.3149 | ⑧ | 44.5° | .068-.088 | .059-.078 | .002 |
| 3.8L/V6-231 | 1991 | .008 | — | .313-.3149 | ⑧ | 44.5° | .068-.088 | .059-.078 | .002 |
| 5.2L/V8-318 | 1989 | ③ | — | .374-.375 | ④ | 45-45.5° | .065-.085 | .080-.100 | .003 |

①—Exhaust, .0030-.0047 inch; intake, .0009-.0026 inch.

②—Exhaust: Std., .0020-.0035 inch; service limit, .006 inch. Intake: Std., .0012-.0024 inch; service limit, .004 inch.

③—Length of span multiplied by .00075.

④—Exhaust, .002-.004 inch; Intake, .001-.003 inch.

⑤—Exhaust, .0020-.0035 inch; intake, .0008-.0020 inch.

⑥—Exhaust, .0020-.0033 inch; intake, .0008-.0019 inch.

⑦—Minimum thickness is overall thickness, less warpage limit, combined with amount of grinding of cylinder block gasket surface.

⑧—Maximum allowable by rocking method. Exhaust, .016 inch; intake, .010 inch.

⑨—Single Overhead Camshaft.

⑩—Dual Overhead Camshaft.

⑪—Monaco.

⑫—Except Monaco & Stealth.

⑬—Stealth.

# ENGINE REBUILDING SPECIFICATIONS

## VALVES

| Engine Liter/CID | Year | Stem Diameter Intake | Stem Diameter Exhaust | Clearance Intake | Clearance Exhaust | Clearance Jet | Installed Height | Maximum Tip Refinish | Face Angle | Margin① Intake | Margin① Exhaust |
|---|---|---|---|---|---|---|---|---|---|---|---|
| 1.5L/4-89.6 | 1989-90 | .260 | .260 | ⑤ | ⑥ | — | — | — | 45-45.5° | .020 | .039 |
| 1.5L/4-89.6 | 1991 | .2585-.2591 | .2571-.2579 | ⑤ | ⑥ | — | — | — | 45-45.5° | .020 | .039 |
| 1.6L/4-97 | 1989-90 | .2585-.2586 | .2571-.2579 | — | — | — | — | — | 45-45.5° | .028 | .039 |
| 1.8L/4-107 | 1990-91 | .31 | .31 | ⑤ | ⑥ | — | — | — | 45-45.5° | .028 | .020 |
| 2.0L/4-122⑧ | 1989-91 | .310 | .310 | ⑦ | ⑦ | — | — | — | 45-45.5° | .028 | .060 |
| 2.0L/4-122⑨ | 1990-91 | .2585-.2591 | .2571-.2579 | — | — | — | — | — | 45-45.5° | .040 | .059 |
| 2.2L/4-135 | 1989-91 | .3124① | .3103① | — | — | — | 1.960-2.009② | .020③ | 45° | ⑫ | ⑬ |
| 2.5L/4-153 | 1989-91 | .3124① | .3103① | — | — | — | 1.960-2.009② | .020③ | 45° | .031 | .0469 |
| 2.6L/4-156 | 1989 | .3150④ | .3150 | — | — | ⑥ | — | — | 45° | .028 | .059 |
| 3.0L/V6-181⑪ | 1989-91 | .313-.314 | .312-.3125 | — | — | — | — | — | 45-45.5° | .047 | .079 |
| 3.0L/V6-181⑩ | 1990-91 | .315 | .315 | — | — | — | — | — | 45° | .059 | .067 |
| 3.0L/V6-181⑭⑧ | 1991 | .314 | .314 | — | — | — | — | — | 45-45.5° | .047 | .079 |
| 3.0L/V6-181⑭⑨ | 1991 | .260 | .260 | — | — | — | — | — | 45-45.5° | .039 | .059 |
| 3.3L/V6-201 | 1990-91 | .312-.313 | .3112-.3119 | — | — | — | — | .002-.005 | 44.5-° | .031 | .0469 |
| 3.8L/V6-231 | 1991 | .312-.313 | .3112-.3119 | — | — | — | — | .002-.005 | 44.5-° | .031 | .0469 |
| 5.2L/V8-318 | 1989 | .372-.373 | .371-.372 | — | — | — | — | — | 44.5-45° | .031 | .0469 |

①—Minimum.
②—Measured between tip of valve and top of seal boss.
③—If more than .020 inch must be ground from valve stem, check clearance between rocker arm and valve spring retainer. If clearance is less than .050 inch, grind rocker arm ears.
④—Jet valve, .169 inch.
⑤—Hot, .0059 inch; cold, .0028 inch.
⑥—Hot, .0098 inch; cold, .0067 inch.
⑦—Hot, .010 inch; cold, .007 inch.
⑧—Single Overhead Camshaft.
⑨—Dual Overhead Camshaft.
⑩—Monaco.
⑪—Except Monaco and Stealth.
⑫—Non-turbo, .031 inch; Turbo, .041 inch.
⑬—Non-turbo, .0469 inch; Turbo, .042 inch.
⑭—Stealth.

## VALVE SPRINGS

| Engine Liter/CID | Year | Free Length | Installed Height | Spring Pressure Pounds @ Inches | Maximum Straightness Deviation |
|---|---|---|---|---|---|
| 1.5L/4-89.6 | 1989-90 | 1.756 | 1.469 | — | 4° |
| 1.5L/4-89.6 | 1991 | ⑪ | 1.469 | ⑫ | 4° |
| 1.6L/4-97 | 1989-90 | 1.803 | 1.469 | — | 4° |
| 1.8L/4-107 | 1990-91 | 1.937 | 1.469 | 62 @ 1.469 | 4° |
| 2.0L/4-122⑤ | 1989-91 | 1.961 | 1.591 | 73 @ 1.591 | 4° |
| 2.0L/4-122⑥ | 1990-91 | 1.902 | — | 66⑩ | 4° |
| 2.2L/4-135 | 1989-91 | ① | 1.62-1.68 | 108-120 @ 1.65 | .079 |
| 2.5L/4-153 | 1989-91 | ① | 1.62-1.68 | 108-120 @ 1.65 | .079 |
| 2.6L/4-156 | 1989 | 1.961 | 1.591 | 73 @ 1.591 | 4° |
| 3.0L/V6-181⑧ | 1989 | 1.988 | 1.591 | 73 @ 1.591 | 4° |
| 3.0L/V6-181⑧ | 1990-91 | 1.960 | 1.591 | 73 @ 1.591 | 4° |
| 3.0L/V6-181⑦ | 1990-91 | 1.909 | — | 76 @ 1.575 | — |
| 3.0L/V6-181⑨⑤ | 1991 | 1.961 | 1.591 | 74 @ 1.591 | 4° |
| 3.0L/V6-181⑨⑥ | 1991 | 1.846 | 1.492 | 62 @ 1.492 | 4° |
| 3.3L/V6-201 | 1990-91 | 1.909 | 1.531-1.593 | 58-63 @ 1.570 | — |
| 3.8L/V6-231 | 1991 | 1.909 | 1.531-1.593 | 58-63 @ 1.570 | — |
| 5.2L/V8-318 | 1989 | ② | 1.625-1.6875 | ③ | ④ |

①—Except turbocharged engines, 2.39 inches; turbocharged engines, 2.28 inches.
②—Except H.P. engines, 2.00 inches; H.P. engines 2.10 inches.
③—Except H.P. engines, 78-88 lbs. @ 1.6875 inches; H.P. engines, 108-118 lbs. @ 1.6563 inches.
④—Except H.P. engines, .0625 inches; H.P. engines, .080 inches.
⑤—Single Overhead Camshaft.
⑥—Dual Overhead Camshaft.
⑦—Monaco.
⑧—Except Monaco and Stealth.
⑨—Stealth.
⑩—At installed height.
⑪—Intake valve spring 1.815 inches; Exhaust valve spring, 1.843 inches.
⑫—Intake, 51 lbs. at 1.469 inches; Exhaust, 64 lbs. at 1.469 inches.

## CRANKSHAFT

| Engine Liter/CID | Year | Crankshaft | | | |
|---|---|---|---|---|---|
| | | Main Bearing Journal Diameter | Connecting Rod Journal Diameter | Maximum Out Of Round All | Maximum Taper All |
| 1.5L/4-89.6 | 1989-91 | 1.89 | 1.65 | .0006 | .0006 |
| 1.6L/4-97 | 1989-90 | 2.24 | 1.77 | .0006 | .0006 |
| 1.8L/4-107 | 1990-91 | 2.24 | 1.77 | .0006 | .0002 |
| 2.0L/4-122 ① | 1989-91 | 2.24 | 1.77 | .0006 | .0002 |
| 2.0L/4-122 ② | 1990-91 | 2.2433-2.2439 | 1.7709-1.7715 | .0006 | .0002 |
| 2.2L/4-135 | 1989-91 | 2.362-2.363 | 1.968-1.969 | .005 | .0004 |
| 2.5L/4-151 | 1989-91 | 2.362-2.363 | 1.968-1.969 | .005 | .0004 |
| 2.6L/4-156 | 1989 | 2.36 | 2.09 | .0006 | .0002 |
| 3.0L/V6-181 ④ | 1989-91 | 2.361-2.362 | 1.968-1.969 | .001 | .0002 |
| 3.0L/V6-181 ③ | 1990-91 | 2.7576-2.7583 | 2.3611-2.3618 | — | — |
| 3.0L/V6-181 ⑤ | 1991 | 2.358 | 1.965 | ⑥ | .0002 |
| 3.3L/V6-201 | 1990-91 | 2.519 | 2.283 | .001 | .001 |
| 3.8L/V6-231 | 1991 | 2.519 | 2.283 | .001 | .001 |
| 5.2L/V8-318 | 1989 | 2.4995-2.5005 | 2.124-2.125 | .001 | .001 |

①—Single Overhead Camshaft.
②—Dual Overhead Camshaft.
③—Monaco.
④—Except Monaco and Stealth.
⑤—Stealth.
⑥—SOHC engines, .0002 inch; DOHC engines, .00012.

## CYLINDER BLOCK

| Engine Liter/CID | Year | Cylinder Bore Diameter (Std.) | Cylinder Bore Taper Max. | Cylinder Bore Out Of Round Max. |
|---|---|---|---|---|
| 1.5L/4-89.6 | 1989-91 | 2.9724-2.9736 | .0008 | .0008 |
| 1.6L/4-97 | 1989-90 | 3.2402-3.2413 | .0004 | .0004 |
| 1.8L/4-107 | 1990-91 | 3.173 | .0004 | .0004 |
| 2.0L/4-122 ① | 1989-91 | 3.346 | .0008 | .0008 |
| 2.0L/4-122 ② | 1990-91 | 3.3465 | .0004 | .0004 |
| 2.2L/4-135 | 1989-91 | 3.44-3.45 | .005 | .002 |
| 2.5L/4-153 | 1989-91 | 3.44-3.45 | .005 | .002 |
| 2.6L/4-156 | 1989 | 3.587 | .0008 | .0008 |
| 3.0L/V6-181 ④ | 1989-91 | 3.586-3.587 | .0008 | .0008 |
| 3.0L/V6-181 ③ | 1990-91 | ⑤ | ⑤ | ⑤ |
| 3.3L/V6-201 | 1990-91 | 3.660 | .002 | .003 |
| 3.8L/V6-231 | 1991 | 3.779 | .002 | .003 |
| 5.2L/V8-318 | 1989 | 3.910-3.912 | .010 | .005 |

①—Single Overhead Camshaft.
②—Dual Overhead Camshaft.
③-Monaco.
④-Except Monaco.
⑤-Cylinder liner.

## BEARINGS & CONNECTING RODS

| Engine Liter/CID | Year | Bearing Clearance | | Connecting Rods | | Crankshaft Endplay |
|---|---|---|---|---|---|---|
| | | Main Bearings | Connecting Rod Bearings | Pin Bore Diameter | Side Clearance | |
| 1.5L/4-89.6 | 1989-90 | .0008-.0018 | .0006-.0017 | — | .0039-.0098 | .0020-.0071 |
| 1.5L/4-89.6 | 1991 | .0008-.0028 | .0008-.0024 | — | .0039-.0098 | .0020-.0071 |
| 1.6L/4-97 | 1989-90 | .0008-.0020 | .0008-.0020 | — | .0039-.0098 | .0020-.0071 |
| 1.8L/4-107 | 1990-91 | .0008-.0020 | .0008-.0020 | — | .0039-.0098 | .0020-.0070 |
| 2.0L/4-122⑤ | 1989-91 | .0008-.0020 | .0006-.0020 | — | .0039-.0098 | .0020-.0071 |
| 2.0L/4-122② | 1990-91 | .0008-.0020 | .0008-.0020 | — | .0040-.0098 | .0020-.0070 |
| 2.2L/4-135 | 1989 | .0004-.0028 | ① | — | .005-.013 | .002-.007 |
| 2.2L/4-135 | 1990-91 | .0004-.0028 | .0008-.0034 | — | .005-.013 | .002-.007 |
| 2.5L/4-151 | 1989 | .0004-.0028 | ① | — | .005-.013 | .002-.007 |
| 2.5L/4-151 | 1990-19 | .0004-.0028 | .0008-.0034 | — | .005-.013 | .002-.007 |
| 2.6L/4-156 | 1989 | .0008-.0018 | .0008-.0020 | — | .0039-.0098 | .0020-.0071 |
| 3.0L/V6-181⑦ | 1989-91 | .0008-.0019 | .0008-.0028 | — | .004-.010 | .002-.010 |
| 3.0L/V6-181⑥ | 1990-91 | .0015-.0035 | — | .9826-.9831 | .008-.015 | .003-.010 |
| 3.0L/V6-181⑧⑤ | 1991 | .0008-.0019 | .0006-.0018 | — | .0039-.0098 | .002-.0098 |
| 3.0L/V6-181⑧② | 1991 | .0007-.0017 | .0006-.0018 | — | .0039-.0098 | .002-.0098 |
| 3.3L/V6-201 | 1990 | ④ | .0005-.0022 | — | .006-.014 | .002-.007 |
| 3.3L/V6-201 | 1991 | .0007-.0022 | .00075-.003 | .9007-.9009 | .005-.015 | .003-.009 |
| 3.8L/V6-231 | 1991 | .0007-.0022 | .00075-.003 | .9007-.9009 | .005-.015 | .003-.009 |
| 5.2L/V8-318 | 1989 | ③ | .0005-.0022 | .9819-.9834 | .006-.014 | — |

①—Except Turbocharged engines, .0008-.0034 inch; turbocharged engines, .0008-.0031 inch.
②—Dual Overhead Camshaft.
③—No. 1, .0005-.0015 inch; No. 2, 3, 4 & 5, .0005-.0020 inch.
④—No. 1, .0005-.0015 inch; No. 2, 3 & 4, .0005-.0020 inch.
⑤—Single Overhead Camshaft.
⑥-Monaco.
⑦-Except Monaco and Stealth.
⑧-Stealth.

## PISTONS, PINS & RINGS

| Engine Liter/CID | Year | Piston Diameter (Std.) | Piston Clearance | Piston Pin Diameter | Piston Pin To Piston Clearance | Piston Ring End Gap ① | | Piston Ring Side Clearance | |
|---|---|---|---|---|---|---|---|---|---|
| | | | | | | Comp. | Oil | Comp. | Oil |
| 1.5L/4-89.6 | 1989-91 | 2.9713-2.9724 | .0008-.0016 | — | — | .0079 | .0079 | ⑱ | — |
| 1.6L/4-97⑳ | 1989-90 | ㉔ | ㉕ | — | — | ㉑ | .0079 | .0012-.0028 | — |
| 1.8L/4-107 | 1990-91 | 3.173 | .0004-.0012 | — | — | ㉖ | .008 | ㉗ | — |
| 2.0L/4-122⑲ | 1989-91 | 3.346 | .0004-.0012 | — | — | ㉓ | .0079 | ㉒ | — |
| 2.0L/4-122⑳ | 1990-91 | 3.3465 | ㉜ | — | — | ㉑ | .0079 | .0012-.0028 | — |
| 2.2L/4-135③ | 1989-91 | 3.443-3.445⑤ | .0005-.0015⑥ | — | — | ㉘ | .015 | ⑦ | .008② |
| 2.2L/4-135④ | 1989-90 | 3.4426-3.4452⑧ | .0005-.0015⑥ | — | — | ⑩ | .015 | ㉙ | .008② |
| 2.2L/4-135④ | 1991 | 3.443-3.444⑧ | .0018-.0028㉟ | — | — | .014-.020 | .010-.020 | ㉙ | .008② |
| 2.5L/4-153③ | 1989-91 | 3.442-3.445㉚ | .0010-.0020⑥ | — | — | ㉘ | .015 | ⑦ | .008② |
| 2.5L/4-153④ | 1989-91 | 3.4434-3.4440㉛ | .006-.0018⑨ | — | — | ⑩ | .015 | ㉙ | .008② |
| 2.6L/4-156 | 1989 | 3.587 | .0012-.0020 | — | — | ⑯ | .0118 | ⑰ | — |
| 3.0L/V6-181㉞ | 1989-91 | 3.585-3.586 | .0012-.0020 | — | — | ⑪ | .012 | ⑫ | ⑬ |
| 3.0L/V6-181㉝ | 1990-91 | — | — | .9839-.9843 | .0015-.0085 | .016-.022 | — | .001-.002 | .0015-.0035 |
| 3.0L/V6-181㊱⑲ | 1991 | 3.5866 | .0012-.0020 | — | — | ㊲ | .0118-.0354 | ⑰ | — |
| 3.0L/V6-181㊱⑳ | 1991 | 3.5866 | .0012-.0020 | — | — | ㊳ | .0079-.0236 | ㉒ | — |
| 3.3L/V6-201 | 1990-91 | 3.6594-3.6602 | .0009-.0022 | .9007-.9009 | .0002-.0008 | .0118 | .0098 | .001-.003 | .0006-.0089 |
| 3.8L/V6-231 | 1991 | 3.7776-3.77832 | .001-.0022 | .9007-.9009 | .0002-.0008 | .0118 | .0098 | .001-.003 | .0006-.0089 |
| 5.2L/V8-318 | 1989 | 3.886-3.891⑭ | ⑮ | .9841-.9843 | .00025-.00075 | .010 | .015 | .0015-.0030 | .0002-.0050 |

①—Minimum.
②—Maximum.
③—Except turbocharged engines.
④—Turbocharged engines.
⑤—Measured at right angle to piston pin, 1.14 inches from top of piston.
⑥—Wear limit, .0027 inch.
⑦—Top, .0015-.0031 inch; limit, .004 inch. 2nd, .0015-.0037 inch; limit, .004 inch.
⑧—Measured at right angle to piston pin, 2.38 inches from top of piston.
⑨—Wear limit, .0030 inch.

*Continued*

⑩—Top, .010 inch; 2nd, .009 inch.
⑪—Top, .012 inch; 2nd, .010 inch.
⑫—Top, .0020-.0035 inch; limit, .0040 inch. 2nd, .0008-.0020 inch; limit, .0039 inch.
⑬—Oil ring side rails must be free to rotate after assembly.
⑭—Measured at right angle to piston pin, 1.045 inches from top of piston.
⑮—Except H.P. engines, .0005-.0015 inch; H.P. engines, .001-.002 inch.
⑯—Top, .0118 inch; 2nd, .0098 inch.
⑰—Top, .0020-.0035 inch; 2nd, .0008-.0024 inch.
⑱—Top, .0012 inch; 2nd, .0008 inch.
⑲—Single Overhead Camshaft.
⑳—Dual Overhead Camshaft.
㉑—Top, .0098 inch; 2nd, .0138 inch.
㉒—Top, .0012-.0028; 2nd, .0008-.0024 inch.
㉓—Top, .0098 inch; 2nd, .0079 inch.
㉔—Except turbocharged engines, 3.2390-3.2402 inch; turbocharged engines, 3.2386-3.2398 inch.
㉕—Except turbocharged engines, .0008-.0016 inch; turbocharged engines, .0012-.0020 inch.
㉖—Top, .0118 inch; 2nd, .0079 inch.
㉗—Top, .0018-.0033 inch; 2nd, .0008-.0024 inch.
㉘—Top, .010 inch; 2nd, .011 inch.
㉙—Top, .0016-.0030 inch; limit, .004 inch. 2nd, .0015-.0037 inch; limit, .004 inch.
㉚—Measured at right angle to piston pin, 1.87 inches from top of piston.
㉛—Measured at right angle to piston pin, 1.48 inches from top of piston.
㉜—Except turbocharged engine, .0008-.0016 inch; turbocharged engine, .0012-.0020 inch.
㉝—Monaco.
㉞—Except Monaco and Stealth.
㉟—Wear limit, .0039 inch.
㊱—Stealth.
㊲—Top, .0118-.0177 inch; 2nd, .0098-.0157 inch.
㊳—Top, .0118-.0177 inch; 2nd, .0177-.0236 inch.

## OIL PUMP

| Engine Liter/ CID | Year | Rotor Backlash | Rotor To Body Clear. | Rotor End Play ① | Rotor Thickness (Minimum) Inner | Rotor Thickness (Minimum) Outer | Outer Rotor Diameter (Minimum) | Maximum Cover Flatness Variation | Relief Spring Free Length | Relief Spring Pressure Lbs. @ Inches |
|---|---|---|---|---|---|---|---|---|---|---|
| 1.5L/4-89.6 | 1989-91 | — | .0039-.0079 | .0016-.0039 | — | — | — | — | 1.835 | 13 @ 1.579 |
| 1.6L/4-97 | 1989-90 | — | ⑦ | — | — | — | — | — | 1.835 | 13.4 @ 1.579 |
| 1.8L/4-107 | 1990-91 | — | .0039-.0063③ | — | — | — | — | — | 1.724 | 8.2 @1.579 |
| 2.0L/4-122⑧ | 1989-91 | — | .010 | — | — | — | — | — | 1.835 | 13.4 @ 1.579 |
| 2.0L/4-122⑨ | 1990-91 | — | ⑦ | — | — | — | — | — | 1.835 | 13.4 @ 1.579 |
| 2.2L/4-135 | 1989-91 | .008② | .0010-.0035③ | .0010-.0035 | — | .944 | 2.469 | .002 | 1.95 | 20 @ 1.34 |
| 2.5L/4-153 | 1989-91 | .008② | .0010-.0035③ | .0010-.0035 | — | .944 | 2.469 | .002 | 1.95 | 20 @ 1.34 |
| 2.6L/4-156 | 1989 | — | .0043-.0059 | ④ | — | — | — | — | 1.835 | 9.5 @ 1.575 |
| 3.0L/V6-181⑪ | 1989-91 | ⑤ | .004-.007 | .0015-.0035 | — | — | — | — | — | ⑥ |
| 3.0L/V6-181⑩ | 1990-91 | — | — | — | — | — | — | — | — | — |
| 3.0L/V6-181⑫ | 1991 | — | .0016-.0037③ | .0039-.0071 | — | — | — | — | 1.724 | 8.3 @ 1.579 |
| 3.3L/V6-201 | 1990-91 | .008 | .022 | — | .301 | .3005 | 3.141 | .003 | — | — |
| 3.8L/V6-231 | 1991 | .008 | .022 | — | .301 | .3005 | 3.141 | .003 | — | — |
| 5.2L/V8-318 | 1989 | .008② | .014③ | .004 | .825 | .825 | 2.469 | .0015 | 1.95 | 19.75 @ 1.34 |

①—Measured between pump cover mounting surface and end of gear, using straightedge and feeler gauge.
②—Maximum inner & outer rotor tip clearance.
③—Maximum clearance between inner and outer rotors and body.
④—Drive gear, .0020-.0043 inch; driven gear, .0016-.0039 inch.
⑤—Inner rotor to case, .006 maximum.
⑥—Relief valve opening pressure, 71.45-85.75 psi.
⑦—Drive gear, .0063-.0083 inch; driven gear, .0051-.0071 inch.
⑧—Single Overhead Camshaft.
⑨—Dual Overhead Camshaft.
⑩—Monaco.
⑪—Except Monaco and Stealth.
⑫—Stealth.

## CAMSHAFT & LIFTERS

| Engine Liter/CID | Year | Camshaft Journal Diameter | Camshaft Bearing Clearance | Camshaft End Play | Lifter Bore Diameter | Lifter Diameter | Lifter To Bore Clearance |
|---|---|---|---|---|---|---|---|
| 1.5L/4-89.6 | 1989-90 | 1.811 | .0015-.0031 | .0020-.0079 | — | — | — |
| 1.5L/4-89.6 | 1991 | 1.811 | .0024-.0039 | .0020-.0079 | — | — | — |
| 1.6L/4-97 | 1989-90 | 1.02 | .0020-.0035 | .004-.008 | — | — | — |
| 1.8L/4-107 | 1990-91 | 1.3360-1.3366 | .0020-.0035 | .004-.008 | — | — | — |
| 2.0L/4-122④ | 1989-91 | 1.34 | .0020-.0035 | .004-.008 | — | — | — |
| 2.0L/4-122⑤ | 1990-91 | 1.0217-1.0224 | .0020-.0035 | .004-.008 | — | — | — |
| 2.2L/4-135 | 1989-90 | ① | — | .005-.013 | — | — | — |
| 2.2L/4-135 | 1991 | ⑧ | — | ⑨ | — | — | — |
| 2.5L/4-153 | 1989-90 | ① | — | .005-.013 | — | — | — |
| 2.5L/4-153 | 1991 | ⑧ | — | ⑨ | — | — | — |
| 2.6L/4-156 | 1989 | 1.34 | .0020-.0035 | .004-.008 | — | — | — |
| 3.0L/V6-181⑦ | 1989-91 | 1.34 | .0020-.0035 | — | — | — | — |

Continued

## CAMSHAFT & LIFTERS—Continued

| Engine Liter/CID | Year | Camshaft Journal Diameter | Camshaft Bearing Clearance | Camshaft End Play | Lifter Bore Diameter | Lifter Diameter | Lifter To Bore Clearance |
|---|---|---|---|---|---|---|---|
| 3.0L/V6-181⑥ | 1990-91 | — | — | .003-.0055 | — | — | — |
| 3.0L/V6-181⑩④ | 1991 | 1.34 | .0020-.0035 | — | — | — | — |
| 3.0L/V6-181⑩⑤ | 1991 | 1.02 | .0020-.0035 | — | — | — | — |
| 3.3L/V6-201 | 1990 | ③ | .001-.003 | .002-.010 | .9051-.9059 | .9035-.9040 | .0011-.0024 |
| 3.3L/V6-201 | 1991 | ⑪ | .001-.004 | .005-.012 | .9051-.9059 | .9035-.9040 | .0011-.0024 |
| 3.8L/V6-231 | 1991 | ⑪ | .001-.004 | .005-.012 | .9051-.9059 | .9035-.9040 | .0011-.0024 |
| 5.2L/V8-318 | 1989 | ② | .001-.003 | .002-.010 | .9048-.9059 | .9035-.9040 | .0008-.0024 |

①—Standard, 1.375-1.376 inch; Oversize, 1.395-1.396 inch. Oversize indicated by green paint marking on camshaft and bearing caps, and "OJS" stamping on rearward oil gallery plug and end of camshaft at air pump end of engine.
②—No. 1, 1.998-1.999 inch; No. 2, 1.982-1.983 inch; No. 3, 1.967- 1.968 inch; No. 4, 1.951-1.952 inch; No. 5, 1.5605-1.5615 inch.
③—No. 1, 1.997-1.999 inch; No. 2, 1.984-1.985 inch; No. 3, 1.953-1.954 inch; No. 4, 1.950-1.951 inch.
④—Single Overhead Camshaft.
⑤—Dual Overhead Camshaft.
⑥—Monaco.
⑦—Except Monaco and Stealth.
⑧—Except 2.2L/4-135 turbo engines, 1.395–1.396 inch; 2.2L/4-135 turbo engine, 1.886–1.887 inch.
⑨—Except 2.2L/4-135 turbo engines, .005–.013 inch; 2.2L/4-135 turbo engines, .001–.008 inch.
⑩—Stealth.
⑪—No. 1, 1.997-1.999 inch; No. 2, 1.980-1.982 inch; No. 3, 1.965-1.967 inch; No. 4, 1.949-1.952 inch.

## BALANCE SHAFTS

| Engine Liter/CID | Year | Journal Diameter | | Oil Clearance | |
|---|---|---|---|---|---|
| | | Front | Rear | Front | Rear |
| 1.8L/4-107 | 1990-91 | ⑤ | 1.4154-1.4160 | ⑥ | .0020-.0036 |
| 2.0L/4-122⑦ | 1989-91 | ④ | 1.614 | .0011-.0024 | .0020-.0036 |
| 2.0L/4-122⑧ | 1990-91 | ⑨ | ⑩ | ⑪ | ① |
| 2.6L/4-156 | 1989 | ③ | 1.69 | ② | .0037-.0053 |

①—Left balance shaft, .0017-.0033 inch; right balance shaft, .0020-.0036 inch.
②—Left balance shaft, .0008-.0024 inch.
③—Left balance shaft, .91 inch; right balance shaft, .83 inch.
④—Left balance shaft, .720 inch; right balance shaft, 1.654 inch.
⑤—Left balance shaft, .7270-.7276 inch; right balance shaft, 1.5338-1.5344 inch.
⑥—Left balance shaft, .0008-.0021 inch; right balance shaft, .0012-.0024 inch.
⑦—Single Overhead Camshaft
⑧—Dual Overhead Camshaft
⑨—Left balance shaft, .7270-.7276 inch; right balance shaft, 1.6519-1.6526 inch.
⑩—Left balance shaft, .1.6126-1.6132 inch; right balance shaft, 1.6122-1.6129 inch.
⑪—Left balance shaft, .0008-.0021 inch; right balance shaft, .0008-.0024 inch.

## INTERMEDIATE SHAFTS

| Engine Liter/CID | Year | Journal Diameter | | Bushing Bore Diameter | | Oil Clearance | |
|---|---|---|---|---|---|---|---|
| | | Outer | Inner | Outer | Inner | Outer | Inner |
| 2.2L/4-135 | 1989-91 | 1.6799-1.6809 | .7744-.7753 | 1.6823-1.6830 | .7763-.7775 | .0013-.0031 | .0001-.0031 |
| 2.5L/4-153 | 1989-91 | 1.6799-1.6809 | .7744-.7753 | 1.6823-1.6830 | .7763-.7775 | .0013-.0031 | .0001-.0031 |

## CYLINDER LINERS

| Engine Liter/CID | Year | Liner Inside Diameter | Liner Base Outside Diameter | Liner Height | Liner Protrusion | |
|---|---|---|---|---|---|---|
| | | | | | Limits | Maximum Variation① |
| 3.0L/V6-180③ | 1990 | ② | 3.85 | 5.16 | .0051-.0078 | — |
| 3.0L/V6-180③ | 1991 | ② | 3.85 | 5.16 | .002-.005 | — |

①—Between Adjacent cylinders.
②—One notch liner, 3.6614-3.6618 inches; two notch liner, 3.6618-3.6622 inches; three notch liner, 3.6622-3.6626 inches.
③-Monaco.

# Eagle

## INDEX



## CYLINDER HEAD, VALVE GUIDES & VALVE SEATS

| Engine Liter/CID | Year | Cylinder Head Warpage Limit | Cylinder head overall thickness | Valve Guides | | Valve Seats | | | |
|---|---|---|---|---|---|---|---|---|---|
| | | | | Inside Diameter | Stem to Guide Clearance | Seat Angle | Seat Width Intake | Seat Width Exhaust | Run Out |
| 1.5L/4-89.6 | 1989-91 | .008 | 4.21③ | — | ① | 44-44.5° | .035-.051 | .035-.051 | — |
| 1.6L/4-97 | 1989-90 | .008 | 5.193-5.201③ | — | ② | 44-44.5° | .035-.051 | .035-.051 | — |
| 1.8L/4-107 | 1990-91 | .008 | 3.484③ | — | ④ | 44-44.5° | .0345-.0512 | .0345-.0512 | — |
| 2.0L/4-122 | 1990-91 | .008 | 5.197③ | — | ⑤ | 45-45.5° | .035-.051 | .035-.051 | — |
| 2.22L/4-132 | 1989 | .002 | 4.394 | .315 | .004 | ⑥ | .07 | .06 | .0025 |
| 2.5L/4-150 | 1989 | .001-.008 | — | .313-.314 | .001-.003 | 44.5° | .040-.060 | .040-.060 | .0025 |
| 3.0L/V6-180 | 1989-91 | .002 | 4.363 | .315 | — | 45° | — | — | — |

①—Exhaust, .0020-.0035 inch; intake, .0010-.0020 inch.
②—Exhaust, .0020-.0035 inch; intake, .0008-.0020 inch.
③—Minimum thickness is overall thickness, less warpage limit, combined with amount of grinding of cylinder block gasket surface.
④—Exhaust, .0020-.0035 inch; intake, .0012-.0024 inch.
⑤—Exhaust, .0020-.0033 inch; intake, .0008-.0019 inch.
⑥—Intake valve, 60°; Exhaust valve, 45°.

## VALVES & VALVE SPRINGS

| Engine Liter/CID | Year | Valves | | | | | | | Valve Springs | |
|---|---|---|---|---|---|---|---|---|---|---|
| | | Stem Diameter | Maximum Tip Refinish | Face Angle | Margin① | Clearance Intake | Clearance Exhaust | Clearance Jet | Free Length | Pressure Pounds @ Inches |
| 1.5L/4-89.6 | 1989-90 | .260 | — | 45-45.5° | ③ | ⑦ | ⑧ | — | 1.756 | — |
| 1.5L/4-89.6 | 1991 | ⑥ | — | 45-45.5° | ③ | ⑦ | ⑧ | — | 1.756 | ⑭ |
| 1.6L/4-97 | 1989-90 | ④ | — | 45-45.5° | ⑤ | — | — | — | 1.803 | — |
| 1.8L/4-107 | 1990-91 | .310 | — | 45-45.4° | ⑨ | — | — | — | 1.937 | 62 @ 1.469 |
| 2.0L/4-122 | 1990-91 | ⑩ | — | 45-45.4° | ⑪ | — | — | — | 1.902 | 66⑫ |
| 2.22L/4-132 | 1989 | .315 | — | ⑬ | — | — | — | — | — | — |
| 2.5L/4-150 | 1989 | .311-.312 | .010 | 45° | — | — | — | — | 1.967 | 80-90 @ 1.640 |
| 3.0L/V6-180 | 1989-90 | .315 | — | 45° | ② | — | — | — | 1.909 | 76 @ 1.575 |
| 3.0L/V6-180 | 1991 | .315 | — | 45° | — | — | — | — | 1.909 | 76 @ 1.575 |

①—Minimum.
②—Intake, .059 inch; exhaust, .067 inch.
③—Intake, .020 inch; exhaust, .039 inch.
④—Intake, .2585-.2586 inch; exhaust, .2571-2579 inch.
⑤—Intake, .028 inch; exhaust, .039 inch.
⑥—Intake, .2585–2591 inch; Exhaust, .2571–.2579 inch.
⑦—.0059 inch hot; .0028 inch cold.
⑧—.0098 inch hot; .0067 inch cold.
⑨—Intake, .039 inch; exhaust, .028 inch.
⑩—Intake, .2585-.2591 inch; exhaust, .2571-.2579 inch.
⑪—Intake, .040 inch; exhaust, .059 inch.
⑫—At installed height.
⑬—Intake valve, 60°; Exhaust valve, 45°.
⑭—Intake, 51 lbs. at 1.469 inches; Exhaust, 64 lbs at 1.469 inches.

# ENGINE REBUILDING SPECIFICATIONS

## CRANKSHAFT & BEARINGS

| Engine Liter/CID | Year | Crankshaft | | | | Bearing Clearance | | Crankshaft Endplay |
|---|---|---|---|---|---|---|---|---|
| | | Main Bearing Journal Diameter | Connecting Rod Journal Diameter | Maximum Out of Round All | Maximum Taper All | Main Bearings | Connecting Rod Bearings | |
| 1.5L/4-89.6 | 1989-91 | 1.89 | 1.65 | .0006 | .0006 | .0008-.0018 | .0006-.0017 | .0020-.0071 |
| 1.6L/4-97 | 1989-90 | 2.24 | 1.77 | .0006 | .0006 | .0008-.0020 | .0008-.0020 | .0020-.0071 |
| 1.8L/4-107 | 1990-91 | 2.24 | 1.77 | .0006 | .0002 | .0008-.0020 | .0008-.0020 | .0020-.0070 |
| 2.0L/4-122 | 1990-91 | 2.2433-2.2439 | 1.7709-1.7715 | .0006 | .0002 | .0008-.0020 | .0008-.0020 | .0020-.0070 |
| 2.22L/4-132 | 1989 | 2.476 | 2.216 | — | — | — | — | .002-.009 |
| 2.5L/4-150 | 1989 | 2.4996-2.5001 | 2.0934-2.0955 | .0005 | .0005 | .0010-.0025 | .0010-.0025 | .0015-.0065 |
| 3.0L/V6-180 | 1989-91 | 2.7576-2.7583 | 2.3611-2.3618 | — | — | .0015-.0035 | — | .003-.010 |

## CONNECTING RODS

| Engine Liter/CID | Year | Pin Bore Diameter | Big End Bore Diameter | Side Clearance |
|---|---|---|---|---|
| 1.5L/4-89.6 | 1989-91 | — | — | .0039-.0098 |
| 1.6L/4-97 | 1989-90 | — | — | .0039-.0098 |
| 1.8L/4-107 | 1990-91 | — | — | .0040-.0098 |
| 2.0L/4-122 | 1990-91 | — | — | .0039-.0098 |
| 2.22L/4-132 | 1989 | .905 | — | .012-.022 |
| 2.5L/4-150 | 1989 | .9288-.9298 | 2.2080-2.2085 | .010-.019 |
| 3.0L/V6-180 | 1989-91 | .9826-.9831 | 2.508 | .008-.015 |

## PISTONS, PINS & RINGS

| Engine Liter/CID | Year | Piston Diameter (Std.)① | Piston Clearance | Piston Pin Bore Diameter | Piston Pin Diameter | Piston Pin To Piston Clearance | Piston Ring End Gap② | | Piston Ring Side Clearance | |
|---|---|---|---|---|---|---|---|---|---|---|
| | | | | | | | Com. | Oil | Com. | Oil |
| 1.5L/4-89.6 | 1989-91 | 2.9713-2.9724 | .0008-.0016 | — | — | — | .0079 | .0079 | ③ | — |
| 1.6L/4-97④ | 1989-90 | 3.239-3.2402 | .0008-.0016 | — | — | — | ⑥ | .0079 | .0012-.0028 | — |
| 1.6L/4-97⑤ | 1989-90 | 3.2386-3.2398 | .0012-.0020 | — | — | — | ⑥ | .0079 | .0012-.0028 | — |
| 1.8L/4-107 | 1990-91 | 3.173 | .0004-.0012 | — | — | — | ⑦ | .0079 | ⑧ | — |
| 2.0L/4-122 | 1990-91 | 3.3465 | .0008-.0016 | — | — | — | ⑥ | .0079 | .0012-.0028 | — |
| 2.0L/4-122 | 1989 | — | — | .905 | .905 | ⑨ | ⑩ | ⑩ | — | — |
| 2.5L/4-150 | 1989 | — | .0013-.0021 | .9308-.9313 | .9304-.9309 | .0004-.0006 | .010 | .015 | .0010-.0032 | .0010-.0085 |
| 3.0L/V6-180 | 1989-91 | — | — | .9844-.9848 | .9839-.9843 | .0015-.0085 | .016 | — | .001-.002 | .0015-.0035 |

①—Measured at 90° angle to piston pin
②—Minimum.
③—Top, .0012-.0028 inch; No. 2, .0008-.0024 inch.
④—Except turbocharged engine.
⑤—Turbocharged engine.
⑥—Top, .0098 inch; No. 2, .0138 inch.
⑦—Top, .0118 inch; No. 2, .0079 inch.
⑧—Top, .0018-.0033 inch; No. 2, .0008-.0024 inch.
⑨—Press fit.
⑩—Pre-Adjusted.

## CYLINDER BLOCK, CAMSHAFT & LIFTERS

| Engine Liter/ CID | Year | Cylinder Bore Diameter (Std.) | Cylinder Bore Taper Max. | Cylinder Bore Out Of Round Max. | Cylinder Block Warpage Max. | Lifter Bore Diameter | Lifter Diameter | Lifter To Bore Clearance | Camshaft Journal Diameter | Camshaft Bearing Clearance |
|---|---|---|---|---|---|---|---|---|---|---|
| 1.5L/4-89.6 | 1989-91 | 2.9724-2.9736 | .0008 | .0008 | .004 | — | — | — | 1.811 | .0015-.0031 |
| 1.6L/4-97 | 1989-90 | 3.2402-3.2413 | .0004 | .0004 | .0039 | — | — | — | 1.02 | .0020-.0035 |
| 1.8L/4-107 | 1990-91 | 3.173 | .0004 | .0004 | .0020 | — | — | — | 1.3360-1.3366 | .0020-.0035 |
| 2.0L/4-122 | 1990-91 | 3.3465 | .0004 | .0004 | .0020 | — | — | — | 1.0217-1.0224 | .0020-.0035 |
| 2.22L/4-132 | 1989 | ② | ② | ② | — | — | — | — | — | — |
| 2.5L/4-150 | 1989 | 3.8751-3.8775 | .001 | .001 | — | .9055-.9065 | .9040-.9045 | .0010-.0025 | ① | .001-.003 |
| 3.0L/V6-180 | 1989-91 | ② | ② | ② | — | — | — | — | — | — |

①—No. 1, 2.029-2.030 inches; No. 2, 2.019-2.020 inches; No. 3, 2.009-2.010 inches; No. 4, 1.999-2.000 inches.
②—Uses cylinder liners.

## OIL PUMP

| Engine Liter/CID | Year | Pump Gear Backlash | Pump Gear To Body Clearance | Pump Gear End Play① |
|---|---|---|---|---|
| 1.5L/4-89.6 | 1989-91 | — | — | .0016-.0039 |
| 1.6L/4-97 | 1989-90 | .0098② | .0098② | .0016-.0039 |
| 1.8L/4-107 | 1990-91 | — | ③ | — |
| 2.0L/4-122 | 1990-91 | — | ④ | — |
| 2.0L/4-132 | 1989 | — | .004② | .005② |
| 2.5L/4-150 | 1989 | — | .002-.004 | .004-.008 |
| 3.0L/V6-180 | 1989-91 | — | — | — |

①—Measured with a feeler gauge.
②—Maximum.
③—Drive gear, .0024-.0047 inch; driven gear, .0016-.0047 inch.
④—Drive gear, .0063-.0083 inch; driven gear, .0051-.0071 inch.

## CYLINDER LINERS

| Engine Liter/CID | Year | Liner Inside Diameter | Liner Base Outside Diameter | Liner Height | Liner Protrusion | |
|---|---|---|---|---|---|---|
| | | | | | Limits | Maximum Variation① |
| 2.22L/4-132 | 1989 | 3.464 | 3.685 | 5.846 | .007-.006② | — |
| 3.0L/V6-180 | 1989-90 | ② | 3.85 | 5.16 | .0051-.0078 | — |
| 3.0L/V6-180 | 1991 | ② | 3.85 | 5.16 | .002-.005 | — |

①—Between Adjacent cylinders.
②—One notch liner, 3.6614-3.6618 inches; two notch liner, 3.6618-3.6622 inches; three notch liner, 3.6622-3.6626 inches.

## BALANCE SHAFTS

| Engine Liter/CID | Year | Journal Diameter | | Oil Clearance | |
|---|---|---|---|---|---|
| | | Front | Rear | Front | Rear |
| 1.8L/4-107 | 1990-91 | ① | 1.4154-1.4160 | ② | .0020-.0036 |
| 2.0L/4-122③ | 1990-91 | ④ | ⑤ | ⑥ | ⑦ |

①—Left balance shaft, .7270-.7276 inch; right balance shaft, 1.5338-1.5344 inch.

②—Left balance shaft, .0008-.0021 inch; right balance shaft, .0012-.0024 inch.

③—Dual Overhead Camshaft

④—Left balance shaft, .7270-.7276 inch; right balance shaft, 1.6519-1.6526 inch.

⑤—Left balance shaft, .1.6126-1.6132 inch; right balance shaft, 1.6122-1.6129 inch.

⑥—Left balance shaft, .0008-.0021 inch; right balance shaft, .0008-.0024 inch.

⑦—Left balance shaft, .0017-.0033 inch; right balance shaft, .0020-.0036 inch.

# FORD MOTOR COMPANY

# FORD MOTOR COMPANY

# FORD CROWN VICTORIA & THUNDERBIRD, MERCURY COUGAR & GRAND MARQUIS

## INDEX OF SERVICE OPERATIONS

**NOTE:** Refer To Rear Of This Manual For Vehicle Manufacturer's Special Service Tool Suppliers.

# INDEX OF SERVICE OPERATIONS—Continued

# Specifications

## GENERAL ENGINE SPECIFICATIONS

| Year | Engine Liter/CID① | Engine VIN Code ② | Fuel System | Bore & Stroke | Compression Ratio | Net H.P. @ RPM③ | Maximum Torque Ft. Lbs. @ RPM | Normal Oil Pressure Psi. |
|---|---|---|---|---|---|---|---|---|
| 1989–90 | 3.8L/V6-232 | 4 | SEFI | 3.80 x 3.40 | 9.0 | 140 @ 3800 | 215 @ 2400 | 40–60④ |
| | 3.8L/V6-232 SC⑤ | C, R | SEFI | 3.80 x 3.40 | 8.2 | 210 @ 4000 | 315 @ 2600 | 40–60④ |
| | 5.0L/V8-302⑥ | F | SEFI | 4.00 x 3.00 | 8.9 | 150 @ 3200 | 270 @ 2000 | 40–60⑦ |
| | 5.0L/V8-302⑧ | F | SEFI | 4.00 x 3.00 | 8.9 | 160 @ 3400 | 280 @ 2200 | 40–60⑦ |
| 1991 | 5.0L/V8-302⑥ | F | SEFI | 4.00 x 3.00 | 8.9 | 150 @ 3200 | 270 @ 2000 | 40–60⑦ |
| | 5.0L/V8-302⑧ | F | SEFI | 4.00 x 3.00 | 8.9 | 160 @ 3400 | 280 @ 2200 | 40–60⑦ |
| 1991–92 | 3.8L/V6-232 | 4 | SEFI | 3.80 x 3.40 | 9.0 | 140 @ 3800 | 215 @ 2400 | 40–60④ |
| | 3.8L/V6-232 SC⑤ | C, R | SEFI | 3.80 x 3.40 | 8.2 | 210 @ 4000 | 315 @ 2600 | 40–60④ |
| | 5.0L/V8-302 HO⑨ | T | SEFI | 4.00 x 3.00 | 9.0 | 200 @ 4000 | 275 @ 3000 | 40–60⑦ |
| 1992 | 4.6L/V8-281⑥ | F | SEFI | 3.60 x 3.60 | 9.0 | 190 @ 4200 | 260 @ 3200 | 40–60⑦ |
| | 4.6L/V8-281⑧ | F | SEFI | 3.60 x 3.60 | 9.0 | 210 @ 4600 | 270 @ 3400 | 40–60⑦ |

SEFI—Sequential Multi-Port Electronic Fuel Injection
①—C.I.D.-Cubic Inch Displacement.
②—The eighth digit of VIN denotes engine code.
③—Ratings are net-as installed in vehicle.
④—At 2500 RPM with engine at operating temperature.
⑤—Supercharged engine.
⑥—Single exhaust.
⑦—At 2000 RPM with engine at operating temperature.
⑧—Dual exhaust.
⑨—Cougar & Thunderbird.

## TUNE UP SPECIFICATIONS

| Engine (VIN Code)① | Spark Plug Gap | Ignition Timing BTDC② Firing Order Fig. ③ | Ignition Timing BTDC② Man. Trans. | Ignition Timing BTDC② Auto. Trans. | Ignition Timing BTDC② Mark Fig. | Curb Idle Speed Man. Trans. | Curb Idle Speed Auto. Trans. ④ | Fast Idle Speed Man. Trans. | Fast Idle Speed Auto. Trans. | Fuel Pump Pressure, Psi. |
|---|---|---|---|---|---|---|---|---|---|---|
| **1989** | | | | | | | | | | |
| 3.8L/V6-232 (4) | .054 | A | — | ⑤ | B | — | 550D⑥ | — | ⑥ | 35–45⑦ |
| 3.8L/V6-232 (C, R) | .054 | C | ⑤ | ⑤ | ⑧ | 700–800⑥ | 550–650D⑥ | ⑥ | ⑥ | 35–45⑦ |
| 5.0L/V8-302 (F) | .050 | D | — | ⑤ | E | — | 625D⑥ | — | ⑥ | 35–45⑦ |
| **1990** | | | | | | | | | | |
| 3.8L/V6-232 (4) | .054 | A | — | ⑤ | B | — | ⑥ | — | ⑥ | 35–45⑦ |
| 3.8L/V6-232 (C, R) | .054 | C | ⑤ | ⑤ | ⑧ | 700–800⑥ | 550–650D⑥ | ⑥ | ⑥ | 35–45⑦ |
| 5.0L/V8-302 (F) | .050 | D | — | ⑤ | E | — | ⑥ | — | ⑥ | 35–45⑦ |
| **1991** | | | | | | | | | | |
| 3.8L/V6-232 (4) | .054 | A | — | ⑤ | B | — | 550–650D⑥ | — | ⑥ | 39.5⑦ |
| 3.8L/V6-232 (C, R) | .054 | C | ⑤ | ⑤ | ⑧ | 700–800⑥ | 550–650⑥ | ⑥ | ⑥ | 35–45⑦ |
| 5.0L/V8-302 (F) | .050 | D | — | ⑤ | E | — | ⑥ | — | ⑥ | 39.2⑦ |
| 5.0L/V8-302 HO (T) | .054 | D | ⑤ | ⑤ | — | 675⑥ | 625N⑥ | ⑥ | ⑥ | 30–40⑦ |
| **1992** | | | | | | | | | | |
| 3.8L/V6-232 (4) | .052–.056 | A | — | ⑤ | — | — | ⑥ | — | ⑥ | 30–45⑦ |
| 3.8L/V6-232 (C, R) | .052–.056 | C | ⑤ | ⑤ | ⑧ | 700⑥ | 600⑥ | ⑥ | ⑥ | 30–60⑦ |
| 4.6L/V8-281 (F) | .054 | 1-3-7-2-6-5-4-8 | — | ⑤ | ⑧ | — | 640N⑥ | — | ⑥ | 36–39⑦ |
| 5.0L/V8-302 HO (T) | .054 | 1-3-7-2-6-5-4-8 | — | ⑤ | — | — | ⑥ | — | ⑥ | 30–40⑦ |

①—The eighth digit of Vehicle Identification Number (VIN) denotes engine code.
②—BTDC: Before Top Dead Center.
③—D:Drive. When checking idle speed, set parking brake & block drive wheels.
④—Before disconnecting wires from distributor cap, determine location of No. 1 wire in cap, as distributor position may have been altered from that shown at the end of this chart.
⑤—Non-adjustable.
⑥—Idle speed is controlled by an automatic idle speed control.
⑦—Wrap shop towel around fuel diagnostic valve to prevent fuel spillage. Connect suitable fuel pressure gauge to fuel diagnostic valve. Energize fuel pump & check pressure gauge reading.
⑧—Equipped with crankshaft sensor.

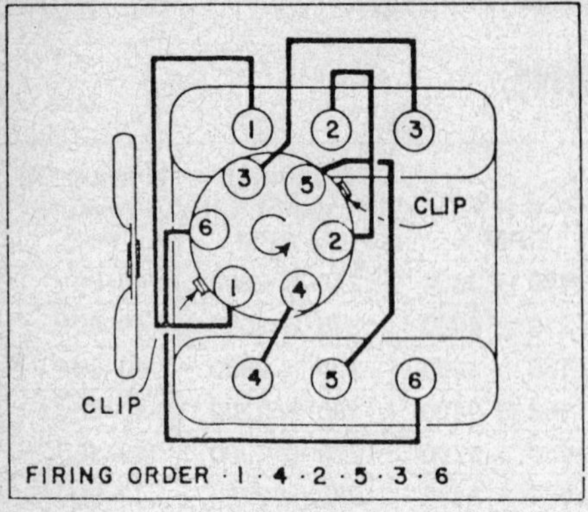


Fig. A

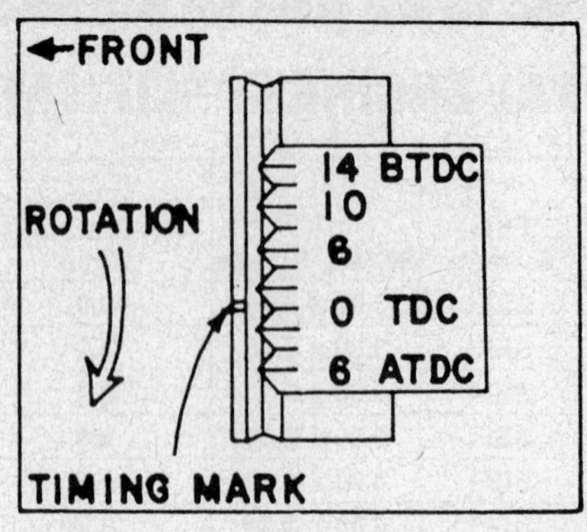


Fig. B

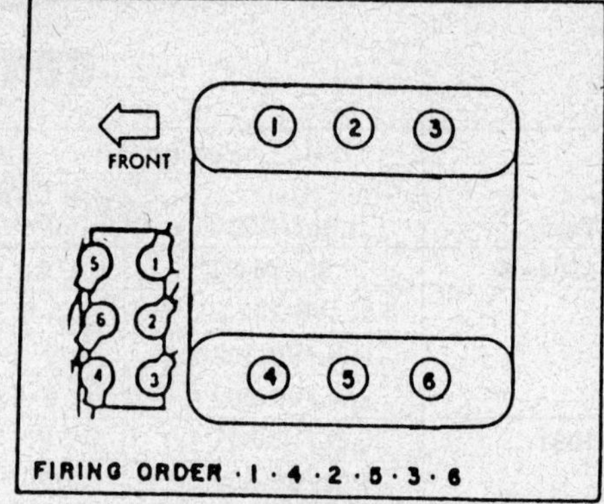


Fig. C

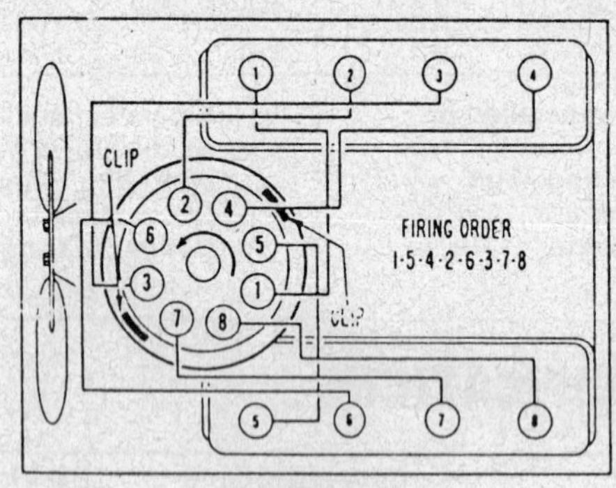


Fig. D

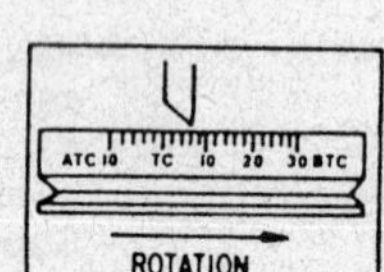


Fig. E

# WHEEL ALIGNMENT SPECIFICATIONS

## FRONT

| Year | Caster Angle, Degrees Limits | Caster Angle, Degrees Desired | Camber Angle, Degrees Limits Left | Camber Angle, Degrees Limits Right | Camber Angle, Degrees Desired Left | Camber Angle, Degrees Desired Right | Toe-In Inch | Toe Out on Turns, Deg. Outer Wheel | Toe Out on Turns, Deg. Inner Wheel |
|---|---|---|---|---|---|---|---|---|---|
| **COUGAR & THUNDERBIRD** | | | | | | | | | |
| 1989–92 | +4.75 to +6.25 | +5.5 | −1.25 to +.25 | −1.25 to +.25 | −.5 | −.5 | 1/8 | 19.73 | 20 |
| **CROWN VICTORIA & GRAND MARQUIS** | | | | | | | | | |
| 1989–91 | +2.5 to +4.5 | +3.5 | −.75 to +.25 | −.75 to +.25 | −.5 | −.5 | 1/16 | 18.51 | 20 |
| 1992 | +4.75 to +6.25 | +5.5 | −1.25 to +.25 | −1.25 to +.25 | −.5 | −.5 | 1/8 | 18.51 | 20 |

## REAR

| Year | Camber Angle, Degrees Limits Left | Camber Angle, Degrees Limits Right | Camber Angle, Degrees Desired Left | Camber Angle, Degrees Desired Right | Toe-In Inch |
|---|---|---|---|---|---|
| **COUGAR & THUNDERBIRD** | | | | | |
| 1989–92 | −1 to 0 | −1 to 0 | −.5 | −.5 | 1/16 |

# COOLING SYSTEM & CAPACITY DATA

| Engine & VIN Code | Cooling Capacity, Qts. | Radiator Cap Relief Pressure, Psi. | Thermo. Opening Temp. | Fuel Tank Gals. | Engine Refill Qts. | Transmission Oil | | | |
|---|---|---|---|---|---|---|---|---|---|
| | | | | | | Man. Trans. Pts. | Auto. Trans. Qts.① | Rear Axle Oil Pts. |
| **1989–90** | | | | | | | | |
| 3.8L/V6-232 (4) | 11.6 | 16 | 197 | 18.8 | 4② | — | 12.3③ | ④ |
| 3.8L/V6-232 SC (C, R) | 12 | 16 | 197 | 18.8 | 4② | 6.3③ | 12.3③ | ⑤ |
| 5.0L/V8-302 (F) | 14.1 | 16 | 197 | 18 | 4② ⑥ | — | 12.3③ | ⑦ |
| **1991** | | | | | | | | |
| 3.8L/V6-232 (4) | 11.8 | 16 | 196 | 19 | 4.5⑧ | — | 12.3③ | 3.1 |
| 3.8L/V6-232 SC (C, R) | 11.8 | 16 | 197 | 19 | 4.5⑧ | 6.3③ | 12.3③ | 3.4 |
| 5.0L/V8-302 (F)⑨ | 14.4 | 16 | 192 | 18 | 4② ⑥ | — | 12.3③ | 3.8 |
| 5.0L/V8-302 HO (T)⑩ | 14.1 | 16 | 195 | 19 | 4② ⑥ | — | 12.3③ | 3.4 |
| **1992** | | | | | | | | |
| 3.8L/V6-232 (4, C, R) | 12.5 | 16 | 197 | 18 | 4.5⑧ | 6.3 | 12.3③ | 3.1⑪ |
| 4.6L/V8-281 (F) | 13.6 | 14–18 | 195 | 20 | 5.0 | — | 12.3③ | 3.8 |
| 5.0L/V8-302 HO (T) | 14.1 | 14–18 | 192–197 | 18 | 4.0② | — | 12.3③ | 3.35 |

①—Approximate, make final check with dipstick.
②—Add 1 qt. with filter change.
③—Use Mercon type transmission fluid.
④—Conventional axle, 3 pts. Traction-Lok axle, 2.75 pts. plus 4 oz. of friction modifier meeting Ford Motor Co. specification EST-M2C118-A.
⑤—Models w/7.5 inch ring gear, conventional axle, 3 pts.; Traction-Lok axle, 2.75 pts. plus 4 oz. of friction modifier meeting Ford Motor Co. specification EST-M2C118-A. Models w/8.8 inch ring gear, conventional axle, 3.5 pts.; traction-Lok axle, 3.75 pts. plus 4 oz. of friction modifier meeting Ford Motor Co. specification EST-M2C118-A.
⑥—Equipped with dual sump oil pan. Remove both drain plugs to fully drain oil. One drain plug is located at front of oil pan. Second drain plug is located at left hand bottom of oil pan.
⑦—Conventional axle, 4 pts. Traction-Lok axle, 3.75 pts. plus 4 oz. of friction modifier meeting Ford Motor Co. specification EST-M2C118-A.
⑧—Add ½ qt. with filter change.
⑨—Crown Victoria & Grand Marquis.
⑩—Cougar & Thunderbird.
⑪—On Super Charged Engines, 3.50 Pts.

# LUBRICANT DATA

| Year | Model | Lubricant Type | | | | |
|---|---|---|---|---|---|---|
| | | Transmission | | | | |
| | | Manual | Automatic | Rear Axle | Power Steering | Brake System |
| 1989–92 | All | Mercon | Mercon | XY-90-QL① | ② | DOT 3 |

①—Traction-Lok axles, add Friction Modifier C8AZ-19B546-A or equivalent.
②—Type F trans. fluid or premium power steering fluid.

# Electrical

## INDEX



## AIRBAG SYSTEM DISARMING

**The electrical circuit necessary for system deployment is powered directly from the battery and a backup power supply. To avoid accidental deployment and possible personal injury, the airbag system must be deactivated prior to servicing or replacing any component located near or related to airbag system activation components.**

### 1989–1991

A back-up power supply is included in the system to provide airbag deployment in the event the battery or battery cables are damaged in an accident before the sensors can close. The power supply is a capacitor that will retain a charge for approximately 15 minutes after the battery ground cable is disconnected. **Backup power supply must be disconnected to deactivate airbag system.** To remove backup power supply, refer to "Airbags" in the "Passive Restraint" section.

1. Disconnect battery ground cable.
2. Disconnect backup power supply.
3. Remove four nut and washer assemblies securing airbag module to steering wheel, then disconnect airbag electrical connector. Attach jumper wire to airbag terminals on clockspring terminals.
4. **On models equipped with passenger-side airbag,** disconnect airbag module connector located behind glove compartment. Attach a jumper wire to airbag terminals on wiring harness side of passenger airbag module connector terminals.
5. **On all models,** reconnect battery and backup power supply if necessary to perform repair procedure.
6. To reactivate, disconnect battery ground cable and backup power supply, then reverse remainder of deactivation procedure. **Torque** airbag module to steering wheel nut assemblies to 24-32 inch lbs. on Crown Victoria and Grand Marquis, or 35-53 inch lbs. on all other models.
7. Verify airbag lamp after reactivating system.

### 1992

1. Disconnect positive battery cable and wait one minute.
2. Remove four nut and washer assemblies securing airbag to steering wheel.
3. Disconnect airbag electrical connector and install airbag simulator tool No. 105-00008 or equivalent.
4. **On models w/passenger side airbag,** remove passenger airbag and disconnect electrical connector.
5. Install airbag simulator tool No. 105-00008 or equivalent.
6. **On all models,** connect positive battery cable.
7. To activate airbag system, disconnect positive battery cable and reverse procedure. **Torque** mounting nut and washer assemblies to 36-49 inch lbs.
8. Verify proper operation of airbag lamp.

## FUSE PANEL & FLASHER LOCATION

### COUGAR & THUNDERBIRD

Fuse panel is on LH side of lower instrument panel.

Combination turn signal/hazard flasher is located to RH side of steering column opening reinforcement, mounted on a bracket.

### CROWN VICTORIA & GRAND MARQUIS

Fuse panel is located behind LH side of instrument panel.

Flashers are located on fuse panel.

## STARTER REPLACE

**STARTER PROBLEMS:** If starter is noisy or if it locks up, before condemning the starter, loosen three mounting bolts enough to hand fit the starter properly into pilot plate. Then tighten mounting bolts, starting with top bolt.

1. Disconnect battery ground cable.
2. Raise and support front of vehicle.
3. Remove starter shield, if equipped.
4. Disconnect starter cable and push on connector, if equipped.
5. **On 1992 LTD Crown Victoria & Grand Marquis models,** remove up-

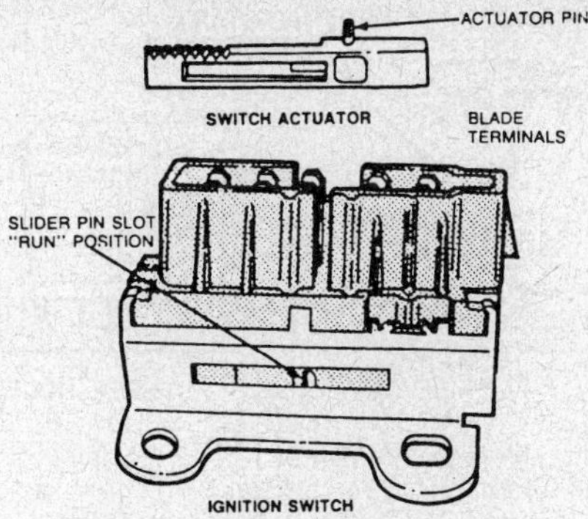


**Fig. 1 Ignition switch replacement**

per mounting bolt using a swivel socket and 22 inch extension. Access is in front of and along side of RH front engine mount.

6. **On all models,** remove mounting bolts and starter. **On some models it may be necessary to turn wheels right or left to remove starter.**
7. Reverse procedure to install. **Torque** bolts to 15-20 ft. lbs.

# DISTRIBUTOR

## REMOVAL

1. Disconnect primary wire connector from distributor.
2. Remove distributor cap, and position aside with spark plug wires attached.
3. Remove distributor rotor.
4. Note position of shaft plate, armature and rotor locating holes for assembly reference, then loosen hold-down bolt and clamp and remove distributor. Some models use special distributor hold-down bolts. To remove these bolts, use tool No. T82L-12270-A or equivalent.

## INSTALLATION

1. Rotate distributor by hand to ensure free rotation.
2. Ensure base O-ring is in place, then position rotor locating holes in original locations.
3. Install distributor, ensuring TFI-IV module is in same position relative to engine as when it was removed.
4. Install hold-down bolt and tighten until distributor can just barely be rotated.
5. Press rotor on distributor shaft.
6. Connect wiring harness to distributor, then install distributor cap and **torque** cap screws to 17-23 inch lbs.
7. Adjust ignition timing to specifications, then **torque** distributor hold-down bolt to 6-8.5 ft. lbs.

# IGNITION LOCK

## REPLACE

### COUGAR & THUNDERBIRD

1. Disconnect battery ground cable.
2. **On models equipped with tilt column,** remove upper extension shroud by detaching from retaining clip at 9 o'clock position.
3. **On all models,** remove both trim shroud halves.
4. Disconnect key warning switch electrical connector.
5. Turn ignition key to "Run." Place gear selector lever in "Park" if equipped with column shift.
6. Insert a 1/8 inch diameter wire pin into hole in casting around lo ck cylinder. Remove lock cylinder while depressing retaining pin with wire.
7. Reverse procedure to install. Lock cylinder must be in "Run" and retaining pin depressed during installation. Following installation, turn key to check for correct operation in all positions.

### CROWN VICTORIA & GRAND MARQUIS

#### 1989

1. Remove steering column trim shroud.
2. Disconnect key warning switch electrical connector.
3. Turn ignition lock to "On" or "Run" position.
4. Using a 1/8 inch pin or punch located in the 4 o'clock hole and 1 1/4 inch from outer edge of lock cylinder housing, depress retaining pin while pulling the lock cylinder from housing.
5. Turn lock cylinder to "On" or "Run" position and insert cylinder into housing. Ensure lock cylinder is fully seated and aligned into interlocking washer before turning key to "Off" position. This will permit retaining pin to extend into lock cylinder housing hole.
6. Rotate key to check for proper mechanical operation.
7. Connect key warning switch electrical connector.

#### 1990–1992

1. Disconnect battery ground cable and turn lock cylinder to "RUN" position.
2. Insert a 1/8 inch diameter wire pin or small drift punch in hole in trim shroud under lock cylinder. Depress retaining pin while pulling out on lock cylinder to remove from column housing.
3. Install lock cylinder by turning to run position and depressing retaining pin. Insert lock cylinder into housing. Ensure cylinder is fully seated and aligned in interlocking washer before turning key to "OFF." This will permit cylinder retaining pin to extend into cylinder housing hole.
4. Using key, rotate lock cylinder. Ensure correct mechanical operation in all positions. Connect battery ground cable.

# IGNITION SWITCH

## REPLACE

### COUGAR & THUNDERBIRD

1. Disconnect battery ground cable.
2. Remove steering column lower shroud, then remove four nuts holding column assembly to column mounting bracket.

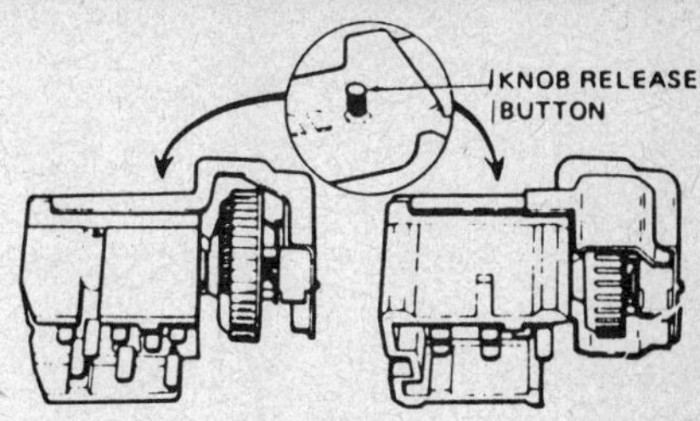


**Fig. 2 Headlamp switch replacement. Crown Victoria & Grand Marquis**

3. Remove steering column shroud attaching screws, then the steering column shroud.
4. Disconnect ignition switch electrical connector, **Fig. 1,** then rotate ignition key lock cylinder to "Run" position.
5. Remove switch to lock cylinder attaching screws.
6. Remove ignition switch from actuator pin.
7. Adjust ignition switch by sliding carrier to "Run" position. **A new replacement switch assembly will be preset in "Run" position.**
8. Place ignition key lock cylinder in "Run" position by rotating cylinder approximately 90° from "Lock" position.
9. Install ignition switch on actuator pin. **Slightly move switch back and forth to align mounting holes with column lock housing threaded holes.**
10. Install switch to lock cylinder attaching bolts and **torque** bolts to 50-60 inch lbs.
11. Connect switch electrical connector.
12. Install steering column trim shrouds, then check ignition for proper operation.

### CROWN VICTORIA & GRAND MARQUIS

1. Disable airbag system as described under "Airbag System Disarming."
2. Remove steering column shroud by removing self-tapping screws. Remove tilt lever if equipped.
3. Remove instrument panel lower steering column cover.
4. Disconnect ignition switch electrical connector.
5. Rotate ignition key lock cylinder to "RUN" position, then remove two screws retaining ignition switch.
6. Disconnect ignition switch from actuator.
7. Reverse procedure to install, noting the following:
   a. If necessary, move switch slightly back and forth to align mounting holes with column mounting holes.
   b. Activate airbag system as described under "Airbag System Disarming."
   c. Ensure proper operation of ignition switch in all positions.

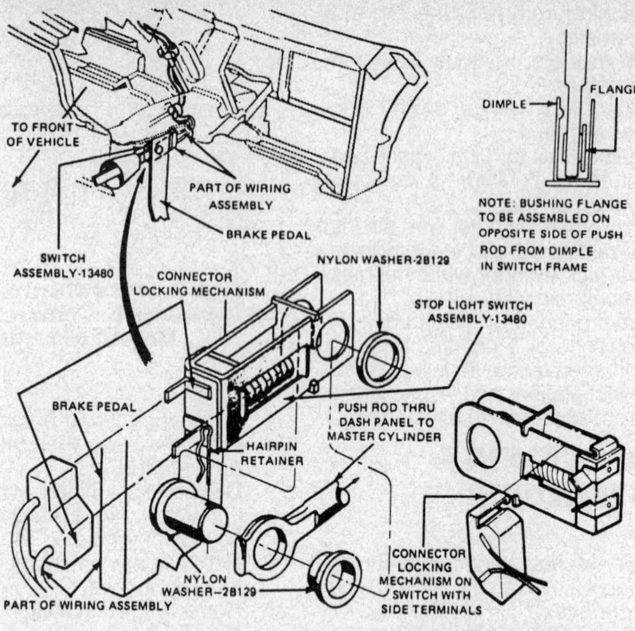


**Fig. 3 Stop lamp switch replacement**

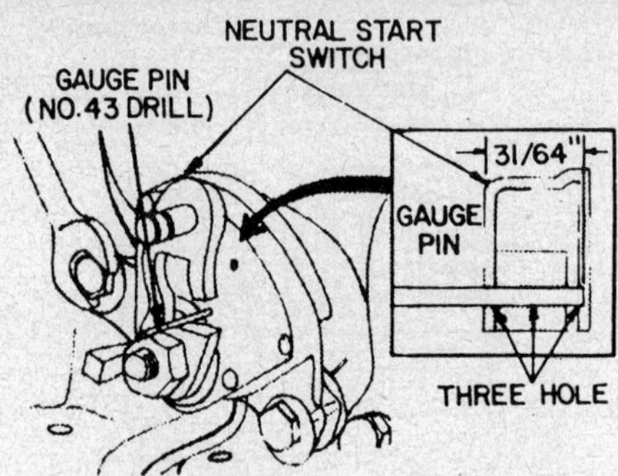


**Fig. 4 Neutral safety switch replacement. Cougar & Thunderbird**

# HEADLAMP SWITCH REPLACE

## COUGAR & THUNDERBIRD

1. Disconnect battery ground cable.
2. Remove two cluster trim panel retaining screws.
3. Pull off headlamp switch knob and snap off cluster trim panel.
4. Disconnect electrical connector to headlamp dimmer sensor assembly.
5. With headlamp switch in full On position, using opening in instrument panel, depress shaft release button on switch and remove shaft.
6. Remove headlamp switch retaining nut and pull switch through opening to disconnect wiring connector.
7. Reverse procedure to install.

## CROWN VICTORIA & GRAND MARQUIS

1. Disable airbag system as described under "Airbag System Disarming."
2. Under instrument panel, depress light switch knob and shaft retainer button on side of switch and, while holding button in, pull knob and shaft assembly from switch, **Fig. 2.**
3. Unscrew trim bezel and remove locknut.
4. From under instrument panel, pull switch from panel while tilting downward, disconnect electrical connector and remove switch.
5. Reverse procedure to install.

# STOP LAMP SWITCH REPLACE

1. Disconnect battery ground cable and disconnect wires at switch connector.
2. Remove hairpin retainer and slide stop light switch, pushrod, nylon washers and bushings away from brake pedal, and remove switch, **Fig. 3.**
3. Reverse procedure to install.

# NEUTRAL SAFETY SWITCH REPLACE

## COUGAR & THUNDERBIRD

### A4LD

1. Remove downshift linkage rod from transmission downshift lever.
2. Apply penetrating oil to downshift lever shaft and nut; then remove downshift outer lever.
3. Remove switch attaching bolts.
4. Disconnect multiple wire connector and remove switch from transmission.
5. Install new switch.
6. With transmission manual lever in neutral, rotate switch and install gauge pin (.43 drill) into gauge pin holes, **Fig. 4. Shank end of drill must be inserted approximately 15/32 inch into each of the gauge pin holes.**
7. Tighten switch attaching bolts and remove gauge pin.
8. Reverse remainder of procedure to install.

### AOD

1. Disconnect battery ground cable.
2. Place transmission gear selector in manual Low position.
3. Raise and support vehicle.
4. Disconnect electrical connector from neutral start switch. Lift connector straight up off switch using a long screwdriver under rubber plug of connector.
5. Remove switch and O-ring using socket No. T74P-77247-A or equivalent. **Use of any tools other than those specified may result in damage to vehicle.**
6. Reverse procedure to install. **Torque** switch to 7-10 ft. lbs.

## CROWN VICTORIA & GRAND MARQUIS

1. Disconnect battery ground cable.
2. Remove air cleaner assembly.
3. Place transmission selector lever in manual low position, then disconnect neutral safety switch electrical connector from switch. Lift connector straight off without any side-to-side motion.
4. Remove switch and O-ring using a 24 inch extension, universal adapter and socket No. T74P-77247-A. **Use of any tools other than those specified may result in damage to vehicle.**
5. Reverse procedure to install. **Torque** switch to 7-10 ft. lbs.

# TURN SIGNAL SWITCH REPLACE

## COUGAR & THUNDERBIRD

1. Disconnect battery ground cable.
2. Remove trim shroud or shroud halves.
3. Remove turn signal switch lever from switch. Grasp lever and use a pulling and twisting motion while pulling lever straight out from switch.
4. Peel back foam shield from turn signal switch, then disconnect two electrical connectors from switch.

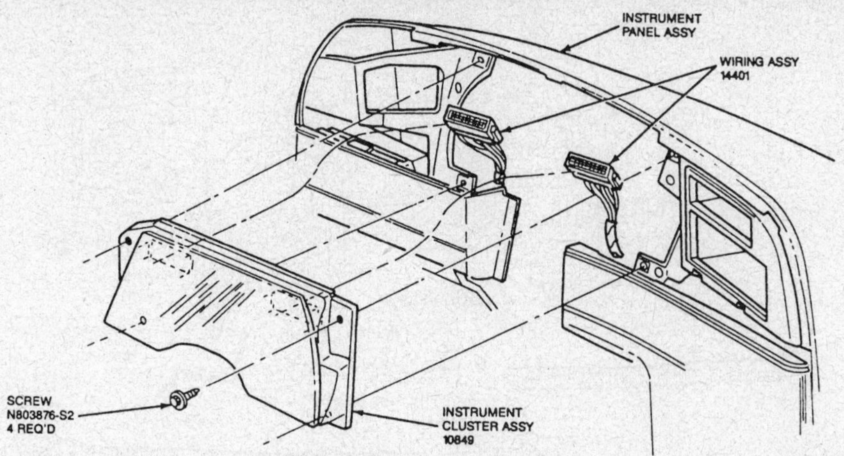


**Fig. 5 Instrument cluster replacement. Cougar & Thunderbird**

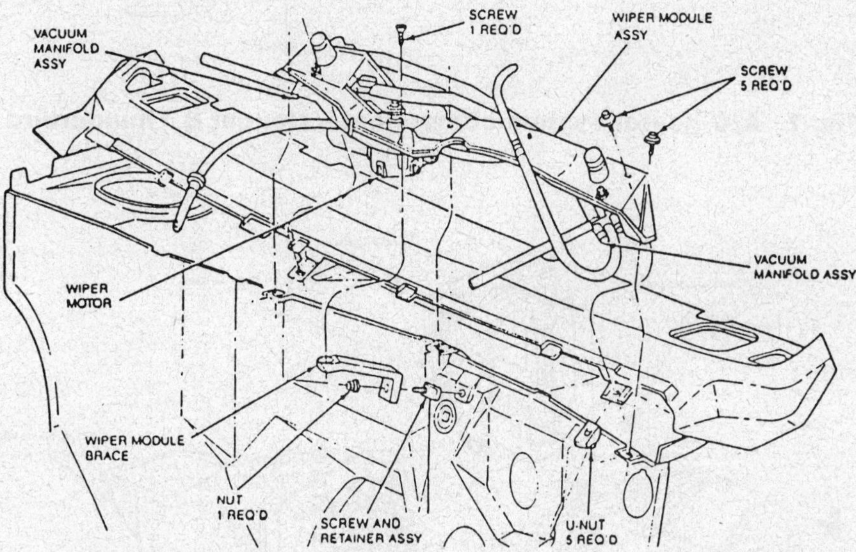


**Fig. 6 Wiper motor replacement. Cougar & Thunderbird**

5. Remove turn signal switch attaching screws, then remove switch.
6. Reverse procedure to install.

## CROWN VICTORIA & GRAND MARQUIS

1. Disconnect battery ground cable.
2. **On models with tilt column,** unsnap extension shroud, located below steering wheel, from retaining clip.
3. **On all models,** remove attaching screws, then remove steering column trim shroud.
4. Remove turn signal switch lever by grasping lever and using a pulling twisting motion of the hand, while pulling lever straight out of switch.
5. Peel foam sight shield from switch, then disconnect two turn signal switch wire connectors.
6. Remove two screws attaching turn signal switch to lock cylinder housing, then disengage switch from housing.
7. Reverse procedure to install.

# MULTI-FUNCTION SWITCH REPLACE

## COUGAR & THUNDERBIRD

1. Disconnect battery ground cable.
2. Remove lower LH finish panel retaining bolts and carefully pull to disengage retaining clips.
3. Remove lower LH reinforcement panel retaining bolts and remove panel.
4. Remove steering column lower shroud retaining screws and remove lower shroud.
5. Remove steering column retaining nuts, then remove column upper shroud.
6. Disconnect switch electrical connectors.
7. Remove switch retaining bolts, then remove switch.
8. Reverse procedure to install.

## CROWN VICTORIA & GRAND MARQUIS

1. Disable airbag system as described under "Airbag System Disarming."
2. Tilt column to lowest position and remove tilt lever, if equipped.
3. Remove ignition lock cylinder.
4. Remove shroud screws, then remove upper and lower shrouds.
5. Remove two screws attaching multi-function switch to steering column casting. Disengage switch from casting.
6. Disconnect two electrical connectors.
7. Reverse procedure to install, noting the following:
   a. **Torque** retaining screws to 18-26 inch lbs.
   b. Activate airbag system as described under "Airbag System Disarming."

# HORN SOUNDER REPLACE

## MODELS EQUIPPED w/TURN SIGNAL MOUNTED SWITCH

Horn sounder is located on the turn signal, headlight dimmer and horn lever. Refer to "Turn Signal Switch, Replace" when replacing switch.

1. Disconnect battery ground cable.
2. Pry switch cover off top. Use caution not to damage cover when removing.
3. Remove switch attaching screws, then lift switch from steering wheel. Use caution not to loose contact spring.
4. Reverse procedure to install.

# STEERING WHEEL REPLACE

## MODELS LESS PASSIVE RESTRAINT SYSTEM

1. Disconnect battery ground cable.
2. Remove horn pad and cover assembly.
3. Disconnect horn wire and speed control wiring, if equipped.
4. Remove and discard steering wheel nut.
5. Mark relationship between steering shaft and steering wheel hub for proper reinstallation.
6. Remove steering wheel with a suitable puller.
7. Reverse procedure to install. **Torque** new steering wheel bolt to 23-33 ft. lbs.

## MODELS w/PASSIVE RESTRAINT SYSTEM

1. Disable airbag system as described under "Airbag System Disarming."
2. Center front wheels to straight ahead position.
3. Remove airbag module from steering wheel.
4. Disconnect speed control wire harness from steering wheel.
5. Remove and discard steering wheel retaining bolt, then install steering wheel puller tool No. T67L-3600-A or equivalent and remove steering wheel.
6. Route contact assembly wire harness through steering wheel as wheel is lifted off of shaft.
7. Reverse procedure to install, noting the following:
   a. Route contact assembly wire harness through steering wheel opening at three o'clock position. Steering wheel and shaft alignment marks should be aligned.
   b. Ensure airbag contact wire is not pinched and speed control wiring does not get trapped between steering wheel and contact assembly.
   c. **Torque** steering wheel retaining bolt to 22-33 ft. lbs.
   d. **Torque** module retaining nuts to 36-47 inch lbs.
   e. Activate airbag system as described under "Airbag System Disarming."

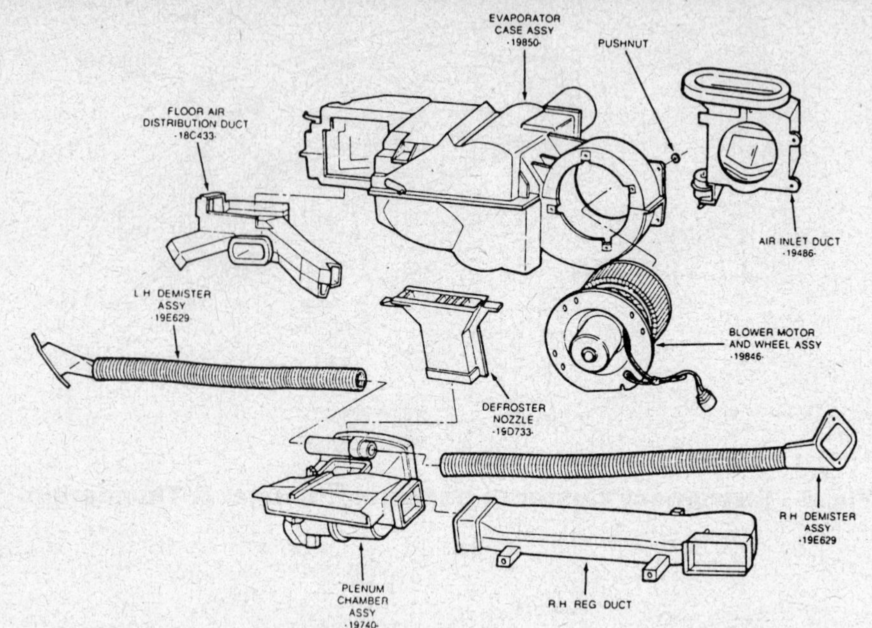


**Fig. 7 A/C-heater system components. Cougar & Thunderbird**

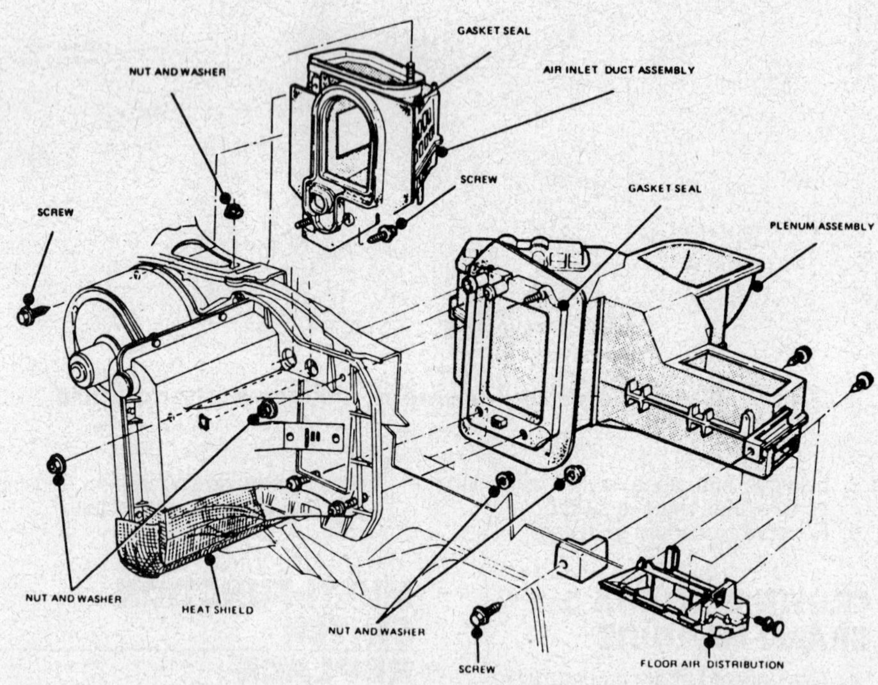


**Fig. 8 A/C-heater system components. Crown Victoria & Grand Marquis**

# INSTRUMENT CLUSTER REPLACE

## COUGAR & THUNDERBIRD

### Standard Cluster

1. Disconnect battery ground cable.
2. Remove two retaining screws from cluster trim panel and remove trim panel.
3. Remove four cluster mounting screws, **Fig. 5,** then pull bottom of cluster towards steering wheel.
4. Reach behind cluster and disconnect two connectors.
5. **On Super Coupe and XR7 models,** disconnect vacuum lines for booster gauge.
6. **On all models,** swing bottom of cluster to clear top of steering column shroud and remove.
7. Reverse procedure to install.

### Electronic Cluster

1. Disconnect battery ground cable.
2. Remove headlamp knob, then remove cluster finish panel by removing two screws located on upper inside surface.
3. Carefully pull away finish panel while detaching spring clips surrounding finish panel.
4. Disconnect connector on rear of switch assembly.
5. Disconnect autolamp module, if equipped.
6. Place clean soft cloth over steering column shroud to prevent damage, then remove four cluster retaining screws and pull bottom of cluster towards steering wheel.
7. Place clean soft cloth over lens, to prevent scratching.
8. Reach behind cluster and disconnect two electrical connectors.
9. Swing bottom of cluster out to clear top of cluster from crash pad and remove.
10. Reverse procedure to install.

## CROWN VICTORIA & GRAND MARQUIS

### Standard Cluster

1. Disable airbag system as described under "Airbag System Disarming."
2. **On 1989-91 models,** disconnect speedometer cable.
3. **On all models,** remove instrument cluster trim cover attaching screws and the trim cover.
4. Remove lower steering column cover attaching screws and the cover.
5. **On Grand Marquis models,** remove knee bolster.
6. **On all models,** remove steering column shroud lower half.
7. Remove screws securing transmission indicator column bracket to steering column. Detach cable loop from pin on shift lever and remove bracket from column.
8. Remove four instrument cluster attaching screws.
9. Disconnect cluster feed plug and remove cluster assembly from vehicle.
10. Reverse procedure to install.

### Electronic Cluster

1. Set parking brake and disable airbag system as described under "Airbag System Disarming."
2. Unsnap center molding on left and right sides of instrument panel.
3. Remove steering column cover and column shroud.
4. Remove knobs from auto dim and auto lamp switches, if equipped.
5. Remove 13 screws retaining instrument panel and pull panel out.
6. Move shift lever to 1 position for access.
7. Disconnect electrical connectors from warning lamp module, switch module and center panel switches, if equipped.
8. Remove instrument panel carefully, using caution to not scratch cluster lens.
9. Disconnect electrical connector from front of cluster.
10. Disconnect PRNDL assembly from cluster by carefully bending bottom tab down and pulling PRNDL assembly forward.
11. Pull cluster out and disconnect electrical connectors on rear of cluster.
12. Remove instrument cluster.
13. Reverse procedure to install. Following installation, activate airbag system as described under "Airbag System Disarming."

# WINDSHIELD WIPER MOTOR REPLACE

## COUGAR & THUNDERBIRD

1. Disconnect battery ground cable.
2. With wipers in Park position, remove arm and blade assemblies.
3. Remove LH cowl vent screen.
4. Remove vacuum manifolds from wiper module, **Fig. 6.**
5. Disconnect wiring connectors, then remove five bolts and one nut from wiper module and remove module.
6. Remove crankpin clip, then disconnect linkage drive arm from motor crankpin.
7. Remove three motor attaching screws, pull motor from opening.
8. Reverse procedure to install, ensuring that wiper motor is in the park position prior to installation.

## CROWN VICTORIA & CROWN VICTORIA

### 1989–91

1. Disconnect battery ground cable.
2. Disconnect right side washer nozzle hose and remove right side wiper arm and blade assembly from pivot shaft.
3. Remove wiper motor/linkage cover.
4. Disconnect linkage drive arm from motor output arm crankpin by removing retaining clip.
5. Disconnect wiring connectors from motor.
6. Remove three bolts retaining motor to dash panel extension and the motor.
7. Reverse procedure to install.

### 1992

1. Disconnect battery ground cable.
2. Remove rear hood seal and wiper arm assemblies.
3. Remove cowl vent screens. Disconnect washer hoses from washer jets.
4. Remove wiper assembly retaining screws and lift assembly out. Disconnect washer hose.
5. Disconnect electrical connectors from wiper motor.
6. Reverse procedure to install.

# WINDSHIELD WIPER SWITCH REPLACE

## COUGAR & THUNDERBIRD

1. Disconnect battery ground cable.
2. Remove four steering column shroud attaching screws, then grasp top and bottom of shroud and separate.
3. Using a screwdriver, disconnect wire connector from wiper switch.
4. Remove two wiper switch attaching screws, then remove switch.
5. Reverse procedure to install.

## CROWN VICTORIA & GRAND MARQUIS

1. Disconnect battery ground cable.
2. Remove steering column cover screws and separate the two halves.
3. Remove wiper switch retaining screws, disconnect wiring connector and remove switch.
4. Reverse procedure to install.

# WINDSHIELD WIPER TRANSMISSION REPLACE

## CROWN VICTORIA & GRAND MARQUIS

1. Disconnect battery ground cable.
2. Remove wiper arm and blade assemblies from pivot shafts. Remove rear hood seal.
3. Remove wiper motor and linkage cover for access to linkage.
4. Disconnect linkage drive arm from motor crank pin by removing retaining clip.
5. Remove six bolts retaining left and right pivot shafts to cowl, and remove the complete linkage assembly.
6. Reverse procedure to install.

# RADIO REPLACE

When installing radio, adjust antenna trimmer for peak performance.

## EXCEPT 1989–91 LTD CROWN VICTORIA & GRAND MARQUIS

1. Disconnect battery ground cable.
2. Install radio removal tool No. T87P-19061-A or equivalent, into face plate. Push tools in approximately one inch to release retaining clips.
3. Slightly spread tools and pull radio from dash.
4. Disconnect power, antenna and speaker leads from radio.
5. Reverse procedure to install. Ensure rear bracket is engaged on lower support rail.

## 1989–91 CROWN VICTORIA & GRAND MARQUIS

### Except All-Electronic Radio

1. Disconnect battery ground cable.
2. Remove radio knobs and screws attaching bezel to instrument panel.
3. Remove radio mounting plate attaching screws.
4. Pull radio to disengage it from lower rear support bracket.
5. Disconnect radio wiring and remove radio.
6. Reverse procedure to install.

### All-Electronic Radio

1. Disconnect battery ground cable.
2. Remove screws attaching bezel to instrument panel.
3. Remove radio attaching screws.
4. Pull radio to disengage it from rear support bracket, then disconnect antenna, power and speaker leads and remove radio.
5. Remove rear support retaining nut and the support.
6. Reverse procedure to install.

# BLOWER MOTOR REPLACE

## COUGAR & THUNDERBIRD

1. Disconnect battery ground cable.
2. Remove glove compartment liner, then disconnect blower motor wire connector.
3. Remove four screws and pull blower motor outward, **Fig. 7.**
4. Remove push nuts from blower motor shaft and slide blower wheel off shaft.
5. Reverse procedure to install.

## CROWN VICTORIA & GRAND MARQUIS

1. Disconnect battery ground cable.
2. Disconnect all blower motor electrical wires and connectors.
3. Remove blower motor cooling tube, then the mounting screws.
4. Rotate blower motor slightly to the right so bottom edge of mounting plate follows contour of wheelwell splash panel. Then, lift blower motor up and out of housing assembly.
5. Reverse procedure to install.

# HEATER CORE REPLACE

## COUGAR & THUNDERBIRD

1. Disconnect battery ground cable.
2. Remove instrument panel as described in the "Dash Panel Service" section.
3. Remove right instrument panel brace located above heater case and attached to cowl.
4. Drain engine coolant and remove hoses from heater core, then plug hoses and the core.
5. Disconnect vacuum supply hose from in-line vacuum check valve in engine compartment.
6. Disconnect blower motor wire harness from resistor and motor lead.
7. Working under the hood, remove three heater assembly to dash panel retaining nuts.
8. In passenger compartment, remove heater assembly support bracket to cowl top panel attaching screw.
9. Remove one bracket to dash panel retaining screw below heater assembly.
10. Carefully remove heater assembly away from dash panel and remove heater assembly from vehicle, **Fig. 7.**
11. Remove four heater core access cover attaching screws, then the access cover from case.
12. Remove seal from heater core tubes, then remove heater core.
13. Reverse procedure to install.

## CROWN VICTORIA & GRAND MARQUIS

1. Disconnect battery ground cable, then drain cooling system.
2. Disconnect heater hoses from heater core. Plug heater hoses and core fittings to prevent coolant spillage.
3. Remove bolt located below windshield wiper motor, attaching left end of plenum to dash panel.
4. Remove nut attaching upper lefthand corner of evaporator or heater case to dash panel.
5. Disconnect vacuum control system supply hose from vacuum source, then push grommet and hose into passenger compartment.
6. **On 1992 models,** remove all instrument panel retaining screws and pull instrument panel back as far as possible without disconnecting any wire harnesses.
7. **On 1989-91 models,** remove glove compartment.
8. **On all models,** loosen righthand door sill plate and remove side cowl trim panel.
9. **On 1989-91 models,** remove bolt attaching righthand side of instrument panel to side cowl.
10. Remove instrument panel pad as follows:
    a. Remove two screws from each defroster nozzle opening in pad.
    b. From front lower edge of panel pad, remove five attaching screws.
    c. From each end of pad, remove one attaching screw.
    d. Lift pad assembly from instrument panel.
11. **On all models,** disengage temperature control cable housing from bracket on top of plenum. Disconnect cable from temperature blend door crank arm.
12. **On models w/automatic temperature control (ATC),** remove cross body brace and disconnect wiring harness from temperature blend door actuator and disconnect ATC sensor tube from evaporator case connector.
13. **On 1989-91 models,** remove push clip attaching center duct bracket to plenum, then rotate bracket upward and to the right.
14. **On all models,** disconnect vacuum harness at vacuum connector near floor air distribution duct.
15. Disconnect white vacuum hose from outside recirculating air door vacuum motor.
16. **On 1992 models,** remove two hush panels.
17. **On all models,** remove one plastic push fastener retaining floor air distribution duct to LH end of plenum. Remove LH screw and loosen RH screw on rear face of plenum. Remove floor air distribution duct.
18. Remove two screws from rear side of floor air distribution duct to plenum, **Fig. 8.** To remove RH screw, it may be necessary to remove the two screws attaching lower panel door vacuum motor to mounting bracket.
19. Remove push fastener attaching floor air distribution duct to left end of plenum, then remove floor air distribution duct.
20. Remove two nuts located along lower flange of plenum.
21. Carefully move plenum rearward, so that heater core tubes and plenum case upper stud clear openings in dash panel, then remove plenum from vehicle by rotating upper portion of the plenum forward, down and out from under instrument panel. It may be necessary to carefully pull lower edge of instrument panel rearward while plenum is being removed from behind instrument panel.
22. Remove retaining screws from heater core cover, then the cover from plenum assembly.
23. Remove retaining screw from heater core inlet and outlet tube bracket.
24. Pull heater core and seal assembly from plenum assembly.
25. Reverse procedure to install.

# EVAPORATOR CORE REPLACE

## COUGAR & THUNDERBIRD

1. Disconnect battery ground cable.
2. Remove instrument panel as described in "Dash Panel Service" section.
3. Discharge A/C refrigerant system.
4. Disconnect and cap high and lower pressure hoses.
5. Disconnect and cap refrigerant line from accumulator drier.
6. Drain engine coolant and remove hoses from heater core, then plug hoses and the core.
7. Disconnect blower motor wiring.
8. Working under the hood, remove three heater assembly to dash panel retaining nuts.
9. In passenger compartment, remove evaporator case assembly support bracket to cowl top panel attaching screw.
10. Remove one bracket to dash panel retaining screw below evaporator case assembly.
11. Carefully remove evaporator case assembly away from dash panel and remove heater assembly from vehicle, **Fig. 7.**
12. Using a small saw, cut top of evaporator case between dotted line, then remove evaporator core.
13. Reverse procedure to install. An evaporator core cover kit is available for installation.

## CROWN VICTORIA & GRAND MARQUIS

1. Disconnect battery ground cable, then drain cooling system.
2. Disconnect and cap suction hose from accumulator drier.
3. Disconnect liquid line from evaporator inlet tube. Position liquid line away from evaporator assembly.
4. Disconnect 2 electrical connectors from de-ice switch in accumulator drier.
5. Disconnect heater hoses from heater core tubes.

6. Remove six right hand hood seal bracket assembly attaching screws, then remove ground strap and fold hood seal toward left hand side.
7. Disconnect and position aside all wiring and vacuum hoses attached to evaporator case.
8. Disconnect blower motor wiring.
9. From passenger side of dash panel, fold carpeting back on right hand side of floor, remove bottom left hand screw that supports inlet recirculation air duct.
10. From engine side of dash panel, one upper and two lower nuts from evaporator case mounting studs. Also remove two screws from blower motor portion of case.
11. Pull bottom of evaporator case assembly away from dash to disengage mounting studs, then pull top of case outward to disengage upper stud.
12. Remove evaporator case from vehicle.
13. Separate evaporator case halves and remove evaporator core.
14. Reverse procedure to install.

# 3.8L/V6-232 Engine

## INDEX



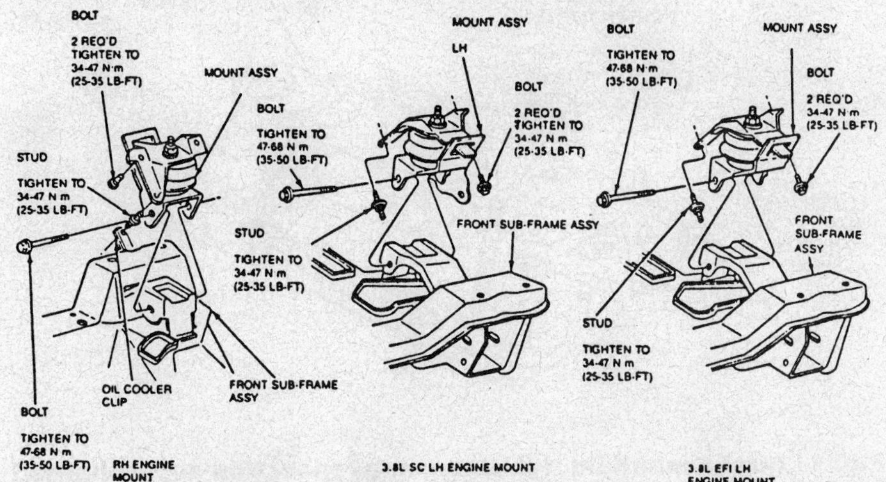


**Fig. 1 Engine mount removal**

## ENGINE MOUNTS
### REPLACE

Whenever self-locking mounting bolts and nuts are removed, they must be replaced with new self-locking bolts and nuts.

1. Remove fan shroud attaching screws, then remove air tube from remote air cleaner.
2. Raise and support vehicle, then support engine using a jack and wood block placed below engine.
3. Remove insulator to front subframe through bolts, **Fig. 1.**
4. Disconnect shift linkage, then raise engine enough to clear clevis brackets.
5. Remove accessories and oil cooler line attaching clips from engine support brackets.
6. Remove bolts attaching insulator bracket assembly to engine, then remove insulator and bracket. **Left front engine mount removal on supercharged engine may require lowering front subframe.**
7. Reverse procedure to install. Tighten to specifications.

## ENGINE
### REPLACE

1. Disconnect battery ground cable and drain engine coolant.
2. Mark position of hood hinges and remove hood.
3. Remove left cowl vent screen and wiper module.
4. Disconnect alternator to voltage regulator wiring harness.
5. **On supercharged engine,** remove upper intercooler tube from supercharger and cooler assemblies. Remove bolt retaining cooler tube to power steering bracket and remove tube.
6. **On all models,** remove radiator upper sight shield, release belt tension and remove belts.
7. Remove air cleaner to throttle body tube assembly, then disconnect cooling fan and motor assembly connector.
8. Remove fan shroud, fan assembly and upper radiator hose.
9. Disconnect automatic transmission oil cooler tubes from radiator, then disconnect heater hoses.
10. Disconnect lower radiator hose at water pump, then remove radiator retaining bolts and radiator assembly.
11. **On supercharged engines,** remove two push pins attaching intercooler to radiator.
12. **On non-supercharged models,** disconnect power steering pump and bracket and position aside.
13. **On all models,** discharge A/C system as described in "Air Conditioning" section.
14. Disconnect A/C compressor clutch electrical connector and compressor lines. Cap or plug open A/C lines.
15. Remove A/C compressor retaining bolts, then the compressor.
16. Remove radiator coolant recovery reservoir.

17. Remove wiring shield, then the accelerator cable mounting bracket and position aside.
18. Release fuel system pressure, then disconnect fuel inlet & return hose.
19. Disconnect ECM electrical connector, engine feed harnesses and vacuum lines.
20. **On non-supercharged models,** disconnect ground wire assembly and coil wire.
21. **On supercharged models,** disconnect DIS module wiring, then remove coil pack retaining bolts and position aside.
22. Remove nuts attaching lower intercooler tube to supercharger elbow, then remove intercooler tube bolts at power steering bracket.
23. Remove alternator bracket bolts, then disconnect alternator wiring and remove alternator.
24. Remove power steering pump, then bracket assembly and position aside.
25. **On all models,** disconnect canister purge line.
26. Disconnect one end of throttle control valve cable.
27. Raise vehicle on hoist, then drain oil and remove oil filter.
28. **On supercharged models,** remove two nuts attaching lower intercooler tube to intercooler, then remove intercooler.
29. **On all models,** remove exhaust pipe-to-manifold nuts, then remove lefthand exhaust shield.
30. Disconnect heated exhaust gas oxygen (HEGO) sensor assembly.
31. Remove inspection plug, then the torque converter bolts.
32. Remove engine to transmission bolts, then remove engine mount bolts.
33. **On supercharged models,** remove lefthand mount retaining strap.
34. **On all models,** remove crankshaft pulley assembly.
35. Remove starter motor assembly, ground cable and starter harness retainers from left and right sides.
36. Disconnect oil level indicator sensor. Partially lower vehicle, then disconnect oil pressure sending unit gauge assembly.
37. Position floor jack under transmission.
38. Position engine lifting equipment and remove engine assembly from vehicle.
39. Reverse procedure to install. Tighten to specifications.

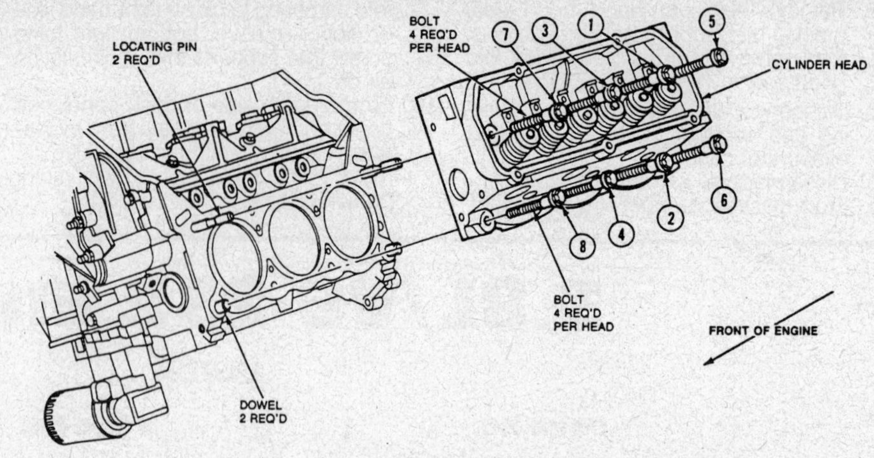


**Fig. 2 Cylinder head tightening sequence**

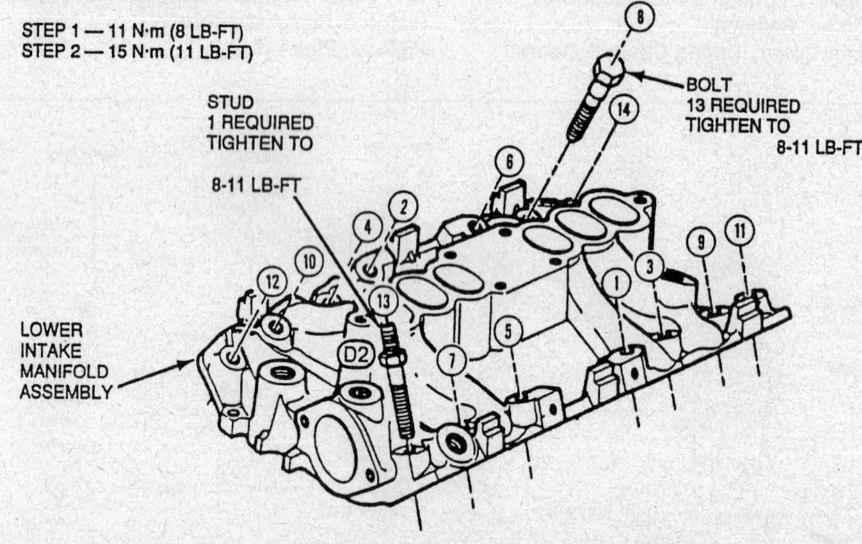


**Fig. 3 Intake manifold tightening sequence. Non-supercharged engines**

# CYLINDER HEAD

## REMOVAL

1. Disconnect battery ground cable and drain cooling system.
2. Remove air cleaner assembly, air intake duct and heat tube.
3. Loosen accessory drive belt idlers and remove drive belts.
4. If LH cylinder head is being removed, proceed as follows:
   a. Remove intercooler and intercooler tubes.
   b. Remove oil filler cap and power steering pump front mounting bracket attaching bolts.
   c. Remove alternator assembly and accessory drive belt main idler.
   d. Remove power steering pump/alternator bracket attaching bolts.
5. **On 1989-90 models,** if RH cylinder head is being removed, proceed as follows:
   a. Disconnect Thermactor tube support bracket from rear of cylinder head.
   b. Remove A/C compressor belt and main drive belt.
   c. Remove Thermactor pump pulley, then remove Thermactor pump.
   d. Remove mounting bracket retaining bolts, leave hoses connected and position compressor aside.
   e. Remove PCV valve.
6. **On 1991-92 models,** if RH cylinder head is being removed, proceed as follows:
   a. Remove A/C compressor belt and main drive belt.
   b. Remove mounting bracket retaining bolts. Leave hoses connected and position compressor aside.
   c. Remove PCV valve.
7. **On all models,** remove upper intake manifold.
8. **On supercharged models,** remove supercharger.
9. **On all models,** remove valve rocker arm cover attaching screws and injec-

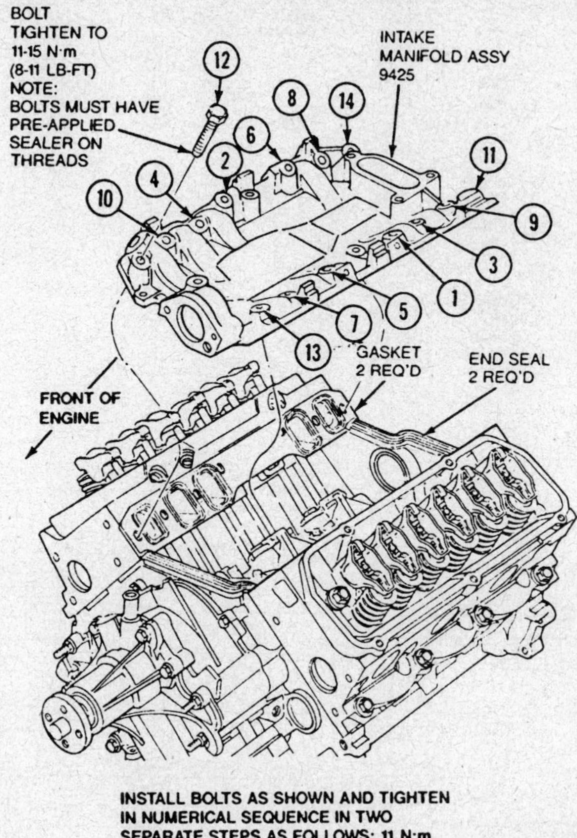


**Fig. 4 Intake manifold tightening sequence. Supercharged engines**

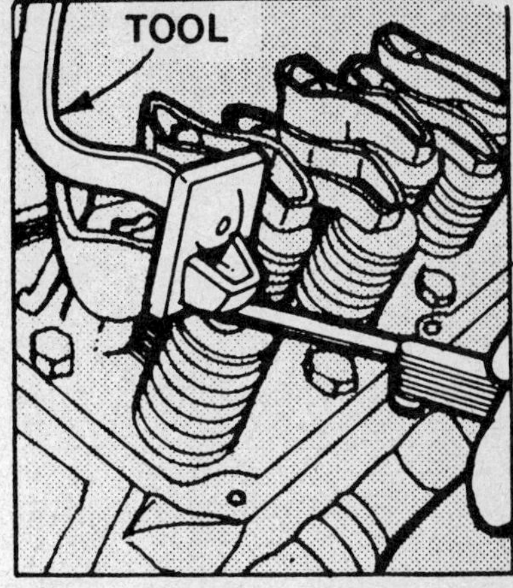


**Fig. 5 Compressing lifter to check valve clearance**

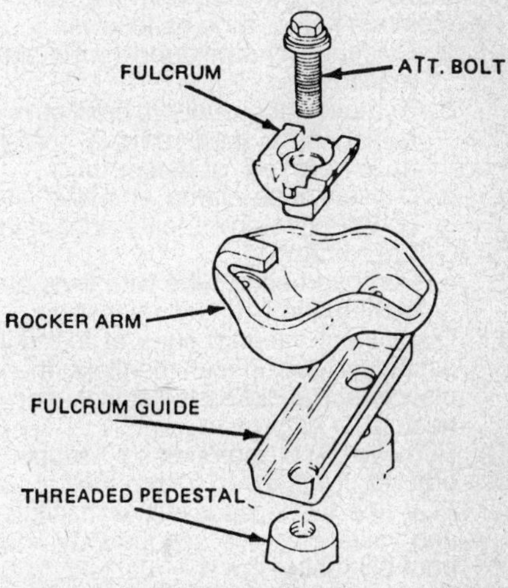


**Fig. 6 Rocker arm assembly**

tor fuel rail assembly.

10. Remove lower intake manifold and exhaust manifolds.
11. Loosen rocker arm fulcrum retaining bolts enough to allow rocker arm to be lifted off push rod and rotate to one side.
12. Remove push rods. Note position of each rod for installation. Push rods must be installed in original position.
13. Remove and discard cylinder head retaining bolts, then remove cylinder head.

## INSTALLATION

**Always use new cylinder head bolts. Torque retention with used bolts can vary, which may result in coolant or compression leakage at cylinder head mating surface.**

1. Position cylinder head and new gasket on dowels for alignment.
2. Apply a thin coating of Pipe Sealant w/Teflon No. D8AZ-19554-A or equivalent to threads of short cylinder head bolts. **Do not apply to long bolts.**
3. Install cylinder head bolts in sequence shown in **Fig. 2. Torque** in following steps:
   a. 37 ft. lbs.
   b. 45 ft. lbs.
   c. 52 ft. lbs.
   d. 59 ft. lbs.
   e. Back off each bolt 2-3 turns.
4. **On supercharged engines,** final torque cylinder head bolts in sequence shown in **Fig. 2,** as follows:
   a. **Torque** to 48-55 ft. lbs.
   b. Rotate an additional 90-110 °.
   c. Go to next bolt in sequence.
5. **On non-supercharged engines,** final torque bolts in sequence shown in **Fig. 2,** as follows:
   a. **Torque** bolts to 11-18 ft. lbs.
   b. Rotate long bolts an additional 85-105 °.
   c. Rotate short bolts an additional 65-85 °.
   d. Go to next bolt in sequence.
6. Dip each push rod end in Oil Conditioner D9AZ-19579-CA or equivalent, then install each push rod in original position.
7. For each valve, rotate crankshaft until valve lifter rests on heel (base circle) of camshaft lobe. **Torque** fulcrum attaching bolts to initial value of 43 inch lbs.
8. Lubricate all rocker arm assemblies with Oil Conditioner D9AZ-19579-CA or equivalent heavy engine oil. Final **torque** fulcrum bolts to 19-25 ft. lbs.
9. Install exhaust manifolds and lower intake manifold.
10. Install injector fuel rail assembly.
11. Install rocker cover and gasket. Tighten to specifications.
12. Install upper intake manifold and supercharger, if equipped. Tighten to specifications.
13. Reverse remainder of removal procedure to complete installation. Tighten specifications.

## INTAKE MANIFOLD REPLACE

**The following procedure has been revised by a Technical Service Bulletin.**

1. Disconnect battery ground cable and drain engine cooling system.
2. Remove air cleaner assembly including air intake duct and heat tube.
3. Disconnect accelerator cable at throttle body assembly, then speed control cable, if equipped.
4. Disconnect transmission linkage at upper intake manifold.
5. Remove bolts from accelerator cable mounting bracket and position cables aside.
6. **On 1989 models,** disconnect Thermactor air supply hose at check valve.
7. **On all models,** disconnect fuel lines at injector fuel rail assembly.
8. **On supercharged models,** remove supercharger.

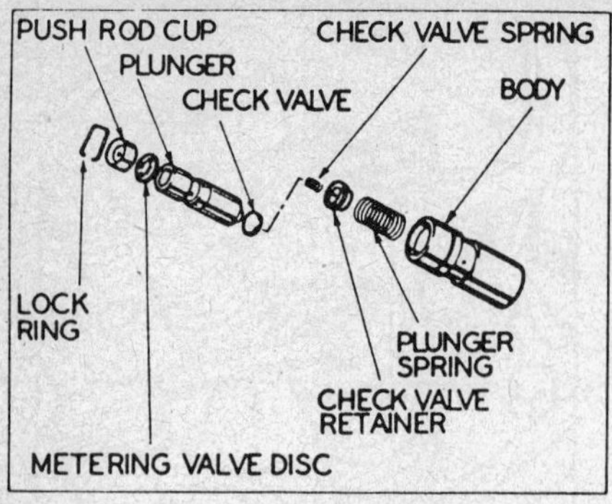


**Fig. 7 Hydraulic valve lifter**

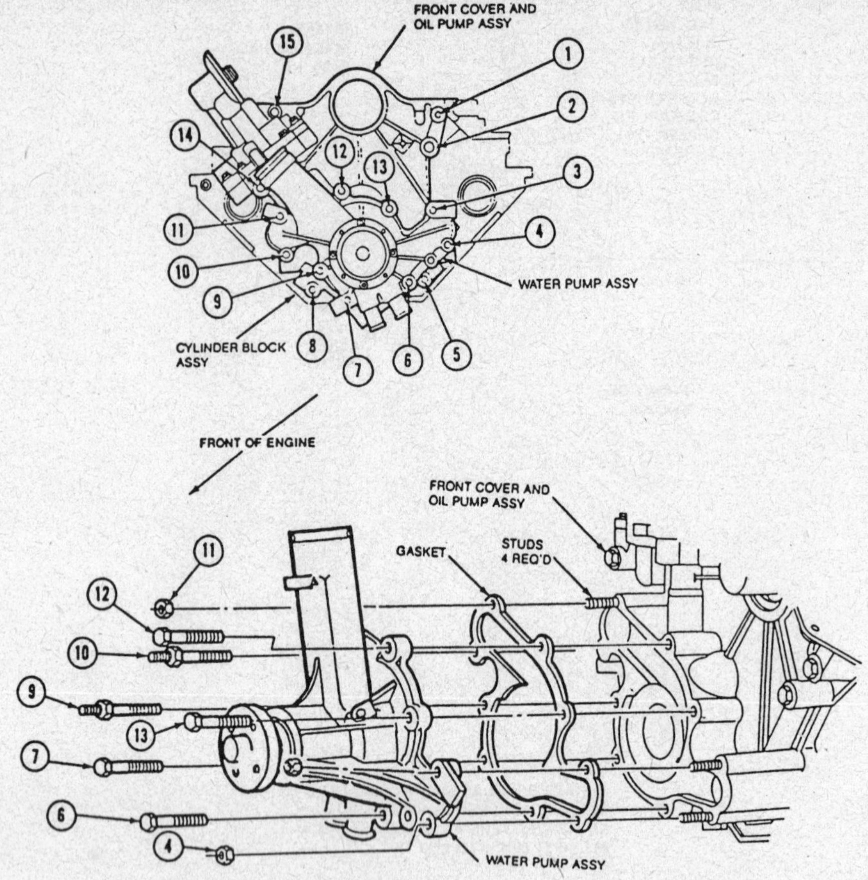


**Fig. 8 Front cover & water pump bolt locations**

9. **On all models,** disconnect radiator hose at thermostat housing, then the coolant bypass hose from manifold.
10. Remove heater tube as follows:
    a. Disconnect heater tube from intake manifold.
    b. Remove tube support bracket retaining nuts, then remove heater hose from rear of heater tube.
    c. Loosen hose clamp at heater elbow, then remove heater tube with hose attached.
    d. Remove heater tube with lines attached and set assembly aside.
11. Disconnect vacuum lines at fuel rail assembly and intake manifold, then disconnect necessary electrical connectors.
12. Remove A/C compressor support bracket, if equipped. Disconnect one PCV line from upper intake manifold and valve. Remove second PCV line from LH rocker cover.
13. Remove throttle body assembly, then the EGR valve assembly from upper manifold.
14. Remove wiring retainer bracket from LH front side of intake manifold and position aside with spark plug wires.
15. Remove upper intake manifold bolts and studs, then the upper intake manifold.
16. Remove injectors and fuel rail assembly.
17. Remove heater water outlet hose, then the lower intake manifold attaching bolts and studs.
18. Remove lower intake manifold. **The manifold is sealed at each end with RTV-type sealer. To break seal, it may be necessary to pry on front of manifold with a screwdriver blade. Use care to prevent damage to machined surfaces when prying with screwdriver.**
19. Remove and discard manifold side gaskets and end seals.
20. Reverse procedure to install, noting the following:
    a. Clean all cylinder head/block to intake manifold contact areas.
    b. Apply a dab of gasket and trim adhesive part No. 19B508-AA or equivalent to each cylinder head mating surface. Press new intake manifold gasket into place over locating dowels.
    c. Apply a 1/8 inch bead of silicone sealer D6AZ-19562-B or equivalent at each corner where cylinder head joins the cylinder block.
    d. Install front and rear intake manifold end seals, then carefully lower intake manifold into position on cylinder block and cylinder heads. Use locating dowels as necessary to guide manifold.
    e. **On non-supercharged engines,** install attaching bolts and studs. **Torque** in two steps; first to 8 ft. lbs., then to 11 ft. lbs, in sequence shown in **Fig. 3.**
    f. **On supercharged engines,** install attaching bolts and studs. **Torque** to 8-11 ft. lbs. in sequence shown in **Fig. 4.**
    g. Tighten EGR valve assembly mounting bolts, throttle body mounting bolts and A/C compressor support bracket bolts to specifications.

# VALVE ARRANGEMENT

## FRONT TO REAR

Right Bank .................. I-E-I-E-I-E
Left Bank.................... E-I-E-I-E-I

# VALVE LIFT SPECIFICATIONS

| Engine | Year | Intake, Inch | Exhaust, Inch |
|---|---|---|---|
| 3.8L/V6-232 | 1989–92 | .424 | .447 |

# CAMSHAFT LOBE LIFT SPECIFICATIONS

| Engine | Year | Intake, Inch | Exhaust, Inch |
|---|---|---|---|
| 3.8L/V6-232 | 1989–92 | .245 | .259 |

# VALVES

## ADJUST

Correct valve clearance is .09-.19 inch.

A .060 inch longer or a .060 inch shorter pushrod is available to compensate for dimensional changes in the valve train. If clearance is less than specified, the .060 inch shorter pushrod should be used. If clearance is more than the maximum specified, the .060 inch longer pushrod should be used.

Using an auxiliary starter switch crankshaft until No. 1 cylinder is at TDC compression stroke, then compress valve lifter using tool T82C-6500-A or equivalent, **Fig. 5.** At this point, the following valves can be

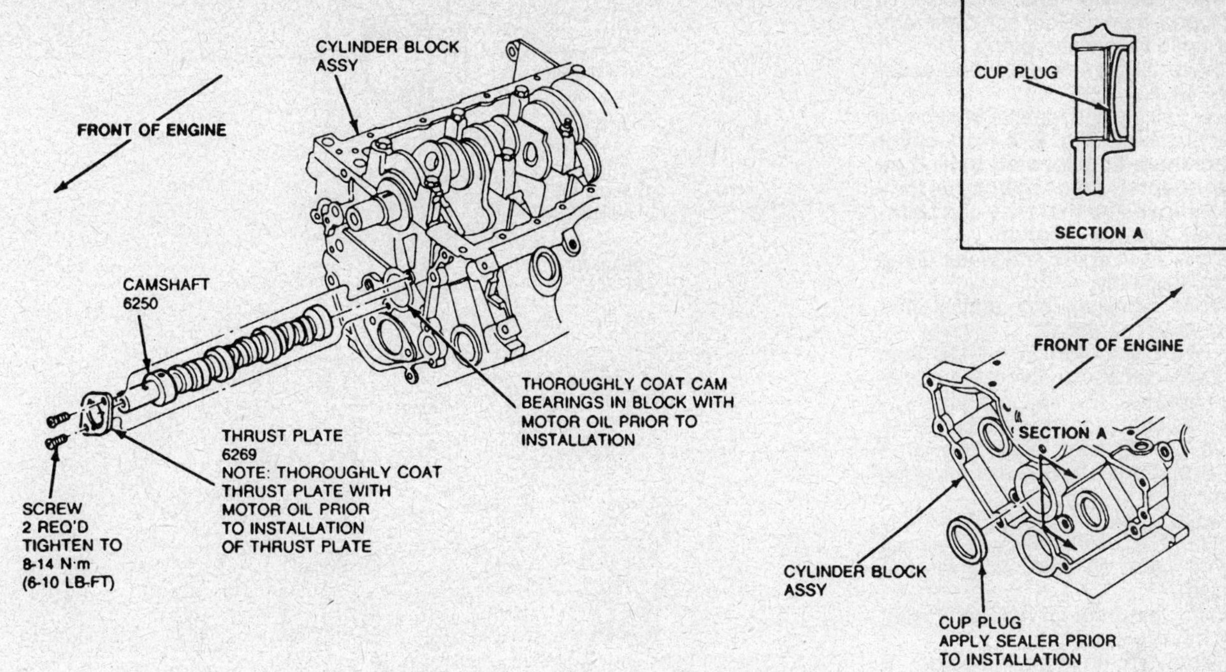


**Fig. 9 Camshaft installation**

checked: intake Nos. 1, 3 and 6; exhaust Nos. 1, 2 and 4.

After clearance on these valves has been checked, rotate crankshaft until No. 5 cylinder is at TDC compression stroke (1 revolution of crankshaft), and then compress valve lifter using tool No. T82C-6500-A or equivalent, **Fig. 5,** and check the following valves: intake Nos. 2, 4 and 5; exhaust Nos. 3, 5 and 6.

# VALVE GUIDES

Valve guides consist of holes bored in the cylinder head. For service the guide holes can be reamed oversize to accommodate valves with oversize stems of .015 and .030 inch.

# ROCKER ARM SERVICE

These engines use stamped steel rocker arms retained by a fulcrum seat which bolts directly to the cylinder head and guides the rocker arm, **Fig. 6. Torque** fulcrum bolts in two steps as follows: For each valve rotate crankshaft until valve lifter rests on heel (base circle) of camshaft lobe and torque fulcrum bolt to 5-11 ft. lbs. After initial torquing of all fulcrum bolts, final torque to 19-25 ft. lbs. Final torque may be done with camshaft in any position.

# VALVE LIFTERS
## REPLACE

1. Disconnect secondary ignition wires from spark plugs using wire remover T74P-6666-A or equivalent. Remove ignition wire routing clips from rocker arm cover attaching bolt studs and position wires aside.
2. Remove intake manifold, refer to "Intake Manifold, Replace."
3. Remove rocker arm covers. On engines with stud mounted rocker arms, loosen stud nuts and rotate rocker arms to one side. On other engines, remove fulcrum bolt, fulcrum, rocker arm and fulcrum guide (if used).
4. Remove pushrods in sequence so they can be installed in their original bores.
5. Remove lifter guide retainer bolts, retainer and guide plate, if equipped.
6. Using a magnet rod, remove lifters and place in a numbered rack so they can be installed in their original bores. If lifters are stuck in bores by excessive varnish, etc., it may be necessary to use a plier-type tool to remove. Rotate lifter back and forth to loosen from gum or varnish.
7. The internal parts of each lifter are matched sets. Do not intermix parts. Keep assemblies intact until they are to be cleaned, **Fig. 7.**

# FRONT COVER, TIMING CHAIN & GEARS
## REPLACE

To replace seal in timing gear cover, it is necessary to remove cover as outlined below.

1. Disconnect battery ground cable and drain cooling system.
2. Remove air cleaner and air intake duct.
3. **On supercharged engines,** remove electric cooling fan assembly.
4. **On non-supercharged engines,** remove fan/clutch assembly.
5. **On all models,** remove drive belts and water pump pulley.
6. Remove power steering pump mounting bracket bolts, if equipped. Leave hoses connected and position pump assembly aside.
7. Remove A/C compressor support bracket, if equipped. Leave compressor in place.
8. Disconnect coolant bypass hose and heater hoses at water pump and upper radiator hose at thermostat housing.
9. Disconnect ignition coil secondary wire from distributor cap, then remove distributor cap with ignition wires attached.
10. **On non-supercharged engines,** with No. 1 cylinder at TDC compression stroke, mark position of rotor to distributor housing and position of distributor housing to front cover.
11. Remove distributor hold-down clamp, then lift distributor from front cover.
12. **On supercharged engines,** remove hold-down clamp and lift camshaft synchronizer from front cover.
13. Raise and support vehicle.
14. Remove crankshaft pulley using crankshaft damper removal tool No. T85P-6316-D and vibration damper removal adapter tool No. T82L-6316-B or equivalents.

15. Remove oil filter and oil cooler, if equipped, then disconnect lower radiator hose from water pump.
16. Remove oil pan as described under "Oil Pan, Replace."
17. Lower vehicle and remove front cover attaching bolts, **Fig. 8. A front cover attaching bolt is located behind oil filter adapter. Also tag bolts as they are removed so that they can be installed at same location.**
18. Remove front cover and water pump as an assembly.
19. Remove camshaft bolt and washer from end of camshaft.
20. Remove distributor drive gear, then remove camshaft sprocket, crankshaft sprocket and timing chain.
21. If crankshaft sprocket is difficult to remove, pry off shaft using two large screwdrivers positioned on both sides of sprocket.
22. Remove chain tensioner assembly from front of cylinder block as follows:
    a. Pull back on ratcheting mechanism.
    b. Install pin through hole in bracket to relieve tension.
    c. Remove three mounting bolts.
23. Reverse procedure to install, noting the following:
    a. If a replacement front cover is to be installed, the water pump, oil pump, oil filter adapter and intermediate shaft must be removed from the front cover to be replaced and reinstalled on the replacement front cover. It may be necessary to rotate crankshaft 180° from the No. 1 cylinder TDC location to position fuel pump eccentric for fuel pump installation. When installing distributor, No. 1 cylinder must be at TDC position and marks made during removal must be aligned.
    b. Lightly oil all bolt and stud threads before installation, except those specifying special sealant.
    c. Rotate crankshaft as necessary to position piston No. 1 at TDC and crankshaft keyway at 12 o'clock position.
    d. Lubricate timing chain and front oil seal with new clean engine oil.
    e. Ensure timing marks are aligned across from each other.
    f. **On non-supercharged engines,** install distributor with rotor pointing at No. 1 cap tower.
    g. Tighten to specifications.

## CAMSHAFT
### REPLACE

1. Drain cooling system and remove radiator and grille.
2. **On engines equipped with air conditioning,** purge refrigerant from system and remove condenser.
3. **On all engines,** remove front cover, timing chain and sprockets.
4. Remove intake manifold.
5. Remove pushrods, lifters and oil pan.
6. Remove thrust plate, then carefully remove camshaft by pulling toward front of engine, **Fig. 9. Use care to avoid damaging camshaft bearings.**
7. Reverse procedure to install, noting the following:
    a. Lubricate cam lobes and bearing surfaces with Oil Conditioner D9AZ-19579-CA or equivalent.
    b. Tighten to specifications.

NOTCH AND BUTTON (TO FRONT OF ENGINE)
PISTON
OIL SQUIRT HOLE (TO RH SIDE OF ENGINE)
BEARING INSERT (UPPER)
BEARING INSERT (LOWER)
BEARING CAP

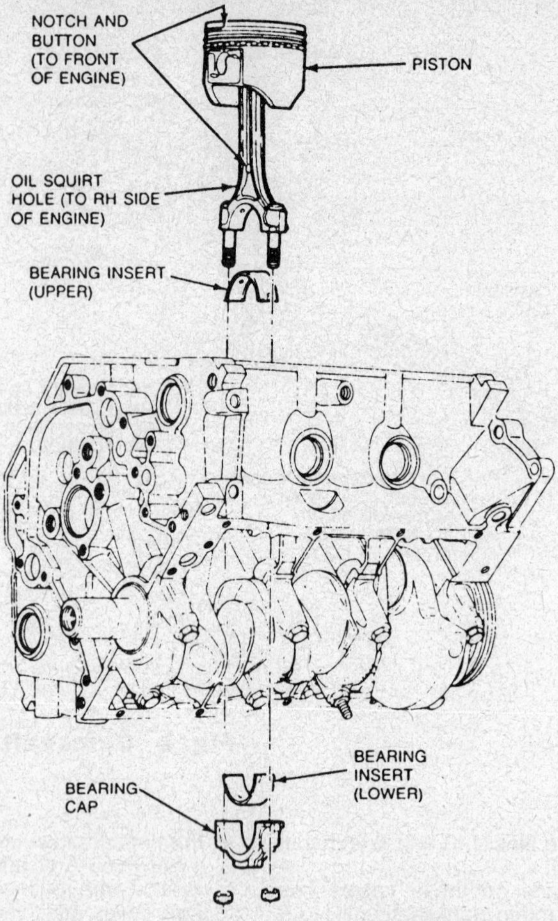

**Fig. 10 Piston & rod assembly**

## PISTON & ROD ASSEMBLY

When installed, piston and rod assembly should have the notch or arrow in piston head toward front of engine with connecting rod numbers positioned as shown in **Fig. 10.** Check side clearance between connecting rods at each crankshaft journal. Correct side clearance is .0047-.0114 Inch.

## PISTONS, PINS & RINGS

Pistons are available in standard sizes and oversizes of .003, .020, .030 and .040 inch. Piston rings are available in standard sizes and oversizes of .020, .030 and .040 inch. Piston pins are available in standard size and oversizes of .001 and .002 inch.

## MAIN & ROD BEARINGS

Main and rod bearings are available in standard sizes and undersizes of .001, .002, .010, .020 and .030 inch.

## CRANKSHAFT REAR OIL SEAL
### REPLACE

1. Using a sharp tool, punch one hole into seal metal surface between seal lip and engine block.
2. Remove seal using slide hammer No. T82L-9533-B or equivalent. Use care to prevent damage to sealing surface.
3. Lubricate new seal with clean engine oil and install using seal installation tool No. T82L-6701-A or equivalent. Tighten bolts alternately to seat seal properly, **Fig. 11.**

## OIL PAN
### REPLACE

1. Disconnect battery ground cable, then remove air cleaner and air intake duct.
2. Remove two bolts attaching sight shield and position shield aside.
3. Remove hood weather seal and wiper assemblies.

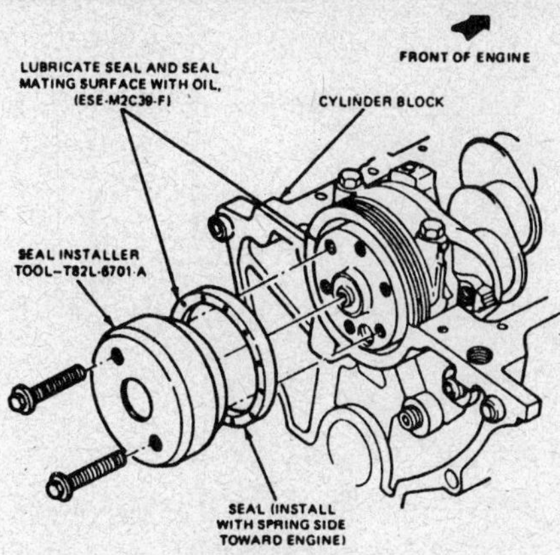


**Fig. 11 Crankshaft rear seal installation**

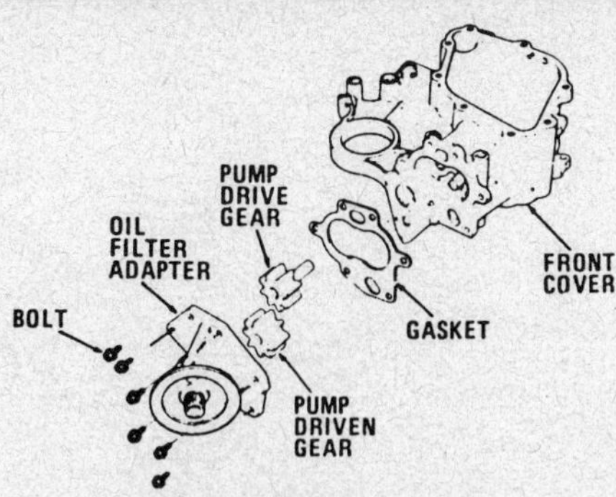


**Fig. 12 Oil pump replacement**

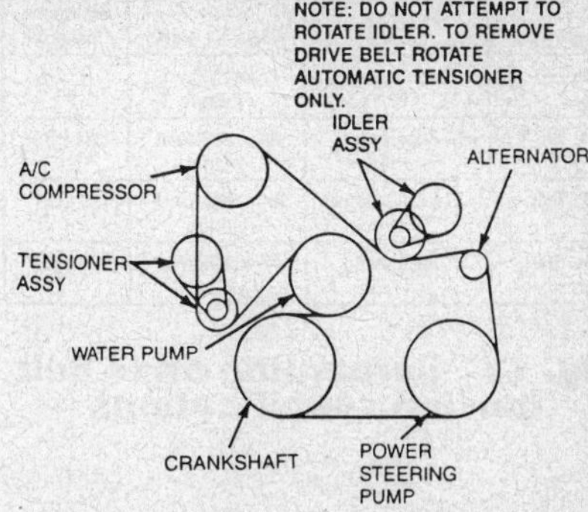


**Fig. 13 Serpentine drive belt routing. Non-supercharged**

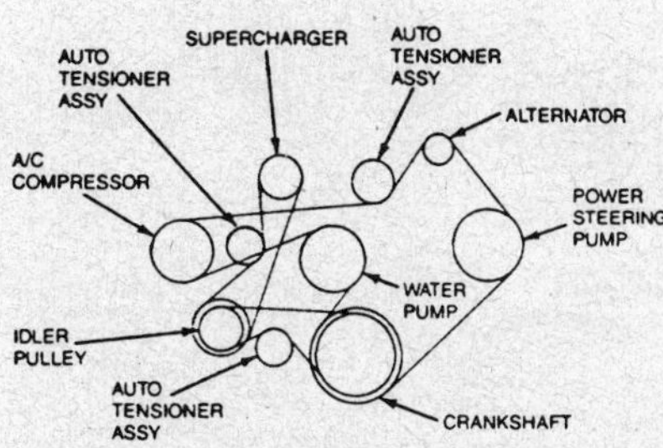


**Fig. 14 Serpentine drive belt routing. Supercharged engines**

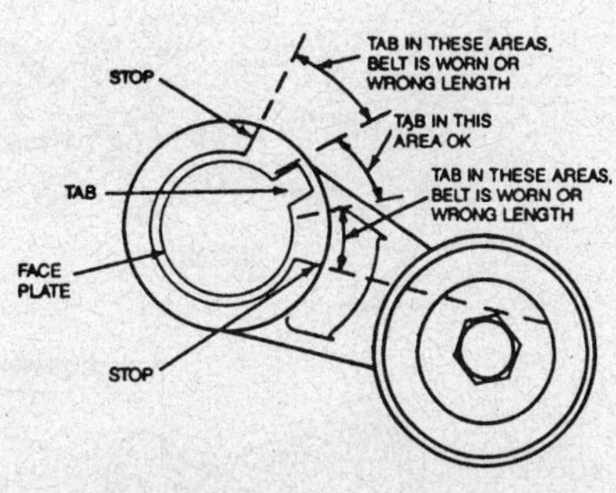


**Fig. 15 Drive belt tensioner**

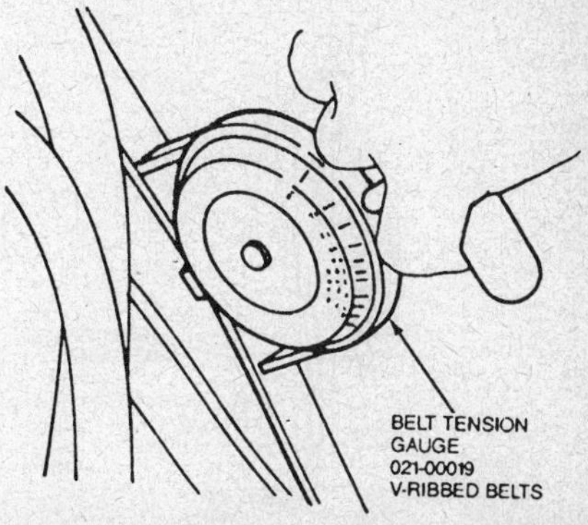


**Fig. 16 Drive belt tension gauge**

4. Remove LH cowl vent screen and wiper module.
5. **On supercharged engines,** remove supercharger.
6. **On all models,** install engine lifting eyes, then engine support fixture D88L-6000-A or equivalent.
7. Raise and support vehicle.
8. Remove engine mount through bolts.
9. **On supercharged engines,** remove left side mount retaining strap.
10. Partially lower vehicle, then raise engine at support fixture.
11. Raise vehicle and remove starter motor assembly.
12. Drain engine oil, then remove oil filter.
13. Remove wire loom, ground strap and automatic transmission cooler lines.
14. Remove oil pan-to-bell housing bolts, then the crankshaft position sensor shield bolts.
15. Remove remaining oil pan retaining bolts.
16. Remove steering shaft pinch bolts and separate steering shaft.
17. Position a transmission jack under front of subframe.
18. Remove six rearward bolts on front of subframe, then loosen two front subframe bolts.
19. Remove lower strut to control arm bolts and nuts on both sides of vehicle.
20. Lower subframe, then remove oil pan.
21. Reverse procedure to install. Tighten to specifications.

## OIL PUMP REPLACE

On these engines, the oil pump is contained within the front cover, **Fig. 12.** To replace oil pump, remove front cover as described under "Front Cover, Timing Chain & Gears, Removal."

## OIL PUMP REPAIRS

Referring to **Fig. 12,** disassemble pump. To remove oil pressure relief valve, insert a self-threading sheet metal screw of the proper diameter into oil pressure relief valve chamber cap and pull cap out of chamber. Remove spring and plunger.

The inner rotor, shaft and outer race are serviced as an assembly. One part should not be replaced without replacing the other.

## SERPENTINE DRIVE BELT ROUTING

Refer to **Figs. 13 and 14** for drive belt installation. This engine is equipped with automatic drive belt tensioners, **Fig. 15.** These tensioners have built in drive belt wear indicators. With engine off, check position of tensioner belt length indicator. If indicator is not between minimum belt length and maximum belt stretch lines, replace drive belt. Belt tension can be checked using a suitable belt tension gauge, **Figs. 16 and 17.** Belt tension should be checked at the middle of longest accessible span.

## COOLING SYSTEM BLEED

These engines do not require a specific bleed procedure. After filling cooling system, start engine and allow to reach operating temperature with radiator cap removed. Air in system will then be automatically bled through cap opening.

## THERMOSTAT REPLACE

1. Partially drain cooling system.
2. Disconnect upper radiator hose at thermostat housing.
3. Remove two mounting bolts, housing and gaskets.
4. Reverse procedure to install. Tighten to specifications.

## WATER PUMP REPLACE

1. Drain cooling system, then remove air cleaner and air intake duct.

| Application | Usage | Width x Length | Minimum Tension |
|---|---|---|---|
| 3.8L EFI | Accessory | 6K x 2510mm ± 6mm | 74 LBS |
| 3.8L S/C | Accessory | 8K x 2280mm ± 6mm | 135 LBS |
| 3.8L S/C | Super Charger | 8K x 996.5mm ± 6mm | 69 LBS |
| 3.8L S/C | Jackshaft | 7K x 1080mm ± 6mm | 56 LBS |

**Fig. 17 Serpentine drive belt tension specifications**

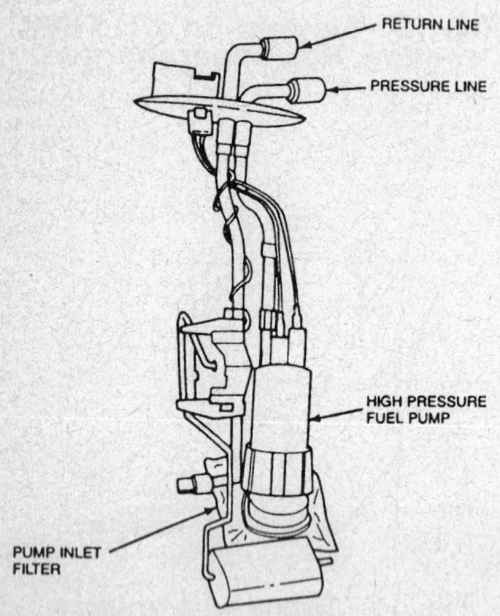


**Fig. 18 Fuel pump replacement**

2. Remove fan shroud attaching screws then the fan and fan clutch attaching bolts. Remove fan and fan clutch and shroud.
3. Loosen accessory drive belt idler, then remove drive belt and water pump pulley, **Fig. 8.**
4. **On models equipped with power steering,** remove pump mounting bracket attaching bolts, position pump aside with hoses attached.
5. **On models equipped with A/C,** remove compressor front support bracket.
6. **On all models,** disconnect lower radiator hose, coolant bypass hose and heat hose from water pump.
7. **On models equipped with Tripminder,** remove fuel flow sensor support bracket. Do not disconnect fuel lines.
8. **On all models,** remove water pump attaching bolts, then remove water pump.
9. Reverse procedure to install.

## FUEL PRESSURE RELIEF

Release pressure from fuel system at the fuel pressure relief valve using tool No. T80L-9974-B or equivalent. When relieving fuel pressure, crank engine with fuel pump electrical connector disconnected.

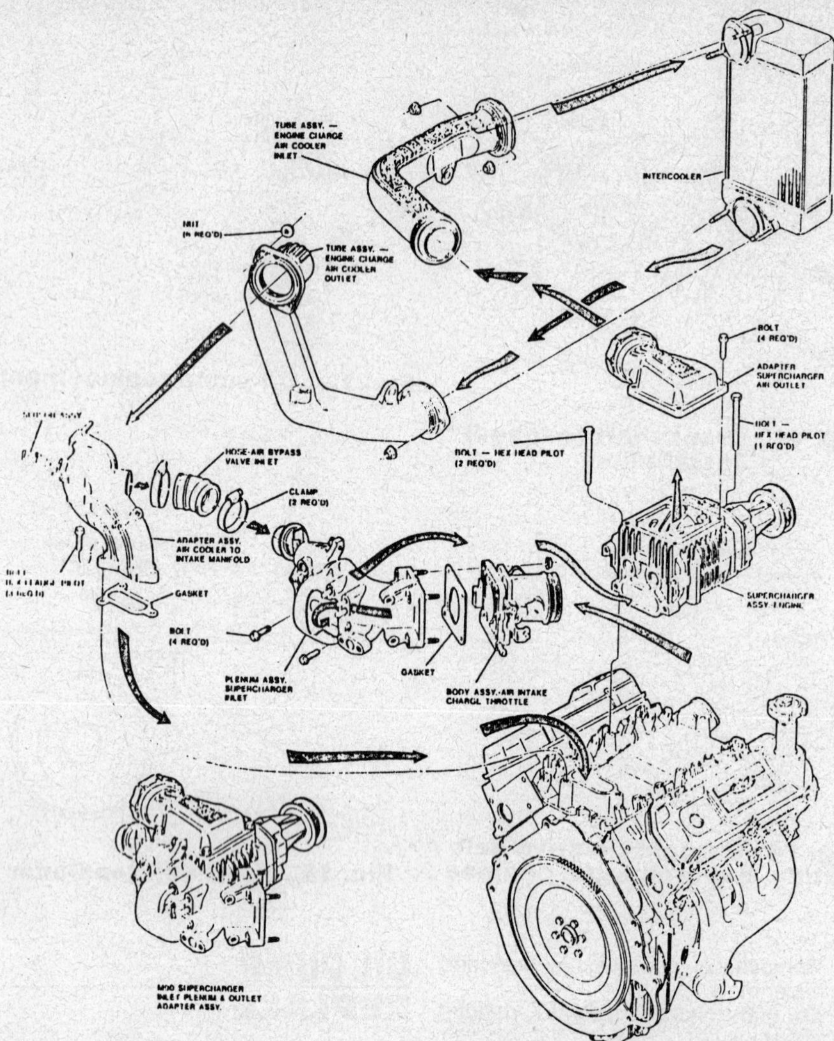


**Fig. 19 Supercharger operation & air flow**

## FUEL PUMP REPLACE

1. Disconnect battery ground cable.
2. Relieve fuel pressure as described above.
3. Remove fuel tank from vehicle as follow:
   a. Drain fuel tank.
   b. Raise and support vehicle, then disconnect and cap fuel and vent lines from fuel tank. Tag lines so they can be installed in same locations. It may be necessary to remove exhaust pipe and shield to gain access to fuel tank.
   c. Disconnect electrical connectors from fuel sender and fuel pump. Tag electrical connections so they can be installed in same locations.
   d. Disconnect fuel filler tube.
   e. Remove fuel tank support straps, then lower fuel tank from vehicle.
4. Rotate fuel pump lock ring counterclockwise, then remove fuel pump, **Fig. 18.**
5. Reverse procedure to install.

## SUPERCHARGED 3.8L/V6-232

This engine is a modified version of the base 3.8L/V6-232. Modifications were necessary to enable the engine to handle added stress and to offset added weight created by the supercharger.

The engine block, cylinder head and crankshaft have been strengthened to contain the gas loads generating by supercharging. The cylinder head is constructed of a special heat treated aluminum.

The pistons are made out of a special hypereutectic alloy. The compression ratio is 8.2:1, compared to the 9.0:1 ratio in the standard engine.

The intake manifold is a newly designed plenum configuration to accommodate the supercharger and related components.

On models with automatic transmission, the camshaft is the same as that of the standard engine. On supercharged models with automatic transmission, the camshaft is a unique design with 8° greater intake duration, 4° less exhaust duration, .0122 inch greater intake lift and .0051 inch greater exhaust lift.

In addition to a conventional radiator, the

supercharged engine uses an air-to-air intercooler. The intercooler cools air which is heated during compression by the supercharger before it is forced into the intake manifold. Cooling the air increases its density, resulting in increased power output.

The supercharger used on this engine is a Roots-type positive displacement pump. It is an engine driven compressor which uses two counter-rotating rotors to trap air inside the supercharger body where it is compressed and forced into the intake manifold and combustion chamber. The increased density of the fuel charge inside the combustion chamber generates the added engine power.

The supercharger is belt-driven indirectly off the engine crankshaft. The supercharger runs at 2.6 times the crankshaft's speed with a maximum speed of 15,600 RPM. Boost pressure is approximately 12 psi at 4,000 engine RPM.

The design of the system's rotors greatly contributes to a reduction in the noise generally associated with supercharged applications. Some Root's type systems use straight lobe rotors that result in uneven pressure pulses causing higher noise levels. This system uses a helical rotor design, which evens out the pressure pulses in the blower, reducing noise levels. The helical rotor design also increases efficiency by reducing the amount of air carried back to the inlet side of the supercharger through the space between the meshing rotors.

Air flows through the supercharged system as shown in **Fig. 19.** Air enters through the remote mounted air cleaner, past the mass air flow meter to the air intake charge throttle body assembly. It then passes through the supercharger inlet plenum assembly into the bottom of the supercharger, is pressurized by the spinning rotors and discharged through the top by the air outlet adapter to the upper tube assembly. The upper tube assembly carries the air into the top of the intercooler where it is cooled and sent through the outlet tube assembly at the bottom. The cooled air passes through the air cooler-to-intake manifold adapter assembly to the intake manifold, then routed to the individual cylinders.

The system also uses a bypass which branches off from the air cooler-to-i ntake manifold adapter assembly. The bypass allows the supercharger to idle when the extra power is not needed by routing excess air back through the supercharger inlet plenum assembly, allowing the engine to run normally aspirated.

## TIGHTENING SPECIFICATIONS

| Year | Component | Torque/Ft. Lbs. |
|---|---|---|
| 1989 | Camshaft Sprocket | 15–22 |
| | Crankshaft Dampner | 93–121 |
| 1989–92 | A/C Compressor Mounting | 30–45 |
| | A/C Lower Mounting Bracket | 30–45 |
| | Alternator Pivot Bolt | 45–57 |
| | Camshaft Thrust Plate | 6–10 |
| | Connecting Rod | 31–36 |
| | Coolant Temperature Switch | 8–12 |
| | Crankshaft Pulley To Dampner | 20–28 |
| | Crankshaft Stud Bolt | 6–8.5 |
| | Cylinder Head | ① |
| | Distributor Hold-Down | 20–29 |
| | ECT Sensor | 6–9 |
| | EGR Valve To Intake Manifold | 15–22 |
| | Fan Clutch Assembly | 12–18 |
| | Fan Shroud | 24–48② |
| | Flywheel | 54–64 |
| | Front Cover | 15–22 |
| | Fuel Rail Assembly Bolt | 6–8 |
| | Fulcrum Bolt | ① |
| | Heater Tube Support Bracket | 15–22 |
| | HEGO Sensor | 28–33 |
| | Intake Manifold (Non-Supercharged Engine) | ① |
| | Intake Manifold (Supercharged Engine) | ① |
| | Intake Manifold Retaining Strap | 34–44 |
| | Low Oil Level Sensor | 20–30 |
| | Main Bearing Cap | 65–81 |
| | Oil Drain Plug | 15–25 |
| | Oil Filter Adapter To Front Cover | 18–22 |
| | Oil Inlet Tube To Cylinder Block | 15–22 |
| | Oil Inlet Tube To Main Bearing Cap | 30–40 |
| | Oil Pan Bolts | 80–106② |
| | Oil Pickup Tube | 15–22 |

*Continued*

## TIGHTENING SPECIFICATIONS—Continued

| Year | Component | Torque/Ft. Lbs. |
|---|---|---|
| | Power Steering Lower Brace Bolt | 18–24 |
| | Power Steering Upper Brace Bolt | 30–45 |
| | Rocker Arm Cover | 7–9 |
| | Rocker Arm Fulcrum Bolt | ① |
| | Spark Plug | 5–11 |
| | Thermostat Housing | 15–22 |
| | Throttle Body Nut | 15–22 |
| | Valve Lifter Guide Plate | 7–10 |
| | Water Pump | 15–22 |
| 1990–92 | Camshaft Sprocket | 30–37 |
| | Crankshaft Dampner | 103–132 |

①—Refer To Text. ②—Inch Lbs.

# 4.6L/V8-281 Engine

**NOTE:** On Vehicles Equipped With Airbags, Disarm Airbag System As Outlined Under "Airbag System Disarming" Before Any Diagnosis, Testing, Troubleshooting Or Repairs Are Performed. After All Diagnosis, Testing, Troubleshooting Or Repairs Have Been Completed, Rearm Airbag System As Outlined Under "Airbag System Disarming."

## INDEX



## AIRBAG SYSTEM DISARMING

**The electrical circuit necessary for system deployment is powered directly from the battery and a backup power supply. To avoid accidental deployment and possible personal injury, the airbag system must be deactivated prior to servicing or replacing any component located near or related to airbag system activation components.**

1. Disconnect positive battery cable and wait one minute.
2. Remove four nut and washer assemblies securing airbag to steering wheel.
3. Disconnect airbag electrical connector and install airbag simulator tool No. 105-00008 or equivalent.
4. **On models with passenger side airbag,** remove passenger airbag and disconnect electrical connector.
5. Install airbag simulator tool No. 105-00008 or equivalent.
6. **On all models,** connect positive battery cable.
7. To activate airbag system, disconnect positive battery cable and reverse procedure. **Torque** mounting nut and washer assemblies to 36-49 inch lbs.
8. Verify proper operation of airbag lamp.

## ENGINE MOUNTS REPLACE

### FRONT

1. Disconnect both battery cables and remove air inlet tube.
2. Drain cooling system, then remove cooling fan and shroud.
3. Relieve fuel system pressure as described under "Fuel System Pressure Relief."
4. Remove upper radiator hose, wiper module and support bracket.
5. Discharge A/C system and disconnect A/C compressor outlet hose, then remove bolt retaining hose assembly to RH coil bracket.
6. Remove engine electrical harness 42-pin connector from bracket on brake vacuum booster.
7. Disconnect engine electrical connector and transmission harness electrical connector.
8. Disconnect throttle valve cable at throttle body, then remove heater outlet hose from RH cylinder head.
9. Remove blower motor resistor.
10. Remove RH engine mount to lower engine bracket attaching bolt. **Fig. 1.**
11. Disconnect EGR valve vacuum hoses and tube.
12. Remove EGR valve mounting bolts, then disconnect Heated Exhaust Gas Oxygen (HEGO) sensors.
13. Raise and support vehicle.
14. Remove engine mount through bolts.

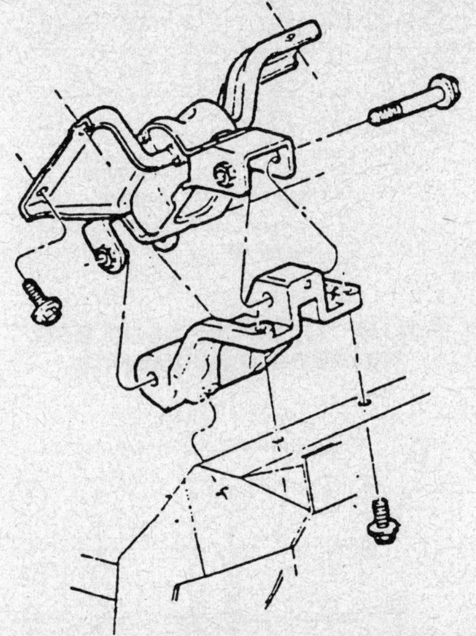

Fig. 1 Front engine mount removal

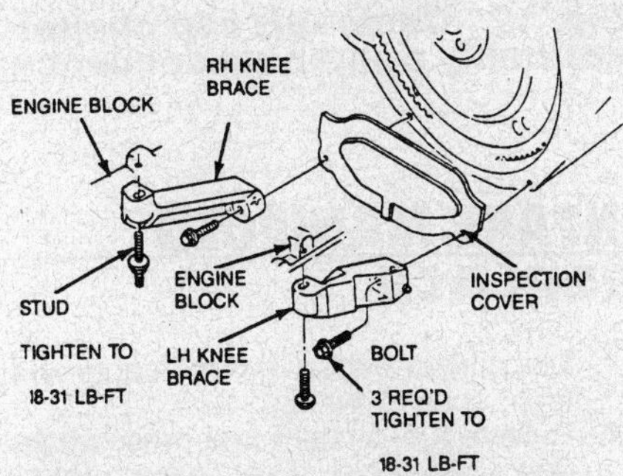


Fig. 4 Transmission line bracket assembly removal

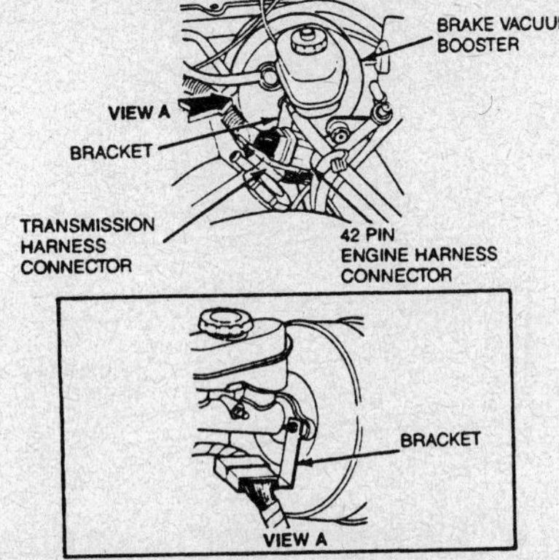


Fig. 2 Engine & transmission harness connectors

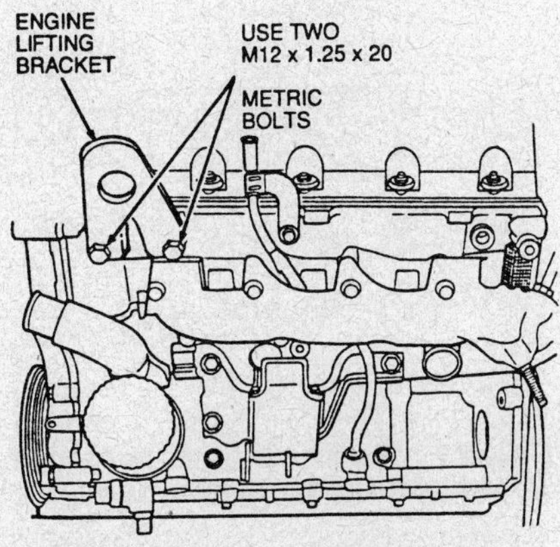


Fig. 5 Engine lift bracket installation

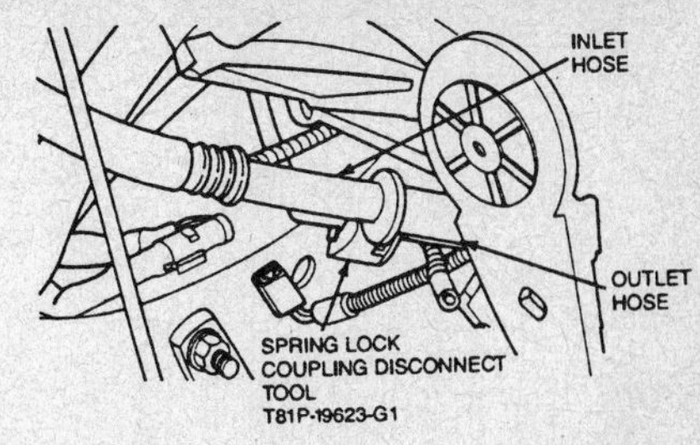


Fig. 3 A/C compressor lines removal

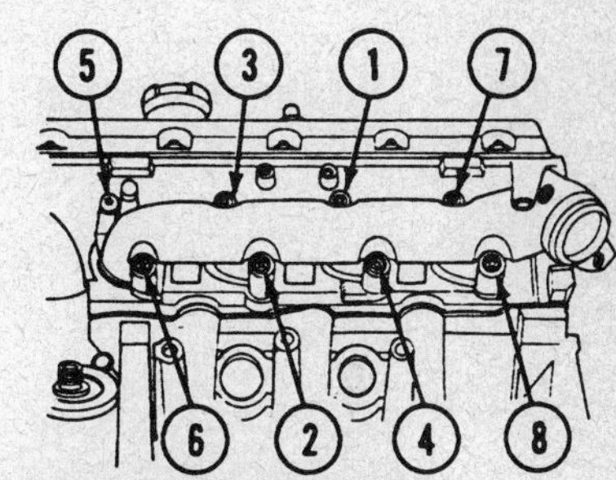


Fig. 6 Exhaust manifold tightening sequence

RH mount has one bolt, LH mount has two bolts.

15. Remove EGR tube line attaching nut at RH exhaust manifold, then remove EGR valve and tube assembly.
16. Disconnect exhaust pipes at manifolds, then lower and secure exhaust at crossmember.
17. Position a jack and wood block under oil pan, rearward of drain plug, then raise engine approximately 4 inches.
18. Install wood block under oil pan, then lower engine onto wood block.
19. Remove three engine mount attaching bolts from RH and LH engine mounts. Remove engine mounts.
20. Reverse procedure to install. Tighten to specifications.

### REAR

1. Raise and support vehicle, then support transmission using a jack and a wood block.
2. Remove two bolts attaching mount to crossmember.
3. Raise transmission with jack and remove mount and retainer assembly.
4. Reverse procedure to install. Tighten to specifications.

## ENGINE REPLACE

1. Disconnect battery cables.
2. Mark position of hood hinges and remove hood.
3. Drain cooling system and discharge A/C system.
4. Relieve fuel system pressure as described under "Fuel System Pressure Relief," then disconnect fuel lines.
5. Remove engine cooling fan, shroud and radiator, then remove wiper module and bracket.
6. Remove air inlet tube and 42-pin electrical harness connector from bracket at brake vacuum booster, **Fig. 2.**
7. Disconnect 42-pin connector and transmission harness electrical connector, then position connectors aside.
8. Disconnect accelerator, seed control cables and throttle valve cable.
9. Disconnect purge solenoid electrical connector and vacuum hose.
10. Disconnect power distribution and starter relay power supply.
11. Disconnect vacuum hose from throttle body port.
12. Disconnect heater hoses, then the alternator electrical harness at fender apron and junction box.
13. Using tool No. T81P-19623-G1, G2 or equivalent, remove A/C compressor inlet and outlet attaching hoses, **Fig. 3.**
14. Disconnect EVO sensor electrical connector from power steering pump.
15. Disconnect body ground strap at dash panel, then raise and support vehicle, then drain engine oil.
16. Disconnect exhaust pipes at manifolds, then lower exhaust system and suspend with wire from crossmember.
17. Remove transmission line bracket attaching nut, then remove engine to transmission knee braces attaching bolts and stud, **Fig. 4.**
18. Remove starter motor, then disconnect power steering pump from engine and position aside.
19. Remove plug to access torque converter attaching nuts, then rotate crankshaft to remove nuts (Four required).
20. Remove six engine to transmission attaching bolts.
21. Remove engine mount through bolts.
22. Lower vehicle and support transmission with suitable jack.
23. Install engine lift brackets, **Fig. 5,** then connect suitable lift equipment.
24. Carefully raise engine and separate from transmission, then remove engine from engine compartment.
25. Reverse procedure to install. Tighten to specifications.

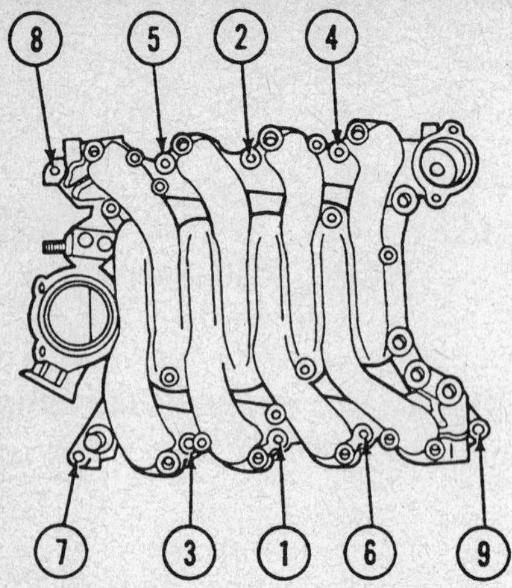

Fig. 7 Intake manifold tightening sequence

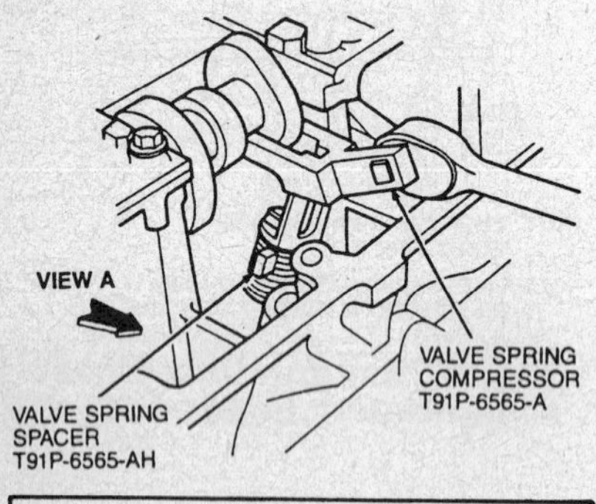


Fig. 10 Valve spring compression

## EXHAUST MANIFOLD REPLACE

1. Disconnect battery ground cables.
2. Remove air intake tube and drain cooling system.
3. Remove cooling fan and shroud, then relieve fuel system pressure as described under "Fuel System Pressure Relief."
4. Disconnect fuel lines and remove upper radiator hose.
5. Remove wiper module and support bracket.
6. Discharge A/C system, then disconnect A/C compressor outlet hose at compressor and remove bolt retaining hose assembly to RH coil bracket.
7. Remove 42-pin engine electrical connector from bracket on brake booster.
8. Disconnect 42-pin electrical connector and transmission harness connector.

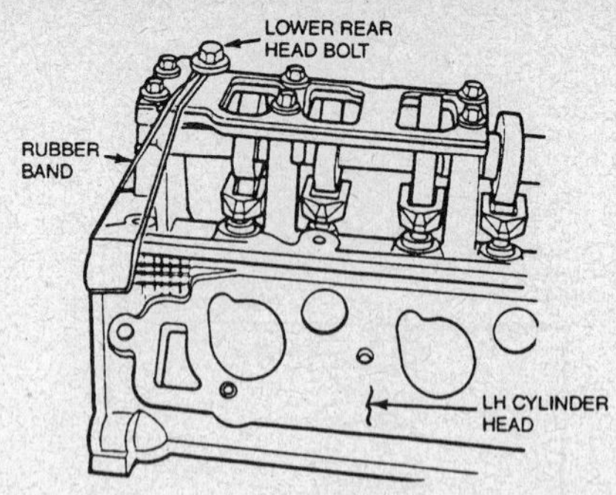


Fig. 8 LH lower rear head bolt removal

Fig. 11 Rear oil seal retainer tightening sequence

9. Disconnect throttle valve cable from throttle body, then disconnect heater outlet hose.
10. Remove ground strap at RH cylinder head and position heater hose aside.
11. Remove blower motor resistor.
12. Remove bolt remaining RH engine mount to lower engine bracket.
13. Disconnect both heated exhaust gas oxygen (HEGO) sensors. Raise and support vehicle.
14. Remove engine mount through bolts.
15. Remove EGR tube line nut from RH exhaust manifold.
16. Disconnect exhaust from manifolds. Lower exhaust and support with wire from crossmember.
17. **For LH exhaust manifold,** remove engine mount from cylinder block and eight bolts retaining exhaust manifold.
18. Position a jack and a block of wood below oil pan, rearward of oil drain hole.
19. Raise engine approximately four inches.
20. **For RH exhaust manifold,** remove eight mounting bolts and remove manifold.
21. Reverse procedure to install, noting the following:
    a. Position manifold to cylinder head and **torque** to 15-22 ft. lbs., in sequence shown in **Fig. 6.**
    b. Tighten to specifications.

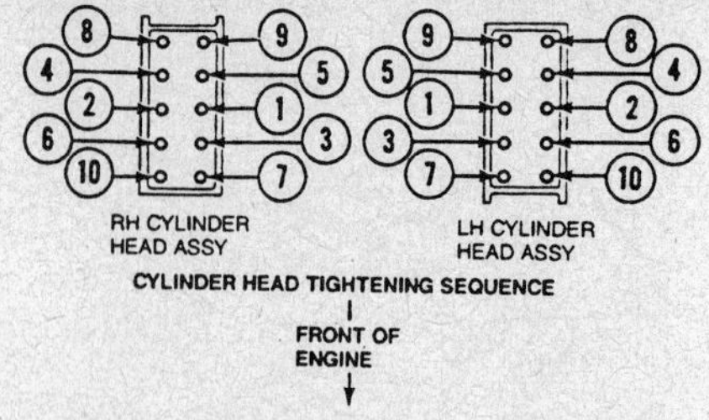


Fig. 9 Cylinder head bolt tightening sequence

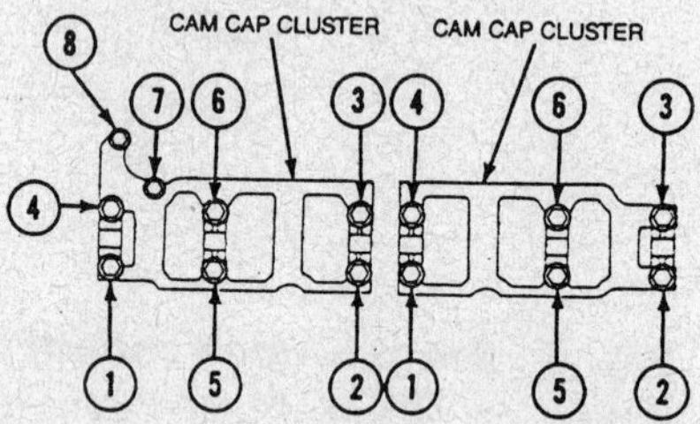


Fig. 12 Camshaft cap cluster assembly tightening sequence

## INTAKE MANIFOLD REPLACE

1. Disconnect battery ground cable and drain cooling system.
2. Relieve fuel system fuel pressure as described under "Fuel System Pressure Relief."
3. Remove wiper module and air inlet tube.
4. Release belt tensioner and remove accessory drive belt.
5. Disconnect spark plug wires from spark plugs and plug wire brackets from camshaft cover studs.
6. Disconnect both ignition coils, CID sensor and ignition wires from both coils.
7. Remove ignition wire tray and ignition wire assembly.
8. Disconnect alternator wiring harness from junction block, fender apron and alternator.
9. Remove alternator and mounting bracket.
10. Raise and support vehicle, then disconnect oil sending unit and EVO sensor. Position aside.
11. Disconnect EGR tube from RH exhaust manifold, then lower vehicle.
12. Disconnect 42-pin connector, A/C compressor, HDR sensor and canister purge solenoid.
13. Remove PCV valve from camshaft cover, then disconnect canister purge vent hose from PCV valve.
14. Disconnect accelerator and speed control cables from throttle body, then remove accelerator cable bracket from intake manifold and position aside.
15. Disconnect throttle valve cable from throttle body.

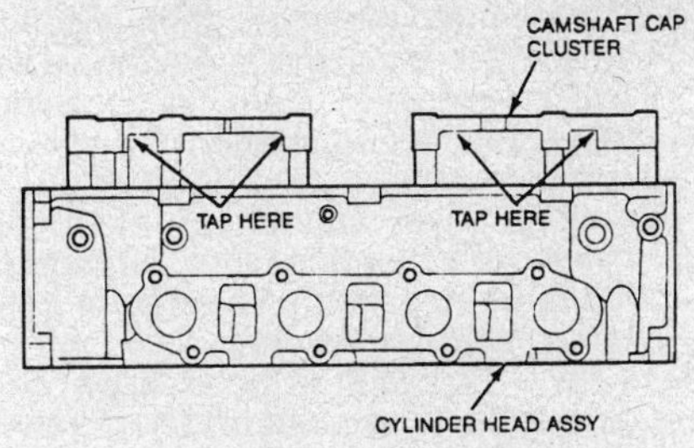


**Fig. 13 Camshaft replacement**

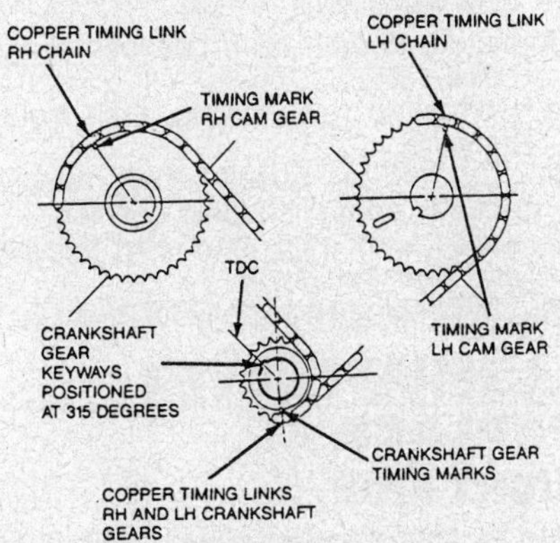


**Fig. 16 LH timing chain installation**

16. Disconnect vacuum hose from throttle body adapter port.
17. Disconnect both HEGO sensors and heater supply hose.
18. Remove thermostat housing, then disconnect upper hose and position aside.
19. Remove bolts attaching intake manifold, then the intake manifold and gaskets.
20. Reverse procedure to install, noting the following:
    a. Clean cylinder head and intake manifold surfaces.
    b. Install new intake manifold gaskets.
    c. **Torque** manifold bolts to 15-22 ft. lbs., in sequence shown, **Fig. 7.**

## CYLINDER HEAD REPLACE

1. Disconnect battery ground cable and drain cooling system. Remove cooling fan and shroud.
2. Relieve fuel system fuel pressure a described under "Fuel System Pressure Relief."
3. Remove air inlet tube and wiper module.
4. Release belt tensioner and remove accessory drive belt.
5. Disconnect ignition wires from spark plugs and ignition wire brackets from camshaft cover studs.

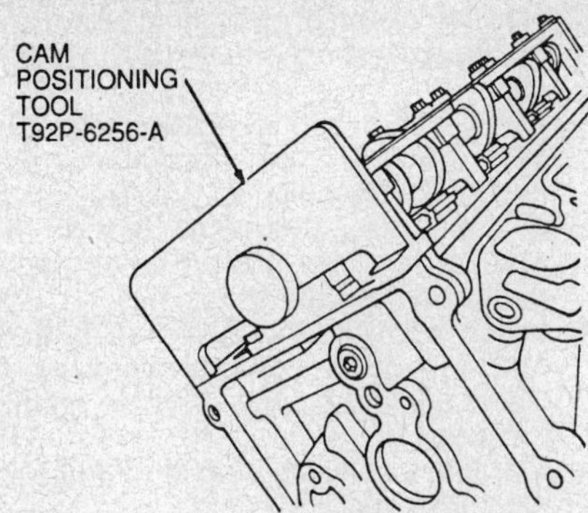


**Fig. 14 Camshaft positioning tool**

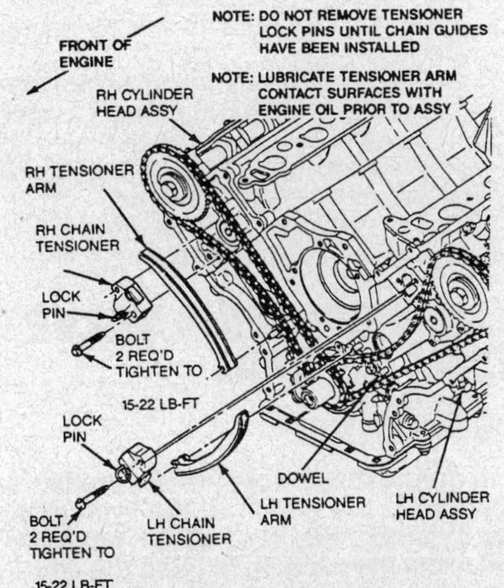


**Fig. 17 Tensioner arm installation**

6. Remove ignition wire tray from coil brackets.
7. Remove bolt securing A/C high pressure line to RH coil bracket.
8. Disconnect both ignition coils and CID sensor, then remove nuts securing both coil brackets to front cover.
9. Slide ignition coil brackets and ignition wire assembly off mounting studs and remove.
10. Remove water pump pulley, then disconnect alternator wiring harness from junction block, fender apron and alternator.
11. Remove alternator and mounting bracket.
12. Disconnect positive battery cable at power distribution box, then remove attaching bolt from positive battery cable bracket located on right side of cylinder head.
13. Disconnect vent hose from canister purge solenoid, then place positive battery cable aside.
14. Disconnect canister purge solenoid vent hose from PCV valve, then remove PCV valve from camshaft cover.

NOTE: WITH EITHER CHAIN POSITIONED AS SHOWN, MARK EACH END AND USE MARKS AS TIMING MARKS

**Fig. 15 Timing chain marks**

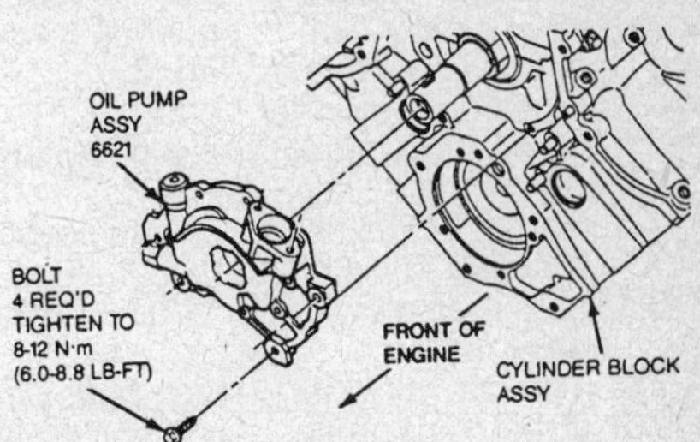


**Fig. 18 Oil pump assembly**

15. Remove 42-pin engine harness connector from retaining bracket on brake vacuum booster, then disconnect and position aside.
16. Disconnect HDR sensor, A/C compressor clutch and canister purge solenoid electrical connectors.
17. Raise and support vehicle, then remove bolts retaining power steering pump to engine block and cylinder front cover. **Front lower bolt on power steering will not come out completely.**
18. Remove bolts attaching oil pan to front cover.
19. Remove crankshaft damper retaining bolt and washer from crankshaft.
20. Install crankshaft damper remover tool No. T58P-6316-D or equivalent on damper, then pull damper from crankshaft.
21. Disconnect EVO sensor and oil sending unit and position aside.
22. Disconnect EGR tube from right exhaust manifold.
23. Disconnect exhaust for right and left manifolds, then suspend with wire.
24. Remove bolt retaining starter wiring harness to rear of right cylinder head, then lower vehicle.
25. Remove right and left camshaft cover to cylinder head.
26. Disconnect accelerator and speed control cables.
27. Remove accelerator bracket from intake manifold and position aside.
28. Disconnect throttle valve cable from throttle body, then the vacuum hose from throttle body elbow port.
29. Disconnect both HEGO sensor and heater supply hose.
30. Remove thermostat housing, then disconnect upper hose and position aside.
31. Remove intake manifold and gaskets.
32. Remove timing chain as described under "Timing Chain, Replace."
33. Remove bolts attaching left cylinder head. **The lower rear bolt cannot be removed due to interference with**

**brake vacuum booster.** Use a rubber band or similar item to hold bolt away from engine as shown, **Fig. 8.**

34. Remove left cylinder head.
35. Remove ground strap retaining heater return line to right cylinder head.
36. Remove bolts attaching right cylinder head. **The lower rear bolt cannot be removed due to interference with evaporator housing.** Use a rubber band or similar item to hold bolt away from engine as shown, **Fig. 8.**
37. Remove right cylinder head.
38. Reverse procedure to install, noting the following:
    a. Rotate crankshaft counterclockwise 45°. This ensures that all pistons are below top of engine block deck face.
    b. **Torque** cylinder head bolts in three steps, in sequence shown in **Fig. 9.** First to 15-22 ft. lbs., then rotate in sequence 85-95°., then an additional 85-95°.
    c. Rotate crankshaft clockwise 45°. This will position crankshaft at TDC No. 1. **Crankshaft must only be rotated in clockwise direction and only as far as TDC.**
    d. Tighten to specifications.

## VALVE LASH SPECIFICATIONS

| Year | Intake, Inch | Exhaust, Inch |
|---|---|---|
| 1992 | .472 | .472 |

## VALVE ARRANGEMENT

### FRONT TO REAR

| | |
|---|---|
| Right Bank | I-E-I-E-I-E-I-E |
| Left Bank | E-I-E-I-E-I-E-I |

## CAMSHAFT LOBE LIFT SPECIFICATIONS

| Year | Intake, Inch | Exhaust, Inch |
|---|---|---|
| 1992 | .2594 | .2594 |

## VALVE CLEARANCE SPECIFICATIONS

Valve clearance is maintained by a hydraulic lash adjuster and roller follower, and is not adjustable. Correct clearance is .020-.069 inch at intake valves and .046-.095 inch at exhaust valves with hydraulic lash adjuster completely collapsed.

## HYDRAULIC LASH ADJUSTER

### REPLACE

1. Remove camshaft covers as described under "Camshaft Cover, Replace."
2. Position piston of cylinder at bottom of stroke and camshaft lobe at base circle.
3. Install valve spring spacer tool No. T91P-6565-AH or equivalent, between spring coils to prevent valve seal damage. **If spacer is not installed, retainer will hit valve stem seal and damage seal.**
4. Install Valve Spring Compressor tool No. T91P-6565-A or equivalent, under camshaft and on top of valve spring retainer, **Fig. 10.**
5. Compress valve spring and remove roller follower.
6. Remove valve spring compressor and spacer.
7. If necessary , remove hydraulic lash adjuster.
8. Repeat steps 2 through 7 for remaining cylinders as required.
9. Reverse procedure to install, noting the following:
    a. Valve lash adjuster must not exceed .059 inch (1.5mm) of plunger travel prior to installation.
    b. When installing roller follower, piston must be at bottom of stroke and camshaft at base circle.
    c. Tighten to specifications.

## VALVE SPRING & VALVE STEM OIL SEAL

### REMOVAL

**If, during this procedure, air pressure has forced the piston to the bottom of the cylinder, any loss of air pressure will allow the valve to fall into the cylinder. A rubber band, tape or string wrapped around the end of the valve stem will prevent this and still allow enough travel to check the valve for binding and excess guide to valve stem clearance.**

1. Remove camshaft covers as described under "Camshaft Cover, Replace."
2. Remove roller followers as described under "Hydraulic Lash Adjuster, Replace."
3. Remove spark plug, then position piston at top of stroke with both valves closed.
4. Install suitable air line with adapter in spark plug opening, then apply air pressure. Failure of air pressure to hold valves closed is an indication of valve or valve seat damage that may require cylinder head removal.
5. Install .40 inch shim between spring coils.
6. Using Valve Spring Compressor tool No. T91P-6565-A or equivalent, compress valve spring.
7. Remove keepers, retainer and valve spring.
8. Use suitable locking pliers, remove valve stem seal.
9. Repeat steps 3 through 8 as required.

### INSTALLATION

1. **Piston must be at Top Dead Center (TDC) of cylinder being serviced.**
2. Remove air pressure, then inspect valve stem for damage. Rotate valve and check valve stem tip eccentric movement during rotation.
3. Position valve up and down through normal travel and check stem for binding. **If valve has been damaged. It will be necessary to remove cylinder head for service.**
4. If valve condition is good, apply engine oil to valve stem and hold valve closed, then apply air pressure in cylinder.
5. Using Valve Stem Seal Replacer tool No. T88T-6571-A or equivalent, install valve stem seal.
6. Position valve spring and retainer over valve stem.
7. Install .40 inch shim between spring coils.
8. Compress valve spring, then install keepers.
9. Turn off air supply, then remove adapter from spark plug opening.
10. Install spark plug, then roller follower and camshaft cover.
11. Start engine and check for leaks.

## CAMSHAFT COVER

### REPLACE

### RIGHT SIDE

1. Disconnect battery ground cable, then disconnect positive battery cable at power distribution box.
2. Remove positive battery cable bracket to cylinder head attaching bolt.
3. Disconnect High Data Rate (HDR) sensor, A/C compressor clutch and canister purge solenoid electrical connectors, then position aside.
4. Disconnect purge solenoid vent hose, then position positive battery cable aside.
5. Disconnect spark plug ignition wires. **Do not remove wires.**
6. Remove ignition wire brackets, then position wires aside.
7. Remove PCV valve and position aside.
8. Remove camshaft cover attaching bolts, then remove camshaft cover.
9. Reverse procedure to install. Tighten to specifications.

### LEFT SIDE

1. Disconnect battery ground cable.
2. Remove air inlet tube.
3. Relieve fuel pressure as outlined under "Fuel System Pressure Relief," then disconnect fuel lines.
4. Raise and support vehicle.
5. Disconnect EVO sensor and oil pressure sending unit electrical connectors, then position electrical harness aside.
6. Lower vehicle, then remove 42-pin electrical harness connector from bracket at brake vacuum booster, **Fig. 2,** then disconnect and position aside.
7. Remove windshield wiper module.
8. Disconnect spark plug ignition wires. **Do not remove wires.**
9. Remove ignition wire brackets, then position wires aside.

10. Remove camshaft cover attaching bolts, then remove camshaft cover.
11. Reverse procedure to install. Tighten to specifications.

## FRONT COVER
### REPLACE

1. Disconnect battery ground cable and remove engine cooling fan and shroud.
2. Loosen water pump pulley bolts and remove serpentine drive belt.
3. Remove water pump pulley.
4. Raise and support vehicle, then remove power steering pump attaching bolts. **Front lower power steering pump pull out completely.**
5. Support power steering pump and position aside.
6. Remove oil pan to front cover attaching bolts.
7. Remove crankshaft damper attaching bolt and washer, then remove damper using removal tool No. T58P-6316-D or equivalent.
8. Lower vehicle, then bolt securing A/C high pressure line to RH coil bracket.
9. Remove camshaft covers front attaching bolts, then loosen remaining cover bolts.
10. Using plastic wedges or suitable tool, prop up camshaft covers.
11. Disconnect ignition coils and Crankshaft Identification (CID) sensor.
12. Remove RH coil bracket attaching nuts, then position power steering hose aside.
13. Remove LH coil bracket attaching nuts, then pull bracket and ignition wires from mounting studs and position aside.
14. Remove front cover attaching bolts and stub bolts, then remove front cover.
15. Reverse procedure to install, noting the following:
    a. Tighten to specifications.
    b. Apply silicone gasket and sealant E3AZ-19562-A or equivalent in damper keyway. Ensure crankshaft key and keyway are aligned, using Crankshaft Damper Replacer T47P-6316-B or equivalent, install crankshaft damper.

## FRONT OIL SEAL
### REPLACE

1. Disconnect battery ground cable.
2. Release belt tensioner and remove serpentine drive belt.
3. Raise and support vehicle, then remove crankshaft damper attaching bolt and washer.
4. Using crankshaft damper removal tool No. T58P-6316-D or equivalent, remove crankshaft damper.
5. Using front cover seal removal tool No. T74P-6700-A or equivalent, remove front cover seal.
6. Reverse procedure to install, noting the following:
    a. Install front cover seal using replacement tool No. T88T-6701-A1, A2 or equivalent.
    b. Apply silicone gasket and sealant E3AZ-19562-A or equivalent in damper keyway. Ensure crankshaft key and keyway are aligned, using Crankshaft Damper Replacer T47P-6316-B or equivalent, install crankshaft.
    c. Tighten to specifications.

## PISTON & ROD ASSEMBLY

If old pistons are serviceable, ensure they are installed on original rods from which they were removed. Check side clearance between connecting rods and crankshaft journal. Correct clearance is .015-.040 inch.

## CRANKSHAFT REAR OIL SEAL
### REPLACE

1. Using a suitable jack, lower transmission and support.
2. Remove flywheel.
3. Remove oil pan as described under "Oil Pan, Replace."
4. Remove rear oil seal retainer attaching bolts.
5. Reverse procedure to install. **Torque** seal retainer to 6.0-8.8 ft. lbs., in sequence shown in **Fig. 11.**

## CAMSHAFT
### REPLACE

1. Disconnect battery ground cable, then remove cooling fan and shroud.
2. Relieve fuel system pressure as described under "Fuel System Pressure Relief."
3. Remove camshaft covers as described under "Camshaft Cover, Replace."
4. Remove front cover as described under "Front Cover, Replace."
5. Remove timing chains as described under "Timing Chains, Gears, Tensioners & Guides, Replace."
6. Rotate crankshaft counterclockwise 45°. Ensure pistons are below top of engine deck face. **Crankshaft must be in position prior to rotating camshafts or piston and/or valve damage may result.**
7. Install Valve Spring Compressor tool No. T91P-6565-A or equivalent, under camshaft and on valve spring retainer.
8. Install .40 inch shim between spring coils and camshaft to prevent damage.
9. Camshaft must be at base circle before compressing valve spring, then rotate camshaft, as required, until roller followers are removed.
10. Compress valve spring, then remove roller follower.
11. Repeat steps 7 through 10 until all roller followers are removed.
12. Remove camshaft cap cluster assembly attaching bolt, **Fig. 12.**
13. Tap upward on camshaft cap, **Fig. 13,** then carefully remove camshaft cap and camshaft.
14. Reverse procedure to install, noting the following:
    a. Refer to **Fig. 12,** for camshaft cap cluster bolt tightening sequence.
    b. Tighten attaching nuts and bolts to specifications.

## TIMING CHAINS, GEARS, TENSIONERS & GUIDES
### REMOVAL

**At no time, when the timing chains are removed and the cylinder heads are installed, may the crankshaft and/or camshaft be rotated. Rotation may result in valve and/or piston damage.**

**If engine has jumped time, cylinder heads must be removed to repair damage to valves and/or pistons.**

1. Remove all necessary components to access timing chains.
2. Remove crankshaft position sensor tooth wheel and rotate engine to No. 1 cylinder TDC.
3. To prevent accidental rotation of camshafts, install cam positioning tools No. T92P-6256-A or equivalents, to flats on camshafts as shown in **Fig. 14.**
4. Remove two bolts retaining RH tensioner to cylinder head and remove tensioner.
5. Remove RH tensioner arm, then remove two bolts securing RH chain guide to cylinder head and remove chain guide.
6. Remove RH crankshaft gear.
7. Remove RH camshaft sprocket retaining bolt, washer, gear and spacer, if necessary.
8. Remove two bolts securing LH tensioner to cylinder head and remove tensioner.
9. Remove LH tensioner arm, then the bolts securing LH chain guide to cylinder head. Remove chain guide.
10. Remove LH chain from camshaft and crankshaft gears.
11. Remove LH crankshaft gear.
12. Remove LH camshaft sprocket retaining bolt, washer, gear and spacer, if necessary.
13. **Do not rotate crankshaft and/or camshaft while timing chains are removed.**

### INSTALLATION

If engine has jumped time, ensure all repairs to engine components and/or valve train are completed. Then rotate engine counterclockwise 45°. This will position all pistons below top of deck face. Install cylinder heads and begin with step 5.

1. Position LH camshaft spacers and gears on camshaft, if removed.
2. Install washer and camshaft gear retaining bolt. Tighten to specifications.
3. Position RH camshaft spacer and gear on camshaft, if removed.
4. Install washer and camshaft gear retaining bolt. Tighten to specifications.

**Cam positioning tools No. T92P-6256-A or equivalent, must be installed on camshaft(s) to prevent from rotating.**

5. Install LH crankshaft gear. Ensure tapered portion of gear faces away from engine block.
6. If copper links of timing chain are not visible, split chain in half and mark two opposing links as shown in **Fig. 15.**
7. Install LH timing chain on camshaft gear. Ensure copper link is aligned with timing mark of camshaft gear. **Fig. 16.**
8. Install LH timing chain on crankshaft gear. Ensure copper link is aligned with timing mark on crankshaft gear.
9. Install RH crankshaft gear. Ensure tapered portion of gear faces toward engine block.
10. Install RH timing chain on camshaft gear. Ensure copper link is aligned with timing mark of camshaft gear.
11. Install RH timing chain on crankshaft gear. Ensure copper link is aligned with crankshaft gear.
12. Lubricate tensioner arm contact surfaces with engine oil and install RH and LH tensioner arms on dowels. **Fig. 17.**
13. Install RH and LH timing chain tensioners. Tighten to specifications. **Do not remove lock pins until timing chain guides are installed.**
14. Install chain guides. Tighten to specifications.
15. Remove lock pins from timing chain tensioners and ensure all timing marks are aligned.
16. Remove cam positioning tools and install all components removed during removal procedure. Tighten to specifications.

## OIL PAN

### REPLACE

1. Disconnect ground and positive battery cables.
2. Remove air inlet tube and drain cooling system. Remove cooling fan and shroud.
3. Relieve fuel system pressure as described under "Fuel System Pressure Relief." Disconnect fuel lines.
4. Remove upper radiator hose, wiper module and support bracket.
5. Discharge A/C system, then disconnect A/C compressor outlet hose. Remove bolt securing hose assembly to RH coil bracket.
6. Remove engine electrical harness 42-pin connector from bracket on brake vacuum booster.
7. Disconnect engine electrical connector, then disconnect transmission harness electrical connector.
8. Disconnect throttle valve cable at throttle body.
9. Disconnect heater outlet hose.
10. Remove RH cylinder head ground strap attaching nut, then remove upper stud and lower bolt securing heater hose to cylinder head.
11. Remove blower motor resistor, then the RH engine mount to lower engine bracket attaching bolt.
12. Disconnect exhaust system from manifolds.
13. Lower exhaust and secure to crossmember with wire.
14. Position a suitable jack and block of wood below oil pan, rearward of drain plug.
15. Raise engine approximately four inches, then insert two wood blocks, approximately 2.5-2.75 inches thick, under each engine mount.
16. Lower engine onto wood blocks and remove jack from below oil pan.
17. Loosen 16 retaining bolts and remove oil pan. **It may be necessary to loosen, without removing, the two nuts on rear transmission mount and raise extension housing of transmission slightly to remove oil pan.**
18. Reverse procedure to install. Tighten to specifications.



**Fig. 19 Serpentine drive belt routing**

## OIL PUMP

### REPLACE

1. Remove camshaft covers, front cover and oil pan as previously described.
2. Remove timing chains as described under "Timing Chains, Gears, Tensioners & Guides, Replace."
3. Remove oil pump mounting bolts, then remove oil pump, **Fig. 18.**
4. Reverse procedure to install, noting the following:
   a. Align oil pump inner rotor with flat of crankshaft.
   b. **Torque** oil pump attaching bolts to 6.-8.8 ft.lbs.

## COOLING SYSTEM BLEED

1. Place heater temperature switch in maximum heat position.
2. Fill reservoir to below filler neck seat.
3. Leave pressure cap off and run engine until thermostat opens.
4. Stop engine and add coolant to reservoir as necessary to adjust level. Install pressure cap.

## THERMOSTAT

### REPLACE

1. Drain coolant level below upper radiator hose and thermostat housing.
2. Disconnect upper radiator hose at thermostat housing, then remove two thermostat housing retaining bolts.
3. Remove O-ring seal and thermostat from intake manifold. Inspect O-ring for damage and replace if necessary.
4. Reverse procedure to install. Tighten bolts to specifications.

## BELT TENSION DATA

Automatic belt tensioners are spring loaded devices which set and maintain drive belt tension. The drive belt should not require tension adjustment for the life of belt. Automatic tensioners have belt wear indicator marks. If indicator mark is not between indicator lines, belt is worn or an incorrect belt is installed.

## SERPENTINE DRIVE BELT

### BELT ROUTING

Refer to **Fig. 19,** for drive belt routing.

### REPLACEMENT

1. Rotate tensioner away from belt using a breaker bar installed in 1/2 inch square hole in tensioner arm.
2. Lift old belt over alternator pulley flange and remove.
3. When installing, position new belt over pulleys. Ensure all V-grooves make proper contact with pulley.
4. Ensure belt is properly installed on each pulley.

## WATER PUMP

### REPLACE

1. Disconnect battery ground cable and drain cooling system.
2. Remove engine cooling fan and shroud.
3. Release belt tensioner and remove accessory drive belt.
4. Remove water pump pulley mounting bolts, then remove water pump pulley.
5. Loosen mounting bolts and remove water pump.
6. Reverse procedure to install. Replace O-ring and tighten to specifications.

## FUEL SYSTEM PRESSURE RELIEF

**Fuel supply lines, will remain pressurized after engine is shut off. Pressure must be relieved prior to any fuel system servicing.**

1. Remove fuel tank cap.
2. Using fuel pressure gauge tool No. T80L-9974-B or equivalent, relieve fuel system pressure at pressure relief valve RH rear fuel rail. **Pressure relief valve cap must be removed.**
3. Using suitable tool, remove pressure relief valve.
4. Reverse procedure to install. **Torque**

fuel pressure relief valve to 48-84 inch lbs. **Torque** fuel pressure relief valve cap to 4-6 inch lbs.

## FUEL PUMP
## REPLACE

1. Relieve fuel system pressure as described under "Fuel System Pressure Relief."
2. Drain fuel tank, then raise and support vehicle.
3. Disconnect fuel supply and return line fittings and vent line.
4. Disconnect fuel pump and sender electrical connectors.
5. Remove fuel tank attaching support straps, then carefully lower fuel tank assembly. Ensure dirt does not enter tank or fuel system.
6. Using Fuel Tank Sender Wrench No. D74P-9275-A or equivalent, turn fuel pump locking ring counterclockwise, then remove locking ring.
7. Remove fuel pump assembly, then remove and discard seal ring.
8. Reverse procedure to install, noting the following:
   a. Once fuel pump is installed, using Fuel Pressure Gauge tool No. T80L-9974-B or equivalent on fuel charging assembly Schrader valve, turn ignition from OFF to ON position for 3 seconds. Repeat OFF to ON switching 5 to 10 times until pressure gauge shows at least 35 psi.
   b. Tighten to specifications.

# TIGHTENING SPECIFICATIONS

| Year | Component | Torque/Ft.Lbs. |
|---|---|---|
| 1992 | A/C Compressor Mounting Bolts | 15–22 |
| | Alternator To Cylinder Block | 15–22 |
| | Camshaft Cover Bolt | 6–8.8 |
| | Camshaft Gear Bolt | 81–95 |
| | Connecting Rod Bolt | ① |
| | Coolant Temperature Switch | 12–17 |
| | Crankshaft Rear Oil Seal Retainer | ① |
| | Cylinder Front Cover Bolt | 15–22 |
| | Cylinder Head Bolt | ① |
| | Damper To Crankshaft Bolt | 114–121 |
| | ECT Sensor | 12–17 |
| | EGR Tube Connector | 33–48 |
| | EGR Valve Line Nut | 26–33 |
| | EGR Valve To Intake Manifold | 15–22 |
| | Engine Mount Attaching Bolts | 45–59 |
| | Engine Mount Through Bolts | 15–22 |
| | Engine To Transmission Bolts | 30–44 |
| | Engine To Transmission Braces | 18–31 |
| | Exhaust Manifold | ① |
| | Exhaust Pipe To Exhaust Manifold | 20–30 |
| | Flywheel Bolts | 54–64 |
| | Front Cover | 15–22 |
| | Fuel Rail Retaining Bolts | 6–8.8 |
| | Fuel Tank Strap | 22–30 |
| | HEGO Sensors | 27–33 |
| | Intake Manifold | ① |
| | Main Bearing Cap | ② |
| | Oil Filter Adapter | 15–22 |
| | Oil Inlet Tube To Main Bearing Cap | 15–22 |
| | Oil Inlet Tube To Oil Pump Bolt | 6–8.8 |
| | Oil Pan Drain Plug | 8–12 |
| | Oil Pan To Cylinder Block | 15–22 |
| | Oil Pump To Cylinder Block | 6–8.8 |
| | Power Steering Pump To Engine | 15–22 |
| | Rear Engine Mount Nuts | 35–47 |
| | Rear Engine Mount To Crossmember Bolts | 51–67 |
| | Rear Oil Seal Retainer | ① |
| | Spark Plug | 6.6–7.3 |

*Continued*

## TIGHTENING SPECIFICATIONS—Continued

| Year | Component | Torque/Ft.Lbs. |
|---|---|---|
| | Thermostat Mounting Bolts | 15–22 |
| | Throttle Body & Adapter Assembly | 6–8.8 |
| | Timing Chain Guides | 6–8.8 |
| | Timing Chain Tensioner Bolts | 15–22 |
| | Torque Converter Nuts | 22–25 |
| | Water Pump Mounting Bolts | 15–22 |
| | Water Pump Pulley Bolts | 15–22 |

①–Refer to text.
②—Tighten in two steps, first to 22–25 ft. lbs., then an additional 85–95°.

# 5.0L/V8-302 & 5.8L/V8-351 Engines

**NOTE:** On Vehicles Equipped With Airbags, Disarm Airbag System As Outlined Under "Airbag System Disarming" Before Any Diagnosis, Testing, Troubleshooting Or Repairs Are Performed. After All Diagnosis, Testing, Troubleshooting Or Repairs Have Been Completed, Rearm Airbag System As Outlined Under "Airbag System Disarming."

## INDEX



## AIRBAG SYSTEM DISARMING

**The electrical circuit necessary for system deployment is powered directly from the battery and a backup power supply. To avoid accidental deployment and possible personal injury, the airbag system must be deactivated prior to servicing or replacing any component located near or related to airbag system activation components.**

### 1989–1991

A back-up power supply is included in the system to provide airbag deployment in the event the battery or battery cables are damaged in an accident before the sensors can close. The power supply is a capacitor that will retain a charge for approximately 15 minutes after the battery ground cable is disconnected. **Backup power supply must be disconnected to deactivate airbag system.** To remove backup power supply, refer to "Airbags" in the "Passive Restraint" section.

1. Disconnect battery ground cable.
2. Disconnect backup power supply.
3. Remove four nut and washer assemblies securing airbag module to steering wheel, then disconnect airbag electrical connector. Attach jumper wire to airbag terminals on clockspring terminals.
4. **On models equipped with passenger-side airbag,** disconnect airbag module connector located behind glove compartment. Attach a jumper wire to airbag terminals on wiring harness side of passenger airbag module connector terminals.
5. **On all models,** reconnect battery and backup power supply if necessary to perform repair procedure.
6. To reactivate, disconnect battery ground cable and backup power supply, then reverse remainder of deactivation procedure. **Torque** airbag module to steering wheel nut assemblies to 24-32 inch lbs.
7. Verify airbag lamp after reactivating system.

### 1992

1. Disconnect positive battery cable and wait one minute.
2. Remove four nut and washer assemblies securing airbag to steering wheel.
3. Disconnect airbag electrical connector and install airbag simulator tool

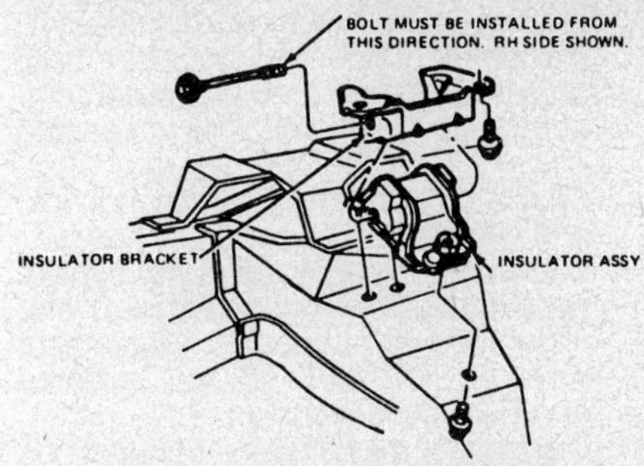


**Fig. 1 Engine mount replacement**

No. 105-00008 or equivalent.
4. **On models w/passenger side airbag,** remove passenger airbag and disconnect electrical connector.
5. Install airbag simulator tool No. 105-00008 or equivalent.
6. **On all models,** connect positive battery cable.
7. To activate airbag system, disconnect positive battery cable and reverse procedure. **Torque** mounting nut and washer assemblies to 36-49 inch lbs.
8. Verify proper operation of airbag lamp.

## ENGINE MOUNTS REPLACE

**Whenever self-locking mounting bolts and nuts are removed, they must be replaced with new self-locking bolts and nuts.**

### CROWN VICTORIA, GRAND MARQUIS, 1991 COUGAR & THUNDERBIRD

1. Remove fan shroud attaching screws, then support engine using a jack and wood block placed below oil pan.
2. Remove bolts attaching insulators to front subframe.
3. Raise engine sufficiently with jack to disengage insulator from subframe.
4. Remove engine insulator and bracket assembly to cylinder block attaching bolts.
5. Remove engine insulator assembly.
6. Reverse procedure to install. Tighten to specifications.

### 1992 COUGAR & THUNDERBIRD

1. Remove fan shroud attaching screws.
2. Support engine using a suitable jack with a wooden block placed under oil pan.
3. Remove nut and through bolt attaching insulator to frame crossmember.
4. Disconnect shift linkage, as required.
5. Raise engine slightly, then remove insulator and heat shield, if equipped, **Fig. 1.**
6. Reverse procedure to install. Tighten to specifications.

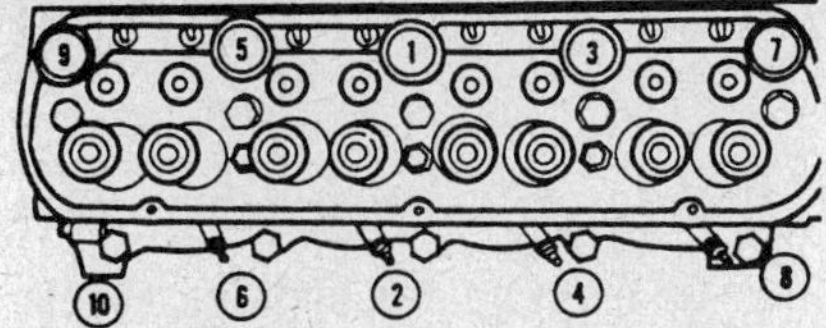


**Fig. 2 Cylinder head tightening sequence**

## ENGINE REPLACE

### COUGAR & THUNDERBIRD

1. Disconnect battery ground cable and drain cooling system.
2. Disconnect engine compartment lamp connector and remove dipstick, then mark hinge positions and remove hood.
3. Discharge A/C system, then disconnect and plug A/C compressor lines.
4. Disconnect compressor clutch electrical connectors, power steering pressure switch and alternator wiring harness.
5. Remove fan shroud and fan assembly, then remove upper radiator hose.
6. Remove air cleaner to throttle body tube assembly. Disconnect transmission oil cooler lines.
7. Disconnect throttle and kickdown cables from throttle body and remove cable bracket retaining bolts. Position cable and bracket assembly clear of area.
8. Disconnect vacuum lines at upper intake manifold vacuum tee, A/C control panel vacuum supply hose, Thermactor valve and EGR valve.
9. Remove upper intake manifold, then disconnect main engine wiring harness connectors at RH side of dash panel.
10. Disconnect heater hoses at engine and position engine wiring harness sot it can be removed with engine.
11. Disconnect wiring harness from coil and distributor. Relieve fuel system pressure.
12. Disconnect fuel hoses from fuel supply manifold. Cap lines and fittings to prevent contamination.
13. Disconnect lower radiator hose from water pump. Remove radiator.
14. Raise and support vehicle, drain engine oil and remove filter.
15. Remove starter motor, then disconnect HEGO sensors from right and left catalytic converters.
16. Disconnect battery ground cable from LH side of engine, then disconnect transmission cooler line brackets, ground straps and starter motor wiring harness from RH side of engine.
17. Remove torque converter inspection cover and mark one of converter studs to flywheel for alignment during installation.
18. Remove torque converter retaining nuts, then the exhaust manifold heat shield at left manifold flange and disconnect exhaust pipe from flange.
19. Disconnect RH exhaust manifold flange. Loosen transmission mount retaining nut.
20. Remove converter housing to engine bolts, then the motor mount through bolts.
21. Lower vehicle and remove power steering lines. Support transmission with suitable floor jack.
22. Install suitable engine lifting sling on engine lifting eyes. Lift engine assembly clear of engine mounts and remove assembly from vehicle.
23. Reverse procedure to install. Tighten to specifications.

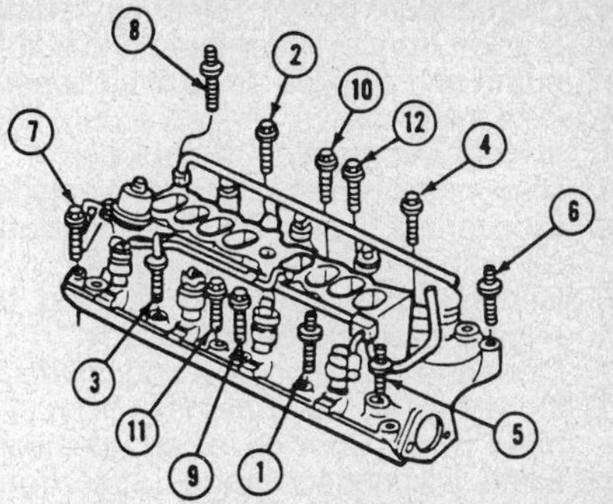


**Fig. 3 Intake manifold tightening sequence. 5.0L/V8-302 & 5.0L/V8-302 HO**

### CROWN VICTORIA & GRAND MARQUIS

**Because of engine compartment tolerances, engine should not be removed or installed with transmission attached.**

1. Disconnect battery and alternator ground cables.
2. Drain cooling system and crankcase.
3. Mark position of hinges and remove hood.
4. Remove air cleaner and intake duct assembly.
5. Disconnect radiator hoses from engine.
6. On models with automatic transmission, disconnect transmission oil cooler lines from radiator.
7. Remove fan shroud attaching bolts, then the radiator, fan, spacer, pulley and shroud.
8. Remove alternator mounting bolts and position alternator aside.
9. Disconnect oil pressure sending unit electrical connector.
10. Relieve fuel pressure, then disconnect fuel tank line at fuel pump and plug line.
11. Disconnect accelerator cable and speed control cable, if equipped, from carburetor or throttle body.
12. Disconnect throttle valve vacuum line from intake manifold, if equipped.
13. Disconnect manual shift rod and retracting spring at shift rod stud.
14. Disconnect transmission filler tube bracket from engine block.
15. Isolate and remove A/C compressor from vehicle, if equipped.

16. Disconnect power steering pump bracket from cylinder head and water pump and position aside, if equipped.
17. Disconnect power brake vacuum line from intake manifold, if equipped.
18. Disconnect heater hoses from engine.
19. Disconnect coolant temperature sending unit electrical connector.
20. Remove upper flywheel housing to engine attaching bolts.
21. Disconnect ignition coil and distributor wiring. Remove harness from left hand rocker arm cover and position aside. Disconnect ground strap from engine block.
22. Raise and support front of vehicle.
23. Disconnect starter motor wiring and remove starter motor.
24. Disconnect exhaust pipes from manifold.
25. Disconnect engine mounts from frame brackets.
26. Disconnect secondary air line to catalytic converter, if equipped.
27. If equipped with manual transmission, remove bolts attaching clutch equalizer bar to frame rail, then the equalizer from engine block. Remove remaining flywheel housing to engine bolts.
28. On models with automatic transmission, detach transmission oil cooler lines from retainer. Remove converter housing inspection cover, then remove converter to flywheel attaching bolts. Secure converter in housing. Remove remaining converter housing to engine bolts.
29. Lower vehicle and support transmission. Attach suitable engine lifting equipment to engine.
30. Raise engine slightly and pull forward to disengage from transmission.
31. Remove engine from vehicle.
32. Reverse procedure to install.

## CYLINDER HEAD REPLACE

1. Disconnect battery ground cable and remove intake manifold.
2. Remove rocker arm cover.
3. Remove A/C compressor, if necessary.
4. **If removing LH cylinder head,** disconnect power steering pump bracket from LH cylinder head. Position pump clear of area. Disconnect oil lever indicator tube from exhaust manifold stud.
5. Remove thermactor crossover tube from rear of cylinder heads.
6. **If removing RH cylinder head,** remove alternator mounting bracket from cylinder head.
7. Remove fuel line clip at front of RH cylinder head.
8. Disconnect exhaust manifold from muffler intake pipe.
9. Loosen rocker arm stud nuts or bolts so that rocker arms can be rotated to the side.
10. Remove pushrods, keeping them in sequence so they may be installed in original locations. Remove exhaust valve stem caps.
11. Loosen cylinder head bolts and lift head off of block. If required, remove exhaust manifolds to gain access to lower attaching bolts. Remove and discard head gasket.
12. Reverse procedure to install, noting the following:
    a. **On 5.0L/V8-302 engines,** slightly tighten cylinder head bolts in a series of two steps in sequence shown in **Fig. 2. Torque** first step to 55-65 ft. lbs., then **torque** all cylinder head bolts again in sequence to 65-72 ft. lbs.
    b. **On 5.8L/V8-351 engines,** slightly tighten cylinder head bolts in a series of two steps in sequence shown in **Fig. 2. Torque** first step to 95-105 ft. lbs., then **torque** all cylinder head bolts again in sequence to 105-112 ft. lbs.
    c. When cylinder head bolts have been tightened following the above step, it is not necessary to retighten bolts after extended operation. Bolts may be checked and retightened, if desired.
    d. Apply Multi-Purpose Grease D0AZ-19584-AA or equivalent, to both ends of push rods and valve stem tips. Install push rods in original positions.
    e. Install rocker arms and check valve clearance.
    f. Tighten all components to specifications.

## EXHAUST MANIFOLD

1. Remove oil dipstick and tube assembly.
2. Remove thermactor hardware, if equipped.
3. Disconnect exhaust manifold from exhaust pipe. Remove spark plug wires and spark plugs.
4. Disconnect oxygen sensor (HEGO sensor).
5. Remove mounting bolts and washers, then remove exhaust manifolds.
6. Reverse procedure to install. Tighten to specifications.

## INTAKE MANIFOLD REPLACE

### 5.0L/V8-302 & 5.0L/V8-302 HO

1. Disconnect battery ground cable and drain cooling system, then disconnect accelerator cable and speed control linkage from throttle body.
2. Disconnect transmission cable and remove accelerator cable bracket.
3. Disconnect vacuum lines at intake manifold fitting.
4. Disconnect spark plug wires. Remove wires and bracket assembly from rocker arm cover attaching stud. Remove distributor cap, adapter and spark plug wire assembly.
5. Relieve fuel system pressure, then disconnect fuel lines.
6. Disconnect distributor wiring connector, then remove distributor hold-down bolt. Remove distributor.
7. Disconnect upper radiator hose from coolant outlet housing and water temperature sending unit wire at sending unit.
8. Disconnect hose from intake manifold and two throttle body cooler hoses.
9. Loosen clamp on water pump bypass hose at coolant outlet housing and slide hose off of housing. Disconnect wires at ECT, ACT, TP, ISC solenoid and EGR sensors.
10. Disconnect injector wire connections and fuel charging assembly wiring.
11. Pull PCV valve out of grommet at rear of lower intake manifold. Disconnect fuel evaporative purge hose from plastic connector at front of upper intake manifold.
12. Remove upper intake manifold.
13. Remove heater tube assembly from lower intake manifold.
14. Remove lower intake manifold. It may be necessary to pry manifold away from cylinder head.
15. Avoid possible damage to gasket sealing surfaces. Remove intake manifold gaskets and seals.
16. Reverse procedure to install, noting the following:
    a. Apply a 1/16 inch bead of sealer to outer end of each intake manifold seal for the full width of seal (four places).
    b. **Torque** intake manifold bolts to 15-20 ft. lbs. in sequence shown in **Fig. 3.**
    c. Following installation, fill and bleed cooling system, then adjust ignition timing.
    d. Operate engine at fast idle and check all hose connections and gaskets for leaks. When engine temperatures have stabilized, tighten intake manifold bolts to 23-25 ft. lbs.

### 5.8L/V8-351

1. Disconnect battery ground cable and drain cooling system.
2. Remove air cleaner, crankcase ventilation hose and intake duct assembly.
3. Disconnect accelerator cable and speed control linkage, if equipped, from carburetor.
4. Disconnect TV rod on AOD transmissions. Remove accelerator cable bracket.
5. Disconnect vacuum lines at intake manifold, then disconnect high tension lead and primary wiring connector from ignition coil.
6. Disconnect spark plug wires. Remove wires and bracket assembly from rocker arm cover attaching stud.
7. Remove distributor cap, adapter and spark plug wire assembly.
8. Relieve fuel system pressure and remove carburetor fuel intake line.
9. Disconnect distributor vacuum hoses from distributor. Disconnect distributor wiring connector and remove distributor hold-down bolt and remove distributor.
10. Disconnect upper radiator hose from coolant outlet housing and water tem-

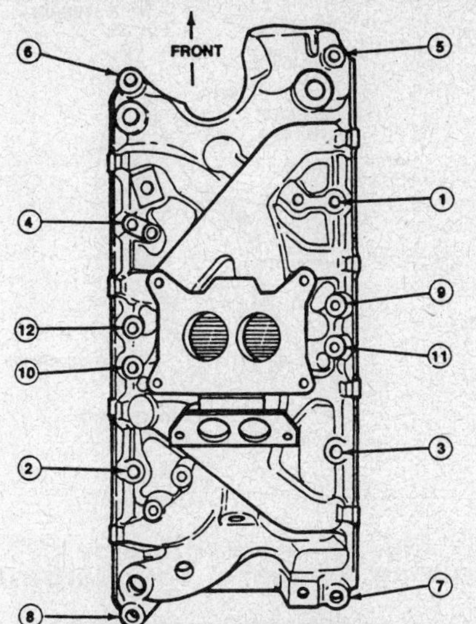


**Fig. 4 Intake manifold tightening sequence. 5.8L/V8-351**

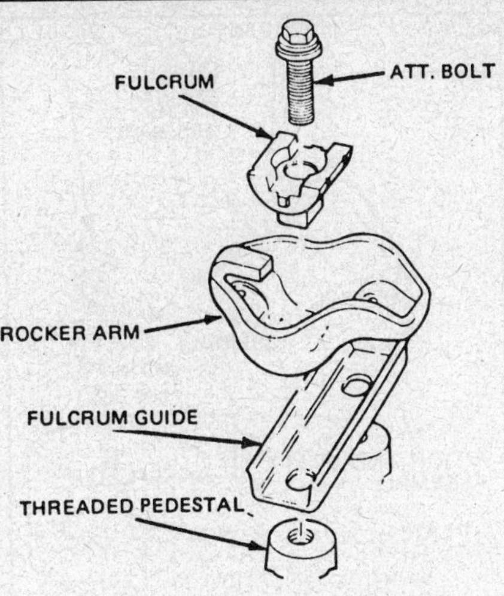


**Fig. 5 Rocker arm**

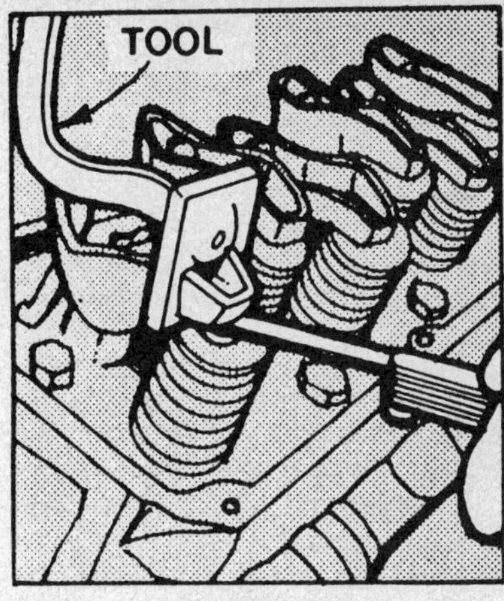


**Fig. 6 Valve clearance adjustment**

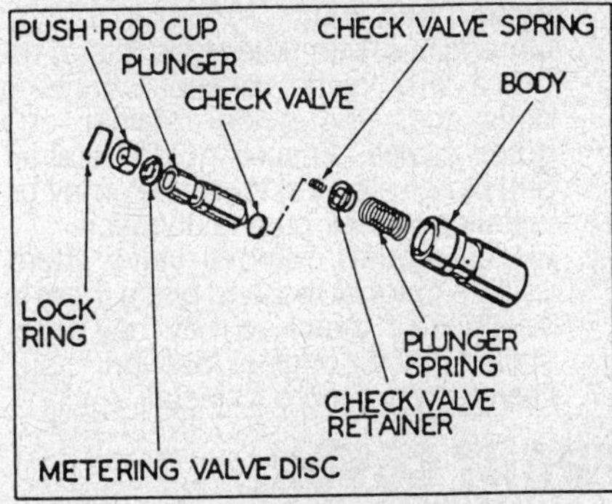


**Fig. 7 Hydraulic valve lifter disassembled**

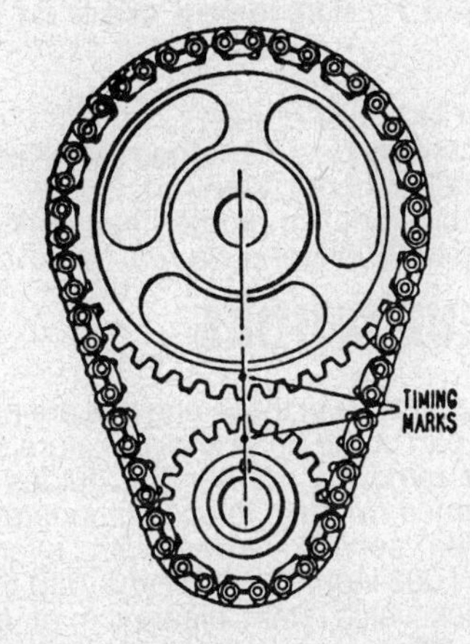


**Fig. 8 Timing mark alignment**

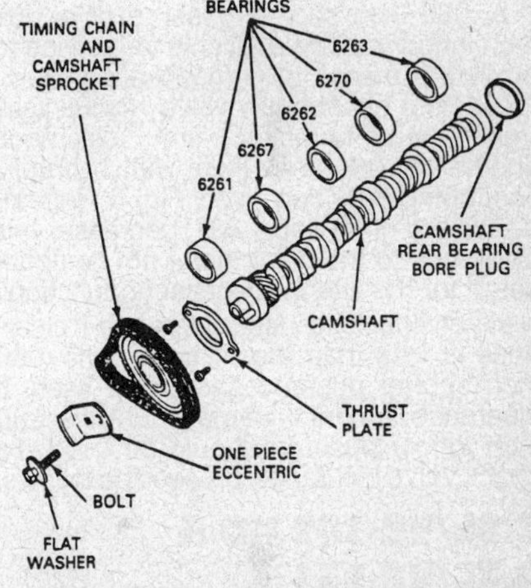


**Fig. 9 Camshaft replacement**

perature sending unit wire at sending unit.

11. Disconnect heater hose from intake manifold, then remove bypass hose from water pump.
12. Disconnect crankcase vent hose assembly at rocker arm cover. Disconnect fuel evaporative purge tube.
13. Remove intake manifold and carburetor as an assembly.
14. Reverse procedure to install, noting the following:
    a. Apply a 1/16inch bead of sealer to outer end of each intake manifold seal for full width of seal (four places).
    b. **Torque** manifold bolts in sequence shown in **Fig. 4**, to 23-25 ft. lbs.
    c. Following installation, fill and bleed cooling system.
    d. Operate engine at fast idle. When engine temperature has stabilized, adjust engine fast idle speed, then retighten intake manifold bolts.

# VALVE ARRANGEMENT

## FRONT TO REAR

Right .................... I-E-I-E-I-E-I-E

Left...................... E-I-E-I-E-I-E-I

# VALVE LIFT SPECIFICATIONS

| Engine | Year | Intake, Inch | Exhaust, Inch |
|---|---|---|---|
| 5.0L/V8-302 | 1989 | .3776 | .3934 |
| 5.0L/V8-302 | 1990-91 | .442 | .450 |
| 5.0L/V8-302 HO | 1991-1992 | .442 | .442 |
| 5.8L/V8-351 | 1989-91 | .442 | .450 |

# CAMSHAFT LOBE LIFT SPECIFICATIONS

| Engine | Year | Intake, Inch | Exhaust, Inch |
|---|---|---|---|
| 5.0L/V8-302 | 1989 | .2375 | .2475 |
| 5.0L/V8-302 | 1990-91 | .278 | .283 |
| 5.0L.V8-302 HO | 1991-1992 | .278 | .278 |
| 5.8L/V8-351 | 1989-91 | .278 | .283 |

# COLLAPSED LIFTER GAP

| Engine | Year | Valve Lash, Inch |
|---|---|---|
| 5.0L/V8-302 | 1989-91 | .071-.171 |
| 5.0L/V8-302 HO | 1991-1992 | .098-.198 |
| 5.8L/V8-351 | 1989-91 | .092-.192 |

# VALVES

## ADJUST

To eliminate the need of adjusting valve lash, a positive stop fulcrum bolt and seat is used, **Fig. 5.**

It is very important that the correct pushrod be used and all components be installed and torqued as follows:

1. Position piston of cylinder being worked on at TDC of its compression stroke.
2. Install rocker arm, fulcrum seat and oil

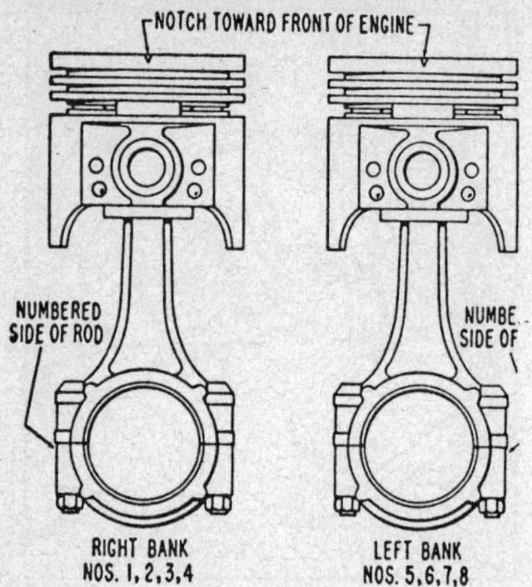


**Fig. 10 Piston & rod assembly**

deflector. Install fulcrum bolt and torque to specification.

A .060 inch shorter pushrod or a .060 inch longer rod are available for service to provide a means of compensating for dimensional changes in valve mechanism. Valve stem-to-rocker arm clearance should be .096-.146 inch, with hydraulic lifter completely collapsed, **Fig. 6.** Repeated valve grind jobs will decrease this clearance to the point that if not compensated for the lifters will cease to function.

When checking valve clearance, if clearance is less than the minimum, the .060 inch shorter pushrod should be used. If clearance is more than maximum, the .060 inch longer pushrod should be used. To check valve clearance, proceed as follows:

## 5.0L/V8-302 HO & 5.8L/V8-351

1. With No. 1 piston at TDC at end of compression stroke, check following valves:
   a. Intake Nos. 1, 4 and 8; exhaust Nos. 1, 3 and 7.
2. Rotate crankshaft 360°. Check following valves:
   a. Intake Nos. 3 and 7; exhaust Nos. 2 and 6.
3. Rotate crankshaft 90°. Check following valves:
   a. Intake Nos. 2, 5 and 6; exhaust Nos. 4, 5 and 8.
4. If clearance is less than specified, install a shorter push rod.
5. If clearance is greater than specified, install a longer push rod.

## 5.0L/V8-302

1. With No. 1 piston at TDC at end of compression stroke, check clearance of following valves:
   a. Intake Nos. 1, 7 and 8; exhaust Nos. 1, 4 and 5.
2. Rotate crankshaft 360°. Check clearance of following valves:
   a. Intake Nos. 4 and 5; exhaust Nos. 2 and 6.
3. Rotate crankshaft 90°. Check clearance of following valves:
   a. Intake Nos. 2, 3 and 6; exhaust

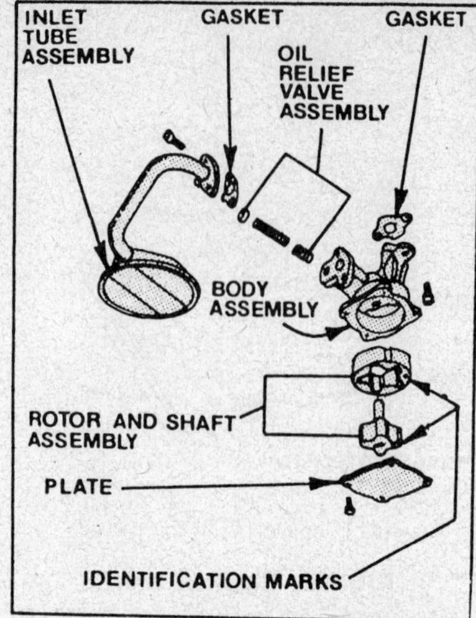


**Fig. 11 Exploded view of oil pump**

Nos. 3, 7 and 8.

4. If clearance is less than specified, install a shorter push rod.
5. If clearance is greater than specified, install a longer push rod.

## VALVE GUIDES

Valve guides in these engines are an integral part of the head and, therefore, cannot be removed. For service, guides can be reamed oversize to accommodate one of three service valves with oversize stems (.003 inch, .015 inch and .030 inch).

Check valve stem clearance of each valve (after cleaning) in its respective valve guide. If clearance exceeds service limits of .0055 inch, ream valve guides to accommodate next oversize diameter valve.

## ROCKER ARMS

These engines use a bolt and fulcrum attachment, **Fig. 5.** To replace, remove attaching bolt, then the fulcrum, rocker arm and fulcrum guide, if opposite rocker arm is being removed.

## VALVE LIFTERS REPLACE

The internal parts of each hydraulic valve lifter assembly are a matched set. If these are mixed, improper valve operation may result. Therefore, disassemble, inspect and test each assembly separately to prevent mixing the parts.

**Fig. 7** illustrates one type of hydraulic lifter used. On some late model engines, a roller type hydraulic lifter is used instead of conventional lifter.

1. Remove intake manifold and related parts.
2. Remove rocker arm covers.
3. Loosen rocker arm stud nuts or bolts and rotate rocker arms to the side.

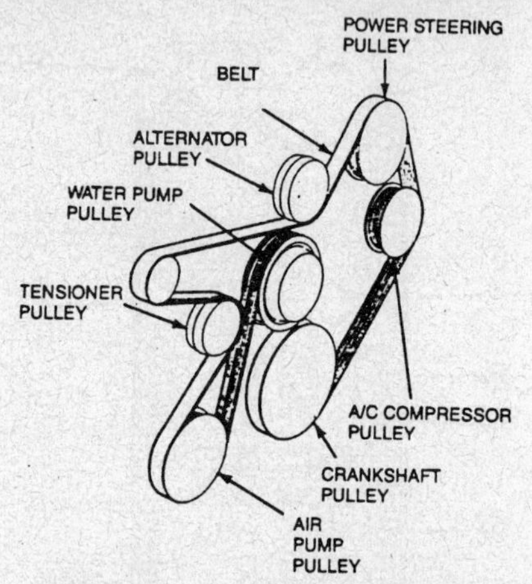


**Fig. 12 Serpentine belt routing. Cougar & Thunderbird**

4. Lift out pushrods, keeping them in sequence in a rack so they may be installed in their original location. **On some late model engines with roller type lifters, pushrods have a collar at upper end and can only be installed one way.**
5. On engines with roller type lifters, remove lifter guide retainer attaching bolts, then the guide retainer and guide plates. Ensure guide retainer and plates are marked so they may be installed in their original location.
6. On all models, remove valve lifters, using a magnet rod, and place them in sequence in a rack so they may be installed in their original location.
7. Reverse procedure to install.

## FRONT COVER REPLACE

1. Refer to "Water Pump, Replace" and perform all steps except removal of water pump. Leave water pump attached to front cover.
2. Drain oil crankcase, then remove crankshaft pulley from crankshaft vibration damper.
3. Remove damper attaching capscrew and washer. Install crankshaft damper removal tool No. T58P-6316-D or equivalent, on crankshaft vibration damper. Remove vibration damper.
4. Remove oil pan to front cover attaching bolts.
5. Carefully separate front cover from oil pan gasket.
6. Remove front cover and water pump as an assembly.
7. Reverse procedure to install, noting the following:
   a. Use care when installing cover to avoid seal damage or possible gasket mis-location.
   b. It may be necessary to force cover downward to slightly compress pan gasket. This can be accomplished by using front cover alignment tool No. T61P-6019-B or equivalent, at front cover attaching hole locations.
   c. Coat threads of attaching screws

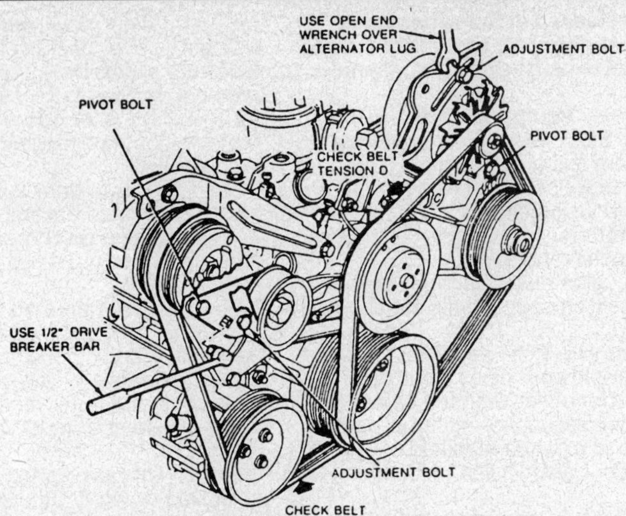


**Fig. 13 Serpentine belt routing. Crown Victoria & Grand Marquis**

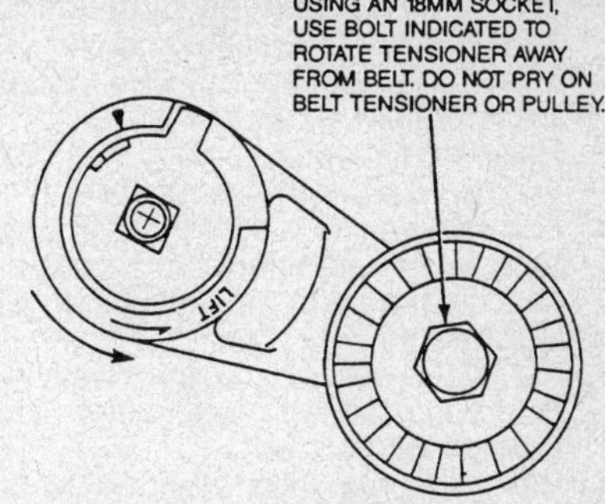


**Fig. 14 Serpentine belt replacement. Cougar & Thunderbird**

with oil resistant pipe sealant with Teflon D8AZ-19554-A or equivalent, and install screws. While pushing in on alignment tool, tighten oil pan to cover attaching screws to specifications.

d. Tighten cover to block attaching screws to specifications, then remove pilot.
e. Apply multi-purpose grease D0AZ-19584-AA or equivalent, to oil seal rubbing surface of vibration damper inner hub to prevent damage to seal. Apply silicone gasket and sealant E3AZ-19562-A or equivalent, to keyway before installing on crankshaft.
f. Align crankshaft vibration damper keyway with key on crankshaft. Install vibration damper on crankshaft using crankshaft sprocket and damper replacement tool No. T52L-6306-AEE or equivalent. Install capscrew and washer and tighten to specifications. Install crankshaft pulley.
g. Fill and bleed cooling system, then adjust ignition timing.

## TIMING CHAIN
## REPLACE

After removing front cover as outlined above, crank engine until timing marks are aligned as shown in **Fig. 8.** Remove camshaft sprocket retaining bolt, washer, fuel pump eccentric and spacer, if equipped. Slide both sprockets and chain forward and remove them as an assembly.

Reverse procedure to install chain and sprockets. Ensure timing marks are aligned.

## CAMSHAFT
## REPLACE

It may be necessary to remove or reposition radiator, A/C condenser and grille components to provide adequate clearance.

1. Remove front cover and timing chain as previously described.
2. Remove intake manifold and related components.
3. Remove EGR valve and rocker arm covers.
4. Loosen rocker arm stud nuts or bolts and rotate rocker arms to one side.
5. Remove pushrods, keeping them in sequence in a rack so they may be installed in their original location.
6. Using a magnet, remove valve lifters and place them in a rack in sequence so they may be installed in their original location.
7. Remove camshaft thrust plate, **Fig. 9**, and carefully pull camshaft from engine, using care to avoid damaging camshaft bearings.
8. Reverse procedure to install, noting the following:
   a. Oil camshaft journals with heavy engine oil SG and apply Multi-Purpose Grease D0AZ-19584-AA or equivalent, to lobes and valve stem tips. Install camshaft thrust plate with groove toward cylinder block.
   b. Lubricate rocker arms and fulcrum seats with heavy engine oil SG.
   c. Tighten to specifications.
   d. Fill and bleed cooling system.

## CAMSHAFT BEARINGS

When necessary to replace camshaft bearings, engine must be removed from vehicle and plug at the rear of the cylinder block must be removed in order to utilize the special camshaft bearing removal and installation tools required to do this job. If properly installed, camshaft bearings require no reaming—nor should this type bearing be reamed or altered in any manner in an attempt to fit bearings.

## PISTON & ROD ASSEMBLY

Assemble pistons to rods so notch or arrow faces toward front of engine and numbered side of rod faces away from center of engine, **Fig. 10.** After installation, check side clearance between connecting rods at each crankshaft journal. Clearance should be .010-.020 inch.

## PISTONS, PINS & RINGS

Pistons and rings are available in standard sizes and oversizes of .003, .020, .030 and .040 inch.

Oversize piston pins of .001 and .002 inch are available.

## MAIN & ROD BEARINGS

Main and rod bearings are available in standard sizes and the following undersizes: .001, .002, .010, .020, .030, .040 inch.

## CRANKSHAFT OIL SEAL
## REPLACE

A one piece crankshaft rear main oil seal must be used when replacement of seal is required.

1. Punch one hole into seal metal surface between seal lip and engine block using a suitable tool.
2. Screw threaded end of suitable slide hammer into hole and remove seal. Use caution not to damage oil seal surface.
3. Lubricate new seal with engine oil, then position seal on rear oil seal installer tool No. T82L-6701-A or equivalent.
4. Position tool and seal on rear of engine, then install tool attaching bolts. Tighten attaching bolts alternately until seal is properly seated.

## OIL PAN
## REPLACE

### COUGAR & THUNDERBIRD

1. Disconnect battery ground cable and remove oil dipstick.
2. Disconnect air filter cover retaining clips to allow free movement when engine is raised.
3. Remove two bolts retaining radiator

shroud to radiator and pull shroud loose from lower retaining clips.
4. Install engine support fixture tool No. D88L-6000-A or equivalent.
5. Raise and support vehicle, then drain engine oil and remove oil filter.
6. Remove engine mount through bolts, then loosen transmission mount nut to allow mount to move when engine is raised.
7. Partially lower vehicle, then raise engine approximately two inches, using support fixture tool.
8. Raise engine and remove power steering cooler line retaining clips. Remove bolt securing transmission lines to engine block.
9. Disconnect electrical connector from low oil level sensor located in oil pan, if equipped.
10. Remove oil pan retaining bolts, then remove steering shaft pinch bolt and separate steering shaft from power steering rack assembly.
11. Position two jack stands below engine support subframe. Remove lower strut-to-control arm bolts and nuts.
12. While supporting engine support subframe on jack stands, remove six rearward bolts on subframe. Loosen two forward bolts on subframe.
13. Lower subframe and remove oil pump/pick-up tube assembly and place it in oil pan.
14. Remove oil pan.
15. Reverse procedure to install, tighten to specifications.

## CROWN VICTORIA & GRAND MARQUIS

1. Disconnect battery ground cable and remove air cleaner assembly.
2. Disconnect accelerator cable and kickdown rod from carburetor or TV cables from throttle body.
3. Remove accelerator mounting bracket bolts and bracket, then the EGR valve, if necessary.
4. Remove fan shroud attaching screws and position shroud over fan.
5. Disconnect wiper motor electrical connector and remove wiper motor.
6. Disconnect windshield washer hose.
7. Remove wiper motor mounting cover.
8. Remove oil level dipstick, then the dipstick tube retaining bolt from exhaust manifold.
9. If equipped with EGR cooler or EEC, remove Thermactor air dump tube retaining clamp, then the Thermactor crossover tube at rear of engine.
10. On all models, raise and support vehicle.
11. Drain oil pan.
12. **On models equipped with EGR cooler or EEC,** remove filler tube from transmission oil pan and drain transmission, then remove starter motor.
13. **On all models,** disconnect fuel line at fuel pump and plug line. **Vehicles equipped with electronic fuel injection use a high pressure electric fuel pump. Prior to disconnecting fuel lines from pump, pressure must be released at Schrader valve on the fuel charging assembly.**
14. Disconnect exhaust pipes from manifolds.
15. **On models equipped with EGR cooler or EEC,** remove exhaust gas sensor from exhaust manifold, then the Thermactor secondary air tube to converter housing clamps.
16. **On all models,** loosen rear engine mount attaching nuts.
17. Remove engine mount through bolts.
18. Remove shift crossover bolts at transmission.
19. If equipped with EGR cooler or EEC, disconnect exhaust pipes from catalytic converter outlet, then the catalytic converter secondary air tube and inlet pipes to exhaust manifold.
20. Disconnect transmission kickdown rod.
21. Remove torque converter housing cover.
22. Remove brake line retainer from front crossmember.
23. With a suitable jack, raise engine as far as possible.
24. Place a block of wood between each engine mount and chassis bracket. When engine is secured in this position, remove jack.
25. Remove oil pan attaching bolts and lower oil pan.
26. Remove oil pickup tube bolts and lower tube in oil pan.
27. Remove oil pan from vehicle.
28. Reverse procedure to install.

# OIL PUMP REPLACE

1. Remove oil pan as described under "Oil Pan, Replace" procedure.
2. Remove oil inlet pickup tube and screen assembly.
3. Remove oil pump attaching bolts, then the oil pump and intermediate drive shaft.
4. Reverse procedure to install, noting the following:
    a. Prime oil pump with engine oil before installing.
    b. Position intermediate drive shaft into distributor sprocket. With intermediate drive shaft firmly seated, the stop on the shaft should contact crankcase surface.
    c. Remove shaft and adjust as necessary. Position pump with intermediate drive shaft insert to cylinder block, then install and tighten attaching bolts to specification.
    d. **Do not force oil pump into position on cylinder block. If pump drive shaft is misaligned with distributor shaft, rotate drive shaft to a new position.**

# OIL PUMP SERVICE

1. With all parts clean and dry, check inside of pump housing and outer race and rotor for damage or excessive wear, **Fig. 11.**
2. Check mating surface of pump cover for wear. Minor scuff marks are normal, but if cover, gears or housing surfaces are excessively worn, scored or grooved, replace pump. Inspect rotor for nicks, burrs or score marks. Remove minor imperfections with an oil stone.
3. Measure inner to outer rotor tip clearance. With rotor assembly removed from pump and resting on a flat surface, clearance must not exceed .012 inch.
4. With rotor assembly installed in housing, place a straightedge over rotor assembly and housing. Measure clearance between straightedge and inner rotor and outer race (rotor endplay). Clearance must not exceed .005 inch.
5. Inspect relief valve spring to see if it is collapsed or worn. Check relief valve spring tension. If spring is worn or damaged, replace pump. Check relief valve piston for free operation in the bore.
6. Internal components are not serviceable. If any component is out of specification, pump assembly must be replaced.

# SERPENTINE DRIVE BELTS

## ROUTING

Refer to **Figs. 12 and 13** for serpentine drive belt routings.

## REPLACEMENT

### Cougar & Thunderbird

1. Rotate tensioner as shown in **Fig. 14,** and remove old belt.
2. Install new belt over pulleys. Ensure all V-grooves make proper contact with pulley.

### Crown Victoria & Grand Marquis

The tensioner arm should be checked to ensure top edge of arm is located between two index marks scribed on circumference next to slot of the tensioner housing. If tensioner arm is not properly aligned, drive belt and pulleys should be inspected for wear and binding. If drive belt and pulleys are satisfactory, tensioner must be replaced as outlined in the following procedure:

1. Insert a 16 inch pry bar or equivalent in slot of tensioner bracket, and using tensioner housing as a fulcrum, push pry bar downward to force tensioner pulley upward, relieving tension on belt, **Fig. 13.**
2. Remove drive belt.
3. Remove bolt securing tensioner assembly to alternator bracket.
4. Remove tensioner assembly.
5. Position tensioner assembly so tang, located on rear of assembly, is placed to fit in the hole or slot in alternator bracket.
6. Install tensioner assembly bolt through hole in alternator bracket and **torque** bolt to 55-80 ft. lbs.

7. Install drive belt by inserting pry bar as outlined in Step 1. Refer to decal located on top of windshield washer/coolant expansion reservoir for proper belt routing.
8. Remove pry bar.
9. The drive belt is automatically tensioned when the tensioner arm is located between two index marks.

# COOLING SYSTEM BLEED

## COUGAR & THUNDERBIRD

1. With engine off, add specified coolant concentrate to radiator, then add water until it reaches radiator filler neck seat.
2. Remove vent plug on water bypass elbow (located on intake manifold behind water outlet connection). **Vent plug must be removed before radiator fill or engine may not fill completely. Do not turn plastic cap under vent plug or gasket may be damaged. Do not try to add coolant through vent plug hole. Install vent plug after filling radiator and before starting engine.**
3. Install radiator pressure cap to first notch.
4. Start and idle engine until upper radiator hose is warm.
5. Carefully remove cap and top off radiator with water.
6. Install cap on radiator. Fill coolant recovery reservoir to FULL COLD mark with coolant, then add water to FULL HOT mark. This will ensure a proper mixture in coolant recovery bottle.
7. Check for leaks at radiator draincock, block plug and vent plug.

## CROWN VICTORIA & GRAND MARQUIS

These models do not require a specific bleed procedure. After filling cooling system, start engine and allow to reach operating temperature with radiator cap removed. Air in system will then be automatically bled through cap opening.

# THERMOSTAT

## REPLACE

1. Partially drain coolant, until level is below thermostat.
2. Disconnect bypass hose from thermostat housing.
3. Mark location of distributor and loosen hold-down clamp.
4. Rotate distributor to gain access, if necessary.
5. Disconnect upper radiator hose and remove two thermostat housing bolts.
6. Remove thermostat, housing and gasket.
7. Reverse procedure to install. Tighten to specifications.

# WATER PUMP

## REPLACE

1. Drain cooling system, then remove upper radiator hose at engine.
2. Remove fan and clutch assembly from water pump shaft using fan clutch holding tool No. T84T-6312-C and fan clutch nut wrench tool No. T84T-6312-D or equivalents. Position fan and clutch in fan shroud.
3. Remove fan shroud and fan/clutch as one assembly.
4. Loosen water pump pulley bolts.
5. Remove accessory drive belt by rotating tensioner away from belt by using pulley retaining bolts only.
6. Remove water pump pulley, then disconnect radiator lower hose, heater hose and water pump bypass hose at water pump.
7. Remove bolts attaching pump to front cover. Remove pump.
8. Reverse procedure to install, noting the following:
   a. Tighten to specifications.
   b. Following installation, fill and bleed cooling system.

# FUEL PRESSURE RELIEF

Fuel lines will remain pressurized for long periods of time after engine is shut off. This pressure must be relieved before servicing any fuel related component.

A valve on fuel charging assembly is used to relieve system pressure. Attach EFI and CFI fuel pressure gauge tool No. T80L-9974-B or equivalent, to schrader valve located on fuel rail. Pressure in fuel system may now be released.

# FUEL PUMP

## REPLACE

1. Disconnect battery ground cable.
2. Release pressure from fuel system at fuel pressure relief valve using Fuel Pressure Gauge tool No. T80L-9974-B or equivalent. When relieving fuel pressure, crank engine with fuel pump electrical connector disconnected.
3. Drain fuel from tank through filler neck, then raise and support vehicle.
4. Remove exhaust pipe and exhaust shield, if necessary for access.
5. Disconnect fuel hoses and tubes. Disconnect one end of vapor crossover hose at rear of driveshaft. Disconnect filler hose. **Plastic fuel tube connections are on top of fuel tank and are inaccessible. Fuel tank must be lowered to gain access to connections.**
6. Place a support below fuel tank and remove bolts from fuel tank straps. Use caution not to damage fuel tank, fuel tank support or straps.
7. Lower fuel tank and disconnect fuel lines and electrical connector from fuel gauge sender. Clean fuel pump retaining flange to prevent fuel contamination.
8. Turn fuel pump locking ring counterclockwise using fuel tank sender wrench tool No. D84P-9275-A or equivalent, and remove locking ring.
9. Remove fuel pump, sender assembly and seal ring.
10. Reverse procedure to install, noting the following:
    a. Ensure locating keyways and seal ring remain in groove.
    b. Hold pump assembly in place and install locking ring finger-tight. Ensure all locking tabs are under tank lock ring tabs.
    c. Install EFI-CFI fuel pressure gauge tool No. T80L-9974-B or equivalent, on fuel charging assembly fuel diagnostic valve. Turn ignition switch from OFF to ON position for three seconds. Turn ignition switch for three seconds repeatedly until pressure gauge shows a minimum 35 psi.

# BELT TENSION DATA

| Year | Model | Belt | New Lbs. | Used Lbs. |
|---|---|---|---|---|
| 1989–91 | Crown Victoria & Grand Marquis | 1/4 inch V Belt | 70 | 50 |
| | | All other V Belts | 110 | 90 |
| | | 5K① | 140 | 120 |
| | | 6K② | 120 | 110 |
| | | 6K③ | 170 | 150 |
| 1991–92 | Cougar & Thunderbird | 6K② | 90 | 90 |

①—5 grooves fixed.
②—6 grooves with tensioner.
③—6 grooves fixed.

# TIGHTENING SPECIFICATIONS

| Year | Component | Torque/Ft. Lbs. |
|---|---|---|
| 1989–92 | Alternator Adjustment Arm To Water Pump Stud Nut | 20–39 |
| | Alternator Adjustment Arm To Alternator Bolt | 24–40 |
| | Camshaft Sprocket Bolt | 40–45 |
| | Camshaft Thrust Plate | 9–12 |
| | Connecting Rod Nut | 19–24 |
| | Crankshaft Damper Bolt | 70–90 |
| | Crankshaft Pulley To Damper | 35–50 |
| | Cylinder Head Bolts | ① |
| | Distributor Hold-Down Bolt | 18–26 |
| | EGR Valve To Spacer | 12–18 |
| | Engine Insulator Assembly | 26–38 |
| | Engine Mount Through Bolts | 45–65 |
| | Exhaust Manifold | 18–24 |
| | Fan Clutch To Water Pump Hub | 35–47 |
| | Fan Shroud Attaching Screws | 27–44② |
| | Flywheel to Crankshaft | 75–85 |
| | Front Cover | 12–18 |
| | Intake Manifold To Cylinder Head | ① |
| | Main Bearing Cap Bolts | 60–70 |
| | Oil Filter Insert To Engine Adapter Bolt | 20–30 |
| | Oil Inlet To Main Bearing Cap | 22–32 |
| | Oil Inlet Tube To Oil Pump | 12–18 |
| | Oil Pan Drain Plug | 15–25 |
| | Oil Pan To Engine | 6–9 |
| | Oil Pump To Engine | 22–32 |
| | Pulley To Damper Bolt | 35–50 |
| | Pump Bracket To Cylinder Head | 40–55 |
| | Rocker Arm Fulcrum Bolt | 18–25 |
| | Rocker Arm Cover | 6–9 |
| | Spark Plugs | 5–10 |
| | Steering Shaft Pinch Bolt | 30–42 |
| | Thermactor Pump Pivot Bolt | 35–50 |
| | Thermostat Housing | 9–12 |
| | Transmission Mount Nut | 65–85 |
| | Throttle Body Attaching Nut | 12–18 |
| | Throttle Body To EGR Spacer & Upper Intake Manifold | 12–18 |
| | Valve Lifter Guide Plate | 71–106② |
| | Water Outlet Housing | 12–18 |
| | Water Pump | 12–18 |

①—Refer to text. ②—Inch Lbs.

# Clutch & Manual Transmission

## INDEX

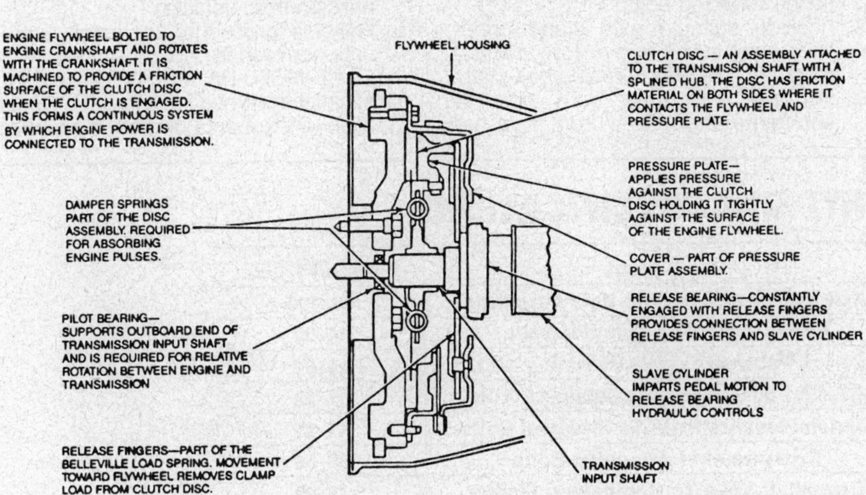

ENGINE FLYWHEEL BOLTED TO ENGINE CRANKSHAFT AND ROTATES WITH THE CRANKSHAFT. IT IS MACHINED TO PROVIDE A FRICTION SURFACE OF THE CLUTCH DISC WHEN THE CLUTCH IS ENGAGED. THIS FORMS A CONTINUOUS SYSTEM BY WHICH ENGINE POWER IS CONNECTED TO THE TRANSMISSION.
FLYWHEEL HOUSING
CLUTCH DISC — AN ASSEMBLY ATTACHED TO THE TRANSMISSION SHAFT WITH A SPLINED HUB. THE DISC HAS FRICTION MATERIAL ON BOTH SIDES WHERE IT CONTACTS THE FLYWHEEL AND PRESSURE PLATE.
PRESSURE PLATE— APPLIES PRESSURE AGAINST THE CLUTCH DISC HOLDING IT TIGHTLY AGAINST THE SURFACE OF THE ENGINE FLYWHEEL.
DAMPER SPRINGS PART OF THE DISC ASSEMBLY. REQUIRED FOR ABSORBING ENGINE PULSES.
COVER — PART OF PRESSURE PLATE ASSEMBLY.
RELEASE BEARING—CONSTANTLY ENGAGED WITH RELEASE FINGERS PROVIDES CONNECTION BETWEEN RELEASE FINGERS AND SLAVE CYLINDER
PILOT BEARING— SUPPORTS OUTBOARD END OF TRANSMISSION INPUT SHAFT AND IS REQUIRED FOR RELATIVE ROTATION BETWEEN ENGINE AND TRANSMISSION
SLAVE CYLINDER IMPARTS PEDAL MOTION TO RELEASE BEARING HYDRAULIC CONTROLS
RELEASE FINGERS—PART OF THE BELLEVILLE LOAD SPRING. MOVEMENT TOWARD FLYWHEEL REMOVES CLAMP LOAD FROM CLUTCH DISC.
TRANSMISSION INPUT SHAFT

**Fig. 1 Cross sectional view of clutch system**

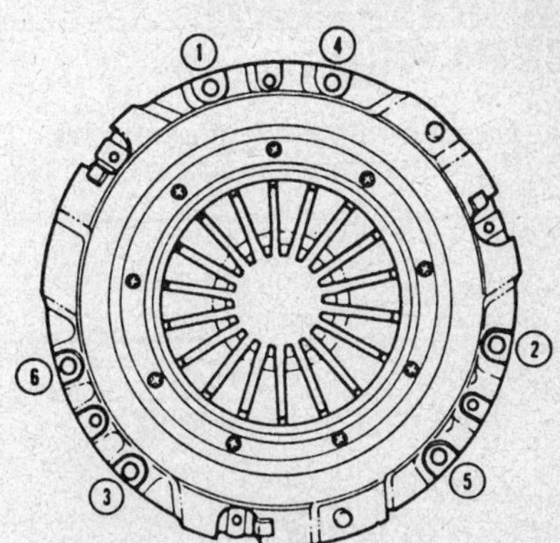

1
2
3
4
5
6

**Fig. 2 Clutch pressure plate tightening sequence**

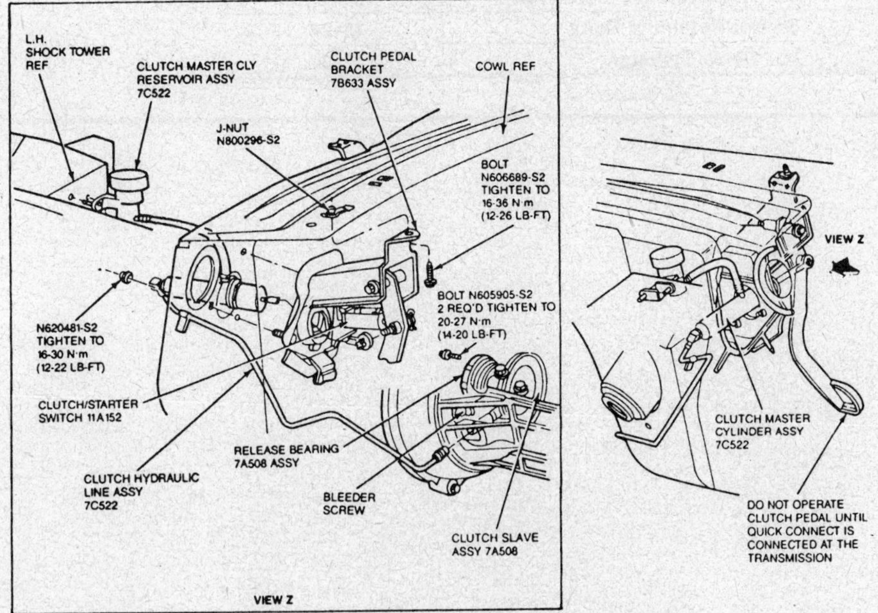

L.H. SHOCK TOWER REF
CLUTCH MASTER CLY RESERVOIR ASSY 7C522
CLUTCH PEDAL BRACKET 7B633 ASSY
COWL REF
J-NUT N800296-S2
BOLT N606689-S2 TIGHTEN TO 16-36 N·m (12-26 LB-FT)
VIEW Z
BOLT N605905-S2 2 REQ'D TIGHTEN TO 20-27 N·m (14-20 LB-FT)
N620481-S2 TIGHTEN TO 16-30 N·m (12-22 LB-FT)
CLUTCH/STARTER SWITCH 11A152
RELEASE BEARING 7A508 ASSY
CLUTCH HYDRAULIC LINE ASSY 7C522
BLEEDER SCREW
CLUTCH SLAVE ASSY 7A508
CLUTCH MASTER CYLINDER ASSY 7C522
DO NOT OPERATE CLUTCH PEDAL UNTIL QUICK CONNECT IS CONNECTED AT THE TRANSMISSION
VIEW Z

**Fig. 3 Clutch hydraulic system**

## CLUTCH
### REPLACE

1. Disconnect negative battery cable.
2. Disconnect clutch cylinder from clutch pedal and dash panel.
3. Raise and support vehicle, then remove starter.
4. Disconnect hydraulic coupling at transmission, using coupling disconnect tool No. T88T-70522-A or equivalent, by sliding white sleeve toward slave cylinder, and apply a slight tug on tube.
5. Remove transmission as described under "Transmission, Replace".
6. Mark assembled position of pressure plate and cover to flywheel for reference during assembly.
7. Loosen pressure plate cover attaching bolts evenly, until pressure plate springs are expanded, then remove the bolts.
8. Remove pressure plate cover assembly, then the clutch disc from flywheel, **Fig. 1.**
9. Reverse procedure to install. Tighten pressure plate attaching bolts to specifications, in sequence shown in **Fig. 2.** Bleed clutch hydraulic system as necessary.

## SLAVE CYLINDER
### REPLACE

1. Raise and support vehicle, then disconnect master cylinder push rod from clutch pedal.
2. Disconnect clutch hydraulic line using clutch coupling tool No. T88T-70522-A or equivalent.
3. Remove transmission.
4. Loosen retaining bolts and remove clutch slave cylinder.
5. Reverse procedure to install, noting the following:
   a. Position slave cylinder over input shaft, aligning bleeder screw and line coupling with holes in transmission housing.
   b. Tighten to specifications and bleed system.

## CLUTCH HYDRAULIC SYSTEM BLEEDING

1. Clean area around bleed valve at clutch actuating (slave) cylinder and clutch reservoir cap, **Fig. 3.**
2. Raise and support vehicle.
3. Attach a suitable length of hose to

clutch actuating cylinder bleed valve.
4. While clutch pedal is being depressed, slightly open clutch actuating cylinder bleed valve.
5. Close bleed valve, then release clutch pedal.
6. Repeat procedure until air is removed from system. While performing procedure, maintain fluid level in clutch master cylinder. Add only DOT 3 type brake fluid to clutch master cylinder.

## TRANSMISSION REPLACE

1. Disconnect battery ground cable.
2. Place transmission shift lever in Neutral position, then remove shift lever knob.
3. Remove console upper cover, then remove shifter retaining bolts and shifter.
4. Raise and support vehicle, then drain oil from transmission.
5. Remove body re-inforcement in front axle.
6. Disconnect exhaust pipe from resonator.
7. Remove driveshaft to companion flange retaining bolts.
8. Position suitable axle stand under front axle, then remove forward and rearward retaining nuts and bolt plate.
9. Remove vent tube from hole in sub-frame, then lower front axle assembly and slide driveshaft from transmission. Position drive shaft on front driveshaft support.
10. Remove catalytic converter.
11. Disconnect clutch hydraulic line from actuating cylinder.
12. Remove starter motor assembly.
13. Position suitable transmission jack under transmission, then remove crossmember.
14. Remove flywheel housing to engine attaching bolts, then remove transmission from vehicle.
15. Reverse procedure to install. Lubricate driveshaft yoke splines with C1AZ-19590-BA or equivalent prior to installation. When installing driveshaft, align index marks on flange on yoke.

## TIGHTENING SPECIFICATIONS

| Year | Component | Torque/Ft. Lbs. |
|---|---|---|
| 1989–92 | Axle Housing Bushing & Retaining Nuts | 68–100 |
| | Clutch Actuating Cylinder Bolts | 14–20 |
| | Clutch Pedal Assembly Retaining Bolts | 16–22 |
| | Clutch Pedal Assembly Retaining Nuts | 12–22 |
| | Clutch Pressure Plate To Flywheel Bolts | 15–25 |
| | Crossmember Attaching Bolts | 35–50 |
| | Driveshaft Yoke To Companion Flange | 70–95 |
| | Flywheel Housing To Engine Bolts | 40–49 |
| | Pressure Plate To Flywheel | 20–28 |
| | Transmission Drain & Filler Plugs | 29–43 |
| | Shifter Retaining Bolts | 18–24 |
| | Slave Cylinder | 14–20 |

# Rear Axle & Suspension

## INDEX



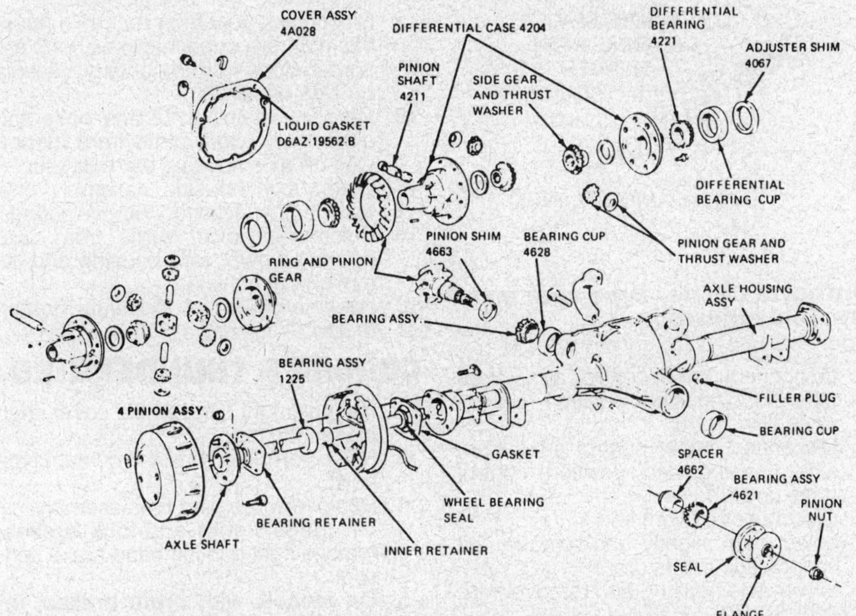


**Fig. 1 Disassembled view of Ford integral carrier type rear axle assembly w/bolt on type axle retention**

## DESCRIPTION

### FORD INTEGRAL CARRIER W/BOLT-ON TYPE AXLE RETENTION

This rear axle, **Fig. 1,** is an integral design hypoid with the center line of the pinion set below the center line of the ring gear. The semi-floating axle shafts are retained in the housing by ball bearings and bearing retainers at axle ends.

The differential is mounted on two opposed tapered roller bearings which are retained in the housing by removable caps. Differential bearing preload and drive gear backlash is adjusted by nuts located behind each differential bearing cup.

The drive pinion assembly is mounted on two opposed tapered roller bearings. Pinion bearing preload is adjusted by a collapsible spacer on the pinion shaft. Pinion and ring gear tooth contact is adjusted by shims between the rear bearing cone and pinion gear.

### FORD INTEGRAL CARRIER W/C-LOCK TYPE AXLE RETENTION

The gear set, **Fig. 2,** consist of a ring gear and an overhung drive pinion which is supported by two opposed tapered roller bearings. Pinion bearing preload is maintained by a collapsible spacer on the pinion shaft and adjusted by the pinion nut. The differential case is a one piece design with two openings to allow assembly of internal components and lubricant flow. The pinion shaft is retained with a threaded bolt assembled to the case. The differential case is mounted in the carrier between two opposed tapered roller bearings. The bearings are retained in the carrier by removable bearing caps. Differential bearing preload and ring gear backlash are adjusted by the use of shims located between the differential bearing cups and the carrier housing. Axle shafts are held in the housing by C-locks positioned in a slot on the axle shaft splined end, **Fig. 3.**

### REAR WHEEL DRIVE HALFSHAFT SYSTEM

This system shown in **Fig. 4,** employs constant velocity (CV) joints at both its inboard (differential) and outboard (wheel) ends for vehicle operating smoothness. The CV joints are connected by an interconnecting shaft which is splined at both ends and retained in the inboard and outboard CV joints by circlips.

The inboard CV joint stub shaft is splined and held in the differential side gear by circlip. The outboard CV joint stub shaft is pressed into the hub and secured with a free-spinning lock nut. The CV joints are lube-for-life with a special CV joint grease and require no periodic lubrication. The CV boots should be periodically inspected and replaced immediately when damage or grease leakage is evident.

Halfshaft removal from the differential is accomplished by applying a load to the back face of the inboard CV joint assembly to overcome the circlip. The outboard joint end must be pressed from the hub.

The inboard tripod CV joints can be disassembled and serviced. Other then the CV boot, the outboard CV joint is serviced only as an assembly with the shaft.

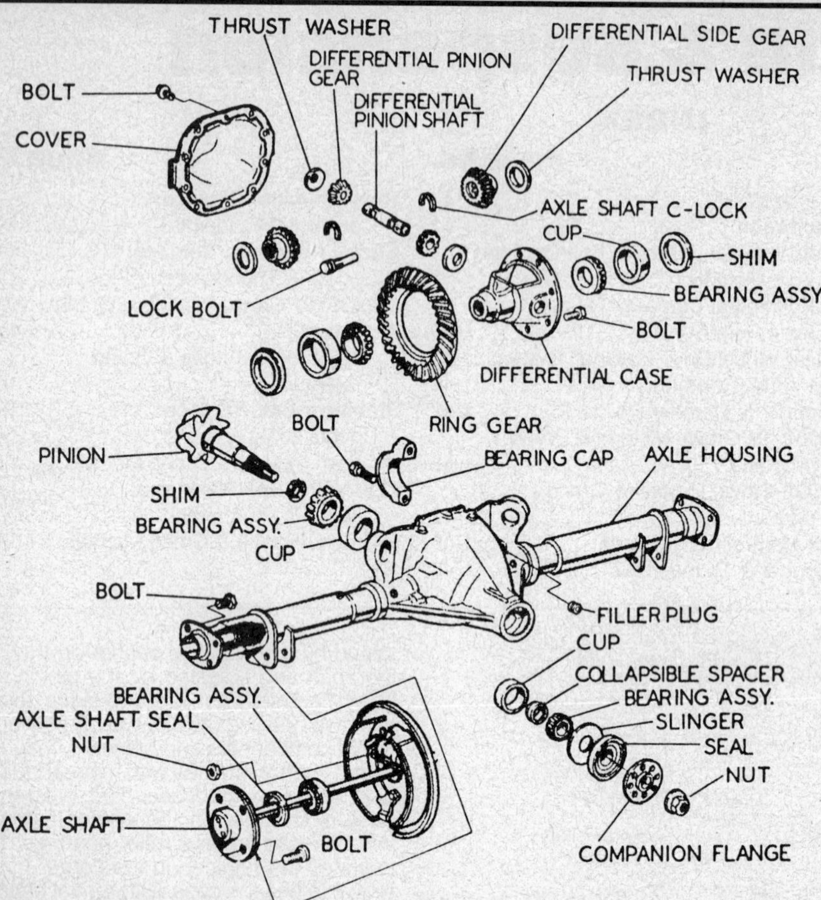


**Fig. 2 Disassembled view of Ford integral carrier type rear axle assembly w/C-lock type axle retention**

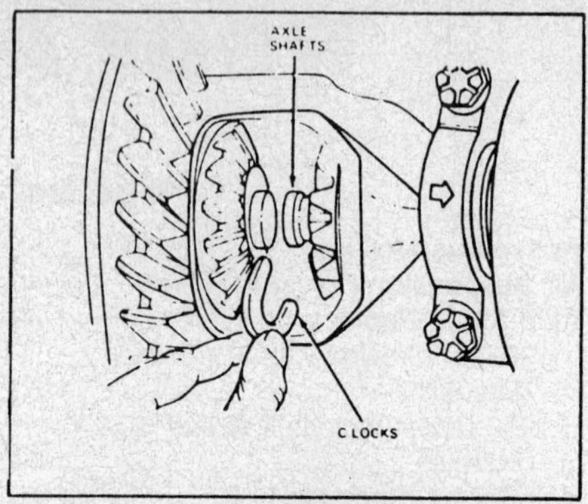


**Fig. 3 Axle shaft C-lock. Crown Victoria & Grand Marquis**

# REAR AXLE REPLACE

## 1989–91 CROWN VICTORIA & GRAND MARQUIS

1. Raise vehicle. Support at frame members and rear axle, then remove wheel and tire assembly.
2. Remove brake drums and disconnect brake lines at wheel cylinders.
3. Make marks on drive shaft yoke and pinion flange for reassembly, then disconnect drive shaft at rear U-joint and remove drive shaft from transmission extension housing. Install seal replacer tool in extension housing to prevent leakage.
4. Position a drain pan under differential carrier, then remove carrier attaching bolts and allow differential to drain.
5. Disconnect stabilizer bar, if equipped.
6. Disconnect shock absorbers from lower mountings.
7. Remove brake lines from retaining clips on rear axle housing, then remove brake line junction block retaining screw.
8. Position a suitable jack under axle housing to prevent housing from tilting when removing control arms.
9. Disconnect lower control arms from axle housing and position control arms downward.
10. Disconnect upper control arms from axle housing and position control arms upward.
11. Disconnect air vent line.
12. Lower axle slightly and remove coil springs and insulators.
13. Lower axle housing and remove from vehicle.

## 1992 CROWN VICTORIA & GRAND MARQUIS

1. Disconnect battery ground cable and switch air suspension OFF.
2. Raise vehicle and position safety stands below rear frame crossmember.
3. Drain axle fluid by removing cover.
4. Remove wheels, rotors, calipers and ABS speed sensor.
5. Remove lock bolt from pinion shaft and remove shaft. **Fig. 5.**
6. Push axle shafts inward to remove C-locks.
7. Remove axle shafts, then remove RH and LH disc brake adapter brackets, bolts and J-nuts. **Fig. 6.**
8. Remove four retaining nuts from each disc brake adapter and support with wire from underbody.
9. Disconnect driveshaft at companion flange and support with wire.
10. Support axle housing with jackstands, then disengage brake line from clips that retain line to axle housing.
11. Release air spring pressure as described under "Air Suspension Pressure Relief." Remove air spring.
12. Disconnect vent from rear axle housing, then disconnect lower shock absorber studs from mounting brackets on axle housing.
13. Remove retaining nut and bolts and disconnect upper arms from mountings on axle housing ear brackets.
14. Lower axle housing assembly until springs are released. Remove springs.
15. Disconnect lower arms from axle housing. Lower axle housing and remove from vehicle.
16. Reverse procedure to install. Tighten to specifications.

## COUGAR & THUNDERBIRD

1. Remove right hand wheel cover, then loosen lug nuts.
2. Raise vehicle on a frame contact type hoist.
3. Remove wheel and tire assembly.
4. **On models with anti-lock brakes,** remove right and left hand brake sensors.
5. **On models with drum brakes,** remove right hand brake drum.
6. **On models with rear disc brakes,** proceed as follows:
   a. Disconnect parking brake cable from right hand caliper.
   b. Remove brake calipers with brake hoses attached. Suspend brake caliper from chassis with wire.
   c. Remove push nuts, then remove brake rotors.
7. **On all models,** Remove upper control arm bolt. Wire upper control arm to upper portion of shock to provide clearance for halfshaft removal.
8. Mark position of lower control arm to knuckle.
9. Remove right hand lower control arm to knuckle bolts and nuts.
10. Using tool No. T89P-3514-A or equivalent, remove right hand halfshaft from differential carrier. Use care not to damage differential oil seals or CV joint boots.
11. Remove halfshaft from knuckle.

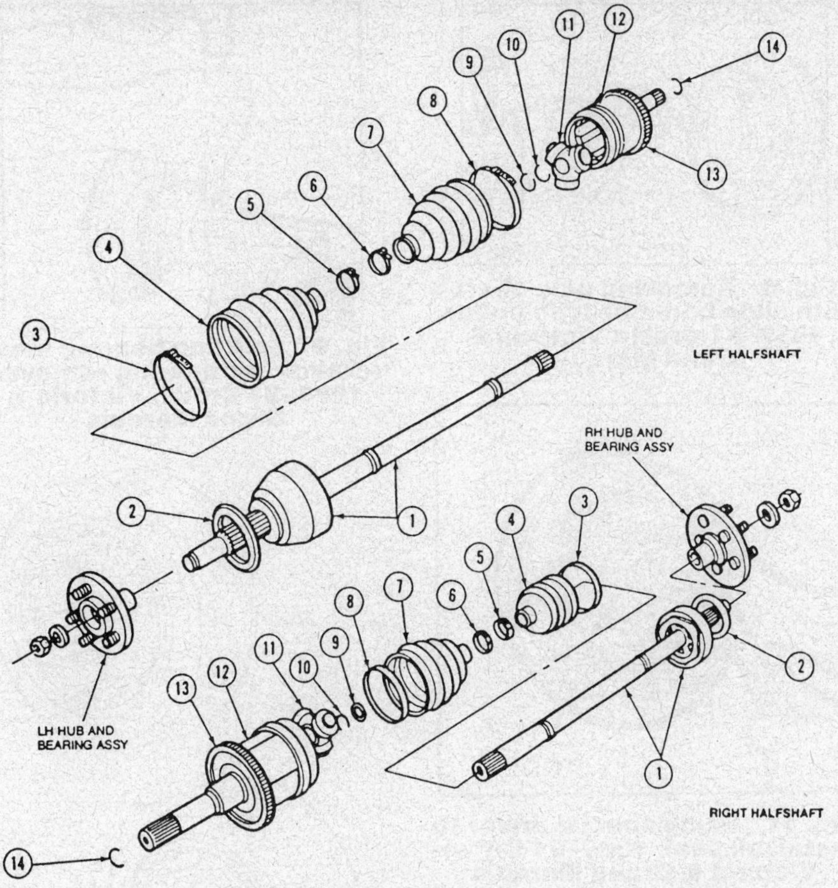


**Fig. 4 Rear wheel drive halfshaft system. Cougar & Thunderbird**

12. Position differential plug No. T89P-4850-B or equivalent into differential housing to prevent fluid loss.
13. Mark position of driveshaft yoke to differential companion flange, then remove driveshaft retaining bolts.
14. Slide driveshaft forward and allow to rest on driveshaft hoop.
15. Using a suitable jack, support rear axle.
16. Remove rear axle mount retaining bolts, then remove rear mount.
17. Remove front axle retaining bolts and nuts.
18. Using tool No. T89P-3514-A or equivalent, remove left hand halfshaft inboard CV joint from differential carrier. Use care not to damage differential oil seals or CV joint boots.
19. While lowering rear axle assembly, move to right and disengage axle from left hand stub shaft.
20. Position differential plug T89P-4850-B or equivalent into differential housing to prevent fluid loss, then lower axle from vehicle.
21. Reverse procedure to install, noting the following:
    a. **New hub retainer nut, CV joint stub shaft circlips and differential seals must be installed.**
    b. Tighten to specifications.

# AXLE SHAFT REPLACE

## 1989–91 CROWN VICTORIA & GRAND MARQUIS

### Ford Integral Carrier w/Bolt On Type Axle Retention

1. Remove wheel and tire assembly, then remove nuts attaching brake drum to axle shaft flange and remove brake drum.
2. Working through opening in axle shaft flange, remove nuts securing axle shaft bearing retainer, **Fig. 7.**
3. Using a suitable puller, pull axle shaft from housing, **Fig. 8.**
4. Remove brake backing plate and attach to frame side rail with a piece of wire.
5. If rear wheel bearing is to be replaced, loosen inner retainer ring by nicking it deeply in several places with a chisel, **Fig. 9,** then slide retainer from axle shaft.
6. Press bearing from axle shaft using tool No. T71P-4621-B or equivalent.
7. Using a hook type puller, remove oil seal from axle housing, **Fig. 10.**
8. Position bearing retainer and bearing on axle shaft, then using press tool No. T62F-4621-A or equivalent, press bearing onto shaft until firmly seated against shoulder.
9. Using bearing installation tool, press inner retainer onto shaft until retainer is firmly seated against bearing.
10. Wipe all lubricant from oil seal area of axle housing, then install oil seal using seal installation tool No. T79P-1177-A, **Fig. 11.**
11. Install gasket on housing flange, then

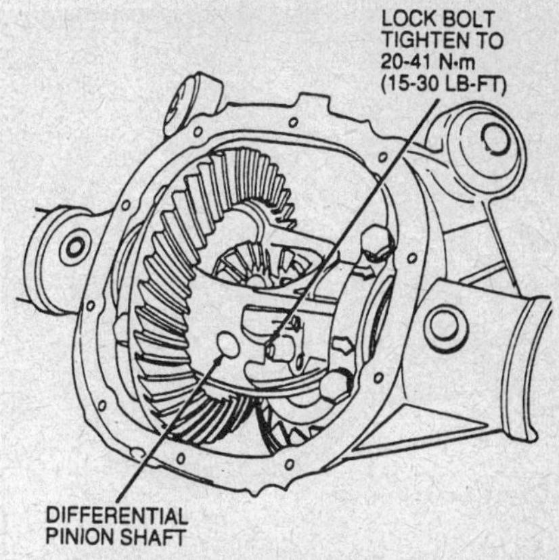


**Fig. 5 Rear axle removal. 1992 Crown Victoria & Grand Marquis**

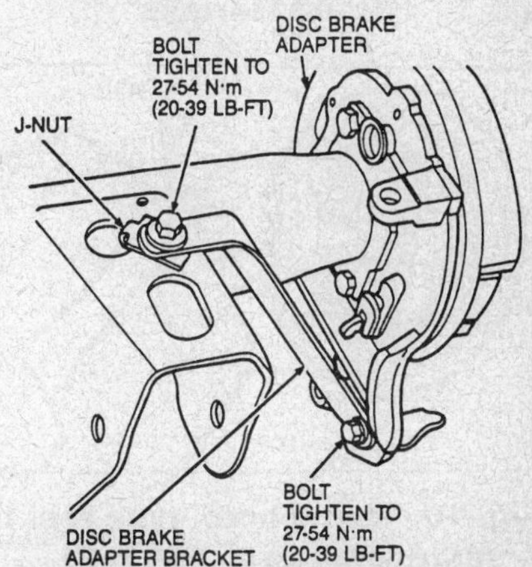


**Fig. 6 Disc brake adapter removal. 1992 Crown Victoria & Grand Marquis**

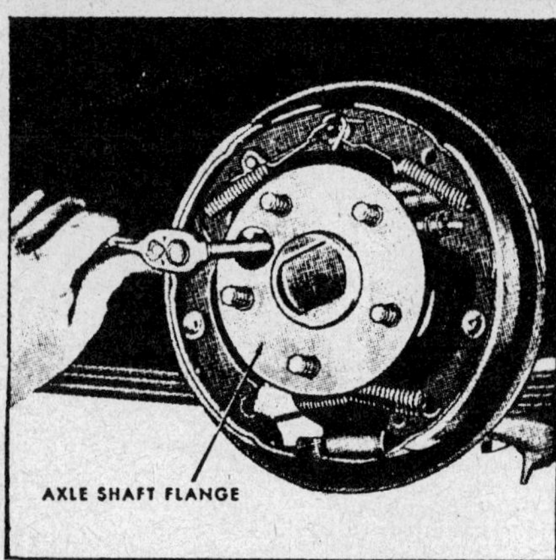


**Fig. 7 Removing nuts from wheel bearing retainer. 1989–91 Crown Victoria & Grand Marquis**

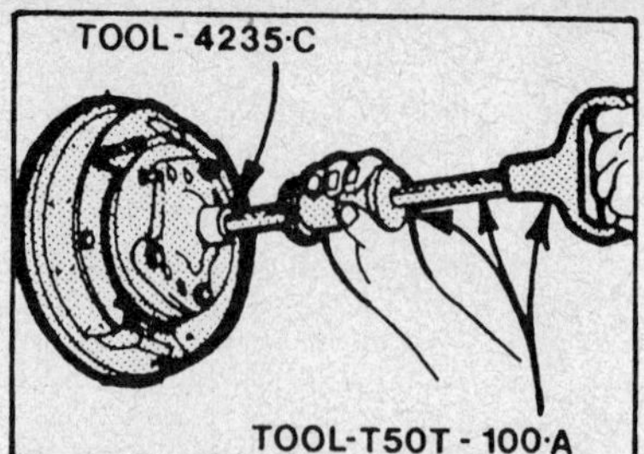


**Fig. 8 Removing axle shaft with slide hammer-type puller. 1989–91 Crown Victoria & Grand Marquis**

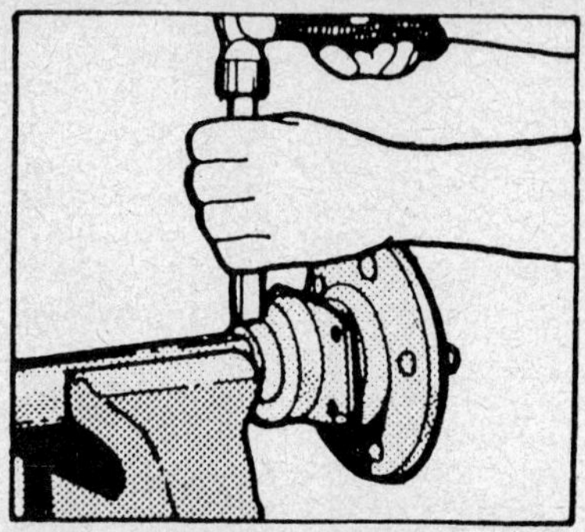

**Fig. 9 Splitting bearing inner retainer for bearing removal. 1989–91 Crown Victoria & Grand Marquis**

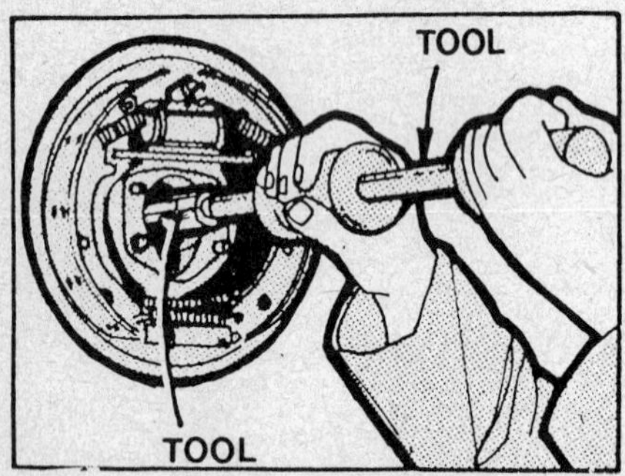


**Fig. 10 Using hook-type tool to remove oil seal. 1989–91 Crown Victoria & Grand Marquis**

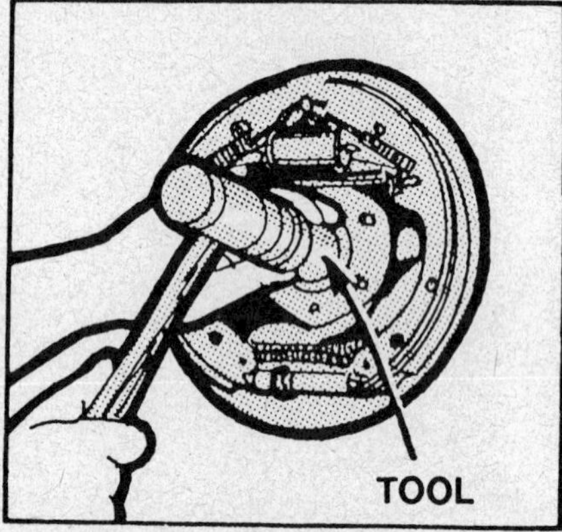


**Fig. 11 Using special driver to install oil seal. 1989–91 Crown Victoria & Grand Marquis**

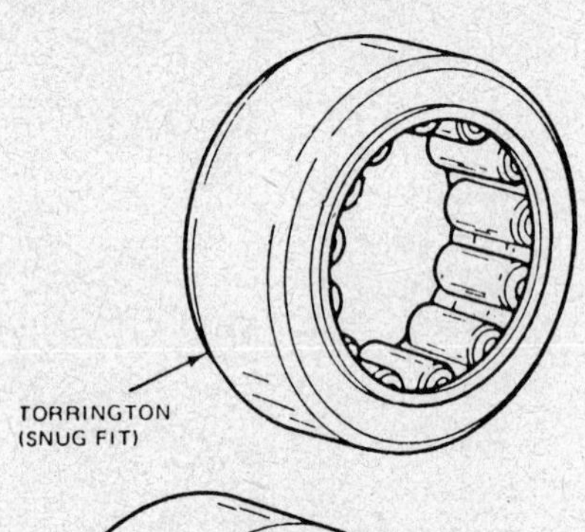


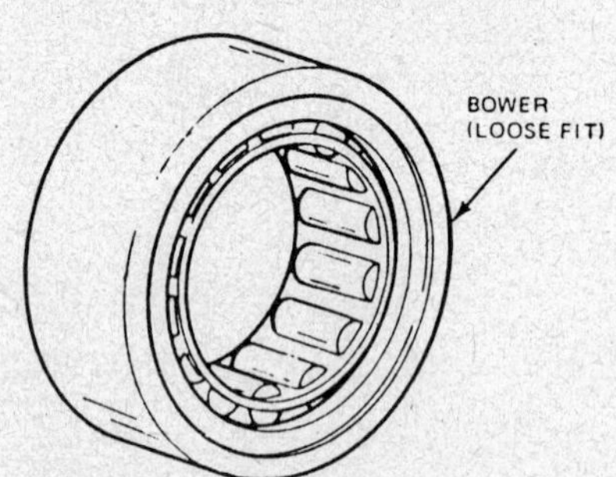


**Fig. 12 Axle shaft bearing identification. 1989–91 Crown Victoria & Grand Marquis**

install brake backing plate.

12. Carefully slide axle shaft into housing using care not to damage oil seal, then install bearing retainer attaching nuts and **torque** to 20 to 40 ft. lbs.
13. Install brake drum and retaining nuts, then install wheel and tire assembly.

### Ford Integral Carrier w/C-Lock Type Axle Retention

1. Raise and support rear of vehicle.
2. Remove wheel and tire assembly and brake drum.
3. Remove rear axle housing cover and drain lubricant.
4. Remove differential pinion lock screw and differential pinion shaft.
5. Remove wheel speed sensor, if equipped. **Damage to sensor may occur if sensor is not removed before axle shaft.**
6. Push axle shafts inward and remove C-locks, **Fig. 3.**
7. Remove axle shaft from housing using care not to damage oil seal.
8. Remove bearing and seal as an assembly using a suitable slide hammer, **Fig. 10**, if necessary. **Two types of bearing are used, Fig. 12. One requires a light press fit in the housing flange, while on the other a loose fit is acceptable. Therefore, if a loose fitting bearing is encountered, it does not indicate excessive wear or damage.**
9. Lubricate bearing with rear axle lubricant and install bearing into housing bore using bearing installation tool No. T78P-1225-A or equivalent.
10. Install axle shaft seal into housing using seal installation tool No. T78P-1177-A or equivalent, **Fig. 11.**
11. Reverse procedure to install axle shaft. Tighten to specifications.

## 1992 CROWN VICTORIA & GRAND MARQUIS

### Removal

1. Disconnect battery ground cable and turn air suspension switch OFF.
2. Raise and support vehicle. Remove rear wheel and tire assembly.
3. Remove disc brake calipers and rotors.
4. Drain rear axle fluid by removing cover.
5. Remove differential pinion shaft lock bolt and differential pinion shaft. **Fig. 5.**
6. Push flanged end of axle shafts toward center of vehicle and remove C-lock from button end of axle shaft. **Fig. 3.**
7. Remove axle shaft from housing, use caution not to damage oil seal and ABS sensor ring.

### Installation

1. Ensure O-ring is present on spline end of axle shaft.
2. Carefully slide axle shaft into axle housing. Use extreme caution to not damage bearing seal or ABS sensor ring.
3. Start splines into side gear and push firmly until button end of axle shaft can be seen in differential case.
4. Install C-lock on button end of axle shaft splines. Push shaft outboard until splines engage and the C-lock seats in counterbore of differential side gear.
5. Position differential pinion shaft through case and pinion gears, aligning hole in shaft with lock bolt hose. Apply rear axle lubricant E0AZ-19580-AA or equivalent, to pinion shaft lock bolt. Tighten to specifications.
6. Install cover and tighten to specifications.
7. Install ABS speed sensor, rotors and calipers. Tighten to specifications.

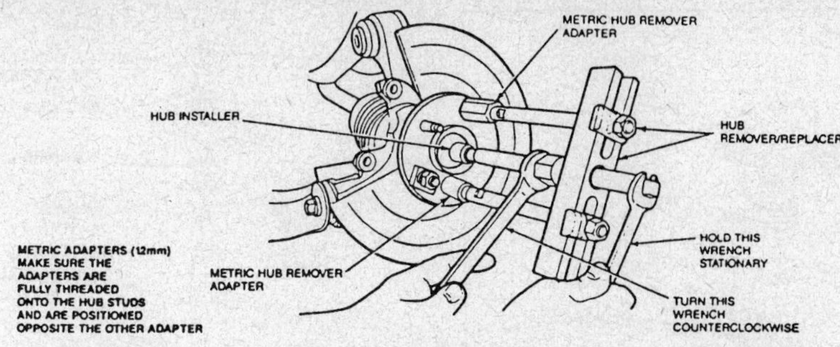


**Fig. 13 Mounting hub removal tool. Cougar & Thunderbird**

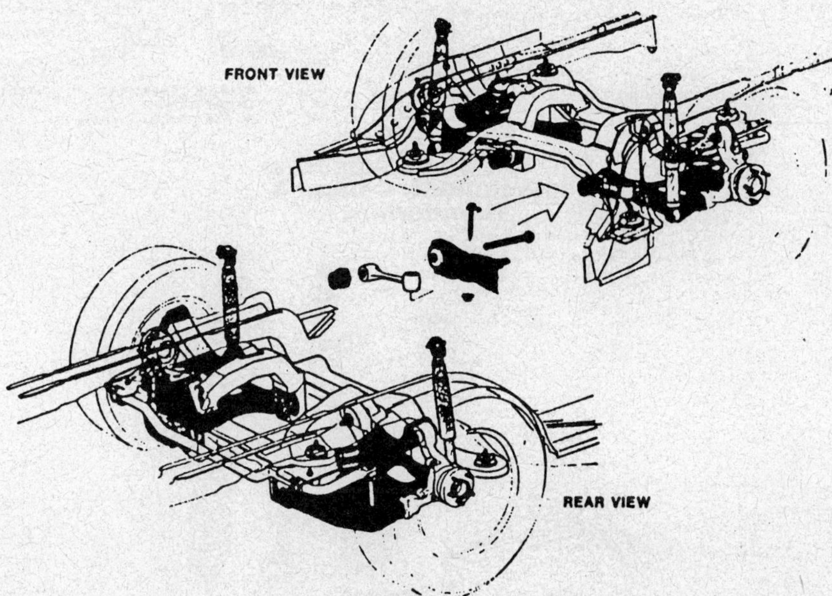


**Fig. 14 Rear suspension. Cougar & Thunderbird**

## REAR HALFSHAFTS REPLACE

### COUGAR & THUNDERBIRD

**Do not begin this removal procedure unless following parts are available; new hub retainer nut; new inboard CV joint stub shaft circlip and new differential oil seal. Once removed, these parts must not be reused during assembly. Their torque holding ability is diminished during removal.**

1. Remove wheel cover/hub cover and remove hub retainer nut, then loosen wheel nuts.
2. Raise and support vehicle on a frame contact hoist.
3. Remove rear wheel and tire assembly.
4. **On models with drum brakes,** remove brake drum.
5. **On models with disc brakes,** proceed as follows:
   a. Remove anti-lock brake sensors.
   b. Pull back on parking brake release lever and at same time pull on cable. This will slacken cable so cable end can be removed from brake caliper attachment.
   c. Remove upper and lower brake caliper attaching bolts.
   d. Remove caliper assembly from rotor, then carefully wire caliper to brake junction bracket.
   e. Remove brake rotor push nuts and remove rotor.
6. **On all models,** remove upper control arm bolts and nuts, then wire upper control arm to upper shock absorber so that it does not damage CV joint boots when halfshaft is removed.
7. Using a paint marker, mark position of lower control arm in relation to knuckle with lower bushings in their relaxed position. When upper control arm bolt is removed from knuckle, lower bushings will return to their relaxed positions. **Failure to mark this position will result in bushing wind-up on assembly and incorrect ride height, causing misalignment and premature tire wear.**
8. Install hub remover T81P-1104-C or equivalent to hub studs as shown in **Fig. 13.**
9. Turn wrench counterclockwise until halfshaft is free in hub.
10. Remove lower control arm attaching bolts.
11. Remove knuckle assembly while supporting outboard CV joint and boot. Carefully rest halfshaft on lower control arm.
12. Insert CV joint removal tool No. T89P-3514-A or equivalent between differential housing and CV joint. Push tool outward until CV joint becomes free from differential side gear. **Extreme care must be taken to prevent damage to the differential oil seal, differential housing, sensor ring and/or CV joint and boot.**
13. Remove halfshaft from vehicle, then plug differential housing to prevent loss of lubricant.
14. Reverse procedure to install, noting the following:
    a. Install new differential oil seal and circlip on inboard CV joint.
    b. Ensure to align reference marks on lower control arm to marks on knuckle/bushing assembly.
    c. If equipped with rear disc brakes, **torque** caliper retaining bolts to 80-100 ft. lbs.
    d. If equipped with anti-lock brakes, **torque** brake sensor retaining bolts to 14-20 ft. lbs.

## SHOCK ABSORBER REPLACE

### COUGAR & THUNDERBIRD

**These vehicles are equipped with gas pressurized rear shock absorbers which will extend unassisted. Do not apply heat or flame to shock tube during removal.**

1. Position vehicle on drive-on hoist or alignment pit, so that rear suspension arms are supported during removal.
2. Remove all upper attaching parts from inside of luggage compartment, **Figs. 14 and 15.**
3. Remove attaching bolt and at lower arm, then remove shock absorber.
4. Reverse procedure to install. Tighten to specifications.

### 1989–91 CROWN VICTORIA & GRAND MARQUIS

1. With rear axle properly supported, disconnect shock absorber at upper mounting and compress it to clear hole in spring seat.
2. Disconnect shock absorber from stud on axle bracket, **Fig. 16.**
3. Reverse procedure to install. Tighten to specifications.

### 1992 CROWN VICTORIA & GRAND MARQUIS

1. Disconnect battery ground cable and turn air suspension switch OFF.
2. Raise and support vehicle.
3. To assist in removing upper attachment on shock absorbers using a plastic dust tube, place an open end

wrench on hex stamped into dust tube's metal cap. For shock absorbers with a steel dust tube, grasp tube to prevent stud rotation when loosening retaining nut.
4. Remove shock absorber retaining nut, washer and insulator assembly from stud on upper side of frame.
5. Compress shock absorber to clear hole in frame and remove inner insulator and washer from upper retaining stud.
6. Remove self-locking nut and disconnect chock absorber lower stud from mounting bracket on rear axle tube.
7. Reverse procedure to install. Tighten to specifications.

# STABILIZER BAR
## REPLACE
### COUGAR & THUNDERBIRD

1. Raise and support vehicle, then remove both rear wheels.
2. Remove both stabilizer bar link upper retaining bolts and nuts.
3. Remove stabilizer bar bracket bolts.
4. Remove rear muffler hanger retaining nuts.
5. Remove stabilizer bar from vehicle.
6. Reverse procedure to install. Tighten to specifications.

### CROWN VICTORIA & GRAND MARQUIS

1. Raise and support vehicle at frame side rails.
2. Support rear axle with a suitable jack and position axle so shock absorbers are fully extended.
3. Remove bolts, nuts and spacers attaching stabilizer bar to lower arms, **Fig. 16.**
4. Remove stabilizer bar from vehicle.
5. Reverse procedure to install. Tighten to specifications.

# COIL SPRING
## REPLACE
### COUGAR & THUNDERBIRD

1. Raise and support vehicle.
2. Remove rear wheel and tire assembly.
3. Remove rear stabilizer bar link nuts at both ends of stabilizer bar. Rotate bar up and out of the way.
4. Disconnect parking brake cable at brake caliper.
5. Install three Spring Cages tool No. 086-00031 or equivalent, to rear springs as follows:
   a. Install one spring cage without an adjuster link to inboard side or innermost bend of spring, **Fig. 17.**
   b. Install two more spring cages, with adjusters, at 120° angles to the previously installed cage.
6. Place a transmission jack or suitable stand under lower rear control arm as far outboard as possible.
7. Support rear knuckle and caliper assembly by wiring upper control arm to body.
8. Remove lower shock absorber mounting bolt and nut.
9. Mark position of toe adjustment cam to subframe for reference. Loosen both inboard pivot bolts on lower control arm. **Control arm must not be lowered until pivot bolts are loose. Do not attempt to remove plastic cap on front of pivot nut.**
10. Remove two bolts and nuts attaching lower control arm to knuckle, **Fig. 18.**
11. Lower control arm by lowering jack. Ensure spring cages properly seat on spring as control arm is dropped.
12. Remove jack, pull control arm down fully by hand and remove rear spring with cages in place.
13. Using coil spring compressor tool No. D78P-5310-A or equivalent, compress spring and remove spring

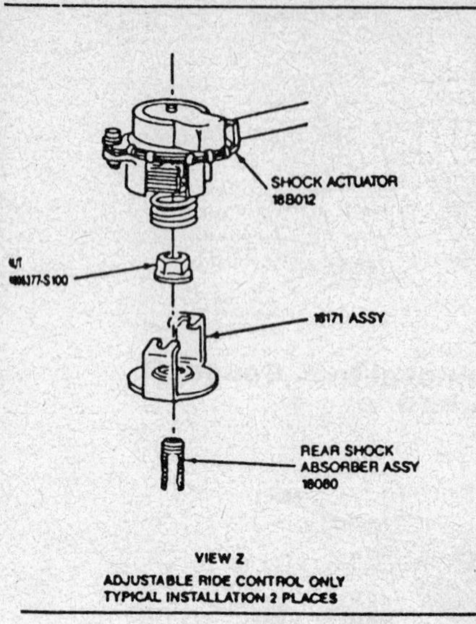


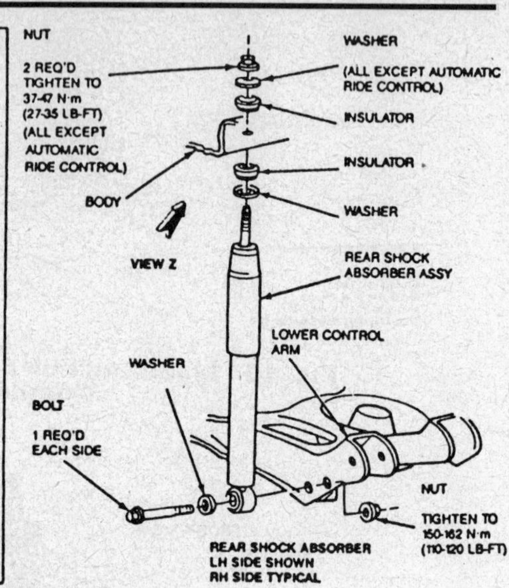


**Fig. 15 Shock absorber replacement. Cougar & Thunderbird**

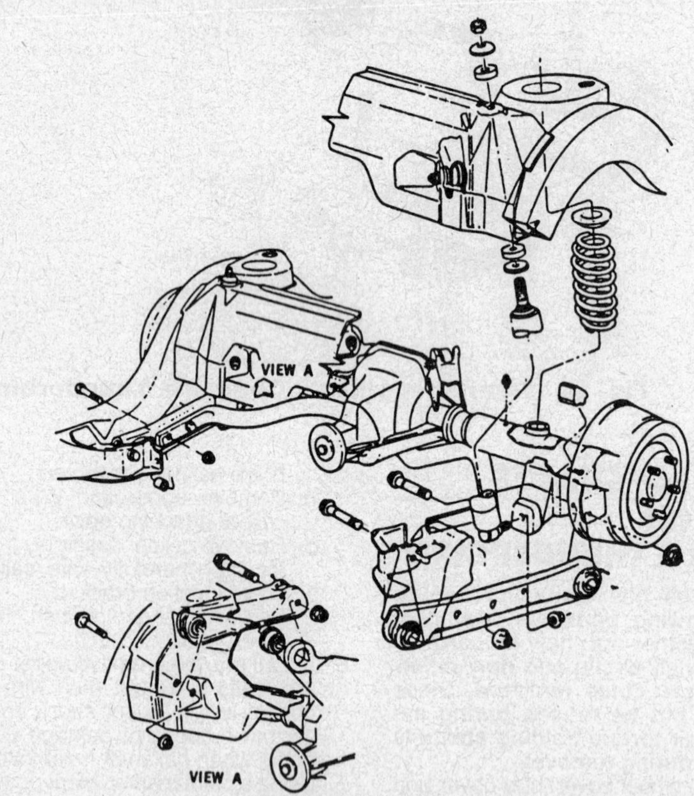


**Fig. 16 Exploded view of rear suspension. Crown Victoria & Grand Marquis**

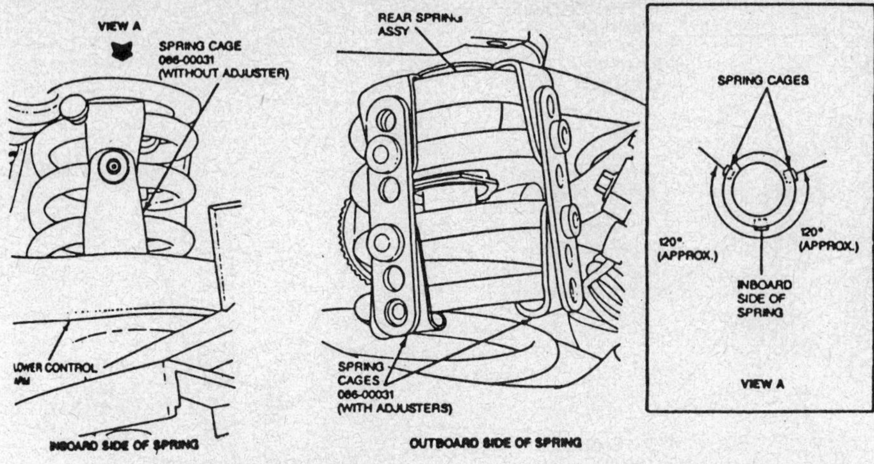


**Fig. 17 Mounting spring cages. Cougar & Thunderbird**

cages.

14. Remove upper and lower spring insulators from spring.
15. Reverse procedure to install, compress spring to approximately 10.5 inches overall length prior to installation.

## CROWN VICTORIA & GRAND MARQUIS

1. Raise rear of vehicle and support at frame. Support rear axle with a suitable jack.
2. Remove rear stabilizer bar, if necessary.
3. Disconnect shock absorbers at lower mountings.
4. **On 1989-91 models,** disconnect brake line from rear brake hose and remove hose to bracket clip.
5. **On all models,** Lower axle to remove springs. **On some models, it may be necessary to disconnect RH parking brake cable from righthand upper arm retainer prior to lowering axle.**
6. Reverse procedure to install. Install an insulator between upper seat and spring, if necessary. Tighten to specifications.

# CONTROL ARMS REPLACE

## COUGAR & THUNDERBIRD

### LOWER ARM

1. Remove coil spring as described in "Coil Spring, Replace".
2. Remove inner control arm pivot bolts and nuts, then remove arm assembly.
3. Remove toe compensating link from control arm.
4. Reverse procedure to install. Tighten to specifications.

### UPPER ARM

1. Raise and support vehicle.
2. Remove rear wheel and tire assembly.
3. Support knuckle and hub assembly so that it cannot swing outward.
4. Remove inner and outer pivot bolts and nuts at upper control arm, then remove upper control arm.
5. Reverse procedure to install, noting that inner pivot bolt used for camber adjustment has a specially-shaped washer under bolt head. Ensure fasteners are used in correct locations. Set camber adjustment as described in "Wheel Alignment". Tighten to specifications.

## 1989–91 CROWN VICTORIA & GRAND MARQUIS

Control arms must be replaced in pairs.

1. Raise rear of vehicle and support at frame. Support axle with a suitable jack.
2. Remove stabilizer bar, if necessary.
3. Lower axle and install a second jack under differential pinion nose.
4. Disconnect parking brake cable from upper arm retainer.
5. Disconnect control arm from axle bracket. On upper arms, disconnect arm from crossmember and on lower arms, disconnect arm from frame attachment bracket.
6. Reverse procedure to install. Tighten to specifications.

## 1992 CROWN VICTORIA & GRAND MARQUIS

**Control arms must be replaced in pairs.**

If both upper control arms and both lower control arms are being removed at same time, remove both coil springs.

### LOWER ARM

1. Disconnect battery ground cable and turn air suspension switch OFF.
2. Mark rear suspension shock tube relative to protective sleeve with vehicle on level ground.
3. Remove rear stabilizer bar, then raise and support vehicle and place jackstands below rear axle.
4. Lower vehicle until rear shocks are fully extended to relieve spring pressure.
5. Support axle below differential pinion nose as well as below axle.
6. Remove and discard lower arm pivot bolt and nut from axle bracket.
7. Disengage lower arm from bracket.
8. Remove and discard pivot bolt and nut from frame bracket. Remove lower control arm.
9. Reverse procedure to install. Tighten to specifications.

### UPPER ARM

Control arms must be replaced in pairs. **Remove and replace one control at a time to prevent axle from rolling or slipping sideways.**

If both upper control arms and both lower control arms are being removed at same time, remove both coil springs.

#### Removal

1. Raise vehicle and support frame side rails with jackstands.
2. Support rear axle.
3. Lower axle and support below differential pinion nose.
4. Remove and discard nut and bolt securing upper arm to axle housing. Disconnect arm from housing.
5. Remove and discard nut and bolt securing upper arm to frame bracket. Remove arm.

#### Installation

1. Hold upper arm in position on front arm bracket. Install new bolt and self-locking nut. Do not tighten.
2. Secure upper arm to axle housing with new nuts and bolts. **Bolts must be pointed toward front of vehicle.**
3. Raise suspension with hoist, until upper arm rear pivot hole is in position with hole in axle bushing. Install new pivot bolt and nut with nut facing inboard.
4. Tighten to specifications.

# REAR KNUCKLE REPLACE

## COUGAR & THUNDERBIRD

**Do not begin this procedure unless a new hub retainer nut is available. Once removed, this part cannot be reused during assembly. Its torque holding and/or retention capability is greatly diminished during removal.**

1. Remove wheelcover/hub cover from wheel and tire assembly, then loosen wheel nuts.
2. Remove and discard hub nut and washer.
3. Raise and support vehicle, then remove wheel and tire assembly.
4. Pull back on parking brake cable release lever and at same time pull on cable. This action will relax cable so it can be removed from brake caliper or backing plate.
5. **On models with disc brakes,** proceed as follows:
   a. Remove parking brake cable from caliper.

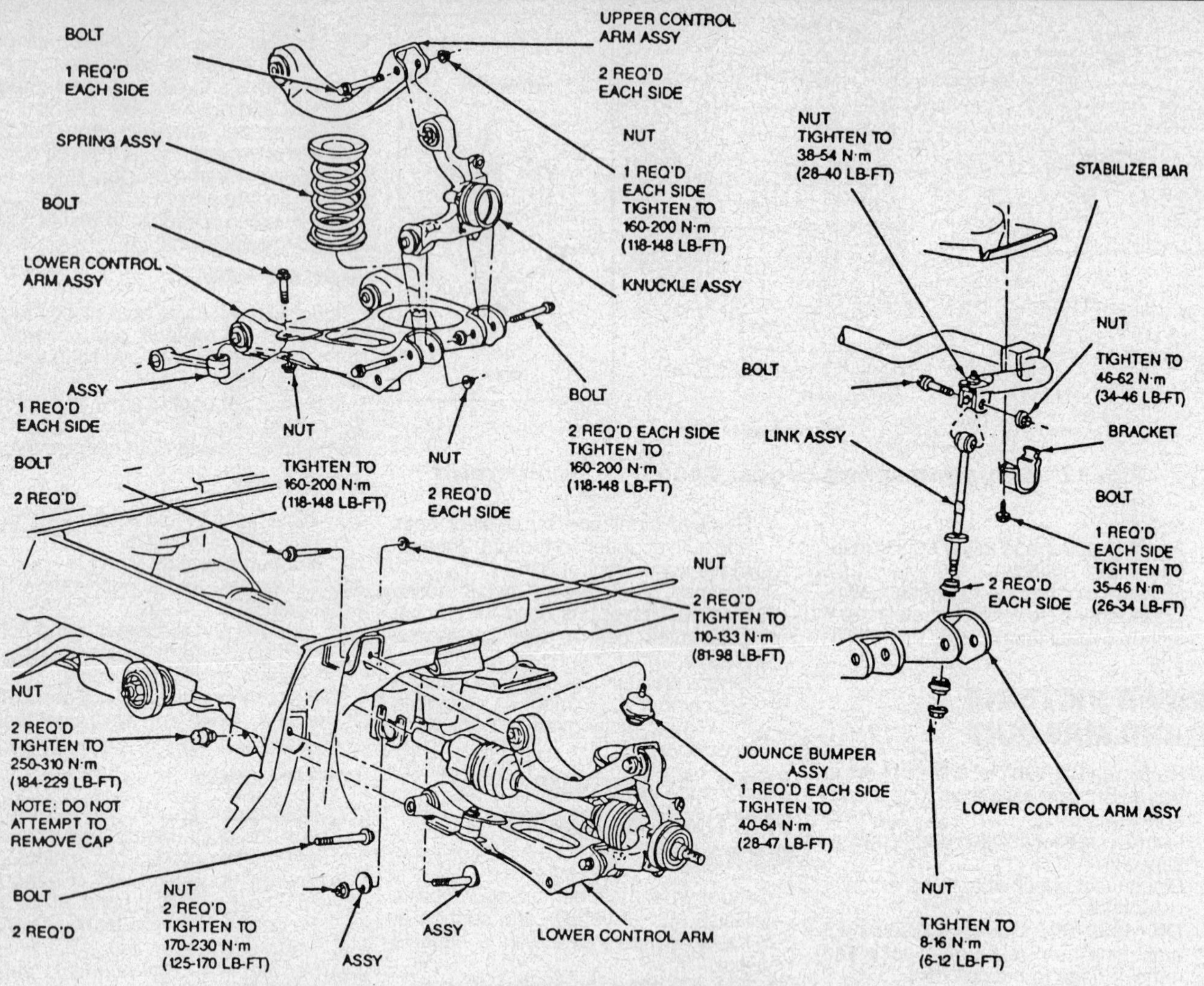


**Fig. 18 Exploded view of rear suspension. Cougar & Thunderbird**

b. Remove upper and lower caliper attaching bolts and remove caliper assembly from rotor.
c. Carefully wire caliper to brake junction bracket.

6. **On all models,** with push on nuts removed, remove brake rotor or drum assembly.
7. Remove three bolts retaining splash shield to knuckle and remove splash shield.
8. Disconnect parking brake cable and disconnect brake line from wheel cylinder.
9. Remove upper control arm nut and bolt.
10. Wire upper control arm to body to prevent damage to CV boots when knuckle and hub assembly is removed.
11. Install hub remover/replacer tool No. T81P-1104-C or equivalent to hub studs. Turn wrench counterclockwise until halfshaft is free in hub.
12. Using a paint marker, mark position of control arm in relation to knuckle with bushings in a relaxed position. When upper control arm bolt is removed from knuckle, lower arm bushings will return to a relaxed position. **Failure to mark position will cause bushing wind up upon assembly and incorrect ride height. These conditions can cause misalignment and premature tire wear.**
13. Note approximate angle of knuckle in relaxed position by measuring distance from upper bushing to any convenient point on vehicle body.
14. Remove lower control arm to knuckle attaching bolts and nuts.
15. Remove knuckle assembly from halfshaft.
16. Reverse procedure to install. Tighten to specifications.

# AIR SUSPENSION PRESSURE RELIEF

Before servicing any air suspension components, disconnect power to system by turning air suspension switch OFF or by disconnect battery ground cable.

**Do not remove an air spring under any circumstances when there is pressure in the air spring. Do not remove any component supporting an air spring without either exhausting the air or providing support for air spring.**

# TIGHTENING SPECIFICATIONS

## COUGAR & THUNDERBIRD

| Year | Component | Torque/ft. lbs. |
|---|---|---|
| 1989–92 | ABS Sensor Bolt | 14–20 |
| | Axle Hub Nut | 250 |
| | Caliper Bolt | 80–100 |
| | Caliper To Knuckle Bolts | 44–60 |
| | Crossmember bolt | 12–17 |
| | Driveshaft Companion Flange Bolts | 70–95 |
| | Driveshaft Hoop Bolt | 30–44 |
| | Exhaust Pipe To Muffler Bolt | 21—29 |
| | Fuel Tank Strap Bolts | 21–29 |
| | Hub Retainer Nut | 188–254 |
| | Jounce Bumper To Body | 28–47 |
| | Lower Control Arm To Toe Compensator Link Nut | 118–148 |
| | Lower Control Arm To Knuckle | 118–148 |
| | Lower Control Arm To Subframe (Front) | 184–229 |
| | Lower Control Arm To Subframe (Rear) | 125–170 |
| | Shock Absorber To Lower Control Arm | 110–120 |
| | Shock Absorber Upper Mount | 27–35 |
| | Splash Shield To Knuckle Bolts | 45–59 |
| | Stabilizer Bar Link To Lower Control Arm | 6–12 |
| | Stabilizer Bar U-Bracket To Subframe | 26–34 |
| | Stabilizer Clevis To Stabilizer Bar | 28–40 |
| | Stabilizer Link To Stabilizer Bar | 34–46 |
| | Upper Control Arm To Knuckle | 118–148 |
| | Upper Control Arm To Subframe | 81–98 |
| | Wheel Lug Nut | 80–106 |

## CROWN VICTORIA & GRAND MARQUIS

| Year | Component | Torque/ft. lbs. |
|---|---|---|
| 1989–92 | Driveshaft Flange Bolts | 70–95 |
| | Disc Brake Adapter Bolts & Nuts | 20–39 |
| | Lower Arm To Axle | 103–133 |
| | Lower Arm To Frame | 120–150 |
| | Pinion Shaft Lock Bolt | 15–29 |
| | Rear Cover Bolts | 19–25 |
| | Shock Absorber To Axle Bracket | 52–85 |
| | Shock Absorber Upper Mount Nut | 14–26 |
| | Speed Sensor Bolt | 40–60 ① |
| | Stabilizer Bar | 70–92 |
| | Stabilizer To Axle | 16–21 |
| | Stabilizer Link To Frame | 13–17 |
| | Upper Arm To Axle | 103–133 |
| | Upper Arm To Frame | 120–150 |
| | Wheel Lug Nuts | 80–106 |

① —Inch Lbs.

# Front Suspension & Steering

## INDEX



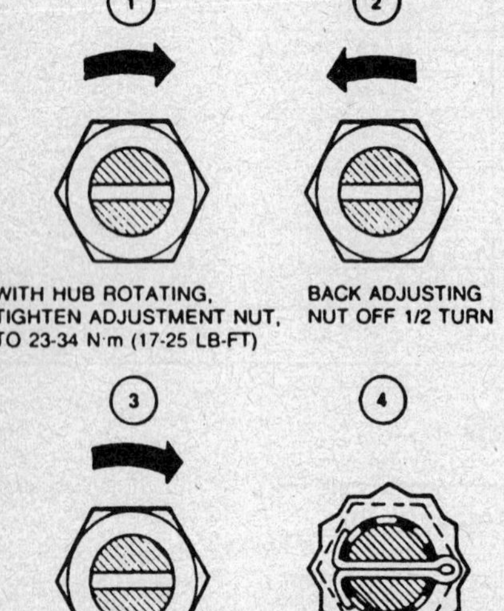

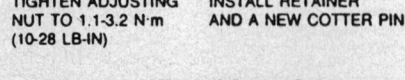

**Fig. 1 Wheel bearing adjustment. 1989–91 Crown Victoria & Grand Marquis**

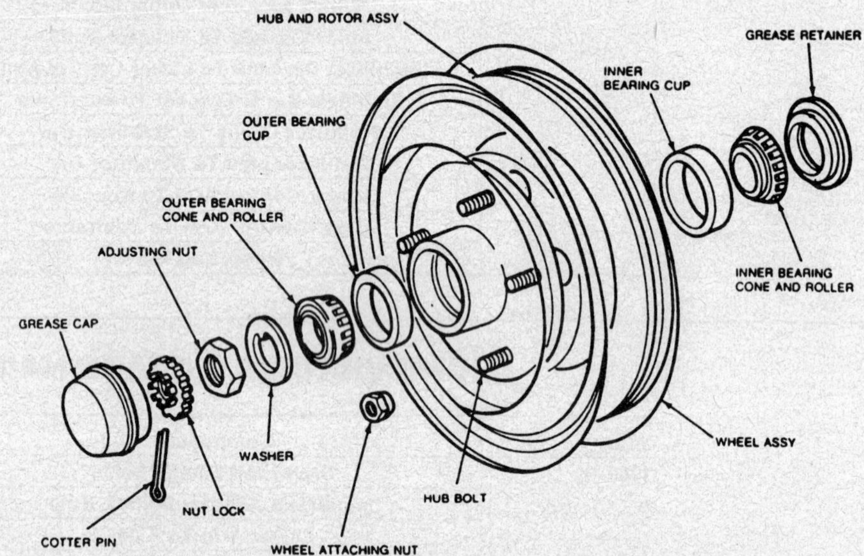


**Fig. 2 Hub & wheel bearing assembly. 1989–91 Crown Victoria & Grand Marquis**

## WHEEL BEARINGS ADJUST

### 1989–91 CROWN VICTORIA & GRAND MARQUIS

1. Raise and support vehicle so front wheels are free to turn.
2. Remove wheel cover, then the grease cap from hub.
3. Clean excess grease from end of spindle, then remove cotter pin and nut lock.
4. Back off adjusting nut three turns, then rock wheel assembly in and out several times to push pad away from rotor.
5. **Torque** adjusting to nut 17-25 ft. lbs. while rotating wheel assembly, **Fig. 1.**
6. Back off adjusting nut 1/2 turn, then retighten nut to 10-28 inch lbs.
7. Install nut lock on nut so castellations on lock are aligned with cotter pin hole in spindle, then install cotter pin.
8. Check wheel rotation. If wheel rotates roughly or makes noise, lubricate or replace bearings as necessary.

### COUGAR, THUNDERBIRD, 1992 CROWN VICTORIA & GRAND MARQUIS

These models are equipped with sealed bearing units which do not require adjustment or maintenance. If bearing is found to be defective, then hub and bearing must be replaced as an assembly.

## WHEEL BEARINGS REPLACE

### 1989–91 CROWN VICTORIA & GRAND MARQUIS

1. Raise and support front of vehicle, then remove tire and wheel assemblies.
2. Remove caliper mounting bolts. **It is not necessary to disconnect brake lines for this operation.**
3. Slide caliper off of disc, inserting a

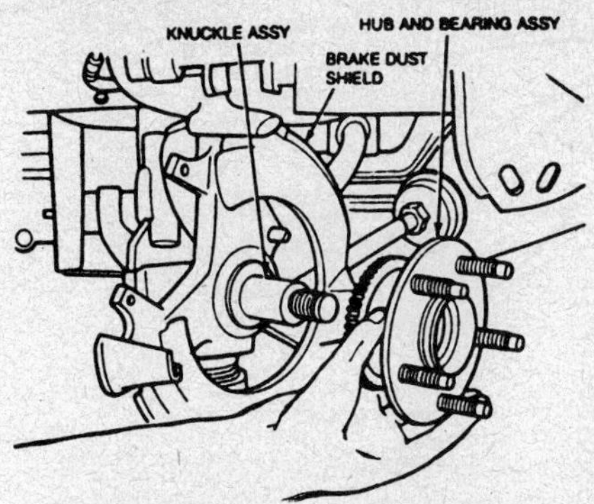


**Fig. 3 Hub & wheel bearing assembly. Cougar, Thunderbird, 1992 Crown Victoria & Grand Marquis**

spacer between shoes to hold in bores after caliper is removed. Position caliper assembly out of the way. **Do not allow caliper to hang by brake hose.**

4. Remove hub and disc assembly. Grease retainer and inner bearing can now be removed, **Fig. 2.**
5. Reverse procedure to install. Adjust wheel bearing as described under "Wheel Bearing, Adjust."

## COUGAR, THUNDERBIRD, 1992 CROWN VICTORIA & GRAND MARQUIS

1. Raise and support front of vehicle, then remove wheel and tire assembly.
2. Remove grease cap from hub.
3. Remove disc brake caliper with brake hose attached. Suspend caliper from suspension with wire. Do not allow caliper to hang from brake hose.
4. Remove brake rotor.
5. Remove hub nut, then remove hub and bearing assembly, **Fig. 3.** If difficulty is encountered in hub removal, use hub removal tool No. T81P-1104-C or equivalent.
6. Reverse procedure to install. Use a new hub nut and tighten to specifications.

# BALL JOINT INSPECTION

## COUGAR & THUNDERBIRD

1. Raise front of vehicle and position jacks under sub-frame.
2. Position a suitable dial indicator to ball joint to be checked, in such a manner that lateral movement between spindle and arm can be measured.
3. Grasp tire at top and bottom, then slowly move tire inward and outward while noting indicator reading.
4. If dial indicator reading exceeds .015 inch, replace ball joint.

## CROWN VICTORIA & GRAND MARQUIS

### Lower Ball Joint

These models are equipped with lower ball joint wear indicators, **Fig. 4.** To check ball joint for wear, support vehicle in normal driving position with both ball joints loaded. Observe the checking surface of ball joint. If checking surface is inside the cover, **Fig. 4**, replace ball joint.

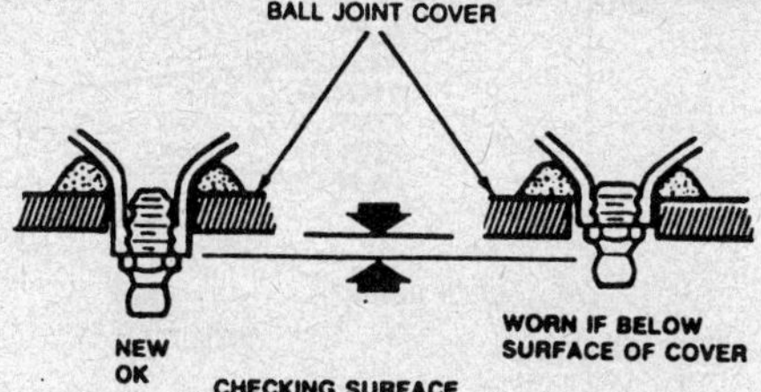


**Fig. 4 Lower ball joint wear indicator. Crown Victoria & Grand Marquis**

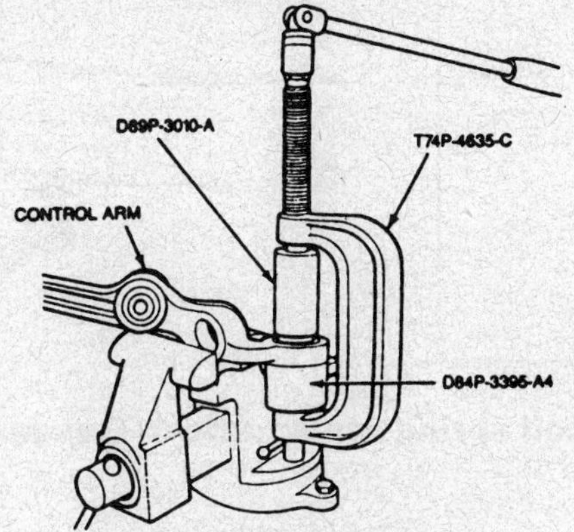


**Fig. 6 Lower ball joint replacement. Cougar & Thunderbird**

### Upper Ball Joint

1. Raise car on floor jacks placed beneath lower control arms.
2. Grasp lower edge of tire and move wheel in and out, **Fig. 5.**
3. As wheel is being moved in and out, observe upper end of spindle and upper arm.
4. Any movement between upper end of spindle and upper arm indicates ball joint wear and loss of preload. If any such movement is observed, replace upper ball joint.

During the foregoing check, lower ball joint will be unloaded and may move. Disregard all such movement of lower ball joint. Also, do not mistake loose wheel bearings for a worn ball joint.

# BALL JOINTS REPLACE

## COUGAR & THUNDERBIRD

### Upper Ball Joint

The upper ball joint and upper control arm must be replaced as an assembly. Refer to "Control Arm, Replace."

### Lower Ball Joint

1. Remove lower control arm as described under "Control Arm, Replace."
2. Remove and discard ball joint boot seal, then position lower control arm in a vise.
3. Press ball joint from lower control arm using removal tools No. D89P-3010-A, D84P-3395-A4 and T74P-4635-C or equivalent, **Fig. 6.**
4. Reverse procedure to install. Do not remove protective cover from ball joint until after it has been installed. Press ball joint into lower control arm until fully seated. After installing lower control arm, check and adjust wheel alignment as necessary. Tighten to specifications.

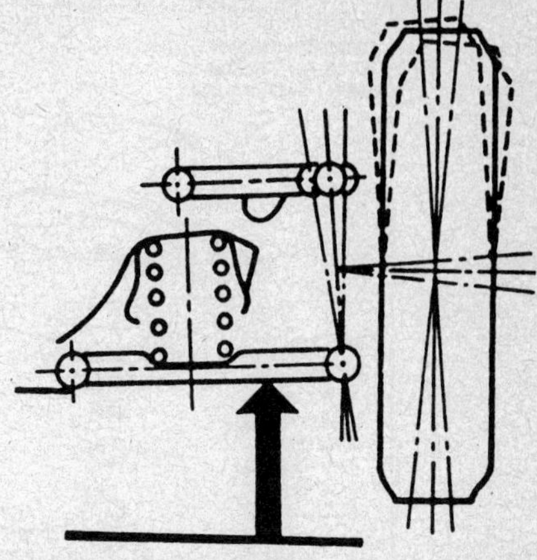

**Fig. 5 Checking upper ball joint for wear. Crown Victoria & Grand Marquis**

## 1989–91 CROWN VICTORIA & GRAND MARQUIS

Ball joint repair kits which do not require control arm replacement, are available and can be installed using the following procedure.

The ball joints are riveted to upper and lower control arms. Ball joints can be replaced on vehicle by removing the rivets and retaining new ball joint to control arm with attaching bolts, nuts and washers furnished with ball joint kit.

When removing a ball joint, use a suitable pressing tool to force ball joint out of spindle.

## 1992 CROWN VICTORIA & GRAND MARQUIS

### Upper Ball Joint

1. Raise and support front of vehicle. Remove wheel assembly.
2. Position jack below lower control arm at the ball joint.
3. Remove retaining nut and punch bolt from upper ball joint stud.
4. Mark position of alignment cams.
5. Remove ball joint retaining nuts.
6. Remove ball joint and spread slot with pry bar to separate ball joint stud from spindle.
7. Reverse procedure to install. Tighten to specifications.

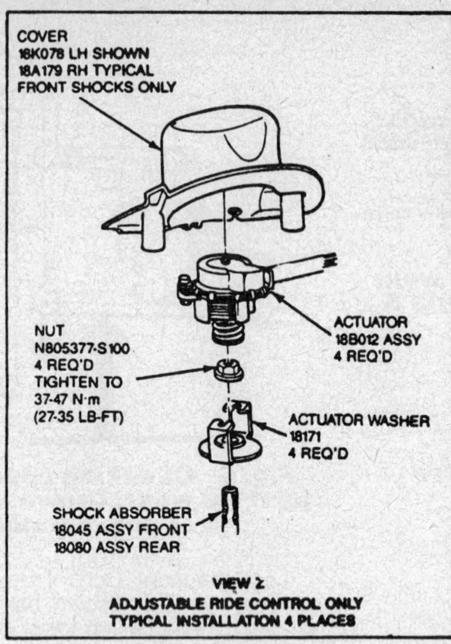


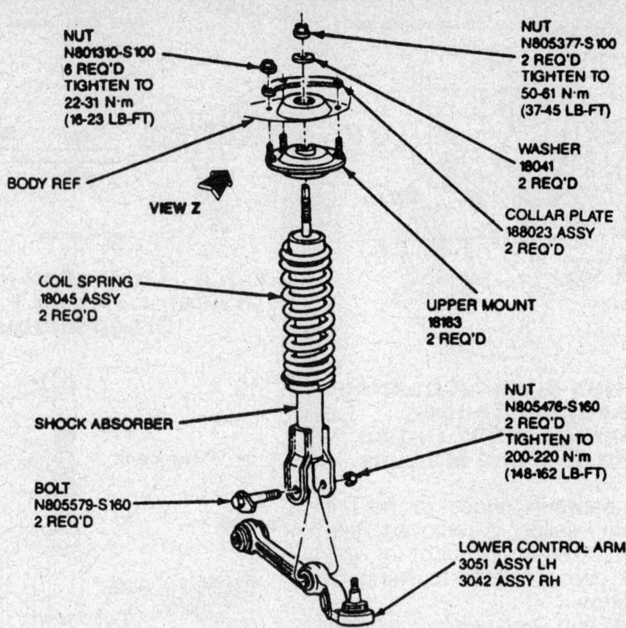


**Fig. 7 Strut & coil spring replacement. Cougar & Thunderbird**

### Lower Ball Joint

The lower ball joint must be replaced as an assembly, with the lower control arm.

## SHOCK ABSORBER REPLACE

### CROWN VICTORIA & GRAND MARQUIS

1. Remove nut, washer and bushing from shock absorber upper end.
2. Raise vehicle and install safety stands.
3. Remove two thread-cutting screws from lower end of shock absorber, then remove shock absorber.
4. Reverse procedure to install. **If threads in lower arm become damaged, reuse original thread-cutting screws along with 5/16-18 locknuts. Tighten to specifications.**

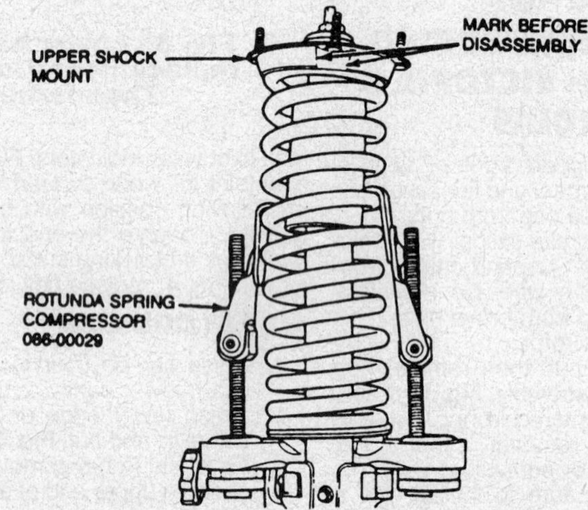


**Fig. 8 Upper mount to spring alignment mark placement. Cougar & Thunderbird**

## STRUT ASSEMBLY REPLACE

### COUGAR & THUNDERBIRD

1. Remove plastic cover at upper shock mount.
2. Remove automatic ride actuator, if equipped.
3. Remove three upper mounting nuts and collar plate from studs in engine compartment.
4. Raise and support vehicle, then remove tire and wheel assemblies.
5. Remove lower shock mounting bolt and nut, **Fig. 7.**
6. Remove nut at stabilizer link upper mounting stud.
7. Separate link from spindle using joint separator tool No. D88L-3006-A or equivalent.
8. Support lower control arm assembly with transmission jack.
9. Raise control arm and spindle with jack until stabilizer link can be completely separated from spindle. Position link out of the way.
10. Remove spindle to upper control arm attaching nut and bolt. Discard nut and bolt.
11. Lower jack to separate spindle from upper control arm. Do not allow spindle to hang free, support with wire or other means.
12. Remove support from lower control arm and remove shock and coil spring assembly.
13. Reverse procedure to install. Tighten to specifications.

## COIL SPRING REPLACE

### COUGAR & THUNDERBIRD

**The upper shock mount cannot be rotated when the shock and spring are assembled. Mark position of upper mount to coil spring with chalk, paint or grease pencil, prior to disassembly, Fig. 8. If upper mount is not properly positioned during assembly it will not install in vehicle. If installing new coil spring or upper mount transfer reference marks from removed parts to new parts.**

1. Remove coil spring and shock strut assembly , **Fig. 7,** from vehicle as de-

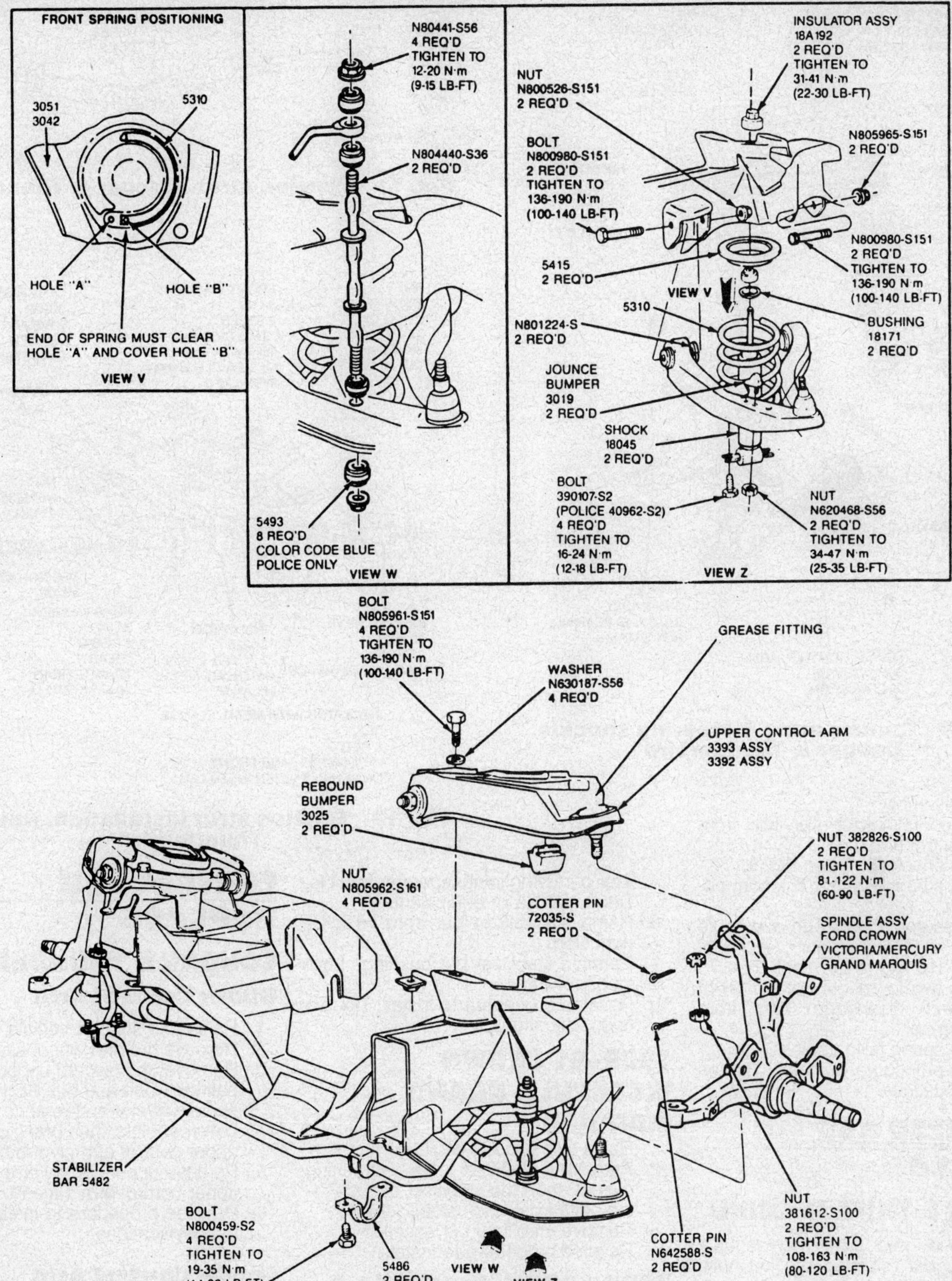


**Fig. 9 Front suspension assembly. Crown Victoria & Grand Marquis**

scribed under "Strut Assembly, Replace."

2. Position shock assembly in Spring Compressor tool No. 086-00029 or equivalent.
3. Compress spring and remove upper mount.
4. Release spring compressor to remove coil spring.
5. Position shock and coil assembly in Spring Compressor tool No. 086-00029 or equivalent and compress spring to install upper mount.
6. Install upper mount aligning reference marks.
7. Install nut and tighten to specification.
8. Release spring compressor, ensuring coil spring is properly seated.
9. Install coil spring and shock strut assembly from vehicle as described under "Strut Assembly, Replace."
10. Tighten to specifications.

## CROWN VICTORIA & GRAND MARQUIS

1. Raise and support vehicle. Remove

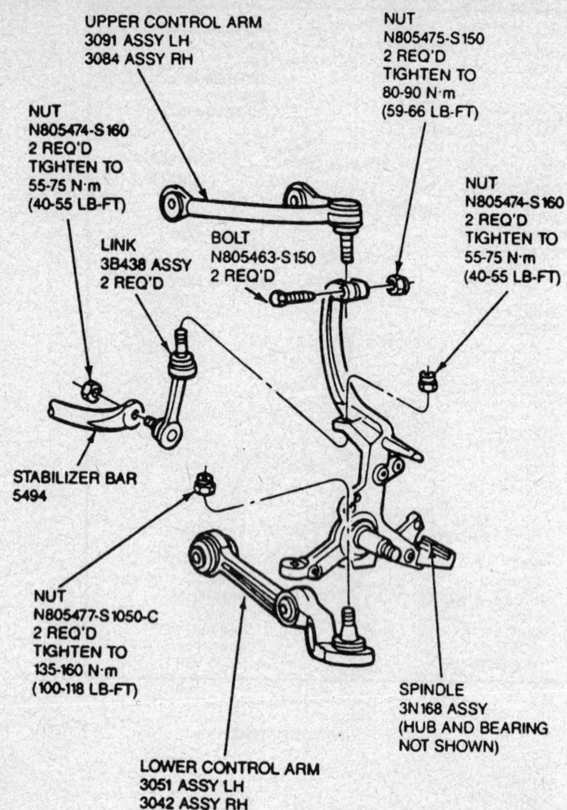


**Fig. 10 Control arms & steering knuckle. Cougar & Thunderbird**

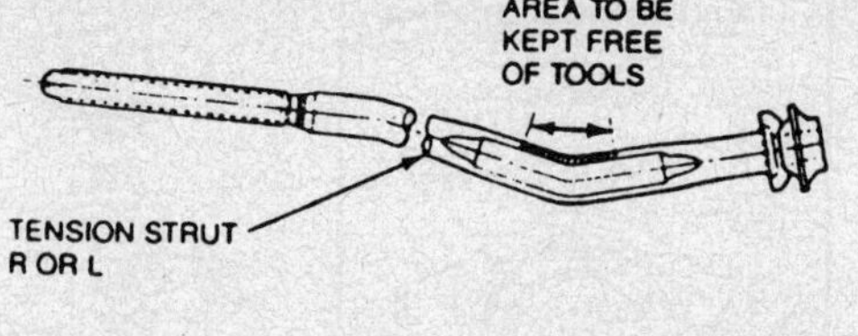


**Fig. 11 Tension strut. Cougar & Thunderbird**

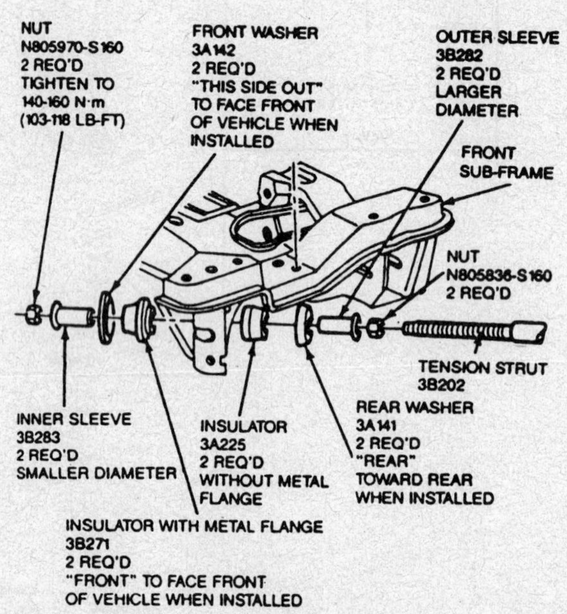


**Fig. 12 Tension strut installation. Cougar & Thunderbird**

wheel assembly.
2. Disconnect stabilizer bar link from lower control arm.
3. Remove shock absorber, **Fig. 9.**
4. Remove steering center link from pitman arm.
5. Compress coil spring with a suitable spring compressor, tool D-78P-5310-A or equivalent.
6. Remove two lower control arm pivot bolts and disengage arm from crossmember.
7. Remove spring from vehicle.
8. Reverse procedure to install. Tighten to specifications.

## STABILIZER BAR REPLACE

### COUGAR & THUNDERBIRD

1. Remove air inlet tube, then remove stabilizer bar retaining bracket bolts and brackets.
2. Remove serpentine drive belt, then raise and support vehicle.
3. Remove front tire and wheel assemblies, then remove crankshaft vibration damper.
4. Remove cotter pins and castellated nuts at rod ends.
5. Separate tie rod ends from spindles using tie rod end removal tool No. 3290-D or equivalent.
6. Remove transmission oil cooler line bracket.
7. Remove stabilizer bar link from stabilizer bar using joint separator tool No. D88L-3006-A or equivalent.
8. Remove stabilizer bar from vehicles right side
9. Remove stabilizer bar bushings from stabilizer bar.
10. Reverse procedure to install. Tighten to specifications.

### 1989–91 CROWN VICTORIA & GRAND MARQUIS

1. Raise and support vehicle.
2. Remove stabilizer bar attaching clamps, then the stabilizer bar attaching bolts from each stabilizer link.
3. Remove stabilizer bar assembly.
4. Reverse procedure to install.

### 1992 CROWN VICTORIA & GRAND MARQUIS

1. Raise and support vehicle.
2. Remove nuts from pinch bolts at both spindles. Remove bolts.
3. Spread slots in spindles with a pry bar to free ball studs.
4. Disconnect stabilizer bar brackets from frame. Pull bar forward until links can be removed from spindle attachments.
5. Reverse procedure to install. Tighten to specifications.

## CONTROL ARM REPLACE

### COUGAR & THUNDERBIRD

#### Upper Control Arm

1. Raise and support vehicle.
2. Remove tire and wheel assembly.
3. Remove and discard upper spindle to ball joint bolt and nut. Slightly spread spindle at slot and remove ball joint.
4. Lower vehicle, then brake off flags on upper control arm pivot bolt heads.
5. Remove upper control arm bolts, then upper control arm, **Fig. 10.**
6. Reverse procedure to install. Tighten to specifications.

#### Lower Control Arm

1. Raise and support vehicle.
2. Remove tire and wheel assembly.
3. Loosen lower ball joint nut three or four turns.
4. Rap spindle to separate ball joint. Leave nut attached.
5. Support spindle by wire to prevent excessive sagging of upper control arm.
6. Mark position of camber adjustment cam.
7. Remove nut attaching tension strut to control arm. hold strut by flats with wrench while turning nut. **Do not hold**

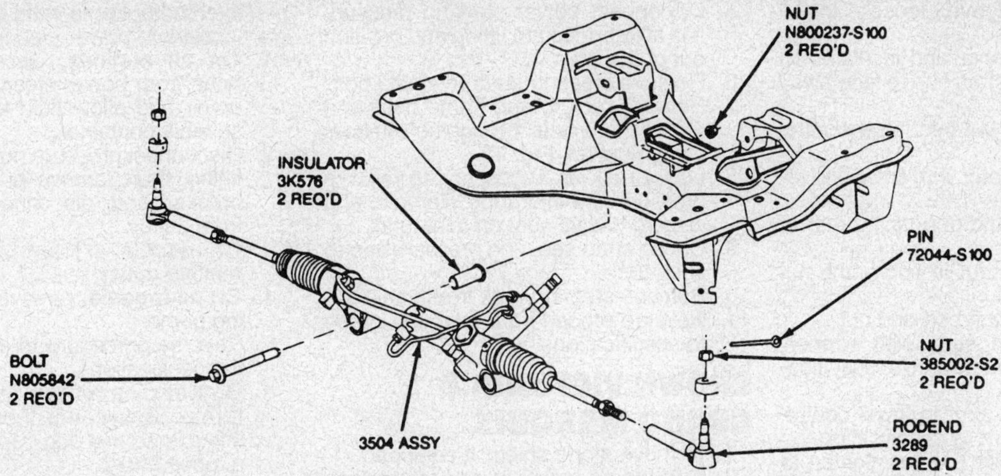


**Fig. 13 Power rack & pinion steering gear installation. Cougar & Thunderbird**

**strut or damage surface in area shown in Fig. 11, damage to tension strut may result.**

8. Remove lower shock bolt and nut.
9. Remove pivot (camber) bolt and nut.
10. Remove nut at lower ball joint and remove control arm, **Fig. 10.**
11. Reverse procedure to install, after installation check front end alignment and adjust as necessary. Tighten to specifications.

## CROWN VICTORIA & GRAND MARQUIS

### Lower Control Arm

1. Raise and support front of vehicle, then remove front wheels.
2. Remove brake caliper, rotor, dust shield and ABS sensor, if equipped.
3. Remove jounce bumper, if equipped.
4. Remove shock absorber.
5. Disconnect stabilizer bar link from lower control arm.
6. Disconnect steering center link from pitman arm.
7. Remove lower ball joint attaching nut cotter pin, then loosen lower ball joint nut one or two turns. **Do not remove nut from stud at this time.**
8. Install ball joint press tool T57P-3006-B or equivalent between upper and lower ball joint studs.
9. Compress ball joint with tool, then tap spindle, near lower stud, to loosen stud in spindle.
10. Remove ball joint press tool, then position a suitable jack under lower control arm.
11. Install suitable coil spring compression tool, then remove coil spring.
12. Remove ball joint nut, then the lower control arm assembly, **Fig. 9.**
13. Reverse procedure to install, noting the following:
    a. Tighten to specifications.
    b. Ensure coil spring is properly aligned, **Fig. 9.**
    c. Check and adjust wheel alignment.

### Upper Control Arm

1. Raise and support front of vehicle, then remove front wheels.
2. Remove upper ball joint attaching nut cotter pin, then loosen upper ball joint nut one or two turns. **Do not remove nut from stud at this time.**
3. Install ball joint press tool T57P-3006-B or equivalent between upper and lower ball joint studs.
4. Compress ball joint with tool, then tap spindle, near upper stud, to loosen stud in spindle.
5. Remove ball joint press tool, then position a suitable jack under lower control arm.
6. Remove upper control arm attaching bolts, then the upper control arm assembly, **Fig. 9.**
7. Reverse procedure to install. Tighten to specifications and check wheel alignment.

# SPINDLE ASSEMBLY REPLACE

## COUGAR & THUNDERBIRD

1. Raise and support vehicle.
2. Remove tire and wheel assembly.
3. Remove brake caliper and rotor.
4. Remove hub and bearing assembly.
5. Remove brake anti-lock sensor and position out of the way.
6. Remove tie rod end cotter pin and loosen castellated nut. Separate tie rod end from spindle using tie rod end remover tool No. 3290-D or equivalent.
7. Remove stabilizer bar link at spindle using joint separator D88L-3006-A or equivalent.
8. Separate lower ball joint from spindle. Loosen nut and rap spindle with hammer. Remove nut.
9. Remove and discard upper spindle to upper control arm bolt and nut. Spread slot slightly and remove spindle from control arm and vehicle.
10. Reverse procedure to install. Tighten to specifications.

# TENSION STRUT REPLACE

## COUGAR & THUNDERBIRD

### Removal

1. Raise and support vehicle.
2. Remove tire and wheel assembly.
3. Hold tension strut on flats with wrench. Remove front sub-frame attaching nut and insulator. **Do not hold strut or damage surface in area shown in Fig. 11, damage to tension strut may result.**
4. Mark position, or note number of visible threads at tension strut rear sub-frame nut.
5. Back off tension strut rear sub-frame nut.
6. Remove tension strut to lower control arm attaching nut.
7. Remove lower shock bolt and nut.
8. Remove brake hose bracket to body attaching bolt.
9. Remove ABS sensor attaching bolt and position sensor out of the way.
10. Pry lower control arm rearward and remove tension strut.

### Installation

1. If front tension strut insulators were removed, de-burr insulator sleeves before reassembly. If new sleeves are used, inner sleeve must be shorter than outer sleeve. Cut up to 1/4 inch off inner sleeve if necessary, **Fig. 12.**
2. Install tension strut retaining nut all the way down on threads. Install with nylon insert facing forward.
3. Install outer sleeve and rear washer. Word REAR must face outward.
4. Install rear insulator (without metal flange) with large end toward sub-frame.
5. Install tension strut in sub-frame.
6. Install front insulator, with the word FRONT toward front of vehicle and metal flange toward sub-frame.
7. Install front washer, with the words "THIS SIDE OUT" toward front of vehicle.

8. Install inner sleeve, loosely install front nut.
9. Install front washer and insulator on rear of tension strut, cup to face away from insulator.
10. Install tension strut into lower control arm.
11. Install rear insulator with small end toward control arm.
12. Install washer and cup facing rear of vehicle.
13. Return torsion strut-to-sub-frame nut to original position.
14. Install lower shock bolt and nut.
15. Holding tension strut with wrench, tighten strut to sub-frame to specification.
16. Tighten tension strut to lower control arm attaching nut to specification.
17. Install brake hose bracket, tighten to specifications.
18. Install ABS sensor, tighten to specifications.
19. Install tire and wheel assembly, check front wheel alignment.

## POWER STEERING GEAR REPLACE

### COUGAR & THUNDERBIRD

1. Raise and support vehicle. Remove both front wheel and tire assemblies.
2. Remove cotter pins at outer tie rod ends and remove castellated nuts at each end. Discard cotter pins.
3. Separate tie rod ends from spindles, using tie rod end removal tool No. 3290-D or equivalent.
4. Disconnect and plug power steering return line hose.
5. Disconnect power steering pressure line at intermediate fitting and position out of the way.
6. Remove steering shaft retaining bolt.
7. Remove rack to sub-frame bolts and nuts, access nuts through hole in front crossmember, **Fig. 13.**
8. Lower rack as necessary, to remove pressure line inlet tube. Remove and discard plastic seal on inlet tube.
9. Cut tie strap securing pressure line to each tube.
10. Remove steering rack from vehicle.
11. Reverse procedure to install. Tighten to specifications.

### CROWN VICTORIA & GRAND MARQUIS

1. Remove stone shield, if equipped.
2. Disconnect pressure and return lines from steering gear. Plug lines and ports in gear to prevent entry of dirt.
3. Remove two bolts that secure flex coupling to steering gear and to column.
4. Raise car and remove sector shaft nut.
5. Use a puller to remove pitman arm.
6. Support steering gear, then remove attaching bolts.
7. Work steering gear free of flex coupling and remove it from car.
8. Reverse procedure to install. Tighten to specifications.

## POWER STEERING PUMP REPLACE

### COUGAR & THUNDERBIRD

**On Supercharged engines,** intercooler and intercooler tubes must be removed to gain access to power steering pump.

1. **On all engines,** disconnect return hose from power steering pump reservoir and allow fluid to drain into a suitable container.
2. Disconnect pressure hose from pump fitting, then remove pump mounting bracket and disconnect drive belt from pulley.
3. **On models w/fixed pump system,** remove pulley.
4. **On all models,** remove power steering pump.
5. Reverse procedure to install. Tighten to specifications.
6. **Do not overtighten pressure hose fitting.** Swivel and/or end play of the fitting is normal and does not indicate a loose fitting.

### CROWN VICTORIA & GRAND MARQUIS

1. Disconnect power steering pump return line and allow power steering pump fluid to drain into a suitable container.
2. Disconnect power steering pump pressure hose from pump fitting.
3. Disconnect drive belt from power steering pump pulley, remove pulley, then remove pump.
4. Reverse procedure to install. Tighten to specifications.
5. **Do not overtighten pressure hose fitting.** Swivel and/or end play of the fitting is normal and does not indicate a loose fitting.

# TIGHTENING SPECIFICATIONS

## COUGAR & THUNDERBIRD

| Year & Model | Component | Torque/Ft. Lbs |
|---|---|---|
| 1989–92 | ABS Sensor Bolt | 40–60① |
| | Brake Caliper Torx Bolts | 25 |
| | Brake Hose Retaining Bolt | 9–11 |
| | Hose Fittings At Gear | 20–25 |
| | Lower Control Arm To Shock | 118–162 |
| | Lower Control Arm To Spindle (Ball Joint) | 80–120 |
| | Lower Control Arm To Sub-frame | 92–125 |
| | Lower Control Arm To Tension Strut | 90–120 |
| | Pressure Hose Fitting At Pump | 10–15 |
| | Pump Mounting Bracket | 30–45 |
| | Stabilizer Bar Bracket | 40–55 |
| | Stabilizer Bar Link To Spindle | 40–55 |
| | Stabilizer Bar Link To Stabilizer Bar | 40–55 |
| | Steering Flex Coupling Nut | 20–30 |
| | Steering Gear To Crossmember | 100–144 |
| | Shock To Upper Mount | 37–45 |
| | Tension Strut To Sub-frame | 90–120 |
| | Tie Rod Ball Socket To Rack | 55–65 |
| | Tie Rod End To Jam Nut | 35–50 |
| | Tie Rod End To Spindle | 39–54 |
| | Upper Control Arm To Body | 55–90 |
| | Upper Control Arm To Spindle (Ball Joint) | 50–65 |
| | Upper Shock Mount To Body | 16–23 |
| | Wheel Hub Nut | 189–254 |
| | Wheel Lug Nuts | 85–106 |

① —Inch Lbs.

## CROWN VICTORIA & GRAND MARQUIS

| Year & Model | Component | Torque/Ft. Lbs |
|---|---|---|
| 1989-91 | Bearing Adjusting Nut | 17-25 |
| 1989-1992 | Ball Joint To Lower Spindle | 80-119 |
| | Ball Joint To Upper Spindle | 51-67 |
| | Brake Caliper Torx Bolts | 24 |
| | Flex Coupling to Gear Input Shaft Bolt | 20-30 |
| | Hub Nut | 189-254 |
| | Lower Arm To Crossmember | 101-140 |
| | Lower Arm To Frame | 101-140 |
| | Pinch Bolt & Nut | 38-49 |
| | Pitman Arm Nut | 44-46 |
| | Pitman Arm To Sector Shaft Retaining Nut | 200-250 |
| | Pressure Hose To Gear | 16-25 |
| | Quick Connect Tube Nut | 35-45 |
| | Return Hose To Gear | 25-34 |
| | Sector Shaft Cover Bolts | 55-70 |
| | Shock Absorber Top Stud Nut | 16-20 |
| | Shock Absorber Upper Mount | 19-27 |
| | Stabilizer Bar Link To Spindle | 41-44 |
| | Stabilizer Link To Bar | 30-40 |
| | Steering Gear To Side Rail Mounting Bolts | 50-65 |
| | Steering Pump To Engine | 15-22 |
| | Upper Ball Joint To Upper Arm | 107-129 |
| | Wheel Lug Nuts | 85-104 |

# Wheel Alignment

INDEX



## COUGAR & THUNDERBIRD

### CASTER

Caster is adjusted by moving the tension strut relative to the front sub-frame. Loosen nuts securing strut to sub-frame and adjust caster by running the nuts in appropriate direction until desired setting is achieved. The setting should be locked by holding adjusting nut and **torquing** locknut to 117 ft. lbs.

### CAMBER

#### Front

Camber is adjusted by rotating a cam bolt at lower control arm inner pivot. Loosen nut securing adjustment and adjust by rotating bolt head. Lock adjustment by holding bolt and **torque** nut to 125 ft. lbs.

#### Rear

Camber is adjusted by rotating a cam bolt at upper control arm inner pivot. Loosen nut securing adjustment and adjust by rotating head of bolt. Lock adjustment by holding bolt and **torque** nut to 98 ft. lbs.

### TOE-IN

#### Front

1. Check to see that steering shaft and steering wheel marks are in alignment and in the top position.
2. Loosen clamp screw on tie rod bellows and free the seal on the rod to prevent twisting of bellows, **Fig. 1.**
3. Place opened end wrench on flats of tie rod socket to prevent socket from turning, then loosen tie rod jam nuts.
4. Use suitable pliers to turn tie rod inner end to correct the adjustment to specifications. Do not use pliers on tie rod threads. Turning to reduce number of threads showing will increase toe-in. Turning in opposite direction will reduce toe-in.
5. **Torque** tie rod jam nuts to 43-50 ft. lbs.

#### Rear

The recommended adjustment sequence for rear alignment is to set toe then camber. Toe should be rechecked before final tightening.

Toe is adjusted by rotating a cam bolt at lower arm inner pivot. Loosen nut securing adjustment and adjust by rotating bolt head. Lock adjustment by holding bolt and **torque** nut to 170 ft. lbs.

## 1989–91 CROWN VICTORIA & GRAND MARQUIS

Wheel balancing differs on vehicles with

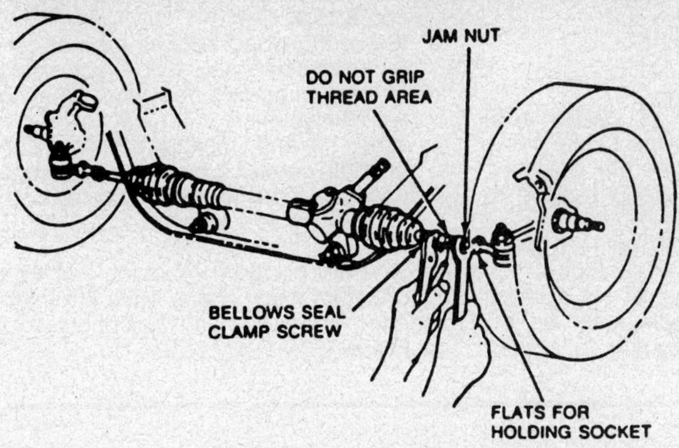


**Fig. 1 Toe-in adjustment. Cougar & Thunderbird**

**Fig. 2 Adjusting caster & camber. 1989–91 Crown Victoria & Grand Marquis**

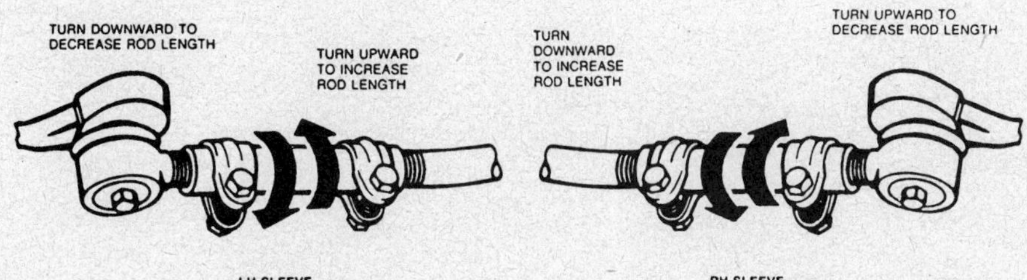


**Fig. 3 Toe-in adjustment. Crown Victoria & Grand Marquis**

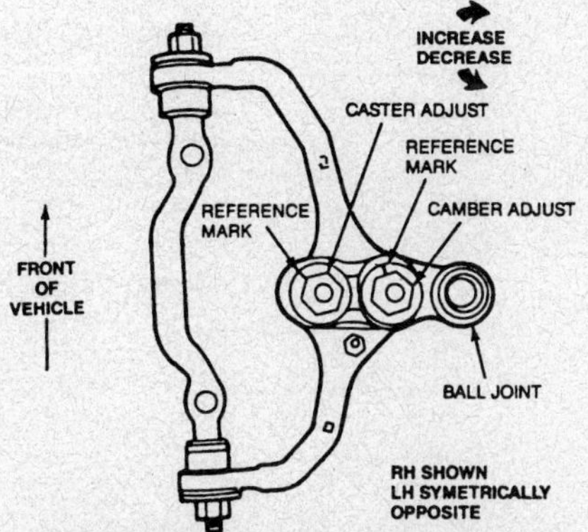


**Fig. 4 Caster & camber adjustment. 1992 Crown Victoria & Grand Marquis**

disc brakes, dynamic balancing of the wheel and tire assembly on vehicle should not be attempted without first pulling back the shoe and lining assemblies from the rotor. If this is not done, brake drag may burn out motor on wheel spinner.

The drag can be eliminated by removing wheel, taking out two bolts holding caliper splash shield, and detaching shield. Then push pistons into their cylinder bores by applying steady pressure on shoes on each side of the rotor for at least a minute. If necessary, use water pump pliers to apply pressure.

After pistons have been retracted, reinstall splash shield and wheel. The wheel and tire assembly can then be dynamically balanced in usual manner. After balancing has been completed, be sure to pump brake pedal several times until shoes are seated and a firm brake pedal is obtained.

Caster and camber can be adjusted by loosening bolts that attach upper suspension arm to shaft at frame side rail, and moving arm assembly in or out in elongated bolt holes, **Fig. 2.** Since any movement of arm affects both caster and camber, both factors should be balanced against one another when making adjustment.

Use alignment tool T79P-3000A or equivalent, **Fig. 2.** Install tool with pins in frame holes and hooks over the upper arm inner shaft. Tighten hook nuts snug before loosening upper arm inner shaft attaching bolts.

## CASTER

1. Tighten the tool front hook nut or loosen the rear hook nut as required to increase caster to desired angle.
2. To decrease caster, tighten rear hook nut or loosen front hook nut as required. **The caster angle can be checked without tightening inner shaft retaining bolts.**
3. Check camber angle to be sure it did not change during caster adjustment and adjust if necessary.
4. **Torque** upper arm inner shaft retaining bolts to 120-140 ft. lbs. and remove tool.

## CAMBER

1. Loosen both inner shaft retaining bolts.
2. Tighten or loosen hook nuts as necessary to increase or decrease camber.
3. Recheck caster and readjust if necessary.

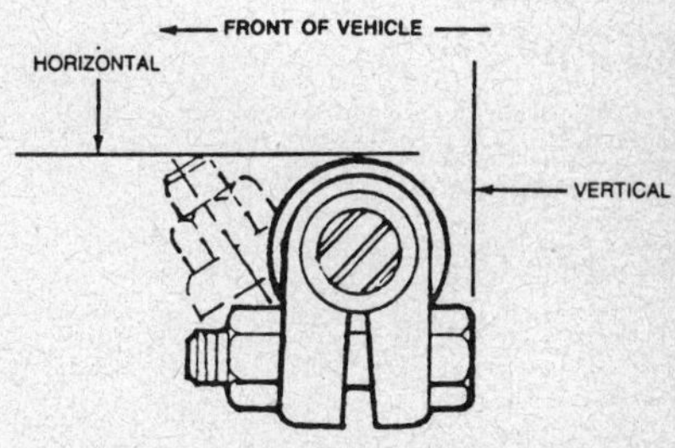


**Fig. 5 Sleeve position**

4. **Torque** upper arm inner shaft retaining bolts to 120-140 ft. lbs.

## TOE-IN

Position front wheels in straight-ahead position. Then turn both tie rod adjusting sleeves an equal amount until desired toe-in setting is obtained, **Fig. 3. Torque** tie rod sleeve clamp bolt to 20-22 ft. lbs.

# 1992 CROWN VICTORIA & GRAND MARQUIS

## CASTER & CAMBER

Camber and Caster adjustment tools No. T79P-3000-A are required to accurately adjust caster and camber.

1. Loosen two nuts on top of adjustment cams. **Fig. 4.**
2. Turn hex cams as required to obtain

desired valve.

3. Adjust camber and caster on each wheel as determined by alignment specification.
4. If correct specification cannot be obtained, ensure upper control arm to frame retaining bolts are centered in slots. Loosen and reposition as required. **Torque** to 101-140 ft. lbs.
5. After proper settings have been obtained, hold each cam and **Torque** nuts to 107-129 ft. lbs.
6. Check toe-in and steering wheel spoke position.

## TOE-IN

Following adjustment of caster and camber, check steering wheel spoke position. If spokes are not in normal position, they can be properly adjusted while toe is being adjusted.

1. Loosen two clamp bolts on each spindle connecting rod sleeve. **Fig. 3.**
2. Adjust toe. If steering wheel spokes are in normal position, lengthen or shorten both rods equally to obtain correct toe.
3. If steering wheel spokes are not correct, make necessary rod adjustments to obtain correct toe and steering wheel alignment.
4. When toe and steering wheel position are both correct, lubricate clamp, bolts and nuts. **Torque** clamp bolts on both connecting rod sleeves to 20-22 ft. lbs.
5. Sleeve position should not be changed when clamp bolts are tightened for proper clamp bolt orientation. Fig. 5.

# FORD TEMPO, MERCURY TOPAZ & 1989–90 FORD ESCORT

## INDEX OF SERVICE OPERATIONS

**NOTE:** Refer To Rear Of This Manual For Vehicle Manufacturer's Special Service Tool Suppliers.

## INDEX OF SERVICE OPERATIONS—Continued



# Specifications

## GENERAL ENGINE SPECIFICATIONS

| Year | Engine | | Fuel System | Bore & Stroke | Comp. Ratio | Net H.P. @ RPM① | Maximum Torque Ft. Lbs. @ RPM | Normal Oil Pressure (psi) |
|---|---|---|---|---|---|---|---|---|
| | Liter/CID | VIN Code | | | | | | |
| 1989-90 | 1.9L/4-116 Except H.O. | 9 | CFI | 3.23 x 3.46 | 9.0 | 90 @ 4600 | 106 @ 3400 | 35-65⑤ |
| | 1.9L/4-116 H.O. | J | EFI | 3.23 x 3.46 | 9.0 | 110 @ 5400 | 115 @ 4200 | 35-65⑤ |
| | 2.3L/4-140③ | X② | EPFI | 3.68 x 3.30 | 9.0 | 98 @ 4400 | 124 @ 2200 | 55-70⑤ |
| | 2.3L/4-140④ | S② | EPFI | 3.68 x 3.30 | 9.0 | 100 @ 4400 | 130 @ 2600 | 55-70⑤ |
| 1991 | 2.3L/4-140③ | X② | EPFI | 3.68 x 3.30 | 9.0 | 98 @ 4400 | 124 @ 2200 | 55-70⑤ |
| | 2.3L/4-140④ | S② | EPFI | 3.68 x 3.30 | 9.0 | 100 @ 4400 | 130 @ 2600 | 55-70⑤ |
| 1992 | 2.3L/4-140③ | X② | EPFI | 3.68 x 3.30 | 9.0 | 98 @ 4400 | 124 @ 2200 | 55-70⑤ |
| | 3.0L/V6-182 | U② | SEPFI | 3.50 x 3.14 | 9.0 | 135@5500 | ⑥ | 55-70⑤ |

①—Ratings are net-as installed in vehicle.
②—Tempo & Topaz.
③—High Swirl Combustion (HSC) engine.
④—High Specific Output (HSO) engine.
⑤—Pressure given is with engine warm and operating at 2000 RPM.
⑥—Manual Trans; 150@3250, Automatic;150@4200.

# FORD TEMPO, MERCURY TOPAZ & 1989–90 FORD ESCORT

## TUNE UP SPECIFICATIONS

| Year & Engine/ VIN Code ① | Spark Plug Gap | Ignition Timing BTDC | | | | Curb Idle Speed③ | | Fast Idle Speed | | Fuel Pump Pressure (psi) |
|---|---|---|---|---|---|---|---|---|---|---|
| | | Firing Order Fig. ② | Man. Trans. | Auto. Trans. | Mark Fig. | Man. Trans. | Auto Trans. | Man. Trans. | Auto. Trans. | |
| **1989–90** | | | | | | | | | | |
| 1.9L/4-116 CFI/9 | .044 | A | 10⑦ | 10⑦ | B | 900-1000 ④ | 900-1000 ④ | ④ | ④ | 14.5-17.5⑤ |
| 1.9L/4-116 EFI/J | .044 | A | 10⑦ | 10⑦ | B | 900-1000 ④ | 900-1000 ④ | ④ | — | 35-45⑤ |
| 2.3L/4-140/S,⑨ | .054 | C | 15⑦ | 15⑦ | ⑥ | 810-890④ | 680-760D ④ | ④ | ④ | 45-60⑤ |
| 2.3L/4-140/X,⑧ | .054 | C | 15⑦ | 15⑦ | ⑥ | 820-880④ | 690-760D④ | ④ | ④ | 45-60⑤ |
| **1991** | | | | | | | | | | |
| 2.3L/4-140/S,⑨ | .054 | C | 15⑦ | 15⑦ | ⑥ | 810-890④ | 680-760D ④ | ④ | ④ | 45-60⑤ |
| 2.3L/4-140/X,⑧ | .054 | C | 15⑦ | 15⑦ | ⑥ | 820-880④ | 690-760D④ | ④ | ④ | 45-60⑤ |
| **1992** | | | | | | | | | | |
| 2.3L/4-140/X,⑧ | .054 | C | 15⑦ | 15⑦ | ⑥ | 820-880④ | 690-760D④ | ④ | ④ | 45-60⑤ |
| 3.0L/V6-182,U | ⑪ | ⑩ | ⑪ | ⑪ | ⑪ | ⑪ | ⑪ | — | — | 36-39 |

①—The eighth digit of The Vehicle Identification Number (VIN) denotes engine code.

②—Before removing wires from distributor cap, determine location of No. 1 wire in cap, as distributor position may have been altered from that shown at the end of this chart.

③—D: Drive.

④—Idle speed controlled by an automatic idle speed control.

⑤—On EFI models equipped with fuel diagnostic valve, wrap shop towel around fitting to prevent fuel spillage. Connect a suitable fuel pressure gauge to fuel diagnostic valve. On CFI models & EFI models less fuel diagnostic valve, disconnect electrical connector at inertia switch, then crank engine for approximately 15 seconds to deplete fuel system pressure. Wrap shop towel around connection to be disconnected to avoid fuel spillage. Connect a suitable fuel pressure gauge between throttle body & fuel filter. On all models, energize fuel pump & check fuel pressure gauge reading. This test is done with ignition key on and engine off.

⑥—Refer to Fig. D for models equipped with manual transaxle. Refer to Fig. E for models with automatic transaxle. On manual transaxle models, a cover plate retained by two screws must be removed to view timing marks. On automatic transaxle models, symbols are indented on outer face of flywheel.

⑦—Disconnect in-line spout connector, then start engine & adjust ignition timing as necessary. After completing adjustment, reconnect spout connector.

⑧—High Swirl Combustion (HSC) engine.

⑨—High Specific Output (HSO) engine.

⑩—Firing order; 1-4-2-5-3-6.

⑪—Refer to Vehicle Emission Information Label located in engine compartment.

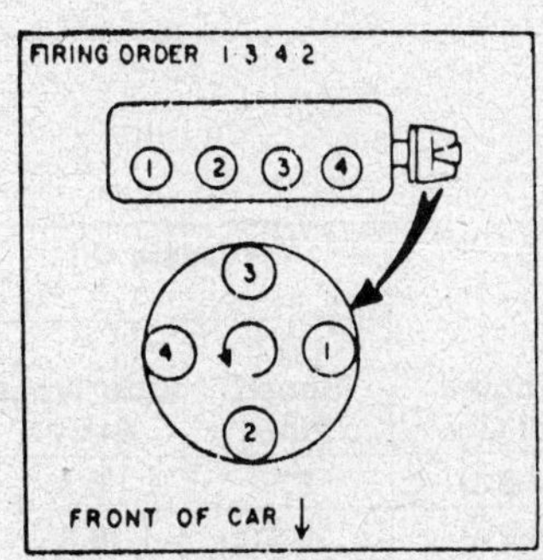


**Fig. A**

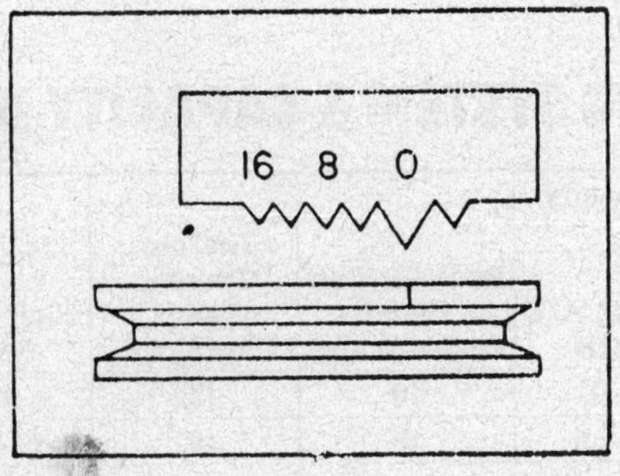


**Fig. B**

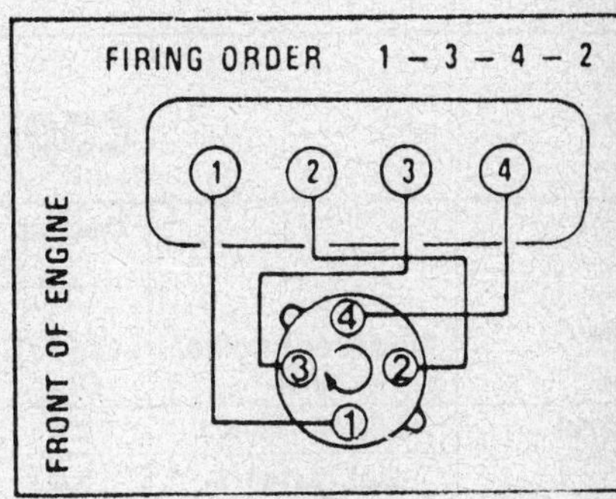


**Fig. C**

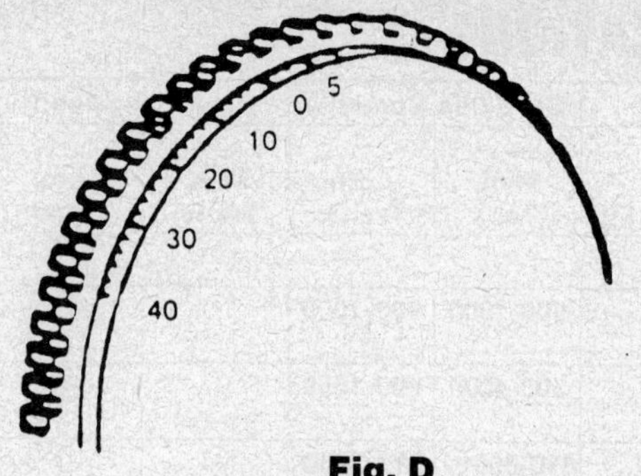

Fig. D

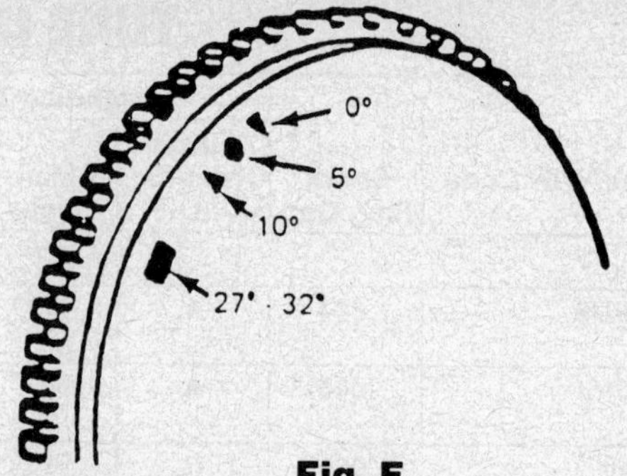

Fig. E

# FRONT WHEEL ALIGNMENT SPECIFICATIONS

| Year | Model | Caster Angle, Degrees | | Camber Angle, Degrees | | | | Toe-In. Inch | Toe Out on Turns, Deg. | |
|---|---|---|---|---|---|---|---|---|---|---|
| | | | | Limits | | Desired | | | | |
| | | Limits | Desired | Left | Right | Left | Right | | Outer Wheel | Inner Wheel |
| 1989 | Escort | +1.57 to +3.17 | +2.32 | +0.43 to +1.93 | -.01 to +1.49 | +1.18 | +0.74 | ① | ② | 20 |
| | Tempo & Topaz | +1.69 to +3.19 | +2.44 | +0.66 to +2.16 | +0.22 to +1.72 | +1.41 | +0.97 | ① | ② | 20 |
| 1990 | Escort Except GT | +1.57 to +3.17 | +2.32 | +0.65 to +2.15 | -0.21 to +1.71 | +1.4 | +0.96 | ① | ② | 20 |
| | Escort GT | +1.57 to +3.17 | +2.32 | +0.25 to +1.75 | -.19 to +1.31 | +1 | +0.56 | ① | ② | 20 |
| | Tempo & Topaz | +1.69 to +3.19 | +2.44 | +0.66 to +2.16 | +0.22 to +1.72 | +1.41 | +0.97 | ① | ② | 20 |
| 1991-92 | Tempo & Topaz | +1.69 to +3.19 | +2.44 | +0.66 to +2.16 | +0.22 to +1.72 | +1.41 | +0.97 | ① | ② | 20 |

①—Toe-out, 0.10 inch.
②—Left wheel, 20 degrees; right wheel 18.2 degrees.

# REAR WHEEL ALIGNMENT SPECIFICATIONS

| Year | Model | Camber Angle, Degrees | | | | Toe-In. Inch |
|---|---|---|---|---|---|---|
| | | Limits | | Desired | | |
| | | Left | Right | Left | Right | |
| 1989-90 | Escort | -1.2 to +0.5 | -1.2 to +0.5 | -.35 | -.35 | .18 |
| 1989-91 | Tempo & Topaz① | -0.04 to +1.09 | -0.4 to +1.9 | +.34 | +.34 | 0 |
| 1989-92 | Tempo & Topaz② | -0.91 to +0.59 | -0.91 to +0.59 | -.16 | -.16 | 0 |

①—All wheel drive models.
②—Except all wheel drive models.

# COOLING SYSTEM & CAPACITY DATA

| Year | Model or Engine/ VIN | Cooling Capacity, Qts. | | Radiator Cap Relief Pressure, psi. | Thermo. Opening Temp. Degrees F. | Fuel Tank Gals. | Engine Refill Qts.① | Transaxle Oil | |
|---|---|---|---|---|---|---|---|---|---|
| | | Less A/C Qts. | With A/C Qts. | | | | | 4 & 5 Speed Pints | Auto Trans. Qts.① |
| 1989-90 | 1.9L/4-116/9,J | 7.9 | ② | 16 | 192 | 13 | 4.0④ | 6.1 | 8.3 |
| | 2.3L/4-140/S | 8.3 | 8.1 | 16 | 192 | 15.4③ | 4.5④ | 6.1 | 8.3 |
| | 2.3L/4-140/X | 8.3 | 8.1 | 16 | 192 | 15.4③ | 4.5④ | 6.1 | 8.3 |
| | 2.3L/4-140/X | 8.3 | 8.1 | 16 | 192 | 15.4③ | 4.5④ | 6.1 | 8.3 |
| 1991 | 2.3L/4-140/S | 8.3 | 8.1 | 16 | 192 | 15.4③ | 4.5④ | 6.1 | 8 .3 |
| | 2.3L/4-140/X | 8.3 | 8.1 | 16 | 192 | 15.4③ | 4.5④ | 6.1 | 8.3 |
| | 2.3L/4-140/X | 8.3 | 8.1 | 16 | 192 | 15.4③ | 4.5④ | 6.1 | 8.3 |
| 1992 | 2.3L/4-140/X | 8.3 | 8.1 | 16 | 192 | 15.4③ | 4.5④ | 6.1 | 8.3 |
| | 2.3L/4-140/X | 8.3 | 8.1 | 16 | 192 | 15.4③ | 4.5④ | 6.1 | 8.3 |
| | 3.0L/V6-182/U | 8.3 | 8.1 | 16 | 192 | 15.4③ | 4.5④ | 6.1 | 8.3 |

①—Approximate. Make final check with dipstick.
②—Models with manual transaxle, 6 qts.; models with automatic transaxle, 7 qts.
③—With all wheel drive 14.2 gallons.
④—Includes filter.

## LUBRICANT DATA

| Year | Model | Lubricant Type | | | | | |
|---|---|---|---|---|---|---|---|
| | | Transaxle | | | | | |
| | | Manual | Automatic | Transfer Case | Rear Axle | Power Steering | Brake System |
| 1989–92 | All | ATF③ | ATF③ | ATF | ① | ATF② | DOT 3 |

①—Hypoid Gear Lubricant.
②—Type F.
③—Mercon XT-2-QDX.

# Electrical

## INDEX

Page No.



## AIRBAG SYSTEM DISARMING

### 1989–91

**The electrical circuit necessary for system deployment is powered directly from the battery and a backup power supply. To avoid accidental deployment and possible personal injury, the airbag system must be deactivated prior to servicing or replacing any system components.**

A back-up power supply is included in the system to provide airbag deployment in the event the battery or battery cables are damaged in an accident before the sensors can close. The power supply is a capacitor that will retain a charge for approximately 15 minutes after the battery ground cable is disconnected or one minute if the positive battery cable is grounded. **Backup power supply must be disconnected to deactivate airbag system.** To remove backup power supply, refer to "Airbags" in the "Passive Restraint" section.

### 1992

#### Deactivation

1. Disconnect positive battery cable.
2. Wait one minute. This is the time required for backup power supply in diagnostic monitor to deplete its stored energy.
3. Remove four nut and washer assemblies retaining driver airbag module to steering wheel. Disconnect driver airbag connector. Connect Rotunda Airbag Simulator tool No. 105-00008 or equivalent to vehicle harness at top of steering wheel.
4. Connect positive battery cable.

#### Reactivation

1. Disconnect positive battery cable.
2. Wait one minute for backup power supply to deplete stored energy.
3. Remove airbag simulator from vehicle harness connector at top of steering column. Reconnect driver airbag connector. Position driver airbag on steering wheel, then install four nut and washer assemblies. **Torque** retaining nuts to 24-32 inch lbs.
4. Connect positive battery cable, then Prove-Out System.

#### Prove-Out System

Prove-out system means to turn the ignition switch from Off to Run and visually monitor the airbag indicator, located on dash panel. The airbag indicator will light continuously for approximately six seconds and then turn off. If an airbag system fault is present, the indicator will either fail to light, remain lit continuously or light in a flashing manner.

The flashing manner may not occur until approximately 30 seconds after the ignition switch has been turned from Off to Run. This is the time needed for the diagnostic monitor to complete testing of the system. If the airbag indicator is inoperative and an airbag system fault exists, a tone will sound in a pattern of five sets of five beeps. If this occurs, the airbag indicator will need to be serviced.

## FUSE PANEL AND FLASHER LOCATION

The fuse panel is located behind the lefthand side of the instrument panel.

The flashers are located on the fuse panel.

## STARTER REPLACE

### EXCEPT 3.0L/V6-182

1. Disconnect battery ground cable.
2. Raise and support vehicle.
3. Disconnect starter cable from starter motor terminal.

4. **On vehicles equipped with manual transmission,** remove three nuts attaching roll restrictor brace to transmission-side starter studs and remove brace.
5. **On all models,** remove two bolts attaching starter rear support bracket.
6. Remove retaining nut from rear of starter stud bolt, then remove bracket.
7. Remove three starter mounting nuts or bolts and the starter.
8. Reverse procedure to install. **Torquing** starter retaining bolts or nuts to 30-40 ft. lbs.

### 3.0L/V6-182

1. Disconnect and insulate battery ground cable.
2. Disconnect starter cable and push on connector from starter solenoid. **When disconnecting the plastic hardshell connector at "S" terminal, grasp the plastic shell, depress the tab and pull lead off. Do not pull separately on wire. Be careful to pull straight off to prevent damage to the "S" solenoid terminal.**
3. Remove upper starter retaining bolt, then lower bolt and starter assembly.
4. Reverse procedure to install, noting the following:
   a. **Torque** starter motor retaining bolts to 16-19 ft. lbs.

## DISTRIBUTOR REPLACE

### REMOVAL

1. Disconnect distributor from wiring harness.
2. Mark position of No. 1 cylinder wire tower on distributor base for reference when installing distributor.
3. Loosen distributor cap hold-down screws, then remove cap. **Pull distributor cap straight off to prevent damage to rotor and spring.**
4. Position cap and wires aside, then remove distributor rotor.
5. Remove distributor hold-down bolts, then distributor.

### INSTALLATION

#### 1.9L/4-116 Engine

1. Install distributor in cylinder head, seating offset tang of drive coupling into groove on end of camshaft.
2. Install hold-down bolts finger tight.
3. Install distributor cap, then **torque** distributor cap retaining screws to 18-23 inch. lbs.
4. Connect distributor to wiring harness.
5. Set distributor base timing, then **torque** distributor hold-down bolts to 44-62 inch. lbs.
6. Check initial timing, adjust if necessary.

#### 2.3L/4-140 Engine

1. Set No. 1 piston at Top Dead Center (TDC) of compression stroke.
2. With No. 1 piston on compression stroke, align timing pointer with TDC on flywheel.
3. Align location boss on rotor with hole on armature. Fully seat rotor on distributor shaft.
4. Rotate distributor shaft so blade on rotor is pointing toward mark on distributor base, that was previously made in step two of removal procedure.
5. While installing distributor, continue rotating rotor slightly so leading edge of the vane is centered in vane switch stator assembly.
6. Rotate distributor in cylinder head to align leading edge of vane and vane switch assembly. Ensure rotor is pointing at No. 1 mark on distributor base.
7. If vane and vane switch stator cannot be aligned by rotating distributor while in cylinder head, remove distributor just enough to disengage distributor gear from camshaft gear. Rotate rotor enough to engage distributor gear on another tooth of camshaft gear. Repeat Step 1 if necessary.
8. Install distributor hold-down clamp and bolt, finger tight.
9. Install distributor cap, then **torque** distributor cap retaining screws to 18-23 inch. lbs.
10. Connect distributor to wiring harness.
11. Set initial base timing, then **torque** distributor retaining bolt to 17-25 ft. lbs.
12. Check ignition base timing, adjust if necessary.

#### 3.0L/V6-182 Engine

1. Disconnect distributor from wiring harness.
2. Mark position on No. 1 cylinder wire tower on distributor base for reference when installing distributor.
3. Loosen distributor cap hold-down screws, then remove cap straight off distributor to prevent damage to rotor blade and spring.
4. Position cap and attached wires aside so as not to interfere with distributor removal.
5. Remove rotor by pulling upward to remove it from the distributor shaft and armature.
6. Remove distributor hold-down bolt and clamp, then distributor assembly from engine.
7. Cover distributor opening with clean shop towel to prevent entry of foreign material or dirt into engine.
8. Remove No. 1 cylinder spark plug, then rotate engine clockwise until No. 1 piston is on the compression stroke.
9. With No. 1 piston on compression stroke, align timing pointer with TDC mark on the crankshaft damper.
10. Align locating boss on rotor with hole on armature. Fully seat rotor on distributor shaft.
11. Rotate distributor shaft so blade on rotor is pointing toward mark on distributor base, that was previously made.
12. While installing distributor, continue rotating rotor slightly so leading edge of the vane is centered in vane switch stator assembly.
13. Rotate distributor in block to align leading of vane and vane switch stator assembly. Ensure rotor is pointing at No. 1 mark on distributor base. If vane and vane switch cannot be aligned by rotating distributor in cylinder block, remove distributor enough to just disengage distributor gear from camshaft gear, then rotate rotor enough to engage distributor gear on another tooth of camshaft gear.
14. Install distributor hold-down clamp and bolt.
15. Install distributor cap, No. 1 spark plug and ignition wires. Ensure that the ignition wires are securely connected to the distributor cap and spark plugs.
16. **Torque** distributor cap hold-down screws to 18-23 inch lbs.
17. Connect distributor electrical connector.
18. Adjust ignition timing to specifications, then **torque** distributor hold-down bolt to 17-25 ft. lbs.

## IGNITION LOCK REPLACE

1. **On models equipped with airbag,** disarm airbag system as described under "Airbag System Disarming."
2. Disconnect battery ground cable.
3. **On tilt columns,** remove upper extension shroud by unsnapping shroud from from retaining clip at 9 o'clock position.
4. **On all models,** remove five screws retaining the two trim shroud halves.
5. Disconnect key warning buzzer electrical connector, then turn the ignition key to the RUN position.
6. Place 1/8 diameter pin or small drift punch into hole in casting surrounding lock cylinder. Depress retaining pin while pulling out on lock cylinder to remove it from column housing.
7. Install lock cylinder by turning it to RUN position and depressing retaining pin. Insert lock cylinder into lock cylinder housing. **Ensure cylinder is fully seated and aligned in the interlocking washer before turning key to the OFF position. This will permit cylinder retaining pin to extend into cylinder housing hole.**
8. Rotate lock cylinder, using lock cylinder key, to ensure correct mechanical operation in all positions.
9. Connect key warning buzzer connector, then install shroud.
10. Connect battery ground cable and ensure proper operation. **Ensure vehicle cannot be started in drive and reverse.**
11. **On models equipped with airbag,** rearm airbag system as described under "Airbag System Disarming."

## IGNITION SWITCH REPLACE

### MODELS LESS PASSIVE RESTRAINT SYSTEM

1. Disconnect battery ground cable, then

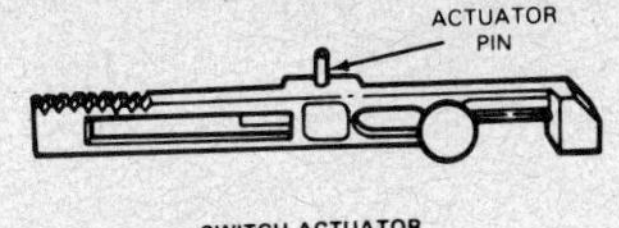


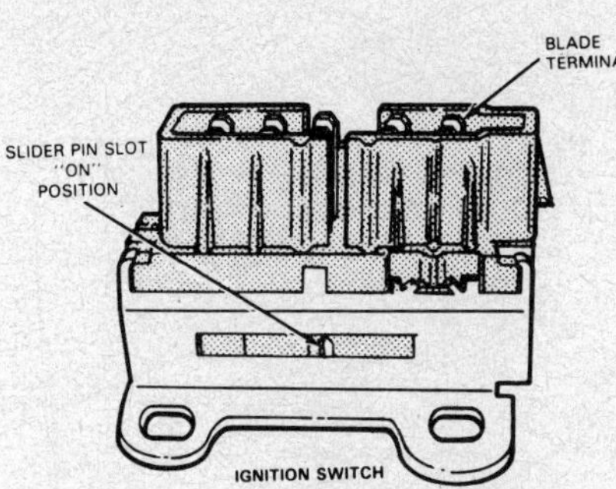


**Fig. 1 Ignition switch**

remove five steering column shroud attaching screws.

2. Remove two bolts and two nuts attaching steering column to column bracket, then lower steering column assembly to seat and remove column shrouds.
3. Disconnect ignition switch wire connector, then rotate ignition switch lock cylinder to the Run position.
4. Remove the two shear bolts using an easy out.
5. Detach ignition switch from actuator pin, then remove switch.
6. Check to ensure that ignition switch actuator pin slot and ignition switch lock cylinder are in the Run position. **Replacement ignition switches are set in the Run position. The Run position on the ignition switch lock cylinder is located approximately 90° from the lock position.**
7. Position ignition switch on actuator pin. It may be necessary to move switch slightly to align switch to column mounting bolt holes, **Fig. 1.**
8. Install and tighten shear bolts until heads break off.
9. Connect wire connector to ignition switch, then connect battery ground cable and check ignition switch for proper operation.
10. Position upper shroud on column, then raise steering column and install column mounting bracket to instrument panel attaching bolts. **Torque** bolts to 15 to 25 ft. lbs.
11. Position lower shroud on column and install attaching bolts.

## MODELS W/PASSIVE RESTRAINT SYSTEM

1. Park vehicle with wheels in the straight ahead position. Turn ignition switch to "Lock" position and rotate steering wheel 16° counterclockwise until locked into position.
2. Disarm airbag system as described under "Airbag System Disarming."
3. Remove five steering column shroud attaching screws.

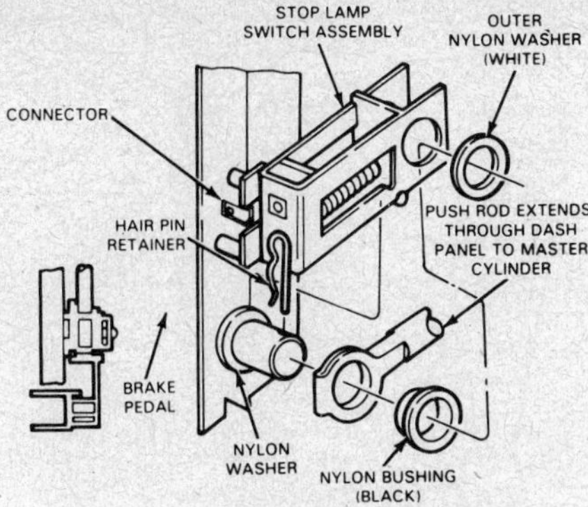


**Fig. 2 Stop light switch**

4. Remove two bolts and two nuts holding steering column assembly to steering column bracket assembly. Lower steering column to seat.
5. Remove steering column shrouds.
6. Disconnect ignition switch electrical connectors slip ring connector to column harness.
7. Rotate ignition lock cylinder to the RUN position.
8. Disengage ignition switch from actuator pin.
9. Reverse procedure to install, noting the following:
   a. Ensure actuator pin slot in ignition switch is in the RUN position.
   b. **Torque** ignition switch retaining screws to 4-6 ft. lbs.
   c. **Torque** steering column to steering column bracket retaining bolts to 15-25 ft. lbs.
   d. Reactivate airbag system As Described Under "Airbag System Disarming."

## STARTER/CLUTCH INTERLOCK SWITCH
## REPLACE

1. **On models equipped with airbag,** disarm airbag system as described under "Airbag System Disarming."
2. Remove trim panel above clutch pedal.
3. Disconnect electrical connector.
4. Remove clutch interlock retaining screw and hairpin clip, then remove switch. **Always install the switch with the self-adjusting clip one inch above end of the rod. The clutch pedal must be fully up (clutch engaged) or the switch may be improperly adjusted.**
5. Insert eyelet end of rod over pin on clutch pedal, then secure with hairpin clip.
6. Align mounting boss with corresponding hole in bracket, then install retaining screw.
7. Reset clutch interlock switch by depressing clutch pedal to floor.
8. Connect electrical connector, then install trim panel.
9. **On models equipped with airbag,** rearm airbag system as described under "Airbag System Disarming."

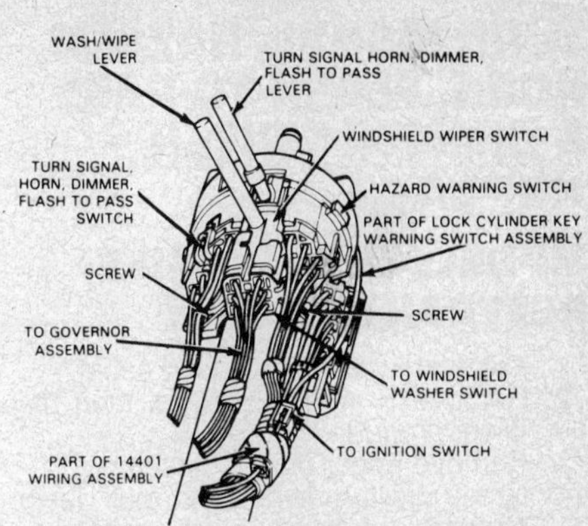


**Fig. 3 Turn signal, hazard, horn, flash-to-pass & dimmer switch**

## HEADLAMP SWITCH
## REPLACE

1. **On models equipped with airbag,** disarm airbag system as described under "Airbag System Disarming."
2. Disconnect battery ground cable.
3. **On models less air conditioning,** remove two lefthand air vent control retaining screws, then place control aside.
4. **On all models,** remove fuse panel bracket retaining screws, then move fuse panel assembly aside to gain access to headlamp switch.
5. Pull headlamp knob out to "On" position.
6. Depress headlamp knob and shaft retainer button on headlamp switch, then remove knob assembly.
7. Remove headlamp switch retaining bezel.
8. Disconnect multiple connector plug, then remove switch from instrument panel.
9. Reverse procedure to install.
10. **On models equipped with airbag,** rearm airbag system as described under "Airbag System Disarming."

## STOP LAMP SWITCH
## REPLACE

1. **On models equipped with airbag,** disarm airbag system as described under "Airbag System Disarming."
2. Disconnect battery ground cable.
3. Remove retainer and outer white nylon washer from pedal pin. Slide switch off brake pedal pin far enough so that outer side of plate of switch clears pin. Remove switch, **Fig. 2.**
4. Reverse procedure to install.
5. **On models equipped with airbag,** rearm airbag system as described under "Airbag System Disarming."

# TURN SIGNAL, HAZARD, HORN, FLASH-TO-PASS & DIMMER SWITCH

## REPLACE

### MODELS LESS PASSIVE RESTRAINT SYSTEM

1. Disconnect battery ground cable.
2. Remove 5 shroud screws, then the lower shroud.
3. Remove upper shroud assembly.
4. Grasp switch lever and pull lever straight out from switch assembly, **Fig. 3.**
5. Peel back foam switch cover from turn signal switch.
6. Disconnect 2 electrical connectors.
7. Remove 2 self tapping screws attaching switch assembly to lock cylinder housing, then disconnect switch from housing.
8. Reverse procedure to install.

### MODELS w/PASSIVE RESTRAINT SYSTEM

1. Disarm airbag system as described under "Airbag System Disarming."
2. Disconnect battery ground cable.
3. Remove five shroud attaching screws, then lower shroud.
4. Remove upper shroud.
5. Remove switch lever by grasping lever and pulling lever straight out from switch.
6. Peel back foam switch cover from turn signal switch.
7. Disconnect two switch electrical connectors and Airbag slip ring connector from column harness.
8. Remove two self tapping screws attaching switch to lock cylinder housing, then disengage switch from housing.
9. Reverse procedure to install.
10. **On models equipped with airbag,** rearm airbag system as described under "Airbag System Disarming."

# INSTRUMENT CLUSTER

## REPLACE

### TEMPO & TOPAZ

1. **On models equipped with airbag,** disarm airbag system as described under "Airbag System Disarming."
2. Disconnect battery ground cable.
3. Remove retaining screws from bottom of steering column opening and snap steering column cover out.
4. Remove steering column trim shroud, **Fig. 4.**
5. Remove lower cluster finish panels.
6. Remove cluster opening finish panel screws and pull panel rearward.
7. Disconnect speedometer cable from transaxle.
8. Remove screws retaining cluster and carefully pull cluster rearward enough to disengage speedometer cable.
9. Carefully pull cluster away from instrument panel.
10. Reverse procedure to install.
11. **On models equipped with airbag,** rearm airbag system as described under "Airbag System Disarming."

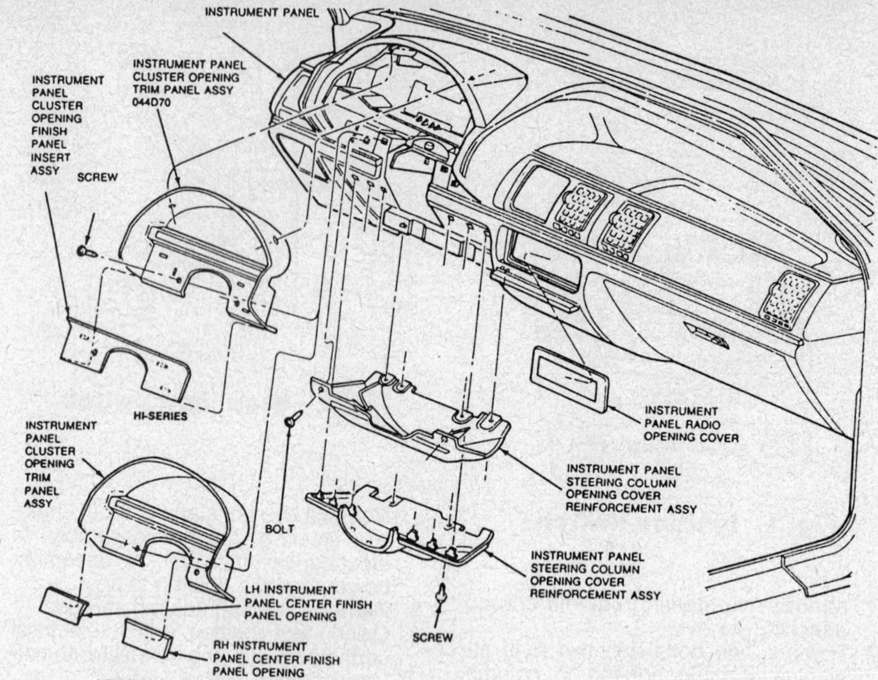


**Fig. 4 Instrument cluster removal. Tempo & Topaz**

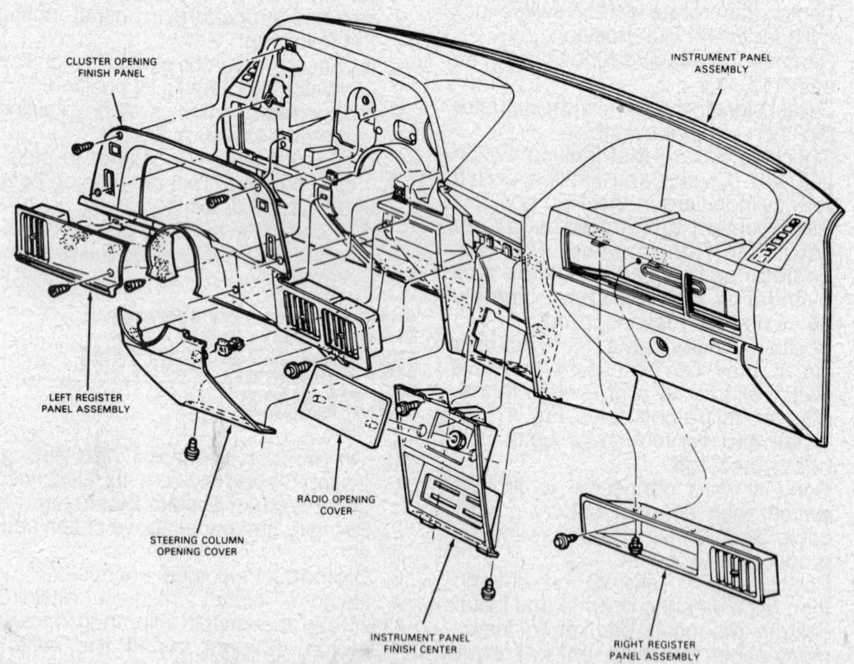


**Fig. 5 Instrument panel. Escort**

### ESCORT

1. Disconnect battery ground cable.
2. Remove retaining screws from bottom of steering column opening and snap steering column cover out.
3. Remove cluster opening finish panel retainer screws and the finish panel.
4. Remove upper and lower screws retaining cluster to instrument panel, **Fig. 5.**
5. Reach under instrument panel and disconnect speedometer cable by pressing down on flat surface of connector.
6. Pull cluster away from instrument panel and disconnect cluster feed plug from its receptacle in printed circuit.
7. Reverse procedure to install.

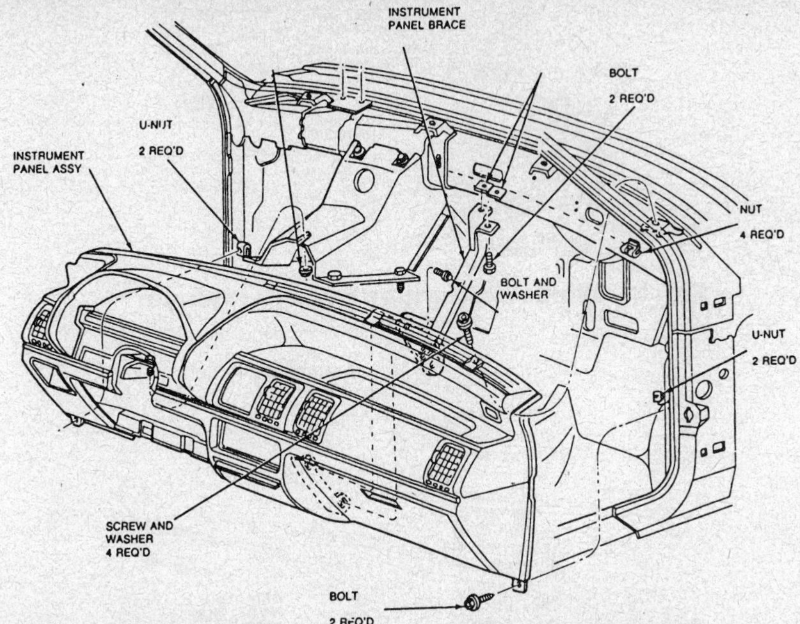


**Fig. 6 Instrument panel. Tempo & Topaz**

## STEERING WHEEL
### REPLACE

1. **On models equipped with airbag,** disarm airbag system as described under "Airbag System Disarming."
2. Disconnect battery ground cable.
3. Remove horn pad retaining screws from rear of wheel, then pad assembly.
4. **On Airbag equipped vehicles,** remove Airbag module assembly retaining screws, then Airbag module.
5. Lift Airbag module from wheel, then disconnect clockspring to module connector.
6. Remove energy absorbing foam from steering wheel assembly.
7. **On all models,** disconnect horn pad wiring connector.
8. Loosen steering wheel attaching bolt four to six turns. Do not remove bolt.
9. **On Airbag equipped vehicles,** remove bolt completely to remove vibration damper, then reinstall bolt loosely on shaft.
10. **On all models,** position steering wheel puller (Tool No. T67L-3600-A) or equivalent on steering wheel.
11. Tighten bolt on removal tool until steering wheel is loose on shaft.
12. Reverse procedure to install, noting the following:
    a. **Torque** steering wheel retaining bolt to 23-33 ft. lbs.
    b. **Torque** Airbag retaining bolts to 35-53 inch lbs.
13. **On models equipped with airbag,** rearm airbag system as described under "Airbag System Disarming."

## HORN SOUNDER
### REPLACE
#### ESCORT

1. Remove screws from back of steering wheel.
2. Remove foam pad, if equipped.
3. Remove wire connector from steering wheel terminals.
4. Reverse procedure to install.

#### TEMPO & TOPAZ
##### Less Passive Restraints

1. Remove two screws from back of steering wheel, then lift off horn cover pad.
2. Remove wire connector from steering wheel terminals.
3. Reverse procedure to install.

##### With Passive Restraints

**On models equipped with Airbag passive restraints,** the horn sounder is located on the turn signal, headlight dimmer and horn lever. Refer to Turn Signal, Hazard, Horn, Flash-To-Pass & Dimmer Switch, Replace when replacing lever.

## AUXILIARY CLUSTER
### REPLACE
#### TEMPO

1. **On models equipped with airbag,** disarm airbag system as described under "Airbag System Disarming."
2. Disconnect battery ground cable.
3. Pull trim cover at bottom edge and slide out of tabs at top edge.
4. Remove three cluster to console attaching screws. **On Tempo models,** remove four cluster to console attaching screws, then pull cluster outward and disconnect electrical connector.
5. Remove cluster from console.
6. Reverse procedure to install.
7. **On models equipped with airbag,** rearm airbag system as described under "Airbag System Disarming."

## GRAPHIC WARNING DISPLAY
### REPLACE

1. **On models equipped with airbag,** disarm airbag system as described under "Airbag System Disarming."
2. Disconnect battery ground cable, then remove console finish panel by prying at bottom edge to disengage retainers.
3. Remove module to console attaching screws, then pull module outward and disconnect electrical connector.
4. Remove module from console.
5. Reverse procedure to install.
6. **On models equipped with airbag,** rearm airbag system as described under "Airbag System Disarming."

## RADIO
### REPLACE

1. **On models equipped with airbag,** disarm airbag system as described under "Airbag System Disarming."
2. Disconnect battery ground cable.
3. Remove radio knobs and instrument panel center trim panel.
4. Remove radio mounting plate screws, then pull radio outward to disengage lower rear support bracket.
5. Disconnect antenna and speaker leads from radio, then remove radio.
6. Remove nuts and washers from radio control shafts. Remove mounting plate.
7. Remove rear support retaining nut and support.
8. Reverse procedure to install.
9. **On models equipped with airbag,** rearm airbag system as described under "Airbag System Disarming."

## WINDSHIELD WIPER MOTOR
### REPLACE

1. Disconnect battery ground cable.
2. Lift passenger side water shield cover from cowl, then disconnect motor electrical connector.
3. Remove linkage retaining clip from motor arm, then the three bolts attaching motor to mounting bracket, **Fig. 6.**
4. Disconnect operating arm from motor, then separate motor from mounting bracket and remove from vehicle.
5. Reverse procedure to install.

## REAR WIPER MOTOR
### REPLACE
#### ESCORT

1. Disconnect battery ground cable.
2. Remove liftgate inner trim panel.
3. **On station wagon models,** remove license plate housing attaching screws, disconnect lamp electrical connector, then the housing.

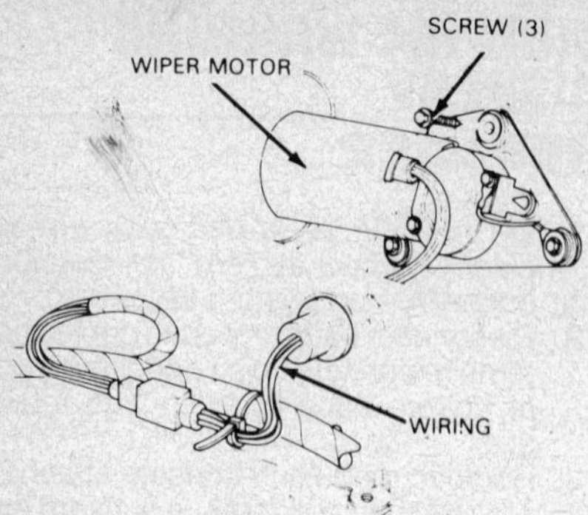


Fig. 7 Windshield wiper motor

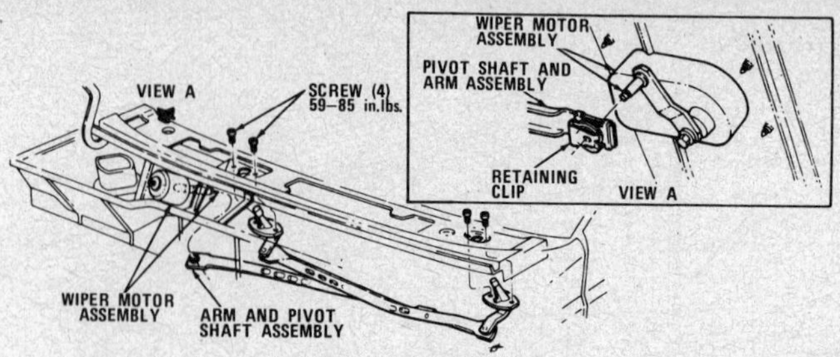


Fig. 8 Windshield wiper linkage replace. Escort

4. **On all models,** pull wiper motor electrical connector clip out from retaining hole.
5. Disconnect electrical connector halves.
6. Remove motor.
7. Reverse procedure to install.

# WINDSHIELD WIPER TRANSMISSION

## REPLACE

1. Remove wiper arm and blade assemblies from pivot shaft.
2. Disconnect battery ground cable, then remove clip and disconnect linkage drive arm from motor crank pin.
3. **On Tempo and Topaz models,** remove top grille from left and right cowl, then the pivot to cowl attaching screws.
4. **On Escort models,** remove pivot shaft retaining nuts.
5. **On all models,** remove linkage and pivots from cowl chamber, **Figs. 7 and 8.**
6. Reverse procedure to install.

# WINDSHIELD WIPER SWITCH

## REPLACE

The switch handle is an integral part of the switch and cannot be removed separately.

### ESCORT w/STANDARD STEERING COLUMN

1. Disconnect battery ground cable.
2. Remove upper steering column trim shroud, then disconnect electrical connector.
3. Pull back shield, then remove two screws securing switch. Remove switch.
4. Reverse procedure to install.

### ESCORT w/TILT STEERING COLUMN

1. Disconnect battery ground cable.
2. Remove steering column shroud and peel back side shield.

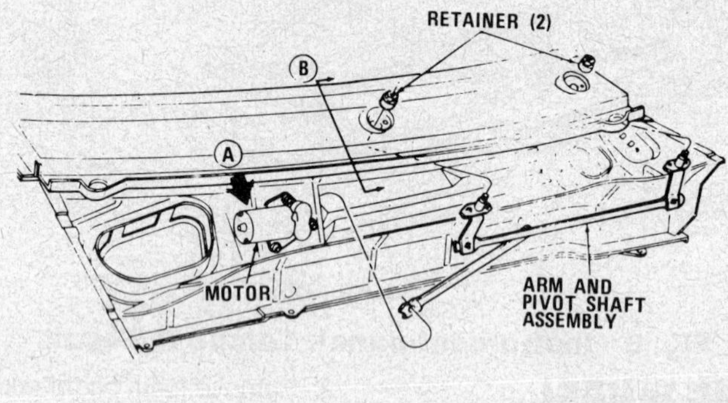


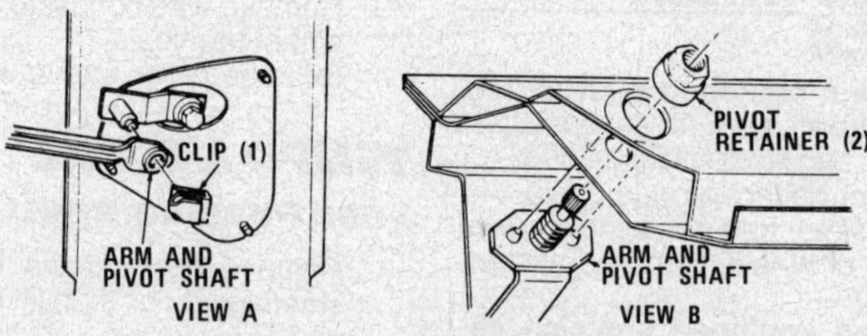


Fig. 9 Windshield wiper linkage replace. Tempo & Topaz

3. Disconnect electrical connector from end of switch wiring.
4. Remove screw attaching wiring retainer to column.
5. Grasp switch handle and pull straight out to disengage wiper switch from turn signal switch.
6. Reverse procedure to install.

### TEMPO & TOPAZ

1. **On models equipped with airbag,** disarm airbag system as described under "Airbag System Disarming."
2. Disconnect battery ground cable.
3. Insert a small screwdriver into small slot on top of switch bezel.
4. While pushing down on screwdriver, work top part of switch bezel away from instrument panel.
5. Insert small screwdriver into small slot on bottom of switch bezel.
6. While pushing up on screwdriver, work bottom part of switch bezel away from instrument panel.
7. Remove switch from instrument panel, then remove connector.
8. Reverse procedure to install.
9. **On models equipped with airbag,** rearm airbag system as described under "Airbag System Disarming."

# BLOWER MOTOR

## REPLACE

### TEMPO & TOPAZ

#### Less Air Conditioning

1. **On models equipped with airbag,** disarm airbag system as described under "Airbag System Disarming."
2. Disconnect battery ground cable.
3. Remove screws securing right ventilator control cable to instrument panel.
4. Remove screw securing right register duct to lower right edge of instrument panel.
5. Remove glove box and hinge bar from instrument panel.
6. Pull right register duct from installed position between air inlet duct and right register opening, **Fig. 9.**
7. Remove ventilator grille from bottom of ventilator assembly, then screws securing right ventilator assembly to blower housing.
8. Remove hub clamp spring from blower wheel hub, **Fig. 10.**
9. Pull blower wheel from blower shaft, then remove three blower motor flange attaching screws.
10. Pull blower motor from housing, disconnect electrical connector, then remove motor from vehicle.

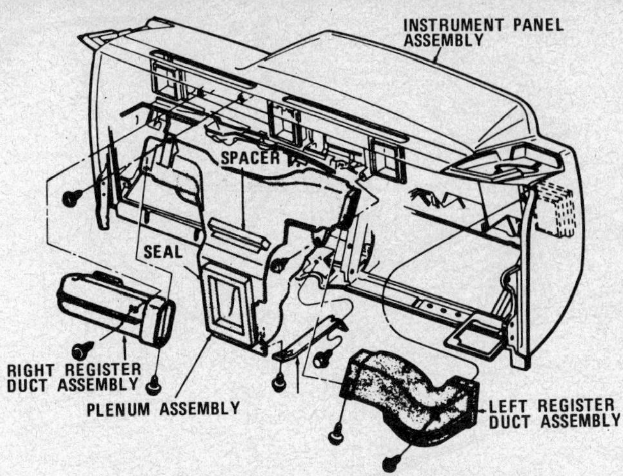


**Fig. 10 Vent assembly removal**

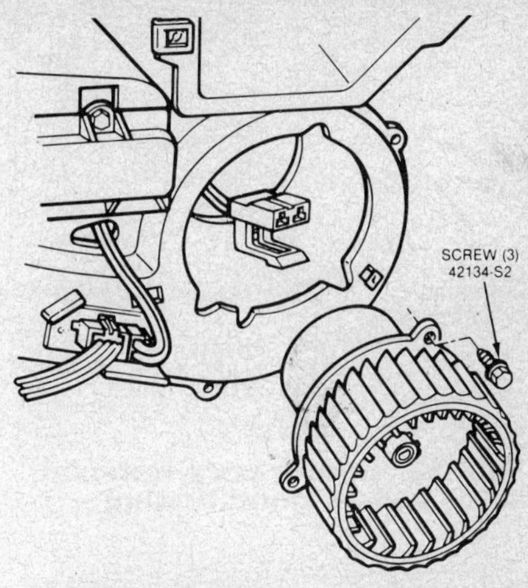


**Fig. 11 Blower motor removal. Less air conditioning**

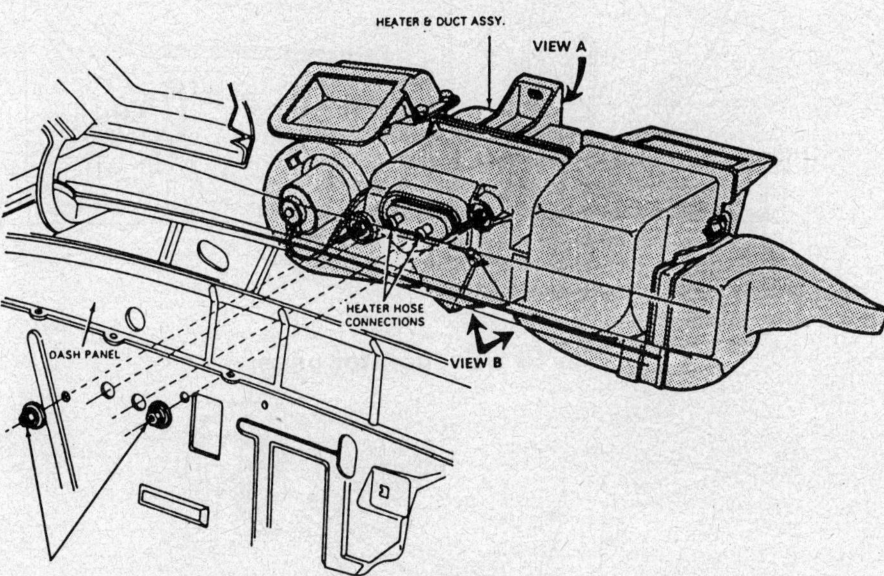


**Fig. 12 Heater case assembly. Escort**

11. Reverse procedure to install.
12. **On models equipped with airbag,** rearm airbag system as described under "Airbag System Disarming."

### With Air Conditioning

1. **On models equipped with airbag,** disarm airbag system as described under "Airbag System Disarming."
2. Disconnect battery ground cable.
3. Remove glove box door and instrument panel lower reinforcement from instrument panel.
4. Disconnect blower motor electrical connector, then remove blower motor and mounting plate from evaporator housing.
5. Rotate motor until mounting plate flats clear edge of glove box opening, then remove motor.
6. Remove hub clamp wheel spring from blower wheel hub and remove blower wheel from motor shaft.
7. Reverse procedure to install.
8. **On models equipped with airbag,** rearm airbag system as described under "Airbag System Disarming."

## ESCORT

1. Disconnect battery ground cable and drain coolant from radiator.
2. Disconnect heater hoses from heater core and plug heater core tubes.
3. Remove instrument panel as described previously.
4. Remove instrument panel center brace from cowl top panel.
5. Remove nut attaching heater case top support to heater case, **Fig. 11.**
6. Working in engine compartment, remove two washer nuts attaching heater case to dash panel.
7. Loosen sound insulation from cowl top panel in area around air inlet opening.
8. Pull heater case assembly away from dash panel to disengage studs and remove case assembly from vehicle.
9. Remove three screws attaching air inlet duct assembly to heater case assembly, then remove air inlet duct.
10. Remove pushnut from blower wheel hub.
11. Pull blower wheel from blower motor shaft.
12. Remove three blower motor flange attaching screws located inside blower housing.
13. Pull blower motor out of housing and disconnect blower motor electrical connector.
14. Reverse procedure to install.

## HEATER CORE REPLACE

### LESS AIR CONDITIONING

1. **On models equipped with airbag,** disarm airbag system as described under "Airbag System Disarming."
2. Disconnect battery ground cable and drain cooling system.
3. Disconnect heater hoses from heater core and plug all open lines and fittings to prevent spillage.
4. Remove glove box and liner and move temperature lever to warm position.
5. Remove heater core cover, then working from engine compartment, loosen two nuts attaching heater case assembly to dash panel.
6. Push heater core toward passenger compartment, then pull heater core through glove box opening and remove from vehicle, **Fig. 12.**
7. Reverse procedure to install.
8. **On models equipped with airbag,** rearm airbag system as described under "Airbag System Disarming."

### WITH AIR CONDITIONING

1. **On models equipped with airbag,** disarm airbag system as described under "Airbag System Disarming."
2. Disconnect battery ground cable and drain cooling system.
3. Disconnect heater hoses from heater core and plug all lines and fittings.
4. Remove floor duct from plenum.
5. Remove screws attaching heater core cover to plenum, then the cover and heater core, **Fig. 13.**
6. Reverse procedure to install.
7. **On models equipped with airbag,**

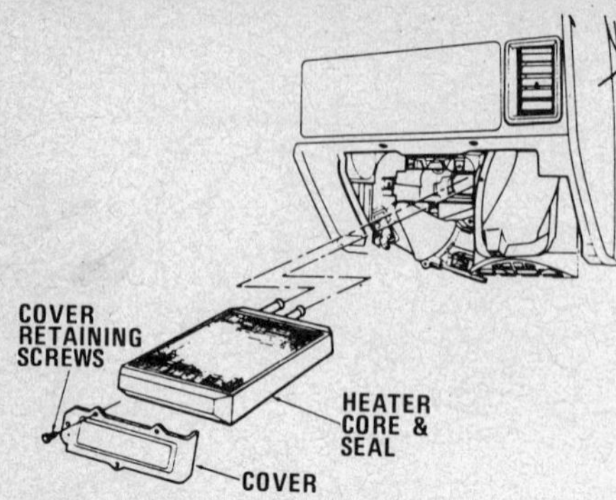


Fig. 13 Heater core removal. Less air conditioning

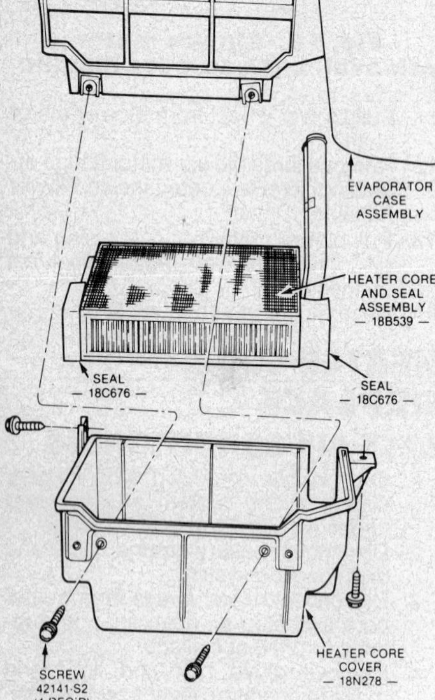


Fig. 14 Heater core removal. With air conditioning

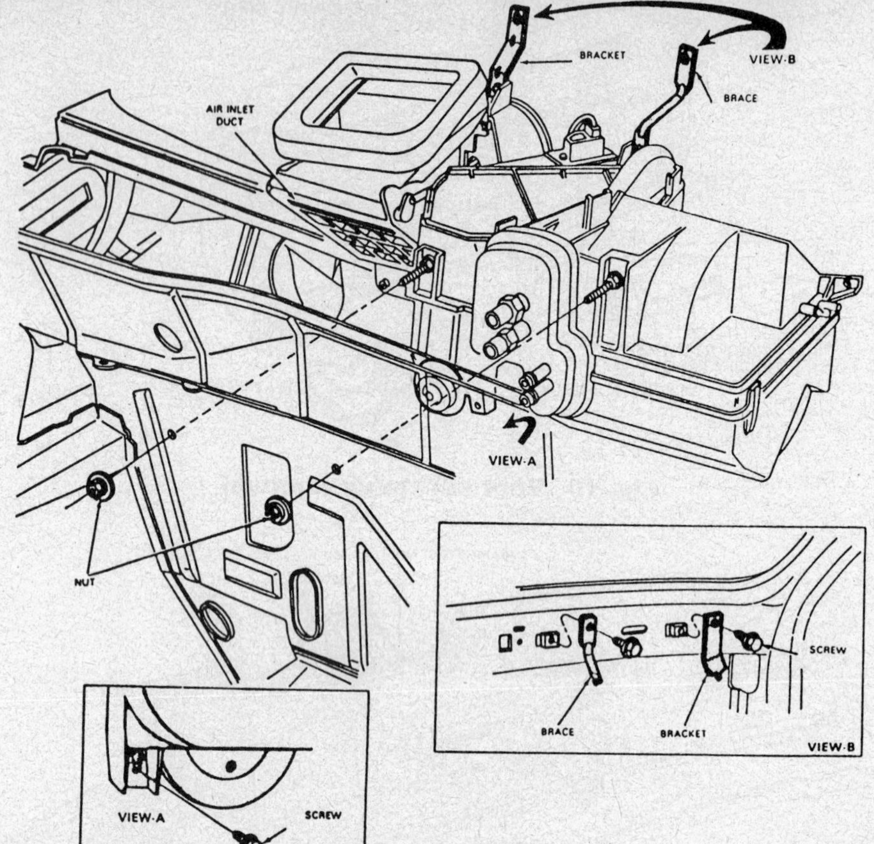


Fig. 15 Evaporator case

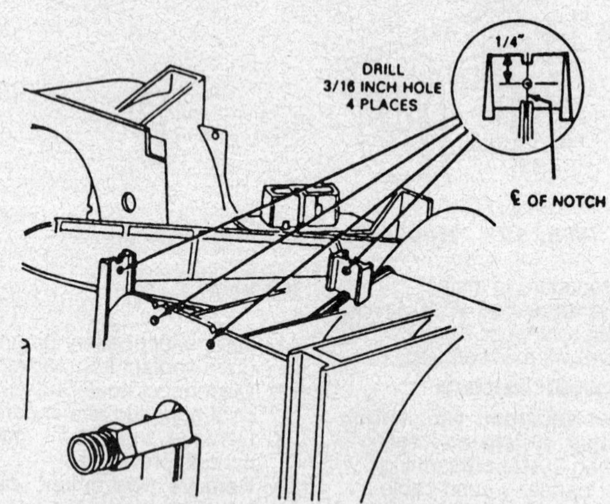


Fig. 16 Locations for drilling holes

rearm airbag system as described under "Airbag System Disarming."

## EVAPORATOR CORE REPLACE

Whenever an evaporator core is replaced, it will be necessary to replace the suction accumulator/dryer.

1. **On models equipped with airbag,** disarm airbag system as described under "Airbag System Disarming."
2. Disconnect battery ground cable.
3. Drain coolant from radiator.
4. Discharge refrigerant from air conditioning system.
5. Working from inside engine compartment, disconnect heater hoses from heater core. Plug heater core tubes or blow any coolant from heater core with low pressure air.
6. Disconnect high pressure line and the accumulator/dryer inlet tubes from evaporator core at dash panel.
7. Cap refrigerant lines and evaporator core to prevent excess dirt and moisture from entering system.
8. Remove dash panel, refer to "Dash Panel Service" for procedure.
9. Disconnect wire harness connector from blower motor resistor.
10. Remove one screw attaching the bottom of evaporator case to dash panel.
11. Remove two nuts attaching evaporator case to dash panel in engine compartment.
12. Loosen sound insulation from the cowl top panel in the area around air inlet opening.
13. Remove two screws attaching support bracket and brace to cowl top panel, **Fig. 14.**
14. Remove air inlet duct from evaporator case (four screws).
15. Remove foam seal from evaporator core tubes.
16. Drill a 3/16 inch hole in both upright tabs on top of evaporator case, **Fig. 15.**
17. Using a small saw blade, cut the top of evaporator case between two raised

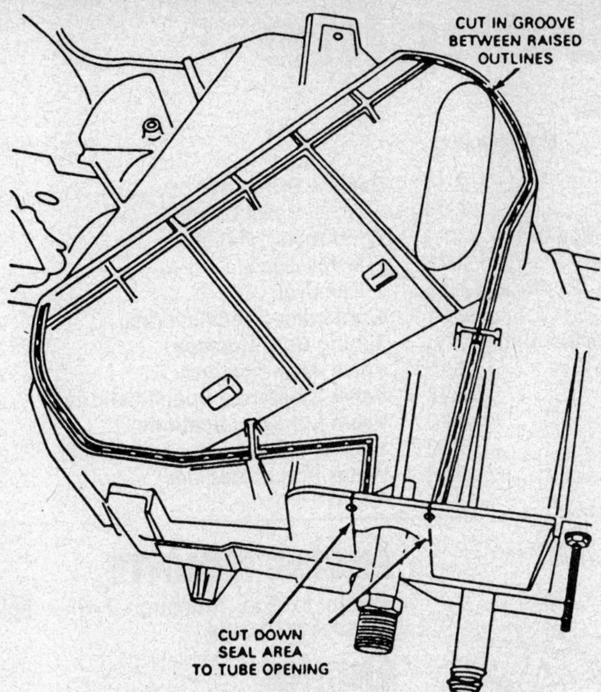


**Fig. 17 Cutting outline locations**

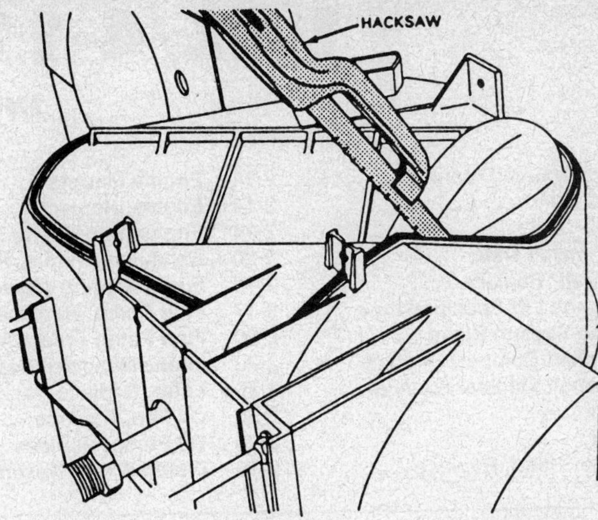


**Fig. 18 Evaporator case cover removal**

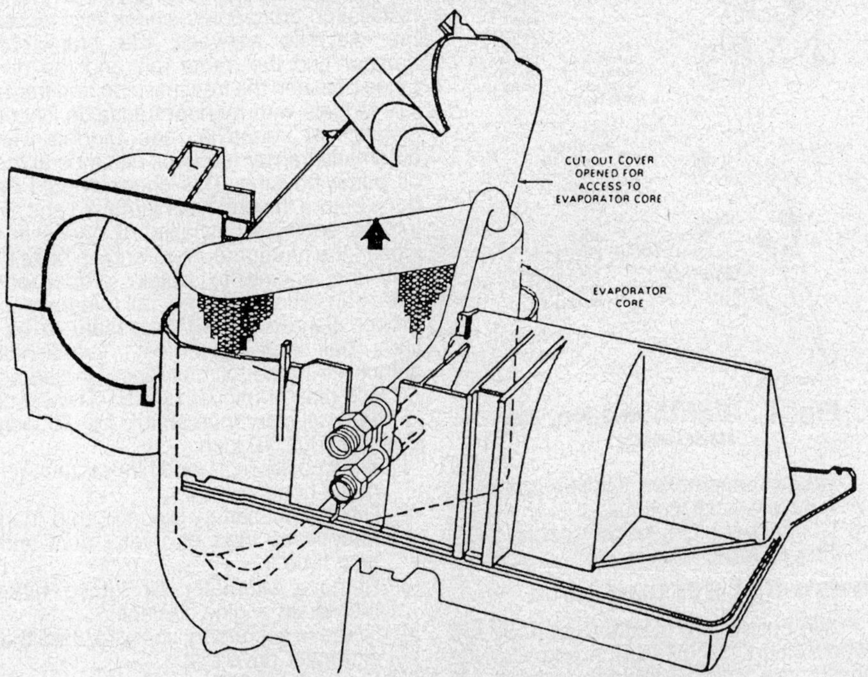


**Fig. 19 Evaporator core removal**

outlines, **Figs. 16 and 17.**

18. Remove two blower motor resistor retaining screws, then blower motor resistor.
19. Fold cutout cover back from case, **Fig. 18.**
20. Remove evaporator core.
21. Reverse procedure to install, noting the following:
    a. Install caulking cord (rope sealer) part No. D9AZ-19560-A or equivalent to seal evaporator case against leakage along cut line.
    b. Install a spring nut on each of the two upright tabs and with the two holes drilled in the front flange. Ensure hole in spring nut is aligned with the 3/16 inch holes drilled in the tab and flange. Install and tighten screw in each spring nut (through the hole in the tab or flange) to secure the cutout cover in the closed position.
    c. **On models equipped with airbag,** rearm airbag system as described under "Airbag System Disarming."

# 1.9L/4-116 Engine

## INDEX



## AIRBAG SYSTEM DISARMING

### 1989–91

**The electrical circuit necessary for system deployment is powered directly from the battery and a backup power supply. To avoid accidental deployment and possible personal injury, the airbag system must be deactivated prior to servicing or replacing any system components.**

A back-up power supply is included in the system to provide airbag deployment in the event the battery or battery cables are damaged in an accident before the sensors can close. The power supply is a capacitor that will retain a charge for approximately 15 minutes after the battery ground cable is disconnected or one minute if the positive battery cable is grounded. **Backup power supply must be disconnected to deactivate airbag system.** To remove backup power supply, refer to "Airbags" in the "Passive Restraint" section.

### 1992

#### Deactivation

1. Disconnect positive battery cable.
2. Wait one minute. This is the time required for backup power supply in diagnostic monitor to deplete its stored energy.
3. Remove four nut and washer assemblies retaining driver airbag module to steering wheel. Disconnect driver airbag connector. Connect Rotunda Airbag Simulator tool No. 105-00008 or equivalent to vehicle harness at top of steering wheel.
4. Connect positive battery cable.

#### Reactivation

1. Disconnect positive battery cable.
2. Wait one minute for backup power supply to deplete stored energy.
3. Remove airbag simulator from vehicle harness connector at top of steering column. Reconnect driver airbag connector. Position driver airbag on steering wheel, then install four nut and washer assemblies. **Torque** retaining nuts to 24-32 inch lbs.
4. Connect positive battery cable, then Prove-Out System.

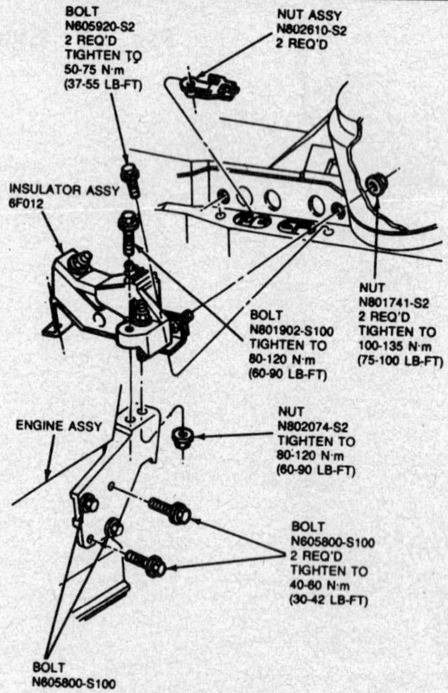


**Fig. 1 Righthand No. 3A insulator**

#### Prove-Out System

Prove-out system means to turn the ignition switch from Off to Run and visually monitor the airbag indicator, located on dash panel. The airbag indicator will light continuously for approximately six seconds and then turn off. If an airbag system fault is present, the indicator will either fail to light, remain lit continuously of light in a flashing manner.

The flashing manner may not occur until approximately 30 seconds after the ignition switch has been turned from Off to Run. This is the time needed for the diagnostic monitor to complete testing of the system. If the airbag indicator is inoperative and an airbag system fault exists, a tone will sound in a pattern of five sets of five beeps. If this occurs, the airbag indicator will need to be serviced.

## ENGINE MOUNTS

Refer to **Figs. 1 through 3** when replacing engine mounts.

## ENGINE

### REPLACE

When performing engine removal and installation procedures, check and record the distance between the crankshaft damper and the frame rail, and the distance between the transmission and frame rail. Models with manual transaxle, check distance at transaxle case. Models with automatic transaxle, check distance at the oil pump housing. This check should be done before the engine is removed and after the engine is installed. If necessary, loosen the motor mount-to-engine bolts to shift the engine to obtain proper engine/transaxle to frame rail clearances. Proper clearances are necessary to ensure half-shaft alignment. Crankshaft damper-to-frame rail clearance should be .62 inch plus or minus .15 inch. Transaxle to frame rail clearance should be .98 inch plus or minus .19 inch.

1. Mark position of hood hinges, then remove hood.
2. Disconnect battery ground cable, then remove air cleaner, intake duct and heat tube.
3. Remove alternator air intake tube, then drain engine coolant.
4. Remove secondary coil wire, then the alternator drive belt.
5. Remove alternator mount bolts, then position alternator aside.
6. **On models with automatic transaxle,** disconnect cooler lines at radiator.
7. **On all models,** disconnect the engine coolant hoses at radiator, then the heater hoses at engine block.
8. Disconnect electric cooling fan, then remove fan and shroud as an assembly.
9. **On models with automatic transaxle,** remove transaxle coolant line routing clip at radiator.
10. **On all models,** remove radiator.
11. Disconnect heater at metal tube, then the necessary engine electrical connectors.

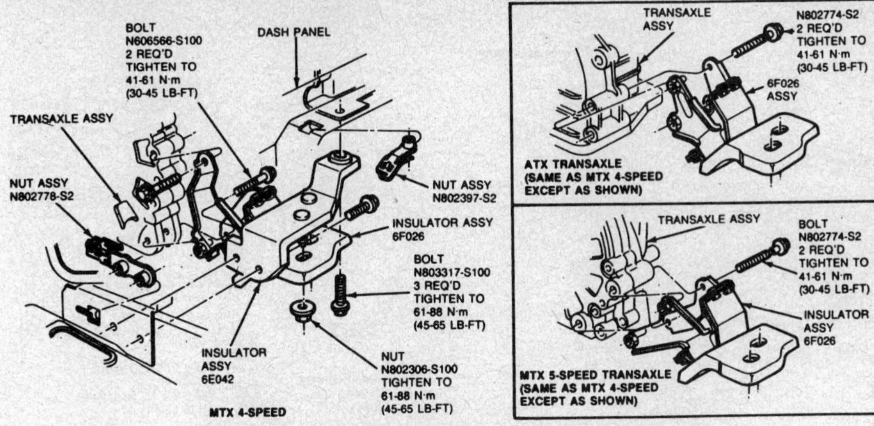


**Fig. 2 Lefthand rear No. 4 insulator**

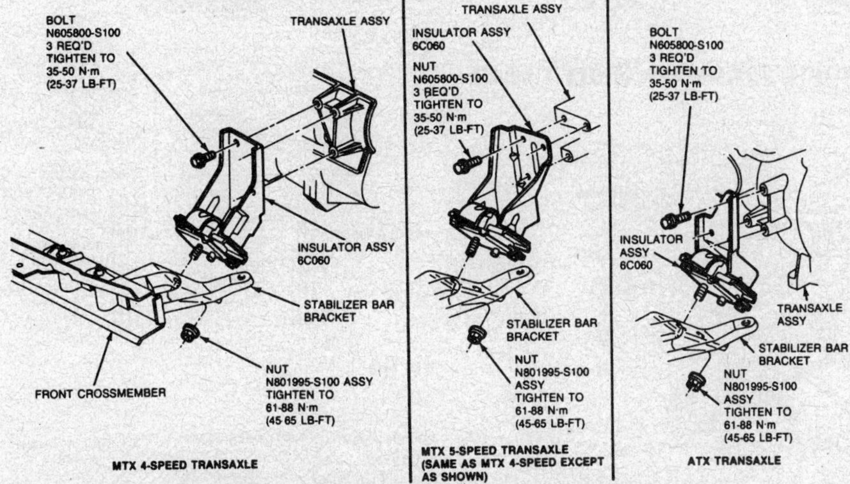


**Fig. 3 Lefthand front No. 1 insulator**

12. Disconnect vacuum hoses, then the fuel pump supply and return lines.
13. **On models with power brakes,** disconnect brake booster vacuum hose at engine.
14. **On models with automatic transaxle,** disconnect kickdown rod at fuel charging assembly.
15. **On all models,** disconnect accelerator cable, then remove cable routing bracket attaching screws.
16. Disconnect vapor hose at carbon canister, then raise and support vehicle.
17. Remove clamp from heater supply and return tubes, then disconnect starter battery cable.
18. Remove starter brace from front of starter motor, then starter from vehicle.
19. Disconnect exhaust pipe, then remove support bracket.
20. Remove converter cover on automatic transaxle models or inspection cover on manual transaxle models, then the crankshaft damper.
21. **On models with automatic transaxle,** remove torque converter to flywheel attaching bolts, then the converter housing lower attaching bolts.
22. **On models with manual transaxle,** remove timing belt cover lower attaching bolts, then the flywheel attaching bolts.
23. **On all models,** loosen coolant bypass hose clamp, then disconnect hose from intake manifold.
24. Remove battery ground cable to engine block attaching bolt, then the No. 3A casting bracket to engine bracket attaching nut and bolt, **Fig. 1.**
25. Lower vehicle, then attach suitable lifting brackets to engine, then attach lifting device to engine brackets.
26. Remove No. 3A casting to insulator retaining nut, then the casting.
27. **On models with manual transaxle,** remove remaining timing belt cover attaching bolts, then the cover.
28. **On all models,** remove insulator attaching bracket from engine, then support transaxle with a suitable jack.
29. **On models with automatic transaxle,** remove upper attaching bolts from converter housing.
30. **On models with manual transaxle,** remove upper attaching bolts from flywheel housing.
31. **On all models,** remove engine from vehicle.
32. Reverse procedure to install.

## INTAKE MANIFOLD
## REPLACE

**Refer to "Fuel Pump, Replace" to relieve fuel system pressure.**

To remove upper intake manifold assembly, proceed as follows:

1. Disconnect engine air cleaner outlet tube from throttle body.
2. Unplug throttle position sensor from wiring harness.
3. Disconnect vacuum lines from upper manifold assembly.
4. Disconnect EGR tube at manifold connection.
5. Unplug air bypass valve connector.
6. Remove manifold upper support bracket top bolt.
7. Remove five upper manifold attaching bolts.
8. Remove upper manifold assembly and gasket.
9. Reverse procedure to install. Tighten retaining nuts in sequence shown, **Fig. 4,** to specifications.

## FUEL CHARGING ASSEMBLY
## REPLACE

1. Remove engine air cleaner outlet between vane air meter and air throttle body by loosening two clamps.
2. Disconnect and remove accelerator and speed control cables, if so equipped, from accelerator mounting bracket and throttle lever.
3. Disconnect top manifold vacuum fitting connectors.
4. Disconnect EGR vacuum line at EGR valve.
5. Disconnect EGR tube from upper intake manifold by supporting connector while loosening compression nut.
6. Disconnect upper support manifold bracket by removing top bolt only.
7. Disconnect electrical connectors at main engine harness (near No. 1 runner) and at ECT sensor located in heater supply tube.
8. Remove fuel supply and return lines.
9. Remove six manifold mounting nuts.
10. Disconnect lower support manifold bracket by removing top bolt only.
11. Remove manifold with wiring harness and gasket.
12. Reverse procedure to install, **Torque** all bolts to specification.

## EXHAUST MANIFOLD
## REPLACE

1. Disconnect battery ground cable, then remove air cleaner tray.
2. Disconnect electric cooling fan electrical connector, then remove radiator shroud attaching bolts and shroud.
3. Disconnect thermactor tube at exhaust manifold, then remove air conditioning hose bracket.
4. Remove exhaust manifold retaining nuts, then raise and support vehicle.
5. Remove anti-roll brace, then disconnect water tube brackets.
6. Disconnect exhaust pipe at catalytic converter, then remove exhaust manifold.
7. Reverse procedure to install. Refer to **Fig. 5,** during installation procedure.

EFI Engine

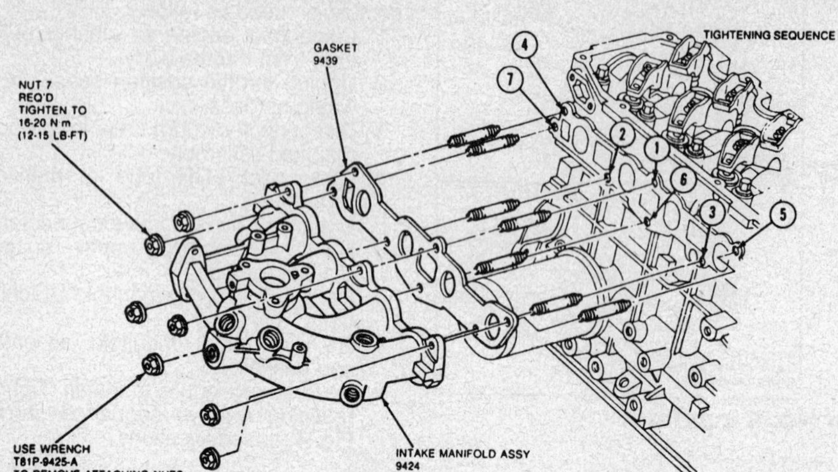


**Fig. 4 Intake manifold bolt tightening sequence (Part 1 of 2)**

EFI HO Engine

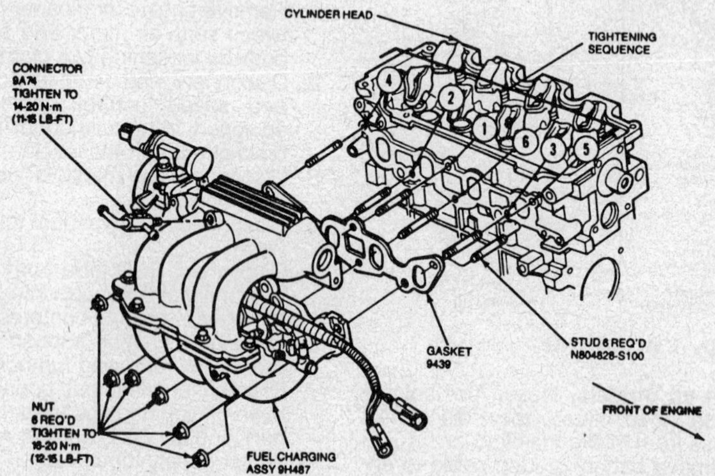


**Fig. 4 Intake manifold bolt tightening sequence (Part 2 of 2)**

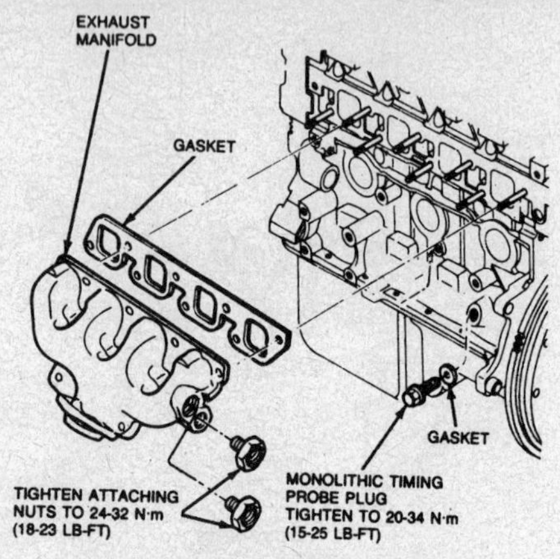


**Fig. 5 Exhaust manifold assembly**

EFI

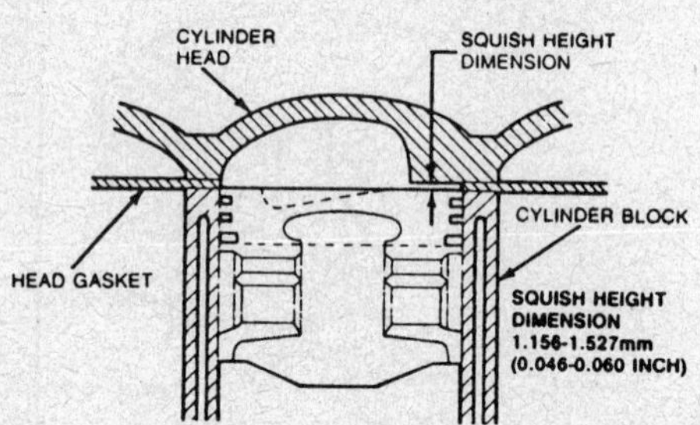


EFI HO

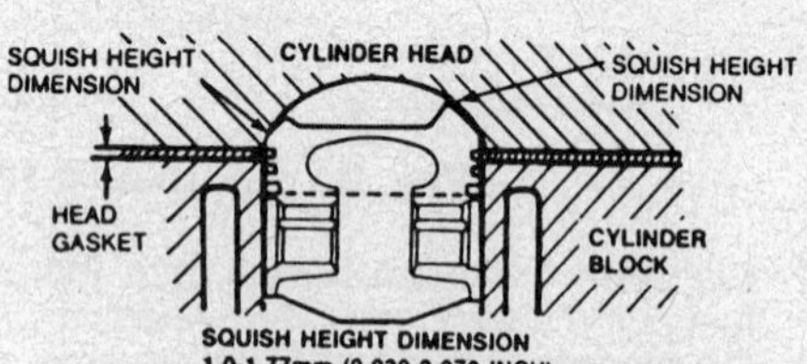


**Fig. 6 Piston squish height (Part 1 of 2)**

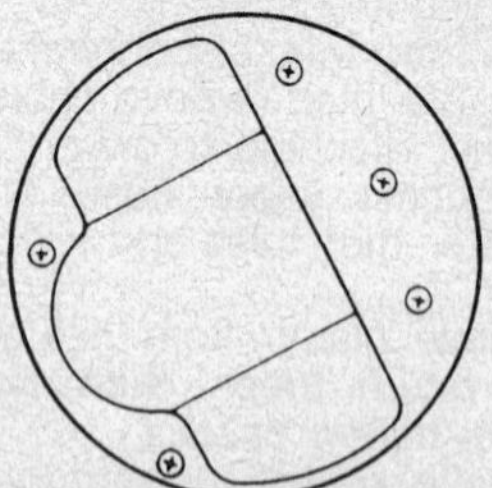

**Fig. 6 Piston squish height (Part 2 of 2)**

# CYLINDER HEAD
## REPLACE

1. Raise and secure hood in open position.
2. Disconnect battery ground cable.
3. Drain cooling system and disconnect heater hose at the fitting located under the intake manifold.
4. Disconnect cooling fan switch electrical connector.
5. Remove air cleaner assembly.
6. Remove PCV hose from air cleaner assembly.
7. Label, then disconnect all electrical connectors and vacuum hoses from cylinder head assembly.
8. Remove rocker arm cover.
9. Remove accessory drive belts.
10. Remove crankshaft damper.
11. Remove timing belt cover.
12. Turn crankshaft until No. 1 cylinder is at TDC of compression stroke.
13. Remove distributor cap and spark plug wires as an assembly.
14. Using torque wrench adapter T88P-6254-A or equivalent, loosen both belt tensioner attaching bolts.
15. Secure belt tensioner as far left toward front of vehicle as possible.
16. Remove timing belt.
17. Disconnect EGR tube from EGR valve.
18. Disconnect fuel supply and return lines from metal connectors, located on the right side of the engine and set rubber lines aside.
19. Disconnect accelerator cable and speed control cable, if equipped.
20. Disconnect alternator from wiring harness.
21. Remove alternator and mounting bracket.
22. Raise and support vehicle.
23. Disconnect exhaust pipe from exhaust manifold.
24. Lower vehicle.
25. Remove and discard cylinder head bolts and washers.
26. Remove cylinder head with exhaust and intake manifolds attached.
27. Remove cylinder head gasket. Do not lay cylinder head flat. Damage to the spark plugs, valves or gasket surfaces may result.
28. Reverse procedure to install. **Before FINAL installation of the cylinder head, check piston squish height. Squish height is the clearance of the piston dome to the cylinder head dome at piston TDC, Fig. 6.** No rework of the cylinder head gasket

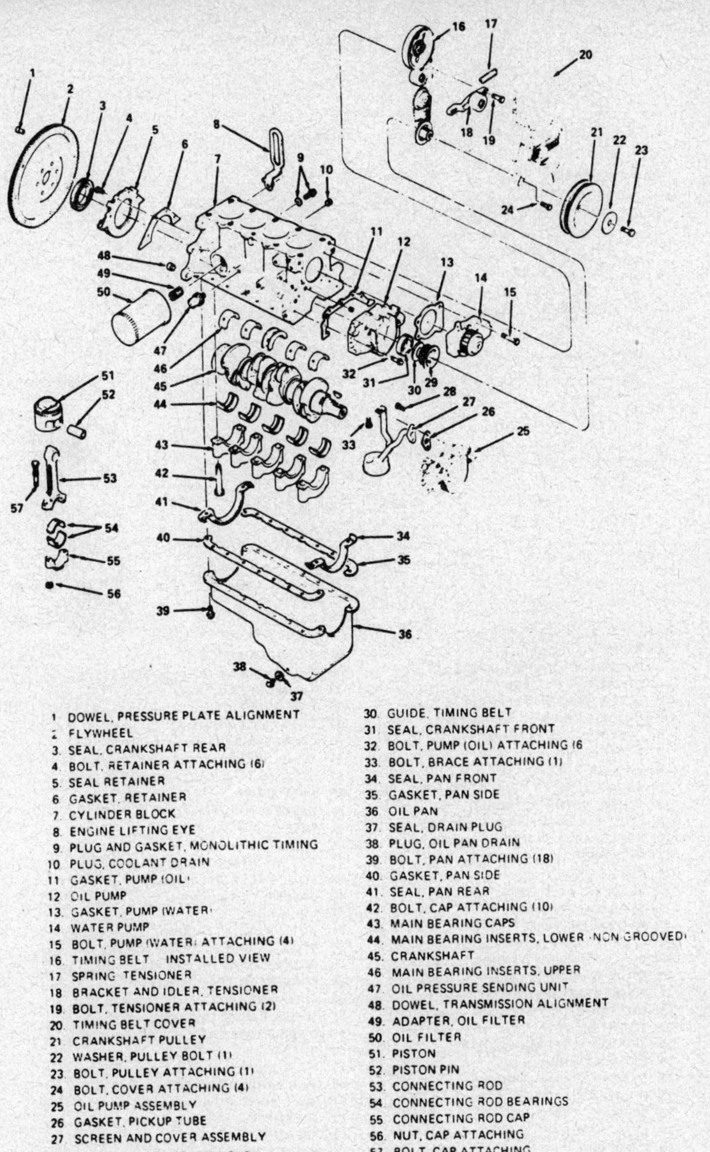


**Exploded view of cylinder block, crankshaft & related components**

surfaces (slabbing) or use of replacement components (crankshaft, piston and connecting rod) causing the assembled squish height to be over or under the tolerance specification is permitted. If no other parts other than the cylinder head gasket are replaced, the piston squish height should be within specification. If parts other than the cylinder head gasket are replaced, check the squish height. If the squish height is out of specification, replace the parts again, and check the piston squish height again. Check squish height as follows:

a. Clean all gasket material from the mating surfaces on the cylinder head and engine block.
b. Place a small amount of soft lead solder of appropriate thickness on the piston spherical areas.
c. Rotate crankshaft to lower the piston in the bore and install the cylinder head gasket. A compressed (used) gasket is preferred.
d. Install the used cylinder head bolts and tighten the head bolts to 30-44 ft. lbs. in sequence.
e. Rotate the crankshaft to move the piston through its TDC position.
f. Remove the cylinder head and measure the thickness of the compressed solder to determine squish height at TDC. The solder should be .046-.060 inch for EFI & .039-.070 inch EFI HO engines. **Before installing the cylinder head the crankshaft must be rotated so that the No. 1 piston is 90 degrees before top dead center (BTDC). To position the piston, turn crankshaft until the**

TIGHTENING SEQUENCE – CYLINDER HEAD ATTACHING BOLTS

| 9 | 3 | 1 | 5 | 7 | |
|---|---|---|---|---|---|
| ○ | ○ | ○ | ○ | ○ | INTAKE |
| ○ | ○ | ○ | ○ | ○ | EXHAUST |
| 8 | 6 | 2 | 4 | 10 | |

**Fig. 7 Cylinder head bolt tightening sequence**

**pulley keyway is at 9 o'clock position. To time the valve train to this piston position, turn the camshaft until keyway is at the 6 o'clock position. The camshaft and the crankshaft must not be turned until after the installation of the timing gears and timing belt.**

29. **Torque** new cylinder head bolts in sequence shown in **Fig. 7,** to 44 ft. lbs. Loosen all attaching bolts approximately two turns, then torque attaching bolts in sequence shown to 44 ft. lbs. After tightening cylinder head bolts, turn all bolts 90 degrees, again in sequence shown. Complete bolt tightening by turning all bolts in sequence an additional 90 degrees.

## VALVE CLEARANCE SPECIFICATIONS

| Year | Engine | Valve Lash, Inch |
|---|---|---|
| 1989-90 | 1.9L/4-116 | .059-.194① |

①—With hydraulic valve lash adjuster completely collapsed.

## VALVE ARRANGEMENT

### FRONT TO REAR

1.9L/4-116① ........... I-I-I-I-E-E-E-E

①—Valves are arranged in sequence shown with intake valves located to the rear of cylinder head and exhaust valves to the front of cylinder head.

## CAMSHAFT LOBE LIFT SPECIFICATIONS

| Engine | Year | Intake, Inch | Exhaust, Inch |
|---|---|---|---|
| 1.9L/4-116 | 1989-90 | .240 | .240 |

## VALVE LIFT SPECIFICATIONS

| Engine | Year | Intake, Inch | Exhaust, Inch |
|---|---|---|---|
| 1.9L/4-116 | 1989-90 | .396 | .396 |

## VALVES

### ADJUST

The 1.9L engine is equipped with an overhead camshaft and hydraulic lash adjuster. Valve stem to rocker arm clearance is measured with tappet completely collapsed. Perform the following procedure when measuring valve tappet clearance:

1. Rotate engine until piston of No. 1 cylinder is at TDC of compression stroke.
2. Position suitable hydraulic lifter compressor tool onto rocker arm, then slowly apply pressure to bleed tappet. Continue to apply pressure until lifter plunger bottoms. Hold tappet in this position and check clearance between rocker arm and valve stem tip using a suitable feeler gauge with less than a 3/8 inch width. Collapsed tappet gap clearance should be .059-.194 inch on 1.9L/4-116 engines. If clearance is less than specified, check for worn or damaged fulcrums, tappets or camshaft lobes.
3. With No. 1 piston on TDC of compression stroke, check the following valves as outlined: Nos. 1 and 2 intake & No. 1 exhaust.
4. Rotate crankshaft 180° from present position, then check the following valves: No. 3 intake & No. 3 exhaust.
5. Rotate crankshaft 180° from present position, then check the following valves: No. 4 intake & Nos. 2 and 4 exhaust.

## TIMING BELT
## REPLACE

1. Disconnect battery ground cable, then remove accessory drive belts.
2. Remove timing cover. **Align timing mark on camshaft sprocket with timing mark on cylinder head, Fig. 8.**
3. Install timing belt cover, then ensure timing mark on crankshaft damper aligns with TDC mark on front cover.
4. Remove timing belt cover.
5. Loosen both timing tensioner attaching bolts using torque wrench adapter T81P-6254-A or equivalent.
6. Pry tensioner away from belt as far as possible, then tighten one attaching bolt.
7. Remove crankshaft damper, then the timing belt. Discard timing belt if damaged.
8. Install timing belt over sprockets in a counterclockwise direction starting at crankshaft. Ensure belt span between crankshaft and camshaft is kept tight as belt is installed over remaining sprocket.
9. Loosen belt tensioner attaching bolt and allow to locate against belt.
10. Tighten one tensioner attaching bolt using previously mentioned tool, then install crankshaft damper, drive plate and pulley attaching bolt.
11. Retain crankshaft damper using strap wrench tool No. D85L-6000-A or equivalent, then **torque** pulley nut to specifications.
12. To seat timing belt on sprocket teeth, proceed as follows:
    a. Connect battery ground cable, then crank engine for approximately 30 seconds.

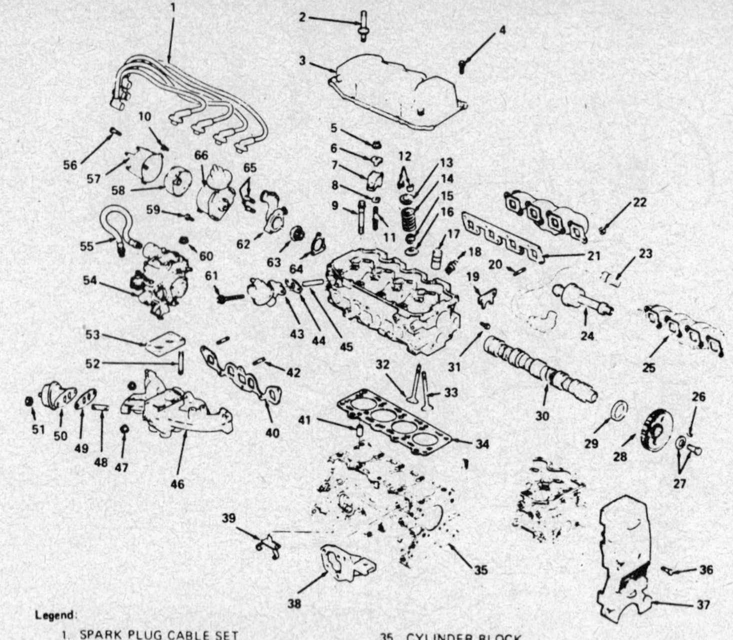

Legend:

1. SPARK PLUG CABLE SET
2. BOLT/STUD, COVER ATTACHING (2)
3. ROCKER ARM COVER
4. SCREW, COVER ATTACHING (7)
5. NUT, FULCRUM ATTACHING (8)
6. FULCRUM, ROCKER ARM
7. ROCKER ARM
8. WASHER, FULCRUM (8)
9. BOLT, CYLINDER HEAD ATTACHING (10)
10. SCREW, ROTOR ATTACHING (2)
11. STUD, FULCRUM ATTACHING (8)
12. KEYS, VALVE SPRING RETAINER
13. RETAINER, VALVE SPRING
14. VALVE SPRING
15. SEAL, VALVE STEM
16. SEAT, VALVE SPRING
17. HYDRAULIC TAPPET
18. SPARK PLUG
19. PLATE, CAMSHAFT THRUST
20. STUD, MANIFOLD ATTACHING (8)
21. GASKET, EXHAUST MANIFOLD
22. NUT, MANIFOLD ATTACHING (8)
23. EGR TUBE
24. CHECK VALVE, AIR INJECTION
25. EXHAUST MANIFOLD
26. SHAFT KEY, CAM SPROCKET
27. BOLT/WASHER SPROCKET ATTACHING (1)
28. SPROCKET, CAMSHAFT
29. SEAL, CAMSHAFT
30. CAMSHAFT
31. BOLT, THRUST PLATE ATTACHING (2)
32. INTAKE VALVE
33. EXHAUST VALVE
34. GASKET, CYLINDER HEAD
35. CYLINDER BLOCK
36. BOLTS (2) & NUTS (2), COVER ATTACHING
37. TIMING BELT COVER
38. ENGINE MOUNT
39. CRANKCASE VENTILATION BAFFLE
40. GASKET, INTAKE MANIFOLD
41. DOWEL, CYLINDER HEAD ALIGNMENT (2)
42. STUD, MANIFOLD ATTACHING (6)
43. FUEL PUMP
44. GASKET, FUEL PUMP
45. PUSH ROD, FUEL PUMP
46. INTAKE MANIFOLD
47. NUT, MANIFOLD ATTACHING (6)
48. STUD, VALVE ATTACHING (2)
49. GASKET, EGR VALVE
50. EGR VALVE
51. NUT, VALVE ATTACHING (2)
52. STUD, CARBURETOR ATTACHING (4)
53. GASKET, CARBURETOR MOUNTING
54. CARBURETOR
55. FUEL LINE
56. SCREW, CAP ATTACHING (2)
57. DISTRIBUTOR CAP
58. ROTOR
59. BOLT, DISTRIBUTOR ATTACHING (3)
60. NUT, CARBURETOR ATTACHING (4)
61. BOLT, PUMP ATTACHING (2)
62. THERMOSTAT HOUSING
63. THERMOSTAT
64. GASKET, HOUSING
65. BOLT, HOUSING ATTACHING (2)
66. DISTRIBUTOR

**Exploded view of cylinder head assembly & related components**

    b. Disconnect battery ground cable, then rotate crankshaft as necessary to align timing pointer on cam sprocket with timing mark on cylinder head.
    c. Position timing belt cover on engine, then ensure timing mark on crankshaft aligns with TDC pointer on cover.
    d. If timing marks do not align, remove belt, align timing marks and repeat steps 8-12.
13. Loosen tensioner attaching bolt, then secure crankshaft and ensure it will not rotate.
14. Using camshaft holding tool No. D81P-6256-A or equivalent and a suitable torque wrench, turn camshaft sprocket counterclockwise. **Torque** belt tensioner attaching bolt to specifications. for new belt or 10 ft. lbs. on new belt. **Ensure engine is cold when applying torque to camshaft sprocket. Do not set torque on hot engine.**
15. Install timing belt cover, accessory drive belts, then connect battery ground cable.

## LIFTER
## REPLACE

Refer to **Fig. 9**, for lifter replacement.

## CAMSHAFT
## REPLACE

1. Disconnect battery ground cable, then remove air cleaner assembly.
2. Remove PCV hose, then the accessory drive belts.

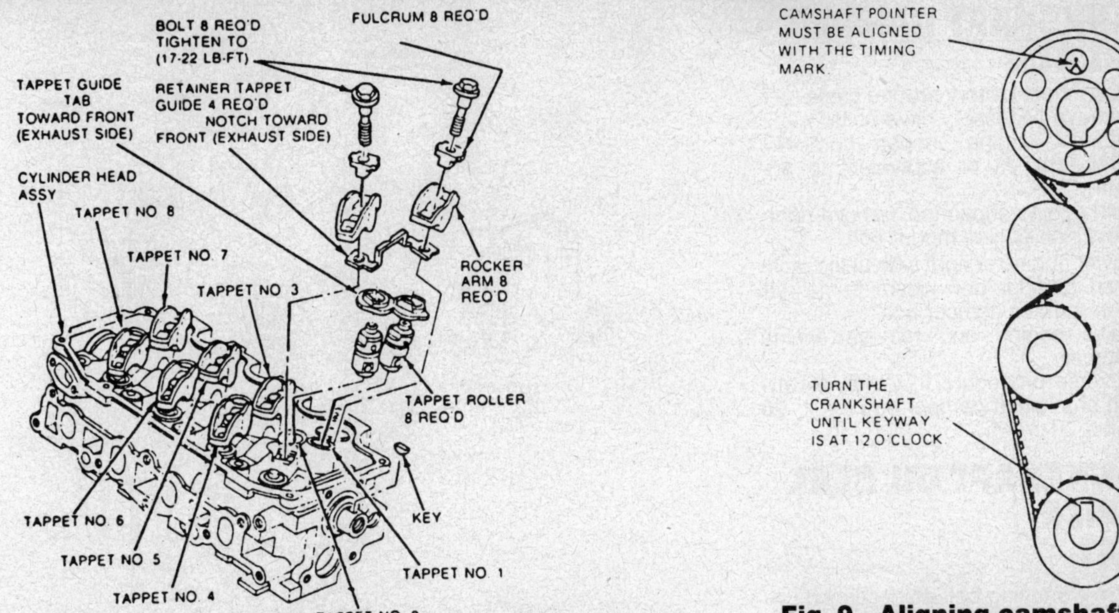


**Fig. 8 Exploded view of lifter components**

**Fig. 9 Aligning camshaft to cylinder head timing marks**

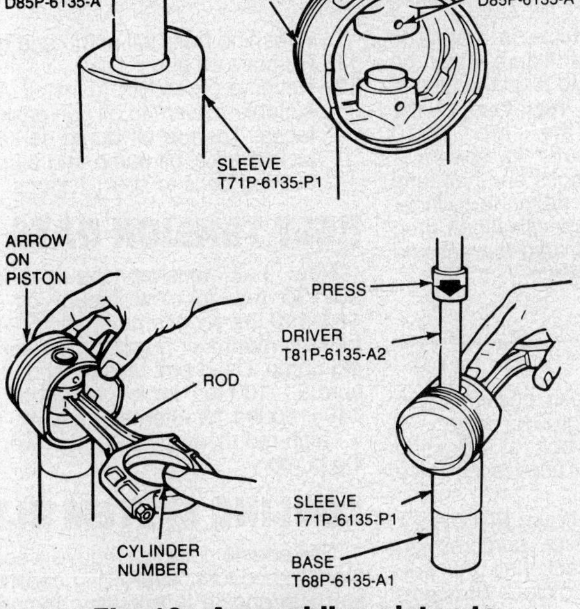


**Fig. 10 Assembling piston to rod**

FRONT OF ENGINE
ASSEMBLY REFERENCE ARROW
PISTON
COMPRESSION RING
PISTON PIN
CONNECTING ROD
OIL SQUIRT HOLE (ON LH SIDE OF ROD)
CONNECTING ROD CAP
OIL CONTROL RING ASSEMBLY (2 CONTROL RINGS, ONE OIL RING SPACER)
BEARING INSERT

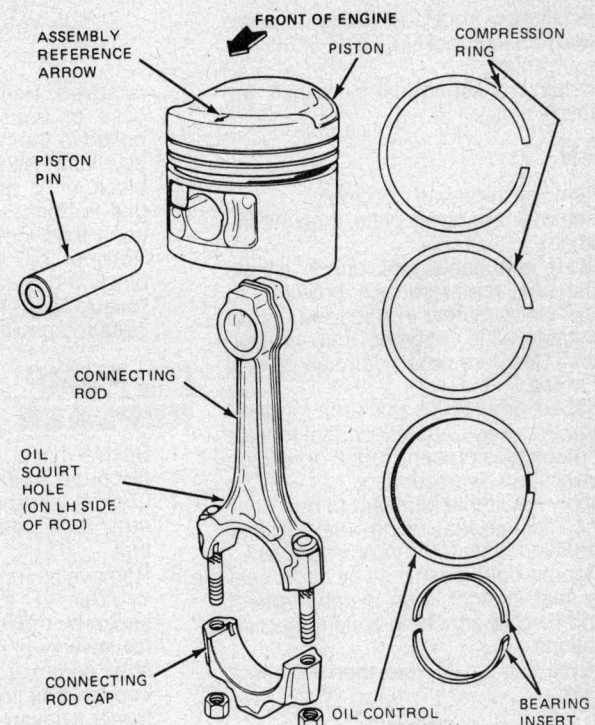

**Fig. 11 Piston & rod assembly**

3. Remove crankshaft damper, then the timing belt cover.
4. Remove valve cover attaching bolts and studs, then the valve cover.
5. Set piston of No. 1 cylinder at TDC of compression stroke, then remove rocker arm hex flange nuts, fulcrums and rocker arms.
6. Remove fulcrum washers, then the tappets.
7. Remove distributor assembly, then loosen timing belt tensioner attaching bolts using torque wrench adapter tool No. T81P-6254-A or equivalent.
8. Remove timing belt, then the camshaft sprocket and key.
9. Remove thrust plate, then the fuel pump.
10. Remove ignition coil and coil bracket.
11. Remove camshaft through rear of head, toward transaxle.
12. Reverse procedure to install.
13. Apply a suitable lubricant to camshaft prior to installation, then check seal for wear and damage and replace as necessary.

## PISTON & ROD ASSEMBLY

Position locator tool D85P-6135-A or equivalent into center hole of sleeve T71P-6135-P1, **Fig. 10,** then place piston onto locator. Locator will align pin bores in piston and rods and will also serve as a pilot for piston pin. Press piston into place using driver tool No. T81P-6135-A2 or equivalent. Assemble piston to rod with arrow facing front of engine and numbered side of rod facing exhaust manifold side of engine, **Fig. 11.** Check side clearance between connecting rods at each crankshaft journal. Clearance should be .004-.011 inch.

## CRANKSHAFT DAMPER
### REPLACE

1. Disconnect battery ground cable.
2. Remove accessory drive belts.
3. Connect engine support (tool No. D88L-6000-A) or equivalent to engine.
4. With engine supported, remove right-hand side engine mount bolt.
5. Lower engine at right side until crankshaft damper bolt clears frame rail, then remove damper bolt.
6. Raise engine and remove engine damper.
7. Reverse procedure to install, **torquing** crankshaft damper bolt to 81-96 ft. lbs.

## CRANKSHAFT OIL SEAL SERVICE
### FRONT

1. Remove timing belt as described under "Timing Belt, Replace."
2. Remove crankshaft damper, then the front seal.
3. Install new front seal using oil pump seal replacer tool No. T81P-6700-A or equivalent.
4. Install crankshaft damper, then the timing belt.

### REAR

1. Remove transaxle assembly.
2. Remove rear cover plate, then the flywheel.
3. Using a suitable tool, punch a hole into seal metal surface between lip and block. Screw in threaded end of suitable slide hammer, then remove seal. Use care not to damage oil seal surface.
4. Inspect crankshaft seal area for damage that may cause new seal to leak. If damage is present, repair or replace crankshaft as necessary.
5. Apply a suitable lubricant to new seal, then install seal using seal installer tool No. T81P-6701-A or equivalent.
6. Tighten bolts evenly as to allow seal to seat straight, then install flywheel and **torque** attaching bolts to specifications.
7. Install rear cover plate, then the transaxle.

## OIL PAN
### REPLACE

1. Disconnect battery ground cable.
2. Raise and support vehicle.
3. Drain oil from engine.
4. Disconnect starter cable.
5. Remove starter motor from engine.
6. Remove two oil pan-to-transaxle attaching bolts.
7. Disconnect exhaust pipe from manifold and converter.
8. Remove oil pan attaching bolts and oil pan.
9. Reverse procedure to install. If the oil pan is installed on engine with engine removed from vehicle, a transaxle case or equivalent fixture must be bolted to the block to align the oil pan up, flush with the rear face of the block. **Torque** the two M-10 pan-to-transaxle bolts to specifications, then loosen bolts one-half turn. **Torque** oil pan flange-to-cylinder block M-8 bolts to specifications, then **torque** two M-10 pan-to-transaxle bolts to specifications.

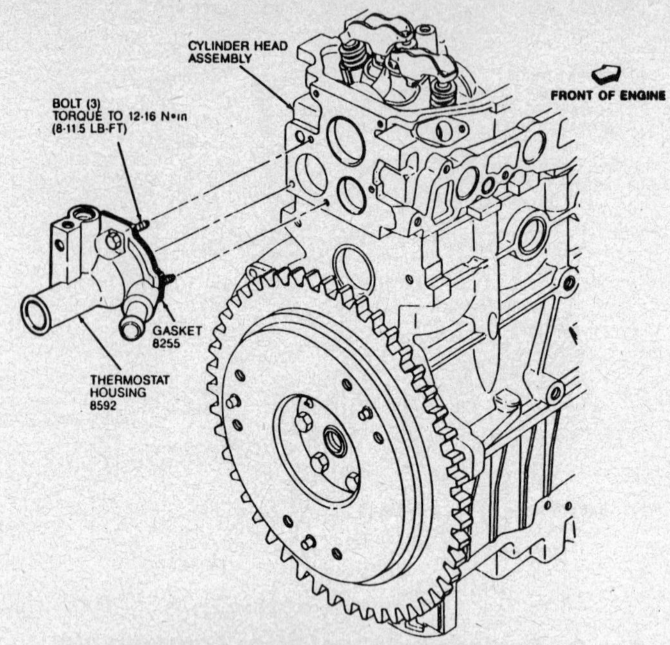


**Fig. 12 Thermostat replacement**

## OIL PUMP
### REPLACE

1. Secure hood in open position, then disconnect battery ground cable.
2. Loosen alternator bolt at adjusting arm, then remove accessory drive belt.
3. Remove timing belt cover. Place No. 1 cylinder at T.D.C. of compression stroke by turning crankshaft until pulley keyway is at 12 o'clock and camshaft sprocket keyway is at 6 o'clock. Loosen belt tensioner, then pry tensioner away from belt and tighten one attaching bolt.
4. Disengage timing belt from camshaft sprocket, water pump sprocket and crankshaft sprocket. Raise vehicle on a suitable hoist, then drain crankcase.
5. Remove timing belt, then the crankshaft drive plate assembly.
6. Remove crankshaft damper, then the crankshaft sprocket.
7. Disconnect starter cable at starter, then remove knee brace from engine.
8. Remove starter, then the rear section of knee brace and inspection plate at transaxle.
9. Remove oil pan retaining bolts, then the oil pan.
10. Remove front and rear oil pan seals and side gaskets, then the oil pump attaching bolts, oil pump and gasket.
11. Remove oil pump seal.
12. Reverse procedure to install. Apply a suitable sealant to oil pan gasket surfaces. **Torque** oil pump screen and pickup tube, oil pump and oil pan attaching bolts to specifications.

## BELT TENSION DATA

New belt tension should measure 90-130 lbs. for low mount air pump, 150-190 lbs. for alternator and 50-90 lbs. for high mount air pump and power steering pump. Used belt tension should measure 80-100 lbs. for low mount air pump, 140-160 lbs. for alternator and 40-60 lbs. for high mount air pump and power steering pump.

## COOLING SYSTEM BLEED

This engine does not require a specified bleed procedure. After filling cooling system, run engine to operating temperature with radiator/pressure cap off. Air will then automatically bleed through cap opening.

## THERMOSTAT
### REPLACE
#### REMOVAL

1. Disconnect battery cable and wiring connector from thermo switch in thermostat housing.
2. Remove radiator cap, then attach a hose to drain tube and open draincock. Drain coolant level until its below water outlet connection. Close the draincock.
3. Loosen upper hose at radiator, **Fig. 12,** then remove water outlet housing retaining bolts. Lift clear of engine and remove thermostat. Do not pry housing off.

## INSTALLATION

1. Clean outlet housing and cylinder head mating surfaces.
2. Position thermostat and seat so it will compress gasket. Position outlet to cylinder head, using a new gasket and install retaining bolts.
3. Connect top hose to radiator and tighten clamp. Ensure that draincock is closed.
4. Fill cooling system with coolant recommended by manufacturer as follows:
   a. Add 50 percent coolant, then add water until radiator is full. Allow coolant level to settle, then add more coolant until radiator remain full.
   b. Install radiator cap to first notch, connect battery cable and wire connector to thermo switch. Start engine and let idle until upper hose is warm, then carefully remove radiator cap and top off coolant level.
   c. Install cap securely and fill reservoir to FULL COLD mark with proper concentrate. Add water to FULL HOT mark. Check for leaks.

## WATER PUMP
## REPLACE

1. Disconnect battery ground cable, then drain cooling system.
2. Remove accessory drive belts, then the engine front timing cover.
3. Place No. 1 cylinder at T.D.C. of compression stroke by turning crankshaft until pulley keyway is at 12 o'clock and camshaft sprocket keyway is at 6 o'clock. Loosen belt tensioner, then pry tensioner away from belt and tighten one attaching bolt.
4. Secure tensioner as far left as possible, then remove timing belt.
5. Remove camshaft sprocket, then the rearward front timing cover stud.
6. Disconnect heater return tube hose connection at water pump inlet tube.
7. Remove water pump inlet tube fasteners, then the tube and gasket.
8. Remove water pump to cylinder block bolts, then the water pump.
9. Reverse procedure to install. Refer to "Timing Belt, Replace" for proper belt tension procedures.

## FUEL PUMP
## REPLACE

Fuel supply lines will remain pressurized for long periods of time after engine shut-down. This pressure must be relieved before any service is attempted. A valve is provided on the fuel rail assembly for this purpose. To relieve system pressure, remove air cleaner assembly and connect pressure gauge tool No. T80L-9974-A or equivalent, onto fuel diagnostic valve on the fuel rail assembly. Gradually release fuel system pressure.

1. Disconnect battery ground cable.
2. Depressurize fuel system as described previously.
3. Raise and support vehicle.
4. Loosen fuel pump mounting bolt until fuel pump can be removed from vehicle.
5. Remove parking brake cable from pump clip.
6. Disconnect electrical connector and fuel pump outlet fitting.
7. Disconnect fuel pump inlet line from pump. **Either drain fuel tank or raise end of fuel line above fuel level in tank to prevent fuel siphon action.**
8. Remove pump from vehicle.
9. Reverse procedure to install. To pressurize fuel system, proceed as follows:
   a. Install pressure tool gauge No. T80L-9974-A or equivalent onto fuel rail pressure fitting.
   b. Turn ignition switch to ON position for 2 seconds and repeat turning ignition switch ON and OFF at 2 second intervals until gauge tool indicates approximately 35 psi.

## SERVICE BULLETINS

### NOISY ROLLER LIFTERS

Some 1989-90 Escorts may experience a loud tapping noise inside the engine compartment. This may be caused by mechanical failure of the lifters or air trapped inside lifter. The air trapped inside will not allow sufficient oil to enter which will cause lifter noise and/or failure. Lifter noise for up to three seconds after initial start up is normal and requires no corrective action.

Check the engine code tag, located on timing belt cover, for one of the following codes: 7G460, 7G461, 7G473, 8G460, 8G461, 8G473, 9G460, 9G461, 9G473, 0G480, 0G481, 0G482 & 0G483. These codes indicate the engine has roller lifters.

Use the following procedure to determine if lifters have air trapped inside or lifter replacement is required.

1. Bring engine to normal operating temperature by running at idle for at least tem minutes.
2. Run engine at 1500-2000 rpm. Listen for lifter noise, which is a constant tapping sound that can be heard at normal operating temperature, at this rpm.
3. If lifter noise is present, purge air from lifter by driving the vehicle for eight minutes at 3000 rpm. **Select appropriate gear to maintain 3000 rpm at a speed consistent with local traffic laws and road conditions.**
4. If lifter noise is still present, locate defective lifter that feels spongy.
5. If any lifter is replaced, align paint dot (blue or orange) on top of tappet retainer clip with oil feed hole in cylinder head lifter bore. Intake lifters should have paint dot facing toward distributor end of cylinder head and exhaust lifters paint dot will face timing belt.

## TIGHTENING SPECIFICATIONS

| Year | Component | Torque/ft. Lbs. |
|---|---|---|
| 1989-90 | Alternator Adjuster Arm To Alternator | 53 |
| | Alternator Brace Arm To Alternator | 18 |
| | Alternator Bracket To Block | 37 |
| | Alternator Pivot Bolt | 51 |
| | Belt Tensioner Attaching Bolt | 27-32 |
| | Camshaft Sprocket To Cam | 71-84 |
| | Camshaft Thrust Plate To Head | 7-11 |
| | Connecting Rod Bolts | ① |
| | Crankshaft Damper bolt | 81-96 |
| | Crankshaft Pulley Nut | 74-90 |
| | Cylinder Head Bolts | 44② |
| | Distributor Clamp | 6-8 |
| | Exhaust Manifold | 15-20 |
| | Exhaust Manifold Nuts | 16-19 |
| | EGR Valve Stud To Intake Manifold | 3.7-7.4 |
| | EGR Valve To Spacer Stud Nut | 13-19 |

*Continued*

## TIGHTENING SPECIFICATIONS—Continued

| Year | Component | Torque/ft. Lbs. |
|---|---|---|
| 1989-90 | Fan Switch To Water Outlet Housing | 5-8 |
| | Flywheel Attaching Bolts | 54-64 |
| | Intake Manifold | 12-15 |
| | M-10 Pan-To-Transaxle Bolts | 30-40 |
| | Main Bearing Cap Bolts | 67-80 |
| | Oil Pan To Engine Block | 15-20 |
| | Oil Pan To Transaxle | 30-40 |
| | Oil Pump Attaching Bolts | 5-7 |
| | Oil Pump Cover | 6-9 |
| | Oil Pump Screen And Pickup Tube Attaching Bolts | 6-9 |
| | Rocker Arm Cover | 6-8 |
| | Rocker Arm Shaft Bracket | 17-22 |
| | Spark Plugs | 8-15 |
| | Timing Tensioner Bolt | 17-20 |
| | Valve Cover To Head | 6-8 |
| | Valve Cover Stud To Head | 6-8 |
| | Vibration Damper Or Pulley | ③ |
| | Water Drain Plug | 5-8 |
| | Water Outlet Housing | 6-8 |
| | Water Pump Inlet Tube To Water Pump | 4-5 |
| | Water Pump To Engine Block | 5-8 |

①—1989; 19-25 ft. lbs., 1990; 26-30 ft. lbs.
②—Then tighten each bolt an additional 180° in 90° increments
③—1989, 74-90 ft. lbs., 1990, 81-96 ft. lbs.

# 2.3L/4-140 Engine

**NOTE:** On Vehicles Equipped With Airbags, Disarm Airbag System As Outlined Under "Airbag System Disarming" Before Any Diagnosis, Testing, Troubleshooting Or Repairs Are Performed. After All Diagnosis, Testing, Troubleshooting Or Repairs Have Been Completed, Rearm Airbag System As Outlined Under "Airbag System Disarming."

## INDEX



## AIRBAG SYSTEM DISARMING

### 1989–91

**The electrical circuit necessary for system deployment is powered directly from the battery and a backup power supply. To avoid accidental deployment and possible personal injury, the airbag system must be deactivated prior to servicing or replacing any system components.**

A back-up power supply is included in the system to provide airbag deployment in the event the battery or battery cables are damaged in an accident before the sensors can close. The power supply is a capacitor that will retain a charge for approximately 15 minutes after the battery ground cable is disconnected or one minute if the positive battery cable is grounded. **Backup power supply must be disconnected to deactivate airbag system.** To remove backup power supply, refer to "Airbags" in the "Passive Restraint" section.

### 1992

#### Deactivation

1. Disconnect positive battery cable.
2. Wait one minute. This is the time required for backup power supply in diagnostic monitor to deplete its stored energy.
3. Remove four nut and washer assemblies retaining driver airbag module to steering wheel. Disconnect driver airbag connector. Connect Rotunda Airbag Simulator tool No. 105-00008 or

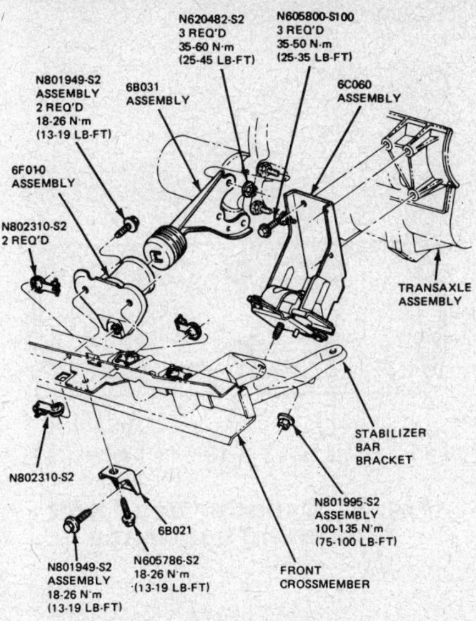


**Fig. 1 Lefthand front No. 1 insulator. 4 & 5 speed manual transaxle**

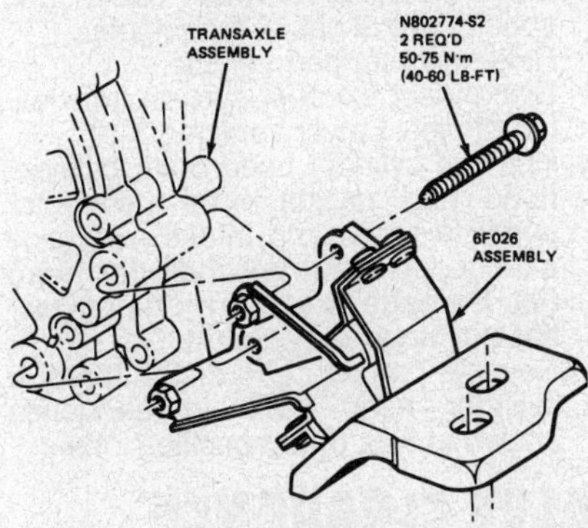


**Fig. 4 Lefthand rear No. 4 insulator. 5 speed manual & automatic transaxle**

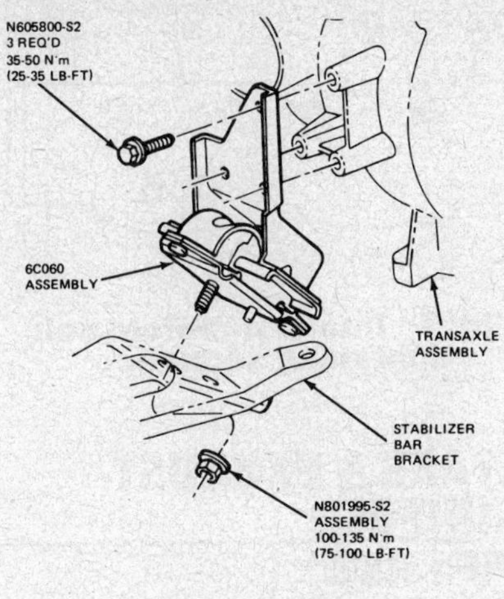


**Fig. 2 Lefthand front No. 1 insulator. Automatic transaxle**

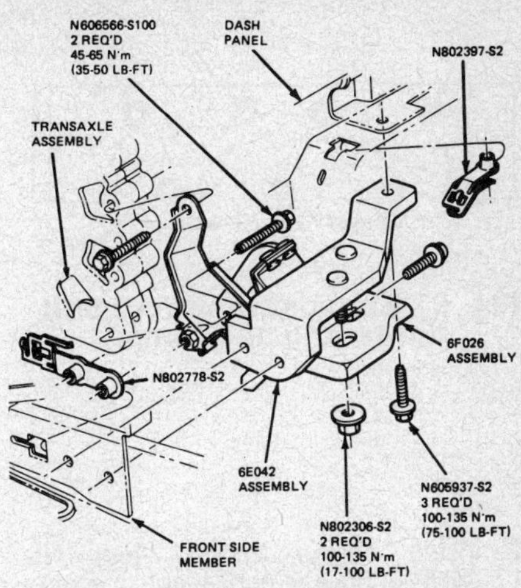


**Fig. 3 Lefthand rear No. 4 insulator. 4 speed manual transaxle**

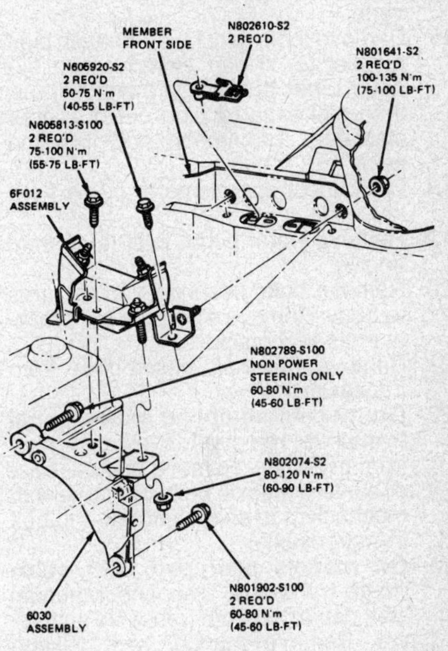


**Fig. 5 Righthand No. 3A insulator**

equivalent to vehicle harness at top of steering wheel.

4. Connect positive battery cable.

### Reactivation

1. Disconnect positive battery cable.
2. Wait one minute for backup power supply to deplete stored energy.
3. Remove airbag simulator from vehicle harness connector at top of steering column. Reconnect driver airbag connector. Position driver airbag on steering wheel, then install four nut and washer assemblies. **Torque** retaining nuts to 24-32 inch lbs.
4. Connect positive battery cable, then Prove-Out System.

### Prove-Out System

Prove-out system means to turn the ignition switch from Off to Run and visually monitor the airbag indicator, located on dash panel. The airbag indicator will light continuously for approximately six seconds and then turn off. If an airbag system fault is present, the indicator will either fail to light, remain lit continuously or light in a flashing manner.

The flashing manner may not occur until approximately 30 seconds after the ignition switch has been turned from Off to Run. This is the time needed for the diagnostic monitor to complete testing of the system. If the airbag indicator is inoperative and an airbag system fault exists, a tone will sound in a pattern of five sets of five beeps. If this occurs, the airbag indicator will need to be serviced.

## ENGINE MOUNTS
## REPLACE

Refer to **Figs. 1 through 5** when replacing engine mounts.

## ENGINE
## REPLACE

Engine and transaxle are removed as an assembly.

1. Mark position of hood hinges, then remove hood.
2. Disconnect battery ground cable, then remove air cleaner assembly.
3. Remove lower radiator hose and drain coolant from engine. Remove upper radiator hose from engine.
4. **On models equipped with automatic transaxle,** disconnect transaxle cooler lines from rubber hoses below radiator.
5. **On all models,** remove coil assembly from cylinder head. Disconnect coolant fan electrical connector.
6. Remove radiator shroud, cooling fan and radiator.
7. Carefully discharge refrigerant from air conditioning system, if equipped. Remove inlet and outlet lines from compressor.
8. Mark and disconnect all electrical and vacuum lines from engine.
9. **On models equipped with automatic transaxle,** disconnect TV linkage from transaxle. **On models equipped with manual transaxle,** disconnect clutch cable from transaxle shift lever.
10. **On all models,** disconnect accelerator linkage, fuel supply and return lines from engine.
11. Disconnect thermactor pump discharge hose from pump.
12. Disconnect power steering pressure and return lines from pump, if equipped. Remove power steering line bracket from cylinder head.

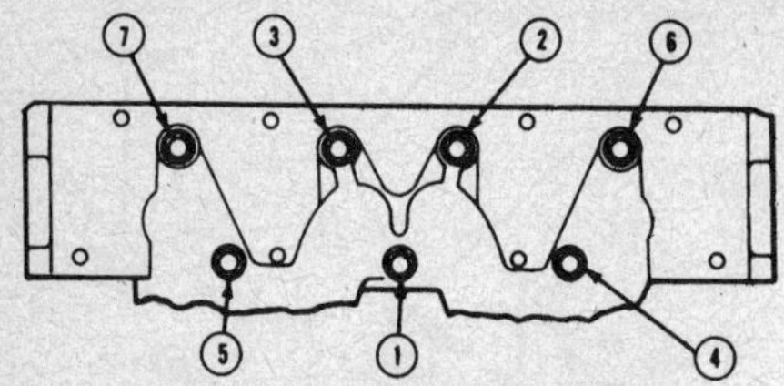

Fig. 6 Exhaust manifold bolt tightening sequence

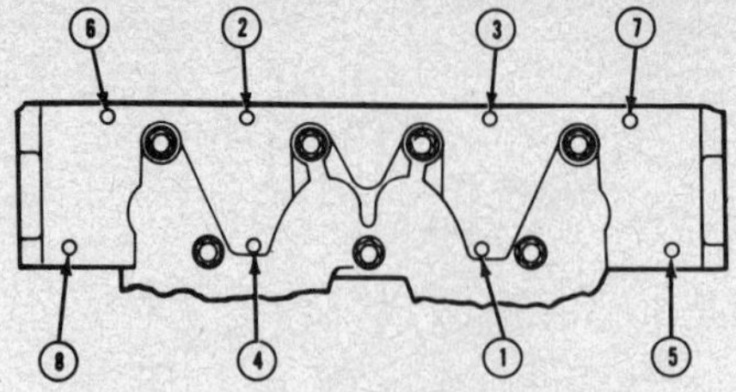

Fig. 7 Intake manifold bolt tightening sequence

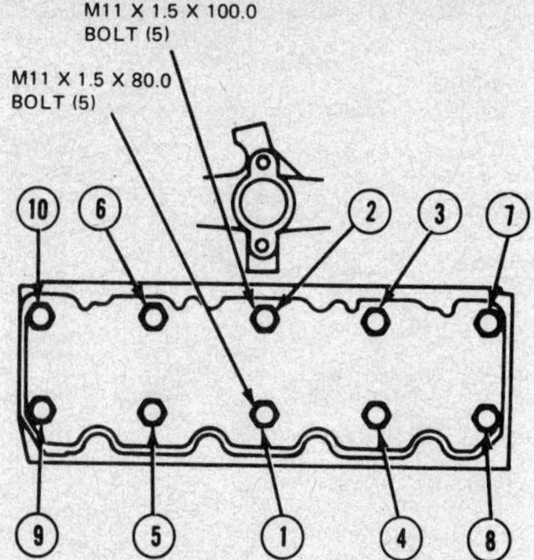


Fig. 8 Cylinder head bolt tightening sequence

13. Install engine support tool No. D79P-6000-A or equivalent, to engine lifting eye.
14. Raise and support vehicle.
15. Remove starter cable from starter.
16. Remove air hose from catalytic converter.
17. Remove bolt securing exhaust pipe bracket to oil pan. Remove two exhaust pipes to exhaust manifold nuts, then pull exhaust pipe out of rubber insulating grommets and position aside.
18. Disconnect speedometer cable from transaxle.
19. Remove water pump inlet hose from engine.
20. Remove bolts securing control arms to body. Remove stabilizer bar bracket bolts and brackets.
21. Remove halfshaft assemblies from transaxle.
22. **On models equipped with manual transaxle,** remove roll restrictor nuts from transaxle. Remove shift stabilizer bar to transaxle bolts. Remove shift mechanism to shift shaft nut and bolt from transaxle.
23. **On models equipped with automatic transaxle,** disconnect manual shift cable clip from transaxle shift lever. Remove manual shift linkage bracket bolts and bracket from transaxle.
24. **On all models,** remove nuts and lefthand rear No. 4 insulator mount bracket from body bracket.
25. Lower vehicle and install suitable lifting hoist to engine. **Do not allow front wheels to touch floor.**
26. Remove engine support tool No. D79L-6000-A or equivalent from engine.
27. Remove righthand No. 3 insulator intermediate bracket to engine bracket bolts and intermediate bracket to insulator nuts. Remove nut on the bottom of double ended stud which secures intermediate bracket to engine bracket. Remove bracket.
28. Carefully lower engine and transaxle assembly from vehicle.
29. Reverse procedure to install. When installing engine/transaxle assembly, position assembly directly below engine compartment. Slowly lower vehicle over engine and transaxle. Do not allow front wheels to contact floor.

# INTAKE & EXHAUST MANIFOLD

## REPLACE

1. Disconnect battery ground cable and drain coolant from engine.
2. Disconnect accelerator cable.
3. Remove air cleaner assembly and heat stove duct from heat shield.
4. Disconnect all vacuum lines from intake manifold.
5. Remove thermactor belt from pulley, thermactor hose and thermactor pump from engine.
6. Remove exhaust pipe to exhaust manifold nuts and disconnect exhaust pipe from exhaust manifold.
7. Remove exhaust manifold heat shield.
8. Disconnect EGO (Exhaust Gas Oxygen) sensor electrical connector.
9. Disconnect thermactor check valve hose from tube assembly. Remove EGR valve bracket nuts and EGR valve bracket.
10. Disconnect water inlet hose from intake manifold.
11. Disconnect EGR hose from EGR valve.
12. Remove bolts, intake manifold and gasket from engine.
13. Remove bolts and exhaust manifold from engine.
14. Reverse procedure to install. **Torque** exhaust manifold bolts in two steps and in sequence shown in **Fig. 6,** to 5-7 ft. lbs., then refer to "Tightening Specifications." **Torque** intake manifold bolts in sequence shown in **Fig. 7** to specifications.

# CYLINDER HEAD

## REPLACE

1. Disconnect battery ground cable.
2. Remove lower radiato r hose and drain coolant from engine.
3. Disconnect heater hose from fitting located under intake manifold.
4. Disconnect upper radiator hose from cylinder head.
5. Disconnect electric cooling fan switch from electrical connector.
6. Remove air cleaner assembly from engine.
7. Mark and disconnect all vacuum hoses from cylinder head.
8. Remove rocker arm cover.
9. Remove all accessory drive belts from engine.
10. Remove distributor cap and spark plug wires as an assembly.
11. Disconnect EGR tube from EGR valve. Disconnect choke cap wire.
12. Disconnect fuel supply and return lines from rubber connector.
13. Disconnect accelerator cable and speed control cable, if equipped.
14. Raise and support vehicle.
15. Disconnect exhaust system from exhaust pipe. Lower vehicle.
16. Remove cylinder head bolts, cylinder head and gasket with thermactor pump, exhaust and intake manifolds attached. **Do not lay cylinder head flat. Damage to spark plugs or gasket surfaces may result.**
17. Reverse procedure to install. **Torque** cylinder head bolts in sequence shown in **Fig. 8,** to specifications.

# VALVE CLEARANCE SPECIFICATIONS

| Year | Engine | Valve Lash, Inch |
|---|---|---|
| 1989-92 | 2.3L/4-140 HSC | .070-.170① |
| 1989-91 | 2.3L/4-140 HSO | .070-.170① |

①—With hydraulic valve lash adjuster completely collapsed.

# VALVE ARRANGEMENT

## FRONT TO REAR

2.3L/4-140 .............. I-E-I-E-E-I-E-I

# CAMSHAFT LOBE LIFT SPECIFICATIONS

| Engine | Year | Intake, Inch | Exhaust, Inch |
|---|---|---|---|
| 2.3L/4-140 HSC | 1989-92 | .249 | .239 |
| 2.3L/4-140 HSO | 1989-91 | .2625 | .2625 |

# VALVE LIFT SPECIFICATIONS

| Engine | Year | Intake, Inch | Exhaust, Inch |
|---|---|---|---|
| 2.3L/4-140 HSC | 1989-92 | .392 | .377 |
| 2.3L/4-140 HSO | 1989-91 | .413 | .413 |

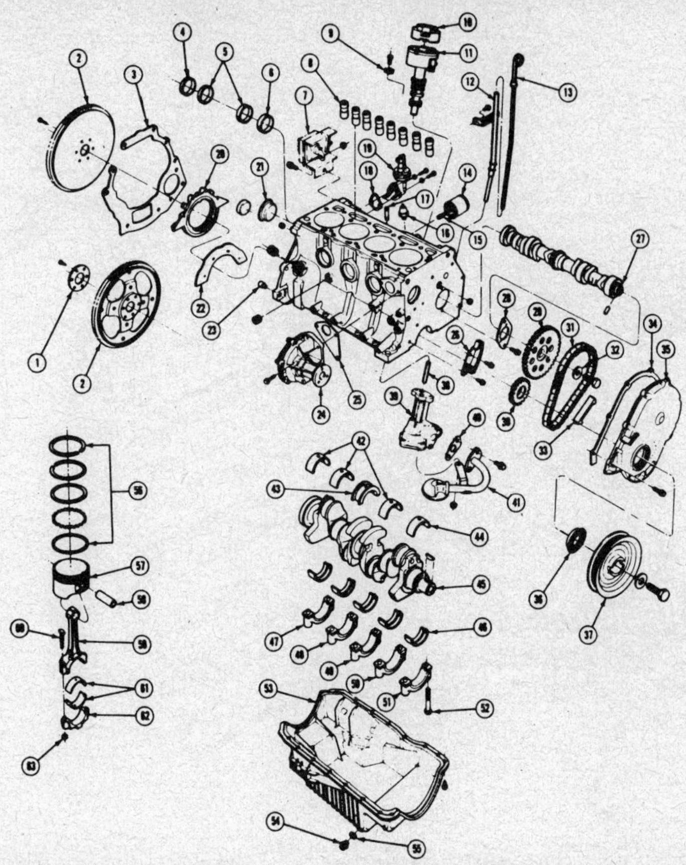

1 REINFORCEMENT PLATE
2 FLYWHEEL
3 REAR COVER PLATE
4 CAMSHAFT BEARING
5 CAMSHAFT BEARING
6 CAMSHAFT BEARING
7 COIL
8 TAPPET ASSEMBLY
9 CLAMP
10 ROTOR
11 DISTRIBUTOR ASSEMBLY
12 TUBE
13 OIL DIPSTICK
14 OIL FILTER
15 INSERT
16 OIL PRESSURE SWITCH
17 FUEL PUMP PUSHROD
18 FUEL PUMP GASKET
19 FUEL PUMP
20 RETAINER ASSEMBLY
21 COVER
22 GASKET
23 DOWEL
24 WATER PUMP ASSEMBLY
25 WATER PUMP GASKET
26 TENSIONER ASSEMBLY
27 CAMSHAFT
28 THRUST PLATE
29 CAMSHAFT SPROCKET
30 CRANKSHAFT SPROCKET
31 TIMING CHAIN ASSEMBLY
32 WASHER
33 TIMING CHAIN DAMPER
34 FRONT COVER GASKET
35 FRONT COVER
36 SEAL
37 CRANKSHAFT PULLEY ASSEMBLY
38 INTERMEDIATE DRIVESHAFT
39 OIL PUMP ASSEMBLY
40 PICK-UP TUBE GASKET
41 PICK-UP TUBE ASSEMBLY
42 UPPER MAIN BEARING
43 UPPER THRUST BEARING
44 UPPER MAIN BEARING FRONT
45 CRANKSHAFT
46 LOWER MAIN BEARING
47 REAR MAIN BEARING CAP
48 MAIN BEARING CAP
49 MAIN BEARING CAP
50 MAIN BEARING CAP
51 MAIN BEARING CAP FRONT
52 BOLT
53 OIL PAN ASSEMBLY
54 DRAIN PLUG
55 WASHER
56 PISTON RINGS
57 PISTON
58 PISTON PIN
59 CONNECTING ROD
60 STUD
61 ROD BEARINGS
62 ROD CAP
63 NUT

**Cylinder head assembly & components**

## HYDRAULIC VALVE LIFTERS

### REPLACE

Before replacing a hydraulic valve lifter for noisy operation, ensure the noise is not caused by improper collapsed tappet gap, worn rocker arms, pushrods or valve tips.

To check collapsed tappet gap, proceed as follows:

1. Rotate camshaft to position A as shown in **Fig. 9.**
2. Check intake and exhaust valves on compression stroke under camshaft position A. With camshaft in position A, tappet gap should be .072-.174 inch with tappet collapsed on base circle. Check No. 1 cylinder intake and exhaust valves. Check No. 2 cylinder intake valve. Check No. 3 cylinder exhaust valve. Tighten fulcrum bolts to specifications.
3. Rotate camshaft 180 degrees to position B as shown in **Fig. 9.** Check No. 2 cylinder exhaust valve. Check No. 3 cylinder intake valve. Check No. 4 cylinder intake and exhaust valve. Tighten fulcrum bolts to specification.

Remove lifters as follows:

1. Remove cylinder head as described previously.
2. Using a suitable magnet, remove lifters from lifter bores.
3. Place valve lifters in a rack so they can be installed in their original positions. **If the lifters are stuck in their bores by excessive varnish or gum buildup, use hydraulic lifter puller tool No. D81-6500-A or equivalent to remove valve lifters.**
4. Reverse procedure to install.

## ROCKER ARM COVER

### REPLACE

1. Disconnect battery ground cable.
2. Remove oil filler cap.
3. Disconnect PCV hose from PCV valve.
4. Disconnect throttle linkage cable from rocker arm cover.
5. Disconnect speed control cable from rocker arm cover, if equipped.
6. Remove rocker arm cover bolts and cover.
7. Reverse procedure to install, **noting the following Technical Service Bulletin:**
   a. If mold-in-place gasket is damaged by cuts longer than 1/8 inch, or by more than three nicks or cuts (any size), replace entire rocker cover assembly.
   b. If damaged, replace rubber isolators (part No. E83Z-6C518-A) or washer bolt and rubber isolator assembly, (part No. E93Z-6C519-A).
   c. Put one drop of adhesive tread lock (part No. ESE-M2G260-AA) on bolts if they are to be reused, failure to do so may result in oil leakage.
   d. **Torque** rocker cover assembly to specifications.

## FRONT COVER OIL SEAL

### REMOVAL

The following removal and installation procedure can only be performed with the engine removed from the vehicle. Remove engine as described under "Engine, Replace."

1. Remove bolt and washer from crankshaft pulley.
2. Using bearing cone remover tool No. T77F-4220-B1 or equivalent, remove crankshaft pulley.
3. Using front cover seal remover tool No. T74P-6700-A or equivalent, remove front cover oil seal.

### INSTALLATION

1. Coat new front cover oil seal with a suitable lubricant.
2. Using pinion oil seal installer tool No. T83T-4676-A or equivalent, install oil seal into front cover. Drive oil seal in until it is fully seated into front cover recess. Check oil seal after installation to ensure spring is properly positioned in oil seal.
3. Install crankshaft pulley, washer and bolt. **Torque** crankshaft pulley bolt to specification.

## FRONT COVER, TIMING CHAIN & SPROCKETS

### REPLACE

The following procedure can only be performed with the engine removed from the vehicle. Remove engine as described under "Engine, Replace."

1. Remove dipstick, crankshaft pulley bolt, washer and pulley.
2. Remove front cover bolts and front cover, **Fig. 10.**
3. Align camshaft and crankshaft

sprocket timing marks as shown in **Fig. 11.**
4. Remove camshaft sprocket bolt and washer.
5. Remove sprockets and timing chain from engine as an assembly, **Fig. 12.** Check timing chain vibration damper for wear. Replace if necessary.
6. Remove oil pan.
7. Reverse procedure to install. Ensure to align timing marks as shown in **Fig. 10.**

## CAMSHAFT
## REPLACE

The following procedure can only be performed with the engine removed from the vehicle. Remove engine as described under "Engine, Replace."

1. Remove dipstick. Drain coolant and oil from engine.
2. Remove accessory drive belts and pulleys.
3. Position No. 1 piston at TDC with distributor rotor at No. 1 firing position, then remove distributor.
4. Remove cylinder head as described under "Cylinder Head, Replace."
5. Using a suitable magnet, remove hydraulic tappets and position in order so that they can be installed in their original locations. If tappets are stuck in their bores, use hydraulic lifter remover tool No. D81L-6500A or equivalent to remove tappets.
6. Loosen then remove fan drive belt, fan and crankshaft pulley.
7. Remove front cover as described under "Front Cover, Timing Chain & Sprockets, Replace."
8. Remove fuel pump, gasket and fuel pump pushrod.
9. Remove timing chain, sprockets and timing chain tensioner as described under "Front Cover, Timing Chain & Sprockets, Replace."
10. Remove camshaft thrust plate. Carefully remove camshaft from engine to avoid damaging camshaft bearings, journals and lobes.
11. Reverse procedure to install. Lubricate camshaft with suitable oil before installing. Ensure No. 1 piston is at TDC with distributor rotor at No. 1 firing position.

## MAIN BEARINGS

Main bearings are available in standard sizes and undersizes of .010, .020, .030 and .040 inch.

## CRANKSHAFT REAR OIL SEAL
## REPLACE

1. Remove engine and transaxle from vehicle as described under "Engine, Replace."
2. Remove transaxle from engine.
3. Remove rear cover plate.
4. Using a suitable tool, punch a hole

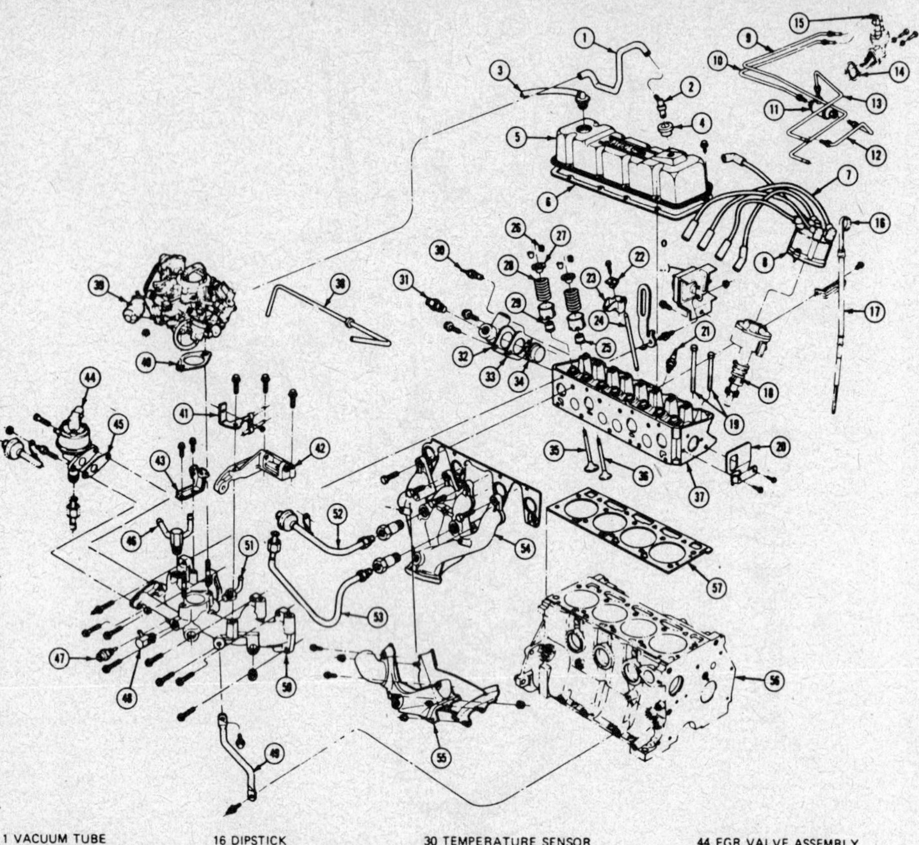

1 VACUUM TUBE
2 VENT VALVE ASSEMBLY
3 TUBE ASSEMBLY
4 GROMMET
5 ROCKER ARM COVER
6 ROCKER ARM COVER GASKET
7 SPARK PLUG WIRES
8 DISTRIBUTOR CAP
9 FUEL LINES
10 FUEL LINES
11 FUEL FILTER
12 FUEL FILTER LINES
13 FUEL FILTER LINES
14 FUEL PUMP GASKET
15 FUEL PUMP ASSEMBLY
16 DIPSTICK
17 DIPSTICK TUBE ASSEMBLY
18 DISTRIBUTOR
19 CYLINDER HEAD BOLTS
20 ENGINE LIFTING EYE
21 SPARK PLUG
22 ROCKER ARM FULCRUM
23 ROCKER ARM
24 PUSHROD
25 EXHAUST VALVE STEM SEAL
26 KEY
27 SPRING RETAINER
28 SPRING
29 INTAKE VALVE STEM SEAL
30 TEMPERATURE SENSOR
31 FAN SWITCH
32 WATER OUTLET CONNECTION
33 WATER OUTLET CONNECTION GASKET
34 THERMOSTAT ASSEMBLY
35 INTAKE VALVE
36 EXHAUST VALVE
37 CYLINDER HEAD
38 CARBURETOR FUEL LINE
39 CARBURETOR ASSEMBLY
40 CARBURETOR GASKET
41 BRACKET
42 BRACKET
43 ACCELERATOR SHAFT BRACKET
44 EGR VALVE ASSEMBLY
45 EGR VALVE GASKET
46 VACUUM FITTING
47 SENSOR
48 VACUUM FITTING
49 BRACE
50 INTAKE MANIFOLD ASSEMBLY
51 VACUUM FITTING
52 TUBE ASSEMBLY
53 TUBE ASSEMBLY
54 EXHAUST MANIFOLD
55 HEAT SHIELD
56 CYLINDER BLOCK
57 CYLINDER HEAD GASKET

**Cylinder block assembly & components**

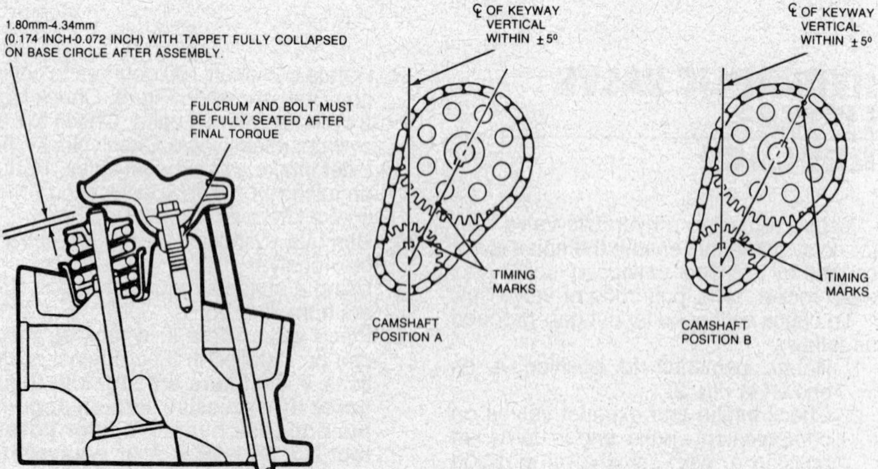


**Fig. 9 Checking collapsed tappet gap**

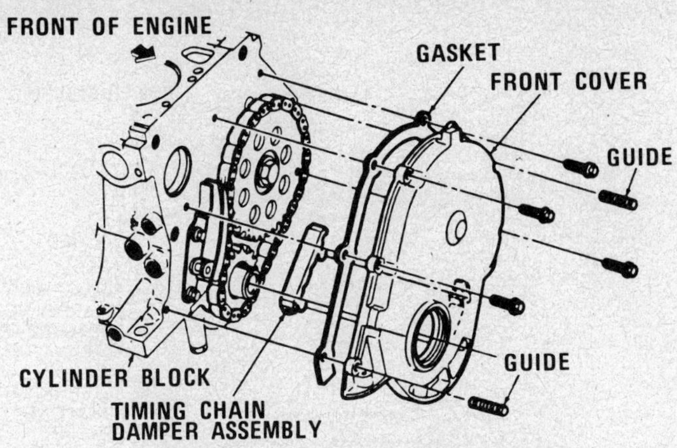


**Fig. 10 Front cover removal**

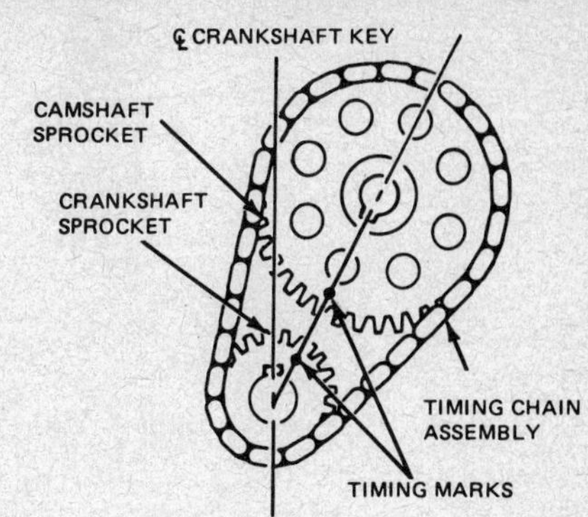


**Fig. 11 Valve timing marks**

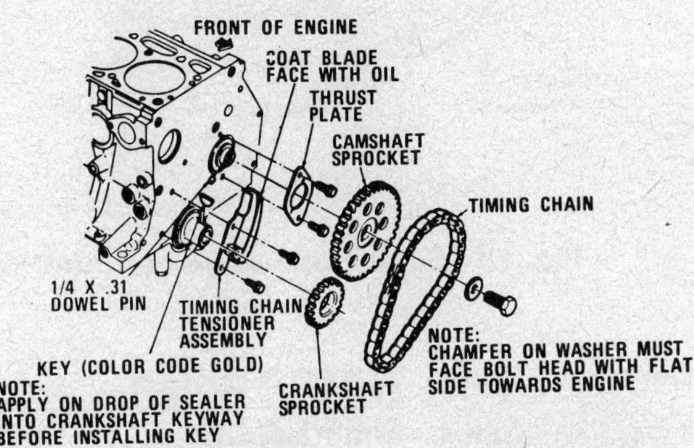


**Fig. 12 Timing chain & sprockets removal**

into the seal metal surface between the lip and block. Using jet plug remover tool No. T77L-9533-B or equivalent, remove seal.

5. Reverse procedure to install.

## OIL PAN
## REPLACE

1. Disconnect battery ground cable.
2. Raise and support vehicle.
3. Drain coolant and oil from engine.
4. **On models equipped with manual transaxle,** remove roll restrictor.
5. **On all models,** remove starter from engine.
6. Disconnect exhaust pipe from oil pan.
7. Remove engine coolant tube located at the lower radiator hose, at the water pump and from tabs on oil pan.
8. Remove oil pan bolts and oil pan, **Fig. 13,** from engine.
9. Reverse procedure to install, noting the following:
   a. Remove all traces of RTV sealant from engine block and oil pan.
   b. Clean block rails, front cover, rear cover retainer and oil pan thoroughly with Dupont(R) Freon (TF) or equivalent solvent.
   c. Remove and clean oil pump pick-up tube and screen assembly.
   d. Apply RTV (part No. E8AZ-19652-A) or equivalent in oil pan groove. Completely fill the oil pan groove with sealer. Sealer Bead should be 3/16 inch wide and 1/8 inch rise above oil pan surface in all areas except half-rounds. The half-rounds should have 3/16 wide bead and 3/16 inch rise above oil pan surface. **Applying RTV in excess of the specified amount will not improve sealing of oil pan.**
   e. RTV sealant needs to cure completely before coming in contact with engine oil, about one hour at 65-75°F ambient temperature.

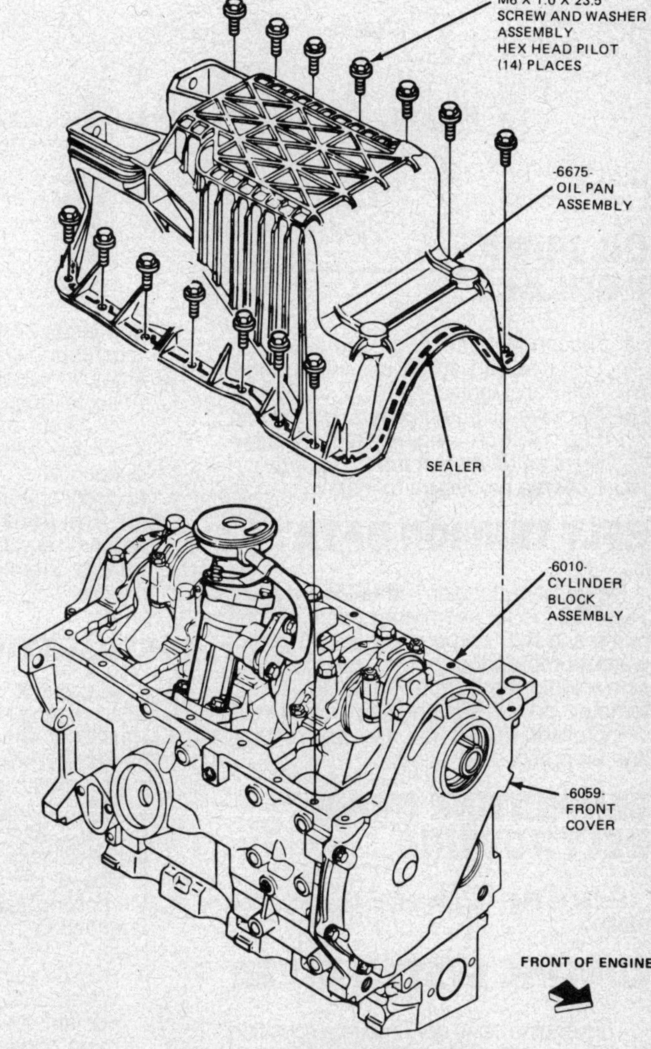


**Fig. 13 Oil pan removal**

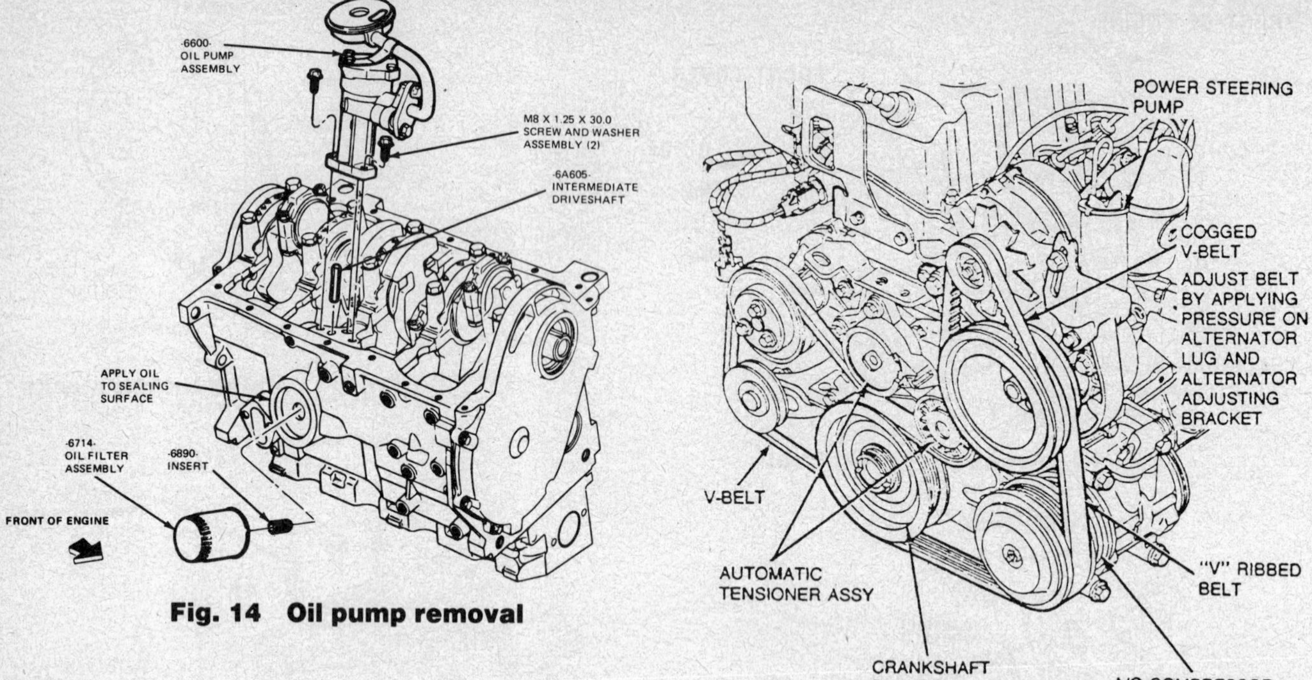


**Fig. 14 Oil pump removal**

**Fig. 15 Serpentine drive belt routing**

## OIL PUMP REPLACE

1. Disconnect battery ground cable.
2. Remove oil pan as described under "Oil Pan, Replace."
3. Remove oil pump bolts and oil pump, **Fig. 14,** from engine. Remove intermediate driveshaft from oil pump.
4. Reverse procedure to install.

## BELT TENSION DATA

New belt tension should measure 150-190 lbs. for alternator, power steering pump and A/C compressor 50-90 lbs. for water pump and air pump. Used belt tension should measure 140-160 lbs. for alternator, power steering pump and A/C compressor 40-60 lbs. for water pump and air pump.

## SERPENTINE DRIVE BELT ROUTING

Refer to **Fig. 15,** for serpentine drive belt routing.

## COOLING SYSTEM BLEED

This engine does not require a specified bleed procedure. After filling cooling system, run engine to operating temperature with radiator/pressure cap off. Air will then automatically bleed through cap opening.

## THERMOSTAT REPLACE

### REMOVAL

1. Disconnect battery cable and wiring connector from thermo switch in thermostat housing.
2. Remove radiator cap, then attach a hose to drain tube and open draincock. Drain coolant level until its below water outlet connection. Close the draincock.
3. Loosen upper hose at radiator, **Fig. 12,** then remove water outlet housing retaining bolts. Lift clear of engine and remove thermostat. Do not pry housing off.

### INSTALLATION

1. Clean outlet housing and cylinder head mating surfaces.
2. Position thermostat and seat so it will compress gasket. Position outlet to cylinder head, using a new gasket and install retaining bolts.
3. Connect top hose to radiator and tighten clamp. Ensure that draincock is closed.
4. Fill cooling system with coolant recommended by manufacturer as follows:
   a. Add 50 percent coolant, then add water until radiator is full. Allow coolant level to settle, then add more coolant until radiator remain full.
   b. Install radiator cap to first notch, connect battery cable and wire connector to thermo switch. Start engine and let idle until upper hose is warm, then carefully remove radiator cap and top off coolant level.
   c. Install cap securely and fill reservoir to FULL COLD mark with proper concentrate. Add water to FULL HOT mark. Check for leaks.

## WATER PUMP REPLACE

1. Disconnect battery ground cable and drain coolant from engine.
2. Loosen thermactor pump adjusting bolt and remove belt.
3. Remove thermactor air pump hose clamp, thermactor pump bracket bolts, pump and bracket assembly from engine.
4. Loosen water pump idler pulley bolt and remove belt from water pump pulley.
5. Remove water pump inlet tube.
6. Remove water pump bolts and water pump, **Fig. 16.**
7. Reverse procedure to install.

## FUEL PUMP REPLACE

Fuel supply lines will remain pressurized for long periods of time after engine shut-down. This pressure must be relieved before any service is attempted. A valve is provided on the fuel rail assembly for this purpose. To relieve system pressure, remove air cleaner assembly and connect pressure gauge tool No. T80L-9974-A or equivalent onto fuel valve on fuel rail assembly.

1. Disconnect battery ground cable.
2. Depressurize fuel system as described previously.
3. Remove fuel from fuel tank by pumping fuel out of fuel filler neck.
4. Raise and support vehicle.
5. Disconnect then remove fuel filler neck.

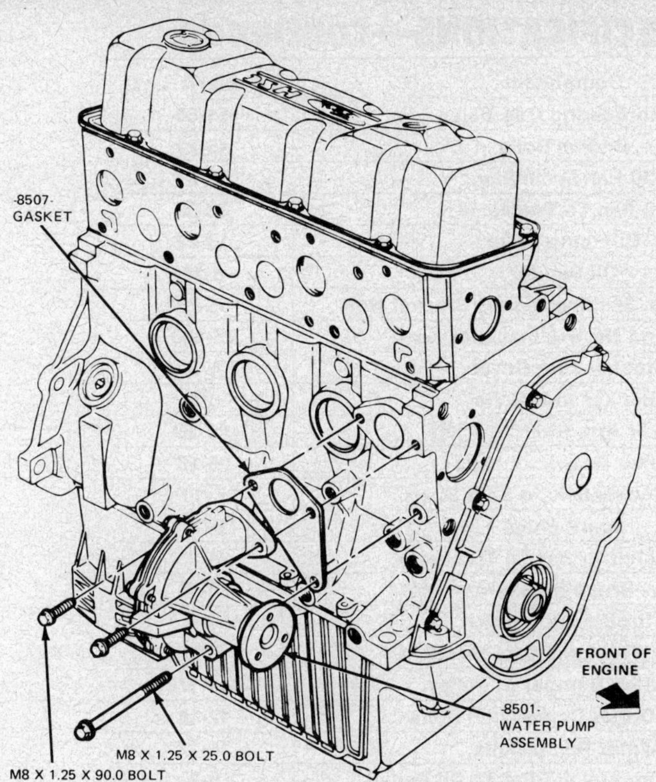


**Fig. 16 Water pump removal**

6. **On all wheel drive models,** remove exhaust system and rear axle assembly.
7. **On all models,** support fuel tank, then remove tank support straps. Lower fuel tank partially and remove fuel lines, electrical connectors and vent lines from tank.
8. Turn fuel pump locking ring counterclockwise and remove locking ring.
9. Remove fuel pump, bracket and gasket assembly.
10. Reverse procedure to install. To pressurize fuel system, proceed as follows:
    a. Install pressure gauge tool No. T80L-9974-A or equivalent onto fuel rail pressure fitting.
    b. Turn ignition switch to ON position for 3 seconds, repeatedly 5 to 10 times until pressure gauge indicates 13 psi.
11. **On all wheel drive models,** proceed as follows:
    a. Lift sender unit up and disconnect jet pump line from electrical connector resistor unit.
    b. Remove fuel pump and bracket assembly.
    c. Remove seal gasket.
    d. Remove jet pump assembly attaching screw.
    e. Remove jet pump assembly.

# SERVICE BULLETINS

## OIL & COOLANT LEAKAGE

On 1989 Tempo & Topaz, engine coolant and oil leaking at the cylinder head-to-engine block mating surface may be caused by the cylinder head gasket. The leakage will appear more often in climates that have extreme temperature changes. Coolant and oil leakage will be most noticeable in areas below the No. 2 and 3 spark plugs. To correct this, a new head gasket made of graphite must be installed. Refer to "Cylinder Head Replace."

# TIGHTENING SPECIFICATIONS

| Year | Component | Torque/ft. Lbs. |
|---|---|---|
| 1989-92 | Accelerator Shaft Bracket Bolt | 7-11 |
| | Camshaft Sprocket Bolt | 41-56 |
| | Camshaft Thrust Plate Bolts | 6-9 |
| | Camshaft Tensioner Bolts | 6-9 |
| | Crankshaft Seal Retainer Bolts | 6-9 |
| | Cooling Fan Switch | 8-18 |
| | Connecting Rod Cap Bolts | 21-26 |
| | Cylinder Head Bolts | ② |
| | Distributor Hold down Bolt | 17-25 |
| | Dipstick Tube | 6-9 |
| | EGR Valve Bolts | 13-19 |
| | EGR Tube Connector | 25-35 |
| | EGR Tube Nuts | 25-35 |
| | Engine Coolant Temperature Sensor | 12-18 |
| | Exhaust Manifold | 20-30 |
| | Flywheel to Crankshaft | 54-64 |
| | Front Cover Bolts | 6-9 |
| | Intake Manifold | 15-22 |
| | Lefthand Front No. 1 Insulator To Transaxle Bolts | 30-42 |
| | Lefthand Front No. 1 Insulator To Bracket Nut | 75-100 |
| | Lefthand Rear No. 4 Insulator To Body Bolts | 75-100 |
| | Lefthand Rear No. 4 Insulator To Transaxle | 35-50 |

Continued

## TIGHTENING SPECIFICATIONS—Continued

| Year | Component | Torque/ft. Lbs. |
|---|---|---|
| | Main Bearing Cap Bolts | 51-56 |
| | Oil Pan Bolts | 15-22 |
| | Oil Pan Drain Plug | 15-25 |
| | Oil Pan To Transaxle | 30-39 |
| | Oil Pump Bolts | 15-22 |
| | Oil Sender | 8-18 |
| | Righthand No. 34 Intermediate Bracket Bolt | 55-75 |
| | Righthand No. 3-A Insulator Nuts | 75-100 |
| | Rocker Arm Cover | 7-10 |
| | Rocker Arm Bolts | ① |
| | Rocker Arm Shaft Bracket | 20-26 |
| | Roller Restrictor Nuts | 25-45 |
| | Shift Mechanism To Shift Shaft | 7-10 |
| | Spark Plugs | 6-10 |
| | Shift Stabilizer Bar To Transaxle | 25-35 |
| | Support Brace-Intake Manifold | 30-40 |
| | Throttle Body Bolts | 6-8 |
| | Vacuum Fittings-Intake Manifold | 6-10 |
| | Vibration Damper or Pulley | 140-170 |
| | Water Outlet Connection Bolts | 12-18 |
| | Water Pump Bolts | 15-22 |
| | Water Pump Inlet Tube To Oil Pan | 6-8 |

①—Tighten in two steps, tighten to 4–7.5 ft. lbs., then 19–26 ft. lbs.

②—Refer to text for tightening sequence, Tighten in two steps, tighten to 51–59 ft. lbs., then 70-76 ft. lbs.

# 3.0L/V6-182 Engine

**NOTE:** Refer To The "Ford Taurus & Mercury Sable" In This Tab Section For Service Procedures On This Engine Not Included In This Section.

**NOTE:** On Vehicles Equipped With Airbags, Disarm Airbag System As Outlined Under "Airbag System Disarming" Before Any Diagnosis, Testing, Troubleshooting Or Repairs Are Performed. After All Diagnosis, Testing, Troubleshooting Or Repairs Have Been Completed, Rearm Airbag System As Outlined Under "Airbag System Disarming."

### INDEX



## AIRBAG SYSTEM DISARMING

### Deactivation

1. Disconnect positive battery cable.
2. Wait one minute. This is the time required for backup power supply in diagnostic monitor to deplete its stored energy.
3. Remove four nut and washer assemblies retaining driver airbag module to steering wheel. Disconnect driver airbag connector. Connect Rotunda Airbag Simulator tool No. 105-00008 or equivalent to vehicle harness at top of steering wheel.
4. Connect positive battery cable.

### Reactivation

1. Disconnect positive battery cable.
2. Wait one minute for backup power supply to deplete stored energy.
3. Remove airbag simulator from vehicle harness connector at top of steering column. Reconnect driver airbag connector. Position driver airbag on steering wheel, then install four nut and washer assemblies. **Torque** retaining nuts to 24-32 inch lbs.
4. Connect positive battery cable, then Prove-Out System.

### Prove-Out System

Prove-out system means to turn the ignition switch from Off to Run and visually monitor the airbag indicator, located on dash panel. The airbag indicator will light continuously for approximately six seconds and then turn off. If an airbag system fault is present, the indicator will either fail to light, remain lit continuously or light in a flashing manner.

The flashing manner may not occur until approximately 30 seconds after the ignition switch has been turned from Off to Run. This is the time needed for the diagnostic monitor to complete testing of the system. If the airbag indicator is inoperative and an airbag system fault exists, a tone will sound in a pattern of five sets of five beeps. If this occurs, the airbag indicator will need to be serviced.

## ENGINE
### REPLACE

1. Disconnect battery cables, then remove battery from vehicle.
2. Remove battery tray and air cleaner as an assembly from vehicle.
3. Scribe hood hinge positions on hood for reference during assembly.
4. Discharge air conditioning system, if equipped. Cap all open lines.
5. Drain engine cooling system.
6. Locate Schraeder valve on fuel rail assembly, then remove protective cap.
7. Cover valve with shop towel, then using a small screwdriver, press inner valve stem inward slowly to release fuel system pressure. **Ensure all pressure is released.**
8. Disconnect all fuel lines from engine assembly, then position them aside.
9. Remove upper radiator hose.
10. Mark and record all electrical connector locations, then disconnect and set aside all wiring looms and connectors at junction blocks.
11. Mark and record all vacuum line connections, then disconnect all vacuum lines and crankcase ventilation hoses.
12. Disconnect power steering high pressure and return lines from power steering pump.
13. Remove power steering reservoir.
14. Disconnect air conditioning lines from condenser, leaving manifold lines attached to compressor.
15. Disconnect accelerator linkage, transaxle throttle valve linkage and speed control cable, if equipped.
16. Disconnect speedometer cable from transaxle.
17. **On models equipped with automatic transaxle,** disconnect transaxle cooler lines from radiator.
18. **On all models,** remove coolant overflow bottle, then lower radiator hose.
19. Remove power steering lines at rear of engine above transaxle.
20. Raise and support vehicle, then drain engine oil.
21. Disconnect heater hoses from engine, then position hoses aside.
22. Remove front wheel and tire assemblies.
23. Support center of exhaust system, then disconnect Y-pipe from engine exhaust manifolds.
24. Remove bolt retaining air conditioning line to engine block.
25. Disconnect tie rod ends from spindle assemblies.
26. Disconnect lower ball joints, then pull down on lower control arms to disengage ball joints from spindle.
27. Remove axle halfshaft assemblies from transaxle, then install plugs.
28. Lower vehicle, then remove ignition coil bracket retaining bolts. Position coil assembly out of the way.
29. Install engine lifting eyes part No. D81L-6001-D or equivalent, at front of righthand cylinder head and rear of lefthand cylinder head.
30. Remove through bolts from engine mounts.
31. Carefully lift engine out of vehicle, using universal load positioning sling tool No. 014-00036 or equivalent to tilt engine vertically to clear master cylinder.
32. Reverse procedure to install, noting the following:
    a. Fill and check transaxle fluid.
    b. Fill and check cooling system for leaks after engine warm up.
    c. If equipped, evacuate and recharge air conditioning system.
    d. Adjust ignition timing, if necessary.
    e. Road test vehicle. **When the battery has been disconnected, some abnormal drive symptoms may occur while the EEC-IV processor relearns its adaptive strategy. The vehicle may need to be driven 10 miles or more to relearn the strategy.**

## OIL PAN & OIL PUMP
### REPLACE

1. Disconnect battery ground cable, then insulate cable end with electrical tape or equivalent.
2. Remove engine oil level dipstick, then raise and support vehicle.
3. If equipped with low oil level sensor, remove electrical connector retainer clip at sensor an disconnect connector.
4. Drain engine oil.
5. Remove starter motor as follows:
    a. Disconnect starter cable and push on connector from starter solenoid. **When disconnecting the plastic hardshell connector at "S" terminal, grasp the plastic shell, depress the tab and pull lead off. Do not pull separately on wire. Be careful to pull straight off to prevent damage to the "S" solenoid terminal.**
    b. Remove upper starter retaining bolt, then lower bolt and starter assembly.
6. Disconnect oxygen sensor electrical connectors.
7. Remove exhaust pipe and catalyst assembly from engine.
8. **On models equipped with automatic transaxle,** remove torque converter access cover from transaxle.
9. **On models equipped with manual transaxle,** remove left and right transaxle support plates.
10. **On all models,** remove oil pan retaining bolts. **Ensure internal pan baffle does not snag on oil pump pickup tube and screen when lowering pan.**
11. Remove oil pan gasket and discard.
12. Remove oil pump retaining bolt, then oil pump from main bearing cap. When oil pump is removed, the intermediate shaft which drives the distributor will remain in the pump. If replacing the pump, remove intermediate shaft by pulling it from the pump. Check retaining clip for damage, replace if necessary.
13. Insert oil pump intermediate shaft assembly into hex drive hole in oil pump assembly until retainer clicks into place.
14. Install oil pump assembly with intermediate shaft through intermediate shaft hole in rear main bearing cap, then position pump over locating pins.
15. Install oil pump retaining bolt, then **torque** to 30–40 ft. lbs.
16. Install a new oil pan gasket to cylinder block using retaining features and gasket & trim adhesive part No. D7AZ-19B508-AA or equivalent. Snug retaining bolts at all four corners and two places on cylinder block sealing rail to support unit until adhesive cures.
17. Apply a 3/16 inch bead of silicone sealer part No. E8AZ-19562-A or equivalent, to the junction of the rear main bearing cap and cylinder block.
18. Apply a 3/16 inch bead of silicone sealer part No. E8AZ-19562-A or equivalent, to the junction of the front cover assembly and cylinder block.
19. Remove bolts retaining gasket to cylinder block, then position oil pan and install retaining bolts and hand tighten.
20. **Torque** four corner bolts to 7–10 ft. lbs, then install and torque remaining bolts.
21. Install left and right transaxle plates on manual transaxles or access plate on automatic transaxles.
22. Install starter motor assembly. **Torque** retaining bolts to 16–19 ft. lbs.
23. Connect oil level sensor connector, then install retainer clip.
24. Fill crankcase with oil.
25. Replace oil level dipstick, then connect battery ground cable.
26. Check vehicle for leaks.

## CYLINDER HEADS
### REPLACE

1. Rotate crankshaft to 0 degrees Top Dead Center (TDC) on the compression stroke.
2. Disconnect battery ground cable, then insulate cable end with electrical tape.
3. Drain engine cooling system.
4. Remove PCV closure hose and clean air flex tube.
5. Remove clean air flex tube from throttle body and mass air flow sensor (MAFS).
6. Locate Schraeder valve on fuel rail above intake manifold, then remove protective cap.

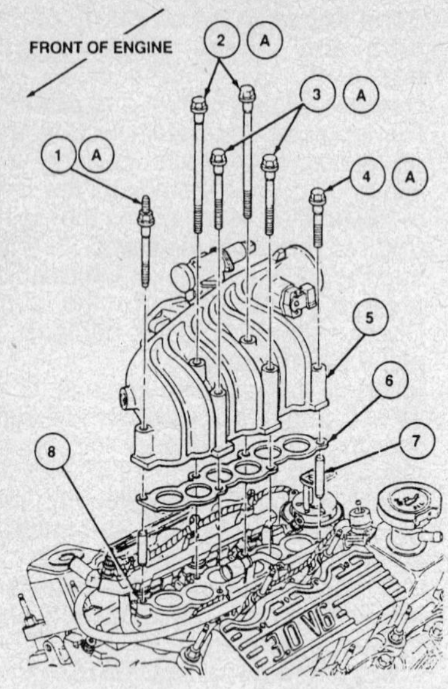


| Item | Part Number | Description |
|---|---|---|
| 1A | — | Stud Bolt |
| 2A | — | Bolt—M8 x 1.25 x 130 |
| 3A | — | Bolt—M8 x 1.25 x 100 |
| 4A | — | Bolt—M8x 1.25 x 68 |
| 5 | 9E926 | Air Intake Throttle Body |
| 6 | 9H486 | Air Intake Throttle Body Gasket |
| 7 | — | Guide Pin |
| 8 | — | Lower Intake Manifold |
| A | | Tighten to 20-30 N-m (15-22 Lb-Ft) |

**Fig. 1 Air intake throttle body bolt locations**

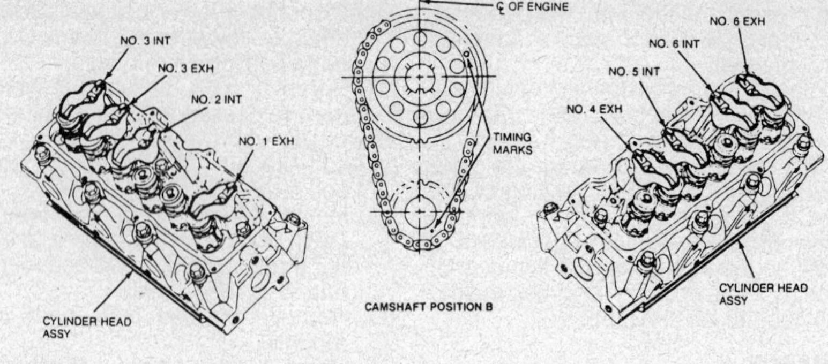


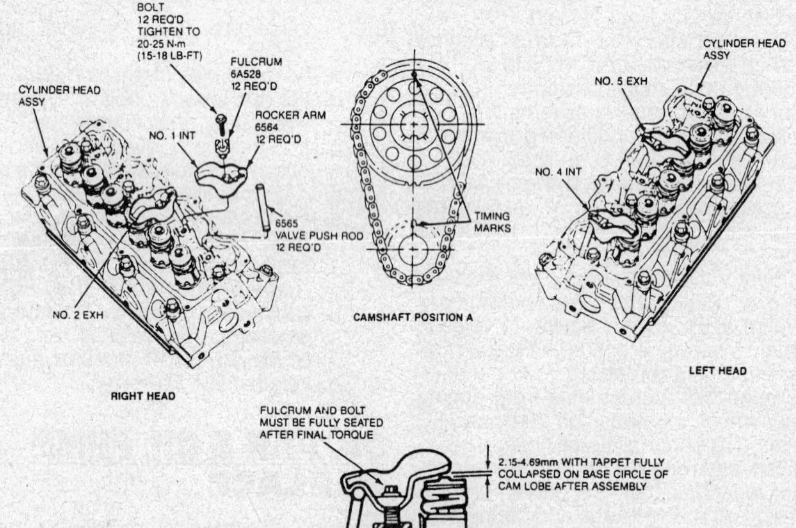


**Fig. 2 Rocker arm & valve locations**

7. Cover valve with shop towel to prevent accidental fuel spray into eyes, then using a small screwdriver or equivalent, slowly release fuel system pressure. **Ensure all pressure is released.**
8. Mark location of vacuum lines, then remove vacuum lines from engine.
9. Disconnect TPS, idle air bypass valve, ECT, PFE, distributor, ignition coil and coolant temperature sending unit electrical connectors.
10. Disconnect upper radiator hose from thermostat housing.
11. Loosen EGR tube retaining nuts, then remove tube.
12. Remove air intake throttle body as follows:
    a. Loosen air cleaner air tube retaining clamps, then remove tube.
    b. Remove air bypass valve solenoid (ISC) snowshield.
    c. Disconnect throttle cable from throttle body lever.
    d. Remove two throttle cable bracket retaining bolts from side of throttle body, then bracket assembly.
    e. Loosen and remove five air intake throttle body retaining bolts and one stud bolt noting their locations, **Fig. 1.**
    f. Remove air intake throttle body assembly from intake manifold. Discard old gasket.
13. Disconnect fuel injector harness retainers from inboard rocker arm cover studs, then electrical connectors at each injector. Remove fuel injector harness from engine.
14. Disconnect heater hose near thermostat housing.
15. Mark spark plug wires for reference during installation, then remove ignition wires from spark plugs.
16. Mark distributor housing to cylinder block and note rotor position in relation to distributor cap.
17. Remove distributor hold-down clamp and bolt, then distributor from engine.
18. Remove oil cooler tube assembly retaining bolt from ignition coil bracket.
19. Remove ignition coil from rear of lefthand cylinder head.
20. Remove rocker arm covers.
21. Loosen cylinder No. 3 intake valve rocker arm retaining nut, then rotate arm off of pushrod and away from top of valve stem, **Fig. 2.** Remove the pushrod.
22. Remove intake manifold retaining bolts. **Before attempting to remove intake manifold, break seal between the manifold and cylinder block. Wedge a large screwdriver between intake and cylinder block in the area between thermostat and transaxle.**
23. Remove intake manifold. **Intake manifold may be removed with fuel supply manifold and injectors in place.**
24. **If removing righthand cylinder head (rear of engine compartment),** proceed as follows:
    a. Remove accessory drive belt. Using a socket, rotate tensioner away from belt.
    b. Remove water pump to front cover hose.
    c. Raise and support vehicle, then remove lower water pump tube.
    d. Remove retaining nut from upper bracket, then bolt from lower bracket. Gently grasp tube at water pump end and pull tube out of water pump. Set assembly aside.
    e. Remove exhaust inlet pipe flange retaining nuts from exhaust manifold studs.
    f. Lower vehicle, then remove heater hose from rear of water pump.
    g. Remove water pump pulley shield, then water pump from bracket.
    h. Remove exhaust manifold heat

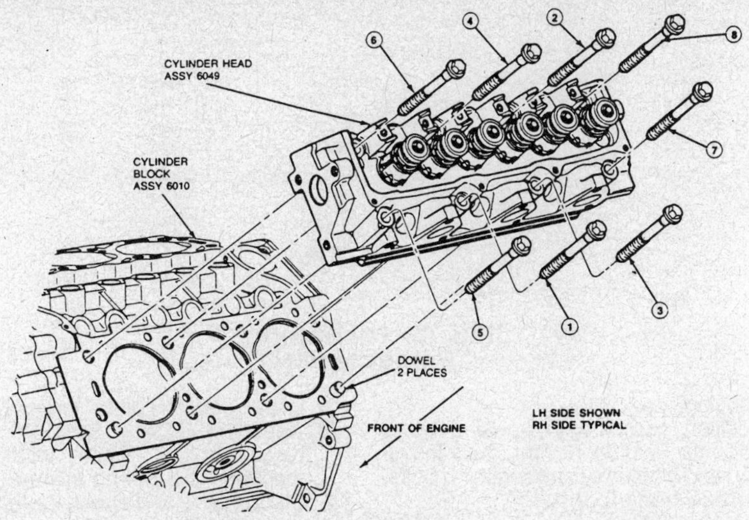


**Fig. 3 Cylinder head bolt tightening sequence**

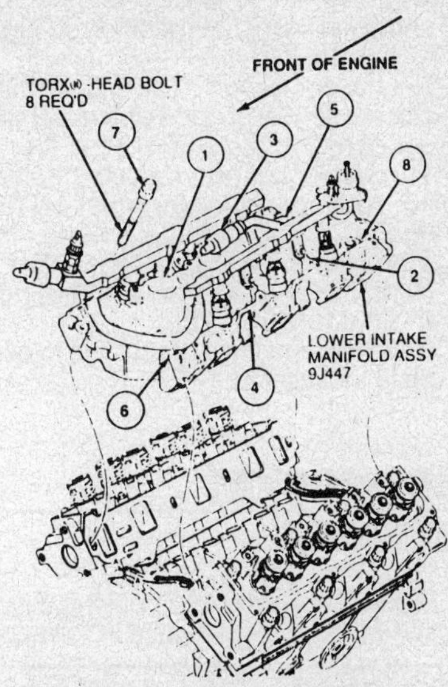


**Fig. 5 Intake manifold tightening sequence**

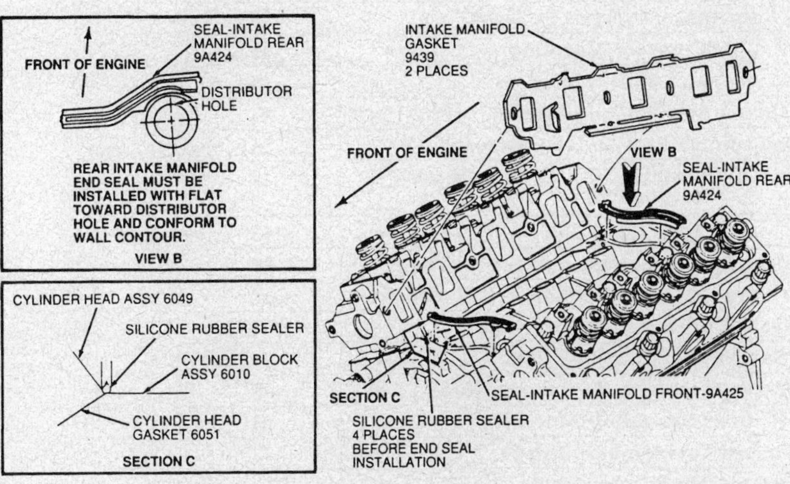


**Fig. 4 Silicone rubber & intake seal installation**

shield, then exhaust manifold.

25. **If removing lefthand cylinder head (front of engine compartment),** proceed as follows:
    a. Remove accessory drive belt. Using a 1/2 inch breaker bar, rotate tensioner away from drive belt.
    b. Remove two power steering pulley shield retaining bolts, then shield.
    c. Remove drive belt tensioner retaining bolt, then tensioner.
    d. Remove three alternator bracket to cylinder head retaining bolts.
    e. Remove upper alternator retaining bolt, then three air conditioning brace retaining bolts and remove brace.
    f. Move assembly away from cylinder head slightly.
    g. Remove exhaust inlet pipe flange retaining nuts from exhaust manifold studs.
    h. Remove exhaust manifold heat shield.
    i. Rotate or remove engine oil dipstick tube out of way.
26. Loosen rocker arm fulcrum retaining bolts enough to allow rocker arm to be lifted off the pushrod and rotated to one side.
27. Remove pushrods. Identify position of each pushrod for installation. **Pushrods should be installed in their original position during reassembly.**
28. Remove cylinder head retaining bolts and discard.
29. Remove cylinder head and discard gasket. If cylinder is stuck, place a heavy steel rod or equivalent into intake port and rock cylinder head to break seal. **When breaking seal, ensure removal tool does not damage machined surfaces or intake valve.**
30. Immediately wipe dry the cylinder bore of any coolant which might have leaked from head removal. Apply a light coating of engine oil to cylinder bore surfaces. **Engine coolant is corrosive to engine bearings and piston rings.**
31. Position new head gasket on cylinder block with V-cut toward front of engine.
32. Position cylinder head to engine block over dowels.
33. Install and hand tighten new cylinder head retaining bolts.
34. **Torque** cylinder head bolts in sequence shown in **Fig. 3** as follows:
    a. **Torque** bolts to 52-66 ft. lbs., then back off all bolts one complete turn.
    b. **Torque** bolts in sequence to 33-41 ft. lbs.
    c. **Torque** bolts in sequence to 63-73 ft. lbs.
35. Apply a 1/4 inch drop of silicone rubber part No. D6AZ-19562-AA or equivalent to intersection of cylinder block and cylinder head assembly at four corners as shown in **Fig. 4.**
36. Position intake gaskets onto cylinder heads, then front and rear intake manifold seals.
37. Carefully lower intake manifold into position aligning manifold bolt holes to those in cylinder heads.
38. Install bolt Nos. 1 through 4, **Fig. 5,** then hand tighten.
39. Install remaining bolts and tighten in two steps as follows:
    a. **Torque** in numerical sequence to 15-22 ft. lbs.
    b. **Torque** in sequence to 19-24 ft. lbs.
40. Completely coat distributor gear teeth with rear axle lubricant part No. XY-90-QL or equivalent, install retaining bolt and clamp and hand tighten.
41. Lubricate pushrods and rocker arms with oil conditioner part No. D9AZ-195579-CA or equivalent and install pushrods.
42. Move rocker arms into position with pushrods, then tighten retaining bolts.
43. Rotate crankshaft 360 degrees (one full turn) in a clockwise direction from 0 degrees TDC.
44. **Torque** rocker arm retaining bolts

shown in camshaft position A, **Fig. 2** to 5-11 ft. lbs.

45. Rotate crankshaft 120 degrees in a clockwise direction. **Torque** remainder of rocker arms to 5-11 ft. lbs.
46. **Torque** rocker arm retaining bolts to 19-28 ft. lbs. **Fulcrum must be fully seated into cylinder head and pushrod must be fully seated in rocker arm and lifter sockets prior to final torque.**
47. Reverse remaining procedure to complete installation.

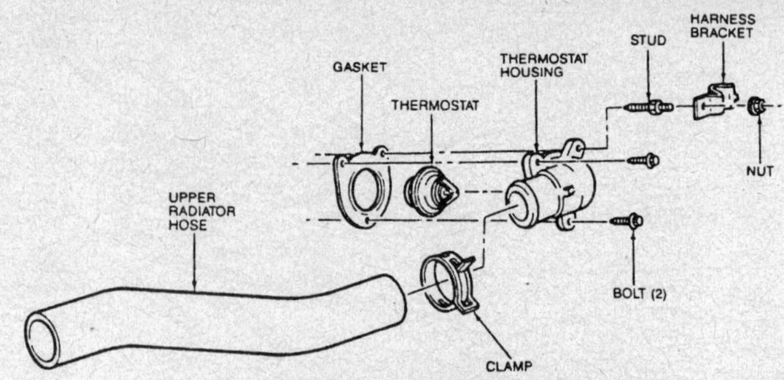


**Fig. 6 Thermostat Replacement**

## THERMOSTAT
### REPLACE

1. Install thermostat into housing, **Fig. 6**, ensuring that jiggle valve in relation to housing.
2. Position gasket onto housing using bolts as holding device, then install housing assembly and retaining bolts. **Torque bolts to 9 ft. lbs.**
3. Install upper radiator hose. Refer to "Bleeding Cooling System," fill and bleed cooling system with recommended amount and mixture.
4. Start engine and check for leaks.

## TIGHTENING SPECIFICATIONS

| Year | Component | Torque/ft. Lbs. |
|---|---|---|
| 1992 | A/C Compressor Bracket To Block | 35 |
| | A/C Compressor Mounting | 35 |
| | ACT Sensor | 15 |
| | Alternator Adjustment Arm (Lock-In Tension Setting) Bolt | 27 |
| | Alternator Adjustment Arm To Cylinder Head Bolt | 35 |
| | Alternator Brace to Adjustment Arm & Throttle Body (2 nuts) | 12 |
| | Alternator Pivot Bolt | 43 |
| | Auto-Tensioner To A/C Compressor Bracket Bolt | 35 |
| | Auto-Tensioner/Power Steering Bracket To Cylinder Head | 35 |
| | Camshaft Sprocket To Camshaft | 37-51 |
| | Camshaft Thrust Plate Bolt | 7 |
| | Coil & Bracket Assembly To Cylinder Head | 35 |
| | Connecting Rod Nut | 26 |
| | Coolant Temperature Switch | 15 |
| | Crankshaft Pulley Nuts | 30-44 |
| | Crankshaft Vibration Damper To Crankshaft | 93-121 |
| | Distributor Hold Down Bolt | 18 |
| | ECT Sensor | 12-17 |
| | EGR To Throttle Body | 15-22 |
| | EGR Tube To EGR Valve & Exhaust Manifold | 26-48 |
| | Exhaust Heat Shield | 12-15 |
| | Exhaust Inlet Pipe To Manifold | 25-34 |
| | Exhaust Manifold | 15-22 |
| | Flywheel To Crankshaft | 59 |
| | Fuel Rail To Intake Manifold | 6-9 |
| | Heater Elbow | 18 |
| | Heater Tube To Intake Manifold | 26 |
| | HEGO Sensor | 30 |
| | Hose Clamp | 28-48① |
| | Idle Speed Control Solenoid | 7 |
| | Low Level Oil Sensor | 20-30 |
| | Main Bearing Cap Bolt | 55-63 |
| | Oil Dipstick Tube To Exhaust Manifold | 11-15 |
| | Oil Drain Plug | 9-12 |
| | Oil Pump To Cylinder Block | 35 |
| | PFE Sensor & Bracket | 7 |
| | Power Steering Bracket To Cylinder Head Bolt | 29-41 |

*Continued*

## TIGHTENING SPECIFICATIONS—Continued

| Year | Component | Torque/ft. Lbs. |
|---|---|---|
| | Rocker Arm bolt | 15-18 |
| | Rocker Arm Cover | 8-10 |
| | Spark Plug | 5-11 |
| | Thermostat Housing | 8-10 |
| | Throttle Body To Intake Manifold | 19 |
| | Throttle Cable Bracket | 13 |
| | Timing Cover To Cylinder Block | 19 |
| | TP Sensor | 22① |
| | Water Pump Hose Clamps | 19-37① |
| | Water Pump Pulley Shield | 7-10 |
| | Water Pump Pulley To Hub | 15-22 |
| | Water Pump To Front Cover | 71-106① |

①—Inch lbs.

# Clutch & Manual Transaxle

## INDEX



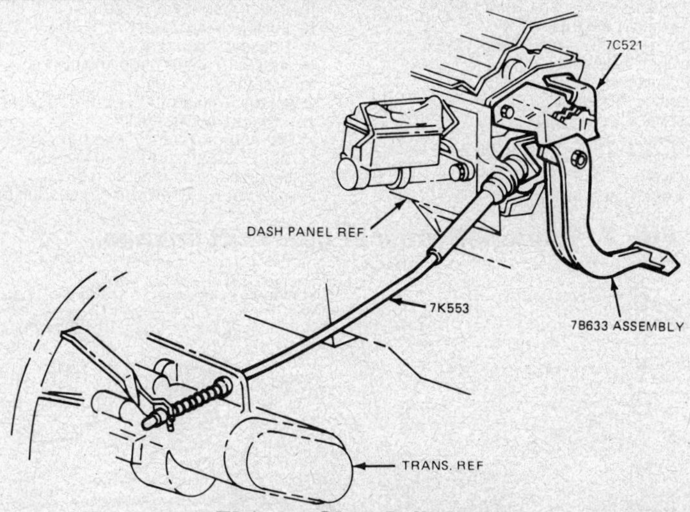


**Fig. 1 Clutch linkage**

## CLUTCH ADJUST

Lift clutch pedal to the uppermost position when connecting or disconnecting the clutch cable. Whenever the clutch cable is disconnected for any reason, such as transmission removal or clutch, clutch pedal components, or clutch cable replacement, it is important that the proper method for installing the clutch cable be followed. Under no circumstances should a prying instrument such as a screwdriver or a pry bar be used to install the cable into the quadrant.

The cable operated clutch control system, **Fig. 1,** is self adjusting and periodic adjustments are not required. If the clutch cable is replaced for any reason, an initial adjustment is performed by pulling the clutch pedal to its full upward position.

## GEARSHIFT LINKAGE ADJUST

Adjustment of the external gearshift linkage is not necessary and no provision is made for adjustment, **Fig. 2.**

## CLUTCH REPLACE

1. Remove transmission as described under "Manual Transaxle, Replace" procedure.
2. Loosen pressure plate cover attaching bolts evenly to avoid distorting cover. If same pressure plate and cover are to be installed, mark cover and flywheel so pressure plate can be installed in original position.
3. Remove pressure plate and clutch disc from flywheel, **Fig. 3.**
4. Position clutch disc and pressure plate onto flywheel with flatter side of clutch disc facing toward flywheel.
5. Ensure three dowel pins on flywheel are aligned with dowel pins on pressure plate.
6. Snug tighten cover attaching bolts, then align clutch disc using clutch aligner tool T81P-7550A or equivalent. **Torque** bolts to 12-24 ft. lbs. (17-32 Nm.).
7. Remove alignment tool, then install transaxle and perform initial clutch adjustment.

## CLUTCH CABLE REPLACE

### REMOVAL

Whenever the clutch cable is disconnected for any reason, such as transaxle or clutch removal, clutch pedal components, or clutch cable replacement, it is imperative that the proper method for installing the clutch cable be followed.

1. Disconnect battery ground cable.
2. Prop up clutch pedal to lift pawl free of quadrant.
3. Remove air cleaner assembly to gain access to clutch cable.
4. Grasp the extended tip of the clutch cable with a pair of pliers, and unhook clutch cable from clutch bearing release lever. **Do not grasp wire strand portion of inner cable since this may cut wires and result in cable failure.**

5. Disconnect cable from insulator that is located on the rib of transaxle.
6. Remove panel above clutch pedal pad.
7. Position clutch shield away from brake pedal support bracket by removing the rear retaining screw.
8. Loosen front retaining screw located near toe board, and rotate shield out of the way.
9. With clutch pedal lifted up to release pawl, rotate gear quadrant forward. Unhook clutch cable from gear quadrant. Allow quadrant to swing rearward. **Do not allow quadrant to snap back.**
10. Pull cable through recess between clutch pedal and gear quadrant, and from insulator on pedal assembly.
11. Withdraw cable through engine compartment.

## INSTALLATION

**The clutch pedal must be lifted to disengage the adjusting mechanism during cable installation. Failure to do so will result in damage to the self-adjuster mechanism.**

**Do not use a prying instrument such as a screwdriver or a pry bar to install the cable into the quadrant.**

1. Insert clutch cable assembly from then engine or passenger compartment through dash panel and dash panel grommet. **Ensure cable is routed under the brake lines and not trapped at the spring tower by the brake lines. If the vehicle is equipped with power steering, the clutch cable is to be routed inboard of the power steering hose.**
2. Push clutch cable through insulator on stop bracket, then through recess between pedal and gear quadrant.
3. With clutch pedal lifted up to release pawl, rotate gear quadrant forward. Hook cable into gear quadrant.
4. Install clutch shield on brake pedal support bracket, then lower instrument trim panel.
5. Secure pedal in upper most position using wire, tape or equivalent.
6. Working inside engine compartment, insert clutch cable through insulator and hook cable into clutch release lever.
7. Remove device used to temporarily secure pedal against stop.
8. Adjust clutch pedal by depressing clutch pedal several times.
9. Install air cleaner assembly, then connect battery ground cable.

DISASSEMBLED VIEW

FRONT OF VEHICLE

1. KNOB – GEAR SHIFT LEVER
2. NUT – SHIFT KNOB LOCKING
3. UPPER BOOT ASSEMBLY – GEAR SHIFT LEVER
4. SCREW – TAPPING ( 4 REQUIRED)
5. LOWER BOOT ASSEMBLY – GEAR SHIFT LEVER
6. BOOT RETAINER ASSEMBLY – GEAR SHIFT LEVER
7. BOLT – BOOT RETAINER (4 REQUIRED)
8. NUT – SPRING (4 REQUIRED)
9. LEVER ASSEMBLY – GEARSHIFT
10. BOLT – TAPPING (4 REQUIRED)
11. SCREW – TAPPING (4 REQUIRED)
12. SUPPORT ASSEMBLY (SHIFT STABILIZER BAR)
13. BUSHING – GEAR SHIFT STABILIZER BAR
14. SLEEVE – GEAR SHIFT ROD
15. SCREW – TAPPING (2 REQUIRED)
16. COVER – CONTROL SELECTOR
17. BUSHING – ANTI TIZZ
18. HOUSING – CONTROL SELECTOR
19. ASSEMBLY – SHIFT ROD AND CLEVIS
20. ASSEMBLY – CLAMP
21. CLAMP – GEAR SHIFT LEVER (2 REQUIRED)
22. NUT – CLAMP ASSEMBLY
23. RETAINING SPRING – GEAR SHIFT TUBE
24. BOLT -- STABILIZER BAR ATTACHING
25. WASHER – FLAT (2 REQUIRED)
26. ASSEMBLY – NUT/WASHER (4 REQUIRED)

**Fig. 2 Exploded view of gearshift linkage**

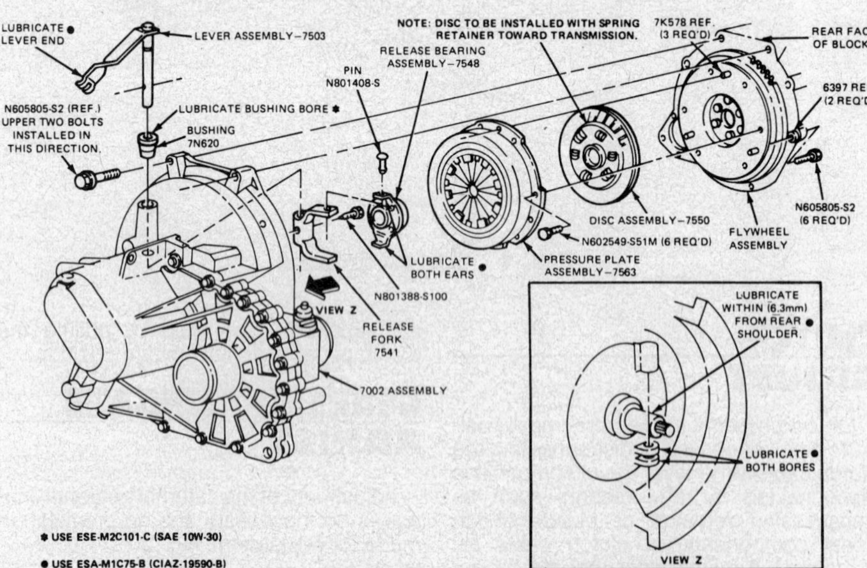


**Fig. 3 Exploded view of clutch assembly**

## MANUAL TRANSAXLE REPLACE

**On models equipped with all wheel drive system, refer to "Transfer Case" Section to remove transfer case.**

## 4 SPEED

### Escort

1. Disconnect battery ground cable.
2. Remove 2 top transaxle to engine mounting bolts.
3. Grasp and pull clutch cable forward, disconnecting cable from clutch release lever.
4. Remove clutch cable casing from rib on the top surface of transaxle case.
5. Raise and support vehicle.
6. Remove brake hose routing clip to suspension strut bracket mounting bolt.
7. Remove bolt securing lower control arm ball joint onto steering knuckle assembly. Pry lower control arm away from knuckle.

8. Using halfshaft remover tool No. D83P-4026-A or equivalent, pry right inboard CV joint assembly from transaxle.
9. Remove inner CV joint from transaxle by grasping righthand steering knuckle and swing knuckle and shaft outward from transaxle.
10. Wire halfshaft assembly in level position to prevent overextending CV joint.
11. Repeat steps 8 through 10 on left inboard CV joint assembly. **If the CV joint cannot be pried from the transaxle, insert differential rotator tool T81P-4026-A or equivalent through right side of case and tap CV joint out.**
12. Remove both front stabilizer bar to control arm attaching nut and washer.
13. Remove 2 front stabilizer bar mounting brackets, then the stabilizer bar.
14. Disconnect speedometer cable from transaxle.
15. Disconnect back-up light switch electrical connector from transaxle switch.
16. Remove clutch housing stiffener brace attaching bolts.
17. Remove shift mechanism stabilizer bar to transaxle attaching bolt.
18. Disconnect then remove transaxle control selector indicator switch and bracket.
19. Remove shift mechanism to shift shaft attaching bolt, then the shift mechanism.
20. Position a suitable jack under transaxle assembly.
21. Loosen rear mount stud nut, then remove bottom rear mount attaching bolt.
22. Remove 3 bolts securing front mount to transaxle case.
23. Lower transaxle slightly until transaxle clears rear mount.
24. Position a suitable jack under engine oil pan.
25. Remove remaining 4 transaxle to engine attaching bolts.
26. Lower transaxle from vehicle.
27. Reverse procedure to install. **During installation of transaxle assembly, ensure transaxle is flush with rear face of engine before installing and tightening attaching bolts.**

### Tempo & Topaz

1. Disconnect battery ground cable.
2. Position a suitable block of wood approximately 7 inches of length under clutch pedal to hold clutch pedal up.
3. Grasp and pull clutch cable forward, disconnecting cable from clutch release shaft lever assembly.
4. Remove clutch casing from top rib of transaxle case.
5. Remove 2 top transaxle to engine attaching bolts.
6. Remove air cleaner assembly.
7. Raise and support vehicle, then remove front stabilizer bar to control arm attaching nut and washer.
8. Remove stabilizer bar mounting brackets.
9. Remove nut and bolt attaching lower control ball joint to steering knuckle assembly.
10. Using a suitable tool, pry lower control arm away from steering knuckle.
11. Using halfshaft remover tool D83P-4026-A or equivalent, pry left inboard CV joint assembly from transaxle. Remove inboard CV joint from transaxle by grasping the lefthand steering knuckle and swinging the knuckle and halfshaft outward from transaxle. **If the CV joint cannot be pried from transaxle, insert differential rotator tool T81P-4026-A or equivalent through right side of case and tap CV joint out.**
12. Wire halfshaft assembly in level position to prevent overextending CV joint.
13. Repeat steps 10 through 12 for other CV joint.
14. Remove back-up light switch electrical connector from transaxle.
15. Remove starter motor and position aside.
16. Remove engine roll restrictor.
17. Remove shift mechanism, shift indicator and bracket assembly.
18. Disconnect speedometer cable from transaxle.
19. Remove oil pan to clutch housing stiffener brace attaching bolts.
20. Position a suitable jack under transaxle assembly.
21. Remove 2 nuts securing lefthand rear No. 4 insulator to body bracket.
22. Remove bolts securing lefthand front No. 1 insulator to body bracket.
23. Lower transaxle slightly until transaxle clears rear mount.
24. Position a suitable jack under engine.
25. Remove 4 transaxle to engine attaching bolts.
26. Lower transaxle from vehicle.
27. Reverse procedure to install.

## 5 SPEED

1. Disconnect battery ground cable and drain transaxle fluid.
2. Wedge a seven inch wood block under clutch pedal.
3. Disconnect clutch cable from clutch release shaft assembly, then remove the clutch cable casing from rib on top surface of transaxle case.
4. Remove two top transaxle to engine mounting bolts.
5. Remove top bolt that secures air management valve bracket to transaxle.
6. Raise vehicle, then remove lower control arm ball joint to steering knuckle attaching nut and bolt. Discard nut and bolt and repeat procedure on opposite side.
7. Pry lower control arm from knuckle on both sides of vehicle using suitable pry bar. Use care not to damage or cut ball joint.
8. Pry left inboard CV joint assembly from transaxle using suitable pry bar. **Lubricant will drain from the seal at this time. Install two plugs.**
9. Remove inboard CV joint from transaxle. Repeat procedure on other side. **If the CV joint assembly cannot be pried from the transaxle, insert differential rotator tool T81P-4026-A or other suitable tool through the left side and tap the joint out. Tool can be used from either side of the transaxle.**
10. Wire left and right halfshaft assemblies in level position.
11. Remove back-up lamp switch connector from transaxle back-up lamp switch.
12. Remove engine roll restrictor bracket.
13. Remove three heater pipe bracket attaching screws, then remove engine roll restrictor.
14. Remove starter.
15. Disconnect shift mechanism from shaft.
16. Disconnect and remove control selector indicator switch arm from shift shaft.
17. Remove shift mechanism stabilizer bar to transaxle attaching bolt, then remove control selector indicator switch and bracket.
18. Remove speedometer cable from transaxle.
19. Remove two stiffener brace attaching bolts from lower position of clutch housing.
20. Position a jack under transaxle.
21. Remove two rear mount and air management valve to transaxle securing bolts, then remove three bolts attaching front mount to transaxle.
22. Lower transaxle support jack until transaxle clears rear mount and support engine with suitable jack. Use a suitable piece of wood between the jack and engine.
23. Remove remaining four engine-to-transaxle attaching bolts.
24. Remove transaxle from rear face of the engine and lower it from vehicle. **The transaxle case casting may have sharp edges. Wear protective gloves when handling the transaxle assembly.**
25. Reverse procedure to install. **Torque** the following as specified, engine-to-transaxle bolts 26-31 ft. lbs., front transaxle mount bolts 25-35 ft. lbs., rear transaxle mount bolts 40-51 ft. lbs., starter stud bolts 30-40 ft. lbs., starter nuts 25-30 ft. lbs.

# TIGHTENING SPECIFICATIONS
## ESCORT

| Year | Component | Torque/ft. Lbs. |
|---|---|---|
| 1989-90 | Air Manage Valve Bracket Bolt To Transaxle | 28–31 |
| | Back-up Lamp Switch | 12–15 |
| | Clutch Lever Cover Screws | 1.5–2.0 |
| | Control Arm To Steering Knuckle | 37–44 |
| | Control Selector Plate | 6–8 |
| | Detent Plunger Retaining Screw | 6–8 |
| | Filler Plug | 9–15 |
| | Front Mount Bracket Bolts | 25–35 |
| | Fork Interlock Sleeve Pin | 12–15 |
| | Rear Mounting Bolts | 35–50 |
| | Reverse Shift Relay Lever Bracket | 6–8 |
| | Roller Restrictor Nuts | 25–30 |
| | Shift Lever Cover Screws | 1.5–2.0 |
| | Shift Stabilizer Bar To Transaxle Case | 25–35 |
| | Speedometer Cable | 2.5–3.5 |
| | Stiffener Brace Bolts | 28–38 |
| | Starter Stud Bolts | 30–40 |
| | Switch Actuator Bracket Bolt | 7–10 |
| | Transaxle Case To Clutch Housing | 13–18 |
| | Transaxle To Engine | 25–35 |
| | Transaxle Mounting Stud | 38–41 |
| | Wheel Nuts | 80–105 |

## TEMPO & TOPAZ EXCEPT ALL WHEEL DRIVE

| Year | Component | Torque/ft. Lbs. |
|---|---|---|
| 1989–92 | Back-up Lamp Switch | 12–15 |
| | Brake Hose Clip Bolt | 8 |
| | Control Selector Plate | 6–8 |
| | Control Arm To Knuckle Nut | 30–45 |
| | Clutch Lever Cover Screws | 1.5–2.0 |
| | Detent Plunger Retaining Screw | 6–8 |
| | Engine Roll Restrictor Attaching Nuts | 14–20 |
| | Filler Plug | 9–15 |
| | Fork Interlock Sleeve Pin | 12–15 |
| | Front Hub Nut | 180–200 |
| | Front Stabilizer Bar Bracket Bolts | 47–55 |
| | Front Stabilizer Bar To Control Arm | 107–125 |
| | Lefthand Front No. 1 Insulator To Body Bracket | 25–35 |
| | Lefthand Rear No. 4 Insulator To Body Bracket | 35–50 |
| | Lower Control Arm Ball Joint To Steering Knuckle Nut | 37–44 |
| | Oil Pan To Transaxle | 28–38 |
| | Pin To Release Fork | 30–40 |
| | Pressure Plate To Flywheel | 12–24 |
| | Reverse Shift Relay Lever Bracket | 6–8 |
| | Shift Lever Cover Screws | 1.5–2.0 |
| | Shift Mechanism To Shift Shaft | 7–10 |
| | Shift Mechanism Stabilizer To Transaxle Bolt | 23–35 |
| | Speedometer Cable | 2–3 |
| | Starter Cable | 5.5–10 |
| | Starter Stud Bolts | 30–40 |
| | Transaxle To Engine Block | 25–35 |
| | Transaxle Case To Clutch Housing | 13–18 |
| | Wheel Lug Nuts | 80–105 |

*Continued*

## TEMPO ALL WHEEL DRIVE

| Year | Component | Torque/ft. Lbs. |
|---|---|---|
| 1989-91 | Back-up Lamp Switch | 12–15 |
| | Bearing Cap Retaining Bolts | 18–24 |
| | Brake Hose Clip Bolt | 8 |
| | Center Support Bearing Retaining Bolts | 23–30 |
| | Clutch Lever Cover Screws | 1.5–2.0 |
| | Cover Plate To Housing | 7–12 |
| | Control Selector Plate | 6–8 |
| | Control Arm To Knuckle Nut | 30–45 |
| | Detent Plunger Retaining Screw | 6–8 |
| | Differential Housing To Support Bracket | 70–80 |
| | Driveshaft To Drive Yoke | 15–17 |
| | Driveshaft To Torque Tube Yoke Flange | 15–17 |
| | Engine Roll Restrictor Attaching Nuts | 14–20 |
| | Filler Plug | 9–15 |
| | Fork Interlock Sleeve Pin | 12–15 |
| | Front Hub Nut | 180–200 |
| | Front Stabilizer Bar Bracket Bolts | 47–55 |
| | Front Stabilizer Bar To Control Arm | 107–125 |
| | Gear Housing To Transfer Case | 7–12 |
| | Lefthand Front No. 1 Insulator To Body Bracket | 25–35 |
| | Lefthand Rear No. 4 Insulator To Body Bracket | 35–50 |
| | Lower Control Arm Ball Joint To Steering Knuckle Nut | 37–44 |
| | Oil Pan To Transaxle | 28–38 |
| | Pin To Release Fork | 30–40 |
| | Pinion Nut | 180–210 |
| | Pressure Plate To Flywheel | 12–24 |
| | Rear Suspension Control Arm Bolt | 60–86 |
| | Reverse Shift Relay Lever Bracket | 6–8 |
| | Shift Lever Cover Screws | 1.5–2.0 |
| | Shift Mechanism To Shift Shaft | 7–10 |
| | Shift Mechanism Stabilizer To Transaxle Bolt | 23–35 |
| | Speedometer Cable | 2–3 |
| | Starter Cable | 5.5–10 |
| | Starter Stud Bolts | 30–40 |
| | Torque Tube To Rear Axle | 40–50 |
| | Torque Tube Mounting Bracket To Crossmember | 28–35 |
| | Torque Tube Mounting Bracket To Torque Tube | 45–50 |
| | Transaxle To Engine Block | 25–35 |
| | Transaxle Case To Clutch Housing | 13–18 |
| | Transfer Case Retaining Bolts | 15–19 |
| | Transfer Case Side Cover Retaining Bolts | 7–12 |
| | U-Joint Retaining Bolts | 15–17 |
| | Vacuum Servo Line Bracket | 7–12 |
| | Vacuum Servo Shield To Transfer Case | 7–12 |
| | Vacuum Solenoids To Shock Tower | 21–30 |
| | Wheel Lug Nuts | 80–105 |

# Transfer Case

INDEX



## TRANSFER CASE

### DESCRIPTION

The transfer case used on Tempo and Topaz models with the All Wheel Drive system, is actuated by an electrically controlled vacuum servo system. When the AWD (All Wheel Drive) switch is turned on, a relay activates the 4WD solenoid valve. The 4WD solenoid valve allows a vacuum to be created in the lefthand chambers of the vacuum servo. Vacuum in the lefthand chambers moves the servo rod and sliding collar into engagement with the transfer case output gears, driveshaft and rear axle. When the AWD switch is turned OFF, a relay activates the 2WD solenoid valve. The 2WD solenoid valve then allows a vacuum to be created in the righthand chambers of the vacuum servo. Vacuum in the righthand chambers then returns the servo rod and sliding collar, disengaging the transfer case, driveshaft and rear axle output gears.

## TRANSFER CASE REPLACE

1. Raise and support vehicle.
2. Drain fluid from transfer case by removing drive housing lower lefthand attaching bolt.
3. Remove vacuum line attaching bracket bolt.
4. Remove drive shaft front attaching bolts and caps. Disconnect front of drive shaft from drive yoke.
5. Remove three bolts attaching vacuum motor shield, then the shield.
6. Remove vacuum lines from servo.
7. Support transfer case assembly, then remove transfer case to transaxle attaching bolts.
8. Remove transfer case.
9. Reverse procedure to install.

# Rear Axle & Suspension

INDEX



## DESCRIPTION

### ESCORT

These vehicles use a modified MacPherson strut independent rear suspension, **Fig. 1.** Each side consists of a shock strut, lower control arm, tie rod, spindle and a coil spring mounted between the lower control arm and body crossmember side rail.

### TEMPO & TOPAZ

These vehicles use a new MacPherson strut independent rear suspension, **Fig. 2.** Each side consists of a shock absorber strut assembly, two parallel control arms per side, tie rod, spindle and a jounce bumper and bracket.

The shock absorber strut assembly includes a rubber isolated top mount, upper spring seat, coil spring insulator, coil spring and a lower spring seat. the strut assembly is attached at the top by two studs, which retain the top mount of the strut to the inner body side panel. The lower end of the assembly is bolted to the spindle. The two control arms are attached to the underbody and spindle with nuts and bolts. The tie rod is attached to the underbody and the spindle. The jounce bumper bracket is bolted to the strut.

## REAR AXLE ASSEMBLY REPLACE

### TEMPO w/ALL WHEEL DRIVE

Remove rear axle assembly to a suitable workbench to conduct all axle repairs.

1. Disconnect battery ground cable.
2. Raise and support vehicle. Position a suitable jack under the rear axle assembly.
3. Disconnect and remove exhaust system components from catalytic converter to rear of vehicle.
4. Remove rear U-joints bolts and caps retaining driveshaft from torque tube yoke flange. Lower driveshaft.
5. Remove four attaching bolts from torque tube support bracket.
6. Remove axle attaching bolt from lefthand differential support bracket.
7. Remove axle attaching bolt from center differential support bracket.
8. Lower axle assembly and remove inboard U-joint attaching bolts and caps from each halfshaft. Remove and wire halfshaft assemblies aside.
9. Reverse procedure to install. **Torque** inboard U-joint cap attaching nuts, differential housing to lefthand and center differential support bracket attaching bolts to specifications. **Torque**

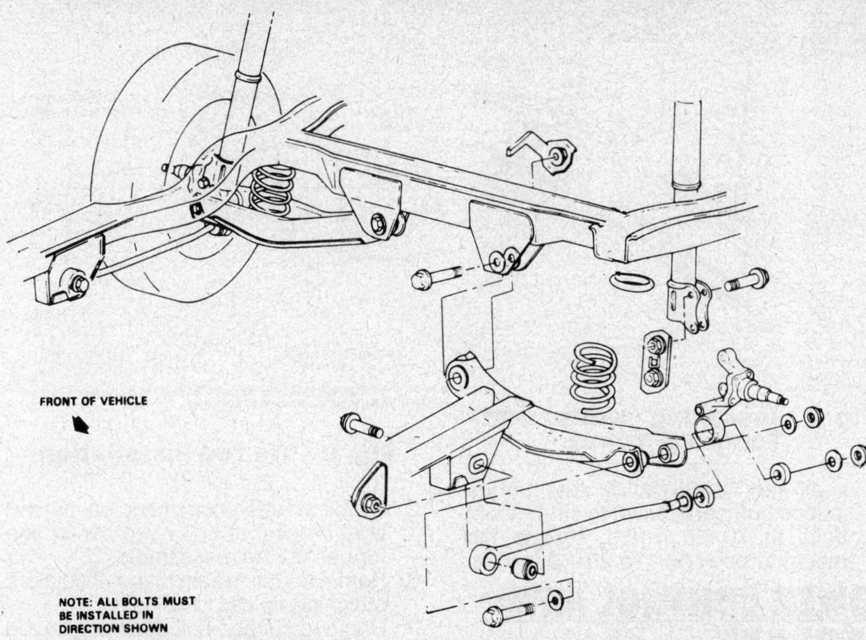


**Fig. 1 Exploded view of rear suspension. Escort**

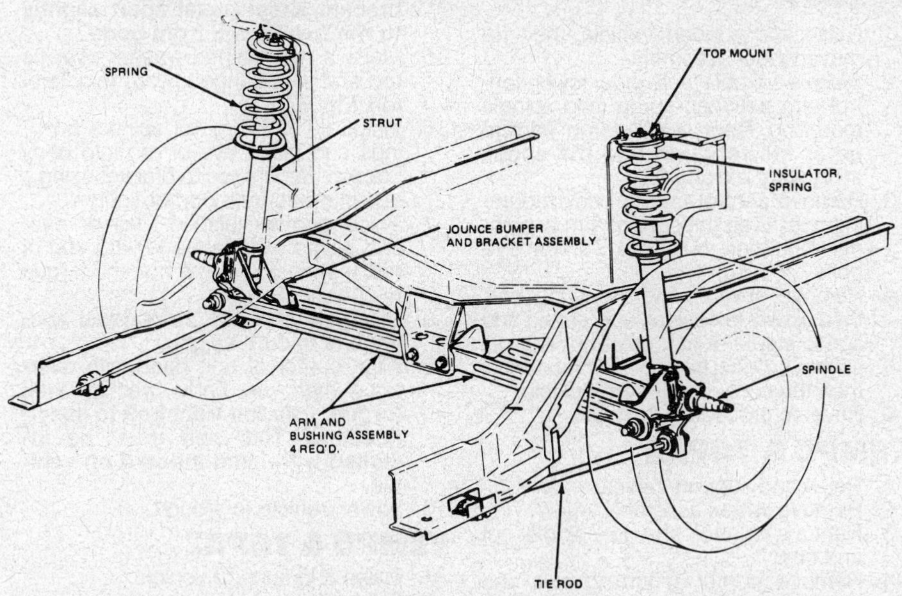


**Fig. 2 Rear suspension components. Tempo & Topaz**

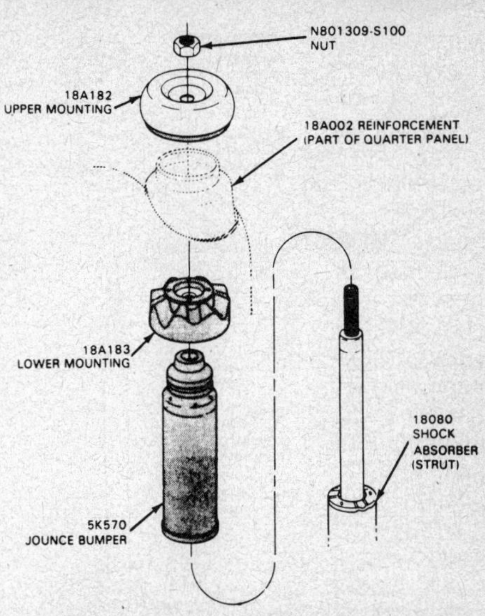


**Fig. 3 Shock absorber strut upper mounting components. Escort**

mounting bracket, torque tube to crossmember attaching bolts, and driveshaft to torque tube yoke flange attaching bolts to specifications.

# HALFSHAFT REPLACE

## TEMPO w/ALL WHEEL DRIVE

1. Remove rear suspension control arm attaching bolt.
2. Remove outboard U-joint attaching bolts and caps.
3. Remove inboard U-joint attaching bolts and caps.
4. Carefully slide shafts together. Do not allow splined shafts to contact with excessive force. Remove halfshafts. **Do not drop the halfshafts as the impact may damage U-joint bearing cups.**
5. Remove and retain bearing cups.
6. Inspect U-joint assemblies for wear and/or damage. Replace U-joints, if necessary.
7. Reverse procedure to install. Note the following:
   a. The inboard shaft has a larger diameter than the outboard shaft.
   b. **Torque** inboard U-joint attaching bolts to 15-17 ft. lbs.
   c. **Torque** outboard U-joint attaching bolts to 15-17 ft. lbs.
   d. **Torque** rear suspension control arm attaching bolt to 60-86 ft. lbs.

# DRIVESHAFT REPLACE

## TEMPO w/ALL WHEEL DRIVE

During removal and installation, support driveshaft using a suitable jack or hoist under the center bearing assembly.

1. To maintain driveshaft balance, mark U-joints so they may be installed in their original positions. **Do not use a sharp tool to place alignment marks on any component.**
2. Remove front U-joint attaching bolts and caps.
3. Slide driveshaft toward rear of vehicle and disengage driveshaft.
4. Remove rear U-joint attaching bolts and caps attaching driveshaft, from torque tube yoke flange.
5. Slide driveshaft toward front of vehicle and disengage driveshaft. **Do not allow splined shafts to contact with excessive force.**
6. Remove center bearing attaching bolts.
7. Remove driveshaft and retain bearing cups with tape, if necessary.
8. Inspect U-joint assemblies for wear or damage. Replace, if necessary.
9. Reverse procedure to install. **Torque** U-joint retaining caps and bolts to 15-17 ft. lbs. **Torque** center bearing and attaching bolts to 23-30 ft. lbs.

# SHOCK STRUT REPLACE

## ESCORT

1. Raise and support vehicle.
2. Remove rear compartment access panels. **On four-door models,** remove quarter trim panel.
3. **On all models,** loosen top shock strut attaching nut, then remove

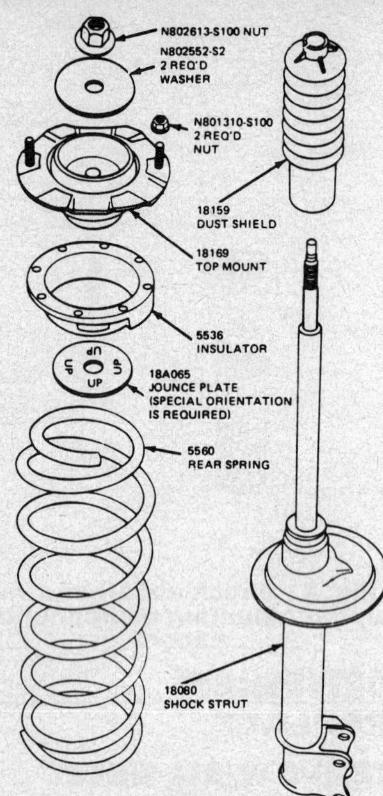


**Fig. 4 Strut, spring & upper mount components. Tempo & Topaz**

wheel assembly.

4. Remove clip retaining brake hose to rear shock and position hose aside.
5. Loosen but do not remove two nuts and bolts securing shock strut to spindle.
6. Remove top mounting nut, washer and rubber insulator, **Fig. 3.**
7. Remove two bottom mounting bolts, then the shock strut from the vehicle.
8. Reverse procedure to install.

# SHOCK STRUT, UPPER MOUNT & SPRING

## REPLACE

### TEMPO & TOPAZ

1. Raise and support vehicle. Loosen upper strut mount to body nuts located in luggage compartment.
2. Remove wheel assembly.
3. Place a suitable jack under control arms.
4. Remove brake hose bracket to strut bolt and position brake hose bracket aside.
5. Remove jounce bumper bracket.
6. Remove two upper mount to body nuts, then the strut.
7. Place strut, spring and upper mount assembly into a suitable spring compressor tool. **Do not remove the spring from the strut without first compressing the spring.**
8. With spring compressed, remove strut shaft to mount nuts. Remove spring, strut and mount, **Fig. 4,** from spring compressor tool.
9. Reverse procedure to install. **Torque** shaft nut to 35-50 ft. lbs., torque jounce bumper bracket to strut mount bolts to 70-96 ft. lbs., **torque** top mount to body nuts to 25-30 ft. lbs.

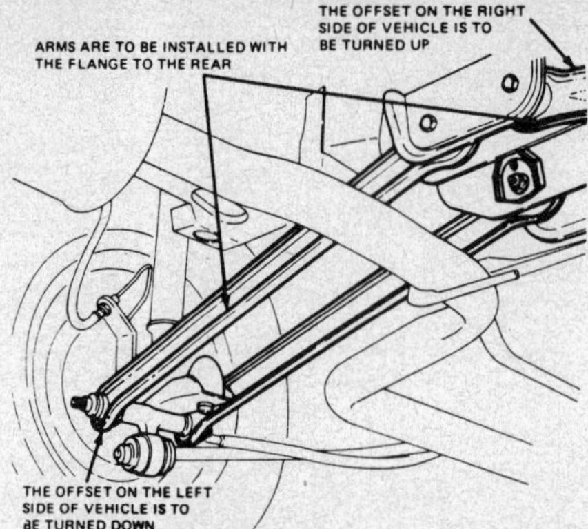


**Fig. 5 Installing control arm. Tempo & Topaz**

# LOWER CONTROL ARM

## REPLACE

### ESCORT

1. Raise and support vehicle, then remove wheel assembly.
2. Place a suitable jack under lower control arm between spring and spindle mounting. **Rear suspension should be at full rebound and the shock strut fully extended.**
3. Remove control arm to body mounting nuts, then the control arm to spindle mounting nuts. Do not remove bolts.
4. Remove spindle end mounting bolt, then slowly lower jack until spring and spring insulator can be removed.
5. Remove bolts from body mountings, then the control arm from vehicle.
6. Reverse procedure to install.

### TEMPO & TOPAZ

1. Raise and support vehicle.
2. Remove wheel assembly.
3. Remove control arm to spindle nut and bolt.
4. Remove center mounting nut and bolt.
5. Remove control arm from vehicle.
6. Reverse procedure to install. **Torque** control arm to body bolt and control arm to spindle nut to specifications. **When installing new control arms the bushing with the 10 mm hole is installed toward the center of the vehicle and the bushing with the 12 mm hole toward the spindle. The offset on the control arm must face up on the right side of the vehicle and down on the left side of the vehicle, Fig. 5. The flanged edge of the control arm stamping must face the rear of the vehicle.**

# TIE ROD

## REPLACE

### ESCORT

1. Raise and support vehicle.

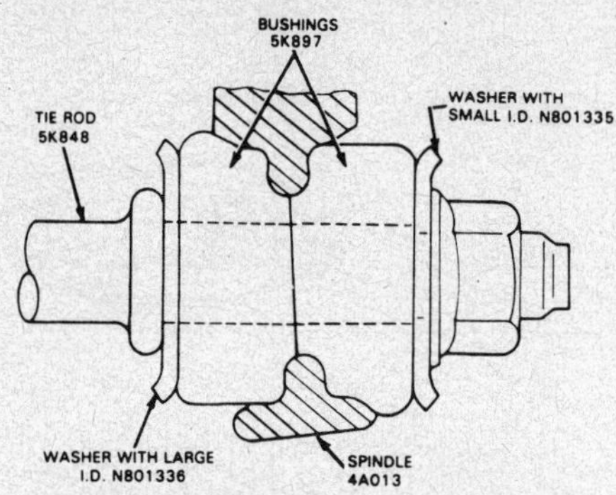


**Fig. 6 Tie rod installation**

2. Scribe a reference mark on tie rod front bracket at bolt head center line for use during reassembly.
3. Remove nut, washer and insulators attaching tie rod to spindle.
4. Remove nut and bolt attaching tie rod to body bracket, then the tie rod. **It may be necessary to pry front bracket sheet metal apart slightly to remove tie rod from body.**
5. Place a new dished washer over tie rod end with flange toward middle of rod, **Fig. 6.**
6. Install tie rod through spindle bushings and place eye of rod into body bracket. Secure rod to bracket using a new nut and bolt. Do not tighten.
7. Place another dished washer over end of rod with flange toward end of rod, then install a new nut and torque to specifications.
8. Using suitable jack, raise lower control arm to curb height.
9. Align center of bolt head with reference mark on body bracket, then **torque tie rod front bolt to specifications. This bolt must be installed with head inboard on vehicle.**
10. Lower vehicle to ground.

### TEMPO & TOPAZ

1. Raise and support vehicle.
2. From inside of luggage compartment, loosen two strut top mount to body nuts.
3. Raise vehicle. Position a suitable jack under lower control arm with a piece of wood between jack and control arm.
4. Remove wheel assembly.
5. Remove two top mount studs, then tie rod to spindle retaining nut.
6. Remove tie rod to body retaining nut.
7. Lower jack until upper strut mount studs clear body mount holes.
8. Move spindle rearward until tie rod can be removed.
9. Place new washers and bushings on both ends of tie rod, **Fig. 6. Front and rear bushings are not interchangeable. The rear bushings have indentations incorporated in them.**
10. Insert tie rod into body bracket, then install new bushing, washer and nut. Do not tighten nut.

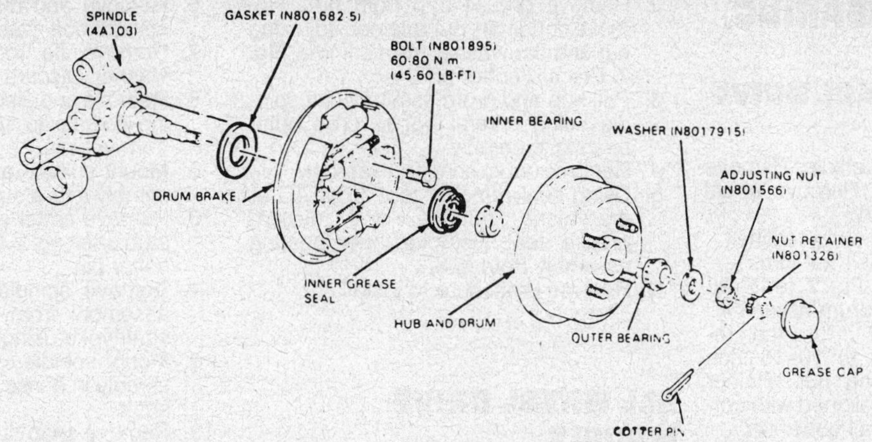


**Fig. 7 Exploded view of rear wheel bearing assembly. Except models w/all wheel drive system**

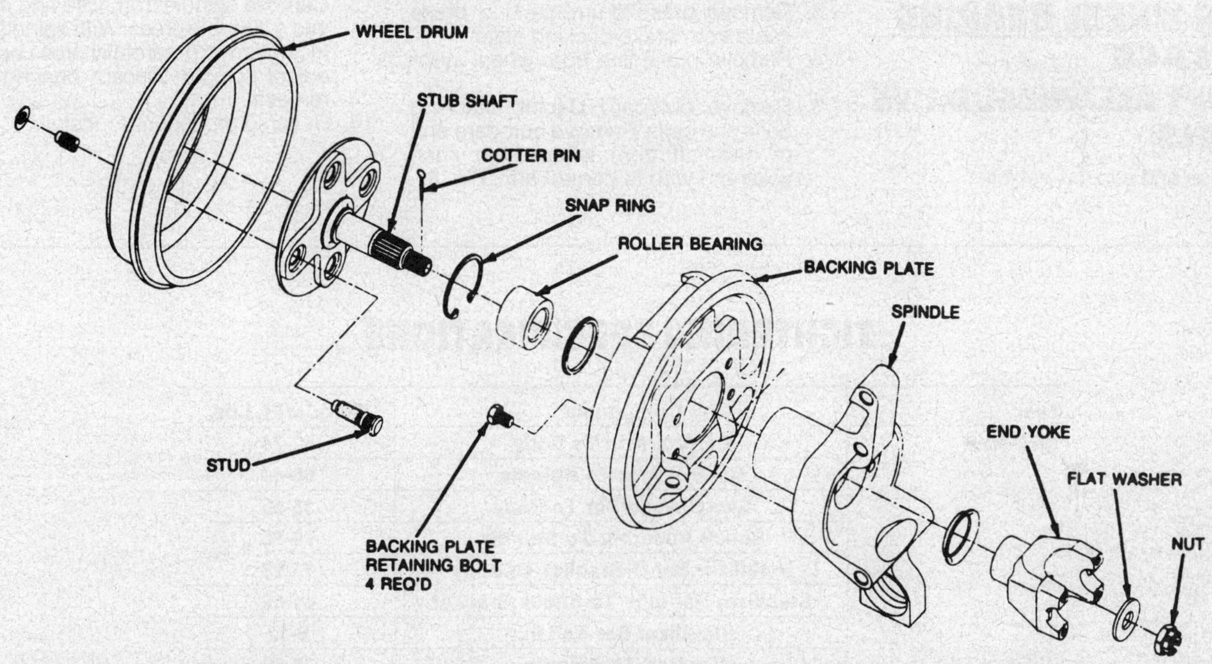


**Fig. 8 Exploded view of rear wheel bearing assembly. Models w/all wheel drive system**

11. Pull back on spindle until tie rod can be installed into the spindle. Install new bushing, washer and nut. Do not tighten nut.
12. Raise jack enough to secure the two strut mounting studs in place.
13. Install two strut to body mount nuts. **Torque** nuts to specifications.
14. Using a suitable jack, raise lower control arm to curb height. Install tie rod nuts and **torque** to specifications.
15. Remove jack and install wheel assembly. Lower vehicle.

# SPINDLE REPLACE

## ESCORT

If a frame contact hoist is used, a jack stand must be placed under lower control arm to raise it to curb height.

1. Raise and support vehicle.
2. Remove wheel assembly, then the brake drum and wheel bearings.
3. Remove brake backing plate assembly, then the tie rod retaining nut and dished washer.
4. Remove two nuts and bolts securing strut to spindle.
5. Remove nut and bolt securing lower control arm to spindle, then the spindle.
6. Reverse procedure to install.

## TEMPO & TOPAZ

1. Raise and support vehicle.
2. Remove wheel assembly.
3. Remove brake drum. Remove brake flex hose bracket to strut bolt.
4. Remove brake backing plate to spindle bolts, then the brake backing plate. **Care should be taken to ensure that brake flex hose is not stretched and brake tube is not bent.**
5. Remove lower control arm to spindle bolt, washer and nut.
6. Remove tie rod nut, bushing and washer.
7. Remove spindle to strut bolts, then the spindle.
8. Reverse procedure to install. **Torque** spindle to strut bolts, tie rod nut and lower control arm to spindle nut to specifications.

# COIL SPRING REPLACE

## ESCORT

1. Raise and support vehicle. Support lower control arm with suitable jack.
2. Remove tire and wheel assembly.
3. Remove nut, bolt and washer securing lower control arm to spindle.
4. Lower control arm until spring can be removed.
5. Reverse procedure to install. A new spring insulator must be used when replacing the spring.

## REAR WHEEL BEARING, ADJUST

### EXCEPT ALL WHEEL DRIVE MODELS

1. Raise and support vehicle. Remove dust cover from hub. Remove wheel assembly, if necessary.
2. Remove cotter pin and nut retainer.
3. Back off adjusting nut 1 full turn.
4. **Torque** adjusting nut, **Fig. 7,** to 17-25 ft. lbs., while rotating drum assembly.
5. Back off adjusting nut 1/2 turn, then retighten adjusting nut to 10-15 inch lbs. Position adjusting nut retainer over nut so slots are aligned with cotter pin hole, then install cotter pin.
6. Install dust cover, wheel assembly, if necessary and lower vehicle to ground.

## REAR WHEEL BEARING REPLACE

### EXCEPT ALL WHEEL DRIVE MODELS

1. Raise and support vehicle.
2. Remove grease cap from hub. Remove cotter pin, nut retainer, adjusting nut and flat washer from spindle, **Fig. 7.** Discard cotter pin.
3. Pull hub and drum assembly off spindle being careful not to drop outer bearing assembly.
4. Remove outer bearing assembly.
5. Using seal removal tool 1175-AC or equivalent, remove and discard grease seal. Remove inner bearing assembly from hub.
6. Reverse procedure to install.

### ALL WHEEL DRIVE MODELS

1. Raise and support vehicle.
2. Remove wheel and tire assembly.
3. Remove brake drum, parking brake cable from brake backing plate.
4. Remove brake line from wheel cylinder.
5. Remove outboard U-joint attaching bolts and caps. Remove outboard end of halfshaft from wheel stub shaft yoke and wire to control arm, **Fig. 8.**
6. Remove and discard control arm to spindle bolt, washers and nut.
7. Remove tie rod nut, bushing and washer. Discard nut.
8. Remove and discard two bolts attaching spindle to strut. Remove spindle from vehicle.
9. Mount spindle and backing plate assembly into a suitable vise.
10. Remove cotter pin and nut attaching stub shaft yoke to stub shaft. Discard cotter pin.
11. Remove spindle and backing plate assembly from vise. Remove stub shaft yoke using a suitable tool.
12. Mount spindle and backing plate assembly in a vise. Remove wheel stub shaft.
13. Remove snap ring retaining bearing.
14. Remove four bolts attaching spindle to backing plate. Remove backing plate.
15. Remove spindle from vise and mount into a suitable press. With spindle side facing upward, carefully press bearing out of spindle. Discard bearing after removal.
16. Reverse procedure to install.

## TIGHTENING SPECIFICATIONS

| Year | Component | Torque/Ft. Lbs. |
|---|---|---|
| 1989-90① | Control Arm To Body | 52-74 |
| | Control Arm To Spindle | 60-80 |
| | Shock Absorber To Body | 35-55 |
| | Shock Absorber To Spindle | 70-96 |
| | Stabilizer Bar U-Bracket To Body | 15-25 |
| | Stabilizer Bar Link To Shock Bracket | 41-55 |
| | Stabilizer Bar To Link | 6-12 |
| | Tie Rod To Spindle | 35-50 |
| | Tie Rod To Body Nut-Front | 52-74 |
| | Wheel Lug Nut | 80-105 |
| 1989-92② | Control Arm To Body | 30-40 |
| | Control Arm To Spindle | 60-80 |
| | Strut Top Mount To Body | 20-30 |
| | Strut To Spindle | 70-96 |
| | Strut To Top Mount | 35-50 |
| | Wheel Lug Nut | 80-105 |

①—Escort.
②—Tempo & Topaz.

# Front Suspension & Steering

INDEX



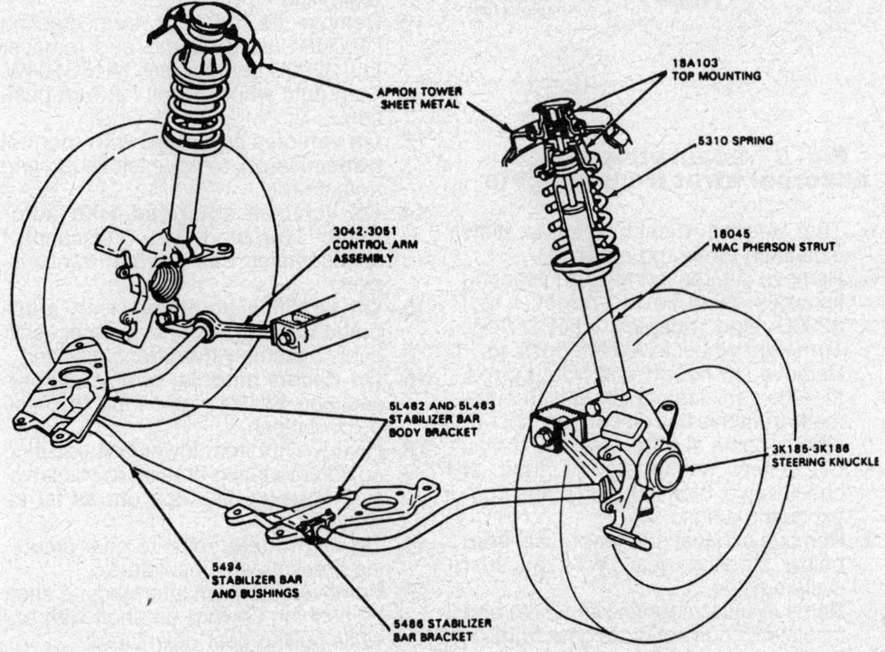


Fig. 1 Front suspension

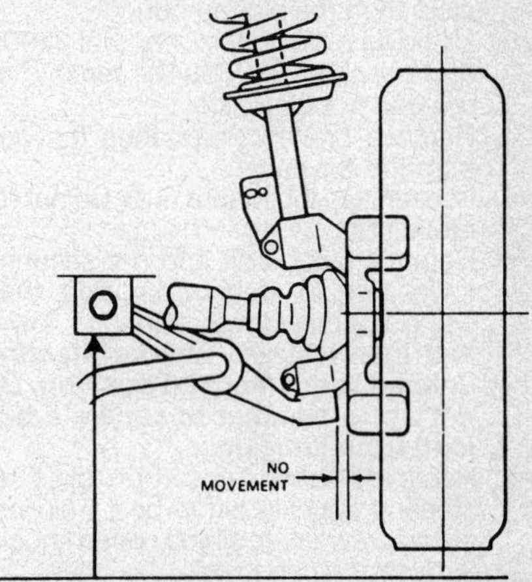


Fig. 2 Checking lower ball joint

## DESCRIPTION

These vehicles use a MacPherson type front suspension with the vertical shock absorber struts attached to the upper fender reinforcements and the steering knuckle, **Fig. 1.** The lower control arms are attached inboard to a crossmember and outboard to the steering knuckle through a ball joint to provide lower steering knuckle position.

## STRUT ASSEMBLY
### REPLACE

1. Raise and support vehicle, then remove tire and wheel assembly.
2. Loosen but do not remove, two top mount-to-shock tower nuts.
3. Remove brake hose retaining bracket from strut.
4. Remove strut-to-knuckle pinch bolt, then using a large screwdriver, slightly spread pinch joint.
5. Using a suitable pry bar, place top of bar under fender apron and pry down on knuckle until strut separates from knuckle. **Be careful not to pinch brake flex line.**
6. Remove two top mount-to-shock tower nuts, then strut from vehicle.
7. Install spring compressor in bench mount.
8. Compress spring with Rotunda spring compressor (tool No. 086-00029) or equivalent.
9. Place 18 mm deep socket tool No. D81P-18045-A1 or equivalent on strut shaft nut. Insert an 8 mm hex deep socket with 1/4-inch drive wrench. Remove top shaft mounting nut from shaft while holding 1/4 inch drive socket with a suitable extension. **Do not attempt to remove shaft nut by turning shaft and holding nut. The nut must be turned and the shaft held to avoid possible damage to shaft.**
10. Loosen spring compressor tool, then remove top mount bracket assembly, bearing insulator and spring.
11. reverse procedure to install.**Torque** strut shaft nut to 35-50 ft. lbs. Install new steering knuckle pinch nut and **torque** to specifications.**Torque** two top mount attaching nuts to specifications.

## CHECKING BALL JOINTS

1. Raise and support vehicle.
2. With suspension in full rebound position, grasp lower edge of tire and move wheel in and out, **Fig. 2.**
3. Observe lower end of knuckle and lower control arm as wheel is being moved in and out. Any movement between lower end of knuckle and lower arm indicates excessive ball joint wear.
4. If any movement is observed, install a new lower control arm assembly. The lower ball joint and control arm are serviced as an assembly only. Refer to Lower Control Arm, Replace in this section.

## LOWER CONTROL ARM
### REPLACE

1. Raise and support vehicle.
2. Remove nut from stabilizer bar, then the large dished washer.
3. Remove lower control arm inner pivot bolt and nut.
4. Remove lower control arm ball joint pinch bolt, then using a screwdriver, separate the control arm from the steering knuckle and remove from vehicle. **Ensure steering column is in**

**unlocked position. Do not use a hammer to separate ball joint from knuckle.**

5. Reverse procedure to install. **Torque** pinch bolt and nut to 38-45 ft. lbs. **Torque** lower control arm inner pivot nut to 98-115 ft. lbs.

## STEERING KNUCKLE
### REPLACE

1. Raise and support vehicle, then remove wheel assembly.
2. Remove cotter pin from tie rod end stud, then the slotted nut.
3. Using tie rod end remover tool 3290C and adapter T81P3504W, remove tie rod end from knuckle.
4. Remove brake caliper, then the hub from the driveshaft.
5. Loosen two top mount nuts. Do not remove nuts.
6. Remove pinch bolt and nut securing lower arm to steering knuckle, then using a screwdriver, separate lower arm from knuckle. **Ensure steering column is in unlocked position. Do not use a hammer to separate ball joint from knuckle.**
7. Remove shock absorber strut to steering knuckle pinch bolt, then using a screwdriver, slightly open knuckle to strut pinch joint.
8. Remove steering knuckle from shock absorber strut, **Fig. 3,** then from the vehicle.
9. Reverse procedure to install. **Torque** steering knuckle, lower control arm to steering knuckle pinch bolt, and two top mount nuts to specifications. Install new slotted nut then **torque** to 28-32 ft. lbs.

## STABILIZER BAR
### REPLACE

1. Raise and support vehicle.
2. Remove stabilizer insulator mounting bracket bolts.
3. Remove stabilizer bar to control arm attaching bolts, then the stabilizer bar assembly.
4. Remove worn insulators from stabilizer bar.
5. Reverse procedure to install. **Torque** stabilizer bar to control arm attaching bolt and stabilizer insulator mounting bracket bolts to specifications.

## STEERING GEAR
### REPLACE
### MANUAL STEERING

1. Disconnect battery ground cable, then turn ignition switch to "On" position.
2. Remove access panel from dash below steering column.
3. Remove intermediate shaft bolts at gear input shaft and at steering column shaft.
4. Using a wide blade screwdriver, spread slots enough to loosen intermediate shaft at both ends.

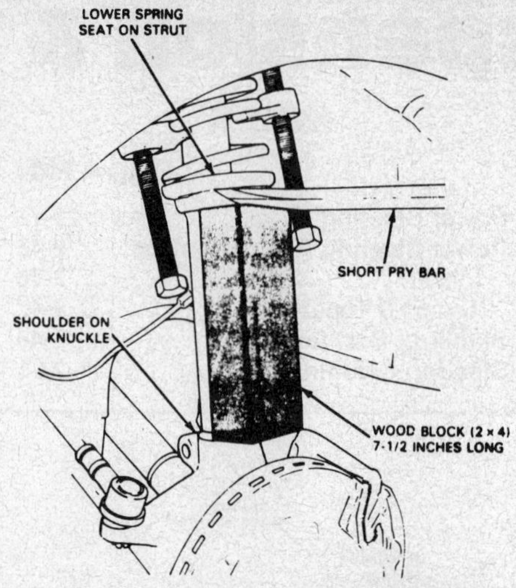


**Fig. 3 Separating shock absorber strut from knuckle**

5. Turn steering wheel fully left to allow clearance for tie rod removal.
6. Remove tie rod ends from steering knuckles using tie rod remover tool 3290D and adapter T81P3504W. Turn right wheel to full left position.
7. Remove left tie rod end from tie rod, then on vehicles equipped with automatic transmission disconnect speedometer cable at transmission.
8. Disconnect secondary air tube at check valve, then exhaust pipes from exhaust manifold.
9. Remove exhaust hanger bracket from below steering gear. Wire exhaust system aside.
10. Remove gear mounting brackets and insulators, then separate gear from intermediate shaft while simultaneously pulling upward on shaft from inside vehicle. **Right and lefthand brackets and insulators are not interchangeable.**
11. Rotate gear forward and downward to clear input shaft.
12. Ensure input shaft is in full left turn position, then remove gear through right side apron opening until left tie rod clears shift linkage.
13. Lower left side of gear and remove gear from vehicle.
14. Reverse procedure to install. Ensure input shaft is at full left turn stop and right wheel assembly is in full left turn position. Use caution not to damage steering gear bellows.

### POWER STEERING

1. Disconnect battery ground cable, then turn ignition switch to On position.
2. Remove access panel from dash below steering column.
3. Remove four screws from dash panel steering column boot, then slide boot along intermediate shaft.
4. Remove intermediate shaft bolts at gear input shaft and from steering column shaft.
5. Using wide blade screwdriver, spread slot wide enough to loosen intermediate shaft at both ends.
6. Turn steering wheel to full left stop to facilitate gear removal.
7. Remove pressure switch.
8. **On Escort models equipped with air conditioning,** secure liquid line above dash opening.
9. **On all models,** disconnect secondary air tube at check valve, then the exhaust pipes from exhaust manifold. Secure exhaust system to the side.
10. Remove exhaust hanger brackets from below steering gear and from side apron.
11. Disconnect pressure and return lines from intermediate connector and drain fluid.
12. Remove tie rod ends from steering knuckles using tie rod end remover tool 3290D and adapter T81P3504W. Turn right wheel to full left turn position.
13. **On vehicles equipped with manual transmission,** remove left tie rod end from tie rod.
14. **On vehicles equipped with automatic transmission,** disconnect speedometer cable from transmission.
15. **On vehicles equipped with automatic transmission,** disconnect shift cable assembly from transmission.
16. **On Escort models,** remove screws securing heater water tube to brace below oil pan.
17. Remove nut from lower bolt securing engine mounting bracket to transmission housing. Tap bolt out as far as possible.
18. **On all models,** remove gear mounting brackets and insulators.
19. Remove gear from intermediate shaft by pushing upward on shaft with bar while pulling gear downward.
20. Rotate gear downward and forward to clear input shaft.
21. Ensure input shaft is in full left turn position, then move gear through right side apron opening until left tie rod clears opening. Use caution to avoid damaging bellows.
22. Lower left side of gear and remove gear from vehicle.
23. Reverse procedure to install.

## POWER STEERING PUMP
### REPLACE
### ESCORT

1. Remove air cleaner, thermactor pump drive belt and thermactor pump.
2. Remove power steering reservoir filler extension. Cover opening to prevent entry of dirt.
3. From underneath vehicle, loosen one power steering pump adjusting bolt and remove one pump to mounting bracket bolt, then disconnect return hose.
4. Form engine compartment, loosen one power steering pump adjusting bolt, then loosen pivot and remove drive belts.
5. Remove the remaining two power steering pump to bracket retaining bolts, then remove pump from bracket

by passing pulley through adjusting bracket opening.

6. Disconnect pressure hose from power steering pump, then remove pump.
7. Reverse procedure to install.

### TEMPO & TOPAZ

1. Remove alternator drive belt.
2. Place alternator in upper most position.
3. Remove radiator overflow bottle.
4. Remove power steering pump drive belt.
5. Disconnect return line from pump.
6. Completely back off power steering pump pressure line nut. The pressure line will separate when the pump bracket is removed.
7. Remove power steering pump mounting bolts and pump.
8. Reverse procedure to install.

## FRONT WHEEL BEARINGS

## REPLACE

The front wheel bearings are cartridge design and are pre-greased, sealed and require no maintenance. The bearings are preset and cannot be adjusted.

1. Raise and support vehicle, then remove tire and wheel assembly.
2. Remove brake caliper and rotor.
3. Disconnect lower control arm and tie rod from knuckle (leave strut attached).
4. Loosen two strut top mount to apron attaching nuts.
5. Using suitable tools, remove hub bearing and knuckle assembly by pushing out constant velocity joint outer shaft until it is free of assembly.
6. Install hub removing tool D80L-1002-L and D80L-625-1 or equivalents, onto knuckle bosses and remove hub.
7. Remove snap ring retaining bearing in knuckle assembly. Discard snap ring.
8. Using a suitable press and bearing remover tools T83P-1104-AH3 and T83P-1104-AH2, press bearing from knuckle assembly. Discard bearing.
9. Remove halfshaft assembly. Place shaft into a suitable vise and remove bearing dust shield. Discard dust shield.
10. Reverse procedure to install.

## INNER TIE ROD

## REPLACE

1. Unlock steering column by turning ignition key.
2. Engage parking brake, then raise and support vehicle.
3. Clean any loose dirt or oil from power steering gear and boot bellows.
4. Disconnect outer tie rod end from steering knuckle.
5. Loosen jamb nut and keep flush with outer tie rod.
6. Remove cotter pin and castle nut, then disconnect outer tie rod from steering knuckle.
7. Mark threads at jamb nut location, then remove outer tie rod end from inner tie rod.
8. Remove jamb nut from inner tie rod spindle.
9. Remove left and right steering gear boot bellows along with breather tube.
10. Remove rollpin or rivet securing inner tie rod to steering rack, **Use a sharp chisel to gently pry up or rivet. Do not cut off.**
11. Use side cutters to remove rivet. **The rivet has a steel core which will deform the steering gear rack threads if it is not completely removed.**
12. If rivet is not accessible, unscrew inner tie rod (less than one full turn). **Have steering gear at or near full turn (lock) position. Use a wrench on rack teeth (flat) to resist rotation and prevent damage to pinion during removal and installation.**
13. Remove inner tie rod from steering gear rack using a wrench on rack teeth in combination Rotunda socket (tool No. D90P-3290-A) or equivalent.
14. Reverse procedure to install, noting the following:
    a. Replenish any grease which may have been removed from rack teeth.
    b. Install roll pin using channel locks.
    c. Check inner tie rod function by moving tie rod spindle. Handshake in various directions.
    d. Apply steering gear grease to inner tie rod groove where bellows attach to tie rod end. This allows for toe-in adjustment without twisting bellows.
    e. **Torque** jamb nut to 42-50 ft.lbs.
    f. **Torque** steering knuckle castle nut to 27 ft. lbs., continue tightening to 27-32 ft. lbs. to nearest hole slot.
    g. Align front end to specification.

## TIGHTENING SPECIFICATIONS

| Year | Component | Torque/ft. lbs. |
|---|---|---|
| 1989-92 | Control Arm To Body | 48-55 |
| | Control Arm To Knuckle | 38-45 |
| | Stabilizer Bar Bracket Assembly To Body | 48-55 |
| | Stabilizer Bar Insulator U-Bracket Clamps To Bracket Assembly | ① |
| | Stabilizer Bar To Control Arm | 98-115 |
| | Strut Top Mount To Body | 25-30 |
| | Strut To Knuckle | 55-81 |
| | Strut To Top Mount | 35-50 |
| | Tie Rod End To Steering Knuckle | 28-32 |
| | Wheel Lug Nut | 80-105 |

①—Escort, 59-68; Tempo & Topaz, 85-100.

# Wheel Alignment

INDEX



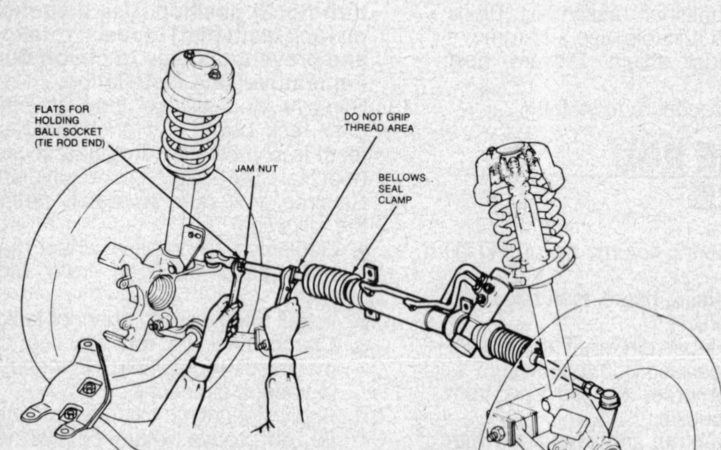


**Fig. 1 Adjusting front wheel toe-in and toe-out**

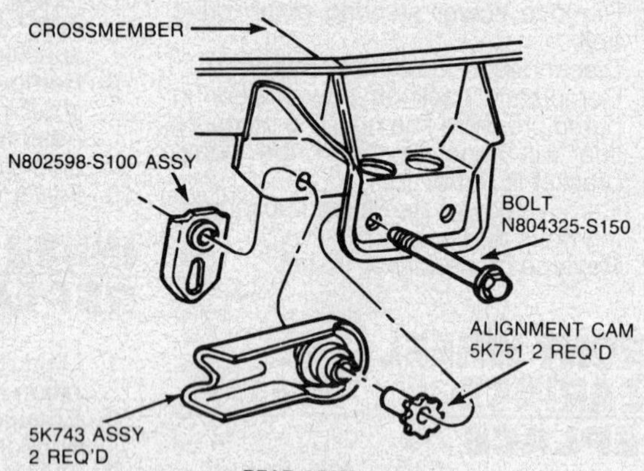


**Fig. 2 Rear wheel toe-in and toe-out alignment cam**

## FRONT WHEEL ALIGNMENT

### CASTER & CAMBER

Caster and camber angles are preset at the factory and cannot be adjusted.

### TOE-IN

To adjust toe-in, **Fig. 1**, lock steering wheel in the straight ahead position using suitable steering wheel holder. Remove small outer clamp from steering boot to prevent boot from twisting during adjustment procedure. Loosen tie rod adjusting nuts, then adjust left and right tie rods until each wheel has 1/2 the desired total toe specification. Tighten tie rod adjusting nuts, replace steering gear rubber boots and tighten clamp. Remove steering wheel holding tool.

## REAR WHEEL ALIGNMENT

### CASTER & CAMBER

Caster and camber cannot be adjusted and factory set.

### TOE-IN & TOE-OUT

Toe-in and toe-out can be adjusted if it is determined that the vehicle is not within alignment specifications. To adjust toe of either wheel, loosen bolt attaching rear control arm to body, **Fig. 2,** and rotate alignment cam until the required alignment setting is obtained. **Torque** control arm attaching bolt to 52-74 ft. lbs.

# LINCOLN

## INDEX OF SERVICE OPERATIONS

**NOTE:** Refer To Rear Of This Manual For Vehicle Manufacturer's Special Service Tool Suppliers.



*Continued*

## INDEX OF SERVICE OPERATIONS—Continued

# Specifications

## GENERAL ENGINE SPECIFICATIONS

| Year | Engine Liter/CID ① | Engine VIN Code ② | Fuel System | Bore & Stroke | Compression Ratio | Net HP @ RPM. ③ | Maximum Torque Ft. Lbs. @ RPM | Normal Oil Pressure Psi. |
|---|---|---|---|---|---|---|---|---|
| 1989-90 | 3.8L/V6-232 | 4 | ④ | 3.80 x 3.40 | 9.0 | 140 @ 3800 | 215 @ 2200 | 40-60 |
| | 5.0L/V8-302 | F | ④ | 4.00 x 3.00 | 8.9 | ⑤ | ⑥ | 40-60 |
| | 5.0L/V8-302 HO | E | ④ | 4.00 x 3.00 | 9.2 | 225 @ 4000 | 300 @ 3200 | 40-60 |
| 1991 | 3.8L/V6-232 | 4 | ④ | 3.80 x 3.40 | 9.1 | 190 @ 4200 | 260 @ 3200 | 40-60 |
| | 4.6L/V8-281 | F | ④ | 3.60 x 3.60 | 9.0 | ⑦ | ⑧ | 40-60 |
| | 5.0L/V8-302 HO | E | ④ | 4.00 x 3.00 | 9.2 | 225 @ 4000 | 300 @ 3200 | 40-60 |
| 1992 | 3.8L/V6-232 | 4 | ④ | 3.80 x 3.40 | 9.1 | 160 @ 4400 | 225 @ 3000 | 40-60 |
| | 4.6L/V8-281 | W | ④ | 3.60 x 3.60 | 9.0 | ⑦ | ⑧ | 40-60 |
| | 5.0L/V8-302 HO | E | ④ | 4.00 x 3.00 | 9.1 | 225 @ 4200 | 300 @ 3200 | 40-60 |

①—CID-cubic inch displacement.
②—The eighth digit of the VIN denotes engine code.
③—Ratings are net-as installed in vehicle.
④—Electronic Fuel Injection.
⑤—Single exhaust, 150 @ 3200; dual exhaust, 160 @ 3400.
⑥—Single exhaust, 270 @ 2000; dual exhaust, 280 @ 2200.
⑦—Single exhaust, 190 @ 4200; dual exhaust, 210 @ 4600.
⑧—Single exhaust, 260 @ 3200; dual exhaust, 270 @ 3400.

## TUNE UP SPECIFICATIONS

| Year & Engine/ VIN Code ① | Spark Plug Gap | Ignition Timing BTDC ② Firing Order Fig. ④ | Ignition Timing BTDC ② Man. Trans. | Ignition Timing BTDC ② Auto. Trans. | Ignition Timing BTDC ② Mark Fig. | Curb Idle Speed ③ Man. Trans. | Curb Idle Speed ③ Auto Trans. | Fast Idle Speed Man. Trans. | Fast Idle Speed Auto. Trans. | Fuel Pump Pressure, Psi. |
|---|---|---|---|---|---|---|---|---|---|---|
| **1989–90** | | | | | | | | | | |
| 3.8L/V6-238(4) | .054 | E | — | 10⑨ | D | — | 620-720D ⑥ | — | ⑥ | 35-45⑧ |
| 5.0L/V8-302(F) | .050 | A | — | 10⑨ | B | — | 525-650D ⑥ | — | ⑥ | 35-45⑦ |
| 5.0L/V8-302(E) HO | .054 | C | — | 10⑨ | B | — | 550-675D ⑥ | — | ⑥ | 35-45⑦ |
| **1991—92** | | | | | | | | | | |
| 3.8L/V6-238(4) | .054 | E | — | 10⑨ | D | — | 620-720D ⑥ | — | ⑥ | 35-45⑧ |
| 4.6L/V8-281(W) | .054 | F | — | — | ⑤ | — | ⑥ | — | ⑥ | 35-45⑦ |
| 5.0L/V8-302(E) HO | .054 | C | — | 10⑨ | B | — | 550-675D ⑥ | — | ⑥ | 35-45⑦ |

①—The eighth digit of the Vehicle Identification Number (VIN) denotes engine code.
②—BTDC: Before Top Dead Center.
③—D: Drive.
④—Before disconnecting wires from distributor cap, determine location of No. 1 wire in cap, as distributor position may have been altered from that shown at the end of this chart.
⑤—Equipped with crankshaft sensor.
⑥—Idle speeds are controlled by the automatic idle control.
⑦—Wrap shop towel around fuel diagnostic valve to prevent fuel spillage. Connect a suitable fuel pressure gauge to fuel diagnostic valve. Energize fuel pump & note fuel pressure gauge reading.
⑧—Wrap shop towel around fitting to prevent fuel spillage, then connect a suitable fuel pressure gauge to fuel diagnostic valve on fuel rail assembly. Connect jumper wire to VIP self test connector FP terminal. The VIP connector is located at the right hand rear of the engine compartment at the electronic control assembly. Place ignition switch in On position, then connect VIP jumper wire to ground & check fuel pressure gauge reading.
⑨—Disconnect in-line spout connector, then start engine & adjust ignition timing as necessary. After completing adjustment, reconnect spout connector.

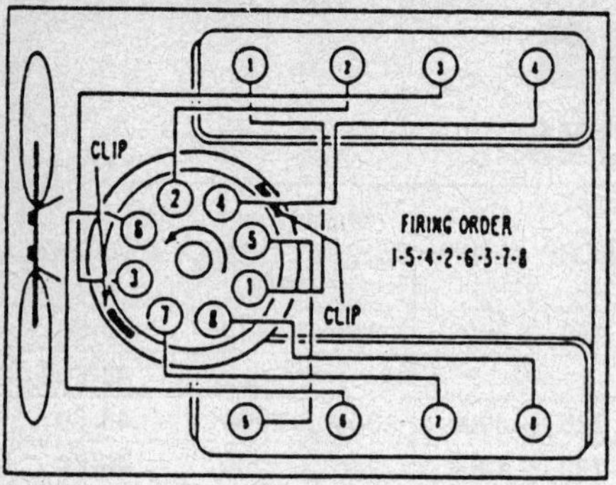


Fig. A

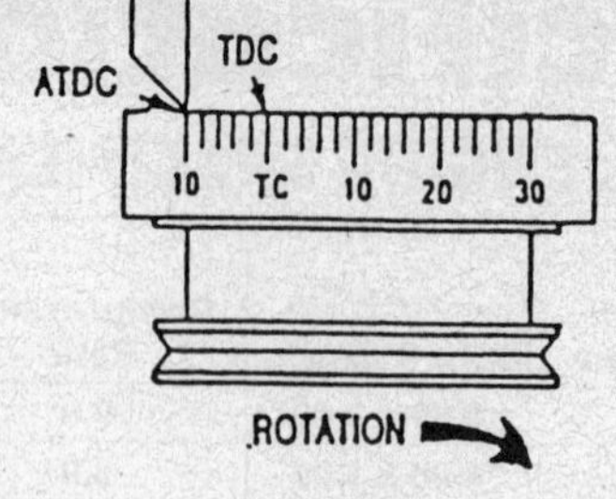


Fig. B

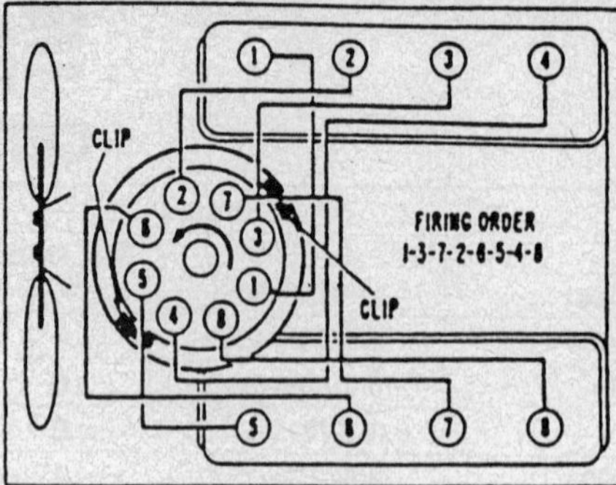


Fig. C

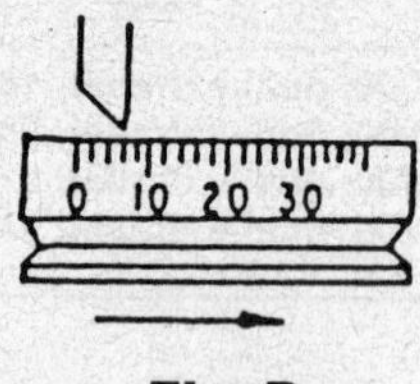


Fig. D

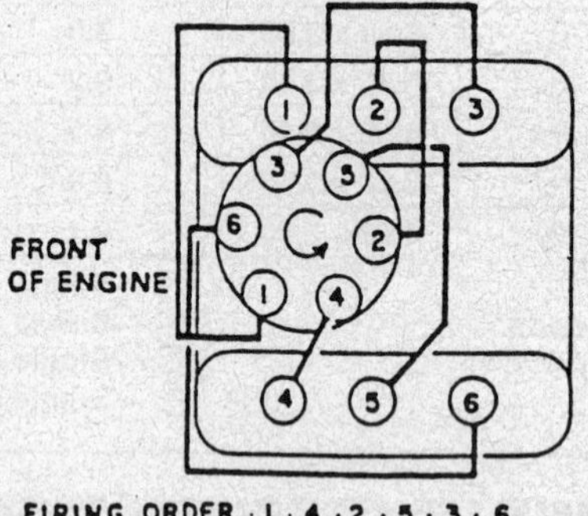


Fig. E

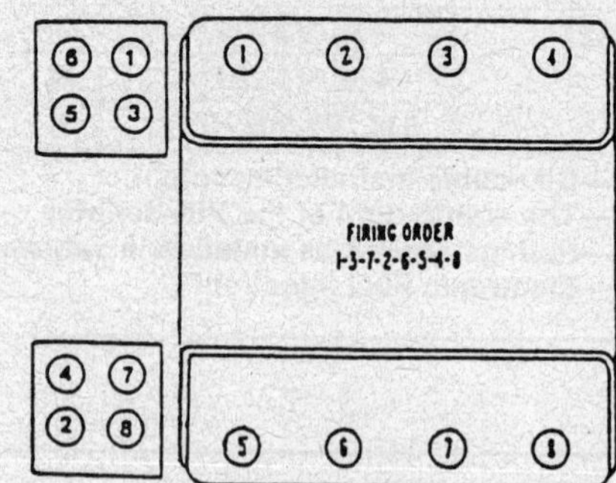


Fig. F

## FRONT WHEEL ALIGNMENT SPECIFICATIONS

| Year | Model | Caster Angle, Degrees | | Camber Angle, Degrees | | | | Toe-In, Inch | Toe Out on Turns, Degrees | |
|---|---|---|---|---|---|---|---|---|---|---|
| | | | | Limits | | Desired | | | | |
| | | Limits | Desired | Left | Right | Left | Right | | Outer Wheel | Inner Wheel |
| 1989–90 | Town Car | +2.5 to +4.5 | +3.5 | −.75 to +.25 | −.75 to +.25 | −.5 | −.5 | 1/16 | 18.51 | 20 |
| | Mark VII | +.6 to +2.7 | +1.5 | −.75 to +.75 | −.75 to +.75 | 0 | 0 | 1/8 | 17.14 | 20 |
| | Continental | +3.6 to +5.2 | +4.4 | −1.7 to −.5 | −1.7 to −.5 | −1.1 | −1.1 | ① | 18.21 | 20 |
| 1991–92 | Town Car | +4.75 to +6.25 | +5.5 | −1.25 to +.25 | −1.25 to +.25 | −.5 | −.5 | 1/16 | 18.51 | 20 |
| | Mark VII | +.6 to +2.7 | +1.5 | −.75 to +.75 | −.75 to +.75 | 0 | 0 | 1/8 | 17.14 | 20 |
| | Continental | +3.6 to +5.2 | +4.4 | −1.7 to −.5 | −1.7 to −.5 | −1.1 | −1.1 | ① | 18.21 | 20 |

①—Total toe, −.20 degrees.

## REAR WHEEL ALIGNMENT SPECIFICATIONS

| Year | Model | Camber Angle, Degrees | | | | Toe-In, Degrees |
|---|---|---|---|---|---|---|
| | | Limits | | Desired | | |
| | | Left | Right | Left | Right | |
| 1989–92 | Continental | −2 to −.6 | −2 to −.6 | −1.3 | −1.3 | ① |

①—Total toe, +.20 degrees.

# COOLING SYSTEM & CAPACITY DATA

| Year | Model or Engine/VIN① | Cooling Capacity, Qts. | Radiator Cap Relief Pressure, Psi. | Thermo. Opening Temp. Deg. F | Fuel Tank Gal. | Engine Oil Refill Qts. | Auto. Trans. Qts. ② | Rear Axle Oil Pints |
|---|---|---|---|---|---|---|---|---|
| 1989–90 | 3.8L/V6-232(4) Continental | 11.1 | 16 | 196 | 18.6 | 4⑤ | 12.8 | ⑥ |
| | 5.0L/V8-302(E) Mark VII | 14.1 | 16 | 192 | 22.1 | 4③④ | 12.3 | 3.75 |
| | 5.0L/V8-302(F) Town Car | 14.1 | 16 | 192 | 22.3 | 4③④ | 12.3 | 3.75 |
| 1991–92 | 3.8L/V6-232(4) Continental | 12.1 | 16 | 196 | 18.6 | 4⑤ | 12.8 | ⑥ |
| | 5.0L/V8-302(E) Mark VII | 14.1 | 16 | 192 | 20 | 4③④ | 12.3 | 3.75 |
| | 4.6L/V8-281(W) Town Car | 14.1 | 16 | 196 | 21 | 5③ | 12.3 | 3.75 |

①—The eighth digit of Vehicle Identification Number (VIN) denotes engine code.
②—Approximate. Make final check with dipstick.
③—Add one quart with filter change.
④—Dual sump oil pan. Remove both drain plugs to fully drain oil. One drain plug located at front of oil pan. Second drain plug located at left side of oil pan.
⑤—Add ½ qt. with filter change.
⑥—Front wheel drive.

# LUBRICANT DATA

| Year | Model | Lubricant Type | | | | | |
|---|---|---|---|---|---|---|---|
| | | Transaxle | | | | | |
| | | Manual | Automatic | Transfer Case | Rear Axle | Power Steering | Brake System |
| 1989–92 | All | — | ATF | — | ① | ATF② | Heavy Duty |

①—Use ESP-M2C154-A (XY90-QL) or equivalent plus four ounces of EST-M2C118-A (C8AZ-19B546-A) friction modifier or equivalent for traction-lok axles.
②—Type F.

# Electrical

## INDEX



## AIRBAG SYSTEM DISARMING

**The electrical circuit necessary for system deployment is powered directly from the battery and a backup power supply. To avoid accidental deployment and possible personal injury, the airbag system must be deactivated prior to servicing or replacing any system components.**

A back-up power supply is included in the system to provide airbag deployment in the event the battery or battery cables are damaged in an accident before the sensors can close. The power supply is a capacitor that will retain a charge for approximately 15 minutes after the battery ground cable is disconnected. **Backup power supply must be disconnected to deactivate airbag system.**

### 1989–91 MODELS

1. Disconnect battery ground cable.
2. Disconnect backup power supply as described under "Backup Power Supply, Replace" in the "Passive Restraint" section.
3. Remove four nut and washer assemblies securing airbag module to steering wheel, then disconnect airbag electrical connector. Attach jumper wire to airbag terminals on clockspring.
4. **On models equipped with passenger-side airbag,** disconnect airbag module connector located behind glove compartment. Attach a jumper wire to airbag terminals on wiring harness side of passenger airbag module connector
5. To reactivate, disconnect battery ground cable and backup power supply, then reverse remainder of deactivation procedure. **Torque** airbag module to steering wheel nut assemblies to 35-53 inch lbs.
6. Verify airbag lamp after reactivating system.

### 1992 MODELS

1. Disconnect positive battery cable and wait one minute.
2. Remove four nut and washer assemblies securing airbag to steering wheel.
3. Disconnect airbag electrical connector and install airbag simulator tool No. 105-00008 or equivalent.
4. **On models with passenger side airbag,** remove passenger airbag and disconnect electrical connector.
5. Install airbag simulator tool No. 105-00008 or equivalent.
6. **On all models,** connect positive battery cable.
7. To activate airbag system, disconnect positive battery cable and reverse procedure. **Torque** mounting nut and washer assemblies to 36-49 inch lbs.
8. Verify proper operation of airbag lamp.

## FUSE PANEL & FLASHER LOCATION

The fuse panel is located under the instrument panel to the lefthand side of the steering column.

The turn signal & hazard flashers are located on the fuse panel.

## STARTER REPLACE

### 1989–91 EXCEPT CONTINENTAL

1. Disconnect battery ground cable, then raise and support vehicle.
2. Disconnect starter cable at starter terminal, then remove starter mounting bolts.
3. Remove starter. On some models, it may be necessary to turn wheels to the left or right to gain clearance for removal.
4. Reverse procedure to install. **Torque** starter cable to starter motor bolt to 70-110 inch lbs.

### 1989–91 CONTINENTAL

1. Disconnect battery ground cable, then the starter electrical cable.
2. If applicable, remove cable support and ground cable connection from upper starter stud bolt.

3. If applicable, remove brace at starter motor and cylinder block.
4. Remove starter mounting bolts, then the starter from area between sub-frame and radiator.
5. Reverse procedure to install.

## 1992 CONTINENTAL, MARK VII & TOWN CAR

**When servicing starter or performing any maintenance in the area of starter, note heavy gauge input lead connected to starter solenoid is Hot at all times. Ensure protective cap is installed over terminal and is replaced after service. When battery has been disconnected and reconnected, some abnormal drive symptoms may occur while the EEC processor relearns its adaptive strategy. The vehicle may need to be driven 10 miles or more to relearn strategy.**

1. Disconnect battery ground cable.
2. Raise and support vehicle.
3. Disconnect starter cable and push on connector from starter solenoid. **When disconnecting hardshell connector at "S" terminal, grasp plastic shell and pull off. Do not pull on wire.**
4. Remove starter motor attaching bolts, then remove starter.
5. Remove lower attaching bolt.
6. Reverse procedure to install. **Torque** starter upper and lower bolts to 16-19 ft. lbs.

# DISTRIBUTOR

## REPLACE

1. Disconnect negative battery cable, then the distributor from wiring harness.
2. Mark position of No. 1 cylinder wire tower on distributor base, for installation reference.
3. Loosen distributor cap hold-down screws. Remove cap straight off distributor to prevent damage to rotor blade and spring.
4. Remove rotor from the distributor shaft and armature, by pulling upward.
5. Remove distributor hold-down clamp, then the distributor. **Cover distributor opening in cylinder block or head to prevent entry of foreign material.**
6. Reverse procedure to install noting the following:
   a. No. 1 piston must be at (TDC) of compression stroke. Remove No. 1 cylinder spark plug and rotate engine clockwise until No. 1 piston is on the compression stroke.
   b. Align timing pointer with (TDC) on the crankshaft damper, then the locating boss on rotor with hole on armature. Fully seat rotor on distributor shaft.
   c. Rotate distributor shaft so blade on rotor is pointing toward mark on distributor base, that was previously made.
   d. While installing distributor continue rotating rotor slightly so leading edge of vane is centered in vane switch stator assembly.
   e. Rotate distributor in block to align leading edge of vane and vane switch stator assembly. Verify rotor is pointing at No. 1 mark on distributor base.
   f. Install hold-down.

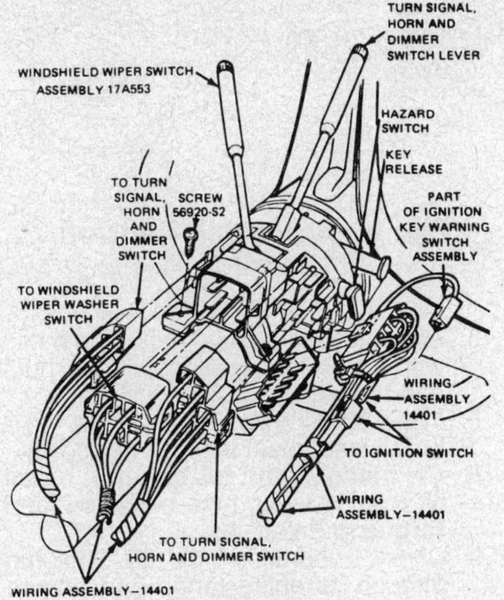


**Fig. 1 Ignition switch installation**

# IGNITION LOCK

## REPLACE

### 1989 MODELS

1. Disable airbag system as described under "Airbag System Disarming."
2. Disconnect battery ground cable.
3. Remove steering column trim shroud.
4. Disconnect key warning switch electrical connector.
5. Turn ignition lock to "On" position.
6. Using a $1/8$ inch pin or punch located in the 4 o'clock hole and $1\frac{1}{4}$ inch from outer edge of lock cylinder housing, depress retaining pin while pulling the lock cylinder from housing.
7. Turn lock cylinder to "On" position and insert cylinder into housing. Ensure that the lock cylinder is fully seated and aligned into the interlocking washer before turning key to "Off" position. This will permit the retaining pin to extend into the lock cylinder housing hole.
8. Rotate key to check for proper mechanical operation.
9. Connect key warning switch electrical connector.
10. Connect battery ground cable.
11. Check for proper operation.
12. Rearm airbag as described under "Airbag System Disarming."

### 1990–92 MODELS

#### FUNCTIONAL LOCK

1. Disable airbag system as described under "Airbag System Disarming."
2. Disconnect battery ground cable.
3. Turn lock cylinder key to Run position.
4. Place a $1/8$ inch punch in hole in trim shroud under lock cylinder.
5. Depress retaining pin with punch and remove lock cylinder by pulling outward.
6. Install lock cylinder by turning it to Run position and depressing retaining pin.
7. Rotate lock cylinder with key to ensure proper operation.
8. Rearm airbag as described under "Airbag System Disarming."
9. Reconnect battery ground cable.

#### NON-FUNCTIONAL LOCK

##### Removal

1. Disable airbag system as described under "Airbag System Disarming."
2. Disconnect battery ground cable.
3. Remove steering wheel.
4. Remove three trim shroud attaching screws, then the two trim shrouds.
5. Disconnect key warning switch electrical connector.
6. Using a $1/8$ inch drill, drill out retaining pin. **Do not drill deeper than $1/2$ inch.**
7. Place a chisel at base of ignition lock cylinder cap, then strike chisel with sharp blows to break cap away from cylinder.
8. Using a $3/8$ inch drill, drill down middle of ignition lock key slot $1\frac{3}{4}$ inches, until lock cylinder breaks loose from breakaway base of lock cylinder.
9. Remove lock cylinder and drill shavings from lock cylinder housing.
10. Remove retainer, washer, ignition switch and actuator, then clean all drill shavings from casting.
11. Inspect lock cylinder housing, if any damage is present, replace housing.

##### Installation

1. Install actuator and ignition switch.
2. Install trim and electrical parts.
3. Install new ignition lock cylinder.
4. Install steering wheel.
5. Ensure lock operates properly.
6. Rearm airbag as described under "Airbag System Disarming."

# IGNITION SWITCH

## REPLACE

### EXCEPT CONTINENTAL

#### Removal

1. Disable airbag system as described under "Airbag System Disarming."
2. Disconnect battery ground cable.
3. Remove steering column shroud.
4. Disconnect ignition switch electrical connector.
5. Rotate ignition key lock cylinder to the Run position.
6. Remove two ignition switch attaching bolts.
7. Disengage ignition switch from actuator pin.
8. Remove ignition switch.

#### Installation

1. Adjust ignition switch by sliding carrier to Run position.
2. Ensure ignition key lock cylinder is in Run position.
3. Install ignition switch pin into actuator hole in column.
4. Install switch attaching screws and **torque** to 50-70 inch lbs.

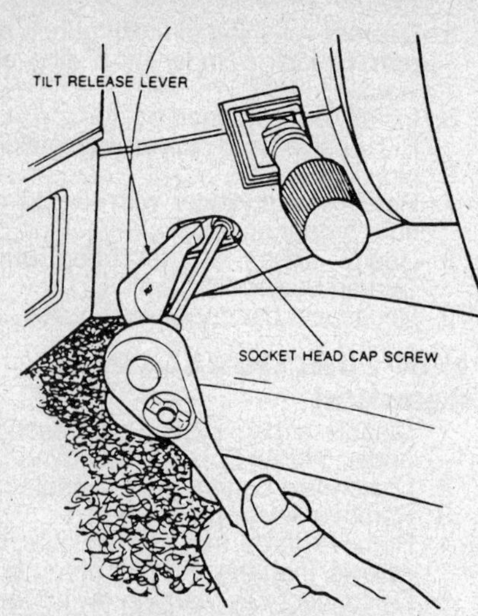


**Fig. 2 Tilt release lever removal**

5. Connect ignition switch electrical connector, **Fig. 1.**
6. Connect battery ground cable.
7. Check ignition switch for proper operation.
8. Install steering column shrouds.
9. Rearm airbag as described under "Airbag System Disarming."

## CONTINENTAL

### Removal

1. Disable airbag system as described under "Airbag System Disarming."
2. Disconnect battery ground cable.
3. Turn lock cylinder key to Run position.
4. Place a 1/8 inch punch in hole in trim shroud under lock cylinder.
5. Depress retaining pin with punch and remove lock cylinder by pulling outward.
6. **On models with tilt columns,** remove tilt release lever by removing one socket head capscrew, **Fig. 2.**
7. **On all models,** remove four instrument panel lower cover retaining screws, then the lower cover.
8. Remove three steering column shroud attaching screws, then the shroud.
9. Remove four steering column to support bracket retaining bolts, then lower column.
10. Remove three screws from diverter plate, then the diverter plate from column.
11. Disconnect ignition switch electrical connector.
12. Remove two tamper resistant Torx screws retaining ignition switch, then the switch.

### Installation

1. Ensure ignition switch is in the Run position by rotating switch fully clockwise to start position and releasing slowly, **Fig. 3.**
2. Install ignition switch and cover assembly, then two Torx retaining screws. **Torque** screws to 30-48 inch lbs.
3. Connect ignition switch electrical connector.
4. Position diverter plate on column and install three attaching screws. **Torque** screw to 30-48 inch lbs.
5. Align steering column mounting holes with support bracket, install four nuts and **torque** to 15-25 ft. lbs.
6. Install steering column shrouds.
7. Install instrument panel lower cover.
8. **On models with tilt column,** install tilt release lever, then capscrew and **torque** to 6-8 ft. lbs.
9. Check operation of tilt column through its entire range and ensure there is no interference with instrument panel.
10. **On all models,** connect batter ground cable.
11. Check column functions as follows:
    a. With shift lever in Park position and ignition lock cylinder in Lock position, ensure steering wheel locks.
    b. With shift lever in Drive position and ignition lock cylinder in run position, rotate lock cylinder toward Lock position until it stops, ensure engine electrical is Off and steering wheel does not lock.
    c. Rotate ignition lock cylinder counterclockwise and ensure radio is energized.
    d. Place shift lever in Park position, then rotate ignition lock cylinder clockwise to the Start position and ensure starter is energized.
    e. Rearm airbag as described under "Airbag System Disarming."

**Fig. 3 Adjusting ignition switch**

# HEADLAMP SWITCH REPLACE

## 1989 MARK VII

1. Disable airbag system as described under "Airbag System Disarming."
2. Remove lens assembly attaching screws and the lens assembly.
3. Remove switch assembly attaching screws, then pull switch out from instrument panel, **Fig. 4.**
4. Disconnect switch electrical connector and remove switch.
5. Reverse procedure to install. Rearm airbag as described under "Airbag System Disarming."

## CONTINENTAL

1. Disable airbag system as described under "Airbag System Disarming."
2. Remove headlamp switch knob and trim panel molding.
3. Remove trim panel retaining screw, then the trim panel.
4. Remove headlamp switch-to-finish panel attaching screws, electrical connector and headlamp switch.
5. Reverse procedure to install. Rearm airbag as described under "Airbag System Disarming."

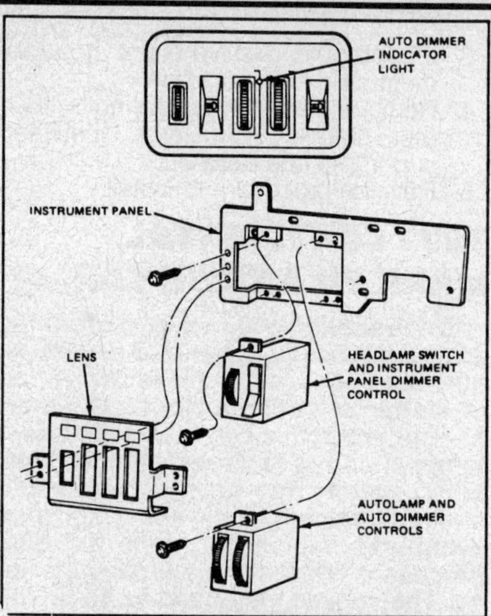


**Fig. 4 Headlamp switch replacement. Mark VII**

## 1990–92 MARK VII

1. Disable airbag system as described under "Airbag System Disarming."
2. Remove center molding, then the headlamp switch knob.
3. Remove five cluster finish panel retaining screws.
4. Remove headlight switch lens by snapping out.
5. Remove two headlamp switch retaining screws.
6. Remove headlamp switch from instrument panel, then disconnect electrical connector.
7. Reverse procedure to install. Rearm airbag as described under "Airbag System Disarming."

## 1989 TOWN CAR

1. Disable airbag system as described under "Airbag System Disarming."
2. Disconnect battery ground cable.
3. Insert a hooked tool into headlight switch knob slot and remove spring tension on knob, then pull off.
4. Remove steering column lower shroud and lower lefthand instrument panel trim bezel.
5. Remove five headlight switch mounting bracket retaining screws.
6. Carefully pull switch and bracket from instrument panel and disconnect switch wiring.
7. Remove locknut and screw retaining switch to switch bracket.
8. Reverse procedure to install. Rearm airbag as described under "Airbag System Disarming."

## 1990–92 TOWN CAR

1. Disable airbag system as described under "Airbag System Disarming."
2. Disconnect battery ground cable.
3. Insert a hooked tool into headlight switch knob slot and remove spring tension on knob, then pull off.
4. Remove headlamp auto dimmer switch knob, if equipped.
5. Remove righthand and lefthand moldings from instrument panel by pulling away from instrument panel and snapping out of retainers.
6. Remove 12 finish panel retaining

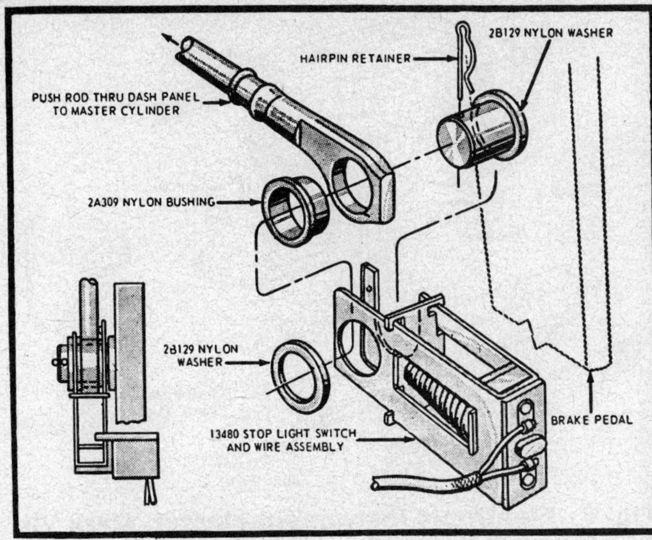


**Fig. 5 Stop light switch**

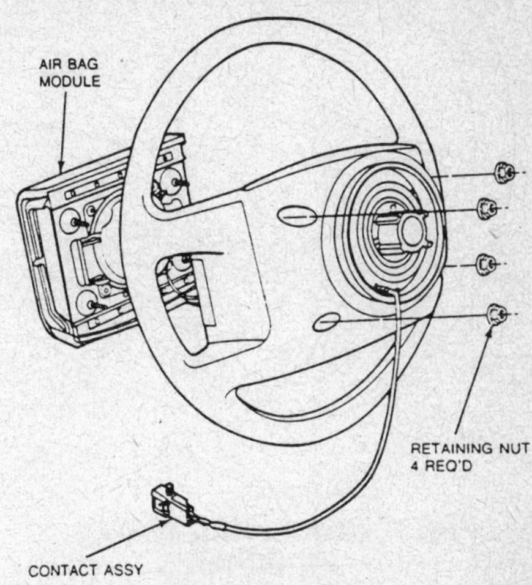


**Fig. 6 Disconnecting contact assembly**

screws.

7. Remove finish panel, then the headlamp switch bracket retaining screws and bracket.
8. Remove switch to bracket retaining nut, then disconnect electrical connector and remove switch.
9. Reverse procedure to install. Rearm airbag as described under "Airbag System Disarming."

# STOP LAMP SWITCH REPLACE

1. Disconnect wires at switch connector.
2. Remove hairpin retainer, slide switch, pushrod and nylon washers and bushing away from brake pedal, and remove switch, **Fig. 5.**
3. Reverse above procedure to install.

# NEUTRAL SAFETY SWITCH REPLACE

## MARK VII & TOWN CAR

1. Disconnect battery ground cable.
2. Position transmission selector lever in "Lo" position.
3. Raise and support vehicle, then working from underneath vehicle, disconnect electrical harness from switch by lifting harness straight up off switch.
4. Using neutral start switch socket tool No. T74P-77247-A or equivalent, remove neutral start switch and O-ring seal by positioning tool over the extension housing area to gain access to switch.
5. Reverse procedure to install. **Torque** switch to 7-10 ft. lbs. using tool mentioned above.

## CONTINENTAL w/AXOD TRANSAXLE

1. Disconnect battery ground cable.
2. Place shift lever in Neutral, then disconnect linkage from manual shift lever.
3. Disconnect switch wiring connector, then remove switch attaching bolts and switch.
4. Install switch and attaching bolts, but do not tighten bolts at this time.
5. Insert a No. 43 (.089 inch) drill bit through hole in switch, then **torque** attaching bolts to 7-9 inch lbs. and remove drill bit.
6. Reconnect switch connector and battery cable, then ensure that starter engages in Neutral or Park positions only.

# MULTI-FUNCTION SWITCH REPLACE

## REMOVAL

1. Disable airbag system as described under "Airbag System Disarming."
2. Disconnect battery ground cable.
3. **On models with tilt column,** place tilt column to lowest position and remove tilt lever.
4. **On all models,** remove ignition lock cylinder.,
5. Remove shroud attaching screws, then the upper and lower shroud.
6. Remove wiring harness retainer, then disconnect electrical connectors.
7. Remove multi-function switch to steering column attaching screws, then the multi-function switch.

## INSTALLATION

1. Connect switch electrical connectors.
2. Install switch and retaining screws, **torque** screws to 18-27 inch lbs.
3. Install wiring harness retainer.
4. Install upper and lower trim shrouds. **Torque** screws to 6-10 inch lbs.
5. Install ignition lock cylinder.
6. Install tilt lever. **Torque** retaining bolt to 6-9 inch lbs.
7. Connect battery ground cable.
8. Check steering column and switch for proper operation.
9. Rearm airbag as described under "Airbag System Disarming."

# STEERING WHEEL REPLACE

## 1989 MARK VII & TOWN CAR

1. Disable airbag system as described under "Airbag System Disarming."
2. Remove steering wheel hub cover.
3. Loosen steering wheel nut four to six turns.
4. If no marks are present, scribe alignment marks on steering wheel and shaft to aid in installation.
5. Using steering wheel puller tool No. T67L-3600-A or equivalent, loosen steering wheel on shaft.
6. Remove steering wheel attaching bolt and discard.
7. Remove steering wheel.
8. Reverse procedure to install. **Torque** new retaining bolt to 21-33 ft. lbs. On vehicles equipped with speed control, check slip ring for damage and slip ring grease for contamination before installing steering wheel.
9. Rearm airbag as described under "Airbag System Disarming."

## 1989–90 CONTINENTAL

### Removal

1. Disable airbag system as described under "Airbag System Disarming."
2. Disconnect battery ground cable.
3. Center front wheels to straight ahead position.
4. Remove lower instrument panel cover.
5. Remove steering column lock cylinder.
6. Remove tilt release lever, then the lower steering column shroud.
7. Disconnect contact assembly from body wire harness, **Fig. 6.**
8. Remove contact assembly ground wire screw, located at lock cylinder housing.
9. Remove four airbag module retaining nuts.
10. Remove airbag module from steering wheel and disconnect contact assembly.

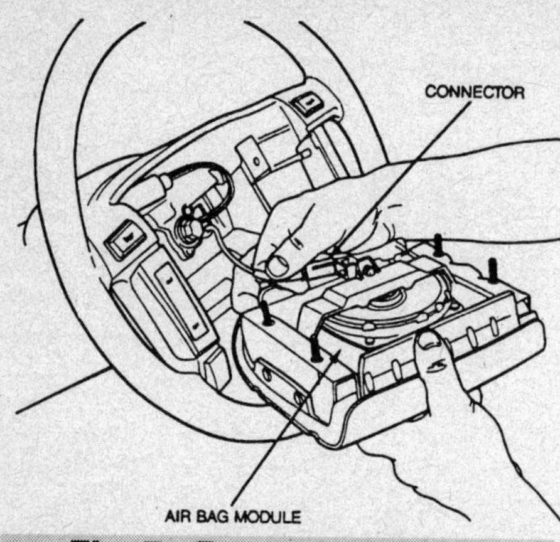


**Fig. 7 Removing airbag module**

11. Remove and discard steering wheel attaching bolt.
12. Remove steering wheel and contact assembly. **Ensure contact assembly is locked in straight ahead position, do not allow contact assembly to rotate out of position.**

### Installation

1. Install steering wheel and contact assembly on steering column. **Ensure that drive pin on speed control/horn brush assembly engages in drive socket of contact assembly housing.**
2. Install new steering wheel bolt. **Torque** to 23-33 ft. lbs.
3. Install ground wire and retaining screw.
4. Connect contact assembly harness connector.
5. Connect contact assembly to module.
6. Install module on steering wheel, then the four retaining nuts.
7. Install lower steering column shroud.
8. Install lock cylinder assembly, then the tilt release lever.
9. Install lower instrument panel cover.
10. Connect battery ground cable.
11. Check steering column for proper operation.
12. Rearm airbag as described under "Airbag System Disarming."

## 1990–92 MARK VII, TOWN CAR & 1991–92 CONTINENTAL

1. Disable airbag system as described under "Airbag System Disarming."
2. Center front wheels to straight ahead position.
3. Disconnect battery ground cable.
4. **On 1991-92 models,** disconnect back-up power supply.
5. **On all models,** remove four airbag module retaining nuts, then lift module off steering wheel, **Fig. 7.**
6. Disconnect airbag wire harness from module, then remove module.
7. Disconnect speed control wire harness from steering wheel.
8. Remove steering wheel retaining bolt.
9. Using steering wheel puller tool No. T67L-3600-A or equivalent, remove steering wheel.
10. Reverse procedure to install, noting the following:
    a. Ensure airbag wire is not pinched.
    b. Install new steering wheel bolt and **torque** to 23-33 ft. lbs.
    c. **Torque** airbag module retaining nuts to 3-4 ft. lbs. d.
    d. Rearm airbag as described under "Airbag System Disarming."

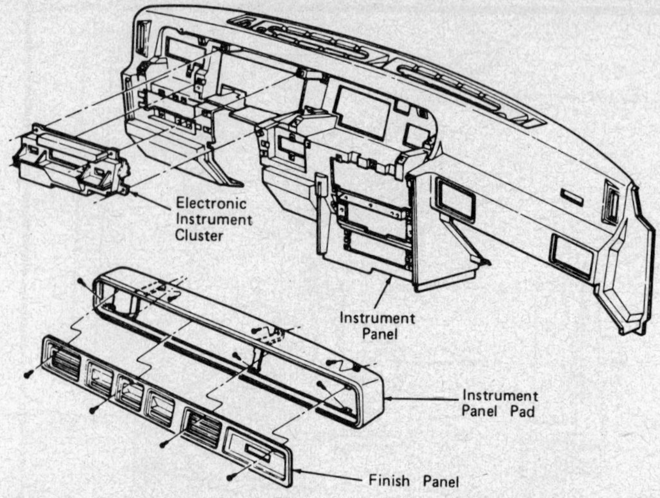


**Fig. 8 Electronic instrument cluster. Mark VII**

# INSTRUMENT CLUSTER REPLACE

## MARK VII

### Less Electronic Cluster

1. Disable airbag system as described under "Airbag System Disarming."
2. Disconnect battery ground cable.
3. Remove instrument cluster finish panel, then disconnect warning lamp module connectors.
4. Remove instrument panel binnacle molding.
5. Remove five mask to back-plate mounting screws. **Do not remove three top screws retaining lens to mask.**
6. Remove lens and mask assembly.
7. Lift main dial assembly from back-plate. **Some effort may be required to pull quick connect terminals from clips.**
8. Install quick connect terminals to clips and position main dial assembly on back-plate. **Ensure foam seal under indicator lamp baffle is correctly positioned.**
9. Install lens and mask assembly, then the five attaching screws.
10. Install instrument panel binnacle molding.
11. Connect warning lamp module connectors, then install instrument cluster finish panel.
12. Connect battery ground cable.

### With Electronic Cluster

1. Disable airbag system as described under "Airbag System Disarming."
2. Remove the four finish panel retaining screws, then rotate top of panel towards steering wheel and remove from vehicle, **Fig. 8.**
3. Remove the six instrument panel pad retaining screws, then rotate pad toward steering wheel and remove from vehicle.
4. Remove the four instrument cluster to instrument panel retaining screws, then pull cluster away from instrument panel.
5. Disconnect cluster electrical connector and remove cluster.
6. Reverse procedure to install. Rearm airbag as described under "Airbag System Disarming."

## CONTINENTAL

1. Disable airbag system as described under "Airbag System Disarming."
2. Disconnect battery ground cable.
3. Position vehicle on a flat surface to prevent movement when gear shift selector is out of position.
4. Turn ignition switch to unlock shift lever, then move lever down from front of electronic instrument cluster (EIC).
5. Tilt steering column down, then remove right and left finish moulding by pulling upward to unsnap clips.
6. Disconnect electrical connectors.
7. Remove five Torx screws below cluster that retain applique.
8. Unsnap applique along top, then pull applique away from panel.
9. Disconnect switch assembly electrical connectors.
10. Remove three attaching screws from bottom of steering column shroud.
11. Lift up top section of shroud and remove clip on left side near steering wheel. Separate upper section of shroud from side section near ignition switch. Slip upper section off shift lever.
12. Remove four Torx screws retaining cluster to instrument panel.
13. Place a soft cloth on steering column to prevent scratching front surface of cluster when removed.
14. Tilt top of cluster slightly toward rear of vehicle, then disconnect two snaps beneath cluster retaining PRNDL assembly.
15. Unplug three connectors behind cluster. **Connectors have locking tabs**

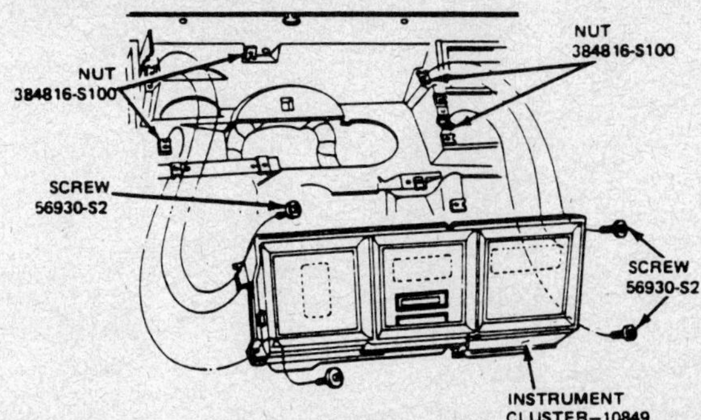


**Fig. 9 Electronic instrument cluster. Town Car**

that must be pressed in to unplug connection.

16. Loosen two clips retaining PRNDL assembly to cluster, then position aside.
17. Push bottom of cluster into instrument panel, then tilt top of cluster toward rear of vehicle and remove cluster.
18. Reverse procedure to install. Rearm airbag as described under "Airbag System Disarming."

## 1989 TOWN CAR

### Less Electronic Cluster

1. Disable airbag system as described under "Airbag System Disarming."
2. Disconnect battery ground cable.
3. Disconnect speedometer cable, then remove trim cover screws and remove trim cover.
4. Remove lower steering column cover screws and remove cover.
5. Remove transmission indicator bracket retaining screw, then disconnect cable loop and bracket pin from steering column. Also remove the column bracket from column.
6. Remove cluster retaining screws, then disconnect electrical feed plug from connector and remove cluster.

### With Electronic Cluster

1. Disconnect battery ground cable.
2. Remove steering column cover, lower instrument panel trim cover, keyboard trim panel and panel on left of column.
3. Remove the ten instrument cluster trim cover retaining screws, then remove trim cover.
4. Remove the four screws retaining instrument cluster to instrument panel and pull cluster forward. Disconnect both electrical plugs and ground wire from their receptacles, then disconnect speedometer cable by pressing on flat surface of plastic connector.
5. Remove transmission indicator cable bracket retaining screw, then disconnect cable loop and bracket pin from steering column.
6. Remove plastic clamp from around steering column, then remove cluster, **Fig. 9.**
7. Reverse procedure to install.
8. Reverse procedure to install. Rearm airbag as described under "Airbag System Disarming."

## 1990–92 TOWN CAR

### Less Electronic Cluster

1. Disable airbag system as described under "Airbag System Disarming."
2. Disconnect battery ground cable.
3. Remove cluster trim cover retaining screws, then the trim cover.
4. Remove lower steering cover retaining screws, then the lower steering cover.
5. Remove lower half of steering column shroud.
6. Remove transmission indicator bracket retaining screw, then disconnect cable loop and bracket pin from steering column. Also remove column bracket from column.
7. Remove cluster retaining screws, then disconnect electrical feed plug from connector and remove cluster assembly.
8. Remove attaching screws from lens and mask assembly.
9. Remove temperature and fuel gauge from cluster.
10. Remove PRNDL retaining screws from speedometer.
11. Remove speedometer.
12. Reverse procedure to install. Rearm airbag as described under "Airbag System Disarming."

### With Electronic Cluster

1. Disable airbag system as described under "Airbag System Disarming."
2. Disconnect battery ground cable.
3. Unsnap center molding on righthand and lefthand sides of instrument panel.
4. Remove steering column cover and shroud.
5. Remove knobs from auto dim and auto lamp, if equipped.
6. Remove 13 instrument panel retaining screws, then pull panel out.
7. Move shift lever to 1 position for easier access.
8. Disconnect electrical connectors from warning module, switch module and center panel switches, if equipped.
9. Remove instrument panel.
10. Disconnect electrical connector from front of cluster.
11. Disconnect PRNDL assembly from cluster, by carefully bending bottom tab down and pulling assembly forward.
12. Pull cluster out and disconnect electrical connector.
13. Remove instrument cluster.
14. Reverse procedure to install. Rearm airbag as described under "Airbag System Disarming."

# WINDSHIELD WIPER MOTOR

## REPLACE

### MARK VII

1. Disable airbag system as described under "Airbag System Disarming."
2. Turn wipers on, then with wiper blades straight up on windshield, turn ignition key to "Off" position.
3. Disconnect battery ground cable and remove arm and blade assemblies.
4. Remove left side cowl top grille.
5. Remove drive arm to motor crankpin retaining clip, then disconnect drive arm from crankpin.
6. Disconnect wiper motor electrical connector, then remove wiper motor retaining screws and the wiper motor from opening.
7. Reverse procedure to install. Rearm airbag as described under "Airbag System Disarming."

### CONTINENTAL

1. Disable airbag system as described under "Airbag System Disarming."
2. Disconnect battery ground cable.
3. Disconnect power lead electrical connector from wiper motor.
4. Remove lefthand windshield wiper arm.
5. Remove linkage retaining clip from arm on motor by lifting locking tab up and pulling clip away from pin.
6. Remove motor and bracket assembly attaching bolts, then the motor.
7. Reverse procedure to install. **Torque** motor attaching bolts to 60-85 inch lbs.
8. Rearm airbag as described under "Airbag System Disarming."

### 1989 TOWN CAR

1. Disable airbag system as described under "Airbag System Disarming."
2. Disconnect battery ground cable.
3. Disconnect right side washer nozzle hose clip and remove right side wiper arm and blade assembly from pivot shaft.
4. Remove wiper motor linkage cover.
5. Disconnect linkage drive arm from the motor output arm crankpin by removing retainer clip.
6. Disconnect the wiring connectors from the motor.
7. Remove three bolts retaining the motor to the dash panel extension and the motor.
8. Reverse procedure to install. Rearm airbag as described under "Airbag System Disarming."

### 1990–92 TOWN CAR

1. Disable airbag system as described under "Airbag System Disarming."
2. Disconnect battery ground cable.
3. Remove rear hood seal, then the wiper arm assemblies.
4. Remove cowl vent screens and disconnect washer hoses from jets.
5. Disconnect electrical connectors from wiper motor.
6. Remove wiper assembly retaining screws, then lift assembly, **Fig. 10.**
7. Unsnap and remove wiper linkage cover.

8. Remove linkage retaining clip from motor operating arm.
9. Remove motor retaining screws, then the motor.
10. Reverse procedure to install. Rearm airbag as described under "Airbag System Disarming."

# WINDSHIELD WIPER TRANSMISSION

## REPLACE

### MARK VII

The wiper transmission is mounted below the cowl top panel and can be reached by raising the hood. Because the pivot shaft and transmission assemblies are connected with unremovable plastic ball joints, the right and left pivot shafts and transmission are serviced as a unit.

1. Perform steps 1 and 2 as outlined under "Windshield Wiper Motor, Replace" procedure.
2. Raise hood, then remove left and right cowl top grilles.
3. Remove drive arm to wiper motor crankpin retaining clip, then disconnect drive arm from crankpin.
4. Remove pivot shaft attaching screws, then guide transmission and pivots from cowl chamber.
5. Reverse procedure to install, ensuring wiper motor is in "Park" position.

### CONTINENTAL

1. Disconnect negative battery cable.
2. Remove wiper arm and blade assembly from pivots shafts.
3. Remove leaf screens.
4. Remove motor crankpin clip, then disconnect linkage drive arm.
5. Remove pivot-to-cowl attaching screws, then the linkage and pivots from cowl chamber.
6. Reverse procedure to install.

### 1989 TOWN CAR

1. Disconnect battery ground cable.
2. Remove wiper arm and blade assemblies from the pivot shafts.
3. Remove wiper motor and linkage cover for access to linkage.
4. Disconnect the linkage drive arm from the motor crankpin by removing the retaining clip.
5. Remove the six bolts retaining the left and right pivot shafts to the cowl, and remove the complete linkage assembly.
6. Reverse procedure to install.

### 1990–92 TOWN CAR

Refer to "Wiper Motor, Replace" for wiper transmission replacement procedures.

# WINDSHIELD WIPER SWITCH

## REPLACE

1. Disable airbag system as described under "Airbag System Disarming."
2. Disconnect battery ground cable.
3. Remove the steering column cover screws and separate the two halves.
4. Remove wiper switch retaining screws, disconnect wiring connector and remove switch.
5. Reverse procedure to install. Rearm airbag as described under "Airbag System Disarming."

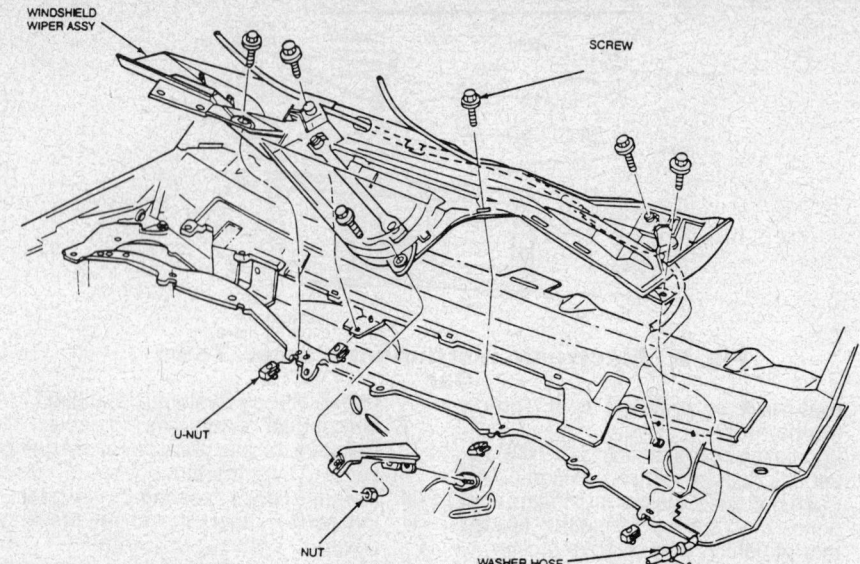

**Fig. 10 Windshield wiper assembly. 1990–92 Town Car**

# RADIO

## REPLACE

When installing radio, ensure to adjust antenna trimmer for peak performance.

### 1989 MARK VII

1. Disable airbag system as described under "Airbag System Disarming."
2. Disconnect battery ground cable.
3. Remove center instrument panel trim panel.
4. Remove four radio and mounting bracket to instrument panel retaining screws.
5. Push radio towards the front of vehicle and raise back end slightly so rear support bracket clears clip in instrument panel and carefully pull out radio.
6. Disconnect radio wiring and remove radio.
7. Remove rear support bracket.
8. Reverse procedure to install. Rearm airbag as described under "Airbag System Disarming."

### CONTINENTAL, 1990–92 MARK VII & TOWN CAR

1. Disable airbag system as described under "Airbag System Disarming."
2. Disconnect battery ground cable.
3. Install radio removal tool No. T87P-19061-A or equivalent into radio face plate, push tool in approximately one inch to release retaining clips.
4. Apply a light spreading force on tools and slowly pull radio from instrument panel.
5. Disconnect wiring connectors and antenna cable.
6. Reverse procedure to install. Rearm airbag as described under "Airbag System Disarming."

### 1989 TOWN CAR

1. Disable airbag system as described under "Airbag System Disarming."
2. Disconnect battery ground able.
3. Remove radio plate to instrument panel retaining screws.
4. Pull radio rearward until the rear support bracket is clear of instrument panel.
5. Disconnect radio wiring and antenna lead. Remove radio.
6. Remove screws securing front bracket to radio and remove, remove rear support bracket.
7. Reverse procedure to install. Rearm airbag as described under "Airbag System Disarming."

# BLOWER MOTOR

## REPLACE

### TOWN CAR

1. Disconnect battery ground cable.
2. Disconnect blower motor lead from wiring harness, then remove blower motor cooling tube from blower motor.
3. Remove the four blower motor retaining screws.
4. Rotate motor and wheel assembly slightly to the right so that bottom edge of mounting plate follows contour of wheelwell splash panel, then lift the motor and wheel assembly up and out of housing.
5. Reverse procedure to install.

### MARK VII

1. Disconnect battery ground cable.
2. Remove glove compartment and shield, then disconnect wire connector from outside recirc actuator.
3. Remove side cowl panel, then instrument panel lower right-to-side attaching bolts.
4. Remove support bracket attaching screws at top of air recirc duct.

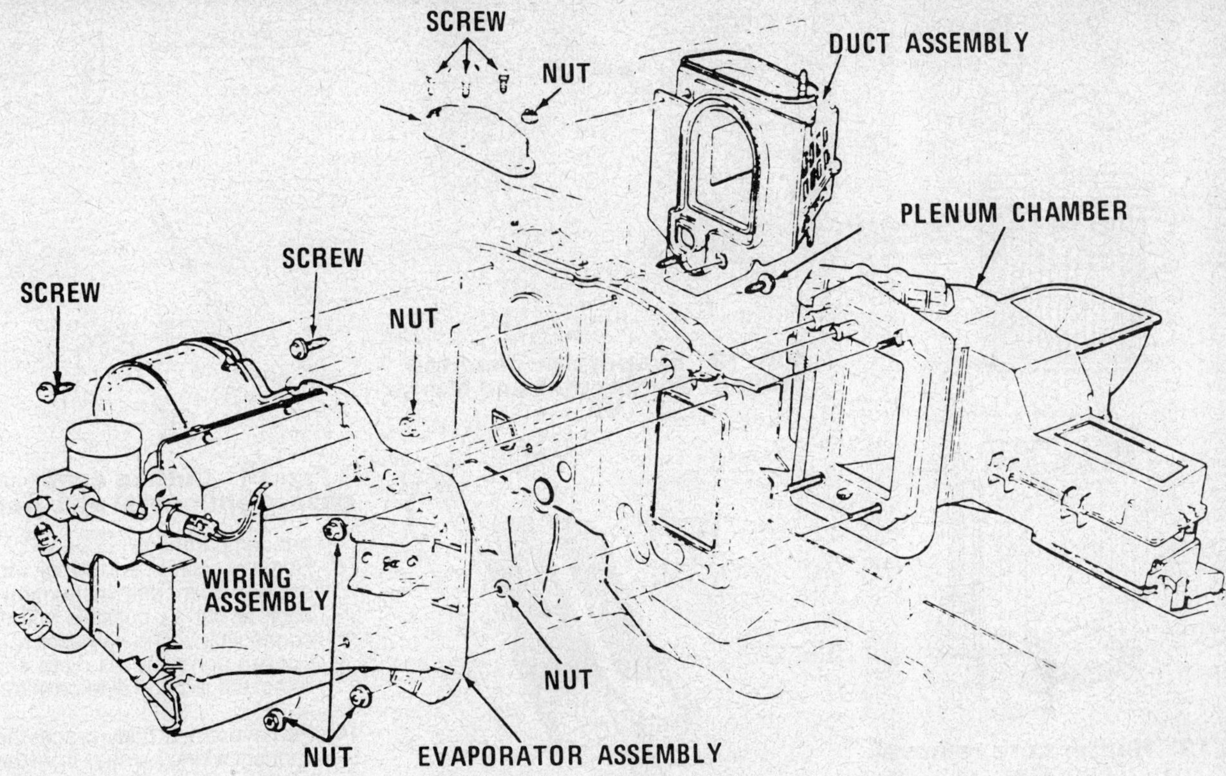


**Fig. 11 Plenum & air inlet duct assembly. Town Car**

5. Remove five recirc duct attaching screws, then remove recirc duct.
6. Remove four blower motor plate attaching screws, then remove the blower motor and wheel assembly from blower housing.
7. Reverse procedure to install.

## CONTINENTAL

1. Remove release retainers and lower glove compartment door.
2. Remove recirc duct support bracket retaining screw.
3. Remove electrical connector retaining screw, then disconnect three connectors from bracket and remove bracket.
4. Remove vacuum connection to recirc door vacuum motor, then disconnect aspirator hoses from muffler.
5. Remove six recirc duct attaching screws.
6. Remove recirc duct from evaporator assembly from between instrument panel and evaporator case.
7. Disconnect blower motor electrical lead.
8. Remove blower motor wheel assembly attaching nut, then remove wheel.
9. Remove four blower motor attaching screws, then remove the motor from evaporator case.
10. Reverse procedure to install.

# HEATER CORE REPLACE

## MARK VII

1. Disable airbag system as described under "Airbag System Disarming."
2. Remove instrument panel.
3. Discharge refrigerant from A/C system, then disconnect high and low pressure hoses. Cap hose ends to prevent entry of dirt and moisture.
4. Drain coolant and disconnect hoses from heater core. Plug hoses and core to prevent spillage.
5. Remove air inlet duct/blower housing assembly support brace to cowl top panel retaining screw.
6. Disconnect A/C wiring, if necessary, then working from engine compartment, remove the two evaporator case to dash panel retaining nuts.
7. Working from passenger compartment, remove evaporator case support bracket to cowl panel attaching screw.
8. Carefully pull evaporator case away from dash panel and remove from vehicle.
9. Remove heater core access cover to evaporator case attaching screws.
10. Remove heater core and seals from case, then remove seals from heater core tubes.
11. Reverse procedure to install. Rearm airbag as described under "Airbag System Disarming."

## CONTINENTAL

1. Disable airbag system as described under "Airbag System Disarming."
2. Remove instrument panel as described under "Dash Panel Service."
3. Remove evaporator case assembly.
4. Remove vacuum source from heater core tube.
5. Remove seal from heater core tubes.
6. Remove three blend door actuator to evaporator case screws, then remove actuator.
7. Remove four heater core access cover attaching screws, then remove cover and seal.
8. Remove heater core and seal.
9. Reverse procedure to install. Rearm airbag as described under "Airbag System Disarming."

## 1989 TOWN CAR

1. Disable airbag system as described under "Airbag System Disarming."
2. Disconnect battery ground cable.
3. Disconnect heater hoses from core. Plug hoses and heater core tubes to prevent coolant loss during core removal.
4. Remove one bolt located below the windshield wiper motor retaining left end of plenum to dash panel.
5. Remove one nut retaining the upper left corner of evaporator case to dash panel.
6. Disconnect vacuum supply hose from vacuum source, then push grommet and hose into passenger compartment.
7. Remove glove compartment, then loosen door sill plates and remove side cowl trim panels. On some models, it may be necessary to lower the steering column to remove the instrument panel. On these models, disconnect harnesses from multiple connectors and transmission shift indicator from column, then remove steering column to instrument panel brace attaching nuts and lower steering column to seat.
8. Disconnect speedometer cable from speedometer and antenna lead from radio.

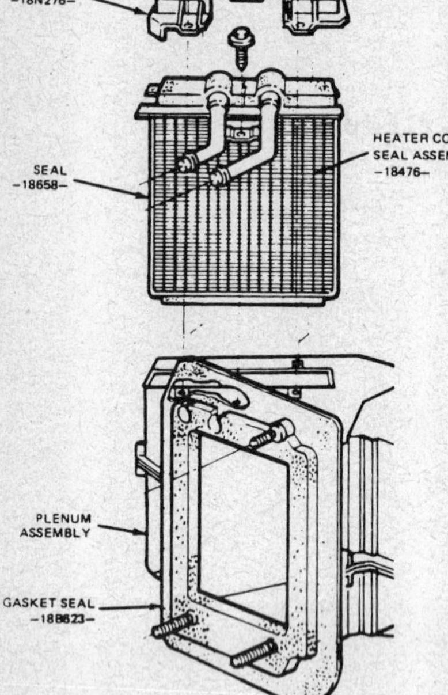


**Fig. 12 Heater core removal. Town Car**

9. Remove bolt retaining lower right end of instrument panel to side cowl, then remove instrument panel pad as follows:
   a. Remove screws retaining instrument panel pad to instrument panel at each defroster opening.
   b. Remove the one screw retaining each outboard end of pad to instrument panel.
   c. Remove the five screws retaining lower edge of instrument panel pad, then pull instrument panel pad rearward and remove it.
10. Disconnect temperature control cable housing from bracket at top of plenum, then disconnect cable from temperature blend door crank arm.
11. Remove push clip retaining the center register duct bracket to the plenum and rotate bracket to the right.
12. Disconnect vacuum jumper harness at multiple vacuum connector near the floor air distribution duct, then disconnect white vacuum hose from the outside-recirculating door vacuum motor.
13. Remove screws retaining the passenger side of floor air distribution duct to the plenum. It may be necessary to remove the two screws retaining the partial (lower) panel door vacuum motor to mounting bracket to gain access to right screw.
14. Remove the plastic push fastener retaining floor air distribution duct to left end of plenum and remove floor air distribution duct.
15. Remove nuts from the two studs along lower edge of plenum.
16. Carefully move plenum rearward to allow heater core tubes and stud at

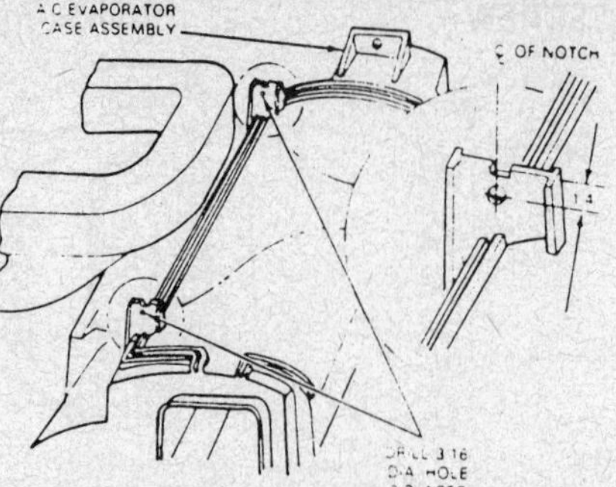


**Fig. 13 Evaporator case tab drilling. Continental and Mark VII**

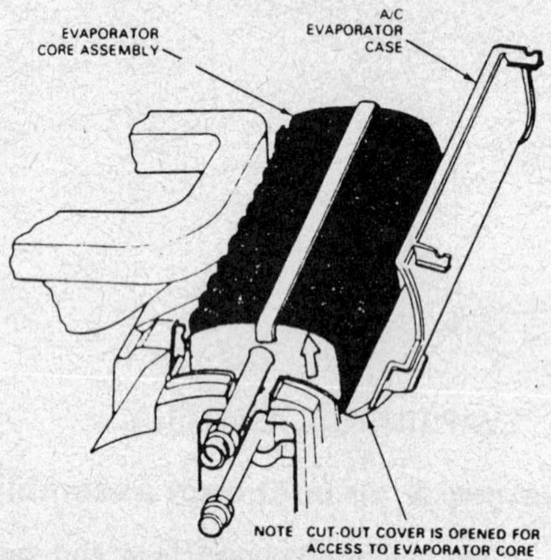


**Fig. 15 Removing evaporator case from core. Continental and Mark VII**

top of plenum to clear holes in dash panel. Remove plenum by rotating top of plenum forward, down and out from under instrument panel. Carefully pull lower edge of instrument panel rearward as necessary while rolling the plenum from behind the instrument panel, **Fig. 11.**

17. Remove the four retaining screws from heater core cover and remove cover from plenum, **Fig. 12.**
18. Remove heater core retaining screw then pull core and seal assembly from plenum assembly.
19. Reverse procedure to install. Rearm airbag as described under "Airbag System Disarming."

## 1990–92 TOWN CAR

1. Disable airbag system as described under "Airbag System Disarming."
2. Disconnect battery ground cable.
3. Disconnect heater hose from heater core tubes, then plug heater hoses and core tubes.
4. Remove three plenum to dash panel attaching nuts located below the windshield wiper motor.
5. Remove one nut retaining upper lefthand corner of evaporator case to dash panel.
6. Remove lefthand and righthand lower instrument panel insulators.
7. Disconnect two vacuum supply hoses from vacuum source, then push vacuum hoses and grommet into passen-

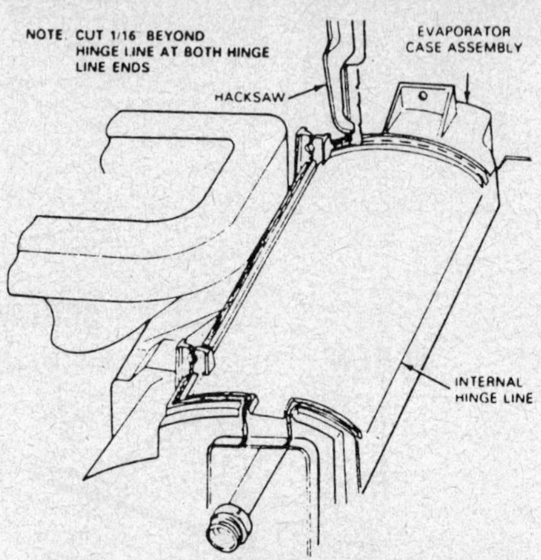


**Fig. 14 Cutting evaporator case. Continental and Mark VII**

ger compartment.

8. Remove instrument panel mounting screws, then pull instrument panel back as far as possible without disconnecting wiring harnesses.
9. Loosen righthand sill plate end, then remove righthand side cowl trim panel.
10. Remove cross body brace, then disconnect wiring harness from temperature blend door actuator.
11. Disconnect ATC sensor tube from evaporator case connector.
12. Disconnect the vacuum jumper harness at the multiple vacuum connector located near floor air distribution duct.
13. Disconnect white vacuum hose from outside-recirculating door vacuum motor.
14. Remove two hush panels, then the floor air distribution duct.
15. Remove two nuts along lower flange of plenum.
16. Carefully move plenum rearward to allow heater core tubes and stud at top of plenum to clear holes in dash panel. Remove plenum by rotating top of plenum forward, down and out from under instrument panel. Carefully pull lower edge of instrument panel rearward as necessary while rolling the plenum from behind the instrument panel.
17. Remove the four retaining screws from heater core cover and remove cover from plenum.
18. Remove heater core and seal assembly from plenum assembly.
19. Reverse procedure to install. Rearm airbag as described under "Airbag System Disarming."

# EVAPORATOR CORE REPLACE

## CONTINENTAL & MARK VII

1. Remove evaporator case as outlined under "Heater Core, Replace."
2. Disconnect and remove vacuum harness.
3. Remove six screws attaching recirculation duct, then remove duct.
4. Remove two screws from air inlet duct

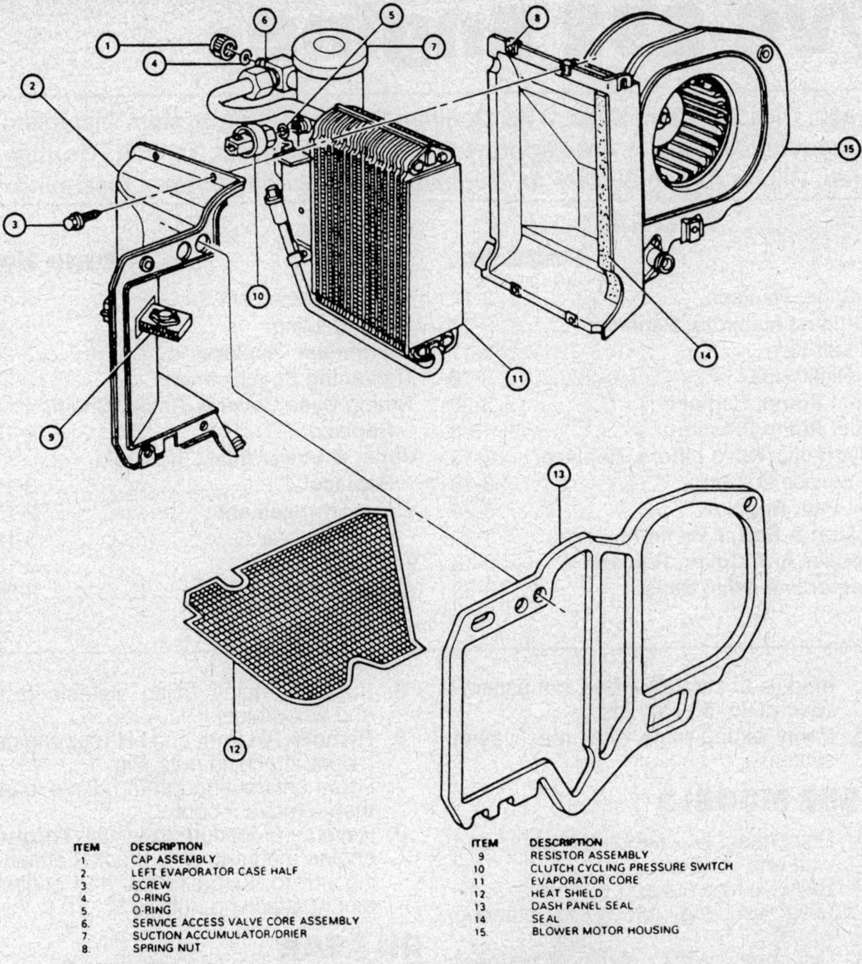


**Fig. 16 Exploded view evaporator case. Town Car**

and remove duct from evaporator case.
5. Remove support bracket, then screws holding electronic connector bracket to recirculation duct.
6. Remove blend door actuator and cold engine lockout switch.
7. Remove molded seal from evaporator core tubes.
8. Drill a (3/16 inch) hole in both upright tabs on top of evaporator case, **Fig. 13.**
9. Using a hot knife or small saw blade, cut top of evaporator case between raised outline, **Fig. 14.**
10. Fold cutout cover back from opening and lift evaporator core from case, **Fig. 15.**
11. Reverse procedure to install noting the following:
    a. Transfer four foam core seals to new evaporator core.
    b. Install caulking cord No. D9AZ-19560-A or equivalent to seal evaporator case against leakage along cut line.

## TOWN CAR

1. Remove evaporator case as outlined under "Heater Core, Replace."
2. Remove dash panel seal, then the heat shield from bottom of evaporator case.
3. Remove six screws attaching two halves of case together.
4. Separate two halves of evaporator case, then remove evaporator core and mounting bracket.
5. Disconnect the suction accumulator/drier inlet from evaporator core outlet tube, **Fig. 16.**
6. Reverse procedure to install noting the following:
    a. Install new O-rings to accumulator/drier.
    b. Apply caulking cord No. D9AZ-19560-A or equivalent to case flange and around evaporator core tubes.
    c. Install a new heat shield on bottom of evaporator case assembly with staples.

# 3.8L/V6-232 Engine

**NOTE: On Vehicles Equipped With Airbags, Disarm Airbag System As Outlined Under "Airbag System Disarming" Before Any Diagnosis, Testing, Troubleshooting Or Repairs Are Performed. After All Diagnosis, Testing, Troubleshooting Or Repairs Have Been Completed, Rearm Airbag System As Outlined Under "Airbag System Disarming."**

## INDEX



## AIRBAG SYSTEM DISARMING

**The electrical circuit necessary for system deployment is powered directly from the battery and a backup power supply. To avoid accidental deployment and possible personal injury, the airbag system must be deactivated prior to servicing or replacing any component located near or related to airbag system activation components.**

A back-up power supply is included in the system to provide airbag deployment in the event the battery or battery cables are damaged in an accident before the sensors can close. The power supply is a capacitor that will retain a charge for approximately 15 minutes after the battery ground cable is disconnected. **Backup power supply must be disconnected to deactivate airbag system.**

### 1989–91 MODELS

1. Disconnect battery ground cable.
2. Disconnect backup power supply as described under "Backup Power Supply, Replace" in the "Passive Restraint" section.
3. Remove four nut and washer assemblies securing airbag module to steering wheel, then disconnect airbag electrical connector. Attach jumper wire to airbag terminals on clockspring.
4. **On models equipped with passenger-side airbag,** disconnect airbag module connector located behind glove compartment. Attach a jumper wire to airbag terminals on wiring harness side of passenger airbag module connector
5. To reactivate, disconnect battery ground cable and backup power supply, then reverse remainder of deactivation procedure. **Torque** airbag module to steering wheel nut assemblies to 35-53 inch lbs.
6. Verify airbag lamp after reactivating system.

### 1992 MODELS

1. Disconnect positive battery cable and wait one minute.
2. Remove four nut and washer assemblies securing airbag to steering wheel.
3. Disconnect airbag electrical connector and install airbag simulator tool No. 105-00008 or equivalent.
4. **On models with passenger side airbag,** remove passenger airbag and disconnect electrical connector.
5. Install airbag simulator tool No. 105-00008 or equivalent.
6. **On all models,** connect positive battery cable.
7. To activate airbag system, disconnect positive battery cable and reverse procedure. **Torque** mounting nut and washer assemblies to 36-49 inch lbs.
8. Verify proper operation of airbag lamp.

## ENGINE MOUNT REPLACE

This vehicle is equipped with two RH (front and rear) and one LH internally restrained hydraulic engine mounts. The two RH mounts are equipped with nylon heat shields. All mounts are located and attached to the front sub-frame assembly.

### RH FRONT

1. Remove A/C compressor and position aside. It is not necessary to discharge A/C system.
2. Raise and support vehicle.
3. Remove engine mount-to-A/C compressor bracket attaching nut.
4. Temporarily attach A/C compressor to A/C bracket using two lower bolts.
5. Support engine using suitable jack and wood block.
6. Remove RH front and LH rear engine mount attaching nuts, **Fig. 1.**
7. Raise engine enough to relieve load, then remove mount.
8. Reverse procedure to install. **Torque** engine mount-to-A/C bracket attaching nut to 40-55 ft. lbs. and engine mount attaching nuts to 55-70 ft. lbs.

### RH REAR

1. Raise and support vehicle.
2. Loosen RH front and LH engine mount attaching nuts, **Fig. 1.**
3. Support engine using suitable equipment, then raise engine approximately one inch.
4. Loosen RH rear engine mount and heat shield retaining nut.
5. Raise and support vehicle.
6. Loosen four sub-frame attaching bolts, then remove engine mount attaching nut and engine mount.
7. Reverse procedure to install. **Torque** engine mount attaching bolts to 55-75 ft. lbs.

### LH MOUNT & SUPPORT ASSEMBLY

1. Raise and support vehicle.
2. Remove tire and wheel assembly.
3. Using a suitable jack support transmission.
4. Remove vertical restrictor assembly, then the nut retaining transaxle mount to support assembly.
5. Remove two through bolts retaining mount to frame.
6. Raise transmission, to release load on mount, then remove bolts retaining support assembly to transmission.
7. Remove mount.
8. Reverse procedure to install. **Torque** support assembly to transmission to 34-44 ft. lbs.

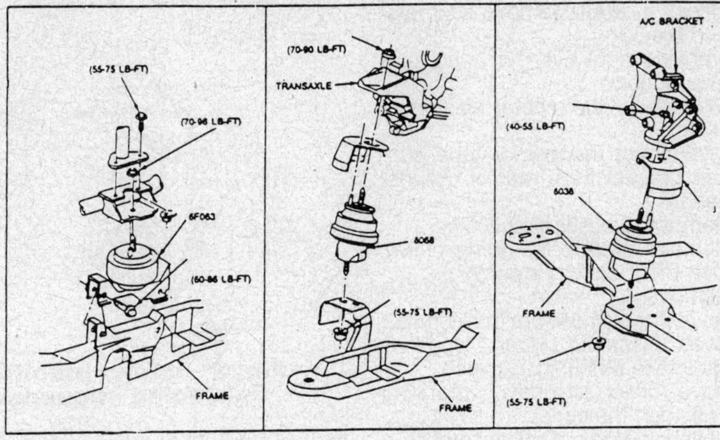


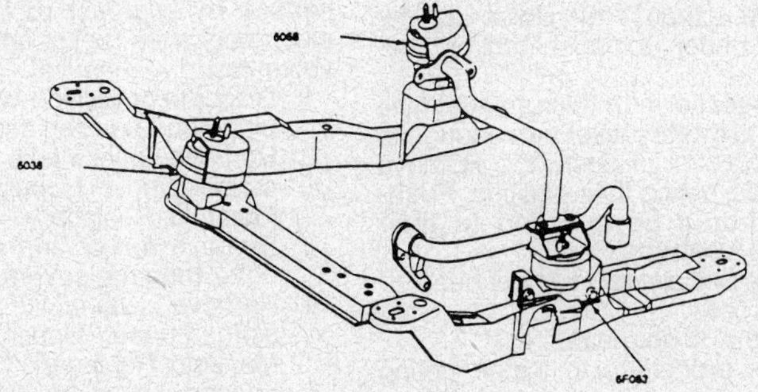


**Fig. 1 Engine mounts**

## ENGINE REPLACE

1. Disconnect battery ground cable.
2. Drain cooling system and engine oil.
3. Mark position of hood hinges and remove hood.
4. Relieve fuel line pressure and discharge air conditioning system.
5. Disconnect the following:
   a. Alternator-to-voltage regulator wiring harness.
   b. Electric cooling fan and motor assembly.
   c. Transaxle oil cooler lines, then the transaxle pressure switch wiring.
   d. Heater hoses at engine block.
   e. Power steering hoses and hose routing brackets.
   f. A/C compressor clutch electrical connector, then the compressor discharge hose.
   g. Fuel lines.
   h. Power steering pump tube bracket.
   i. Electronic engine control (EEC-IV) wiring assembly.
   j. Vacuum lines and ground wires.
   k. Throttle cable at throttle valve.
6. Remove engine oil dipstick, then the upper radiator sight shield.
7. Remove integrated controller relay and position aside.
8. Remove air cleaner assembly, fan shroud, upper radiator hose and coolant recovery reservoir.
9. Remove wiring shield, then the accelerator cable mounting bracket.
10. Remove air suspension compressor and position aside.
11. Remove transaxle support assembly attaching bolts, then the support assembly.
12. Remove A/C compressor mounting bolts, then the compressor.
13. Raise and support vehicle.
14. Remove oil filter.
15. Disconnect exhaust gas oxygen sensor.
16. Release tension of drive belts, then remove crankshaft pulley and drive belt tensioner.
17. Remove starter motor.
18. Remove catalytic converter housing cover, then the converter and inlet pipe assembly.
19. Remove engine mount attaching nuts, then the torque converter-to-flywheel attaching nuts.
20. Remove oil level indicator sensor.
21. Disconnect lower radiator hose.
22. Loosen engine-to-transaxle attaching bolts, leaving bolts loosely installed.
23. Remove wheel and tire assemblies.
24. Remove drive belts.
25. Remove water pump pulley attaching bolts, then the pulley.
26. Remove radiator.
27. Remove distributor cap and position aside. Remove distributor rotor.
28. Remove exhaust manifold lock bolts.
29. Remove thermactor air pump attaching bolts, then the pump.
30. Disconnect oil pressure sending unit.
31. Remove engine-to-transaxle bolts.
32. Install suitable engine lifting device and position transmission jack under transaxle.
33. Raise transaxle assembly, then lift engine from vehicle.
34. Reverse procedure to install.

## UPPER & LOWER INTAKE MANIFOLD REPLACE

1. Drain cooling system.
2. Remove air cleaner assembly.
3. Disconnect accelerator cable at throttle body. On models with speed control, disconnect speed control cable.
4. **On all models,** disconnect transaxle linkage at upper intake manifold, then remove accelerator cable mounting bracket attaching bolts and position cables aside.
5. Disconnect thermactor air supply hose from check valve.
6. Disconnect flexible fuel lines from steel lines over rocker cover, then the fuel lines at injector fuel rail assembly.
7. Disconnect upper radiator hose from thermostat housing, then the coolant bypass hose.
8. Disconnect heater tube from intake manifold, then remove tube support bracket attaching nut. Remove heater hose from rear of tube, then loosen hose clamp at heater elbow and remove tube with hose and fuel lines attached and set aside.
9. Disconnect vacuum lines and all necessary electrical connectors.
10. **On models equipped with A/C,** remove compressor support bracket.
11. **On all models,** disconnect PCV lines from upper intake manifold and left-hand rocker cover, then remove throttle body assembly.
12. Remove EGR valve assembly from upper manifold.
13. Remove wiring retainer bracket and position aside.
14. Remove upper intake manifold attaching bolts, then the manifold, **Fig. 2.**
15. Remove fuel injectors and fuel rail assembly.
16. Remove heater outlet hose.
17. Remove lower manifold attaching bolts, the then lower manifold. **It may be necessary to pry on front of lower manifold to break the seal. Do not damage sealing surfaces.**
18. Reverse procedure to install, noting the following:
   a. Apply a 1/8 inch bead of silicone at each corner where cylinder head meets the block.
   b. Torque manifold bolts to specifications in sequence as shown in **Fig. 3.**
   c. Torque throttle body bolts to specifications in a cross pattern.
   d. **Torque** EGR attaching bolts to 15-22 ft. lbs.

## EXHAUST MANIFOLD REPLACE

### LEFT SIDE

1. Remove oil dipstick tube support bracket.
2. Disconnect spark plug wires.
3. Raise and support vehicle.

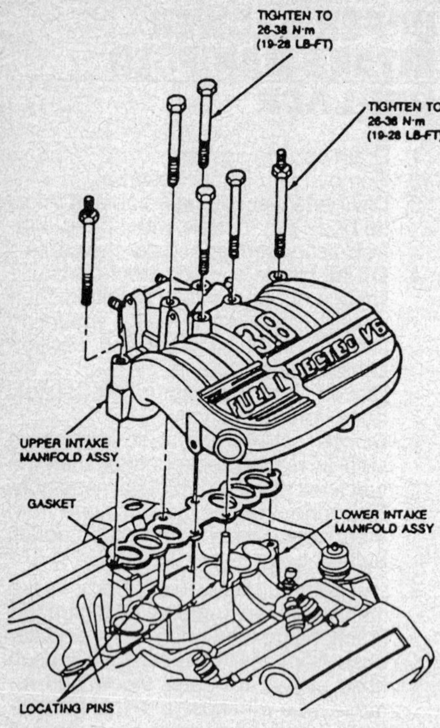


**Fig. 2 Upper intake manifold**

4. Remove manifold-to-exhaust pipe attaching nuts.
5. Lower vehicle.
6. Remove exhaust manifold attaching bolts, then the manifold.
7. Reverse procedure to install. Torque manifold attaching bolts to specifications.

### RIGHT SIDE

1. Remove air cleaner outlet tube assembly.
2. Disconnect coil wire, then the spark plug wires.
3. Disconnect EGR tube.
4. Raise and support vehicle.
5. Remove manifold-to-exhaust pipe attaching nuts, then lower vehicle.
6. Remove exhaust manifold attaching bolts, then the manifold.
7. Reverse procedure to install. Torque manifold attaching bolts to specifications.

## CYLINDER HEAD
## REPLACE

1. Drain cooling system
2. Disconnect negative battery cable.
3. Remove air cleaner assembly and drive belts.
4. If removing left cylinder head, proceed as follows:
   a. Remove oil fill cap.
   b. Remove power steering pump with hoses connected, positioning pump aside.
   c. **On models with A/C,** remove compressor mounting bracket bolts and position compressor aside.
   d. **On all models,** remove alternator and bracket.
5. If removing right cylinder head, proceed as follows:
   a. Disconnect thermactor air control valve
   b. Disconnect thermactor tube support bracket from rear of cylinder head
   c. Remove accessory drive idler.
   d. Remove thermactor pump pulley, then the thermactor pump.
   e. Remove PCV valve.
6. Remove upper and lower intake manifolds as described under ""Upper & Lower Intake Manifold, Replace."
7. Remove rocker arm cover attaching screws, then the cover.
8. Remove injector fuel rail assembly.
9. Remove exhaust manifolds as described under "Exhaust Manifold, Replace".
10. Loosen rocker arm fulcrum attaching bolts and rotate rocker arm enough to allow removal of pushrods. Remove pushrods, noting their position. **Pushrods should be installed in their original position.**
11. Remove and discard cylinder head attaching bolts.
12. Remove cylinder head.
13. Reverse procedure to install, noting the following:
    a. Apply suitable sealer to short cylinder head bolts, then lightly oil all other bolts.
    b. Torque rocker arm fulcrum attaching bolts, rocker arm cover bolts to specifications.
    c. **Torque** cylinder head bolts in sequence shown, **Fig. 4.** Torque bolts in for steps; 37 ft. lbs, 45 ft. lbs, 52 ft. lbs, and 59 ft. lbs., then back off all bolts 2-3 turns.
    d. **Torque** long bolts to 11-18 ft. lbs., then an additional 85-105°.
    e. **Torque** short bolts to 11-18 ft. lbs., then an additional 65-85°.

## VALVE ARRANGEMENT
### FRONT TO REAR

Right Side .................... E-I-I-E-I-E
Left Side .................... E-I-E-I-I-E

## CAM LOBE LIFT SPECIFICATIONS

Exhaust .................... .259inch
Intake .................... .245inch

## VALVES
## ADJUST

This engine is equipped with hydraulic lifters. No adjustments are required.

## HYDRAULIC VALVE LIFTERS
## REPLACE

Before replacing hydraulic valve lifters

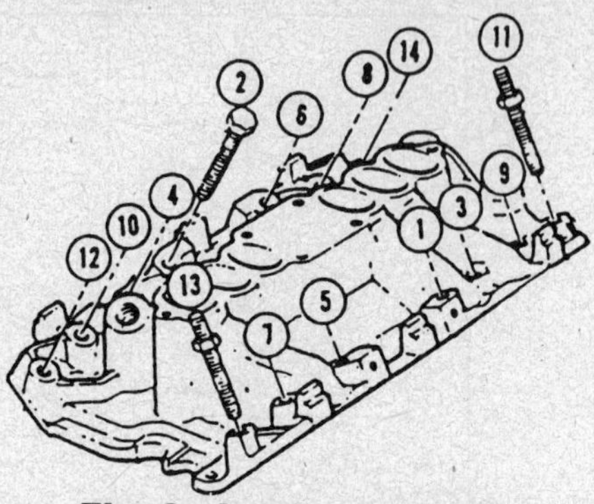


**Fig. 3 Intake manifold tightening sequence**

for noisy operation, ensure the noise is not caused by improper rocker arm-to-stem clearance, worn rocker arms, pushrods or valve tips.

1. Disconnect ignition wires from spark plugs and position aside.
2. Remove upper intake manifold as described under "Upper & Lower Intake Manifold, Replace."
3. Remove rocker arm cover attaching bolts, then the covers.
4. Remove lower intake manifold as described under "Upper & Lower Intake Manifold, Replace."
5. Loosen rocker arm fulcrum attaching bolts, lift rocker arms off pushrods and rotate to side.
6. Remove pushrods, then the lifters. Keep lifters and pushrods in order, as they should be installed in their original position.
7. Reverse procedure to install. Lubricate lifters, pushrods and rocker arms with suitable lubricant. Torque rocker arm fulcrum bolts to specifications. **Ensure pushrods and rocker arms are fully seated prior to tightening bolts.**

**SERVICE BULLETIN:** A low medium pitch noise such as a squeak, chirp or knock that can be heard under the hood in the engine compartment may be caused by the fulcrum and rocker assemblies. The noise is most noticeable at engine idle with engine at normal operating temperature.

Use the following diagnostic procedure to determine if a Break-In Additive will eliminate the noise or if a set of rocker arm assemblies are required.

1. Bring engine to normal operating temperature.
2. Using a stethoscope on the rocker arm cover, determine which rocker arms are noisy.
3. If noisy arms are present, add one container of Break-In Additive No. E9SZ-19579-A to the crankcase.
4. Continue to idle engine for ten minutes.
5. Test drive vehicle for no less than five minutes.
6. If noise persists rocker new rocker assemblies are required.

## ROCKER ARM COVER
## REPLACE

1. Disconnect ignition wires from spark

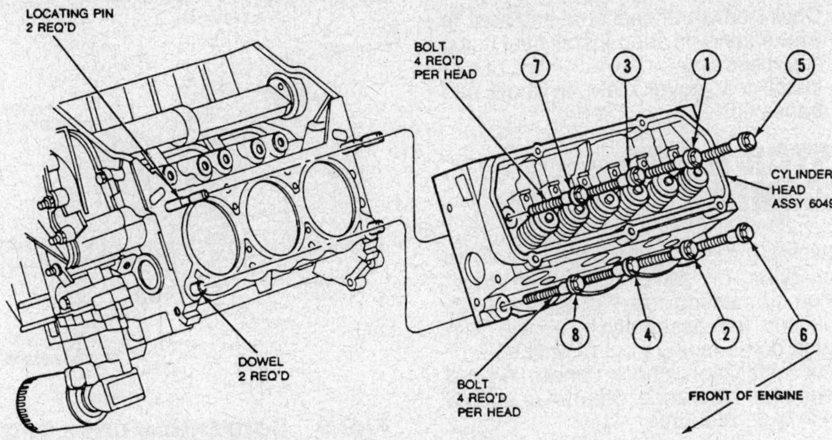


**Fig. 4 Cylinder head tightening sequence**

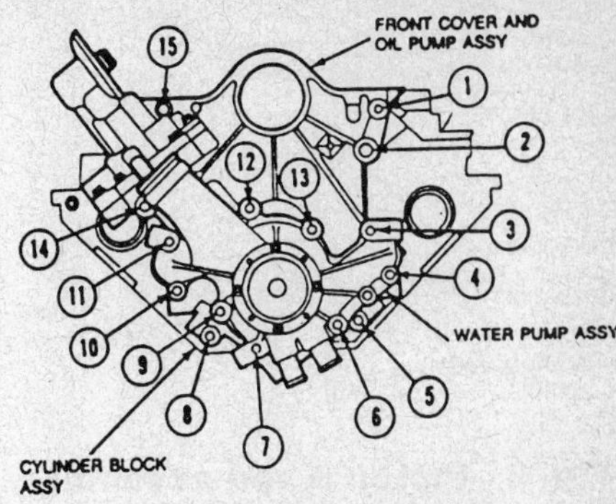


**Fig. 5 Front cover bolt locations**

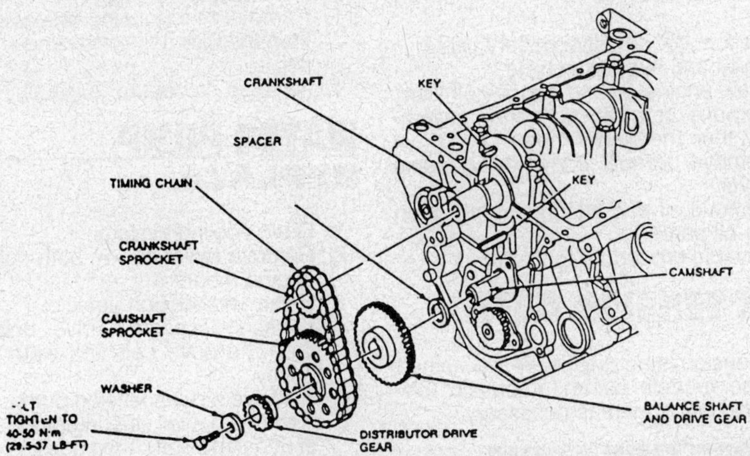


**Fig. 6 Timing chain & sprocket removal**

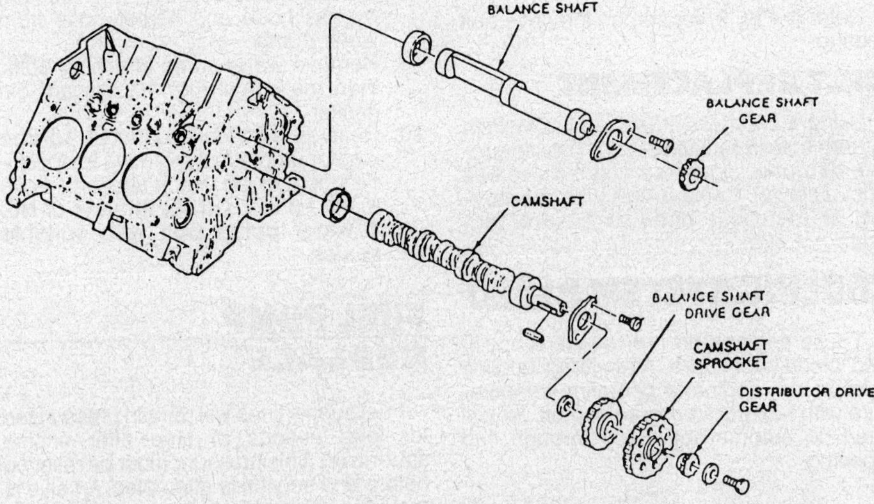


**Fig. 7 Balance shaft assembly**

plugs and position aside.

2. Remove air cleaner assembly, oil fill cap and PCV valve.
3. Remove rocker arm cover attaching screws, then the covers.
4. Reverse procedure to install. Torque attaching screws to specifications.

# TIMING CASE COVER & TIMING CHAIN

## REPLACE

1. Drain cooling system.
2. Disconnect negative battery cable.
3. Loosen accessory drive belt idler, then remove drive belt and water pump pulley.
4. Remove power steering pump mounting bracket attaching bolts, then remove assembly with hoses connected, positioning pump aside.
5. **On models with A/C,** remove compressor front support bracket, leaving compressor in place.
6. **On all models,** disconnect coolant bypass hose and heater hose at water pump, then the upper radiator hose at thermostat housing.
7. Disconnect coil wire from distributor cap, then remove cap with plug wires attached. Remove distributor hold-down clamp and distributor.
8. Raise and support vehicle.
9. Remove crankshaft pulley and damper using suitable puller. If crankshaft pulley and damper have to be separated, mark damper and pulley for reassembly reference, as damper and pulley are balanced as a unit and should be installed back to their original position.
10. Remove oil filter and disconnect lower radiator hose.
11. Remove oil pan as described under "Oil Pan, Replace."
12. Lower vehicle.
13. Remove front cover attaching bolts, **Fig. 5. Ensure attaching bolt behind oil filter adapter is removed to avoid damaging cover upon removal.**
14. Remove ignition timing indicator.
15. Remove front cover and water pump as an assembly. Remove and discard cover gasket.
16. Remove camshaft bolt and washer from end of camshaft.
17. Remove distributor drive gear.
18. Remove camshaft sprocket, crankshaft sprocket and timing chain, **Fig. 6.**. If crankshaft sprocket is difficult to remove, pry it off the shaft using two large screwdrivers.
19. Reverse procedure to install. Align timing chain and sprockets by placing No. 1 cylinder at TDC and crankshaft keyway at 12 o'clock position.

# CAMSHAFT

## REPLACE

1. Remove engine from vehicle as de-

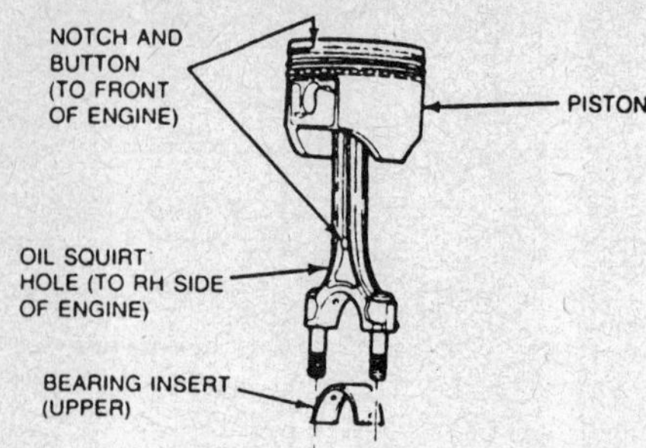


**Fig. 8 Piston & rod assembly**

scribed under "Engine, Replace."

2. Remove intake manifolds as described under "Upper & Lower Intake Manifold, Replace."
3. Remove valve lifters as described under "Hydraulic Valve Lifters, Replace."
4. Remove timing case cover and timing chain as described under "Timing Case Cover & Timing chain, Replace."
5. Remove oil pan as described under "Oil Pan, Replace."
6. Remove camshaft through front of engine. **Do not damage bearing surfaces during removal.**
7. Reverse procedure to install. Lubricate cam lobes and bearings with suitable lubricant.

## BALANCE SHAFT
### REPLACE

A balance shaft system is used on 3.8L/V6-232 to provide increased engine smoothness. The counter-rotating shaft, driven by a gear mounted on the camshaft snout between the camshaft thrust plate and sprocket, is located above the camshaft in the cylinder block valley area. The balance shaft is retained in the cylinder block by a thrust plate, and rides on bearings very similar to that of the camshaft.

1. Remove engine from vehicle as described under "Engine, Replace."
2. Remove timing case cover and timing chain as described under "Timing Case Cover & Timing chain, Replace."
3. Remove oil pan as described under "Oil Pan, Replace."
4. Remove balance shaft thrust plate, **Fig. 7,** then the balance shaft. **Do not damage bearings during removal.**
5. Reverse procedure to install. Lubricate balance shaft bearing journals with suitable lubricant.

## CRANKSHAFT REAR OIL SEAL
### REPLACE

1. Remove transaxle and flywheel as described under "Transaxle, Replace" in the "Automatic Transmissions/Transaxles" section.
2. Remove rear cover plate.
3. Using suitable tool, punch hole in seal metal between seal lip and cylinder block. Using suitable slide hammer remove seal.
4. Coat crankshaft seal area and seal lip with engine oil, then install seal using suitable driver.
5. Install rear cover plate, flywheel and transaxle.

## PISTON & ROD ASSEMBLY

Assemble rod to piston with notch on piston dome on same side as oil squirt hole on connecting rod, **Fig. 8.** Assemble piston and rod assembly in engine with notch in dome facing front of engine.

After installation, check connecting rod big end side clearance. Clearance should be .0047-.0114 inch.

## OIL PAN
### REPLACE

1. Disconnect negative battery cable.
2. Raise and support vehicle.
3. Drain engine oil and remove oil filter.
4. Remove catalytic convertor assembly, then the starter motor.
5. Remove torque convertor housing cover.
6. Remove oil pan attaching bolts, then the oil pan.
7. Reverse procedure to install.

## BELT TENSION DATA

Belt tension is automatically maintained on these models by an automatic tensioner. No adjustment is necessary.

## SERPENTINE DRIVE BELTS

### BELT ROUTING

Refer to **Fig. 9,** for serpentine drive belt routing.

### BELT REPLACEMENT

Using a breaker bar installed in 1/2 inch square hole in tensioner behind pulley, rotate tensioner clockwise and remove belt from pulley(s). **Use caution when removing or installing belts to ensure tool does not slip.**

## COOLING SYSTEM BLEED

These engines do not require a specified bleed procedure. After filling cooling system, run engine to operating temperature with radiator/pressure cap off. Air will then be automatically bled through cap opening.

## THERMOSTAT
### REPLACE

Do not remove the radiator cap while engine is operating or while engine is still under pressure.

1. Drain cooling system until coolant level is below thermostat.

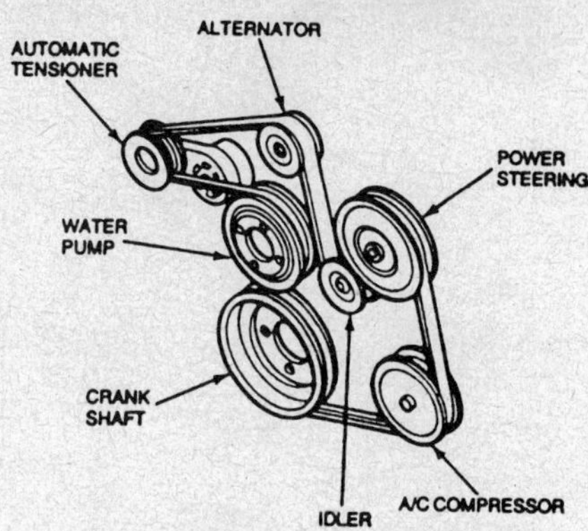


**Fig. 9 Serpentine drive belt routing**

2. Disconnect upper radiator hose at thermostat housing.
3. Remove two housing retaining bolts, then the thermostat housing and gasket.
4. Reverse procedure to install.

## WATER PUMP
### REPLACE

1. Drain cooling system.
2. Remove lower nut on both righthand engine mounts.
3. Raise and support vehicle.
4. Loosen accessory drive belt idler, then the drive belt and water pump pulley.
5. Remove air suspension pump.
6. Remove power steering pump bracket attaching bolts, then position bracket and pump aside.
7. **On models equipped with A/C,** remove compressor front support bracket, leaving compressor in place.
8. **On all models,** disconnect coolant bypass hose and heater hose from water pump.
9. Remove water pump attaching bolts, then the pump, **Fig. 10.** Discard old gasket.
10. Reverse procedure to install. **Torque** water pump attaching bolts to specifications and fan clutch attaching bolts to 12-18 ft. lbs. **Coat threads of No. 1 water pump bolt with suitable sealer.**

## FUEL PUMP
### REPLACE

Fuel supply lines will remain pressurized for long periods of time after engine shut-down. This pressure must be relieved before any service is attempted. A valve is provided on the fuel rail assembly for this purpose. To relieve system pressure, remove air cleaner assembly and connect pressure gauge tool No. T80L-9974-B or equivalent onto fuel valve on fuel rail assembly.

1. Disconnect battery ground cable.
2. Relieve fuel system pressure as described previously.
3. Remove fuel from fuel tank by pump-

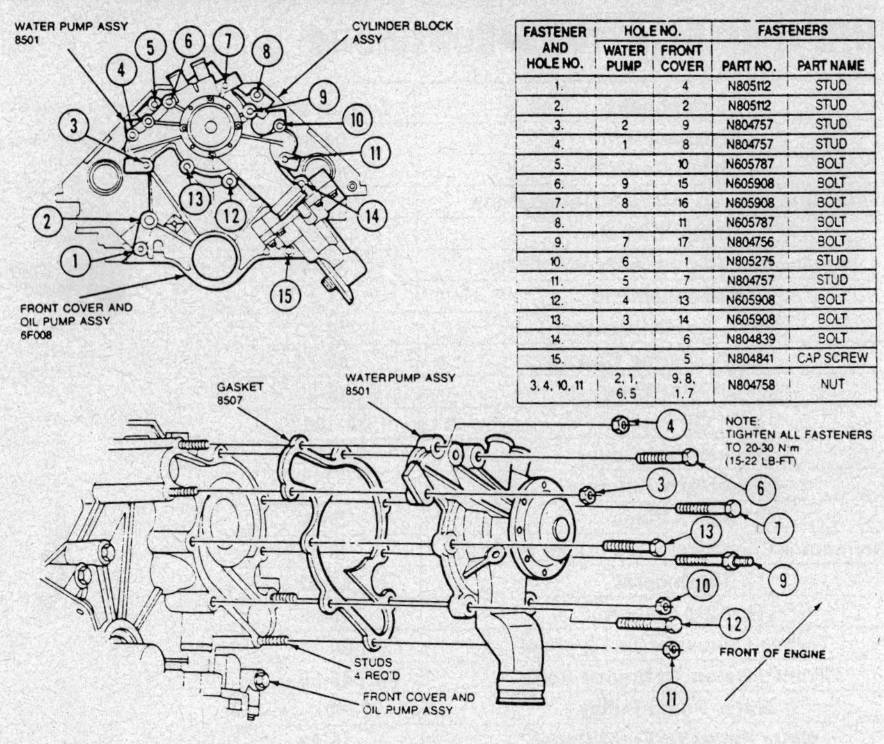

| FASTENER AND HOLE NO. | HOLE NO. | | FASTENERS | |
|---|---|---|---|---|
| | WATER PUMP | FRONT COVER | PART NO. | PART NAME |
| 1. | | 4 | N805112 | STUD |
| 2. | | 2 | N805112 | STUD |
| 3. | 2 | 9 | N804757 | STUD |
| 4. | 1 | 8 | N804757 | STUD |
| 5. | | 10 | N605787 | BOLT |
| 6. | 9 | 15 | N605908 | BOLT |
| 7. | 8 | 16 | N605908 | BOLT |
| 8. | | 11 | N605787 | BOLT |
| 9. | 7 | 17 | N804756 | BOLT |
| 10. | 6 | 1 | N805275 | STUD |
| 11. | 5 | 7 | N804757 | STUD |
| 12. | 4 | 13 | N605908 | BOLT |
| 13. | 3 | 14 | N605908 | BOLT |
| 14. | | 6 | N804839 | BOLT |
| 15. | | 5 | N804841 | CAP SCREW |
| 3, 4, 10, 11 | 2, 1, 6, 5 | 9, 8, 1, 7 | N804758 | NUT |



**Fig. 10 Water pump assembly**

ing fuel out of fuel filler neck.

4. Raise and support vehicle.
5. Disconnect and remove fuel filler neck.
6. Support fuel tank, then remove tank support straps. Lower fuel tank partially and remove fuel lines, electrical connectors and vent lines from tank. Remove tank.
7. Turn fuel pump locking ring counterclockwise and remove locking ring.
8. Remove fuel pump, bracket and gasket assembly.
9. Reverse procedure to install. Pressurize fuel system as follows:
   a. Install pressure gauge tool No. T80L-9974-B or equivalent onto fuel rail pressure fitting.
   b. Turn ignition switch to On position for 3 seconds, repeatedly 5 to 10 times until pressure gauge indicates 30 psi.

## TIGHTENING SPECIFICATIONS

| Year | Component | Torque/ft. lbs. |
|---|---|---|
| 1989-92 | Air Pump Brace To Bracket | 52-70 |
| | Air Pump Brace To Crankshaft Pulley Nut | 15-22 |
| | Air Pump Bracket To Engine | 30-40 |
| | Air Pump Pivot Bolt | 30-40 |
| | Air Pump Pulley | 71-101③ |
| | Alternator Brace To Alternator | 30-44 |
| | Alternator Brace To Intake Manifold Nut | 15-22 |
| | Alternator Brace To Water Pump | 15-22 |
| | Alternator Pivot Bolt | 45-57 |
| | Camshaft Sprocket Bolt | 30-36 |
| | Connecting Rod Nut | 31-36 |
| | Crankshaft Damper Bolt | 104-132 |
| | Crankshaft Pulley | 20-28 |
| | Cylinder Head Bolt | ① |
| | Distributor Cap | 18-23③ |
| | Distributor Hold-Down | 20-29 |
| | ECT Sensor | 6-9 |
| | EGR Valve To Intake Manifold | 15-22 |

*Continued*

## TIGHTENING SPECIFICATIONS—Continued

| Year | Component | Torque/ft. lbs. |
|---|---|---|
| 1989–92 | Flywheel Bolt | 54-64 |
| | Front Cover | 15-22 |
| | Fuel Injection To Intake Manifold Bolts | 71-104③ |
| | Heater Elbow | 15-17 |
| | Heater Tube To Intake Manifold Stud | 8-10 |
| | Intake Manifold | ② |
| | Low Level Oil Sensor | 18-22 |
| | Main Bearing Cap | 65-74 |
| | Oil Inlet Tube | 15-22 |
| | Oil Pan | 80-106③ |
| | Rocker Arm Cover | 80-106③ |
| | Rocker Arm Fulcrum | ④ |
| | Spark Plugs | 5-11 |
| | Thermactor Check Valve To Intake Manifold | 16-19 |
| | Thermostat | 15-22 |
| | Throttle Body Nut | 15-22 |
| | Torque Converter To Flywheel | 20-34 |
| | Transmission To Engine Bolts | 40-50 |
| | Water Pump Pulley | 71-101③ |
| | Water Pump To Front Cover | 15-22 |

①—Refer to text.
②—Torque bolts in three steps as follows: 7 ft. lbs., 15 ft. lbs., 24 ft. lbs.
③—Inch lbs.
④—Torque to 44 inch lbs., then retorque to 18–25 ft. lbs.

# 4.6L/V8-281 Engine

**NOTE:** On Vehicles Equipped With Airbags, Disarm Airbag System As Outlined Under "Airbag System Disarming" Before Any Diagnosis, Testing, Troubleshooting Or Repairs Are Performed. After All Diagnosis, Testing, Troubleshooting Or Repairs Have Been Completed, Rearm Airbag System As Outlined Under "Airbag System Disarming."

## INDEX



## AIRBAG SYSTEM DISARMING

**The electrical circuit necessary for system deployment is powered directly from the battery and a backup power supply. To avoid accidental deployment and possible personal injury, the airbag system must be deactivated prior to servicing or replacing any system components.**

A back-up power supply is included in the system to provide airbag deployment in the event the battery or battery cables are damaged in an accident before the sensors can close. The power supply is a capacitor that will retain a charge for approximately 15 minutes after the battery ground cable is disconnected. **Backup power supply must be disconnected to deactivate airbag system.**

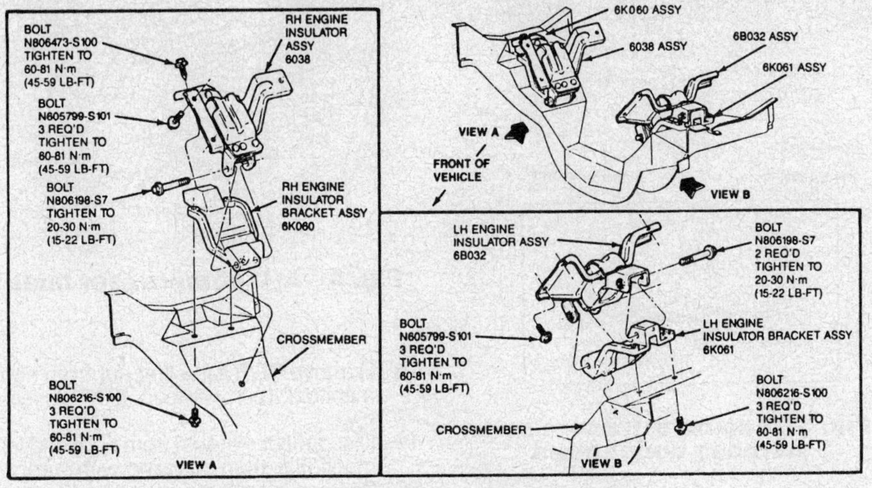


**Fig. 1 Front engine mounts**

## 1989–91 MODELS

1. Disconnect battery ground cable.
2. Disconnect backup power supply as described under "Backup Power Supply, Replace" in the "Passive Restraint" section.
3. Remove four nut and washer assemblies securing airbag module to steering wheel, then disconnect airbag electrical connector. Attach jumper wire to airbag terminals on clockspring.
4. **On models equipped with passenger-side airbag,** disconnect airbag module connector located behind glove compartment. Attach a jumper wire to airbag terminals on wiring harness side of passenger airbag module connector
5. To reactivate, disconnect battery ground cable and backup power supply, then reverse remainder of deactivation procedure. **Torque** airbag module to steering wheel nut assemblies to 35-53 inch lbs.
6. Verify airbag lamp after reactivating system.

## 1992 MODELS

1. Disconnect positive battery cable and wait one minute.
2. Remove four nut and washer assemblies securing airbag to steering wheel.
3. Disconnect airbag electrical connector and install airbag simulator tool No. 105-00008 or equivalent.
4. **On models with passenger side airbag,** remove passenger airbag and disconnect electrical connector.
5. Install airbag simulator tool No. 105-00008 or equivalent.
6. **On all models,** connect positive battery cable.
7. To activate airbag system, disconnect positive battery cable and reverse procedure. **Torque** mounting nut and washer assemblies to 36-49 inch lbs.
8. Verify proper operation of airbag lamp.

# ENGINE MOUNT REPLACE

## FRONT

1. Disconnect ground and positive battery cables.
2. Remove air inlet tube.
3. Drain cooling system, then remove cooling fan and shroud.
4. Relieve fuel system pressure as outlined under "Fuel System Pressure Relief."
5. Remove upper radiator hose.
6. Remove wiper module and support bracket.
7. Discharge A/C system.
8. Disconnect A/C compressor outlet hose, then remove hose assembly to righthand coil bracket attaching bolt.
9. Remove engine electrical harness 42-pin connector from bracket on brake vacuum booster.
10. Disconnect engine electrical connector, then disconnect transmission harness electrical connector.
11. Disconnect throttle valve cable at throttle body.
12. Disconnect heater outlet hose.
13. Remove heater outlet hose assembly to righthand cylinder head upper attaching stud, then loosen lower bolt bolt and position aside.
14. Remove blower motor resistor.
15. Remove righthand engine mount to lower engine bracket attaching bolt.
16. Disconnect EGR valve vacuum hoses and tube.
17. Remove EGR valve to intake manifold attaching bolts.
18. Disconnect Heated Exhaust Gas Oxygen (HEGO) sensors.
19. Raise and support vehicle.
20. Remove righthand front engine mount two through bolts, then remove lefthand front engine mount through bolt, **Fig. 1.**
21. Remove EGR tube line attaching nut at righthand exhaust manifold, then remove EGR valve assembly.
22. Disconnect exhaust pipes at exhaust manifolds, then lower and support exhaust at crossmember.
23. Position suitable jack and wood block under oil pan, rearward of drain plug, then raise engine approximately 4 inches.
24. Install wood block under oil pan, then lower engine onto wood block.
25. Remove engine mount attaching bolts.
26. Reverse procedure to install, noting the following:
    a. **Torque** EGR valve and tube assembly to exhaust manifold line nut to 26-33 ft. lbs.
    b. **Torque** exhaust manifold to exhaust attaching bolts to 20-30 ft. lbs.
    c. **Torque** EGR valve to intake manifold attaching bolts to 15-22 ft. lbs.
    d. **Torque** heater outlet hose to righthand cylinder head attaching stud, bolt and ground strap to 15-22 ft. lbs.
    e. Refer to **Fig. 1,** for engine mount torque specifications.

## REAR

1. Raise and support vehicle, then using suitable jack and wood block support transmission.
2. Remove rear mount to crossmember attaching bolts.
3. Remove mount to transmission attaching bolt, **Fig. 2.**
4. Raise transmission with suitable jack, then remove mount assembly.
5. Reverse procedure to install. Refer to **Fig. 2,** for rear engine mount torque specifications.

# ENGINE REPLACE

1. Disconnect ground and positive battery cables.
2. Mark hood for installation alignment, then remove hood.
3. Drain cooling system, then discharge A/C system.
4. Relieve fuel system pressure as outlined under "Fuel System Pressure Relief," then disconnect fuel lines.
5. Remove engine cooling fan, shroud and radiator.
6. Remove wiper module and bracket.
7. Remove air inlet tube.
8. Remove 42-pin electrical harness connector from bracket at brake vacuum booster, **Fig. 3.**
9. Disconnect 42-pin connector and transmission harness electrical connector, then position connectors aside.
10. Using suitable tool, disconnect accelerator and speed control cables.

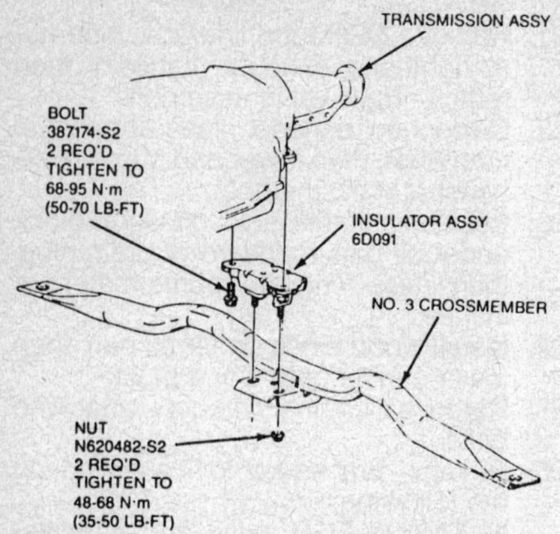


**Fig. 2 Rear engine mount**

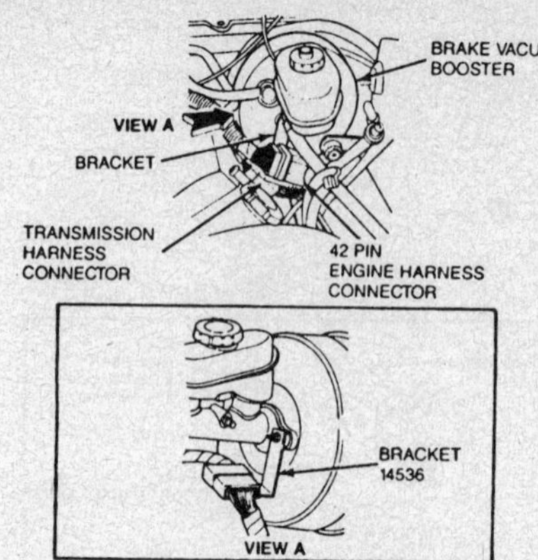


**Fig. 3 Engine & transmission harness connectors**

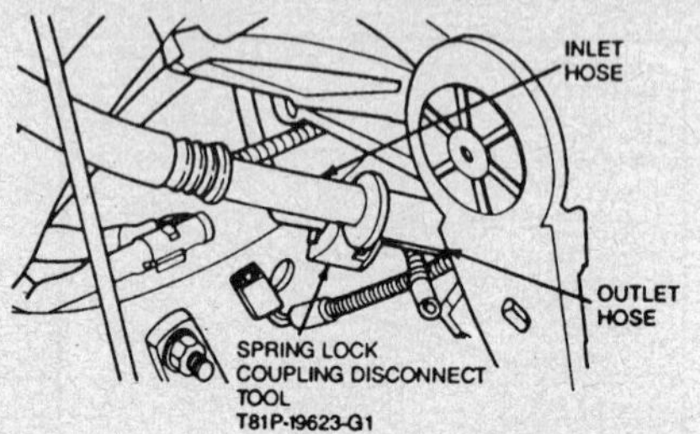


**Fig. 4 A/C compressor lines**

11. Disconnect throttle valve cable.
12. Disconnect purge solenoid electrical connector and vacuum hose.
13. Disconnect power distribution and starter relay power supply.
14. Disconnect throttle body elbow vacuum port supply hose.
15. Disconnect heater inlet and return hoses.
16. Disconnect alternator electrical harness at fender apron and junction box.
17. Using tool No. T81P-19623-G1, G2 or equivalent, remove A/C compressor inlet and outlet attaching hoses, **Fig. 4.**
18. Disconnect EVO sensor electrical connector.
19. Disconnect body ground strap at dash panel.
20. Raise and support vehicle, then drain engine oil.
21. Disconnect exhaust pipes at exhaust manifolds, then lower and support exhaust at crossmember.
22. Remove transmission line bracket attaching nut, then remove engine to transmission knee braces attaching bolts and stud, **Fig. 5.**
23. Remove starter assembly.
24. Remove power steering pump attaching nuts and position pump aside.
25. Remove engine block plug to gain access to torque converter attaching nuts, then rotate crankshaft to remove attaching nuts.
26. Remove engine to transmission attaching bolts.
27. Remove righthand front engine mount two through bolts, then remove lefthand front engine mount through bolt.
28. Lower vehicle, using suitable jack, support transmission.
29. Install engine lift brackets, **Fig. 6,** then connect suitable lift equipment.
30. Carefully raise engine and separate from transmission, then remove engine.
31. Reverse procedure to install, noting the following:
    a. **Torque** engine to transmission attaching bolt to 30-44 ft. lbs.
    b. Refer to **Fig. 1,** for engine mount torque specifications.
    c. **Torque** torque converter attaching nuts to 22-25 ft. lbs.
    d. **Torque** power steering pump attaching nuts to 15-22 ft. lbs.
    e. Refer to **Fig. 5,** for transmission brace torque specifications.
    f. **Torque** exhaust to exhaust manifold attaching bolts to 20-30 ft. lbs.

## EXHAUST MANIFOLD REPLACE

1. Disconnect battery ground cable.
2. Remove air inlet tube.
3. Drain cooling system, then remove cooling fan and shroud.
4. Relieve fuel system fuel pressure. **Refer to "Relieving Fuel System Pressure" elsewhere in this section.**
5. Remove upper radiator hose.
6. Remove wiper module and support bracket, then discharge refrigerant from system.
7. Disconnect A/C compressor outlet hose at compressor, then remove bolt retaining hose assembly to right coil bracket.
8. Remove 42-pin engine harness connector from retaining bracket on brake vacuum booster.
9. Disconnect 42-pin connector and transmission harness connector, **Fig. 7.**
10. Remove oil dipstick tube, on left exhaust manifold, then disconnect throttle valve cable from throttle body.
11. Disconnect heater outlet hose, then remove ground strap to right cylinder head.
12. Remove upper stud, then loosen lower bolt retaining heater outlet hose to right cylinder head and position aside.
13. Remove blower motor resistor.
14. Remove right engine insulator, then disconnect vacuum hoses from EGR valve and EGR tube.
15. Remove EGR valve assembly attaching bolts, then disconnect HEGO sensor.
16. Raise and support vehicle.
17. Remove two through bolts for left engine insulator and one through bolt for the right.
18. Remove EGR tube line nut from right manifold, then remove EGR assembly.
19. Disconnect exhaust from right and left manifolds, then suspend with wire.
20. Position a suitable jack and block of wood under oil pan, then raise engine approximately 4 inches.
21. If removing left manifold, remove engine insulator from cylinder block, then remove attaching bolts and manifold.
22. If removing right manifold, remove attaching bolts and manifold.
23. Reverse procedure to install. Torque manifold bolts to specification in sequence shown in **Fig. 8.**

## INTAKE MANIFOLD REPLACE

1. Disconnect battery ground cable.
2. Drain cooling system.
3. Relieve fuel system fuel pressure. **Refer to "Relieving Fuel System Pressure" elsewhere in this section.**
4. Remove wiper module and air inlet tube.
5. Release belt tensioner and remove accessory drive belt.
6. Disconnect ignition plug wires from spark plugs. **Do not pull on wire(s).**
7. Disconnect ignition wire brackets from camshaft cover studs.
8. Disconnect both ignition coils, CID sensor and ignition wires from both coils.
9. Remove ignition wire tray and ignition wire assembly.
10. Disconnect alternator wiring harness from junction block, fender apron and alternator.
11. Remove alternator and mounting bracket.
12. Raise and support vehicle.
13. Disconnect oil sending unit and EVO sensor, then position aside.
14. Disconnect EGR tube from right exhaust manifold, then lower vehicle.
15. Disconnect 42-pin connector, A/C compressor, HDR sensor and canister purge solenoid.
16. Remove PCV valve from camshaft cover, then disconnect canister purge vent hose from PCV valve.
17. Disconnect accelerator and speed control cables from throttle body, then remove accelerator cable bracket from intake manifold and position aside.

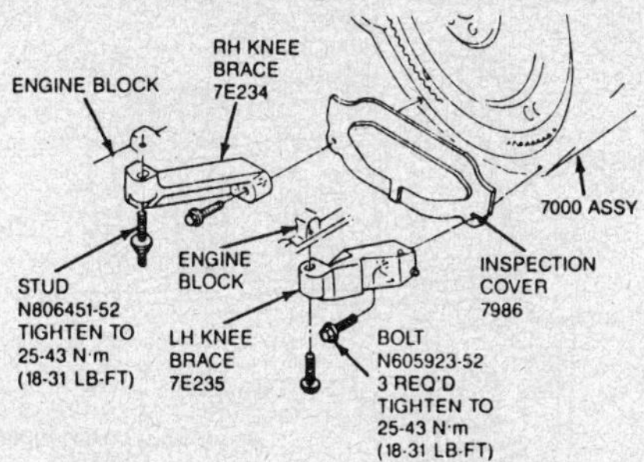


**Fig. 5 Transmission line bracket assembly**

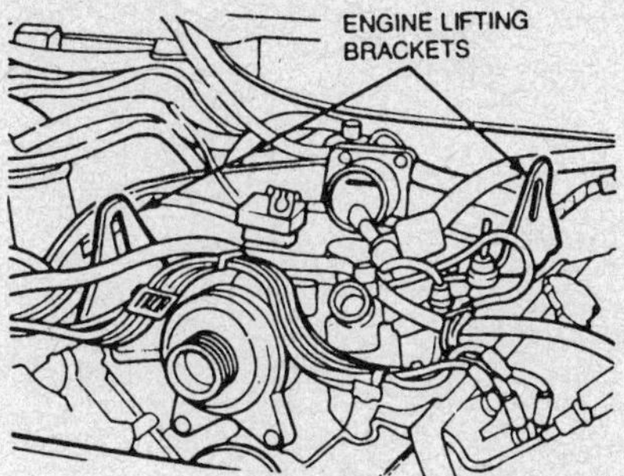


**Fig. 6 Engine lift brackets**

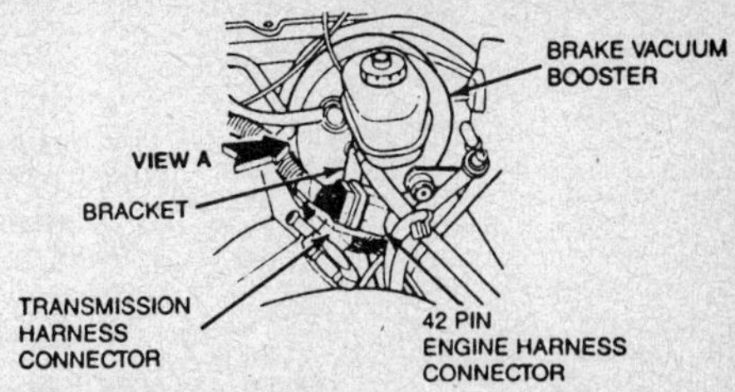


**Fig. 7 Engine & transmission harness connectors**

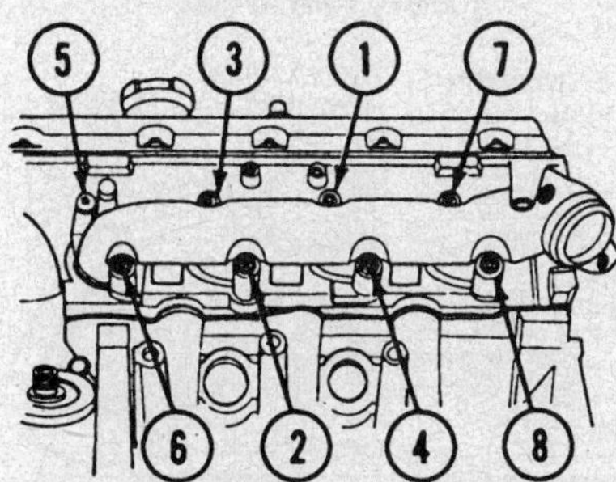


**Fig. 8 Exhaust manifold tightening sequence**

18. Disconnect throttle valve cable from throttle body.
19. Disconnect vacuum hose from throttle body adapter port.
20. Disconnect both HEGO sensors and heater supply hose.
21. Remove thermostat housing, then disconnect upper hose and position aside.
22. Remove bolts attaching intake manifold, then the intake manifold and gaskets.
23. Reverse procedure to install, noting the following:
    a. Clean cylinder head and intake manifold surfaces.
    b. Install new intake manifold gaskets.
    c. Torque manifold bolts to specifications in sequence shown, **Fig. 9.**

# CYLINDER HEAD
## REPLACE

1. Disconnect battery ground cable.
2. Drain cooling system, then remove cooling fan and shroud.
3. Relieve fuel system fuel pressure. **Refer to "Relieving Fuel System Pressure" elsewhere in this section.**
4. Remove air inlet tube and wiper module.
5. Release belt tensioner, then remove accessory drive belt.
6. Disconnect ignition wires from spark plugs. **Do not pull on ignition wire(s).**
7. Disconnect ignition wire brackets from camshaft cover studs.
8. Remove bolt attaching A/C high pressure line to right coil bracket.
9. Disconnect both ignition coils and CID sensor.
10. Remove right and left coil bracket to front cover attaching nuts.
11. Slide ignition coil brackets and ignition wire assembly off mounting studs, then remove from vehicle.
12. Remove water pump pulley, then disconnect alternator wiring harness from junction block, fender apron and alternator.
13. Remove alternator and mounting bracket.
14. Disconnect positive battery cable at power distribution box, then remove attaching bolt from positive battery cable bracket located on right side of cylinder head.
15. Disconnect vent hose from canister purge solenoid, then place positive battery cable aside.
16. Disconnect canister purge solenoid vent hose from PCV valve, then remove PCV valve from camshaft cover.
17. Remove 42-pin engine harness connector from retaining bracket on brake vacuum booster, then disconnect and position aside.
18. Disconnect HDR sensor, A/C compressor clutch and canister purge solenoid electrical connectors.
19. Raise and support vehicle.
20. Remove bolts retaining power steering pump to engine block and cylinder front cover. **Front lower bolt on power steering will not come all the way out.**
21. Remove bolts attaching oil pan to front cover.
22. Remove crankshaft damper retaining bolt and washer from crankshaft.
23. Install crankshaft damper remover tool No. T58P-6316-D or equivalent on damper, then pull damper from crankshaft.
24. Disconnect EVO sensor and oil sending unit and position aside.
25. Disconnect EGR tube from right exhaust manifold.
26. Disconnect exhaust for right and left manifolds, then suspend with wire.
27. Remove bolt retaining starter wiring harness to rear of right cylinder head, then lower vehicle.
28. Remove right and left camshaft cover to cylinder head.
29. Disconnect accelerator and speed control cables.
30. Remove accelerator bracket from intake manifold and postion aside.
31. Disconnect throttle valve cable from throttle body, then the vacuum hose from throttle body elbow port.

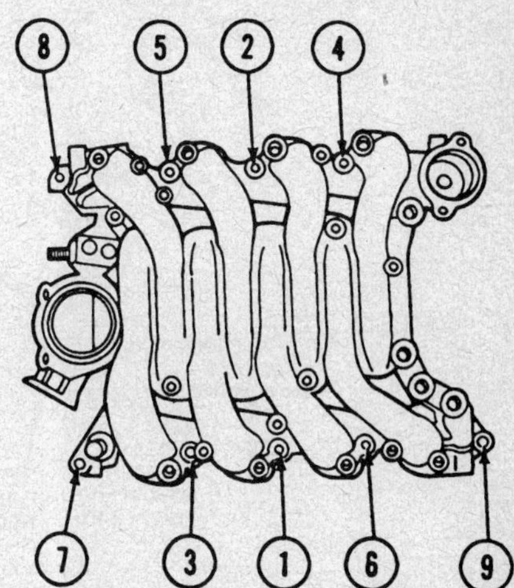


**Fig. 9 Intake manifold tightening sequence**

32. Disconnect both HEGO sensor and heater supply hose.
33. Remove thermostat housing, then disconnect upper hose and position aside.
34. Remove bolts attaching intake manifold, then the intake manifold and gaskets, **Fig. 10.**
35. Remove timing chain as described under "Timing Chain, Replace."
36. Remove bolts attaching left cylinder head. **The lower rear bolt cannot be removed due to interference with the brake vacuum booster. Use a rubber band or similar item to hold bolt away from engine as shown, Fig. 11.**
37. Remove left cylinder head.
38. Remove ground strap retaining heater return line to right cylinder head.
39. Remove bolts attaching right cylinder head. **The lower rear bolt cannot be removed due to interference with the evaporator housing. Use a rubber band or similar item to hold bolt away from engine as shown, Fig. 12.**
40. Remove right cylinder head.
41. Reverse procedure to install, noting the following:
    a. Rotate crankshaft counterclockwise 45°. This ensures that all pistons are below top of engine block deck face.
    b. **Torque** cylinder head bolts in sequence shown, **Fig. 13.** 15-22 ft. lbs., then rotate in sequence

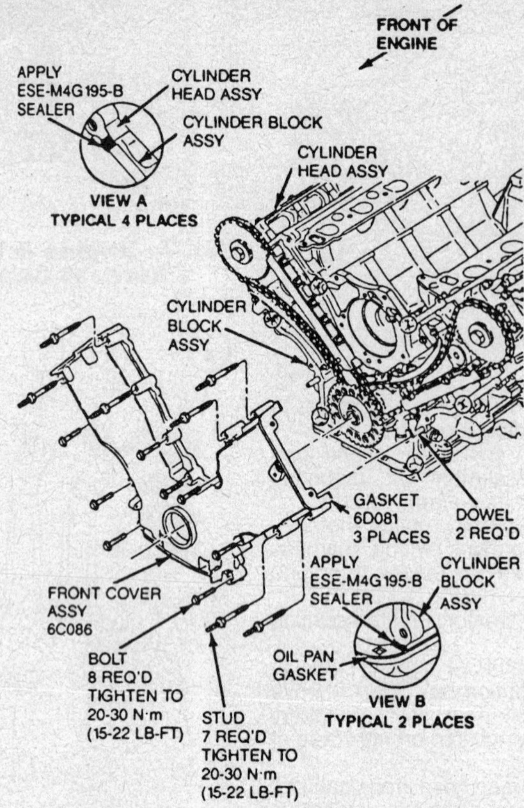


**Fig. 10 Front cover removal**

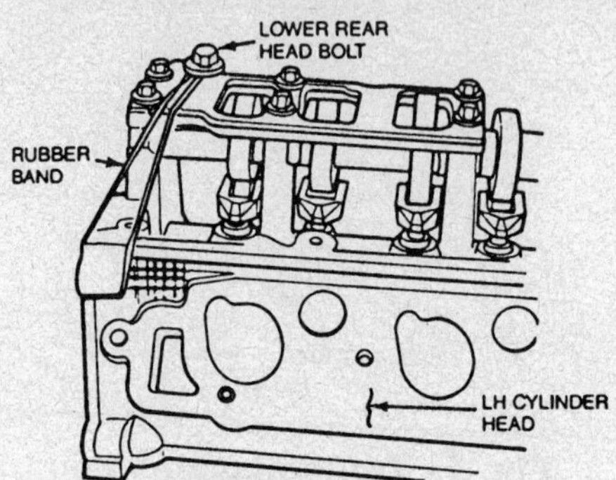


**Fig. 11 LH lower rear head bolt removal**

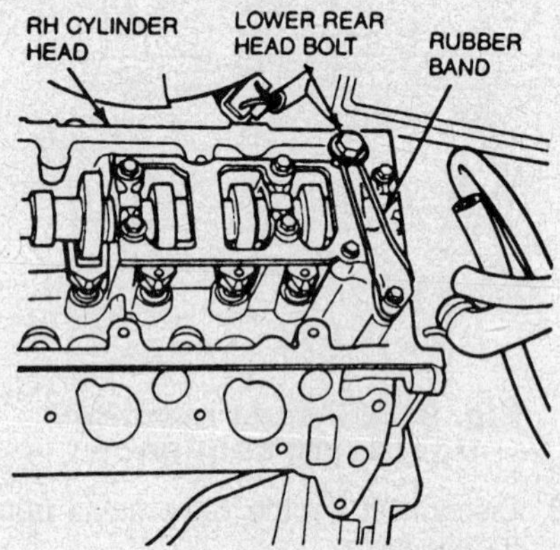


**Fig. 12 RH lower rear head bolt removal**

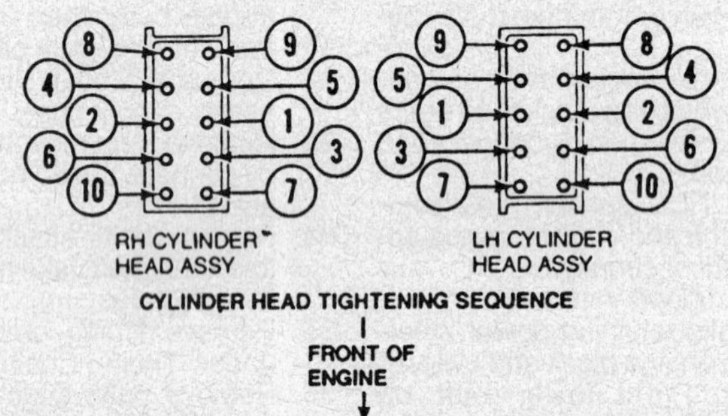


**Fig. 13 Cylinder head tightening sequence**

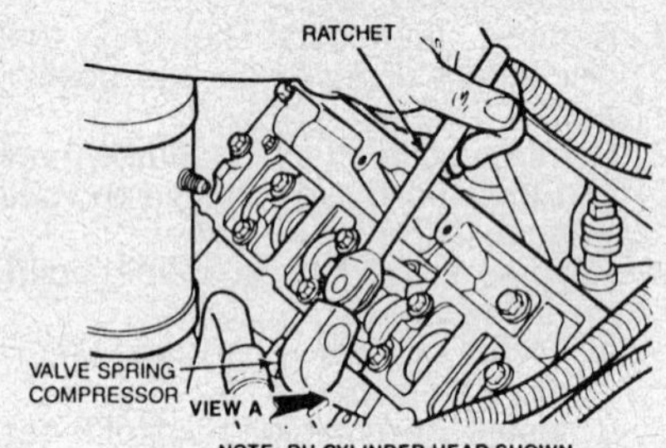


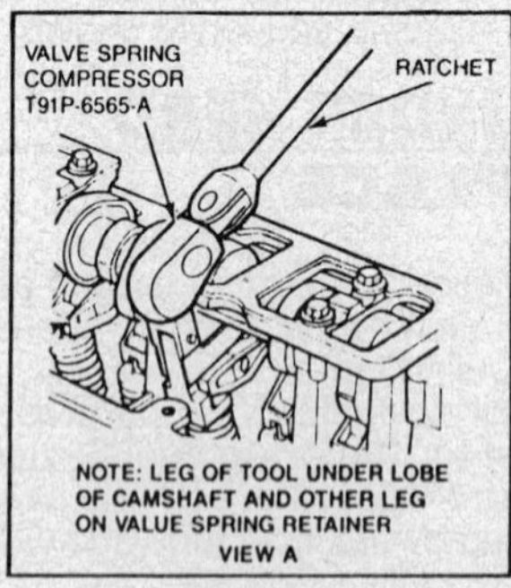


**Fig. 14 Valve spring compressor**

85-95°., then additional 85-95°.

c. Rotate crankshaft clockwise 45°. This will position crankshaft at TDC No. 1. **Crankshaft must only be rotated in the clockwise direction and only as far as TDC.**

# FUEL SYSTEM PRESSURE RELIEF

**Fuel supply lines, on models equipped with fuel injected engines, will remain pressurized after the engine is shut off. Pressure must be relieved prior to any fuel system servicing.**

1. Remove fuel tank cap.
2. Using fuel pressure gauge tool No. T80L-9974-B or equivalent, relieve fuel system pressure at pressure relief valve righthand rear fuel rail. **Pressure relief valve cap must be removed.**
3. Using suitable tool, remove pressure relief valve.
4. Reverse procedure to install. **Torque** fuel pressure relief valve to 48-84 inch lbs. **Torque** fuel pressure relief valve cap to 4-6 inch lbs.

# VALVE ARRANGEMENT

## FRONT TO REAR

Right Side................I-E-I-E-I-E-I-E
Left Side.................E-I-E-I-E-I-E-I

# VALVE CLEARANCE SPECIFICATIONS

Valve lift should measure .020-.069 inch at intake valves and .046-.095 inch at exhaust valves with hydraulic lash adjuster completely collapsed.

# CAM LOBE LIFT SPECIFICATIONS

Intake & Exhaust..................2549

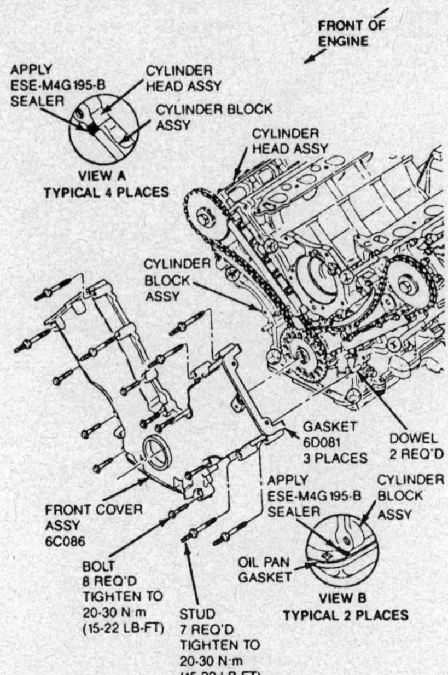


**Fig. 15 Front engine cover assembly**

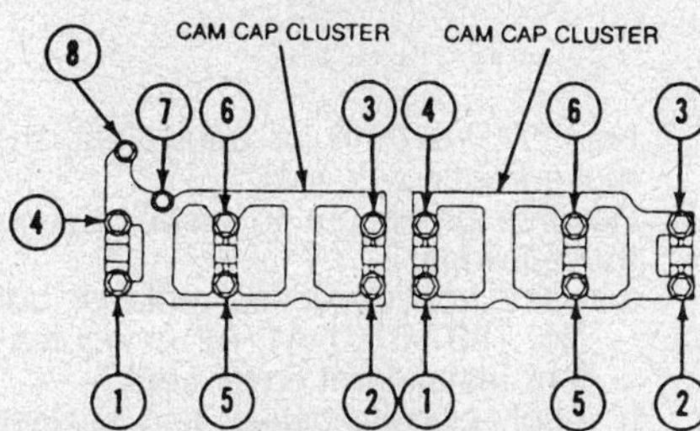


**Fig. 18 Camshaft cap cluster assembly**

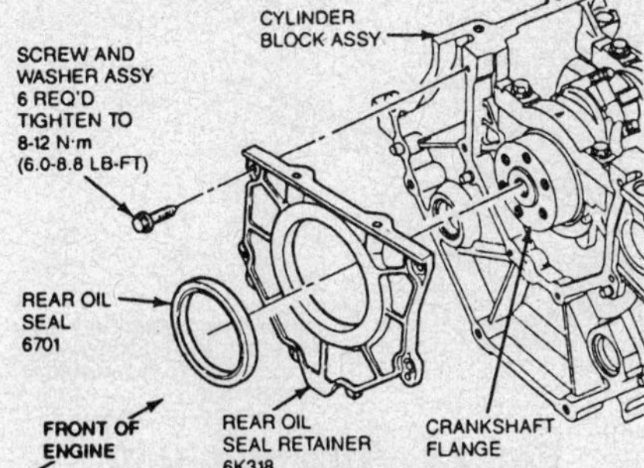


**Fig. 16 Crankshaft rear oil seal**

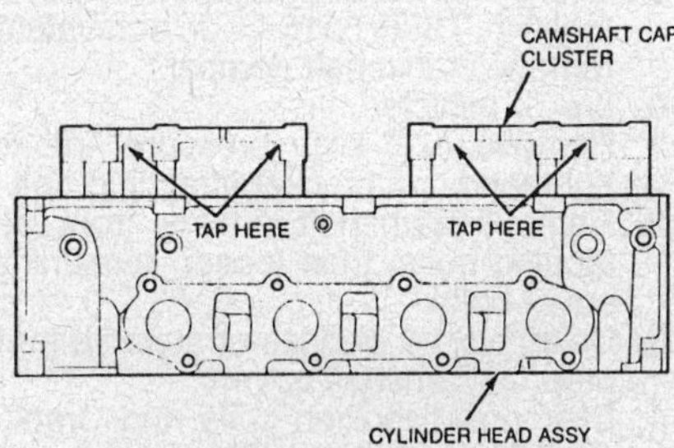


**Fig. 19 Camshaft cap cluster**

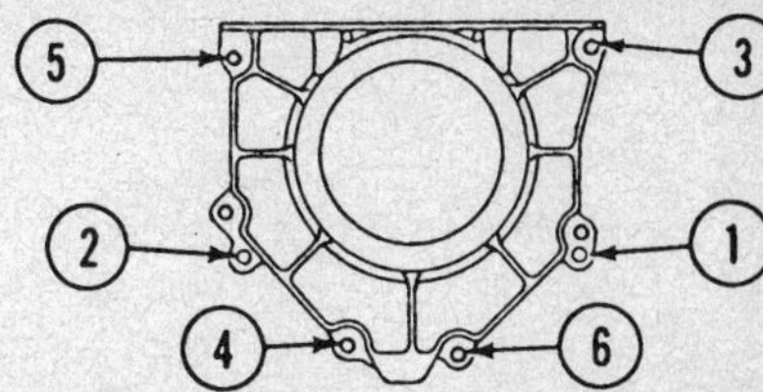


**Fig. 17 Rear oil seal retainer tightening sequence**

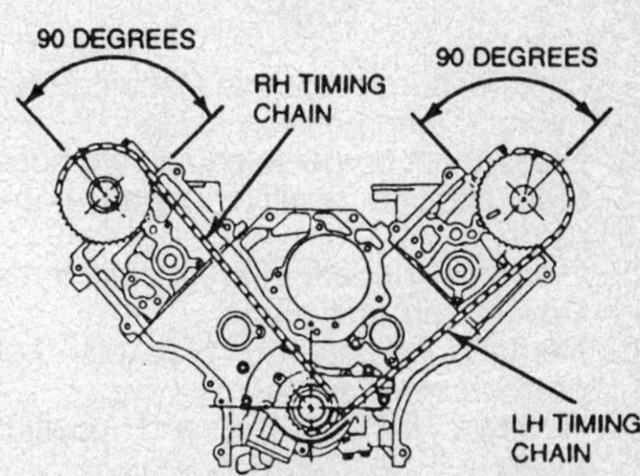


**Fig. 20 Engine rotation to TDC**

# HYDRAULIC LASH ADJUSTER
## REPLACE

1. Remove camshaft covers as outlined under "Camshaft Cover, Replace."
2. Position piston of cylinder at bottom of stroke and camshaft lobe at base circle.
3. Install .40 inch shim between spring coils to prevent damage.
4. Install Valve Spring Compressor tool No. T91P-6565-A or equivalent, under camshaft and on valve spring retainer, **Fig. 14.**
5. Compress valve spring, then remove roller follower.
6. Remove valve spring compressor and shim.
7. Remove hydraulic lash adjuster, as required.
8. Repeat steps 2 through 7 as required.
9. Reverse procedure to install, noting the following:
   a. Valve lash adjuster must have no more than 1.5mm of plunger travel prior to installation.
   b. When installing roller follower, piston must be at bottom of stroke and camshaft at base circle.

# VALVE SPRING & VALVE STEM OIL SEAL
## REPLACE
### REMOVAL

**If, during this procedure, air pressure has forced the piston to the bottom of the cylinder, any loss of air pressure will allow the valve to fall into the cylinder. A rubber band, tape or string wrapped around the end of the valve stem will prevent this and still allow enough travel to check the valve for binding and excess guide to valve stem clearance.**

1. Remove camshaft covers as outlined under "Camshaft Cover, Replace."
2. Remove roller followers as outlined under "Hydraulic Lash Adjuster, Replace."
3. Remove spark plug, then position piston at top of stroke with both valves closed.
4. Install suitable air line with adapter in spark plug opening, then apply air pressure. Failure of air pressure to hold the valves closed is an indication of valve or valve seat damage that may require cylinder head removal.
5. Install .40 inch shim between spring coils.
6. Using Valve Spring Compressor tool No. T91P-6565-A or equivalent, compress valve spring.
7. Remove keepers, retainer and valve spring.
8. Use suitable locking pliers, remove valve stem seal.
9. Repeat steps 3 through 8 as required.

### INSTALLATION

1. **Piston must be at Top Dead Center (TDC) of cylinder being serviced.**
2. Remove air pressure, then inspect valve stem for damage. Rotate valve and check valve stem tip eccentric movement during rotation.
3. Position valve up and down through normal travel and check the stem for binding. **If the valve has been damaged. It will be necessary to remove cylinder head for service.**
4. If valve condition is good, apply engine oil to valve stem and hold valve closed, then apply air pressure in cylinder.
5. Using Valve Stem Seal Replacer tool No. T88T-6571-A or equivalent, install valve stem seal.
6. Position valve spring and retainer over valve stem.
7. Install .40 inch shim between spring coils.
8. Compress valve spring, then install keepers.
9. Turn off air supply, then remove adapter from spark plug opening.
10. Install spark plug, then roller follower and camshaft cover.
11. Start engine and check for leaks.

# CAMSHAFT COVER
## REPLACE
### RIGHT SIDE

1. Disconnect battery ground cable, then disconnect positive battery cable at power distribution box.
2. Remove positive battery cable bracket to cylinder head attaching bolt.
3. Disconnect High Data Rate (HDR) sensor, A/C compressor clutch and

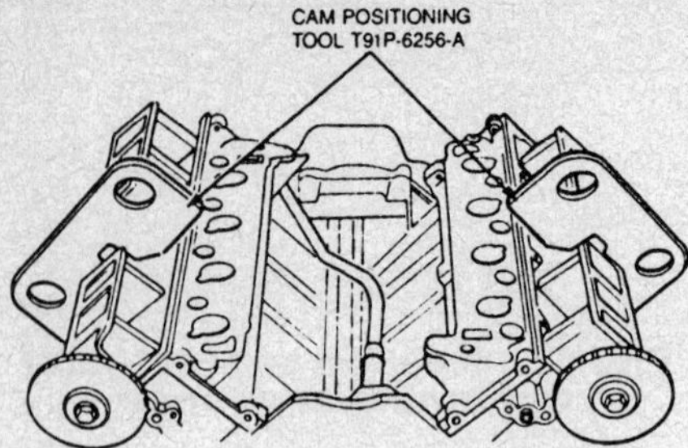


**Fig. 21 Camshaft positioning tool**

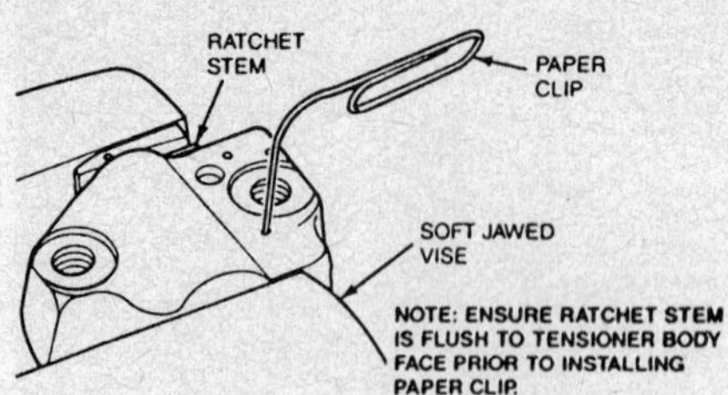


**Fig. 22 Timing chain tensioner bleed**

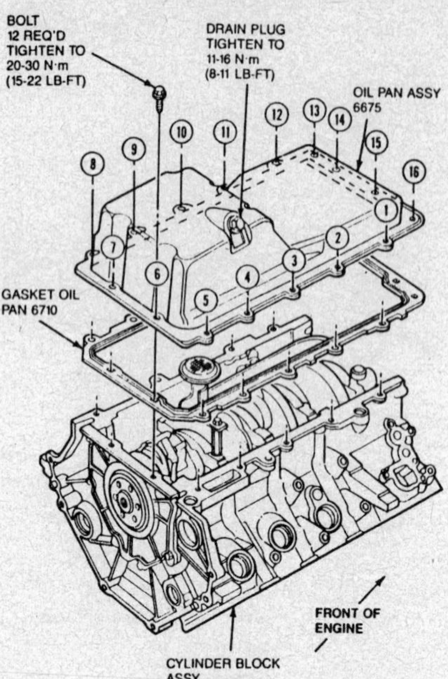


**Fig. 23 Oil pan tightening sequence**

canister purge solenoid electrical connectors, then position aside.

4. Disconnect purge solenoid vent hose, then position positive battery cable aside.
5. Disconnect spark plug ignition wires. **Do not remove wires.**
6. Remove ignition wire brackets, then position wires aside.
7. Remove PCV valve and position aside.
8. Remove camshaft cover attaching bolts, then remove camshaft cover.
9. Reverse procedure to install. **Torque** camshaft cover bolts to 6-8.8 ft. lbs.

## LEFT SIDE

1. Disconnect battery ground cable.
2. Remove air inlet tube.
3. Relieve fuel pressure as outlined under "Fuel System Pressure Relief," then disconnect fuel lines.
4. Raise and support vehicle.
5. Disconnect EVO sensor and oil pressure sending unit electrical connectors, then position electrical harness aside.
6. Lower vehicle, then remove 42-pin electrical harness connector from bracket at brake vacuum booster, **Fig. 3,** then disconnect and position aside.
7. Remove windshield wiper module.
8. Disconnect spark plug ignition wires. **Do not remove wires.**
9. Remove ignition wire brackets, then position wires aside.
10. Remove camshaft cover attaching bolts, then remove camshaft cover.
11. Reverse procedure to install. **Torque** camshaft cover bolts to 6-8.8 ft. lbs.

# FRONT ENGINE COVER
## REPLACE

1. Remove engine cooling fan and shroud.
2. Loosen water pump pulley attaching bolts, then remove serpentine drive belt.
3. Remove water pump pulley attaching bolts, then remove pulley.
4. Raise and support vehicle.
5. Remove power steering pump attaching bolts. **Front lower power steering pump bolt will not come out.**
6. Support power steering pump and position aside.
7. Remove oil pan to front cover attaching bolts.
8. Remove crankshaft damper attaching bolt and washer.
9. Using crankshaft damper remover tool No T58P-6316-D or equivalent, remove crankshaft damper.
10. Lower vehicle.
11. Remove A/C high pressure line to righthand coil bracket attaching bolt.
12. Remove camshaft covers front attaching bolts, then loosen remaining cover bolts.
13. Using plastic wedges or suitable tool, prop up camshaft covers.
14. Disconnect ignition coils and Crankshaft Identification (CID) sensor.
15. Remove righthand coil bracket attaching nuts, then position power steering hose aside.
16. Remove lefthand coil bracket attaching nuts, then pull bracket and ignition wires from mounting studs and position aside.
17. Remove front cover attaching bolts and stub bolts, **Fig. 15,** then remove front cover.
18. Reverse procedure to install, noting the following:
    a. **Refer to Fig. 15,** for front cover tightening specifications.
    b. **Torque** coil bracket attaching nuts, oil pan attaching bolts, power steering pump attaching bolts and water pump pulley attaching bolts to 15-22 ft. lbs.
    c. **Torque** camshaft cover attaching bolts to 6-8.8 ft. lbs.
    d. Apply silicone gasket and sealant E3AZ-19562-A or equivalent in damper keyway. Ensure crankshaft key and keyway are aligned, using Crankshaft Damper Replacer T47P-6316-B or equivalent, install crankshaft damper.
    e. **Torque** crankshaft damper attaching bolt and washer to 114-121 ft. lbs.

# FRONT OIL SEAL
## REPLACE

1. Disconnect battery ground cable.
2. Release belt tensioner, then remove serpentine drive belt.
3. Raise and support vehicle.
4. Remove crankshaft damper attaching bolt and washer.
5. Using crankshaft damper remover tool No. T58P-6316-D or equivalent, remove crankshaft damper.
6. Using front cover seal remover tool No. T74P-6700-A or equivalent, remove front cover seal.
7. Reverse procedure to install, noting the following:
    a. Using front cover seal replacer tool No. T88T-6701-A1, A2 or equivalent, install front cover seal.
    b. Apply silicone gasket and sealant E3AZ-19562-A or equivalent in damper keyway. Ensure crankshaft key and keyway are aligned, using Crankshaft Damper Replacer T47P-6316-B or equivalent, install crankshaft.
    c. **Torque** crankshaft damper attaching bolt and washer to 114-121 ft. lbs.

# PISTON & ROD ASSEMBLY

If the old pistons are serviceable, make certain that they are installed on the rods from which they were removed. Check side clearance between connecting rods and crankshaft journal. Clearance should be .015-.040 inch.

# CRANKSHAFT REAR OIL SEAL
## REPLACE

1. Using a suitable jack, lower transmission and support.
2. Remove flexplate assembly.
3. Remove oil pan as outlined under "Oil Pan, Replace."
4. Remove rear oil seal retainer attaching bolts, **Fig. 16.**
5. Reverse procedure to install. Refer to **Fig. 17,** for rear oil seal retainer attaching bolts tightening sequence.

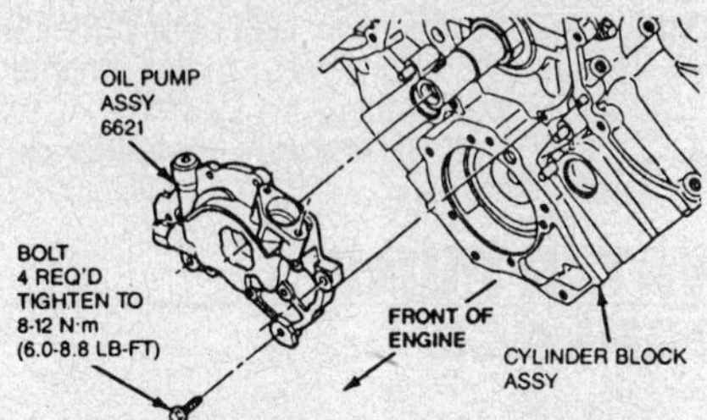


**Fig. 24 Oil pump assembly**

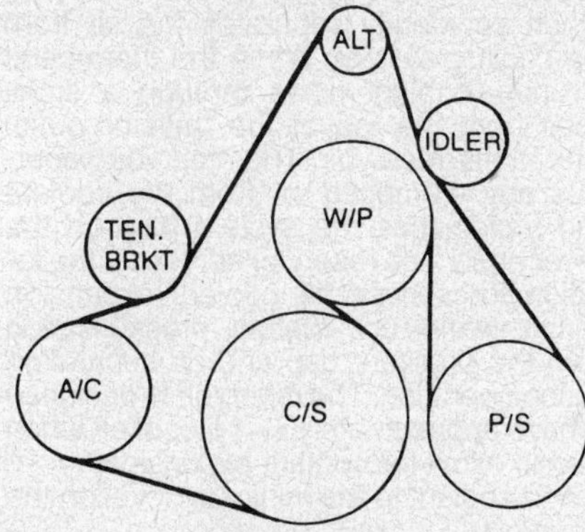


**Fig. 25 Serpentine drive belt routing**

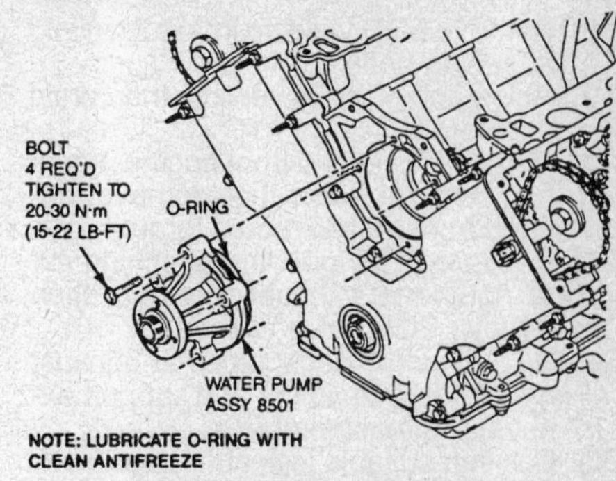


**Fig. 26 Water pump replacement**

# CAMSHAFT
## REPLACE

1. Remove camshaft covers as outlined under "Camshaft Cover, Replace."
2. Remove engine front cover as outlined under "Front Engine Cover, Replace."
3. Remove timing chains as outlined under "Timing Chains, Gears, Tensioners & Guides, Replace."
4. Rotate crankshaft counterclockwise 45°, ensuring pistons are below top of engine deck face. **Crankshaft must be in position prior to rotating camshafts or piston and/or valve damage may result.**
5. Install Valve Spring Compressor tool No. T91P-6565-A or equivalent, under camshaft and on valve spring retainer.
6. Install .40 inch shim between spring coils and camshaft to prevent damage.
7. Camshaft must be at base circle before compressing valve spring, then rotate camshaft, as required, until roller followers are removed.
8. Compress valve spring, then remove roller follower.
9. Repeat steps 5 through 8 until all roller followers are removed.
10. Remove camshaft cap cluster assembly attaching bolt, **Fig. 18.**
11. Tap upward on camshaft cap, **Fig. 19,** then carefully remove camshaft cap and camshaft.
12. Reverse procedure to install, noting the following:
    a. Refer to **Fig. 18,** for camshaft cap cluster bolt tightening sequence.
    b. Torque attaching nuts and bolts to specifications.

# TIMING CHAINS, GEARS, TENSIONERS & GUIDES
## REPLACE

**At no time, when the timing chains are removed and the cylinder heads are installed, may the crankshaft and/or camshaft be rotated. Rotation may result in valve and/or piston damage.**

1. Remove camshaft covers as outlined under "Camshaft Cover, Replace."
2. Remove front engine cover as outlined under "Front Engine Cover, Replace."
3. Remove cylinder head as outlined under "Cylinder Head, Replace."
4. Remove High Data Rate (HDR) wheel, then rotate engine to No. 1 TDC, **Fig. 20.**
5. Install Cam Positioning tool No. T91P-6256-A or equivalent on camshaft flats, **Fig. 21.**
6. Remove righthand tensioner attaching bolts, then remove tensioner and arm.
7. Remove righthand chain guide attaching bolts, then remove chain guide.
8. Remove righthand timing chain, then remove righthand crankshaft gear.
9. Remove righthand camshaft gear attaching bolt, washer, gear and spacer, if required.
10. Remove lefthand tensioner attaching bolts, then remove tensioner and arm.
11. Remove lefthand chain guide attaching bolts, then remove chain guide.
12. Remove lefthand timing chain, then remove lefthand crankshaft gear.
13. Remove lefthand camshaft gear attaching bolt, washer, gear and spacer, if required.
14. Reverse procedure to install, noting the following:
    a. If engine has jumped time, ensure all repairs to engine components and/or valve train are completed. Then rotate engine counterclockwise 45°. This will position all pistons below top of deck face.
    b. **Torque** camshaft and washer attaching bolt to 81-95 ft. lbs.
    c. Bleed timing chain tensioner as outlined under "Timing Chain Tensioner, Bleed."
    d. **Torque** timing chain tensioner attaching bolts to 15-22 ft. lbs.
    e. **Torque** timing chain guide attaching bolts to 6-8.8 ft. lbs.

# TIMING CHAIN TENSIONER
## BLEED

1. Position timing chain tensioner in suitable soft-jawed vise.
2. Using suitable tool, position ratchet lock mechanism from ratchet stem, then slowly compress tensioner plunger by rotating vise handle. **Tensioner must be compressed slowly or internal seal damage may result.**
3. When tensioner plunger bottoms in tensioner bore, continue holding ratchet lock mechanism, then push ratchet mechanism down until flush with tensioner face.
4. While holding ratchet stem flush to tensioner face, release ratchet lock mechanism, then install paper clip or suitable tool to lock tensioner in collapsed position, **Fig. 22.**
5. **Do not remove paper clip or suitable tool until timing chain, tensioner, tensioner arm and timing chain guide are installed on engine.**

# OIL PAN
## REPLACE

1. Disconnect ground and positive battery cables.
2. Remove air inlet tube.
3. Drain cooling system, then remove cooling fan and shroud.
4. Relieve fuel system pressure as outlined under "Fuel System Pressure Relief," then disconnect fuel lines.
5. Remove upper radiator hose.
6. Remove wiper module and support bracket.
7. Discharge A/C system.
8. Disconnect A/C compressor outlet hose, then remove hose assembly to righthand coil bracket attaching bolt.
9. Remove engine electrical harness 42-pin connector from bracket on brake vacuum booster.
10. Disconnect engine electrical connector, then disconnect transmission harness electrical connector.
11. Disconnect throttle valve cable at throttle body.
12. Disconnect heater outlet hose.
13. Remove righthand cylinder head grounds strap attaching nut.
14. Remove heater outlet hose assembly to righthand cylinder head upper attaching stud, then loosen lower bolt bolt and position aside.
15. Remove blower motor resistor.
16. Remove righthand engine mount to lower engine bracket attaching bolt.
17. Disconnect EGR valve vacuum hoses and tube.

18. Remove EGR valve to intake manifold attaching bolts.
19. Raise and support vehicle, then drain engine oil.
20. Remove righthand front engine mount two through bolts, then remove left-hand front engine mount through bolt.
21. Remove EGR tube line attaching nut at righthand exhaust manifold, then remove EGR valve assembly.
22. Disconnect exhaust pipes at exhaust manifolds, then lower and support exhaust at crossmember.
23. Position suitable jack and wood block under oil pan, rearward of drain plug, then raise engine approximately 4 inches.
24. Install two wood blocks approximately 2.5-2.75 inch thick under each engine mount.
25. Lower engine to wood blocks, then remove jack.
26. Remove oil pan attaching bolts. It may be necessary to loosen rear transmission mount attaching nuts and with suitable jack, raise extension housing slightly to remove oil pan.
27. Remove oil pan.
28. Reverse procedure to install. Refer to **Fig. 23,** for oil pan bolt tightening sequence and torque specifications.

## OIL PUMP
### REPLACE

1. Remove camshaft covers as outlined under "Camshaft Covers, Replace."
2. Remove front cover as outlined under "Front Engine Cover, Replace."
3. Remove oil pan as outlined under "Oil Pan, Replace."
4. Remove timing chains as outlined under "Timing Chains, Gears, Tensioners & Guides, Replace."
5. Remove oil pump attaching bolts, then remove oil pump, **Fig. 24.**
6. Reverse procedure to install, noting the following:
   a. Align oil pump inner rotor with flat of crankshaft.
   b. **Torque** oil pump attaching bolts to 6.-8.8 ft.lbs.

## COOLING SYSTEM BLEED

A pressurized reservoir system is used which constantly separates the air from the cooling system. When the thermostat is open, coolant flows through a small hose from the top of the radiator outlet tank to the reservoir. The reservoir seperates any entrapped air from the coolant and replenishes the system through the lower hose. The reservoir serves as the location for service fill, coolant expansion during warm up, system pressurization from the pressure cap and air separation during operation. The reservoir is designed to have approximately .5-1 liter of air when cold to allow for coolant expansion.

Add coolant to the minimum level on the reservoir.

## THERMOSTAT
### REPLACE

1. Drain coolant level below upper radiator hose and thermostat housing.
2. Disconnect upper radiator hose at thermostat housing, then remove two thermostat housing retaining bolts.
3. Remove O-ring seal and thermostat from intake manifold. Inspect O-ring for damage and replace if necessary.
4. Reverse procedure to install. Torque bolts to specifications.

## BELT TENSION DATA

Automatic belt tensioners are spring loaded devices which set and maintain the drive belt tension. The drive belt should not require tension adjustment for the life of the belt. Automatic tensioners have belt wear indicator marks. If the indicator mark is not between the indicator lines, the belt is worn or an incorrect belt is installed.

## SERPENTINE DRIVE BELTS

### BELT ROUTING

Refer to **Fig. 25,** for drive belt routing.

### BELT REPLACEMENT

1. Rotate tensioner away from belt using a breaker bar installed in 1/2 inch square hole in tensioner arm.
2. Lift old belt over alternator pulley flange and remove.
3. When installing new belt over pulleys. Ensure all V-grooves make proper contact with pulley.
4. Ensure belt is properly installed on each pulley.

## WATER PUMP
### REPLACE

1. Drain cooling system, then remove engine cooling fan and shroud.
2. Release belt tensioner, then remove accessory drive belt, **Fig. 26.**
3. Remove water pump pulley attaching bolts, then remove water pump pulley.
4. Remove water pump attaching bolts, then remove water pump.
5. Reverse procedure to install. **Torque** water pump and water pump pulley attaching bolts to 15-22 ft. lbs.

## FUEL PUMP
### REPLACE

1. Relieve fuel system pressure as outlined under "Fuel System Pressure Relief."
2. Using suitable tool, drain fuel tank at fuel filler neck.
3. Raise and support vehicle.
4. Disconnect fuel supply and return line fittings and vent line.
5. Disconnect fuel pump and sender electrical connectors.
6. Remove fuel tank attaching support straps, then carefully lower fuel tank assembly. Ensure dirt does not enter tank or fuel system.
7. Using Fuel Tank Sender Wrench No. D74P-9275-A or equivalent, turn fuel pump locking ring counterclockwise, then remove locking ring.
8. Remove fuel pump assembly, then remove and discard seal ring.
9. Reverse procedure to install, noting the following:
   a. Once fuel pump is installed, using Fuel Pressure Gauge tool No. T80L-9974-B or equivalent on the fuel charging assembly Schrader valve, turn ignition from OFF to ON position for 3 seconds. Repeat OFF to ON switching 5 to 10 times until pressure gauge shows at least 35 psi.

## TIGHTENING SPECIFICATIONS

| Year | Component | Torque/Ft.Lbs. |
|---|---|---|
| 1991–92 | Alternator To Cylinder Block | 15-22 |
| | Camshaft Bolt | 81-95 |
| | Camshaft Cover Bolt | 6-8.8 |
| | Connecting Rod Bolt | ① |
| | Cylinder Front Cover Bolt | 15-22 |
| | Cylinder Head Bolt | ② |
| | Damper To Crankshaft Bolt | 114-121 |
| | EGR Valve To INtake Manifold | 15-22 |
| | Exhaust Manifold To Cylinder Head Bolt | 15-22 |
| | Exhaust Pipe To Exhaust Manifold | 20-30 |
| | Front Engine Mount Attaching Bolts | 45-59 |
| | Front Engine Mount Through Bolts | 15-22 |
| | Intake Manifold To Cylinder Head Bolt | 53-64③ |
| | Oil Inlet Tube To Main Bearing Cap | 15-22 |
| | Oil Inlet Tube To Oil Pump Bolt | 6-8.8 |
| | Oil Pan Drain Plug | 7-9 |
| | Oil Pan To Cylinder Block | 15-22 |
| | Oil Pump To Cylinder Block | 6-8.8 |
| | Rear Engine Mount Attaching Bolt | 50-70 |
| | Rear Engine Mount Attaching Nut | 35-50 |
| | Spark Plug | 6.6-7.3 |
| | Thermostat Housing | 15-22 |
| | Water Pump To Cylinder Block | 15-22 |
| | Water Pump To Pulley Bolt | 15-22 |

①—Tighten to 18–25 ft. lbs., then rotate 85–95°.
②—Tighten to 15–22 ft. lbs., then rotate 85–95 °, then rotate again 85–95 °.
③—Retorque assembly with engine hot.

# 5.0L/V8-302 Engine

**NOTE:** On Vehicles Equipped With Airbags, Disarm Airbag System As Outlined Under "Airbag System Disarming" Before Any Diagnosis, Testing, Troubleshooting Or Repairs Are Performed. After All Diagnosis, Testing, Troubleshooting Or Repairs Have Been Completed, Rearm Airbag System As Outlined Under "Airbag System Disarming."

## INDEX



## AIRBAG SYSTEM DISARMING

**The electrical circuit necessary for system deployment is powered directly from the battery and a backup power supply. To avoid accidental deployment and possible personal injury, the airbag system must be deactivated prior to servicing or replacing any component located near or related to airbag system activation components.**

A back-up power supply is included in the system to provide airbag deployment in the event the battery or battery cables are damaged in an accident before the sensors can close. The power supply is a capacitor that will retain a charge for approximately 15 minutes after the battery ground cable is disconnected. **Backup power supply must be disconnected to deactivate airbag system.**

### 1989–91 MODELS

1. Disconnect battery ground cable.
2. Disconnect backup power supply as described under "Backup Power Supply, Replace" in the "Passive Restraint" section.
3. Remove four nut and washer assemblies securing airbag module to steering wheel, then disconnect airbag electrical connector. Attach jumper wire to airbag terminals on clockspring.
4. **On models equipped with passenger-side airbag,** disconnect airbag module connector located behind glove compartment. Attach a jumper wire to airbag terminals on wiring harness side of passenger airbag module connector
5. To reactivate, disconnect battery ground cable and backup power supply, then reverse remainder of deactivation procedure. **Torque** airbag module to steering wheel nut assemblies to 35-53 inch lbs.
6. Verify airbag lamp after reactivating system.

### 1992 MODELS

1. Disconnect positive battery cable and wait one minute.
2. Remove four nut and washer assemblies securing airbag to steering wheel.
3. Disconnect airbag electrical connector and install airbag simulator tool No. 105-00008 or equivalent.
4. **On models with passenger side airbag,** remove passenger airbag and disconnect electrical connector.
5. Install airbag simulator tool No. 105-00008 or equivalent.
6. **On all models,** connect positive battery cable.
7. To activate airbag system, disconnect positive battery cable and reverse procedure. **Torque** mounting nut and washer assemblies to 36-49 inch lbs.
8. Verify proper operation of airbag lamp.

## ENGINE MOUNT

## REPLACE

### TOWN CAR

Whenever self-locking mounting bolts and nuts are removed, they must be replaced with new self-locking bolts and nuts.

1. Remove fan shroud attaching screws, if necessary.
2. Remove the nut and through bolt attaching the insulator to the support bracket, **Fig. 1.**
3. Remove three bolts attaching insulators assembly to frame.
4. Raise the engine slightly with a jack and a wood block placed under the oil pan.
5. Remove insulator assembly.
6. Reverse procedure to install.

### MARK VII

1. Remove fan shroud attaching screws.
2. Raise and support engine using a jack and wood block placed under engine.
3. Remove insulator attaching nuts to No. 2 crossmember, **Fig. 2.**
4. Disconnect shift linkage.
5. Raise engine sufficiently with jack so insulator stud is remove from crossmember.
6. Remove transmission brace attached at righthand engine mount bracket.
7. Remove engine insulator attaching bolts from cylinder block, then remove insulator.
8. Reverse procedure to install.

## ENGINE

## REPLACE

On models equipped with Thermactor system, remove or disconnect components that will interfere with engine removal or installation.

1. Drain cooling system and crankcase.
2. Remove hood, then disconnect battery and alternator ground cables from cylinder block.
3. Remove air cleaner and duct assembly.
4. Disconnect upper and lower radiator hoses from engine block and transmission oil cooler lines from radiator.
5. Remove bolts attaching fan shroud to radiator.
6. Remove radiator, fan, spacer, pulley and fan shroud.
7. Remove alternator mounting bolts and position alternator aside.
8. Disconnect oil pressure sending unit wire connector and fuel line at fuel pump. Plug fuel tank line. On models equipped with electronic fuel injection, relieve pressure at the Schraeder type valve on the fuel charging valve before disconnecting fuel lines.
9. Disconnect accelerator cable from throttle and throttle valve vacuum line at intake manifold.
10. Disconnect transmission manual shift rod, then disconnect retracting spring at shift rod stud.
11. Disconnect transmission oil filler tube bracket from engine block.
12. **On models equipped with A/C,** isolate and remove compressor.
13. **On all models,** remove power steering pump bracket from cylinder head and position pump aside. Position pump so that fluid will not drain from reservoir.
14. Disconnect heater hoses from water pump and intake manifold and temperature sending unit wire connector.
15. Remove converter housing to engine upper attaching bolts.
16. Disconnect primary wire connector from ignition coil, then remove wiring harness from left rocker arm cover and position out of way. Disconnect ground strap from block. On EEC-IV equipped vehicles, disconnect wiring at sensors.
17. Raise front of vehicle and remove starter.
18. Disconnect exhaust pipes from exhaust manifold, then remove engine support insulators from brackets on frame.
19. Disconnect transmission oil cooler lines from retainer and remove converter housing inspection cover.
20. Disconnect flywheel from converter, secure converter to converter housing.
21. Remove remaining converter housing to engine attaching bolts, then lower vehicle and support transmission using a suitable jack.
22. Attach engine lifting device to lifting brackets on intake manifold, then raise engine slightly and disconnect from transmission.
23. Carefully lift engine from engine compartment.
24. Reverse procedure to install.

## INTAKE MANIFOLD

## REPLACE

1. Disconnect battery ground cable and drain cooling system.
2. Remove air cleaner, PCV hose and air intake duct, then disconnect electric choke heater tube, if applicable.
3. Remove accelerator cable bracket, then disconnect speed control linkage, TV cable and all vacuum lines from manifold.
4. Disconnect high tension lead and primary wiring connector from ignition coil, then remove coil and support bracket from manifold.
5. Disconnect high tension leads from spark plugs, then remove distributor cap, adapter and high tension leads as an assembly.
6. Disconnect fuel return and supply lines. **Relieve fuel pressure at valve on metal fuel rail located at LH front corner of engine before disconnecting fuel lines.**
7. Disconnect electrical leads from distributor, then remove hold down bolt and distributor. Mark position of rotor to aid installation.
8. Disconnect upper radiator hose, coolant temperature sending wire and throttle body cooler hoses at manifold.
9. Loosen hose clamp, then slide bypass hose off outlet housing.
10. Disconnect all remaining electrical connections that will interfere with manifold removal.
11. Disconnect crankcase vent hose assembly at rear of lower intake manifold, then the fuel evaporative purge tube, if so equipped.
12. Remove attaching bolts, then the upper intake manifold.
13. Remove lower intake manifold, together with fuel rails.
14. Reverse procedure to install, following tightening sequence **Fig 3.**

## CYLINDER HEAD

## REPLACE

Before installing cylinder head, wipe off engine block gasket surface and be cer-

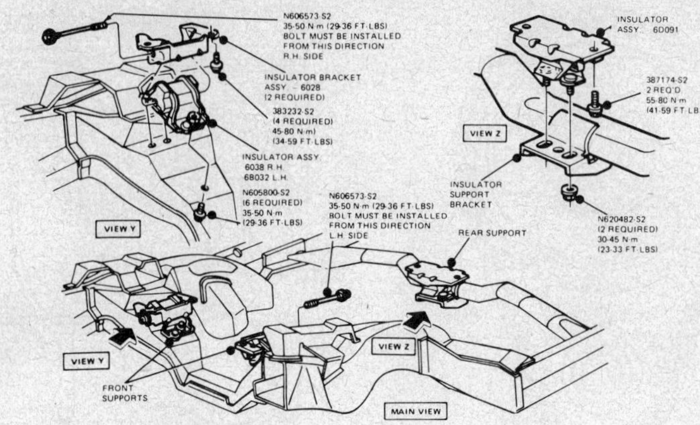


**Fig. 1 Engine mounts. Town Car**

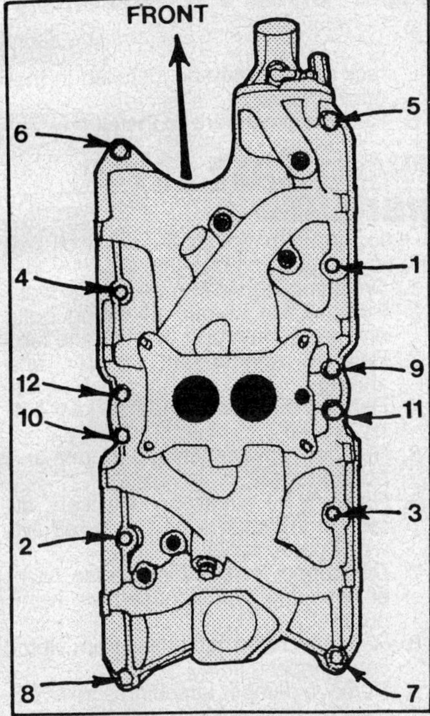


**Fig. 3 Intake manifold tightening sequence**

tain no foreign material has fallen into cylinder bores, bolt holes or in the valve lifter area. It is good practice to clean out bolt holes with compressed air.

Some cylinder head gaskets are coated with a special lacquer to provide a good seal once the parts have warmed up. Do not use any additional sealer on such gaskets. If the gasket does not have this lacquer coating, apply suitable sealer to both sides.

Tighten cylinder head bolts a little at a time in three steps in the sequence shown in the **Fig. 4.** Final tightening should be to the torque specifications. After the bolts have been torqued to specifications, they should not be disturbed.

1. Remove intake manifold.
2. Disconnect battery ground cable at cylinder head.

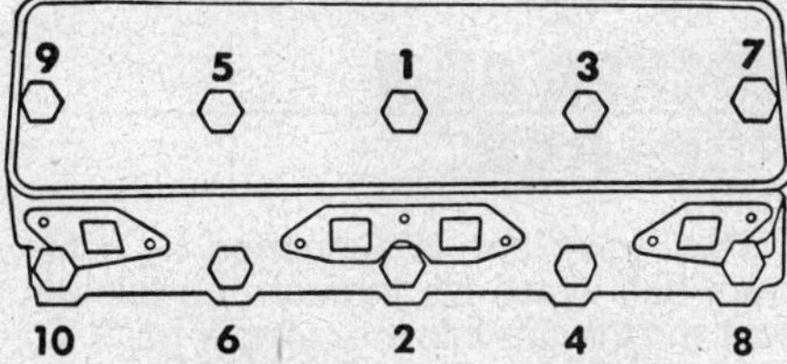


**Fig. 4 Cylinder head tightening sequence**

3. On Mark VII, if left head is being removed, remove A/C compressor (if equipped). Also remove and wire power steering pump out of the way. If equipped with Thermactor System, disconnect hose from air manifold on left cylinder head.
4. **On Town Car,** if left head is being removed, remove power steering pump (if equipped).
5. **On Mark VII,** If right head is to be removed, remove alternator mounting bracket bolt and spacer, ground wire and air cleaner inlet duct, and A/C compressor bracket.
6. **On Town Car,** if right head is to be removed, remove air conditioning compressor and mounting bracket (if equipped).
7. **On all models,** if right head is to be removed on an engine with Thermactor System, remove air pump from bracket. Disconnect hose from air manifold.
8. Disconnect exhaust manifolds at exhaust pipes.
9. Remove rocker arm covers. If equipped with Thermactor System, remove check valve from air manifold.
10. Remove fulcrum bolts, oil deflectors (if used), fulcrums and rocker arms. On all engines, remove pushrods. Keep rocker arms and pushrods in order so they can be installed in the same position.
11. Remove head bolts and lift head off block.
12. Reverse procedure to install. **Torque** cylinder head bolts in sequence shown in **Fig. 4.** 55-65 ft. lbs., then **torque** to 65-72 ft. lbs.

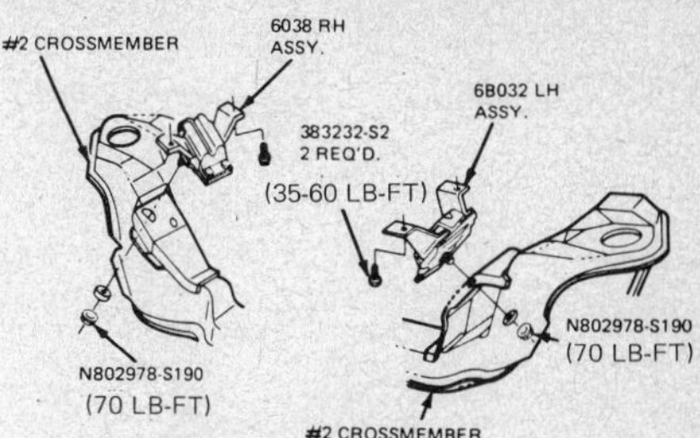


**Fig. 2 Engine mounts. Mark VII**

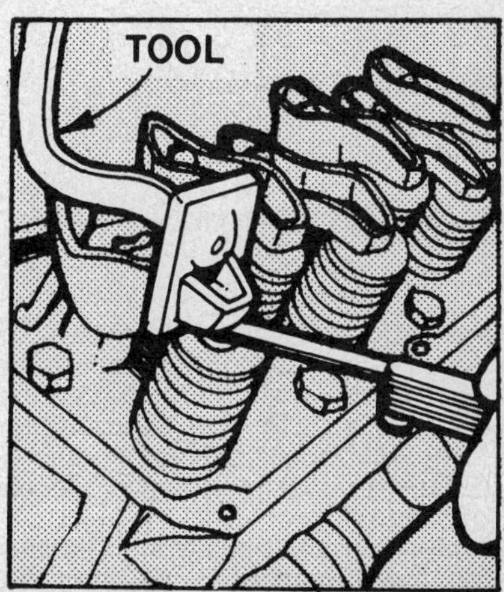


**Fig. 5 Compressing lifter to check valve clearance**

## VALVE CLEARANCE SPECIFICATIONS

| Engine | Int. | Exh. |
|---|---|---|
| 5.0L/V8-302 | .096-.146① | .096-.146① |
| 5.0L/V8-302 H.O. | .123-.146① | .123-.146① |

**①—With hydraulic lifter fully collapsed.**

## VALVES

### ADJUST

To eliminate the need of adjusting valve lash, a positive stop nut fulcrum bolt and seat is used on these engines.

It is very important that the correct pushrod be used and all components be installed and torqued as follows:

1. Position the piston of the cylinder being worked on at TDC of its compression stroke.
2. Install rocker arm, fulcrum seat and oil deflector. Install fulcrum bolt and torque to specifications.

A .060 inch shorter pushrod or a .060 inch longer rod is available for service to provide a means of compensating for dimensional changes in the valve mechanism. Valve stem-to-rocker arm clearance should be as specified, with the hydraulic lifter completely collapsed, **Fig. 5.** Repeated valve grind jobs will decrease this clearance to the point that if not compensated for the lifters will cease to funct-

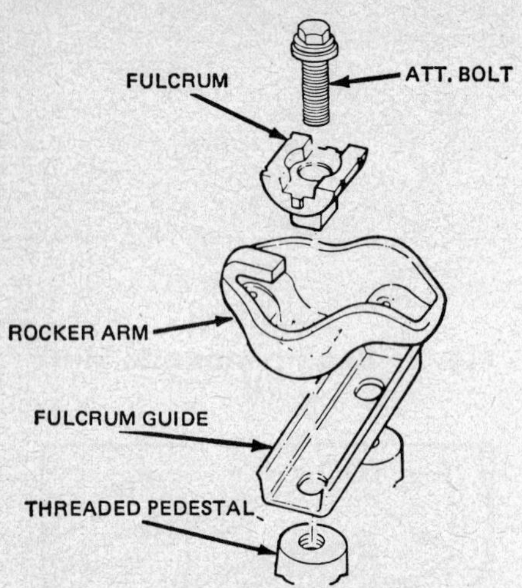


**Fig. 6 Rocker arm & related parts**

When checking valve clearance, if the clearance is less than the minimum, the .060 inch shorter pushrod should be used. If clearance is more than the maximum, the .060 inch longer pushrod should be used. To check valve clearance, proceed as follows:

1. Mark crankshaft pulley at three locations, with number 1 location at TDC timing mark (end of compression stroke), number 2 location one half turn (180°) clockwise from TDC and number 3 location three quarter turn clockwise (270°) from number 2 location.
2. Turn the crankshaft to the number 1 location and check the clearance on the following valves:
   a. 5.0L/V8-302: intake Nos. 1, 7 and 8; exhaust Nos. 1, 4 and 5.
   b. 5.0L/V8-302 H.O.: intake Nos. 1, 4 and 8; exhaust Nos. 1, 3 and 7.
3. Turn the crankshaft to the number 2 location and check the clearance on the following valves:
   a. 5.0L/V8-302: intake Nos. 4 and 5; exhaust Nos. 2 and 6.
   b. 5.0L/V8-302 H.O.: intake Nos. 3 and 7; exhaust Nos. 2 and 6.
4. Turn the crankshaft to the number 3 location and check the clearance on the following valves:
   a. 5.0L/V8-302: intake Nos. 2, 3 and 6; exhaust Nos. 3, 7 and 8.
   b. 5.0L/V8-302 H.O.: intake Nos. 2, 5 and 6; exhaust Nos. 4, 5 and 8.

## VALVE ARRANGEMENT
### FRONT TO REAR

5.0L/V8-302, Right Bank. . . I-E-I-E-I-E-I-E
5.0L/V8-302, Left Bank . . . . E-I-E-I-E-I-E-I

## VALVE LIFT SPECIFICATIONS

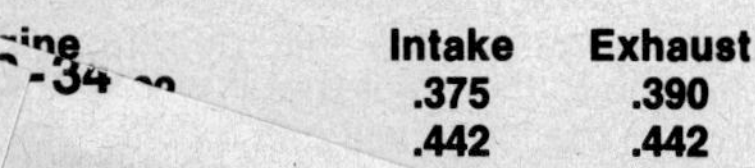

| [illegible]ine | Intake | Exhaust |
|---|---|---|
| [illegible] | .375 | .390 |
| [illegible] | .442 | .442 |

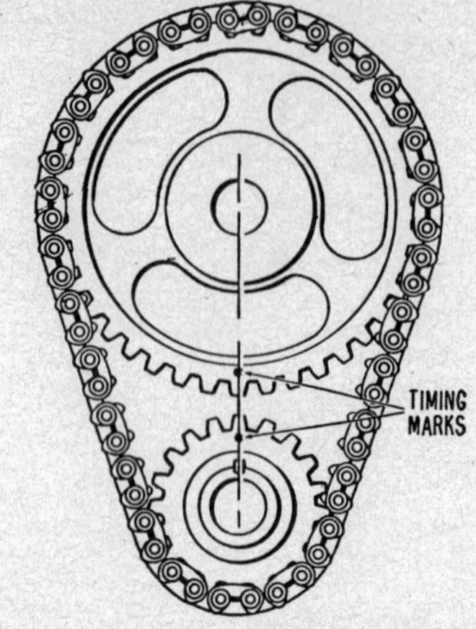


**Fig. 7 Valve timing marks**

## ROCKER ARM
### REPLACE

The rocker arm is supported by a fulcrum bolt which fits through the fulcrum seat and threads into the cylinder head. To disassemble, remove the bolt, fulcrum seat, fulcrum guide and rocker arm, **Fig. 6.**

## VALVE GUIDES

Valve guides in these engines are an integral part of the head and, therefore, cannot be removed. For service, guides can be reamed oversize to accommodate one of three service valves with oversize stems (.003 inch, .015 inch and .030 inch).

Check the valve stem clearance of each valve (after cleaning) in its respective valve guide. If the clearance exceeds the service limits of .0055 inch, ream the valve guides to accommodate the next oversize diameter valve.

## HYDRAULIC VALVE LIFTERS
### REPLACE

The internal parts of each hydraulic valve lifter assembly are a matched set. If these are mixed, improper valve operation may result. Therefore, disassemble, inspect and test each assembly separately to prevent mixing the parts.

All 5.0L/V8-302 engines are equipped with roller hydraulic lifters. Pushrods used on these engines have a collar at the upper end and must be installed in this position. To replace valve lifters, proceed as follows:

1. Remove intake manifold and related parts.
2. Remove rocker arm covers.
3. Loosen rocker arm stud nuts or bolts and rotate rocker arms to the side.
4. Lift out pushrods, keeping them in sequence in a rack so they may be installed in their original location.
5. Using a magnet rod, remove valve lifters and place them in sequence in a rack so they may be installed in their original location.
6. Reverse procedure to install.

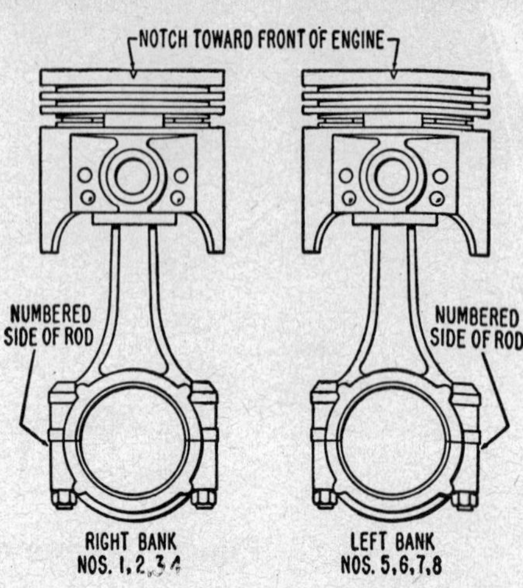


**Fig. 8 Piston & rod assembly**

## TIMING CASE COVER
### REPLACE

If necessary to replace the cover oil seal the cover must first be removed.

1. Drain cooling system and crankcase.
2. Remove fan shroud attaching bolts and position shroud over engine fan.
3. Remove engine fan, spacer and shroud.
4. Remove drive belts and A/C idler pulley bracket.
5. Remove power steering pump and position aside.
6. Remove all accessory brackets attached to water pump, then remove water pump pulley.
7. Disconnect lower radiator hose, heater hose and bypass hose from water pump.
8. Remove crankshaft pulley from vibration damper.
9. Remove damper attaching screw and washer, then using a suitable puller, remove damper.
10. If applicable, disconnect fuel pump outlet line, then remove fuel pump attaching bolts and position pump aside.
11. Remove oil level dipstick.
12. Remove oil pan to front cover attaching bolts.
13. Remove front cover to engine block attaching bolts, then remove front cover and water pump as an assembly. **Use a thin blade knife to cut oil pan gasket flush with cylinder block face prior to separating front cover from cylinder block.**
14. Reverse procedure to install.

## TIMING CHAIN
### REPLACE

1. Remove timing case cover as outlined previously.
2. Crank the engi ne until the timing mark on the camshaft sprocket is ad-

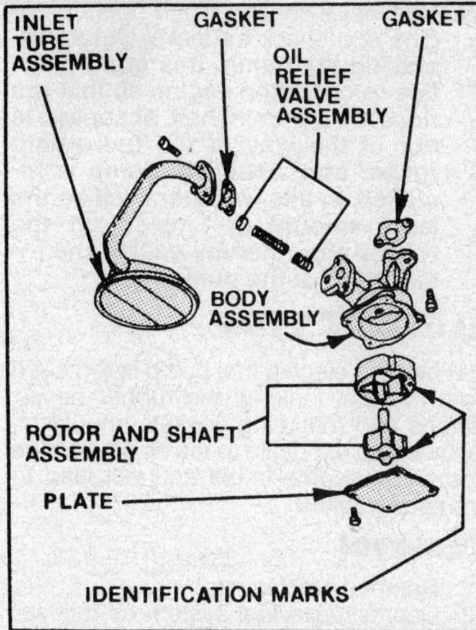


**Fig. 9 Oil pump assembly**

jacent to the timing mark on the crankshaft sprocket, **Fig. 7.**

3. Remove capscrews, lock plate and fuel pump eccentric from front of camshaft.
4. Place a screwdriver behind the camshaft sprocket and carefully pry the sprocket and chain off the camshaft.
5. Reverse the foregoing procedure to install the chain, being sure to align the timing marks as shown in **Fig. 7.**

## CAMSHAFT

### REPLACE

If it is necessary to replace the camshaft only, it may be accomplished without removing the engine from the chassis. However, if the camshaft bearings are to be replaced, the engine will have to be removed. To remove the camshaft, refer to the procedure outlined below. **It may be necessary to remove or reposition radiator, A/C compressor and grille components to provide adequate clearance.**

1. To remove camshaft, remove front cover and timing chain.
2. Remove distributor cap and spark plug wires, then remove distributor.
3. Disconnect automatic transmission oil cooler lines from radiator and remove radiator.
4. Remove intake manifold and TBI as an assembly.
5. Remove rocker arm covers.
6. Loosen rocker arm fulcrum or bolts and rotate rocker arms to one side.
7. Remove pushrods, keeping them in sequence in a rack so they may be installed in their original location.
8. Using a magnet, remove valve lifters and place them in a rack in sequence so they may be installed in their original location.
9. Remove camshaft thrust plate, and carefully pull camshaft from engine, using care to avoid damaging camshaft bearings.
10. Reverse procedure to install. **Prior to installation of the camshaft, lubricate pushrods and camshaft lobes with lubricant part No. D0AZ-19584-A or equivalent for 5.0L/V8-302 engines. Using engine oil SF, lubricate valve tappets & bores.**

## PISTON & ROD ASSEMBLY

If the old pistons are serviceable, make certain that they are installed on the rods from which they were removed. The assembly must be assembled as shown in **Fig. 8.**

Check side clearance between connecting rods and crankshaft journal. Clearance should be .010-.020 inch.

## PISTONS, RINGS & PINS

Pistons are available in oversizes of .003, .020, .030 and .040 inch.

Piston pins are available in oversizes of .001 and .002 inch.

Rings are available in oversizes of .020, .030 and .040 inch.

## MAIN & ROD BEARINGS

Main and rod bearings are available in standard size and undersizes of .001, .002, .010, 020, .030 and .040 inch.

## CRANKSHAFT REAR OIL SEAL

### REPLACE

A one-piece rear oil seal is used on these engines. To replace seal, proceed as follows:

1. Using a sharp awl, punch one hole into seal metal surface between seal lip and engine block.
2. Using slide hammer tool No. T82L-9533-B or equivalent, screw tool into hole in seal and remove seal by gently pulling rearward. Use caution to avoid damaging sealing surface.
3. Lubricate new seal with engine oil, then position seal on installer tool No. T82L-6701-A, or equivalent.
4. With spring end of seal facing towards engine, install tool, then alternately tighten bolts until rear face of seal is within .005 inch of the engine block.

## OIL PAN

### REPLACE

1. Disconnect battery ground cable and remove air cleaner assembly.
2. Disconnect accelerator cable and kickdown rod from throttle.
3. Remove accelerator mounting bracket bolts and bracket, then the EGR valve and cooler, if applicable.

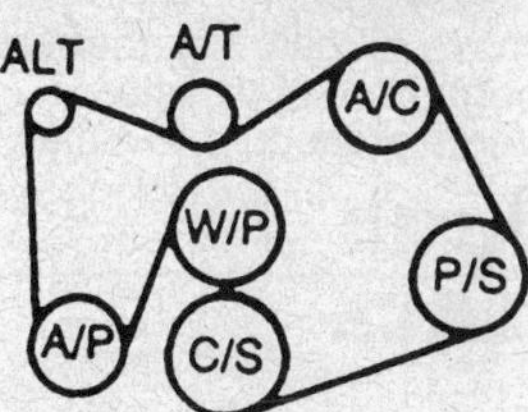


**Fig. 10 Serpentine drive belt routing**

4. Remove fan shroud attaching screws and position shroud over fan.
5. Disconnect wiper motor electrical connector and remove wiper motor.
6. Disconnect windshield washer hose.
7. Remove wiper motor mounting cover.
8. Remove oil level dipstick, then the dipstick tube retaining bolt from exhaust manifold.
9. If equipped with EGR cooler, remove Thermactor air dump tube retaining clamp, then the Thermactor crossover tube at rear of engine.
10. Raise and support vehicle, then drain engine oil.
11. Remove starter motor.
12. Disconnect fuel tank fuel line at fuel pump and plug line. **Vehicles equipped with electronic fuel injection have high pressure at the electric fuel pump. Pressure must be relieved at the schraeder type valve on the fuel charging assembly (CFI), or at valve on metal fuel rail located at LH front corner of engine (SFI) before disconnecting fuel lines.**
13. Disconnect exhaust pipes from manifolds.
14. **If equipped with EGR cooler,** remove thermactor secondary air tube to converter housing clamps.
15. **On all models,** remove dipstick tube from oil pan.
16. Loosen transmission mount attaching nuts.
17. Remove engine mount through bolts.
18. Remove shift crossover bolts at transmission.
19. Disconnect transmission kickdown rod.
20. Remove brake line retainer from front crossmember.
21. With a suitable jack, raise engine as far as possible.
22. Place a block of wood between each engine mount and chassis bracket. When engine is secured in this position, remove jack, then the low oil level sensor, if equipped.
23. If equipped, remove stabilizer bar attaching bolts and lower stabilizer bar.
24. Remove transmission cooling line clamp retaining bolt, then position cooling lines aside.
25. Remove oil pan attaching bolts and lower pan to crossmember.
26. Remove oil pickup tube and oil pump retaining nuts and bolts, then lower tube and oil pump into oil pan.

27. Remove oil pan, together with pump, through front of vehicle.
28. Reverse procedure to install.

## OIL PUMP REPLACE

The oil pan must be removed to gain access to the oil pump. Refer to "Oil Pan, Replace" for procedure.

## OIL PUMP SERVICE

To disassemble, remove the pump cover plate, **Fig. 9**, and lift out the rotor and shaft. Remove cotter pin that secures relief valve plug in pump housing. Drill a small hole and insert a self-tapping screw into plug, then using pliers remove plug from pump housing. Then remove the retainer spring and relief valve from the pump housing. Inspect the pump as follows:

1. With all parts clean and dry, check the inside of the pump housing and the outer race and rotor for damage or excessive wear.
2. Check the mating surface of the pump cover for wear. If this surface is worn, scored or grooved, replace the cover.
3. Measure the clearance between the outer race and housing. This clearance should be .001-.013.
4. With the rotor assembly installed in the housing, place a straightedge over the rotor assembly and housing. Measure the clearance between the straightedge and the rotor and outer race. Recommended limits are .0016-.004 inch.
5. Check the driveshaft to housing bearing clearance by measuring the O.D. of the shaft and the I.D. of the housing bearing. The recommended clearance limits are .0015-.0030 inch.
6. Inspect the relief valve spring for a collapsed or worn condition.
7. Check the relief valve piston for scores and free operation in the bore. The specified clearance is .0015-.0030 inch.

## BELT TENSION DATA

| Belt | New | Used |
|---|---|---|
| **1989–91** | | |
| **Except 1/4 inch** | **140** | **105** |
| **4 Ribs Except Air Pump** | **130** | **115** |
| **4 Ribs Air Pump** | **110** | **105** |
| **5 Ribs** | **150** | **135** |
| **6 Ribs①** | **160** | **145** |
| **6 Ribs②** | **113** | **110** |

**①—w/tensioner.**
**②—w/absorber.**

## SERPENTINE DRIVE BELTS

### BELT ROUTING

Refer to **Fig. 10**, for serpentine drive belt routing.

### BELT REPLACEMENT

1. Lift or rotate automatic tensioner.
2. Remove old belt.
3. Install new belt over pulleys. Ensure all V-grooves make proper contact with pulley.

## COOLING SYSTEM BLEED

These engines do not require a specified bleed procedure. After filling cooling system, run engine to operating temperature with radiator/pressure cap off. Air will then be automatically bled through cap opening.

## THERMOSTAT REPLACE

1. Drain cooling system until coolant level is below the thermostat.
2. Disconnect bypass hose at thermostat housing.
3. Mark location of distributor, then loosen hold down clamp and rotate distributor to gain access.
4. Disconnect upper radiator hose at thermostat housing, then remove two housing retaining bolts.
5. Remove thermostat housing and gasket.
6. Reverse procedure to install. Torque bolts to specifications.

## WATER PUMP REPLACE

1. Drain cooling system, then remove fan shroud attaching bolts and position shroud over fan.
2. Remove fan, spacer and shroud.
3. Remove drive belts, then remove A/C idler pulley bracket.
4. Remove power steering pump and position aside.
5. Remove all accessory brackets which attach to water pump, then remove water pump pulley.
6. Remove lower radiator hose, heater hose and bypass hose from water pump.
7. Remove water pump to front cover attaching bolts, then remove water pump.
8. Reverse procedure to install.

## FUEL PUMP REPLACE

### MECHANICAL TYPE

1. Disconnect fuel lines from fuel pump.
2. Remove fuel pump attaching bolts and the fuel pump and gasket.
3. Remove all gasket material from the pump and block gasket surfaces. Apply sealer to both sides of new gasket.
4. Position gasket on pump flange and hold pump in position against its mounting surface. Make sure rocker arm is riding on camshaft eccentric.
5. Press pump tight against its mounting. Install retaining screws and tighten them alternately.
6. Connect fuel lines. Then operate engine and check for leaks. **Before installing the pump, it is good practice to crank the engine so that the nose of the camshaft eccentric is out of the way of the fuel pump rocker arm when the pump is installed. In this way there will be the least amount of tension on the rocker arm, thereby easing the installation of the pump.**

### ELECTRIC TYPE

When the electric fuel pump is removed from the fuel tank, all the rubber hoses, clamps and mounting gaskets should be replaced, as exposure to the air causes the hoses to become brittle and will lead to premature failure.

#### Removal

1. Remove air cleaner.
2. Depressurize fuel system as follows:
   a. **On CFI engines,** attach fuel pressure gauge tool No. T80L-9974-B or equivalent to fuel diagnostic valve on the fuel charging assembly, then slowly depressurize fuel system.
   b. **On EFI engines,** depressurize fuel system at valve located in fuel rail on LH front corner of engine.
3. **On all models,** siphon fuel from fuel tank, then raise and support vehicle.
4. Disconnect fuel supply, return and vent lines at the left and right side rear axle frame kickdowns.
5. Disconnect electrical connector in front of fuel tank.
6. Disconnect and remove fuel filler tube.
7. Remove fuel tank support straps, then the fuel tank.
8. Clean all dirt accumulated around fuel pump attaching flange, then disconnect supply and return line fittings and the electrical connector.
9. Turn fuel pump lock ring counterclockwise and remove lock ring.
10. Remove fuel pump and bracket assembly from fuel tank. Discard seal ring.

#### Installation

1. Clean fuel tank mounting surface and seal ring groove.
2. Lightly coat new seal ring with heavy grease to hold it in place, then install into fuel ring groove.
3. Carefully install fuel pump and bracket assembly into tank, ensuring filter is not damaged during installation. Ensure locating keys are positioned in keyways and seal ring remains in groove.
4. Holding pump assembly in place, install lock ring finger tight, ensuring all locking tabs are positioned under fuel tank ring tabs. Continue to turn lock ring clockwise until ring contacts stop.
5. Connect fuel pump electrical connector, then lubricate fittings and reconnect fuel lines.
6. Install fuel tank and tighten support straps.

7. Reconnect fuel sender and fuel pump wiring harness, then lower vehicle.
8. Install fuel filler tube and reconnect vent line.
9. Lubricate fittings at right and lefthand side of rear axle frame, reconnect finger tight, then tighten an additional 1/4 turn.
10. Fill fuel tank with at least 10 gallons of fuel and check for leaks.
11. Activate fuel pump until system is fully pressurized, then check all fittings for leakage. Repair leaks as necessary.
12. Start engine and recheck for leaks.

# TIGHTENING SPECIFICATIONS

| Year | Component | Torque/ft. lbs. |
|---|---|---|
| 1989-92 | Alternator Adjustment Arm To Water Pump Stud Nut | 20-39 |
| | Alternator Adjustment Arm To Alternator Bolt | 24-40 |
| | Alternator And Thermactor Pump Bracket To Cylinder Head | ③ |
| | Camshaft Sprocket Gear Bolt | 40-45 |
| | Camshaft Thrust Plate | 9-12 |
| | Connecting Rod Nut | 19-24 |
| | Crankshaft Damper Bolt | 70-90 |
| | Cylinder Head Bolt | ① |
| | Distributor Hold-Down Bolt | 18-26 |
| | EGR Valve To Spacer Intake Manifold | 12-18 |
| | Exhaust Manifold | 18-24 |
| | Fan To Water Pump Hub Bolt | 15-22 |
| | Flywheel Bolt | 75-85 |
| | Front Cover Bolts | 12-18 |
| | Intake Manifold Lower | 12-18 |
| | Intake Manifold To Cylinder Head | ② |
| | Intake Manifold Upper | 12-18 |
| | Main Bearing Cap | 60-70 |
| | Oil Filter Insert To Cylinder Block Adapter Bolt | 20-30 |
| | Oil Inlet Tube To Oil Pump Bolt | 12-18 |
| | Oil Inlet Tube To Main Bearing Cap Nut | 22-32 |
| | Oil Pan | 6-9 |
| | Oil Drain Plug | 15-25 |
| | Oil Pump To Cylinder Block | 22-32 |
| | Pulley To Damper Bolt | 35-50 |
| | Rocker Arm Cover | 10-13 |
| | Rocker Arm Fulcrum | 18-25 |
| | Spark Plugs | 5-10 |
| | Thermactor Pump Pivot Bolt | 35-50 |
| | Thermactor Pump Adjustment Arm To Pump | 22-32 |
| | Thermactor Pump Pulley To Pump Hub | ④ |
| | Thermostat Housing | 17-25 |
| | Throttle Body Attaching Nut | 12-18 |
| | Vacuum fittings To Intake Manifold | 10-13⑤ |
| | Water Outlet Housing | 12-18 |
| | Water Pump To Cylinder Block Front Cover | 12-18 |

①—Torque to 55-65 ft. lbs., then torque to 65-72 ft. lbs.
②—Torque to 15-20 ft. lbs., then torque to 23-25 ft. lbs.
③—3/8 inch bolt 22-32 ft. lbs.; 7/16 inch bolt 40-55 ft. lbs.
④—Inch lbs.
⑤—Apply Teflon Tape.

# Rear Axle & Suspension, Rear Wheel Drive Models

## INDEX



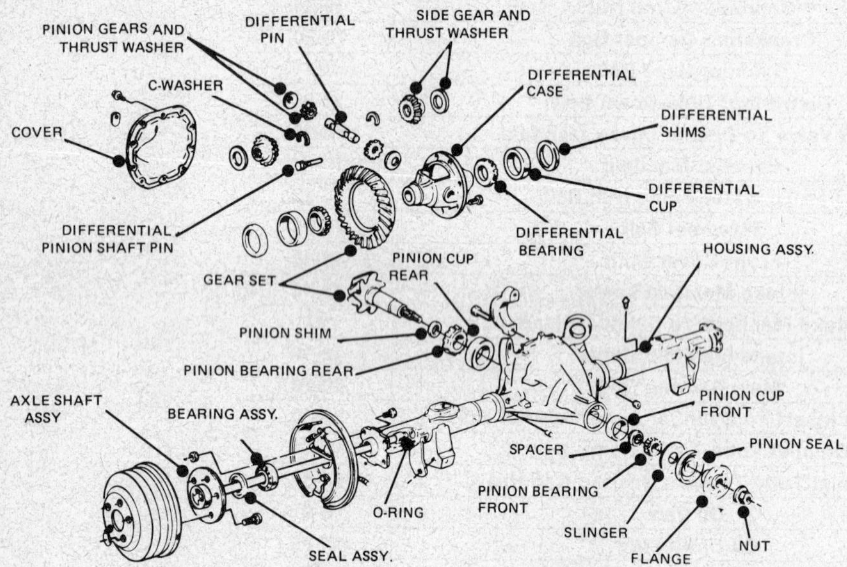


**Fig. 1 Integral carrier type rear axle assembly (typical)**

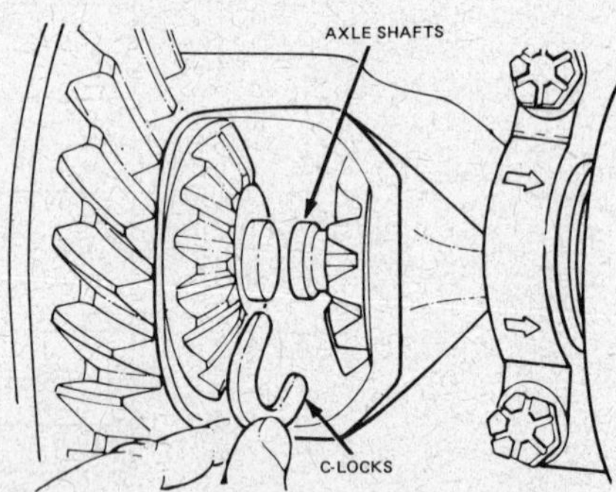


**Fig. 2 Axle shaft "C" locks**

## DESCRIPTION

**Fig. 1** illustrates the rear axle assembly used on these vehicles. When necessary to overhaul these units, refer to the rear axle specifications table at the beginning of this chapter.

The gear set consists of a ring gear and an overhung drive pinion which is supported by two opposed tapered roller bearings, **Fig. 1.** The differential case is a one-piece design with openings allowing assembly of the internal parts and lubricant flow. The differential pinion shaft is retained with a threaded bolt (lock) assembled to the case.

The roller type wheel bearings have no inner race, and the rollers directly contact the bearing journals of the axle shafts. The axle shafts do not use an inner and outer bearing retainer. Rather, they are held in the axle by means of C-locks. These C-locks also fit into a machined recess in the differential side gears within the differential case. There is no retainer bolt access hole in the axle shaft flange.

## REAR AXLE

### REPLACE

1. Raise vehicle and position safety stands under the rear frame crossmember.
2. Disconnect driveshaft at companion flange and secure it to vehicle using wire.
3. Remove wheels and brake drums. If equipped with rear disc brakes, remove calipers from anchor plates and rotors from shafts.
4. **The rear anti-lock brake sensor ring must be removed before axle shafts are removed.** The sensor ring is located between the brake drum and axle shaft.
5. Support axle housing with floor jack.
6. Disconnect brake line from clips that retain line to axle housing, then disconnect vent from rear axle housing. Some axle vents may be secured to the housing assembly through the brake junction block. When reinstalling, apply thread locking compound E0AZ-19554-B or equivalent to ensure proper retention.
7. Disconnect shock absorbers from axle housing.
8. Disconnect upper control arms from mountings on axle housing.
9. Lower axle housing assembly until coils springs are released, then remove springs.
10. Disconnect lower control arms from mountings on axle housing, then lower the axle housing and remove it from vehicle.
11. Reverse procedure to install.

## AXLE SHAFT, BEARING & SEAL

### REPLACE

1. Raise car on hoist and remove wheels.
2. Drain differential lubricant.
3. Remove brake drums.
4. Remove differential housing cover.
5. Position safety stands under rear frame member and lower hoist to allow axle to lower as far as possible.
6. Working through differential case opening, remove pinion shaft lock bolt and pinion shaft.
7. Push axle shaft inward toward center of axle housing and remove C-lock(s) from housing, **Fig. 2.**
8. Remove axle shaft, using extreme care to avoid contact of shaft seal lip

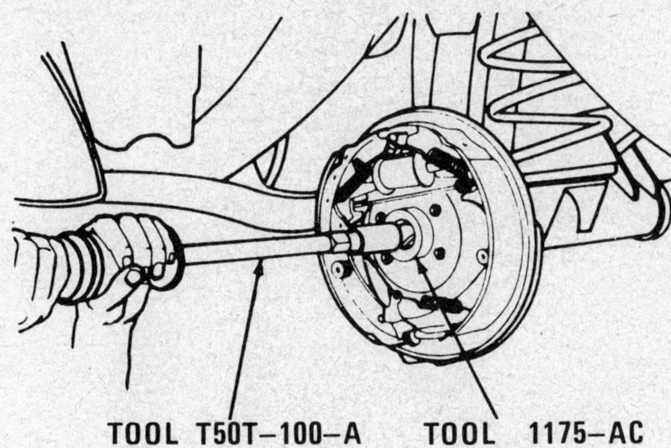
TOOL T50T–100–A
TOOL 1175–AC

**Fig. 3 Removing axle shaft seal and bearing**

with any portion of axle shaft except seal journal.

9. Use a hook-type puller to remove seal and bearing, **Fig. 3.**
10. Reverse procedure to install, using suitable driving tools to install seal and bearing. Lubricate new bearing with rear axle lubricant and apply grease between the lips of the seal. Apply silicone sealant to carrier casting face as shown, **Fig. 4**, then install housing cover. **Torque** cover bolts to 30 ft. lbs.

## PROPELLER SHAFT REPLACE

To maintain proper drive line balance, mark the driveshaft, universal joints, slip yoke and companion flange before removing the shaft assembly so it can be reinstalled in its original position.

1. Remove companion flange to drive pinion flange attaching bolts.
2. Pull driveshaft rearward until slip yoke clears transmission extension housing.
3. Reverse procedure to install.

## SHOCK ABSORBER REPLACE

### MARK VII & 1990–92 TOWN CAR

**Turn air suspension switch off before replacing shock absorber.**

1. Open trunk to gain access to upper shock absorber attachment.
2. Remove rubber cap if equipped, from shock absorber stud, then remove nut, washer and insulator.
3. Raise vehicle and support rear axle.
4. Remove lower shock absorber protective cover, then remove cross bolt and nut from lower shock absorber mounting bracket.
5. From underneath vehicle, compress shock absorber to clear hole in upper shock tower, then remove shock absorber. **These models are equipped with gas pressurized shock absorbers which extend unassisted during removal. Do not apply heat or flame to the shock absorber tube during removal.**
6. Reverse procedure to install. While holding shock absorber in position, **torque** lower cross bolt to 59 ft. lbs. Lower vehicle and install upper mounting nut, washer and insulator and **torque** nut to 24 to 26 ft. lbs.

### 1989 TOWN CAR

1. With the rear axle supported properly disconnect shock absorber at upper mounting and compress it to clear hole.
2. Disconnect shock absorber from lower attachment.
3. Reverse procedure to install. **The Town Car is equipped with gas pressurized shock absorbers which extend unassisted during removal. Do not apply heat or flame to the shock absorber tube during removal.**

## COIL SPRINGS REPLACE

### TOWN CAR

1. Raise rear of vehicle and support at frame side sills. Support rear axle with a suitable jack.
2. Disconnect shock absorbers and stabilizer bar from axle housing, **Fig. 5.**
3. Disconnect righthand parking brake cable from righthand upper arm retainer.
4. Lower the axle housing until coil springs are released.

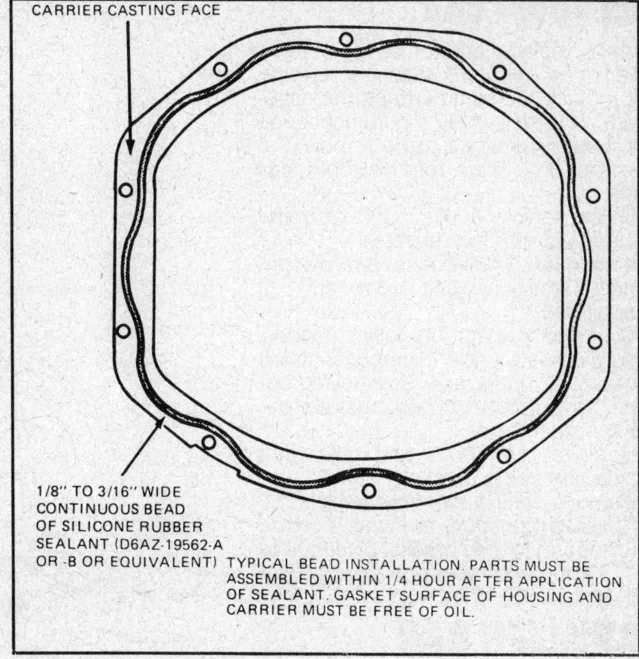
CARRIER CASTING FACE
1/8" TO 3/16" WIDE CONTINUOUS BEAD OF SILICONE RUBBER SEALANT (D6AZ-19562-A OR -B OR EQUIVALENT)
TYPICAL BEAD INSTALLATION. PARTS MUST BE ASSEMBLED WITHIN 1/4 HOUR AFTER APPLICATION OF SEALANT. GASKET SURFACE OF HOUSING AND CARRIER MUST BE FREE OF OIL.

**Fig. 4 Applying sealant to carrier casting face**

5. Remove springs and insulators, **Fig. 5.**
6. Reverse procedure to install.

## CONTROL ARMS REPLACE

### MARK VII & 1990–92 TOWN CAR

#### Upper Arm

Always replace control arm in pairs. If one arm requires replacement, replace the same arm on the opposite side of the vehicle.

1. Turn air suspension switch off.
2. Raise and support vehicle, then disconnect rear height sensor from side arm. Note position of sensor adjustment bracket to aid in reassembly.
3. Remove upper arm to axle and upper arm to frame bracket pivot bolts and nuts.
4. Remove upper control arm.
5. Reverse procedure to install. **Torque** pivot bolts to 100 ft. lbs.

#### Lower Arm

1. Turn air suspension switch to off position, then raise and support vehicle and remove wheel assembly.
2. Vent air springs to atmosphere by removing air spring solenoid.
3. Remove the two air spring to lower control arm retaining bolts, and remove air spring from lower arm.
4. Remove control arm to frame and control arm to axle bracket pivot bolts and nuts.
5. Remove lower control arm.
6. Reverse procedure to install. **Torque** pivot bolts to 100 ft. lbs.

## 1989 TOWN CAR

Always replace control arms in pairs. Therefore, if one arm requires replacement, replace the same arm on the opposite side of vehicle. Also, if both upper and lower control arms are to be removed at the same time, first remove both coil springs.

1. Raise vehicle and support at frame side rails with jack stands.
2. If removing lower control arm, disconnect stabilizer bar from arm (if equipped).
3. With shock absorbers fully extended, support axle under differential pinion nose and under axle. If removing upper arm, disconnect parking brake cable from retainer.
4. Remove pivot bolts and nuts from axle and frame brackets, **Fig. 5.**
5. Remove control arm from vehicle.
6. Reverse procedure to install. **Torque** lower arm to axle bracket pivot bolt to 118 ft. lbs. and lower arm to frame pivot bolt to 135 ft. lbs.

# STABILIZER BAR REPLACE

## MARK VII & 1990–92 TOWN CAR

1. Turn air suspension switch off, then raise and support vehicle.
2. Remove stabilizer bar to link attaching nuts.
3. Remove stabilizer bar to bushing U-clamp attaching nuts, then the stabilizer bar.
4. Reverse procedure to install.

## 1989 TOWN CAR

1. Raise rear of vehicle and support at frame side sills.
2. Lower axle housing until shock absorbers are fully extended.
3. Remove the four bolts, nuts and spacers retaining stabilizer bar lower control arms, then remove stabilizer bar.
4. Reverse procedure to install. **Torque** bolts to 70-92 ft. lbs.

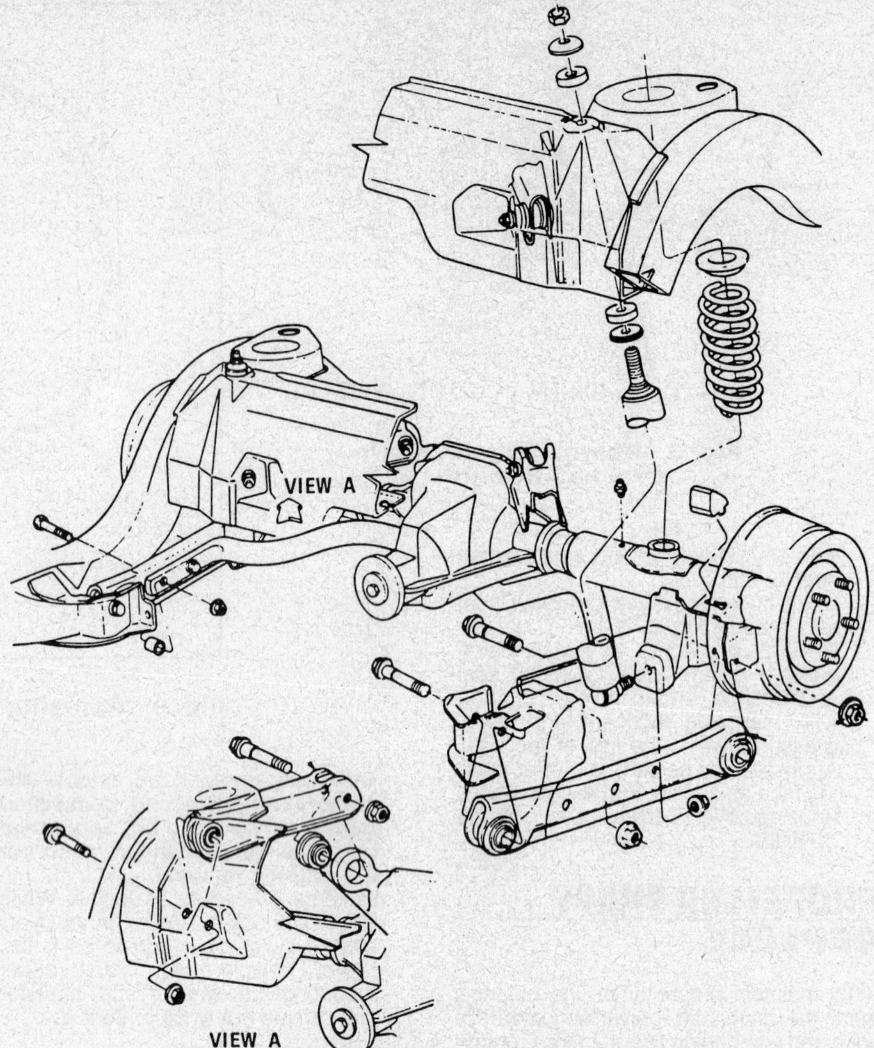


**Fig. 5 Rear suspension. Town Car**

# TIGHTENING SPECIFICATIONS

| Year | Component | Torque/ft. lbs. |
|---|---|---|
| 1989① | Brake Backing Plate Bolts | 20-40 |
| | Differential Bearing Cap Bolt | 70-85 |
| | Differential Pinion Shaft Lock Bolt | 15-30 |
| | Lower Arm To Axle | 70-100 |
| | Lower Arm To Frame | 80-105 |
| | Lug Nuts | 85-104 |
| | Oil Filler Plug | 15-30 |
| | Rear Cover Screws | ④ |
| | Ring Gear Attaching Bolts | 70-85 |
| | Shock Absorber (Upper) | 19-27 |
| | Shock Absorber To Axle Bracket | 52-85 |
| | Upper Arm To Frame | 80-105 |
| | Upper Arm To Axle | 70-100 |
| | Stabilizer Bar To Lower Arm | 32-52 |

## TIGHTENING SPECIFICATIONS—Continued

| Year | Component | Torque/ft. lbs. |
|---|---|---|
| 1989-92② | Air Spring To Lower Arm | 25-35 |
| | Brake Backing Plate Bolts | 20-40 |
| | Clevis Bracket To Axle | 55-70 |
| | Differential Bearing Cap Bolt | 70-85 |
| | Differential Pinion Shaft Lock Bolt | 15-30 |
| | Lower Arm To Axle | 90-100 |
| | Lower Arm To Frame | 80-105 |
| | Lug Nuts | 85-104 |
| | Oil Filler Plug | 15-30 |
| | Rear Cover Screws | ④ |
| | Ring Gear Attaching Bolts | 70-85 |
| | Sensor Lower Bracket To Frame | 7-10 |
| | Sensor Upper Bracket To Frame | 110-150③ |
| | Shock Absorber To Frame | 17-27 |
| | Shock Absorber To Clevis Bracket | 45-60 |
| | Stabilizer Bar To Axle | 13-20 |
| | Stabilizer Bar To Body | 13-18 |
| | Upper Arm To Axle | 70-100 |
| | Upper Arm To Frame | 80-105 |

①—Except air suspension.
②—Air suspension.
③—Inch lbs.
④—Plastic cover 15-20 ft. lbs.; metal cover 25-35 ft. lbs.

# Rear Suspension, Front Wheel Drive Models

## INDEX



## DESCRIPTION

The Continental utilizes a fully independent rear suspension consisting of MacPherson struts with integral air springs and dual-damping shock absorbers, counterbalancing torsion springs and a height sensor.

The air suspension and dual damping functions are controlled by a microcomputer based module which receives inputs for vehicle speed, door switch position, damping actuator feedback, steering wheel turning rate and angle, engine vacuum, throttle position, brake actuation, ignition switching, and vehicle ride height. The dual-damping function automatically switches from a soft to firm ride when the driving situation (hard cornering, acceleration or braking, etc.) dictates the need for increased damping effect.

The rear struts, **Fig. 1**, use a dual path mount which separates the strut and air spring mounting surfaces, to help provide for maximum isolation. The counterbalancing torsion springs, fitted between the strut and lower control arm, produce an outward force on the strut that tends to offset the binding forces induced by the rear wheels. The rotary design Hall effect type height sensor, **Fig. 2**, permits multiple height positions to be defined, resulting in specialized leveling during all types of driving and load characteristics.

## SERVICE PRECAUTION

**Always place the air suspension switch in the Off position before performing any work, or whenever raising the rear suspension.**

## STRUT ASSEMBLY REPLACE

1. Position suitable jack or hoist under vehicle, then raise just enough to contact body.
2. Disconnect air suspension electrical wiring and all related parts that will interfere with strut removal.
3. Loosen, but do not remove, the strut to inner body attaching nuts.
4. Raise and support vehicle, then remove wheel and tire assembly.
5. Remove brake hose to strut bracket attaching clip, then position hose aside.
6. If applicable, remove stabilizer bar attaching hardware and insulators, then separate stabilizer bar from link.
7. If applicable, remove tension strut to spindle attaching nut, washer and insulator, then move spindle rearward until it can be separated from tension strut.
8. Mark position of notch on toe adjustment cam, **Fig. 3.**
9. Remove strut to spindle pinch bolt, then using a pry bar or other suitable tool, separate pinch joint as necessary to allow for strut removal.
10. Disengage strut from pinch joint, then lower vehicle as necessary to allow removal of upper attaching nuts.
11. Remove strut from vehicle.
12. Reverse procedure to install.

## TENSION STRUT REPLACE

1. If necessary, disconnect air suspension electrical wiring and all related parts that will interfere with tension strut removal.
2. Raise vehicle on frame contact hoist using lift pads located rearward of front wheels and forward of rear wheels. Raise hoist only enough to contact body.
3. Loosen, but do not remove, the upper strut to inner body attaching nuts, then raise and support vehicle.
4. Remove wheel and tire assembly.
5. Remove tension strut to spindle and tension strut to body attaching nuts.
6. While moving spindle rearward, remove tension strut from vehicle.
7. Reverse procedure to install, using new washers and bushings.

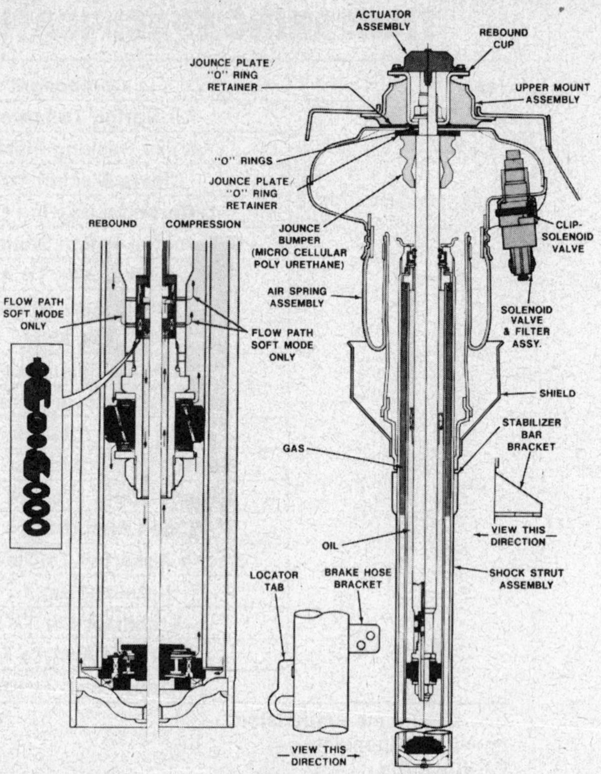

Fig. 1 Cross sectional view of rear strut assembly

## STABILIZER BAR REPLACE

1. If necessary, disconnect air suspension electrical wiring and all related parts that will interfere with stabilizer bar removal.
2. Raise and support vehicle.
3. Remove stabilizer bar to link attaching nuts, washers and insulators.
4. Remove U-bracket attaching bolts, then the stabilizer bar.
5. Reverse procedure to install, using new attaching parts.

## LOWER CONTROL ARM REPLACE

1. If necessary, disconnect air suspension electrical wiring and all related parts that will interfere with control arm removal.
2. Raise and support vehicle.
3. Mark position of notch on toe adjustment cam, **Fig. 3.**
4. Remove control arm to spindle attaching bolt, nut, and washer.
5. Remove control arm to body attaching bolt and nut, then the control arm.
6. Reverse procedure to install, then check rear wheel alignment and adjust as necessary.

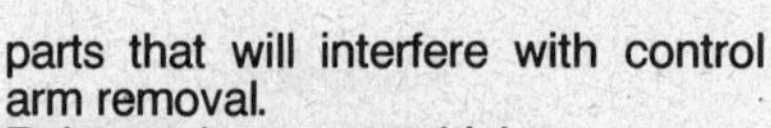

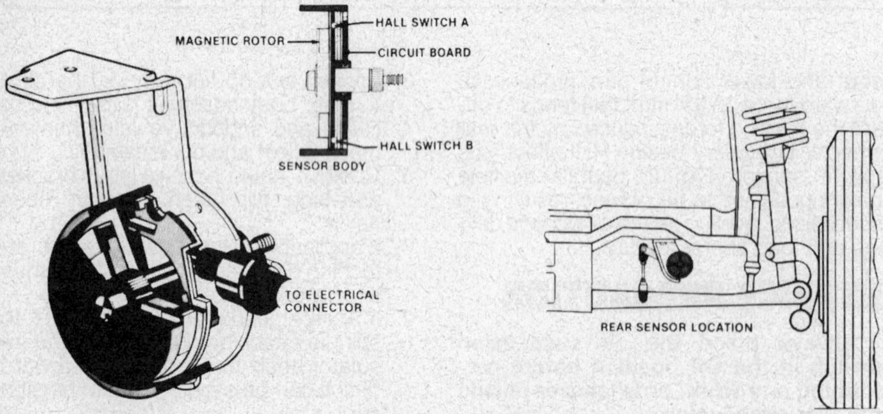

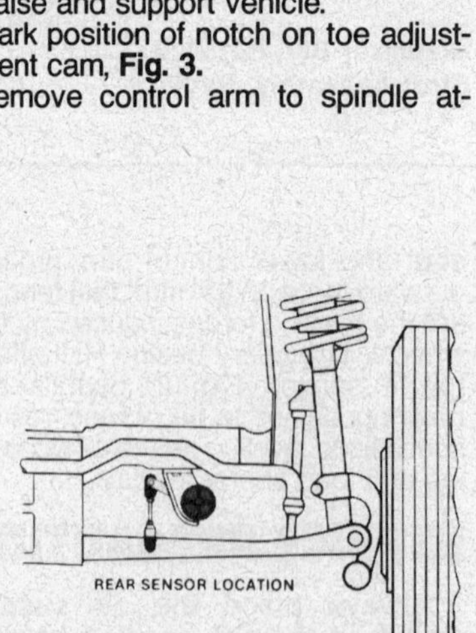


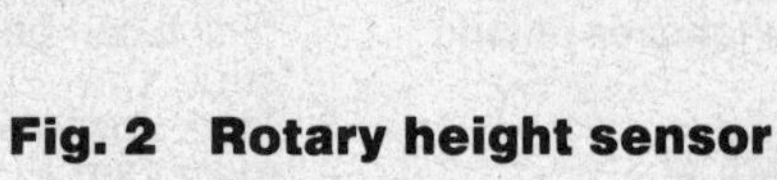

Fig. 2 Rotary height sensor

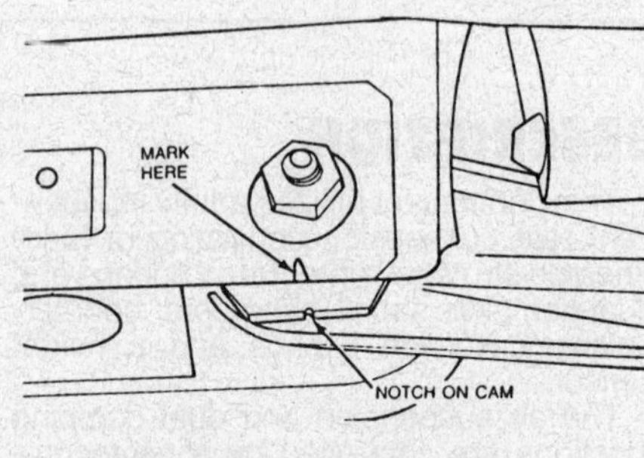


Fig. 3 Marking toe adjustment cam.

## TIGHTENING SPECIFICATIONS

| Year | Component | Torque/Ft. Lbs. |
|---|---|---|
| 1989-92 | Arm Inner Pivot Retainer | 45-65 |
| | Control Arm To Body | 45-65 |
| | Control Arm To Spindle | 42-57 |
| | Lug Nuts | 85-104 |
| | Spring To Stud Nut | 10-15 |
| | Spring Clamp To Spindle Bolt | 10-15 |
| | Strut Top Mount To Body | 19-26 |
| | Strut To Spindle | 51-70 |
| | Strut To Top Mount | 35-50 |
| | Stud To Arm Nut | 17-24 |
| | Tension Strut To Body | 35-50 |
| | Tension Strut To Spindle | 35-50 |
| | Stabilizer Bar Link | 5-7 |
| | Stabilizer U-Bracket | 25-37 |

# Front Suspension & Steering, Rear Wheel Drive Models

**NOTE:** On Models Equipped With Air Suspension, Refer To Air Suspension Section For Service Procedures.

## INDEX



## WHEEL BEARINGS

### ADJUST

#### MARK VII & 1989–90 TOWN CAR

1. With wheel rotating, **torque** adjusting nut to 17-25 ft. lbs, **Fig. 1.**
2. Back off adjusting nut 1/2 turn and **torque** nut to 10-15 inch lbs.
3. Place nut lock on nut so that castellations on lock are aligned with cotter pin hole in spindle and install cotter pin.
4. Check front wheel rotation, if it rotates noisily or rough, clean, inspect or replace wheel bearings as necessary.

#### 1991–92 TOWN CAR

On these models the wheel bearings are preset and cannot be adjusted.

## WHEEL BEARINGS

### REPLACE

#### MARK VII & 1989–90 TOWN CAR

1. Raise car and remove front wheels.
2. Remove caliper mounting bolts. **It is not necessary to disconnect the brake line for this operation.**
3. Slide caliper off of the disc, inserting a spacer between the shoes to hold them in their bores after the caliper is removed. Position caliper assembly out of the way. **Do not allow caliper to hang by brake hose.**
4. Remove hub and disc. Grease retainer and inner bearing can now be removed.
5. Reverse procedure to install.

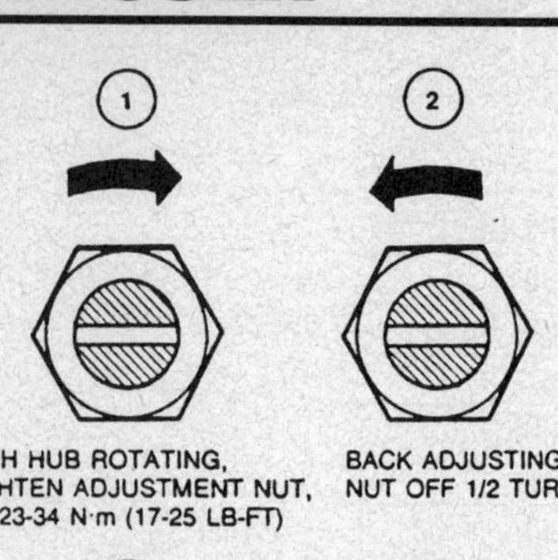


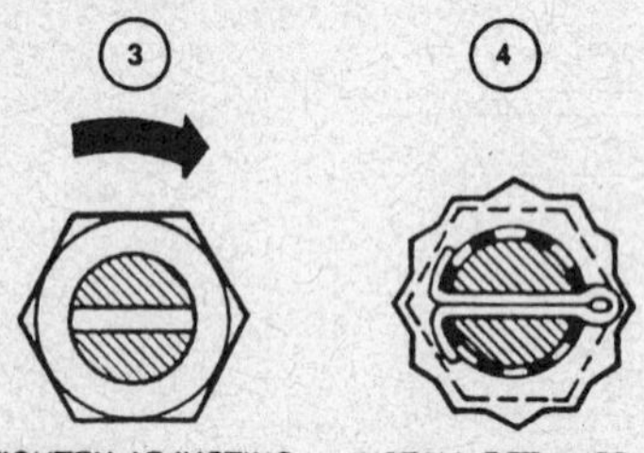


**Fig. 1 Front wheel bearing adjustment. Mark VII & 1989–90 Town Car**

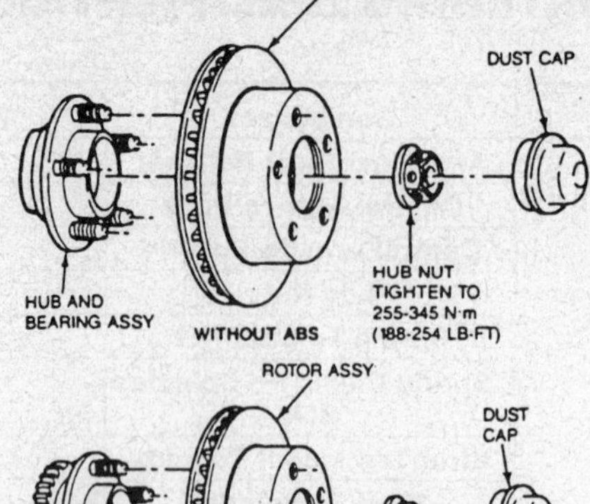


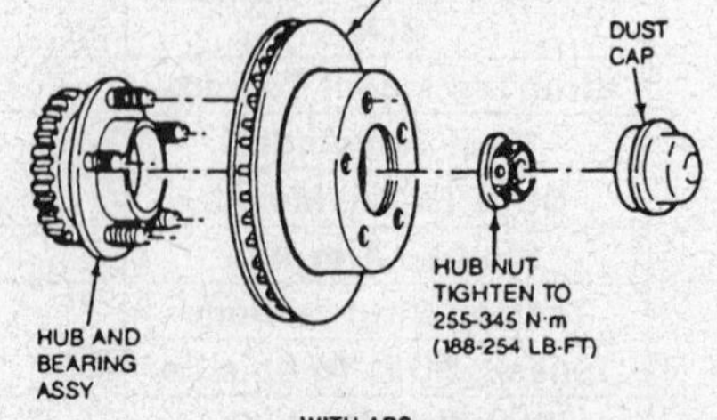


**Fig. 2 Hub & bearing assembly. 1991–92 Town Car**

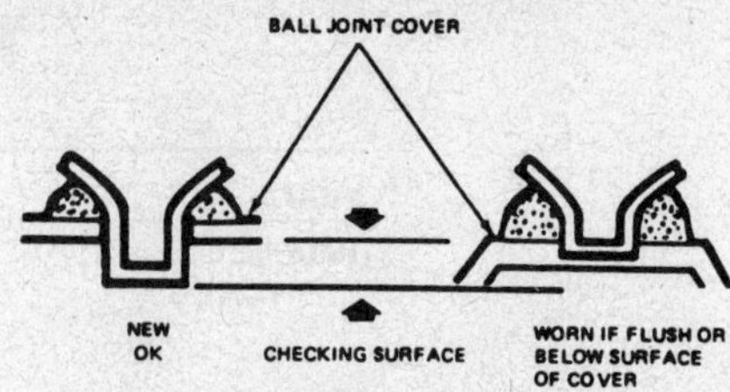


**Fig. 3 Lower ball joint wear indicator**

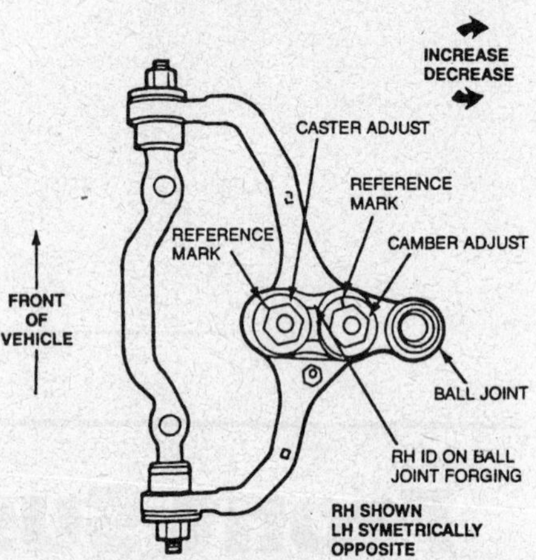


**Fig. 4 Upper control assembly. 1991–92 Town Car**

## 1991–92 TOWN CAR

1. Raise and support front of vehicle, then remove wheel and tire assembly.
2. Remove grease cap from hub.
3. Remove brake caliper and suspend from chassis with wire. Do not allow caliper to hang from brake hose.
4. Remove push clips, if equipped, then remove brake rotor, **Fig. 2.**
5. Remove hub nut, then remove hub and bearing assembly. If difficulty is encountered, use front hub remover tool No. T81P-1104-C or equivalent to remove hub and bearing assembly.
6. Reverse procedure to install. A new hub and bearing retaining nut should be installed. **Torque** hub bearing nut to 189-254 ft. lbs.

# CHECKING BALL JOINTS FOR WEAR

## UPPER BALL JOINT

### Town Car

1. Raise car on floor jacks placed beneath lower control arms.
2. Grasp lower edge of tire and move wheel in and out.
3. As wheel is being moved in and out, observe upper end of spindle and upper arm.
4. Any movement between upper end of spindle and upper arm indicates ball joint wear and loss of preload. If such movement is observed, replace upper ball joint. **During the foregoing check, the lower ball joint will be unloaded and may move. Disregard all such movement of the lower joint. Also, do not mistake loose wheel bearings for a worn ball joint.**

## LOWER BALL JOINT

### Mark VII

1. Support vehicle in normal driving position with both ball joints loaded.
2. Clean area around grease fitting and checking surface. **The checking surface is the round boss into which the grease fitting is installed.**
3. The checking surface should project outside the cover, **Fig. 3.** If surface is inside cover replace lower arm assembly.

### Town Car

These models are equipped with lower ball joint wear indicators, **Fig. 3.** To check ball joint for wear, support vehicle in normal driving position with both ball joints loaded. Observe the checking surface of the ball joint. If the checking surface is inside the cover, replace the ball joint.

# BALL JOINTS REPLACE

## MARK VII

These ball joints are not serviceable. If they require replacement, the control arm and ball joint must be replaced as an assembly. Torque ball joint stud to specifications

## 1989–90 TOWN CAR

Ford Motor Company recommends that new ball joints should not be installed on used control arms, and that the control arm be replaced if ball joint replacement is required. However, aftermarket ball joint repair kits which do not require control arm replacement, are available and can be installed using the following procedure.

When replacing a riveted joint, remove the rivets and retain the new joint in its control arm with the bolts, nuts and washers furnished with the ball joint kit.

Use a suitable pressing tool to force the ball joint from the spindle.

## 1991–92 TOWN CAR

1. Raise and support vehicle, then remove wheel and tire assembly. Position jack stands under both sides of frame just to the rear of lower control arm.
2. Position a suitable jack under lower control arm.
3. Remove nut from upper ball joint to steering knuckle pinch bolt, then tap out pinch bolt.
4. Mark positions of caster and camber adjusting cams for use during installation, **Fig. 4.**
5. Remove two bolts attaching ball joint to upper control arm.
6. Using a suitable pry bar, spread slot to release ball joint from steering knuckle and remove.
7. Reverse procedure to install. Align caster and camber marks made during removal. After completing installation, check front wheel alignment.

# SHOCK STRUT REPLACE

## MARK VII

Turn air suspension switch off before removing shock strut.

1. Place ignition switch in the Unlocked position so that front wheels are free to move.

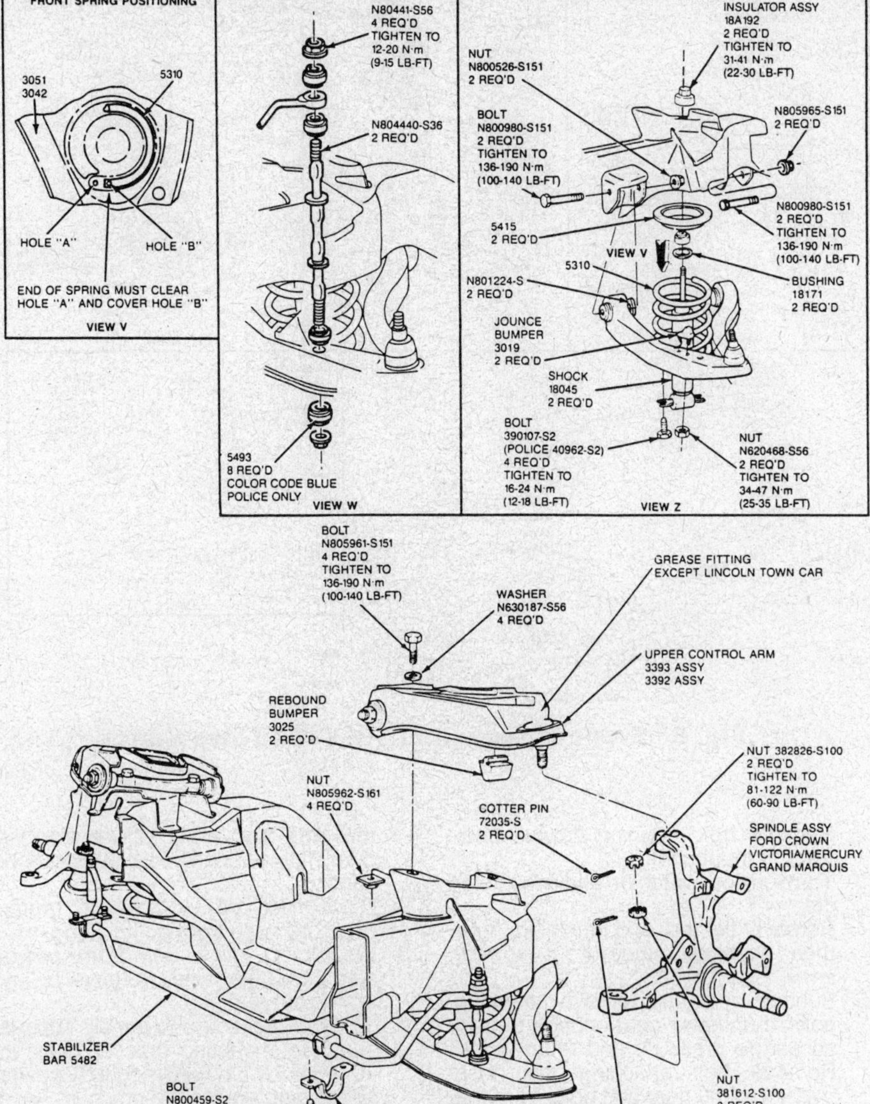


**Fig. 5 Front suspension. 1989–90 Town Car**

2. From engine compartment, remove one strut to upper mounting nut. Use a screwdriver in rod slot to hold rod stationary when removing nut.
3. Raise front of vehicle by lower control arms, then place safety stands under frame jack pads located rearward of wheels.
4. Remove wheel and tire assembly, then remove brake caliper, rotor assembly and dust shield.
5. Remove two nuts and bolts attaching lower strut to spindle. **When removing the second lower strut to spindle nut, hold strut firmly as gas pressure will cause strut to fully extend.**
6. Lift strut upward from spindle to compress rod, then pull downward and remove strut.
7. Reverse procedure to install.

## SHOCK ABSORBER REPLACE

### TOWN CAR

1. Remove nut, washer and bushing from upper end of shock absorber.
2. Raise and support vehicle.
3. Remove screws retaining shock absorber to lower control arm and remove shock absorber.
4. **These models are equipped with gas pressurized shock absorbers which extend unassisted during removal. Do not apply heat or flame during removal.**
5. Reverse procedure to install.

## COIL SPRING REPLACE

### TOWN CAR

1. Raise and support vehicle.
2. Remove wheel and tire assembly.
3. Disconnect stabilizer bar link from lower control arm.
4. Remove shock absorber.
5. Remove steering center link from Pitman arm.
6. Compress coil spring with a suitable spring compressor.
7. Remove two lower control arm pivot bolts and disengage arm from crossmember.
8. Remove spring from vehicle.
9. Reverse procedure to install. Torque stabilizer bar to lower control arm nuts and lower control arm to crossmember bolts to specifications.

## STABILIZER BAR REPLACE

### TOWN CAR

1. Raise and support vehicle.
2. Remove stabilizer bar attaching clamps, then the stabilizer bar attaching bolts from each stabilizer link.
3. Remove stabilizer bar assembly, **Figs. 5 and 6.**
4. Reverse procedure to install.

## CONTROL ARM REPLACE

### LOWER CONTROL ARM

#### Town Car

1. Raise and support front of vehicle, then remove front wheels.
2. Remove brake caliper, rotor, dust shield and ABS sensor, if equipped.
3. Remove jounce bumper, if equipped.
4. Remove shock absorber.
5. Disconnect steering center link from pitman arm.
6. Remove lower ball joint attaching nut cotter pin, then loosen lower ball joint nut one or two times, **Figs. 5 and 6.** Do not remove nut from stud at this time.
7. Tap spindle boss sharply to relieve stud pressure, then tap near lower stud to loosen stud in spindle.
8. Position a suitable jack under lower control arm.
9. Install suitable coil spring compression tool, then remove coil spring.
10. Remove ball joint nut, then the lower control arm assembly.
11. Reverse procedure to install, noting the following:
    a. Torque ball joint attaching nut specifications.
    b. Ensure coil spring is properly aligned, **Fig. 5.**
    c. Torque control arm to crossmember attaching bolts and nuts to specifications.
    d. Check wheel alignment.

## UPPER CONTROL ARM

### 1989–90 Town Car

1. Raise and support front of vehicle, then remove front wheels.
2. Remove upper ball joint attaching cotter pin, then loosen upper ball joint nut one or two turns. **Do not remove nut from stud at this time.**
3. Install ball joint press tool No. T57P-3006-B or equivalent between upper and lower ball joints studs.
4. Compress ball joint with tool, then tap spindle, near upper stud to loosen stud in spindle.
5. Remove ball joint press tool, then position a suitable jack under lower control arm.
6. Remove upper control arm attaching bolts, then the upper control arm assembly, **Fig. 5.**
7. Reverse procedure to install, noting the following:
   a. Torque ball joint attaching nut to specifications.
   b. Torque upper control arm attaching bolts to specifications.
   c. Check wheel alignment.

### 1991–92 Town Car

1. Raise and support vehicle, then remove wheel and tire assembly. Position jack stands under both side of frame just to the rear of lower control arm.
2. Position a suitable jack under lower control arm.
3. Remove nut from upper ball joint to steering knuckle pinch bolt, then tap out pinch bolt.
4. Mark positions of caster and camber adjusting cams for use during installation, **Fig. 4.**
5. Using a suitable pry bar, spread slot to release ball joint from steering knuckle.
6. Remove upper control arm attaching bolts, then remove upper arm assembly, **Fig. 6.**
7. Reverse procedure to install. Align caster and camber marks made during removal. After completing installation, check front end alignment.

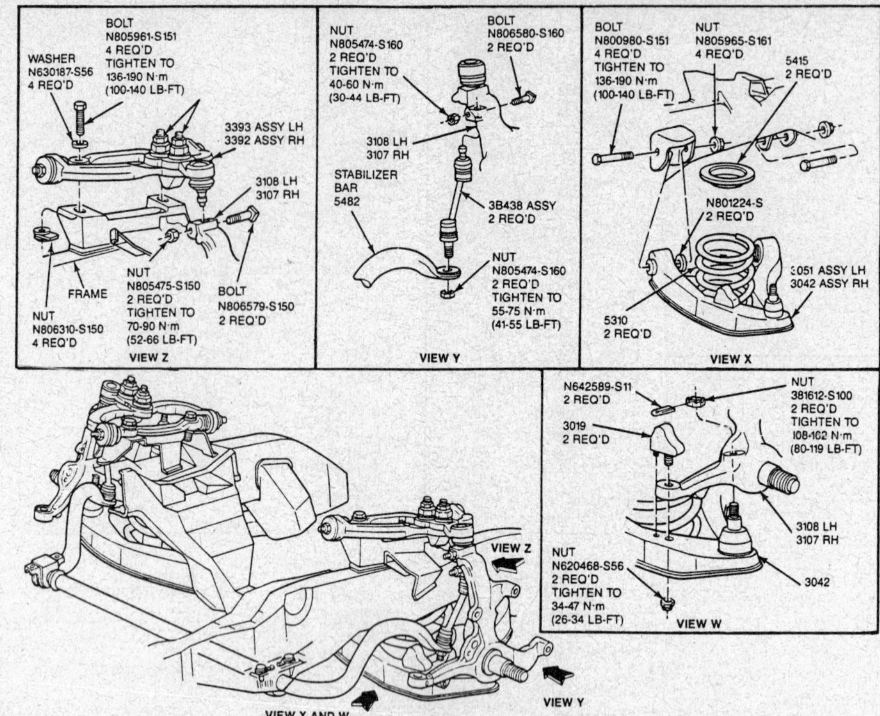

**Fig. 6 Front suspension. 1991–92 Town Car**

## POWER STEERING GEAR REPLACE

### TOWN CAR

1. Remove stone shield, if equipped.
2. Disconnect pressure and return lines from steering gear. Plug lines and ports in gear to prevent entry of dirt.
3. Remove two bolts that secure flex coupling to steering gear and to column.
4. Raise car and remove sector shaft nut.
5. Use a puller to remove pitman arm.
6. Support steering gear, then remove attaching bolts.
7. Work steering gear free of flex coupling and remove it from car.
8. Reverse procedure to install.

### MARK VII

#### Integral Power Rack & Pinion

1. Disconnect battery ground cable.
2. Remove bolt retaining flexible coupling to input shaft.
3. Turn ignition switch on and raise vehicle.
4. Remove tie rod end retaining nuts, then separate studs from spindle arms.
5. Support gear and remove attaching bolts, then lower gear enough to gain access to pressure and return lines. Remove bolt attaching the hose bracket to the gear and bolts from the crossmember.
6. Disconnect and cap pressure and return lines, then remove steering gear.
7. Reverse procedure to install.

#### Integral Power Steering Gear

1. Disconnect lines from steering gear and plugs lines and ports.
2. Remove the two bolts securing flex coupling to steering gear and to column.
3. Raise vehicle and remove sector shaft nut and Pitman arm. **Do not damage the seals.**
4. Support steering gear and remove three attaching bolts. Remove flex coupling clamp bolt and work steering gear free of coupling, then remove steering gear.
5. Reverse procedure to install.

## POWER STEERING PUMP REPLACE

### TOWN CAR

1. Disconnect power steering pump return line and allow power steering pump fluid to drain into a suitable container.
2. Disconnect power steering pump pressure hose from pump fitting.
3. Disconnect drive belt from power steering pump pulley, remove pulley, then remove pump.
4. Reverse procedure to install. **Torque** pump to mounting bracket bolts to 30-45 ft. lbs. On Ford model CII power steering pump, **torque** pressure hose to pump fitting to 10-15 ft. lbs. Endplay on this fitting is normal and does not indicate a loose fitting.

### MARK VII

1. Disconnect fluid return hose from reservoir and drain power steering fluid into a container.
2. Remove pressure hose from pump fitting. Do not remove fitting from pump.
3. Disconnect belt from pulley. If necessary, remove pulley from pump installing pulley removal tool No. T75L-3733-A or equivalent so small diameter threads engage in pump shaft. While holding small hex head, rotate tool nut to remove pulley. Do not apply in and out pressure on pump shaft as this will damage the internal thrust areas.
4. Remove pump.
5. If pulley was removed, install tool and while holding small hex head, turn tool nut clockwise to install pulley. Pulley must be flush within .010 inch of the end of the pump. Do not apply in and out pressure on shaft. Remove tool.

# TIGHTENING SPECIFICATIONS

| Year | Component | Torque/ft. lbs. |
|---|---|---|
| 1989① | Lower Arm To No. 2 Crossmember | 110-150 |
| | Lower Ball Joint To Spindle | 80-120 |
| | Lug Nuts | 85-104 |
| | Pitman Arm To Sector Shaft Retaining Nut | 200-250 |
| | Pressure Hose To Gear | 16-25 |
| | Return Hose To Gear | 25-34 |
| | Sector Shaft Cover Bolts | 55-75 |
| | Shock Strut Upper Mount | 50-75 |
| | Shock Upper Mount To Body | 50-75 |
| | Stabilizer Bar Mounting Clamp | 40-55 |
| | Stabilizer Bar To Frame | 14-26 |
| | Stabilizer Bar To Lower Arm | 9-12 |
| | Spindle To Shock Strut | 140-200 |
| | Steering Gear To No. 2 Crossmember | 90-100 |
| | Tie Rod End To Spindle Nut | 35-47 |
| | Upper Arm To Frame | 100-140 |
| | Upper Ball Joint To Spindle | 60-90 |
| 1989-92② | Air Compressor To Bracket | 30-40③ |
| | Ball Joint To Spindle | 100-120 |
| | Compressor Bracket To Frame | 30-40③ |
| | Front Bolts To Support Bracket | 30-45 |
| | Lower Arm To No. 2 Crossmember | 110-150 |
| | Lug Nuts | 85-104 |
| | Pinion Bearing Plug | 40-60 |
| | Pinion Bearing Locknut | 30-40 |
| | Pivot Bolt | 30-45 |
| | Pressure Hose Fitting To Pump | 10-15 |
| | Pump Bracket To Rear Support | 18-24 |
| | Pump To Bracket | 30-45 |
| | Rear Support To Engine Head | 30-45 |
| | Return Hose To Pump | 12-24③ |
| | Sensor Lower Attachment To Arm | 8-12 |
| | Sensor Upper Attachment To Frame | 26-34 |
| | Shock Upper Mount To Body | 62-75 |
| | Shock Strut Upper Mount | 55-92 |
| | Spindle To Shock Strut | 140-200 |
| | Stabilizer Bar Mounting Clamp | 40-55 |
| | Stabilizer Bar To Lower Arm | 9-12 |
| | Steering Gear To No. 2 Crossmember | 90-100 |
| | Support Bracket To Engine | 30-45 |
| | Support Bracket To Water Pump | 30-45 |
| | Tie Rod Ball Socket Assembly To Rack | 55-65 |
| | Tie Rod End To Jam Nut | 35-50 |
| | Tie Rod End To Spindle Nut | 35-47 |

①—Except air suspension.
②—Air suspension.
③—Inch lbs.

# Front Suspension & Steering, Front Wheel Drive Models

## INDEX



## DESCRIPTION

The Continental front suspension consists of MacPherson struts with integral air springs and dual-damping shock absorbers, and two height sensors, one at each control arm.

The air suspension and dual damping functions are controlled by a microcomputer based module which receives inputs for vehicle speed, door switch position, damping actuator feedback, steering wheel turning rate and angle, engine vacuum, throttle position, brake actuation, ignition switching, and vehicle ride height. The dual-damping function automatically switches from a soft to firm ride when the driving situation (hard cornering, acceleration or braking, etc.) dictates the need for increased damping effect.

The front struts, **Fig. 1**, are mounted to the body through a precision ball bearing and rubber mount system. The ball bearing provides a durable pivot for the strut/wheel assembly, while the rubber mount provides for a smooth ride on rough roads with minimal noise. The rotary design Hall effect type height sensor, identical to the rear sensor, permits multiple height positions to be defined, resulting in specialized leveling during all types of driving and load characteristics.

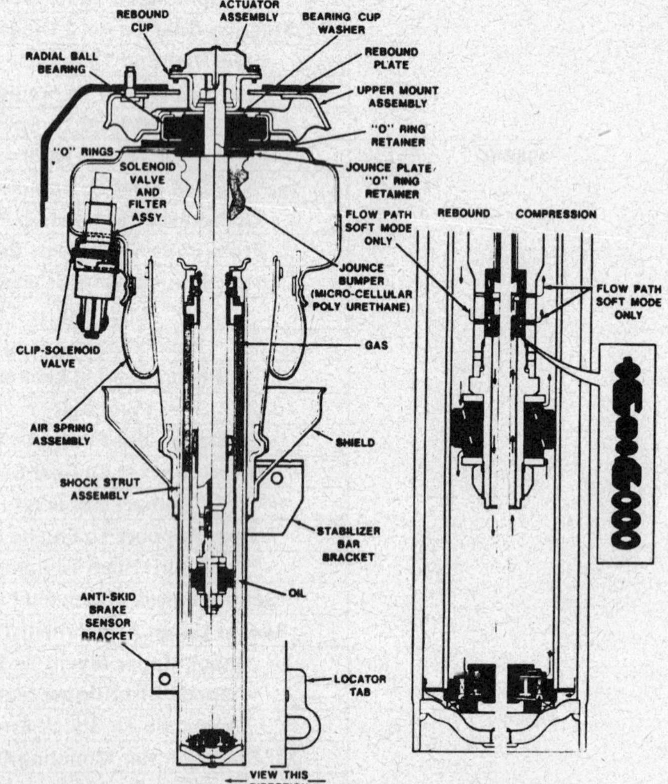


**Fig. 1 Cross-sectional view of front strut assembly**

## SERVICE PRECAUTION

**Always place the air suspension switch in the Off position before performing any work, or whenever raising the front suspension.**

## STRUT ASSEMBLY
### REPLACE

1. Remove hub nut and loosen the upper strut attaching nuts, then raise and support vehicle. **Do not lift vehicle from lower control arm.**
2. Disconnect air suspension electrical wiring and all related parts that will interfere with strut removal.
3. Remove wheel and tire assembly.
4. Remove brake caliper and support with suitable wire, then disconnect tie rod end.
5. Remove stabilizer bar link nut, then remove link from strut.
6. Remove lower control arm to steering knuckle pinch nut and bolt, then spread joint as necessary and disengage control arm from knuckle.
7. Using a suitable hub installation/removal tool, press axle from hub/rotor assembly. Wire axle shaft as necessary to maintain level position. **Do not permit axle shaft to move outward during disengagement from hub, since damage to CV joints could result.**
8. Remove strut to steering knuckle pinch bolt, then spread joint and remove steering knuckle and hub assembly.
9. Remove strut upper attaching nuts, then remove strut from vehicle.
10. Reverse procedure to install.

## LOWER CONTROL ARM
### REPLACE

1. Raise and support vehicle.
2. Disconnect air suspension electrical wiring and all related parts that will interfere with control arm removal.
3. Remove wheel and tire assembly, then the tension strut nut and washer.
4. Remove lower control arm to steering knuckle pinch nut and bolt, then

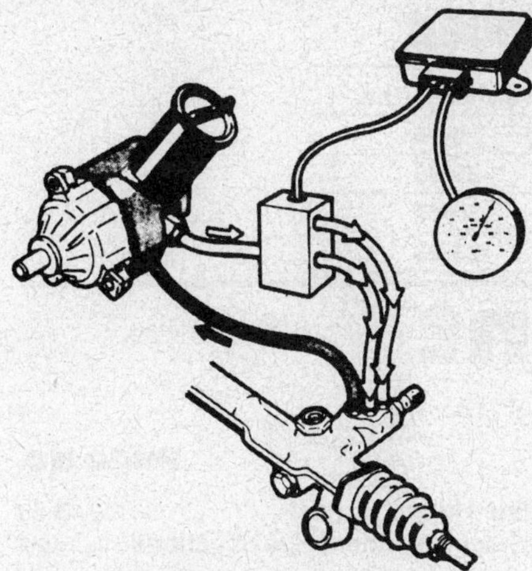

Fig. 2 Variable assist power rack & pinion steering gear system

# POWER RACK & PINION STEERING GEAR SYSTEM

The Continental uses a new electro-hydraulic, speed sensitive variable assist rack and pinion power steering system. The system is designed to generate higher levels of power assist during low vehicle speeds and while parking, while progressively reducing power assist as vehicle speed increases.

The system is comprised of a new control valve, an electro-hydraulic actuator valve, and an electronic control module that is programmed to provide the right amount of assist during all vehicle speeds, **Figs. 2 and 3.**

The control module also has built-in diagnostic capabilities, which enables quicker troubleshooting in the event of a system malfunction.

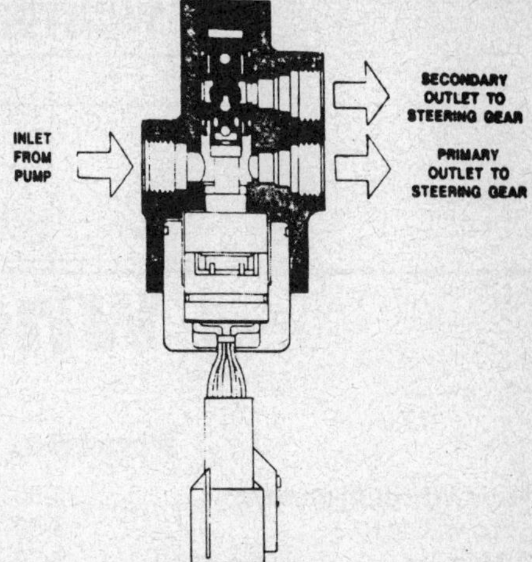


Fig. 3 Cross-sectional view of actuator valve

spread joint and separate ball joint from knuckle.

5. Remove lower control arm inner pivot bolt and nut, then the lower control arm.
6. Reverse procedure to install.

# STABILIZER BAR
## REPLACE

1. Raise and support vehicle.
2. Remove stabilizer bar link to strut and link to bar attaching nuts.
3. Remove stabilizer bar mounting brackets, then the stabilizer bar. It may be necessary to move steering gear from sub-frame and lower rear of sub-frame to gain access to mounting brackets.
4. Reverse procedure to install.

# POWER STEERING GEAR
## REPLACE

1. Remove steering column boot attachments, then the intermediate shaft retaining bolts and shaft.
2. Remove secondary steering column boot from inside of passenger compartment.
3. Raise and support vehicle.
4. Remove tie rod ends from from spindle, then gear to sub-frame attaching bolts.
5. Remove both height sensor attachments, then both rear sub-frame to body attaching bolts.
6. Remove exhaust pipe to catalytic converter.
7. Carefully lower sub-frame assembly approximately four inches.
8. Remove heat shield band and fold down shield.
9. Rotate gear to clear bolts from sub-frame and pull left to allow room for line fitting removal.
10. Remove line fittings, then drain using a suitable pan.
11. Remove lefthand sway bar link, then gear assembly through lefthand wheel housing.
12. Reverse procedure to install.

# POWER STEERING PUMP
## REPLACE

1. Disconnect battery ground cable.
2. Loosen tensioner assembly and rotate tensioner pulley clockwise.
3. Remove belt from alternator and power steering pulley.
4. Remove three bolts retaining pump to bracket and remove pump.
5. Reverse procedure to install.

# TIGHTENING SPECIFICATIONS

| Year | Component | Torque/ft. lbs. |
|---|---|---|
| 1989-92 | Control Arm To Knuckle | 40-55 |
| | Control Arm To Sub-Frame | 70-95 |
| | Front Bolts To Support Bracket | 30-41 |
| | Intermediate Shaft To Steering Column Nuts | 15-25 |
| | Intermediate Shaft To Steering Column Nuts | 15-25 |
| | Lug Nuts | 85-104 |
| | Outlet Fitting To Valve Cover | 25-34 |
| | Pivot Bolt | 45-57 |
| | Pressure Hose Tube Nut To Pump Pressure Fitting | 20-25 |
| | Pump To Bracket | 30-45 |
| | Return Hose To Pump Hose Clamp | 8-24③ |
| | Stabilizer Bar Bracket To Sub-Frame | 21-32 |
| | Stabilizer Bar Link Assembly To Bar | 35-48 |
| | Stabilizer Bar Link Assembly To Strut | 55-75 |
| | Strut Top Mount To Body | 22-32 |
| | Strut To Knuckle | 70-95 |
| | Strut To Top Mount | 35-50 |
| | Support Bracket To Cylinder Head | 15-22 |
| | Tension Strut To Control Arm | 70-95 |

## TIGHTENING SPECIFICATIONS–Continued

| Year | Component | Torque/ft. lbs. |
|---|---|---|
| | Tension Strut To Sub Frame | 70-95 |
| | Tie Rod Ball Socket Assembly To Rack | 55-65 |
| | Tie Rod End To Spindle Nut | 35-47 |
| | Tie Rod End To Steering Knuckle | 23-25 |

# Wheel Alignment

## INDEX



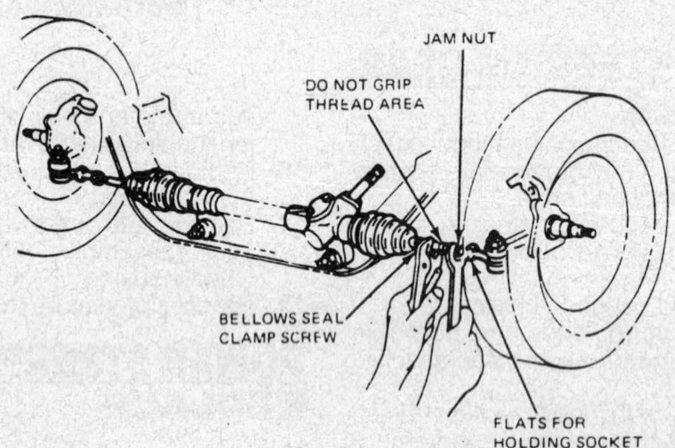


**Fig. 1 Toe-in adjustment. Mark VII**

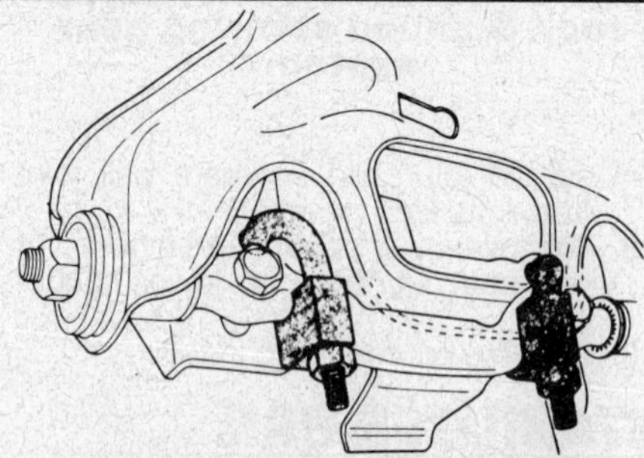

**Fig. 2 Caster & camber adjusting tools. Town Car**

## FRONT WHEEL ALIGNMENT

### MARK VII

Before performing wheel alignment check on these vehicles, ensure vehicle ride height is correct.

#### Caster & Camber

Caster is pre-set at the factory and is not adjustable.

To adjust camber, drill out pop rivet located on top of camber plate. Loosen the camber plate to body apron retaining nuts, then move the top of the shock strut to the desired location. Retighten the retaining nuts. It is not necessary to replace the pop rivet after the camber adjustment is completed.

#### Toe-In

1. Check to see that steering shaft and steering wheel marks are in alignment and in the top position.
2. Loosen clamp screw on the tie rod bellows and free the seal on the rod to prevent twisting of the bellows, **Fig. 1.**
3. Place open end wrench on flats of tie rod socket to prevent socket from turning, then loosen tie rod jam nuts.
4. Use suitable pliers to turn the tie rod inner end to correct the adjustment to specifications. Do not use pliers on tie rod threads. Turning to reduce number of threads showing will increase toe-in. Turning in the opposite direction will reduce toe-in.

### TOWN CAR

Caster and camber can be adjusted by loosening the bolts that attach the upper suspension arm to the shaft at the frame side rail, and moving the arm assembly in or out in the elongated bolt holes. Since any movement of the arm affects both caster and camber, both factors should be balanced against one another when making the adjustment.

#### Caster, Adjust

1. To adjust caster, install the adjusting tool as shown in **Fig. 2.**
2. Loosen both upper arm inner shaft retaining bolts and move either front or rear of the shaft in or out as necessary to increase or decrease caster angle. Then tighten bolt to retain adjustment.

#### Camber, Adjust

1. Loosen both upper arm inner retaining bolts and move both front and rear ends of shaft inward or outward as necessary to increase or decrease camber angle.
2. Tighten bolts and recheck caster and readjust if necessary.

#### Toe-In

Position the front wheels in their straight-ahead position. Then turn both tie rod adjusting sleeves an equal amount until the desired toe-in setting is obtained.

### CONTINENTAL

#### Toe-In

To adjust toe-in, lock steering wheel in straight ahead position using suitable steering wheel holder. Loosen, then slide off small outer clamps from steering boot to prevent boot from twisting during adjustment procedure. Loosen tie rod adjusting and jam nuts, then adjust length of left and right tie rods until each wheel has 1/2 the desired total toe specification. After adjustment is completed, tighten jam nuts, reinstall outer clamps and remove steering wheel holder.

## REAR WHEEL ALIGNMENT

### CONTINENTAL

#### Camber

Camber is factory set and cannot be adjusted.

#### Toe-In

Toe-In is adjusted by rotating the cams located inside the rear inner lower control arm bushings.

## RIDE HEIGHT ADJUST

Refer to "Air Suspension" section for ride height adjustment procedures.

# FORD MUSTANG

## INDEX OF SERVICE OPERATIONS

**NOTE:** Refer To The Rear Of This Manual For Vehicle Manufacturer's Special Service Tool Suppliers.

## INDEX OF SERVICE OPERATIONS—Continued



# Specifications

## GENERAL ENGINE SPECIFICATIONS

| Year | Engine | | Fuel System | Bore & Stroke | Compression Ratio | Net H.P. @ RPM③ | Maximum Torque Ft. Lbs. @ RPM | Normal Oil Pressure, psi |
|---|---|---|---|---|---|---|---|---|
| | Liter/CID① | VIN Code② | | | | | | |
| 1989—92 | 2.3L/4-140 | A | E.F.I.④ | 3.78 X 3.12 | 9.5 | 88 @ 4000 | 132 @ 2600 | 40-60⑤ |
| | 5.0L/V-8 302 | E | S.E.F.I.⑥ | 4.0 X 3.0 | 9.0 | 225 @ 4200 | 300 @ 3200 | 40-60⑤ |

①—CID-cubic inch displacement.
②—The eighth digit denotes engine code.
③—Net rating-as installed on vehicle.
④—Multi-port electronic fuel injection
⑤—Engine hot, at 2000 RPM
⑥—Multi-port sequential electronic fuel injection

## TUNE UP SPECIFICATIONS

| Year & Engine/ VIN Code ① | Spark Plug Gap | Ignition Timing BTDC | | | | Curb Idle Speed③ | | Fast Idle Speed | | Fuel Pump Pressure, psi |
|---|---|---|---|---|---|---|---|---|---|---|
| | | Firing Order Fig. ② | Man. Trans. | Auto. Trans. | Mark Fig. | Man. Trans. | Auto Trans. | Man. Trans. | Auto. Trans. | |
| **1989** | | | | | | | | | | |
| 2.3L/4-140/A | .044 | A | 10⑥ | 10⑥ | B | ④ | ④ | ④ | ④ | 35-45⑤ |
| 5.0L/V8-302 H.O./E | .054 | C | 10⑥ | 10⑥ | D | ④ | ④ | ④ | ④ | 35-45⑤ |
| **1990-92** | | | | | | | | | | |
| 2.3L/4-140/A Except Calif. | .044 | A | 10⑥ | 10⑥ | B | 770-830④ | 770-830D④ | ④ | ④ | 35-45⑤ |
| 2.3L/4-140/A Calif. | .044 | A | 10⑥ | 10⑥ | B | 830-890④ | 790-850D④ | ④ | ④ | 35-45⑤ |
| 5.0L/V8-302 H.O./E | .054 | C | 10⑥ | 10⑥ | D | ④ | ④ | ④ | ④ | 35-45⑤ |

①—The eighth digit of the Vehicle Identification Number (V.I.N.) denotes engine code.
②—Before removing wires from distributor cap, determine location of No. 1 wire in cap, as distributor position may have been altered from that shown at the end of this chart.
③—D: Drive. When checking idle speed, set parking brake & block drive wheels.
④—Idle speed controlled by an automatic idle speed control.
⑤—Wrap shop towel around fuel diagnostic valve to prevent fuel spillage. Connect suitable fuel pressure gauge to fuel diagnostic valve. Energize fuel pump & check pressure gauge reading.
⑥—Disconnect in-line spout connector, then start engine & adjust ignition timing as necessary. After completing adjustment, reconnect spout connector.

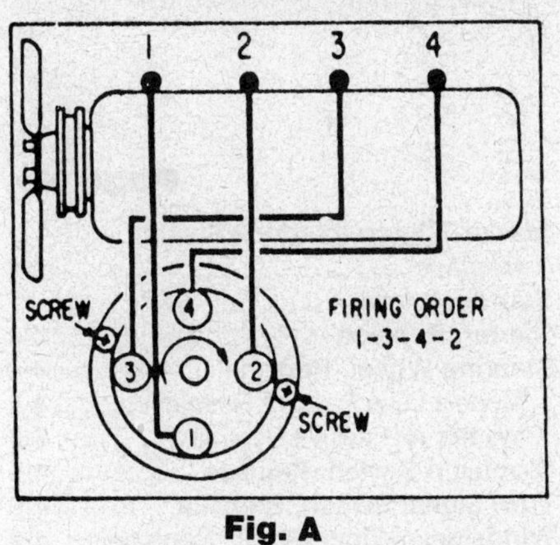


Fig. A

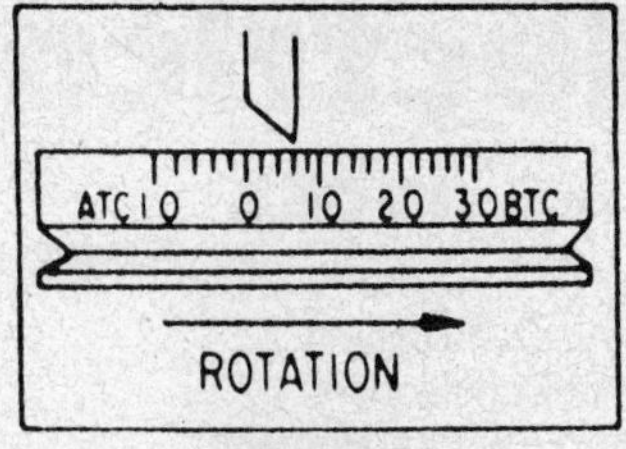


Fig. B

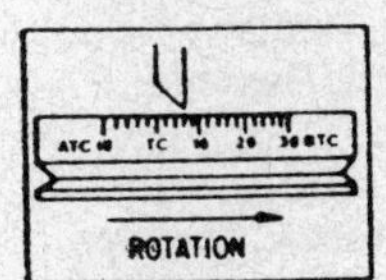


Fig. D

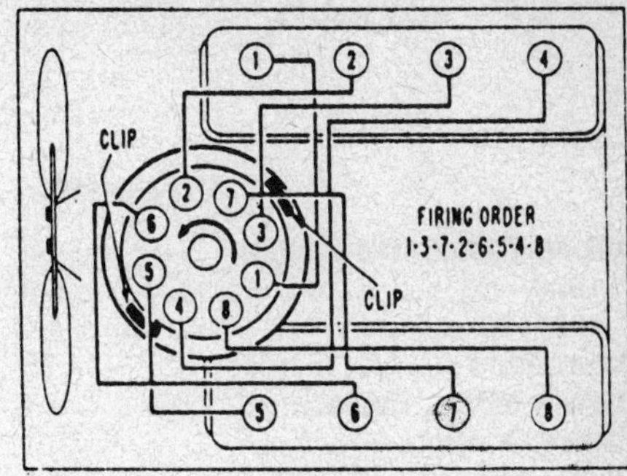


Fig. C

# COOLING SYSTEM & CAPACITY DATA

| Year | Model or Engine/VIN | Cooling Capacity, Qts. | | Radiator Cap Relief Pressure, Lbs. | Thermo. Opening Temp, °F | Fuel Tank, Gals. | Engine Oil Refill, Qts. ① | Transmission Oil | | |
|---|---|---|---|---|---|---|---|---|---|---|
| | | Less A/C | With A/C | | | | | 5 Speed, Pints | Auto. Trans., Qts. ② | Rear Axle Oil Pints |
| 1989–90 | 2.3L/4-140 | 10 | 10 | 16 | 192 | 15.4 | 4 | 5.6 | 9.7 | 3.5 |
| | 5.0L/V8-302 H.O./E | 14.1 | 14.1 | 16 | 196 | 15.4 | 4 | 5.6 | 12.3 | 3.75 |
| 1991–92 | 2.3L/4-140 | 8.6 | 9.2 | 16 | 192 | 15.4 | 5 | 5.6 | 10 | 3.3 |
| | 5.0L/V8-302/E | 14.1 | 14.1 | 16 | 195 | 15.4 | 4 | 5.6 | 10 | 3.3 |

①—Add 1 qt. with filter change unless otherwise noted.

②—Approximate. Make final check with dipstick.

# LUBRICANT DATA

| Year | Model | Lubricant Type | | | | | |
|---|---|---|---|---|---|---|---|
| | | Transaxle | | | | | |
| | | Manual | Automatic | Transfer Case | Rear Axle | Power Steering | Brake System |
| 1989–92 | All | ATF③ | ATF③ | — | ① | ATF② | Dot 3 |

①—XY-90-QL Gear Lubricant and four ounces of Friction Modifier.

②—Type F.

③—Mercon XT-2-QDX.

# WHEEL ALIGNMENT SPECIFICATIONS

| Year | Model | Caster Angle, Degrees | | Camber Angle, Degrees | | | | Toe-In Inch | Toe-Out On Turns, Degrees | |
|---|---|---|---|---|---|---|---|---|---|---|
| | | | | Limits | | Desired | | | | |
| | | Limits | Desired | Left | Right | Left | Right | | Outer Wheel | Inner Wheel |
| 1989 | Except 5.0L GT | +.4 to +1.9 | +1.15 | −.85 to +.65 | −.85 to +.65 | -.1 | -.1 | .19 | 19.84 | 20 |
| | 5.0L GT | +.5 to +2 | +1.27 | −.6 to +.9 | −.6 to +.9 | +.14 | +.14 | .19 | 19.84 | 20 |
| 1990–92 | 2.3L/4-140 | +1.15 to +2.65 | +1.9 | −1.25 to +.25 | −1.25 to +.25 | -.5 | -.5 | ① | 19.84 | 20 |
| | 5.0L GT | +1.15 to +2.65 | +1.9 | −1.35 to +.15 | −1.35 to +.15 | -.6 | -.6 | ① | 19.84 | 20 |

①—Total toe. -.12 inch.

# Electrical

## INDEX



## AIRBAG SYSTEM DISARMING

**The electrical circuit necessary for system deployment is powered directly from the battery and a backup power supply. To avoid accidental deployment and possible personal injury, the airbag system must be deactivated prior to servicing or replacing any component located near or related to airbag system activation components.**

### 1990

A back-up power supply is included in the system to provide airbag deployment in the event the battery or battery cables are damaged in an accident before the sensors can close. The power supply is a capacitor that will retain a charge for approximately 15 minutes after the battery ground cable is disconnected. **Backup power supply must be disconnected to deactivate airbag system.** To remove backup power supply, refer to "Airbags" in the "Passive Restraint" section.

1. Disconnect battery ground cable.
2. Disconnect backup power supply.
3. Remove four nut and washer assemblies securing airbag module to steering wheel, then disconnect airbag electrical connector. Attach jumper wire to airbag terminals on clockspring terminals.
4. Reconnect battery and backup power supply if necessary to perform repair procedure.
5. To reactivate, disconnect battery ground cable and backup power supply, then reverse remainder of deactivation procedure. **Torque** airbag module to steering wheel nut assemblies to 24-32 inch lbs.
6. Verify airbag lamp after reactivating system.

### 1991–92

1. Disconnect positive battery cable, then ground cable end to frame or engine. Wait one minute for back-up power supply to discharge.
2. Remove four nut and washer assemblies securing airbag to steering wheel.
3. Disconnect airbag electrical connector and install airbag simulator tool No. 105-00008 or equivalent.
4. Install airbag simulator tool No. 105-00008 or equivalent.
5. Connect positive battery cable.
6. To activate airbag system, disconnect positive battery cable and reverse procedure. **Torque** mounting nut and washer assemblies to 36-49 inch lbs.
7. Verify proper operation of airbag lamp.

## FUSE PANEL & FLASHER LOCATION

The fuse panel is located to the lefthand side of the steering column under the instrument panel.

The hazard and turn signal flashers are located on the fuse panel.

## STARTER REPLACE

1. Disconnect battery ground cable.
2. Raise and support front of vehicle.
3. Disconnect starter cable from starter.
4. Remove starter motor attaching bolts and the starter.
5. Reverse procedure to install, **torque** starter retaining bolts to 15-20 ft. lbs.

## DISTRIBUTOR REPLACE

### REMOVAL

1. Disconnect primary wire connector from distributor.
2. Using a screwdriver, remove distributor cap, and position aside with wires attached.
3. Remove distributor rotor.
4. Note position of shaft plate, armature and rotor locating holes for assembly reference, then remove distributor hold-down bolt and clamp and the distributor. Some models use special distributor hold-down bolts. To remove these bolts, use tool No. T82L-12270-A or equivalent.

### INSTALLATION

1. Rotate distributor by hand to ensure free rotation.
2. Ensure base O-ring is in place, then position rotor locating holes in original locations.
3. Install distributor, ensuring TFI-IV module is in same position relative to engine as when it was removed.
4. Install hold-down bolt and tighten until distributor can just barely be rotated.
5. Press rotor on distributor shaft.
6. Connect wiring harness to distributor, then install distributor cap and **torque** cap screws to 17-23 inch lbs.
7. Adjust ignition timing to specifications, then **torque** distributor hold-down bolt to 6-8.5 ft. lbs.

## MULTI-FUNCTION SWITCH REPLACE

1. **On models equipped with airbag,** disarm airbag system as described under "Airbag System Disarming."
2. **On all models,** disconnect battery ground cable and isolate cable end with electrical tape.
3. Remove steering column shroud retaining screws, then the upper and lower shrouds.
4. Remove electrical connectors.
5. Remove two self-tapping screws, attaching multi-function switch to the steering column.
6. Remove switch from column.
7. Reverse procedure to install, noting the following:

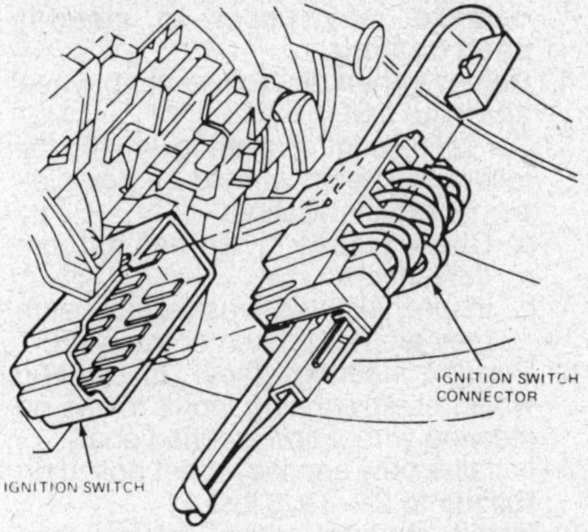


**Fig. 1 Ignition switch**

a. **Torque** self-tapping screws to 17-25 ft. lbs.
b. **Torque** shroud screws to 6-10 inch lbs.
c. Check switch for proper operation.
d. Reactivate airbag system.

## IGNITION LOCK REPLACE

1. **On models equipped with airbag,** disarm airbag system as described under "Airbag System Disarming."
2. **On all models,** disconnect battery ground cable and isolate with electrical tape.
3. **On models with tilt steering column,** remove upper extension shroud. Unsnap shroud from retaining clip located at the 9 o'clock position.
4. **On all models,** remove trim shroud or shroud halves, then disconnect key warning switch electrical connector.
5. Place gear shift lever in PARK on models with automatic trans. or in any gear on models with manual trans.
6. Insert a 1/8 inch diameter pin in the hole in casting surrounding lock cylinder. Pull lock cylinder out of housing while depressing retaining pin.
7. To install, turn lock cylinder to RUN position and depress retaining pin.
8. Install lock cylinder into housing. Turn key to OFF position after checking that cylinder is fully seated and aligned in the interlocking washer.
9. Turn the key to check for proper operation in all positions.
10. Install trim shroud and extension shroud if applicable.
11. Reconnect battery ground cable.
12. Reactivate airbag system.

## IGNITION SWITCH REPLACE

### REMOVAL

1. **On models equipped with airbag,** disarm airbag system as described under "Airbag System Disarming."
2. **On all models,** disconnect battery ground cable and isolate cable end with electrical tape.

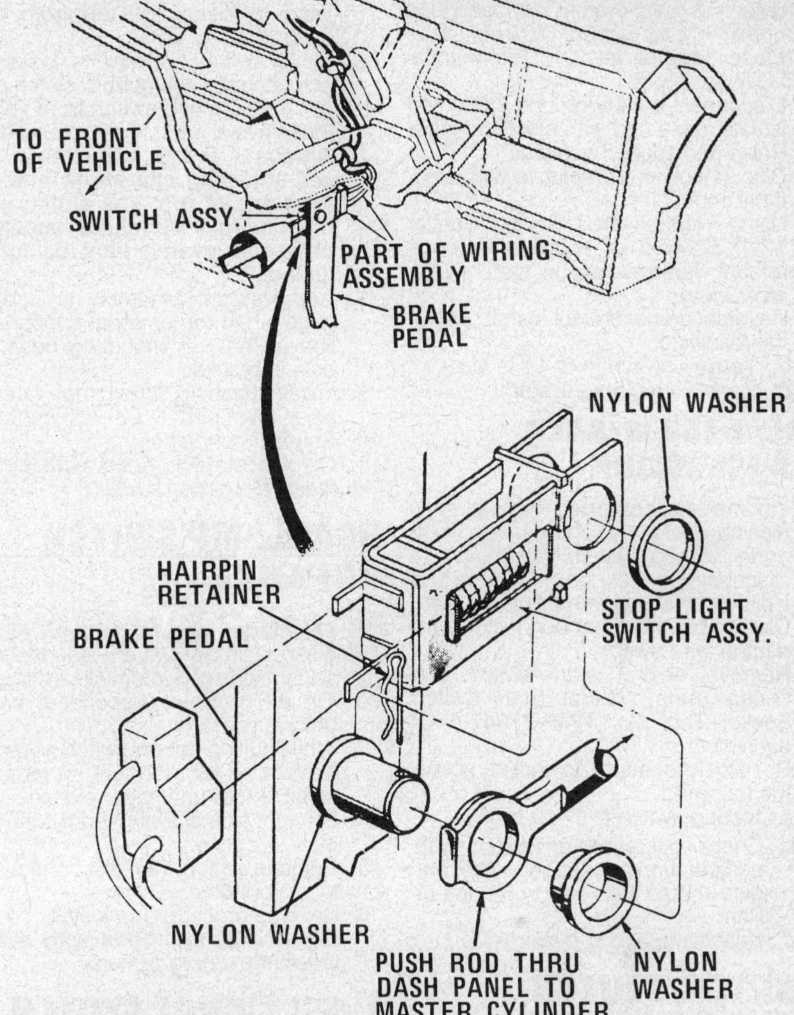


**Fig. 2 Stop light switch installation**

3. Remove steering column trim shroud. **On models with tilt column,** remove upper extension shroud.
4. **On all models,** remove electrical connector from switch, **Fig. 1.**
5. Rotate ignition key to (Run) position.
6. Remove two ignition switch-to-lock cylinder housing attaching screws.
7. Disengage switch from the actuator pin.
8. Reactivate airbag system.

### INSTALLATION

1. Adjust switch by sliding the carrier to the switch On (Run) position.
2. Check to ensure that the ignition key lock cylinder is in the On (Run) position by rotating the key lock cylinder approximately 90 degrees from the Lock position.
3. Install switch onto the actuator pin.
4. **Torque** attaching screws to 50-70 inch lbs.
5. Connect electrical connector to switch.
6. Install steering column trim shroud. **For tilt column only, install upper extension shroud.**
7. Connect battery ground cable.
8. Check for proper operation.
9. Reactivate airbag system.

## STOPLAMP SWITCH REPLACE

1. **On models equipped with airbag,** disarm airbag system as described under "Airbag System Disarming."
2. **On all models,** disconnect wires at connector.
3. Remove hairpin retainer, slide switch, pushrod and nylon washers and bushing away from the pedal and remove the switch, **Fig. 2.**
4. Reverse procedure to install.
5. **On models equipped with airbag,** reactivate airbag system.

## NEUTRAL SAFETY SWITCH REPLACE

### 5.0L/V8-302 w/AOD TRANSMISSION

1. **On models equipped with airbag,**

disarm airbag system as described under "Airbag System Disarming."
2. Place selector lever in the manual LOW position.
3. Disconnect battery ground cable and isolate cable end with electrical tape.
4. Raise and support vehicle.
5. Disconnect neutral safety switch electrical connector.
6. Using Neutral Start Switch Socket T74P-77247-A or equivalent, and a ratchet, remove neutral start switch and O-ring.
7. Reverse procedure to install, noting the following:
   a. **Torque** switch to 8-11 ft. lbs.
   b. Reactivate airbag system.

### 2.3L/4-140 W/A4LD TRANSMISSION

1. **On models equipped with airbag,** disarm airbag system as described under "Airbag System Disarming."
2. Disconnect battery ground cable and isolate cable end with electrical tape.
3. Disconnect electrical connector from neutral start switch.
4. Remove neutral start switch and O-ring using Neutral Start Switch Socket Tool No. T74P-77247-A or equivalent.
5. Reverse procedure to install, noting the following:
   a. **torque** switch to 7-10 ft.lbs.
   b. Check operation of switch with parking brake engaged. The engine should start only in Neutral or Park.
   c. Reactivate airbag system.

## STARTER/CLUTCH INTERLOCK SWITCH REPLACE

The starter/clutch interlock switch is designed to prevent starting the engine unless the clutch pedal is fully depressed. The switch is connected between the ignition switch and the starter motor relay coil and maintains an open circuit with the clutch pedal in the up position (clutch engaged).

The switch is designed to automatically self-adjust the first time the clutch pedal is pressed to the floor. The self-adjuster consists of a two piece clip snapped together over a serrated rod. When the plunger or rod is extended, the clip bottoms out on the serrations to a position determined by the clutch pedal travel. In this way, the switch is set to close the starter circuit when the clutch is pressed all the way to the floor (clutch Disengaged). To replace interlock switch proceed as follows:

1. **On models equipped with airbag,** disarm airbag system as described under "Airbag System Disarming."
2. **On all models,** disconnect electrical connector.
3. Remove retaining pin from clutch pedal.
4. Remove switch bracket attaching screw.
5. Lift switch and bracket assembly upward to disengage tab from pedal support.
6. Move switch outward to disengage actuating rod eyelet from clutch pedal pin, then remove switch from vehicle.
7. Place eyelet end of rod onto pivot pin. **Always install switch with self-adjusting clip about one inch from end of rod. The clutch pedal must be fully up (clutch engaged), otherwise switch may be misadjusted.**
8. Swing switch assembly around, engage tab in top of pedal support, and line up hole in mounting boss with hole in bracket.
9. Install attaching screw, then retaining pin in pivot pin.
10. Connect connector.
11. **On models equipped with airbag,** reactivate airbag system.

## HEADLAMP SWITCH REPLACE

1. **On models equipped with airbag,** disarm airbag system as described under "Airbag System Disarming."
2. **On all models,** disconnect battery ground cable.
3. While pulling out on switch assembly, push in on left side locking tabs with suitable tool until tabs release.
4. Pry right side of switch from dash panel.
5. Remove switch, then disconnect electrical connectors.
6. Reverse procedure to install.
7. **On models equipped with airbag,** reactivate airbag system.

## TURN SIGNAL SWITCH REPLACE

1. **On models equipped with airbag,** disarm airbag system as described under "Airbag Systom Disarming."
2. **On all models,** disconnect battery ground cable and isolate with electrical tape.
3. Remove column cover attaching screws, then the cover.
4. Disconnect switch electrical connector.
5. Remove switch attaching screws, then the switch.
6. Reverse procedure to install.
7. Reactivate airbag system.

## STEERING WHEEL REPLACE

### MODELS LESS PASSIVE RESTRAINT SYSTEM

1. Remove steering wheel cover.
2. Loosen steering wheel bolt four to six turns, but do not remove.
3. Use steering wheel remover T67L-3600-A, or equivalent, to remove steering wheel. **Do not use knock-off type puller, or strike attaching bolt with a hammer, as damage may occur to steering shaft bearing.**
4. Remove, then discard steering wheel attaching bolt.
5. For speed control steering wheels, the following checks should be completed prior to installation:
   a. Check grease in slip ring for contamination.
   b. Inspect slip ring brushes to ensure they are not broken or trapped.
6. Position steering wheel on steering wheel shaft, aligning index marks on steering wheel and steering shaft.
7. Install a new service wheel bolt, then **torque** to 21-33 ft. lbs.
8. Install steering wheel cover, then check for proper operation.

### MODELS W/PASSIVE RESTRAINT SYSTEM

1. **On models equipped with airbag,** disarm airbag system as described under "Airbag System Disarming."
2. Disconnect battery ground cable and isolate cable end with electrical tape.
3. Remove four airbag retaining nuts.
4. Remove airbag module from steering wheel, then disconnect electrical connector.
5. Remove and discard steering wheel attaching bolt.
6. Remove steering wheel from column.
7. To replace, position steering wheel on column shaft.
8. Install a new steering wheel bolt, then **torque** to 23-32 ft. lbs.
9. Connect airbag electrical connector, position module to wheel, installing retaining nuts, then **torque** to 3-4 ft. lbs.
10. Connect battery ground cable, then reactivate airbag system.

## HORN SOUNDER REPLACE

1. **On models equipped with airbag,** disarm airbag system as described under "Airbag System Disarming."
2. **On all models,** disconnect battery ground cable, then remove steering column cover attaching screws and steering column cover.
3. With wire connectors exposed, carefully lift connector retaining tabs and disconnect connectors.
4. Remove switch attaching screws and the switch.
5. Reverse procedure to install, then reactivate airbag system.

## INSTRUMENT CLUSTER REPLACE

1. **On models equipped with airbag,** disarm airbag system as described under "Airbag System Disarming."
2. **On all models,** disconnect battery ground cable and isolate cable end with electrical tape.
3. Remove switch assemblies from righthand and lefthand sides of cluster assembly:

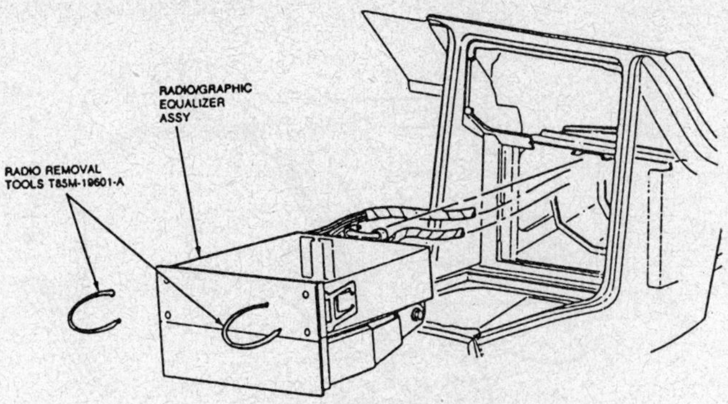


**Fig. 3 Radio removal.**

a. While pulling out on switch assembly, push in on locking tabs with suitable tool until tabs release.
b. Pull switch from dash panel.
c. Remove switch, then disconnect electrical connectors.

4. Remove two upper and three lower retaining screws from instrument cluster trim cover, then the trim cover.
5. Pull cluster from panel slightly and disconnect speedometer cable and the printed circuit electrical connectors.
6. Remove instrument cluster from instrument panel.
7. Reverse procedure to install, then reactivate airbag system, if equipped.

# WINDSHIELD WIPER MOTOR
## REPLACE

1. Disconnect battery ground cable and isolate cable end with electrical tape, then remove righthand wiper arm and blade assembly.
2. Remove cowl grille, then remove clip and disconnect linkage drive arm from motor crank pin.
3. Disconnect wiper motor wire connector, then remove three motor attaching screws and pull motor through opening.
4. Reverse procedure to install.

# WINDSHIELD WIPER TRANSMISSION
## REPLACE

1. Disconnect battery ground cable and isolate cable end with electrical tape, then remove right wiper arm and blade assembly from pivot shaft.
2. Remove cowl top grille, then remove clip and disconnect linkage drive arm from wiper motor crank pin.
3. Remove two screws retaining righthand pivot shaft to cowl and large nut and spacer from left pivot shaft, then remove linkage assembly.
4. Reverse procedure to install.

# WINDSHIELD WIPER SWITCH
## REPLACE

1. **On models equipped with airbag,** disarm airbag system as described under "Airbag System Disarming."
2. **On all models,** disconnect battery ground cable and isolate cable end with electrical tape.
3. Remove steering column shroud attaching screws and the shroud.
4. Disconnect electrical connector from wiper switch.
5. Remove wiper switch attaching screws and the switch.
6. Reverse procedure to install.
7. **On models equipped with airbag,** reactivate airbag system.

# RADIO
## REPLACE

1. **On models equipped with airbag,** disarm airbag system as described under "Airbag System Disarming."
2. **On all models,** disconnect negative battery cable and isolate cable end with electrical tape.
3. Using radio removing tool No. T87P-19061 or equivalent, spread radio face plate. **Fig. 3.**
4. Remove radio, then disconnect antenna and electrical connectors.
5. **On models equipped with airbag,** reactivate airbag system.

# BLOWER MOTOR
## REPLACE

1. **On models equipped with airbag,** disarm airbag system as described under "Airbag System Disarming."
2. **On all models,** disconnect battery ground cable and isolate cable end with electrical tape.
3. Loosen glove compartment assembly by squeezing sides of glove compartment together to disengage retainer tabs.
4. Let glove compartment and door hang in front of instrument panel.
5. Remove blower motor cooling hose.
6. Remove four screws that retain blower motor assembly to blower motor housing.
7. Disconnect electrical connector from wiring harness.
8. Carefully pull blower motor assembly from housing.
9. Reverse procedure to install.
10. **On models equipped with airbag,** reactivate airbag system.

# HEATER CORE
## REPLACE
### LESS AIR CONDITIONING

1. **On models equipped with airbag,** disarm airbag system as described under "Airbag System Disarming."
2. **On all models,** drain cooling system, then disconnect battery ground cable and isolate cable end with electrical tape.
3. Disconnect heater hoses from heater core and plug core openings.
4. Remove glove box liner.
5. Remove instrument panel to cowl brace retaining screws and the brace.
6. Move temperature control lever to warm position.
7. Remove the four heater core cover retaining screws, then the cover through the glove box opening.
8. Remove heater core assembly mounting stud nuts from engine compartment.
9. Push core tubes and seal toward passenger compartment to loosen core from case assembly.
10. Remove heater core from case through the glove box opening, **Fig. 4.**
11. Reverse procedure to install, noting the following:
    a. Reactivate airbag system, if equipped.

### WITH AIR CONDITIONING

1. **On models equipped with airbag,** disarm airbag system as described under "Airbag System Disarming."
2. **On all models,** remove instrument panel and lay it on front seat as outlined in "Dash Panel Service" section.
3. Discharge refrigerant from air conditioning system.
4. **On models equipped with 2.3L/4-140 engine,** remove speed control servo.
5. **On all models,** working from inside engine compartment, disconnect air conditioning lines from evaporator core at dash panel.
6. Remove low pressure line from accumulator/dryer, then cap all open lines to prevent contamination of system.
7. Disconnect heater hoses from heater core tubes and plug hoses with suitable 5/8 inch and 3/4 inch plugs.
8. Cap heater core tubes to prevent coolant loss from heater core during removal of evaporator core.
9. Working from inside passenger compartment, remove screw attaching air inlet duct and blower housing assembly support brace to cowl top panel.

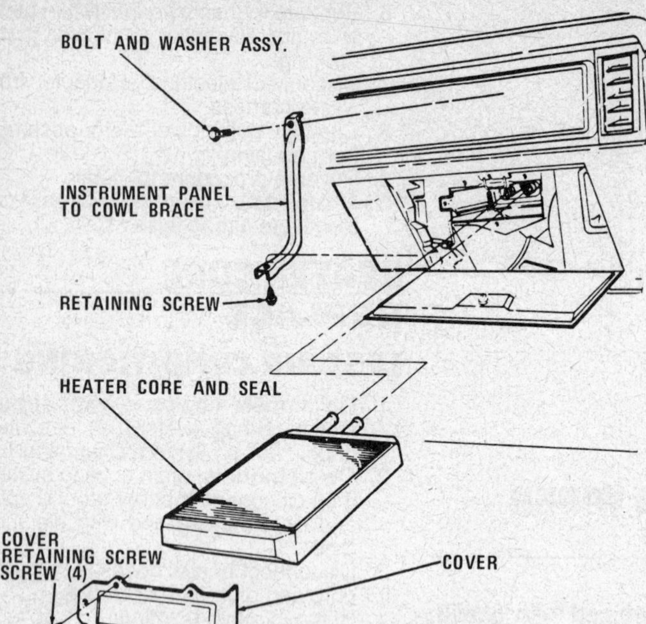


**Fig. 4 Heater core replacement. Less A/C**

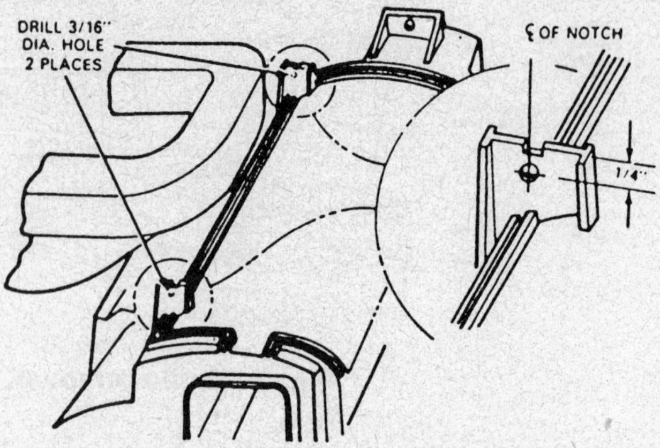

10. Disconnect vacuum supply hose (black) from in-line vacuum check valve in engine compartment.
11. Disconnect blower motor wires from wire harness, then wire harness from blower motor resistor.
12. Working from inside engine compartment, remove two nuts retaining evaporator case to dash panel.
13. Working from inside passenger compartment, remove two screws attaching evaporator case support brackets to cowl top panel.
14. Remove one screw retaining bracket below evaporator case to dash panel.
15. Carefully pull evaporator case from dash panel, then remove case from vehicle.
16. Remove four heater core access cover attaching screws, then cover from case.
17. Lift heater core from case.
18. Remove seal from heater core tubes.
19. Reverse procedure to install, noting the following:
    a. Reactivate airbag system, if equipped.

## EVAPORATOR CORE REPLACE

Whenever an evaporator core is replaced, it will be necessary to replace the suction/accumulator dryer.

1. **On models equipped with airbag,** disarm airbag system as described under "Airbag System Disarming."
2. **On all models,** remove instrument panel and lay it on front seat as outlined in "Dash Panel Service" section.
3. Discharge refrigerant from air conditioning system.
4. **On models equipped with 2.3L/4-140 engine,** remove speed control servo.
5. **On all models,** working from inside engine compartment, disconnect air conditioning lines from evaporator core at dash panel.
6. Remove low pressure line from accumulator/dryer, then cap all open lines to prevent contamination of system.
7. Disconnect heater hoses from heater core tubes and plug hoses with suitable 5/8 inch and 3/4 inch plugs.
8. Cap heater core tubes to prevent coolant loss from heater core during removal of evaporator core.
9. Working from inside passenger compartment, remove screw attaching air inlet duct and blower housing assembly support brace to cowl top panel.
10. Disconnect vacuum supply hose (black) from in-line vacuum check valve in engine compartment.
11. Disconnect blower motor wires from wire harness, then wire harness from blower motor resistor.
12. Working from inside engine compartment, remove two nuts retaining evaporator case to dash panel.
13. Working from inside passenger compartment, remove two screws attaching evaporator case support brackets to cowl top panel.
14. Remove one screw retaining bracket below evaporator case to dash panel.
15. Carefully pull evaporator case from dash panel, then remove case from vehicle.
16. Remove four screws retaining air inlet duct to evaporator case, then duct.
17. Remove foam seal from evaporator core tubes.
18. Drill 3/16 inch hole in both upright tabs as shown in **Fig. 5.**
19. Using a small saw blade, cut top of evaporator case between raised outlines as shown in **Fig. 6.**
20. Remove two screws retaining blower motor resistor to evaporator case, then resistor.
21. Fold cutout flap from opening and lift evaporator core from case.
22. Reverse procedure to install, reactivate airbag system, if equipped.

**Fig. 5 Locations for drilling holes in case tabs**

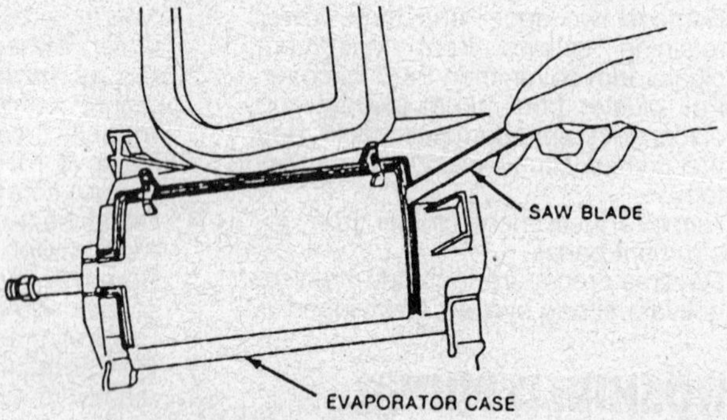

**Fig. 6 Cutting between raised outlines of evaporator case**

# 2.3L/4-140 Engine

**NOTE:** On Vehicles Equipped With Airbags, Disarm Airbag As Outlined Under "Airbag System Disarming" Before Any Diagnosis, Testing, Troubleshooting Or Repairs Are Performed. After All Diagnosis, Testing, Troubleshooting Or Repairs Have Been Completed, Rearm Airbag As Outlined Under "Airbag System Disarming."

## INDEX



## AIRBAG SYSTEM DISARMING

**The electrical circuit necessary for system deployment is powered directly from the battery and a backup power supply. To avoid accidental deployment and possible personal injury, the airbag system must be deactivated prior to servicing or replacing any component located near or related to airbag system activation components.**

### 1990

A back-up power supply is included in the system to provide airbag deployment in the event the battery or battery cables are damaged in an accident before the sensors can close. The power supply is a capacitor that will retain a charge for approximately 15 minutes after the battery ground cable is disconnected. **Backup power supply must be disconnected to deactivate airbag system.** To remove backup power supply, refer to "Airbags" in the "Passive Restraint" section.

1. Disconnect battery ground cable and isolate cable end with electrical tape.
2. Disconnect backup power supply, located behind glove compartment.
3. Remove four nut and washer assemblies securing airbag module to steering wheel, then disconnect airbag electrical connector. Attach jumper wire to airbag terminals on clockspring terminals.
4. Reconnect battery and backup power supply if necessary to perform repair procedure.
5. To reactivate, disconnect battery ground cable and backup power supply, then reverse remainder of deactivation procedure. **Torque** airbag module to steering wheel nut assemblies to 24-32 inch lbs.
6. Verify airbag lamp after reactivating system.

### 1991-92

1. Disconnect positive battery cable, then ground cable end to frame or engine for one minute to discharge back-up power supply.
2. Remove four nut and washer assemblies securing airbag to steering wheel.
3. Disconnect airbag electrical connector.
4. Install airbag simulator tool No. 105-00008 or equivalent.
5. Connect positive battery cable.
6. To activate airbag system, disconnect positive battery cable and reverse procedure. **Torque** mounting nut and washer assemblies to 24-32 inch lbs.
7. Verify proper operation of airbag lamp.

## ENGINE MOUNTS

### REPLACE

1. Support engine using a wood block and jack placed under the engine.
2. Remove fan shroud, if necessary.
3. Remove screw attaching fuel pump shield to lefthand support bracket, if so equipped.
4. Remove nut and washer assemblies attaching both insulators to the crossmember, **Figs. 1 through 3.**
5. Disconnect transmission shift linkage.
6. Raise engine sufficiently to clear the insulator studs from the crossmember.
7. Remove bolts attaching insulator and bracket assembly from engine and remove insulator and bracket assembly.
8. Reverse procedure to install. **Torque** insulator and bracket assembly to 33-45 ft. lbs.
9. **Torque** cross member nut assemblies onto insulator studs to 65-85 ft. lbs.

## ENGINE

### REPLACE

1. Raise hood and secure in vertical position.
2. Drain coolant from radiator and oil from crankcase.
3. Remove air cleaner and exhaust manifold shroud.
4. Disconnect battery ground cable.
5. Remove radiator hoses and remove radiator and fan.
6. Disconnect heater hoses from water pump and carburetor choke fitting.
7. Disconnect wires from alternator and starter and disconnect accelerator cable from carburetor. On A/C vehicles, remove compressor from bracket and position it out of way with lines attached.
8. Disconnect flex fuel line from tank line and plug tank line.
9. Disconnect primary wire at coil and disconnect oil pressure and temperature sending unit wires at sending units.
10. Remove starter and raise vehicle to remove the flywheel or converter housing upper attaching bolts.
11. Disconnect inlet pipe at exhaust manifold. Disconnect engine mounts at underbody bracket and remove flywheel or converter housing cover.
12. **On vehicle with manual shift,** remove flywheel housing lower attaching bolts.
13. **On vehicle with automatic transmission,** disconnect converter from flywheel and remove converter housing lower attaching bolts. Disconnect transmission oil cooler lines if attached to engine at pan rail.
14. **On all models,** lower vehicle and support transmission and flywheel or converter housing with a jack.

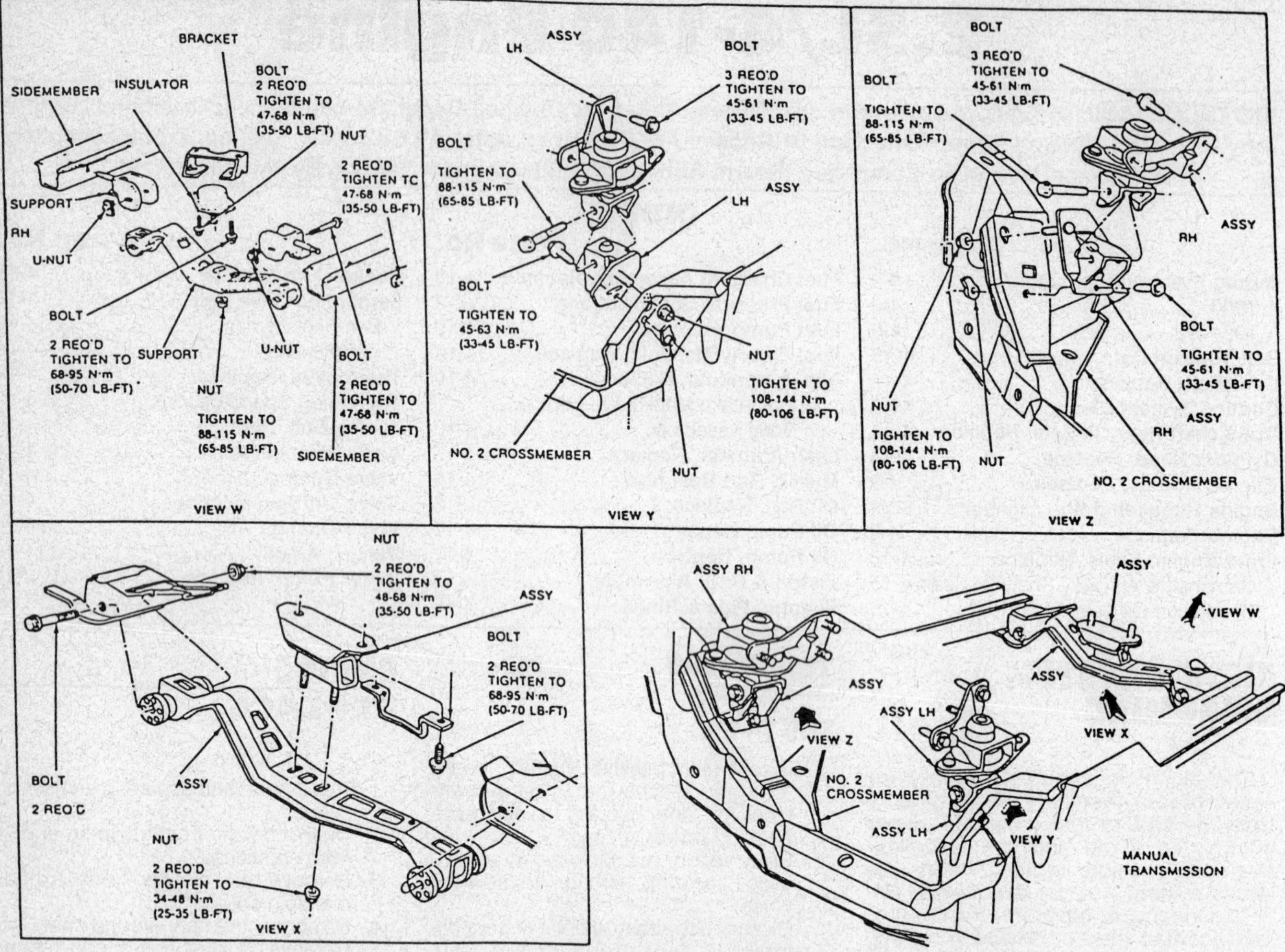


**Fig. 1 Engine mount installation. Hard top models w/T5 transmission**

15. Attach engine lifting hooks to brackets and carefully lift engine out of engine compartment.

# INTAKE MANIFOLD REPLACE

## UPPER INTAKE MANIFOLD & THROTTLE BODY ASSEMBLY

1. Disconnect battery ground cable.
2. Label, then disconnect all electrical connectors and vacuum lines from manifold assembly.
3. Release pressure from fuel system at the fuel pressure relief valve using fuel pressure gauge tool T80L-9974-B or equivalent. The fuel pressure relief valve is located on the fuel line in the upper righthand corner of the engine compartment.
4. Disconnect throttle linkage, cruise control and kickdown cables. Loosen, then position aside accelerator cable.
5. Disconnect air hose from crankcase vent hose.
6. Disconnect PCV system by disconnecting hose from upper intake manifold fitting.
7. Disconnect EGR tube from EGR valve.
8. Remove four upper intake manifold mounting bolts, **Fig. 4.**
9. Remove upper intake manifold assembly.
10. Reverse procedure to install.

# FUEL CHARGING ASSEMBLY REPLACE

1. Disconnect battery ground cable.
2. Remove fuel filler cap to relieve fuel tank pressure.
3. Drain coolant from radiator.
4. Release pressure from fuel system at the fuel pressure relief valve using tool No. T80L-9974-B (EFI Pressure Gauge) or equivalent. The fuel pressure relief valve is located on the fuel line in the upper righthand corner of engine compartment.
5. Disconnect electrical connectors at:
   a. Throttle position sensor, then injector wiring harness.
   b. Knock sensor, then air charge temperature sensor.
   c. Engine coolant temperature sensor, then air bypass valve.
   d. Fan switch, then EGR valve.
6. Label vacuum lines for installation at upper intake manifold vacuum tree, then disconnect vacuum lines.
7. Disconnect vacuum line to fuel pressure regulator.
8. Disconnect throttle linkage, cruise control and kickdown cable.
9. Remove accelerator cable from bracket, then position out of way.
10. Disconnect air intake hose.
11. Disconnect PCV hose from fitting on underside of upper intake manifold.
12. Disconnect water bypass line at lower intake manifold.
13. Disconnect EGR tube from EGR valve.
14. Remove engine oil dipstick retaining screw.
15. Remove four upper intake manifold retaining nuts.
16. Remove upper intake manifold and air throttle assembly.
17. Disconnect EVAP canister purge hose from throttle body.
18. Remove spring lock coupling retaining clips from fuel inlet and return fittings.
19. Disconnect fuel supply manifold and fuel return lines using quick connect removal tool No. D87L-9280-A or B or equivalents.

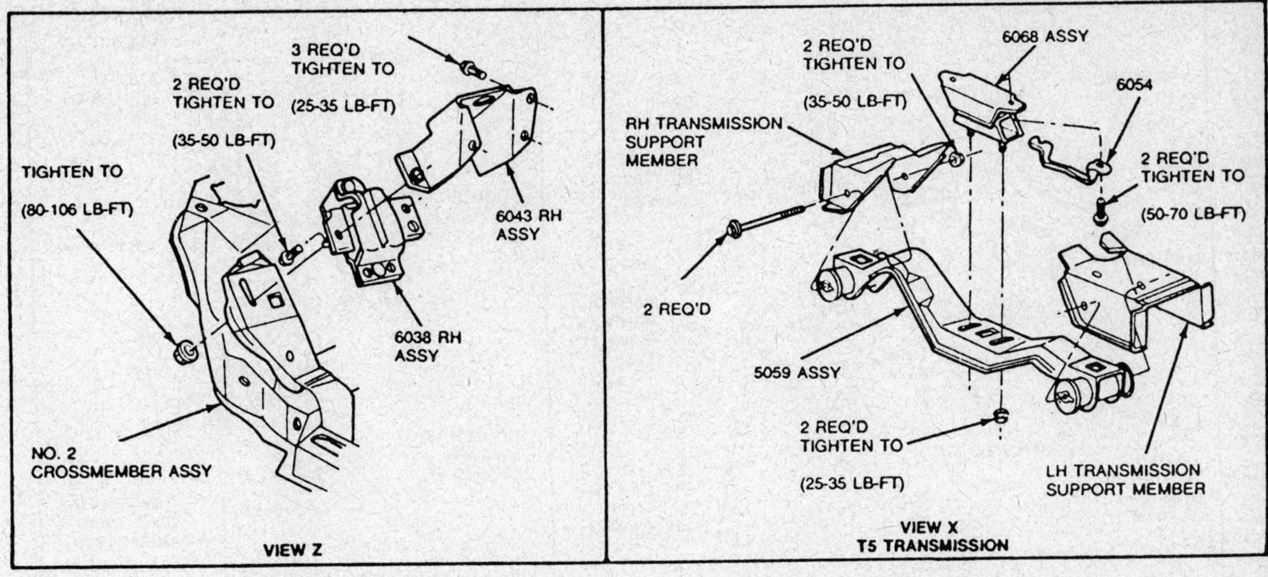


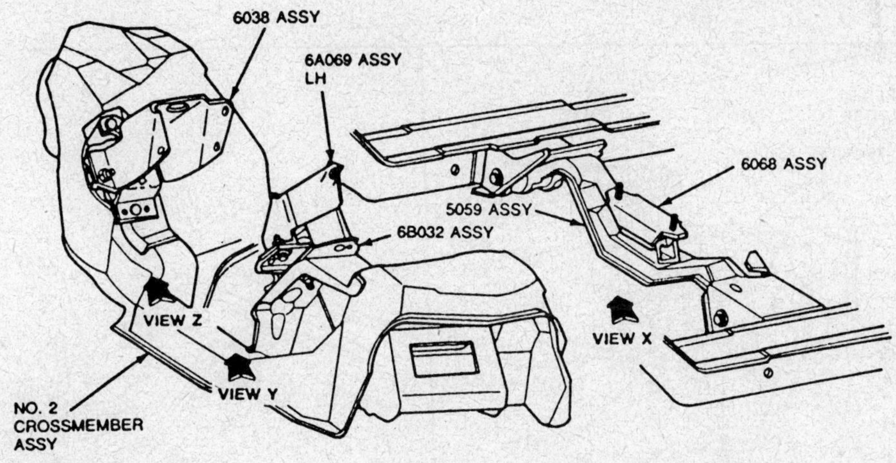


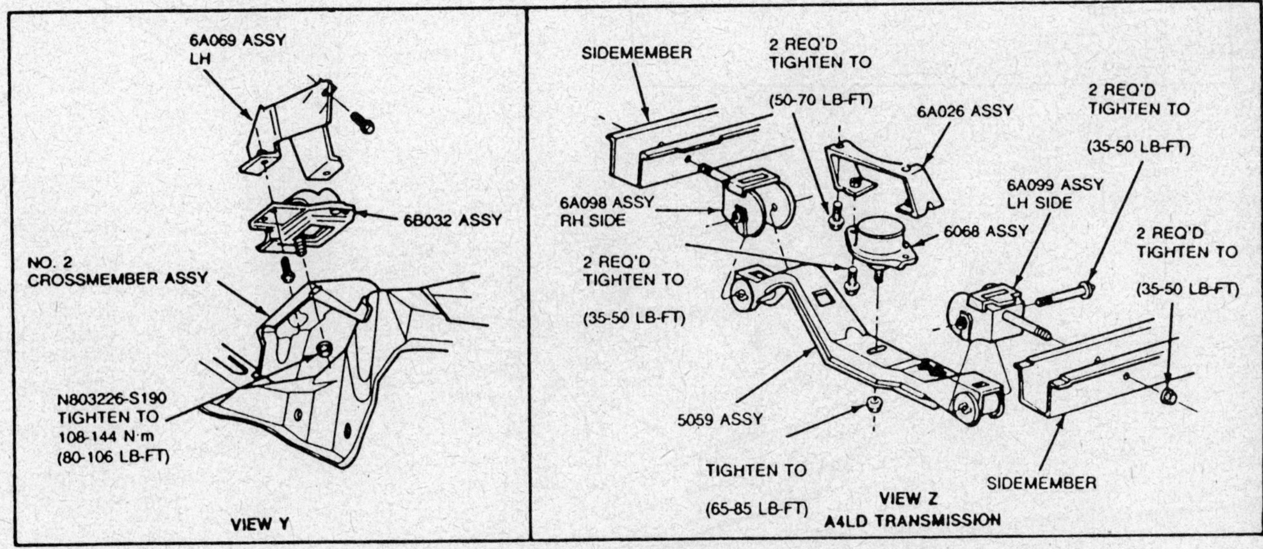


**Fig. 2 Engine mount installation. Convertible models w/T5 transmission**

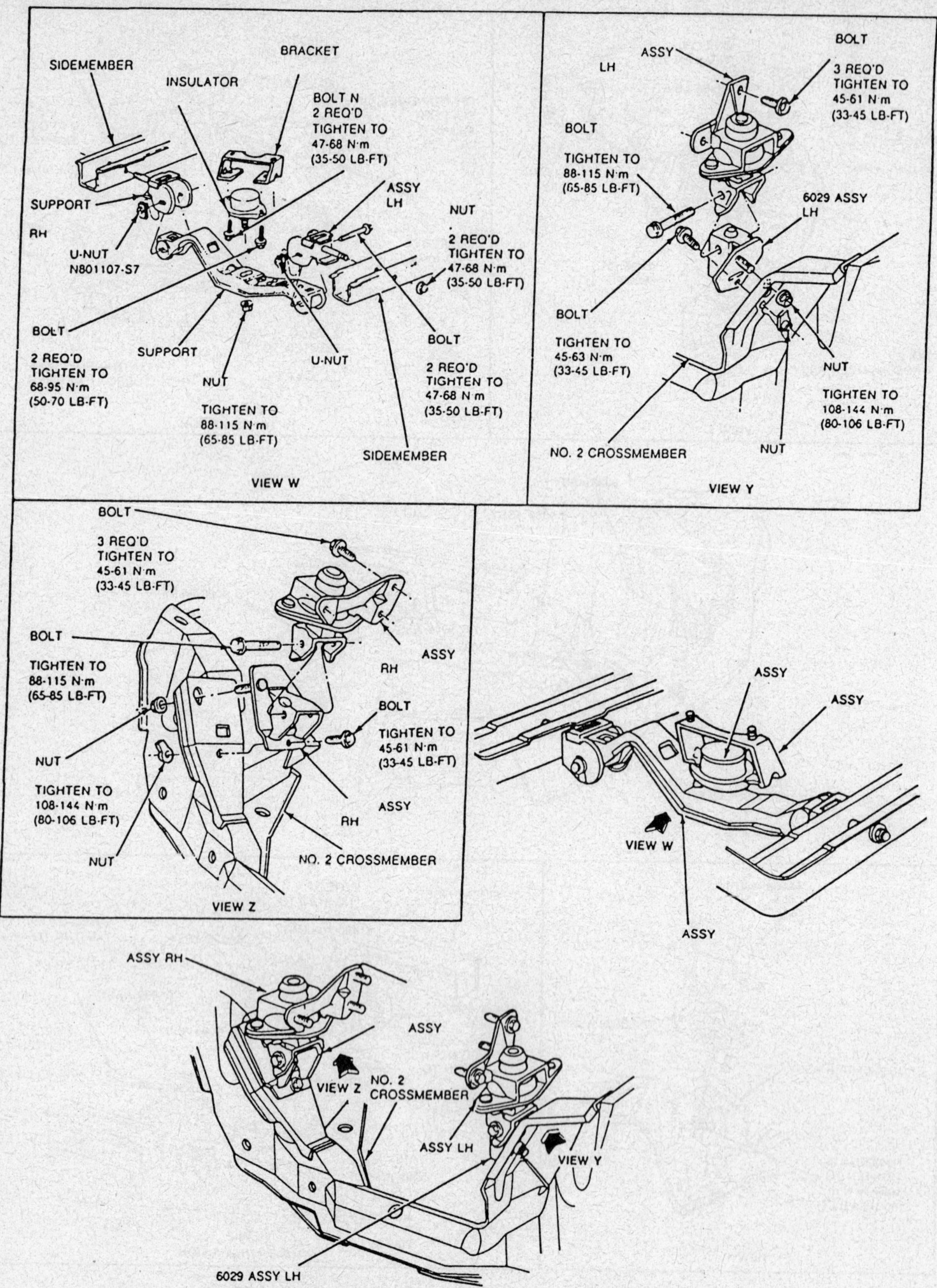


**Fig. 3 Engine mount installation. Models w/A4LD transmission**

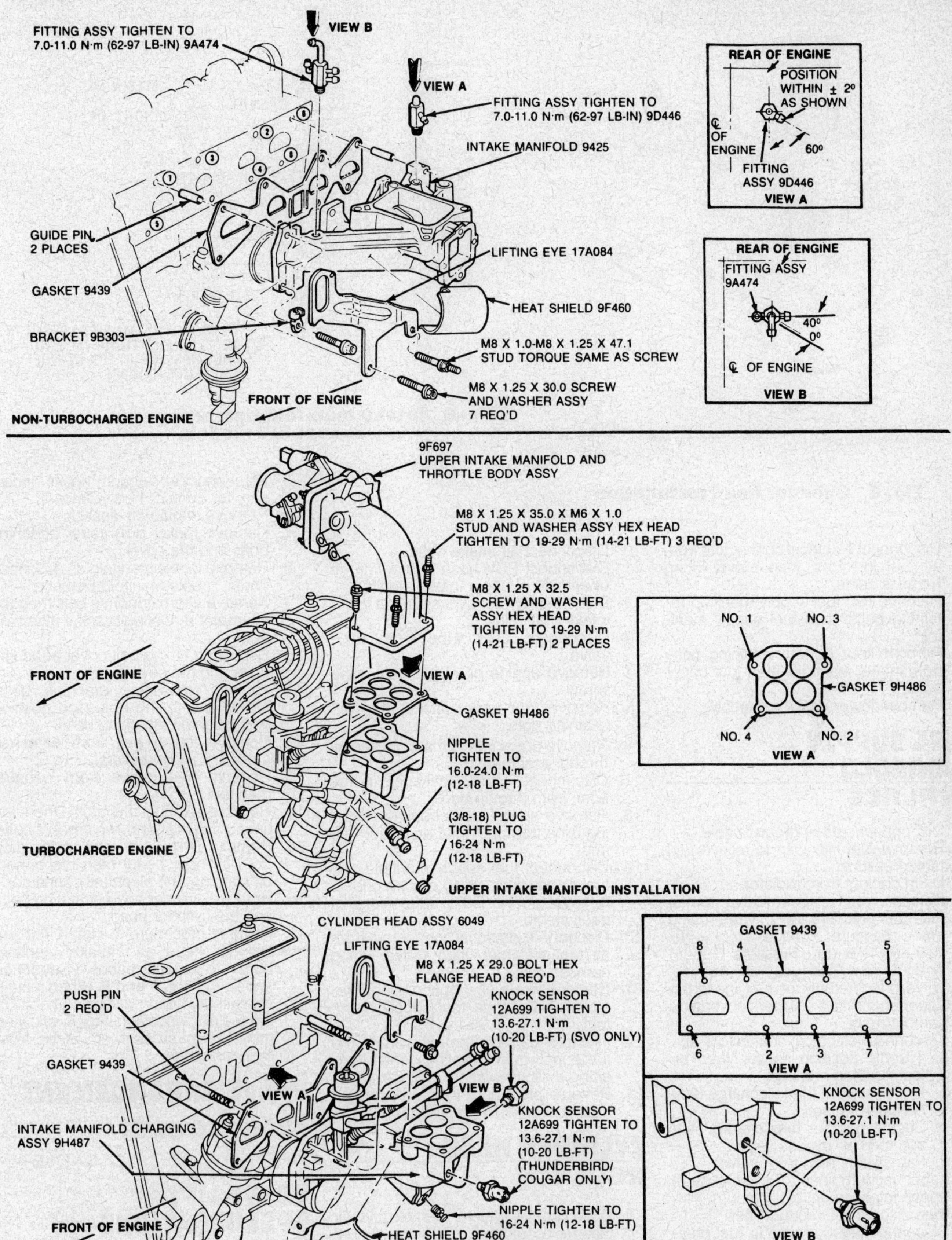


**Fig. 4 Intake manifold assembly. EFI models**

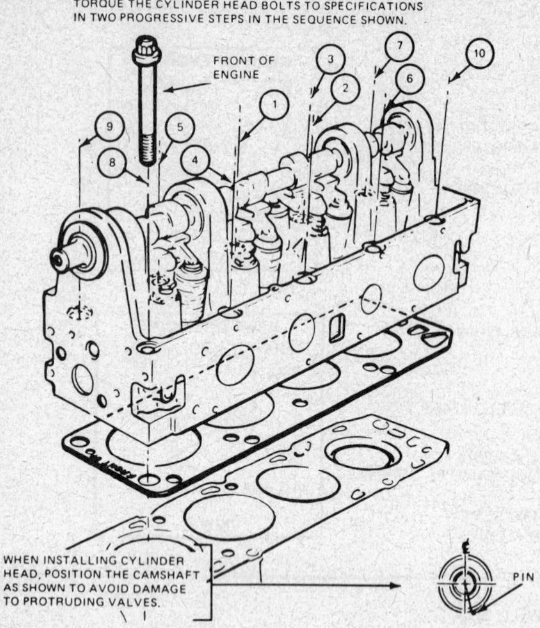
TORQUE THE CYLINDER HEAD BOLTS TO SPECIFICATIONS IN TWO PROGRESSIVE STEPS IN THE SEQUENCE SHOWN.
FRONT OF ENGINE
WHEN INSTALLING CYLINDER HEAD, POSITION THE CAMSHAFT AS SHOWN TO AVOID DAMAGE TO PROTRUDING VALVES.
PIN

**Fig. 5 Cylinder head installation**

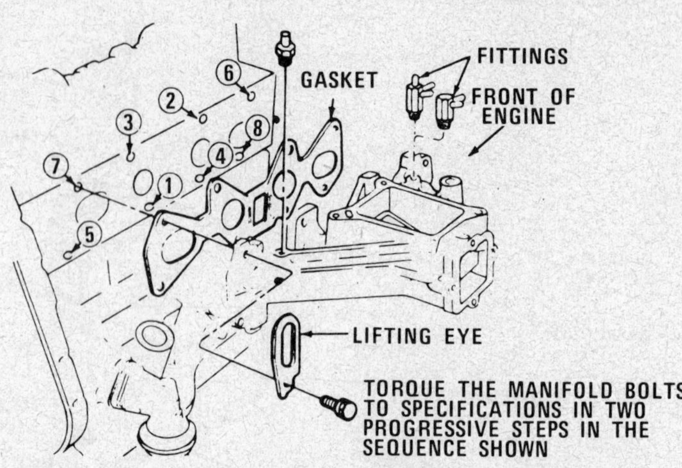
GASKET
FITTINGS
FRONT OF ENGINE
LIFTING EYE
TORQUE THE MANIFOLD BOLTS TO SPECIFICATIONS IN TWO PROGRESSIVE STEPS IN THE SEQUENCE SHOWN

**Fig. 6 Intake manifold tightening sequence. Except EFI models**

20. Disconnect electrical connectors from all fuel injectors, then move wiring harness aside.
21. Remove two fuel supply manifold retaining bolts, then fuel supply manifold.
22. Remove four bottom retaining bolts from intake manifold, then four upper bolts.
23. Remove lower intake assembly.

## FUEL SUPPLY MANIFOLD REPLACE

1. Disconnect battery ground cable.
2. Remove fuel filler cap to relieve fuel tank pressure.
3. Drain coolant from radiator.
4. Release pressure from fuel system at the fuel pressure relief valve using fuel pressure gauge tool No. T80L-9974-B (EFI Pressure Gauge) or equivalent. The fuel pressure relief valve is located on the fuel line in the upper righthand corner of engine compartment.
5. Disconnect electrical connectors at:
   a. Throttle position sensor, then injector wiring harness.
   b. Knock sensor, then air charge temperature sensor.
   c. Engine coolant temperature sensor, then air bypass valve.
   d. Fan switch, then EGR valve.
6. Label vacuum lines for installation at upper intake manifold vacuum tree, then disconnect vacuum lines.
7. Disconnect vacuum line to fuel pressure regulator.
8. Disconnect throttle linkage, cruise control and kickdown cable.
9. Remove accelerator cable from bracket, then position out of way.
10. Disconnect air intake hose.
11. Disconnect PCV hose from fitting on underside of upper intake manifold.
12. Disconnect water bypass line at lower intake manifold.
13. Disconnect EGR tube from EGR valve.
14. Remove engine oil dipstick retaining screw.
15. Remove four upper intake manifold retaining nuts.
16. Remove upper intake manifold and air throttle assembly.
17. Disconnect EVAP canister purge hose from throttle body.
18. Remove spring lock coupling retaining clips from fuel inlet and return fittings.
19. Disconnect fuel supply manifold and fuel return lines using quick connect removal tool No. D87L-9280-A or B or equivalents.
20. Disconnect electrical connectors from all fuel injectors, then move wiring harness aside.
21. Remove two fuel supply manifold retaining bolts, then fuel supply manifold.
22. Injectors can be removed from the fuel supply manifold at this time by exerting a slight twisting/pulling motion.
23. Reverse procedure to install, **torque** nuts and bolts to specification.

## CYLINDER HEAD REPLACE

1. Drain cooling system, then remove air cleaner assembly.
2. Remove heater hose-to-rocker arm cover retaining screw.
3. Remove distributor cap and ignition wires.
4. Remove spark plugs.
5. Disconnect all vacuum hoses necessary for cylinder head removal.
6. Remove engine oil dipstick.
7. Remove rocker arm cover attaching bolts and the cover.
8. Remove intake manifold as described under "Intake Manifold Replace."
9. Remove alternator drive belt, then the alternator mounting bracket attaching bolts.
10. Removing timing belt cover attaching bolts and the cover.
11. Loosen cam idler attaching bolts. Move idler to the unloaded position and retighten attaching bolts.
12. Remove timing belt from camshaft and auxiliary sprockets.
13. Remove heat stove from exhaust manifold.
14. Remove exhaust manifold, then the timing belt idler and two bracket bolts.
15. Remove timing belt idler spring stop from cylinder head, then disconnect oil sending unit electrical connector.
16. Remove cylinder head attaching bolts and the cylinder head.
17. Reverse procedure to install. **Torque** cylinder head and intake manifold bolts to specifications. Sequence shown in **Figs. 5 and 6.** When installing cylinder head, position camshaft in the 5 o'clock position, **Fig. 5,** allowing minimum protrusion of valves from cylinder head.

## VALVE ARRANGEMENT

### FRONT TO REAR

2.3L/4-140 Engine........ E-I-E-I-E-I-E-I

## VALVE LIFT SPECIFICATIONS

| Engine | Year | Intake, Inch | Exhaust, Inch |
|---|---|---|---|
| 2.3L/4-140 | 1989–92 | .3900 | .3900 |

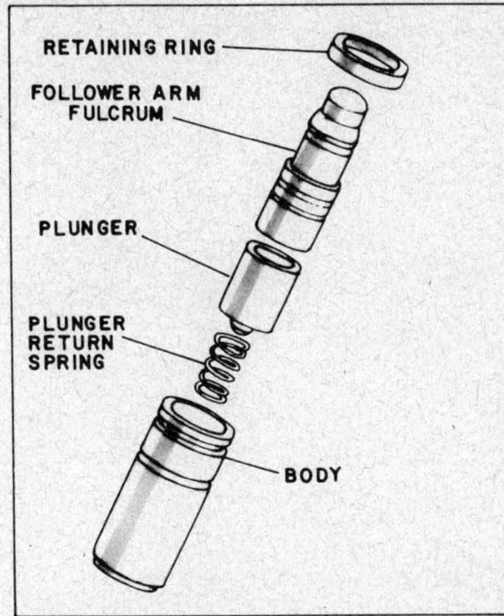


Fig. 7 Valve lash adjuster. Type I

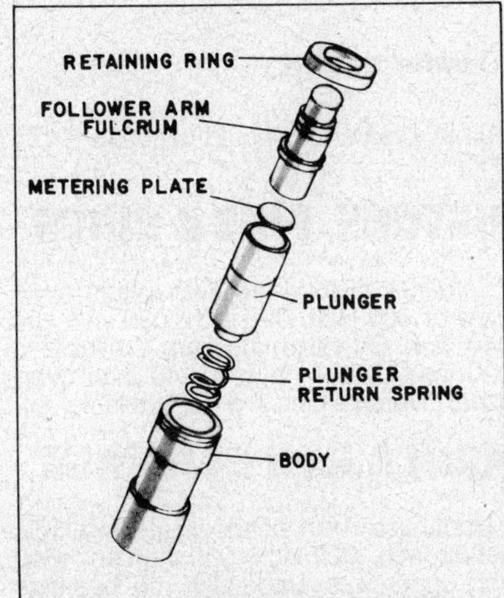


Fig. 8 Valve lash adjuster. Type II

# VALVE TIMING

## INTAKE OPENS BEFORE TDC

| Engine | Year | Degrees |
|---|---|---|
| 2.3L/4-140 | 1989–92 | 22 |

# VALVES ADJUST

The valve lash on this engine cannot be adjusted due to the use of hydraulic valve lash adjusters. However, the valve train can be checked for wear as follows:

1. Crank engine to position camshaft with flat section of lobe facing rocker arm of valve being checked.
2. Remove rocker arm retaining spring. **Late models do not incorporate the retaining spring.**

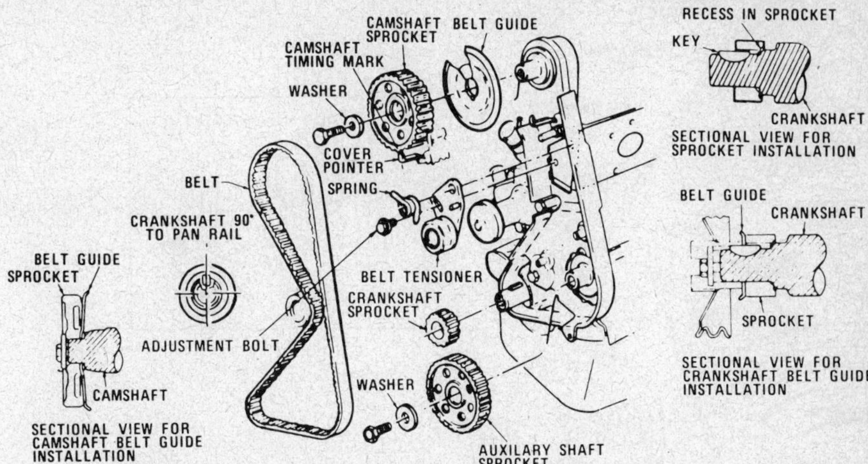


Fig. 9 Drive belt & sprockets installation. 2.3L/4-140 engine

3. Collapse lash adjuster with valve spring compressor tool T74P-6565B and insert correct size feeler gauge between rocker arm and camshaft lobe. Clearance should be .040-.050 inch. If not, remove rocker arm and check for wear and replace as necessary. If rocker arm is found satisfactory, check valve spring assembled height and adjust as needed. Valve spring assembled height should be 1.53 to 1.59 inch. If not, remove lash adjuster, and clean or replace parts as necessary.

# VALVE GUIDES

Valve guides consist of holes bored in the cylinder head. For service the guides can be reamed oversize to accommodate valves with oversize stems of .003, .015 and .030 inch.

# ROCKER ARM SERVICE

1. Remove rocker arm cover.
2. Rotate camshaft until flat section of lobe faces rocker arm being removed.
3. With valve spring compressor tool T74P-6565B, collapse lash adjuster and, if necessary, valve spring and slide rocker arm over lash adjuster.
4. Reverse procedure to install. **Before rotating camshaft, ensure that lash adjuster is collapsed to prevent valve train damage.**

# LASH ADJUSTER REPLACE

The hydraulic valve lash adjusters can be removed after rocker arm removal. There are two types of lash adjusters available, Type 1, being the standard lash adjuster, **Fig. 7,** and Type II, having a .020 inch oversize outside diameter, **Fig. 8.**

# FRONT ENGINE SEALS REPLACE

To gain access to the front engine seals, remove the timing belt cover and proceed as follows:

## CRANKSHAFT OIL SEAL

1. Without removing cylinder front cover, remove crankshaft sprocket with crankshaft sprocket remover tool T74P-6306A.
2. Remove crankshaft oil seal with front cover seal remover tool T74P-6700B.
3. Install a new crankshaft oil seal with shaft seal installer tool T74P-6150A.
4. Install crankshaft sprocket with recess facing engine block.

## CAMSHAFT & AUXILIARY SHAFT OIL SEALS

1. Remove camshaft or auxiliary shaft sprocket with camshaft sprocket remover/holding tool T74P-6256A.
2. Remove oil seal with front cover seal remover tool T74P-6700B.
3. Install a new oil seal with shaft seal installer tool T74P-6150A.
4. Install camshaft or auxiliary shaft sprocket with camshaft sprocket holding tool T74P-6256A with center arbor removed.

# TIMING BELT REPLACE

1. Position crankshaft at TDC, No. 1 cylinder compression stroke.
2. Remove timing belt cover, loosen belt tensioner, and remove belt from sprockets, **Fig. 9.** Tighten tensioner bolt, holding tensioner in position. **Do not rotate crankshaft or camshaft after belt is removed. Rotating either component will result in improper valve timing.**
3. To install belt, ensure timing marks are aligned, **Fig. 10,** and place belt over sprockets.
4. Loosen tensioner bolt, allowing tensioner to move against belt.
5. Rotate crankshaft two complete turns, removing slack from belt. Torque tensioner adjustment and pivot bolts and

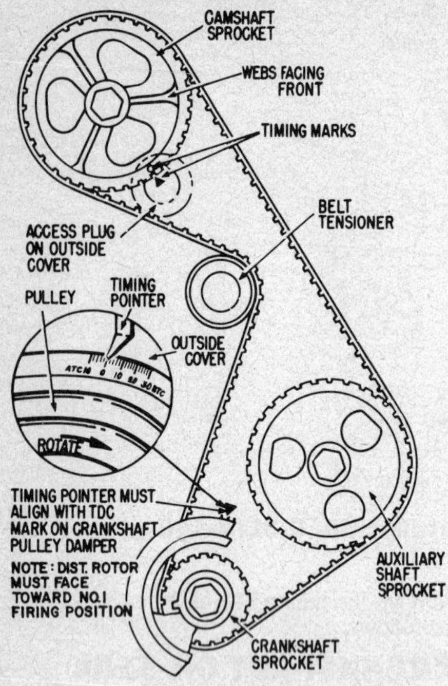


**Fig. 10 Valve timing marks**

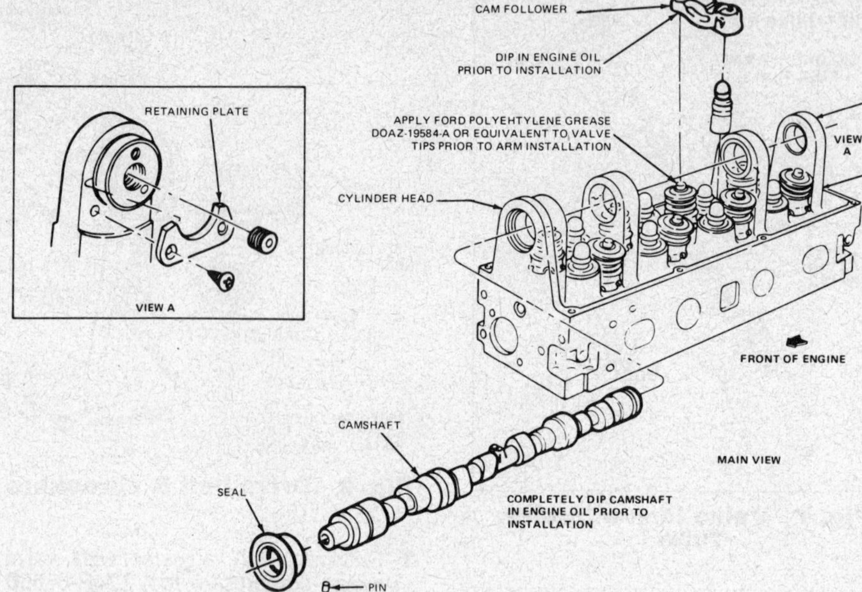


**Fig. 11 Camshaft replacement**

check alignment of timing marks, **Fig. 10.**

6. Install timing belt cover.

## CAMSHAFT REPLACE

1. Drain cooling system, then remove air cleaner assembly.
2. Disconnect ignition wires from spark plugs and rocker arm cover and position aside.
3. Disconnect all vacuum hoses necessary for camshaft removal.
4. Remove rocker arm cover attaching bolts and the cover.
5. Remove alternator drive belt.
6. Remove alternator mounting bracket attaching bolts and position bracket aside.
7. Remove upper radiator hose and disconnect lower hose.
8. Remove fan shroud. On models equipped with electric fan, remove fan and shroud as an assembly.
9. Remove timing belt cover attaching bolts and the cover.
10. Loosen cam idler attaching bolts. Move idler to the unloaded position and retighten attaching bolts.
11. Remove timing belt from camshaft and auxiliary sprockets.
12. Raise and support vehicle.
13. Remove right and left engine mount nuts and washers.
14. Raise engine as far as possible using a suitable transmission jack with a block of wood positioned between jack and engine. Install wood blocks between No. 2 crossmember pedestals and engine mounts, then remove jack and lower vehicle.
15. Depress valve springs using valve spring compressor tool No. T74P-6565-A or equivalent and remove camshaft followers.
16. Remove camshaft sprocket attaching bolt, then the sprocket using camshaft sprocket holding/removing tool No. T-74P-6256-B, or equivalent.
17. Remove seal using front cover seal remover tool No. T74P-6700-A, or equivalent.
18. Remove camshaft rear retainer attaching screws, then retainer.
19. Remove camshaft from cylinder head, **Fig. 11.**
20. Reverse procedure to install. **The camshaft sprocket attaching bolt should be replaced.** If a new bolt is not available, coat threads of original bolt with D8AZ-19554-A pipe sealer or equivalent.

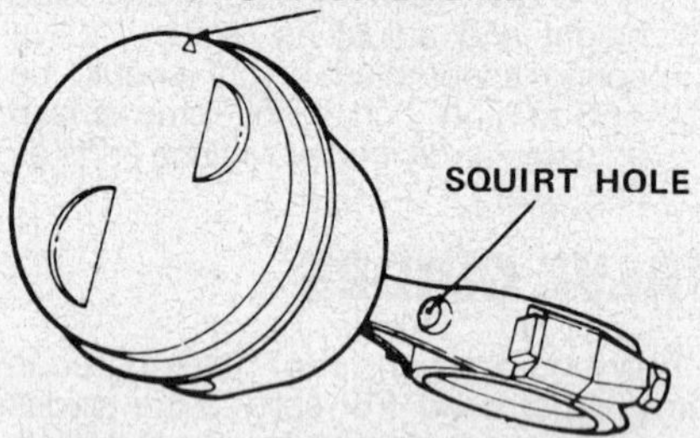


**Fig. 12 Piston & rod assembly**

## PISTON & ROD, ASSEMBLY

Assemble the rod to the piston with the arrow or notch on top of piston facing front of engine, **Fig. 12.**

Check side clearance between connecting rods at each connecting rod crankshaft journal. Clearance should be .0035-.0105 inch.

## PISTONS, PINS & RINGS

Oversize pistons are available in oversizes of .003 inch, .020 inch, .030 inch and .040 inch. Oversize rings are available in .020 inch, .030 inch and .040 inch oversizes. Oversize pins are not available.

## MAIN & ROD BEARINGS

Undersize main bearings are available in .002 inch, .020 inch, .030 inch and .040 inch undersizes. Undersize rod bearings are available in undersizes of .002 inch, .010 inch, .020 inch, .030 inch and .040 inch.

The crankshaft and main bearings are installed with arrows on main bearing caps facing front of engine, **Fig. 13.** Install PCV baffle between bearing journals No. 3 and 4.

## CRANKSHAFT REAR OIL SEAL REPLACE

1. Remove oil pump, if necessary, as described under "Oil Pump, Replace."
2. Punch one hole into metal surface between seal and block using a sharp awl.
3. Screw the threaded end of slide hammer, tool No. T77L-9533-B or equivalent, into seal and remove seal. Use care to avoid damaging oil seal mating surface.
4. Apply suitable sealer to seal and block mating surfaces.
5. Position seal on crankshaft seal installer tool No. T82L-6701-A or equivalent, **Fig. 14,** and install seal. Tighten

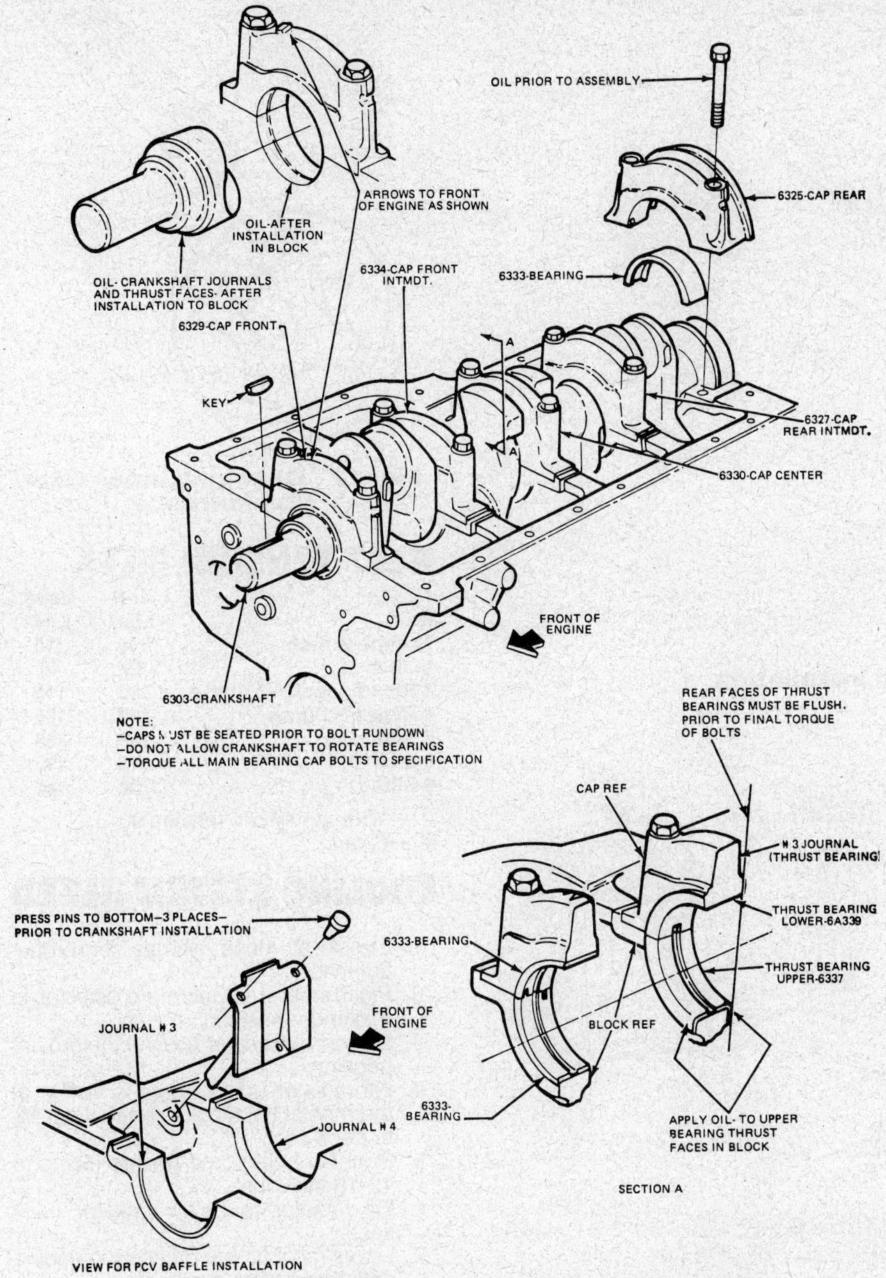

**Fig. 13 Crankshaft & main bearing installation**

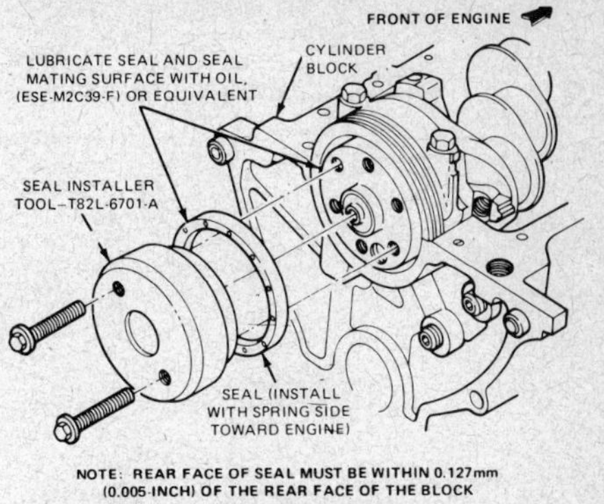

**Fig. 14 Crankshaft rear oil seal installation. 2.3L/4-140 engine**

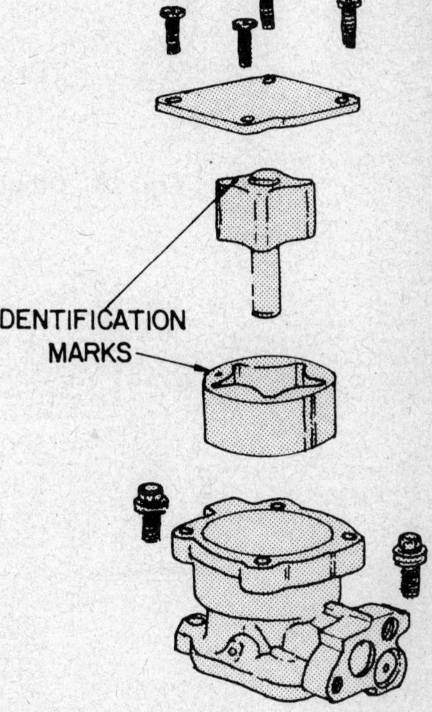


**Fig. 15 Oil pump exploded view**

bolts alternately to ensure proper seating of the seal.

6. Install oil pump if previously removed.

## OIL PAN REPLACE

1. Disconnect battery ground cable.
2. Remove fan shroud. If equipped with electric fan, remove fan and shroud as an assembly.
3. Drain cooling system, then disconnect upper and lower hoses from radiator.
4. Raise and support vehicle.
5. Drain engine oil, then remove right and left engine mount nuts and bolts or washers.
6. Raise engine as far as possible using a suitable jack with a block of wood positioned between jack and engine. Install wood blocks between mounts and chassis brackets or No. 2 crossmember pedestals, then remove jack.
7. Remove shake brace, then the sway bar attaching bolts and lower the sway bar.
8. Remove starter motor.
9. Remove steering gear attaching bolts and lower the gear.
10. Remove oil pan attaching bolts and the oil pan. **The number four piston must be in the up position to allow clearance between crankshaft and rear of oil pan for oil pan removal.**
11. Reverse procedure to install.

## OIL PUMP REPLACE

The oil pump, **Fig. 15**, can be removed after oil pan removal, **Fig. 16.**

## OIL PUMP REPAIRS

1. Remove end plate and withdraw O-ring from groove in body.
2. Check clearance between inner rotor tip and outer rotor lobe, **Fig. 17.** This should not exceed .012 inch. Rotors are supplied only in a matched pair.
3. Check clearance between outer rotor and the housing. This should not exceed .013 inch.
4. Place a straightedge across face of pump body. Clearance between face

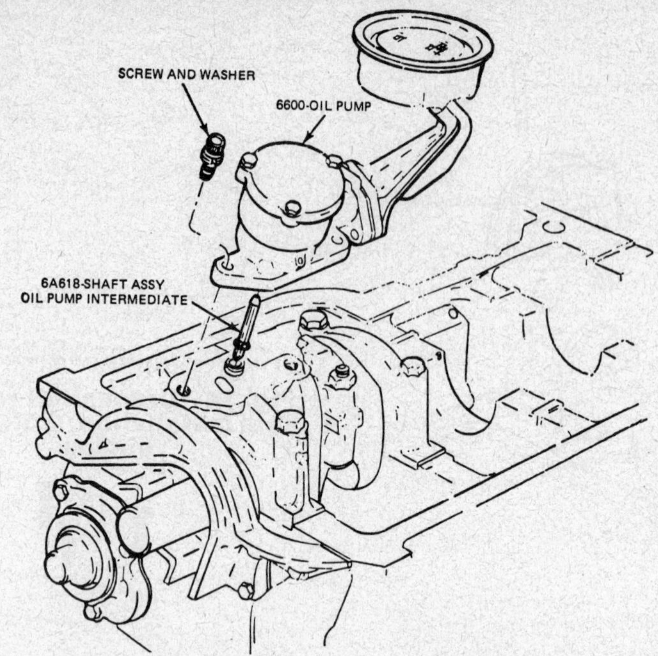


Fig. 16 Oil pump installation

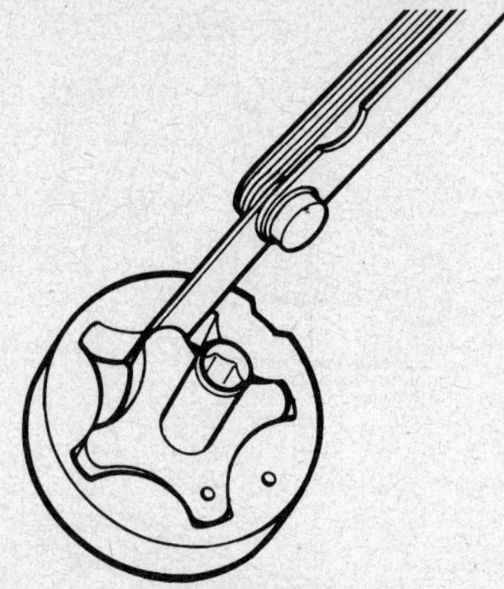

Fig. 17 Checking inner rotor tip clearance

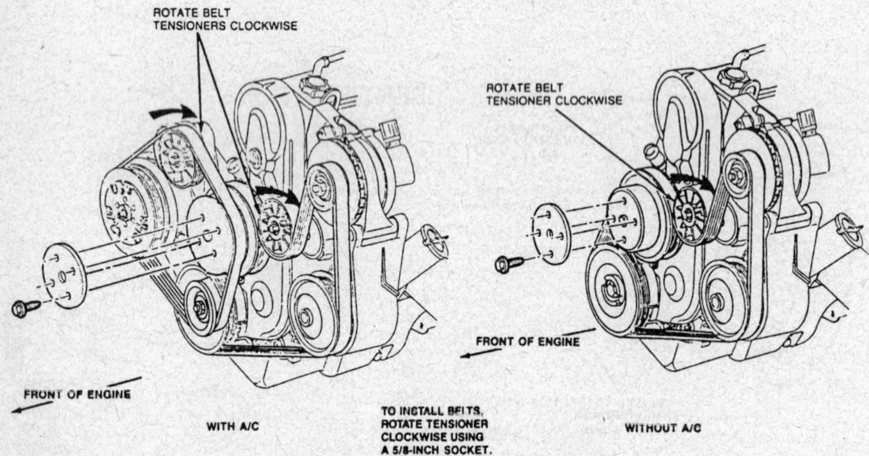


Fig. 18 Serpentine Belt Routing

of rotors and straightedge should not exceed .004 inch.

5. If necessary to replace rotor or drive shaft, remove outer rotor and then drive out retaining pin securing the skew gear to drive shaft and pull off the gear.
6. Withdraw inner rotor and drive shaft.

## SERPENTINE DRIVE BELTS

Conditions requiring belt replacement are excessive wear, rib chunk-out, severe glazing and frayed cords. Replace any belt exhibiting one of these conditions. Cracks on the rib side of a belt are considered acceptable.

If the belt has chunks missing from the ribs it should be replaced. If two or more adjacent ribs have lost sections a 1/2 inch or longer, or if the missing chunks are creating a noise or vibration condition. Replace the belt.

### BELT ROUTING

Refer to **Fig. 18** for proper belt routing.

### BELT REPLACEMENT

1. Lift or rotate automatic tensioner.
2. Remove belt(s).
3. Install new belt over pulleys. Ensure that all V-grooves make proper contact with the pulley.
4. Rotate tensioner over belt.

## BELT TENSION DATA

| Belt | New Lbs. | Used Lbs. |
|---|---|---|
| Except 1/4 inch | 140 | 110 |
| 1/4 inch | 65 | 40 |
| 4 Ribs Except Air Pump | 130 | 115 |
| 4 Ribs Air Pump | 110 | 105 |
| 5 Ribs | 150 | 135 |
| 6 Ribs① | 113 | 110 |
| 6 Ribs② | 160 | 145 |

①—With automatic tensioner.
②—Fixed.

## COOLING SYSTEM BLEED

1. Check all hose clamps for proper tightness.
2. Place heater temperature selector in maximum position.
3. Disconnect heater hose at thermostat housing.
4. Fill radiator until coolant is visible at thermostat housing or radiator cap filler neck seat.
5. Connect heater and **torque** clamp to 12-18 inch. lbs.
6. Fill radiator to below radiator neck seat.
7. Leave radiator cap off and run engine until thermostat opens.
8. Stop engine and add coolant to radiator as necessary to adjust level.

## THERMOSTAT REPLACE

1. Disconnect battery cable, then wiring connector from thermo switch in thermostat housing.
2. Remove radiator cap, then attach a hose to drain tube and open draincock. Drain coolant until level is below water outlet connection. Close the draincock.
3. Loosen upper hose at radiator, then remove water outlet housing retaining bolts.
4. Remove thermostat housing, then the thermostat. Do not pry housing off.
5. Clean outlet housing and cylinder head mating surfaces.

6. Position thermostat and seat so it will compress gasket. Position outlet to cylinder head, using a new gasket, then install retaining bolts.
7. Connect top hose to radiator and tighten clamp. Ensure that draincock is closed.
8. Fill cooling system with coolant as follows:
   a. Add 50 percent coolant, then add water until radiator is full. Allow coolant level to settle, then add more coolant until radiator remains full.
   b. Install radiator cap to first notch, connect battery cable and wire connector to thermo switch. Start engine and let idle until upper hose is warm, then carefully remove radiator cap and top off coolant level.
   c. Install cap securely and fill reservoir to FULL COLD mark with proper concentrate of coolant. Add water to FULL HOT mark. Check for leaks.

## WATER PUMP REPLACE

A provision for wrench clearance has been made in the timing belt inner cover, so only the outer cover must be removed in order to replace water pump.

1. Drain cooling system and disconnect hoses from pump.
2. Loosen alternator and remove drive belt.
3. Remove fan, spacer and pulley.
4. Remove drive belt cover.
5. Remove water pump attaching bolts and water pump.

## FUEL PUMP REPLACE

1. Disconnect battery ground cable.
2. Release pressure from fuel system as described under "Intake Manifold, Replace."
3. Drain fuel tank through filler neck using tool No. 034-00002 (Rotunda Fuel Storage Tanker) and tool No. 034-00011 (Adapter Hose) or Equivalent.
4. Raise and support vehicle.
5. Disconnect and remove fuel filler tube.
6. Remove fuel tank support straps and support fuel tank in vehicle.
7. Remove fuel lines and vent hose, then disconnect electrical connectors.
8. Remove fuel tank from vehicle.
9. Remove any dirt around fuel pump retaining flange, then turn fuel pump locking ring counterclockwise using fuel tank sender wrench tool No. D84P-9275-A or equivalent.
10. Remove locking ring, then fuel pump and bracket assembly.
11. Remove seal gasket and discard.
12. Reverse procedure to install.

## TIGHTENING SPECIFICATIONS

| Year | Component | Torque/ft. lbs. |
|---|---|---|
| 1989-92 | Air Cleaner Housing To Vane Air Meter | 15–22 |
| | Auxiliary Shaft Gear Bolt | 28–40 |
| | Auxiliary Shaft Thrust Plate Bolt | 6–9 |
| | Belt Tensioner (Timing Pivot Bolt) | 28–40 |
| | Belt Tensioner (Timing Adjusting Bolt) | 14–21 |
| | Camshaft Gear Bolt | 50–71 |
| | Camshaft Thrust Plate Bolt | 6–9 |
| | Connecting Rod Cap Bolts | ④ |
| | Cylinder Front Cover Bolt | 14–21 |
| | Cylinder Head Bolts | ① |
| | Distributor Clamp Bolt | 14–21 |
| | EGR Valve To Spacer Bolt | 14–21 |
| | EGR Tube To Exhaust Manifold Connector | 9–12 |
| | EGR Tube Nut | 9–12 |
| | Exhaust Manifold | ③ |
| | Flywheel To Crankshaft | 56-64 |
| | Fuel Charging Assembly To Intake Manifold (Stud) | 5–7.5 |
| | Fuel Charging Assembly To Intake Manifold (Nut) | 12–15 |
| | Fuel Charging Assembly To Intake Manifold (Bolt) | 12–15 |
| | Fuel Charging Assembly To Cylinder Head | 14–21 |
| | Fuel Injector Manifold To Fuel Charging Assembly | 15–22 |
| | Injector Wiring Harness Bracket | 15–22 |
| | Intake Manifold To Cylinder Head | 14–21 |
| | Main Bearing Cap Bolts | ⑤ |
| | Oil Pump Pickup To Pump | 14–21 |
| | Oil Return Fitting To Upper Block | 6–9 |
| | Oil Pump To Block | 14–21 |
| | Oil Pan Drain Plug to Pan | 15–25 |
| | Oil Pan To Block | 10–13.5 |
| | Oil Filter Insert To Cylinder Block | 20–35 |
| | Oil Filter To Engine Block | ② |

*Continued*

## TIGHTENING SPECIFICATIONS—Continued

| Year | Component | Torque/ft. lbs. |
|---|---|---|
| 1989–92 | Rocker Arm Cover | 5-8 |
| | Spark Plugs | 5-10 |
| | Temperature Sending Unit To Block | 8–18 |
| | Throttle Body To Upper Intake Manifold | 12–15 |
| | Timing Belt Cover Stud (Inner) | 14–21 |
| | Timing Belt Cover Bolt (Outer) | 6-9 |
| | Vibration Damper Or Pulley | ⑥ |
| | Vane Air Meter Mounting Screws | 15–22 |
| | Water Bypass Line | 12–20 |
| | Water Jacket Drain Plug To Block | 23–28 |
| | Water Pump To Block (Bolt) | 14–21 |
| | Water Outlet Connection Bolt | 14–21 |

①—Torque in 2 steps: step 1, 50–60 ft. lbs.; step 2, 80–90 ft. lbs.
②—Torque in 2 steps: step 1, 5–7 ft. lbs.; step 2, 14–21 ft. lbs.
③—Torque in 2 steps: step 1, 14–17 ft. lbs., step 2, 20–30 ft. lbs.
④—Torque in 2 steps: 1, 25–30 ft. lbs.; 2, 30–36 ft. lbs.
⑤—Step 1, 50–60 ft. lbs., step 2, 75–85 ft. lbs.
⑥—1989–90; 103–133 ft. lbs. 1991–92; 114–151 ft. lbs.

# 5.0L/V8-302 Engine

**NOTE:** On Vehicles Equipped With Airbags, Disarm Airbag As Outlined Under "Airbag System Disarming" Before Any Diagnosis, Testing, Troubleshooting Or Repairs Are Performed. After All Diagnosis, Testing, Troubleshooting Or Repairs Have Been Completed, Rearm Airbag As Outlined Under "Airbag System Disarming."

**NOTE:** Refer To Chapter 1 "Cougar, Thunderbird, Crown Victoria & Grand Marquis" In This Tab Section For Service Procedures On This Engine Not Included In This Section.

## INDEX



## AIRBAG SYSTEM DISARMING

**The electrical circuit necessary for system deployment is powered directly from the battery and a backup power supply. To avoid accidental deployment and possible personal injury, the airbag system must be deactivated prior to servicing or replacing any component located near or related to airbag system activation components.**

### 1990

A back-up power supply is included in the system to provide airbag deployment in the event the battery or battery cables are damaged in an accident before the sensors can close. The power supply is a capacitor that will retain a charge for approximately 15 minutes after the battery ground cable is disconnected. **Backup power supply must be disconnected to deactivate airbag system.** To remove backup power supply, refer to "Airbags" in the "Passive Restraint" section.

1. Disconnect battery ground cable and isolate cable end with electrical tape.
2. Disconnect backup power supply, located behind glove compartment.
3. Remove four nut and washer assemblies securing airbag module to steering wheel, then disconnect airbag electrical connector. Attach jumper wire to airbag terminals on clockspring terminals.
4. Reconnect battery and backup power supply if necessary to perform repair procedure.
5. To reactivate, disconnect battery ground cable and backup power supply, then reverse remainder of deactivation procedure. **Torque** airbag module to steering wheel nut assemblies to 24-32 inch lbs.
6. Verify airbag lamp after reactivating system.

### 1991–92

1. Disconnect positive battery cable, then ground cable end to frame or engine for one minute to discharge back-up power supply.
2. Remove four nut and washer assemblies securing airbag to steering wheel.
3. Disconnect airbag electrical connector.
4. Install airbag simulator tool No. 105-00008 or equivalent.
5. Connect positive battery cable.
6. To activate airbag system, disconnect positive battery cable and reverse procedure. **Torque** mounting nut and washer assemblies to 24-32 inch lbs.
7. Verify proper operation of airbag lamp.

## ENGINE MOUNTS REPLACE

1. Remove fan shroud attaching screws, if necessary.
2. Remove nuts attaching insulators to lower bracket, **Fig. 1.**
3. Raise engine with a suitable jack and a block of wood placed under oil pan.
4. Remove insulator to engine block attaching bolts.
5. Remove insulator from vehicle.
6. Reverse procedure to install.

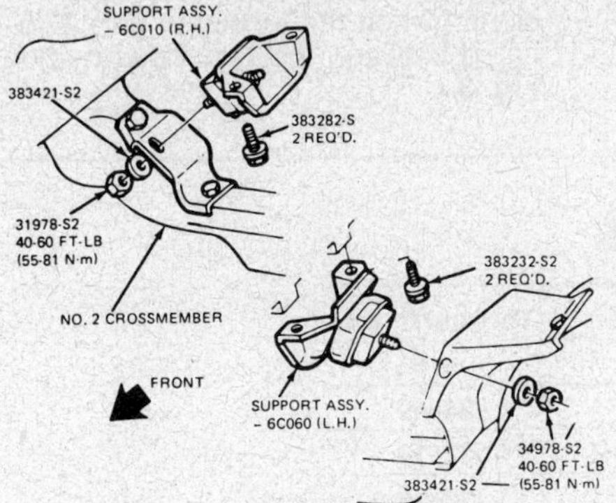


**Fig. 1 Engine mounts**

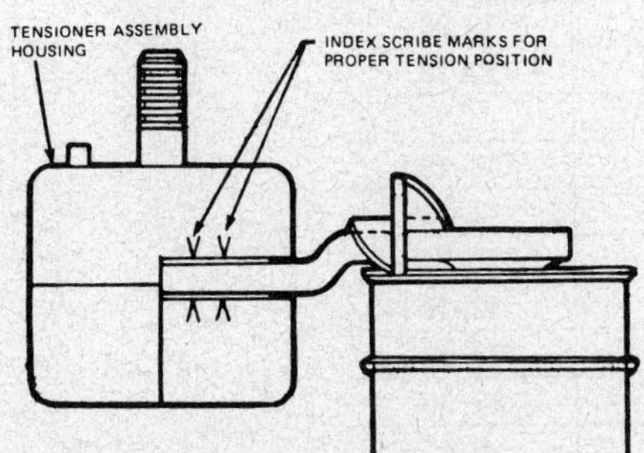


**Fig. 2 Serpentine drive belt**

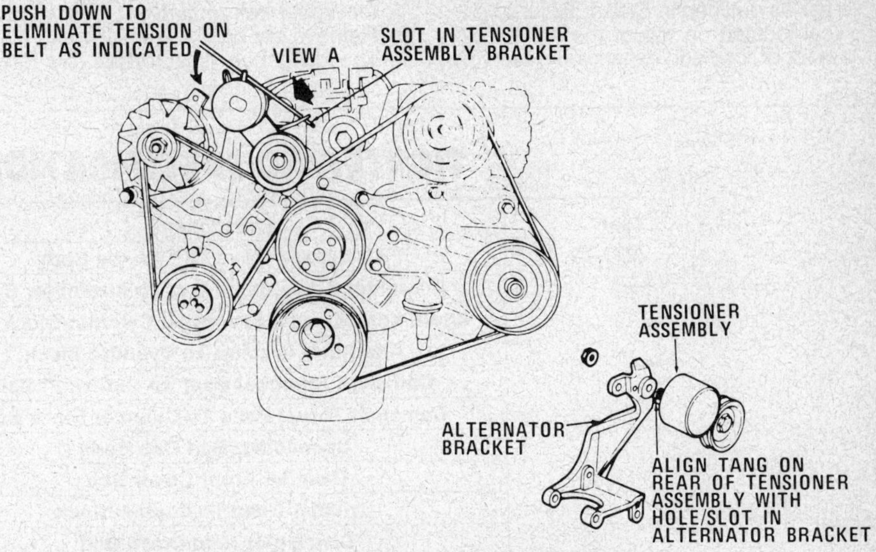


**Fig. 3 Serpentine drive belt tensioner alignment marks**

# VALVE CLEARANCE SPECIFICATIONS

| Year | Engine | Valve Lash |
|---|---|---|
| 1989–92 | 5.0L/V8-302 H.O. | ① ② |

①—**Measurement is with hydraulic lash adjuster completely collapsed.**

②—**Allowable measurement is .098–.198 inch., desired measurement is . 123–.146 inch.**

# VALVE CLEARANCE

## ADJUST

A .060 inch shorter pushrod or .060 inch longer pushrod is available for service to provide a means of compensating for dimensional changes in the valve mechanism. Valve stem-to-valve rocker arm clearance should be within specification with the hydraulic lifter completely collapsed.

Repeated valve reconditioning operations (valve seat and/or valve refacing) will decrease the valve opening clearance. The positive stop rocker arm bolt eliminates the necessity of adjusting the valve clearance. However, to obtain the specified valve clearance, it is important that all valve components be in a serviceable condition and tightened to specification.

If the clearance is less than specified, install a shorter pushrod. If the clearance is greater than specified, install a longer pushrod. To determine whether a shorter or longer pushrod is necessary, follow the procedure outlined below:

1. Disconnect brown lead (I terminal), then red and blue lead (S terminal) at starter relay.
2. Install auxiliary starter switch between battery and S terminals of starter relay.
3. Crank engine with ignition switch (off) to position number 1 piston at TDC at the end of the compression stroke, then check the following valves:
   a. No. 1 intake, No. 1 exhaust.
   b. No. 4 intake, No. 3 exhaust.
   c. No. 8 intake, No. 7 exhaust.
4. Rotate crankshaft 360 degrees (one revolution) clockwise. Check the following valves:
   a. No. 3 intake, No. 2 exhaust.
   b. No. 7 intake, No. 6 exhaust.
5. Rotate crankshaft 90 degrees (1/4 revolution) clockwise. Check the following valves:
   a. No. 2 intake, No. 4 exhaust.
   b. No. 5 intake, No. 5 exhaust.
   c. No. 6 intake, No. 8 exhaust.
6. Replace pushrods as necessary.

# OIL PAN

## REPLACE

1. Disconnect battery cables.
2. Remove fan shroud retaining bolts and position fan shroud over fan.
3. Remove dipstick and tube assembly.
4. Raise and support vehicle, then drain crankcase. **Some oil pans have dual oil sumps. Make sure to remove both drain plugs to thoroughly drain oil.**
5. Remove the two bolts retaining steering gear to main crossmember and allow steering gear to rest on frame away from oil pan.
6. Remove engine mount retaining bolts, then raise engine and place a 2 x 4 inch wooden block between each engine mount and vehicle frame.
7. Remove rear K-braces.
8. Remove oil pan retaining bolts and lower oil pan onto frame.
9. Remove oil pump retaining bolts and the inlet tube retaining nut from No. 3 main bearing cap stud. Lower the oil pump assembly into the oil pan.
10. Remove oil pan. If necessary, rotate engine so that crankshaft throws clear oil pan rail.
11. Reverse procedure to install.

# SERPENTINE DRIVE BELT

Some engines are equipped with a serpentine drive belt, **Fig. 2,** to drive the accessories in place of the usual arrangement. This "V" ribbed belt drives the fan/water pump, alternator, secondary air pump, optional A/C compressor and optional power steering pump.

The tensioner arm should be checked to ensure that the top edge of the arm is located between the two index marks scribed on the circumference next to the slot of the tensioner housing, **Fig. 3.** If the tensioner arm is not properly aligned, the drive belt and pulleys should be inspected for wear and binding. If the drive belt and pulleys are satisfactory, the tensioner must be replaced as outlined in the following procedure:

1. Insert a 16 inch pry bar or equivalent in the slot of the tensioner bracket, and using the tensioner housing as a fulcrum, push the pry bar downward to force the tensioner pulley upward, relieving tension on belt, **Fig. 2.**
2. Remove drive belt.
3. Remove bolt securing tensioner assembly to alternator bracket.
4. Remove tensioner assembly.
5. Position tensioner assembly so the tang, located on the rear of the assembly, is placed to fit in the hole or slot in alternator bracket.
6. Install the tensioner assembly bolt through the hole in the alternator bracket and **torque** bolt to 55-80 ft. lbs.
7. Install drive belt by inserting the pry

bar as outlined in Step 1. Refer to decal located on top of the windshield washer/coolant expansion reservoir for proper belt routing.

8. Remove pry bar.
9. The drive belt is automatically tensioned when the tensioner arm is located between the two index marks, **Fig. 3.**

## TIGHTENING SPECIFICATIONS

| Year | Component | Torque/ft. lbs. |
|---|---|---|
| 1989–92 | Air Bypass Valve To Throttle Body | 6–8 |
| | Alternator Adjustment Arm To Alternator Bolt | 24–40 |
| | Alternator Adjustment Arm To Cylinder Block Bolt | 12–18 |
| | Alternator Bracket To Cylinder Block | 12–18 |
| | Camshaft Sprocket Gear To Camshaft Bolt | 40–45 |
| | Camshaft Thrust Plate To Cylinder Block Bolt | 9–12 |
| | Connecting Rod Cap Bolts | 19-24 |
| | Cylinder Front Cover Bolt | 12–18 |
| | Cylinder Head To Engine Block | ① |
| | Distributor Hold Down Bolt | 18–26 |
| | EGR Valve To Intake Manifold Spacer | 12–18 |
| | Exhaust Manifold To Cylinder Head | 18–24 |
| | Fan To Water Pump Hub | 12–18 |
| | Flywheel To Crankshaft | 75-85 |
| | Fuel Charging Assembly To Head | 23-25 |
| | Fuel Rail Assembly To Intake Manifold | 6–8 |
| | Intake Manifold | ② |
| | Main Bearing Cap Bolts | 60-70 |
| | Oil Filter Insert To Cylinder Block Adapter Bolt | 20–30 |
| | Oil Filter To Cylinder Block | ③ |
| | Oil Inlet Tube To Oil Pump Bolt | 12–18 |
| | Oil Pan Drain Plug | 15–25 |
| | Oil Pan To Cylinder Block | 6-9 |
| | Oil Pump To Cylinder Block | 22-32 |
| | Oil Inlet Tube To Main Bearing Cap | 22-32 |
| | Pulley To Vibration Damper | 35-50 |
| | Rocker Arm Fulcrum To Cylinder Head | 18–25 |
| | Rocker Arm Cover | 6-9 |
| | Rocker Arm Shaft Bracket | 18-25 |
| | Spark Plugs | 5-10 |
| | Throttle Body To EGR Spacer And Upper Intake Manifold | 12–18 |
| | Throttle Cable To Manifold | 8–10 |
| | Timing Chain Front Cover | 19-27 |
| | Upper Intake To Fuel Charging Assembly | 12–18 |
| | Vacuum Fittings To Intake Manifold | 6–10④ |
| | Vibration Damper/Pulley | 70-90 |
| | Water Outlet Housing | 9–12 |
| | Water Pump To Cylinder Block Front Cover | 12–18 |

①—Refer to text for proper tightening sequence, then torque in 2 steps: step 1, 55–65 ft. lbs.; step 2, 65–72 ft. lbs.

②—Torque in 2 steps: step 1, 11–15 ft. lbs., step 2, 20–25 ft. lbs. After assembly, retorque with engine hot.

③—½ turn after gasket contacts sealing surface.

④—Install with teflon tape.

# Clutch & Manual Transmission

INDEX



## CLUTCH PEDAL
## ADJUST

A self adjusting type clutch mechanism is used. The adjust mechanism consists of a spring loaded ratchet quadrant attached to the clutch cable. To accomplish this adjustment, grasp clutch pedal and pull upward, then slowly depress clutch pedal. If a click is heard during the procedure, an adjustment was necessary and has been accomplished. This procedure should be performed at least every 5000 miles.

## TRANSMISSION
## REPLACE

1. Raise and support vehicle.
2. Remove four bolts retaining catalytic converter, then converter.
3. Mark driveshaft so that it may be installed in the same relative position, then remove driveshaft. Cover extension housing to prevent leakage.
4. Disconnect electrical leads and speedometer cable from transmission.
5. Support rear of engine and transmission, then remove crossmember.
6. Lower transmission assembly to expose two bolts securing shift handle to shift tower, then remove bolts and handle assembly.
7. Disconnect wiring harness from back-up lamp switch.
8. **On 5.0L/V8-302 engines,** disconnect neutral sensing switch.
9. **On all models,** Remove bolt from speedometer cable retainer, then speedometer driven gear from transmission.
10. Move transmission and jack rearward until transmission input shaft clears flywheel housing. If necessary, lower the engine enough to obtain clearance for transmission removal.

## CLUTCH
## REPLACE

### 2.3L/4-140 ENGINE

Prior to installing throw-out bearing, apply a light film of lithium base lubricant part No. C1AZ-19590-B or equivalent to transmission front bearing retainer outside diameter, the clutch release fork and anti-rattle spring where they contact the release bearing hub and to the throw-out bearing where the bearing contacts the pressure plate release fingers. In addition, fill the throw-out bearing grease groove with the same lubricant. Wipe off all excess lubricant.

1. Lift clutch pedal to its uppermost position to disengage pawl and quadrant. Push quadrant forward, unhook cable from quadrant and allow it to slowly swing rearward.
2. Raise and support vehicle.
3. Remove retainer pin and clevis pin from lower end of bellcrank.
4. Remove retaining clip, then clutch cable from flywheel housing.
5. Remove starter electrical connectors, then starter motor from flywheel housing.
6. Remove transmission.
7. Remove flywheel housing-to-engine attaching bolts, then flywheel housing.
8. Disconnect short cable from release lever by pushing cable and release lever boot approximately 1/2 inch toward release bearing and pull cable rearward through hole in boot.
9. Remove release lever boot from flywheel housing.
10. Remove clutch release lever from housing by pulling it through window in housing until spring is disengaged from pivot.
11. Remove release bearing from release lever.
12. Loosen six pressure plate cover attaching bolts evenly to release spring tension gradually and avoid distorting cover. If same pressure plate and cover is to be installed, mark cover and flywheel so pressure plate can be located in original position.
13. Remove pressure plate and clutch disc from flywheel.
14. Position clutch disc and pressure plate assembly on flywheel. The three dowel pins on flywheel must be properly aligned with pressure plate. Bent, damaged or missing dowel pins must be replaced.
15. Start cover attaching bolts but do not tighten.
16. Align clutch disc using proper alignment tool inserted in pilot bearing. To avoid pressure destortion, alternately tighten bolts a few turns at a time, until seated. **Torque** pressure plate to 12-24 ft. lbs.
17. Remove alignment tool.
18. Apply light film of long life lubricant part No. C1AZ-19590-BA or equivalent to:
    a. Outside diameter of transmission front bearing retainer.
    b. Release lever fork and anti-rattle spring where they contact release bearing hub.
    c. Release bearing surface that contacts pressure plate release fingers.
    d. Release lever ball pivot and mating release lever pocket.
    e. Fill grease groove of release bearing hub. Clean all excess grease from inside bore of bearing hub or contamination of clutch disc will occur.
19. Attach clutch release bearing to release lever.
20. Attach release lever and release bearing to flywheel housing.
21. Install release lever boot in housing with hole toward transmission.
22. Install short cable in release lever boot, then into keyhole slot in release lever, by pushing boot toward release bearing.
23. Install flywheel housing to engine block and **torque** to specification.
24. Install flywheel inspection plate.
25. Connect clutch cable to flywheel housing and connect retaining clip.
26. Place clevis over end fitting of cable, then install clevis pin and retaining pin.
27. Install starter motor, then transmission assembly.
28. Install clutch cable assembly by lifting clutch pedal to disengage pawl and quadrant. Then, push quadrant forward and hook end of cable over rear of quadrant.
29. Cycle clutch pedal several times to adjust cable.

### 5.0L/V8-302 ENGINE

1. Lift clutch pedal to its uppermost position to disengage pawl and quadrant. Push quadrant forward, unhook cable from quadrant and allow it to slowly swing rearward.
2. Raise and support vehicle.
3. Remove dust shield.
4. Remove retaining clip, then clutch cable from flywheel housing.
5. Remove flywheel inspection plate from front of clutch housing.
6. Remove transmission.
7. Remove clutch housing retaining bolts, then housing.
8. Remove clutch release lever from housing by pulling it through window in housing until retainer spring is disengaged from pivot.
9. Remove release bearing from release lever.
10. Loosen six pressure plate cover attaching bolts evenly to release spring tension gradually and avoid distorting cover. If same pressure plate and cover is to be installed, mark cover and flywheel so pressure plate can be located in original position.
11. Remove pressure plate and clutch disc from flywheel.
12. Reverse procedure to install. **Torque** all components to specification.

## TIGHTENING SPECIFICATIONS

| Year | Component | Torque/ft. lbs. |
|---|---|---|
| 1989–92 | Back-up Lamp Switch | ① |
| | Bearing Retainer | 11–20 |
| | Catalytic Converter Attaching Bolts | 20–30 |
| | Cluster Gear Rear bearing Retainer | 11–15 |
| | Drain Plug | 15–30 |
| | Driveshaft Bolts | 42–57 |
| | Extension Housing | 20–45 |
| | Flywheel Bolts, 2.3L/4-140 | 56–64 |
| | Flywheel Bolts, 5.0L/V8-302 | 75–85 |
| | Flywheel Housing To Engine, 2.3L/4-140 | 28–38 |
| | Flywheel Housing To Engine, 5.0L/V8-302 | 39–54 |
| | Neutral Sensing Switch | ① |
| | Pressure Plate To Flywheel, 2.3L/4-140 & 5.0L/V8-302 | 12–24 |
| | Shift Boot To Floor Pan | 3–7 |
| | Shift Cover | 6–11 |
| | Shift Lever To Transmission | 23–32 |
| | Speedometer Cable Retaining Screw | 3–5 |
| | Transmission To Flywheel Housing | 45–65 |
| | Transmission Extension Housing Bolts | 25–35 |
| | Transmission Support | 36–50 |
| | Top Gear Sensing Switch | ① |
| | Turret Cover | 11–15 |

①—1989–91; 12–18 ft. lbs. 1992; 20–35 ft. lbs.

# Rear Axle & Suspension

## INDEX



## REAR AXLE

### DESCRIPTION

This rear axle, **Fig. 1,** is an integral design hypoid with the center line of the pinion set below the center line of the ring gear. The semi-floating axle shafts are retained in the housing by ball bearings and bearing retainers at axle ends.

The differential is mounted on two opposed tapered roller bearings which are retained in the housing by removable caps. Differential bearing preload and drive gear backlash is adjusted by nuts located behind each differential bearing cup.

The drive pinion assembly is mounted on two opposed tapered roller bearings. Pinion bearing preload is adjusted by a collapsible spacer on the pinion shaft. Pinion and ring gear tooth contact is adjusted by shims between the rear bearing cone and pinion gear.

## REAR AXLE

### REPLACE

1. Raise and support vehicle, then position safety stands at rear frame members.
2. Drain lubricant from axle.
3. Mark drive shaft and pinion flanges for reassembly, then disconnect drive shaft at rear axle U-joint and remove drive shaft from transmission extension housing. Install seal replacer tool in extension housing to prevent leakage.
4. Disconnect shock absorbers at lower mountings.
5. Remove rear wheels and brake drums, then disconnect brake lines at wheel cylinders.
6. Disconnect vent hose from vent tube, then remove vent tube from brake junction and axle housing.
7. Remove clips retaining brake lines to axle housing.
8. Support rear axle housing using a suitable jack.
9. Disconnect upper control arms from mountings on axle housing, then carefully lower axle assembly until spring tension is relieved and remove coil springs. Disconnect lower control arms from axle housing.
10. Lower rear axle and remove from vehicle.
11. Reverse procedure to install.

## AXLE SHAFT, BEARING & OIL SEAL

### REPLACE

#### 7½ INCH RING GEAR

1. Raise and support vehicle.
2. Remove wheel and tire assembly, then the brake drum.
3. Clean all dirt from carrier cover area.
4. Remove housing cover to drain lubricant from rear axle.

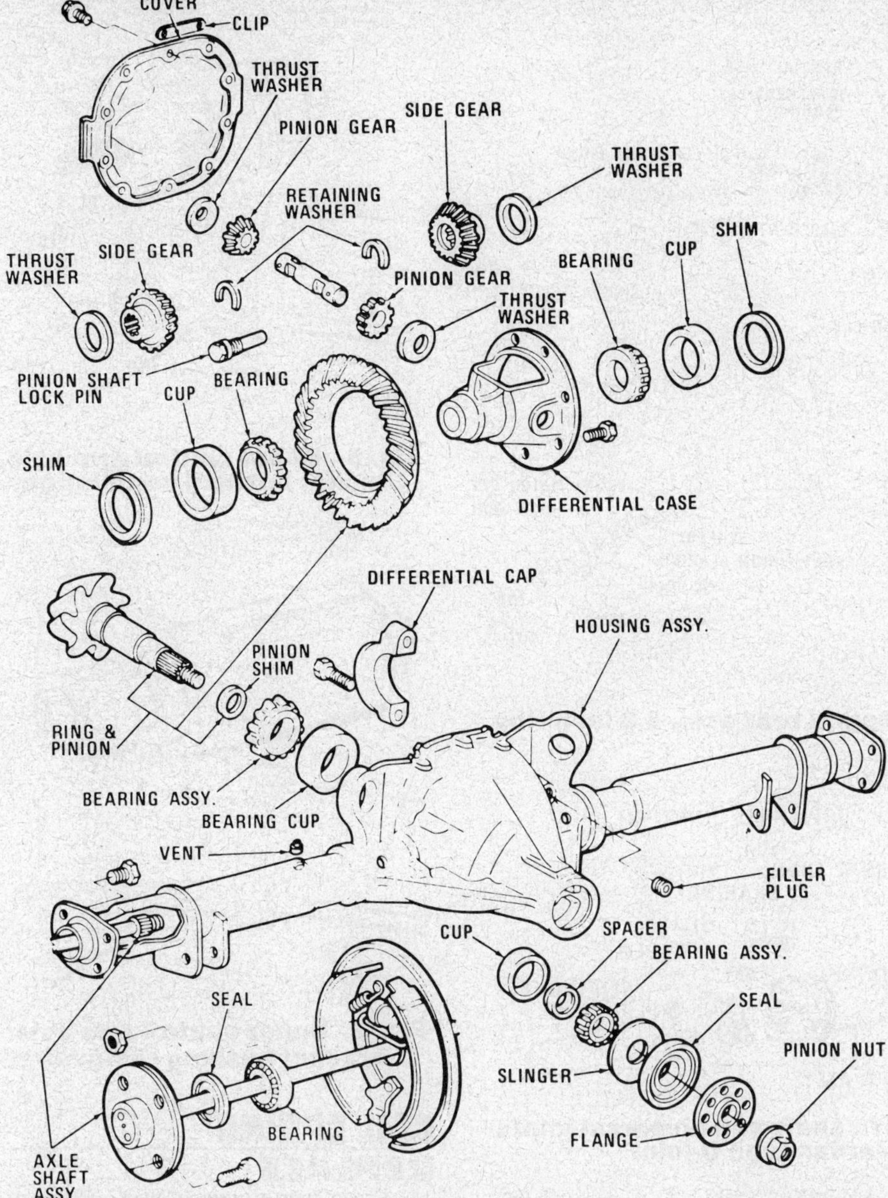


**Fig. 1 Disassembled view of integral rear axle. 7½ inch ring gear**

5. Remove differential pinion shaft lock bolt and the shaft.
6. Move flanged end of axle shafts toward center of vehicle and remove "C" clip from button end of shaft.
7. Remove axle shaft from housing. Use care to avoid damaging the oil seal.
8. Remove bearing and seal as an assembly using a suitable slide hammer.
9. Reverse procedure to install. Lubricate new bearing with rear axle lubricant prior to installation. Apply suitable grease between lips of oil seal. **The bearing should be installed using wheel bearing installer tool No. T78P-1225-A or equivalent, and the seal using wheel seal installer tool No. T78P-1177-A or equivalent. If proper tools are not used, early bearing or seal failure may result. If seal becomes cocked in the bore during installation, it must be removed and replaced with a new one.**

## 8.8 INCH RING GEAR

1. Raise and support vehicle, then remove rear wheel and tire assembly.
2. Clean all dirt from carrier cover area with a wire brush and/or cloth.
3. Remove axle housing cover and drain lubricant from axle, **Fig. 2.**
4. Remove differential pinion shaft lock bolt and differential pinion shaft.
5. Push flanged end of axle shaft toward center of the vehicle, then remove C-lock from button end of axle shaft assembly.
6. Remove axle shaft from housing. Ensure not to damage oil seal.
7. Insert seal removing tool 1175-AC or equivalent, into housing bore and position it behind bearing so tangs on tool engage bearing outer race. Using slide hammer tool T50T-100-A or equivalent, remove bearing and seal as a unit.
8. Reverse procedure to install, noting the following:
   a. Lubricate new bearing with lubricant E0AZ-19580-A or equivalent, and install bearing into housing bore using wheel bearing installing tool T78P-1225-A or equivalent.
   b. Install axle shaft seal using wheel seal installer tool T78P-1177-A or equivalent. Apply lubricant C1AZ-19590-B or equivalent, between the lips of the seal. **Installation of bearing or seal assembly without proper tool may result in an early bearing or seal failure. If seal becomes cocked in bore during installation, remove it and install a new one.**
   c. Check for presence of axle shaft O-ring on the spline end of the shaft and install if not present.

# PROPELLER SHAFT
## REPLACE

1. To maintain balance, mark relationship of rear drive shaft yoke and the drive pinion flange of the axle if alignment marks are not visible.
2. Disconnect rear U-joint from companion flange, **Fig. 3.** Wrap tape around loose bearing caps to prevent them from falling off spider. Pull drive shaft toward rear of car until slip yoke clears transmission extension housing and the seal. Install tool in extension housing to prevent lubricant leakage.

# SHOCK ABSORBER
## REPLACE

On all models except Mustang 3-door, open the luggage compartment to gain access to the upper shock stud. On Mustang 3-door models, entry to the upper shock attachment is made by opening the hatch door and removing the trim panel access door.

**These vehicles are equipped with gas pressurized shock absorbers which will extend unassisted. Do not apply heat or flame to the shock absorber tube during removal.**

1. From inside luggage compartment, remove rubber cap, if so equipped.
2. Remove attaching nut, washer and insulator assembly from shock absorber upper stud.
3. Raise and support vehicle, then support rear axle.
4. Remove attaching nut, washer and insulator assembly from shock absorber lower stud.
5. From underside of vehicle, compress shock absorber to clear it from hole in upper shock tower.
6. Remove shock absorber.
7. Reverse procedure to install, **torque** attaching bolts to specification.

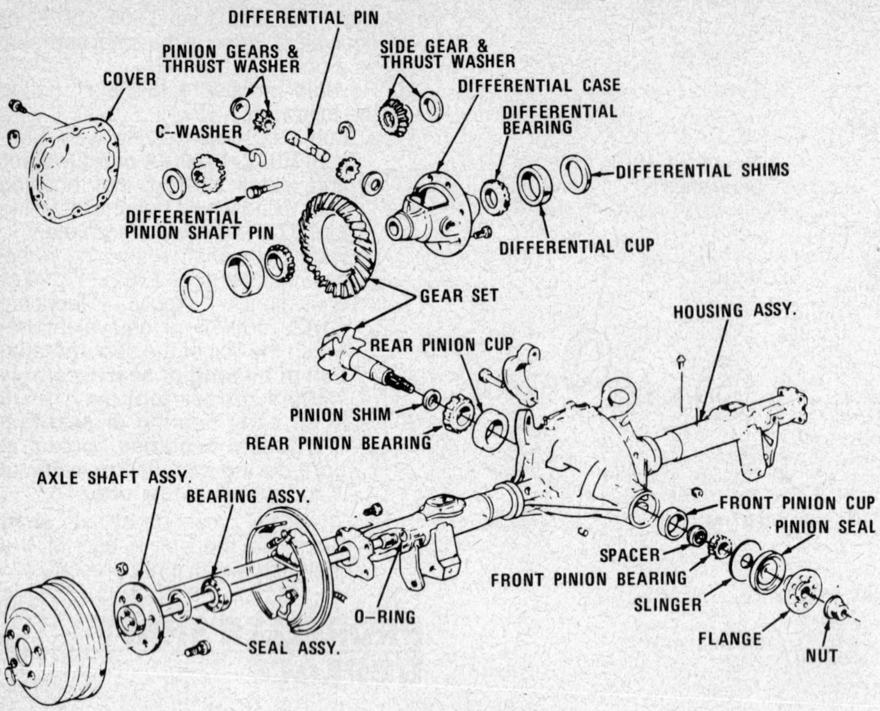


**Fig. 2 Disassembled view of integral rear axle. 8.8 inch ring gear**

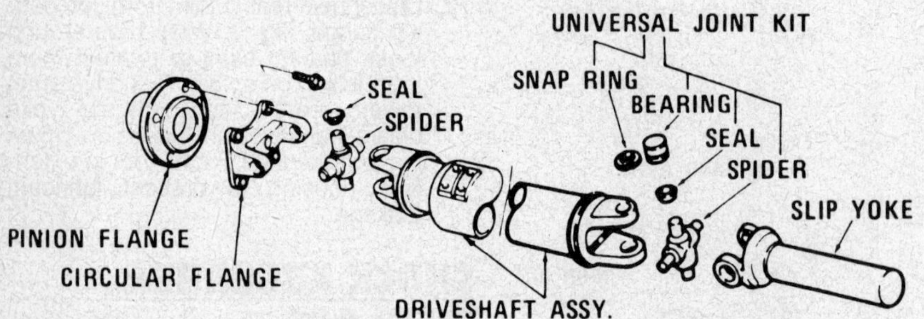


**Fig. 3 Disassembled view of drive shaft and universal joints disassembled. Single Cardan type U-joint**

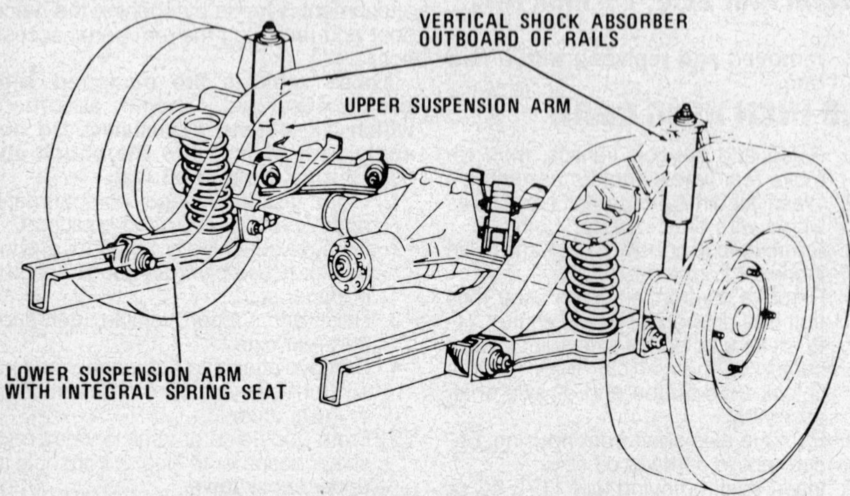


**Fig. 4 Coil spring rear suspension**

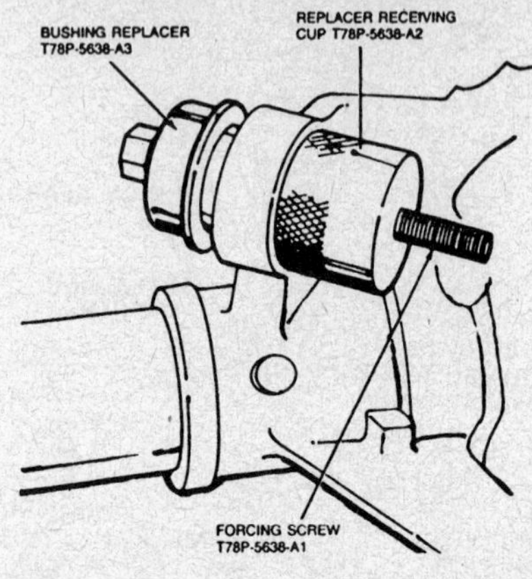


**Fig. 5 Upper control arm axle bracket bushing installation**

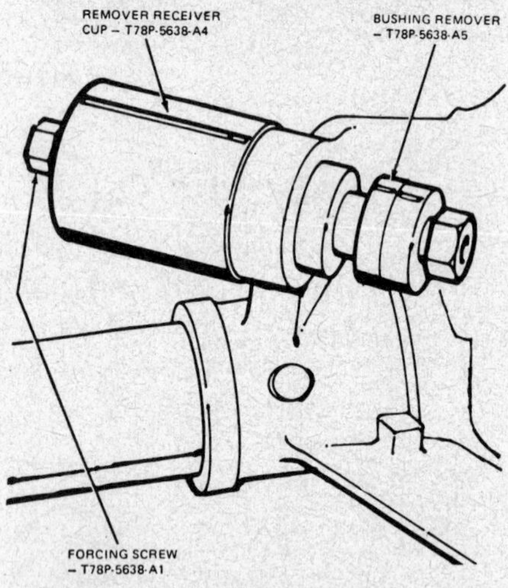


**Fig. 6 Upper control arm axle bracket bushing removal**

# COIL SPRING

## REPLACE

1. Raise rear of vehicle and support at rear body crossmember.
2. Remove stabilizer bar, if equipped, **Fig. 4.**
3. Lower axle housing until shock absorbers are fully extended. **The axle housing must be supported with a suitable jack.**
4. Position a suitable jack under lower control arm rear pivot bolt to support control arm, then remove pivot bolt.
5. Carefully lower the lower control arm until spring tension is relieved, then remove coil spring and insulator.
6. Reverse procedure to install. Torque lower control arm pivot bolt to specifications, with suspension at curb height.

# CONTROL ARMS & BUSHINGS

## REPLACE

### UPPER CONTROL ARM

1. Raise rear of vehicle and support at

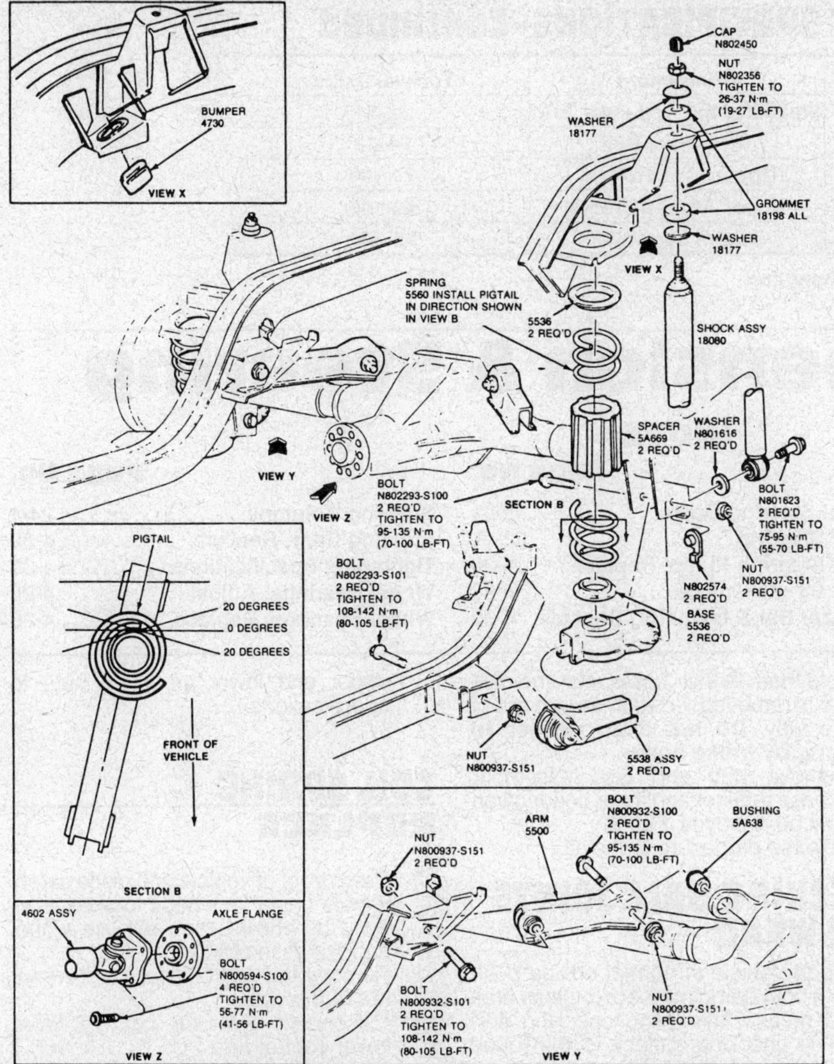


**Fig. 7 Exploded view of rear suspension**

rear body crossmember.

2. Remove upper control arm rear and front pivot bolts, then remove control arm.
3. If control arm axle bracket bushings are to be replaced, refer to **Figs. 5 and 6.**
4. Position upper control arm into side rail bracket, then install front pivot bolt. Do not tighten bolt at this time.
5. Raise rear axle until upper control arm rear pivot bolt hole is aligned with hole in axle housing, then install rear pivot bolt. Do not tighten bolt at this time.

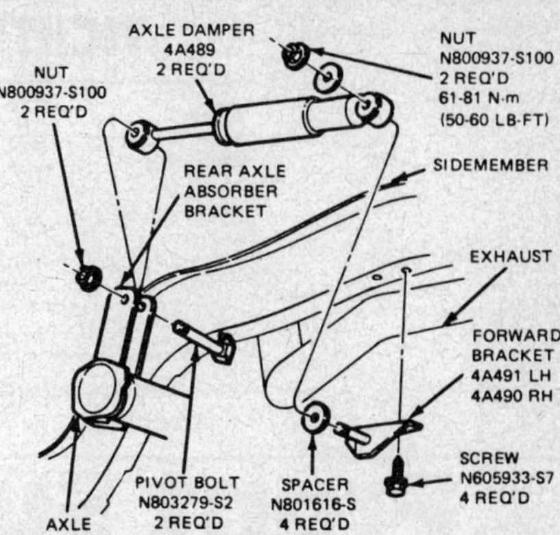


**Fig. 8 Axle damper assembly. Mustang GT**

6. Position suspension at curb height. Torque front pivot bolt to specifications.

## LOWER CONTROL ARMS

1. Remove coil spring as described under "Coil Spring, Replace."
2. Remove lower control arm front pivot bolt and nut, then remove control arm, **Fig. 7.**
3. Reverse procedure to install. Torque front pivot bolt to specifications. Torque rear pivot bolt to specifications.

## STABILIZER BAR
### REPLACE

1. Raise and support rear of vehicle.
2. Remove four bolts attaching stabilizer bar to brackets on lower control arms.
3. Remove stabilizer bar from vehicle.
4. Reverse procedure to install. **Torque** all bolts to 45-50 ft. lbs.

## AXLE DAMPERS
### REPLACE

1. Raise vehicle and support rear axle.
2. Remove rear wheel, then the axle damper rear attaching nut and pivot bolt, **Fig. 8.**
3. Remove axle damper forward attaching nut, the axle damper and spacer.
4. Reverse procedure to install. **Torque** attaching bolts to 50-60 ft. lbs.

## TIGHTENING SPECIFICATIONS

| Year | Component | Torque/ft. lbs. |
|---|---|---|
| 1989-92 | Axle Damper Front Bolt | 57-75 |
| | Axle Damper Rear Nut | 57-75 |
| | Axle Flange Bolt | 41-56 |
| | Bracket Retaining Bolt | 7-12 |
| | Bumper To Bracket Nut | 12-20 |
| | Clevis Bracket To Axle | 55-70 |
| | Lower Arm To Axle | 70-100 |
| | Lower Arm To Frame | 80-105 |
| | Shock Absorber (lower attachment) | 57-75 |
| | Shock Absorber (upper attachment) | 20-27 |
| | Shock Absorber To Clevis Bracket① | 45-60 |

Continued

## TIGHTENING SPECIFICATIONS—Continued

| Year | Component | Torque/ft. lbs. |
|---|---|---|
| 1989–92 | Stabilizer Bar To Lower Arm | 33-51 |
| | Torx Drive Bolt | 31-39 |
| | Upper Arm To Axle | 70-100 |
| | Upper Arm To Frame | 80-105 |
| | Wheel Lug Nuts | 85-104 |

①—Vehicle equipped with handling package

# Front Suspension & Steering

## INDEX



## FRONT SUSPENSION

The front suspension, **Fig. 1,** is of the modified MacPherson strut design, which uses shock struts and coil springs. The springs are mounted between the lower control and a spring pocket in the crossmember.

## WHEEL BEARINGS
### ADJUST

1. Raise vehicle until wheel and tire clear floor.
2. Remove wheel cover and dust cap from hub.
3. Remove cotter pin and locknut.
4. Loosen adjusting nut 3 turns, then rock wheel, hub and rotor assembly in and out several times to move shoe and linings away from rotor.
5. While rotating wheel assembly, **torque** the adjusting nut to 17-25 ft. lbs. to seat the bearings. **Fig. 2.**
6. Back off the adjusting nut one half turn. Retighten the nut to 10-12 inch lbs. with a torque wrench or finger tight.
7. Locate the nut lock on the adjusting nut so the castellations on the lock are aligned with the cotter pin hole in the spindle.
8. Install new cotter pin and replace dust cap and wheel cover.

## WHEEL BEARINGS
### REPLACE

1. Raise vehicle and remove front wheels.
2. Remove caliper mounting bolts. **It is not necessary to disconnect the brake lines for this operation.**
3. Slide caliper off of disc, inserting a clean spacer between the shoes to hold them in their bores after the caliper is removed. Position caliper out of the way. **Do not allow caliper to hang by brake hose.**
4. Remove hub and disc assembly. Grease retainer and inner bearing can now be removed. **Fig. 3.**
5. Reverse procedure to install.

## CHECKING BALL JOINTS FOR WEAR

Support vehicle in normal driving position with both ball joints loaded. Clean area around grease fitting and checking surface. The checking surface is the round boss into which the grease fitting is installed. The checking surface should project outside the ball joint cover, **Fig. 4.** If checking surface is inside the cover replace the lower control arm assembly.

## SHOCK STRUT
### REPLACE

Due to the preload pressure in the strut assembly, it will take up to 50 lbs of force to push the strut rod down into the cylinder assembly (lower can). **This is normal and does not indicate a binding condition.**

1. Place ignition switch in the unlocked position.
2. From engine compartment, remove upper shock absorber mounting nut.
3. Raise front of vehicle and support lower control arms. Position safety stands under frame jacking pads located rearward of wheels.
4. Remove wheel and tire assembly.
5. Remove caliper, rotor and dust shield.
6. Remove two bolts attaching shock absorber to spindle.
7. Lift strut upward from spindle to compress rod, then pull downward and remove shock absorber.
8. Remove jounce bumper, if equipped.
9. Reverse procedure to install. Torque upper and lower mounting nuts to specifications.

## COIL SPRING
### REPLACE

1. Raise front of vehicle and place safety stands under jack pads located rearward of wheels, then remove wheel and tire assembly.
2. Remove the brake caliper and wire it out of the way.
3. Disconnect stabilizer bar link from lower control arm.
4. Remove steering gear retaining bolts if necessary, then position the gear so that the suspension arm bolt may be removed.
5. Using tie rod end remover tool 3290-D or equivalent, disconnect tie rod from spindle.
6. Install spring compressor No. T82P-5310-A on models equipped with 2.3L engine, or No. D78P-5310-A on models with 5.0L engine, then compress coil spring until it is free of the spring seat. **Ensure spring compressor is properly installed before compressing spring. Also ensure spring is sufficiently compressed to permit removal of lower control arm pivot bolts.**
7. Remove two lower control arm pivot bolts, then disengage lower control arm and remove spring assembly, **Fig. 1. Measure compressed length of spring and amount of curvature to aid in compressing and installing spring.**
8. Reverse procedure to install. Ensure lower spring end is positioned between two holes in lower control arm spring pocket. Torque stabilizer bar and steering gear to No. 2 crossmember to specifications. **Torque** tie rod to steering spindle to 35 ft. lbs.

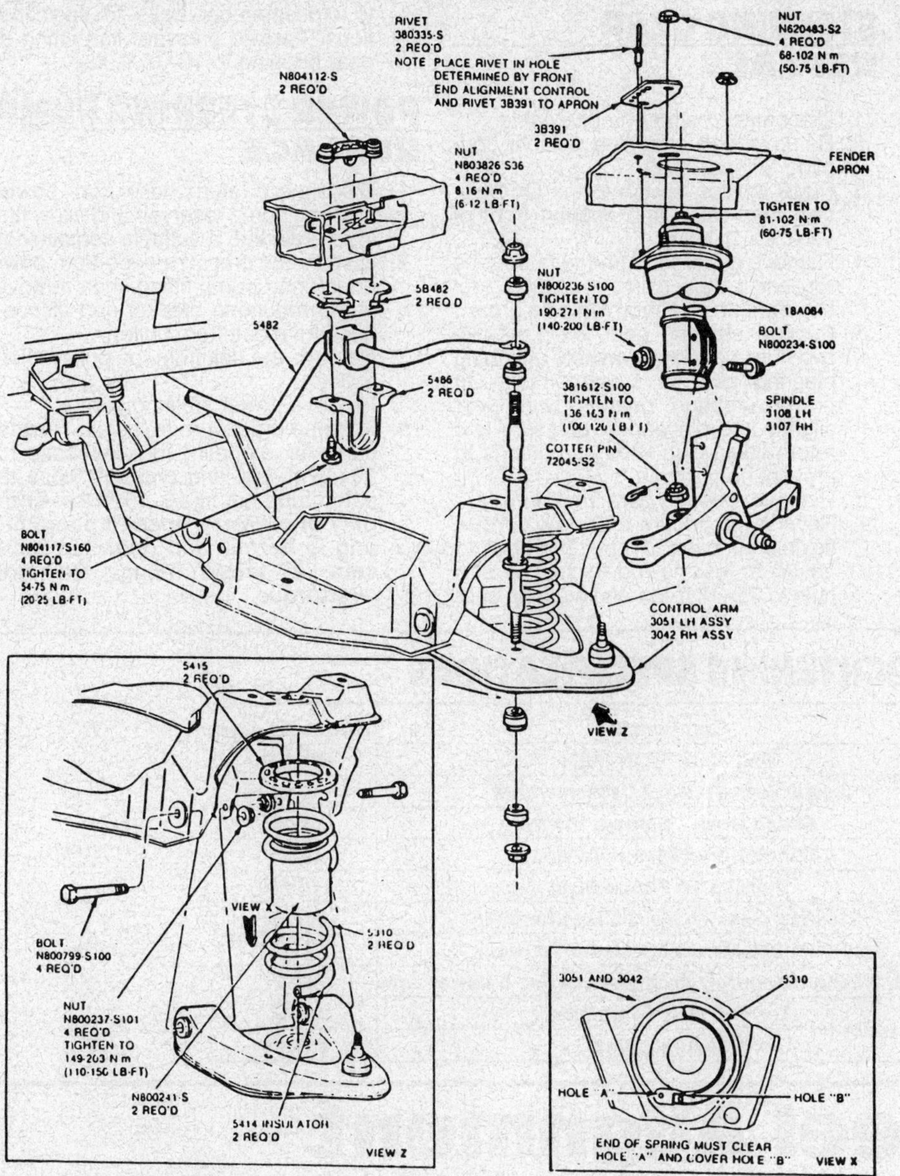


**Fig. 1 Front suspension assembly**

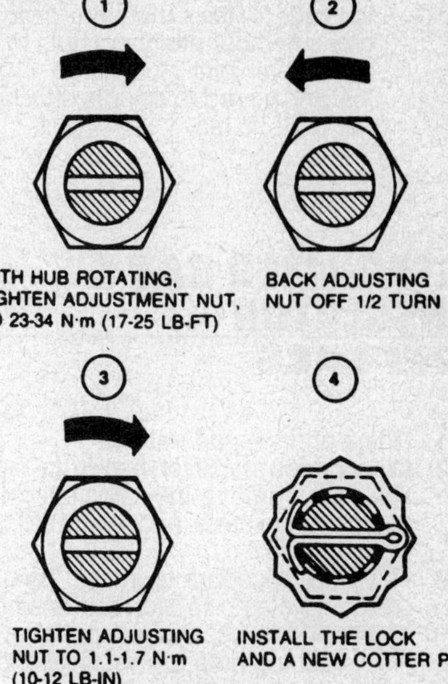


**Fig. 2 Wheel bearing adjustment**

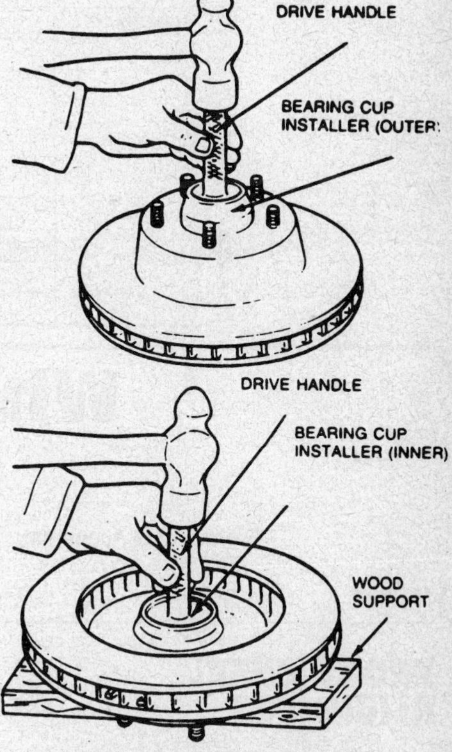


**Fig. 3 Wheel bearing replacement**

## BALL JOINTS
### REPLACE

The lower ball joint and lower control arm must be replaced as an assembly.

## CONTROL ARM
### REPLACE

1. Raise and support vehicle, allowing control arm to hang freely.
2. Remove brake caliper, rotor and dust shield, then disconnect tie rod from spindle using suitable tool.
3. If necessary, remove steering gear attaching bolts and position gear as necessary to gain access to control arm attaching bolts.
4. Remove cotter pin, then loosen ball joint stud nut approximately two turns. **Do not remove stud nut at this time.**

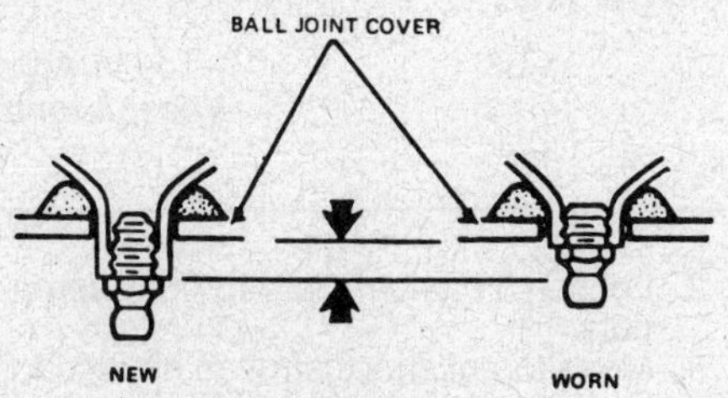


**Fig. 4 Checking lower ball joint for wear**

5. Tap spindle boss with suitable mallet to disengage ball joint stud from spindle.
6. Use spring compressor tool No. T82P-5310-A on models with 2.3L engine, or tool No. D78P-5310-A on 5.0L models, then compress the coil spring slightly.
7. Remove ball joint stud nut, then raise strut and spindle assembly and wire in place to gain increased working area for control arm removal.
8. Remove control arm to crossmember pivot bolts and nuts, then the control arm.
9. Reverse procedure to install, noting the following:
   a. When installing coil spring, ensure lower spring end is positioned between the two holes in control arm spring pocket as shown in **Fig. 1.**

b. **Torque** control arm attaching nuts to 130 ft. lbs., steering gear to crossmember attaching nuts to 95 ft. lbs., ball joint stud nut to 110 ft. lbs. and tie rod to spindle attaching nut to 35 ft. lbs.

## STABILIZER BAR & INSULATOR
### REPLACE

1. Raise and support vehicle.
2. Disconnect stabilizer bar from each link, then remove insulator attaching clamps, insulators and stabilizer bar from vehicle.
3. Reverse procedure to install. **Torque** attaching clamp to side rail retaining bolts to 48 ft. lbs. and stabilizer bar to link attaching nuts to specifications.

## STEERING GEAR
### REPLACE

1. Disconnect battery ground cable.
2. Remove bolt attaching flexible coupling to input shaft.
3. Place ignition switch in the On position, then raise and support front of vehicle.
4. Remove cotter pins and nuts from tie rod ends, then using a suitable tool separate tie rods from spindle arms.
5. Support steering gear, then remove two nuts, bolts and washers attaching steering gear to crossmember. On power steering gears, lower gear slightly and disconnect pressure and return lines. Cap lines and fittings to prevent entry of dirt.
6. Remove steering gear from vehicle.
7. Reverse procedure to install. **Torque** flexible coupling to input shaft bolt to 20-30 ft. lbs., tie rod to spindle arm nuts to 35-47 ft. lbs. and steering gear to crossmember bolts to specifications. **Torque** pressure line fitting at gear housing to 10-15 ft. lbs.

## POWER STEERING PUMP
### REPLACE

1. Disconnect return hose from power steering pump reservoir and allow fluid to drain into a suitable container.
2. Disconnect pressure hose from power steering pump fitting, then remove pump mounting bracket and disconnect drive belt from pulley.
3. Remove the belt from the pulley, then pulley.
4. Remove power steering pump.
5. Reverse procedure to install. **Torque** pump to mounting bracket bolts to 30-45 ft. lbs. and pressure hose to pump tube nut to 10-15 ft. lbs. **Endplay of pressure hose to pump fitting is normal and does not indicate a loose fitting. Do not overtorque.**

## TIGHTENING SPECIFICATIONS

| Year | Component | Torque/Ft. Lbs. |
|---|---|---|
| 1989-92 | Ball Joint To Spindle | 80-120 |
| | Lower Arm To No. 2 Crossmember | 110-150 |
| | Shock Strut To Upper Mount | 50-75 |
| | Shock Upper Mount To Body | 50-75 |
| | Spindle To Shock Strut | 140-200 |
| | Steering Gear To No. 2 Crossmember | 90-100 |
| | Stabilizer Bar Mounting Clamp To Bracket | 37-50 |
| | Stud & Washer Assembly To Stabilizer Bar & Lower Arm | 6-12 |
| | Tie Rod End To Spindle | 35-47 |
| | Wheel Lug Nuts | 85-104 |

# Wheel Alignment

### INDEX



## FRONT WHEEL ALIGNMENT

### CASTER

The caster angle of this suspension is factory pre-set and cannot be adjusted.

### CAMBER

1. Remove pop rivet from camber plate.
2. Loosen 3 camber plate-to-body apron nuts.
3. Move top of shock strut as needed to bring camber angle within specifications, then tighten nuts. **It is not necessary to replace the pop rivet.**

### TOE-IN, ADJUST

1. Check to see that steering shaft and steering wheel marks are in alignment and in the top position.
2. Loosen clamp screw on the tie rod bellows and free the seal on the rod to prevent twisting of the bellows.
3. Loosen tie rod jam nut.
4. Use suitable pliers to turn the tie rod inner end to correct the adjustment to specifications. Do not use pliers on tie rod threads. Turning to reduce number of threads showing will increase toe-in. Turning in the opposite direction will reduce toe-in. **Torque** to 43-50 ft. lbs.

# FORD TAURUS & MERCURY SABLE

## INDEX OF SERVICE OPERATIONS

**NOTE:** Refer To The Rear Of This Manual For Vehicle Manufacturer's Special Service Tools.



*Continued*

## INDEX OF SERVICE OPERATIONS—Continued

# Specifications

## GENERAL ENGINE SPECIFICATIONS

| Year | Engine Liter/CID① | Engine VIN Code② | Fuel System | Bore & Stroke | Comp. Ratio | Net H.P. @ RPM ③ | Maximum Torque/Ft. Lbs. @ RPM | Normal Oil Pressure Pounds |
|---|---|---|---|---|---|---|---|---|
| 1989–90 | 2.5L/4-153 | D | CFI④ | 3.7 x 3.3 | 9.0 | 90 @ 4400 | 130 @ 2600 | 55-60⑥ |
| | 3.0L/V6-182 | U | EFI⑤ | 3.5 x 3.1 | 9.2 | 140 @ 4800 | 160 @ 3000 | 55-60⑥ |
| | 3.0L/V6-182⑦ | Y | EFI | 3.5 x 3.15 | 9.8 | 220 @ 6000 | 200 @ 4800 | — |
| | 3.8L/V6-232 | 4 | EFI | 3.8 x 3.4 | 9.0 | 140 @ 3800 | 215 @ 2400 | 40-60⑥ |
| 1991 | 2.5L/4-153 | D | EFI⑤ | 3.7 x 3.3 | 9.0 | 90 @ 4400 | 130 @ 2600 | 55-60⑥ |
| | 3.0L/V6-182 | U | SEFI | 3.5 x 3.1 | 9.2 | 140 @ 4800 | 160 @ 3000 | 55-60⑥ |
| | 3.0L/V6-182⑦ | Y | SEFI | 3.5 x 3.15 | 9.8 | 220 @ 6000 | 200 @ 4800 | — |
| | 3.8L/V6-232 | 4 | SEFI | 3.8 x 3.4 | 9.0 | 140 @ 3800 | 215 @ 2400 | 40-60⑥ |
| 1992 | 3.0L/V6-182 | U | SEFI | 3.5 x 3.14 | 9.3 | 140 @ 4800 | 160 @ 3000 | 55-60⑥ |
| | 3.0L/V6-182⑦ | Y | SEFI | 3.5 x 3.15 | 9.8 | 220 @ 6200 | 200 @ 4800 | — |
| | 3.8L/V6-232 | 4 | SEFI | 3.8 x 3.4 | 9.0 | 140 @ 3800 | 215 @ 2200 | 40-60⑥ |

①—CID-Cubic inch displacement.
②—The eighth digit of the VIN denotes engine code.
③—Ratings are net-as installed in vehicle.
④—Central (single point) Fuel Injection.
⑤—Electronic (multi-point) Fuel Injection.
⑥—At 2000 RPM.
⑦—SHO w/double overhead cam engine.

## TUNE UP SPECIFICATIONS

| Liter/CID (VIN Code)① | Spark Plug Gap | Ignition Timing BTDC, Degrees: Firing Order Fig. ② | Ignition Timing: Man. Trans. | Ignition Timing: Auto. Trans. | Ignition Timing: Mark Fig. | Curb Idle Speed③: Man. Trans. | Curb Idle Speed③: Auto Trans. | Fast Idle Speed: Man. Trans. | Fast Idle Speed: Auto. Trans. | Fuel Pump Pressure, Psi |
|---|---|---|---|---|---|---|---|---|---|---|
| **1989** | | | | | | | | | | |
| 2.5L/4-153 (D) | .044 | A | 10⑤ | 10⑤ | B | ④ | 675–725④ | ④ | ④ | 13–16⑥ |
| 3.0L/V6-182 (U) | .044 | E | — | 10⑤ | D | — | ④ | — | ④ | 35–45⑥ |
| 3.0L/V6-182 (Y) | .044 | F | ⑦ | ⑦ | ⑧ | ④ | ④ | ④ | ④ | 35–45⑥ |
| 3.8L/V6-238 (4) | .054 | C | — | 10⑤ | D | — | ④ | — | ④ | 35–45⑥ |
| **1990–91** | | | | | | | | | | |
| 2.5L/4-153 (D,N) | .044 | A | 10⑤ | 10⑤ | B | ④ | 675–725④ | ④ | ④ | 13–16⑥ |
| 3.0L/V6-182 (U) | .044 | E | — | 10⑤ | D | — | ④ | — | ④ | 35–45⑥ |
| 3.0L/V6-182 (Y) | .044 | F | 10⑦ | — | ⑧ | 760–830④ | — | ④ | — | 35–45⑥ |
| 3.8L/V6-238 (4) | .054 | C | — | 10⑤ | D | — | 650–750④ | — | ④ | 35–45⑥ |
| **1992** | | | | | | | | | | |
| 3.0L/V6-182 (U) | .044 | E | — | 10⑤ | D | — | ④ | — | ④ | 35–45⑥ |
| 3.0L/V6-182 (Y) | .044 | F | 10⑦ | — | ⑧ | 760–830④ | — | ④ | — | 35–45⑥ |
| 3.8L/V6-238 (4) | .054 | C | — | 10⑤ | D | — | 650–750④ | — | ④ | 35–45⑥ |

①—The eighth digit of the VIN denotes engine code.
②—Before disconnecting wires from distributor cap, determine location of No. 1 wire in cap, as distributor position may have been altered from that shown at the end of this chart.
③—D: Drive.
④—Idle speed is controlled by an automatic idle control system.
⑤—Disconnect in-line spout connector, then start engine & adjust ignition timing as necessary. After completing adjustment, reconnect spout connector.
⑥—Wrap shop towel around fitting to prevent fuel spillage, then connect a suitable fuel pressure gauge to fuel diagnostic valve on fuel rail assembly. Connect jumper wire to VIP self test connector FP terminal. On 2.5L/4-153 engines, the VIP connector is located at rear of engine on right hand side near the valve cover. On 3.0L/V6-182 & 3.8L/V6-238 engines, the VIP connector is located at the right hand rear of the engine compartment at the electronic control assembly. Place ignition switch in On position, then connect VIP jumper wire to ground check fuel pressure gauge reading.
⑦—Non-adjustable.
⑧—Equipped w/crankshaft position sensor.

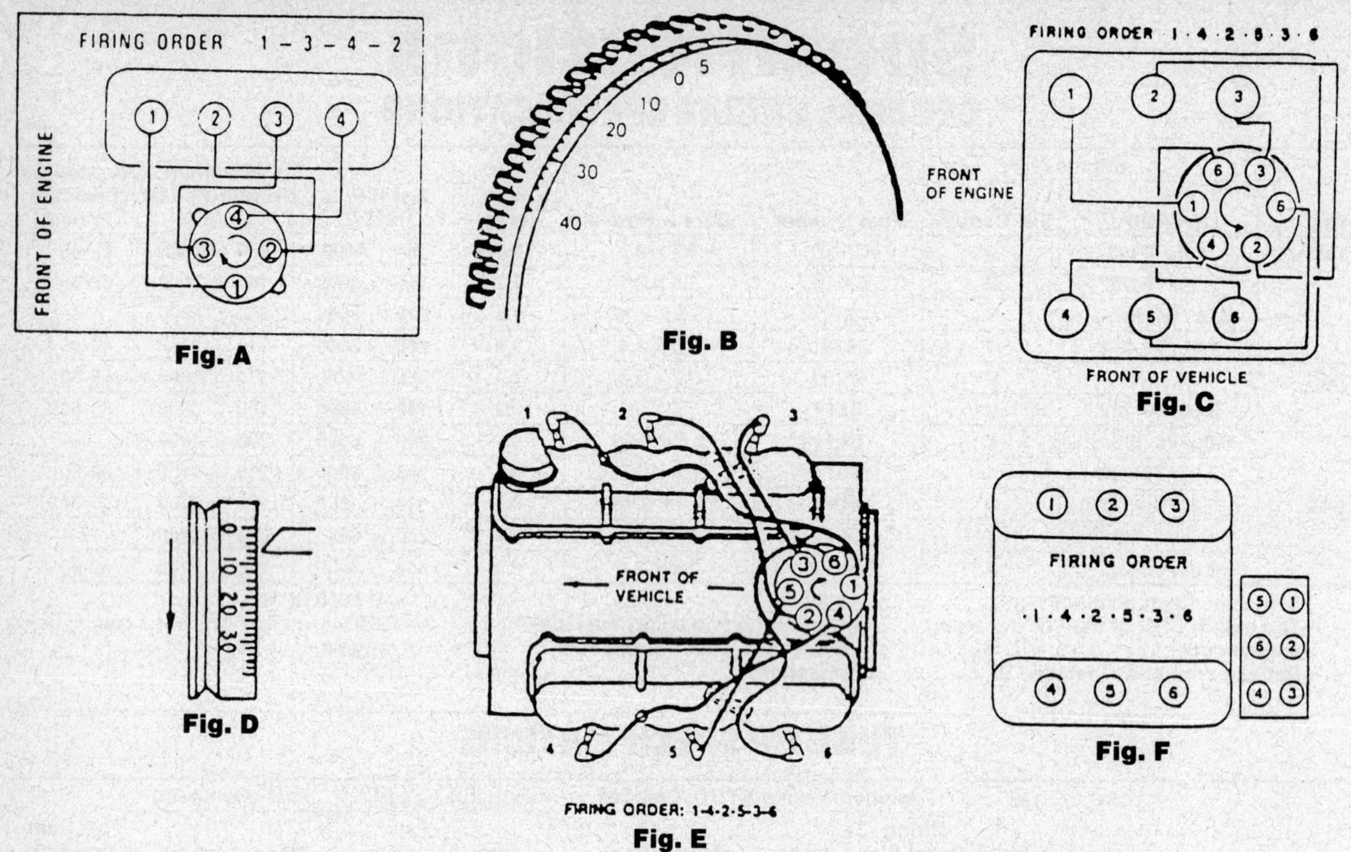


Fig. A

Fig. B

Fig. C

Fig. D

Fig. E

Fig. F

## FRONT WHEEL ALIGNMENT SPECIFICATIONS

| Year | Model | Caster Angle, Degrees | | Camber Angle, Degrees | | | | Toe-In Inch | Toe Out on Turns, Degrees | |
|---|---|---|---|---|---|---|---|---|---|---|
| | | | | Limits | | Desired | | | | |
| | | Limits | Desired | Left | Right | Left | Right | | Outer Wheel | Inner Wheel |
| 1989 | Taurus Sedan | +2.8 to +5.8 | +3.8 | −1.1 to +.1 | −1.1 to +.1 | −.5 | −.5 | ① | 18.25 | 20 |
| | Sable Sedan | +2.7 to +5.7 | +3.7 | −1.1 to +.1 | −1.1 to +.1 | −.5 | −.5 | ① | 18.25 | 20 |
| | All Sta. Wag. | +2.8 to +5.8 | +3.8 | −1.04 to +.16 | −1.04 to +.16 | −.44 | −.44 | ① | 18.25 | 20 |
| 1990 | Taurus Sedan | +2.8 to +5.8 | +3.8 | −1.1 to +.1 | −1.1 to +.1 | −.5 | −.5 | ① | 18.25 | 20 |
| | Sable Sedan | +2.7 to +5.7 | +3.7 | −1.1 to +.1 | −1.1 to +.1 | −.5 | −.5 | ① | 18.25 | 20 |
| | All Sta. Wag. | +2.6 to +5.6 | +3.6 | −1.05 to +.15 | −1.05 to +.15 | −.45 | −.45 | ① | 18.25 | 20 |
| 1991 | Taurus Sedan | +2.8 to +5.8 | +3.8 | −1.1 to +.1 | −1.1 to +.1 | −.5 | −.5 | ① | 18.25 | 20 |
| | Sable Sedan | +2.7 to +5.7 | +3.7 | −1.1 to +.1 | −1.1 to +.1 | −.5 | −.5 | ① | 18.25 | 20 |
| | All Sta. Wag. | +2.6 to +5.6 | +3.6 | −1.05 to +.15 | −1.05 to +.15 | −.45 | −.45 | ① | 18.25 | 20 |
| 1992 | Taurus Sedan | +2.8 to +5.8 | +3.8 | −1.1 to +.1 | −1.1 to +.1 | −.5 | −.5 | ① | 18.25 | 20 |
| | Sable Sedan | +2.7 to +5.7 | +3.7 | −1.1 to +.1 | −1.1 to +.1 | −.5 | −.5 | ① | 18.25 | 20 |
| | All Sta. Wag. | +2.7 to +5.7 | +3.7 | −1 to +.2 | −1 to +.2 | −.4 | −.4 | ① | 18.25 | 20 |

①—Total toe, −.10 inch.

## REAR WHEEL ALIGNMENT SPECIFICATIONS

| Year | Model | Camber Angle, Degrees | | Toe-In Inch |
|---|---|---|---|---|
| | | Limits | Desired | |
| 1989 | Sedan | −1.6 to −.2 | −.9 | +.06 |
| | Wagon | −1.32 to +.08 | −.062 | +.06 |
| 1990 | All | −1.6 to −.2 | −.9 | +.06 |
| 1991 | Sedan | −1.6 to −.2 | −.9 | +.06 |
| | Wagon | −1.9 to +.1 | −.9 | +.06 |
| 1992 | Sedan | −1.6 to −.2 | −.9 | +.06 |
| | Wagon | −1.9 to +.1 | −.9 | +.06 |

## COOLING SYSTEM & CAPACITY DATA

| Year | Model | Engine Liter/CID (VIN) | Cooling Capacity, Qts. | | Radiator Cap Relief Pressure, Lbs. | Thermo. Opening Temp. | Fuel Tank Gals. | Engine Oil Refill, Qts. | Transaxle Capacity | |
|---|---|---|---|---|---|---|---|---|---|---|
| | | | Less A/C | With A/C | | | | | Manual Pts. | Automatic Qts.① |
| 1989–91 | Sedan | 2.5L/4-153 (D,N) | 8.3 | 8.3 | 16 | 192 | ④ | 5⑤ | — | 8.4 |
| | Sedan | 3.0L/V6-182 (U) | 11 | 11 | 16 | 197 | ④ | 4② | — | 12.8 |
| | Wagon | 3.0L/V6-182 (U) | 11.8 | 11.8 | 16 | 197 | ④ | 4② | — | 12.8 |
| | Sedan | 3.0L/V6-182 (Y)③ | 11.6 | 11.6 | 16 | 197 | ④ | 5⑤ | 6.1 | — |
| | Sedan | 3.8L/V6-232 (4) | 12.1 | 12.1 | 16 | 197 | ④ | 4⑥ | — | 12.8 |
| | Wagon | 3.8L/V6-232 (4) | 12.1 | 12.1 | 16 | 197 | ④ | 4⑥ | — | 12.8 |
| 1992 | Sedan | 3.0L/V6-182 (U) | 11 | 11 | 16 | 197 | ④ | 4.5⑤ | 6.2 | 12.8 |
| | Wagon | 3.0L/V6-182 (U) | 11.8 | 11.8 | 16 | 197 | ④ | 4.5⑤ | 6.2 | 12.8 |
| | Sedan | 3.0L/V6-182 (Y)③ | 11.6 | 11.6 | 16 | 192 | 18.4 | 5⑤ | 6.2 | 12.8 |
| | Sedan | 3.8L/V6-232 (4) | 12.1 | 12.1 | 16 | 197 | ④ | 4.5⑤ | 6.2 | 13.1 |
| | Wagon | 3.8L/V6-232 (4) | 12.1 | 12.1 | 16 | 197 | ④ | 4.5⑤ | 6.2 | 13.1 |

①—Approximate, make final check w/dipstick.
②—Add ½ qt. w/filter change.
③—SHO w/double overhead cam engine.
④—Standard tank, 16.0 gals.; optional extended range tank, 18.6 gals.
⑤—Includes filter.
⑥—Add 1 qt. w/filter change.

## LUBRICANT DATA

| Year | Model | Lubricant Type | | | |
|---|---|---|---|---|---|
| | | Transmission | | Power Steering | Brake System |
| | | Manual | Automatic | | |
| 1989–90 | All | Type F or MERCON ATF | MERCON ATF | Type F ATF | DOT 3 |
| 1991–92 | All | MERCON ATF | MERCON ATF | Type F ATF | DOT 3 |

# Electrical

## INDEX



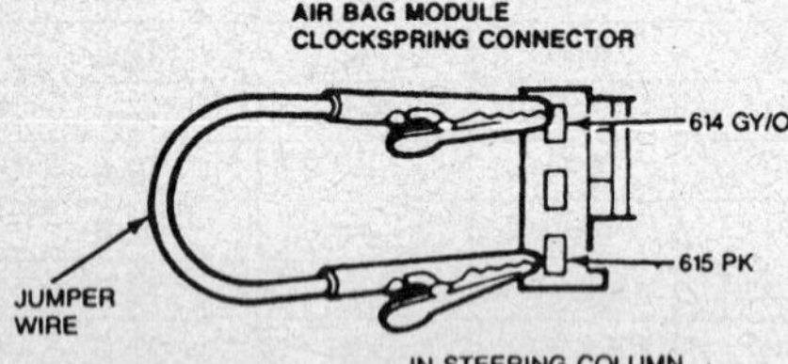


**Fig. 1 Jumper wire at airbag terminals. Except 1992**

## AIRBAG SYSTEM DISARMING

### EXCEPT 1992 MODELS

1. Disconnect battery ground cable, then open glove compartment down past its stops.
2. Disconnect electrical connector from backup power supply, located to the right of the glove compartment opening.
3. Remove four nut and washer assemblies securing driver air bag module to steering wheel.
4. Disconnect air bag electrical connector, then attach a jumper wire between air bag terminals on clockspring, **Fig. 1.** If necessary, reconnect battery and backup power supply.
5. To reactivate, disconnect battery ground cable and backup power supply, then reverse remainder of deactivation procedure. **Torque** airbag module to steering wheel attaching nut assemblies to 35-53 inch lbs.

### 1992 MODELS

1. Disconnect positive battery cable, wait one minute, then proceed to step 2.
2. Remove four airbag module to steering wheel attaching nuts and washers.
3. Disconnect airbag electrical connector.
4. Install Rotunda airbag simulator tool No. 105-00008 or equivalent, to clockspring to simulate airbag, **Fig. 2.**
5. Reconnect positive battery terminal.
6. Reverse procedure to activate system. **Torque** airbag module attaching nuts to 36-49 inch lbs. Turn ignition switch from Off to Run, airbag indicator will light for about six seconds, if light remains lite, does not light or flashes, airbag system failure is indicated.

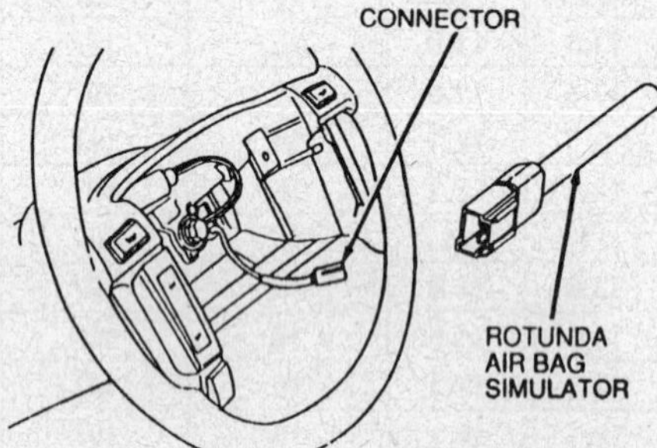


**Fig. 2 Airbag simulator. 1992**

## FUSE PANEL & FLASHER LOCATION

The fuse panel is located under the instrument panel left of the steering column. The combination turn signal/hazard flasher is located behind on the lefthand side instrument panel reinforcement above the fuse panel.

## STARTER
### REPLACE

If the starter motor is noisy or if it locks up, before replacing the starter, loosen the mounting bolts enough to hand fit the starter properly into the pilot plate. Tighten the mounting bolts, starting with the top one.

1. Disable airbag system as described under "Airbag System Disarming."
2. Disconnect battery ground cable, then the starter electrical cable.
3. Remove cable support and ground cable connection from upper starter stud bolt.
4. Remove starter brace from cylinder block and starter.
5. Remove starter mounting bolts.
6. **On models with automatic transmission,** remove starter from between sub-frame and radiator.
7. **On models with manual transmission,** remove starter from between sub-frame and engine.
8. **On all models,** reverse procedure to install.

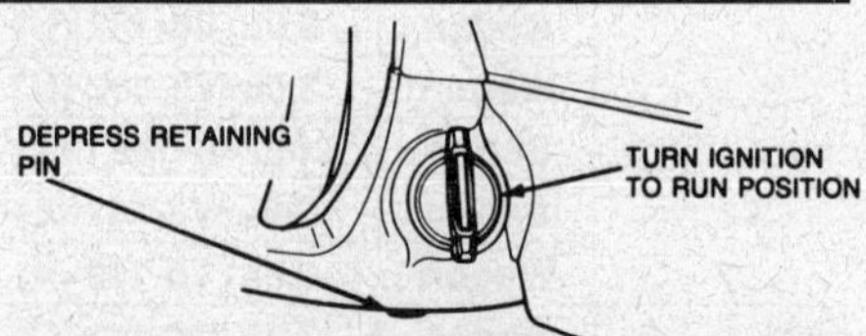


**Fig. 3 Ignition lock cylinder removal**

## IGNITION LOCK
### REPLACE

1. **On models equipped with airbag,** disarm airbag system as outlined under "Airbag System Disarming."
2. **On all models,** disconnect battery ground cable.
3. Rotate ignition switch to the Run position, then working through steering column lower shroud, **Fig. 3,** depress lock cylinder retaining pin with suitable 1/8 inch drill.
4. Pull ignition lock cylinder from housing.
5. Rotate replacement lock cylinder to the RUN position, then while depressing retaining pin, insert lock cylinder into housing. To ensure proper installation, rotate ignition switch through travel.
6. Install battery ground cable, then ensure ignition lock operates properly.
7. **On models equipped with airbag,** reactivate airbag system as outlined under "Airbag System Disarming."

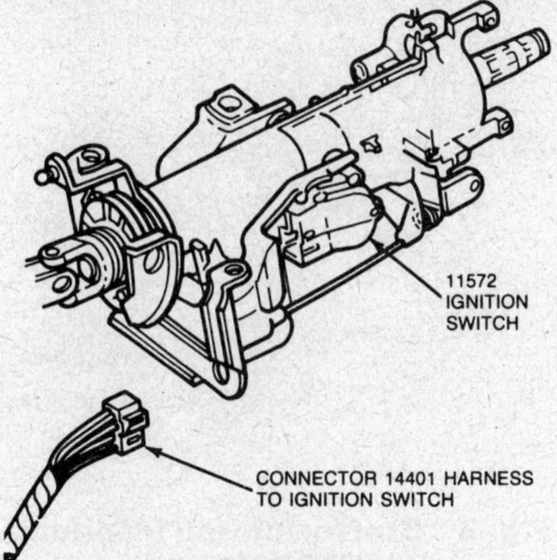


**Fig. 4 Ignition switch electrical connector removal. 1989 models**

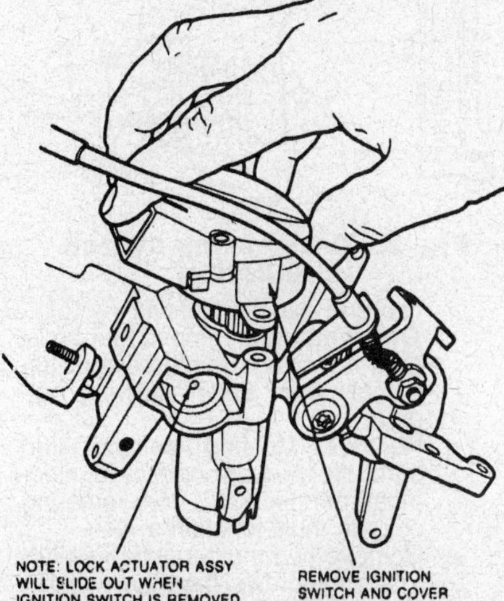


**Fig. 6 Ignition switch removal. 1989 models**

# IGNITION SWITCH
## REPLACE
### 1989

1. Remove ignition lock as described in "Ignition Lock, Replace."
2. **On models with tilt columns,** remove tilt release lever attaching screw then the lever.
3. **On all models,** remove lower instrument panel attaching screws, then the panel.
4. Remove steering column shroud attaching screws, then the shroud.
5. Remove steering column to support bracket attaching nuts and bolts, then lower steering column.
6. Disconnect ignition switch electrical connector, **Fig. 4.**
7. Remove lock actuator cover plate attaching bolt, **Fig. 5,** then the cover plate. **The lock actuator assembly is free to slide out of cylinder housing.**
8. Remove ignition switch attaching screws, then the ignition switch, **Fig. 6.**

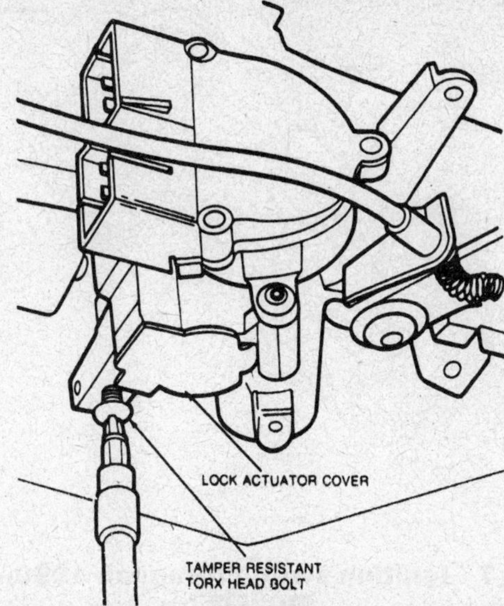


**Fig. 5 Lock actuator cover plate removal. 1989 models**

9. Ensure replacement ignition switch is in the Run position by fully rotating driveshaft clockwise to Start position and releasing.
10. Install lock actuator assembly to a depth of .46-.54 inch from the bottom of actuator assembly to bottom of lock cylinder housing.
11. While holding actuator at proper depth, install ignition switch and cover. Attach with two tamper-resistant Torx head screws. **Torque** screws to 30-48 inch lbs.
12. Install lock cylinder, then rotate ignition switch to the Lock position. Measure depth of actuator assembly as outlined in step 10 above. Actuator assembly must be .92-1.00 inch inside lock cylinder housing. If measurement is not within specifications, actuator assembly must be removed and reinstalled.
13. Install lock actuator cover plate with tamper-resistant Torx head screw. **Torque** screw to 30-48 inch lbs.
14. Install ignition switch electrical connector, then connect battery ground cable.
15. Ensure ignition switch works properly at all functions and the steering column locks functions properly.
16. Remove ignition lock cylinder as outlined elsewhere in this section.
17. Align steering column mounting bracket with steering column bracket and install mounting bolts and nuts. **Torque** to 15-25 ft. lbs.
18. Install steering column shrouds, then instrument panel lower cover.
19. **On models with tilt columns,** install tilt lever and tilt lever mounting screw. **Torque** screw to 6.5-8.5 inch lbs.
20. **On all models,** install ignition lock cylinder.

### 1990–92
#### Removal

1. **On models equipped with airbag,** disarm airbag system as outlined under "Airbag System Disarming."
2. **On all models,** disconnect battery ground cable.
3. Remove four or five steering column shroud attaching screws, then the shroud.
4. **On models with tilt steering,** remove tilt lever.
5. **On 1992 models,** remove instrument panel lower steering column cover.
6. **On all models,** disconnect ignition switch electrical connector **Fig. 7.**
7. Rotate lock cylinder to RUN position, then remove two ignition switch attaching screws.
8. Disengage ignition switch from actuator pin.

#### Installation

1. Set ignition lock and switch to their RUN positions, then install ignition switch onto the actuator pin.
2. Install switch attaching screws, moving switch slightly back and forth to align switch mounting holes with column lock housing threaded holes. **Torque** screws to 50-70 inch lbs.
3. Connect electrical connector and battery ground cable.
4. Check switch for proper function, including START and ACC positions. Ensure steering column locks with switch in LOCK position.
5. Install instrument panel lower steering column cover, trim shrouds and tilt lever.
6. **On models equipped with airbag,** reactivate airbag system as outlined under "Airbag System Disarming."

# STARTER/CLUTCH INTERLOCK SWITCH
## REPLACE

1. **On models equipped with airbag,** disarm airbag system as outlined under "Airbag System Disarming."

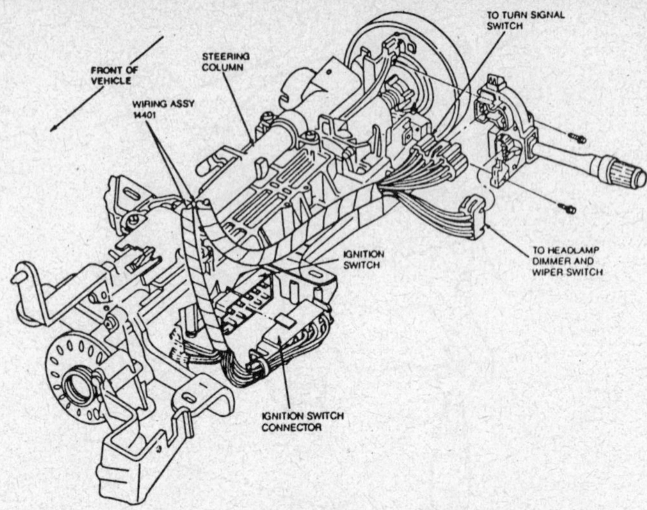


**Fig. 7 Ignition switch removal. 1990–92 models**

2. **On all models,** disconnect battery ground cable.
3. Remove panel above clutch pedal, then disconnect starter/clutch interlock switch wiring.
4. Remove starter/clutch interlock switch attaching screw and hairpin clip, then remove switch.
5. Depress barb at end of rod, then pull rod from clutch pedal.
6. Install switch with self-adjusting clip about one inch from end of rod. **During installation of switch, the clutch pedal must be fully up, otherwise the switch may become misadjusted.**
7. Insert eyelet end of rod over clutch pedal pin, then install hairpin clip, **Fig. 8.**
8. Align switch mounting hole with mounting bracket hole, then install and tighten attaching screw.
9. Adjust starter/clutch interlock switch by pressing clutch pedal to floor.
10. Connect wiring connector, then install panel above clutch pedal.
11. Connect battery ground cable, then check switch for proper operation.
12. **On models equipped with airbag,** reactivate airbag system as outlined under "Airbag System Disarming."

# NEUTRAL SAFETY SWITCH
## REPLACE

1. Disconnect battery ground cable.
2. Set shift lever in Neutral position.
3. Remove linkage from transmission manual shift lever.
4. Disconnect neutral safety switch wiring connector.
5. Remove neutral safety switch attaching bolts, then the switch.
6. Install replacement switch on manual shaft.
7. Install neutral safety switch attaching bolts. Do not tighten at this time.
8. Insert a No. 43 (.089 inch) drill bit through hole provided in switch.
9. **Torque** attaching bolts to 7-9 inch lbs., then remove drill bit.
10. Connect neutral safety switch wiring connector, then battery negative terminal.
11. Ensure starter operates in Neutral and Park positions only.

# LAMP SWITCH
## REPLACE

### 1989

#### Sable

1. Disconnect battery ground cable.
2. Remove lower lefthand side finish panel.
3. Remove two headlamp switch attaching screws, then disconnect switch electrical connector.
4. Remove lamp switch.
5. Reverse procedure to install.

#### Taurus

1. Disconnect battery ground cable.
2. Pull off lamp switch knob.
3. Remove bezel retaining nut, then the bezel.
4. Remove instrument cluster finish panel.
5. Remove two headlamp switch attaching screws, then pull switch out of instrument panel and disconnect electrical connector. Remove switch.
6. Reverse procedure to install.

### 1990–92

1. **On models equipped with airbag,** disarm airbag system as outlined under "Airbag System Disarming."
2. **On all models,** disconnect battery ground cable.
3. Pull off headlamp switch knob and remove retaining nut.
4. Remove instrument cluster finish panel as follows:
   a. Engage parking brake and remove ignition lock cylinder as described in "Ignition Lock, Replace."
   b. **On models with tilt column,** set tilt column lever to full down position and remove tilt lever.
   c. **On all models,** remove four bolts, then cover and reinforcement assembly from under steering column.
   d. Remove steering column trim shrouds, then disconnect all electrical connections from steering column multi-function switch.
   e. Remove two multi-function switch retaining screws, then the switch.
   f. Pull gear shift lever to its lowest down position.
   g. Remove four cluster opening finish panel retaining screws.
   h. Pull finish panel away from instrument panel, then disconnect wiring from switches, clock and warning lamps.
5. Remove two headlamp to instrument panel retaining screws.
6. Pull switch out of instrument panel, then disconnect electrical connector and remove switch.
7. Reverse procedure to install.
8. **On models equipped with airbag,** reactivate airbag system as outlined under "Airbag System Disarming."

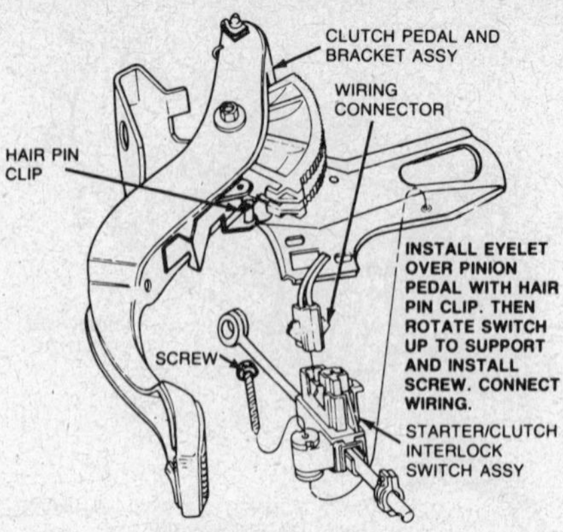


**Fig. 8 Starter/clutch interlock switch removal**

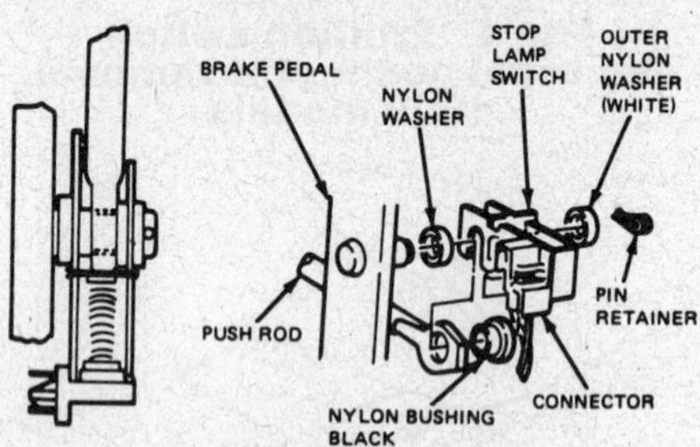


**Fig. 9 Brake lamp switch installation**

# STOP LAMP SWITCH
## REPLACE

1. **On models equipped with airbag,** disarm airbag system as outlined under "Airbag System Disarming," then lift stop lamp switch wire harness connector locking tab, remove wire connector.
2. Remove hairpin retainer and white nylon washer, then slide switch and pushrod assembly away from brake

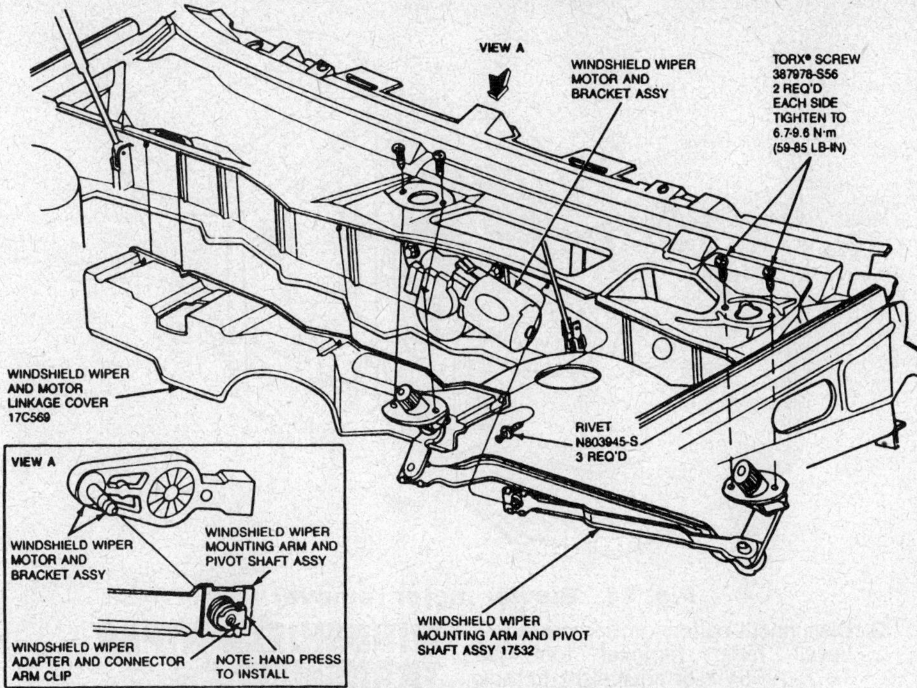


**Fig. 10 Windshield wiper transmission removal**

pedal. Remove switch by sliding up and/or down. **Since switch side plate nearest switch is slotted, it is not necessary to remove master cylinder pushrod, black bushing or one white bushing, nearest the brake pedal from brake pedal pin, Fig. 9.**

3. Position switch so U-shaped side is nearest brake pedal and directly over brake pedal pin. **The black bushing must be in position in pushrod eyelet with washer face on side away from pedal arm.**
4. Slide switch up and down as necessary to trap black plastic bushing and pushrod between the two side plates of the switch, then push switch and pushrod assembly towards brake pedal arm.
5. Install white nylon washer on pedal pin, then the hairpin retainer. **Do not substitute other types of pin retainers. Replace only with production type hairpin retainer.**
6. Connect wire harness connector to switch, then check stop lamps for proper operation. The brake lamps should illuminate with less than 6 lbs. of force applied at the brake pedal pad.
7. **On models equipped with airbag,** reactivate airbag system as outlined under "Airbag System Disarming."

## MULTI-FUNCTION SWITCH REPLACE

1. **On models equipped with airbag,** disarm airbag system as outlined under "Airbag System Disarming."
2. **On all models,** disconnect battery ground cable.
3. **On models with tilt steering column,** move column to lowest position and remove tilt lever attaching screw and the lever.
4. **On all models,** remove ignition lock as described in "Ignition Lock, Replace."
5. Remove upper and lower steering column shrouds.
6. Remove wiring harness retainer, then the three multi-function switch wiring connectors.
7. Remove multi-function switch attaching screws, then disengage switch from casting and remove.
8. Reverse procedure to install, noting the following:
   a. **Torque** multi-function attaching screws to 18-27 inch lbs.
   b. **Torque** tilt lever attaching screw (if equipped) to 6-8.5 inch lbs.
   c. **On models equipped with airbag,** reactivate airbag system as outlined under "Airbag System Disarming."

## STEERING WHEEL REPLACE

### 1989

#### Removal

1. Disconnect battery ground cable.
2. Remove two horn pad cover retaining screws from back of steering wheel.
3. **On models equipped with speed control,** disconnect speed control electrical connector.
4. **On all models,** remove steering wheel retaining bolt.
5. Remove steering wheel from column upper shaft by grasping rim of steering wheel and pulling off.

#### Installation

**The multi-function switch lever must be in the neutral position before installing steering wheel or damage to the switch cam may result.**

1. Align mark on steering column with mark on shaft to ensure that straight-ahead steering wheel position corresponds with straight-ahead position of the front wheels.
2. Install steering wheel retaining bolt and **torque** to 23-33 ft. lbs.
3. Install steering wheel horn pad.
4. Connect battery ground cable, then check steering column for proper operation.

### 1990–92

1. **On models equipped with airbag,** disarm airbag system as outlined under "Airbag System Disarming."
2. **On all models,** center front wheels to straight-ahead position.
3. Disconnect speed control wire harness from steering wheel.
4. Remove steering wheel retaining bolt.
5. Using steering wheel puller tool No. T67L-3600-A or equivalent, remove steering wheel. Route contact assembly wire harness through steering wheel as wheel is lifted off shaft.
6. Reverse procedure to install, noting the following:
   a. Ensure vehicle front wheels are in straight-ahead position.
   b. Route contact assembly wire harness through steering column opening at the three o'clock position.
   c. Align steering shaft alignment marks.
   d. **Torque** steering wheel retaining nut to 23-33 ft. lbs.
   e. **On models equipped with airbag,** reactivate airbag system as outlined under "Airbag System Disarming."

## INSTRUMENT CLUSTER REPLACE

### CONVENTIONAL

1. **On models equipped with airbag,** disarm airbag system as outlined under "Airbag System Disarming."
2. Disconnect battery ground cable.
3. Remove ignition lock assembly as outlined under "Ignition Lock, Replace."
4. Remove steering column trim shrouds.
5. Remove lower lefthand and radio trim panel attaching screws, then pull rearward to unclip.
6. **On Taurus models,** remove clock assembly.
7. **On all models,** remove cluster finish panel attaching screws and jam nut located behind headlamp switch, then rock finish panel outer edge rearward to remove.
8. **On models equipped with column shift,** disconnect PRND1 indicator from column.

9. **On 1989 models,** disconnect speedometer cable at transaxle.
10. **On 1990-92 models,** disconnect upper speedometer cable from lower cable in engine compartment.
11. **On all models,** remove four instrument cluster attaching screws, then pull cluster rearward.
12. Disconnect cluster electrical connectors, then depress cable latch to disengage speedometer cable while pulling cable from cluster.
13. Remove instrument cluster.
14. Reverse procedure to install.
15. **On models equipped with airbag,** reactivate airbag system as outlined under "Airbag System Disarming."

### ELECTRONIC

1. **On models equipped with airbag,** disarm airbag system as outlined under "Airbag System Disarming."
2. Disconnect battery ground cable.
3. Remove two lower trim panels.
4. Remove steering column cover, then PRNDL cable to cluster attaching screws.
5. Pull cluster trim panel rearward, disconnect switch module, then remove trim panel.
6. Remove four cluster attaching screws, then pull cluster bottom rearward.
7. Reach behind and underneath cluster, then disconnect electrical connectors.
8. Pull cluster bottom rearward to remove.
9. Reverse procedure to install.
10. **On models equipped with airbag,** reactivate airbag system as outlined under "Airbag System Disarming."

## RADIO

### REPLACE

### EXCEPT 1992 MODELS

1. **On models equipped with airbag,** disarm airbag system as outlined under "Airbag System Disarming," then disconnect battery ground cable.
2. **On Taurus models,** remove radio opening finish panel attaching screw (in lower part of panel) then, on Taurus and Sable models, remove radio finish panel by snapping out.
3. **On all models,** remove radio bracket to instrument panel attaching screws, then push radio to front and raise back end of radio slightly so rear support bracket clears clip in instrument panel. Carefully remove radio from instrument panel.
4. Disconnect radio wiring connector and antenna lead.
5. Reverse procedure to install.
6. **On models equipped with airbag,** reactivate airbag system as outlined under "Airbag System Disarming."

### 1992 MODELS

1. **On models equipped with airbag,** disarm airbag system as outlined under "Airbag System Disarming."
2. Disconnect battery ground cable.
3. Install radio removal tool No. T87P-19061-A or equivalent, to radio face plate, push tool inward about one inch to release radio clips. **Do not push tool with excessive force or radio damage may result.**
4. Apply light even force on tool, then pull radio from instrument panel.
5. Disconnect radio electrical connector and antenna lead.
6. Reverse procedure to install.
7. **On models equipped with airbag,** reactivate airbag system as outlined under "Airbag System Disarming."

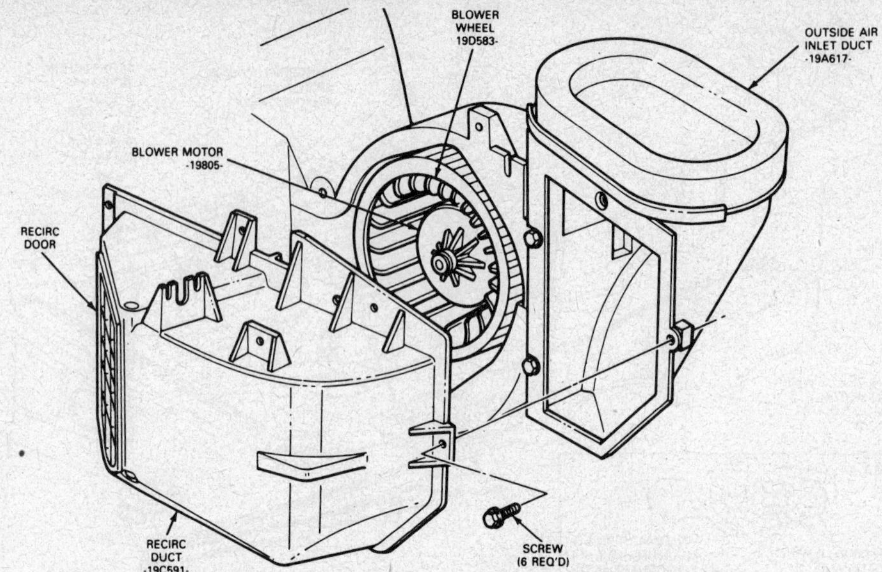


**Fig. 11 Blower motor removal**

## WINDSHIELD WIPER MOTOR

### REPLACE

### FRONT

1. Disconnect battery ground cable.
2. Disconnect wiper motor electrical connector.
3. Remove left side wiper arm. Lift water shield cover from passenger side cowl.
4. Remove linkage retaining clip from wiper motor arm.
5. Remove wiper motor attaching bolts, then the wiper motor.
6. Reverse procedure to install. **Torque** wiper motor attaching bolts to 60-80 inch lbs.

### REAR

1. Disconnect battery ground cable, then remove wiper arm and blade.
2. Remove pivot shaft attaching nut and washers, then disconnect wiper motor electrical connector. **Pull connector only. Do not pull wires.**
3. Remove wiper motor attaching nut, then the motor.
4. Reverse procedure to install.

## WINDSHIELD WIPER TRANSMISSION

### REPLACE

1. Disconnect battery ground cable.
2. Remove wiper arm and blade assemblies from windshield wiper pivot arms.
3. Remove leaf screens from both sides of cowl.
4. Remove linkage drive arm to motor crank arm retaining clip, then separate linkage drive arm from motor crank arm, **Fig. 10.**
5. Remove pivot arm to cowl attaching screws, then withdraw windshield wiper transmission from cowl chamber.
6. Reverse procedure to install. **Torque** pivot arm attaching screws to 60-84 inch lbs.

## WINDSHIELD WIPER SWITCH

### REPLACE

### FRONT

The Windshield wiper switch is an integral part of the multi-function switch. For replacement procedures, refer to "Multi-Function Switch, Replace."

### REAR

1. **On models equipped with airbag,** disarm airbag system as outlined under "Airbag System Disarming."
2. Remove four instrument cluster finish panel attaching screws, then remove by rocking upper edge of finish panel towards drivers seat.
3. Disconnect rear washer switch wiring connector.
4. Remove washer switch from instrument panel.
5. Reverse procedure to install.
6. **On models equipped with airbag,**

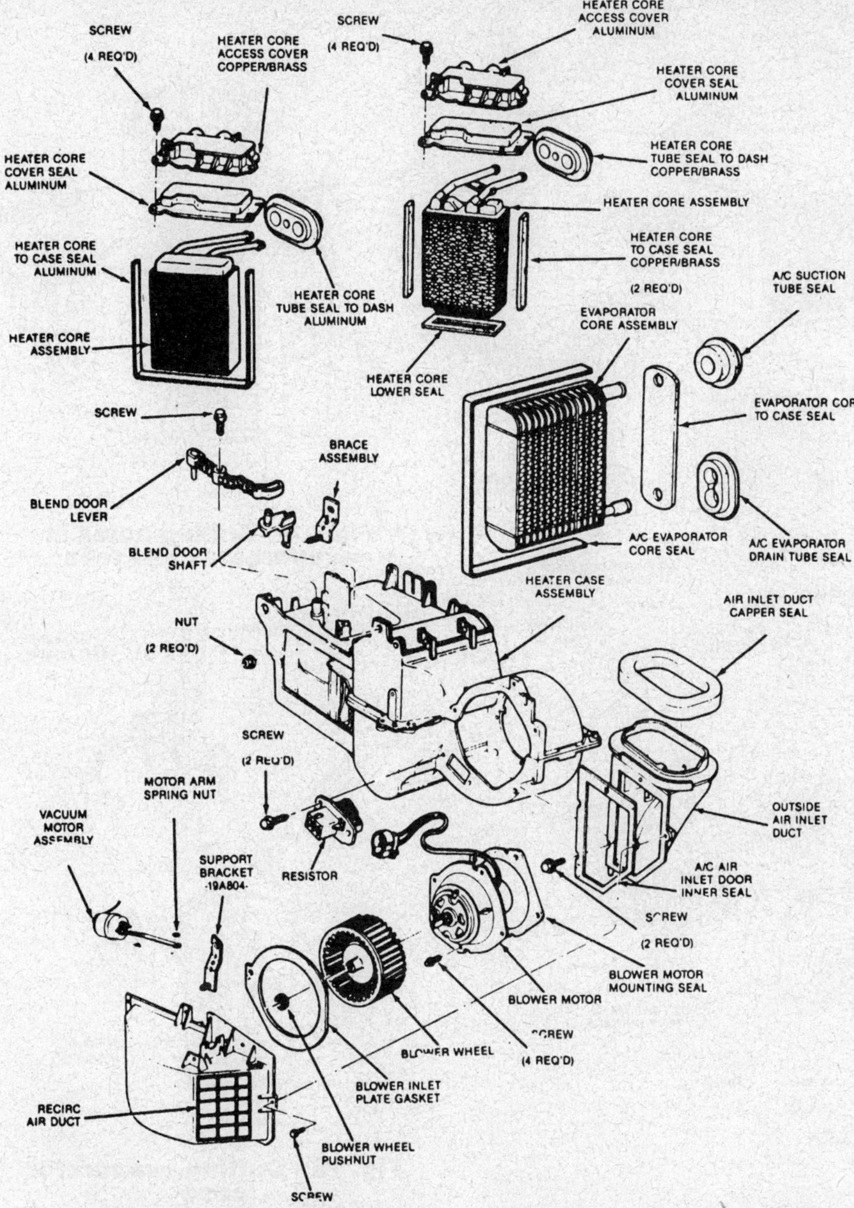


**Fig. 12 Heater & evaporator case assembly. Less ATC**

reactivate airbag system as outlined under "Airbag System Disarming."

## BLOWER MOTOR REPLACE

1. **On models equipped with airbag,** disarm airbag system as outlined under "Airbag System Disarming," then disconnect battery ground cable.
2. Open glove compartment door, then release retainers and allow glove box door to swing downward. Remove recirculation duct support bracket to cowl attaching screw, then the recirculation door motor vacuum connection.
3. Remove six recirculation duct to heater case attaching screws, **Fig. 11,** then lower duct from between instrument panel and heater case and remove.
4. Disconnect blower motor electrical connection.
5. Remove blower wheel attaching clip and the blower wheel.
6. Remove blower motor attaching bolts, then the blower motor from the evaporator case.
7. Reverse procedure to install.
8. **On models equipped with airbag,** reactivate airbag system as outlined under "Airbag System Disarming."

## HEATER CORE REPLACE

### LESS A/C

1. **On models equipped with airbag,** disarm airbag system as outlined under "Airbag System Disarming."
2. Disconnect battery ground cable.
3. Drain cooling system into suitable container.
4. Disconnect heater hoses from heater core, then plug heater core tubes.
5. Disconnect vacuum supply hose from inline check valve located in engine compartment.
6. Remove instrument panel as described in "Dash Panel Service."
7. Remove instrument panel to heater case shake brace attaching screw, then the instrument panel shake brace.
8. Remove floor register to heater case attaching bolts, then floor register.
9. Remove heater case to dash panel attaching nuts located in engine compartment.
10. Remove screws attaching top brackets to cowl top panel, then carefully pull heater assembly from dash panel and remove from vehicle.
11. Remove vacuum source line from heater core tube seal, then remove heater core tube seal.
12. Remove heater core access cover attaching screws, then the access cover.
13. Remove heater core and seals from heater case.
14. Reverse procedure to install.
15. **On models equipped with airbag,** reactivate airbag system as outlined under "Airbag System Disarming."

### WITH A/C

1. **On models equipped with airbag,** disarm airbag system as outlined under "Airbag System Disarming."
2. Remove instrument panel as described in "Dash Panel Service" section.
3. Remove evaporator case as described under "Evaporator Core, Replace."
4. Remove vacuum source line from heater core tube seal, then the seal from heater core tubes, **Figs. 12 and 13.**
5. Remove four heater core access cover attaching screws, then the access cover and seal from evaporator case.
6. Lift heater core and seals from evaporator case.
7. Reverse procedure to install.
8. **On models equipped with airbag,** reactivate airbag system as outlined under "Airbag System Disarming."

## EVAPORATOR CORE REPLACE

1. **On models equipped with airbag,** disarm airbag system as outlined under "Airbag System Disarming," then disconnect battery ground cable.
2. Drain coolant from radiator and discharge A/C system.
3. Disconnect heater hoses from heater core. Plug heater core tubes.
4. Disconnect vacuum supply hose from in-line vacuum check valve in engine compartment.
5. Disconnect liquid line and accumulator from evaporator core at dash panel. Cap refrigerant lines and evapora-

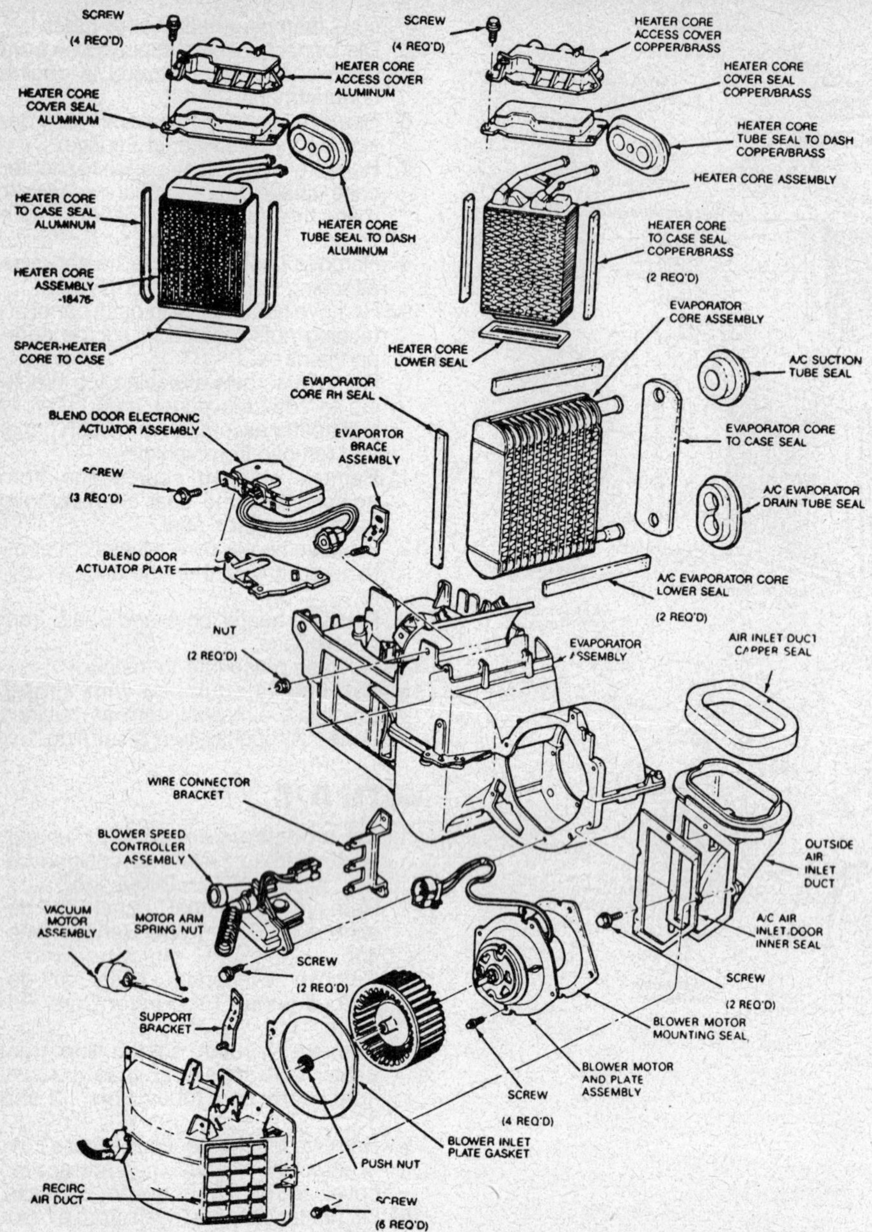


**Fig. 13 Heater & evaporator case assembly. With ATC**

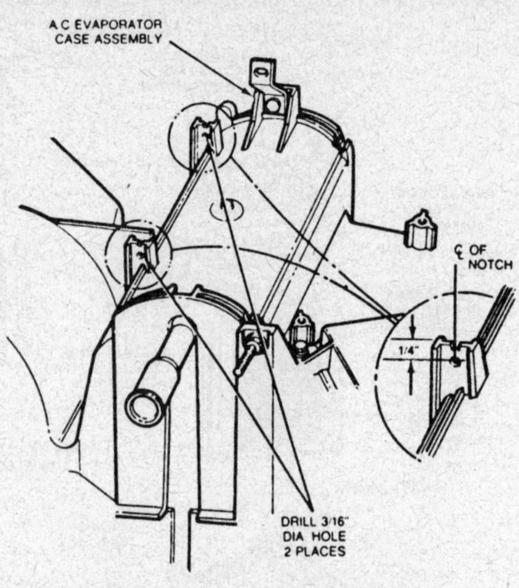


**Fig. 14 Drilling holes in evaporator case tabs**

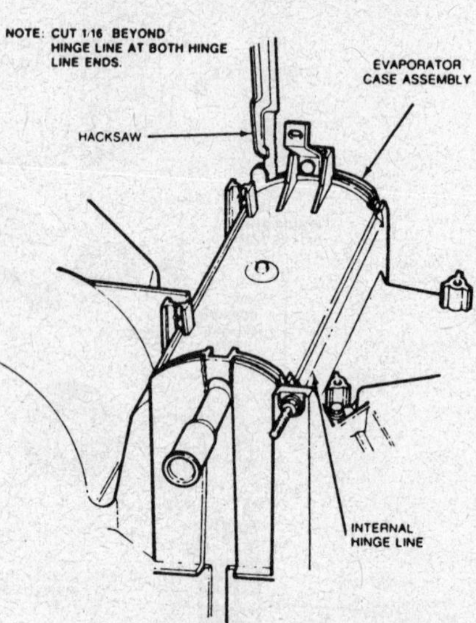


**Fig. 15 Cutting evaporator case**

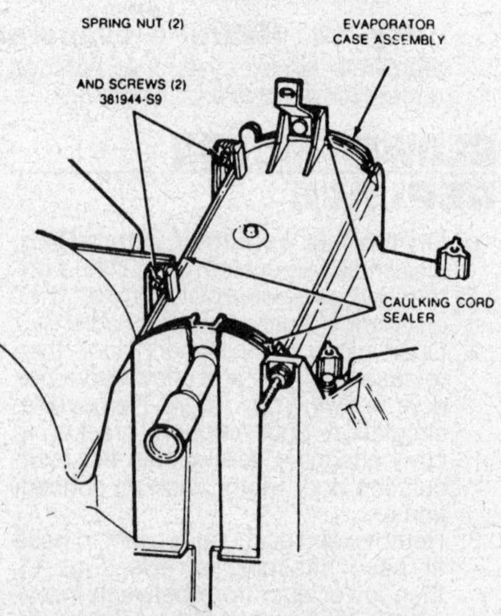


**Fig. 16 Securing & caulking evaporator case cover**

tor core to prevent entrance of dirt and excess moisture.

6. Remove instrument panel as described in "Dash Panel Service" section.
7. Remove evaporator case to instrument panel shake brace attaching screw, then the shake brace.
8. Remove two screws holding floor register and floor ducts to bottom of evaporator case.
9. Remove three evaporator case to dash panel retaining nuts, located in engine compartment.
10. Remove two support brackets to cowl top panel attaching screws, **Fig. 12.**
11. Carefully pull evaporator case assembly away from dash panel and remove it from vehicle. **Whenever the evaporator case is removed from the vehicle it will be necessary to replace the suction accumulator/drier.**
12. Disconnect and remove vacuum harness from vacuum motor.
13. Remove six recirc duct screws from evaporator, then the recirc duct.
14. Remove two air inlet to evaporator attaching screws.
15. Remove support bracket from evaporator case, then the moulded seals from evaporator tubes.
16. **On models with automatic temperature control,** remove screws holding electronic connector bracket to recirc duct, **Fig. 13.**
17. Disconnect engine harness 14401 from blower speed control connector, then release three connectors from bracket and remove bracket.
18. Disconnect aspirator hose and remove blend door actuator.
19. **On all models,** drill a 3/16 inch hole in each of two upright tabs on top of evaporator case as shown in **Fig. 14.**

20. Using a small saw blade or equivalent, cut top of evaporator case between raised outlines as shown in **Fig. 15.**
21. Fold cutout cover back from opening and lift out evaporator core from case.
22. Reverse procedure to install, noting the following:
    a. Transfer two foam core seals to new evaporator core.
    b. Install spring nut on each of two upright tabs and adjacent holes drilled in front flange. Align hole in spring nuts with 3/16 inch holes drilled in tab and flange. Install screw in each spring nut to secure cutout cover in closed position, **Fig. 16.**
    c. Using caulking cord No. D9AZ-19560-A or equivalent, seal evaporator case along cut line as shown in **Fig. 16.**
    d. **On models equipped with airbag,** reactivate airbag system as outlined under "Airbag System Disarming."

# 2.5L/4-153 Engine

**NOTE: On Vehicles Equipped With Airbags, Disarm Airbag System As Outlined Under "Airbag System Disarming" Before Any Diagnosis, Testing, Troubleshooting Or Repairs Are Performed. After All Diagnosis, Testing, Troubleshooting Or Repairs Have Been Completed, Rearm Airbag System As Outlined Under "Airbag System Disarming."**

## INDEX



## AIRBAG SYSTEM DISARMING

1. Disconnect battery ground cable, then open glove compartment down past its stops.
2. Disconnect electrical connector from backup power supply, located to the right of the glove compartment opening.
3. Remove four nut and washer assemblies securing driver air bag module to steering wheel.
4. Disconnect air bag electrical connector, then attach a jumper wire between air bag terminals on clockspring, **Fig. 1.** If necessary, reconnect battery and backup power supply.
5. To reactivate, disconnect battery ground cable and backup power supply, then reverse remainder of deactivation procedure. **Torque** airbag module to steering wheel attaching nut assemblies to 35-53 inch lbs.

## ENGINE MOUNTS REPLACE

### LH INSULATOR & SUPPORT ASSEMBLY

#### Models w/Automatic Transmission

1. Raise and support vehicle, then remove left front wheel and tire assembly.
2. Support transmission with suitable jack and block of wood positioned near insulator.

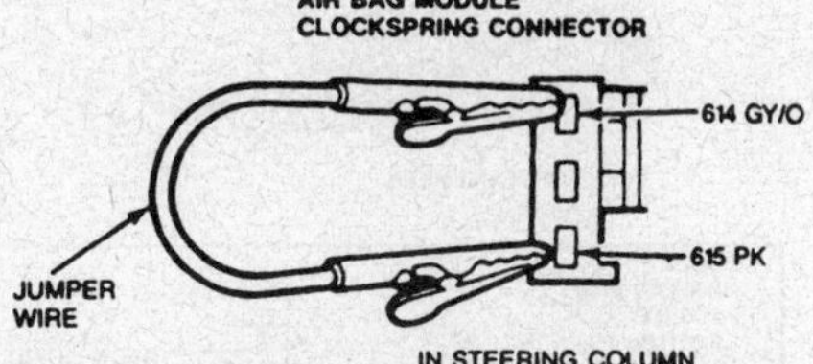


**Fig. 1 Airbag terminal jumper wire**

3. Remove insulator to support assembly attaching nuts, **Fig. 2.**
4. Remove insulator to frame through bolts, then using jack, raise transmission enough to unload insulator.
5. Remove support assembly to transmission attaching bolts, then remove insulator and/or transmission support assembly.
6. Reverse procedure to install.

#### Models w/Manual Transmission

1. Raise and support vehicle, then remove left front wheel and tire assembly.
2. Support transmission with suitable jack and block of wood positioned near insulator.
3. Remove insulator to frame attaching bolts, **Fig. 3,** then using jack, raise transmission enough to unload insulator.
4. Remove insulator to transmission attaching bolts, then the mount.
5. Reverse procedure to install.

### RH FRONT OR REAR INSULATOR

1. Remove lower damper nut from right side of engine.
2. Raise and support vehicle, then support engine with suitable jack and block of wood positioned near insulator.
3. Remove insulator to frame attaching nut, **Figs. 2 and 3,** then raise engine enough to unload insulator.
4. Remove insulator to engine bracket attaching bolts, then the insulator.
5. Reverse procedure to install.

## ENGINE REPLACE

1. Relieve fuel system pressure by disconnecting electrical connector at inertia switch, then crank engine for 15 seconds.
2. Remove timing window cover at transaxle and rotate engine until flywheel timing marker is aligned with timing pointer.
3. Mark crankshaft pulley at 12 o'clock (TDC) position. Rotate crankshaft pulley to 6 o'clock (BDC) position.
4. Disconnect battery ground cable.
5. Mark position of hood hinges for installation reference, then remove hood.
6. Remove air cleaner assembly and drain engine coolant.

7. Disconnect upper radiator hose at engine.
8. Disconnect and mark wiring assembly and vacuum lines for installation reference.
9. Disconnect crankcase ventilation hose at valve cover and intake manifold.
10. Disconnect fuel lines and heater hoses at throttle body.
11. Disconnect ground wire at engine.
12. Disconnect accelerator cable and throttle valve control cable at throttle body.
13. **On models with A/C,** discharge A/C system and pressure and suction lines from compressor.
14. **On all models,** remove drive belt and water pump pulley.
15. Remove air cleaner to canister hose, then raise and support vehicle.
16. Drain engine oil and remove oil filter.
17. Disconnect starter cable and remove starter motor.
18. Remove converter nuts, then position mark on crankshaft pulley as close to 6 o'clock position (BDC) as possible with converter stud visible. **The flywheel timing must be in a 6 o'clock position for proper engine removal and installation.**
19. Remove engine insulator nuts, then disconnect exhaust pipe from manifold.
20. Disconnect canister and halfshaft brackets from the engine.
21. Remove lower engine to transaxle attaching bolts, then disconnect lower radiator hose at tube.
22. Lower vehicle and position a floor jack under transaxle.
23. Disconnect power steering lines at pump.
24. Attach suitable engine lifting device to engine, then remove upper engine to transaxle attaching bolts.
25. Remove engine from vehicle.
26. Reverse procedure to install.

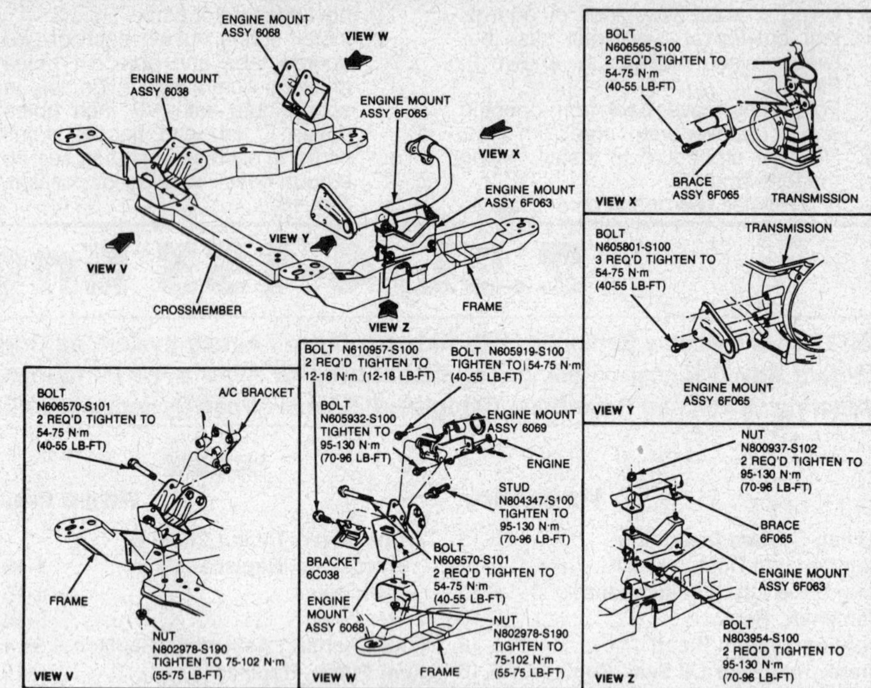


**Fig. 2 Engine mounts. Models w/auto. trans.**

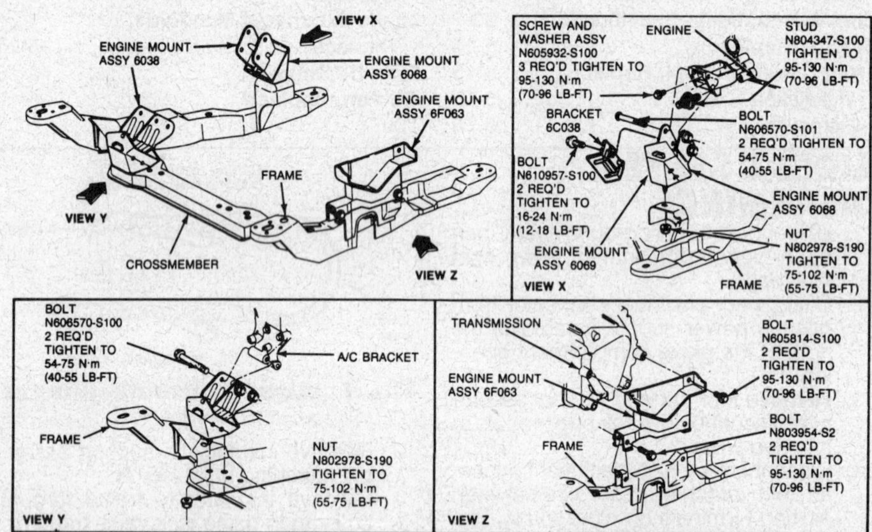


**Fig. 3 Engine mounts. Models w/man. trans.**

## INTAKE & EXHAUST MANIFOLDS
### REPLACE

1. Disconnect battery ground cable, then drain cooling system.
2. Remove accelerator cable, air cleaner assembly and heat stove tube at heat shield.
3. Mark vacuum lines for reference, then remove necessary vacuum lines.
4. Remove Thermactor belt, hose and pump assembly. If equipped.
5. Remove exhaust pipe to exhaust manifold attaching nuts, then the manifold heat shroud.
6. Disconnect Exhaust Gas Oxygen (EGO) sensor wire connector.
7. Disconnect Thermactor check valve hose from tube assembly, if equipped. Then remove bracket to EGR valve attaching nuts.
8. Disconnect water inlet hose from intake manifold, then EGR tube from EGR valve.
9. Remove intake manifold attaching bolts, then intake manifold and gasket.
10. Remove exhaust manifold attaching bolts, then exhaust manifold.
11. Reverse procedure to install. Refer to **Figs. 4 and 5,** for tightening sequence. **Torque** exhaust manifold in two steps; first step 5-7 ft. lbs.; second step to 20-30 ft. lbs. **Torque** intake manifold to 23 ft. lbs.

## FUEL CHARGING ASSEMBLY
### REPLACE

1. Remove air tube at fuel charging assembly inlet.
2. Disconnect electrical connector at inertia switch located on lefthand side of luggage compartment.
3. Remove fuel cap and release tank pressure, then release fuel system pressure by cranking engine for 15 seconds.
4. **On models with manual transaxle,** disconnect throttle cable.
5. **On models with automatic transaxle,** disconnect throttle valve lever.
6. **On all models,** disconnect electrical connectors at idle speed control, throttle position sensor and fuel injector.
7. Disconnect fuel inlet, outlet connections and PCV vacuum line at fuel

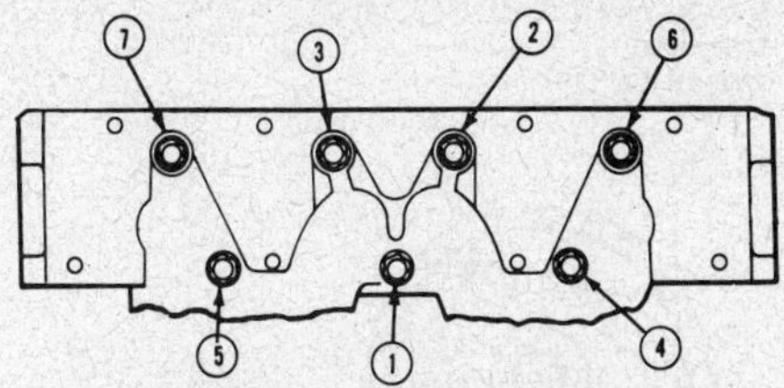

Fig. 4 Exhaust manifold bolt tightening sequence

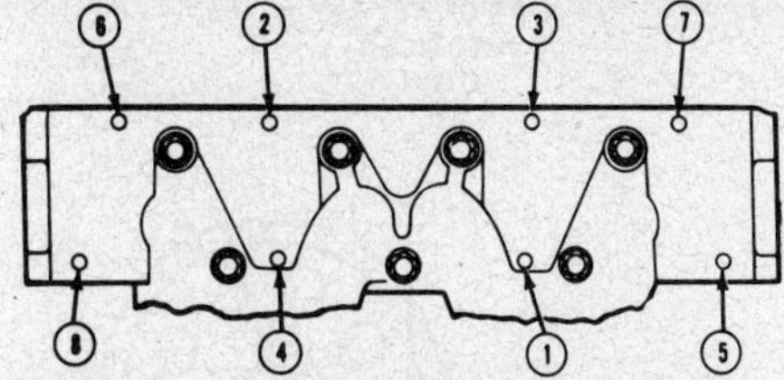

Fig. 5 Intake manifold bolt tightening sequence

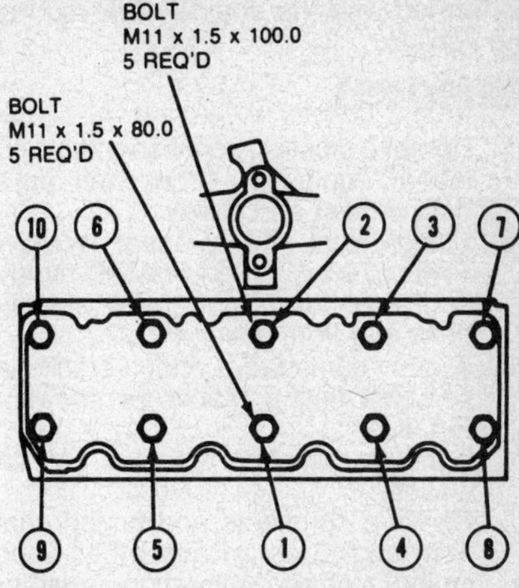


Fig. 6 Cylinder head bolt tightening sequence

charging assembly.

8. Remove two fuel charging assembly retaining nuts, then the fuel charging assembly.
9. Remove charging assembly mounting gasket from intake manifold.
10. Reverse procedure to install.

## CYLINDER HEAD

### REPLACE

**If cylinder head is being removed to replace a leaking cylinder head gasket, refer to "Service Bulletins" for possible cause and repair assistance.**

1. Disconnect battery ground cable.
2. Remove lower radiator hose and drain cooling system.
3. Disconnect heater hose from fitting located under intake manifold.
4. Disconnect upper radiator hose from cylinder head.
5. Disconnect electric cooling fan switch electrical connector.
6. Remove air cleaner assembly from engine.
7. Mark and disconnect all vacuum hoses from cylinder head.
8. Remove rocker arm cover.
9. Remove all accessory drive belts from engine.
10. Remove distributor cap and spark plug wires as an assembly.
11. Disconnect EGR tube from EGR valve, then disconnect choke cap wire.
12. Disconnect fuel supply and return lines from rubber connector.
13. Disconnect accelerator cable and speed control cable, if equipped.
14. Loosen thermactor pump belt pulley, if equipped.
15. Raise and support vehicle.
16. Disconnect exhaust system from exhaust pipe, then lower vehicle.
17. Remove cylinder head bolts, cylinder head and gasket with thermactor pump, exhaust and intake manifolds attached. **Do not lay cylinder head flat. Damage to spark plugs or gasket surfaces may result.**
18. Reverse procedure to install. Refer to **Fig. 6**, for cylinder head bolt tightening sequence. **Torque** bolts in two steps; first step 52-59 ft. lbs.; second step 70-76 ft. lbs.

## VALVE ARRANGEMENT

### FRONT TO REAR

2.5L/4-153 .............. I-E-I-E-E-I-E-I

## CAM LOBE LIFT SPECIFICATIONS

Exhaust .......................239 inch
Intake .........................249 inch

## VALVES

### ADJUST

Hydraulic valve lifters are used in this engine. No adjustment is required. To check intake and exhaust valve stem to rocker arm tip clearance, refer to "Hydraulic Valve Lifters, Service."

## HYDRAULIC VALVE LIFTER SERVICE

### DIAGNOSIS

Before replacing a hydraulic valve lifter for noisy operation, ensure the noise is not caused by improper collapsed tappet gap, worn rocker arms, pushrods or valve tips.

To check for collapsed tappet gap, proceed as follows:

1. Rotate camshaft to position A as shown in **Fig. 7.**
2. Check intake and exhaust valve stem to rocker arm tip clearance on compression stroke under camshaft position A. With camshaft in position A, gap should be .072-.174 inch with tappet collapsed on base circle. Check No. 1 cylinder intake and exhaust valves. Check No. 2 cylinder intake valve. Check No. 3 cylinder exhaust valve. Tighten fulcrum bolts to specifications.
3. Rotate camshaft 180° to position B as shown in **Fig. 7.** Check No. 2 cylinder exhaust valve. Check No. 3 cylinder intake valve. Check No. 4 cylinder intake and exhaust valve. Tighten fulcrum bolts to specification.

### REPLACE

1. Remove cylinder head as described previously.
2. Using a suitable magnet, remove lifters from lifter bores.
3. Place valve lifters in order so they can be installed in their original positions. **If the lifters are stuck in their bores by excessive varnish or gum buildup, use tool No. T70L-6500-A or equivalent to remove valve lifters.**
4. Reverse procedure to install.

## ROCKER ARM COVER

### REPLACE

1. Disconnect battery ground cable.
2. Remove oil filler cap.
3. Disconnect PCV hose from PCV valve.
4. Disconnect throttle linkage cable from rocker arm cover.
5. Disconnect speed control cable from rocker arm cover, if equipped.
6. Remove rocker arm cover bolts and cover.
7. Reverse procedure to install. Torque attaching bolts to specifications.

## FRONT COVER OIL SEAL

### REPLACE

#### REMOVAL

The following removal and installation procedure can only be performed with the engine removed from the vehicle.

1. Remove bolt and washer from crankshaft pulley.
2. Using tool No. T77F-4220-B1 or equivalent, remove crankshaft pulley.
3. Using tool No. T74P-6700-A or equivalent, remove front cover oil seal.

#### INSTALLATION

1. Coat new front cover oil seal with a suitable lubricant.
2. Using tool No. T83T-4676-A or equivalent, install oil seal into front cover. Drive oil seal in until it is fully seated into front cover recess. Check oil seal after installation to ensure spring is properly positioned in oil seal.
3. Lubricate crankshaft pulley hub, then install pulley, washer and bolt. Torque crankshaft pulley bolt to specifications.

## FRONT COVER, TIMING CHAIN & SPROCKETS

### REPLACE

The following procedure can only be

performed with the engine removed from the vehicle.

## REMOVAL

1. Remove dipstick, accessory drive pulley (if equipped), crankshaft pulley bolt, washer and pulley.
2. Using front cover seal remover T74P-6700-A or equivalent, remove front seal, then front cover attaching bolts and front cover, **Fig. 7.**
3. Align camshaft and crankshaft sprocket timing marks as shown in **Fig. 8.**
4. Remove camshaft sprocket bolt and washer.
5. Remove sprockets and timing chain from engine as an assembly. Check timing chain vibration damper (located inside front cover) for wear. Replace if necessary.
6. Remove oil pan.

## INSTALLATION

1. Install sprockets and timing chain. Align timing marks as shown in **Fig. 9.** Oil timing chain, sprockets and tensioner after installation.
2. With front cover seal removed, position front cover on engine.
3. Position front cover alignment tool T84P-6019-C or equivalent onto end of crankshaft. Ensure crankshaft pulley key is aligned with keyway in tool.
4. Install front cover bolts. Torque bolts to specifications, then remove front cover alignment tool.
5. Coat new front cover oil seal with a suitable lubricant.
6. Using tool No. T83T-4676-A or equivalent, install oil seal into front cover. Drive oil seal in until it is fully seated into front cover recess. Check oil seal after installation to ensure spring is properly positioned in oil seal.
7. Lubricate crankshaft pulley hub, then install pulley. Do not install washer and bolt at this time.
8. Install oil pan and accessory drive pulley (if equipped).
9. Install crankshaft pulley bolt and washer. Torque crankshaft pulley bolt to specifications.

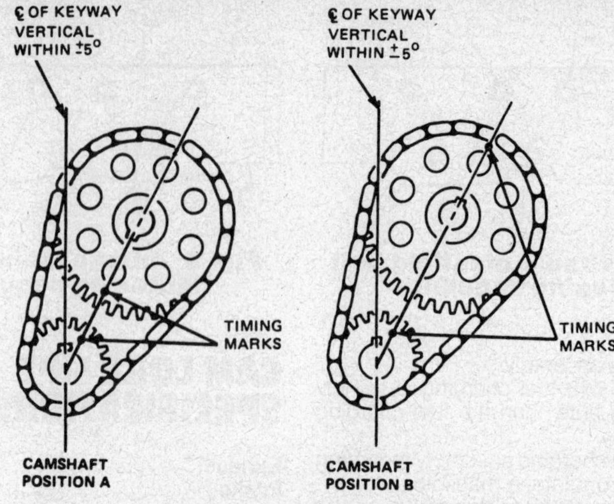


**Fig. 7 Positioning camshaft to check for collapsed tappet gap**

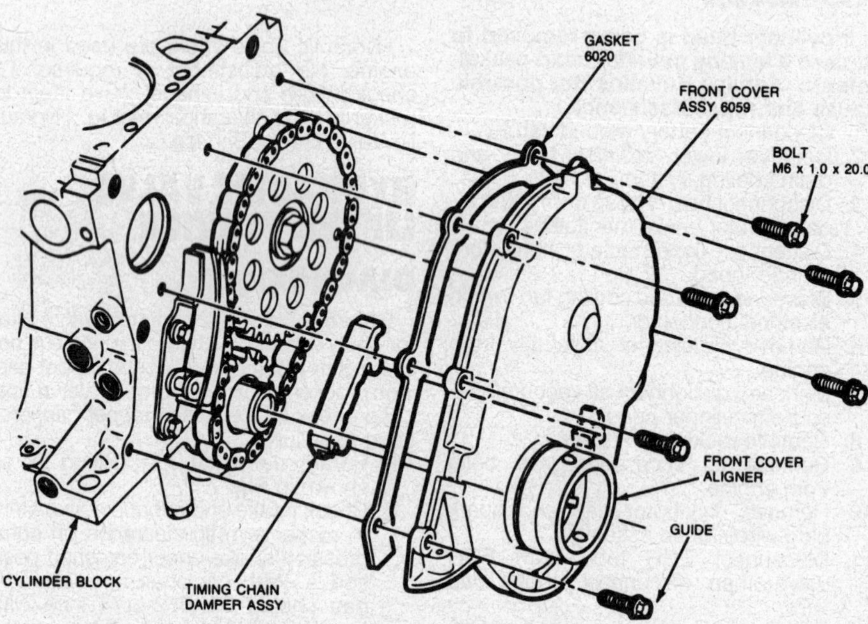


**Fig. 8 Front cover removal**

# CAMSHAFT

## REPLACE

The following procedure can only be performed with the engine removed from the vehicle.

1. Remove dipstick, then drain cooling system and crankcase.
2. Remove accessory drive belts and pulleys.
3. Position No. 1 piston at TDC with distributor rotor at No. 1 firing position, then remove distributor.
4. Remove cylinder head as described under "Cylinder Head, Replace."
5. Using a suitable magnet, remove hydraulic tappets and position in order so that they can be installed in their original locations. If tappets are stuck in their bores, use tool No. T70L-6500A or equivalent to remove tappets.
6. Remove crankshaft pulley bolt, washer and pulley.
7. Remove front cover as described under "Front Cover, Timing Chain & Sprockets, Replace."
8. Remove oil pan as described under "Oil Pan, Replace."
9. Remove timing chain, sprockets and timing chain tensioner as described under "Front Cover, Timing Chain & Sprockets, Replace."
10. Remove camshaft thrust plate. Carefully remove camshaft from engine to avoid damaging camshaft bearings, journals and lobes.
11. Reverse procedure to install. Lubricate camshaft with suitable oil before installing. Ensure No. 1 piston is at TDC with distributor rotor at No. 1 firing position.

# MAIN BEARINGS

Main bearings are available in standard sizes and undersizes of .001, .002, .010, .020, .030 and .040 inch.

# CRANKSHAFT REAR OIL SEAL

## REPLACE

1. Remove transaxle, then the flywheel.
2. Remove rear cover plate.
3. Using a suitable tool, punch a hole into the seal metal surface between the seal lip and block. Using slide hammer, Tool No. T77L-9533-B or equivalent, remove seal.

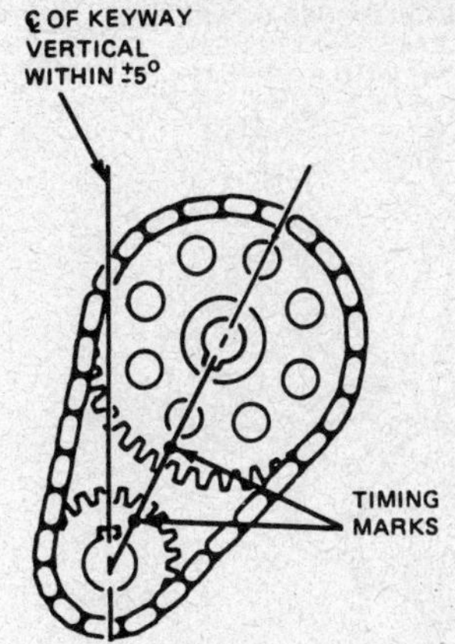


Fig. 9 Valve timing marks

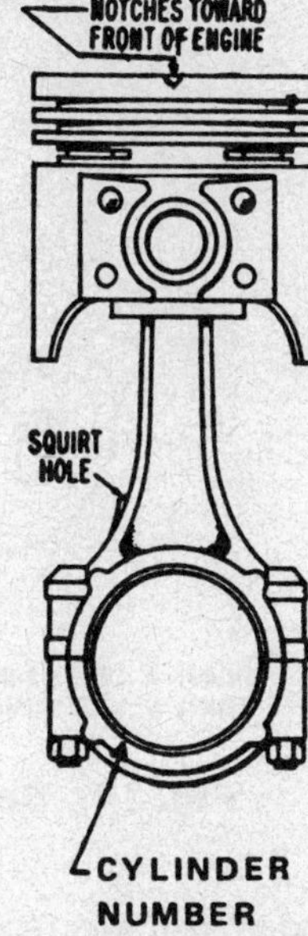


Fig. 10 Piston & rod assembly

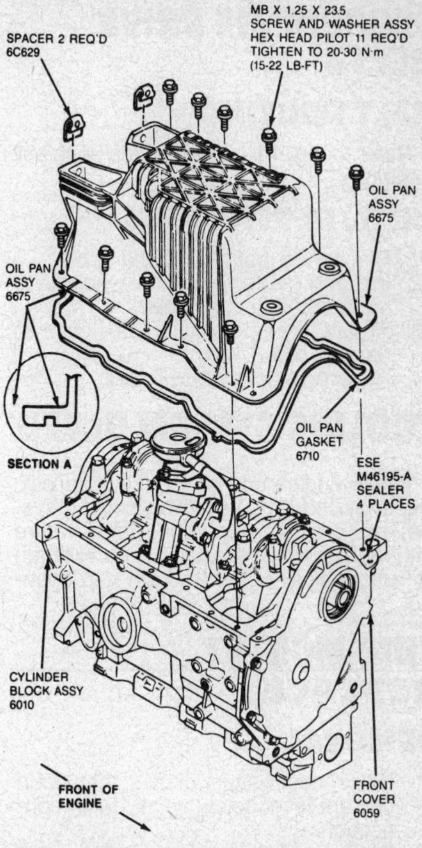


Fig. 11 Oil pan removal

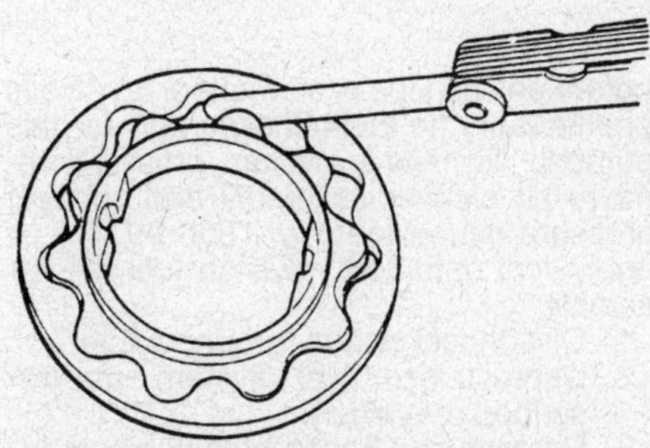

Fig. 12 Oil pump tip clearance

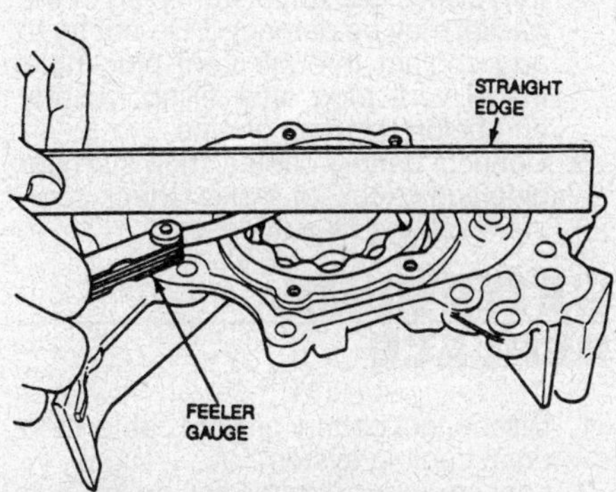


Fig. 13 Oil pump rotor endplay

4. Coat crankshaft seal area and seal lip with engine oil, then using tool No. T81P-6701-A, install seal.
5. Install rear cover plate and two dowels.
6. Install flywheel. Torque bolts to specifications.

## PISTON & ROD ASSEMBLY

Assemble the rod to the piston with the notch on top of piston facing front of engine, **Fig. 10.**

After installation, check connecting rod big end side clearance. Clearance should be .0035-.0105 inch.

## OIL PAN

### REPLACE

1. Disconnect battery ground cable.
2. Raise and support vehicle.
3. Drain cooling system and crankcase.
4. **On models with manual transaxle,** remove roll restrictor.
5. **On all models,** remove starter motor.
6. Disconnect exhaust pipe from oil pan.
7. Remove engine coolant tube located at the lower radiator hose, at the water pump and from tabs on oil pan. On models with A/C, position A/C line off to side.
8. Remove oil pan bolts and oil pan, **Fig. 11,** from engine.
9. Clean oil pan and cylinder block surfaces with Dupont Freon TF or equivalent.
10. Remove oil pump screen and pickup tube and clean thoroughly, then reinstall.
11. Reverse steps 1-9 to assemble, noting the following. **Torque** oil pan to transaxle attaching bolts to 30-39 ft. lbs. to align oil pan, then loosen bolts 1/2 turn. **Torque** oil pan to cylinder block attaching bolts to 15-23 ft. lbs., then the oil pan to transaxle attaching bolts to 30-39 ft. lbs.

## OIL PUMP

### REPLACE

1. Disconnect battery ground cable.
2. Remove oil pan as described under "Oil Pan, Replace."
3. Remove oil pump attaching bolts, then oil pump from engine. Remove intermediate driveshaft from oil pump.
4. Reverse procedure to install.

## OIL PUMP INSPECTION

1. Wash all parts in suitable solvent, then dry with compressed air.
2. Ensure all dirt and particles are removed.
3. Inspect inner pump housing for wear or damage.
4. Inspect pump cover mating surface for wear, scuff marks are normal, if surface is worn or grooved, replace pump assembly.
5. Inspect rotor for nicks, burrs or score marks, remove imperfections with suitable oil stone.
6. Using suitable feeler gauge, measure inner tip to outer rotor tip clearance, **Fig. 12,** clearance on 1989 models, should not exceed .010 inch, clearance on 1990-91 models, should not exceed .012 inch.
7. Install suitable straightedge, then using feeler gauge, measure rotor endplay, **Fig. 13,** clearance should not exceed .005 inch.
8. If any inspection is not as indicated, replace oil pump assembly.

## BELT TENSION DATA

Belt tension is automatically maintained on these models by an automatic tensioner. Therefore, no adjustment is necessary.

## SERPENTINE DRIVE BELTS

### BELT ROUTING

Refer to **Fig. 14.** for serpentine drive belt routing.

### BELT, REPLACE

1. Disconnect battery ground cable.
2. Install suitable 1/2 inch flex handle to square hole in tensioner.
3. Rotate tensioner counterclockwise to remove belt.
4. Reverse procedure to install.

## COOLING SYSTEM BLEED

These engine do not require a specific bleed procedure. After filling cooling system, run engine to operating temperature with radiator/pressure cap off. Air will then be automatically bled through cap opening.

## THERMOSTAT REPLACE

### REMOVAL

1. Disconnect battery cables, then drain coolant level below water outlet connection.
2. Remove vent plug from water outlet connection, then loosen top radiator hose clamp at radiator.
3. Remove water outlet retaining bolts, lift clear of engine and remove thermostat. Do not pry housing off.

### INSTALLATION

1. Clean water outlet and cylinder head mating surfaces. Ensure that outlet pocket and air vent passage are free from rust. Clean vent plug and gasket.
2. Place thermostat fully inserted so it will compress gasket and press into water outlet connection to secure. Position cater outlet connection to intake manifold with a new gasket and secure with retaining bolts.
3. Tighten bolts to specifications, position top radiator hose and tighten clamps. Ensure that drain cock is closed.
4. Fill cooling system with recommended coolant mixture. The vent plug must be removed before radiator fill or engine may not fill completely. Do not turn plastic cap under vent plug or the gasket may be damaged. Do not try to add coolant through vent plug hole. Install vent plug after filling radiator and before starting engine.
5. Connect battery cables, then start engine and check for leaks. Check coolant level and fill if necessary.

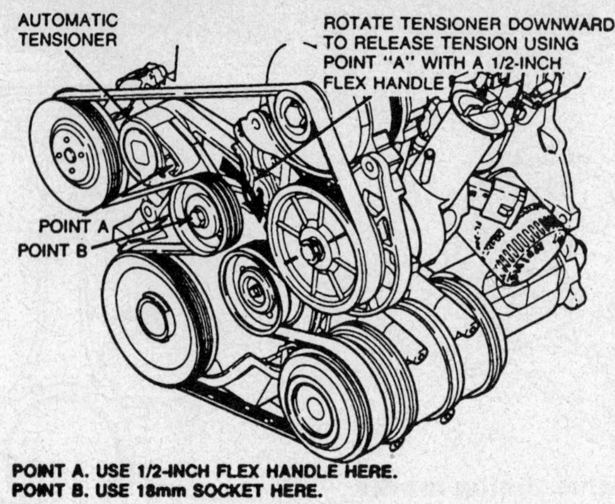


**Fig. 14 Serpentine drive belt routing**

## WATER PUMP REPLACE

1. Disconnect battery ground cable, then drain cooling system.
2. Loosen water pump idler pulley bolt and remove belt from water pump pulley.
3. Remove water pump inlet tube.
4. Remove water pump bolts and water pump.
5. Reverse procedure to install.

## FUEL PUMP REPLACE

Fuel supply lines will remain pressurized for long periods of time after engine shut-down. This pressure must be relieved before any service is attempted. A valve is provided on the fuel rail assembly for this purpose. To relieve system pressure, remove air cleaner assembly and connect pressure gauge tool No. T80L-9974-A or equivalent onto fuel valve on fuel rail assembly.

1. Disconnect battery ground cable.
2. Depressurize fuel system as described previously.
3. Remove fuel from fuel tank by pumping fuel out of fuel filler neck.
4. Raise and support vehicle.
5. Disconnect and remove fuel filler neck.
6. Support fuel tank, then remove tank support straps. Lower fuel tank partially and remove fuel lines, electrical connectors and vent lines from tank. Remove tank and place on suitable workbench.
7. Turn fuel pump locking ring counterclockwise and remove locking ring.
8. Remove fuel pump, bracket and gasket assembly.
9. Reverse procedure to install. To pressurize fuel system, proceed as follows:
   a. Install pressure gauge tool No. T80L-9974-A or equivalent onto fuel rail pressure fitting.
   b. Turn ignition switch to ON position for 3 seconds, repeatedly 5 to 10 times until pressure gauge indicates 13 psi, then check for leaks.

## TIGHTENING SPECIFICATIONS

| Year | Component | Torque/Ft. Lbs. |
|---|---|---|
| 1989–91 | Camshaft Sprocket Bolts | 41-46 |
| | Camshaft Tensioner Bolts | 35-53 |
| | CFI Throttle Body Nuts | 15-25 |
| | Connecting Rod Cap Bolts | 35-53 |
| | Connecting Rod Cap Nuts | 21-26 |
| | Crankshaft Pulley Bolt | 140-170 |
| | Cylinder Head Bolts | ① |
| | Damper To Engine | 8-12 |
| | Distributor Hold-Down Bolts | 17-25 |
| | EGR Tube Connector | 25-35 |
| | EGR Valve Bolts | 13-19 |
| | Engine Coolant Temperature Sensor | 8-18 |
| | Exhaust Manifold | ① |
| | Flywheel Bolts | 54-64 |
| | Fuel Charging Assembly To Intake Manifold | 15-25 |
| | Fuel Pump Cover Bolts | 15-23 |
| | Insulator To Engine Bracket | 40-55 |
| | Insulator To Frame | 55-75 |
| | Insulator To Support | 55-75 |
| | Intake Manifold | ① |
| | LH Front No. 1 Insulator to Bracket Nut | 75-100 |
| | LH Front No. 1 Insulator to Transaxle | 25-37 |
| | LH Rear No. 4 Insulator to Body Bolts | 75-100 |
| | LH Rear No. 4 Insulator to Transaxle | 35-50 |
| | LH Shift Stabilizer Bar to Transaxle | 25-35 |
| | Low Oil Lever Sensor | 20-30 |
| | Main Bearing Cap Bolts | 51-66 |
| | Oil Pan Bolts | 15-23 |
| | Oil Pan Drain Plug | 15-25 |
| | Oil Pump Bolts Bolts | 15-23 |
| | Rocker Arm Bolts | ② |
| | Rocker Arm Cover Bolts | 6-8 |
| | Spark Plugs | 6-10 |
| | Support Assembly To Transmission | 60-86 |
| | Thermostat Housing | 12–18 |
| | Water Outlet Connection Bolts | 12-18 |
| | Water Pump Bolts | 15-23 |
| | Water Pump Inlet Tube to Oil Pan | 6-8 |

①—Refer to text.
②—First step, torque to 4.5-7.5 ft. lbs.; second step, torque to 19.5-26.5 ft. lbs.

# 3.0L/V6-182 Engine, Except SHO

**NOTE: On Vehicles Equipped With Airbags, Disarm Airbag System As Outlined Under "Airbag System Disarming" Before Any Diagnosis, Testing, Troubleshooting Or Repairs Are Performed. After All Diagnosis, Testing, Troubleshooting Or Repairs Have Been Completed, Rearm Airbag System As Outlined Under "Airbag System Disarming."**

## INDEX



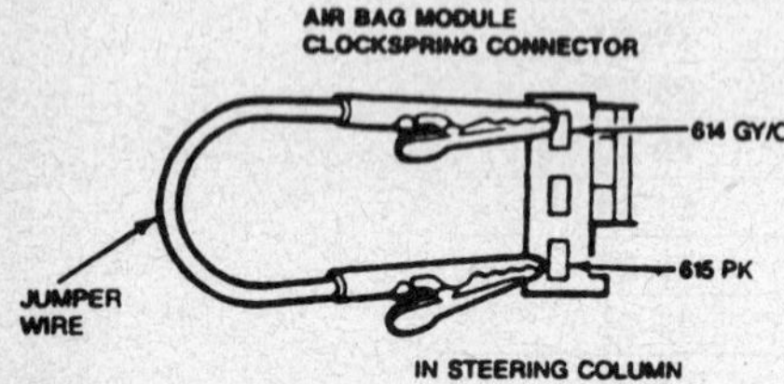


**Fig. 1 Airbag terminal jumper wire. Except 1992**

## AIRBAG SYSTEM DISARMING

### EXCEPT 1992 MODELS

1. Disconnect battery ground cable, then open glove compartment down past its stops.
2. Disconnect electrical connector from backup power supply, located to the right of the glove compartment opening.
3. Remove four nut and washer assemblies securing driver air bag module to steering wheel.
4. Disconnect air bag electrical connector, then attach a jumper wire between air bag terminals on clockspring, **Fig. 1.** If necessary, reconnect battery and backup power supply.
5. To reactivate, disconnect battery ground cable and backup power supply, then reverse remainder of deactivation procedure. **Torque** airbag module to steering wheel attaching nut assemblies to 35-53 inch lbs.

### 1992 MODELS

1. Disconnect positive battery cable, wait one minute, then proceed to step 2.
2. Remove four airbag module to steering wheel attaching nuts and washers.
3. Disconnect airbag electrical connector.
4. Install Rotunda airbag simulator tool No. 105-00008 or equivalent, to clockspring to simulate airbag, **Fig. 2.**
5. Reconnect positive battery terminal.
6. Reverse procedure to activate system. **Torque** airbag module attaching nuts to 36-49 inch lbs. Turn ignition switch from Off to Run, airbag indicator will light for about six seconds, if light remains lite, does not light or flashes, airbag system failure is indicated.

## FUEL SYSTEM PRESSURE RELIEF

**Fuel supply lines will remain pressurized for long periods of time after engine shut-down. This pressure must be relieved before any service is attempted. A valve is provided on the fuel rail assembly for this purpose. To relieve system pressure, remove air cleaner assembly and connect pressure gauge tool No. T80L-9974-A or T80L-9974-B or equivalent onto fuel valve on fuel rail assembly. To pressurize fuel system, proceed as follows:**

a. Install pressure gauge tool No. T80L-9974-A or T80L-9974-B equivalent onto fuel rail pressure fitting.
b. Turn ignition switch to On position for 3 seconds, repeatedly 5 to 10 times until pressure gauge indicates 13 psi.

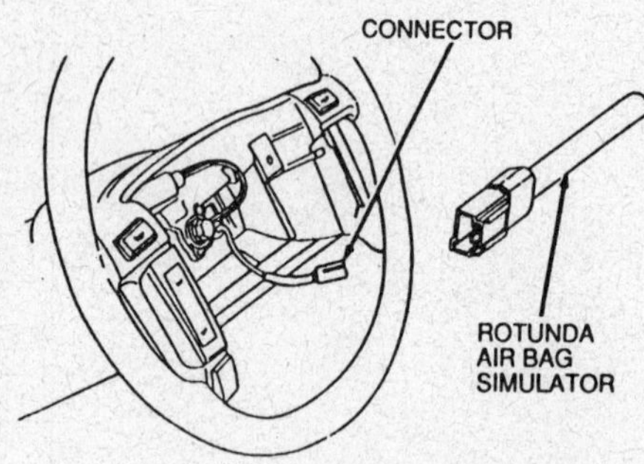


**Fig. 2 Airbag simulator. 1992**

## ENGINE MOUNTS REPLACE

### LH INSULATOR & SUPPORT ASSEMBLY

1. Raise and support vehicle.
2. Remove left front tire and wheel assembly, then support transaxle using suitable jack and block of wood.
3. Remove insulator to support attaching nuts, **Figs. 3 and 4.**
4. Remove insulator to frame through bolts, then raise transaxle enough to unload insulator.

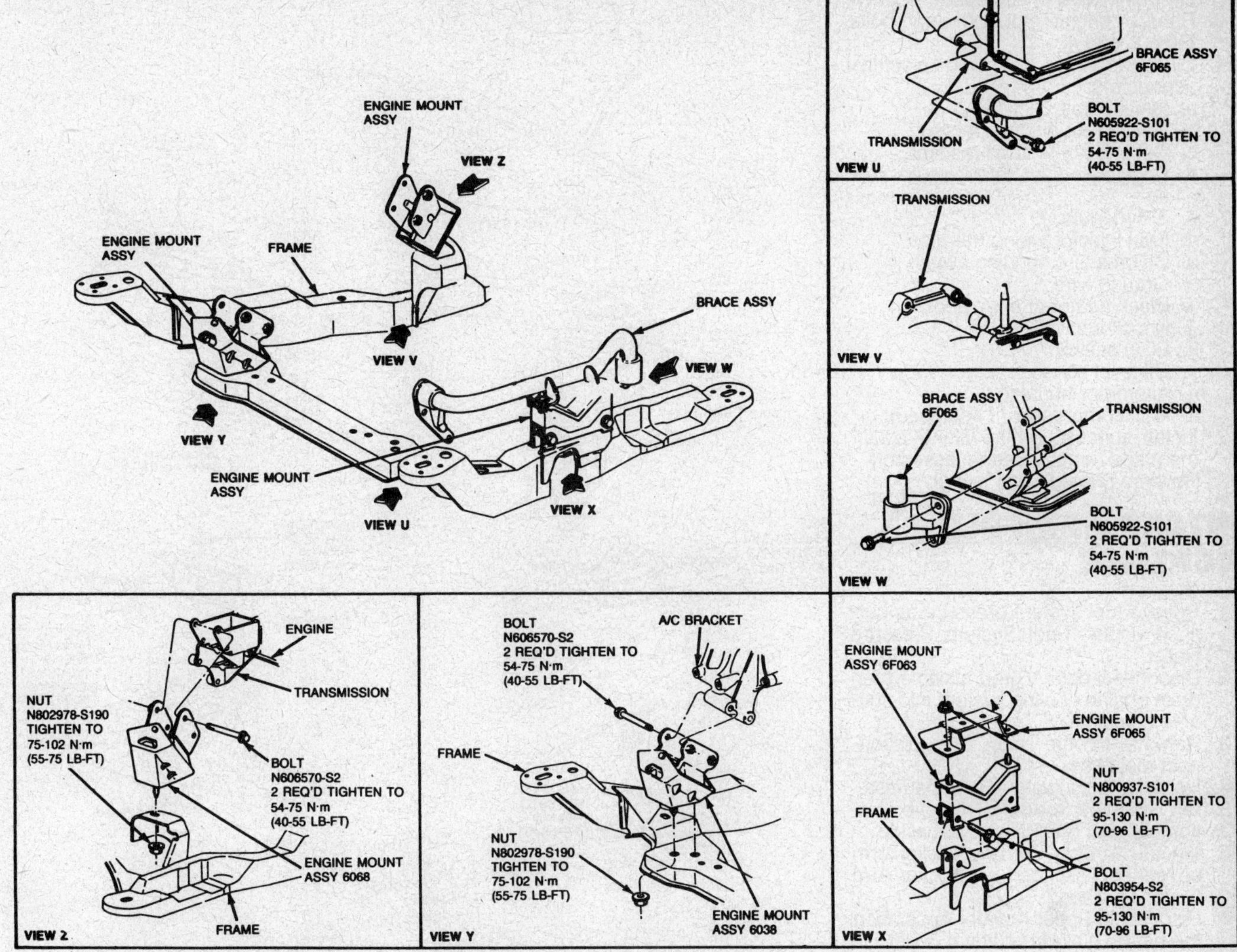


**Fig. 3 Engine mounts. 1989–90**

5. Remove support assembly to transaxle attaching bolts.
6. **On 1989-90 models,** remove insulator and/or support assembly.
7. **On 1991-92 models,** rotate support assembly counterclockwise to remove from upper stud.
8. **On all models,** reverse procedure to install.

## RH FRONT NO. 2 & RH REAR NO. 3

1. **On 1989-90 models,** remove lower insulator bolt from righthand side of engine. Refer to "Engine Damper RH, Replace."
2. **On all models,** raise and support vehicle.
3. Place jack and wood block under engine block.
4. Remove nuts retaining righthand front and righthand rear insulators to frame, **Figs. 3 and 4.**
5. Raise engine enough to unload insulator, then remove through bolts and engine mounts.
6. Reverse procedure to install.

# ENGINE DAMPER REPLACE

## RH SIDE

**Do not clamp damper tube or piston rod.**

1. Remove bolt attaching lower end of damper to engine bracket, **Fig. 5.**
2. Remove upper end of damper to engine bracket attaching bolt.
3. Remove engine damper.
4. Reverse procedure to install.

## LH SIDE

**Do not clamp damper tube or piston rod.**

1. Remove speed control servo and bracket assembly.
2. Remove bolt and flag nut attaching lower end of damper to engine mount attaching bracket, **Fig. 6.**
3. Remove bolts attaching upper damper bracket to side rail bracket.
4. Remove engine damper.
5. Reverse procedure to install.

# ENGINE REPLACE

1. Relieve fuel system pressure as outlined under "Fuel System Pressure Relief."
2. Disconnect battery ground cable, then drain engine coolant and oil into suitable containers.
3. Discharge A/C system (if equipped).
4. Remove air cleaner assembly, battery, battery tray, integrated relay controller, cooling fan assembly and bounce damper bracket.
5. Disconnect hoses from radiator, then remove radiator assembly.
6. Disconnect evaporative emission control hose.
7. Disconnect starter brace, then the exhaust pipes from manifolds.
8. Disconnect power steering hoses, fuel lines and vacuum hoses.
9. Disconnect engine ground strap, heater hoses, accelerator cable linkage, throttle valve linkage and speed

control linkage (if equipped).
10. Remove engine mount through bolts, **Figs. 3 and 4.**
11. Disconnect the following electrical connectors:
    a. Ignition coil.
    b. Radio frequency supressor.
    c. Cooling fan voltage resistor.
    d. Engine coolant temperature sensor.
    e. TFI module.
    f. Fuel injector wiring harness.
    g. Oil pressure sending switch.
    h. Ground wire.
    i. Block heater (if equipped).
    j. Knock sensor.
    k. EGO sensor.
    l. Oil level sensor.
    m. Alternator harness.
    n. A/C compressor (if equipped).
12. Install suitable engine lifting equipment and remove engine assembly.
13. Reverse procedure to install.

## INTAKE MANIFOLD
### REPLACE

1. Relieve fuel system pressure as outlined under "Fuel System Pressure Relief."
2. Disconnect battery ground cable, then drain engine cooling system into suitable container.
3. Remove throttle body, then disconnect fuel lines.
4. Remove fuel injector wiring harness.
5. **On 1990-92 models,** remove ignition coil and bracket and set aside.
6. **On all models,** remove rocker arm covers as described in "Rocker Arm Cover, Replace."
7. Disconnect upper radiator hose, then the heater hose from water outlet.
8. Mark distributor rotor and body with reference marks, then remove distributor assembly.
9. Remove intake manifold attaching bolts, then the intake manifold.
10. Reverse procedure to install, noting the following:
    a. Tighten intake manifold bolts in sequence shown in **Fig. 7.**
    b. **On 1989 models, torque** bolts in three steps, first to 11 ft. lbs., then to 18 ft. lbs., then to 24 ft. lbs.
    c. **On 1990-91 models, torque** bolts in two steps, first to 11 ft. lbs., then to 22 ft. lbs.
    d. **On 1992 models, torque** bolts in two steps, first to 15-22 ft. lbs., then to 19-24 ft. lbs.

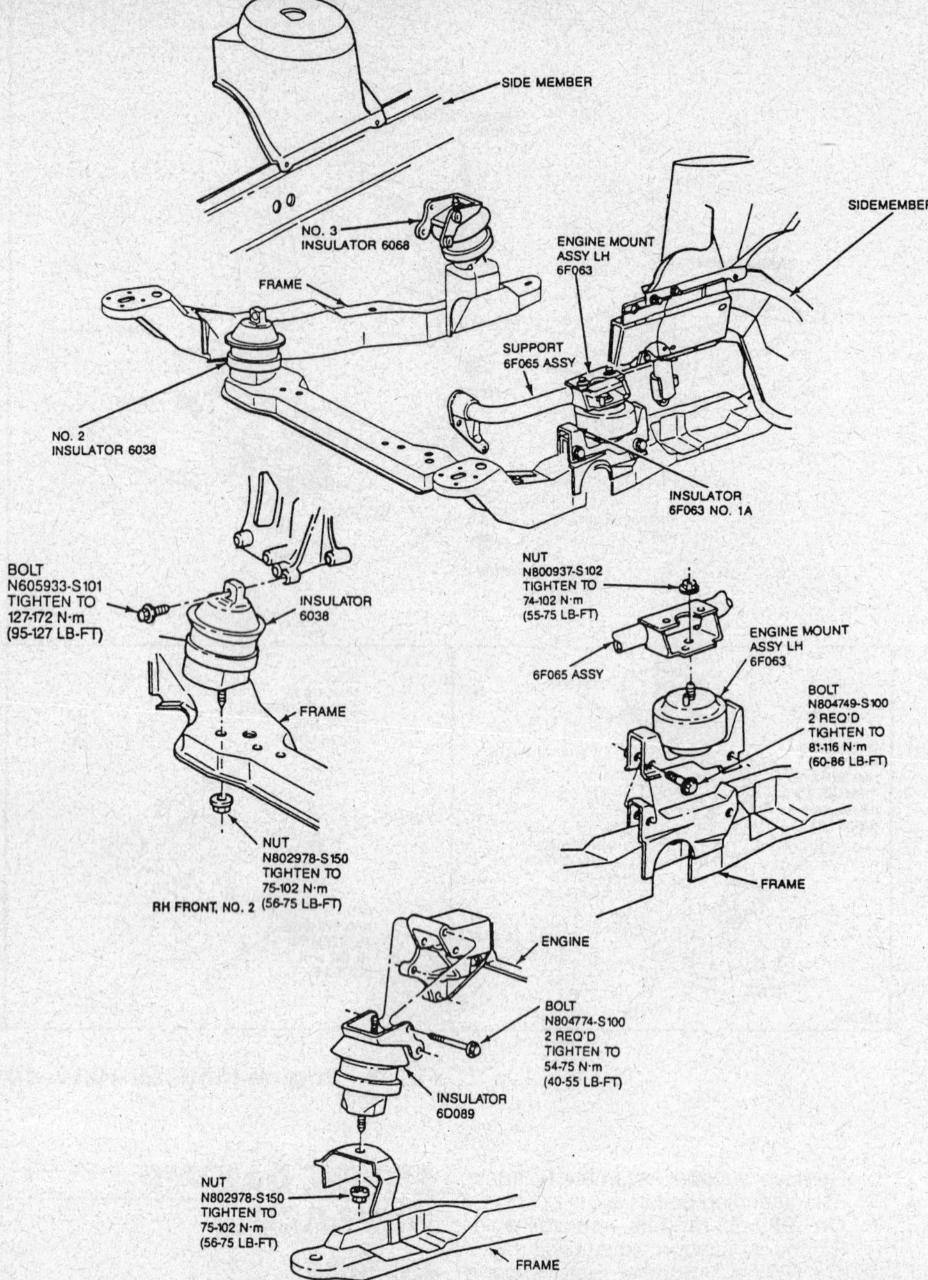


**Fig. 4 Engine mounts. 1991—92**

## EXHAUST MANIFOLD
### REPLACE

#### LEFT SIDE

1. Relieve fuel system pressure as outlined under "Fuel System Pressure Relief."
2. Remove dipstick tube support bracket, then remove exhaust pipe to manifold attaching nuts.
3. Remove exhaust manifold to cylinder head attaching bolts, then the manifold.
4. Reverse procedure to install, noting the following:
    a. Lightly lubricate nuts and bolts with suitable oil.
    b. Torque manifold attaching bolts to specifications.
    c. Torque exhaust pipe to manifold attaching nuts to specifications.

#### RIGHT SIDE

1. Relieve fuel system pressure as outlined under "Fuel System Pressure Relief."
2. **On 1989-90 models,** remove heater hose support bracket, then disconnect heater hoses.
3. **On all models,** using suitable back-up wrench on EGR tube lower adapter, remove EGR tube from exhaust manifold.
4. **On 1992 models,** remove coolant bypass tube.
5. **On all models,** remove exhaust pipe to manifold attaching nuts.
6. Remove exhaust manifold to cylinder head attaching bolts, then the manifold.

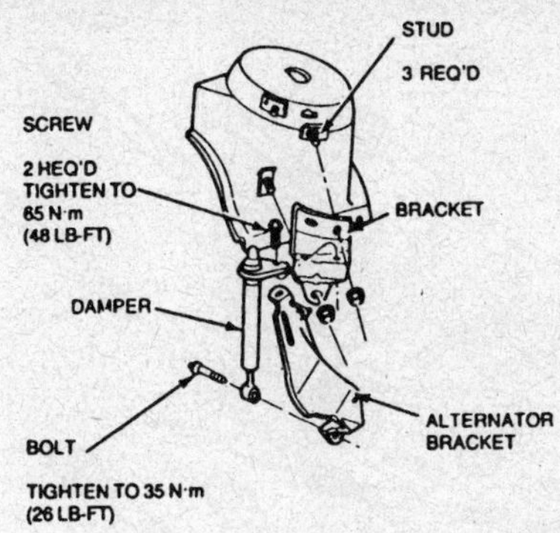


**Fig. 5 RH engine damper assembly**

7. Reverse procedure to install, noting the following.
   a. Lightly lubricate nuts and bolts with suitable oil.
   b. Torque manifold attaching bolts to specifications.
   c. Torque exhaust pipe to manifold attaching nuts to specifications.
   d. Torque EGR tube to specifications.

# CYLINDER HEAD
## REPLACE

**If cylinder head is leaking engine coolant, refer to "Service Bulletins" in this section prior to removing cylinder head.**

1. Relieve fuel system pressure as outlined under "Fuel System Pressure Relief."
2. Rotate crankshaft to 0° TDC of the compression stroke.
3. Disconnect battery ground cable, then drain cooling system.
4. Remove air cleaner outlet tube.
5. Remove intake manifold as described in "Intake Manifold, Replace."
6. Remove accessory drive belt. If right side head is being removed, remove accessory belt idler. If left side head is being removed, remove alternator adjusting arm.
7. **On models w/power steering,** remove pump bracket attaching bolts, then the pump and bracket as an assembly with hoses attached. Position pump and bracket assembly aside in an upright position to prevent leakage of fluid.
8. **On all models,** if left side cylinder head is being removed, remove coil bracket and dipstick tube. If right side cylinder head is being removed, remove ground strap and throttle cable support bracket.
9. Remove exhaust manifolds, then the PCV valve and rocker arm covers.
10. Loosen rocker arm fulcrum bolts enough to allow the rocker arms to be swung aside and the pushrods removed. Keep pushrods in order so they can be installed in original position.
11. Remove cylinder head attaching bolts, then the cylinder head(s) and gasket(s). Discard gaskets(s).
12. Reverse procedure to install, noting the following:
    a. Lightly oil bolt threads prior to installation.
    b. Replace any damaged gasket alignment dowels.
    c. Tighten bolts in sequence shown in **Fig. 8.**
    d. **On 1989 models, torque** bolts in two steps, first to 33-41 ft. lbs., then to 63-73 ft. lbs.
    e. **On 1990-92 models, torque** bolts in two steps, first to 37 ft. lbs., then to 68 ft. lbs.
    f. Prior to installation, dip each pushrod end in oil conditioner D9AZ-19579-C or other suitable heavy engine oil.
    g. Lubricate rocker arm assemblies with oil conditioner D9AZ-19579-C or other suitable heavy engine oil.

# VALVE ARRANGEMENT
## FRONT TO REAR

Right Side.................... I-E-I-E-I-E
Left Side.................... E-I-E-I-E-I

# CAM LOBE LIFT SPECIFICATIONS

Exhaust ...................... .260 inch
Intake ...................... .260 inch

# VALVES
## ADJUST

Hydraulic valve lifters are used in this engine. No adjustment is required.

# HYDRAULIC VALVE LIFTERS
## REPLACE

Before replacing a hydraulic valve lifter for noisy operation, ensure the noise is not caused by improper rocker arm to stem clearance, worn rocker arms, pushrods or valve tips.

1. Disconnect battery ground cable, then drain engine coolant.
2. Remove throttle body, then the spark plug wire routing clips mounted on valve cover attaching bolt studs. Lay spark plug wires with the routing clips attached towards rear of engine.
3. Remove intake manifold as described in "Intake Manifold, Replace."
4. Loosen rocker arm fulcrum attaching bolt(s) a sufficient amount to swing rocker arm aside to allow the pushrod(s) to be removed, then remove pushrod(s). Keep pushrods in order so they can be returned to their original position.
5. Using a suitable magnet, remove lifter(s) from lifter bores. **If the lifters are stuck in their bores by excessive varnish or gum buildup, use tool No. T70L-6500-A or equivalent to remove valve lifters.**
6. Place valve lifters in a rack so they can be installed in their original positions.
7. Reverse procedure to install, noting the following:
   a. Lubricate lifter(s), lifter bores, rocker arms and pushrod(s) with oil conditioner D9AZ-19579-A or suitable heavy engine oil.
   b. Torque bolts to specifications.

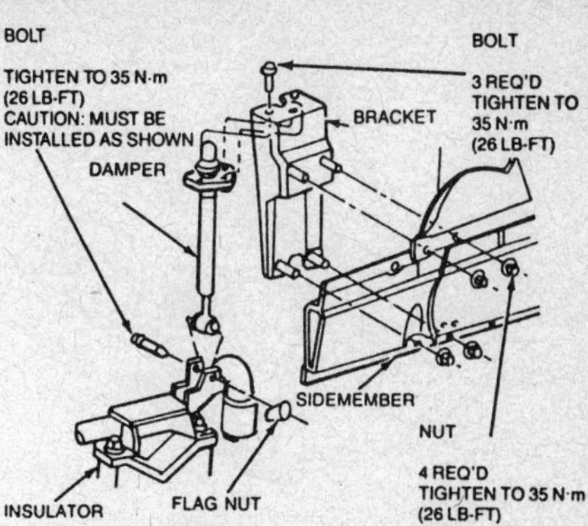


**Fig. 6 LH engine damper assembly**

# ROCKER ARM COVER
## REPLACE

1. Relieve fuel system pressure as outlined under "Fuel System Pressure Relief."
2. Disconnect battery ground cable, then disconnect spark plug wires from spark plugs.
3. Remove spark plug wire separators from rocker arm cover attaching bolt studs.
4. If left side rocker arm cover is being removed, performing the following:
   a. Disconnect crankcase breather hose and remove oil filler cap.
   b. Remove fuel injector harness stand-offs from inboard rocker arm cover studs and position harness out of the way.
5. If right side rocker arm cover is removed, perform the following:
   a. Remove throttle body assembly.
   b. Disconnect EGR tube and heater hoses.
   c. Remove PCV valve and move fuel injector harness out of the way.
6. Remove rocker arm cover attaching bolts, then the cover.
7. Reverse procedure to install, noting the following:
   a. Lightly oil bolt and stud threads prior to installation.
   b. Apply bead of RTV sealant at cylinder head to intake manifold rail step.
   c. Torque rocker arm cover attaching bolts and EGR tube to specifications.

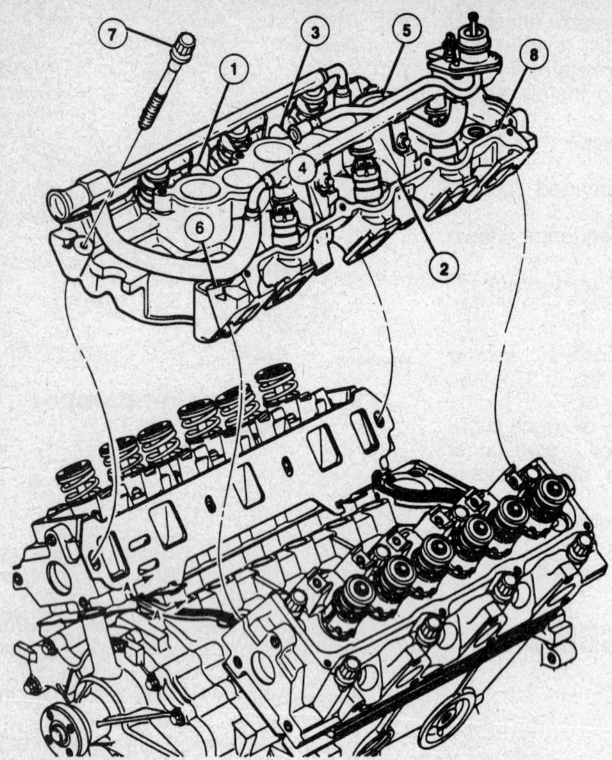

Fig. 7 Intake manifold bolt tightening sequence

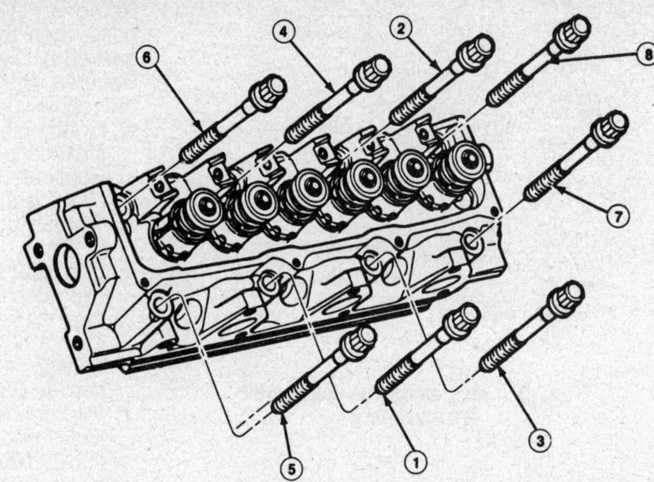

Fig. 8 Cylinder head bolt tightening sequence

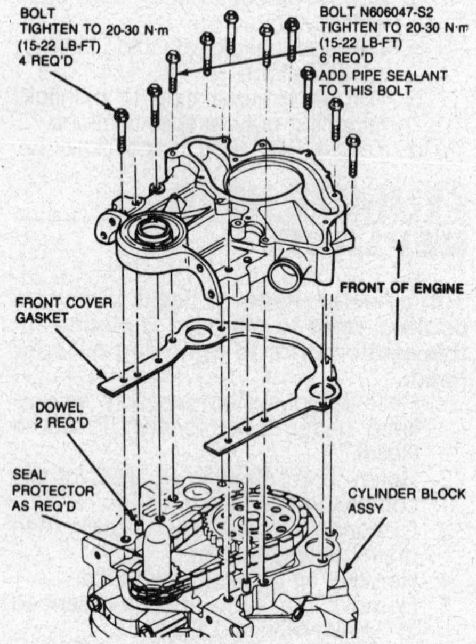


Fig. 9 Front cover removal & installation. 1989

# FRONT OIL SEAL
## REPLACE

1. Loosen accessory drive belts, then remove right front wheel.
2. Remove four crankshaft pulley to damper attaching bolts, then remove accessory drive belt and pulley.
3. Remove vibration damper attaching bolt, then using suitable puller, remove vibration damper.
4. Using flat bladed screwdriver or other suitable tool, pry seal from front timing cover. **Use caution not to damage front cover or crankshaft.**
5. Lubricate replacement seal lip with clean engine oil, then install seal with suitable seal installer.
6. Lubricate inner hub surface of vibration damper with clean engine oil, then apply RTV sealant to keyway of inner hub surface of vibration damper.
7. Install vibration damper. Torque attaching bolt to specification.
8. Install crankshaft pulley. Torque bolts to specifications.
9. Install accessory drive belts, then install right front wheel.
10. Start engine and check for oil leaks.

# FRONT COVER, TIMING CHAIN & SPROCKETS
## REPLACE
### 1989

1. Remove idler pulley and bracket assembly, then the drive and accessory belts.
2. Remove water pump as described elsewhere in this section.
3. Remove crankshaft pulley and damper. Refer to Front Oil Seal, Replace.
4. Remove lower radiator hose, then the oil pan to timing cover bolts.
5. Remove front cover to cylinder block attaching bolts, then remove front cover, **Fig. 9.**
6. Cover oil pan opening to prevent dirt entry, then rotate crankshaft until No. 1 piston is at TDC compression stroke and timing marks are aligned as shown, **Fig. 10.**
7. Remove camshaft sprocket attaching bolt and washer, then slide crankshaft sprocket, timing chain and camshaft sprocket from engine as an assembly.
8. Install replacement camshaft sprocket, timing chain and crankshaft sprocket as an assembly with timing marks aligned, **Fig. 10.**
9. Carefully cut, then remove exposed portion of oil pan gasket. Coat oil pan gasket surface with sealing compound B54-19554-A or equivalent. Cut and position necessary gaskets on oil pan gasket surface and apply sealing compound above, at the corners and on gasket surface.
10. Lubricate replacement seal lip with clean engine oil, then install seal with suitable seal installer. Install front cover, refer to **Fig. 9,** for torque specifications. **Use suitable sealant on front cover bolt which extends through water jacket.**
11. Lubricate inner hub surface of vibration damper with clean engine oil, then apply RTV sealant to keyway of inner hub surface of vibration damper.
12. Reverse steps 1 through 4 to complete installation.

### 1990–92

1. Relieve fuel system pressure as outlined under "Fuel System Pressure Relief."
2. Disconnect battery ground cable, then loosen four water pump pulley bolts with drive belt in place.
3. Loosen alternator belt-adjuster jackscrew to provide sufficient slack in belt for removal.
4. Drain cooling system, then remove lower radiator hose and heater hose from water pump.
5. Remove crankshaft pulley and damp-

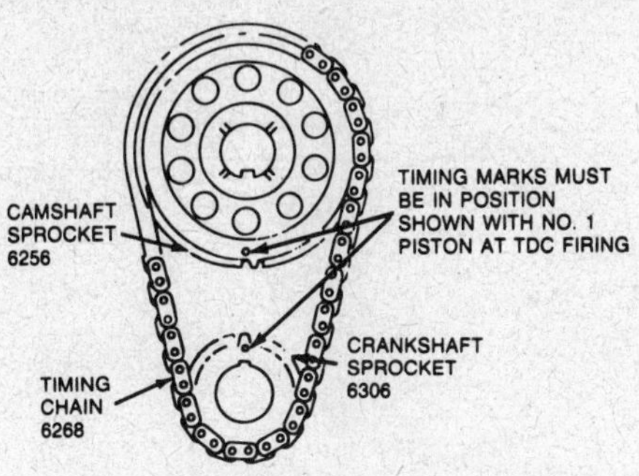


**Fig. 10 Valve timing mark alignment**

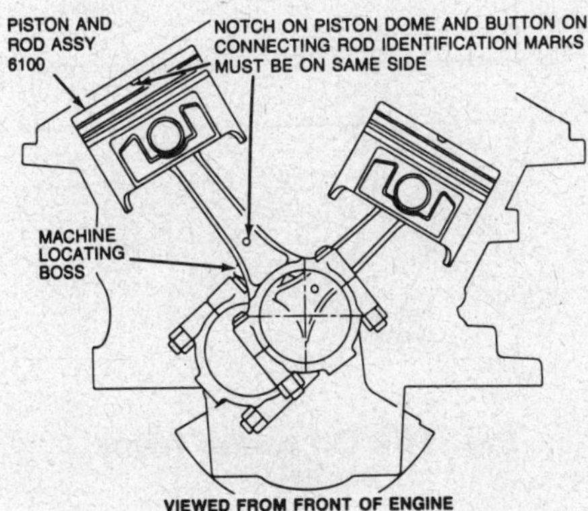


**Fig. 12 Piston & rod assembly**

er as described in "Front Oil Seal, Replace."

6. Drain and remove oil pan as described under "Oil Pan, Replace."
7. Remove timing cover to block retaining bolts, **Fig. 11. Timing cover and water pump may be removed as an assembly by not removing bolts Nos. 11-15 as shown in Fig. 11.**
8. After cover is pulled away from block, remove water pump pulley and bolts.
9. Reverse procedure to install, noting the following:
   a. Carefully clean all gasket material from timing cover and cylinder block. **The aluminum timing cover gouges easily, use care when scraping gasket.**
   b. Inspect timing cover crankshaft seal, replace if necessary.
   c. Before installing bolt Nos. 1, 2 and 3, apply pipe sealant No. D6AZ-19558-A or equivalent.
   d. Tighten front cover bolts to sequence shown in **Fig. 11.**
   e. **On 1990-91 models, torque** bolts 1 through 10 to 19 ft. lbs., then bolts 11 through 15 to 7 ft. lbs.
   f. **On 1992 models, torque** bolts 1 through 10 to 15-22 ft. lbs., then bolts 11 through 15 to 71-106 inch lbs.

## CAMSHAFT
### REPLACE

1. Remove engine from vehicle and mount in suitable work stand.
2. Remove front cover and timing chain as described in " Front Cover, Timing Chain & Sprockets, Replace."
3. Remove intake manifold and hydraulic valve lifters as described in "Hydraulic Valve Lifters, Replace."
4. Remove camshaft thrust plate, then carefully pull camshaft from cylinder block. Use caution to avoid damaging bearings, journals and lobes.
5. Reverse procedure to install, noting the following:
   a. Torque camshaft thrust plate attaching screws to specification.
   b. Lubricate lifters, lifter bores, rocker arms and pushrods with oil conditioner D9AZ-19579-A or suitable heavy engine oil.

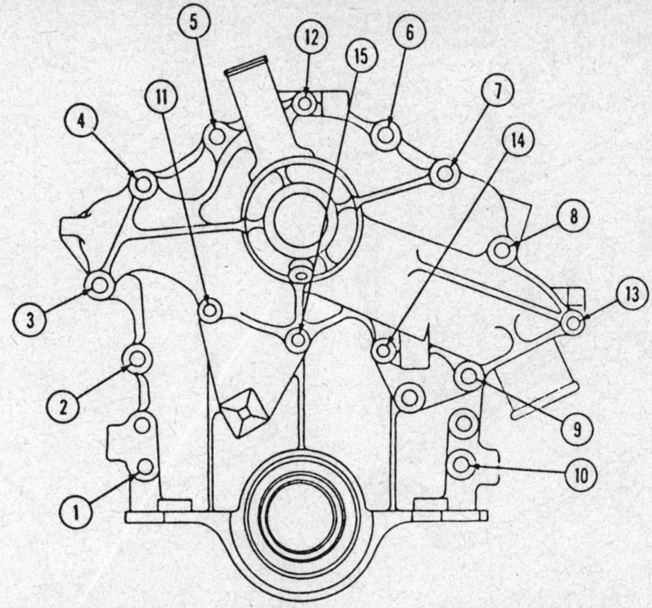

| FASTENER AND HOLE NO. | FASTENERS SIZE | FASTENER APPLICATION |
|---|---|---|
| 1 | M8 x 1.25 x 43.5 | F/C TO BLOCK |
| 2 | M8 x 1.25 x 43.5 | F/C TO BLOCK |
| 3 | M8 x 1.25 x 70 | W/P & F/C TO BLOCK |
| 4 | M8 x 1.25 x 70 | W/P & F/C TO BLOCK |
| 5 | M8 x 1.25 x 42 | F/C TO BLOCK |
| 6 | M8 x 1.25 x 70 | W/P & F/C TO BLOCK |
| 7 | M8 x 1.25 x 70 | W/P & F/C TO BLOCK |
| 8 | M8 x 1.25 x 70 | W/P & F/C TO BLOCK |
| 9 | M8 x 1.25 x 70 | W/P & F/C TO BLOCK |
| 10 | M8 x 1.25 x 42 | F/C TO BLOCK |
| 11 | M6 x 1 x 25 | W/P TO F/C |
| 12 | M6 x 1 x 25 | W/P TO F/C |
| 13 | M6 x 1 x 25 | W/P TO F/C |
| 14 | M6 x 1 x 25 | W/P TO F/C |
| 15 | M6 x 1 x 25 | W/P TO F/C |

W/P — Water Pump Assy
F/C — Front Cover Assy
T/P — Timing Pointer

**Fig. 11 Removing timing cover & water pump. 1990–92**

## MAIN BEARINGS

Main bearings are available in standard sizes and undersizes of .001, .002, .010, .020, .030 and .040 inch.

## CRANKSHAFT REAR OIL SEAL
### REPLACE

1. Remove transaxle, then the flywheel.
2. Remove rear cover plate.
3. Using a suitable tool, punch a hole into the seal metal surface between the lip and block. Using slide hammer, Tool No. T77L-9533-B or equivalent, remove seal.
4. Coat crankshaft seal area and seal lip with engine oil, then using tool No. T82L-6701-A, install seal.
5. Install rear cover plate and two dowels.
6. Install flywheel. Torque bolts to specifications.

## PISTON & ROD ASSEMBLY

Assemble the rod to the piston with the notch on the piston dome on the same

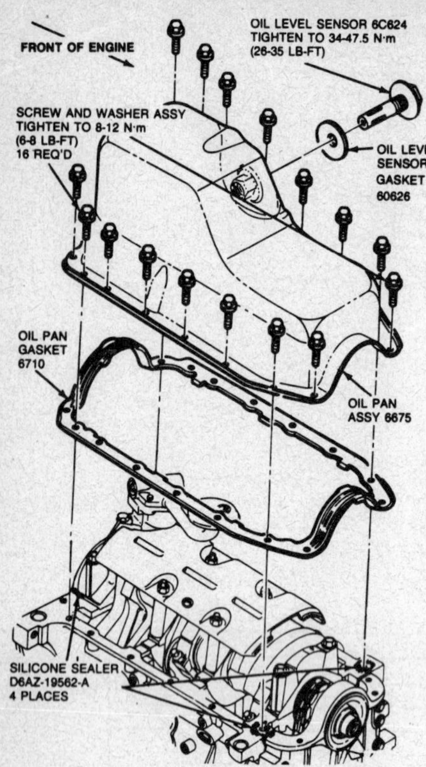


Fig. 13 Oil pan

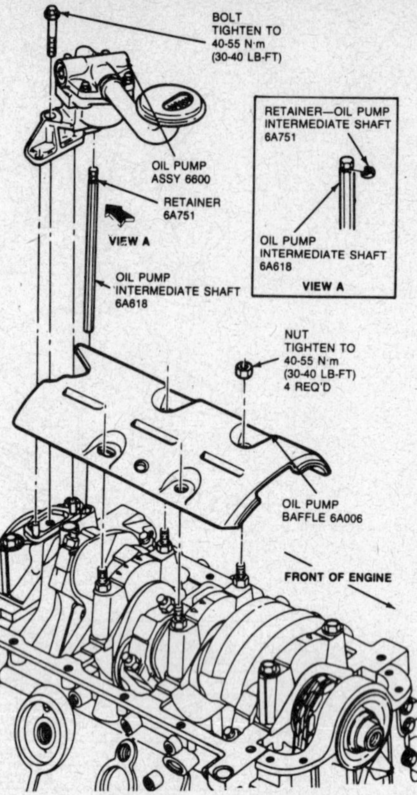


Fig. 14 Oil pump removal

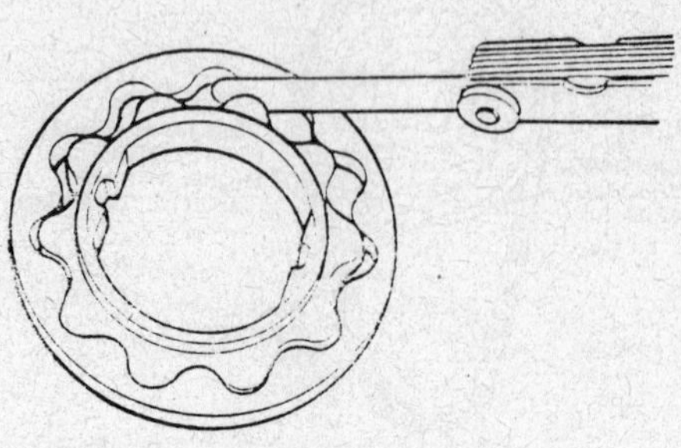

Fig. 15 Oil pump tip clearance

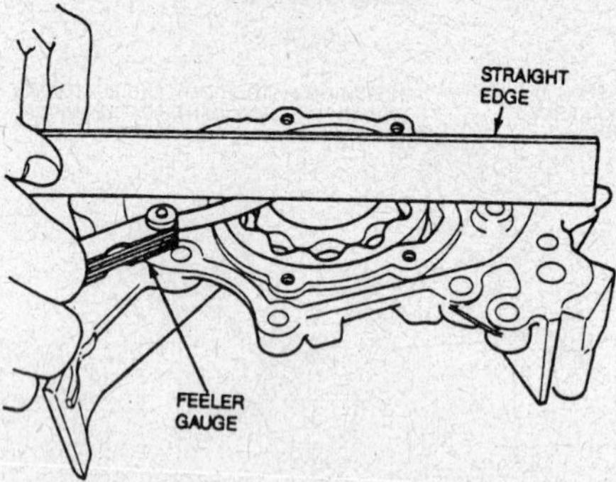


Fig. 16 Oil pump rotor endplay

side as the button on the connecting rod identification marks. Assemble piston and rod assembly in engine with notch in dome facing front of engine, **Fig. 12.**

After installation, check connecting rod big end side clearance. Clearance should be .006-.014 inch.

## OIL PAN
### REPLACE

1. Relieve fuel system pressure as outlined under "Fuel System Pressure Relief."
2. Disconnect battery ground cable, then remove oil dipstick, then raise and support vehicle.
3. **On models with low oil level sensor,** remove retainer clip at sensor and disconnect sensor electrical connector.
4. **On all models,** drain crankcase.
5. Remove starter motor, then disconnect Exhaust Gas Oxygen (EGO) sensor electrical connector.
6. Remove head pipe and catalytic converter assembly.
7. Remove lower engine/flywheel dust cover from converter/flywheel housing.
8. Remove oil pan to cylinder block and front cover attaching screws, **Fig. 13,** then the oil pan and gasket.
9. Reverse procedure to install, noting the following:
   a. Apply 1/8 inch bead of suitable silicone sealer to junction of front and rear main bearing caps with cylinder block, prior to installing new gasket.
   b. Torque oil pan bolts to specifications and low oil level sensor (if equipped) to specifications.

## OIL PUMP
### REPLACE

1. Remove oil pan as described in "Oil Pan, Replace."
2. Remove oil pump attaching bolts, **Fig. 14.**
3. Remove oil pump and intermediate shaft.
4. If necessary, pull intermediate shaft from oil pump.
5. Reverse procedure to install, when installing intermediate shaft into replacement pump ensure shaft retainer clicks into position.

## OIL PUMP INSPECTION

1. Wash all parts in suitable solvent, then dry with compressed air.
2. Ensure all dirt and particles are removed.
3. Inspect inner pump housing for wear or damage.
4. Inspect pump cover mating surface for wear, scuff marks are normal, if surface is worn or grooved, replace pump assembly.
5. Inspect rotor for nicks, burrs or score marks, remove imperfections with suitable oil stone.
6. Using suitable feeler gauge, measure inner tip to outer rotor tip clearance, **Fig. 15,** clearance on 1989 models, should not exceed .010 inch, clearance on 1990-91 models, should not exceed .012 inch, on 1992 models, clearance should be .0024-.0071 inch.
7. Install suitable straightedge, then using feeler gauge, measure rotor endplay, **Fig. 16,** on 1989-91 models, clearance should not exceed .005 inch, on 1992 models, clearance should be .0012-.0035 inch.
8. If any inspection is not as indicated, replace oil pump assembly.

## BELT TENSION DATA

| Belt | New, Lbs | Used, Lbs. |
|---|---|---|
| 5-Rib | 140-160 | 110-130 |
| 6-Rib | ① | ① |

①—Auto tensioner.

## SERPENTINE DRIVE BELTS

### BELT ROUTING

Refer to **Fig. 17.** for serpentine drive belt routing.

### BELT, REPLACE

#### Less Auto Tensioner

1. Disconnect battery ground cable.
2. Loosen adjusting arm and pivot bolts.
3. Turn alternator belt adjusting screw

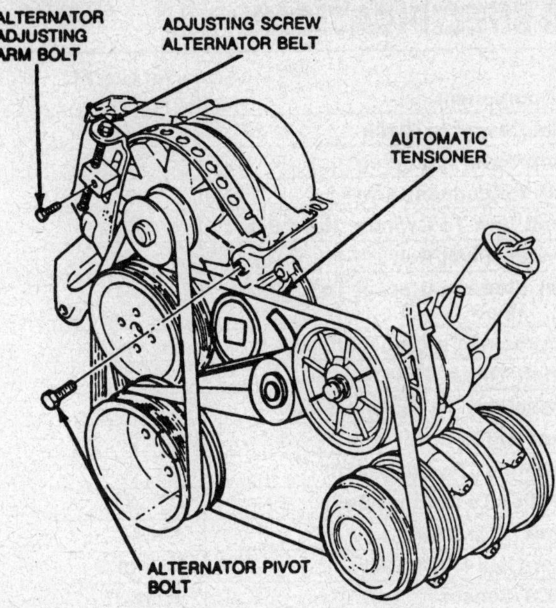


**Fig. 17 Serpentine drive belt routing**

counterclockwise, until belt can be removed.
4. Reverse procedure to install.

### With Auto Tensioner

1. Disconnect battery ground cable.
2. Install suitable 1/2 inch flex handle in square hole in tensioner.
3. Rotate tensioner counterclockwise, then remove belt.
4. Reverse procedure to install.

## COOLING SYSTEM BLEED

These engine do not require a specific bleed procedure. After filling cooling system, run engine to operating temperature with radiator/pressure cap off. Air will then be automatically bled through cap opening.

## THERMOSTAT REPLACE

### REMOVAL

1. Drain cooling system below level of upper radiator hose.
2. Remove upper radiator hose, then three retaining bolts from thermostat housing.
3. Remove housing and thermostat as an assembly, discarding old gasket. Clean sealing surfaces with gasket scraper. Ensure not to gouge aluminum surfaces as these gouges may form leaks.

### INSTALLATION

1. Install thermostat into housing, ensuring that jiggle valve in relation to housing.
2. Position gasket onto housing using bolts as holding device, then install housing assembly and retaining bolts.
3. Install upper radiator hose. Refer to "Bleeding Cooling System," fill and bleed cooling system with recommended amount and mixture.
4. Start engine and check for leaks.

## WATER PUMP REPLACE

1. Relieve fuel system pressure as outlined under "Fuel System Pressure Relief."
2. Disconnect battery ground cable, then drain cooling system.
3. Loosen accessory drive belt idler, then remove drive belts, then remove accessory drive belt idler bracket from engine.
4. Disconnect heater hose from water pump.
5. Remove water pump pulley to pump hub attaching bolts. **The pump pulley cannot be removed at this time due to insufficient clearance between body and pump.**
6. Remove 11 water pump attaching bolts, **Fig. 11,** then lift the water pump and pulley assembly up and out of vehicle and remove pulley.
7. Lightly lubricate all bolts and stud threads with oil.
8. Position pulley on replacement pump, then install pump/pulley assembly. Tighten attaching bolts in sequence shown in **Fig. 11,** to specifications as outlined under "Front Cover, Timing Chain & Sprockets."
9. Install water pump pulley to pump hub attaching bolts and torque to specifications.
10. Reverse steps 1 through 4 to complete installation.

## FUEL PUMP REPLACE

1. Relieve fuel system pressure as outlined under "Fuel System Pressure Relief."
2. Disconnect battery ground cable.
3. Remove fuel from fuel tank by pumping fuel out of fuel filler neck.
4. Raise and support vehicle.
5. Disconnect then remove fuel filler neck.
6. Support fuel tank, then remove tank support straps. Lower fuel tank partially and remove fuel lines, electrical connectors and vent lines from tank. Remove tank and place on suitable workbench.
7. Turn fuel pump locking ring counterclockwise and remove locking ring.
8. Remove fuel pump, bracket and gasket assembly.
9. Reverse procedure to install.

## TIGHTENING SPECIFICATIONS

| Year | Component | Torque/Ft. Lbs. |
|---|---|---|
| 1989–92 | A/C Compressor to Block | 35 |
| | A/C Compressor Mounting | 35 |
| | Alternator Adjustment Arm | 27 |
| | Alternator Adjustment Arm To Cylinder Head Bolt | 35 |
| | Alternator Pivot Bolt | 43 |
| | Auto Tensioner/Power Steering Bracket To Cylinder Head | 35 |
| | Camshaft Sprocket To Camshaft | 46 |
| | Camshaft Thrust Plate | 7 |
| | Coil & Bracket Assembly To Cylinder Head | 35 |
| | Connecting Rod Nut | 26 |
| | Crankshaft Damper To Crankshaft | ④ |
| | Crankshaft Pulley To Damper Bolts | ⑤ |
| | Cylinder Head Bolt | ① |
| | Distributor Hold-Down Bolt | 18 |
| | ECT Sensor | 12-17 |
| | EGR Spacer To Intake Manifold Bolt | 18 |
| | EGR Tube To EGR Valve & Exhaust Manifold | ⑥ |
| | EGR Valve To Throttle Body | 18 |
| | Engine Mounts | ① |
| | Exhaust Manifold | 19 |
| | Flywheel To Crankshaft | 59 |
| | Fuel Rail To Intake Manifold | 7 |
| | Front Cover | ① |
| | Intake Manifold To Cylinder Head | ① |
| | Low Level Oil Sensor | ⑦ |
| | Main Bearing Cap | ⑧ |
| | Oil Drain Plug | 10 |
| | Oil Indicator Tube To Exhaust Manifold | 13 |
| | Oil Inlet Tube To Cylinder Block | 15-22 |
| | Oil Inlet To Main Bearing Cap | 30-40 |
| | Oil Insert To Cylinder Block | 25 |
| | Oil Pan To Cylinder Block | ⑨ |
| | Power Steering Bracket To Cylinder Head Bolt | 29-41 |
| | Rocker Arm Cover To Cylinder Head Bolt | ⑨ |
| | Rocker Arm Fulcrum To Cylinder Head Bolt | ③ |
| | Spark Knock Sensor | 29-40 |
| | Spark Plug To Cylinder Head | 5-11 |
| | Tensioner Locknut | 25-37 |
| | Thermostat Housing | 6-9 |
| | Throttle Body To Intake Manifold | 19 |
| | Timing Cover To Cylinder Block | 19 |
| | Water Pump Pulley To Hub | ⑩ |
| | Water Pump To Front Cover | ② |

①—Refer to text.
②—1989–91, 6–8 ft. lbs., 1992, 71–106 inch lbs.
③—1989, first step, tighten to 5.1–11 ft. lbs.; second step, ighten to 20–28 ft. lbs. 1990–91, first step, tighten to 8 ft. lbs.; second step, tighten to 24 ft. lbs. 1992, first step, tighten to 5–11 ft. lbs.; second step, tighten to 19–28 ft. lbs.
④—1989, 141–169 ft. lbs., 1990–91, 107 ft. lbs., 1992, 93–121 ft. lbs.
⑤—1989–90, 26 ft. lbs., 1991–92, 37 ft. lbs.
⑥—1989–91, 37 ft. lbs., 1992, 26–48 ft. lbs.
⑦—1989–90, 26–35 ft. lbs., 1991–92, 20–30 ft. lbs.
⑧—1989–90, 63–69 ft. lbs., 1991–92, 55–63 ft. lbs.
⑨—1989–90, 80–106 inch lbs., 1991, 7–9 ft. lbs., 1992, 8–10 ft. lbs.
⑩—1989–90, 12–19 tf. lbs., 1991, 26 ft. lbs., 1992, 15–22 ft. lbs.

# 3.0L/V6-182 SHO Engine

**NOTE: On Vehicles Equipped With Airbags, Disarm Airbag System As Outlined Under "Airbag System Disarming" Before Any Diagnosis, Testing, Troubleshooting Or Repairs Are Performed. After All Diagnosis, Testing, Troubleshooting Or Repairs Have Been Completed, Rearm Airbag System As Outlined Under "Airbag System Disarming."**

## INDEX



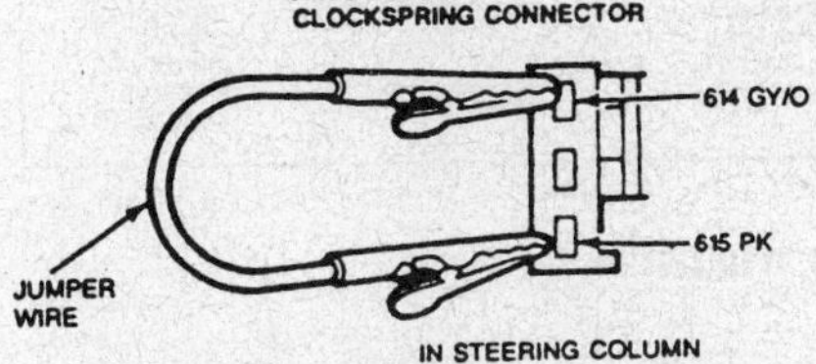


**Fig. 1 Airbag jumper wire. Except 1992**

## AIRBAG SYSTEM DISARMING

### EXCEPT 1992 MODELS

1. Disconnect battery ground cable, then open glove compartment down past its stops.
2. Disconnect electrical connector from backup power supply, located to the right of the glove compartment opening.
3. Remove four nut and washer assemblies securing driver air bag module to steering wheel.
4. Disconnect air bag electrical connector, then attach a jumper wire between air bag terminals on clockspring, **Fig. 1.** If necessary, reconnect battery and backup power supply.
5. To reactivate, disconnect battery ground cable and backup power supply, then reverse remainder of deactivation procedure. **Torque** airbag module to steering wheel attaching nut assemblies to 35-53 inch lbs.

### 1992 MODELS

1. Disconnect positive battery cable, wait one minute, then proceed to step 2.
2. Remove four airbag module to steering wheel attaching nuts and washers.
3. Disconnect airbag electrical connector.
4. Install Rotunda airbag simulator tool No. 105-00008 or equivalent, to clockspring to simulate airbag, **Fig. 2.**
5. Reconnect positive battery terminal.
6. Reverse procedure to activate system. **Torque** airbag module attaching nuts to 36-49 inch lbs. Turn ignition switch from Off to Run, airbag indicator will light for about six seconds, if light remains lite, does not light or flashes, airbag system failure is indicated.

## FUEL SYSTEM PRESSURE RELIEF

**Fuel supply lines will remain pressurized for long periods of time after engine shut-down. This pressure must be relieved before any service is attempted. A valve is provided on the fuel rail assembly for this purpose. To relieve system pressure, remove air cleaner assembly and connect pressure gauge tool No. T80L-9974-A or T80L-9974-B or equivalent onto fuel valve on fuel rail assembly. To pressurize fuel system, proceed as follows:**

1. Install pressure gauge tool No. T80L-9974-A or T80L-9974-B equivalent onto fuel rail pressure fitting.
2. Turn ignition switch to On position for 3 seconds, repeatedly 5 to 10 times until pressure gauge indicates 13 psi.

## ENGINE MOUNTS REPLACE

### LH INSULATOR & SUPPORT ASSEMBLY

1. Remove bolt attaching roll damper, then position aside.
2. Remove back-up lamp switch, then the energy management bracket.
3. Raise and support vehicle.

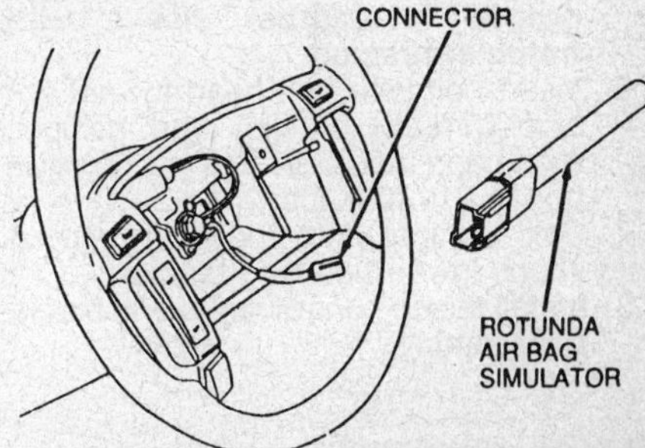


**Fig. 2 Airbag simulator. 1992**

4. Remove left front tire and wheel assembly, then support transaxle using suitable jack and block of wood.
5. Remove nuts attaching lower damper bracket to engine mount, **Fig. 3.**
6. Remove insulator to subframe through bolts, then raise transaxle enough to unload insulator.
7. Remove insulator and lower damper bracket.
8. Reverse procedure to install.

### RH FRONT OR REAR INSULATOR

1. Remove lower damper attaching bolt from RH side of engine, **Fig. 3.**
2. Raise and support vehicle, then place suitable jack and block of wood under engine.
3. Remove nuts attaching roll damper to engine mount, then the roll damper.
4. Raise engine enough to unload insulator.
5. Remove two attaching bolts, then insulator from engine bracket.
6. Reverse procedure to install.

## ENGINE DAMPER REPLACE

### RIGHTHAND DAMPER

**Do not clamp damper tube or piston rod.**

1. Remove nuts retaining lower end of

damper to engine bracket.

2. Remove bolts retaining upper damper bracket to shock tower bracket.
3. Remove engine damper.
4. Position engine damper lower sleeve to line up with engine bracket notch, secure with new nut. **Torque** to 21-30 ft. lbs.
5. Position engine damper with upper bracket to shock tower bracket, secure with new nut. **Torque** to 40-55 ft. lbs.

### LEFTHAND DAMPER

**Do not clamp damper tube or piston rod.**

1. Remove speed control servo and bracket assembly.
2. Remove bolt and flag nut retaining lower end of damper to No. 1A engine mount retaining bracket.
3. Remove bolts retaining upper damper bracket to side rail bracket.
4. Remove engine damper.
5. Insert lower end of damper into engine mount retaining bracket, **align groove in damper sleeve with notch in bracket.**
6. Insert bolt with bolt head toward engine through bracket and damper, then hand start new flag nut. **Torque** bolt to 21-30 ft. lbs.
7. Pull damper into position against shock tower mounting bracket.
8. Install speed control servo and bracket assembly.

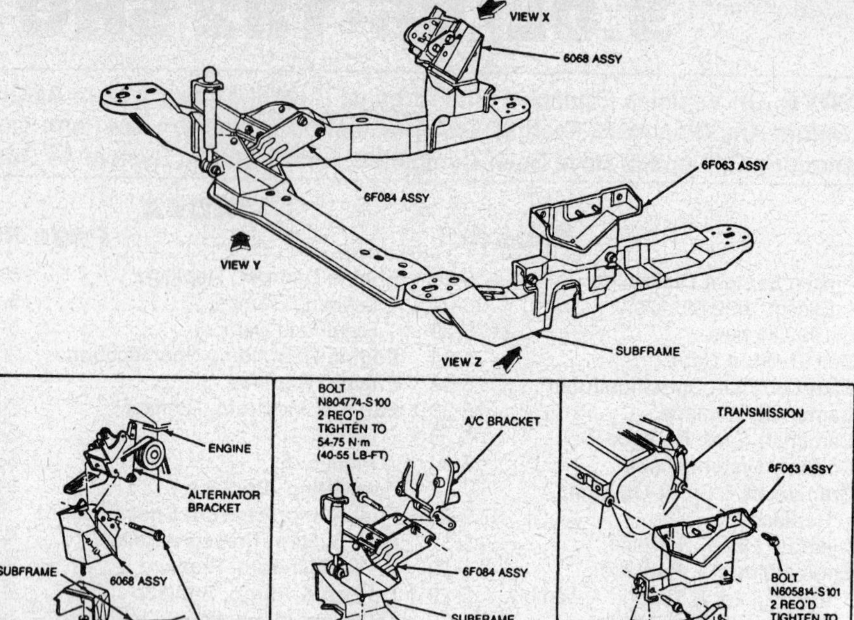


**Fig. 3 Engine mounts**

## ENGINE
## REPLACE

1. Relieve fuel system pressure as outlined under "Fuel System Pressure Relief."
2. Disconnect battery ground cable, then drain cooling system.
3. Remove battery and battery tray assembly.
4. Disconnect under hood lamp electrical connector, then mark position of hood hinges and remove hood.
5. Remove oil dipstick tube, then disconnect alternator to voltage regulator wiring harness.
6. Remove radiator upper sight shield, discharge A/C system, then remove radiator coolant reservoir assembly.
7. Remove integrated relay controller.
8. Remove air cleaner hose assembly and upper radiator hose.
9. Disconnect electric fan and shroud, then remove lower radiator hose and radiator assembly.
10. Bleed fuel system, then disconnect fuel hoses.
11. Remove power steering reservoir and position aside.
12. Disconnect reservoir hose from power steering pump.
13. Disconnect throttle linkage, then vacuum and heater hoses.
14. Disconnect electrical connector from harness on rear of engine.
15. Remove belts from A/C compressor, alternator and power steering pump.
16. Disconnect cycling switch on top of suction accumulator/drier.
17. Disconnect A/C line at dash panel, then remove accumulator and bracket assembly.
18. Remove alternator assembly, then disconnect A/C discharge hose.
19. Remove A/C compressor and bracket assembly.
20. Raise and support vehicle.
21. Drain engine oil and remove oil filter.
22. Remove wheel and tires assemblies, then disconnect oil level sensor electrical connector.
23. Remove RH lower ball joint, tie rod end and stabilizer bar.
24. Remove center support bearing bracket, then RH CV joint from transaxle.
25. Disconnect heater exhaust gas oxygen sensor assembly.
26. Remove four exhaust catalyst to engine retaining bolts.
27. Remove starter mounting bolts, then starter assembly.
28. Remove lower transaxle mounting bolts, then engine mount to sub-frame attaching nuts.
29. Remove crankshaft pulley assembly, then lower vehicle.
30. Remove upper transaxle mounting bolts.
31. Install suitable engine lifting equipment.
32. Remove engine assembly.
33. Reverse procedure to install.

## INTAKE MANIFOLD
## REPLACE

1. Relieve fuel system pressure as outlined under "Fuel System Pressure Relief."
2. Drain cooling system, then disconnect battery ground cable.
3. Disconnect electrical connectors and vacuum lines from intake assembly, then remove air cleaner tube, then disconnect coolant lines and cables from throttle body.
4. Remove upper intake attaching bolts and upper intake brackets, then loosen four lower bolts and remove brackets.
5. Remove 12 intake manifold attaching bolts, **Fig. 4.**
6. Remove intake assembly and gaskets.
7. Reverse procedure to install, noting the following:
   a. Intake gasket is reuseable.
   b. Torque 12 manifold retaining bolts to specification.
   c. When installing manifold brackets, bracket with stud must be installed in same location from which it was removed, **Fig. 5.**

## EXHAUST MANIFOLD
## REPLACE

### LEFT SIDE

1. Relieve fuel system pressure as outlined under "Fuel System Pressure Relief."

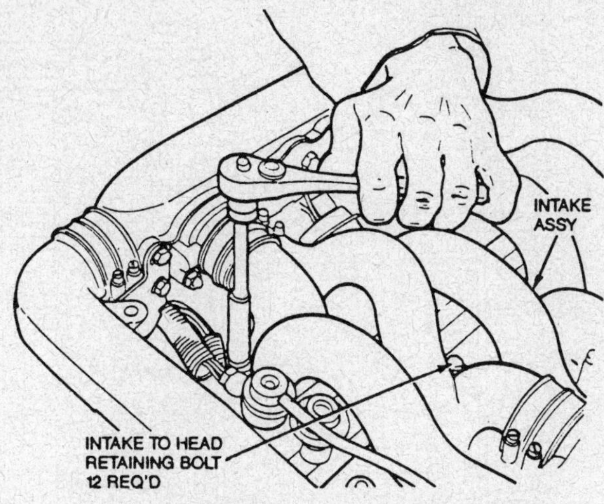


**Fig. 4 Removing intake bolts**

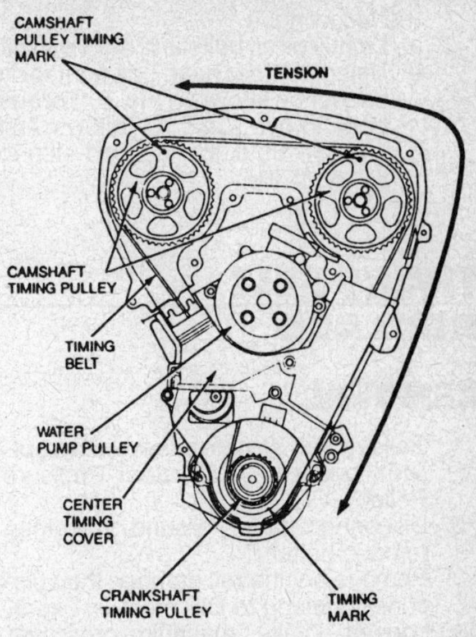


**Fig. 6 Timing mark alignment**

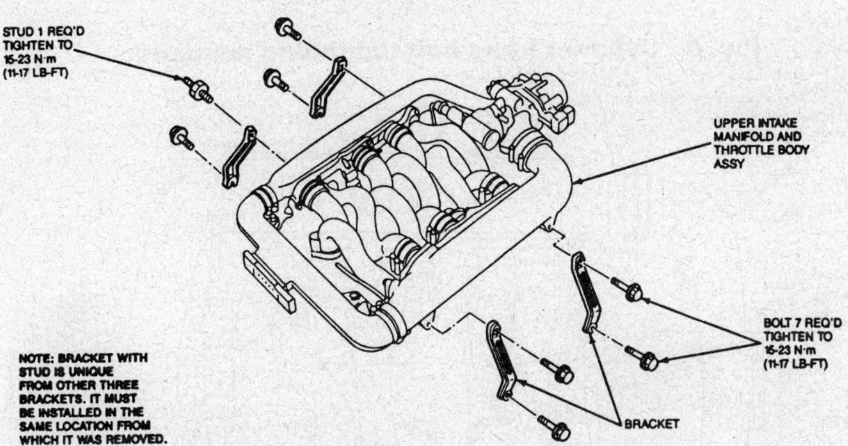


**Fig. 5 Upper intake manifold assembly**

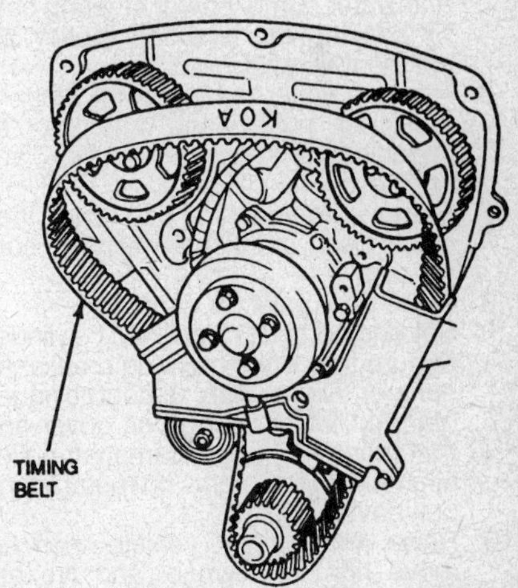


**Fig. 7 Installing timing belt**

2. Remove oil dipstick tube support bracket and power steering pressure and return hoses.
3. Remove exhaust pipe to manifold attaching nuts, then heat shield attaching bolts.
4. Remove exhaust manifold attaching nuts, then the manifold.
5. Reverse procedure to install, noting the following:
   a. Lightly lubricate bolts and nuts with oil.
   b. Torque manifold attaching nuts to specifications.
   c. Torque heat shield attaching bolts to specifications.
   d. Torque exhaust pipe attaching nuts to specifications.

### RIGHT SIDE

1. Remove right cylinder head as described in "Cylinder Head, Replace."
2. Remove heat shield attaching bolts.
3. Remove exhaust manifold attaching nuts, then the manifold.
4. Reverse procedure to install, noting the following:
   a. Lightly lubricate bolts and nuts with oil.
   b. Torque manifold attaching nuts to specifications.
   c. Torque heat shield attaching bolts to specifications.
   d. Install right cylinder as described in "Cylinder Head, Replace."

## CYLINDER HEAD REPLACE

1. Relieve fuel system pressure as outlined under "Fuel System Pressure Relief."
2. Disconnect battery ground cable, then drain cooling system.
3. Remove air cleaner assembly and outlet tube, then remove intake manifold as described previously.
4. Remove drive belts, then upper timing belt cover.
5. Remove LH idler pulley and bracket assembly.
6. Raise and support vehicle, then remove RH wheel and inner fender splash shield.
7. Remove crankshaft damper pulley, then lower timing belt cover.
8. Align timing marks as shown, **Fig. 6.**
9. Release tension on timing belt by loosening tensioner attaching nut, then rotate tensioner with a hex head wrench.
10. Lower vehicle until wheels touch and keep supported on hoist.
11. Disconnect crankshaft sensor wiring assembly, then the center cover.
12. Remove timing belt, ensure location of KOA on timing belt for proper installation, **Fig. 7.**
13. Remove cylinder head covers.
14. Remove camshaft timing pulleys.
15. Remove upper rear and center timing belt covers.
16. If left side head is being removed, remove coil bracket and dipstick tube. If right side head is being removed, remove coolant outlet hose.
17. Remove exhaust manifold on left cylinder head. On right cylinder head, ensure exhaust manifold is removed with the head.
18. Reverse procedure to install, noting

the following:
a. Lightly oil all bolts and nuts with oil.
b. Using cylinder head bolt tightening sequence shown in **Fig. 8. Torque** bolts in two steps as follows; first step 37-50 ft. lbs., second step to 62-68 ft. lbs.

## TIMING BELT REPLACE

### REMOVAL

1. Relieve fuel system pressure as outlined under "Fuel System Pressure Relief."
2. Disconnect battery ground cable, then remove battery.
3. Remove engine roll damper, then disconnect wiring to DIS module, **Fig. 9.**
4. Loosen intake manifold crossover tube hose clamps.
5. Remove alternator/air conditioning and water pump/power steering belts by backing out tensioner pulley adjustment screws.
6. Remove water pump/power steering tensioner pulley and alternator/air conditioning tensioner pulley and bracket.
7. Remove upper timing belt cover, then disconnect crankshaft sensor connectors.
8. Place gear selector in neutral.
9. Set engine to TDC on No. 1 cylinder. Ensure that white mark on crankshaft damper aligns with 0 degree index mark on lower timing belt cover and that marks on intake camshaft pulley align with index marks on metal timing belt cover, **Fig. 10.**
10. Raise and support vehicle, then remove righthand wheel and tire assembly.
11. Loosen fender splash shield and position out of the way.
12. Using puller tool No. T67L-3600-A, adapter tool No. D80L-630-3 and screws tool No. T89P-6701-A or equivalent, remove crankshaft damper.
13. Remove lower and center timing belt covers, then disconnect crankshaft sensor wire and grommet from slot in cover and stud on water pump.
14. Loosen timing belt tensioner, rotate pulley 180° clockwise and tighten tensioner nut to hold pulley in "unload" position, **Fig. 11.**
15. Lower vehicle and remove timing belt.

### INSTALLATION

**Do not let new timing belt come in contact with gasoline, oil, water or coolant prior to installation.**

1. Ensure engine is at TDC on No. 1 cylinder. Check that camshaft pulley marks line up with index marks on upper steel belt cover and that crankshaft pulley aligns with index mark on oil pump housing, **Fig. 12.**

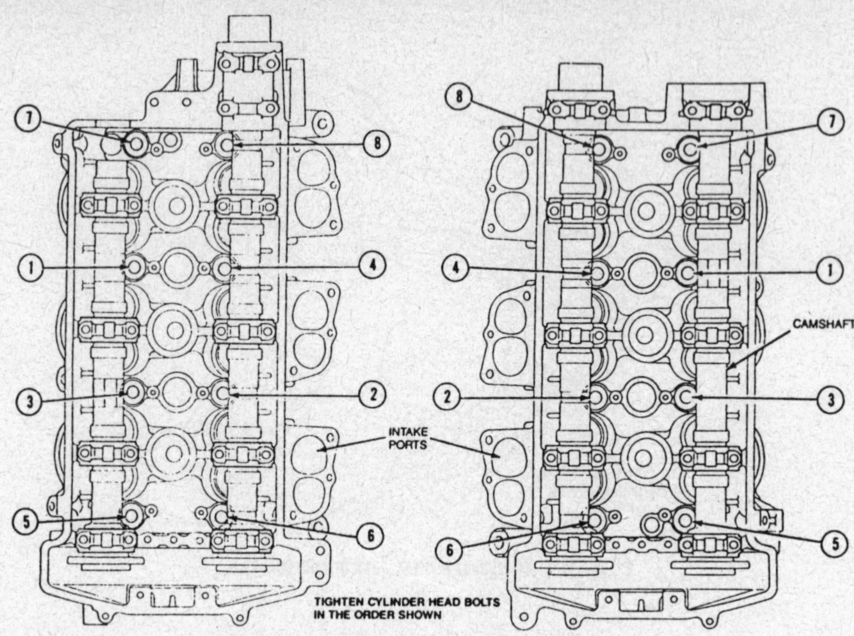


**Fig. 8 Cylinder head bolt tightening sequence**

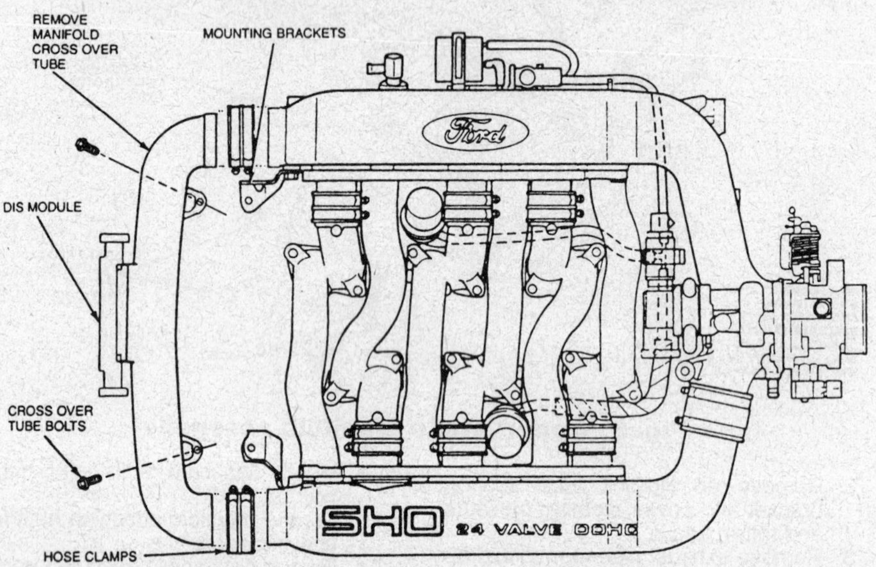


**Fig. 9 Intake manifold assembly**

2. Install timing belt on crankshaft pulley and route to camshaft pulley as shown in **Fig. 7.** Ensure yellow lines on belt are aligned with index marks on pulleys.
3. Release tensioner locknut and leave nut loose, then raise and support vehicle.
4. Install center timing belt cover, connect crankshaft sensor wire and install grommet in slot. Ensure wire is routed properly, torque bolts to specifications.
5. Install lower timing belt cover, torque bolts to specifications.
6. Install crankshaft damper, then rotate crankshaft two revolutions in the clockwise direction until yellow mark on damper aligns with 0 degree mark on lower timing belt cover.
7. Remove plastic access door on lower timing belt cover, torque tensioner locknut to specification.
8. Rotate crankshaft 60° more in clockwise direction until white mark on damper aligns with 0 degree index mark on lower timing cover.
9. Lower vehicle, check that marks on camshaft pulleys align with marks on rear metal timing belt cover, **Fig. 10.**
10. Route crankshaft sensor wiring and connect with engine wiring harness.
11. Install upper timing belt cover, torque bolts to specifications.
12. Install water pump/power steering and alternator/air conditioning tensioner pulleys and torque to specifications.
13. Install drive belts and set tension according to specifications, refer to "Belt

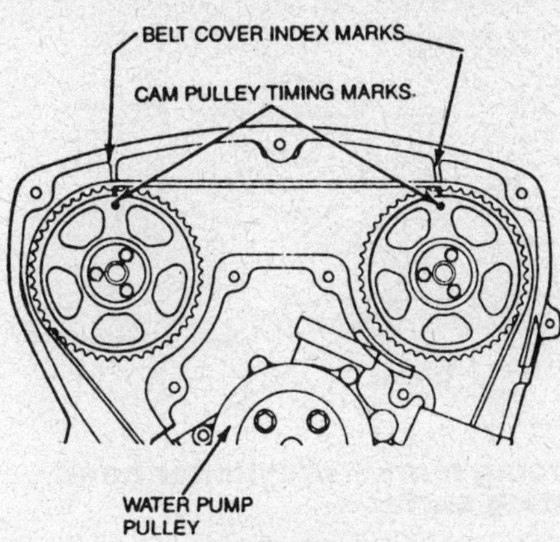


**Fig. 10 Camshaft timing mark alignment**

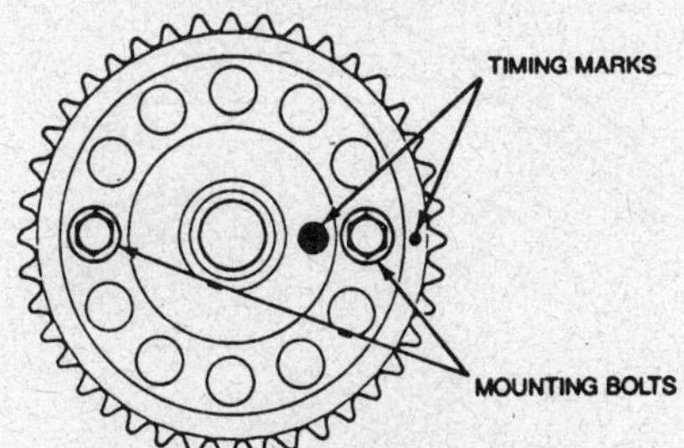


**Fig. 13 Chain sprocket alignment marks**

Tension Data." Torque idler pulley nuts to specification.

14. Install intake manifold cross over tube, torque bolts to specification.
15. Install engine roll damper and battery, then connect battery cables and raise vehicle.
16. Install splash shield, tire and wheel assembly, then lower vehicle.

# CAMSHAFT

## REPLACE

1. Place engine to TDC on No. 1 cylinder.
2. Remove intake manifold as described under "Intake Manifold, Replace."
3. Remove timing belt as described under "Timing Belt, Replace."
4. Remove cylinder head covers.
5. Remove camshaft pulleys, noting location of dowel pins.
6. Remove upper rear timing belt cover.
7. Loosen camshaft bearing caps uniformly. **If camshaft bearing caps are not loosened uniformly camshaft damage may result.**
8. Remove bearing caps, noting their position for proper installation.
9. Remove camshaft chain tensioner attaching bolts, then remove camshaft together with chain and tensioner.
10. Remove and discard oil seal.
11. Remove chain sprocket from camshaft.
12. Reverse procedure to install, noting the following:
    a. When installing chain sprockets, align timing marks on sprockets with camshaft as shown in **Fig. 13.**

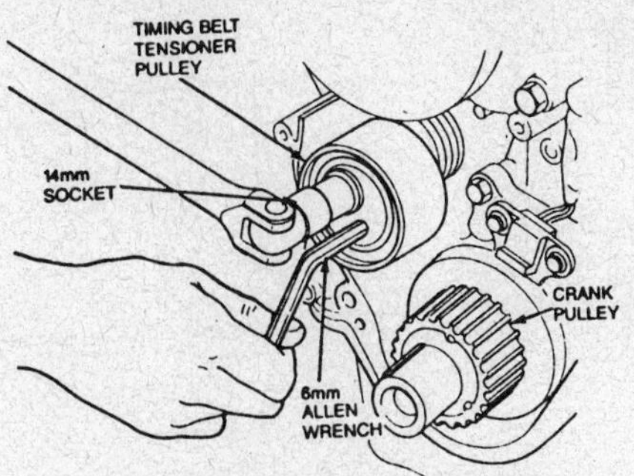


**Fig. 11 Timing belt removal**

Tighten attaching bolts to specifications.

b. Align white painted link with timing mark on sprocket, **Fig. 14.**
c. Rotate camshaft approximately 60 degrees counterclockwise and install chain tensioners. **LH and RH chain tensioners are not interchangeable.**
d. Lubricate camshaft journals with suitable lubricant.
e. Using tightening sequence shown in **Fig. 15,** torque bearing caps in two steps to specification.
f. Tighten chain tensioner to specifications, then rotate camshafts 60° clockwise to ensure proper alignment of timing marks. Marks on camshaft sprockets should align with cylinder mating surfaces as shown in **Fig. 16.**
g. Set camshaft positioning tool No. T89P-6256-C or equivalent on camshafts to check for correct positioning as shown in **Fig. 17.** Flats on tool should align with flats on camshaft. If tool does not line up, repeat installation procedure.

# CAMSHAFT SEAL

## REPLACE

1. Set engine to TDC on No. 1 cylinder.
2. Remove timing belt upper cover as described under "Timing Belt, Replace."
3. Remove timing belt from camshaft pulleys.
4. Remove crankshaft pulleys, noting location of dowel pins.
5. Using seal puller tool No. T78P-3504-N or equivalent, remove camshaft seal.
6. Reverse procedure to install, applying silicone sealer D6AZ-19562-A or equivalent to new seal outer diameter and seal seating surface prior to installation.

# CAM LOBE LIFT SPECIFICATIONS

| | |
|---|---|
| Exhaust | .315inch |
| Intake | .335inch |

# VALVES

## ADJUST

The valves are adjusted by the use of

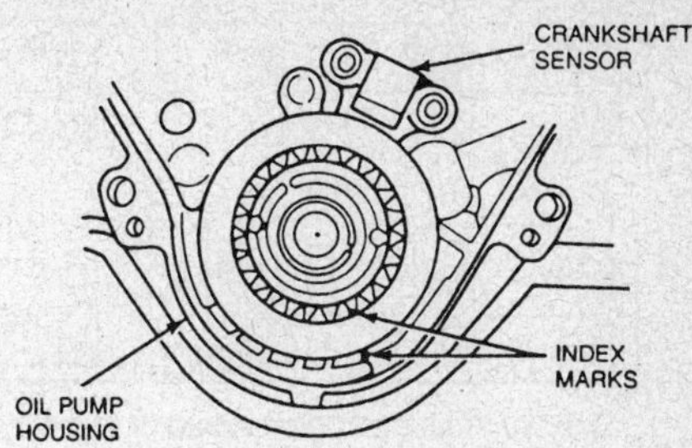


**Fig. 12 Crankshaft pulley alignment marks**

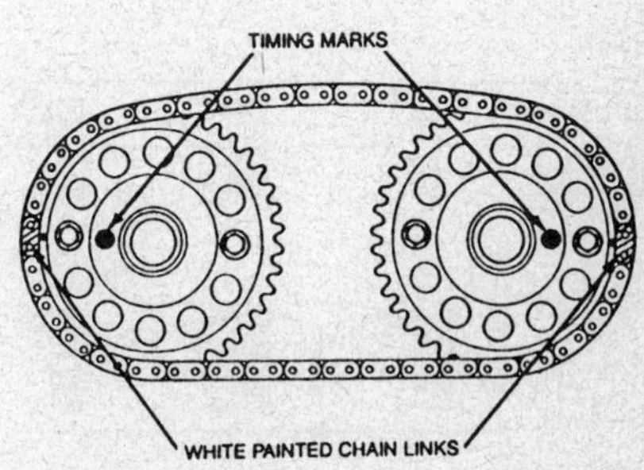


**Fig. 14 Timing chain & sprocket installation**

shims placed between the camshaft and valve spring retainer.

# CRANKSHAFT & FRONT OIL SEAL

## REPLACE

1. Loosen accessory drive belts, then remove RH front wheel.
2. Remove damper attaching bolt.
3. Remove drive belts from crankshaft damper.
4. Using suitable puller tool No. T67L-3600-A or equivalent, remove crankshaft damper from crankshaft.
5. Remove timing belt as described under "Timing Belt, Replace."
6. Using suitable puller or equivalent, remove crankshaft timing gear. **Ensure not to damage crankshaft sensor or shutter.**
7. Using seal puller tool No. T78P-3504-N or equivalent, remove front oil seal.
8. Reverse procedure to install.

# PISTON & ROD ASSEMBLY

Refer to **Fig. 18.** for piston and rod assemble.

# OIL PAN & PUMP

## REPLACE

1. Relieve fuel system pressure as outlined under "Fuel System Pressure Relief."

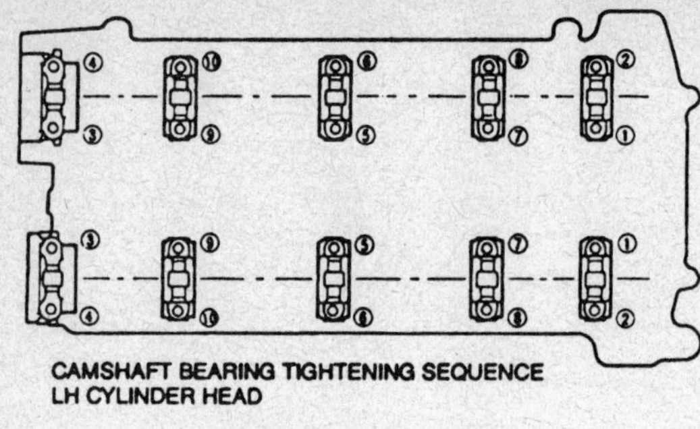


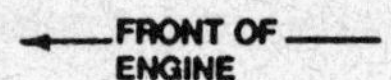


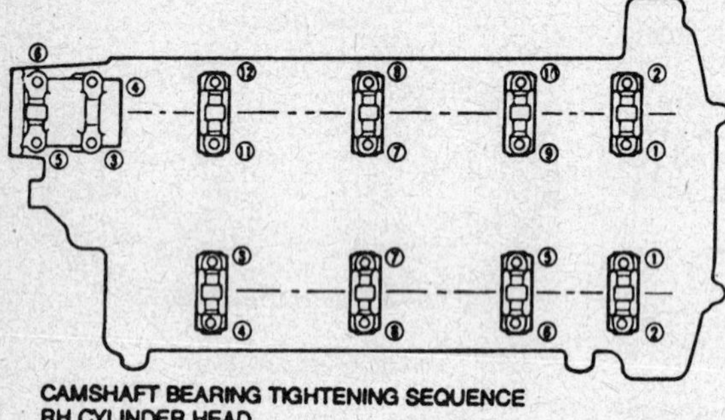


**Fig. 15 Camshaft bearing tightening sequence**

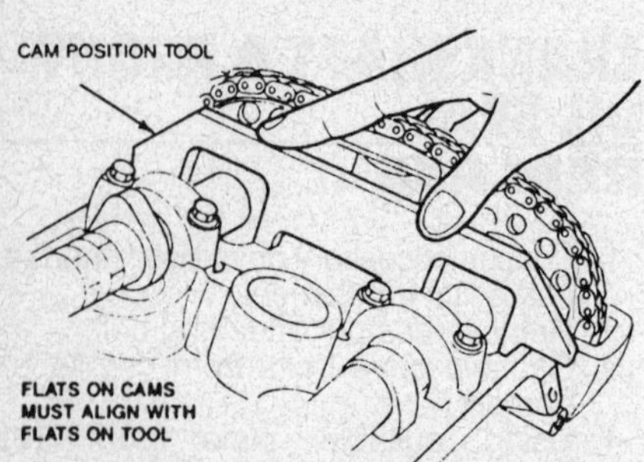


**Fig. 17 Checking cam for proper position**

2. Disconnect battery ground cable, then remove oil dipstick.
3. Remove accessory drive belts, then timing belt as described under "Timing Belt, Replace."
4. Raise and support vehicle. On models with low oil sensor, remove retainer clip at sensor, then disconnect sensor electrical connector, **Fig. 19.**
5. Drain crankcase.
6. Remove starter motor, then disconnect Heater Exhaust Gas Oxygen (HEGO) sensor electrical connector.
7. Remove catalyst and pipe assembly.
8. Remove lower engine/flywheel dust cover from converter housing.
9. Remove oil pan gasket, then timing belt pulley as described under "Timing Belt, Replace."
10. Remove sump pump to oil pump attaching bolts.
11. Remove oil pump to block attaching bolts, then remove pump.
12. Reverse procedure to install, noting the following:
    a. Torque oil pump bolts to specifications.
    b. Torque oil pan bolts to specifications, in sequence, **Fig. 20.**

## OIL PUMP INSPECTION

1. Wash all parts in suitable solvent, then dry with compressed air.
2. Ensure all dirt and particles are removed.
3. Inspect inner pump housing for wear or damage.
4. Inspect pump cover mating surface for wear, scuff marks are normal, if surface is worn or grooved, replace pump assembly.
5. Inspect rotor for nicks, burrs or score marks, remove imperfections with suitable oil stone.
6. Using suitable feeler gauge, measure inner tip to outer rotor tip clearance, **Fig. 21,** clearance on 1989 models, should not exceed .010 inch, clearance on 1990-92 models, clearance should be .0024-.0071 inch.
7. Install suitable straightedge, then using feeler gauge, measure rotor endplay, **Fig. 22,** on 1989-91 models, clearance should not exceed .005 inch, on 1992 models, clearance should be .0012-.0035 inch.
8. If any inspection is not as indicated, replace oil pump assembly.

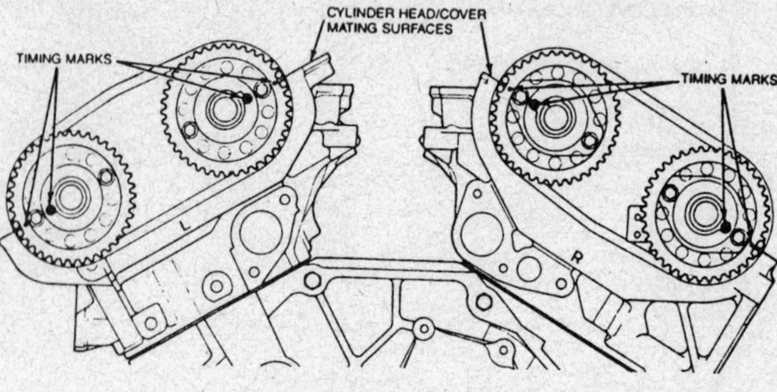


**Fig. 16 Aligning timing marks w/cylinder head mating surface**

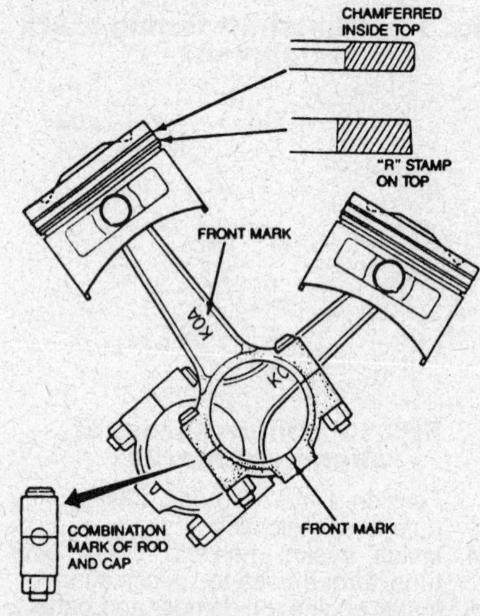


**Fig. 18 Piston & rod assembly**

## BELT TENSION DATA

| Belt | New | Used |
|---|---|---|
| Air Conditioning & Alternator | 220-265 | 148-192 |
| Power Steering & Water Pump | 154-198 | 112-157 |

## SERPENTINE DRIVE BELTS

### BELT ROUTING

Refer to **Fig. 23.** for serpentine drive belt routing.

### BELT, REPLACE

1. Disconnect battery ground cable.
2. Loosen idler pulley nut.
3. Loosen idler adjusting screw until belt can be removed.
4. Reverse procedure to install.

## COOLING SYSTEM BLEED

These engine do not require a specific bleed procedure. After filling cooling system, run engine to operating temperature with radiator/pressure cap off. Air will then be automatically bled through cap opening.

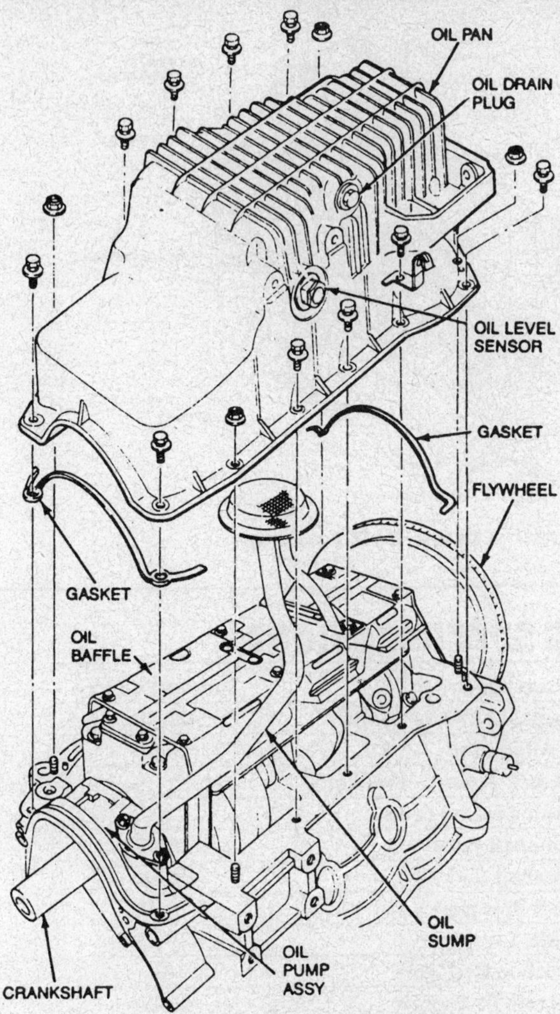


**Fig. 19 Oil pan & pump removal**

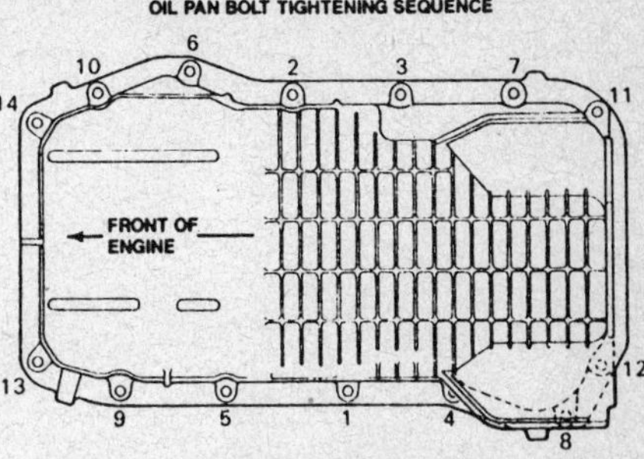


**Fig. 20 Oil pan tightening sequence**

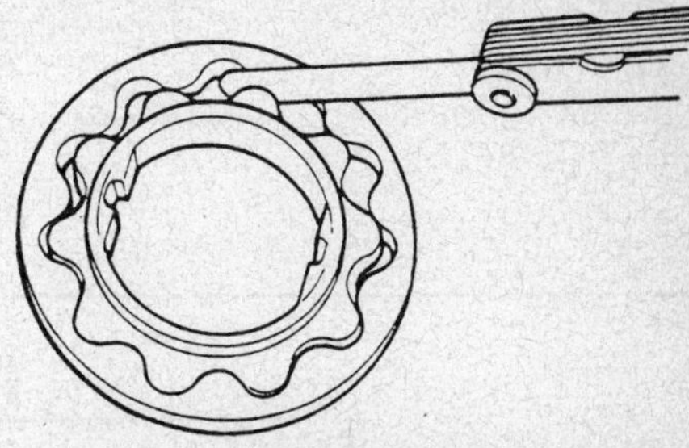

**Fig. 21 Oil pump tip clearance**

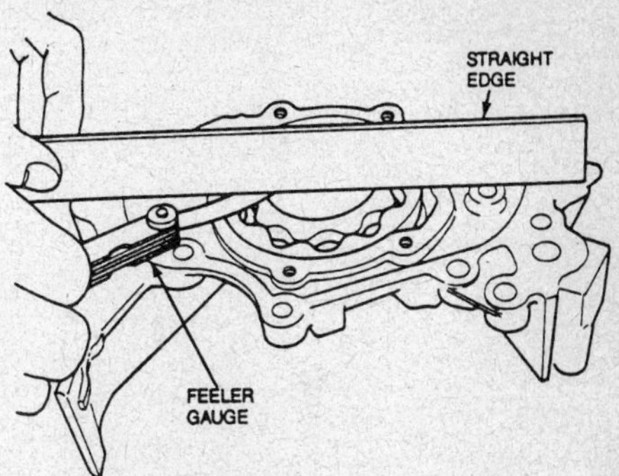


**Fig. 22 Oil pump rotor endplay**

# THERMOSTAT

## REPLACE

### REMOVAL

1. Drain cooling system below level of upper radiator hose.
2. Remove upper radiator hose, then three retaining bolts from thermostat housing.
3. Remove housing and thermostat as an assembly, discarding old gasket. Clean sealing surfaces with gasket scraper. Ensure not to damage aluminum surfaces as leak may form.

### INSTALLATION

1. Install thermostat into housing, ensuring that jiggle valve in relation to housing.
2. Position gasket onto housing using bolts as holding device, then install housing assembly and retaining bolts.
3. Install upper radiator hose. Refer to "Bleeding Cooling System," fill and bleed cooling system with recommended amount and mixture.
4. Start engine and check for leaks.

# WATER PUMP

## REPLACE

1. Relieve fuel system pressure as outlined under "Fuel System Pressure Relief."
2. Drain cooling system, then disconnect battery cable.
3. Remove battery and battery tray, then drive belt and accessory belts.
4. Remove attaching bolts, retaining A/C, alternator idler pulley and bracket.
5. Disconnect electrical connector from ignition module and ground strap.
6. Loosen four clamps on upper intake connector tube, then remove two retaining bolts.
7. Remove upper intake connector tube.
8. Remove RH tire and wheel assembly and splash panel.
9. Remove upper timing belt cover, then the crankshaft pulley.
10. Remove lower timing belt cover.
11. Remove attaching bolts from center timing belt cover and position aside.
12. Remove water pump attaching bolts, then the pump.
13. Reverse procedure to install.

# FUEL PUMP

## REPLACE

1. Relieve fuel system pressure as outlined under "Fuel System Pressure Relief."
2. Disconnect battery ground cable.
3. Remove fuel from fuel tank by pumping fuel out of fuel filler neck.
4. Raise and support vehicle.
5. Disconnect then remove fuel filler neck.
6. Support fuel tank, then remove tank support straps. Lower fuel tank partially and remove fuel lines, electrical connector and vent lines from tank. Remove tank and place on suitable workbench.
7. Turn fuel pump locking ring counterclockwise and remove locking ring.
8. Remove fuel pump, bracket and gasket assembly.
9. Reverse procedure to install.

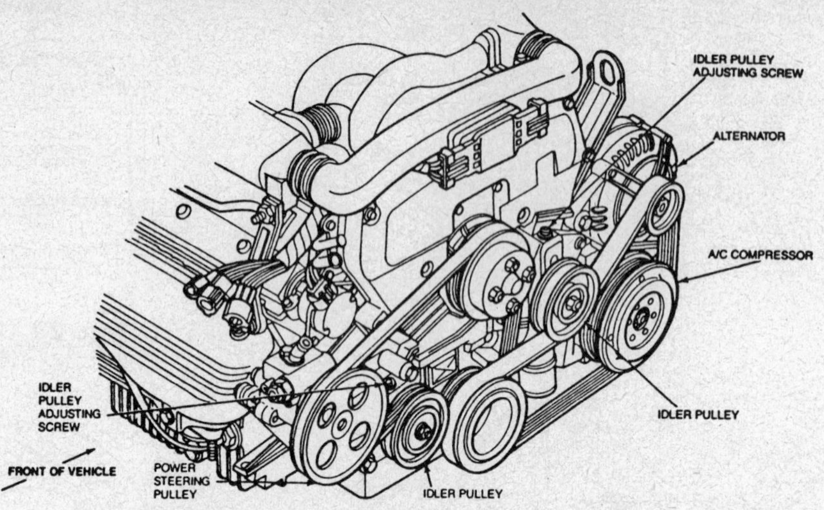


**Fig. 23 Serpentine drive belt routing**

## TIGHTENING SPECIFICATIONS

| Year | Component | Torque/Ft. Lbs. |
|---|---|---|
| 1989–92 | A/C Compressor Bracket Bolts | 27–40 |
| | Alternator | 25–36 |
| | Alternator & A/C Pulley & Bracket | 11–16 |
| | Camshaft Bearing Caps | ③ |
| | Camshaft Pulley | 15–18 |
| | Camshaft Sensor | 6–8 |
| | Camshaft Sprocket Bolts | 10–13 |
| | Chain Tensioner | 11–14 |
| | Connecting Rod Nuts | ④ |
| | Converter To Engine | 19–34 |
| | Crankshaft Pulley Bolt | 113–126 |
| | Crankshaft Sensor Bolts | 13–22② |
| | Cylinder Head Bolts | ① |
| | EGR Tube To Exhaust Manifold | 11–16 |
| | Engine Coolant Temperature Sensor | 12–17 |
| | Engine Mount | ① |
| | Exhaust Manifold To Cylinder Head | 26–38 |
| | Exhaust Pipe To Manifold | 16–24 |
| | Flywheel | ⑦ |
| | Front Cover Bolts | 60–90② |
| | Fuel Rail | 11–16 |
| | Heat Shield | 11–16 |
| | Idler Pulley Nut | 25–36 |
| | Ignition Coil Pack Bracket | 21–31 |
| | Ignition Coil Pack Screws | 3.3–5.2 |
| | Intake Manifold | 11–16 |
| | Intake Manifold Crossover Tube | 11–16 |
| | Knock Sensor | 22–28 |
| | Main Bearing Caps | ⑤ |
| | Main Bearing Support Beam | ⑥ |
| | Oil Drain Plug | 15–24 |
| | Oil Level Sensor | 16–24 |
| | Oil Pick Up Tube | 60–90② |
| | Oil Pressure Sending Switch | 12–17 |
| | Oil Pump | 11–16 |

*Continued*

## TIGHTENING SPECIFICATIONS—Continued

| Year | Component | Torque/Ft. Lbs. |
|---|---|---|
| 1989-92 | Oil Screen | 6-8 |
| | Oil Seal Carrier Bolts | 55-82② |
| | Oil Sump To Oil Pump | 6-8 |
| | Power Steering Pump Pulley | 40-50 |
| | Pressure Plate | 12-24 |
| | Rocker Arm Cover Bolts | 8-11 |
| | Spark Plugs | 17-19 |
| | Tension Locknut | 25-37 |
| | Thermostat Housing | 5-8 |
| | Throttle Body Bolts | 12-16 |
| | Throttle Position Sensor | 18-26② |
| | Timing Belt Rear Cover | 70② |
| | Transaxle To Engine | 25-35 |
| | Upper Oil Baffle | 11-16 |
| | Water Pump Pulley | 11-16 |
| | Water Pump | ⑧ |

①—Refer to text.
②—Inch lbs.
③—Tighten in two steps, first to 71–106 inch lbs., then to 12–16 ft. lbs.
④—1989, 28 ft. lbs., 1990–92, tighten in two steps, first to 22–26 ft. lbs., then to 33–36 ft. lbs.
⑤—1989, tighten in two steps, first to 37–50 ft. lbs., then to 58–60 ft. lbs., 1990–92, tighten in two steps, first to 34–50 ft. lbs., then to 58–65 ft. lbs.
⑥—1989, 11–17 ft. lbs., 1990–92, 15–24 ft. lbs.
⑦—Tighten in two steps, first to 29–43 ft. lbs., then to 51–58 ft. lbs.
⑧—1989–90, 5–6 ft. lbs., 1991, 12–17 ft. lbs., 1992, 12–16 ft. lbs.

# 3.8L/V6-232 Engine

**NOTE:** On Vehicles Equipped With Airbags, Disarm Airbag System As Outlined Under "Airbag System Disarming" Before Any Diagnosis, Testing, Troubleshooting Or Repairs Are Performed. After All Diagnosis, Testing, Troubleshooting Or Repairs Have Been Completed, Rearm Airbag System As Outlined Under "Airbag System Disarming."

## INDEX



## AIRBAG SYSTEM DISARMING

### EXCEPT 1992 MODELS

1. Disconnect battery ground cable, then open glove compartment down past its stops.
2. Disconnect electrical connector from backup power supply, located to the right of the glove compartment opening.
3. Remove four nut and washer assemblies securing driver air bag module to steering wheel.
4. Disconnect air bag electrical connector, then attach a jumper wire between air bag terminals on clockspring, **Fig. 1.** If necessary, reconnect battery and backup power supply.
5. To reactivate, disconnect battery

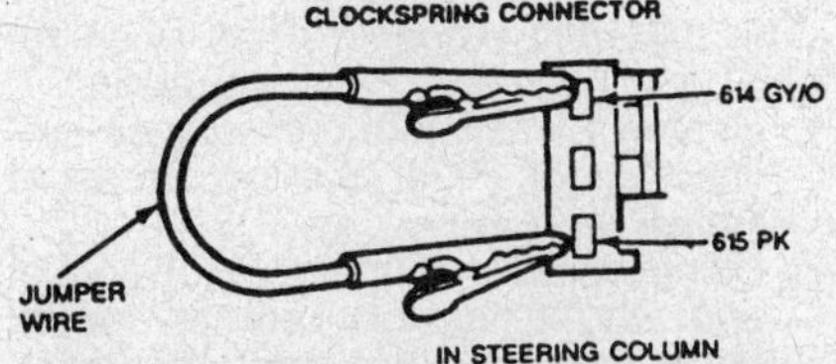


**Fig. 1 Airbag jumper wire. Except 1992**

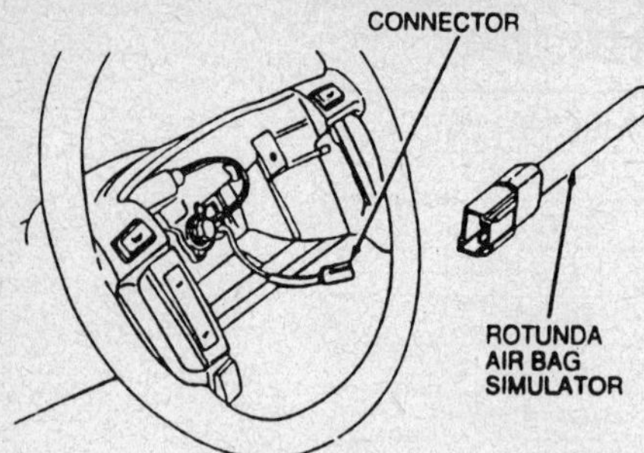


**Fig. 2 Airbag simulator. 1992**

ground cable and backup power supply, then reverse remainder of deactivation procedure. **Torque** airbag module to steering wheel attaching nut assemblies to 35-53 inch lbs.

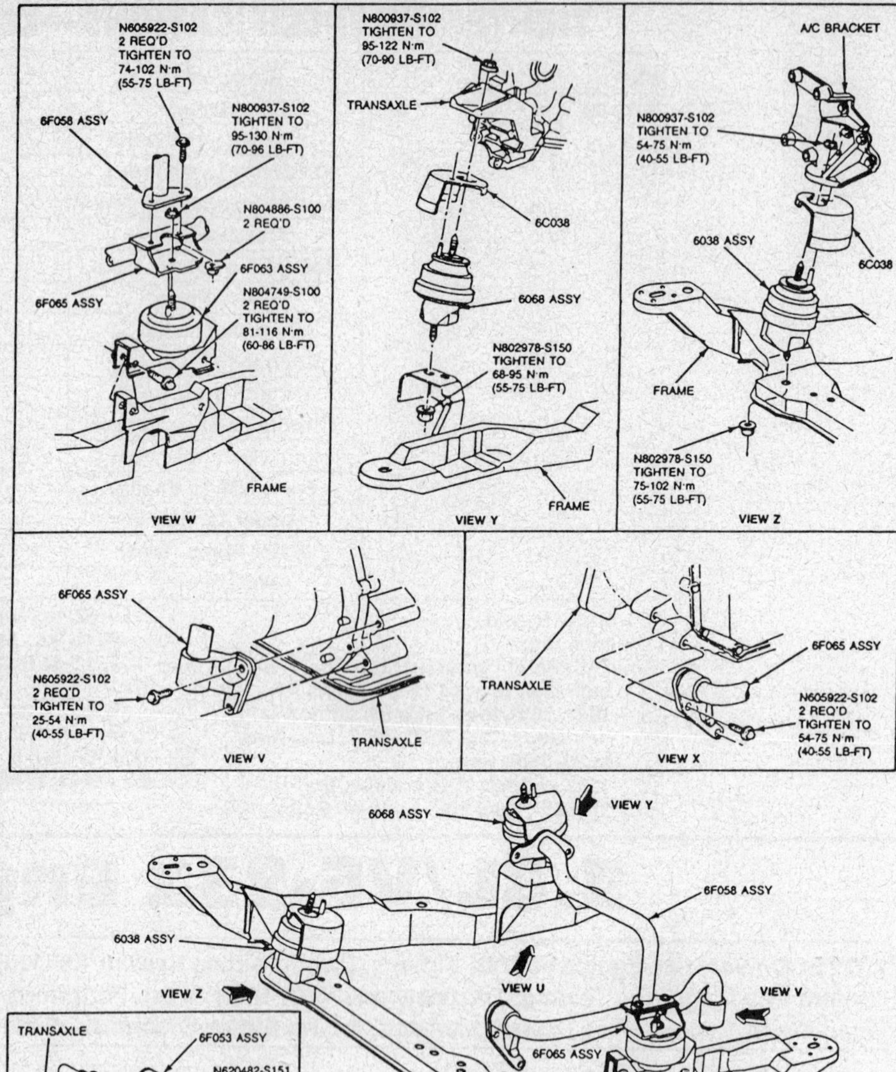


**Fig. 3 Engine mounts**

## 1992 MODELS

1. Disconnect positive battery cable, wait one minute, then proceed to step 2.
2. Remove four airbag module to steering wheel attaching nuts and washers.
3. Disconnect airbag electrical connector.
4. Install Rotunda airbag simulator tool No. 105-00008 or equivalent, to clockspring to simulate airbag, **Fig. 2.**
5. Reconnect positive battery terminal.
6. Reverse procedure to activate system. **Torque** airbag module attaching nuts to 36-49 inch lbs. Turn ignition switch from Off to Run, airbag indicator will light for about six seconds, if light remains lite, does not light or flashes, airbag system failure is indicated.

# FUEL SYSTEM PRESSURE RELIEF

**Fuel supply lines will remain pressurized for long periods of time after engine shut-down. This pressure must be relieved before any service is attempted. A valve is provided on the fuel rail assembly for this purpose. To relieve system pressure, remove air cleaner assembly and connect pressure gauge tool No. T80L-9974-A or T80L-9974-B or equivalent onto fuel valve on fuel rail assembly. To pressurize fuel system, proceed as follows:**

a. Install pressure gauge tool No. T80L-9974-A or T80L-9974-B equivalent onto fuel rail pressure fitting.
b. Turn ignition switch to On position for 3 seconds, repeatedly 5 to 10 times until pressure gauge indicates 13 psi.

# ENGINE MOUNTS

# REPLACE

## LH INSULATOR & SUPPORT ASSEMBLY

1. Raise and support vehicle.
2. Remove left front tire and wheel assembly, then support transaxle using suitable jack and block of wood.
3. Remove insulator to support attaching nuts, **Fig. 3.**
4. Remove insulator to frame through bolts, **Fig. 3.**, then raise transaxle enough to unload insulator.
5. Remove support assembly to transaxle attaching bolts, then the insulator and/or support assembly.
6. Reverse procedure to install.

## RH FRONT

The following procedure has been revised per a Technical Service Bulletin.

1. Relieve fuel system pressure as outlined under "Fuel System Pressure Relief."
2. Using suitable 18mm swivel socket and long extension, remove mount upper attaching nut through engine compartment.
3. Raise and support vehicle.
4. Loosen, but do not remove, RH rear lower mount attaching nut.
5. Loosen, but do not remove, RH front lower mount attaching nut.
6. Lower vehicle.
7. Install suitable engine lifting equipment, then lift engine about one inch.
8. Raise and support vehicle, then remove engine mount.
9. Reverse procedure to install.

## RH REAR

1. Raise and support vehicle.
2. Loosen RH front and RH rear insulator attaching nuts, **Fig. 3.**
3. Remove catalytic converter, then lower vehicle.
4. Using suitable engine support equipment, raise engine one inch and support.
5. Raise and support vehicle.
6. Loosen four sub-frame attaching

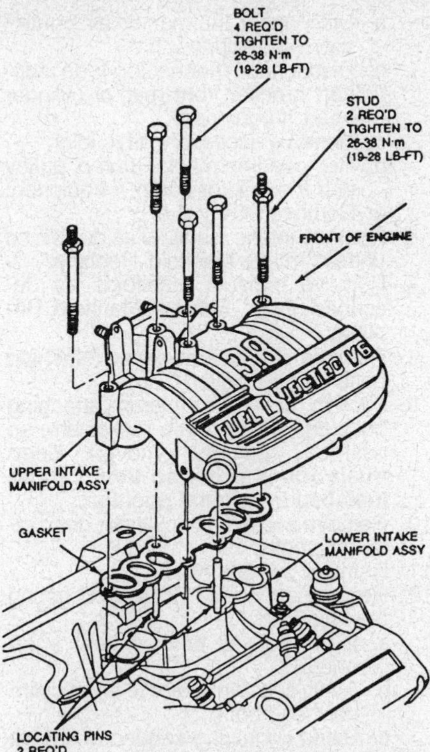


Fig. 4 Upper intake manifold assembly

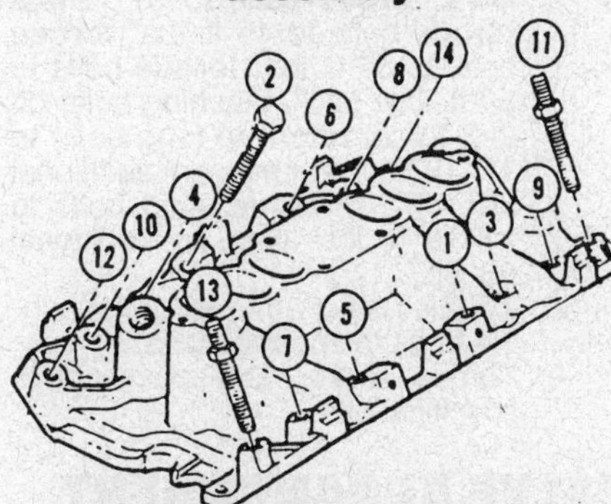

Fig. 6 Intake manifold bolt tightening sequence

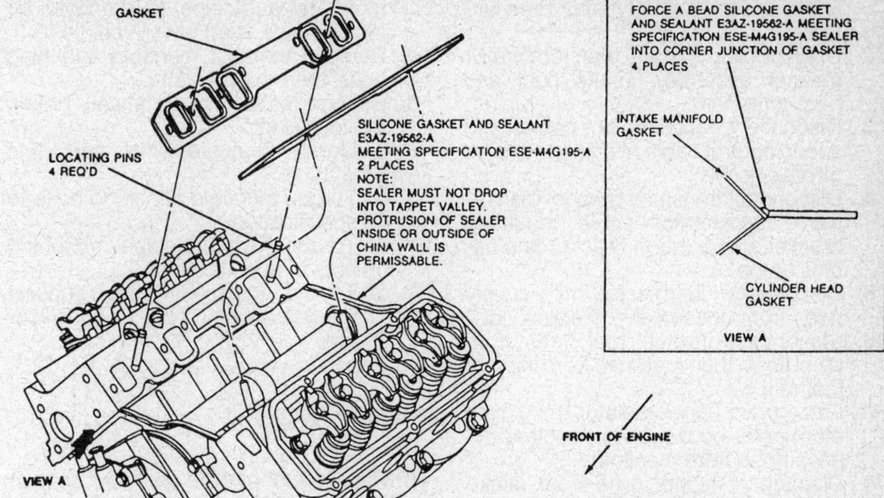


Fig. 5 Intake manifold sealant application

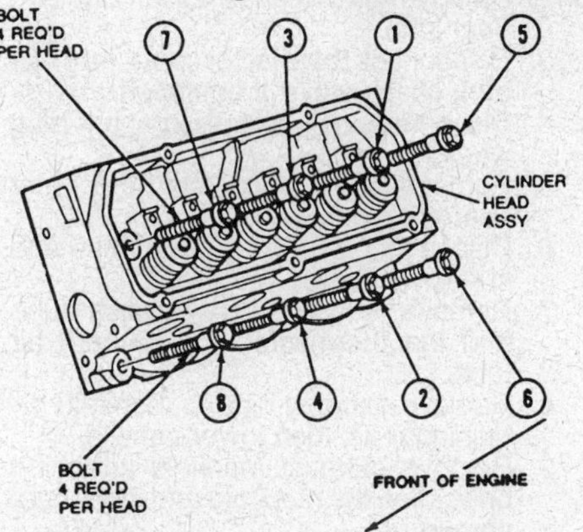


Fig. 7 Cylinder head bolt tightening sequence

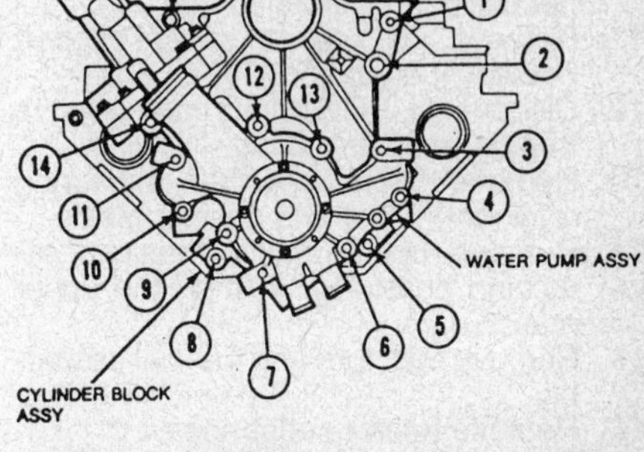


Fig. 8 Front cover attaching bolt locations

bolts, then remove insulator attaching nut and insulator.

7. Reverse procedure to install.

## ENGINE

### REPLACE

1. Relieve fuel system pressure as outlined under "Fuel System Pressure Relief."
2. Disconnect battery ground cable, then drain cooling system.
3. Disconnect underhood lamp electrical connector, then mark position of hood hinges and remove hood.
4. Remove oil dipstick tube, then disconnect alternator to voltage regulator wiring harness.
5. Remove radiator upper sight shield, then cooling fan motor relay attaching bolts, then position relay aside.
6. Remove air cleaner assembly.
7. Disconnect engine cooling fan.
8. Remove fan shroud, then the upper radiator hose.
9. Disconnect transaxle oil cooler tubes, then the heater hoses.
10. Disconnect power steering pump pressure hose, then the A/C compressor electrical connector.
11. Discharge A/C system, then disconnect compressor to condenser line.
12. Remove coolant recovery reservoir.
13. Remove wiring shield and accelerator cable mounting bracket.
14. Disconnect fuel hoses, then the power steering pump pressure and return tube bracket.
15. Disconnect engine control sensor electrical connector.
16. Disconnect vacuum hoses and ground wire assembly.
17. Remove duct assembly, then disconnect throttle control valve cable.
18. Disconnect bulkhead electrical connector, then transaxle pressure switches.
19. Remove transaxle support assembly attaching bolts.
20. Remove transaxle support assembly.
21. Raise and support vehicle.
22. Drain engine oil and remove oil filter, then disconnect exhaust gas oxygen sensor.
23. Remove drive belt, then the crankshaft pulley.
24. Remove drive belt tensioner, then the starter motor.
25. Remove converter housing assembly, then the inlet pipe converter assembly.
26. Remove engine support insulator retaining nuts.
27. Remove converter to flywheel attaching nuts.
28. Disconnect oil level sensor electrical connector.
29. Disconnect lower radiator hose, then remove engine to transaxle attaching bolts.
30. Remove wheel and tire assemblies.
31. Remove water pump pulley attaching bolts.
32. Remove water pump, then the distributor cap and position aside.
33. Remove distributor rotor, then the exhaust manifold bolt lock retaining bolts.
34. Remove thermactor air pump attaching bolts and the pump, if equipped.
35. Disconnect oil pressure sender electrical connector.
36. Install suitable engine lifting equipment.
37. Remove engine assembly.
38. Reverse procedure to install.

## INTAKE MANIFOLD

### REPLACE

1. Relieve fuel system pressure as out-

lined under "Fuel System Pressure Relief."
2. Drain cooling system, then remove air cleaner assembly, intake duct and heat tube.
3. Disconnect accelerator cable and speed control cable (if equipped) from throttle body.
4. Disconnect transaxle linkage, then remove accelerator cable mounting bracket and position bracket and cables aside.
5. Disconnect thermactor air supply hose from check valve, if equipped.
6. Disconnect flexible fuel lines from steel lines, then fuel lines from injector fuel rail.
7. Disconnect upper radiator hose from thermostat housing, then coolant bypass hose from manifold.
8. Disconnect heater tube from intake manifold, then remove tube support bracket attaching nut.
9. Disconnect heater hose from rear of tube, then remove tube.
10. Disconnect vacuum lines, then all necessary electrical connectors.
11. Remove A/C compressor support bracket, if equipped.
12. Disconnect PCV lines, then remove throttle body assembly.
13. Remove EGR valve, then the wiring retainer bracket and position aside.
14. Remove upper intake manifold attaching bolts, **Fig. 4,** then the upper manifold.
15. Remove injectors and fuel rail assembly.
16. Remove heater outlet hose.
17. Remove lower manifold attaching bolts and lower manifold. **It may be necessary to pry on front of lower manifold to break the seal. Ensure care is taken not to damage sealing surfaces.**
18. Reverse procedure to install, noting the following:
    a. Apply a 1/8 inch bead of silicone at each corner where cylinder head meets the block, **Fig. 5.**
    b. Using tightening sequence shown in **Fig. 6,** torque manifold bolts in two steps as follows: first step 8 ft. lbs and second step 11 ft. lbs. As revised per Technical Service Bulletin.
    c. Torque throttle body attaching bolts to specification in a crisscross pattern.
    d. Torque EGR attaching bolts to specifications.

## EXHAUST MANIFOLD REPLACE

### LEFT SIDE

1. Relieve fuel system pressure as outlined under "Fuel System Pressure Relief."
2. Remove oil dipstick tube support bracket, then disconnect spark plug wires.
3. Raise and support vehicle, then remove exhaust pipe to manifold attaching nuts, then lower vehicle.
4. Remove exhaust manifold attaching bolts, then the manifold.
5. Reverse procedure to install, noting the following:
    a. Lightly lubricate bolts and nuts with oil.
    b. Torque manifold attaching bolts to specification.
    c. Torque exhaust pipe attaching nuts to specification.
    d. Torque dipstick tube support bracket attaching nut to specification.

### RIGHT SIDE

1. Relieve fuel system pressure as outlined under "Fuel System Pressure Relief."
2. Remove air cleaner assembly and heat tube.
3. Disconnect thermactor hose from air tube check valve, if equipped.
4. Disconnect coil wire, then spark plug wires.
5. Remove spark plugs, then the outer heat shroud.
6. Disconnect EGR tube, then raise and support vehicle.
7. Remove transmission dipstick tube and the thermactor downstream air tube.
8. Remove exhaust pipe to manifold attaching nuts, then lower vehicle.
9. Remove exhaust manifold attaching bolts, then the manifold and inner heat shroud.
10. Reverse procedure to install, noting the following:
    a. Lightly lubricate bolts and nuts with oil.
    b. Torque manifold attaching bolts to specifications.
    c. Torque exhaust pipe attaching nuts to specifications.
    d. Torque outer heat shroud attaching screws specification.

## CYLINDER HEAD REPLACE

1. Relieve fuel system pressure as outlined under "Fuel System Pressure Relief."
2. Disconnect battery ground cable, then drain cooling system.
3. Remove air cleaner assembly, intake duct and heat tube.
4. Remove drive belt, then if removing left cylinder head, proceed as follows:
    a. Remove power steering pump and position aside, then remove oil fill cap.
    b. Remove A/C compressor mounting bracket and position aside, if equipped.
    c. Remove alternator and bracket.
5. If removing right cylinder head, proceed as follows:
    a. Disconnect thermactor air control valve, if equipped.
    b. Disconnect thermactor tube support bracket from rear of cylinder head, if equipped.
    c. Remove accessory drive idler.
    d. Remove thermactor pump pulley and thermactor pump, if equipped.
    e. Remove PCV valve.
6. Remove intake manifold as described under ""Intake Manifold, Replace."
7. Remove exhaust manifolds as described under "Exhaust Manifold, Replace."
8. Remove rocker arm cover attaching bolts and the cover.
9. Loosen rocker arm fulcrum attaching bolts enough to rotate rocker arm so pushrod can be removed. **Keep pushrods in order so they can be installed in original position.**
10. Remove and discard cylinder head attaching bolts.
11. Remove cylinder head.
12. Reverse procedure to install, noting the following:
    a. Lightly oil all bolts except short ones.
    b. Apply suitable sealer to short cylinder head bolts.
    c. Using tightening sequence shown in **Fig. 7, torque** cylinder head attaching bolts in six steps as follows: **torque** bolts to 37 ft. lbs.; **torque** bolts to 45 ft. lbs.; **torque** bolts to 52 ft. lbs.; **torque** bolts to 59 ft. lbs.; back attaching bolts off 2-3 turns; **retorque** long bolts to 11-18 ft. lbs., then an additional 85-105°; **retorque** short bolts to 11-18 ft. lbs., then an additional 65-85°.
    d. Torque rocker arm fulcrum attaching bolts to specifications.
    e. Torque rocker arm cover bolts specifications.

## VALVE ARRANGEMENT

### FRONT TO REAR

Right Side .................... E-I-I-E-I-E
Left Side .................... E-I-E-I-I-E

## CAM LOBE LIFT SPECIFICATIONS

Exhaust ...................... .241 inch
Intake ........................ .240 inch

## VALVES ADJUST

This engine is equipped with hydraulic lifters. No adjustments are required.

## HYDRAULIC VALVE LIFTERS REPLACE

Before replacing hydraulic valve lifters

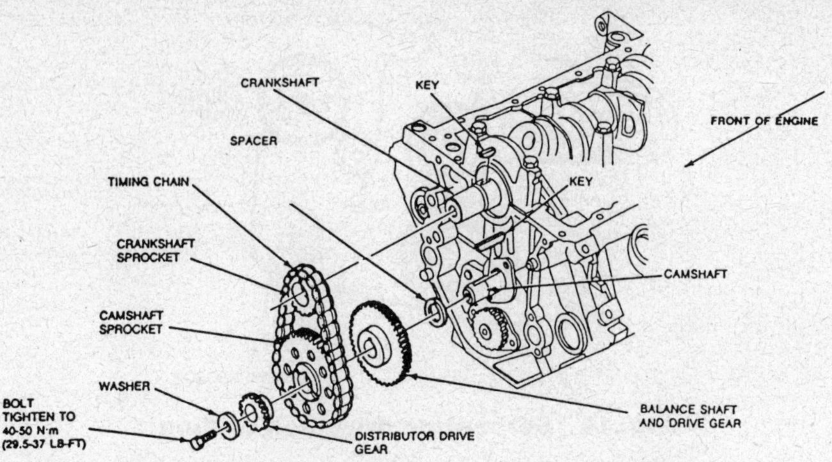


**Fig. 9 Timing chains & sprocket removal**

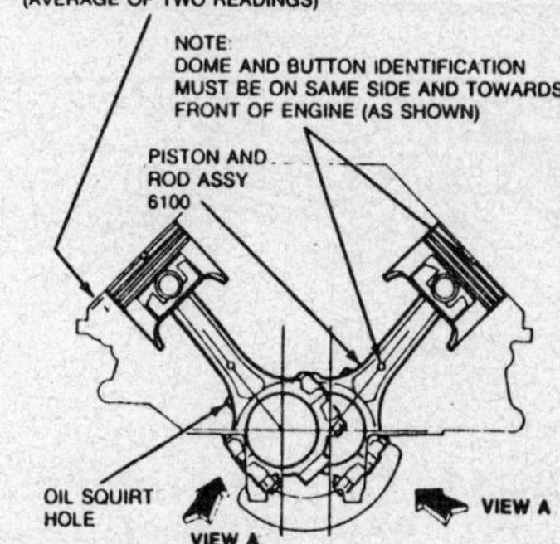


**Fig. 11 Piston & rod assembly**

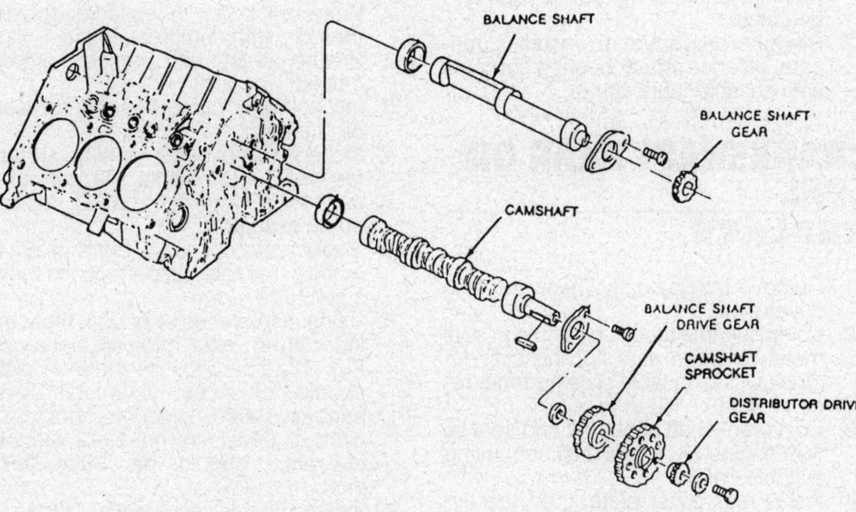


**Fig. 10 Balance shaft assembly**

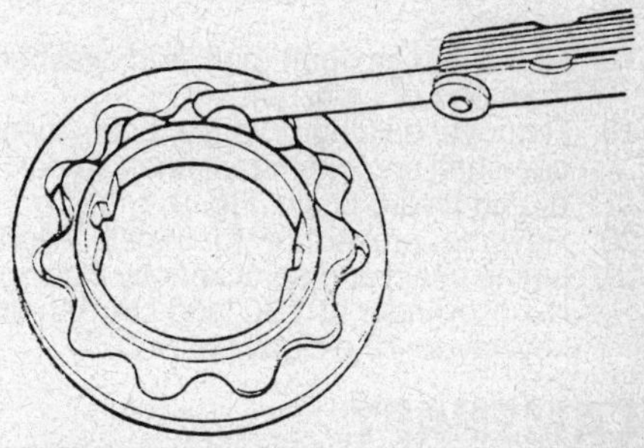

**Fig. 12 Oil pump tip clearance**

for noisy operation, ensure the noise is not caused by improper rocker arm to stem clearance, worn rocker arms, pushrods or valve tips.

1. Disconnect spark plug wires from spark plugs and position aside.
2. Remove intake manifolds as described under "Intake Manifold, Replace."
3. Remove rocker arm cover attaching bolts and the covers.
4. Loosen rocker arm fulcrum attaching bolts enough so rocker arm can be lifted of pushrod and rotated aside.
5. Remove pushrods, then the lifters. Keep lifters and pushrods in order, so they can be installed in their original position.
6. Reverse procedure to install, noting the following:
   a. Lubricate lifters, pushrods and rocker arms with suitable lubricant.
   b. Torque rocker arm fulcrum bolts to specifications. **Prior to torquing bolts, ensure pushrods and rocker arms are fully seated.**

## ROCKER ARM COVER REPLACE

1. Disconnect spark plug wires from spark plugs and position aside.
2. Remove air cleaner assembly, oil fill cap and PCV valve.
3. Remove rocker arm cover attaching bolts and the covers.
4. Reverse procedure to install. Torque cover attaching bolts to specifications.

## FRONT COVER, TIMING CHAIN & SPROCKETS REPLACE

1. Relieve fuel system pressure as outlined under "Fuel System Pressure Relief."
2. Disconnect battery ground cable, then drain cooling system.
3. Remove air cleaner assembly and air intake duct.
4. Remove cooling fan shroud attaching bolts, cooling fan clutch attaching bolts, then cooling fan clutch assembly and the fan shroud.
5. Remove drive belt, then the water pump pulley.
6. Remove power steering pump bracket attaching bolts, then position bracket and pump aside.
7. Remove A/C compressor front support bracket, if equipped.
8. Disconnect coolant bypass hose and heater hose from water pump.
9. Disconnect upper radiator hose from thermostat housing.
10. Disconnect coil wire from distributor cap, then remove cap and plug wires.
11. Remove distributor hold-down clamp, then the distributor.
12. Raise and support vehicle.
13. Remove crankshaft pulley and damper using suitable puller.
14. Remove oil filter, then disconnect lower radiator hose from water pump.
15. Remove oil pan as described under "Oil Pan, Replace."
16. Lower vehicle, then remove front cover attaching bolts, **Fig. 8. Be sure to remove attaching bolt located be-**

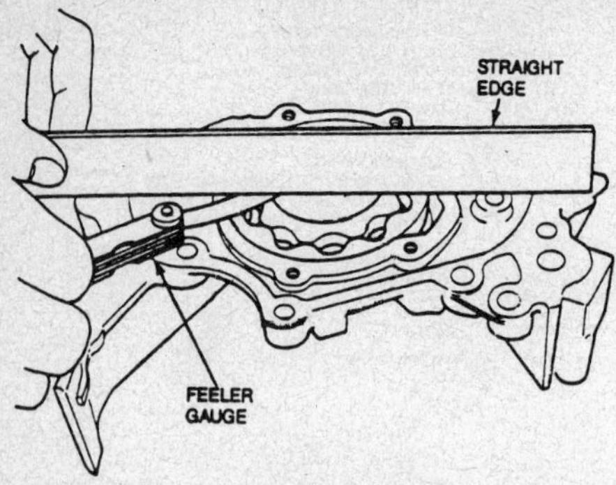

Fig. 13 Oil pump rotor endplay

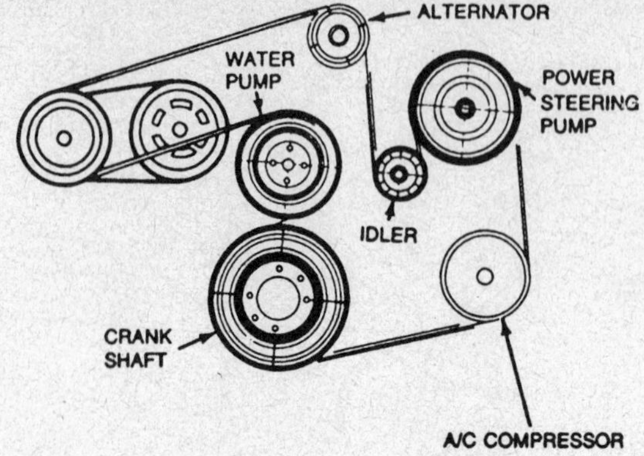


Fig. 14 Serpentine drive belt routing

**hind oil filter adapter. Cover will be damaged if pried on prior to bolt removal.**

17. Remove ignition timing indicator, then front cover and water pump as an assembly.
18. Remove camshaft bolt and washer from end of camshaft.
19. Remove distributor drive gear, then camshaft sprocket, crankshaft sprocket and timing chain, **Fig. 9.**
20. Reverse procedure to install. Align timing chain and sprockets by placing No. 1 cylinder at TDC and crankshaft keyway to 12 o'clock position.

## CAMSHAFT

### REPLACE

1. Disconnect battery ground cable, then drain cooling system.
2. Remove radiator, then A/C condenser (if equipped).
3. Remove grille.
4. Remove intake manifolds as described under "Intake Manifold, Replace."
5. Remove lifters as described under "Hydraulic Valve Lifters, Replace."
6. Remove front cover and timing chain as described under "Front Cover, Timing chain & Sprockets, Replace."
7. Remove oil pan as described under "Oil Pan, Replace."
8. Remove camshaft from front of engine, ensuring not to damage bearings or lobes.
9. Reverse procedure to install. Lubricate cam lobes and bearings with suitable lubricant.

## BALANCE SHAFT

### REPLACE

1. Disconnect battery ground cable, then drain cooling system.
2. Remove radiator, then A/C condenser (if equipped).
3. Remove grille.
4. Remove front cover and timing chain as described under "Front cover, Timing Chain & Sprockets, Replace."
5. Remove oil pan as described under "Oil Pan, Replace."
6. Remove balance shaft thrust plate, **Fig. 10,** then balance shaft from front of engine, ensuring not to damage bearings.
7. Reverse procedure to install. Lubricate balance shaft bearing journals with suitable lubricant.

## CRANKSHAFT REAR OIL SEAL

### REPLACE

1. Remove transaxle, flywheel and rear cover plate.
2. Using suitable tool, punch hole in seal metal between seal lip and cylinder block. Using suitable slide hammer remove seal.
3. Coat crankshaft seal area and seal lip with engine oil, then install seal using suitable driver.
4. Install rear cover plate, then the flywheel and transaxle. Torque all bolts to specifications.

## PISTON & ROD ASSEMBLY

Assemble rod to piston with notch on piston dome on the same side as oil squirt hole on connecting rod. Assemble piston and rod assembly in engine with notch in dome facing front of engine, **Fig. 11.**

## OIL PAN

### REPLACE

1. Relieve fuel system pressure as outlined under "Fuel System Pressure Relief."
2. Disconnect battery ground cable then, raise and support vehicle.
3. Drain crankcase, then remove oil filter.
4. Remove catalytic converter assembly.
5. Remove starter motor, then torque converter housing cover.
6. Remove oil pan attaching bolts and oil pan.
7. Reverse procedure to install.

## OIL PUMP INSPECTION

1. Wash all parts in suitable solvent, then dry with compressed air.
2. Ensure all dirt and particles are removed.
3. Inspect inner pump housing for wear or damage.
4. Inspect pump cover mating surface for wear, scuff marks are normal, if surface is worn or grooved, replace pump assembly.
5. Inspect rotor for nicks, burrs or score marks, remove imperfections with suitable oil stone.
6. Using suitable feeler gauge, measure inner tip to outer rotor tip clearance, **Fig. 12,** clearance on 1989 models, should not exceed .010 inch, clearance on 1990-91 models, should not exceed .012 inch, on 1992 models, clearance should be .0024-.0071 inch.
7. Install suitable straightedge, then using feeler gauge, measure rotor endplay, **Fig. 13,** on 1989-91 models, clearance should not exceed .005 inch, on 1992 models, clearance should be .0012-.0035 inch.
8. If any inspection is not as indicated, replace oil pump assembly.

## BELT TENSION DATA

Belt tension is automatically maintained on this engine by an automatic tensioner. Therefore, no adjustment is necessary.

## SERPENTINE DRIVE BELTS

### BELT ROUTING

Refer to **Fig. 14.** for serpentine drive belt routing.

### BELT, REPLACE

1. Disconnect battery ground cable.
2. Install suitable 1/2 inch flex handle in square hole in tensioner.
3. Rotate tensioner counterclockwise, then remove belt.

4. Reverse procedure to install.

## COOLING SYSTEM BLEED

These engine do not require a specific bleed procedure. After filling cooling system, run engine to operating temperature with radiator/pressure cap off. Air will then be automatically bled through cap opening.

## THERMOSTAT

### REPLACE

#### REMOVAL

Do not remove the radiator cap while engine is operating or while engine is still under pressure.

1. Drain cooling system until coolant level is below thermostat.
2. Disconnect upper radiator hose at thermostat housing.
3. Remove two housing retaining bolts, then the thermostat housing and gasket.

#### INSTALLATION

So that the thermostat is correctly installed, the water outlet casting on all engines contains a locking recess into which the thermostat is turned and locked.

1. Clean gasket surface on thermostat housing and intake manifold, then position the thermostat in the housing, with the bridge section in the outlet casting. Turn the thermostat clockwise to lock it in position.
2. Position new gasket and thermostat housing on the manifold, then install two retaining bolts.
3. Connect upper hose to housing, then fill cooling system with recommended coolant.
4. Start engine and check for leaks.

## WATER PUMP

### REPLACE

1. Relieve fuel system pressure as outlined under "Fuel System Pressure Relief."
2. Drain cooling system, then remove air cleaner assembly and air intake duct.
3. Remove fan shroud attaching screws, then fan clutch attaching bolts.
4. Remove fan clutch, then fan shroud then, remove drive belt, then water pump pulley, **Fig. 15.**
5. Remove power steering pump bracket attaching bolts, then position bracket and pump aside.
6. Remove A/C compressor front support bracket, if equipped.
7. Disconnect coolant bypass hose and heater hose from water pump.
8. Remove water pump attaching bolts and pump.
9. Reverse procedure to install. **Coat threads of No. 1 water pump bolt with suitable sealer.**

## FUEL PUMP

### REPLACE

1. Relieve fuel system pressure as outlined under "Fuel System Pressure Relief."
2. Disconnect battery ground cable.
3. Remove fuel from fuel tank by pumping fuel out of fuel filler neck.
4. Raise and support vehicle.
5. Disconnect and remove fuel filler neck.
6. Support fuel tank, then remove tank support straps. Lower fuel tank partially and remove fuel lines, electrical connectors and vent lines from tank. Remove tank and place on suitable workbench.
7. Turn fuel pump locking ring counterclockwise and remove locking ring.
8. Remove fuel pump, bracket and gasket assembly.
9. Reverse procedure to install.

## TIGHTENING SPECIFICATIONS

| Year | Component | Torque/Ft. Lbs. |
|---|---|---|
| 1989–92 | Alternator Bracket | 30–40 |
| | Balance Shaft Thrust Plate | 6–10 |
| | Camshaft Sprocket To Camshaft | ③ |
| | Camshaft Thrust Plate | 6–10 |
| | Connecting Rod | 31–36 |
| | Crankshaft Damper To Crankshaft | 103–132 |
| | Crankshaft Pulley To Damper | 20–28 |
| | Cylinder Headbolt | ① |
| | Distributor Hold-Down Bolt | 20–29 |
| | EGR Valve To Intake Manifold | 15–22 |
| | Engine Mounts | ① |
| | Exhaust Manifold | 15–22 |
| | Fan Clutch Assembly | 12–18 |
| | Flywheel To Crankshaft | 54–64 |
| | Front Cover To Cylinder Block | 15–22 |
| | Fuel Pump To Front Cover | 15–22 |
| | Heater Tube To Intake Manifold | 8–10 |
| | Intake Manifold To Cylinder Head | ① |
| | Low Level Oil Sensor | 20–30 |
| | Main Bearing Cap | 65–81 |
| | Oil Inlet Tube Main Bearing | 30–40 |
| | Oil Inlet Tube To Cylinder Block | 15–22 |
| | Oil Pan To Cylinder Block | 80–106② |
| | Oil Pump Cover | 18–22 |

Continued

## TIGHTENING SPECIFICATIONS—Continued

| Year | Component | Torque/Ft. Lbs. |
|---|---|---|
| 1989–92 | Rocker Arm Cover To Cylinder Head | 80–106② |
| | Rocker Arm Fulcrum To Cylinder Head | ④ |
| | Spark Plug To Cylinder Head | ⑤ |
| | Throttle Body | 15–22 |
| | Water Pump Front Cover | 15–22 |

①—Refer to text.
②—Inch pounds.
③—1989, 15–22 ft. lbs., 1990–92, 30–37 ft. lbs.
④—1989, first step, tighten to 5.1–11 ft. lbs., second step, tighten to 18.4–-25.8 ft. lbs. 1990–91, first step, tighten to 44 inch lbs.; second step, tighten to 18.4–25.8 ft. lbs. 1992, first step, tighten to 44 inch lbs.; second step, tighten to 25 ft. lbs.
⑤—1989–91, 5–11 ft. lbs., 1992, 62–132 inch lbs.

# Clutch & Manual Transaxle

## INDEX



## CLUTCH
### ADJUST

These models incorporate a self-adjusting clutch mechanism, **Fig. 1.** The self-adjust mechanism consists of a spring loaded ratchet quadrant attached to the clutch cable. During clutch cable replacement or whenever clutch adjustment is necessary, grasp the clutch pedal and pull upwards, then slowly depress clutch pedal several times.

Whenever the clutch cable is disconnected for any reason, the clutch pedal assembly must be restrained in the uppermost position during both removal and replacement of the components. After the clutch cable is installed and the clutch allowed to rest in its normal position, adjust clutch by slowly depressing clutch several times.

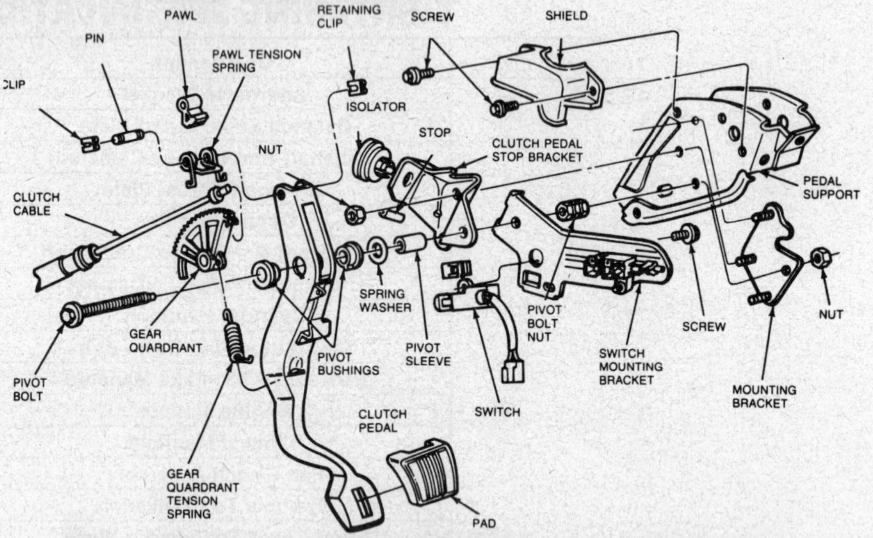

**Fig. 1 Exploded view of clutch pedal & self-adjusting mechanism**

## CLUTCH
### REPLACE

1. Remove transaxle as described under "Manual Transaxle, Replace" procedure.
2. Loosen pressure plate attaching bolts evenly to avoid distortion. If pressure plate is to be reused, scribe reference marks between plate and flywheel for reference during assembly.
3. Remove pressure plate and clutch disc from flywheel, **Fig. 2. These models do not use a pilot bearing.**
4. Position clutch disc and pressure plate onto flywheel with flatter side of clutch disc facing toward flywheel.
5. Ensure three dowel pins on flywheel are aligned with holes in pressure plate, then install mounting bolts. Do not tighten at this time.
6. Using clutch alignment tool T81P-7550-A or equivalent, align clutch disc with flywheel. Alternately tighten pressure plate mounting screws until fully seated, then torque bolts to specifications.
7. Remove alignment tool, than install transaxle.

## GEARSHIFT LINKAGE
### ADJUST

Adjustment of the gearshift linkage is not necessary and no provision for adjustment is provided, **Fig. 3.**

## MANUAL TRANSAXLE
### REPLACE

1. Disconnect battery ground cable.

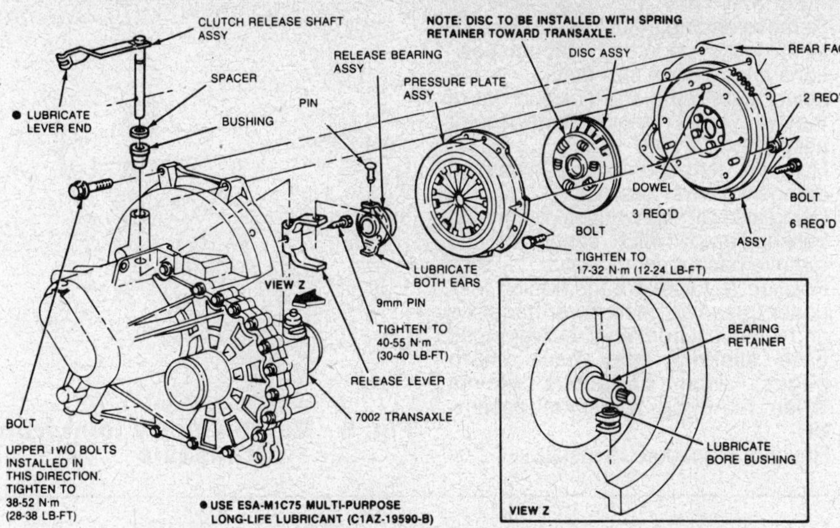


**Fig. 2 Exploded view of clutch assembly**

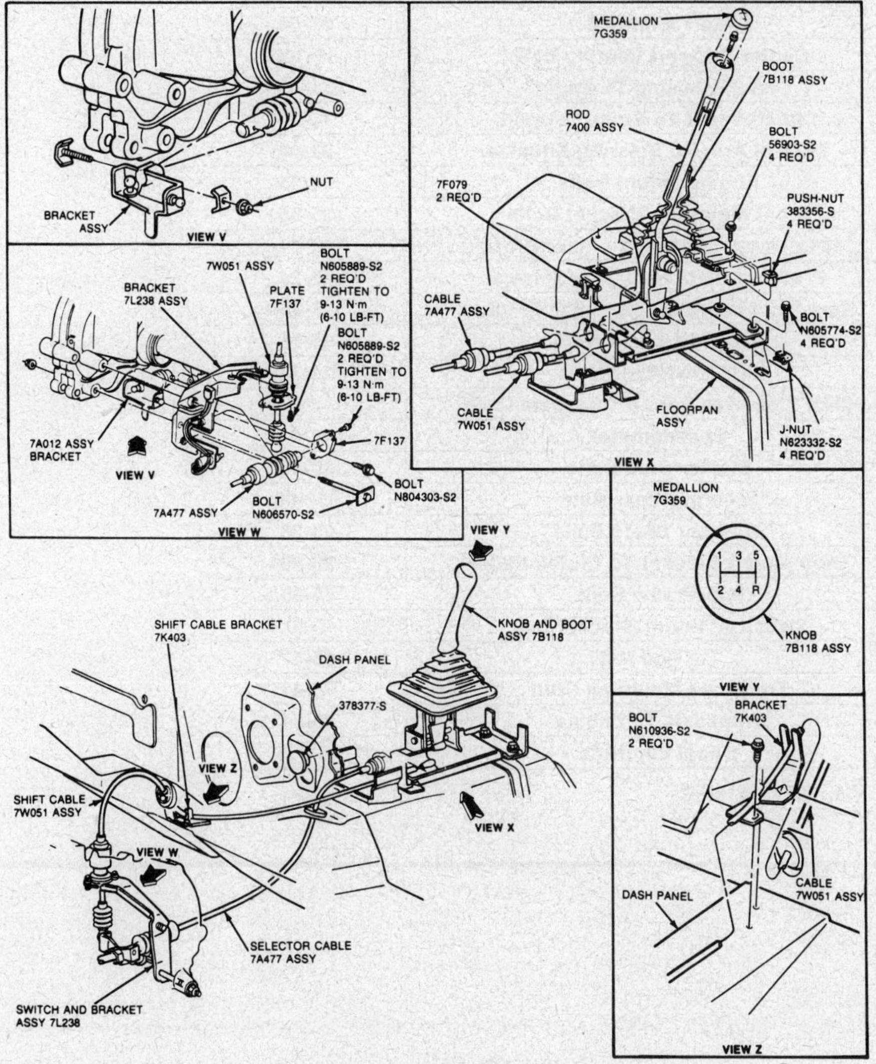


**Fig. 3 Gearshift linkage**

2. Wedge a block of wood approximately seven inches in length under clutch pedal to hold pedal up slightly higher than it normal position.
3. Remove air cleaner hose.
4. Grasp clutch cable end with fingers and pull forward, disconnect end from clutch release shaft assembly.
5. Remove clutch cable casing from rib on top surface of transaxle case.
6. Install engine lifting eyes, then tie up wiring harness and power steering cooler hoses.
7. Disconnect speedometer cable and speed sensor wire.
8. Using engine support fixture tool No. 014-00750 or equivalent, support engine.
9. Raise and support vehicle, then remove tire and wheel assemblies.
10. Remove nut and bolt attaching lower control arm ball joint to steering knuckle. Discard removed nut and bolt, then repeat procedure on opposite side.
11. Using halfshaft remover tool No. D83P-4026-A or equivalent, pry lower control arm away from steering knuckle as shown in **Fig. 4.** Repeat procedure on opposite side. **Use care not to damage or cut ball joint boot. Pry bar must not contact the lower arm.**
12. Remove upper nut from stabilizer bar and separate stabilizer from knuckle.
13. Remove tie rod nut and separate tie rod end from knuckle.
14. Disconnect Heated Exhaust Oxygen Gas (HEGO) sensor, then remove exhaust catalyst assembly.
15. Disconnect power steering cooler from subframe and position out of the way.
16. Disconnect battery cable bracket from subframe.
17. Using a large pry bar, pry lefthand inboard CV joint assembly from transaxle. To prevent lubricant leaking from the seal, install transaxle plugs part No. T81P-1177-B or equivalent into transaxle. Repeat procedure on righthand side. **Use care when prying CV joint assembly so as not to damage the differential oil seal.**
18. Remove inboard CV joint from transaxle by grasping lefthand steering knuckle and swinging knuckle and halfshaft outward from the transaxle. Repeat procedure on righthand side. **If CV joint assembly cannot be pried out of transaxle, insert differential rotator tool No. T81P-4026-A or equivalent through side of transaxle and tap joint out, Fig. 5.**
19. Wire halfshaft assemblies in a near level position to prevent damage to assembly during remaining operations.
20. Remove center support bearing retaining bolts, then the righthand halfshaft from transaxle.
21. Remove two steering gear retaining nuts from sub-frame. Support steering gear by wiring up tie rod ends to coil springs.
22. Remove transaxle to engine retaining bolts, then disconnect two shift cables from transaxle.

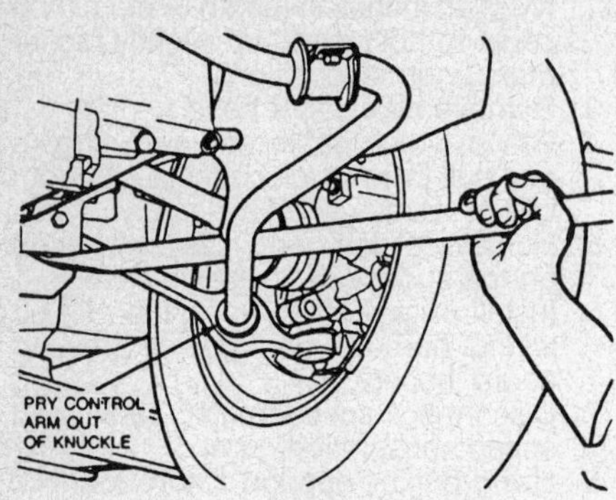


**Fig. 4 Separating control arm & steering knuckle**

23. Remove engine mount bolts, then position jacks underbody mount positions and remove four bolts.
24. Lower sub-frame and position out of the way, then remove starter motor assembly.
25. Remove lefthand engine vibration dampener lower bracket.
26. Using a small screwdriver, disconnect backup lamp switch connector and remove backup lamp switch.
27. Position a suitable transmission jack under transaxle, then lower transaxle and remove it from engine. **Transaxle case castings may have sharp edges, wear protective gloves when handling transaxle assembly.**
28. Reverse procedure to install.

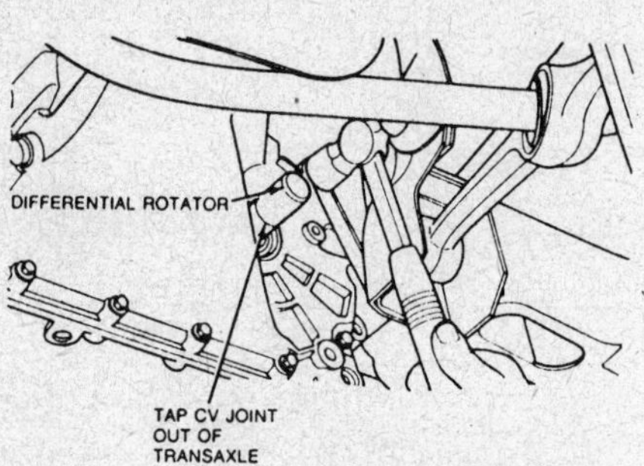


**Fig. 5 Removing CV joint from transaxle**

## TIGHTENING SPECIFICATIONS

| Year | Component | Torque/Ft. Lbs. |
|---|---|---|
| 1989–92 | Air Manage Valve Bracket Bolt To Transaxle | 28-31 |
| | Ball Joint Nut | 37-44 |
| | Center Support Bearing Bolts | 85-100 |
| | Clutch Housing To Engine | 31–39 |
| | Clutch Pedal To Brake Support | 15–25 |
| | Control Arm To Steering Knuckle | 37-44 |
| | Engine Mount Bolts | 40-55 |
| | Front Mounting Bracket Bolts | 25-35 |
| | Lower Mount Bracket To Inner Bracket | 45-61 |
| | Pressure Plate Mounting Screws | 12-24 |
| | Rear Mount Bracket To Lower Bracket | 45-61 |
| | Rear Mounting Bolts | 35-50 |
| | Roll Restrictor Nuts | 25-30 |
| | Shift Stabilizer Bar To Transaxle Case | ① |
| | Speedometer | 3-4 |
| | Starter Stud Bolts | 30-40 |
| | Steering Gear Nuts | 85-100 |
| | Stiffener Brace Bolts | 28-38 |
| | Stop Mount Bracket To Clutch Pedal | 26-29 |
| | Sub-Frame Bolts | 65-85 |
| | Switch Actuator Bracket Bolt | 7-10 |
| | Tie Rod Nut | 35-47 |
| | Transaxle Mounting Stud | 38-41 |
| | Transaxle To Engine | 28-31 |
| | Wheel Lug Nuts | 85-105 |

①—1989–91, 23–35 ft. lbs., 1992, 35–46 ft. lbs.

# Rear Suspension

## INDEX



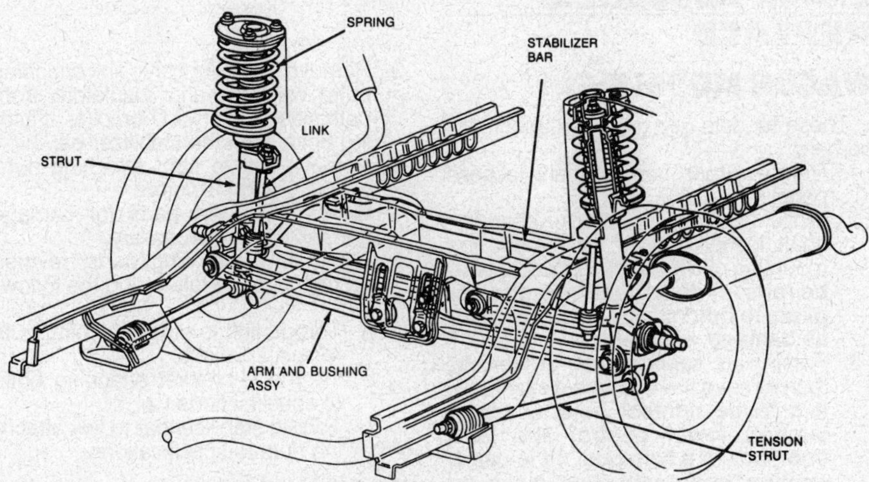


**Fig. 1 Rear suspension. Sedan**

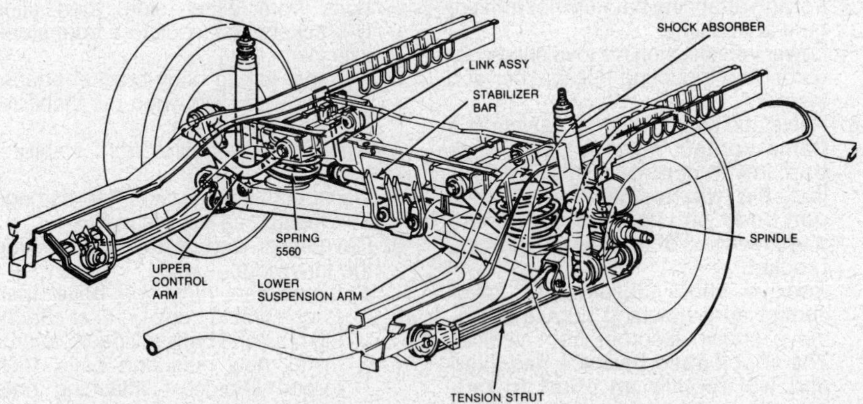


**Fig. 2 Rear suspension. Wagon**

## DESCRIPTION

### SEDAN MODELS

These models utilize an independent rear suspension. Each side consists of a MacPherson strut, an upper mount and washers, two parallel lower control arms, a tension strut, a spindle and a stabilizer bar mounted on the strut.

The top of the MacPherson strut is attached to the inner body side panel, while the lower end of the strut is attached to the spindle with a pinch clamp and bolt. The parallel lower control arms attach to the underbody with nuts and bolts. The tension strut attaches to the lower part of the spindle and to the underbody, **Fig. 1**.

### WAGON MODELS

These models also utilize an independent rear suspension. Each side consists of an upper and lower control arm, a shock absorber, a two piece spindle tension control strut and a coil spring.

The top of the shock absorber is attached to the body side panel by a rubber insulated top mount assembly and to the lower control arms by two nuts. The upper control arm attaches to the crossmember and the upper part of the spindle. The lower control arm attaches to the underbody and lower part of the spindle. The coil spring operates against the lower control arm and is located inboard of the shock absorber, **Fig. 2**.

## STRUT, UPPER MOUNT & SPRING REPLACE

### SEDAN MODELS

1. Position suitable jack or hoist under vehicle, then raise just enough to contact body.
2. Working in trunk, loosen, but do not remove, the three strut to inner body attaching nuts.
3. Raise and support vehicle, then remove tire and wheel assembly from side being worked on.
4. Remove brake differential valve to control arm attaching bolt.
5. Using suitable wire suspend control arm to body to ensure proper support after strut removal.
6. Remove brake hose to shock strut bracket attaching clip and position hose aside.
7. If equipped with stabilizer bar, remove U-bracket from body, then the stabilizer bar attaching nut, washer and insulator. Separate stabilizer bar from link.
8. Remove tension strut to spindle attaching nut, washer and insulator, then move spindle rearward enough to separate it from tension strut.
9. Remove strut to spindle pinch bolt, then using a pry bar or other suitable tool, separate pinch joint as necessary to allow for strut removal.

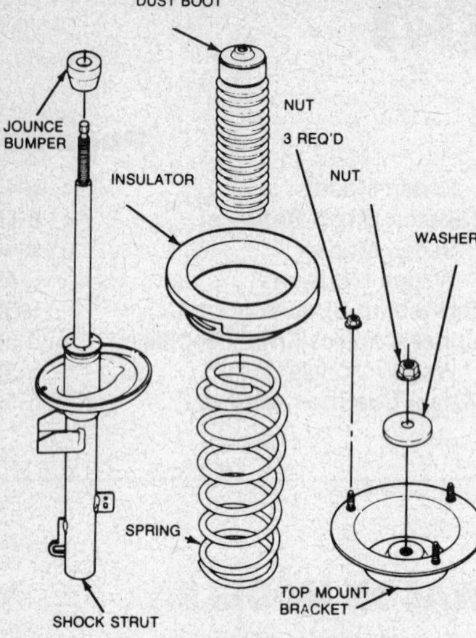


**Fig. 3 MacPherson strut components. Sedan**

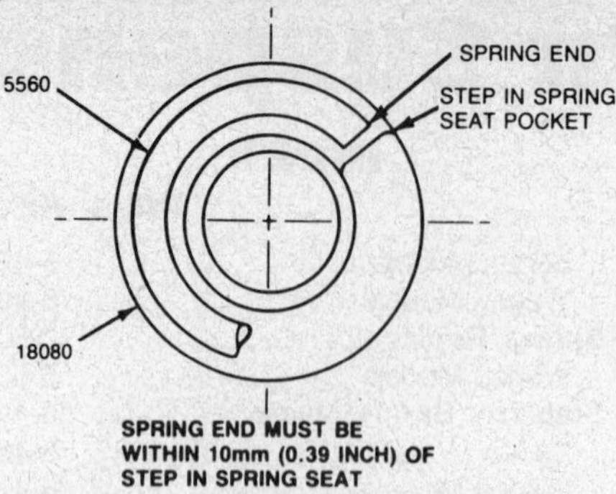


**Fig. 4 Coil spring installation**

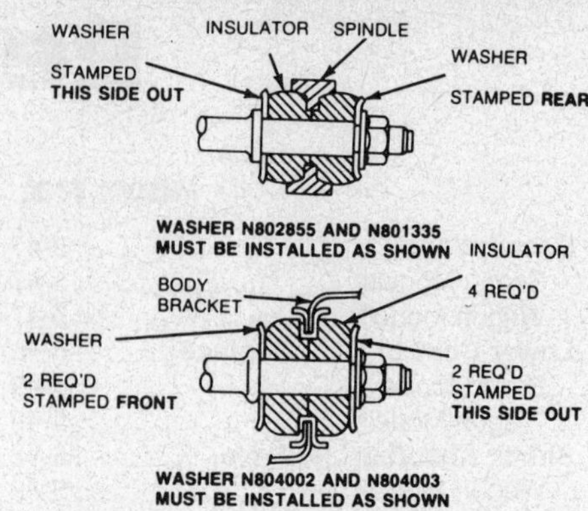


**Fig. 5 Tension strut bushing installation. Sedan**

10. Remove strut from pinch joint, then lower vehicle as necessary to allow removal of bolts loosened in step 2. Remove strut from vehicle. **During strut removal, use care not to stretch the rear brake hose or kink the steel brake line.**
11. Remove link attaching nut, washer and insulator, then the link from the strut.
12. Mark location of insulator to top mount, then place strut, spring and upper mount assembly in suitable spring compressor and compress spring.
13. While restraining strut shaft from turning, remove strut upper shaft mounting nut. **If strut is to be reused, do not use vise grips or pliers to hold strut shaft as damage will result.**
14. Carefully loosen spring compressor tool, then remove top mount bracket assembly, spring insulator and spring, **Fig. 3.**
15. Using new attaching parts, reverse procedure to install, noting the following:
    a. When installing spring on strut, ensure spring is properly located in upper and lower spring seats. Refer to **Fig. 4,** for spring end placement.
    b. When tightening strut nut, restrain strut shaft from turning. Torque strut nut to specification.
    c. Torque stabilizer link to strut attaching nut to specifications.
    d. Torque strut pinch bolt to specifications.
    e. Torque tension strut to spindle attaching nut to specifications.
    f. Torque stabilizer link to stabilizer bar attaching nut to specifications.
    g. Torque stabilizer bar U-bracket attaching bolt to specifications.
    h. Torque strut top mount to body attaching nuts to specification.

## SHOCK ABSORBER REPLACE

### WAGON MODELS

These models use gas filled shock absorbers.

1. Remove rear compartment access panels.
2. While restraining shock absorber shaft, loosen, but do not remove top mounting nut. **If shock absorber is to be reused, do not use vise grips or pliers to hold shock absorber shaft as damage will result.**
3. Raise and support rear of vehicle, then remove tire and wheel assembly. **If a frame contact hoist is used, support lower control arm with floor jack. If a twin post lift is used, support body with floor jacks on lifting pads forward of tension strut body bracket.**
4. Loosen shock absorber to lower control arm attaching nuts. Do not remove nuts at this time.
5. Lower vehicle, then remove shock absorber top mounting nut, washer and insulator.
6. Raise and support rear of vehicle. **If a frame contact hoist is used, support lower control arm with floor jack. If a twin post lift is used, support body with floor jacks on lifting pads forward of tension strut body bracket.**
7. Remove shock absorber to lower control arm attaching nuts, then remove shock absorber from vehicle. **The shock absorbers are gas filled and will require an effort to collapse them for removal.**
8. Reverse procedure to install, noting the following:
    a. Torque shock absorber top mounting nut to specifications.
    b. Torque shock absorber to lower control arm mounting nuts to specifications.

## STABILIZER BAR REPLACE

### SEDAN MODELS

1. Raise and support vehicle.
2. Remove stabilizer bar to link attaching nuts, washers and insulators from both sides. Remove U-bracket attaching bolts, then the stabilizer bar.
3. Remove link to strut attaching nuts, washers and insulators.
4. Inspect attaching parts for damage and replace as necessary.
5. Using new attaching parts, reverse procedure to install, noting the following:
    a. Torque link to strut attaching nuts to specifications.
    b. Torque U-bracket attaching bolts to specifications.
    c. Torque stabilizer bar to link attaching nuts to specifications.

### WAGON MODELS

1. Raise and support vehicle.
2. Remove U-bracket retaining nuts and bolts from either side, then slide U-brackets and insulators from stabilizer bar.
3. Remove link to body bracket attaching nuts and bolts, then the stabilizer and link assemblies.
4. Slide link assemblies from stabilizer bar.
5. Inspect attaching parts for damage and replace as necessary.
6. Reverse procedure to install, noting the following:
    a. Install new nuts and bolts, then torque link to body bracket attaching nuts and bolts to specifications.
    b. Install new nuts and bolts, then torque U-bracket attaching nuts and bolts to specifications.

## TENSION STRUT REPLACE

### SEDAN MODELS

1. Raise vehicle on frame contact hoist using lift pads located rearward of front wheels and forward of rear wheels. Raise hoist only enough to contact body.
2. Working inside trunk, loosen, but do not remove, three strut to inner body attaching nuts.

3. Raise vehicle, then remove tire and wheel assembly.
4. Remove tension strut to spindle attaching nut.
5. Remove tension strut to body attaching nut.
6. While moving spindle rearward, remove tension strut.
7. Install new inner washers and bushings on both ends of tension strut. Refer to **Fig. 5,** for bushing and washer identification.
8. Install tension strut end into body bracket, then install outer bushing, washers and nut. Do not tighten nut at this time.
9. While moving spindle rearward, install tension strut in spindle, then install outer bushing, washer and nut.
10. Ensure bushings are correctly seated in mountings, **Fig. 5.**
11. Support spindle with suitable jack stand, then working inside trunk, remove three strut to inner body attaching nuts. Install new nuts and torque to specification.
12. Remove jack stand, then install tire and wheel assembly.
13. Lower vehicle.

### WAGON MODELS

1. Raise vehicle on frame contact hoist, then position suitable jack under lower control arm and raise arm to normal curb height.
2. Remove wheel and tire assembly, then tension strut to lower control arm attaching nut and bolt.
3. Remove tension strut to body bracket attaching nut and bolt, then the tension strut.
4. Insert front end of replacement torsion strut in body bracket, then install new attaching nut and bolt. Do not tighten at this time.
5. Position rear end of torsion strut in lower control arm, then install new attaching nut and bolt.
6. Torque torsion strut to body bracket attaching nut and bolt to specifications.
7. Install wheel and tire assembly, then remove jack and lower vehicle.

## SPINDLE REPLACE

### SEDAN MODELS

1. Raise and support vehicle, then remove tire and wheel assembly.
2. Remove brake drum, then the brake hose to strut retaining clip.
3. Remove brake backing plate attaching bolts, then the plate. Wire backing plate out of the way.
4. Remove control arm to spindle attaching bolts, washers and nuts, then the tension strut nut, washer and bushing.
5. Remove spindle to strut pinch bolt, then the spindle.
6. Position replacement spindle onto tension strut, then onto shock strut.
7. Install new strut to spindle pinch bolt. Do not tighten at this time.
8. Install tension strut bushing, washer and new nut. Do not tighten at this time.
9. Install new control arm to spindle attaching bolts.
10. Using suitable jack, raise lower control arm to normal curb height, then tighten nuts and bolts as follows:
    a. Torque spindle to strut bolt to specification.
    b. Torque tension strut nut to specification.
    c. Torque control arm to spindle attaching nuts to specification.
11. Install brake backing plate and brake hose to strut retaining clip.
12. Install brake drum and wheel and tire assembly.
13. Lower vehicle.

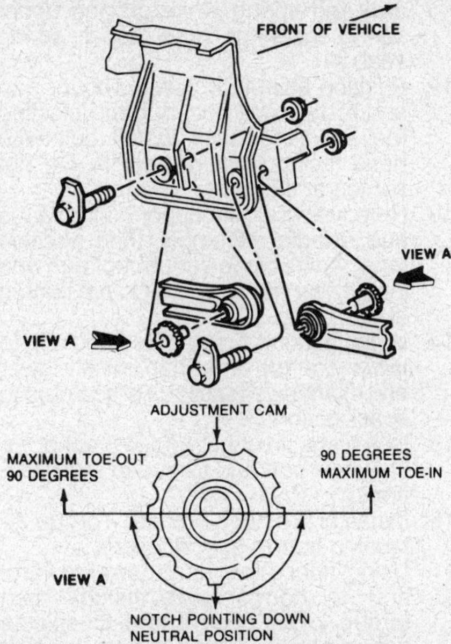


**Fig. 6 Lower control arm bushing & cam installation. Sedan**

### WAGON MODELS

1. Raise and support vehicle, then remove tire and wheel assembly. **If vehicle is raised on frame contact hoist, position suitable jack under lower control arm to raise arm to normal curb height.**
2. Remove brake drum and wheel bearings, then the brake backing plate.
3. Remove upper control arms to crossmember attaching nuts and bolts.
4. Remove bolt, one washer, adjusting cam and nut attaching spindle to lower control arm.
5. Remove spindle and upper control arm as an assembly, then remove upper control arm to spindle attaching nut and the spindle.
6. Install upper control arms to spindle using a new nut. Do not tighten at this time.
7. Position spindle and upper control arm assembly on lower control arm. Install new nut and washer, existing adjusting cam and new nut. Do not tighten at this time.
8. Position front and rear upper control arms to body bracket, then install new nuts and bolts. Do not tighten at this time.
9. Ensure lower control arm is at normal curb height, then proceed as follows:
    a. Torque upper control arms to body bracket attaching bolts to specifications.
    b. Torque upper control arms to spindle attaching nut to specifications.
    c. Torque spindle to lower control arm attaching nut to specifications.
    d. Install brake backing plate, brake drum and wheel bearings.
    e. Install tire and wheel assembly, then remove jack assembly and lower vehicle.

## LOWER CONTROL ARM REPLACE

### SEDAN MODELS

1. Raise and support vehicle.
2. Disconnect brake proportioning valve from left side front control arm, then the parking brake cable from control arms.
3. Remove control arm to spindle attaching bolt, nut and washer.
4. Remove control arm to body bracket attaching bolt and nut, then the control arm.
5. Position control arm (and cam where required, **Fig. 6**), at body bracket, then install new nut and bolt. Do not tighten at this time. **When installing control arms, the offset must face up (the arms are stamped "bottom" on lower edge). The flange edge of the right side rear arm stamping must face the front of the vehicle. The other three must face the rear of the vehicle. During installation, note that the control arms have two adjustment cams that fit inside the bushings at the control arm to body attachment. The cam is installed from the rear on the left arm and from the front on the right arm, Fig. 6.**
6. Position outer end of arm at spindle, then install new bolt, washer and nut. Torque nut to specifications.
7. Torque control arm to body bracket attaching nut to specifications.
8. Attach parking brake cables and brake proportioning valve to control arms.
9. Lower vehicle, then check rear toe and reset as necessary.

### WAGON MODELS

1. Raise and support rear of vehicle, then remove tire and wheel assembly.
2. Remove rear spring. Refer to" Spring, Replace" for procedure.
3. Remove lower control arm to body bracket attaching bolt, then the control arm.
4. Position lower control arm in body bracket, then install new nut and bolt with bolt head toward front of vehicle. Do not tighten at this time.

5. Install rear spring. Refer to" Spring, Replace" for procedure.
6. Using suitable jack, support lower control arm at normal curb height, then torque control arm to body bracket attaching bolt to specifications.
7. Torque lower control arm to spindle attaching bolt to specifications.
8. Install tire and wheel assembly, then lower vehicle.

## SPRING
## REPLACE

### WAGON MODELS

1. Raise vehicle on frame contact hoist, then using suitable floor jack, raise lower control arm to normal curb height.
2. Remove tire and wheel assembly.
3. Remove brake hose bracket from body, then the stabilizer bar U-bracket from lower control arm.
4. Remove shock absorber to lower control arm attaching nuts, then the parking brake cable and clip from lower control arm.
5. Remove tension strut to lower control arm attaching nut and bolt, then wire upper control arms and spindle to keep them from dropping down.
6. Remove lower control arm to spindle attaching nut, bolt and toe adjusting cam.
7. Carefully lower control arm with floor jack until spring can be removed.
8. Remove spring and insulators.
9. Install lower spring insulator on control arm. Ensure insulator is seated properly.
10. Position upper insulator on spring, then install spring on lower control arm. Ensure spring is properly seated.
11. Using floor jack, raise lower control arm and spring while guiding upper spring insulator onto upper spring seat.
12. Position spindle in lower control arm and install new bolt, nut and existing toe adjusting cam. Install bolt with head facing front of vehicle. Do not tighten at this time.
13. Remove wire from upper control arms and spindle assembly, then position tension strut in lower control arm and install new nut and bolt. Do not tighten at this time.
14. Install parking brake cable and clip to lower control arm, then install lower end of shock absorber. Torque nuts to specifications.
15. Install stabilizer bar and U-bracket. Install new bolt and torque to specifications.
16. Install brake hose bracket. Torque attaching bolt to specifications.
17. Using floor jack, raise lower control arm to normal curb height, then torque lower control arm to spindle nut and tension strut to body bracket bolt to specifications.
18. Install tire and wheel assembly, then remove floor jack and lower vehicle.
19. Check rear end alignment.

## UPPER CONTROL ARMS
## REPLACE

### WAGON MODELS

1. Raise vehicle on frame contact hoist, then using suitable floor jack, raise lower control arm to normal curb height.
2. Remove wheel and tire assembly, then brake hose bracket from body.
3. Loosen spindle to upper control arms attaching nut.
4. Loosen spindle to lower control arm attaching nut.
5. Remove upper control arms to body brackets attaching nuts and bolts. Ensure spindle does not fall outward.
6. Carefully tilt upper part of spindle outward until upper control arms are clear of body brackets. Wire spindle in this position.
7. Remove spindle to upper control arms attaching nut, then the upper control arms.
8. Install upper control arms on spindle and install new nut. Do not tighten at this time.
9. Position upper control arms in body brackets, then install new nuts and bolts. Torque to specification. Remove wire from spindle.
10. Torque upper control arms to spindle attaching nut to specification.
11. Torque lower control arm to spindle attaching nut to specification.
12. Install brake hose bracket on body, then the tire and wheel assembly.
13. Remove floor jack and lower vehicle.
14. Check rear wheel alignment and correct as necessary.

## WHEEL BEARINGS
## ADJUST

1. Raise and support rear of vehicle, then remove grease cap.
2. Remove cotter pin and nut retainer.
3. Back of adjusting nut one full turn, then while rotating hub and drum assembly to seat bearings, **torque** adjusting nut to 17-25 ft. lbs.
4. Loosen adjusting nut one-half turn, then **retorque** to 10-15 inch lbs.
5. Install nut retainer and cotter pin. Bend over ends of cotter pin over retainer flange. **Properly adjusted wheel bearings may have a slightly loose feel which is considered normal.**

## TIGHTENING SPECIFICATIONS

| Year | Component | Torque/Ft. Lbs. |
|---|---|---|
| 1989–92① | Control Arm To Spindle | 42-57 |
| | Control Arm To Body | 45-65 |
| | Stabilizer Bar Link To Stabilizer Bar | 5-7 |
| | Stabilizer Bar Link To Strut | 5-7 |
| | Stabilizer U-Bracket To Body | 25-34 |
| | Strut Top Mount To Body | 19-26 |
| | Strut To Top Mount | 35-50 |
| | Strut To Spindle | 50-67 |
| | Tension Strut To Spindle | 35-50 |
| | Tension Strut To Body | 35-50 |
| | Wheel Lug Nut | 85–105 |
| 1989–92② | Brake Hose Bracket | 8-12 |
| | Lower Control Arm To Body | 40-52 |
| | Shock Absorber To Body | 19-27 |
| | Shock Absorber To Lower Suspension Arm | 12-20 |
| | Spindle To Lower Control Arm | ③ |
| | Stabilizer Bar U-Bracket To Lower Suspension Arm | 20-30 |
| | Stabilizer Link Assembly To Body | 40-52 |

*Continued*

## TIGHTENING SPECIFICATIONS—Continued

| Year | Component | Torque/Ft. Lbs. |
|---|---|---|
| 1989-92② | Tension Strut To Body | 40-52 |
| | Tension Strut To Lower Suspension Arm | 40-52 |
| | Upper Control Arms To Body | 70-95 |
| | Upper Control Arms To Spindle | 150-190 |
| | Upper Suspension Arm To Spindle | 40-55 |
| | Wheel Lug Nuts | 85-105 |

①—Sedan models.
②—Wagon models.
③—1989-91, 60-86 ft. lbs., 1992, 40-55 ft. lbs.

# Front Suspension & Steering

## INDEX



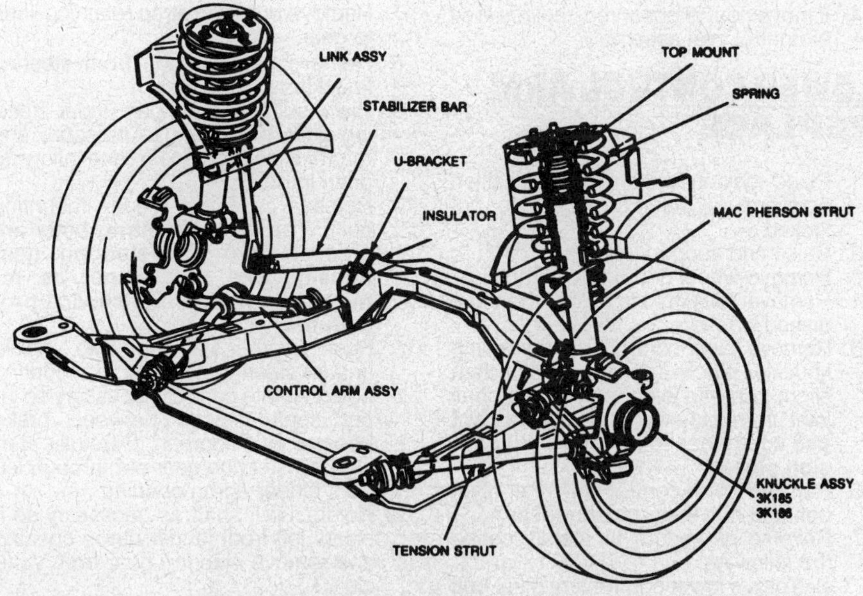


**Fig. 1 Front suspension assembly**

## DESCRIPTION

This suspension is of the gas filled MacPherson strut type, **Fig. 1.** The strut top mount consists of a rubber insulated bearing and seat and coil spring insulator. The top mount is attached to the body side apron by three bolts. The lower part of the strut is mounted in the steering knuckle and is retained by a pinch bolt. A forged lower control arm is attached to the sub-frame and to the steering knuckle. A tension strut is connected to the lower control arm and to the forward part of the sub-frame.

## STRUT ASSEMBLY REPLACE

1. Place ignition switch in Off position and ensure steering wheel is not locked.
2. Remove hub nut and loosen three strut attaching nuts, then raise and support vehicle. Do nut raise vehicle with lower control arm.
3. Remove wheel and tire assembly.
4. Remove brake caliper and wire it aside.
5. Remove brake rotor and tie rod end.
6. Remove stabilizer bar link nut, then remove link from strut.
7. Remove lower control arm to steering knuckle pinch nut and bolt, then slightly spread joint and remove lower control arm.
8. Using suitable hub remover/installer, press axle from hub. Wire axle shaft to body to maintain level position. **Do not allow axle shaft to move outward. Over extension of the constant velocity (CV) joint could result in separation of internal parts, which could cause CV joint failure.**
9. Remove strut to steering knuckle pinch bolt, then spread joint slightly and remove steering knuckle and hub assembly.
10. Remove strut attaching nuts, then remove strut assembly from vehicle.
11. Compress strut spring with coil spring compressor D85P-7178-A or equivalent.
12. Using a 10 mm box wrench, restrain strut shaft, then remove strut mounting nut with suitable 21 mm crow foot socket. **Do not allow strut shaft to rotate.**

13. Loosen compressor tool, then remove strut top mount bracket assembly, bearing and seat assembly and spring, **Fig. 2.**
14. Reverse procedure to install, noting the following:
    a. Torque strut to steering knuckle pinch bolt to specification.
    b. Torque lower control arm to steering knuckle pinch bolt to specifications.
    c. Torque stabilizer bar assembly to strut to specifications.
    d. Torque tie rod end attaching nut to specification.
    e. Torque strut attaching nuts to specifications.
    f. With vehicle on ground, torque hub nut to specification.

## STEERING KNUCKLE
### REPLACE

1. Place ignition switch in Off position and ensure steering wheel is not locked.
2. Remove hub nut and loosen three strut attaching nuts, then raise and support vehicle. Do not raise vehicle with lower control arm.
3. Remove wheel and tire assembly.
4. Remove brake caliper and wire it aside.
5. Remove brake rotor and tie rod end.
6. Remove stabilizer bar link nut, then remove link from strut.
7. Remove lower control arm to steering knuckle pinch nut and bolt, then slightly spread joint and remove lower control arm.
8. Using suitable hub remover/installer, press axle from hub. Wire axle shaft to body to maintain level position. **Do not allow axle shaft to move outward. Over extension of the constant velocity (CV) joint could result in separation of internal parts, which could cause CV joint failure.**
9. Remove rotor splash shield (if equipped).
10. Remove strut to steering knuckle pinch bolt, then spread joint slightly and remove steering knuckle and hub assembly.
11. Reverse procedure to install, noting the following:
    a. Torque strut to steering knuckle pinch bolt to specification.
    b. Torque lower control arm to steering knuckle pinch bolt to specification.
    c. Torque stabilizer bar assembly to strut to specifications.
    d. Torque tie rod end attaching nut to specification.
    e. Torque strut attaching nuts to specifications.
    f. With vehicle on ground, torque hub nut to specification.

## BALL JOINT INSPECTION

1. Raise vehicle until wheels fall to a full down position.

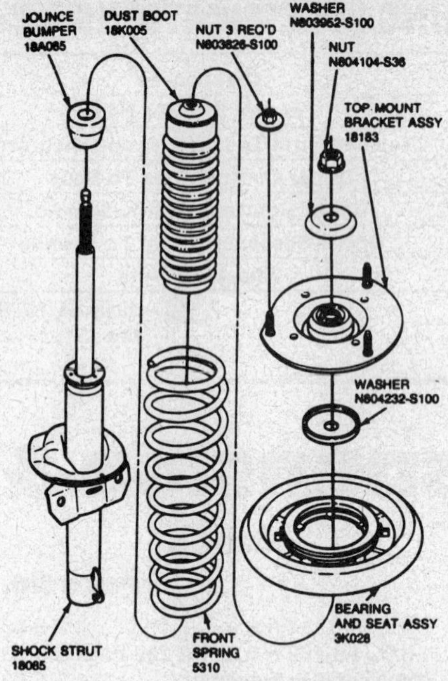


**Fig. 2 MacPherson strut assembly**

2. Grasp lower edge of tire and move wheel assembly in and out.
3. As wheel is being moved, observe lower end of knuckle and lower control arm. Any movement would indicate abnormal ball joint wear.
4. If movement is observed, replace lower control arm assembly.

## LOWER CONTROL ARM
### REPLACE

1. Place ignition switch in Off position and ensure steering wheel is not locked.
2. Raise and support vehicle.
3. Remove wheel and tire assembly.
4. Remove tension strut nut, then the dished washer.
5. Remove lower control arm to steering knuckle pinch nut and bolt, then slightly spread joint and separate ball joint from steering knuckle. **Do not use a hammer to separate suspension pieces.**
6. Remove lower control arm inner pivot bolt and nut, then the control arm.
7. Reverse procedure to install, noting the following:
    a. Torque lower control arm pivot bolt to specification.
    b. Torque lower control arm to steering knuckle attaching bolt to specifications.
    c. Torque tension strut nut to specification.

## STABILIZER BAR
### REPLACE

1. Raise and support vehicle.
2. Remove stabilizer bar link to strut attaching nuts.
3. Remove stabilizer bar link to stabilizer bar attaching nuts.
4. Remove steering gear to sub-frame attaching bolts, then move steering gear off sub-frame.
5. Support sub-frame with suitable safety stands, then remove rear sub-frame attaching bolts. Lower rear part of sub-frame to gain access to stabilizer bar mounting brackets.
6. Remove mounting brackets, then the stabilizer bar.
7. Reverse procedure to install, noting the following:
    a. Torque stabilizer bar mounting brackets to specifications.
    b. Torque sub-frame attaching bolts to specification.
    c. Torque stabilizer bar link attaching nuts to specification.

## STEERING GEAR
### REPLACE

1. Disconnect battery ground cable.
2. Remove steering shaft weather boot to dash panel attaching bolts.
3. Remove intermediate shaft to steering column shaft attaching bolts.
4. Move weather boot aside, then remove steering gear input shaft pinch bolt and remove intermediate shaft.
5. Raise and support vehicle.
6. Remove left front wheel and heat shield.
7. Remove bundling strap retaining lines to gear.
8. Remove tie rod ends from steering knuckles.
9. Place suitable drain pan under steering gear, then remove pressure and return lines from gear and allow to drain into pan.
10. Remove nuts from gear mounting bolts. **The gear mounting bolts are pressed into the steering gear housing and should not be removed during normal service procedures.**
11. Push weather boot end into vehicle and lift steering gear out of mounting holes. Rotate gear as necessary so input shaft passes between brake booster and floorpan. Carefully start working steering gear out through left front fender apron opening.
12. Rotate input shaft as necessary so it clears left front fender apron opening and remove steering gear from vehicle.
13. Reverse procedure to install, noting the following:
    a. Prior to installing hydraulic hoses, install new plastic seals on fittings.
    b. Torque steering gear attaching nuts to specification.
    c. Torque hydraulic pressure hose and hydraulic return hose fittings to specifications. **When hydraulic fittings are properly installed, the hoses are free to swivel.**
    d. Fill power steering system with automatic transmission fluid type F.
    e. Set toe-in to specifications.

## POWER STEERING PUMP REPLACE

### 2.5L/4-153 ENGINE

1. Disconnect battery ground cable.
2. Using suitable 1/2 inch drive socket wrench, rotate tensioner pulley clockwise and remove alternator and power steering belts.
3. Position suitable drain pan under pump, then disconnect pressure and return lines and allow fluid to drain.
4. Using hub puller T69L-10300-B or equivalent, remove pulley from shaft.
5. Remove three pump to bracket attaching bolts, then the pump.
6. Reverse procedure to install.

### 3.0L/V6-182 & 3.8L/V6-232 ENGINES

1. Disconnect battery ground cable.
2. Loosen idler pulley, then remove power steering belt.
3. Using hub puller T69L-10300-B or equivalent, remove pulley from shaft.
4. Position suitable drain pan under pump, then disconnect return line and allow fluid to drain.
5. Completely back off pressure line fitting. Line will separate during pump removal.
6. Remove three pump to bracket attaching bolts, then the pump.
7. Reverse procedure to install.

## TIGHTENING SPECIFICATIONS

| Year | Component | Torque/Ft. Lbs. |
|---|---|---|
| 1989–92 | Control Arm Pivot Bolt | 70-95 |
| | Control Arm To Knuckle | 40-55 |
| | Control Arm To Sub-Frame | 70-95 |
| | Hub Nut | 180-200 |
| | Power Steering High Pressure Hose | 20-25 |
| | Power Steering Return Hose | 15-20 |
| | Stabilizer Bar Bracket To Sub-Frame | 22-39 |
| | Stabilizer Bar Link Assembly To Stabilizer Bar | 35-48 |
| | Stabilizer Bar Link Assembly To Shock Strut | 55-75 |
| | Stabilizer Bar Mounting Brackets | 85-100 |
| | Steering Gear Attaching Nuts | 85-100 |
| | Strut Top Mount To Body | 22-32 |
| | Strut To Top Mount | 35-50 |
| | Strut To Knuckle | 70-95 |
| | Tension Strut To Control Arm | 70-95 |
| | Tension Strut To Sub-Frame | 70-95 |
| | Tie Rod End To Steering Knuckle | 23-36 |
| | Wheel Lug Nuts | 85-105 |

# Wheel Alignment

INDEX



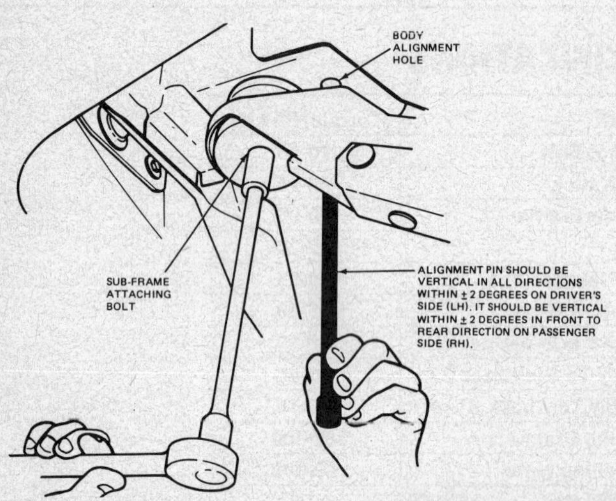


**Fig. 1 Aligning front suspension**

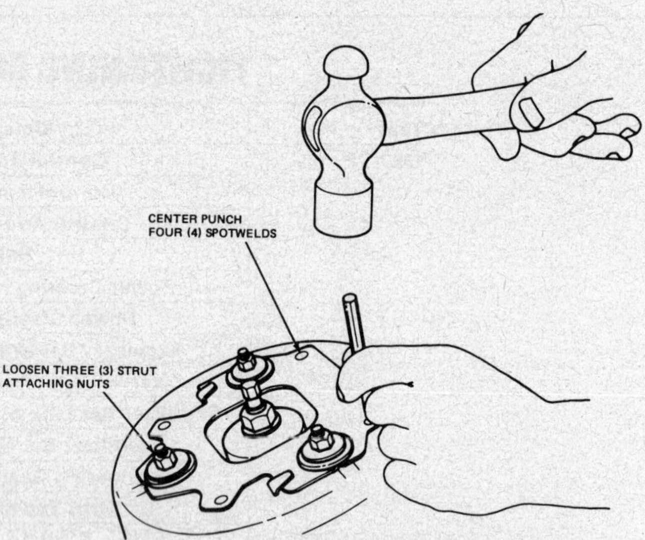


**Fig. 2 Loosening alignment plate**

## FRONT WHEEL ALIGNMENT

### CASTER & CAMBER

1. Prior to aligning the front end, the sub-frame alignment must be checked using the following procedure.
   a. Loosen sub-frame to body attaching bolts.
   b. Install a 3/4 inch outside diameter pipe or similar tool into left front sub-frame and body alignment holes, **Fig. 1.**
   c. Align left front sub-frame and body alignment holes, then slightly tighten left front sub-frame attaching bolt.
   d. Repeat steps b and c on right front alignment holes, then recheck left front alignment.
   e. Torque sub-frame attaching bolts to specifications.
2. Center punch spot welds on both strut alignment plates, then loosen strut attaching nuts, **Fig. 2.**
3. Using Rotunda Spot-Eze or equivalent, remove spot welds. **Do not drill deeper than thickness of alignment plates.**
4. Remove strut attaching nuts, then the alignment plates.

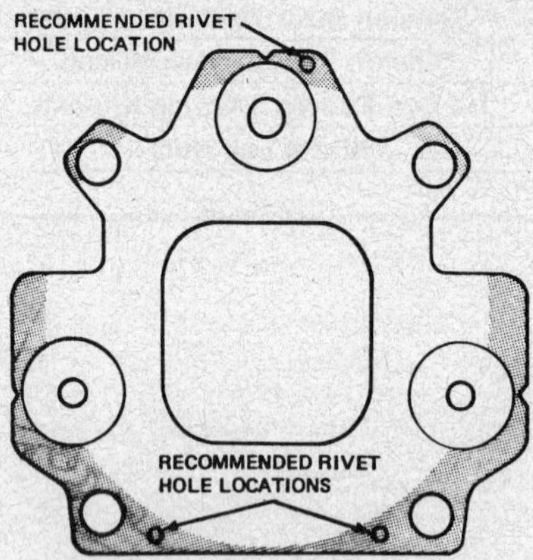


**Fig. 3 Rivet hole location**

5. Remove burrs from strut towers and alignment plates, then paint all exposed metal on strut towers and alignment plates.
6. Install alignment plates, then loosely install strut attaching nuts.
7. Align front end, then torque strut attaching nuts to specifications.
8. Drill three 1/8 inch holes as indicated in **Fig. 3,** through alignment plates and strut towers, then paint exposed metal. **Do not drill deeper than 3/8 inch into strut tower.**
9. Install three 1/8 inch diameter pop rivets with a grip range of 1/4 inch into alignment plate/strut tower.

### TOE-IN

To adjust toe-in, lock steering wheel in straight ahead position using suitable steering wheel holder. Loosen and slide off small outer clamps from steering boot to prevent boot from twisting during adjustment procedure. Loosen tie rod adjusting, then adjust left and right tie rods until each wheel has 1/2 the desired total toe specification. Tighten tie rod adjusting nuts and install clamps. Remove steering wheel holding tool.

## REAR WHEEL ALIGNMENT

### CASTER & CAMBER

The caster and camber angles are factory set and cannot be adjusted.

### TOE-IN

On sedan models, toe-in is adjusted by rotating the cams located inside the rear inner lower control arm bushings.

On wagon models, toe-in is adjusted by rotating the cams located inside the outer lower control arm bushings.

# FORD PROBE

**NOTE:** Refer To Rear Of This Manual For Vehicle Manufacturer's Special Service Tool Suppliers.

## INDEX OF SERVICE OPERATIONS-Continued

## INDEX OF SERVICE OPERATIONS-Continued



# Specifications

## GENERAL ENGINE SPECIFICATIONS

| Year | Engine Liter/CID ① | Engine VIN Code ② | Fuel System | Bore & Stroke | Compression Ratio | Net H.P. @ RPM | Maximum Torque Ft. Lbs. @ RPM | Normal Oil Pressure Psi |
|---|---|---|---|---|---|---|---|---|
| 1989-92 | 2.2L/4-133 | C | Fuel Injection | 3.39 x 3.70 | 8.6 | 110 @ 4700 | 130 @ 3000 | 43-57 |
| | 2.2L/4-133 Turbo | L | Fuel Injection | 3.39 x 3.70 | 7.8 | 145 @ 4300 | 190 @ 3500 | 43-57 |
| 1991-92 | 3.0L/V6-182 | U | Fuel Injection | 3.50 x 3.14 | 9.3 | 145 @ 4800 | 165 @ 3400 | 43-57 |

①—CID-Cubic inch displacement.
②—The eighth digit denotes engine code.

## TUNE UP SPECIFICATIONS

| Year & Engine/VIN Code ① | Spark Plug Gap | Ignition Timing BTDC② Firing Order Fig. ④ | Ignition Timing BTDC② Man. Trans. | Ignition Timing BTDC② Auto. Trans. | Ignition Timing BTDC② Mark Fig. | Curb Idle Speed③ Man. Trans. | Curb Idle Speed③ Auto Trans. | Fast Idle Speed Man. Trans. | Fast Idle Speed Auto. Trans. | Fuel Pump Pressure, Psi. |
|---|---|---|---|---|---|---|---|---|---|---|
| **1989** | | | | | | | | | | |
| 2.2L/4-133/C | .041 | ⑥ | 6⑦ | 6⑦ | ⑧ | 750 | 750N | ⑤ | ⑤ | 27–40⑨ |
| 2.2L/4-133/L Turbo | .041 | ⑥ | 9⑩ | 9⑩ | ⑧ | 750 | 750N | ⑤ | ⑤ | 27–40⑨ |
| **1990–92** | | | | | | | | | | |
| 2.2L/4-133/C | .041 | ⑥ | 6⑦ | 6⑦ | ⑧ | 750 | 750N | ⑤ | ⑤ | 27–40⑨ |
| 2.2L/4-133/L Turbo | .041 | ⑥ | 9⑩ | 9⑩ | ⑧ | 750 | 750N | ⑤ | ⑤ | 27–40⑨ |
| 3.0L/V6-182/U | .041 | A | 10⑪ | 10⑪ | B | ⑫ | ⑫ | ⑫ | ⑫ | 30–45⑬ |

*Continued*

## TIGHTENING SPECIFICATIONS—Continued

①—The eighth digit of the Vehicle Identification Number (VIN) denotes engine code.
②—BTDC: Before Top Dead Center.
③—N: Neutral.
④—Before disconnecting wires from distributor cap, determine location of No. 1 wire in cap, as distributor position may have been altered from that shown at the end of this chart.
⑤—Computer controlled, non-adjustable.
⑥—Timed at No. 1 cylinder, front of engine. Firing order, 1-3-4-2.
⑦—With distributor vacuum hoses disconnected & plugged.
⑧—Timing mark located on crankshaft pulley.
⑨—Prior to disconnecting fuel lines, start engine, then disconnect fuel pump relay. After engine has stalled, turn ignition switch to off position. Disconnect fuel line located between fuel filter & fuel rail, install a suitable fuel pressure gauge. After connecting fuel pressure gauge, install fuel pump relay & check fuel system pressure at various engine speeds.
⑩—With test connector grounded. The test connector is located near the left hand strut tower above the brake master cylinder.
⑪—Disconnect in-line spout connector, then start engine & adjust ignition timing as necessary. After completing adjustment, reconnect spout connector.
⑫—Idle speed is controlled by an automatic idle control system.
⑬—Wrap shop towel around fitting to prevent fuel spillage, then connect a suitable fuel pressure gauge to fuel diagnostic valve on fuel rail assembly. Place ignition switch in On position & check fuel pressure gauge reading.

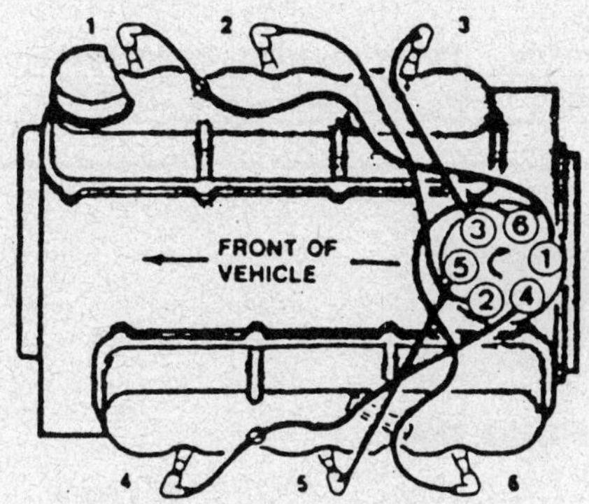

Fig. A

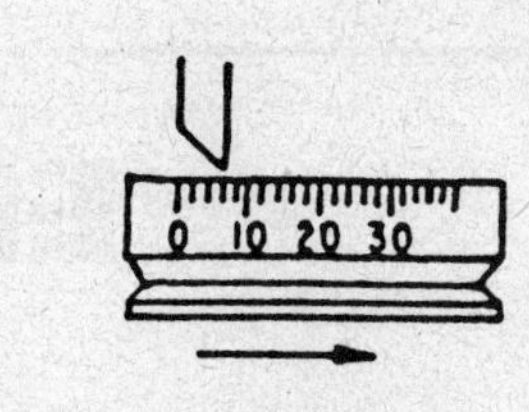


Fig. B

## FRONT WHEEL ALIGNMENT SPECIFICATIONS

| Year | Caster Angle, Degrees | | Camber Angle, Degrees | | | | Toe-In, Inch | King Pin Inclination |
|---|---|---|---|---|---|---|---|---|
| | | | Limits | | Desired | | | |
| | Limits | Desired | Left | Right | Left | Right | | |
| 1989–90 | +.47 to +1.97 | +1.22 | −.47 to +1.03 | −.47 to +1.03 | +.28 | +.28 | 0 | 12.78 |
| 1991–92 | +1 3/20 to +2 13/20 | +1 9/10 | −29/60 to +1 1/60 | − −29/60 to +1 1/60 | +4/15 | +4/15 | .12 | — |

## REAR WHEEL ALIGNMENT SPECIFICATIONS

| Year | | Camber Angle, Degrees | | | |
|---|---|---|---|---|---|
| | | Limits | | Desired | |
| | Left | Right | Left | Right | Toe-In, Inch |
| 1989–90 | −.25 to +1.25 | −.25 to +1.25 | +.5 | +.5 | .12 |
| 1991–92 | −1 11/60 to +19/60 | −1 11/60 to +19/60 | −13/60 | −13/60 | .12 |

## COOLING SYSTEM & CAPACITY DATA

| Year | Engine/VIN ① | Cooling Capacity Less A/C Qts. | Cooling Capacity With A/C Qts. | Radiator Cap Relief Pressure, Psi. | Thermo. Opening Temp. Deg. F | Fuel Tank Gals. | Engine Oil Refill Qts. | Transaxle Oil ② 5 Speed Pts. | Transaxle Oil ② Auto. Trans. Qts. |
|---|---|---|---|---|---|---|---|---|---|
| 1989–92 | 2.2L/4-133/C | 7.9 | 7.9 | 13 | 185 | 15.1 | 4.5③ | 7.2 | 8.3 |
| | 2.2L/4-133/L Turbo | 7.9 | 7.9 | 13 | 185 | 15.1 | 4.5③ | 7.8 | 8.3 |
| 1990–92 | 3.0L/V6-182/U | 9.9 | 9.9 | 16 | 197 | 15.1 | 4③ | 7.1 | 8.3 |

①—The eighth digit of Vehicle Identification Number (VIN) denotes engine code.

②—Approximate. Make final check with dipstick.

③—Add ½ qt. with filter change.

## LUBRICANT DATA

| Year | Model | Transaxle Manual | Transaxle Automatic | Power Steering | Brake System |
|---|---|---|---|---|---|
| 1989–92 | All | Mercon | Mercon | Mercon | DOT 3 |

# Electrical

## INDEX



## FUSE PANEL & FLASHER LOCATION

The main fuse panel is located on the lefthand side of the engine compartment, near the battery. The interior fuse panel is located just above the lefthand side kick panel.

The flasher relay box is mounted below the lefthand side of the instrument panel, on the bulkhead.

## STARTER REPLACE

### 2.2L/4-133 ENGINE

1. Disconnect battery ground cable.
2. **On models with manual transaxles,** remove exhaust pipe bracket.
3. **On all models,** remove transaxle to engine bracket, then the intake manifold to engine bracket.
4. Disconnect wiring from starter motor.
5. Remove three starter motor attaching bolts, then the starter motor from the vehicle.
6. Reverse procedure to install, noting the following:
   a. **Torque** starter motor attaching bolts to 23-34 ft. lbs.
   b. **Torque** intake manifold to engine bracket bolts to 14-22 ft. lbs.
   c. **On automatic transaxle models,** when installing the transaxle to engine bracket, **torque** bellhousing bolt to 66-86 ft. lbs., then the remaining three bracket bolts to 27-38 ft. lbs.
   d. **On manual transaxle models,** when installing the transaxle to engine bracket, **torque** bracket bolts to 32-45 ft. lbs.

### 3.0L/V6-182 ENGINE

**When servicing starter or performing any maintenance in the area of starter, note heavy gauge input lead connected to starter solenoid is Hot at all times. Ensure protective cap is installed over terminal and is replaced after service.**

1. Disconnect battery ground cable.
2. **On models with automatic transaxle,** remove kickdown cable routing bracket from engine block.
3. **On all models,** disconnect wire from

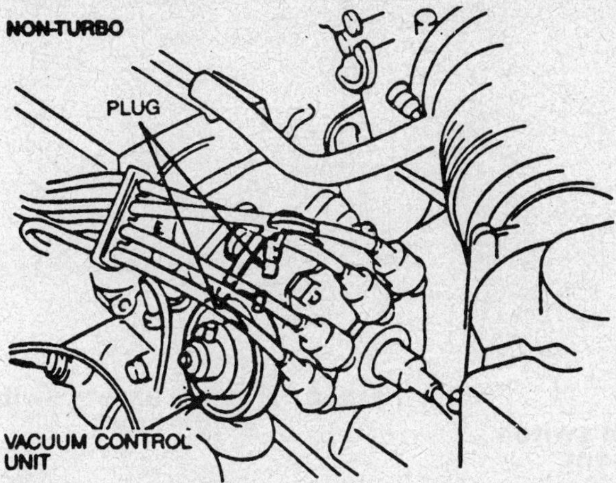


**Fig. 1 Distributor vacuum hose location**

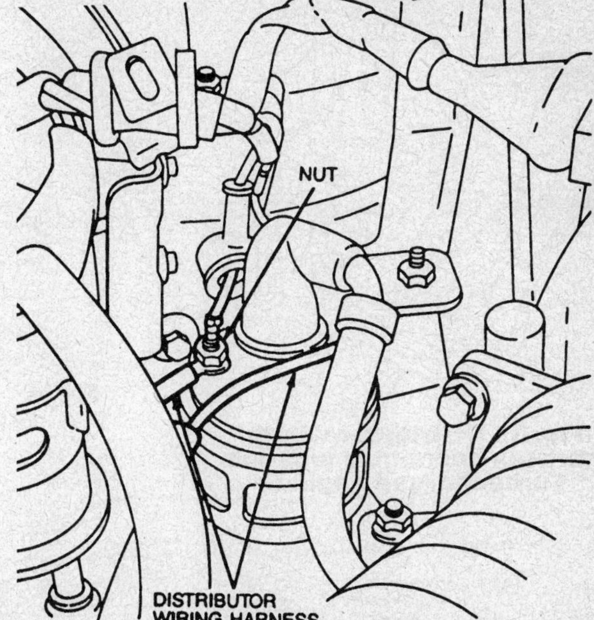


**Fig. 2 Distributor wiring harness connector location. Non-turbocharged engines**

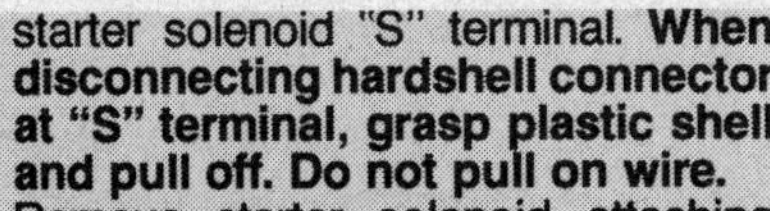

starter solenoid "S" terminal. **When disconnecting hardshell connector at "S" terminal, grasp plastic shell and pull off. Do not pull on wire.**

4. Remove starter solenoid attaching nut, then disconnect cable from terminal.
5. Remove starter mounting bolts, then the starter motor.
6. Reverse procedure to install. **Torque starter mounting bolts to 15-20 ft. lbs.**

# DISTRIBUTOR
## REPLACE

### 2.2L/4-133 ENGINE

1. Disconnect battery ground cable.
2. **On non-turbocharged engines,** disconnect distributor vacuum hoses, noting location for reference during installation, **Fig. 1,** then disconnect distributor electrical connector from coil, **Fig. 2.**
3. **On turbocharged engines,** disconnect distributor electrical connector near distributor, **Fig. 3.**
4. **On all models,** remove distributor cap and position aside.
5. Position No. 1 piston at TDC on compression stroke.
6. Mark position of distributor in engine and position of rotor on distributor housing for installation reference.
7. Remove distributor hold-down bolts, then lift distributor out of engine. **Do not crank engine after distributor has been removed.**
8. Reverse procedure to install, noting the following:
   a. Ensure No. 1 piston is at TDC on the compression stroke.
   b. Install new O-ring onto distributor shaft and lubricate O-ring with engine oil.
   c. Install distributor, ensuring to engage drive gear into camshaft slot.

### 3.0L/V6-182 ENGINE

1. Disconnect battery ground cable.
2. Disconnect primary wiring connector from distributor.
3. Remove spark plug from No. 1 cylinder. **When removing distributor cap, mark position of the No. 1 wire tower on distributor base for installation reference.**
4. Remove distributor cap and position aside.
5. Rotate crankshaft pulley until rotor points to No. 1 wire tower TDC on distributor.
6. Disconnect TFI-IV harness connector.
7. Remove distributor hold-down bolt and clamp, then lift distributor out of engine. On vehicles equipped with security type hold-down bolt, use distributor wrench tool No. T82L-12270-A or equivalent to remove hold-down bolt.
8. Reverse procedure to install, noting the following:
   a. Ensure No. 1 piston is at TDC on the compression stroke.
   b. Tighten distributor hold-down bolt to 17-25 ft. lbs.
   c. Check initial timing. Adjust if necessary.

# IGNITION SWITCH
## REPLACE

1. Disconnect battery ground cable.
2. Remove steering column upper mounting bolts, then the steering column pivot lock assembly. Allow steering column to hang down. **It may be necessary to remove the instrument panel lower panel, lap duct, then defroster duct for access.**
3. Remove ignition switch to ignition switch housing attaching screw, **Fig. 4.**
4. Disconnect four ignition switch snap connectors from left of steering column. **Note location of each wire in the four wire connector. The two key-in warning buzzer wires (green and the red/orange tracer) may be removed by disengaging tang with a paper clip or other tool.**
5. Remove protective looming from ignition switch wiring.
6. Remove ignition switch from vehicle.
7. Install the two key-in warning buzzer wires by aligning the flat side of the wire end with grooved portion of connector, then pushing wire into connector until locking tang engages wire end. Connect the other two ignition switch wires.
8. Install protective looming around ignition switch wiring.
9. Connect the four snap electrical connectors by pushing together until locking tangs engage.
10. Install ignition switch to ignition switch housing attaching screw.
11. Install upper steering column mounting bolts. Install instrument panel lower panel, lap duct, then defroster duct, if removed.

# CLUTCH ENGAGE SWITCH
## REPLACE

1. Disconnect battery ground cable.
2. Disconnect switch wiring from switch.
3. Remove switch from clutch pedal bracket.
4. Reverse procedure to install.

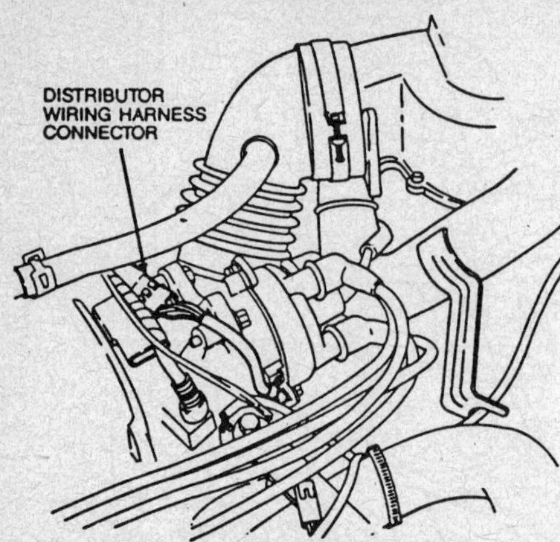


**Fig. 3 Distributor wiring harness connector location. Turbocharged engines**

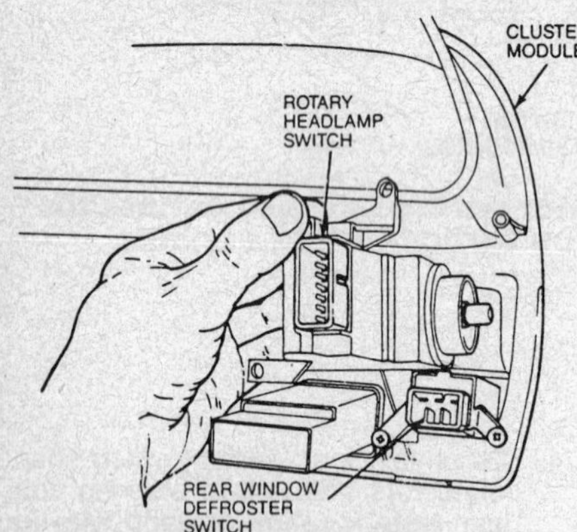


**Fig. 6 Rotary light switch replacement**

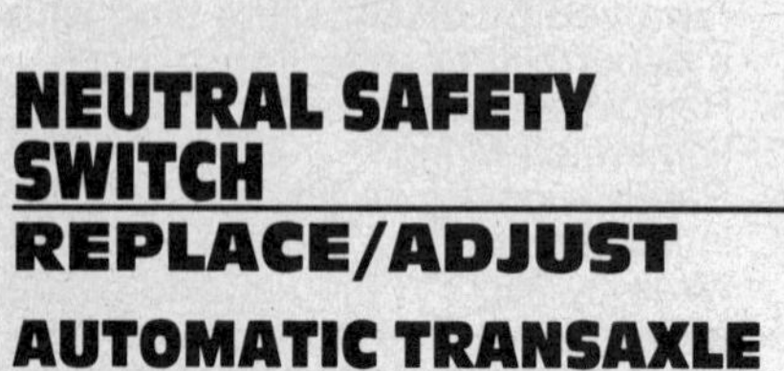

# NEUTRAL SAFETY SWITCH

## REPLACE/ADJUST

### AUTOMATIC TRANSAXLE

1. Disconnect battery ground cable.
2. Set shift lever in Neutral position.
3. Disconnect neutral safety switch wiring connector.
4. Remove neutral safety switch from transaxle.
5. Install replacement switch.
6. Install neutral safety switch attaching bolts. Do not tighten at this time.
7. Insert a .079 inch drill bit through hole provided in switch, **Fig 5.**
8. **Torque** attaching bolts to 69-95 inch lbs., then remove drill bit.
9. Connect neutral safety switch wiring connector, then battery negative terminal.
10. Ensure starter operates in Neutral and Park positions only.

# ROTARY LIGHT SWITCH

## REPLACE

1. Disconnect battery ground cable.
2. Remove turn signal switch as outlined elsewhere in this section.
3. Pull rotary switch knob from switch stem.
4. Remove light switch attaching screws, then the switch, **Fig. 6.**
5. Reverse procedure to install.

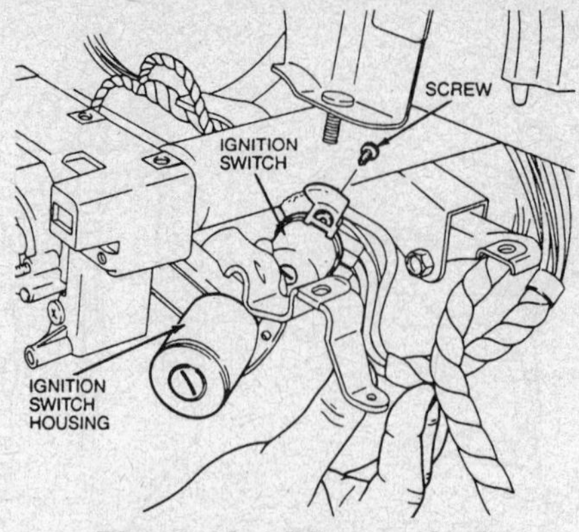


**Fig. 4 Ignition switch replacement**

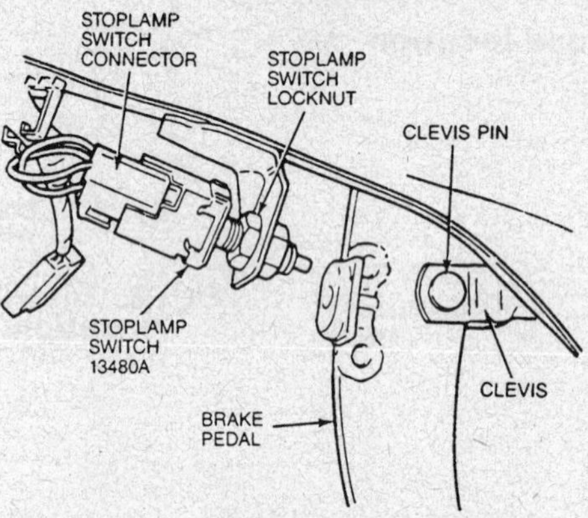


**Fig. 7 Stop lamp switch replacement/adjustment**

# STOP LIGHT SWITCH

## REPLACE

1. Disconnect battery ground cable.
2. Disconnect electrical connector from stop light switch, **Fig. 7.**
3. Loosen locknut securing stop light switch, then rotate switch counterclockwise to remove.
4. Install nuts securing stop light switch to bracket. Do not tighten nuts at this time.
5. Connect electrical connector to switch.
6. Adjust switch for proper operation by rotating the switch to obtain a brake pedal height of 8.54-8.74 inches as measured from the firewall.

# TURN SIGNAL SWITCH

## REPLACE

1. Disconnect battery ground cable.
2. Remove steering wheel as outlined elsewhere in this section.
3. Remove two center cover attaching screws, then the cover.
4. Remove cluster module attaching screws, then disconnect electrical connectors fr om cluster module.
5. Remove cluster module by pulling away from instrument cluster.
6. Remove turn signal arm attaching screw, then the arm.
7. Remove two turn signal switch attaching screws, then the switch from rear of cluster module, **Fig. 8.**
8. Reverse procedure to install.

**Fig. 5 Neutral safety switch adjustment**

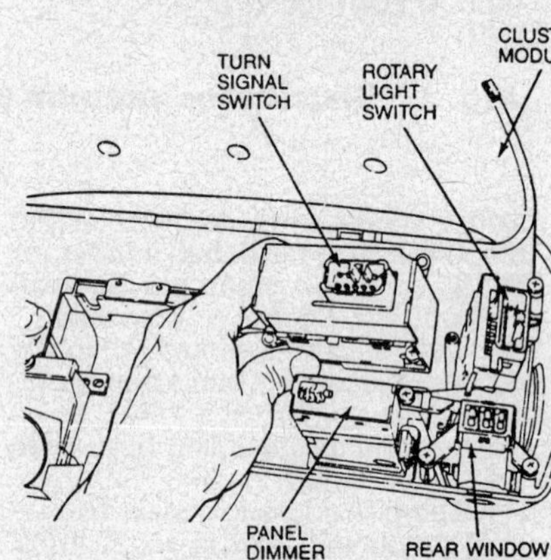


**Fig. 8 Turn signal switch replacement**

# STEERING WHEEL

## REPLACE

1. Disconnect battery ground cable.
2. Remove two screws from back of steering wheel.
3. Pull steering wheel cover pad from steering wheel, then disconnect horn wire from pad. Remove steering wheel hub cover, then the horn switch assembly.
4. Remove steering wheel attaching nut.
5. Place an alignment mark between the steering wheel and steering shaft.
6. Using steering wheel puller T76L-3600-A, or equivalent, remove steering wheel.
7. Reverse procedure to install. **Torque** steering wheel attaching nut to 29-36 ft. lbs.

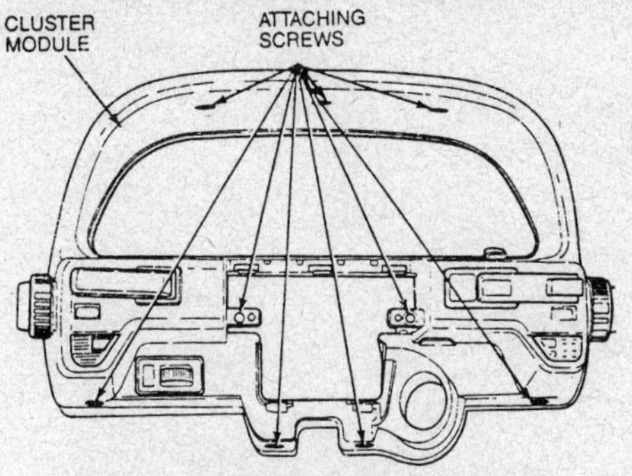


**Fig. 9 Instrument cluster module attaching screw location**

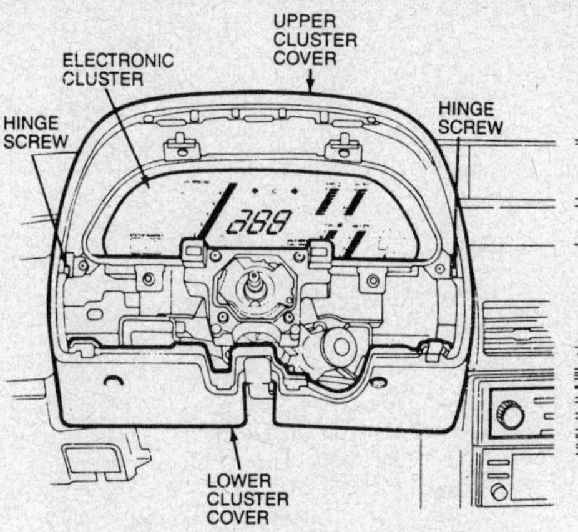


**Fig. 10 Instrument cluster covers, electronic cluster**

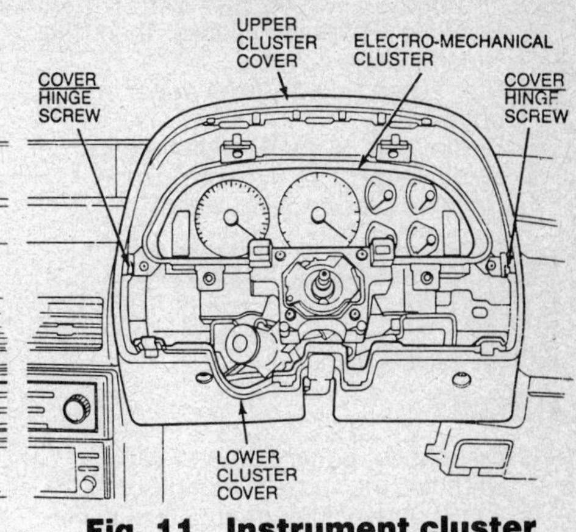


**Fig. 11 Instrument cluster covers, electro-mechanical cluster**

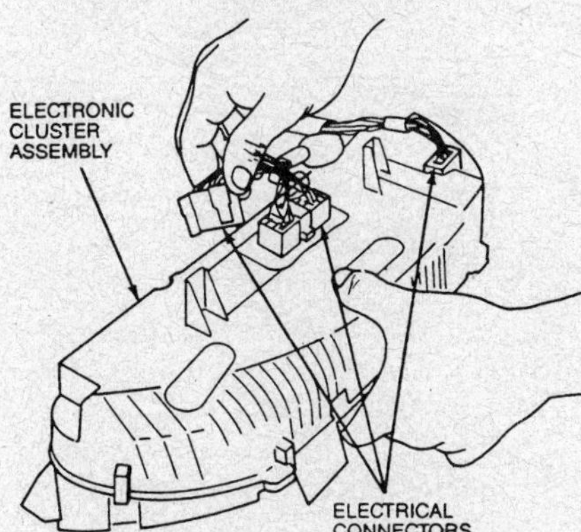


**Fig. 12 Disconnecting instrument cluster electrical connectors, electronic cluster**

# INSTRUMENT CLUSTER
## REPLACE

### LESS ELECTRONIC CLUSTER

1. Disconnect battery ground cable.
2. Remove steering wheel as outlined elsewhere in this section.
3. Remove cluster module.
4. Loosen two cover hinge screws.
5. Remove six upper cluster cover attaching screws, then the cover. **Use caution not to tear rubber seal that joins upper and lower portions of cluster cover panels.**
6. Remove lower cluster cover panel.
7. Remove four cluster mounting screws, then disconnect two electrical connectors from rear of cluster.
8. Disconnect speedometer cable, then remove cluster from vehicle.
9. Reverse procedure to install.

### WITH ELECTRONIC CLUSTER

1. Disconnect battery ground cable.
2. Remove steering wheel as outlined elsewhere in this section.
3. Remove two steering column cover screws, then the cover.
4. Remove nine cluster module attaching screws, **Fig. 9.**

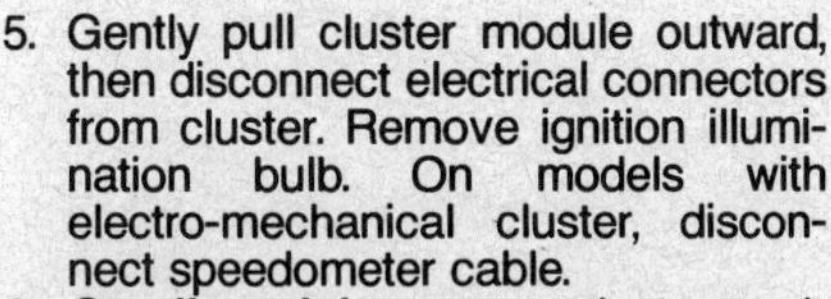

5. Gently pull cluster module outward, then disconnect electrical connectors from cluster. Remove ignition illumination bulb. On models with electro-mechanical cluster, disconnect speedometer cable.
6. **On all models,** remove cluster module.
7. Loosen two cover hinge screws, **Figs. 10 and 11,** , then remove six screws from instrument cluster cover. Remove cover.
8. Remove lower cluster cover panel. **Use caution not to rip the rubber seal that joins the upper and lower sections of the cluster cover panel.**
9. Remove four instrument cluster attaching screws, then disconnect the electrical connectors from rear of cluster, **Figs. 12 and 13.**. Remove cluster from vehicle.
10. Reverse procedure to install.

# RADIO
## REPLACE

1. Disconnect battery ground cable.
2. Remove ash tray.
3. **On manual transaxle models,** remove gearshift and boot trim panel. On automatic transaxle models, remove selector trim panel.
4. **On all models,** remove cigar lighter assembly.
5. Disconnect cigar lighter lamp by twisting the socket.
6. Remove two radio to instrument panel attaching screws.
7. Pull radio from panel, then disconnect electrical connectors and antenna cable.
8. Reverse procedure to install.

# WINDSHIELD WIPER MOTOR
## REPLACE

### FRONT

1. Disconnect battery ground cable.
2. Remove arm and blade assemblies.
3. Disconnect hose from washer jet.

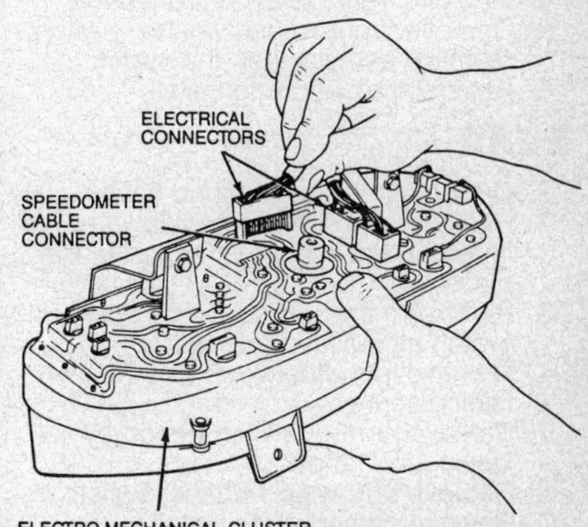


**Fig. 13 Disconnecting instrument cluster electrical connectors, electro-mechanical cluster**

4. Remove lower moulding, then the wiper linkage cover.
5. Pull wiper linkage from wiper motor output arm.
6. Disconnect electrical connectors from wiper motor.
7. Remove wiper motor attaching bolts, then the wiper motor.
8. Reverse procedure to install.

### REAR

1. Disconnect battery ground cable, then remove wiper arm and blade.
2. Remove pivot shaft boot, then the attaching nut and mount.
3. Pry off liftgate interior trim panel.
4. Disconnect wiper motor electrical connector.
5. Remove wiper motor attaching bolts, then the wiper motor.
6. Reverse procedure to install.

# WINDSHIELD WIPER TRANSMISSION
## REPLACE

### FRONT

1. Disconnect battery ground cable.
2. Remove wiper arm and blade assemblies.

3. Remove lower moulding, then the wiper linkage cover.
4. Pull wiper linkage from wiper motor output arm.
5. Remove pivot shaft retaining caps.
6. Remove pivot shafts and linkage.
7. Reverse procedure to install.

# WINDSHIELD WIPER SWITCH

## REPLACE

### FRONT

1. Disconnect battery ground cable.
2. Remove the cluster module as outlin"ed under "Instrument Cluster, Replace."
3. Remove front washer/interval rate control switch.
4. Remove front wiper control switch.
5. Remove front wiper/washer switch retaining screws, then the switch.
6. Reverse procedure to install.

### REAR

1. Disconnect battery ground cable.
2. Remove the cluster module as outlin"ed under "Instrument Cluster, Replace."
3. Remove the front wiper/washer switch as outlined previously.
4. Remove rear wiper/washer switch retaining screws.
5. Remove control switch button by releasing the tangs.
6. Remove rear wiper/washer switch.
7. Reverse procedure to install.

# BLOWER MOTOR

## REPLACE

1. Disconnect battery ground cable.
2. Remove passenger side sound deadening panel.
3. Remove glove box and brace.
4. Remove blower motor cooling hose from blower motor.
5. Disconnect blower motor electrical connector from blower housing.
6. Remove three blower motor housing attaching screws, then the blower motor from vehicle.
7. Remove blower wheel retaining clip, then pull wheel from blower motor shaft.
8. Reverse procedure to install.

# HEATER CORE

## REPLACE

### LESS AIR CONDITIONING

**To replace the heater core, it will be necessary to remove the entire instrument panel, Fig. 14.**

1. Disconnect battery ground cable.
2. Remove steering column.
3. Remove instrument cluster.
4. Remove floor console.
5. Remove hood release handle.
6. Remove ash tray and the cigar lighter assembly.
7. Remove left and right console kick panels.

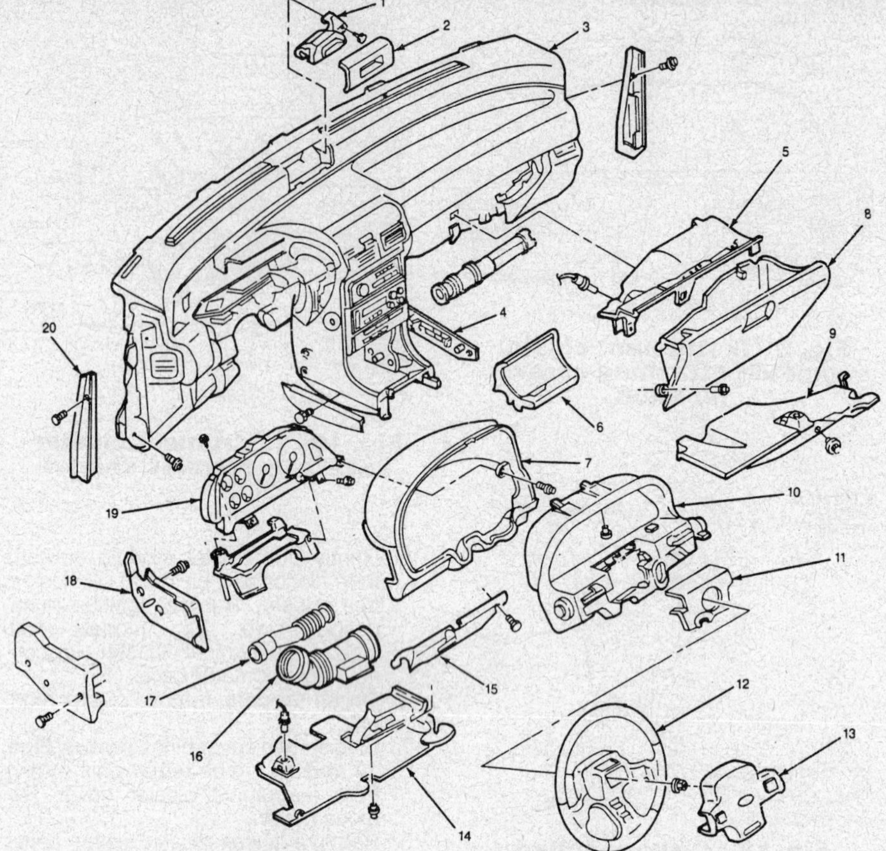

1. TRIP COMPUTER
2. TRIP COMPUTER COVER
3. INSTRUMENT PANEL
4. DASH SIDE COVER
5. GLOVE COMPARTMENT PANEL
6. LAP DUCT
7. CLUSTER COVER
8. GLOVE COMPARTMENT
9. RIGHT SOUND DEADENING PANEL
10. SWITCH MODULE
11. COLUMN COVER
12. STEERING WHEEL
13. STEERING WHEEL COVER
14. LEFT SOUND DEADENING PANEL
15. LOWER PANEL
16. LAP DUCT
17. DEFROST DUCT
18. DASH SIDE WALL
19. INSTRUMENT CLUSTER
20. DASH SIDE COVER

**Fig. 14 Instrument panel assembly**

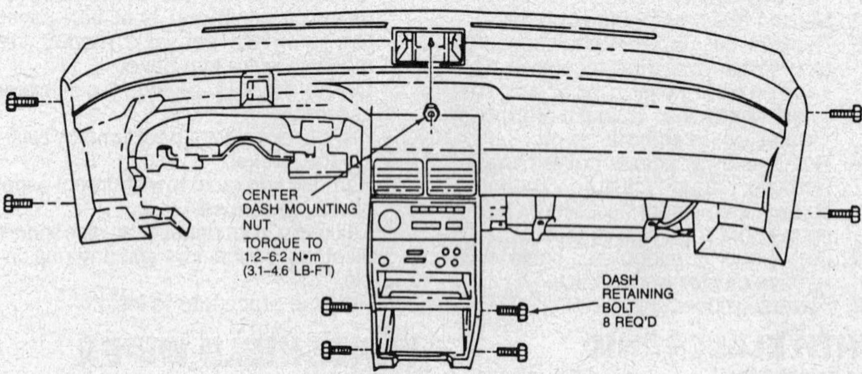


**Fig. 15 Instrument panel attachments**

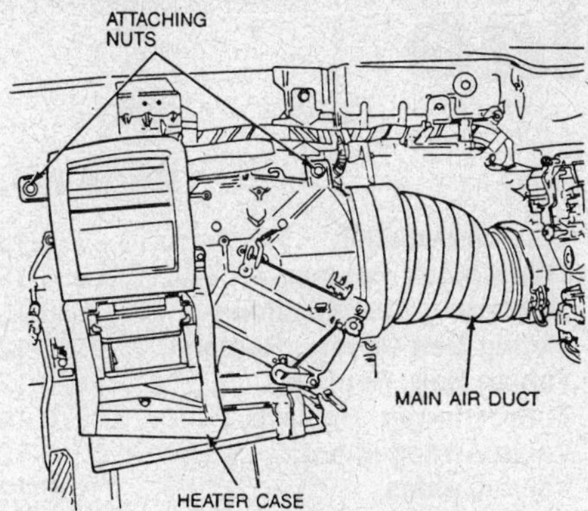


**Fig. 16 Main air duct & heater case attachments, less air conditioning**

8. Remove right and left instrument panel dash side covers.
9. Remove heater or A/C control panel.
10. Remove radio.
11. Remove trip computer.
12. Remove access cover to reach the center instrument panel dash mounting nut, then the nut, **Fig. 15.**
13. Remove eight remaining instrument panel mounting bolts, then the instrument panel, **Fig. 15.**
14. Drain cooling system.
15. Disconnect heater hoses from heater core. Plug core tubes and heater hoses to prevent coolant spillage into passenger compartment.
16. Remove main air duct, **Fig. 16.**
17. Remove heater case mounting nuts, **Fig. 16,** then pull heater case straight out. **Use caution not to bend core tubes.**
18. Remove two heater core tube braces to heater case attaching screws, then the braces.
19. Remove heater core from case by lifting straight up.
20. Reverse procedure to install.

## WITH AIR CONDITIONING

**To replace the heater core, it will be necessary to remove the entire instrument panel, Fig. 14.**

1. Perform steps 1 through 15 as outlined for models "Less Air Conditioning."
2. Discharge refrigerant from A/C system.

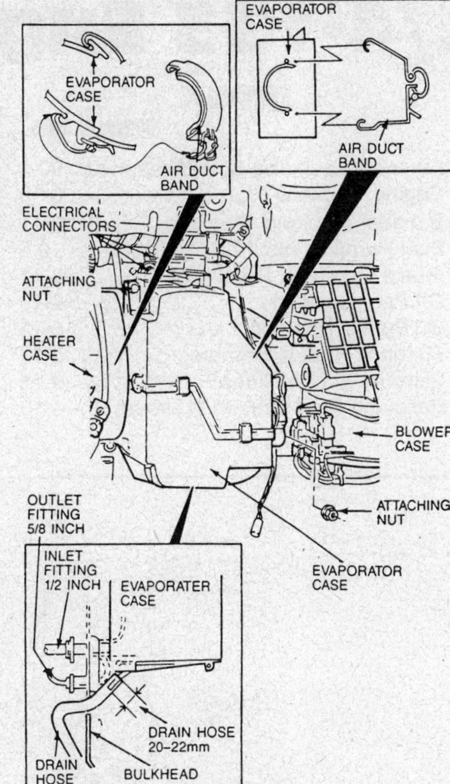


**Fig. 17 Evaporator case assembly**

3. Remove charcoal canister from vehicle.
4. Disconnect refrigerant lines from evaporator. Plug evaporator and lines to prevent entry of dirt and moisture.
5. Disconnect the A/C relay electrical connectors from top of evaporator case.
6. Remove air duct bands, **Fig. 17.**
7. Remove evaporator case attaching nuts, **Fig. 17,** then the evaporator case from vehicle.
8. Remove three heater case mounting nuts, **Fig. 18,** then pull heater case straight out. **Use caution not to bend core tubes.**
9. Remove two heater core tube braces to heater case attaching screws, then the braces.
10. Remove heater core from case by lifting straight up.
11. Reverse procedure to install.

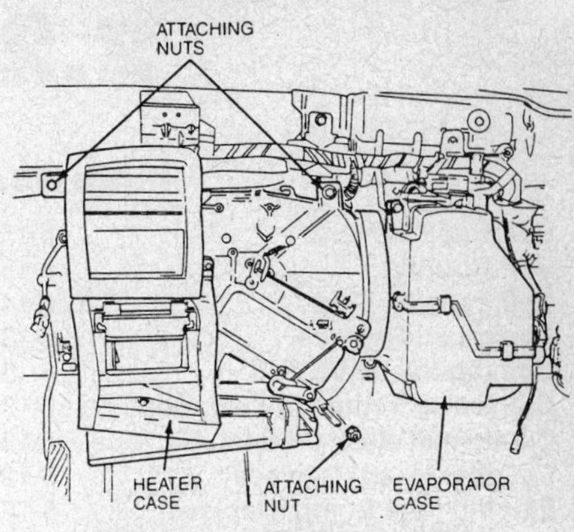


**Fig. 18 Heater case attachments, with air conditioning**

# EVAPORATOR CORE REPLACE

1. Remove instrument panel Fig. 14, as outlined in "Dash Panel Service" section.
2. Disconnect battery ground cable.
3. Discharge refrigerant from system, then remove carbon canister from vehicle.
4. Disconnect A/C lines from evaporator, then plug ends to prevent dirt and moisture from entering system, **Fig. 17.**
5. Fit spring lock coupling tools No. T81P-19623-G2 1/2 inch or tool No. T83P-19623-C 5/8 inch to coupling.
6. Close tool and push into open side of cage to expand garter spring and release female fitting. Garter spring may not release if tool is cocked while pushing into cage opening.
7. After garter spring is expanded, pull fitting apart and remove tool from coupling.
8. Disconnect electrical connectors from A/C relays at top of evaporator core.
9. Remove air duct bands and drain hose.
10. Remove evaporator case attaching nuts, then the evaporator case from vehicle.
11. Carefully remove evaporator case from vehicle.
12. Remove foam seals at inlet and outlet of the cooling unit by peeling them away from evaporator case.
13. Remove seven retaining clips from housing, then separate case halves and remove evaporator.

# 2.2L/4-133 Engine

## INDEX



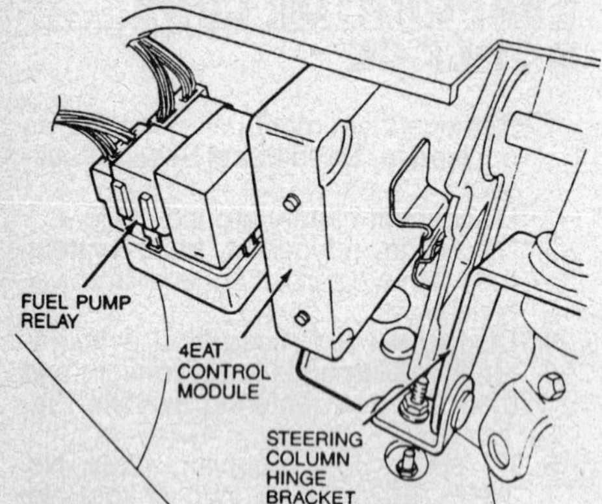


**Fig. 1 Fuel pump relay location**

## RELIEVING FUEL SYSTEM PRESSURE

**On this engine, it is necessary to relieve the fuel system pressure before disconnecting any fuel lines or hoses.**

1. Start engine.
2. Disconnect fuel pump relay, **Fig. 1.**
3. After the engine stalls, turn ignition switch OFF.
4. Reconnect fuel pump relay.

## ENGINE MOUNTS

### REPLACE

Refer to "3.0L/V6-182 engine" section for engine mount replacement.

## ENGINE

### REPLACE

1. Relieve fuel system pressure. **Refer to "Relieving Fuel System Pressure" elsewhere in this section.**
2. Disconnect battery cables, then remove battery.
3. Mark hood hinge locations, then remove hood.
4. Drain cooling system, engine oil, automatic transaxle fluid.

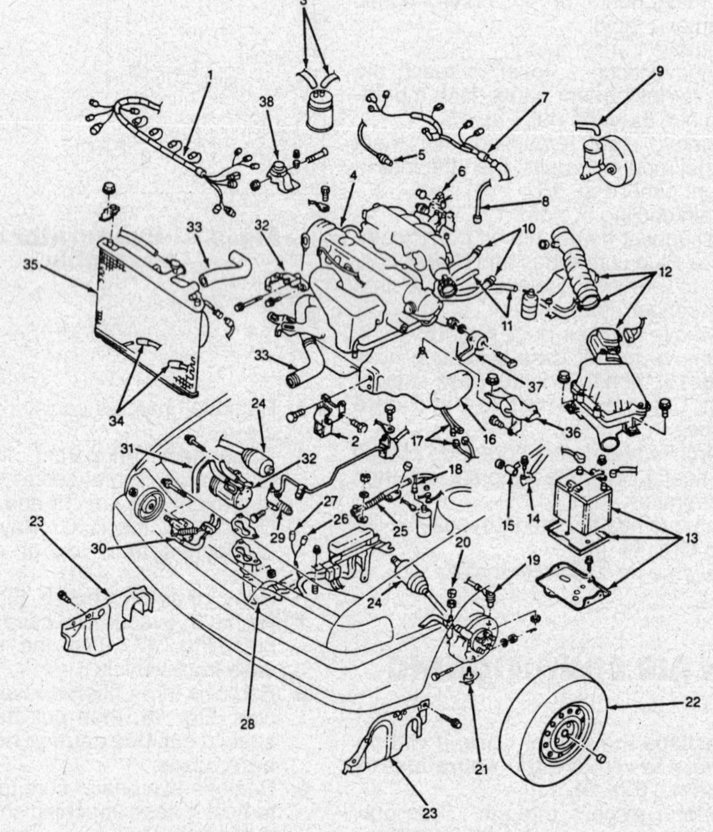

1. EFI HARNESS
2. ENGINE MOUNT #2
3. CANISTER HOSE
4. ENGINE AND TRANSAXLE
5. ACCELERATOR CABLE
6. THREE-WAY SOLENOID ASSEMBLY
7. ENGINE HARNESS
8. SPEEDOMETER CABLE
9. BRAKE VACUUM HOSE
10. HEATER HOSE
11. FUEL HOSE
12. AIR CLEANER ASSEMBLY
13. BATTERY AND BATTERY CARRIER
14. CHANGE ROD (MTX)
15. EXTENSION BAR (MTX)
16. TRANSAXLE
17. TRANSAXLE HARNESS
18. HIGH TENSION LEAD
19. TIE ROD END
20. STABILIZER CONTROL ROD
21. LOWER ARM BUSHING
22. FRONT WHEEL
23. ENGINE SIDE COVER
24. HALFSHAFT
25. CONTROL CABLE (ATX)
26. HEAT GAUGE UNIT CONNECTOR
27. RADIATOR TEMPERATURE SWITCH
28. EXHAUST PIPE
29. CLUTCH RELEASE CYLINDER (MTX)
30. POWER STEERING OIL PUMP
31. DRIVE BELT
32. A/C COMPRESSOR AND BRACKET
33. RADIATOR HOSE
34. ATF HOSE (ATX)
35. RADIATOR AND COOLING FAN
36. ENGINE MOUNT #4
37. ENGINE MOUNT #1
38. ENGINE MOUNT #3

**Fig. 2 Engine compartment component location. Less turbo**

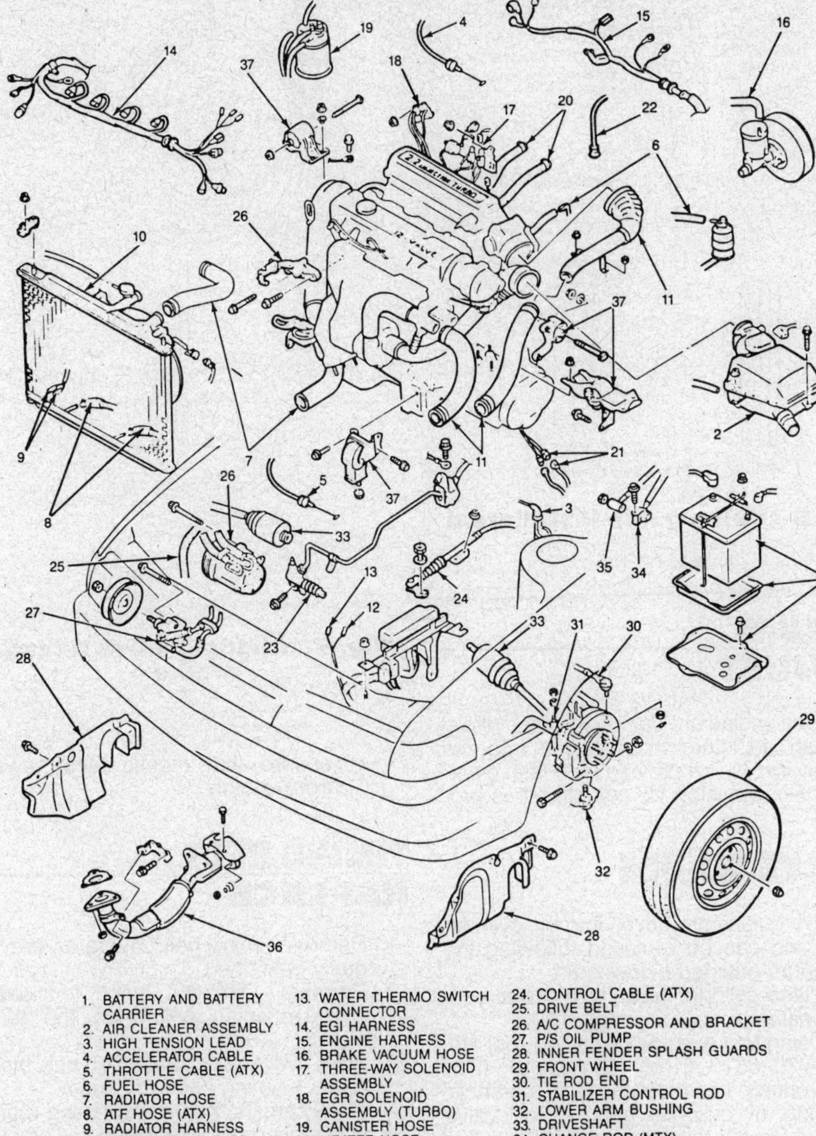


**Fig. 3 Engine compartment component location. With turbo**

5. **On all models,** disconnect or remove the following, **Figs. 2 and 3.**
   a. Battery carrier and fuse holder.
   b. Air filter assembly and duct.
   c. Engine and EFI wiring harnesses.
   d. Distributor wiring at coil and three sensors at thermostat housing
   e. Oxygen sensor.
   f. Radiator and cooling fan electrical connectors.
   g. Automatic transaxle models: transaxle oil cooler lines.
   h. Manual transaxle models: clutch release cylinder.
   i. Front section of exhaust pipe.
   j. Discharge A/C system.
   k. A/C lines on compressor and the A/C compressor clutch electrical connector.
   l. Power steering lines.
   m. Engine ground strap.
   n. Heater hoses and fuel lines.
   o. Vacuum lines to brake booster, charcoal canister, firewall mounted solenoids and distributor.
   p. Automatic transaxle electrical connectors.
   q. Speedometer cable.
6. **On turbocharged models,** disconnect or remove the following:
   a. Turbocharger hoses and pipe.
   b. Driveshafts.
   c. Transaxle shift cable or rod.
7. Install engine lifting equipment.
8. Remove engine mount bolts.
9. Remove engine and transaxle as an assembly from vehicle.
10. Reverse procedure to install.

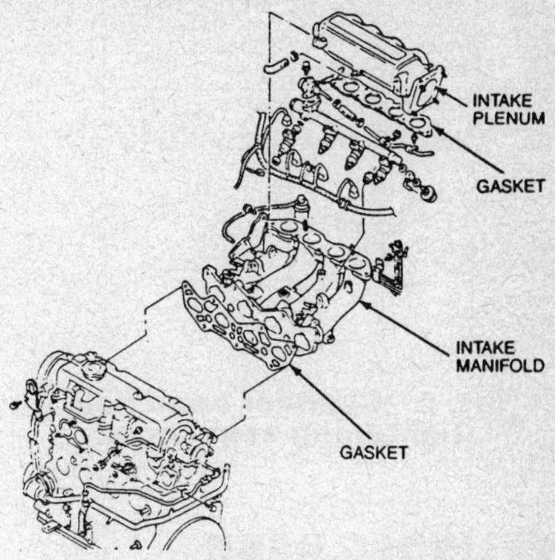


**Fig. 4 Intake manifold & plenum**

## INTAKE MANIFOLD REPLACE

1. Relieve fuel system pressure. **Refer to "Relieving Fuel System Pressure" elsewhere in this section.**
2. Disconnect battery ground cable, then drain cooling system.
3. Remove water hose from bottom of intake manifold.
4. Remove intake plenum, **Fig. 4.**
5. Disconnect EGR pipe and tag, remove wiring, then hoses that may interfere with manifold removal.
6. Remove intake manifold attaching bolts and nuts.
7. Remove intake manifold bracket, then the intake manifold, **Fig. 4.**
8. Clean cylinder head and intake manifold mating surfaces.
9. Install new intake manifold gasket.
10. Install intake manifold, attaching nuts and bolts.
11. Install intake plenum.
12. Install intake manifold bracket, then tighten to specifications.
13. Install remaining components in reverse order.

## EXHAUST MANIFOLD REPLACE

1. Disconnect exhaust gas oxygen sensor electrical connector, then remove sensor from manifold.
2. Remove turbocharger assembly, if applicable.
3. Disconnect exhaust pipe from exhaust manifold, then remove outer heat shield.
4. Remove exhaust manifold attaching bolts, the exhaust manifold, inner heat shield and gaskets.
5. Reverse procedure to install. Tightening to specifications.

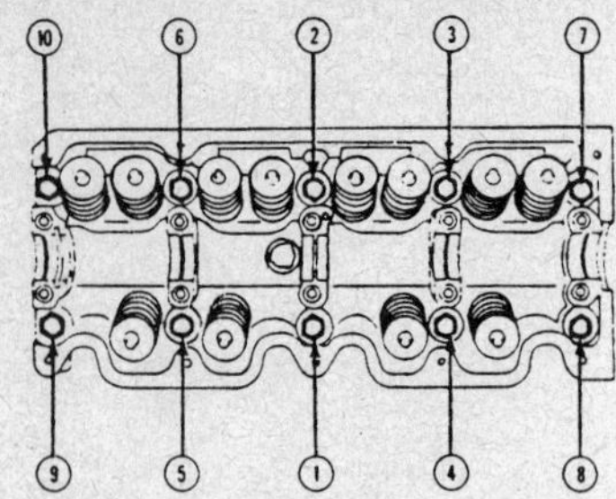

Fig. 5 Cylinder head bolt tightening sequence

## CYLINDER HEAD
### REPLACE

1. Relieve fuel system pressure. **Refer to "Relieving Fuel System Pressure" elsewhere in this section.**
2. Disconnect battery ground cable, then drain cooling system.
3. Remove upper radiator hose and the water bypass hose.
4. Remove accessory drive belts.
5. Remove righthand inner fender panel.
6. Remove crankshaft pulley attaching bolts, pulley, then baffle plate.
7. Remove two nuts, dowels from righthand engine mount, then the engine mount from vehicle.
8. Remove seven timing belt cover attaching bolts, then the cover.
9. Remove timing belt tensioner, spring, then attaching bolt.
10. Mark direction of rotation on timing belt. **Direction of rotation must be mark ed to assure that belt is installed in original direction of rotation.** Remo ve timing belt.
11. Remove rocker arm cover, then rocker shaft assembly.
12. Remove intake, then exhaust manifolds as outlined elsewhere in this section.
13. Remove spark plug wires, spark plugs, then the distributor.
14. Remove front and rear engine lifting eyes, then the engine ground wire.
15. Disconnect three electrical connectors from thermostat housing.
16. Remove cylinder head attaching bolts, cylinder head and the gasket.
17. Reverse procedure to install. **Torque** cylinder head bolts in sequence shown, **Fig. 5.** 29-32 ft. lbs., then 59-64 ft. lbs. **When installing timing belt, align mark on crankshaft sprocket with mark on oil pump housing and align mark on camshaft sprocket with mark on cylinder head.**

## VALVE ARRANGEMENT

The valves are arranged with two intake valves, both on the same side of the cylinder head and one exhaust valve, opposite each intake valve.

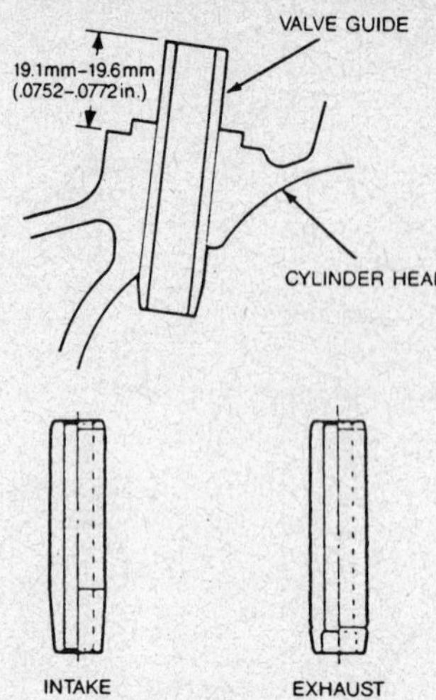


Fig. 6 Valve guide installation

## VALVES
### ADJUST

These engine are equipped with hydraulic lash adjusters incorporated into the rocker arm, which provide zero lash clearance. No provision for adjustment is provided.

## VALVE GUIDES

Valve guides are driven into the cylinder head and can be replaced following the procedure outlined below.

1. Place cylinder head in a water bath heated to approximately 190°F.
2. Using valve guide removing tool No. T87C-6510-A or equivalent, then working from combustion chamber side of cylinder head, drive valve guides out toward camshaft.
3. Using tool mentioned above, drive in new guides. When properly installed, guides should protrude .752-.772 inch above cylinder head as shown in **Fig. 6.**

## TIMING BELT COVERS
### REPLACE

1. Remove accessory drive belts.
2. Remove crankshaft pulley as follows:
   a. Remove right inner fender panel.
   b. Remove bolts, the crankshaft pulley, then baffle plate.
3. Support engine.
4. Remove attaching nuts, dowels from right engine mount, then remove mount from engine.
5. Remove attaching bolts, the upper, then lower covers as needed.
6. Reverse procedure to install, noting the following:
   a. Install covers using new gaskets, then **torque** attaching bolts to 61-87 inch lbs.
   b. When installing crankshaft pulley, ensure that recess faces away from engine.

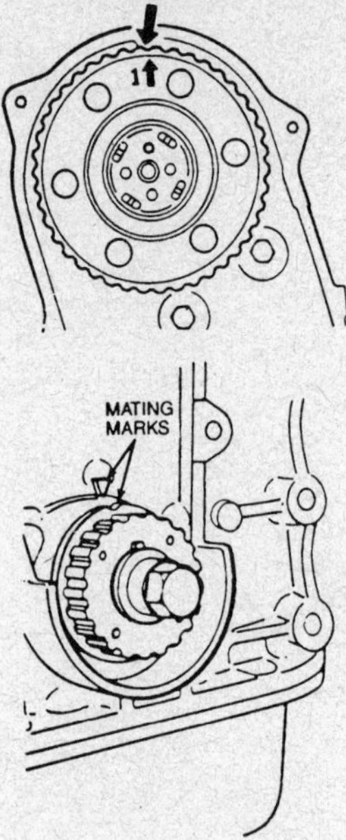


Fig. 7 Aligning valve timing marks

## TIMING BELT
### REPLACE

1. Remove timing belt covers as previously described.
2. Remove timing belt tensioner spring,retaining bolt, then the tensioner.
3. Mark direction of rotation on belt, then remove timing belt from engine.
4. Align camshaft sprocket timing mark with mark on cylinder head and crankshaft sprocket timing mark with mark on oil pump housing, **Fig. 7.**
5. Install timing belt. If reusing old belt, ensure belt is installed with rotation mark in same direction as noted in step 3.
6. Place timing belt tensioner and spring in position, then temporarily secure tensioner with spring fully extended.
7. With timing belt securely positioned against idler pulley side, loosen tensioner bolt and allow tensioner to retract.
8. Turn crankshaft two revolutions in normal direction of rotation, then ensure timing marks are still aligned as outlined in step 4.
9. Tighten tensioner retaining bolt to specifications, then apply 22 lbs. of pressure to belt. Measure belt deflection between idler pulley and camshaft sprocket. Belt deflection should be .30-.33 inch.
10. If belt deflection is not as specified, repeat steps 6 through 9. If deflection is still not as specified, replace tensioner.
11. Reinstall timing belt covers.

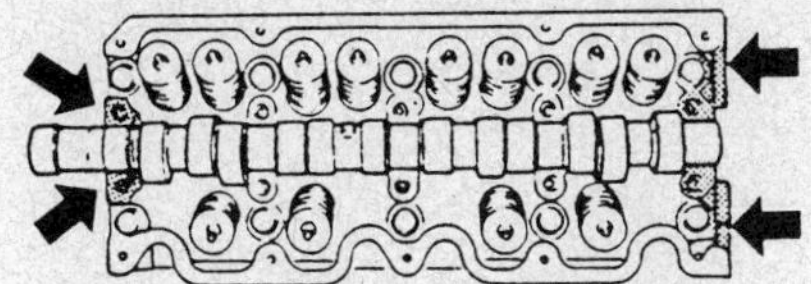

Fig. 8 Applying sealer to cylinder head

## CAMSHAFT
### REPLACE

1. Remove timing belt as previously described.
2. Remove rocker cover, front, then rear housings.
3. Prevent camshaft sprocket from rotating using a screwdriver, remove retaining bo lt, then sprocket.
4. Remove rocker arm shaft assembly retaining bolts and the rocker shaft, then camshaft bearing caps.
5. Lift camshaft upward, then remove from cylinder head.
6. Clean camshaft journals, then position camshaft into cylinder head.
7. Position plastigauge on camshaft journals and install bearing caps, then rocker shaft assembly. **Torque** rocker shaft retaining bolts in two steps to 13-20 ft. lbs., remove shaft, bearing caps, then measure bearing clearance. Bearing clearance should be .0014-.0033 inch for front and rear journals, or .0026-.0045 inch for the three center journals. Maximum clearance should not exceed .0059 inch. If bearing clearance is not as specified, replace cylinder head and/or camshaft.
8. Apply silicone sealant to areas shown, **Fig. 8,** then reinstall bearing caps, rocker shaft, then **torque** shaft retaining bolts in two steps to 13-20 ft. lbs. Install front and rear housings.
9. Install camshaft sprocket, aligning No. 1 mark on sprocket with dowel on camshaft, **Fig. 9.**
10. Install sprocket retaining bolt, prevent sprocket from rotating, then tighten retaining bolt to specifications.
11. Install timing belt, then rocker cover to complete installation.

## PISTON & ROD ASSEMBLE

Assemble piston to connecting rod with F mark on piston and oil hole in connecting rod positioned as shown, **Fig. 10.**

## PISTONS, PINS & RINGS

Pistons and rings are available in standard sizes, then .010 and .020 inch oversizes. Piston pins are available in standard size only. Maximum piston to bore clearance should not exceed .006 inch.

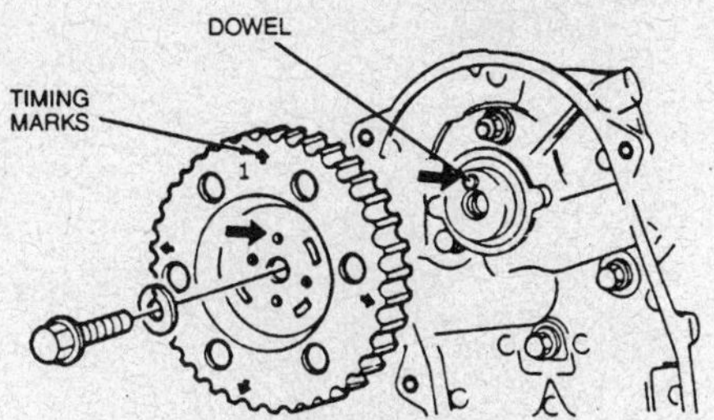


Fig. 9 Installing camshaft sprocket

## CRANKSHAFT FRONT OIL SEAL
### REPLACE

The crankshaft front seal is incorporated into the oil pump housing. Refer to "Oil Pump, Replace" for procedure.

## CRANKSHAFT REAR OIL SEAL
### REPLACE

1. Remove transaxle.
2. Remove clutch assembly, if applicable, then the flywheel.
3. Remove starter mounting plate as necessary.
4. Remove crankshaft rear oil seal retainer, then press seal from retainer.
5. Clean seal retainer surface, then coat new seal with engine oil.
6. Position seal into retainer with hollow side of seal facing engine, then drive seal into retainer using rear crank seal replacer tool No. T88C-6701-BH or equivalent.
7. Install seal and retainer using new gasket, then tighten retainer attaching bolts to specifications.
8. Trim excess gasket material from retainer, install starter mounting plate, then **torque** retaining bolts to 14-22 ft. lbs.
9. Install clutch assembly, if applicable, then the flywheel.
10. Install transaxle.

## OIL PAN
### REPLACE

1. Disconnect battery ground cable, then raise and support vehicle.
2. Remove splash shield from right inner fender well, then drain engine oil.
3. Remove engine to flywheel housing support bracket, disconnect front section of exhaust pipe, then remove exhaust pipe support.

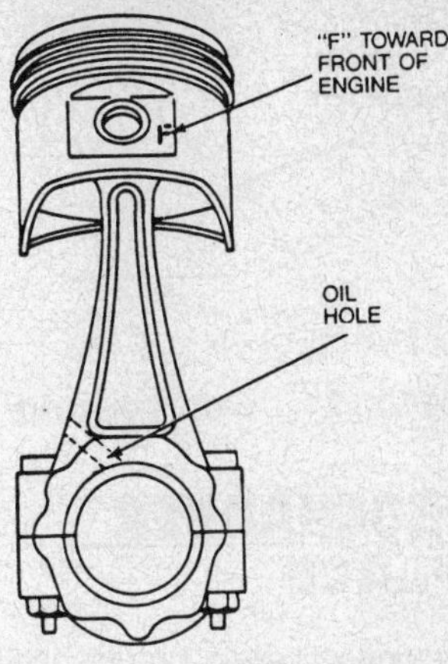


Fig. 10 Assembling piston to connecting rod

4. Remove flywheel housing dust cover.
5. Remove oil pan attaching bolts, lower pan, disconnect oil strainer from pump, then allow to fall into pan.
6. Remove oil pan, oil strainer, then stiffener.
7. Clean mounting surfaces on cylinder block, oil pan, then stiffener.
8. Apply continuous bead of silicone sealer to both sides of stiffener on inside edge of bolt holes.
9. Install stiffener, oil strainer, then oil pan. Tighten pan attaching bolts to specifications.
10. Perform steps 1 through 4 in reverse order to complete installation.

## OIL PUMP
### REPLACE

1. Remove timing belt as previously described.
2. Remove crankshaft sprocket retaining bolt, then the sprocket and key.
3. Remove oil pan as outlined previously.
4. With oil strainer disconnected from pump, remove pump to cylinder block attaching bolts and the pump, then gasket.
5. Pry front crankshaft seal from pump using screwdriver, clean seal bore, then install new seal using front crank seal replacer tool No. T88C-6701-AH or equivalent.
6. If reusing old pump, install new O-ring into pump body.
7. Apply continuous bead of silicone sealer to contact surface of oil pump. **Ensure sealer does not enter into outlet hole in pump or cylinder block.**
8. Install oil pump and gasket, tightening to specifications.
9. Perform steps 1 through 4 in reverse order to complete installation. Tightening crankshaft sprocket retaining bolt to specifications.

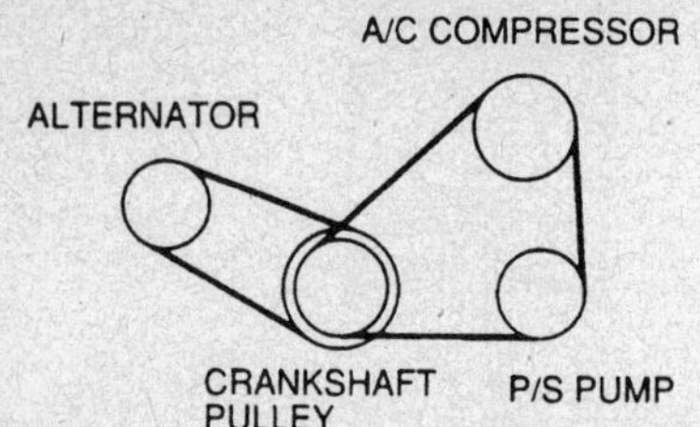


**Fig. 11 Belt routing**

## TURBOCHARGER REPLACE

1. Disconnect battery ground cable, then drain cooling system.
2. Remove inlet and outlet air hoses from turbocharger assembly.
3. Remove heat shields from exhaust manifold and turbocharger assembly. **It may be necessary to disconnect EGO sensor electrical connector to remove heat shield from turbocharger.**
4. Disconnect oil feed and return lines, the coolant inlet, then outlet hoses from turbocharger assembly.
5. Remove EGR tube from exhaust manifold.
6. Disconnect turbo boost control solenoid valve electrical connector, then remove air tube from solenoid valve at turbocharger outlet air hose.
7. Remove mounting bolt from retaining bracket under turbocharger assembly.
8. Discharge A/C system, if applicable, then disconnect refrigerant lines from compressor.
9. Remove EGO sensor from exhaust manifold.
10. Disconnect converter inlet pipe from turbocharger joint pipe.
11. Remove exhaust manifold attaching bolts, the exhaust manifold, then turbocharger as an assembly.
12. Reverse procedure to install, noting the following:
    a. Before connecting oil feed line, fill turbocharger inlet fitting with approximately 1 ounce of engine oil.
    b. Before starting engine, disconnect electrical connector from ignition coil, then crank engine for 20 seconds. Reconnect connector to coil and start engine, then allow to idle for approximately 30 seconds. Stop engine, disconnect battery ground cable, then depress brake pedal for at least 5 seconds before reconnecting cable. **The preceding procedure must be performed to cancel the malfunction code that will be stored in the computer memory.**

## BELT TENSION DATA

To check belt tension for the alternator belt, apply approximately 22 lbs. of pressure to belt. Belt deflection should be .27-.35 inch for a used belt or .27-.35 inch for a new belt.

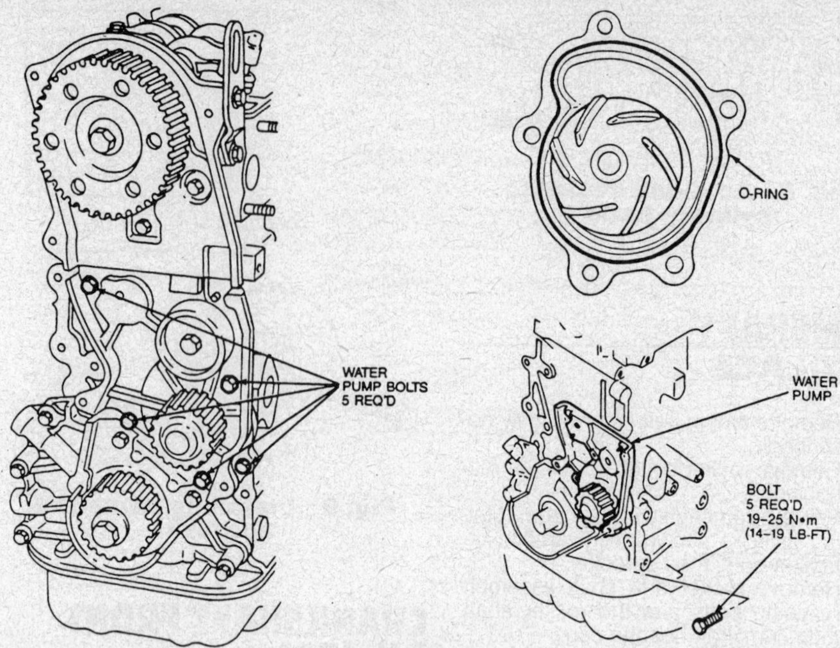


**Fig. 12 Water pump mounting bolt location**

**Fig. 13 Positioning O-ring onto water pump**

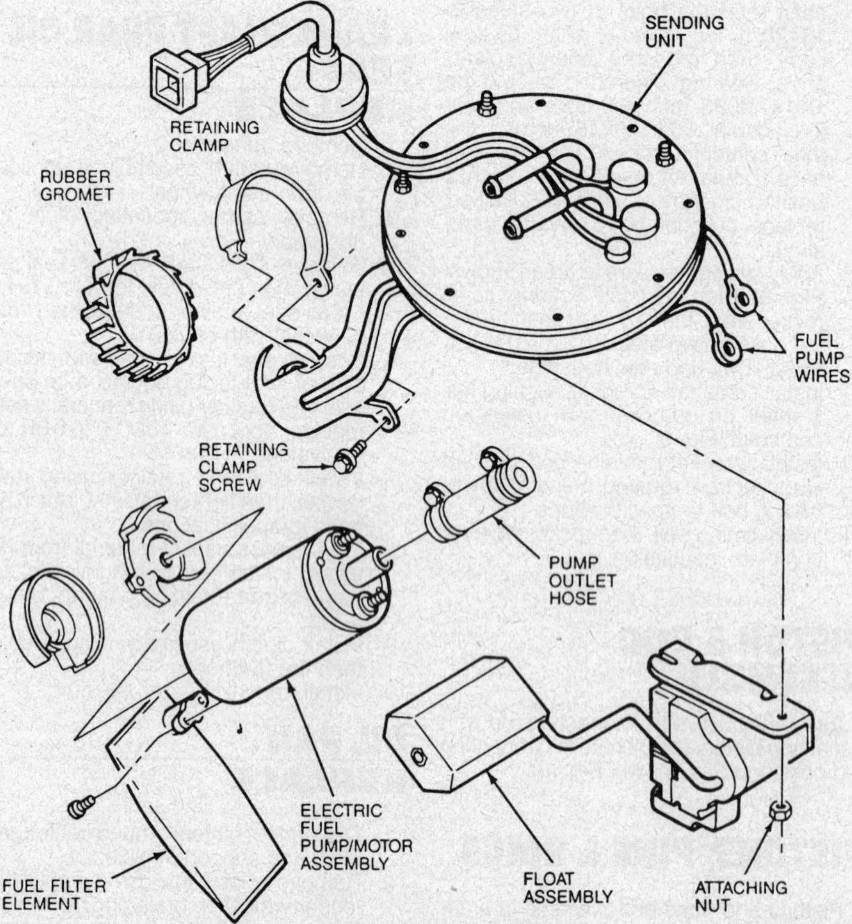


**Fig. 14 Fuel sending unit & pump**

To check belt tension for the power steering belt, apply approximately 22 lbs. of pressure to belt between pulleys. Belt deflection should be .31-.39 inch for a new belt or .35-.43 inch for a used belt.

## BELT ROUTING

Refer to **Fig. 11.** for belt routing.

## BELT REPLACEMENT

1. Loosen A/C compressor drive belt adjusting bolts, then rotate compressor toward engine and remove belt.
2. Loosen alternator pivot bolt and adjuster bolt, then rotate alternator toward engine and remove drive belt(s).
3. Reverse procedure to install.

## COOLING SYSTEM BLEED

This engine does not require a specified bleed procedure. After filling cooling system, run engine to operating temperature with radiator/pressure cap off. Air will then be automatically bled through the cap opening.

## THERMOSTAT

### REPLACE

1. Drain radiator to below level of thermostat.
2. Disconnect coolant temperature switch at thermostat housing.
3. Using pliers, clamp hose clamps, then slide toward center of hose.
4. Remove upper radiator hose.
5. Remove two attaching nuts, thermostat housing, thermostat and gasket. **Do not pry housing off.**
6. Reverse procedure to install. Tightening to specifications.

## WATER PUMP

### REPLACE

1. Drain cooling system.
2. Remove timing belt as previously described.
3. Remove water pump attaching bolts, then the water pump, **Fig. 12.**
4. Clean water pump, then cylinder block mating surface.
5. Position new O-ring on water pump as shown, **Fig. 13.**
6. Install water pump, attaching bolts, then tighten bolts to specifications.
7. Install timing belt, covers, then fill cooling system.

## ELECTRIC FUEL PUMP

### REPLACE

The electric fuel pump is located in the fuel tank and is integral with the fuel sending unit.

1. Relieve fuel system pressure as outlined at the beginning of this section.
2. Disconnect battery ground cable.
3. Remove rear seat cushion.
4. Disconnect fuel sending unit electrical connector, remove sending unit access cover attaching screws, then the access cover.
5. Remove clamps, disconnect fuel supply, then return hoses from sending unit.
6. Remove sending unit attaching screws, then the sending unit.
7. Disassemble sending unit to remove pump as shown in **Fig. 14.**

## SERVICE BULLETINS

On these models, with build dates prior to May 1, 1989 a rough engine idle, engine miss, poor performance, fouled spark plugs or oil consumption may be caused by a hairline crack in the cylinder head near an intake valve guide. This crack can cause engine oil to build-up in the valve area and combustion chamber. To correct this problem, inspect cylinder head to determine if replacement is required. Refer to "Cylinder Head, Replace" for replacement procedure.

## TIGHTENING SPECIFICATIONS

| Year | Component | Torque/ft. lbs. |
|---|---|---|
| 1989-92 | Camshaft Sprocket Bolt | 35–48 |
| | Connecting Rod Nuts | 48–51 |
| | Crankshaft Pulley Bolts | 109–152① |
| | Crankshaft Seal Retainer Bolts | 69–104① |
| | Crankshaft Sprocket | 108–116 |
| | Crankshaft To Flywheel Bolts | 71–76 |
| | Crankshaft To Flywheel Support Bracket Bolts | 27–38 |
| | Cylinder Head Bolts | ② |
| | Exhaust Manifold Bolts | 16–21 |
| | Exhaust Pipe To Exhaust Manifold Bolts | 23–34 |
| | Front/Rear Housing | 14–19 |
| | Flywheel Housing Dust Cover Bolts | 49–95① |
| | Flywheel Housing Support Bracket Bolts | 27–38 |
| | Intake Manifold Bracket Bolts | 14–22 |
| | Intake Manifold Bolts | 14–22 |
| | Main Bearing Cap Bolts | 61–65 |
| | Oil Pan Bolts | 69–104① |
| | Outer Heat Shield Bolts | 14–22 |
| | Rear Engine Plate | 14–22 |
| | Rocker Arm Cover Retaining Bolts | 52–69① |
| | Rocker Arm Shaft Bolt | 13–20 |
| | Spark Plug | 11–17 |
| | Thermostat Housing Bolts | 14–22 |
| | Timing Belt Cover | 61–87① |
| | Water Pump | 14–19 |

①—Inch lbs.
②—Refer to text.

# 3.0L/V6-182 Engine

INDEX



## ENGINE MOUNTS

### REPLACE

Refer to **Fig. 1.** when replacing engine mounts.

## ENGINE

### REPLACE

**Engine and transaxle are removed as an assembly.**

1. Disconnect battery ground cables.
2. Mark hood hinge locations, then remove hood.
3. Drain cooling system and discharge A/C system.
4. Remove air cleaner assembly.
5. Remove vacuum valve assembly from righthand shock tower.
6. Disconnect fuel lines and position aside.
7. Relieve fuel pressure as follows:
   a. Start engine.
   b. Disconnect fuel pump relay.
   c. After engine stalls, turn ignition switch Off.
   d. Reconnect fuel pump relay.
8. Remove upper radiator hose.
9. Disconnect all electrical connectors and looms and position aside.
10. Disconnect or remove the following:
    a. Alternator.
    b. A/C compressor clutch.
    c. Ignition coil.
    d. Engine coolant temperature sensor.
    e. Injector wiring harness including six injector connectors.
    f. Air charge temperature sensor and throttle position sensor.
    g. Oil pressure sending switch.
    h. Engine ground straps.
    i. Block heater (if equipped).
    j. Knock sensor and EGR sensor.
    k. Oil lever sensor.
    l. Vacuum lines, crankcase ventilation hoses.
    m. Heater hoses and power steering pump return lines.
11. Disconnect A/C lines from condenser and chassis, leaving manifold lines attached to compressor.
12. Disconnect accelerator linkage, transmission throttle valve linkage and speed control cable (if equipped).

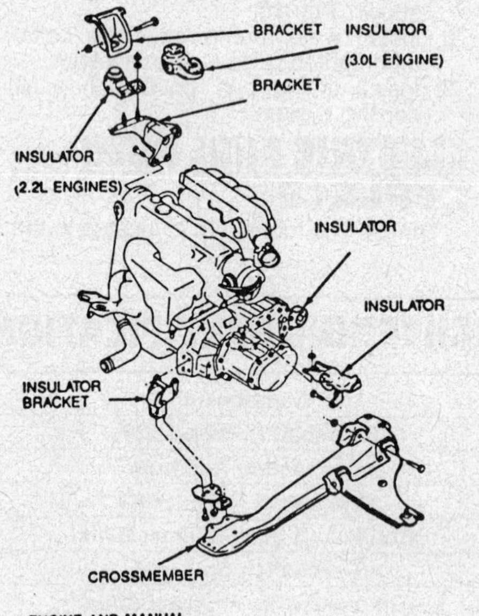


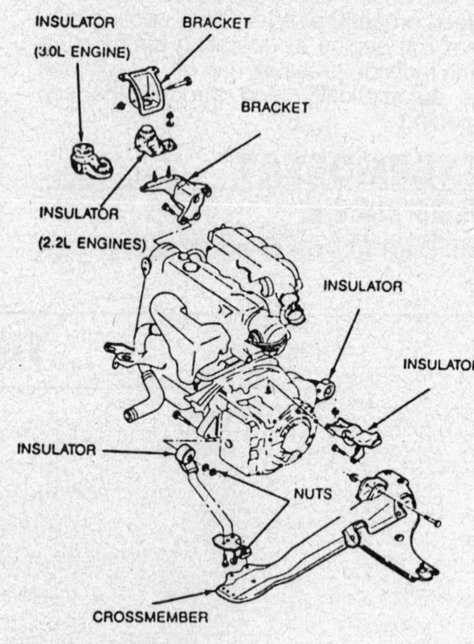


**Fig. 1 Engine mounts**

13. Remove battery and tray.
14. Remove fuse box and position aside.
15. Disconnect speed control servo and position aside.
16. **On models with automatic transaxle,** disconnect shift cable and electrical connectors and position aside.
17. **On models with analog cluster,** disconnect speedometer.
18. **On models with electronic cluster,** disconnect vehicle speed sensor connector.
19. **On models with manual transaxle,** remove clutch release cylinder with hose still attached and position aside.
20. **On all models,** remove radiator, cooling fan and shroud.
21. Raise and support vehicle.
22. Remove wheels and tires assemblies.
23. Remove lower radiator hose and front exhaust pipe.
24. Remove starter motor.
25. **On models with automatic transaxle,** remove torque converter nuts.
26. **On models with manual transmission,** remove shift control rod and extension bar.
27. **On all models,** remove stabilizer links and tie rod ends from lower control arms.
28. Disconnect lower ball joints, then pull down on control arms to disengage them from spindle.
29. Remove three bolts from dynamic damper bracket on righthand halfshaft assembly. Pulling outward on righthand brake and spindle assembly, disengage right halfshaft from transaxle.
30. Pulling outward on left hand brake and spindle assembly, disengage left halfshaft assemblies.
31. Install two transaxle plugs T88C-7025-AH or equivalent into differential side gears. **Failure to install transaxle plugs may allow differen-**

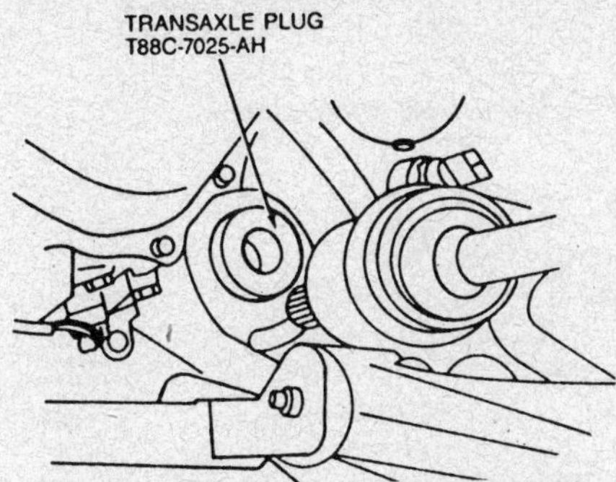


**Fig. 2 Transaxle plug location**

**tial side gears to become mispositioned, Fig. 2.**

32. Disconnect lower rear transmission mount.
33. Lower vehicle and attach a suitable lifting device, **Fig. 3.**
34. Disconnect lower front engine mount and righthand upper engine mount at timing cover.
35. Disconnect lefthand upper engine mount at transaxle case.
36. Carefully lift engine and transaxle assembly from vehicle.
37. Reverse procedure to install.

# INTAKE MANIFOLD
## REPLACE

1. Disconnect battery ground cable, then drain cooling system.
2. Remove air cleaner outlet flex hose to throttle body.
3. Mark vacuum lines for reference, then remove vacuum lines to throttle body.
4. Remove ignition wires from spark plugs, then harnesses from rocker cover retaining studs.
5. Remove throttle body, then relieve pressure at fuel supply manifold Schrader valve. **Cover valve with shop towel to prevent accidental fuel spray into eyes.**
6. Remove fuel line safety clips, then disconnect fuel lines from fuel supply manifold. Ensure to cover fuel lines ends with a clean shop towel to prevent dirt from entering opening.
7. Remove fuel injector wiring harness from engine, then fuel supply manifold and injectors. Injectors and fuel supply manifold may be removed with intake manifold as an assembly.
8. Remove ignition coil and bracket and position aside.
9. Remove rocker arm covers, then disconnect upper radiator and heater hoses.
10. Disconnect EGR tube attaching nut from EGR valve (if equipped).
11. Disconnect PFE sensor hose from EGR tube nipple. Loosen lower tube attaching nut and rotate tube away from valve.
12. Mark and remove distributor assembly, then disconnect engine coolant temperature sensor connector.
13. Remove intake manifold retaining bolts. It may be necessary to pry intake manifold upward to break the silicone seal.
14. Reverse procedure to install, noting the following:
    a. Ensure surfaces are clean and free of old silicone sealer.
    b. When using silicone rubber sealer, assembly must occur within 15 minutes after sealer application.
    c. **Torque** manifold bolts in numerical sequence shown in **Fig. 4.** In two steps, first to 11 ft. lbs., then to 18 ft. lbs.

# EXHAUST MANIFOLD
## REPLACE

### LEFT SIDE

1. Remove dipstick tube support bracket and heatshield retaining nuts.
2. Raise and support vehicle.
3. Remove exhaust manifold to front exhaust pipe attaching nuts, then lower vehicle.
4. Remove exhaust manifold attaching nuts, then the manifold.
5. Reverse procedure to install, noting the following:
    a. Lightly lubricate bolts with suitable oil.
    b. Tighten manifold attaching bolts to specifications.
    c. Tighten heat shield attaching to specifications.

### RIGHT SIDE

1. Raise and support vehicle.
2. Using back-up wrench on EGR tube lower adapter, remove EGR supply tube from exhaust manifold (if equipped).
3. Remove spark plugs and heatshield retaining nuts.
4. Remove manifold to exhaust pipe attaching nuts.
5. Remove exhaust manifold attaching bolts, then the manifold.
6. Reverse procedure to install, noting the following:
    a. Lightly lubricate nuts and bolts with suitable oil.
    b. Tighten manifold attaching bolts to specifications.
    c. Tighten exhaust pipe to manifold attaching nuts to specifications.
    d. Tighten EGR tube to specifications.

# CYLINDER HEAD
## REPLACE

1. Disconnect battery ground cable, then drain cooling system.
2. Remove air cleaner duct tube.
3. Remove intake manifold as previously described.
4. Remove accessory drive belts. If front cylinder head is being removed, remove power steering pump.
5. Remove alternator/accessory support bracket.
6. Remove oil level dipstick and tube.
7. Remove ignition coil and bracket.
8. Remove exhaust manifold as previously described.

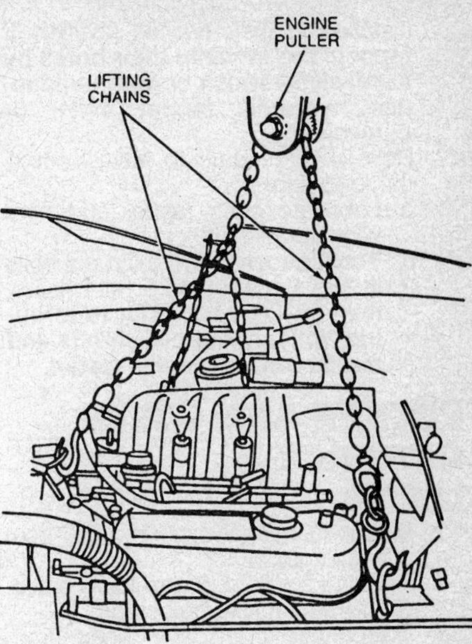


**Fig. 3 Engine removal**

9. Loosen rocker arm fulcrum attaching bolt enough to rotate rocker arm so pushrod can be removed. **Keep pushrods in order so they can be installed in original position.**
10. Remove cylinder head attaching bolts.
11. Remove cylinder head(s).
12. Remove and discard cylinder head gasket(s).
13. Reverse procedure to install, noting the following:
    a. Lightly oil all bolts.
    b. **Torque** cylinder head bolts as shown, **Fig. 5.** in two steps first to 33-41 ft. lbs., then 63-73 ft. lbs.

# VALVES
## ADJUST

This engine is equipped with hydraulic lifters. No adjustment is required.

# HYDRAULIC VALVE TAPPETS
## REPLACE

Before replacing hydraulic valve tappets for noisy operation, ensure the noise is not caused by improper valve-to-rocker arm clearance, worn rocker arms, pushrods or rocker arm cover baffle clearance.

1. Disconnect battery ground cable, then drain cooling system.
2. Remove air intake throttle body.
3. Remove rocker arm covers and intake manifold assembly.
4. Loosen rocker arm fulcrum attaching bolts enough so rocker arm can be lifted off pushrod and rotated aside.
5. Remove pushrods. Keep pushrods in order, so they can be installed in their original position.
6. Using a magnet, remove tappets. Keep tappets in order, so they can be

installed in their original position. **If tappets are stuck in their bores by excessive varnish or gum buildup, use hydraulic tappet puller or equivalent.**

7. Reverse procedure to install, noting the following:
   a. Lubricate each tappet and bore with suitable lubricant.
   b. **Torque** rocker arm fulcrums bolts in two steps first to 5.1-11 ft. lbs., then 20-28 ft. lbs. **Prior to torquing bolts, ensure pushrods and rocker arms are fully seated.**

## ROCKER ARM COVER REPLACE

### LEFT SIDE

1. Disconnect spark plug wire from spark plugs.
2. Remove spark plug wire loom brackets from attaching bolt studs.
3. Disconnect crankcase hose from rocker cover.
4. Disconnect alternator harness loom retainers from rocker arm cover studs, then pull injector harness and position aside.
5. Remove two attaching bolts and six studs from rocker arm cover.
6. Remove rocker arm cover and gasket.
7. Reverse procedure to install, noting the following:
   a. Lightly oil bolt and stud threads prior to installation.
   b. Apply bead of Silicone Sealer or equivalent at cylinder head intake manifold rail step.
   c. Tighten rocker arm cover bolt to specifications.

### RIGHT SIDE

1. Disconnect battery ground cable.
2. Disconnect air cleaner tube from throttle body, then remove plastic shield from throttle body.
3. Disconnect EGR supply tube, if equipped and all vacuum hoses from air intake throttle body.
4. Disconnect ACT sensor, **Fig. 6.**
5. Disconnect ISC servo.
6. Disconnect TPS, then remove EVP sensor (if equipped).
7. **On models with manual transaxle,** disconnect throttle cable.
8. **On models with automatic transaxle,** disconnect throttle valve control cable.
9. **On all models,** remove fuel rail bracket bolt from throttle body.
10. Remove air intake attaching bolts, then lift off throttle body.
11. Disconnect spark plug wires, then position injector harness aside.
12. Remove rocker arm cover attaching bolts, then the cover.
13. Reverse procedure to install, noting the following:
    a. Lightly oil bolt and stud threads prior to installation.
    b. Apply bead of Silicone Sealer or equivalent at cylinder head intake manifold rail step.
    c. Tighten rocker arm cover bolt to specifications.

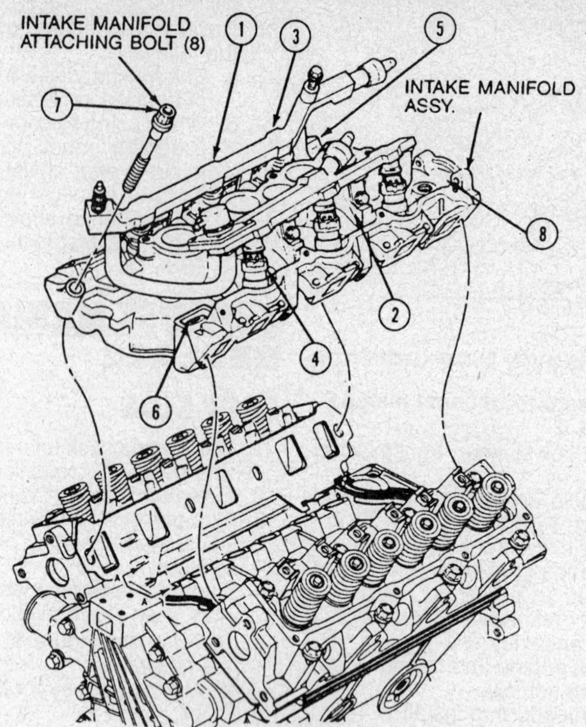


**Fig. 4 Intake manifold bolt tightening sequence**

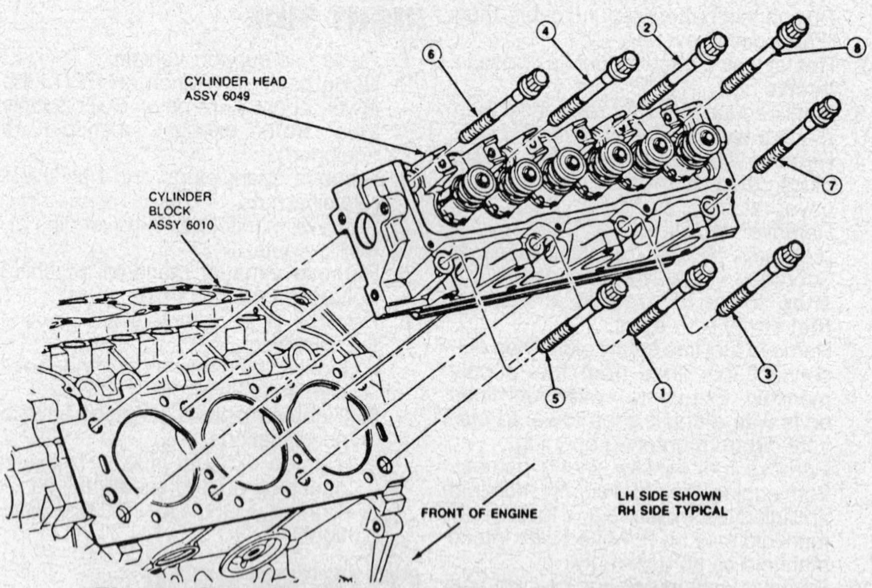


**Fig. 5 Cylinder head bolt tightening sequence**

   d. **Torque** EGR supply tube 37 ft. lbs.

## CRANKSHAFT REPLACE

1. Remove accessory drive belts.
2. Raise and support vehicle, then remove right front wheel.
3. Remove plastic inner fender shield.
4. Remove water pump belt, then lower vehicle.
5. Support engine with suitable jack.
6. **On models with manual transaxle,** remove righthand engine mount.
7. **On models with automatic transaxle,** remove spacer from water pump bracket.
8. **On all models,** remove right upper engine mount to timing cover.
9. Lower jack carefully allowing engine to rest on remaining mounts.
10. Raise and support vehicle.
11. Remove crankshaft damper bolt and flat washer.
12. Using puller crankshaft damper remover tool No. T58P-6316-D or equivalent, remove crankshaft damper from crankshaft.
13. When removing damper, remove

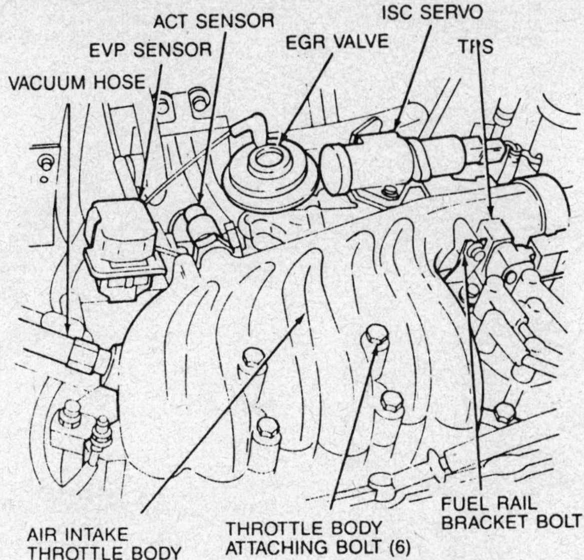


**Fig. 6 Rocker arm cover removal**

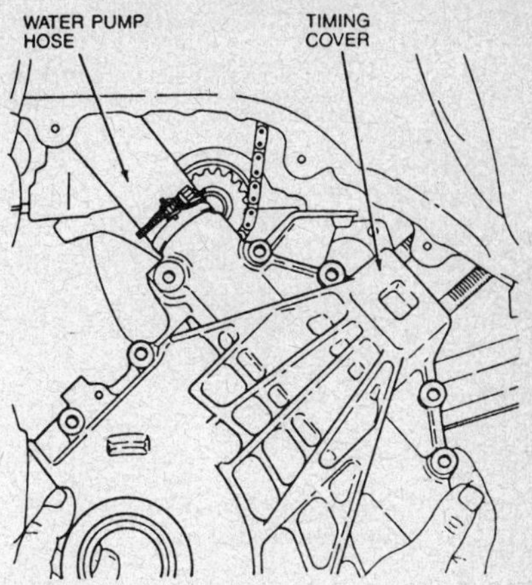


**Fig. 7 Timing cover removal**

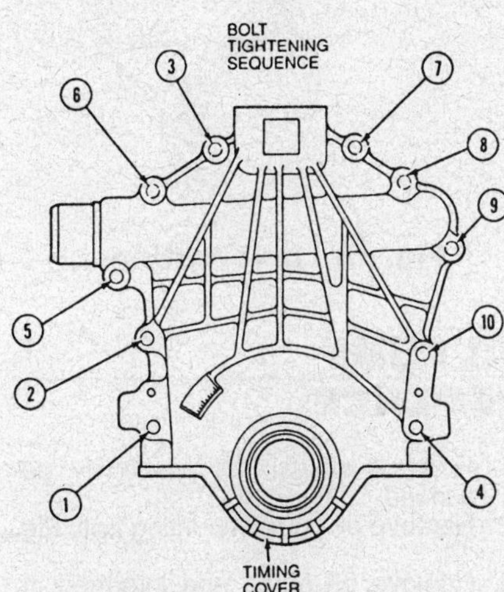


**Fig. 8 Timing cover bolt tightening sequence**

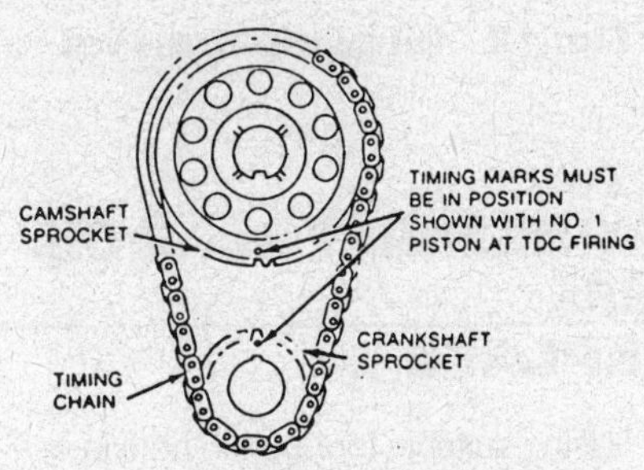


**Fig. 9 Aligning timing marks**

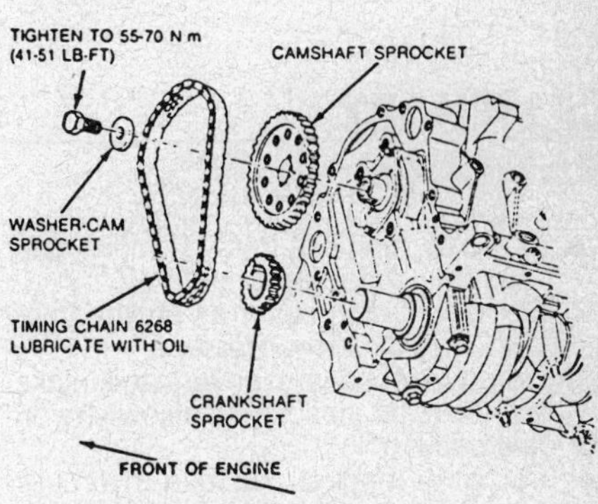


**Fig. 10 Timing chain & sprockets installation**

three nuts and one bolt that attach right side of subframe to body. Pull down slightly to provide clearance for damper removal.

14. Reverse procedure to install, noting the following:
    a. Lubricate crankshaft damper sealing surface with clean engine oil.
    b. Apply sealer to keyway of damper.
    c. Tighten vibration damper to specifications.

## TIMING COVER OIL SEAL
## REPLACE

1. Remove crankshaft damper as previously described.
2. Using remover front cover seal remover tool No. T70P-6B070-B or equivalent, remove oil seal.
3. Reverse procedure to install.

## TIMING COVER
## REPLACE

1. Disconnect battery ground cable.
2. Remove crankshaft damper as outlined under "Crankshaft, Replace."
3. Drain oil, then remove oil pan.
4. Remove timing cover bottom bolts, then lower vehicle.
5. Remove remaining timing cover bolts.
6. Carefully insert a flat bladed screwdriver between timing cover and cylinder block. Pry timing cover from block.
7. Pull timing cover over end of crankshaft, then lower it through engine compartment. **Timing cover may be removed with water pump upper hose attached, Fig. 7.**
8. Reverse procedure to install, noting the following:
    a. Clean gasket mating surfaces on cylinder block and timing cover.
    b. Ensure cover is correctly seated on dowels.
    c. Refer to **Fig. 8.** for bolt tightening sequence. Apply suitable sealant D6AZ-19558-A on threads.
    d. Tighten timing cover bolts to specifications.

## TIMING CHAIN & SPROCKETS
## REPLACE

1. Disconnect battery ground cable, then drain cooling system.
2. Drain crankcase, then remove crankshaft pulley and damper as outlined under "Crankshaft Replace."
3. Remove timing cover as outlined under "Timing Cover, Replace."
4. Rotate crankshaft until No. 1 piston is at TDC compression stroke and timing marks are aligned as shown, **Fig. 9.**
5. Remove camshaft sprocket attaching bolt and washer, then slide crankshaft sprocket, timing chain and camshaft sprocket from engine as an assembly.
6. Reverse procedure to install, noting the following:
    a. Clean and inspect parts before installation.
    b. Install replacement sprockets and timing chain as an assembly with timing marks aligned, **Fig. 10.**
    c. **Camshaft retaining bolt has a drilled oil passage for timing chain lubrication. If damaged, do not replace with standard bolt. Clean oil passage with solvent.**

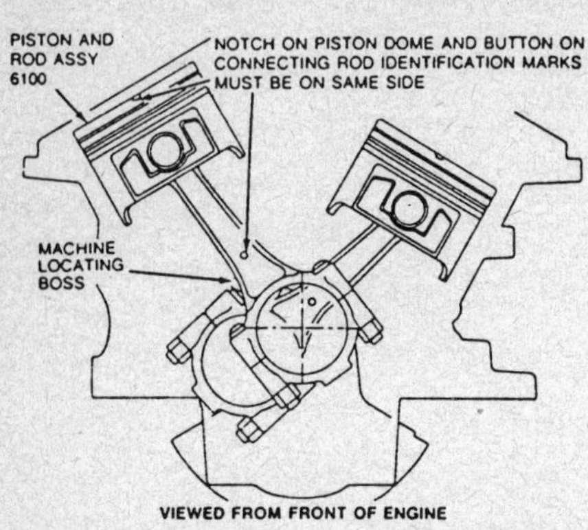


**Fig. 11 Piston & rod assembly**

## CAMSHAFT
### REPLACE

1. Remove engine from vehicle and mount in suitable work stand.
2. Remove timing cover as outlined under "Timing Cover, Replace."
3. Remove rocker arm covers and intake manifold as described elsewhere in this section.
4. Using a magnet, remove hydraulic tappets. Keep tappets in order, so they can be installed in their original position. **If tappets are stuck in their bores by excessive varnish or gum buildup, use hydraulic tappet puller or equivalent.**
5. Check camshaft endplay. If endplay is greater than .005 inch replace thrust plate.
6. Remove timing chain and sprockets.
7. Remove camshaft thrust plate, then carefully pull camshaft from front of engine. Use caution to avoid damaging bearings, journals and lobes.
8. Reverse procedure to install, noting the following:
   a. Prior to installation, lubricate camshaft lobes and journals with SAE 50 weight oil.
   b. Tighten camshaft thrust plate to specifications.
   c. Lubricate tappets and tappet bores with heavy engine oil.

## PISTON & ROD ASSEMBLE

Ensure notch in piston dome faces front of engine and machine locating boss is facing righthand side of engine as shown, **Fig. 11.**

## PISTON, PINS & RINGS

Pistons and rings are available in standard sizes and in oversizes. Standard sizes are color-coded red or blue or have .0003 OS stamped on the dome. Maximum piston to bore clearance should not exceed .0032 inch.

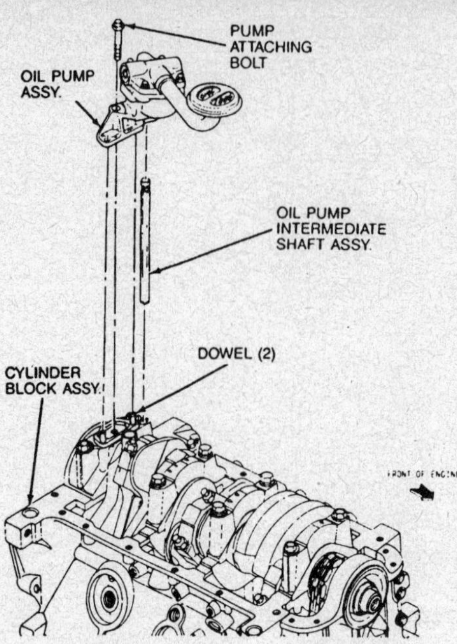


**Fig. 12 Oil pump removal**

## CRANKSHAFT REAR OIL SEAL
### REPLACE

1. Using suitable tool, punch hole in seal metal between seal lip and cylinder block.
2. Using jet plug remover tool No. T77L-95333-B or equivalent screw in threaded end, then using slide hammer remove seal.
3. Use care to avoid damaging oil seal surface.
4. Install oil seal.

## OIL PAN
### REPLACE

1. Disconnect battery ground cable.
2. Raise and support vehicle, then drain crankcase.
3. Remove starter motor.
4. Remove front and rear transaxle to engine braces, then disconnect low oil level sensor electrical connector.
5. Remove exhaust inlet pipe from manifolds and position aside.
6. Drain cooling system, then remove water pump as outlined in "Water Pump, Replace."
7. Remove water pump bracket and idler pulley.
8. Remove attaching bolts from front of righthand crossmember.
9. Loosen but do not remove attaching bolts from rear of righthand crossmember. **Allow crossmember to drop as low as possible to permit removal of oil pan.**
10. Remove oil pan attaching bolts and the oil pan.
11. Reverse procedure to install.

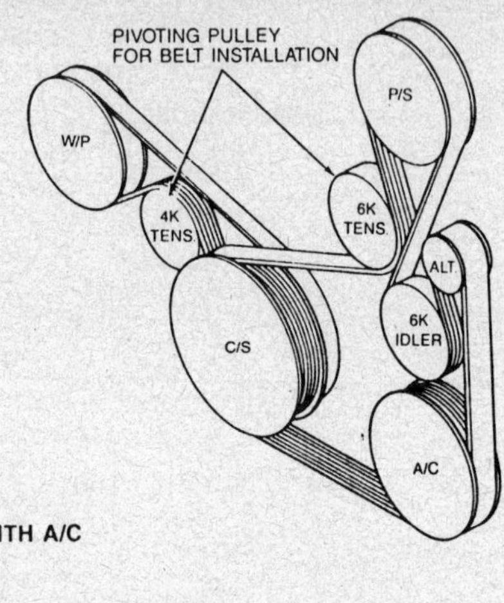


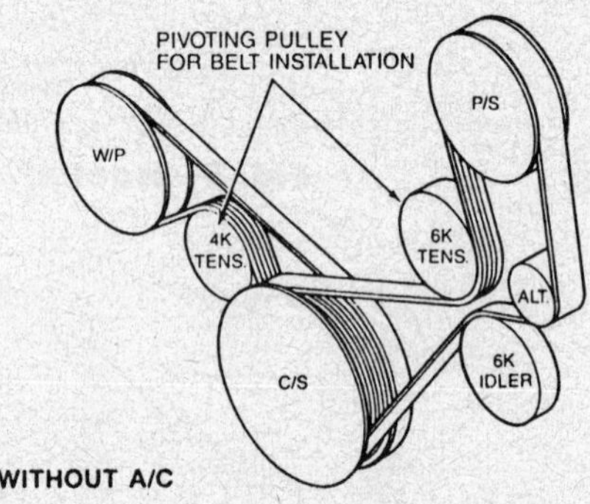


**Fig. 13 Belt routing**

## OIL PUMP
### REPLACE

1. Remove oil pan as previously described.
2. Remove oil pump mounting bolt, **Fig. 12.**
3. Remove oil pump and intermediate shaft from rear main bearing cap.
4. Pull intermediate shaft out of oil pump.
5. Reverse procedure to install, noting the following:
   a. Install intermediate shaft into drive hole in pump assembly.
   b. Install oil pump. Tightening to specifications.
   c. Install oil pan.

## BELT TENSION DATA

Belt tension is automatically maintained on these models by an automatic tensioner. Therefore, no adjustment is necessary.

## SERPENTINE BELT
### BELT ROUTING

Refer to **Fig. 13**, for belt routing.

### BELT REPLACEMENT

Mark direction of rotation on drive belt with a marking pen to ensure correct installation if the belt is to be reused. Failure to do so may result in belt noise.

1. Remove plastic belt shield from pow-

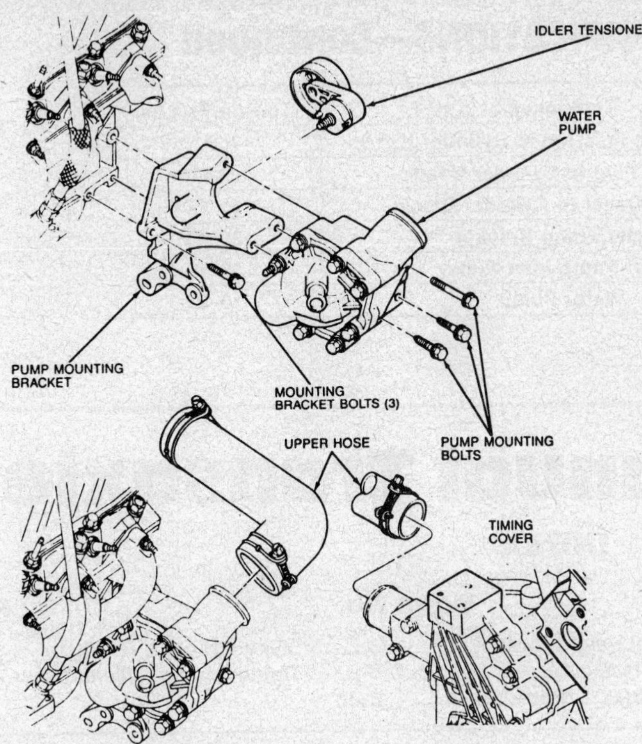


**Fig. 14 Water pump removal**

er steering pump.
2. Using a 1/2 inch drive breaker bar or equivalent inserted in idler pulley tensioner, release tension on drive belt.
3. While releasing belt tension, move drive belt off of tensioner pulley.
4. Release tensioner, then remove belt from engine.
5. Reverse procedure to install.

## COOLING SYSTEM BLEED

This engine does not require a specified bleed procedure. After filling cooling system, run engine to operating temperature with radiator/pressure cap off. Air will then be automatically bled through the cap opening.

## THERMOSTAT REPLACE

1. Drain cooling system.
2. Loosen upper radiator hose clamp, then disconnect hose from thermostat housing.
3. Remove attaching nut securing harness bracket.
4. Remove upper radiator radiator hose.
5. Remove attaching nuts, thermostat housing, thermostat and gasket. **Do not pry housing off.**
6. Reverse procedure to install.

## WATER PUMP REPLACE

1. Raise and support vehicle.
2. Drain cooling system, then remove water pump belt.
3. Remove upper hose and heater hose from pump, **Fig. 14.**
4. Remove lower radiator hose from water pump steel tube.
5. Remove steel tube brace bolt from mounting bracket.
6. Remove water pump attaching bolts, then the pump.
7. Reverse procedure to install.

## TIGHTENING SPECIFICATIONS

| Year | Component | Torque/Ft. Lbs. |
|---|---|---|
| 1990-92 | Camshaft Sprocket to Camshaft | 40–51 |
| | Camshaft Thrust Plate | 6–8 |
| | Connecting Rod Nut | 23–39 |
| | Coolant Temp Switch | 12–18 |
| | Crankshaft Damper | 92–122 |
| | Cylinder Head | ① |
| | EGR Supply Tube to Exhaust Manifold | 25–48 |
| | EGR Tube Fitting to Exhaust Manifold | 25–48 |
| | EGR Valve to Throttle Body | 15–22 |
| | Exhaust Manifold | 15–22 |
| | Flywheel to Crankshaft Bolt | 54–64 |
| | Fuel Rail to Intake Manifold | 6–8 |
| | Intake Manifold to Cylinder Head | ① |
| | Low Level Oil Sensor | 20–30 |
| | Main Bearing Cap Bolt | 55–63 |
| | Oil Filter to Adapter | 89–132② |
| | Oil Indicator Tube to Exhaust Manifold | 11–15 |
| | Oil Pan to Cylinder Block | 7–10 |
| | Oil Pan Drain Plug | 8–12 |
| | Oil Pressure Sending Unit | 12–16 |
| | Oil Pump to Main Cap Bolt | 30–40 |

*Continued*

## TIGHTENING SPECIFICATIONS—Continued

| Year | Component | Torque/Ft. Lbs. |
|---|---|---|
| 1990-92 | Rocker Arm Fulcrum to Cylinder Head | ① |
| | Spark Plug to Cylinder Head | 5–11 |
| | Timing Cover to Cylinder Block | 15–22 |
| | Water Pump Bracket | 30–40 |
| | Water Pump Idler Pulley | 30–40 |
| | Water Pump | 15–22 |

①—See text for procedure.
②—Inch lbs.

# Clutch & Manual Transaxle

## INDEX



## CLUTCH PEDAL HEIGHT
### ADJUST

1. Measure distance from the bulkhead to the upper center of the pedal pad, **Fig. 1.**
2. Distance should be 8.5-8.7 inches.
3. If adjustment is required, remove lower dash panel, then air ducts.
4. Loosen locknut, then turn stopper bolt until pedal height is within specification.
5. After adjustment, tighten locknut, install air ducts, then lower dash panel.

## CLUTCH PEDAL FREE PLAY
### ADJUST

1. Measure clutch pedal free play distance, **Fig. 1.**
2. Free play should be .20-.51 inch.
3. If an adjustment is required, remove lower dash panel, then air ducts.
4. Loosen locknut, then turn push rod until pedal free play is within specification.
5. Measure distance from the floor to center of the pedal pad when the pedal is fully depressed. The distance should be 2.7 inch or more.
6. Tighten the locknut.
7. Install air ducts, then lower dash panel.

## CLUTCH
### REPLACE

1. Disconnect battery ground cable.
2. Remove transaxle from vehicle.
3. Install flywheel lock tool No. T84P-6375-A or equivalent, into transaxle mounting hole on the engine, then engage the tooth of the locking tool into the flywheel ring gear. **To avoid dropping the clutch disc when the bolts are removed, use clutch aligning tool No. T71P-7137-H for 2.2L/4-133 turbo and 3.0L/V6-182 models or No. T74P-7137-K on non-turbocharged models.**
4. Remove bolts attaching pressure plate assembly to flywheel and the pressure plate assembly, **Fig. 2.**
5. Remove clutch disc and the clutch aligning tool.
6. Reverse procedure to install. Tightening to specifications.

## SLAVE CYLINDER
### REPLACE

1. Disconnect pressure line from slave cylinder, then plug line to prevent leakage.
2. Remove slave cylinder attaching bolts, then the cylinder.
3. Reverse procedure to install. Tightening to specifications.

## CLUTCH BLEED

The clutch hydraulic system must be bled whenever the pressure line is disconnected.

**The fluid in the reservoir must be maintained at the 3/4 level or higher during air bleeding.**

1. Remove bleeder cap from slave cylinder and attach vinyl hose to bleeder screw, place other end of hose in container.
2. Slowly pump clutch pedal several times.
3. With clutch pedal depressed, loosen bleeder screw to release trapped air.
4. Tighten bleeder screw.
5. Repeat steps 2 through 4 until no air bubbles appear in fluid.

## CLUTCH MASTER CYLINDER
### REPLACE

1. Remove ABS relay box, if equipped.
2. Disconnect clutch pressure line from master cylinder.
3. Remove mounting nuts, then master cylinder.
4. Reverse procedure to install, noting the following:
   a. Tighten slave cylinder mounting nuts to specifications.
   b. Bleed air from system.

## MANUAL TRANSAXLE
### REPLACE

1. Disconnect battery ground cable.
2. Disconnect or isolate main fuse block assembly.
3. Disconnect center lead from distributor terminal.
4. Disconnect airflow meter electrical connector from air cleaner assembly.
5. **On non-turbocharged models,** remove resonance chamber, then bracket. On turbocharged models, remove throttle body to intercooler air hose, then the air cleaner to turbocharger air hose.
6. Disconnect speedometer cable (analog cluster) or harness (digital cluster).

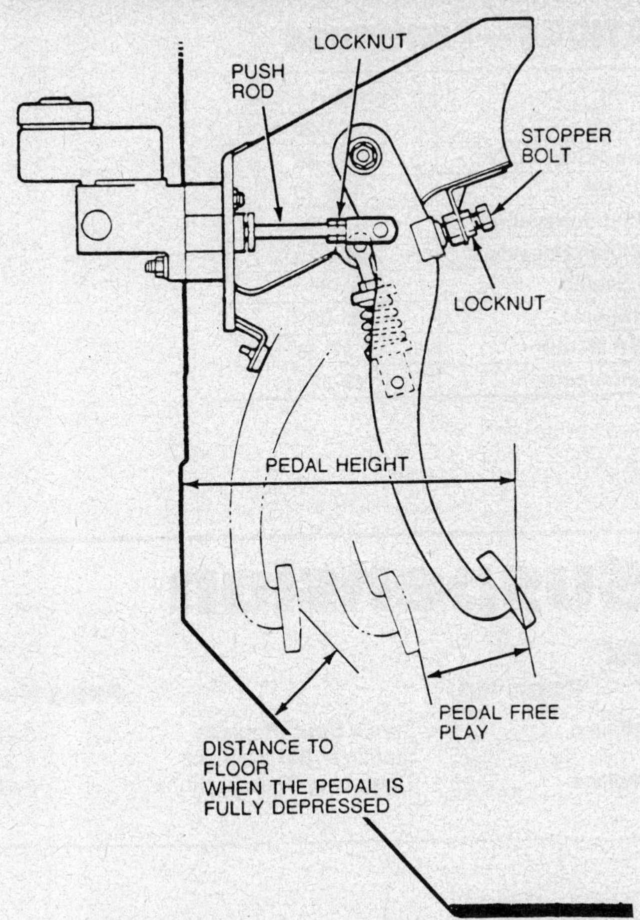


**Fig. 1 Clutch adjustment**

**Fig. 2 Clutch assembly**

7. **On models with 3.0L/V6-182 engine,** position pan under radiator and drain coolant, then close valve.
8. Remove upper radiator hose.
9. Disconnect two ground wires from transaxle case.
10. **On all models,** raise and support vehicle.
11. Remove front tire and wheel assembly.
12. Remove splash shields.
13. Drain fluid from transaxle assembly.
14. Remove slave cylinder from transaxle.
15. Remove tie rod nuts, cotter pins, then disconnect tie rod ends.
16. Remove stabilizer link assemblies.
17. Remove bolts and nuts from lower control arm ball joints.
18. Pull lower control arms down to separate them from the steering knuckles.
19. Remove righthand joint shaft bracket.
20. Remove halfshaft assemblies from transaxle.
21. Install two transaxle plugs tool No. T88C-7025-AH or equivalent, between the differential side gears. **Failure to install the transaxle plugs may allow the differential side gears to become incorrectly positioned.**
22. Remove gusset plate to transaxle attaching bolts.
23. **On models with 3.0L/V6-182 engine,** remove front exhaust pipe.
24. **On all models,** disconnect extension bar and control rod.
25. **On models except 3.0/V6-182 engine,** remove flywheel inspection cover.
26. **On all models,** remove starter motor, then access brackets.
27. Install engine support bar tool No. D87L-6000-A or equivalent, then attach it to the engine hanger.
28. Remove center transaxle mount, then bracket.
29. Remove left transaxle mount.
30. Remove nut and bolt attaching right transaxle mount to vehicle frame.
31. Remove crossmember and left side lower control arm as an assembly.
32. Position jack under transaxle, then secure transaxle to jack.
33. Remove engine to transaxle attaching bolts.
34. Lower transaxle from vehicle.
35. Reverse procedure to install. Noting that during installation of the stabilizer link assemblies, turn the nuts on each assembly until 1 inch of bolt thread can be measured from the upper nut. When this length is obtained, secure the upper nut, then back off the lower nut until a **torque** of 12-17 ft. lbs. is reached.

## TIGHTENING SPECIFICATIONS

| Year | Component | Torque/Ft. Lbs. |
|---|---|---|
| 1990-92 | Clutch Master Cylinder Nuts | 14–19 |
| | Extension Bar to Transaxle | 40–51 |
| | Center Transaxle Mount Bolts | 27–40 |
| | Center Transaxle Mount Nuts | 47–66 |
| | Crossmember Bolts | 27–40 |
| | Crossmember Nuts | 55–69 |
| | Flywheel | 71–75 |
| | Flywheel Inspection Cover | 69–95④ |
| | Gusset Plate to Transaxle | 27–38 |
| | Left Mount to Bracket | 49–69① |

Continued

## TIGHTENING SPECIFICATIONS—Continued

| Year | Component | Torque/Ft. Lbs. |
|---|---|---|
| 1990-92 | Pressure Plate | 13–20 |
| | Right Transaxle Mount | 63–86 |
| | Slave Cylinder | 14–19 |
| | Transaxle Case to Clutch Housing | 13–14 |
| | Transaxle Case to Clutch Housing | 37–52① |
| | Transaxle to Engine | 66–86③ |
| | Transaxle to Engine | 47–66② |
| | Transaxle to Left Mount | 27–38 |
| | Transaxle to Left Mount | 49–69① |

①—2.2L/4-133 turbo & 3.0L/V6-182 engine.
②—3.0L/V6-182 engine.
③—Except 3.0L/V6-182 engine.
④—Inch lbs.

# Rear Axle & Suspension

## INDEX



## DESCRIPTION

The rear suspension, **Fig. 1,** is fully independent utilizing rear MacPherson struts at each wheel. If the vehicle is equipped with the programmed ride control system, the rear strut towers locate the programmed ride control actuators and the strut assemblies. A forged rear spindle bolts to the shock absorber, double rear lateral links and a single trailing arm.

## SHOCK STRUT

### REPLACE

1. Disconnect battery ground cable.
2. Remove tire and wheel assembly.
3. Remove upper trunk side garnish, then lower trunk side trim to gain access to the strut assembly.
4. Disconnect programmed ride control module electrical connector from top of strut assembly, if equipped.
5. Remove programmed ride control module, if equipped.
6. Remove ABS harness and bracket, if equipped.
7. Remove rear brake drum and backing plate assembly or rear disc brake caliper, then rotor assembly.
8. Remove brake line U-clip from the strut housing.
9. Loosen the trailing arm bolt, **Fig. 2.** Remove spindle to shock absorber attaching bolts.
10. Remove the strut attaching nuts from inside the vehicle. Remove strut assembly, **Fig. 3.**
11. Reverse procedure to install. Tightening bolts to specifications.

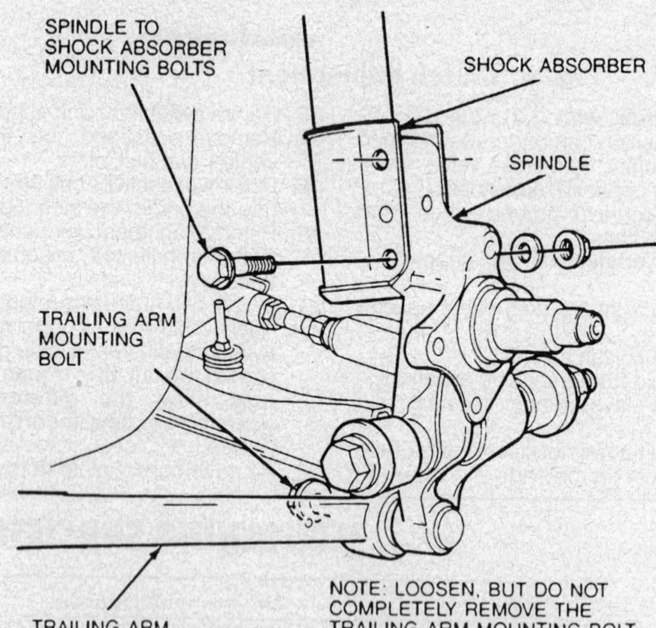


**Fig. 1 Rear suspension components**

## LATERAL LINK, TRAILING ARM & REAR CROSSMEMBER

### REPLACE

1. Disconnect battery ground cable.
2. Remove spindle from vehicle.
3. Remove rear stabilizer.
4. Remove nut from lateral link mounting bolt at the rear crossmember. Remove lateral link.
5. Remove parking brake attaching bolts from trailing arm assembly.
6. Remove the trailing arm mounting bolt from the body mounting bracket.
7. Remove trailing arm from the vehicle.
8. Remove exhaust mounting bolts and

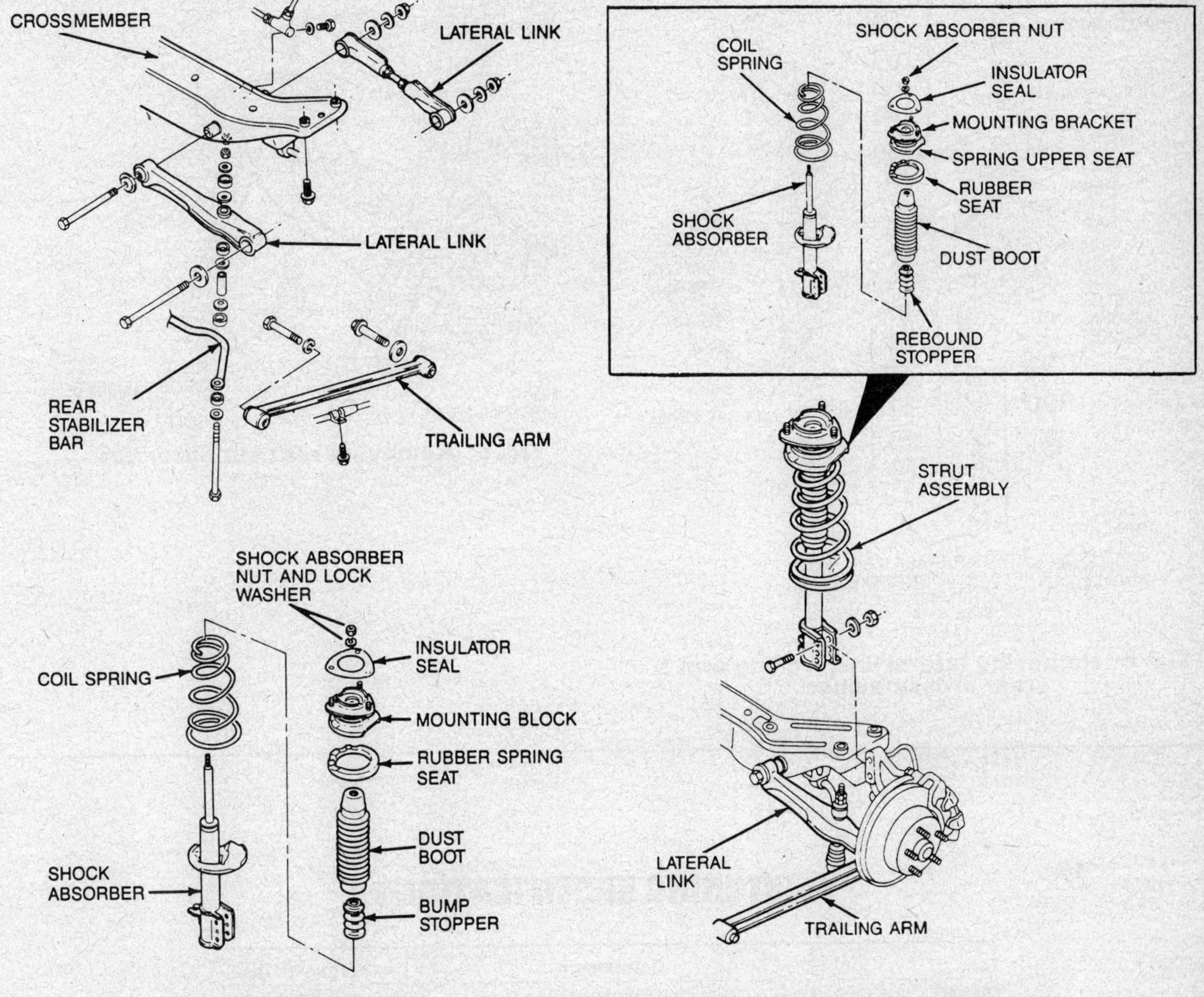


**Fig. 2 Removing spindle**

**Fig. 3 Removing shock strut**

brake line retaining bracket from rear crossmember.

9. Remove mounting bolts from end of the crossmember.
10. Remove rear crossmember and front lateral link as an assembly.
11. Remove common lateral link mounting bolt from the rear crossmember.
12. Remove front lateral link from rear crossmember, **Fig. 4.**
13. Reverse procedure to install. Tightening bolts to specifications.

## STABILIZER BAR
### REPLACE

1. Remove mounting bolt assembly from front lateral link, **Fig. 5.**
2. Remove stabilizer bushing, then bracket from rear crossmember.
3. Reverse procedure to install. Tightening bolts to specifications.

## REAR WHEEL BEARING ENDPLAY
### ADJUST

1. Ensure parking brake is fully released.
2. Remove wheel and tire assembly.
3. Rotate brake drum to ensure no brake drag.
4. Using a dial indicator, check wheel bearing end play. End play should not exceed .008 inch.
5. If measurement exceeds specification, replace bearing.

## REAR WHEEL BEARING
### REPLACE

1. Remove rear brake drum or rotor from vehicle.
2. Remove dust seal and rear bearing.
3. Reverse procedure to install.

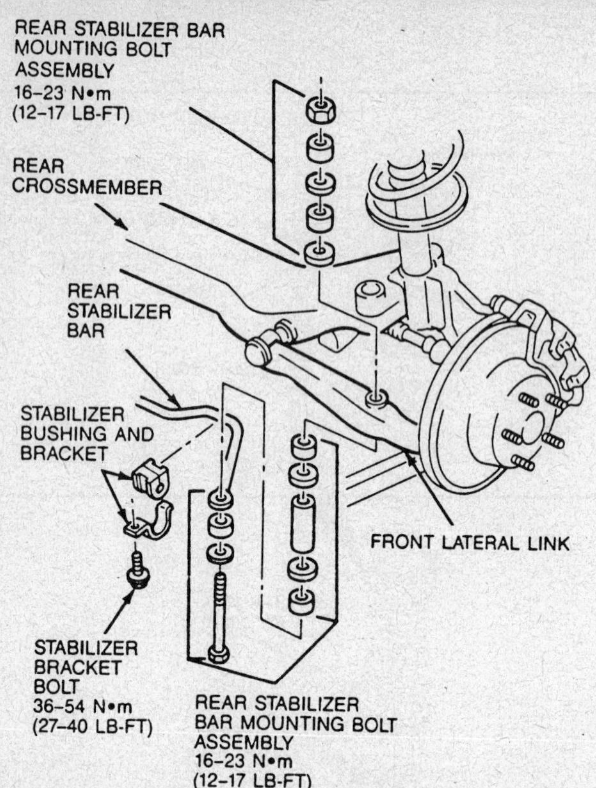


**Fig. 4 Removing lateral link, trailing arm & rear crossmember**

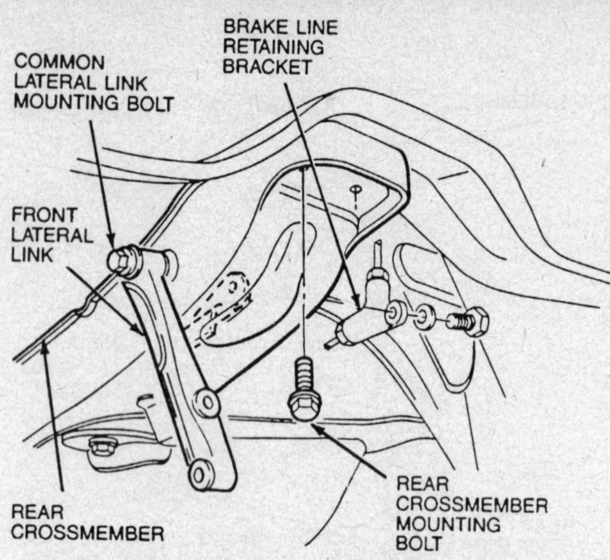


**Fig. 5 Removing rear stabilizer bar**

# TIGHTENING SPECIFICATIONS

| Year | Component | Torque/ft. lbs. |
|---|---|---|
| 1989-92 | Crossmember Mounting Bolts | 27–40 |
| | Hub Spindle To Back Plate | 33–43 |
| | Hub Spindle To Shock Absorber | 69–86 |
| | Lateral Link Mounting Bolt | 64–86 |
| | Shock Absorber Tower Nut | 47–67 |
| | Stabilizer Bar Mounting Bolt | 12–17 |
| | Stabilizer Bracket Attaching Bolt | 27–40 |
| | Strut Attaching Nuts | 34–46 |
| | Trailing Arm Mounting Bolt (Front) | 46–69 |
| | Trailing Arm Mounting Bolt (Rear) | 64–86 |
| | Wheel Lug Nuts | 65–87 |

# Front Suspension & Steering

## INDEX



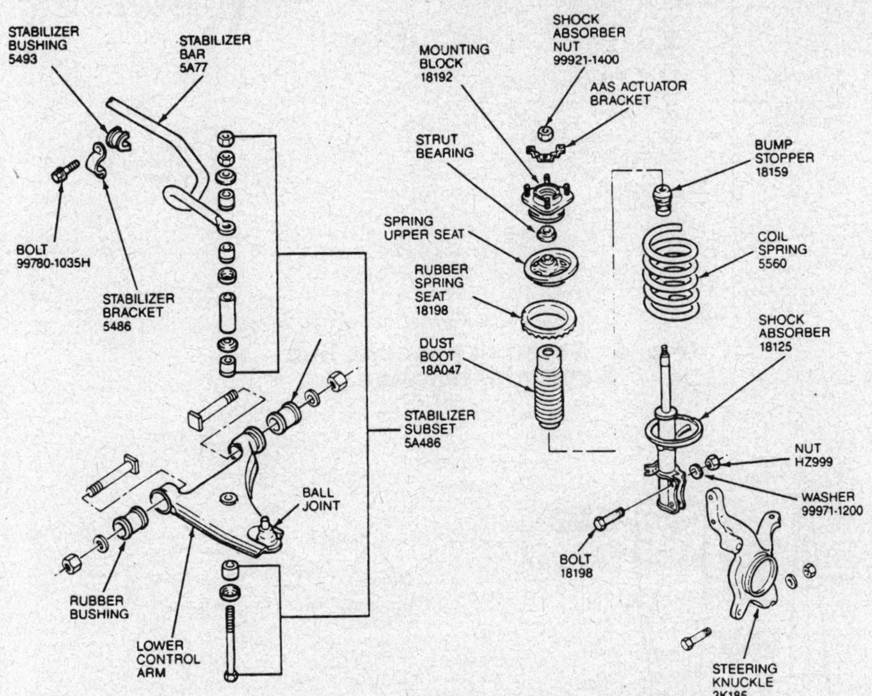


Fig. 1 Front suspension (Part 1 of 2)

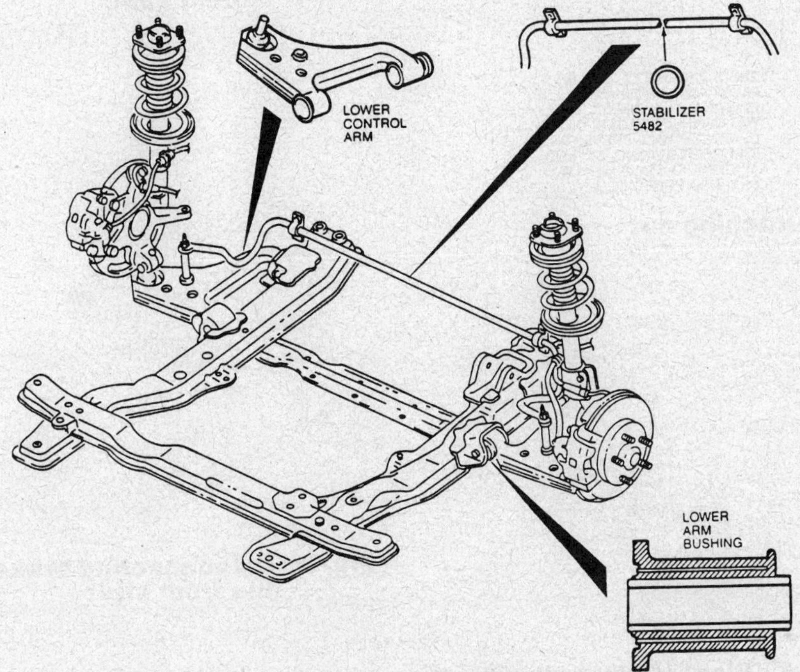


Fig. 1 Front suspension (Part 2 of 2)

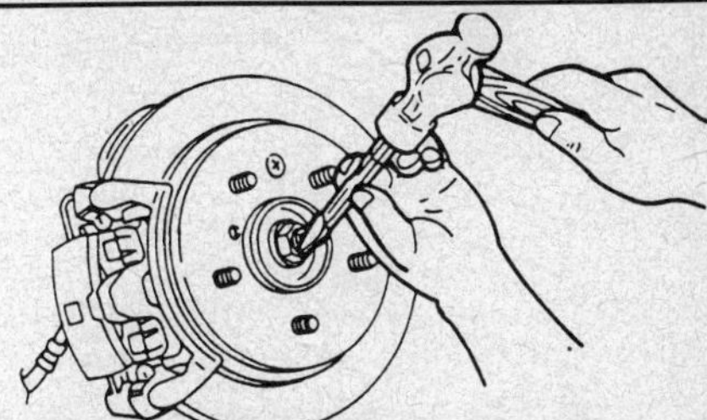

**Fig. 2 Removing stake from halfshaft attaching nut**

## DESCRIPTION

This suspension is of the MacPherson strut type, **Fig. 1.** The strut towers are located in the wheelwells and position the upper ends of the struts. If the vehicle is equipped with the optional Programmed Ride Control system, the ride control actuator bolts to the top of the strut mounting block that houses a rubber mounted strut bearing. The upper end of the coil spring rides in a rubber sprint seat. A forged steering knuckle is bolted to the shock absorber.

If the vehicle is not equipped with the Programmed Ride Control System, the struts used are the conventional non-adjustable type. These struts are not interchangeable.

The lower ball joints are pressed into the lower control arm that is attached to the steering knuckle. The control arms are supported by rubber bushings at each end. A hollow stabilizer bar is connected to the control arms.

## WHEEL HUB/STEERING KNUCKLE ASSEMBLY

### REPLACE

1. Raise and support vehicle.
2. Remove tire and wheel assembly.
3. Carefully raise the staked portion of the halfshaft attaching nut using a small cape chisel, **Fig. 2.**
4. Remove halfshaft attaching nut. When loosening the nut, lock the hub in position by having a helper lock the brakes. **Discard the nut, it should not be reused.**
5. Remove stabilizer bar link bolts.
6. Separate tie rod end from steering knuckle, **Fig. 3.**
7. Remove caliper, then anchor bracket assembly. Suspend caliper from coil spring. **Do not allow to hang from brake line.**
8. Remove brake rotor, **Fig. 4.**

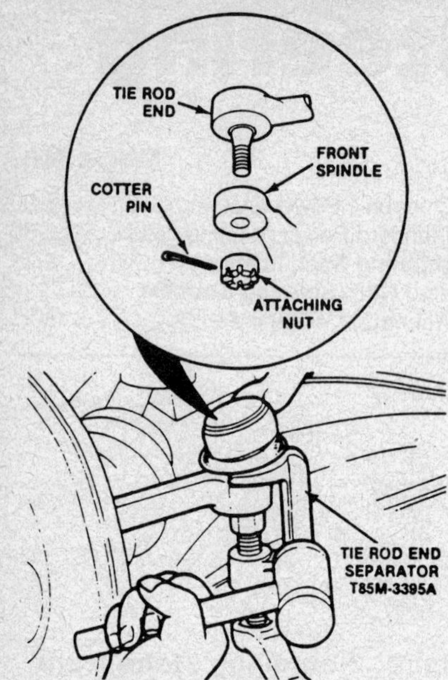


**Fig. 3 Separating tie rod end from steering knuckle**

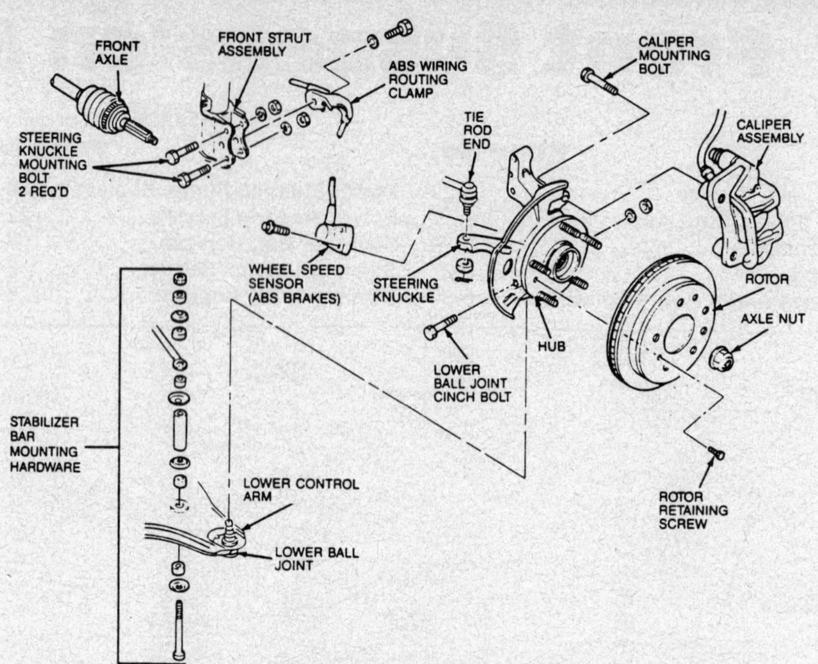


**Fig. 4 Steering knuckle, hub & rotor installation**

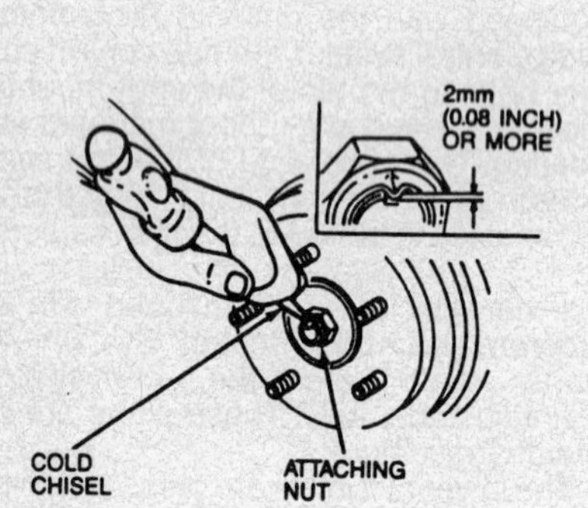

THE STAKING TOOL CAN BE FABRICATED FROM AN EXISTING HARDENED CHISEL. THE CORRECT RADIUS ON THE CHISEL TIP WILL PREVENT IMPROPER STAKING. DO NOT ATTEMPT TO STAKE WITH A SHARPED EDGED TOOL.

**Fig. 5 Staking halfshaft attaching nut**

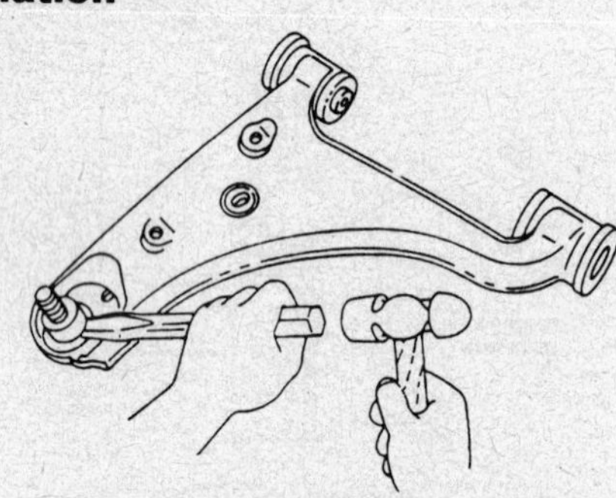

**Fig. 6 Removing ball joint dust boot**

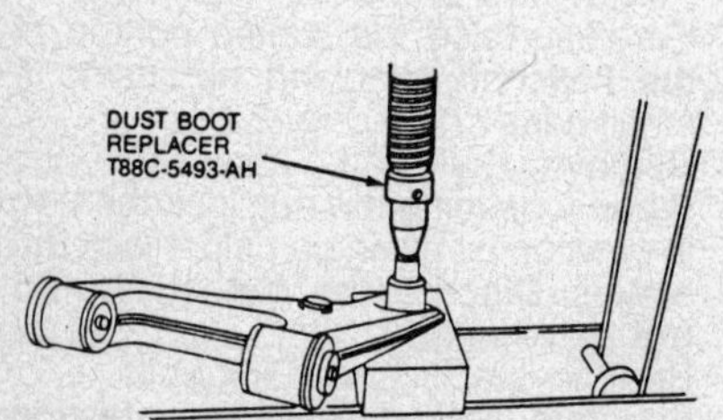


**Fig. 7 Installing ball joint dust boot**

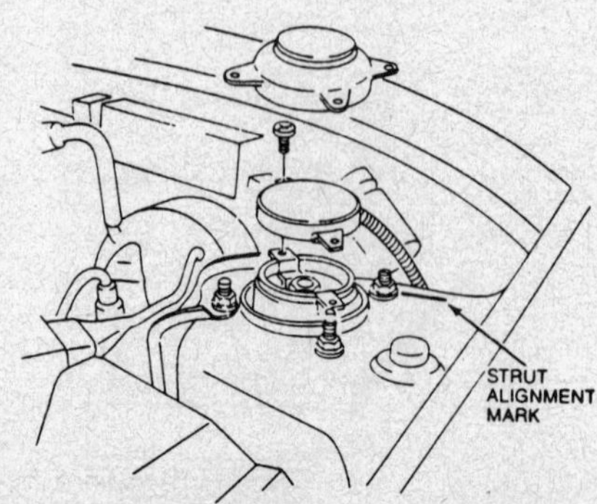


**Fig. 8 Placing strut alignment mark**

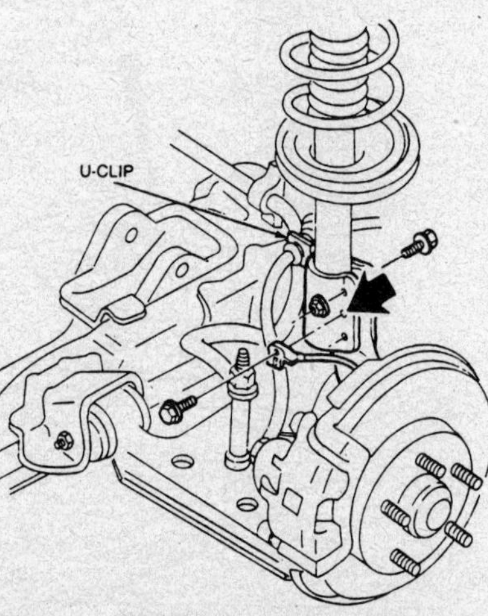


**Fig. 9 Disconnecting brake line from strut**

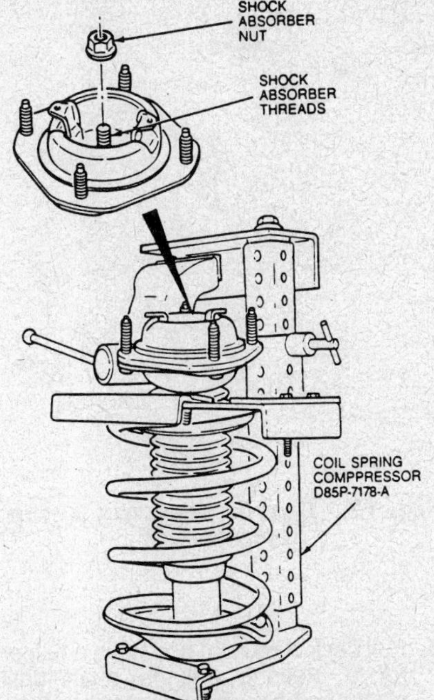


**Fig. 10 Spring compressor installation**

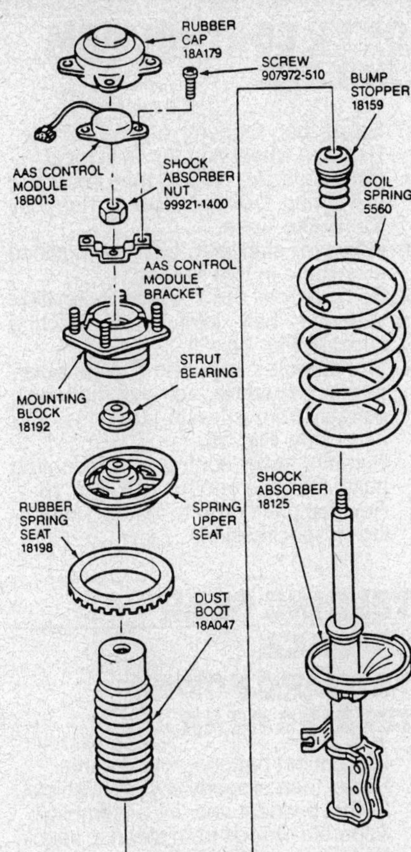


**Fig. 11 Strut disassembled**

STABILIZER BUSHING 5493 — BOLT 99780-1035H — STABILIZER BAR — STABILIZER BRACKET 5486 — STABILIZER LINK ASSEMBLY SUBSET 5A486 — LOWER CONTROL ARM

**Fig. 12 Stabilizer bar installation**

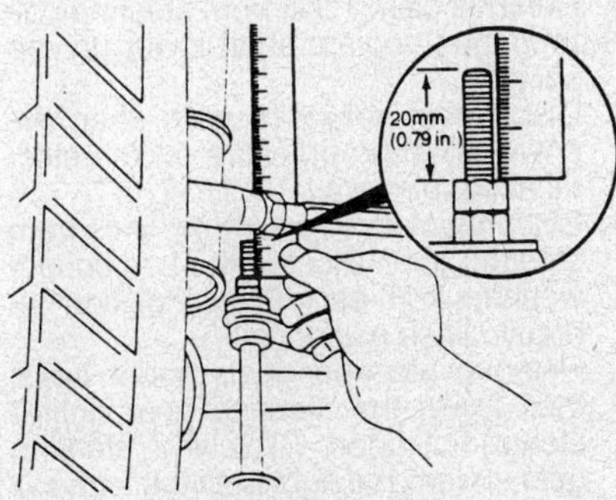


**Fig. 13 Stabilizer bar link installation**

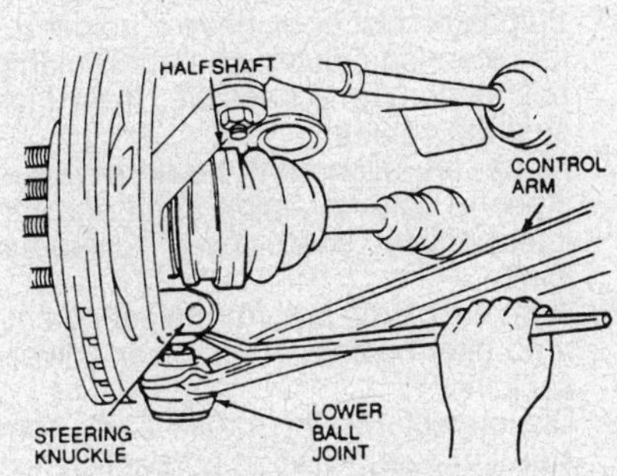


**Fig. 14 Separating ball joint from control arm**

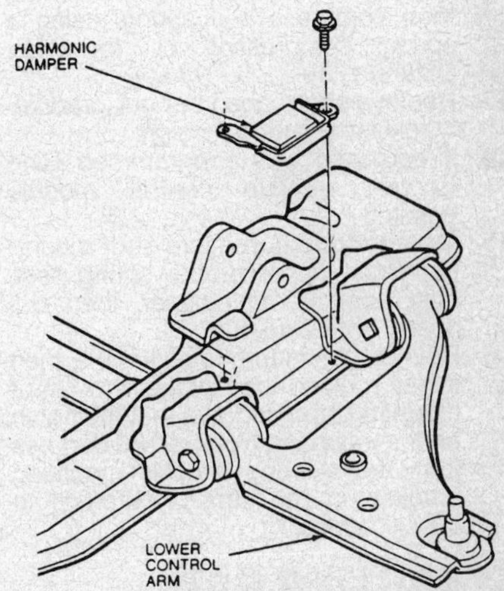


**Fig. 15 Harmonic damper installation**

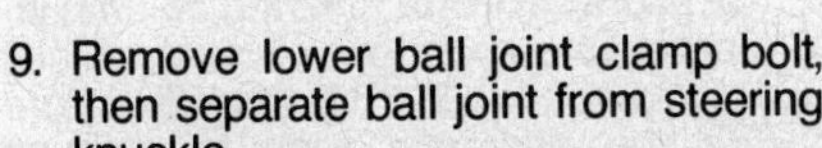

9. Remove lower ball joint clamp bolt, then separate ball joint from steering knuckle.
10. Remove steering knuckle to strut attaching bolts.
11. Slide front hub/steering knuckle assembly from strut bracket and halfshaft, **Fig. 4. Use caution not to damage grease seals. If the hub binds on the halfshaft splines, lightly tap end of halfshaft with a plastic hammer. If the halfshaft splines become rusted to the hub, use a two-jawed puller or a hub puller to separate.**
12. Reverse procedure to install. Tightening to specifications, then stake nut, **Fig. 5. Torque** tie rod ending attaching nut to 22-33 ft. lbs.

# BALL JOINT SERVICE

**The ball joints on this vehicle are not serviceable parts. Only the dust boots are replaceable.**

1. Remove lower control arm as outlined elsewhere in this section.
2. Place control arm in a vise.
3. Remove dust boot with a chisel, **Fig. 6. Use caution not to damage ball joint.**
4. Liberally coat inside of new dust boot with lubricant C1AZ-19590-B or equivalent.
5. Install dust boot with dust boot installer tool No. T88C-5493-AH or equivalent, **Fig. 7.**
6. Install lower control arm.

# COIL SPRING/STRUT ASSEMBLY

## REPLACE

1. Raise and properly support front of vehicle.
2. Remove rubber cap from strut mounting block. If equipped with Programmed Ride Control, disconnect control module connector.
3. Place an alignment mark between the inside of the strut mounting block and the chassis strut tower, **Fig. 8.**

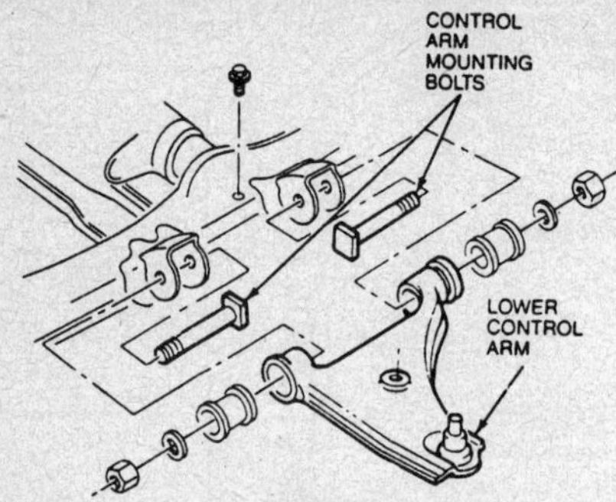


**Fig. 16 Lower control arm installation**

4. If equipped with Programmed Ride Control, remove control module.
5. If equipped with anti-lock brake system, remove system harness and bracket.
6. **On all models,** remove brake caliper, the U-clip from brake line hose, then slide from strut bracket, **Fig. 9.**
7. Remove steering knuckle to strut attaching bolts.
8. Remove vane airflow meter assembly, then the ignition coil bracket from strut tower.
9. Remove strut mounting bolts from tower, then the strut assembly from vehicle.
10. Place strut assembly in a vise.
11. Loosen, but do not remove shock absorber nut, **Fig. 10.**
12. Remove strut assembly from vise, then compress coil spring, using a spring compressor or tool No. D85P-7178-A.
13. Remove shock absorber nut, gradually releasing spring tension.
14. If equipped with Programmed Ride Control, remove control module bracket.
15. **On all models,** remove strut mounting block, upper rubber spring seat, dust boot, bump stopper, then coil spring from strut, **Fig. 11.**
16. Reverse procedure to assemble, then install. When installing the strut mounting block, ensure that the notch on the mounting block is 180 degrees from the steering knuckle mounting bracket on the strut. Tightening to specifications.

## STABILIZER BAR
### REPLACE

1. Raise and properly support vehicle.
2. Remove wheel and tire assembly.
3. Remove stabilizer bar link assembly from lower control arm, **Fig. 12.**
4. Remove mount bolt from stabilizer bar bushing.
5. Remove stabilizer bar from vehicle.
6. Reverse procedure to install. Tightening to specifications. Tighten stabilizer bar link nut until .79 inch of threads protrude above nut, **Fig. 13.**

## LOWER CONTROL ARM
### REPLACE

1. Raise, then properly support vehicle.
2. Remove wheel and tire assembly.
3. Remove brake caliper, then secure to coil spring. **Do not allow to hang by the brake hose.**
4. Remove stabilizer bar as outlined elsewhere in this section.
5. Remove ball joint clamp bolt, then separate ball joint from steering knuckle, **Fig. 14.**
6. **On vehicles equipped with automatic transaxle,** remove harmonic damper from chassis subframe, lefthand side, **Fig. 15.**
7. Remove lower control arm mounting bolts, then the control arm, **Fig. 16.**
8. Reverse procedure to install. Tightening to specifications.

## STEERING GEAR
### REPLACE
### STANDARD POWER STEERING GEAR

1. Disconnect battery ground cable.
2. Raise, then properly support vehicle.
3. Remove wheel and tire assemblies.
4. Separate tie rods from steering knuckles.
5. Remove plastic dust shield from both sides of lower inner fender.
6. Pull back dust boot, have a helper rotate steering column shaft until clamp bolt becomes accessible, then lock steering column.
7. Place an alignment mark between steering column pinion shaft and the intermediate shaft lower universal joint.
8. Remove clamp bolt from steering column intermediate shaft lower universal joint.
9. Disconnect two hydraulic lines from steering gear. Position hydraulic lines aside.
10. Remove steering gear mount bolts, then lower the steering gear until it clears bulkhead. Slide the steering gear toward the right until the lefthand tie rod clears the left lower control arm. Slide steering gear to the left, then remove from vehicle.
11. Reverse procedure to install. Tightening to specifications.

### ELECTRONIC POWER STEERING GEAR

1. Disconnect battery ground cable.
2. Raise, then properly support vehicle.
3. Remove wheel and tire assemblies.
4. Separate tie rods from steering knuckles.
5. Remove plastic dust shield from both sides of lower inner fender.

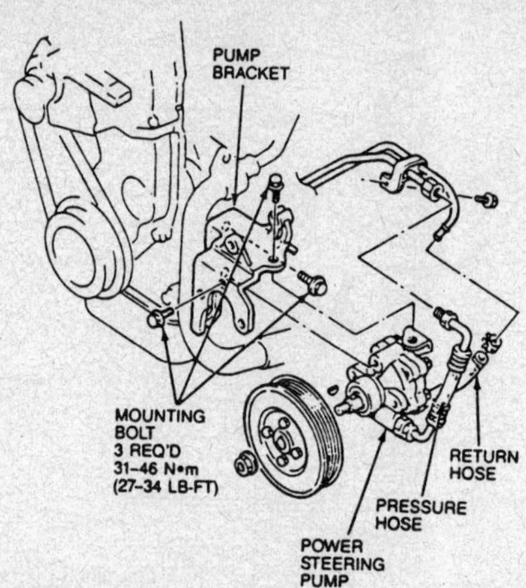


**Fig. 17 Power steering pump installation**

6. Pull back dust boot and have a helper rotate steering column shaft until clamp bolt becomes accessible, then lock steering column.
7. Place an alignment mark between steering column pinion shaft and the intermediate shaft lower universal joint.
8. Remove clamp bolt from steering column intermediate shaft lower universal joint.
9. Disconnect solenoid valve, then the power steering pressure switch electrical connectors.
10. Disconnect three hydraulic lines from steering gear. Discard the two copper washers from each fitting. Position hydraulic lines aside.
11. Remove steering gear mount bolts, then lower the steering gear until it clears bulkhead. Slide the steering gear toward the right until the lefthand tie rod clears the left lower control arm. Then, slide steering gear to the left and remove from vehicle.
12. Reverse procedure to install. Tightening steering gear mount bolts to specifications. **Torque** steering column intermediate shaft lower universal joint clamp bolt to 13-20 ft. lbs. When connecting hydraulic lines to steering gear, install new copper washers.

## POWER STEERING PUMP
### REPLACE

1. Disconnect battery ground cable.
2. Remove righthand inner fender splash shield.
3. Remove drive belt.
4. Disconnect power steering pressure and return hoses from pump.
5. Remove three power steering pump mounting bolts and the pump, **Fig. 17.**
6. Reverse procedure to install. Tightening to specifications.

## TIGHTENING SPECIFICATIONS

| Year | Component | Torque/ft. lbs. |
|---|---|---|
| 1989-92 | Ball Joint Clamp Bolt | 32-40 |
| | Control Arm Rod Jam Nuts | 41-59 |
| | Dynamic Damper Mounting Bolts | 31-46 |
| | Halfshaft Attaching Nut | 116-174 |
| | Lower Control Arm Mounting Bolts | 69-93 |
| | Power Steering Pump Mounting Bolts | 27-34 |
| | Stabilizer Bar Bushing | 27-40 |
| | Steering Gear Mount Bolts | 27-40 |
| | Steering Knuckle To Strut | 69-86 |
| | Strut Attaching Nuts | 34-46 |
| | Strut Tower Nut | 47-69 |
| | Tie Rod End Jam Nuts | 51-72 |
| | Wheel Lug Nuts | 65-87 |

# Wheel Alignment

INDEX



## PRELIMINARY ADJUSTMENT

Before measuring and setting front wheel alignment, rest front wheels on turn plates.

Before setting rear toe, rest rear wheels on slider plates or turn plates. Before setting any alignment angle, jounce the vehicle three times at each end to establish trim height.

Special adapters are available for using a magnetic hub gauge at rear wheels. Depending on type of equipment used, these may not be necessary. After removing hub cap and bearing cap, hub gauge will snap into place on brake drum. Magnetic mounting toe gauges may also be installed in the same manner.

Always perform wheel alignment on a level alignment rack. Do not attempt to check or adjust front wheel alignment without first inspecting front end components.

Check all factors of front wheel alignment except turning angle before making any adjustments. Check the turning angle only after camber and toe have been adjusted to specification. Check front wheel alignment under following curb load conditions:

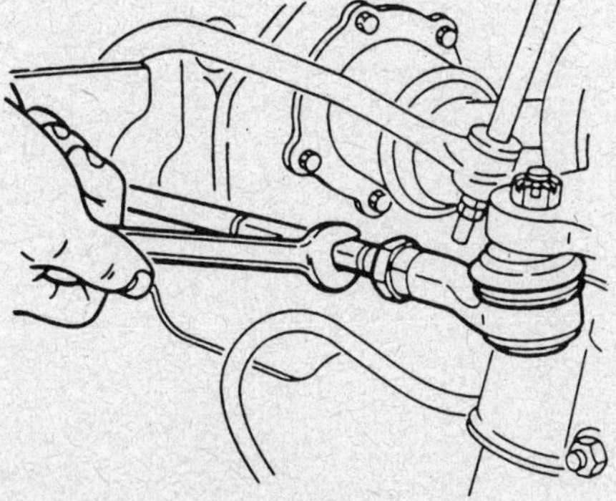

Fig. 1 Adjusting front toe-in

1. Establish standing curb height.
2. Remove heavy weights from trunk.
3. Ensure all tires are inflated to specification (cold).
4. Ensure Fuel tank, oil reservoir and radiator are filled to specification. If necessary, add six pounds of weight to trunk for each gallon of gasoline missing from tank.
5. Place front seats in full rear position.
6. Check rear toe adjustment.
7. Always road test vehicle after adjusting alignment. If vehicle still pulls, switch front tires. If vehicle still pulls in same direction, recheck alignment and rear tracking. If vehicle pulls in opposite direction, rotate tires, then road test again.

## FRONT WHEEL ALIGNMENT

Always adjust rear toe before setting front alignment angles.

### CASTER

Front caster adjustment is not a separate procedure on this vehicle. Front caster should fall within specification when front camber is adjusted. If caster does not fall within specification, check control arms, stabilizers and bushings. If these components are satisfactory, check vehicle body for distortion at suspension mounting points.

### CAMBER

1. Raise vehicle and support at body so that front suspension is unloaded.

2. Remove tire and wheel assembly.
3. Remove upper strut attaching nuts.
4. Lower strut, then rotate strut mounting block until camber is within specification.
5. Reinstall strut in strut tower.
6. **Torque** strut attaching nuts to 34-46 ft. lbs, then recheck camber adjustment.

## TOE-IN

1. Loosen jam nuts at tie rod ends, then release clips at small ends of steering gear boots. **Ensure boots are free on tie rod ends so that they will not be twisted when tie rods are turned.**
2. Turn tie rods into or out of tie rod ends an equal amount on each side, **Fig.1**. To increase toe-in, turn right tie rod toward front of vehicle, and turn left tie rod toward read of vehicle. To decrease toe-in, turn tie rods in opposite direction. One turn of each side tie rod changes toe-in by approximately .28inch.
3. Check front tracking. **Always set tracking immediately after setting toe.** Set tracking by by using rear wheels as a reference point. Follow equipment manufacture's instructions to check tracking. The angle of each front wheel in relationship to rear wheels must be the same.
4. Ensure toe-in is still within specifications, then **torque** jam nuts to 51-72 ft. lbs. Ensure steering gear boot ends are correctly positioned on appropriate sections of tie rods, then install boot clips.
5. Measure turning angle by placing front wheels on a turning-radius gauge and fully turning wheels to the left, then right. Inner turning angle should be 36.44° and outer turning angle should be 30.99°.

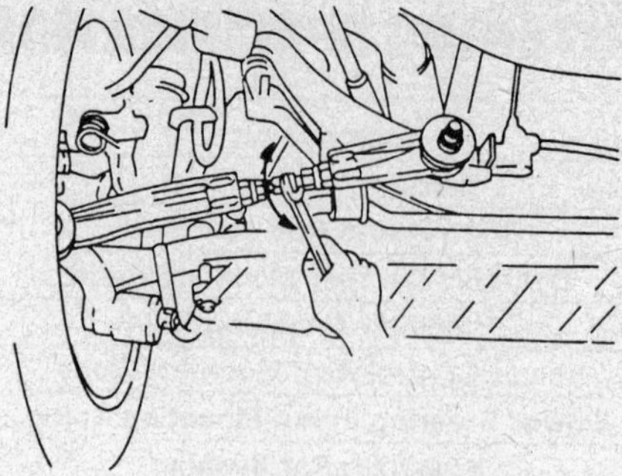

**Fig. 2 Adjusting rear toe-in**

# REAR WHEEL ALIGNMENT

## TOE-IN

1. Loosen jam nuts clockwise on right control arm, then loosen jam nuts counterclockwise on left control arm.
2. To increase toe-in, turn right control arm rod counterclockwise and turn left control arm rod clockwise, **Fig. 2.**
3. To decrease toe-in, turn right control arm clockwise and turn left control arm counterclockwise. **Turn control arm rods into or out of control arm ends an equal amount on each side.** One turn of each control arm rod changes toe by .46 inch.
4. **Torque** control arm jam nuts to 41-59 ft. lbs.

# MERKUR

## INDEX OF SERVICE OPERATIONS

**NOTE:** Refer To The Rear Of This Manual For Vehicle Manufacturer's Special Tool Suppliers.

Page No.

## INDEX OF SERVICE OPERATIONS—Continued



# Specifications

## GENERAL ENGINE SPECIFICATIONS

| Year | Engine | | Fuel System | Bore x Stroke Inches | Comp. Ratio | Net HP @ RPM③ | Maximum Torque Ft. Lbs @ RPM | Normal Oil Pressure Psi |
|---|---|---|---|---|---|---|---|---|
| | CID①/Liter | VIN Code② | | | | | | |
| 1989 | 2.3L/4-140④ | T | Fuel Inj. | 3.780 x 3.126 | 8.0 | 145 @ 4400 | 180 @ 3000 | 40–60⑤ |
| | 2.3L/4-140⑥ | T | Fuel Inj. | 3.780 x 3.126 | 8.0 | 175 @ 5000 | 200 @ 3000 | 40–60⑤ |
| 1989 | 2.9L/V6-177 | V | Fuel Inj. | 3.66 x 2.83 | 9.0 | 144 @ 5500 | 162 @ 3000 | 40–60⑤ |

①—CID: Cubic Inch Displacement.
②—The eighth digit of the VIN denotes engine code.
③—Ratings are net, as installed in vehicle.
④—Auto. trans.
⑤—At 2000 RPM.
⑥—Man. Trans.

## TUNE UP SPECIFICATIONS

| Year & Engine/ VIN Code | Spark Plug Gap | Ignition Timing BTDC① | | | | Curb Idle Speed | | Fast Idle Speed | | Fuel Pump Pressure Psi |
|---|---|---|---|---|---|---|---|---|---|---|
| | | Firing Order Fig. | Man. Trans. | Auto. Trans. | Mark Fig. | Man. Trans. | Auto. Trans.② | Man. Trans. | Auto. Trans. | |
| **1989** | | | | | | | | | | |
| 4-140(2.3L)/T | .034 | A | 13③ | 10③ | B | 825–975④ | 925–1075N④ | ⑤ | ⑤ | 35–45⑥ |
| **1989** | | | | | | | | | | |
| V6-177(2.9L)/V | .044 | C | 10③ | 10③ | D | 850⑤ | 850N⑤ | ⑤ | ⑤ | 43.5⑦ |

①—BTDC: Before Top Dead Center.
②—N: Neutral.
③—With spout wire disconnected. The spout wire is located near the distributor, within 6 inches of the TFI module.
④—With idle bypass valve electrical connector connected. When adjusting, disconnect idle bypass valve electrical connector & set idle screw to 725–775 RPM.
⑤—Controlled by idle speed control motor.
⑥—With fuel pressure gauge connected to schrader valve on fuel supply manifold, start engine & check fuel pressure.
⑦—Connect a fuel pressure gauge to schrader valve on fuel rail. Connect a jumper wire to blue/red wire terminal of the diagnostic test connector. The six pin diagnostic test connector is located on the right hand fender apron, to the rear of the strut tower. Place ignition switch in On position (do not start engine), then connect jumper wire to ground for approximately 1 minute and note fuel pressure gauge reading.

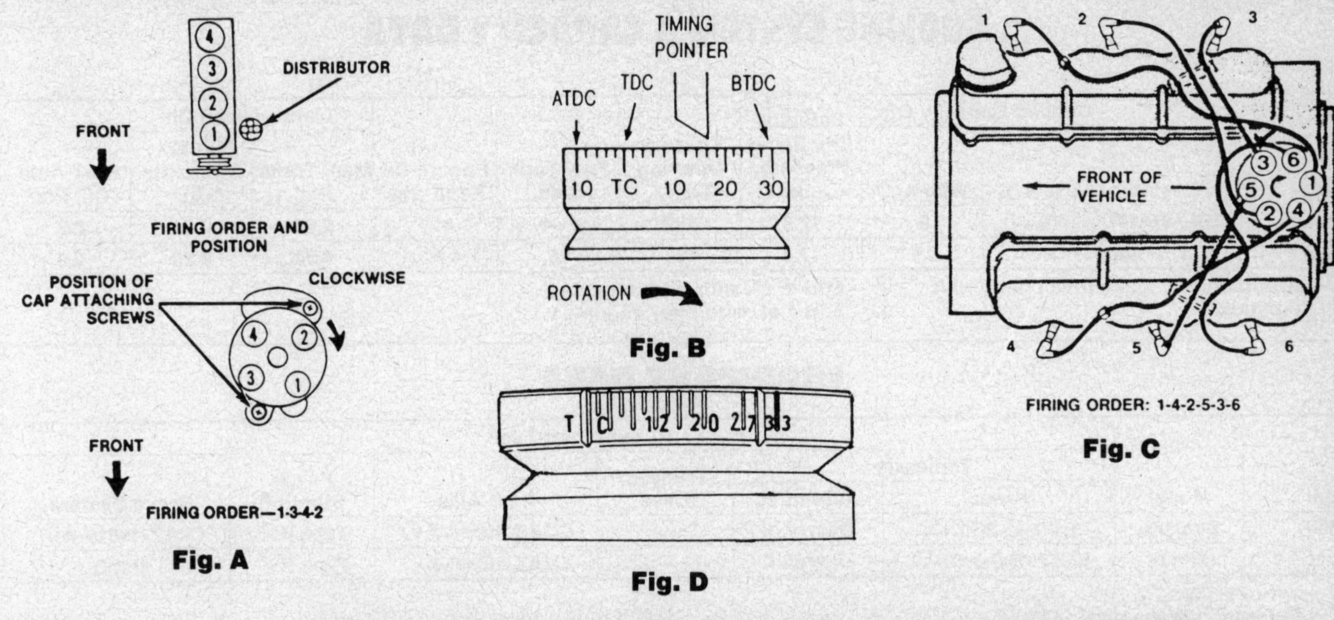


Fig. A

Fig. B

Fig. C

Fig. D

# FRONT WHEEL ALIGNMENT SPECIFICATIONS

| Year | Model | Caster Angle, Degrees | | Camber Angle, Degrees | | | | Toe-In Inch | Wheel Turning Angle ① | |
|---|---|---|---|---|---|---|---|---|---|---|
| | | | | Limits | | Desired | | | | |
| | | Limits | Desired | Left | Right | Left | Right | | Left | Right |
| 1989 | XR4Ti | +29/30 to +2 29/30 | +1 29/30 | −1 8/15 to +7/15 | −1 8/15 to +7/15 | −8/15 | −8/15 | 5/64 | — | — |
| 1989 | Scorpio | +1 to +3 | +2 | −1 7/16 to +9/16 | −1 7/16 to +9/16 | −7/16 | −7/16 | 9/64 | 20 | 19.2 |

①—At outside wheel with inside wheel turned at 20°.

# REAR WHEEL ALIGNMENT SPECIFICATIONS

Camber angle varies with ride height. Measure ride height from center of rear wheel to bottom of wheel opening molding.

| Model | Toe In Inch | Ride Height Inches | Camber Angle Degrees |
|---|---|---|---|
| XR4Ti | 3/64 | 13.78 to 14.13 | −2 5/6 to −1/2 |
| | 3/64 | 14.17 to 14.53 | −2 7/15 to −2/15 |
| | 3/64 | 14.57 to 14.92 | −2 1/10 to +1/4 |
| | 3/64 | 14.96 to 15.31 | −1 43/60 to +37/60 |
| | 3/64 | 15.35 to 15.71 | −1 7/20 to +1 |
| | 3/64 | 15.75 to 16.10 | −29/30 to +1 11/30 |
| | 3/64 | 16.14 to 16.50 | −3/5 to +1 3/4 |
| | 3/64 | 16.54 to 16.89 | −13/60 to +2 7/60 |
| Scorpio | 1/20 | 14.17 to 14.53 | −2 1/60 to −1/60 |
| | 1/20 | 14.56 to 14.92 | −1 19/30 to +11/30 |
| | 1/20 | 14.96 to 15.31 | −1 4/15 to +11/15 |
| | 1/20 | 15.35 to 15.70 | −53/60 to +1 7/60 |
| | 1/20 | 15.75 to 16.10 | −31/60 to +1 29/60 |
| | 1/20 | 16.14 to 16.50 | −2/15 to +1 13/15 |
| | 1/20 | 16.54 to 16.89 | +7/30 to +2 7/30 |
| | 1/20 | 16.92 to 17.28 | +37/60 to +2 37/60 |

## COOLING SYSTEM & CAPACITY DATA

| Year | Engine | Cooling Capacity Qts. Less A/C | Cooling Capacity Qts. With A/C | Radiator Cap Relief Pressure, Lbs. | Thermo. Opening Temp. | Fuel Tank Gals. | Engine Oil Refill Qts. | Transmission Oil Man. Trans. Pts. | Transmission Oil Auto. Trans. Qts. ① | Rear Axle Oil, Pts. |
|---|---|---|---|---|---|---|---|---|---|---|
| 1989 | 2.9L/V6-177 | 9 | 9 | 17.5 | 192 | — | 4③ | 2.36 | 9.25 | 2.7 |
| 1989 | 2.3L/4-140 | 9.5 | 9.5 | 17.4 | 192 | 15 | 4.5② | 2.64 | 9.25 | 2.8 |

①—Approximate, make final check with dipstick.
②—Add ½ qt. with filter change.
③—Add 1 qt. with filter change.

## LUBRICANT DATA

| Year | Model | Lubricant Type: Transaxle Manual | Transaxle Automatic | Transfer Case | Rear Axle | Power Steering | Brake System |
|---|---|---|---|---|---|---|---|
| 1989 | Scorpio | ESD-M-2C175A | Dexron II | — | EOAZ-19580-A① | Type F② | C6AZ-19542-A① |
| | XR4Ti | E5RY-19C-547A① | Dexron II | — | EOAZ-19580-A① | Type F② | Dot 3 |

①—Ford Part No.
②—Automatic Transmission Fluid.

# Electrical

## INDEX



## FUSE PANEL & FLASHER LOCATION

The fuse panel is located in the cowl area, near the lefthand rear corner of the engine compartment. Flashers are centrally located behind the instrument panel.

## STARTER MOTOR REPLACE

### SCORPIO

#### Removal

1. Disconnect battery ground cable, then raise and support vehicle.
2. Disconnect starter cable from solenoid, then the starter motor relay-to-solenoid wire.
3. Remove starter attaching bolts and the starter.

#### Installation

1. Position starter motor to engine and **torque** attaching bolts to 20-25 ft. lbs.
2. Connect starter cable to motor and **torque** to 41-44 inch lbs.
3. Connect starter relay to solenoid wire, then lower vehicle and connect battery ground cable.

### XR4Ti

#### Removal

1. Disconnect battery ground cable, then raise and support vehicle.
2. Disconnect starter cable from starter motor terminal.
3. Remove bolt attaching heat shield to cylinder block.
4. Remove starter attaching bolts, heat shield rear support bracket, transmission to cylinder block brace and the starter.

#### Installation

1. Position starter, bracket, brace and heat shield.
2. Install attaching bolts, **torquing** to 15-20 ft. lbs.
3. Install heat shield attaching bolt.
4. Tighten starter support bracket at cylinder block, then at starter.
5. Connect starter cable, lower vehicle and connect battery ground cable.

# DISTRIBUTOR
## REPLACE
### SCORPIO

1. Disconnect battery negative cable.
2. Use a screwdriver to remove the distributor cap, then position aside.
3. Rotate engine until No.1 piston is at TDC.
4. Remove the rotor.
5. Disconnect wiring connector from the TFI module.
6. Remove distributor hold-down and clamp.
7. Gently pull distributor from block.
8. Reverse procedure to install.

### XR4Ti

1. Disconnect battery negative cable.
2. Disconnect wiring connector from the TFI module, then the coil wire.
3. Use a screwdriver to remove the distributor cap, then position aside.
4. Remove the rotor.
5. Note the position of the shaft plate, armature and rotor locating holes.
6. Remove distributor hold-down and clamp.
7. Gently pull distributor from block.
8. Reverse procedure to install.

# STEERING WHEEL
## REPLACE

1. Disconnect battery negative cable.
2. Center steering wheel, ensure wheels are also centered.
3. Remove steering wheel center hub cover, then loosen steering wheel attaching nut.
4. Turn ignition switch to the run position.
5. Pull steering wheel straight up, to release from the taper on steering shaft.
6. Remove the attaching nut, then steering wheel.
7. Reverse procedure to install, noting the following:
   a. Align turn signal cam with the turn signal switch cancelling lever.
   b. Ensure the tab on the turn signal cancelling cam engages the slot on the underside of the steering wheel hub.
   c. **Torque** steering wheel attaching nut to 33-40 ft. lbs.
   d. Remove ignition key, then check steering wheel lock for proper operation.

# IGNITION SWITCH
## REPLACE
### REMOVAL

1. Disconnect battery ground cable.
2. Remove steering column shroud.
3. Insert key in ignition switch and turn key to ACC.
4. Depress key cylinder leaf spring through access hole in lock housing, then gently jiggle key back and forth until lock barrel and key cylinder come free.
5. Remove circlip from lock barrel, being careful not to damage circlip location in lock barrel.
6. Withdraw key approximately .2 inch, then remove key barrel from cylinder.

### INSTALLATION

1. Insert key fully into key barrel, then withdraw key approximately .2 inch.
2. Insert key barrel into cylinder.
3. Insert key fully and ensure that key and barrel turn freely.
4. Turn key to ACC position and install retaining circlip, ensuring that open jaws of clip align with keyway register of cylinder.
5. Insert cylinder assembly into housing, ensuring that cylinder is firmly seated in housing so that leaf spring fits into undercut slot in housing. Jiggle key back and forth as necessary to achieve proper alignment.
6. Check operation of lock assembly in all positions.

# LIGHT SWITCH
## REPLACE
### SCORPIO

1. Disconnect battery ground cable.
2. Remove cluster trim panel attaching screws and the trim panel.
3. Depress tabs on both sides of switch, then pull switch rearward.
4. Disconnect electrical connector, then remove switch.
5. Reverse procedure to install.

### XR4Ti

1. Disconnect battery ground cable.
2. Remove retaining screws, then the upper and lower steering column shrouds.
3. Remove two screws attaching multiswitch assembly to steering column, then guide multiswitch away from steering column.
4. Disconnect multiconnector and ground wire connector, then remove multiswitch.
5. Reverse procedure to install.

# STOP LIGHT SWITCH
## REPLACE
### REMOVAL

1. Disconnect battery ground cable.
2. Remove lower instrument panel.
3. Disconnect electrical connector from stop light switch.
4. Twist stop light switch counterclockwise and remove.

### INSTALLATION

1. Insert switch into lock ring opening and push in until switch barrel touches pedal. Ensure that pedal is not removed from its stop.
2. Twist switch clockwise to lock, then reconnect electrical connector and check operation of switch.
3. Install lower instrument panel and reconnect battery ground cable.

# NEUTRAL SAFETY SWITCH
## REPLACE

1. Disconnect battery ground cable, then the electrical connector from the switch.
2. Using a socket, remove switch.
3. Remove and discard switch O-ring.
4. Reverse procedure to install, using new O-ring, and **torque** switch to 7-10 ft. lbs.

# TURN SIGNAL SWITCH
## REPLACE
### SCORPIO

1. Disconnect battery ground cable.
2. Remove retaining screws, then the upper and lower steering column shrouds.
3. Rotate steering wheel 90° left of center, then remove two switch attaching screws and guide switch away from steering column.
4. Disconnect electrical connector from switch, then remove the switch.
5. Reverse procedure to install.

### XR4Ti

When replacing turn signal switch, refer to "Light Switch, Replace" procedure.

# INSTRUMENT CLUSTER
## REPLACE
### SCORPIO

1. Disconnect battery ground cable.
2. Remove four instrument finish panel attaching screws and the panel.
3. Remove four instrument panel-to-cluster attaching screws.
4. Pull cluster away from instrument panel, then disconnect electrical connectors and remove cluster. **Insert screwdriver in graphic display connector and pry retainer out of display prior to pulling connector from display.**
5. Reverse procedure to install.

### XR4Ti

1. Disconnect battery ground cable.
2. Remove screw from upper steering column shroud and remove shroud.
3. Remove instrument panel illumination control and intermittent wiper control rheostats.
4. Remove four bezel retaining screws, then the bezel.
5. Remove four instrument cluster to instrument panel attaching screws and pull cluster toward steering wheel.
6. Disconnect speedometer cable, harness connector, and turbo boost gauge vacuum line from rear of cluster assembly and remove cluster.
7. Reverse procedure to install.

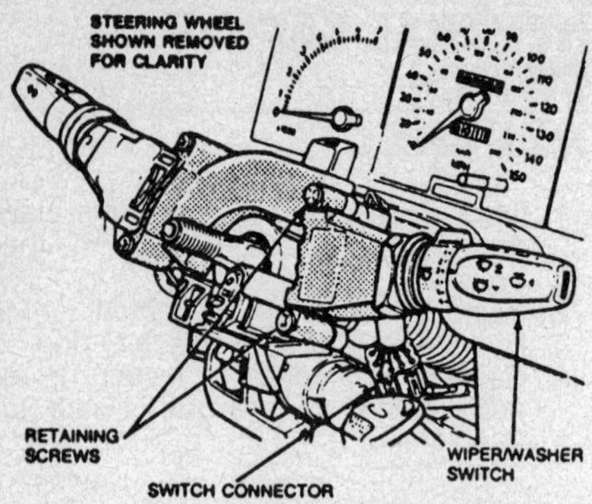


**Fig. 1 Removing windshield wiper switch. Scorpio**

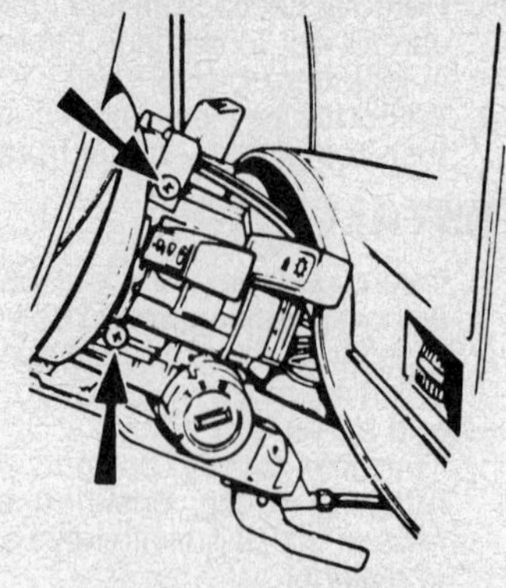

**Fig. 2 Removing windshield wiper switch. XR4Ti**

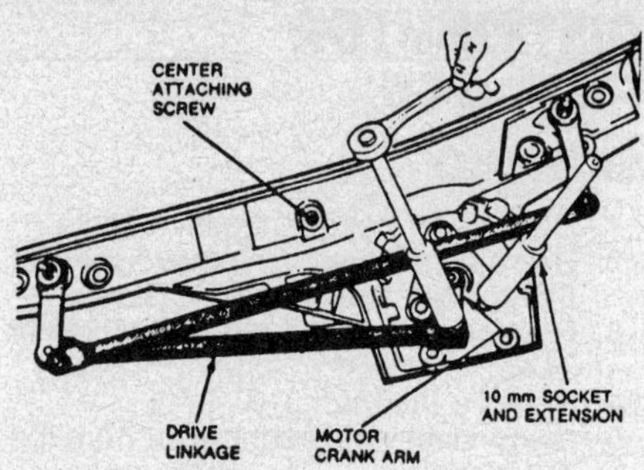


**Fig. 3 Front wiper crank arm removal & installation. Scorpio**

# WIPER SWITCH
## REPLACE
### REMOVAL

1. Disconnect battery ground cable, then remove steering column upper and lower shrouds.
2. Remove two Phillips head screws and the guide switch assembly from the steering column, **Figs. 1 and 2.**
3. Disconnect electrical connectors from switch, then remove switch.

### INSTALLATION

1. Connect electrical connectors at switch.
2. Position switch on mounting bracket and retain with two Phillips head screws.
3. Install upper and lower steering column shrouds and reconnect battery ground cable.

# WINDSHIELD WIPER MOTOR
## REPLACE
### SCORPIO
#### FRONT WIPER
##### Removal

1. Disconnect battery ground cable.
2. Remove wiper arm-to-pivot shaft retaining nuts, then pull wiper arms from shafts.
3. Remove four Torx screws securing cowl top panel to dash panel.
4. Remove eight Torx screws securing wiper motor, bracket and linkage to dash panel.
5. Disconnect electrical connectors from wiper motor, then remove motor, bracket and linkage from vehicle.
6. Remove crank arm nut and the crank arm from wiper motor as shown in **Fig. 3.**
7. Remove motor-to-bracket attaching bolts, then the motor bracket and cover.

##### Installation

1. Install motor cover and bracket. **Torque** bracket attaching bolts to 6-7 ft. lbs.
2. Position crank arm on motor shaft and install retaining nut. Block arm to prevent movement, then **torque** nut to 17-18 ft. lbs.
3. Position motor, bracket and linkage assembly in vehicle and connect electrical connectors.
4. Position motor and linkage assembly as shown in **Fig. 3,** then install retaining screws and **torque** to 4.5-6 ft. lbs.
5. Install cowl top panel. **Torque** attaching screws to 4.5-6 ft. lbs.
6. Connect battery ground cable, then cycle wiper motor to Park position.
7. Install wiper arms, **torquing** retaining nuts to 18-20 ft. lbs.

#### REAR WIPER

1. Disconnect battery ground cable.
2. Lift cap on wiper arm and remove arm retaining nut and washer.
3. Carefully pry wiper arm from motor shaft.
4. Open liftgate, then remove lower trim panel attaching screws and the trim panel.
5. Remove wiper motor ground cable retaining screw from liftgate, then disconnect motor electrical connector.
6. Remove motor bracket attaching screws, then the motor and bracket assembly.
7. Remove bracket attaching screws and separate motor from bracket.
8. Reverse procedure to install.

### XR4Ti
#### FRONT WIPER
##### Removal

1. Turn wiper motor ON, then when blades are straight up, turn key OFF.
2. Remove arm and blade assemblies, then disconnect battery ground cable.
3. Remove locknut from motorshaft, then remove motor arm from motor.
4. Remove three motor attaching bolts, then the motor.
5. Disconnect electrical connector from motor.

##### Installation

1. Connect electrical connector at motor, place motor in position and **torque** retaining bolts to 7-9 ft. lbs.
2. Connect wiper motor arm to shaft of windshield wiper motor, ensuring that key of motor arm is aligned to shaft, and **torque** locknut to 13-15 ft. lbs.
3. Connect battery ground cable.
4. Before installing arm and blade assembly on pivot shaft, cycle motor to ensure that it is in P position.

#### REAR WIPER
##### Removal

1. Unclip plastic clip from base of wiper arm, unscrew wiper arm securing nut and remove nut and washer.
2. Open liftgate and carefully pry out liftgate trim panel clips from their locations, then remove trim panel.
3. Remove three bolts attaching wiper motor bracket to liftgate, and the screw attaching ground lead, then disconnect electrical connector motor.
4. Remove motor from liftgate, disconnecting rear washer supply hose from wiper.

##### Installation

1. Reconnect rear washer supply hose to wiper motor, then position motor in liftgate by pushing output shaft through grommet in liftgate outer panel and **torque** three attaching bolts to 4-5 ft. lbs.
2. Install wiper arm and securing nut, **torquing** nut to 12-13 ft. lbs.
3. Install liftgate trim panel, then check operation of system.

# RADIO
## REPLACE
### REMOVAL

1. Disconnect battery ground cable.
2. Insert radio removing tool Nos., T85M-19061-A or equivalents, one on each side of radio, into access holes until click is heard.
3. Apply an outward side pressure to release locking tangs and slide radio from dash.
4. Disconnect antenna, speaker, ground and power leads from radio.
5. Disengage special tool by depressing locking tangs on sides of radio while applying slight inward pressure on tool, then pull tool from access holes.
6. Remove plastic support bracket and locating plate from rear of receiver.

## INSTALLATION

1. Connect power supply, speaker plugs and antenna cable to rear of receiver.
2. Install locating plate and plastic support bracket to rear of receiver and slide receiver into opening until retaining tangs lock.
3. Reconnect battery ground cable.

## HEATER CORE REPLACE

### SCORPIO

1. Disconnect battery ground cable.
2. Drain cooling system, then disconnect heater hoses from heater core.
3. Carefully blow compressed air into heater core to remove residual coolant.
4. Remove heater core water connector cover plate and gasket from bulkhead.
5. Remove center console and bracket, then the gear shift boot if equipped.
6. Remove vent nozzle bezel, then the instrument cluster finish panel and panel pad.
7. Remove glove box and ashtray.
8. Remove radio assembly as previously described.
9. Remove ECA and anti-lock brake modules.
10. Remove lower right hand instrument panel trim plate.
11. Disconnect hoses on heater housing from demister and fresh air vent nozzles.
12. Remove center fresh air vent nozzle hose and Bowden cables from heater housing.
13. Disconnect rear heater system hoses from heater housing.
14. Disconnect electrical connectors from discharge temperature sensor and actuator temperature and distribution flaps.
15. Remove two heater assembly attaching nuts and the heater assembly.
16. Remove heater core attaching screws and the heater core.
17. Reverse procedure to install.

### XR4Ti

1. Disconnect battery ground cable.
2. Drain engine coolant from cooling system and remove hoses from heater core, plugging hoses and core.
3. Carefully blow air into upper of two connecting pipes to remove residual coolant.
4. Remove cover plate and gasket from firewall.
5. Remove center console, drawing it rearward.
6. Remove side trim panel in right hand footwell.
7. Disconnect heater control lever and the leads from the glove compartment light, A/C blower switch and cigar lighter, then remove lower right hand dash panel.
8. Disconnect all duct hoses from heater housing.
9. Disconnect bowden cables from heater housing.
10. Remove heater from firewall and draw it in until the water connectors of the heater core are clear of the firewall, then pull heater assembly to the right.
11. Remove two heater core retaining screws and slide heater core out of housing.
12. Reverse procedure to install.

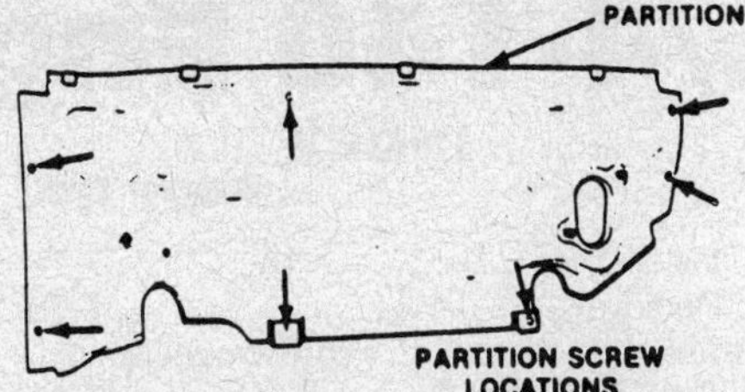


**Fig. 4 Partition retaining bolt location. XR4Ti**

## BLOWER MOTOR/EVAPORATOR REPLACE

### SCORPIO

1. Disconnect battery ground cable, then discharge and evacuate A/C system.
2. Remove air cleaner, then the line gasket from dash panel.
3. Remove Torx head retaining screw, then disconnect compressor suction line and receiver dryer fluid line from expansion valve. Remove and discard seals.
4. Remove rubber seal from dash panel extension.
5. Remove nut securing hot water shut-off valve and bracket to extension.
6. Disconnect de-ice thermostat electrical connector from plug.
7. Disconnect vacuum line from vacuum switch, then remove de-ice thermostat wiring, vacuum line and rubber grommet from bulkhead extension.
8. Remove bulkhead extension attaching screws and the extension.
9. Disconnect fan motor electrical connector and ground strap.
10. Remove attaching screws and nuts, then the evaporator housing and fan assembly.
11. Remove vacuum switch linkage to vacuum switch attaching screw.
12. Remove blower speed regulator cover attaching screws.
13. Disconnect electrical connector from blower speed regulator.
14. Remove evaporator housing attaching screws and the housing.
15. Remove access cover attaching screws and the cover from evaporator housing.
16. Remove lower evaporator case attaching screws, then the de-ice thermostat.
17. Remove evaporator case clips, then separate case halves.
18. Remove blower motor attaching screw and the blower motor.
19. Reverse procedure to install. **Ensure de-ice thermostat is properly aligned during installation.**

### XR4Ti

1. Disconnect both battery terminals.
2. Discharge A/C system refrigerant at service access gauge port valve.
3. Remove engine valve cover and the cowl insulator cover.
4. Pull water valve out of retaining clip and remove clip.
5. Remove two battery shield attaching screws and the shield.
6. Disconnect vacuum hose from EGR valve, then disconnect EGR valve by removing bolt attaching it to manifold and position valve out of way.
7. Remove two nuts retaining air conditioning hose plate and seal at the partition between the engine compartment and evaporator, then remove plate and seal.
8. Disconnect wiring harness from partition, pulling harness forward to disconnect tabs connecting harness to partition.
9. Remove No. 30 torx bolt retaining refrigerant lines to expansion valve.
10. Disconnect suction and liquid lines from expansion valve.
11. Remove weather seal from upper edge of partition.
12. Remove seven retaining screws attaching partition, Fig. 4. **If screws are damaged during removal, replace with 10 mm hex head screws and washers.**
13. Remove left and right drainage valves, then the partition, by pulling partition up and out.
14. Disconnect de-icer wire from connector, then the ground wire on the evaporator.
15. Remove evaporator to firewall attaching bolts.
16. Remove cowl grille panel, then disconnect windshield wiper to windshield wiper motor arm.
17. Slide evaporator case assembly upward and forward out of engine compartment checking and replacing seal as necessary.
18. Remove three access cover attaching bolts, then pry cover open using screwdriver.
19. Remove two screws on blower scrolls to lower case and the two screws attaching the de-ice thermostat.
20. Separate evaporator case halves by removing connecting clips sealing case.
21. Remove one screw retaining blower motor to case, then the blower motor.
22. Reverse procedure to install.

# 2.3L/4-140 Engine

## INDEX



## ENGINE REPLACE

1. Disconnect battery ground cable.
2. Mark hood hinge location, disconnect ground strap near right hinge and remove hood.
3. Using vacuum pump D80P-250-A or equivalent, release pressure from EFI fuel system at fuel pressure regulator valve.
4. Remove cap from cooling system expansion tank and drain coolant.
5. Disconnect radiator upper hose from radiator, then on vehicles equipped with manual transmission, disconnect radiator air vent hose from radiator.
6. Remove radiator upper attaching bolts and disconnect cooling fan electrical connector.
7. Remove oil dipstick.
8. Disconnect vacuum hose from EGR valve.
9. Disconnect fuel injector electrical connector located between upper intake manifold and oil dipstick.
10. Carefully disconnect electrical connectors from EEC-IV engine coolant temperature sensor, engine knock sensor, oil pressure sending unit, cooling fan temperature switch, throttle air bypass valve and the throttle position sensor. **When disconnecting EEC-IV system related component electrical connectors, ensure that vehicle battery ground cable is disconnected to avoid serious EEC-IV system and related component damage.**
11. Disconnect fuel line from pulse damper.
12. Using tool No. T82L-9500-AH or equivalent, disconnect fuel return line.
13. Disconnect throttle cable and, if equipped, the transmission kickdown cable.
14. Remove accelerator cable bracket attaching screws and the bracket from the upper intake manifold, then position bracket and accelerator cable, and transmission kickdown cable if equipped, out of way.
15. Disconnect supply hose from vacuum tree located on dash panel.
16. Disconnect electrical connector from distributor TFI module.
17. Remove alternator from mounting bracket and secure out of way.
18. Remove power steering pump from mounting bracket and secure out of way.
19. Remove turbocharger air inlet tube and disconnect orange ground wire from turbocharger air inlet elbow.
20. Disconnect electrical connector from exhaust gas oxygen sensor and the vacuum hose from the turbocharger air inlet elbow.
21. Remove A/C compressor from its mounting bracket and secure out of way.
22. **On vehicles equipped with automatic transmission,** remove transmission dipstick tube attaching nut at turbocharger outlet flange.
23. **On all vehicles,** disconnect coolant supply and return hoses from heater control valve.
24. **On vehicles equipped with automatic transmission,** disconnect transmission oil cooling lines from radiator.
25. **On all vehicles,** raise and support vehicle.
26. **On vehicles equipped with manual transmission,** disconnect radiator refill tube at refill hose.
27. **On all vehicles,** disconnect radiator lower hose from radiator, then remove bolts attaching radiator to side rail and remove radiator through bottom of vehicle.
28. Remove bolt attaching chassis ground wire to A/C compressor bracket, then remove starter.
29. Remove nuts attaching catalytic converter inlet pipe to turbocharger.
30. Remove catalytic converter to converter inlet pipe flange attaching bolts and the catalytic converter support bracket bolt.
31. Remove inlet pipe.
32. **On vehicles equipped with manual transmission,** remove bolt attaching engine rear cover to flywheel housing.
33. **On vehicles equipped with automatic transmission,** remove torque converter to drive plate attaching nuts through starter opening. **To bring bolts into position, turn crankshaft with ratchet handle and socket applied to crankshaft pulley attaching bolt. Always turn crankshaft clockwise. Counterclockwise rotation may cause timing belt to jump time.**
34. **On all vehicles,** remove stud nuts attaching engine mounts to cross member.
35. Remove converter/flywheel housing attaching bolts. If removal of bolts at

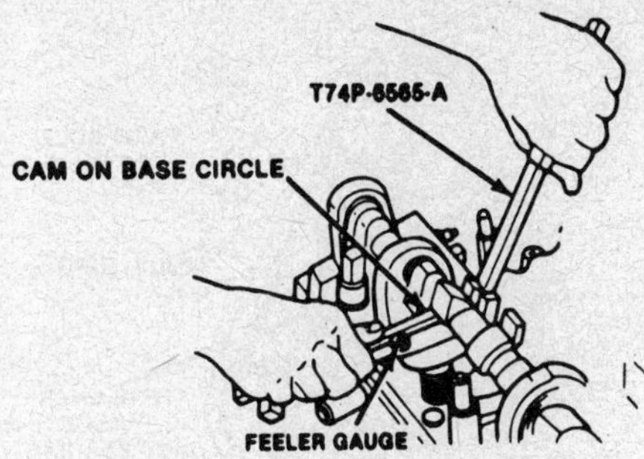


**Fig. 1 Adjusting valves**

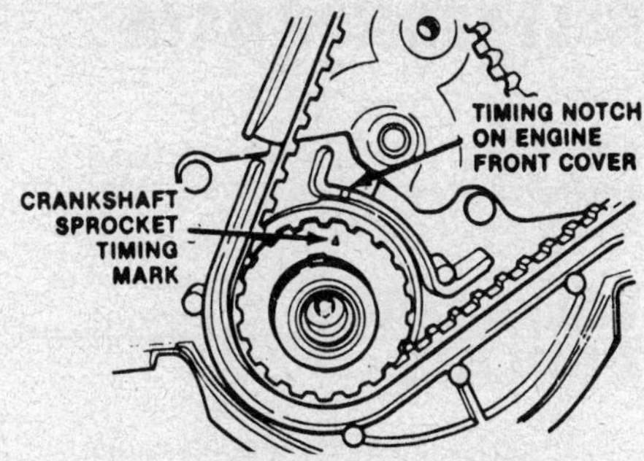


**Fig. 2 Align timing marks on crankshaft sprocket & engine front cover**

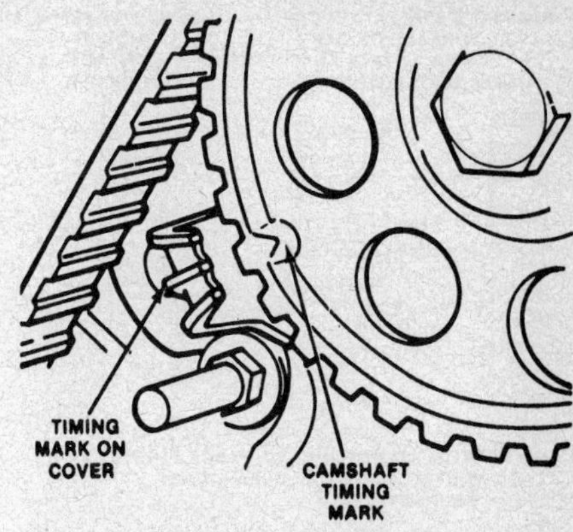


**Fig. 3 Aligning timing marks on camshaft sprocket & inner timing belt cover**

top of housing is prevented by contact with body, leave them loose and in position. If necessary, to gain access to housing to engine bolts, support transmission with jack and remove nuts securing transmission mount to underbody. Remove nuts securing driveshaft center bearing support to underbody. Lower transmission and remove converter/flywheel housing to engine bolts, then raise transmission and secure transmission mount to underbody.

36. Lower vehicle.
37. Install engine lifting device on engine lifting attachments.
38. Support transmission with jack and raise engine until front support lower studs clear crossmember.
39. Remove bolts attaching front support brackets to engine and remove mounts and brackets as assemblies.
40. Pull engine forward to separate it from transmission, then carefully raise engine out of engine compartment.
41. Reverse procedure to install.

# VALVES

## ADJUST

1. Remove valve cover.
2. Position camshaft so that base circle of lobe is facing cam follower of valve to be checked. To position camshaft lobes, turn crankshaft using ratchet handle and socket on crankshaft pulley attaching bolt. **Always turn crankshaft clockwise. Counterclockwise rotation may cause timing belt to jump time.**
3. Using valve spring compressor T74P-6565-A or equivalent, slowly apply pressure on lash adjuster side of cam follower until lash adjuster is completely collapsed. Holding follower in this position, measure clearance between base circle of cam and the follower using a feeler gauge, **Fig. 1.**
4. Clearance should be .0035-.0055 inch. If clearance exceeds .0055 inch, remove cam follower and inspect for damage.
5. If cam follower appears to be intact, and not excessively worn, measure valve spring assembled height.

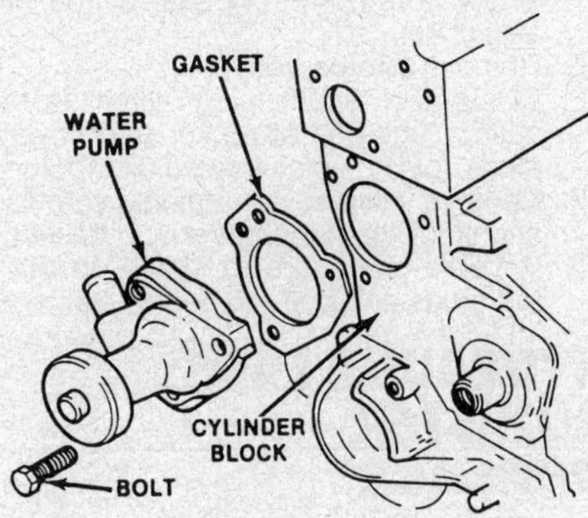


**Fig. 4 Water pump location**

6. If assembled height is correct, check dimensions of camshaft.
7. If camshaft dimensions are within specifications, remove, clean and test lash adjuster.

# CAMSHAFT TIMING

## CHECK

**An access plug is provided in the cam drive belt cover so that camshaft timing can be checked without removal of the cover or any other engine components.**

1. Disconnect battery ground cable.
2. Remove access plug from the cam drive belt cover.
3. Set crankshaft to TDC by aligning the TC mark on the timing belt cover with notch on the crankshaft pulley. Align timing marks by turning the crankshaft pulley attaching bolt. **Always turn the crankshaft clockwise, which is the normal direction of rotation. Reverse rotation (counterclockwise) may cause the timing belt to jump time due to the arrangement of the timing belt tensioner.**
4. Look through the access hole in the belt cover to ensure timing mark on the camshaft drive sprocket is aligned with the pointer on the inner timing belt cover assembly.
5. If the mark is not in sight, turn the crankshaft one complete revolution clockwise and check timing mark alignment.
6. If the timing marks are properly aligned, the camshaft is correctly timed to the crankshaft.
7. If the timing marks do not align, proceed with the camshaft timing adjustment procedure.

## ADJUSTMENT

1. Disconnect battery ground cable.
2. Remove drive belts.
3. Remove water pump pulley.
4. Remove timing belt cover as outlined under "Timing Belt, Replace."
5. Remove crankshaft damper and pulley.
6. Remove spark plugs, if necessary.
7. Turn crankshaft clockwise to alignment timing mark on the crankshaft sprocket with the timing mark on the engine front cover, **Fig. 2.**
8. Turn camshaft to align timing mark on the camshaft sprocket with the timing mark on the inner timing belt cover assembly, **Fig. 3.**
9. Remove distributor cap and position aside. Set distributor rotor to the number one firing position by turning the auxiliary shaft.
10. Install timing belt as outlined under "Timing Belt, Replace," and check timing mark alignment.

# WATER PUMP

## REPLACE

Refer to **Fig. 4,** when performing this procedure.

1. Disconnect battery ground cable.
2. Remove drive belts, water pump pulley and timing belt cover.
3. Loosen cap on coolant expansion tank and drain coolant from radiator.
4. Remove radiator lower hose and the heater return hose from water pump.
5. Remove water pump attaching bolts and the pump.
6. Clean gasket mating surfaces, then install new gasket, pump and attaching bolts, torquing bolts to specifications.
7. **Torque** water pump pulley bolts to 13-19 ft. lbs.

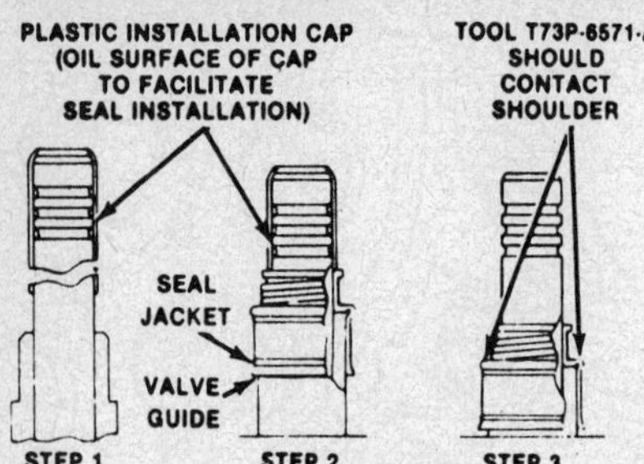


STEP #1— WITH VALVES IN HEAD, PLACE PLASTIC INSTALLATION CAP OVER END OF VALVE SYSTEM.

STEP #2— START VALVE STEM SEAL CAREFULLY OVER CAP. PUSH SEAL DOWN UNTIL JACKET TOUCHES TOP OF GUIDE.

STEP #3— REMOVE PLASTIC INSTALLATION CAP. USE INSTALLATION TOOL T73P-6571-A OR SCREWDRIVERS TO BOTTOM SEAL ON VALVE GUIDE.

**Fig. 5 Installing valve springs & seals**

8. Reverse steps 1 through 4 to complete installation.

## THERMOSTAT
### REPLACE

1. Drain cooling system.
2. Disconnect upper radiator hose and heater hose from thermostat housing.
3. Remove thermostat housing attaching bolts, then the housing.
4. Remove the thermostat.
5. Clean gasket surfaces, then install new gaskets coated with suitable sealer.
6. Install thermostat in housing, then turn thermostat left or right until it locks in the housing. **Ensure heater coolant outlet is open.**
7. Install housing to cylinder head, then install bolts and **torque** to 14-21 ft. lbs.
8. Install heater and radiator hoses, then fill cooling system.

## COOLING SYSTEM BLEED

1. Refill cooling system with equal parts of specified anti-freeze and water.
2. Fill expansion tank to the MAX. level indicator.
3. Install pressure cap to the first stop. **Do not install cap completely.**
4. Run engine at fast idle until thermostat opens, then turn engine off. Upper radiator hose should feel warm when thermostat opens.
5. Check fluid level in the expansion tank. Fill to the MAX. indicator as needed.
6. Install pressure cap completely.

## BELT TENSION DATA

| Belt | New | Used |
|---|---|---|
| Alternator | 140 | 120 |
| A/C | 140 | 120 |

## VALVE COVER
### REPLACE

1. Disconnect battery ground cable.
2. Loosen clamp on PCV hose at oil separator on valve cover and disconnect hose.
3. Disconnect coolant hose that passes over rear of rocker arm cover.
4. Remove coolant pipes retaining clip screw from right front side of rocker arm cover.
5. Remove throttle body.
6. Disconnect spark plug wires from spark plugs and at rocker arm cover studs, folding wires toward distributor.
7. Remove valve cover retaining screws and studs, then the cover and gasket.
8. Reverse procedure to install, **torquing** studs and bolts to 5-8 ft. lbs.

## HYDRAULIC LASH ADJUSTER
### REPLACE

1. Disconnect battery ground cable, then remove valve cover.
2. Rotate engine in normal direction of rotation until base circle of camshaft lobe of selected valve is contacting cam follower.
3. Using valve spring compressing tool No. T74P-6565-A or equivalent, compress valve spring until cam follower can be removed out and over the hydraulic lash adjuster.
4. Lift out hydraulic lift adjuster.
5. Repeat steps 2 through 4 as required for remaining lash adjusters.
6. Reverse procedure to install.

## VALVE SPRINGS & SEALS
### REPLACE

1. Disconnect battery ground cable, then remove valve cover.
2. Rotate engine in direction of normal rotation until base circle of camshaft lobe of selected valve is contacting cam follower. Ensure that other valve of that cylinder is also closed.
3. Using valve spring compressor tool No. T74P-6565-A or equivalent, compress valve spring until cam follower can be removed out and over the hydraulic lash adjuster.
4. Install a compressed air adapter in spark plug hole with a minimum of 140 psi air pressure available, then turn on air pressure to hold that cylinder's valves against their seats. **Both valves must be closed to hold air pressure.**

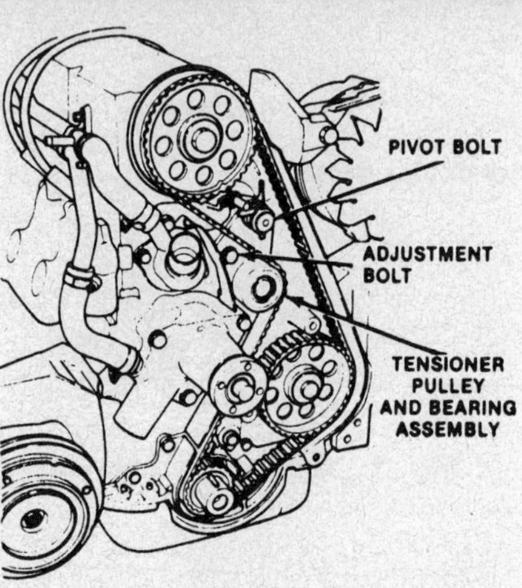


**Fig. 6 Timing belt tensioner bolt location**

5. Depress valve spring and remove locks, spring retainer, spring and seal.
6. Fasten rubber band or string to valve key groove to prevent losing valve if a valve is opened or the air pressure drops.
7. Inspect valve stems for scores, sticking, excessive or obvious stem to guide clearance and eccentricity or wobbling when rotated. If any of these conditions exist, the cylinder head must be removed for further inspection and service.
8. Apply air pressure through spark plug holes to hold valves closed. Install new valve stem seals using valve seal installer T73P-6571-A or equivalent and the plastic installation caps, **Fig. 5.**
9. Install valve springs, spring retainers and keys and remove air pressure adapter.
10. Depress valve springs and install cam followers.
11. Install valve cover and throttle body.

## TIMING BELT
### REPLACE
#### REMOVAL

1. Disconnect battery ground cable.
2. Remove access plug from cam drive belt cover.
3. Set crankshaft to TDC by aligning the TDC mark on the timing belt cover with notch on crankshaft pulley. Align timing marks by turning the crankshaft pulley attaching bolt. **Always rotate crankshaft clockwise, which is the normal direction of rotation. Reverse rotation (counterclockwise) may cause the timing belt to jump time due to the arrangement of the timing belt tensioner.**
4. Look through the access hole in the belt cover to ensure timing mark on the camshaft drive sprocket is aligned with the pointer on the inner timing belt cover assembly.

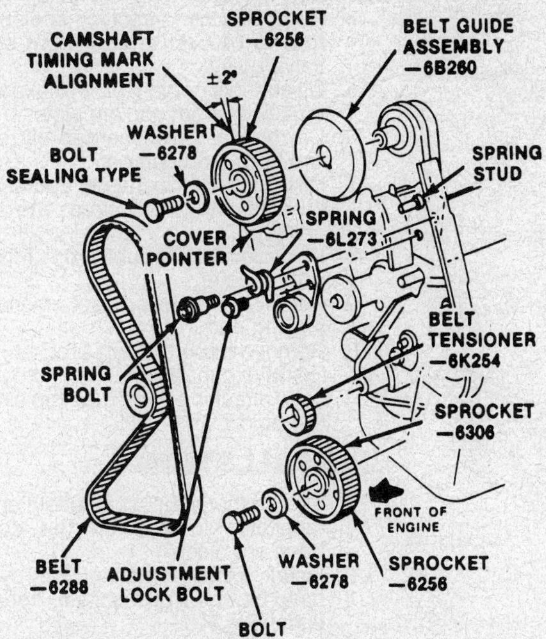


Fig. 7 Installing timing belt

Fig. 8 Installing camshaft sprocket & seal

5. If the mark is not in sight, turn crankshaft one complete revolution clockwise and check timing mark alignment.
6. Remove drive belts, water pump pulley, timing belt cover, and crankshaft damper and pulley.
7. Loosen timing belt tensioner adjusting bolt, **Fig. 6.**
8. Using camshaft belt tensioner tool No. T74P-6254-A or equivalent, pry tensioner away from timing belt.
9. While holding tensioner away from belt, secure it in released position by tightening belt tensioner adjustment bolt.
10. Remove timing belt.

### INSTALLATION

1. Ensure that belt and sprockets are clean and not worn or damaged, and that timing marks are aligned as outlined in removal procedure.
2. Move belt tensioner to no tension position, tighten the adjustment lock bolt and install the belt.
3. Loosen adjustment lock bolt and allow the tensioner to tighten the belt.
4. **Torque** pivot and adjustment lock bolts to specifications, **Fig. 7.**
5. Install crankshaft damper and pulley, timing belt cover, water pump pulley and drivebelts.

## CAMSHAFT SPROCKET & SEAL

## REPLACE

### REMOVAL

1. Disconnect battery ground cable.
2. Remove drive belts, water pump pulley, timing belt cover, crankshaft damper and pulley and timing belt.
3. Using camshaft sprocket holding/removing tool No. T74P-6256-B or equivalent, remove camshaft sprocket.
4. Remove camshaft sprocket belt guide.
5. Using front cover seal remover T74P-6700-B or equivalent, remove camshaft seal.

### INSTALLATION

1. Ensure seal and seal surface on camshaft are clean and not damaged.
2. Lubricate camshaft seal surface and the seal lip with engine oil.
3. Install seal on front seal replacer tool No. T74P-6150-A or equivalent, then thread tool arbor into camshaft.
4. Turn nut on tool arbor until the seal is bottom in its bore in the camshaft front bearing tower.
5. Remove tool from camshaft.
6. Install camshaft sprocket belt guide.
7. Install camshaft sprocket, using tool No. T74P-6256-B or equivalent as a holding fixture, and the sprocket retaining bolt to push the sprocket onto the camshaft, **Fig. 8.**
8. Using new camshaft sprocket bolt or Teflon tape when installing. **Torque** sprocket bolt to specifications.
9. Install timing belt as outlined under "Timing Belt, Replace," timing belt cover, crankshaft damper and pulley, water pump pulley and drive belts.

## CRANKSHAFT DAMPER & PULLEY

## REPLACE

1. Disconnect battery ground cable, then remove drive belts.
2. Remove crankshaft damper and pulley bolt.
3. Using tool No. T74P-6316-A or equivalent, remove crankshaft damper and pulley.
4. Reverse procedure to install, torquing bolt to specifications.

## TIMING BELT TENSIONER

## REPLACE

1. Disconnect battery ground cable, then remove drive belts.
2. Remove water pump pulley, timing belt cover, crankshaft damper and pulley and timing belt as outlined under "Timing Belt, Replace."
3. Remove timing belt tensioner adjustment and spring retaining bolts, then the timing belt tensioner.
4. Reverse procedure to install, installing bolts finger tight.

## AUXILIARY SHAFT SPROCKET & SEAL

## REPLACE

### REMOVAL

1. Disconnect battery ground cable.
2. Remove drive belts, water pump pulley, timing belt cover, crankshaft damper and pulley and timing belt as outlined under "Timing Belt, Replace."
3. Using tool No. T74P-6256-B or equivalent, remove auxiliary shaft sprocket.
4. Using tool No. T74P-6700-B or equivalent, remove auxiliary shaft seal.
5. Remove auxiliary shaft cover.
6. Remove auxiliary shaft, being careful not to scratch bearings.

### INSTALLATION

1. Ensure that auxiliary shaft and bearings are clean and not worn or damaged.
2. Dip auxiliary shaft in engine oil.
3. Install auxiliary shaft in bearing bores, being careful not to scratch bearings.
4. Install auxiliary shaft retaining plate.
5. Install auxiliary shaft gasket and cover without seal, torquing bolts to specifications.
6. Install auxiliary shaft seal.
7. Using tool No. T74P-6256-B or equivalent, install auxiliary shaft sprocket. Remove center arbor, as tool is used as a holding fixture. The sprocket retaining bolt presses the sprocket onto the shaft. **Torque** bolt to specifications.
8. Install timing belt as outlined under "Timing Belt, Replace," crankshaft damper and pulley, timing belt cover, water pump pulley and drive belts.

## CRANKSHAFT SPROCKET, FRONT COVER & SEAL

## REPLACE

### REMOVAL

1. Disconnect battery ground cable.
2. Remove drive belts, water pump pulley, timing belt cover, crankshaft damper and pulley and timing belt as outlined under "Timing Belt, Replace."
3. Using tool No. T74P-6306-A or equivalent, remove crankshaft sprocket.
4. Remove camshaft sprocket belt guide.
5. Using tool, remove front cover seal.
6. Remove engine front cover.

### INSTALLATION

1. Ensure that front of cylinder block and front cover are clean.
2. Position front cover gasket on cylinder block, retaining with grease. **It may be necessary to trim ends of oil pan to cylinder block front seal if installing a cover without replacing oil pan gasket.**
3. Install front cover without seal in it, starting attaching bolts but leaving them loose.
4. Insert front cover alignment tool No. T74P-6019-B, or equivalent, into cover to align it with crankshaft, torque bolts to specifications, then remove tool.
5. Oil inner lip of cover seal, then install.
6. Thread tool and seal onto crankshaft, then, with outer nut, force tool and seal toward engine until seal bottoms in front cover. Remove tool.
7. Install crankshaft sprocket, timing belt as outlined under "Timing Belt, Replace," crankshaft damper and pulley, timing belt cover, water pump and drive belts.

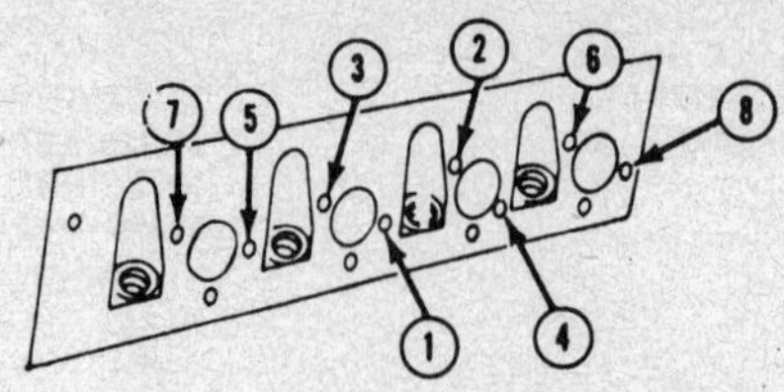


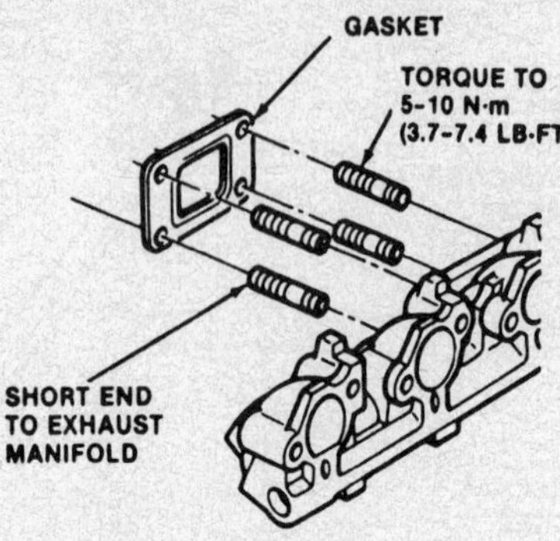

**Fig. 9 Installing exhaust manifold**

## TIMING BELT INNER COVER

## REPLACE

1. Disconnect battery ground cable.
2. Remove drive belts, water pump pulley, timing belt cover, crankshaft damper and pulley, timing belt as outlined under "Timing Belt, Replace," camshaft sprocket, timing belt tensioner and auxiliary sprocket.
3. Remove attaching bolts and the timing belt inner cover.
4. Reverse procedure to install, torquing bolts to specifications.

## EXHAUST MANIFOLD

## REPLACE

### REMOVAL

1. Disconnect battery ground cable.
2. Loosen cap on coolant expansion tank and drain coolant from radiator.
3. Remove heater return hose at water pump.
4. Remove screw attaching coolant pipe routing bracket to right front side of valve cover.
5. Disconnect coolant pipe to expansion tank hose from coolant pipe.
6. Disconnect turbocharger oil supply line from turbocharger.
7. Disconnect turbocharger coolant supply and return tube from the turbocharger.
8. Disconnect PCV tube from turbo air inlet adapter.
9. Remove turbo to exhaust manifold attaching nuts.
10. Remove turbo support bracket.
11. Remove exhaust manifold to cylinder head attaching bolts, then the exhaust manifold.

### INSTALLATION

1. Ensure that exhaust manifold and the manifold surfaces on the cylinder head are clean.
2. Install exhaust manifold to cylinder head bolts. Torque bolts to specifications, **Fig. 9.**
3. Install turbocharger support bracket and the turbo to exhaust manifold nuts.
4. Connect PCV tube at turbo air inlet adapter.
5. Connect turbo coolant and oil supply lines at turbocharger.
6. Install heater pipe to coolant expansion tank hose at heater pipe.
7. Install coolant pipe retaining clip screw at valve cover.
8. Install coolant hose at water pump and refill cooling system.

## UPPER INTAKE MANIFOLD

## REPLACE

### REMOVAL

1. Disconnect battery ground cable.
2. **On vehicles equipped with automatic transmission,** disconnect kickdown cable from throttle linkage.
3. **On all vehicles,** disconnect accelerator cable from throttle linkage.
4. Remove accelerator cable bracket attaching screws and the bracket from upper intake manifold, position bracket, accelerator cable and kickdown cable, if equipped, out of way.
5. Disconnect fuel pressure regulator vacuum hose, PCV hose and the vacuum tree supply hose at intake manifold fittings.
6. Loosen hose clamps and remove turbocharger outlet hose.
7. Remove EGR flange attaching bolts.
8. Remove nut attaching pulse damper to bracket.
9. Disconnect low oil level sensor connector, then remove oil dipstick.
10. Remove oil dipstick bracket attaching screw.
11. Cut fuel injector wiring harness routing strap at pulse damper bracket as necessary.
12. Remove two pulse damper bracket attaching nuts and the bracket.

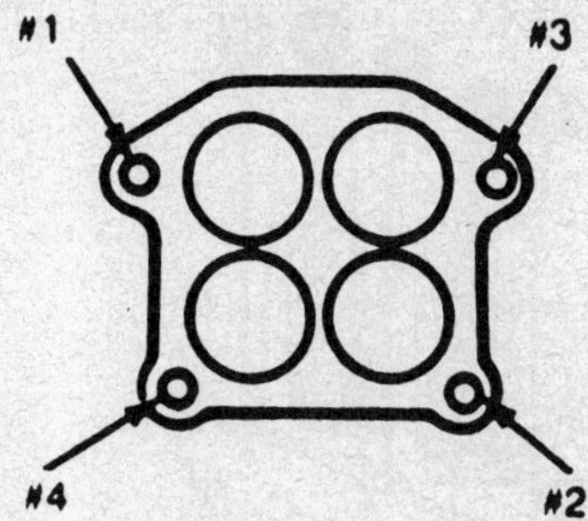


**Fig. 10 Upper intake manifold bolt tightening sequence**

13. Remove two upper attaching screws and two lower attaching nuts connecting throttle body assembly to upper intake manifold.
14. Remove upper intake manifold attaching bolts, the manifold and gaskets.

### INSTALLATION

1. Ensure both gasket surfaces on upper intake manifold and upper surface of lower intake manifold are clean.
2. Place new gasket on lower intake manifold and place upper intake manifold in position, then install four attaching bolts, torquing to specification in proper sequence, **Fig. 10.**
3. Install two EGR flange attaching bolts and torque to specifications.
4. Place pulse damper bracket on upper intake manifold and install attaching nuts.
5. Install new fuel injection wiring harness routing strap as necessary.
6. Install oil dipstick bracket attaching screw.
7. Install oil dipstick and connect low oil level sensor connector.
8. Place pulse damper on bracket and install attaching nut.
9. Install new gasket and the throttle body attaching screws and nuts, torquing to specifications.
10. Connect vacuum tree source hose and PCV hose to fitting on upper intake manifold.
11. Connect fuel pressure regulator vacuum hose to fuel pressure regulator and the fittings on upper intake manifold.
12. Place accelerator cable bracket against upper intake manifold and install attaching screws.
13. Connect accelerator cable.
14. Connect kickdown cable, if equipped.
15. Install turbocharger outlet hose and tighten clamp.

# LOWER INTAKE MANIFOLD

## REPLACE

### REMOVAL

1. Disconnect battery ground cable, then drain cooling system.
2. Disconnect electrical connectors from knock sensor, fan temperature sensor, fuel injection wiring harness and instrument cluster coolant temperature sender.
3. Disconnect coolant bypass line from lower intake manifold.
4. Depressurize EFI fuel system using a hand operated vacuum pump. Connect pump hose at fuel system pressure regulator and apply at least 25 inches vacuum. **Fuel supply lines will remain pressurized for some period of time after engine is shut off. System pressure must be relieved before disconnecting any fuel lines.**
5. Disconnect vacuum pump from fuel pressure regulator.
6. Disconnect fuel supply line from fuel supply manifold.
7. Disconnect fuel return line using tool No. T82L-950-AH or equivalent.
8. Remove nut attaching pulse damper to bracket and position pulse damper and fuel supply line out of way.
9. Remove upper intake manifold as previously described.
10. Disconnect EEC coolant temperature sensor.
11. Remove four upper and four lower attaching bolts and the lower intake manifold and gasket.
12. Remove two attaching bolts, disengage each injector and remove fuel supply manifold assembly.

### INSTALLATION

1. Clean and inspect mounting surfaces of lower intake manifold and the cylinder head, ensuring that both surfaces are clean and flat.
2. Install new gasket.
3. Position lower intake manifold on cylinder head and install four upper attaching bolts finger tight.
4. Install four lower manifold bolts and torque to specifications, in proper sequence, **Fig. 11.**
5. Install fuel supply manifold assembly by pressing each injector into place on lower intake manifold and installing two attaching bolts.
6. Ensure that gasket surfaces of upper and lower intake manifolds are clean.
7. Install EEC coolant temperature sensor.
8. Install upper intake manifold and two gaskets.
9. Connect fuel return line.
10. Place pulse damper on bracket and connect fuel supply line.
11. Connect coolant bypass line to lower intake manifold.
12. Connect electrical connectors at knock sensor, fan temperature sensor, fuel injection wiring harness and the instrument cluster coolant temperature sender.
13. Connect battery ground cable and refill cooling system.

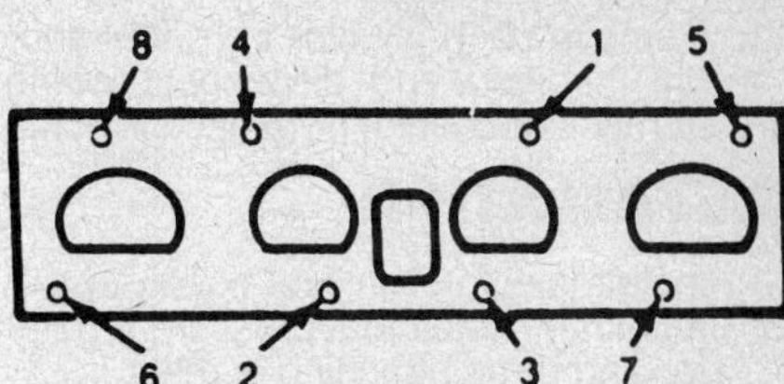


**Fig. 11 Lower intake manifold bolt tightening sequence**

# FUEL SUPPLY MANIFOLD

## REPLACE

### REMOVAL

1. Disconnect battery ground cable.
2. **On vehicles equipped with automatic transmission,** disconnect kickdown cable from throttle linkage.
3. **On all vehicles,** disconnect accelerator cable from throttle linkage.
4. Remove screws attaching accelerator cable bracket to upper intake manifold and position bracket, accelerator cable and kickdown cable, if equipped, out of way.
5. Disconnect fuel pressure regulator vacuum hose from fuel pressure regulator and the upper intake manifold fitting.
6. Disconnect PCV hose from upper intake manifold fitting.
7. Disconnect coil wire from distributor cap and position out of way.
8. Remove distributor cap attaching screws and the cap, positioning cap and attached wires out of way.
9. Depressurize EFI fuel system using a hand operated vacuum pump. Connect pump hose to fuel system pressure regulator and apply at least 25 inches vacuum.
10. Disconnect vacuum pump from fuel pressure regulator.
11. Disconnect fuel supply line from fuel supply manifold.
12. Using tool No. T82L-9500-AH or equivalent, disconnect fuel return line.
13. Remove nut attaching fuel pulse damper to mounting bracket.
14. Cut fuel injection wiring harness routing strap at fuel pulse damper as necessary.
15. Disconnect fuel injection wiring harness connector.
16. Disconnect electrical connector from coolant temperature sender in cylinder block.
17. Remove fuel supply manifold assembly front attaching bolt.
18. Remove fuel supply manifold assembly rear attaching bolt.
19. Remove fuel supply manifold assembly by disengaging each fuel injector from lower intake manifold, then carefully pulling whole assembly out from under upper intake manifold toward front of engine.
20. Remove three Allen head attaching screws and the fuel pressure regulator from fuel supply manifold.

21. Remove each injector from fuel supply manifold and disconnect wiring harness connector from each injector.

### INSTALLATION

1. Install injectors on fuel supply manifold, then install fuel pressure regulator and three attaching screws.
2. Connect wiring harness connector to each fuel injector, then position fuel supply manifold assembly under upper intake manifold and insert each injector into its opening in lower intake manifold.
3. Install front and rear fuel supply manifold attaching bolts, **torquing** to 15-22 ft. lbs.
4. Connect electrical connectors at coolant temperature sender and fuel injection wiring harness.
5. Install new fuel injection wiring harness routing strap on fuel pulse damper bracket as necessary.
6. Place fuel pulse damper in mounting bracket and install attaching nut.
7. Connect fuel supply line and install retaining clip, then connect fuel return line.
8. Install distributor cap and attaching screws and connect coil wire to distributor cap.
9. Connect PCV hose and the vacuum hoses to fuel pressure regulator and upper intake manifold fittings.
10. Position accelerator cable bracket on upper intake manifold and install attaching screws.
11. Connect accelerator cable to throttle linkage.
12. **On vehicles equipped with automatic transmission,** connect kickdown cable to throttle linkage.
13. **On all vehicles,** connect battery ground cable.

## CYLINDER HEAD REPLACE

### REMOVAL

1. Disconnect battery ground cable.
2. Remove drive belts, water pump pulley, timing belt cover, crankshaft damper and pulley, valve cover, timing belt, camshaft sprocket, timing belt tensioner and timing belt inner cover.
3. Remove alternator and mounting bracket to cylinder head bolts.
4. Remove exhaust manifold to cylinder head attaching bolts.
5. Remove timing belt tensioner spring stop stud from cylinder head.
6. Remove cylinder head attaching bolts and the cylinder head.

### INSTALLATION

1. Ensure that cylinder head and cylinder block gasket surfaces are clean.
2. Position new cylinder head gasket on block.
3. Ensure that crankshaft sprocket and camshaft sprocket timing marks align as shown in **Figs. 2 and 3,** then lower cylinder head assembly onto cylinder block, ensuring head fits over two dowels on head surface of block.
4. Install valve cover gasket on valve cover using sealant and place cover aside.
5. Oil cylinder head bolts and install in cylinder head, **torquing** in two steps in proper sequence, **Fig. 12. Torque** first to 50-60 ft. lbs., then to 80-90 ft. lbs.
6. Install timing belt tensioner spring stop stud into cylinder head, torquing to specifications.
7. Position exhaust manifold on cylinder head and install attaching bolts, torquing in two steps in proper sequence, **Fig. 9.** to specifications.
8. Install alternator bracket to cylinder head bolts.
9. Install fuel supply manifold, timing belt inner cover, auxiliary sprocket, timing belt tensioner, camshaft sprocket and seal, timing belt, crankshaft damper and pulley, timing belt cover, water pump pulley, drive belts and valve cover.

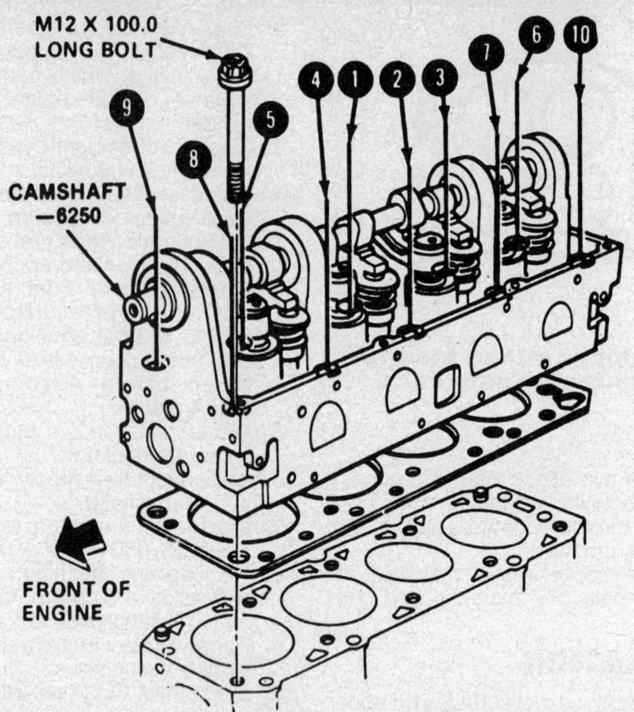


**Fig. 12 Cylinder head bolt tightening sequence**

## OIL PAN REPLACE

### REMOVAL

1. Disconnect battery ground cable.
2. Disconnect oil level sensor electrical connector, then remove oil dipstick.
3. Install engine support tool No. D79P-6000-B or equivalent.
4. Raise and support vehicle, then drain engine oil.
5. Remove starter.
6. Remove pinch bolt at steering column to steering gear coupling.
7. Remove engine mount studs to crossmember attaching bolts.
8. Lower vehicle and, using support tool, raise engine as far as possible.
9. Raise vehicle, then remove steering gear to crossmember attaching bolts.
10. Disengage steering gear from steering column and pull forward, away from steering column, being careful not to bend or stretch power steering gear hoses and lines.
11. Position jack under crossmember, then remove crossmember to side rail attaching bolts.
12. Lower transmission jack and crossmember, then remove oil pan attaching bolts and the oil pan.

### INSTALLATION

1. Clean gasket surfaces on oil pan and cylinder block.
2. Apply even coat of sealant to oil pan side gaskets and allow sealant to dry past wet stage, then install on oil pan.
3. Apply 1/4 inch bead of sealant along seam between cylinder block and front cover, and along seam between cylinder block and rear main bearing cap.
4. Install oil pan end seals in front cover and rear main bearing cap, **Fig. 13.**
5. Position oil pan and install attaching bolts.
6. Torque corner attaching bolts to specifications, beginning at hole "A," **Fig. 13,** working clockwise around pan.
7. Raise crossmember into position and install crossmember to side member attaching bolts, torque bolts to specifications and remove jack.
8. Position steering gear on crossmember and connect to steering column, then install attaching bolts and

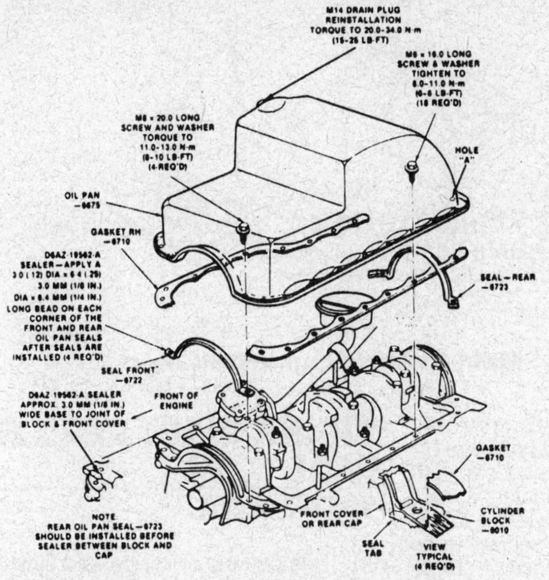


Fig. 13 Installing oil pan

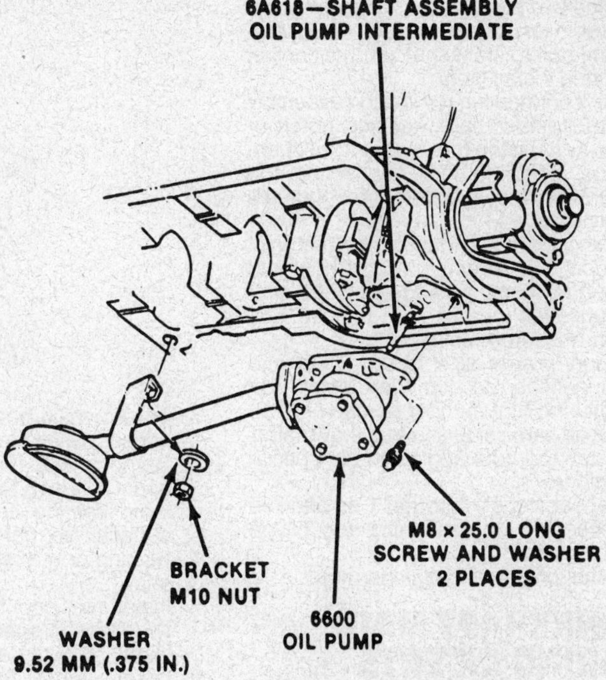


Fig. 14 Removing oil pump

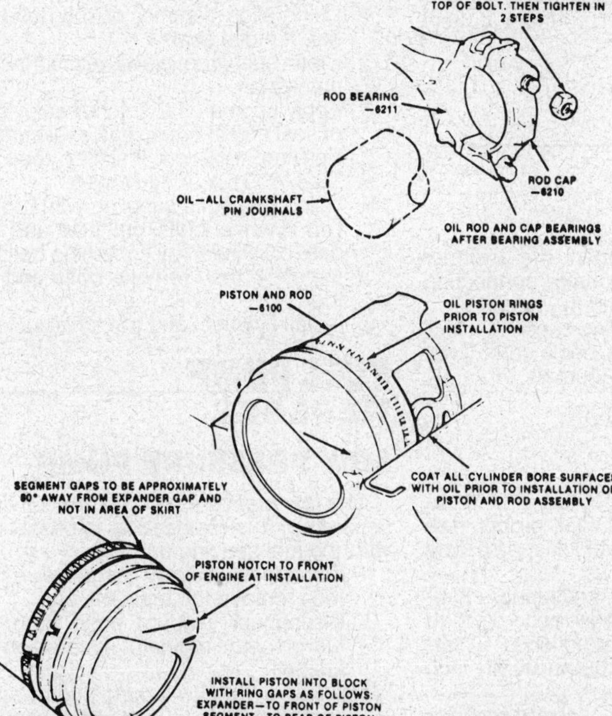


Fig. 15 Installing connecting rod & piston

**torque** to 10 ft. lbs. plus additional 1/4 turn.

9. Torque steering column to gear pinch bolt to specifications.
10. Lower vehicle and remove engine support tool, then raise vehicle.
11. Install engine mount attaching nuts, torquing to specification.
12. Install starter, then lower vehicle.
13. Fill crankcase and connect electrical connector at oil level sensor, if equipped.
14. Connect battery ground cable, then start engine and check for oil leaks along edge of oil pan.

## OIL PUMP

### REPLACE

1. Remove oil pan as previously described.
2. Remove oil pickup tube and screen support bracket nut from No 4 main bearing cap, **Fig. 14.**
3. Remove two oil pump attaching screws and the oil pump.
4. Remove oil pump intermediate shaft.
5. Reverse procedure to install.

## CONNECTING ROD & PISTON

### REPLACE

#### REMOVAL

1. Disconnect battery ground cable.
2. Remove cylinder head and oil pan as previously described.
3. Turn crankshaft until connecting rod to be removed is in down position.
4. Remove carbon from upper portion of cylinder bore. If ridge can be felt or seen at top of bore, it must be removed.
5. If necessary, install ridge reamer in cylinder bore and, following tool manufacturer's instructions, remove ridge until bore is straight to top edge of cylinder.
6. Repeat steps 3 through 5 as necessary.
7. Remove connecting rod nuts, then rod cap and bearing half.
8. Using hammer handle or piece of wood or plastic, tap rod and piston upward until piston rings clear top of cylinder block.
9. Remove rod and piston assembly from top of cylinder bore.
10. Repeat steps 3 through 9 as necessary.

#### INSTALLATION

1. Install proper size connecting rod bearing half into connecting rod and coat it with engine oil. The installed connecting rod bearing to crankshaft clearance should be .0008-0026 inch (0.020-0.066 mm).
2. Properly space piston ring gaps, **Fig. 15,** dip piston in engine oil and install and tighten piston ring compressor tool.

3. Slide two pieces of snug fitting rubber hose over connecting rod bolts to prevent bolt to crankshaft journal contact during installation.
4. Start connecting rod/piston assembly into cylinder bore, keeping notch or arrow in piston top toward front of engine, ensuring that connecting rod number and cylinder bore numbers coincide.
5. Using hammer handle or piece of wood, tap piston/rod assembly into cylinder bore, guiding rod bolts over crankshaft journal, then remove rubber hose from bolts.
6. Insert proper size bearing half into connecting rod cap, then install cap, ensuring that number on cap and rod are on same side and that they match.
7. Install rod nuts and torque to specifications.
8. Repeat steps 1 through 7 as often as necessary on remaining rod/piston assemblies.
9. Install oil pan and cylinder head.

## CRANKSHAFT MAIN BEARING INSERTS

## REPLACE

### REMOVAL

1. Disconnect battery ground cable, then remove starter.
2. Remove oil pan and oil pump as previously described.
3. Remove main bearing cap attaching bolts. **If bearing inserts are to be replaced with engine in vehicle, leave at least two main bearing caps tight while servicing others.**
4. Remove main bearing caps and bearing inserts.
5. Remove upper bearing inserts. Insert tool in crankshaft journal oil hole and turn crankshaft in normal direction of rotation to remove upper bearing half. **Always turn crankshaft clockwise. Counterclockwise rotation may cause timing belts to jump time.**
6. If bearing clearance is to be measured in vehicle using Plastigage, support crankshaft with piece of wood and jack to avoid false reading.

### INSTALLATION

1. After inspecting crankshaft for nicks, scoring and wear, measure crankshaft to select proper bearing to crankshaft clearance. Clearance should be .0008-.0026 inch (0.020-0.066 mm). Always keep two bearing caps tight while measuring others.
2. Install new bearings in caps and cylinder block, matching bearing tangs with notch in cap and block.
3. Install upper bearing half.
4. Ensure that bearing caps are properly located, **Fig. 16,** torque cap bolts to specifications. After each cap is tightened, ensure that crankshaft can be rotated manually. If not, remove one bearing cap at a time, until problem is located.

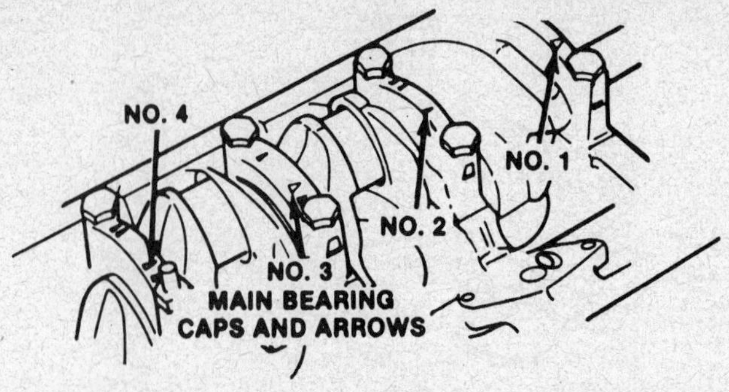


**Fig. 16 Main bearing cap installation**

5. Torque main bearing caps to specifications. Check for crankshaft rotation.
6. Remove rear main bearing cap and apply a 1/8 inch bead of sealant across main bearing cap to cylinder block surface. Do not apply sealant onto bearing or rear seal surface of crankshaft.
7. Install rear cap, torquing cap bolts in two steps to specification.
8. Install oil pump and oil pan.
9. Install starter, then connect battery ground cable.

## CRANKSHAFT

## REPLACE

### REMOVAL

1. Remove engine, then the cylinder head, oil pan, oil pump, connecting rods and pistons and flywheel.
2. Remove main bearing caps.
3. Remove crankshaft, being careful not to damage bearing journals.

### INSTALLATION

1. After cleaning, inspecting and measuring crankshaft, install proper size bearings in cylinder block and bearing caps.
2. Install crankshaft, measuring clearance with Plastigage according to manufacturer's instructions. Clearance should be .0008-.0026 inch (0.020-0.066 mm).
3. Ensure that bearing caps are properly positioned, **Fig. 16,** then torque cap bolts to specifications.
4. After each cap is tightened, ensure that crankshaft can be rotated manually. If not, remove one cap at a time, until source of interference is found.
5. Remove rear main bearing cap and apply 1/8 inch bead of sealant across main bearing cap to cylinder block surface. Do not apply sealant onto bearing or rear seal surface of crankshaft.
6. Install rear cap, torquing bolts to specification in two steps.
7. Install connecting rods and pistons, oil pump, crankshaft rear oil seal, oil pan, flywheel and cylinder head, then the engine.

## CRANKSHAFT REAR OIL SEAL

## REPLACE

1. Remove transmission and flywheel.
2. Punch small hole in metal portion of rear face of seal.
3. Install sheet metal screw in punched hole.
4. Using slide hammer or roll head pry bar, remove seal.
5. Clean seal groove and seal surface of crankshaft.
6. Apply engine oil to interior sealing lip of seal and to crankshaft seal surface.
7. Position seal on installer tool No. T82L-6701-A or equivalent.
8. Using two bolts supplied with tool, or two flywheel bolts, pull seal and tool onto crankshaft by tightening bolts alternately, then remove bolts and the tool.
9. Install flywheel and transmission.

## FUEL PUMP

## REPLACE

### LOW PRESSURE PUMP

The low pressure pump is not serviced separately, it is replaced as an assembly with the fuel sending unit.

1. Disconnect battery negative cable, then remove the fuel tank cap.
2. Disconnect vacuum hose from the fuel pressure regulator (located on the fuel rail).
3. Using a hand vacuum pump, apply approximately 25 inch Hg of vacuum to the pressure regulator. It may take up to three minutes to relieve fuel system pressure.
4. Remove as much fuel as possible from the fuel tank, using a safety approved pump.
5. Remove the filler door/filler neck housing attaching screws and the filler door.
6. Remove the filler neck to housing attaching screws, then the filler cap and tether assembly.
7. Raise and support vehicle.
8. Remove the filler neck support bracket attaching bolt, then disconnect fuel supply and return lines from the routing clip located above the righthand halfshaft.

9. Support the fuel tank with a jack, using safety straps to secure tank to jack.
10. Remove the fuel tank shield attaching screws, then the fuel tank strap attaching bolts.
11. Lower the fuel tank slightly, then remove the vapor line, fuel level sending unit connector, fuel pump wiring connector and the fuel supply and return lines.
12. Move the fuel tank to the left to separate from the filler neck.
13. Push the tank rearward to clear the tank shield, then lower the tank from vehicle.
14. Using lock ring tool No. D84P-9275-A or equivalent, remove sending unit/fuel pump lock ring.
15. Remove lock ring, seal ring and sending unit/fuel pump from fuel tank.
16. Reverse procedure to install. Apply a light coat of grease onto new seal ring before installing.

## HIGH PRESSURE PUMP

1. Depressurize EFI fuel system using a hand operated vacuum pump. Connect pump hose to fuel system pressure regulator and apply at least 25 inches vacuum. **Fuel supply lines will remain pressurized for some period of time after engine is shut off. System pressure must be relieved before disconnecting any fuel lines.**
2. Disconnect battery ground cable.
3. Raise and support vehicle, then disconnect fuel pump electrical connector.
4. Disconnect fuel lines from pump inlet and outlet fittings.
5. Remove pump bracket attaching screws and the pump.
6. Remove pump and foam insulator from mounting bracket.
7. Disconnect wiring harness from pump.
8. Reverse procedure to install.

# TURBOCHARGER

The turbocharger is basically an air compressor that is connected into the air induction system to increase air flow to the engine. The turbocharger used on this vehicle is a blow-through system, the fuel injectors are mounted downstream from the turbocharger rather than upstream as they would be in a draw-through system. The energy required to compress the air is taken from the engine exhaust gases. By using pressure and heat normally discharged by the exhaust system, a turbocharged engine can increase wide-open and heavy throttle power levels while maintaining fuel economies at part load. The turbocharger converts this normally wasted energy into rotating mechanical force. The rotational force of the turbine is transferred to the compressor side of the turbocharger through the interconnecting shaft.

At operating speed, the spinning compressor wheel creates its own suction or vacuum at the air inlet elbow. This vacuum draws more air into the engine than the normal vacuum created by piston movement. This additional air pumped into the intake manifold where it is mixed with fuel supplied by electronically controlled fuel injectors. As the turbocharger pressure forces the air/fuel mixture into the cylinders, it becomes tightly packed. This heavier and denser mixture burns with increased force that boosts torque and horsepower in comparison with non-turbocharged engines of the same displacement.

The rotating assembly is supported on two pressure lubricated bearings and, because a turbocharger can operate at speeds up to 120,000 RPM, lubrication of the bearings which support the shaft is important for cooling and friction reduction.

The turbocharger bearings are lubricated with engine oil supplied through a tube routed from the turbocharger center housing to a supply fitting threaded into the oil pressure sending unit port.

A piston ring seal is used on the turbine wheel shaft end to prevent engine oil leakage into the turbine wheel housing. A carbon face seal is used on the compressor wheel shaft end to prevent engine oil leakage into the compressor wheel housing.

The engine oil drains from the turbocharger through a return hole in the center housing and returns to the engine through an oil return tube connected between the bottom of the turbocharger and the side of the engine block.

The turbocharger is also cooled by engine coolant circulating through the center housing. Coolant is routed to the turbocharger from the cylinder block, circulates through the center housing and returns to the radiator through the heater return tube.

During turbocharger boost, more and more exhaust gases are created which spin the compressor and turbine wheels at an increasing rate. This gas flow to turbine speed increase cycle could continue until a boost became great enough to damage engine. A wastegate is used to limit the amount of boost. The wastegate is located in the turbine housing and it allows exhaust gases to bypass the turbine wheel once maximum allowable boost pressure has been reached. Position of the wastegate is controlled by a diaphragm and spring actuator assembly that senses manifold pressure and correctly positions the lever and valve assembly to obtain the desired amount of bypassed exhaust gases.

The amount of pressure applied to the diaphragm is controlled by a boost control solenoid located on the right side of the engine compartment in front of the cooling system expansion tank. Hoses connect the solenoid to the pressure and vacuum sides of the turbocharger. Solenoid function is controlled by the EEC-IV electronic control assembly. When boost pressures reaches approximately 15 psi on vehicles with manual transmission, or 13 psi on vehicles with automatic transmission, the ECA will use the boost control solenoid to open the wastegate, bypassing exhaust gases away from the turbine blades.

If turbo boost rises above the safe limit, the operator is alerted to this condition through an overboost warning buzzer. The buzzer circuit is completed through a pressure sensitive switch located in the left rear corner of the engine compartment. The switch receives its signal through a hose connected to the vacuum tree, which is connected directly to the intake manifold. If pressure exceeds 18 psi, the switch contacts close and the warning buzzer sounds.

1. Raise and support vehicle, then install a clutch housing alignment adapter tool No. T75L-4201-A or equivalent, installed to a dial indicator with a magnetic base at the end of the actuator.
2. Set dial indicator to zero.
3. Connect a gauged air pressure line to the actuator inlet port. To obtain a gauged air pressure, use a combination air pressure regulator and an air pressure dial tool No. T79P-6634-A or equivalent, connected to a source line (shop air supply).
4. Starting with zero air pressure, slowly increase air pressure until the actuator arm moves approximately .015 inch. The pressure gauge should indicate between 9.5-10.5 psi.
5. If reading is not within specification, or if no movement is measured at 10.5 psi, replace turbocharger assembly.

# TIGHTENING SPECIFICATIONS

| Year | Component | Torque/Ft. lbs. |
|---|---|---|
| 1989 | Auxiliary Gear Shaft Bolt | 28-40 |
| | Auxiliary Shaft Cover Bolt | 6-9 |
| | Auxiliary Shaft Thrust Plate Bolt | 6-9 |
| | Belt Tensioner (Timing Pivot Bolt) | 28-40 |
| | Belt Tensioner (Timing Adjusting Bolt) | 14-21 |
| | Camshaft Gear Bolt | 50-71 |
| | Camshaft Thrust Plate Bolt | 6-9 |
| | Catalytic Converter To Inlet Pipe Bolts | 26-30 |
| | Flywheel Housing To Block | 23-38 |
| | Connecting Rod Nut | 30-36 ① |
| | Crankshaft Damper Bolt | 103-133 |
| | Crossmember To Side Member Bolts | 38-47 |
| | Cylinder Front Cover Bolt | 6-9 |
| | Cylinder Head Bolt | 80-90 ② |
| | Cylinder Head Passage Plugs | 23-28 |
| | Distributor Clamp Bolt | 14-21 |
| | Driveshaft Center Bearing Support Nuts | 55-60 |
| | EGR Tube Nut | 9-12 |
| | EGR Tube To Exhaust Manifold Connection | 9-12 |
| | EGR Valve To Spacer | 14-21 |
| | Engine Mount Attaching Nuts | 50-70 |
| | Engine Mount To Front Crossmember Nuts | 38-47 |
| | Engine Mount To Underbody | 15-20 |
| | Exhaust Manifold To Cylinder Head Bolt, Stud, Or Nut | 20-30 ③ |
| | Flywheel To Crankshaft | 56-64 |
| | Front Cover Bolts | 6-9 |
| | Intake Manifold Bolt (Lower) | 14-21 |
| | Intake Manifold To Cylinder Head Bolt, Or Nut | 14-21 |
| | Main Bearing Cap Bolts | ② |
| | Oil Filter Insert To Cylinder Block | 20-35 |
| | Oil Pan Drain Plug | 15-25 |
| | Oil Pan To Block | 10-13.5 |
| | Oil Pressure Sending Unit To Block | 8-18 |
| | Oil Pump Cover | 90-130 ⑤ |
| | Oil Pump To Block | 14-21 |
| | Oil Pump Pickup Tube To Pump | 14-21 |
| | Oil Supply Line Nut | 20-30 |
| | Oil Supply Line Fitting Nut | 9-12 |
| | Oil Return To Turbocharger Bolt | 14-21 |
| | Oil Return To Fitting Nut | 9-22 |
| | Oil Return To Fitting To Upper Block | 6-9 |
| | Radiator Lower Mount Bolts | 15-19 |
| | Radiator Upper Mounting Studs | 6-9 |
| | Rocker Arm Cover | 5-8 |
| | Spark Plug | 7-15 |
| | Starter Bolts | 15-20 |
| | Steering Column To Gear Pinch Bolts | 12-15 |
| | Steering Gear Attaching Bolts | 10 ④ |
| | Temperature Sending Unit | 8-18 |
| | Thermostat Housing Bolts | 14-21 |
| | Throttle Body To Upper Intake Nut | 12-15 |
| | Timing Belt Inner Cover Stud | 14-21 |
| | Timing Belt Outer Cover Retaining Bolts | 6-9 |

*Continued*

## TIGHTENING SPECIFICATIONS-Continued

| Year | Component | Torque/Ft. lbs. |
|---|---|---|
| 1989 | Torque Converter Housing To Block | 22-27 |
| | Torque Converter Support To Transmission Mount Bolt | 37-42 |
| | Torque Converter-To-Drive Plate Nuts | 26-28 |
| | Turbocharger To Manifold Nut | 28-40 |
| | Turbocharger Air Inlet | 15-22 |
| | Water Jacket Drain Plug | 23-28 |
| | Water Pump | 14-21 |
| | Water Outlet Connection Bolt | 14-21 |

①—Torque in sequence in two steps: Step 1; 25-30 ft. lbs., step 2; 30-36 ft. lbs.
②—Torque in sequence in two steps: Step 1; 50-60 ft. lbs., step 2; 75-85 ft. lbs. Check crankshaft rotation after each torquing.
③—Torque in sequence in two steps: Step 1; 15-17 ft. lbs., step 2; 20-30 ft. lbs.
④—Then an additional 90°.
⑤—Inch lbs.
⑥—Torque in sequence in two steps: Step 1; 50-60 ft. lbs., step 2; 80-90 ft. lbs.

# 2.9L/V6-177 Engine

## INDEX



## ENGINE MOUNTS REPLACE

1. Raise and support vehicle.
2. Remove engine mount to crossmember attaching nuts, then lower vehicle.
3. Remove mount-to-support bracket attaching nuts, **Fig. 1.**
4. Raise engine using a jack and remove mounts.
5. Reverse procedure to install, torquing mount attaching nuts to specifications. **Ensure upper locating pins align with holes in support bracket during installation.**

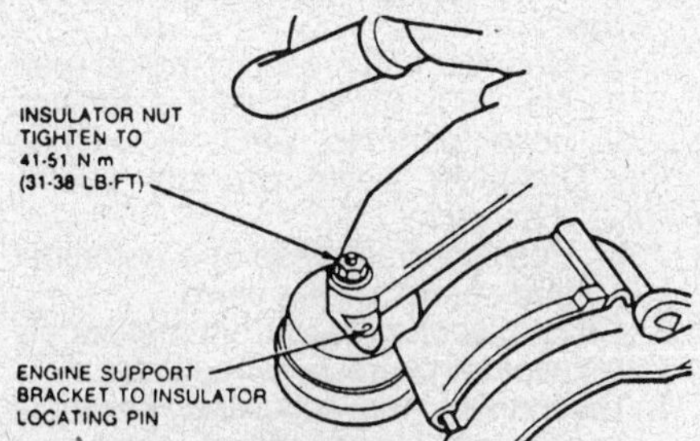


**Fig. 1 Engine mount replacement**

## ENGINE REPLACE

### REMOVAL

1. Disconnect battery ground cable, then drain cooling system.
2. Disconnect engine compartment lamp electrical connector on inboard side of battery.
3. Disconnect windshield washer hose from reservoir and plug reservoir outlet.
4. Disconnect hood ground strap, mark hood hinge locations, then remove hood.
5. Disconnect inlet air hoses from throttle body.
6. Remove air cleaner cover, air box and inlet air hoses.
7. Remove radiator upper shroud and cooling fan assembly.
8. Unfasten power steering pump and alternator and position components aside.
9. **On models equipped with Thermactor,** remove Thermactor retaining bolts, hose and air pump and position aside.
10. **On all models,** disconnect hoses from heater valve.
11. Disconnect coolant hoses from water pump and thermostat housing.
12. Disconnect throttle cable from throttle body linkage. Remove throttle cable bracket attaching bolts position aside.
13. Release fuel system pressure as follows:
    a. Connect fuel pressure gauge (part No. T80L-9974-B) with extension hose (part No. D85L-9974-B) to Schrader valve on fuel supply manifold.
    b. Position drain hose in a container and depress drain valve.
14. Disconnect fuel supply and return lines.
15. Remove distributor cap, rotor, distributor electrical connector and spark plug wires.
16. Label and disconnect ignition coil electrical connectors.
17. Label and disconnect vacuum hoses from front and rear of upper intake manifold and EGR fitting.

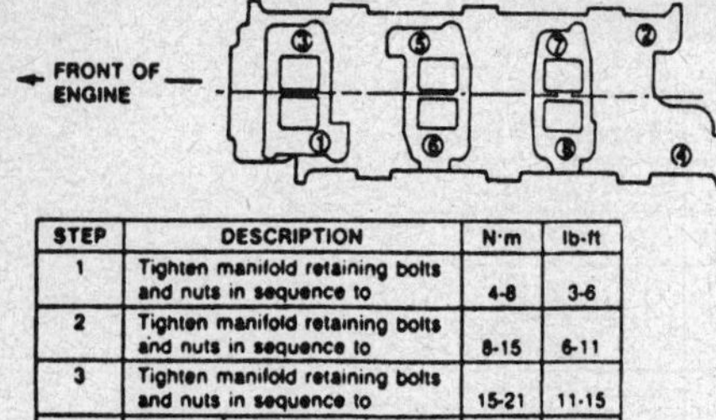


| STEP | DESCRIPTION | N·m | lb-ft |
|---|---|---|---|
| 1 | Tighten manifold retaining bolts and nuts in sequence to | 4-8 | 3-6 |
| 2 | Tighten manifold retaining bolts and nuts in sequence to | 8-15 | 6-11 |
| 3 | Tighten manifold retaining bolts and nuts in sequence to | 15-21 | 11-15 |
| 4 | Tighten manifold retaining bolts and nuts in sequence to | 21-25 | 15-18 |

**Fig. 2 Intake manifold bolt tightening sequence**

18. Remove carbon canister with bracket and vacuum line.
19. Disconnect the following electrical connectors and position aside: air charge temperature sensor, idle speed control valve, oil pressure switch, engine coolant temperature sensor, throttle position sensor, A/C compressor clutch and fuel injectors.
20. Disconnect ground wire from spade terminal on LH fender apron.
21. Disconnect manifold absolute pressure sensor under cowl weatherstrip and position aside.
22. Raise and support vehicle.
23. Remove exhaust manifold-to-exhaust pipe retaining nuts.
24. **On models equipped with automatic transmission,** disconnect transmission oil cooler lines from radiator.
25. **On all models,** remove two radiator attaching bolts, then disengage upper retaining clips and lower radiator from vehicle.
26. Disconnect starter wiring, then remove starter attaching bolts and the starter.
27. Remove engine insulator lower retaining nuts and washers.
28. Remove side and lower converter housing or clutch-to-engine attaching bolts.
29. **On models equipped with automatic transmission,** remove inspection plate, then the converter-to-flywheel attaching nuts.
30. **On all models,** loosen A/C compressor retaining bolt and pivot bolts, then lower vehicle.
31. Install engine lifting device on engine lifting attachments.
32. Support transmission with a jack, then remove two upper converter housing or clutch attaching bolts.
33. Raise engine enough to allow A/C compressor to be removed, then unfasten the compressor and wire aside.
34. Raise engine until insulators are cleared, then pull engine forward to separate it from transmission and carefully raise engine out of engine compartment.

### INSTALLATION

Reverse procedure to install, noting the following:

1. Torque transmission-to-engine attaching bolts to specification.

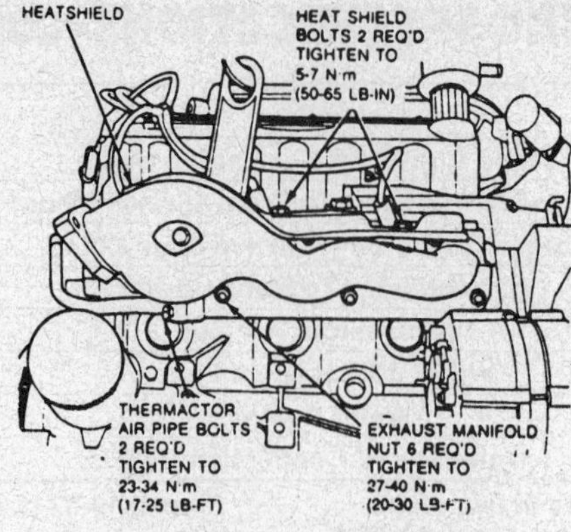


**Fig. 3 Exhaust manifold replacement. Right side**

2. Temporarily install A/C compressor prior to lowering engine into vehicle.
3. Torque left side engine support bracket attaching bolts to specification.
4. **On models equipped with automatic transmission,** torque converter-to-flywheel retaining nuts to specification.
5. **On all models,** torque exhaust manifold-to-exhaust pipe attaching bolts to specification.
6. **Torque** throttle cable bracket attaching bolts to 11-15 ft. lbs.

## INTAKE MANIFOLD REPLACE

1. Disconnect battery ground cable.
2. Remove air inlet hoses from air cleaner and throttle body.
3. Disconnect throttle cable from linkage from throttle body.
4. Remove throttle cable bracket attaching bolts, then position cable and bracket aside.
5. Release fuel system pressure as follows:
   a. Connect fuel pressure gauge (part No. T80L-9974-B) with extension hose (part No. D85L-9974-B) to Schrader valve on fuel supply manifold.
   b. Position drain hose in a container and depress drain valve.
6. Disconnect fuel lines from fuel supply manifold and pressure regulator.
7. Disconnect the following electrical connectors and position aside: air charge temperature sensor, idle speed control valve, throttle position sensor and engine coolant temperature sensor.
8. Label, then disconnect vacuum hoses from intake manifold, manifold plenum and throttle body.
9. Drain cooling system, then remove hose from thermostat housing to radiator.
10. Unfasten and remove EGR tube from throttle body.
11. Remove throttle body/plenum assembly attaching bolts and the assembly from intake manifold.
12. Remove distributor cap and wires as an assembly, then disconnect distributor electrical connector.

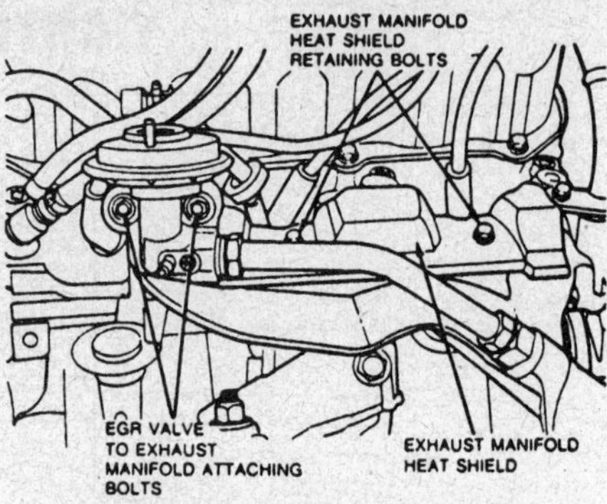


**Fig. 4 Exhaust manifold replacement. Left side**

13. Mark position of distributor rotor and housing for assembly reference, then remove hold-down screw, clamp and the distributor assembly.
14. Remove valve cover attaching bolts and the valve cover.
15. Remove intake manifold attaching bolts and the intake manifold. **Note length of attaching bolts for assembly reference.**
16. Reverse procedure to install, noting the following:
   a. Apply sealant to manifold prior to gasket installation.
   b. Ensure tab on right hand cylinder head gasket fits in cutout on intake manifold.
   c. Hand-tighten retaining nuts onto studs 3 and 4, then torque retaining nuts and bolts as shown in **Fig. 2.**
   d. Torque valve cover attaching bolts and EGR tube-to-throttle body attaching bolts to specification.
   e. Torque throttle body/plenum assembly attaching bolts to specifications in two steps.

## EXHAUST MANIFOLD REPLACE

### RIGHT SIDE

1. Disconnect battery ground cable.
2. Remove heat shield attaching bolts and the heat shield, **Fig. 3.**
3. Remove exhaust pipe attaching bolts and the exhaust pipe.
4. Unfasten and remove Thermactor pipe, if equipped, from manifold.
5. Remove exhaust manifold attaching bolts and the manifold.
6. Reverse procedure to install. Torque attaching bolts to specification.

### LEFT SIDE

1. Disconnect battery ground cable.
2. Remove EGR valve-to-manifold attaching bolts, **Fig. 4.**
3. Remove EGR tube attaching screws and disconnect tube from throttle body.
4. Remove manifold heat shield attaching bolts and the heat shield.
5. Raise and support vehicle.
6. Remove exhaust manifold-to-exhaust pipe attaching nuts.

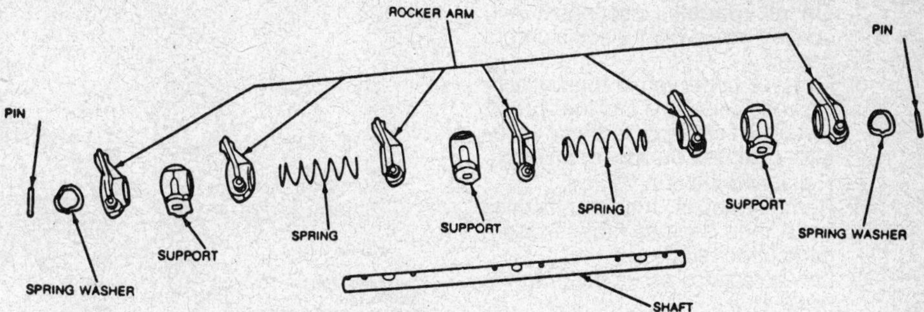


**Fig. 7 Exploded view of rocker arm assembly**

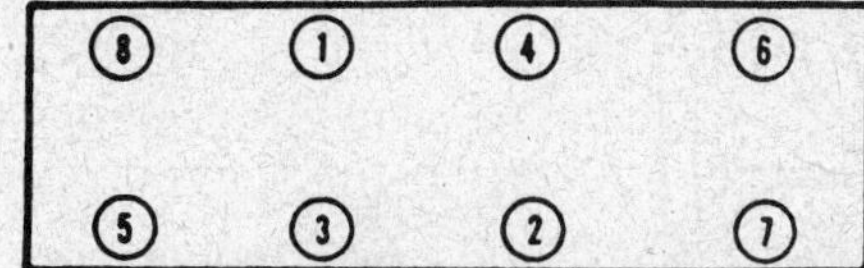


STEP 1: TIGHTEN IN SEQUENCE TO 30 N·m (22 LB-FT)
STEP 2: TIGHTEN IN SEQUENCE TO 70-75 N·m (51-55 LB-FT)
STEP 3: WAIT 5 MINUTES
STEP 4: IN SEQUENCE, TURN ALL BOLTS 90 DEGREES.

**Fig. 5 Cylinder head bolt tightening sequence**

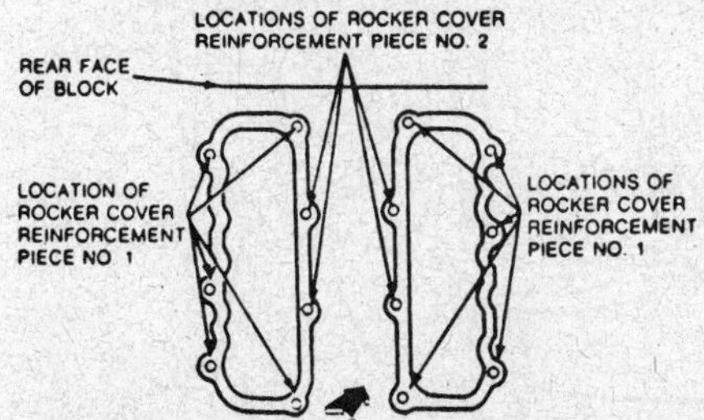


CAUTION:
IF ROCKER COVER IS TIGHTENED WITHOUT LOAD DISTRIBUTION WASHERS, DEFORMATION OF THE ROCKER COVER WILL OCCUR. INSTALLING REINFORCEMENT PIECE AFTERWARD WILL NO LONGER PREVENT LEAKS.

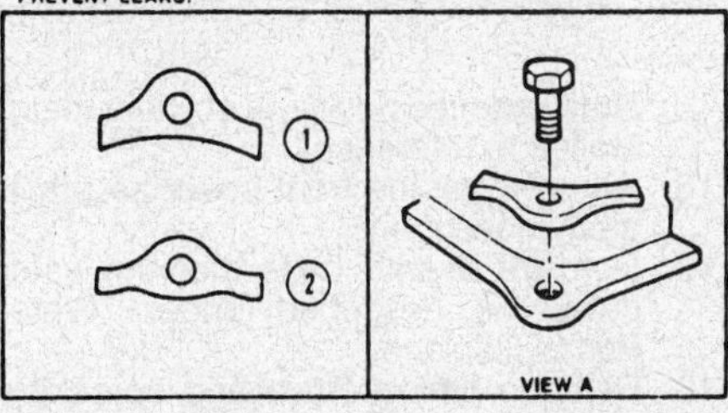


**Fig. 6 Valve cover installation**

7. Remove bolts attaching Thermactor air pipe, if equipped, to manifold.
8. Remove exhaust manifold attaching nuts and the manifold.
9. Reverse procedure to install. Torque attaching bolts to specification.

# CYLINDER HEAD
## REPLACE

1. Disconnect battery ground cable, then drain cooling system.
2. Remove intake hoses from throttle body, then disconnect throttle linkage.
3. Remove distributor cap and wires as an assembly, then disconnect distributor electrical connector.
4. Mark position of distributor rotor and housing for assembly reference, then remove hold-down screw and clamp and the distributor assembly.
5. Remove upper radiator hose, then the valve cover and shaft. **When removing rocker arm shaft, loosen bolts two turns at a time.**
6. Release fuel system pressure as follows:
   a. Connect fuel pressure gauge (part No. T80L-9974-B) with extension hose (part No. D85L-9974-B) to Schrader valve on fuel supply manifold.
   b. Position drain hose in a container and depress drain valve.
7. Disconnect fuel line from fuel rail, then remove intake manifold as previously described.
8. Remove pushrods. Note installed positions for assembly reference.
9. Remove exhaust manifolds as previously described.
10. Remove cylinder head attaching bolts and the cylinder head. **Discard head gaskets and attaching bolts.**
11. Reverse procedure to install, noting the following:
    a. Left hand and right hand gaskets are not interchangeable.
    b. Guide cylinder heads onto cylinder block with fabricated alignment dowels positioned in block.
    c. Tighten cylinder head attaching bolts in sequence shown in **Fig. 5.**

# VALVES
## ADJUST

1. Position cams so tappets are in the base circle area on cylinder to be adjusted.
2. Loosen adjusting screws until a distinct lash between roller arm pad and valve tip end can be noticed. Tappet plunger should now be fully extended.
3. Screw in adjustment screws until rocker arms slightly touch valves.
4. Turn adjustment screw in an additional 1½ turns (equivalent to .079 inch plunger travel into lifter) to achieve normal operating position.

# VALVE COVER & ROCKER ARM SHAFT
## REPLACE

1. Remove spark plug wires, then the PCV valve and hose as necessary.
2. Remove valve cover attaching screws and washers. **Washers must be installed in their original positions.**
3. **On models equipped with automatic transmission,** disconnect throttle linkage and kickdown linkage.
4. **On all models,** tap valve cover to break seal and remove the cover.
5. Remove rocker arm shaft by loosening bolts two turns at a time.
6. Reverse procedure to install, noting the following:
   a. Tighten rocker arm shaft support attaching bolts two turns at a time until torque specification is obtained.
   b. Adjust valves as previously described.
   c. Apply silicone sealant to mating surfaces of valve covers and cylinder head prior to installing new gasket, **Fig. 6.**
   d. Torque valve cover attaching screws to specifications after ensuring all load distribution washers are installed in their original positions.

# ROCKER ARM ASSEMBLY SERVICE

1. Remove rocker arm shaft assembly as previously described.
2. Remove spring washer and pin from each end of rocker arm shaft, **Fig. 7.**
3. Remove rocker arms, springs and shaft supports from shaft. **Mark components for assembly reference.**
4. If necessary to remove shaft plugs, drill plug on one end, knock out plug on opposite end, then knock out remaining plug from remaining end.
5. Drive new shaft plugs into position using a blunt tool. **Ensure cup side of plugs face out.**
6. Install spring washer and pin on one end of shaft, then lubricate shaft with heavy engine oil and install components in same sequence as they were removed.
7. Install remaining spring washer and pin, then apply heavy engine oil to rocker arm pads.
8. Install rocker arm shaft assembly, ensuring oil holes in shaft point down.

# ENGINE FRONT COVER
## REPLACE

1. Remove oil pan as described under "Oil Pan, Replace."
2. Remove radiator as follows:
   a. Drain cooling system, then disconnect upper and lower hoses from radiator.
   b. **On models equipped with automatic transmission,** disconnect and plug transmission oil cooler lines from radiator.

c. **On all models,** disconnect A/C cooling fan switch electrical connector.
d. Remove upper fan shroud attaching bolts and rivets and the shroud. **Retain rivets and radiator insulators for use during installation.**
e. Raise and support vehicle.
f. Remove lower mount attaching bolts, then depress tabs to disengage upper studs.
g. Lower radiator assembly from vehicle.

3. Unfasten A/C compressor and Thermactor air pump and bracket and position aside.
4. Remove power steering pump and bracket, then the alternator and drive belts.
5. Remove engine driven cooling fan. **Viscous clutch nut nas left hand threads which must be rotated clockwise for removal.**
6. Remove water pump as described under "Water Pump, Replace."
7. Remove heater and radiator hoses, then the crankshaft drive pulley.
8. Remove front cover attaching bolts and the front cover.
9. Reverse procedure to install, noting the following:
   a. With new gasket in place on front cover, position cover on engine and start all retaining screws two or three turns.
   b. Install alignment tool No. T74P-6019-A or equivalent to crankshaft, then position cover over tool.
   c. Ensure front cover-to-oil pan mating flange properly aligns with lower edge of cylinder block, then torque front cover attaching bolts to specifications.
   d. Upon completion of installation, operate engine for a period, then **re-torque** front cover attaching bolts to specifications.

## TIMING CHAIN REPLACE

1. Drain cooling system and engine oil.
2. Remove engine front cover as previously described.
3. Remove camshaft sprocket attaching bolt, then the sprocket and timing chain.
4. If necessary, remove crankshaft sprocket using tool No. T71P-7137-H or equivalent.
5. Reverse procedure to install, noting the following:
   a. Ensure sprocket keyways are properly aligned when installing gears.
   b. Check camshaft endplay as shown in **Fig. 8.** Position dial indicator point on camshaft attaching screw, then zero the dial indicator. Position a screwdriver between sprocket and engine block, then pull camshaft forward and release it. If reading exceeds .009 inch, replace thrust plate.
   c. Ensure timing marks are properly aligned when installing crankshaft sprocket.
   d. Torque camshaft sprocket attaching bolt to specification.

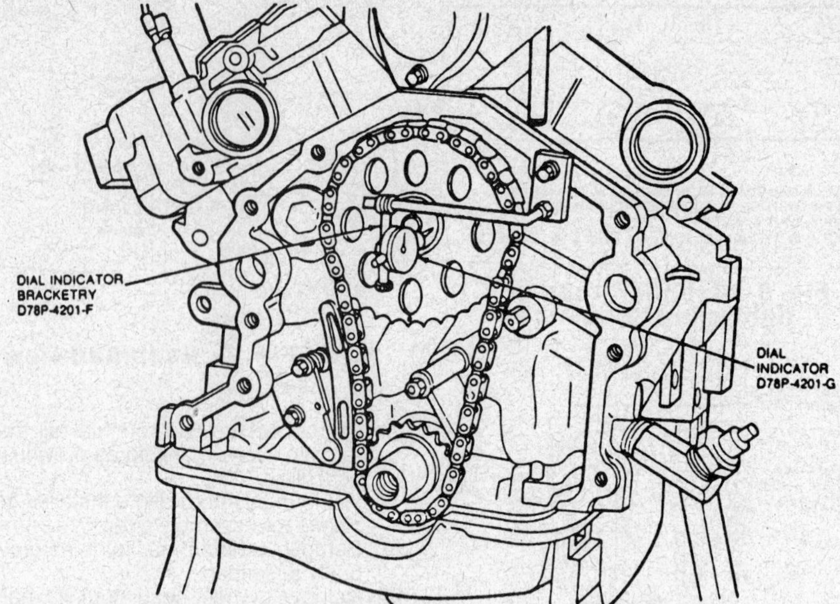


**Fig. 8 Camshaft endplay measurement**

## CAMSHAFT REPLACE

1. Disconnect battery ground cable.
2. Remove upper fan shroud attaching bolts and rivets and the shroud. **Retain rivets and radiator insulators for use during installation.**
3. Remove engine driven cooling fan. **Viscous clutch nut nas left hand threads which must be rotated clockwise for removal.**
4. Drain cooling system, then disconnect upper and lower hoses from radiator.
5. **On models equipped with automatic transmission,** disconnect and plug transmission oil cooler lines from radiator.
6. **On all models,** disconnect A/C cooling fan switch electrical connector.
7. Raise and support vehicle.
8. Remove lower mount attaching bolts, then depress tabs to disengage upper studs.
9. Lower radiator assembly from vehicle.
10. Loosen A/C condenser retaining bolts.
11. Remove upper and lower engine mount retaining nuts, then lower vehicle.
12. Remove grille attaching screws and the grille.
13. Remove A/C condenser attaching bolts, then lower condenser and cooling fan from vehicle.
14. Remove cylinder head as previously described.
15. Remove valve lifters using a magnet. Note installed positions of lifters for installation reference.
16. Remove engine front cover as previously described.
17. Remove all drive belts, then the water pump as described under "Water Pump, Replace."
18. Remove timing chain and sprockets as previously described.
19. Raise and support engine and transmission assembly to provide adequate clearance for camshaft removal.
20. Remove camshaft thrust plate and attaching bolts, then carefully slide camshaft from engine.
21. Reverse procedure to install, noting the following:
    a. Lubricate camshaft journals and cam lobes with heavy engine oil prior to installation.
    b. Install spacer ring with chamfered side toward camshaft, then install camshaft key.
    c. Install thrust plate to cover main oil gallery, **Fig. 9**, and torque attaching bolts to specification.
    d. Torque upper and lower engine mount retaining nuts to specifications.

## VALVE SPRING RETAINER & STEM SEAL REPLACE

Provided the valve or valve seat is not damaged, broken valve springs or leaking stem seals can be replaced without removing the cylinder head.

1. Remove valve cover and rocker arm shaft as previously described.
2. Remove spark plug and both pushrods of cylinder being serviced.
3. Apply compressed air to spark plug hole, **Fig. 10. Exercise extreme cau-**

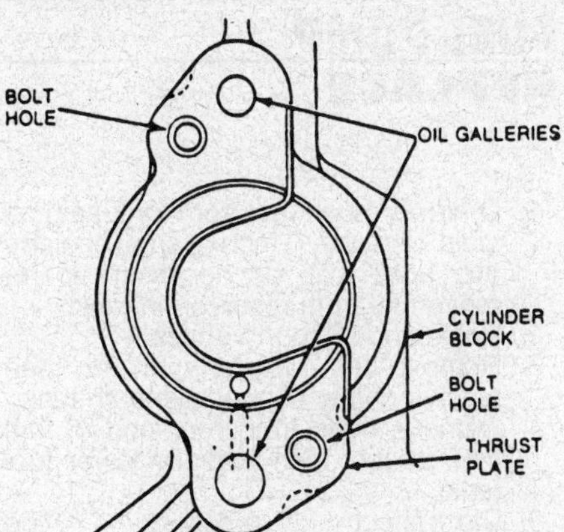


**Fig. 9 Camshaft thrust plate installation**

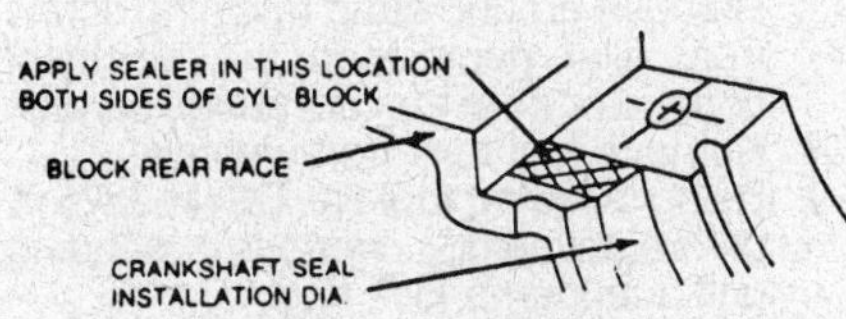


**Fig. 12 Rear main bearing cap installation**

**tion as air pressure may force rotation of the crankshaft.**

4. Compress valve spring using a spring compressor, then remove valve spring retainer locks, spring retainer and spring. If air pressure does not hold valve in closed position, the valve is likely damaged or improperly seated and the cylinder head should be removed for further inspection.
5. Remove valve stem seal.
6. Reverse procedure to install. Lubricate, then install new valve stem seal using tool No. T37P-6571-A or equivalent.

## CRANKSHAFT REAR OIL SEAL

### REPLACE

1. Remove transmission assembly and, on models equipped with manual transmission, then clutch pressure plate and disc.
2. Remove flywheel, flywheel housing and rear plate.
3. Punch two holes in seal on opposite sides of crankshaft directly above bearing cap-to-cylinder block split line. Insert a sheet metal screw into each hole.
4. Remove oil seal by prying against screws with two screwdrivers. **Use care to avoid scratching crankshaft oil seal surface.**
5. Clean oil seal groove in main bearing cap and cylinder block.
6. Apply lubricant to new seal and install using tool No. T72C-6165 or equivalent, **Fig. 11.**

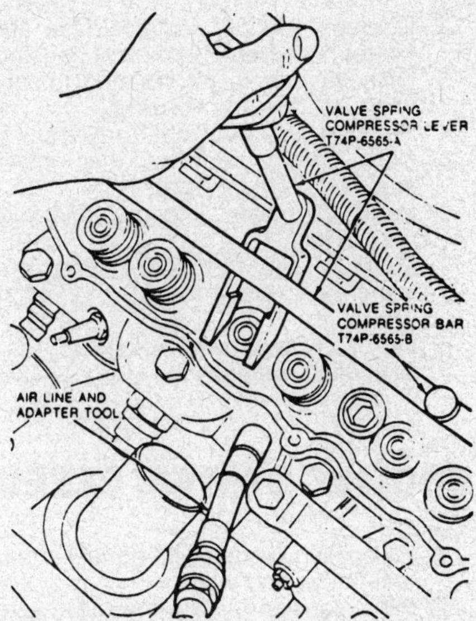


**Fig. 10 Valve spring removal**

## OIL PAN

### REPLACE

1. Disconnect battery ground cable.
2. Disconnect distributor cap and rotor and position aside.
3. Disconnect fuel return line in front of ABS power brake unit.
4. Remove upper fan shroud attaching bolts and rivets and the shroud. **Retain rivets for use during installation.**
5. Raise and support vehicle.
6. Remove two lower engine mount to crossmember retaining nuts.
7. Disconnect starter motor wiring, then remove starter motor attaching bolts and the starter.
8. Disconnect exhaust pipe from exhaust manifold, then lower vehicle.
9. Using engine support bar (tool No. D79P-6000-B or equivalent), lift engine until transmission contacts dash panel.
10. Raise and support vehicle.
11. Remove lower heater hose attaching bolts, then drain engine oil.
12. Remove two lower transmission attaching bolts.
13. Remove lower steering shaft flange coupler attaching bolts and nuts.
14. Position transmission jack under No. 1 front crossmember.
15. Remove clips from front flexible brake line.
16. Remove crossmember attaching bolts, then lower crossmember two inches.
17. Remove oil pan attaching bolts and nuts and the oil pan.
18. Reverse procedure to install, noting the following:
    a. If all gasket material does not come out of groove in rear main bearing cap, remove cap and clean block and the cap. Apply sealant to cylinder block, **Fig. 12**, then install and torque bearing cap. Ensure bearing cap is flush within .005 inch of cylinder block rear face.
    b. Remove all gasket material from block and oil pan mating surfaces, then apply silicone sealant and install new gasket, **Fig. 13.**

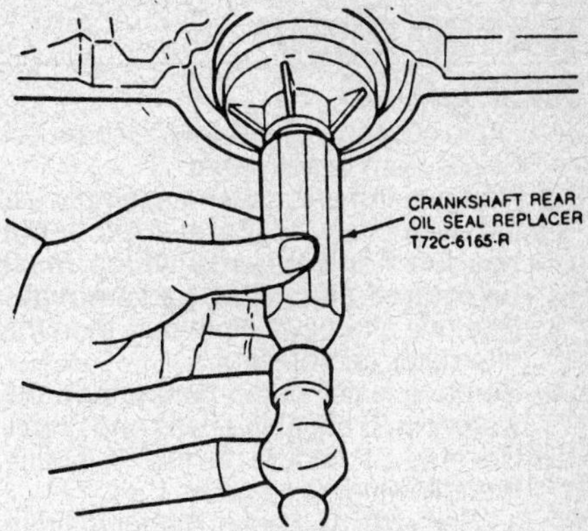


**Fig. 11 Crankshaft rear oil seal installation**

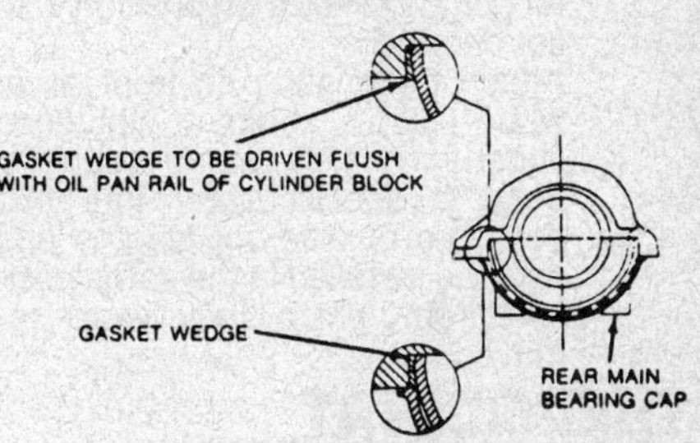


**Fig. 13 Oil pan gasket installation**

## OIL PUMP

### REPLACE

The oil pump is not serviceable and must be replaced as an assembly.

### REMOVAL

1. Remove oil pan as previously described.
2. Remove oil pump attaching bolts, then the oil pump and pump driveshaft.

### INSTALLATION

1. Fill either inlet or outlet port of pump with clean engine oil, then rotate pump shaft to prime pump.
2. Install pump driveshaft into block with pointed end facing inward.
3. Position oil pump with new gasket onto engine. Torque attaching bolts to specifications.
4. Install oil pan, then operate engine and check for oil leaks.

## BELT TENSION DATA

| Belt Type | New Lbs. | Used Lbs. |
|---|---|---|
| 3/8 | 80–100 | 50–80 |
| 1/2 | 100–120 | 80–100 |

## WATER PUMP
### REPLACE

1. Drain cooling system, then disconnect hoses from water pump.
2. Remove fan and clutch assembly using wrenches. **Viscous clutch nut nas left hand threads which must be rotated clockwise for removal.**
3. Remove alternator drive belt, then the alternator and bracket.
4. Remove water pump pulley, then the water pump attaching bolts and pump.
5. Reverse procedure to install, noting the following:
   a. Remove all gasket material from water pump and front cover mating surfaces.
   b. Apply sealant to both sides of water pump gasket, then position gasket on pump.
   c. Attach water pump to front cover with two bolts tightened finger-tight, then torque attaching bolts to specification. Note that bolts are of different lengths and must be installed in the same position from which they were removed.

## THERMOSTAT
### REPLACE

1. Drain cooling system.
2. Disconnect upper radiator hose and heater hose from thermostat housing.
3. Remove thermostat housing attaching bolts, then the housing.
4. Remove the thermostat from housing.
5. Clean gasket surfaces, then install seal ring on thermostat.
6. Install thermostat into manifold with vent at top.
7. Install housing to cylinder head, then install bolts and **torque** to 12-15 ft. lbs.
8. Install heater and radiator hoses, then fill cooling system.

## COOLING SYSTEM BLEED

1. Fill cooling system with equal parts of anti-freeze and water.
2. Fill expansion tank to the MAX. level indicator.
3. Install pressure cap to the first stop. **Do not install cap completely.**
4. Run engine at fast idle until thermostat opens, then turn engine off. Upper radiator hose should feel warm when thermostat opens.
5. Check fluid level in the expansion tank. Fill to the MAX. indicator as needed.
6. Install pressure cap completely.

## FUEL PUMP
### REPLACE

1. Drain as much fuel from tank as possible. Use of a $1/4$ inch or smaller diameter hose may be necessary to remove fuel from reservoir in tank.
2. Raise and support vehicle.
3. Remove the fuel tank shield, then place a safety support beneath tank.
4. Remove bolts from rear end of fuel tank straps, then partially lower fuel tank.
5. Disconnect pressure line push-connect fitting (hairpin type), then swing tank straps out of the way.
6. Disconnect righthand and lefthand vapor tubes from vapor valve assemblies.
7. Remove ground strap retaining screw from filler neck, then the electrical connector from the fuel gauge sender.
8. Remove fuel tank from vehicle.
9. Using lock ring tool No. D84P-9275-A or equivalent, remove sending unit/fuel pump lock ring.
10. Remove lock ring, seal ring and sending unit/fuel pump from fuel tank.
11. Reverse procedure to install. Apply a light coat of grease onto new seal ring before installing.

## TIGHTENING SPECIFICATIONS

| Year | Component | Torque/Ft. lbs. |
|---|---|---|
| 1989 | Air Conditioning Pulley To Crank Pulley | 19-28 |
| | Main Bearing Cap | 65-75 |
| | Camshaft Sprocket | 19-28 |
| | Connecting Rod | 19-24 |
| | Crankshaft Pulley | 85-96 |
| | Front Cover To Block | 13-16 |
| | Intake Manifold Stud | 10-12 |
| | Starter Mounting Bolts | 20-25 |
| | Throttle Body To Upper Intake | 6-10 |
| | Alternator Adjustment Arm To Alternator | 60-70 |
| | Alternator Adjustment Arm To Front Cover | 60-70 |
| | Alternator Mounting Bracket To Cylinder Block | 29-40 |
| | Alternator Mounting Bracket To Cylinder Head | ① |
| | Alternator Pivot Bolt | 45-61 |
| | Camshaft Thrust Plate Bolts | 13-16 |
| | EGR To Carburetor Spacer | 2-7 |
| | EGR Valve To Plenum | 15-18 |
| | EGR Tube To Throttle Body | 6-9 |
| | Engine Lower Insulator Retaining Nuts | 31-38 |
| | Engine Lower Retaining Nuts | 31-38 |
| | Engine Rear Cover Plate | 47-52 |
| | Engine Support Bracket-LH | 31-42 |
| | Engine Support Bracket To Insulator Nuts | 31-38 |

*Continued*

## TIGHTENING SPECIFICATIONS–Continued

| Year | Component | Torque/Ft. lbs. |
|---|---|---|
| 1989 | Engine To Clutch Housing | 30-38 |
| | Engine To Converter Housing | 23-26 |
| | Exhaust Manifold To Cylinder Head | 20-30② |
| | Fan Clutch To Water Pump Hub | 15-25 |
| | Fan To Fan Clutch | 6-8 |
| | Flywheel Bolts | 47-52 |
| | Fuel Pressure Regulator To Fuel Rail | 7-10 |
| | Fuel Rail To Intake Manifold | 7-10 |
| | Heat Shield Manifold Stud | 50-65④ |
| | Idle Air Bypass Valve To Plenum | 7-10 |
| | Knock Sensor Assembly To Block | 30-40 |
| | Oil Filter Adapter To Cylinder Block | 15-30 |
| | Oil Level Indicator Tube To Manifold Nut Stud | 30-40 |
| | Oil Pan Drain Plug | 15-21 |
| | Oil Pan To Cylinder Block | 5-8 |
| | Oil Pickup Tube To Support To Main Cap | 12-15 |
| | Oil Pump Case | 6-10 |
| | Oil Pump Pickup Tube To Pump | 6-10 |
| | Pulley/Water Pump | 14-22 |
| | Rocker Arm Shaft Support Bolt | 43-50 |
| | Rocker Cover To Cylinder Head | 3-5 |
| | Spark Plug | 18-28 |
| | Thermactor Air Pipe To Exhaust Manifold | 14-22 |
| | Timing Chain Guide To Block | 7-10 |
| | Timing Chain Tensioner To Block | 7-10 |
| | Timing Pointer To Front Cover | 5-7 |
| | Torque Converter To Flywheel | 22-30 |
| | Transmission To Engine Bolts-Upper | ③ |
| | Water Jacket Drain Plug | 14-18 |
| | Water Outlet Connection | 6-9 |
| | Water Pump To Front Cover | 7-9 |
| | Y-Pipe To Exhaust Manifold | 26-29 |
| | Cylinder Head | ⑤ |
| | Intake Manifold Bolts | ⑥ |

①—M-8 bolts, 14-22 ft. lbs., M-10 bolts, 29-40 ft. lbs.
②—Bolts and studs.
③—Automatic transmission, 22-30 ft. lbs. Manual transmission, 23-38 ft. lbs.
④—Inch lbs.
⑤—Tighten bolts in sequence in three steps: step one, 22 ft. lbs.; step two, 51-55 ft. lbs.; step three, tighten an additional 90°.
⑥—Tighten bolts in sequence in four steps: step one, 3-6 ft. lbs.; step two, 6-11 ft. lbs.; step three, 11-15 ft. lbs.; step four, 15-18 ft. lbs.

# Clutch & Manual Transmission

## INDEX



## CLUTCH REPLACE

### REMOVAL

Do not get grease or oil on clutch disc facing. Even a small trace of grease or oil may cause clutch grabbing or slipping. Handle disc by its edges and do not touch facings. The clutch assembly is equipped with a self adjuster which automatically adjusts cable length to maintain correct pedal height and throw out bearing preload.

1. Remove transmission as described under "Transmission, Replace."
2. If old pressure plate is to be reused, scribe alignment marks on pressure plate and flywheel for proper assembly.
3. Remove pressure plate attaching bolts, loosening bolts one turn at a

time to release pressure plate spring tension evenly, then remove pressure plate and clutch disc.

## INSTALLATION

1. When installing new clutch, sand friction surfaces on pressure plate and flywheel using medium-fine emery cloth or equivalent aluminum oxide paper. Sand lightly until friction surfaces are covered with fine scratch lines that run across the surface.
2. After sanding, remove all traces of grit and oil using shop towel saturated with denatured alcohol.
3. Coat crankshaft pilot bearing with small amount of lubricant.
4. Position clutch disc and pressure plate on flywheel, aligning marks made during disassembly, then install clutch alignment tool T71P-7137-H or equivalent. **Ensure that clutch disc faces in proper direction. New discs are stamped FLYWHEEL to indicate proper installation direction. When installed correctly, damper springs will face away from flywheel.**
5. **Torque** pressure plate attaching bolts one turn at a time to specifications.
6. Remove clutch disc alignment tool, then install transmission.

# TRANSMISSION REPLACE

## SCORPIO

1. Wedge a block of wood approximately seven inches long under clutch pedal.
2. Disconnect battery ground cable, then remove distributor cap and rotor.
3. Remove gearshift lever knob.
4. Remove center console attaching screws, then the center console and shift boot.
5. Remove center console bracket, then the four retaining screws, frame and noise-dampening pad.
6. Remove gear lever attaching screws and the gear lever.
7. Disconnect oxygen sensor electrical connector in engine compartment and release sensor wiring from routing clip.
8. Raise and support vehicle.
9. Remove four stabilizer bar-to-side member attaching bolts.
10. Disconnect ground strap from exhaust pipe.
11. Remove exhaust system from manifolds to front muffler.
12. Remove catalytic converter heat shield quick fasteners and the heat shield.
13. Disconnect driveshaft from rear axle flange.
14. Scribe reference marks around both sides of center bearing support bracket attaching bolt flat washers, then remove support bearing bracket and attaching bolts. **Spacers installed between support bearing bracket and floorpan must be installed in their original positions to avoid driveline vibration.**
15. Remove driveshaft from extension housing, then plug housing to prevent fluid leakage.
16. Support engine using a jack.
17. Disconnect radio ground strap, then remove transmission rear mount attaching nuts and the mount.
18. Disconnect speedometer sensor, sensor ground strap, neutral gear switch and back-up lamp switch from transmission.
19. Disconnect starter motor wiring, then remove two starter attaching bolts.
20. Pull dust boot aside, then disconnect clutch cable from release lever.
21. Remove clutch cable and dust boot from housing.
22. Remove engine rear cover plate-to-flywheel housing attaching bolt.
23. Remove two flywheel housing attaching bolts from top of housing.
24. Remove four remaining flywheel housing attaching bolts, then the starter heat shield.
25. Pull transmission rearward until flywheel contacts body.
26. Raise rear of transmission and pull rearward to clear body, then lower rear of transmission and pull rearward to remove.
27. Reverse procedure to install, torquing the following to specifications:
    a. Flywheel housing side attaching bolts and the engine rear cover attaching bolt.
    b. Rear mount attaching bolts.
    c. Rear axle flange bolts.
    d. Center bearing attaching bolts.
    e. Upon completion of installation, press clutch pedal to floor several times to adjust clutch cable freeplay.

## XR4Ti

1. Wedge a block of wood approximately seven inches long under clutch pedal.
2. Disconnect battery ground cable, then raise and support vehicle.
3. Remove catalytic converter inlet pipe to turbocharger attaching nuts.
4. Remove attaching nuts at catalytic converter outlet to muffler inlet flange and the catalytic converter support bracket.
5. Remove catalytic converter and inlet pipe as an assembly.
6. Remove driveshaft, installing plug in extension housing seal.
7. Remove starter, then the front stabilizer bar to body U-brackets and the body stiffener rod.
8. Position block of wood between stabilizer bar and body side rail.
9. Support transmission with jack and remove bolt attaching rear mount to transmission.
10. Remove bolts attaching rear mount to body and remove mount, then loosen engine mount attaching nuts until only two or three threads are visible on end of stud.
11. Position block of wood against engine oil pan and raise front of engine with stand. Raise engine until stud nuts on engine mounts contact the crossmember and, as engine tilts downward, lower jack supporting transmission.
12. Disconnect electrical connectors from back-up light switch and neutral safety switch.
13. Remove attaching bolts and raise transmission shift lever out of extension housing.
14. Remove snap ring and pull speedometer cable out of extension housing.
15. Remove clutch release lever cover, then pull rearward on clutch release cable and disengage from release lever.
16. Remove attaching screws from speedometer cable routing clips and position cable out of way on left side of vehicle.
17. Remove bolt attaching engine rear cover plate to flywheel housing.
18. Remove flywheel housing attaching bolts located at top of housing, then the four remaining flywheel housing attaching bolts.
19. Pull transmission rearward until flywheel housing contacts body.
20. Raise rear of transmission and pull rearward to clear body, then lower rear of transmission and pull rearward to remove.
21. Reverse procedure to install, torquing the following to specifications:
    a. Flywheel housing attaching bolts to specifications.
    b. Engine rear cover attaching bolt to specifications.
    c. Engine mount stud nuts to specifications.
    d. Rear mount to body attaching bolts to specifications.
    e. Rear mount to transmission attaching bolt to specifications.
    f. U-bracket and body stiffener rod attaching bolts to specifications.
    g. Attaching nuts at converter outlet and at turbocharger to specifications.
22. After installation is completed, press clutch pedal to floor several times to adjust clutch cable freeplay.

# SERVICE BULLETINS

## CLUTCH CONTROLS—CLICKING & CRACKLING NOISE

### 1989 Merkur Scorpio & XR4Ti

This condition may exist due to the self adjusting pawl slipping over the adjusting sector or a sticking clutch cable. To correct this condition, proceed as follows:

1. Listen for clicking noise while fully depressing and slowly releasing clutch pedal.

2. Ensure clutch pedal travel is not obstructed and clutch cable is installed correctly.
3. Ensure clutch cable enters straight into adjusting sector.
4. If clicking noise still exists, install new clutch cable.
5. If crackling noise is present after new clutch cable has been installed, remove self adjusting clutch mechanism from vehicle.
6. Install new service self adjusting pawl and adjusting sector (part No. E9RY-7L583-A).

# TIGHTENING SPECIFICATIONS

## SCORPIO

| Year | Component | Torque/Ft. lbs. |
|---|---|---|
| 1989 | Back-Up Lamp Switch | 7-10 |
| | Converter Outlet To Muffler Inlet | 21-30 |
| | Cover To Case | 7-8 |
| | Driveshaft Center Bearing Bolts | 13-17 |
| | Driveshaft To Rear Axle Flange | 47-55 |
| | Engine Mount Stud Nut | 50-70 |
| | Engine Rear Cover To Flywheel Housing | 28-38 |
| | Extension Housing To | 33-36 |
| | Fifth Gear Attaching Nut | 89-111② |
| | Flywheel Housing To Case | 52-67 |
| | Flywheel Housing To Engine | 28-38 |
| | Flywheel To Crankshaft Bolts | 56-64 |
| | Front Bearing Retainer To Case | 7-8 |
| | Interlock Plate To Case | 16-19 |
| | Neutral Drive Switch | 7-10 |
| | Pressure Plate To Flywheel | 15-19① |
| | Rear Mount To Body | 25-35 |
| | Rear Mount To Transmission | 50-70 |
| | Shift Detent Plug | 13-14 |
| | Shift Lever Attaching Bolts | 16-19 |
| | Stabilizer Bracket To Body | 33-41 |
| | Starter Motor To Flywheel Housing | 15-20 |
| | Turbocharger Attaching Bolts | 25-35 |
| | U-Bracket | 33-41 |

①—Tighten one complete turn at a time.
②—Use a 1 7/16 (36 mm), 12-point socket.

## XR4Ti

| Year | Component | Torque/ft. lbs. |
|---|---|---|
| 1989 | Air Baffle Stud Nut | 17-19 |
| | Converter Outlet To Muffler Inlet | 21-30 |
| | Cover To Case | 14-15 |
| | Engine Mount Stud Nut | 50-70 |
| | Engine Rear Cover To Flywheel Attaching Bolt | 28-38 |
| | Exhaust Inlet Pipe To Turbocharger | 25-35 |
| | Extension Housing To Case | 33-36 |
| | Fifth Gear Attaching Nut | 89-111 |
| | Flywheel Housing To Case | 52-67 |
| | Flywheel Housing To Engine | 28-38 |
| | Flywheel To Crankshaft | 56-64 |
| | Front Bearing Retainer To Case | 7-8 |
| | Interlock Plate To Case | 16-19 |
| | Pressure Plate To Flywheel | 15-19 |
| | Rear Mount To Body | 25-35 |
| | Rear Mount To Transmission | 50-70 |
| | Shift Detent Plug | 13-14 |
| | Stabilizer Brackets To Body | 33-41 |
| | Starter Motor To Flywheel Housing | 15-20 |

# Rear Axle & Suspension

## INDEX



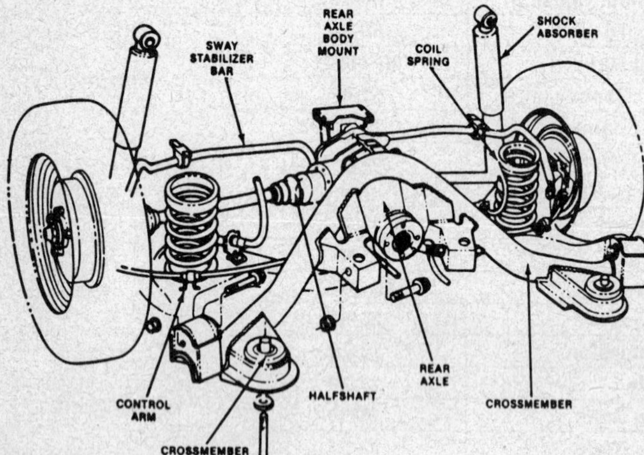


**Fig. 1 Exploded view of rear suspension. Scorpio**

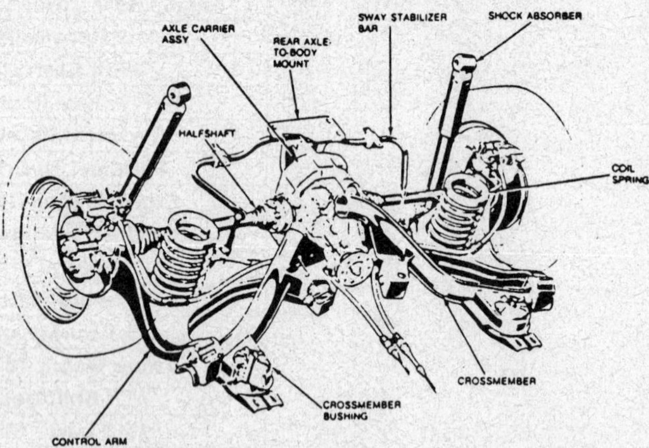


**Fig. 2 Exploded view of rear suspension. XR4Ti**

## SHOCK ABSORBER REPLACE

### SCORPIO

1. Remove luggage compartment floor covering.
2. Remove trim panels from wheelhousing and side panel.
3. Remove shock absorber trim cover from rear wheelhousing.
4. Raise and support rear of vehicle.
5. Position jack under control arm and raise it enough to relieve tension from shock absorber.
6. Remove nut and bolt attaching upper end of shock absorber.
7. Remove lower nut and bolt and the shock absorber.
8. Reverse procedure to install. **Torque** upper and lower attaching nuts to 30-36 ft. lbs. and lower bolt to 33-40 ft. lbs.

### XR4Ti

1. Remove rear parcel shelf.
2. Remove shock absorber trim cover from rear wheel housing.
3. Raise and support rear of vehicle.
4. Position jack under control arm and raise it enough to relieve coil spring tension from shock absorber.
5. Remove nut and bolt attaching upper end of shock absorber.
6. Remove cap from bottom of shock absorber.
7. Remove nut and bolt attaching lower end of shock absorber to control arm bracket.
8. Reverse procedure to install, **torquing** upper and lower attaching nuts and bolts to 30-37 ft. lbs.

## COIL SPRING REPLACE

### SCORPIO

#### Removal

1. Raise and support vehicle with rear wheels and suspension hanging free.
2. Remove bolts attaching halfshaft to wheel stub shaft, **Fig. 1.** To prevent damage to constant velocity joints, tie halfshaft to convenient underbody component.
3. Unfasten stabilizer bar from link rod.
4. Disconnect brake line from bracket on body and unclip line from floor assembly. **When removing left side spring, the brake line distribution piece must be unscrewed from floor panel.**
5. Remove clip attaching rear brake hose to routing bracket on control arm.
6. Using line wrenches, disconnect brake tube from brake hose.
7. Using jack, raise lower control arm enough to relieve coil spring tension from shock absorber.
8. Remove shock absorber-to-control arm bracket attaching nut and bolt.
9. Remove rear axle front crossmember guide plate-to-body attaching bolts and the bushing attaching bolts.
10. Slowly and carefully lower jack until spring and seat can be removed.

#### Installation

1. Install spring upper seat on spring end with color code and plastic sleeve, ensuring end of coil seats against step in spring seat and that seat tabs are positioned between first and second coil.
2. Position coil spring and seat assembly on control arm. **The spring and seat must be installed dry.**
3. Raise control arm to compress coil spring enough to allow installation of the shock absorber lower attaching bolt.

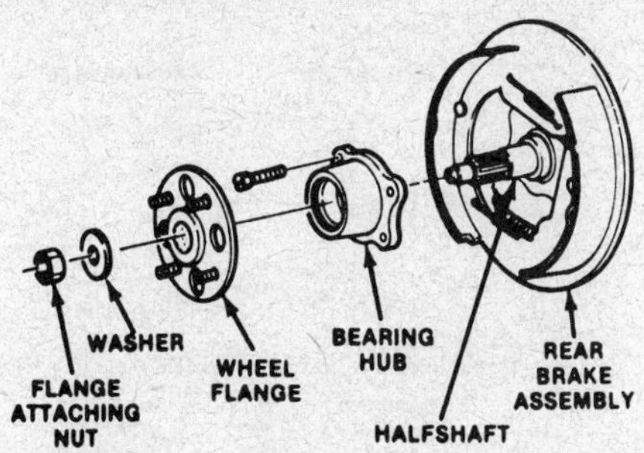


**Fig. 3 Removing wheel flange. XR4Ti**

4. Install attaching nut on shock absorber bolt, **torquing** nut to 30-37 ft. lbs., or bolt to 33-40 ft. lbs.
5. Install bushing attaching bolt and **torque** to 59-73 ft. lbs.
6. Install rear axle front crossmember guide plate-to-body attaching bolts and **torque** to 31-37 ft. lbs.
7. Secure brake line to floor assembly and body bracket.
8. Position brake hose through routing bracket on control arm and connect it to brake tube.
9. Install brake hose retaining clip.
10. Position halfshaft and install attaching bolts. **Torque** bolts to 28-31 ft. lbs.
11. Connect stabilizer bar link to control arm.
12. Bleed brake system.

### XR4Ti

#### Removal

1. Raise and support vehicle with rear wheels and suspension hanging free.
2. Remove bolts attaching halfshaft to wheel stub shaft, **Fig. 2.** To prevent damage to constant velocity joints, tie halfshaft to convenient underbody component.
3. Remove clip attaching rear brake hose to routing bracket on control arm.
4. Using line wrenches, disconnect brake tube from brake hose.
5. Remove cap from bottom of shock absorber.
6. Using jack, raise lower control arm enough to relieve coil spring tension from shock absorber.
7. Remove lower shock absorber attaching nut and bolt.
8. Slowly and carefully lower jack until it can be removed.
9. Support axle housing using jack.
10. Remove rear axle mount to body attaching bolts and disconnect axle vent tube.
11. Slowly and carefully lower jack until coil spring and its seat can be removed. Do not remove support from rear axle. Lower axle only enough to allow removal of coil spring.

#### Installation

1. Install spring upper seat on spring end with color code and plastic sleeve, ensuring that end of coil seats against step in spring seat and that seat tabs are positioned between first and second coil.
2. Install coil spring and seat assembly, then raise rear axle into position and install body mount attaching bolts. **Torque** two inner bolts to 37-41 ft. lbs. and four outer bolts to 37-50 ft. lbs. **The body mount bolts must be cleaned, and new Loctite applied.**
3. Remove axle support and position it under control arm, then raise jack until coil spring is compressed enough to allow installation of lower shock absorber attaching bolt.
4. Install attaching nut on shock absorber bolt, **torquing** nut to 30-37 ft. lbs., or bolt to 33-40 ft. lbs.
5. Remove control arm support and install shock absorber cap.
6. Position brake hose through routing bracket on control arm and connect it to brake tube.
7. Install brake hose retaining clip.
8. Position halfshaft and install attaching bolts, **torquing** bolts to 28-31 ft. lbs.
9. Connect axle vent hose located at top right hand corner of axle housing.
10. Ensure that stabilizer bar link is connected to control arm.
11. Bleed brake system.

## CONTROL ARM & BEARING HUB

## REPLACE

### SCORPIO

1. Remove coil spring as previously described.
2. Using screwdriver, open routing clamp and disengage parking brake cable from control arm.
3. Unfasten brake caliper and position aside, leaving brake line attached.
4. Remove stub shaft nut, then pull off wheel hub.
5. Working from under vehicle, pull wheel stub shaft out of control arm.
6. Remove control arm inner and outer attaching bolts and the control arm.
7. Reverse procedure to install, noting the following:
   a. When installing control arm attaching bolts, ensure bolt heads face inboard. Use blue bolts and nuts for outboard side and gold bolts and nuts for inboard side.
   b. With vehicle weight on tires, **torque** control arm attaching bolts to 63-74 ft. lbs.

### XR4Ti

1. Remove coil spring as previously described.
2. Using screwdriver, open routing clamp and disengage parking brake cable from control arm.
3. Disconnect sway stabilizer link from control arm.
4. Remove wheel flange attaching nut and washer, then wheel flange, **Fig. 3.**
5. Remove rear bearing hub and tie brake backing plate out of way.
6. Working from under vehicle, pull wheel stub shaft out of control arm.
7. Remove control arm inner and outer attaching bolts and the control arm.

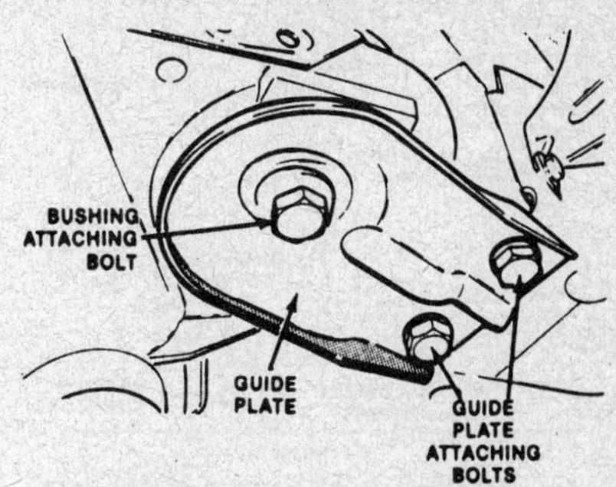


**Fig. 4 Location of crossmember bushing to body attaching bolt**

8. Reverse procedure to install, noting the following:
   a. When installing control arm attaching bolts, ensure bolt heads face inboard.
   b. With vehicle weight on tires, **torque** control arm attaching bolts to 63-74 ft. lbs.

## CONTROL ARM BUSHINGS

## REPLACE

### REMOVAL

1. Remove control arm as previously described.
2. Using drawbolt T78P-5638-A1, receiver cup T85M-5638-A2, a 7/16 inch 20 UNF hex nut and a 7/16 inch flat washer, or equivalents, remove larger control arm bushing.
3. Using drawbolt T78P-5638-A1, receiver cup T85M-5638-A1, a 7/16 inch 20 UNF nut and a 7/16 inch flat washer, or equivalents, remove smaller control arm bushing.

### INSTALLATION

1. Lubricate bushings with non petroleum lubricant.
2. Using drawbolt T78P-5638-A1, replacer cup T85M-5638-A3, a 7/16 inch 20 UNF nut and a 7/16 inch flat washer, or equivalents install new larger control arm bushing.
3. Using drawbolt T78P-5638-A1, replacer cup T78P-5638-A3, a 7/16 inch 20 UNF nut and a 7/16 inch flat washer, or equivalents, install new smaller control arm bushing.

## REAR CROSSMEMBER BUSHING

## REPLACE

### REMOVAL

1. Raise and support vehicle with suspension and tires hanging free.
2. Position jack under control arm and raise enough to support control arm against downward pressure of coil spring. **Ensure control arm is securely supported before removing bushing to body attaching bolt.**

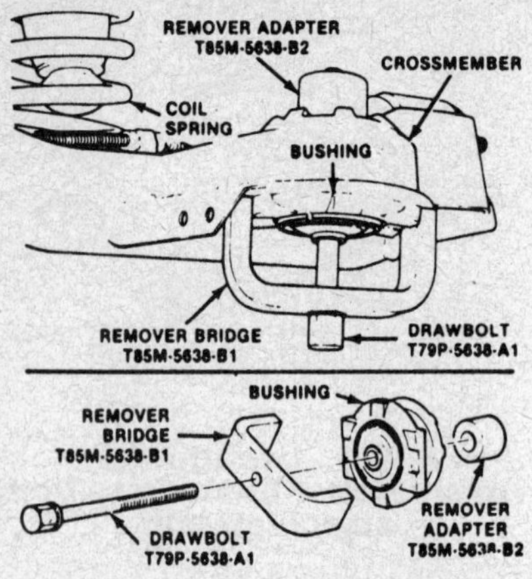


**Fig. 5 Removing crossmember bushing**

3. Remove crossmember bushing to body attaching bolt, **Fig. 4.**
4. Remove bushing guide plate attaching bolts and the guide plate.
5. Carefully lower crossmember to provide clearance for bushing removal and installation tools.
6. Remove crossmember bushing, **Fig. 5.**

## INSTALLATION

1. Lubricate replacement bushing with non-petroleum lubricant.
2. Install crossmember bushing, **Fig. 6.**
3. Carefully raise crossmember into position.
4. Position bushing guide plate and install attaching bolts, **torquing** to 30-37 ft. lbs.
5. Install bushing to body attaching bolt and washer, **torquing** bolt to 59-74 ft. lbs.

# REAR AXLE & SUSPENSION ASSEMBLY

## REPLACE

### REMOVAL

1. Remove coil springs, driveshaft and muffler and silencer assembly.
2. Remove nylon lockpin, if equipped, then loosen parking brake adjuster sleeve locknut, then thread adjuster sleeve away from body routing bracket.
3. Remove clip and clevis pin attaching parking brake cable equalizer to parking brake lever rod.
4. Disengage parking brake cable from body routing brackets.
5. Remove stabilizer bar U-brackets.
6. Position jack under rear axle and secure crossmember to jack.
7. Remove crossmember bushing attaching bolt on both sides of vehicle.
8. Remove crossmember bushing guide plate attaching bolts and the guide plate on both sides of vehicle.
9. Remove bolts attaching axle mount to body, then carefully lower crossmember out of vehicle.

### INSTALLATION

1. Raise crossmember into position on vehicle.
2. Install but do not tighten axle mount attaching bolts.
3. Position crossmember insulator guide plates and install attaching bolts.
4. Install crossmember bushing attaching bolts and washers, **torquing** guide plate attaching bolts to 30-38 ft. lbs. and the crossmember bushing attaching bolts to 59-74 ft. lbs.
5. **On Scorpio models, torque** four axle mount attaching bolts to 37-49 ft. lbs. On XR4Ti models, **torque** two inner axle mount attaching bolts to 37-41 ft. lbs. and four outer bolts to 37-50 ft. lbs.
6. **On all models,** route parking brake cable through body brackets, then position parking brake equalizer and install clevis pin and retaining clip.
7. Install stabilizer bar U-brackets, **torquing** attaching bolts to 15-18 ft. lbs.
8. Install muffler and silencer assembly, driveshaft and coil springs.
9. Bleed rear brake system and adjust parking brake.

# STABILIZER BAR

## REPLACE

1. Loosen wheel lug nuts, then raise and support rear of vehicle and remove wheel.
2. Disconnect stabilizer bar links from lower control arm using screwdriver.
3. Place a piece of tape on stabilizer bar next to U-bracket and insulator for proper alignment during installation.
4. Remove U-brackets to body attaching bolts, then disengage U-brackets and remove stabilizer bar.
5. Reverse procedure to install, **torquing** U-brackets to body attaching bolts to 15-18 ft. lbs.

# REAR AXLE

## REPLACE

### SCORPIO

#### Removal

1. Raise and support vehicle.
2. Unfasten tail pipe from rear insulator.
3. Disconnect driveshaft from drive flange and center bearing from floor assembly. Retain spacer washers for reuse.
4. Remove driveshaft from transmission extension housing and rest it on exhaust system. Plug transmission opening to prevent leakage.
5. Disconnect and suspend both rear axle shafts from inner driveshaft flanges.
6. Disconnect left side stabilizer bar bracket from floor crossmember to gain access to rear mounting bolts.
7. Support rear axle assembly with a jack and remove four attaching bolts from floor crossmember.

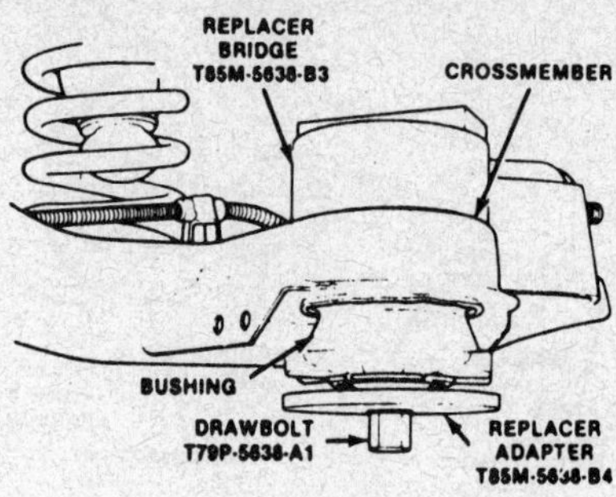


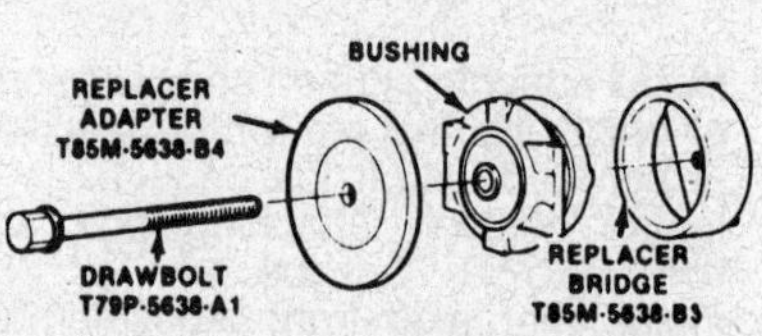


**Fig. 6 Installing crossmember bushing**

8. Lower rear axle assembly, then remove two rear body mount-to-axle cover attaching bolts.
9. Remove front end axle housing to crossmember attaching bolts and shims, if equipped.
10. Remove axle housing to crossmember through bolt and nut.
11. Lower axle and remove from vehicle.
12. Remove rear mount attaching bolts and the mount.

#### Installation

1. If axle case, axle assembly or suspension crossmember is replaced, check flange clearance as follows:
   a. Install rear mount on axle housing rear cover, **torquing** attaching bolts to 37-41 ft. lbs.
   b. Lift assembly into position between crossmember flanges.
   c. Install through bolt and four axle bolts to crossmember attaching bolts but do not tighten bolts.
   d. Position axle housing rear mount against body and secure with four bolts, **torquing** bolts to 14-18 ft. lbs.
   e. **Torque** front lower attaching bolt to 51-66 ft. lbs.
   f. **Torque** through bolt to 51-66 ft. lbs.
   g. Using feeler gauge, check clearance between crossmember flanges and the rear axle mounting boss, **Fig. 7.**
   h. Select appropriate shims to be installed between crossmember and axle.
2. Install shims, if required, and **torque** attaching bolts to 51-66 ft. lbs.
3. Install stabilizer bar bracket bolt and **torque** to 15-18 ft. lbs.
4. Connect axle halfshafts to stub shaft flanges and install attaching bolts, **torquing** to 28-32 ft. lbs.
5. Remove plug from transmission, then guide splined end of driveshaft into extension housing.

6. Loosely attach center bearing housing to floor assembly, then secure driveshaft to flange and **torque** attaching bolts to 42-55 ft. lbs.
7. Attach tail pipe to rear insulator.
8. Check rear axle oil level, then lower vehicle.

## XR4Ti

### Removal

1. Disconnect axle halfshafts from stub shaft flanges on each side of housing. Before releasing halfshafts, support them from body floor in approximately their normal position.
2. Remove driveshaft, then support rear axle housing with jack and remove rear body mount attaching bolts.
3. Remove four bolts and two shims, if equipped, attaching front end of axle housing to crossmember brackets, then remove nut and through bolt attaching axle housing to crossmember.
4. Lower axle housing clear of rear suspension and remove it, then remove rear mount.

### Installation

1. If axle case, axle assembly or suspension crossmember is replaced, check flange clearance as follows:
   a. Install rear mount on axle housing rear cover, **torquing** attaching bolts to 37-41 ft. lbs.
   b. Lift assembly into position between crossmember flanges.
   c. Install through bolt and four axle bolts to crossmember attaching bolts but do not tighten bolts.

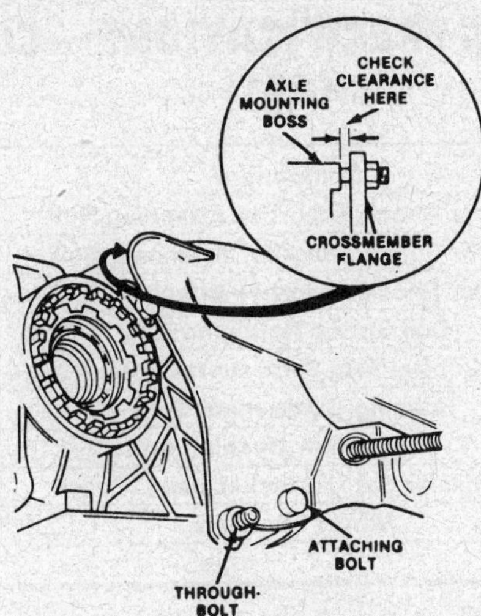


**Fig. 7 Checking mounting flange clearance**

   d. Position axle housing rear mount against body and secure with four bolts, **torquing** bolts to 14-18 ft. lbs.
   e. **Torque** front lower attaching bolt to 51-66 ft. lbs.
   f. **Torque** through bolt to 51-66 ft. lbs.
   g. Using feeler gauge, check clearance between crossmember flanges and the rear axle mounting boss, **Fig. 7.**
   h. Select appropriate shims to be installed between crossmember and axle.
2. Install shims, if required, and **torque** attaching bolts to 51-66 ft. lbs.
3. Install driveshaft.
4. Connect axle halfshafts to stub shaft flanges and install attaching bolts, **torquing** bolts to 28-31 ft. lbs.

# HALFSHAFTS

## REPLACE

### REMOVAL

1. Ensure that transmission is in neutral and parking brake is fully released.
2. Raise and support rear of vehicle with rear wheels hanging free.
3. Remove bolts attaching halfshaft to wheel stub shaft, turning driveshaft as necessary to bring bolts into accessible position.
4. **On Scorpio models,** position halfshaft in grooved area of the rear suspension control arm.
5. **On XR4Ti models,** hang halfshaft from floor of vehicle.
6. **On all models,** remove bolts attaching halfshaft to rear axle stub shaft and remove halfshaft.

### INSTALLATION

**Halfshafts are different lengths and must be installed on the correct side of vehicle, with longer shaft being installed on right side of vehicle.**

1. Pack CV joints with lubricant.
2. **On Scorpio models,** position halfshaft in grooved area of the rear suspension control arm.
3. **On XR4Ti models,** hang halfshaft from floor of vehicle.
4. **On all models,** position halfshaft to axle stub shaft and install attaching bolts.
5. Release halfshaft from vehicle floor and position it to axle stub shaft, installing attaching bolts.
6. **Torque** attaching bolts to 28-31 ft. lbs.

# TIGHTENING SPECIFICATIONS

## SCORPIO

| Year | Component | Torque/Ft. lbs. |
|---|---|---|
| 1989 | Axle Mounting Bolts | 22-25 |
| | Upper Shock Absorber Attaching Nut | 30-36 |
| | Lower Shock Absorber Attaching Bolt | 33-40 |
| | Lower Shock Absorber Attaching Nut | 30-36 |
| | Halfshaft Attaching Bolts | 28-31 |
| | Control Arm Attaching Nuts | 63-73 |
| | Bushing Guide Plate Attaching Bolts | 31-37 |
| | Bushing To Body Attaching Bolt | 59-73 |
| | Crossmember Bushing Attaching Bolts | 59-73 |
| | Stabilizer Bar O-Bracket Bolts | 15-18 |
| | Rubber Axle Casting Mounting | 15-18 |
| | Wheel Lug Nuts | 75-101 |

*Continued*

## TIGHTENING SPECIFICATIONS—Continued

### XR4Ti

| Year | Component | Torque/Ft. lbs. |
|---|---|---|
| 1989 | Lower Shock Absorber Attaching Nut | 33-40 |
| | Lower Shock Absorber Attaching Bolt | 30-37 |
| | Upper Shock Absorber Attaching Nut | 30-37 |
| | Coil Spring Retaining Nut | 38-48 |
| | Control Arm Pivot Bolts (Rear) | 63-74 |
| | Bushing Guide Plate Bolts | 30-38 |
| | Crossmember Bushing Bolts | 59-74 |
| | Stabilizer Bar U-Bracket Bolts (Rear) | 14-19 |
| | Wheel Lug Nuts | 75-101 |

# Front Suspension & Steering

## INDEX



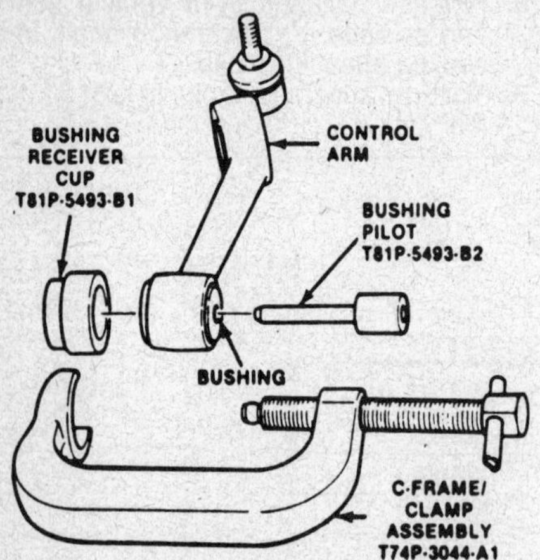


**Fig. 1 Removing control arm bushings**

## CONTROL ARM AND/OR STABILIZER BAR BUSHINGS REPLACE

### SCORPIO

#### Removal

1. Remove pivot bolt, nut and washer securing control arm to crossmember.
2. Remove stabilizer bar-to-control arm attaching nut.

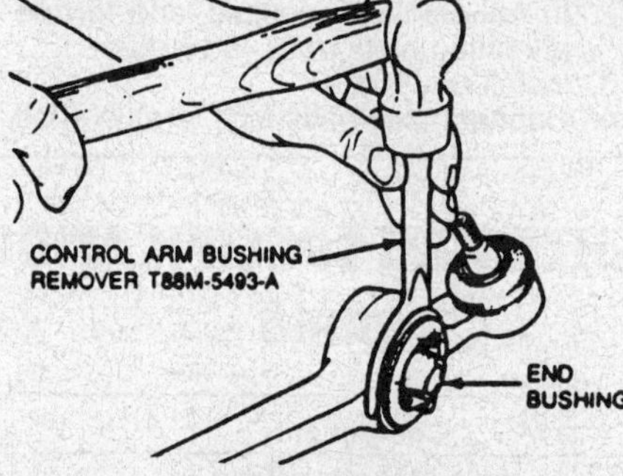


**Fig. 2 Stabilizer bar bushing removal. Scorpio**

3. Remove front washer and cover from end of stabilizer bar.
4. Raise and support vehicle.
5. Remove and discard cotter pin and nut from control arm ball joint, then lower control arm from vehicle.
6. Remove control arm and stabilizer bar bushings, **Figs. 1 and 2.**

#### Installation

1. Install control arm bushing as follows:
   a. Apply rubber lubricant to control arm bore and outer surface of bushing.
   b. Install bushing using tools shown in **Fig. 3.** Install bushing with a quick, continuous motion to avoid damage.
2. Install stabilizer bar bushing as follows:

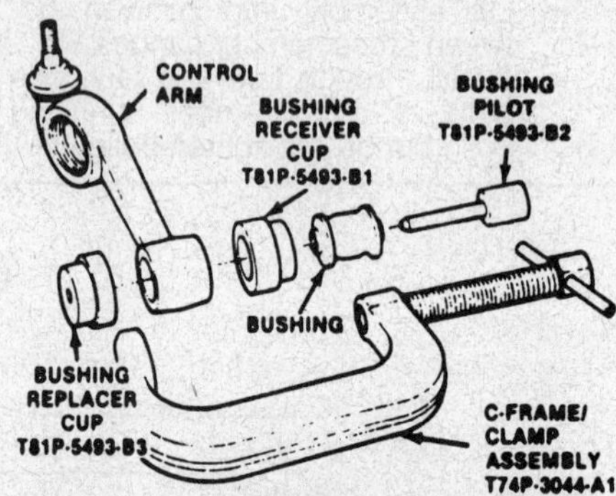


**Fig. 3 Installing control arm bushings**

   a. Secure control arm in a vise.
   b. Install one bushing using tool No. T88M-5493-B or equivalent, then tighten screw to seat bushing.
   c. Invert control arm and install second bushing.
3. Slide control arm onto stabilizer bar, ensuring rear washer is properly positioned on stabilizer.
4. Install front washer cover and the stabilizer bar-to-control arm attaching nut. Do not tighten nut at this time.
5. Install ball joint into spindle carrier. **Torque** nut to 48-62 ft. lbs., then install new cotter pin.
6. Pull bottom of tire inward until control arm enters crossmember and aligns with bolt holes. Secure arm in this position using a drift punch.
7. Install control arm pivot bolt, washer

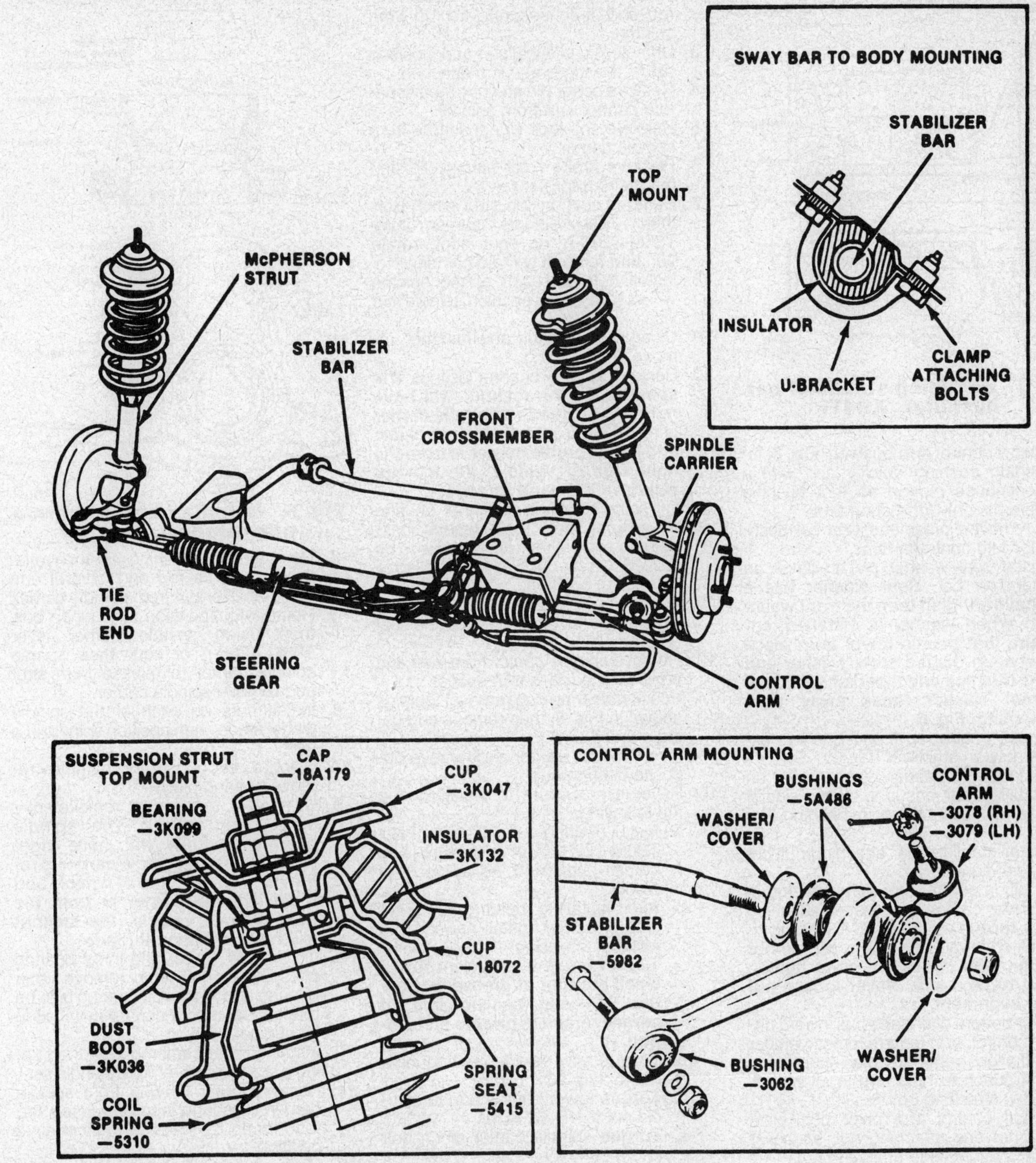

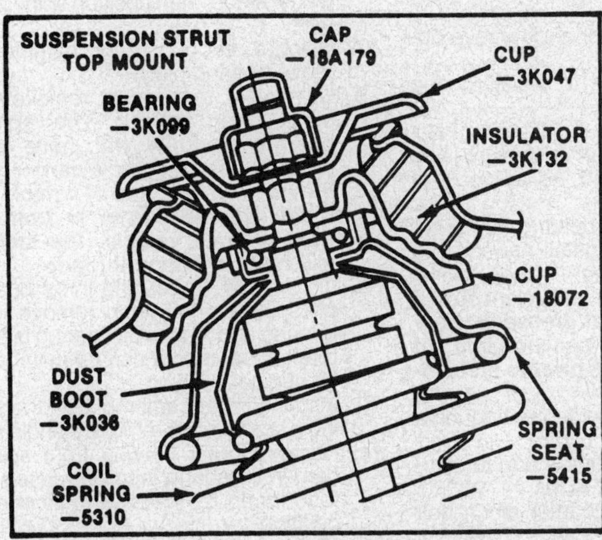


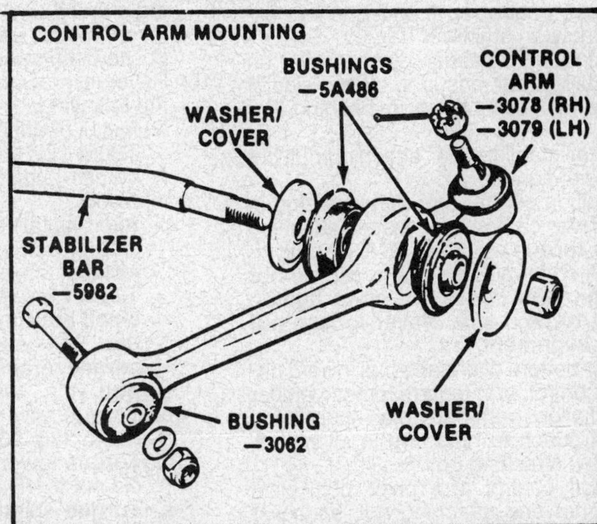


**Fig. 4 Front suspension. XR4Ti**

and attaching nut. Snug nut but do not tighten at this time.

8. Lower vehicle, then **torque** control arm pivot bolt to 22 ft. lbs.
9. **Torque** stabilizer bar-to-control arm attaching nut to 52-81 ft. lbs.

## XR4Ti

### Removal

1. Remove cotter pin and attaching nut and separate control arm from spindle carrier. **With spindle carrier and control arm disconnected, the spindle carrier can easily cause damage to control arm ball joint boot.**
2. Remove pivot bolt attaching control arm to crossmember.
3. Remove stabilizer bar to control arm attaching nut, **Fig. 4.**
4. Remove front washer/plastic cover from end of stabilizer bar.
5. Remove control arm and bushings as an assembly.
6. Remove rear washer/plastic cover from end of stabilizer bar.
7. Remove bushings from control arm as necessary, **Fig. 1.**

### Installation

**Stabilizer bar bushings are designed to allow control arm to move backward and forward somewhat.**

1. Coat control arm bore and outer surface of bushing with non-petroleum lubricant.

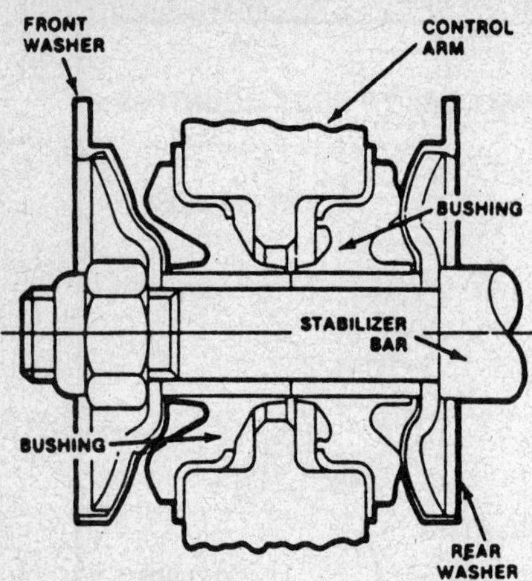


**Fig. 5 Installing stabilizer bar bushings. XR4Ti**

2. Install control arm bushing, **Fig. 3,** inserting bushing quickly and with a continuous motion so that bushing deforms only for a short time.
3. If removed, press stabilizer bar bushings into control arm.
4. Install rear washer/plastic cover on stabilizer bar. **Rear washer has a shallower dish than the front washer. When washer is installed, ensure that plastic cover is in place between dished steel washer and the bushing and that dished side of steel washer faces away from bushing, Fig. 5.**
5. Install control arm and bushing assembly on stabilizer bar.
6. Install front washer/plastic cover on stabilizer bar, ensuring dished side of washer faces away from bushing, **Fig. 5.**
7. Install stabilizer bar attaching nut, but do not tighten.
8. Position control arm ball joint stud in spindle carrier and install attaching nut, **torque** nut to 48-65 ft. lbs. and install cotter pin. **If slots in nut do not align with cotter pin hole, tighten nut to next slot. Never loosen nut for alignment.**
9. Grip bottom of tire and pull inward until control arm enters crossmember and aligns with bolt holes, then, using drift punch to hold arm in alignment, install attaching bolt.
10. Install control arm pivot bolt, plain washer and attaching nut, snugging but not tightening attaching nut.
11. Lower vehicle.
12. With vehicle weight on tires, **torque** control arm pivot bolt nut to 11 ft. lbs. then additional 90°, and the stabilizer bar attaching nut to 52-81 ft. lbs.

## HUB, ROTOR & BEARING REPLACE

### SCORPIO

1. Raise and support vehicle, then remove wheel and tire assembly.
2. Remove cotter pin and nut from tie rod end, then separate tie rod from spindle.
3. Unfasten brake caliper and position aside, leaving brake line attached.
4. Remove cotter pin and nut, then separate control arm from spindle.
5. Remove anti-lock wheel sensor from spindle carrier.
6. Remove brake rotor spring clip and the brake rotor.
7. Remove suspension strut pinch bolt, then using spindle carrier lever T85M-3206-A or equivalent, rotate 90° and remove spindle carrier.
8. Install nuts on each of the spindle wheel studs, then position spindle in a vise.
9. Using a drift punch and hammer, remove bearing plug.
10. Remove spindle bearing locknut. **The spindle bearing locknut will have right hand threads if spindle carrier is removed from left side of vehicle and if the spindle carrier is from the right side of vehicle, the locknut will have left hand threads.**
11. Lift spindle carrier and inner bearing off spindle shaft, then remove inner bearing and washer. If bearing is to be reused, tag it so it can be installed in its original position.
12. Install spindle carrier in vise, then using a screwdriver remove spindle seal and remaining bearing.
13. Remove spindle carrier from vise and position in a press with spacer.
14. Position bearing cup removal tools as shown in **Fig. 6,** then remove cup using a press.
15. Invert spindle carrier and remove opposite bearing cup.
16. Reverse procedure to install, noting the following:
    a. Install bearing cups using tool No. T88M-1225-C or equivalent with carrier supported by a block of wood.
    b. After installing bearing on outer side of carrier, install new grease retainer using tool No. T88M-1249-A or equivalent. **Add a small amount of grease to cavities between sealing lips of grease retainers prior to installation.**
    c. **Torque** new spindle bearing locknut to 288-331 ft. lbs.
    d. **Torque** lower control arm to spindle nut to 48-62 ft. lbs.
    e. **Torque** spindle carrier pinch bolt to 59-66 ft. lbs.
    f. **Torque** tie rod end nut to 15-23 ft. lbs.

### XR4Ti

**The hub and rotor are a matched and balanced assembly. Before removing rotor locate the paint mark or etch mark that indicates proper hub to rotor alignment. If marks are not present, mark hub and rotor for assembly alignment.**

1. Raise and support vehicle, then remove wheel and tire assembly.
2. Remove anchor plate plate attaching bolts, then lift caliper and anchor plate assembly off rotor and tie out of way.

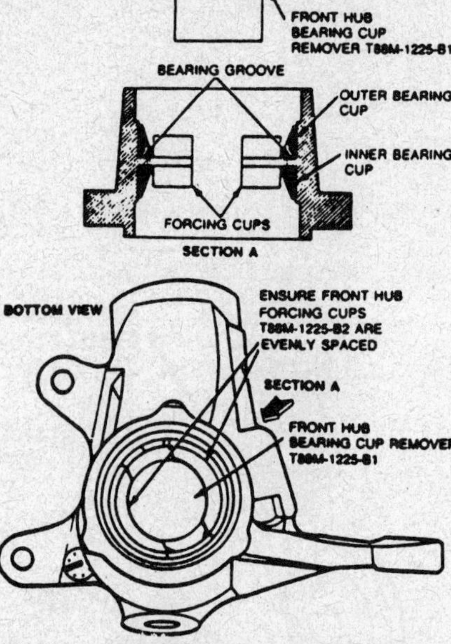


**Fig. 6 Spindle carrier bearing cup removal. Scorpio**

3. Remove rotor retaining clip, then rotor.
4. Disconnect tie rod end, control arm and stabilizer bar from spindle carrier.
5. Remove suspension strut pinch bolt, then using spindle carrier lever T85M-3206-A or equivalent, spread spindle carrier to release from strut and remove spindle carrier.
6. Install nuts on each of the spindle wheel studs, then position spindle in a vise.
7. Using a drift punch and hammer, remove bearing plug.
8. Using a 41 mm socket, remove spindle bearing locknut. **The spindle bearing locknut will have right hand threads if spindle carrier is removed from left side of vehicle and if the spindle carrier is from the right side of vehicle, the locknut will have left hand threads.**
9. Lift spindle carrier and inner bearing off spindle shaft, then remove inner bearing and washer. If bearing is to be reused, tag it so it can be installed in its original position.
10. Install spindle carrier in vise, then using a screwdriver remove spindle seal.
11. Remove outer bearing from spindle carrier. If bearing is to be reused, tag it so it can be installed in its original position.
12. Reverse procedure to install, noting the following:
    a. Install spindle bearing locknut and **torque** to 229-250 ft. lbs.
    b. **Torque** tie rod end ball joints to 18-22 ft. lbs.
    c. **Torque** strut pinch bolt to 59-66 ft. lbs.
    d. **Torque** anchor plate to spindle carrier attaching bolts to 43-44 ft. lbs.
    e. **Torque** control ball joint stud in spindle carrier to 48-63 ft. lbs.
    f. **Torque** stabilizer bar attaching nut to 52-81 ft. lbs. and control arm pivot bolt nut to 11 ft. lbs.

13. If rotor has been removed without alignment marks, proceed as follows:
    a. Install rotor on hub, then wheel lug nuts.
    b. Using a dial indicator and a holding fixture, measure rotor runout. The indicator stylus should contact the rotor approximately 7/16 inch from the end.
    c. Rotate hub and disc assembly and record dial indicator reading.
    d. If indicator reading is .003 inch or less, this positioning of rotor may be used during assembly.
    e. If indicator reading is greater than .003 inch, reposition rotor on hub in 90° increments until lowest reading is obtained.
    f. When a reading of no more than .003 inch is obtained, mark alignment of hub and rotor.

# STABILIZER BAR

## REPLACE

### SCORPIO

#### Removal

1. Remove four bolts securing two U-brackets to chassis.
2. Raise and support vehicle.
3. Remove attaching nuts and front washers/covers from ends of stabilizer bar.
4. Remove one control arm pivot bolt and pull control arm out of crossmember.
5. Pull stabilizer out of lower control arms and remove from vehicle.
6. Remove rear washers/covers from stabilizer bar.
7. Remove insulators from stabilizer bar. It may be necessary to pry insulators slightly open. **Do not pry any more than necessary to avoid damaging the integral metal sleeve.**

#### Installation

1. Apply rubber lubricant to stabilizer bar, then install stabilizer bar insulators with split facing forward.
2. Install rear washers/covers onto stabilizer bar.
3. Position stabilizer bar through control arms, then install front washers/covers and attaching nuts. Do not tighten nuts at this time.
4. Install lower control arm to crossmember, then lower vehicle. Do not tighten pivot bolt at this time.
5. Attach stabilizer bar to chassis. Install U-brackets and **torque** attaching bolts to 52-66 ft. lbs.
6. With vehicle weight on tires, **torque** control arm pivot bolt to 22 ft. lbs. plus an additional 90°.
7. **Torque** stabilizer bar-to-control arm attaching nuts to 52-81 ft. lbs.

### XR4Ti

#### Removal

1. Remove attaching nuts and front washers/covers from ends of stabilizer bar.

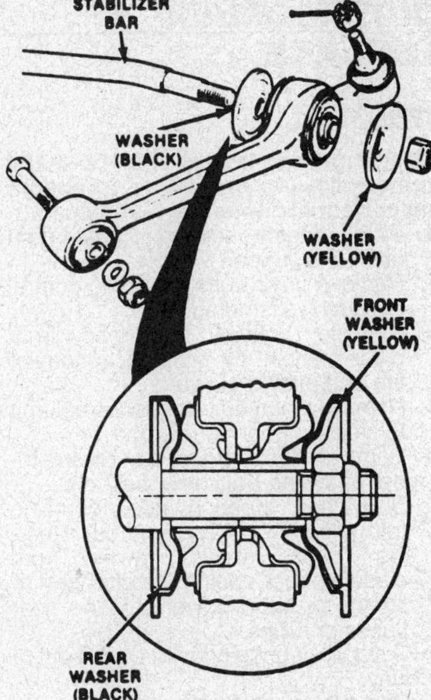


**Fig. 7 Installing stabilizer bar. XR4Ti**

2. Remove four bolts securing two U-brackets and torque brace to body.
3. Remove one control arm pivot bolt and pull control arm out of crossmember.
4. Pull stabilizer out of lower control arms and remove from vehicle.
5. Remove rear washers/covers from stabilizer bar.
6. Remove insulators from stabilizer bar.

#### Installation

1. Coat inside of stabilizer bar bushings and bushing surfaces on stabilizer bar with non-petroleum lubricant, then install body insulators on stabilizer bar.
2. Install rear washers/plastic covers on stabilizer bar. **Rear washer has a shallower dish than front washer. When washer is installed, ensure plastic cover is in place between dished steel washer and the bushing and that dished side of steel washer faces away from bushing, Fig. 7.**
3. Install stabilizer bar into control arms bushings and install control arm into crossmember with pivot bolt, washer and nut, snugging but not tightening attaching nut.
4. Install U-brackets on insulators and install attaching bolts, **torquing** to 42-52 ft. lbs.
5. Install front washers/plastic covers on stabilizer bar. **Ensure dished side of steel washer faces away from bushing, with plastic cover in place between bushing and steel washer.**
6. Install stabilizer bar attaching nuts, snugging but not tightening.
7. Lower vehicle.
8. With vehicle weight on tires, **torque** stabilizer bar attaching nut to 52-81 ft. lbs. and the control arm pivot bolt nut to 11 ft. lbs. plus an additional 90°.

# STRUT

## REPLACE

### SCORPIO

#### Removal

1. Disconnect battery ground cable.
2. Raise and support vehicle.
3. Remove wheel and tire assembly, then unfasten brake caliper assembly and position aside, leaving brake line attached.
4. Remove wheel sensor from spindle carrier.
5. Remove cotter pin and nut, then separate tie rod end from spindle.
6. Remove control arm as previously described.
7. Using a pry bar, pry down on control arm and stabilizer bar and pull strut clear of control arm.
8. Remove brake pad sensor wiring from strut clip.
9. Remove dust cap from top strut mount.
10. Support strut and spindle carrier assembly, then remove three upper locknuts and washers and lower strut assembly and top mount from inner fender.
11. Remove suspension strut pinch bolt, then using spindle carrier lever T85M-3206-A or equivalent, rotate 90° and remove spindle carrier.
12. Remove strut assembly from vehicle.

#### Installation

1. Position spindle carrier lever T85M-3206-A or equivalent into spindle carrier slot and rotate 90°. Slide spindle carrier assembly over strut, then install new pinch bolt and **torque** to 59-66 ft. lbs.
2. Position strut assembly into inner fender, then install washers and locknuts. **Torque** locknuts to 15-17 ft. lbs.
3. Install control arm into spindle carrier, **torquing** nut to 48-62 ft. lbs.
4. Attach tie rod end to spindle carrier. **Torque** nut to 19-22 ft. lbs., then install cotter pin.
5. Secure brake pad sensor wiring into strut clip.
6. Install wheel sensor and caliper assembly.
7. Install wheel and tire assembly, then lower vehicle.
8. Install top mount dust cap, then connect battery ground cable.

### XR4Ti

#### Removal

**If twin post hoist is used to perform this procedure, front of vehicle must be supported on safety stands to allow lowering of front post. If front post is not lowered, the lower control may contact lift and prevent removal of strut.**

1. Remove wheel and raise and support vehicle.

2. Remove strut pinch bolt from spindle carrier.
3. Insert spindle carrier lever T85M-3206-A or equivalent into slot in spindle carrier and rotate it through 90° to open slot.
4. Push downward on brake rotor to disengage spindle carrier from strut. **When releasing spindle carrier from strut, be careful not to damage brake hose. Place jack under control arm bushing boss to keep being pushed down too far.**
5. Remove cap from top mount attaching nut.
6. Hold piston shaft with 6 mm Allen wrench and loosen top mount attaching nut.
7. Support strut from below and remove top mount nut, retainer and strut, discarding nut.

### Installation

1. Position strut through top mount insulation and install retainer and a new top mount attaching nut but do not tighten nut.
2. Position strut in spindle by pulling outward on strut and lifting spindle using brake rotor. Use spindle carrier lever or equivalent to spread spindle carrier to allow strut to center correctly. When strut enters spindle, grip rotor and pivot spindle into position. **If strut is not pulled outward to match spindle angle, it will jam as the spindle is pivoted into position.**
3. Install strut pinch bolt, **torquing** to 59-66 ft. lbs.
4. Ensure top of strut is centered in suspension tower and **torque** top mount attaching nut to 29-38 ft. lbs., holding piston shaft as necessary with 6 mm Allen wrench.
5. Install cap on top mount attaching nut and install wheel.

# TOP MOUNT INSULATOR REPLACE

## XR4Ti

1. Remove cap from top mount attaching nut.
2. Hold piston shaft with 6 mm Allen wrench and remove and discard top mount attaching nut.
3. Remove retainer from piston shaft.
4. Using pry bar, force suspension assembly downward, being careful not to stretch brake hose.
5. Remove top mount insulator.
6. Reverse procedure to install, noting the following:
   a. Ensure top of strut is centered in suspension tower before installing retainer and attaching nut.
   b. **Torque** new top mount attaching nut to 29-38 ft. lbs., holding piston shaft with 6 mm Allen wrench as necessary.

# CROSSMEMBER REPLACE

## REMOVAL

**Steering must be set straight ahead during following procedure to ensure that correct alignment is maintained.**

1. Install engine support fixture, then raise and support vehicle.
2. Remove pivot bolts attaching control arms to crossmember.
3. Remove control arm end from crossmember by gripping bottom of tire and pulling outward.
4. Remove pinch bolt at steering column to steering gear coupling.
5. Remove steering gear to crossmember attaching bolts and washers.
6. Disengage steering gear coupling from steering column and pull steering gear forward away from crossmember, being careful not to stretch or bend power steering gear hoses or tubes.
7. Support steering gear by tying it out of way.
8. Remove engine mounts to crossmember attaching stud nuts.
9. **On Scorpio models,** remove brake line clips from crossmember and carefully slide brake lines out from locator slots.
10. **On all models,** position jack under crossmember and secure with safety chain.
11. Remove crossmember to side rail attaching bolts and washers.
12. Lower crossmember and remove from under vehicle.

## INSTALLATION

1. Raise crossmember into position and install crossmember to side rail attaching bolts and washers.
2. **Torque** attaching bolts to 51-66 ft. lbs. and remove jack.
3. Position steering gear on crossmember and connect coupling to steering column, ensuring that block splines are properly mated.
4. Install steering gear attaching bolts and washers, snugging bolt to 11 ft. lbs. plus an additional 90°.
5. Install steering coupling pinch bolt, **torquing** to 15-22 ft. lbs. on Scorpio models, or 18-22 ft. lbs. on XR4Ti models.
6. Install engine mount attaching bolts, **torquing** to 31-42 ft. lbs. on Scorpio models, or 38-47 ft. lbs. on XR4Ti models.
7. Grip bottom of tire and pull inward until control arm enters crossmember, aligning control arm with bolt holes and install pivot bolt. Use drift punch to hold control arm in alignment while pivot bolt is installed.
8. Install pivot bolt and washer, snugging but not tightening bolt.
9. Lower vehicle.
10. With weight of vehicle on front tires, **torque** control arm pivot bolt to 22 ft. lbs. on Scorpio models, or 11 ft. lbs. on XR4Ti models, plus an additional 90° on all models.
11. Remove engine support fixture.

# STRUT SERVICE

## SCORPIO

### Disassembly

1. Clamp strut spring compressor 086-00029 or equivalent in a vise and adjust tool to Start position following manufacturer's instructions.
2. Position strut assembly in tool and carefully compress spring.
3. Hold piston rod with a 6 mm Allen wrench and remove coil spring locknut and retainer, **Fig. 8.**
4. Remove top mount, bearing and spring seat, then the spring and spring compressor.
5. Remove dust boot and stop bumper from piston.

### Assembly

1. Position stop bumper and dust boot over piston.
2. Ensure both springs are free of dirt and grease, then position compressed spring onto strut lower spring seat.
3. Install upper spring seat, bearing, top mount and retainer. Ensure bearing is installed with small hole facing up.
4. Hold piston rod with a 6 mm Allen wrench, then install locknut and **torque** to 29-38 ft. lbs.
5. Carefully release strut spring compressor.
6. Ensure bearing is properly positioned in upper spring seat and spring is properly positioned in both seats, then remove assembly from spring compressor.

## XR4Ti

### Disassembly

1. Clamp strut spring compressor 086-00016 or equivalent in a vise and adjust tool to Start position following tool manufacturer's instructions.
2. Using tool, carefully compress coil spring.
3. Hold piston shaft with a 6 mm Allen wrench and remove coil spring retaining nut.
4. Release coil spring tension.
5. Remove top mount cup, bearing, upper spring seat and dust boot, **Fig. 9.**
6. Slide jounce bumper off piston shaft and remove coil spring.

### Assembly

1. Install coil spring, then jounce bumper, dust boot, upper spring seat, bearing and top mount cup.
2. Compress spring using spring compressor.
3. Install coil spring retaining nut, **torquing** to 38-48 ft. lbs., holding piston shaft with 6 mm Allen wrench as necessary.
4. Release coil spring tension and remove strut from spring compressor.

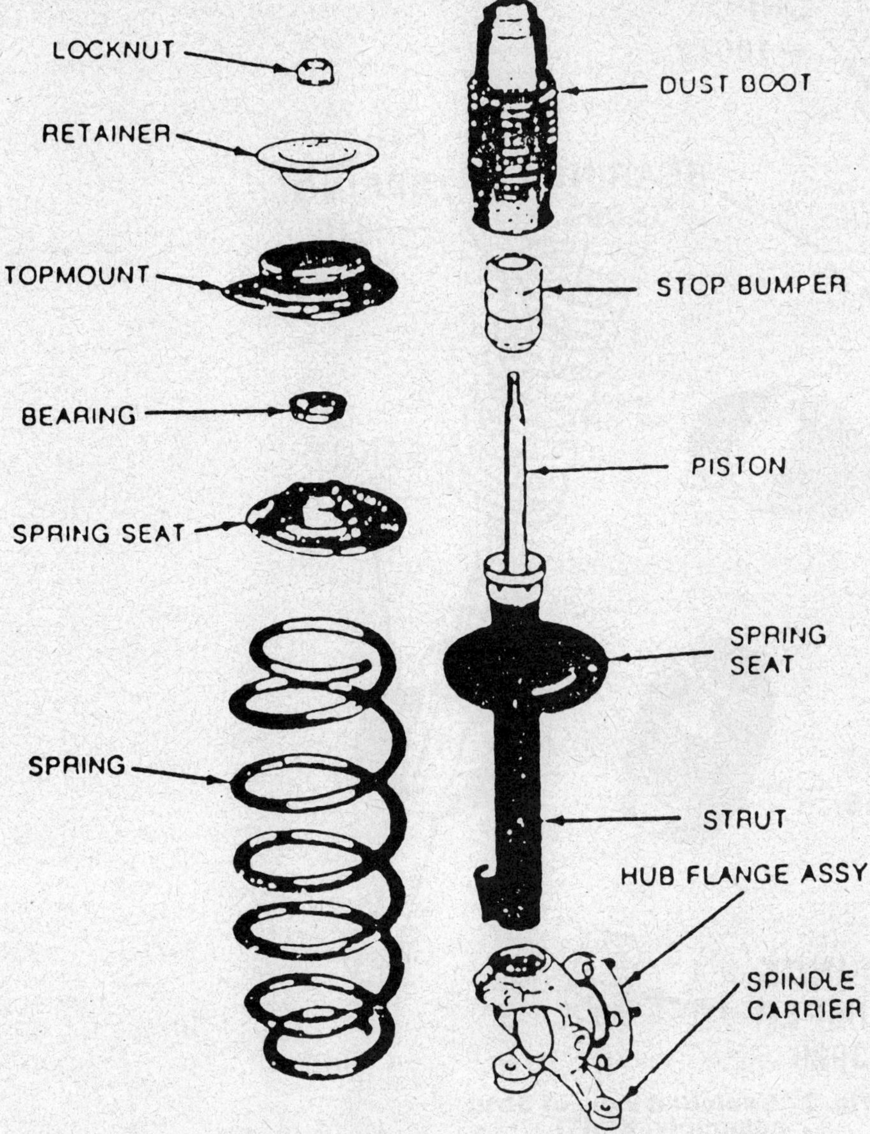


**Fig. 8 Exploded view of Strut assembly. Scorpio**

## POWER STEERING GEAR REPLACE

Scorpio models are equipped with a ZF power steering gear. XR4Ti models may be equipped with either a TRW or ZF steering gear.

### TRW GEAR

#### Removal

1. Disconnect battery ground cable, then turn ignition key to On position.
2. Remove cotter pins and nuts attaching tie rod ends to spindle carriers.
3. Separate tie rod ends from spindle carriers.
4. Remove pinch bolt from flexible coupling, rotating coupling as necessary to gain access to pinch bolt.
5. Position drain pan and disconnect power steering hoses from steering gear by removing routing clamp and the washer-head screw securing pump line plate assembly to gear housing and pulling assembly free. Plug housing port to prevent entry of foreign matter.
6. Remove steering gear mounting bolts and the gear.

#### Installation

1. Center steering wheel and turn ignition key to Off position.
2. Center steering gear as follows:
   a. Turn steering gear input shaft clockwise to full left turn stop.
   b. Turn input shaft counterclockwise and count number of turns required to move rack from full left turn stop to full right turn stop.
   c. From right turn stop, turn input shaft clockwise exactly 1/2 the turns previously counted.
3. Position steering gear on crossmember, engaging flexible coupling with input shaft, rocking coupling as necessary to align blind splines on shaft and coupling.
4. Turn ignition key to On position, then turn steering column as necessary to align blind splines on coupling and the steering shaft.
5. Connect steering gear to steering column and position on crossmember.
6. Install steering coupling pin bolt, **torquing** to 18-22 ft. lbs.
7. Plug pump line assembly into steering gear supply and return ports and secure line plate with washer-head screw and routing clamp.
8. Install new steering gear mounting bolts and **torque** to approximately 11 ft. lbs. plus an additional 90°.
9. Connect tie rods to spindle carriers and install castle nuts, **torque** nuts to 15-23 ft. lbs. and install new cotter pins. **If slots in nut do not align with cotter pin holes, tighten nut to next slot. Never loosen nut for alignment.**
10. Turn ignition key to Off position.
11. Connect battery ground cable.
12. Fill power steering pump to correct level.

### ZF GEAR

#### Removal

1. Turn steering wheel to straight-ahead position.
2. Raise and support vehicle.
3. Remove lower pinch bolt securing flex coupling to steering gear pinion shaft.
4. Remove nuts and cotter pins securing tie rod ends to spindle carriers.
5. Separate tie rod ends from spindle carriers.
6. Position drain pan and disconnect power steering hoses from steering gear by removing routing clamp and the bolt securing pump line plate assembly to gear housing and pulling assembly free. Plug housing port to prevent contamination.
7. Remove steering gear attaching bolts and the steering gear.

#### Installation

1. Position steering gear on engine front crossmember. **Torque** two attaching bolts to 11 ft. lbs., then an additional 90°.
2. Remove plugs from fluid lines and gear housing ports.
3. Install new O-rings on pressure and return lines, then connect lines to gear.
4. Install routing clamp screw and clamp plate bolt. **Torque** bolt to .6-.9 ft. lbs.
5. Connect tie rod ends to spindle carriers. **Torque** attaching nuts to 19-22 ft. lbs., then install cotter pins.
6. Install steering column coupling shaft onto pinion shaft. Install pinch bolt and **torque** to 19-22 ft. lbs. **Ensure block splines on coupling and pinion shaft are properly aligned.**

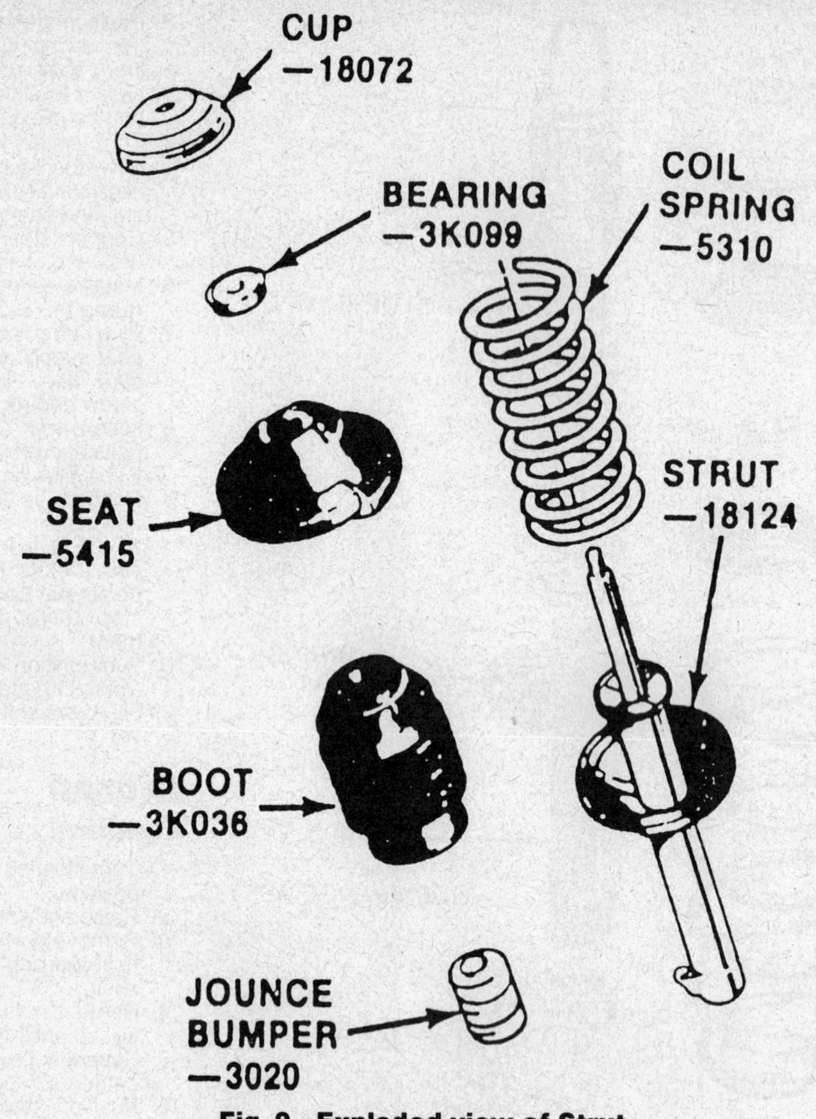


**Fig. 9 Exploded view of Strut assembly. XR4Ti**

## TIGHTENING SPECIFICATIONS

### SCORPIO

| Year | Component | Torque/Ft. lbs. |
|---|---|---|
| 1989 | Control Arm To Spindle Attaching Nut | 48-62 |
| | Control Arm Pivot Bolt | 22① |
| | Crossmember To Chassis Bolts | 52-66 |
| | Engine Mount Attaching Nut | 31-42 |
| | Stabilizer Bar Attaching Nut | 52-81 |
| | Stabilizer Bar U-Brackets | 52-66 |
| | Spindle Carrier Pinch Bolt | 59-66 |
| | Steering Coupling Pinch Bolt | 18-22 |
| | Strut Top Mount Nut | 15-17 |
| | Tie Rod To Spindle Carrier | 19-22 |
| | Steering Column Shaft Pinch Bolt | 15-22 |
| | Steering Gear Bolts | 11 |
| | Strut Piston Rod Locknut | 30-38 |
| | Wheel Lug Nuts | 75-101 |

### XR4Ti

| Year | Component | Torque/Ft. lbs. |
|---|---|---|
| 1989 | Coil Spring Retaining Nut | 38-48 |
| | Control Arm Ball Joint Nut | 48-63 |
| | Control Arm Pivot Bolt | 11① |
| | Crossmember Bolts | 51-66 |
| | Engine Mount Attaching Nut | 38-47 |
| | Shock Absorber Lower Attaching Bolt | 30-37 |
| | Shock Absorber Lower Attaching Nut | 33-40 |
| | Stabilizer Bar Attaching Nut | 52-81 |
| | Stabilizer Bar U-Brackets | 46-52 |
| | Steering Coupling Pinch Bolt | 18-22 |
| | Steering Gear Bolts | 11① |
| | Strut Pinch Bolt | 59-66 |
| | Strut Top Mount Nut | 29-38 |
| | Wheel Lug Nuts | 75-101 |

①—Then an additional 90°.

# Wheel Alignment

## INDEX

**Page No.**



## DESCRIPTION

The angles at which suspension components operate in relation to the vehicle and wheel centerlines, are calculated during vehicle design to provide maximum tire contact with the road throughout the full range of suspension travel. The checking of caster, camber and wheel toe-in or out is the measurement of these suspension angles at the wheels, and the possible adjustments are performed to ensure that the tires make maximum contact with the road at all times and cause the vehicle to track in a straight line when the front wheels are centered. Proper alignment of the front and rear wheels with the vehicle chassis and each other is essential for acceptable handling and to minimize tire wear.

Prior to checking wheel alignment, ensure that tires are properly matched (same size tires on each axle set), correctly inflated and uniformly worn. Ensure that wheel bearings are properly adjusted and that suspension components are not damaged or worn. Wheel alignment should be checked with the vehicle unloaded, as any abnormal or uneven loads affect ride height which, in turn, affects suspension operating angles (wheel alignment).

Only wheel toe-in or out is adjustable on these models. Caster and camber are not adjustable. However, they should be checked as possible causes of handling or tire wear complaints. If caster and camber are not within limits suspension components should be inspected for wear and damage, and replaced as needed. If control arms, stabilizers and bushings are in good condition, check vehicle body for distortion at suspension mounting points or for collision damage.

## TOE-IN & STEERING WHEEL CENTERING ADJUSTMENT

If the steering wheel is not properly centered when vehicle is driven straight ahead, mark its position with a piece of tape across the gap between steering wheel hub and steering column shroud.

If toe-in is to be adjusted, the operation can be combined with steering wheel centering. But, to avoid complications, one should be completed before starting the other. To center the steering wheel, the tie rods must be turned into one tie rod end and out of the other, in equal amounts to avoid changing the toe setting. This shifts the steering rack right or left, turning the pinion, steering column and wheel to its desired position. Center steering as follows:

1. Mark the tie rod and tie rod ends with paint or a grease pencil to indicate their original relative positions.
2. Loosen and back off the tie rod end jam nuts, then release the steering gear boot clips. Ensure boots are free on the tie rods to avoid twisting.
3. Screw tie rods into one tie rod end and out of the other, depending on which way the steering wheel is to be moved and how much. Example: if left tie rod is screwed in and right tie rod is

screwed out, the steering rack moves to the left and the steering wheel movement is counterclockwise as seen from the drivers seat. For clockwise correction, the rack must be moved to the right. If the road wheels are positioned and locked in the straight ahead position during this operation, using the steering wheel tape mark as a starting point, the wheel will turn during adjustment and the centered position can be judged visually. One revolution of the tie rods will result in a steering wheel correction of approximately 19°. Check marks on tie rods and tie rod ends, to ensure tie rods are turned equal amounts. Adjust toe-in as follows:

a. Loosen jam nuts at tie rod ends and release clips at small ends of steering gear boots, ensuring boots are free on tie rods so they will not be twisted when tie rods are turned.
b. Turn tie rods into or out of tie rod ends an equal amount on each side to keep steering wheel centered.
c. When toe-in is within specifications, **torque** tie rod end jam nuts to 42-50 ft. lbs., then ensure steering gear boot ends are positioned in the reduced-diameter sections of the tie rods and install boot clips.

## RIDE HEIGHT

Refer to "Rear Wheel Alignment Specifications" at the front of this chapter for ride height specifications.

# 1989 MERCURY TRACER

## INDEX OF SERVICE OPERATIONS

**NOTE:** Refer To The Rear Of This Manual For Vehicle Manufacturer's Special Tool Suppliers.

# Specifications

## GENERAL ENGINE SPECIFICATIONS

| Year | Engine CID①/Liter | Engine VIN Code② | Fuel System | Bore & Stroke | Comp. Ratio | Net Brake HP @ RPM③ | Maximum Torque Ft. Lbs. @ RPM | Normal Oil Pressure Psi |
|---|---|---|---|---|---|---|---|---|
| 1989 | 4-97.5/1.6L | 5 | EFI④ | 3.07 x 3.29 | 9.3 | 82 @ 5000 | 92 @ 2500 | 50–64⑤ |

①—CID: Cubic Inch Displacement.
②—The eighth digit of the VIN denotes engine code.
③—Ratings are net, as installed in vehicle.
④—Nippondenso Port Fuel Injection.
⑤—At 3000 RPM.

## TUNE UP SPECIFICATIONS

| Year & Engine/ VIN Code | Spark Plug Gap | Ignition Timing BTDC① Firing Order Fig. | Man. Trans. | Auto. Trans. | Mark Fig. | Curb Idle Speed Man. Trans. | Auto. Trans. ② | Fast Idle Speed Man. Trans. | Auto. Trans. | Fuel Pump Pressure Psi |
|---|---|---|---|---|---|---|---|---|---|---|
| 1989 | | | | | | | | | | |
| 4-97.5(1.6L)/5 | .041 | A | ⑤ | ⑤ | B | 850 | 850N | ③ | ③ | 64–85.3④ |

①—BTDC: Before Top Dead Center.
②—N: Neutral.
③—Controlled by ECA (Electronic Control Assembly).
④—Prior to checking fuel pump pressure, release fuel system by starting engine and disconnecting vane air flow meter. After engine has stalled, place ignition switch in the Off position. Remove rear seat, then open fuel pump access cover. Connect a suitable fuel pressure gauge to fuel pump outlet connection. Connect a jumper wire between fuel pump test connector terminals, then place ignition switch in On position and check fuel pressure.
⑤—With distributor vacuum advance hose disconnected & plugged, 2° BTDC; with distributor vacuum advance hose connected, approximately 7° BTDC.

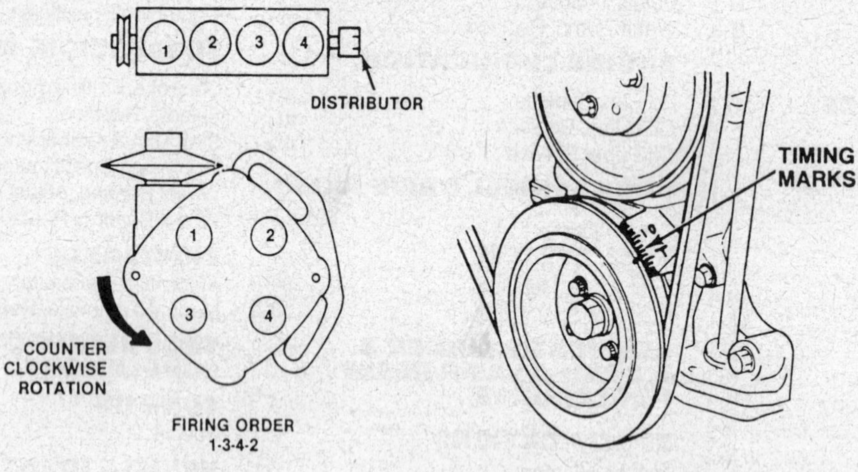


Fig. A

Fig. B

## FRONT WHEEL ALIGNMENT SPECIFICATIONS

| Year | Model | Caster Angle, Degrees Limits | Caster Desired | Camber Angle, Degrees Limits | Camber Desired | Toe-In Inch | King Pin Inclination | Steering Angle Degrees Inner | Outer |
|---|---|---|---|---|---|---|---|---|---|
| 1989 | All | +5/6 to +2 1/3 | +1 7/12 | +1/20 to +1 23/60 | +4/5 | .08 | +12 11/30 | 40 | 33 |

## REAR WHEEL ALIGNMENT SPECIFICATIONS

| Year | Model | Camber Angle, Degrees | | Toe-In Inch |
|---|---|---|---|---|
| | | Limits | Desired | |
| 1989 | All | −3/4 to +3/4 | 0 | .08 |

## COOLING SYSTEM & CAPACITY DATA

| Year | Model | Cooling Capacity Qts. | | Radiator Cap Relief Pressure, Lbs. | Thermo. Opening Temp. °F. | Fuel Tank Gals. | Engine Oil Refill Qts. | Transmission Oil | | |
|---|---|---|---|---|---|---|---|---|---|---|
| | | Less A/C | With A/C | | | | | 4 Speed Pints | 5 Speed Pints | Auto. Trans. Qts. ① |
| 1989 | All | ② | ② | 11–15 | ④ | 11.9 | ③ | 6.8 | 6.8 | 6 |

①—Approximate, make final check with dipstick.
②—Man. trans. models, 5.3 qts.; auto. trans. models, 6.3 qts.
③—Less filter change, 3.2 qts.; with filter change, 3.5 qts.
④—Sub-valve, 185°F; main valve, 190.4°F.

## LUBRICANT DATA

| Year | Model | Lubricant Type | | | | | |
|---|---|---|---|---|---|---|---|
| | | Transaxle | | Transfer Case | Rear Axle | Power Steering | Brake System |
| | | Manual | Automatic | | | | |
| 1989 | All | Dexron II① | Type F① | — | — | Dexron II① | Dot 3 |

①—Automatic Transmission Fluid.

# Electrical

## INDEX



## FUSE PANEL & FLASHER LOCATION

The fuse panel is located above the lefthand kick panel. The fuse block is located on the lefthand side of the engine compartment.

The turn signal/hazard flasher is located under the lefthand side of the instrument panel.

## STARTER MOTOR
### REPLACE

1. Disconnect battery ground cable.
2. Disconnect starter motor electrical connections.
3. Remove starter motor to engine support bracket, **Fig. 1.**
4. Remove starter to flywheel housing attaching bolts, then remove starter motor from vehicle.
5. Reverse procedure to install.

## DISTRIBUTOR
### REPLACE

1. Disconnect battery ground cable.
2. Remove two screws retaining distributor cap, then position cap and wires aside.
3. Remove distributor cap gasket.
4. Label, then remove vacuum hoses from distributor.
5. Disconnect distributor harness and note wire location for correct installation.
6. Mark relationship of the distributor housing to the cylinder head for reference during installation.
7. Mark relationship of the rotor tip in relation to the distributor hold down bolts for reference during installation.
8. Remove two hold down bolts, then the distributor assembly. **If crankshaft is turned while the distributor is removed, the rotor to distributor alignment mark made during removal can no longer be used to correctly time the distributor to the camshaft. The drive dog of the distributor is offset so as to allow only one installation position.**

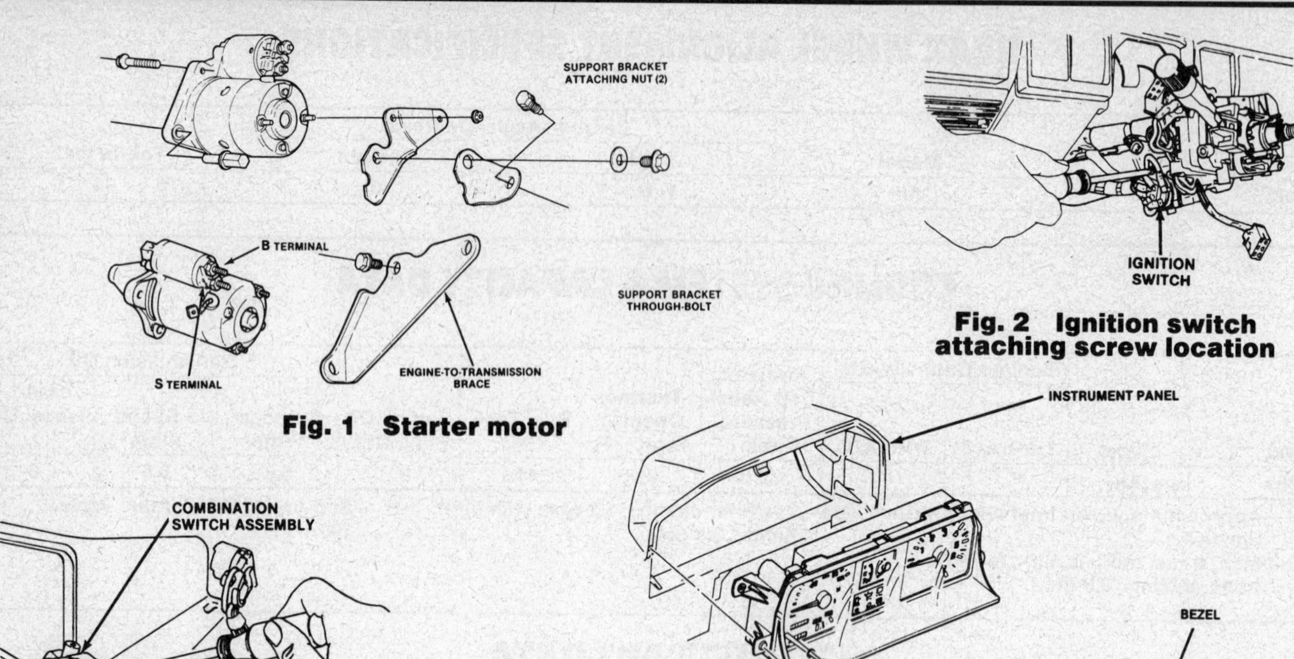


**Fig. 1 Starter motor**

**Fig. 2 Ignition switch attaching screw location**

COMBINATION SWITCH ASSEMBLY

CLAMP

**Fig. 3 Loosening combination switch clamp**

BEZEL

INSTRUMENT CLUSTER

**Fig. 4 Instrument cluster**

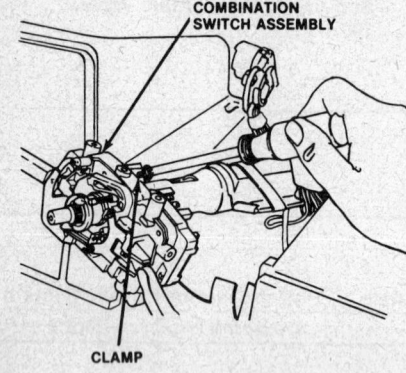

9. Reverse procedure to install. Insert distributor and rotate rotor until drive dog falls into slot of camshaft.

## STEERING WHEEL & HORN SOUNDER
### REPLACE

1. Disconnect battery ground cable.
2. From rear side of steering wheel, remove two screws attaching steering wheel cover pad to steering wheel, then remove cover pad.
3. Remove steering wheel attaching nut.
4. Remove two steering wheel cover pad bracket attaching screws, then remove bracket.
5. Place alignment marks on steering wheel and steering shaft.
6. Using a suitable steering wheel puller, remove steering wheel.
7. Reverse procedure to install. When installing steering wheel align marks on steering wheel and shaft made during removal.

## IGNITION SWITCH
### REPLACE

1. Disconnect battery ground cable.
2. Remove trim ring from around ignition lock, by grasping and pulling straight out.
3. If necessary, remove under cover and side lap duct cover from drivers side of instrument panel.
4. Remove screw attaching A/C duct assembly to access panel support bracket, if equipped.
5. Remove two attaching screw, then remove access panel support bracket.
6. Remove side window defroster duct located under steering column, by grasping ends of duct and pulling outward with a slight twisting motion.
7. Remove ignition switch wiring harness snap retainer and strap connector, by disengaging lock tangs.
8. Remove four bolts attaching steering column to instrument, then lower steering column.
9. Remove screw attaching ignition switch to housing, **Fig. 2,** then grasp body of switch and pull straight out.
10. Disconnect electrical connectors from ignition switch. **Note location of wires for installation.**
11. Reverse procedure to install.

## STOP LAMP SWITCH
### REPLACE

1. Disconnect battery ground cable.
2. Disconnect electrical connector from stop lamp switch.
3. Remove nuts securing stop lamp switch to bracket, then remove stop lamp switch.
4. Reverse procedure to install. When installing stop lamp switch, adjust switch until brake pedal height is 8.62 to 8.82 inches, then tighten locknut.

## COMBINATION SWITCH
### REPLACE

1. Disconnect battery ground cable.
2. Mark steering column shaft and steering wheel, then remove steering wheel and steering column covers.
3. Loosen combination switch clamp, **Fig. 3,** then slide combination switch upward and disconnect combination switch electrical connectors.
4. Remove combination switch from steering column.
5. Reverse procedure to install.

## INSTRUMENT CLUSTER
### REPLACE

1. Disconnect battery ground cable.
2. Remove steering wheel, refer to "Steering Wheel and Horn Sounder, Replace."
3. Remove attaching screws, then remove instrument cluster bezel, **Fig. 4.**

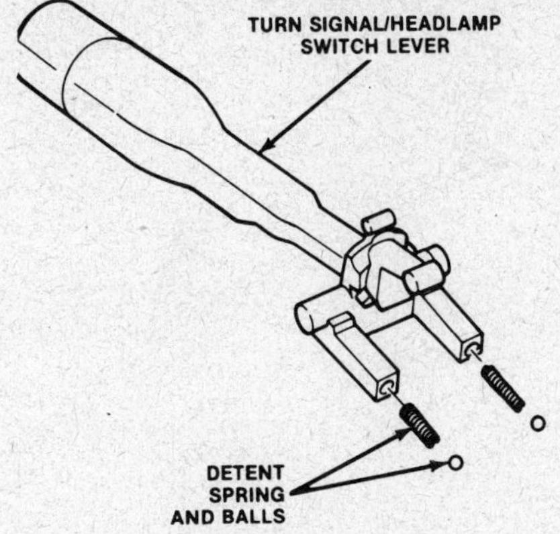


**Fig. 5 Turn signal/headlamp switch lever**

**Fig. 6 Front wiper switch removal**

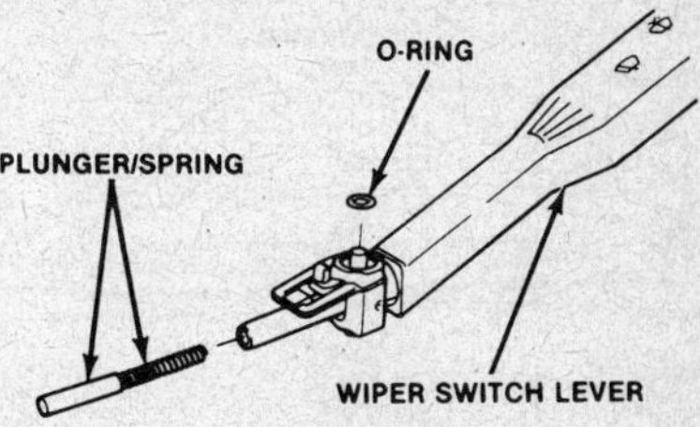


**Fig. 7 Front wiper switch lever**

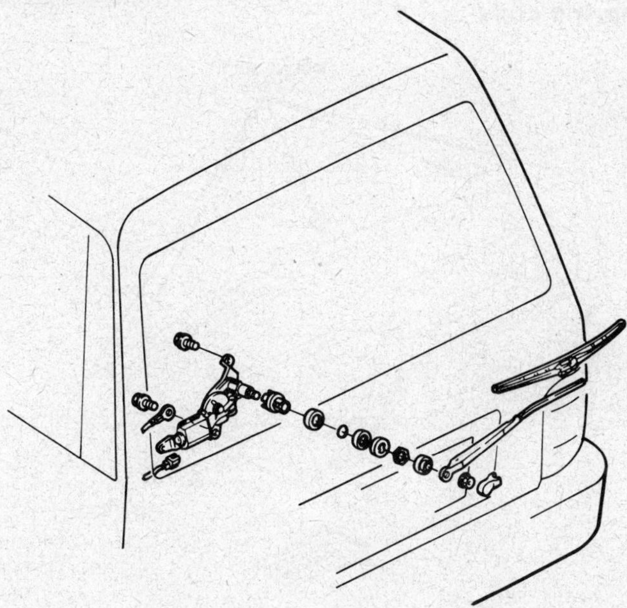

**Fig. 8 Rear wiper motor**

4. Remove instrument cluster attaching bolts, then pull cluster slightly outward and disconnect speedometer cable and electrical connectors.
5. Remove instrument cluster from instrument panel.
6. Reverse procedure to install.

## RADIO
## REPLACE

1. Disconnect battery ground cable.
2. Remove trim plate, then remove four screws retaining radio to instrument panel.
3. Slide radio toward rear of vehicle to gain access to electrical connectors.
4. Disconnect electrical connectors and antenna lead from radio.
5. Remove nut, then disconnect ground connection and alignment pin from stud at rear of radio.
6. Remove radio from instrument panel.
7. Reverse procedure to install.

## WIPER SWITCH
## REPLACE

### FRONT

1. Disconnect battery ground cable.
2. Remove steering wheel as described under "Steering Wheel and Horn Sounder, Replace."
3. Remove combination switch as described under "Combination Switch, Replace."
4. Remove turn signal/headlamp switch lever retainer attaching screws, then carefully remove lever from combination switch, **Fig. 5. Use care not lose lever detent balls.**
5. Remove wiper switch to combination switch attaching screws, then remove wiper switch, **Fig. 6.**
6. Remove wiper switch lever from combination switch, **Fig. 7. Use care not lose O-ring, retaining pin detent plunger and spring.**
7. Reverse procedure to install.

### REAR

1. Disconnect battery ground cable.
2. Remove wiper switch from instrument panel by gently prying on outer edge of switch.
3. Disconnect electrical connector and remove switch.
4. Reverse procedure to install.

## WIPER MOTOR
## REPLACE

### FRONT

1. Disconnect battery ground cable.
2. Remove three retainers from shield, then remove plastic shield.
3. Remove locknut and washer from motor shaft.
4. Disconnect electrical connectors from wiper motor.
5. Remove four bolts and insulators attaching wiper to firewall, then remove wiper motor.
6. Reverse procedure to install.

### REAR

1. Disconnect battery ground cable.
2. Remove wiper arm and blade assembly, **Fig. 8.**
3. Remove nut, washers and packings from wiper motor shaft.
4. Remove trim panel from liftgate.
5. Disconnect electrical connector from wiper motor.
6. Remove bolts and insulators attaching wiper motor to tailgate.
7. Disconnect ground wire connection at tailgate, then remove wiper motor.
8. Reverse procedure to install.

## WINDSHIELD WIPER TRANSMISSION
## REPLACE

1. Disconnect battery ground cable.
2. Remove wiper arm and blade assemblies.
3. Remove cowl panel attaching screws, **Fig. 9**, then release four spring clips, **Fig. 10.**
4. Lift cowl panel upward and disconnect hoses from washer nozzles, then remove cowl panel.
5. Remove nut and washer attaching wiper transmission to wiper motor, then disconnect linkage from wiper motor.

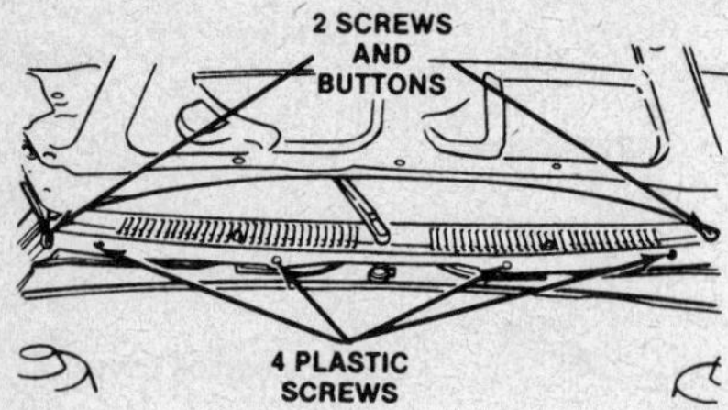


**Fig. 9 Cowl panel attaching screw locations**

6. Remove two bolts attaching each wiper pivot shaft, **Fig. 11**,, then remove wiper transmission through cowl opening.
7. Reverse procedure to install.

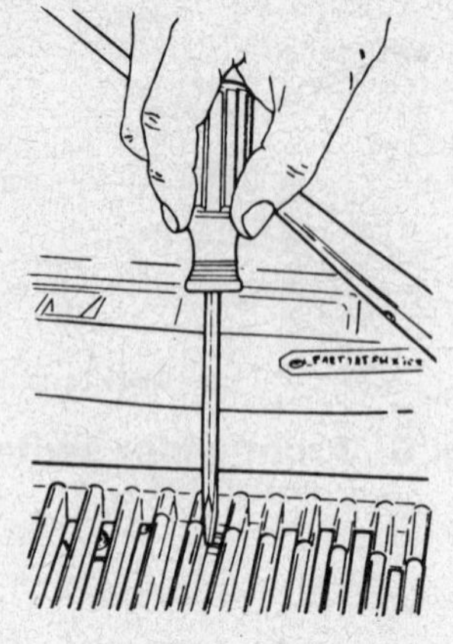

**Fig. 10 Releasing cowl panel spring clips**

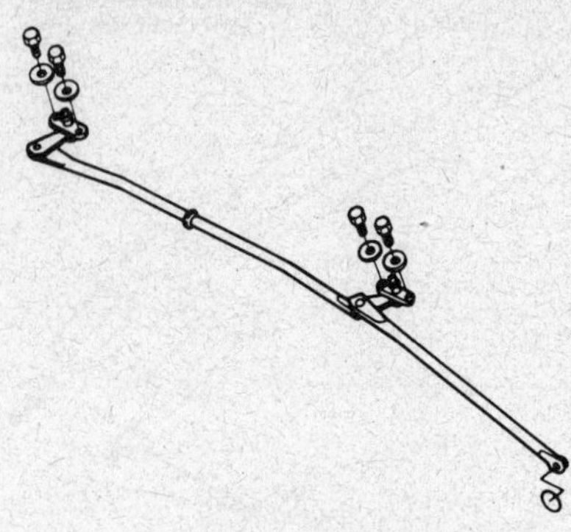

**Fig. 11 Windshield wiper transmission**

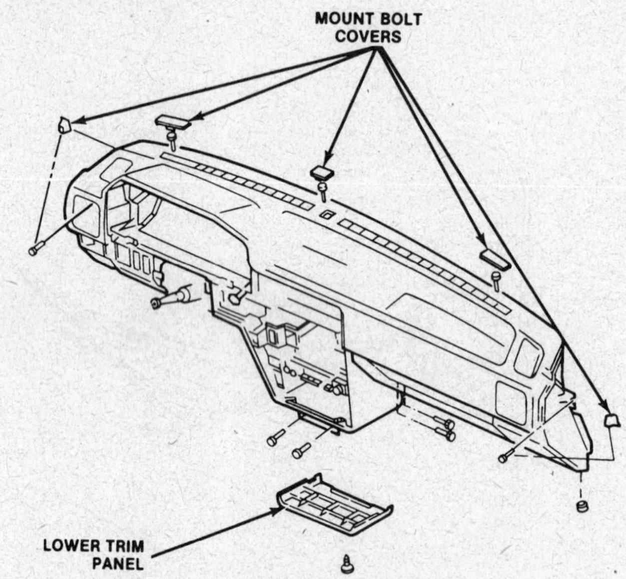


**Fig. 12 Instrument panel attaching bolt and nut locations**

# HEATER CORE
## REPLACE

1. Disconnect battery ground cable.
2. Remove instrument panel as follows:
   a. Remove instrument panel under covers.
   b. Remove lap duct panel from instrument panel.
   c. Disconnect heater control cables at doors located on blower case.
   d. Disconnect speedometer cable, then disconnect three electrical connectors from rear of instrument cluster.
   e. Remove brace located below lap duct, then remove lap duct and defroster duct.
   f. Remove steering column lower cover, then remove four steering column mounting bolts and lower steering column.
   g. Remove glove box attaching screws, then remove glove box from instrument panel.
   h. Remove nut attaching hood release cable to instrument panel and position cable aside.
   i. Position front seats in the full forward position, the remove two rear console attaching screws.
   j. Position front seats in the full rearward position, then remove two screws attaching rear console to rear console.
   k. Pull rear console upward and rearward to remove.
   l. Remove gear shift lever knob, then remove four front console attaching screws.
   m. Remove front console and side panels.
   n. Remove lower trim panel located beneath radio, then remove instrument panel mounting bolt covers, **Fig. 12.**
   o. Remove nine instrument panel attaching bolts and two attaching nuts.
   p. Lift upward on instrument panel and pull slightly outward, then disconnect antenna lead, radio electrical connectors, blower electrical connector and three instrument panel electrical connectors located at lower left corner of instrument panel.
   q. Carefully remove instrument panel.
3. Drain cooling system, then disconnect heater hoses at heater core. Cap heater core tubes to prevent coolant spillage during removal.
4. Disconnect defroster and main air duct from heater case.
5. Remove carpet panel from beneath heater case.
6. Detach wiring harness braces from heater case.
7. Remove three lower brace attaching screws, then remove brace.
8. Remove two lower heater case mounting bolts, then two upper heater case mounting nuts.
9. Remove mounting nut from passenger side of heater case, then disconnect lower duct from heater case.
10. Pull heater case straight rearward, using care not to damage heater core tubes.
11. Remove three attaching screws, then remove heater core cover, **Fig. 13.**
12. Remove heater core tube braces, then remove heater core by pulling straight out.
13. Remove clip, then remove extension outlet tube.
14. Loosen clamp, then remove extension inlet tube.
15. Reverse procedure to install.

# BLOWER MOTOR
## REPLACE

1. Disconnect battery ground cable.
2. Remove passenger side instrument panel under cover.
3. Disconnect blower motor electrical connector, then remove three blower motor cover attaching screws, **Fig. 14.**
4. Remove cover, cooling tube and blower motor.
5. Reverse procedure to install.

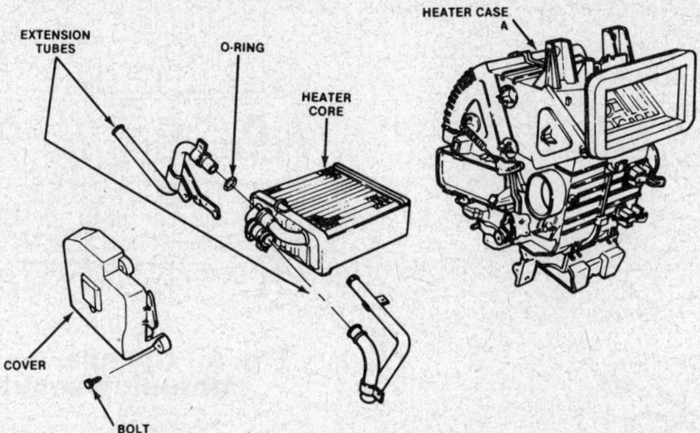


Fig. 13 Heater core & case

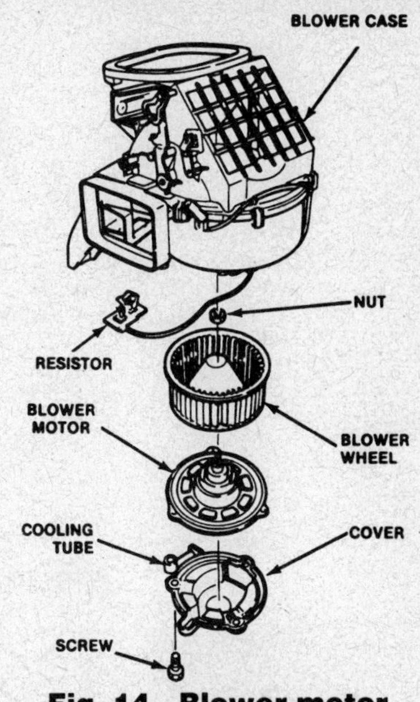


Fig. 14 Blower motor assembly

## EVAPORATOR CORE
### REPLACE

1. Disconnect battery ground cable, then discharge refrigerant from A/C system.
2. Disconnect A/C lines from evaporator and plug ends, then remove evaporator tube grommets from bulkhead.
3. Remove glove box, then disconnect electrical connectors.
4. Remove air duct bands and drain hose, then unit mounting bolts and nuts.
5. Remove cooling unit.
6. Reverse procedure to install. **Add .845-1.014 fl. oz. of compressor oil to evaporator if replaced.**

# Engine
## INDEX



## ENGINE
### REPLACE

1. Disconnect battery ground cable.
2. Mark hood hinge location, then remove hood from vehicle. Ensure ground strap near right hand hood hinge is disconnected before removing hood.
3. Drain cooling system, crankcase and transaxle.
4. Remove battery and battery tray, **Fig. 1.**
5. Remove air cleaner and oil dipstick.
6. Remove engine cooling fan and shroud.
7. Disconnect accelerator cable and speed control cable, if equipped.
8. Disconnect speedometer cable from transaxle.
9. Relieve fuel system pressure by starting engine and disconnecting vane air flow meter. After engine has stalled, place ignition switch in the Off position.
10. Disconnect and cap fuel hoses as necessary permit engine removal.
11. Disconnect radiator and heater hoses.
12. **On models with automatic transaxle, loosen transaxle oil cooler line clamps, then disconnect oil cooler lines at transaxle.**
13. **On all models, disconnect power brake unit vacuum hose.**
14. Disconnect evaporative emission control canister hoses.
15. Disconnect engine wiring harness connectors and engine ground strap.
16. Disconnect exhaust pipe from exhaust manifold.
17. Remove A/C compressor and power steering pump and position aside with hoses attached, if equipped.
18. Separate halfshafts from transaxle as follows:
    a. Raise and support front of vehicle, then remove necessary underbody covers.
    b. Remove stabilizer bar to control arm attaching bolts, nuts, bushings and washers.
    c. Remove wheel and tire assemblies.
    d. Remove lower ball joint clamp bolt, then separate lower ball joint from steering knuckle.
    e. **On models with manual transaxle, pull outward on steering knuckle and brake assembly to separate halfshaft from transaxle. If halfshaft is difficult to remove, insert a suitable pry bar between halfshaft and transaxle case. Lightly tap end of pry bar until halfshaft loosens from differential side gear. Suspend halfshaft from chassis using a piece of wire.**
    f. **On models with automatic transaxle, position a suitable pry bar between transaxle case and halfshaft. Light tap end of pry bar until halfshaft loosens from differential side gear. Carefully pull halfshaft out of transaxle and suspend from chassis using a piece wire.**
    g. **On all models, when reinstalling halfshafts, a replacement circlip must be installed.**
19. **On models equipped with manual transaxle, disconnect clutch cable.**
20. **On all models, disconnect shift control cable or rod.**
21. Remove engine splash shield and inner fender panel.
22. Remove engine mounting attaching bolts, then remove engine and transmission from vehicle as an assembly.
23. Separate engine from transmission.
24. Reverse procedure to install. When installing halfshafts, do not move joints to angles greater than 20 degrees, as damage to seals and boots may result. The halfshaft is properly seated when the shaft circlip snaps into the differential side gear groove.

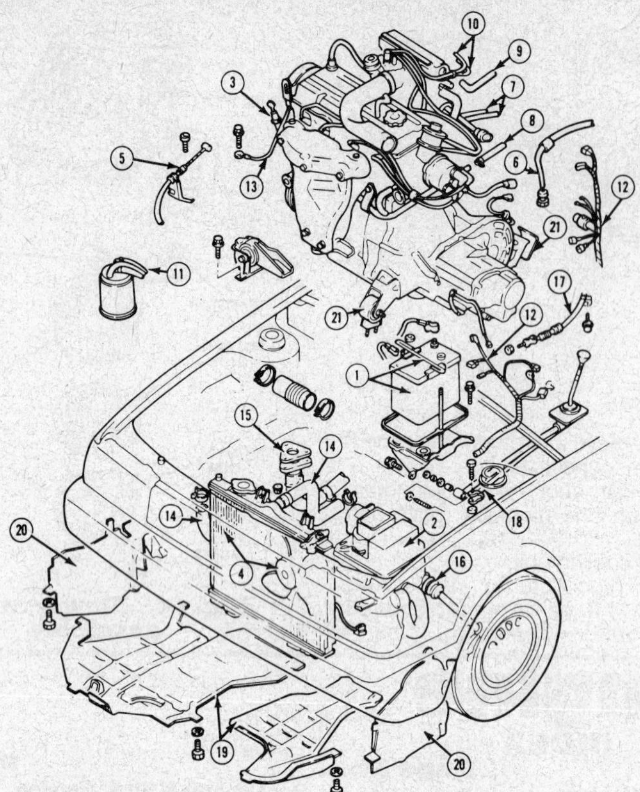

1. BATTERY AND BATTERY CARRIER
2. AIR CLEANER ASSEMBLY
3. OIL LEVEL GAUGE
4. COOLING FAN AND RADIATOR COWLING
5. ACCELERATOR CABLE AND CRUISE CONTROL CABLE (IF EQUIPPED)
6. SPEEDOMETER CABLE
7. FUEL HOSES
8. HEATER HOSES
9. BRAKE VACUUM HOSE
10. IDLE-UP SOLENOID VALVE HOSES
11. CANISTER HOSE
12. ENGINE HARNESS CONNECTORS
13. ENGINE GROUND
14. UPPER AND LOWER RADIATOR HOSE
15. EXHAUST PIPE
16. DRIVE SHAFTS
17. CLUTCH CONTROL CABLE (MTX)
18. SHIFT CONTROL ROD
19. ENGINE SPLASH SHIELD
20. INNER FENDER PANEL
21. ENGINE MOUNTS

**Fig. 1 Engine replacement**

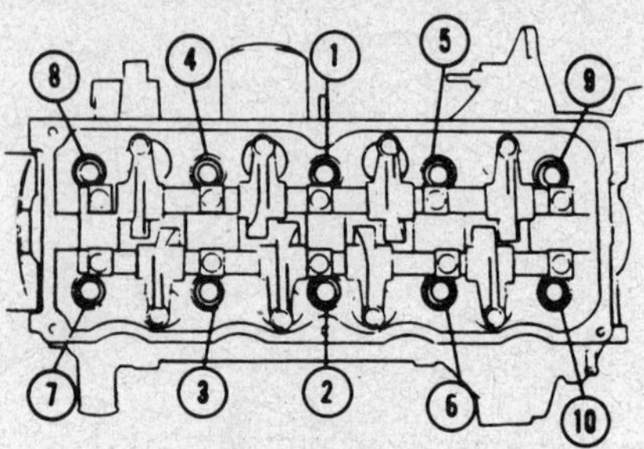

**Fig. 2 Cylinder head bolt tightening sequence**

20. **On all models, disconnect shift control cable or rod.**
21. Remove engine splash shield and inner fender panel.
22. Remove engine mounting attaching bolts, then remove engine and transmission from vehicle as an assembly.
23. Separate engine from transmission.
24. Reverse procedure to install. When installing halfshafts, do not move joints to angles greater than 20 degrees, as damage to seals and boots may result. The halfshaft is properly seated when the shaft circlip snaps into the differential side gear groove.

## INTAKE MANIFOLD REPLACE

1. Disconnect battery ground cable, then drain cooling system.
2. Remove intake plenum, then disconnect hoses and electrical connectors, as necessary, to permit intake manifold removal.
3. Remove intake manifold attaching bolts, then remove intake manifold and gasket.
4. Reverse procedure to install. When installing intake manifold, tighten attaching bolts alternately and evenly.

## EXHAUST MANIFOLD REPLACE

1. Disconnect oxygen sensor wire connector.
2. Remove exhaust manifold insulator shields.
3. Disconnect exhaust pipe from exhaust manifold.
4. Remove exhaust manifold to cylinder head attaching bolts, then remove exhaust manifold.
5. Reverse procedure to install.

## CYLINDER HEAD REPLACE

1. Disconnect battery ground cable.
2. Remove alternator and A/C compressor drive belts, if equipped.
3. Remove right hand fender inner panel.
4. Remove water pump pulley to hub attaching bolts, then remove water pump pulley.
5. Remove bolts, spacer and crankshaft outer pulley.
6. Remove spacer, screws and crankshaft inner pulley.
7. Remove seven timing belt cover attaching bolts, then remove covers.
8. Remove timing belt tensioner spring and retaining bolt.
9. Mark direction of rotation on timing so that it can be reinstalled in the same direction, then remove timing belt as described under "Timing Belt, Replace."
10. Remove air duct, then disconnect accelerator and speed control cables, if equipped.
11. Disconnect vent hose from front of rocker arm cover, then detach spark plug wires from retainers.
12. Remove rocker arm cover attaching bolts, then remove rocker arm cover.
13. Disconnect oxygen sensor electrical connector, then remove exhaust manifold insulator.
14. Disconnect exhaust pipe from exhaust manifold.
15. Remove exhaust manifold to cylinder head attaching bolts, then remove exhaust manifold.
16. Drain cooling system, then remove intake plenum.
17. Disconnect hoses and electrical connectors as necessary permit intake manifold removal. Tag hoses and electrical connectors for installation.
18. Remove intake manifold to cylinder head attaching bolts, then remove intake manifold.
19. Remove spark plugs, then remove distributor.
20. Remove front and rear engine lifting eyes and engine ground cable.
21. Disconnect electrical connectors as necessary to permit cylinder head removal.
22. Disconnect upper radiator hose, then remove bypass hose and bracket.
23. Remove cylinder head attaching bolts, then remove cylinder head.
24. Reverse procedure to install. When installing cylinder head, torque bolts alternately and evenly in sequence shown in **Fig. 2.**

## ROCKER ARM & SHAFT SERVICE

1. Remove rocker arm cover.
2. Alternately and evenly loosen rocker shaft attaching bolts, then carefully lift rocker shaft assemblies from cylinder head.
3. Remove rocker arms and springs from rocker shaft. Do not remove hydraulic valve lash adjusters from rocker arms unless necessary.

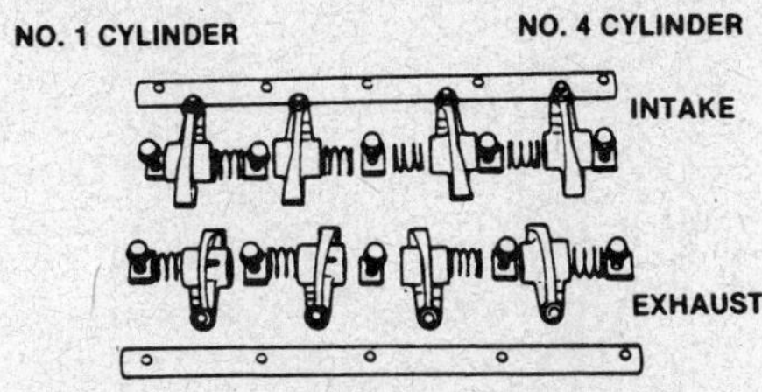


**Fig. 3 Rocker arm & shaft assembly**

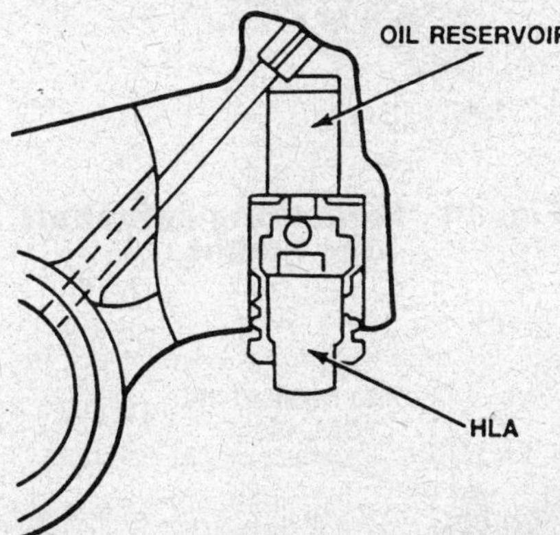


**Fig. 6 Hydraulic lash adjuster (HLA)**

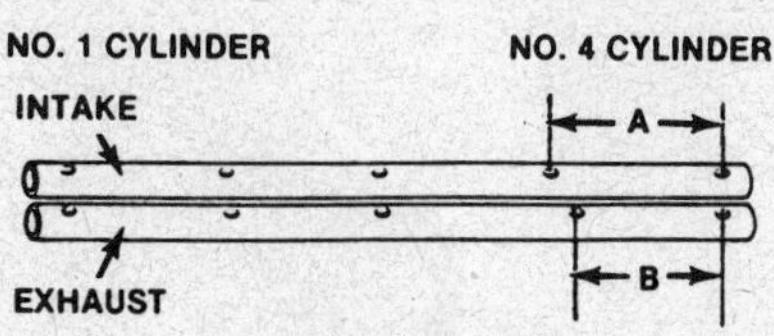


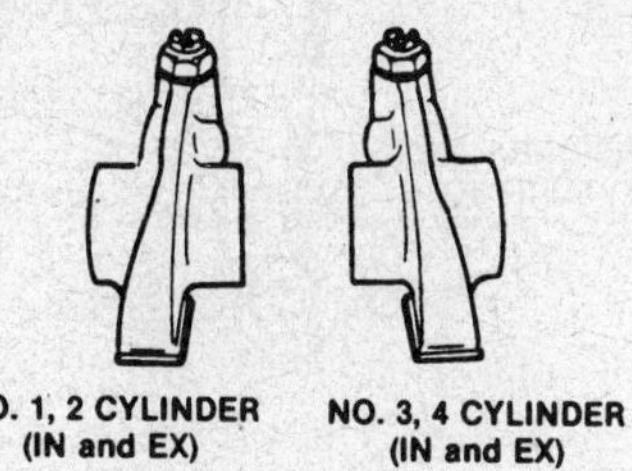


**Fig. 4 Rocker arm & shaft identification**

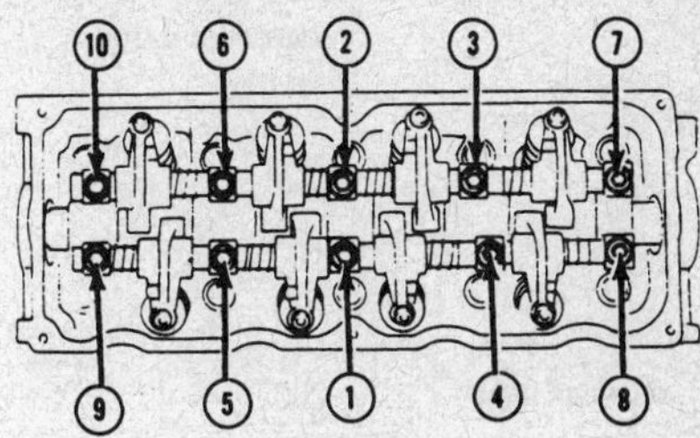


**Fig. 5 Rocker arm shaft bolt tightening sequence**

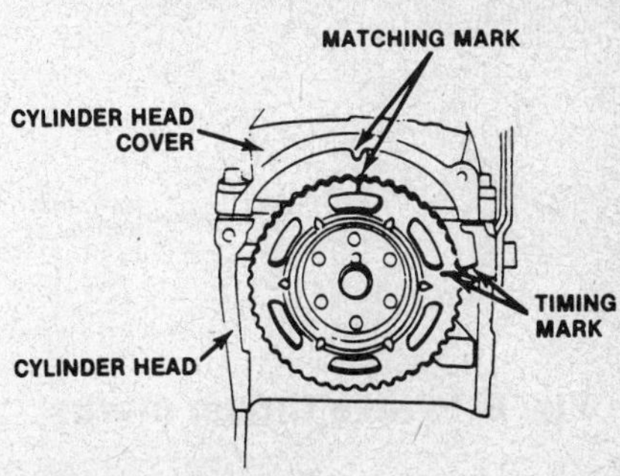


**Fig. 8 Camshaft timing marks**

4. Measure outside diameter of rocker shaft and inside diameter of rocker arm shaft bore. The maximum difference between these two measurements should not exceed .0039 inch. Also check hydraulic valve lash adjuster for wear and damage and replace as necessary.
5. Pour engine oil into rocker reservoir.
6. If removed, apply engine oil to hydraulic valve lash adjuster and install in rocker arm. Use care not damage O-ring when installing.
7. Assemble rocker arms and springs to rocket shaft, **Fig. 3.** Rocker arms and shafts can be identified as shown in **Fig. 4.**
8. Install assembled rocker shaft assemblies, with oil holes facing down, to cylinder head and torque attaching bolts alternately and evenly in sequence shown in **Fig. 5.**

# VALVES
## ADJUST

These engines are equipped with hydraulic valve lash adjusters, which are not adjustable, **Fig. 6.**

# HYDRAULIC VALVE LASH ADJUSTERS

The hydraulic valve lash adjusters are located in the rocker arms, **Fig. 6.** Refer to "Rocker Arm & Shaft Service" procedure.

# VALVE GUIDES

Valve guides can be replaced using tool No. T87C-6510-A. When removing valve guide, drive out toward camshaft side of cylinder head. When installing valve guide, drive in until clip just contacts cylinder head, **Fig. 7.**

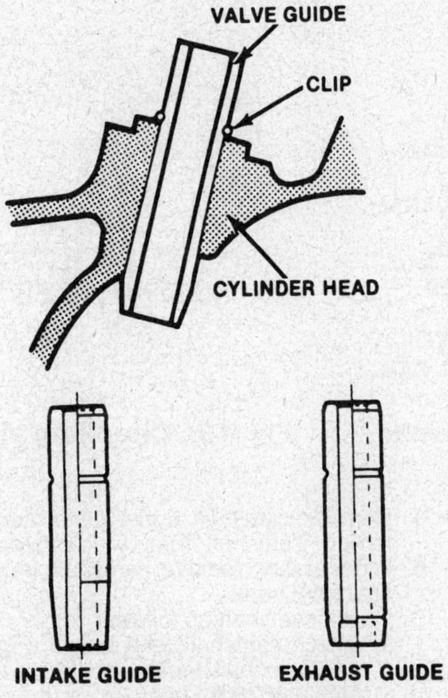


**Fig. 7 Valve guide identification**

# CAMSHAFT TIMING CHECK

1. Remove timing belt upper cover.
2. Align crankshaft pulley timing notch with TC mark on timing belt cover tab.
3. Camshaft timing marks should be aligned, **Fig. 8.** If camshaft timing cannot be viewed, rotate crankshaft pulley one revolution, aligning notch with timing cover TC mark.
4. If camshaft timing marks are aligned, the camshaft is properly timed to the crankshaft. If camshaft timing marks are not properly aligned, refer to "Timing Belt, Replace" procedure.

# TIMING BELT COVER
## REPLACE

1. Remove alternator and A/C compressor drive belts, if equipped.
2. Remove right hand fender inner panel.
3. Remove bolts attaching water pump pulley to pump hub, then remove pulley.
4. Remove bolts, spacer and outer crankshaft pulley.
5. Remove spacer, screw and inner crankshaft pulley and baffle.
6. Remove timing belt cover attaching screws, then remove timing belt covers.
7. Reverse procedure to install.

# TIMING BELT
## REPLACE

**Whenever the timing belt has broken or slipped significantly, a possibility of internal engine damage is present.**

1. Remove timing belt covers, as described under "Timing Belt Cover, Replace."
2. Remove timing belt tensioner spring and retaining bolt.
3. Mark direction of rotation on timing belt, so it can be reinstalled in the same direction.
4. Remove timing belt from sprockets.
5. Check timing belt, tensioner and sprockets for wear and damage.
6. Align camshaft and crankshaft timing marks, **Fig. 9.**
7. Install timing belt with rotation mark placed during removal facing in the same direction.
8. Position timing belt tensioner to engine, then install tensioner bolt finger tight, **Fig. 10.**

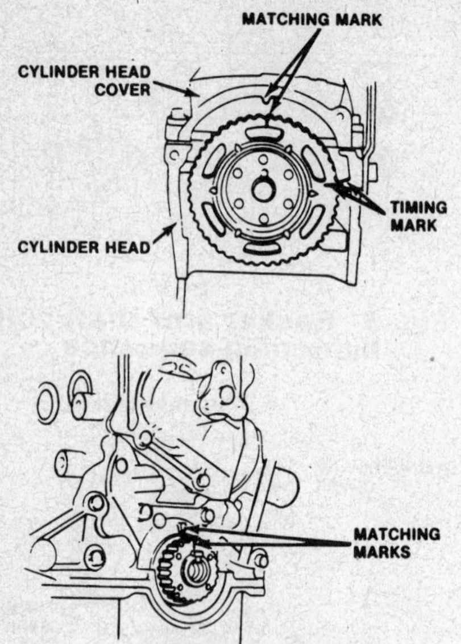


**Fig. 9 Valve timing marks**

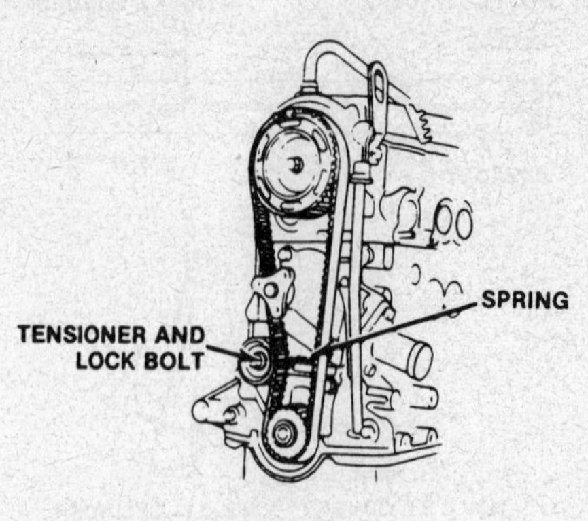


**Fig. 10 Timing belt tensioner**

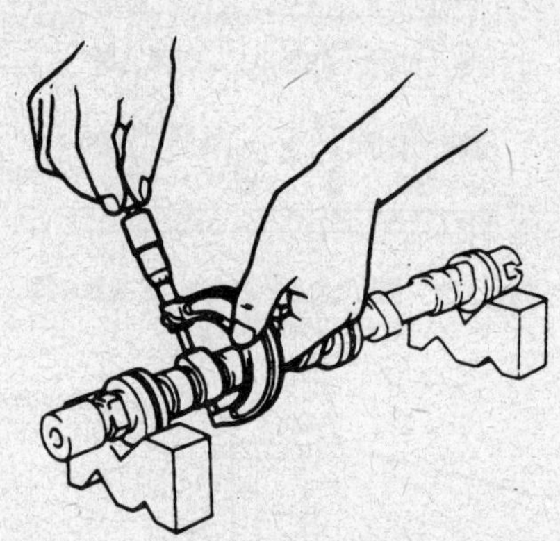

**Fig. 11 Measuring camshaft lobe height**

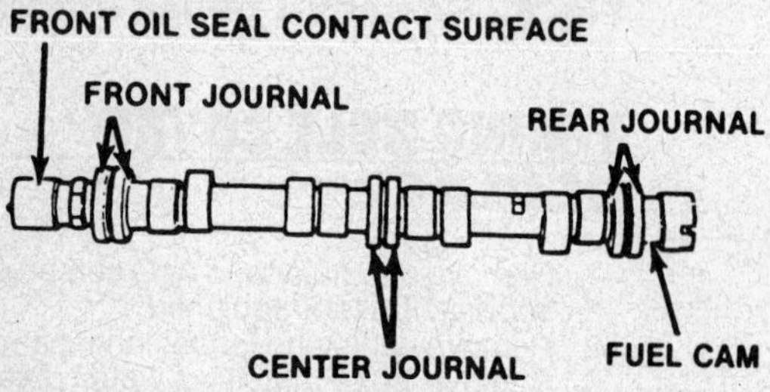

FRONT OIL SEAL CONTACT SURFACE
FRONT JOURNAL
REAR JOURNAL
CENTER JOURNAL
FUEL CAM

**Fig. 12 Measuring camshaft journal diameters**

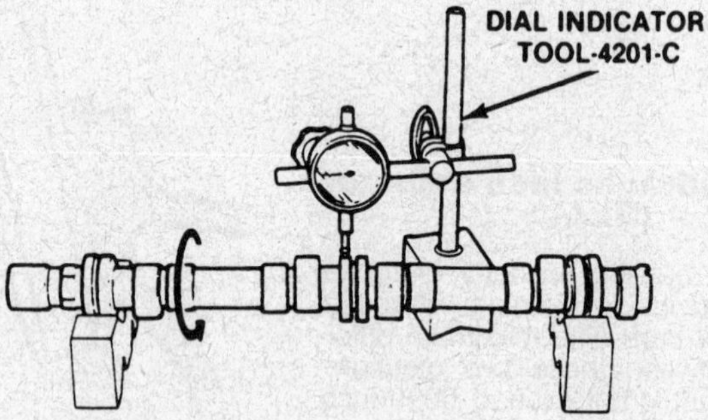

DIAL INDICATOR TOOL-4201-C

**Fig. 13 Checking camshaft for straightness**

9. Rotate crankshaft in direction of rotation two revolutions, aligning camshaft and crankshaft timing marks, **Fig. 9.**
10. Check to ensure timing marks are properly aligned. If not, realign.
11. Tighten timing belt tensioner bolt.
12. Measure deflection between crankshaft and camshaft sprockets. Deflection should be .35 to .39 inch at 22 pounds pressure. If deflection is not within limits, repeat steps 9 through 12.
13. Install timing belt covers as described under "Timing Belt Cover, Replace."

## CAMSHAFT REPLACE

1. Remove timing belt as described under "Timing Belt, Replace."
2. Remove camshaft sprocket attaching bolt, sprocket and dowel pin. Use a screwdriver or other suitable tool to prevent sprocket from turning when removing attaching bolt.
3. Remove cylinder head as described under "Cylinder Head, Replace."
4. Remove rocker arm arm shaft assemblies as described under "Rocket Arm Service."
5. Remove camshaft thrust plate, then remove camshaft from cylinder head.
6. If necessary, remove camshaft front seal from bore.
7. Check camshaft as follows:
   a. Check camshaft lobe height, **Fig. 11.** Camshaft lobes should measure 1.4378 to 1.4437 inch. If any lobe measures less than 1.4329 inch, replace camshaft.
   b. Measure front and rear camshaft bearing journals, **Fig. 12.** Front and camshaft bearing journals should measure between 1.7103 to 1.7112 inch.
   c. Measure center camshaft bearing journal, **Fig. 12.** Center camshaft bearing journal should measure 1.70791 to 1.71000 inch.
   d. Measure front seal contact surface **Fig. 12.** Front seal contact surface should measure 1.1796 to 1.1811 inch.
   e. Check all camshaft bearing journals for out of round. The out of round limit is .002 inch.
   f. Measure fuel cam height, **Fig. 12.** Fuel pump cam height should be between 1.331 to 1.346, with a limit of 1.323 inch.
   g. Check camshaft for bend condition, **Fig. 13.** The limit at the center journal is .0012 inch.
   h. Position camshaft and thrust plate in cylinder head and measure camshaft end play, **Fig. 14.** End play should be .002 to .007 inch. If end play exceeds .008 inch, replace thrust plate or camshaft as necessary.
   i. Check camshaft journal to bearing clearance, **Fig. 15.** Clearance should not exceed .006 inch.
8. Reverse procedure to install. When installing camshaft front seal use tool No. T87C-6019-A or equivalent.

## PISTON & ROD ASSEMBLY

Assemble piston to rod so that front F mark on piston and oil groove on connection rod are positioned as shown in **Fig. 16.** When installing piston and rod assembly, numbered side of cap should be on same side as numbered side of rod.

## PISTONS, PINS & RINGS

Pistons and rings are available in standard size and oversizes of .010, .020, .030 and .040 inch. Pistons and piston pins are available as an assembly.

When assembled to crankshaft, connecting rod side clearance should not exceed .012 inch.

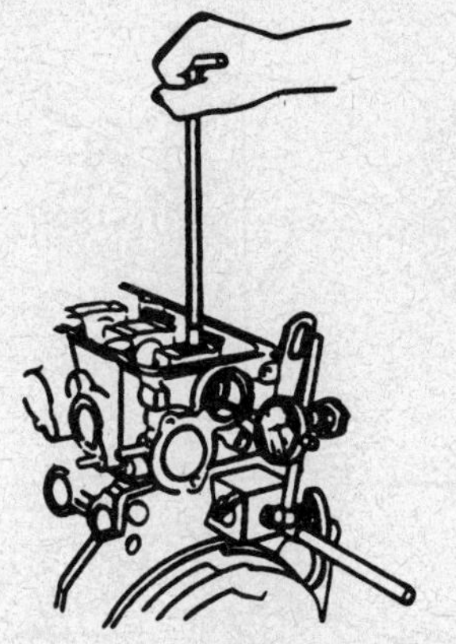

Fig. 14 Checking camshaft end play

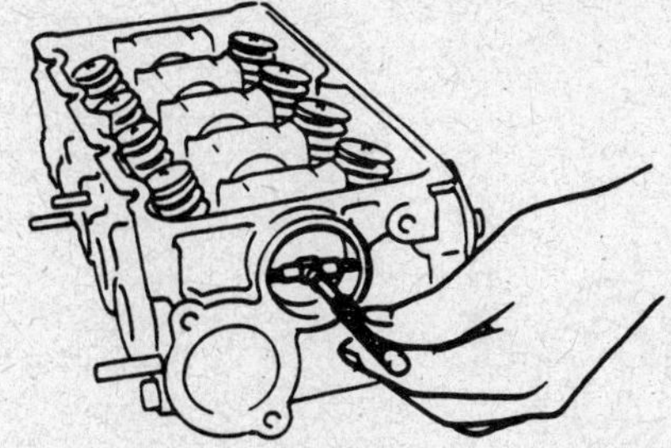

Fig. 15 Measuring camshaft bearing bore

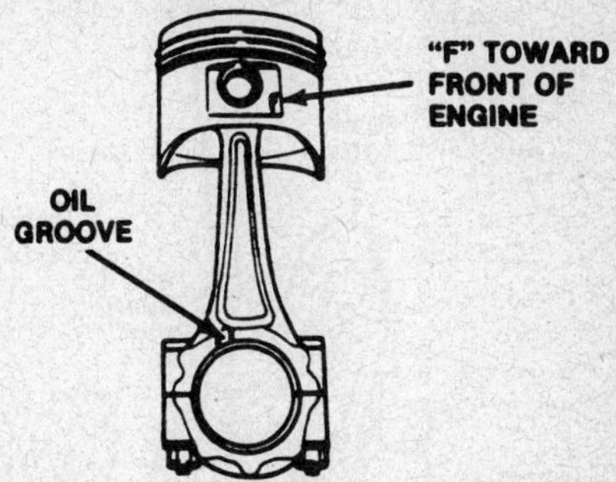


Fig. 16 Piston & rod assembly

Fig. 18 Oil pan installation

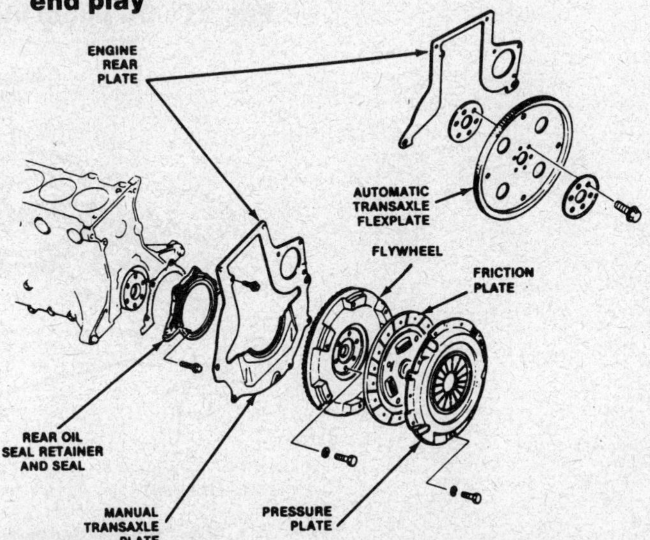


Fig. 17 Crankshaft rear seal replacement

# MAIN & ROD BEARINGS

Main and rod bearings are available in standard size and undersizes of .010, .020 and .030 inch.

# CRANKSHAFT REAR OIL SEAL

## REPLACE

1. Disconnect battery ground cable.
2. Remove transaxle from vehicle.
3. If equipped with manual transaxle, remove clutch and pressure plate.
4. On all models, remove flywheel attaching bolts and flywheel, **Fig. 17.**
5. Remove engine rear plate, if necessary.
6. Remove crankshaft rear seal retainer, then press out seal.
7. Reverse procedure to install. When installing seal onto retainer, position hollow side of seal toward engine. Use tool No. T87C-6701-A or equivalent to install seal. When installing halfshafts to transaxle, use a new circlip, position gap in circlip to top of circlip groove.

# OIL PAN

## REPLACE

1. Disconnect battery ground cable.
2. Remove under body shield and right hand inner fender panel, then drain crankcase.
3. Remove engine to flywheel housing support bracket bolts at engine.
4. Remove flywheel housing dust cover.
5. Remove oil pan attaching bolts, then remove oil pan and gaskets. It maybe necessary to rotate crankshaft to provide clearance for oil pan removal.
6. Reverse procedure to install. Before installing oil pan, apply a suitable sealer across joint lines of cylinder block and front and rear covers, **Fig. 18.**

# OIL PUMP

## REPLACE

1. Remove timing belt as described under "Timing Belt, Replace."
2. On models equipped with manual transaxle, place shift lever in fourth gear position and apply parking brake.
3. On models equipped with automatic

DIPSTICK AND TUBE
OIL PUMP
GASKET
CYLINDER BLOCK
INLET PIPE AND SCREEN

Fig. 19 Oil pump replacement

transaxle, remove flywheel housing dust cover and hold flywheel in position using tool No. T84P-6375-A or equivalent.

4. On all models, remove crankshaft sprocket attaching bolt, then remove sprocket and key.
5. Remove oil pan as described under "Oil Pan, Replace."
6. Remove bolts attaching oil pump to engine block, then remove oil pump, **Fig. 19.**
7. Reverse procedure to install. When applying sealer to oil pump gasket, do not allow sealer to enter oil pump outlet port or engine block.

# OIL PUMP SERVICE

1. Remove oil pump pickup tube and

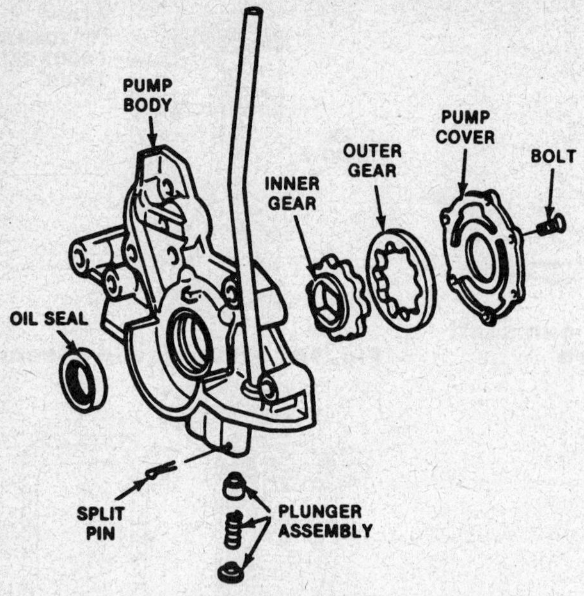


Fig. 20 Exploded view of oil pump

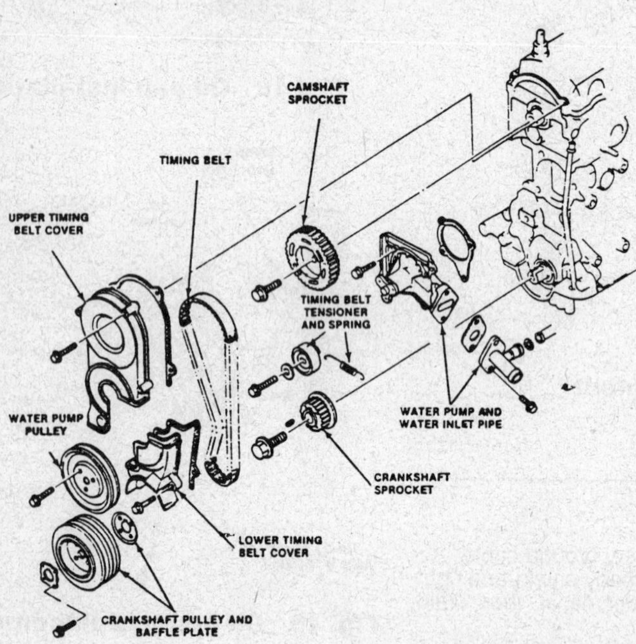


Fig. 22 Water pump replace

screen, **Fig. 20.**

2. Remove oil pump cover attaching screws, then remove cover and inner and outer gears.
3. Pry oil seal from pump body, then remove cotter pin retainer, spring and relief valve from pump.
4. Check pump body for wear and damage and replace as necessary. Light scoring is acceptable.
5. Check pump body to outer gear clearance, **Fig. 21.** Clearance should not exceed .0087 inch.
6. Check inner gear to outer clearance at point of least clearance, **Fig. 21.** Clearance should not exceed .0078 inch.
7. Using a straight edge and feeler gauge, measure gear end play **Fig. 21.** End play should not exceed .0055 inch.
8. Check relief for wear and damage and replace as necessary.
9. Install relief valve, spring, retainer and cotter pin on pump housing.
10. Using tool T87C-6019-A or equivalent, install replacement seal into pump body.
11. Install inner and outer gears into pump body, then install cover and attaching screws. Apply a suitable thread locking compound to cover attaching screws before installing.
12. Install gasket, pickup tube and screen.

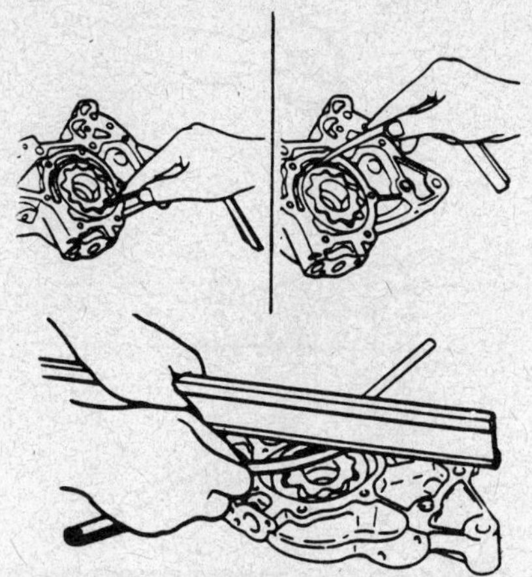

Fig. 21 Oil pump inspection

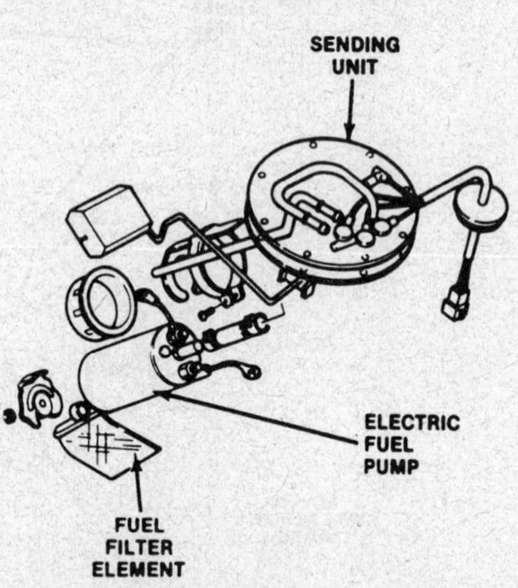


Fig. 23 Electric fuel pump/sending unit assembly

## WATER PUMP REPLACE

1. Remove timing belt as described under "Timing Belt, Replace."
2. Drain cooling system, then disconnect lower radiator and heater hoses from water pump.
3. Remove water pump attaching bolts and the water pump, **Fig. 22.**
4. Reverse procedure to install.

## THERMOSTAT REPLACE

1. Disconnect cooling fan electrical connector from thermostat housing.
2. Drain cooling system, then disconnect upper radiator hose at thermostat housing.
3. Remove thermostat housing attaching bolts, then the housing.
4. Remove thermostat and gasket.
5. Install thermostat into cylinder head, valve end first. **Ensure jiggle valve is at top.**
6. Install new gasket coated with suitable sealer. **Painted side of gasket must face thermostat.**

7. Install housing and attaching bolts. **Torque** bolts to 14-22 ft. lbs.
8. Connect upper hose, then fill cooling system.

## COOLING SYSTEM BLEED

These engine do not require a specified bleed procedure. After filling cooling system,run engine to operating temperature with radiator/pressure cap off. Air will then be automatically bled through cap opening.

## BELT TENSION DATA

Alternator, water pump, power steering and A/C compressor drive belts should be tensioned to 110 to 132 lbs.

## FUEL PUMP

### REPLACE

1. Relieve fuel system pressure by starting engine and disconnecting vane air flow meter. After engine has stalled, place ignition switch in the Off position.
2. Remove rear seat cushion, then open fuel pump access cover and disconnect fuel pump electrical connector.
3. Disconnect fuel pump ground wire, then remove access cover.
4. Disconnect and cap fuel supply and return lines.
5. Remove sending unit/fuel pump assembly to fuel tank attaching bolts, then remove sending unit/fuel pump assembly and gasket from tank.
6. Remove fuel filter from fuel pump, then disconnect fuel pump electrical leads from sending unit.
7. Remove retaining clamp screw, then remove fuel pump outlet hose clamp.
8. Remove fuel pump from sending unit, **Fig. 23.**
9. Reverse procedure to install.

## TIGHTENING SPECIFICATIONS

***Torque Specifications Are For Clean And Lightly Lubricated Threads Only. Dry Or Dirty Threads Produce Increased Friction Which Prevents Accurate Measurement Of Tightness.**

| Year | Component | Torque/ft. lbs. |
|---|---|---|
| 1989 | Camshaft Sprocket Bolt | 36-45 |
| | Camshaft Thrust Plate Bolt | 6-9 |
| | Connecting Rod Nut | 37-41 |
| | Coolant Temperature Sender | 4-7 |
| | Crankshaft Damper Bolt | 71-76 |
| | Cylinder Head Bolts | 56-60 |
| | Exhaust Manifold To Cylinder Head | 12-17 |
| | Flexplate to Crankshaft | 71-76 |
| | Flywheel To Crankshaft | 71-76 |
| | Ignition Distributor Clamp Bolt | 14-22 |
| | Intake Manifold To Cylinder Head | 14-19 |
| | Main Bearing Cap Bolts | 40-43 |
| | Oil Pan Drain Plug | 22-30 |
| | Oil Pan To Engine | 5.7-6.5 |
| | Oil Pressure Sending Unit | 9-13 |
| | Oil Pump Cover To Pump | ① |
| | Oil Pump Pickup Tube To Pump | 5.5-7.9 |
| | Oil Pump To Engine | 14-19 |
| | Pressure Plate To Flywheel | 13-20 |
| | Rocker Arm Cover To Cylinder Head | 3.6-6.4 |
| | Rocker Arm Shaft To Cylinder Head | 16-21 |
| | Spark Plug | 11-17 |
| | Starter Motor To Engine | 23-34 |
| | Timing Belt Cover | 5.7-8 |
| | Timing Belt Tensioner Adjusting Bolt | 14-19 |
| | Torque Converter To Flex Plate | 25-36 |
| | Transaxle To Engine | 47-66 |
| | Water Outlet To Engine | 14-19 |
| | Water Pump To Engine | 14-19 |

①—**Apply locking compound to screw threads, then install hand tight.**

# Clutch & Manual Transaxle

## INDEX



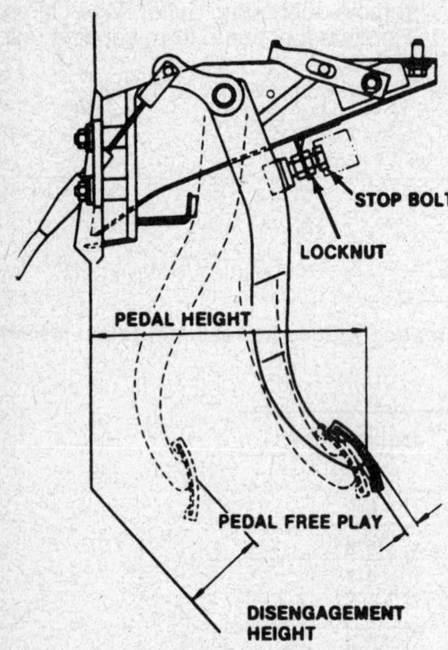


**Fig. 1 Clutch pedal height & free play check**

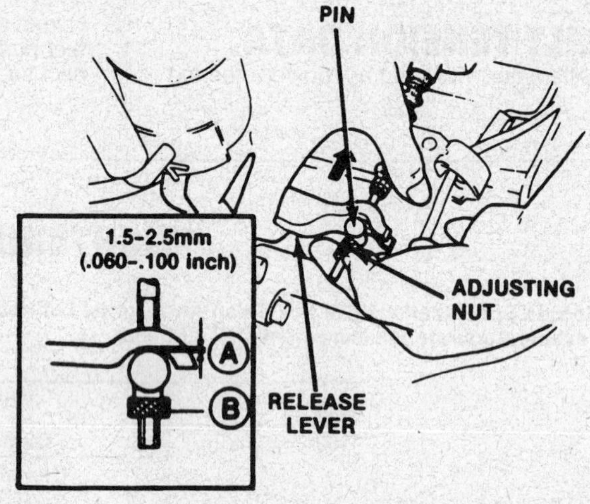


**Fig. 2 Clutch pedal free play adjustment**

## CLUTCH PEDAL
## ADJUST

### PEDAL HEIGHT

1. Measure distance from upper center of clutch pedal pad to firewall, **Fig. 1.** Clutch pedal height should be 8.4 to 8.6 inches.
2. If clutch pedal height is not within specification, remove instrument panel components as necessary to gain access to clutch pedal.
3. Loosen locknut on clutch pedal stop, then rotate stop bolt until correct clutch pedal height is obtained, **Fig. 1.**
4. Tight clutch pedal stop locknut and install instrument panel components that were removed to gain access to clutch pedal.

### PEDAL FREEPLAY

1. Lightly depress clutch pedal and measure freeplay, **Fig. 1.** Clutch pedal freeplay should be .35 to .59 inch.
2. If clutch pedal freeplay is not with limits, depress clutch release lever and pull pin away from lever, **Fig. 2.**
3. Rotate adjusting nut (B), **Fig. 2,** until a clearance .06 to .10 inch is obtained.
4. After completing adjustment, ensure clutch pedal to floor pan free play is as described in step 1.

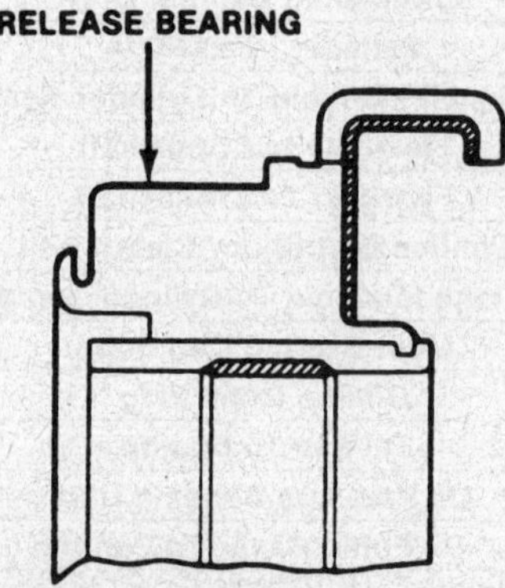


**Fig. 3 Apply lubricant to release bearing shaded areas**

## CLUTCH
## REPLACE

1. Remove transaxle as described under "Manual Transaxle, Replace."
2. Install flywheel locking tool T84P-6375-A or equivalent.
3. Using a suitable clutch pilot tool to hold clutch plate in position, alternately and evenly loosen pressure plate attaching bolts.
4. Remove pressure plate, then remove clutch pilot tool and clutch plate.
5. Reverse procedure to install. Apply lubricant C1AZ-19590-B or equivalent to clutch release bearing, **Fig. 3, and clutch disc and input shaft splines. Use care not to allow lubricant to contact clutch face. Position clutch disc to flywheel as shown in** **Fig. 4.** When installing pressure plate, **torque pressure plate attaching bolts alternately and evenly to 13 to 20 ft. lbs.**

## MANUAL TRANSAXLE
## REPLACE

1. Disconnect battery ground cable, then remove air cleaner.
2. Disconnect speedometer cable from transaxle, then disconnect clutch cable from release fork.
3. Remove bolt attaching clutch cable bracket and ground wire.
4. Remove coolant pipe bracket.
5. Remove secondary air pipe and EGR pipe bracket.
6. Disconnect neutral safety switch and back-up lamp switch electrical connectors.
7. Disconnect body ground connector, then remove two upper transaxle to engine attaching bolts.
8. Support engine using a suitable engine support bar.
9. Raise and support vehicle, then drain transaxle lubricant.
10. Remove front wheel and tire assemblies, then remove engine compartment side and under covers.
11. Remove front stabilizer bar, then remove lower ball joint to steering knuckle bolts. Pull lower control arms downward to separate lower arms from steering knuckles. Use care not to damage ball joint boots.
12. Pull front hubs outward to separate

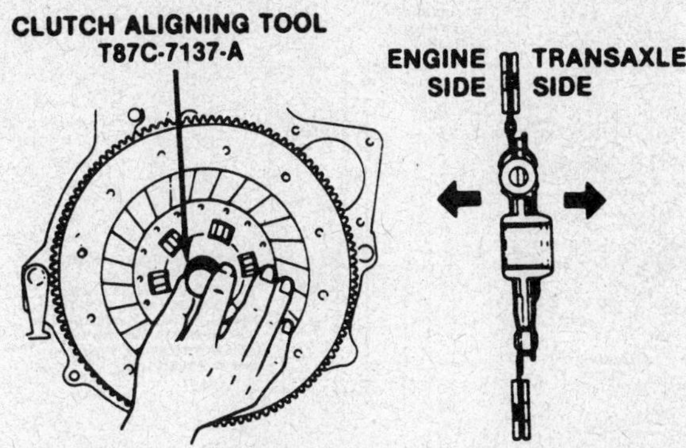


**Fig. 4 Positioning clutch plate to flywheel**

halfshafts from transaxle and suspend shafts from body with wire. Use care when removing halfshafts from transaxle, as damage to oil seals may result. Hold halfshafts during removal, as movement of joint through angles in excess of 20 degrees may result in damage to boots.

13. Remove crossmember attaching bolts, then remove crossmember.
14. Remove nut and bolt attaching shift control rod to transaxle, then position control rod aside.
15. Remove bolt attaching shift extension mounting bracket, then slide extension from mounting bracket.
16. Remove starter motor, then remove bolts attaching end plate to transaxle.
17. Lower transaxle by loosening engine support bar, then support transaxle using a suitable jack.
18. Remove bolt attaching engine mount to transaxle.
19. Remove remaining transaxle to engine attaching bolts, then remove transaxle.
20. Reverse procedure to install. Apply lubricant C1AZ-19590-A or equivalent to input shaft splines. **Torque transaxle to engine attaching bolts to 47 to 66 ft. lbs.** When installing halfshafts, use a new circlip, positioning gap in circlip at top of circlip groove.

## TIGHTENING SPECIFICATIONS

| Year | Component | Torque/ft. lbs. |
|---|---|---|
| 1989 | Clutch Pressure Plate Retaining Bolts | 13-20 |
| | Differential Crown Wheel Retaining Bolts | 45-54 |
| | Flywheel Retaining Bolts | 60-65 |
| | Gate Lock Bold | 8.7–11.6 |
| | Gear Shaft Lock Nut① | 96–155 |
| | Guide Bolt | 6.5–10.1 |
| | Rear Cover① | 6–8 |
| | Ring Gear | 51-62 |
| | Reverse Idle Shaft Lock Bolt | 15.2–22.4 |
| | Transcase | 13.0–18.8 |
| | Transaxle Case To Clutch Housing Bolts | 14-20 |

①—5 Speed transmission.

# Rear Suspension

## INDEX



## WHEEL BEARING ADJUST

1. Block front wheels, then raise and support rear of vehicle.
2. Remove wheel and tire assembly.
3. Ensure parking brake is fully released, then remove grease cap and raise staked portion of wheel bearing adjusting nut using a suitable chisel.
4. Remove wheel bearing adjusting nut and discard. To loosen adjusting nut on left hand side of vehicle, turn nut counterclockwise. To loosen adjusting nut on right hand side of vehicle, turn nut clockwise.
5. Position replacement adjusting nut on spindle, then **torque nut to 18.1 to 21.7 ft. lbs.,** while rotating brake drum to seat bearings.
6. Loosen locknut slightly, so that nut can be rotated by hand.
7. Install lug nut on stud, then position stud at 12 o'clock position. Using an inch torque wrench on lug nut, measure and record amount of force required to start rotation of brake drum, **Fig. 1.** This measurement is seal drag.
8. To determine preload setting, add the required amount of preload, which is 1.3 to 4.3 inch lbs., to the seal drag reading obtained in step 7.
9. Tighten wheel bearing adjusting nut slightly, then using inch lb. torque wrench as described in step 7, measure wheel bearing preload. Continue to tighten wheel bearing adjusting nut a little at a time until wheel bearing preload determined in step 8 is obtained.
10. After proper preload setting has been obtained, stake wheel bearing adjusting nut, **Fig. 2.** If nut is damaged during staking, it must be replaced.
11. Install grease cap, then install wheel and tire assembly.

## WHEEL BEARING REPLACE

1. Raise and support rear of vehicle, then remove wheel and tire assembly.
2. Using a suitable chisel, carefully raise staked portion of wheel bearing adjusting nut.
3. Remove wheel bearing adjusting nut and discard, **Fig. 3.** To loosen adjusting nut on left hand side of vehicle, turn nut counterclockwise. To loosen

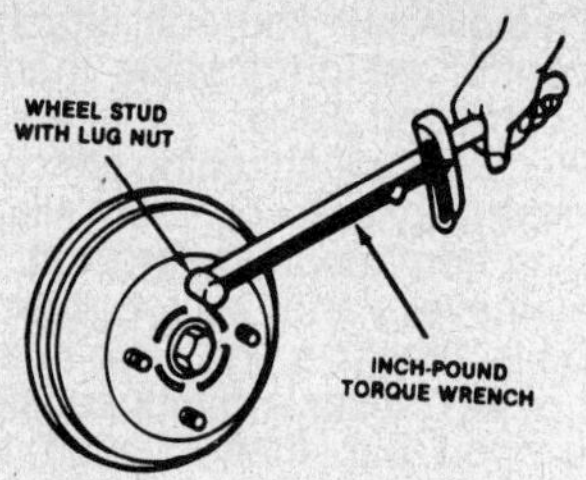


**Fig. 1 Wheel bearing adjustment**

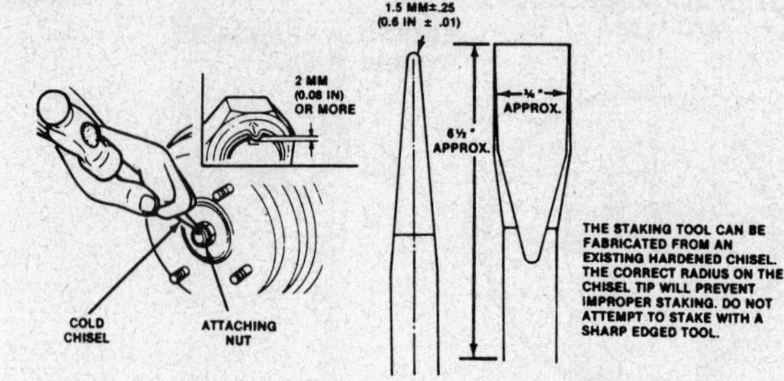


**Fig. 2 Staking wheel bearing adjusting nut**

adjusting nut on right hand side of vehicle, turn nut clockwise.

4. Remove outer wheel bearing from hub, then remove brake drum and hub assembly.
5. Remove grease seal, then remove inner bearing from hub.
6. If necessary, bearing races can be driven from hub using a suitable brass drift.
7. Reverse procedure to install. Prior to installation, pack wheel bearings and hub cavity with suitable wheel bearing grease. Also apply grease to seal lip. After installing bearings, adjust wheel bearing preload as described under "Wheel Bearing, Adjust."

## STRUT UNIT & COIL SPRING

### REPLACE

1. Raise and support rear of vehicle, then remove wheel and tire assembly.
2. Remove rear brake drum and hub assembly as described under "Wheel Bearing, Replace."
3. Remove trailing arm and spindle to strut unit attaching bolt, **Figs. 4 and 5.**
4. Place alignment mark on strut rubber mounting bracket, then from inside vehicle, remove strut attaching nuts and remove strut from tower.
5. Using a suitable spring compressor, compress coil spring.
6. With coil spring compressed, remove remove strut nut, rubber mounting bracket, spring upper seal and spring seat.
7. Carefully release spring compressor and remove coil spring.
8. Reverse procedure to install. Tighten spindle to strut attaching bolts to torque listed at the end of this section.

## CONTROL & TRAILING ARMS

### REPLACE

1. Raise rear of vehicle and remove wheel and tire assembly.
2. Remove brake drum and hub as described under "Wheel Bearing, Replace."
3. On hatchback models, place alignment marks on rear toe adjusting cam and control arm, **Fig. 4.**
4. On all models, place alignment marks

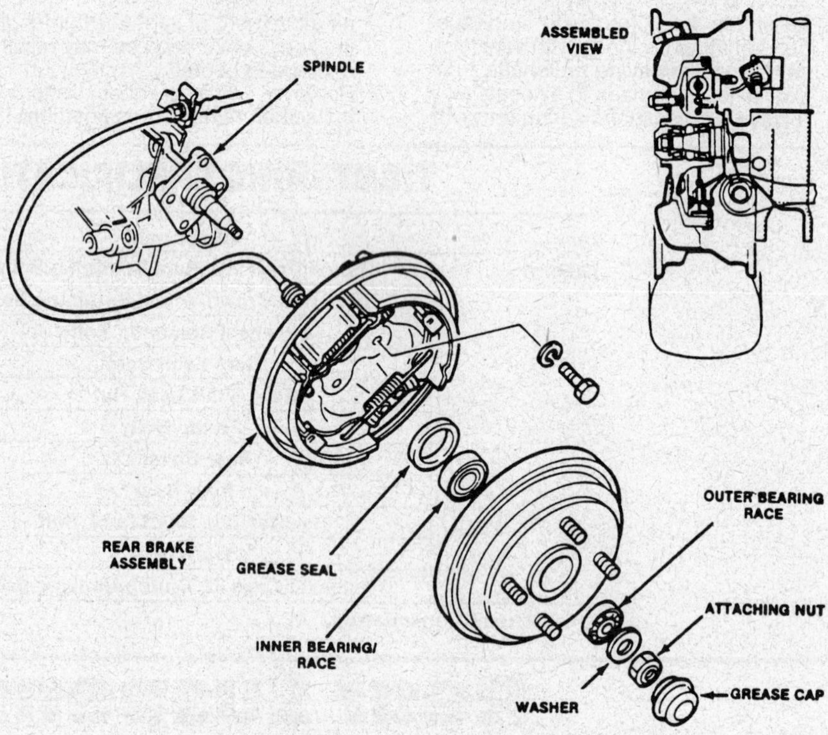


**Fig. 3 Wheel bearings & hub**

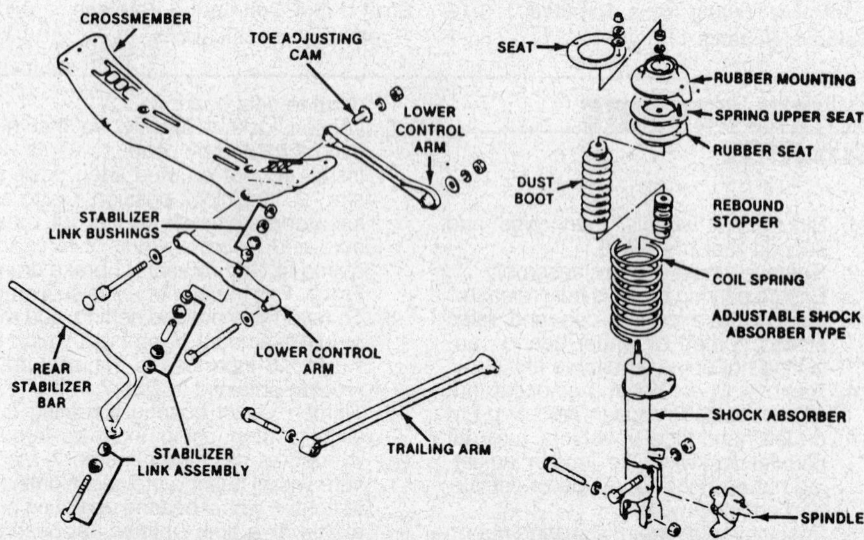


**Fig. 4 Rear suspension. Hatchback models**

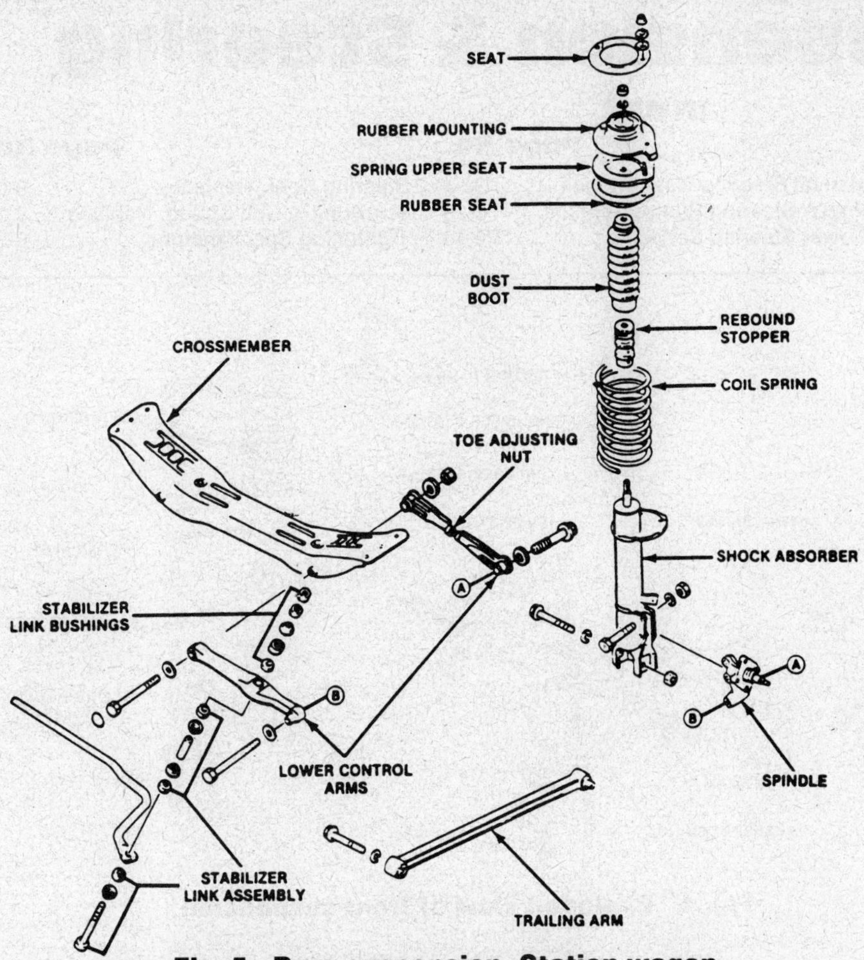


**Fig. 5 Rear suspension. Station wagon**

on control arm and control arm bushing.

5. On all models, place alignment marks on each side of trailing arm and crossmember.
6. Remove stabilizer bar link, then remove stabilizer bar and bushings, **Figs. 4 and 5.**
7. Loosen inner and outer trailing arm bolts, then loosen spindle to strut unit attaching bolts.
8. Remove parking brake attaching bolt from rear trailing arm assembly.
9. Loosen trailing arm to strut attaching bolts, then remove control and trailing arm.
10. Reverse procedure to install. When installing control and trailing arms, align all marks made during removal. When installing stabilizer link bolt, tighten until .31 inch of thread is exposed beyond nut. After vehicle has been lowered to ground, retighten stabilizer link bolt.

## SPINDLE REPLACE

1. Raise and support rear of vehicle, then remove wheel and tire assembly.
2. Remove brake drum and hub as described under "Wheel Bearing, Replace."
3. Remove spindle to strut unit attaching bolts, then remove control bolt, **Figs. 4 and 5.**
4. Remove spindle from strut unit.
5. Reverse procedure to install.

## TIGHTENING SPECIFICATIONS

| Year | Component | Torque/ft. lbs. |
|---|---|---|
| 1989 | Brake Line Fittings | 9-16 |
| | Control Arm Jam Nuts | 41-47 |
| | Control Arm Inner Bolt | 69-86 |
| | Control Arm To Spindle | 69-86 |
| | Lateral Link Through Bolt | 69-86 |
| | Spindle To Backing Plate | 33-49 |
| | Spindle To Strut Unit Bolts | 69-86 |
| | Stabilizer Bar Bushing Bracket Bolts | 32-40 |
| | Wheel Cylinder To Backing Plate | 7.2-9.4 |
| | Wheel Lug Nuts | 65-87 |

# Front Suspension & Steering

## INDEX



## STRUT UNIT & COIL SPRING

### REPLACE

1. Raise and support front vehicle, then remove wheel and tire assembly.
2. Remove rotor and hub as described in "Front Drive Axle."
3. Place alignment marks on inside of strut mounting block.
4. Remove steering knuckle to strut attaching bolts, **Fig. 1.**
5. Remove clip attaching brake hose to strut unit, then slide hose out of bracket.
6. Remove strut mounting bolts at strut tower, then remove strut and coil spring unit from vehicle.
7. Using a suitable spring compressor, compress coil spring.
8. Remove strut nut, then carefully release coil spring compressor.
9. Remove coil spring and upper mounting components.
10. Reverse procedure to install.

MOUNTING BLOCK
SPRING UPPER SEAT
RUBBER SEAT
BUMP STOPPER
STABILIZER BAR
COIL SPRING
RUBBER SEAT
SHOCK ABSORBER
STEERING KNUCKLE
LOWER ARM
RUBBER BUSHING
BALL JOINT

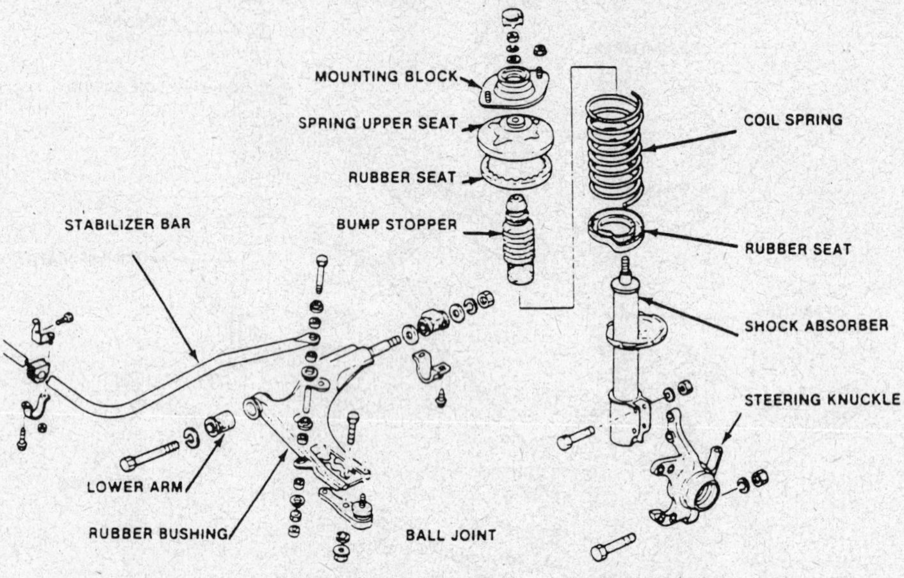

**Fig. 1 Exploded view of front suspension**

## BALL JOINT

### REPLACE

1. Raise and support front of vehicle, then remove wheel and tire assembly.
2. Remove caliper and suspend from coil spring with brake hose attached.
3. Remove stabilizer link from control arm, **Fig. 1.**
4. Remove tie rod end from steering knuckle using a suitable puller.
5. Remove ball joint to steering knuckle clamp bolt, then using a suitable pry bar, pull downward on lower control arm to separate ball joint stud from steering knuckle.
6. Remove two ball joint to control arm attaching nuts, then remove ball joint from lower control arm.
7. Reverse procedure to install. When installing stabilizer link, tighten until .43 inch of thread extends beyond nut.

## CONTROL ARM

### REPLACE

1. Raise and support front of vehicle, then remove wheel and tire assembly.
2. Remove brake caliper and suspend from coil spring with brake hose attached.
3. Remove stabilizer link, **Fig. 1.**
4. Place alignment marks on rear control arm bushing and mounting bracket,

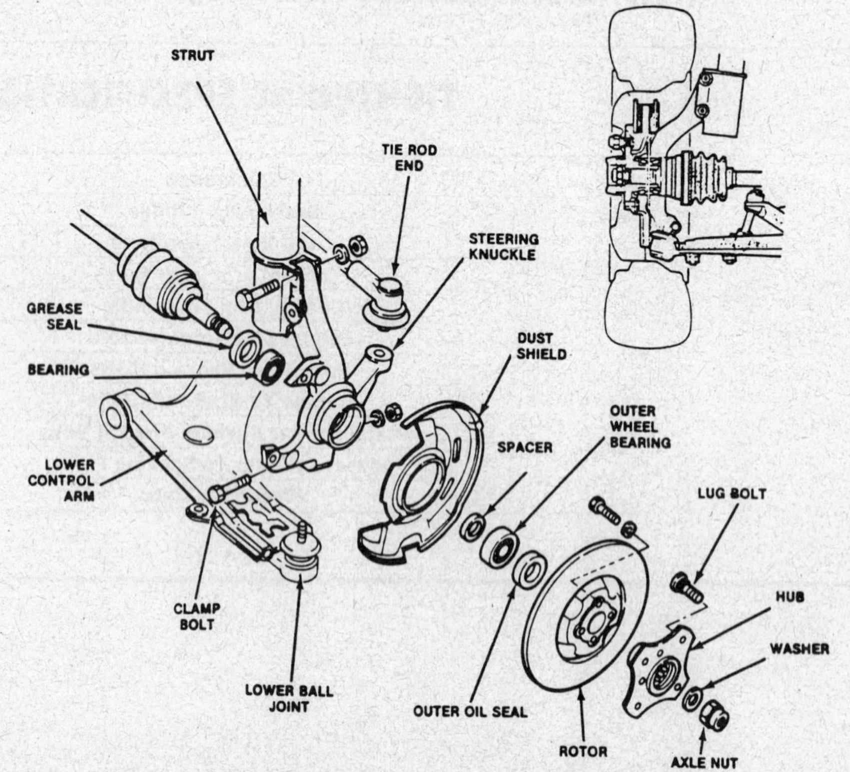


**Fig. 2 Hub & steering knuckle assembly**

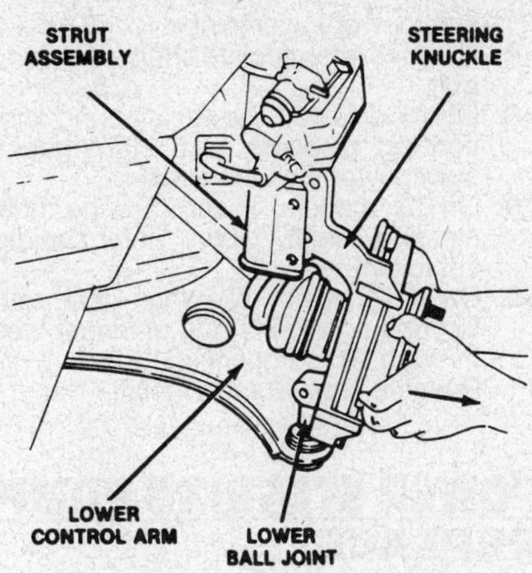


**Fig. 3 Separating hub & steering knuckle assembly from halfshaft**

**Fig. 4 Removing bearing from hub**

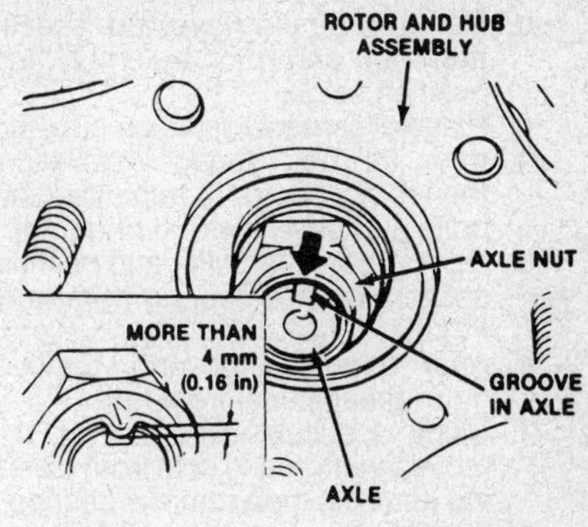


**Fig. 5 Staking axle nut**

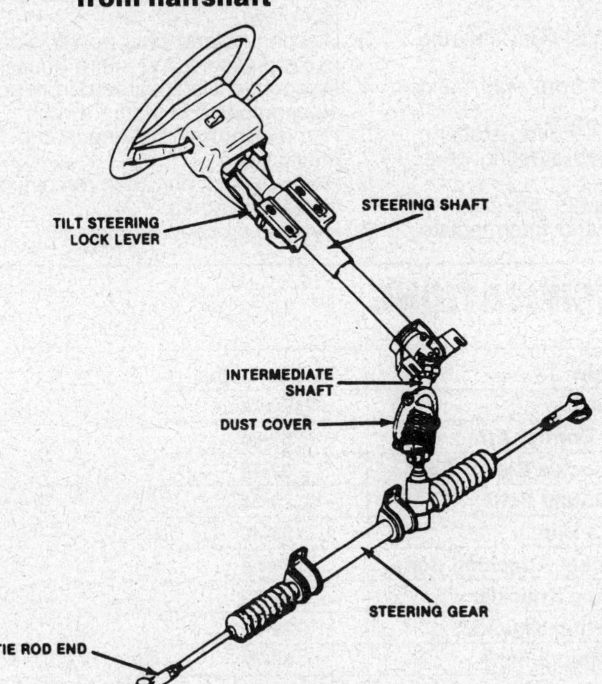


**Fig. 6 Manual steering gear replacement**

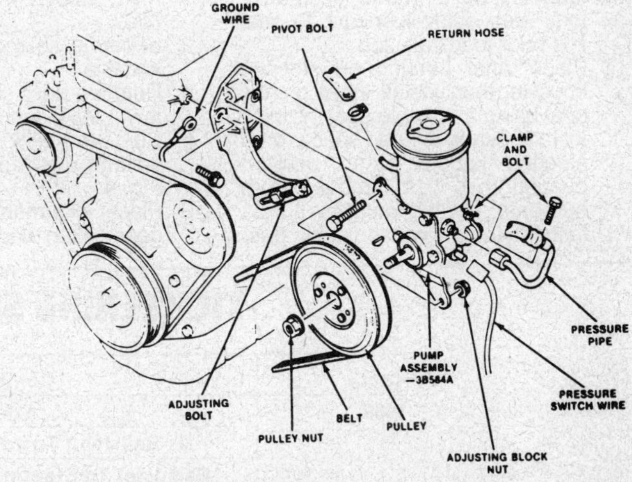


**Fig. 7 Power steering pump replacement**

then place alignment marks on front control arm bushing and control arm.

5. Remove ball joint to steering knuckle clamp bolt.
6. Loosen lower control arm front bushing nut and rear bushing bolt.
7. Remove lower control front bushing bracket attaching bolts and remove bracket.
8. Remove lower control arm rear bushing bolt and remove lower control arm.
9. If necessary, remove lower control arm from bushing nut and bushing.
10. If necessary, replace control arm rear bushing as follows:
    a. Using a hacksaw remove rear flange from rear control arm bushing.
    b. Using tool No. T87C-5493-B, press rear bushing from control arm.
    c. Position replacement lower control arm rear bushing, then press in using tool.
11. Reverse procedure to install. When installing stabilizer link, tighten until .43 inch of thread extends beyond nut. Recheck stabilizer bar bushing bracket attaching bolts torque after vehicle has been lowered.

## HUB & STEERING KNUCKLE REPLACE

### REMOVAL

1. Raise and support front of vehicle, then remove wheel and tire assembly.
2. Using a suitable chisel, carefully raise staked portion of axle nut.
3. With brakes applied, remove and discard axle nut, **Fig. 2.**
4. Remove stabilizer to control arm attaching bolt.
5. Remove cotter pin and retaining nut, then separate tie rod end from steering knuckle using a suitable tool.
6. Remove U-clip attaching brake hose to strut unit.
7. Remove caliper assembly with brake hose attached and suspend from coil spring using wire.
8. Remove bolt retaining ball joint to steering knuckle, then pry downward on lower control arm to separate ball joint from steering knuckle.
9. Remove steering knuckle to strut unit attaching bolts, then slide hub and steering knuckle out of strut unit bracket and off end of halfshaft, **Fig. 3.** If hub and steering knuckle binds on halfshaft, tap end of halfshaft with a soft faced mallet. If halfshaft splines are rusted, a suitable two jawed or hub puller must be used to separate halfshaft from hub. Use care when separating, as damage to grease seals may result.
10. If bearings are to be replaced, proceed as follows:
    a. Using tool No. T87C-1104-A, separate steering knuckle from hub and rotor.

b. Remove bearing preload spacer from hub and rotor assembly and position aside.
c. Place alignment marks on hub and rotor for use during installation, then remove rotor to hub attaching bolts and separate hub and rotor.
d. Using a suitable puller and bearing splitter, remove bearing from hub, **Fig. 4.**
e. After removing bearing, remove outer grease seal from hub.
f. Using a suitable screwdriver, remove inner grease seal from steering knuckle, then remove bearing.
g. If necessary, remove dust shield from steering knuckle.
h. Using tool No. T87C-1175-B, install dust shield on steering knuckle, if removed.
i. Pack bearings and hub cavity with lubricant C1AZ-1959D or equivalent. Also apply lubricant to seal lips prior to installation.
j. Place inner bearing on steering knuckle, then install inner grease seal using a suitable seal installer.
k. Install bearing preload spacer onto steering knuckle, then position bearing that was removed from hub onto steering knuckle.
l. Install outer grease seal onto steering knuckle using a suitable seal installer.
m. Position rotor to hub alignment marks, then install.
n. Press hub and rotor assembly onto steering knuckle.

11. Reverse procedure to install hub and knuckle assembly. Tighten axle nut to torque listed at the end of this section. After tightening axle nut, stake nut in place, **Fig. 5.** Tighten stabilizer link until .43 inch of thread extends beyond nut.

## STEERING GEAR REPLACE

1. Remove battery from vehicle.
2. Raise and support front of vehicle, then remove wheel and tire assemblies.
3. Separate tie rod ends from steering knuckle.
4. Remove dust shield from right hand lower inner fender.
5. Remove plastic tie securing steering column dust cover to steering gear, **Fig. 6.**
6. Place alignment marks on steering gear pinion flange and intermediate shaft lower lower joint.
7. Remove intermediate shaft lower joint bolt.
8. On models with power steering, disconnect pressure and return hoses from power steering gear.
9. On all models, lower steering until steering shaft clears intermediate shaft joint.
10. Carefully slide steering gear out through right hand side of fender well through tie rod opening.
11. Reverse procedure to install.

## POWER STEERING PUMP REPLACE

1. Remove power steering pump drive belt, **Fig. 7.**
2. Disconnect ground wire from engine lifting eye.
3. Disconnect and plug power steering pump pressure and return hoses.
4. Disconnect electrical lead from power steering pump pressure switch.
5. Remove power steering pump from bracket.
6. Remove pivot bolt, then remove power steering pump.
7. Reverse procedure to install.

## TIGHTENING SPECIFICATIONS

| Year | Component | Torque/ft. lbs. |
|---|---|---|
| 1989 | Axle Nut | 116-174① |
| | Ball Joint To Lower Control Arm | 69-86 |
| | Ball Joint To Steering Knuckle Clamp Bolt | 32-40 |
| | Brake Caliper Mounting Bolts | 29-36 |
| | Brake Disc To Hub | 33-40 |
| | Stabilizer Bar Bushing Bracket Attaching Bolts | 44-54 |
| | Strut Unit To Steering Knuckle. | 69-72 |
| | Tie Rod End To Steering Knuckle | 22-33 |
| | Tie Rod to Rack (Man. Steer.) | 58-72 |
| | Tie Rod to Rack (Power Steer.) | 43.4-57.9 |
| | Wheel Lug Nuts | 65-87 |

**①—Stake nut using a suitable chisel. If axle nut is damaged during staking, replace nut.**

# Wheel Alignment

## INDEX

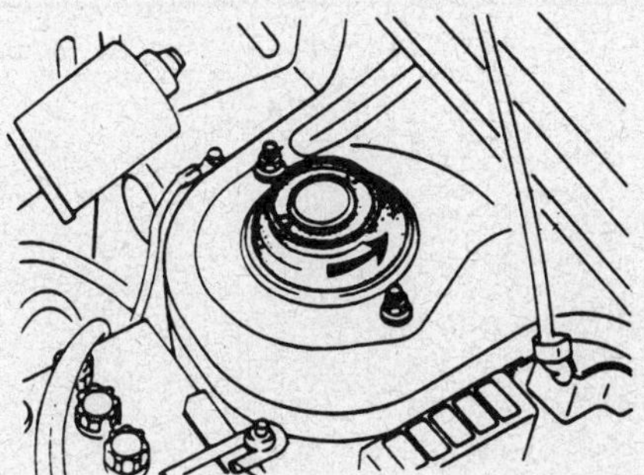

**Fig. 1 Rotating strut bearing to adjust front camber**

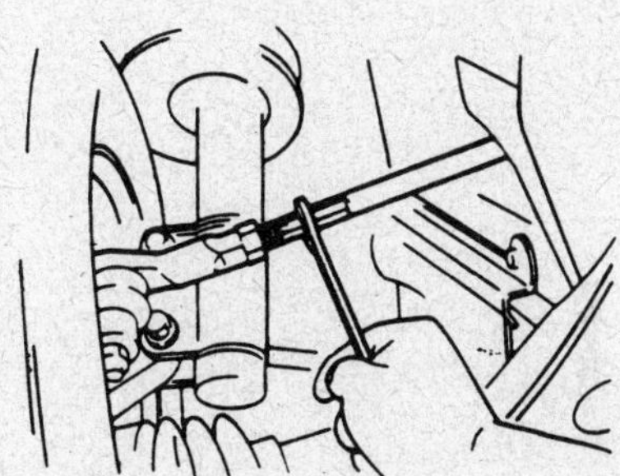

**Fig. 2 Adjusting front toe-in**

## FRONT WHEEL ALIGNMENT

### CASTER

When checking caster ensure tires are properly inflated. Caster angles are not adjustable. If caster is not within specifications, check for damaged or distorted control arm or stabilizer bar or worn bushings.

### CAMBER

Camber angle can be changed by 28 minutes by the strut bearing one half turn.

1. Raise and support vehicle by body so that front suspension is unloaded.
2. Remove wheel and tire assembly.
3. Remove strut to strut tower attaching nuts, then lower strut from tower.
4. Rotate strut bearing 180 degrees, **Fig. 1.**
5. Position strut to strut tower, then install attaching nuts.
6. Install wheel and tire assembly, then recheck camber setting.

### TOE-IN

1. Loosen jam nuts at tie rod ends, then release clips securing boots to tie rod.
2. Turn tie rods in or out of tie rod ends as necessary, **Fig. 2.** Rotate tie rods an equal amount on each side to maintain steering center.

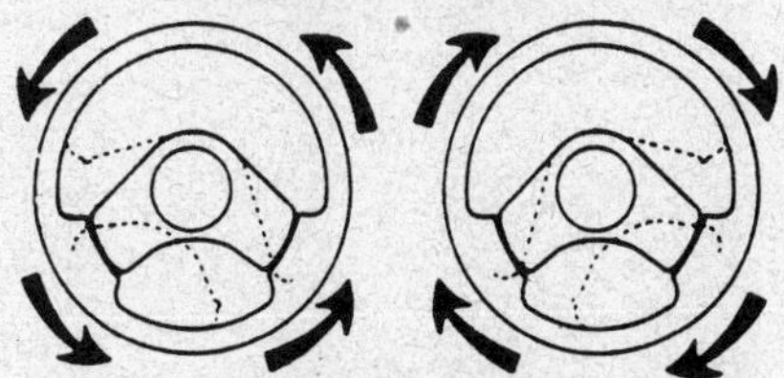

CLOCKWISE ANGULAR ERROR TURN BOTH TIE-RODS AN EQUAL AMOUNT COUNTERCLOCKWISE TO CORRECT
COUNTER-CLOCKWISE ANGULAR ERROR TURN BOTH TIE-RODS AN EQUAL AMOUNT CLOCKWISE TO CORRECT
CLOCKWISE AND COUNTERCLOCKWISE ARE AS VIEWED FROM THE LEFT SIDE OF THE VEHICLE

**Fig. 3 Centering steering wheel**

3. Check vehicle front tracking. Refer to alignment manufacturers instruction for front track check procedure.
4. After setting front track, recheck toe-in setting.
5. **Torque tie rod end jam nuts to 25.3 to 28.9 ft. lbs.,** then install clips retaining boots to tie rods.

### CENTERING STEERING WHEEL

After completing front toe-in and front track adjustments, steering wheel should be centered, if not proceed as follows:

1. Using a grease pencil, place alignment marks on tie rod ends and tie rods.
2. Loosen tie rod end jam nuts, then remove clips securing boots to tie rods.
3. Rotate tie rods in equal amounts as indicated in **Fig. 3.** Refer to alignment marks made with grease pencil to ensure both tie rods are being rotated equal amounts.
4. After completing adjustment, **torque jam nuts to 25.3 to 28.9 ft. lbs.,** then install boot to tie rod retaining clips.

## REAR WHEEL ALIGNMENT

### CAMBER

Rear camber angle cannot be adjusted on these models. If rear camber is not within specifications, check chassis and body to chassis mountings for damage and distortion.

### TOE-IN

#### HATCHBACK MODELS

Rear toe-in on these models is adjusted by rotating adjusting cams located on the control arms.

### STATION WAGON

1. Loosen jam nuts at control arms.
2. To increase toe-in, rotate right control arm clockwise and left control arm counterclockwise, **Fig. 4.** To decrease toe-in, rotate right control arm counterclockwise and left control arm clockwise. Rotate both control arms by equal amounts.
3. After completing rear toe-in adjustment, check vehicle rear tracking as per alignment equipment manufacturers instructions.
4. **Torque jam nuts to 41 to 47 ft. lbs.**

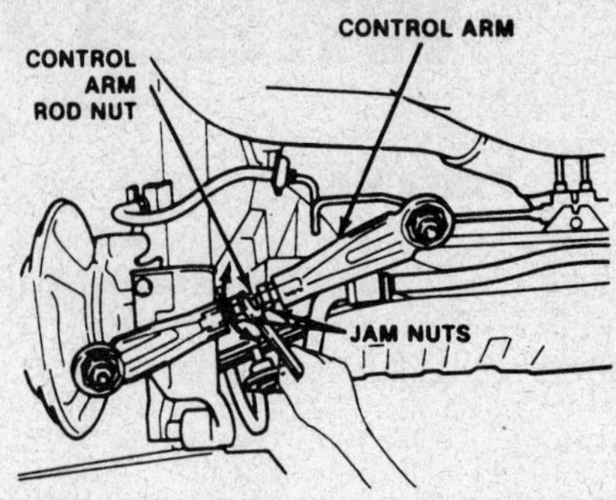


**Fig. 4 Rear toe-in adjustment**

# MERCURY CAPRI

## INDEX OF SERVICE OPERATIONS

**NOTE:** Refer To Rear Of This Manual For Vehicle Manufacturer's Special Service Tool Suppliers.

# Specifications

## GENERAL ENGINE SPECIFICATIONS

| Year | Engine Liter/CID | Engine VIN Code | Fuel System | Bore and Stroke | Compression Ratio | Net H.P. @ RPM | Maximum Torque Ft. Lbs. @ RPM | Normal Oil Pressure Pounds |
|---|---|---|---|---|---|---|---|---|
| 1991-92 | 1.6L/4-98 | Z | MPI | 3.07 x 3.29 | 9.4 | 63 @ 5000 | 73 @ 3000 | 50-64① |
| 1991-92 | 1.6L/4-98② | 6 | MPI | 3.07 x 3.29 | 7.9 | 132 @ 6000 | 136 @ 3000 | 50-64① |

①—At 3000 RPM.
②—Turbocharged engine

## TUNE UP SPECIFICATIONS

| Year & Engine/VIN Code | Spark Plug Gap | Ignition Timing BTDC① Firing Order Fig. | Ignition Timing BTDC① Man. Trans. | Ignition Timing BTDC① Auto. Trans. | Ignition Timing BTDC① Mark Fig. | Curb Idle Speed Man. Trans. | Curb Idle Speed Auto. Trans. | Fast Idle Speed Man. Trans. | Fast Idle Speed Auto. Trans. | Fuel Pump Pressure Psi |
|---|---|---|---|---|---|---|---|---|---|---|
| **1991-92** | | | | | | | | | | |
| 1.6L/4-98 | .39-.43 | ① | ② | ② | B | 800-900 | 800-900③ | — | ④ | ⑤ |

①—Inline 1-3-4-2.
②—Base Timing Inspection: Disconnect and plug hoses from vacuum diaphragm. Run engine to operating temperature and with electrical loads off, set/check idle to 800-900 RPM. Check timing at 1°-3° (BTDC)for non-Turbo and 11°-13° (BTDC) for turbo.
③—Turbo Models w/automatic transaxle.
④—The ECM controls the rate of fuel injection in response to information received from driver controls, sensors and switches which monitor engine conditions during operation.
⑤—Fuel pump outlet fuel pressure is 64-85 psi. Fuel injection pressure (Engine running) is 37-41 psi.

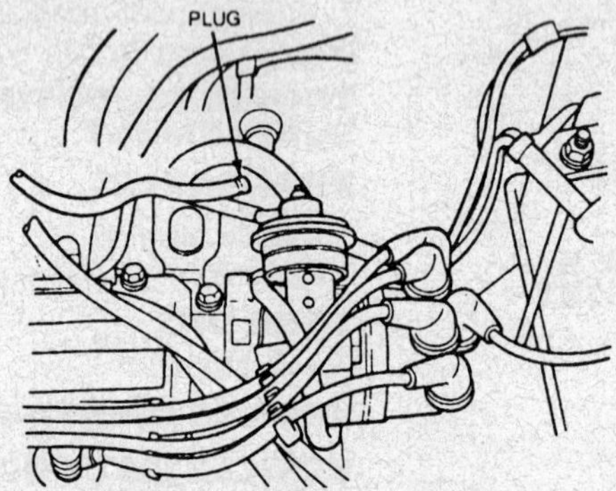

Fig. A Ignition timing

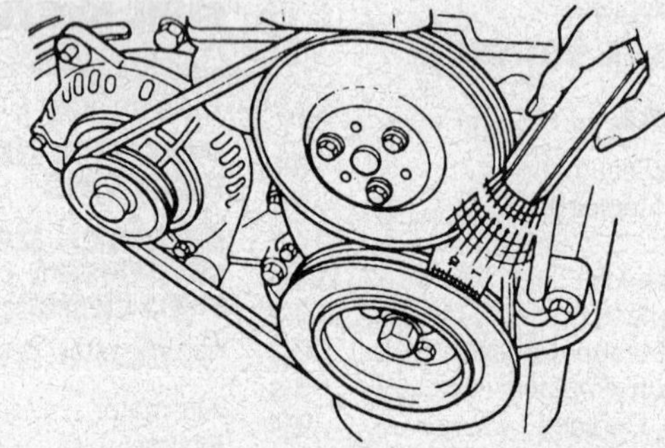
Fig. B Timing marks (BTDC)

## WHEEL ALIGNMENT SPECIFICATIONS

| Year | Caster Angle, Degrees Limits | Caster Angle, Degrees Desired | Camber Angle, Degrees Limits | Camber Angle, Degrees Desired | Toe-In Inch |
|---|---|---|---|---|---|
| **Front** | | | | | |
| 1991-92 | +.83 to +2.33 | +1.58 | +.5 to +1.55 | +.80 | +.08 |
| **Rear** | | | | | |
| 1991-92 | — | — | −1.17 to +.33 | −.42 | +0 |

## COOLING SYSTEM & CAPACITY DATA

| Year | Model or Engine/VIN | Cooling Capacity, Qts. | | Radiator Cap Relief Pressure, Lbs. | Thermo. Opening Temp. | Fuel Tank Gals. | Engine Oil Refill Qts. | Transaxle Oil | |
|---|---|---|---|---|---|---|---|---|---|
| | | Less A/C | With A/C | | | | | Manual Transaxle Qts. | Auto. Transaxle Qts.③ |
| 1991-92 | 1.6L/4-98 | ① | ① | 15-19 | ④ | 11.1 | 3.5 | 3.4 | 6.0③ |

①—1.6L engine less turbocharger; 5.3 qts. 1.6L engine with turbocharger; 6.3 qts. Fill radiator with 50/50 mixture of Premium Cooling System Fluid (Anti-Freeze) and water.

②—Thermostat sub valve at 190.5°–193.5° and main valve at 196.5°–199.5°

③—Use dipstick to determine when system is full.

## LUBRICANT DATA

| Year | Model | Lubricant Type | | | | | |
|---|---|---|---|---|---|---|---|
| | | Transaxle | | | | | |
| | | Manual | Automatic | Transfer Case | Rear Axle | Power Steering | Brake System |
| 1991-92 | All | ATF① | ATF① | — | — | ATF① | DOT 3 |

①—Mercon XT-2-QDX or XT-2-DDX.

# Electrical

## INDEX



## AIRBAG SYSTEM DISARMING

### AIRBAG SYSTEM DEACTIVATION

**The electrical circuit necessary for system deployment is powered directly from the battery. To avoid accidental deployment and possible personal injury, the battery and back-up power supply must be disconnected prior to servicing or replacing any system components.**

1. Disconnect battery ground cable and isolate cable end with electrical tape.
2. Open glove compartment, then lower the door fully by depressing the stops.
3. Detach the battery back-up which is a blue rectangular box on the outer left-hand side of the glove compartment, then disconnect electrical connector.
4. Remove four nut and washer assemblies retaining the airbag to the steering wheel.
5. Disconnect the airbag connector from the clockspring.
6. Attach a jumper wire between the gray/orange (GY/O) wire terminal and pink (PK) wire terminal of the clockspring connector.

### AIRBAG SYSTEM REACTIVATION

1. Remove jumper wire from airbag terminals on clockspring.
2. Connect airbag module to clockspring connector.
3. Position airbag module on steering wheel, then install four nut and washer assemblies. **Torque** nuts to 17-26 Inch. Lbs.
4. Connect battery ground cable, then back-up power supply.
5. Verify airbag indicator lamp operation.

## FUSE PANEL & FLASHER LOCATION

The fuse panel is located under the left side of the instrument panel. The hazard flasher is located inside the lefthand bottom edge of the instrument panel. The turn signal flasher is located on the relay panel above the fuse panel.

## STARTER REPLACE

1. Disconnect battery ground cable, then isolate cable end with electrical tape.
2. Disconnect starter electrical connectors, then remove starter motor upper attaching bolts.
3. Remove intake manifold upper support bracket attaching bolts.
4. Raise and support vehicle, then remove starter support bracket to intake manifold support bracket attaching bolt.
5. Remove intake manifold lower support bracket attaching bolts.
6. Loosen exhaust hangers, if necessary, then remove starter attaching bolts.
7. Reverse procedure to install noting the following:
   a. **Torque** starter to support bracket attaching nuts to 54-70 inch lbs.
   b. **Torque** starter support bracket to manifold support bracket attaching bolt to 14-19 ft. lbs.
   c. **Torque** upper and lower starter attaching bolts to 23-30 ft. lbs.
   d. **Torque** upper and lower intake manifold bracket attaching bolts to 22-34 ft. lbs.

## DISTRIBUTOR REPLACE

1. Disconnect battery ground cable, then

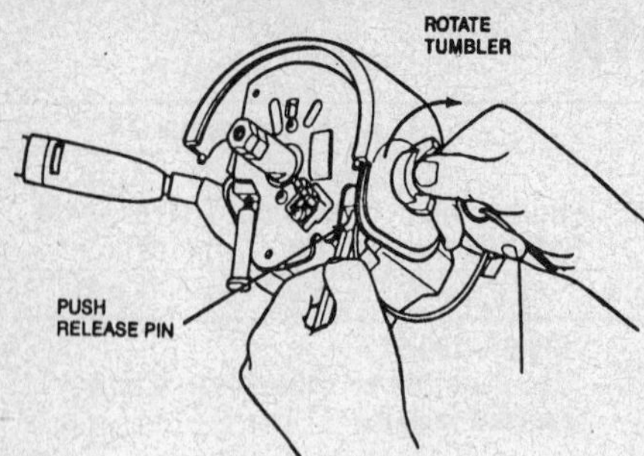


**Fig. 1 Ignition lock replace**

isolate cable end with electrical tape.
2. Disconnect distributor high tension cable and mark for installation.
3. Disconnect remaining electrical connectors.
4. Remove distributor attaching bolt, then remove distributor.
5. Reverse procedure to install

# IGNITION LOCK
## REPLACE

1. Disarm airbag system as described under "Airbag System Disarming."
2. Disconnect battery ground cable.
3. Remove steering wheel as outlined under "Steering Wheel, Replace."
4. Remove steering column lower shroud.
5. Install ignition key, then rotate tumbler while pushing release pin with 0.125 inch drift, **Fig. 1.**
6. Remove lock from housing.
7. Reverse procedure to install.
8. Reactivate airbag system as described under "Airbag System Disarming."

# IGNITION SWITCH
## REPLACE

1. Disarm airbag system as described under "Airbag System Disarming."
2. Disconnect battery ground cable.
3. Remove steering column lower shroud.
4. Remove center access panel and lower steering column trim panel.
5. Remove lefthand defroster connector tube.
6. Remove upper steering column attaching bolts, then lower steering column to rest on instrument panel brace. **Ensure wires are not pinched when steering column is lowered.**
7. Remove ignition lock as outlined under "Ignition Lock, Replace."
8. Remove upper steering column cover.
9. Remove column lock shield.
10. Disconnect ignition switch electrical connector.
11. Remove switch attaching screws, then remove switch.
12. Reverse procedure to install. **Torque** ignition switch attaching screws to 50-70 inch lbs. **Torque** steering column lock shield attaching screws to 11-14 ft. lbs. **Torque** upper steering column attaching bolts to 17-23 ft. lbs.
13. Reactivate airbag system as described under "Airbag System Disarming."

# STOP LAMP SWITCH
## REPLACE
### REMOVAL

1. Disarm airbag system as described under "Airbag System Disarming."
2. Disconnect stop lamp switch electrical connectors.
3. Remove stop lamp switch attaching nut, then remove switch.

### INSTALLATION

1. Install switch, then finger tighten attaching nut.
2. Ensure distance from brake pedal to stop lamp switch is .078 inch. If distance is not as indicated, adjust by rotating stop lamp switch.
3. Tighten locknut, then reconnect electrical connectors.
4. Reactivate airbag system as described under "Airbag System Disarming."

# NEUTRAL SAFETY SWITCH
## REPLACE

1. Disarm airbag system as described under "Airbag System Disarming."
2. Disconnect battery ground cable.
3. Place shift indicator in "Neutral" position.
4. Remove air cleaner assembly.
5. Remove shift cable attaching nut, then disconnect cable, **Fig. 2.**
6. Remove neutral switch harness from metal retainer, then separate harness from sheathing.
7. Disconnect switch electrical connectors.
8. Remove switch attaching bolts, then remove switch.
9. Reverse procedure to install, noting the following:
   a. Ensure switch and shaft are in "Neutral" position.
   b. Loosely install switch attaching bolts, then remove cover screw and align internal hole with cover screw hole.
   c. Ensure alignment by inserting a .079 inch pin through opening.
   d. **Torque** switch attaching screws to 69-95 inch lbs.
   e. Remove alignment pin, then **torque** cover screw to 3-6 inch lbs.
   f. **Torque** shift cable attaching nut to 33-47 ft lbs.
   g. Reactivate airbag system as described under "Airbag System Disarming."

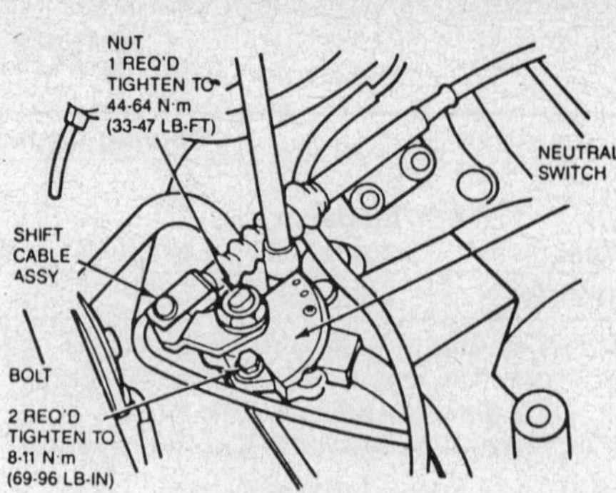


**Fig. 2 Neutral safety switch replace**

# HEADLIGHT SWITCH
## REPLACE

1. Disarm airbag system as described under "Airbag System Disarming."
2. Disconnect battery ground cable.
3. Remove instrument cluster bezel.
4. Disconnect headlamp switch electrical connectors.
5. Depress switch tangs, then remove switch from bezel.
6. Reverse to install.
7. Reactivate airbag system as described under "Airbag System Disarming."

# TURN SIGNAL SWITCH
## REPLACE

1. Disarm airbag system as described under "Airbag System Disarming."
2. Disconnect battery ground cable.
3. Remove center trim panel and steering column lower access cover.
4. Remove steering column lower shroud.
5. Remove upper steering column attaching bolts, then lower steering column to rest on instrument panel brace. **Ensure wires are not pinched when lowering steering column.**
6. Remove turn signal switch attaching screws, then remove switch assembly.
7. Carefully pull multi-function lever out of switch, then disconnect switch electrical connectors.
8. Reverse procedure to install. **Torque** steering column attaching bolts to 17-23 ft. lbs.
9. Reactivate airbag system as described under "Airbag System Disarming."

# STEERING WHEEL
## REPLACE

1. Disarm airbag system as described under "Airbag System Disarming."
2. Remove airbag module attaching nuts at rear of steering wheel.
3. Disconnect airbag module electrical connector.
4. Loosen steering wheel attaching bolt four to six turns.

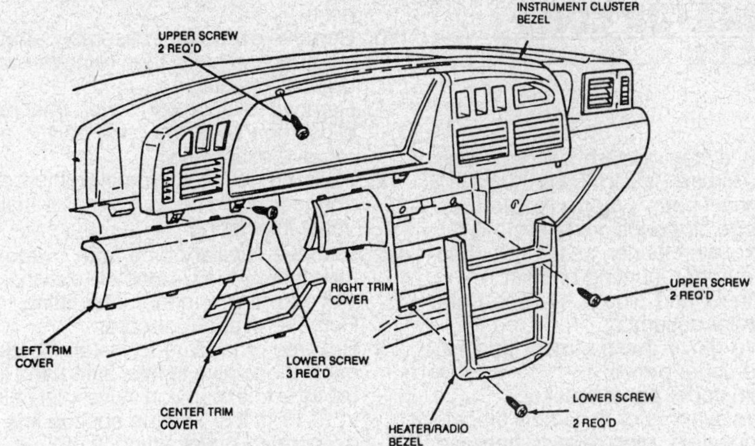


**Fig. 3 Instrument cluster replace**

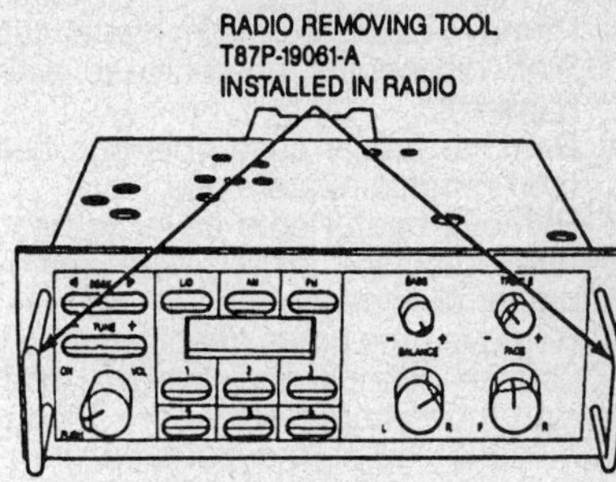


**Fig. 4 Radio replace**

5. Install steering wheel puller tool No. T67L-3600-A or equivalent, then remove steering wheel attaching bolt.
6. Remove steering wheel. **Ensure not to damage airbag clockspring or module when removing steering wheel.**
7. Reverse procedure to install. **Torque** steering wheel attaching bolt to 23-33 ft. lbs. **Torque** airbag module attaching screws to 17-26 inch lbs.
8. Reactivate airbag system as described under "Airbag System Disarming."

## INSTRUMENT CLUSTER
### REPLACE

1. Disarm airbag system as described under "Airbag System Disarming."
2. Disconnect battery ground cable.
3. Remove radio/heater control bezel, steering column covers and instrument panel bezel attaching screws, **Fig. 3.**
4. Disconnect speedometer cable at transaxle.
5. Remove instrument cluster attaching screws.
6. Pull instrument cluster rearward, then disconnect speedometer cable from cluster.
7. Disconnect attaching electrical connectors, then remove instrument cluster.
8. Reverse procedure to install. **Torque** instrument cluster attaching screws to 2-3 ft. lbs.
9. Reactivate airbag system as described under "Airbag System Disarming."

## RADIO
### REPLACE

1. Disarm airbag system as described under "Airbag System Disarming."
2. Disconnect battery ground cable.
3. Remove radio/heater control bezel.
4. Install radio removal tool No. T87P-19061-A or equivalent, **Fig. 4.**
5. Slide radio rearward to gain access.
6. Disconnect radio electrical connectors, then disconnect antenna.
7. Remove radio rear support attaching nut, then remove rear radio support.
8. Reverse procedure to install.
9. Reactivate airbag system as described under "Airbag System Disarming."

## WINDSHIELD WIPER MOTOR
### REPLACE

1. Disconnect battery ground cable.
2. Gently pry windshield wiper linkage from ball socket at motor.
3. Disconnect motor electrical connectors.
4. Remove motor to dash panel attaching bolts and rubber insulators, then remove wiper motor.
5. Reverse procedure to install. **Torque** motor to dash panel attaching bolts and insulators to 5-7 ft. lbs.

## WINDSHIELD WIPER TRANSMISSION
### REPLACE

1. Remove wiper arms as follows:
   a. Lift cover, then remove wiper arm attaching nut from shaft.
   b. Carefully pry arm from shaft.
2. Remove lower windshield molding.
3. Gently pry linkage from ball socket at windshield wiper motor.
4. Remove attaching caps and bolts from pivot shafts.
5. Remove windshield wiper linkage.
6. Reverse procedure to install. **Torque** pivot shaft attaching bolts to 7-9 ft. lbs.

## WINDSHIELD WIPER SWITCH
### REPLACE

1. Disarm airbag system as described under "Airbag System Disarming."
2. Remove center trim panel and lower steering column access panel.
3. Remove steering column lower shroud attaching screws, then remove lower shroud.
4. Disconnect wiper switch electrical connector and pull wiring out of routing clip.
5. Pull switch and lever assembly to remove.
6. Reverse procedure to install.
7. Reactivate airbag system as described under "Airbag System Disarming."

## BLOWER MOTOR
### REPLACE

1. Disarm airbag system as described under "Airbag System Disarming."
2. Disconnect battery ground cable.
3. Disconnect blower motor electrical connector.
4. Remove blower motor and cover to lower case attaching screws.
5. Remove cover, cooling tube and blower motor.
6. Remove blower wheel to blower motor attaching nut, then remove blower wheel.
7. Remove blower motor gasket.
8. Reverse procedure to install.
9. Reactivate airbag system as described under "Airbag System Disarming."

## HEATER CORE
### REPLACE

1. Disarm airbag system as described under "Airbag System Disarming."
2. Remove floor console and instrument panel assembly.
3. Drain cooling system.
4. Disconnect and plug heater hoses from heater core extension tubes.
5. Remove defroster hoses and plastic rivets.
6. Remove main air duct connecting heater case to blower case or air conditioning unit, if equipped.
7. Roll back carpet to gain access to lower duct and heater case mounting bolts, then disconnect lower duct from heater case.

8. Remove cable ends from heater case, then disconnect heater case wiring harness.
9. Remove heater case nuts and bolts, then remove heater case.
10. Remove heater core cover to heater case attaching screws, then remove heater core cover.
11. Remove tube brace attaching screws.
12. Loosen clamps and remove extension tubes from heater core, then remove O-ring from outlet tube.
13. Pull heater core outward, then remove any remaining extension tubes and grommets.
14. Reverse procedure to install. **Torque** heater case upper, lower and center attaching nuts and bolts to 5-7 ft. lbs. **Torque** heater hose clamps to 3-4 ft. lbs.
15. Reactivate airbag system as described under "Airbag System Disarming."

## EVAPORATOR CORE REPLACE

1. Disarm airbag system as described under "Airbag System Disarming."
2. Disconnect battery ground cable, then discharge air conditioning system.
3. Remove air cleaner assembly, then remove front mounting bracket.
4. Disconnect and plug A/C lines from evaporator assembly.
5. Remove glove compartment assembly and upper panel.
6. Remove upper panel bracket.
7. Remove evaporator assembly electrical connectors, then release harness retainers.
8. Remove defroster tube, then remove air duct bands.
9. Remove evaporator assembly drain hose.
10. Remove evaporator assembly attaching nuts and bolts, then remove evaporator assembly.
11. Remove evaporator cover attaching clips, then separate case halves and remove evaporator.
12. Remove de-ice thermostat, then disconnect liquid tube from expansion valve inlet fitting.
13. Remove capillary tube from evaporator outlet, then remove expansion valve from evaporator inlet fitting.
14. Remove evaporator core.
15. Reverse procedure to install. **Torque** expansion valve to inlet fitting and liquid tube to expansion valve inlet fitting to 9-11 ft. lbs. **Torque** suction line to evaporator outlet fitting to 22-25 ft. lbs.
16. Reactivate airbag system as described under "Airbag System Disarming."

# 1.6L/4-97 Engine

**NOTE: On Vehicles Equipped With Airbags, Disarm Airbag System As Outlined Under "Airbag System Disarming" Before Any Diagnosis, Testing, Troubleshooting Or Repairs Are Performed. After All Diagnosis, Testing, Troubleshooting Or Repairs Have Been Completed, Rearm Airbag System As Outlined Under "Airbag System Disarming."**

## INDEX



## AIRBAG SYSTEM DISARMING

### AIRBAG SYSTEM DEACTIVATION

**The electrical circuit necessary for system deployment is powered directly from the battery. To avoid accidental deployment and possible personal injury, the battery and back-up power supply must be disconnected prior to servicing or replacing any system components.**

1. Disconnect battery ground cable and isolate cable end with electrical tape.
2. Open glove compartment, then lower the door fully by depressing the stops.
3. Detach the battery back-up which is a blue rectangular box on the outer lefthand side of the glove compartment, then disconnect electrical connector.
4. Remove four nut and washer assemblies retaining the airbag to the steering wheel.
5. Disconnect the airbag connector from the clockspring.
6. Attach a jumper wire between the gray/orange (GY/O) wire terminal and pink (PK) wire terminal of the clockspring connector.

### AIRBAG SYSTEM REACTIVATION

1. Remove jumper wire from airbag terminals on clockspring.
2. Connect airbag module to clockspring connector.
3. Position airbag module on steering wheel, then install four nut and washer assemblies. **Torque** nuts to 17-26 Inch. Lbs.
4. Connect battery ground cable, then back-up power supply.
5. Verify airbag indicator lamp operation.

## FUEL SYSTEM PRESSURE RELIEVE

**Fuel pressure must be relieved prior to servicing any fuel system component.**

1. Remove back seat cushion.
2. Disconnect fuel pump connector.
3. Run engine until engine stalls.
4. Connect fuel pump connector and install back seat cushion.

## ENGINE MOUNTS REPLACE

### RIGHTHAND

1. Support engine assembly with a suitable floor jack.
2. Remove mount to engine bracket nuts, **Fig. 1.**
3. Remove mount through bolt.
4. Remove bracket to body bolts.
5. Remove mount.
6. Reverse procedure to install.

### FRONT

1. Support engine with engine support fixture tool No. D88l-6000-a, or equivalent.

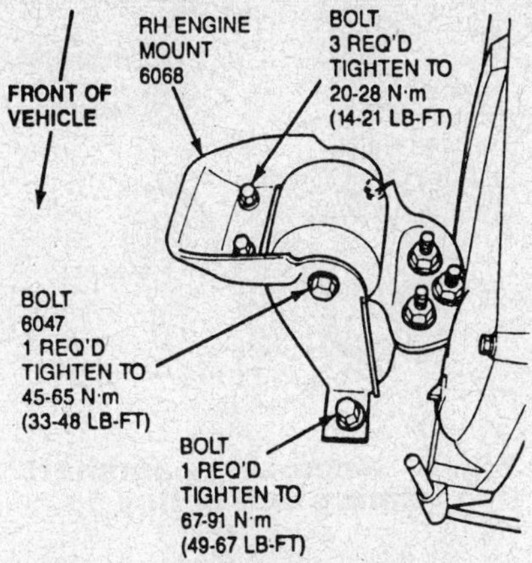


**Fig. 1 Righthand engine mount**

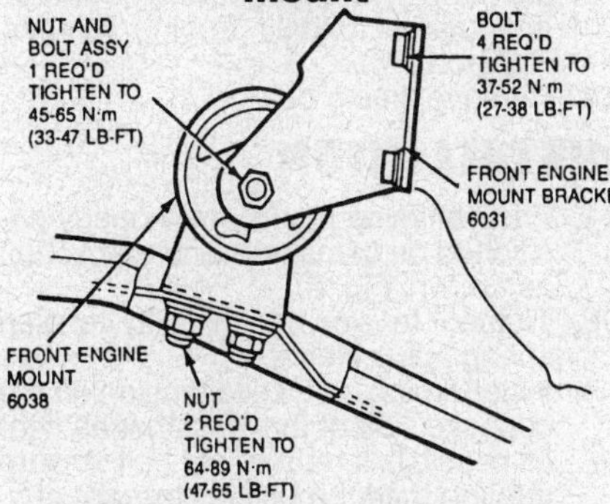


**Fig. 3 Rear engine mount**

**Fig. 2 Front engine mount**

2. Raise and support vehicle.
3. Remove engine mount nuts from crossmember, **Fig. 2.**
4. Remove engine mount bolts from transaxle.
5. Remove mount.
6. Reverse procedure to install.

### REAR

1. Support engine with engine support fixture tool No. D88l-6000-a, or equivalent.
2. Raise and support vehicle.
3. Remove engine mount to crossmember nuts, **Fig. 3.**
4. Remove lefthand A-arm bolts. Remove engine support crossmember nuts and bolts.
5. Remove rear engine mount bolts and mount.
6. Reverse procedure to install.

## ENGINE

### REPLACE

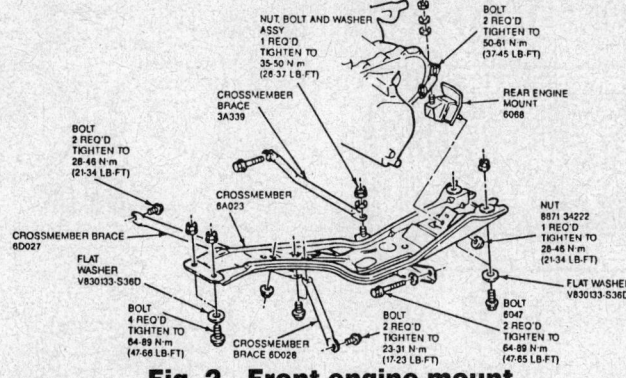

1. Relieve fuel system pressure as outlined under "Fuel System Pressure Relieve."
2. Disconnect and remove battery, battery tray and battery tray support bracket.
3. Discharge A/C system.
4. Disconnect windshield washer hose at hood. Mark then remove hood assembly.
5. Disconnect intake air tube and wiring to ignition coil and vane air flow meter.
6. Remove air cleaner and air flow meter assembly.
7. Disconnect intercooler hoses from turbocharger, if equipped.
8. Drain cooling system and remove radiator assembly.
9. Disconnect accelerator cable and remove retaining bracket.
10. Disconnect speedometer cable at connection located under hood.
11. Disconnect and plug fuel lines at fuel filter and pressure regulator.
12. Disconnect power brake booster vacuum hose and disconnect heater hoses at heater core.
13. Mark then disconnect all necessary vacuum hoses.
14. **On models with manual transaxle turbocharged engines,** disconnect clutch cable and remove support bracket and cable from transaxle.
15. **On models with manual transaxle naturally aspirated engines,** disconnect clutch slave cylinder hydraulic line.
16. **On models with automatic transaxles,** remove transaxle cooler lines.
17. **On all models,** disconnect starter and alternator wiring connectors.
18. Disconnect engine coolant sensors located at the rear of engine block.
19. remove ground strap connection at thermostat cover.
20. Disconnect EGO sensor wire, main wiring harness, throttle position and knock sensor connector, distributor wiring and transaxle wiring.
21. Disconnect ground wire and strap at front of engine.
22. Install lifting eye on engine.
23. Remove engine oil dipstick tube.
24. Remove power steering pump and mounting bracket assembly and position aside.
25. **On models with A/C,** remove upper A/C compressor mounting bolts.
26. **On all models,** raise and support vehicle and drain engine oil.
27. **On models with A/C,** remove lower A/C compressor mounting bolts and position compressor aside.
28. **On all models,** remove front tire and wheel assemblies.
29. Separate ball joints from steering knuckles.
30. Remove splash shields and drain transaxle oil.
31. Remove drive shafts as outlined under "Drive Shaft, Replace" in the "Front Drive Axle" section.
32. Disconnect front exhaust exhaust pipe from engine.
33. Remove frame support bar to engine support bolt.
34. Loosen right control arm bolt and pivot support bar downward.
35. Remove exhaust hangers and allow exhaust system to hand down six inches and support with mechanic's wire.
36. Disconnect transaxle shift linkage and stabilizer bar at transaxle.
37. Remove nuts from front and rear engine mounts.
38. Lower vehicle.
39. Position engine lifting crane tool No. 077-00043, or equivalent. Attach chains onto eyes located on sides of cylinder head.
40. Support engine with crane and remove righthand engine mount through bolt.
41. Raise engine off mounts and slightly pivot engine/transaxle assembly.
42. disconnect oil pressure sensor and route starter/alternator wiring harness from engine.
43. Lift engine out of vehicle by turning assembly to clear brake master cylinder, shift linkage, radiator support and A/C lines.
44. Remove intake manifold support bracket and starter assembly.
45. Mark location and remove transaxle to engine retaining bolts.
46. Separate transaxle from engine.
47. Reverse procedure to install.

## INTAKE MANIFOLD

### REPLACE

1. Relieve fuel system pressure as outlined under "Fuel System Pressure Relieve."
2. Disconnect battery ground cable and drain cooling system.
3. Disconnect intercooler tube and/or air intake tube and air bypass hoses.
4. Disconnect main engine harness connection and TPS connector.
5. Disconnect necessary vacuum hoses from throttle body.
6. Disconnect fuel lines at fuel filter and pressure regulator.
7. Disconnect throttle cable and hoses from BCA valve.
8. remove BCA valve nut and bolt.
9. Remove intake manifold bolts and nuts from support bracket and cylinder head.

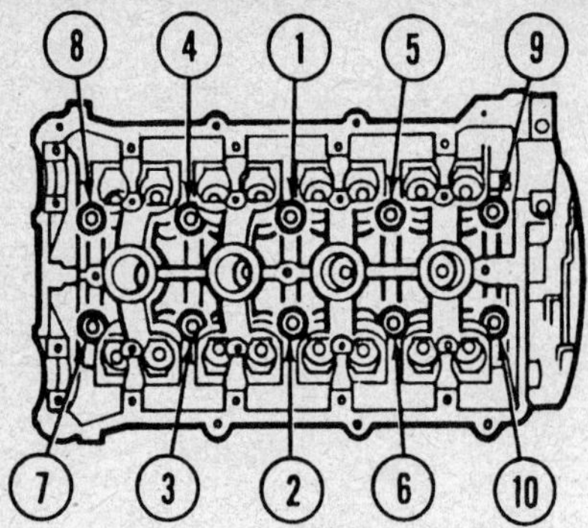


**Fig. 4 Cylinder head tightening sequence**

10. Remove intake manifold and throttle body assembly.
11. Reverse procedure to install.

# EXHAUST MANIFOLD REPLACE

## EXCEPT TURBOCHARGED ENGINE

1. Remove intake air tube.
2. Remove front exhaust pipe to exhaust manifold nuts.
3. Remove exhaust support bracket.
4. Disconnect EGO sensor.
5. Remove exhaust manifold nuts and manifold.
6. Reverse procedure to install.

## TURBOCHARGED ENGINE

Refer to "Turbocharger, Replace" for exhaust manifold replacement procedures.

# CYLINDER HEAD REPLACE

1. Relieve fuel system pressure as outlined under "Fuel System Pressure Relieve."
2. Disconnect battery ground cable and drain cooling system.
3. Remove air intake tube from throttle body.
4. Remove spark plug wires and retainers.
5. Remove air intake tube from air cleaner.
6. Disconnect cooling hose from thermostat cover.
7. Disconnect vacuum hoses and cooling hoses from throttle body and intake manifold.
8. Disconnect throttle cable.
9. Disconnect fuel lines at fuel filter and pressure regulator.
10. Disconnect main harness connector.
11. Disconnect EGO sensor connector and remove ground.
12. Disconnect intercooler tubes from turbocharger, if equipped.
13. Disconnect ground wire and straps from cylinder head.
14. Remove timing belt covers and timing belt as outlined under "Timing Belt and Covers."

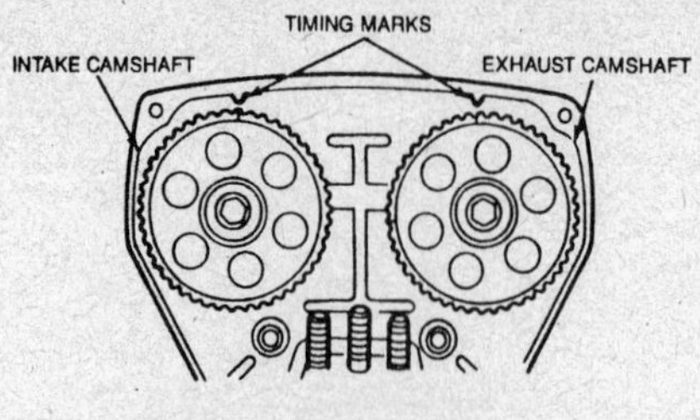


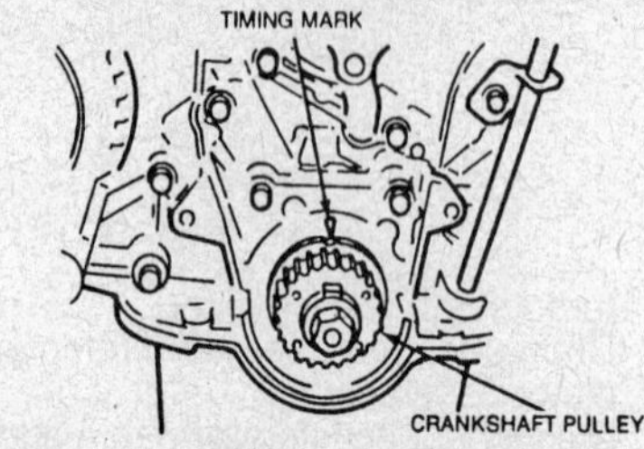


**Fig. 5 Engine timing marks**

15. **On turbocharged engines,** remove exhaust manifold and turbocharger assembly as outlined under "Turbocharger, Replace."
16. **On non-turbocharged engines,** disconnect front exhaust pipe from exhaust manifold.
17. **On all models,** remove intake manifold support upper bolts.
18. Remove cylinder head cover.
19. Remove cylinder head and intake manifold as an assembly.
20. Reverse procedure to install noting the following:
    a. Ensure coolant passage opening in intake manifold gasket align with manifold and cylinder head.
    b. Tighten cylinder head bolts in sequence shown in **Fig. 4** in two steps. First **torque** bolts to 14-25 ft. lbs. then repeat sequence and **torque** bolts to 56-60 ft. lbs.

# VALVE ADJUST

These engines use hydraulic lash adjusters, no adjustments are required.

# TIMING BELT & COVERS REPLACE

## REMOVAL

1. Raise and support vehicle.
2. Remove right front tire and wheel assembly and splash guard.
3. Lower vehicle.
4. Remove spark plugs and set No. 1 cylinder at top dead center (TDC).
5. Remove alternator and power steering belts.
6. Remove oil dipstick.
7. Remove water pump and crankshaft pulleys.
8. Remove crankshaft damper and baffle.
9. Remove upper, center and lower timing belt covers.
10. Remove timing belt tension spring.
11. Mark timing belt rotation direction.
12. Loosen timing belt tension pulley.
13. Support engine with a suitable floor jack and remove right engine mount as outlined under "Engine Mounts, Replace."
14. Remove timing belt.

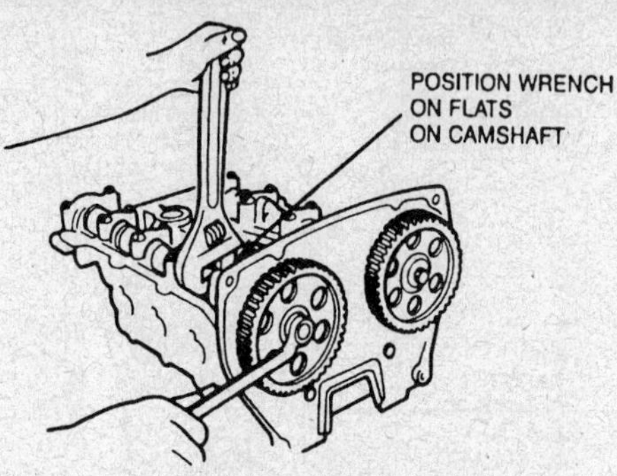


**Fig. 6 Removing camshaft timing belt pulley**

## INSTALLATION

1. Ensure timing marks are properly positioned on camshafts and crankshaft as shown, **Fig. 5.**
2. Tighten tension pulley with tension spring fully extended.
3. Install timing belt. Keep tension on the opposite side of the tensioner as tight as possible. If reusing old belt, ensure rotation mark on belt is correct.
4. Loosen tension pulley retaining bolt to allow tension spring to tighten belt.
5. Rotate engine two full turns. Check alignment of timing marks. If timing marks do not align repeat steps 1 through 4.
6. Tighten tension pulley retaining bolt and repeat step 5.
7. Measure timing belt tension between camshaft pulleys. Belt deflection should be .33-.45 inch. If deflection is not within specification, replace tension spring.
8. Reverse steps 1 through 9 of "Removal" procedure to complete installation.

# CAMSHAFT, CAMSHAFT PULLEY & OIL SEAL REPLACE

1. Relieve fuel system pressure as outlined under "Fuel System Pressure Relieve."
2. Disconnect battery ground cable and drain cooling system.
3. Disconnect air bypass hoses and remove intake air tube.
4. Disconnect throttle cable and remove retaining bracket.
5. Remove cylinder head cover.
6. Remove timing belt as outlined under" Timing Belt & Covers, Replace."
7. Remove camshaft pulleys by holding camshaft with wrench then remove pulley retaining bolt, **Fig. 6.**
8. Remove seal plate then camshaft seal using seal removing tool No. T78P-3504-N, or equivalent.
9. If removing intake camshaft, remove

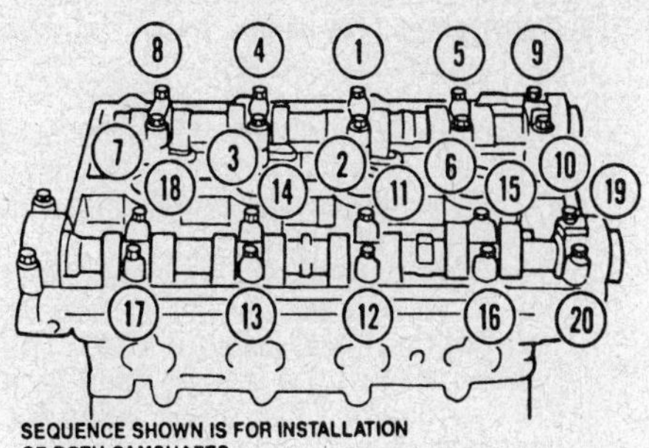


**Fig. 7 Camshaft bearing cap tightening sequence**

distributor as outlined under "Distributor, Replace" in the "Electrical" section.

10. Note cylinder number and rotation direction of each camshaft bearing cap, then remove camshaft bearing cap bolts alternator and gradually.
11. Remove the camshaft.
12. Reverse procedure to install noting the following:
    a. Align timing marks on camshaft as outlined under "Timing Belt & Covers, Replace."
    b. Tighten bearing caps is sequence shown in **Fig. 7** to specification.
    c. Install new camshaft seals using seal installation tool Nos. T90P-6256-BH and T90P-6256-AH or equivalent.

## CRANKSHAFT OIL SEALS REPLACE

### FRONT

1. Remove timing belt as outlined under "Timing Belt & Covers, Replace."
2. Remove crankshaft timing belt pulley.
3. remove crankshaft seal using seal remover tool No. T78P-3504-N, or equivalent.
4. Coat seal with oil and install seal using seal installation tool No. T87P-6019-A.
5. Reverse procedure to install.

### REAR

1. Remove transaxle assembly.
2. Remove clutch cover and disc, if equipped.
3. Remove flywheel.
4. Remove seal using seal remover tool No. T78P-3504-N, or equivalent.
5. Coat seal with oil and install seal using seal installation tool Nos. T87C-6701-A and T90P- 6701-AH.
6. Reverse procedure to install.

## OIL PAN REPLACE

1. Raise and support vehicle.
2. Drain engine oil into a suitable container.
3. Remove frame brace bolt. Loosen righthand A-arm front bolt and pivot brace downward.
4. Disconnect front exhaust pipe from engine.
5. Remove exhaust hangers and allow exhaust system to hang supported by mechanic's wire.
6. **On turbocharged models,** disconnect turbocharger oil return hose.
7. **On all models,** remove oil pan bolts.
8. Pry oil pan loose from cylinder block.
9. Reverse procedure to install.

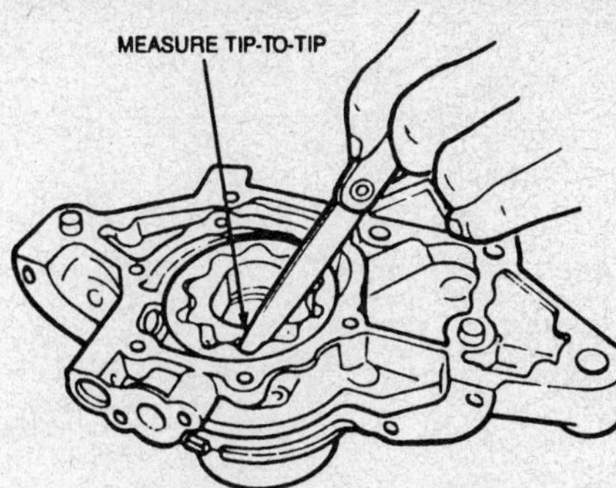


**Fig. 8 Measuring inner to outer rotor clearance**

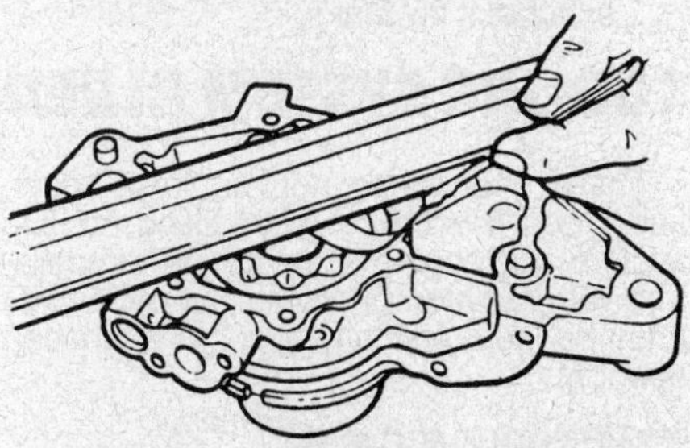

**Fig. 10 Measuring rotor to pump cover clearance**

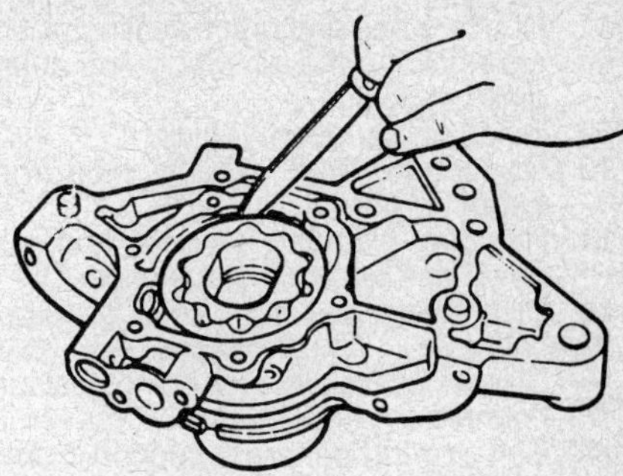

**Fig. 9 Measuring outer rotor to body clearance**

## OIL PUMP SERVICE

### REMOVAL

1. Remove timing belt as outlined under "Timing Belt & Covers, Replace."
2. Remove oil pan as outlined under "Oil Pan, Replace."
3. Remove crankshaft timing belt pulley.
4. Remove oil strainer/pickup tube.
5. Remove oil pump bolts and oil pump.

### DISASSEMBLY

1. Remove oil pump cover.
2. Remove outer and inner rotors.
3. Remove cotter pin and remove pressure piston, cap and spring.
4. Remove oil seal using seal remover tool No. T78P-3504-N, or equivalent.

### INSPECTION

1. Inspect pressure spring for weakness or breakage.
2. Pressure spring free length should be 1.791 inch.
3. Inner to outer rotor clearance should not exceed .0079 inch, **Fig. 8.**
4. Outer rotor to pump body clearance should not exceed .0087 inch, **Fig. 9.**
5. Rotor to pump body clearance should not exceed .0055 inch, **Fig. 10.**

### ASSEMBLY

1. Install oil seal flush with pump body.
2. Install pressure piston, cap and spring with a new cotter pin.
3. install inner and outer rotors.
4. Install oil pump cover.

### INSTALLATION

1. Clean gasket surface.
2. Install oil pump with new gasket.
3. Install oil pump bolts and torque to specification.
4. Install crankshaft timing pulley, oil pan and timing belt and covers as outlined.

## BELT TENSION DATA

New belts (no run time) should measure 0.31-.035 inch deflection with 22 lbs. of applied force, or 110-132 lbs., using a gauge.

Used belts (more that 10 minutes of run time) should measure 0.35-.039 inch deflection with 22 lbs. of applied force, or 110-132 lbs., using a gauge.

## TURBOCHARGER REPLACE

1. Disconnect battery ground cable and drain cooling system.
2. Remove throttle body air intake tube.
3. Disconnect intercooler hose from turbocharger assembly and position out of the way.
4. Disconnect the EGO sensor.
5. Remove bolts retaining lower heat shield to turbocharger and remove heat shield.
6. Remove bolts retaining upper and side heat shields, then the heat shields.
7. Remove power steering pump and bracket and position aside.
8. Disconnect lower radiator hose from water pump.
9. Remove screws retaining air cleaner duct tube, loosen tube and position duct tube aside.
10. Disconnect coolant return hose at turbocharger.

11. Remove bolt and brass sealing washers retaining the oil supply line at engine block.
12. Raise and support vehicle.
13. Disconnect front exhaust pipe from turbocharger.
14. Remove exhaust hangers and pull down and left on exhaust pipe.
15. Disconnect oil return hose at turbocharger.
16. Disconnect coolant return hose at turbocharger.
17. Remove turbocharger support bracket bolts.
18. Remove coolant bypass tube bolts from water pump.
19. Lower vehicle.
20. Loosen retaining clamp on coolant bypass tube at rear of cylinder head.
21. Remove 11 nuts from exhaust manifold.
22. Pull coolant bypass tube bracket from exhaust stud and position aside.
23. Pull exhaust manifold off stud and move assembly slightly to the right-hand side of engine compartment to clear cooling fan. Remove turbocharger and exhaust manifold assembly from vehicle.
24. Working on bench, remove four nuts retaining turbocharger to exhaust manifold, separate assembly and discard gasket.
25. Reverse procedure to install. If turbocharger was replaced proceed as follows:
    a. Disconnect ignition coil.
    b. Crank engine for 20 seconds.
    c. Connect ignition coil.
    d. Start engine and run at idle for 30 seconds.
    e. Check for leaks.

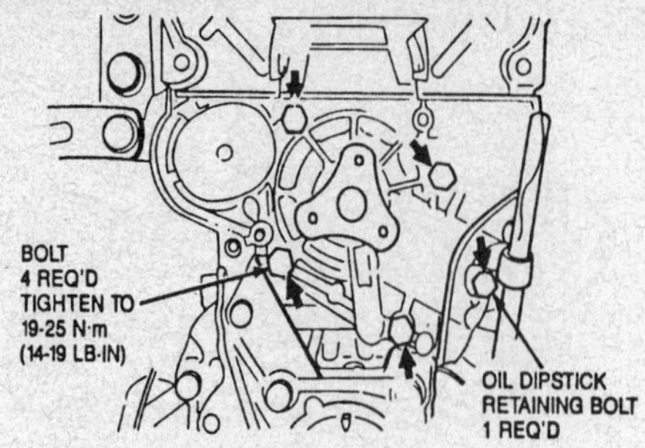


**Fig. 11 Water pump removal**

## COOLING SYSTEM BLEED

These engines do not require a specified bleed procedure. After filling cooling system, run engine to operating temperature with radiator/pressure cap off. Air will then be automatically bled through cap opening.

## THERMOSTAT REPLACE

1. Disconnect cooling fan switch connector from switch on thermostat housing.
2. Remove radiator pressure cap. **Ensure engine is cool prior to servicing.**
3. Drain cooling system to a level below thermostat housing.
4. Disconnect upper radiator hose from thermostat housing, then remove housing retaining bolts.
5. Remove thermostat and gasket.
6. Clean mating surfaces of housing and cylinder head, then install thermostat in cylinder head, valve end first with jiggle valve at the top.
7. Coat new gasket with water resistant sealer B5A-19554-A or equivalent, and position it on cylinder head. The painted side of the gasket must face the thermostat. Ensure bolt holes are correctly aligned.
8. Install thermostat housing, ensuring that the gasket does not shift. Install two retaining bolts and **Torque to 14-22 ft. lbs.**
9. Connect upper radiator hose to thermostat housing, then fill system with recommended coolant mixture and install pressure cap.
10. Connect cooling fan switch connector, then start engine and allow to run until warm.
11. Ensure system is pressurized, then check for leaks.

## WATER PUMP REPLACE

1. Remove timing belt as outlined under "Timing Belt & Covers, Replace."
2. Drain cooling system.
3. Remove timing belt tensioner and idler pulleys.
4. Remove engine oil dipstick.
5. Remove power steering pump and bracket then position aside.
6. Remove water pump outlet.
7. Remove water pump assembly, **Fig. 11.**

## TIGHTENING SPECIFICATIONS

| Year | Component | Torque/ft. lbs. |
|---|---|---|
| 1991-92 | A-Arm Front Bolt | 69-86 |
| | A/C Compressor Bolt | 30-40 |
| | Ball Joint | 32-40 |
| | Camshaft Bearing Bolt | 100-126① |
| | Camshaft Pulley | 36-45 |
| | Chassis Cross Brace Bolt | 26-37 |
| | Clutch Pressure Plate Bolt | 13-19 |
| | Connecting Rod Bearing Nut | 35-38 |
| | Crankshaft Main Bearing Bolt | 40-43 |
| | Crankshaft Pulley Bolt | 109-152① |
| | Crankshaft Rear Seal Flange Bolt | 69-95① |
| | Crankshaft Timing Pulley | 80-87 |
| | Cylinder Head Bolt | 56-60④ |
| | Cylinder Head Cover Bolt | 69-95① |
| | Engine End Plate | 69-95① |
| | Exhaust Manifold Nut | 29-42 |
| | Exhaust Pipe To Manifold Nut | 29-42 |
| | Flywheel Bolt | 71-76 |
| | Front Engine Mount Nut | 47-66 |
| | Front Engine Mount Through Bolt | 33-48 |

*Continued*

## TIGHTENING SPECIFICATIONS—Continued

| Year | Component | Torque/ft. lbs. |
|---|---|---|
| 1991-92 | Front Engine To Transaxle Bolt | 27–38 |
| | Front Exhaust Pipe To Support Bracket Bolt | 32–45 |
| | Gusset Plate Bolt | 27–38 |
| | Intake Manifold Bolt | 14–19 |
| | Intake Manifold Nut | 14–19 |
| | Intake Manifold Support Bracket Bolt | 23–34 |
| | Intermediate Axle Shaft Bearing Support Bolt | 27–38 |
| | Knock Sensor | 14–25 |
| | Oil Cooler Nut | 22–29 |
| | Oil Pan Bolt | 69–95 ① |
| | Oil Pressure Sensor | 104–156 ① |
| | Oil Pump Assembly Bolt | 14–19 |
| | Oil Pump Cover | 14–19 |
| | Oil Pump Pickup Bolt | 69–95 ① |
| | Oil Spray Nozzle Bolt | 104–156 ① |
| | Power Steering Pivot Bolt | 23–34 |
| | Power Steering Pump Bracket Bolt | 35–48 |
| | Power Steering Pump Bracket Nut | 35–48 |
| | Power Steering Adjusting Nut | 27–38 |
| | Radiator Bracket Bolt | 69–95 ① |
| | Rear Engine Mount Bolt | 27–38 |
| | Rear Engine Mount Nut | 47–66 |
| | Righthand Engine Mount Body Bracket Bolt | 14–21 |
| | Righthand Engine Mount Body Bracket Bolt | 49–67 |
| | Seal Plate Bolt | 69–95 ① |
| | Shift Cable Pivot Nut ③ | 33–47 |
| | Shift Cable Retaining Bolt | 69–95 ① |
| | Shift Linkage Rod Nut | 12–17 |
| | Shifter stabilizer nut | 23–34 |
| | Starter Bolt | 25–34 |
| | Starter Bracket to Support Bracket Bolt | 14–19 |
| | Timing Belt Cover Bolts | 69–95 ① |
| | Timing Belt Pulley Bolt | 27–38 |
| | Torque Converter Bolt | 25–36 |
| | Torque Convertor Cover Plate Bolt | 61–87 ① |
| | Transaxle To Engine Bolt | ② |
| | Water Pump Outlet Bolt | 14–19 |
| | Water Pump Pulley Bolt | 69–95 ① |
| | Wheel Lug Nuts | 67–88 |

①—Inch lbs.
②—Manual transaxle, upper 66–86 ft. lbs., lower 27–38 ft. lbs.; automatic transaxle, upper, 41–59 ft. lbs.
③—Automatic transaxle.
④—Tighten first to 14–25 ft. lbs. in sequence, then to 56–60 ft. lbs.

# Clutch & Manual Transaxle

## INDEX



## CLUTCH PEDAL HEIGHT

### ADJUST

1. Measure distance from upper center of the pedal pad to dash panel, **Fig. 1.**
2. Distance should be 8.4-8.6 inches on turbocharged models and 9.02-9.22 inches on non-turbocharged models.
3. Loosen locknut, then turn stopper bolt until pedal height is within specifications.
4. Tighten locknut.

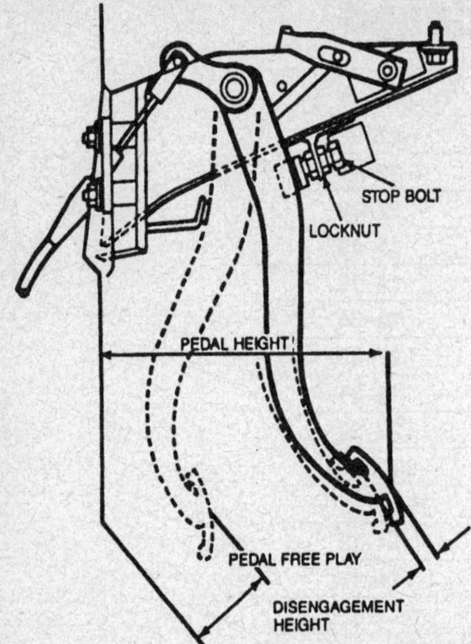


**Fig. 1 Clutch adjustment. Turbocharged models**

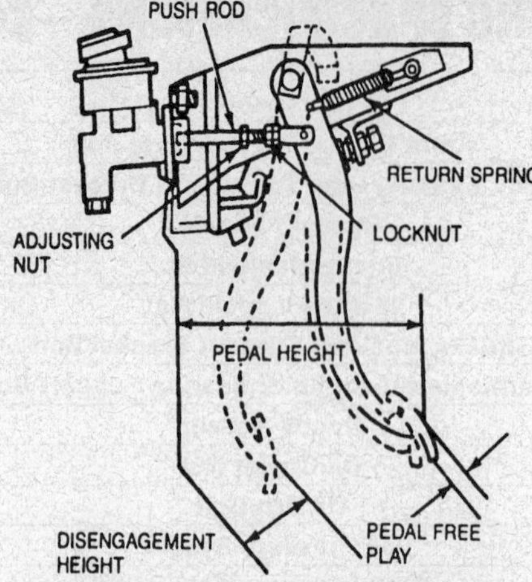


**Fig. 2 Clutch adjustment. Non-turbocharged models**

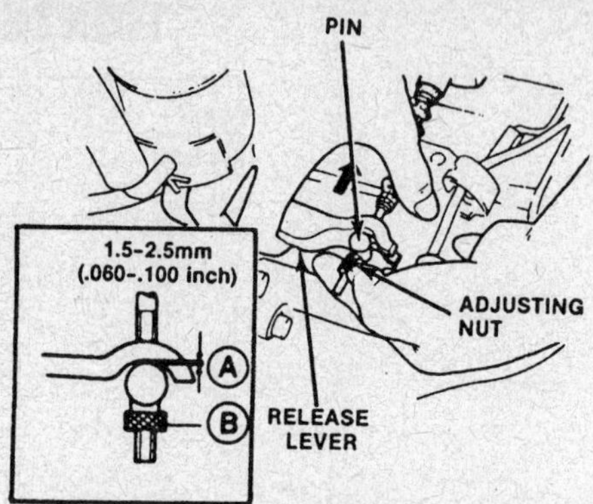


**Fig. 3 Clutch pedal free play adjustment. Turbocharged models**

## CLUTCH PEDAL FREE PLAY

### ADJUST

1. Lightly depress pedal and measure freeplay, **Fig. 1.**
2. Freeplay should measure .350-.590 inches on turbocharged models and 0.02-1.2 inches on non-turbocharged models.
3. **On non-turbocharged models,** loosen locknut, then turn push rod until pedal free play is within specification, **Fig. 2.**
4. Tighten locknut to 17-25 ft. lbs. Ensure pedal height is 9.02-9.22 inch.
5. **On turbocharged models,** if clutch pedal freeplay is not within specification, depress clutch release lever and pull pin away from lever.
6. Rotate adjusting nut (B), until a clearance 0.06-0.100 inch is obtained, **Fig. 3.**
7. Measure distance from floor and upper center of pedal pad when the pedal is fully depressed. Distance should be 3.3 inches.

## CLUTCH

### REPLACE

1. Disconnect battery ground cable.
2. Remove transaxle from vehicle.
3. Install flywheel lock tool T74P-6375-A or equivalent, into transaxle mounting hole on engine, then engage tooth of locking tool into flywheel ring gear. **To avoid dropping clutch disc when bolts are removed, use clutch aligning tool T87C-7137-A or equivalent.**
4. Remove bolts attaching pressure plate to flywheel, then remove pressure plate assembly, **Fig. 4.**
5. Remove clutch disc and clutch aligning tool. **Use care when removing the last bolt to prevent dropping flywheel.**
6. Reverse procedure to install. **Torque** pressure plate assembly attaching bolts to 13-20 ft. lbs.

## SLAVE CYLINDER

### REPLACE

This vehicle uses two types of clutch release systems. Turbocharged vehicles with type G transaxles use a mechanical cable system. Non-turbocharged vehicles with type F2 transaxles use a hydraulic clutch system.

1. Disconnect hydraulic line from slave cylinder and plug to prevent fluid loss.
2. Remove two retaining bolts, then slave cylinder.
3. Reverse procedure to install, noting the following:
   a. **Torque** retaining bolts to 12-16 ft. lbs.
   b. Fill reservoir and bleed clutch system.

## CLUTCH SYSTEM BLEED

1. Raise and support vehicle.
2. Attach a hose to bleeder valve on clutch slave cylinder.
3. Depress clutch pedal to floor and hold.
4. Open bleeder valve 1/2 turn.
5. Watch for air bubbles in brake fluid while bleeding. **Keep reservoir full of fluid while bleeding.**
6. Close bleeder screw, then release clutch pedal.
7. Open bleeder valve 1/4 turn, then push pedal down as far as it will go. Close valve and release pedal.
8. Fill reservoir, then check clutch for proper operation. Repeat procedure as necessary.

## CLUTCH MASTER CYLINDER

### REPLACE

1. Remove battery, then windshield wiper motor.
2. Disconnect hydraulic line fitting at retaining bracket on transaxle case, then drain fluid from clutch master cylinder. Reconnect fitting after draining fluid.
3. Disconnect hydraulic line from master cylinder.
4. Remove master cylinder retaining nuts, then clutch master cylinder.
5. Reverse procedure to install, noting the following:
   a. **Torque** clutch master cylinder retaining nuts to 14-19 ft. lbs.
   b. Bleed hydraulic clutch system.

## MANUAL TRANSAXLE

### REPLACE

### NON-TURBOCHARGED MODELS

1. Disconnect battery ground cable.
2. Remove air cleaner assembly, then loosen both front wheel lug nuts.
3. Disconnect speedometer cable from transaxle.
4. Remove clutch slave hydraulic line retaining bracket and nut.
5. Remove bolts retaining ground wire and engine harness bracket to transaxle. Pull harness out of routing clip.
6. Disconnect ground strap at front of transaxle.
7. Install engine support bar tool D88L-6000-A or equivalent, then remove upper transaxle to engine retaining bolts.
8. Remove upper starter retaining bolts, then disconnect neutral safety switch and back-up lamp switch electrical connectors.
9. Raise and support vehicle, then remove front tire and wheel assemblies.
10. Remove splash shields.
11. Drain fluid from transaxle assembly.
12. Remove front stabilizer bar.
13. Remove bolts and nuts from lower control arm ball joints.
14. Pull lower control arms down to separate them from the steering knuckles. **Use care not to damage ball joint dust boot.**
15. Remove inner left fender splash shield.

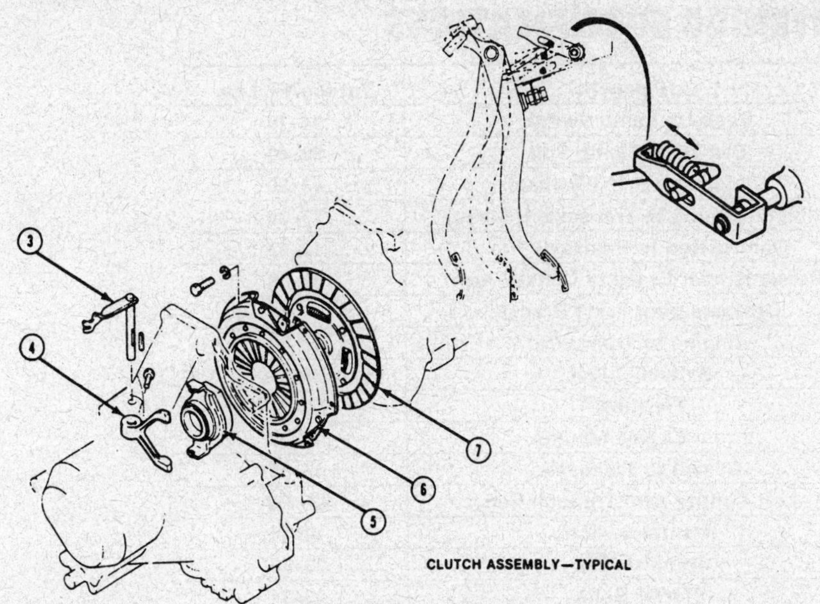


1. CLUTCH PEDAL
2. CLUTCH CABLE
3. RELEASE LEVER
4. RELEASE FORK
5. RELEASE BEARING
6. PRESSURE PLATE ASSEMBLY
7. CLUTCH DISC
8. CLUTCH SWITCH

**Fig. 4 Clutch assembly**

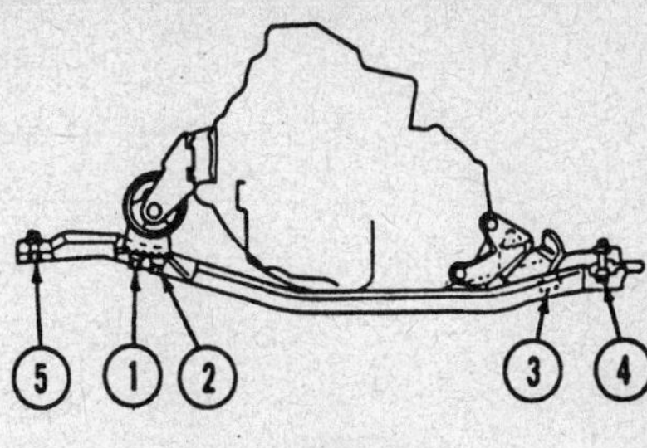


**Fig. 5 Removing crossmember bolts**

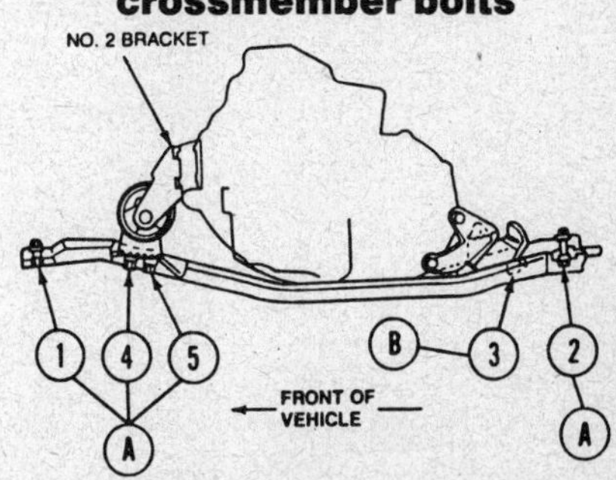


**Fig. 6 Installing crossmember bolts**

16. Separate both halfshafts by pulling front hub outward as follows:
    a. Withdraw halfshafts horizontally from transaxle to prevent damage to oil lip seals.
    b. Hold halfshafts during removal to prevent damage to boots and joints caused by moving the joint through angles in excess of 20°.
    c. Suspend halfshafts in a horizontal position using a wire hanger or tie to vehicle.
17. Remove two crossmember braces, then remove crossmember brace to control arm support bolts.
18. Remove left control arm through bolt, then exhaust hanger from crossmember.
19. Remove remaining crossmember bolts in sequence shown, then the crossmember, **Fig. 5.**
20. Remove bolt attaching shift control rod to transaxle, then position aside.
21. Remove nut attaching shift extension bar mounting bracket, then slide extension bar off stud.
22. Remove bolts retaining clutch slave cylinder and set wire aside.
23. Remove lower bolt retaining starter motor, then remove bolts attaching end plate to transaxle.
24. Remove nut and washer retaining support bracket to exhaust manifold.
25. Remove gusset plate to transaxle attaching bolt.
26. Position jack under transaxle, then secure transaxle to jack.
27. Remove front engine mount and bracket from transaxle.
28. Remove bolts attaching transaxle to engine.
29. Remove the transaxle.
30. Reverse procedure to install. Install crossmember bolts in numerical sequence, then **torque** to specifications, **Fig. 6.**

## TURBOCHARGED MODELS

1. Disconnect battery ground cable.
2. Remove air cleaner assembly, then loosen both front wheel lug nuts.
3. Disconnect speedometer cable from transaxle.
4. Remove clutch cable from release lever by removing adjusting nut and pin.
5. Remove intake air bypass valve mounting nut.
6. Remove clutch cable mounting bracket from transaxle.
7. Remove ground wire retaining bolt, then the ground wire.
8. Remove coolant pipe bracket and wire harness clip.
9. Disconnect neutral safety switch and back-up lamp switch electrical connectors.
10. Disconnect body ground connector, then remove two upper transaxle to engine attaching bolts.
11. Remove upper starter mounting bolts.
12. Install engine support bar tool D89L-6000-A or equivalent, then attach it to engine hanger.
13. Raise and support vehicle.
14. Drain fluid from transaxle assembly.
15. Remove front tire and wheel assemblies.
16. Remove front stabilizer bar.
17. Remove ball joint clamp bolts, then pull lower control arms down to separate them from the steering knuckles. **Use care not to damage ball joint dust boot.**
18. Separate both halfshafts by pulling front hub outward as follows:
    a. Withdraw halfshafts horizontally from transaxle to prevent damage to oil lip seals.
    b. Hold halfshafts during removal to prevent damage to boots and joints caused by moving the joint through angles in excess of 20 degrees.
    c. Suspend halfshafts in a horizontal position using a wire hanger or tie to vehicle.
    d. **On turbocharged models,** it will be necessary to remove intermediate shaft and support bearing assembly.
19. Remove two front crossmember braces.
20. Remove crossmember brace to A-arm support bolts.
21. Remove exhaust hanger from crossmember.
22. Remove remaining crossmember bolts in sequence shown, then the crossmember, **Fig. 5.**
23. Remove bolt attaching shift control rod to transaxle, then position aside.
24. Remove attaching bolt from shift extension bar mounting bracket, then slide extension bar off bracket.
25. Remove lower bolt retaining starter motor, then remove bolts attaching end plate to transaxle.
26. Lower transaxle by loosening engine bracket bar hook bolt.
27. Position jack under transaxle, then secure transaxle to jack.
28. Remove front engine mount and bracket from transaxle.
29. Remove bolts attaching transaxle to engine.
30. Remove the transaxle.
31. Reverse procedure to install. Install crossmember bolts in numerical sequence, then **torque** to specifications, **Fig. 6.**

## TIGHTENING SPECIFICATIONS

| Year | Component | Torque/Ft. Lbs. |
|---|---|---|
| 1991-92 | Back-Up Lamp Switch | 14–18 |
| | Ball Joint Clamp Bolt | 32–40 |
| | Clutch Cover to Flywheel | 13–20 |
| | Clutch Housing to Transaxle Housing | 27–38 |
| | Control Rod to Transaxle Nut | 12–17 |
| | Crossmember Brace to Control Arm | 69–86 |
| | Crossmember Front Braces | 23–43 |
| | Engine to Transaxle | 47–66 |
| | Extension Bar | 23–34 |
| | Flywheel | 60–65 |
| | Front Engine Mounts | 27–38 |
| | Gusset to Transaxle | 47–66 |
| | Left Control Arm Through Bolt | 93–117 |
| | Neutral Switch | 14–18 |
| | Stabilizer Bar | 23–33 |
| | Starter Bolts | 23–34 |
| | Wheel Lug Nuts | 67–88 |

# Rear Suspension

## INDEX



## DESCRIPTION

The rear suspension is fully independent utilizing rear MacPherson struts at each wheel. Rear strut towers locate the spring and strut. Forged rear spindle bolts to the strut double lower control arms and a single trailing arm locate the rear suspension, **Fig. 1**.

Both of the control arms and the trailing arms have rubber bushings at each end. The control arms are attached to the rear crossmember and also to the spindle with a common bolt at each end. The trailing arm bolts to the strut and a bracket on the floorpan.

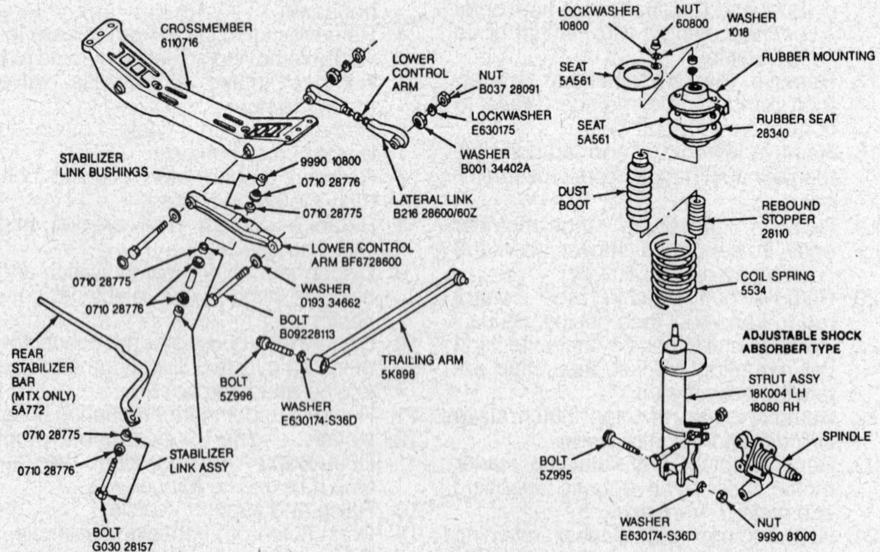


**Fig. 1 Rear suspension**

## HUB & BEARING ASSEMBLY
### REPLACE

1. Ensure parking brake is fully released.
2. Raise and support vehicle, then remove wheel and tire assembly.
3. Remove two caliper guide pin bolts, then lift caliper of disc with hose and cable attached, then tie caliper assembly to strut spring.
4. Remove grease cap, **Fig. 2.**
5. Raise staked portion of locknut using suitable tool.
6. Remove and discard locknut. **Locknuts are threaded left and right. The lefthand threaded locknut is located on the righthand side of the vehicle. Turn this locknut clockwise to loosen. The righthand threaded locknut is turned counterclockwise to loosen.**
7. Remove washer and outer bearing from bearing hub.
8. Remove brake rotor/bearing hub assembly.
9. Remove bearing grease seal using suitable tool.
10. Remove inner bearing from bearing hub. **If bearings are to be reused, they should be tagged to be installed in their original position.**

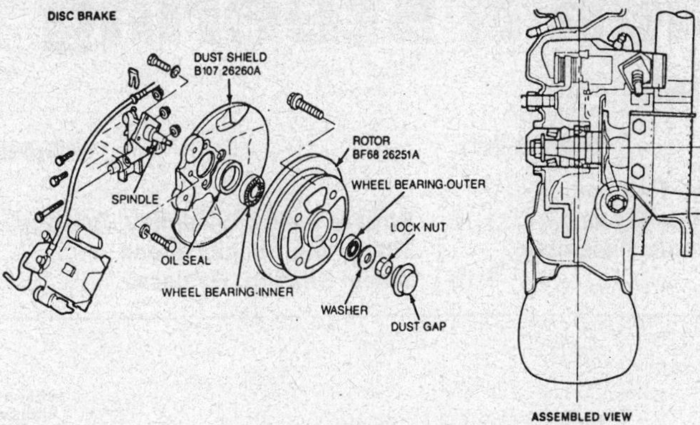


**Fig. 2 Rear hub & bearing assembly**

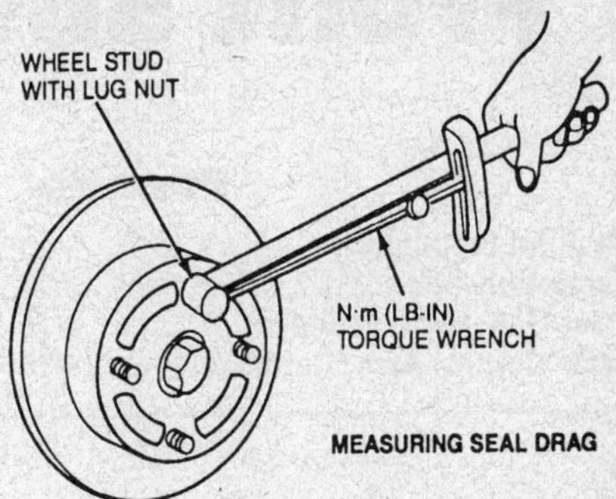


**Fig. 3 Measuring rear wheel bearing preload**

11. Reverse procedure to install, noting the following:
    a. Install new grease seal using tool No. T87C-1175-A or equivalent.
    b. Torque all attaching nuts and bolts to specifications.
    c. **Torque** locknut to 18.1-21.7 ft. lbs. to seat bearings.
    d. Adjust bearing preload as outlined under "Wheel Bearing Preload, Adjust."

## WHEEL BEARING PRELOAD

### ADJUST

1. Loosen bearing hub locknut.
2. Measure seal drag, place a torque wrench on a lug nut positioned at twelve o'clock and measure amount of force required to turn the brake rotor, note torque wrench reading when rotation starts, **Fig. 3.**
3. Add amount of seal drag to required preload which is 1.3-4.3 inch lbs.
4. Finger tighten wheel bearing locknut, then place torque wrench on lug nut positioned at twelve o'clock, continue tightening locknut until indicated preload is with specifications.

## SPINDLE ASSEMBLY

### REPLACE

1. Remove rear wheel and tire assemblies.
2. Remove rear disc brake caliper and rotor assemblies.
3. Loosen spindle to strut attaching bolts.
4. Loosen outer rear control arm nut and bolt.
5. Remove spindle to strut mount attaching bolt, then remove outer control arm bolt and nut.
6. Remove spindle assembly from strut.
7. Reverse procedure to install. Torque attaching nuts and bolts to specifications.

## STRUT & SPRING ASSEMBLY

### REPLACE

1. Remove rear wheel and tire assemblies.
2. Remove rear disc brake caliper and rotor assemblies.
3. Loosen trailing arm attaching bolt, then loosen spindle to shock absorber attaching bolts.
4. Remove trailing arm and spindle attaching bolts.
5. Mark alignment on strut rubber mounting bracket.
6. Inside trunk, remove upper strut attaching nuts.
7. Compress coil spring using tool No. T81P-5310-A or equivalent.
8. With spring compressed, remove strut rod attaching nut, rubber mounting bracket, spring upper and lower seat, then the rubber spring seat.
9. Release coil spring and remove spring compressor tool.
10. Remove coil spring, dust boot and rebound bumpers.
11. Reverse procedure to install. Torque attaching nuts and bolts to specifications.

## CONTROL ARMS & TRAILING ARM

### REPLACE

1. Remove rear wheel and tire assemblies.
2. Remove rear disc brake caliper and rotor assemblies.
3. Mark control arm and control arm bushings for alignment at installation.
4. Mark trailing arm and crossmember for alignment at installation.
5. Remove stabilizer link assembly.
6. Remove stabilizer bar and bushings.
7. Loosen inner and outer lower control arm attaching bolts.
8. Loosen spindle to strut attaching bolts.
9. Remove parking brake to rear trailing assembly attaching bolt.
10. Loosen trailing arm to strut attaching bolts.
11. Once all control arm and trailing arm attaching bolts are loosen, then remove all bolts and remove control arms and trailing arm.
12. Reverse procedure to install. Torque all attaching nuts and bolts to specifications.

## TIGHTENING SPECIFICATIONS

| Year | Component | Torque/Ft. Lbs. |
|---|---|---|
| 1991-92 | Control Arm Bolt | 69-86 |
| | Control Arm To Spindle | 69-86 |
| | Inner Control Arm Bolts | 69-86 |
| | Rear Stabilizer Bracket | 32-39 |
| | Spindle To Strut Bolt | 69-86 |
| | Wheel Bearing Locknut | 67-88 |
| | Wheel Lug Nuts | 67-88 |

# Front Suspension & Steering

## INDEX



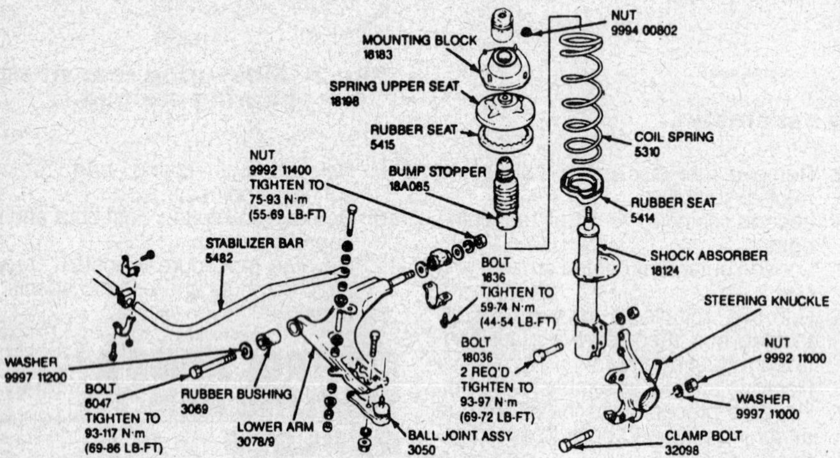


**Fig. 1 Front suspension**

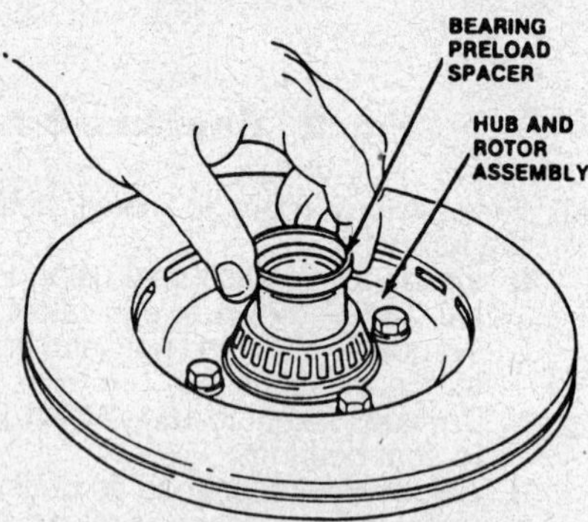


**Fig. 2 Front wheel bearing preload spacer**

## DESCRIPTION

The front suspension consists of MacPherson struts, coil springs and single control arms, **Fig. 1.** Strut towers located in the wheel wells locate the upper ends of the struts. The strut mounting blocks house rubber mounted strut bearings. Both the upper and lower end of the coil springs ride in heavy rubber spring seats. A forged steering knuckle bolts to each strut assembly.

Ball joints connect the control arms to the steering knuckles. The wide control arms are supported by rubber bushings at each end. Body lean on turns is controlled by a hollow stabilizer bar that connects to both lower control arms.

## WHEEL BEARING
### REPLACE

1. Remove steering knuckle and hub assembly as outlined under "Steering Knuckle & Hub Assembly, Replace."
2. Remove hub and brake rotor assembly from steering knuckle using tool No. T87C-1104-A or equivalent.
3. Remove front bearing preload spacer, **Fig. 2. The spacer between bearings determines preload, do not discard.**
4. Mark hub and rotor assembly for installation alignment.
5. Place hub and rotor assembly in soft-jawed vise or equivalent, then remove hub and rotor attaching bolts.
6. Remove wheel hub bearing using tool Nos. D84L-1123-A and D80L-927-A or equivalents.
7. Remove hub outer grease seal, then remove inner grease seal from steering knuckle with suitable tool.
8. Remove steering knuckle bearing.
9. Reverse procedure to install. Torque all attaching nuts and bolts to specifications.

## BALL JOINT INSPECTION

1. Raise and support vehicle.
2. Move front wheel and tire assembly vertically while observing ball joint in lower control arm at bottom of steering knuckle.
3. If movement is detected between steering knuckle and control arm, ball joint should be replaced.

## LOWER BALL JOINT
### REPLACE

1. Raise and support vehicle, then remove wheel and tire assembly.
2. Remove ball joint clamp attaching bolt from steering knuckle.
3. Using a small pry bar or equivalent, pull lower control arm downward to separate from steering knuckle.
4. Remove lower ball joint attaching blots.
5. Using a small pry bar or equivalent, pull ball joint from control arm.
6. Reverse procedure to install. Torque all attaching bolts to specifications.

## LOWER CONTROL ARM
### REPLACE

1. Raise and support vehicle, then remove wheel and tire assembly.
2. Disconnect stabilizer bar from control arm, if equipped, **Fig. 1.**
3. Remove ball joint clamp attaching bolt.
4. Remove control arm front attaching bolt.
5. Remove control arm rear bracket and attaching bolts, then remove control arm.
6. Reverse procedure to install.

## STEERING KNUCKLE & HUB ASSEMBLY
### REPLACE

1. Raise and support vehicle, then remove wheel and tire assembly.
2. Carefully raise the staked portion of the halfshaft attaching nut using a suitable tool.
3. Remove halfshaft attaching nut, then discard nut. **When loosening the nut, apply brakes to lock hub.**
4. Remove stabilizer bar to control arm attaching nut, bolt, washer and bushings.
5. Remove tie rod end cotter pin, then remove attaching nut.
6. Separate tie rod end from steering knuckle using tool No. T85M-3395-A or equivalent.
7. Remove attaching clip at center of brake caliper flex hose.
8. Remove brake caliper attaching bolts, then support and position aside.

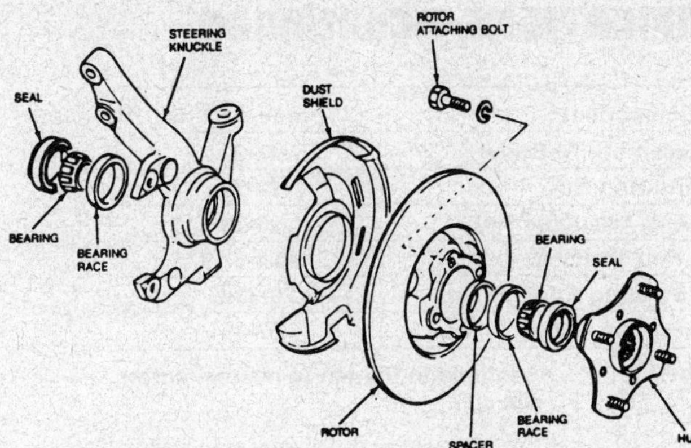


**Fig. 3 Front wheel bearing**

9. Remove lower ball joint clamp attaching nut and bolt.
10. Using suitable tool, pry control arm downward to separate ball joint from steering knuckle.
11. Remove steering knuckle to strut attaching bolts.
12. Remove steering knuckle and hub assembly from halfshaft, Fig. 3. **Use caution not to damage seals. If hub binds on halfshaft splines, loosen by lightly tapping end of halfshaft with plastic face hammer. Do not use metal faced hammer as constant velocity joint internal damage may result.**
13. Reverse procedure to install. Torque attaching nuts and bolts to specifications.

## STRUT & SPRING ASSEMBLY

### REPLACE

1. Raise and support vehicle, then remove wheel and tire assembly.
2. Remove brake caliper, then support and position aside.
3. Mark inside strut mounting block for installation alignment.
4. Remove steering knuckle to strut attaching nuts and bolts.
5. Remove brake line hose to strut attaching clip, then position brake line hose aside.
6. Remove strut mount to strut tower attaching nuts.
7. Remove strut and spring assembly, then compress spring using Rotunda Spring Compressor tool No. 086-00029 or equivalent.
8. Remove strut rod nut, then carefully release spring compressor.
9. Remove strut mounting block, upper spring seat, bump stopper, coil spring and lower spring seat from strut.
10. Reverse procedure to install.

## POWER STEERING GEAR

### REPLACE

1. Remove battery assembly.
2. Raise and support vehicle, then remove front tire and wheel assemblies.
3. Separate tie rod ends from steering knuckle as follows:
   a. Remove tie rod end cotter pin and attaching nut.
   b. Using tool No. T85M-3395-A or equivalent separate tie rod end from steering knuckle.
   c. Mark tie rod end, jamb nut and tie rod for installation alignment.
   d. Loosen tie rod end jamb nut, then remove tie rod end.
4. Remove righthand lower inner fender dust shield.
5. Lower vehicle. **Do not allow anything but rear wheels to touch ground.**
6. Using suitable cutters, cut plastic wire tie clamping steering column dust boot to steering gear.
7. Pull dust boot back, then rotate steering column shaft until clamp bolt is accessible, then lock steering column.
8. Mark steering column pinion shaft and intermediate shaft lower universal joint for installation alignment.
9. Remove intermediate shaft lower universal joint attaching clamp bolt.
10. Disconnect power steering gear return line.
11. Remove power steering gear pressure hose banjo bolt, then position hose aside. **Do not reuse copper washers from fitting.**
12. Remove steering gear attaching bolts.
13. Carefully lower steering gear, then remove steering gear through righthand fenderwell.
14. Reverse procedure to install. Torque all attaching nuts and bolts to specifications.

## POWER STEERING PUMP ASSEMBLY

### REPLACE

1. Disconnect battery ground cable.
2. Remove righthand radiator support and brace.
3. Disconnect intercooler outlet hose at throttle inlet and position aside, if equipped.
4. Remove engine lifting eye ground wire.
5. Place drain pan below power steering pump, then disconnect power steering pump inlet and return lines, then plug lines.
6. Remove power steering pressure switch electrical connector.
7. Remove pump bracket adjusting screw, nut and block, then remove pivot bolt.
8. Position pump below bracket, then remove bracket attaching nut and bolts.
9. Remove pump bracket, then remove pump assembly.
10. Reverse procedure to install. Torque all attaching nuts and bolts to specifications.

## TIGHTENING SPECIFICATIONS

| Year | Component | Torque/Ft. Lbs. |
|---|---|---|
| 1991-92 | Ball Joint Clamp Bolt | 32-40 |
| | Ball Joint To Control Arm | 69-86 |
| | Brake Caliper Bolts | 29-36 |
| | Control Arm Bracket | 44-54 |
| | Control Arm (Front Bolt) | 69-86 |
| | Control Arm (Rear Nut) | 55-69 |
| | Halfshaft Nuts | 116-174 |
| | Hub To Rotor Bolts | 33-40 |
| | Power Steering Pump Bracket | 27-38 |
| | Stabilizer Link Bolts | ① |
| | Steering Knuckle To Strut | 69-86 |

*Continued*

## TIGHTENING SPECIFICATIONS—Continued

| Year | Component | Torque/Ft. Lbs. |
|---|---|---|
| 1991-92 —Cont'd | Strut Assembly To Body | 17-22 |
| | Strut Rod Nut | 22-27 |
| | Tie Rod End Attaching Nut | 26-29 |
| | Tie Rod To Rack | 43.4-57.9 |
| | Tie Rod To Steering Knuckle Nut | 22-33② |
| | Wheel Lug Nuts | 67-88 |

①—Tighten nut until .43 inch of the bolt threads extend beyond the nut.

②—Torque to specifications, then continue to tighten to nearest cotter pin slot.

# Wheel Alignment

## INDEX



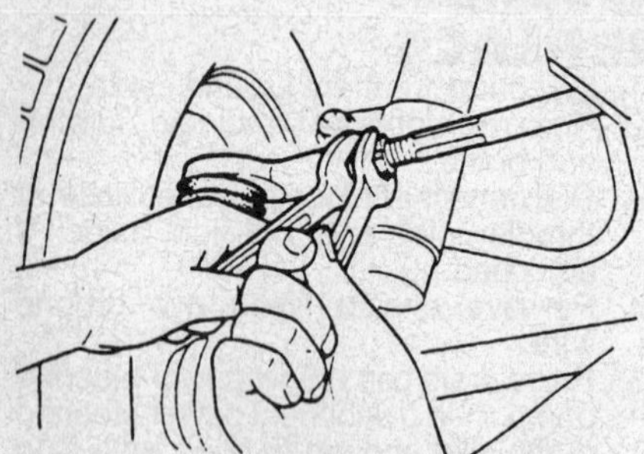

Fig. 1 Adjusting front toe-in

## PRELIMINARY CHECK

Before measuring and setting front wheel alignment, rest front wheels on turn plates.

Before setting rear toe, rest rear wheels on slider plates or turn plates. Before setting any alignment angle, jounce the vehicle three times at each end to establish trim height.

Special adapters are available for using a magnetic hub gauge at rear wheels. Depending on type of equipment used, these may not be necessary. After removing hub cap and bearing cap, hub gauge will snap into place on brake drum. Magnetic mounting toe gauges may also be installed in the same manner.

Always perform wheel alignment on a level alignment rack. Before doing alignment, check the following.

1. Worn suspension parts.
2. Standing curb height.
3. Remove heavy weights from trunk.
4. Wheel bearings.
5. Full tank of gas.
6. Place front seats in full rear position.
7. Check rear toe adjustment.
8. Always road test vehicle after adjusting alignment. If vehicle still pulls, switch front tires. If vehicle still pulls in same direction, check alignment and rear tracking. If vehicle pulls in opposite direction, rotate tires, then road test again.

## FRONT WHEEL ALIGNMENT

### CASTER

While caster is pre-set at the factory and not adjustable, it should be checked as a possible cause of suspension complaints. When checking caster ensure tires are properly inflated. If caster does not fall within specification, check control arms, stabilizers and bushings. If these components are satisfactory, check vehicle body for distortion at suspension mounting points.

### CAMBER

1. Raise vehicle and support at body so that front suspension is unloaded.
2. Remove tire and wheel assembly.
3. Loosen and remove four top strut attaching nuts from mounting studs.
4. Lower strut, then rotate strut and rotate bearing 180°.
5. Install strut in strut tower.
6. Install and tighten four attaching nuts.
7. Check camber is set correctly.

### TOE-IN

1. Loosen jam nuts at tie rod ends, then release clips at small ends of steering gear boots. **Ensure boots are free on tie rod ends so that they will not be twisted when tie rods are turned.**
2. Turn tie rods into or out of tie rod ends an equal amount on each side, **Fig. 1.** to keep steering wheel centered.
3. Check front tracking. **Always set tracking immediately after setting toe.** Set tracking by using rear wheels as a reference point. Follow equipment manufacture's instructions to check tracking. The angle of each front wheel in relationship to rear wheels must be the same.
4. Check toe setting after setting tracking.
5. When toe is correct, tighten tie rod end locknuts to 26-28 ft. lbs. Verity that steering gear boot ends are positioned in the reduced diameter sections of tie rods and install boot clips.

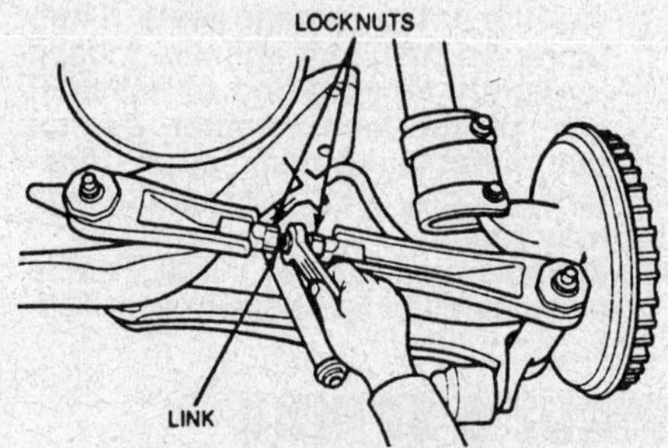


Fig. 2 Adjusting rear toe

## REAR WHEEL ALIGNMENT

### TOE ADJUSTMENT

Rear toe should always be checked whenever an alignment on the front wheels is required. Rear toe should be adjusted prior to setting the front alignment angles. Rear toe is adjusted by loosening the locknuts and rotating the adjustment link on the rear control arms, **Fig. 2.** One turn of the link will change toe .044 inch.

# 1991–92 FORD ESCORT & MERCURY TRACER

## INDEX OF SERVICE OPERATIONS

**NOTE:** Refer To Rear Of This Manual For Vehicle Manufacturer's Special Service Tool Suppliers.

# Specifications

## GENERAL ENGINE SPECIFICATIONS

| Year | Engine Liter/CID | Engine VIN Code | Fuel System | Bore and Stroke | Compression Ratio | Net H.P. @ RPM | Maximum Torque Ft. Lbs. @ RPM | Normal Oil Pressure, psi |
|---|---|---|---|---|---|---|---|---|
| 1991-92 | 1.8L/4-112 | 8 | MPFI | 3.27 x 3.35 | 9.0 | 127 @ 6500 | 114 @ 4500 | — |
| | 1.9L/4-116 | J | SMPFI | 3.23 x 3.46 | 9.0 | 88 @ 4400 | 108 @ 3800 | 35-65① |

①—With engine at normal operating temperature and 2000 RPM.

## TUNE UP SPECIFICATIONS

| Year & Engine/ VIN Code① | Spark Plug Gap | Ignition Timing BTDC② Firing Order Fig. ④ | Ignition Timing BTDC② Man. Trans. | Ignition Timing BTDC② Auto. Trans. | Ignition Timing BTDC② Mark Fig. | Curb Idle Speed③ Man. Trans. | Curb Idle Speed③ Auto. Trans. | Fast Idle Speed Man. Trans. | Fast Idle Speed Auto. Trans. | Fuel Pump Pressure Psi |
|---|---|---|---|---|---|---|---|---|---|---|
| 1991-92 | | | | | | | | | | |
| 1.8L/4-112, 8 | .041 | ⑦ | 10⑤ | 10⑤ | B | 750 | 750N | ⑥ | ⑥ | 38-46⑧ |
| 1.9L/4-116, J | .041 | C | — | — | ⑨ | ⑩ | ⑩ | ⑩ | ⑩ | 35-40⑧ |

①—The eighth digit of the Vehicle Identification Number (VIN) denotes engine code.
②—BTDC. Before Top Dead Center.
③—N:Neutral
④—Before disconnecting wires from distributor cap, determine location of No. 1 wire in cap, as distributor position may have been altered from that shown.
⑤—With STI connector grounded, refer to Fig. D.
⑥—Computer controlled, non-adjustable.
⑦—Firing order, 1-3-4-2. Refer to Fig. A for spark plug wire connections at distributor cap.
⑧—Wrap shop towel around fitting to prevent fuel spillage, then connect a suitable pressure gauge to fuel diagnostic valve on fuel rail assembly. Place ignition switch in On position & check fuel pressure gauge reading.
⑨—Equipped with a crankshaft position sensor.
⑩—Idle speed controlled by an automatic idle speed control (ISC) valve.

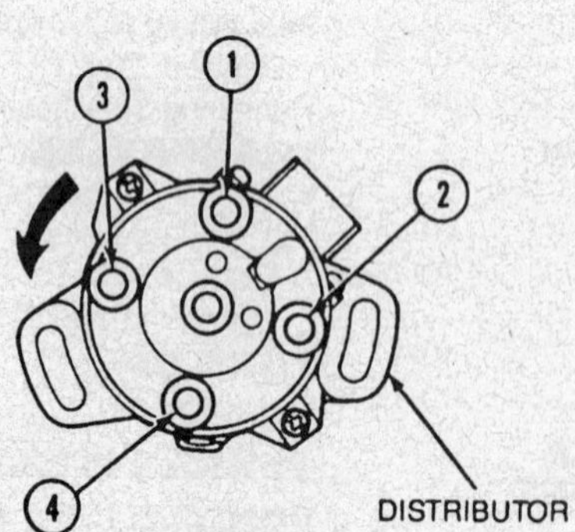

Fig. A

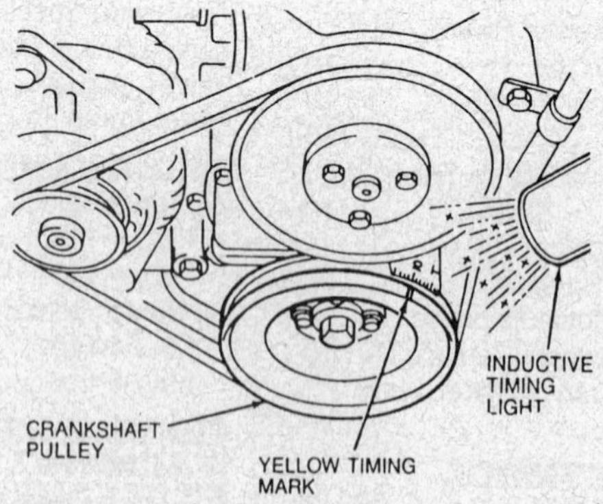

Fig. B

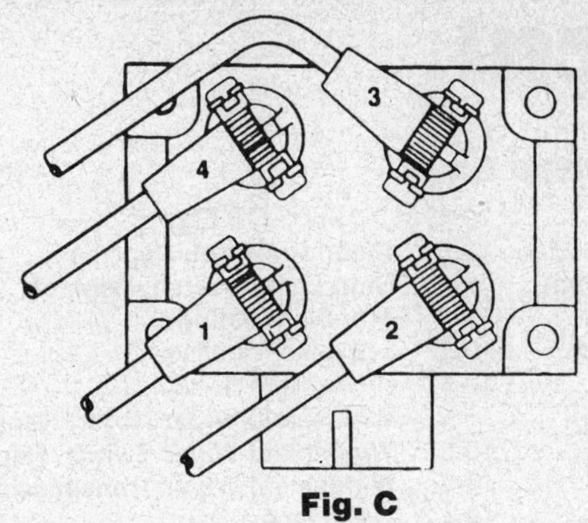


Fig. C

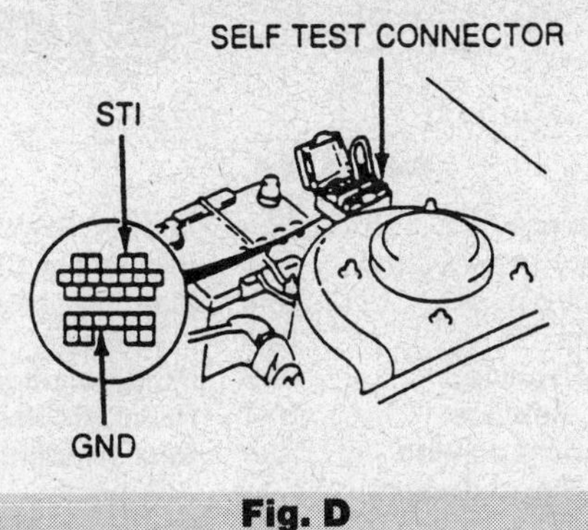


Fig. D

## WHEEL ALIGNMENT SPECIFICATIONS

| Year | Caster Angle, Degrees | | Camber Angle, Degrees | | Toe-In Inch |
|---|---|---|---|---|---|
| | Limits | Desired | Limits | Desired | |
| **Front** | | | | | |
| 1991-92 | +1 to +2 5/6 | +1 11/12 | −5/16 to +2/3 | −1/12 | .08 |
| **Rear** | | | | | |
| 1991-92 | — | — | −1 1/12 to +5/12 | −1/3 | .08 |

## COOLING SYSTEM & CAPACITY DATA

| Year | Model or Engine/VIN | Cooling Capacity, Qts. | | Radiator Cap Relief Pressure, Lbs. | Thermo. Opening Temp. | Fuel Tank Gals. | Engine Oil Refill Qts. | Transaxle Oil | |
|---|---|---|---|---|---|---|---|---|---|
| | | Manual Transaxle | Automatic Transaxle | | | | | Manual Transaxle Qts. | Auto. Transaxle Qts. |
| 1991-92 | 1.8L/4-112, 8 | 5.3 | 6.3 | 15 | 192 | 13.2 | 4.0① | 3.55 | 6.1 |
| | 1.9L/4-116, J | 5.3 | 6.3 | 16 | 195 | 11.9 | 4.0① | 2.83 | 6.1 |

①—Includes filter.

## LUBRICANT DATA

| Year | Model | Lubricant Type | | | | | |
|---|---|---|---|---|---|---|---|
| | | Transaxle | | Transfer Case | Rear Axle | Power Steering | Brake System |
| | | Manual | Automatic | | | | |
| 1991–92 | All | ATF① | ATF① | — | — | ATF① | DOT 3 |

①—Mercon XT-2-QDX or XT-2-DDX.

# Electrical

## INDEX



## FUSE PANEL & FLASHER LOCATION

These vehicles use two fuse panels. The passenger compartment fuse panel is located below the instrument panel, to the left of the steering wheel. The engine compartment fuse panel is located on the left side of the engine compartment.

The flasher unit is located below the left-hand side of the instrument panel.

## STARTER REPLACE

### 1.8L/4-112 ENGINE

1. Disconnect battery ground cable, then remove air duct from throttle body to resonance chamber.
2. Remove starter motor upper mount bolts, then raise and support vehicle.
3. Remove intake plenum support bracket, then disconnect "S" terminal connector from starter solenoid. When disconnecting connector from "S" terminal, grasp connector and depress plastic tab to remove.
4. Remove "B" terminal attaching nut and disconnect cable from terminal.
5. Remove starter motor lower mounting bolt, then the starter motor.
6. Reverse procedure to install. **Torque** upper and lower mounting bolts to 15-20 ft. lbs. and "B" terminal attaching nut to 7-12 ft. lbs.

### 1.9L/4-116 ENGINE

1. Disconnect battery ground cable.
2. **On models equipped with automatic transaxle,** remove kickdown cable routing bracket from engine block.
3. **On all models,** disconnect wire from starter solenoid "S" terminal. When disconnecting connector from "S" terminal, grasp connector and depress plastic tab to remove.
4. Remove "B" terminal attaching nut and disconnect cable from terminal.

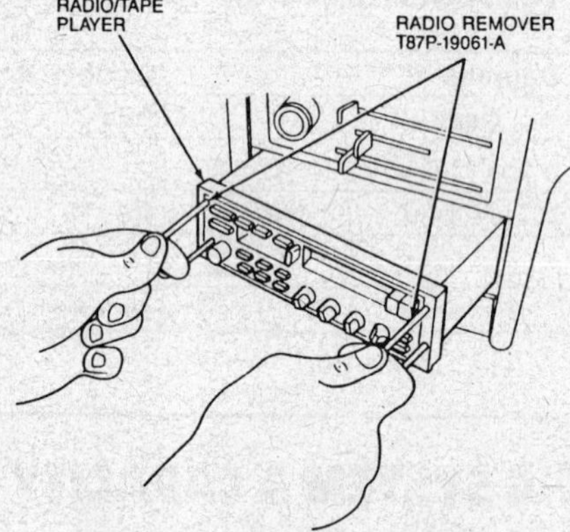


**Fig. 1 Radio removal**

5. Remove starter motor mounting bolts, then the starter motor.
6. Reverse procedure to install. **Torque** mounting bolts to 15-20 ft. lbs. and "B" terminal attaching nut to 7-12 ft. lbs.

## DISTRIBUTOR REPLACE

### 1.8L/4-112 ENGINE

1. Disconnect battery ground cable, then disconnect coil wire from distributor.
2. Remove distributor cap screws, then pull off cap and swing it aside.
3. Disconnect distributor electrical connector.
4. If distributor unit is not being replaced, scribe a reference mark across distributor base flange and cylinder head. This reference mark will allow installation without changing timing.
5. Remove distributor mounting bolts, then the distributor.
6. Reverse procedure to install noting the following:
   a. Ensure that drive tangs engage with camshaft slots.
   b. **Torque** distributor mounting bolts to 14-19 ft. lbs.
   c. If a new distributor has been installed, ignition timing should be checked and adjusted.

### 1.9L/4-116 ENGINE

This engine uses a distributorless ignition.

## IGNITION SWITCH REPLACE

1. Remove multi-function switch as described under "Multi-Function Switch, Replace."
2. Disconnect ignition switch electrical connector.
3. Remove three mounting screws, then the ignition switch.
4. Reverse procedure to install.

## HEADLAMP & TURN SIGNAL SWITCHES REPLACE

The headlamp and turn signal switches are serviced with the multi-function switch as a unit. Refer to "Multi-Function Switch, Replace" for procedure.

## FOG LAMP SWITCH REPLACE

1. Disconnect battery ground cable.
2. Detach hood release cable from left lower dash trim panel, then remove four retaining screws and left lower dash trim panel.
3. Disconnect electrical connector from fog lamp switch, then squeeze two lock tabs and remove fog lamp switch through front of trim panel.
4. Reverse procedure to install.

## STOP LAMP SWITCH REPLACE

1. Disconnect battery ground cable, then disconnect stop lamp switch electrical connector.
2. Remove stop lamp locknut, then the stop lamp switch.

3. Reverse procedure to install, adjust stop lamp switch by turning the switch until it contacts the brake pedal, then turn an additional half turn.

## MULTI-FUNCTION SWITCH
### REPLACE

1. Disconnect battery ground cable, then remove steering wheel as described under "Steering Wheel, Replace."
2. Remove four retaining screws from steering column lower cover, then remove lower cover.
3. Remove steering column upper cover, then disconnect three multi-function switch electrical connectors.
4. Remove multi-function switch retaining screw, then pull electrical connectors from retaining brackets and remove switch.
5. Reverse procedure to install.

## INSTRUMENT PANEL DIMMER SWITCH
### REPLACE

1. Disconnect battery ground cable.
2. Detach hood release cable from left lower dash trim panel, then remove four retaining screws and left lower dash trim panel.
3. Disconnect electrical connector from dimmer switch, then squeeze two lock tabs and remove dimmer switch through front of trim panel.
4. Reverse procedure to install.

## RADIO
### REPLACE

1. Disconnect battery ground cable.
2. Using radio remover No. T87P-19061-A or equivalent, pull radio out from its mounting position and disconnect antenna and electrical connectors, **Fig. 1.**
3. Remove radio from vehicle.
4. Reverse procedure to install.

## STEERING WHEEL
### REPLACE

1. Disconnect battery ground cable.
2. Remove steering wheel cover retaining screws from back side of wheel, then remove cover.
3. Disconnect horn and speed control electrical connectors.
4. Remove steering wheel mounting nut, then steering wheel using puller No. T67L-3600-A or equivalent.
5. Reverse procedure to install. **Torque** steering wheel mounting nut to 29-36 ft. lbs.

## INSTRUMENT CLUSTER
### REPLACE

1. Disconnect battery ground cable.
2. Remove four bolts securing steering

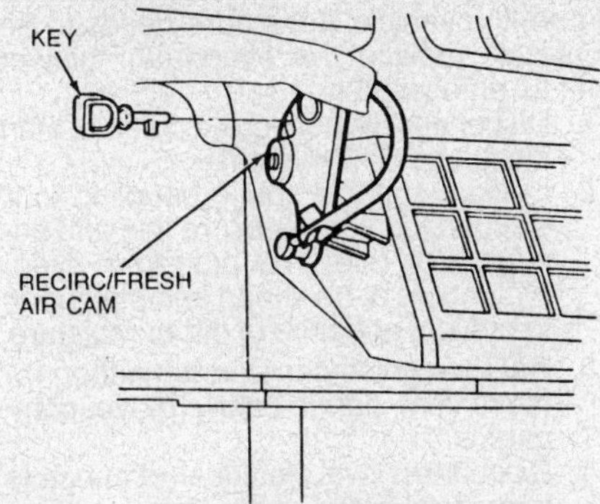


**Fig. 2 Adjusting Recirc/Fresh air cable**

column to instrument panel frame, then lower steering column.
3. Remove cap screws securing instrument cluster bezel to instrument panel, then the instrument cluster bezel.
4. Disconnect speedometer cable at transaxle by pulling cable out of vehicle speed sensor.
5. Remove screws and bolts securing instrument cluster to instrument panel, then pull cluster out slightly and disconnect electrical connectors.
6. Disconnect speedometer cable from instrument cluster, then remove cluster from instrument panel.
7. Reverse procedure to install.

## WINDSHIELD WIPER MOTOR
### REPLACE

1. Disconnect battery ground cable.
2. Remove wiper arm attaching nut cover, then attaching nut and pull wiper arm from pivot shaft.
3. With hood closed, remove seven screw covers from cowl grille screws.
4. Remove seven cowl grille screws, then cowl grille.
5. Pry up four baffle retaining clips, then remove baffle trim piece.
6. Remove wiper linkage retaining clip, then disconnect wiper linkage from motor. Ensure that wiper motor is in the PARK position before disconnecting linkage.
7. Disconnect two motor electrical connectors, then remove three mounting bolts and motor.
8. reverse procedure to install. **Torque** wiper motor mounting bolts to 61-87 inch lbs.

## REAR WIPER MOTOR
### REPLACE

1. Disconnect battery ground cable.
2. Lift wiper arm attaching nut cover and remove nut, then pull wiper arm from pivot shaft.
3. Remove shaft seal from outer bushing attaching nut, then remove outer bushing attaching nut and outer bushing.
4. Remove liftgate trim panel as follows:
   a. Remove three push-in retainers and hi-mount stop lamp cover.
   b. Remove liftgate seaming welt from along trim panel, then disengage 10 retaining clips and remove trim panel.
   c. Remove cargo area lamp.
5. Disconnect wiper motor electrical connector, then remove three wiper motor mounting bolts and wiper motor.
6. Reverse procedure to install noting the following:
   a. **Torque** wiper motor mounting bolts to 61-87 inch lbs. and outer bushing attaching nut to 35-52 inch lbs.
   b. Turn wiper switch to the ON position and allow pivot shaft to move through three or four cycles, then turn wiper switch off.
   c. Position wiper arm on pivot shaft so tip of blade is .79-.98 inch from rear window molding.
   d. **Torque** wiper arm attaching nut to 61-87 inch lbs.

## WINDSHIELD WIPER TRANSMISSION
### REPLACE

1. Disconnect battery ground cable.
2. With hood closed, remove seven screw covers from cowl grille screws.
3. Remove seven cowl grille screws, the cowl grille.
4. Pry up four baffle retaining clips, then remove baffle trim piece.
5. Remove two retaining screws from each pivot shaft, then remove pivot shaft and wiper linkage assembly.
6. Reverse procedure to install. **Torque** pivot shaft retaining screws to 61-87 inch lbs.

## WINDSHIELD WIPER SWITCH
### REPLACE

The windshield wiper switch is serviced with the multi-function switch as a unit. Refer to "Multi-Function Switch, Replace" for procedure.

## BLOWER MOTOR
### REPLACE

1. Disconnect battery ground cable, then remove trim panel below glove compartment.
2. Remove wiring bracket and bolt, then disconnect blower motor electrical connector.
3. Remove three blower motor attaching bolts, then blower motor.
4. Remove blower wheel retaining clip, then blower wheel from blower motor.
5. Reverse procedure to install.

## HEATER CORE

### REPLACE

1. Disconnect battery ground cable.
2. Disconnect heater hoses at bulkhead, then remove instrument panel.
3. Disconnect mode selector and temperature control cables from cams and retaining clips.
4. Loosen capscrew that secures heater to blower clamp, then remove three heater unit mounting nuts.
5. Disconnect antenna lead from retaining clip, then remove heater unit.
6. Remove insulator, then four brace capscrews and brace.
7. Remove heater core from heater unit.
8. Reverse procedure to install.

## EVAPORATOR CORE

### REPLACE

If a leaking evaporator core is suspected, leak test the core before removing it from the vehicle. If the core needs to be replaced, replace the evaporator/blower unit as an assembly.

1. Disconnect battery ground cable, then discharge A/C system.
2. Using a suitable spring coupling tool, disconnect high-pressure line and accumulator/drier inlet tube from evaporator core at bulkhead and plug ports to prevent entrance of dirt or moisture.
3. Remove glove compartment, then remove trim panel below glove compartment.
4. Disconnect two electrical connectors from resistor assembly, then electrical connector from blower motor.
5. Remove right dash side panel, then right lower dash trim panel and capscrews.
6. Remove support bar and bolts, then support plate and bolts.
7. Disconnect cable from recirc/fresh air cam and retaining clip.
8. Loosen capscrew that secures evaporator to heater clamp, then remove four mounting nuts from evaporator/blower unit.
9. Remove evaporator/blower unit.
10. Reverse procedure to install, adjusting Recirc/Fresh air cable as follows:
    a. Move air cable to the FRESH position on climate control assembly.
    b. Remove glove compartment.
    c. Insert Cable Locating Key tool No. E7GH-18C408-A or equivalent through the fresh air door cam key slot and recirc door key boss opening to secure cam in its proper position as shown in **Fig. 2.**
    d. Disconnect cable from retaining clip next to Recirc/Fresh air cam, then connect cable to retaining clip.
    e. Remove cable locating key, then ensure that Recirc/Fresh air lever moves its full stroke.
    f. Leak test, evacuate and charge A/C system.

# 1.8L/4-112 Engine

## INDEX



## RELIEVING FUEL SYSTEM PRESSURE

1. Start engine, then remove rear seat cushions to gain access to fuel pump electrical connections.
2. Disconnect fuel pump electrical connections and wait for engine to stall.
3. Connect fuel pump electrical connections and install rear seat cushion.

## ENGINE MOUNT

### REPLACE

1. Install a suitable engine removal sling onto engine lifting brackets.
2. Place an engine hoist into position and support engine.
3. Remove engine vibration dampener, then the engine mount.
4. Reverse procedure to install.

## ENGINE

### REPLACE

### AUTOMATIC TRANSAXLE

1. Relieve fuel system pressure as described in "Relieving Fuel System Pressure."
2. Disconnect battery ground cable.
3. Marking hinge locations for installation reference, remove hood.
4. Discharge A/C system, then drain cooling system.
5. Remove air duct connecting throttle body to resonance chamber.
6. Disconnect power brake vacuum supply hose from power brake, then any necessary vehicle speed control vacuum hoses from intake plenum.
7. Disconnect the following electrical connectors:
    a. Power steering pump.
    b. Water thermoswitch.
    c. Temperature sending unit.
    d. Oil pressure switch.
    e. Fuel injector wiring harness.
    f. Oxygen sensor.
    g. Throttle position sensor.
    h. Distributor.
8. Disconnect all engine ground straps, then the ignition coil high-tension lead from the distributor.
9. Disconnect accelerator and kickdown cable bracket from throttle cam.
10. Remove accelerator and kickdown cable bracket from intake plenum and set assembly aside.
11. Disconnect heater core inlet and outlet hoses at bulkhead.
12. Remove necessary fuel line clips, then disconnect fuel pressure and return lines from the fuel rail.
13. Remove upper radiator hose, then disconnect cooling fan electrical connector.
14. Disconnect radiator thermoswitch

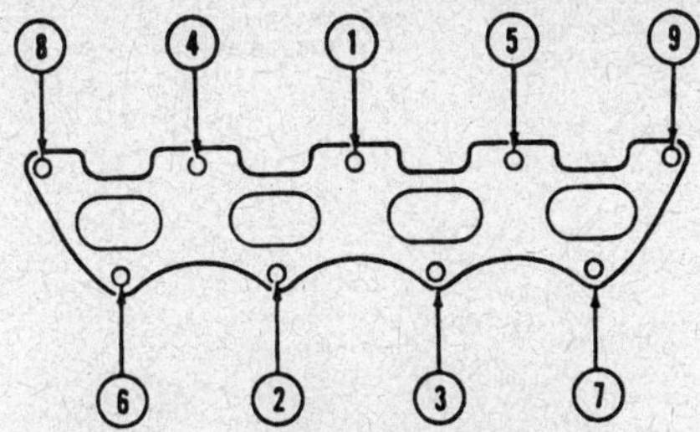

Fig. 1 Intake manifold nut tightening sequence

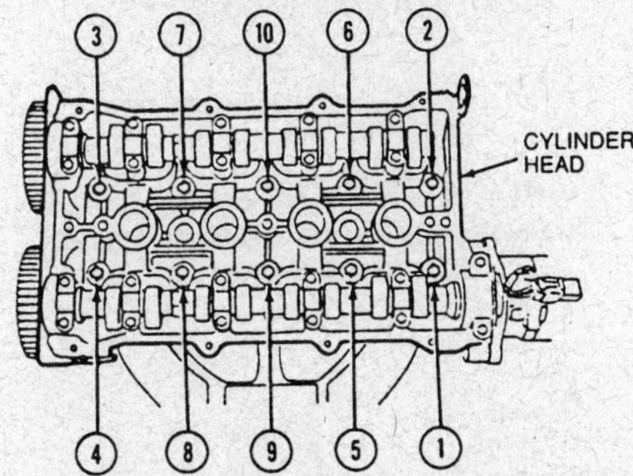


Fig. 3 Cylinder head bolt removal sequence

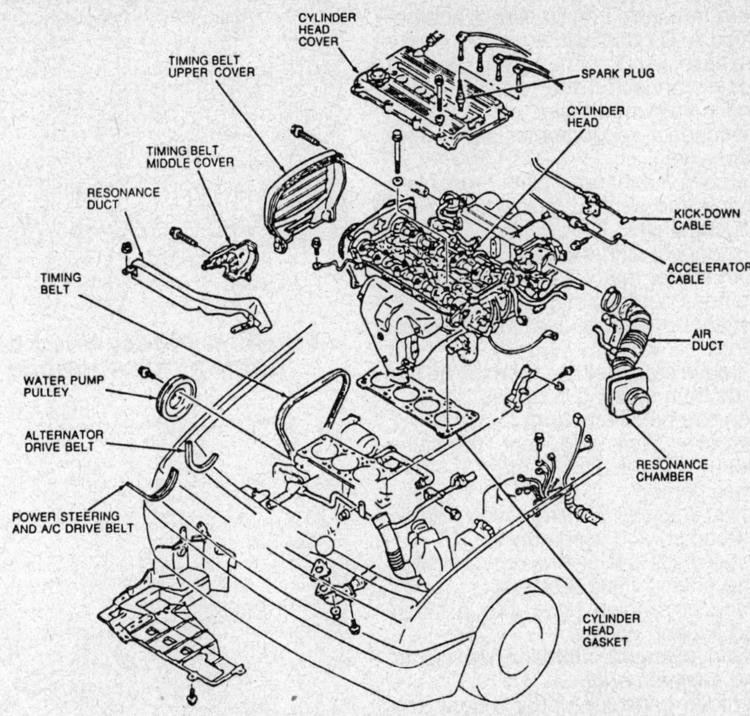


Fig. 2 Removing & installing cylinder head

electrical connector, then remove starter motor.

15. Raise and support vehicle.
16. Remove righthand upper, righthand lower and lefthand lower splash shields.
17. Remove lower radiator hose, then disconnect two transaxle cooling lines from the radiator and plug lines.
18. Remove A/C line mounting bracket from radiator and position aside.
19. Remove halfshaft bearing support, then the inspection plate from oil pan.
20. Place a wrench on the crankshaft pulley, then rotate crankshaft and remove the torque converter nuts.
21. Remove power steering and A/C accessory drive belt.
22. Remove timing belt as described in "Timing Belt, Replace."
23. Remove crankshaft pulley mounting bolts from crankshaft pulley guide plate.
24. Remove crankshaft pulley, crankshaft pulley guide plate ann timing belt outer and inner guide plates.
25. Remove exhaust flex-pipe and mounting assembly from exhaust manifold.
26. Remove A/C compressor, then remove power steering pump and bracket assembly leaving hoses connected. Suspend pump with wire and position out of the way.
27. Remove all accessible transaxle to engine bolts from engine block.
28. Lower vehicle, then remove radiator mounting brackets and resonance duct.
29. Remove radiator, fan and shroud assembly from vehicle.
30. Remove vacuum chamber canister, then pressure regulator and bracket assembly.
31. Remove shutter valve actuator and bracket assembly, position aside.
32. Remove water pump and alternator accessory drive belt, then remove alternator.
33. Install a suitable engine removal sling onto engine lifting brackets, then place an engine hoist into position and support engine.
34. Remove oil pan to transaxle attaching bolts and remaining transaxle to engine bolts from engine block.
35. Remove engine vibration dampener, then the front engine mount.
36. Carefully separate engine from transaxle, then remove engine from the vehicle.
37. Reverse procedure to install.

## MANUAL TRANSAXLE

1. Relieve fuel system pressure as described in "Relieving Fuel System Pressure."
2. Disconnect battery ground cable.
3. Marking hinge locations for installation reference, remove hood.
4. Discharge A/C system, then drain cooling system.
5. Remove resonance duct and air cleaner assembly.
6. Remove battery and battery tray.
7. Disconnect accelerator cable from throttle cam, then remove cable bracket from intake plenum.
8. Remove upper radiator hose from thermostat housing and radiator.
9. Disconnect radiator thermoswitch electrical connectors, then remove radiator overflow hose from the radiator filler neck.
10. Disconnect cooling fan electrical connectors, then remove radiator mounting brackets.
11. Disconnect the following electrical connectors:
    a. Alternator and oil pressure switch.
    b. Throttle position sensor and idle speed control.
    c. Manual lever position switch and fuel injector wiring harness.
    d. Back-up lamp switch and water thermoswitch.
    e. Oxygen sensor, power steering pump and distributor.
12. Disconnect all engine ground straps, then the ignition coil high tension lead from the distributor.
13. Disconnect fuel pressure and return lines.
14. Disconnect heater core inlet and outlet hoses.
15. Disconnect power brake supply, purge control and speed control vacuum hoses.
16. Raise and support vehicle.
17. Remove righthand upper and lower splash shields.
18. Remove clutch slave cylinder pipe bracket from transaxle leaving hose connected. Position slave cylinder aside, taking care not to damage pipe or hose.
19. Disconnect shift control rod and extension bar from transaxle.
20. Remove battery duct, then disconnect lower radiator hose from radiator.
21. Disconnect transaxle cooling lines from radiator, then remove power steering and A/C accessory drive belt.
22. Remove power steering pump and bracket assembly leaving hoses connected.
23. Position power steering assembly aside and suspend it with wire.
24. Remove A/C hose routing bracket

from transaxle crossmember and position A/C hose aside.
25. Remove A/C compressor leaving hoses connected, then position aside and suspend with wire.
26. Disconnect speedometer cable from transaxle.
27. Remove exhaust pipe mounting flange and support bracket from exhaust manifold.
28. Disconnect starter motor "S" terminal from starter motor solenoid.
29. Remove nut from starter solenoid "B" terminal and disconnect wire from terminal.
30. Remove stabilizer bar, then the tie rod ends from steering knuckles.
31. Remove halfshafts from transaxle.
32. Remove front and rear transaxle mount attaching nuts from crossmember.
33. Lower vehicle, then remove radiator, fan and shroud assembly.
34. Install a suitable engine removal sling onto engine lifting brackets.
35. Place an engine hoist into position and support engine.
36. Remove engine vibration dampener and engine mount.
37. Remove transaxle upper mount and support bracket.
38. Remove engine and transaxle as an assembly.
39. Remove engine intake plenum support bracket.
40. Remove starter motor from transaxle housing, then the transaxle front mount.
41. Remove oil pan to transaxle bolts and transaxle to engine attaching bolts from the engine block.
42. Separate transaxle from engine, then remove clutch assembly from engine.
43. Reverse procedure to install.

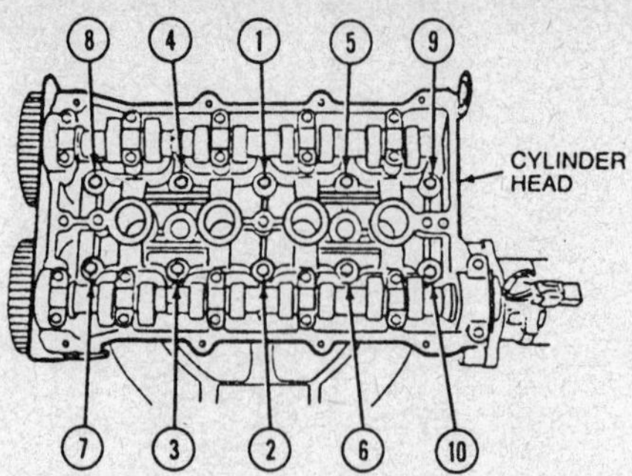

**Fig. 4 Cylinder head bolt tightening sequence**

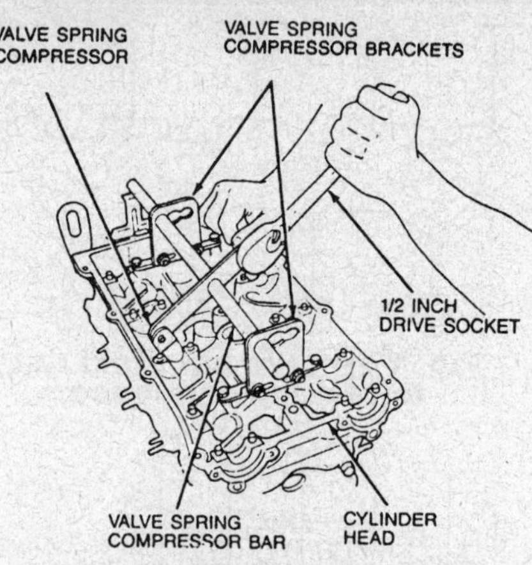

**Fig. 5 Removing valve keepers, valve seats, valve springs & valve**

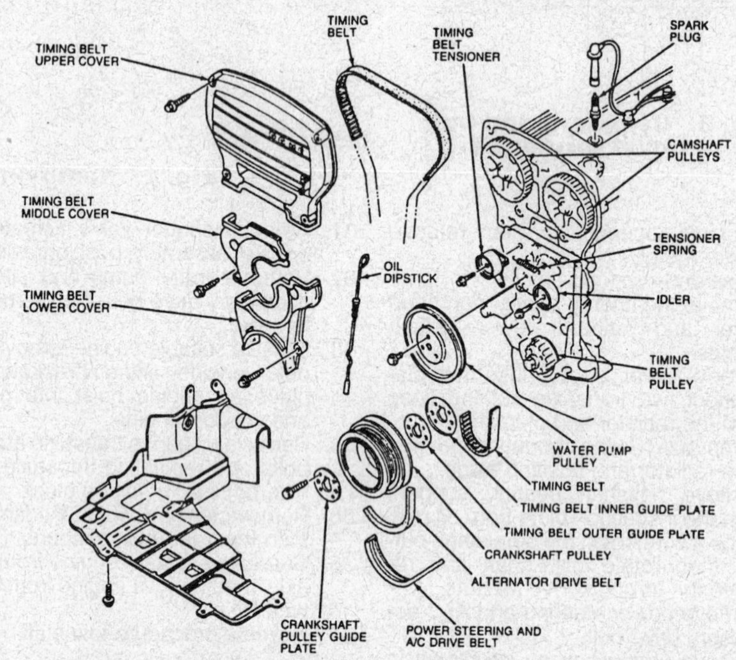

**Fig. 6 Exploded view of timing belt assembly**

## INTAKE MANIFOLD
### REPLACE

1. Relieve fuel system pressure as described in "Relieving Fuel System Pressure."
2. Disconnect battery ground cable.
3. Disconnect necessary vacuum hoses from intake manifold and plenum.
4. Remove vacuum chamber canister from intake plenum.
5. Disconnect idle speed control and bypass air hoses from intake plenum.
6. Disconnect accelerator and kickdown cables from throttle cam, then remove bracket from intake plenum.
7. Disconnect throttle body electrical connector, then remove fuel rail assembly from manifold.
8. Remove two bolts from transaxle vent tube and remove vent tube from intake plenum.
9. Remove intake manifold upper retaining nuts, then raise and support vehicle.
10. Remove intake plenum support bracket, then the intake manifold lower retaining nuts.
11. Lower vehicle and remove intake manifold, intake plenum and throttle body as an assembly.
12. Reverse procedure to install, install intake manifold retaining nuts in order shown in **Fig. 1. Torque** nuts to 14-19 ft. lbs.

## EXHAUST MANIFOLD
### REPLACE

1. Disconnect battery ground cable.
2. Remove resonance duct, then disconnect upper radiator hose.
3. Remove cooling fan, then raise and support vehicle.
4. Remove exhaust pipe from exhaust manifold and remove gasket.
5. Remove two bolts from exhaust pipe support bracket.
6. Remove lefthand side lower splash shield, then the cooling fan lower mounting bolts.
7. Lower vehicle and disconnect oxygen sensor electrical connector.
8. Remove manifold heat shield, then manifold mounting nuts and manifold assembly.
9. Remove all gasket material from cylinder head and manifold.
10. Reverse procedure to install.

## CYLINDER HEAD
### REPLACE

1. Relieve fuel system pressure as described in "Relieving Fuel System Pressure."
2. Disconnect battery ground cable.
3. Drain cooling system, then remove timing belt upper and middles covers, **Fig. 2.**

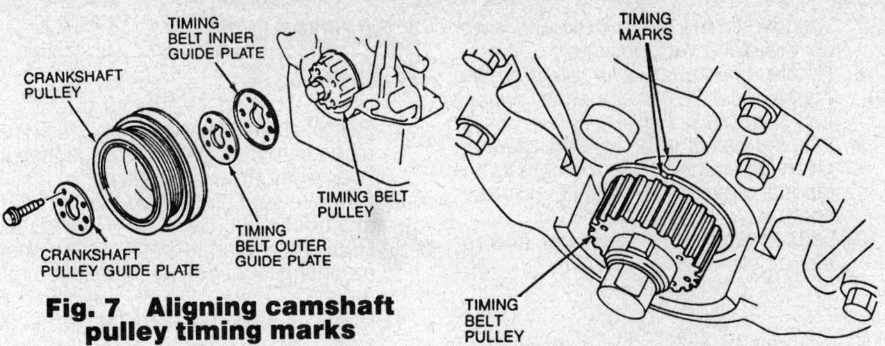


**Fig. 7 Aligning camshaft pulley timing marks**

**Fig. 8 Aligning timing belt pulley timing marks**

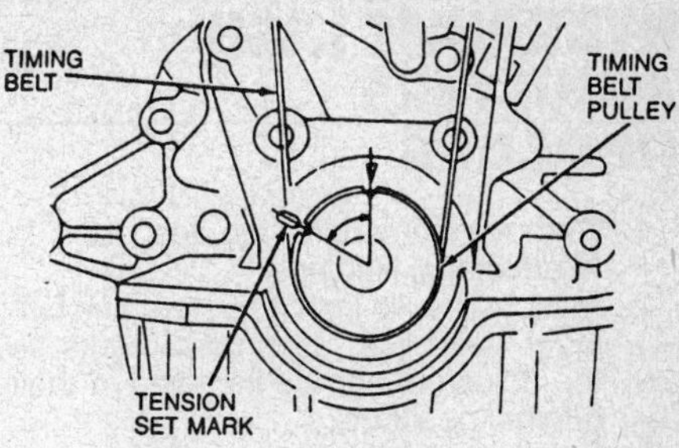


**Fig. 9 Aligning timing belt pulley with tension set mark**

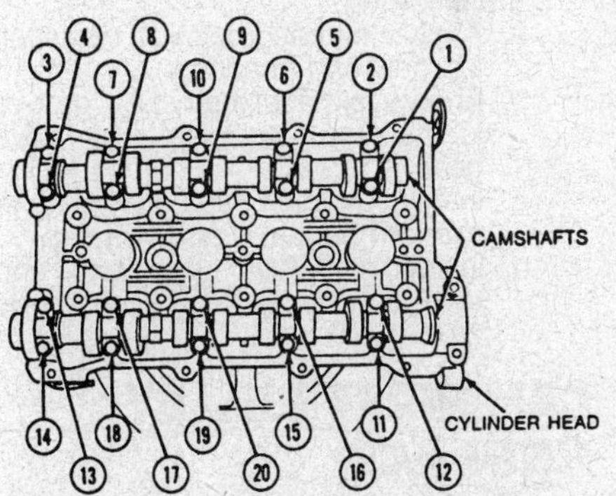


**Fig. 10 Camshaft cap bolt loosening sequence**

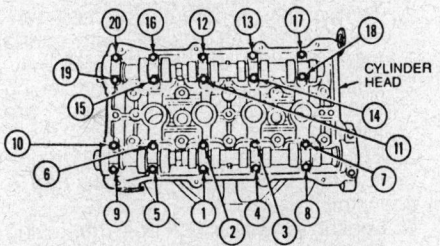

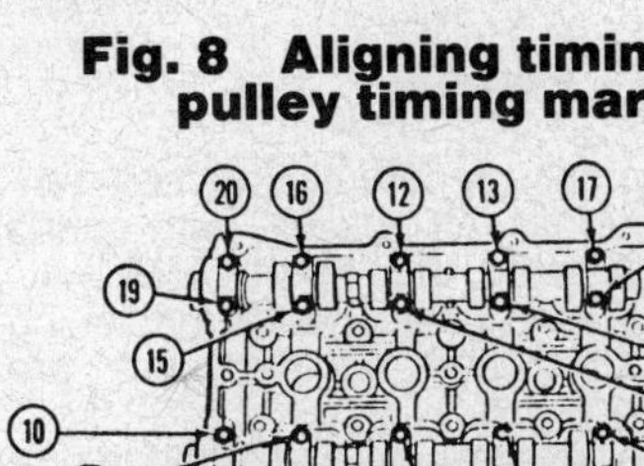


**Fig. 11 Camshaft cap bolt tightening sequence**

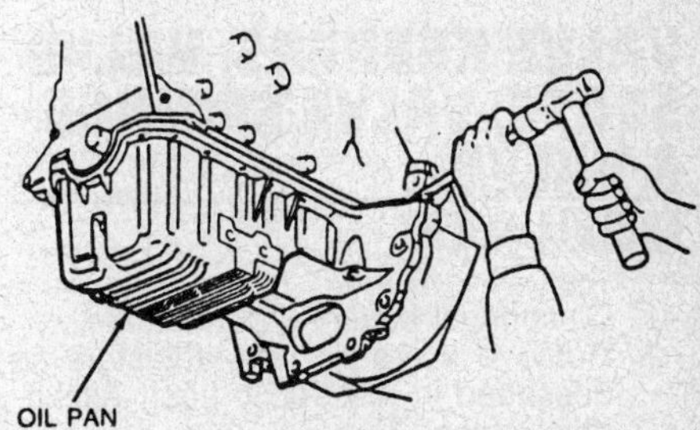


**Fig. 12 Oil pan removal**

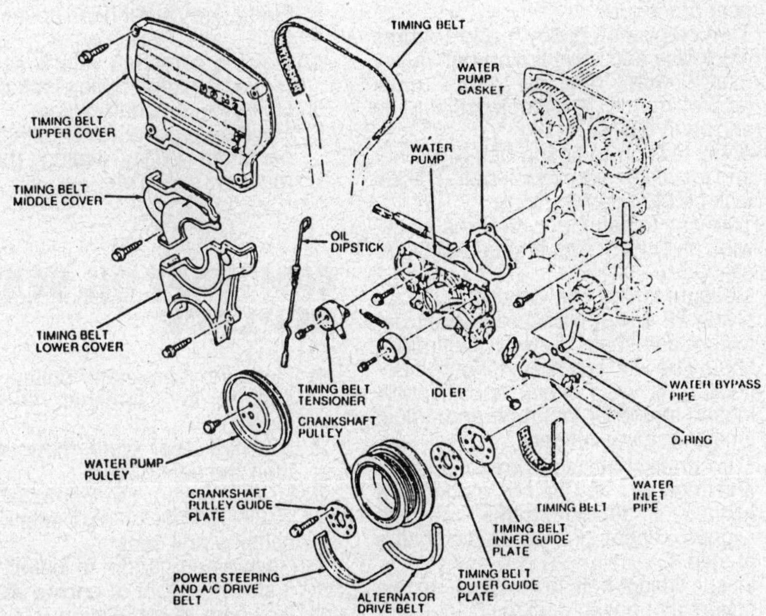


**Fig. 13 Removing water pump**

4. Rotate crankshaft and align timing marks located on camshaft pulleys and seal plate.
5. Loosen timing belt tensioner lock bolt and temporarily secure tensioner spring in the fully extended position.
6. Remove timing belt from camshaft pulleys and position so that it is not damaged during the removal and installation of the cylinder head. **Do not allow timing belt to be contaminated by oil or grease.**
7. Disconnect vacuum hoses from cylinder head cover, then spark plug wires from spark plugs.
8. Remove cylinder head cover and gasket, then the air duct from resonance chamber to throttle body.
9. Disconnect accelerator and kickdown cables from throttle cam, then remove accelerator and kickdown cable bracket from intake plenum.
10. Disconnect all vacuum lines from intake plenum, then all necessary electrical connectors from cylinder head, exhaust manifold, intake plenum and throttle body.
11. Disconnect ground straps, then remove upper radiator hose.
12. Remove transaxle to engine block upper righthand bolt.
13. Disconnect fuel pressure and return lines and plug lines.
14. Disconnect ignition coil high tension lead from distributor, then all necessary hoses from cylinder head and intake plenum.
15. Remove two bolts from transaxle vent tube routing brackets, then raise and support vehicle.
16. Remove bolt from water pump to cylinder head hose bracket.
17. Remove exhaust mounting flange and exhaust pipe support bracket from exhaust manifold.
18. Remove intake plenum support bracket, then lower vehicle.
19. Remove cylinder head bolts in sequence shown in **Fig. 3.**
20. Remove cylinder head assembly along with intake plenum and exhaust manifold from vehicle.
21. Reverse procedure to install, noting the following:
    a. **Torque** cylinder head bolts to 56-60 ft. lbs. in sequence shown in **Fig. 4.**
    b. Perform steps 6-12 in "Installation" procedure of "Timing Belt, Replace."

## HYDRAULIC LASH ADJUSTERS

### REPLACE

1. Remove camshafts as described in "Camshafts, Replace."
2. Mark hydraulic lash adjusters and cylinder head with alignment marks so the adjusters can be installed in their original positions.
3. Remove adjusters from cylinder head.
4. Reverse procedure to install, applying clean engine oil to adjusters before installation.

## VALVE KEEPERS, VALVE SEATS, VALVE SPRINGS & VALVE

### REPLACE

1. Disconnect battery ground cable.
2. Remove hydraulic lash adjusters as described in "Hydraulic Lash Adjusters, Replace."
3. Install two Valve Spring Compressor Brackets tool No. T89P-6565-A2 or equivalent, onto necessary camshaft cap bolt holes as shown in **Fig. 5.**
4. Install Valve Spring Compressor Bar tool No. T87C-6565-A or equivalent through bracket assemblies.
5. Install a 1/2 drive socket handle onto spring compressor.
6. Align spring compressor squarely over valve spring upper seat, then compress spring and remove valve keepers with a magnet.
7. Release spring compressor and remove valve spring upper seat, valve spring, valve spring lower seat and valve.
8. Reverse procedure to install, noting the following:
   a. Lubricate valve stem prior to installation.
   b. When installing valve spring ensure compressed end of spring goes into cylinder head first.
   c. After installation tap end of valve stem lightly with a plastic hammer to ensure that keepers are fully seated.

## TIMING BELT

### REPLACE

#### REMOVAL

1. Remove upper timing belt cover and gasket, **Fig. 6.**
2. Loosen water pump pulley attaching bolts, then remove water pump and alternator accessory drive belt.
3. Remove water pump pulley, then raise and support vehicle.
4. Remove right wheel, then righthand upper and lower splash shields.
5. Remove A/C and power steering accessory drive belts.
6. Remove crankshaft pulley, crankshaft pulley guide plate and timing belt outer and inner guide plates.
7. Remove timing belt middle and lower covers along with gaskets.
8. Rotate crankshaft and align timing marks located on camshaft pulleys and seal, plate, **Fig. 7.**
9. If timing belt is to be reused, mark an arrow on timing belt to indicate its rotational direction for installation reference.
10. Loosen timing belt tensioner and remove belt.

#### INSTALLATION

1. Temporarily secure timing belt tensioner in far left position with spring fully extended, then tighten lock bolt.
2. Ensure that timing marks on timing belt pulley and engine block are aligned, **Fig. 8.**
3. Ensure timing marks on camshaft pulleys and seal plate are aligned, **Fig. 7.**
4. Install timing belt.
5. Loosen tensioner lock bolt, then using a suitable prying tool, position timing belt tensioner so that timing belt is taut, tighten lock bolt.
6. Turn crankshaft pulley two turns clockwise and align timing belt pulley mark with mark on engine block.
7. Ensure camshaft pulley marks are aligned with seal plate marks. If marks are not aligned, remove belt and repeat procedure.
8. Turn crankshaft pulley 1 and 5/6 turns clockwise and align timing belt pulley mark with tension set mark (approximately 10 o'clock position) as shown in **Fig. 9.**
9. Apply tension to timing belt tensioner and install tensioner lock bolt. Torque lock bolt to specifications.
10. Turn crankshaft 2 and 1/6 turns clockwise and check that timing marks are aligned.
11. Measure timing belt deflection by applying 22 lbs. of pressure on belt between camshaft pulleys. Deflection should be within 0.35-0.45 inch. If deflection is not within specification, loosen tensioner lock bolt and adjust tensioner as necessary.
12. Turn crankshaft two turns clockwise and ensure all timing marks are aligned. If timing marks are not aligned, repeat procedure beginning at step 4.
13. Install timing belt lower and middle covers along with gaskets.
14. Install timing belt inner and outer guide plates, crankshaft pulley and crankshaft pulley guide plate. Torque bolts to specification.
15. Install A/C and power steering accessory drive belt.
16. Install righthand upper and righthand lower splash shields.
17. Install water pump pulley, then alternator and water pump pulley accessory drive belt.
18. Install right wheel, then lower vehicle.
19. Install timing belt upper cover and gasket. Torque bolts to specification.

## CAMSHAFTS

### REPLACE

1. Remove distributor assembly, then remove camshaft pulley as described in "Camshaft Pulley, Replace."
2. Remove seal plate, then loosen camshaft bolts in order shown in **Fig. 10.**
3. Remove camshaft caps noting their mounting locations for installation reference.
4. Remove camshaft and camshaft oil seal.
5. Reverse procedure to install, noting the following:
   a. Apply clean engine oil to camshaft journals and bearings.
   b. Ensure exhaust camshaft groove is installed into distributor drive gear.
   c. Install camshaft caps according to cap numbers and arrow marks.
   d. Install camshaft cap bolts and **torque** in sequence shown in **Fig. 11** to 8-10 ft. lbs.

## CAMSHAFT PULLEY

### REPLACE

1. Remove timing belt as described in "Timing Belt, Replace."
2. Disconnect vacuum hoses from cylinder head cover, then spark plug wires from spark plugs.
3. Remove cylinder head cover and gasket.
4. Holding camshaft with a wrench, remove camshaft pulley lock bolt.
5. Remove camshaft pulley.
6. Reverse procedure to install, aligning camshaft pulley timing mark with mark on seal plate.

## CAMSHAFT OIL SEAL

### REPLACE

1. Remove camshaft pulley as described in "Camshaft Pulley, Replace."
2. Remove seal plate mounting bolts, then the seal plate.
3. Using Locknut Pin Remover tool No. T78P-3504-N or equivalent, remove camshaft oil seal.
4. Reverse procedure to install, applying a small amount of engine oil to lip of seal prior to installation.

## VALVE STEM SEAL

### REPLACE

1. Remove valve keepers, valve seats, valve spring as described in "Valve Keepers, Valve Seats, Valve Springs & Valve, Replace."
2. Assemble Valve Stem Seal Remover tool No. T89P-6510-D and Slide Hammer tool No. T59L-100-B or equivalent, and remove valve seal from cylinder head.
3. Reverse procedure to install.

## CRANKSHAFT REAR COVER & OIL SEAL

### REPLACE

1. Remove flywheel (manual transmission) or flexplate (automatic transmission).
2. Remove rear cover mounting bolts and rear cover.
3. Using a screwdriver protected with a rag, remove crankshaft rear oil seal.
4. Reverse procedure to install, applying a small amount of engine oil to lip of new oil seal.

## OIL PAN

### REPLACE

1. Raise and support vehicle.
2. Drain engine oil, then remove righthand upper slash shield.
3. Remove righthand and lefthand lower splash shields.
4. Remove exhaust pipe front mounting flange and exhaust pipe support bracket from exhaust manifold.
5. Remove oil pan to transaxle mounting bolts, then support oil pan with a jack stand.
6. Remove oil pan to engine block attaching bolts. **Do not force a prying tool between engine block and oil pan when trying to remove pan. This may cause damage to oil pan contact surface.**
7. Using a suitable prying tool, carefully pry oil pan from engine block at point shown in **Fig. 12.**
8. Reverse procedure to install.

## OIL PUMP

### REPLACE

1. Remove timing belt as described in "Timing Belt, Replace."
2. Remove timing belt pulley lock bolt.
3. Using a steering wheel puller remove timing belt pulley, then the woodruff key.
4. Remove oil pan and oil strainer as described in "Oil Pan, Replace" and Oil Strainer, Replace."
5. Remove A/C compressor mounting bolts and position compressor aside.
6. Remove A/C compressor mounting bracket, then the mounting bolt from oil dipstick tube bracket.
7. Remove alternator lower mounting bolt.
8. Remove oil pump mounting bolts and oil pump.
9. Reverse procedure to install.

## OIL STRAINER

### REPLACE

1. Remove oil pan as described in "Oil Pan, Replace."
2. Remove oil strainer mounting bolts, oil strainer and gasket.
3. Reverse procedure to install.

## BELT TENSION DATA

### ALTERNATOR/WATER PUMP BELT

Adjust the tension of the belt using either Belt Tension Gauge tool No. 021-0028A or equivalent, or deflection method.

Using Belt Tension Gauge tool No. 021-0028A or equivalent, position the gauge on the longest accessible span of the belt and use the following specifications: **New Belt** (no run time), adjust tension to 85.8-103.4 lbs. Run the engine for 10 minutes, then readjust belt tension. **Used Belt** (more than 10 minutes of run time), adjust tension to 68.2-85.8 lbs.

Using the deflection method, **New Belt** (no run time), belt deflection measurement should be 0.31-0.35 inch. **Used Belt** (more than 10 minutes of run time), belt deflection measurement should be 0.35-0.39 inch.

### POWER STEERING & A/C COMPRESSOR BELT

Adjust the tension of the belt using either Belt Tension Gauge tool No. 021-0028A or equivalent, or deflection method.

Using Belt Tension Gauge tool No. 021-0028A or equivalent, position the gauge on the longest accessible span of the belt and use the following specifications, **New Belt** (no run time), adjust tension to 110-132 lbs. Run the engine for 10 minutes and readjust tension. **Used Belt** (more than 10 minutes of run time), adjust tension to 95-110 lbs.

If you are using the deflection method, **New Belt** (no run time) belt deflection measurement should be 0.31-0.35 inch. **Used Belt** (more than 10 minutes of run time), belt deflection measurement should be 0.35-0.39 inch.

## COOLING SYSTEM BLEED

After filling cooling system, run engine for approximately 12 minutes with radiator pressure cap off, then top off radiator. Secure cap, then and with engine running, fill coolant reservoir to FULL HOT mark with coolant.

## THERMOSTAT

### REPLACE

1. Ensure that engine is cool, remove radiator cap and open draincock. Allow coolant to drain below level of thermostat housing.
2. Remove air intake tube and disconnect water thermoswitch connector.
3. Disconnect engine wiring harness ground strap from connector above housing.
4. Disconnect exhaust gas oxygen sensor electrical connector, then remove upper radiator hose from housing.
5. Remove thermostat housing retaining bolt and nut, then the thermostat and gasket.
6. Clean mating surfaces of housing and cylinder head, then install thermostat in cylinder head.
7. Position gasket and thermostat housing on cylinder head and install housing bolt and nut, **torquing to 14-19 ft. lbs.**
8. Install upper radiator hose and connect EGO sensor electrical connector.
9. Connect engine ground strap to connector above housing, then the water thermoswitch connector.
10. Install air intake tube and refill cooling system with 50/50 coolant mixture. Add coolant until radiator remains full.
11. Start engine until upper hose is warm. Check for leaks and refill if necessary.
12. Run engine for 12 minutes, then top off radiator. Securely install radiator cap with engine running.
13. Fill coolant recovery reservoir to the Full Hot mark with 50/50 mixture.

## WATER PUMP

### REPLACE

1. Drain cooling system, then remove timing belt as described in "Timing Belt, Replace."
2. Raise and support vehicle, then remove oil dipstick tube bracket bolt from water pump.
3. Remove bolts and gasket from water inlet pipe, **Fig. 13.**
4. Remove all but uppermost water pump mounting bolt, then lower vehicle.
5. Remove upper mounting bolt and water pump assembly.
6. Remove gasket material from water pump.
7. Reverse procedure to install, refer to "Timing Belt, Replace" for timing belt installation.

## SERVICE BULLETINS

### LACK OF HEAT

On some 1991 Escort and Tracer models, poor heater performance may be experienced due to restricted coolant flow. This condition may be caused by a piece of casting flash that is attached to the water jacket inside the cylinder head. The casting flash restricts coolant flow through the heater pipe inlet next to the thermostat jacket. **The engine temperature will operate in the normal range with or without the casting flash.** Inspect the thermostat jacket using the following procedure:

1. Drain cooling system, then remove the thermostat housing and thermostat.
2. Visibly check and confirm by feeling with your finger for any piece of casting flash attached to the heater pipe inlet beside the thermostat jacket.
3. Remove any casting flash from the thermostat jacket.
4. Install thermostat housing and thermostat using a new thermostat gasket.
5. Fill cooling system, then check heater performance.

## TIGHTENING SPECIFICATIONS

| Year | Component | Ft. Lbs. |
|---|---|---|
| 1991-92 | Accelerator & Kickdown Cable Bracket | 6-8 |
| | A/C Compressor Mounting Bracket | 30-40 |
| | Alternator Lower Mounting Bolt | 27-38 |
| | Camshaft Cap | ① |
| | Camshaft Pulley Lock Bolt | 36-45 |
| | Clutch Release Cylinder | 12-17 |
| | Connecting Rod Cap | 35-37 |
| | Crankshaft Pulley | 9-12 |
| | Crankshaft Rear Cover | 6-8 |
| | Cylinder Head | ① |
| | Cylinder Head Cover | 4-6 |
| | Distributor Mounting Bolts | 14-19 |
| | Exhaust Flex Pipe To Converter | 51-69 |
| | Engine Coolant Temperature Sensor | 4-6 |
| | Engine Lifting Bracket | 27-38 |
| | Engine Mount Through Bolt | 49-69 |
| | Engine Mount To Engine Block | 49-69 |
| | Engine Oil Dipstick Bracket | 6-8 |
| | Engine Support Bracket | 69-86 |
| | Engine Vibration Dampener | 41-59 |
| | Exhaust Manifold Heat Shield | 6-8 |
| | Exhaust Manifold Nuts | 28-34 |
| | Exhaust Mounting Flange To Exhaust Manifold | 23-34 |
| | Flexplate Bolts | 71-76 |
| | Flywheel Bolts | 71-76 |
| | Fuel Rail Mounting Bolts | 14-19 |
| | Halfshaft Bearing Support | 31-46 |
| | Idler Mounting Bolt | 27-38 |
| | Intake Plenum & Manifold Assembly To Cylinder Head Nuts | ① |
| | Main Bearing Cap | 40-43 |
| | Oil Pan Drain Plug | 22-30 |
| | Oil Pan To Engine Block | 6-8 |
| | Oil Pan To Transaxle | 27-38 |
| | Oil Pressure Switch | 9-13 |
| | Oil Pump | 14-19 |
| | Oil Strainer | 6-8 |
| | Power Steering Pump Bracket | 27-38 |
| | Radiator Mounting Bracket | 6-8 |
| | Seal Plate | 6-8 |
| | Shift Control Rod To Transaxle | 12-17 |
| | Spark Plugs | 11-17 |
| | Starter Motor | 27-38 |
| | Temperature Gauge Sending Unit | 4-6 |
| | Thermostat Housing Bolt & Nut | 14-19 |
| | Timing Belt Lower Cover | 6-8 |
| | Timing Belt Middle Cover | 6-8 |
| | Timing Belt Pulley | 80-87 |
| | Timing Belt Tensioner | 27-38 |
| | Timing Belt Upper Cover | 6-8 |
| | Torque Converter Nuts | 25-36 |
| | Transaxle Front Mount | 27-38 |
| | Transaxle To Engine | ② |

*Continued*

## TIGHTENING SPECIFICATIONS—Continued

| Year | Component | Ft. Lbs. |
|---|---|---|
| 1991-92 —Cont'd | Transaxle Upper Mount Bolts | 32-45 |
| | Transaxle Upper Mount Nuts | 49-69 |
| | Water Pump Bolts | 14-19 |
| | Water Pump Inlet Fitting To Water Pump | 14-19 |
| | Water Pump Pulley | 6-8 |

①—Refer to text.
②—Automatic transaxle, 41–59; manual transaxle, 47–66.

# 1.9L/4-116 Engine

## INDEX



## FUEL SYSTEM PRESSURE RELIEVE

**Fuel pressure must be relieved prior to servicing any fuel system component.**

1. Remove back seat cushion.
2. Disconnect fuel pump connector.
3. Run engine until fuel in system is consumed.
4. Reconnect fuel pump connector and install back seat cushion.

## ENGINE MOUNTS

Refer to "Engine Mount, Replace" procedure in "1.8L/4-112" section when replacing engine mounts.

## ENGINE REPLACE

Refer to "Engine, Replace" procedure in "1.8L/4-112" section.

## INTAKE MANIFOLD REPLACE

1. Relieve fuel system pressure as outlined under "Fuel System Pressure Relief."
2. Disconnect battery ground cable and drain coolant system.
3. Remove air intake tube.
4. Disconnect fuel injector harness from EEC-IV harness.
5. Disconnect crankshaft position sensor.
6. Disconnect fuel supply and return lines.
7. Disconnect camshaft position sensor.
8. Remove throttle and kick down cables from throttle lever.
9. Remove throttle cable bracket.
10. Remove power brake vacuum supply and PCV hoses.
11. Remove vacuum hose from bottom of throttle body.
12. Remove nuts from intake manifold.
13. Remove intake manifold from vehicle.
14. Reverse procedure to install.

## EXHAUST MANIFOLD REPLACE

1. Disconnect battery ground cable.
2. Remove accessory drive belt.
3. Remove alternator and cooling fan and shroud assembly.
4. Remove exhaust manifold heat shield.
5. Raise and support vehicle.
6. Disconnect catalytic converter inlet pipe.
7. Lower vehicle.
8. Remove exhaust manifold nuts and remove the exhaust manifold.
9. Reverse procedure to install.

## CYLINDER HEAD REPLACE

1. Raise and secure hood.
2. Relive fuel pressure refer to "Fuel System Pressure Relief" procedure.
3. Disconnect battery ground cable.
4. Drain cooling system and disconnect heater hose at fitting located under intake manifold.
5. Remove air cleaner assembly.
6. Remove PCV hose from air cleaner assembly.
7. Label, then disconnect and or remove all electrical connectors, vacuum hoses, accelerator and transaxle kick-down cables and brackets from cylinder head assembly.
8. Remove upper radiator hose.
9. Remove oil level tube mounting nut from cylinder head stud.
10. Remove power steering hose and A/C line retainer bracket bolts from alternator bracket.
11. Remove accessory drive belt, then alternator and drive belt automatic tensioner.
12. Raise vehicle, then remove right side splash shield.
13. Remove crankshaft dampener, catalytic converter inlet pipe and starter motor wiring harness retaining clip below intake manifold.
14. Set engine No. 1 cylinder to TDC.
15. Lower vehicle.
16. Support engine with floor jack.
17. Remove righthand engine mount dampener, then right hand mount retaining bolts from mount bracket on engine.
18. Loosen righthand engine mount thru-bolt and roll mount back out of way.

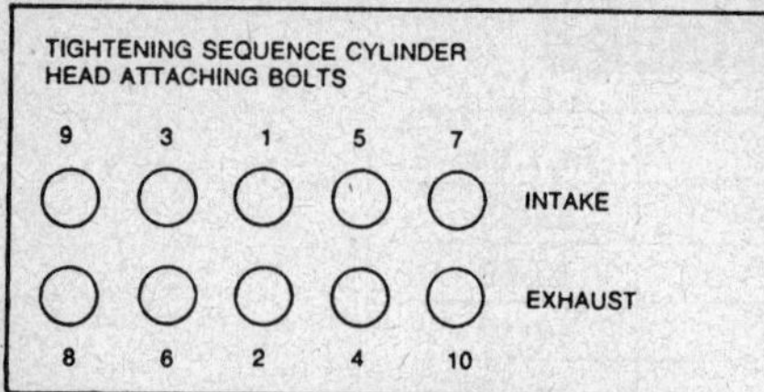


**Fig. 1 Cylinder head bolt tightening sequence**

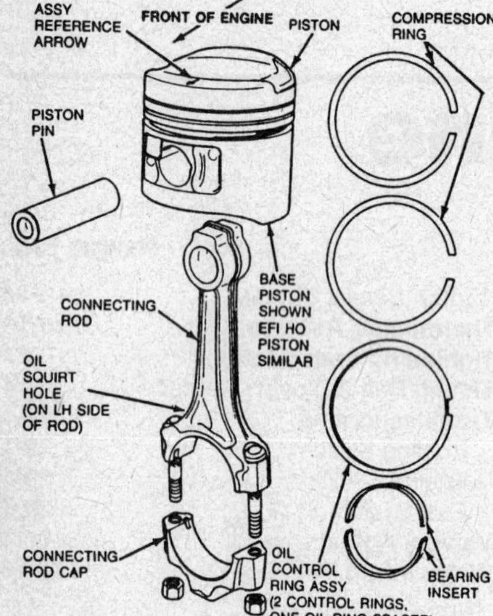


**Fig. 4 Piston & rod assembly**

19. Remove timing belt cover.
20. Loosen belt tensioner attaching bolt, then pry tensioner as far forward as possible. Tighten attaching bolt in this position.
21. Remove timing belt.
22. Roll righthand engine mount bracket back into position, then install mounting bolts.
23. Lower floor jack, then remove heater hose support bracket retaining bolt (starter motor bolt).
24. Remove alternator bracket to cylinder head mounting bolt.
25. Remove rocker arm cover.
26. Remove and set aside cylinder head bolts and washers (used if needed for squish height check). **New bolts must be used for final assembly.**
26. Remove cylinder head with exhaust and intake manifolds attached.
27. Remove cylinder head gasket. **Do not lay cylinder head flat. Damage to the spark plugs, valves or gasket surfaces may result.**
28. Reverse procedure to install, noting the following:
    a. Before final installation of the cylinder head, check piston squish height as described in "Squish Height Check."
    b. **Torque** new cylinder head bolts in sequence shown in **Fig. 1,** first to 44 ft. lbs. Loosen bolts approximately two turns, then torque bolts in sequence to 44 ft. lbs. Turn bolts

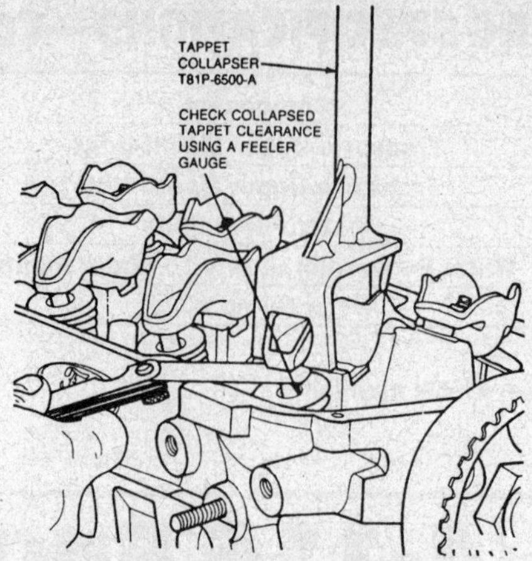


**Fig. 2 Checking tappet clearance**

an additional 90 degrees in sequence, then an additional 90 degrees.
    c. Crankshaft must be rotated so that the No. 1 piston is 90 degrees before top dead center (BTDC). Turn crankshaft until the pulley keyway is at 9 o'clock position, then time valve train by turning camshaft until keyway is at the 6 o'clock position. **Camshaft and crankshaft must not be turned until after the installation of the timing gears and timing belt.**

## SQUISH HEIGHT CHECK

Squish height is the clearance of the piston dome to the cylinder head dome at TDC. No rework of the cylinder head gasket surfaces (slabbing) or use of replacement components (crankshaft, piston and connecting rod) causing the assembled squish height to be over or under the tolerance specification is permitted. If no other parts other than the cylinder head gasket are replaced, the piston squish height should be within specification. If parts other than the cylinder head gasket are replaced, squish height must be checked.

1. Clean all gasket material from cylinder head mating surfaces.
2. Place a small amount of soft lead solder on piston spherical areas.
3. Rotate crankshaft to lower the piston in the bore and install the cylinder head gasket. A used gasket is preferred.
4. Install used cylinder head bolts and **torque** to 30-44 ft. lbs. in sequence shown in **Fig. 1.**
5. Rotate crankshaft to move piston through its TDC position.
6. Remove cylinder head and measure thickness of compressed solder to determine squish height at TDC. The solder should be within .039-.070 inch.

## VALVES
### ADJUST

The 1.9L engine is equipped with an

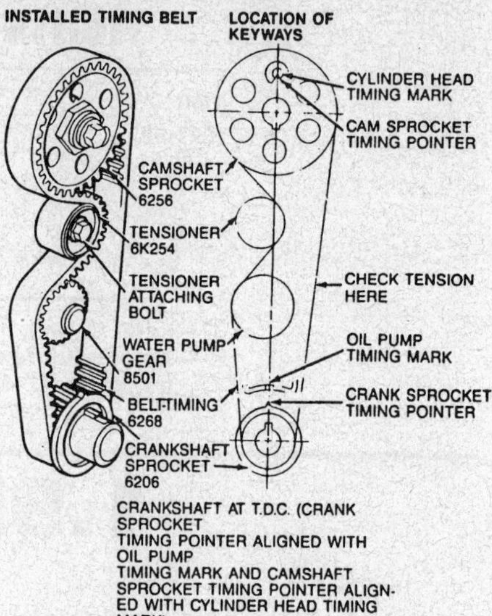


**Fig. 3 Aligning timing marks**

overhead camshaft and hydraulic lash adjuster. Valve stem to rocker arm clearance is measured with tappet completely collapsed. Perform the following procedure when measuring valve tappet clearance:

1. Connect an auxiliary starter switch, then crank engine with ignition switch OFF until No. 1 piston is on TDC after compression stroke.
2. Position tappet collapser tool No. T8 1P-6500-A or equivalent on rocker arm, then slowly apply pressure to bleed tappet. Continue to apply pressure until lifter plunger bottoms. Hold tappet in this position and check clearance between rocker arm and valve stem tip using a suitable feeler gauge, **Fig. 2.** Collapsed tappet clearance should be .000-.177 inch, with prefered clearance of .087 inch. If clearance is less than specified, check for worn or damaged fulcrums, tappets or camshaft lobes.
3. With No. 1 piston at TDC end of compression stroke, check the following valves as outlined: No. 1 and 2 intake and No. 1 exhaust.
4. Rotate crankshaft 180° from present position, then check the following valves: No. 3 intake & No. 3 exhaust.
5. Rotate crankshaft 180° from present position, then check the following valves: No. 4 intake & Nos. 2 and 4 exhaust.

## TIMING BELT & COVER
### REPLACE

1. Disconnect battery ground cable.
2. Remove accessory drive belt.
3. Remove drive belt tensioner.
4. Remove timing belt cover retaining nuts.
5. Remove timing belt cover.
6. Align timing mark on camshaft sprocket with timing mark on cylinder head, **Fig. 3.** Ensure crankshaft sprocket is aligned with the timing mark on the oil pump housing.

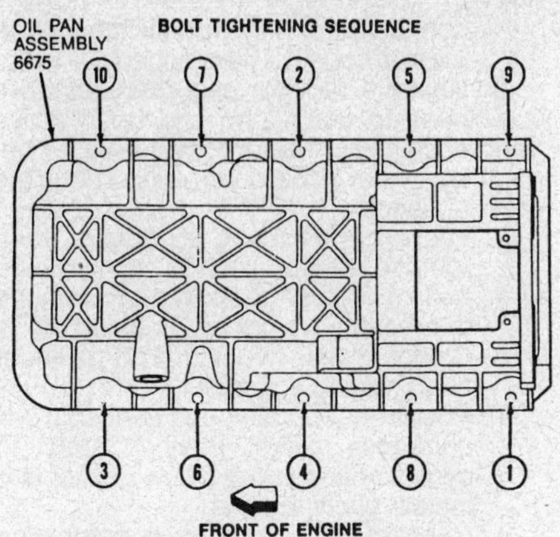


**Fig. 5 Oil pan tightening sequence**

7. Loosen the timing belt tensioner bolt.
8. Pry tensioner away from timing belt and tighten bolt.
9. Remove spark plugs.
10. Raise and support vehicle.
11. Remove righthand splash shield.
12. Remove crankshaft dampener.
13. Remove timing belt from vehicle.
14. Reverse procedure to install, noting the following:
    a. Install timing belt over sprockets in a counterclockwise direction starting at crankshaft. Keep belt span between the crankshaft and camshaft tight while installing over remaining sprockets.
    b. Loosen tensioner bolt and allow tensioner to contact timing belt.
    c. Rotate engine two complete turns. Ensure timing marks align and tighten tensioner bolt.
    d. Tighten attaching bolts to specifications.

## CAMSHAFT
### REPLACE

1. Disconnect battery ground cable and remove air intake duct.
2. Remove rocker arm cover.
3. Remove accessory drive belt.
4. Remove timing belt as outlined under "Timing Belt & Cover, Replace."
5. Remove rocker arms and tappets as follows:
    a. Remove hex flange nut.
    b. Remove fulcrums and rocker arms.
    c. Remove tappet guide retainers and tappet guides.
    d. Remove tappets.
6. Remove EDIS coil assembly.
7. Remove camshaft sprocket and key.
8. Remove camshaft thrust plate.
9. Remove cup plug from rear of cylinder head.
10. Remove camshaft through rear of cylinder head toward transaxle. Use care not to damage bearing surfaces.
11. Reverse procedure to install, noting the following:
    a. Coat camshaft lobes and bearing surfaces with oil prior to installation.

1.9L DRIVE BELT ROUTING

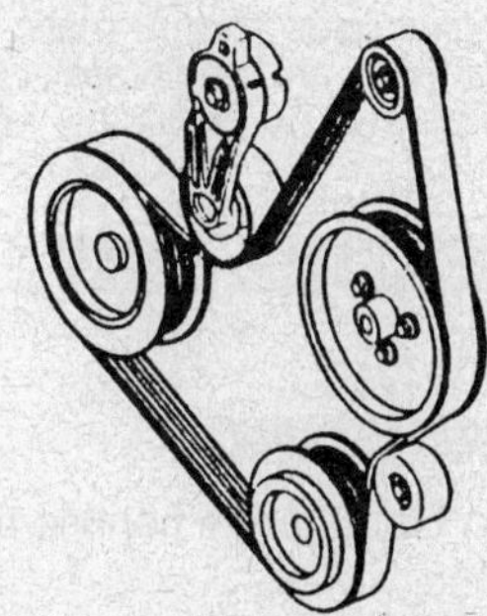

A/C, POWER STEERING, ALTERNATOR

ALTERNATOR ONLY

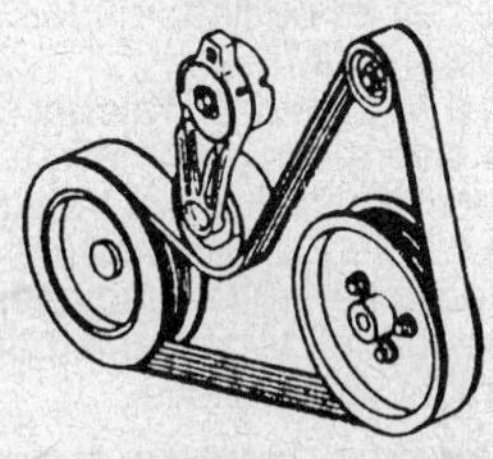

POWER STEERING, ALTERNATOR

**Fig. 6 Serpentine belt routing**

    b. Adjust valves as outlined under "Valves Adjust."
    c. Install cup plug using sealant part No. ESE-M46217-A, or equivalent. **Use sparingly, excess sealant can clog oil holes in camshaft.**

## CAMSHAFT SEAL
### REPLACE

1. Disconnect battery ground cable.
2. Remove accessory drive belt.
3. Remove timing belt as outlined under "Timing Belt & Cover, Replace."
4. Remove camshaft sprocket.
5. Using a suitable tool, remove camshaft seal.
6. Reverse procedure to install, using seal installing tool No. T81P-6292-A, or equivalent.

## PISTON & ROD ASSEMBLE

Assemble piston to connecting rod with connecting rod oil squirt hole and arrow on piston in position shown in **Fig. 4.**

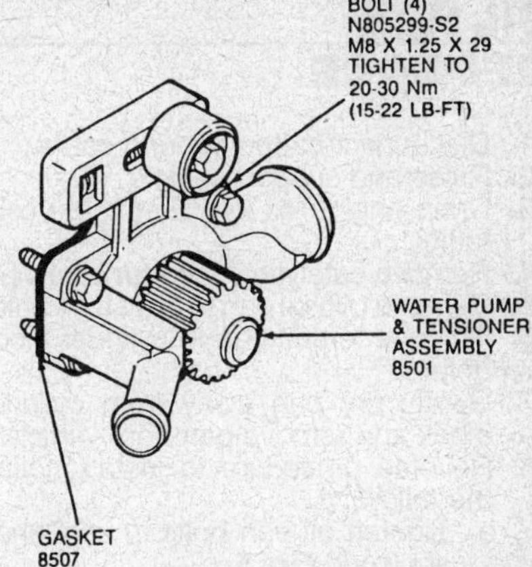


**Fig. 7 Water pump assembly**

## CRANKSHAFT DAMPENER
### REPLACE

1. Disconnect battery ground cable.
2. Remove accessory drive belt.
3. Raise and support vehicle.
4. Remove right side splash shield.
5. Remove flywheel inspection cover.
6. Hold flywheel using a suitable tool.
7. Remove crankshaft dampener bolt and washer and dampener.
8. reverse procedure to install.

## CRANKSHAFT OIL SEAL
### REPLACE

#### FRONT

1. Disconnect battery ground cable.
2. Remove accessory drive belt.
3. Raise and support vehicle.
4. Remove righthand splash shield.
5. Remove timing belt as outlined under "Timing Belt & Cover, Replace."
6. Remove crankshaft sprocket and belt guide.
7. Remove front crankshaft seal from oil pump body using a suitable seal remover.
8. Reverse procedure to install, using seal installer tool No. T81P-6700-A, or equivalent.

#### REAR

1. Disconnect battery ground cable.
2. Remove transaxle and flywheel assembly.
3. Remove engine cover plate.
4. With a sharp awl, punch a hole in metal part of rear crankshaft seal.
5. Remove seal using jet plug remover tool No. T77L-9533-B, or equivalent.
6. Reverse procedure to install, using seal installation tool Nos. T88P-6701-B2 and T88P-6701-B1, or equivalent.

## OIL PAN
### REPLACE

1. Disconnect battery ground cable.
2. Raise and support vehicle.
3. Drain engine oil into a suitable container.
4. Remove catalytic converter inlet pipe.
5. Remove two oil pan to transaxle bolts.
6. Remove ten oil pan to cylinder block bolts.
7. Gently pry pan away from cylinder block and remove pan from vehicle.
8. Reverse procedure to install, noting the following:
   a. Tighten oil pan bolts in sequence shown in **Fig. 5.**
   b. Ensure oil pan is lined up flush with rear face of cylinder block.

## OIL PUMP
### REPLACE

1. Disconnect battery ground cable.
2. Remove accessory drive belt and tensioner.
3. Support engine with a suitable floor jack.
4. Remove right engine mount dampener.
5. Remove right engine mount bolts from mount bracket.
6. Loosen mount through bolt and roll engine mount aside.
7. Remove timing belt as outlined under "Timing Belt & Cover, Replace."
8. Raise and support vehicle.
9. Remove right side splash shield.
10. Remove catalytic converter inlet pipe.
11. Drain engine oil and remove oil pan as outlined under "Oil Pan, Replace."
12. Remove crankshaft sprocket and timing belt guide.
13. Disconnect crank angle sensor.
14. Remove six oil pump to engine bolts.
15. Remove oil pump assembly from engine.
16. Reverse procedure to install, noting the following:
    a. Position pump drive gear to allow pump to pilot over crankshaft and seat firmly on cylinder block.
    b. When oil pump bolts are tighten, gasket must not be below cylinder block sealing surface.

## BELT TENSION DATA

This engine uses an automatic belt tensioner that sets and maintains drive belt tension. There is no provision for adjustment.

## SERPENTINE DRIVE BELT

### BELT ROUTING

Refer to **Fig. 6** for serpentine belt routing.

### BELT, REPLACE

#### Removal

1. Using a 3/8 inch drive ratchet or breaker bar inserted in automatic tensioner, pull tool toward front of vehicle.
2. While releasing belt tension, remove drive belt from tensioner pulley and slip it off remaining accessory pulleys.

#### Installation

1. Route belt as outlined under "Serpentine Drive Belt."
2. Using a 3/8 inch drive ratchet or breaker bar inserted in automatic tensioner, pull tool toward front of vehicle.
3. While holding tool, slip drive belt behind tensioner pulley and release tool.
4. Ensure that all V-grooves make proper contact with pulleys.

### TENSIONER, REPLACE

1. Remove accessory drive belt as outlined under "Serpentine Drive Belt."
2. Remove automatic tensioner mounting bolt.
3. Remove tensioner from engine.
4. Reverse procedure to install.

## COOLING SYSTEM BLEED

After filling cooling system, run engine for approximately 12 minutes with radiator pressure cap off, then top off radiator. Secure cap, then and with engine running, fill coolant reservoir to FULL HOT mark with coolant.

## THERMOSTAT
### REPLACE

1. Disconnect battery cable and wiring connector from thermo switch in thermostat housing, if equipped.
2. Remove radiator cap, then attach a hose to drain tube and open draincock. Drain coolant level until its below water outlet connection. Close the draincock.
3. Loosen upper hose at radiator, then remove water outlet housing retaining bolts. Lift clear of engine and remove thermostat. Do not pry housing off.
4. Clean outlet housing and cylinder head mating surfaces.
5. Position thermostat and seat so it will compress gasket. Position outlet to cylinder head, using a new gasket and install retaining bolts.
6. Connect top hose to radiator and tighten clamp. Ensure that draincock is closed.
7. Fill cooling system with recommended coolant as follows:
   a. Add 50 percent coolant, then add water until radiator is full. Allow coolant level to settle, then add more coolant until radiator remain full.
   b. Install radiator cap to first notch, connect battery cable and wire connector to thermo switch. Start engine and let idle until upper hose is warm, then carefully remove radiator cap and top off coolant level.
   c. Install cap securely and fill reservoir to FULL COLD mark with proper concentrate. Add water to FULL HOT mark. Check for leaks.

## WATER PUMP
### REPLACE

1. Disconnect battery ground cable and drain cooling system.
2. Remove accessory drive belt and tensioner.
3. Remove timing belt as outlined under "Timing Belt & Cover, Replace."
4. Raise and support vehicle.
5. Remove lower radiator hose.
6. Disconnect heater hose from water pump.
7. Lower vehicle.
8. Support engine with a suitable floor jack.
9. Remove right engine mount bolts and pivot mount aside.
10. Remove water pump bolts, raise engine and remove water pump, **Fig. 7.**
11. Reverse procedure to install.

## TIGHTENING SPECIFICATIONS

| Year | Component | Torque/ft. Lbs. |
|---|---|---|
| 1991-92 | Alternator To Alternator Brace Arm | 15–22 |
| | Alternator Bracket To Engine Block | 30–40 |
| | Alternator Pivot Attaching Bolt | 30–40 |
| | Camshaft Position Sensor To Head | 15–22 |
| | Camshaft Sprocket To Cam | 70–85 |
| | Camshaft Thrust Plate To Head | 6–9 |
| | Coil Bracket To Head | 6–8 |
| | Coil To Bracket | 3–5 |
| | Connecting Rod Cap To Rod | 26–30 |
| | Crankshaft Damper Attaching Bolt | 81–96 |
| | Crankshaft Position Sensor To Oil Pump | 2–2.5 |
| | Crankshaft Rear Seal Retainer To Block | 15–22 |
| | Cylinder Head To Block | ① |
| | EGR Valve To Intake Manifold | 4–7② |
| | Engine To Transaxle | 27–38 |
| | Exhaust Manifold To Cylinder Head | 16–19 |
| | Flywheel To Crankshaft | 54–67 |
| | Heat Shield To Exhaust Manifold Nut | 4–5 |
| | Heat Shield To Exhaust Manifold Stud | 2–7 |
| | Intake Manifold To Head | 12–15 |
| | Main Bearing Cap To Block | 67–80 |
| | Oil Filter Adapter To Oil Pump | 21–26 |
| | Oil Gallery Pipe Plugs | 8–12 |
| | Oil Pan Drain Plug | 15–22 |
| | Oil Pan To Block | 15–22 |
| | Oil Pan To Transaxle | 30–40 |
| | Oil Pump To Block | 8–12 |
| | Oil Separator To Block | 6–8 |
| | Pick-up and Screen To Pump | 7–9 |
| | Rocker Arm Bolt | 17–22 |
| | Rocker Arm Cover To Head | 4–9 |
| | Spark Plug | 8–15 |
| | Thermostat Housing To Head | 6–9 |
| | Timing Belt Cover Stud To Block | 7–9 |
| | Timing Belt Cover Stud To Block Stud Nut | 3–5 |
| | Timing Tensioner Attaching Bolt | 17–22 |
| | Transaxle To Engine | 40–59 |
| | Water Pump To Block | 15–22 |

①—Refer to text for torque and tightening sequence.
②—California models.

# Clutch & Manual Transaxle

## INDEX



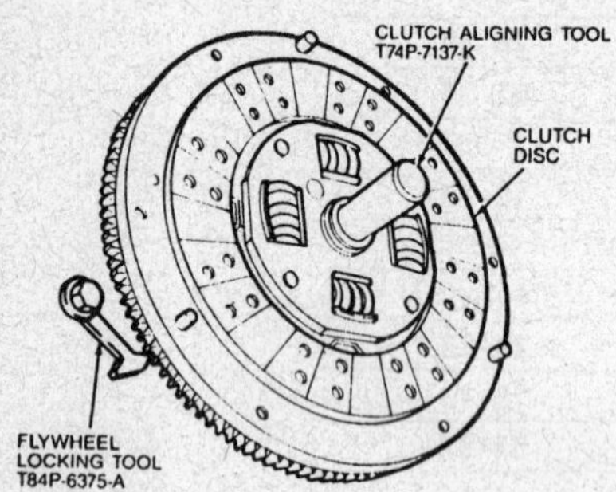


**Fig. 1 Installing clutch disc**

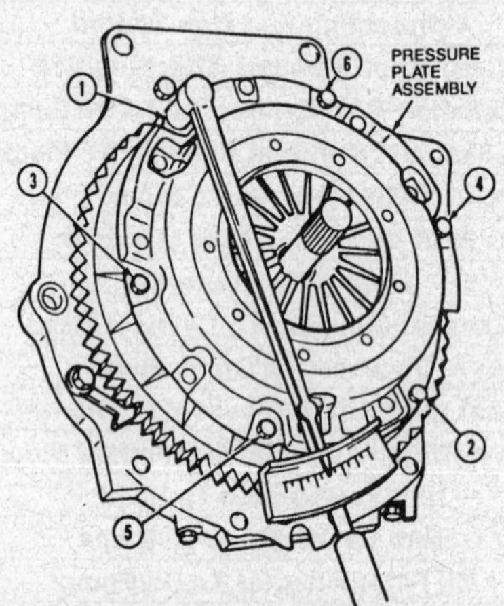


**Fig. 2 Pressure plate tightening sequence**

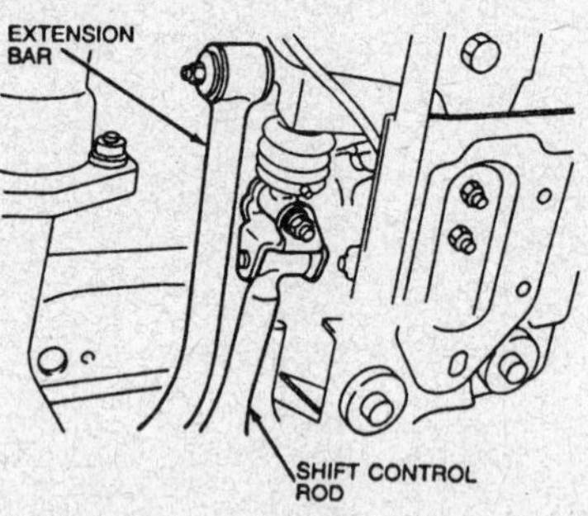


**Fig. 3 Extension bar and shift control rod**

## CLUTCH
### ADJUST

The 1991-92 Escort and Tracer use a hydraulic clutch control system. This system consists of a fluid reservoir, master cylinder, pressure line and slave cylinder. The clutch master cylinder is mounted on the bulkhead near the brake master cylinder. This hydraulic system utilizes brake fluid from the brake master cylinder reservoir. This system has no provisions for adjustment.

## CLUTCH PEDAL
### ADJUST

To determine if the pedal height requires adjustment, measure the distance from the bulkhead to the upper center of pedal pad. The distance should be 7.72-8.03 inches. Use the following procedure if adjustment is required.

1. Disconnect clutch switch electrical connector.
2. Loosen clutch switch locknut.
3. Turn clutch switch until correct height is achieved.
4. **Torque** locknut to 10-13 ft. lbs.
5. Measure pedal freeplay, pedal freeplay travel should be between 0.20-0.51 inch.
6. Connect electrical connector.

## CLUTCH PEDAL FREEPLAY ADJUSTMENT

To determine if the pedal freeplay requires adjustment, depress clutch pedal by hand until clutch resistance is felt. Measure the distance between upper pedal height and where the resistance is felt. Freeplay should be 0.20-0.51 inch. Use the following procedure if adjustment is necessary.

1. Loosen clutch pedal push rod locknut.
2. Turn push rod until pedal freeplay is within specification.
3. Check that disengagement height is correct when the pedal is fully depressed. Minimum disengagement height is 1.6 inches.
4. **Torque** pushrod locknut to 9-12 ft. lbs.

## CLUTCH
### REPLACE

1. Remove transaxle as described in "Manual Transaxle, Replace."
2. Install Flywheel Locking Tool No. T84P-6375-A or equivalent in a transaxle mounting hole on engine block, then engage tooth of locking tool into flywheel ring gear.
3. Loosen pressure plate cover attaching bolts evenly to avoid distorting cover. If same pressure plate and cover are to be installed, mark cover and flywheel so pressure plate can be installed in original position.
4. Remove pressure plate and clutch disc from flywheel.
5. Reverse procedure to install, noting the following:
   a. Clean splines on clutch disc and transaxle input shaft, then apply a small amount of Clutch Grease part No. C1AZ-19590-B or equivalent to clutch disc and input shaft splines. **Avoid getting grease on on clutch face.**
   b. Position clutch disc plate onto flywheel as shown in **Fig. 1.**
   c. Ensure three dowel pins on flywheel are aligned with dowel pins on pressure plate.
   d. Finger tighten cover attaching bolts, then align clutch disc using tool T74P-7137-K or equivalent.
   e. Evenly **torque** bolts to 13-20 ft. lbs. in sequence shown, **Fig. 2.**
   f. Remove alignment tool, then install transaxle and perform clutch bleed procedure.

## CLUTCH SLAVE CYLINDER
### REPLACE

1. Disconnect pressure line from slave cylinder, then plug line to prevent leakage.
2. Remove slave cylinder retaining bolts, then cylinder.
3. Reverse procedure to install. **Torque** slave cylinder retaining bolts to 12-17 ft. lbs.

## HYDRAULIC CLUTCH BLEED

The clutch hydraulic system must be bled whenever the pressure line is disconnected.

**The fluid in the reservoir must be maintained at the 3/4 level or higher during air bleeding.**

1. Remove bleeder cap from slave cylinder and attach vinyl hose to bleeder screw, place other end of hose in container.
2. Slowly pump clutch pedal several times.
3. With clutch pedal depressed, loosen bleeder screw to release trapped air.
4. Tighten bleeder screw.
5. Repeat steps 2 through 4 until no air bubbles appear in fluid.

## CLUTCH MASTER CYLINDER

### REPLACE

1. Remove battery and battery tray assembly.
2. Disconnect clutch pressure line from master cylinder.
3. Using needle nose vise grips or equivalent. clamp off brake fluid feed line to clutch master cylinder.
4. Disengage clamp, then remove brake fluid feed hose from clutch master cylinder.
5. From inside vehicle, remove master cylinder retaining nut.
6. From inside engine compartment, remove master cylinder retaining nut, then master cylinder.
7. Align clutch pedal push rod, then install master cylinder. **Torque** retaining nuts to 14-19 ft. lbs.
8. Connect master cylinder pressure line, then torque pressure line retaining nut to 10-16 ft. lbs.
9. Install hose and clamp assembly, then battery and tray.
10. Bleed air from system.

## MANUAL TRANSAXLE

### REPLACE

1. Remove battery and battery tray assembly.
2. Remove air duct hose and resonance chamber from engine.
3. Disconnect speedometer cable at transaxle assembly.
4. Remove retaining clip from slave cylinder line, then disconnect slave cylinder line from slave cylinder and plug hose.
5. Disconnect ground strap from transaxle.
6. Remove tie wrap, then disconnect three electrical connectors located above transaxle.
7. Remove electrical connector support bracket.
8. Mount Engine Support Bar tool No. D88L-6000-A or equivalent, and attach it to engine hangers.
9. Remove three nuts from upper transaxle mounts.
10. Loosen upper mount pivot nut, then rotate mount out of way.
11. Remove three bolts, then upper transaxle mount bracket.
12. Remove two upper transaxle-to-engine bolts.
13. Raise and support vehicle.
14. Remove front wheel and tire assemblies.
15. Remove inner fender splash shields.
16. Drain transaxle fluid.
17. Remove halfshaft assemblies from transaxle, refer to "Front Suspension" section in this chapter for this procedure.
18. Install two Transaxle Plugs (part No. T88C-7025-AH) or equivalent, between differential side gears.
19. Remove plenum support bracket.
20. Remove starter motor, refer to "Electrical Section" in this chapter for this procedure.
21. Remove extension bar from transaxle, **Fig. 3.**
22. Remove shift control rod from transaxle assembly, **Fig. 3.**
23. Remove both lower splash shields.
24. Remove two transaxle mount-to-crossmember nuts.
25. Remove lower crossmember.
26. Remove front transaxle mount.
27. Position transmission jack or equivalent, under transaxle, then secure jack to transaxle assembly.
28. Remove five lower engine-to-transaxle bolts.
29. Lower transaxle out of vehicle.
30. Reverse procedure to install. **Torque** all bolts to specification.

## TIGHTENING SPECIFICATIONS

| Year | Component | Torque/ft. Lbs. |
|---|---|---|
| 1991-92 | Back-up Lamp Switch | 14–22 |
| | Control Arm, Front Bolt | 69–86 |
| | Control Arm, Rear Nut | 55–69 |
| | Extension Bar Nut | 12–17 |
| | Flywheel Bolts | ② |
| | Front Transaxle Mount Bolts | 12–17 |
| | Guide Plate Lower Bolts | 16–25 |
| | Guide Plate Upper Bolt | 69–100① |
| | Lower Engine To Transaxle Bolts | 27–38 |
| | Lower Crossmember Nuts | 47–66 |
| | Lower Crossmember Bolts | 47–66 |
| | Neutral Switch | 14–22 |
| | Pressure Plate To Flywheel | 13–20 |
| | Rear Cover Bolts | 68–95① |
| | Shaft Locknuts | 94–145 |
| | Shift Arm | 104–122① |
| | Shift Control Rod Bolt/Nut | 23–34 |
| | Speedometer Driven Gear Retaining Bolt | 69–104① |
| | Steering Knuckle To Strut bolts | 69–86 |
| | Transaxle Drain Plug | 29–43 |
| | Transaxle Mount To Crossmember Nuts | 27–38 |
| | Transaxle To Engine Bolts (Lower) | 27–38 |
| | Transaxle To Engine Bolts (Upper) | 47–66 |
| | Wheel Lug Nut | 65–88 |

**①—Inch lbs.**
**②—1.8L/4-112, 71–76 ft. lbs.; 1.9L/4-116, 54–67 ft. lbs.**

# Rear Suspension

## INDEX



## DESCRIPTION

The rear suspension uses double-acting, oil filled shock/strut assemblies with straight wound coil springs. the rear wheels and brake drums/rotors are supported by a sealed roller bearing mounted on a spindle. A staked nut is used to retain the bearing and hub in position on the spindle. The staked nut cannot be reused. **Rear lateral links base part No. 5A995 are available in a solid (left side) and adjustable (right side) type. Both types are interchangeable side-to-side. When replacement of the solid link is necessary, an adjustable link should be installed.**

## REAR WHEEL HUB BEARING

### ADJUST

1. Raise and support vehicle, then remove rear wheel.
2. **On models with disc brakes,** remove brake caliper and rotor.
3. **On models with drum brakes,** remove brake drum.
4. **On all models,** position a dial indicator to wheel hub.
5. Push and pull wheel hub by hand and measure wheel bearing play.
6. If wheel bearing play exceeds .002 inch, check and adjust locknut torque or replace wheel bearing if necessary.

## LATERAL LINKS & TRAILING LINK

### REPLACE

1. Raise and support vehicle, then remove rear wheel.
2. Remove rear stabilizer bar as described under "Rear Stabilizer Bar, Replace."
3. Remove cap covering front and rear lateral link pivot bolts, then position a floor jack stand under rear suspension crossmember.
4. Remove bolts securing rear suspension crossmember to vehicle frame, then lower floor jack stand to allow rear suspension crossmember to be lowered from vehicle frame.
5. Remove front and rear lateral link pivot nut, washer and bolt from the crossmember, then remove front and rear lateral links from crossmember.
6. Remove bolt, washers and nut securing front and rear lateral links to rear wheel spindle, then remove front and rear lateral links.
7. Remove nuts securing parking brake cable and cable bracket to trailing link.
8. Remove trailing link bolts and washers from vehicle frame and rear wheel spindle, then remove rear trailing link.
9. Reverse procedure to install noting the following:
   a. **Torque** trailing link front bolt to 46-69 ft.lbs. and rear bolt to 69-93 ft. lbs.
   b. **Torque** front and rear lateral link nut at rear spindle to 63-86 ft. lbs.
   c. **Torque** front and rear lateral link nut at rear suspension crossmember to 50-70 ft. lbs.
   d. Install stabilizer bar washers, bushings, sleeve and nut and tighten so that .64-.72 inches of thread is exposed.

## REAR WHEEL HUB/SPINDLE ASSEMBLY

### REPLACE

#### DISC-TYPE BRAKES

1. Raise and support vehicle, then remove rear wheel.
2. Remove cap from rear wheel hub, then remove brake caliper and rotor.
3. Remove nut securing rear wheel hub to rear wheel spindle and hub, then remove bolts securing brake dust shield.
4. Remove nuts and bolts securing rear shock/strut assembly to rear wheel spindle.
5. Remove bolt and washer securing rear trailing arm to rear wheel spindle.
6. Remove rear stabilizer bar as described under "Rear Stabilizer Bar, Replace."
7. Remove nuts and bolts securing front and rear lateral links to rear wheel spindle, then remove spindle.
8. Reverse procedure to install. **Torque** rear wheel spindle to rear shock/strut assembly bolts and trailing arm to spindle bolt to 69-93 ft. lbs. and front and rear lateral links to spindle to 63-86 foot lbs.

#### DRUM-TYPE BRAKES

1. Raise and support vehicle, then remove rear wheel.
2. Remove cap from rear wheel hub, then remove rear brake drum.
3. Remove nut securing rear wheel hub to rear wheel spindle, then the hub from the spindle.
4. Remove drum brake backing plate from spindle.
5. Remove nuts and bolts securing rear shock/strut assembly to rear wheel spindle.
6. Remove bolt and washer securing rear trailing arm to rear wheel spindle.
7. Remove rear stabilizer bar as described under "Rear Stabilizer Bar, Replace."
8. Remove nuts and bolts securing front and rear lateral links to rear wheel spindle, then remove spindle.
9. Reverse procedure to install. **Torque** rear wheel spindle to rear shock/strut assembly bolts and trailing arm to spindle bolt to 69-93 ft. lbs. and front and rear lateral links to spindle to 63-86 foot lbs.

## REAR SHOCK/STRUT ASSEMBLY

### REPLACE

1. Raise and support vehicle, then remove rear wheel.
2. Remove clip securing flexible brake hose to rear shock/strut assembly.
3. Remove nuts and bolts securing rear shock/strut assembly to rear wheel spindle assembly.
4. **On hatchback and wagon models,** remove quarter lower trim panel.
5. **on all models,** remove mounting block nuts, then rear shock/strut assembly from vehicle.
6. Reverse procedure to install. **Torque** mounting block nuts to 22-27 ft. lbs. and lower rear shock/strut bolts to 69-93 ft. lbs.

## COIL SPRING

### REPLACE

1. Remove rear shock/strut assembly as described under "Rear Shock/Strut Assembly, Replace."
2. Position rear shock/strut assembly into a vise and secure assembly at mounting block.
3. Remove cap and loosen piston rod nut one turn. Do not remove piston rod nut at this time.

4. Install an appropriate coil spring compressor onto coil spring and compress spring.
5. Remove piston rod nut, washer, retainer and mounting block and coil spring.
6. Reverse procedure to install. **Torque** piston rod nut to 41-50 ft. lbs.

## REAR STABILIZER BAR

### REPLACE

1. Raise and support vehicle, then remove stabilizer nuts, washers, bushings, sleeves and bolts.
2. Remove bolts securing stabilizer bar brackets and grommets to rear suspension crossmember, then remove stabilizer bar from vehicle.
3. Reverse procedure to install noting the following:
   a. **Torque** stabilizer bar bracket bolts to 32-43 ft. lbs.
   b. Install stabilizer bar washers, bushings, sleeve and nut and tighten so that .64-.72 inches of thread is exposed.

## TIGHTENING SPECIFICATIONS

| Year | Component | Torque/ft. lbs. |
|---|---|---|
| 1991-92 | Front Trailing Arm Bolt | 69-93 |
| | Lateral Link Nut At Wheel Spindle | 63-86 |
| | Lateral Link To Crossmember Nut | 50-70 |
| | Rear Shock/Strut Mounting Block Nuts | 22-27 |
| | Rear Shock/Strut Piston Rod Nut | 41-50 |
| | Rear Shock/Strut To Rear Wheel Spindle | 69-93 |
| | Rear Trailing Arm Bolt | 49-69 |
| | Rear Wheel Hub Nut | 130-174 |
| | Stabilizer Bar To Rear Suspension Crossmember | 32-43 |
| | Wheel Lug Nuts | 65-88 |

# Front Suspension & Steering

## INDEX



## DESCRIPTION

The front suspension is a MacPherson strut design with cast steering knuckles. The shock absorber strut assembly includes a mounting block, a thrust bearing, an upper spring seat, a rubber spring seat, a bound stopper and coil spring mounted to the shock strut.

The front wheels and brake rotors are supported by a sealed roller bearing mounted in the steering knuckle. A snap ring holds the bearing in the knuckle. The halfshaft is secured to the front hub assembly with a staked nut. The staked nut cannot be reused.

## FRONT HUB/STEERING KNUCKLE ASSEMBLY

### REPLACE

1. Raise and support vehicle, then remove front wheel, brake caliper and rotor.
2. Remove nut securing halfshaft to hub, then remove outer tie rod at steering knuckle.
3. Remove nuts and bolts securing shock/strut assembly to steering knuckle, then separate shock/strut assembly from steering knuckle.
4. Remove nut and bolt securing lower ball joint to steering knuckle, then separate ball joint from steering knuckle.
5. Remove front hub/steering knuckle assembly from halfshaft.
6. Reverse procedure to install. **Torque** ball joint nut to 32-43 ft. lbs., shock/strut assembly bolts to 69-93 ft. lbs. and front hub nut to 174-235 ft. lbs.

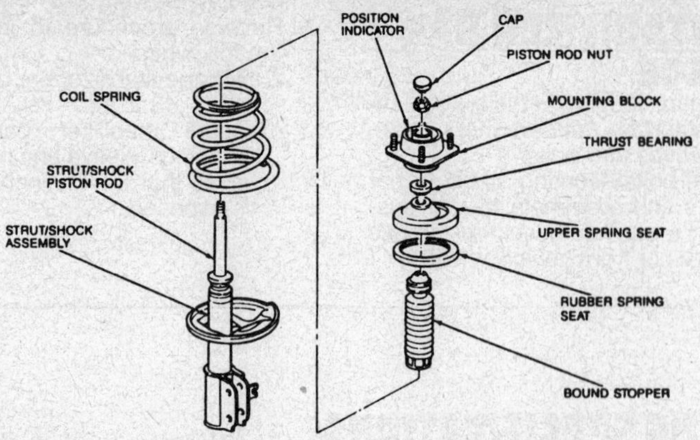


**Fig. 1 Front shock/strut assembly exploded view.**

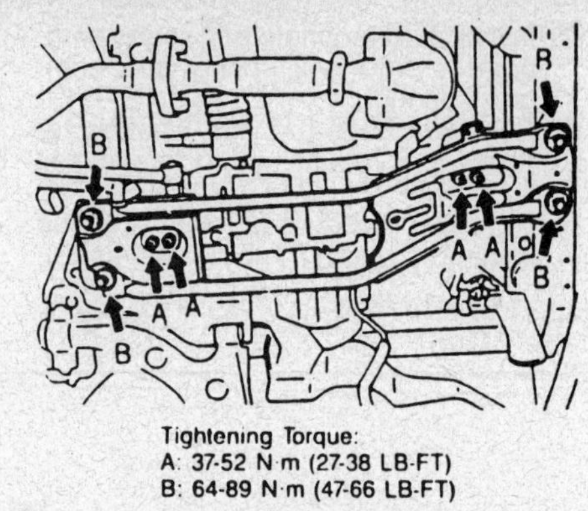


**Fig. 2 Crossmember bolt torquing sequence.**

## WHEEL BEARINGS

### ADJUST

1. Raise and support vehicle, then remove front wheel, brake caliper and rotor.
2. Position a dial indicator to wheel hub, then push and pull wheel hub by hand and measure wheel bearing play.
3. If wheel bearing play exceeds .002 inch, check and adjust locknut torque or, if necessary, replace wheel bearing.
4. Install brake rotor, caliper and wheel, then lower vehicle.

## WHEEL BEARINGS

### REPLACE

1. Remove front hub/steering knuckle assembly as described under "Front Hub/Steering Knuckle, Replace."
2. Position front hub/steering knuckle assembly on a press and press front hub out of steering knuckle using a suitable removal tool.
3. Remove E-clip from steering knuckle, then position steering knuckle onto a press.
4. Using a suitable bearing remover, press bearing out of steering knuckle.
5. Reverse procedure to install.

## LOWER BALL JOINT INSPECTION

**This procedure has been altered by a factory service bulletin.**

Secure ball joint bracket into a vise. Thread ball joint attaching nut onto ball joint stud until nut bottoms out on stud. Install a torque wrench onto nut and measure torque required to keep stud in motion. Correct turning torque should be 14-25 ft. lbs.

## LOWER BALL JOINTS

### REPLACE

1. Remove nut and bolt securing ball joint to steering knuckle.
2. Remove nuts securing ball joint to lower control arm, then remove ball joint.
3. Reverse procedure to install.

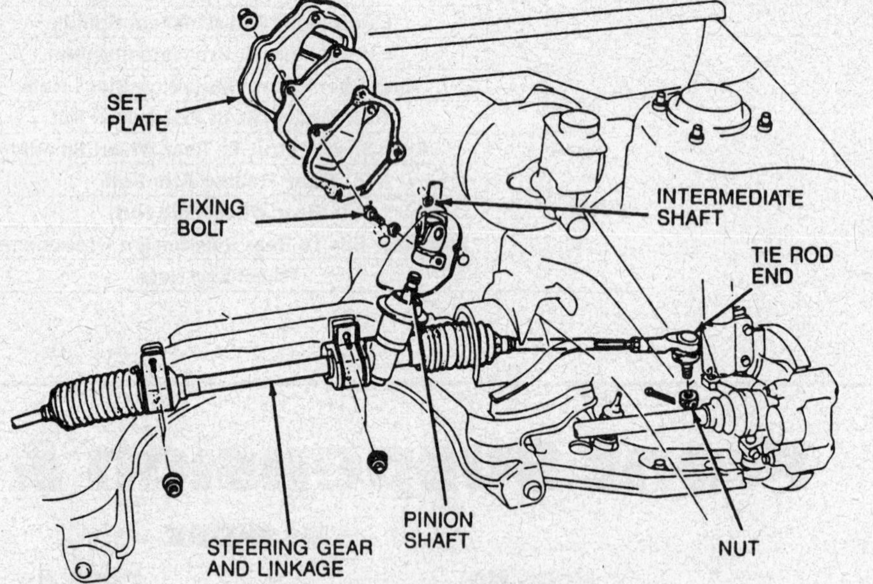


**Fig. 3 Manual steering gear exploded view.**

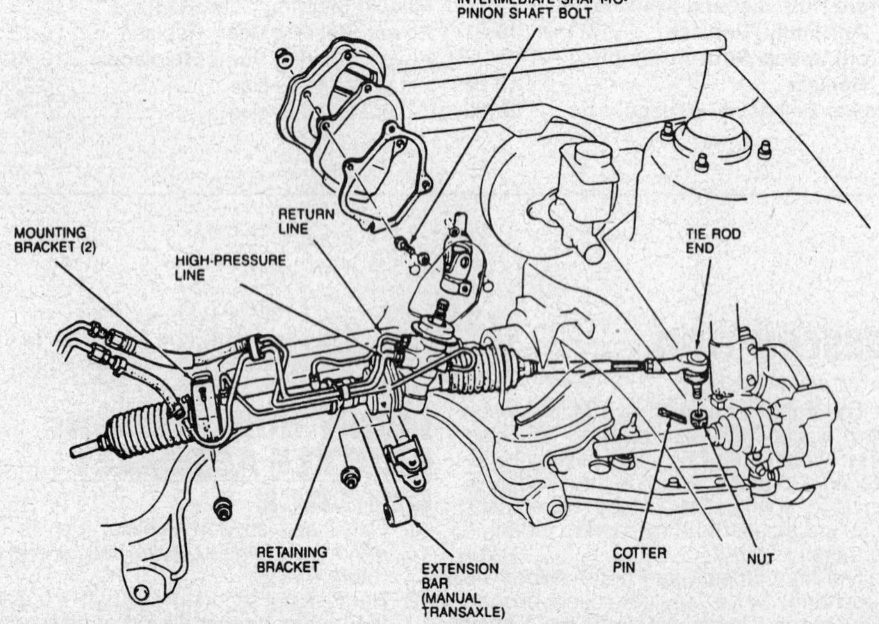


**Fig. 4 Power steering gear exploded view.**

## FRONT SHOCK/STRUT ASSEMBLY

### REPLACE

1. Raise and support vehicle, then remove front wheel>
2. Remove clip securing flexible brake hose to shock/strut assembly.
3. Remove two nuts and bolts securing shock/strut assembly to steering knuckle.
4. Remove upper mounting block nuts on strut tower, then remove shock/strut assembly.
5. Reverse procedure to install noting the following:
   a. Position shock/strut assembly into wheel housing ensuring that direction indicator on mounting block faces inboard.
   b. **Torque** upper mounting block to strut tower nuts to 22-30 ft. lbs. and shock/strut assembly bolts to 69-93 ft. lbs.

## COIL SPRING

### REPLACE

1. Remove front shock/strut assembly as described under "Front Shock/Strut Assembly, Replace."
2. Remove cap from top of shock/strut assembly.
3. Secure shock/strut assembly mounting block in a vise, then turn piston rod nut one full revolution to loosen.
4. Install an appropriate spring compressor onto shock/strut spring, then compress spring.
5. Remove nut, mounting block, thrust bearing, upper spring seat, rubber spring seat, coil spring and bound stopper. **Fig. 1.**
6. Reverse procedure to install. **Torque** piston rod nut to 58-81 ft. lbs.

## STABILIZER BAR

### REPLACE

1. Support engine with three bar engine support No. D88L-6000-A or equivalent, then raise and support vehicle.
2. Remove front wheels, then remove nuts securing steering gear mounting brackets.
3. Position steering gear slightly forward, then remove stabilizer bar nuts, washers, bushings, sleeves and bolts from lower control arm.
4. Remove rear crossmember nuts from rear transaxle mount and vehicle frame.
5. Loosen front crossmember bolts and nuts from front transaxle mount and vehicle frame, then lower rear end of crossmember.
6. Remove nuts and bolts securing chassis frame to vehicle frame, then lower chassis frame. **Engine and transaxle mounts will support the chassis frame when unbolting chassis frame from vehicle frame.**
7. Unbolt stabilizer bar from chassis frame and remove stabilizer bar from vehicle.
8. Reverse procedure to install noting the following:
   a. **Torque** stabilizer bar to chassis frame bolts to 32-43 ft. lbs.
   b. **Torque** chassis frame to vehicle frame bolts to 69-93 ft. lbs.
   c. **Torque** crossmember to vehicle frame and transaxle mounts as shown in **Fig. 2.**
   d. Install stabilizer bar bolts, sleeves, bushings, washers and nuts and tighten so that .67-.75 inches of thread is showing.
   e. **Torque** steering gear bracket nuts to 28-38 ft. lbs.

## LOWER CONTROL ARM

### REPLACE

1. Raise and support vehicle, then remove stabilizer bar nuts, washers, bushings, sleeves and bolts.
2. Remove lower control arm front bushing bolt and washer, then remove bolts securing lower control arm rear bushing retaining strap.
3. Remove nut and bolt securing lower ball joint to steering knuckle, then separate steering knuckle from lower ball joint.
4. Remove lower control arm.
5. Reverse procedure to install noting the following:
   a. **Torque** lower control arm pivot bolt nut to 69-86 ft. lbs.
   b. **Torque** ball joint retaining bolt and nut to 32-43 ft. lbs.
   c. **Torque** lower control arm rear bushing retaining strap bolts to 69-86 ft. lbs.
   d. **Torque** lower control arm front pivot bolt to 69-93 ft. lbs.
   e. Install stabilizer bar bolts, sleeves, bushings, washers and nuts and tighten so that .67-.75 inches of thread is showing.

## MANUAL STEERING GEAR

### REPLACE

Refer to **Fig. 3** when replacing manual steering gear.

1. From inside of vehicle, remove nuts securing set plate, remove set plate.
2. Remove intermediate shaft to pinion shaft bolt from inside of vehicle.
3. Raise and support vehicle, then remove front wheels.
4. Remove cotter pins and nuts securing tie rod ends to steering knuckles.
5. Separate tie rod end from steering knuckle using tie rod end separator No. T85M-3395-A or equivalent.
6. **On vehicles equipped with manual transaxle,** disconnect extension bar.
7. **On all vehicles,** remove nuts securing steering gear brackets to bulkhead, n remove the brackets.
8. Remove steering gear from vehicle.
9. Reverse procedure to install noting the following:
   a. **Torque** steering gear bracket nuts to 27-38 ft. lbs.
   b. **On vehicles equipped with a manual transaxle, torque** extension bar nut to 23-34 ft. lbs.
   c. **On all vehicles, torque** tie rod end nut to 31-42 ft. lbs.
   d. **Torque** intermediate shaft to pinion shaft bolt to 13-20 ft. lbs.

## POWER STEERING GEAR

### REPLACE

Refer to **Fig. 4** when replacing power steering gear.

1. From inside of the vehicle, remove nuts securing set plate, then remove set plate.
2. Remove intermediate shaft to pinion shaft bolt from inside of vehicle.
3. Raise and support vehicle, then remove front wheels.
4. Remove cotter pins and nuts securing tie rod ends to steering knuckles.
5. Separate tie rod end from steering knuckle using a suitable tie rod end separator.
6. Remove two screws from power steering line retaining bracket, then remove bracket from steering gear housing.
7. Disconnect return and the high-pressure line from steering gear and plug lines.
8. **On vehicles equipped with a manual transaxle,** disconnect extension bar and shift control rod from transaxle.
9. **On all vehicles,** remove nuts from two steering gear mounting brackets, then remove splash shield from left wheel well.
10. Remove steering gear from left side of vehicle.
11. Reverse procedure to install noting following:
    a. **Torque** steering gear mounting bracket nuts to 27-38 ft. lbs.
    b. **On vehicles equipped with a manual transaxle, torque** extension bar nut to 23-34 ft. lbs. and shift control rod nut to 12-17 ft. lbs.
    c. **On vehicles equipped with a 1.9L/4-116 engine,** install a new strap to hold power steering lines to gear housing.
    d. **On all vehicles, torque** return line and high-pressure line flare nuts to 22-28 ft. lbs.
    e. **Torque** tie rod end nuts to 31-42 ft. lbs.
    f. **Torque** intermediate shaft to pinion shaft bolt to 13-20 ft. lbs.

## POWER STEERING PUMP

### REPLACE

### 1.8L/4-112 ENGINE

1. Loosen reservoir to pump hose clamp and pull hose from reservoir, then plug hose.
2. Remove two reservoir mounting bolts and lift reservoir from its mounting position.
3. Loosen return hose clamp and pull return hose from reservoir, then plug hose.
4. Remove reservoir from vehicle.
5. Disconnect electrical connector from power steering pressure switch.
6. Loosen high-pressure line flare nut and disconnect line from pump, then plug line.
7. Raise and support vehicle, then remove five front undercover bolts and

remove undercover.
8. Remove belt tensioner adjustment bolt, then accessory drive belt from pulley.
9. Lower vehicle, then remove three pump mounting bracket bolts and pump and bracket.
10. Reverse procedure to install. **Torque** pump mounting bolts to 27-38 ft. lbs. and high-pressure line flare nut to 12-17 ft. lbs.

## 1.9L/4-116 ENGINE

**This procedure has been altered by a factory service bulletin.**

1. Drain radiator, then loosen belt tensioner and remove drive belt from pulley.
2. Remove belt tensioner bolt, then tensioner.
3. Support engine with a floor jack, then remove engine vibration dampener nut and bolt and remove dampener.
4. Remove two front engine mount nuts, then loosen engine mount pivot bolt and position engine mount aside.
5. Raise engine to access power steering pump pulley, then hold pulley in position with a suitable tool and remove three pulley mounting bolts and pulley.
6. Lower engine, then position engine mount and install two nuts.
7. Raise and support vehicle, then loosen clamp and disconnect return line from pump.
8. Loosen flare nut from high-pressure line and disconnect line from pump.
9. Remove two passenger side splash shields, then remove four A/C compressor mounting bolts and position compressor aside.
10. Remove lower radiator hose, then remove three power steering pump mounting bolts and pump.
11. Reverse procedure to install noting the following:
    a. **Torque** A/C compressor mounting bolts to 30-40 ft. lbs.
    b. Position power steering pump pulley, then hold in position with a suitable tool and install and **torque** mounting bolts to 15-22 ft. lbs.
    c. **Torque** belt tensioner mounting bolt to 30-41 ft. lbs.

## TIGHTENING SPECIFICATIONS

| Year | Component | Torque/ft. lbs. |
|---|---|---|
| 1991-92 | Ball Joint Turning Torque | 14-25 |
| | Chassis Frame To Vehicle Frame | 69-93 |
| | Lower Ball Joint To Lower Control Arm | 69-86 |
| | Lower Ball Joint To Steering Knuckle | 32-43 |
| | Lower Control Arm Front Pivot Nut | 69-93 |
| | Lower Control Arm Retaining Strap | 69-86 |
| | Halfshaft Locknut | 174-235 |
| | Shock/Strut Assembly To Steering Knuckle | 69-93 |
| | Shock/Strut Piston Nut | 58-81 |
| | Shock/Strut Upper Mounting Block Nuts | 22-30 |
| | Stabilizer Bar To Chassis Frame | 32-43 |
| | Steering Gear To Vehicle Frame | 28-38 |
| | Wheel Lug Nuts | 65-88 |

# Wheel Alignment

## INDEX



## DESCRIPTION

The independent front and rear suspension system is designed for minimum maintenance. Other than incorrect front toe, front chamber and rear toe, suspension misalignment can only result from wear or damage to suspension parts or distortion of body structure due to collision damage.

## FRONT WHEEL ALIGNMENT

### CAMBER

1. Raise and support front of vehicle.
2. From inside engine compartment, remove mounting block nuts located on top of strut tower.
3. Push mounting block downward and turn to desired position, **Fig. 1.**
4. Install mounting block nuts, then **torque** to 22-30 ft. lbs.

### TOE-IN

1. Loosen left and right tie rod locknuts.
2. Release clips at small ends of steering gear boots.
3. Turn tie rods equally until desired toe-in setting is reached. **Left and right tie rods are both righthand threads. One turn of the tie rod (both sides) makes a toe-in change of about 0.24 inch.**
4. **Torque**tie rod locknuts to 25-29 ft. lbs.

## REAR WHEEL ALIGNMENT

### TOE ADJUSTMENT

Only the righthand link is adjustable. If the thrust angle is not within specification, install an adjustable link on the lefthand side of vehicle, then readjust rear toe.

1. Loosen lateral link locknuts.
2. Turn lateral link adjustment link to adjust. One turn of link is about 0.44 inch.
3. **Torque** locknuts to 41-47 ft.lbs.

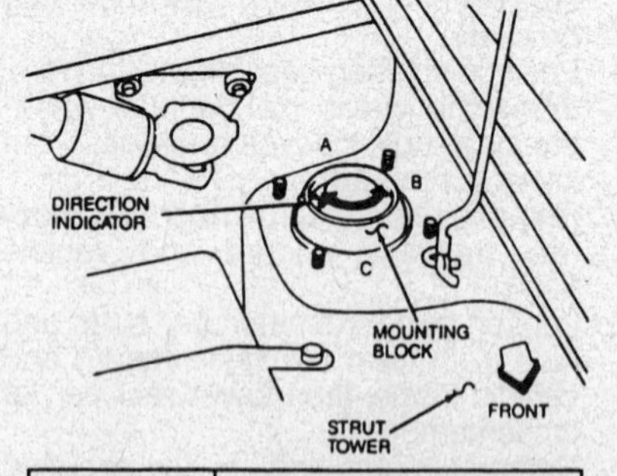


| Direction Indicator | Difference from Standard Position | |
|---|---|---|
| | Camber Angle | Caster Angle |
| A | + 14' | + 14' |
| B | + 29' | 0° |
| C | + 14' | – 14' |

**Fig. 1 Adjusting front wheel chamber**

# FORD FESTIVA

## INDEX OF SERVICE OPERATIONS

## INDEX OF SERVICE OPERATIONS—Continued



# Specifications

## GENERAL ENGINE SPECIFICATIONS

| Year | Engine Liter/CID① | Engine VIN Code② | Fuel System | Bore x Stroke Inches | Comp. Ratio | Net HP @ RPM③ | Maximum Torque Ft. Lbs. @ RPM | Normal Oil Pressure Psi |
|---|---|---|---|---|---|---|---|---|
| 1989 | 1.3L/4-80.8 | K | 2 Bbl.④ | 2.78 x 3.29 | 9.0 | 58 @ 5000 | 73 @ 3500 | 50-64⑥ |
| | 1.3L/4-80.8 | H | EFI⑤ | 2.78 x 3.29 | 9.7 | 63 @ 5000 | 73 @ 3000 | 50-64⑥ |
| 1990-92 | 1.3L/4-80.8 | H | EFI⑤ | 2.78 x 3.29 | 9.7 | 63 @ 5000 | 73 @ 3000 | 50-64⑥ |

①—CID: Cubic Inch Displacement.
②—The eighth digit of the VIN denotes engine code.
③—Ratings are net, as installed in vehicle.
④—Aisin Kogyo carburetor.
⑤—Aisin Kogyo port fuel injection.
⑥—At 3000 RPM with engine hot.

## TUNE UP SPECIFICATIONS

| Year & Engine/VIN Code | Spark Plug Gap | Ignition Timing BTDC① Firing Order Fig. | Ignition Timing BTDC① Man. Trans. | Ignition Timing BTDC① Auto. Trans. | Ignition Timing BTDC① Mark Fig. | Curb Idle Speed② Man. Trans. | Curb Idle Speed② Auto. Trans. | Fast Idle Speed Man. Trans. | Fast Idle Speed Auto. Trans. | Fuel Pump Pressure psi |
|---|---|---|---|---|---|---|---|---|---|---|
| **1989** | | | | | | | | | | |
| 1.3L/4-80.8/K 2Bbl. | .041 | A | TDC③ | TDC③ | B | 700-750 | 700-750N | 1650-2150 | 1650-2150 | 3-6 |
| 1.3L/4-80.8/H EFI | .041 | A | 2③ | 2③ | B | 800-900 | 800-900N | ④ | ④ | 64-85⑤ |
| **1990-92** | | | | | | | | | | |
| 1.3L/4-80.8/H EFI | .041 | A | 10⑥ | 10⑥ | B | 700 | 850N | ④ | ④ | 64-85⑤ |

①—BTDC: Before Top Dead Center.
②—N: Neutral., P:Park.
③—With distributor advance disconnected.
④—Controlled by ECA (Electronic Control Assembly).
⑤—Removing rear seat cushion, then release fuel system by starting engine and disconnecting fuel pump electrical connector. After engine has stalled, place ignition switch in the Off position. Connect a suitable fuel pressure gauge to fuel pump outlet connection. Connect a jumper wire between fuel pump test connector terminals, then place ignition switch in On position and check fuel pressure.
⑥—With STI connector grounded, refer to Fig. C.

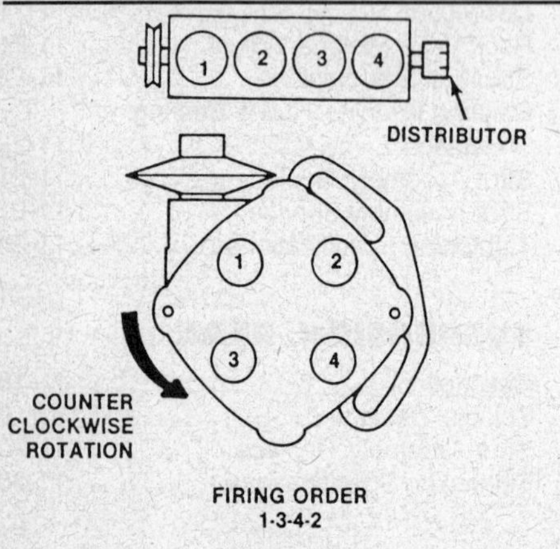


**Fig. A**

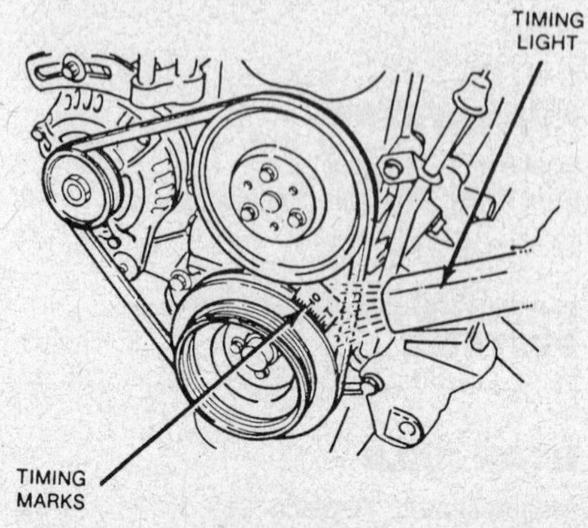


**Fig. B**

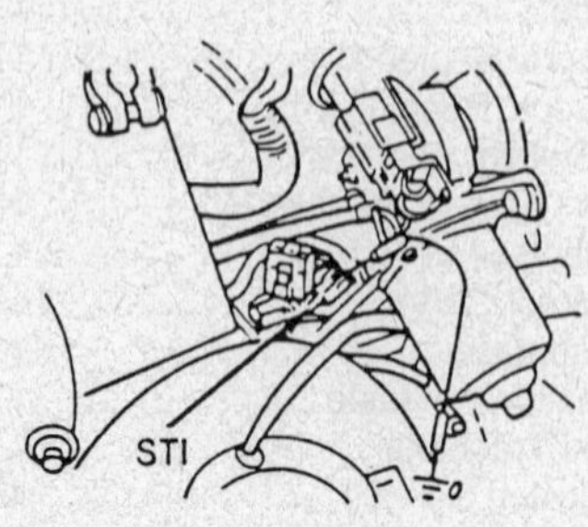


**Fig. C**

## FRONT WHEEL ALIGNMENT SPECIFICATIONS

| Year | Model | Caster Angle, Degrees | | Camber Angle, Degrees | | | | Toe-In, Inch | King Pin Inclination Degrees |
|---|---|---|---|---|---|---|---|---|---|
| | | | | Limits | | Desired | | | |
| | | Limits | Desired | Left | Right | Left | Right | | |
| 1989–90 | All | +1/3 to +1 5/6 | +1 7/12 | −1/4 to +1 7/12 | −1/4 to +1 7/12 | +2/3 | +2/3 | .02 to .26 | 14 11/60 |
| 1991—92 | All | +1 1/3 to +1 5/6 | +1 7/12 | −5/12 to +1 5/12 | −5/12 to +1 5/12 | +1/2 | +1/2 | .02 to .26 | — |

## REAR WHEEL ALIGNMENT SPECIFICATIONS

| Year | Model | Camber | | Toe-In Inch |
|---|---|---|---|---|
| | | Limits | Desired | |
| 1989–92 | All | +1/15 to +13/30 | +1/4 | 0 to .24 |

## COOLING SYSTEM & CAPACITY DATA

| Year | Engine | Cooling Capacity, Qts. | | Radiator Cap Relief Pressure Psi. | Thermo. Opening Temp. | Fuel Tank Gals. | Engine Oil Refill Qts.① | Transaxle Oil | |
|---|---|---|---|---|---|---|---|---|---|
| | | Less A/C | With A/C | | | | | Man. Trans. Pts. | Auto. Trans. Qts② |
| 1989–92 | 1.3L/4-80.8 | 5.3 | 5.3 | 13 | ③ | 10 | 3.6 | 5.3 | ④ |

①—Includes filter change.
②—Approximate, make final check with dipstick.
③—Sub-valve, 185°; main valve, 190°.
④—Oil pan only, 3 qts.; total capacity, 8.4 qts.

## LUBRICANT DATA

| Year | Model | Lubricant Type | | | | | |
|---|---|---|---|---|---|---|---|
| | | Transaxle | | Transfer Case | Rear Axle | Power Steering | Brake System |
| | | Manual | Automatic | | | | |
| 1989–92 | All | Mercon XT-2-QDX | Mercon XT-2-QDX | — | — | E6AZ-195882-AA① | DOT 3 |

①—Ford part No. or equivalent.

# Electrical

## INDEX



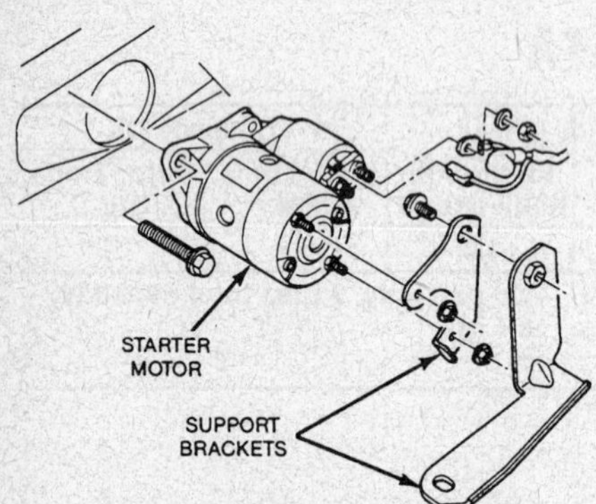


**Fig. 1 Starter motor replacement**

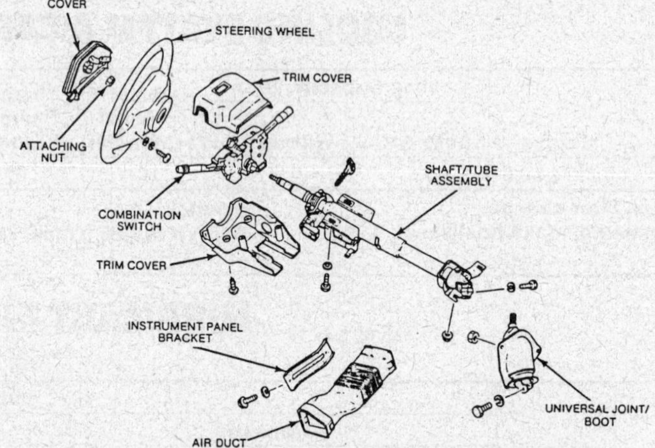


**Fig. 2 Upper steering column components**

## FUSE PANEL & FLASHER LOCATION

The fuse panel is located left side of the steering column, behind access panel. The flashers are located below instrument panel in upper left hand corner, behind ECA.

## STARTER REPLACE

### AUTOMATIC TRANSAXLE

1. Disconnect battery ground cable.
2. Remove two upper starter motor mounting bolts.
3. Raise and support vehicle.
4. Remove two manifold to cylinder block bracket bolts, then the bracket.
5. Remove mounting bracket to support bracket bolt.
6. Remove support bracket.
7. Remove two nuts and washers that secure mounting bracket to starter motor.
8. Disconnect the "B" and "S" terminal connectors at starter solenoid.
9. Remove lower starter motor mounting bolt.
10. Remove starter motor.
11. Reverse procedure to install, **torque** starter motor retaining bolts to 23-34 ft.lbs.

### MANUAL TRANSAXLE

1. Disconnect battery ground cable, then raise and support front of vehicle.
2. Disconnect all electrical connections at starter, **Fig. 1.**
3. Remove starter motor support bracket to transaxle attaching bolts.
4. Remove starter motor attaching bolts and the starter motor.
5. Reverse procedure to install, **torque** starter motor retaining bolts to 23-34 ft.lbs.

## DISTRIBUTOR REPLACE

1. Disconnect battery ground cable.
2. Disconnect coil wire from from distributor.
3. Remove distributor cap attaching screws.
4. Pull off distributor cap and swing it aside.
5. Disconnect distributor electrical connector.
6. If the distributor is not being replaced, scribe a reference mark across distributor base flange and cylinder head. This reference mark will allow installation without changing timing.
7. Remove distributor unit, then O-ring at base of distributor.
8. Reverse procedure to install, noting the following:
   a. Install new O-ring.
   b. During installation of distributor, ensure offset tangs engage with camshaft slots.
   c. If distributor unit was not replaced, align scribe marks made during removal and tighten mounting bolts to 14-18 ft. lbs.
   d. If a new distributor is being installed, the ignition timing should be checked and adjusted.

## COMBINATION SWITCH REPLACE

1. Disconnect battery ground cable.
2. Remove steering wheel as outlined previously.
3. Remove upper and lower steering column trim covers, **Fig. 2.**
4. Disengage wire harness retaining clip, then disconnect harness connectors from back of switch.

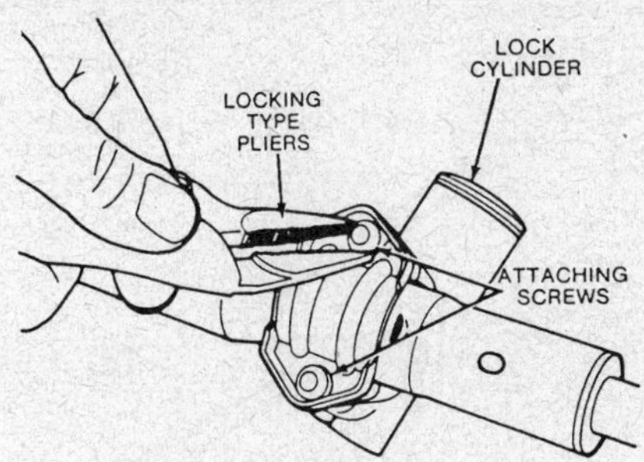


**Fig. 3 Ignition lock removal**

5. Working from below steering column, loosen band clamp securing switch hub to steering column jacket, then pull switch assembly off steering column.
6. Reverse procedure to install.

# IGNITION LOCK
## REPLACE

1. Disconnect battery ground cable.
2. Remove steering wheel, combination switch and ignition switch as outlined previously.
3. Using suitable locking pliers, remove attaching screws, then the mounting cap and lock housing from steering column jacket, **Fig. 3.**
4. To install ignition lock, proceed as follows:
   a. Position lock housing on steering column jacket, then install mounting cap and new attaching screws. Tighten screws only enough to hold lock housing in position on column jacket.
   b. Turn lock mechanism with ignition key to verify correct operation of lock. If lock binds, reposition on jacket slightly until mechanism functions properly.
   c. Tighten attaching screws until heads break off, then reinstall parts removed in step 1 to complete installation.

# IGNITION SWITCH
## REPLACE

1. Disconnect battery ground cable.
2. Remove upper and lower steering column trim covers.
3. Disengage switch harness from retaining clip, then remove retaining screw and ignition switch from lock housing, **Fig. 4.**
4. To install switch, proceed as follows:
   a. Push ignition switch into lock housing bore until switch tang engages lock cylinder. **If necessary, turn lock cylinder with ignition key until switch tang aligns with switch slot.**
   b. Install switch retaining screw, position wire harness as necessary, then close harness retaining clip.
   c. Reinstall upper and lower trim covers.

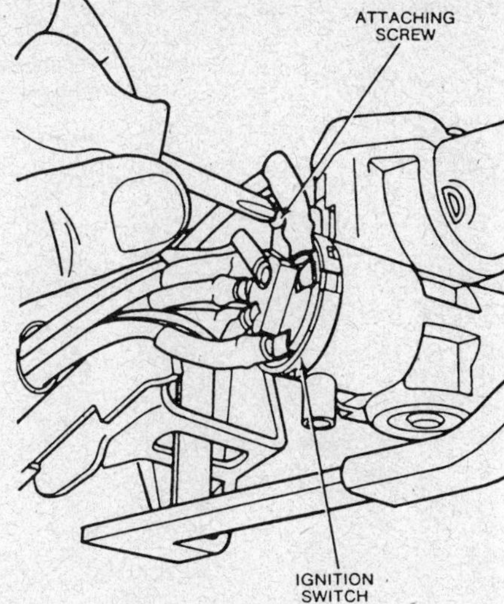


**Fig. 4 Ignition switch attaching screw location**

# HEADLAMP & TURN SIGNAL SWITCH
## REPLACE

The headlamp/turn signal switch is mounted on the steering column as part of the combination switch assembly.

1. Disconnect battery ground cable.
2. Remove combination switch as outlined previously.
3. Remove attaching screws, then separate headlamp/turn signal switch from combination switch.
4. Rotate switch handle to parking light detent.
5. Remove switch handle attaching screws and plate, then rotate handle out of switch body. **Use care to prevent loss of detent balls and springs.**
6. Reverse procedure to install.

# STOP LIGHT SWITCH
## REPLACE

1. Disconnect battery ground cable.
2. Disconnect wiring from switch.
3. Remove locknut, then the switch from brake pedal support, **Fig. 5.**
4. Reinstall switch and locknut, then adjust switch as follows:
   a. Connect ohmmeter across switch terminals.
   b. Rotate switch toward brake pedal until ohmmeter indicates infinite resistance.
   c. Rotate switch toward brake pedal an additional 1/2 turn, then tighten locknut and reconnect wiring.

# STEERING WHEEL
## REPLACE

### 1989 MODELS

1. Carefully pry out center insert of steering wheel trim pad.

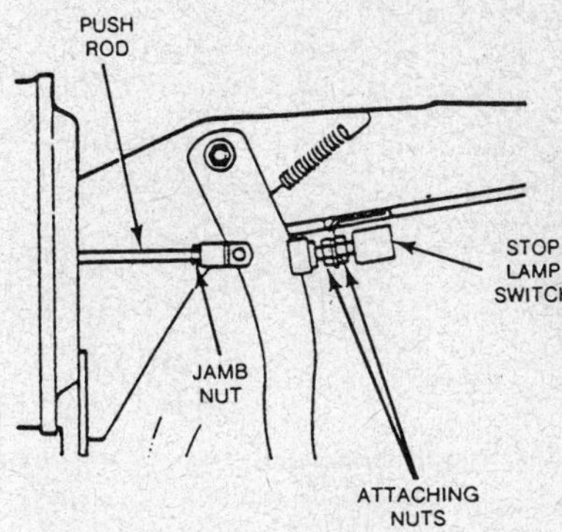


**Fig. 5 Stop light switch replacement**

2. Remove steering wheel retaining nut.
3. Remove two trim pad retaining screws from rear of steering wheel.
4. Disconnect horn wire, then remove trim pad assembly.
5. Mark steering wheel and column shaft for reference during assembly, then remove steering wheel using steering wheel puller tool No. T67L-3600-A or equivalent.
6. Reverse procedure to install, **torquing** steering wheel retaining nut to 29-36 ft. lbs.

### 1990–92 MODELS

1. Remove two screws from back of steering wheel, then disconnect horn wire.
2. Remove steering wheel cover, then steering wheel retaining nut.
3. Mark steering wheel and column shaft for reassembly.
4. Remove steering wheel with steering wheel puller tool No. T67L-3600-A or equivalent.
5. Reverse procedure to install, **torquing** steering wheel retaining nut to 29-36 ft. lbs.

# INSTRUMENT CLUSTER
## REPLACE

1. Disconnect battery ground cable.
2. **On models equipped with tilt steering column, release tilt lock, then lower steering column to seat. On models equipped with conventional steering column, remove upper and lower steering column trim covers.**
3. **On all models,** remove cluster bezel attaching screws and pull bezel away from cluster.
4. If applicable, disconnect electrical wiring from rear window defogger or wiper switch.
5. Remove instrument cluster attaching screws, then pull cluster outward and disconnect speedometer cable and electrical connectors from rear of cluster.
6. Remove cluster from vehicle, **Fig. 6.**
7. Reverse procedure to install.

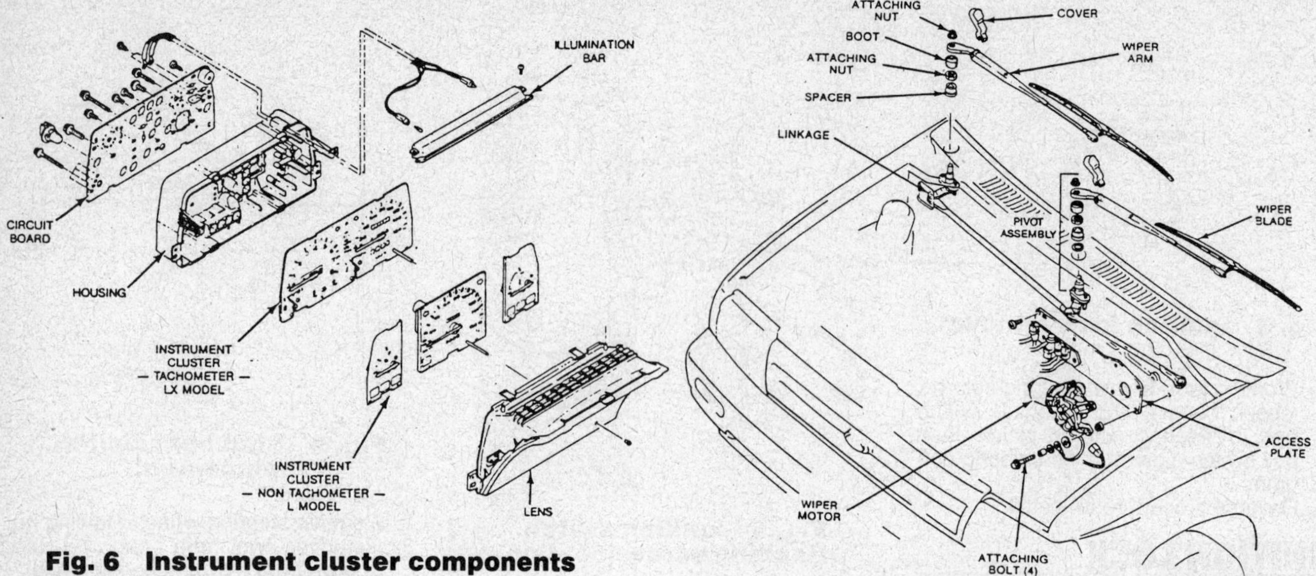


**Fig. 6 Instrument cluster components**

**Fig. 7 Windshield wiper motor replacement**

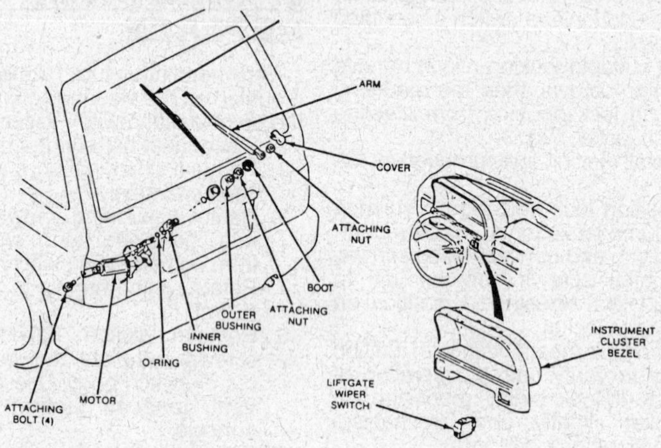


**Fig. 8 Rear wiper motor replacement**

# RADIO

## REPLACE

1. Disconnect battery ground cable.
2. Remove radio/heater control panel bezel attaching screws, then the bezel.
3. Remove radio to instrument panel attaching screws.
4. Pull radio outward, disconnect antenna lead and all electrical connections, then remove radio from instrument panel.
5. Reverse procedure to install.

# WIPER MOTOR

## REPLACE

### FRONT

1. Disconnect battery ground cable.
2. Disconnect electrical connector, then remove wiper motor to dash panel attaching bolts, **Fig. 7.**
3. Remove mounting plate attaching screws and pull plate away from dash panel.
4. Using suitable tool, pry linkage pivot from motor output arm, then remove wiper motor from vehicle.
5. Reverse procedure to install, ensuring ground wire is securely fastened to left upper attaching bolt of motor.

### REAR

1. Disconnect battery ground cable.
2. Lift cover, then remove wiper arm attaching nut and the wiper arm, **Fig. 8.**
3. Pull off shaft seal and remove outer bushing attaching nut and outer bushing.
4. Using suitable tool, pry trim panel off inner portion of liftgate.
5. Peel back wire harness electrical tape, then disconnect wiper motor electrical connector.
6. Remove wiper motor to liftgate attaching bolts, then the wiper motor.
7. Check inner and outer bushings and shaft O-ring for damage, and replace parts as necessary.
8. Reverse procedure to install. Cycle wiper motor several times to ensure motor is in Park position before installing wiper arm. When properly installed, tip of wiper blade should be approximately 3 inches from edge of liftgate window seal.

# WIPER SWITCH

## REPLACE

### WINDSHIELD WIPER SWITCH/INTERVAL WIPER MODULE

The wiper switch and interval wiper module (if equipped) are mounted on the steering column as part of the combination switch assembly.

1. Disconnect battery ground cable.
2. Remove combination switch as outlined previously.
3. Remove wiper switch/interval wiper module attaching screws, then disengage switch from combination switch, **Fig. 9.**
4. Using a thin screwdriver, disengage switch handle lock tab and pull handle from switch assembly.
5. Remove plunger, spring and O-ring from handle.
6. Reverse procedure to install.

### REAR WIPER

1. Disconnect battery ground cable.
2. **On models equipped with tilt steering column, release tilt lock, then lower steering column to seat. On models equipped with conventional steering column, remove upper and lower steering column trim covers.**
3. **On all models,** remove cluster bezel attaching screws and pull bezel away from cluster.

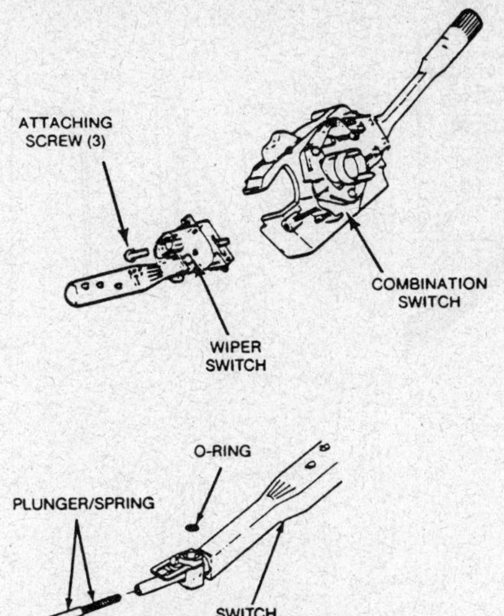


**Fig. 9 Windshield wiper switch & interval wiper module replacement**

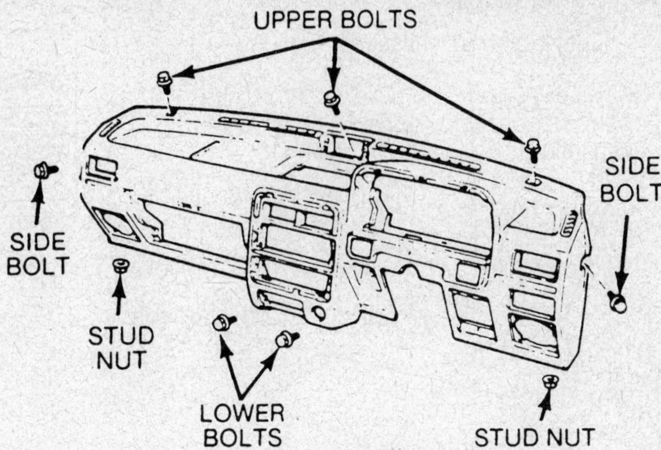


**Fig. 10 Instrument panel attaching bolt & nut location**

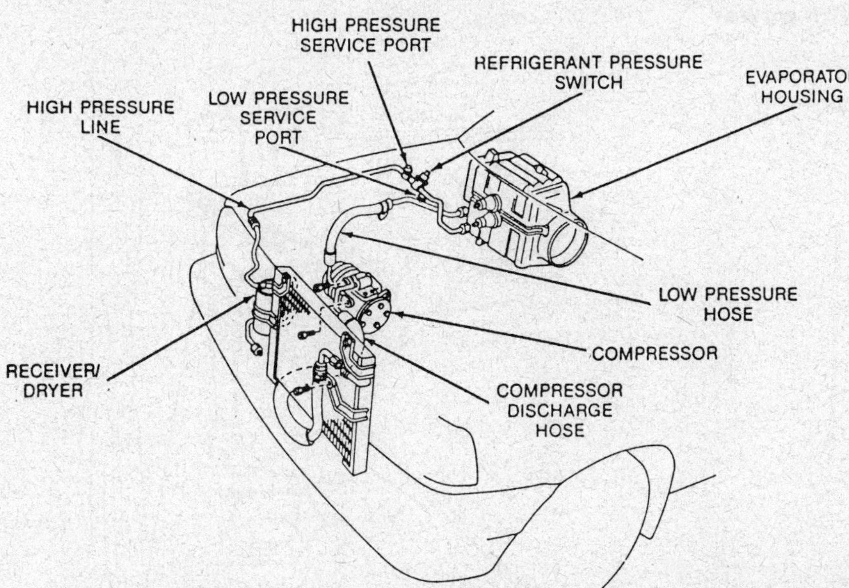


**Fig. 11 Evaporator hose routing. Less power steering**

4. Depress switch lock tabs, then disconnect electrical connector and remove switch from bezel, **Fig. 8.**
5. Reverse procedure to install.

# FRONT WIPER MOTOR LINKAGE
## REPLACE

1. Remove front wiper motor as outlined previously.
2. Remove wiper arms, then the pivot assembly protective boots, **Fig. 7.**
3. Remove pivot attaching nuts and spacers, then the linkage through opening in dash panel.
4. Reverse procedure to install.

# BLOWER MOTOR
## REPLACE

1. Disconnect battery ground cable.
2. Remove instrument panel spacer brace and air flow duct located below steering column.
3. Disconnect blower motor electrical wiring.
4. Remove blower motor attaching screws and the blower motor.
5. Remove blower wheel retaining nut and washer, then pull wheel off blower motor shaft.
6. Reverse procedure to install.

# HEATER CORE
## REPLACE

1. Disconnect battery ground cable.
2. Remove combination switch as outlined previously.
3. Remove instrument panel hood attaching screws, then push hood rearward to gain access to switch electrical connections. Disconnect all switch wiring as necessary, then remove hood.
4. Remove instrument cluster as outlined previously.
5. Working from underneath center of instrument panel, remove center mounting bracket bolts, then the mounting bracket.
6. Disconnect and remove lefthand and righthand heater ducts.
7. Remove glove box.
8. Remove fuse panel cover, then the fuse panel attaching screws. Push fuse panel forward, but do not remove from vehicle.
9. Remove shift lever console and radio.
10. Remove air conditioning/heater control panel, then disconnect cigar lighter electrical connector.
11. Working from underneath instrument panel, disconnect all air conditioning/heater control cables that will interfere with instrument panel removal.
12. Remove trim inserts concealing instrument panel attaching bolts.
13. Remove the seven attaching bolts and two stud nuts retaining instrument panel, **Fig. 10.**
14. Disconnect any remaining electrical wiring, then remove instrument panel from vehicle.
15. Working from engine compartment, disconnect hoses from heater core.
16. Disconnect wiring from blower motor and blower motor resistor.
17. Disengage wiring harness and antenna lead from bracket on front of plenum.
18. Loosen screw securing connector duct to plenum, then remove upper and lower plenum to cowl panel attaching nuts.

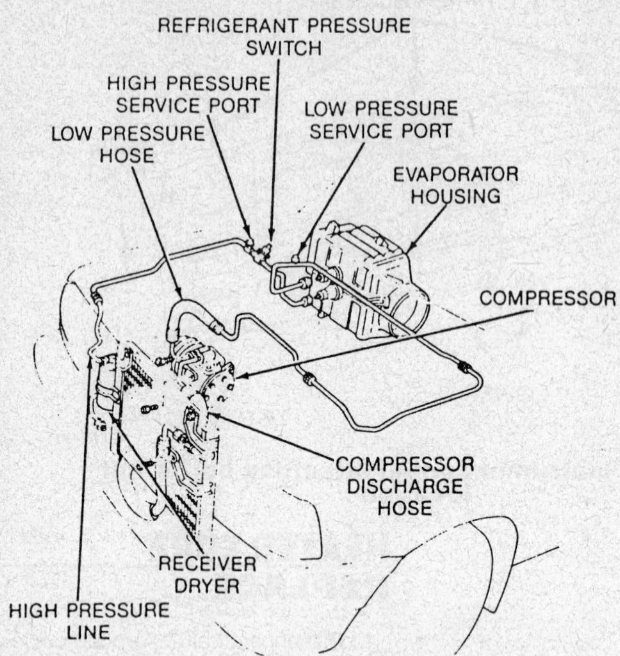


**Fig. 12 Evaporator hose routing. With power steering**

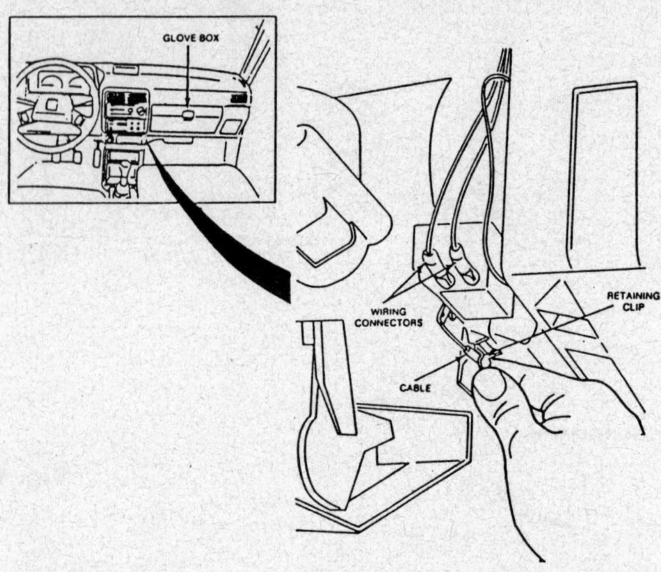


**Fig. 13 Evaporator case electrical connections**

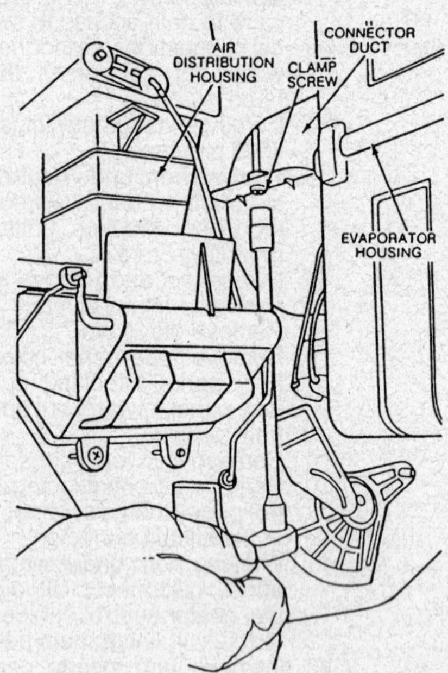


**Fig. 14 Evaporator case clamp screw location**

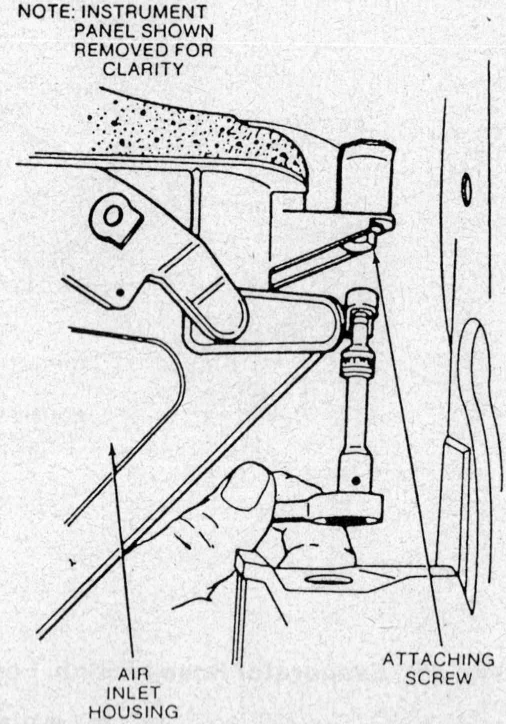


**Fig. 15 Air inlet attaching bolt**

19. Disengage plenum from defroster ducts, then pull outward and remove plenum from vehicle.
20. Disconnect link connecting the two defroster doors, then remove screws and clips securing plenum halves together.
21. Separate plenum halves and remove heater core.
22. Remove tube insert from bottom of heater core.
23. Reverse procedure to install.

## EVAPORATOR CORE REPLACE

1. Disconnect battery ground cable.
2. Discharge refrigerant from A/C system.
3. Working from inside engine compartment, disconnect low and high pressure lines from evaporator outlet fitting, **Figs. 11 and 12.**
4. Remove two glove box retaining screws, then glove box assembly.
5. Disconnect two electrical connectors from thermostat, **Fig. 13.**
6. Disconnect cable from thermostat.
7. Disengage wire harness retaining clamps from top of evaporator housing.
8. Loosen clamp screw securing connector duct to evaporator housing, **Fig. 14.**
9. Disconnect drain hose from evaporator housing.
10. Remove air inlet duct attaching bolt, **Fig. 15.**
11. Remove bolt attaching base of evaporator housing to dash panel.

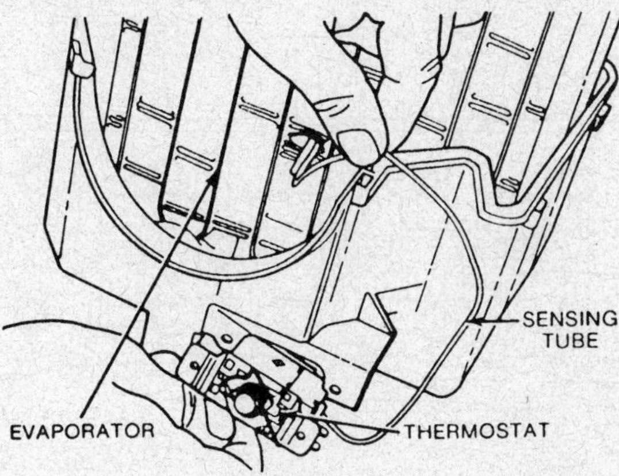


**Fig. 16 Thermostat & sensing tube removal**

12. Remove nuts attaching top of evaporator housing to dash panel.
13. Remove evaporator housing.
14. Remove the ten clips securing the upper evaporator housing to lower housing.
15. Remove upper evaporator housing.
16. Remove thermostat retaining screws, then thermostat. **Fig. 16.**
17. Pull sensing tube from between evaporator core fins as the thermostat is removed.
18. Remove evaporator core from lower housing, then tube separation insert from between inlet and outlet tubes.
19. Remove staples securing capillary tube insulator.
20. Remove expansion valve and capillary tube from evaporator core.
21. Reverse procedure to install. Install new O-ring seals.

# Engine

## INDEX



## ENGINE MOUNTS REPLACE

### FRONT MOUNT

1. Remove mount through bolt attaching nut.
2. Support engine using suitable tool, then remove through bolt.
3. Raise and support front of vehicle.
4. Remove front mount to crossmember attaching nuts, raise engine as necessary, and remove mount from crossmember.
5. Reverse procedure to install, positioning mount as shown in **Fig. 1.**

### REAR MOUNT

1. Raise and support front of vehicle.
2. Support engine using suitable tool, then remove rear mount to crossmember attaching nut.
3. Remove mount to engine bracket attaching bolts, raise engine as necessary, then remove mount from crossmember.
4. Reverse procedure to install.

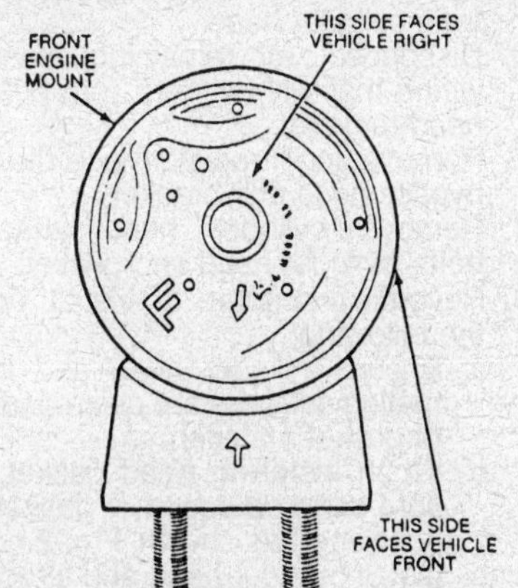


**Fig. 1 Installing front engine mount**

## ENGINE REPLACE

The engine and transaxle are removed as an assembly on these vehicles.

1. Disconnect battery cables, then remove battery and battery tray.
2. Scribe alignment marks on hood and hood hinges to facilitate installation, then remove hood.
3. Drain cooling system, crankcase and transaxle, then discharge air conditioning system.
4. Remove air cleaner and oil dipstick.
5. Disconnect electrical connectors and hoses, then remove cooling fan and radiator as an assembly.
6. Disconnect accelerator cable at carburetor and bracket.
7. Disconnect speedometer cable.
8. Disconnect and mark all remaining hoses, lines and electrical connections that will interfere with engine/transaxle removal.
9. Raise and support vehicle, then disconnect catalytic converter from exhaust system.
10. Remove A/C compressor, if equipped, and position aside. **Do not disconnect lines from compressor.**
11. Disconnect lower control arms from steering knuckles.
12. Separate halfshafts from transaxle and install suitable holding tool for differential side gear.
13. **On vehicles with automatic transaxles,** remove nut which connects shift lever to manual shaft assembly, then shift cable from transaxle.

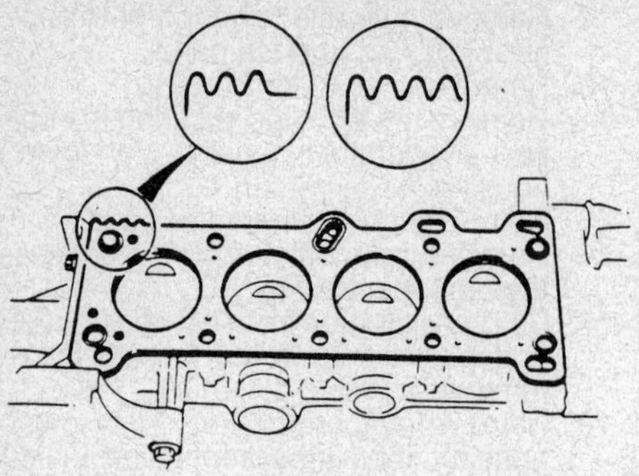

Fig. 2 Positioning head gasket

14. **On vehicles with manual transaxles,** disconnect clutch control cable, then the shift control rod from transaxle.
15. **On all models,** disconnect stabilizer bar from transaxle, then support engine using suitable tool.
16. Remove rear crossmember to chassis attaching bolts.
17. Working through access hole in crossmember, remove front engine mount attaching nut.
18. Remove rear engine mount to crossmember attaching nut.
19. Remove crossmember to chassis attaching bolts, then lower and remove crossmember from vehicle.
20. Lower vehicle, attach suitable hoist to engine, then raise vehicle again to gain clearance for engine/transaxle removal.
21. Remove right engine mount through bolt, raise engine/transaxle assembly slightly, then guide assembly out through bottom of vehicle.
22. Reverse procedure to install.

# INTAKE MANIFOLD
## REPLACE

1. Disconnect battery ground cable, then drain cooling system.
2. Remove air cleaner assembly, then disconnect accelerator cable from carburetor.
3. Disconnect and mark all hoses, lines and electrical connections that will interfere with manifold removal.
4. Remove retaining bolts, then the intake manifold.
5. Clean manifold and cylinder head mating surfaces, then reinstall manifold using new gasket.

# EXHAUST MANIFOLD
## REPLACE

1. Raise and support vehicle.
2. Remove catalytic converter inlet pipe to manifold and pulse air tube to inlet pipe attaching nuts and washers.
3. Remove inlet pipe support bracket attaching bolts, then lower vehicle.
4. Remove air cleaner assembly, then the exhaust manifold heat shroud.
5. Remove oxygen sensor wiring from routing bracket, then disconnect sensor electrical connector.
6. Remove pulse air tube routing bracket attaching bolt and clamp, then the pulse air tube and gaskets.
7. Remove exhaust manifold to cylinder head attaching nuts, then the manifold.
8. Reverse procedure to install using new gaskets.

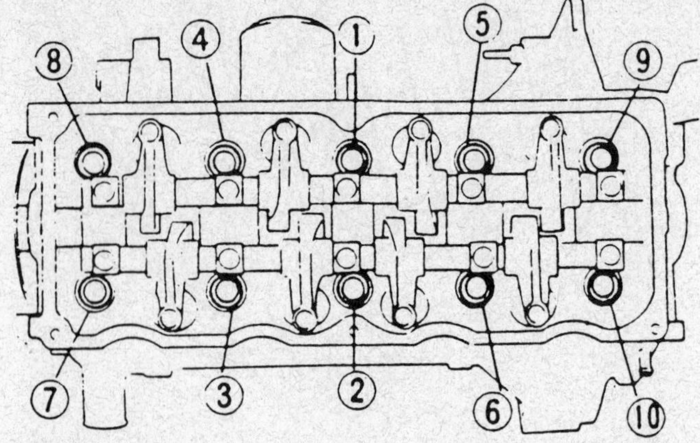


Fig. 3 Cylinder head bolt tightening sequence

# CYLINDER HEAD
## REPLACE

1. Remove timing belt covers and timing belt as outlined previously.
2. Remove intake and exhaust manifolds.
3. Disconnect spark plug wires and remove spark plugs from cylinder head.
4. Disconnect distributor electrical connections, scribe alignment marks on distributor base flange and cylinder head, then remove distributor mounting bolts and the distributor.
5. Remove front and rear engine lifting eyes, then disconnect ground wire from cylinder head.
6. Disconnect all remaining electrical wiring that will interfere with cylinder head removal.
7. Remove upper radiator hose, then the bypass hose and bracket.
8. Remove cylinder head attaching bolts, cylinder head and gasket.
9. Reverse procedure to install, noting the following:
   a. Ensure cylinder head and block mating surfaces are clean and free of gasket material.
   b. When installing head gasket, ensure serrated edges of gasket are positioned as shown, **Fig. 2.**
   c. Install cylinder head and attaching bolts, then tighten bolts in sequence shown, **Fig. 3.**

# VALVE CLEARANCE SPECIFICATIONS

| Year | Engine | Int. | Exh. |
|---|---|---|---|
| **1989** | **1.3L/4-80.8①** | **.012H** | **.012H** |
| **1989–92** | **1.3L/4-80.8②** | ③ | ③ |

**①—Carbureted engine.**
**②—EFI engine.**
**③—Equipped with hydraulic valve lash adjusters, no adjustment.**

# VALVE ARRANGEMENT
## FRONT TO REAR

1.3L/4-80.8. . . . . . . . . . . . . . . . I-E-I-E-E-I-E-I

# VALVES
## ADJUST
### CARBURETED ENGINES

The following procedure should be performed with engine at normal operating temperature.

1. Remove rocker cover.
2. Position No. 1 cylinder at TDC of compression stroke. With engine in this position, notch on crankshaft pulley should align with TDC mark on belt cover and both valves for No. 1 cylinder should be closed.
3. With engine in this position, adjust the following valves: Intake, No. 1 and 2; Exhaust, No. 1 and 3. To adjust valves, loosen locknut on adjusting screw, then position specified feeler gauge between valve stem and adjusting screw, **Fig. 4.** Turn adjusting screw until slight drag is felt at feeler gauge, then tighten locknut.
4. Turn crankshaft one full turn in normal direction of rotation to bring No. 4 cylinder to TDC of compression stroke. With engine in this position, adjust remaining valves as outlined in previous step.
5. Reinstall rocker cover using new gasket.

### EFI ENGINES

These engines are equipped with hydraulic valve lash adjusters, **Fig. 5,** which are not adjustable.

# HYDRAULIC VALVE LASH ADJUSTERS

The hydraulic valve lash adjusters are located in the rocker arms, **Fig. 5.** Refer to "Rocker Arm & Shaft Service" procedure.

# VALVE GUIDES

Valve guides can be replaced using valve guide remover tool No.

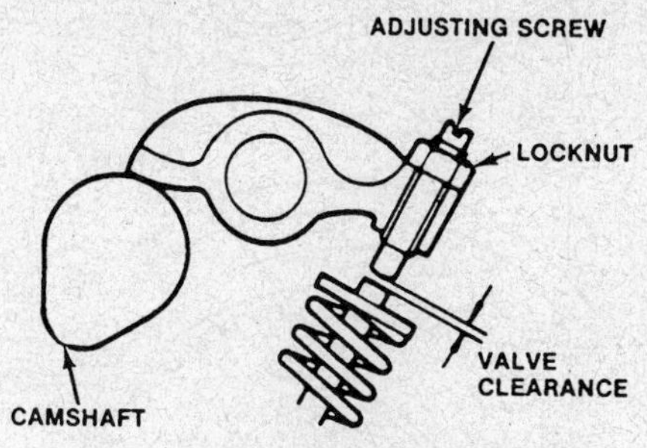


**Fig. 4 Valve clearance adjustment**

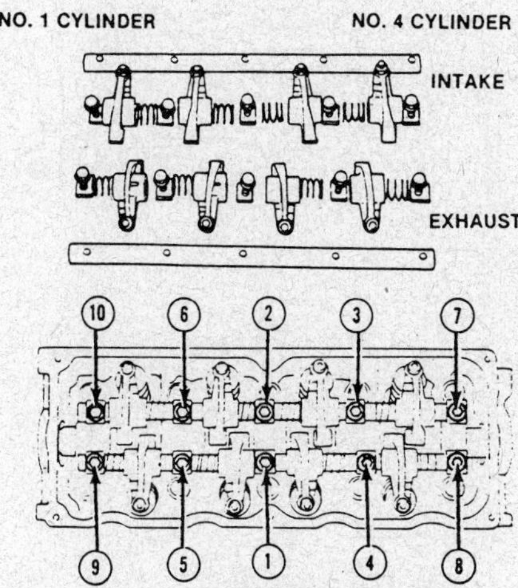


**Fig. 7 Rocker arm & assembly & bolt tightening sequence**

T87C-6510-A. When removing valve guide, drive out toward camshaft side of cylinder head. When installing valve guide, drive in until clip just contacts cylinder head, **Fig. 6.**

## ROCKER ARM & SHAFT SERVICE

1. Remove rocker arm cover.
2. Alternately and evenly loosen rocker shaft attaching bolts, then carefully lift rocker shaft assemblies from cylinder head.
3. Remove rocker arms and springs from rocker shaft. **On EFI engines, do not remove hydraulic valve lash adjusters from rocker arms unless necessary.**
4. Measure outside diameter of rocker shaft and inside diameter of rocker arm shaft bore. The maximum difference between these two measurements should not exceed .004 inch. **On EFI engines,** also check hydraulic valve lash adjuster for wear and damage and replace as necessary.
5. **On EFI engines,** pour engine oil into rocker reservoir.
6. **On EFI engines,** apply engine oil to hydraulic valve lash adjuster and install in rocker arm, if removed. Use care not to damage O-ring when installing.

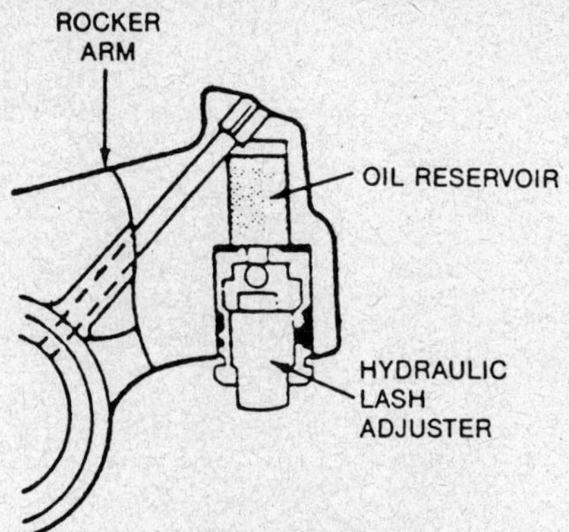


**Fig. 5 Hydraulic valve lash adjuster assembly**

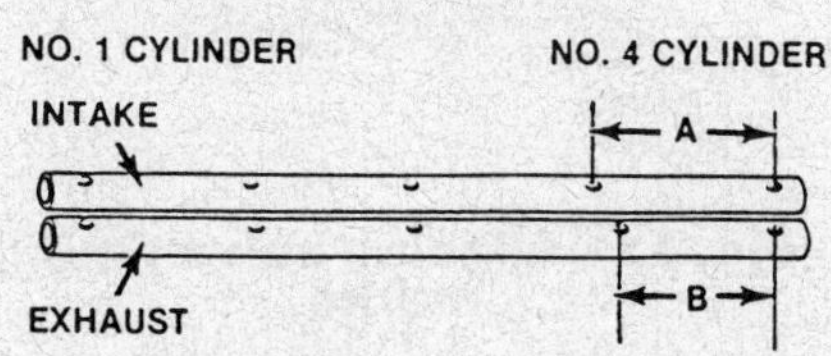


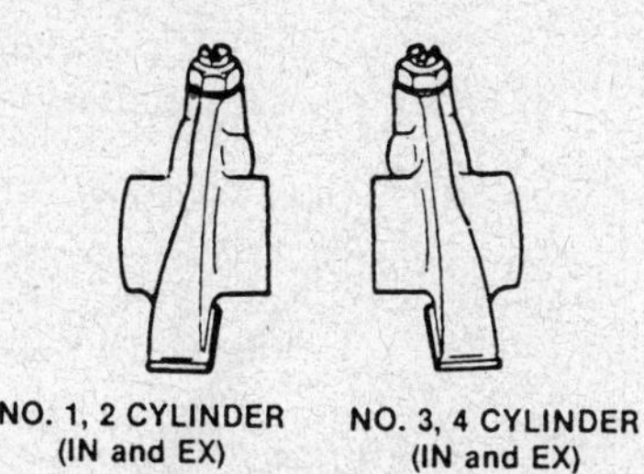


**Fig. 8 Rocker arm & shaft identification.**

7. **On all engines,** assemble rocker arms and springs to rocket shaft, **Fig. 7.** Rocker arms and shafts can be identified as shown in **Fig. 8.**
8. Install assembled rocker shaft assemblies, with oil holes facing down, to cylinder head and **torque** attaching bolts alternately and evenly in sequence shown in **Fig. 7** to value listed at rear of this section. When tightening rocker shaft attaching bolts, pull back on rocker arm springs.

## TIMING BELT COVERS
## REPLACE

1. Remove accessory drive belts.
2. Remove water pump pulley to pump hub attaching bolts, then the pulley.
3. Remove right inner fender panel to gain access to crankshaft pulley.
4. Remove outer crankshaft pulley attaching bolts, then the outer stiffener/spacer and outer pulley, **Fig. 9.**
5. Remove inner stiffener/spacer, attaching screws, inner pulley and baffle plate.
6. Remove attaching bolts, then the upper and lower timing covers.
7. Reverse procedure to install. When installing crankshaft pulley, ensure curved lip on baffle plate and deep recess of inner pulley face outward.

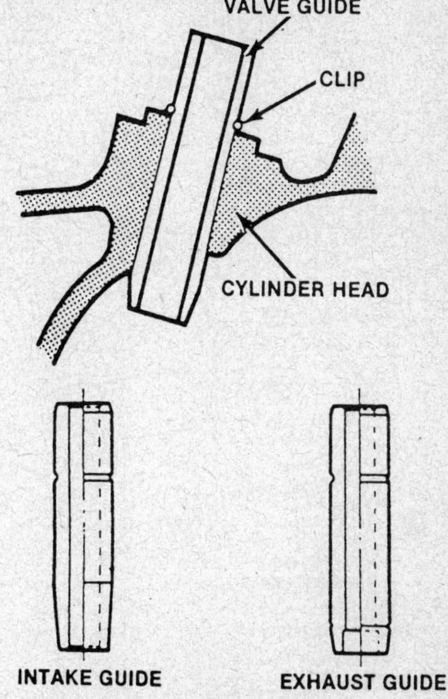


**Fig. 6 Valve guide replacement.**

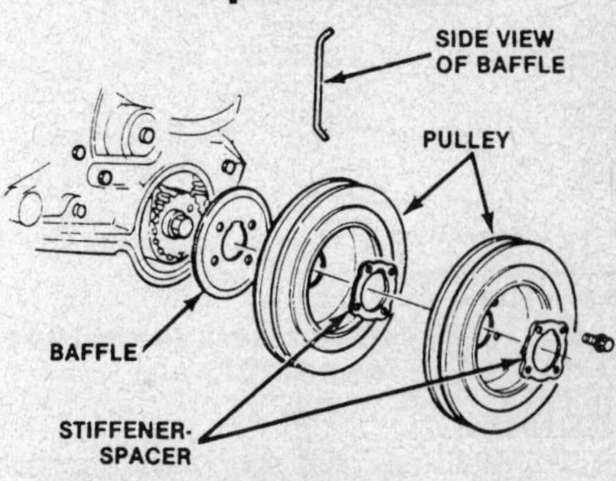


**Fig. 9 Crankshaft pulley assembly**

## TIMING BELT
## REPLACE

1. Remove timing belt covers as outlined previously.
2. Remove timing belt tensioner pulley attaching bolt, then the tensioner pulley, spring and spring cover, **Fig. 10.**
3. If reusing old belt, mark direction of rotation on belt to aid installation.
4. Remove timing belt from crankshaft and camshaft sprockets.
5. Check crankshaft and camshaft sprockets, tensioner pulley and timing belt for wear or damage. Replace components as necessary.
6. Align camshaft and crankshaft sprocket timing marks with marks on cylinder head and oil pump housing, **Fig. 11.**
7. Install timing belt. If reusing old belt, ensure belt is installed so that direction of rotation mark made during removal is positioned correctly.
8. Install spring and spring cover onto tensioner pulley, **Fig. 10,** then install pulley and attaching bolt. Do not tighten bolt at this time.

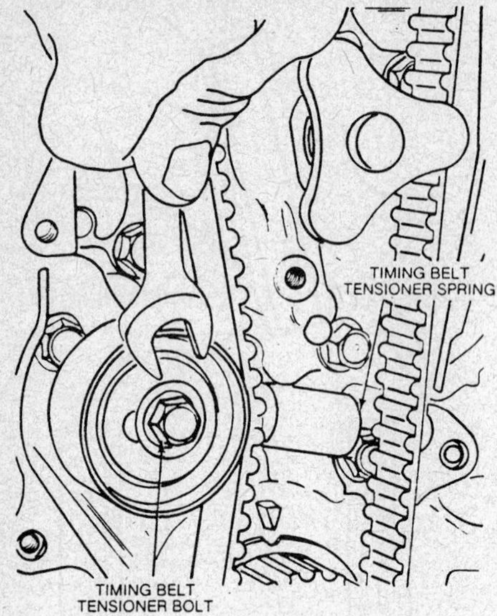


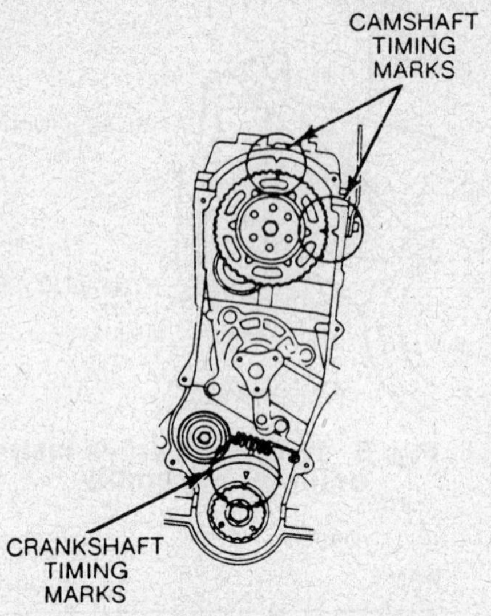


**Fig. 11 Aligning valve timing marks**

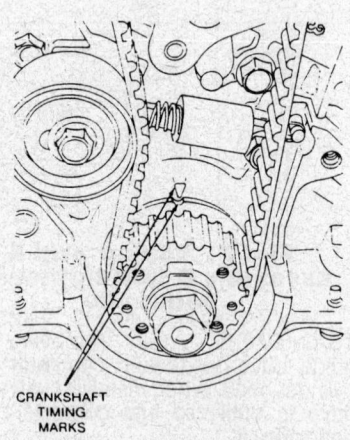

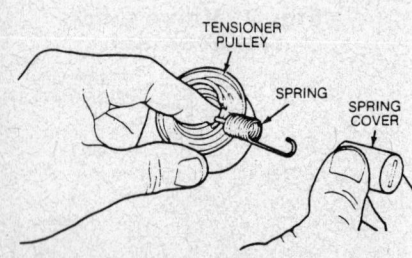

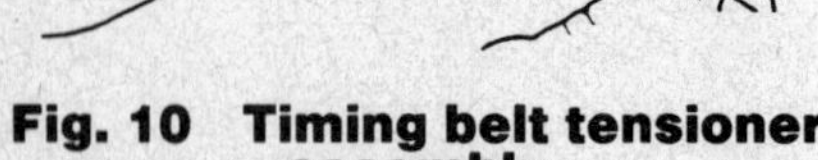

**Fig. 10 Timing belt tensioner assembly**

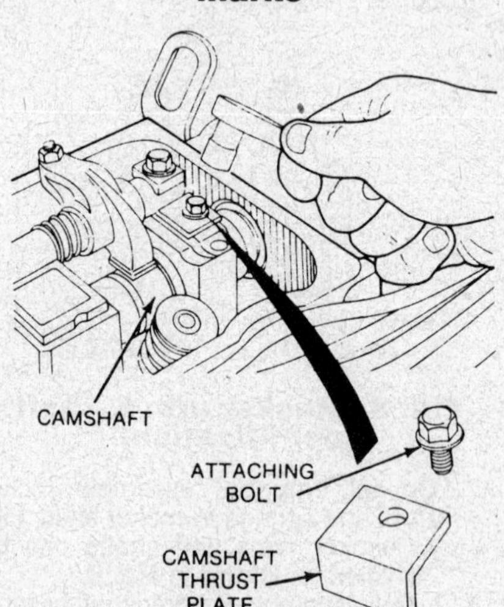


**Fig. 13 Camshaft thrust plate**

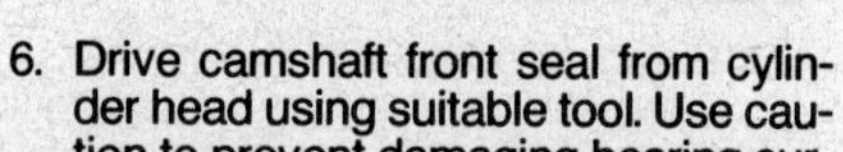


**Fig. 12 Camshaft & crankshaft valve timing marks**

9. Install tensioner spring onto anchor, then tighten pulley attaching bolt to torque listed at the end of this section.
10. Reinstall timing belt covers.

## CAMSHAFT TIMING CHECK

1. Align crankshaft pulley timing notch with TC mark on timing belt cover tab.
2. Remove timing belt upper cover.
3. Camshaft timing marks should be aligned, **Fig. 12.** If camshaft timing cannot be viewed, rotate crankshaft pulley one revolution, aligning notch with timing cover TC mark.
4. If camshaft timing marks are aligned, the camshaft is properly timed to the crankshaft. If camshaft timing marks are not properly aligned, refer to "Timing Belt, Replace" procedure.

## CAMSHAFT REPLACE

1. Remove cylinder head as outlined previously.
2. Remove rocker arm shaft assembly retaining bolts, then the rocker shaft assemblies.
3. To prevent camshaft rotation, position suitable open end wrench on flats on front part of camshaft, then remove camshaft sprocket retaining bolt and camshaft sprocket.
4. Remove camshaft thrust plate attaching bolt, then the thrust plate, **Fig. 13.**
5. Carefully slide camshaft out of cylinder head.

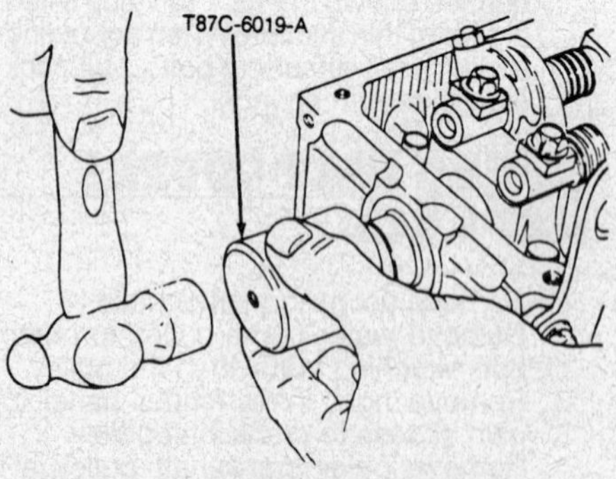


**Fig. 14 Installing camshaft front seal**

6. Drive camshaft front seal from cylinder head using suitable tool. Use caution to prevent damaging bearing surface.
7. Lubricate camshaft journals and lobes, then install camshaft and thrust plate.
8. Lubricate front seal bore and seal lip with engine oil, then drive new seal into cylinder head using tool No. T87C-6019-A or equivalent, **Fig. 14.**
9. Install camshaft sprocket and retaining bolt. Hold sprocket with large screwdriver, then tighten retaining bolt.
10. Install rocker shaft assemblies, refer to "Rocker Arm & Shaft Service."
11. Reinstall cylinder head.

## PISTON & ROD, ASSEMBLE

Assemble piston to connecting rod so that "F" mark on piston pin bore and oil

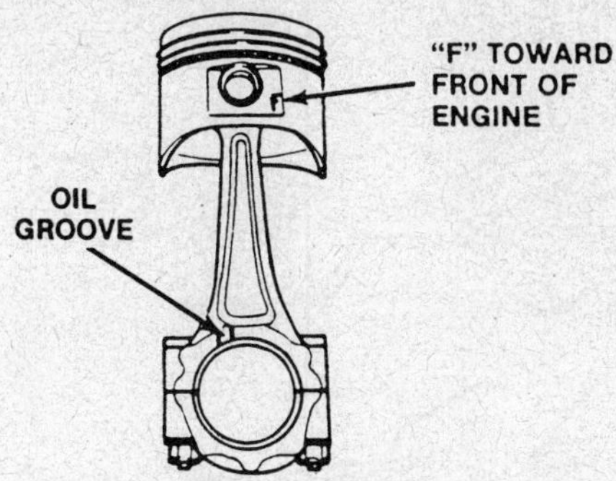


Fig. 15 Piston & rod assembly

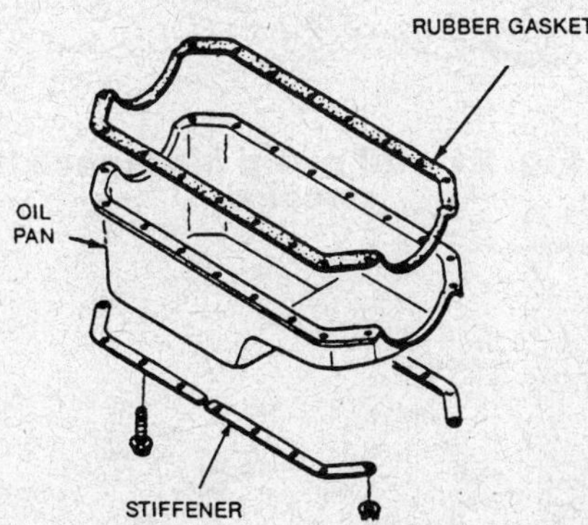


Fig. 18 Oil pan replacement

groove on connecting rod face toward front of engine, **Fig. 15.** After installing connecting rod, check side clearance with feeler gauge. Clearance should not exceed .012 inch.

## CRANKSHAFT SPROCKET & FRONT OIL SEAL

### REPLACE

1. Remove timing belt as outlined previously.
2. Position shift lever in 4th gear, then apply parking brake.
3. Remove crankshaft sprocket retaining bolt, then the sprocket and key.
4. Using suitable tool, pry old seal from oil pump assembly.
5. Clean seal bore, then press in new seal using suitable tool, **Fig. 16.**
6. Reinstall key and sprocket onto crankshaft.
7. Coat sprocket retaining bolt threads with non-hardening type sealer, then install bolt.
8. Reinstall timing belt.

## CRANKSHAFT REAR OIL SEAL

### REPLACE

1. Remove transaxle as outlined in "Clutch & Manual Transaxle."
2. Remove flywheel attaching bolts and flywheel, then the engine rear cover plate, **Fig. 17.**

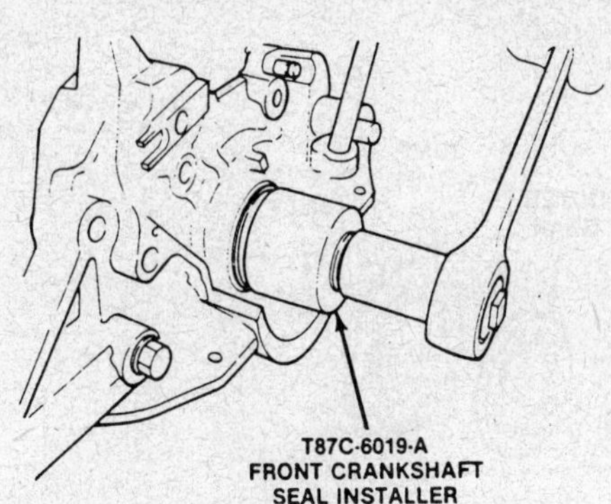


Fig. 16 Installing crankshaft front seal

3. Remove seal retainer attaching bolts and seal retainer, then carefully pry out oil seal using suitable tool.
4. Lubricate, then install seal using suitable tool. **Ensure that hollow side of seal faces toward engine.**
5. Install seal retainer and tighten attaching bolts. Trim off excess gasket material after installation.
6. Install engine rear cover plate and tighten attaching bolts.
7. Install flywheel and tighten attaching bolts.
8. Reinstall transaxle.

## OIL PAN

### REPLACE

1. Disconnect battery ground cable, raise and support vehicle, then drain crankcase.
2. Remove flywheel housing dust cover.
3. Remove oil pan to cylinder block attaching bolts, nuts and stiffeners, **Fig. 18.**
4. Remove oil pan from vehicle. **If crankshaft interferes with pan removal, it may be necessary to rotate the crankshaft to provide clearance between pan and counterweights.**
5. **On models equipped with EFI, remove oil pan baffle.**
6. Reverse procedure to install, noting the following:
   a. Before installing pan, ensure that pan and cylinder block mating surfaces are free from oil and old gasket material.
   b. Apply suitable sealer across joint line of cylinder block and front and rear engine covers as shown in **Fig. 19.**

## OIL PUMP

### REPLACE

### REMOVAL

1. Remove crankshaft sprocket and oil pan as outlined previously.
2. Remove oil pump to cylinder block attaching bolts, then the oil pump.

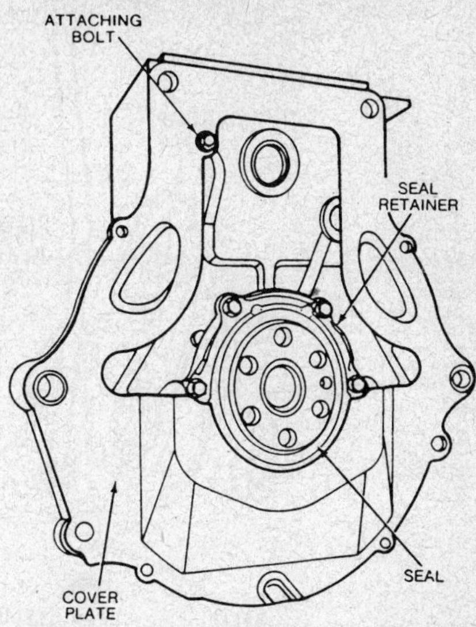


Fig. 17 Rear cover assembly

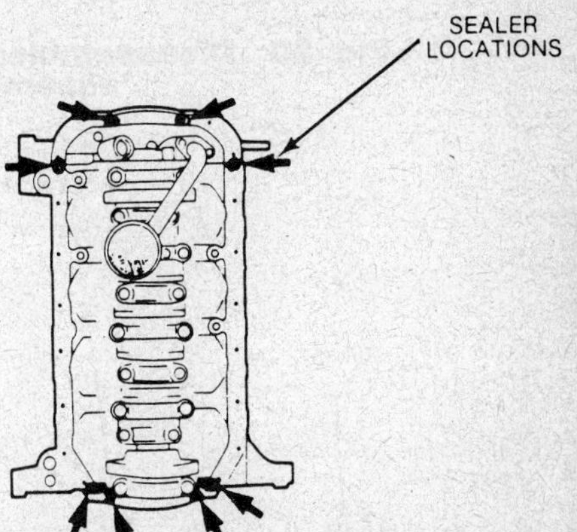


Fig. 19 Applying sealant to cylinder block

### INSTALLATION

1. Ensure that oil pump and cylinder block mating surfaces are clean and free from old gasket material.
2. Apply a thick film of sealer to both sides of oil pump gasket, then install gasket, oil pump and attaching bolts.
3. Install pickup tube and screen assembly using new gasket.
4. Install crankshaft sprocket and oil pan.

## OIL PUMP SERVICE

### DISASSEMBLY

1. Remove pickup tube and screen assembly.
2. Remove oil pump cover attaching bolts, then the cover and inner and outer gears, **Fig. 20.**
3. If necessary, pry oil seal from pump body.
4. Remove split pin, then the relief valve plunger assembly from pump body.

### INSPECTION

1. Inspect pump body gear pocket and

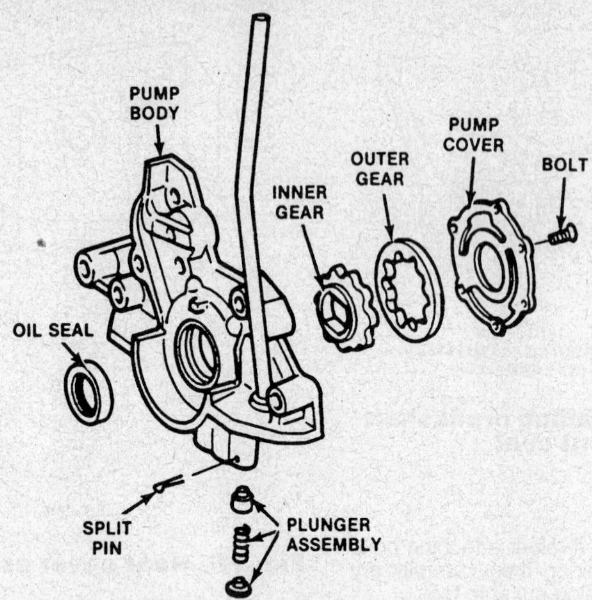


**Fig. 20 Disassembled view of oil pump assembly**

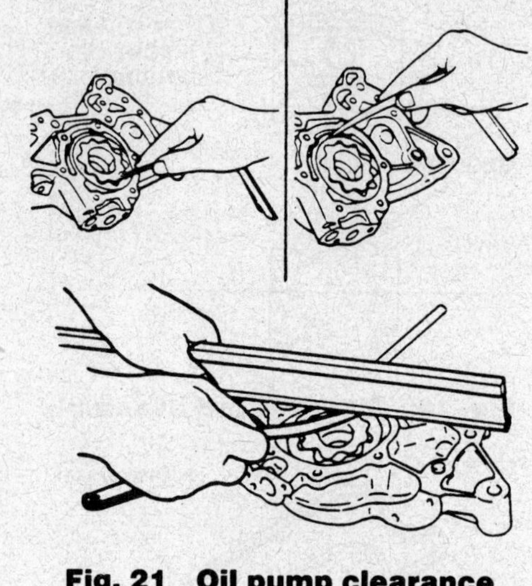

**Fig. 21 Oil pump clearance checks**

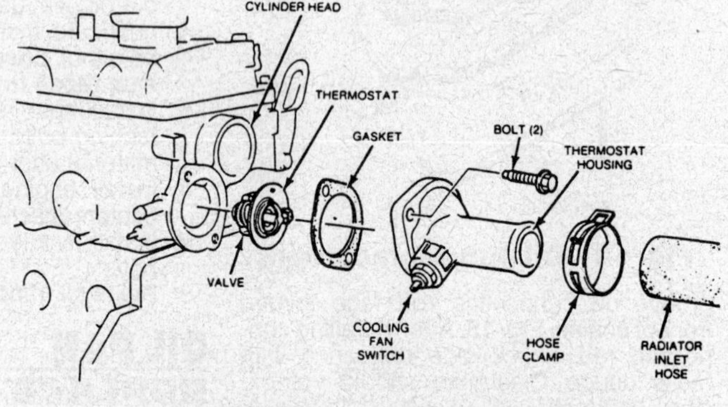


**Fig. 23 Thermostat replacement**

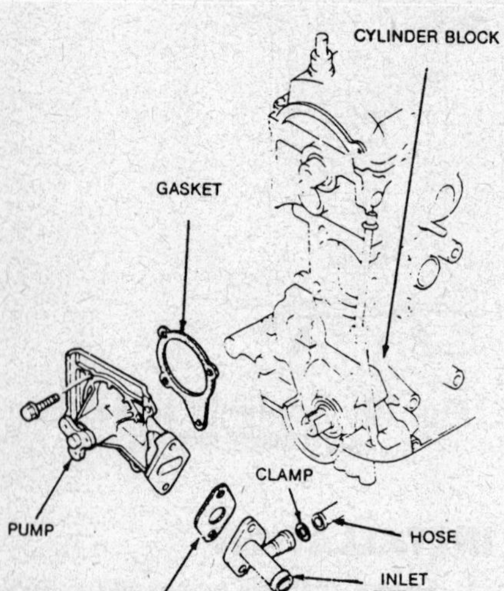


**Fig. 22 Water pump replacement**

relief valve bore for excessive wear or scoring. Replace pump body, if necessary.

2. Inspect relief valve plunger assembly for scoring, burrs or excessive wear. Replace plunger assembly as necessary.
3. Reinstall inner and outer gears into pump body.
4. Measure clearance between inner gear tip and outer gear as shown in **Fig. 21.** Clearance should not exceed .0078 inch.
5. Measure outer gear to pump body clearance. Clearance should not exceed .0087 inch.
6. Using a suitable straightedge, measure gear end play as shown in **Fig. 12.** End play should not exceed .0055 inch.
7. If above clearances are beyond specified limits, replace gears or pump body as required.

## ASSEMBLY

1. Place relief valve plunger assembly into pump body, then install split pin.
2. If oil seal was removed, drive in new seal using seal installing tool No. T87C-6019-A or equivalent.
3. Lubricate, then install gears into pump body.
4. Install pump cover and attaching bolts. Coat bolt threads with Loctite or equivalent before installation.

## WATER PUMP REPLACE

1. Drain cooling system.
2. Remove timing belt as outlined previously.
3. Disconnect lower radiator and heater hoses from water pump inlet.
4. Remove water pump attaching bolts and the water pump, **Fig. 22.**
5. Ensure that water pump and cylinder block mating surfaces are clean and free from old gasket material.

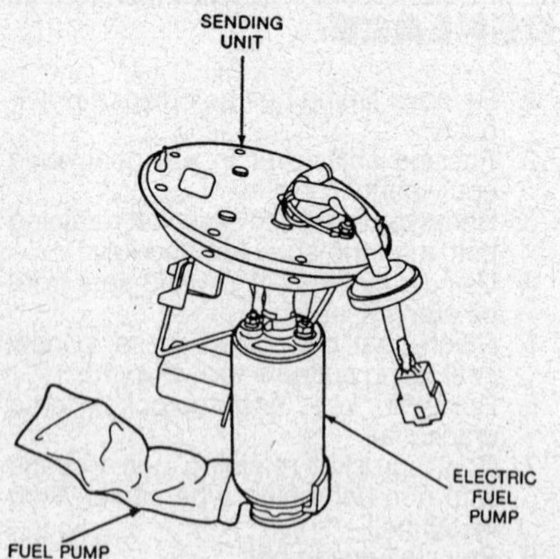


**Fig. 24 Fuel pump & sending unit assembly**

6. Coat both sides of water pump gasket with suitable sealer, then install gasket, water pump and attaching bolts.
7. Connect lower radiator and heater hoses to pump inlet.
8. Install timing belt.

## COOLING SYSTEM BLEED

This engine does not require a specified bleed procedure. After filling cooling system, run engine to operating temperature with radiator/pressure cap off. Air will then automatically be bled through cap opening.

## THERMOSTAT REPLACE

**To avoid possibility of personal injury or damage to vehicle, ensure ignition switch is in Off position before disconnecting wire from cooling fan temperature switch. If wire is disconnected from temperature switch with ignition switch in On position, cooling fan will turn On.**

1. Remove radiator pressure cap from radiator filler neck.
2. Drain coolant level below radiator upper hose.
2. Disconnect electrical connector from cooling fan switch on thermostat housing, **Fig. 23.**
3. Disconnect upper radiator hose at thermostat housing, then remove two thermostat housing retaining bolts from cylinder head.
4. Remove thermostat housing and gasket.
5. Remove thermostat.
6. Reverse procedure to install.

## BELT TENSION DATA

| Belt | Tension In Lbs. New | Tension In Lbs. Used |
|---|---|---|
| A/C Comp. | 110–125 | 92–110 |
| Alternator | 110–132 | 95–110 |

## FUEL PUMP REPLACE

### CARBURETED ENGINES

1. Remove air cleaner assembly.
2. Mark, then disconnect fuel lines from pump.
3. Loosen fuel pump attaching bolts one or two turns, then grasp pump and loosen from cylinder head mounting pad.
4. To reduce pressure on pump and aid installation, crank engine until pump arm rests on low side of cam circle.
5. Remove attaching bolts, then the fuel pump, gaskets and insulator.
6. Reverse procedure to install, using new gaskets.

### EFI ENGINES

1. Relieve fuel system pressure as follows:
   a. Remove rear seat cushion.
   b. Start engine and disconnect fuel pump electrical connector.
   c. After engine has stalled, place ignition switch in the Off position.
2. Disconnect and cap fuel supply and return lines.
3. Remove sending unit/fuel pump assembly to fuel tank attaching bolts, then remove sending unit/fuel pump assembly and gasket from tank, **Fig. 24.**
4. Remove fuel filter from fuel pump, then disconnect fuel pump electrical leads from sending unit.
5. Remove retaining clamp screw, then remove fuel pump outlet hose clamp.
6. Remove fuel pump from sending unit.
7. Reverse procedure to install.

## TIGHTENING SPECIFICATIONS

***Torque specifications are for clean and lightly lubricated threads only. Dry or dirty threads produce increased friction which prevents accurate measurement of tightness.**

| Year | Component | Torque/ft. lbs. |
|---|---|---|
| 1989-92 | Camshaft Sprocket | 36-45 |
| | Connecting Rod Cap Bolts | 22-25 |
| | Cover Plate | 5.7-7.9 |
| | Crankshaft Pulley Bolts | 9-12.6 |
| | Crankshaft Rear Seal Retainer | 5.7-7.9 |
| | Crankshaft Sprocket | 80-87 |
| | Crossmember Bolts | 47-66 |
| | Cylinder Head Bolts | 56-60 |
| | Engine Mount (Front) To Crossmember Nuts | 32-38 |
| | Engine Mount (Rear) To Crossmember Nut | 21-34 |
| | Engine To Transaxle | 41-59 |
| | Exhaust Manifold To Cylinder Head | 12-17 |
| | Flywheel Cover | 5-7.2 |
| | Flywheel To Crankshaft | 71-76 |
| | Gusset Plate | 27-38 |
| | Heat Shroud Bolts | 12-17 |
| | Intake Manifold To Cylinder Head | 14-20 |
| | Main Bearing Cap Bolts | 40-43 |
| | Oil Pan To Engine | 5.7-6.5 |
| | Oil Pump Attaching Bolts | 14-19 |
| | Oil Pump Inlet Tube | 5.7-7.9 |
| | Rocker Arm Cover | 4-7 |
| | Rocker Arm Shaft | 16-21 |
| | Side Mount Nuts | 28-40 |

## TIGHTENING SPECIFICATIONS

| Year | Component | Torque/ft. lbs. |
|---|---|---|
| 1989-92 | Spark Plug | 11-17 |
| | Tensioner Bolt | 14-19 |
| | Thermostat Housing Attaching Bolts | 14-22 |
| | Timing Belt Cover Attaching Bolts | 5.7-7.9 |
| | Torque Converter To Flex Plate | 26-36 |
| | Water Pump Pulley Attaching Bolts | 36-45 |
| | Water Pump To Engine | 14-19 |

# Clutch & Manual Transaxles

INDEX



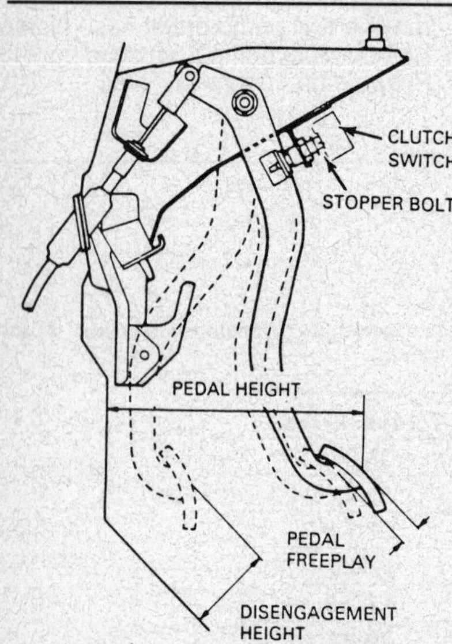


**Fig. 1 Clutch pedal adjustments**

## ADJUSTMENTS

### CLUTCH PEDAL HEIGHT

1. Disconnect clutch cable at release lever so that cable will not interfere with measurement.
2. Move carpeting and insulation away from pedal area.
3. Measure distance from upper center of pedal to dash panel as shown in **Fig. 1.** Measurement should be 8.2-8.4 inch. If distance is not as specified, proceed to next step.
4. Inspect clutch pedal mounting for damaged, worn or missing parts. Replace parts as necessary. If pedal mounting is satisfactory, proceed to next step.
5. Remove instrument panel bracket and air duct located underneath steering column.
6. Loosen clutch switch locknut, then turn switch in or out as required until pedal height is as specified in step 3. Tighten locknut.
7. Reconnect clutch cable to release lever, then adjust pedal freeplay as outlined below.
8. Recheck pedal height measurement. If height adjustment is not within specification, check clutch cable for binding or damage.
9. Reinstall air duct and instrument panel bracket.

### PEDAL FREEPLAY

1. Move clutch pedal back and forth and measure freeplay, **Fig. 1.**
2. Pedal freeplay should be .350-.590 inch. If freeplay is not as specified, proceed to next step.
3. Pull back on release lever, then measure clearance between lever and cable pin, **Fig. 2.** Clearance should be .060-.100 inch.
4. If clearance is not as specified, thread adjuster in or out until specified clearance is obtained.
5. Recheck freeplay. If freeplay is still not within specified limits, inspect clutch release components for damage.

## CLUTCH

### REPLACE

1. Remove transaxle as described further on in this section.
2. If pressure plate will be reused, scribe alignment marks on pressure plate and flywheel to aid installation.
3. Prevent flywheel from turning using suitable tool, then loosen pressure plate attaching bolts one turn at a time until all spring tension is released.
4. Remove attaching bolts, pressure plate and clutch disc, **Fig. 3.**
5. If new clutch disc is being installed, sand friction surfaces of pressure plate and flywheel with medium grit

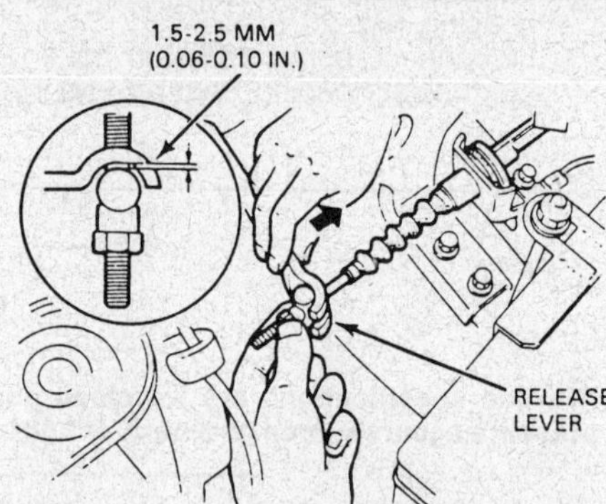


**Fig. 2 Checking clearance between release lever & cable pin**

emery cloth to break glaze on surface. After sanding is completed, remove grit with an alcohol soaked shop towel.
6. Install clutch disc with damper springs facing **away** from flywheel, then install pressure plate and attaching bolts.
7. Install suitable clutch alignment tool, then **torque** attaching bolts evenly to 17 ft. lbs. Remove tool.
8. Reinstall transaxle.

## MANUAL TRANSAXLE

### REPLACE

1. Disconnect battery ground cable, then raise and support vehicle.
2. Disconnect all electrical wiring and speedometer cable from transaxle.
3. Loosen clutch cable adjuster nut and disengage cable from release lever.
4. Remove starter motor, then the two bolts located at top of clutch housing, **Fig. 4**
5. Support engine using suitable support fixture.
6. Remove shift rod to input shaft rail attaching nut and bolt.
7. Remove lower control arm to steering

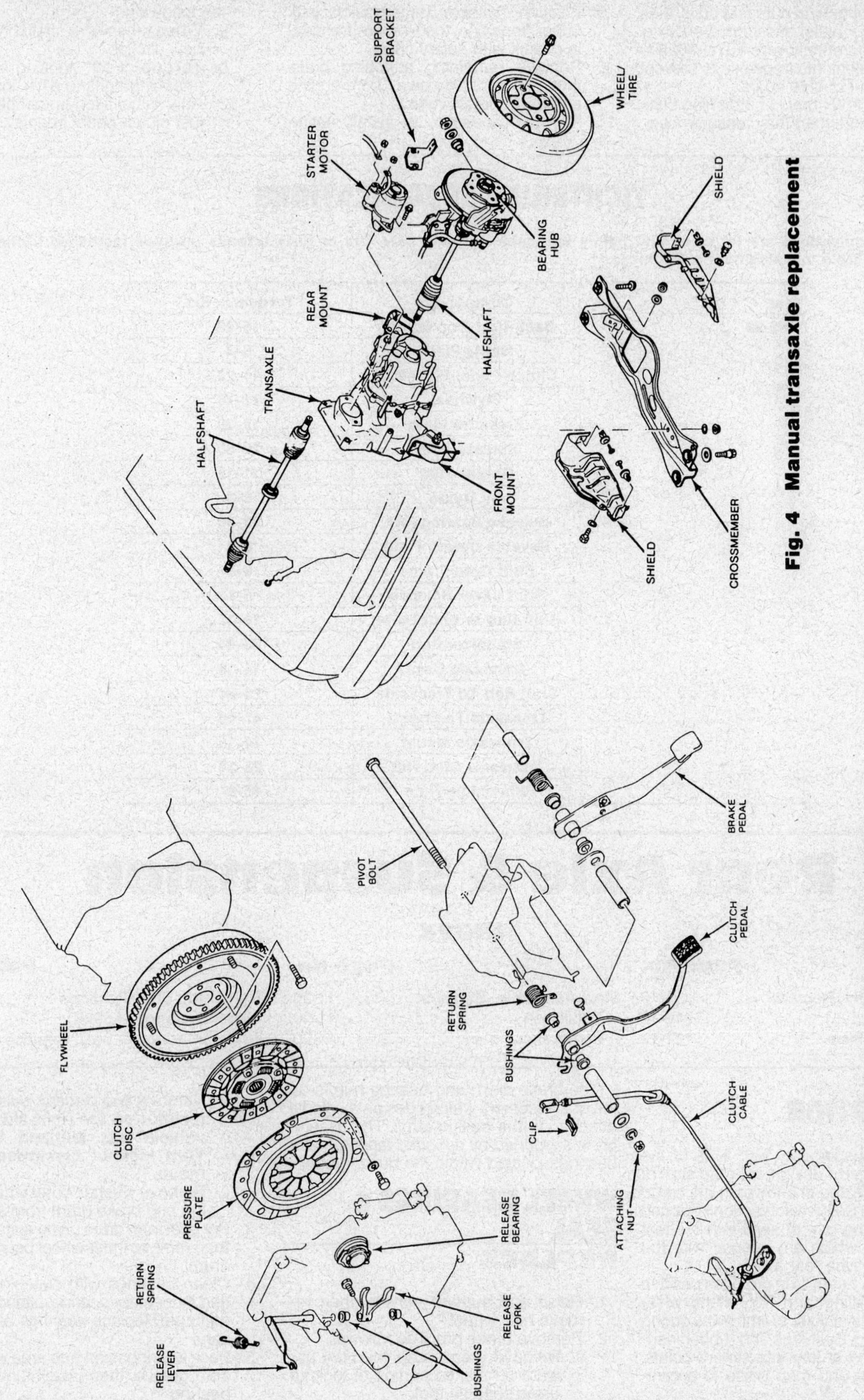


**Fig. 3 Clutch system components**

**Fig. 4 Manual transaxle replacement**

knuckle attaching nuts and bolts, then disengage halfshafts from transaxle. Install differential plugs T87C-7025-C or equivalent into transaxle to prevent movement of side gears.
8. Remove NVH bracket attaching bolts and bracket, then the crossmember.
9. Position suitable transmission jack under transaxle, then secure transaxle to jack with safety chain.
10. Remove remaining attaching bolts, then pull transaxle away from engine and lower out of vehicle.
11. Reverse procedure to install, noting the following:
    a. When installing halfshafts, use new circlips.
    b. **Torque** clutch housing to engine attaching bolts to 57 ft. lbs.
12. After installation is completed, adjust clutch pedal freeplay.

## TIGHTENING SPECIFICATIONS

***Torque specifications are for clean and lightly lubricated threads only. Dry or dirty threads produce increased friction which prevents accurate measurement of tightness.**

| Year | Component | Torque/ft. lbs. |
|---|---|---|
| 1989-92 | Back-Up Lamp Switch | 15–22 |
| | Baffle Plate | 6–8 |
| | Clutch Pedal Pivot Bolt | 14–25 |
| | Flywheel | 71–76 |
| | Pressure Plate | 13–20 |
| | Release Fork | 26–30 |
| | Detent Plug | 11–15 |
| | Oil Guide | 6–8 |
| | Release Bearing fork | 26–30 |
| | Reverse Detent Plate | 6–8 |
| | Shift Gate Frame | 6–8 |
| | Shift Lever Housing | 5–7 |
| | Shift Rod to Shift Lever | 12–17 |
| | Stabilizer Rod | 23–34 |
| | Transaxle Case | 14–19 |
| | Shift Rod To Transaxle | 23–34 |
| | Transaxle To Engine | 47–66 |
| | Transaxle Mount | 14–19 |
| | Transaxle Stud Nut | 23–34 |
| | Wheel Lug Nuts | 65-87 |

# Rear Axle & Suspension

## INDEX



## DESCRIPTION

The rear suspension, **Fig. 1**, is of the MacPherson strut design, with the strut at each wheel seated in a tower in the cargo compartment. Suspension action is carried out through the use of semi-independent trailing arms, which are integral with the torsion beam type rear axle.

The torsion beam axle provides positive control of trailing arm alignment, while doubling as a stabilizer to limit sway during hard cornering. Bushings and rubber insulators, installed at key attachment points, keep vibration and road noise to a minimum.

The brake drum and bearing hub is an integral assembly which rides on a spindle attached to the trailing arms. The assembly is supported by opposed tapered roller bearings located within the bearing hub.

## WHEEL BEARINGS & SEAL

### REPLACE

1. Raise and support vehicle, then remove rear wheel.
2. Remove brake drum as follows:
    a. Remove grease cap, then pry upward on staked portion of locknut using suitable tool.
    b. Remove and discard locknut. **The locknut on the right side of the vehicle has lefthand threads. Turn locknut clockwise to remove.**
    c. Remove washer, outer wheel bearing and brake drum from spindle.
3. Pry seal from drum using suitable tool, then remove inner wheel bearing from drum.
4. Clean bearings with suitable solvent and inspect for scoring, pitting or heat damage. Replace bearings as necessary.
5. Pack bearings and hub area with suitable grease, then install inner wheel bearing.

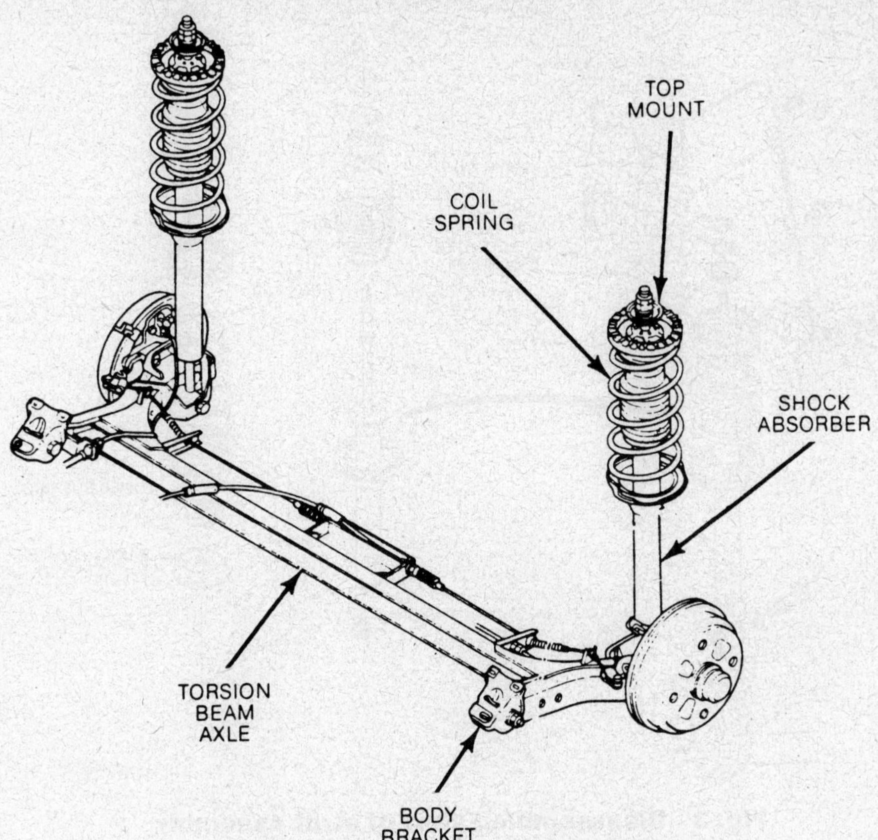


**Fig. 1 Rear axle & suspension**

6. Lubricate new seal, then install into drum using suitable driver.
7. Install drum, outer wheel bearing, washer and locknut.
8. Adjust wheel bearing preload as outlined under "Wheel Bearings, Adjust" procedure.
9. Install grease cap and rear wheel, then lower vehicle.

## WHEEL BEARINGS
### ADJUST

1. Raise and support vehicle, then remove rear wheel and grease cap.
2. While rotating brake drum, **torque** locknut to 18-22 ft. lbs.
3. Loosen locknut until it can be turned by hand, then measure seal drag as follows:
   a. Install a lug nut onto brake drum and place nut at 12 o'clock position.
   b. Using an inch lb. torque wrench, measure amount of force needed to start rotation of drum. Record seal drag measurement.
4. To determine specified preload, add seal drag measurement recorded in previous step to required bearing preload of 1.3-4.3 inch lbs.
5. Tighten locknut slightly, then measure amount of force needed to start rotation of drum.
6. Continue to tighten locknut until preload determined in step 4 is reached.
7. After adjustment is completed, stake locknut to spindle with rounded chisel. **If splitting or cracking occurs after staking, replace locknut.**
8. Install grease cap and rear wheel, then lower vehicle.

## SPINDLE
### REPLACE

1. Raise and support vehicle, then remove brake drum.
2. Wire backing plate in position, then working from rear side of plate, remove spindle attaching nuts. **Do not confuse mounting stud nuts with spindle nuts. The spindle nuts are located underneath the vehicle on the inboard side of the trailing arm.**
3. Position backing plate, then install spindle. Tighten spindle attaching nuts.
4. Reinstall brake drum, then lower vehicle.

## AXLE ASSEMBLY
### REPLACE

1. Raise and support rear of vehicle so that struts are fully extended, then remove rear wheels.
2. Remove struts as outlined further on in this section.
3. Disconnect all brake lines that will interfere with axle removal.
4. Disconnect parking brake cable at backing plates, then remove equalizer and cables from axle.
5. If necessary, remove backing plates and spindles from trailing arms.
6. Remove axle assembly to body bracket pivot bolts, then lower axle assembly out of vehicle.
7. If axle bushings require replacement, proceed as follows:
   a. Using bushing remover tool No. D80L-1002-L or equivalent, press bushings out of trailing arm from inboard side.
   b. Lubricate new bushings with soapy water, then position on outboard edges of trailing arm. Ensure that marks on bushing face are aligned parallel with trailing arm axis, **Fig. 2.** Press bushings into trailing arms using tool mentioned in previous step. **To distinguish between right and left bushings, note the "F" and "R" marks molded into the bushing. When properly installed, the letters should be right side up with the "F" facing toward front of vehicle.**
8. Raise axle assembly, then align pivot bolt holes and install pivot bolts. Do not tighten bolts at this time.
9. If removed, install backing plates and spindles.
10. Install parking brake equalizer assembly on axle, then connect parking brake cables to parking brake levers at backing plates.
11. Connect brake lines at routing brackets and clip in place.
12. Install struts and rear wheels, then lower vehicle to allow suspension to reach normal ride height.
13. With vehicle on level surface, tighten pivot bolts.
14. After installation is completed, check rear suspension alignment as follows:
    a. Mark center of underbody at a position equidistant between left and right body bracket inboard mounting bolts.
    b. Measure distance from center mark obtained in previous step to centers of right and left strut lower mounting bolts.
    c. If measurement obtained on right and left sides are not within .200 inch, shift body brackets side to side to center suspension.
    d. After adjustment is completed, tighten upper body bracket bolts.

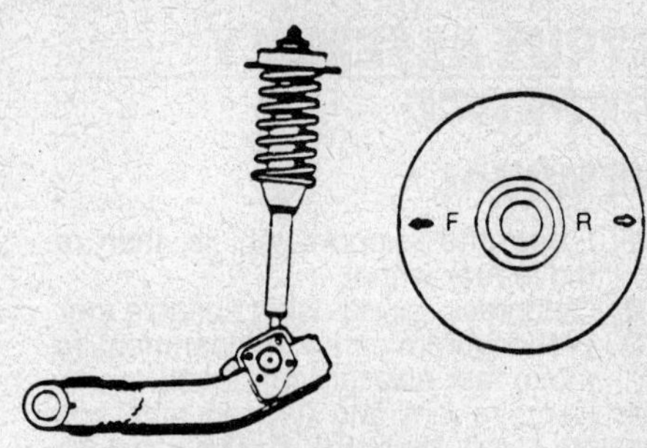


**Fig. 2 Positioning bushing on trailing arm**

## STRUT ASSEMBLY REPLACE

### REMOVAL

1. Raise and support vehicle, then remove rear wheel.
2. Compress spring using suitable tool.
3. Working from cargo compartment, remove rear quarter trim panel.
4. Remove jam and flanged nuts from strut rod, then the bushing washer and upper bushing, **Fig. 3.**
5. Remove lower mounting bolt, then pull strut downward and separate it from spring and seat insulator.
6. Remove lower bushing and jounce bumper seat from strut rod, then slide jounce bumper and shield off strut.
7. Inspect all bushings, bumpers and insulators for damage or deterioration. Replace components as necessary.

### INSTALLATION

1. Slide jounce bumper, shield, bumper seat and lower bushing onto strut rod.
2. If upper spring seat insulator requires replacement, install insulator onto upper end of spring so that end of coil seats firmly against step in insulator.
3. Position spring on strut, ensuring end of coil seats firmly against step in strut spring seat.
4. Compress spring, then working from wheel well area, guide upper end of strut rod into tower mounting hole.
5. Line up lower end of strut with mounting hole in trailing arm, then install lower mounting bolt several turns to hold strut in position.
6. Install upper bushing, bushing washer and flanged nut onto upper end of strut rod. Tighten flanged nut, then lock in position with jam nut.
7. Tighten lower mounting bolt, then remove spring compressor.
8. Install wheel, then lower vehicle.

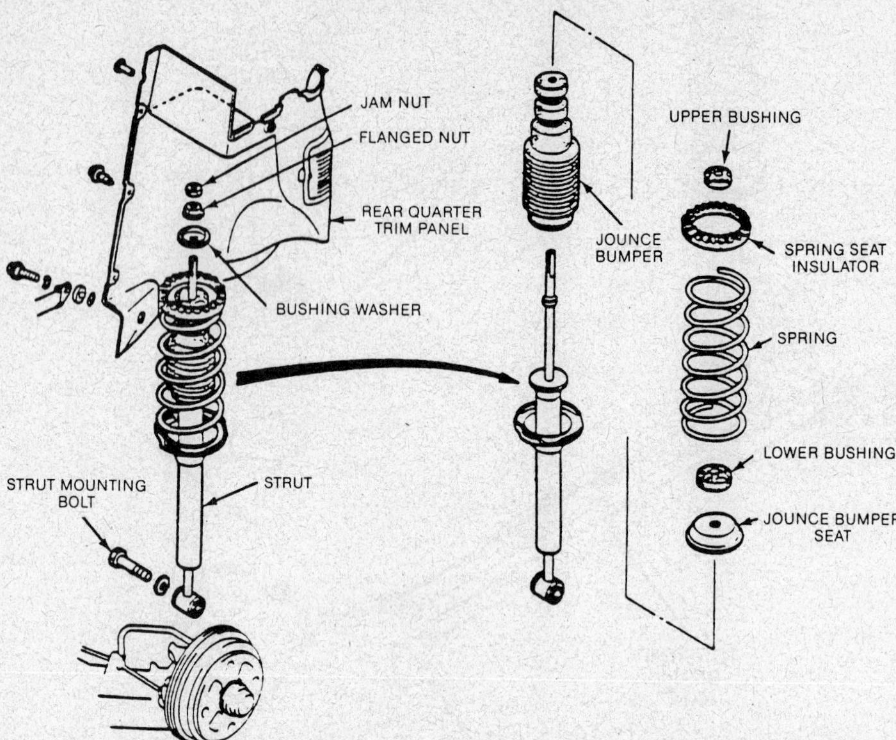


**Fig. 3 Disassembled view of strut assembly**

## TIGHTENING SPECIFICATIONS

***Torque specifications are for clean and lightly lubricated threads only. Dry or dirty threads produce increased friction which prevents accurate measurement of tightness.**

| Year | Component | Torque/ft. lbs. |
|---|---|---|
| 1989-92 | Body Bracket Lower Mounting Bolt | 69-87 |
| | Body Bracket Upper Mounting Bolt | 40-50 |
| | Brake Backing Plate | 32-45 |
| | Strut Lower Attaching Bolt | 40-50 |
| | Strut Rod Upper Nut | 12-18 |
| | Torsion Beam Pivot Bolt | 69-87 |
| | Wheel Spindle Support Nut | 32-45 |
| | Wheel Lug Nuts | 65-87 |

# Front Suspension & Steering

## INDEX



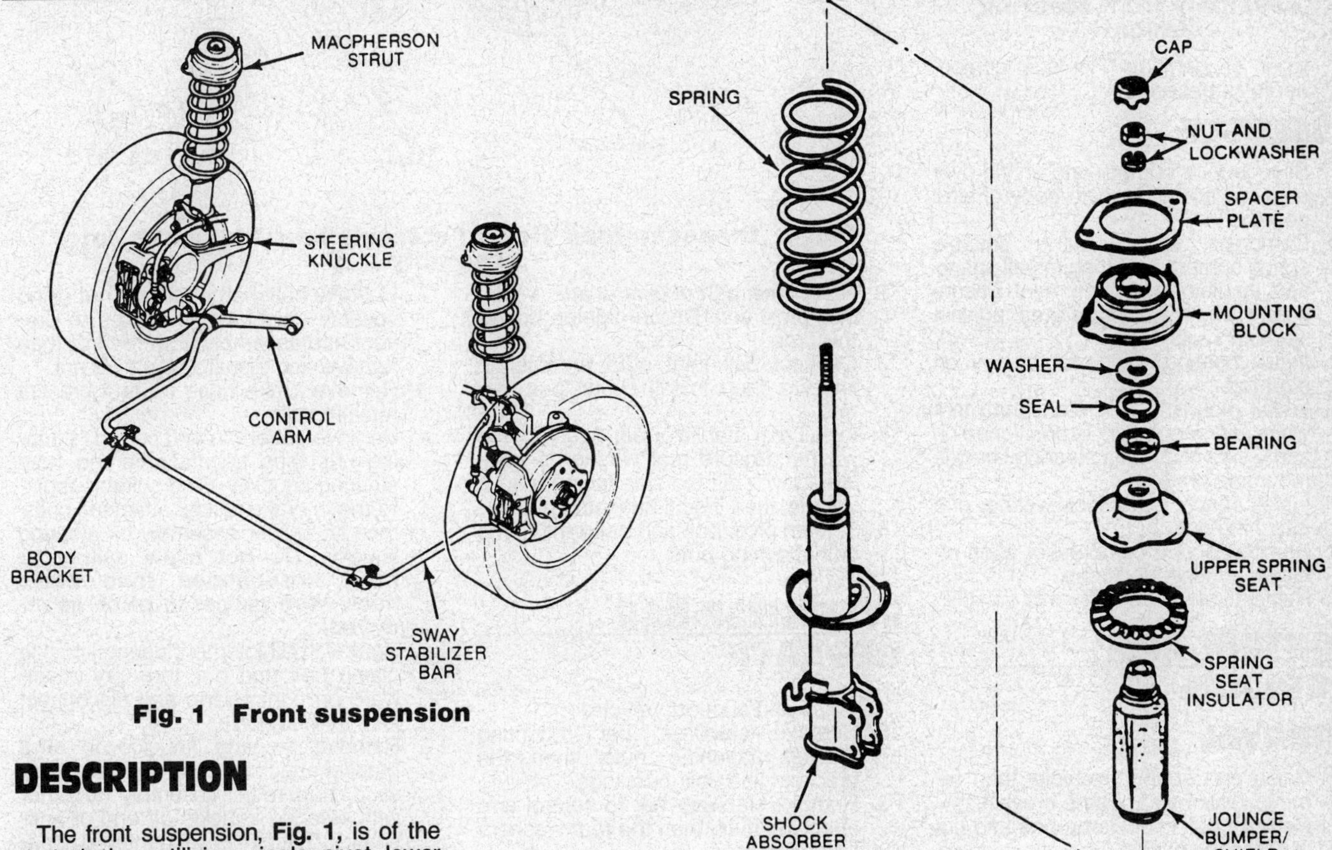


**Fig. 1 Front suspension**

**Fig. 2 Disassembled view of front strut assembly**

## DESCRIPTION

The front suspension, **Fig. 1**, is of the strut design, utilizing single pivot lower control arms with integral ball joints. The front wheels ride on forged steering knuckles, which are clamped to the ball joints on the lower end, and bolted to the lower bracket of the strut assembly on the upper end. A front stabilizer bar, connected to the lower control arms, is used to limit body sway during hard cornering and doubles as a trailing arm to maintain lower control arm alignment.

## STRUT ASSEMBLY REPLACE

### REMOVAL

1. Raise and support vehicle, ensuring strut is fully extended, then remove front wheel.
2. Remove brake line clip, then disengage brake line from strut assembly.
3. Remove strut to steering knuckle attaching bolts and nuts.
4. Working from engine compartment, remove nuts securing strut mounting block to shock tower.
5. Pull lower end of strut outward to disengage strut from steering knuckle, then lower strut assembly and remove from vehicle.

### INSTALLATION

1. Position strut, together with spacer plate, into shock tower, ensuring white alignment mark faces outward.
2. Install mounting block attaching nuts.
3. Connect steering knuckle to lower strut bracket, then install attaching bolts and nuts.
4. Position brake line in cutout in strut lower bracket, then install retaining clip.
5. Install front wheel, then lower vehicle.

## STRUT ASSEMBLY SERVICE

### DISASSEMBLY

1. Remove strut as outlined previously.
2. Compress spring using suitable spring compressor.
3. Pry out mounting block cap, then remove upper attaching nut and lockwasher, **Fig. 2.**
4. Remove spacer plate, mounting block, washer, seal and bearing from strut rod.
5. Remove upper spring seat, seat insulator and spring, then the jounce bumper and shield.
6. Inspect all components for excessive

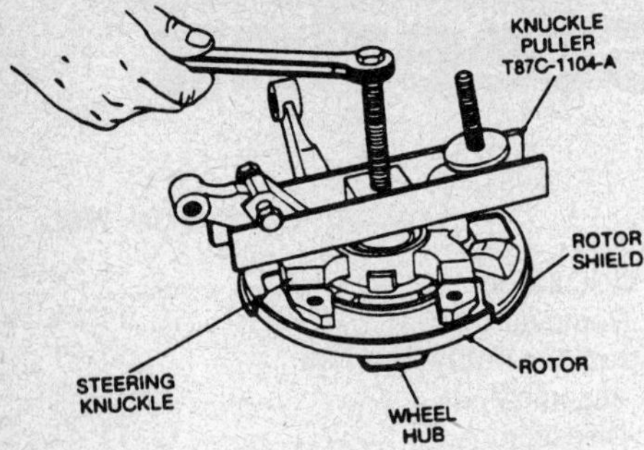


**Fig. 3 Separating hub/rotor assembly from steering knuckle**

wear or damage. Replace components as necessary.

### ASSEMBLY

1. Slide jounce bumper and shield over strut rod and onto main body of strut assembly.
2. Compress spring using suitable spring compressor, then install spring, seat insulator and upper seat. Ensure spring ends are positioned against steps in seats.
3. Install bearing, seal and washer on strut rod.
4. Install mounting block, ensuring that white alignment mark is positioned on same side of strut as steering knuckle mounting bracket.
5. Install spacer plate, lock washer and attaching nut.
6. Remove spring compressor, then install mounting block cap.
7. Reinstall strut assembly into vehicle.

## CONTROL ARM REPLACE

### REMOVAL

1. Raise and support vehicle, then remove pivot bolt at frame bracket.
2. Remove ball joint clamp bolt and nut at steering knuckle.
3. Remove stabilizer bar bushing retaining nut from rear of control arm, then remove bushing washer and bushing.
4. Pry ball joint stud out of steering knuckle, then disengage control arm from stabilizer bar and remove from vehicle.

### INSPECTION

1. Check control arm for cracks and pivot bushing for deterioration. If bushing requires replacement, remove and install bushing using suitable tools.
2. Check ball joint stud rotating torque with suitable torque wrench. Rotating torque should be 16-27 inch lbs. If rotating torque is not as specified, replace control arm.

### INSTALLATION

1. Install stabilizer bar into control arm. If removed, ensure front bushing washer is positioned with dished side facing front of vehicle.
2. Raise inner part of control arm and install pivot bolt. Do not tighten bolt at this time.
3. Connect ball joint stud to steering knuckle, then install clamp bolt and nut.
4. Install rear stabilizer bar bushing and washer. Ensure rear washer is positioned with dished side facing rear of vehicle, then install attaching nut.
5. Tighten pivot bolt and ball joint clamp bolt attaching nuts.

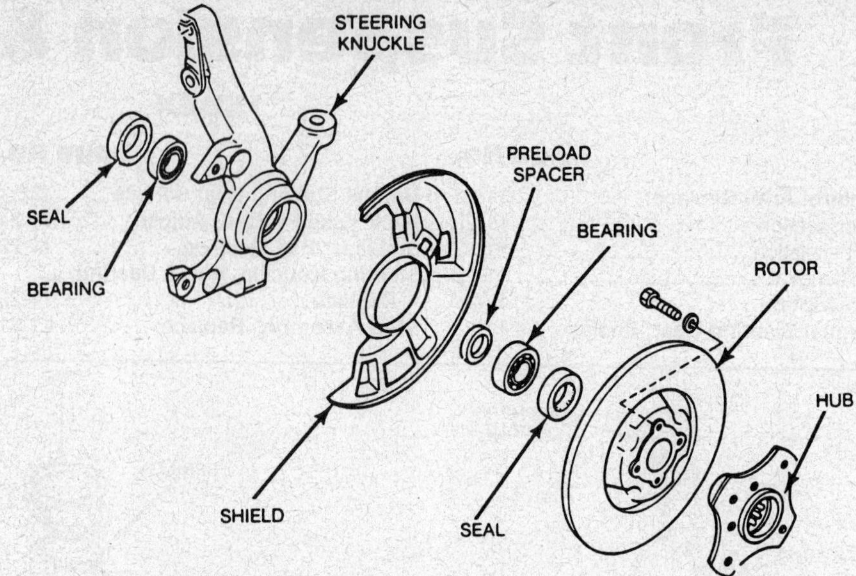


**Fig. 4 Disassembled view of steering knuckle & hub/rotor assembly**

## STABILIZER BAR REPLACE

1. Raise and support vehicle.
2. Remove stabilizer bar mounting bracket attaching nuts, then the brackets and split bushings.
3. Remove stabilizer bar to control arm attaching nuts, then the rear washers and bushings.
4. Pull stabilizer bar forward and remove from vehicle. If necessary, remove front bushings and washers from bar.
5. Reverse procedure to install, noting the following:
   a. When installing bushing washers, ensure that front washer is installed with dished side facing front of vehicle and rear washer is positioned with dished side facing rear of vehicle.
   b. When installing split bushings, ensure that split side faces forward and that bushings are positioned next to white locating marks on bar.

## STEERING KNUCKLE, HUB & BEARING REPLACE

1. Raise and support vehicle, then remove front wheel.
2. Unstake halfshaft attaching nut using suitable chisel, apply brakes to prevent hub assembly from turning, then remove and discard attaching nut.
3. Remove brake hose to strut bracket retaining clip.
4. Remove cotter pin and tie rod attaching nut, then separate tie rod from steering knuckle using suitable tool.
5. Remove brake caliper attaching bolts, then lift caliper assembly off steering knuckle. **Do not allow caliper to hang unsupported from brake hose. Wire caliper in place as required.**
6. Remove ball joint to steering knuckle clamp bolt and nut, then pry downward on control arm and disconnect joint from knuckle.
7. Remove steering knuckle to strut bracket attaching bolts and nuts, then slide hub/rotor assembly together with steering knuckle off end of halfshaft. If difficulty is encountered separating hub from halfshaft, tap end of shaft with plastic mallet to facilitate removal.
8. Separate hub/rotor assembly from steering knuckle using tool shown in **Fig. 3.**
9. Remove bearing preload spacer from hub, **Fig. 4. The spacer is pre-selected to yield correct bearing preload. Save spacer to use during reassembly.**
10. Clamp hub/rotor assembly in soft jaw vise, scribe alignment marks on hub and rotor, then remove hub to rotor attaching bolts and separate rotor from hub.
11. Using suitable bearing remover, press hub shaft from outer bearing, then remove outer grease seal from hub.
12. Using suitable seal remover, pry inner grease seal from steering knuckle bore, then remove inner bearing.
13. Inspect bearings, hub, steering knuckle and dust shield for damage or excessive wear. Replace components

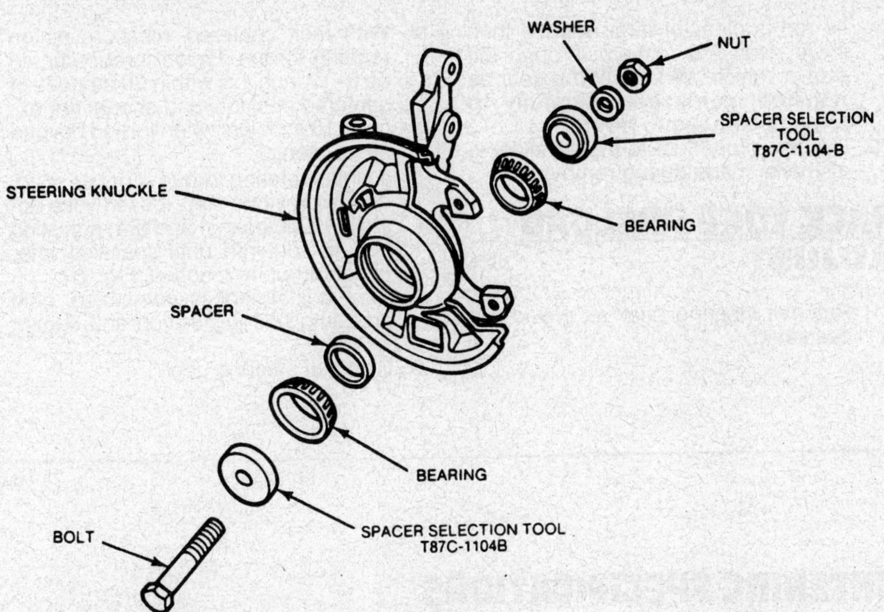


**Fig. 5 Bearing preload spacer selection tool installation**

| Stamped mark | Thickness |
|---|---|
| 1 | 6.285 mm (0.2474 in) |
| 2 | 6.325 mm (0.2490 in) |
| 3 | 6.365 mm (0.2506 in) |
| 4 | 6.405 mm (0.2522 in) |
| 5 | 6.445 mm (0.2538 in) |
| 6 | 6.485 mm (0.2554 in) |
| 7 | 6.525 mm (0.2570 in) |
| 8 | 6.565 mm (0.2586 in) |
| 9 | 6.605 mm (0.2602 in) |
| 10 | 6.645 mm (0.2618 in) |
| 11 | 6.685 mm (0.2634 in) |
| 12 | 6.725 mm (0.2650 in) |
| 13 | 6.765 mm (0.2666 in) |
| 14 | 6.805 mm (0.2682 in) |
| 15 | 6.845 mm (0.2698 in) |
| 16 | 6.885 mm (0.2714 in) |
| 17 | 6.925 mm (0.2730 in) |
| 18 | 6.965 mm (0.2746 in) |
| 19 | 7.005 mm (0.2762 in) |
| 20 | 7.045 mm (0.2778 in) |
| 21 | 7.085 mm (0.2794 in) |

**Fig. 6 Bearing preload spacer identification chart**

as necessary.

14. If original bearings and steering knuckle are being used, proceed to step 15. If bearings or steering knuckle require replacement, proceed as follows to select proper bearing preload spacer:
    a. Drive new inner and outer bearing races into steering knuckle using suitable tools.
    b. Lubricate races and new bearings with engine oil, then install bearings into steering knuckle.
    c. Install spacer selection tool kit T87C-1104-B, original spacer and hardware shown in **Fig. 5** onto steering knuckle, then clamp steering knuckle in soft jaw vise.
    d. Tighten center bolt in increments. After bolt is tightened to specification, remove assembly from vise and rotate steering knuckle to seat bearings.
    e. Again clamp steering knuckle in vise, then measure the amount of torque necessary to start rotation of center bolt using an inch lb. torque wrench.
    f. If torque reading is 2.2-10.4 inch lbs., spacer is correct thickness. If torque reading is less than 2.2 inch lbs., a thinner spacer must be used. If torque reading is greater than 10.4 inch lbs., a thicker spacer must be used. Twenty one spacers of various thicknesses are available for service. Each spacer has a number stamped on it for identification purposes, **Fig. 6.** Changing the spacer by one number, either up or down, will result in a 1.7-3.5 inch lb. change in bearing preload.
15. Pack bearings and hub with suitable high temperature grease, then install inner bearing into steering knuckle.
16. Lubricate seal lip, then install new inner seal using suitable tool.
17. Place original bearing preload spacer,

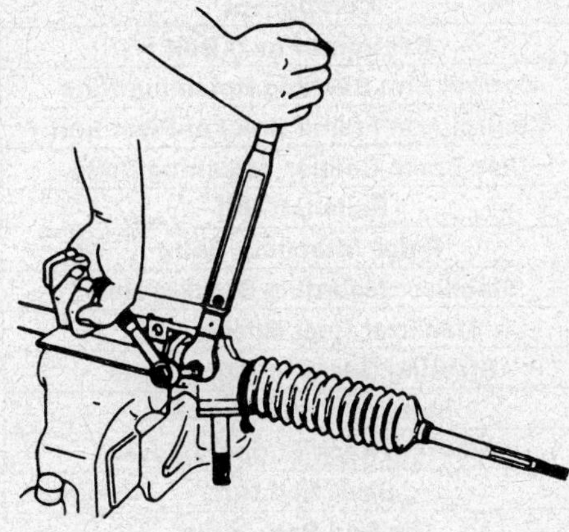

**Fig. 7 Adjusting rack yoke preload**

or spacer selected in step 14, into steering knuckle.

18. Lubricate seal lip, then install outer wheel bearing and new outer seal into knuckle.
19. Position rotor onto hub, aligning marks made during disassembly, then install attaching bolts.
20. Place hub/rotor assembly into steering knuckle bore, then press assembly fully into knuckle using suitable tools.
21. Follow steps 1 through 7 in reverse order to complete installation and note the following:
    a. Apply a thin coat of grease to halfshaft splines before installing steering knuckle and hub/rotor assembly.
    b. When installing new halfshaft attaching nut, apply brakes to prevent hub assembly from turning. Stake nut into groove on halfshaft after tightening.

c. Tighten tie rod end to steering knuckle attaching nut, then install new cotter pin. **If holes in attaching nut do not line up with hole in ball stud, tighten nut as required until cotter pin can be installed. Never loosen nut when installing cotter pin.**

## MANUAL STEERING GEAR

### REPLACE

1. Disconnect battery cables and remove battery.
2. Scribe alignment marks on steering column lower universal joint and steering gear pinion shaft, then remove steering column as follows:
    a. Working from underneath steering column, remove instrument panel brace and air duct.
    b. Remove upper and lower steering column covers, release harness clip, then disconnect harness connectors from back of combination switch.
    c. Remove ignition switch as outlined in the "Electrical Section."
    d. Remove steering column upper mounting bracket to instrument panel attaching nuts, then lower column.
    e. Scribe alignment marks on column shaft and intermediate shaft upper universal joint, then remove clamp screw from joint.
    f. Remove steering column hinge bracket to pedal support attaching nuts, then pull steering column rearward and remove from vehicle.

3. Cut plastic tie strap securing steering column boot to steering gear.
4. Raise and support vehicle, then remove front wheels.
5. Remove tie rod to steering knuckle attaching nuts, then separate tie rods from knuckle.
6. Remove catalytic converter.
7. Remove tie rod splash shield from right inner fender.
8. Remove steering gear mounting bolts and lower gear until free from steering column boot.
9. Slide steering gear to the right until left tie rod is clear of inner fender, then lower gear and remove through left side of vehicle. **When sliding gear as required, guide gear carefully to prevent damage to boots.**
10. Reverse procedure to install, aligning all marks made during removal.

## RACK YOKE PRELOAD ADJUST

1. Remove steering gear as previously described.
2. With rack centered, measure pinion rotating torque. Pinion torque should be 8-12 inch lbs. within 90 degrees of centered position, and should not exceed 13 inch lbs. when turned beyond 90° of center.
3. If pinion rotating torque is not as specified in previous step, loosen yoke adjusting bolt locknut and turn adjusting bolt as required until specified rotational torque is reached, **Fig. 7.**
4. After adjustment is completed, hold adjusting bolt in position and tighten locknut.
5. Reinstall steering gear.

## TIGHTENING SPECIFICATIONS

***Torque specifications are for clean and lightly lubricated threads only. Dry or dirty threads produce increased friction which prevents accurate measurement of tightness.**

| Year | Component | Torque/ft. lbs. |
|---|---|---|
| 1989-92 | Ball Joint Pinch Bolt | 32-40 |
| | Control Arm Bushing Retaining Nuts | 47-57 |
| | Control Arm Frame Bracket Pivot Bolt | 32-40 |
| | Disc Brake Caliper Attaching Bolts | 29-36 |
| | Halfshaft Nut | 116-174 |
| | Rotor Attaching Bolts | 33-40 |
| | Stabilizer Mounting Bracket Nuts | 40-50 |
| | Stabilizer Rear Bushing Nut | 43-52 |
| | Steering Gear Mounting Bolts | 23-34 |
| | Steering Knuckle Bolts | 69-86 |
| | Steering Rack Support Cover | 29-43 |
| | Strut Rod Nut | 40-50 |
| | Tie Rod Ball Joints | 43-58 |
| | Tie Rod End Nut | 22-33 |
| | Upper Mounting Block Bolts | 22-27 |
| | Wheel Lug Nuts | 65-87 |

# Wheel Alignment

## INDEX



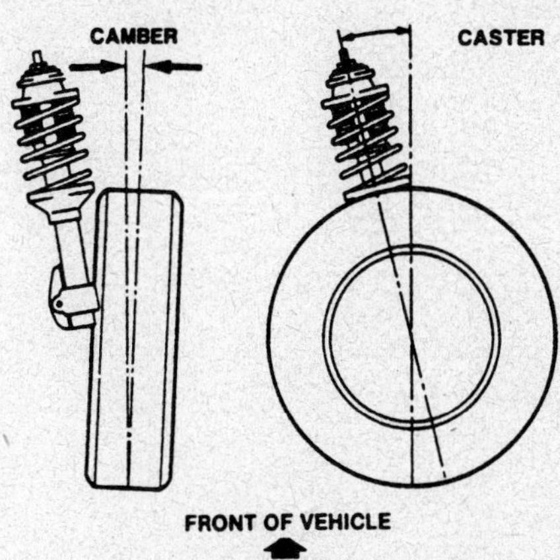


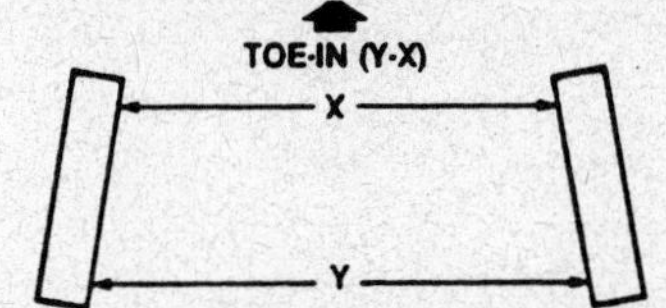


**Fig. 1 Front wheel alignment settings**

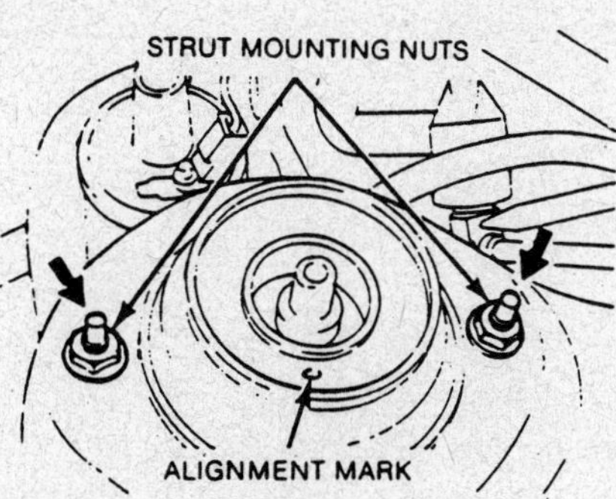


**Fig. 2 Front strut camber alignment mark**

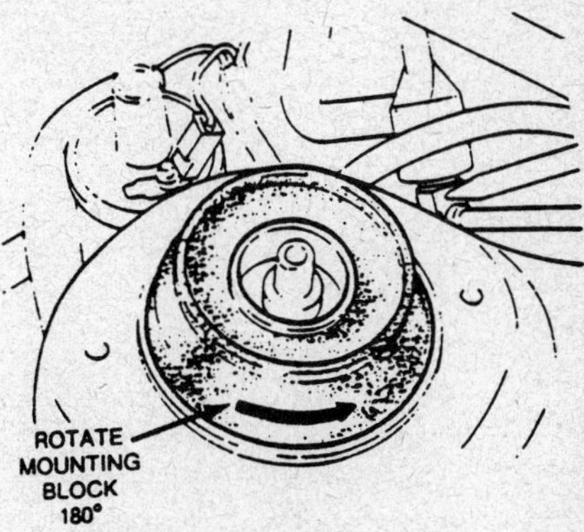


**Fig. 3 Front camber adjustment**

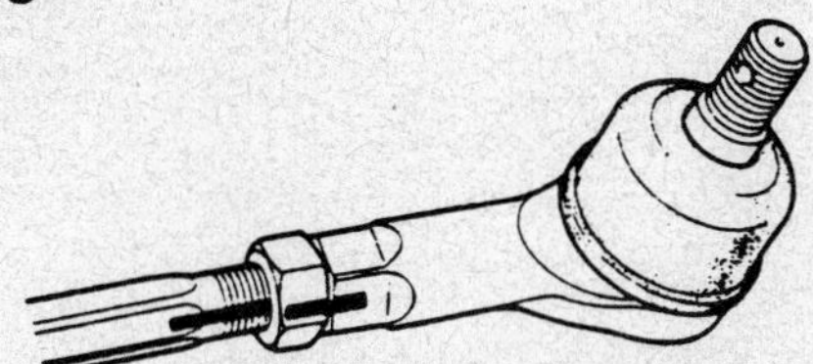

**Fig. 4 Marking position of tie rod, tie rod end & jam nut**

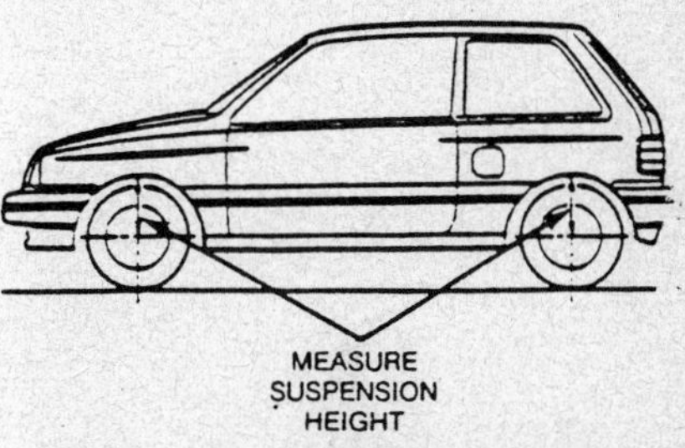


**Fig. 5 Suspension height measurement**

## FRONT WHEEL ALIGNMENT

### CASTER

Caster is not adjustable, **Fig. 1.** If caster angles are not within specification, check for damaged or bent suspension components, deteriorated bushings, or distorted body mounting points.

### CAMBER

Camber angle, **Fig. 1,** is controlled by the position of the strut mounting block in the shock tower. The mounting block can be positioned in the tower in two ways, resulting in a camber variation of approximately 1/2°. If the camber setting has not been changed previously, the white alignment mark on the mounting block will be positioned on the outboard side of the strut assembly, **Fig. 2.** Changing the position of the alignment mark 180° will increase camber angle approximately 1/2°, **Fig. 3.** If the alignment mark is already positioned inboard of the strut, changing the mounting block position can only result in camber being reduced by approximately 1/2°. To adjust camber setting, proceed as follows:

1. Raise and support vehicle and remove front wheels.
2. Remove upper strut attaching nuts.
3. Lower strut sufficiently so that mounting studs clear tower, then rotate mounting block 180° as necessary.
4. Reposition strut in tower, then install attaching nuts and **torque** to 32 to 45 ft. lbs.

### TOE-IN

1. Ensure that tires are properly inflated, then position vehicle on suitable alignment rack.
2. Bounce vehicle several times to normalize ride height, then check toe setting. If toe setting is not within specification, proceed to next step.
3. Mark relationship between tie rods, tie rod ends and jam nuts, then loosen tie rod boot clamps to prevent twisting or damage to boots, **Fig. 4.**
4. Adjust toe-in by turning **both** tie rods in or out an equal amount until toe setting is within specification.
5. After adjustment is completed, tighten jam nuts and boot clamps.

## REAR WHEEL ALIGNMENT

Rear camber and toe-in are determined by the configuration of the trailing arms on the torsion beam rear axle. No provision for adjustment is provided. The only rear suspension adjustment possible is the lateral positioning of the rear axle. This adjustment should only be performed if replacing the rear axle assembly. Refer to "Axle Assembly, Replace" procedure in

"Rear Axle & Suspension" section for adjustment procedure.

## SUSPENSION HEIGHT

Prior to checking suspension height, remove heavy items from vehicle, such as tool boxes etc. Suspension height is measured from ground to the fender cut out above the center of the wheel and tire assembly, **Fig. 5.** This measurement should be performed at all four wheels. Readings from side to side and front to rear should not vary by more than .4 inch. **It should be noted that uneven tire wear will increase the variance in the measurements and should be taken into consideration. If variance is more than .4 inch, check springs and suspension components for wear and damage.**

# AIR CONDITIONING

## TABLE OF CONTENTS



# System Testing

## INDEX



## GENERAL PRECAUTIONS

### SAFETY

The freon refrigerant used in car A/C systems is also known as R-12. It is colorless and odorless both as a gas and a liquid. Since it boils (vaporizes) at −21.7°F, it will usually be in a vapor state when being handled in a repair shop. But if a portion of the liquid coolant should come in contact with the hands or face, note that its temperature momentarily will be at least 22° below zero.

Protective goggles should be worn when opening any refrigerant lines. If liquid coolant does touch the eyes, bathe the eyes quickly in cold water. Then apply a bland disinfectant oil to the eyes. See an eye doctor.

When checking a system for leaks with a torch type leak detector, do not breathe the vapors coming from the flame. Do not discharge refrigerant in the area of a live flame. A poisonous phosgene gas is produced when R-12 is burned. While the small amount of this gas produced by a leak detector is not harmful unless inhaled directly at the flame, the quantity of refrigerant released into the air when a system is purged can be extremely dangerous if allowed to come in contact with an open flame. Thus, when purging a system, be sure that the discharge hose is routed to a well ventilated place where no flame is present. Under these conditions the refrigerant will be quickly dissipated into the surrounding air.

Never allow the temperature of refrigerant drums to exceed 125°F. The resultant increase in temperature will cause a corresponding increase in pressure which may cause the safety plug to release or the drum to burst.

If it is necessary to heat a drum of refrigerant when charging a system, the drum should be placed in water that is no hotter than 125°F. Never use a blowtorch, or other open flame. If possible, a pressure release mechanism should be attached before the drum is heated.

### CLEANLINESS

Air conditioning systems are extremely sensitive to moisture and dirt. The importance of clean working conditions is extremely important, as the smallest particle of foreign matter in an air conditioning system will contaminate the refrigerant, causing rust, ice or damage to the compressor. For this reason, all replacement parts are sold in vacuum sealed containers and should not be opened until they are to be installed in the system. If, for any reason, a part has been removed from its container for any length of time, the part must be completely flushed using only R-12 to remove any dust or moisture that may have accumulated during storage. In cases of collision repairs where the system has been open for any length of time, the entire system must be purged completely and a new receiver-drier must be installed because the element of the existing unit will have become saturated and unable to remove any moisture from the system once the system is recharged.

When making gauge connections, purge the gauge lines first by cracking the charging valve and allowing a small amount of refrigerant to flow through the lines, then connect the lines immediately.

Cleanliness is especially important when servicing compressors because of the very close tolerances used in these units. Consequently, repairs to the compressor itself should not be attempted unless all proper tools are at hand and a virtually spotless work area is provided.

### GENERAL SERVICE

Use care when disconnecting or connecting refrigerant lines; always use a backup wrench and be careful not to overtighten any connection. Overtightening may result in a line or flare seat distortion and a system leak.

When making pressure checks on systems having service valves, be sure valve is in the intermediate position. If turned in too far, the hose connection will be closed, a position used for isolating the compressor. When closing the gauge port, do not overtighten the valve or damage to the seat will result.

After disconnecting gauge lines, check the valve areas to be sure service valves are correctly seated and schraeder valves, if used, are not leaking.

## EXERCISE SYSTEM

An important fact most car owners ignore is that the A/C system must be used periodically. Car manufacturers caution that when the air conditioner is not used regularly, particularly during cold months, it should be turned on for a few minutes once every two or three weeks while the engine is running. This keeps the system in good operating condition.

Checking out the system for the effects of disuse before the onset of summer is one of the most important aspects of A/C system servicing.

First clean out the condenser core, mounted in most cases at the front of the vehicle's radiator. All obstructions, such as leaves, bugs, and dirt, must be removed, as they will reduce heat transfer and impair the efficiency of the system. Make sure the space between the condenser and the radiator also is free of foreign matter.

Ensure the evaporator water drain is open. The evaporator cools and dehumidifies the air before it enters the car.

# PERFORMANCE TEST

## EXCEPT CAPRI, FESTIVA, PROBE, SCORPIO, TRACER, XR4Ti & 1991 ESCORT

Refrigerant system problems are diagnosed by checking refrigerant pressures and clutch cycle rate and times. Compare pressures and cycle time to charts shown in **Fig. 1 and 2.** Conditional requirements for refrigerant system tests must be satisfied to obtain accurate pressure readings. If findings do not fall between lines on respective charts, refer to **Fig. 3**, to determine specific cause of improper readings.

After necessary repairs have been performed, take pressure readings while meeting conditional requirements to ensure problem has been corrected.

Visual inspection of the system may determine problems with the refrigerant system. By making a visual inspection, some of the following problems can be diagnosed: obstructed air passages, broken belts, disconnected or broken wires, loose or broken mounting brackets and refrigerant leaks.

A refrigerant leak will usually appear as an oily residue at the leakage point in the system.

## CAPRI

1. Connect manifold gauge set to system.
2. Turn A/C system on and operate blower motor at high speed with engine running at 2000 RPM.
3. Open all windows and move recirc/fresh air lever to Recirc position.
4. Position one thermometer in center console duct and another thermometer in blower inlet under righthand side of dash.
5. Allow A/C system to stabilize for 5-10 minutes, then note high pressure gauge reading which should be 199-220 psi. If necessary, attempt to raise excessively low pressure by covering the condenser or lower high pressure by spraying water through condenser. If pressure cannot be brought within specifications, record stabilized pressure and perform necessary system diagnosis.

## FESTIVA

1. Connect manifold gauge set to system.
2. Turn A/C system on and operate blower motor at high speed with engine running at 2000 RPM.
3. Open all windows and move recirc/fresh air lever to Recirc position.
4. Position one thermometer in center console duct and another thermometer in blower inlet under righthand side of dash.
5. Measure and record relative humidity at blower inlet using a psycrometer.
6. Allow A/C system to stabilize for 5-10 minutes, then note high pressure gauge reading which should be 199-220 psi. If necessary, attempt to raise excessively low pressure by covering the condenser or lower high pressure by spraying water through condenser. If pressure cannot be brought within specifications, record stabilized pressure and perform necessary system diagnosis.
7. Determine difference in temperatures at air inlet and center console duct and compare temperature difference to relative humidity on graph, **Fig. 4.** If intersection of lines on graph are within hatched lines, the A/C system is operating satisfactorily.

## PROBE

1. Connect manifold gauge set to system.
2. Start and run engine at 2000 RPM, then turn A/C system On.
3. Set temperature control to cool and blower motor to high.
4. If compressor clutch does not engage, jumper battery power to green/black wire at clutch connector.
5. Wait until air conditioning system stabilizes, then check readings at high and low pressure gauges.
6. Normal reading for high pressure gauge should be 199-220 psi. Normal reading for low pressure gauge should be 19-21 psi. for 1989-90 models or 28-43 psi. for 1991 models.
7. If pressure is not within specifications, record stabilized pressure and perform necessary system diagnosis.

## 1989 TRACER

### No Cooling Or Insufficient Cooling

1. Check A/C drive belt for proper tension. If A/C belt has proper tension, proceed to step 2. If not adjust as necessary.
2. Ensure A/C compressor rotates freely. If compressor rotates freely, proceed to step 3. If not, repair or replace as necessary.
3. With an A/C manifold set, check both high and low side pressures. If pressures are not correct, proceed to step 4. If both pressures are correct, proceed to step 5.
4. Check A/C system for leaks with a pump style halogen leak detector and repair or replace any leaking components. If no leaks are found, proceed to step 5.
5. Check for water in the system. If there is water, the receiver could be oversaturated causing an obstruction in refrigerant circulation. If water is found, replace receiver/drier and compressor, then recharge system. If no water is found, proceed to step 6.
6. If A/C manifold set reads 245kPa on low pressure side and 2257kPa on high pressure side and low pressure side piping is not cold when touched, air could be in the system. If air is found in the system, bleed down system and recharge. If no air is found in the system, proceed to step 7.
7. Using A/C manifold set check that refrigerant is circulating properly throughout the system. If refrigerant is not circulating properly, replace thermostatic expansion valve. If refrigerant is circulating properly, proceed to step 8.
8. Check for proper air distribution through evaporator and air ducts. If air is not circulating properly, repair as required. If air is circulating properly, proceed to step 9.
9. Inspect magnetic clutch, wiring fuses and circuit breaker for proper operation. Repair and replace as necessary. If no problems are found, proceed to step 10.
10. Jump battery voltage to magnetic clutch black/white terminal. If magnetic clutch fails to operate, replace clutch. If clutch operates, proceed to step 11.
11. With A/C and blower on, check if there is 12 volts at magnetic clutch black/white lead. If there is not 12 volts, check ground connection of magnetic clutch and repair as required. If there is 12 volts, proceed to step 12.
12. With A/C and blower on, check for 12 volts at A/C cut relay black/white terminal. If there is not 12 volts, locate and repair open circuit between A/C cut relay and magnetic clutch. If there is 12 volts, proceed to step 13.
13. With A/C off, check for continuity between A/C cut relay red/black and yellow/green terminals. If there is no continuity, replace A/C cut relay. If there is continuity, proceed to step 14.
14. With A/C and blower on, check for 12 volts at A/C cut relay yellow/green terminal. If there is not 12 volts, locate and repair open or short in wiring harness between A/C cut relay and main relay. If there is 12 volts, proceed to step 15.
15. With A/C off, check for continuity between A/C cut relay yellow/green terminal and ground. If there is no continuity, locate and repair open or short in wiring harness between A/C cut relay red/black terminal and ECA 1S terminal. If there is continuity, proceed to step 16.
16. With A/C and blower on, check for 12 volts at A/C cut relay black/green terminal. If there is not 12 volts, replace A/C cut relay. If there is 12 volts, proceed to step 17.
17. With A/C off, check for continuity between refrigerant pressure switch black/green terminals. If there is no continuity, replace refrigerant pressure switch. If there is continuity, proceed to step 18.
18. With A/C off, check for continuity green and black/green terminals on

**IMPORTANT — TEST REQUIREMENTS**

The following test conditions must be established to obtain accurate clutch cycle rate and cycle time readings:

- Run engine at 1500 rpm for 10 minutes.
- Operate A/C system on max A/C (recirculating air).
- Run blower at max speed.
- Stabilize in car temperature @ 70°F to 80°F (21°C to 22°C).

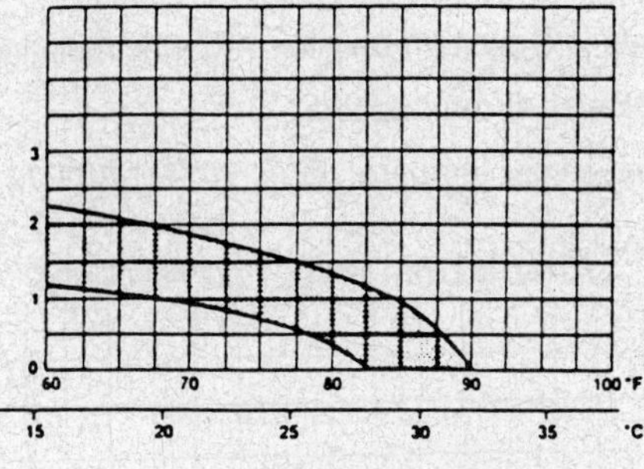


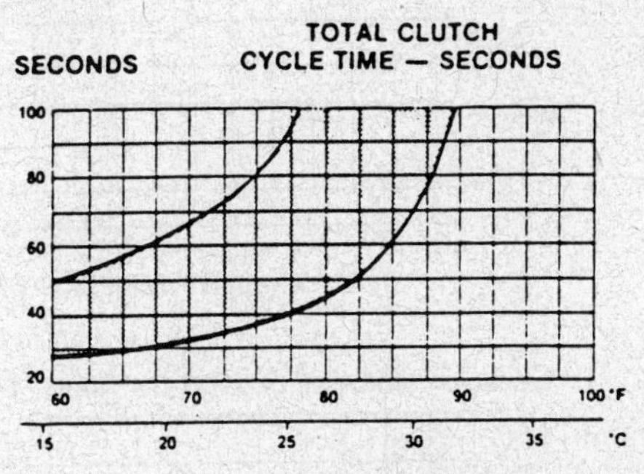


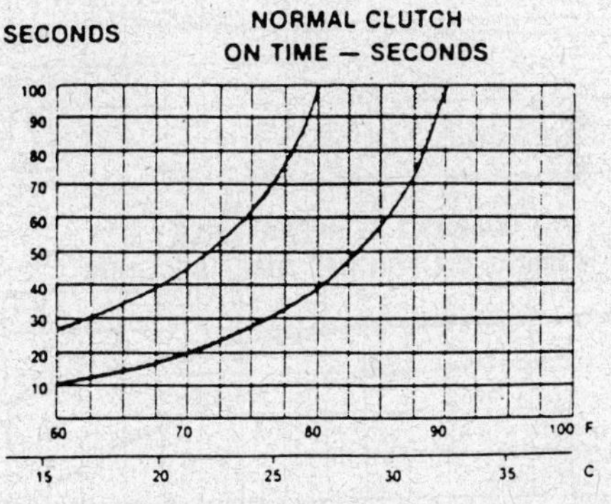


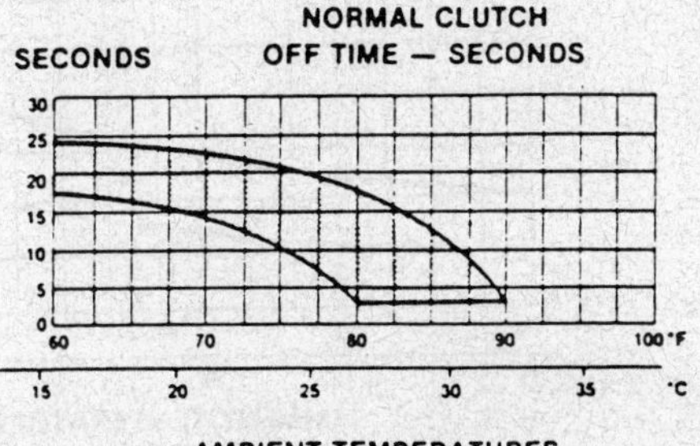


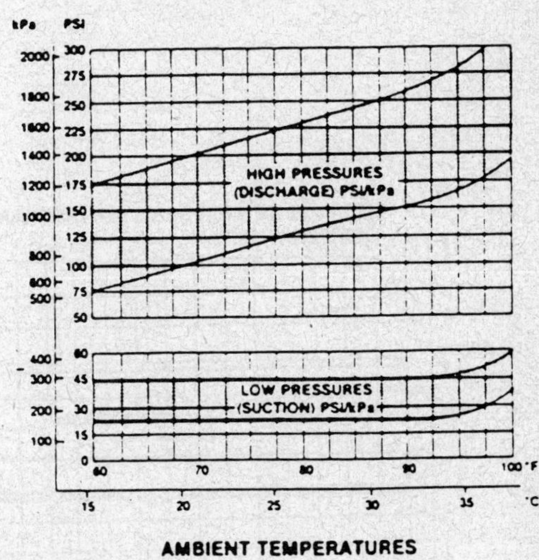


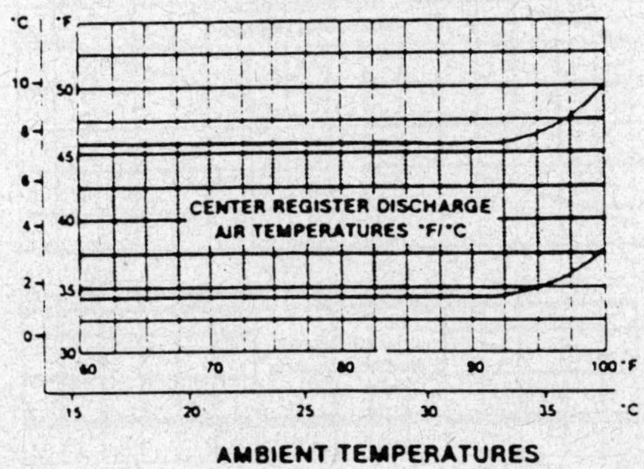


**Fig. 1 Refrigerant pressure & temperature charts. Continental, Cougar, Escort, Mark VII, Mustang, Sable, Taurus, Tempo, Topaz & Thunderbird**

**IMPORTANT — TEST REQUIREMENTS**

The following test conditions must be established to obtain accurate clutch cycle rate and cycle time readings:

- Run engine at 1500 rpm for 10 minutes.
- Operate A/C system on max A/C (recirculating air).
- Run blower at max speed.
- Stabilize in car temperature @ 70°F to 80°F (21°C to 22°C).

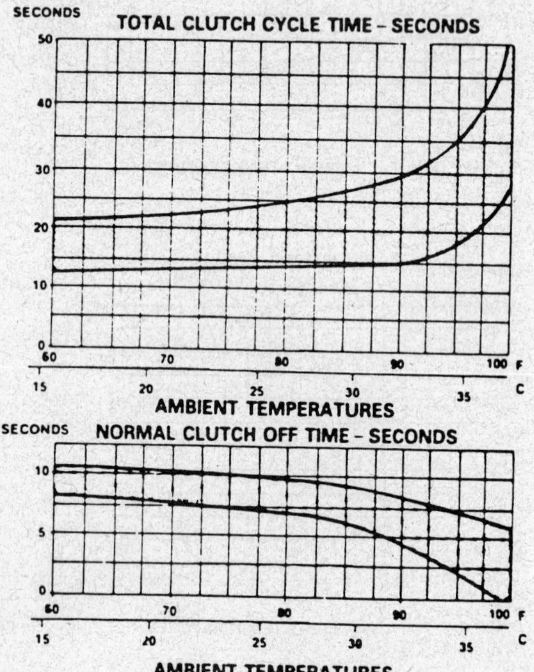

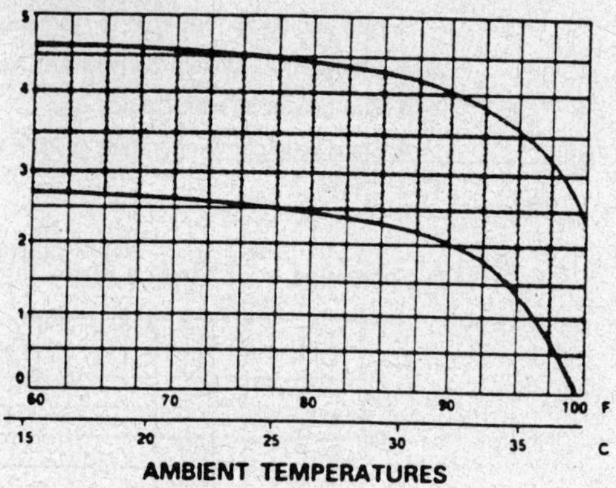


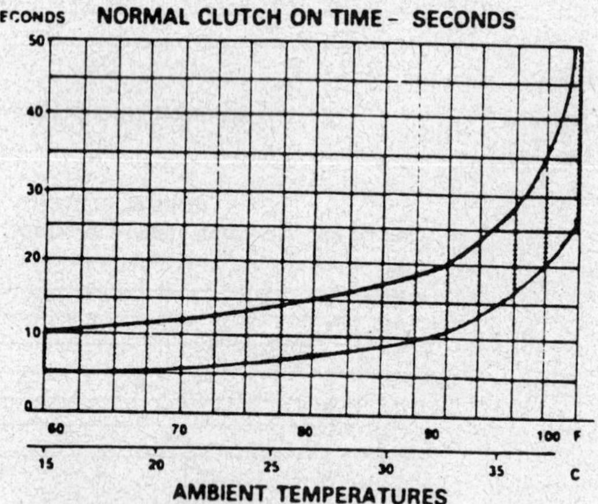


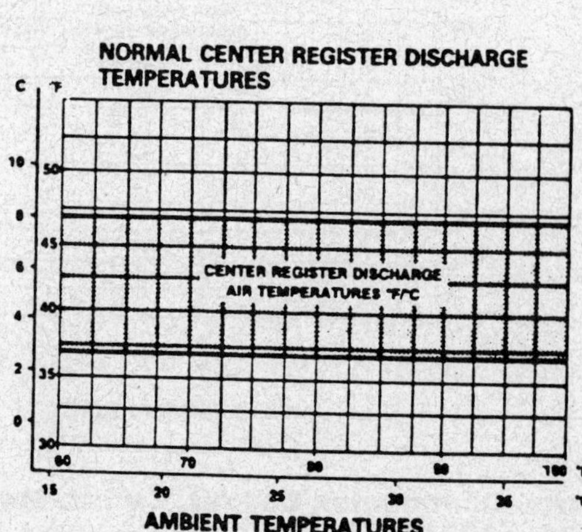


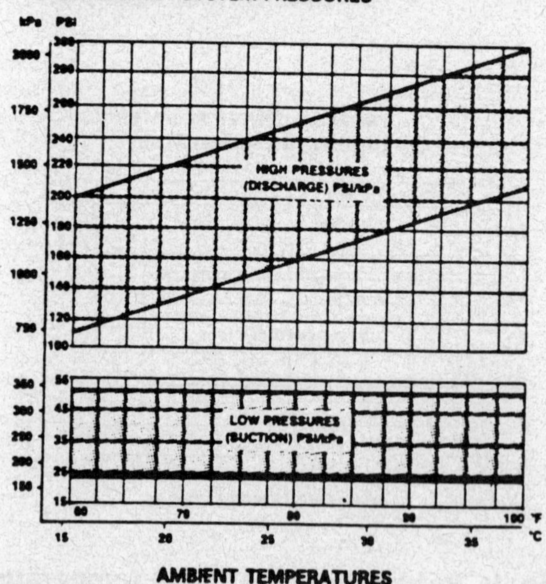


**Fig. 2 Refrigerant pressure & temperature charts. Crown Victoria, Grand Marquis & Town Car**

**NOTE: System test requirements must be met to obtain accurate test readings for evaluation. Refer to the normal refrigerant system pressure/temperature and the normal clutch cycle ratio and times charts.**

| High (Discharge) Pressure | Low (Suction) Pressure | Clutch Cycle Time | | | Component — Causes |
|---|---|---|---|---|---|
| | | Rate | On | Off | |
| High | High | Continuous Run | | | Condenser — Inadequate Airflow |
| High | Normal to High | | | | Engine Overheating |
| Normal to High | Normal | | | | Air in Refrigerant<br>Refrigerant Overcharge (a)<br>Humidity or Ambient Temp Very High (b) |
| Normal | High | | | | Fixed Orifice Tube — Missing<br>O Rings Leaking/Missing |
| Normal | High | Slow | Long | Long | Clutch Cycling Switch — High Cut In |
| Normal | Normal | Slow or No Cycle | Long or Continuous | Normal or No Cycle | Moisture in Refrigerant System<br>Excessive Refrigerant Oil |
| | | Fast | Short | Short | Clutch Cycling Switch — Low Cut In or High Cut Out |
| Normal | Low | Slow | Long | Long | Clutch Cycling Switch — Low Cut Out |
| Normal to Low | High | Continuous Run | | | Compressor — Low Performance |
| Normal to Low | Normal to High | | | | A/C Suction Line — Partially Restricted or Plugged (c) |
| Normal to Low | Normal | Fast | Short | Normal | Evaporator — Restricted Airflow |
| | | | Short to Very Short | Normal to Long | Condenser fixed orifice Tube or A/C Liquid Line — Partically Restricted or Plugged |
| | | | Short to Very Short | Short to Very Short | Low Refrigerant Charge |
| | | | Short to Very Short | Long | Evaporator Core — Partially Restricted or Plugged |
| Normal to Low | Low | Continuous Run | | | A/C Suction Line — Partially Restricted or Plugged (d)<br>Clutch Cycling Switch — Sticking Closed |
| Low | Normal | Very Fast | Very Short | Very Short | Clutch Cycling Switch — Cycling Range Too Close |
| Erratic Operation or Compressor Not Running | | — | — | — | Clutch Cycling Switch — Dirty Contacts or Sticking Open<br>Poor Connection at A/C Clutch Connector or Clutch Cycling Switch Connector<br>A/C Electrical Circuit Erratic |

Additional Possible Cause Components Associated with Inadequate Compressor Operation

- Compressor Drive Belt — Loose
- Compressor Clutch — Slipping
- Clutch Coil Open — Shorted or Loose Mounting
- Control Assembly Switch — Dirty Contacts or Sticking Open
- Clutch Wiring Circuit — High Resistance Open or Blown Fuse

Additional Possible Cause Components Associated with a Damaged Compressor

- Compressor Clutch — Seized
- Clutch Cycling Switch — Sticking Closed
- Suction Accumulator Drier — Refrigerant Oil Bleed Hole Plugged
- Refrigerant Leaks

(a) Compressor may make noise on initial run. This is slugging condition caused by excessive liquid refrigerant.
(b) Compressor clutch may not cycle in ambient temperatures above 80°F depending on humidity conditions.
(c) Low pressure reading will be normal to high if pressure is taken at accumulator and if restriction is downstream of service access valve.
(d) Low pressure reading will be low if pressure is taken near the compressor and restriction is upstream of service access valve.

**Fig. 3 Refrigerant system pressure evaluation chart**

the thermostatic switch. If there is no continuity, replace thermostatic switch. If there is continuity, proceed to step 19.

19. With A/C and blower on, check for 12 volts A/C relay No. 3 green terminal. If there are 12 volts, locate and repair open or short in wiring harness between A/C relay No. 3 and A/C cut relay. If there is not 12 volts, proceed to step 20.
20. With A/C and blower on, check for 12 volts at A/C relay No. 3 blue/black terminal. If there is not 12 volts, locate and repair open or short in wiring harness between A/C relay No. 3 and battery. If there is 12 volts, proceed to step 21.
21. With A/C off, check for continuity between A/C relay No. 3 yellow and blue terminals. If there is no continuity, replace A/C relay No. 3. If there is continuity, proceed to step 22.
22. With A/C and blower on, check for 12 volts at A/C relay No. 3 yellow terminal. If there is not 12 volts, locate and repair open or short in wiring harness between A/C relay No. 3 and ignition switch. If there is 12 volts, proceed to step 23.
23. With A/C and blower on and ignition off, check for continuity between A/C relay No. 3 blue terminal and ground. If there is continuity, replace A/C relay. If there is no continuity, proceed to step 24.
24. Check for continuity between A/C relay No. 3 blue terminal and A/C switch blue terminal. If there is no continuity, locate and repair open in blue wire between A/C relay No. 3 and A/C switch. If there is continuity, proceed to step 25.
25. With A/C on and ignition off, check for continuity between A/C switch blue and yellow terminals. If there is no continuity, replace A/C switch. If there is continuity, proceed to step 26.
26. With A/C off, check for continuity between A/C switch blue/yellow terminal and blower control switch blue/yellow terminal. If there is no continuity, repair blue/yellow wire between A/C switch and blower control switch. If there is continuity refer to "No Heater Blower Operation" step 3.

### No Engine Cooling Fan Operation

1. With A/C and blower on, check for 12 volts at A/C relay No. 1 black/green wire. If there is not 12 volts, refer to "No Cooling Or Insufficient Cooling" step 18. If there is 12 volts, proceed to step 2.
2. With A/C off, check for continuity across A/C relay No. 1 black/green wire to black wire. If there is no continuity, replace A/C relay No. 1. If there is continuity, proceed to step 3.
3. Check for continuity between A/C relay No. 1 and both A/C relay black wires to ground. If there is no continuity, repair ground connections as required. If there is continuity, proceed to step 4.
4. With A/C relay No. 1 connector disconnected, A/C and blower on and engine below 97°C, check for 12 volts at A/C relay yellow/green terminal. If there is not 12 volts, locate and repair open in yellow/green lead between A/C relay and cooling fan motor. If there is 12 volts, replace A/C relay No. 1.

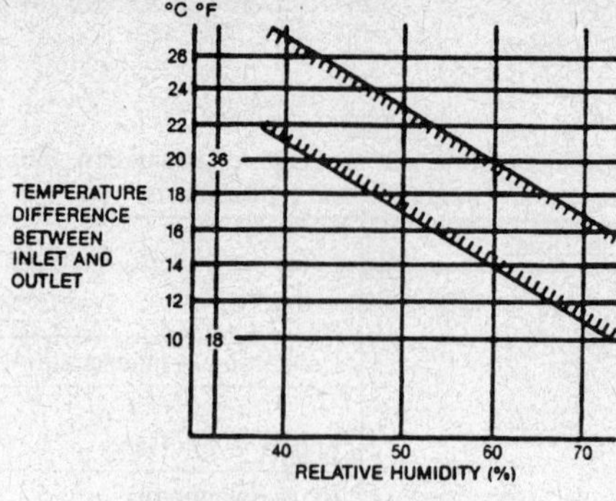


**Fig. 4 A/C system performance chart. Festiva**

### No Condenser Fan Motor Operation

1. With A/C and blower on, check for 12 volts at A/C relay No. 2 black/green wire. If there is not 12 volts, refer to "No Cooling Or Insufficient Cooling" step 18. If there is 12 volts, proceed to step 2.
2. With A/C off, check for continuity across A/C relay No. 2 black/green wire, to black wire. If there is no continuity, replace A/C relay No. 2. If there is continuity, proceed to step 3.
3. Check for continuity at both A/C relay No. 2 black wires to ground. If there is no continuity, repair grounds as required. If there is continuity, proceed to step 4.
4. With A/C relay No. 2 green/red wire disconnected from relay, A/C and blower on, check for 12 volts at A/C relay green/red wire. If there is 12 volts, replace A/C No. 2 relay. If there is not 12 volts, proceed to step 5.
5. With A/C off, check for continuity from A/C relay No. 2 green/red wire to condenser fan motor connector green/red wire. If there is no continuity, repair wire as required. If there is continuity, proceed to step 6.
6. With A/C on, check for 12 volts at condenser fan motor blue wire. If there is not 12 volts, check ignition switch circuit. If there is 12 volts, replace condenser fan motor.

### Improper Cold Air Distribution

1. Set A/C for maximum cold position. Ensure mix door is in proper position. If air mix door is not in the proper position adjust cable as required. If door is in proper position, proceed to step 2.
2. With A/C set for maximum cold, check that fresh air door is in the proper position so as to allow only interior air to pass through or around the evaporator. If door is not in proper position, adjust cable as required. If door is in proper position, proceed to step 3.
3. With A/C set for maximum cold, check that function control door is in position so that air is distributed through center and side vents. If door is not in proper position, adjust cable as required. If door is in proper position, check for blockage in ducts and repair as required.

## 1991 ESCORT & TRACER

1. Connect manifold gauge set to system.
2. Start and run engine at 2000 RPM, then turn A/C system On.
3. Set temperature control to MAX and blower motor to III.
4. Wait until air conditioning system stabilizes, then check readings at high and low pressure gauges.
5. Normal reading for high pressure gauge should be 171-235 psi. Normal reading for low pressure gauge should be 21-23 psi.
6. If pressure is not within specifications, record stabilized pressure and perform necessary system diagnosis.

## SCORPIO & XR4Ti

The most common complaints associated with an air conditioning system are inadequate, erratic or non-existent cooling. To diagnose a fault correctly, proceed as follows:

1. Connect a manifold gauge set.
2. Close both hand valves on manifold gauge set.
3. Place A/C system in operation as follows:
   a. Close both hand valves on manifold gauge set.
   b. Set A/C system to maximum cooling and the fan to "Speed II" and "recirculated air," then insert a thermometer into the center vent nozzle approximately .20-.28 inch.
   c. Apply parking brake, close all windows and doors and run engine at 1500 RPM for approximately 3 minutes.
   d. Read the temperature on the thermometer. The temperature should be within specifications, which vary according to ambient air temperature, **Fig. 5.**
4. Compare manifold gauge readings with specifications, **Figs. 6 and 7,** then proceed to proper diagnosis and match test results.

# LEAK TESTS

Testing the refrigerant system for leaks is one of the most important phases of troubleshooting. One or more of the methods outlined will prove useful in detecting leaks or checking connections if service work is performed. Before beginning any leak test, attach a manifold gauge set and note pressure. If little or no pressure is indicated, a partial charge must be installed. Check all connections, compressor head gasket, oil filler plug and compressor shaft seal for leaks.

| Ambient Temperature | | Temperature at Center Vent Nozzle | |
|---|---|---|---|
| °C | °F | °C | °F |
| 15 | 60 | 4-6 | 40-42 |
| 20 | 68 | 4-6 | 40-42 |
| 26 | 79 | 4-7 | 40-45 |
| 32 | 90 | 5-8 | 41-46 |
| 37 | 100 | 7-10 | 45-50 |

**Fig. 5 Temperature comparison chart. Scorpio & XR4Ti**

| Ambient Temperature | | Low-Pressure Side | |
|---|---|---|---|
| °C | °F | kPa | psi |
| 15 | 60 | *60-99 | *8.7-14.4 |
| 20 | 68 | *60-120 | *8.7-17.4 |
| 26 | 79 | *60-140 | *8.7-20.3 |
| 32 | 90 | *60-193 | *8.7-28.0 |
| 37 | 100 | 116-212 | 16.8-30.8 |

**Fig. 6 Low pressure side test pressure range chart. Scorpio & XR4Ti**

| Ambient Temperature | | High-Pressure | |
|---|---|---|---|
| °C | °F | kPa | p |
| 15 | 60 | 496-965 | 72- |
| 20 | 68 | 496-1,158 | 72-1 |
| 26 | 79 | 965-1,179 | 140-17 |
| 32 | 90 | 1,400-1,738 | 203-25 |
| 37 | 100 | 1,593-1,979 | 231-287 |

**Fig. 7 High pressure side test pressure range chart. Scorpio & XR4Ti**

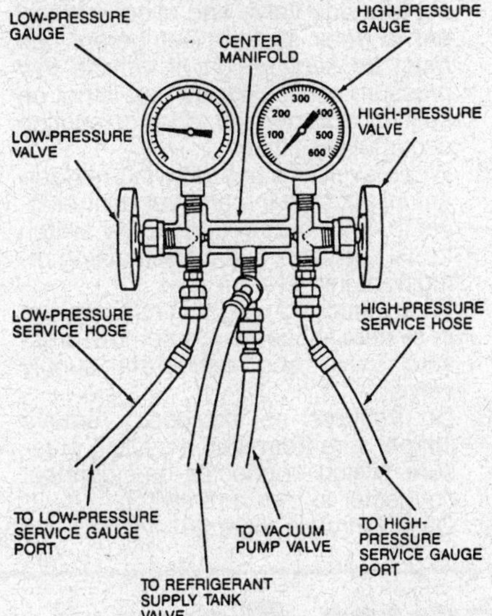


**Fig. 8 Refrigerant system service connections**

## ELECTRONIC LEAK DETECTORS

There are a number of electronic leak detectors available to perform leak tests. Refer to operating instructions for the unit being used and observe these general procedures:

1. Move the detector probe one inch per second in areas of suspected leaks.
2. Position the probe below the test point, as refrigerant gas is heavier than air.
3. Be sure to check service access gauge port valve fittings, particularly when valve caps are missing, as dirt accumulations can destroy the sealing area of valve core when manifold gauge set is attached. Replace missing valve caps after cleaning valve core area. **Valve caps should only be finger tightened. Using pliers to tighten valve caps may distort sealing surface of valve.**
4. Check for leaks in manifold gauge set and hoses, as well as the rest of the system.

## FLAME-TYPE (HALIDE) LEAK DETECTORS

**When using flame-type detectors, avoid inhaling fumes produced by burning refrigerant. Do not use this type detector where concentrations of combustible or explosive gases, dusts or vapors may exist.**

1. Adjust detector flame as low as possible to obtain maximum sensitivity. Be sure copper element is cherry red and not burned away. The flame will be almost colorless.
2. Slowly move detector along areas of suspected leaks. A slight leak will cause the flame to change to a bright yellow-green color. A significant leak will be indicated by a brilliant blue flame. Position detector under areas being tested as refrigerant gas is heavier than air. **The presence of dust in the pickup hose may cause a change in the color of the flame. If not recognized, a false diagnosis could be made. Store leak detector in a clean place and ensure hose is free of dust before leak testing.**
3. Check for leaks in the manifold gauge set and hoses, as well as the rest of the system.
4. Use a small fan to ventilate areas where the leak detector indicates refrigerant constantly. These areas are contaminated with refrigerant and must be ventilated before leak can be pinpointed.

## FLUID LEAK DETECTORS

Apply leak detector solution around joints to be tested. A cluster of bubbles will form immediately if there is a leak. A white foam that forms after a short while will indicate an extremely small leak. In some confined areas such as sections of the evaporator and condenser, electronic leak detectors will be more useful.

## DISCHARGING SYSTEM

The use of refrigerant recovery and recycling stations allows the recovery and reuse of refrigerant after contaminants and moisture have been removed.

When using a recovery or recycling station, follow the manufacturer's operating instructions, noting the following:

1. **Use extreme caution and observe all safety and service precautions related to use of refrigerants.**
2. Connect refrigerant recycling station hose(s) to vehicle A/C service port(s) and recovery station inlet fitting. Hoses used should have shut off devices or check valves within 12 inches of hose ends to minimize introduction of air into recycling station and to minimize amount of refrigerant released when hose(s) is disconnected.
3. Turn recycling station On to start recovery process. Allow recycling station to pump refrigerant from A/C system until station pressure gauge indicates vacuum.
4. After vehicle A/C system has been evacuated, close station inlet valve, if equipped.
5. Turn station Off. On some stations the pump will automatically be turned Off by a low pressure switch.
6. Allow vehicle A/C system to remain closed for approximately two minutes. Observe vacuum level indicated on gauge. If pressure does not rise, disconnect recycling station hose(s).
7. If system pressure rises, repeat steps 3 through 6 until vacuum level remains stable for two minutes.
8. Service A/C system as necessary, then evacuate and recharge A/C system.

## EVACUATING SYSTEM WITH VACUUM PUMP

Vacuum pumps suitable for removing air and moisture from A/C systems are commercially available. A specification for system pump down used here is 28-29½ inches vacuum. This reading can be attained at or near sea level only. For each 1000 feet of altitude this operation is performed, the reading will be 1 inch vacuum higher. For example, at 5000 feet elevation, only 23-24½ inches of vacuum can be obtained. **The system must be completely discharged before it can be evacuated. Damage to the vacuum pump will result if pressurized refrigerant is allowed to enter.**

1. Connect vacuum pump to gauge manifold. With gauges connected into system, remove cap from vacuum hose connector. Install center hose from gauge manifold to vacuum pump connector. Midposition high and low side compressor service valve (if used). Open high and low side gauge manifold hand valves.
2. Operate vacuum pump a minimum of 30 minutes for air and moisture removal. Watch compound gauge to see that system pumps down into a vacuum. System will reach 28-29½ inches Hg vacuum in a maximum of 5 minutes. If system does not pump down, check all connections and leak test if necessary.
3. Close gauge manifold hand valves and shut off vacuum pump.
4. Check ability of system to hold vacuum. Watch compound gauge to see that gauge does not rise at a faster

han 1 inch vacuum every 4 or 5 tes. If compound gauge rises at apid a rate, install partial charge leak test. Then discharge system outlined above.

ystem holds vacuum, charge sys- with refrigerant.

## RGING SYSTEM

**umber of manufacturers are pro- ing refrigerant products which are escribed as being direct replacements for refrigerant R-12. The use of any unauthorized substitute refrigerant may severely damage A/C components. R-12 is the only authorized refrigerant to be used in any air conditioning system for Ford vehicle.**

Refer to "A/C Data Table" for refrigerant capacities.

**When charging from small cans, do not open manifold gauge set high pressure (discharge) gauge valve, as this can cause the containers to explode.**

1. Connect manifold gauge set **Fig. 8**, then set valves closed to center hose, disconnect vacuum pump from manifold gauge set.
2. Connect center hose of manifold gauge set to refrigerant supply.
3. Purge air from center hose by loosening hose at manifold gauge set and open refrigerant drum valve. When refrigerant escapes from hose, tighten center hose connection at manifold gauge set.
4. On vehicles so equipped, disconnect wire harness connector at clutch cycling pressure switch. Install jumper wire across terminals of connector.
5. On all models, open manifold gauge set low side valve and allow refrigerant to enter system. Refrigerant can must be kept upright if vehicle low pressure service gauge port is not on suction accumulator/drier or suction accumulator fitting.
6. When system stops drawing refrigerant in, start engine and set control lever to A/C position and blower switch to "HI" position to draw remaining refrigerant into system.
7. When specified weight of refrigerant is in system, close gauge set low pressure valve and refrigerant supply valve.
8. On vehicles so equipped, remove jumper wire from clutch cycling pressure switch connector and connect connector to pressure switch.
9. On all models, operate system until pressures stabilize to check operation and system pressures. During high ambient temperatures, a high volume fan may be necessary to blow air through the radiator and condenser to cool engine and prevent excessive refrigerant system pressures.
10. When charging is complete and system operating pressures are normal, disconnect manifold gauge set from vehicle and install protective caps on service gauge port valves.

## SERVICE BULLETINS

### INTERMITTENT OR INOPERATIVE A/C SYSTEM

#### 1991 Escort & Tracer w/1.9L/4-114 Engine

The above condition may be caused by an A/C clutch that does not engage. This may be caused by an A/C clutch wire that was damaged because it was routed too close to the A/C idler pulley.

To correct this condition, repair damaged section of wire and reroute wire to inboard side of lower radiator hose.

# System Servicing

## INDEX



## OIL CHARGE

### EXCEPT CAPRI, FESTIVA, SCORPIO, XR4Ti & TRACER

#### Nippondenso 10P13 Compressor

A new service replacement compressor contains 7.75 ounces of a special paraffin base refrigerant oil (part No. Motorcraft YN-9). Before installing replacement compressor, drain oil from old and new compressors. If three to five ounces of oil was drained from old compressor, install the same amount of oil drained from old compressor. If more than five ounces was drained from old compressor, install five ounces of new refrigerant oil in new compressor. If less than three ounces was removed from old compressor, install three ounces in new compressor.

When replacing the accumulator/dryer drill a 1/2 inch hole in old accumulator body and drain oil from hole. Add same amount of new oil plus two ounces to new accumulator/dryer.

When other air conditioning system components are replace add the following quantities of refrigerant oil: Evaporator core, 3 fluid ounces; Condenser, 1 fluid ounce.

Replacement of other components such as an orifice tube or hoses does not require the addition of any refrigerant oil.

#### Ford FS6 & Nippondenso 6P148 Compressors

A new service replacement compressor contains 10 fluid ounces of refrigerant oil. Before installing replacement compressor, drain 4 fluid ounces of oil from compressor in order to maintain total system oil charge within specified limits.

When other air conditioning system components are replace add the following quantities of 500 viscosity refrigerant oil: Accumulator, same amount drained from old accumulator plus 1 ounce (drain accumulator through pressure switch fitting); Evaporator core, 3 fluid ounces; Condenser, 1 fluid ounce.

Replacement of other components such as valves or hoses does not require the addition of any refrigerant oil.

#### Tecumseh HR-980 Compressors

A new service replacement 4 cylinder compressor contains 8 fluid ounces of refrigerant oil. Before installing replacement compressor, drain 4 fluid ounces of oil from compressor in order to maintain total system oil charge within specified limits.

When other air conditioning system components are replace add the following quantities of 500 viscosity refrigerant oil: Accumulator, same amount drained from old accumulator plus 1 ounce (drain accumulator through pressure switch fitting); Evaporator core, 3 fluid ounces; Condenser, 1 fluid ounce.

Replacement of other components such as valves or hoses does not require the addition of any refrigerant oil.

#### Nippondenso 10P15 Series Compressors

A new service replacement compressor contains 8 fluid ounces of refrigerant oil. Before installing replacement compressor, drain oil from compressor into a clean graduated container, then pour 5 ounces of clean refrigerant oil into compressor to maintain total system oil charge limits.

When other air conditioning system components are replace add the following quantities of refrigerant oil: Accumulator, same amount drained from old accumulator plus 1 ounce (drain accumulator by drilling 1/2 inch hole in accumulator body); Evaporator core, 3 fluid ounces; Condenser, 1 fluid ounce.

Replacement of other components such as valves or hoses does not require the addition of any refrigerant oil.

### Nippondenso 10PA17 Compressor

A new service replacement compressor contains 8 ounces of refrigerant oil. Before installing replacement compressor, drain oil from old compressor. If three to five ounces of oil was drained from old compressor, drain new compressor and install the same amount of oil drained from old compressor. If more than five ounces was drained from old compressor, install five ounces of new refrigerant oil in new compressor. If less than three ounces was removed from old compressor, install three ounces in new compressor.

When other air conditioning system components are replace add the following quantities of refrigerant oil: Accumulator, same amount drained from old accumulator plus 2 ounces; Evaporator core, 3 fluid ounces; Condenser, 1 fluid ounce.

Replacement of other components such as an orifice tube or hoses does not require the addition of any refrigerant oil.

### Ford FX-15 Axial 10 Cylinder Compressor

A new service replacement compressor contains 7 fluid ounces of refrigerant oil. Before installing replacement compressor, drain oil from old compressor. If three to five ounces of oil were drained from old compressor, then drain new compressor and install the same amount of oil drained from old compressor. If more than five ounces were drained from old compressor, install five ounces of new refrigerant oil in new compressor. If less then three ounces was removed from old compressor, install three ounces in new compressor.

When other air conditioning system components are replace add the following quantities of refrigerant oil: Accumulator, same amount drained from old accumulator plus 1 ounce; Evaporator core, 3 fluid ounces; Condenser, 1 fluid ounce.

Replacement of other components such as valves or hoses does not require the addition of any refrigerant oil.

### CAPRI

When replacing system components, add the following quantities of refrigerant oil: Compressor, 2.0-3.4 ounces; Condenser, 1 ounce; Evaporator 1 ounce; Receiver-drier, .5 ounce.

### FESTIVA

When replacing system components, add or drain the following quantities of refrigerant oil: Compressor, drain 1.2 ounces; Condenser, add 1.0 ounce; Evaporator, add 3.0 ounces; Receiver-dr amount drained from old drier ounce.

### 1989 TRACER

When replacing system compon add the following quantities of refrige oil: Compressor, 2.0-3.4 ounces; C denser, .85-1.0 ounce; Evaporator, .85-1 ounces; Receiver-drier, .5-.7 ounces.

### 1991 TRACER

Refer to "Nippondenso 10P13 Compressor," for oil charge specifications.

### XR4Ti

When replacing system components, add or drain the following quantities of refrigerant oil: When installing new compressor, drain 1/2 ounce oil from replacement compressor. Add 1/2 ounce oil when replacing condenser or evaporator, .2 ounce oil when replacing receiver-drier or .1 ounce oil when replacing any refrigerant hose.

### SCORPIO

When replacing system components, add or drain the following quantities of refrigerant oil: When installing new compressor, drain .7 ounce oil from replacement compressor. Add 1/2 ounce oil when replacing condenser or evaporator, .7 ounce oil when replacing receiver-drier.

# Charging Valve Location

| Model | High Pressure Fitting | Low Pressure Fitting |
|---|---|---|
| **FORD & MERCURY** | | |
| Except Crown Victoria, Festiva, Grand Marquis, Sable & Taurus | High Pressure Line From Compressor | Low Pressure Line From Compressor |
| Festiva | High Pressure Line Next to Pressure Switch | Low Pressure Line From Compressor |
| Crown Victoria, Grand Marquis, Sable & Taurus | High Pressure Line From Compressor | Accumulator |
| **LINCOLN** | | |
| Except Mark VII | High Pressure Line From Compressor | Accumulator |
| Mark VII | High Pressure Line From Compressor | Low Pressure Line From Compressor |
| **MERKUR** | | |
| XR4TI | Accumulator | Accumulator |
| Scorpio | Accumulator | Receiver/Drier |

# A/C Data Table

| | Model & Engine | Refrigerant Capacity, Lbs. | A/C Compressor Model | Refrigeration Oil | | | Compressor Clutch Air Gap Inch |
|---|---|---|---|---|---|---|---|
| | | | | Viscosity | Total System Capacity, Ounces | Compressor Oil Level Check, Inches | |
| **…ROWN VICTORIA & MERCURY GRAND MARQUIS** | | | | | | | |
| [illegible] | All | 3.25 | Nippondenso 10PA17 | ② | 8 | ① | .014-.026 |
| [illegible] | All | 3.0 | Ford FX-15 | ② | 7 | ① | .018-.033 |
| **…ORD ESCORT & TEMPO; MERCURY TOPAZ** | | | | | | | |
| 1989–91 | Tempo & Topaz | 2.25 | Nippondenso 10P15 | 500 | 8 | ① | .021-.036 |
| 1989–90 | Escort | 2.25 | Nippondenso 10P15 | 500 | 8 | ① | .021-.036 |
| 1991 | Escort | 2.13 | Nippondenso 10P13 | ② | 7.75 | ① | .021-.036 |
| **FORD FESTIVA & MERCURY TRACER** | | | | | | | |
| 1989–91 | Festiva | 1.56 | — | 500 | 10 | ① | .016-.028 |
| 1989 | Tracer | 1.55 | — | 500 | 10 | ① | .016-.028 |
| 1991 | Tracer | 2.13 | Nippondenso 10P13 | ② | 7.75 | ① | .021-.036 |
| **FORD MUSTANG** | | | | | | | |
| 1989 | 2.3L/4-140 | 2.5 | Tecumseh HR980 | 500 | 8 | ① | .009-.041 |
| 1990–91 | 2.3L/4-140 | 2.5 | Nippondenso 10P15 | ② | 8 | ① | .021-.036 |
| 1989–91 | 5.0L/V8-302 | 2.5 | Nippondenso 6P148 | ② | 10 | ① | .21-.36 |
| **FORD PROBE** | | | | | | | |
| 1989–91 | 2.2L/4-133 | 2.5 | Nippondenso 10P15A | 500 | 3.3 | ① | .016-.028 |
| 1990–91 | 3.0L/V6-182 | 2.5 | Nippondenso 10P15 | ② | 8 | ① | .021-.036 |
| **FORD TAURUS & MERCURY SABLE** | | | | | | | |
| 1989–90 | 2.5L/4-153 | 2.75 | Ford FS-6 | 500 | 10 | ① | .021-.036 |
| | 3.0L/V6-182 | 2.75 | Ford FX-15 | ② | 7 | ① | .018-.033 |
| | 3.0L/V6-182 SHO | 2.75 | Nippondenso 10P15F | ② | 8 | ① | .021-.036 |
| | 3.8L/V6-232 | 2.5 | Nippondenso 10P15 | ② | 8 | ① | .021-.043 |
| 1991 | 2.5L/4-153 | 2.75 | Ford FS-6 | 500 | 10 | ① | .021-.036 |
| | 3.0L/V6-182 | 2.75 | Ford FX-15 | ② | 7 | ① | .018-.033 |
| | 3.0L/V6-182 SHO | 2.75 | Nippondenso 10P15F | ② | 8 | ① | .021-.036 |
| | 3.8L/V6-232 | 2.5 | Ford FX-15 | ② | 7 | ① | .018-.033 |
| **FORD THUNDERBIRD & MERCURY COUGAR** | | | | | | | |
| 1989–91 | All | 2.6 | FX-15 | ② | 7 | ① | .018-.033 |
| **LINCOLN** | | | | | | | |
| 1989–90 | Town Car | 3.0 | Nippondenso 10PA17 | ② | 8 | ① | .021-.036 |
| | Continental | 2.5 | Nippondenso 10P15C | ② | 8 | ① | .021-.043 |
| | Mark VII | 2.5 | Nippondenso 10PA17 | ② | 8 | ① | .014-.026 |
| 1991 | Town Car | 2.5 | Ford FX-15 | ② | 7 | ① | .018-.033 |
| | Continental | 2.5 | Ford FX-15 | ② | 7 | ① | .018-.033 |
| | Mark VII | 2.5 | Nippondenso 10PA17 | ② | 8 | ① | .014-.026 |
| **MERCURY CAPRI** | | | | | | | |
| 1991 | All | 1.4 | — | 500 | 10 | ① | .016-.028 |
| **MERKUR** | | | | | | | |
| 1989 | Scorpio | — | Nippondenso 10P15 | 500 | 8 | ① | .021-.036 |
| 1989 | XR4TI | — | Nippondenso 10P15 | 500 | 8 | ① | .021-.036 |

①—Note that "Oil Level Inches" cannot be checked. Refer to total capacity in ounces. See text for procedure.

②—Paraffin base viscosity refrigerant oil, part No. Motorcraft YN-9.

# ENGINE COOLING FANS

## TABLE OF CONTENTS



# Variable Speed Fans

## INDEX



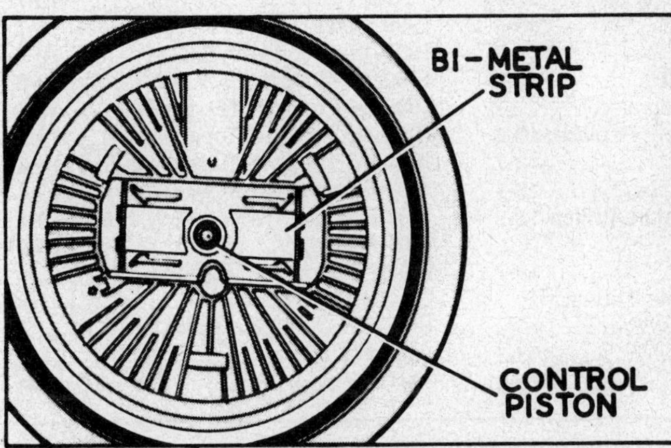


**Fig. 1 Variable-speed fan with flat bi-metal thermostatic spring**

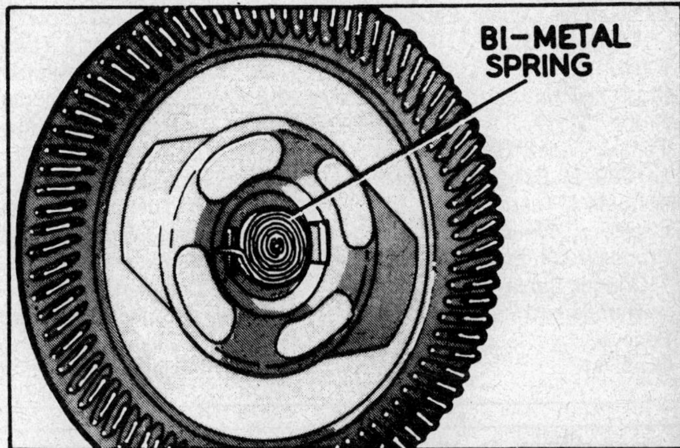


**Fig. 2 Variable-speed fan with coiled bi-metal thermostatic spring**

## DESCRIPTION

The fan drive clutch is a fluid coupling containing silicone oil. Fan speed is regulated by the torque-carrying capacity of the silicone oil. The more silicone oil in the coupling the greater the fan speed, and the less silicone oil the slower the fan speed.

Two types of fan drive clutches are in use. On one, **Fig. 1**, a bi-metallic strip and control piston on the front of the fluid coupling regulates the amount of silicone oil entering the coupling. The bi-metallic strip bows outward with an increase in surrounding temperature and allows a piston to move outward. The piston opens a valve regulating the flow of silicone oil into the coupling from a reserve chamber. The silicone oil is returned to the reserve chamber through a bleed hole when the valve is closed.

On the other type of fan drive clutch, **Fig. 2**, a heat-sensitive, bi-metal spring connected to an opening plate brings about a similar result. Both units cause the fan speed to increase with a rise in temperature and to decrease as the temperature goes down.

In some cases a Flex-Fan is used instead of a Fan Drive Clutch. Flexible blades vary the volume of air being drawn through the radiator, automatically increasing the pitch at low engine speeds.

## FAN DRIVE CLUTCH TEST

Do not operate the engine until the fan has been first checked for possible cracks and separations.

Run the engine at a fast idle speed (1000 RPM) until normal operating temperature is reached. This process can be speeded up by blocking off the front of the radiator with cardboard. Regardless of temperatures, the unit must be operated for at least five minutes immediately before being tested.

Stop the engine and, using a glove or a cloth to protect the hand, immediately check the effort required to turn the fan. If considerable effort is required, it can be assumed that the coupling is operating satisfactorily. If very little effort is required to turn the fan, it is an indication that the coupling is not operating properly and should be replaced.

If the clutch fan is the coiled bi-metal spring type, it may be tested while the vehicle is being driven. To check, disconnect the bi-metal spring and rotate 90° counterclockwise. This disables the temperature-controlled free-wheeling feature and the clutch performs like a conventional fan. If this cures the overheating condition, replace the clutch fan.

## SERVICE PROCEDURE

**To prevent silicone fluid from draining into fan drive bearing, do not store or place drive unit on bench with rear of shaft pointing downward.**

The removal procedure for either type of fan clutch assembly is generally the same for all cars. Merely unfasten the unit from the water pump and remove the assembly from the car.

The variable speed fan with flat bi-metal thermostatic spring may be partially disassembled for inspection and cleaning. Remove screws holding the assembly together and separate the fan from the drive clutch. Next remove the metal strip on the front by pushing one end of it toward the fan clutch body so it clears the retaining bracket. Then push the strip to the side so that its opposite end will spring out of place. Now remove the small control piston underneath it.

Check the piston for free movement of the coupling device. If the piston sticks, clean it with emery cloth. If the bi-metal strip is damaged, replace the entire unit. These strips are not interchangeable.

When reassembling, install the control piston so that the projection on the end of it will contact the metal strip. Then install the metal strip. After reassembly, clean the clutch drive with a cloth soaked in solvent. Avoid dipping the clutch assembly in any type of liquid. Install the assembly in the reverse order of removal.

The coil spring type of fan clutch cannot be disassembled, serviced or repaired. If it does not function properly it must be replaced with a new unit.

# Electric Cooling Fans

**NOTE:** Wire Code Identification And Symbol Identification Located At The Front Of This Manual Can Be Used As An Aid When Using Wiring Circuits Found In This Section.

## INDEX



**CAUTION:** The Battery Ground Cable Should Be Disconnected Whenever Underhood Service Is Performed.

## DESCRIPTION

### CAPRI & 1991 ESCORT & TRACER

The electric cooling fan draws air through the radiator to dissipate heat absorbed by coolant. The fan will operate when the coolant has reached a specific temperature. The coolant temperature switch matches fan operation to coolant heat load. At 212°F, the switch will open and begin fan operation. When the coolant temperature drops to 200°F, the switch will close, stopping the fans operation. The 1.9L/4-116 Escort cooling fan is controlled by the ECA.

### CONTINENTAL, COUGAR, SABLE, TAURUS & THUNDERBIRD

The electric drive cooling fan system consists of a fan and a two-speed electric motor. This fan motor will only run when the ignition switch is in the Run position.

The cooling fan is controlled during engine operation by the integrated relay control module (IRCM) and the EEC-IV module. These controls cause the fan to run at low speed when the engine temperature reaches approximately 215°F, or when the A/C is on and vehicle does not provide enough air flow. The fan will continue to run until engine temperature drops to approximately 210°F.

The cooling fan will run at high speed when fan has been operating at low speed, but engine temperature is still above 230°F, or during idle when engine temperature has reached approximately 236°F. The cooling fan will begin to operate at low speed when engine temperature drops to approximately 224°F. The cooling fan does not cycle with A/C.

### TEMPO, TOPAZ, 1989 TRACER & 1989–90 ESCORT

The electric fan system consists of a fan and electric motor. This system uses a coolant temperature switch, mounted in the thermostat housing, to sense coolant temperature. Vehicles equipped with A/C have a cooling fan controller and a cooling fan relay. On Tempo and Topaz models equipped with a standard heater, the cooling fan is powered through the cooling fan relay.

On Tempo and Topaz models, the cooling fan is wired to operate only when the ignition switch is in the Run position. On Escort models, the cooling fan will run whenever the cooling fan temperature switch is closed.

On vehicles equipped with A/C, the cooling fan motor will be energized whenever the A/C cycling pressure switch closes, with the select lever in the A/C or Defrost position. The A/C clutch coil will be energized once voltage is supplied to the fan motor. The A/C clutch will cycle with the A/C clutch cycling pressure switch. The fan motor will stay energized as the clutch cycles, if the cycling pressure switch "open intervals" are less than 2-3 minutes. If the coolant temperature switch closes in the A/C mode at approximately 210°F, the fan motor will run until coolant temperature drops below approximately 193°F.

### FESTIVA

The cooling fan system consists of an electro-mechanical fan, a temperature switch and a temperature relay.

The temperature switch, located in the thermostat housing, senses engine coolant temperature; while the relay, located in the left front corner of the engine compartment between the battery and headlamp, provides the ground path to complete the circuit.

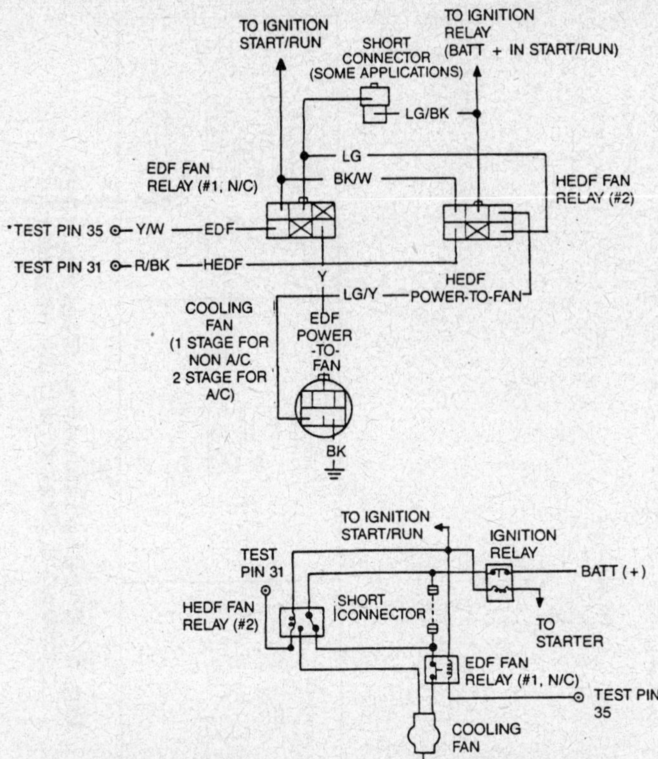


**Fig. 1 Cooling fan pinpoint test wiring diagram. Continental, Cougar, Sable, Taurus, Thunderbird & Probe w/3.0L engine**

When coolant temperature is below approximately 194°F, the temperature switch is closed, while the relay contacts are held open by the magnetism produced in the relay coil. When temperature is above approximately 207°F, the temperature switch is opened, allowing the relay contacts to close, thereby completing the ground circuit and activating the cooling fan.

Vehicles equipped with air conditioning have an added relay in the circuit, allowing the bypassing of the engine temperature portion of the circuit, and enabling fan activation any time the air conditioning system is in use.

## MUSTANG

This system consists of a single speed fan, which operates only when the ignition switch is in the run position. On 1989-90 models, the cooling fan is controlled during vehicle operation by the EEC-IV module. On 1991 models, the cooling fan is controlled during vehicle operation by the integrated relay control module (IRCM) and EEC-IV module. The cooling fan should operate when coolant temperature reaches 221°F, or with the air conditioning on and vehicle speed below 43 mph. The fan will continue to run until coolant temperature drops to 201°F, or vehicle speed reaches at least 48 mph.

## PROBE

### 2.2L/4-134 ENGINE

#### Manual Transaxle

A single normally closed relay supplies power to the fan motor. The fan motor is controlled by the coolant temperature switch. When the air conditioning is being used, the wide-open throttle-A/C cutoff relay controls the cooling fan relay to operate the fan. An electric signal is sent to the ECA to maintain idle quality.

#### Electronic Automatic Transmission

A two-speed cooling fan is used on these models. The cooling fan relay (CFR) and high speed fan relay (HSFR) combine to provide both speeds. The CFR produces the low speed operation. The HSFR provides high speed operation when excessive temperature is reached, or when the A/C compressor is operating.

### 3.0L/V6-183 ENGINE

Cooling fan operation is controlled entirely by the Electronic Control Assembly (ECA) and integral relay controller.

## DIAGNOSIS & TESTING

Refer to the wiring diagrams in **Figs. 1 through 16,** when performing diagnosis and testing procedures.

Perform visual inspection prior to performing any diagnosis and testing procedures.

1. Check coolant level and condition.
2. Check condition of radiator, thermostat and hoses.
3. Check for fan blade interference.
4. Check for proper mounting of fan motor.
5. Check for proper fan blade attachment to motor.
6. Check for blown fuses.
7. Check wiring harnesses for damaged wires and poor or corroded connectors.
8. Ensure battery is fully charged.

## CAPRI

### Condition Charts

Refer to **Fig. 17** for condition diagnosis charts.

### Test Step Diagnosis

Refer to **Fig. 18** for diagnostic test steps.

## PROBE W/3.0L ENGINE, CONTINENTAL, COUGAR, SABLE, TAURUS & THUNDERBIRD

### READING CODES

#### Star Tester

1. Turn ignition switch to the Off position.
2. Connect color coded adapter cable to the Star tester, **Fig. 19.**
3. Connect adapter cable leads to Self-Test connectors.
4. Start engine, then turn Star-Tester power switch to the On position. The number 88 will appear in the display.
5. When the 88 changes to 00, the tester is ready to receive codes.
6. Depress the Push button at front of tester. The button will latch down and a colon will appear in the display. Colon must be displayed to receive codes.
7. Tester will display the latest code received.

#### Analog Volt/Ohm Meter (VOM)

1. Turn ignition switch to the Off position.
2. Set VOM on a DC range of 0-15 volts.
3. Connect VOM from battery positive to the Self-Test output pin of large Self-Test connector, **Fig. 20.**
4. Continuous memory codes are separated from Key On Engine Off codes by a six second delay, a single half-second sweep, then another six second delay.

### FAN PINPOINT TEST

Refer to **Fig. 21** for wiring diagram and pinpoint test steps.

### INTEGRATED CONTROLLER PINPOINT TEST

The integral relay control module interfaces with the EEC-IV to provide control of the cooling fan. Refer to **Fig. 22** for terminal identification.

Refer to **Fig. 23** for pinpoint test steps.

## TEMPO, TOPAZ, 1989 TRACER & 1989–90 ESCORT

### Less A/C

Voltage readings can be obtained using Rotunda digital volt/ohm meter 007-00001, or equivalent.

Refer to **Figs. 24 and 25** for diagnosis of the cooling fan system less air conditioning.

### With A/C

Refer to **Figs. 26 and 27** for diagnosis of the cooling fan system w/A/C.

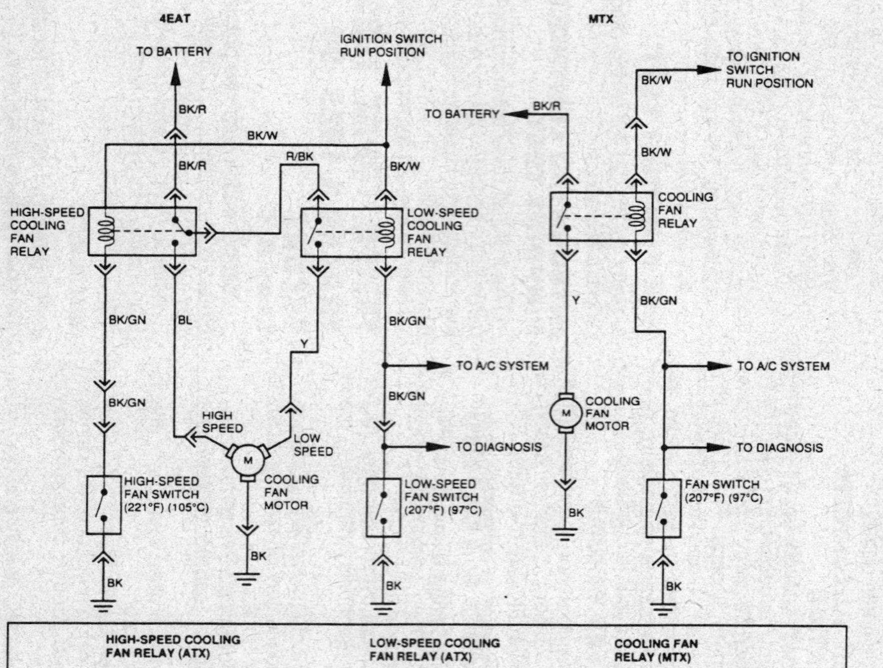


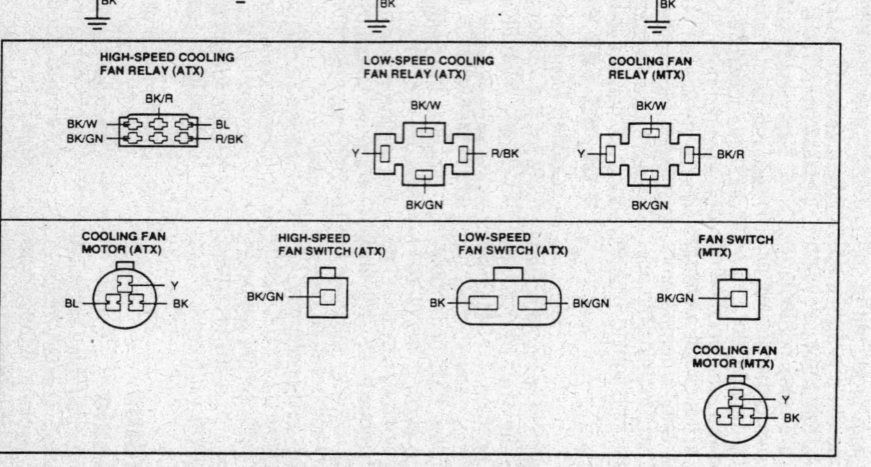


**Fig. 2 Cooling fan wiring diagram. 1991 Escort & Tracer w/1.8L engine**

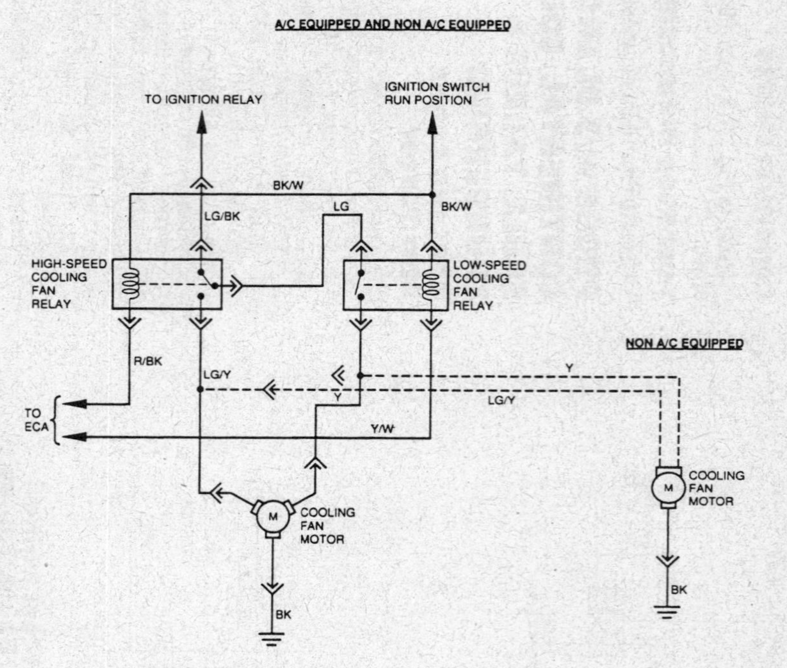


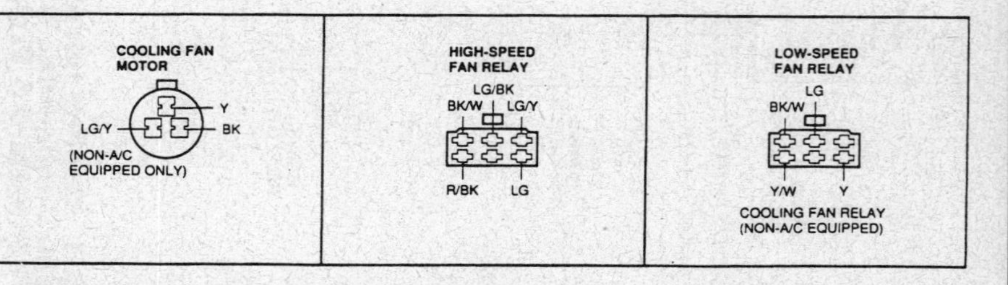


**Fig. 3 Cooling fan wiring diagram. 1991 Escort & Tracer w/1.9L engine**

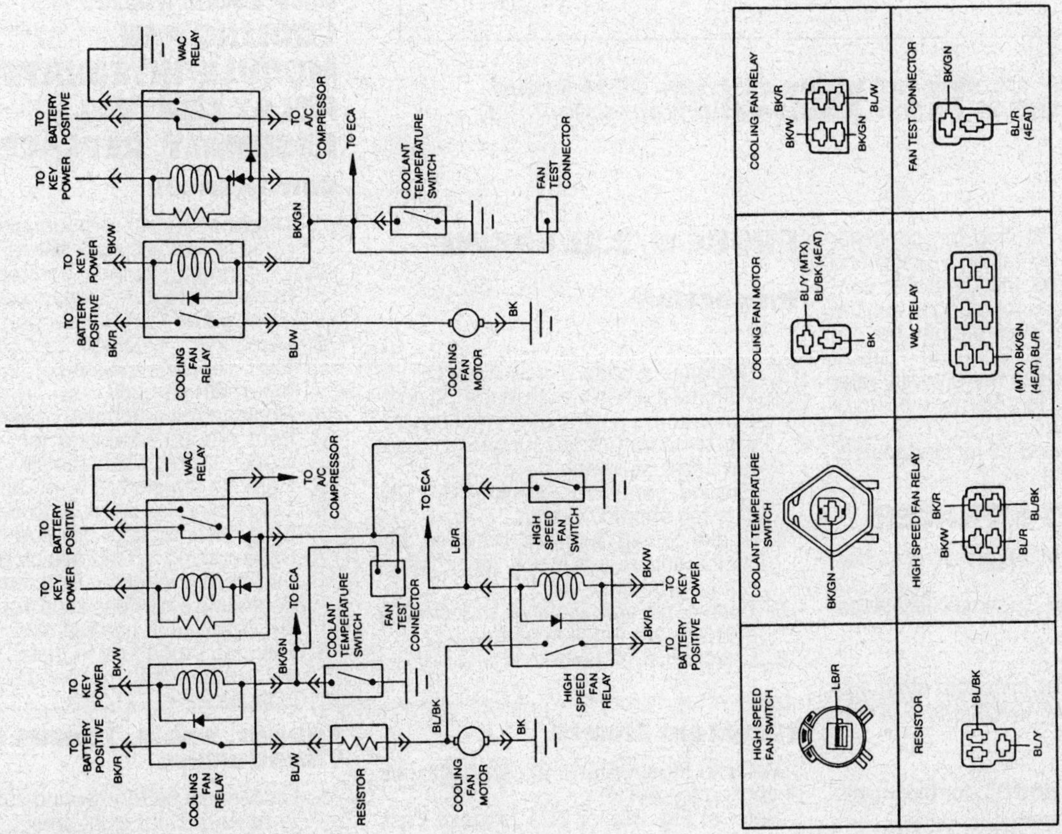

| HIGH SPEED FAN SWITCH | COOLANT TEMPERATURE SWITCH | COOLING FAN MOTOR | COOLING FAN RELAY |
|---|---|---|---|
| LB/R | BK/GN | BL/Y (MTX) BL/BK (4EAT) BK | BK/R BK/W BK/GN BL/W |
| **RESISTOR** | **HIGH SPEED FAN RELAY** | **WAC RELAY** | **FAN TEST CONNECTOR** |
| BL/BK BL/Y | BK/R BK/W BL/R BL/BK | (MTX) BK/GN (4EAT) BL/R | BK/GN BL/R (4EAT) |

**Fig. 4 Cooling fan wiring diagram. 1989–90 Probe w/2.2L engine & manual transaxle**

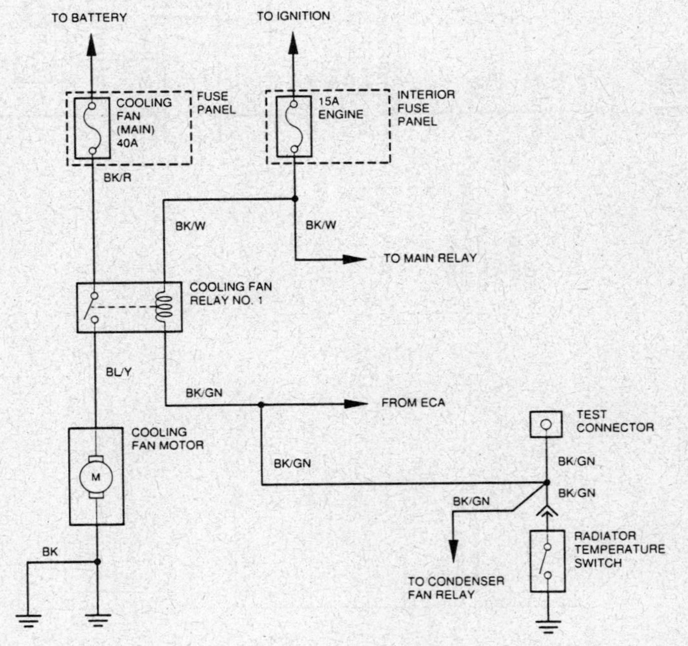


| COOLING FAN MOTOR | COOLING FAN RELAY | TEST CONNECTOR | RADIATOR TEMPERATURE SWITCH |
|---|---|---|---|
| BL/Y BK | BL/Y BK/GN BK/R BK/W | BK/GN | BK |

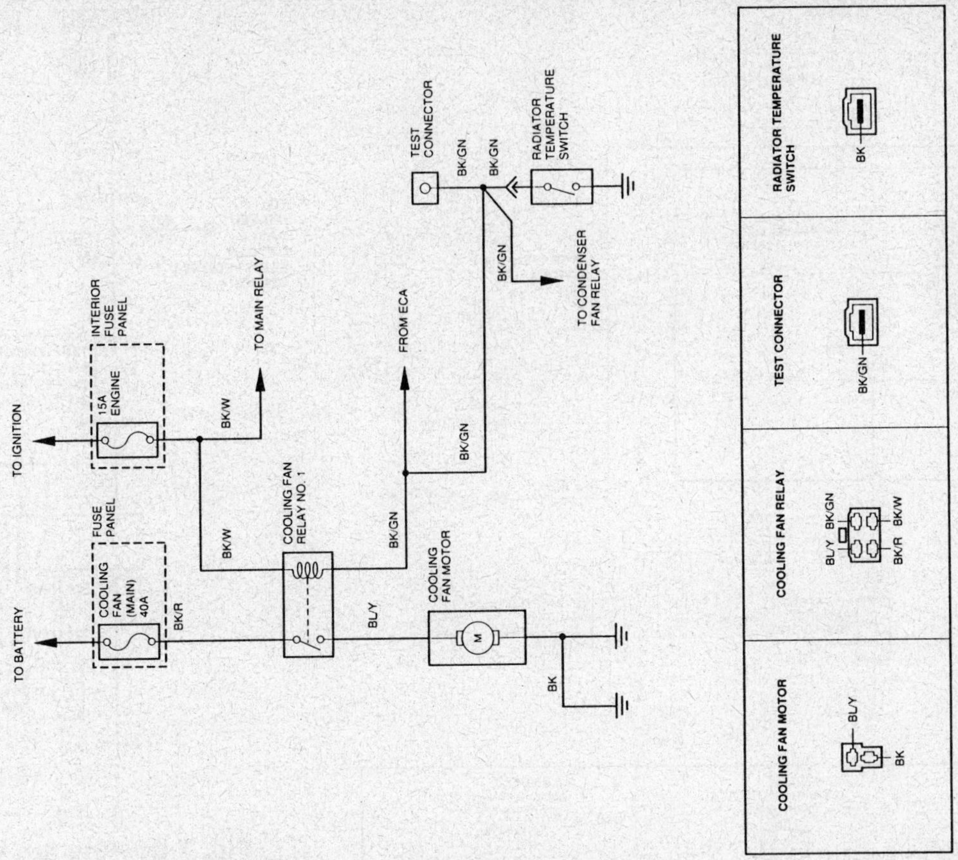

**Fig. 5 Cooling fan wiring diagram. 1991 Probe w/2.2L engine & manual transaxle**

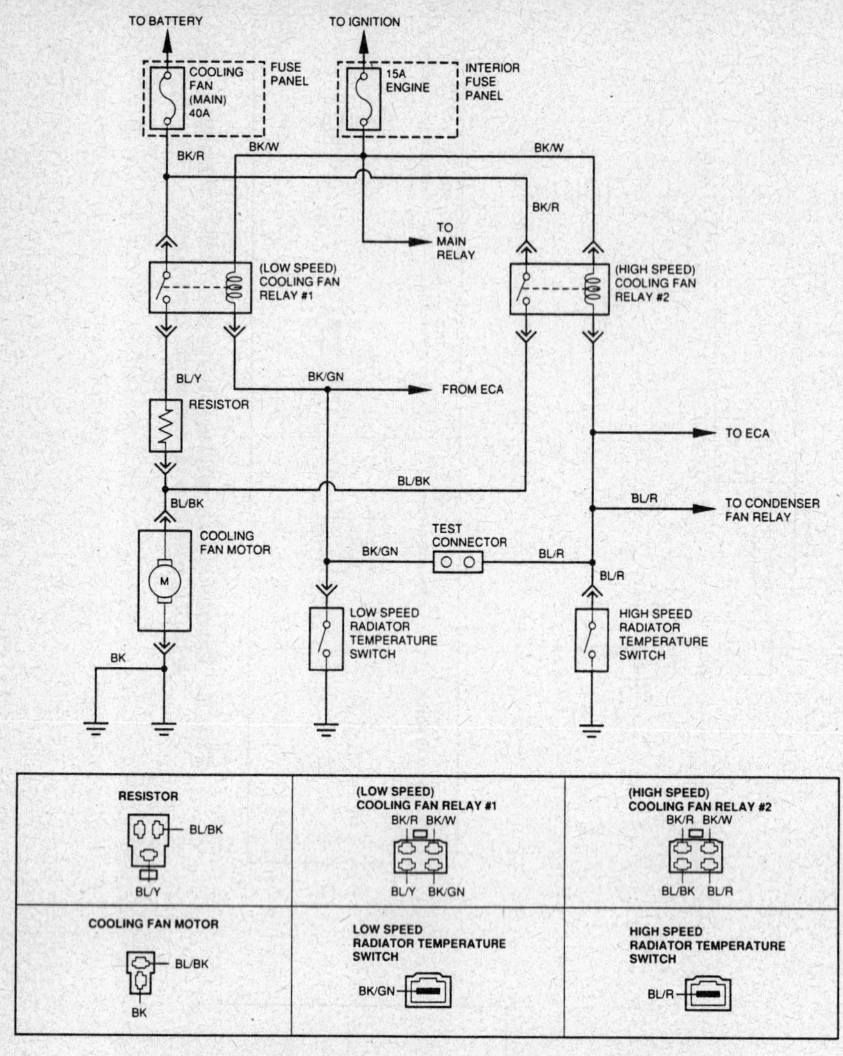


**Fig. 6 Cooling fan wiring diagram. 1991 Probe w/2.2L engine & automatic transaxle**

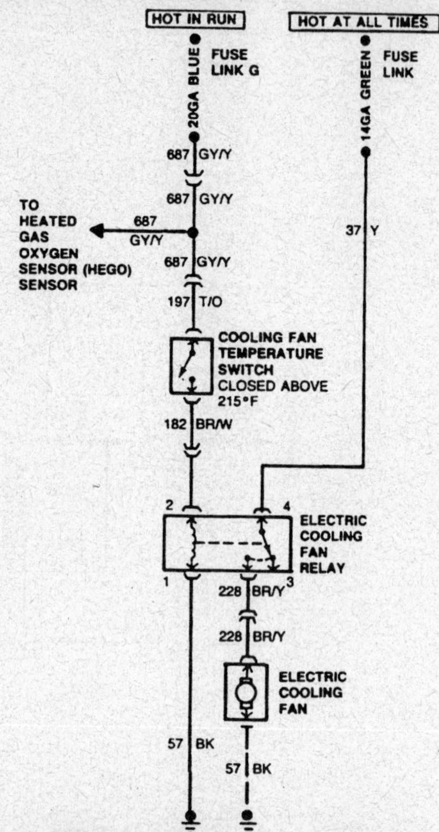


**Fig. 7 Cooling fan wiring diagram. Tempo & Topaz less A/C**

Diagnosis of the cooling fan controller can be performed by taking voltage and continuity readings at the controller connector, with the connector plugged into the controller. The readings should be obtained at the indicated connector pins. if the indicated reading is not present, refer to system diagnosis to determine origin of problem.

Refer to **Figs. 28 and 29** for diagnosis of cooling fan controller.

## 1991 ESCORT & TRACER

Refer to **Fig. 30** for diagnostic condition chart.

Refer to **Fig. 31** for diagnostic test steps.

## FESTIVA

Refer to **Fig. 32** for symptom chart and **Fig. 33** for diagnostic test steps.

## MUSTANG

Refer to **Figs. 34 and 35**, for diagnostic test steps.

## PROBE w/2.2L ENGINE

### Inspection

1. Disconnect battery ground cable.
2. With the ignition switch in the On position and the engine at normal operating temperature, disconnect coolant temperature switch.
3. Ground connector terminal BK/GN. The fan should operate.
4. Shake wiring harness between fan motor and relays. Look for signs of opens or shorts.
5. Ensure air conditioning and cooling systems are functioning properly.
6. Check ECA pinpoint test.

### Symptom Charts

Refer to **Figs. 36 and 37**, for diagnosis of cooling fan system.

Refer to **Fig. 38**, for ECA Pinpoint Test.

# COMPONENT REPLACEMENT

## COOLING FAN MODULE/INTEGRATED RELAY CONTROL ASSEMBLY, REPLACE

### Continental

1. Disconnect battery ground cable, then remove radiator sight shield.
2. Disconnect electrical connector, then remove integrated relay control assembly from radiator support, **Fig. 39.**
3. Disconnect electrical fan connector, then separate connector located at top of fan shroud.
4. Remove male terminal connector clip from shroud mounting tab, then remove air bag crash sensor.
5. Remove fan shroud from radiator.
6. Lift cooling fan module to disengage from lower radiator clip and end tab.
7. Slide cooling fan module clear of radiator hose connector, then remove two engine wire harness clips from side of fan shroud. Lift module past radiator.
8. Reverse procedure to install. **Torque** shroud to radiator nuts and bolts to 36 inch lbs.

### Cougar, Sable, Taurus & Thunderbird

1. Disconnect battery ground cable, then remove radiator sight shield.

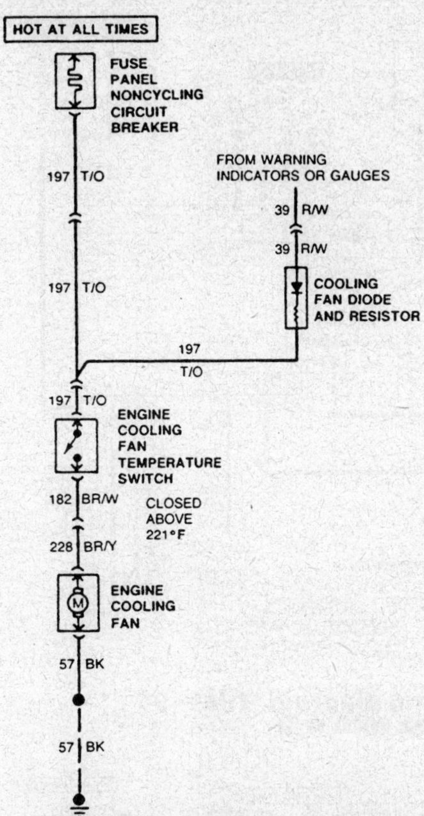


Fig. 8 Cooling fan wiring diagram. 1989 Tracer & 1989-90 Escort less A/C

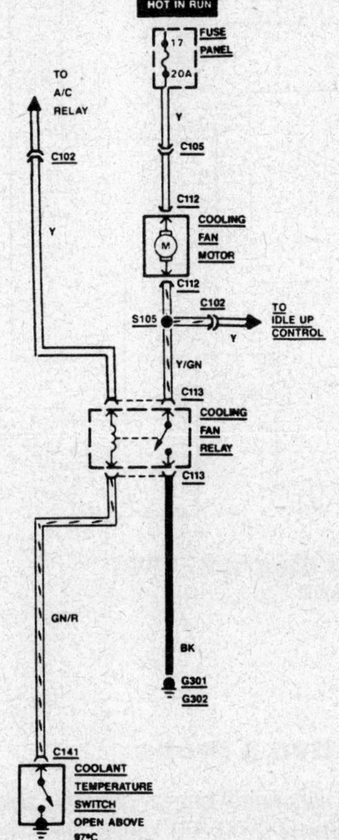


Fig. 10 Cooling fan wiring diagram. 1989 Tracer with A.C

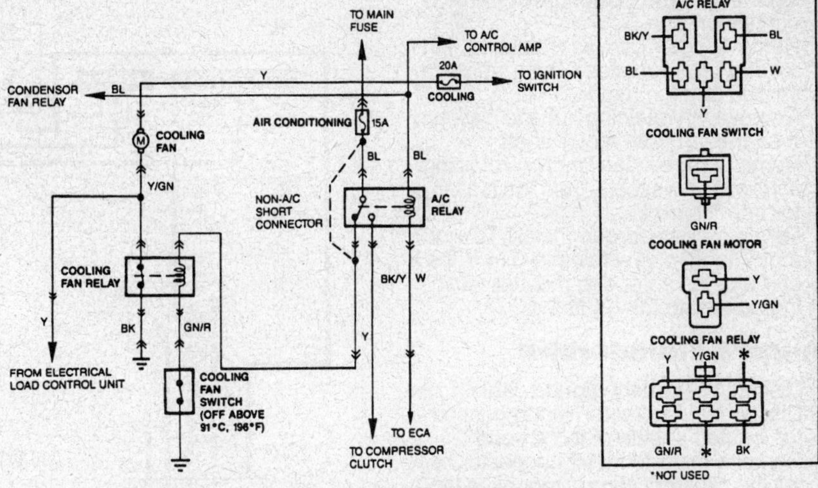


Fig. 9 Cooling fan wiring diagram. Capri

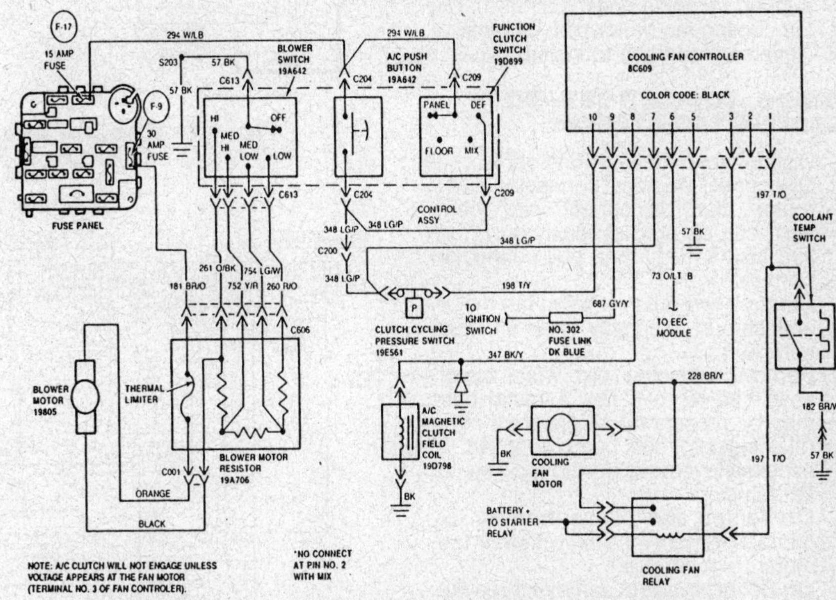


Fig. 11 Cooling fan wiring diagram. 1989–90 Escort with A/C

2. Disconnect electrical connector, then remove integrated relay control assembly from radiator support.
3. Reverse procedure to install.

## COOLING FAN RELAY

### Capri & Festiva

The cooling fan relay is located near the lefthand headlamp.

1. Disconnect battery ground cable.
2. Remove the screw from the top of the relay.
3. Remove protective boot.
4. Disconnect electrical connector.
5. Reverse procedure to install.

### 1991 Escort & Tracer

The cooling fan main relays are located in the fuse block on the lefthand side of the engine compartment. The high and low speed cooling fan relays (2 and 3) are mounted on a single bracket inside the lefthand front fender apron. The air cleaner assembly must be removed to gain access to the relays. Disconnect battery ground cable prior to servicing.

### Probe

The cooling fan relays are located in the lefthand side of the bulkhead within the main relay box. A bracket is used to attach each relay to the bulkhead, **Fig. 40.**

1. Disconnect battery ground cable, then remove the relay from the bracket.
2. Disconnect electrical connector.
3. Reverse procedure to install.

## COOLING FAN MOTOR, REPLACE

### Capri

1. Disconnect battery ground cable.
2. Remove fan wiring harness from rout-

ing clamps, then disconnect harness connector.

3. Remove four screws retaining fan shroud to radiator, then remove shroud and fan motor.
4. Remove fan retaining nut and washer, then the fan from motor shaft.
5. Remove three fan motor retaining screws and washers, then the fan motor from shroud.
6. Reverse procedure to install. **Torque** motor to shroud screws to 3-4 ft. lbs. and four fan shroud to radiator retaining screws to 23-34 ft. lbs.

### Cougar & Thunderbird

1. Disconnect battery ground cable.
2. Disconnect fan motor wiring connector located at side of fan shroud.
3. Remove male terminal connector retaining clip from shroud mounting tab.
4. Remove overflow hose from shroud, then two upper shroud to radiator support retaining bolts.
5. Lift cooling fan motor past radiator.
6. Reverse procedure to install.

### Tempo, Topaz, 1989–90 Escort & 1989 Tracer

1. Disconnect battery ground cable.
2. Disconnect electrical connector at fan motor, then disconnect wire loom from clip on shroud (push down on two lock fingers, then pull connector from motor end).
3. Remove two nuts retaining fan motor and shroud assembly, then lift from vehicle.
4. Remove retaining clip from motor shaft and remove fan. A metal burr may be present on motor shaft after retaining clip has been removed. If necessary, remove burr to facilitate in fan removal.
5. **On Tempo and Topaz models,** remove three screws, then withdraw fan motor from shroud.
6. **On Escort models,** remove three nut and washer assemblies, then the fan motor from shroud.
7. Reverse procedure to install, noting the following:
   a. **Torque** motor to shroud attaching nuts and washers to 44-66 inch lbs.
   b. **Torque** fan, motor, and shroud assembly to radiator retaining nut to 35-41 inch lbs.
   c. **Torque** fan, motor, and shroud assembly to radiator retaining screw to 23-33 inch lbs., on Escort or 31-41 inch lbs. on Tempo and Topaz.

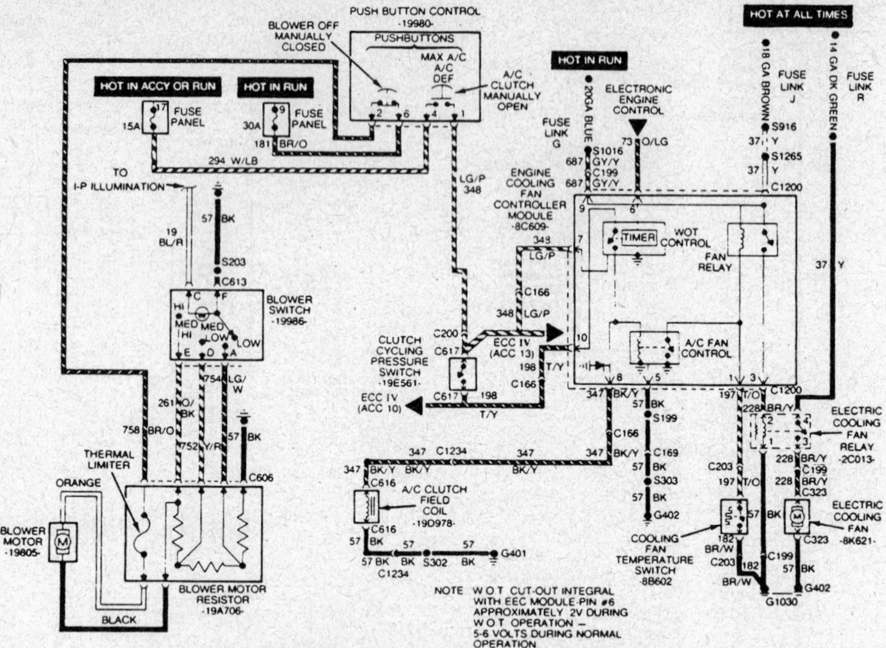


**Fig. 12 Cooling fan wiring diagram. 1989–90 Tempo & Topaz with A/C**

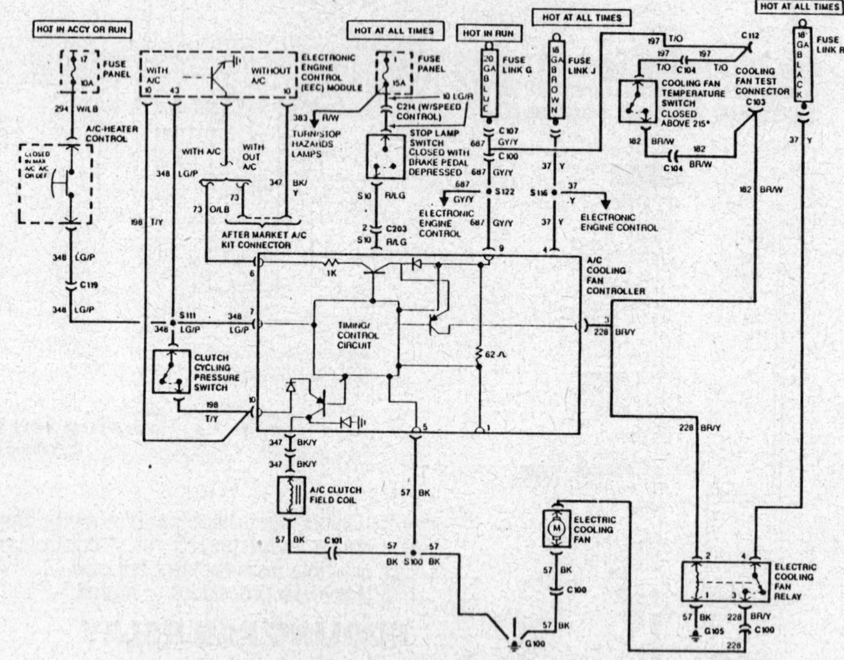


**Fig. 13 Cooling fan wiring diagram. 1991 Tempo & Topaz**

### 1991 Escort & Tracer

1. Disconnect battery ground cable.
2. **On 1.8L/4-110 models,** remove the resonance duct from the radiator isomounts.
3. **On all models,** disconnect cooling fan electrical connector.
4. Remove three radiator shroud attaching bolts from radiator, then lift shroud and fan motor assembly out from vehicle.
5. Remove cooling fan retainer clip, then the fan from motor.
6. Disconnect cooling fan motor electrical harness retainers, then remove harness from retainers.
7. Remove cooling fan motor attaching screws, then the motor from shroud.
8. Reverse procedure to install.

### Festiva & Probe

1. Disconnect battery ground cable, then the cooling fan wiring harness connectors from routing clamps.
2. Remove four screws attaching fan and shroud to radiator, then the fan and shroud.

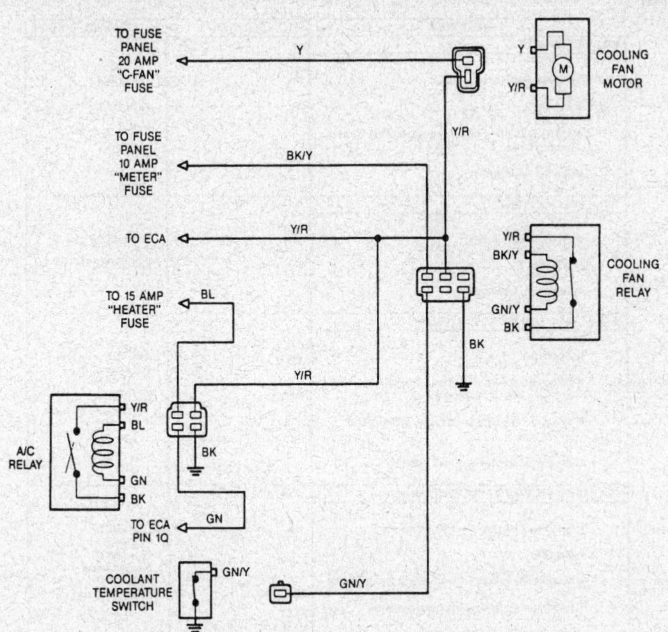


**Fig. 14 Cooling fan wiring diagram. Festiva**

**Fig. 15 Cooling fan wiring diagram. 1989–90 Mustang**

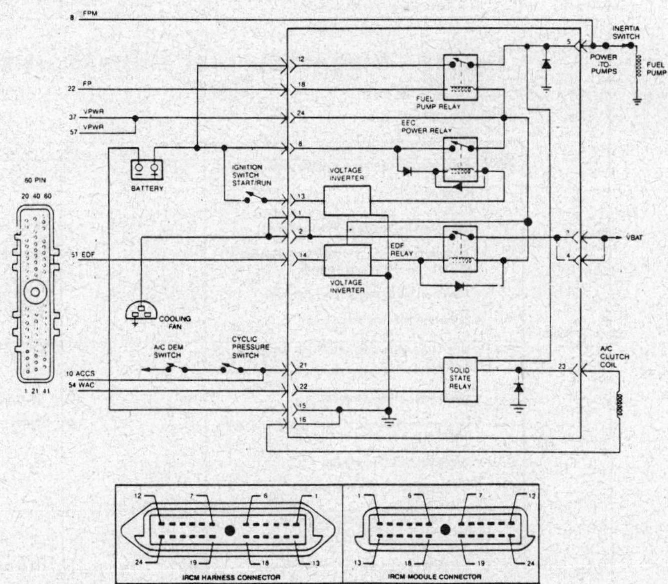

**Fig. 16 Cooling fan wiring diagram. 1991 Mustang**

3. Remove fan attaching nut and washer, then the fan from motor shaft.
4. Remove attaching screws, then separate fan motor from shroud.
5. Reverse procedure to install, noting the following for Probe models only:
   a. **Torque** fan motor to shroud bolts to 23-46 ft. lbs.
   b. **Torque** fan to fan motor attaching nut and washer to 69-95 inch lbs.
   c. **Torque** shroud to radiator bolts to 61-87 inch lbs.

### Mustang

1. Disconnect battery ground cable, then remove fan wiring harness from routing clips.
2. Disconnect wiring harness from fan motor connector (pull up on single lock finger to separate connector).
3. Remove shroud retaining screws, then the fan assembly from vehicle.
4. Remove retaining clip from end of motor shaft, then the fan. A small metal burr may be present on motor after retaining clip is removed. Removal of clip may be necessary prior to fan removal.
5. Remove fan motor to shroud retaining nuts, then the fan motor.
6. Reverse procedure to install. **Torque** motor to shroud nuts to 48.5-62.0 inch lbs. and shroud to radiator screws to 70-95 inch lbs.

### Sable & Taurus

Refer to **Fig. 41,** for models with 2.5L/4-153 and 3.0L/V6-183 engines and **Fig. 42,** for models with 3.0L/V6-183 SHO and 3.8L/V6-232 engines.

1. Disconnect battery ground cable, then remove radiator sight shield.
2. Disconnect fan motor wiring connector.
3. Remove bolts attaching fan and shroud assembly to radiator.
4. **On models with 2.5L/4-153 and 3.0L/V6-183 engines,** rotate fan and shroud assembly, then lift past radiator.
5. Remove fan U-spring retainer from motor shaft, then the fan.
6. Remove fan motor to shroud bolts, then remove motor.
7. On models with 3.8L/V6-232 engines, slide cooling fan module clear of radiator hose connector, then lift past radiator.
8. Reverse procedure to install.

## ENGINE COOLANT TEMPERATURE SWITCH

### Capri, Festiva & Probe

The cooling fan will run if the coolant temperature switch wire is disconnected, with the ignition switch in the Run position. Ensure ignition switch is in the Off position prior to disconnecting wire.

1. Disconnect battery ground cable, then drain cooling system.
2. Disconnect switch connector.
3. Remove switch from thermostat housing.
4. Reverse procedure to install. Coat switch threads with pipe sealant containing Teflon.

| CONDITION | POSSIBLE SOURCE | ACTION |
|---|---|---|
| • Overheating | • Fuse.<br>• Cooling fan switch.<br>• Cooling fan relay.<br>• Cooling fan motor.<br>• A/C relay.<br>• Circuit. | • Go to EC1.<br>• Go to EC17.<br>• Go to EC15.<br>• Go to EC12.<br>• Go to EC7.<br>• Go to EC4. |

**Fig. 17 Condition diagnosis charts (Part 1 of 2). Capri**

| CONDITION | POSSIBLE SOURCE | ACTION |
|---|---|---|
| • Fan Runs Erratically or Intermittently | • Cooling fan switch.<br>• Cooling fan relay.<br>• Cooling fan motor.<br>• A/C relay.<br>• Circuit. | • Go to EC17.<br>• Go to EC15.<br>• Go to EC12.<br>• Go to EC7.<br>• Go to EC4. |
| • Fan Runs Continuously | • Cooling fan relay.<br>• Cooling fan switch.<br>• A/C relay.<br>• Circuit. | • Go to EC15.<br>• Go to EC17.<br>• Go to EC7.<br>• Go to EC4. |
| • Fan Does Not Run When A/C is ON | • A/C relay.<br>• Cooling fan relay.<br>• Cooling fan motor.<br>• Circuit. | • Go to EC7.<br>• Go to EC15.<br>• Go to EC12.<br>• Go to EC4. |

**Fig. 17 Condition diagnosis charts (Part 2 of 2). Capri**

| TEST STEP | RESULT | ACTION TO TAKE |
|---|---|---|
| **EC6 CHECK THE LEAD TO A/C CONTROL AMPLIFIER (A/C ONLY)** | | |
| • Key OFF | Yes ▶ | GO to EC7. |
| • Measure the resistance of the BL wire between the A/C relay and the A/C control amplifier. | No ▶ | SERVICE BL wire. |
| • Is the resistance less than 5 ohms? | | |
| **EC7 CHECK A/C RELAY (A/C ONLY)** | | |
| • Disconnect A/C Relay. | Yes ▶ | GO to EC8. |
| • Measure the resistance between the following terminals and verify the resistances:<br>From — To — Resistances<br>BL — Y — Less than 5 ohms<br>BL — BK/Y — Greater than 10,000 ohms | No ▶ | SERVICE/REPLACE A/C relay. |
| • Apply 12 volts to the BL terminal as shown below. | | |
| • Ground the W terminal. | | |
| • Measure the resistance between the following terminals and verify the resistances:<br>From — To — Resistances<br>BL — Y — Greater than 10,000 ohms<br>BL — BK/Y — Less than 5 ohms | | |
| A/C RELAY<br>+ 12 VOLTS; BK/Y; BL; BL; W; Y<br>MEASURE RESISTANCE FROM THIS BL TERMINAL TO EITHER THE Y OR THE BK/Y TERMINAL AS DIRECTED ABOVE. | | |
| • Are the resistances correct? | | |

**Fig. 18 Diagnostic test steps (Part 2 of 5). Capri**

| TEST STEP | RESULT | ACTION TO TAKE |
|---|---|---|
| **EC1 CHECK FUSES** | | |
| • Locate interior fuse panel. | Yes ▶ | GO to EC4. |
| • Key OFF. | No ▶ | GO to EC2. |
| • Check the 15 amp air conditioning and the 20 amp cooling fuses. | | |
| • Are the fuses good? | | |
| **EC2 CHECK SYSTEM** | | |
| • Replace blown fuse(s). | Yes ▶ | GO to EC3. |
| • Key ON. | No ▶ | GO to EC4. |
| • Did fuse(s) blow again? | | |
| **EC3 CHECK FOR SHORTS TO GROUND** | | |
| • Key OFF. | Yes ▶ | SERVICE wire(s) in question. |
| • Disconnect the BL wire at the air conditioning fuse and the Y wire at the cooling fuse. | No ▶ | GO to EC4. |
| • Measure the resistance of the BL and then the Y wire to ground. | | |
| • Are the resistances less than 5 ohms? | | |
| **EC4 CHECK SUPPLY TO COOLING FAN MOTOR** | | |
| • Disconnect cooling fan motor connector. | Yes ▶ | GO to EC5. (A/C only). GO to EC11. (non A/C only) |
| • Key ON. | | |
| • Measure the voltage on the Y wire at the connector. | | |
| • Reconnect the cooling fan motor connector. | No ▶ | SERVICE Y wire. |
| • Is the voltage greater than 10 volts? | | |
| **EC5 CHECK SUPPLY TO A/C RELAY (A/C ONLY)** | | |
| • Disconnect the A/C relay connector. | Yes ▶ | GO to EC6. |
| • Measure the voltage on the BL wire at the relay connector. | No ▶ | SERVICE BL wire. |
| • Reconnect the A/C relay connector. | | |
| • Is the voltage greater than 10 volts? | | |

**Fig. 18 Diagnostic test steps (Part 1 of 5). Capri**

| TEST STEP | RESULT | ACTION TO TAKE |
|---|---|---|
| **EC8 CHECK LEAD BETWEEN A/C RELAY AND COOLING FAN RELAY (A/C ONLY)** | | |
| • Disconnect the cooling fan relay connector.. | Yes ▶ | GO to EC9. |
| • Measure the resistance of the Y wire between the A/C relay and the cooling fan relay. | No ▶ | SERVICE Y wire. |
| • Reconnect the cooling fan relay connector. | | |
| • Is the resistance less than 5 ohms? | | |
| **EC9 CHECK LEAD BETWEEN A/C RELAY AND ECA (A/C ONLY)** | | |
| • Disconnect the ECA connector. | Yes ▶ | GO to EC10. |
| • Measure the resistance of the W wire between the A/C relay and the ECA. | No ▶ | SERVICE W wire. |
| • Reconnect the ECA connector. | | |
| • Is the resistance less than 5 ohms? | | |
| **EC10 CHECK LEAD BETWEEN A/C RELAY AND COMPRESSOR CLUTCH (A/C ONLY)** | | |
| • Disconnect the compressor clutch connector. | Yes ▶ | GO to EC11. |
| • Measure the resistance on the BK/Y wire between the A/C relay and the compressor clutch. | No ▶ | SERVICE BK/Y wire. |
| • Reconnect the compressor clutch connector. | | |
| • Is the resistance less than 5 ohms? | | |
| **EC11 CHECK SUPPLY TO COOLING FAN RELAY (NON-A/C ONLY)** | | |
| • Access cooling fan relay connector. | Yes ▶ | GO to EC12.. |
| • Key ON. | No ▶ | SERVICE Y wire. |
| • Measure the voltage on the Y wire at the cooling fan relay. | | |
| • Is the voltage greatrr than 10 volts? | | |
| **EC12 CHECK COOLING FAN MOTOR** | | |
| • Locate the cooling fan motor connector. | Yes ▶ | GO to EC13. |
| • Ground the Y/GN wire at the connector. | No ▶ | SERVICE/REPLACE cooling fan motor. |
| • Does the cooling fan motor turn on? | | |

**Fig. 18 Diagnostic test steps (Part 3 of 5). Capri**

| TEST STEP | RESULT ▶ | ACTION TO TAKE |
|---|---|---|
| **EC13** CHECK LEAD BETWEEN COOLING FAN RELAY AND COOLING FAN MOTOR | | |
| • Key OFF.<br>• Measure the resistance of the Y/GN wire between the cooling fan relay and the cooling fan motor.<br>• Is the resistance less than 5 ohms? | Yes ▶<br>No ▶ | GO to EC14.<br>SERVICE Y/GN wire. |
| **EC14** CHECK COOLING FAN RELAY GROUND | | |
| • Measure the resistance of the BK wire between the cooling fan relay and ground.<br>• Is the resistance less than 5 ohms? | Yes ▶<br>No ▶ | GO to EC15.<br>SERVICE BK wire. |
| **EC15** CHECK COOLING FAN RELAY | | |
| • Disconnect the cooling fan relay connector.<br>• Measure the resistance between the Y/GN terminal and the BK terminal at the relay.<br>• Is the resistance less than 5 ohms?<br>• Apply 12 volts to the Y terminal at the relay.<br>• Ground the GN/R terminal at the relay.<br>• Measure the resistance between the Y/GN terminal and the BK terminal at the relay.<br>• Reconnect the cooling fan relay.<br>• Is the resistance greater than 10,000 ohms? | Yes ▶<br>No ▶ | GO to EC16.<br>SERVICE/REPLACE cooling fan relay. |
| **EC16** CHECK LEAD BETWEEN COOLING FAN RELAY AND COOLING FAN SWITCH | | |
| • Measure the resistance of the GN/R wire between the cooling fan relay and the cooling fan switch.<br>• Is the resistance less than 5 ohms? | Yes ▶<br>No ▶ | GO to EC17.<br>SERVICE GN/R wire. |

**Fig. 18 Diagnostic test steps (Part 4 of 5). Capri**

| TEST STEP | RESULT ▶ | ACTION TO TAKE |
|---|---|---|
| **EC17** FAN SWITCH FUNCTION | | |
| • Disconnect the cooling fan switch connector.<br>• Using a VOM check the continuity of the switch from terminal GN/R to ground.<br>• Start up the engine and observe the continuity of the switch on the VOM as engine warms up.<br>• If continuity is still present in the switch by the time the engine is hot, remove the fan switch from the engine.<br>• Place the switch in a 50% water and glycol mixture with a 150°C (250°F) range thermometer.<br>• Heat the water and monitor the switch continuity, using VOM, and verify the opening and closing temperature as the water is heated then cooled. 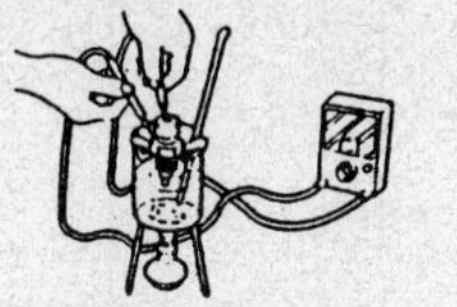<br>• Does the switch operate at the approximate specified temperatures? Refer to Specifications. | Yes ▶<br>Yes ▶<br>No ▶ | RETURN to condition chart.<br>GO to EC18. (A/C only)<br>SERVICE/REPLACE cooling fan switch. |
| **EC18** CHECK SYSTEM FOR OPERATION WHEN A/C IS TURNED ON (A/C ONLY) | | |
| • Turn the A/C on.<br>• Does the cooling fan motor turn on? | Yes ▶<br>No ▶ | RETURN to condition chart.<br>SERVICE/REPLACE cooling fan motor. |

**Fig. 18 Diagnostic test steps (Part 5 of 5). Capri**

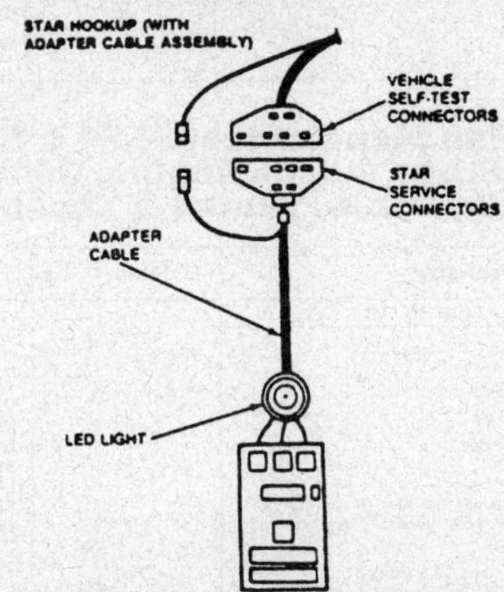


**Fig. 19 Star Tester connections. Probe w/3.0L Engine, Continental, Cougar, Sable, Taurus & Thunderbird**

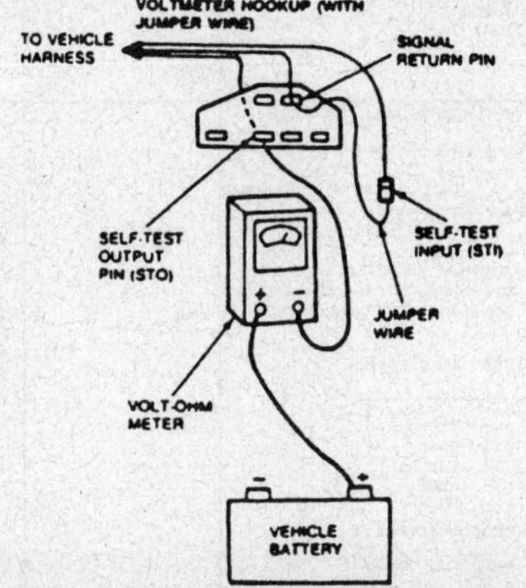


**Fig. 20 Volt/Ohm meter (VOM) connections. Probe w/3.0L Engine, Continental, Cougar, Sable, Taurus & Thunderbird**

| TEST STEP | RESULT ▶ | ACTION TO TAKE |
|---|---|---|
| **KF1** SERVICE CODE 83/88: CHECK FOR IGNITION START/RUN CIRCUIT VOLTAGE AT HEDF/EDF RELAY | | |
| Service Code 83 indicates a HEDF primary circuit failure.<br>Service Code 88 indicates an EDF primary circuit failure.<br>Possible causes are:<br>— Open or shorted circuit.<br>— Faulty fan relay.<br>— Faulty processor.<br>— Faulty A/C high pressure switch (Code 83).<br>**NOTE: During diagnosis, use the chart below to determine the correct pin number, circuit and relay being tested.**<br>• Key off.<br>• Disconnect EDF or HEDF relay.<br>• DVOM on 20 volt scale.<br>• Key on.<br>• Measure voltage between IGN Start/Run circuit at the EDF/HEDF relay vehicle harness connector and chassis ground.<br>• Is voltage greater than 10.5 volts? | Yes ▶<br>No ▶ | GO to KF2.<br>SERVICE open circuit. RECONNECT EDF/HEDF relay. |

| Code | Circuit | Test Pin Number | Fan Relay |
|---|---|---|---|
| 83 | HEDF | 31 | HEDF(#2) |
| 88 | EDF | 35 | EDF(#1) |

**Fig. 21 Fan pinpoint test KF1 (Part 1 of 11). Probe w/3.0L Engine, Continental, Cougar, Sable, Taurus & Thunderbird**

| TEST STEP | RESULT ▶ | ACTION TO TAKE |
|---|---|---|
| **KF2** ENTER OUTPUT STATE CHECK (REFER TO QUICK TEST APPENDIX) | | |
| **NOTE: Do not use STAR tester for this Step, use VOM/DVOM.**<br>• Key off, wait 10 seconds.<br>• DVOM on 20 volt scale.<br>• Disconnect electrical connector on the speed control servo; if equipped.<br>• Connect DVOM negative test lead to STO at the Self-Test connector and positive test lead to the battery positive post.<br>• Jumper STI to SIG RTN at the Self-Test connector.<br>• Perform Key On Engine Off Self-Test until the completion of the Continuous Memory Codes.<br>• DVOM will indicate less than 1.0 volt when test complete.<br>• Depress and release throttle.<br>• **Does voltage increase to greater than 10.5 volts?** | Yes ▶<br><br>No ▶ | REMAIN in Output State Check. GO to KF3.<br><br>DEPRESS throttle to WOT and RELEASE. |
| **KF3** CHECK FOR EDF/HEDF CIRCUIT CYCLING | | |
| • Still in Output State Check.<br>• EDF or HEDF relay disconnected.<br>• DVOM on 20 volt scale.<br>• Connect DVOM positive test lead to the IGN Start/Run circuit and the negative test lead to the EDF or HEDF circuit at the EDF/HEDF relay vehicle harness connector.<br>• While observing DVOM, depress throttle. For EDF, wait until "CHECK ENGINE" light flashes once (10 seconds). For HEDF, wait until "CHECK ENGINE" light flashes twice (15 seconds). Release throttle. EDF/HEDF outputs are now "on". To cycle "off", depress and release throttle.<br>• **Does voltage cycle high and low (about 1 volt change)?** | Yes ▶<br><br>No ▶ | REPLACE EDF or HEDF relay. REMOVE jumper.<br><br>REMOVE jumper. GO to KF4. |

**Fig. 21 Fan pinpoint tests KF2 & KF3 (Part 2 of 11). Probe w/3.0L Engine, Continental, Cougar, Sable, Taurus & Thunderbird**

| TEST STEP | RESULT ▶ | ACTION TO TAKE |
|---|---|---|
| **KF4** CHECK CONTINUITY OF EDF/HEDF CIRCUIT | | |
| • Key off.<br>• EDF or HEDF relay disconnected.<br>• Disconnect processor 60 pin connector. Inspect for damaged or pushed out pins, corrosion, loose wires, etc. Service as necessary.<br>• Install breakout box, leave processor disconnected.<br>• DVOM on 200 ohm scale.<br>**For Code 83:**<br>— Measure resistance between Test Pin 31 at the breakout box and HEDF circuit at the HEDF relay vehicle harness connector.<br>**For Code 88:**<br>— Measure resistance between Test Pin 35 at the breakout box and EDF circuit at the EDF relay vehicle harness connector.<br>• **Is resistance less than 5.0 ohms?** | Yes ▶<br><br>No ▶ | GO to KF5.<br><br>SERVICE open circuit. REMOVE breakout box. RECONNECT all components. RERUN Quick Test. |
| **KF5** CHECK EDF/HEDF CIRCUIT FOR SHORT TO POWER | | |
| • Key on.<br>• Breakout box installed, processor disconnected.<br>• EDF or HEDF relay disconnected.<br>• DVOM on 20 volt scale.<br>• Measure voltage between Test Pin 31 (HEDF) or 35 (EDF) at the breakout box and battery negative post.<br>• **Is voltage less than 1.0 volts?** | Yes ▶<br><br>No ▶ | GO to KF6.<br><br>SERVICE short circuit. REMOVE breakout box. RECONNECT all components. If code is still present, REPLACE processor. |

**Fig. 21 Fan pinpoint tests KF4 & KF5 (Part 3 of 11). Probe w/3.0L Engine, Continental, Cougar, Sable, Taurus & Thunderbird**

| TEST STEP | RESULT ▶ | ACTION TO TAKE |
|---|---|---|
| **KF6** CHECK EDF/HEDF CIRCUIT FOR SHORT TO GROUND | | |
| • Key off.<br>• Breakout box installed, processor disconnected.<br>• EDF or HEDF relay disconnected.<br>• DVOM on 200,000 ohm scale.<br>• Measure resistance between Test Pin 31 (HEDF) or 35 (EDF) and Test Pins 40 and 60 at the breakout box.<br>• **Is resistance greater than 10,000 ohms?** | Yes ▶<br><br>No ▶ | REPLACE processor. REMOVE breakout box. RECONNECT all components.<br><br>SERVICE short circuit. (For Code 83, first VERIFY that A/C high pressure switch is open). REMOVE breakout box. RECONNECT all components. |
| **KF10** LOW SPEED (EDF) AND/OR HIGH SPEED (HEDF) COOLING FAN DOES NOT OPERATE: CHECK FOR VOLTAGE TO EDF RELAY | | |
| • Key off.<br>• Disconnect EDF relay.<br>• DVOM on 20 volt scale.<br>• Key on.<br>• Measure voltage between the short connector input pin at the EDF relay vehicle harness connector and battery negative post.<br>• **Is voltage greater than 10.5 volts?**<br>TO SHORT CONNECTOR<br>TO HEDF RELAY<br>WITH A/C<br>EDF RELAY VEHICLE HARNESS CONNECTOR | Yes ▶<br><br>No ▶ | GO to KF13.<br><br>**For A/C equipped vehicles:**<br>GO to KF11.<br>**For non A/C vehicles:**<br>VERIFY condition of jumper at short connector and operation of IGN relay. If OK, SERVICE open circuit. RECONNECT EDF relay. RE-EVALUATE symptom. |

**Fig. 21 Fan pinpoint tests KF6 & KF10 (Part 4 of 11). Probe w/3.0L Engine, Continental, Cougar, Sable, Taurus & Thunderbird**

| TEST STEP | RESULT ▶ | ACTION TO TAKE |
|---|---|---|
| **KF11** CHECK FOR VOLTAGE TO HEDF RELAY | | |
| • Key off.<br>• EDF relay disconnected.<br>• Disconnect HEDF relay.<br>• DVOM on 20 volt scale.<br>• Key on.<br>• Measure voltage between the IGN relay input pin at the HEDF relay vehicle harness connector and battery negative post.<br>• **Is voltage greater than 10.5 volts?**<br>TO IGNITION RELAY<br>HEDF RELAY VEHICLE HARNESS CONNECTOR | Yes ▶<br><br>No ▶ | GO to KF12.<br><br>VERIFY operation of IGN relay. If OK, SERVICE open circuit. RECONNECT EDF and HEDF relays. RE-EVALUATE symptoms. |
| **KF12** CHECK CONTINUITY BETWEEN EDF AND HEDF RELAYS | | |
| • Key off.<br>• EDF and HEDF relays disconnected.<br>• DVOM on 200 ohm scale.<br>• Measure resistance between the HEDF input pin at the EDF relay vehicle harness connector and the output to EDF pin at the HEDF relay vehicle harness connector.<br>• **Is resistance less than 5.0 ohms?**<br>EDF RELAY<br>HEDF RELAY<br>VEHICLE HARNESS CONNECTORS | Yes ▶<br><br>No ▶ | REPLACE HEDF relay. RECONNECT all components. RE-EVALUATE symptom.<br><br>SERVICE open circuit. RECONNECT EDF and HEDF relays. RE-EVALUATE symptom. |

**Fig. 21 Fan pinpoint tests KF11 & KF12 (Part 5 of 11). Probe w/3.0L Engine, Continental, Cougar, Sable, Taurus & Thunderbird**

| TEST STEP | RESULT ▶ | ACTION TO TAKE |
|---|---|---|
| **KF13** CHECK CIRCUITS FROM EDF RELAY TO FAN | | |
| • Key off.<br>• EDF relay disconnected.<br>• Insert jumper wire from short connector input pin to Power-To-Fan pin at the EDF relay vehicle harness connector.<br>• Key on.<br>• **Does fan run?**<br>JUMPER WIRE<br>EDF RELAY VEHICLE HARNESS CONNECTOR | Yes ▶ | **For A/C equipped vehicles:** REMOVE jumper. GO to KF16.<br>**For Non A/C vehicles:** REPLACE EDF relay. REMOVE jumper. RE-EVALUATE symptom. |
| | No ▶ | REMOVE jumper. GO to KF14. |
| **KF14** CHECK EDF POWER-TO-FAN CIRCUIT CONTINUITY | | |
| • Key off.<br>• EDF relay disconnected.<br>• Disconnect cooling fan.<br>• DVOM on 200 ohm scale.<br>• Measure resistance between the EDF Power-To-Fan output pin at the EDF vehicle harness connector and the EDF Power-To-Fan input pin at the cooling fan vehicle harness connector.<br>• **Is resistance less than 5.0 ohms?**<br>EDF RELAY — POWER TO FAN — COOLING FAN<br>VEHICLE HARNESS CONNECTORS | Yes ▶ | GO to KF15. |
| | No ▶ | SERVICE open circuit. RECONNECT all components. RE-EVALUATE symptom. |

**Fig. 21 Fan pinpoint tests KF13 & KF14 (Part 6 of 11). Probe w/3.0L Engine, Continental, Cougar, Sable, Taurus & Thunderbird**

| TEST STEP | RESULT ▶ | ACTION TO TAKE |
|---|---|---|
| **KF15** CHECK COOLING FAN GROUND CIRCUIT | | |
| • Key off.<br>• EDF relay disconnected.<br>• Cooling fan disconnected.<br>• DVOM on 200 ohm scale.<br>• Measure resistance between GND circuit at the cooling fan vehicle harness connector and battery negative post.<br>• **Is resistance less than 5.0 ohms?** | Yes ▶ | REPLACE cooling fan. RECONNECT all components. RE-EVALUATE symptom. |
| | No ▶ | SERVICE open circuit. RECONNECT all components. RE-EVALUATE symptom. |
| **KF16** CHECK CIRCUITS FROM HEDF RELAY TO FAN | | |
| • Key off.<br>• EDF relay disconnected.<br>• Disconnect A/C high pressure (A/C HP) switch.<br>• Insert a jumper wire between the two pins of the A/C HP switch vehicle harness connector.<br>• Key on.<br>• **Does fan run at high speed?** | Yes ▶ | REPLACE EDF relay. REMOVE jumper. RECONNECT A/C high pressure switch. RE-EVALUATE symptom. |
| | No ▶ | REMOVE jumper. RECONNECT EDF relay. GO to KF17. |

**Fig. 21 Fan pinpoint tests KF15 & KF16 (Part 7 of 11). Probe w/3.0L Engine, Continental, Cougar, Sable, Taurus & Thunderbird**

| TEST STEP | RESULT ▶ | ACTION TO TAKE |
|---|---|---|
| **KF17** VERIFY CONTINUITY OF CIRCUITS FROM A/C HIGH PRESSURE SWITCH | | |
| • Key off.<br>• A/C HP switch disconnected.<br>• Disconnect HEDF relay.<br>• DVOM on 200 ohm scale.<br>• Measure continuity from GND circuit at A/C HP switch vehicle harness connector and battery negative post.<br>• Measure continuity between output to HEDF relay pin at A/C HP switch vehicle harness connector and A/C HP switch input pin at the HEDF relay vehicle harness connector.<br>• **Is each resistance less than 5.0 ohms?**<br>HEDF RELAY<br>TEST PIN 31<br>A/C HIGH PRESSURE SWITCH<br>VEHICLE HARNESS CONNECTORS | Yes ▶ | GO to KF18. |
| | No ▶ | SERVICE open circuit. RECONNECT all components. RE-EVALUATE symptom. If symptom is still present, continue diagnosis at KF16. |

**Fig. 21 Fan pinpoint test KF17 (Part 8 of 11). Probe w/3.0L Engine, Continental, Cougar, Sable, Taurus & Thunderbird**

| TEST STEP | RESULT ▶ | ACTION TO TAKE |
|---|---|---|
| **KF18** CHECK HEDF POWER-TO-FAN VOLTAGE AT FAN WITH A/C HP SWITCH GROUNDED | | |
| • Key off<br>• A/C HP switch disconnected.<br>• Reconnect HEDF relay.<br>• Disconnect cooling fan.<br>• DVOM on 20 volt scale.<br>• Again insert a jumper wire between the two pins of the A/C HP switch vehicle harness connector.<br>• Key on.<br>• Measure voltage between HEDF Power-To-Fan circuit at the cooling fan vehicle harness connector and battery negative post.<br>• **Is voltage greater than 10.5 volts?**<br>HEDF POWER-TO-FAN<br>COOLING FAN VEHICLE HARNESS CONNECTOR | Yes ▶ | REPLACE cooling fan. REMOVE jumper. RECONNECT all components. RE-EVALUATE symptom. |
| | No ▶ | REMOVE jumper. RECONNECT A/C HP switch. GO to KF19. |
| **KF19** CHECK HEDF POWER-TO-FAN CIRCUIT CONTINUITY | | |
| • Key off.<br>• Cooling fan disconnected.<br>• Disconnect HEDF relay.<br>• DVOM on 200 ohm scale.<br>• Measure resistance between the HEDF Power-To-Fan output pin at the HEDF vehicle harness connector and the HEDF Power-To-Fan input pin at the cooling fan vehicle harness connector.<br>• **Is resistance less than 5.0 ohms?**<br>HEDF POWER-TO-FAN<br>HEDF RELAY VEHICLE HARNESS CONNECTOR | Yes ▶ | REPLACE HEDF relay. RECONNECT all components. RE-EVALUATE symptom. |
| | No ▶ | SERVICE open circuit. RECONNECT all components. RE-EVALUATE symptom. |

**Fig. 21 Fan pinpoint tests KF18 & KF19 (Part 9 of 11). Probe w/3.0L Engine, Continental, Cougar, Sable, Taurus & Thunderbird**

| TEST STEP | RESULT ▶ | ACTION TO TAKE |
|---|---|---|
| **KF25** LOW SPEED (EDF) OR HIGH SPEED (HEDF) COOLING FAN ALWAYS ON: VERIFY IGNITION RELAY IS OPENING | | |
| **NOTE: Verify that A/C is off during testing.**<br>• **Is cooling fan always on with key off, but operating normally with key on?** | Yes ▶ | VERIFY that IGN relay contacts are not always closed. If OK, CHECK circuit from IGN relay to fan relay(s) for short to BATT(+). |
| | No ▶ | GO to KF26. |
| **KF26** CHECK FOR EDF RELAY ALWAYS CLOSED | | |
| • Key off.<br>• Disconnect EDF relay.<br>• Key on.<br>• **Does fan continue to run?** | Yes ▶ | **For A/C equipped vehicles:**<br>GO to KF27.<br>**For non A/C vehicles:**<br>SERVICE short to power in EDF Power-To-Fan circuit. RECONNECT EDF relay. RE-EVALUATE symptom. |
| | No ▶ | REPLACE EDF relay. RE-EVALUATE symptom. |
| **KF27** CHECK HEDF RELAY | | |
| • Key off.<br>• EDF relay disconnected.<br>• Disconnect HEDF relay.<br>• Key on.<br>• **Does fan continue to run?** | Yes ▶ | GO to KF28. |
| | No ▶ | REPLACE HEDF relay. RECONNECT EDF relay. RE-EVALUATE symptom. |

**Fig. 21 Fan pinpoint tests KF25, KF 26 & KF27 (Part 10 of 11). Probe w/3.0L Engine, Continental, Cougar, Sable, Taurus & Thunderbird**

| TEST STEP | RESULT ▶ | ACTION TO TAKE |
|---|---|---|
| **KF28** CHECK EDF POWER-TO-FAN CIRCUIT FOR SHORT TO POWER | | |
| • Key off.<br>• EDF and HEDF relay disconnected.<br>• Disconnect cooling fan.<br>• DVOM on 20 volt scale.<br>• Key on.<br>• Measure voltage between EDF Power-To-Fan circuit at the cooling fan vehicle harness connector and battery negative post.<br>• **Is voltage greater than 1.0 volt?**<br>EDF POWER-TO-FAN<br>HEDF POWER-TO-FAN<br>COOLING FAN VEHICLE HARNESS CONNECTOR | Yes ▶ | SERVICE Short-To-Power in EDF Power-To-Fan circuit. RECONNECT all components. RE-EVALUATE symptom. |
| | No ▶ | SERVICE Short-To-Power in HEDF Power-To-Fan circuit. RECONNECT all components. RE-EVALUATE symptom. |

**Fig. 21 Fan pinpoint test KF28 (Part 11 of 11). Probe w/3.0L Engine, Continental, Cougar, Sable, Taurus & Thunderbird**

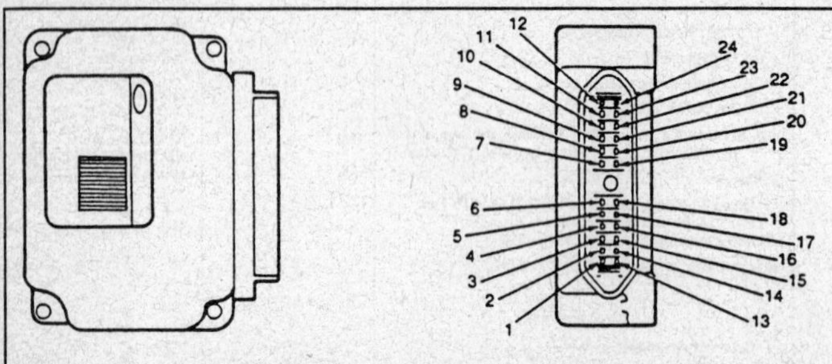


**Fig. 22 Integral relay control module terminal identification. Probe w/3.0L Engine, Continental, Cougar, Sable, Taurus & Thunderbird**

| TEST STEP | RESULT ▶ | ACTION TO TAKE |
|---|---|---|
| **X1** CHECK BATTERY VOLTAGE | | |
| • Key on, engine off.<br>• DVOM on 20 volt scale.<br>• Measure voltage across battery terminals.<br>• **Is voltage greater than 10.5 volts?** | Yes ▶ | GO to X2. |
| | No ▶ | SERVICE discharged battery. |
| **X2** CHECK BATTERY GROUND | | |
| • Key on, engine off.<br>• DVOM on 20 volt scale.<br>• Measure voltage between battery negative post and SIG RTN circuit in the Self-Test connector.<br>• **Is voltage greater than 0.5 volts?** | Yes ▶ | GO to X3. |
| | No ▶ | GO to X8. |
| **X3** GROUND FAULT ISOLATION | | |
| • Key off.<br>• Disconnect processor 60 pin connector. Inspect for damaged or pushed out pins, corrosion, loose wires etc. Service as necessary.<br>• Install breakout box and connect processor to breakout box.<br>• DVOM on 20 volt scale.<br>• Key on, engine off.<br>• Measure voltage between battery negative post and Test Pins 40 and 60 at the breakout box.<br>• **Is each voltage less than 0.5 volts?** | Yes ▶ | GO to X4. |
| | No ▶ | SERVICE open ground circuit. REMOVE breakout box. RECONNECT processor. |
| **X4** PROCESSOR GROUND FAULT ISOLATION | | |
| • Key off, wait 10 seconds.<br>• Breakout box installed, processor connected.<br>• DVOM on 200 ohm scale.<br>• Measure resistance between Test Pin 46 and Test Pins 40 and 60 at the breakout box.<br>• **Is each resistance less than 5 ohms?** | Yes ▶ | GO to X5. |
| | No ▶ | REPLACE processor. REMOVE breakout box. |

**Fig. 23 Integrated controller pinpoint tests X1, X2, X3 & X4 (Part 1 of 30). Probe w/3.0L Engine, Continental, Cougar, Sable, Taurus & Thunderbird**

| TEST STEP | RESULT ▶ | ACTION TO TAKE |
|---|---|---|
| **X5 CHECK SIG RTN CIRCUIT CONTINUITY** | | |
| • Key off, wait 10 seconds.<br>• Breakout box installed, processor connected.<br>• DVOM on 200 ohm scale.<br>• Measure resistance between Test Pin 46 at the breakout box and SIG RTN circuit at Self-Test connector.<br>• **Is resistance less than 5.0 ohms?** | Yes ▶ | System OK. REMOVE breakout box. RECONNECT processor. |
| | No ▶ | SERVICE open circuit. REMOVE breakout box. RECONNECT processor. |
| **X6 MEASURE VOLTAGE AND GROUND TO INTEGRATED CONTROLLER** | | |
| • Key off.<br>• Disconnect Integrated Controller.<br>• DVOM on 20 volt scale.<br>• Measure voltage between pin 8 and pin 15 at the Integrated Controller vehicle harness connector.<br>• **Is voltage greater than 10.5 volts?** | Yes ▶ | GO to X7. |
| | No ▶ | GO to X9. |
| **X7 CHECK KEY POWER TO INTEGRATED CONTROLLER** | | |
| • Key off.<br>• Integrated Controller disconnected.<br>• DVOM on 20 volt scale.<br>• Key on, engine off.<br>• Measure voltage between Pin 13 and Pin 15 at the Integrated Controller vehicle harness connector.<br>• **Is voltage greater than 10.5 volts?** | Yes ▶ | GO to X8. |
| | No ▶ | SERVICE open between Pin 13 and ignition switch. RECONNECT Integrated Controller. |

**Fig. 23 Integrated controller pinpoint tests X5, X6, & X7 (Part 2 of 30). Probe w/3.0L Engine, Continental, Cougar, Sable, Taurus & Thunderbird**

| TEST STEP | RESULT ▶ | ACTION TO TAKE |
|---|---|---|
| **X8 CHECK VPWR CIRCUIT CONTINUITY** | | |
| • Key off.<br>• Integrated Controller disconnected.<br>• Disconnect processor 60 pin connector. Inspect for damaged or pushed out pins, corrosion, loose wires, etc. Service as necessary.<br>• Install breakout box, leave processor disconnected.<br>• DVOM on 200 ohm scale.<br>• Measure resistance between Test Pins 37 and 57 at the breakout box and Pin 24 at the Integrated Controller vehicle harness connector.<br>• **Is resistance greater than 5.0 ohms?** | Yes ▶ | SERVICE open in VPWR circuit. REMOVE breakout box. RECONNECT all components. |
| | No ▶ | REPLACE Integrated Controller. REMOVE breakout box. RECONNECT processor. |
| **X9 MEASURE CONTINUITY OF POWER GROUND TO INTEGRATED CONTROLLER** | | |
| • Key off.<br>• Integrated Controller disconnected.<br>• DVOM on 200 ohm scale.<br>• Measure resistance between battery negative post and Pin 15 at the Integrated Controller vehicle harness connector.<br>• **Is resistance greater than 5.0 ohms?** | Yes ▶ | SERVICE open in battery ground to Pin 15 (Integrated Controller harness connector). RECONNECT Integrated Controller. |
| | No ▶ | SERVICE open in battery positive to Pin 8 (Integrated Controller harness connector). RECONNECT Integrated Controller. |

**Fig. 23 Integrated controller pinpoint tests X8, & X9 (Part 3 of 30). Probe w/3.0L Engine, Continental, Cougar, Sable, Taurus & Thunderbird**

| TEST STEP | RESULT ▶ | ACTION TO TAKE |
|---|---|---|
| **X10 SERVICE CODE 72: CHECK VPWR CIRCUIT FOR INTERMITTENT OPEN** | | |
| Service Code 72 indicates that while Key Power was present, VPWR was interrupted or interference from electrical noises caused the processor to reset, resulting in possible stalls, high idle rpm, lack of power on acceleration or other drive symptoms.<br>Possible Causes:<br>— Intermittent open in VPWR circuit from integrated controller to processor.<br>— EEC power relay intermittent malfunction.<br>— Intermittent open in VBAT circuit to integrated controller.<br>— Intermittent open in KEY POWER circuit to integrated controller.<br>— EEC harness too close to the distributor spark plug wires and other vehicle harnesses.<br>• Enter Continuous Monitor Mode (Engine Running) Observe VOM or STAR LED for indication of a fault while performing the following:<br>• Shake, bend and twist vehicle harness from Integrated Controller to the processor, to the ignition switch and to battery positive post.<br>• **Is a fault indicated or does Code 72 reappear in Continuous Memory if Quick Test is rerun?** | Yes ▶ | CHECK for proper routing of EEC harness. SERVICE as necessary. If OK SERVICE intermittent VPWR circuit. |
| | No ▶ | INSPECT component and harness connectors of Integrated Controller and processor, for loose or damaged pins, corrosion, etc. SERVICE as necessary. If OK, ROAD TEST vehicle through a variety of drive modes. If symptom exists, REPLACE Integrated Controller, otherwise testing complete. |
| **X11 CHECK POWER-TO-PUMP(S) CIRCUIT VOLTAGE** | | |
| • Key on, engine off.<br>• Locate and disconnect fuel pump(s).<br>• DVOM on 20 volt scale.<br>• Measure voltage between CHASSIS GROUND and POWER-TO-PUMP(s) circuit at the fuel pump vehicle harness connector during crank mode.<br>• **Is voltage greater than 8.0 volts during crank?** | Yes ▶ | GO to Electric Fuel Pump |
| | No ▶ | GO to X12. |

**Fig. 23 Integrated controller pinpoint tests X10 & X11 (Part 4 of 30). Probe w/3.0L Engine, Continental, Cougar, Sable, Taurus & Thunderbird**

| TEST STEP | RESULT ▶ | ACTION TO TAKE |
|---|---|---|
| **X12 CHECK POWER-TO-PUMP(S) CIRCUIT CONTINUITY** | | |
| • Key off.<br>• Disconnect Integrated Controller.<br>• Fuel pump(s) disconnected.<br>• DVOM on 200 ohm scale.<br>• Measure resistance between Pin 5 at the Integrated Controller vehicle harness connector and POWER-TO-PUMP(s) circuit at the fuel pump vehicle harness connector.<br>• **Is resistance less than 5.0 ohms?** | Yes ▶ | REPLACE Integrated Controller. RECONNECT all components. |
| | No ▶ | SERVICE open in POWER-TO-PUMP(s) circuit. RECONNECT all components. |
| **X14 CHECK POWER-TO-PUMP(S) CIRCUIT FOR SHORTS TO POWER** | | |
| • Key off.<br>• Disconnect Integrated Controller.<br>• Disconnect fuel pump(s).<br>• DVOM on 200,000 ohm scale.<br>• Measure resistance between Pin 5 and Pin 24 at the Integrated Controller vehicle harness connector.<br>• Measure resistance between Pin 5 at the Integrated Controller vehicle harness connector and battery positive post.<br>• **Is each resistance greater than 10,000 ohms?** | Yes ▶ | REPLACE Integrated Controller. RECONNECT fuel pump. |
| | No ▶ | SERVICE short circuit. RECONNECT all components. ATTEMPT to start vehicle. If vehicle runs. If vehicle will not run, REPLACE Integrated Controller. |

**Fig. 23 Integrated controller pinpoint tests X12 & X14 (Part 5 of 30). Probe w/3.0L Engine, Continental, Cougar, Sable, Taurus & Thunderbird**

| TEST STEP | RESULT ▶ | ACTION TO TAKE |
|---|---|---|
| **X15** SERVICE CODE 87/83: CHECK CONTINUITY OF FUEL PUMP CIRCUIT | | |
| Service Code 87 or 83 indicates that the voltage output for the high or low fuel pump circuit did not change when activated during Key On Engine Off Self-Test. | Yes ▶ | GO to X16. |
| Possible causes are: — Open or grounded fuel pump circuit. — Open or grounded processor output driver. | No ▶ | SERVICE open in fuel pump circuit. REMOVE breakout box. RECONNECT all components. |
| • Key off.<br>• Disconnect Integrated Controller.<br>• Disconnect processor 60 pin connector. Inspect for damaged or pushed out pins, corrosion, loose wires, etc. Service as necessary.<br>• Install breakout box, leave processor disconnected.<br>• DVOM on 200 ohm scale.<br>**For Service Code 87 (except 3.0L SHO):**<br>• Measure resistance between Test Pin 22 at the breakout box and Pin 18 at the Integrated Controller vehicle harness connector.<br>**For Service Code 87 (3.0L SHO):**<br>• Measure resistance between Test Pin 41 at the breakout box and Pin 11 at the Integrated Controller vehicle harness connector.<br>**For Service Code 83 (3.0L SHO):**<br>• Measure resistance between Test Pin 22 at the breakout box and Pin 18 at the Integrated Controller vehicle harness connector.<br>• **Is resistance less than 5.0 ohms?** | | |

**Fig. 23 Integrated controller pinpoint test X15 (Part 6 of 30). Probe w/3.0L Engine, Continental, Cougar, Sable, Taurus & Thunderbird**

| TEST STEP | RESULT ▶ | ACTION TO TAKE |
|---|---|---|
| **X16** CHECK APPROPRIATE FUEL PUMP CIRCUIT FOR SHORTS TO POWER AND GROUND | | |
| • Key off.<br>• Breakout box installed, processor disconnected.<br>• Integrated Controller disconnected.<br>• DVOM on 200,000 ohm scale.<br>**For Service Code 87 (except 3.0L SHO):**<br>• Measure resistance between Test Pin 22 and Test Pins 37, 57 and battery positive post and between Test Pin 22 and Test Pins 40, 60 and battery negative post.<br>**For Service Code 87 (3.0L SHO):**<br>• Measure resistance between Test Pin 41 and Test Pins 37, 57 and battery positive post and between Test Pin 41 and Test Pins 40, 60 and battery negative post.<br>**For Service Code 83 (3.0L SHO):**<br>• Measure resistance between Test Pin 22 at the breakout box and Pin 18 at the Integrated Controller vehicle harness connector.<br>• **Is each resistance greater than 10,000 ohms?** | Yes ▶<br>No ▶ | GO to X17.<br>SERVICE the appropriate fuel pump circuit shorts to power or ground. REMOVE breakout box. RECONNECT all components. If code 87 or 83 is still present, GO to X17. |
| **X17** CHECK FUEL PUMP RELAY COIL RESISTANCE | | |
| • Key off.<br>• Breakout box installed, processor disconnected.<br>• Integrated Controller disconnected.<br>• DVOM on 200 ohm scale.<br>• Measure resistance of Integrated Controller from Pin 18 to 24 or from Pin 11 to 24 as appropriate.<br>• **Is resistance between 65 and 100 ohms?** | Yes ▶<br>No ▶ | REPLACE processor. REMOVE breakout box. RECONNECT Integrated Controller.<br>REPLACE Integrated Controller. REMOVE breakout box. RECONNECT processor. |

**Fig. 23 Integrated controller pinpoint tests X16 & X17 (Part 7 of 30). Probe w/3.0L Engine, Continental, Cougar, Sable, Taurus & Thunderbird**

| TEST STEP | RESULT ▶ | ACTION TO TAKE |
|---|---|---|
| **X18** NO HIGH OR LOW FAN | | |
| • Key off.<br>• Disconnect Integrated Controller.<br>• DVOM on 20 volt scale.<br>• Key on, engine off.<br>• Measure voltage between battery negative post and Pins 1, 2, 6 and 7, (for 3.8L, Pins 3 and 4) respectively at the Integrated Controller vehicle harness connector.<br>• **Is each voltage greater than 10.5 volts?** | Yes ▶<br>No ▶ | GO to X19.<br>SERVICE open in battery power circuit. RECONNECT Integrated Controller. RE-EVALUATE symptom. |
| **X19** CHECK FAN MOTOR OPERATION | | |
| • Key off.<br>• Integrated Controller disconnected.<br>• Jumper Pin 3 to Pin 6 at Integrated Controller vehicle harness connector.<br>• **Does fan run?** | Yes ▶<br>No ▶ | **For 3.8L:** GO to X20. **For all others:** GO to X25.<br>GO to X21. |
| **X20** CHECK FAN MOTOR OPERATION | | |
| • Key off.<br>• Integrated Controller disconnected.<br>• Jumper Pin 3 to Pin 2 at Integrated Controller vehicle harness connector.<br>• **Does fan run?** | Yes ▶<br>No ▶ | GO to X25.<br>GO to X23. |
| **X21** MEASURE BATTERY VOLTAGE SUPPLY AT FAN — BYPASSING INTEGRATED CONTROLLER | | |
| • Key off.<br>• Disconnect cooling fan.<br>• Integrated Controller disconnected.<br>• Jumper Pin 3 to Pin 6 at Integrated Controller vehicle harness connector.<br>• DVOM on 20 volt scale.<br>• Measure voltage at cooling fan vehicle harness connector.<br>• **Is voltage greater than 8.0 volts?** | Yes ▶<br>No ▶ | REPLACE fan motor. RECONNECT Integrated Controller. RE-EVALUATE symptom.<br>GO to X22. |

**Fig. 23 Integrated controller pinpoint tests X18, X19, X20 & X21 (Part 8 of 30). Probe w/3.0L Engine, Continental, Cougar, Sable, Taurus & Thunderbird**

| TEST STEP | RESULT ▶ | ACTION TO TAKE |
|---|---|---|
| **X22** VERIFY COOLING FAN GROUND | | |
| • Key off.<br>• Cooling fan disconnected.<br>• Integrated Controller disconnected.<br>• Jumper Pin 3 to Pin 6 at Integrated Controller vehicle harness connector.<br>• DVOM on 20 volt scale.<br>• Measure voltage between voltage positive at cooling fan vehicles harness connector and battery negative post.<br>• **Is voltage greater than 8.0 volts?** | Yes ▶<br>No ▶ | SERVICE open in ground circuit to fan. RECONNECT all components. RE-EVALUATE symptom.<br>SERVICE open in power-to-fan circuit from Pin 3 and Pin 4 (for 3.8L, Pin 6 and Pin 7) of Integrated Controller vehicle harness connector to cooling fan vehicle harness connector. RECONNECT all components. RE-EVALUATE symptom. |
| **X23** MEASURE BATTERY VOLTAGE SUPPLY AT FAN-BYPASSING INTEGRATED CONTROLLER | | |
| • Key off.<br>• Disconnect cooling fan.<br>• Integrated Controller disconnected.<br>• Jumper Pin 3 to Pin 2 at Integrated Controller vehicle harness connector.<br>• DVOM on 20 volt scale.<br>• Measure voltage at cooling fan vehicle harness connector.<br>• **Is voltage greater than 8.0 volts?** | Yes ▶<br>No ▶ | REPLACE fan motor. RECONNECT Integrated Controller. RE-EVALUATE symptom.<br>GO to X24. |

**Fig. 23 Integrated controller pinpoint tests X22 & X23 (Part 9 of 30). Probe w/3.0L Engine, Continental, Cougar, Sable, Taurus & Thunderbird**

| TEST STEP | RESULT ▶ | ACTION TO TAKE |
|---|---|---|
| **X24** VERIFY COOLING FAN GROUND | | |
| • Key off.<br>• Cooling fan disconnected.<br>• Integrated Controller disconnected.<br>• Jumper Pin 3 to Pin 2 at Integrated Controller vehicle harness connector.<br>• DVOM on 20 volt scale.<br>• Measure voltage between voltage positive at cooling fan vehicle harness connector and battery negative post.<br>• **Is voltage greater than 8.0 volts?** | Yes ▶<br><br>No ▶ | SERVICE open in ground circuit to fan. RECONNECT all components. RE-EVALUATE symptom.<br><br>SERVICE open in power-to-fan circuit from Pin 1 and Pin 2 of Integrated Controller vehicle harness connector to cooling fan vehicle harness connector. RECONNECT all components. RE-EVALUATE symptom. |
| **X25** CHECK FAN RUNNING MODE (LOW) | | |
| • Key off.<br>• Disconnect processor.<br>• Reconnect Integrated Controller.<br>• Key on, engine off.<br>• **Does fan run at low speed?** | Yes ▶<br><br>No ▶ | GO to X26.<br><br>REPLACE Integrated Controller. RECONNECT processor. RE-EVALUATE symptom. |

**Fig. 23 Integrated controller pinpoint tests X24 & X25 (Part 10 of 30). Probe w/3.0L Engine, Continental, Cougar, Sable, Taurus & Thunderbird**

| TEST STEP | RESULT ▶ | ACTION TO TAKE |
|---|---|---|
| **X26** JUMPER HIGH ELECTRIC-DRIVE SIGNAL (HEDF) TO GROUND | | |
| • Key off.<br>• Inspect processor 60 pin connector for damaged or pushed out pins, corrosion, loose wires, etc. Service as necessary<br>• Install breakout box, leave processor disconnected.<br>• Integrated Controller connected.<br>• Key on, engine off.<br>• For 3.8L:<br>— Jumper Test Pin 41 to Test Pin 40 at breakout box.<br>• For all others:<br>— Jumper Test Pin 52 to Test Pin 40 at breakout box.<br>• **Does fan speed change from low to high?** | Yes ▶<br><br>No ▶ | GO to X27.<br><br>REPLACE Integrated Controller. REMOVE breakout box. RECONNECT processor. RE-EVALUATE symptom. |
| **X27** CHECK ECT SENSOR | | |
| • Key off, wait 10 seconds.<br>• Breakout box installed.<br>• Connect processor to breakout box.<br>• Check engine coolant level.<br>• Warm engine to operating temperature before taking ECT resistance measurement.<br>• Key off, wait 10 seconds.<br>• Disconnect ECT sensor.<br>• DVOM on 200,000 ohm scale.<br>• Measure resistance of the ECT sensor.<br>• **Is the resistance between 1500 ohms and 2000 ohms?** | Yes ▶<br><br>No ▶ | For 3.8L SEFI SC: GO to X28.<br>For all others: REPLACE processor. REMOVE breakout box. RECONNECT all components. RE-EVALUATE symptom.<br><br>REPLACE ECT sensor. REMOVE breakout box. RECONNECT all components. RE-EVALUATE symptom. |

**Fig. 23 Integrated controller pinpoint tests X26 & X27 (Part 11 of 30). Probe w/3.0L Engine, Continental, Cougar, Sable, Taurus & Thunderbird**

| TEST STEP | RESULT ▶ | ACTION TO TAKE |
|---|---|---|
| **X28** CHECK A/C PRESSURE SWITCH HARNESS CONTINUITY | | |
| • Key off.<br>• Breakout box installed, processor connected.<br>• Disconnect A/C pressure switch.<br>• DVOM on 200 ohm scale.<br>• Measure resistance between Test Pin 2 at the breakout box and A/C pressure circuit at switch vehicle harness connector.<br>• Measure resistance between Test Pin 46 at the breakout box and SIG RTN circuit at the switch vehicle harness connector.<br>• **Is each resistance less than 5 ohms?** | Yes ▶<br><br>No ▶ | GO to X29.<br><br>SERVICE open circuit. REMOVE breakout box. RECONNECT all components. |
| **X29** VERIFY HEDF OPERATION | | |
| • Key off.<br>• Breakout box installed, processor connected.<br>• A/C pressure switch disconnected.<br>• Jumper A/C pressure circuit to SIG RTN circuit at the switch vehicle harness connector.<br>• Key on.<br>• **Is HEDF on?** | Yes ▶<br><br>No ▶ | REPLACE A/C PRESSURE switch. RE-EVALUATE symptom.<br><br>REPLACE processor. REMOVE breakout box. |
| **X30** SERVICE CODE 83: CHECK HEDF CONTROLLER RESISTANCE | | |
| Service Code 83 indicates a High Electro Drive Fan (HEDF)/circuit failure.<br>• Key off.<br>• Disconnect Integrated Controller.<br>• DVOM on 200 ohm scale.<br>• Measure resistance between Pin 17 and Pin 24 at the Integrated Controller.<br>• **Is resistance between 50 ohms and 100 ohms?** | Yes ▶<br><br>No ▶ | GO to X31.<br><br>REPLACE Integrated Controller. |

**Fig. 23 Integrated controller pinpoint tests X28, X29 & X30 (Part 12 of 30). Probe w/3.0L Engine, Continental, Cougar, Sable, Taurus & Thunderbird**

| TEST STEP | RESULT ▶ | ACTION TO TAKE |
|---|---|---|
| **X31** CHECK HEDF CIRCUIT CONTINUITY | | |
| • Key off.<br>• Disconnect processor 60 pin connector. Inspect for damaged or pushed out pins, corrosion, loose wires, etc. Service as necessary.<br>• Install breakout box, leave processor disconnected.<br>• Integrated Controller disconnected.<br>• DVOM on 200 ohm scale.<br>For 3.8L:<br>— Measure resistance between Test Pin 41 at the breakout box and Pin 17 of the Integrated Controller vehicle harness connector.<br>For all others:<br>— Measure resistance between Test Pin 52 at breakout box and Pin 17 of Integrated Controller vehicle harness connector.<br>• **Is resistance less than 5 ohms?** | Yes ▶<br><br>No ▶ | GO to X32.<br><br>SERVICE open in HEDF circuit. REMOVE breakout box. RECONNECT all components. |
| **X32** CHECK HEDF CIRCUIT FOR SHORTS TO GROUND | | |
| • Key off.<br>• Breakout box installed, processor disconnected.<br>• Integrated Controller disconnected.<br>• DVOM on 200,000 ohm scale.<br>For all 3.8L:<br>— Measure resistance between Test Pin 41 and Test Pin 40 at the breakout box.<br>For all others:<br>— Measure resistance between Test Pin 52 and Test Pin 40 at the breakout box.<br>• **Is resistance greater than 10,000 ohms?** | Yes ▶<br><br>No ▶ | GO to X33.<br><br>SERVICE short to ground in HEDF circuit. REMOVE breakout box. RECONNECT all components. |

**Fig. 23 Integrated controller pinpoint tests X31 & X32 (Part 13 of 30). Probe w/3.0L Engine, Continental, Cougar, Sable, Taurus & Thunderbird**

| TEST STEP | RESULT ▶ | ACTION TO TAKE |
|---|---|---|
| **X33** CHECK HEDF CIRCUIT FOR SHORTS TO POWER | | |
| • Key off.<br>• Breakout box installed, processor disconnected.<br>• Integrated Controller disconnected.<br>• DVOM on 200,000 ohms scale.<br>For 3.8L:<br>— Measure resistance between Test Pin 41 and Test Pin 37 at the breakout box.<br>For all others:<br>— Measure resistance between Test Pin 52 and Test Pin 37 at the breakout box.<br>• Is resistance greater than 10,000 ohms? | Yes ▶<br><br>No ▶ | REPLACE Processor. REMOVE breakout box. RECONNECT all components.<br><br>SERVICE short to power. REMOVE breakout box. RECONNECT all components. If code 83 is still present, REPLACE processor. |
| **X35** LOW SPEED FAN ALWAYS ON | | |
| • Key off.<br>• Disconnect processor 60 pin connector. Inspect for damaged or pushed out pins, corrosion, loose wires. Service as necessary.<br>• Install breakout box, leave processor disconnected.<br>• Disconnect Integrated Controller.<br>• DVOM on 200 ohm scale.<br>• Measure the resistance between Test Pin 55 at the breakout box and Pin 14 at the Integrated Controller vehicle harness connector.<br>• Is resistance less than 5 ohms? | Yes ▶<br><br>No ▶ | GO to X36.<br><br>SERVICE open in EDF circuit. REMOVE breakout box. RECONNECT all components. RE-EVALUATE symptom. |
| **X36** CHECK EDF CIRCUIT FOR SHORTS TO POWER | | |
| • Key off.<br>• Breakout box installed, processor disconnected.<br>• Integrated Controller disconnected.<br>• DVOM on 200,000 ohm scale.<br>• Measure resistance between Test Pin 55 and Test Pin 37 and between Test Pin 55 and battery positive post.<br>• Is each resistance greater than 10,000 ohms? | Yes ▶<br><br>No ▶ | GO to X37.<br><br>SERVICE short to power in EDF circuit. GO to X37. |

**Fig. 23 Integrated controller pinpoint tests X33, X35 & X36 (Part 14 of 30). Probe w/3.0L Engine, Continental, Cougar, Sable, Taurus & Thunderbird**

| TEST STEP | RESULT ▶ | ACTION TO TAKE |
|---|---|---|
| **X37** CHECK EDF FOR SHORT TO GROUND | | |
| • Key on, engine off.<br>• Breakout box installed, processor disconnected.<br>• Connect Integrated Controller.<br>• Jumper Test Pin 55 to Test Pin 40 or 60 at the breakout box.<br>• Does fan continue to run? | Yes ▶<br><br>No ▶ | REPLACE controller. REMOVE breakout box. RECONNECT processor. RE-EVALUATE symptom.<br><br>REPLACE processor. REMOVE breakout box. RECONNECT controller. REEVALUATE symptom. |
| **X38** CHECK A/C PRESSURE SWITCH INPUT | | |
| • Key off.<br>• Disconnect A/C pressure switch.<br>• Key on, engine off.<br>• Does fan still run? | Yes ▶<br><br>No ▶ | RECONNECT A/C pressure switch. GO to X39.<br><br>REPLACE the A/C pressure switch. RE-EVALUATE symptom. |
| **X39** CHECK A/C PRESSURE SWITCH CIRCUIT FOR SHORTS TO GROUND | | |
| • Key on.<br>• Disconnect processor 60 pin connector. Inspect for damaged or pushed out pins, corrosion, loose wires. Service as necessary.<br>• Install breakout box, leave processor disconnected.<br>• Disconnect Integrated Controller.<br>• DVOM on 200,000 ohm scale.<br>• Measure resistance between Test Pin 2 and Test Pins 40, 46 and 60 at the breakout box.<br>• Is each resistance greater than 10,000 ohms? | Yes ▶<br><br>No ▶ | GO to X35.<br><br>SERVICE short circuit. REMOVE breakout box. RECONNECT all components. RE-EVALUATE the symptom. |

**Fig. 23 Integrated controller pinpoint tests X37, X38 & X39 (Part 15 of 30). Probe w/3.0L Engine, Continental, Cougar, Sable, Taurus & Thunderbird**

| TEST STEP | RESULT ▶ | ACTION TO TAKE |
|---|---|---|
| **X40** CHECK FAN VOLTAGE | | |
| • Key off.<br>• Disconnect Integrated Controller.<br>• DVOM on 20 volt scale.<br>• Measure voltage between battery negative post and Pins 1 and 2 at the Integrated Controller vehicle harness connector.<br>• Is each voltage greater than 10.5 volts? | Yes ▶<br><br>No ▶ | GO to X41.<br><br>SERVICE open in battery power circuit. RECONNECT Integrated Controller. RE-EVALUATE symptom. |
| **X41** CHECK FAN MOTOR OPERATION | | |
| • Key off.<br>• Integrated Controller disconnected.<br>• Jumper Pin 1 to Pin 3 at Integrated Controller vehicle harness connector.<br>• Does fan run? | Yes ▶<br><br>No ▶ | GO to X42.<br><br>GO to X43. |
| **X42** CHECK FAN RUNNING MODE | | |
| • Key off.<br>• Disconnect processor.<br>• Connect Integrated Controller.<br>• Key on, engine off.<br>• Does fan run? | Yes ▶<br><br>No ▶ | GO to X46.<br><br>GO to X44. |
| **X43** MEASURE BATTERY VOLTAGE SUPPLY AT FAN — BYPASSING INTEGRATED CONTROLLER | | |
| • Key off.<br>• Disconnect cooling fan.<br>• Integrated Controller disconnected.<br>• Jumper Pin 1 to Pin 3 at Integrated Controller vehicle harness connector.<br>• DVOM on 20 volt scale.<br>• Measure voltage at cooling fan vehicle harness connector.<br>• Is voltage greater than 8.0 volts? | Yes ▶<br><br>No ▶ | REPLACE FAN. RECONNECT all components. RE-EVALUATE symptom.<br><br>GO to X45. |

**Fig. 23 Integrated controller pinpoint tests X40, X41, X42 & X43 (Part 16 of 30). Probe w/3.0L Engine, Continental, Cougar, Sable, Taurus & Thunderbird**

| TEST STEP | RESULT ▶ | ACTION TO TAKE |
|---|---|---|
| **X44** CHECK EDF CIRCUIT FOR SHORT TO GROUND | | |
| • Key off.<br>• Processor and Integrated Controller disconnected.<br>• DVOM on 200,000 ohm scale.<br>• Measure resistance from Pin 14 to Pin 15 at Integrated Controller vehicle harness connector.<br>• Is resistance greater than 10,000 ohms? | Yes ▶<br><br>No ▶ | REPLACE Integrated Controller. RECONNECT processor. RE-EVALUATE symptom.<br><br>SERVICE short to ground in EDF circuit. RECONNECT all components. RE-EVALUATE symptom. |
| **X45** VERIFY COOLING FAN GROUND | | |
| • Key off.<br>• Cooling fan disconnected.<br>• Integrated Controller disconnected.<br>• Jumper Pin 1 to Pin 3 at Integrated Controller vehicle harness connector.<br>• DVOM on 20 volt scale.<br>• Measure voltage between voltage positive at cooling fan vehicle harness connector and negative battery post.<br>• Is voltage greater than 8.0 volts? | Yes ▶<br><br>No ▶ | SERVICE open in ground circuit to fan. RECONNECT all components. RE-EVALUATE symptom.<br><br>SERVICE open in power-to-fan circuit from Pin 3 and Pin 4 of Integrated Controller vehicle harness connector to cooling fan vehicle harness connector. RECONNECT all components. RE-EVALUATE symptom. |

**Fig. 23 Integrated controller pinpoint tests X44 & X45 (Part 17 of 30). Probe w/3.0L Engine, Continental, Cougar, Sable, Taurus & Thunderbird**

| TEST STEP | RESULT ▶ | ACTION TO TAKE |
|---|---|---|
| **X46** CHECK ECT SENSOR | | |
| • Key off.<br>• Reconnect processor.<br>• Check engine coolant level.<br>• Warm engine to operating temperature before taking ECT resistance measurement.<br>• Key off, wait 10 seconds.<br>• Disconnect ECT sensor.<br>• DVOM on 200,000 ohm scale.<br>• Measure resistance of the ECT sensor.<br>• Is the resistance between 1500 ohms and 2000 ohms? | Yes ▶<br><br>No ▶ | REPLACE processor. RECONNECT ECT sensor. RE-EVALUATE symptom.<br><br>REPLACE ECT sensor. RECONNECT all components. RE-EVALUATE symptom. |
| **X50** CHECK FOR VOLTAGE AT A/C CLUTCH | | |
| • Disconnect A/C clutch.<br>• Key on, engine off.<br>• A/C demand switch to A/C ON position.<br>• Start engine.<br>• DVOM on 20 volt scale.<br>• Check voltage at A/C clutch vehicle harness connector.<br>• Is voltage greater than 10.5 volts? | Yes ▶<br><br>No ▶ | Perform A/C Diagnosis.<br><br>GO to X51. |
| **X51** CHECK FOR CONTINUITY FROM INTEGRATED CONTROLLER TO A/C CLUTCH | | |
| • Key off.<br>• A/C clutch disconnected.<br>• Disconnect Integrated Controller.<br>• DVOM on 200 ohm scale.<br>• Measure resistance between Pin 23 of the Integrated Controller vehicle harness connector and power side of the A/C clutch vehicle harness connector and between Pin 16 of the Integrated Controller vehicle harness connector and ground side of the A/C clutch vehicle harness connector.<br>• Is each resistance less than 5 ohms? | Yes ▶<br><br>No ▶ | RECONNECT Integrated Controller. GO to X52.<br><br>SERVICE open in power to A/C clutch or ground to A/C clutch. RECONNECT Integrated Controller. RE-EVALUATE symptom. |

**Fig. 23 Integrated controller pinpoint tests X46, X50 & X51 (Part 18 of 30). Probe w/3.0L Engine, Continental, Cougar, Sable, Taurus & Thunderbird**

| TEST STEP | RESULT ▶ | ACTION TO TAKE |
|---|---|---|
| **X52** ENTER OUTPUT STATE CHECK (REFER TO QUICK TEST APPENDIX) | | |
| NOTE: Do not use STAR tester for this Step, use VOM/DVOM.<br>• Key off, wait 10 seconds.<br>• Disconnect processor 60 pin connector. Inspect for damaged or pushed out pins, corrosion, loose wires, etc. Service as necessary.<br>• Install breakout box and connect processor to breakout box.<br>• Disconnect electrical connector on the speed control servo; if so equipped.<br>• DVOM on 20 volt scale.<br>• Connect DVOM negative test lead to STO and positive test lead to battery positive.<br>• Jumper STI to SIGNAL RETURN.<br>• Perform Key On Engine Off Self-Test until the completion of the Continuous Test Codes.<br>• DVOM will indicate zero volts.<br>• Depress and release the throttle.<br>• Did DVOM reading change to a high voltage reading? | Yes ▶<br><br>No ▶ | REMAIN in Output State Check. GO to X53.<br><br>DEPRESS throttle to WOT and RELEASE. |
| **X53** CHECK WAC OUTPUT FOR PROPER ELECTRICAL OPERATION | | |
| • Key on, engine off.<br>• A/C demand switch to A/C ON position.<br>• Breakout box installed, processor connected.<br>• DVOM on 20 volt scale.<br>• Connect DVOM positive test lead to Test Pin 37 and negative test lead to Test Pin 54 at the breakout box.<br>• While observing DVOM, depress and release the throttle several times.<br>• Does voltage output change? | Yes ▶<br><br>No ▶ | GO to X54.<br><br>GO to X57. |

**Fig. 23 Integrated controller pinpoint tests X52 & X53 (Part 19 of 30). Probe w/3.0L Engine, Continental, Cougar, Sable, Taurus & Thunderbird**

| TEST STEP | RESULT ▶ | ACTION TO TAKE |
|---|---|---|
| **X54** CHECK FOR VOLTAGE AT A/C CLUTCH SWITCH | | |
| • Key on, engine off.<br>• A/C demand switch to A/C ON position.<br>• DVOM on 20 volt scale.<br>• Breakout box installed, processor connected.<br>• Measure voltage between Test Pin 10 and Test Pin 40 at the breakout box.<br>• Is voltage greater than 10.5 volts? | Yes ▶<br><br>No ▶ | GO to X55.<br><br>GO to X56. |
| **X55** CHECK CONTINUITY OF ACCS CIRCUIT TO INTEGRATED CONTROLLER | | |
| • Key off, wait 10 seconds.<br>• Breakout box installed.<br>• Disconnect processor.<br>• Disconnect Integrated Controller.<br>• DVOM on 200 ohm scale.<br>• Measure resistance between Test Pin 10 at the breakout box and Pin 21 at the Integrated Controller vehicle harness connector.<br>• Is resistance less than 5 ohms? | Yes ▶<br><br>No ▶ | REPLACE Integrated Controller. REMOVE breakout box. RECONNECT processor. RE-EVALUATE symptom.<br><br>SERVICE open in ACCS circuit. REMOVE breakout box. RECONNECT all components. RE-EVALUATE symptom. |
| **X56** CHECK ACCS CIRCUIT CONTINUITY | | |
| • Key off, wait 10 seconds.<br>• Breakout box installed, processor connected.<br>• A/C demand switch to A/C ON position.<br>• DVOM on 200 ohm scale.<br>• Measure resistance between Test Pin 10 at the breakout box and A/C demand switch.<br>• Is resistance less than 5 ohms? | No ▶<br><br>Yes ▶ | SERVICE open in circuit. REMOVE breakout box. RECONNECT all components.<br><br>EEC-IV system OK. REMOVE breakout box. RECONNECT all components. |

**Fig. 23 Integrated controller pinpoint tests X54, X55 & X56 (Part 20 of 30). Probe w/3.0L Engine, Continental, Cougar, Sable, Taurus & Thunderbird**

| TEST STEP | RESULT ▶ | ACTION TO TAKE |
|---|---|---|
| **X57** CHECK CONTINUITY IN WAC TO INTEGRATED CONTROLLER CIRCUIT | | |
| • Key off, wait 10 seconds.<br>• Breakout box installed.<br>• Disconnect processor.<br>• Disconnect Integrated Controller.<br>• DVOM on 200 ohm scale.<br>• Measure resistance between Test Pin 54 at the breakout box and Pin 22 at Integrated Controller harness.<br>• Is resistance less than 50 ohms? | No ▶<br><br>Yes ▶ | SERVICE open in WAC circuit. REMOVE breakout box. RECONNECT all components. RE-EVALUATE symptom.<br><br>GO to X58. |
| **X58** CHECK WAC CIRCUIT FOR SHORTS TO GROUND | | |
| • Key off, wait 10 seconds.<br>• Breakout box installed, processor disconnected.<br>• Integrated Controller disconnected.<br>• DVOM on 200,000 ohm scale.<br>• Measure resistance between Test Pin 54 and Test Pin 40 and between Test Pin 54 and Test Pin 46 and between Test Pin 54 and battery negative post.<br>• Is each resistance greater than 10,000 ohms? | Yes ▶<br><br>No ▶ | GO to X59.<br><br>SERVICE shorts to ground in WAC circuit. REMOVE breakout box. RECONNECT all components. RE-EVALUATE symptom. |
| **X59** CHECK WAC CIRCUIT FOR SHORTS TO POWER | | |
| • Key off, wait 10 seconds.<br>• Breakout box installed, processor disconnected.<br>• Integrated Controller disconnected.<br>• DVOM on 200,000 ohm scale.<br>• Measure resistance between Test Pin 54 and Test Pin 37 and between Test Pin 54 and battery positive.<br>• Is each resistance greater than 10,000 ohms? | Yes ▶<br><br>No ▶ | GO to X60.<br><br>SERVICE short to power in WAC circuit. REMOVE breakout box. RECONNECT all components. GO to X60. |

**Fig. 23 Integrated controller pinpoint tests X57, X58 & X59 (Part 21 of 30). Probe w/3.0L Engine, Continental, Cougar, Sable, Taurus & Thunderbird**

| TEST STEP | RESULT ▶ | ACTION TO TAKE |
|---|---|---|
| **X60** CHECK FOR VOLTAGE AT A/C CLUTCH | | |
| • Key off, wait 10 seconds.<br>• Breakout box installed, processor disconnected.<br>• Connect Integrated Controller.<br>• Disconnect A/C clutch.<br>• A/C demand switch to A/C ON position.<br>• DVOM on 20 volt scale.<br>• Key on, engine off.<br>• Measure voltage at A/C clutch harness connection.<br>• **Is voltage greater than 10.5 volts?** | Yes ▶<br><br>No ▶ | REPLACE processor. REMOVE breakout box. RECONNECT all components. RE-EVALUATE symptom.<br><br>REPLACE Integrated Controller. REMOVE breakout box. RECONNECT all components. RE-EVALUATE symptom. |
| **X80** SERVICE CODE 88: CHECK EDF PROCESSOR SIGNAL TO INTEGRATED CONTROLLER FOR SHORTS TO GROUND | | |
| **For fan always on with Code 88:** GO to X82.<br>**For all others:**<br>• Key off.<br>• Disconnect processor 60 pin connector. Inspect for damaged or pushed out pins, corrosion, and loose wires, etc. Service as necessary.<br>• Install breakout box, leave processor disconnected.<br>• Disconnect Integrated Controller.<br>• DVOM on 200,000 ohm scale.<br>• Measure resistance between Test Pin 55 and Test Pin 40 at the breakout box.<br>• **Is resistance less than 10,000 ohms?** | Yes ▶<br><br>No ▶ | SERVICE short to ground in EDF circuit. RECONNECT all components.<br><br>GO to X81. |

**Fig. 23 Integrated controller pinpoint tests X60 & X80 (Part 22 of 30). Probe w/3.0L Engine, Continental, Cougar, Sable, Taurus & Thunderbird**

| TEST STEP | RESULT ▶ | ACTION TO TAKE |
|---|---|---|
| **X81** CHECK FAN RUNNING MODE | | |
| • Key off.<br>• Breakout box installed, processor disconnected.<br>• Connect integrated controller.<br>• Key on, engine off.<br>• **Does fan run at low speed?** | Yes ▶<br><br>No ▶ | REPLACE processor. REMOVE breakout box. RECONNECT all components.<br><br>REPLACE Integrated Controller. REMOVE breakout box. RECONNECT all components. |
| **X82** FAN ALWAYS ON WITH CODE 88: CHECK EDF PROCESSOR SIGNAL TO INTEGRATED CONTROLLER CONTINUITY | | |
| • Key off.<br>• Disconnect processor 60 pin connector. Inspect for damaged or pushed out pins, corrosion, and loose wires, etc. Service as necessary.<br>• Install breakout box, leave processor disconnected.<br>• Disconnect Integrated Controller.<br>• DVOM on 200 ohm scale.<br>• Measure resistance between Test Pin 55 at the breakout box and Pin 14 at the Integrated Controller vehicle harness connector.<br>• **Is resistance less than 5 ohms?** | Yes ▶<br><br>No ▶ | GO to X83.<br><br>SERVICE open in EDF circuit. REMOVE breakout box. RECONNECT all components. |
| **X83** CHECK EDF CIRCUIT FOR SHORTS TO POWER | | |
| • Key off.<br>• Breakout box installed, processor disconnected.<br>• Integrated Controller disconnected.<br>• DVOM on 200,000 ohm scale.<br>• Measure resistance between Test Pin 55 and Test Pin 37, and between Test Pin 55 and battery positive.<br>• **Is each resistance less than 10,000 ohms?** | Yes ▶<br><br>No ▶ | SERVICE short to power in EDF circuit, then GO to X84.<br><br>GO to X84. |

**Fig. 23 Integrated controller pinpoint tests X81, X82 & X83 (Part 23 of 30). Probe w/3.0L Engine, Continental, Cougar, Sable, Taurus & Thunderbird**

| TEST STEP | RESULT ▶ | ACTION TO TAKE |
|---|---|---|
| **X84** CHECK EDF CIRCUIT FOR SHORTS TO GROUND | | |
| • Key off.<br>• Breakout box installed, processor disconnected.<br>• Connect Integrated Controller.<br>• Key on, engine off.<br>• Jumper Test Pin 55 to Test Pin 40 or 60 at the breakout box.<br>• **Does fan continue to run?** | Yes ▶<br><br>No ▶ | REPLACE Integrated Controller. REMOVE breakout box. RECONNECT all components.<br><br>REPLACE processor. REMOVE breakout box. RECONNECT all components. |
| **X90** SERVICE CODE 95: CHECK INERTIA SWITCH | | |
| Key On Engine Off Service Code 95 indicates that one of the following has occurred:<br>— Open circuit in or between the fuel pump and FPM circuit (see schematic)<br>— Poor fuel pump ground<br>— FUEL PUMP circuit short to power<br>— Fuel pump relay contacts always closed<br>• Key off, wait 10 seconds.<br>• Locate and disconnect fuel pump inertia switch.<br>• DVOM on 200 ohm scale.<br>• Measure resistance of the fuel pump inertia switch.<br>• **Is resistance less than 5.0 ohms?** | Yes ▶<br><br>No ▶ | RECONNECT inertia switch. GO to X91.<br><br>REPLACE or RESET inertia switch. |
| **X91** VERIFY THAT FUEL PUMP IS OFF | | |
| • Key off.<br>• Listen for motor noise from fuel pump.<br>• **Is fuel pump off?** | Yes ▶<br><br>No ▶ | GO to X93.<br><br>GO to X92. |

**Fig. 23 Integrated controller pinpoint tests X84, X90 & X91 (Part 24 of 30). Probe w/3.0L Engine, Continental, Cougar, Sable, Taurus & Thunderbird**

| TEST STEP | RESULT ▶ | ACTION TO TAKE |
|---|---|---|
| **X92** CHECK FOR FUEL PUMP RELAY ALWAYS CLOSED | | |
| • Key off.<br>• Locate and disconnect Integrated Controller.<br>• **Does fuel pump shut off when Integrated Controller is disconnected?** | Yes ▶<br><br>No ▶ | REPLACE Integrated Controller.<br><br>SERVICE short to power in POWER-TO-PUMP/FPM circuit. RECONNECT Integrated Controller. |
| **X93** CHECK FPM CIRCUIT CONTINUITY | | |
| • Key off.<br>• Disconnect processor 60 pin connector. Inspect for damaged or pushed out pins, corrosion, loose wires, etc. Service as necessary.<br>• Install breakout box, leave processor disconnected.<br>• Disconnect Integrated Controller.<br>• DVOM on 200 ohm scale.<br>• Measure resistance between FPM circuit at the breakout box and Pin 5 at the Integrated Controller vehicle harness connector.<br>• **Is resistance less than 5.0 ohms?** | Yes ▶<br><br>No ▶ | GO to X94.<br><br>SERVICE open circuit. REMOVE breakout box. RECONNECT all components. |
| **X94** CHECK FOR CONTINUITY BETWEEN FPM CIRCUIT AND GROUND | | |
| • Key off.<br>• Breakout box installed, processor disconnected.<br>• Integrated Controller disconnected.<br>• DVOM on 200 ohm scale.<br>• Measure resistance between FPM circuit at the breakout box and battery negative post.<br>• **Is resistance less than 5.0 ohms?** | Yes ▶<br><br>No ▶ | REPLACE processor. REMOVE breakout box. RECONNECT Integrated Controller.<br><br>REMOVE breakout box. RECONNECT all components. |

**Fig. 23 Integrated controller pinpoint tests X92, X93 & X94 (Part 25 of 30). Probe w/3.0L Engine, Continental, Cougar, Sable, Taurus & Thunderbird**

| TEST STEP | RESULT ▶ | ACTION TO TAKE |
|---|---|---|
| X95 SERVICE CODE 96: CHECK POWER-TO-PUMP(S) CIRCUIT CONTINUITY | | |
| Service Code 96 indicates that when the fuel pump is being activated, power is not being supplied to the fuel pump.<br>• Key off, wait 10 seconds.<br>• Disconnect processor 60 pin connector. Inspect for damaged pins, corrosion, loose wires, etc. Service as necessary.<br>• Install breakout box, leave processor disconnected.<br>• Disconnect Integrated Controller.<br>• DVOM on 200 ohm scale.<br>• Measure resistance between the FPM circuit at the breakout box and Pin 5 at the Integrated Controller vehicle harness connector.<br>• **Is resistance less than 5.0 ohms?** | Yes ▶<br>No ▶ | GO to X96.<br>SERVICE open in POWER-TO-PUMP circuit between FPM splice and the Integrated Controller. REMOVE breakout box. RECONNECT all components. |
| X96 CHECK FUEL PUMP OPERATION | | |
| • Key off.<br>• Breakout box installed.<br>• Connect processor to breakout box.<br>• Connect Integrated Controller.<br>• DVOM on 20 volt scale.<br>• Connect DVOM between FPM circuit and Test Pin 40 at the breakout box.<br>• While observing DVOM, turn key to on.<br>• **Does voltage increase to greater than 9.8 volts for about 1 second after key is turned to on?** | Yes ▶<br>No ▶ | REPLACE processor. REMOVE breakout box.<br>REPLACE Integrated Controller. REMOVE breakout box. RECONNECT processor. |
| X97 MEASURE IDLE FUEL PUMP RELAY POWER CIRCUIT CONTINUITY | | |
| Service Code 59 indicates the idle fuel pump is not receiving the appropriate supplied voltage.<br>• Key off.<br>• Disconnect Integrated Controller.<br>• DVOM on 200 ohm scale.<br>• Measure resistance between Pin 10 at the Integrated Controller vehicle harness connector and battery positive post.<br>• **Is resistance between 1.0 and 1.2 ohms?** | Yes ▶<br>No ▶ | GO to X95<br>SERVICE Idle Fuel Pump circuit. RECONNECT Integrated Controller. |

**Fig. 23 Integrated controller pinpoint tests X95, X96 & X97 (Part 26 of 30). Probe w/3.0L Engine, Continental, Cougar, Sable, Taurus & Thunderbird**

| TEST STEP | RESULT ▶ | ACTION TO TAKE |
|---|---|---|
| X100 CONTINUOUS MEMORY CODE 95: CHECK EEC-IV HARNESS | | |
| A Continuous Memory Code 95 indicates that one of the following intermittent conditions has occurred:<br>— Open circuit in or between the fuel pump and FPM circuit in the processor (see schematic X).<br>— Poor fuel pump ground.<br>• Start engine.<br>• Check for engine stall/stumble while performing the following (also, if possible, listen for fuel pump turning off).<br>— Shake, wiggle, bend the power-to-pump circuit between the Integrated Controller Pin 5 and the fuel pump.<br>— Shake, wiggle, bend the fuel pump ground circuit from the fuel pump to ground.<br>— Lightly tap the inertia switch and the fuel pump to simulate road shock.<br>• Key off.<br>• Inspect the fuel pump electrical connector and the fuel pump ground for corrosion, damaged pins, etc.<br>• **Is fault indicated/found?** | Yes ▶<br>No ▶ | ISOLATE fault and SERVICE as necessary. CLEAR Continuous Memory Code 95<br>GO to X101. |

**Fig. 23 Integrated controller pinpoint test X100 (Part 27 of 30). Probe w/3.0L Engine, Continental, Cougar, Sable, Taurus & Thunderbird**

| TEST STEP | RESULT ▶ | ACTION TO TAKE |
|---|---|---|
| X101 CHECK FPM CIRCUIT | | |
| • Key off.<br>• Disconnect processor 60 pin connector. Inspect for damaged or pushed out pins, corrosion, loose wires, etc. Service as necessary.<br>• Install breakout box, leave processor disconnected.<br>• Connect a test lamp between FPM circuit and Test Pin 37 at the breakout box.<br>• Key on, engine off.<br>• Observe test lamp for an indication of a fault while performing the following (The light will go out when a fault is found indicating an open):<br>— Shake, wiggle, bend the fuel pump monitor circuit (Pin 8) between the processor and splice into the POWER-TO-PUMP(s) circuit.<br>• **Is fault found/indicated?** | Yes ▶<br>No ▶ | ISOLATE fault and SERVICE as necessary. REMOVE breakout box. RECONNECT processor. CLEAR Continuous Memory Code 95<br>Unable to duplicate and/or identify fault at this time.<br>All others, CLEAR Continuous Memory |
| X102 CONTINUOUS MEMORY CODE 59 or 96: CHECK FOR CONTINUOUS MEMORY CODE 83 or 87 | | |
| • **Is Continuous Memory Code 83 or 87 also present?** | Yes ▶<br>No ▶ | GO to X104.<br>GO to X103. |

**Fig. 23 Integrated controller pinpoint tests X101 & X102 (Part 28 of 30). Probe w/3.0L Engine, Continental, Cougar, Sable, Taurus & Thunderbird**

| TEST STEP | RESULT ▶ | ACTION TO TAKE |
|---|---|---|
| X103 CHECK EEC-IV HARNESS | | |
| A Continuous Memory Code 59 or 96, without the presence of a Continuous Memory Code 83 or 87, indicates that during vehicle operation, one of the following has occurred:<br>— Fuel pump relay contacts opened.<br>— Open in the POWER-TO-PUMP(s) circuit from the Integrated Controller Pin 5 to the FPM splice.<br>• Start engine.<br>• Check for engine stall/stumble while performing the following (also, if possible, listen for fuel pump turning off):<br>— Shake, wiggle, bend the POWER-TO-PUMP circuit from the Integrated Controller to the FPM splice.<br>— Lightly tap the Integrated Controller (to simulate road shock).<br>• Key off.<br>• Inspect the Integrated Controller 24 pin connectors for corrosion, damaged pins, etc.<br>• **Is fault indicated/found?** | Yes ▶<br>No ▶ | ISOLATE fault and SERVICE as necessary. CLEAR Continuous Memory<br>Unable to duplicate and/or identify fault at<br>All others, CLEAR Continuous Memory |

**Fig. 23 Integrated controller pinpoint test X103 (Part 29 of 30). Probe w/3.0L Engine, Continental, Cougar, Sable, Taurus & Thunderbird**

| TEST STEP | RESULT ▶ | ACTION TO TAKE |
|---|---|---|
| X104 CONTINUOUS MEMORY CODE 83 or 87: CHECK EEC-IV HARNESS | | |
| A Continuous Memory Code 83 or 87 indicates that one of the following intermittent conditions has occurred:<br>— Open VPWP circuit in the Integrated Controller.<br>— Open coil in fuel pump relay.<br>— Open in fuel pump primary circuit. | Yes ▶ | ISOLATE fault and SERVICE as necessary. CLEAR Continuous Memory Service Code(s) |
| • Start engine.<br>• Check for engine stall/stumble while performing the following (also, if possible, listen for fuel pump turning off):<br>— Shake, wiggle, bend the EEC-IV Harness fuel pump circuit (Pin 22) between the processor and the Integrated Controller (Pin 18).<br>or:<br>— Shake, wiggle, bend the EEC-IV harness fuel pump circuit (Pin 41) between the processor and the Integrated Controller (Pin 11).<br>— Lightly tap the Integrated Controller (to simulate road shock).<br>• Key off.<br>• Inspect the processor 60 pin connectors and the Integrated Controller 24 pin connector for corrosion, damaged pins, etc.<br>• **Is fault indicated/found?** | No ▶ | Unable to duplicate and/or identify fault at this time.<br><br>All others, CLEAR Continuous Memory |

**Fig. 23 Integrated controller pinpoint test X104 (Part 30 of 30). Probe w/3.0L Engine, Continental, Cougar, Sable, Taurus & Thunderbird**

ENGINE COOLING FAN DIAGNOSIS

| TEST | RESULT ▶ | ACTION TO TAKE |
|---|---|---|
| **1** | | |
| • Disconnect motor lead. Jumper motor negative to ground and motor positive to B+. | Motor does not run ▶ | REPLACE motor. |
| | Motor runs ▶ | CONNECT motor lead and GO to Test 2. |
| **2** | | |
| • Disconnect electrical connector at cooling fan temperature switch. | (OK) ▶ | GO to Test 3. |
| • With ignition switch in RUN position, check for voltage on Circuit 197 (T/O). Should equal battery voltage. | (ØK) ▶ | CHECK for open or short circuit in Circuit 197 (T/O). SERVICE as necessary. CHECK cooling fan operation. |
| **3** | | |
| • Jumper cooling fan temperature switch connector pins together.<br>• With ignition switch in RUN position, cooling fan motor should run. | (OK) ▶ | REPLACE cooling fan temperature switch. CHECK cooling fan operation. |
| | (ØK) ▶ | LEAVE jumper connected. GO to Test 4. |
| **4** | | |
| • Disconnect connector at fan relay (on radiator support LH side near headlamp). | (OK) ▶ | GO to Test 5. |
| • Check for voltage at Terminals No. 2 (relay coil) and No. 4 (relay output to fan motor). | (ØK) ▶ | SERVICE Circuit 182 and 37 at relay connector. CONNECT the temperature switch. CHECK cooling fan operation. |
| **5** | | |
| • Connect connector at fan relay.<br>• Jumper Circuits 37 to 28 at fan relay (Terminals No. 3 and No. 4). | Motor runs ▶ | REPLACE relay. CHECK cooling fan operation. |
| | Motor does not run ▶ | GO to Test 6. |
| **6** | | |
| • Disconnect connector at fan motor. | (OK) ▶ | GO to Test 7. |
| • Check for voltage on Circuit 228 (BR/Y).<br>• With ignition switch in RUN position and cooling fan temperature switch connector jumpered, Circuit 228 (BR/Y) should have battery voltage. | (ØK) ▶ | *CHECK Circuit 228 BR/Y for open. SERVICE wiring between fan motor and cooling fan temperature switch. CONNECT cooling fan relay connector. CHECK cooling fan operation. |

*Service non-cycling circuit breaker as required.

**Fig. 25 Cooling fan system diagnosis. Tempo & Topaz, less A/C**

ENGINE COOLING FAN DIAGNOSIS — ESCORT

| TEST | RESULT ▶ | ACTION TO TAKE |
|---|---|---|
| **1** | | |
| • Disconnect motor lead. Jumper negative to ground and positive to B+. | Motor does not run ▶ | REPLACE motor. |
| | Motor runs ▶ | CONNECT motor lead and GO to Test 2. |
| **2** | | |
| • Disconnect electrical connector at cooling fan temperature switch. | (OK) ▶ | GO to Test 3. |
| • Check for voltage on Circuit 197. Should equal battery voltage.<br>• Ignition in OFF position. | (ØK) ▶ | CHECK for open or short circuit in Circuit 197 and/or circuit breaker. SERVICE as necessary. CHECK cooling fan operation. |
| **3** | | |
| • Jumper cooling fan temperature switch connector pins together.<br>• Cooling fan motor should run.<br>• Ignition in OFF position. | (OK) ▶ | REPLACE cooling fan temperature switch. CHECK cooling fan operation. |
| | (ØK) ▶ | LEAVE jumper connected. GO to Test 4. |
| **4** | | |
| • Disconnect connector at fan motor. | (OK) ▶ | GO to Test 5 |
| • Check for voltage on Circuit 228 (BR/Y).<br>• With cooling fan temperature switch connector jumpered, Circuit 228 (BR/Y) should have battery voltage.<br>• Ignition in OFF position. | (ØK) ▶ | *CHECK Circuits 228 BR/Y and 182 BR/W for open. SERVICE wiring between fan motor and cooling fan temperature switch. CONNECT cooling fan temperature switch connector. CHECK cooling fan operation. |
| **5** | | |
| • Check ground, Circuit 57 (BK) for continuity. | (OK) ▶ | CHECK cooling fan operation. |
| | (ØK) ▶ | SERVICE open in Circuit 57 BK. CONNECT cooling fan motor connector. CONNECT cooling fan temperature switch connector. CHECK cooling fan operation. |

*Service non-cycling circuit breaker as required.

**Fig. 24 Cooling fan system diagnosis. Escort, less A/C**

ENGINE COOLING FAN DIAGNOSIS

| TEST STEP | RESULT ▶ | ACTION TO TAKE |
|---|---|---|
| **1** | | |
| • Check fuses and fuse link for the 294, 687 and 37 Circuits. | Good ▶ | GO to Step 2. |
| | Bad ▶ | REPLACE fuse and RE-TEST. |
| **2** | | |
| • Determine when fan does or does not operate.<br>**NOTE: The fan controller incorporates internal circuit protection that opens the circuit to the fan motor in case of a stall or short circuit.*** | A. Operates during A/C operation only. ▶ | GO to Step 3. |
| | B. Does not operate during A/C operation or during high engine coolant temperatures. ▶ | GO to Step 11. |
| | C. Operates during high engine coolant temperatures only. ▶ | GO to Step 6. |
| **3** | | |
| • Unplug connector at coolant temperature switch. Jumper connector terminals. | Fan motor runs ▶ | REPLACE coolant temperature switch. |
| | Fan motor does not run ▶ | GO to Step 4. |
| **4** | | |
| • Check the coolant switch ground (Circuits 57 and 182). Check that the coolant has exceeded 105°C (221°F) by idling a cold engine for approximately 25 minutes. Vehicles with temperature gauge should indicate toward the high end of normal band. | Ground OK ▶ | GO to Step 5. |
| | Ground not OK ▶ | SERVICE ground circuit. |
| **5** | | |
| • With the engine off, unplug connector from coolant temperature switch and check for battery voltage at Circuit 197. | Battery voltage ▶ | VERIFY cooling system at 105°C (221°F). |
| | No battery voltage ▶ | SERVICE circuit. |
| **6** | | |
| • Check fan controller ground at terminal 5 of fan controller. | Ground OK ▶ | GO to Step 7. |
| | Ground Not OK ▶ | SERVICE ground. |
| **7** | | |
| • Remove connector from cooling fan controller. Turn ignition switch to RUN. Check for voltage at Circuits 198, 348 and 687 with mode switch in A/C or Defrost. | No voltage ▶ | GO to Step 8. |
| | Voltage OK ▶ | REPLACE fan controller. |

**Fig. 26 Cooling fan system diagnosis (Part 1 of 2). Escort w/1.9L/4-116 & A/C**

ENGINE COOLING DIAGNOSIS — Continued

| TEST STEP | RESULT ▶ | ACTION TO TAKE |
|---|---|---|
| **8** | | |
| • Remove connector from clutch cycling pressure switch and jumper across the connector. Check to see if the fan motor engages.* | Fan motor engages ▶ | GO to Step 9. |
| | Fan motor does not engage ▶ | GO to Step 10. |
| **9** | | |
| • Check A/C system for refrigerant charge 344.75 kPa (50 psi) pressure at ambient temperatures about 10°C (50°F).* | No refrigerant charge ▶ | LEAK TEST, SERVICE, RE-CHARGE system. |
| | Refrigerant pressures above 344.75 kPa (50 psi) ▶ | REPLACE clutch cycling pressure switch. |
| **10** | | |
| • Remove connector from A/C control assembly. Jumper Circuit 348 to 294. Check for voltage at Circuit 198. | Voltage OK ▶ | REPLACE A/C push button switch. GO to Step 7. |
| | No voltage ▶ | SERVICE open circuits. |
| **11** | | |
| • Unplug connector at cooling fan motor. Jumper B+ and ground to motor. | Fan motor runs ▶ | GO to Step 12. |
| | Fan motor does not run ▶ | REPLACE motor. |
| **12** | | |
| • Remove jumper wires and connect harness connector to fan motor. Unplug connector from cooling fan controller and turn ignition switch to RUN. Check for voltage at Circuits 37, 687, 182, 198 and 348, and fan controller ground (Circuit 57). | No voltage at one or both circuits ▶ | SERVICE circuit(s). CHECK cooling operations. |
| | Voltage and ground OK ▶ | GO to Step 13. |
| **13** | | |
| • Jumper Circuit 37 to Circuit 228 at the cooling fan relay (bypasses relay contacts). | Fan motor runs ▶ | GO to Step 15. |
| | Fan motor does not run ▶ | GO to Step 14. |
| **14** | | |
| • Check continuity between terminal 3 of the fan relay and the 228A Circuit (fan motor). | Circuits OK ▶ | System OK. VERIFY fan motor operation, Step 11. |
| | Circuits open ▶ | SERVICE circuits. |
| **15** | | |
| • Unplug connector at coolant temperature switch and jumper across connector terminals. Check for ground in Circuit 197 at terminal No. 1 of cooling fan relay and terminal No. 1 of cooling fan controller. | Ground OK ▶ | REPLACE cooling fan relay. |
| | Ground not OK ▶ | SERVICE circuits. |

*Fan controllers with prefix E5EZ or later, refer to Engine Cooling Fan Diagnosis for vehicles with A/C.

**Fig. 26 Cooling fan system diagnosis (Part 2 of 2). Escort w/1.9L/4-116 & A/C**

ENGINE COOLING FAN DIAGNOSIS — Continued

| TEST STEP | RESULT ▶ | ACTION TO TAKE |
|---|---|---|
| **8** | | |
| • Remove connector from clutch cycling pressure switch and jumper across the connector. Check to see if the fan motor engages.* | Fan motor engages ▶ | GO to Step 9. |
| | Fan motor does not engage ▶ | GO to Step 10. |
| **9** | | |
| • Check A/C system for refrigerant charge 344.75 kPa (50 psi) pressure at ambient temperatures about 10°C (50°F).* | No refrigerant charge ▶ | LEAK TEST, SERVICE, RE-CHARGE system. |
| | Refrigerant pressures above 344.75 kPa (50 psi) ▶ | REPLACE clutch cycling pressure switch. |
| **10** | | |
| • Remove connector from A/C control assembly. Jumper Circuit 294 to Circuit 348 and check for voltage. | Voltage OK ▶ | REPLACE A/C push button switch. GO to Step 11. |
| | No voltage ▶ | SERVICE open Circuits 348, 299. GO to Step 11. |
| **11** | | |
| • Remove connector from clutch cycling pressure switch and jumper across the connector. Check to ensure fan motor engages. | Fan motor engages ▶ | Fan OK |
| | Fan motor does not engage. ▶ | SERVICE fan controller. Circuits 348 and 198 between A/C pressure switch and fan controller. |
| **12** | | |
| • Unplug connector at cooling fan motor. Jumper B+ and ground to motor. | Fan motor runs ▶ | GO to Step 13. |
| | Fan motor does not run ▶ | REPLACE motor. |
| **13** | | |
| • Remove jumper wires and connect harness connector to fan motor. Unplug connector from cooling fan controller and turn ignition switch to RUN. Check for voltage at Circuits 37, 687, 198 and 348, and fan controller ground. | No voltage at one or both circuits ▶ | SERVICE circuit(s). |
| | Voltage and ground OK at circuits ▶ | GO to Step 14. |
| **14** | | |
| • Jumper Circuit 37 to Circuit 228A (terminal No. 2 of fan relay) at the cooling fan controller. | Fan motor runs ▶ | REPLACE fan controller. |
| | Fan motor does not run ▶ | GO to Step 15. |

*Fan controllers with prefix E5EZ or later, refer to Engine Cooling Fan Diagnosis for vehicles with A/C.

**Fig. 27 Cooling fan system diagnosis (Part 2 of 3). Tempo & Topaz, w/A/C**

ENGINE COOLING FAN DIAGNOSIS

| TEST STEP | RESULT ▶ | ACTION TO TAKE |
|---|---|---|
| **1** | | |
| • Check fuse and fuse link. | Good ▶ | GO to Step 2. |
| | Bad ▶ | REPLACE fuse and RE-TEST. |
| **2** | | |
| • Determine when fan does or does not operate. NOTE: The fan controller incorporates internal circuit protection that opens the fan circuit in case of a short in the fan relay coil. | A. Operates during A/C operation only. ▶ | GO to Step 3. |
| | B. Does not operate during A/C operation or during high engine coolant temperatures. ▶ | GO to Step 12. |
| | C. Operates during high engine coolant temperatures only. ▶ | GO to Step 6. |
| **3** | | |
| • Turn the ignition switch to RUN, and unplug connector at coolant temperature switch. Jumper connector to ground with A/C and DEFROST off. | Fan motor runs ▶ | GO to Step 4. |
| | Fan motor does not run ▶ | GO to Step 5. |
| **4** | | |
| • Verify the coolant switch ground by checking the ground circuit (No. 182) for continuity. Verify the coolant has exceeded 210°F (84.7°C) by idling a cold engine for approximately 25 minutes. Vehicles with temperature gauge should indicate toward the high end of normal band. | Fan motor runs ▶ | Cooling fan system is OK. |
| | Fan motor does not run ▶ | REPLACE coolant temperature switch. |
| **5** | | |
| • Unplug connector from cooling fan controller and check continuity of Circuit 197 from controller coolant temperature switch. | Continuity ▶ | REPLACE cooling fan controller. |
| | No continuity ▶ | SERVICE circuit. |
| **6** | | |
| • Check fan controller system ground at terminal 5 of the fan controller.① | Ground OK ▶ | GO to Step 7. |
| | Ground not OK ▶ | SERVICE ground. |
| **7** | | |
| • Remove connector from cooling fan controller. Check for voltage at Circuits 198 and 348.① | No voltage at one or both circuits ▶ | GO to Step 8. |
| | Voltage OK ▶ | REPLACE fan controller. |

①For fan controllers with prefix E5FZ or later, see Engine Cooling Fan Diagnosis for vehicles with A/C.

**Fig. 27 Cooling fan system diagnosis (Part 1 of 3). Tempo & Topaz, w/A/C**

ENGINE COOLING FAN DIAGNOSIS — Continued

| TEST STEP | RESULT ▶ | ACTION TO TAKE |
|---|---|---|
| **15** | | |
| • Jumper Circuit 37 to Circuit 228 | Fan motor runs ▶ | GO to Step 17. |
| | Fan motor does not run ▶ | GO to Step 16. |
| **16** | | |
| Unplug the 5-way connector of the engine compartment mounted fan relay. Jumper Circuit 37 to Circuit 228 (fan motor). | Fan motor runs ▶ | GO to Step 17. |
| | Fan motor does not run ▶ | SERVICE fan motor ground. |
| **17** | | |
| Jumper 57 Circuit to terminal 1 of fan relay. Jumper 37 circuit to the 228A Circuit. | Fan motor runs ▶ | SERVICE circuits |
| | Fan motor does not run. ▶ | REPLACE fan relay. |

**Fig. 27 Cooling fan system diagnosis (Part 3 of 3). Tempo & Topaz, w/A/C**

COOLING FAN CONTROLLER DIAGNOSIS
1.9L with A/C②

| Cooling Fan Relay Near Headlamps (LH) | Coolant Temperature Switch | Clutch Cycling Pressure Switch | Ignition Switch | A/C Control Assy. | WOT Signal from EEC | ①Engine Cooling Fan Motor | A/C Clutch Field Coil |
|---|---|---|---|---|---|---|---|
| | | | C | | | | |
| | | | C | | G | | |
| | | | C | C | | | |
| | | | C | C | C | | |
| | | C | C | | | | |
| | | C | C | | C | | |
| | | C | C | | | | |
| | | C | C | | C | | |
| E | | C | C | C | | E | E |
| E | | C | C | C | G | E | |
| E | C | | | | | E | |
| E | C | | C | | | E | |
| E | C | C | C | C | | E | E |
| E | C | C | C | C | G | E | |

C — Closed
E — Energized
G — EEC Ground at WOT
①For fan controllers with prefix E5EZ or later, the cooling fan motor will remain energized if the WOT switch opens. In addition, the fan motor will remain energized up to three minutes if the A/C cycling switch opens.
②A fan relay, located on the LH radiator support, has been added for 1.9L A/C models. This relay increases the fan motor voltage. Its operation is similar to that of the fan relay located on the printed circuit board (PCB) in the fan controller.

**Fig. 28 Cooling fan controller diagnosis (Part 1 of 4). 1990 Escort**

TEST 1: IGNITION SWITCH OFF

| Connector Pin Number | Voltmeter should read |
|---|---|
| 1 | 12-volts with coolant temperature switch open. |
| 2 | (not used) |
| 3 | 0 voltage (with coolant temperature switch open) |
| 4 | (not used) |
| 5 | 0-volts |
| 6 | 0-volts |
| 7 | 0-volts |
| 8 | 0-volts |
| 9 | 0-volts |
| 10 | 0-volts |

**Fig. 28 Cooling fan controller diagnosis, ignition switch Off (Part 2 of 4). 1990 Escort**

TEST 2: IGNITION SWITCH IN RUN, ENGINE RUNNING AND A/C/DEFROST OFF

| Connector Pin Number | Voltmeter should read |
|---|---|
| 1 | Battery voltage with coolant temperature switch open — Less than 1-volt with coolant temperature switch closed. |
| 2 | (not used) |
| 3 | 0-volts with coolant temperature switch open — Battery voltage with coolant temperature switch closed. |
| 4 | (not used) |
| 5 | 0-volts |
| 6 | 6-volts |
| 7 | 0-volts |
| 8 | 0-volts |
| 9 | Battery voltage |
| 10 | 0-volts |

**Fig. 28 Cooling fan controller diagnosis, engine running & A/C Off (Part 3 of 4). 1990 Escort**

TEST 3: IGNITION SWITCH IN RUN, ENGINE RUNNING AND A/C/DEFROST ON

| Connector Pin Number | Voltmeter should read |
|---|---|
| 1 | Less than 1.0-volt with coolant temperature switch closed. |
| 2 | (not used) |
| 3 | Battery voltage with temperature switch and/or clutch cycling pressure cut-out switch closed — 0-volts if both switches are open.(1) |
| 4 | (not used) |
| 5 | 0-volts |
| 6 | Wide-open throttle: 0-volts<br>Not wide-open throttle: 6-volts |
| 7 | Battery voltage |
| 8 | Battery voltage with clutch cycling, switch closed or not wide-open throttle 0-volts if A/C cycling switch open or wide-open throttle. |
| 9 | Battery voltage |
| 10 | Battery voltage with clutch cycling pressure switch closed. |

(1)On fan controllers with prefix E5EZ or later, the fan motor will stay energized when the WOT switch is open. The fan motor will stay energized if the A/C cycling pressure switch opens for less than 2-3 minutes.

**Fig. 28 Cooling fan controller diagnosis, engine running & A/C On (Part 4 of 4). 1990 Escort**

| Cooling Fan Relay Terminal No. 3 | Wide-Open Throttle Cutout Switch | Engine Coolant Temp. Switch | Clutch Cycling Pressure Switch | A/C Control Assy. (A/C or Defrost Position) | Ignition Switch | (3)Engine Cooling Fan Motor (Terminal 3) | A/C Clutch Field Coil (Terminal 8) |
|---|---|---|---|---|---|---|---|
| | G | | | | C | | |
| | G | | | C | C | | |
| | G | | C | | C | | |
| | G | C | C | C | | | |
| | G | | C | C | | | |
| E | G | | C | C | C | E | |
| | G | C | | | | | |
| E | G | C | | | C | E | |
| E | G | C | C | C | C | E | |
| | | | | | C | | |
| | | | | C | C | | |
| E | | | C | C | C | E | E(1) |
| E | | C | | | C | E | |
| E | | C | | C | C | E | |
| E | | C | C | C | C | E | E |

C — Closed
E — Energized
G — EEC Ground
(1)2-4 Second Time Delay Before Closing On Earlier Models
(3)For fan controllers with prefix E53Z or later, the fan will stay energized for 2-3 minutes after the A/C cycling pressure switch opens.

**Fig. 29 Cooling fan controller diagnosis (Part 1 of 4). Tempo & Topaz**

TEST 1 — IGNITION SWITCH OFF — TEMPO/TOPAZ

| Connector Pin Number | Voltmeter should read |
|---|---|
| 1 | 0-volts |
| 2 | (not used) |
| 3 | 0-volts |
| 4 | (not used) |
| 5 | 0-volts |
| 6 | 0-volts |
| 7 | 0-volts |
| 8 | 0-volts |
| 9 | 0-volts |
| 10 | 0-volts |

**Fig. 29 Cooling fan controller diagnosis, ignition switch Off (Part 2 of 4). Tempo & Topaz**

TEST 2 — IGNITION SWITCH IN RUN — ENGINE AND A/C OR DEFROST OFF TEMPO/TOPAZ — 50 STATES

| Connector Pin Number | Voltmeter should read |
|---|---|
| 1 | Battery voltage with coolant temperature switch open. |
| 2 | (not used) |
| 3 | 0-volts with coolant temperature switch open — Battery voltage with coolant temperature switch closed. |
| 4 | (not used) |
| 5 | 0-volts — continuity with ground |
| 6 | 6-volts |
| 7 | 0-volts |
| 8 | 0-volts |
| 9 | Battery voltage |
| 10 | 0-volts |

**Fig. 29 Cooling fan controller diagnosis, ignition switch in Run engine & A/C Off (Part 3 of 4). Tempo & Topaz**

TEST 3: IGNITION SWITCH IN RUN — ENGINE RUNNING AND A/C OR DEFROST ON — TEMPO/TOPAZ

| Connector Pin Number | Voltmeter should read |
|---|---|
| 1 (c) | 0-volts with clutch cycling pressure switch closed/or coolant temperature switch closed. |
| 2 | (not used) |
| 3 (c), (d) | Battery voltage with coolant temperature switch closed and/or clutch cycling pressure switch closed (a) — 0-volts otherwise. |
| 4 | (not used) |
| 5 | 0-volts |
| 6 | 6-volts during normal operation — 0-volts during wide-open throttle operation (b). |
| 7 | Battery voltage |
| 8 (a), (d) | Battery voltage when A/C clutch cycling pressure switch is closed and throttle is normal (c) — 0-volts with cycling switch open or throttle closed. |
| 9 | Battery voltage |
| 10 | Battery voltage when A/C clutch cycling pressure switch and high pressure cut-out switch closed — 0-volts if switch is open. |

(a) When Pin 6 is grounded, Pin 8 will have 0 volts.

(b) High pressure cutout switch (if used) must also be closed.

(c) On fan controllers with prefix E53Z or later the fan motor will stay energized when the WOT switch is open. The fan motor will stay energized if the A/C cycling pressure switch opens for less than 2-3 minutes.

(d) 0 volts if short/overload occurs in fan relay coil circuits.

NOTE: Indicated voltages in the 50 states and Canada procedures can vary, depending on the type of meter used.

**Fig. 29 Cooling fan controller diagnosis, engine running & A/C On (Part 4 of 4). Tempo & Topaz**

| CONDITION | POSSIBLE SOURCE | ACTION |
|---|---|---|
| • Cooling Fan Always Runs | • Relay(s).<br>• Circuit.<br>• ECA.<br>• Motor.<br>• Switch. | • GO to EC4.<br><br><br><br>• GO to EC10. (1.8L) |
| • Cooling Fan Never Runs (Overheating) | • Relay(s).<br>• Circuit.<br>• ECA.<br>• Motor.<br>• Switch. | • GO to EC1.<br><br><br><br>• GO to EC10. (1.8L) |
| • Cooling Fan Runs but No High Speed | • Relay(s).<br>• Circuit.<br>• ECA.<br>• Motor.<br>• Switch. | • GO to EC2.<br><br><br><br>• GO to EC10. (1.8L) |
| • Cooling Fan Runs but No Low Speed | • Relay(s).<br>• Circuit.<br>• ECA.<br>• Motor.<br>• Switch. | • GO to EC2.<br><br><br><br>• GO to EC10. (1.8L) |

**Fig. 30 Diagnostic condition chart. 1991 Escort & Tracer**

| TEST STEP | RESULT ► | ACTION TO TAKE |
|---|---|---|
| **EC1** CHECK FUSE | | |
| • Access the interior fuse panel.<br>• Check the 15 amp engine fuse.<br>• Is the fuse good?<br>NOTE: If the fuse blows again, check for a short in the "BK/W" wire. | Yes ►<br>No ► | GO to EC2.<br>REPLACE the engine fuse. |

**Fig. 31 Diagnostic test step EC1 (Part 1 of 11). 1991 Escort & Tracer**

| TEST STEP | RESULT ► | ACTION TO TAKE |
|---|---|---|
| **EC2** CHECK VOLTAGE TO RELAY(S) | | |
| • Key ON.<br>• Measure the voltage on the "BK/W" wire at low-speed cooling fan relay.<br>• Is the voltage greater than 10 volts?<br>**If equipped with 1.8L 4EAT or 1.9L A/C:**<br>• Measure the voltage on the "BK/W" wire at high speed cooling fan relay.<br>• Is the voltage greater than 10 volts? | Yes ►<br>No ► | GO to EC3.<br>REPAIR/REPLACE the "BK/W" wire. |

**Fig. 31 Diagnostic test step EC2 (Part 2 of 11). 1991 Escort & Tracer**

| TEST STEP | RESULT ► | ACTION TO TAKE |
|---|---|---|
| **EC3** CHECK VOLTAGE TO RELAY(S) | | |
| • Key ON.<br>• Measure the voltage on the "BK/R" (1.8L) or "LG/BK" (1.9L) wire at high-speed cooling fan relay.<br>• Is the voltage greater than 10 volts?<br>**If equipped with 1.9L A/C or 1.8L 4EAT:**<br>• Measure the resistance of the "LG" (1.9L) or "R/BK" (1.8L) wire between high-speed cooling fan relay and low-speed cooling fan relay.<br>• Is the resistance less than 5 ohms? | Yes ►<br>No ► | GO to EC4.<br>REPAIR/REPLACE the wire(s). |

**Fig. 31 Diagnostic test step EC3 (Part 3 of 11). 1991 Escort & Tracer**

| TEST STEP | RESULT ► | ACTION TO TAKE |
|---|---|---|
| **EC4** CHECK COOLING FAN RELAY | | |
| • Key ON.<br>• Ground the "Y/W" (1.9L) or "BK/GN" (1.8L) at cooling fan relay (1.8L MTX or 1.9L non-A/C) or low-speed cooling fan relay (1.8L 4EAT or 1.9L A/C).<br>• Measure the resistance between the following wire colors at the relay: | Yes ►<br>No ► | GO to EC5.<br>REPAIR/REPLACE cooling fan relay. |

| Vehicle Type | Wire Colors | Resistance |
|---|---|---|
| 1.8L 4EAT | "R/BK", "Y" | less than 5 ohms |
| 1.8L MTX | "BK/R", "Y" | less than 5 ohms |
| 1.9L Non-A/C | "LG/BK", "Y" | less than 5 ohms |
| 1.9L A/C | "LG", "Y" | less than 5 ohms |

• Are the resistances less than 5 ohms?

**Fig. 31 Diagnostic test step EC4 (Part 4 of 11). 1991 Escort & Tracer**

| TEST STEP | RESULT ► | ACTION TO TAKE |
|---|---|---|
| **EC5** CHECK COOLING FAN RELAY | | |
| **With 1.8L 4EAT or 1.9L A/C only:**<br>• Ground the "BK/GN" (1.8L) or "R/BK" (1.9L) wire at the high-speed cooling fan relay.<br>• Measure the resistances between the following wires at the relay:<br>1.8L — "BK/R" and "BL"<br>1.9L — "LG/BK" and "LG/Y"<br>• Turn the ignition switch to the ON position.<br>• Measure the resistances between the following wires at the relay:<br>1.8L — "BK/R" and "R/BK"<br>1.9L — "LG/BK" and "LG"<br>• Are the resistances less than 5 ohms? | Yes ►<br>No ► | GO to EC6.<br>REPAIR/REPLACE high speed cooling fan relay. |

**Fig. 31 Diagnostic test step EC5 (Part 5 of 11). 1991 Escort & Tracer**

| TEST STEP | RESULT ► | ACTION TO TAKE |
|---|---|---|
| **EC6** CHECK CONTINUITY BETWEEN RELAYS AND MOTOR | | |
| • Key OFF.<br>• Access the cooling fan relays.<br>• Measure the resistance of the "Y" wire between cooling fan relay (1.8L MTX or 1.9L Non-A/C) or low-speed cooling fan relay (1.8L 4EAT or 1.9 A/C) and the cooling fan motor.<br>**If equipped with 1.8L 4EAT or 1.9L A/C only:**<br>• Measure the resistance of the "LG/Y" (1.9L) or "BL" (1.8L) wire between high-speed cooling fan relay and the cooling fan motor.<br>• Are the resistances less than 5 ohms? | Yes ►<br>No ► | GO to EC7.<br>REPAIR/REPLACE the wires. |

**Fig. 31 Diagnostic test step EC6 (Part 6 of 11). 1991 Escort & Tracer**

| TEST STEP | RESULT ► | ACTION TO TAKE |
|---|---|---|
| **EC7** CHECK COOLING FAN MOTOR GROUND | | |
| • Key OFF.<br>• Access the cooling fan motor.<br>• Measure the resistance of the "BK" wire to the ground.<br>• Is the resistance less than 5 ohms? | Yes ►<br>No ► | GO to EC8.<br>REPAIR/REPLACE the "BK" wire. |

**Fig. 31 Diagnostic test step EC7 (Part 7 of 11). 1991 Escort & Tracer**

| TEST STEP | RESULT ► | ACTION TO TAKE |
|---|---|---|
| **EC8** CHECK COOLING FAN MOTOR | | |
| • Key OFF.<br>• Apply 12 volts to the "Y" wire at the motor.<br>• Does the motor run at low speed?<br>**If equipped with 1.8L 4EAT or 1.9L A/C:**<br>• Apply 12 volts to the "BL" wire (1.8L) or the "LG/Y" (1.9L) at the motor.<br>• Does the motor run at high speed? | Yes ►<br><br>No ► | GO to EC9. (1.9L)<br>GO to EC10. (1.8L)<br>REPLACE the motor. |

**Fig. 31 Diagnostic test step EC8 (Part 8 of 11). 1991 Escort & Tracer**

| TEST STEP | RESULT ► | ACTION TO TAKE |
|---|---|---|
| EC9 CHECK CONTINUITY FROM RELAYS TO ECA (1.9L ONLY) | | |
| • Key ON.<br>• Ground the "Y/W" wire at the ECA.<br>• Does the motor run at low speed?<br>If equipped with A/C:<br>• Disconnect the "Y/W" wire at the ECA.<br>• Ground the "R/BK" wire at the ECA.<br>• Does the motor run at high speed? | Yes ►<br><br>No ► | Engine/Emissions<br><br>REPAIR/REPLACE the wires. |

Fig. 31 Diagnostic test step EC9 (Part 9 of 11). 1991 Escort & Tracer

| TEST STEP | RESULT ► | ACTION TO TAKE |
|---|---|---|
| EC10 FAN MOTOR FUNCTION WITH BYPASSED FAN SWITCH (1.8L ONLY) | | |
| • Disconnect the cooling fan switch connector (at the water outlet connection).<br>WARNING: TO AVOID PERSONAL INJURY AND COMPONENT DAMAGE, KEEP HANDS CLEAR OF THE FAN BLADES AT ALL TIMES.<br>• Ground the "BK/GN" terminal in the connector and note whether the fan motor runs.<br>• Does the fan motor run with the "BK/GN" terminal grounded? | Yes ►<br>No ► | GO to EC11 .<br>SERVICE the "BK/GN" wire. |

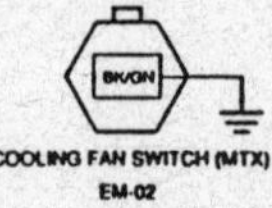


Fig. 31 Diagnostic test step EC10 (Part 10 of 11). 1991 Escort & Tracer

| TEST STEP | RESULT ► | ACTION TO TAKE |
|---|---|---|
| EC11 FAN SWITCH FUNCTION (1.8L ONLY) | | |
| • Disconnect the cooling fan switch connector.<br>• Start up the engine.<br>• Using a VOM as the engine warms up, check the continuity of the switch.<br>• If no continuity exists by the time the engine is hot, remove the switch from the engine.<br>• Place the switch in 50% glycol and water with a 150° C (250° F), range thermometer.<br>• Heat the water and monitor the switch continuity using a VOM.<br>• Verify that the switch closes and opens at the specified temperature. (See the specifications.)<br>• Does the switch show continuity when the engine becomes hot, or does it operate at specified temperatures? | Yes ►<br>No ► | RETURN to the symptom chart.<br>REPLACE the cooling fan switch. |

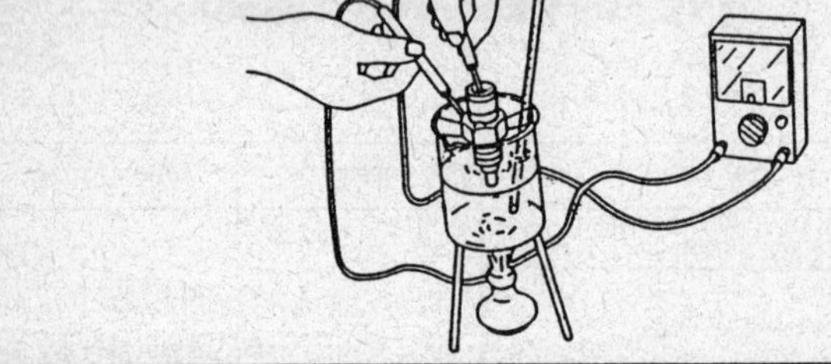

Fig. 31 Diagnostic test step EC11 (Part 11 of 11). 1991 Escort & Tracer

| SYMPTOM | POSSIBLE CAUSE | ACTION TO TAKE |
|---|---|---|
| Cooling fan never runs or runs improperly | • Fuse<br>• Cooling fan relay<br>• Coolant temperature switch<br>• Harness<br>• Fan motor<br>• A/C Relay | Go to CF1 |
| Cooling fan always runs | • Cooling fan relay<br>• Coolant temperature switch<br>• Harness<br>• Fan motor<br>• A/C Relay | Go to CG1 |
| Cooling fan does not run with A/C on | • A/C Relay<br>• Circuit | Go to CG4 |

Fig. 32 Symptom chart. Festiva

| TEST STEP | RESULT ► | ACTION TO TAKE |
|---|---|---|
| CF2 CHECK VOLTAGE SUPPLY | | |
| • Key on, engine off.<br>• Measure voltage at cooling fan motor yellow terminal.<br>• Is voltage greater than 10V? | Yes ►<br>No ► | GO to CF3 .<br>SERVICE yellow wire from 20 amp "cooling fan" fuse to cooling fan motor. |

Fig. 33 Test Step CF2 (Part 2 of 14). Festiva

| TEST STEP | RESULT ► | ACTION TO TAKE |
|---|---|---|
| CF1 SYSTEM INTEGRITY CHECK | | |
| • Check for fully charged battery.<br>• Check for blown fuses, corrosion, poor electrical connections, signs of opens, shorts or damage to the wiring harness. Check the cooling fan and shroud for obstruction, loose fan blade, misalignment of fan and other damage.<br>• Key on, engine off.<br>• Coolant temperature switch disconnected.<br>• Shake the wiring harness vigorously from the cooling fan motor to the cooling fan relay, the coolant temperature switch and the fuse panel; look for signs of opens or shorts.<br>• Tap each connector, the cooling fan relay, the 20 amp cooling fan fuse and look for signs of bad connections, bad crimps or loose wires.<br>• Does the system appear to be in good condition? | Yes ►<br>No ► | GO to CF2 .<br>REPAIR or Replace faulty components as required.<br>NOTE: If a blown 20 amp "cooling fan" fuse is replaced and fails immediately, there is a short to ground in the yellow wire from fuse panel to the cooling fan motor. |

Fig. 33 Test Step CF1 (Part 1 of 14). Festiva

| TEST STEP | RESULT ► | ACTION TO TAKE |
|---|---|---|
| CF3 GROUND COOLING FAN MOTOR | | |
| • Key on, engine off.<br>• Ground Y/R terminal at cooling fan motor with jumper wire.<br>• Does cooling fan operate? | Yes ►<br>No ► | GO to CF4 .<br>SERVICE motor side of cooling fan harness; if all OK, replace cooling fan motor. |

Fig. 33 Test Step CF3 (Part 3 of 14). Festiva

| TEST STEP | RESULT ► | ACTION TO TAKE |
|---|---|---|
| **CF4** CHECK POWER AT RELAY | | |
| • Key on, engine off.<br>• Disconnect cooling fan relay.<br>• Measure voltage at cooling fan relay Y/R wire.<br>• Is voltage greater than 10V? | Yes ►<br>No ► | GO to CF5.<br>SERVICE Y/R wire from Cooling Fan Motor to cooling fan relay, A/C relay and ECA. |

**Fig. 33 Test Step CF4 (Part 4 of 14). Festiva**

| TEST STEP | RESULT ► | ACTION TO TAKE |
|---|---|---|
| **CF5** CHECK VOLTAGE SUPPLY TO RELAY | | |
| • Key on, engine off.<br>• Cooling fan relay disconnected.<br>• Measure voltage at cooling fan relay BK/Y terminal.<br>• Is voltage greater than 10V? | Yes ►<br>No ► | GO to CF6.<br>SERVICE BK/Y wire from cooling fan relay to 10 amp "METER" fuse. |

**Fig. 33 Test Step CF5 (Part 5 of 14). Festiva**

| TEST STEP | RESULT ► | ACTION TO TAKE |
|---|---|---|
| **CF6** CHECK RELAY OPERATION | | |
| • Key off.<br>• Remove cooling fan relay.<br>• Apply battery power to relay "A" terminal.<br>• Measure resistance between relay "B" and "C" terminals.<br>• Ground relay "D" terminal with a jumper wire.<br>• Is resistance greater than 10,000 ohms with "D" terminal grounded and less than 5 ohms with "D" terminal ungrounded?<br>D C<br>A B<br>NOTE: Connector shown looking into relay. | Yes ►<br>No ► | RECONNECT relay, GO to CF7.<br>REPLACE cooling fan relay. |

**Fig. 33 Test Step CF6 (Part 6 of 14). Festiva**

| TEST STEP | RESULT ► | ACTION TO TAKE |
|---|---|---|
| **CF7** CHECK COOLANT TEMPERATURE SWITCH VOLTAGE | | |
| • Key on, engine off.<br>• Coolant temperature switch disconnected.<br>• Measure voltage at coolant temperature switch GN/R terminal.<br>• Is voltage greater than 10V? | Yes ►<br>No ► | GO to CF8.<br>SERVICE GN/R wire from cooling fan relay to coolant temperature switch. |

**Fig. 33 Test Step CF7 (Part 7 of 14). Festiva**

| TEST STEP | RESULT ► | ACTION TO TAKE |
|---|---|---|
| **CF8** CHECK COOLANT TEMPERATURE SWITCH OPERATION | | |
| • Let engine cool completely.<br>• Remove radiator cap.<br>• Place thermometer/pyrometer probe in radiator (under coolant surface).<br>• Measure resistance between coolant temperature switch terminal and ground.<br>• Start engine. Run until coolant temperature exceeds 97°C (207°F), and then shut engine off.<br>SWITCH OPERATION (see table below)<br>• Does switch open at 97°C (207°F) and then close when coolant temperature falls below 90°C (194°F)? | Yes ►<br>No ► | SERVICE cooling fan relay ground (BK wire).<br>REPLACE cooling fan switch. |

SWITCH OPERATION

| COOLANT | TEMPERATURE | RESISTANCE |
|---|---|---|
| Below opening temp. | 97°C (rising) | 10,000 ohms or greater |
| Above | 97°C | 0-5 ohms |
| Below closing temp. | 90°C (falling) | 10,000 ohms or greater |

**Fig. 33 Test Step CF8 (Part 8 of 14). Festiva**

| TEST STEP | RESULT ► | ACTION TO TAKE |
|---|---|---|
| **CG1** SYSTEM INTEGRITY CHECK | | |
| • Turn key on.<br>• Check for signs of shorted wires, worn insulation and signs of damage to the wiring harness.<br>• Shake the wiring harness vigorously and look for signs of shorts.<br>• Inspect the cooling fan motor, look for signs of shorting or damage to the motor.<br>• Check "METER" fuse.<br>• Does the system appear to be in good condition? | Yes ►<br>No ► | GO to CG2.<br>REPAIR or replace faulty component(s) as required. |

**Fig. 33 Test Step CG1 (Part 9 of 14). Festiva**

| TEST STEP | RESULT ► | ACTION TO TAKE |
|---|---|---|
| **CG2** CHECK FOR SHORTS | | |
| • Key off.<br>• Disconnect cooling fan motor.<br>• Disconnect cooling fan relay.<br>• Disconnect A/C relay.<br>• Disconnect ECA.<br>• Measure resistance between cooling fan motor connector Y/R terminal and ground.<br>• Is resistance greater than 10,000 ohms? | Yes ►<br>No ► | GO to CG3.<br>SERVICE shorts in Y/R from cooling fan motor to cooling fan relay, A/C relay and ECA. |

**Fig. 33 Test Step CG2 (Part 10 of 14). Festiva**

| TEST STEP | RESULT ► | ACTION TO TAKE |
|---|---|---|
| **CG3** CHECK FAN MOTOR | | |
| • Key on, engine off.<br>• Disconnect Y/R wire from cooling fan motor connector (pull wire out of connector).<br>• Does cooling fan motor continue to operate? | Yes ►<br>No ► | RECONNECT Y/R wire. Replace cooling fan motor, shorted internal.<br>RECONNECT Y/R wire. GO to CG4. |

**Fig. 33 Test Step CG3 (Part 11 of 14). Festiva**

| TEST STEP | RESULT ► | ACTION TO TAKE |
|---|---|---|
| **CG4** CHECK POWER TO RELAY | | |
| • Disconnect ECA.<br>• Key on.<br>• A/C on, blower on.<br>• Measure voltage at the A/C relay connector.<br>Vehicle: 1.3L EFI — Wire Color: Y/R and BL<br>• Are both readings greater than 10V? | Yes ►<br>No Y/R ►<br>No BL ► | GO to CG5.<br>SERVICE Y/R wire from cooling fan motor to A/C relay and ECA. If all OK, SERVICE GN wire from A/C Relay to ECA.<br>SERVICE BL wire or 15 amp HEATER fuse as required. |

| Vehicle | Wire Color |
|---|---|
| 1.3L EFI | Y/R and BL |

**Fig. 33 Test Step CG4 (Part 12 of 14). Festiva**

| TEST STEP | RESULT ▶ | ACTION TO TAKE |
|---|---|---|
| **CG5** CHECK RELAY OPERATION | | |
| • Remove A/C relay.<br>• Jump battery power to A/C relay "A" terminal.<br>• Measure resistance between A/C relay "B" and "C" terminals.<br>• Ground A/C relay "D" terminal with a jumper wire.<br>• Is reading greater than 10,000 ohms with "D" terminal open and less than 5 ohms with relay terminal grounded? | Yes ▶<br><br>No ▶ | REINSTALL relay.<br>GO to CG6.<br><br>REPLACE A/C relay. |
| B A<br>C D | | |

**Fig. 33 Test Step CG5 (Part 13 of 14). Festiva**

FAN MOTOR INOPERATIVE

| TEST | RESULT ▶ | ACTION TO TAKE |
|---|---|---|
| **TEST 1** | | |
| • Disconnect motor lead. Jumper negative to ground and positive to B+ at motor. | Motor does not run ▶ | REPLACE motor. |
| | Motor runs ▶ | CONNECT motor lead and GO to Test 2. |
| **TEST 2** | | |
| • Unplug connector at cooling fan temperature switch. Jumper from connector to ground on Circuit 45. Turn ignition switch to RUN. | Motor runs ▶ | CHECK switch ground. If ground is OK, REPLACE coolant temperature switch. |
| | Motor does not run ▶ | GO to Test 3. |
| **TEST 3** | | |
| • Turn ignition switch to OFF and remove jumper installed in Test 2. Check continuity of Circuit 45 from cooling fan controller (terminal 1) to cooling fan temperature switch. | Continuity (OK crossed out) ▶ | CHECK Circuit 45 for an open. |
| | Continuity (OK) ▶ | JUMPER coolant temperature switch wire to ground and GO to Test 4. |
| **TEST 4** | | |
| • Jumper from B+ to Circuit 687 at cooling fan controller (terminal 8). Do not disconnect wiring connector from controller. | Motor runs ▶ | CHECK ignition feed Circuit 687 for an open. |
| | Motor does not run ▶ | REMOVE jumper and GO to Test 5. |
| **TEST 5** | | |
| • Disconnect the wiring connector at the cooling fan controller. Jumper B+ to Circuit 228 (terminal 5). | Motor does not run ▶ | CHECK Circuit 228 for an open. |
| | Motor runs ▶ | REMOVE jumper and GO to Test 6. |
| **TEST 6** | | |
| • Connect a jumper from Circuit 68 to 228 (terminals 2 and 5) at the cooling fan controller connector. | Motor does not run ▶ | CHECK Circuit 68 for an open. |
| | Motor runs ▶ | REPLACE cooling fan controller and REMOVE jumper from temperature switch wire. |

**Fig. 34 Diagnostic chart, fan motor inoperative. Mustang**

FAN MOTOR OPERATES WHEN ENGINE TEMPERATURE REACHES SWITCH SET POINT BUT DOES NOT OPERATE IN THE A/C MODE — Continued

| TEST | RESULT ▶ | ACTION TO TAKE |
|---|---|---|
| **TEST 8** | | |
| • Check for voltage on 883 Circuit at Pin 6 of cooling fan controller. | Voltage ▶ | GO to Test 9. |
| | No voltage ▶ | SERVICE open 883 Circuit to controller. |
| **TEST 9** | | |
| • Ground 57 Circuit at Pin 4 of controller — controller must be connected. | Electro-drive fan runs ▶ | SERVICE ground circuit. |
| | Electro-drive fan does not run ▶ | REPLACE controller. |

**Fig. 35 Diagnostic chart, fan does not operate in A/C mode (Part 2 of 2). Mustang**

| TEST STEP | RESULT ▶ | ACTION TO TAKE |
|---|---|---|
| **CG6** CHECK POWER FROM RELAY | | |
| • Key on.<br>• Disconnect thermostatic switch.<br>• Disconnect ECA.<br>• Measure resistance at A/C Relay.<br>• A/C on, blower on.<br>Terminals / Resistance: BK—Ground, GN—Ground: 0-5 ohms<br>• Are resistances OK? | No ▶<br><br>Yes ▶ | SERVICE relay ground (BK wire), or SERVICE GN wire as required.<br><br>GO to CF4. |

**Fig. 33 Test Step CG6 (Part 14 of 14). Festiva**

FAN MOTOR OPERATES WHEN ENGINE TEMPERATURE REACHES SWITCH SET POINT BUT DOES NOT OPERATE IN THE A/C MODE

NOTE: A/C CLUTCH CIRCUIT WILL NOT ENERGIZE WITHOUT BATTERY VOLTAGE AT PINS OF COOLING FAN CONTROLLER.

| TEST | RESULT ▶ | ACTION TO TAKE |
|---|---|---|
| **TEST 1** | | |
| • Place A/C function selector switch in an A/C or DEFROST position. Start engine and wait five seconds. | Fan motor does not engage ▶ | GO to Test 2. |
| | Fan motor engages and disengages repeatedly ▶ | GO to Test 9. |
| **TEST 2** | | |
| • Check 20 amp fuse in fuse panel. | Blown ▶ | REPLACE. |
| | Good fuse ▶ | GO to Test 3. |
| **TEST 3** | | |
| • Disconnect A/C clutch cycling pressure switch. Jump across connector. | Fan motor engages ▶ | GO to Test 4. |
| | Fan motor does not engage ▶ | GO to Test 6. |
| **TEST 4** | | |
| • Check A/C system for loss of refrigerant charge. | No refrigerant charge ▶ | Leak test, SERVICE and CHARGE system. |
| | Refrigerant system has charge with low pressure above 344.75 kPa (50 psi) ▶ | GO to Test 5. |
| **TEST 5** | | |
| • Check for continuity across the A/C clutch cycling pressure switch. Remove switch connector. | No continuity ▶ | REPLACE the A/C clutch cycling pressure switch |
| | Continuity ▶ | GO to Test 8. |
| **TEST 6** | | |
| • Check for voltage on Circuit 348 at A/C clutch cycling pressure switch. | Voltage (OK) ▶ | GO to Test 8. |
| | No voltage ▶ | GO to Test 7. |
| **TEST 7** | | |
| • Check for voltage on Circuits 296 and 348 at function selector switch in instrument panel. | Voltage on Circuit 296 but not on 348 ▶ | SERVICE A/C control assembly. |
| | No voltage on Circuit 296 ▶ | TRACE Circuits 296 and 297 toward Ignition switch. |

**Fig. 35 Diagnostic chart, fan does not operate in A/C mode (Part 1 of 2). Mustang**

| SYMPTOM | POSSIBLE CAUSE | ACTION TO TAKE |
|---|---|---|
| • Cooling Fan never runs - May cause overheating. | • Fuses<br>• Motor<br>• Cooling Fan Relay<br>• Resistor (4EAT only).<br>• Motor ground.<br>• Coolant Temperature Switch<br>• Resistor (2.2L 4EAT only) | • INSPECT, REPLACE.<br>• GO to CF1. |
| • Cooling Fan Runs constantly. | • Coolant Temperature Switch<br>• High Speed Fan Switch<br>• High Speed Fan Relay<br>• Cooling Fan Relay<br>• Circuit<br>• ECA | • GO to EC1. |
| • No High Speed Fan (2.2L 4EAT only). | • High Speed Fan Relay<br>• High Speed Fan Switch<br>• Resistor<br>• Circuit | • GO to HS1. |
| • No Fan Operation with A/C on.<br>NOTE: Confirm A/C System functions properly. | • WAC Relay<br>• Circuit | JUMP WAC Relay BK/GN (MTX) or BL/R (4EAT) to ground. If fan operates, REPLACE WAC Relay. If fan does not operate, SERVICE BK/GN or BL/R wires. |

**Fig. 36 Symptom chart. Probe w/2.2L Engine**

| TEST STEP | RESULT ► | ACTION TO TAKE |
|---|---|---|
| **CF1** DISCONNECT COOLANT TEMPERATURE SWITCH | | |
| • Key on.<br>• Engine cold.<br>• Disconnect Coolant Temperature Switch (CTS).<br>• Ground CTS Connector BK/GN terminal.<br>• Does Cooling Fan run? | Yes ►<br>No ► | REPLACE Coolant Temperature Switch.<br>GO to CF2 . |

**Fig. 37 Diagnostic chart CF1 (Part 1 of 18). Probe w/2.2L Engine**

| TEST STEP | RESULT ► | ACTION TO TAKE |
|---|---|---|
| **CF2** GROUND CFR | | |
| • Key on.<br>• Engine cold.<br>• Ground BK/GN terminal of Cooling Fan Relay.<br>• Does Cooling Fan run? | Yes ►<br>No ► | SERVICE BK/GN from Cooling Fan Relay to CTS.<br>GO to CF3 . |

**Fig. 37 Diagnostic chart CF2 (Part 2 of 18). Probe w/2.2L Engine**

| TEST STEP | RESULT ► | ACTION TO TAKE |
|---|---|---|
| **CF3** CHECK POWER TO RELAY | | |
| • Key on.<br>• Measure voltage at Cooling Fan Relay BK/R and BK/W terminals.<br>• Are both readings 10V or greater? | Yes ►<br>No ► | GO to CF4 .<br>SERVICE wire in question. |

**Fig. 37 Diagnostic chart CF3 (Part 3 of 18). Probe w/2.2L Engine**

| TEST STEP | RESULT ► | ACTION TO TAKE |
|---|---|---|
| **CF4** CHECK RELAY OPERATION | | |
| • Key on.<br>• Measure voltage at Cooling Fan Relay BL/W terminal.<br>• Ground Relay BK/GN terminal.<br>• Is voltage greater than 10V with BK/GN grounded and less than 1V with BK/GN open? | Yes ►<br>No ► | GO to CF5 .<br>REPLACE Relay. |

**Fig. 37 Diagnostic chart CF4 (Part 4 of 18). Probe w/2.2L Engine**

| TEST STEP | RESULT ► | ACTION TO TAKE |
|---|---|---|
| **CF5** JUMP POWER TO MOTOR | | |
| • Key on.<br>• Jump battery power to Engine Cooling Fan Motor Harness Connector BL/Y terminal (MTX vehicles) or BL/BK terminal (4EAT vehicles).<br>• Does motor run? | Yes (4EAT) ►<br>Yes (MTX) ►<br>No ► | GO to CF6 .<br>SERVICE BL/W wire from Cooling Fan Relay to Cooling Fan Motor for opens or shorts.<br>SERVICE motor ground connection (BK wire). If all OK, REPLACE Cooling Fan Motor. |

**Fig. 37 Diagnostic chart CF5 (Part 5 of 18). Probe w/2.2L Engine**

| TEST STEP | RESULT ► | ACTION TO TAKE |
|---|---|---|
| **CF6** JUMP ACROSS RESISTOR | | |
| • Key on.<br>• Jump CTS BK/GN wire to ground.<br>• Disconnect Resistor.<br>• Jump Resistor Harness Connector BL/W and BL/BK together.<br>• Does fan motor run? | Yes ►<br>No ► | REPLACE resistor.<br>SERVICE BL/W or BL/BK wires. |

**Fig. 37 Diagnostic chart CF6 (Part 6 of 18). Probe w/2.2L Engine**

| TEST STEP | RESULT ► | ACTION TO TAKE |
|---|---|---|
| **HS1** CHECK HIGH SPEED FAN SWITCH | | |
| • Key on.<br>• Disconnect High Speed Fan Switch (HSFS).<br>• Ground HSFS LB/R terminal.<br>• Does fan motor run? | Yes ►<br>No ► | REPLACE High Speed Fan Switch.<br>GO to HS2 . |

**Fig. 37 Diagnostic chart HS1 (Part 7 of 18). Probe w/2.2L Engine**

| TEST STEP | RESULT ► | ACTION TO TAKE |
|---|---|---|
| **HS2** GROUND RELAY | | |
| • Key on.<br>• Ground LB/R terminal of High Speed Fan Relay.<br>• Does fan motor run? | Yes ►<br>No ► | SERVICE LB/R wire.<br>GO to HS3 . |

**Fig. 37 Diagnostic chart HS2 (Part 8 of 18). Probe w/2.2L Engine**

| TEST STEP | RESULT ► | ACTION TO TAKE |
|---|---|---|
| **HS3** CHECK POWER TO RELAY | | |
| • Key on.<br>• Measure voltage at High Speed Fan Relay BK/W and BK/R terminals.<br>• Are both readings 10V or greater? | Yes ►<br>No ► | GO to HS4 .<br>SERVICE wire in question. |

**Fig. 37 Diagnostic chart HS3 (Part 9 of 18). Probe w/2.2L Engine**

| TEST STEP | RESULT ► | ACTION TO TAKE |
|---|---|---|
| **HS4** CHECK RELAY OPERATION | | |
| • Key on.<br>• Measure voltage at High Speed Fan Relay BL/BK terminal.<br>• Ground LB/R terminal.<br>• Is voltage greater than 10V with LB/R grounded, and 0V with LB/R open? | Yes ►<br>No ► | GO to HS5 .<br>REPLACE relay. |

**Fig. 37 Diagnostic chart HS4 (Part 10 of 18). Probe w/2.2L Engine**

| TEST STEP | RESULT ► | ACTION TO TAKE |
|---|---|---|
| **HS5** CHECK RESISTOR | | |
| • Key off.<br>• Disconnect Resistor.<br>• Measure resistance across Resistor (BL/W to BL/BK).<br>• Is resistance between 100 and 10,000 ohms? | Yes ►<br>No ► | SERVICE BL/BK wire from High Speed Fan Relay to Fan Motor.<br>REPLACE Resistor. |

**Fig. 37 Diagnostic chart HS5 (Part 11 of 18). Probe w/2.2L Engine**

| TEST STEP | RESULT ► | ACTION TO TAKE |
|---|---|---|
| **EC1** DISCONNECT CTS | | |
| • Key on.<br>• Cold engine.<br>• Disconnect Coolant Temperature Switch.<br>• Does fan stop? | Yes ►<br>No ► | REPLACE Coolant Temperature Switch.<br>GO to EC2 . |

**Fig. 37 Diagnostic chart EC1 (Part 12 of 18). Probe w/2.2L Engine**

| TEST STEP | RESULT ► | ACTION TO TAKE |
|---|---|---|
| EC2 DISCONNECT ECA | | |
| • Key on.<br>• Cold engine.<br>• Disconnect ECA.<br>• Does fan stop? | Yes MTX ► | SERVICE BK/GN wire from Cooling Fan Relay and WAC Relay to ECA. |
| | Yes 4EAT ► | SERVICE BK/GN wire from Cooling Fan Relay to ECA - or - BL/R wire from High Speed Fan Relay and WAC Relay to ECA. |
| | No ► | GO to EC3 . |

Fig. 37 Diagnostic chart EC2 (Part 13 of 18). Probe w/2.2L Engine

| TEST STEP | RESULT ► | ACTION TO TAKE |
|---|---|---|
| EC3 CHECK CFR BK/BL FOR SHORTS | | |
| • Key off.<br>• Disconnect Cooling Fan Relay (CFR).<br>• Disconnect ECA.<br>• Disconnect Coolant Temperature Switch (CTS).<br>• Measure resistance between Cooling Fan Relay (CFR) Connector BK/GN terminal and ground.<br>• Is resistance greater than 10,000 ohms? | Yes ► | RECONNECT CFR. RECONNECT CTS. GO to EC4 . |
| | No ► | SERVICE BK/GN for shorts. |

Fig. 37 Diagnostic chart EC3 (Part 14 of 18). Probe w/2.2L Engine

| TEST STEP | RESULT ► | ACTION TO TAKE |
|---|---|---|
| EC4 CHECK RELAY OPERATION | | |
| • Key on, cold engine.<br>• Disconnect ECA.<br>• Disconnect Cooling Fan Relay.<br>• Does fan stop? | Yes ► | REPLACE Cooling Fan Relay. |
| | No MTX ► | SERVICE BL/W from Cooling Fan Relay to Fan Motor (shorted to power). If all OK, REPLACE Fan Motor. |
| | No 4EAT ► | GO to EC5 . |

Fig. 37 Diagnostic chart EC4 (Part 15 of 18). Probe w/2.2L Engine

| TEST STEP | RESULT ► | ACTION TO TAKE |
|---|---|---|
| EC5 DISCONNECT HSFS | | |
| • Key on, cold engine.<br>• Disconnect High Speed Fan Switch.<br>• Does fan stop? | Yes ► | REPLACE High Speed Fan Switch. |
| | No ► | GO to EC6 . |

Fig. 37 Diagnostic chart EC5 (Part 16 of 18). Probe w/2.2L Engine

| TEST STEP | RESULT ► | ACTION TO TAKE |
|---|---|---|
| EC6 CHECK HSF RELAY BL/R FOR SHORTS | | |
| • Key off. | No ► | SERVICE BL/R wire. |
| • Disconnect ECA.<br>• Disconnect High Speed Fan Switch<br>• Disconnect High Speed Fan Relay<br>• Measure resistance between HSF Relay BL/R and ground.<br>• Is resistance greater than 10,000 ohms? | Yes ► | GO to EC7 |

Fig. 37 Diagnostic chart EC6 (Part 17 of 18). Probe w/2.2L Engine

| TEST STEP | RESULT ► | ACTION TO TAKE |
|---|---|---|
| EC7 CHECK HSF RELAY OPERATION | | |
| • Key on, cold engine.<br>• Disconnect High Speed Fan Relay.<br>• Does fan stop? | Yes ► | REPLACE High Speed Fan Relay. |
| | No ► | SERVICE BL/BK from HSF Relay to Fan Motor (shorted to power). If all OK, REPLACE Fan Motor. |

Fig. 37 Diagnostic chart EC7 (Part 18 of 18). Probe w/2.2L Engine

| TEST STEP | RESULT ► | ACTION TO TAKE |
|---|---|---|
| KF1 SERVICE CODE 83/88: CHECK FOR IGNITION START/RUN CIRCUIT VOLTAGE AT HEDF/EDF RELAY | | |
| Service Code 83 indicates a HEDF primary circuit failure.<br>Service Code 88 indicates an EDF primary circuit failure.<br>Possible causes are:<br>— Open or shorted circuit.<br>— Faulty fan relay.<br>— Faulty processor.<br>— Faulty A/C high pressure switch (Code 83).<br>**NOTE: During diagnosis, use the chart below to determine the correct pin number, circuit and relay being tested.** | Yes ► | GO to KF2 . |
| | No ► | SERVICE open circuit. RECONNECT EDF/ HEDF relay. |

| Code | Circuit | Test Pin Number | Fan Relay |
|---|---|---|---|
| 83 | HEDF | 31 | HEDF(# 2) |
| 88 | EDF | 35 | EDF(# 1) |

• Key off.
• Disconnect EDF or HEDF relay.
• DVOM on 20 volt scale.
• Key on.
• Measure voltage between IGN Start/Run circuit at the EDF/HEDF relay vehicle harness connector and chassis ground.
• Is voltage greater than 10.5 volts?

Fig. 38 Pinpoint test step KF1 (Part 1 of 11). Probe w/2.2L Engine

| TEST STEP | RESULT ▶ | ACTION TO TAKE |
|---|---|---|
| **KF2** ENTER OUTPUT STATE CHECK (REFER TO QUICK TEST APPENDIX) | | |
| **NOTE: Do not use STAR tester for this Step, use VOM/DVOM.**<br>• Key off, wait 10 seconds.<br>• DVOM on 20 volt scale.<br>• Disconnect electrical connector on the speed control servo; if equipped.<br>• Connect DVOM negative test lead to STO at the Self-Test connector and positive test lead to the battery positive post.<br>• Jumper STI to SIG RTN at the Self-Test connector.<br>• Perform Key On Engine Off Self-Test until the completion of the Continuous Memory Codes.<br>• DVOM will indicate less than 1.0 volt when test complete.<br>• Depress and release throttle.<br>• **Does voltage increase to greater than 10.5 volts?** | Yes ▶<br><br>No ▶ | REMAIN in Output State Check. GO to KF3.<br><br>DEPRESS throttle to WOT and RELEASE. If STO voltage does not go high, leave equipment hooked up and GO to QC2. |
| **KF3** CHECK FOR EDF/HEDF CIRCUIT CYCLING | | |
| • Still in Output State Check.<br>• EDF or HEDF relay disconnected.<br>• DVOM on 20 volt scale.<br>• Connect DVOM positive test lead to the IGN Start/Run circuit and the negative test lead to the EDF or HEDF circuit at the EDF/HEDF relay vehicle harness connector.<br>• While observing DVOM, depress throttle. For EDF, wait until "CHECK ENGINE" light flashes once (10 seconds). For HEDF, wait until "CHECK ENGINE" light flashes twice (15 seconds). Release throttle. EDF/HEDF outputs are now "on". To cycle "off", depress and release throttle.<br>• **Does voltage cycle high and low (about 1 volt change)?** | Yes ▶<br><br>No ▶ | REPLACE EDF or HEDF relay. REMOVE jumper. RERUN Quick Test.<br><br>REMOVE jumper. GO to KF4 |

**Fig. 38 Pinpoint test steps KF2 & KF3 (Part 2 of 11). Probe w/2.2L Engine**

| TEST STEP | RESULT ▶ | ACTION TO TAKE |
|---|---|---|
| **KF4** CHECK CONTINUITY OF EDF/HEDF CIRCUIT | | |
| • Key off.<br>• EDF or HEDF relay disconnected.<br>• Disconnect processor 60 pin connector. Inspect for damaged or pushed out pins, corrosion, loose wires, etc. Service as necessary.<br>• Install breakout box, leave processor disconnected.<br>• DVOM on 200 ohm scale.<br>**For Code 83:**<br>— Measure resistance between Test Pin 31 at the breakout box and HEDF circuit at the HEDF relay vehicle harness connector.<br>**For Code 88:**<br>— Measure resistance between Test Pin 35 at the breakout box and EDF circuit at the EDF relay vehicle harness connector.<br>• **Is resistance less than 5.0 ohms?** | Yes ▶<br><br>No ▶ | GO to KF5.<br><br>SERVICE open circuit. REMOVE breakout box. RECONNECT all components. |
| **KF5** CHECK EDF/HEDF CIRCUIT FOR SHORT TO POWER | | |
| • Key on.<br>• Breakout box installed, processor disconnected.<br>• EDF or HEDF relay disconnected.<br>• DVOM on 20 volt scale.<br>• Measure voltage between Test Pin 31 (HEDF) or 35 (EDF) at the breakout box and battery negative post.<br>• **Is voltage less than 1.0 volts?** | Yes ▶<br><br>No ▶ | GO to KF6.<br><br>SERVICE short circuit. REMOVE breakout box. RECONNECT all components. If code is still present, REPLACE processor. |

**Fig. 38 Pinpoint test steps KF4 & KF5 (Part 3 of 11). Probe w/2.2L Engine**

| TEST STEP | RESULT ▶ | ACTION TO TAKE |
|---|---|---|
| **KF6** CHECK EDF/HEDF CIRCUIT FOR SHORT TO GROUND | | |
| • Key off.<br>• Breakout box installed, processor disconnected.<br>• EDF or HEDF relay disconnected.<br>• DVOM on 200,000 ohm scale.<br>• Measure resistance between Test Pin 31 (HEDF) or 35 (EDF) and Test Pins 40 and 60 at the breakout box.<br>• **Is resistance greater than 10,000 ohms?** | Yes ▶<br><br>No ▶ | REPLACE processor. REMOVE breakout box. RECONNECT all components.<br><br>SERVICE short circuit. (For Code 83, first VERIFY that A/C high pressure switch is open). REMOVE breakout box. RECONNECT all components. |
| **KF10** LOW SPEED (EDF) AND/OR HIGH SPEED (HEDF) COOLING FAN DOES NOT OPERATE: CHECK FOR VOLTAGE TO EDF RELAY | | |
| • Key off.<br>• Disconnect EDF relay.<br>• DVOM on 20 volt scale.<br>• Key on.<br>• Measure voltage between the short connector input pin at the EDF relay vehicle harness connector and battery negative post.<br>• **Is voltage greater than 10.5 volts?**<br>TO SHORT CONNECTOR<br>TO HEDF RELAY<br>WITH A/C<br>EDF RELAY VEHICLE HARNESS CONNECTOR | Yes ▶<br><br>No ▶ | GO to KF13.<br><br>**For A/C equipped vehicles:**<br>GO to KF11.<br>**For non A/C vehicles:**<br>VERIFY condition of jumper at short connector and operation of IGN relay. If OK, SERVICE open circuit. RECONNECT EDF relay. RE-EVALUATE symptom. |

**Fig. 38 Pinpoint test steps KF6 & KF10 (Part 4 of 11). Probe w/2.2L Engine**

| TEST STEP | RESULT ▶ | ACTION TO TAKE |
|---|---|---|
| **KF11** CHECK FOR VOLTAGE TO HEDF RELAY | | |
| • Key off.<br>• EDF relay disconnected.<br>• Disconnect HEDF relay.<br>• DVOM on 20 volt scale.<br>• Key on.<br>• Measure voltage between the IGN relay input pin at the HEDF relay vehicle harness connector and battery negative post.<br>• **Is voltage greater than 10.5 volts?**<br>TO IGNITION RELAY<br>HEDF RELAY VEHICLE HARNESS CONNECTOR | Yes ▶<br><br>No ▶ | GO to KF12.<br><br>VERIFY operation of IGN relay. If OK, SERVICE open circuit. RECONNECT EDF and HEDF relays. RE-EVALUATE symptoms. |
| **KF12** CHECK CONTINUITY BETWEEN EDF AND HEDF RELAYS | | |
| • Key off.<br>• EDF and HEDF relays disconnected.<br>• DVOM on 200 ohm scale.<br>• Measure resistance between the HEDF input pin at the EDF relay vehicle harness connector and the output to EDF pin at the HEDF relay vehicle harness connector.<br>• **Is resistance less than 5.0 ohms?**<br>EDF RELAY<br>HEDF RELAY<br>VEHICLE HARNESS CONNECTORS | Yes ▶<br><br>No ▶ | REPLACE HEDF relay. RECONNECT all components. RE-EVALUATE symptom.<br><br>SERVICE open circuit. RECONNECT EDF and HEDF relays. RE-EVALUATE symptom. |

**Fig. 38 Pinpoint test steps KF11 & KF12 (Part 5 of 11). Probe w/2.2L Engine**

| TEST STEP | RESULT ▶ | ACTION TO TAKE |
|---|---|---|
| **KF13** CHECK CIRCUITS FROM EDF RELAY TO FAN | | |
| • Key off.<br>• EDF relay disconnected.<br>• Insert jumper wire from short connector input pin to Power-To-Fan pin at the EDF relay vehicle harness connector.<br>• Key on.<br>• **Does fan run?**<br>JUMPER WIRE<br>EDF RELAY VEHICLE HARNESS CONNECTOR | Yes ▶ | **For A/C equipped vehicles:** REMOVE jumper. GO to KF16.<br>**For Non A/C vehicles:** REPLACE EDF relay. REMOVE jumper. RE-EVALUATE symptom. |
| | No ▶ | REMOVE jumper. GO to KF14. |
| **KF14** CHECK EDF POWER-TO-FAN CIRCUIT CONTINUITY | | |
| • Key off.<br>• EDF relay disconnected.<br>• Disconnect cooling fan.<br>• DVOM on 200 ohm scale.<br>• Measure resistance between the EDF Power-To-Fan output pin at the EDF vehicle harness connector and the EDF Power-To-Fan input pin at the cooling fan vehicle harness connector.<br>• **Is resistance less than 5.0 ohms?**<br>POWER TO FAN<br>EDF RELAY<br>COOLING FAN<br>VEHICLE HARNESS CONNECTORS | Yes ▶ | GO to KF15. |
| | No ▶ | SERVICE open circuit. RECONNECT all components. RE-EVALUATE symptom. |

**Fig. 38 Pinpoint test steps KF13 & KF14 (Part 6 of 11). Probe w/2.2L Engine**

| TEST STEP | RESULT ▶ | ACTION TO TAKE |
|---|---|---|
| **KF15** CHECK COOLING FAN GROUND CIRCUIT | | |
| • Key off.<br>• EDF relay disconnected.<br>• Cooling fan disconnected.<br>• DVOM on 200 ohm scale.<br>• Measure resistance between GND circuit at the cooling fan vehicle harness connector and battery negative post.<br>• **Is resistance less than 5.0 ohms?** | Yes ▶ | REPLACE cooling fan. RECONNECT all components. RE-EVALUATE symptom. |
| | No ▶ | SERVICE open circuit. RECONNECT all components. RE-EVALUATE symptom. |
| **KF16** CHECK CIRCUITS FROM HEDF RELAY TO FAN | | |
| • Key off.<br>• EDF relay disconnected.<br>• Disconnect A/C high pressure (A/C HP) switch.<br>• Insert a jumper wire between the two pins of the A/C HP switch vehicle harness connector.<br>• Key on.<br>• **Does fan run at high speed?** | Yes ▶ | REPLACE EDF relay. REMOVE jumper. RECONNECT A/C high pressure switch. RE-EVALUATE symptom. |
| | No ▶ | REMOVE jumper. RECONNECT EDF relay. GO to KF17. |

**Fig. 38 Pinpoint test steps KF15 & KF16 (Part 7 of 11). Probe w/2.2L Engine**

| TEST STEP | RESULT ▶ | ACTION TO TAKE |
|---|---|---|
| **KF17** VERIFY CONTINUITY OF CIRCUITS FROM A/C HIGH PRESSURE SWITCH | | |
| • Key off.<br>• A/C HP switch disconnected.<br>• Disconnect HEDF relay.<br>• DVOM on 200 ohm scale.<br>• Measure continuity from GND circuit at A/C HP switch vehicle harness connector and battery negative post.<br>• Measure continuity between output to HEDF relay pin at A/C HP switch vehicle harness connector and A/C HP switch input pin at the HEDF relay vehicle harness connector.<br>• **Is each resistance less than 5.0 ohms?**<br>HEDF RELAY<br>TEST PIN 31<br>A/C HIGH PRESSURE SWITCH<br>VEHICLE HARNESS CONNECTORS | Yes ▶ | GO to KF18. |
| | No ▶ | SERVICE open circuit. RECONNECT all components. RE-EVALUATE symptom. If symptom is still present, continue diagnosis at KF16. |

**Fig. 38 Pinpoint test step KF17 (Part 8 of 11). Probe w/2.2L Engine**

| TEST STEP | RESULT ▶ | ACTION TO TAKE |
|---|---|---|
| **KF18** CHECK HEDF POWER-TO-FAN VOLTAGE AT FAN WITH A/C HP SWITCH GROUNDED | | |
| • Key off.<br>• A/C HP switch disconnected.<br>• Reconnect HEDF relay.<br>• Disconnect cooling fan.<br>• DVOM on 20 volt scale.<br>• Again insert a jumper wire between the two pins of the A/C HP switch vehicle harness connector.<br>• Key on.<br>• Measure voltage between HEDF Power-To-Fan circuit at the cooling fan vehicle harness connector and battery negative post.<br>• **Is voltage greater than 10.5 volts?**<br>HEDF POWER-TO-FAN<br>COOLING FAN VEHICLE HARNESS CONNECTOR | Yes ▶ | REPLACE cooling fan. REMOVE jumper. RECONNECT all components. RE-EVALUATE symptom. |
| | No ▶ | REMOVE jumper. RECONNECT A/C HP switch. GO to KF19. |
| **KF19** CHECK HEDF POWER-TO-FAN CIRCUIT CONTINUITY | | |
| • Key off.<br>• Cooling fan disconnected.<br>• Disconnect HEDF relay.<br>• DVOM on 200 ohm scale.<br>• Measure resistance between the HEDF Power-To-Fan output pin at the HEDF vehicle harness connector and the HEDF Power-To-Fan input pin at the cooling fan vehicle harness connector.<br>• **Is resistance less than 5.0 ohms?**<br>HEDF POWER-TO-FAN<br>HEDF RELAY VEHICLE HARNESS CONNECTOR | Yes ▶ | REPLACE HEDF relay. RECONNECT all components. RE-EVALUATE symptom. |
| | No ▶ | SERVICE open circuit. RECONNECT all components. RE-EVALUATE symptom. |

**Fig. 38 Pinpoint test steps KF18 & KF19 (Part 9 of 11). Probe w/2.2L Engine**

| TEST STEP | RESULT ▶ | ACTION TO TAKE |
|---|---|---|
| **KF25** LOW SPEED (EDF) OR HIGH SPEED (HEDF) COOLING FAN ALWAYS ON: VERIFY IGNITION RELAY IS OPENING | | |
| **NOTE: Verify that A/C is off during testing.**<br>• **Is cooling fan always on with key off, but operating normally with key on?** | Yes ▶ | VERIFY that IGN relay contacts are not always closed. If OK, CHECK circuit from IGN relay to fan relay(s) for short to BATT(+). |
| | No ▶ | GO to KF26. |
| **KF26** CHECK FOR EDF RELAY ALWAYS CLOSED | | |
| • Key off.<br>• Disconnect EDF relay.<br>• Key on.<br>• **Does fan continue to run?** | Yes ▶ | **For A/C equipped vehicles:**<br>GO to KF27.<br>**For non A/C vehicles:**<br>SERVICE short to power in EDF Power-To-Fan circuit. RECONNECT EDF relay. RE-EVALUATE symptom. |
| | No ▶ | REPLACE EDF relay. RE-EVALUATE symptom. |
| **KF27** CHECK HEDF RELAY | | |
| • Key off.<br>• EDF relay disconnected.<br>• Disconnect HEDF relay.<br>• Key on.<br>• **Does fan continue to run?** | Yes ▶ | GO to KF28. |
| | No ▶ | REPLACE HEDF relay. RECONNECT EDF relay. RE-EVALUATE symptom. |

**Fig. 38 Pinpoint test steps KF25, KF26 & KF27 (Part 10 of 11). Probe w/2.2L Engine**

| TEST STEP | RESULT ▶ | ACTION TO TAKE |
|---|---|---|
| **KF28** CHECK EDF POWER-TO-FAN CIRCUIT FOR SHORT TO POWER | | |
| • Key off.<br>• EDF and HEDF relay disconnected.<br>• Disconnect cooling fan.<br>• DVOM on 20 volt scale.<br>• Key on.<br>• Measure voltage between EDF Power-To-Fan circuit at the cooling fan vehicle harness connector and battery negative post.<br>• **Is voltage greater than 1.0 volt?**<br>EDF POWER-TO-FAN<br>HEDF POWER-TO-FAN<br>COOLING FAN VEHICLE HARNESS CONNECTOR | Yes ▶ | SERVICE Short-To-Power in EDF Power-To-Fan circuit. RECONNECT all components. RE-EVALUATE symptom. |
| | No ▶ | SERVICE Short-To-Power in HEDF Power-To-Fan circuit. RECONNECT all components. RE-EVALUATE symptom. |

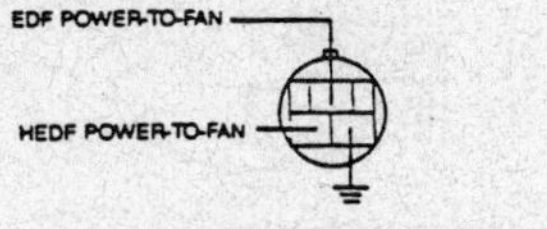

**Fig. 38 Pinpoint test step KF28 (Part 11 of 11). Probe w/2.2L Engine**

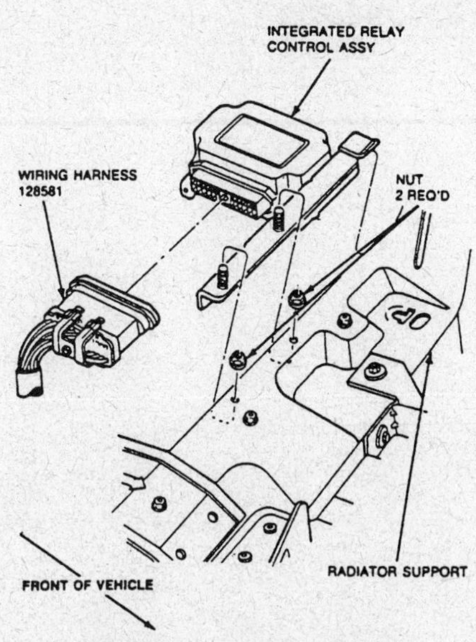


**Fig. 39 Cooling fan module/integrated relay replace. Continental**

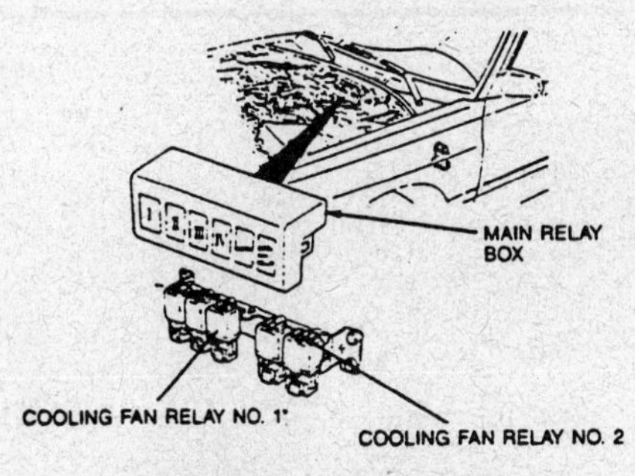


**Fig. 40 Cooling fan relay replace. Probe**

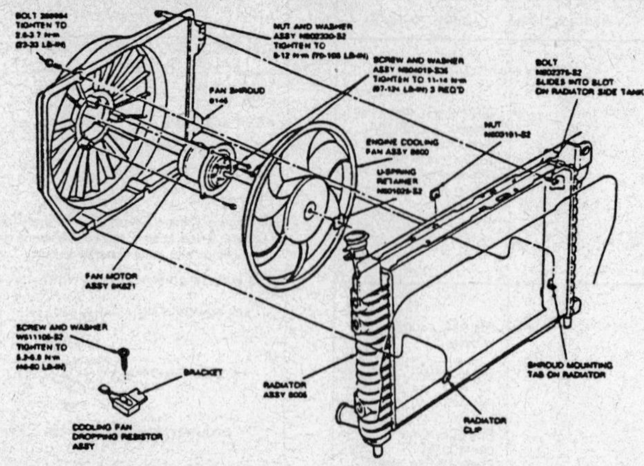


**Fig. 41 Cooling fan motor replace. Sable & Taurus w/2.5L/4-153 or 3.0L/V6-183**

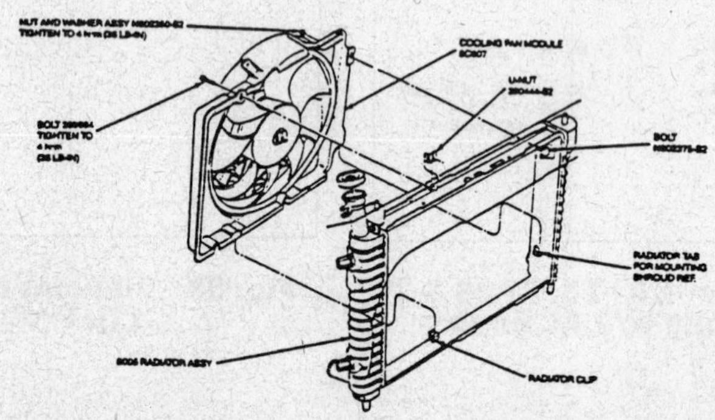


**Fig. 42 Cooling fan motor replace. Sable & Taurus w/3.0L/V6-183 SHO or 3.8L/V6-232**

# DASH GAUGES

## INDEX



# FUEL LEVEL INDICATING SYSTEM

## DESCRIPTION

### Magnetic Type

The fuel level indicating system is a magnetic type system, which consists of the sending unit located in the fuel tank, an anti-slosh module located on the back of the instrument cluster, and a fuel gauge located in the instrument cluster.

The sending unit changes resistance according to the level of fuel in the fuel tank, which varies the current flow through the gauge. The pointer position varies proportionately to the current flow. In this system, the sending unit resistance is low when the fuel level is low and high when the fuel level is high.

The pointer of the magnetic gauge remains in position when the ignition is turned to the Off position. O some models, an anti-slosh module is used to dampen out fluctuating fuel signals from the sender.

Some vehicles are equipped with a low fuel warning indicator. The anti-slosh module will also actuate the low fuel indicator when the fuel level in the tank reaches 1/16 to 1/8 full.

### Bimetal Type

The fuel level indicator gauge pointer is attached to a wire wound bimetal strip, which, when heated by a signal from the fuel sender unit, produces the appropriate level indication. When the current is low there is little heating effect and the point moves a short distance. As the current increases, it produces a greater heating effect, causing the pointer to move a greater distance.

## CALIBRATION TEST

### Magnetic Type

The required test equipment consists of a Rotunda Gauge Tester part No. 021-00055 or equivalent, a pair of 22 ohm and 145 ohm resistor or another fuel sender of known quality.

1. Perform test with resistors as follows:
   a. Disconnect wiring connector at sender unit, then connect resistor between gauge lead and a suitable ground.
   b. Turn ignition switch to On position.
   c. With 145 ohm resitor, the gauge pointer should contact the Full mark.
   d. With 22 ohm resistor, the gauge pointer should contact the Empty mark.
2. Perform test with fuel sender of known quality as follows:
   a. Turn ignition switch to Off position.
   b. Disconnect wiring connector from sender and connect it to test sender.
   c. Move float rod away from fuel filter against Full stop position. Wait approximately 30 seconds, then turn ignition switch to On position. The gauge should read on or above the Full mark.
   d. Move float rod toward fuel filter against Empty stop position. Turn ignition switch to Off position. Wait approximately 30 seconds, then turn ignition switch to On position. The gauge should read on or below the Empty mark.
   e. If gauge performs as indicated, perform fuel sender unit tests. Refer to "System Diagnosis" for fuel sender unit tests.
   f. If gauge is out of calibration at the Empty mark, or both the Empty and Full mark, replace gauge.

### Bimetal Type

The required test equipment consists of a Rotunda Gauge Tester part No. 021-00055 or equivalent, a pair of 10 ohm and 75 ohm resistor or another fuel sender of known quality.

1. Perform test with resistors as follows:
   a. Disconnect wiring connector at sender unit, then connect resistor between gauge lead and a suitable ground.
   b. Turn ignition switch to On position.
   c. With 10 ohm resitor, the gauge pointer should contact the Full mark.
   d. With 75 ohm resistor, the gauge pointer should contact the Empty mark.
2. Perform test with fuel sender of known quality as follows:
   a. Turn ignition switch to Off position.
   b. Disconnect wiring connector from sender and connect it to test sender.
   c. Move float rod away from fuel filter against Full stop position. Wait approximately 30 seconds, then turn ignition switch to On position. The gauge should read on or above the Full mark.
   d. Move float rod toward fuel filter against Empty stop position. Turn ignition switch to Off position. Wait approximately 30 seconds, then turn ignition switch to On position. The gauge should read on or below the Empty mark.
   e. If gauge performs as indicated, perform fuel sender unit tests. Refer to "System Diagnosis" for fuel sender unit tests.
   f. If gauge is out of calibration at the Empty mark, or both the Empty and Full mark, replace gauge.

## SYSTEM DIAGNOSIS

### Magnetic Type

Refer to **Fig. 1**, for fuel indicating system diagnosis.

### Bimetal Type

Refer to **Figs. 2 through 4**, for fuel indicating system diagnosis.

# COOLANT TEMPERATURE INDICATING SYSTEM

## DESCRIPTION

### Magnetic Type

The temperature indicating system is a magnetic type system, which consists only of the sending unit located in the engine block or cylinder head and a temperature

FUEL GAUGE INOPERATIVE—
POINTER DOES NOT MOVE—PINPOINT TEST A

| | TEST STEP | RESULT | ACTION TO TAKE |
|---|---|---|---|
| A1 | VERIFY CONDITION | | |
| | • Verify condition. | Gauge pointer does not move | GO to A2. |
| | | Gauge pointer moves | GO to D1. |
| A2 | CHECK OTHER GAUGES | | |
| | • Check power to cluster. With ignition ON, observe other gauges and warning indicators for proper operation. If necessary, use Rotunda Digital Volt-Ohmmeter 007-00001 or equivalent or a test lamp to verify voltage at B+ terminal of cluster connector. | Other gauges and warning indicators operate properly; voltage present at cluster | GO to C1. |
| | | Other gauges and warning indicators do not operate properly; no voltage present at cluster | GO to B1. |

PINPOINT TEST B: FUEL GAUGE INOPERATIVE

| | TEST STEP | RESULT | ACTION TO TAKE |
|---|---|---|---|
| B1 | VERIFY POWER AT FUSE PANEL | | |
| | • Use voltmeter to verify system voltage at load side of warning indicators fuse. | System voltage present at load side of fuse | GO to C1. |
| | | System voltage NOT present at load side of fuse | GO to B2. |
| B2 | VERIFY POWER AT FUSE PANEL | | |
| | • Use voltmeter to verify system voltage at feed side of warning indicator fuse. | System voltage present at feed side of fuse | REPLACE fuse. GO to A1. |
| | | System voltage NOT present at feed side of fuse | SERVICE wiring to fuse panel. GO to A1. |

**Fig. 1 Fuel indicating system diagnosis (Part 1 of 5). Models w/magnetic gauge**

PINPOINT TEST C: CLUSTER DIAGNOSIS

| | TEST STEP | RESULT | ACTION TO TAKE |
|---|---|---|---|
| C1 | VERIFY POWER AT CLUSTER | | |
| | • Cluster connectors installed.<br>• Partially remove cluster.<br>• Check for voltage at cluster connector and gauge terminal.<br>• Use Rotunda Digital Volt-Ohmmeter 007-00001 or equivalent. | Voltage present at cluster connector and gauge terminal | GO to C2. |
| | | Voltage not present at cluster and/or gauge terminal | SERVICE circuit. GO to A1. |
| C2 | VERIFY GROUND CIRCUIT AT CLUSTER | | |
| | • Use Rotunda Digital Volt-Ohmmeter 007-00001 or equivalent to check continuity of cluster and gauge ground circuits. | Continuity | GO to D1. |
| | | No continuity or high resistance | SERVICE circuit. GO to A1. |

PINPOINT TEST D: FUEL GAUGE DIAGNOSIS

| | TEST STEP | RESULT | ACTION TO TAKE |
|---|---|---|---|
| D1 | TEST BOX CHECK (LOW) | | |
| | • Turn ignition to OFF position.<br>• Insert Rotunda Gauge System Tester 021-00055 or equivalent in sender circuit.<br>• Disconnect 14405 connector under instrument panel and connect tester to cluster side of connector.<br>• Set tester to 22 ohms.<br>• Turn ignition to RUN position, wait 60 seconds and read fuel gauge. | Fuel gauge reads empty | GO to D4. |
| | | Fuel gauge does not read empty | GO to D2. |
| D2 | TEST BOX CHECK (RETEST) | | |
| | • Turn ignition switch to OFF position.<br>• Turn ignition switch to RUN position.<br>• Tap lightly on instrument panel, wait 60 seconds and read fuel gauge. | Fuel gauge reads empty | GO to D4. |
| | | Fuel gauge does not read empty | GO to D3. |
| D3 | SLOSH MODULE BYPASS TEST | | |
| | • Turn ignition switch to OFF position.<br>• Remove instrument cluster and inspect flexible circuit.<br>• Remove anti-slosh module and connect a jumper wire from Gauge Tester directly to fuel gauge "S" terminal.<br>• Install instrument cluster.<br>• Turn ignition switch to RUN position and read fuel gauge. | Fuel gauge reads empty | REMOVE anti-slosh module. GO to D1. |
| | | Fuel gauge does not read empty | REPLACE fuel gauge. INSTALL anti-slosh module. GO to D1. |
| D4 | TEST BOX CHECK (HIGH) | | |
| | • Turn ignition switch to OFF position.<br>• With Rotunda Gauge System Tester 021-00055 or equivalent connected as in Step D1, set tester to 145 ohms.<br>• Turn ignition switch to RUN position.<br>• Wait 60 seconds and read fuel gauge. | Fuel gauge reads full | GO to D6. |
| | | Fuel gauge does not read full | GO to D5. |

**Fig. 1 Fuel indicating system diagnosis (Part 2 of 5). Models w/magnetic gauge**

PINPOINT TEST D: FUEL GAUGE DIAGNOSIS (Continued)

| | TEST STEP | RESULT | ACTION TO TAKE |
|---|---|---|---|
| D5 | ANTI-SLOSH MODULE BYPASS TEST | | |
| | • Turn ignition switch to OFF position.<br>• Remove instrument cluster and inspect flexible circuit.<br>• Remove anti-slosh module.<br>• Connect a jumper wire from tester to fuel gauge "S" terminal.<br>• Turn ignition switch to RUN position and read fuel gauge. | Fuel gauge reads full | REPLACE anti-slosh module. GO to D1. |
| | | Fuel gauge does not read full | REPLACE fuel gauge. GO to D1. |
| D6 | INSPECT FUEL TANK | | |
| | • Inspect fuel tank for damage or distortion. | Damaged | REPLACE fuel tank. |
| | | Not damaged | GO to E1. |

PINPOINT TEST E: FUEL SENDER DIAGNOSIS

| | TEST STEP | RESULT | ACTION TO TAKE |
|---|---|---|---|
| E1 | TEST BOX CHECK—EMPTY STOP | | |
| | • Connect one lead of Digital Volt-Ohmmeter 007-00001 or equivalent to the fuel sender signal lead and the other lead to ground.<br>NOTE: Float rod is against empty stop (closest to filter). | Ohmmeter reads 14-18 ohms | GO to E2. |
| | | Ohmmeter reads less than 14 ohms or greater than 18 ohms | REPLACE fuel sender. |
| E2 | TEST BOX CHECK—FULL STOP | | |
| | • Connect one lead of Digital Volt-Ohmmeter 007-00001 or equivalent to the fuel sender signal and the other lead to sender ground.<br>NOTE: Float rod is against full stop. | Ohmmeter reads 155-165 ohms | GO to E3. |
| | | Ohmmeter reads less than 155 ohms or greater than 165 ohms | REPLACE fuel sender. |
| E3 | TEST BOX CHECK—FLOAT ROD TRAVEL | | |
| | • Connect one lead of Digital Volt-Ohmmeter 007-00001 or equivalent to the fuel sender signal lead and the other lead to sender ground.<br>• Slowly move float rod from full stop to empty stop. | Ohmmeter reading jumps to open condition while decreasing | REPLACE fuel sender. |
| | | Ohmmeter reading decreases slowly | GO to E4. |
| E4 | FUEL SENDER INSPECTION | | |
| | • Inspect fuel sender.<br>• Inspect float and float rod. | Float rod is distorted | REPLACE sender. |
| | | Float is badly distorted/damaged hitting the filter. | REPLACE sender. |

**Fig. 1 Fuel indicating system diagnosis (Part 3 of 5). Models w/magnetic gauge**

PINPOINT TEST E: FUEL SENDER DIAGNOSIS (Continued)

| | TEST STEP | RESULT | ACTION TO TAKE |
|---|---|---|---|
| E5 | HARNESS CONNECTOR CHECK—EMPTY STOP | | |
| | • Attach all fuel indication connectors.<br>• Move float rod to empty stop position.<br>• Turn ignition to the RUN position.<br>• Wait 60 seconds.<br>• Read fuel gauge. | Gauge reads empty | GO to E6. |
| | | Gauge reads greater than empty | GO to A1. |
| E6 | HARNESS CONNECTOR CHECK—FULL STOP | | |
| | • Attach all fuel indication connectors.<br>• Move float rod to full stop position.<br>• Turn ignition to the RUN position.<br>• Wait 60 seconds.<br>• Read fuel gauge. | Gauge reads full | Fuel sender OK. |
| | | Gauge reads less than full | GO to A1. |

PINPOINT TEST F: INDICATOR STAYS ON
CONTINUALLY—MORE THAN 1/4 TANK OF FUEL

| | TEST STEP | RESULT | ACTION TO TAKE |
|---|---|---|---|
| F1 | VERIFY CONDITION | | |
| | • Verify condition. | Indicator stays on with more than 1/4 tank of fuel | GO to F2. |
| F2 | CHECK ELFW MODULE | | |
| | • Turn ignition to the OFF position.<br>• Disconnect Circuit 14405 connector under instrument panel and connect a 56 ohm resistor between fuel sender feed to gauge and ground.<br>• Turn ignition to the RUN position.<br>• Wait two minutes. | Indicator on, gauge at 1/4 | GO to F3. |
| | | Indicator off | REPLACE ELFW/Anti-Slosh module at instrument cluster. |
| F3 | CHECK GAUGE AND INDICATOR | | |
| | • Turn ignition to the OFF position.<br>• Replace the resistor from Test F2 with a 33 ohm resistor.<br>• Turn ignition to the RUN position.<br>• Wait two minutes. | Indicator off | GO to G3. |
| | | Indicator on, gauge pointer indicates 1/4 tank or above | GO to A1. |
| | | Indicator on, gauge indicates 1/8 to 1/4 tank | ELFW/Anti-Slosh module operating properly. |

PINPOINT TEST G: INDICATOR STAYS OFF
CONTINUALLY

| | TEST STEP | RESULT | ACTION TO TAKE |
|---|---|---|---|
| G1 | VERIFY CONDITION | | |
| | • Verify condition. | Indicator stays off | GO to F2. |

**Fig. 1 Fuel indicating system diagnosis (Part 4 of 5). Models w/magnetic gauge**

PINPOINT TEST G: INDICATOR STAYS OFF
CONTINUALLY (Continued)

| | TEST STEP | RESULT | ACTION TO TAKE |
|---|---|---|---|
| G2 | CHECK ELFW MODULE | | |
| | • Turn ignition to the OFF position.<br>• Disconnect circuit 14405 connector under instrument panel and connect a 33 ohm resistor between fuel sender feed to gauge and ground.<br>• Turn ignition to ON position.<br>• Wait two minutes, read gauge. | Indicator off | GO to H3. |
| | | Indicator on, gauge at 1/4 or above | GO to A1. |
| | | Indicator on, gauge at 1/8 to 1/4 | Low fuel warning operating properly. |
| G3 | CHECK INDICATOR | | |
| | • With ignition switch in the ON/ACC position, ground indicator circuit between indicator and low fuel module. | Indicator on | REPLACE ELFW/Anti-Slosh module on instrument cluster. |
| | | Indicator off | CHECK power circuit to lamp. REPLACE lamp. |

**Fig. 1 Fuel indicating system diagnosis (Part 5 of 5). Models w/magnetic gauge**

FUEL SENDER DIAGNOSIS — PINPOINT TEST

| TEST STEP | | RESULT ► | ACTION TO TAKE |
|---|---|---|---|
| A1 | | | |
| | • Inspect fuel tank for distortion or damage. | Damaged ► | REPLACE fuel tank. |
| | | Not damaged ► | GO to B1. |

FUEL SENDER DIAGNOSIS PINPOINT TEST

| TEST STEP | | RESULT ► | ACTION TO TAKE |
|---|---|---|---|
| B1 | TEST BOX CHECK — EMPTY STOP | | |
| | • Connect one lead of Digital Volt Ohm Meter 007-00001 or equivalent to the fuel sender signal lead and the other lead to ground. | Meter reads 60-80 ohms ► | GO to B2. |
| | **NOTE: Float rod is against empty stop (closest to filter).** | Meter reads less than 60 ohms or greater than 80 ohms ► | REPLACE fuel sender. |
| B2 | TEST BOX CHECK — FULL STOP | | |
| | • Connect one lead of Digital Volt Ohm Meter 007-00001 or equivalent to the fuel sender signal lead and the other lead to sender ground. | Meter reads 8-12 ohms ► | GO to B3. |
| | **NOTE: Float rod is against full stop.** | Meter reads less than 8 ohms or greater than 12 ohms ► | REPLACE fuel sender. |
| B3 | TEST BOX CHECK — FLOAT ROD TRAVEL | | |
| | • Connect one lead of Digital Volt Ohm Meter 007-00001 or equivalent to the fuel sender signal lead and the other lead to sender ground.<br>• Slowly move float rod from full stop to empty stop. | Ohm Meter reading jumps to open condition while increasing ► | REPLACE fuel sender. |
| | | Ohm Meter reading increases slowly ► | GO to B4. |
| B4 | HARNESS CONNECTOR CHECK — EMPTY STOP | | |
| | • Attach all fuel indication connectors.<br>• Move float rod stop to empty position. | Gauge reads empty ► | GO to B5. |
| | • Turn ignition switch to the RUN position.<br>• Wait 60 seconds.<br>• Read fuel gauge. | Gauge reads greater than empty ► | CHECK fuel gauge and IVR calibration. |

**Fig. 2 Fuel indicating system diagnosis (Part 1 of 2). Models w/bimetal gauge except Capri & Probe**

FUEL SENDER DIAGNOSIS PINPOINT TEST

| TEST STEP | | RESULT ► | ACTION TO TAKE |
|---|---|---|---|
| B5 | HARNESS CONNECTOR CHECK — FULL STOP | | |
| | • Attach all fuel indication connectors.<br>• Move float rod to full stop position. | Gauge reads full ► | GO to B6. |
| | • Turn ignition to the RUN position.<br>• Wait 60 seconds.<br>• Read fuel gauge. | Gauge reads less than full ► | CHECK fuel gauge and IVR calibration. |
| B6 | FUEL SENDER INSPECTION | | |
| | • Inspect fuel sender.<br>• Inspect float and float rod. | Float rod is distorted ► | REPLACE sender. |
| | | Float is badly distorted/damaged, hitting the filter. Loose on float rod ► | REPLACE sender. |

**Fig. 2 Fuel indicating system diagnosis (Part 2 of 2). Models w/bimetal gauge except Capri & Probe**

| TEST STEP | | RESULT ► | ACTION TO TAKE |
|---|---|---|---|
| FG1 | INSTRUMENT RELATED SYSTEM CHECK (FUEL GAUGE NOT WORKING) | | |
| | • Turn ignition switch to ON position (engine off).<br>• Check the following items for proper operation:<br>– Fuel gauge<br>– Warning lights (Anti-Lock, Seat belt, Engine, Brake) | Warning lights not working and fuel gauge reads empty ► | GO to FG2. |
| | | Fuel gauge always reads empty (warning lights OK) ► | GO to FG3. |
| | | Fuel gauge always reads full ► | GO to FG6. |
| | | Fuel gauge not accurate ► | GO to FG8. |

| TEST STEP | | RESULT ► | ACTION TO TAKE |
|---|---|---|---|
| FG2 | INSTRUMENT (METER) FUSE CHECK (WARNING LIGHTS NOT WORKING, FUEL GAUGE READS EMPTY) | | |
| | • Check instrument (METER) fuse.<br>• Is fuse OK? | Yes ► | Repair BK/Y wire from fuse panel to instrument cluster. |
| | | No ► | REPLACE fuse. (Read note) |
| NOTE: If fuse blows again, check for shorts to ground in "BK/Y" wires between instruments and fuse panel. Repair "BK/Y" wires as needed. | | | |

**Fig. 4 Fuel indicating system diagnosis (Part 1 of 6). Probe**

| CONDITION | POSSIBLE SOURCE | ACTION |
|---|---|---|
| • Fuel Gauge Always Reads Empty | • Open or damaged wires.<br>• Damaged fuel gauge.<br>• Blown fuse.<br>• Damaged fuel sender. | • Go to FG1. |
| • Fuel Gauge Always Reads Full | • Yellow wire shorted to ground.<br>• Damaged fuel gauge.<br>• Damaged fuel sender. | • Go to FG6. |
| • Fuel Gauge Reads Inaccurately | • Corroded connections.<br>• Damaged fuel gauge. | • Go to FG7. |

| TEST STEP | | RESULT ► | ACTION TO TAKE |
|---|---|---|---|
| FG1 | FUEL GAUGE FUSE CHECK | | |
| | • Access fuse panel.<br>• Check the 10 amp meter fuse.<br>• Is the fuse OK? | Yes ►<br>No ► | GO to FG4.<br>GO to FG2. |
| FG2 | CHECK FUEL GAUGE SYSTEM | | |
| | • Replace fuse.<br>• Key ON.<br>• Does the fuse blow again? | Yes ►<br>No ► | GO to FG3.<br>GO to FG4. |
| FG3 | CHECK FOR SHORTS TO GROUND | | |
| | • Replace fuse.<br>• Measure resistance of BK/Y wire and ground.<br>• Measure resistance of BK/Y wire from 10 amp meter fuse.<br>• Is resistance less than 5 ohms? | Yes ►<br>No ► | SERVICE BK/Y wire.<br>GO to FG4. |
| FG4 | CHECK FOR POWER TO FUEL GAUGE | | |
| | • Key ON.<br>• Access instrument cluster.<br>• Measure voltage on the BK/Y wire and ground.<br>• Is voltage greater than 10 volts? | Yes ►<br>No ► | GO to FG5.<br>SERVICE BK/Y wire. |
| FG5 | FUEL GAUGE CHECK (FUEL GAUGE ALWAYS READS EMPTY) | | |
| | • Ground Y wire at instrument cluster.<br>• Does fuel gauge read full? | Yes ►<br>No ► | GO to FG6.<br>REPLACE fuel gauge. |
| FG6 | FUEL GAUGE CHECK (FUEL GAUGE ALWAYS READS FULL) | | |
| | • Apply 12 volts to Y wire at fuel gauge.<br>• Does fuel gauge read empty? | Yes ►<br>No ► | GO to FG7.<br>REPLACE fuel gauge. |
| FG7 | FUEL GAUGE CONTINUITY CHECK (FUEL GAUGE ALWAYS READS EMPTY) | | |
| | • Remove the back seat cushion.<br>• Ground the Y wire at the fuel pump.<br>• Does the fuel gauge read full? | Yes ►<br>No ► | GO to FG8.<br>SERVICE Y wire between instrument cluster and fuel pump. |

**Fig. 3 Fuel indicating system diagnosis (Part 1 of 2). Capri**

| TEST STEP | | RESULT ► | ACTION TO TAKE |
|---|---|---|---|
| FG8 | FUEL SENDER GROUND CHECK | | |
| | • Measure resistance between the BK wires from the fuel sender to ground.<br>• Is the resistance less than 5 ohms? | Yes ►<br>No ► | GO to FG9.<br>SERVICE ground as needed. |
| FG9 | FUEL GAUGE SYSTEM CHECK | | |
| | • Key ON.<br>• Does the fuel gauge system operate correctly? | Yes ►<br>No ► | RETURN to condition chart.<br>REPLACE fuel sender unit. |

**Fig. 3 Fuel indicating system diagnosis (Part 2 of 2). Capri**

| TEST STEP | | RESULT ► | ACTION TO TAKE |
|---|---|---|---|
| FG3 | FUEL GAUGE CHECK (FUEL GAUGE ALWAYS READS EMPTY, WARNING LIGHTS OK) | | |
| | • Ground "Y" wire at instrument (METER) connector.<br>• Cycle the ignition switch OFF and ON.<br>• Does fuel gauge read full? | Yes ►<br>No ► | GO to FG4.<br>REPLACE fuel gauge (analog cluster) |
| CONVENTIONAL INSTRUMENTS<br>Y | | | |

| TEST STEP | | RESULT ► | ACTION TO TAKE |
|---|---|---|---|
| FG4 | FUEL GAUGE CONTINUITY CHECK NO. 1 (FUEL GAUGE ALWAYS READS EMPTY, WARNING LIGHTS OK) | | |
| | • Ground "Y" wire at fuel tank sender unit connector.<br>• Cycle the ignition switch OFF and ON.<br>• Does fuel gauge read full? | Yes ►<br>No ► | GO to FG5.<br>REPAIR "Y" wire between instruments and fuel tank sender unit. |

**Fig. 4 Fuel indicating system diagnosis (Part 2 of 6). Probe**

| TEST STEP | | RESULT ► | ACTION TO TAKE |
|---|---|---|---|
| FG5 | FUEL GAUGE CONTINUITY CHECK NO. 2 (FUEL GAUGE ALWAYS READS EMPTY, WARNING LIGHTS OK) | | |
| A | • Ground "BK/LG" wire at fuel tank sender unit connector. • Cycle the ignition switch OFF and ON. • Does fuel gauge read correctly? | Yes ► | REPAIR "BK/LG" wire between fuel tank sender unit and ground. |
| | | No ► | GO to B. |
| B | • Ground "BK/LG" wire at harness connector (at instrument cluster). • Cycle the ignition switch OFF and ON. • Does fuel gauge read correctly? | Yes ► | REPAIR "BK/LG" wire between harness connector and instrument cluster. |
| | | No ► | REPLACE fuel tank sender unit. NOTE: Before replacing the sender unit, inspect the float arm assembly for proper attachment to the pump housing. |

| TEST STEP | | RESULT ► | ACTION TO TAKE |
|---|---|---|---|
| FG6 | FUEL GAUGE SHORT CHECK NO. 1 (FUEL GAUGE ALWAYS READS FULL) | | |
| | • Disconnect the small instrument (METER) connector. • Cycle the ignition switch OFF and ON. • Does fuel gauge still read full? | Yes ► | REPLACE fuel gauge (analog cluster) |
| | | No ► | GO to FG7. |

Fig. 4 Fuel indicating system diagnosis (Part 3 of 6). Probe

| TEST STEP | | RESULT ► | ACTION TO TAKE |
|---|---|---|---|
| FG8 | FUEL GAUGE CHECK (FUEL GAUGE NOT ACCURATE) | | |
| | • Disconnect fuel tank sender unit connector. • Connect one lead of Rotunda Gauge Tester (Read note) to the "Y" wire of the connector and the other lead to ground. • Set tester to resistance values shown. • Turn ignition switch to ON position and check to see that needle indicator displays correct values. • Continue inspections for two minutes each, to correctly judge the condition. • The allowable error is twice the width of the needle. • Are fuel gauge readings correct? | Yes ► | GO to FG9. |
| | | No ► | REPLACE fuel gauge. |
| NOTE: Use Rotunda "Gauge System Tester" No. 021-00055 or equivalent. | | | |

CONVENTIONAL

7 Ω
18.5 Ω
32.5 Ω
51 Ω
95 Ω
FUEL

Fig. 4 Fuel indicating system diagnosis (Part 5 of 6). Probe

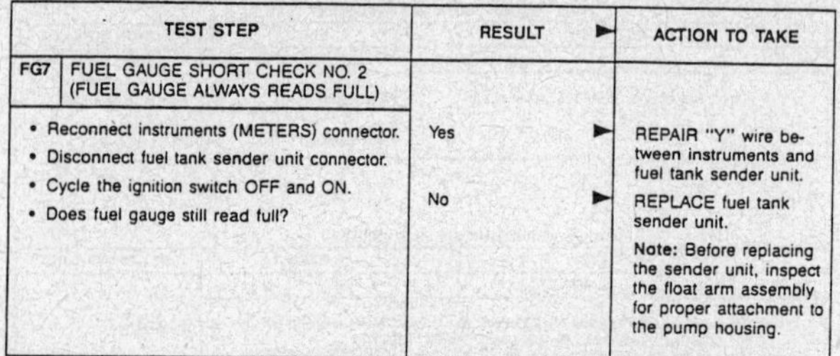

| TEST STEP | | RESULT ► | ACTION TO TAKE |
|---|---|---|---|
| FG7 | FUEL GAUGE SHORT CHECK NO. 2 (FUEL GAUGE ALWAYS READS FULL) | | |
| | • Reconnect instruments (METERS) connector. • Disconnect fuel tank sender unit connector. • Cycle the ignition switch OFF and ON. • Does fuel gauge still read full? | Yes ► | REPAIR "Y" wire between instruments and fuel tank sender unit. |
| | | No ► | REPLACE fuel tank sender unit. Note: Before replacing the sender unit, inspect the float arm assembly for proper attachment to the pump housing. |

Fig. 4 Fuel indicating system diagnosis (Part 4 of 6). Probe

| TEST STEP | | RESULT ► | ACTION TO TAKE |
|---|---|---|---|
| FG9 | FUEL GAUGE UNIT CHECK (FUEL GAUGE NOT ACCURATE) | | |
| | • Remove fuel tank sender unit: – Remove the service hole cover. – Disconnect the connector from the fuel tank sender unit. – Disconnect the main fuel hose. – Use a screwdriver to remove the fuel tank sender unit. • Connect an ohmmeter to fuel tank sender unit. • Are resistance values as listed? | Yes ► | CHECK for loose or dirty connections at fuel tank sender unit (connector C401). |
| | | No ► | REPLACE fuel tank sender unit. NOTE: Before replacing the sender unit, inspect the float arm assembly for proper attachment to the pump housing. |
| WARNING: WHEN REMOVING FUEL TANK SENDER UNIT, KEEP SPARKS, CIGARETTES, AND OPEN FLAMES AWAY FROM FUEL TANK. | | | |

(F)
1—5 Ω
29—36 Ω
46—56 Ω
103—117 Ω
(E)
137mm (5.4 in.)
72mm (2.8 in.)
49mm (2.0 in.)
18.5mm (0.7 inch)

Fig. 4 Fuel indicating system diagnosis (Part 6 of 6). Probe

gauge in the instrument cluster. The sending unit changes resistance according to the temperature of engine coolant, which varies the current flow through the gauge. The pointer position varies proportionally to the current flow. The sender resistance is high when coolant temperature is low, and low when coolant temperature is high.

The pointer of the magnetic gauge remains in position when ignition is turned to the Off position. It will move to the correct indication whenever the ignition is turned back to On position.

### Bimetal Type

The temperature lamp system provides the driver with an indication of engine coolant temperature by means of a switch mounted in the intake manifold and a red engine lamp mounted on the instrument panel. The temperature switch has a temperature sensitive bimetallic arm which completes the lamp circuit through the switch to engine ground.

## CALIBRATION TEST

### Magnetic Type

1. Turn ignition switch to On or ACC position.
2. Connect a 10 ohm resistor between gauge lead and ground. The centerline of pointer should fall within the band around the H mark.
3. Connect a 73 ohm resistor between gauge lead and ground. The centerline of pointer should fall within the band around the C mark.
4. If gauge tests within calibration, replace sender.
5. If gauge is out of calibration, replace gauge.

### Bimetal Type

The instrument voltage regulator (IVR) supplies a common regulated voltage for temperature, oil pressure and fuel gauges. The IVR is malfunctioning only if all gauges show similar problems.

## SYSTEM DIAGNOSIS

Refer to **Fig. 16,** for multiple function warning indicator system diagnosis.

Test temperature gauge with Rotunda Gauge Tester 021-00055 or equivalent or with a 10 ohm resistor for high calibration and a 75 ohm resistor for low calibration as follows:

1. Turn ignition switch to On or ACC position.
2. Connect a 10 ohm resistor between gauge lead and ground. The centerline of pointer should fall within the band around the H mark.
3. Connect a 75 ohm resistor between gauge lead and ground. The centerline of pointer should fall within the band around the C mark.
4. If gauge tests within calibration, replace sender.
5. If gauge is out of calibration, replace IVR and retest.
6. If gauge is out of calibration, replace gauge.

## SYSTEM DIAGNOSIS

Refer to **Figs. 5 and 6,** for coolant temperature indicating system diagnosis.

MAGNETIC TEMP GAUGE
INOPERATIVE—POINTER DOES NOT MOVE—PINPOINT TEST A

| | TEST STEP | RESULT | ► | ACTION TO TAKE |
|---|---|---|---|---|
| A1 | VERIFY CONDITION | | | |
| | • Verify condition. | Gauge pointer does not move | ► | GO to A2. |
| | | Gauge pointer moves | ► | GO to B1. |

MAGNETIC TEMP GAUGE
INOPERATIVE—POINTER DOES NOT MOVE—PINPOINT TEST A (Continued)

| | TEST STEP | RESULT | ► | ACTION TO TAKE |
|---|---|---|---|---|
| A2 | CHECK OTHER GAUGES | | | |
| | • Check power to cluster. With ignition on, observe other gauges and warning indicators for proper operation. If necessary, use Rotunda Digital Volt-Ohmmeter 007-00001 or equivalent or test lamp to verify voltage at B+ terminal of cluster connector. | Other gauges and warning indicators operate correctly; voltage present at cluster | ► | GO to B1. |
| | | Other gauges and warning indicators do not operate correctly; no voltage present at cluster | ► | SERVICE power to cluster. |

TEMPERATURE GAUGE INACCURATE—
PINPOINT TEST B

| | TEST STEP | RESULT | ► | ACTION TO TAKE |
|---|---|---|---|---|
| B1 | TEST BOX CHECK | | | |
| | • Insert Instrument Gauge, System Tester, Rotunda 021-00055 or equivalent in sender circuit. Disconnect connector at sender and connect tester to cluster side of connector. Set tester to LOW (73 ohms). | Gauge reads C | ► | GO to B2. |
| | | Pointer does not move | ► | GO to B3. |
| B2 | TEST BOX CHECK | | | |
| | • Set tester to HIGH (10 ohms). | Gauge reads H | ► | REPLACE sender. |
| | | Gauge does not read H | ► | GO to B3. |
| B3 | CHECK SENDER WIRING | | | |
| | • Check sender circuit wiring for shorts or open with ohmmeter, using Rotunda Digital Volt-Ohmmeter 007-00001 or equivalent. | Okay | ► | REPLACE gauge. |
| | | Not Okay | ► | SERVICE wiring. |

**Fig. 5 Temperature indicating system diagnosis. Except Capri**

| CONDITION | POSSIBLE SOURCE | ACTION |
|---|---|---|
| • Temperature Gauge Always Reads Cold | • Temperature gauge wire open.<br>• Damaged temperature gauge sending unit.<br>• Damaged temperature gauge.<br>• Blown 10 amp meter fuse.<br>• Open power wire. | • Go to TG1. |
| • Temperature Gauge Always Reads Hot | • Short to ground.<br>• Damaged temperature gauge sending unit.<br>• Temperature gauge. | • Go to TG7. |
| • Temperature Gauge Inaccurate | • Open wires.<br>• Temperature gauge sending unit. | • Go to TG10. |

| | TEST STEP | RESULT | ► | ACTION TO TAKE |
|---|---|---|---|---|
| TG1 | TEMPERATURE GAUGE FUSE CHECK | | | |
| | • Access fuse panel. | Yes | ► | GO to TG4. |
| | • Check 10 amp meter fuse. | No | ► | GO to TG2. |
| | • Is fuse OK? | | | |
| TG2 | CHECK TEMPERATURE GAUGE SYSTEM | | | |
| | • Replace fuse. | Yes | ► | GO to TG3. |
| | • Key ON. | No | ► | GO to TG4. |
| | • Does fuse blow again? | | | |
| TG3 | CHECK FOR SHORTS TO GROUND | | | |
| | • Replace fuse. | Yes | ► | SERVICE BK / Y wire. |
| | • Disconnect BK / Y wire from 10 amp meter fuse. | No | ► | GO to TG4. |
| | • Measure resistance of BK / Y wire and ground. | | | |
| | • Is resistance less than 5 ohms? | | | |
| TG4 | CHECK FOR POWER TO TEMPERATURE GAUGE | | | |
| | • Key ON. | Yes | ► | GO to TG5. |
| | • Locate instrument cluster connector. | No | ► | SERVICE BK / Y wire. |
| | • Measure voltage on the BK / Y wire and ground. | | | |
| | • Is voltage greater than 10 volts? | | | |
| TG5 | TEMPERATURE GAUGE CHECK (TEMPERATURE GAUGE ALWAYS READS COLD) | | | |
| | • Locate instrument cluster connector. | Yes | ► | GO to TG6. |
| | • Place a jumper wire from the Y / W wire at instrument cluster to ground. | No | ► | REPLACE temperature gauge. |
| | • Does temperature gauge read hot? | | | |
| TG6 | TEMPERATURE SENSOR CHECK (TEMPERATURE GAUGE ALWAYS READS COLD) | | | |
| | • Place a jumper wire from Y / W wire at the temperature gauge sending unit to ground. | Yes | ► | GO to TG7. |
| | • Does the temperature gauge read hot? | No | ► | SERVICE Y / W wire between the temperature gauge, sending unit and temperature gauge. |

**Fig. 6 Temperature indicating system diagnosis (Part 1 of 3). Capri**

| | TEST STEP | RESULT | ► | ACTION TO TAKE |
|---|---|---|---|---|
| TG7 | TEMPERATURE GAUGE SHORT CHECK (TEMPERATURE GAUGE ALWAYS READS HOT) | | | |
| | • Remove Y / W wire from the temperature gauge sending unit. | Yes | ► | GO to TG8. |
| | • Does the temperature gauge read cold? | No | ► | REPLACE the sending unit. |
| TG8 | TEMPERATURE GAUGE SHORT CHECK (TEMPERATURE GAUGE ALWAYS READS HOT) | | | |
| | • Disconnect instrument cluster connector. | Yes | ► | REPLACE temperature gauge. |
| | • Does the temperature gauge still read hot? | No | ► | GO to TG9. |
| TG9 | CHECK TEMPERATURE GAUGE GROUND | | | |
| | • Locate instrument cluster connector. | Yes | ► | GO to TG10. |
| | • Disconnect instrument cluster connector. | No | ► | SERVICE BK wire. |
| | • Measure resistance between temperature gauge BK wire and ground. | | | |
| | • Is the resistance less than 5 ohms? | | | |

**Fig. 6 Temperature indicating system diagnosis (Part 2 of 3). Capri**

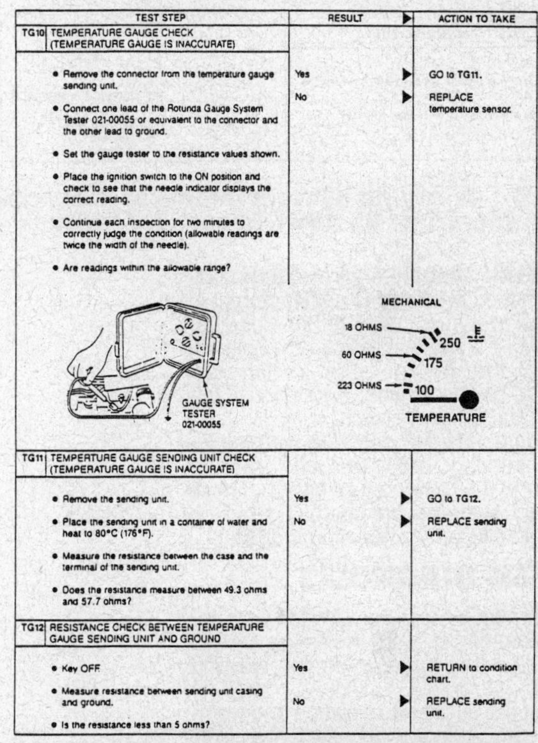

| | TEST STEP | RESULT | ► | ACTION TO TAKE |
|---|---|---|---|---|
| TG10 | TEMPERATURE GAUGE CHECK (TEMPERATURE GAUGE IS INACCURATE) | | | |
| | • Remove the connector from the temperature gauge sending unit. | Yes | ► | GO to TG11. |
| | • Connect one lead of the Rotunda Gauge System Tester 021-00055 or equivalent to the connector and the other lead to ground. | No | ► | REPLACE temperature sensor. |
| | • Set the gauge tester to the resistance values shown. | | | |
| | • Place the ignition switch to the ON position and check to see that the needle indicator displays the correct reading. | | | |
| | • Continue each inspection for two minutes to correctly judge the condition (allowable readings are twice the width of the needle). | | | |
| | • Are readings within the allowable range? | | | |
| TG11 | TEMPERTURE GAUGE SENDING UNIT CHECK (TEMPERATURE GAUGE IS INACCURATE) | | | |
| | • Remove the sending unit. | Yes | ► | GO to TG12. |
| | • Place the sending unit in a container of water and heat to 80°C (176°F). | No | ► | REPLACE sending unit. |
| | • Measure the resistance between the case and the terminal of the sending unit. | | | |
| | • Does the resistance measure between 49.3 ohms and 57.7 ohms? | | | |
| TG12 | RESISTANCE CHECK BETWEEN TEMPERATURE GAUGE SENDING UNIT AND GROUND | | | |
| | • Key OFF. | Yes | ► | RETURN to condition chart. |
| | • Measure resistance between sending unit casing and ground. | No | ► | REPLACE sending unit. |
| | • Is the resistance less than 5 ohms? | | | |



**Fig. 6 Temperature indicating system diagnosis (Part 3 of 3). Capri**

# CHARGING SYSTEM INDICATOR

## DESCRIPTION

A red alternator charge indicator is located in the instrument cluster. This indicator glows when there is no alternator output.

If the system is working normally, the following conditions will be present.

1. With ignition switch Off, charge indicator is Off.
2. With ignition switch in Run (engine not running), charge indicator is On.
3. With ignition switch in Run (engine running), charge indicator is Off.

## SYSTEM DIAGNOSIS

### Except 1991 Escort & Tracer

If charge indicator does not come on with the ignition switch in Run position and the engine not running, check the I circuit (ignition switch to regulator I terminal) for an open circuit or burned out charge indicator. Replace indicator, if necessary.

### 1991 Escort & Tracer

Refer to Fig. 7, for charging indicating system diagnosis.

# OIL PRESSURE INDICATOR, LAMP TYPE

## DESCRIPTION

A red warning indicator glow when the oil pressure is below a prescribed valve. The indicator should come on when the ignition switch is first turned to the Run position. The indicator should go out within a

| SYMPTOM | POSSIBLE CAUSE | ACTION |
|---|---|---|
| • Electrical Power Warning Light Stays On (During Engine Running) | • Warning light supply (alternator).<br>• Wiring harness. | • GO to CH1. |
| • Electrical Power Warning Light Will Not Turn On | • Warning light.<br>• Warning light supply (fuse).<br>• Wiring harness. | • GO to CH2. |

| TEST STEP | RESULT ► | ACTION TO TAKE |
|---|---|---|
| CH1 METER FUSE CHECK (LIGHT DOES NOT TURN ON) | | |
| • Ignition OFF.<br>• Remove and inspect the (15 amp) meter fuse.<br>• Is the fuse OK? | Yes ►<br>No ► | GO to CH2.<br>REPLACE 15 amp fuse. |

| TEST STEP | RESULT ► | ACTION TO TAKE |
|---|---|---|
| CH2 CHECK SUPPLY TO INSTRUMENT CLUSTER | | |
| • Ignition ON.<br>• Measure voltage on the "BK/Y" wire at the instrument cluster.<br>• Is the voltage greater than 10 volts? | Yes ►<br>No ► | GO to CH3.<br>SERVICE or REPLACE the "BK/Y" wire between "METER" fuse and the instrument cluster. |

**Fig. 7 Charging system indicator diagnosis (Part 1 of 2). 1991 Escort & Tracer**

| TEST STEP | RESULT ► | ACTION TO TAKE |
|---|---|---|
| CH3 ELECTRICAL POWER WARNING LIGHT CHECK (LIGHT DOES NOT TURN ON) | | |
| • Place the ignition switch in the ON position.<br>• Verify 12 volts at "BK/Y."<br>• Ground the "W/BK" wire at the instrument cluster connector.<br>• Does the charge warning light turn ON? | Yes ►<br>No ► | GO to CH4.<br>SERVICE or REPLACE charge warning light. |

| TEST STEP | RESULT ► | ACTION TO TAKE |
|---|---|---|
| CH4 ELECTRICAL POWER WARNING CONTINUITY CHECK (LIGHT DOES NOT TURN ON) | | |
| • Check for continuity on the "W/BK" wire between the instrument cluster and the alternator.<br>• Is there continuity? | Yes ►<br>No ► | GO to CH5.<br>REPAIR the "W/BK" wire between the instrument cluster and the alternator. |

| TEST STEP | RESULT ► | ACTION TO TAKE |
|---|---|---|
| CH5 ELECTRICAL POWER SUPPLY CHECK (LIGHT DOES NOT TURN OFF) | | |
| • Place the ignition switch in the ON position.<br>• Measure voltage on the "W/BK" wire at the alternator.<br>• Is the voltage greater than 10 volts? | Yes ►<br>No ► | RETURN to the Symptom Chart.<br>SERVICE battery/alternator. |

**Fig. 7 Charging system indicator diagnosis (Part 2 of 2). 1991 Escort & Tracer**

few seconds after the engines starts, indicating that oil pressure is satisfactory.

The oil switch is calibrated to close between 4.5-7.5 psi. The indicator is connect between the oil pressure switch unit (mounted on the engine) and the coil terminal of the ignition switch.

On some vehicles only one warning indicator serving both the oil pressure switch and the temperature switch. These combined systems are identified by the word ENGINE on the warning indicator.

## SYSTEM DIAGNOSIS

Disconnect temperature switch wire before testing oil pressure indicating system on vehicles that have an engine warning indicator.

To test the oil pressure switch and warning indicator, turn ignition switch to Run, but do not start the engine. The warning indicator should come on. If the indicator does not come on, remove the wire from the switch terminal and connect wire to ground. If the indicator now comes on, the oil pressure switch is inoperative. Replace switch. If indicator does not come on with the switch wire connected to ground, the warning indicator is burned out or the system wiring is open. Replace indicator or service wiring.

If indicator stays on with engine running and engine has adequate oil pressure, disconnect wire from oil pressure switch. The indicator should go out. If indicator goes out, replace oil pressure switch. If indicator does not go out, service shorted wiring between switch and indicator.

# OIL PRESSURE INDICATOR, GAUGE TYPE

## DESCRIPTION

### Except Capri

The oil pressure indicating system is a magnetic type system, which consists of three primary coils, one of which is wound at a 90° angle to the other two. The coils form a magnetic field which varies in direction according to the variable resistance of the sender unit which is connected between two of them. A primary magnet, to which a shaft and pointer are attached, rotates to align to this primary field, resulting in pinter position. The bobbin/coil assembly is pressed into a metal housing which as two hoes for dial mounting. The is no adjustment, calibration or maintenance required for these gauges.

OIL GAUGE INOPERATIVE — POINTER DOES NOT MOVE
PINPOINT TEST A

| TEST STEP | RESULT ► | ACTION TO TAKE |
|---|---|---|
| A1 VERIFY CONDITION | | |
| • Verify Condition. | Gauge pointer does not move ►<br>Gauge pointer moves ► | GO to A2.<br>GO to B1. |
| A2 CHECK OTHER GAUGES | | |
| • Check power to cluster. With ignition on, observe other gauges and warning lamps for proper operation. If necessary, use voltmeter or test lamp to verify voltage at B+ terminal of cluster connector. | Other gauges and warning lamps operate correctly; voltage present at cluster ►<br>Other gauges and warning lamps do not operate correctly; no voltage present at cluster ► | GO to B1.<br>SERVICE power to cluster. |

OIL GAUGE INACCURATE
PINPOINT TEST B

| TEST STEP | RESULT ► | ACTION TO TAKE |
|---|---|---|
| B1 TEST BOX CHECK | | |
| • Insert Instrument Gauge, System Tester, Rotunda 021-00055 or equivalent in sender circuit. Disconnect connector at sender and connect tester to cluster side of connector. Set tester to LOW (73 ohms). | Gauge reads L ►<br>Pointer does not move ► | GO to B2.<br>GO to B3. |
| B2 SENDER TEST | | |
| • Ground wire to engine at sender. | Gauge reads in the middle of scale ►<br>Gauge does not read in middle of scale ► | REPLACE sender.<br>GO to B3. |
| B3 CHECK SENDER WIRING | | |
| • Check sender circuit wiring for shorts or open with ohmmeter. | (OK) ►<br>(NOT OK) ► | REPLACE gauge.<br>SERVICE wiring. |

**Fig. 8 Gauge type oil pressure indicator diagnosis. Except Capri**

### Capri

The oil pressure indicating system consists of a sender unit mounted on the right-hand side of the engine block and a gauge mounted in the instrument cluster.

When engine oil pressure is low, the sender resistance is high, resulting in low current flow through the gauge and little pointer movement.

## SYSTEM DIAGNOSIS

Refer to **Figs. 8 and 9**, for oil pressure indicating system diagnosis.

| CONDITION | POSSIBLE SOURCE | ACTION |
|---|---|---|
| • Oil Pressure Gauge Always Reads Low | • Open signal wire.<br>• Damaged pressure sensor.<br>• Damaged pressure gauge.<br>• Blown fuse.<br>• Open power wire. | • Go to OG1. |
| • Oil Pressure Gauge Always Reads High | • Oil pressure gauge wire shorted to ground.<br>• Damaged oil pressure sensor.<br>• Damaged oil pressure gauge. | • Go to OG7. |
| • Oil Pressure Gauge Reads Inaccurately | • Corroded connections.<br>• Damaged oil pressure sensor. | • Go to OG10. |

| TEST STEP | | RESULT | ▶ ACTION TO TAKE |
|---|---|---|---|
| OG1 | OIL PRESSURE GAUGE FUSE CHECK | | |
| | • Access fuse panel.<br>• Check the 10 amp meter fuse.<br>• Is fuse OK? | Yes<br>No | ▶ GO to OG4.<br>▶ GO to OG2. |
| OG2 | CHECK OIL PRESSURE GAUGE SYSTEM | | |
| | • Replace fuse.<br>• Key ON, engine running.<br>• Does fuse blow again? | Yes<br>No | ▶ GO to OG3.<br>▶ GO to OG4. |
| OG3 | CHECK FOR SHORTS TO GROUND | | |
| | • Replace fuse.<br>• Disconnect BK wire from 10 amp meter fuse.<br>• Measure resistance of BK / Y wire and ground.<br>• Is resistance less than 5 ohms? | Yes<br>No | ▶ GO to OG4.<br>▶ SERVICE / REPLACE BK wire. |
| OG4 | CHECK FOR POWER TO THE OIL PRESSURE GAUGE | | |
| | • Access instrument cluster.<br>• Key ON, engine running.<br>• Measure voltage between the BK / Y wire and ground.<br>• Is voltage greater than 10 volts? | Yes<br>No | ▶ GO to OG5.<br>▶ SERVICE / REPLACE BK / Y wire. |
| OG5 | OIL PRESSURE GAUGE CHECK (OIL PRESSURE GAUGE ALWAYS READS LOW) | | |
| | • Key OFF.<br>• Place a jumper wire from the Y / R wire at instrument cluster to ground.<br>• Does the oil pressure gauge read high? | Yes<br>No | ▶ GO to OG6.<br>▶ REPLACE oil pressure gauge. |
| OG6 | OIL PRESSURE GAUGE CHECK (OIL PRESSURE GAUGE ALWAYS READS LOW) | | |
| | • Place a jumper wire from Y / R wire at the oil pressure switch to ground.<br>• Does the oil pressure gauge read high? | Yes<br>No | ▶ GO to OG7.<br>▶ SERVICE / REPLACE Y / R wire between oil pressure switch and oil pressure gauge. |

**Fig. 9 Gauge type oil pressure indicator diagnosis (Part 1 of 2). Capri**

| TEST STEP | | RESULT | ▶ ACTION TO TAKE |
|---|---|---|---|
| OG7 | OIL PRESSURE GAUGE SHORT CHECK (OIL PRESSURE GAUGE ALWAYS READS HIGH) | | |
| | • Remove Y / R wire from the oil pressure switch.<br>• Does oil pressure gauge read low? | Yes<br>No | ▶ GO to OG8.<br>▶ REPLACE oil pressure switch. |
| OG8 | OIL PRESSURE GAUGE SHORT CHECK (OIL PRESSURE GAUGE ALWAYS READS HIGH) | | |
| | • Disconnect instrument cluster connector.<br>• Does the oil pressure gauge still read low? | Yes<br>No | ▶ REPLACE oil pressure switch.<br>▶ GO to OG9. |
| OG9 | CHECK OIL PRESSURE GAUGE GROUND | | |
| | • Disconnect instrument cluster connector.<br>• Measure resistance between the oil pressure gauge BK wire and ground.<br>• Is the resistance less than 5 ohms? | Yes<br>No | ▶ GO to OG10<br>▶ SERVICE / REPLACE BK wire. |
| OG10 | OIL PRESSURE GAUGE CHECK (OIL PRESSURE GAUGE IS INACCURATE) | | |
| | • Disconnect oil pressure switch.<br>• Connect one lead of Rotunda Gauge System Tester 021-00038 or equivalent to the Y / R wire of the connector and the other lead to ground.<br>• Set the tester to resistance values shown.<br>• Place the ignition switch to the ON position and check to see that the needle indicator displays the correct values.<br>• Continue each inspection for two minutes to correctly judge the condition (allowable readings are twice the width of the needle).<br>• Are readings within the allowable range? | Yes<br>No | ▶ REPLACE oil pressure switch.<br>▶ REPLACE oil pressure gauge. |

**Fig. 9 Gauge type oil pressure indicator diagnosis (Part 2 of 2). Capri**

# OIL PRESSURE, COOLANT TEMPERATURE GAUGES & WARNING LIGHTS

## PROBE, 1991 ESCORT & TRACER

### System Diagnosis

Refer to **Figs. 10 and 11,** for oil pressure coolant temperature and warning lamp indicating systems diagnosis.

# LOW OIL LEVEL WARNING INDICATOR

## DESCRIPTION

This system is used to indicate when engine oil level is 1½ quarts or more below the specified level. The system consist an instrument panel warning lamp, electronic relay and a float type sensor which is located in the oil pan. The warning lamp will be illuminated during engine starting. If oil level is sufficient, the lamp will go out when engine is operating. If oil level is low, the lamp will remain on until engine oil is added or until ignition switch is placed in the off position. The module will take approximately 5 minutes to reset. If engine is started during this reset period, the last reading obtained will be displayed.

## SYSTEM CHECK

With oil at Full mark on dipstick and engine warm, start engine. Warning indicator should come on briefly in Start for bulb test, then go out. Turn engine Off. Drain 2 quarts of oil from engine. Wait for 5 minutes, then restart engine. Warning indicator should come On and stay On.

If indicator does not come On, check the following; indicator, fuse, oil level relay and/or oil level sensor.

## SENSOR TEST

If is best to conduct test with sensor in oil pan with hot oil to ensure oil properly drains from sensor. If removed from pan, sensor must first be submerged in warm oil to ensure proper positioning of float before testing. The sensor must be held horizontally during bench testing to ensure float remains correctly positioned.

Connect positive lead of digital volt/ohmmeter to sensor terminal and negative lead to sensor housing. With sensor submerged in oil (engine full), meter should read Open. Resistance should be greater than 100,000 ohms. With sensor out of oil (oil drained), resistance should be less than 1000 ohms.

## SYSTEM DIAGNOSIS

Refer to **Fig. 12,** for low oil level indicating system diagnosis.

# VOLTMETER

## DESCRIPTION

### Except Capri & 1991 Probe

The voltmeter indicates battery voltage when the ignition is in the Run position (engine off). After starting the engine, the pointer will move to indicate charging system voltage. Voltmeter is not adjustable and should be replaced if inoperative.

### Capri

The voltmeter indicates voltage potential at the battery.

## SYSTEM DIAGNOSIS

### Except Capri & 1991 Probe

To test the voltmeter, turn the ignition switch On, turn headlamps On and set heater blower fan on High with engine stopped. The meter pointer should move toward the lower portion of the normal band (white portion of scale). If no movement of needle is observed, check battery to circuit breaker and circuit breaker to cluster wire connections. If connections are tight, and meter shows no movement, check fuse and wire continuity. If fuse and wire continuity are satisfactory, remove cluster from vehicle. Check for flex circuit to clip terminal continuity. If circuit is satisfactory, replace gauge.

### Capri & 1991 Probe

Refer to **Figs. 13 and 14,** for voltmeter diagnosis.

# TURBO BOOST INDICATING SYSTEM

## DESCRIPTION

The turbo boost indicating system consists of an electrically operated gauge mounted in the instrument cluster and a sensor mounted in the engine compartment. The sensor converts a vacuum signal to electrical input for the gauge.

## SYSTEM DIAGNOSIS

Refer to **Fig. 15,** for turbo boost indicating system diagnosis.

*Continued on page 14-12*

| CONDITION | POSSIBLE SOURCE | ACTION |
|---|---|---|
| • Temperature Gauge and Warning Lights Not Working | • "Meter" fuse.<br>• Circuit.<br>• Open grounds. | • GO to A1. |
| • Temperature Gauge Always Reads Cold | • Temperature gauge.<br>• Temperature sender.<br>• Circuit.<br>• Open grounds. | • GO to A1. |
| • Temperature Gauge Always Reads Hot | • Temperature gauge.<br>• Temperature sender.<br>• Circuit. | • GO to A1. |
| • Temperature Gauge Works but Is Inaccurate | • Temperature gauge.<br>• Temperature sender. | • GO to A1. |
| • Warning Lights Do Not Operate Correctly | • Circuit.<br>• Coolant level sender.<br>• ECA.<br>• Fuse. | • GO to TG1. |

| TEST STEP | | RESULT | ACTION TO TAKE |
|---|---|---|---|
| A1 | VERIFY COMPLAINT | | |
| | • Observe the gauge performance. | Gauge pointer does NOT move | GO to A2. |
| | | Gauge pointer moves | GO to D1. |
| A2 | VERIFY CLUSTER PERFORMANCE | | |
| | • With the ignition ON, observe the other gauges and warning lights for proper operation. | Other gauges and warning lights operate correctly | GO to C1. |
| | | Other gauges and warning lights do NOT operate correctly | GO to B1. |

| TEST STEP | | RESULT | ACTION TO TAKE |
|---|---|---|---|
| B1 | VERIFY POWER AT FUSE PANEL | | |
| | • Use a voltmeter to verify system voltage at the load side of the warning indicators fuse. | System voltage present at the load side of the fuse | GO to C1. |
| | | System voltage is NOT present at the load side of the fuse | GO to B2. |
| B2 | VERIFY POWER AT FUSE PANEL | | |
| | • Use voltmeter to verify the system voltage at the feed side of the warning indicator fuse. | System voltage is present at the feed side of the fuse | REPLACE the 15A meter fuse; RETURN to A1. |
| | | System voltage is NOT present at the feed side of the fuse | REPAIR the wiring to the fuse panel; RETURN to A1. |

**Fig. 10 Oil pressure, coolant temperature gauges & warning lights diagnosis (Part 1 of 4). 1991 Escort & Tracer**

| TEST STEP | | RESULT | ACTION TO TAKE |
|---|---|---|---|
| C1 | VERIFY POWER AT CLUSTER | | |
| | • Have cluster connector(s) remain intact.<br>• Partially remove the cluster from the instrument panel. Use a voltmeter to verify system voltage at the cluster connector and/or gauge terminal/warning light. | Voltage is present at the cluster connector and gauge terminal/warning light socket | REPLACE bulb. GO to C2. |
| | | System voltage is NOT present at the cluster connector and/or gauge terminal/warning light socket | REPAIR the circuitry. (CHECK wiring harness, flex circuit, ECA.) RETURN to A1. |
| C2 | VERIFY GROUND CIRCUITRY AT CLUSTER | | |
| | • Use an ohmmeter to check the continuity of the cluster and gauge ground circuitry. | Ground circuitry is good | GO to D1. |
| | | There is excessive resistance (greater than 5 ohms) in the ground circuitry | REPAIR the circuitry; RETURN to A1. |

| TEST STEP | | RESULT | ACTION TO TAKE |
|---|---|---|---|
| D1 | TEST SENDER CIRCUIT AT LOW | | |
| | • Insert Gauge System Tester, Rotunda 021-00055. Disconnect the connector at the sender and connect the tester to the cluster side of the connector. Set to 74 ohms. | Gauge reads C | GO to D2. |
| | | Gauge does NOT read C | GO to D2. |
| | | Gauge Pointer does NOT move | GO to D3. |
| D2 | TEST SENDER CIRCUIT AT HIGH | | |
| | • Set the Gauge System Tester to 9.7 ohms. | Gauge reads H | GO to D4. |
| | | Gauge does NOT read H | GO to D3. |
| D3 | CHECK SENDER CIRCUIT WIRING | | |
| | • Check the sender circuit wiring for shorts or opens with an ohmmeter. | Wiring is OK | REPLACE the gauge. |
| | | Wiring is shorted or open | REPAIR the wiring; RETURN to A1. |
| D4 | TEMPERATURE SENDER CHECK (TEMPERATURE GAUGE IS INACCURATE) | | |
| | • Remove the temperature sender.<br>• Place the temperature sender in a container of water and heat to 176°F (80°C).<br>• Use an ohmmeter to measure the resistance between the case and the terminal of the temperature sender.<br>• Does the resistance measure between 49 ohms and 58 ohms? | Yes | Repair Engine Cooling. |
| | | No | REPLACE the temperature sender. |

**Fig. 10 Oil pressure, coolant temperature gauges & warning lights diagnosis (Part 2 of 4). 1991 Escort & Tracer**

| TEST STEP | | RESULT | ACTION TO TAKE |
|---|---|---|---|
| TG1 | CHECK METER FUSE | | |
| | • Key OFF.<br>• Remove and inspect the 15 amp "meter" fuse.<br>• Is the fuse OK? | Yes<br>No | GO to TG2.<br>REPLACE the "meter" fuse. |
| TG2 | CHECK THE RESISTANCE TO INSTRUMENT CLUSTER | | |
| | • Key OFF.<br>• Measure resistance between the 15 amp "meter" fuse and the instrument cluster.<br>• Is the resistance less than 5 ohms? | Yes<br>No | GO to TG3.<br>REPAIR/REPLACE the "BK/Y" wire. |
| TG3 | CHECK INSTRUMENT CLUSTER GROUND | | |
| | • Access the instrument cluster.<br>• Measure resistance from the instrument cluster "BK" to ground.<br>• Is the resistance less than 5 ohms? | Yes<br>No | GO to TG4.<br>REPAIR/REPLACE the grounds as needed. |
| TG4 | FAULT MENU | | |
| | • "Check Engine" warning light does not operate correctly.<br>• "Check Coolant" warning light does not operate correctly.<br>• Tachometer does not operate correctly. | Yes<br>No | GO to TG5.<br>GO to TG5.<br>GO to TG6.<br>GO to T1. |
| TG5 | CHECK ENGINE LIGHT TEST WARNING | | |
| | • Key ON.<br>• Using a jumper wire, ground the "Y/BK" wire at the instrument panel.<br>• Does the "Check Engine" light turn on? | Yes<br>No | GO to TG6.<br>REPAIR/REPLACE the "Check Engine" light or SERVICE the instrument cluster. |
| TG6 | RESISTANCE CHECK BETWEEN INSTRUMENT CLUSTER AND ECA | | |
| | • Disconnect the instrument cluster.<br>• Measure resistance from the instrument cluster "Y/BK" to ECA.<br>• Is the resistance less than 5 ohms? | Yes<br>No | GO to TG7.<br>REPAIR/REPLACE the "Y/BK" wire. |
| TG7 | CHECK COOLANT WARNING LAMP TEST | | |
| | • Key ON.<br>• Using a jumper wire, ground the "Y/GN" wire at the instrument panel.<br>• Does the "Check Coolant" light go on? | Yes<br>No | GO to TG8.<br>REPLACE the bulb. |
| TG8 | RESISTANCE CHECK BETWEEN INSTRUMENT CLUSTER AND COOLANT LEVEL SENDER | | |
| | • Disconnect the instrument cluster.<br>• Measure resistance from the instrument cluster "Y/GN" to the coolant level sender.<br>• Is the resistance less than 5 ohms? | Yes<br>No | GO to TG9.<br>REPAIR/REPLACE the "Y/GN" wire. |

**Fig. 10 Oil pressure, coolant temperature gauges & warning lights diagnosis (Part 3 of 4). 1991 Escort & Tracer**

| TEST STEP | | RESULT | ACTION TO TAKE |
|---|---|---|---|
| TG9 | VOLTAGE CHECK TO COOLANT LEVEL SENDER | | |
| | • Measure the voltage from the "meter" fuse "BK/Y" wire to the coolant level sender.<br>• Is the voltage 10 volts or greater? | Yes<br>No | GO to TG10.<br>REPAIR/REPLACE the "BK/Y" wire from "meter" fuse to coolant level sender. |
| TG10 | CHECK COOLANT LEVEL GROUND | | |
| | • Measure resistance from the coolant level sender "BK/GN" to ground.<br>• Is the resistance less than 5 ohms? | Yes<br>No | GO to TG11.<br>REPAIR/REPLACE the "BK/GN" wire to ground. |
| TG11 | CHECK COOLANT LEVEL SENDER | | |
| | • Key ON.<br>• Using a jumper wire, jump the coolant level sender "Y/GN" wire to ground.<br>• Does the "Check Coolant" light turn on? | Yes<br>No | REPLACE the coolant level sender.<br>REPAIR/REPLACE the "Check Coolant" light, or SERVICE the instrument cluster. |
| TG12 | OIL PRESSURE INDICATOR SHORT CHECK (OIL PRESSURE INDICATOR LAMP STAYS ON) | | |
| | • Disconnect the "Y/R" wire from oil pressure switch connector.<br>• Does oil pressure indicator lamp go off? | No | REPAIR "Y/R" wire between oil pressure indicator lamp and oil pressure switch. |
| | | Yes | GO to TG13. |
| TG13 | OIL PRESSURE INDICATOR CONTINUITY CHECK #1 (OIL PRESSURE INDICATOR LAMP WILL NOT LIGHT) | | |
| | • Ground "Y/R" wire at oil pressure switch connector.<br>• Does oil pressure indicator lamp light? | No<br>Yes | GO to TG14.<br>REPLACE oil pressure switch. |
| TG14 | OIL PRESSURE INDICATOR CONTINUITY CHECK #2 (OIL PRESSURE INDICATOR LAMP WILL NOT LIGHT) | | |
| | • Ground "Y/R" wire at instrument connector.<br>• Does oil pressure indicator lamp light? | No<br>Yes | REPLACE lamp.<br>REPAIR "Y/R" wire between oil pressure indicator lamp and oil pressure switch. |

**Fig. 10 Oil pressure, coolant temperature gauges & warning lights diagnosis (Part 4 of 4). 1991 Escort & Tracer**

| TEST STEP | RESULT ► | ACTION TO TAKE |
|---|---|---|
| **BG1** BOOST SENSOR SUPPLY CHECK (BOOST GAUGE NOT WORKING) | | |
| • Check for 12 volts (±1 volt) on "BK/Y" wire at boost sensor connector.<br>• Is there 12 volts? | Yes ►<br>No ► | GO to BG2 .<br>REPAIR "BK/Y" wire between boost sensor and fuse panel. |

| TEST STEP | RESULT ► | ACTION TO TAKE |
|---|---|---|
| **BG2** BOOST SENSOR OUTPUT CHECK (BOOST GAUGE NOT WORKING) | | |
| • Check for 2.5 volts (±.5 volt) on "LG/Y" wire at boost sensor connector.<br>• Is there 2.5 volts? | Yes ►<br>No ► | GO to BG4 .<br>GO to BG3 . |

| TEST STEP | RESULT ► | ACTION TO TAKE |
|---|---|---|
| **BG3** BOOST SENSOR GROUND CHECK (BOOST GAUGE NOT WORKING) | | |
| • Check for continuity between ground and "BK" wire at boost sensor connector.<br>• Is there continuity? | Yes ►<br>No ► | REPLACE boost sensor.<br>REPAIR "BK" wire between boost sensor and ground. |

| TEST STEP | RESULT ► | ACTION TO TAKE |
|---|---|---|
| **BG4** BOOST SENSOR OUTPUT CHECK (BOOST GAUGE NOT WORKING) | | |
| • Check for 2.5 volts (±.5 volt) on "LG/Y" wire at instruments connector.<br>• Is there 2.5 volts? | Yes ►<br>No ► | GO to BG5 .<br>REPAIR "LG/Y" wire between instruments and boost sensor. |

| TEST STEP | RESULT ► | ACTION TO TAKE |
|---|---|---|
| **BG5** BOOST GAUGE CHECK (BOOST GAUGE NOT WORKING) | | |
| • Disconnect boost sensor (connector C281).<br>• Place a jumper between Y/BL and LG/Y wires at instruments connectors<br>• Does boost gauge read full scale? | Yes ►<br>No ► | REPLACE boost sensor.<br>REPLACE boost gauge. |

**Fig. 11 Oil pressure, coolant temperature gauges & warning lights diagnosis (Part 1 of 7). Probe**

| TEST STEP | RESULT ► | ACTION TO TAKE |
|---|---|---|
| **OP1** INSTRUMENT RELATED SYSTEM CHECK (OIL GAUGE NOT WORKING) | | |
| • Turn ignition switch to ON position (engine off).<br>• Check the following items for proper operation:<br>– Oil pressure gauge<br>– Warning lights<br>– Anti-lock<br>– Seat belt<br>– Brake<br>– Engine | Warning lights not working, oil pressure gauge reads low ►<br>Oil pressure gauge always reads low ►<br>Oil pressure gauge always reads high ►<br>Oil pressure gauge not accurate ► | GO to OP2 .<br>GO to OP3 .<br>GO to OP5 .<br>GO to OP7 . |

| TEST STEP | RESULT ► | ACTION TO TAKE |
|---|---|---|
| **OP2** INSTRUMENT (METER) FUSE CHECK (WARNING LIGHTS NOT WORKING, OIL PRESSURE GAUGE READS LOW) | | |
| • Check instrument (METER) fuse.<br>• Is fuse OK? | Yes ►<br>No ► | Repair the BK/Y wire between the fuse panel and the instrument cluster.<br>REPLACE fuse. (Read note) |
| NOTE: If fuse blows again, service shorts to ground in "BK/Y" wires between instruments and fuse panel. | | |

| TEST STEP | RESULT ► | ACTION TO TAKE |
|---|---|---|
| **OP3** GAUGE CHECK (OIL PRESSURE GAUGE ALWAYS READS LOW) | | |
| • Ground "Y/R" wire at instrument (METER) connector.<br>• Does oil pressure gauge read high? | Yes ►<br>No ► | GO to OP4 .<br>REPLACE oil pressure gauge. |

**Fig. 11 Oil pressure, coolant temperature gauges & warning lights diagnosis (Part 2 of 7). Probe**

| TEST STEP | RESULT ► | ACTION TO TAKE |
|---|---|---|
| **OP4** GAUGE CONTINUITY CHECK NO. 1 (OIL PRESSURE GAUGE ALWAYS READS LOW) | | |
| • Ground "Y/R" wire at oil pressure sender unit connector.<br>• Does oil pressure gauge read high? | Yes ►<br>No ► | REPLACE oil pressure sender unit.<br>REPAIR "Y/R" wire between instruments and oil pressure sender unit. |

| TEST STEP | RESULT ► | ACTION TO TAKE |
|---|---|---|
| **OP5** GAUGE SHORT CHECK NO. 1 (OIL PRESSURE GAUGE ALWAYS READS HIGH) | | |
| • Disconnect the small instrument (METER) connector.<br>• Does oil pressure gauge still read high? | Yes ►<br>No ► | REPLACE oil pressure gauge (part of combination gauge).<br>GO to OP6 . |

| TEST STEP | RESULT ► | ACTION TO TAKE |
|---|---|---|
| **OP6** GAUGE SHORT CHECK NO. 2 (OIL PRESSURE GAUGE ALWAYS READS HIGH) | | |
| • Reconnect instruments (METERS) connector.<br>• Disconnect oil pressure sender unit connector.<br>• Does oil pressure gauge still read high? | Yes ►<br>No ► | REPAIR "Y/R" wire between instruments oil pressure sender unit and condenser.<br>REPLACE oil pressure sender unit. |

**Fig. 11 Oil pressure, coolant temperature gauges & warning lights diagnosis (Part 3 of 7). Probe**

| TEST STEP | RESULT ► | ACTION TO TAKE |
|---|---|---|
| **OP7** OIL PRESSURE GAUGE CHECK (OIL PRESSURE GAUGE NOT ACCURATE) | | |
| • Disconnect oil pressure sender unit connector.<br>• Connect one lead of Rotunda Gauge Tester (Read note) to the "Y/R" wire of the connector and the other lead to ground.<br>• Set tester to resistance values shown.<br>• Turn ignition switch to ON position and check to see that needle indicator displays correct values.<br>• Continue inspections for two minutes each to correctly judge the condition.<br>• The allowable error is twice the width of the needle.<br>• Are oil pressure gauge readings correct? | Yes ►<br>No ► | REPLACE oil pressure sender unit.<br>REPLACE oil pressure gauge.<br>NOTE: If the oil pressure gauge is still not operating correctly, the oil pressure circuit board (analog clusters only) may need to be replaced. |
| NOTE: Use Rotunda "Gauge System Tester" No. 021-00038 or equivalent. | | |

ANALOG CLUSTER
OIL PRESSURE CIRCUIT BOARD
0 Ω
±1.8 Ω
OIL

**Fig. 11 Oil pressure, coolant temperature gauges & warning lights diagnosis (Part 4 of 7). Probe**

| TEST STEP | | RESULT ► | ACTION TO TAKE |
|---|---|---|---|
| TG1 | INSTRUMENTS (METER) SYSTEM CHECK (TEMPERATURE GAUGE NOT WORKING) | | |
| • Start engine and allow a warm-up time of 15 minutes.<br>• Shut engine off. Turn ignition to the ON position.<br>• Check the following items for proper operation:<br>– Temperature gauge<br>– Warning lights (Anti-lock, Seat Belt, Engine, Brake) | | No warning lights illuminate and temperature gauge always reads cold ► | GO to TG2. |
| | | Warning lights illuminate and temperature gauge always reads cold ► | GO to TG3. |
| | | Temperature gauge always reads hot ► | GO to TG5. |
| | | Temperature gauge is not accurate ► | GO to TG7. |

| TEST STEP | | RESULT ► | ACTION TO TAKE |
|---|---|---|---|
| TG2 | INSTRUMENTS (METER) FUSE CHECK (TEMPERATURE GAUGE ALWAYS READS COLD/NO WARNING LIGHTS ILLUMINATE) | | |
| • Check instrument (METER) fuse.<br>• Is fuse OK? | | Yes ► | REPAIR BK/Y wire between instrument cluster and fuse panel. |
| | | No ► | REPLACE fuse. (Read note) |
| NOTE: If fuse blows again, check for shorts to ground in "BK/Y" wires between instruments and fuse panel. Repair "BK/Y" wire as needed. | | | |

**Fig. 11 Oil pressure, coolant temperature gauges & warning lights diagnosis (Part 5 of 7). Probe**

| TEST STEP | | RESULT ► | ACTION TO TAKE |
|---|---|---|---|
| TG3 | TEMPERATURE GAUGE CHECK (TEMPERATURE GAUGE ALWAYS READS COLD/WARNING LIGHTS OK) | | |
| • Ground "Y/GN" wire at instrument connector.<br>• Does temperature gauge still read cold? | | Yes ► | REPLACE temperature gauge for conventional instruments |
| | | No ► | GO to TG4. |

| TEST STEP | | RESULT ► | ACTION TO TAKE |
|---|---|---|---|
| TG4 | TEMPERATURE GAUGE CONTINUITY CHECK (TEMPERATURE GAUGE ALWAYS READS COLD/WARNING LIGHTS OK) | | |
| • Ground "Y/GN" wire at water temperature sensor connector.<br>• Does temperature gauge still read cold? | | Yes ► | REPAIR "Y/GN" wire between instruments (METERS) and water temperature sensor. |
| | | No ► | REPLACE water temperature sensor. |

| TEST STEP | | RESULT ► | ACTION TO TAKE |
|---|---|---|---|
| TG5 | TEMPERATURE GAUGE SHORT CHECK NO. 1 (TEMPERATURE GAUGE ALWAYS READS HOT) | | |
| • Remove "Y/GN" wire from water temperature sensor.<br>• Does temperature gauge still read hot? | | Yes ► | GO to TG6. |
| | | No ► | REPLACE water temperature sensor. |

| TEST STEP | | RESULT ► | ACTION TO TAKE |
|---|---|---|---|
| TG6 | TEMPERATURE GAUGE SHORT CHECK NO. 2 (TEMPERATURE GAUGE ALWAYS READS HOT) | | |
| • Reconnect "Y/GN" wire connector at water temperature sensor.<br>• Disconnect instrument (METER) connector.<br>• Does temperature gauge still read hot? | | Yes ► | REPLACE temperature gauge. |
| | | No ► | REPAIR "Y/GN" wire between water temperature sensor and instrument. |

**Fig. 11 Oil pressure, coolant temperature gauges & warning lights diagnosis (Part 6 of 7). Probe**

| TEST STEP | | RESULT ► | ACTION TO TAKE |
|---|---|---|---|
| TG7 | TEMPERATURE GAUGE CHECK (TEMPERATURE GAUGE IS NOT ACCURATE) | | |
| • Remove connector from the water temperature sensor.<br>• Connect one lead of the Rotunda Gauge System Tester 021-00055 (or equivalent) to the "Y/GN" wire at the connector and the other lead to ground as shown.<br>• Set the gauge tester to the resistance values shown.<br>• Turn ignition switch to ON position and check to see that the needle indicator displays the correct values.<br>• Continue each inspection for two minutes to correctly judge the condition (Allowable readings are twice the width of needle).<br>• Is reading within allowable range? | | Yes ► | GO to TG8. |
| | | No ► | REPLACE temperature gauge for conventional instruments cluster |
| NOTE: Use Rotunda "Gauge System Tester" No. 021-00055 or equivalent. | | | |

TEMP 12.4 Ω 18.5 Ω 104.1 Ω 153.9 Ω

| TEST STEP | | RESULT ► | ACTION TO TAKE |
|---|---|---|---|
| TG8 | TEMPERATURE SENSOR CHECK (TEMPERATURE GAUGE IS NOT ACCURATE) | | |
| • Remove the water temperature sensor.<br>• Place water temperature sensor in a container of water and heat to 80ºC (176ºF).<br>• Use an ohmmeter to measure the resistance between the case and terminal of the water temperature sensor.<br>• Does resistance read between 150 ohms and 180 ohms? | | Yes ► | Repair Engine Cooling. |
| | | No ► | REPLACE water temperature sensor. |

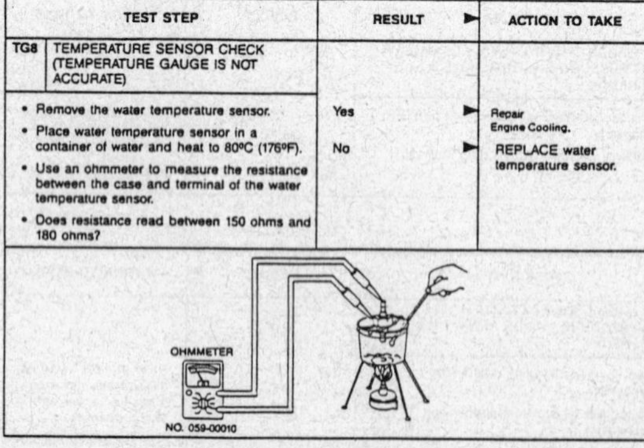


**Fig. 11 Oil pressure, coolant temperature gauges & warning lights diagnosis (Part 7 of 7). Probe**

TEST EQUIPMENT: VOM

| TEST STEP | | RESULT | ACTION TO TAKE |
|---|---|---|---|
| LAMP STAYS ON AFTER STARTING ENGINE — OIL NOT LOW | | | |
| 1A | • Verify oil level is full then check electronic relay ground by disconnecting wire from sensor and restart engine. | Lamp goes off ▶<br>Lamp stays on ▶ | CHECK sensor resistance. If less than 100 K ohms, REPLACE sensor. If greater than 100 K ohms — REPLACE electronic relay.<br>GO to Step 2A. |
| 2A | • Check wiring circuit between oil sensor and terminal No. 4 of electronic relay. | Wire shorted to ground ▶<br>Wire OK ▶ | SERVICE wiring.<br>REPLACE electronic relay. |
| LAMP DOES NOT STAY ON WHEN LOW ON OIL 1.9 LITRES (TWO QUARTS) | | | |
| 1B | • Check electronic relay by disconnecting wire from terminal No. 4. Wait approximately five minutes. Then short terminal to ground. Start engine. | Lamp stays on ▶<br>Lamp does not stay on ▶ | RECONNECT wire. GO to Step 2B.<br>REPLACE electronic relay. |
| 2B | • Check sensor resistance between sensor terminal and ground. | Greater than 1K ohms ▶<br>Less than 1K ohms ▶ | REPLACE sensor.<br>CHECK wiring or connector to sensor for open circuit. |
| NOTE: Ignition should be turned OFF for five minutes between checks to be sure that the electronic relay has "reset." | | | |
| LAMP BLINKS INTERMITTENTLY WHILE DRIVING | | | |
| 1C | • Check for loose connections to relay or bulb. | Not OK ▶<br>Connection OK ▶ | SERVICE connections.<br>REPLACE electronic relay. |

**Fig. 12 Low oil level indicator diagnosis**

| TEST STEP | | RESULT | ACTION TO TAKE |
|---|---|---|---|
| VM1 | INSTRUMENTS (METER) FUSE CHECK (VOLTMETER NOT WORKING)<br>• Check instrument (METER) fuse.<br>• Is fuse OK? | Yes ▶<br>No ▶ | GO to VM2.<br>REPLACE fuse. (Read note) |
| NOTE: If fuse blows again, check for shorts to ground in "BK/Y" wire at instruments. Repair "BK/Y" wire as needed. | | | |

| TEST STEP | | RESULT | ACTION TO TAKE |
|---|---|---|---|
| VM2 | INSTRUMENTS SUPPLY CHECK (VOLTMETER NOT WORKING)<br>• Check for 12 volts (±1 volt) on "BK/Y" wire at instruments connector.<br>• Are there 12 volts? | Yes ▶<br>No ▶ | GO to VM3.<br>REPAIR "BK/Y" wire between instrument cluster connector and fuse panel. |

| TEST STEP | | RESULT | ACTION TO TAKE |
|---|---|---|---|
| VM3 | INSTRUMENTS GROUND CHECK (VOLTMETER NOT WORKING)<br>• Check for 12 volts (±1 volt) on "BK" wire at instruments connector.<br>• Is there 12 volts? | Yes ▶<br>No ▶ | REPAIR "BK" wire between instruments and ground.<br>REPLACE voltmeter. |

**Fig. 13 Voltmeter diagnosis. Probe**

| CONDITION | POSSIBLE SOURCE | ACTION |
|---|---|---|
| • Gauge Always Reads Low | • Open signal wire.<br>• Open power wires.<br>• Damaged voltmeter.<br>• Corroded or loose connections.<br>• Charging system. | • Go to VM1. |
| • Gauge Always Reads High | • Damaged voltmeter.<br>• Corroded or loose connections.<br>• Charging system. | • Go to VM1. |
| • Gauge Is inaccurate | • Damaged voltmeter.<br>• Corroded or loose connections. | • Go to VM1. |

| TEST STEP | | RESULT | ACTION TO TAKE |
|---|---|---|---|
| VM1 | VOLTMETER FUSE CHECK<br>• Access fuse panel.<br>• Check 10 amp meter fuse.<br>• Is fuse OK? | Yes ▶<br>No ▶ | GO to VM4.<br>GO to VM2. |
| VM2 | CHECK VOLTMETER SYSTEM<br>• Replace fuse.<br>• Key ON.<br>• Does fuse blow again? | Yes ▶<br>No ▶ | GO to VM3.<br>GO to VM4. |
| VM3 | CHECK FOR SHORTS TO GROUND<br>• Replace fuse.<br>• Disconnect BK/Y wire from 10 amp meter fuse.<br>• Measure resistance of BK/Y wire and ground.<br>• Is resistance less than 5 ohms? | Yes ▶<br>No ▶ | SERVICE BK/Y wire.<br>GO to VM4. |
| VM4 | CHECK FOR POWER TO VOLTMETER<br>• Key ON.<br>• Access instrument cluster.<br>• Measure voltage at instrument cluster BK/Y wire and ground.<br>• Is voltage greater than 10 volts? | Yes ▶<br>No ▶ | GO to VM5.<br>SERVICE BK/Y wire between instrument cluster and fuse panel. |
| VM5 | VOLTMETER GROUND CHECK<br>• Key ON.<br>• Measure voltage on the BK wire at instrument cluster.<br>• Is voltage greater than 10 volts? | Yes ▶<br>No ▶ | SERVICE BK wire between instrument cluster and ground.<br>REPLACE voltmeter. |

**Fig. 14 Voltmeter diagnosis. Capri**

| CONDITION | POSSIBLE SOURCE | ACTION |
|---|---|---|
| • Turbo Boost Gauge Always Reads Low | • Open wires.<br>• Damaged boost sensor.<br>• Damaged boost gauge.<br>• Blown fuse.<br>• Corroded or loose connections. | • Go to BG1. |
| • Turbo Boost Gauge Always Reads High | • Damaged signal wire.<br>• Damaged boost sensor.<br>• Damaged boost gauge. | • Go to BG4. |
| • Turbo Boost Gauge Is Erratic | • Corroded or loose connections.<br>• Damaged boost sensor.<br>• Damaged boost gauge. | • Go to BG4. |

| TEST STEP | | RESULT | ACTION TO TAKE |
|---|---|---|---|
| BG1 | BOOST GAUGE FUSE CHECK<br>• Access fuse panel.<br>• Check the 10 amp meter fuse.<br>• Is fuse OK? | Yes ▶<br>No ▶ | GO to BG4.<br>GO to BG2. |
| BG2 | CHECK SYSTEM<br>• Replace fuse.<br>• Key ON.<br>• Does fuse blow again? | Yes ▶<br>No ▶ | GO to BG3.<br>GO to BG4. |
| BG3 | CHECK FOR SHORTS TO GROUND<br>• Replace fuse.<br>• Disconnect BK/Y wire from 10 amp meter fuse.<br>• Measure resistance of BK/Y wire and ground.<br>• Is resistance less than 5 ohms? | Yes ▶<br>No ▶ | GO to BG4.<br>SERVICE BK/Y wire. |
| BG4 | CHECK FOR POWER TO THE BOOST GAUGE<br>• Access instrument cluster.<br>• Key ON.<br>• Measure voltage on the BK/Y wire and ground.<br>• Is voltage greater than 10 volts? | Yes ▶<br>No ▶ | GO to BG5.<br>SERVICE BK/Y wire. |
| BG5 | CHECK BLACK WIRE TO GROUND<br>• Disconnect instrument cluster 8 pin connector and the boost sensor connector.<br>• Measure the resistance on the BK wire from each connector to ground.<br>• Is the resistance less than 5 ohms? | Yes ▶<br>No ▶ | GO to BG6.<br>SERVICE BK wire. |

**Fig. 15 Turbo boost indicating system diagnosis (Part 1 of 2)**

| TEST STEP | | RESULT | ACTION TO TAKE |
|---|---|---|---|
| BG6 | CHECK VOLTAGE AT BOOST SENSOR | | |
| | • Access boost sensor connector.<br>• Disconnect boost sensor connector.<br>• Key ON.<br>• Measure voltage across Y / GN and BK wires at the boost sensor connector..<br>• Is the voltage greater than 10 volts? | Yes<br>No | ► GO to BG7.<br>► SERVICE Y / GN and BK wires as needed, going to the boost sensor. |
| BG7 | CHECK BOOST GAUGE SIGNAL WIRE | | |
| | • Access instrument cluster.<br>• Disconnect instrument cluster 8-pin connector.<br>• Disconnect boost sensor.<br>• Measure resistance across the W / BL wire from instrument cluster to boost sensor connector.<br>• Is the resistance less than 5 ohms? | Yes<br>No | ► GO to BG8.<br>► SERVICE W / BL wire. |
| BG8 | CHECK BOOST GAUGE | | |
| | • Disconnect instrument cluster 8 pin connector.<br>• Key ON.<br>• Ground W / BL wire at boost gauge.<br>• Does boost gauge read low?<br>• Apply 12 volts to W / BL wire at boost gauge.<br>• Does boost gauge read high? | Yes<br>No | ► GO to BG9.<br>► REPLACE boost gauge. |
| BG9 | BOOST SENSOR CHECK | | |
| | • Disconnect boost sensor.<br>• Place a jumper wire between Y / GN and W / BL wires on connector.<br>• Does the boost gauge read full? | Yes<br>No | ► REPLACE boost sensor.<br>► RETURN to condition chart. |

**Fig. 15 Turbo boost indicating system diagnosis (Part 2 of 2)**

# LOW COOLANT WARNING SYSTEM

## ESCORT

### DESCRIPTION

The low coolant warning system consist of an instrument panel warning lamp and a sensor assembly, which is located in the coolant recovery bottle. This system is in operation whenever the ignition switch is in the On position. When coolant lever drops 1/4 to 3/4 inch below the Cold Full mark on the coolant recovery bottle, the low coolant lamp on the instrument panel will be illuminated. When coolant level is approximately 1/4 inch above the Cold Full mark on the coolant recovery bottle, the low coolant warning lamp should not be illuminated. When coolant level is slightly below the Cold Full mark, the warning lamp may flash on during turns and hard stops. Coolant level should be maintained approximately 1/2 inch above the Cold Full mark.

### SYSTEM DIAGNOSIS

#### Warning Lamp Does Not Illuminate With Low Coolant Level Condition

1. Place ignition switch in the On position. Low coolant warning lamp on instrument panel should be illuminated, if not, check for the following:
   a. Check bulb and replace if necessary.
   b. If bulb is satisfactory, proceed to step 2.
2. With coolant level in coolant recovery bottle 1 inch below the Cold Full mark, check if instrument panel warning lamp is illuminated with engine operating and note the following:
   a. If lamp is illuminated, system is operating properly.
   b. If lamp is not illuminated, proceed to step 3.
3. Disconnect low coolant sensor electrical connector and connect a jumper wire between electrical connector terminals. Place ignition switch in the Run position and note the following:
   a. If instrument panel warning lamp is not illuminated, check for open circuit between sensor and warning lamp and repair as necessary.
   b. If lamp is illuminated, proceed to step 4.
4. Remove low coolant sensor from coolant recovery bottle and check for continuity between sensor terminals, with float at lowest position of travel. Note the following:
   a. If continuity exist, sensor is satisfactory.
   b. If continuity does not exist, replace sensor.

#### Warning Lamp Remains Illuminated With Sufficient Coolant Level

1. Ensure coolant level is 1/2 inch above the Cold Full mark on coolant recovery bottle. Add coolant as necessary to bring coolant to proper level and check warning lamp. If warning lamp is still illuminated, proceed to step 2.
2. Disconnect electrical connector from coolant sensor and check for the following:
   a. If low coolant level warning lamp is still illuminated, check for short in circuit between sensor and instrument panel warning lamp and repair as necessary.
   b. If instrument panel warning lamp is now not illuminated, replace low coolant sensor.

# MULTIPLE FUNCTION WARNING INDICATOR

## 1989 MUSTANG GT

### DESCRIPTION

This system monitors the engine oil, cooling, fuel and washer fluid for low fluid level conditions. The system consist of four warning lamps, electronic module, three sensors and the fuel sending unit. A bulb check mode is incorporated into the system, which is activated during engine start up. After approximately 3 seconds, when bulb check mode is completed, low fluid level conditions will be verified, if present. The warning lamps are located at the lower right of the instrument cluster. The electronic control module is located above glove compartment.

The coolant, fuel and washer fluid indicator lamps may blink when vehicle is operated on steep grades. This condition should be considered normal.

#### Engine Oil Level Indicator

When engine oil level falls 1 1/2 quarts below the full mark, the "Check Oil" warning lamp will be illuminated. The oil level is sensed by a low oil level sensor located on the engine oil pan, after the bulb check mode has been completed. Once the oil level has been sensed and displayed, the indication will not change until the engine has been stopped and re-started. The module has a built in 90 to 150 second delay mode when the engine is stopped with a sufficient oil level condition, which allows time for the oil to drain back into the oil pan. If the engine is re-started during this delay period, a sufficient oil level condition will be indicated no matter what the true oil level. Whenever the engine is stopped with a low oil level condition, a new oil level reading will be taken upon engine re-start. The oil level sensor is located on the side of the engine oil pan.

#### Low Fuel Indicator

When fuel level drops to approximately 1/8 tank capacity, the low fuel warning indicator will be illuminated. At 1/8 fuel tank capacity, the fuel sending unit outputs a voltage of approximately 3.4 volts to the fluid module. At voltages of 3.4 volts or lower, the fluid module will illuminate the low fuel warning lamp. The low fuel warning lamp will remain illuminated until the fluid module receives a steady voltage of at least 4 volts from the fuel sending unit.

#### Low Coolant Indicator

When coolant level is below the Cold Full mark on the coolant recovery bottle, the "Low Coolant" warning lamp will be illuminated. At this level, the float type switch located in the coolant recovery bottle closes, sending battery voltage to the fluid module, which in turn illuminates the indicator lamp. When coolant level is above the Cold Full mark, the float type switch is open and the indicator lamp is not illuminated.

#### Low Washer Fluid Indicator

When washer fluid level is at approximately 1/3 capacity, the float type switch, located in the washer fluid bottle, closes sending a battery voltage signal to the fluid module. The fluid module will illuminate the "Washer Fluid" warning lamp whenever battery voltage is sensed. When washer fluid level is above the 1/3 capacity level, the float type switch is open and the warning lamp is not illuminated.

PINPOINT TEST A: No Indicators Illuminate When Ignition Is Switched to RUN (No Bulb "Prove-Out")

| TEST STEP | RESULT ▶ | ACTION TO TAKE |
|---|---|---|
| **A1** CHECK FUSE | | |
| • Check fuse 18 in fuse panel (Circuit 640 R/Y). | OK ▶ | GO to **A2**. |
| | ~~OK~~ ▶ | REPLACE fuse. CHECK system operation. |
| **A2** CHECK GROUND | | |
| • Connect one lead of ohmmeter to Circuit 57 BK (ground) at fluid module connector.<br>• Connect other lead to vehicle body ground.<br>• The meter reading should indicate a closed circuit. | OK ▶ | GO to **A3**. |
| | ~~OK~~ ▶ | SERVICE or REPLACE wiring harness and/or connectors. CHECK system operation. |
| **A3** CHECK INDICATOR LAMP OUTPUT CIRCUITS | | |
| • Turn ignition switch to OFF.<br>• Jumper terminals listed in table below.<br>• Turn ignition switch to RUN and observe indicators. They should all turn on.<br>• Remove jumpers.<br>Short terminal: 208 GY, 215 Y/BK, 42 R/W, 82 PK — To terminal: 57 BK, 57 BK, 57 BK, 57 BK<br>**NOTE: Place jumpers on back side of fluid module connector. The fluid module does NOT have to be disconnected.**<br>(Diagram: MODULE, GRAY, GREEN, JUMPER WIRE, HARNESS) | OK ▶ | REPLACE fluid module. CHECK system operation. |
| | ~~OK~~ ▶ | SERVICE or REPLACE wiring harness and/or connectors. CHECK system operation. |

**Fig. 16 Multiple function indicator system diagnosis (Part 1 of 20). 1989 Mustang**

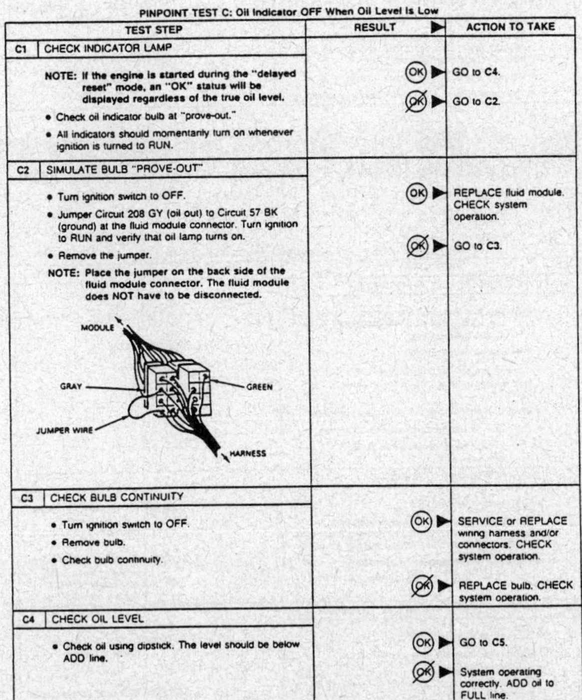

PINPOINT TEST C: Oil Indicator OFF When Oil Level Is Low

| TEST STEP | RESULT ▶ | ACTION TO TAKE |
|---|---|---|
| **C1** CHECK INDICATOR LAMP | | |
| **NOTE: If the engine is started during the "delayed reset" mode, an "OK" status will be displayed regardless of the true oil level.**<br>• Check oil indicator bulb at "prove-out."<br>• All indicators should momentarily turn on whenever ignition is turned to RUN. | OK ▶ | GO to C4. |
| | ~~OK~~ ▶ | GO to C2. |
| **C2** SIMULATE BULB "PROVE-OUT" | | |
| • Turn ignition switch to OFF.<br>• Jumper Circuit 208 GY (oil out) to Circuit 57 BK (ground) at the fluid module connector. Turn ignition to RUN and verify that oil lamp turns on.<br>• Remove the jumper.<br>**NOTE: Place the jumper on the back side of the fluid module connector. The fluid module does NOT have to be disconnected.**<br>(Diagram: MODULE, GRAY, GREEN, JUMPER WIRE, HARNESS) | OK ▶ | REPLACE fluid module. CHECK system operation. |
| | ~~OK~~ ▶ | GO to C3. |
| **C3** CHECK BULB CONTINUITY | | |
| • Turn ignition switch to OFF.<br>• Remove bulb.<br>• Check bulb continuity. | OK ▶ | SERVICE or REPLACE wiring harness and/or connectors. CHECK system operation. |
| | ~~OK~~ ▶ | REPLACE bulb. CHECK system operation. |
| **C4** CHECK OIL LEVEL | | |
| • Check oil using dipstick. The level should be below ADD line. | OK ▶ | GO to C5. |
| | ~~OK~~ ▶ | System operating correctly. ADD oil to FULL line. |

**Fig. 16 Multiple function indicator system diagnosis (Part 3 of 20). 1989 Mustang**

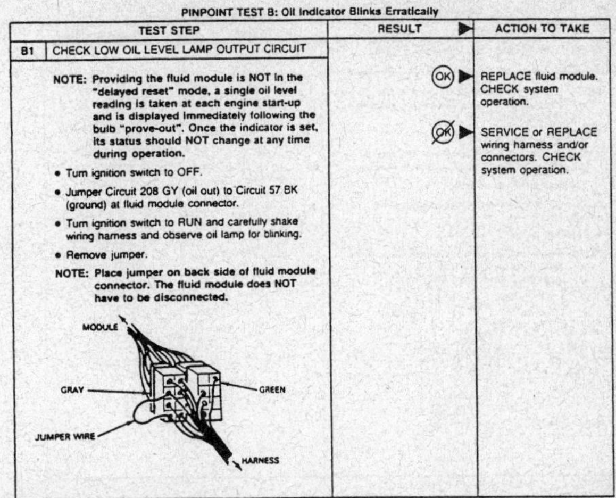

PINPOINT TEST B: Oil Indicator Blinks Erratically

| TEST STEP | RESULT ▶ | ACTION TO TAKE |
|---|---|---|
| **B1** CHECK LOW OIL LEVEL LAMP OUTPUT CIRCUIT | | |
| **NOTE: Providing the fluid module is NOT in the "delayed reset" mode, a single oil level reading is taken at each engine start-up and is displayed immediately following the bulb "prove-out". Once the indicator is set, its status should NOT change at any time during operation.**<br>• Turn ignition switch to OFF.<br>• Jumper Circuit 208 GY (oil out) to Circuit 57 BK (ground) at fluid module connector.<br>• Turn ignition switch to RUN and carefully shake wiring harness and observe oil lamp for blinking.<br>• Remove jumper.<br>**NOTE: Place jumper on back side of fluid module connector. The fluid module does NOT have to be disconnected.**<br>(Diagram: MODULE, GRAY, GREEN, JUMPER WIRE, HARNESS) | OK ▶ | REPLACE fluid module. CHECK system operation. |
| | ~~OK~~ ▶ | SERVICE or REPLACE wiring harness and/or connectors. CHECK system operation. |

**Fig. 16 Multiple function indicator system diagnosis (Part 2 of 20). 1989 Mustang**

PINPOINT TEST C: Oil Indicator OFF When Oil Level Is Low — Continued

| TEST STEP | RESULT ▶ | ACTION TO TAKE |
|---|---|---|
| **C5** CHECK SENSOR RESISTANCE | | |
| • Turn ignition switch to OFF.<br>• Connect one lead of ohmmeter to Circuit 258 W/PK (oil in) and connect other lead to Circuit 57 BK (ground).<br>**NOTE: Make both connections at fluid module connector.**<br>• The meter should read LESS than 1.0K ohms. | OK ▶ | REPLACE fluid module. CHECK system operation. |
| | ~~OK~~ ▶ | GO to C6. |
| **C6** CHECK SENSOR RESISTANCE (Continued) | | |
| • Turn ignition switch to OFF.<br>• Disconnect connector to oil level sensor.<br>• Connect one lead of ohmmeter to sensor connector terminal and connect other lead to Circuit 258 W/PK (oil in) at fluid module connector.<br>• Meter reading should indicate a closed circuit. | OK ▶ | GO to C7. |
| | ~~OK~~ ▶ | SERVICE or REPLACE wiring harness and/or connectors. CHECK system operation. |
| **C7** SIMULATE LOW OIL CONDITION | | |
| • Turn ignition switch to OFF.<br>• Drain 0.95 liter (1 quart) of engine oil.<br>• Repeat Test Step C5.<br>• Resistance should be less than 1.0K ohms.<br>**NOTE: Add oil to FULL mark after test.** | OK ▶ | CHECK system operation. |
| | ~~OK~~ ▶ | REPLACE oil level sensor. CHECK system operation. |

**Fig. 16 Multiple function indicator system diagnosis (Part 4 of 20). 1989 Mustang**

PINPOINT TEST D: Oil Indicator ON When Oil Level Is Normal

| TEST STEP | RESULT ▶ | ACTION TO TAKE |
|---|---|---|
| **D1** CHECK OIL LEVEL | | |
| **NOTE: If the vehicle is serviced for low oil and the engine is restarted before oil level settles, a false level will be displayed.**<br>• Check oil using dipstick. The level must be above ADD line. | OK ▶ | GO to D2. |
| | ~~OK~~ ▶ | ADD oil as required. CHECK system operation. |
| **D2** CHECK FOR SHORT TO GROUND | | |
| • Turn ignition switch to OFF.<br>• Connect one lead of ohmmeter to negative terminal of oil lamp Circuit 208 GY and connect other lead to Circuit 57 BK (ground) at fluid module connector.<br>• The meter reading should indicate an open circuit. | OK ▶ | GO to D3. |
| | ~~OK~~ ▶ | SERVICE or REPLACE wiring harness and/or connectors. CHECK system operation. |
| **D3** CHECK OIL SENSOR RESISTANCE | | |
| • Turn ignition switch to OFF.<br>• Connect one lead of an ohmmeter to Circuit 258 GY (oil in) and connect other lead to Circuit 57 BK (ground).<br>**NOTE: Make both connections at fluid module connector.**<br>• The meter should read greater than 8.2K ohms. | OK ▶ | REPLACE fluid module. CHECK system operation. |
| | ~~OK~~ ▶ | GO to D4. |
| **D4** CHECK SHORT TO GROUND | | |
| • Turn ignition switch to OFF.<br>• Disconnect harness to oil level sensor connector.<br>• Connect one terminal of ohmmeter to sensor connector terminal and connect other terminal to Circuit 258 W/PK at fluid module connector.<br>• The meter reading should indicate an OPEN CIRCUIT. | OK ▶ | REPLACE oil level sensor. CHECK system operation. |
| | ~~OK~~ ▶ | SERVICE or REPLACE wiring harness and/or connectors. CHECK system operation. |

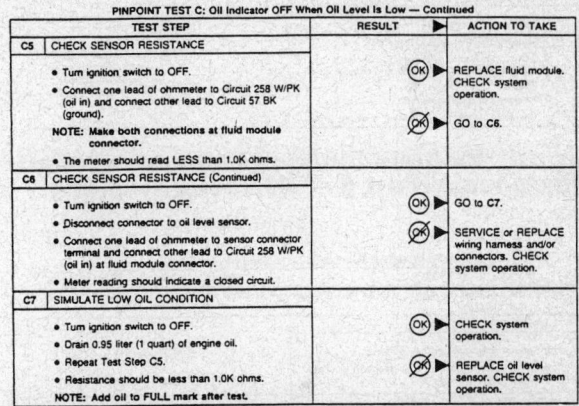

**Fig. 16 Multiple function indicator system diagnosis (Part 5 of 20). 1989 Mustang**

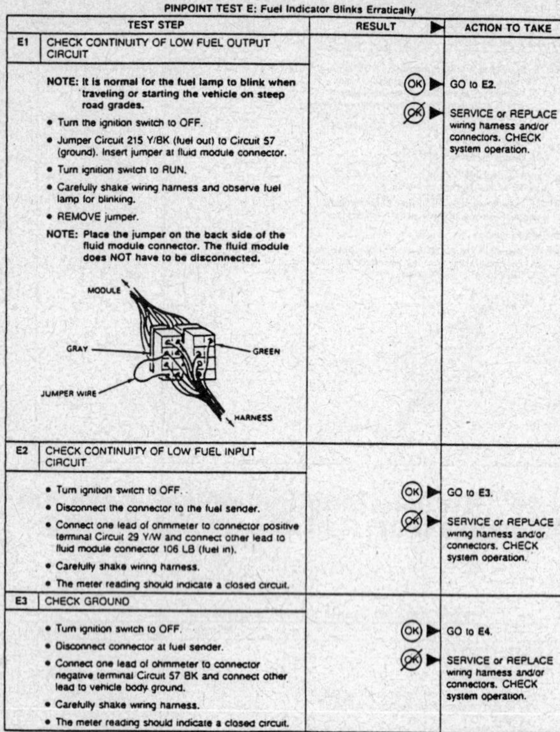

PINPOINT TEST E: Fuel Indicator Blinks Erratically

| | TEST STEP | RESULT ▶ | ACTION TO TAKE |
|---|---|---|---|
| E1 | CHECK CONTINUITY OF LOW FUEL OUTPUT CIRCUIT | | |
| | **NOTE: It is normal for the fuel lamp to blink when traveling or starting the vehicle on steep road grades.**<br>• Turn the ignition switch to OFF.<br>• Jumper Circuit 215 Y/BK (fuel out) to Circuit 57 (ground). Insert jumper at fluid module connector.<br>• Turn ignition switch to RUN.<br>• Carefully shake wiring harness and observe fuel lamp for blinking.<br>• REMOVE jumper.<br>**NOTE: Place the jumper on the back side of the fluid module connector. The fluid module does NOT have to be disconnected.** | OK ▶<br>~~OK~~ ▶ | GO to E2.<br>SERVICE or REPLACE wiring harness and/or connectors. CHECK system operation. |
| E2 | CHECK CONTINUITY OF LOW FUEL INPUT CIRCUIT | | |
| | • Turn ignition switch to OFF.<br>• Disconnect the connector to the fuel sender.<br>• Connect one lead of ohmmeter to connector positive terminal Circuit 29 Y/W and connect other lead to fluid module connector 106 LB (fuel in).<br>• Carefully shake wiring harness.<br>• The meter reading should indicate a closed circuit. | OK ▶<br>~~OK~~ ▶ | GO to E3.<br>SERVICE or REPLACE wiring harness and/or connectors. CHECK system operation. |
| E3 | CHECK GROUND | | |
| | • Turn ignition switch to OFF.<br>• Disconnect connector at fuel sender.<br>• Connect one lead of ohmmeter to connector negative terminal Circuit 57 BK and connect other lead to vehicle body ground.<br>• Carefully shake wiring harness.<br>• The meter reading should indicate a closed circuit. | OK ▶<br>~~OK~~ ▶ | GO to E4.<br>SERVICE or REPLACE wiring harness and/or connectors. CHECK system operation. |



**Fig. 16 Multiple function indicator system diagnosis (Part 6 of 20). 1989 Mustang**

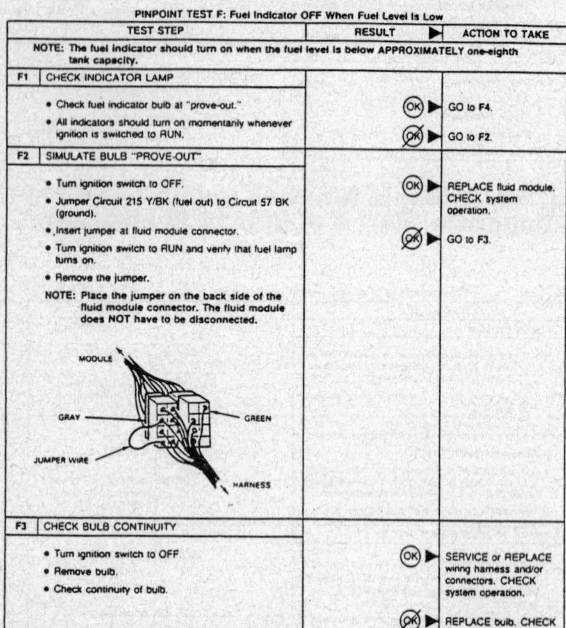

PINPOINT TEST F: Fuel Indicator OFF When Fuel Level Is Low

| | TEST STEP | RESULT ▶ | ACTION TO TAKE |
|---|---|---|---|
| | **NOTE: The fuel indicator should turn on when the fuel level is below APPROXIMATELY one-eighth tank capacity.** | | |
| F1 | CHECK INDICATOR LAMP | | |
| | • Check fuel indicator bulb at "prove-out."<br>• All indicators should turn on momentarily whenever ignition is switched to RUN. | OK ▶<br>~~OK~~ ▶ | GO to F4.<br>GO to F2. |
| F2 | SIMULATE BULB "PROVE-OUT" | | |
| | • Turn ignition switch to OFF.<br>• Jumper Circuit 215 Y/BK (fuel out) to Circuit 57 BK (ground).<br>• Insert jumper at fluid module connector.<br>• Turn ignition switch to RUN and verify that fuel lamp turns on.<br>• Remove the jumper.<br>**NOTE: Place the jumper on the back side of the fluid module connector. The fluid module does NOT have to be disconnected.** | OK ▶<br>~~OK~~ ▶ | REPLACE fluid module. CHECK system operation.<br>GO to F3. |
| F3 | CHECK BULB CONTINUITY | | |
| | • Turn ignition switch to OFF.<br>• Remove bulb.<br>• Check continuity of bulb. | OK ▶<br>~~OK~~ ▶ | SERVICE or REPLACE wiring harness and/or connectors. CHECK system operation.<br>REPLACE bulb. CHECK system operation. |



**Fig. 16 Multiple function indicator system diagnosis (Part 8 of 20). 1989 Mustang**

PINPOINT TEST E: Fuel Indicator Blinks Erratically — Continued

| | TEST STEP | RESULT ▶ | ACTION TO TAKE |
|---|---|---|---|
| E4 | CHECK "FUEL SLOSH" TIME DELAY | | |
| | • Turn ignition switch to OFF.<br>• Disconnect connector at fuel sender.<br>• Apply a 75 ohm resistance across connector in place of sender. (An instrument gauge system tester may be used).<br>• Turn ignition switch to RUN. Observe low fuel indicator. It should go OFF after bulb "prove-out" (1-3 seconds). | OK ▶<br>~~OK~~ ▶ | WAIT four minutes before proceeding to E5. LEAVE ignition in RUN.<br>ENSURE that jumper used in E1 has been removed. CHECK system operation. |
| E5 | CHECK "FUEL SLOSH" TIME DELAY (Continued) | | |
| | • With ignition switch in RUN, carefully replace 75 ohm resistor with a 10 ohm resistor. (An instrument gauge system tester may be used).<br>• The fuel lamp should turn on within 25 seconds, but no sooner than five seconds. | OK ▶<br>~~OK~~ ▶ | The fluid module is OK. CHECK fuel sender/gauge assembly.<br>REPLACE fluid module. CHECK system operation. |

**Fig. 16 Multiple function indicator system diagnosis (Part 7 of 20). 1989 Mustang**

PINPOINT TEST F: Fuel Indicator OFF When Fuel Level Is Low — Continued

| | TEST STEP | RESULT ▶ | ACTION TO TAKE |
|---|---|---|---|
| F4 | CHECK FUEL SENDER RESISTANCE | | |
| | • Turn ignition switch to OFF.<br>• Connect one lead of ohmmeter to Circuit 106 (Fuel in) and connect other lead to Circuit 57 BK (ground).<br>• Make both connections at fluid module connector.<br>• The meter should read 10 to 40 ohms.<br>**NOTE: Ignition must be off when taking measurement.** | OK ▶<br>~~OK~~ ▶ | REPLACE fluid module. CHECK system operation.<br>GO to F5. |
| F5 | CHECK INPUT CIRCUIT | | |
| | • Turn ignition switch to OFF.<br>• Disconnect connector at fuel sender.<br>• Connect one lead of ohmmeter to connector positive terminal Circuit 29 Y/W and connect other lead to Circuit 106 LB (Fuel in) at fluid module connector.<br>• The meter reading should indicate a closed circuit. | OK ▶<br>~~OK~~ ▶ | GO to F6.<br>SERVICE or REPLACE wiring harness and/or connectors. CHECK system operation. |
| F6 | CHECK GROUND | | |
| | • Turn ignition switch to OFF.<br>• Disconnect connector to fuel sender.<br>• Connect one lead of ohmmeter to connector negative terminal Circuit 57 BK and connect other lead to vehicle body ground.<br>• Carefully shake wiring harness.<br>• The meter reading should indicate a closed circuit. | OK ▶<br>~~OK~~ ▶ | CHECK fuel sender/gauge assembly.<br>SERVICE or REPLACE wiring harness and/or connectors. CHECK system operation. |

**Fig. 16 Multiple function indicator system diagnosis (Part 9 of 20). 1989 Mustang**

PINPOINT TEST G: Fuel Indicator ON When Fuel Level Is NOT Low

| | TEST STEP | RESULT ▶ | ACTION TO TAKE |
|---|---|---|---|
| G1 | CHECK FUEL SENDER RESISTANCE | | |
| | **NOTE: The fuel indicator should turn on when the fuel level is below APPROXIMATELY one-eighth tank capacity.**<br>• Turn ignition switch to OFF.<br>• Connect one lead of ohmmeter to Circuit 106 LB (fuel in) and connect other lead to Circuit 57 BK (ground).<br>• Make both connections at fluid module connector.<br>• The meter should read between 40-200 ohms.<br>**NOTE: Ignition must be off when taking measurement.** | OK ▶<br>~~OK~~ ▶ | GO to G2.<br>GO to G3. |
| G2 | CHECK FOR SHORT TO GROUND | | |
| | • Turn ignition switch to OFF.<br>• Connect one lead of ohmmeter to fuel lamp negative terminal 215 Y/BK and connect other lead to Circuit 57 BK (ground) at fluid module connector.<br>• The meter should indicate an open circuit. | OK ▶<br>~~OK~~ ▶ | REPLACE fluid module. CHECK system operation.<br>SERVICE or REPLACE wiring harness and/or connectors. CHECK system operation. |
| G3 | CHECK FOR SHORT TO GROUND (Continued) | | |
| | • Turn ignition switch to OFF.<br>• Disconnect connector from fuel sender.<br>• CONNECT one lead of ohmmeter to Circuit 106 LB (Fuel in) and connect other lead to Circuit 57 BK (Ground).<br>• Make both connections at fluid module connector.<br>• The meter should indicate an open circuit. | OK ▶<br>~~OK~~ ▶ | CHECK fuel sender/gauge assembly.<br>SERVICE or REPLACE wiring harness and/or connectors. CHECK system operation. |

**Fig. 16 Multiple function indicator system diagnosis (Part 10 of 20). 1989 Mustang**

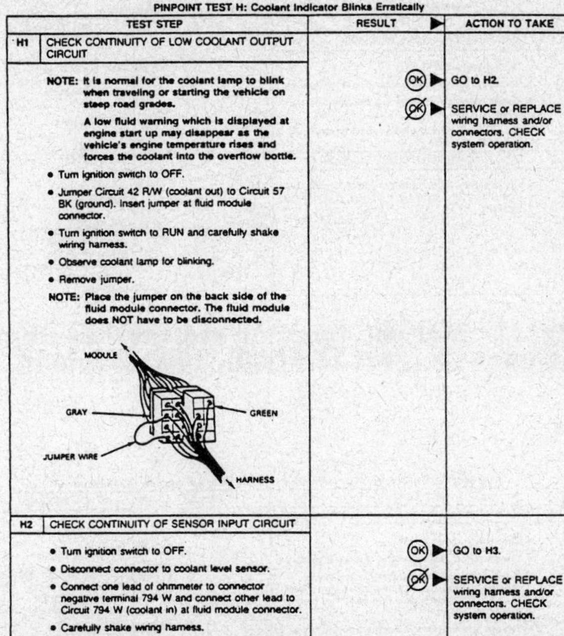

PINPOINT TEST H: Coolant Indicator Blinks Erratically

| TEST STEP | | RESULT | ACTION TO TAKE |
|---|---|---|---|
| H1 | CHECK CONTINUITY OF LOW COOLANT OUTPUT CIRCUIT | | |
| | **NOTE: It is normal for the coolant lamp to blink when traveling or starting the vehicle on steep road grades.** **A low fluid warning which is displayed at engine start up may disappear as the vehicle's engine temperature rises and forces the coolant into the overflow bottle.** • Turn ignition switch to OFF. • Jumper Circuit 42 R/W (coolant out) to Circuit 57 BK (ground). Insert jumper at fluid module connector. • Turn ignition switch to RUN and carefully shake wiring harness. • Observe coolant lamp for blinking. • Remove jumper. **NOTE: Place the jumper on the back side of the fluid module connector. The fluid module does NOT have to be disconnected.** MODULE / GRAY / GREEN / JUMPER WIRE / HARNESS | OK ▶ <br> Not OK ▶ | GO to H2. <br> SERVICE or REPLACE wiring harness and/or connectors. CHECK system operation. |
| H2 | CHECK CONTINUITY OF SENSOR INPUT CIRCUIT | | |
| | • Turn ignition switch to OFF. • Disconnect connector to coolant level sensor. • Connect one lead of ohmmeter to connector negative terminal 794 W and connect other lead to Circuit 794 W (coolant in) at fluid module connector. • Carefully shake wiring harness. • The meter reading should indicate a closed circuit. | OK ▶ <br> Not OK ▶ | GO to H3. <br> SERVICE or REPLACE wiring harness and/or connectors. CHECK system operation. |

**Fig. 16 Multiple function indicator system diagnosis (Part 11 of 20). 1989 Mustang**

PINPOINT TEST H: Coolant Indicator Blinks Erratically — Continued

| TEST STEP | | RESULT | ACTION TO TAKE |
|---|---|---|---|
| H3 | CHECK CONTINUITY OF POWER CIRCUIT | | |
| | • Turn ignition switch to OFF. • Disconnect connector to coolant level sensor. • Connect one lead of ohmmeter to connector positive terminal 640 R/Y and connect other lead to battery Circuit 640 R/Y. • Carefully shake wiring harness. • The meter reading should indicate a closed circuit. | OK ▶ <br> Not OK ▶ | GO to H4. <br> SERVICE or REPLACE wiring harness and/or connectors. CHECK system operation. |
| H4 | CHECK "COOLANT SLOSH" TIME DELAY | | |
| | • Turn ignition switch to OFF. • Disconnect connector to coolant level sensor. • Jumper connector terminals together and turn ignition to RUN. • The coolant lamp should remain on after bulb "prove-out." | OK ▶ <br> Not OK ▶ | WAIT two minutes before proceeding to H5. LEAVE ignition on. <br> CHECK system operation. |
| H5 | CHECK "COOLANT SLOSH" TIME DELAY (Continued) | | |
| | • With ignition in RUN, carefully remove jumper. • The coolant lamp should turn off in no sooner than 15 seconds. | OK ▶ <br> Not OK ▶ | System operates correctly. <br> ENSURE that jumper from H1 has been removed. If it has, REPLACE fluid module. CHECK system operation. |

**Fig. 16 Multiple function indicator system diagnosis (Part 12 of 20). 1989 Mustang**

PINPOINT TEST J: Coolant Indicator OFF When Coolant Level Is Low

| TEST STEP | | RESULT | ACTION TO TAKE |
|---|---|---|---|
| J1 | CHECK INDICATOR LAMP | | |
| | **NOTE: A low fluid warning which is displayed at engine start up may disappear as the vehicle's engine temperature rises and forces coolant into the overflow bottle.** • Check coolant indicator bulb at "prove-out." • All indicators should turn on momentarily whenever ignition is switched to RUN. | OK ▶ <br> Not OK ▶ | GO to J4. <br> GO to J2. |
| J2 | SIMULATE BULB PROVE-OUT | | |
| | • Turn ignition switch to OFF. • Jumper Circuit 42 R/W (coolant out) to Circuit 57 BK (ground). • Insert jumper at fluid module connector. • Turn ignition and VERIFY that fuel lamp turns on. • Remove jumper. **NOTE: Place the jumper on the back side of the fluid module connector. The fluid module does NOT have to be disconnected.** MODULE / GRAY / GREEN / JUMPER WIRE / HARNESS | OK ▶ <br> Not OK ▶ | REPLACE fluid module. CHECK system operation. <br> GO to J3. |
| J3 | CHECK BULB CONTINUITY | | |
| | • Turn ignition switch to OFF. • Remove bulb. • Check bulb continuity. | OK ▶ <br> Not OK ▶ | SERVICE or REPLACE wiring harness and/or connectors. CHECK system operation. <br> REPLACE bulb. CHECK system operation. |
| J4 | CHECK COOLANT LEVEL | | |
| | • Ensure that fluid level is below COLD FULL mark on coolant overflow bottle. | OK ▶ <br> Not OK ▶ | GO to J5. <br> DRAIN coolant. CHECK system operation. |

**Fig. 16 Multiple function indicator system diagnosis (Part 13 of 20). 1989 Mustang**

PINPOINT TEST J: Coolant Indicator OFF When Coolant Level Is Low — Continued

| TEST STEP | | RESULT | ACTION TO TAKE |
|---|---|---|---|
| J5 | CHECK INPUT VOLTAGE | | |
| | • With ignition in RUN, carefully connect one lead of a voltmeter to Circuit 794 W (coolant in) and other to Circuit 57 BK (ground). • Make both connections at fluid module connector. • The meter should read battery voltage. | OK ▶ <br> Not OK ▶ | REPLACE fluid module. CHECK system operation. <br> GO to J6. |
| J6 | CHECK CONTINUITY OF INPUT CIRCUIT | | |
| | • Turn ignition switch to OFF. • Disconnect connector from coolant level sensor. • Connect one lead of ohmmeter to sensor connector negative terminal 794 W and connect other lead to Circuit 794 W (coolant in) at fluid module connector. • The meter reading should indicate a closed circuit. | OK ▶ <br> Not OK ▶ | GO to J7. <br> SERVICE or REPLACE wiring harness and/or connectors. CHECK system operation. |
| J7 | CHECK CONTINUITY OF POWER CIRCUIT | | |
| | • Turn ignition switch to OFF. • Disconnect connector from coolant level sensor. • Connect one lead of ohmmeter to connector positive terminal 640 green and connect other lead to battery Circuit 640 green. • The meter reading should indicate a closed circuit. | OK ▶ <br> Not OK ▶ | GO to J8. <br> SERVICE or REPLACE wiring harness and/or connectors. CHECK system operation. |
| J8 | CHECK CONTINUITY OF SENSOR | | |
| | • Remove coolant level sensor switch unit from overflow bottle. • Using ohmmeter, check continuity across sensor terminals. A closed circuit should be detected only with float in lowest position. • Inspect float for free movement. • Clean unit if necessary. | OK ▶ <br> Not OK ▶ | INSTALL sensor switch unit. CHECK system operation. <br> REPLACE sensor switch unit. CHECK system operation. |

**Fig. 16 Multiple function indicator system diagnosis (Part 14 of 20). 1989 Mustang**

PINPOINT TEST K: Coolant Indicator ON When Coolant Is NOT Low

| TEST STEP | | RESULT | ACTION TO TAKE |
|---|---|---|---|
| K1 | CHECK VOLTAGE | | |
| | **NOTE: A low fluid warning which is displayed at engine start up may disappear as the vehicle's engine temperature rises and forces coolant into the overflow bottle.** • With ignition in RUN, carefully connect one lead of voltmeter to Circuit 794 W (coolant in) and connect other to Circuit 57 BK (ground). Make both connections at fluid module connector. • The meter should read zero voltage. | OK ▶ <br> Not OK ▶ | GO to K2. <br> GO to K3. |
| K2 | CHECK SHORT TO GROUND | | |
| | • Turn ignition switch to OFF • Connect one lead of ohmmeter to coolant lamp negative terminal 42 R/W and connect other lead to Circuit 57 BK (ground) at fluid module connector. • The meter should indicate and open circuit. | OK ▶ <br> Not OK ▶ | REPLACE fluid module. CHECK system operation. <br> SERVICE or REPLACE wiring harness and/or connectors. CHECK system operation. |
| K3 | CHECK COOLANT LEVEL | | |
| | • Ensure that fluid level is between COLD FULL and HOT FULL marks on coolant overflow bottle. | OK ▶ <br> Not OK ▶ | GO to K4. <br> ADD coolant. CHECK system operation. |
| K4 | CHECK SENSOR CONTINUITY | | |
| | • Remove coolant level sensor switch unit from overflow bottle. • Using an ohmmeter, check continuity across sensor terminals. A closed circuit should be detected only when float is in its lowest position. • Inspect float for free movement. • Clean unit if necessary. | OK ▶ <br> Not OK ▶ | INSTALL sensor switch unit. CHECK system operation. <br> REPLACE sensor switch unit. CHECK system operation. |

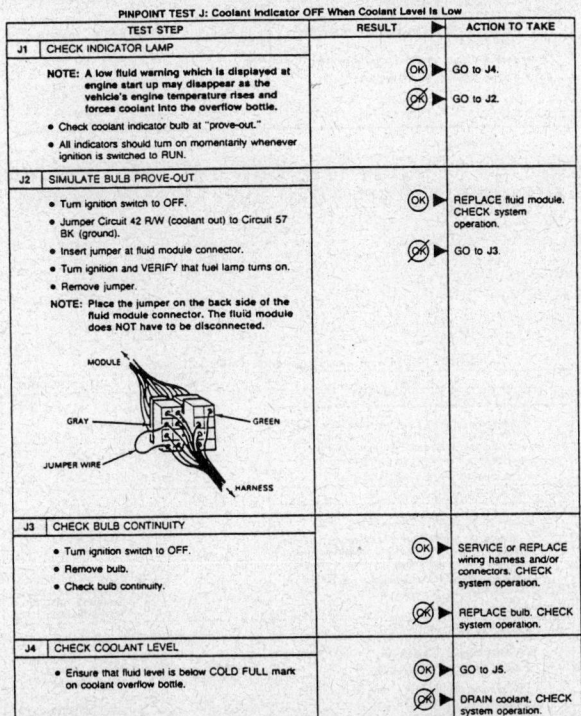

**Fig. 16 Multiple function indicator system diagnosis (Part 15 of 20). 1989 Mustang**

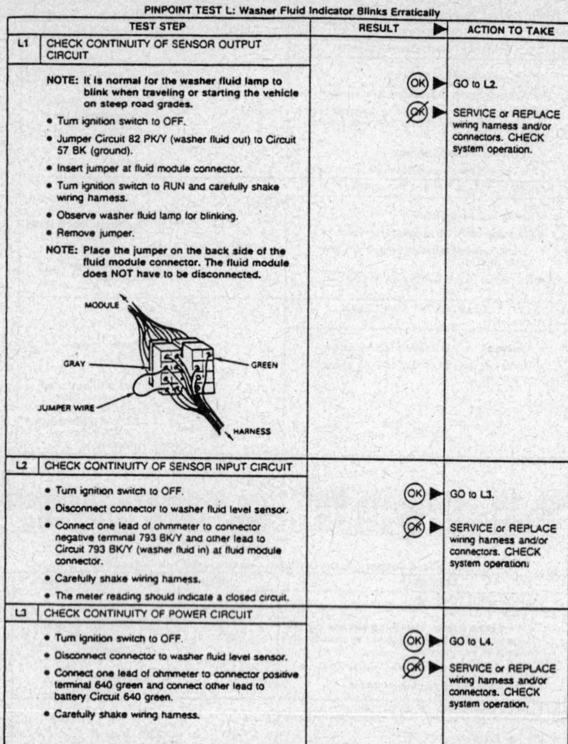

**PINPOINT TEST L: Washer Fluid Indicator Blinks Erratically**

| TEST STEP | | RESULT | ACTION TO TAKE |
|---|---|---|---|
| L1 | CHECK CONTINUITY OF SENSOR OUTPUT CIRCUIT | | |
| | **NOTE: It is normal for the washer fluid lamp to blink when traveling or starting the vehicle on steep road grades.**<br>• Turn ignition switch to OFF.<br>• Jumper Circuit 82 PK/Y (washer fluid out) to Circuit 57 BK (ground).<br>• Insert jumper at fluid module connector.<br>• Turn ignition switch to RUN and carefully shake wiring harness.<br>• Observe washer fluid lamp for blinking.<br>• Remove jumper.<br>**NOTE: Place the jumper on the back side of the fluid module connector. The fluid module does NOT have to be disconnected.** | OK ▶<br>~~OK~~ ▶ | GO to L2.<br>SERVICE or REPLACE wiring harness and/or connectors. CHECK system operation. |
| L2 | CHECK CONTINUITY OF SENSOR INPUT CIRCUIT | | |
| | • Turn ignition switch to OFF.<br>• Disconnect connector to washer fluid level sensor.<br>• Connect one lead of ohmmeter to connector negative terminal 793 BK/Y and other lead to Circuit 793 BK/Y (washer fluid in) at fluid module connector.<br>• Carefully shake wiring harness.<br>• The meter reading should indicate a closed circuit. | OK ▶<br>~~OK~~ ▶ | GO to L3.<br>SERVICE or REPLACE wiring harness and/or connectors. CHECK system operation. |
| L3 | CHECK CONTINUITY OF POWER CIRCUIT | | |
| | • Turn ignition switch to OFF.<br>• Disconnect connector to washer fluid level sensor.<br>• Connect one lead of ohmmeter to connector positive terminal 640 green and connect other lead to battery Circuit 640 green.<br>• Carefully shake wiring harness. | OK ▶<br>~~OK~~ ▶ | GO to L4.<br>SERVICE or REPLACE wiring harness and/or connectors. CHECK system operation. |



**Fig. 16 Multiple function indicator system diagnosis (Part 16 of 20). 1989 Mustang**

**PINPOINT TEST M: Washer Fluid Indicator OFF When Fluid Level Is Low**

| TEST STEP | | RESULT | ACTION TO TAKE |
|---|---|---|---|
| M1 | CHECK INDICATOR LAMP | | |
| | • Check washer fluid indicator bulb at "prove-out."<br>• All indicators should momentarily turn on when ignition is switched to RUN. | OK ▶<br>~~OK~~ ▶ | GO to M4.<br>GO to M2. |
| M2 | SIMULATE BULB PROVE-OUT | | |
| | • Turn ignition switch to OFF.<br>• Jumper Circuit 82 PK/Y (washer fluid out) to Circuit 57 BK (ground).<br>• Insert jumper at fluid module connector.<br>• Turn ignition switch to RUN and verify that washer fluid lamp turns on.<br>• Remove jumper.<br>**NOTE: Place the jumper on the back side of the fluid module connector. The fluid module does NOT have to be disconnected.** | OK ▶<br>~~OK~~ ▶ | REPLACE fluid module. CHECK system operation.<br>GO to M3. |
| M3 | CHECK BULB CONTINUITY | | |
| | • Turn ignition switch to OFF.<br>• Remove bulb.<br>• Check bulb continuity. | OK ▶<br>~~OK~~ ▶ | SERVICE or REPLACE wiring harness and/or connectors. CHECK system operation.<br>REPLACE bulb. CHECK system operation. |
| M4 | CHECK INPUT VOLTAGE | | |
| | • With ignition on, carefully connect one lead of voltmeter to Circuit 793 BK/Y (washer fluid in) and other to Circuit 57 BK (ground).<br>• Make both connections at fluid module connector.<br>• The meter should read battery voltage. | OK ▶<br>~~OK~~ ▶ | REPLACE fluid module. CHECK system operation.<br>GO to M5. |

MODULE — GRAY — GREEN — JUMPER WIRE — HARNESS

**Fig. 16 Multiple function indicator system diagnosis (Part 18 of 20). 1989 Mustang**

**PINPOINT TEST L: Washer Fluid Indicator Blinks Erratically — Continued**

| TEST STEP | | RESULT | ACTION TO TAKE |
|---|---|---|---|
| L4 | CHECK "WASHER FLUID SLOSH" TIME DELAY | | |
| | • Turn ignition switch to OFF.<br>• Disconnect connector to washer fluid level reservoir.<br>• Jumper connector terminals together and turn ignition to RUN.<br>• The washer fluid lamp should remain on after bulb "prove-out." | OK ▶<br>~~OK~~ ▶ | WAIT two minutes before proceeding to L5. LEAVE ignition on.<br>CHECK system operation. |
| L5 | CHECK "WASHER FLUID SLOSH" TIME DELAY | | |
| | • With ignition in RUN, carefully remove jumper. The washer fluid lamp should turn off no sooner than 15 seconds. | OK ▶<br>~~OK~~ ▶ | System operates correctly.<br>ENSURE that jumper from L1 has been removed. If it has, REPLACE fluid module. CHECK system operation. |

**Fig. 16 Multiple function indicator system diagnosis (Part 17 of 20). 1989 Mustang**

**PINPOINT TEST M: Washer Fluid Indicator OFF When Fluid Level Is Low — Continued**

| TEST STEP | | RESULT | ACTION TO TAKE |
|---|---|---|---|
| M5 | CHECK CONTINUITY OF SENSOR INPUT CIRCUIT | | |
| | • Turn ignition switch to OFF.<br>• Disconnect connector to washer fluid level sensor.<br>• Connect one lead of ohmmeter to connector negative terminal 793 Y/BK and connect other lead to Circuit 793 Y/BK (washer fluid in) at fluid module connector.<br>• The meter reading should indicate a closed circuit. | OK ▶<br>~~OK~~ ▶ | GO to M6.<br>SERVICE or REPLACE wiring harness and/or connectors. CHECK system operation. |
| M6 | CHECK CONTINUITY OF SENSOR POWER CIRCUIT | | |
| | • Turn ignition switch to OFF.<br>• Disconnect connector to washer fluid level sensor.<br>• Connect one lead of ohmmeter to connector positive terminal 941 BK/W and connect other lead to battery Circuit 640 Green.<br>• The meter should indicate a closed circuit. | OK ▶<br>~~OK~~ ▶ | GO to M7.<br>SERVICE or REPLACE wiring harness and/or connectors. CHECK system operation. |
| M7 | CHECK SENSOR CONTINUITY | | |
| | • Remove washer fluid reservoir. Ensure that fluid is below sensor.<br>• Measure contact resistance using ohmmeter.<br>• A closed circuit should be detected. | OK ▶<br>~~OK~~ ▶ | INSTALL washer fluid reservoir. CHECK system operation.<br>SERVICE or REPLACE washer fluid reservoir. CHECK system operation. |

**Fig. 16 Multiple function indicator system diagnosis (Part 19 of 20). 1989 Mustang**

**PINPOINT TEST N: Washer Fluid Indicator ON When Washer Fluid Is NOT Low**

| TEST STEP | | RESULT | ACTION TO TAKE |
|---|---|---|---|
| N1 | CHECK SENSOR INPUT VOLTAGE | | |
| | • With ignition in RUN, carefully connect one lead of voltmeter to Circuit 793 BK/Y (washer fluid in) and connect other to Circuit 57 BK (ground). Make both connections at fluid module connector.<br>• The meter should read zero voltage. | OK ▶<br>~~OK~~ ▶ | GO to N2.<br>GO to N3. |
| N2 | CHECK FOR SHORT TO GROUND | | |
| | • Turn ignition switch to OFF.<br>• Connect one lead of ohmmeter to washer fluid lamp negative terminal 793 BK/Y and connect other lead to Circuit 57 BK (ground) at fluid module connector.<br>• The meter should indicate an open circuit. | OK ▶<br>~~OK~~ ▶ | REPLACE fluid module. CHECK system operation.<br>SERVICE or REPLACE wiring harness and/or connectors. CHECK system operation. |
| N3 | CHECK SENSOR CONTINUITY | | |
| | • Remove washer fluid reservoir.<br>• Ensure that fluid is above sensor.<br>• Measure contact resistance using an ohmmeter.<br>• An open circuit should be detected. | OK ▶<br>~~OK~~ ▶ | INSTALL washer fluid reservoir. CHECK system operation.<br>SERVICE or REPLACE washer fluid reservoir. CHECK system operation. |

**Fig. 16 Multiple function indicator system diagnosis (Part 20 of 20). 1989 Mustang**

# STARTER MOTORS

## TABLE OF CONTENTS



# General Information

## INDEX



## STARTER TROUBLE CHECK-OUT

When trouble develops in the starting motor circuit, and the starter cranks the engine slowly or not at all, several preliminary checks can be made to determine whether the trouble lies in the battery, in the starter, in the wiring between them, or elsewhere. Many conditions besides defects in the starter itself can result in poor cranking performance.

To make a quick check of the starter system, turn on the headlights. They should burn with normal brilliance. If they do not, the battery may be run down.

If the battery is in a charged condition so that lights burn brightly, operate the starting motor. Any one of three things will happen to the lights: (1) They will go out, (2) dim considerably or (3) stay bright without any cranking action taking place.

### IF LIGHTS GO OUT

If the lights go out as the starter switch is closed, it indicates that there is a poor connection between the battery and starting motor. This poor connection will most often be found at the battery terminals. Correction is made by removing the cable clamps from the terminals, cleaning the terminals and clamps, replacing the clamps and tightening them securely. A coating of corrosion inhibitor (petroleum jelly will do) may be applied to the clamps and terminals to retard the formation of corrosion.

### IF LIGHTS DIM

If the lights dim considerably as the starter switch is closed and the starter operates slowly or not at all, the battery may be run down, or there may be some mechanical condition in the engine or starting motor that is throwing a heavy burden on the starting motor. This imposes a high discharge rate on the battery which causes noticeable dimming of the lights.

Check the battery state of charge. If it is charged, the trouble probably lies in either the engine or starting motor itself. In the engine, tight bearings or pistons or heavy oil place an added burden on the starting motor. Low temperatures also hamper starting motor performance since it thickens engine oil and makes the engine considerably harder to crank and start. Also, a battery is less efficient at low temperatures.

In the starting motor, a bent armature, loose pole shoe screws or worn bearings, any of which may allow the armature to drag, will reduce cranking performance and increase current draw.

In addition, more serious internal damage is sometimes found. Thrown armature windings or commutator bars, which sometimes occur on over-running clutch drive starting motors, are usually caused by excessive overrunning after starting. This is the result of such conditions as the driver keeping the starting switch closed too long after the engine has started, the driver opening the throttle too wide in starting, or improper carburetor fast idle adjustment. Any of these subject the over-running clutch to extra strain so it tends to seize, spinning the armature at high speed with resulting armature damage.

Another cause may be engine backfire during cranking which may result, among other things, from ignition timing being too far advanced.

To avoid such failures, the driver should pause a few seconds after a false start to make sure the engine has come completely to rest before another start is attempted. In addition, the ignition timing should be checked if engine backfiring has caused the trouble.

### LIGHTS STAY BRIGHT, NO CRANKING ACTION

This condition indicates an open circuit at some point, either in the starter itself, the starter switch or control circuit. The solenoid control circuit can be eliminated momentarily by placing a heavy jumper lead across the solenoid main terminals to see if the starter will operate. This connects the starter directly to the battery and, if it operates, it indicates that the control circuit is not functioning normally. The wiring and control units must be checked to locate the trouble.

If the starter does not operate with the jumper attached, it will probably have to be removed from the engine so it can be examined in detail.

### CHECKING CIRCUIT WITH VOLTMETER

Excessive resistance in the circuit between the battery and starter will reduce cranking performance. The resistance can be checked by using a voltmeter to measure voltage drop in the circuits while the starter is operated. There are three checks to be made:

1. Voltage drop between car frame and grounded battery terminal post (not cable clamp).
2. Voltage drop between car frame and starting motor field frame.
3. Voltage drop between insulated battery terminal post and starting motor terminal stud (or the battery terminal stud of the solenoid).

Each of these should show no more than one-tenth (0.1) volt drop when the starting motor is cranking the engine. Do not use the starter for more than 30 seconds at a time to avoid overheating it.

If excessive voltage drop is found in any of these circuits, make correction by disconnecting the cables, cleaning the connections carefully, and then reconnecting the cables firmly in place. A coating of petroleum jelly on the battery cables and terminal clamps will retard corrosion.

**On some cars,** extra long battery cables may be required due to the location of the battery and starter. This may result in somewhat higher voltage drop than the above recommended 0.1 volt. The only means of determining the normal voltage drop in such cases is to check several of these vehicles. Then when the voltage drop is well above the normal figure for all cars checked, abnormal resistance will be indicated and correction can be made as already explained.

## SOLENOID SWITCHES

The solenoid switch on a cranking motor not only closes the circuit between the battery and the cranking motor but also shifts the drive pinion into mesh with the engine flywheel ring gear. This is done by means of a linkage between the solenoid switch plunger and the shift lever on the cranking motor.

There are two windings in the solenoid; a pull-in winding and a hold-in winding. Both windings are energized when the external control switch is closed. They produce a magnetic field which pulls the plunger in so that the drive pinion is shifted into mesh, and the main contacts in the solenoid switch are closed to connect the battery directly to the cranking motor. Closing the main switch contacts shorts out the pull-in winding since this winding is connected across the main contacts. The magnetism produced by the hold-in winding is sufficient to hold the plunger in, and shorting out the pull-in winding reduces drain on the battery. When the control switch is opened, it disconnects the hold-in winding from the battery. When the hold-in winding is disconnected from the battery, the shift lever spring withdraws the plunger from the solenoid, opening the solenoid switch contacts and at the same time withdrawing the drive pinion from mesh. Proper operation of the switch depends on maintaining a definite balance between the magnetic strength of the pull-in and hold-in windings.

This balance is established in the design by the size of the wire and the number of turns specified. An open circuit in the hold-in winding or attempts to crank with a discharged battery will cause the switch to chatter.

## STARTING MOTOR SERVICE

To obtain full performance data on a starting motor or to determine the cause of abnormal operation, the starting motor should be submitted to a no-load and torque test. These tests are best performed on a starter bench tester with the starter mounted on it.

From a practical standpoint, however, a simple torque test may be made quickly with the starter in the car. Make sure the battery is fully charged and that the starter circuit wires and terminals are in good condition. Then operate the starter to see if the engine turns over normally. If it does not, the torque developed is below standard and the starter should be removed for further checking.

## STARTER DRIVE TROUBLE

Starter drive troubles are easy to diagnose and they usually cannot be confused with ordinary starter difficulties. If the starter does not turn over at all or if it drags, look for trouble in the starter or electrical supply system. Concentrate on the starter drive or ring gear if the starter is noisy, if it turns but does not engage the engine, or if the starter won't disengage after the engine is started. After the starter is removed, the trouble can usually be located quickly.

Worn or chipped ring gear or starter pinion are the usual causes of noisy operation. Before replacing either or both of these parts try to find out what caused the damage. With the Bendix type drive, incomplete engagement of the pinion with the ring gear is a common cause of tooth damage. The wrong pinion clearance on starter drives of the over-running clutch type leads to poor meshing of the pinion and ring gear and too rapid tooth wear.

A less common cause of noise with either type of drive is a bent starter armature shaft. When this shaft is bent, the pinion gear alternately binds and then only partly meshes with the ring gear. Most manufacturers specify a maximum of .003 inch radial runout on the armature shaft.

## WHEN CLUTCH DRIVE FAILS

The over-running clutch type drive seldom becomes so worn that it fails to engage since it is directly activated by a fork and lever. The only thing that is likely to happen is that, once engaged, it will not turn the engine because the clutch itself is worn out. A much more frequent difficulty and one that rapidly wears ring gear and teeth is partial engagement. Proper meshing of the pinion is controlled by the end clearance between the pinion gear and the starter housing or pinion stop, if used.

**On some starters,** the solenoids are completely enclosed in the starter housing and the pinion clearance is not adjustable. If the clearance is not correct, the starter must be disassembled and checked for excessive wear of solenoid linkage, shift lever mechanism, or improper assembly of parts.

Failure of the over-running clutch drive to disengage is usually caused by binding between the armature shaft and the drive. If the drive, particularly the clutch, shows signs of overheating it indicates that it is not disengaging immediately after the engine starts. If the clutch is forced to over-run too long, it overheats and turns a bluish color. For the cause of the binding, look for rust or gum between the armature shaft and the drive, or for burred splines. Excess oil on the drive will lead to gumming, and inadequate air circulation in the flywheel housing will cause rust.

Over-running clutch drives cannot be overhauled in the field so they must be replaced. In cleaning, never soak them in a solvent because the solvent may enter the clutch and dissolve the sealed-in lubricant. Wipe them off lightly with kerosene and lubricate them sparingly with Lubriplate 777 or equivalent.

## WHEN BENDIX DRIVE FAILS

When a Bendix type drive doesn't engage the cause usually is one of three things: either the drive spring is broken, one of the drive spring bolts has sheared off, or the screw shaft threads won't allow the pinion to travel toward the flywheel. In the first two cases, remove the drive by unscrewing the set screw under the last coil of the drive spring and replace the broken parts. Gummed or rusty screw shaft threads are fairly common causes of Bendix drive failure and are easily cleaned with a little kerosene or steel wool, depending on the trouble. Here again, as in the case of over-running clutch drives, use light oil sparingly, and be sure the flywheel housing has adequate ventilation. There is usually a breather hole in the bottom of the flywheel housing which should be open.

The failure of a Bendix drive to disengage or to mesh properly is most often caused by gummed or rusty screw shaft threads. When this is not true, look for mechanical failure within the drive itself.

# Bosch Starter Motors

## INDEX



**STARTER FAILS TO OPERATE**
- WEAK BATTERY – DEAD BATTERY CELL – LOOSE OR CORRODED CABLE TERMINALS
- IGNITION SWITCH FAULTY OR MISADJUSTED
- OPEN CIRCUIT BETWEEN IGNITION STARTER SWITCH AND #4 TERMINAL ON STARTER RELAY
- STARTER RELAY DEFECTIVE
- FAULTY STARTER*

**RELAY OPERATES BUT SOLENOID DOES NOT**
- LEAD OR CONNECTIONS BROKEN INSIDE SOLENOID COVER OR OPEN HOLD-IN WIRE
- FAULTY WIRING

**STARTER FAILS TO OPERATE AND LIGHTS DIM**
- WEAK BATTERY OR DEAD BATTERY CELL
- LOOSE OR CORRODED BATTERY CABLE TERMINALS
- INTERNAL GROUND IN WINDINGS
- GROUNDED STARTER FIELDS
- ARMATURE RUBBING ON POLE SHOES

**STARTER TURNS BUT ENGINE DOES NOT ROTATE**
- STARTER CLUTCH SLIPPING
- BROKEN CLUTCH HOUSING
- PINION SHAFT RUSTED, DIRTY OR DRY DUE TO LACK OF LUBRICATION
- STARTER ARMATURE SHAFT SHEARED
- BROKEN TEETH ON ENGINE RING GEAR

**STARTER RELAY DOES NOT CLOSE**
- BATTERY DISCHARGED
- FAULTY WIRING
- NEUTRAL SAFETY SWITCH ON AUTOMATIC TRANSMISSION FAULTY
- STARTER RELAY FAULTY

**STARTER OPERATES BUT WILL NOT DISENGAGE WHEN IGNITION STARTER SWITCH IS RELEASED**
- IGNITION SWITCH LINKAGE HANGING UP
- FAULTY IGNITION STARTER SWITCH
- SOLENOID CONTACT SWITCH PLUNGER STUCK IN SOLENOID
- NO CLEARANCE BETWEEN WINDING LEADS TO SOLENOID TERMINAL AND MAIN CONTACT IN SOLENOID
- FAULTY RELAY

**WARNING: BEFORE TESTING STARTER, PLACE AUTOMATIC TRANSMISSION IN PARK OR NEUTRAL. ON MANUAL TRANSMISSION BE ABSOLUTELY CERTAIN TO PLACE TRANSMISSION IN NEUTRAL AS THERE IS NO SAFETY LOCKOUT SWITCH ON THIS VEHICLE. SET BRAKES AND DISCONNECT WIRING CONNECTOR FROM ELECTRONIC IGNITION CONTROL UNIT. OR SPARK CONTROL COMPUTER**

**SOLENOID PLUNGER VIBRATES BACK AND FORTH WHEN SWITCH IS ENGAGED.**
- BATTERY LOW
- LEAD OR CONNECTIONS BROKEN INSIDE SWITCH COVER OR OPEN HOLD-IN WIRE
- FAULTY WIRING

**Fig. 1 Starter motor diagnosis**

## DESCRIPTION

Bosch starters have two types, direct drive and gear reduction. Direct drive starters incorporate an overrunning clutch type starter drive. A solenoid switch is mounted on the starter motor.

The other Bosch starter is a gear reduction starter. This starter uses six permanent magnets in place of conventional wound field magnets to save weight, eliminate field winding to case shorts, and improve cold start performance. The gear reduction system uses a planetary gear train to transmit armature rotation to the pinion shaft. A solenoid switch is mounted on the starter motor drive end shield.

## DIAGNOSIS

Refer to **Fig. 1** for starter diagnosis.

## IN-VEHICLE TESTING

**Before starting any tests, ensure that battery is fully charged and that all connections are good.**

## AMPERAGE DRAW TEST

1. Run engine until it reaches operating temperature, then turn engine off.
2. Connect a suitable battery-starter tester according to manufacturer's instructions.
3. Turn battery-starter tester control knob to "Off" position.
4. Turn voltmeter selector knob to "16 Volt" position.
5. Turn battery-starter function selector to "Starter System Test" (0-500 amp scale).
6. Connect red positive ammeter lead to positive battery terminal and the black negative ammeter lead to negative battery terminal.
7. Connect red positive voltmeter lead to positive battery terminal and the black negative voltmeter lead to the negative battery terminal.
8. Connect a remote starter jumper according to manufacturer's instructions. **Do not crank engine excessively during testing.**
9. Disconnect coil wire from distributor cap center tower and secure to good ground.
10. Crank engine with remote starter switch and observe exact voltmeter reading, then stop cranking engine.
11. Turn tester control knob clockwise until voltmeter reads exactly the same as when engine was being cranked. On direct drive starters, ammeter should read 120-160 amps. On reduction gear starters, ammeter should read 150-210 amps.

## STARTER RESISTANCE TEST

1. Disconnect positive battery cable and connect 0-300 scale ammeter between disconnected lead and battery terminal post.
2. Connect a voltmeter, graduated in tenths, between positive post on battery and starter relay terminal on starter solenoid.
3. Crank engine while observing reading on voltmeter and ammeter. A voltage reading exceeding .3 volts indicates

high resistance caused by loose circuit connections, a faulty cable, burned starter relay or solenoid switch contacts. A high current combined with slow cranking speed indicates need for starter repair.
4. Reconnect positive battery lead to battery.

### INSULATED CIRCUIT TEST

1. Turn voltmeter selector knob to 4 volt position.
2. Disconnect ignition coil secondary cable.
3. Connect voltmeter positive lead to battery positive post and voltmeter negative lead to solenoid connector that connects to starter field coils. **It may be necessary to peel back rubber boot on solenoid to reach solenoid connection.**
4. Connect remote control starter switch to battery solenoid terminal of starter relay.
5. Crank engine with remote control starter switch while observing voltmeter reading. If voltmeter reading exceeds .3 volt, there is high resistance in starter insulated coil, proceed as follows:
   a. Remove voltmeter lead from solenoid connector and connect to following points, repeating test at each connection. Starter terminal of solenoid, battery terminal of solenoid, battery cable terminal at solenoid, starter relay and cable clamp at battery.
   b. A small change will occur each time a normal portion of the circuit is removed from test. A definite change in voltmeter reading indicates that last part eliminated in test is at fault.

### STARTER GROUND TEST

1. Connect voltmeter positive lead to starter through bolt and negative voltmeter lead to battery negative post.
2. Crank engine with remote control starter switch and observe voltmeter reading.
3. If voltmeter reading exceeds .2 volt, make following tests to isolate points of excessive voltage loss, repeating test at each connection; starter drive housing, cable terminal at engine, cable clamp at battery.
4. A small change will occur each time a normal portion of circuit is removed from test. A definite change in voltmeter reading indicates last part eliminated in test is at fault.

### STARTER SOLENOID TEST

1. Connect heavy jumper wire on starter relay between battery and solenoid terminals. If engine cranks, perform starter relay test.
2. If engine does not crank or solenoid chatters, check wiring and connectors from relay to starter for loose or corroded connections.
3. Repeat test, if engine still does not crank properly, repair or replace starter as necessary.

### STARTER SOLENOID BENCH TEST

1. Disconnect field coil wire from field coil terminal.
2. Check for continuity between solenoid terminal and field coil terminal. There should be continuity.
3. Check for continuity between solenoid terminal and solenoid housing. There should be continuity.
4. If there is no continuity in either test, replace solenoid assembly.
5. Connect field coil wire to field coil terminal.

### STARTER RELAY TEST

1. Place transmission in Neutral and apply parking brake.
2. Check for battery voltage between starter relay battery terminal and ground.
3. Connect jumper wire on starter relay between battery and ignition terminals.
4. If engine does not crank, connect a second jumper wire to starter relay between ground terminal and good ground and repeat test.
5. If engine cranks in step 4, transmission linkage is improperly adjusted or neutral safety switch is defective.
6. If engine does not crank in step 4, starter relay is defective.

## STARTER MOTOR SPECIFICATIONS
### MERKUR

| Engine | Current Draw Under Normal Load | Current Draw Under No Load | Normal Engine Cranking Speed RPM | New Brush Length Inches | Brush Wear Limit Inches | Brush Spring Tension Oz. | Starter Relay Pull In Winding Resistance | Maximum Voltage Drop | Maximum Commutator Runout Inches |
|---|---|---|---|---|---|---|---|---|---|
| 4-140 | 150–250 | 80 | 180–250 | .45 | .25 | 80 | 3–5 | .5 | .005 |
| V6-177 | 200–300 | 75 | 160–200 | .45 | .32 | — | — | .5 | .005 |

# Ford Motorcraft Starters

## INDEX



## FORD MOTORCRAFT STARTER w/INTEGRAL POSITIVE ENGAGEMENT DRIVE

### DESCRIPTION

This type starting motor, **Fig. 1,** is a four pole, series parallel unit with a positive engagement drive built into the starter. The drive mechanism is engaged with the flywheel by lever action before the motor is energized.

When the ignition switch is turned on to the start position, the starter relay is energized and supplies current to the motor. The current flows through one field coil and a set of contact points to ground. The magnetic field given off by the field coil pulls the moveable pole, which is part of the lever, downward to its seat. When the pole is pulled down, the lever moves the drive assembly into the engine flywheel, **Fig. 2.**

When the moveable pole is seated, it functions as a normal field pole and opens

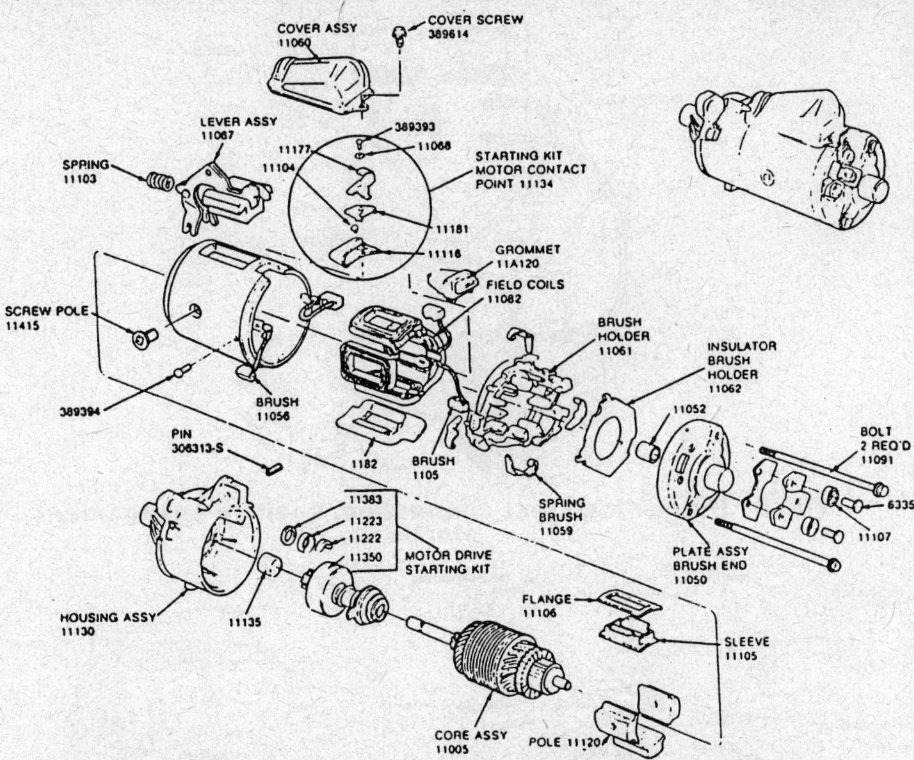


**Fig. 1 Ford Motorcraft positive engagement starting motor**

| CONDITION | POSSIBLE CAUSE | RESOLUTION |
|---|---|---|
| Engine will not crank — starter spins. | 1. Starter motor.<br>2. Flywheel ring gear. | 1. Remove starter, inspect for broken or worn starter drive components. Repair or replace as required.<br>2. Inspect ring gear teeth. Replace flywheel and ring gear if necessary. |
| Engine will not crank. | 1. Loose or corroded battery cables.<br>2. Undercharged battery.<br>3. Burned fusible link in main wire feed to ignition switch.<br>4. Starter relay.<br>5. Loose or broken cables.<br>6. Loose or open wiring through neutral switch to relay.<br>7. Starter motor. | 1. Clean and tighten cable connections.<br>2. Check battery. Charge or replace.<br>3. Check fusible link — correct wiring problem.<br>4. Replace starter relay.<br>5. Tighten or replace cable.<br>6. Repair, adjust or replace as required.<br>7. Repair or replace as required. |
| Engine cranks slowly. | 1. Loose connections or corroded battery cables.<br>2. Undercharged battery.<br>3. Starter motor. | 1. Clean and tighten cable connections.<br>2. Check battery. Charge or replace.<br>3. Repair or replace as required. |

**Fig. 3 Diagnosis chart**

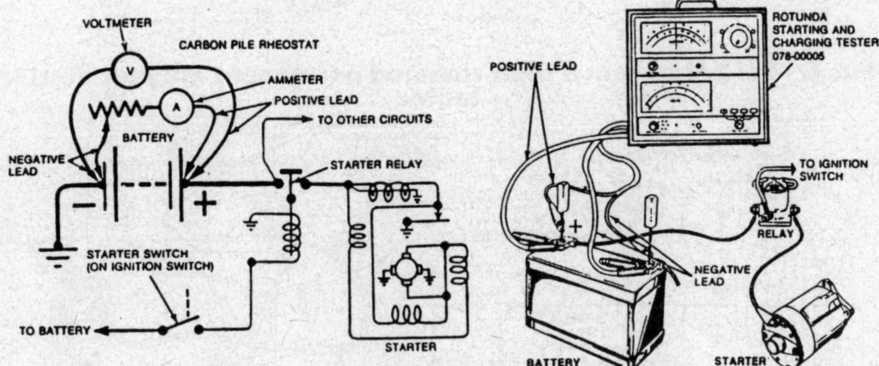


**Fig. 4 Starter cranking circuit test connections**

the contact points. With the points open, current flows through the starter field coils, energizing the starter. At the same time, current also flows through a holding coil to hold the movable pole in its seated position.

When the ignition switch is released from the start position, the starter relay opens the circuit to the starting motor. This allows the return spring to force the lever

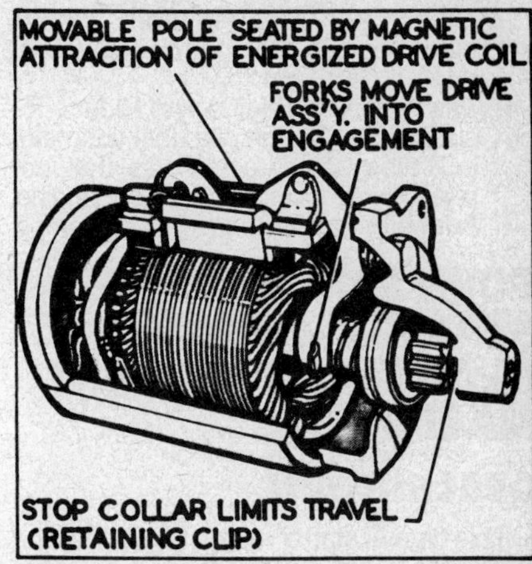


**Fig. 2 Starter drive engaged**

back, disengaging the drive from the flywheel and returning the movable pole to its normal position.

## DIAGNOSIS

When diagnosing this starter motor, refer to **Fig. 3.**

## IN-VEHICLE TESTING

Disconnect vacuum line to Thermactor bypass valve before performing any cranking tests. After tests, run engine 3 minutes before connecting vacuum line.

### Starter Cranking Circuit Test

1. Make test connections as shown in **Fig. 4.**
2. Disconnect ignition coil and crank engine.
3. Connect remote control starter switch from battery terminal of starter relay to S terminal of relay.
4. Maximum allowable voltage drop should be as follows:
   a. .5 volt with voltmeter negative lead connected to starter terminal and positive lead connected to battery positive terminal.
   b. .1 volt with voltmeter negative lead connected to starter relay (battery side) and positive lead connected to positive terminal of battery.
   c. .3 volt with voltmeter negative lead connected to starter relay (starter side) and positive lead connected to positive terminal of battery.
   d. .3 volt with voltmeter negative lead connected to negative terminal of battery and positive lead connected to engine ground.

### Starter Load Test

1. Connect test equipment as shown in **Fig. 5.**
2. Ensure that no current is flowing through ammeter and heavy duty carbon pile rheostat portion of circuit.
3. Crank engine with ignition off and determine exact reading on voltmeter. This test is accomplished by disconnecting push-on connector S at starter relay and by connecting a remote

control starter switch from positive battery terminal to S terminal of starter relay.

4. Stop cranking engine and reduce resistance of carbon pile until voltmeter indicates same reading as that obtained while starter cranked engine. Ammeter should read 150-250 amps.

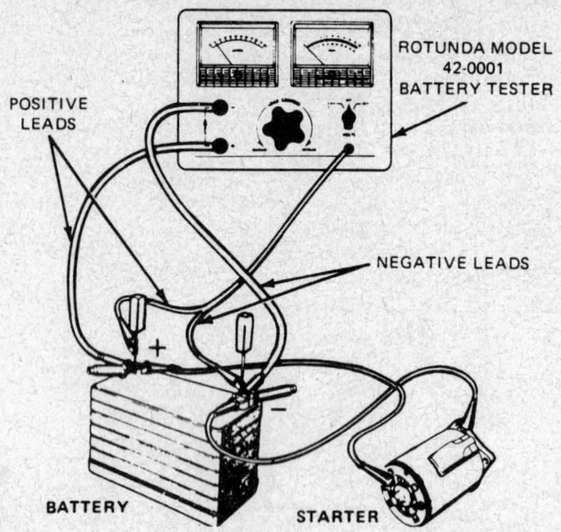


**Fig. 5 Starter load test connection. Positive engagement starter**

# FORD MOTORCRAFT STARTER W/GEAR REDUCED PERMANENT MAGNET

## DESCRIPTION

This type of starter motor, **Fig. 6,** has the starter solenoid mounted on the starter housing. The starter relay connects battery power to the starter solenoid, causing it to energize. On models equipped with manual transmission, a clutch switch in the starter control circuit prevents operation unless the clutch pedal is depressed. On models equipped with automatic transmission, a neutral safety switch in the starter control circuit prevents operation of the starter unless the selector lever is in the "Neutral" or "Park" position.

When the starter solenoid is energized, a magnetic field is created in the solenoid windings. The plunger core is drawn to the solenoid coil and a lever connected to the drive assembly engages the drive pinion gear into the flywheel ring gear. When the plunger is all the way in, its contact disk closes the circuit between the battery and the motor feed terminals. This sends current to the motor and the drive pinion gear cranks the flywheel to start the engine. When the current flows to the engine, the solenoid pull-in coil is bypassed and the hold-in coil keeps the drive pinion gear engaged with the flywheel until the ignition switch is released from the "On" position.

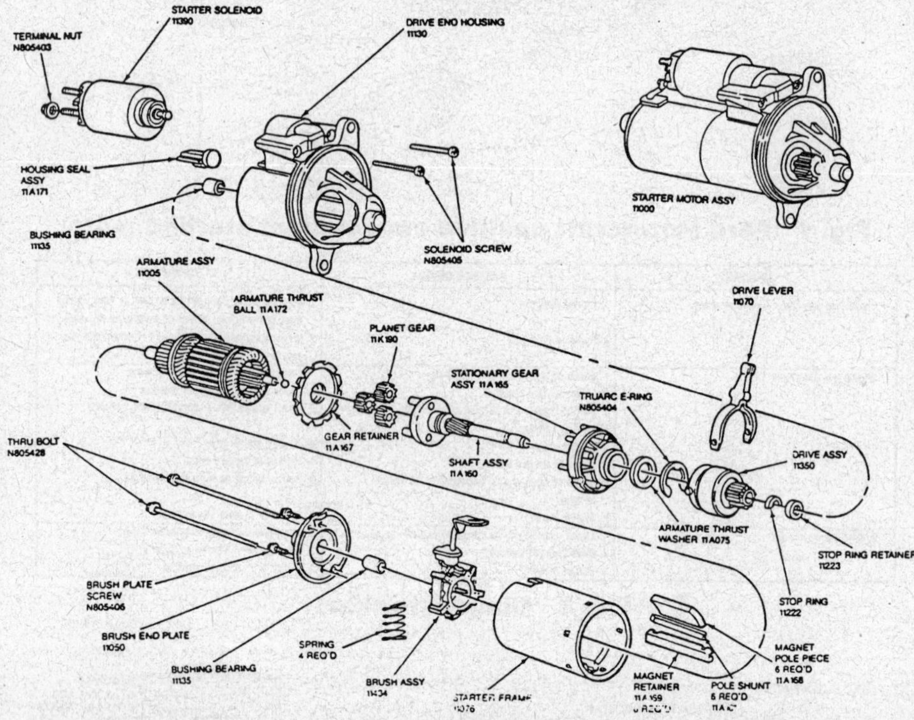


**Fig. 6 Ford Motorcraft gear reduced permanent magnet starter motor**

## DIAGNOSIS

### Starter Load Test

1. Connect test equipment as shown in **Fig. 7,** ensuring no current is flowing through ammeter and heavy duty carbon pile rheostat portion of circuit.
2. Disconnect push-on "S" connector at starter relay, then connect remote control starter switch between positive battery terminal and "S" terminal.
3. Using remote starter, crank engine with ignition in the "Off" position, then determine exact reading on voltmeter.
4. Stop cranking engine, then reduce resistance of carbon pile until voltmeter indicates same reading as obtained with starter cranking the engine. Ammeter should indicate 140-200 amps.

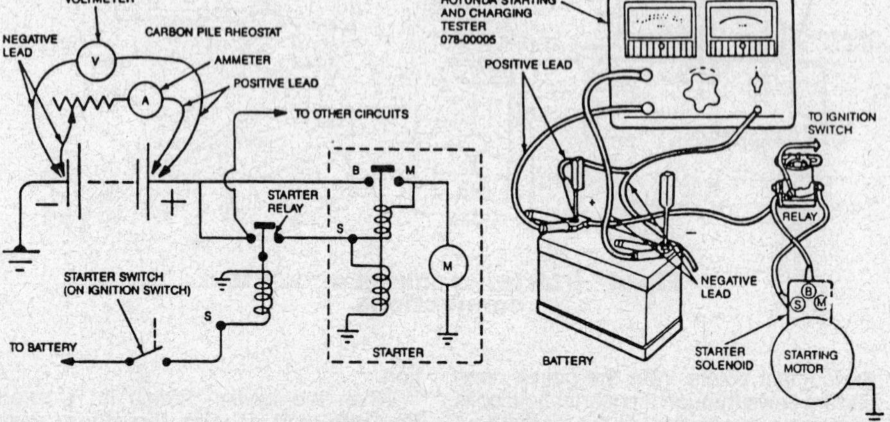


**Fig. 7 Gear reduced permanent magnet starter cranking circuit test connections**

### Starter No-Load Test

1. Connect test equipment as shown in **Fig. 8.** Ensure current is not flowing through ammeter. Ensure starter is securely mounted in vise.
2. Disconnect starter from battery, then reduce resistance of rheostat until

voltmeter indicates reading obtained while starter was running.

3. Ammeter should indicate starter no load current draw, refer to "Starter Motor Specifications."
4. If current exceeds specifications, check for rubbing armature, bent starter shaft, binding starter bearings, or electrical shorts in armature or starter brush assembly.

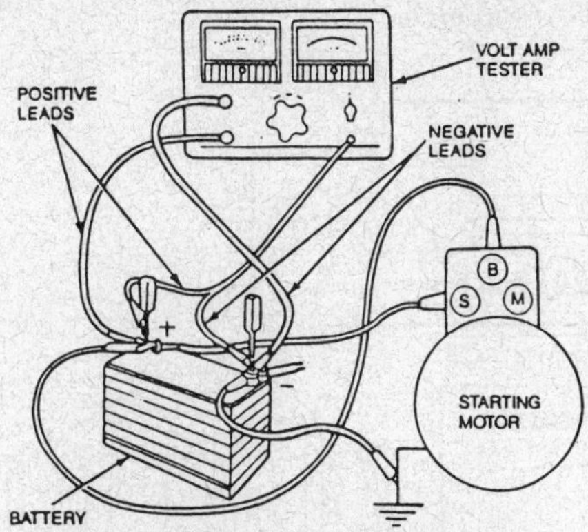


**Fig. 8 Starter no load test connection. Gear reduced permanent magnet starter motor**

## STARTER MOTOR SPECIFICATIONS

| Starter Model Number | Brush Spring Tension, Ounces | No Load Amps | Maximum Load Amps | Normal Load Current Draw (Amps) | Normal Engine Cranking RPM | Minimum Stall Ft. Lbs. @ 5 Volts |
|---|---|---|---|---|---|---|
| EFHD | 64 | 70 | 800 | 130–190 | 200–250 | 10.0 |
| E4AF-AA | 80 | 80 | 500 | 150–250 | 180–250 | 9.5 |
| E4DF-BA | 80 | 80 | ① | 150–250 | 180–250 | 9.5 |
| E6EF-AA | 80 | 80 | ① | 150–250 | 190–260 | 9.5 |
| E6DF-BA | 80 | 80 | ① | 150–250 | 190–260 | 9.5 |
| E7DF-AA | 80 | 80 | ① | 150–250 | 190–260 | 9.5 |
| E7ZF-AA | 80 | 80 | ① | 150–250 | 180–250 | 9.5 |
| E8DF-AA | 80 | 80 | ① | 150–250 | 190–260 | 9.5 |
| E9OF-AA | 64 | 70 | 800 | 150–210 | 170–210 | 11.0 |
| E9OF-BA | 64 | 70 | 800 | 140–200 | 200–250 | 11.0 |
| E9SF-AA | 64 | 70 | 800 | 150–210 | 170–210 | 11.0 |
| E9SF-AA② | 64 | 65 | 580 | 100–200 | 130–180 | 11.5 |
| E9SF-BA | 64 | 70 | 800 | 140–200 | 130–180 | 11.0 |
| FIVU-AA | 64 | 70 | 800 | 160–220 | 110–160 | 11.0 |
| FO2F-AA | 64 | 70 | 800 | 140–200 | 200–250 | 11.0 |

①—1989 models, No Load Amps 500; 1990 models, No Load Amps 800.

②—1989 Thunderbird 3.8L/V6-232 with Gear reduced permanent magnet starter motor.

# Mitsubishi Starter

## INDEX



## DESCRIPTION

This starter system has two electrical circuits a low current and high current. The low current is the control circuit. It includes ignition switch, starter solenoid, neutral safety switch or clutch switch. The high current connects starter to the battery positive terminal. This circuit uses heavy gauge cables because of high current flow required to operate the starter motor, **Fig. 1.**

## IN-VEHICLE TESTING

### PINION DEPTH ADJUSTMENT

1. Connect one 12 volt battery as shown, **Fig. 2.**
2. Disconnect field coil connector from "M" terminal.
3. With battery connected, solenoid should released pinion gear.
4. With pinion extended, measure gap between pinion gear and collar. Pinion clearance should be .020-.080 inch, **If test must be repeated, allow solenoid to cool.**
5. If clearance is not within limits, check for improper installation or worn parts and replace as necessary. Clearance may be adjusted by adding or removing shims between solenoid and the drive end housing as necessary.

### NO LOAD TEST

1. Connect test equipment as shown, **Fig. 3.**

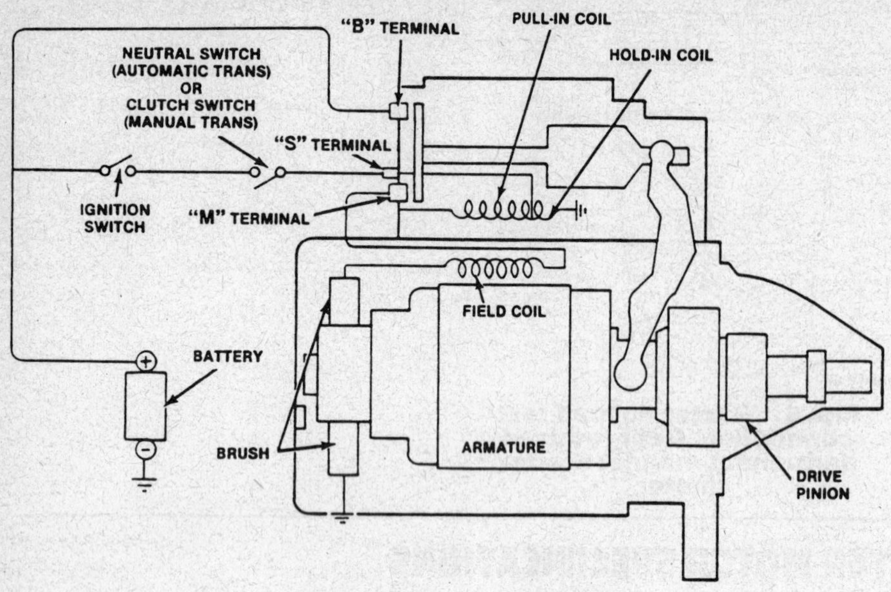


Fig. 1 Mitsubishi starter motor

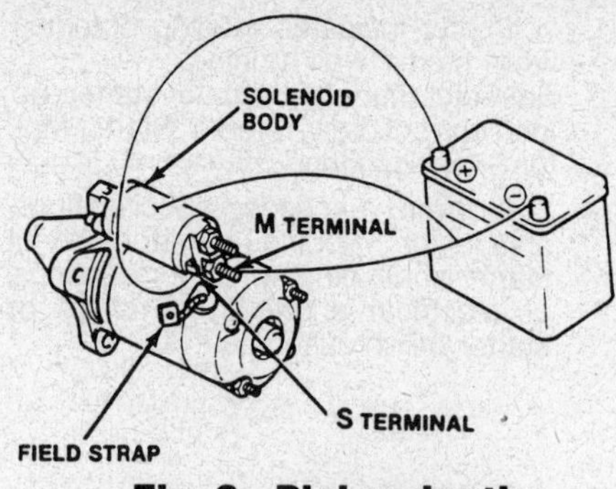


Fig. 2 Pinion depth adjustment

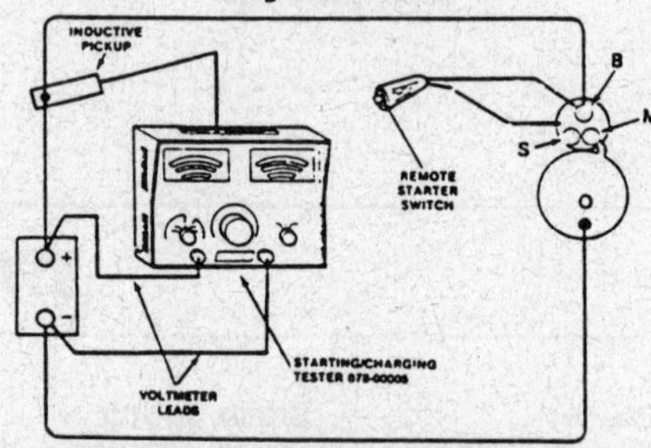


Fig. 3 Starter load test connection

2. Connect remote starter switch, ensuring starter turns smoothly.
3. **On Festiva and Tracer models,** voltmeter should read no less than 11.5 volts and ammeter should read no more than 60 amps.
4. **On Probe models,** voltmeter should read no less than 11 volts and ammeter should read no more than 90 amps.
5. **On all models,** if voltage is lower or amperage is higher, check battery or repair starter as necessary.

# STARTER MOTOR SPECIFICATIONS

## FORD FESTIVA

| Year | Current Draw Under Normal Load | Current Draw Under No Load | Normal Engine Cranking Speed RPM | New Brush Length Inches | Brush Wear Limit Inches | Brush Spring Tension Oz. | Starter Relay Pull In Winding Resistance | Maximum Voltage Drop | Maximum Commutator Runout Inches |
|---|---|---|---|---|---|---|---|---|---|
| 1989 | 150-250 | 60 | 180-250 | .67 | .217 | 80 | 3-5 | .5 | .005 |
| 1990-91① | 150-250 | 60 | 180-250 | .67 | .45 | 80 | 3-5 | .5 | .002 |

①—Mando Machinery, Inc.

## FORD PROBE

| Year | No Load Test | | Brush Spring lbs | Pinion Gap Inches | Commutator Groove Depth Inches | Commutator Outer Depth Inches | Maximum Commutator Runout Inches |
|---|---|---|---|---|---|---|---|
| | Amps | Volts | | | | | |
| 1989-91① | 90 | 11.0 | 1.5-5.3 | 0.02-0.08 | .020-.031 | 1.13 | .002 |

①—1990 2.2L/133 engine

## MERCURY TRACER

| Year | Engine | No Load Test | | Min. Brush Length In. |
|---|---|---|---|---|
| | | Amps | Volts | |
| 1989 | 4-97.5/1.6L | 60 | 11.5 | .453 |

# ALTERNATORS

## TABLE OF CONTENTS



# General Information

## INDEX



## INTRODUCTION

Alternators are composed of the same functional parts as the conventional D.C. generator but they operate differently: The field is called a rotor and is the turning portion of the unit. A generating part, called a stator, is the stationary member, comparable to the armature in a D.C. generator. The regulator, similar to those used in a D.C. system, regulates the output of the alternator-rectifier system.

The power source of the system is the alternator. Current is transmitted from the field terminal of the regulator through a slip ring to the field coil and back to ground through another slip ring. The strength of the field regulates the output of the alternating current. This alternating current is then transmitted from the alternator to the rectifier where it is converted to direct current.

These alternators employ a three-phase stator winding in which the phase windings are electrically 120° apart. The rotor consists of a field coil encased between interleaved sections producing a magnetic field with alternate north and south poles. By rotating the rotor inside the stator the alternating current is induced in the stator windings. This alternating current is rectified (changed to D.C.) by silicon diodes and brought out to the output terminal of the alternator.

## DIODE RECTIFIERS

Six silicon diode rectifiers are used and act as electrical one-way valves. Three of the diodes have ground polarity and are pressed or screwed into a heat sink which is grounded. The other three diodes (ungrounded) are pressed or screwed into and insulated from the end head; these diodes are connected to the alternator output terminal.

Since the diodes have a high resistance to the flow of current in one direction and a low resistance in the opposite direction, they may be connected in a manner which allows current to flow from the alternator to the battery in the low resistance direction. The high resistance in the opposite direction prevents the flow of current from the battery to the alternator. Because of this feature no circuit breaker is required between the alternator and battery.

## SERVICE PRECAUTIONS

1. Be certain that battery polarity is correct when servicing units. Reversed battery polarity will damage rectifiers and regulators.
2. If booster battery is used for starting, be sure to use correct polarity in hook up.
3. When a fast charger is used to charge a vehicle battery, the vehicle battery cables should be disconnected unless the fast charger is equipped with a special Alternator Protector, in which case the vehicle battery cables need not be disconnected. Also the fast charger should never be used to start a vehicle as damage to rectifiers will result.
4. Unless the system includes a load relay or field relay, grounding the alternator output terminal will damage the alternator and/or circuits. This is true even when the system is not in operation since no circuit breaker is used and the battery is applied to the alternator output terminal at all times. The field or load relay acts as a circuit breaker in that it is controlled by the ignition switch.
5. When adjusting the voltage regulator, do not short the adjusting tool to the regulator base as the regulator may be damaged. The tool should be insulated by taping or by installing a plastic sleeve.
6. Before making any "on vehicle" tests of the alternator or regulator, the battery should be checked and the circuit inspected for faulty wiring or insulation, loose or corroded connections and poor ground circuits.
7. Check alternator belt tension to be sure the belt is tight enough to prevent slipping under load.
8. The ignition switch should be off and the battery ground cable disconnected before making any test connections to prevent damage to the system.
9. The vehicle battery must be fully charged or a fully charged battery may be installed for test purposes.

# Bosch Alternators

## INDEX



## DESCRIPTION

This alternator is conventional design, **Fig. 1.**, with rotor magnetic field spinning within the stationary stator windings. The rotor is supported in the housing on ball bearings which are pressed on the shaft. Field current is supplied through the brush set that rides against the rotor slip rings. Because voltage is induced in "Wye" wound stator which produces alternating current, a rectifier assembly is installed between stator and alternator output terminal. The recifier assembly contains six positive and six negative silicon diodes that allow only the positive side of alternating current to reach the output terminal.

## IN-VEHICLE TESTING

Refer to **Fig. 2**, when testing alternator.

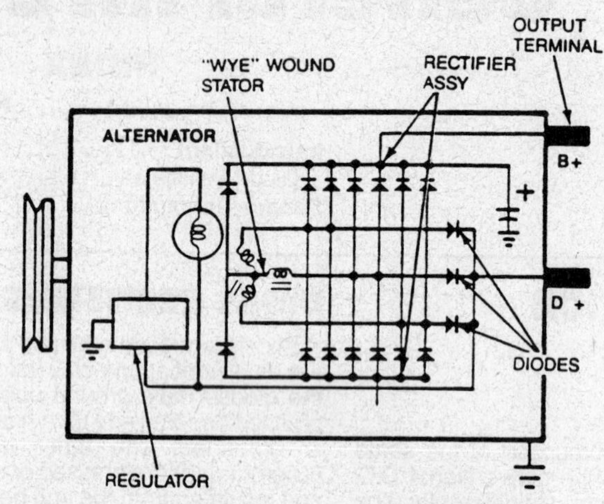


**Fig. 1 Bosch 90 amp alternator**

| TEST STEP | RESULT ▶ | ACTION TO TAKE |
|---|---|---|
| **A1** CHARGE LAMP FUNCTION CHECK | | |
| • Without starting engine, turn ignition switch to RUN (position II). Charge lamp and oil pressure lamp should come on.<br>• Disconnect D+ lead at alternator. Charge lamp should go off.<br>• Ground disconnected D+ lead to engine. Charge lamp should come on. | Lamp functions properly ▶ | GO to **A2**. |
| | Lamp does not come on ▶ | REPLACE lamp fuse or lamp bulb or SERVICE open in lamp feed circuit. |
| | Lamp does not go off ▶ | SERVICE short to ground in D+ wire. |
| | Lamp comes on only with D+ lead grounded ▶ | SERVICE open circuit. CHECK rotor, brushes, or regulator. |
| **A2** BATTERY CONDITION | | |
| • Perform sealed battery voltage/load test. | OK ▶ | GO to **A3**. |
| | Not OK ▶ | REPLACE battery. |
| **A3** B+ WIRING CHECK | | |
| • With ignition switch OFF (position 0), use a voltmeter, Rotunda Number 014-00407, to test for battery voltage at alternator B+ terminal.<br>• Voltage should be within 0.2 volts of battery voltage.<br>B+ TERMINAL / GROUND / NEGATIVE LEAD / POSITIVE LEAD<br>**NOTE: Test step must be performed with alternator installed and all wiring connected. Alternator shown removed for clarity only.** | OK ▶ | GO to **A4**. |
| | Not OK ▶ | SERVICE loose, corroded or damaged B+ wire. |

**Fig. 2 Alternator charging test (Part 1 of 5)**

| TEST STEP | RESULT ▶ | ACTION TO TAKE |
|---|---|---|
| **A4** D+ WIRING CHECK | | |
| • With ignition switch off (position 0), use a voltmeter to test for voltage at alternator D+ terminal. There should be NO VOLTAGE.<br>O-VOLTS, D+ TERMINAL, GROUND, NEGATIVE LEAD, POSITIVE LEAD<br>**NOTE: Test step must be performed with alternator installed, all wiring connected, and ignition switch in RUN (position II). Alternator shown removed for clarity only.** | OK ▶<br>NOT OK ▶ | GO to **A5**.<br>rectifier diode testing. |
| **A5** BATTERY GROUND | | |
| • Use a voltmeter to check voltage drop from battery negative post to ground.<br>• Voltage drop should be less than 0.2 volts. | OK ▶<br>NOT OK ▶ | GO to **A6**.<br>SERVICE loose or corroded connections or damaged ground cable. |
| **A6** ALTERNATOR GROUND | | |
| • Use a voltmeter to check voltage drop from alternator frame to engine ground.<br>• Voltage drop should not exceed 0.2 volts. | OK ▶<br>NOT OK ▶ | GO to **A7**.<br>SERVICE excessive resistance in alternator mounting. |

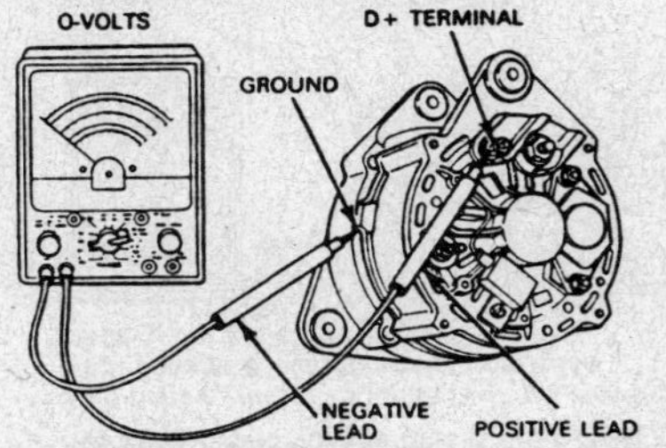

**Fig. 2 Alternator charging test (Part 2 of 5)**

| TEST STEP | RESULT ▶ | ACTION TO TAKE |
|---|---|---|
| **A7** BATTERY DRAIN TEST — KEY OFF | | |
| • Turn ignition to off (position 0).<br>• Disconnect battery positive cables.<br>• Connect an ammeter or test lamp between battery positive terminal and positive cables.<br>• Current draw should be no more than .05 amps (clock draw). Test lamp should not light. | OK ▶<br>NOT OK ▶ | GO to **A8**.<br>CHECK vehicle circuits for drain by pulling fuses from fuse panel one at a time until affected circuit is found. SERVICE as necessary. |
| **A8** REGULATOR BYPASS | | |
| • Connect voltmeter across B+ terminal and ground.<br>• Start engine and run at an idle.<br>• Use a screwdriver or other similar tool to ground connecting strip between brush assembly and regulator to alternator frame.<br>• Increase engine speed slowly while monitoring voltage at B+ terminal.<br>• Alternator should be capable of producing 16 volts.<br>**CAUTION: Do not increase engine speed any more than necessary to produce a 16 volt output. An unregulated alternator can produce excessively high voltage at high speed.** | OK ▶<br>NOT OK ▶ | REPLACE regulator.<br>GO to **A9**. |

**Fig. 2 Alternator charging test (Part 3 of 5)**

BRUSH ASSY/ REGULATOR CONNECTING STRIP

ALTERNATOR FRAME

BRIDGING BRUSH ASSY/ REGULATOR CONNECTING STRIP TO ALTERNATOR FRAME (GROUND)

| TEST STEP | RESULT ▶ | ACTION TO TAKE |
|---|---|---|
| **A9** BASE VOLTAGE AND NO-LOAD TEST | | |
| • Connect voltmeter across battery terminals. Read and record voltage (this is base reading).<br>• Start engine, run at 1500 rpm with no electrical load. Voltage should increase from base reading, but not more than 2.5 volts. | OK ▶ | GO to **A10**. |
| | NOT OK ▶ | SERVICE or REPLACE alternator or regulator. |

13.8V

14.2V

GROUND

B+ TERMINAL

NEGATIVE LEAD

POSITIVE LEAD

**NOTE: Test step must be performed with alternator installed. Engine should be running at approximately 1500 rpm. Alternator shown removed for clarity only.**

**Fig. 2 Alternator charging test (Part 4 of 5)**

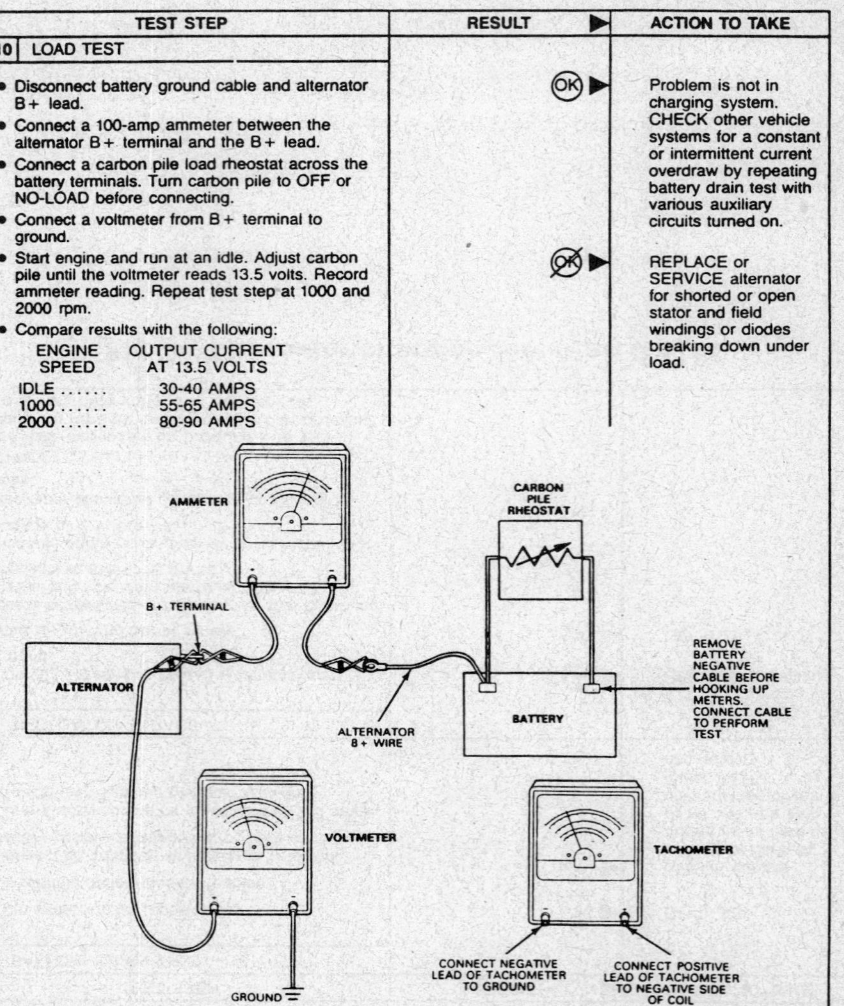


| TEST STEP | RESULT ▶ | ACTION TO TAKE |
|---|---|---|
| **A10** LOAD TEST | | |
| • Disconnect battery ground cable and alternator B+ lead.<br>• Connect a 100-amp ammeter between the alternator B+ terminal and the B+ lead.<br>• Connect a carbon pile load rheostat across the battery terminals. Turn carbon pile to OFF or NO-LOAD before connecting.<br>• Connect a voltmeter from B+ terminal to ground.<br>• Start engine and run at an idle. Adjust carbon pile until the voltmeter reads 13.5 volts. Record ammeter reading. Repeat test step at 1000 and 2000 rpm.<br>• Compare results with the following:<br>ENGINE SPEED — OUTPUT CURRENT AT 13.5 VOLTS<br>IDLE ...... 30-40 AMPS<br>1000 ...... 55-65 AMPS<br>2000 ...... 80-90 AMPS | OK ▶ | Problem is not in charging system. CHECK other vehicle systems for a constant or intermittent current overdraw by repeating battery drain test with various auxiliary circuits turned on. |
| | NOT OK ▶ | REPLACE or SERVICE alternator for shorted or open stator and field windings or diodes breaking down under load. |

**Fig. 2 Alternator charging test (Part 5 of 5)**

## ALTERNATOR SPECIFICATIONS
### MERKUR

| Year | Rating |
|---|---|
| 1989 | 90 |

# Ford Motorcraft Alternator

## INDEX



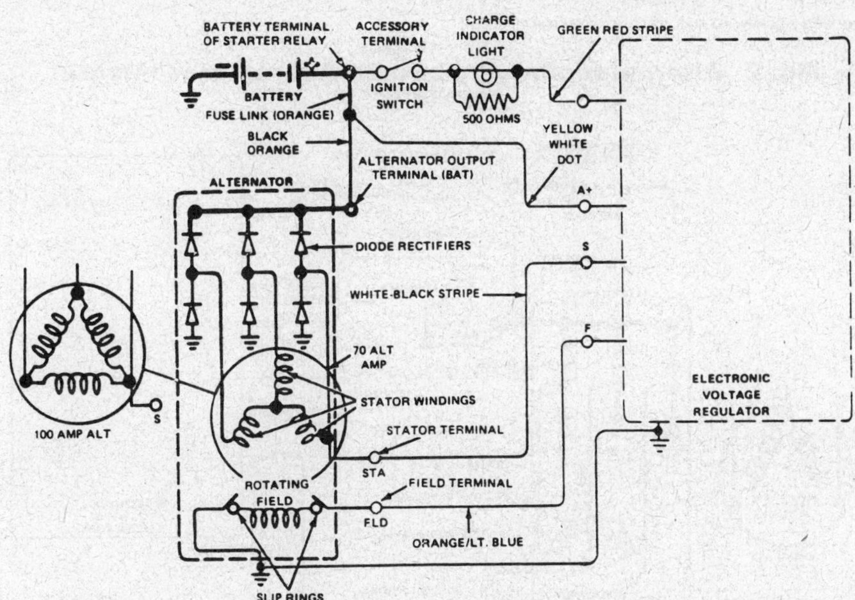


**Fig. 1 Indicator light charging circuit. Except alternator w/integral regulator**

## GENERAL DESCRIPTION

A charge indicator lamp or ammeter can be used in charging system.

If a charge indicator lamp is used in the charging system, **Figs. 1 and 2,** the system operation is as follows: when the ignition switch is turned ON, a small electrical current flows through the lamp filament (turning the lamp on) and through the alternator regulator to the alternator field. When the engine is started, the alternator field rotates and produces a voltage in the stator winding. When the voltage at the alternator stator terminal reaches about 3 volts, the regulator field relay closes. This puts the same voltage potential on both sides of the charge indicator lamp causing it to go out. When the field relay has closed, current passes through the regulator A terminal and is metered to the alternator field.

If an ammeter is used in the charging system, **Figs. 2 and 3,** the regulator 1 terminal and the alternator stator terminal are not used. When the ignition switch is turned ON, the field relay closes and electrical current passes through the regulator A terminal and is metered to the alternator field. When the engine is started, the alternator field rotates causing the alternator to operate.

Some vehicles are equipped with electronic voltage regulators. These solid state regulators are used in conjunction with other components in the charging system such as an alternator with a high field current requirement, a warning indicator lamp shunt resistor (500 ohms) and a wiring harness with a regulator connector. Some vehicles are equipped with Integral Alternator/Regulator (IAR) charging system. This system has a solid state voltage regulator located in the rear of the alternator.

When replacing system components, note the following precautions:

1. Always use the proper alternator in the system.
2. Do not use an electro-mechanical regulator in the system since the wiring harness connector will not index properly with this type of regulator.
3. **On models with external voltage regulator,** the electronic regulators are color coded for proper installation. The black color coded unit is installed in systems equipped with a warning indicator lamp. The blue color coded regulator is installed in systems equipped with an ammeter.
4. The systems use a 500 ohm resistor on the rear of the instrument cluster on vehicles equipped with a warning indicator lamp.

**On systems with an indicator lamp,** closing the ignition switch energizes the warning lamp and turns on the regulator output stage. The alternator receives maximum field current and is ready to generate an output voltage. As the alternator rotor speed increases, the output and stator terminal voltages increase from zero to the system regulation level determined by the regulator setting. When the ignition switch is turned off, the solid state relay circuit turns the output stage off, interrupting current flow through the regulator so there is not a current drain on the battery.

**On vehicles equipped with an ammeter,** the operating principle is similar.

The ammeter indicates current flow into (charge) or out of (discharge) the vehicle battery.

## IN-VEHICLE TESTING

The operations and on vehicle test procedures for the side terminal alternator are same as for rear terminal alternator. However, the internal wiring and bench test procedures differ.

## INDICATOR LAMP SYSTEM

### External Voltage Regulator (EVR) System

1. If charge indicator lamp does not come with the ignition key in the run position and engine not running, check the I wiring circuit (ignition switch to regulator I terminal) for open circuit or burned out charge indicator lamp.
2. If charge indicator lamp does not come on, disconnect electrical connector from regulator and connect a jumper wire, **Fig. 4**, from the I terminal of the regulator wiring plug to negative battery post cable clamp.
3. Charge indicator lamp should go on with ignition key turned to RUN position.
4. If charge indicator lamp does not go on, check for presence of bulb socket resistor. If resistor is missing, replace bulb socket. If resistor is present, check for contact of bulb socket leads to the flexible printed circuit. If satisfactory, check indicator bulb for continuity and replace if burned out.
5. If bulb and socket are satisfactory and socket leads are in contact with the flexible circuit, open circuit exists between ignition switch and regulator.
6. Check 500 ohm resistor across indicator lamp.

### Integral Alternator Regulator (IAR) System

The Integral Alternator Regulator (IAR) has a circuit in the regulator that will indicate a high battery voltage condition. With the IAR system, three conditions can cause the charge indicator to come on during vehicle operation: no alternator output, over-voltage condition or under-voltage condition.

1. If charge indicator does not come on, disconnect wiring connector from regulator **Fig. 5** and connect a jumper wire from wiring connector I to battery post cable clamp.
2. Turn ignition to run position with engine off. If indicator lamp does not light, check for presence of bulb socket resistor. If resistor is missing, replace bulb socket. If resistor is present, check for contact of bulb contact leads to the flexible printed circuit. If satisfactory, check indicator bulb for continuity and replace bulb if burned out. If bulb is satisfactory, perform regulator I circuit test.
3. If indicator lamp does light, remove jumper wire and reconnect electrical connector to regulator. Connect voltmeter negative lead to battery negative post cable clamp and contact voltmeter positive lead to regulator A terminal screw. Battery voltage should be indicated. If battery voltage is not indicated, service A wiring circuit.

## CHARGING SYSTEM TEST

All lights and electrical systems in the off position, parking brake applied, transmission in neutral and a charged battery (at least 1.200 specific gravity).

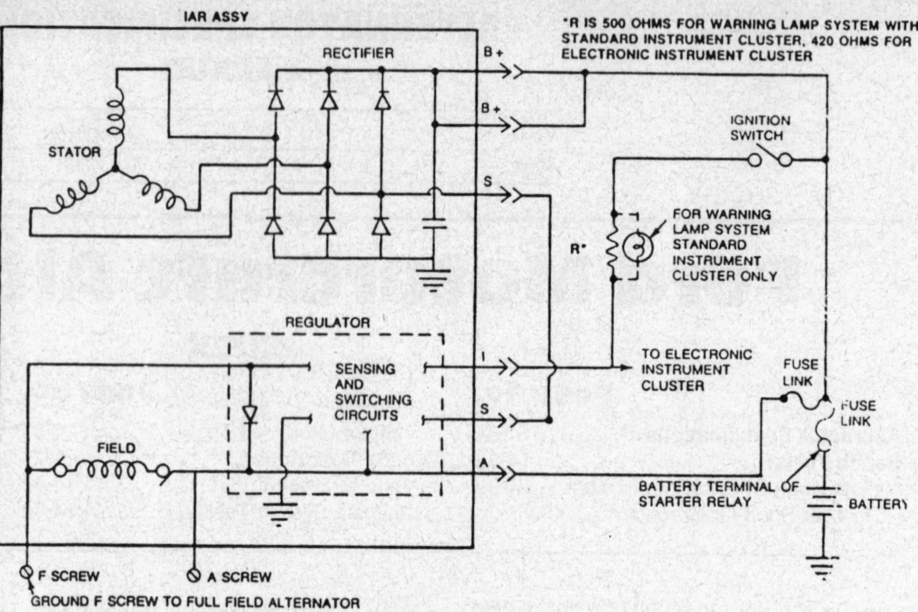


**Fig. 2 Alternator charging circuit. Alternator w/integral regulator**

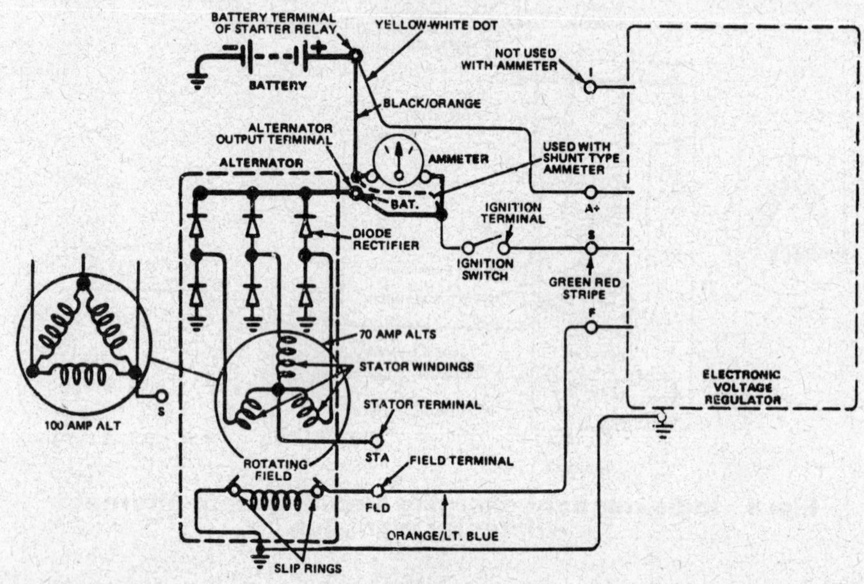


**Fig. 3 Ammeter charging circuit. Except alternator w/integral regulator**

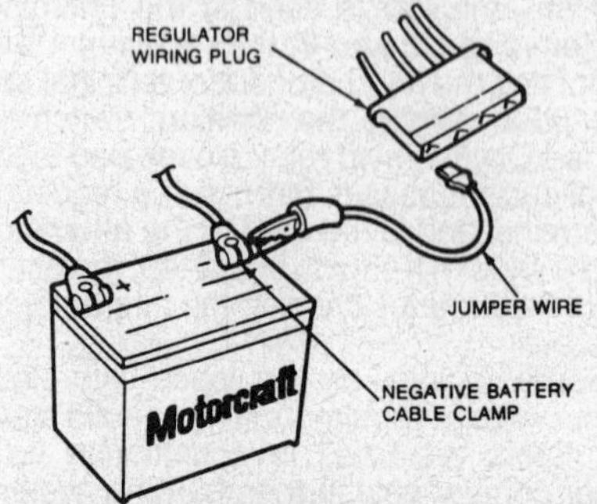


**Fig. 4 Indicator lamp test. External Voltage Regulator (EVR)**

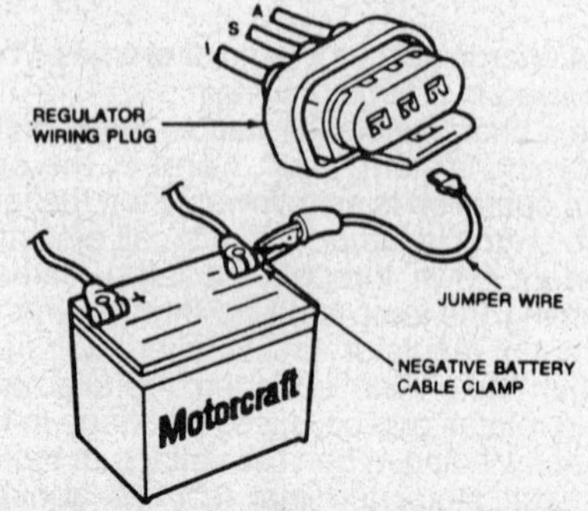


**Fig. 5 Indicator lamp test. Integral Alternator Regulator (IAR)**

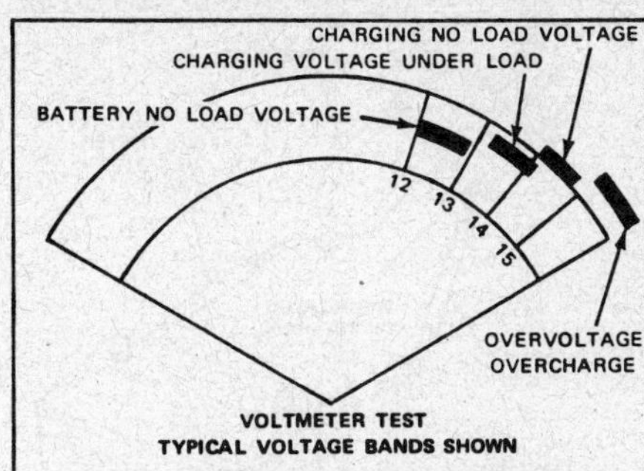


**Fig. 6 Voltmeter test scale**

1. Connect the negative lead of the voltmeter to the negative battery cable clamp (not bolt or nut).
2. Connect the positive lead of the voltmeter to the positive battery cable clamp (not bolt or nut).
3. Record the battery voltage reading shown on the voltmeter scale.
4. Connect the red lead of a tachometer to the distributor terminal of the coil and the black tachometer lead to a good ground.
5. Then, start and operate the engine at approximately 1500 RPM. With no other electrical load (foot off brake pedal and car doors closed), the voltmeter reading should increase but not exceed (2 volts) above the first recorded battery voltage reading. The reading should be taken when the voltmeter needles stops moving.
6. With the engine running, turn on the heater and/or air conditioner blower motor to high speed and headlights to high beam.
7. Increase the engine speed to 2000 RPM. The voltmeter should indicate a minimum reading of 0.5 volts above the battery voltage, **Fig. 6. If the above tests indicate proper voltage readings, the charging system is operating normally. Proceed to "Test Results" if a problem still exists.**

## TEST RESULTS

### Except Alternators w/Integral Regulators

1. If voltmeter reading indicates 2 volts over battery voltage (over voltage), proceed as follows:
   a. Stop the engine and check the ground connections between the regulator and alternator and/or regulator to engine. Clean and tighten connections securely and repeat the Charging System Test Procedures.
   b. If over voltage condition still exists, disconnect regulator wiring plug from regulator and repeat the Charging System Test Procedures.
   c. If over voltage still exists with the regulator wiring plug disconnected, repair the short in the wiring harness between the alternator and regulator. Then, replace the regulator and connect the regulator wiring plug to the regulator and repeat the Charging System Test Procedures.

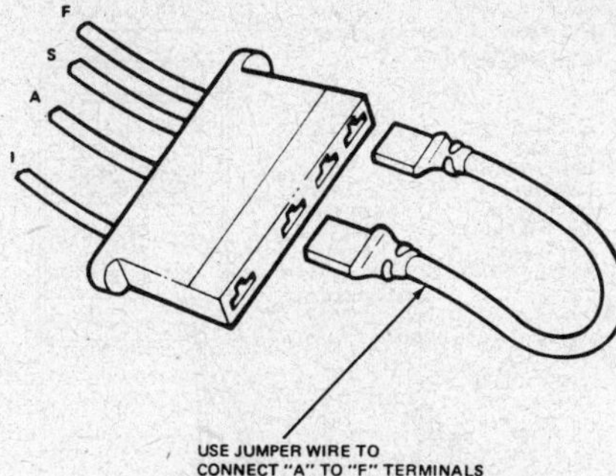


**Fig. 7 Regulator plug jumper wire connection**

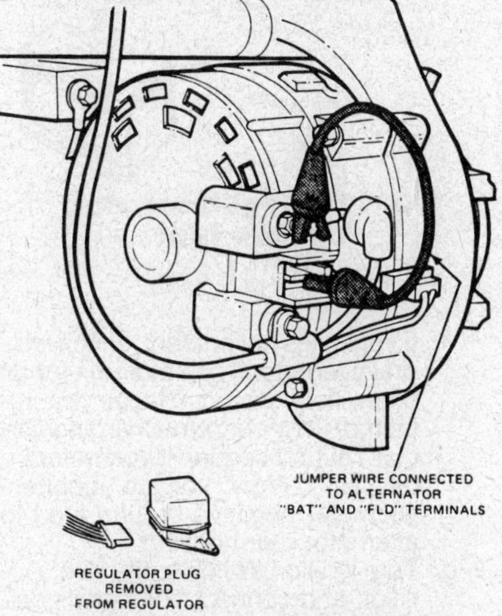


**Fig. 9 Side terminal alternator. Jumper wire connection.**

2. If voltmeter does not indicate more than 1/2 volt above battery voltage, proceed as follows:
   a. Disconnect voltage regulator wire connector and connect an ohmmeter between wire connector "F" terminal and ground. If reading is less or 2.4 ohms, repair grounded field circuit and repeat Charging System Test procedure.
   b. If ohmmeter reading is more than 2.4 ohms, connect a jumper wire between voltage regulator wire connector terminals A and F, **Fig. 7,** then repeat Charging System Test procedure. If voltmeter reading is now more than 1/2 volt above battery voltage, the voltage regulator or wiring is defective, refer to Regulator Test.
   c. If voltmeter still indicates less than 1/2 volt, disconnect jumper wire from voltage regulator wire connector and leave connector disconnected from regulator. Connect a jumper wire between alternator FLD and BAT terminals, **Figs. 8 and 9,** then repeat Charging System Test procedures.

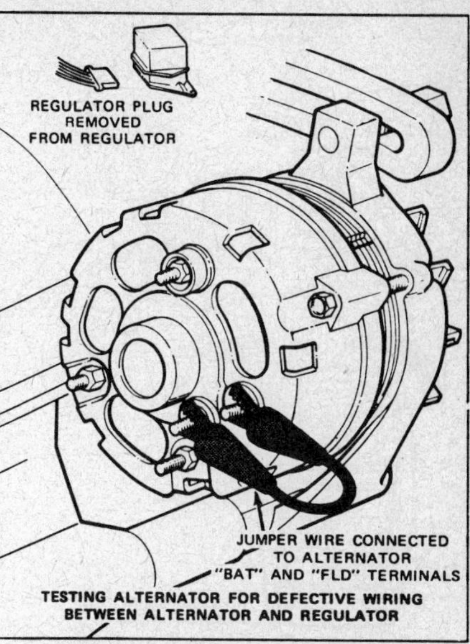


**Fig. 8 Rear terminal alternator. Jumper wire connection**

   d. If voltmeter reading now indicates 1/2 volt or more above battery voltage, repair alternator to regulator wiring harness.
   e. If voltmeter still indicates less than 1/2 volt above battery voltage, stop engine and move voltmeter positive lead to alternator BAT terminal.
   f. If voltmeter now indicates battery voltage, the alternator should be removed, inspected and repaired. If zero volts is indicated, repair BAT terminal wiring.

### Alternators w/Integral Regulators

1. If voltmeter reading indicates 2 volts or over battery voltage (over voltage), proceed as follows:
   a. Stop engine and place ignition switch in the "On" position, then connect voltmeter negative lead to the alternator rear housing.
   b. Connect voltmeter positive lead first to the alternator output connection at the starter solenoid, then to the regulator "A" screw head, **Fig. 10.**
   c. If the voltage difference between the two locations is greater than .5 volts, repair the "A" wiring circuit to eliminate the high resistance condition indicated by the excessive voltage drop.
   d. If over voltage condition still exists, check for loose regulator to alternator grounding screws. **Torque** regulator grounding screws to 15-26 inch lbs.
   e. If over voltage condition still exists, connect voltmeter negative lead to the alternator rear housing.
   f. Place ignition switch in the "Off" position, then connect voltmeter positive lead first to the regulator "A" screw head and then to the regulator "F" screw head, **Fig. 10.**
   g. Different voltage readings at the

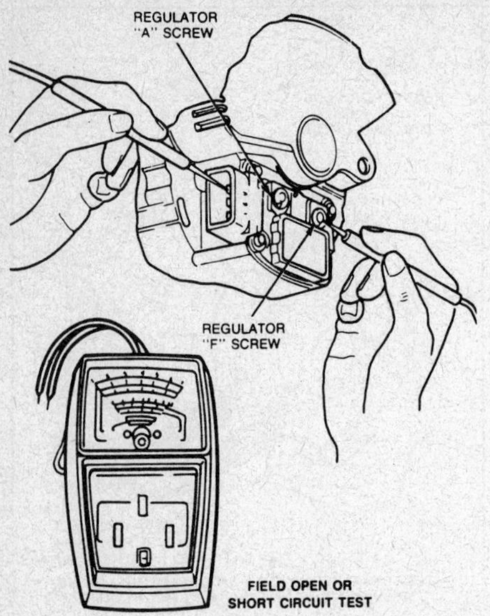


**Fig. 10 Charging circuit test points. Alternator w/integral regulator**

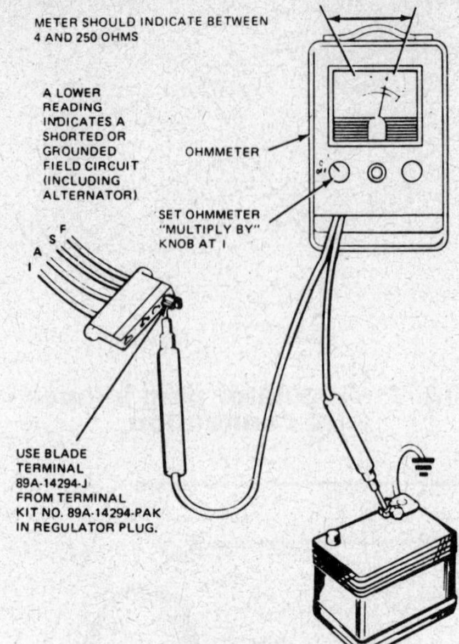


**Fig. 11 Regulator plug voltage test**

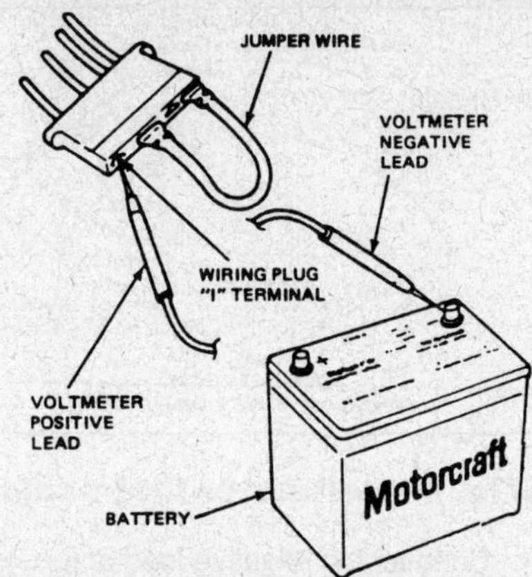


**Fig. 12 Testing regulator S &/or I circuit. External Voltage Regulator (EVR)**

two screw heads in step 1f indicates a defective regulator, grounded brush lead or grounded rotor coil. Repair or replace as required.

h. If battery voltage is obtained at both screw heads in step 1f, replace regulator.

2. If voltmeter does not indicate more than .5 volts over battery voltage, proceed as follows:
   a. Disconnect wiring plug from regulator, then connect an ohmmeter between regulator "A" and "F" terminal screws, **Fig. 10.** Meter should indicate more than 2.4 ohms.
   b. If meter indicates less than 2.4 ohms in step 2a, check integral alternator/regulator unit for a defective regulator, then check the alternator for a shorted rotor or field circuit. Perform Charging System Test procedure after servicing alternator. **Do not replace the regulator until a shorted rotor coil or field circuit has been serviced.**
   c. If meter indicates greater than 2.4 ohms in step 2a, reconnect regulator wiring plug. Connect voltmeter ground lead to the alternator rear housing and voltmeter positive lead to the regulator "A" terminal screw.
   d. Meter should read battery voltage. If battery voltage is not present, repair "A" wiring circuit, then perform Charging Circuit Test procedure. If battery voltage is present, connect the voltmeter ground lead to the alternator rear housing.
   e. Place ignition switch in the "Off" position, then connect voltmeter positive lead to the regulator "F" terminal screw. Meter should indicate battery voltage.
   f. If voltage is not present, check integral alternator/regulator unit for an open field circuit. Repair as required, then perform Charging Circuit Test procedure. If voltmeter indicates battery voltage, connect voltmeter negative ground lead to alternator rear housing.
   g. Turn ignition switch to the "On" position and connect voltmeter positive probe lead to the regulator "F" terminal screw. Voltmeter should indicate 1.5 volts or less.
   h. If more than 1.5 volts is present, proceed to "I Circuit Test." If "I Circuit" is satisfactory, replace the regulator and perform Charging Circuit Test procedure. If 1.5 volts or less is present, disconnect alternator wiring plug and connect suitable jumper wires between the alternator B(+) terminal and mating wiring connector terminals.
   i. Perform Charging System Test procedure, but connect voltmeter positive terminal to one of the B(+) jumper wire terminals.
   j. If voltage rises more than .5 volts above battery voltage, check alternator and starter relay wiring, then repeat Charging System Test procedure, measuring voltage at battery cable clamps.
   k. If voltage does not rise more than .5 volts above battery voltage, connect jumper wire from alternator rear housing to the regulator "F" terminal.
   l. Repeat Charging System Tests procedure with voltmeter positive lead connected to one of the jumper wire terminals.
   m. If voltage rises more than .5 volts, replace regulator. If voltage does not rise more than .5 volts, service the alternator.

# REGULATOR TESTS

## S CIRCUIT TEST—WITH AMMETER

### Except Alternators w/Integral Regulator

1. Connect the positive lead of the voltmeter to the S terminal of the regulator wiring plug **Fig. 11.** Turn the ignition switch to the "On." position. Do not start the engine.
2. The voltmeter reading should indicate battery voltage.
3. If there is no voltage reading, disconnect the positive voltmeter lead from the positive battery clamp and repair the S wire lead from the ignition switch to the regulator wiring plug.
4. Connect the positive voltmeter lead to the positive battery cable terminal and repeat the Charging System Test Procedures.

### Alternators w/Integral Regulator

For test procedures, refer to "S and I Circuit Test-With Indicator Light."

## S AND I CIRCUIT TEST—WITH INDICATOR LIGHT

### Except Alternators w/Integral Regulator

1. Disconnect regulator wiring plug, then install a suitable jumper wire between connector "A" and "F" terminals, **Fig. 12.**
2. With the engine idling and negative voltmeter lead connected to battery ground, connect positive lead of voltmeter to S terminal and then to I terminal of regulator wiring plug, **Fig. 11.** Voltage of S circuit should read approximately 1/2 of the I circuit. If voltage readings are as specified, remove jumper wire, replace regulator and connect wiring plug.
3. If no voltage is present, the wiring is at fault. Service the faulty circuit.

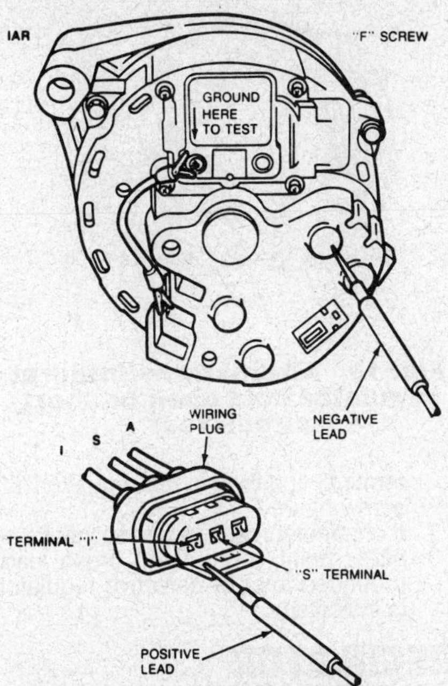


**Fig. 13 Testing regulator S &/or I circuit. Integral Alternator Regulator (IAR)**

### Alternators w/Integral Regulator

1. Disconnect electrical connector from regulator. Connect a jumper wire from the regulator A lead to connector plug A lead. Add a jumper wire from the regulator F screw to the alternator rear housing, **Fig. 13.**
2. With engine idling and voltmeter negative lead connected to alternator rear housing, connect voltmeter positive lead to S terminal and then to I terminal of regulator electrical connector. Voltage at S circuit should read approximately one-half of the I circuit. If voltage readings are normal, remove jumper wire. Replace regulator and connect electrical connector to regulator.
3. If no voltage is present, remove jumper wires and service faulty circuit or alternator.
4. Connect voltmeter positive lead to positive battery terminal.
5. Connect electrical connector to regulator and replace bulb, if equipped.

## FIELD CIRCUIT DRAIN TEST

### Alternators w/Integral Regulator

Connect voltmeter negative lead to the alternator rear housing for all of the following voltage readings.

1. Turn ignition switch to the "Off" position, then connect voltmeter positive lead to the regulator "F" terminal screw. Battery voltage should be present.
2. If less than battery voltage is present, disconnect regulator electrical connector and connect voltmeter positive lead to connector I terminal. No voltage should be present.
3. If voltage is present, repair circuit between I lead and ignition switch. If no voltage is present, proceed to step 4.
4. Connect voltmeter positive lead to the connector S terminal.
5. No voltage should be present. If voltage is present, disconnect alternator electrical connector. Again, connect voltmeter positive lead to the regulator connector S terminal.
6. If voltage is still present, repair circuit between S lead and alternator connector. If no voltage is present, replace alternator rectifier assembly.

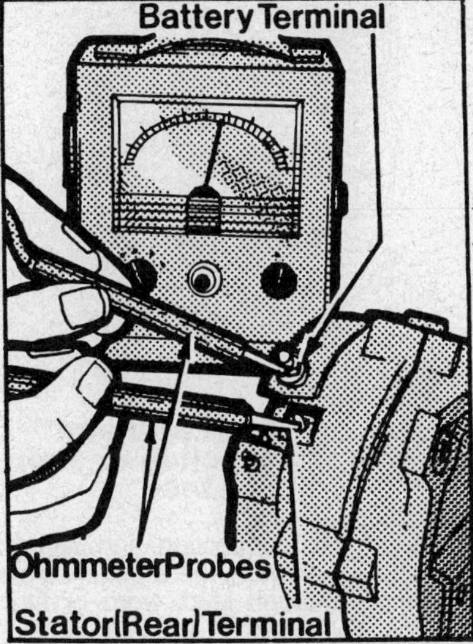


**Fig. 14 Side terminal alternator rectifier short or grounded & stator grounded test**

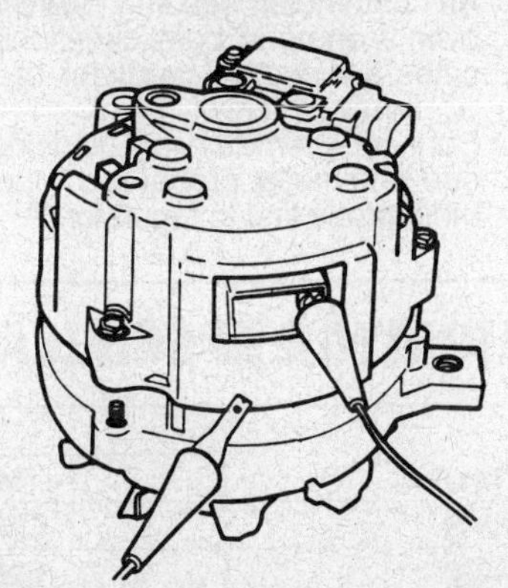

**Fig. 16 Alternator w/integral regulator rectifier short or grounded & stator grounded test**

## BENCH TESTS

## RECTIFIER SHORT OR GROUNDED & STATOR GROUNDED TEST

Using a suitable ohmmeter, connect one probe to the alternator BAT or B+ terminal, **Figs. 14, 15 and 16,** the other probe to the STA terminal (rear blade terminal). Then, reverse the ohmmeter probes and repeat the test. A reading of about 6-6.5 ohms should be obtained in one direction and no needle movement with the probes reversed. A reading in both directions indicates a bad positive diode, a grounded positive diode plate, grounded BAT or B+ terminal or a shorted radio suppression capacitor, if equipped.

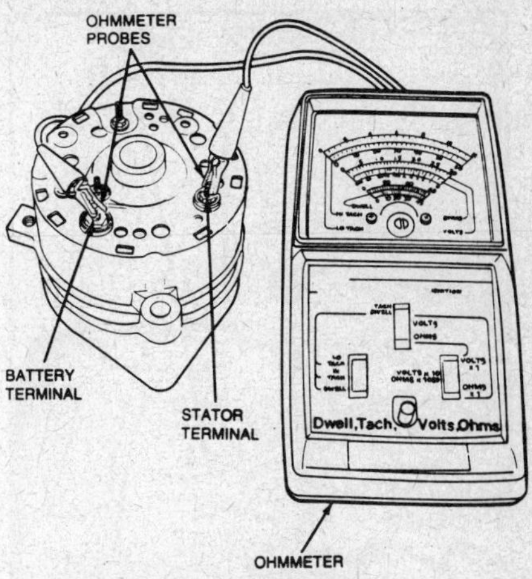


**Fig. 15 Rear terminal alternator rectifier short or grounded & stator grounded test**

Perform the same test using the STA and GND (ground) terminals of the alternator. A reading in both directions indicates either a bad negative diode, a grounded stator winding, a grounded stator terminal, a grounded positive diode plate, or a shorted radio capacitor, if equipped.

Infinite readings (no needle movement) in all four probe positions in the proceeding tests indicates an open terminal lead connection inside the alternator.

## FIELD OPEN OR SHORT CIRCUIT TEST

### Except Alternators w/Integral Regulators

Using a suitable ohmmeter, connect the alternator field terminal with one probe and the ground terminal with the other probe, **Figs. 17 and 18.** Then, spin the alternator pulley. The ohmmeter reading should be 2.4 and 100 ohms, and should fluctuate while the pulley is turning. An infinite reading (no meter movement) indicates an open brush lead, worn or stuck brushes, or a bad rotor assembly. An ohmmeter reading less than 2.4 ohms indicates a grounded brush assembly, a grounded field terminal or a bad rotor.

### Regulators w/Integral Regulator

1. Using a suitable ohmmeter, connect regulator A blade terminal with one probe and the regulator "F" screw head with the other probe, **Fig. 19.**
2. Spin the alternator pulley and note meter reading, then reverse probes and repeat step 1. In one probe direc-

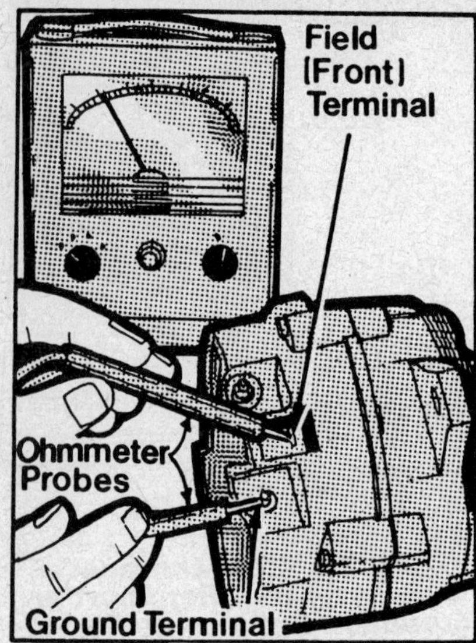


**Fig. 17 Side terminal alternator field open or short circuit test**

tion ohmmeter reading should be between 2.2 and 100 ohms and may fluctuate while pulley is turning. In the other direction, reading should fluctuate between 2.2 and approximately 9 ohms.

3. An infinite reading, no meter movement, in one direction and approximately 9 ohms in the other, indicates an open brush lead, worn or stuck brushes, defective rotor or a loose regulator to brush holder attaching screw.
4. An ohmmeter reading less than 2.2 ohms in both directions indicates a shorted or defective regulator.
5. An ohmmeter reading significantly over 9 ohms in both directions indicates a defective regulator or loose "F" terminal screw.
6. Connect alternator rear housing with one ohmmeter probe and touch the other probe first to regulator "A" blade terminal and then to the regulator "F" screw head.
7. If ohmmeter reads less than infinite at either point, a grounded brush lead, grounded rotor or defective regulator is indicated.

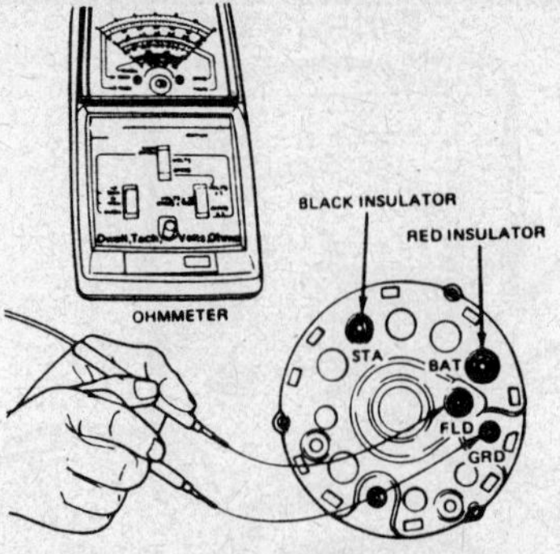


**Fig. 18 Rear terminal alternator field open or short circuit test**

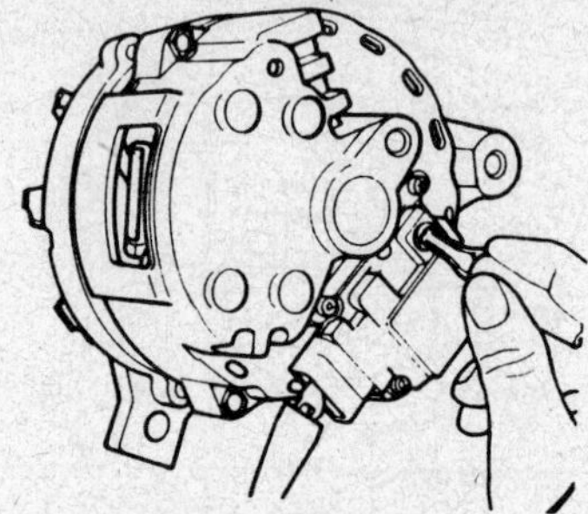

**Fig. 19 Alternator w/integral regulator field open or short circuit test**

## REGULATOR ADJUSTMENTS

These regulators are factory calibrated and sealed and no adjustment is possible. If regulator calibration values are not within specifications, the regulator must be replaced.

## ALTERNATOR SPECIFICATIONS

| Vehicle Application | Year | Alternator | |
|---|---|---|---|
| | | Model | Amp Rating |
| Continental | 1989 | E8DF-CA | 100 |
| | 1990 | E9DF-EA | 100 |
| | 1991 | FODF-BA | 130 |
| Cougar | 1989–90 | E7ZF-CA | 75 |
| | 1989–90 | E9SF-DA | 110 |
| | 1991 | F1SF-BA | 95 |
| Crown Victoria & Grand Marquis | 1989–91 | E7AF-DA | 65 |
| Escort | 1989–90 | E7EF-FB | 60 |
| | 1991 | EFHD | 75 |
| Mark VII | 1989–90 | E7VF-AA | 100 |
| | 1991 | FOLU-AA | 100 |
| Mustang | 1989–91 | E7SF-MA | 75 |
| Sable | 1989 | E8DF-DA | 100 |
| | | E8DF-CA | 100 |
| | 1990 | E9DF-DA | 100 |
| | | E9DF-EA | 100 |
| | 1991 | F1DF-AA | 130 |
| | | F0DF-BA | 130 |

Continued

## ALTERNATOR SPECIFICATIONS —Continued

| Vehicle Application | Year | Alternator Model | Alternator Amp Rating |
|---|---|---|---|
| Taurus | 1989–91 | FODF-AA | 95 |
| Tempo & Topaz | 1989–90 | E73F-CA | 65 |
| | 1989–91 | E73F-BA | 75 |
| | 1991 | F13U-AA | 95 |
| Thunderbird | 1989–90 | E7ZF-CA | 75 |
| | 1989–91 | E9SF-DA | 110 |
| | 1991 | E8SF-BA | 65 |
| Town Car | 1989–90 | E7AF-DA | 65 |
| | 1991 | FIVU | 95 |
| Tracer | 1991 | EFHD | 75 |

# Mitsubishi Alternator

## INDEX



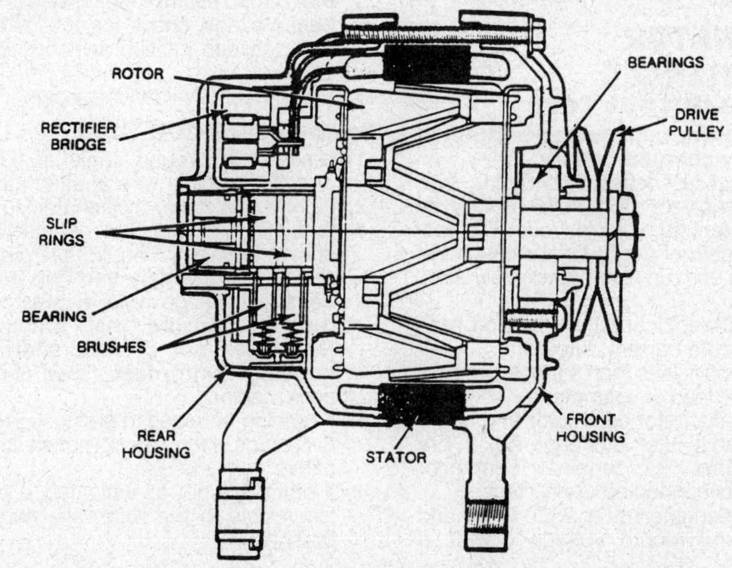


**Fig. 1 Mitsubishi alternator**

## DESCRIPTION

This unit produces alternating current which is changed to direct current by rectifier diodes for distribution to the vehicle electrical system. The electronic voltage regulator is part of the rotor, brush and brush holder assembly. No regulated adjustments are required on this unit, **Fig. 1.**

## IN-VEHICLE TESTING

### BASE VOLTAGE TEST

1. Ensure battery is fully charged.
2. With ignition switch and all electrical accessories off, connect suitable voltmeter to battery terminals.
3. Read and record battery voltage reading. This reading will be used for subsequent tests outlined below.

### ALTERNATOR UNDERCHARGES

#### Current Output Test

1. Connect test leads of charging system analyzer tool 078-00005 or equivalent to vehicle, following tool manufacturer's instructions.
2. Turn on all electrical accessories, then start engine and allow to run between 2500-3000 RPM.
3. Read and record maximum current output. Current output should be within 10 percent of rated alternator output.
4. If current output is within specifications outlined in previous step, alternator is functioning properly. If current output is below specification, proceed to "Voltage Output Test."

#### Voltage Output Test

**The following test must be performed with a fully charged battery.**

1. With charging system analyzer connected as outlined in previous test, start engine and run at approximately 2500 RPM.
2. With all electrical accessories off, read and record current output.
3. If recorded reading is less than 5 amps, proceed to next step. If current reading is greater than 5 amps, voltage loss in charging circuit is indicated. Check battery, alternator and engine ground cable connections. Clean or repair connections as necessary.
4. Connect positive lead of voltmeter to "L" terminal of alternator connector and negative lead to alternator case, **Fig. 2.** Ensure that "L" terminal connector remains connected during test.
5. If reading obtained at "L" terminal is less than 14.4 volts, proceed to "Regulator Power Source Test." If reading obtained is 14.4-15 volts, a problem exists in alternator stator or rectifier.

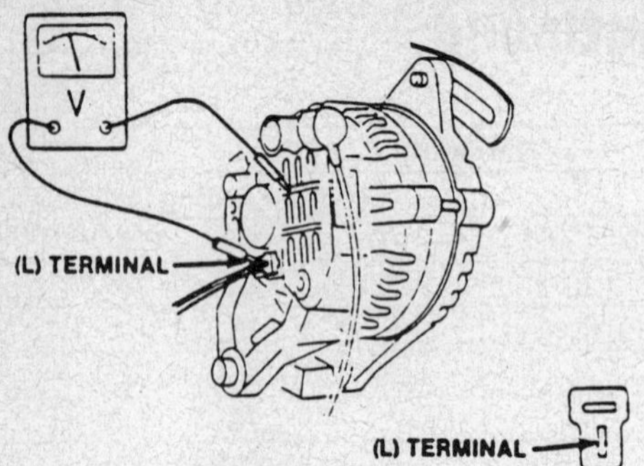


Fig. 2 Voltage output test connections

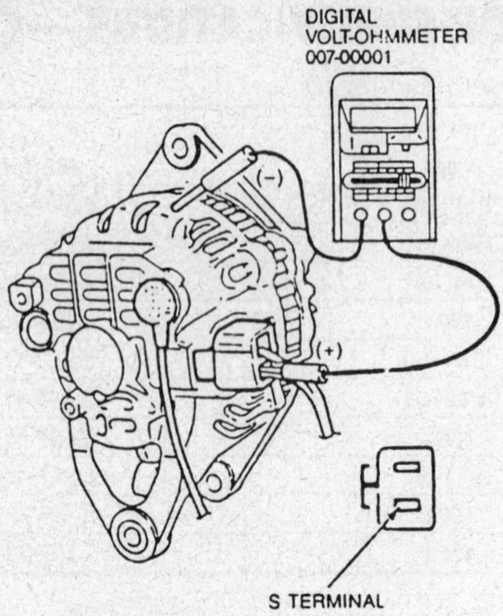


Fig. 3 Regulator power source test connections

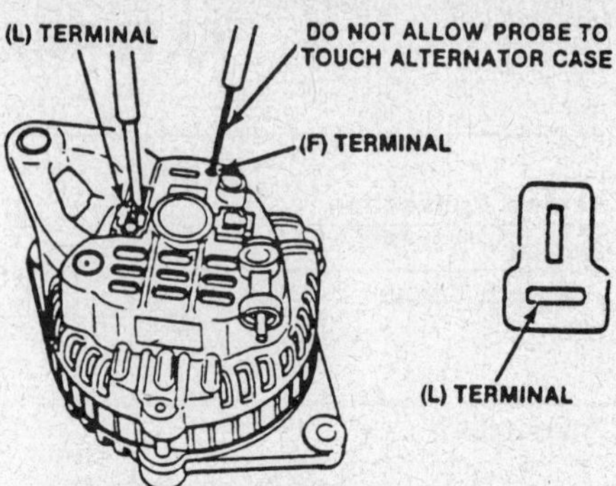


Fig. 4 Rotor field coil test connections

### Regulator Power Source Test

1. Turn ignition switch On, but do not start engine.
2. Disconnect "R" terminal connector from rear of alternator, then connect voltmeter positive lead to "R" terminal connector harness and negative lead to alternator case, **Fig. 3.** Read and record voltage.
3. If reading obtained is at base voltage recorded earlier, proceed to "Rotor Field Coil Test." If reading is less than base voltage, check for defective circuit between battery and "R" terminal.

### Rotor Field Coil Test

1. Disconnect ground cable at battery and "B" terminal wire at alternator.
2. Connect suitable ohmmeter to "L" and "F" terminals of alternator as shown in **Fig. 4. The "F" terminal is mounted internally and can be accessed through hole in rear of alternator. Ensure that ohmmeter lead does not contact alternator housing during test.** Read and record reading.
3. If reading obtained in previous step is 3-6 ohms, field coil is satisfactory. Proceed to "L Terminal Voltage Test."
4. If ohms are not as indicated, a problem exists in the rotor, slip rings or brushes.

### "L" Terminal Voltage Test

1. Reconnect battery ground cable and output wire to "B" terminal at rear of alternator.
2. With ignition switch "On," connect voltmeter positive lead to "L" terminal metal connector, and negative lead to alternator case. Read and record reading.
3. If reading obtained in previous step is 1-3 volts, a problem exists in the stator or rectifier. If reading obtained is above 3 volts, a problem exists in the regulator.

## ALTERNATOR OVERCHARGES

### Voltage Output Test

**The following test must be performed with a fully charged battery.**

1. Connect test leads of charging system analyzer tool 078-00005 or equivalent to vehicle, following tool manufacturer's instructions, then start engine and run at approximately 2500 RPM.
2. With all electrical accessories off, read and record current output.
3. If reading is less than 5 amps, connect positive lead of voltmeter to "L" terminal of alternator connector and negative lead to alternator case, **Fig. 2.** Ensure that "L" terminal connector remains connected during test.
4. Restart engine, run at 2500 RPM, and read and record voltage output. If reading is 14.4-15 volts, alternator is operating properly. If reading is greater than 15 volts, proceed to "Regulator Power Source Test."

### Regulator Power Source Test

1. Turn ignition switch On, but do not start engine.
2. Disconnect "S" terminal connector from rear of alternator, then connect voltmeter positive lead to "S" terminal connector harness and negative lead to alternator case, **Fig. 3.** Read and record voltage.
3. If reading obtained is at base voltage recorded earlier, proceed to "Rotor Field Coil Test." If reading is less than base voltage, check for defective circuit between ignition switch and "S" terminal.
4. Reconnect terminal connector.

### Rotor Field Coil Test

1. Disconnect ground cable at battery and "B" terminal wire at alternator.
2. Connect suitable ohmmeter to "L" and "F" terminals of alternator as shown in **Fig. 4. The "F" terminal is mounted internally and can be accessed through hole in rear of alternator. Ensure that ohmmeter lead does not contact alternator housing during test.** Read and record reading.
3. If reading obtained in previous step is 3-6 ohms, a regulator problem is indicated.
4. If ohms are not as indicated, a problem exists in the rotor, slip rings or brushes.

## ALTERNATOR SPECIFICATIONS

| Vehicle Application | Year | Alternator | |
|---|---|---|---|
| | | Model | Amp Rating |
| Capri | 1991 | — | 70 |
| Escort | 1991 | — | 65 |
| Festiva | 1989-91 | — | 50 |
| Probe | 1989-91 | — | 70 |
| | 1991 | — | 80 |
| | 1991 | — | 90 |
| Taurus | 1990-91 | E9DF-BB | 90 |
| Topaz | 1989-90 | E83F-BA | 75 |
| Tracer | 1989 & 1991 | — | 60 |

# DISC BRAKES

## TABLE OF CONTENTS



# General Information

## INDEX



## GENERAL PRECAUTIONS

1. Grease or any other foreign material must be kept off the caliper, surfaces of the disc and external surfaces of the hub, during service procedures. Handling the brake disc and caliper should be done in a way to avoid deformation of the disc and nicking or scratching brake linings.
2. If inspection reveals rubber piston seals are worn or damaged, they should be replaced immediately.
3. During removal and installation of a wheel assembly, exercise care so as not to interfere with or damage the caliper splash shield, or bleeder screw.
4. Front wheel bearings should be adjusted to specifications.
5. Be sure vehicle is centered on hoist before servicing any of the front end components to avoid bending or damaging the disc splash shield on full right or left wheel turns.
6. Before the vehicle is moved after any brake service work, be sure to obtain a firm brake pedal.
7. The assembly bolts of the two caliper housings should not be disturbed unless the caliper requires service.

## INSPECTION

Remove wheels and inspect brake disc, caliper and linings. The wheel bearings should be inspected at this time and repacked if necessary. Do not get any grease on the linings.

If the caliper is cracked or fluid leakage through the casting is evident, it must be replaced as a unit.

Should it become necessary to remove the caliper for installation of new parts, clean all parts in alcohol, wipe dry using lint free cloths. Using an air hose, blow out drilled passages and bores. Check dust boots for punctures or tears. If punctures or tears are evident, new boots should be installed upon reassembly.

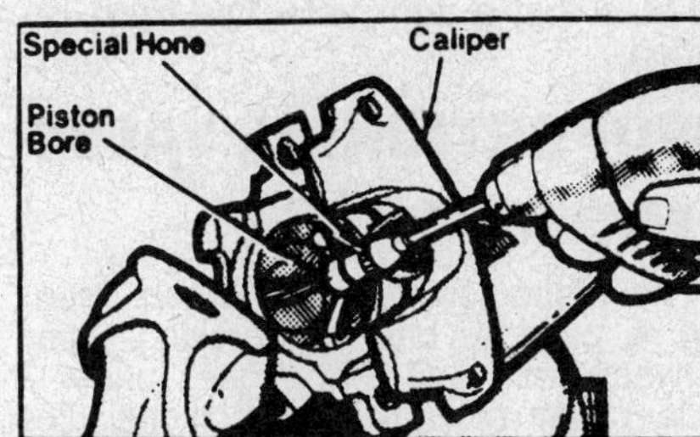


**Fig. 1 Honing caliper piston bore**

Inspect piston bores in both housings for scoring or pitting. Bores that show light scratches or corrosion can usually be cleaned with crocus cloth. However, bores that have deep scratches or scoring may be honed, provided the diameter of the bore is not increased more than .002 inch. If the bore does not clean up within this specification, a new caliper housing should be installed (black stains on the bore walls are caused by piston seals and will do no harm).

When using a hone, **Fig. 1**, be sure to install the hone baffle before honing bore. The baffle is used to protect the hone stones from damage. Use extreme care in cleaning the caliper after honing. Remove all dust and grit by flushing the caliper with alcohol. Wipe dry with clean lint free cloth and then clean a second time in the same manner.

## BRAKE DISC SERVICE

Servicing of disc brakes is extremely critical due to the close tolerances required in machining the brake disc to insure proper brake operation.

The maintenance of these close controls of the shape of the rubbing surfaces is necessary to prevent brake roughness. In addition, the surface finish must be non-directional and maintained at a micro inch finish. This close control of the rubbing surface finish is necessary to avoid pulls and erratic performance and promote long lining life and equal lining wear of both left and right brakes.

In light of the foregoing remarks, refinishing of the rubbing surfaces sh ould not be attempted unless precision equipment, capable of measuring in micro inches (millionths of an inch) is available.

To check lateral run-out of a disc, mount a dial indicator on a convenient part (steering knuckle, tie rod, disc brake caliper housing) so that the plunger of the dial indicator contacts the disc at a point one inch from the outer edge, **Fig. 2.** If the total indicated run-out exceeds specifications, install a new disc.

To check parallelism (thickness variation), mount dial indicators, **Fig. 3,** so the plunger contacts rotor approximately 1 inch from outer edge. If parallelism exceeds specifications, replace rotor.

## BRAKE ROUGHNESS

The most common cause of brake chatter on disc brakes is a variation in thickness of the disc. If roughness or vibration is encountered during highway operation or if pedal pumping is experienced at low speeds, the disc may have excessive thickness variation. To check for this condition, measure the disc at 12 points with a micrometer at a radius approximately one inch from edge of disc. If thickness measurements vary by more than .0005 inch, the disc should be replaced with a new one.

Excessive lateral run-out of braking disc

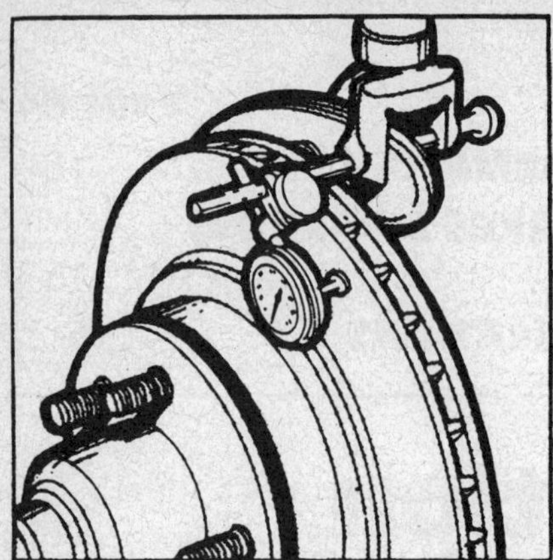

**Fig. 2 Checking rotor for lateral run-out**

**Fig. 3 Checking rotor parallelism (thickness variation)**

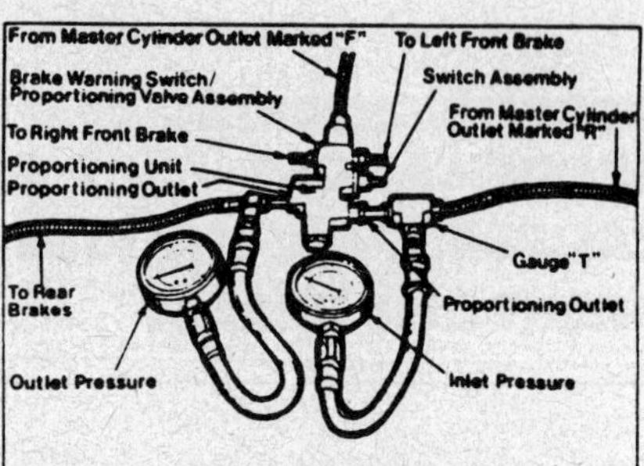


**Fig. 4 Gauge hook-up for testing proportioning valve (typical)**

may cause a "knocking back" of the pistons, possibly creating increased pedal travel and vibration when brakes are applied.

Before checking the run-out, wheel bearings should be adjusted. The readjustment is very important and will be required at the completion of the test to prevent bearing failure. Be sure to make the adjustment according to the recommendations given under "Front Wheel Bearings, Adjust" in the car chapters.

## BLEEDING DISC BRAKES

Pressure bleeding is recommended for all hydraulic disc brake systems.

The disc brake hydraulic system can be bled manually or with pressure bleeding equipment. **On vehicles with disc brakes,** the brake pedal will require more pumping and frequent checking of fluid level in master cylinder during bleeding operation.

Never use brake fluid that has been drained from hydraulic system when bleeding the brakes. Be sure the disc brake pistons are returned to their normal positions and that the shoe and lining assemblies are properly seated. Before driving the vehicle, check brake operation to be sure that a firm pedal has been obtained.

## PROPORTIONING VALVE

### DESCRIPTION

The proportioning valve (when used), **Fig. 4,** provides balanced braking action between front and rear brakes under a wide range of braking conditions. The valve regulates the hydraulic pressure applied to the rear wheel cylinders, thus limiting rear braking action when high pressures are required at the front brakes. In this manner, premature rear wheel skid is prevented.

### TESTING

When a premature rear wheel slide is obtained on a brake application, it usually is an indication that the fluid pressure to the rear wheels is above the 50% reduction ratio for the rear line pressure and that malfunction has occurred within the proportioning valve.

To test the valve, install gauge set shown in **Fig. 4** in brake line between master cylinder and proportioning valve, and at output end of proportioning valve and brake line as shown. Be sure all joints are fluid tight.

Have a helper exert pressure on brake pedal (holding pressure). Obtain a reading on master cylinder output of approximately 700 psi. While pressure is being held as above, reading on valve outlet should be 550-610 psi. If the pressure readings do not meet these specifications, the valve should be removed and a new valve installed.

# Front Disc Brakes

## INDEX



## OPERATION

The caliper assembly consists of a pin slider caliper housing, inner and outer shoe and lining assemblies and a single piston, **Figs. 1 and 2.** The caliper slides on two pins which also act as attaching bolts between caliper and the combination anchor plate and spindle. The outer brake shoe and lining assembly is longer than the inner brake shoe and lining assembly. Inner and outer shoe and lining assemblies are attached to the caliper by spring clips riveted to the shoe surfaces. The inner shoe is attached to the caliper by installing the spring clip to the inside of the caliper piston. The outer shoe clips directly to the caliper housing. A wear indicator is incorporated which emits a noise when the lining is worn to a point when replacement is necessary. Inner and outer shoes are of left and right hand and are not interchangeable.

The inner shoe and lining on Mustang with V8-302 engine has a replaceable single finger anti-rattle clip and an insulator held in position by the clip. The shoe is slotted to accept the snap on clip which loads the assembly against the caliper bridge. The inner shoe on the Mustang with 2300cc engine has a single finger anti-rattle clip, holding the shoe down against the spindle ledge. The clip does not lock into the piston. The insulator is also riveted to the shoe and is not replaceable.

## BRAKE PADS REPLACE

### REMOVAL

#### Except Capri, Festiva, Tracer, Scorpio, XR4Ti, Probe & 1991 Escort

1. Remove brake fluid until reservoir is

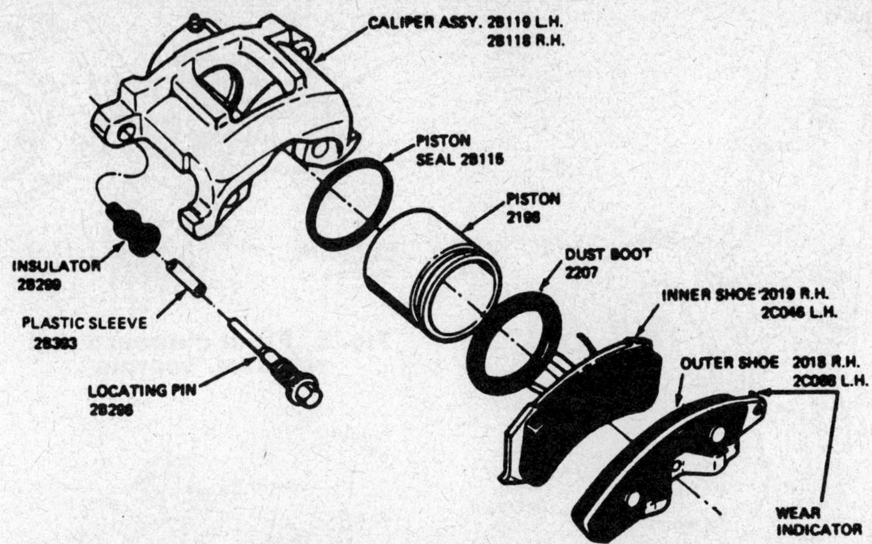


**Fig. 1 Front pin sliding disc brake caliper. Cougar, Crown Victoria, Grand Marquis, LTD, Mark VI & VII, Marquis, Mustang & Thunderbird**

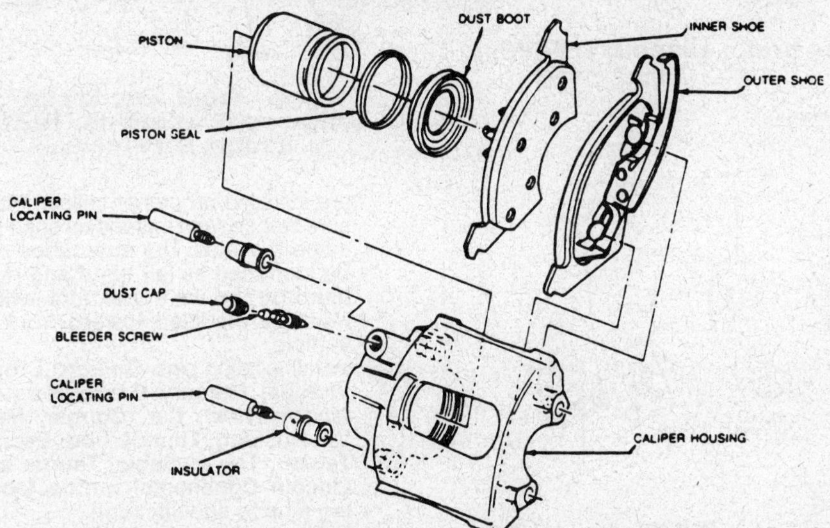


**Fig. 2 Front pin sliding disc brake caliper. Escort, Continental, Sable, Taurus, Tempo and Topaz**

half full.

2. Raise and support front of vehicle, then remove wheel and tire assembly.
3. Remove caliper locating pins.
4. Lift caliper assembly from adapter plate, then remove outer shoe from caliper assembly. **On some models, slip shoe down caliper leg until clip is disengaged.**
5. Remove inner shoe and lining assembly. **On some models, pull shoe straight out of piston. This should require a force as high as 20-30 lbs.**
6. Suspend caliper from inner fender housing with wire to avoid damaging brake hose.
7. Remove and discard locating pin insulators and plastic sleeves.

## Festiva

1. Drain approximately 1/3 of brake fluid from master cylinder.
2. Raise and support front of vehicle, then remove wheel.
3. Remove brake pad pin retainer, then disengage anti-rattle spring from brake pads, **Fig. 3.**
4. Remove brake pad pins and anti-rattle spring, then pull brake pads and shims out of caliper. **Do not discard shims found behind inner brake pad.**

## 1989 Tracer

1. Remove approximately 2/3 of brake fluid from master cylinder.
2. Raise and support front of vehicle.
3. Remove wheel and tire assembly, then, using suitable needle nose pliers, remove retainer locking brake pads to retainer pins, **Fig. 4.**
4. Using a suitable punch, remove brake pad retaining pins.
5. Using a screwdriver, pry caliper outward, then remove outboard pad and shim. **Do not damage caliper piston boots.** Note location of shim for assembly reference.
6. Push caliper inward, then remove inboard pad and shim.
7. Remove anchor plate clips and tag for assembly reference.

## Scorpio & XR4Ti

1. Raise and support vehicle.
2. Remove wheel and tire assembly.
3. Disconnect brake pad wear sensor electrical connector from main harness. Remove connector from clip, leaving clip in position under bleed screw.
4. Remove spring retaining clip from caliper housing.
5. Unfasten caliper assembly and position aside. **Do not disconnect brake line.**
6. Remove inboard brake pad from piston.
7. Force piston into caliper housing using tool No. D79L-2196-A or equivalent, **Fig. 5**, then remove outboard pad.

## 1991 Escort & Tracer

1. Remove wheel and tire assembly.
2. Remove the two brake pad retaining pins from caliper assembly.
3. Remove "M" spring, then the "W" spring, **Fig. 6.**
4. Remove brake pads and shims from the caliper assembly.

## Capri

1. Remove approximately two-thirds of the brake fluid from the master cylinder.
2. Raise and support vehicle.
3. Remove wheel and tire assembly.
4. Using needle nose pliers, remove the pad retainer spring that locks in the disc pad retainer pins.
5. Using a hammer and pin punch, remove the disc pad retainer pins shown in **Fig. 7.**
6. Using a screwdriver, pry the caliper outward to compress the caliper piston inward, then remove the outboard brake pad and shim.
7. Mark the shims with a permanent marker so they can be installed in their original position.
8. Push the caliper inward with one hand, then remove the inboard brake pad with the other hand.
9. Remove the anchor plate clips from the caliper anchor plate. Label the anchor plate clips "top" and "bottom" as they are removed.

## Probe

1. Remove approximately 2/3 of brake fluid from master cylinder.
2. Raise and support vehicle.
3. Remove wheel and tire assembly.
4. Using a screwdriver, pry caliper outboard.
5. Remove caliper mounting bolt, **Fig. 8,** then slide caliper upward.
6. Slide caliper off guide pin, then tag anti-rattle shims so shims can be reinstalled in their original position.
7. Remove brake pads from caliper anchor.
8. Remove retaining clips from brake pads.

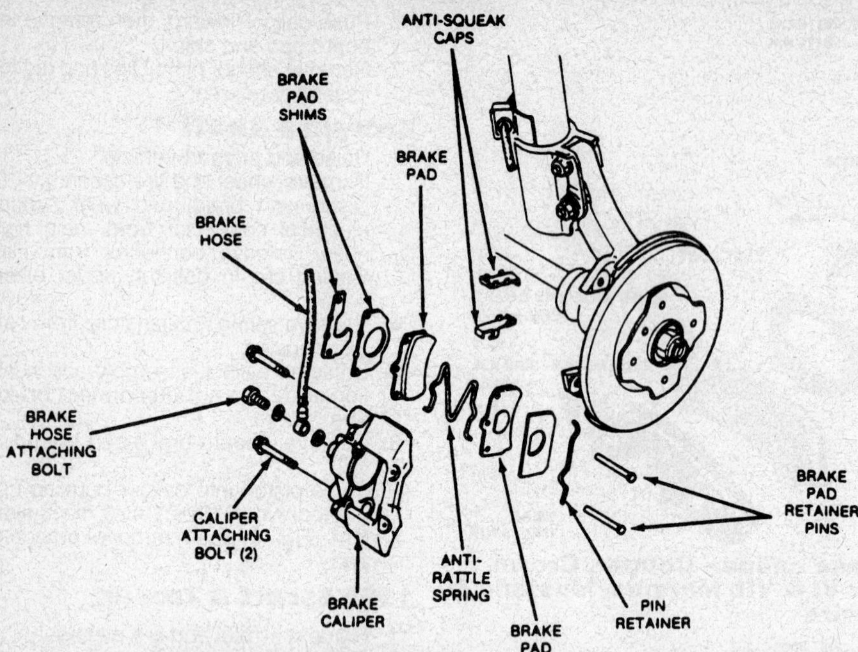


**Fig. 3 Exploded view of front disc brake assembly. Festiva**

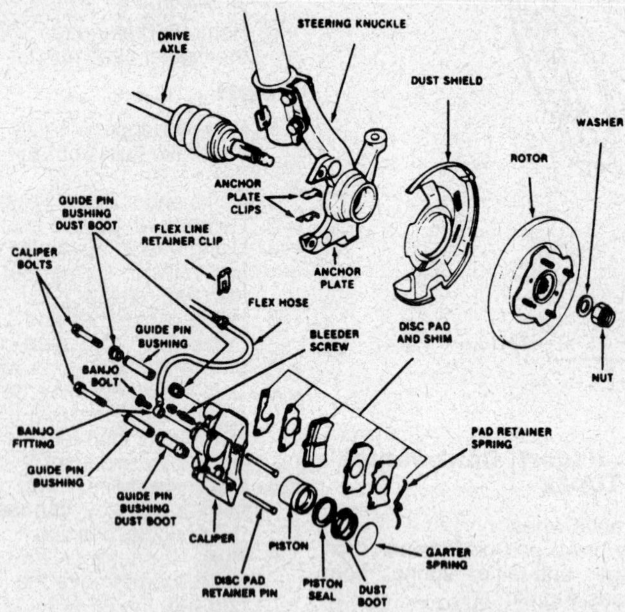


**Fig. 4 Front disc brake assembly. Tracer**

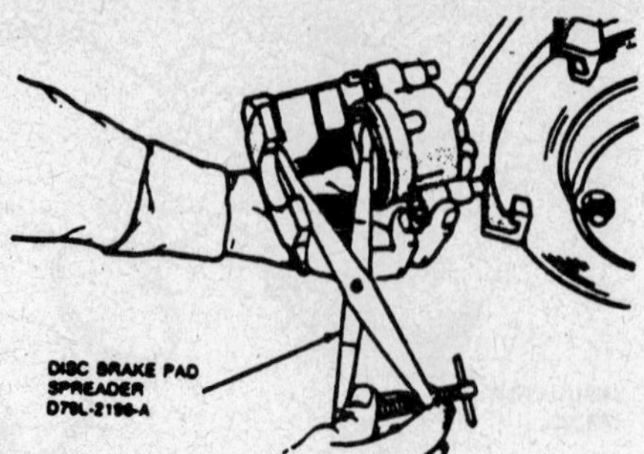


**Fig. 5 Front outboard pad removal. Scorpio**

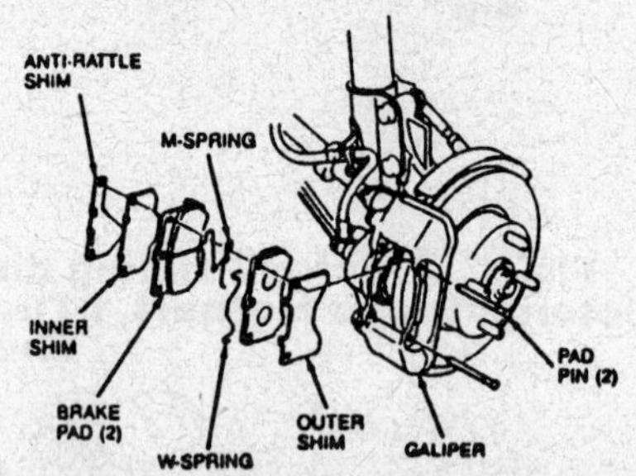


**Fig. 6 Front disc brake component locations. 1991 Escort & Tracer**

# INSTALLATION

## Except Capri, Festiva, Tracer, Scorpio, XR4Ti, Probe & 1991 Escort

1. Using a 4 inch C-clamp and a block of wood 2¾ x 1 inch and approximately ¾ inch thick, seat caliper piston in bore, then remove C-clamp and wooden block. **On some models,** the piston is made of phenolic material. Do not seat piston in bore by applying C-clamp directly to piston. Extra care must be taken during this procedure to prevent damage to the piston. Metal or sharp objects cannot come into direct contact with the piston or damage may result.
2. Install locating pin insulators and plastic sleeves on caliper housing. Ensure insulators and sleeves are properly positioned.
3. Install inner shoe and lining assembly on caliper piston, **Fig. 9. Some inner brake shoes are marked LH (left hand) and RH (right hand) and must be installed on the proper caliper. Use care to not bend spring clips too far during installation in piston, otherwise distortion and rattles may result.**
4. Install outer brake shoe and lining assembly, **Fig. 10.** Ensure that shoes are installed on proper caliper. Make sure that clip and buttons on shoe are properly seated. **The outer shoe can be identified as left hand and right hand by the wear indicator which must be installed toward front of vehicle.**
5. Install locating pins. **On Ford Crown Victoria, Mercury Grand Marquis, Lincoln Town Car, Cougar, Mark VII, Mustang, Thunderbird, Escort, Tempo, Topaz, Sable, Taurus and Lincoln Continental torque locating pins to specification.**
6. Refill master cylinder, then install wheel and tire assembly and lower vehicle.
7. Pump brake pedal several times to position brake linings before moving vehicle.

## Festiva

1. Push piston back fully into caliper bore.
2. Apply suitable brake grease to both sides of inner shim and to back of inner brake pad.
3. Install brake pads and shims, ensuring shims are positioned correctly.
4. Install brake pad pins, anti-rattle spring and pin retainer.
5. Install wheel and lower vehicle, then check and adjust master cylinder fluid level as required.

## 1989 Tracer

1. Install anchor plate clips in same order as removed.
2. Push caliper inboard, then install inboard brake pad and shims.
3. Pry caliper outboard, then install outboard brake pad and shim.

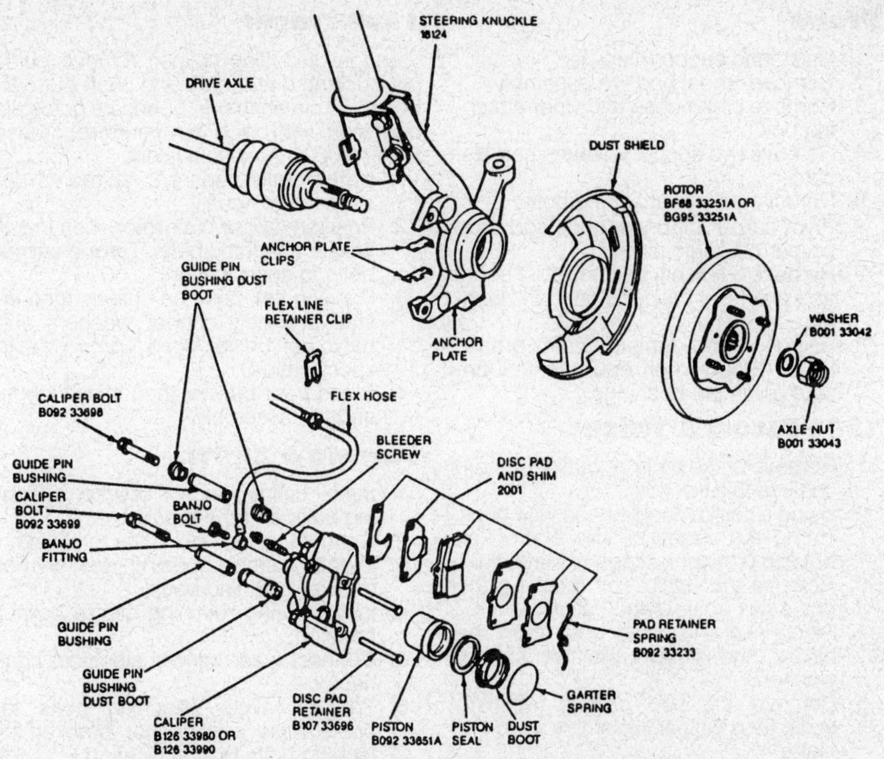


**Fig. 7 Front disc brake assembly. Capri**

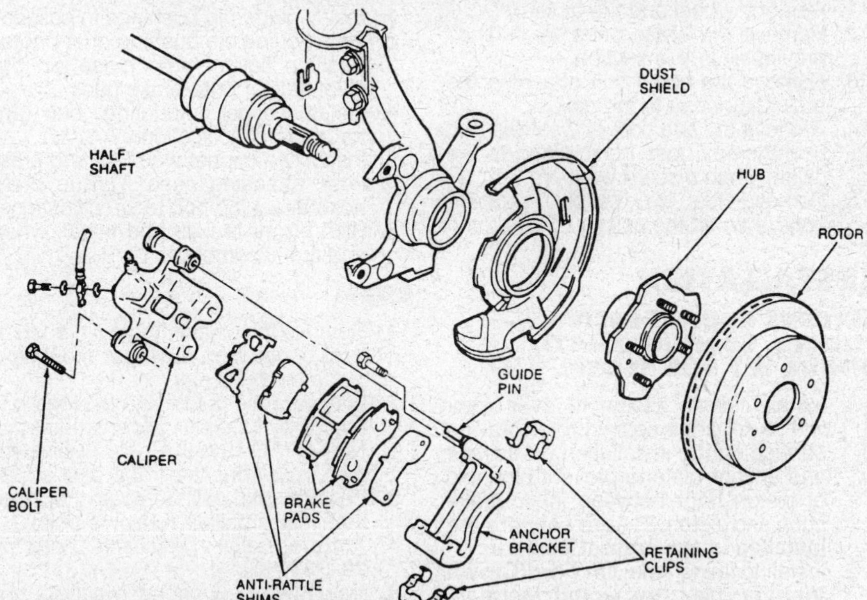


**Fig. 8 Exploded view of front disc brake assembly. Probe**

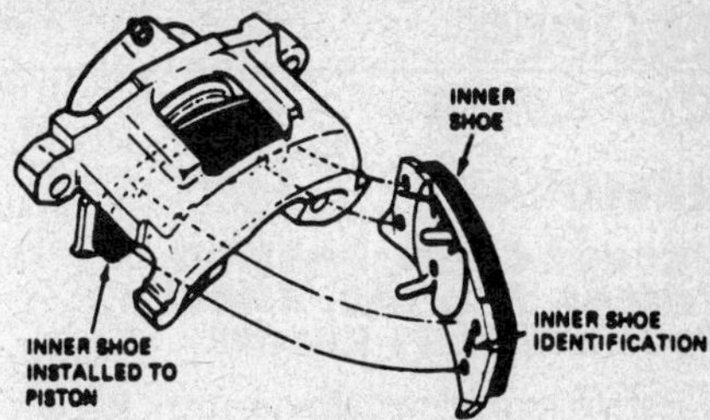


**Fig. 9 Installing inner brake shoe on caliper**

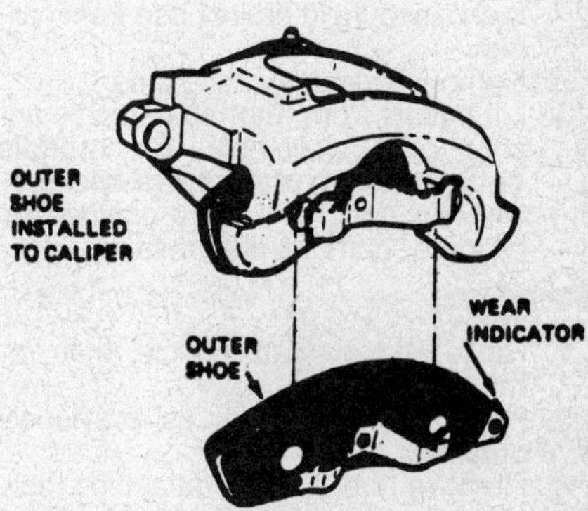


**Fig. 10 Installing outer brake shoe on caliper**

4. Install brake pad retaining pins and springs.
5. Install tire and wheel assembly, then pump brake pedal several times to seat brake pads.

### Scorpio & XR4Ti

1. Install inboard pad into caliper piston, then the outboard pad into anchor bracket.
2. Install pad sensor wiring clip, then the caliper assembly. Torque caliper bolts to specification.
3. Install wheel and tire assembly, then lower vehicle.
4. Pump brake pedal several times to properly position brake pads before moving vehicle.
5. Verify proper operation of pad wear warning lamp, then road test vehicle.

### Probe

1. Install retaining clips on brake pads.
2. Install brake pads into caliper anchor.
3. Install caliper onto guide pin and pivot caliper down over brake pads.
4. Install caliper mounting bolt and torque to specification, **Fig. 8.**
5. Install wheel and tire assembly and torque lug nuts to specification.
6. Pump brake pedal several times to seat brake pads.

### 1991 Escort & Tracer

1. Push the piston fully into the caliper bore.
2. Apply grease between the shims and the brake pad guide plates, then position the brake pads and shims into the caliper.
3. Install the "W" spring, then "M" spring.
4. Install the two brake pad retaining pins, then wheel and tire assembly.

### Capri

1. Install the anchor plate clips. **If the clips are not placed in their original positions, the locating tabs may contact the brake rotor.**
2. Push the caliper assembly inward and install the inboard brake pad and shims.
3. Pry the caliper outward and install the outboard pad and shim. **Ensure the spring tabs on the back of the brake are properly aligned and fully seated in the caliper piston.**
4. Install the brake pad retaining pins, then pin retaining spring.
5. Install wheel and tire assembly. **Torque** wheel lug nuts to 65-88 ft. lbs.
6. Correct level of brake fluid in master cylinder as necessary.

# CALIPER REPLACE

## REMOVAL

### Except Capri, Festiva, Tracer, Scorpio, XR4Ti, Probe & 1991 Escort

Before removing calipers, mark left and right hand calipers so they can be installed in the same position.

1. Raise and support front of vehicle, then remove wheel and tire assembly.
2. Loosen brake tube fitting which connects brake tube to fitting on frame and plug brake tube. Remove retaining clip from brake hose and bracket, then disconnect brake hose from caliper.
3. Remove caliper locating pins.
4. Lift caliper from rotor and spindle anchor plate assembly. **On models equipped with phenolic caliper piston,** do not pry directly against the piston or damage may result.

### Festiva

1. Raise and support vehicle, then remove wheel.
2. Remove brake pads as previously outlined.
3. Remove brake hose attaching bolt, then disconnect hose from caliper. Discard seal washers located between brake hose connection and caliper.
4. Remove caliper attaching bolts and the caliper.
5. Reverse procedure to install using new seal washers. Torque caliper attaching bolts to specification, then bleed brake system.

### 1989 Tracer

1. Raise and support front of vehicle.
2. Remove wheel and tire assembly, then remove brake pads as described previously.
3. Remove brake hose-to-caliper fitting, **Fig. 4.**
4. Remove two caliper attaching bolts, then lift caliper from rotor.

### Scorpio & XR4Ti

1. Raise and support vehicle.
2. Remove wheel and tire assembly.
3. Disconnect electrical connector from brake pad wear sensor.
4. Remove spring retaining clip from caliper housing.
5. Remove piston housing bolts and the housing from anchor bracket.
6. Disconnect brake hose from caliper. Plug line to prevent leakage and contamination.
7. Remove caliper anchor bracket attaching bolts and the bracket, if necessary.
8. Reverse procedure to install, noting the following:
   a. Torque caliper attaching bolts, brake hose and anchor bracket attaching bolts to specification.
   b. Following completion of installation, bleed front brake system.

### Probe

1. Raise and support vehicle.
2. Remove wheel and tire assembly.
3. Remove brake hose to caliper attaching bolt.
4. Remove two copper washers and discard.
5. Remove caliper attaching bolts.
6. Pivot caliper off brake pads and slide caliper off guide pin.
7. Remove guide pin bushing dust boots and push out caliper guide pin bushing.
8. Using high temperature grease D7AZ-19590-A or equivalent, lubricate guide pin bushings.

### 1991 Escort & Tracer

1. Remove brake pads as outlined previously in this section.
2. Using a pair of needle nose vise grips, clamp the center of the brake flex hose to prevent leakage of brake fluid.
3. Remove the banjo bolt retaining the brake flex hose to the caliper.
4. Disconnect the brake hose from the caliper and discard the two copper washers.
5. Remove the two caliper retaining bolts, then caliper assembly from vehicle.

### Capri

1. Remove wheel and tire assembly.
2. Remove the brake pads as outlined previously in this section.
3. Remove the banjo bolt attaching the brake flex hose to the caliper.
4. Remove the two copper washers that seal the flex hose banjo fitting to the caliper, then discard washers.
5. Remove the two caliper retaining bolts, then lift the caliper off the rotor.

## INSTALLATION

### Except Capri, Festiva, Tracer, Scorpio, XR4Ti, Probe & 1 991 Escort

1. Install caliper assembly over rotor with outer shoe against rotor braking surface during installation on spindle and anchor plate to prevent pinching of piston boot between inner brake shoe and piston. **Ensure calipers are installed in the correct position.**
2. Install locating pins. **On Ford Crown Victoria, Mercury Grand Marquis, Lincoln Town Car, Cougar, Mark VII, Mustang, Thunderbird, Escort, Tempo, Topaz, Sable, Taurus and Lincoln Continental torque locating pins to specification.**
3. Connect brake hose to caliper and tighten hose fitting.
4. Position upper end of brake hose in bracket and install retaining clip. Remove plug from brake line, then connect brake hose fitting to brake line.
5. Bleed brake system.
6. Install wheel and tire assembly, then lower vehicle.
7. Pump brake pedal several times to position brake shoes before moving vehicle.

### 1989 Tracer

Before installing caliper, remove guide pin bushing dust boots and push out caliper guide pin bushings. Lubricate guide pin bushings with high temperature grease D7AZ-19590-A or equivalent.

1. Install brake pads and shims as described previously.
2. Position caliper over rotor, then install caliper attaching bolts. Torque caliper bolts to specification.
3. Position flex hose on caliper, then install two new copper washers and banjo bolt on flex hose. Torque bolt to specification.
4. Bleed front brakes, then install wheel and tire assembly.

### Scorpio & XR4Ti

1. Install caliper anchor bracket attaching bolts and the bracket.
2. Connect caliper flex hose to caliper.
3. Install piston housing to anchor bracket retaining bolts.
4. Install spring retaining clip to caliper housing.
5. Connect wear sensor electrical connector.
6. Torque caliper attaching bolts to, brake hose and anchor bracket attaching bolts to specification.

### Probe

1. Install guide pin bushings in caliper.
2. Install guide pin bushing dust boots.
3. Position caliper onto guide pin and pivot caliper onto brake pads.
4. Install caliper mounting bolt and torque to specification.
5. Install two copper washers and brake hose attaching hose. Torque brake hose attaching bolt to specification.
6. Bleed front brakes and install wheel and tire assembly.

### Capri

1. Remove the caliper guide pin bushing dust boots, then push out the caliper guide pin bushings.
2. Lubricate the guide pin bushings with Disc Brake Caliper Slide Grease part No. D7AZ-19590-A or equivalent, then install bushings and dust boots.
3. Position the caliper over the rotor, then install caliper retaining bolts.
4. **Torque** caliper retaining bolts to 29-36 ft. lbs.
5. Install two new copper washers and banjo bolt on brake flex hose, then position the flex hose on the caliper assembly.
6. **Torque** banjo bolt to 17-21 ft. lbs.
7. Install brake pads and shims as previously outlined in this section.
8. Bleed brake system, then install wheel and tire assembly.
9. **Torque** wheel lug nuts to 65-88 ft. lbs.

### 1991 Escort & Tracer

1. Position the caliper and install the two caliper mounting bolts. **Torque** caliper mounting bolts to 29-36 ft. lbs.
2. Install two new copper washers to the brake hose.

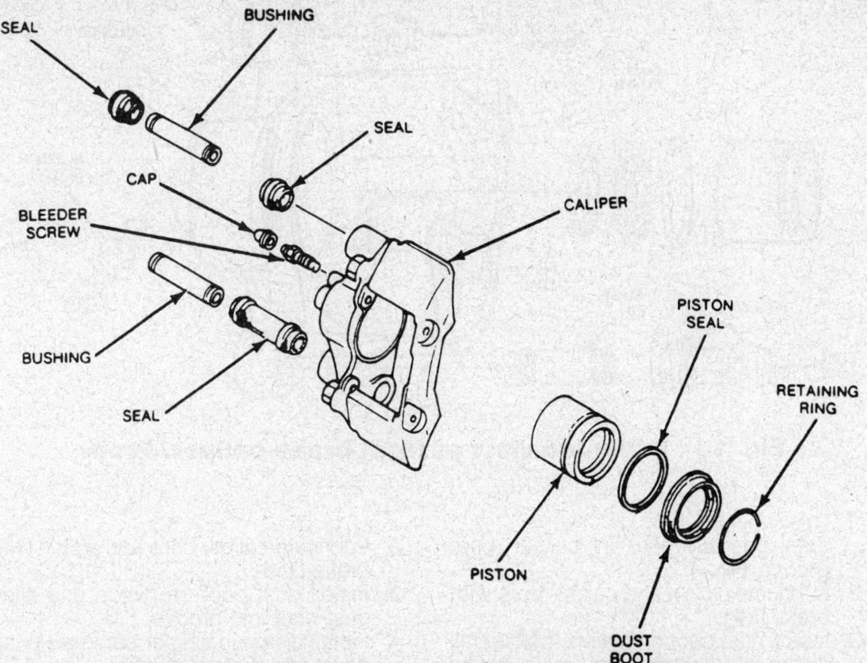


**Fig. 11 Exploded view of brake caliper. Festiva**

3. Position the brake hose onto the caliper, then install the banjo bolt. **Torque** banjo bolt to 16-22 ft. lbs.
4. Remove needle nose vise grips from brake flex hose.
5. Install brake pads as previously outlined in this section.
6. Correct brake fluid level in master cylinder as necessary.
7. Bleed brake system.

# ROTOR

## REPLACE

### 1991 CAPRI, ESCORT & TRACER

#### Removal

1. Raise and support vehicle, then remove wheel and tire assembly.
2. Using a chisel, unstake and remove halfshaft retaining nut and washer. **Discard nut and washer.**
3. Remove brake pads and caliper from the steering knuckle as outlined previously in this section. Support the caliper by a wire strung from the coil spring. Do not disconnect the brake line from the caliper.
4. Using tie rod end separator tool No. T85M-3395-A or equivalent, disconnect the tie rod end from the steering knuckle.
5. Remove ball joint pinch bolt. Separate control arm from steering knuckle.
6. Remove steering knuckle to strut assembly retaining bolts.
7. Using knuckle puller tool No. T87C-1104-A and step plate tool No. D80L-630-3 or equivalents, remove the rotor and hub assembly from the steering knuckle. **The dust shield is pressed onto the steering knuckle. If the bearings are not being serviced, leave the dust shield attached to the knuckle.**

#### Installation

1. Install rotor to the hub. **Torque** retaining bolts to 33-39 ft. lbs.
2. Press the hub and rotor assembly into the steering knuckle.
3. Position the steering knuckle on the Macpherson strut, then install the retaining bolts. **Torque** bolts to 69-86 ft. lbs.
4. Raise the lower control arm and position the lower ball joint stud in the steering knuckle, then install the ball joint pinch bolt.
5. **Torque** pinch bolt 32-39 ft. lbs.
6. Install caliper and brake pads as previously outlined in this section.
7. Install new halfshaft retaining nut, then **torque** nut to 116-174 ft. lbs.
8. Install wheel and tire assembly, then **torque** wheel lug nuts to 65-88 ft. lbs.

# CALIPER OVERHAUL

## DISASSEMBLY

### Except Capri, Festiva, Tracer, Scorpio, XR4Ti, Probe & 1991 Escort

1. Remove caliper assembly from vehicle as described under "Caliper, Replace."
2. Position fiber block and shop towels between caliper piston and caliper housing, then apply compressed air to caliper brake line fitting bore to force piston from caliper.
3. Remove dust boot from caliper assembly, **Figs. 1 and 2.**
4. Remove piston seal from cylinder and discard.

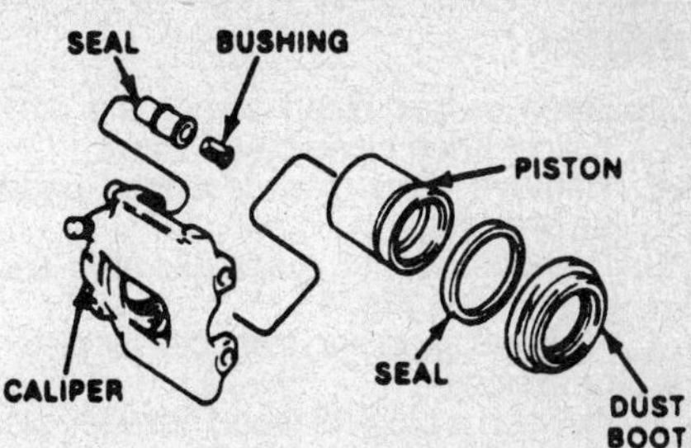


**Fig. 12 Exploded view of front brake caliper. Scorpio**

### Festiva

1. Remove brake pads and caliper as outlined previously.
2. Remove bleeder screw, drain remaining fluid from caliper, then reinstall screw.
3. Remove dust boot retaining ring, **Fig. 11.**
4. Position a block of wood between piston and caliper, then apply compressed air to fluid inlet port and blow piston from caliper bore. **Apply only enough pressure to ease piston out of bore.**
5. Remove dust boot from piston, then using a suitable wooden pick, carefully pry piston seal from caliper bore.
6. Remove bleeder screw, then the caliper bushings and bushing seals.
7. Wash all parts in denatured alcohol and dry with compressed air.

### Capri, Tracer & 1991 Escort

1. Open caliper bleed screw and drain caliper, then close bleed screw.
2. Remove caliper as described under as previously outlined.
3. Remove caliper guide bushing and dust boots, **Fig. 4.**
4. Remove snap ring from caliper piston dust boot.
5. Position a wooden block or shop towels between caliper and piston, then apply air pressure to brake hose fitting to remove piston from caliper. Use only enough air pressure to ease piston from caliper bore. Keep hands and fingers away from piston, as personal injury may result.
6. Remove dust boot from caliper, then using a wooden or plastic pick, remove piston seal from caliper bore.

### Scorpio & XR4Ti

1. Remove caliper assembly and brake pads as previously described.
2. Open bleeder screw and drain fluid from caliper, then close bleeder screw.
3. Position block of wood between piston and caliper, then apply air pressure through fluid inlet port to remove piston. **Apply only enough air pressure to ease piston out of caliper.**
4. Remove dust boot from piston and discard, **Fig. 12.**
5. Remove piston seal from caliper and discard.
6. Remove caliper anchor pin bushing, then the anchor pin seal.

### Probe

1. Open caliper bleed screw and drain caliper, then close bleed screw.
2. Remove caliper as described under as previously outlined.
3. Remove caliper guide bushing and dust boots, **Fig. 13.**
4. Remove snap ring from caliper piston dust boot.
5. Position a block of wood between piston and caliper.
6. Apply air pressure to through brake hose fitting. **Do not use excessive air pressure to remove piston.**
7. Remove dust boot and discard.
8. Remove piston seal from caliper and discard.

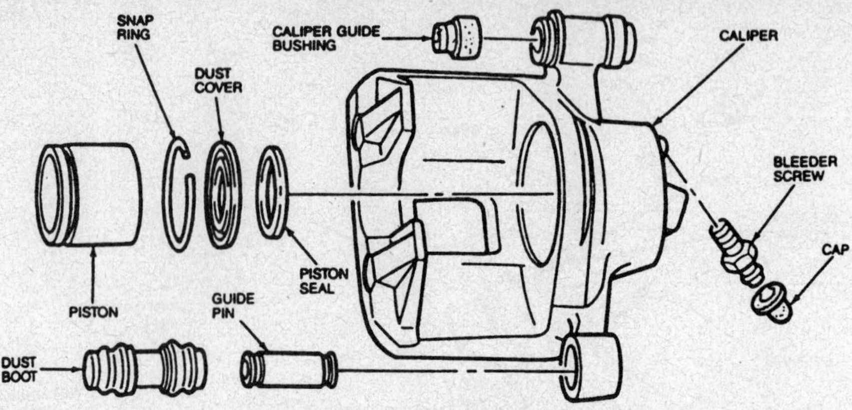


**Fig. 13 Exploded view of front brake caliper. Probe**

## INSPECTION

1. Check piston for scratches, scoring or damage. Replace, if necessary.
2. Check caliper bore for scratches, scoring or corrosion. Light scratches or slight corrosion can be polished out using crocus cloth.
3. Check that bleeder screw and bleeder screw bore hole in caliper are fully open.
4. Check caliper bushings for corrosion and dust boot retaining ring for damage or tension loss. Replace parts as necessary.

## ASSEMBLY

### Except Capri, Festiva, Tracer, Scorpio, XR4Ti, Probe & 1991 Escort

1. Lubricate piston seal with clean brake fluid, then install seal in caliper bore. **Ensure seal is firmly seated in groove.**
2. Install dust boot in outer groove of caliper bore, **Figs. 1 and 2.**
3. Coat piston with clean brake fluid and install piston in caliper bore. Spread dust boot over piston as it is installed. Seat dust boot in piston groove.
4. Install caliper assembly as described under "Caliper, Replace."

### Festiva

1. Lubricate piston seal with suitable brake grease or clean brake fluid, then install into caliper bore.
2. Lubricate piston, then partially install into caliper bore. Ensure dust boot groove on piston remains above caliper bore.
3. Lubricate dust boot with suitable brake grease, then install onto piston.
4. Press piston fully inward until it bottoms in bore, then install dust boot retaining ring.
5. Install bleeder screw.
6. Install caliper bushings and new bushing seals. Lubricate inner surface of bushing seal and outer surface of bushings with suitable brake grease before installation.

### Capri, Tracer & 1991 Escort

1. Lubricate piston seal with brake fluid, then position seal in caliper bore groove, **Fig. 4.**
2. Lubricate piston and caliper bore with brake fluid.
3. Install dust boot on piston, then install piston into caliper bore. Use a gentle rocking motion to bottom piston in caliper bore.
4. Slide dust boot over caliper bore boss and install retaining ring.
5. Install caliper assembly as described under "Caliper, Replace."
6. After completing installation, bleed brake system, then cycle brake pedal several times to seat brake pads and to ensure system is function properly.

### Scorpio & XR4Ti

1. Install caliper anchor pin seal, spraying seal with silicone lubricant to aid installation.
2. Install caliper anchor pin bushing, overlapping edges of bushing slightly to fit bushing into seal. After installation, press bushing against seal to remove overlapping. When properly installed, the ends of the bushing must abut against each other.
3. Lubricate new piston seal with brake fluid and install in seal groove, ensuring that seal does not become twisted but is firmly seated in groove.
4. Position dust boot at bottom of piston and, holding dust boot on piston, pull on seal lip until seal unfolds, allowing lip seal to extend beyond bottom of piston.
5. While holding dust boot on piston, fit seal lip in caliper bore and push piston into caliper. As piston enters bore, the dust boot will refold to its original shape.

### Probe

1. Lubricate mew piston seal with brake fluid and install seal in caliper groove. **Ensure seal does not become twisted in caliper bore.**
2. Lubricate caliper bore and piston with brake fluid.
3. Install dust boot on piston and slide dust boot into groove.
4. Install piston in caliper bore and push down into bottom of bore.
5. Slide dust boot over boss on caliper bore and install snap ring.
6. Install caliper guide bushing, dust boot and guide pin.
7. Install caliper bolt and torque to specification.
8. Bleed front brakes, then pump brake pedal several times to seat brake pads.
9. Check fluid level and add if necessary.
10. With vehicle in Neutral, spin each rotor to ensure brakes are not dragging.
11. Install wheel and tire assemblies.

## SERVICE BULLETINS

### COMPOSITE ROTORS

#### Continental, Sable & Taurus

The disc rotor is a hat section-type composite rotor of steel and cast iron. A Rotunda Rotor Mounting Adapter tool No. 054-00032 or equivalent is required for use on the brake lathe for refinishing. **Failure to use the adapter will result in gouging the brake disc, making it unfit for use.**

A new design full cast front disc brake rotor is now available for service use. If service is required, install the new full cast front disc rotors part No. F10Y-1125-B **in pairs only. Never install a full cast rotor on one side of the vehicle with a composite rotor on the other side.**

The new full cast front disc rotor will not fit 1991 Continental, Sable & Taurus vehicles built after January, 1991. Vehicles built after January, 1991, use a full cast rotor with a larger pilot diameter, part No. F2DZ-1125-A.

The composite rotor, part No. E80Y-1125-A can still be used on the re ar of 1989 Continental vehicles.

# Rear Disc Brakes & Parking Brakes

## INDEX



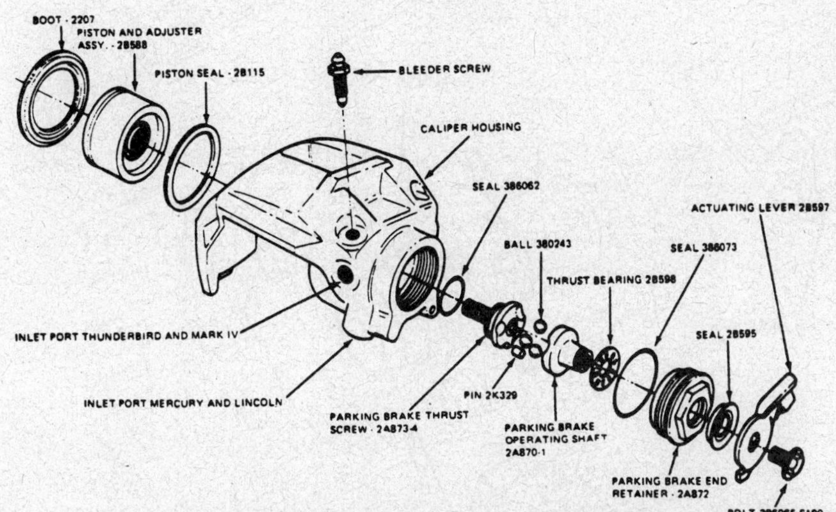


**Fig. 1 Rear disc brake caliper assembly. Mark VII**

## OPERATION

### CONTINENTAL, MARK VII & THUNDERBIRD

Sliding caliper rear disc brakes are used on Continental, Mark VII & Thunderbird, **Figs. 1 and 2.** The caliper is basically the same as the larger front wheel caliper, however, a parking brake mechanism and a larger inner brake shoe anti-rattle spring have been added.

The parking brake lever, located at the rear of the caliper, is actuated by a cable system similar to rear drum brake applications. When the parking brake is applied, the cable rotates the lever and operating shaft, driving the caliper piston and brake shoe assembly against the rotor. An automatic adjuster in the assembly compensates for lining wear and maintains proper clearance in the parking brake mechanism.

The cast iron rotors are ventilated by curved fins located between the braking surfaces and are designed to cause the rotor to act as an air pump when the vehicle is traveling forward. The rotors are not interchangeable and are identified by a Right or Left marking cast inside the hat section of the rotor. The rotor is secured to the axle flange in the same manner as a rear brake drum. A splash shield is bolted to a forged axle adapter to protect the inboard rotor surface.

### CAPRI & PROBE

Rear braking is provided by self-adjusting single piston, floating caliper disc brakes. The caliper slides on two hollow, stainless steel guide pins in bushings.

One guide pin is secured to the anchor bracket by a bolt. The other guide pin is held in position by the caliper retaining bolt.

The disc pads are held in the anchor bracket by two retaining clips and a "V" spring. The caliper must be removed to replace the disc pads.

During normal operation, hydraulic pressure from the master cylinder pushes the piston forward and applies pressure on the inboard brake pad. This pressure also causes the caliper to slide inward on the guide pins. As the brakes are applied, the square cut piston seal distorts. When the brake pedal is released, The square cut seal returns the piston to its normal position. If the piston moves no further than the square cut deformation limit, no self-adjustment takes place. If the movement of the piston is greater than the deformation limit of the square cut seal, the piston and sleeve nut will travel on the threads of the spindle. This is because the loosened adjuster spring allows the sleeve nut to rotate. When the brake pedal is released, the piston returns the amount the square cut seal was deformed but it does not return to its original position. This is because the tightened adjuster spring does not allow the sleeve nut to rotate and travel on the thread. The piston can adjust outward from the caliper housing but it cannot move inward.

When the parking brake is applied inside the vehicle, the parking brake cable moves the caliper mounted parking brake lever. This causes force to be applied to the connecting link, which pushes the piston against the inboard pad. The pressure of the piston against the inboard pad causes the caliper to slide on the guide pins, applying pressure to the outboard pad. As the piston moves outward in the caliper housing, it causes the square cut piston seal to distort. When the parking brake is released inside the vehicle, the square cut seal returns the piston to its normal position and releases the brakes.

### TRACER & 1991 ESCORT

The rear disc brake system consists of a solid disc rotor and a single piston caliper. The brake pads are held in position between the caliper and the rotor by two guides, two shims and an "M" spring. It is not necessary to remove the caliper completely to replace the brake pads; the pads can be removed simply by pivoting the caliper on its mounting bracket.

The parking brake cable is attached to the caliper at the operating lever. When the parking brake is applied, the operating lever pushes the connecting link against the piston which forces application of the brake pads. When the parking brake is released, pressure against the piston is released and the brake pads return to their unapplied position.

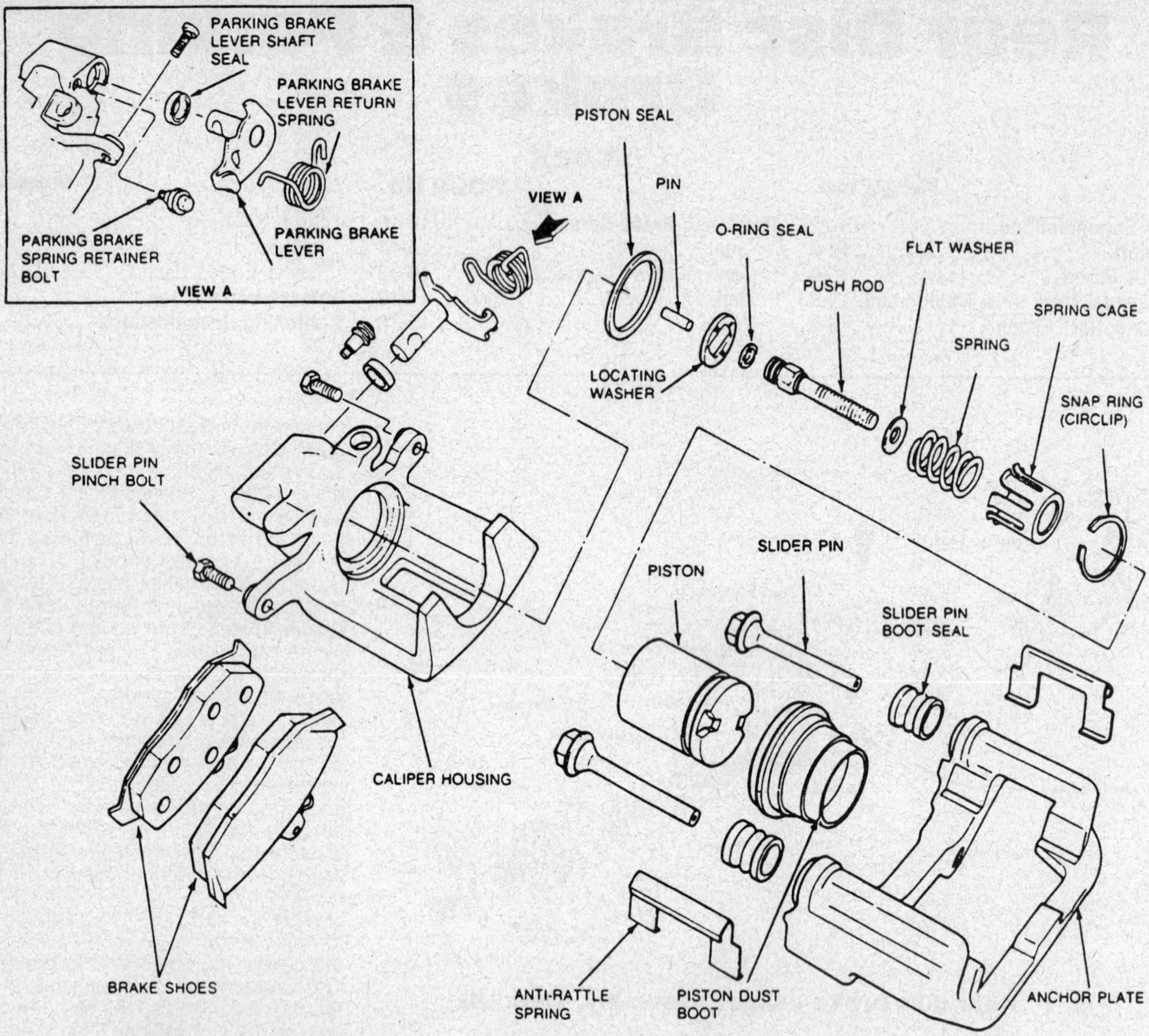

**Fig. 2 Rear disc brake caliper assembly. Thunderbird & Continental**

# REAR DISC BRAKE SERVICE

**After performing any service work, obtain a firm brake pedal before moving vehicle.**

## MARK VII

### CALIPER, REPLACE

#### Removal

1. Raise vehicle and support on safety stands, then remove tire and wheel assemblies.
2. Disconnect fitting on rear brake tube from hose end fitting at frame mounted bracket and plug end of brake tube to prevent loss of fluid and entry of dirt. Remove horse shoe retaining clip from hose fitting and disengage hose from bracket.
3. Disconnect parking cable from lever, **Fig. 3,** using care to avoid kinking or cutting cable or return spring, then remove retaining screw from caliper retaining key, **Fig. 4**, then remove caliper locating pins.

**Fig. 3 Parking lever & cable installation**

4. Slide caliper retaining key and support spring from anchor plate, **Fig. 4.** If necessary, use a hammer and brass drift, being careful to avoid damaging key on sliding ways or hitting parking brake lever. **If caliper cannot be removed due to rust build-up on outer edge of rotor, scrape off loose scale, being careful not to damage braking surfaces. If rotor wear or scoring prevents removal of caliper, it will be necessary to loosen caliper end retainer 1/2 turn maximum, to allow piston to be forced back into its bore. To loosen end retainer, remove parking brake lever and mark or scribe end retainer and caliper housing to be sure that end retainer is not loosened more than 1/2 turn, then force piston back in its bore, Fig. 5, and move caliper back and forth to center rotor and remove caliper. If retainer must be loosened more than 1/2 turn, use caution, as the seal between the thrust screw and housing may be broken and brake fluid will enter parking brake mechanism chamber. In this case, the end retainer must be removed and the internal parts cleaned and lubricated.**

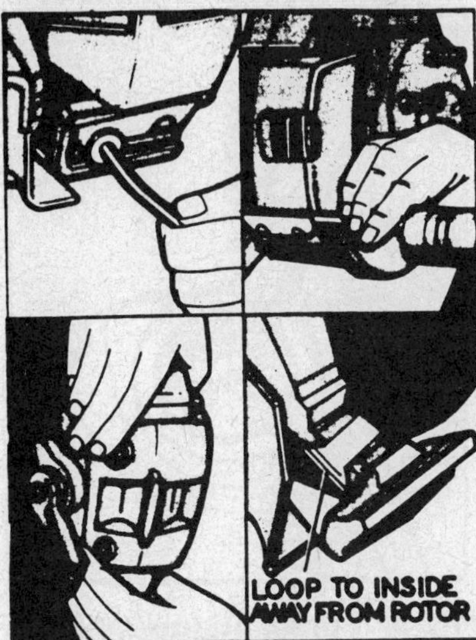


**Fig. 4 Removing rear caliper assembly**

5. Remove outer shoe and lining assembly from anchor plate, then remove rotor retainer nuts and rotor from axle shaft.
6. Remove inner brake shoe and lining assembly from anchor plate and mark each shoe for identification if they are to be reused.
7. Remove anti-rattle clip from anchor plate, then remove flexible hose from caliper by removing hollow retaining bolt.

## Cleaning & Inspection

Clean caliper, anchor plate and rotor assembly and inspect for signs of brake fluid leakage, excessive wear or damage. The caliper must be inspected for leakage both in piston boot area and operating shaft seal area. Lightly sand or wire brush any rust or corrosion from caliper and anchor plate sliding surfaces and inner brake shoe abutment surfaces in anchor plate. Inspect brake shoes for wear. Linings must not be worn to within less than 1/8 inch of shoe surface.

## Installation

1. If end retainer has been loosened only 1/2 turn, reinstall caliper in anchor plate using key. Do not install shoe and lining assembly. Torque end retainer to specification, then install parking brake actuating lever on its keyed spline. Lever arm must point down and rearward so that parking brake cable will pass freely under axle. Torque retainer screw to specification. **Parking brake lever must rotate freely after torquing retainer screw.**
2. Remove caliper from anchor plate. If new shoe and lining assemblies are to be installed, the piston must be bottomed in caliper bore using tool No. T75P-2588-B to provide clearance. Remove rotor and install caliper without lining and shoe assemblies in anchor plate using key only. Install tool and while holding shaft, rotate tool handle counterclockwise until the tool seats firmly against piston, **Fig. 5.**

**Fig. 5 Adjusting piston depth for lining installation**

Loosen handle about 1/4 turn, and while holding handle rotate tool shaft clockwise until piston is fully bottomed in bore (piston will continue to turn even after it is bottomed). Turn tool handle until there is no further inward movement of piston and there is a firm seating force, then remove caliper from mounting plate and reinstall rotor. **For use on some vehicles, tool No. T75P-2588-B must be slightly modified, Fig. 6.**

3. Making certain that brake shoe anti-rattle clip is in place in lower inner brake shoe support on anchor plate with loop of clip toward inside of anchor plate, **Fig. 4,** position inner brake shoe and lining assembly on anchor plate, then install rotor and two retaining nuts.
4. Install outer brake shoe with lower flange ends against caliper abutments and brake shoe upper flanges over shoulders on caliper legs. The shoe upper flanges fit tightly against machined shoulder surfaces. **If old brake shoes and lining assemblies are reused, be certain the shoes are installed in their original positions as marked for identification during removal.**
5. Lubricate caliper and anchor sliding ways with D7AE-019590 grease, using care to prevent lubricant from getting on braking surfaces, then position caliper housing lower V-groove on anchor plate lower abutment surfaces.
6. Rotate caliper until it is completely over rotor, being careful not to damage piston dust boot, then pull caliper outboard until inner shoe and lining is firmly seated against rotor. Measure clearance between outer lining and rotor, clearance must be between 1/32 and 3/32 inch. If it is greater, remove caliper and move piston outward to narrow gap. Follow procedure in step 2 and note that 1/4 turn of the shaft counterclockwise, moves piston about 1/16 inch. **A clearance greater than specified limit may allow adjuster to be pulled out of piston when service brake is applied, causing parking brake to fail to adjust. It will then be necessary to replace piston/adjuster assembly.**
7. While holding caliper against anchor

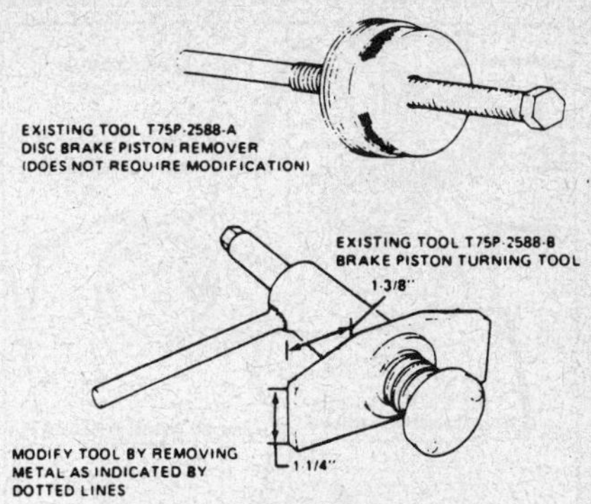


**Fig. 6 Disc brake tool modification**

plate upper abutment surfaces, center caliper over lower anchor plate abutment, then position caliper support spring and key in slot and slide them into opening between lower end of caliper and lower anchor plate abutment until key semi-circular slot is centered over retaining screw threaded hole in anchor plate.

8. Install key retaining screw and torque to specification, then reinstall brake hose on caliper. Place a new gasket on each side of the fitting outlet, then install the attaching bolt through the washers and fitting and torque to specification.
9. Lubricate pins and inside of insulator with D7AZ-19A331-A or equivalent silicone grease and add one drop of Loctite EOAC-19554-A, or equivalent, to locating pin threads. Install locating pins through caliper insulators and into anchor plate and torque to specification.
10. Connect parking brake lever to lever on caliper.
11. Bleed brake system, then with engine running pump brake pedal lightly about 40 times allowing 1 second between pedal applications. An alternate with engine off is to pump brake pedal lightly about 10 times to discharge accumulator, then pump brake pedal firmly about 30 times. Check parking brake for excessive travel or very light effort, if so, repeat pumping brake pedal, and if necessary check parking brake cable tension.
12. Install wheel and torque nuts to specification. **Before moving vehicle, make certain that a firm brake pedal has been obtained.**

## DISC BRAKE PADS, REPLACE

To remove shoe and lining assemblies, follow "Caliper Removal" procedure and omit step 2 as it is not necessary to disconnect brake hose. After removing caliper, support it with a length of wire to avoid damaging brake hose. To install shoe and lining assemblies, follow "Caliper Installation" procedure, making certain that proper parking brake adjustment is obtained.

## CALIPER OVERHAUL

### Disassembly

1. Remove caliper assembly as described previously.

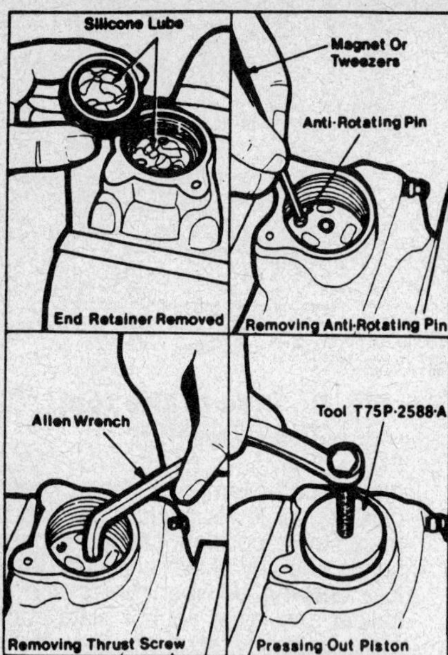


**Fig. 7 Disassembling rear disc brake caliper**

2. Remove caliper end retainer, operating shaft, thrust bearing and balls, **Fig. 1.**
3. Remove thrust screw anti-rotation pin with a magnet or tweezers. If pin cannot be removed with a magnet or tweezers, proceed with the following procedure:
   a. With tool No. T75P-2588B, force piston approximately one inch from caliper bore.
   b. Push piston back into caliper housing with tool, then with tool in position, hold tool shaft in place and rotate handle counterclockwise until thrust screw clears anti-rotation pin. Remove thrust screw and anti-rotation pin.
4. Remove thrust screw by rotating with 1/4 inch Allen wrench.
5. Install Tool No. T75P-2588-A through back of caliper housing and remove piston assembly, **Fig. 7. Use care not to damage polished surface in thrust screw bore and do not attempt to remove or press adjuster can, as it is a press fit in piston.**
6. Remove and discard piston seal, boot, thrust O-ring seal, end retainer, O-ring and end retainer lip seal.

## Cleaning & Inspection

1. Clean all metal parts with alcohol, then using clean, dry compressed air, blow out and dry all grooves and passages making sure the caliper bore and component parts are free of any foreign material.
2. Inspect caliper bore for damage or excessive wear. The thrust screw must be smooth and free of pits. If piston is pitted, scored or chrome plating is worn, replace piston and adjuster assembly.
3. Adjuster can must be bottomed in piston to be properly seated and provide consistent brake operation. If adjuster

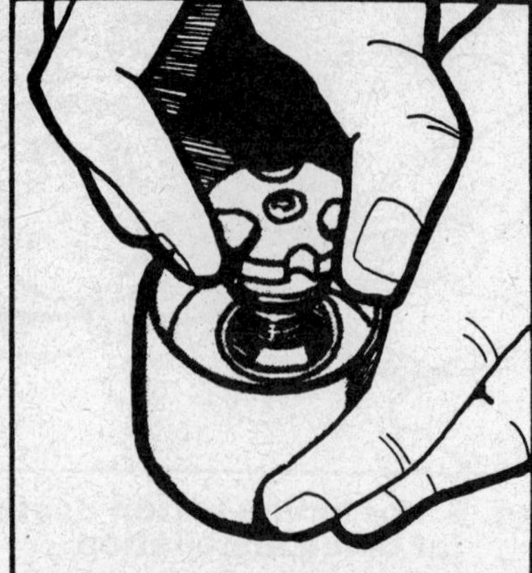

**Fig. 8 Checking parking brake adjuster operation**

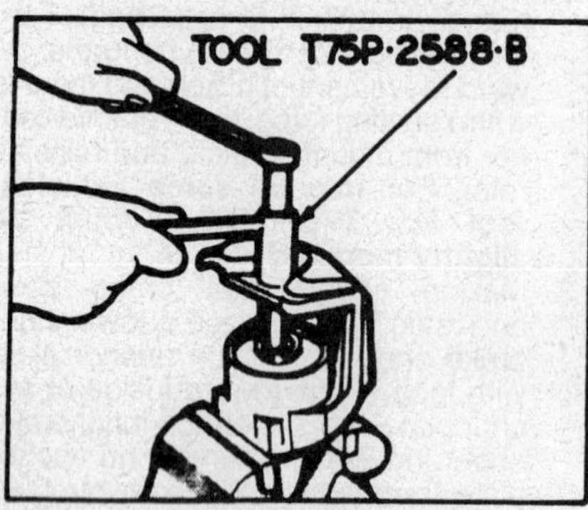


**Fig. 10 Bottoming piston in caliper**

can is loose, appears high in piston, is damaged, or if brake adjustment is usually too tight, too loose or not functioning, replace piston/adjuster assembly. Check adjuster operation by assembling thrust screw into piston/adjuster assembly, then pull the two parts apart about 1/4 inch and release them, **Fig. 8.** When pulling on the two parts, the brass drive ring must remain stationary causing the nut to rotate. When releasing the two parts, the nut must remain stationary and drive ring must rotate. If action does not follow this pattern, replace piston/adjuster assembly.
4. Inspect ball pockets, threads, grooves, bearing surfaces of thrust screw, operating shaft, balls and anti-rotation pin for wear, brinelling or pitting. Replace operating shaft, balls, thrust screw and anti-rotation pin if any of these parts are worn or damaged. A polished appearance on the ball paths is acceptable if there is no sign of wear into the surface.
5. Inspect thrust bearing for corrosion, pitting or wear and replace as necessary.
6. Inspect end plug bearing surface for wear or brinelling and replace as necessary. A polished appearance on bearing surface is acceptable if there is no sign of wear into surface.

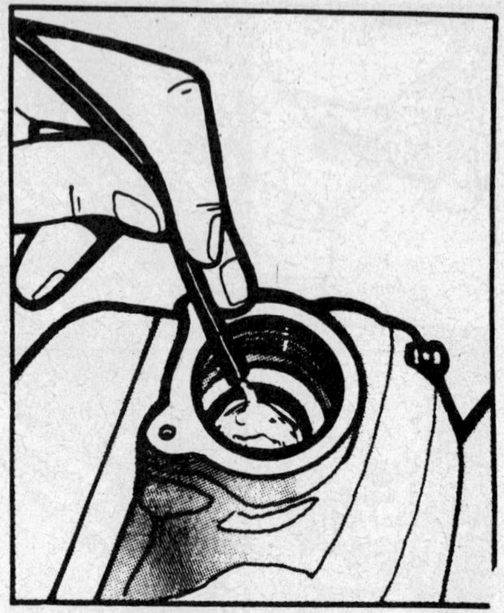

**Fig. 9 Filling piston/adjuster assembly**

7. Inspect operating lever for damage and replace as necessary.

## Assembly

1. Coat new caliper piston seal with clean brake fluid and install it in caliper making certain that seal is not twisted and is fully seated in groove.
2. Install new dust boot by seating flange squarely in outer groove of caliper bore, then coat piston/adjuster assembly with clean brake fluid and install it in caliper bore. Spread dust boot over piston as it is installed and seat dust boot in piston groove.
3. Install caliper in vise, **Fig. 9,** and fill piston/adjuster assembly with clean brake fluid.
4. Coat new thrust screw O-ring with clean brake fluid and install it in thrust screw groove, then install thrust screw into piston adjuster assembly until top surface of thrust screw is flush with bottom of threaded bore, being careful to avoid cutting O-ring seal. Index notches on thrust screw and caliper housing and install anti-rotation pin. **The thrust screw and operating shafts are not interchangeable from side to side since the ramp direction in the ball pockets are different. The pocket surfaces of the operating shaft and thrust screws are stamped "R" (Right) and "L" (Left).**
5. Place a ball in each of three pockets of thrust screw and apply a liberal amount of silicone grease M1C-169-A on parking brake components, then install operating shaft on balls.
6. Coat thrust bearing with silicone grease and install it on operating shaft, then install a new lip seal and O-ring on end retainer.
7. Lightly coat O-ring seal and lip seal with silicone grease and install end retainer in caliper. Firmly hold operating shaft against internal mechanism while installing end retainer to prevent misalignment of balls. If lip seal moves out of position, reseat seal. Torque end retainer to specification. **Parking**

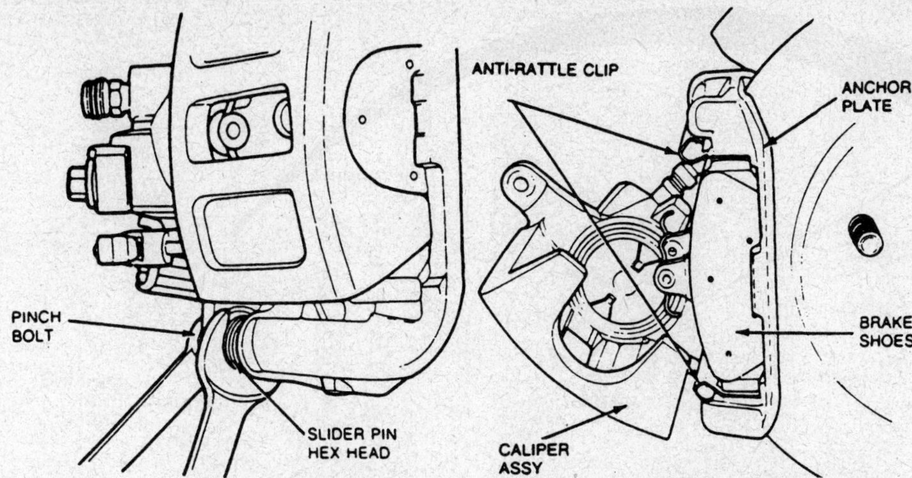


**Fig. 11 Removing slider pin**

**Fig. 12 Positioning anti-rattle clips**

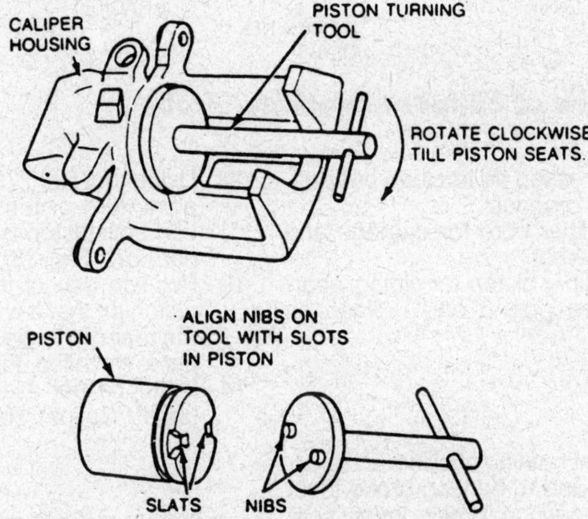


**Fig. 13 Seating caliper piston**

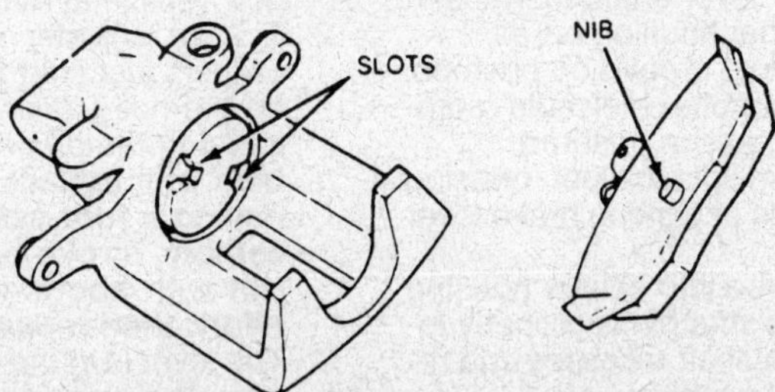


**Fig. 14 Positioning caliper piston to brake pad nib**

**brake lever must rotate freely after torquing.**

8. Install parking brake lever on keyed spline facing down and rearward. Torque retaining screw to specification.
9. Bottom piston using tool No. T75P-2588-B, **Fig. 10,** and install caliper as described previously.

## PARKING BRAKE, ADJUST

1. Fully release parking brake, then place transmission in neutral and support vehicle at rear axle.
2. Tighten adjuster nut until levers on calipers just begin to move, then loosen adjuster nut until levers just return to stop position.
3. Apply and release parking brake. Check levers on caliper to determine if they are fully returned by attempting to pull lever rearward. If lever moves, the adjustment is too tight and must be readjusted.

# CONTINENTAL & THUNDERBIRD

## CALIPER, REPLACE

### Removal

1. Raise and support rear of vehicle, then remove wheel and tire assembly.
2. Disconnect brake hose from caliper assembly.
3. Remove retaining clip, then disconnect parking brake cable from lever arm.
4. Using an open end wrench to hold slider pin in position, remove pinch bolts, **Fig. 11.**
5. Lift caliper assembly from anchor plate, then remove slider pins and boots.

### Installation

1. Apply a suitable silicone dielectric compound to slider pins and inside of boots.
2. Place slider pins and boots on anchor plate, then position caliper assembly on anchor plate. Check to be sure that brake pads and anti-rattle springs are properly positioned, **Fig. 12.**
3. Apply suitable sealer and thread locking compound to pinch bolt threads, then install pinch bolts. While using an open end wrench to hold slider pin in position, torque pinch bolts to specification.
4. Attach parking brake cable to lever arm, then install retaining clip.
5. Using replacement washers, connect brake hose to caliper. Torque retaining bolt to specification.
6. Bleed brake system, then install wheel and tire assembly.
7. Cycle brake pedal several times to position brake pads and caliper piston.

## DISC BRAKE PADS, REPLACE

### Removal

1. Raise and support rear of vehicle, then remove wheel and tire assembly.
2. Remove screw attaching brake hose bracket to shock unit bracket.
3. Remove retaining clip, then disconnect parking brake cable from lever.
4. Using an open end wrench to hold slider pin in position, remove upper pinch bolt, **Fig. 11.** Loosen, but do not lower slider pin pinch bolt.
5. Carefully rotate caliper away from rotor, then remover inner and outer brake pads and anti-rattle springs from anchor plate.

### Installation

1. Using tool No. T87P-2588-A or outer suitable tool, rotate caliper piston clockwise until fully seated, **Fig. 13.** Position one of the two piston slots so that it will engage the nib on the rear of the brake pad, **Fig. 14.**
2. Position inner and outer brake pads on anchor plate, then install anti-rattle springs.
3. Carefully rotate caliper assembly over brake rotor. Ensure brake pads and anti-rattle springs are properly positioned, **Fig. 12.**

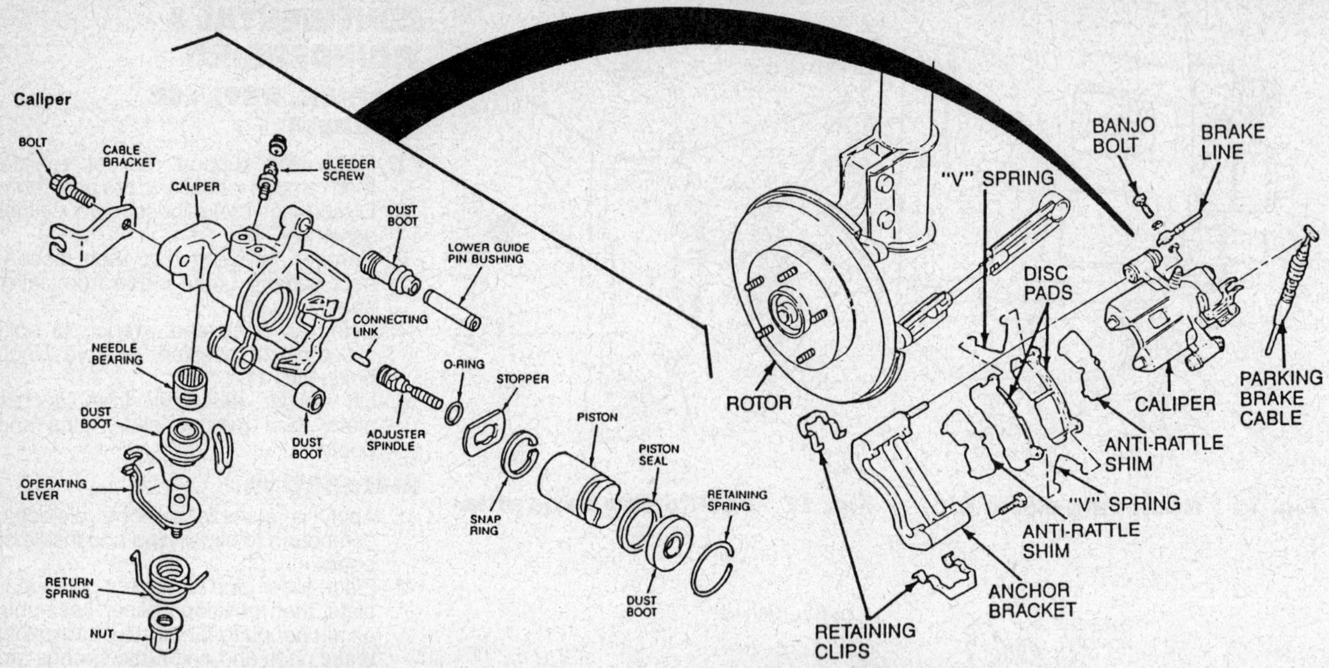


**Fig. 15 Exploded view of caliper assembly. Probe**

4. Apply a suitable thread sealer and locking compound to pinch bolt threads. Install and torque pinch bolts to specification, while holding slider pin in position with a suitable open end wrench.
5. Position parking brake cable to lever, then install retaining clip.
6. Position brake hose and bracket to shock unit bracket and install attaching bolt.
7. Install wheel and tire assembly, then lower vehicle.
8. Cycle brake pedal several times to position brake pads and caliper piston.

## CALIPER OVERHAUL

### Disassembly

1. Remove caliper assembly from vehicle as described under "Caliper, Replace."
2. Position caliper assembly in a soft jawed vise.
3. Using tool No. T75P-2588-B or equivalent, rotate caliper piston counterclockwise to remove from caliper bore, **Fig. 13.**
4. Remove piston dust boot and seal from caliper piston bore, **Fig. 2.**.
5. Remove snap ring retaining pushrod to caliper. Use care when removing, as the snap ring and spring cover are under spring load.
6. Remove spring cover, spring, washer, key plate and pushrod and strut pin from caliper.
7. Remove O-ring from pushrod.
8. Remove parking brake lever return spring, then remove brake lever stop bolt and pull lever from caliper.

### Cleaning & Inspection

1. Clean all metal components with isopropyl alcohol.
2. Use compressed air to clean out passages and grooves.
3. Inspect caliper bore for damage and excessive wear.
4. Inspect caliper piston for pitting, scoring or worn plating and replace as necessary.

### Assembly

1. Apply a light coating of silicone dielectric compound to parking brake lever bore and parking brake lever seal, then position seal into caliper bore, **Fig. 2.**
2. Apply silicone dielectric compound to parking brake lever shaft, then insert shaft into caliper housing bore.
3. Install O-ring into groove on pushrod, then apply silicone dielectric compound to recesses in pushrod.
4. Place strut pin into caliper housing and into recess of parking brake lever shaft.
5. Position pushrod into caliper housing bore, ensuring strut pin is properly located between shaft recesses and recess at end of pushrod.
6. Position key plate over pushrod, so that washer nib is located in hole in caliper housing.
7. Install flat washer, spring and spring cage into caliper bore.
8. Install snap ring using tool No. T87P-2588-P or equivalent. Ensure snap ring is properly seated in recess.
9. Lubricate replacement piston seal with clean brake fluid, then install seal into caliper bore groove.
10. Lubricate piston and dust boot with clean brake fluid, then install dust boot into caliper bore.
11. Position piston into dust boot, seating dust boot in piston groove.
12. Using tool No. T75P-2588-B or equivalent, turn piston in clockwise direction until piston is fully seated in caliper bore, **Fig. 13.**
13. Position one of the two slots on the piston so that it will engage the nib on the rear of the disc pad when the caliper is installed, **Fig. 14.**
14. Install caliper assembly as described under "Caliper, Replace."

## PARKING BRAKE, ADJUST

1. Fully release parking brake, then place transmission in neutral and support vehicle at rear axle.
2. Tighten adjuster nut until levers on calipers just start to move, then loosen the nut just enough to obtain full travel to the off position. **If brake cables are replaced in any system having a foot-actuated control assembly, stroke parking brake control with about 100 pounds pedal effort, then repeat adjustment.**
3. The lever is in the off position when a 1/4 inch diameter pin can be freely inserted past the side of the lever into the 1/4 inch diameter holes in the cast iron housing.
4. Apply and release the parking brake, then apply and release the service brake pedal with moderate force. Check parking brake levers on calipers to determine if they are fully returned to the off position. **If the 1/4 inch pin cannot be freely inserted, the adjustment is too tight. Repeat adjustment procedure. Also, if levers do not return to off position, parking and service brake function will be affected as the vehicle is driven.**

## PROBE

### DISC BRAKE PADS, REPLACE

#### Removal

1. Remove approximately two thirds of the brake fluid from the master cylinder.
2. Raise and support vehicle, then remove wheel and tire assembly.
3. Loosen the parking brake cable housing adjusting nut, then remove the cable housing from the bracket and the parking lever.
4. Remove the lower caliper retaining bolt, then pivot the caliper to clear the brake pads. If necessary, pry the caliper outward.
5. Remove the caliper, then support caliper with wire from strut assembly.
6. Remove the V-springs from the disc pads, then remove the disc pads, anti-rattle shims and retaining clips. If disc pads and anti-rattle shims are to be reused, they must be installed in their original position, **Fig. 15.**
7. If necessary, remove and resurface the rotor at this time. **The rotor must be machined while it is bolted to the hub. The rotor and hub are mounted as an assembly on the rotor lathe to decrease the possibility of rotor runout.**

#### Installation

1. Install the disc pad retaining clips, then position the anti-rattle shims on the disc pads.
2. Position the disc pads into the caliper anchor bracket.
3. Install the V-springs into the disc pads.
4. Lubricate the guide pin bushings with High Temperature Grease part No. D7AZ-19590-A or equivalent.
5. Install the caliper on the guide pin, then pivot the caliper over the brake disc pads.
6. Install the caliper retaining bolt, then **torque** to 12-17 ft. lbs.
7. Bleed brake system.
8. Position the parking brake cable into the parking brake lever and bracket.
9. Adjust the parking brake cable so there is no clearance between the cable end and the parking brake lever.
10. **Torque** the parking brake cable locknut to 14-21 ft. lbs.
11. Install wheel and tire assembly.

### CALIPER, REPLACE

#### Removal

1. Raise and support vehicle, then remove wheel and tire assembly.
2. Loosen the parking brake cable housing adjustment nut, then remove the cable housing from the bracket and the parking brake lever.
3. Remove the banjo bolt attaching the brake flex hose to the caliper.
4. Remove two copper washers from the banjo fitting, then discard washers.
5. Remove lower caliper retaining bolt.
6. Pivot the caliper off the disc pads, then slide caliper off the guide pin.

#### Installation

1. Lubricate the guide pin bushings with High Temperature Grease part No. D7AZ-19590-A or equivalent.
2. Install the caliper onto the guide pin, then pivot caliper over disc pads.
3. Install lower caliper retaining bolt, then **torque** bolt to 12-17 ft. lbs.
4. Install two new copper washers and the banjo bolt on the brake flex hose banjo fitting.
5. Position the flex hose on the caliper. **Torque** banjo bolt to 16-20 ft. lbs.
6. Position the parking brake cable into the parking brake lever and bracket.
7. Adjust the parking brake cable so there is no clearance between the cable end and the parking brake lever.
8. **Torque** the parking brake cable locknut to 14-21 ft. lbs.
9. Install wheel and tire assembly.

### CALIPER OVERHAUL

#### Disassembly

1. Remove caliper as previously outlined.
2. Open the bleeder screw and drain the brake fluid from the caliper through the brake flex hose fitting. After draining the fluid, close the bleeder screw.
3. Remove the caliper guide bushing and dust boots, **Fig. 15.**
4. Pry the retaining spring off the dust boot with a screwdriver, then remove piston.
5. remove the dust boot and discard boot.
6. Remove the piston seal from the caliper and discard. **Use a plastic or wooden pick to remove seal. A metal tool can scratch or nick the seal groove resulting in a possible seal leak.**
7. Remove the stopper snap ring.
8. Remove the adjusting spindle, stopper and connecting link. Separate the adjuster spindle and the stopper.
9. Remove the O-ring from the adjuster spindle, then discard O-ring.
10. Remove the parking brake return spring, then the operating lever nut and lockwasher.
11. Mark the relationship between the operating lever and the shaft, then remove the operating lever from the shaft.
12. Remove the seal from the caliper housing.
13. Remove the shaft from the caliper housing, then the needle bearings.

#### Inspection

The caliper bore, piston seal groove and piston must be inspected for cuts, deep scratches and pitting whenever the caliper is rebuilt. The piston and piston bore may be lightly polished with crocus cloth, if deep scratches cannot be removed, the component must be replaced.

The seal groove in the caliper must be free of deep scratches that would prevent the seal from operating properly.

Inspect the upper guide pin and lower guide pin bushing for wear.

Inspect bushing dust boots for damage or poor sealing.

#### Assembly

1. Lubricate the needle bearings with the orange grease included in the caliper rebuilding kit part No. FOJY-2221-A.
2. Align the opening in the bearing with the bore in the caliper housing, then install the needle bearing.
3. Install the operating shaft into the caliper housing.
4. Install the operating lever. Align the marks made during removal.
5. Install lockwasher nut.
6. Install the connecting link into the operating shaft.
7. Install O-ring onto the adjuster spindle, then position the stopper onto the adjuster spindle so that the pin will align with the caliper housing.
8. Install the adjuster spindle in the caliper by aligning the pins of the adjuster spindle with the holes of the caliper.
9. Install the parking brake return spring.
10. Lubricate a new piston seal with brake fluid and install in caliper groove, then lubricate the caliper bore and caliper piston with brake fluid.
11. Install the dust boot in the caliper bore.
12. Install the piston in the caliper bore by rotating the piston until seated.
13. Install the upper guide pin dust boot, then the lower guide pin bushing dust boot.
14. Install the caliper upper guide pin, then the lower guide pin bushing.

### PARKING BRAKE, ADJUST

1. Normal parking brake adjustment is made at the hand lever between the seat. Remove the six attaching screws in the center console, then remove console.
2. Tighten parking brake adjusting nut on the left side of the parking brake lever. This shortens the equalizer cable. Tighten the adjusting nut until it takes seven to ten notches to fully set the parking brake.

## SCORPIO

### DISC BRAKE PAD, REPLACE

#### Removal

1. Raise and support vehicle.
2. Remove wheel and tire assembly.
3. Disconnect parking brake cable from bracket, **Fig. 16.**
4. Remove front caliper slide pin bolt securing piston housing to anchor bracket, **Fig. 17.**
5. Separate piston assembly from brake rotor, then remove brake pads from carrier bracket.
6. Turn piston clockwise into housing using piston adjuster tool No. T87P-2588-A or equivalent. **Ensure one slot in piston will engage with tab on back of brake pad during installation.**

#### Installation

1. Position brake pads in carrier bracket,

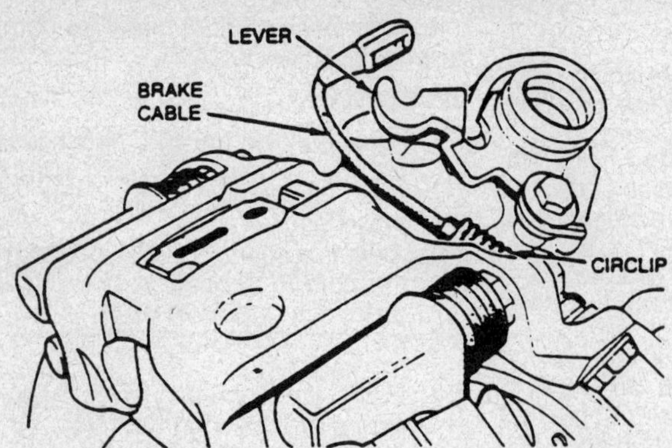


Fig. 16 Removing parking brake cable

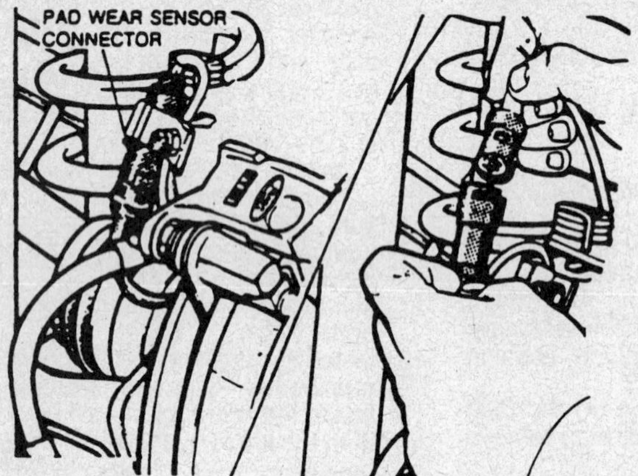


Fig. 18 Disconnecting brake pad wear sensor

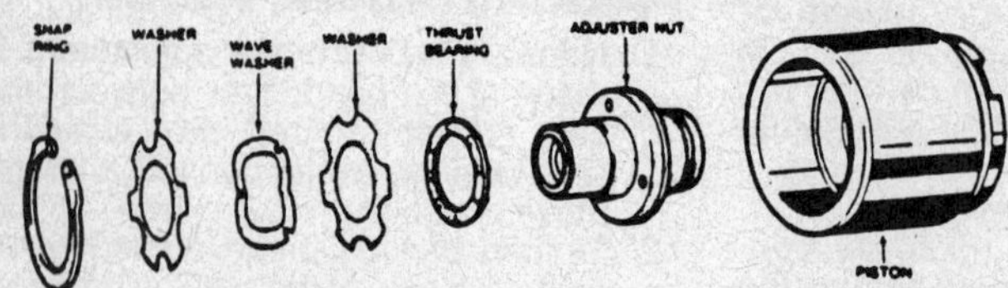


Fig. 20 Exploded view of caliper piston

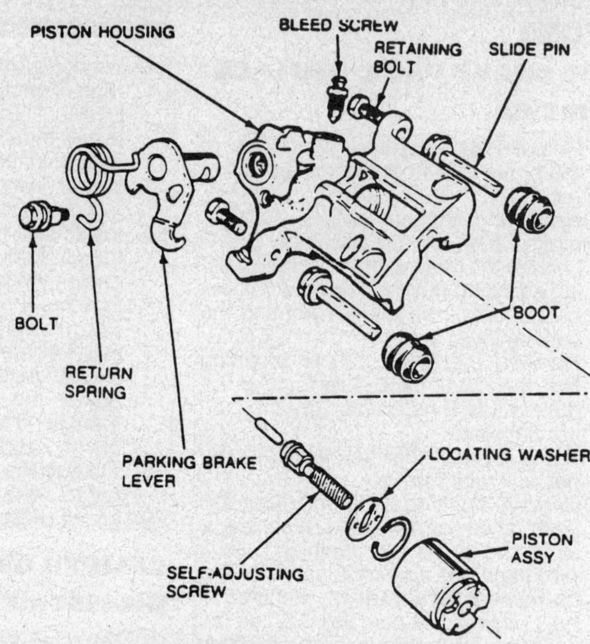


Fig. 17 Exploded view of caliper assembly. Scorpio

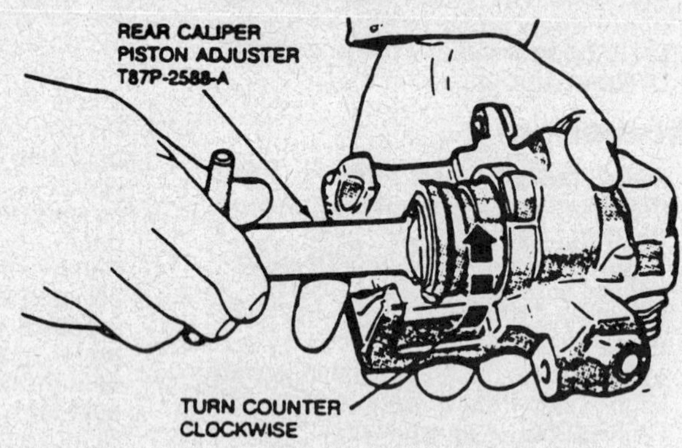


Fig. 19 Removing caliper piston

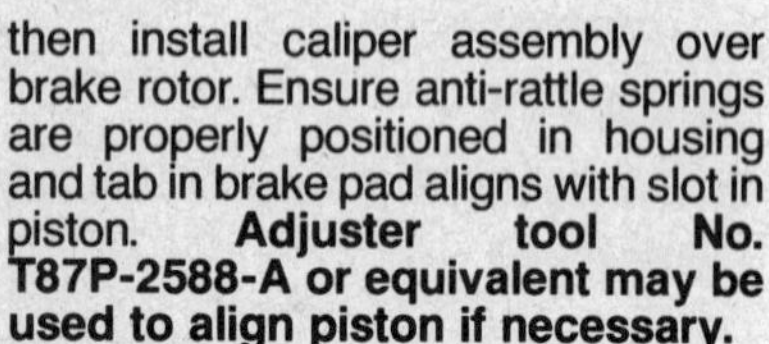

then install caliper assembly over brake rotor. Ensure anti-rattle springs are properly positioned in housing and tab in brake pad aligns with slot in piston. **Adjuster tool No. T87P-2588-A or equivalent may be used to align piston if necessary.**

2. Install front caliper bolt, **Fig. 17,** and torque to specification.
3. Connect parking brake cable, then install wheel and tire assembly.
4. Lower vehicle, then pump brake pedal several times to properly position brake pads before operation.

## CALIPER, REPLACE

1. Apply brake pedal several times to relieve system pressure.
2. Raise and support vehicle.
3. Remove wheel and tire assembly.
4. Disconnect electrical connector from brake pad wear sensor, **Fig. 18.**
5. Disconnect brake line from flex hose and flex hose from housing. Plug lines to prevent leakage and contamination.
6. Disconnect parking brake cable from retaining bracket.
7. Remove caliper assembly attaching bolts and the caliper.
8. Reverse procedure to install, noting the following:
   a. Torque caliper attaching bolts to specification.
   b. Following completion of installation, bleed rear brake system.

## CALIPER OVERHAUL

### Disassembly

1. Remove caliper assembly and brake pads as previously described.
2. Remove slide pin bolts and the slide pins from anchor bracket.
3. Secure caliper assembly in a suitable vise.
4. Turn caliper piston counterclockwise using piston adjuster tool No. T87P-2588-A or equivalent, until it protrudes approximately .8 inch, **Fig. 19.**
5. Disengage piston boot cover from piston groove, then turn piston fully out of housing using adjuster tool.
6. Remove piston boot, then the piston body snap ring, **Fig. 20.**
7. Remove adjuster nut with thrust washers, wave washers and thrust bearing.
8. Remove and discard adjuster nut seal. **Note direction of seal lip for installation reference.**
9. Clean adjuster nut clutch surface and ensure piston breather port in piston groove is not restricted.
10. Remove piston seal from caliper body.
11. Remove circlip, then the washer, spring and spring cover housing from caliper.
12. Remove fast thread adjuster and snap ring retaining key plate from caliper. Remove and discard O-ring from adjuster.
13. Remove parking brake strut from bore.
14. Remove parking brake lever return spring from lever, then remove stop bolt, **Fig. 21.**

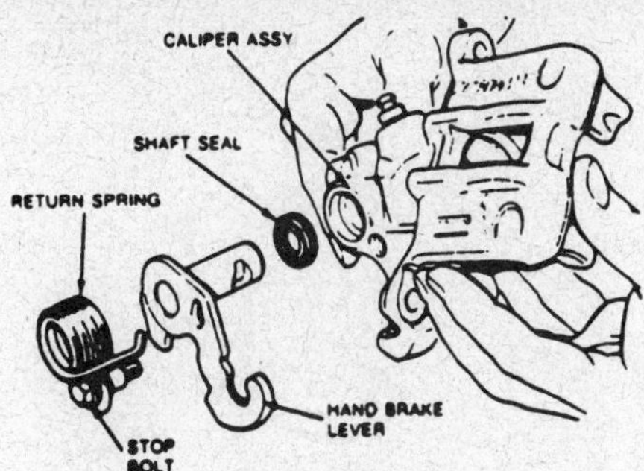


**Fig. 21 Parking brake lever return spring**

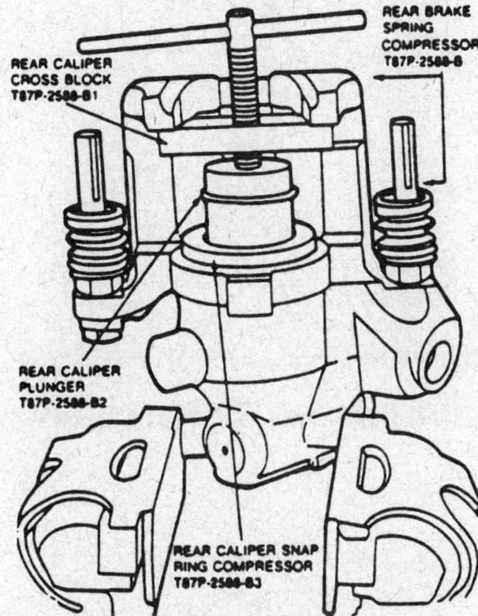


**Fig. 24 Rear caliper brake spring compressor tool installation**

15. Remove parking brake lever return spring from caliper bore. Remove and discard shaft seal.
16. Clean and inspect all caliper components, replacing as necessary.

### Assembly

1. Install new lever shaft bushing, if previously removed, to a depth of .29 inch from lower seal lip, **Fig. 22.** Ensure cutout in bushing is properly aligned with pushrod bore.
2. Apply suitable grease to lever shaft and bushing.
3. Press shaft seal into housing until it is fully seated on shoulder.
4. Slide lever into housing through seal, using care to avoid damaging seal lip.
5. Install parking brake stop bolt and spring, torquing bolt to specification.
6. Apply suitable grease to bore area around strut, then position parking brake strut into caliper bore.
7. Install new O-ring onto fast thread adjuster, then position adjuster in caliper bore.
8. Install key plate and snap ring. Ensure dimple on plate is properly positioned prior to installing snap ring.
9. Position snap ring compressor

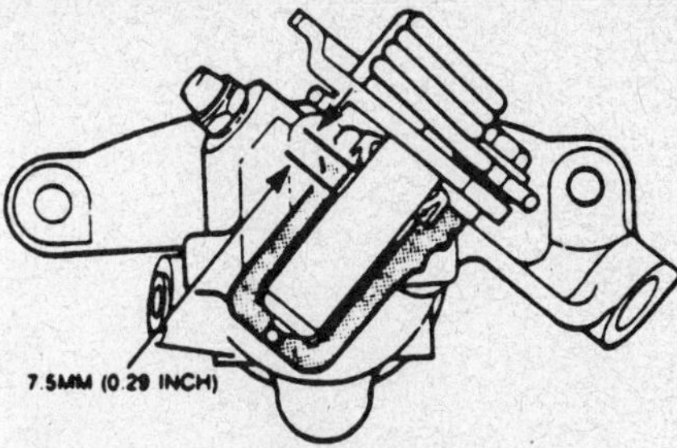


**Fig. 22 Rear caliper lever shaft bushing installation**

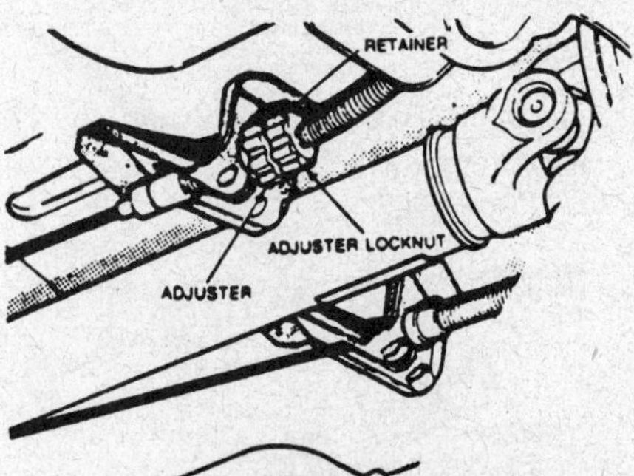


**Fig. 25 Parking brake cable adjusting locknut**

T87P-2588-B3 or equivalent into caliper bore, then insert washer, spring, spring retainer and snap ring into compressor.

10. Position rear brake spring compressor T87P-2588-B or equivalent, **Fig. 23,** as shown in **Fig. 24,** and turn screw clockwise until snap ring is firmly seated.
11. Lubricate caliper body bore with clean hydraulic fluid, then install piston seal into groove.
12. Assemble piston assembly, then install new seal on adjuster nut.
13. Apply brake fluid to piston adjuster nut contact face, then install thrust bearing, thrust washers, wave washer and snap ring.
14. Install piston protective boot into caliper body groove. Stretch boot over piston, then start thread of adjuster nut on fast thread.
15. Screw piston onto fast thread adjuster using piston adjuster T87P-2588-A or equivalent, then compress into caliper base.
16. Secure piston protective cover into piston groove.
17. Apply suitable grease to slide pin bores and inside of boot, then install slide pins and slide pin bolts into anchor bracket. Secure protective boot in grooves.

## PARKING BRAKE, ADJUST

1. Release parking brake lever.
2. Raise and support vehicle.
3. Remove adjusting locknut retainer, **Fig. 25.**
4. Loosen adjuster locknut and adjuster until both parking brake levers on calipers have fully returned to stop.

**Fig. 23 Rear caliper assembly tools**

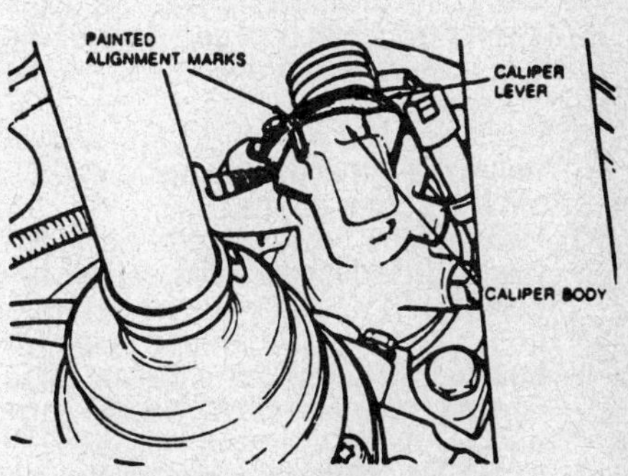


**Fig. 26 Caliper lever alignment marks**

5. Mark caliper lever and caliper housing, **Fig. 26.**
6. Rotate cable adjuster against body abutment bracket until either parking brake caliper lever starts to move from alignment marks.
7. Tighten adjuster locknut finger-tight, then using a wrench, tighten an additional 3-6 clicks. **One complete turn of the adjuster equals six clicks.**
8. Install locknut retainer, then lower vehicle and check parking brake operation.

# CAPRI

## DISC BRAKE PADS, REPLACE

1. Remove approximately 2/3 of brake fluid from master cylinder.
2. Raise and support vehicle.
3. Remove wheel and tire assembly.
4. Using needle nose pliers, remove parking brake return springs at back of caliper. **Fig. 27.**
5. Loosen parking brake cable housing adjusting nut, then remove cable housing from bracket on rear lower control arm.
6. Loosen attaching bolt connecting parking brake cable bracket to rear caliper.
7. Remove parking brake cable from rear caliper, then loosen lower caliper bolt.
8. Pivot caliper upward on upper caliper guide pin.
9. Remove disc pad retaining spring, then the disc pad and shims.
10. Remove anchor plate clips from caliper anchor plate.
11. Remove and resurface rotor if necessary.

## CALIPER, REPLACE

1. Raise and support vehicle, then remove wheel and tire assembly.

2. Remove brake pads as previously outlined.
3. Remove clip retaining the brake flex hose to the strut assembly.
4. Remove the banjo bolt retaining the brake flex hose to the caliper assembly.
5. Remove the two copper washers that seal the flex hose banjo fitting, then discard washers.
6. Remove the lower caliper retaining bolt.
7. Using a cold chisel, remove the upper caliper guide pin dust cap. This will allow access to the allen head on the guide pin.
8. Using an allen wrench, loosen and remove the upper caliper guide pin.
9. Lift the caliper off the rotor.
10. Remove the guide pin and guide pin bushing dust boots from caliper assembly.
11. Lubricate the guide pin and guide pin bushing with Disc Brake Caliper Slide Grease part No. D7AZ-19590-A or equivalent.
12. Install the guide pin and guide pin bushing dust boots.
13. Install the brake pads and shims as previously outlined.
14. Position the caliper over the rotor. **To provide the necessary clearance, it may be necessary to rotate the caliper piston.**
15. Tighten the upper guide pin, then install the dust cap with a plastic hammer.
16. Install the lower caliper retaining bolt through the lower caliper guide pin bushing. **Torque** the lower retaining bolt to 29-36 ft. lbs.
17. Install the flex hose banjo bolt with two new copper washers onto the brake flex hose.
18. Position the flex hose on the caliper, **torque** banjo bolt to 17-21 ft. lbs.
19. Bleed braking system, then install wheel and tire assembly.

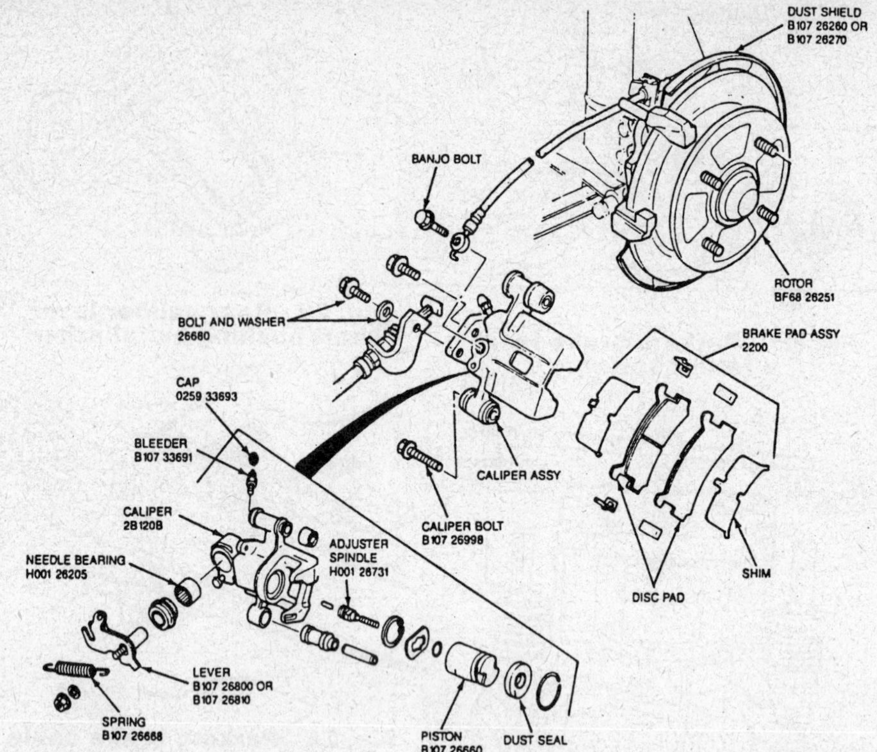


**Fig. 27 Exploded view of rear disc brake assembly. Capri**

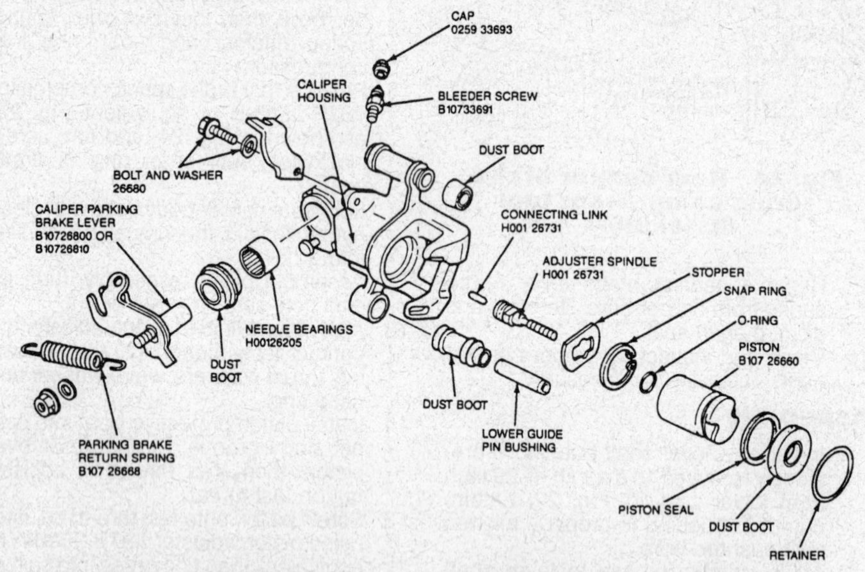


**Fig. 28 Exploded view of rear caliper assembly. Capri**

## CALIPER OVERHAUL

### Disassembly

1. Remove caliper as previously outlined.
2. Open the bleeder screw and drain the brake fluid from the caliper through the brake flex hose fitting. After draining the fluid, close the bleeder screw.
3. Remove the caliper guide bushing and dust boots, **Fig. 28.**
4. Pry the retaining spring off the dust boot with a screwdriver, then remove piston.
5. remove the dust boot and discard boot.
6. Remove the piston seal from the caliper and discard. **Use a plastic or wooden pick to remove seal. A metal tool can scratch or nick the seal groove resulting in a possible seal leak.**
7. Remove the parking brake mechanism from the caliper housing.

### Inspection

The caliper bore, piston seal groove and piston must be inspected for cuts, deep scratches and pitting whenever the caliper is rebuilt. The piston and piston bore may be lightly polished with crocus cloth, if deep scratches cannot be removed, the component must be replaced.

The seal groove in the caliper must be free of deep scratches that would prevent the seal from operating properly.

Inspect the upper guide pin and lower guide pin bushing for wear.

Inspect bushing dust boots for damage or poor sealing.

### Assembly

1. Lubricate the needle bearings with the special grease included in the caliper rebuilding kit part No. FOJY-2221-A as shown in **Fig. 29.**
2. Install the adjuster spindle in the caliper by aligning the pins of the adjuster spindle with the holes of the caliper as shown in **Fig. 30.**
3. Lubricate a new piston seal with brake fluid and install in caliper groove, then lubricate the caliper bore and caliper

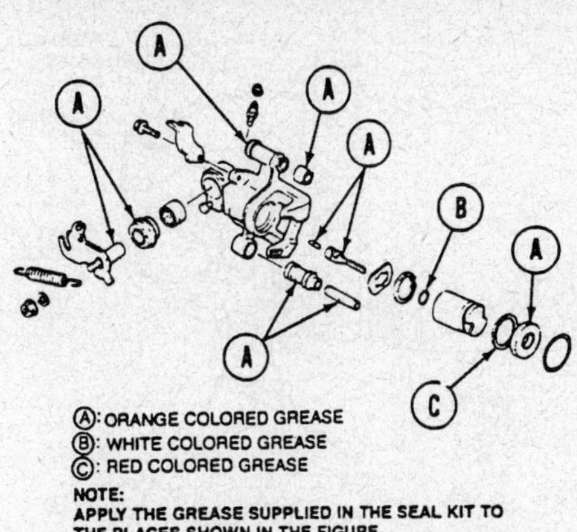


**Fig. 29 Lubrication points of rear caliper assembly. Capri**

piston with brake fluid.

4. Install the dust boot in the caliper bore, then the wire retainer spring.
5. Install the piston in the caliper bore by rotating the piston until seated.
6. Install the upper guide pin dust boot, then the lower guide pin bushing dust boot.
7. Install the caliper upper guide pin, then the lower guide pin bushing.
8. Install the brake pads as previously outlined in this section.
9. Tighten the upper guide pin with allen wrench, then install dust cap with plastic hammer.
10. Install the lower caliper bolt, then **torque** bolt to 29-36 ft. lbs.
11. Bleed braking system, then pump brake pedal several times to seat the pads.
12. Check fluid level in master cylinder, then spin each rotor to ensure the brakes are not dragging.
13. Install wheel and tire assembly. **Torque** wheel lug nuts to 65-88 ft. lbs.

# TRACER & 1991 ESCORT

## DISC BRAKE PADS, REPLACE

1. Raise and support vehicle, then remove rear wheel assembly.
2. If necessary, remove screw plug, then turn adjustment gear counterclockwise with allen wrench to pull the piston fully inward, **Fig. 31.**
3. Remove caliper lower lock bolt.
4. Using a screwdriver, pivot caliper on its mounting bracket to access brake pads as shown in **Fig. 32. If upper lock bolt requires lubrication or service, remove and suspend caliper using wire or equivalent.**
5. Reverse procedure to install noting the following:
   a. Lubricate caliper lock bolt, then **torque** to 33-43 ft. lbs.
   b. If necessary, turn adjustment gear clockwise with allen wrench until brake pads just touch rotor, then loosen gear 1/3 of a turn. Install screw plug, then **torque** to 9-12 ft. lbs.

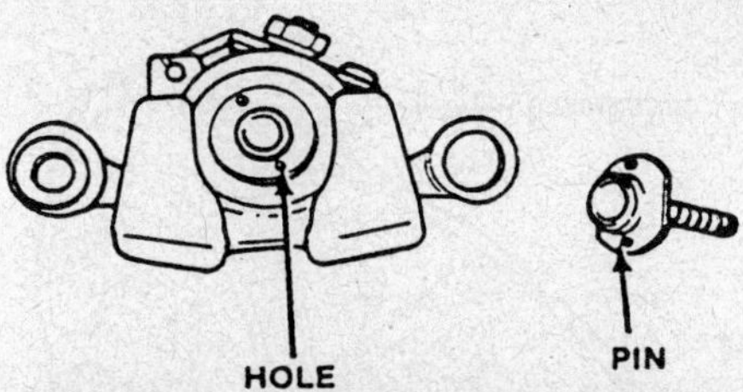


**Fig. 30 Alignment of the adjuster spindle pins. Capri**

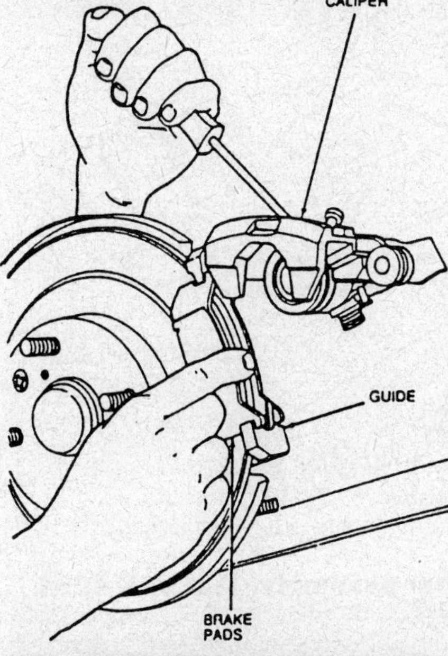


**Fig. 32 Rear disc brake pad removal. Tracer & 1991 Escort**

## CALIPER, REPLACE

### Removal

1. Remove wheel and tire assembly, then brake pads as previously outlined.
2. Remove brake flex hose retaining clip from strut assembly bracket.
3. Remove the banjo bolt attaching the brake flex hose to the caliper, **Fig. 33.**
4. Remove the two copper washers that seal the flex hose banjo fitting, then discard washers.
5. Remove the lower caliper retaining bolt.
6. Using a cold chisel, remove the upper caliper guide pin dust cap. This will give access to the Allen head guide pin.
7. Using an Allen wrench, loosen and remove upper caliper guide pin.
8. Lift caliper off the rotor.

### Installation

Before installation, remove upper and lower guide pin bushings and lubricate with high temperature grease D7AZ-19590-A or equivalent.

1. Install brake pads and shims as previously outlined.
2. Position caliper over rotor, then install caliper retaining bolts and torque to specification.

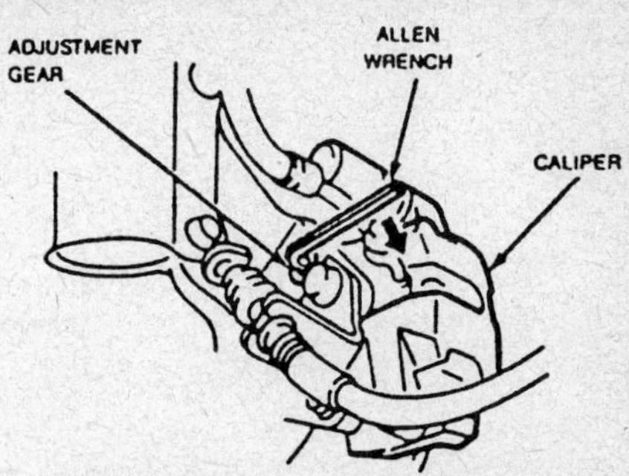


**Fig. 31 Rear disc brake adjustment gear location. Tracer & 1991 Escort**

3. Install two new copper washers and banjo bolt on flex hose banjo fitting.
4. Position flex hose on caliper and install banjo bolt. Torque bolt to specification.
5. Bleed brake system, then install wheel and tire assembly.

## CALIPER OVERHAUL

### Disassembly

1. Remove disc pads as previously outlined, then disconnect brake hose from caliper.
2. Open bleeder screw and drain brake fluid from caliper.
3. Remove caliper guide bushing and dust boots, **Fig. 33.**
4. Pry retaining spring off dust boot, then remove piston.
5. Remove dust boot and discard, then remove piston seal from caliper and discard.
6. Remove parking brake mechanism from caliper housing.

### Assembly

Clean caliper, anchor plate and rotor assembly and inspect for signs of brake fluid leakage, excessive wear or damage. The caliper must be inspected for leakage both in piston boot area and operating shaft seal area. Lightly sand or wire brush any rust or corrosion from caliper and anchor plate sliding surfaces and inner brake shoe abutment surfaces in anchor plate. Inspect brake shoes for wear. Linings must not be worn to less than 1/8 inch of shoe surface.

Lubricate all new seals with brake fluid before installation.

1. Install needle bearings, dust boot and parking brake lever, **Fig. 33.**
2. Install adapter spindle in caliper.
3. Install dust boot into caliper bore, then install retaining spring.
4. Install caliper piston.
5. Install upper and lower guide pin dust boots.
6. Install anchor plate clips, brake pads, shims and spring retainer.
7. Install caliper on anchor plate, then tighten upper guide pin and install dust cap.
8. Install lower guide pin and torque to specification.
9. Bleed brake system, them pump brake pedal several times to seat brake pads.
10. Check brake fluid level, adding fluid as

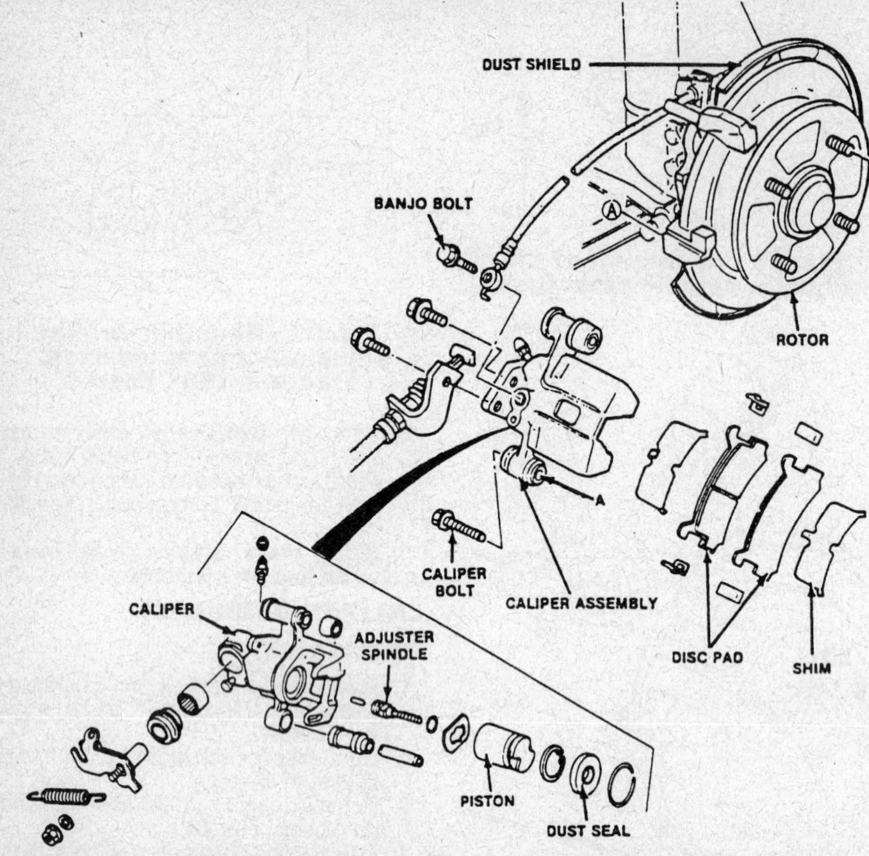


**Fig. 33 Exploded view of caliper assembly. Tracer & 1991 Escort**

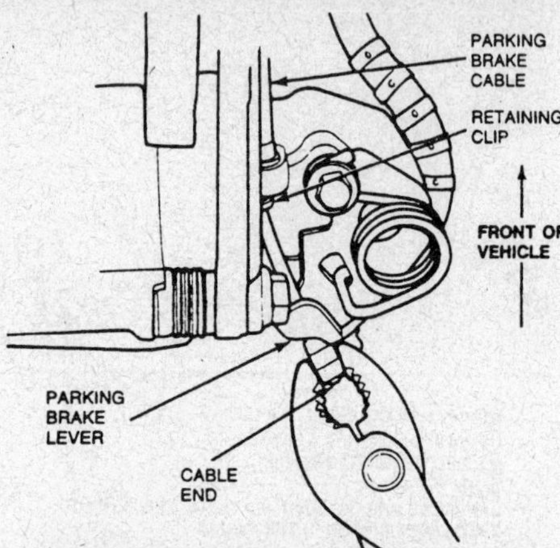


**Fig. 34 Parking brake retaining clip location. Sable & Taurus**

necessary, then install wheel and tire assembly.

## PARKING BRAKE, ADJUST

1. Start engine and shift gearshift lever into the reverse position.
2. With the vehicle moving in reverse, depress brake pedal several times.
3. Shift gearshift lever into park position, then stop engine.
4. Remove parking brake console.
5. Turn adjusting nut until parking brake lever stroke is five to seven notches when pulled with a force of 22 lbs.
6. Install parking brake console.

# SABLE & TAURUS

## DISC BRAKE PADS, REPLACE

### Removal

1. Raise and support vehicle, then remove wheel and tire assembly.
2. Remove screw retaining brake hose bracket to shock absorber bracket.
3. Remove retaining clip from parking brake cable at caliper, then cable end from parking brake lever.
4. Hold slider pin hex heads with an open end wrench, then remove upper caliper pinch bolt.
5. Rotate caliper away from rotor, then remove inner and outer brake pads.

### Installation

1. Using Brake Piston Turning tool No. T87P-2588-A or equivalent, rotate piston clockwise until fully seated. **Ensure that one of the two slots in piston face is positioned so it will engage nub on brake pad.**
2. Install inner and outer brake pads in anchor plate.
3. Rotate caliper assembly over rotor into position on anchor plate. **Ensure brake pads are installed properly.**
4. Remove residue from the upper pinch bolt threads, then apply one drop of Threadlock and Sealer part No. EOAZ-19554-BA or equivalent.
5. Install and **torque** pinch bolts 23-26 ft. lbs., while holding slider pins with an open end wrench.
6. Attach cable end to parking brake lever, then install cable retaining clip on caliper assembly.
7. Position brake flex hose and bracket assembly to shock absorber bracket, then install retaining bolt. **Torque** retaining bolt to 8-11 ft. lbs.
8. Install wheel and tire assembly. **Torque** wheel lug nuts to 85-104 ft. lbs.

## CALIPER, REPLACE

### Removal

During service, handle caliper assembly and rotor in such a way as to avoid nicking, scratching or contaminating the brake pads or deforming the rotor.

After any service, pump the brake pedal to obtaining a firm brake pedal before moving the vehicle. Riding the brake pedal (common with left foot application) must be avoided while driving.

1. Raise and support vehicle, then remove wheel and tire assembly.
2. Remove brake flex hose from caliper assembly.
3. Remove retaining clip from parking brake at caliper, then disengage parking brake cable end from lever arm shown in **Fig. 34.**
4. Hold slider pin hex-heads with open end wrench, then remove pinch bolts.
5. Lift caliper assembly away from anchor plate.
6. Remove slider pins and boots from anchor plate.

### Installation

1. Apply Silicone Dielectric Compound part No. D7AZ-19A331-A or equivalent to inside of slider pin boots and to slider pins.
2. Position slider pins and boots in anchor plate.
3. Position caliper assembly on anchor plate. **Ensure brake pads are installed properly.**
4. Remove residue from the pinch bolt threads, then apply one drop of Threadlock and Sealer part No. EOAZ-19554-BA or equivalent.
5. Install pinch bolts, then **torque** pinch bolts to 23-26 ft. lbs., while holding slider pins with an open end wrench.
6. Attach cable end to parking brake lever, then install cable retaining clip on caliper assembly.
7. Using new copper washers, connect brake flex hose to caliper. **Torque** banjo retaining bolt to 8-11 ft. lbs.
8. Bleed brake system, then install wheel and tire assembly.
9. **Torque** wheel lug nuts to 85-104 ft. lbs.

## CALIPER OVERHAUL

Refer to **Figs. 35 and 36,** during disassembly and assembly procedures.

### Disassembly

1. Remove caliper assembly as previously outlined in this section.
2. Mount caliper assembly in soft jawed vise, or use vise jaw protectors.

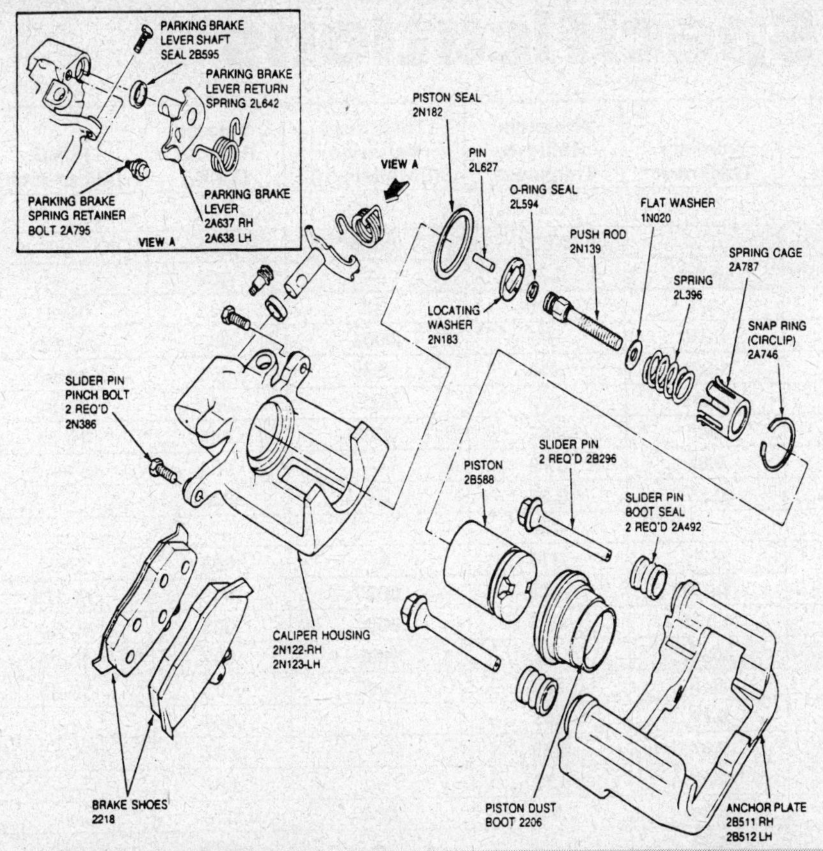


**Fig. 35 Exploded view of rear caliper assembly. Sable & Taurus**

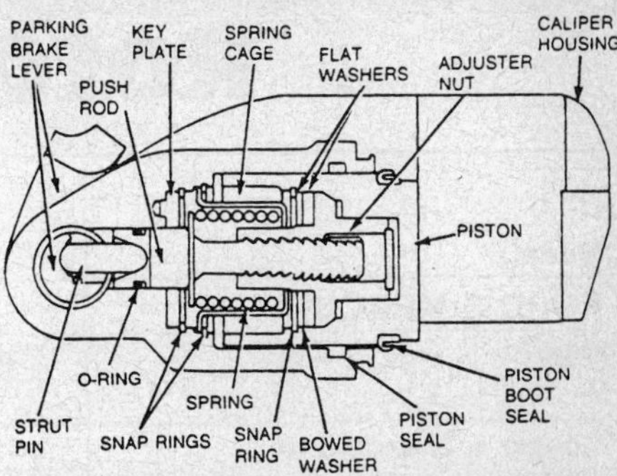


**Fig. 36 Cross sectional view of rear caliper component locations. Sable & Taurus**

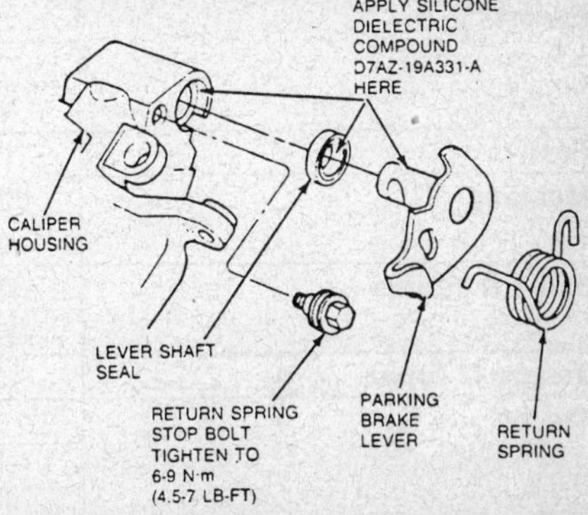


**Fig. 37 Parking brake lever lubrication points. Sable & Taurus**

3. Using Brake Piston Turning Tool No. T87P-2588-A or equivalent, turn piston counterclockwise to remove piston from caliper piston bore.
4. Remove and discard piston dust boot seal and piston seal from caliper bore.
5. Using snap ring (circlip) pliers, remove snap ring retaining push rod assembly from caliper. **The snap ring and spring cover are under spring load. Care should be taken when removing the snap ring.**
6. Remove spring cover, spring, washer, key plate from cylinder bore, then pull out push rod and strut pin.
7. Remove and discard O-ring seal from push rod.
8. Remove parking brake lever return spring, then unscrew parking brake lever stop bolt. Pull parking brake lever out of caliper housing, **Fig. 37.**

## Inspection

1. Clean all metal parts with Isopropyl Alcohol. Use clean, dry compressed air to clean out and dry grooves and passages. Ensure caliper bore and component parts are completely free of any foreign material.
2. Inspect caliper bores for damage or excessive wear. If piston is pitted, scored or plating is worn off, replace piston assembly.

## Assembly

1. Lightly grease parking brake lever bore and lever shaft seal with Silicone Dielectric Compound part No. D7AZ-19A331-A. Press parking brake lever shaft seal into caliper bore.
2. Grease parking brake shaft recess and slightly grease parking brake lever shaft, **Fig. 37.** Insert shaft into bore in caliper housing.
3. Screw lever stop bolt into caliper housing. **Torque** stop bolt to 4.5-7 ft. lbs.
4. Attach parking brake lever return spring to stop bolt, then insert free end into parking brake lever slot.
5. Install new O-ring seal in groove of push rod. Grease recess at push rod end with Silicone Dielectric Compound.
6. Position strut pin into caliper housing and in recess of parking brake lever shaft. Insert push rod into push rod bore of caliper housing. Ensure pin is positioned correctly between shaft recess and recess at the end of the rod.
7. Place key plate over push rod so that the locating nib fits into drilled locating hole in caliper housing. Install flatwasher, push rod, spring and spring cover.
8. Insert outer spacer into piston bore.
9. Insert inner spacer into piston bore, then install snap ring inside of inner spacer.
10. Position spring compressor tool No. T87P-2588-B as shown in **Fig. 38.** Lightly screw tool clockwise to compress spring. Install snap ring. **Snap ring should click into place. Do not overcompress spring.**
11. Lubricate piston seal with brake fluid, then install New piston seal in groove in caliper housing.
12. Coat piston and piston dust boot with clean brake fluid, then install dust boot into piston bore of caliper.
13. Spread dust boot over piston, then seat dust boot in piston groove.
14. Using Brake Piston Turning Tool No. T87P-2588-A or equivalent, rotate piston clockwise until piston is fully seated. **Ensure one slot in piston face is positioned so it will engage with nib on brake pad.**
15. Install caliper as outlined previously in this section.

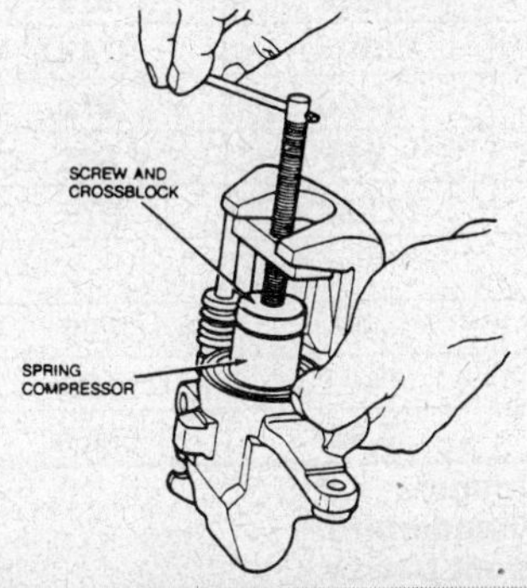


**Fig. 38 Installation of spring, spring cage and snap ring. Sable & Taurus**

## PARKING BRAKE, ADJUST

The parking brake is self adjusting. No initial adjustment is necessary.

# Rotor Specifications

| Model | Year | Nominal Thickness | Minimum Refinish Thickness | Thickness Variation (Parallelism) | Lateral Run-out (T.I.R.) | Finish (Micro-Inch) |
|---|---|---|---|---|---|---|
| **FORD & MERCURY** | | | | | | |
| Capri | 1991⑥ | 0.71 | 0.630 | .0006 | .004 | — |
| | ⑦ | 0.39 | 0.35 | — | .004 | — |
| Cougar & Thunderbird | 1989④ | .870 | .810 | ② | .003 | 10-81 |
| | 1989⑤ | 1.030 | .972 | .0005 | .003 | 15-125 |
| | 1990-91 | 1.024 | .935 | .0005 | .003 | 10-80 |
| Crown Victoria & Grand Marquis | 1989-91 | 1.030 | .972 | .0005 | .003 | 10-80 |
| Escort | 1989-90 | .945 | .882 | .0005 | .003 | 10-80 |
| | 1991⑥ | 0.87 | 0.79 | — | .004 | — |
| | 1991⑦ | 0.35 | 0.28 | — | .004 | — |
| Festiva | 1989-91 | — | .460 | — | — | — |
| Mustang | 1989-91① | .870 | .810 | ② | .003 | 10-81 |
| | 1989③ | 1.030 | .972 | .0005 | .003 | 15-125 |
| Sable & Taurus | 1989-91⑥ | 1.024 | .974 | .0005 | .003 | 10-80 |
| | 1990-91⑦ | .094 | .90 | .0005 | .002 | 16-25 |
| Tempo & Topaz | 1989-91 | .945 | .882 | .0005 | .003 | 10-80 |
| Tracer | 1989 | 0.71 | 0.63 | — | .004 | — |
| | 1991⑥ | 0.87 | 0.79 | — | .004 | — |
| | 1991⑦ | 0.35 | 0.28 | — | .004 | — |
| Probe | 1989-91⑥ | 0.94 | 0.860 | .004 | .003 | — |
| | ⑦ | 0.39 | 0.350 | — | .003 | — |
| **LINCOLN** | | | | | | |
| Continental | 1989-91⑥ | 1.020 | .970 | .0004 | .002 | 10-80 |
| | 1989-91⑦ | 1.020⑧ | .974⑧ | .0005 | .002 | 10-80 |
| Mark VII | 1989-91⑥ | 1.030 | .972 | .0005 | .003 | 15-125 |
| | 1989-91⑦ | .945 | .895 | .0005 | .004 | 16-125 |
| Town Car | 1989-91 | 1.030 | .972 | .0005 | .003 | 10-80 |
| **MERKUR** | | | | | | |
| Scorpio | 1989⑥ | — | 0.90 | .0039 | — | — |
| | 1989⑦ | — | 0.35 | .0039 | — | — |
| XR4Ti | 1989 | 0.95 | 0.898 | — | — | — |

①—Less w/V8-302 engine.
②—Models w/steel wheels, .0005 inch; models w/aluminum wheels, .0003 inch.
③—w/V8-302 engine.
④—Cougar.
⑤—Thunderbird.
⑥—Front brakes.
⑦—Rear brakes.
⑧—On 1990 Continental, nominal rotor thickness; 0.945, minimum rotor thickness; 0.896. These measurements have been revised by Technical Service Bulletin No. 90-10T-8.

# Caliper Specifications

| Model | Year | Caliper Bore Dia. Inch |
|---|---|---|
| **FORD & MERCURY** | | |
| Capri | 1991 | — |
| Cougar & Thunderbird | 1989③ | 2.36 |
| | 1989④ | ⑤ |
| | 1990–91 | ⑥ |
| Crown Victoria & Grand Marquis | 1989-91 | 2.88 |

*Continued*

## SPECIFICATIONS—Continued

| Model | Year | Caliper Bore Dia. Inch |
|---|---|---|
| **FORD & MERCURY -Cont.** | | |
| Escort | 1989-90 | 2.362 |
| | 1991 ⑧ | 2.12 |
| | 1991 ⑨ | 1.19 |
| Festiva | 1989-91 | 2.12 |
| Mustang | 1989-91 ① | 2.36 |
| | 1989-91 ② | 2.87 |
| Probe | 1989-91 | ⑩ |
| Sable & Taurus | 1989-91 | ⑥ |
| Tempo & Topaz | 1989-91 | 2.362 |
| Tracer | 1989 | — |
| | 1991 ⑧ | 2.12 |
| | 1991 ⑨ | 1.19 |
| **LINCOLN** | | |
| Continental | 1989-91 | ⑥ |
| Mark VII | 1989-91 | ⑦ |
| Town Car | 1989-91 | 2.88 |
| **MERKUR** | | |
| Scorpio | 1989 | — |
| XR4Ti | 1989 | — |

①—Except Mustang w/V8-302 engine.
②—Mustang w/V8-302 engine.
③—Cougar.
④—Thunderbird.
⑤—Front, 2.87 inch; rear, 1.789 inch.
⑥—Front, 2.598 inch; rear, 1.79 inch.
⑦—Front, 2.87 inch; rear, 2.1 inch.
⑧—Front brakes.
⑨—Rear brakes.
⑩—Front, 2.12 inch; rear, 1.19 inch.

# DRUM BRAKES

**Refer to "Applications" to determine which type brakes are used on vehicle being serviced.**

## TABLE OF CONTENTS



# Applications

| Vehicle | Type No. |
|---|---|
| 1989 Cougar | 1 |
| 1990-91 Cougar | 9 |
| 1989 Crown Victoria | 1 |
| 1990-91 Crown Victoria | 2 |
| 1989-90 Escort 2 Door Less Styled Steel Wheels | 3 |
| 1989-90 Escort Except 2 Door Less Styled Steel Wheels | 4 |
| 1991 Escort | 7 |
| 1989-91 Festiva | 6 |
| 1989 Grand Marquis | 1 |
| 1990-91 Grand Marquis | 2 |
| 1989-91 Mustang | 2 |
| 1989-91 Probe | 7 |
| 1989-91 Sable | 5 |
| 1989-91 Taurus | 5 |
| 1989-91 Tempo | 4 |
| 1989 Thunderbird | |
| Less Heavy Duty Brakes | 2 |
| With Heavy Duty Brakes | 1 |
| 1990-91 Thunderbird | 9 |
| 1989-91 Topaz | 4 |
| 1989 Town Car | 1 |
| 1990-91 Town Car | 2 |
| 1989 Tracer | 7 |
| 1991 Tracer | 7 |
| 1989 XR4Ti | 8 |

# General Information

## INDEX



## SERVICE PRECAUTIONS

When working on or around brake assemblies, care must be taken to prevent breathing asbestos dust, as many manufacturers incorporate asbestos fibers in the production of brake linings. During routine service operations the amount of asbestos dust from brake lining wear is at a low level, due to a chemical break down during use and a few precautions will minimize exposure. **Do not sand or grind brake linings unless suitable local exhaust ventilation equipment is used to prevent excessive asbestos exposure.**

The brake shoe and lining assemblies should be replaced if the lining is worn to within 1/32 inch of rivet heads (riveted linings) or brake shoe (bonded linings). It is recommended that both front and/or rear wheel sets be replaced whenever a respective shoe and lining assembly is replaced.

If a visual inspection does not adequately determine the condition of the linings, the brake shoe and lining assemblies should be removed and inspected. If shoes do not require replacement, reinstall them in their original positions. Brake shoes and linings should also be replaced if cracked or damaged.

1. Wear a suitable respirator approved for asbestos dust use during all repair procedures.
2. When cleaning brake dust from brake parts, use a vacuum cleaner with a highly efficient filter system. If a suitable vacuum cleaner is not available, use a water soaked rag. **Do not use compressed air or dry brush to clean brake parts.**
3. Keep work area clean using same equipment as for cleaning brake parts.
4. Properly dispose of rags and vacuum cleaner bags by placing them in plastic bags.
5. Do not smoke or eat while working on brake systems. **Never use gasoline, kerosene, alcohol, motor oil, transmission fluid, or any fluid containing mineral oil to clean brake system components. These fluids will damage the rubber caps and seals. If system contamination is suspected, check brake fluid in the reservoir for dirt, discoloration, or separation (break down) of the brake fluid into distinct layers. Drain and flush the hydraulic system with clean brake fluid if contamination is suspected.**

## GENERAL INSPECTION

### BRAKE DRUMS

Any time the brake drums are removed for brake service, the braking surface diameter should be checked with a suitable brake drum micrometer at several points to determine if they are within the safe oversize limit stamped on the brake drum outer surface. If the braking surface diameter exceeds specifications, the drum must be replaced. If the braking surface diameter is within specifications, drums should be cleaned and inspected for cracks, scores, deep grooves, taper, out of round and heat spotting. If drums are cracked or heat spotted, they must be replaced. Minor scores should be removed with sandpaper. Grooves and large scores can only be removed by machining with special equipment, as long as the braking surface is within specifications stamped on brake drum outer surface. Any brake drum sufficiently out of round to cause vehicle vibration or noise while braking or showing taper should also be machined, removing only enough stock to true up the brake drum.

After a brake drum is machined, wipe the braking surface diameter with a denatured alcohol soaked cloth. If one brake drum is machined, the other should also be machined to the same diameter to maintain equal braking forces.

### BRAKE LININGS & SPRINGS

Inspect brake linings for excessive wear, damage, oil, grease or brake fluid contamination. If any of the above conditions exists, brake linings should be replaced. Do not attempt to replace only one set of brake shoes. They should be replaced as an axle set only to maintain equal braking forces. Examine brake shoe webbing, hold-down and return springs for signs of overheating indicated by a slight blue color. If any component exhibits overheating signs, replace hold-down and return springs with new ones. Overheated springs lose their pull and could cause brake linings to wear out prematurely. Inspect all springs for sags, bends and external damage and replace as necessary.

Inspect hold-down retainers and pins for bends, rust and corrosion. If any of the above is found, replace as required.

### BACKING PLATE

Inspect backing plate shoe contact surface for grooves that may restrict shoe movement and cannot be removed by lightly sanding with emery cloth or other suitable abrasive. If backing plate exhibits above condition, it should be replaced. Also inspect for signs of cracks, warpage and excessive rust, indicating need for replacement.

### ADJUSTER MECHANISM

Inspect all components for rust, corrosion, bends and fatigue. Replace as necessary. **On adjuster mechanism equipped with adjuster cable,** inspect cable for kinks, fraying or elongation of eyelet and replace as necessary.

### PARKING BRAKE CABLE

Inspect parking brake cable end for kinks, fraying and elongation and replace as necessary. Use a small hose clamp to compress clamp where it enters backing plate to remove.

# Types 1 & 2

### INDEX



## REMOVAL

1. Raise and support rear of vehicle, then remove tire and wheel assembly.
2. Remove brake drum. If brake lining is dragging on brake drum, back off brake adjustment by rotating adjustment screw. Refer to individual car chapter for procedure. **If brake drum is rusted or corroded to axle flange and cannot be removed, lightly tap axle flange to drum mounting surface with a suitable hammer.**
3. Install suitable wheel cylinder clamp over ends of wheel cylinder to retain pistons in bore.
4. **On type 1 brakes, Fig 1,** remove parking brake lever retaining clip.
5. **On both types, Figs. 1 and 2,** remove adjuster lever spring, primary and secondary shoe return springs using a suitable pair of brake spring pliers.
6. Remove shoe guide plate, if equipped and adjuster cable and guide plate.
7. Using suitable tool, compress hold-down springs, then remove spring retainers, hold-down springs and pins.
8. Separate springs and remove from backing plate.
9. **On type 2 brake,** disengage parking brake lever from secondary shoe.
10. **On all types,** remove parking brake lever from cable.
11. Separate all components from brake shoes.
12. Clean dirt from brake drum, backing plate and all other components. **Do not use compressed air or dry brush to clean brake parts. Many brake parts contain asbestos fibers which, if inhaled, can cause serious injury. Clean brake parts with a water soaked rag or a suitable vacuum cleaner to minimize airborne dust.**

## INSPECTION

1. Inspect components for damage and unusual wear. Replace as necessary.
2. Inspect wheel cylinders. Boots which are torn, cut, or heat damaged indicate need for wheel cylinder replacement. Fluid spilling from boot center hole, or wetness around wheel cylinder ends indicates cup leakage and need for wheel cylinder replacement. **A small amount of fluid is always present and is considered normal, acting as a lubricant for the cylinder pistons.**
3. Inspect backing plate for evidence of seal leakage. If leakage exists, refer to individual car chapters for axle seal replacement procedure.
4. Inspect backing plate attaching bolts and ensure they are tight.
5. Check adjuster screw operation. If satisfactory, lightly lubricate adjusting screw and washer with suitable brake lube. If operation is unsatisfactory, replace.
6. Using fine emery cloth or other suitable abrasive, clean rust and dirt from shoe contact surfaces on backing plate.

## INSTALLATION

1. Lightly lubricate backing plate shoe contact surfaces with suitable brake lube.
2. **On type 1 brakes,** assemble parking brake lever to secondary shoe and secure with spring washer and retaining clip. Crimp ends of clip with suitable pliers. **On type 2 brakes,** engage parking brake lever tang with secondary shoe.
3. Position brake shoes on backing plate, primary (short lining) shoe facing front of vehicle and secondary (long lining) facing rear. Secure brake shoes with hold-down springs, pins and retainers.
4. Install parking brake link and spring between shoes.
5. Loosen parking brake adjustment nut, then install parking brake cable on parking brake lever.

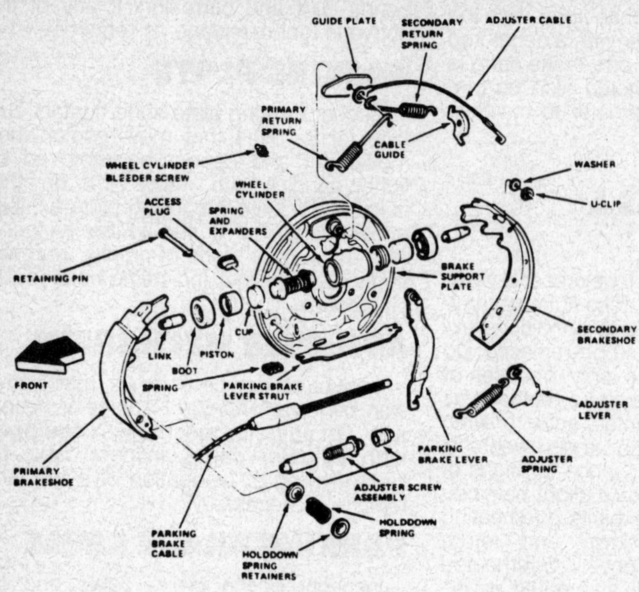


**Fig. 1 Drum brake assembly. Type 1**

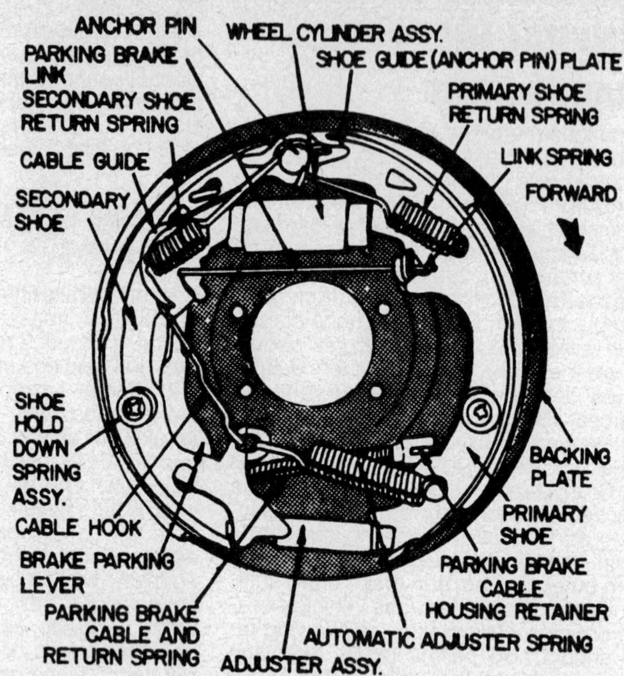


**Fig. 2 Drum brake assembly. Type 2**

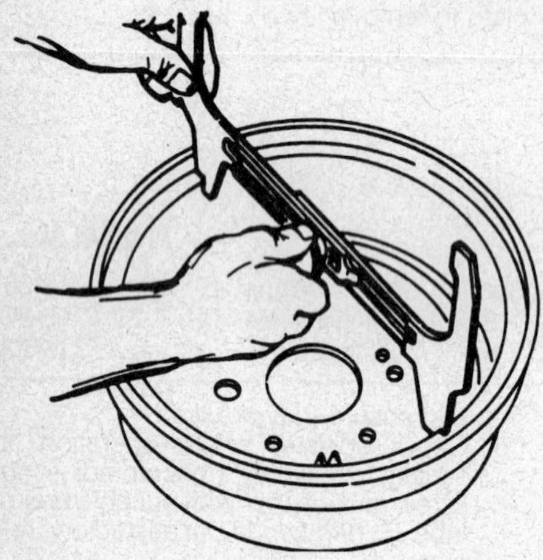

**Fig. 3 Measuring brake drum inside diameter**

6. Install shoe guide plate and adjuster cable eyelet on anchor. Ensure adjuster cable crimp faces out.
7. Ensure parking brake link is properly positioned between brake shoes and wheel cylinder links are engaged in shoe web.
8. Using suitable brake spring pliers, install primary return spring from brake shoe to anchor, then secondary return spring from brake shoe to anchor.
9. **On all types,** remove wheel cylinder clamp installed during removal of brake shoes.
10. Tighten adjuster screw assembly to thread limit and back off 1/2 turn.
11. Install adjuster screw assembly between shoes. Ensure toothed wheel is on secondary shoe side. **Adjuster screw assemblies are stamped R (right) and L (left). To ensure proper adjuster operation, they must be installed on their respective sides.**
12. Hook adjuster cable hook into adjuster lever hole, then position adjuster spring hook in large hole in primary shoe web. Using suitable brake spring pliers, install adjuster spring in adjuster lever hole.
13. Ensure adjuster cable is properly seated in cable guide, then pull adjuster lever, cable and adjuster spring down and towards the rear, engaging lever pivot hook in the large hole of secondary shoe web.
14. After installation, check adjuster operation by pulling adjuster cable between cable guide and adjuster lever towards secondary shoe sufficiently to lift adjuster lever past one tooth on adjuster screw assembly. The adjuster lever should snap into position behind the next tooth, then upon release of adjuster cable, rotate toothed wheel one notch. If operation is not satisfactory, recheck installation.
15. Ensure brake shoe upper ends are seated against anchor pin and shoe assemblies are centered on backing plate. If not, back off parking brake adjustment.
16. Using suitable brake drum to shoe gauge, **Fig. 3,** measure brake drum inside diameter. Adjust brake shoes to dimension obtained on outside portion of gauge using adjuster screw.
17. Install brake drum, wheel and tire assembly.
18. If any hydraulic brake connections have been opened, bleed brake system.
19. Adjust parking brake. Refer to individual car chapter for procedures.
20. Inspect all hydraulic lines and connections for leakage and repair as necessary.
21. Check master cylinder fluid level and replenish as necessary.

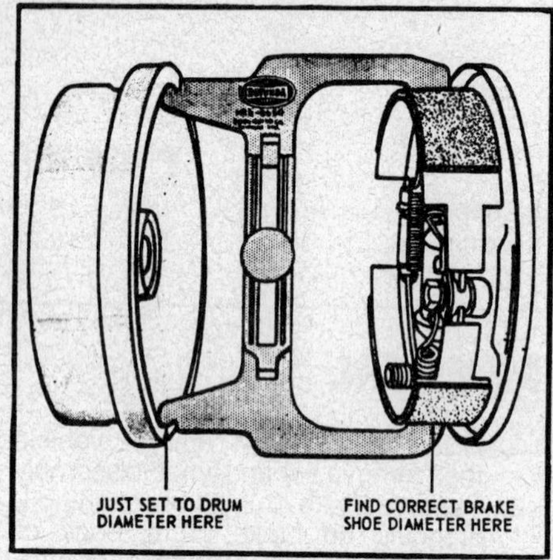


**Fig. 4 Brake adjustment gauge**

22. Check brake pedal for proper feel and return.
23. Lower vehicle and road test. **Do not severely apply brakes immediately after installation of new brake linings or permanent damage may occur to linings, and/or brake drums may become scored. Brakes must be used moderately during first several hundred miles of operation to ensure proper burnishing of linings.**

## SERVICE BRAKES

### ADJUST

1. Use the brake shoe adjustment gauge shown in **Fig 4** to obtain the drum inside diameter as shown. Tighten the adjusting knob on the gauge to hold this setting.

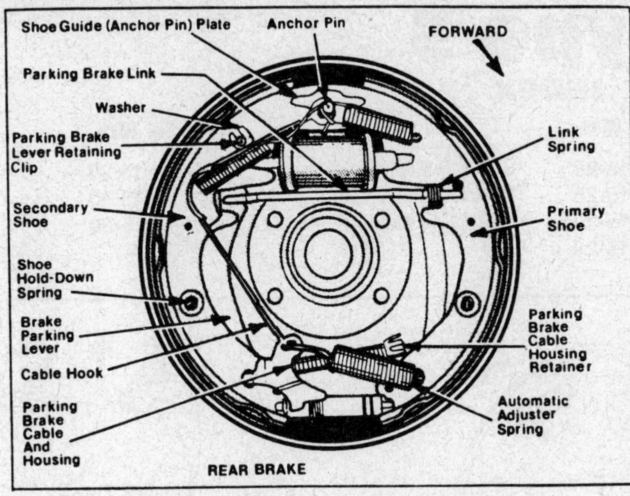


**Fig. 5 Rear drum type brakes**

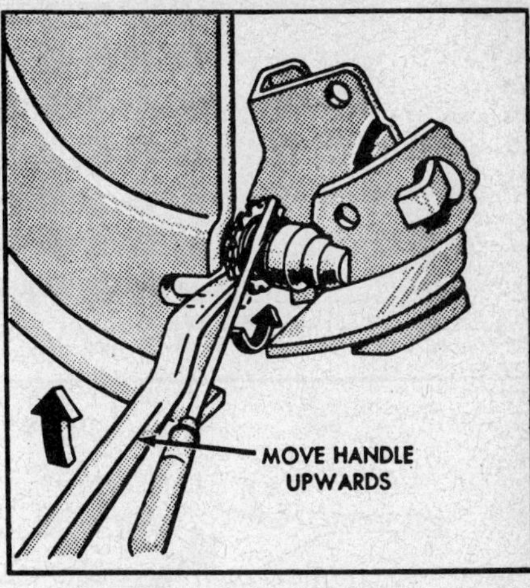


**Fig. 6 Backing off brake adjustment by disengaging adjusting lever**

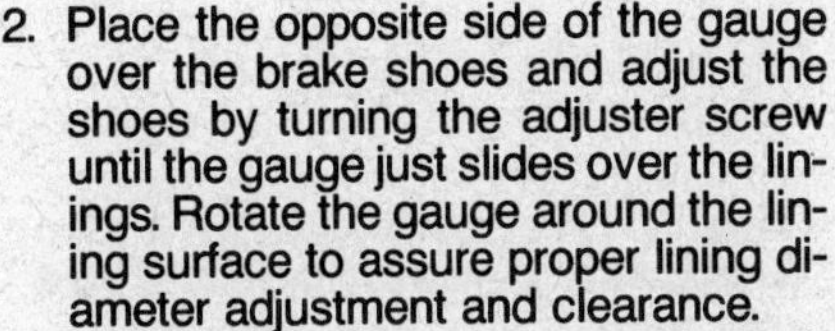

2. Place the opposite side of the gauge over the brake shoes and adjust the shoes by turning the adjuster screw until the gauge just slides over the linings. Rotate the gauge around the lining surface to assure proper lining diameter adjustment and clearance.
3. Install brake drum and wheel, final adjustment is accomplished by making several firm reverse stops, using the brake pedal.

## SELF-ADJUSTING BRAKES

The self adjusting brakes, **Fig. 5**, have self-adjusting shoe mechanisms that assure correct lining-to-drum clearances at all times. The automatic adjusters operate only when the brakes are applied as the vehicle is moving rearward.

Although the brakes are self-adjusting, an initial adjustment is necessary after the brake shoes have been relined or replaced, or when the length of the star wheel adjuster has been changed during some other service operation.

Frequent usage of an automatic transmission forward range to halt vehicle motion may prevent the automatic adjusters from functioning, thereby inducing low pedal heights. Should low pedal heights be encountered, it is recommended that numerous forward and reverse stops be performed with a firm pedal effort until satisfactory pedal height is obtained.

If a low pedal height condition cannot be corrected by making numerous reverse stops (provided the hydraulic system is free of air), it indicates that the self-adjusting mechanism is not functioning. It will be necessary to remove brake drums, clean, free up and lubricate the adjusting mechanism. Then adjust the brakes, being sure the parking brake is fully released.

## INITIAL ADJUSTMENT

1. Remove adjusting hole cover from brake backing plate and from the backing plate side, turn the adjusting screw upward with a screwdriver or other suitable tool to expand the shoes until a slight drag is felt when the drums are rotated.
2. Remove the drum.
3. While holding the adjuster lever out of engagement with the adjusting screw, **fig. 6,** back off the adjusting screw about one full turn with the fingers. **If finger movement will not turn the screw, free it up. If this is not done, the adjusting lever will not turn the screw during vehicle operation. Lubricate the screw during with oil and coat with wheel bearing grease. Any other adjustment procedure may cause damage to the adjusting screw with consequent self-adjuster problems.**
4. Install wheel and drum, and adjusting hole cover. Adjust brakes on remaining wheels in the same manner.
5. If pedal height is not satisfactory, drive the vehicle and make sufficient reverse stops with a firm pedal effort until proper pedal height is obtained.

## PARKING BRAKE ADJUST

1. Make sure parking brake is released.
2. Place transmission in neutral and raise the vehicle.
3. Tighten the adjusting nut against the cable equalizer to cause rear brakes to drag.
4. Loosen the adjusting nut until the rear wheels are fully released. There should be no drag.
5. Lower vehicle and check operation.

# Type 3

## INDEX



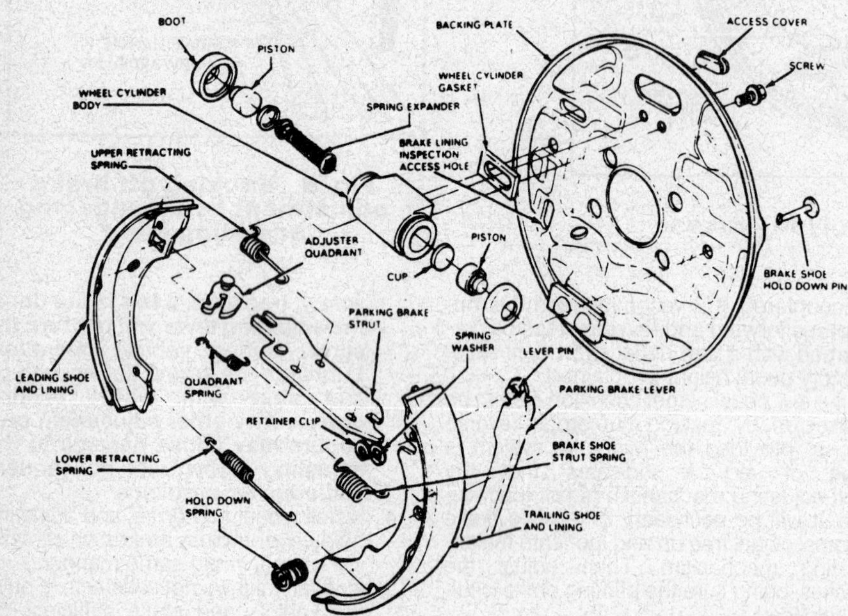


Fig. 1 Drum brake assembly. Type 3

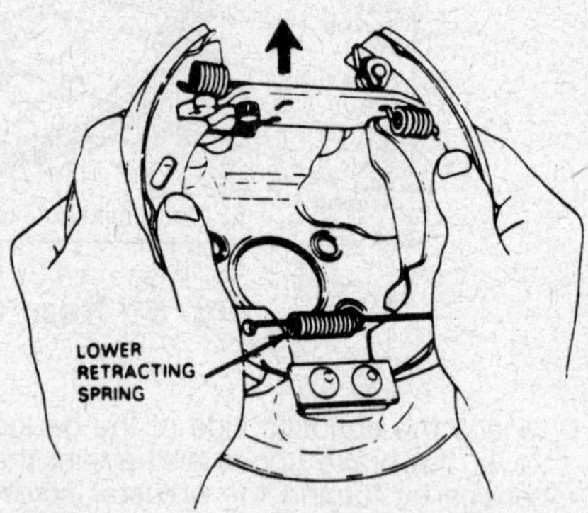


Fig. 2 Removing brake shoe & adjuster assemblies. Type 3

# REMOVAL

1. Raise and support rear of vehicle, then remove tire and wheel assembly.
2. Remove brake drum. If brake lining is dragging on brake drum, back off brake adjustment. Refer to individual car chapters for procedure.
3. Using suitable tool, remove hold-down retainers, springs and pins, **Fig. 1.**
4. Remove brake shoe and adjuster assemblies from backing plate by lifting up and away from anchor block and shoe guide, **Fig. 2. When removing brake shoe and adjuster assemblies, use care not to damage wheel cylinder boots.**
5. Remove parking brake cable from parking brake lever.
6. Remove lower retracting spring from leading and trailing shoes.
7. While holding brake shoe and adjuster assemblies, remove leading shoe upper retracting spring by rotating leading shoe over adjuster quadrant until spring is slack, then remove spring. Remove leading shoe from adjuster assembly.
8. Remove parking brake strut from trailing shoe by pulling strut outward from shoe assembly, then twisting strut downward until spring tension is released. Unhook brake shoe strut spring, then remove parking brake strut and adjuster assembly from trailing shoe.
9. If adjuster disassembly is required, pull adjuster quadrant away from knurled pin in parking brake strut and rotate quadrant in either direction until quadrant teeth are disengaged from strut pin. Remove spring and slide quadrant out of strut. **Do not over stress quadrant spring during removal.**
10. Remove parking brake lever retaining clip and spring washer, then the parking brake lever.
11. Clean dirt from brake drum, backing plate and all other components. **Do not use compressed air or dry brush to clean brake parts. Many brake parts contain asbestos fibers which, if inhaled, can cause serious injury. Clean brake parts with a water soaked rag or a suitable vacuum cleaner to minimize airborne dust.**

# INSPECTION

1. Inspect components for damage and unusual wear. Replace as necessary.
2. Inspect wheel cylinders. Boots which are torn, cut or heat damaged indicate need for wheel cylinder replacement. Peel back lower edge of boot. If fluid spills out, cup leakage is indicated and wheel cylinder should be replaced. **A slight amount of fluid is always present and is considered normal, acting as a lubricant for the cylinder pistons.**
3. Inspect backing plate attaching bolts and ensure they are tight.
4. Using fine emery cloth or other suitable abrasive, clean rust and dirt from shoe contact surfaces on backing plate.

# INSTALLATION

1. Lightly lubricate backing plate shoe contact surfaces with suitable brake lube.
2. Remove brake drum hub grease seal and bearings, then clean and repack bearings and reinstall. Install new grease seal.
3. Lightly lubricate strut to adjuster quadrant contact surfaces with suitable brake lube.
4. Position adjuster quadrant pin in strut slot and install quadrant spring, then pivot quadrant until it engages with strut knurled pin in third or fourth notch of outboard end of quadrant.
5. Assemble parking brake lever to trailing shoe, then install spring washer and retaining clip. Using suitable pliers, crimp retaining clip until securely fastened.
6. Assemble parking brake strut to trail-

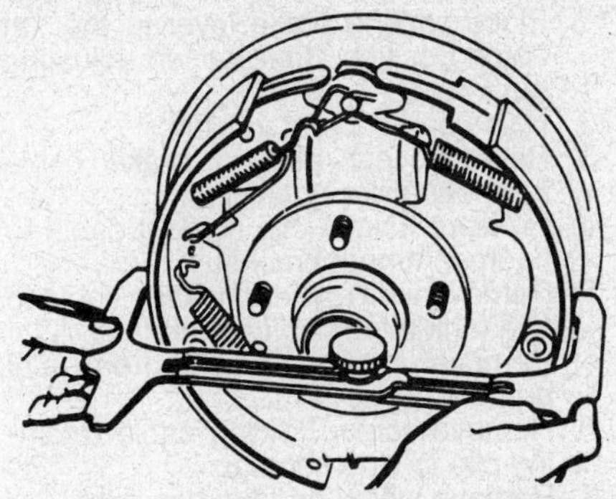

Fig. 3 Adjusting brake shoes to brake drum inside diameter. Type 3

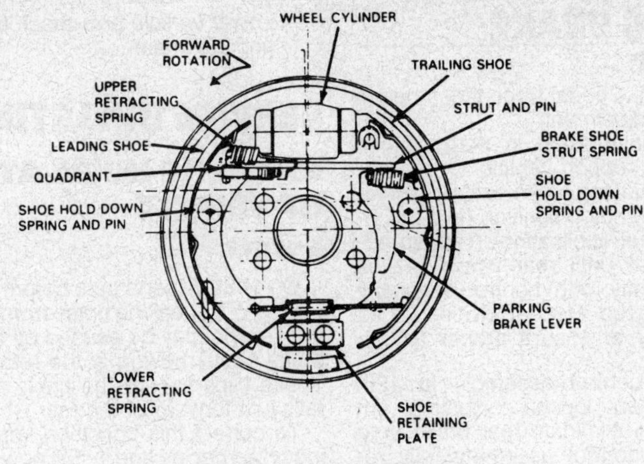


Fig. 4 Rear brake drum assembly

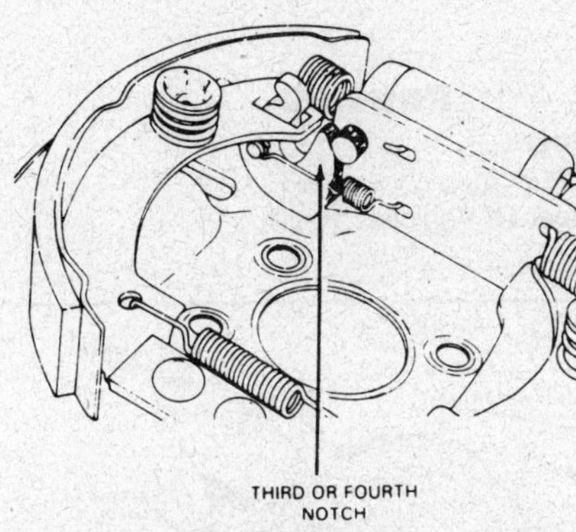


Fig. 5 Initial brake Adjustment

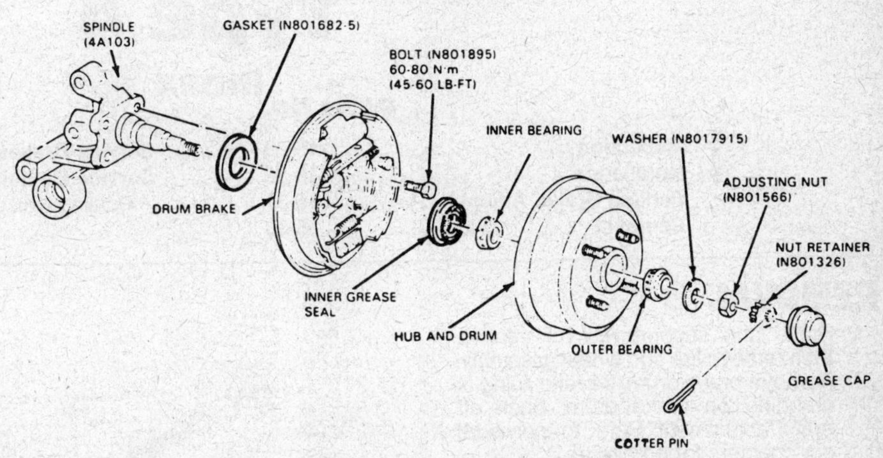


Fig. 6 Rear wheel bearing assembly

ing shoe by attaching brake shoe strut spring to slots in shoe web and strut, and pivoting strut into position, tension spring and holding assembly in place. **Ensure end of spring with hook parallel to the center line of spring coils is installed in shoe web hole. Installed spring should be flat against shoe web and parallel to parking brake strut.**

7. Install lower retracting spring between shoes. Ensure spring hook with longest straight piece fits into trailing shoe hole, **Fig. 1.**
8. Install upper retracting spring by installing hooks in leading shoe web and other end in parking brake strut, then pivot leading shoe over adjuster quadrant and into position.
9. Spread shoe and strut assemblies sufficiently to fit over anchor plate and wheel cylinder piston inserts, and install onto backing plate. **When installing brake shoe and adjuster assemblies, use care not to damage wheel cylinder boots.**
10. Connect parking brake cable to parking brake lever.
11. Using suitable tool, install hold-down springs, retainers and pins.
12. Using suitable brake drum to shoe gauge, measure brake drum inside diameter. Adjust brake shoes to dimension obtained on outside portion of gauge, **Fig. 3.**
13. Install brake drum. Refer to individual car chapters for wheel bearing adjustment procedure.
14. Install tire and wheel assembly.
15. If any hydraulic connections have been opened, bleed brake system.
16. Adjust parking brake. Refer to individual car chapters for procedure.
17. Inspect all hydraulic lines and connections for leakage and repair as necessary.
18. Check master cylinder fluid level and replenish as necessary.
19. Check brake pedal for proper feel and return.
20. Lower vehicle and road test. **Do not severely apply brakes immediately after installation of new brake linings or permanent damage may occur to lining, and/or brake drums may become scored. Brakes must be used moderately during first several hundred miles of operation to ensure proper burnishing of linings.**

## SERVICE BRAKES
## ADJUST

Although the brakes are self-adjusting, **Fig. 4,** an initial adjustment will be necessary after a brake repair. The initial adjustment can be obtained as follows:

1. Pivot adjuster quadrant until it meshes with knurled pin and is in third or fourth notch of the outboard end of the quadrant, **Fig. 5.**
2. Install drum and wheel assembly, then adjust wheel bearings as described in **Fig. 6.**
3. Complete adjustment by applying brakes several times, then check brake operation by making several stops from varying speeds. **If brake drum cannot be removed for brake servicing, remove rubber plug from backing plate inspection hole.**
4. Insert a suitable tool into the hole until it contacts adjuster assembly pivot. Apply pressure sideways on the pivot point allowing adjuster quadrant to ratchet and release the brake adjustment.

## PARKING BRAKE

### ADJUST

1. Pump brake pedal three times before making adjustment.
2. Place transmission in neutral, then raise and support vehicle.
3. Position parking brake control assembly in 12th notch position (two notches from full application). Tighten adjusting nut until rear wheel brakes drag slightly with control assembly fully released. Repeat procedure as necessary to ensure proper adjustment.
4. Position control assembly in 12th notch, then loosen adjusting nut enough to eliminate rear brake drag with the control assembly fully released.
5. Lower vehicle and check operation of parking brake.

## SERVICE BULLETINS

### RATTLING NOISE AT REAR OF VEHICLE

#### Escort

On 1989 Escorts built before 9-16-88, a rattling or squeaking noise from the rear of the vehicle may be caused by the parking brake cable moving in the retaining clips. These clips secure the cable to the side rails just forward of the rear wheels.

To correct this condition, replace parking brake cables and install new vinyl coated clips, part No. E6FZ-2860-A, as follows:

1. Place parking brake lever in the 7th notch position, then loosen adjusting nut.
2. Raise and support vehicle.
3. Remove rear parking brake cable from equalizer bracket.
4. Remove hairpin clip holding cable to floorpan tunnel bracket.
5. Remove wire retainer holding cable to fuel tank mounting bracket.
6. Remove cable and clip from fuel pump bracket.
7. Remove screw holding cable retaining clip to sidemember.
8. Remove wheel and tire assembly.
9. Disengage cable end from brake assembly parking lever.
10. Depress cable prongs holding cable to backing plate, then remove cable.
11. Reverse procedure to install.

# Type 4

## INDEX



## REMOVAL

1. Raise and support rear of vehicle, then remove tire and wheel assembly.
2. Remove brake drum. If brake lining is dragging on brake drum, back off brake adjustment. Refer to individual car chapters for procedure.
3. Using suitable tool, remove hold-down retainers, springs and pins, **Fig. 1.**
4. Remove brake shoes and adjuster assemblies from backing plate by lifting up and away from wheel cylinder assembly. **When removing brake shoe and adjuster assemblies, use care not to bend adjusting lever.**
5. Remove parking brake cable from parking brake lever.
6. Remove lower retracting spring, adjuster screw retracting spring and adjuster lever.
7. Separate brake shoes, then remove parking brake lever retaining clip and spring washer and slide lever off parking brake lever pin on the trailing shoe.
8. Clean dirt from brake drum, backing plate and all other components. **Do not use compressed air or dry brush to clean brake parts. Many brake parts contain asbestos fibers which, if inhaled, can cause serious injury. Clean brake parts with a water soaked rag or a suitable vacuum cleaner to minimize airborne dust.**

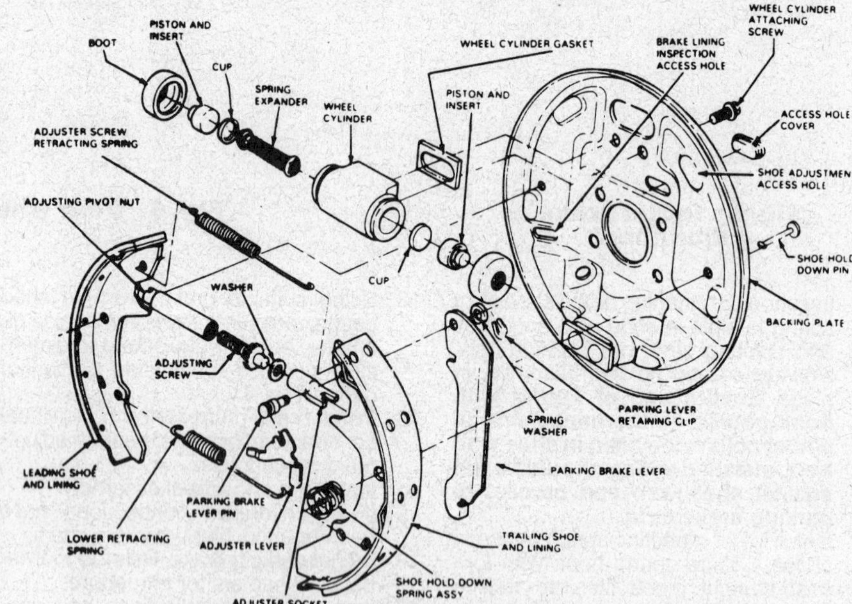


**Fig. 1 Drum brake assembly. Type 4**

## INSPECTION

1. Inspect components for damage and unusual wear. Replace as necessary.
2. Inspect wheel cylinders. Boots which are torn, cut or heat damaged indicate need for wheel cylinder replacement. Peel back lower edge of boot. If fluid spills out, cup leakage is indicated and wheel cylinder should be replaced. **A small amount of fluid is always present and is considered normal, acting as a lubricant for the cylinder pistons.**
3. Inspect backing plate attaching bolts and ensure they are tight.
4. Using fine emery cloth or other suitable abrasive, clean rust and dirt from shoe contact surfaces on backing plate.
5. Check adjuster screw operation. If satisfactory, lightly lubricate adjusting screw and washer with suitable brake lube. If operation is unsatisfactory, replace.

## INSTALLATION

1. Lightly lubricate backing plate shoe

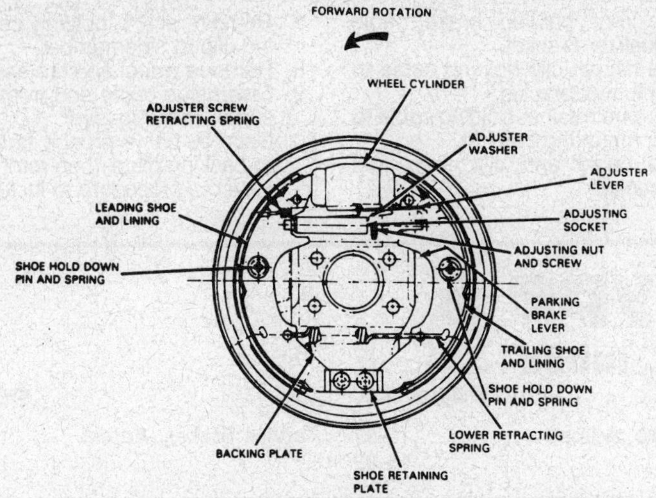


**Fig. 2 Adjusting drum brake assembly**

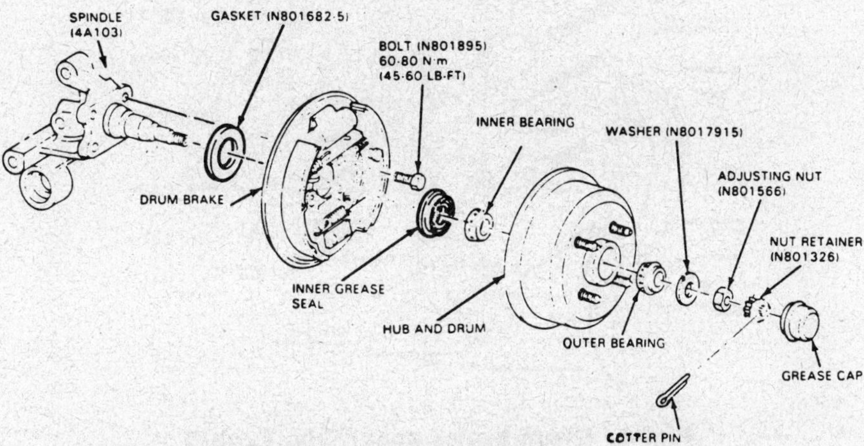


**Fig. 3 Rear wheel bearing assembly**

contact surfaces with suitable brake lubrication.

2. Remove brake drum hub grease seal and bearings, then clean and repack bearings and reinstall. Install new grease seal.
3. Assemble parking brake lever to trailing shoe, then install spring washer and retaining clip. Using suitable pliers, crimp retaining clip until securely fastened.
4. Attach parking brake cable to parking brake lever.
5. Assemble lower retracting spring to leading and trailing shoe assemblies, then spread lower part of shoes and install on backing plate.
6. Using suitable tool, install hold-down springs.
7. Tighten adjuster assembly, then back off 1/2 turn. Install adjuster assembly between leading shoe slot and trailing shoe/parking brake lever slot. The adjuster socket end slot must fit into trailing shoe/parking brake lever. **Adjuster assemblies are stamped R (right) and L (left). To ensure proper adjuster operation, they must be installed on their respective sides. The letter must be installed in the upright position, facing wheel cylinder to ensure the deeper of the two slots in the adjuster socket fits in the parking brake lever.**
8. Install adjuster lever in the parking brake lever groove and into the adjuster socket slot.
9. Using suitable brake spring pliers, install adjusting screw retracting spring from leading shoe slot to adjuster lever notch.
10. Install brake drum. Refer to individual car chapters for wheel bearing adjustment procedure.
11. Install tire and wheel assembly.
12. If any hydraulic connections have been opened, bleed brake system.
13. Adjust parking brake. Refer to individual car chapters for procedure.
14. Inspect all hydraulic lines and connection for leakage, and repair as necessary.
15. Check master cylinder fluid level and replenish as necessary.
16. Check brake pedal for proper feel and return.
17. Lower vehicle and road test. **Do not severely apply brakes immediately after installation of new brake linings or permanent damage may occur to linings, and/or brake drums may become scored. Brakes must be used moderately during first several hundred miles of operation to ensure proper burnishing of linings.**

## SERVICE BRAKES

### ADJUST

Although the brakes are self-adjusting, **Fig. 2,** an initial adjustment will be necessary after a brake repair. The initial adjustment can be obtained as follows:

1. Determine inside diameter of drum brake surface using brake shoe gauge tool No. D81L-1103-A or equivalent. Adjust brake shoe diameter to fit gauge. Hold automatic adjusting lever out of engagement while rotating adjusting screw and ensure that screw turns freely.
2. Install drum and wheel assembly, then adjust wheel bearings as described in **Fig. 3.**
3. Complete adjustment by applying brakes several times, then check brake operation by making several stops from varying speeds. **If brake drum cannot be removed for brake servicing, remove rubber plug from backing plate inspection hole.**
4. Remove the brake line to axle retention bracket. This will allow sufficient room for insertion of a suitable tool to disengage adjusting lever and back off the adjusting screw.

## PARKING BRAKE

### ADJUST

1. Pump brake pedal three times before making adjustment.
2. Place transmission in neutral, then raise and support vehicle.
3. Position parking brake control assembly in 12th notch position (two notches from full application). Tighten adjusting nut until rear wheel brakes drag slightly with control assembly fully released. Repeat procedure as necessary to ensure proper adjustment.
4. Position control assembly in 12th notch, then loosen adjusting nut enough to eliminate rear brake drag with the control assembly fully released.
5. Lower vehicle and check operation of parking brake.

## SERVICE BULLETINS

### RATTLING NOISE AT REAR OF VEHICLE

#### Escort

On 1989 Escorts built before 9-16-88, a rattling or squeaking noise from the rear of the vehicle may be caused by the parking brake cable moving in the retaining clips.

These clips secure the cable to the side rails just forward of the rear wheels.

To correct this condition, replace parking brake cables and install new vinyl coated clips, part No. E6FZ-2860-A, as follows:

1. Place parking brake lever in the 7th notch position, then loosen adjusting nut.
2. Raise and support vehicle.
3. Remove rear parking brake cable from equalizer bracket.
4. Remove hairpin clip holding cable to floorpan tunnel bracket.
5. Remove wire retainer holding cable to fuel tank mounting bracket.
6. Remove cable and clip from fuel pump bracket.
7. Remove screw holding cable retaining clip to sidemember.
8. Remove wheel and tire assembly.
9. Disengage cable end from brake assembly parking lever.
10. Depress cable prongs holding cable to backing plate, then remove cable.
11. Reverse procedure to install.

# Type 5

## INDEX



## REMOVAL

1. Raise and support rear of vehicle, then remove tire and wheel assembly.
2. Remove brake drum. If brake lining is dragging on brake drum, back off brake adjustment. Refer to individual car chapters for procedures.
3. Using suitable tool, remove shoe hold-down springs and pins, **Fig. 1.**
4. Lift brake shoes, springs and adjuster assembly off backing plate and wheel cylinder assembly, being careful not to bend adjusting lever.
5. Remove parking brake cable from parking brake lever.
6. Remove retracting springs from lower brake shoe attachments and upper shoe to adjusting lever attachment points, then separate shoes and disengage adjuster mechanism.
7. Clean dirt from brake drum, backing plate and all other components. **Do not use compressed air or dry brush to clean brake parts. Many brake parts contain asbestos fibers which, if inhaled, can cause serious industry. Clean brake parts with a water soaked rag or a suitable vacuum cleaner to minimize airborne dust.**

## INSPECTION

1. Inspect components for damage and unusual wear. Replace as necessary.
2. Inspect wheel cylinders. Boots which are torn, cut or heat damaged indicate need for wheel cylinder replacement. Peel back lower edge of boot. If fluid spills out, cup leakage is indicated and wheel cylinder should be replaced. **A small amount of fluid is always present and is considered normal, acting as a lubricant for the cylinder pistons.**
3. Inspect backing plate attaching bolts and ensure they are tight.
4. Using fine emery cloth or other suitable abrasive, clean rust and dirt from shoe contact surfaces on backing plate.
5. Check adjuster screw operation. If satisfactory, lightly lubricate adjusting screw and washer with suitable brake lube. If operation is unsatisfactory, replace.

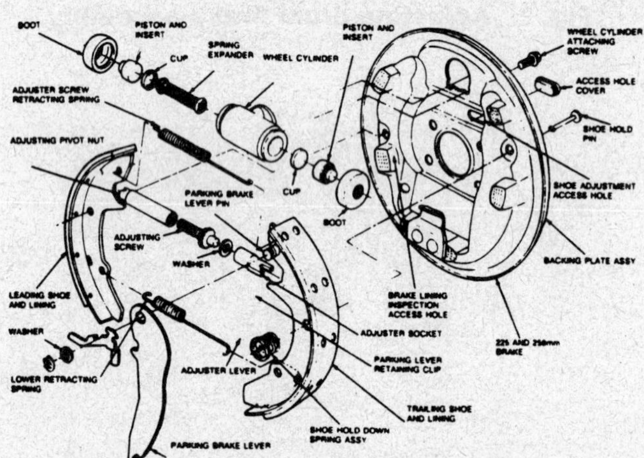


**Fig. 1 Drum brake assembly. Type 5**

## INSTALLATION

1. Lightly lubricate backing plate shoe contact surfaces with suitable brake lubrication.
2. Apply a thin uniform coat of suitable brake lube to adjuster screw threads and socket end of adjusting screw.
3. Install stainless steel washer over socket end of adjusting screw and install socket, then turn adjusting screw fully into adjusting pivot nut and back off 1/2 turn.
4. Assemble parking brake lever to trailing shoe and lining assembly by installing spring washer and a new horseshoe retaining clip. Crimp the clip until it retains lever to shoe securely.
5. Attach parking brake cable to parking brake lever.
6. Attach lower shoe retracting spring to leading and trailing shoe assemblies and install on backing plate. It will be necessary to stretch retracting spring as shoes are installed downward over anchor plate to inside of shoe retaining plate.
7. Install adjuster screw assembly between leading shoe slot and the slot in the trailing shoe and parking brake lever. The adjuster socket end slot must fit into the trailing shoe and parking brake lever. **The adjuster socket blade is marked "R" or "L" for right and left side brake assemblies. The R or L adjuster blade must be installed with the letter R or L in the upright position (facing wheel cylinder) on the correct side to ensure that the deeper of two slots in adjuster sockets fits into the parking brake lever.**
8. Assemble adjuster lever in groove located in parking brake lever pin and into slot of adjuster socket that fits into trailing shoe web.
9. Attach upper retracting spring to leading shoe slot and, using suitable tool, stretch other end of spring into notch on adjuster lever. **If adjuster lever does not contact star wheel after installing spring, adjuster socket may be improperly installed.**
10. Install brake drum. Refer to individual car chapters for wheel bearing adjustment procedure.
11. Install tire and wheel assembly.
12. If any hydraulic connections have

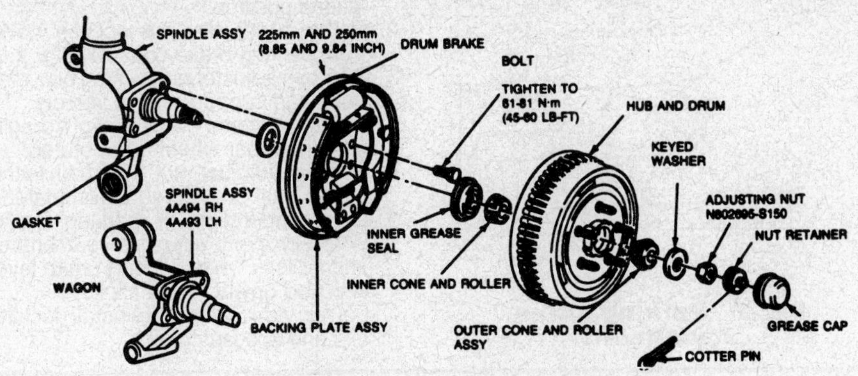


**Fig. 2 Drum assembly**

been opened, bleed brake system.

13. Adjust parking brake. Refer to individual car chapters for procedure.
14. Inspect all hydraulic lines and connections for leakage, repairing as necessary.
15. Check master cylinder fluid level and replenish as necessary.
16. Check brake pedal for proper feel and return.
17. Lower vehicle and road test. **Do not severely apply brakes immediately after installation of new brake linings or permanent damage may occur to linings., and/or brake drums may become scored. Brakes must be used moderately during first several hundred miles of operation to ensure proper burnishing of linings.**

## SERVICE BRAKES

### ADJUST

Although the brakes are self-adjusting, an initial adjustment will be required after a brake repair. The initial adjustment is performed as follows:

1. Determine inside diameter of brake drum surface using brake shoe gauge tool No. D81L-1103-A or equivalent. Adjust brake shoe diameter to fit gauge. Hold automatic adjusting lever out of engagement while rotating adjusting screw and ensure that screw rotates freely.
2. Install brake drum, **Fig 2,** then tire and wheel assembly.

## PARKING BRAKE

### ADJUST

1. Ensure parking brake is released.
2. With transmission in neutral, raise and support vehicle.
3. Tighten parking brake nut against brake equalizer until rear brakes drag, then loosen nut until rear brakes are fully released.
4. Lower vehicle, then check parking brake operation.

# Type 6

## INDEX



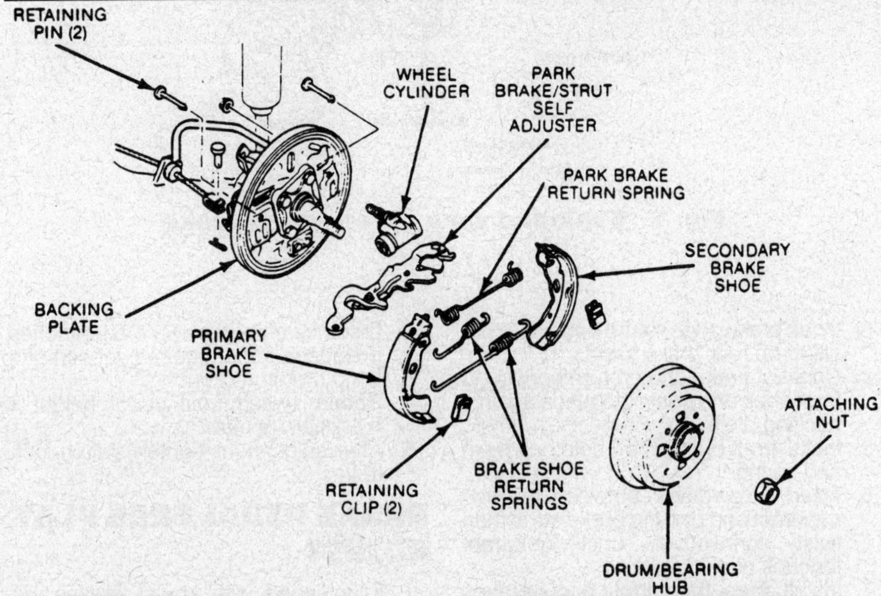


**Fig. 1 Disassembled view of drum brake assembly**

## REMOVAL

1. Raise and support vehicle, then remove rear wheel
2. Remove locknut and brake drum. **The locknut on the right side of the vehicle has lefthand threads. Turn locknut clockwise to remove.**
3. Remove hold down clips and retaining pins, **Fig. 1.**
4. Remove all return springs, then the primary and secondary brake shoes.
5. Remove cotter pin, then the clevis pin from parking brake strut/self adjuster. Disengage parking cable from self adjuster.

## INSTALLATION

1. Clean backing plate with a factory approved vacuum cleaner.
2. Lubricate backing plate shoe pads with suitable high temperature brake grease.
3. Install and position parking brake strut/self adjuster onto backing plate.
4. Install upper return spring to primary brake shoe, then position shoe on backing plate and install retaining pin and hold down clip, **Fig. 1.**
5. Connect upper return spring to secondary brake shoe, then position secondary shoe on backing plate and install retaining pin and hold down clip.
6. Install parking brake return spring.
7. Install lower return spring onto primary and secondary shoes.
8. Connect parking cable onto self adjuster, then install clevis and cotter pins.
9. Push on adjuster cam with screwdriver to position self adjuster in fully released position.
10. Install brake drum and locknut, push brake pedal down several times to set self adjuster, then install rear wheel.
11. Adjust parking brake as required.

## SERVICE BRAKES

### ADJUST

These models are equipped with self-adjusting drum brake mechanisms, which require no adjustment. The brakes are adjusted as necessary, whenever the service brakes are applied.

## PARKING BRAKE

### ADJUST

1. Ensure parking lever is in fully released position.
2. Remove adjuster nut access cover from parking brake console, **Fig. 2.**
3. Remove adjuster nut locking clip, then raise and support rear of vehicle.
4. Tighten adjuster nut until slight drag is felt when rear wheels are rotated.
5. Loosen adjuster nut in small increments until brake drag is eliminated.
6. Check operation of parking brake. When properly adjusted, rear brakes should lock when parking brake lever is pulled upward 8-11 clicks.
7. Lower vehicle, then reinstall locking clip and access cover.

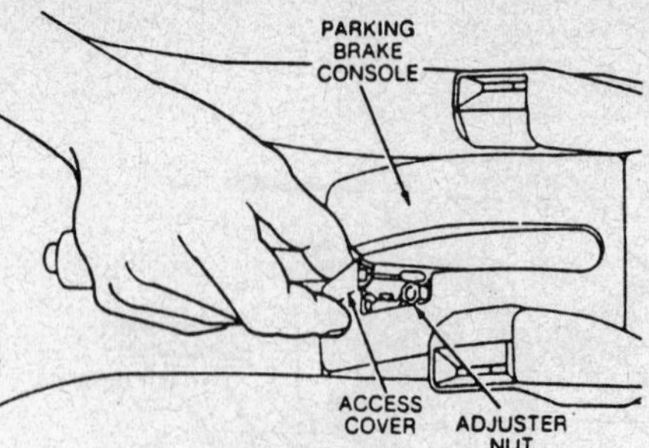


**Fig. 2 Parking brake adjustment**

# Type 7

## INDEX



## REMOVAL

1. Raise and support rear of vehicle.
2. Remove wheel and tire assembly, then the grease cap.
3. Using a suitable chisel, raise staked portion of wheel bearing locknut.
4. Remove rear bearing locknut. To do so, turn the locknut at the lefthand rear wheel bearing counterclockwise and the locknut at the righthand rear wheel bearing clockwise.
5. Remove outer wheel bearing, then remove brake drum and bearing hub assembly.
6. Remove brake shoe hold-down springs, then pull front shoe away from backing plate, disconnect return springs and remove front shoe, **Fig. 1.**
7. Remove return springs from rear shoe, then disconnect anti-rattle spring attaching rear shoe to parking brake strut and remove rear shoe.
8. If necessary, remove adjuster assembly.

**Fig. 1 Exploded view of rear drum brake**

## INSPECTION

Inspect lining material for wear beyond service limits, uneven wear, cracks, scoring, gouges, and contamination from brake fluid or grease. Inspect wheel cylinders for signs of leakage. Inspect the anti-rattle and return springs for signs of heat damage, bends, or damage to coils, and loss of tension. Inspect brake drum for scratches, scoring and out of round conditions.

## INSTALLATION

1. Lubricate the six shoe contact pads with high temperature grease D7AZ-19590-A or equivalent, then the adjuster mechanism toothed quadrant and the anchor plate.
2. Position rear brake shoe in the parking brake strut and install rear hold down pin and spring.
3. Hook brake shoe return springs in position on rear brake shoe.
4. Connect brake shoe return springs to front shoe and push into place against backing plate.
5. Install front brake shoe hold down pin and spring.
6. Insert screwdriver between knurled quadrant and parking brake strut, then twist screwdriver until quadrant touches backing plate.
7. Install drum, then firmly apply brakes two or three times to adjust rear brakes.

## BRAKE ADJUSTMENTS

### BRAKE PEDAL HEIGHT

1. Check distance from center of pedal pad to floor.
2. Distance should be 8.74-8.94 inches.
3. If adjustment is required, loosen stop lamp switch locknut.
4. Rotate switch until pedal height is 8.74-8.94 inches.
5. After adjustment, tighten switch locknut.

### BRAKE PEDAL FREE PLAY, ADJUST

1. If equipped with power brakes, depress pedal a few times in order eliminate the vacuum in the power booster.
2. Depress brake pedal by hand, then check brake free play (until the valve plunger contacts the stopper plate, then resistance is felt). Free play should be .16-.28 inch.
3. If adjustment is required, loosen clevis locknut on brake pedal pushrod.

4. Turn clevis to obtain .16-.28 inch free play.
5. After adjustment, tighten clevis locknut.

## PARKING BRAKE, ADJUST

1. Normal parking brake adjustment is made at the hand lever between the seats. Remove the six attaching screws in the center console, then the console.
2. Tighten parking brake adjusting nut on the left side of the parking brake lever. This shortens the equalizer cable. Tighten the adjusting nut until it takes seven to ten notches to fully set the parking brake.

# Type 8

## INDEX



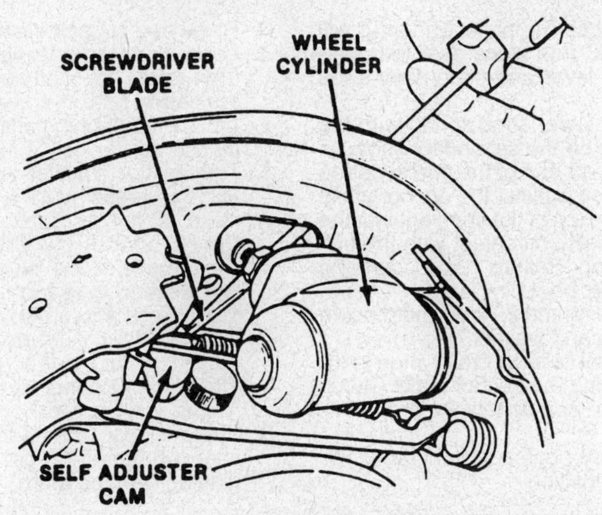


**Fig. 1 Releasing self-adjuster mechanism for brake drum removal**

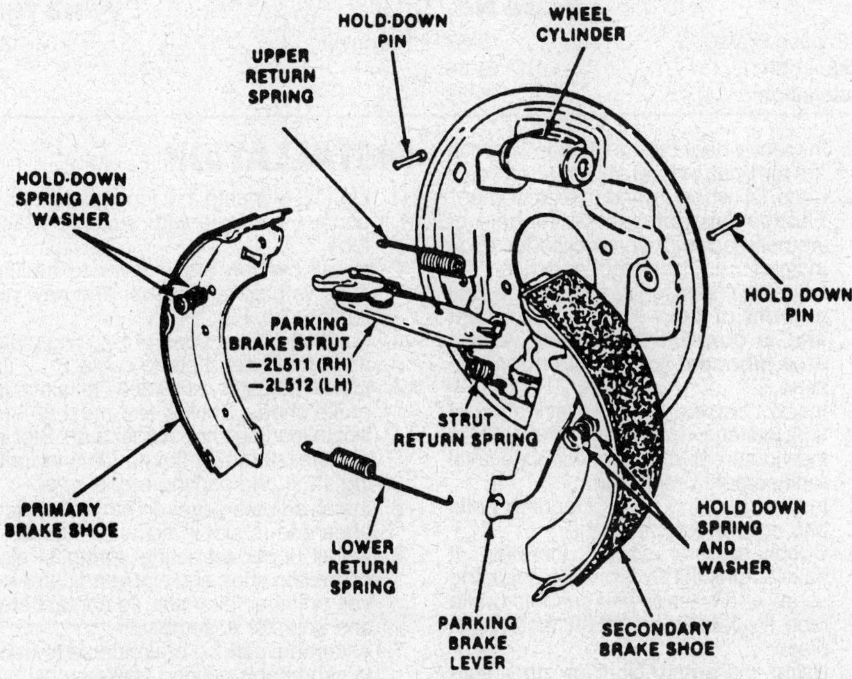


**Fig. 2 Exploded view of brake drum assembly**

## REMOVAL

1. Disconnect battery ground cable.
2. Raise and support vehicle.
3. Remove rear tire and wheel assembly.
4. Remove brake drum. Discard brake drum retaining clip.
5. Should difficulty be experienced in removal of the brake drum due to the action of the automatic self-adjuster mechanism, the self-adjuster may be released and brake drum removed, as follows:
   a. Remove wheel cylinder attaching bolts.
   b. Push wheel cylinder away from the brake backing plate to provide an access opening in the backing plate.
   c. Insert a screwdriver through the backing plate and rotate self-adjuster cam to the released position, **Fig. 1.**
   d. Remove brake drum.
   e. Correctly position wheel cylinder and install attaching bolts. Torque bolts to specification.
6. Remove both brake shoe hold-down springs, **Fig. 2.** To prevent rotation during removal, hold each hold-down pin head with a suitable tool.
7. Pry lower end of the primary shoe from its position against the anchor.
8. Remove lower return spring.
9. Remove shoes and strut by passing the strut between the wheel cylinder and hub assembly.
10. Pull top of primary shoe away from the secondary shoe to disconnect strut from the secondary shoe.
11. Disconnect the parking brake cable from the secondary shoe lever.
12. Remove strut return spring from the secondary shoe.
13. Remove adjuster cam spring.
14. Pull primary shoe away from the strut while rotating the cam to the fully released position.
15. Remove the primary shoe spring.
16. Remove the primary shoe from the strut.

## INSPECTION

Inspect lining material for wear beyond service limits, uneven wear, cracks, scoring, gouges, and contamination from brake fluid or grease. Inspect wheel cylinders for signs of leakage. Inspect the anti-rattle and return springs for signs of heat damage, bends, or damage to coils, and loss of tension. Inspect brake drum for scratches, scoring and out of round conditions.

## INSTALLATION

**Before installing the brake shoes, ensure the wheel cylinder and wheel hub are tightened to specification.**

1. Apply a light coating of grease supplied with the new brake shoes or high temperature grease D7AZ-19590-A, or equivalent, to support ledges where the brake shoes contact the backing plate.
2. Connect parking brake cable to the secondary shoe lever. To connect the cable, position the cable end through the lever and grip the cable end with locking type pliers, then push lever against the spring until it can be rotated over the cable. When properly installed, the plastic washer will be between the spring and lever.
3. Position the secondary shoe and install the hold-down spring.
4. Install the strut and cam assembly on the primary shoe.
5. Rotate the cam to the fully released position.
6. Install the adjuster cam spring.
7. Install the primary shoe spring.
8. Install the strut spring in the secondary shoe and then into the strut.
9. Place the strut on the parking brake lever and move the primary shoe toward the backing plate. The strut will then "click" into place over the parking brake lever and secondary shoe web.
10. Install the lower shoe spring with the longer leg on the secondary shoe.
11. Pry the lower end of the primary shoe into position against the anchor while holding the top of the shoe against the backing plate, in contact with the cylinder piston. Ensure not to damage the cylinder boot.
12. Install the primary shoe hold-down pin, spring and washer.
13. Ensure heel of each brake shoe is located behind the anchor plate. Check each brake component for proper installation.
14. If necessary, push adjuster cam to the released position.
15. Install brake drum(s).
16. Push brake pedal hard twice to set the self-adjuster cam position. The cam will make a ratcheting sound as it resets.
17. Adjust parking brake cable as necessary.

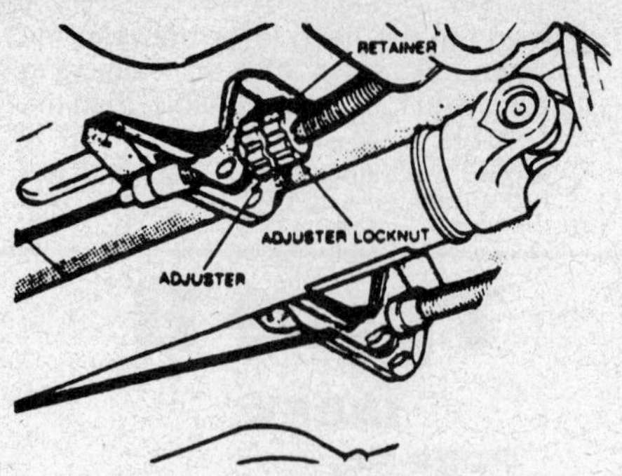


**Fig. 3 Parking brake cable adjusting locknut**

## PARKING BRAKE

### ADJUST

1. Release parking brake lever.
2. Pump the brake pedal to ensure the brake lining self-adjuster is properly set.
3. Raise and support vehicle.
4. Loosen the adjuster locknut, **Fig. 3,** then rotate adjuster sleeve along cable casing until in-and-out movement can be felt at both parking brake stop plungers.
5. Tighten the adjuster against the retaining bracket until a slight movement is felt at each stop plunger. **When added together, the total movement of the plungers should not exceed 0.16 inch. (4.0 mm)—a very slight movement.**
6. Tighten the locknut by hand against the sleeve as much as possible.
7. Tighten the locknut an additional two "clicks" using pliers.
8. Turn the rear wheels by hand to ensure the brake linings are not dragging against the drum.

# Type 9

## INDEX



## REMOVAL

1. Raise and support rear of vehicle, then remove tire and wheel assembly.
2. Remove brake drum.
3. Install suitable wheel cylinder clamp over ends of wheel cylinder to retain pistons in bore.
4. Disconnect parking brake cable from parking brake lever.
5. Remove two brake shoe hold down retainers, springs and pins, **Fig. 1.**
6. Spread brake shoes over piston shoe guide slots, then lift brake shoes, springs and adjuster off backing plat as an assembly.
7. Remove adjuster spring.
8. Remove retracting springs to separate shoes.
9. Remove parking brake lever retaining clip, spring and washer.
10. Remove lever from pin.

## INSPECTION

1. Inspect components for damage and unusual wear. Replace as necessary.
2. Inspect wheel cylinders. Boots which are torn, cut, or heat damaged indicate need for wheel cylinder replacement. Fluid spilling from boot center hole, or wetness around wheel cylinder ends indicates cup leakage and need for wheel cylinder replacement. **A small amount of fluid is always present and is considered normal, acting as a lubricant for the cylinder pistons.**
3. Inspect backing plate for evidence of seal leakage. If leakage exists, refer to individual car chapters for axle seal replacement procedure.
4. Inspect backing plate attaching bolts and ensure they are tight.
5. Check adjuster screw operation. If satisfactory, lightly lubricate adjusting screw and washer with suitable brake lube. If operation is unsatisfactory, replace.
6. Using fine emery cloth or other suitable abrasive, clean rust and dirt from shoe contact surfaces on backing plate.

## INSTALLATION

1. Lightly lubricate backing plate shoe contact surfaces with suitable brake lube.
2. Install parking brake lever to trailing shoe with spring washer and new retaining clip, **Fig. 1.**
3. Position trailing shoe or backing plate and attach hand brake cable.
4. Install adjuster assembly to slots in brake shoes. Socket end must fit into slot in leading shoe (wider slot). Slot in adjuster nut must fit into slots in trailing shoe and parking brake lever.
5. Install adjuster lever on pin on leading shoe and to slot in adjuster socket.
6. Install upper retracting spring in slot on trailing shoe and slot in adjuster lever. Adjuster lever should contact star and adjuster assembly.
7. Assemble parking brake cable to trailing shoe and parking brake lever.
8. Install lower retracting spring to leading-trailing shoe.
9. Install assembly to backing plate fit-

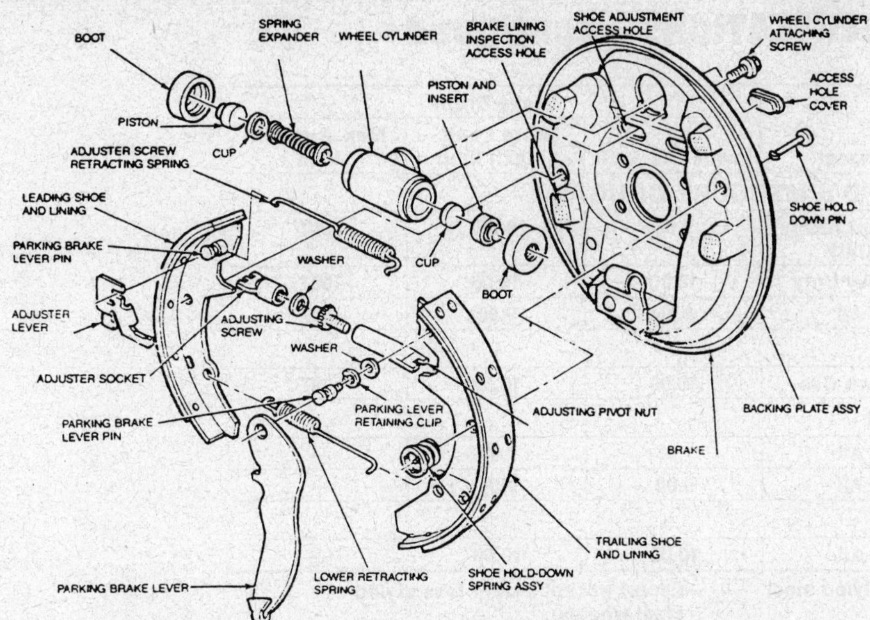


**Fig. 1 Exploded view of brake drum assembly**

ting shoes into wheel cylinder piston slots.

10. Install adjuster socket to leading shoe and lining assembly.
11. Install brake shoe anchor pis, springs and retainers.
12. Remove brake cylinder clamp and install brake drum.

## BRAKE ADJUSTMENTS

### BRAKE PEDAL HEIGHT

1. Run engine at normal operating condition.
2. Measure the distance to the top center of the brake pedal pad.
3. Free height should be approximately 7.35 inches.
4. If brake pedal is not within specification, check the brake pedal, booster or master cylinder to ensure the correct parts are installed. Replace worn or damaged parts.

### BRAKE PEDAL TRAVEL

1. With engine running in neutral or park position, block drive wheels, then release parking brake.
2. Install brake pedal effort gauge No. 021-00001 or equivalent and check pedal travel, with 25 lbs. of pressure applied to brake pedal, travel should not exceed 3.0 inches.
3. If pedal travel exceeds specification, make several reverse stops with a forward stop before each.
4. If travel still exceeds specification, remove brake drums and check brake adjusters, system may require bleeding.

### PARKING BRAKE

1. Apply and release parking brake several times, then place transmission in neutral position.
2. Raise and support vehicle.
3. Release tensioner by rotating locking lever away from threaded rod. Tensioner spring will take up slack and preload cables. **Do not pull down on locking lever as it will pull cables down and cause improper tension.**

# Drum Brake Specifications

| Year | Model | Brake Drum | | |
|---|---|---|---|---|
| | | Inside Dia. Inch | Bore Limit (Max.) Inch | Max. Run-out Inch |
| **FORD CROWN VICTORIA & MERCURY GRAND MARQUIS** | | | | |
| 1989 | Except Sta. Wag. | 10.00 | 10.03 | .007 |
| 1989–91 | Sta. Wag. | 11.03 | 11.09 | .007 |
| 1990–91 | Except Sta. Wag. | 10.00 | 10.06 | .007 |
| **FORD ESCORT** | | | | |
| 1989–90 | All① | 7.08 | 7.14 | .005 |
| | All② | 8.00 | 8.06 | .005 |
| 1991 | All | 9.00 | 9.04 | — |
| **FORD FESTIVA** | | | | |
| 1989–91 | All | 9.00 | — | — |
| **FORD MUSTANG** | | | | |
| 1989–91 | All | 9.00 | 9.06 | .007 |
| **FORD PROBE** | | | | |
| 1989–91 | All | — | 9.06 | — |
| **FORD TAURUS & MERCURY SABLE** | | | | |
| 1989–91 | Except Sta. Wag. | 8.85 | 8.91 | .005 |
| | Sta. Wag. | 9.84 | 9.90 | .005 |
| **FORD TEMPO & MERCURY TOPAZ** | | | | |
| 1989–91 | All | 8.00 | 8.06 | .005 |

*Continued*

## SPECIFICATIONS—Continued

| Year | Model | Brake Drum: Inside Dia. Inch | Brake Drum: Bore Limit (Max.) Inch | Brake Drum: Max. Run-out Inch |
|---|---|---|---|---|
| **FORD THUNDERBIRD & MERCURY COUGAR** | | | | |
| 1989 | Except Heavy Duty | 9.00 | 9.06 | .007 |
| | Heavy Duty | 10.00 | 10.06 | .007 |
| 1990–91 | All | 9.80 | 9.90 | .007 |
| **LINCOLN** | | | | |
| 1989–91 | Town Car | 10.00 | 10.06 | .007 |
| **MERCURY TRACER** | | | | |
| 1989 | All | 7.87 | 7.91 | — |
| 1991 | All | 9.00 | 9.04 | — |
| **MERKUR XR4Ti** | | | | |
| 1989 | All | 10.00 | 10.06 | — |

①—Escort 2 door less styled steel wheels.

②—Escort except 2 door less styled steel wheels.

# Brake Tightening Specifications

## FRONT BRAKES

| Component | Torque/Ft. lbs. |
|---|---|
| Anchor Bracket Attaching Bolts④ | 15–18 |
| Brake Hose Attaching Bolt | ③ |
| Caliper Mounting Bolt | ② |
| Locating Pins | ① |
| Wheel Lug Nuts | 65–88⑤ |

①—On Ford Crown Victoria, Mercury Grand Marquis and Lincoln Town Car models, torque locating pins to 40–60 ft. lbs. On Cougar, Mark VII, Mustang and Thunderbird, torque locating pins to 45 to 65 ft. lbs. On Escort, Tempo and Topaz, Sable, Taurus and Lincoln Continental torque to 18–25 ft. lbs.

②—On Festiva torque caliper attaching bolts to 33 ft. lbs.; Probe 23–30 ft. lbs.; Scorpio & XR4Ti 37–48 ft. lbs.; Escort & Tracer 29–36 ft. lbs.

③—On Scorpio & XR4Ti torque brake hose to 15–18 ft. lbs.; Probe 16–22 ft. lbs.; Escort & Tracer 16–22 ft. lbs.

④—Scorpio & XR4Ti.

⑤—Mark VII, Sable & Taurus; 65–104 ft. lbs.

## REAR BRAKES

| Component | Torque/Ft. lbs. |
|---|---|
| Caliper Attaching Bolt | ① |
| Brake Hose To Caliper Retaining Bolt | ② |
| End Retainer③ | 75–95 |
| Front Caliper Bolt⑤ | 37–48 |
| Key Retaining Screw③ | 12–16 |
| Locating Pins③ | 29–37 |
| Lower Guide Pin④ | 29–36 |
| Wheel Lug Nuts | 65–88⑥ |
| Parking Brake Stop Bolt⑤ | 8–9 |
| Pinch Bolts③ | 30–35 |
| Retainer Screw③ | 16–22 |
| Wheel Cylinder Attaching Bolts | 5–7 |

①—On Mark VII models torque caliper attaching bolt to 20–30 ft. lbs.; Probe & Tracer 29–36 ft. lbs.; Scorpio 37–48 ft. lbs.

②—On Mark VII models torque brake hose to caliper retaining bolt to 30–44 ft. lbs. On Probe & Tracer torque flex hose banjo bolt 16–22 ft. lbs.

③—Mark VII.

④—Probe & Tracer.

⑤—XR4Ti.

⑥—Mark VII, Sable & Taurus; 65–104 ft. lbs.

# AUTOMATIC TRANSMISSIONS/TRANSAXLES

TABLE OF CONTENTS



# Ford A4LD Automatic Overdrive Transmission

INDEX



## TRANSMISSION IDENTIFICATION

This transmission may be identified by the tag attached to the lower lefthand extension attaching bolt. The tag includes model prefix and suffix, a service identification number and a build data code, **Fig. 1.**

## DESCRIPTION

The A4LD, **Fig. 2,** is a 4 speed overdrive automatic transmission with a lockup torque converter.

The hydraulic lockup and unlock function of the torque converter is electronically controlled by the EEC-IV system.

The EEC-IV system controls a converter

clutch solenoid in the main control which hydraulically operates a piston/plate clutch in the converter to provide a solid drive transmission function.

The electronics also prevents the clutch application in engine modes where noise, vibration or harness concerns are most evident in solid drive transmissions.

## TROUBLESHOOTING

### CONVERTER CLUTCH DOES NOT ENGAGE

1. Converter clutch solenoid not energized electrically.
2. Wires to solenoid shorted or circuit open.
3. Transmission case connector not seated.
4. Open or shorted circuit inside solenoid.
5. Malfunctioning engine coolant temperature sensor.
6. Malfunctioning throttle position sensor.
7. Malfunctioning manifold absolute pressure (MAP) sensor.
8. Vacuum line disconnected from MAP sensor.
9. Malfunctioning brake switch.
10. Malfunctioning EEC-IV processor.
11. Converter clutch shuttle valve stuck in the unlock position (against plug) or too high a spring load.
12. Torque converter internal malfunction.
13. Converter clutch solenoid is energized electrically but foreign matter on hydraulic part of solenoid valve prevents closure.

### CONVERTER CLUTCH ALWAYS ENGAGED

1. Converter clutch shift valve stuck in lock position.
2. Converter clutch shuttle valve stuck in locked position.
3. Lockup piston in torque converter will not disengage.

### CONVERTER CLUTCH WILL NOT DISENGAGE DURING COAST DOWN

1. Malfunctioning throttle position sensor.
2. Converter clutch solenoid sticking.

### SLOW INITIAL ENGAGEMENT

1. Incorrect fluid level.
2. Damaged or incorrectly adjusted manual linkage.
3. Contaminated fluid.
4. Incorrect clutch and band application, or low main control pressure.

### ROUGH INITIAL ENGAGEMENT IN FORWARD OR REVERSE

1. Incorrect fluid level.

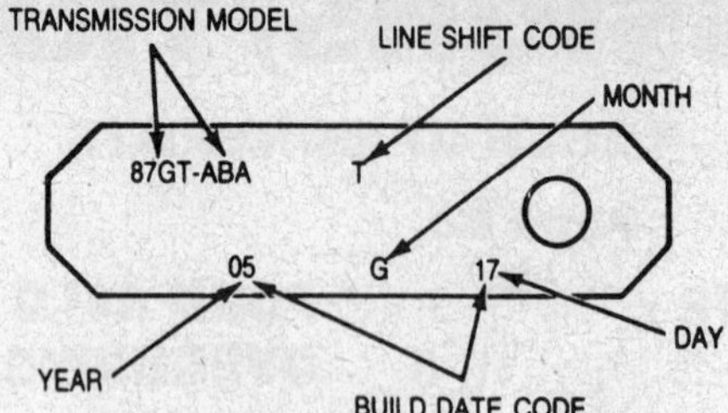


**Fig. 1 Identification tag**

2. High engine idle.
3. Automatic choke on.
4. Loose driveshaft, U-joints or engine mounts.
5. Incorrect clutch or band application or oil control pressure.
6. Sticking or dirty valve body.
7. Converter clutch not disengaging.

### HARSH ENGAGEMENT W/ENGINE WARM

1. Incorrect fluid level.
2. Engine curb idle speed too high.
3. Loose or tight valve body bolts.
4. Sticking or dirty valve body valves.

### NO/DELAYED FORWARD ENGAGEMENT

1. Incorrect fluid level.
2. Incorrect adjusted manual linkage.
3. Low main control pressure.
4. Damaged forward clutch assembly.
5. Loose or tight valve body bolts.
6. Sticking or dirty valve body valves.
7. Restricted transmission filter.
8. Leaking or damaged pump.

### NO/DELAYED REVERSE ENGAGEMENT

1. Incorrect fluid level.
2. Incorrectly adjusted manual linkage.
3. Low main control pressure in reverse.
4. Damaged reverse clutch assembly.
5. Loose valve body bolts.
6. Sticking or dirty valve body valves.
7. Damaged pump.
8. Leaking reverse servo piston seal.
9. Transmission filter plugged.

### NO ENGAGEMENT/DRIVE IN FORWARD

1. Incorrect fluid level.
2. Low main control pressure.
3. Mechanical damage.

### NO ENGAGEMENT/DRIVE IN D

1. Incorrectly adjusted manual linkage.
2. Damaged rear one-way clutch.
3. Dirty or contaminated transmission fluid.
4. Overdrive one-way clutch damage.

### VEHICLE CREEPING IN N

1. Forward clutch failing to disengage.

### NO DELAYED REVERSE ENGAGEMENT/NO ENGINE BRAKING IN MANUAL LOW

1. Incorrect fluid level.
2. Linkage improperly adjusted.
3. Low reverse servo piston leaking.
4. Overdrive clutch damaged.
5. Low/reverse drum polished or glazed.
6. Rear one way clutch damaged.

### NO ENGINE BRAKING IN MANUAL SECOND GEAR

1. Incorrectly adjusted intermediate band.
2. Incorrect band or clutch application.
3. Leaking intermediate servo.
4. Overdrive clutch, overdrive one-way clutch damaged.
5. Glazed band.

### FORWARD ENGAGEMENT SLIPS/SHUDDERS/CHATTERS

1. Incorrect fluid level.
2. Incorrectly adjusted manual linkage.
3. Low main control pressure.
4. Loose or tight valve body bolts.
5. Sticking or dirty valve body valves.
6. Incorrectly seated or leaking forward clutch piston ball.
7. Worn or damaged forward clutch piston seals.
8. Overdrive one-way clutch damaged.
9. Rear one-way clutch damaged.

### REVERSE SHUDDER/CHATTER/SLIPPING

1. Incorrect fluid level.
2. Low main control pressure in reverse.
3. Overdrive and/or rear one-way clutch damaged.
4. Overdrive and/or rear reverse high clutch drum bushing damaged.
5. Overdrive and/or rear reverse high clutch center support seal rings and ring grooves damaged.
6. Low reverse servo piston damaged.
7. Low reverse band out of adjustment.
8. Blockage in cooler lines.
9. Loose U-joints or engine mounts.

### NO DRIVE, SLIPS/CHATTERS IN 1ST GEAR IN OD OR D

1. Worn or damaged overdrive or rear one-way clutch.

### NO DRIVE, SLIPS/CHATTERS IN 2ND GEAR

1. Incorrectly adjusted intermediate band.
2. Improper band or clutch application, or control pressure.
3. Worn or damaged intermediate servo piston and/or internal leaks.
4. Dirty or sticking valve body.

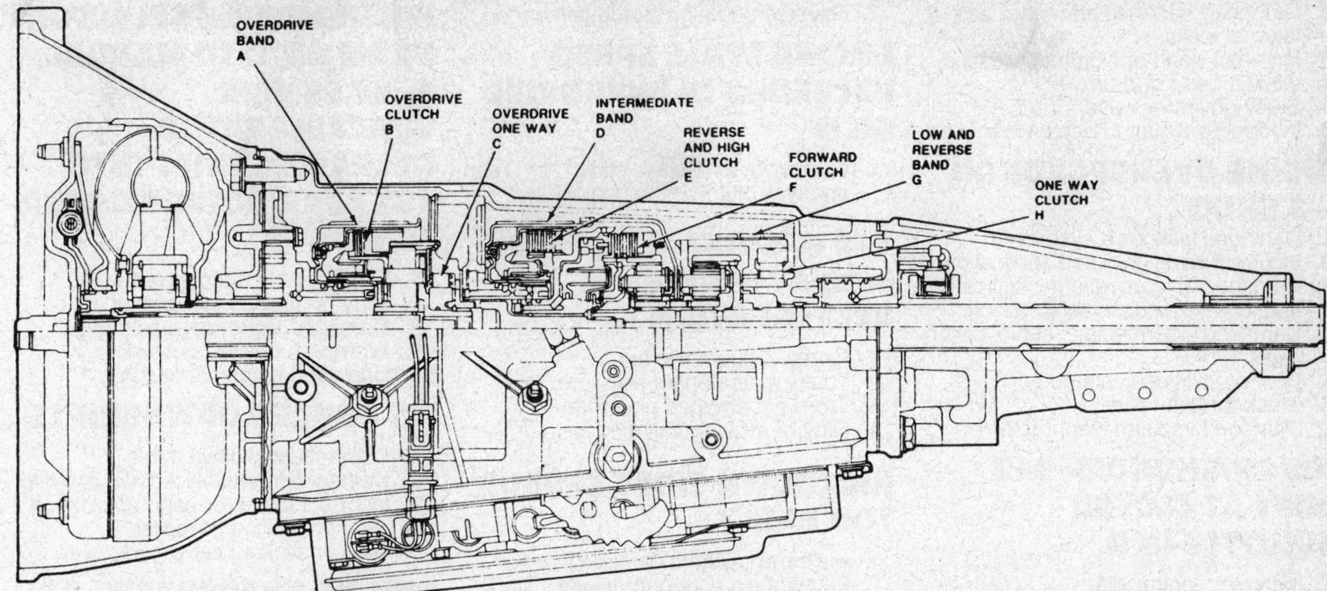


**Fig. 2 Sectional view of Ford A4LD Automatic Overdrive Transmission**

5. Polished or glazed intermediate band or drum.

## STARTS UP IN 2ND OR 3RD

1. Improper band and/or clutch application, or oil pressure control system.
2. Damaged, worn or sticking governor.
3. Loose valve body.
4. Dirty or sticking valve body.
5. Cross leaks between valve body and case mating surface.

## SHIFT POINTS INCORRECT

1. Incorrect fluid level.
2. Vacuum line damaged, clogged or leaking.
3. Malfunctioning EGR system.
4. Speedometer gear incorrectly installed.
5. Incorrect band or clutch application, or oil pressure control system.
6. Worn or damaged governor.
7. Vacuum diaphragm bent, sticking or leaking.
8. Dirty or sticking valve body.

## ALL UPSHIFTS HARSH AND/OR DELAYED/NO UPSHIFTS

1. Incorrect fluid level.
2. Incorrectly adjusted manual linkage.
3. Sticking governor.
4. Main control pressure too high.
5. Valve body bolts improperly torqued.
6. Valve body dirty or sticking valves.
7. Vacuum leak to diaphragm unit.
8. Vacuum diaphragm bent, sticking or leaking.

## MUSHY OR EARLY UPSHIFTS

1. Low main control pressure.
2. Valve body bolts incorrectly torqued.
3. Valve body or throttle control valve sticking.
4. Sticking governor valve.
5. Damaged, sticking or incorrectly adjusted kickdown linkage.

## NO 1–2 UPSHIFT

1. Incorrect fluid level.
2. Damaged kickdown system.
3. Incorrectly adjusted manual linkage.
4. Sticking governor valve.
5. Incorrectly adjusted intermediate band.
6. Vacuum leak to diaphragm unit.
7. Loose or tight valve body bolts.
8. Sticking or dirty valve body valves.
9. Damaged intermediate band and/or servo.
10. Intermediate band improperly adjusted.

## ROUGH/HARSH/DELAYED 1–2 UPSHIFT

1. Incorrect fluid level.
2. Poor engine output.
3. Incorrectly adjusted kickdown linkage.
4. Incorrectly adjusted intermediate band.
5. Excessively high main control pressure.
6. Damaged intermediate servo.
7. Engine vacuum leak.
8. Loose or tight valve body bolts.
9. Vacuum leak to diaphragm unit.
10. Leaking or damaged vacuum diaphragm.

## MUSHY, EARLY, SOFT OR SLIPPING 1–2 UPSHIFT

1. Incorrect fluid level.
2. Poor engine output.
3. Incorrectly adjusted kickdown linkage.
4. Incorrectly adjusted intermediate band.
5. Low main control pressure.
6. Valve body bolts incorrectly torqued.
7. Valve body dirty or sticking valves.
8. Sticking governor valve.
9. Damaged intermediate servo or band.
10. Polished or glazed band or drum.

## NO 2–3 UPSHIFT

1. Incorrect fluid level.
2. Damaged kickdown system.
3. Low main control pressure to reverse high clutch.
4. Loose or tight valve body bolts.
5. Sticking or dirty valve body valves.
6. Sticking governor valve.
7. Damaged intermediate servo or band.

## HARSH/DELAYED 2–3 UPSHIFT

1. Poor engine output.
2. Engine vacuum leak.
3. Damaged kickdown system.
4. Damaged or worn intermediate servo.
5. Loose or tight valve body bolts.
6. Sticking or dirty valve body valves.
7. Damaged vacuum diaphragm.
8. Stuck throttle valve.

## SOFT, EARLY OR MUSHY 2–3 UPSHIFT

1. Incorrectly adjusted kickdown linkage.
2. Valve body bolts incorrectly torqued.
3. Valve body dirty or sticking valves.
4. Vacuum diaphragm bent, sticking or leaking.
5. Throttle valve stuck.

## ERRATIC SHIFTS

1. Poor engine performance.
2. Damaged vacuum line.
3. Loose or tight valve body bolts.
4. Stuck governor valve.
5. Damaged output shaft collector body seal rings.

## SHIFTS 1–3 IN OVERDRIVE OR D

1. Incorrectly adjusted intermediate band.

2. Damaged intermediate servo and/or internal leaks.
3. Incorrect band or clutch application.
4. Glazed band or drum.
5. Stuck governor valve.
6. Incorrectly adjusted kickdown linkage.

## ENGINE OVERSPEEDS ON 2–3 SHIFT

1. Damaged kickdown system.
2. Incorrect band or clutch application.
3. Damaged or worn reverse high clutch and/or intermediate servo piston.
4. Damaged intermediate servo piston seals.
5. Dirty or sticking valve body.
6. Stuck throttle valve.
7. Damaged vacuum diaphragm.

## ROUGH/SHUDDER 3–2 SHIFT AT CLOSED THROTTLE IN D

1. Incorrect engine idle.
2. Incorrect kickdown linkage adjustment.
3. Incorrect clutch or band application.
4. Incorrect governor operation.
5. Dirty or sticking valve body.

## NO 3–4 UPSHIFT, MUSTANG ONLY

1. Damaged kickdown system.
2. Damaged vacuum line.
3. Damaged vacuum diaphragm.
4. Sticking throttle valve.
5. Damaged overdrive servo.
6. Glazed overdrive band.
7. Dirty of sticking valve body.

## NO 3–4 OR 4–3 SHIFT, THUNDERBIRD ONLY

1. 3-4 solenoid is not being energized.
2. Dirty or sticking solenoid valve.
3. 3-4 shift valve stuck.

## NO 3–4 UPSHIFT, MERKUR SCORPIO ONLY

1. Incorrectly adjusted kickdown linkage.
2. Damaged or leaking overdrive servo.
3. Polished or glazed overdrive band or drum.
4. Dirty or sticking valve body.
5. Vacuum line damaged.
6. Vacuum diaphragm damaged.
7. Throttle valve sticking.

## SLIPPING 4TH GEAR

1. Overdrive servo damaged or leaking.
2. Glazed overdrive band or drum.

## ENGINE STALL SPEED EXCEEDED IN OVERDRIVE, D OR R

1. Faulty vacuum system.
2. Low main control pressure.

## ENGINE STALL SPEED EXCEEDED IN R

1. Low/reverse servo/band damaged.
2. Reverse and high clutch damaged.

## ENGINE STALL SPEED EXCEEDED IN OVERDRIVE OR D

1. Overdrive one-way clutch or rear one-way clutch damaged.

## 1–2 UPSHIFT IS ABOVE 40 mph AT MODERATE ACCELERATION

1. Faulty vacuum system.
2. Faulty main control pressure.
3. Worn or damaged governor.
4. Dirty or sticking valve body.

## KICKDOWN SHIFT SPEEDS TOO EARLY

1. Kickdown system damaged.
2. Faulty main control pressure.
3. Damaged or worn governor.

## NO KICKDOWN INTO 2ND GEAR BETWEEN 40–60 mph IN OVERDRIVE OR D

1. Damaged kickdown system.
2. Faulty main control pressure.
3. Dirty or sticking valve body.

## NO SHIFT INTO 2ND GEAR BETWEEN 40–60 mph IN OVERDRIVE OR D

1. Faulty main control pressure.
2. Damaged or worn governor.
3. Dirty or sticking valve body.

## WHEN MOVING SELECTOR FROM OD/D TO MANUAL 1, AT 55 mph w/ACCELERATOR RELEASED, NO BRAKING FELT FROM DOWNSHIFT TO 2ND GEAR

1. Faulty main control pressure.
2. Incorrectly adjusted intermediate band.
3. Damaged overdrive clutch.

## WHEN MOVING SELECTOR FROM OD/D TO MANUAL 1, AT 55 mph w/ACCELERATOR RELEASED, SHIFT INTO 1ST GEAR OCCURS OVER 45 mph

1. Faulty main control pressure.
2. Dirty or sticking valve body.
3. Worn or damaged governor.
4. Incorrectly adjusted kickdown linkage.

## WHEN MOVING SELECTOR FROM OD/D TO MANUAL 1, AT 55 mph w/ACCELERATOR RELEASED, SHIFT INTO 1ST GEAR OCCURS UNDER 15 mph

1. Faulty main control pressure.
2. Dirty or sticking valve body.
3. Damaged low or reverse servo.
4. Worn or damaged governor.
5. Damaged overdrive clutch

## NO FORCED DOWNSHIFTS

1. Damaged kickdown cable.
2. Damaged internal kickdown linkage.
3. Incorrect clutch or band application.
4. Dirty or sticking governor.
5. Dirty or sticking valve body.

## ENGINE OVERSPEEDS ON 3–2 DOWNSHIFT

1. Incorrectly adjusted linkage.
2. Incorrectly adjusted intermediate band.
3. Damaged or worn intermediate servo.
4. Glazed band or drum.
5. Dirty or sticking valve body.

## SHIFT EFFORT HIGH

1. Manual shaft linkage damaged.
2. Inner manual lever nut loose.
3. Manual retainer pin damaged.

## TRANSMISSION OVERHEATS

1. Incorrect fluid level.
2. Poor engine output.
3. Restriction in cooler or lines.
4. Seized converter one-way clutch.
5. Dirty or sticking valve body.

## LEAKING TRANSMISSION

1. Restricted case breather vent.
2. Leaking gaskets and seals.

## POOR VEHICLE ACCELERATION

1. Poor engine output.
2. Torque converter one-way clutch locked.

## NOISY TRANSMISSION/VALVE RESONANCE

1. Incorrectly fluid level.
2. Incorrectly adjusted linkage.
3. Incorrect band or clutch application.
4. Cooler lines grounding.
5. Dirty or sticking valve body.
6. Internal leakage or pump cavitation.

# MAINTENANCE

Ford Motor Company recommends the use of Mercon type automatic transmission fluid in this transmission. If Mercon

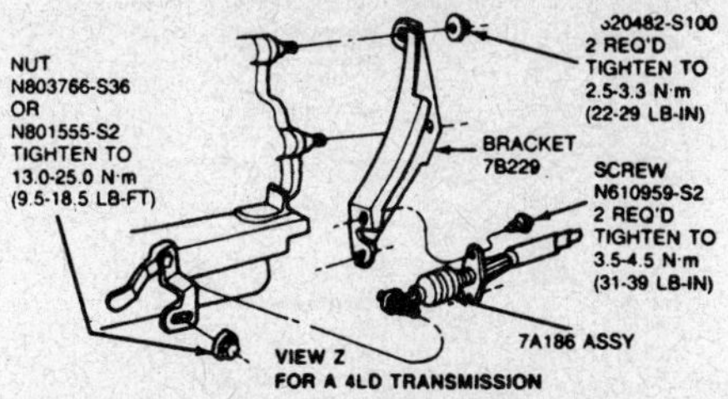


**Fig. 3 Manual linkage, adjust. Thunderbird Turbo Coupe models**

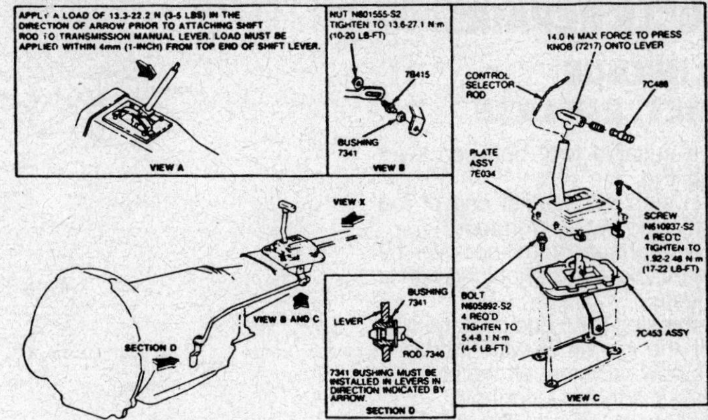


**Fig. 4 Manual linkage, adjust. Mustang w/2.3L/4-140 engine**

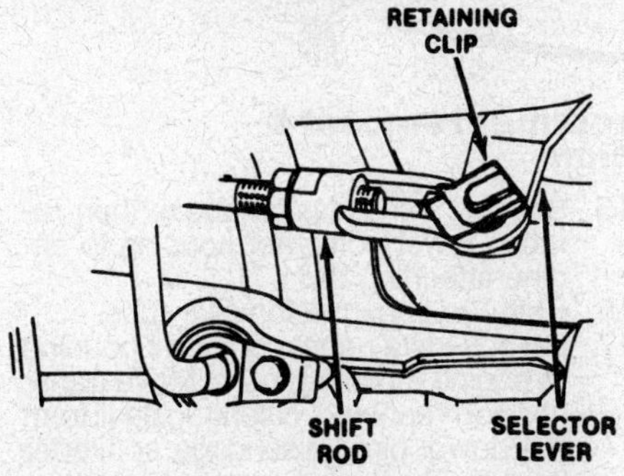


**Fig. 5 Disengaging shift rod from selector lever. Merkur Scorpio**

type fluid is not available, Dexron-II Series D automatic transmission fluid may be used. Use of a fluid other than specified may result in transmission malfunction or failure.

## CHECKING FLUID LEVEL

1. With transmission at operating temperature, park vehicle on a level surface.
2. Run engine at idle speed with service and parking brakes applied and move selector lever through each range. Return selector lever to P.
3. With engine idling, remove dipstick and check fluid level. Fluid level should be between the Add and Full marks.
4. Add specified fluid as required to bring the fluid to the proper level.

## CHANGING FLUID

Normal maintenance and lubrication requirements do not necessitate periodic fluid changes. If vehicle accumulates 5000 or more miles per month or it is used in continuous stop and go service, change fluid every 30,000 miles.

When filling a dry transmission and converter, install 9.5 quarts of specified fluid. Start engine, shift the selector lever through all ranges and place it at P position. Check fluid level and add enough to raise the level in the transmission to the F (full) mark on the dipstick. When a partial drain and refill is required, proceed as follows:

1. Loosen oil pan attaching bolts and allow pan to drain the oil.
2. Remove and clean pan and replace screen.

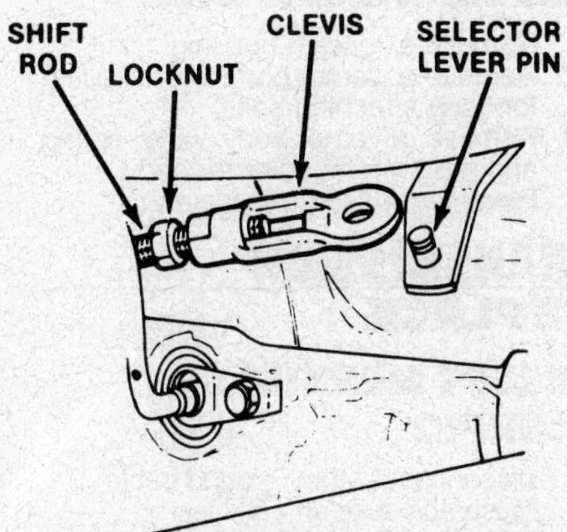


**Fig. 6 Sliding shift rod clevis over selector lever pin. Merkur Scorpio**

3. Place a new gasket on pan and install pan and screen.
4. Add three quarts of specified fluid to transmission.
5. Run engine at a fast idle until it reaches normal operating temperature.
6. Shift selector lever through all ranges and then place it in P position.
7. Add fluid as required to bring the level to the full mark.

## IN-VEHICLE ADJUSTMENTS

## MANUAL LINKAGE, ADJUST

### Thunderbird Turbo Coupe

1. Position transmission selector lever in Overdrive against stop. **When adjusting hold lever against overdrive stop.**
2. Raise and support vehicle, then loosen manual lever shift cable attaching nut, **Fig. 3.**
3. Move transmission manual lever to the Overdrive position, third detent position from the full counterclockwise position.
4. With transmission selector and manual levers in the Overdrive position, **torque** attaching nut to 9.5-18.5 ft. lbs.
5. Check transmission operation.

### Mustang w/2.3L/4-140 Engine

1. Position transmission selector lever into Overdrive. Ensure lever is held tightly against rearward overdrive stop.
2. Raise and support vehicle, then loosen manual lever shift rod retaining nut, **Fig. 4.**
3. Move transmission manual lever to the Overdrive position, third detent position from the full counterclockwise position.
4. With transmission selector lever and manual lever in the Overdrive position, **torque** attaching nut to 10-20 ft. lbs.
5. Check transmission operation.

### Merkur Scorpio

1. Raise and support vehicle.
2. Remove retaining clip, then disconnect shift rod from selector lever, **Fig. 5.**
3. Rotate transmission shift lever as far as possible toward front of vehicle.
4. Rotate transmission shift lever three detent positions toward rear of vehicle.
5. Without moving selector or transmission levers, attempt to slide shift rod clevis in or out to obtain proper fit, **Fig. 6.**
6. If clevis slides into pin, linkage is properly adjusted.
7. If clevis does not slide into pin, loosen locknut and thread clevis in or out to obtain proper fit.
8. After adjustment, tighten clevis locknut. **Ensure linkage adjustment has not affected proper operation of neutral safety switch. With service and parking brakes applied, try to start engine in each gear shift lever position. The engine must start only in N or P positions. If engine cranks in any other shift position, check linkage adjustment and neutral safety switch operation.**

# IN-VEHICLE REPAIRS

## SHIFT LINKAGE GROMMET, REPLACE

1. Place a suitable tool, between lever and rod, **Fig. 7.**
2. Position stop pin against end of rod and force rod out of grommet.
3. Remove grommet from the lever by cutting off the large shoulder with a sharp knife.
4. Adjust the stop to 1/2 and coat the outside of the grommet with lubricant. Place a new grommet on the stop pin and force it into the lever hole.
5. Turn grommet several times to ensure it is properly seated.
6. Squeeze rod into bushing until the stop washer seats against the grommet.

## CONTROL VALVE BODY, REPLACE

1. Raise and support vehicle.
2. Loosen pan attaching bolts, then drain fluid from transmission.
3. Remove attaching bolts, pan and gasket.
4. Remove filter screen and O-ring.
5. Remove low/reverse servo cover, piston, spring and gasket.
6. Disconnect electrical connectors from converter clutch solenoid on Mustang models and two additional electrical connectors at 3-4 shift solenoid on Thunderbird models.
7. Remove bolts from control valve body.
8. Reverse procedure to install.

## LOW/REVERSE SERVO, REPLACE

1. Raise and support vehicle.
2. Loosen pan attaching bolts and allow transmission fluid to drain.
3. Remove all pan attaching bolts except two bolts at the front to allow fluid to drain further.
4. Remove oil filter screen and gasket.
5. Remove retaining screws, low/reverse servo cover, piston and spring and gasket.
6. Reverse procedure to install.

## EXTENSION HOUSING, REPLACE

1. Raise and support vehicle.
2. Remove driveshaft.
3. Support transmission with a suitable jack.
4. Disconnect speedometer cable from extension housing.
5. Remove rear support to crossmember attaching bolts or nuts.
6. Raise transmission slightly and remove rear support from extension housing.
7. Loosen extension housing attaching bolt and allow transmission fluid to drain.
8. Remove extension housing attaching bolts.

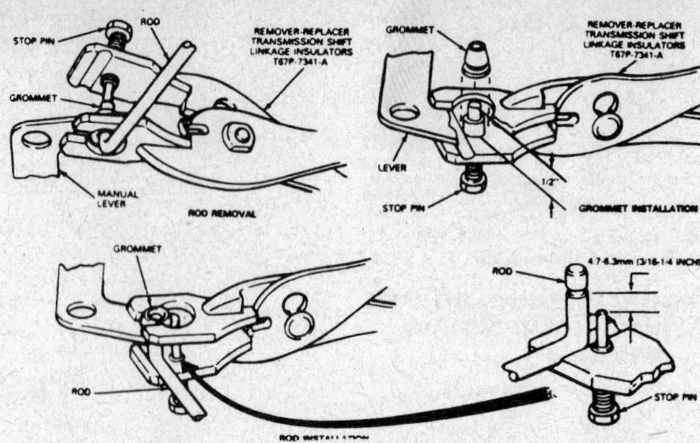


**Fig. 7 Shift linkage grommet removal & installation**

## GOVERNOR, REPLACE

1. Remove extension housing.
2. Remove governor body to coil collector body attaching bolts.
3. Remove governor body, valve, spring and weight from collector body.
4. Reverse procedure to install.

## TRANSMISSION REPLACE

### EXCEPT MERKUR SCORPIO

1. Disconnect battery ground cable.
2. Raise and support vehicle.
3. Drain fluid from transmission.
4. Remove converter access cover and adapter plate attaching bolts from lower lefthand side of converter housing.
5. Rotate crankshaft pulley clockwise (as viewed from the front) to gain access to each attaching bolt, then remove flywheel to converter attaching bolts. **On belt driven overhead cam engines, never rotate the pulley in a counterclockwise direction (as view from the front).**
6. Place an alignment mark on driveshaft and rear axle flange, then remove driveshaft. **Do not use a sharp tool to place alignment mark.**
7. Disconnect and remove speedometer sensor from extension housing.
8. Disconnect shift rod from transmission on Mustang models or shift cable from transmission on Thunderbird models.
9. Remove starter motor.
10. Label, then disconnect all electrical connectors, vacuum lines and fluid cooler lines from transmission.
11. Position a suitable jack under transmission.
12. Remove crossmember to frame side support attaching bolts. Remove crossmember insulator support and damper.
13. Lower jack carefully and slightly and allow transmission to hang.
14. Position a jack to front of engine. Raise engine to gain access to the two upper converter housing to engine attaching bolts.
15. Support transmission again, then remove lower converter housing to engine attaching bolts.
16. Remove transmission filler tube.
17. Remove two upper converter housing to engine attaching bolts. Move transmission rearward, disengaging it from the dowel pins. Disengage converter from flywheel.
18. Lower transmission from vehicle.
19. Reverse procedure to install. **Proper installation of the converter requires full engagement of the converter hub in the pump gear. To accomplish this, the converter must be pushed and at the same time rotated through what feels like two "notches" or bumps. When completely seated, rotation of the converter will usually result in a clicking noise, caused by the converter surface touching the housing to case attaching bolts. This should not be a concern, but an indication of correct converter installation. The converter should rotate without binding. For reference a properly installed converter will have a pilot nose from face to converter housing outer face dimension of 7/16 inch minimum to 9/16 inch maximum.**

### MERKUR SCORPIO

1. Disconnect battery ground cable.
2. Disconnect oxygen sensor electrical connector and release sensor wiring from routing clip.
3. Raise and support vehicle.
4. Remove four stabilizer bar-to-side member attaching bolts.
5. Disconnect ground strap from exhaust pipe, then remove exhaust system from manifolds to front muffler.
6. Remove catalytic converter heat shield fasteners, then the heat shield.
7. Disconnect driveshaft from rear axle flange.
8. Scribe reference marks around both sides of center bearing support bracket attaching bolt flat washers, then remove support bearing bracket and attaching bolts. **Spacers installed between support bearing bracket and floorpan must be installed in their original positions to avoid driveline vibration.**

9. Remove driveshaft from extension housing, then plug housing to prevent fluid leakage.
10. Support engine using a suitable jack, then remove transmission mount attaching nuts and the mount.
11. Position a suitable drain pan under transmission. Loosen transmission fluid pan attaching bolts from rear to front and allow fluid to drain into pan.
12. Remove transmission oil pan attaching bolts and the pan. Remove and discard gasket.
13. Temporarily install oil pan using two bolts on each side.
14. Remove converter access cover and adapter plate attaching bolts from lower end of converter housing.
15. Remove flywheel-to-converter attaching nuts. Turn crankshaft pulley clockwise as necessary to gain access to all four nuts.
16. Remove speed sensor and sensor ground strap from extension housing.
17. Disconnect shift rod from transmission manual lever.
18. Disconnect electrical connector from transmission downshift solenoid.
19. Unfasten starter motor and position aside.
20. Disconnect neutral start switch and converter clutch solenoid electrical connectors.
21. Disconnect vacuum line from transmission vacuum modulator, then remove transmission oil filler tube.
22. Raise transmission assembly slightly with a suitable jack, then secure transmission to jack with a safety chain.
23. Disconnect oil cooler lines from transmission. Plug openings to prevent contamination.
24. Support rear of engine with a suitable jack, then remove transmission mount attaching nuts and the mount.
25. Lower transmission jack to gain access to upper converter housing-to-engine attaching bolts, then remove the bolts.
26. Remove lower converter housing-to-engine attaching bolts and the starter heat shield.
27. Move transmission rearward and carefully lower assembly from vehicle.
28. Reverse procedure to install, noting the following **torques:** lower converter housing-to-engine attaching bolts, 22-30 ft. lbs.; transmission mount attaching nuts, 28-38 ft. lbs.; transmission oil filler tube attaching bolt, 22-30 ft. lbs.; starter attaching bolts, 15-20 ft. lbs.; flywheel-to-converter attaching nuts, 22-30 ft. lbs.; converter adapter plate bolt, 6-7 ft. lbs.; transmission oil pan attaching bolts, 12-17 ft. lbs.; center bearing support bracket attaching bolts, 25-35 ft. lbs.

# TIGHTENING SPECIFICATIONS

| Component | Torque/Ft. Lbs. |
|---|---|
| Center Support (O/D) To Case | 80–115① |
| Cooler Line To Case Connector | 18–23 |
| Cooler Line To Connector Tube Nut | 12–18② |
| Converter Housing & Pump To Case | 27–39 |
| Converter Housing Lower Cover To Converter Housing | 12–16 |
| Converter To Flywheel Attaching Nut | 20–34 |
| Detent Spring To Valve Body | 80–107① |
| Extension Housing To Case | 27–39 |
| Governor Assembly To Oil Collector Body | 84–120① |
| Intermediate Band Adjusting Screw Locknut To Case | 35–45 |
| Main Control To Case | 71–97① |
| Manual Lever Nut | 30–40 |
| Neutral Start Switch To Case | 84–120① |
| Oil Pan To Case | 8–10 |
| Oil Pump To Converter Housing | 17–20 |
| Outer Downshift Lever To Inner Lever Shaft Nut | 7–11 |
| Overdrive Band Adjusting Screw Locknut To Case | 35–45 |
| Pressure Plug To Case | 7–11 |
| Push Connect Cooler Line Fitting To Case | 18–23 |
| Reverse Servo To Case | 80–115① |
| Seperator Plate To Valve Body | 54–72① |
| Transmission To Engine | 28–38 |
| Vacuum Diaphragm Retainer Clip To Case | 80–106① |

①—Inch lbs.
②—Torque to specification while holding transmission fitting.

# Ford Automatic Overdrive Transmission

## INDEX



## TRANSMISSION IDENTIFICATION

This transmission may be identified by the tag attached to the upper righthand extension housing to transmission case bolt. The tag includes model prefix and suffix, a service identification number and a build date code, **Fig. 1.** The service identification number indicates changes in service details which affect interchangeability when the transmission model is not changed. For interpretation of this number the Ford Master Parts Catalog should be consulted.

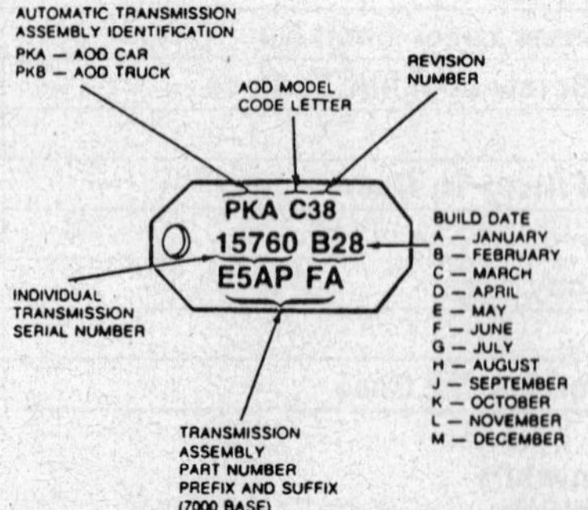


**Fig. 1 Identification tag**

## DESCRIPTION

This unit is a 4 speed automatic transmission incorporating an integral overdrive feature. With selector lever in 1 position, the transmission will start and remain in first gear until the selector lever is moved to another position. In 3 position, the transmission will automatically shift through 1-2-3 range, but will not engage overdrive. In D position, the transmission will automatically select the appropriate time to shift into overdrive (4th gear). The design of the transmission features a split torque path in third gear, where 40% of the engine torque is transmitted hydraulically through the torque converter and 60% is transmitted mechanically through solid connections (direct drive input shaft) to the driveshaft. When transmission is in overdrive (4th gear), 100% of engine torque is transmitted through the direct drive input shaft.

The transmission consists essentially of a torque converter assembly, compound planetary gear train and a hydraulic control system, **Fig. 2.** For gear control the transmission has four friction clutches, two one-way roller clutches and two bands. Overdrive is accomplished by the addition of a band to lock the reverse sun gear while driving the planet carrier. The torque converter operation is similar to other types of automatic transmission, but has an added damper assembly and input shaft for 3rd gear and overdrive. The direct drive input shaft couples the engine directly to the direct clutch. This shaft is driven by the torque converter cover through the damper assembly which cushions engine shock to the transmission.

## TROUBLESHOOTING

### ROUGH INITIAL ENGAGEMENT

1. Improper fluid level.

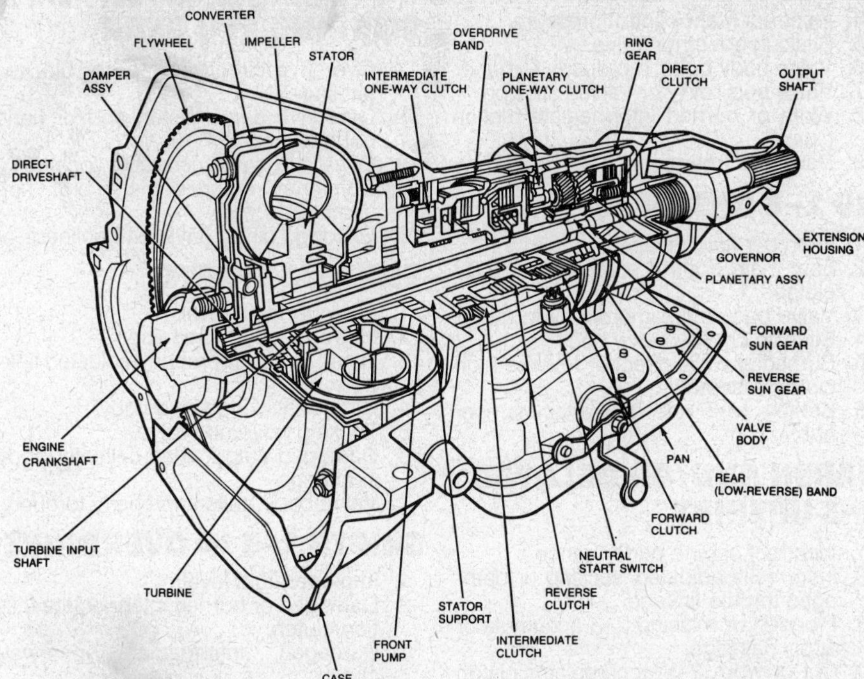


**Fig. 2 Sectional view of Ford Automatic Overdrive Transmission**

2. High engine idle.
3. Loose driveshaft, engine mounts or U-joints.
4. Sticking or dirty valve body.
5. Improper clutch or band application, or low oil control pressure.
6. Incorrectly adjusted automatic choke.

## SLOW INITIAL ENGAGEMENT

1. Improper fluid level.
2. Damaged or improperly adjusted linkage.
3. Contaminated fluid.
4. Low main control pressure or improper clutch and band application.

## HARSH ENGAGEMENTS w/WARM ENGINE

1. Improper fluid level.
2. Damaged or improperly adjusted linkage.
3. High engine idle.
4. Sticking or dirty valve body.
5. Throttle linkage return spring disconnected.
6. Valve body bolts improperly torqued.

## NO OR DELAYED FORWARD ENGAGEMENT

1. Improper fluid level.
2. Damaged or improperly adjusted linkage.
3. Low main control pressure.
4. Forward clutch stator support seal rings Nos. 3 and/or 4 leaking.
5. Burned and/or damaged forward clutch assembly.
6. Forward clutch cylinder check ball and/or piston seal rings leaking.
7. Valve body bolts improperly torqued.
8. Valve body dirty or valves sticking.
9. Clogged transmission filter.
10. Damaged or leaking pump.

## NO OR DELAYED REVERSE ENGAGEMENT

1. Improper fluid level.
2. Damaged or improperly adjusted linkage.
3. Low main control pressure.
4. Leaking high reverse clutch or reverse clutch stator support seal rings Nos. 1 and/or 2.
5. Burned or worn reverse clutch assembly.
6. Leaking reverse clutch piston check ball and/or piston seal rings.
7. Valve body bolts improperly torqued.
8. Valve body dirty or valves sticking.
9. Clogged transmission filter.
10. Damaged pump.

## NO OR DELAYED REVERSE ENGAGEMENT AND/OR NO ENGINE BRAKING IN MANUAL LOW

1. Improper fluid level.
2. Damaged or improperly adjusted linkage.
3. Leaking low reverse servo piston seal.
4. Burned or worn low reverse servo piston.
5. Damaged planetary low one-way clutch.
6. Endplay clearance too tight.

## NO ENGINE BRAKING IN MANUAL 2ND

1. Improper fluid level.
2. Damaged or improperly adjusted linkage.
3. Improper clutch or band application.
4. Improper control system pressure.
5. Leaking intermediate servo.
6. Damaged intermediate one-way clutch.

## FORWARD ENGAGEMENT SLIPS, SHUDDERS AND/OR CHATTERS

1. Improper fluid level.
2. Incorrectly adjusted or damaged linkage.
3. Low main control pressure.
4. Valve body bolts improperly torqued.
5. Valve body dirty or valves sticking.
6. Forward clutch piston check ball leaking and/or not seating.
7. Cut and/or worn forward clutch piston seal.
8. Leaking forward clutch stator support seal rings Nos. 3 and 4.
9. Damaged low one-way clutch (planetary).

## REVERSE SHUDDERS, CHATTERS AND/OR SLIPS

1. Improper fluid level.
2. Low main control pressure in reverse.
3. Leaking low reverse servo.
4. Damaged planetary low one-way clutch.
5. Damaged reverse clutch drum bushing.
6. Worn or damaged reverse clutch stator support seal rings or grooves.
7. Cut and/or worn reverse clutch piston.
8. Damaged reverse band.
9. Loosen driveshaft, engine mounts or U-joints.

## NO DRIVE, SLIPS OR CHATTERS IN 1ST GEAR IN D OR OVERDRIVE

1. Damaged planetary low one-way clutch.

## NO DRIVE, SLIPS OR CHATTERS IN 2ND GEAR

1. Worn or damaged friction clutch or one-way clutch.
2. Intermediate clutch piston belled hole clogged or not positioned at 12 o'clock.
3. Control pressure or improper band or clutch application.
4. Internal leakage.
5. Dirty valve body or sticking valves.

## INITIAL DRIVE IN 2ND OR 3RD

1. Improper fluid level.
2. Damaged or improperly adjusted linkage.
3. Oil pressure control system or improper clutch and/or band application.
4. Intermediate clutch pack clearance too tight.
5. Damaged, worn or sticking governor.

6. Sticking or dirty valve body.
7. Valve body bolts too loose.
8. Cross leaks between valve body and case mating surface.

### IMPROPER SHIFT POINTS

1. Improper fluid level.
2. Damaged or improperly adjusted linkage.
3. Improper speedometer gear installed.
4. Improper clutch or band application.
5. Improper control system pressure.
6. Damaged or worn governor.
7. Sticking or dirty valve body.

### HARSH, DELAYED OR NO UPSHIFTS

1. Improper fluid level.
2. Damaged or improperly adjusted linkage.
3. Throttle return spring disconnected.
4. Damaged or incorrectly adjusted manual linkage.
5. Governor sticking.
6. High main control pressure.
7. Valve body bolts improperly torqued.
8. Sticking or dirty valve body.

### MUSHY AND/OR EARLY UPSHIFTS OR UPSHIFT PILEUP

1. Improper fluid level.
2. Damaged or improperly adjusted linkage.
3. Low main control pressure.
4. Sticking throttle control valve or valve body.
5. Sticking governor valve.
6. Valve body bolts improperly torqued.

### NO 1–2 UPSHIFTS

1. Improper fluid level.
2. Damaged or improperly adjusted linkage.
3. Low main control pressure to intermediate friction clutch.
4. Sticking, leaking or bent diaphragm unit.
5. Sticking or dirty valve body.
6. Burned intermediate clutch, band or servo.
7. Valve body bolts improperly torqued.

### ROUGH, HARSH AND/OR DELAYED 1–2 UPSHIFT

1. Improper fluid level.
2. Poor engine performance.
3. Incorrectly adjusted or damaged throttle linkage.
4. Main control pressure too high.
5. Sticking governor valve.
6. Valve body bolts improperly torqued.
7. Valve body dirty or valves sticking.

### MUSHY, EARLY, SOFT AND/OR SLIPPING 1–2 UPSHIFT

1. Improper fluid level.
2. Improperly tuned engine.
3. Damaged or improperly adjusted linkage.
4. Incorrect main control pressure.
5. Sticking governor valve.
6. Valve body bolts improperly torqued.
7. Valve body dirty or valves sticking.
8. Worn or burned intermediate friction clutch.
9. Damaged intermediate servo.

### NO 2–3 UPSHIFTS

1. Improper fluid level.
2. Low main control pressure to direct clutch.
3. Valve body bolts improperly torqued.
4. Sticking or dirty valve body.
5. Burned or worn direct or reverse-high clutch assembly.
6. Broken weld on converter damper hub.

### HARSH AND/OR DELAYED 2–3 UPSHIFT

1. Incorrect engine performance.
2. Incorrectly adjusted, sticking or damaged throttle linkage.
3. Plugged or missing 2-3 accumulator apply passage.
4. Cut or worn 2-3 accumulator piston seals.
5. Damaged 2-3 accumulator.
6. Valve body bolts improperly torqued.
7. Valve body dirty.
8. Sticking 2-3 capacity modulator valve.
9. Bent, sticking or leaking vacuum diaphragm or T.V. control rod.

### SOFT, EARLY AND/OR MUSHY 2–3 UPSHIFT

1. Improper fluid level.
2. Improperly tuned engine.
3. Damaged or improperly adjusted linkage.
4. Valve body bolts improperly torqued.
5. Burned or worn direct clutch assembly or reverse/high clutch.
6. Damaged accumulator.
7. Dirty or sticking valve body.
8. Bent, sticking or leaking vacuum diaphragm or T.V. control rod.

### NO 3–4 UPSHIFTS

1. Low fluid level.
2. Damaged or improperly adjusted linkage.
3. Direct clutch circuit leakage.
4. Sticking or dirty valve body.
5. Distorted main control gasket.
6. Distorted case.
7. Leaking governor.

### HARSH AND/OR DELAYED 3–4 UPSHIFT

1. Improper fluid level.
2. Damaged or improperly adjusted linkage.
3. Throttle return spring disconnected.
4. Valve body bolts improperly torqued.
5. Valve body dirty or valves sticking.
6. Incorrect engine performance.
7. Cut or worn 3-4 accumulator piston seals.
8. Clogged 3-4 accumulator piston drain passage.

### SLIPPING 4TH GEAR

1. Overdrive circuit leakage or blocked passage.
2. Overdrive servo piston and/or band not applying.
3. Overdrive band incorrectly located.
4. Converter damper plate and hub damaged.
5. Distorted direct driveshaft splines.

### ERRATIC SHIFTS

1. Improper fluid level.
2. Improperly tuned engine.
3. Damaged or improperly adjusted linkage.
4. Dirty or sticking valve body.
5. Sticking governor valve.
6. Damaged output shaft collector body seal rings.
7. Valve body bolts improperly torqued.

### SHIFTS 1–3 IN OVERDRIVE

1. Improper fluid level.
2. Damaged or burned intermediate friction clutch.
3. Damaged intermediate one-way clutch.
4. Improper control system pressure or clutch application.
5. Sticking or dirty valve body.
6. Sticking governor valve.

### ENGINE OVERSPEEDS ON 2–3 SHIFT

1. Improper fluid level.
2. Damaged or improperly adjusted linkage.
3. Improper control system pressure or clutch application.
4. Damaged or worn high clutch or intermediate servo.
5. Sticking or dirty valve body.
6. Broken converter damper hub.
7. Cut or leaking intermediate servo piston seals.

### SHIFT HUNTING 3–4 OR 4–3

1. Improperly tuned engine.
2. Damaged or improperly adjusted linkage.
3. Worn or damaged EGR solenoid.

### NO FORCED DOWNSHIFTS

1. Improper fluid level.
2. Damaged or improperly adjusted linkage.
3. Improper control system pressure or clutch application.
4. Sticking or dirty valve body.
5. Sticking or dirty governor.

### ROUGH SHUDDER 3–1 SHIFT AT CLOSED THROTTLE IN OVERDRIVE

1. Improper fluid level.
2. Improperly tuned engine.
3. Damaged or improperly adjusted linkage.
4. Improper control system pressure or clutch application.
5. Improper governor operation.

6. Sticking or dirty valve body.

### ROUGH OR MUSHY 4–2 OR 3–1 SHIFT

1. Improper fluid level.
2. Improperly tuned engine.
3. Damaged or improperly adjusted linkage.
4. Improper application of intermediate friction and one-way clutch.
5. Sticking or dirty valve body.

### HIGH SHIFT EFFORT

1. Damaged or improperly adjusted linkage.
2. Loose manual lever nut.
3. Damaged manual lever retainer pin.

### TRANSMISSION OVERHEATS

1. Improper fluid level.
2. Improperly tuned engine.
3. Improper control system pressure or clutch application.
4. Restricted cooler or lines.
5. Seized converter one-way clutch.
6. Sticking or dirty valve body.

### CLUNK OR SQUAWK IN 1–2 OR 2–3

1. Blocked intermediate bleed hole or bleed hole not at 12 o'clock position.
2. Incorrectly aligned anti-clunk spring.

### HARSH DOWNSHIFT COASTING CLUNK

1. Improperly seated anti-clunk spring.
2. Damaged or improperly adjusted linkage.

### TRANSMISSION LEAKS

1. Case breather vent.
2. Leakage at gaskets or seals.

### POOR VEHICLE ACCELERATION

1. Improperly tuned engine.
2. Seized torque converter one-way clutch.

### SLIPPING SHIFT FOLLOWED BY SUDDEN ENGAGEMENT

1. Throttle valve linkage set too short.

### TRANSMISSION NOISY (VALVE RESONANCE)

Gauges may aggravate any hydraulic resonance.

1. Improper fluid level.
2. Damaged or improperly adjusted linkage.
3. Improper control system pressure or clutch application.
4. Cooler lines contacting frame, floor pan or other components.
5. Sticking or dirty valve body.
6. Internal leakage or pump cavitation.

### TRANSMISSION NOISY (OTHER THAN VALVE RESONANCE)

1. Improper fluid level.
2. Damaged or improperly adjusted linkage.
3. Contaminated fluid.
4. Loose converter to flywheel housing bolts or nuts.
5. Loose or worn speedometer driven gear.
6. Damaged or worn extension housing bushing seal or driveshaft.
7. Damaged or worn front or rear planetary and/or one-way clutch.

### HARSH COASTING DOWNSHIFT CLUNK

1. Improperly seated anti-clunk spring.
2. Incorrectly adjusted throttle linkage.
3. Sticking throttle linkage return spring.

### INITIAL ENGAGEMENT CLUNK w/ENGINE WARM

1. Engine idle speed incorrect.
2. Incorrectly adjusted throttle linkage.
3. Worn, damaged or loose universal joints, slip yoke, rear axle or suspension.
4. Excessive transmission endplay.

### VEHICLE WILL NOT START

1. Incorrectly adjusted ignition switch.
2. Defective ignition switch.
3. Defective neutral start switch.

## THROTTLE VALVE LINKAGE DIAGNOSIS

Refer to the following for T.V. linkage conditions and subsequent shift troubles.

### T.V. CONTROL LINKAGE ADJUSTED TOO SHORT

1. Early or soft upshifts.
2. Harsh light throttle shift into and out of overdrive.
3. No forced downshift at proper speeds.

### T.V. CONTROL LINKAGE ADJUSTED TOO LONG

1. Harsh idle engagement after engine warm up.
2. Clunking when throttle is released after heavy acceleration.
3. Harsh coasting downshifts out of overdrive.

### INTERFERENCE PREVENTING RETURN OF T.V. CONTROL ROD

1. Delayed or harsh upshifts.
2. Harsh idle engagement.

### BINDING GROMMETS PREVENTING T.V. LINKAGE RETURN

1. Delayed or harsh upshifts.
2. Harsh idle engagement.

### T.V. CONTROL ROD DISCONNECTED

1. Delayed or harsh upshifts.
2. Harsh idle engagement.

### CLAMPING BOLT ON TRUNNION AT LOWER END OF T.V. CONTROL ROD LOOSE

1. Delayed or harsh upshifts.
2. Harsh idle engagement.

### LINKAGE LEVER RETURN SPRING BROKEN OR DISCONNECTED.

1. Delayed or harsh upshifts.
2. Harsh idle engagements.

## MAINTENANCE

Ford Motor Company recommends the use of Mercon type automatic transmission fluid in this transmission. If Mercon type fluid is not available, Dexron-II Series D automatic transmission fluid may be used. Use of a fluid other than specified may result in transmission malfunction of failure.

### CHECKING FLUID LEVEL

1. With transmission at operating temperature, park vehicle on a level surface.
2. Run engine at idle speed with service and parking brakes applied and move selector lever through each range. Return selector lever to P.
3. With engine idling, remove dipstick and check fluid level. Fluid level should be between the Add and Full marks.
4. Add specified fluid as required to bring the fluid to the proper level.

### CHANGING FLUID

Normal maintenance and lubrication requirements do not necessitate periodic fluid changes. If vehicle accumulates 5000 or more miles per month or it is used in continuous stop and go service, change fluid every 30,000 miles.

When filling a dry transmission and converter, install approximately 12 quarts of specified fluid. Start engine, shift the selector lever through all ranges and place it at P position. Check fluid level and add enough to raise the level in the transmission to the F (full) mark on the dipstick. When a partial drain and refill is required, proceed as follows:

1. Loosen oil pan bolts and allow pan to drain.

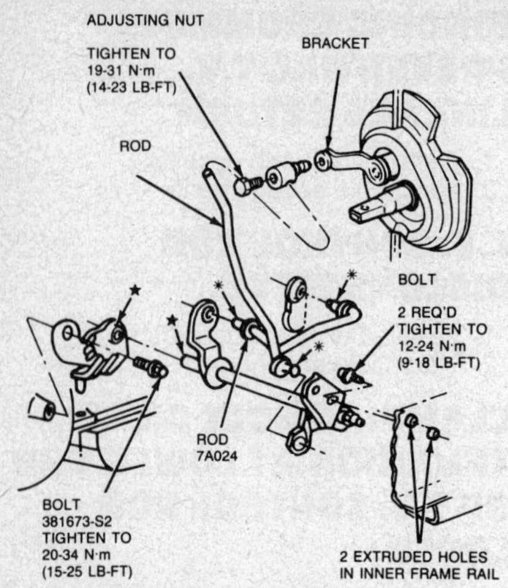


* LUBRICATE WITH ESE-M2C96-E ENGINE OIL
★ LUBRICATE ID OF BEARING LIBERALLY WITH ESA-MIC75-B

**Fig. 3 Manual linkage. 1989 Crown Victoria, Grand Marquis & Town Car**

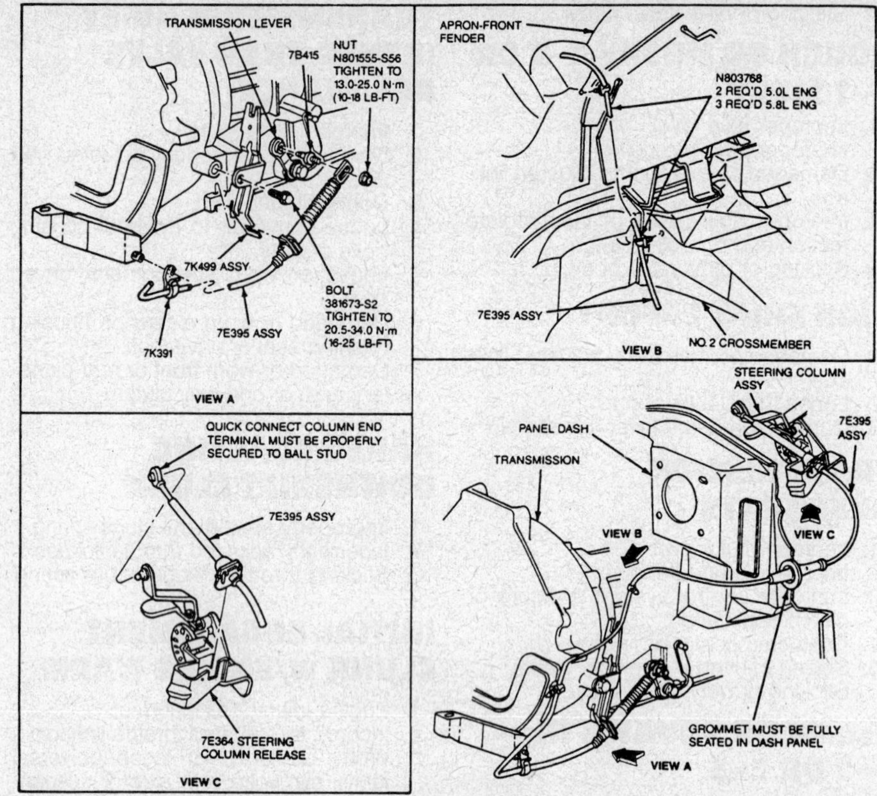


**Fig. 4 Manual linkage. 1990–91 Crown Victoria, Grand Marquis & Town Car**

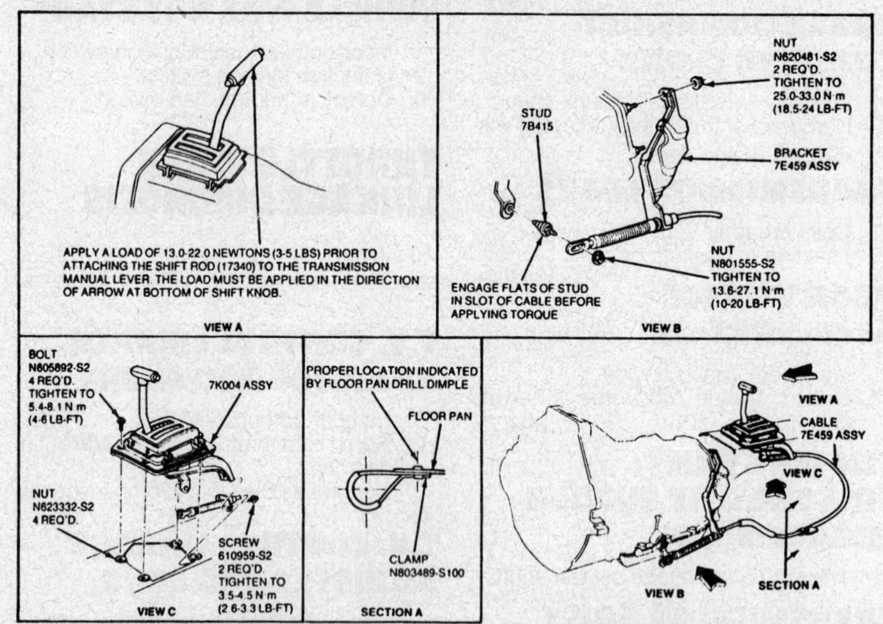


**Fig. 5 Manual linkage. Mustang**

2. Working from rear and both sides of transmission oil pan, remove bolts, allowing pan to drop and drain slowly.
3. Remove and clean pan and replace screen.
4. Place a new gasket on pan and install pan and screen.
5. Add three quarts of specified fluid to transmission.
6. Run engine at a fast idle until it reaches normal operating temperature.
7. Shift selector lever through all ranges and then place it in P position.
8. Add fluid as required to bring the level to the full mark.

# IN-VEHICLE ADJUSTMENTS

## MANUAL LINKAGE, ADJUST

### COLUMN SHIFT

#### 1989 Models

1. Place selector lever in overdrive position, tight against overdrive stop, and hang 8 lb. weight from selector lever to ensure lever remains in overdrive.
2. Raise and support vehicle as necessary and loosen adjusting bolt or nut, **Fig. 3.**
3. Shift transmission into overdrive, ensure that selector lever has not moved from overdrive and tighten adjusting bolt or nut, then check transmission operation in all selector positions.

#### 1990–91 Models

1. Loosen adjusting stud nut at transmission shift lever, **Fig. 4.**
2. Place steering column selector lever in Overdrive and hold selector lever in position by placing a 3 lb. weight on lever.
3. Rotate transmission manual lever to low (clockwise), then return it two detent positions to Overdrive position (counterclockwise).
4. Align flats of adjusting stud with flats of cable slot, then install cable on stud.
5. Tighten adjusting stud nut and washer assembly. **Torque** to 10–18 ft. lbs.
6. Check shift lever for proper operation.

### Floor Shift

1. Place transmission selector lever in overdrive position. **Shift lever should be held against the rearward overdrive stop while linkage is adjusted.**

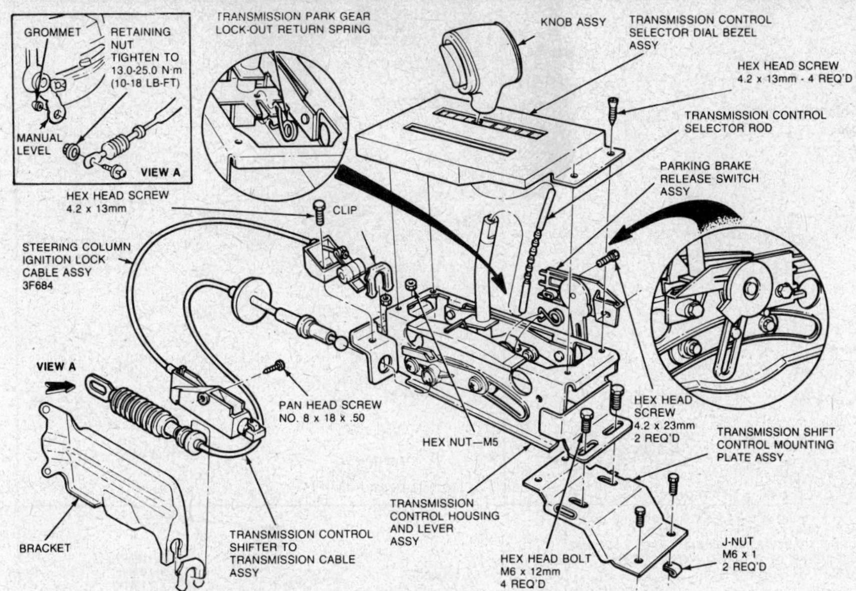


**Fig. 6 Manual linkage. 1989 Mark VII**

2. Raise and support vehicle and loosen manual lever shift rod retaining nut, **Figs. 5 through 8.**
3. Move transmission manual lever to overdrive position and tighten attaching nut.
4. Check transmission operation in all selector lever positions.

## THROTTLE VALVE LINKAGE, ADJUST

**On 1989-91 models equipped with 5.0L/V8-302 engine,** adjustments can be made only by using throttle valve pressure as outlined further on.

### EXCEPT 1989–91 COUGAR & THUNDERBIRD

#### At Transmission

1. **On models less idle speed control (ISC),** proceed as follows:
   a. Check and adjust curb idle speed to specifications with and without throttle solenoid positioner (anti-dieseling solenoid energized, if equipped).
   b. Shut off engine and remove air cleaner.
   c. De-cam fast idle cam on carburetor so that throttle lever is against idle stop or throttle solenoid positioner stop.
2. **On models with idle speed control,** proceed as follows:
   a. Locate self test connector and self test input connector in engine compartment. These connectors are generally located in the area of the righthand fender apron, adjacent to each other.
   b. Connect a jumper wire between self test input connector and signal return ground on self test connector, **Fig. 9.**
   c. Turn ignition key to Run position without starting engine and wait approximately 10 seconds for ISC plunger to fully retract.
   d. Shut off key and remove jumper wire and air cleaner.
3. **On all models,** place shift lever in N and apply parking brake.
4. Set linkage lever adjustment screw at approximately mid-range.
5. If a new T.V. control rod assembly is being installed, connect rod to linkage lever at carburetor or throttle body.
6. Raise and support vehicle.
7. Loosen bolt on sliding trunnion block on T.V. control rod assembly, removing any corrosion from control rod and freeing up trunnion block so that it slides freely on control rod.
8. Push up on lower end of control rod to ensure linkage lever at carburetor or throttle body is firmly against throttle lever, then release force on rod and ensure rod stays up.
9. Push T.V. control lever on transmission up against it's internal stop with a force of approximately 5 lbs., then tighten bolt on trunnion block. **Do not relax force on lever until bolt is tightened.**
10. Lower vehicle and ensure throttle lever is still against stop and, if not, repeat procedure.

#### At Carburetor Or Throttle Body

1. Position throttle lever at idle stop, place shift lever in N and apply parking brake (engine off).
2. Turn linkage lever adjusting screw counterclockwise until end of screw is flush with throttle lever face.
3. Turn adjusting screw clockwise to provide .005 inch clearance between end of screw and throttle lever. Continue turning adjusting screw an additional three turns. If screw travel is limited, one turn is acceptable.
4. If adjusting screw cannot be turned at least one turn, refer to "At Transmission" procedure. **Whenever idle speed is adjusted by more than 50 RPM, the adjustment screw on the linkage lever at the carburetor should also be adjusted as listed in the "Idle Speed/Throttle Valve Linkage Adjustment Chart," Fig. 10. If idle speed was adjusted, ensure that .005 inch clearance exists between linkage lever adjusting screw and the throttle lever. The throttle lever should be at the idle stop and the shift lever in N.**

### 1989–91 Cougar & Thunderbird

1. Remove air cleaner cover and inlet tube from throttle body inlet to gain access to throttle lever and cable assembly.
2. Using a wide blade screwdriver, pry grooved pin on cable out of grommet on throttle body lever.
3. Using a small screwdriver, push out the white locking tab from plastic block on end of cable assembly.
4. Ensure plastic block with pin and tab slides freely on notched rod. If plastic block does not slide freely, white locking tab may not be pushed out far enough.
5. While holding throttle lever firmly against idle stop, push grooved pin into grommet on throttle lever as far as it will go. **While pushing pin into grommet, ensure throttle lever does not move away from idle stop.**
6. Install air cleaner cover and air inlet tube.

## THROTTLE VALVE PRESSURE ADJUSTMENT

### Vehicles w/T.V. Rod Linkage

1. Check curb idle speed, adjusting as necessary. Ensure curb idle speed is set to specification with and without throttle solenoid positioner (anti-diesel solenoid) energized, if equipped.
2. Using adapter fitting tool No. D80L-77001-A or equivalent, attach suitable pressure gauge to T.V. port on transmission, using enough flexible hose so that gauge can be read while operating engine.
3. Obtain T.V. control pressure gauge block tool No. D84P-70332-A or fabricate a block .390-.404 inch thick, **Fig. 11.**
4. Run engine until it reaches normal operating temperature and the throttle lever is off fast idle, or the idle speed control (ISC) plunger, if equipped, is at its normal idle position. Ensure transmission fluid temperature is approximately 100-150°F.
5. Apply parking brake, place shift selector in N, remove air cleaner and shut off air conditioner. If equipped with a vacuum operated throttle modulator, disconnect and plug vacuum line to

this unit. If equipped with a throttle solenoid positioner or an idle speed control, do not disconnect either of these units.

6. With engine idling in N and no accessory load on engine, insert gauge block between carburetor throttle lever and adjustment screw on the T.V. linkage lever at the carburetor, **Fig. 10.** The T.V. pressure should be 30-40 psi. For optimum setting, use adjusting screw to set pressure as close to 33 psi as possible, as pressure will rise approximately 2 psi when shifted from N to D. Turning the screw in will raise the pressure 1.5 psi per turn and backing out the screw will lower the pressure. If equipped with idle speed control, some "hunting" may occur and an average pressure reading will have to be determined. If the adjusting screw does not have enough adjustment range to bring T.V. pressure within specification, first adjust rod at transmission as previously described.
7. Remove gauge block, allowing T.V. lever to return to idle. With engine still idling in N, T.V. pressure must be less than 5 psi. If not, back out adjusting screw until T.V. pressure is less than 5 psi, then reinstall gauge block and ensure T.V. pressure is still 30-40 psi.

### Vehicles w/T.V. Cable Linkage

1. Attach T.V. pressure gauge with hose, tool No. T86L-70002-A, or equivalent, to T.V. port on transmission, using enough hose to make gauge accessible while operating engine.
2. If necessary, remove air cleaner cover and inlet tube from throttle body inlet.
3. Insert tapered end of cable T.V. gauge tool No. T86L-70332-A or equivalent between crimped slug on end of cable and plastic cable fitting that attaches to throttle lever, **Fig. 12.**
4. Push gauge tool in, forcing the crimped slug away from the plastic fitting, ensuring gauge block is pushed in as far as it will go.
5. Run engine until it reaches normal operating temperature and temperature of transmission fluid is 100-150°F.
6. Apply parking brake and place shift selector in N. T.V. pressure should be 30-40 psi. For best results, set T.V. pressure as close to 33 psi as possible as follows:
   a. Using suitable tool, pry up white toggle lever on cable adjuster located immediately behind throttle body cable mounting bracket. The adjuster preload spring should cause the adjusting slider to move away from the throttle body and T.V. pressure should increase.
   b. Push on slider from behind bracket until T.V. pressure is 33 psi and, while still holding slider, push down on toggle lever as far as it will go, locking slider in position.
7. Remove gauge tool, allowing cable to return to its normal idle position.
8. If T.V. pressure is not less than 5 psi, reinstall gauge block and repeat step 6, setting T.V. pressure to a pressure of less than 33 psi but not less than 30 psi.
9. Remove gauge block and ensure T.V. pressure is less than 5 psi.

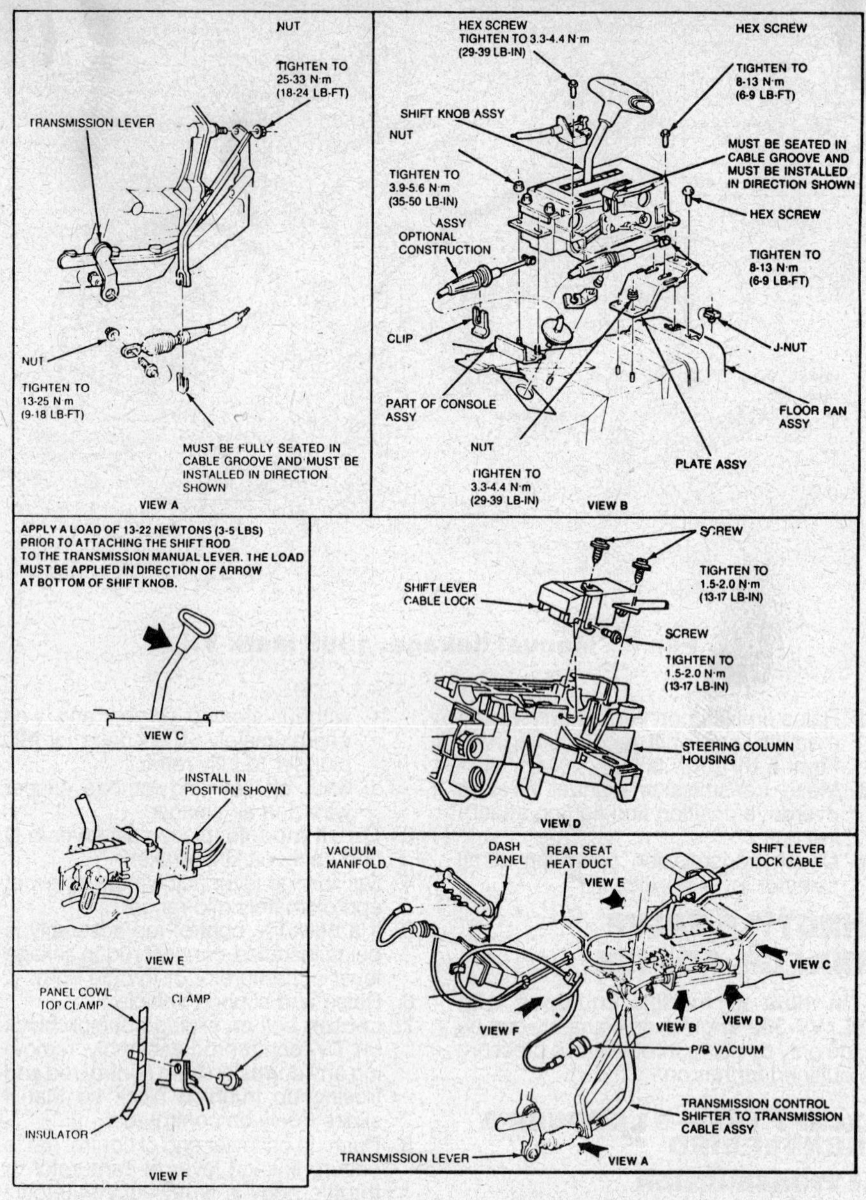


**Fig. 7 Manual linkage. 1990–91 Mark VII**

## IN-VEHICLE REPAIRS

### MANUAL SHIFT LINKAGE GROMMET, REPLACE

The automatic transmission linkage system incorporates a polyurethane plastic grommet to connect the various rods, levers and adjusting stud. Whenever a rod is disconnected from a grommet type connector, the old grommet must be removed and a new one installed.

1. Place lower jaw of shift linkage insulator tool No. T67P-7341-A, or equivalent, between lever and rod, **Fig. 13. For limited work space applications, use grommet tool No. T84P-7341-A or equivalent, Fig. 14.**
2. Position stop pin against end of control rod and force rod out of grommet.
3. Remove grommet from lever by cutting off large shoulder with sharp knife.
4. Adjust stop pin to 1/2 inch and coat outside of grommet with suitable lubricant.
5. Place a new grommet on the stop pin and force it into the lever hole, then turn grommet several times to ensure it is properly seated.
6. Readjust stop pin to proper height, **Fig. 13,** coating ends of rods with suitable lubricant.
7. With pin height properly adjusted, position rod on tool and force rod into grommet until groove in rod seats on inner retaining lip of grommet. **Use grommet tool No. T84P-7341-B for**

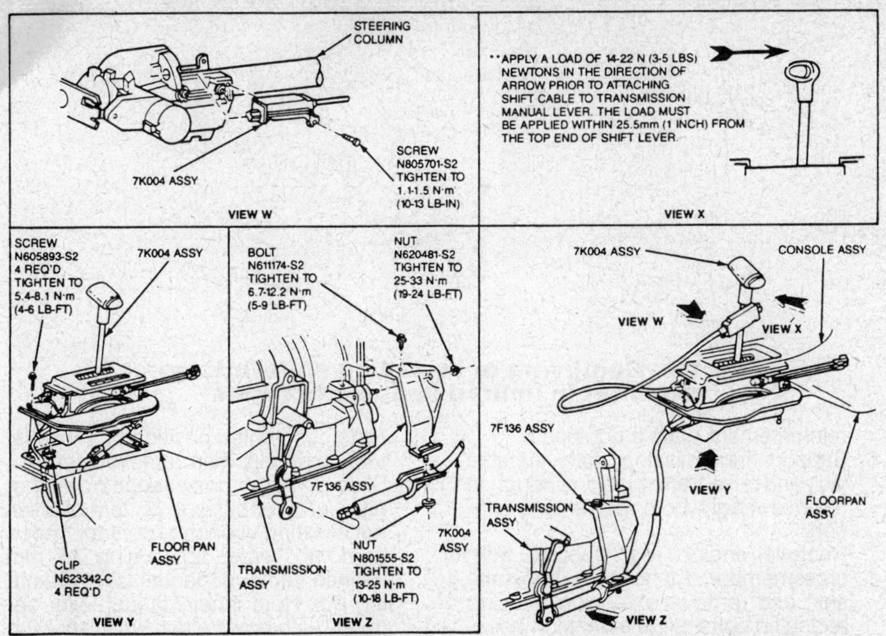


**Fig. 8 Manual linkage. 1989–91 Cougar & Thunderbird**

**Fig. 9 Connecting jumper wire between self test input connector & signal return ground**

| Change on Linkage Lever Adj. Screw | Idle Speed Change |
|---|---|
| No change. | Less than 50 RPM |
| 1½ turns counterclockwise | 50–100 RPM increase |
| 1½ turns clockwise | 50–100 RPM decrease |
| 2½ turns counterclockwise | 100–150 RPM increase |
| 2½ turns clockwise | 100–150 RPM decrease |

**Fig. 10 Idle Speed/Throttle Valve Linkage Adjustment Chart**

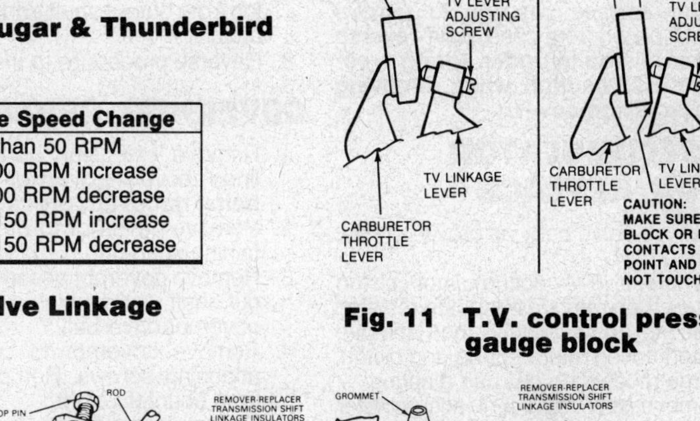


**Fig. 11 T.V. control pressure gauge block**

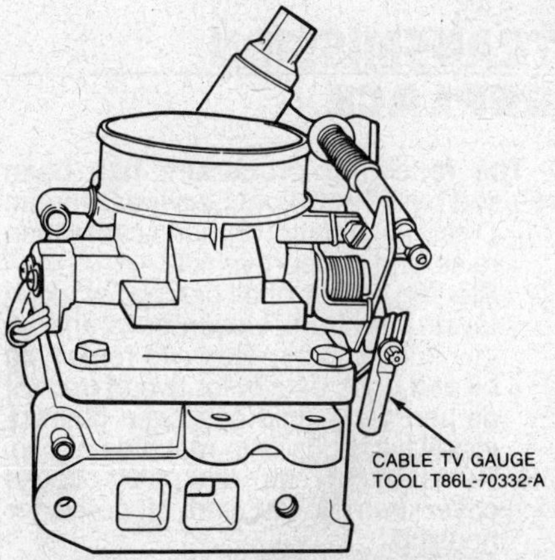


**Fig. 12 Installing cable T.V. gauge tool. 1989 models**

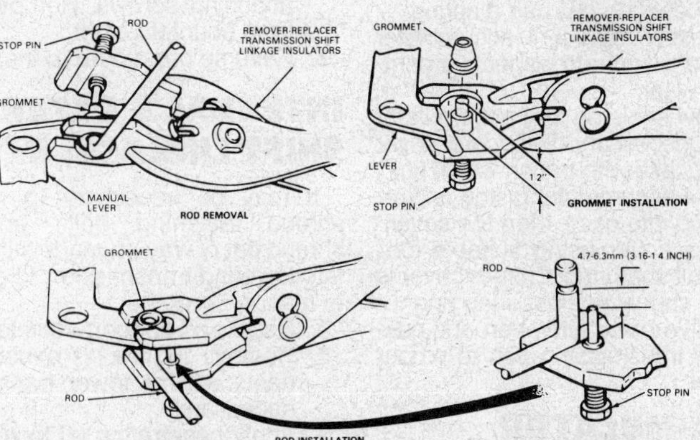


**Fig. 13 Removing or installing shift linkage grommet**

**limited work space applications, Fig. 14.**

## CONTROL VALVE BODY, REPLACE

Some models may require removal of interfering exhaust system components to gain access to control valve body.

1. Raise and support vehicle, drain transmission fluid, then remove transmission pan, gasket and filter.
2. Remove detent spring attaching bolt, then the spring.
3. Remove valve body to case attaching bolts, then the valve body.
4. Reverse procedure to install, noting the following:
   a. Use suitable guide pins to align valve body to case.
   b. **Torque** valve body-to-case attaching bolts to 6.5-8.1 ft. lbs.
   c. **Torque** detent spring attaching bolt to 6.5-8.1 ft. lbs.
   d. **Torque** filter attaching bolts to 6.5-8.1 ft. lbs.
   e. **Torque** oil pan attaching bolts to 6-9 ft. lbs.

## OVERDRIVE SERVO ASSEMBLY, REPLACE

1. Remove valve body as previously described.
2. Compress overdrive servo piston cover with a suitable tool, then remove snap ring retainer.
3. Using servo piston removal tool No. T80L-77030-B or equivalent, apply

compressed air to servo piston release passage and remove the overdrive servo piston cover and spring. Remove piston from cover, then the rubber seal from piston and cover.
4. Install new servo piston and cover seals on the servo piston and cover.
5. Lubricate all seals, piston and piston bore with transmission fluid.
6. Install servo piston into cover, then the return spring into servo piston.
7. Install overdrive piston assembly into overdrive servo bore.
8. Compress overdrive piston using suitable tool, then install snap ring retainer.
9. Install valve body, filter, pan and gasket. Refill transmission to proper fluid level.

## LOW-REVERSE SERVO ASSEMBLY, REPLACE

1. Refer to "Overdrive Servo Assembly, Replace" procedure for replacement. Apply compressed air to the servo piston release passage to remove servo piston from case. **Low-reverse servo piston is under spring pressure. Use caution when removing servo piston cover.**

## 3-4 ACCUMULATOR PISTON, REPLACE

1. Remove valve body as previously described.
2. Compress 3-4 accumulator piston cover, then remove snap ring retainer.
3. Release cover slowly, then remove piston cover, return spring and piston. Some models do not use a spring.
4. Remove seal from 3-4 accumulator cover and piston and inspect for damage and wear.
5. Install new seals on 3-4 accumulator cover, if necessary. Lubricate cover pocket of case with transmission fluid.
6. Install 3-4 accumulator piston and return spring into case, then the cover.
7. Compress cover using suitable tool, then install snap ring. Ensure cover is reseated snugly against snap ring.
8. Install valve body, filter, pan and gasket. Refill transmission pan to proper fluid level.

## 2-3 ACCUMULATOR PISTON, REPLACE

1. Refer to "3-4 Accumulator Piston, Replace" procedure for replacement.

## EXTENSION HOUSING, REPLACE

1. Raise and support vehicle.
2. Disconnect parking brake cable from equalizer, if necessary.
3. Disconnect driveshaft from rear axle flange, then remove driveshaft from transmission.
4. Disconnect speedometer cable from extension housing.
5. Remove engine rear support to extension housing attaching bolts, then the reinforcement plate if equipped.
6. Support transmission with suitable jack and raise transmission enough to remove weight from rear engine support.
7. Remove engine rear support from crossmember, then lower transmission and remove extension housing attaching bolts. Slide extension housing from output shaft and allow fluid to drain.
8. Reverse procedure to install.

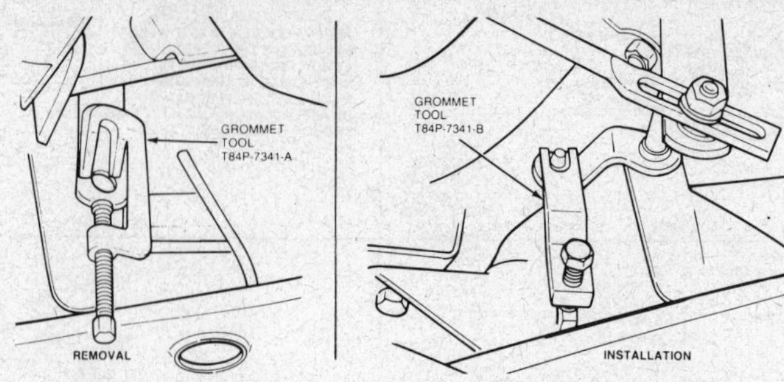


**Fig. 14 Removing or installing shift linkage grommet in limited space situations**

## GOVERNOR, REPLACE

1. Remove extension housing as outlined above. **If governor body only is being removed, proceed to step 4.**
2. Remove governor to output shaft retaining snap ring.
3. Remove governor assembly from output shaft using suitable tool. Remove governor drive ball.
4. Remove governor to counterweight attaching screws. Remove governor from counterweight.
5. Reverse procedure to install.

## INTERNAL & EXTERNAL SHIFT LINKAGE, REPLACE

It may be necessary to remove fan shroud attaching bolts and position shroud out of way on models that necessitate lowering transmission to gain access to manual lever.

1. Raise and support vehicle.
2. Remove interfering exhaust components and/or lower transmission as necessary.
3. Apply penetrating oil to outer throttle lever attaching nut to prevent breaking inner throttle lever.
4. Grasp outer throttle lever and hold firmly, then remove outer throttle lever attaching nut and lock washer and position lever and T.V. rod or cable assembly out of way.
5. Carefully disconnect manual rod from transmission manual lever at transmission using shift linkage grommet removal tool No. T84P-7341-A or equivalent.
6. Remove oil pan, gasket and filter.
7. Remove manual lever detent spring and roller assembly.
8. Remove manual lever retaining pin by carefully prying with sharp narrow screwdriver.
9. Note assembled position of T.V. lever torsion spring, then remove spring.
10. Slide a 5/8 inch box wrench over inner manual lever close to bottom of lever, not allowing wrench to contact "rooster comb" area, and, using 21 mm wrench, remove manual lever attaching nut. Hold inner manual lever securely with box wrench while applying break torque to manual lever attaching nut.
11. Remove outer manual lever from case.
12. Remove inner throttle lever and shaft assembly.
13. Remove inner manual lever and park pawl actuating rod assembly.
14. Disconnect park pawl actuating rod from inner manual assembly.
15. Remove and discard manual lever oil seal.
16. Reverse procedure to install, then adjust manual and throttle linkages.

# TRANSMISSION REPLACE

**The following procedure has been revised by a Technical Service Bulletin.**

1. Disconnect battery ground cable, then raise and support vehicle.
2. Starting at rear of oil pan and working toward the front, loosen bolts and allow fluid to drain. Remove remaining oil pan bolts except for two at front of oil pan. After fluid has been drained, install two bolts onto rear side of pan.
3. Remove converter drain plug access cover from lower end of converter housing.
4. Remove converter-to-flywheel attaching nuts.
5. Turn converter until drain plug is accessible. Remove plug and drain fluid.
6. Install converter drain plug.
7. Remove driveshaft, mark rear driveshaft yoke and companion flange so driveshaft can be installed to its original position.
8. Position a suitable plug into extension housing to prevent fluid leakage.
9. Remove starter motor and disconnect neutral start switch electrical connector.
10. Remove rear mount-to-crossmember and two crossmember-to-frame bolts.
11. Remove engine rear

support-to-extension housing bolts, then disconnect T.V. linkage rod from transmission T.V. lever and manual rod from manual lever at transmission.

12. Remove bolts securing bellcrank bracket to converter housing.
13. Using a suitable jack, raise transmission and remove crossmember from side supports. Disconnect and remove any interfering exhaust system components.
14. Lower transmission and disconnect oil cooler lines from transmission.
15. Disconnect speedometer cable from extension housing.
16. Lower transmission to gain access to oil cooler lines, then disconnect each oil line.
17. Remove bolt and transmission filler tube from transmission.
18. Secure transmission to jack using a suitable chain.
19. Remove converter housing-to-cylinder block bolts.
20. Carefully move transmission and converter assembly away from engine and at the same time, lower jack to permit the transmission to clear the underside of vehicle.
21. Reverse procedure to install, noting the following:
    a. Lubricate converter pilot with chassis grease prior to installation.
    b. **Torque** converter drain plug to 8-28 ft. lbs.
    c. **Torque** engine-to-transmission bolts to 40-50 ft. lbs.
    d. **Torque** oil cooler lines to 18-23 ft. lbs.
    e. **Torque** crossmember-to-side support attaching bolts to 70-100 ft. lbs.
    f. **Torque** converter-to-flywheel attaching nuts to 20-34 ft. lbs.
    g. **Torque** converter housing access cover attaching bolts to 12-16 ft. lbs.

## TIGHTENING SPECIFICATIONS

| Component | Torque/Ft. Lbs. |
|---|---|
| Converter Housing Access Cover | 12–16 |
| Converter Plug To Converter | 8–28 |
| Converter To Flywheel | 20–34 |
| Detent Spring Attaching Bolt | 80–120① |
| Extension Housing To Case | 16–20 |
| Filter To Valve Body | 80–120① |
| Front Pump To Case | 10–20 |
| Governor Body Cover To Governor Body | 20–30① |
| Governor Body To Counterweight | 50–60① |
| Inner Manual Lever To Shaft | 19–27 |
| Neutral Start Switch To Case | 8–11 |
| Oil Pan To Case | 6–10 |
| Outer Throttle Lever To Shaft | 12–16 |
| Pressure Plug To Case | 6–12 |
| Push Connect Fitting To Case | 18–23 |
| Reinforcing Plate To Valve Body | 80–120① |
| Stator Support To Pump Body | 12–16 |
| Transmission To Engine | 40–50 |
| Valve Body To Case | 80–100① |

①—Inch lbs.

# Ford C3 Automatic Transmission

## INDEX



## TRANSMISSION IDENTIFICATION

The transmission may be identified by the tag attached to the low-reverse servo cover bolt, **Fig. 1.** The tag includes the model prefix and suffix, a service identification number and a build date code. The service identification number indicates changes to service details which affect interchangeability when the transmission model is not changed. For interpretation of this number the Ford Master Parts Catalog should be consulted.

## DESCRIPTION

The main control incorporates a manually selective first and second gear range. The transmission features a drive range that provides for fully automatic upshifts and downshifts, and manually selected low and second gears.

The transmission consists essentially of a torque converter, a compound planetary gear train, two multiple disc clutches, a one-way clutch and a hydraulic control system, **Fig. 2.**

For all normal driving the selector lever is moved to the green dot under D on the selector quadrant on the steering column or on the floor console. As the throttle is advanced from the idle position, the transmission will upshift automatically to intermediate gear and then to high.

The driver can force downshift the transmission from high to intermediate at speeds up to 65 mph. A detent on the downshift linkage warns the driver when the carburetor is wide open. Accelerator pedal depression through the detent will bring in the downshift.

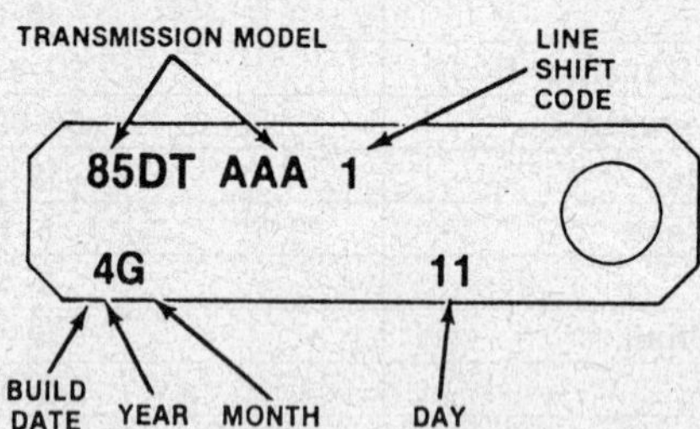


**Fig. 1 C3 identification tag**

With the throttle closed the transmission will downshift automatically as the car speed drops to about 10 mph. With the throttle open at any position up to the detent, the downshifts will come in automatically at speeds above 10 mph and in proportion to throttle opening. This prevents engine lugging on steep hill climbing, for example.

When the selector lever is moved to L with the transmission in high, the transmission will downshift to intermediate or to low depending on the road speed. At speed above 25 mph, the downshift will be from high to intermediate. At speeds below 25 mph, the downshift will be from high to low. With the selector lever in the L position the transmission cannot upshift.

## TROUBLESHOOTING

### ROUGH INITIAL ENGAGEMENT IN D1 OR D2

1. Engine idle speed.
2. Vacuum diaphragm unit or tubes restricted, leaking or incorrectly adjusted.
3. Check control pressure.
4. Pressure regulator.
5. Valve body.
6. Forward clutch.

### 1–2 OR 2–3 SHIFT POINTS ERRATIC

1. Check fluid level.
2. Vacuum diaphragm unit or tubes restricted, leaking or incorrectly adjusted.
3. Immediate servo.
4. Manual linkage adjustment.
5. Governor.
6. Check control pressure.
7. Valve body.
8. Make air pressure check.

### ROUGH 1–2 UPSHIFTS

1. Vacuum diaphragm unit or tubes restricted, leaking or incorrectly adjusted.
2. Intermediate servo.
3. Intermediate band.
4. Check control pressure.
5. Valve body.
6. Pressure regulator.

### ROUGH 2–3 UPSHIFTS

1. Vacuum diaphragm unit or tubes restricted, leaking or incorrectly adjusted.
2. Intermediate servo.
3. Check control pressure.
4. Pressure regulator.
5. Intermediate band.
6. Valve body.
7. Make air pressure check.
8. Reverse-high clutch.

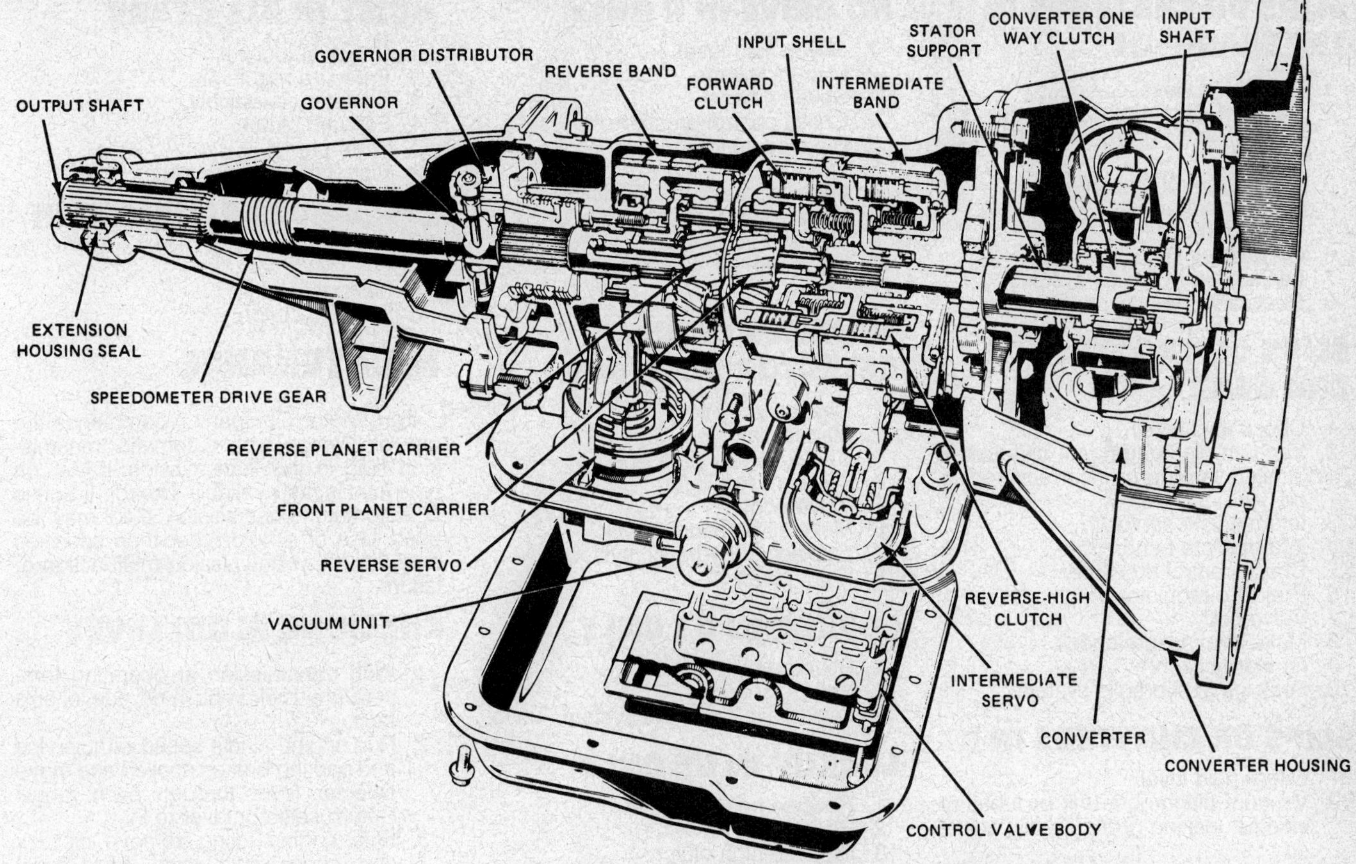


**Fig. 2 C3 Dual Range Automatic**

9. Reverse-high clutch piston air bleed valve.

## DRAGGED OUT 1–2 SHIFT

1. Check fluid level.
2. Vacuum diaphragm unit or tubes restricted, leaking or incorrectly adjusted.
3. Intermediate servo.
4. Check control pressure.
5. Intermediate band.
6. Valve body.
7. Pressure regulator.
8. Make air pressure check.
9. Leakage in hydraulic system.

## ENGINE OVERSPEEDS ON 2–3 SHIFT

1. Manual linkage.
2. Check fluid level.
3. Vacuum diaphragm unit or tubes restricted, leaking or incorrectly adjusted.
4. Reverse servo.
5. Check control pressure.
6. Valve body.
7. Pressure regulator.
8. Intermediate band.
9. Reverse-high clutch.
10. Reverse-high clutch piston air bleed valve.

## NO 1–2 OR 2–3 SHIFT

1. Manual linkage.
2. Downshift linkage, including inner lever position.
3. Vacuum diaphragm unit or tubes restricted, leaking or incorrectly adjusted.
4. Governor.
5. Check control pressure.
6. Valve body.
7. Intermediate band.
8. Intermediate servo.
9. Reverse-high clutch.
10. Reverse-high clutch piston air bleed valve.

## NO 3–1 SHIFT IN D1 OR 3–2 SHIFT IN D2

1. Governor.
2. Valve body.

## NO FORCED DOWNSHIFTS

1. Downshift linkage, including inner lever position.
2. Valve body.
3. Vacuum diaphragm unit or tubes restricted, leaking or incorrectly adjusted.

## RUNAWAY ENGINE ON FORCED 3–2 DOWNSHIFT

1. Check control pressure.
2. Intermediate servo.
3. Intermediate band.
4. Pressure regulator.
5. Valve body.
6. Vacuum diaphragm unit or tubes restricted, leaking or incorrectly adjusted.
7. Leakage in hydraulic system.

## ROUGH 3–2 OR 3–1 SHIFT AT CLOSED THROTTLE

1. Engine idle speed.
2. Vacuum diaphragm unit or tubes restricted, leaking or incorrectly adjusted.
3. Intermediate servo.
4. Valve body.
5. Pressure regulator.

## SHIFTS 1–3 IN D1 AND D2

1. Intermediate band.
2. Intermediate servo.
3. Vacuum diaphragm unit or tubes restricted, leaking or incorrectly adjusted.
4. Valve body.
5. Governor.
6. Make air pressure check.

## NO ENGINE BRAKING IN 1ST GEAR—MANUAL LOW

1. Manual linkage.
2. Reverse band.
3. Reverse servo.
4. Valve body.
5. Governor.
6. Make air pressure check.

### SLIPS OR CHATTERS IN 1ST GEAR—D1

1. Check fluid level.
2. Vacuum diaphragm unit or tubes restricted, leaking or incorrectly adjusted.
3. Check control pressure.
4. Pressure regulator.
5. Valve body.
6. Forward clutch.
7. Leakage in hydraulic system.
8. Planetary one-way clutch.

### SLIPS OR CHATTERS IN 2ND GEAR

1. Check fluid level.
2. Vacuum diaphragm unit or tubes restricted, leaking or incorrectly adjusted.
3. Intermediate servo.
4. Intermediate band.
5. Check control pressure.
6. Pressure regulator.
7. Valve body.
8. Make air pressure check.
9. Forward clutch.
10. Leakage in hydraulic system.

### SLIPS OR CHATTERS IN R

1. Check fluid level.
2. Vacuum diaphragm unit or tubes restricted, leaking or incorrectly adjusted.
3. Reverse band.
4. Check control pressure.
5. Reverse servo.
6. Pressure regulator.
7. Valve body.
8. Make air pressure check.
9. Reverse-high clutch.
10. Leakage in hydraulic system.
11. Reverse-high piston air bleed valve.

### NO DRIVE IN D1 ONLY

1. Check fluid level.
2. Manual linkage.
3. Check control pressure.
4. Valve body.
5. Make air pressure check.
6. Planetary one-way clutch.

### NO DRIVE IN D2 ONLY

1. Check fluid level.
2. Manual linkage.
3. Check control pressure.
4. Intermediate servo.
5. Valve body.
6. Make air pressure check.
7. Leakage in hydraulic system.
8. Planetary one-way clutch.

### NO DRIVE IN L ONLY

1. Check fluid level.
2. Manual linkage.
3. Check control pressure.
4. Valve body.
5. Reverse servo.
6. Make air pressure check.
7. Leakage in hydraulic system.
8. Planetary one-way clutch.

### NO DRIVE IN R ONLY

1. Check fluid level.
2. Manual linkage.
3. Reverse band.
4. Check control pressure.
5. Reverse servo.
6. Valve body.
7. Make air pressure check.
8. Reverse-high clutch.
9. Leakage in hydraulic system.
10. Reverse-high clutch piston air bleed valve.

### NO DRIVE IN ANY SELECTOR POSITION

1. Check fluid level.
2. Manual linkage.
3. Check control pressure.
4. Pressure regulator.
5. Valve body.
6. Make air pressure check.
7. Leakage in hydraulic system.
8. Front pump.

### LOCKUP IN D1 ONLY

1. Reverse-high clutch.
2. Parking linkage.
3. Leakage in hydraulic system.

### LOCKUP IN D2 ONLY

1. Reverse band.
2. Reverse servo.
3. Reverse-high clutch.
4. Parking linkage.
5. Leakage in hydraulic system.
6. Planetary one-way clutch.

### LOCKUP IN L ONLY

1. Intermediate band.
2. Intermediate servo.
3. Reverse-high clutch.
4. Parking linkage.
5. Leakage in hydraulic system.

### LOCKUP IN R ONLY

1. Intermediate band.
2. Intermediate servo.
3. Forward clutch.
4. Parking linkage.
5. Leakage in hydraulic system.

### PARKING LOCK BINDS OR WON'T HOLD

1. Manual linkage.
2. Parking linkage.

### MAXIMUM SPEED TOO LOW, POOR ACCELERATION

1. Engine performance.
2. Brakes bind.
3. Converter one-way clutch.

### NOISY IN N OR P

1. Check fluid level.
2. Pressure regulator.
3. Front pump.
4. Planetary assembly.

### NOISY IN ALL GEARS

1. Check fluid level.
2. Pressure regulator.
3. Planetary assembly.
4. Forward clutch.
5. Front pump.
6. Planetary one-way clutch.

### CAR MOVES FORWARD IN N

1. Manual linkage.
2. Forward clutch.

## MAINTENANCE

Ford Motor Company recommends the use of Mercon type automatic transmission fluid in this transmission. If Mercon type fluid is not available, Dexron-II Series D automatic transmission fluid may be used. Use of a fluid other than specified may result in transmission malfunction of failure.

### CHECKING FLUID LEVEL

1. With transmission at operating temperature, park vehicle on a level surface.
2. Run engine at idle speed with service and parking brakes applied and move selector lever through each range. Return selector lever to P.
3. With engine idling, remove dipstick and check fluid level. Fluid level should be between the Add and Full marks.
4. Add specified fluid as required to bring the fluid to the proper level.

### CHANGING FLUID

Normal maintenance and lubrication requirements do not necessitate periodic fluid changes. If vehicle accumulates 5000 or more miles per month or it is used in continuous stop and go service, change fluid every 30,000 miles. If a major failure has occurred in the transmission, it will have to be removed for service. At this time the converter must be thoroughly flushed to remove any foreign matter.

When filling a dry transmission and converter, install five quarts of specified fluid. Start engine, shift the selector lever through all ranges and place it at P position. Check fluid level and add enough to raise the level in the transmission to the F (full) mark on the dipstick. When a partial drain and refill is required, proceed as follows:

1. Loosen and remove all but two oil pan bolts and drop one edge of the pan to drain the oil.
2. Remove and clean pan and screen.
3. Place a new gasket on pan and install pan and screen.
4. Add three quarts of specified fluid to transmission.
5. Run engine at idle speed for about two minutes.
6. Check oil level and add oil as necessary.
7. Run engine at a fast idle until it reaches normal operating temperature.

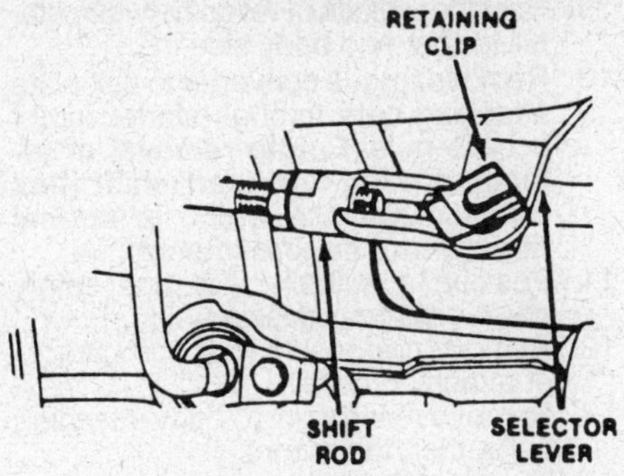


**Fig. 3 Disengaging shift rod from selector lever**

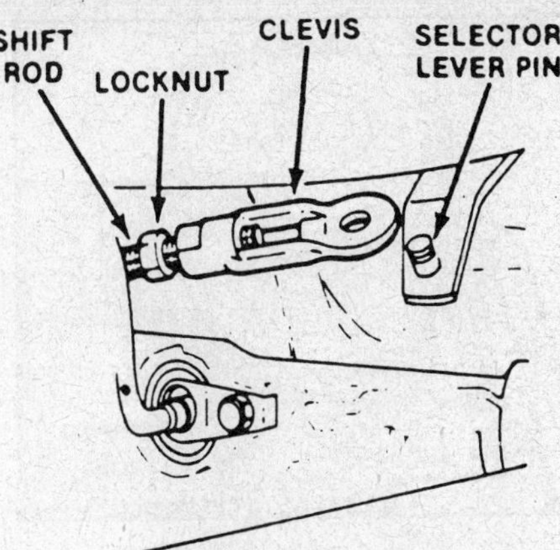


**Fig. 4 Sliding shift rod clevis over selector lever pin**

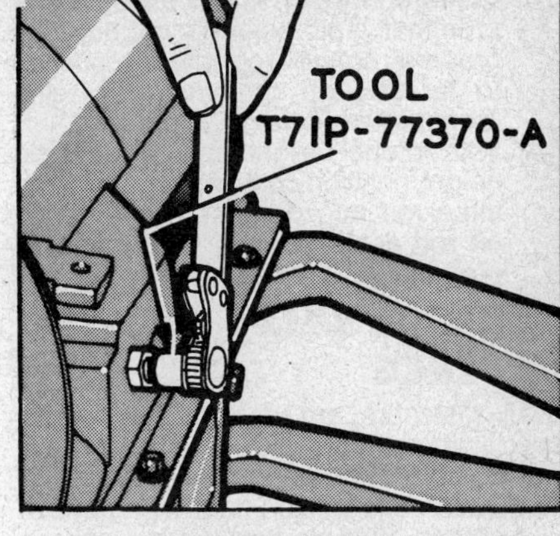


**Fig. 5 Intermediate band adjustment**

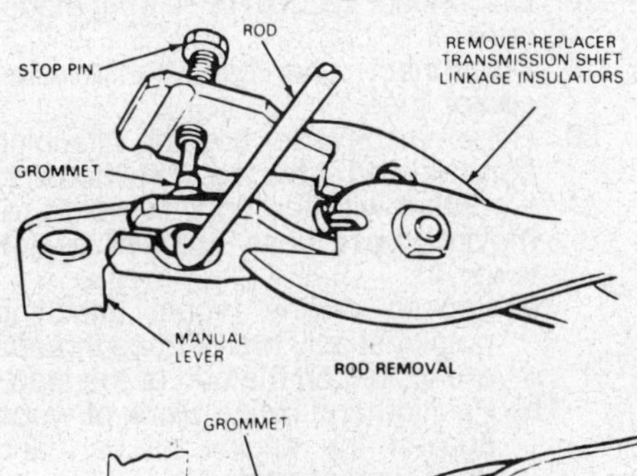


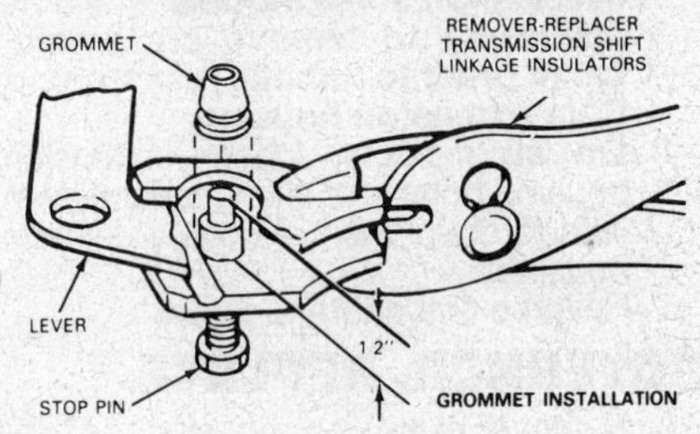


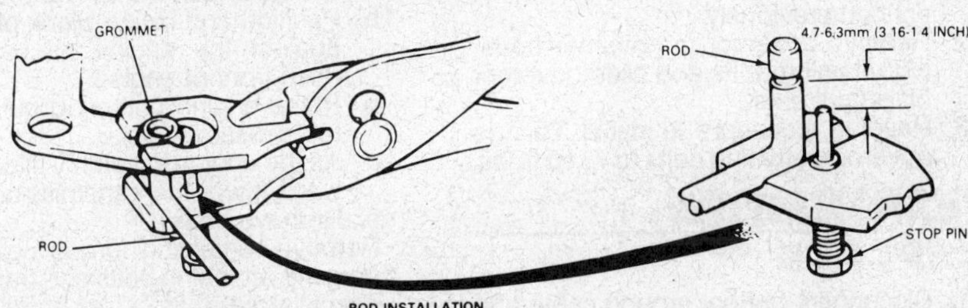


**Fig. 6 Removing or installing shift lever grommet**

8. Shift selector lever through all ranges and then place it in P position.
9. Add fluid as required to bring the level to the full mark.

# IN-VEHICLE ADJUSTMENTS

## MANUAL LINKAGE, ADJUST

1. Raise and support vehicle.
2. Remove retaining clip, then disconnect shift rod from selector lever, **Fig. 3.**
3. Rotate transmission shift lever as far as possible toward front of vehicle.
4. Rotate transmission shift lever two detent positions toward the rear of the vehicle.
5. Lower vehicle and place selector lever in D position, then raise and support vehicle.
6. Without moving the selector or transmission levers, attempt to slide the shift rod clevis in or out to obtain the proper fit, **Fig. 4.**
7. If the clevis slides into the pin, the linkage is properly adjusted.
8. If the clevis does not slide into the pin, loosen locknut and thread the clevis in or out to obtain the proper fit.
9. After adjustment, tighten clevis locknut. **Ensure the linkage adjustment has not affected proper operation of the neutral safety switch. With the brake applied and service brakes applied, try to start the engine in each gear shift lever position. The engine must crank only in the N or P positions. If the engine cranks in any of the other shift positions, check linkage adjustment and neutral safety switch operation.**

## THROTTLE & DOWNSHIFT LINKAGE, ADJUST

1. Apply parking brake and place selector lever in N.
2. Run engine at normal idle speed.
3. Connect tachometer to engine.
4. Adjust engine idle speed to specified RPM with selector lever in either D position. **The carburetor throttle lever must be against the hot idle speed adjusting screw at specified idle speed.**
5. Proceed with adjustments as outlined below.

## BANDS, ADJUST

The intermediate and low-reverse bands adjusting screw locknut must be discarded and a new one installed each time a band is adjusted.

### INTERMEDIATE BAND

1. Disconnect downshift linkage from transmission lever.
2. Discard adjusting screw locknut and install a new locknut.
3. With tools shown in **Fig. 5,** tighten adjusting screw until tool handle clicks. This tool is a pre-set torque wrench which clicks and overruns when the **torque** on the adjusting screw reaches 10 ft. lbs.
4. Back off adjusting screw two turns.
5. Hold adjusting screw from turning and tighten locknut.
6. Connect downshift linkage to transmission lever.

# IN-VEHICLE REPAIRS

## SHIFT LEVER GROMMET, REPLACE

**On some shift lever assemblies, Fig. 6,** an oil impregnated plastic grommet is incorporated in the end of the lever arm. A special tool is required to install the grommet in the manual lever, and to install the manual linkage rod into the grommet.

This grommet should be replaced each time the manual linkage rod is disconnected from shift lever.

1. Place lower jaw of tool between manual lever and shift rod. Position stop in against end of control rod and force rod out of grommet. Remove grommet from lever by cutting off large shoulder with a knife.
2. Before installing a new grommet, adjust stop pin to 1/2 inch and coat outside of grommet with lubricant. Place grommet on stop pin and force into hole in manual lever. Turn grommet several times to seat properly.
3. Adjust height of stop pin as shown in **Fig. 6.** Height is determined by length

of rod end which is to be installed in grommet. If pin height is not adjusted properly, control rod may be pushed to far through grommet, damaging grommet and retaining lip.

4. With proper alignment of stop pin height, position control rod on tool and force rod into grommet until groove on rod seats on inner retainer lip of grommet.

## CONTROL VALVE BODY, REPLACE

All fasteners are designed to metric specifications.

1. Raise and support vehicle.
2. Drain transmission fluid, then remove oil pan, fluid screen, gasket and on early units, remove three spacers.
3. Remove rear servo cover and gasket.
4. Remove control valve body attaching bolts. Note the different length and location of each bolt.
5. Carefully remove control valve body while unlocking and detaching selector lever connecting rod.
6. After installing valve body, **torque** attaching bolts to 72-96 inch lbs. **Torque** rear servo cover attaching bolts to 84-120 inch lbs.

## REAR SERVO, REPLACE

1. Raise and support vehicle, then drain transmission fluid.
2. Remove oil filter screws, gasket and on early models, three spacers.
3. Remove servo cover retaining screws, servo cover, piston and spring, **Fig. 7.**
4. Reverse procedure to install.

## EXTENSION HOUSING, REPLACE

1. Raise and vehicle, then remove driveshaft. **Scribe marks on driveshaft yoke and companion flange, to insure proper positioning of driveshaft during assembly.**
2. Support transmission with suitable jack and disconnect speedometer cable. **On some models, it will be necessary to disconnect the exhaust system from the exhaust manifolds to perform the following step.**
3. Remove engine rear support to crossmember attaching bolts or nuts, then raise transmission slightly and remove rear support from extension housing. **On some models, it will be necessary to remove crossmember in order to remove rear support from extension housing.**

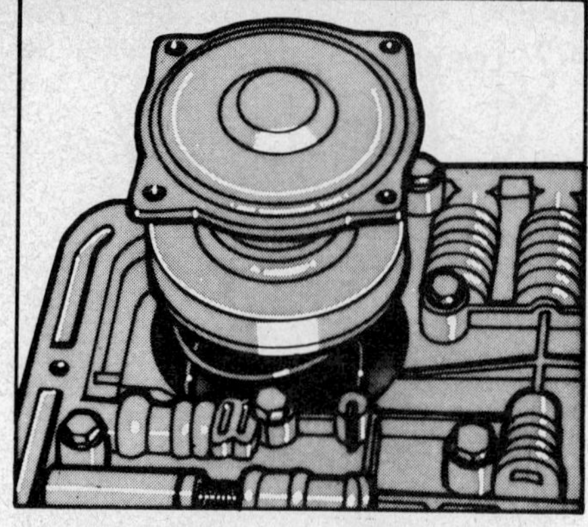

**Fig. 7 Rear servo removal**

4. **On all models,** loosen extension housing bolts and allow transmission fluid to drain, then remove extension housing.
5. Reverse procedure to install.

## GOVERNOR, REPLACE

1. Remove extension housing as described previously.
2. Remove governor to governor housing retaining bolts and slide governor off output shaft.
3. Reverse procedure to install. **Torque** governor retaining bolts to 7-10 ft. lbs.

## TRANSMISSION REPLACE

1. Disconnect battery ground cable and remove transmission fluid dipstick.
2. Raise and support vehicle.
3. Remove nuts attaching catalytic converter inlet pipe to the turbocharger assembly.
4. Remove attaching nuts at converter to muffler inlet flange.
5. Remove support bracket attaching bolt, then the converter and inlet pipe as an assembly.
6. Disconnect driveshaft from transmission.
7. Remove starter motor from engine.
8. Remove stabilizer bar U-brackets and body stiffener rod.
9. Position a block of wood between stabilizer bar and body side rail.
10. Remove torque converter to flex plate attaching nuts through starter motor access hole. **During removal of attaching nuts, turn crankshaft (flex plate) clockwise which is normal direction of engine rotation.**
11. Position a suitable jack and safety chain onto transmission.
12. Remove rear mount to support bracket attaching bolts.
13. Remove rear mount to body attaching bolts, then the mount.
14. Lower transmission.
15. Disconnect speedometer cable.
16. Disconnect electrical connectors from transmission.
17. Disconnect linkages from transmission.
18. Disconnect vacuum hose from modulator.
19. Disconnect and cap transmission cooler lines.
20. Remove converter housing attaching bolts located at the top of the housing.
21. If contact with the body prevents removing these bolts, proceed as follows:
    a. Loosen engine mount attaching nuts until only two or three threads are visible on the end of the stud.
    b. Position and jack a block of wood against the engine oil pan and raise front of engine.
    c. Raise engine until stud nuts contact crossmember.
    d. As the engine assembly tilts downward, lower the transmission jack.
    e. Remove bolts.
22. Remove remaining torque converter housing attaching bolts and transmission filler tube.
23. Pull transmission rearward and lower from vehicle.
24. Reverse procedure to install, noting the following **torques:** converter attaching bolts, 28-38 ft. lbs.; engine mount stud nuts, 50-70 ft. lbs.; rear mount bolts, 25-35 ft. lbs.; rear mount-to-transmission support bracket attaching bolts, 50-70 ft. lbs.; converter attaching nuts, 12-16 ft. lbs.; U-brackets and body stiffener rod attaching bolts, 33-41 ft. lbs.; exhaust system attaching nuts, 20-30 ft. lbs.; converter outlet-to-turbocharger assembly nuts, 25-35 ft. lbs.

## TIGHTENING SPECIFICATIONS

| Component | Torque/Ft. Lbs. |
|---|---|
| Connector To Case | 10–15 |
| Converter Drain Plug | 20–30 |
| Converter Housing To Case | 27–39 |
| Converter Housing To Engine | 28–38 |
| Cooler Line Fittings | 7–10 |
| Downshift Lever Nut | 7–11 |
| Extension Housing To Case | 27–39 |
| Flywheel To Converter | 27–49 |
| Front Band Adjusting Locknut | 35–45 |
| Governor To Collector Body | 7–10 |
| Main Control To Case | 71–97① |
| Manual Lever Nut | 30–40 |
| Neutral Switch To Case | 10–14 |
| Oil Pan To case | 12–17 |
| Oil Pump To Converter Housing | 10–14 |
| Plate To Valve Body | 7–9 |
| Servo Cover To Case | 10–14 |
| Vacuum Diaphragm Retaining Clip To Case | 80–106① |

①—Inch lbs.

# Ford Automatic Transaxle

## INDEX



## TRANSAXLE IDENTIFICATION

The transaxle identification tag, **Fig. 1**, is located near the valve body (upper) cover.

## DESCRIPTION

This transaxle, **Fig. 2**, combines a three speed automatic transaxle with a front wheel driving axle into a single unit.

The transaxle section uses a torque converter with a planetary gear set, one band and three friction elements. The planetary gear set is used to split input power between mechanical and hydraulic in some gears. On 1989-91 Tempo and Topaz and 1989-90 Sable and Taurus, a Fluidically Linked Converter (FLC) that eliminates the converter lock up feature is used.

Other unique features of this transaxle are that there are two input shafts from the converter to the gear train, the valve body is mounted on top of the case, the oil pump is installed at the end opposite the converter and the parking gear is installed in the final drive.

Output from the transmission goes through a final drive assembly to the differential to drive the front axle shafts. The final drive consists of an input gear, idler gear and final drive gear (ring) gear.

## TROUBLESHOOTING

### SLOW INITIAL ENGAGEMENT

1. Improper fluid level.
2. Damaged or improperly adjusted

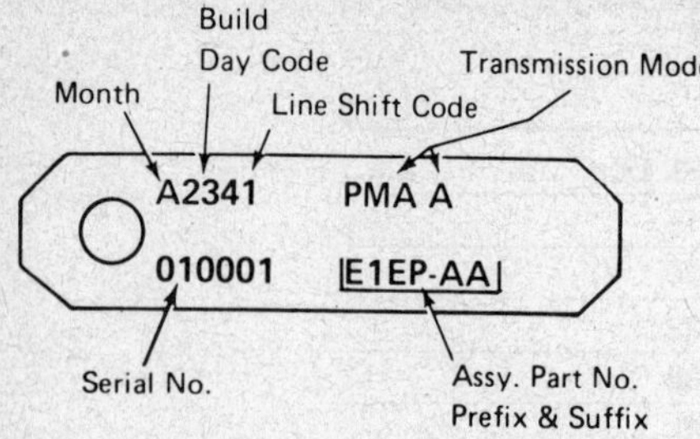


**Fig. 1 Transaxle identification tag**

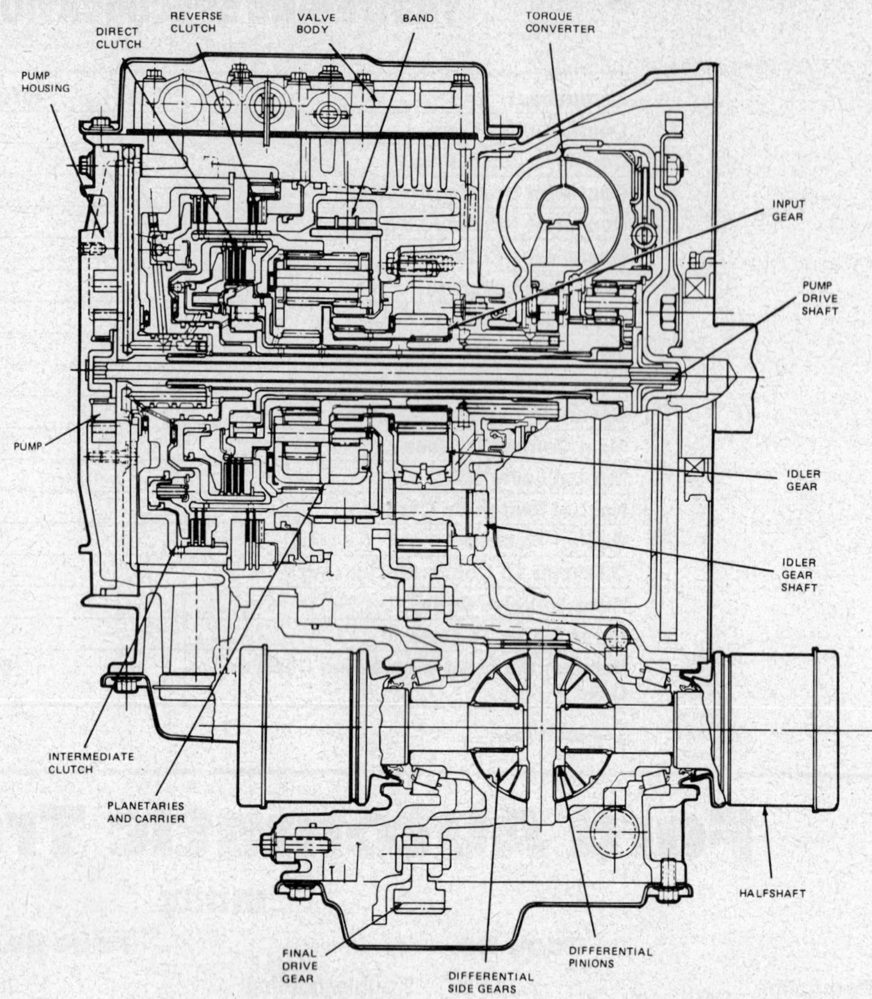


**Fig. 2 Sectional view of automatic transaxle**

manual linkage.
3. Incorrect throttle valve linkage adjustment.
4. Contaminated fluid.
5. Improper clutch or band application or oil control pressure.
6. Dirt in valve body.

## ROUGH INITIAL ENGAGEMENT IN FORWARD OR REVERSE

1. Improper fluid level.
2. Engine idle too high.
3. Automatic choke closed on warm engine.
4. Play in half shafts, constant velocity joints or engine mounts.
5. Improper clutch or band application or oil control pressure.
6. Incorrect throttle valve linkage adjustment.
7. Dirt in valve body.

## NO DRIVE, ANY GEAR

1. Improper fluid level.
2. Damaged or improperly adjusted manual linkage.
3. Improper clutch or band application or oil control pressure.
4. Internal leak.
5. Loose valve body.
6. Damaged or worn clutches or bands.
7. Valve body sticking or dirty.

## NO DRIVE IN 1, 2 OR D

1. Improper fluid level.
2. Damaged or improperly adjusted manual linkage.
3. Improper one-way clutch or band application.
4. Incorrect oil pressure.
5. Damaged or worn band, servo or clutches.
6. Loose valve body.
7. Valve body sticking or dirty.

## NO REVERSE OR SLIPS IN REVERSE

1. Improper fluid level.
2. Damaged or improperly adjusted manual linkage.
3. Play in half shafts, constant velocity joints or engine mounts.
4. Improper oil pressure control.
5. Damaged or worn reverse clutch.
6. Loose valve body.
7. Valve body sticking or dirty.

## NO START IN P OR N

1. Neutral start switch improperly adjusted.
2. Neutral start wire damaged.
3. Manual linkage improperly adjusted.

## NO DRIVE OR SLIPS IN D

1. Damaged or worn one-way clutch.
2. Improper fluid level.
3. Damaged or worn band.
4. Incorrect throttle valve linkage adjustment.

## NO DRIVE OR SLIPS IN 2

1. Improper fluid level.
2. Incorrect throttle valve linkage adjustment.
3. Damaged or worn intermediate friction clutch.
4. Improper clutch application.
5. Internal leakage.
6. Valve body dirty or sticking.
7. Band or drum glazed.

## TAKE OFF IN 2ND OR 3RD

1. Improper fluid level.
2. Damaged or improperly adjusted manual linkage.
3. Improper band or clutch application.
4. Damaged or worn governor.
5. Loose valve body.
6. Valve body sticking or dirty.
7. Leaks between valve body and case mating surface.

## INCORRECT SHIFT POINTS

1. Improper fluid level.
2. Throttle valve linkage improperly adjusted.
3. Improper clutch or band application.
4. Improper oil control pressure.
5. Damaged or worn governor.
6. Valve body dirty or sticking.

## NO UPSHIFT IN D

1. Improper fluid level.
2. Throttle valve linkage improperly adjusted.
3. Improper band or clutch application.
4. Improper oil control pressure.
5. Damaged or worn governor.
6. Valve body sticking or dirty.

## SHIFT 1–3 IN D

1. Improper fluid level.
2. Damaged or worn intermediate friction clutch.
3. Improper clutch application.

4. Improper oil control pressure.
5. Valve body sticking or dirty.

## RUNAWAY UPSHIFTS

1. Improper fluid level.
2. Improper band or clutch application.
3. Improper oil pressure.
4. Damaged or worn direct clutch or servo.
5. Valve body sticking or dirty.

## DELAYED 1–2 SHIFT

1. Improper fluid level.
2. Improper engine performance.
3. Improper throttle valve linkage adjustment.
4. Improper intermediate clutch application.
5. Improper oil control pressure.
6. Damaged intermediate clutch.
7. Valve body sticking or dirty.

## ROUGH 1–2 UPSHIFT

1. Improper fluid level.
2. Improper throttle valve linkage adjustment.
3. Incorrect engine idle or performance.
4. Improper intermediate clutch application.
5. Improper oil control pressure.
6. Valve body sticking or dirty.

## ROUGH 2–3 UPSHIFT

1. Improper fluid level.
2. Incorrect engine performance.
3. Improper band release or direct clutch application.
4. Improper oil control pressure.
5. Valve body sticking or dirty.
6. Damaged or worn servo release and direct clutch piston check ball.
7. Improper throttle valve linkage adjustment.

## ROUGH 3–2 DOWNSHIFT AT CLOSED THROTTLE IN D

1. Improper fluid level.
2. Incorrect engine idle or performance.
3. Improper throttle valve linkage adjustment.
4. Improper band or clutch application.
5. Improper oil control pressure.
6. Improper governor operation.
7. Valve body sticking or dirty.

## NO FORCED DOWNSHIFTS

1. Improper fluid level.
2. Improper clutch or band application.
3. Improper oil control pressure.
4. Damaged internal kickdown linkage.
5. Throttle valve linkage improperly adjusted.
6. Valve body sticking or dirty.
7. Dirty or sticking governor.

## DOWNSHIFT RUNAWAY

1. Improper fluid level.
2. Throttle valve linkage improperly adjusted.
3. Band improperly adjusted.
4. Improper band or clutch application.
5. Improper oil control pressure.
6. Damaged or worn servo.
7. Glazed band or drum.
8. Valve body sticking or dirty.

## NO ENGINE BRAKING IN 1

1. Improper fluid level.
2. Throttle valve linkage improperly adjusted.
3. Damaged or improperly adjusted manual linkage.
4. Improperly adjusted band or clutch.
5. Improper oil control pressure.
6. Glazed band or drum.
7. Valve body sticking or dirty.

## NO ENGINE BRAKING IN 2

1. Improper fluid level.
2. Throttle valve linkage improperly adjusted.
3. Manual linkage improperly adjusted.
4. Improper band or clutch application.
5. Improper oil control system.
6. Leaking servo.
7. Glazed band or drum.

## NOISE PRESENT DURING ALL DRIVE RANGES

1. Damaged speedometer driven gear or C.V. joints.
2. Damaged halfshaft or engine mounts.

## NOISE PRESENT DURING INITIAL ENGAGEMENT

1. Loose convertor to flywheel attaching nuts.
2. Damaged convertor or missing convertor studs.
3. Damaged oil pump.

## NOISE PRESENT IN LOW & REVERSE

1. Damaged planetary gear.

## NOISE PRESENT IN THIRD GEAR ONLY

1. Damaged final drive gear.

## TRANSAXLE NOISY/VALVE RESONANCE

1. Improper fluid level.
2. Improper band or clutch application.
3. Cooler lines grounding.
4. Dirty or sticking valve body.
5. Internal leakage.

## TRANSAXLE OVERHEATS

1. Excessive tow loads.
2. Improper fluid level.
3. Incorrect idle speed.
4. Improper clutch or band application.
5. Restriction in cooler lines.
6. Seized convertor one-way clutch.
7. Dirty or sticking valve body.

## TRANSAXLE FLUID LEAKS

1. Improper fluid level.
2. Leakage at gaskets or seals.

# MAINTENANCE

Ford Motor Company recommends the use of Mercon type automatic transmission fluid in this transmission. If Mercon type fluid is not available, Dexron-II Series D automatic transmission fluid maybe used. Use of a fluid other than specified may result in transmission malfunction or failure.

## CHECKING FLUID LEVEL

To check fluid level, apply parking brake, operate engine at idle speed with vehicle on level surface and transmission in P position. Add fluid as necessary to bring mark on dipstick between Add and Full marks.

## CHANGING FLUID

Fluid and filter changes are not required for average passenger car use. Severe usage such as commercial use or prolonged periods of idling require fluid and filter be changed every 30,000 miles.

1. Raise and support vehicle.
2. Loosen transaxle oil pan attaching bolts and allow fluid to drain.
3. Remove oil pan and clean thoroughly.
4. Install new gasket onto pan, then the pan onto transaxle.
5. Fill transaxle to correct fluid level, then operate engine at idle. With parking brake applied, move selector lever to each position. Place lever in P position and check fluid level with engine at operating temperature. Add fluid as necessary.

# IN-VEHICLE ADJUSTMENTS

## GEARSHIFT LINKAGE, ADJUST

1. Position selector lever in D position against rearward stop.
2. Raise and support vehicle, then loosen manual lever to control cable retaining nut or adjusting bolt.
3. Position transmission manual lever at second detent from most rearward position. This is D position.
4. **Torque** attaching nut to 10-15 ft. lbs. on all models except Sable and Taurus or 16-27 ft. lbs. on Sable and Taurus.
5. Lower vehicle and check for proper operation of transmission in each selector lever position.

## THROTTLE VALVE LINKAGE, ADJUST

### 1989 w/2.3L/4-140 Engine

1. Simultaneously hold throttle open to maintain 1000 RPM while pressing lightly on the ISC motor shaft.
2. After the shaft retracts completely, release throttle and quickly disconnect ISC motor electrical connector.
3. Loosen bolt on sliding trunnion block on T.V. control rod assembly, **Fig. 3.** A minimum of one turn is necessary.
4. Remove any surface corrosion from the control rod and ensure trunnion block moves freely on control rod assembly.

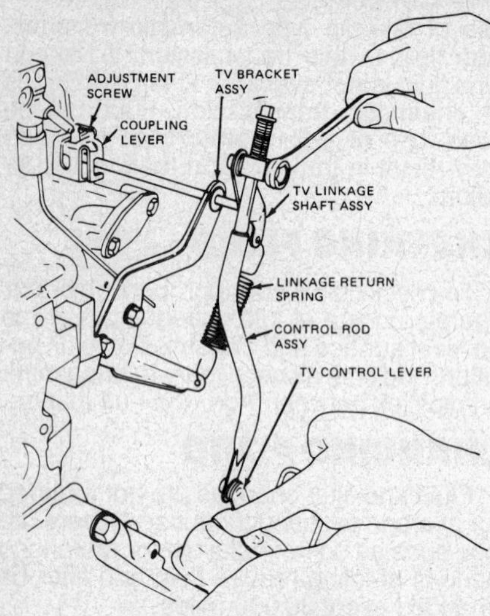


**Fig. 3 Adjusting throttle valve control linkage**

5. With ISC plunger retracted and trunnion block loosened, rotate transaxle T.V. control lever upward, using approximately a one lb. force to ensure T.V. control lever is completely against its internal idle stop. Without releasing force on T.V. control lever, **torque** trunnion block attaching bolt, 7-11 ft. lbs.

### 1990–91 w/2.3L/4-140 Engine

1. Remove splash shield from cable retainer bracket.
2. Loosen trunnion bolt on TV rod.
3. Install plastic clip using adjustment tool No. T91P-7000-A or equivalent to bottom of TV rod. Ensure clip keeps from telescoping, **Fig. 4.**
4. Ensure TV return spring is connected between TV rod and retaining bracket to hold transmission TV lever at its idle position.
5. Ensure throttle lever is resting on throttle return control screw.
6. Tighten trunnion bolt on TV rod, then remove plastic clip.
7. Install splash shield and check for proper operation.

### 1989–90 Models w/1.9L/4-114 Engines

1. Start engine and ensure engine idle speed is as specified.
2. Apply parking brake and place transaxle selector in P.
3. Loosen bolt on sliding trunnion block on T.V. control rod assembly, **Fig. 3.** A minimum of one turn is necessary.
4. Remove any surface corrosion from the control rod and ensure trunnion block moves freely on control rod assembly.
5. Connect a jumper wire between STI connector and signal return ground on self-test connector.
6. Turn ignition key to Run position. **Do not start engine.** The ISC plunger will retract. Wait approximately ten seconds or until plunger is fully retracted.
7. Turn key to Off position and remove jumper wire.
8. Rotate transaxle T.V. control lever upward, using approximately a one lb. force to ensure T.V. control lever is completely against its internal idle stop.
9. Allow trunion to slide on rod to its natural position.
10. Without releasing force on T.V. control lever, **torque** trunnion block attaching bolt to 4-7 ft. lbs.

### 1989–90 Sable & Taurus

1. Locate self-test connector and self-test input STI connector in engine compartment. The two connectors are located next to each other near the dash panel on passenger side of vehicle or righthand fender apron.
2. Connect a jumper wire between STI connector and signal return ground on self-test connector.
3. Turn ignition key to Run position. **Do not start engine.** The ISC plunger will retract. Wait approximately ten seconds or until plunger is fully retracted.
4. Loosen bolt on sliding trunnion block on T.V. control rod assembly, **Fig. 3.** A minimum of one turn is necessary.
5. Remove any surface corrosion from the control rod and ensure trunnion block moves freely on control rod assembly.
6. With engine idling in P, rotate transaxle T.V. control lever upward, using approximately a one lb. force to ensure T.V. control lever is completely against its internal idle stop. Without releasing force on T.V. control lever, **torque** trunnion block attaching bolt to 4-7 ft. lbs.
7. Turn key to Off position and remove jumper wire.

## IN-VEHICLE REPAIRS

### VALVE BODY, REPLACE

1. Remove battery and battery tray.
2. **On all models except Sable and Taurus,** remove ignition coil.
3. **On Sable and Taurus models,** remove air cleaner assembly.
4. **On all models,** remove transaxle oil dipstick.
5. **On all models except Sable and Taurus,** disconnect all hoses and lines from air management valve, then remove the valve from transaxle valve body cover. Also, disconnect fuel evaporator hose from frame rail.
6. **On all models,** disconnect neutral safety switch electrical connector.
7. Disconnect fan motor and temperature sending unit electrical connectors.
8. Remove valve body cover bolts, then the valve body cover and gasket.
9. Remove valve body bolts, then the valve body and gaskets.
10. Reverse procedure to install. Install guide pins to properly align valve body before tightening attaching bolts. One alignment pin may have to be temporarily removed to allow attachment of manual valve. Ensure roller on end of throttle valve plunger engages cam on end of throttle lever shaft. **Torque** valve body bolts to 6-8 ft. lbs. and valve body cover bolts to 7-9 ft. lbs.

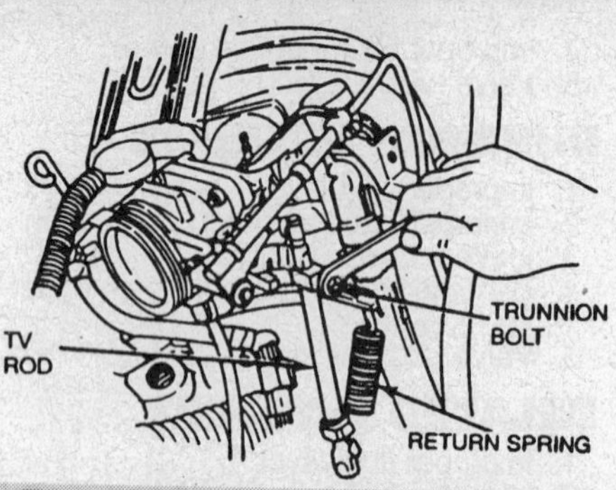


**Fig. 4 Adjusting throttle valve control linkage. Tempo & Topaz**

### GOVERNOR, REPLACE

1. Disconnect battery ground cable, and on carbureted engines, all hoses and lines from air management valve.
2. **On models with 1.9L/4-97.6 carbureted engines,** remove managed air valve supply hose band to intermediate shift control bracket attaching screw.
3. **On all models,** remove air cleaner, then using a long screwdriver, remove governor cover retaining clip.
4. Remove governor cover and governor.
5. Reverse procedure to install.

### SERVO, REPLACE

1. Disconnect battery ground cable.
2. Disconnect electrical connectors from fan motor and temperature sending unit.
3. Disconnect FM capacitor wiring, if equipped.
4. Remove two fan shroud to radiator attaching nuts, then the fan and fan shroud.
5. Remove filler tube to case attaching bolt, then the filler tube and dipstick.
6. Remove lower left side mount to case attaching bolt.
7. Remove servo cap and snap ring using servo installation tool No. T81P-70027A or equivalent.
8. Reverse procedure to install.

## TRANSAXLE REPLACE

### TEMPO, TOPAZ & 1989–90 ESCORT

Due to case configuration, righthand half shaft assembly must be removed first using half shaft removal tool No. D83P-4026-A or equivalent. The lefthand inboard CV joint assembly is then driven from case by inserting differential rotator tool No. T81P-4026-A or equivalent into transaxle.

1. Position vehicle on hoist, then disconnect battery ground cable.

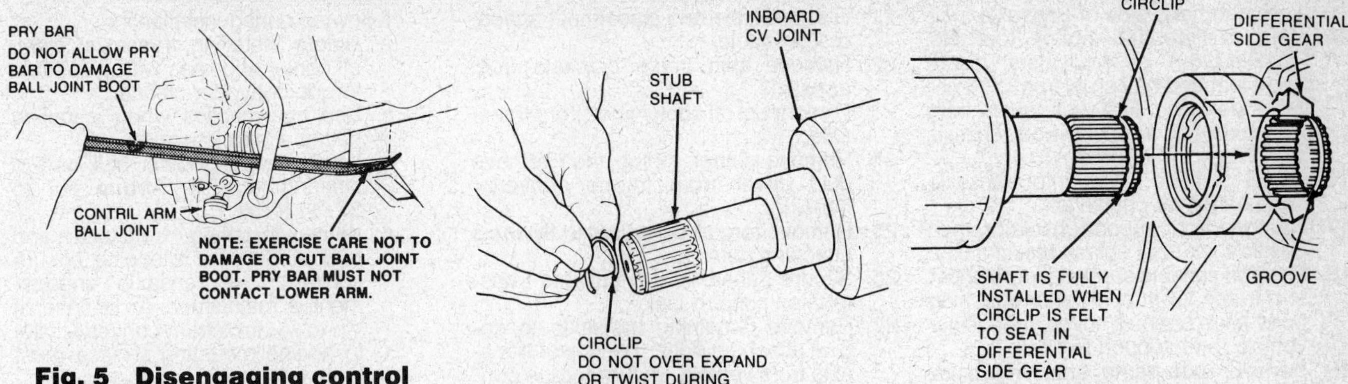
PRY BAR
DO NOT ALLOW PRY BAR TO DAMAGE BALL JOINT BOOT
CONTRIL ARM BALL JOINT
NOTE: EXERCISE CARE NOT TO DAMAGE OR CUT BALL JOINT BOOT. PRY BAR MUST NOT CONTACT LOWER ARM.
INBOARD CV JOINT
STUB SHAFT
CIRCLIP
DO NOT OVER EXPAND OR TWIST DURING INSTALLATION
CIRCLIP
DIFFERENTIAL SIDE GEAR
SHAFT IS FULLY INSTALLED WHEN CIRCLIP IS FELT TO SEAT IN DIFFERENTIAL SIDE GEAR
GROOVE

**Fig. 5 Disengaging control arm from steering knuckle**

**Fig. 6 Replacing circlip on CV stub shaft**

**Fig. 7 Seating half shaft**

2. Disconnect managed air valve from transaxle valve body cover, if equipped.
3. **On 1989-91 models,** remove air cleaner assembly, then back out Thermactor hose attaching bolts and position valve and hoses aside.
4. **On all models,** disconnect electrical connector from neutral safety switch.
5. Disconnect throttle valve linkage and manual lever cable from levers.
6. **On 1989-91 models,** disconnect ground strap located above upper engine mount, then remove ignition coil and bracket assembly.
7. **On all models,** remove two transaxle-to-engine upper bolts located below and to either side of distributor.
8. Raise and support vehicle.
9. Remove front wheel and tire assemblies.
10. Remove nut from control arm to steering knuckle bolt, on both sides of vehicle, then drive bolts out using punch and hammer. **The bolts and nuts must be discarded.**
11. Disengage control arm from steering knuckle, on both sides of vehicle, using a suitable pry bar, **Fig. 5. Use care to avoid damaging ball joint boot. Pry bar must not contact lower arm. Do not use hammer on knuckle to remove ball joints. Plastic splash shield behind rotor has pocket into which lower ball joint fits. When disconnecting lower control arm from knuckle, shield should be bent back to clear ball joint and avoid damaging the shield.**
12. Remove and discard stabilizer bar bracket bolts from both sides of vehicle.
13. Remove and discard stabilizer-to-control arm nut and washer from both side of vehicle, then slide stabilizer bar out of control arms.
14. Remove brake hose routing clip attaching bolts from suspension strut bracket on both sides of vehicle.
15. Disconnect tie rod from steering knuckle on both sides of vehicle.
16. Pry half shaft out of right side of transaxle and position shaft on transaxle housing. **If difficulty is encountered when prying half shaft, remove transaxle oil pan and discard gasket. Insert a large blade screwdriver between differential pinion shaft and inboard CV joint stub shaft. Tap screwdriver handle to dislodge circlip from side gear and free half shaft from differential. Prior to installation of the half shaft, install a new circlip on inboard stub shaft. Also, use a new gasket when installing oil pan.**
17. Disconnect left half shaft from differential side gear using differential rotator tool No. T81P-4026-A or equivalent.
18. Slide half shaft out of transaxle and support end of shaft. **Do not allow end of driveshaft to hang unsupported, as damage to outboard CV joint may result.**
19. Install seal plug tools No. T81P-1177-B or equivalent into differential seals.
20. Unfasten starter support bracket, then disconnect starter cable and remove starter from vehicle. **On some fuel injected models, it will be necessary to disconnect hoses from starter motor.**
21. Remove transaxle support bracket, then the torque converter housing dust cover.
22. Remove torque converter-to-flywheel attaching nuts. Rotate crankshaft as necessary to provide access to each nut.
23. Position a suitable jack under transaxle and remove rear support bracket attaching nuts.
24. Remove left front body bracket attaching nuts and bolts and the bracket.
25. Disconnect cooler lines from transaxle.
26. Remove manual lever bracket attaching bolts from transaxle case.
27. Ensure engine is properly supported, then position a suitable jack under transaxle and remove remaining transaxle-to-engine attaching bolts.
28. Insert a screwdriver between flywheel and torque converter and carefully move transaxle and converter away from engine. When converter studs clear flywheel, lower transaxle several inches and disconnect speedometer cable.
29. Lower transaxle and remove from vehicle.
30. Reverse procedure to install, noting the following:
    a. Replace circlip on CV joint stub shaft, **Fig. 6.** Avoid spreading the circlip any more than necessary.
    b. When inserting half shaft in transaxle, push CV joint into differential until circlip seats in side gear, **Fig. 7.** A rubber mallet may be used to tap the outboard CV joint stub shaft, if necessary.
    c. When attaching lower ball joint to steering knuckle, use care to avoid damaging ball joint boot. Install new pinch bolt and nut. **Torque** nut 40-54 ft. lbs. **Do not torque bolt.**

## SABLE & TAURUS

1. Disconnect battery ground cable.
2. Remove air cleaner assembly, then position engine control wiring out of way.
3. Disconnect throttle valve linkage and manual linkage at transaxle.
4. Remove power steering hose brackets, then remove two upper engine to transaxle mounting bolts.
5. Attach a suitable engine support fixture to engine.
6. Raise and support vehicle, then remove wheel and tire assemblies.
7. Disconnect catalytic converter from inlet pipe.
8. Disconnect engine exhaust air hose assembly.
9. Disconnect tie rod end from spindle.
10. Remove attaching nuts and bolts, then separate lower ball joints from strut units.
11. Remove lower control arms from spindles, then disconnect stabilizer bar.
12. Remove nuts attaching rack and pinion steering gear to sub-frame, then disconnect and remove auxiliary cooler. Position rack and pinion steering gear away from sub-frame and secure with wire.
13. Remove retaining bolts from front righthand axle support and bearing.
14. Remove half shaft and link assembly

from righthand side of transaxle.

15. Using differential rotator tool No. T81P-4026-A or equivalent, disengage lefthand half shaft from differential side gear. Pull half shaft from transaxle and suspend from chassis with wire.
16. Install suitable plugs into transaxle case half shaft openings.
17. Remove front support insulator, then position left front splash shield aside.
18. Position suitable support fixture under sub-frame for support after attaching bolts have been removed, then lower vehicle to to support fixture.
19. Remove sub-frame attaching bolts, then remove sub-frame.
20. Disconnect neutral safety switch electrical connector.
21. Raise vehicle and disconnect speedometer cable.
22. Remove shift cable brackets from transaxle.
23. Disconnect oil cooler lines from transaxle.
24. Remove starter motor, then remove dust cover from torque converter housing.
25. Remove torque converter to flywheel attaching nuts.
26. Secure transaxle to a suitable transmission support jack.
27. Remove remaining transaxle to engine attaching bolts, then lower transaxle from vehicle. Ensure torque converter studs are clear of flywheel before lowering transaxle.
28. Reverse procedure to install. Note the following during installation:
    a. Before installing transaxle, clean oil cooler and lines with a suitable torque converter cleaner.
    b. Use new circlips when installing half shafts to transaxle.
    c. When installing lower ball joint to steering knuckle, **torque** nut to 37-44 ft. lbs.
    d. When installing transaxle and torque converter to engine, ensure converter to transaxle engagement is maintained. A distance of 7/16 to 9/16 inch from converter pilot to engine mounting surface must be maintained.
    e. After installing transaxle, adjust linkages and check transaxle fluid level.

## TIGHTENING SPECIFICATIONS

| Component | Torque/Ft. Lbs. |
|---|---|
| Converter Drain Plug | 8–12 |
| Cooler Tube Fitting To Case | 18–23 |
| Differential Retainer To Case | 15–19 |
| Filler Tube Bracket To Case | 7–9 |
| Filter To Case | 7–9 |
| Idler Shaft Attaching Nut | 110–130 |
| Inner Manual Lever To Shaft Nut | 32–48 |
| Neutral Safety Switch To Case | 7–9 |
| Oil Pan To Case | 15–19 |
| Pressure Test Port Plugs To Case | 8–11 |
| Pump Assembly To Case | 7–9 |
| Pump Support To Pump Body | 6–8 |
| Reactor Support To Case | 6–8 |
| Seperator Plate To Valve Body | 6–8 |
| Transfer Housing To Case | 18–23 |
| TV Adjuster Locknut | 24–36 |
| Valve Body Cover To Case | 7–9 |
| Valve Body To Case | 7–9 |

# Ford AXOD & AXOD-E Automatic Overdrive Transaxle

## INDEX



TRANSMISSION ASSY NO. MIRROR IMAGE PRINT MODEL AND NO.
UD
ASSY E6DP-BA
SN-000001
BD-6D015
BUILD DATE
SERIAL NO.
AAAB1000001

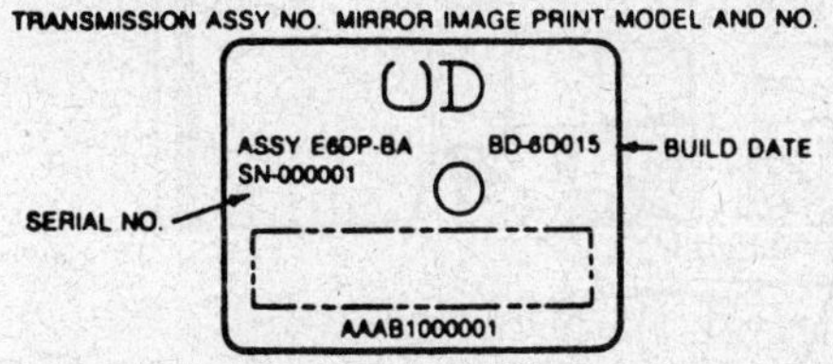

**Fig. 1 Identification tag. 1989**

## TRANSAXLE IDENTIFICATION

The identification tags, **Fig. 1 and 2,** located on top of the converter housing, includes transaxle assembly number, serial number and build date. For interpretation of these numbers, refer to Ford Master Parts Catalog.

## DESCRIPTION

The AXOD and AXOD-E transaxle, **Fig. 3,** has two planetary gear sets and a combination planetary/differential gear set. Four multiple plate clutches, two band assemblies and two one-way clutches act together for proper operation of the planetary gear sets.

A lockup torque converter is coupled to the engine crankshaft and transmits engine power to the gear train by means of a drive link assembly (chain) that connects the drive and driven sprockets. Converter clutch application is controlled through an electronic control integrated in the on-board EEC-IV system. These controls, along with the hydraulic controls in the valve body, operate a piston plate clutch in the torque converter to provide improved fuel economy by eliminating converter slip when applied.

## MAIN COMPONENTS & FUNCTIONS

### TORQUE CONVERTER

#### Converter

The torque converter couples the engine to the turbine shaft. It also provides torque multiplication and absorbs engine shock of gear shifting.

#### Piston Plate Clutch & Damper Assembly

The piston plate clutch and damper assembly transmit engine power to the turbine from the converter cover during lockup.

#### Converter Cover

The converter cover transmits power from the engine into the converter. Also, the oil pump driveshaft is splined to the converter cover.

#### Turbine

The turbine is splined to the drive sprocket turbine shaft and driven by fluid by the impeller.

#### Impeller

The impeller is driven by the converter cover, together with the reactor it supplies torque multiplication.

#### Reactor

The reactor, also called the stator, contains a one-way clutch to hold it stationary only when "reaction" is required. It also causes hydraulic reaction during torque multiplication.

### GEAR TRAIN

#### Forward Clutch

The forward clutch locks the driven sprocket to the low one-way clutch.

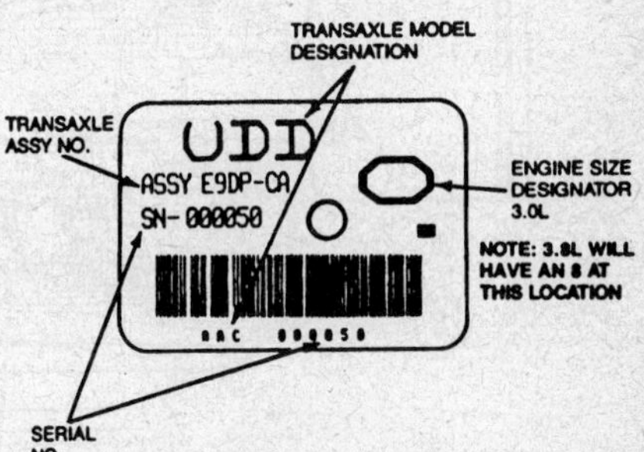


**Fig. 2 Identification tag. 1990–91**

#### Low One-Way Clutch

The low one-way clutch transmits torque from the driven sprocket to the sun gear of the forward planetary gear set in first gear. It also provides engine braking in third gear in connection with the forward clutch.

#### Overdrive Band

The overdrive band holds the sun gear of the forward planetary gear set stationary in fourth gear (overdrive).

#### Direct Clutch

The direct clutch locks the sun gear of the planetary assembly of the forward planetary gear set to the direct one-way clutch in third gear.

#### Direct One-Way Clutch

The direct one-way clutch transmits torque from the driven sprocket to the sun gear of the forward planetary gear set in third gear, and provides engine braking in manual low.

#### Intermediate Clutch

The intermediate clutch locks the driven sprocket to the planetary assembly of the

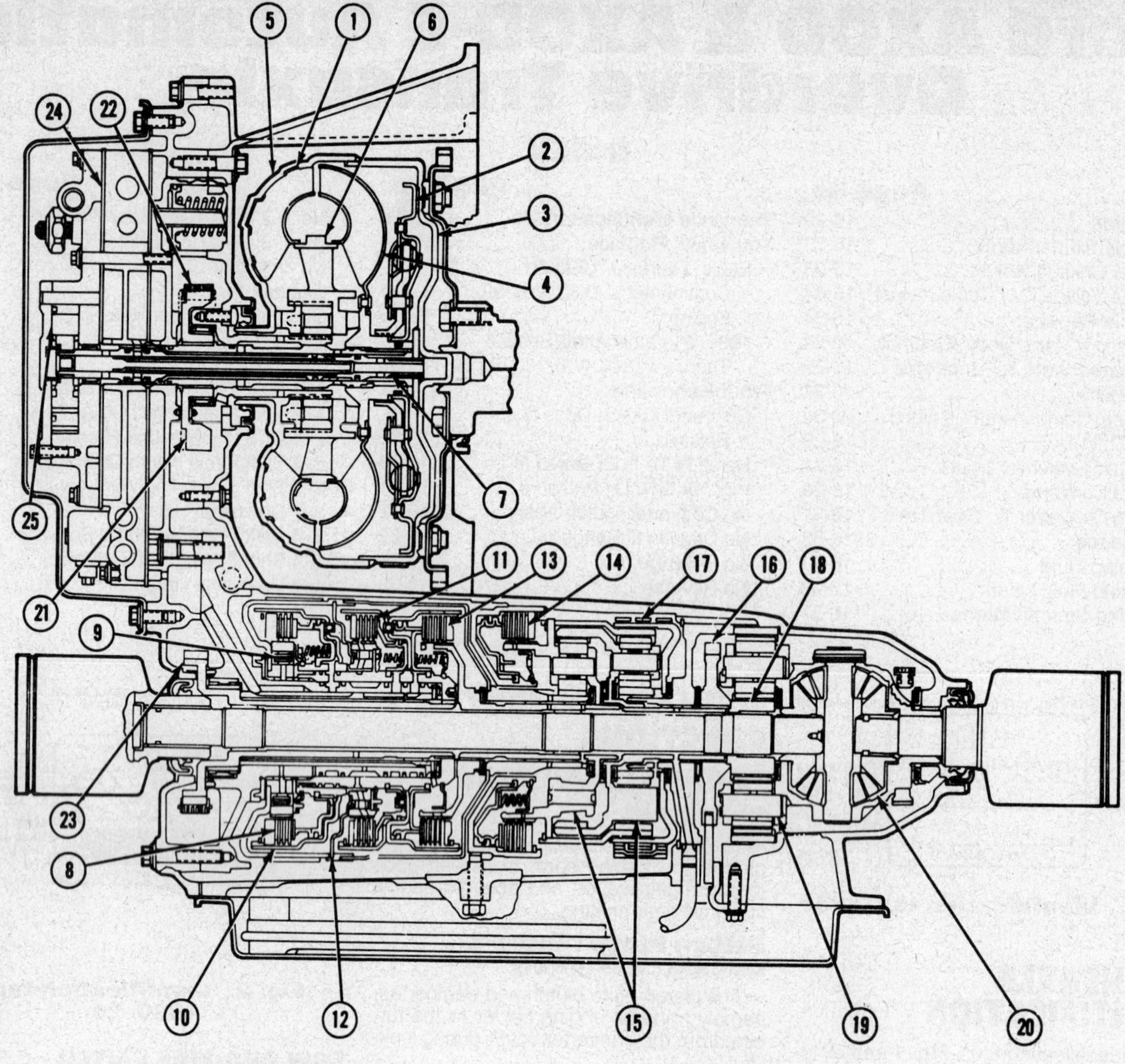


1. TORQUE CONVERTER
2. CONVERTER CLUTCH (PISTON PLATE CLUTCH AND DAMPER ASSEMBLY)
3. CONVERTER COVER
4. TURBINE
5. IMPELLER
6. REACTOR
7. OIL PUMP DRIVESHAFT
8. FORWARD CLUTCH
9. LOW ONE-WAY CLUTCH
10. OVERDRIVE BAND
11. DIRECT CLUTCH
12. DIRECT ONE-WAY CLUTCH
13. INTERMEDIATE CLUTCH
14. REVERSE CLUTCH
15. PLANETARY GEARS
16. PARKING GEAR
17. LOW-INTERMEDIATE BAND
18. FINAL DRIVE SUN GEAR
19. FINAL DRIVE PLANET
20. DIFFERENTIAL ASSEMBLY
21. DRIVE SPROCKET
22. DRIVE LINK ASSEMBLY (CHAIN)
23. DRIVEN SPROCKET
24. VALVE BODY (MAIN CONTROL ASSEMBLY)
25. OIL PUMP

**Fig. 3 Sectional view of Ford AXOD automatic transaxle**

forward planetary gear set in second and third gear.

## Reverse Clutch

The reverse clutch holds the planetary assembly of the forward planetary gear set, and the ring gear of the rear planetary gear set stationary in reverse gear.

## Planetary Gears

Two planetary gear sets are used to provide four forward speeds, including reverse, depending upon clutch and/or band applications.

## Parking Gear

The parking gear allows the output (axle) shaft to be mechanically locked by the parking pawl anchored in the case.

## Low Intermediate Band

The low intermediate band holds the sun gear of the rear planetary gear set stationary in low, first and second gears.

## Final Drive Sun Gear

The final drive sun gear transfers torque from the transmission output to the final drive planetary assembly.

## Final Drive Planet

The final drive planet drives the differential assembly.

## Differential Assembly

The differential assembly drives the

front axle shafts and provides the differential action if driving wheels are turning at different speeds.

## TORQUE CONVERTER TO GEAR TRAIN

### Drive Sprocket

The drive sprocket transmits power from the converter to the drive link assembly (chain).

### Drive Link Assembly (Chain)

The drive link assembly transmits converter power to the gear train.

## HYDRAULIC SYSTEM

### Valve Body

The valve body or main control assembly directs fluid (oil) under pressure to the torque converter, band servos, clutches and governor to control transaxle operation.

### Oil Pump

The oil pump provides a supply of fluid (oil) under pressure to operate, lubricate and cool the transaxle. The pump is a variable capacity vane and rotor pump with output flow proportional to demand. It is located within the transaxle control valve and pump assembly.

### Overdrive Servo

The overdrive servo applies overdrive band in fourth gear.

### Low-Intermediate Servo

The low-intermediate servo applies low-intermediate band in manual, low, first and second gears.

### Governor

The governor provides a "road speed" signal to the hydraulic control system for shift control, and is driven by a gear on the differential assembly.

### Reservoir

Two reservoir areas are used to control oil level, dependent on fluid temperature. Along with the lower sump, a fluid reservoir is located in the lower section of the valve body cover. As fluid temperature in the reservoir increases, a thermostatic element closes, retaining fluid in the upper reservoir.

## ELECTRICAL COMPONENT FUNCTION

### Neutral Pressure Switch (NPS)

The NPS signals the EEC-IV of transaxle engagement shift into R or D for engine control functions.

### 3/2 Pressure Switch

The 3/2 pressure switch signals the EEC-IV of hydraulic transaxle gear shifts for bypass clutch solenoid control. Detects 3-2 shift.

### 4/3 Pressure Switch

The 4/3 pressure switch signals the EEC-IV of hydraulic transaxle gear shifts for bypass clutch solenoid control. Detects 4-3 shift.

### Bypass Clutch Solenoid

The bypass clutch solenoid applies the torque converter bypass clutch when energized or releases it when de-energized.

## DOWNSHIFTS

Under certain conditions the transaxle will downshift automatically to a lower gear range without moving the shift selector lever. There are three different types of downshift categories:

### Coastdown

The coastdown downshift occurs when vehicle is coasting down to a stop.

### Torque Demand

The torque demand downshift occurs during part throttle acceleration when demand for torque is greater than the engine can provide at that gear ratio. The axle will disengage the converter clutch to provide added acceleration, if applied.

### Kickdown

The kickdown downshift occurs when the accelerator pedal is depressed fully to the floor. A forced downshift into second gear is possible below 55 mph. Below approximately 25 mph a forced kickdown to first gear will occur. All shift speed specifications will vary due to tire size and engine calibration requirements.

# TROUBLESHOOTING

## OIL LEAK

1. Side or bottom pan attaching bolts incorrectly torqued.
2. Side or bottom pan gasket or pan rail damaged.
3. Side or bottom pan distorted.
4. T.V. cable, fill tube or electrical connector loose or damaged.
5. Manual shaft seal damaged.
6. Governor or servo cover O-ring seal damaged.
7. Cooler fittings or pressure taps incorrectly torqued or damaged.
8. Converter weld seal leaking.
9. Cooler or converter seal damaged or garter spring missing.
10. Half shaft seals damaged or garter spring missing.
11. Speedometer cable or speed sensor O-ring seal damaged.

## OIL VENTING OR FOAMING

1. Transaxle overfilled.
2. Transaxle fluid contaminated with antifreeze or engine overheating.
3. Bi-metallic element stuck open.
4. Oil filter O-ring damaged.

## HIGH OR LOW OIL PRESSURE

1. Incorrect oil level.
2. T.V. cable/linkage stuck or damaged.
3. Pressure regulator spring damaged.
4. Pressure regulator valve or valve bore nicked or scored.
5. Pressure relief valve damaged or relief valve ball and/or spring missing.
6. Oil pump slide stuck.
7. Oil pump seals and/or vanes damaged.
8. Oil pump driveshaft broken or damaged.

## NO 1–2 SHIFT (FIRST GEAR ONLY)

1. Governor assembly weights binding.
2. Governor assembly springs and gears damaged.
3. Governor shaft seal missing or damaged.
4. Governor valve (ball) stuck or missing.
5. Governor tube leaking or damaged.
6. Intermediate clutch plates damaged or missing.
7. Intermediate clutch assembly piston or seals damaged.
8. Intermediate clutch check ball assembly stuck or missing.
9. Intermediate clutch cylinder damaged.
10. Direct/intermediate clutch hub seals damaged or missing.
11. Direct/intermediate clutch hub holes blocked.
12. Driven sprocket support seals damaged or missing.
13. Driven sprocket support holes blocked.
14. 1-2 shift valve stuck, nicked or damaged.
15. 1-2 throttle delay valve stuck, nicked or damaged.
16. 1-2 accumulator capacity modulator valve stuck, nicked or damaged.
17. Number 9 check ball missing.
18. Control assembly attaching bolts incorrectly torqued.
19. Carrier damaged.
20. Intermediate clutch tap plug loose or missing.

## 1–2 SHIFT FEELS HARSH OR SOFT

1. Incorrect oil pressure.
2. 1-2 accumulator regulator valve stuck, nicked or damaged.
3. 1-2 accumulator regulator valve spring missing or damaged.
4. 1-2 accumulator capacity modulator valve stuck, nicked or damaged.
5. 1-2 accumulator capacity modulator valve spring missing or damaged.
6. 1-2 accumulator assembly piston stuck or damaged.
7. 1-2 accumulator assembly seal damaged or missing.
8. 1-2 accumulator assembly springs damaged or missing.

## 1–2 SHIFT SPEED HIGH OR LOW

1. Governor weights binding.
2. Governor springs and gear damaged.
3. Governor shaft seal or valve stuck or missing.

4. Governor tube leaking or damaged.
5. T.V. control valve, T.V. plunger, T.V. line modulator valve and 1-2 throttle delay valve stuck, nicked or damaged.
6. T.V. control valve, T.V. plunger, T.V. line modulator valve and 1-2 throttle delay valve springs missing or damaged.

## NO 2–3 SHIFT (1–2 SHIFT OK)

1. Governor weights binding.
2. Governor springs and gear damaged.
3. Governor shaft seal or valve stuck or missing.
4. Governor tube leaking or missing.
5. Low/intermediate servo apply rod too long.
6. Low/intermediate servo bore or piston damaged.
7. Low/intermediate piston seals damaged or missing.
8. Low/intermediate servo return spring or retaining clip missing or broken.
9. Direct clutch plates damaged or missing.
10. Direct clutch piston or seals damaged.
11. Direct clutch check ball assembly stuck or missing.
12. Direct clutch cylinder damaged.
13. Direct/intermediate clutch hub seals damaged or missing.
14. Direct/intermediate clutch hub holes blocked.
15. Driven sprocket support seals damaged or missing.
16. Driven sprocket support holes blocked.
17. Direct one-way clutch assembly cage, rollers or springs damaged.
18. Direct one-way clutch assembly rollers missing.
19. Direct one-way clutch assembly inner race incorrectly assembled.
20. Control assembly attaching bolts incorrectly torqued.
21. 2-3 shift valve stuck, nicked or damaged.
22. Number 4 check ball missing.
23. Bypass solenoid not energized during wide open throttle upshift.
24. Case servo release passage blocked.
25. Servo release tube leaking or improperly installed.
26. Direct clutch pressure tap plug loose or missing.

## 2–3 SHIFT FEELS HARSH OR SOFT

1. Low oil pressure.
2. Low/intermediate servo apply rod length incorrect.
3. Low/intermediate servo piston, seal, springs and rod damaged.
4. 2-3 servo regulator valve stuck, nicked or damaged.
5. 2-3 servo regulator valve spring damaged.
6. Back-out valve stuck, nicked or damaged.
7. Back-out valve spring damaged.

## 2–3 SHIFT SPEED HIGH OR LOW

1. Governor weights binding.
2. Governor springs and gear damaged.
3. Governor shaft seal or valve damaged or missing.
4. Governor tube leaking or damaged.
5. T.V. cable damaged or disconnected.
6. T.V. control valve, T.V. plunger, T.V. line modulator valve and 2-3 throttle modulator valve stuck, nicked or damaged.
7. T.V. control valve, T.V. plunger, T.V. line modulator valve and 2-3 throttle modulator valve springs missing or damaged.
8. Governor tube leaking.

## NO 3–4 SHIFT

1. Governor weights binding.
2. Governor springs and gear damaged.
3. Governor shaft seal or valve leaking or missing.
4. Overdrive band assembly not holding.
5. Overdrive servo assembly apply rod too long.
6. Overdrive servo bore or piston damaged.
7. Overdrive servo assembly piston seals damaged or missing.
8. Overdrive servo assembly return spring or retaining clip missing or broken.
9. Forward clutch assembly return springs and piston damaged.
10. Front ring gear damaged.
11. Control assembly attaching bolts incorrectly torqued.
12. 3-4 shift valve stuck, nicked or damaged.
13. 3-4 shift valve spring damaged.
14. 3-4 modulator valve stuck, nicked or damaged.
15. 3-4 modulator valve spring missing.
16. 4-3 scheduling valve stuck, nicked or damaged.
17. 4-3 scheduling valve spring missing.

## 3–4 SHIFT FEELS HARSH OR SOFT

1. Incorrect oil pressure.
2. 3-4 accumulator piston stuck or damaged.
3. 3-4 accumulator piston seal missing or damaged.
4. 3-4 accumulator springs missing or damaged.
5. Number 14 check ball missing.

## 3–4 SHIFT SPEED HIGH OR LOW

1. Governor weights binding.
2. Governor springs and gear damaged.
3. Governor shaft seal or valve missing or damaged.
4. Governor tube leaking.
5. T.V. cable damaged or disconnected.
6. T.V. control valve, T.V. plunger, T.V. line modulator valve and 3-4 modulator valve stuck, nicked or damaged.
7. T.V. control valve, T.V. plunger, T.V. line modulator valve and 3-4 modulator valve springs missing or damaged.

## NO CONVERTER CLUTCH APPLY

1. No lockup signal to the electronic engine control.
2. Bypass solenoid damaged or inoperative.
3. Transaxle bulkhead electrical connector damaged or electrical system wires pinched.
4. 3-2 or 4-3 pressure switch inoperative.
5. Converter clutch blow off check ball not seating or damaged.
6. Turbine shaft seals damaged.
7. Bypass clutch control valve stuck.
8. Bypass clutch control valve plunger stuck.
9. Pump shaft seals missing or damaged.
10. Valve body pilot sleeve damaged or incorrectly aligned.

## CONVERTER CLUTCH DOES NOT RELEASE

1. No unlock signal to the electronic engine control.
2. Bypass solenoid damaged or inoperative.
3. Bypass clutch control valve or plunger valve stuck, nicked or damaged.

## 2–1 OR 3–1 DOWNSHIFT HARSH

1. Low/intermediate servo piston or seal damaged.
2. Low/intermediate servo assembly springs missing or damaged.
3. Low/intermediate servo apply rod length incorrect.
4. Number 9 check ball missing (3-1 only).

## 3–2 DOWNSHIFT HARSH

1. Low/intermediate servo assembly springs missing or damaged.
2. Low/intermediate servo apply rod length incorrect.
3. 3-2 control valve stuck, nicked or damaged.
4. Number 5 check ball missing.

## 4–3 DOWNSHIFT HARSH

1. Overdrive servo assembly apply rod length incorrect.
2. Overdrive servo piston or seal damaged.
3. Overdrive servo assembly springs missing or damaged.

## NO DRIVE IN D RANGE

1. Low oil level.
2. Low oil pressure.
3. Linkage improperly adjusted, disconnected, damaged, broken or bent.
4. T.V. linkage disconnected or missing.
5. Oil pump worn or damaged.
6. Oil pump driveshaft damaged.
7. Drive chain assembly damaged or broken.
8. Drive sprocket shaft to converter turbine spline damaged.

9. Driven sprocket shaft to direct/intermediate clutch hub damaged.
10. Forward clutch plates burned or missing.
11. Forward clutch piston seals or pistons damaged.
12. Forward clutch check ball assembly missing or damaged.
13. Forward clutch driven sprocket support seals damaged or missing.
14. Forward clutch oil holes blocked.
15. Forward clutch direct intermediate hub seals damaged or missing.
16. Low one-way clutch improperly assembled or damaged sprag.
17. Front sun gear/shell damaged.
18. Front and rear carrier pistons/lugs to rear ring gear damaged.
19. Rear ring gear/lugs to forward carrier damaged.
20. Low/intermediate band assembly burned or broken.
21. Low/intermediate servo assembly apply rod too short.
22. Low/intermediate servo assembly piston, seal or rod damaged.
23. Low/intermediate servo oil tubes damaged.
24. Final drive assembly or final drive sun gear shaft pistons or gears damaged.
25. Output shaft incorrectly aligned with axles or damaged shaft splines.
26. Half shaft disengaged from transaxle or damaged shaft splines.

## NO REVERSE

1. Low oil level or pressure.
2. Linkage improperly adjusted, disconnected, damaged, broken or bent.
3. T.V. linkage disconnected or missing.
4. Oil pump worn or damaged.
5. Oil pump driveshaft damaged.
6. Drive chain assembly damaged or broken.
7. Drive sprocket shaft to converter turbine spline damaged.
8. Driven sprocket shaft to direct/intermediate clutch hub damaged.
9. Reverse clutch plates missing or burned.
10. Forward clutch plates missing or burned.
11. Forward clutch piston seals or pistons damaged.
12. Forward clutch check ball assembly missing or damaged.
13. Forward clutch driven sprocket support seals damaged or missing.
14. Forward clutch oil holes blocked.
15. Forward clutch direct intermediate hub seals damaged or missing.
16. Low one-way clutch improperly assembled or damaged sprag.
17. Front and rear carrier pistons/lugs to rear ring gear damaged.
18. Reverse apply tube leaking or improperly installed.

## NO P RANGE

1. Chipped or broken parking pawl or park gear.
2. Broken park pawl return spring.
3. Bent or broken actuating rod.
4. Manual linkage improperly adjusted.

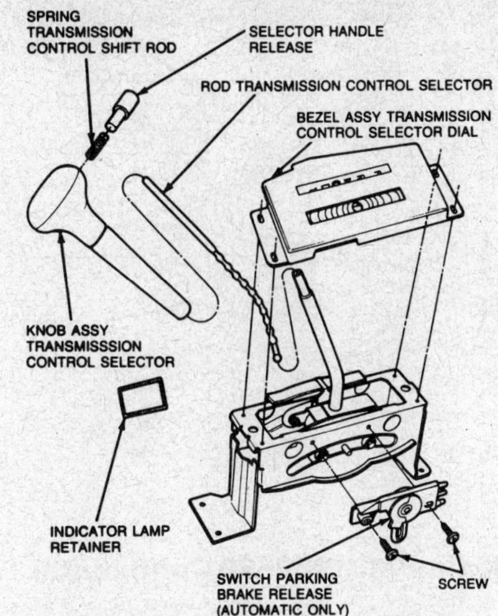


**Fig. 4 Manual control cable adjustment. Sable & Taurus**

## HARSH N TO R OR HARSH N TO D

1. Low/intermediate servo assembly springs damaged or missing.
2. Low/intermediate servo apply rod length incorrect.
3. 3-2 control valve stuck, nicked or damaged.
4. Number 5 ball missing.
5. N/D accumulator piston stuck.
6. N/D accumulator seal damaged or missing.
7. N/D accumulator springs damaged or missing.
8. Number 1 check ball missing.
9. Main control separator plate thermal elements do not close when warm.

## TRANSAXLE OVERHEATS

1. Excessive tow loads.
2. Incorrect fluid level.
3. Incorrect engine idle or performance.
4. Incorrect clutch or band application or oil pressure control system.
5. Restriction in cooler or lines.
6. Seized converter one-way clutch.
7. Dirty or sticking valve body.

## TRANSAXLE FLUID LEAKS

1. Incorrect oil level.
2. Defective gaskets, seals, etc.

# MAINTENANCE

Ford Motor Company recommends the use of Mercon type automatic transmission fluid in this transmission. If Mercon type fluid is not available, Type H automatic transmission fluid maybe used. Use of a fluid other than specified may result in transmission malfunction or failure.

## CHECKING FLUID LEVEL

1. Start engine and allow to reach normal operating temperature.
2. Move transaxle selector lever through each range, allowing enough time in each range for transaxle to engage. Return selector lever to the P position and apply parking brake. **Do not turn engine off during fluid level check.**
3. Clean all dirt from transaxle fluid dipstick cap before removing dipstick from filler tube.
4. Remove dipstick from tube and wipe it clean, then push it all the way back into the tube. Ensure dipstick is fully seated.
5. Pull dipstick out of tube and check fluid level. Fluid should be between the arrows.
6. If necessary, add fluid through the filler tube to raise level to the correct position. **Adding approximately 8 ounces of fluid will raise level from bottom arrow to top arrow. Use caution not to overfill transaxle.**

## CHANGING FLUID

Normal maintenance and lubrication requirements do not necessitate periodic fluid change. If vehicle is operated under abnormal conditions, fluid should be changed every 30,000 miles. If major failure has occurred in the transaxle, it will have to be removed for service. At this time, the converter should be thoroughly flushed to remove any foreign matter.

1. Raise and support vehicle, then position a suitable drain pan under transaxle.
2. Loosen pump and valve body cover attaching bolts and drain oil.
3. Loosen lower oil pan attaching bolts and drain fluid from transaxle.
4. When fluid has drained to the level of the oil pan flange, remove pan attaching bolts working from the righthand side, allowing pan to drop and drain slowly.
5. When fluid has stopped draining, remove and clean pan and screen. Discard pan gasket.
6. Install pan using a new gasket.
7. Tighten pump and valve body cover attaching bolts, then refill transaxle to correct level.

# IN-VEHICLE ADJUSTMENTS

## MANUAL LINKAGE, ADJUST

### Sable & Taurus

1. Position selector lever in the Overdrive position against rearward stop, **Fig. 4. Shift lever should be held in the rearward position while linkage is being adjusted.**
2. Loosen manual lever to control cable attaching nut.
3. Place transaxle lever in the Overdrive position, second detent from most rearward position, then **torque** cable attaching nut to 12-20 ft. lbs. on 1989-90 models.
4. Check operation of transaxle in each selector position. Ensure park and neutral switch operates satisfactorily.

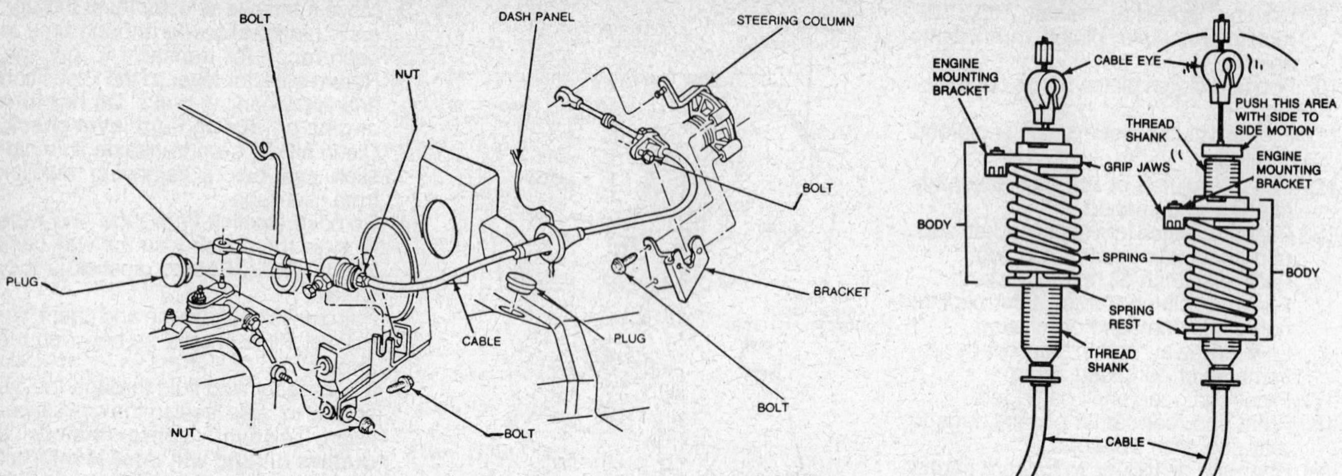


**Fig. 5 Manual control cable adjustment. 1989–90 Continental**

**Fig. 6 T.V. cable adjustment**

### 1989–90 Continental

1. Disconnect control cable from transaxle lever pivot ball, **Fig. 5.**
2. Loosen cable trunnion adjusting bolt located at transaxle retaining bracket, then free cable from trunnion.
3. Place transaxle shift lever in Overdrive position. Place an 8 pound weight on transaxle shift lever to lever in position.
4. Rotate transaxle lever clockwise to low position, then rotate counterclockwise to Overdrive position.
5. Connect control cable to transaxle lever pivot ball.
6. **Torque** cable adjusting screw on trunnion to 11 to 14 ft. lbs.

## THROTTLE VALVE (T.V.) CABLE, ADJUST

**The following procedure has been revised by a Technical Service Bulletin.**

The T.V. cable normal does not require adjustment. The only time cable should be adjusted is if one of the following components is replaced: main control assembly, T.V. cable, T.V. cable engine mounting bracket, throttle control lever link or lever assembly, engine throttle body or transaxle assembly.

The T.V cable adjuster spring rest consists of two pieces, (180° segments.)

1. Span the crack between these two segments **Fig. 6,** using a screwdriver.
2. Compress the spring by pushing the rod with your hand bearing on both segments of the spring rest.
3. While spring is compressed, push white shank toward spring with your index and middle fingers.
4. Unclip T.V. cable from righthand intake manifold clip.
5. Rotate throttle body primary lever to wide open throttle.
6. Clip the T.V. cable into top position of righthand intake manifold clip.

DO NOT REMOVE THIS BOLT

REMOVE 22 8mm VALVE BODY BOLTS INDICATED BY ARROWS

DO NOT REMOVE SIX OIL PUMP COVER BOLTS

DO NOT REMOVE THIS BOLT

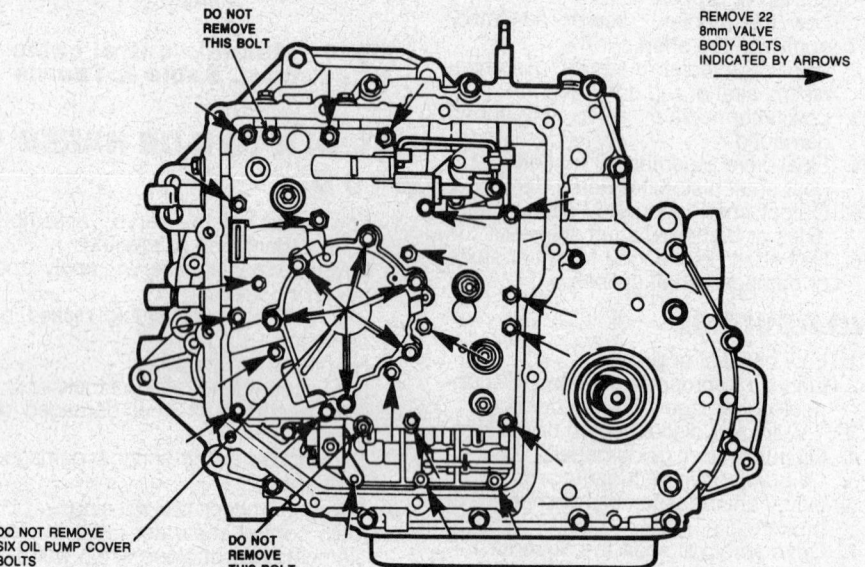

**Fig. 7 Removing oil pump & valve body attaching bolts. AXOD**

# IN-VEHICLE REPAIRS

## OIL PUMP & VALVE BODY ASSEMBLY

### AXOD

#### Removal

1. Disconnect battery ground cable, then remove battery and battery tray.
2. Remove air cleaner assembly, then position all hoses, vacuum lines and wiring away from pump and valve body cover.
3. Raise and support vehicle, then support engine and transaxle assembly using a suitable jack.
4. Remove lefthand engine mounts and supports.
5. Loosen pump and valve body cover attaching bolts and drain transaxle fluid. After fluid has drained, remove cover and gasket.
6. Remove 22 pump and valve body attaching bolts, **Fig. 7.**
7. Pull pump and valve body assembly out enough to clear throttle valve bracket, then rotate valve body clockwise and disconnect manual valve link, **Fig. 8.**
8. Remove pump and valve body assembly from vehicle.

#### Installation

1. Install new pump and valve body to chain cover guide.
2. Slide pump and valve body assembly into oil pump shaft.
3. Rotate pump and valve body assembly toward dash panel, then engage manual valve link with manual valve.
4. Rotate or jiggle pump and valve body assembly to engage spline on oil pump shaft with splines on oil pump rotor. Valve body should slide flush onto chain cover without force. If full engagement of the pump and valve body is not obtained, perform one of the two following methods:
   a. Rotate engine using 7/8 inch deep

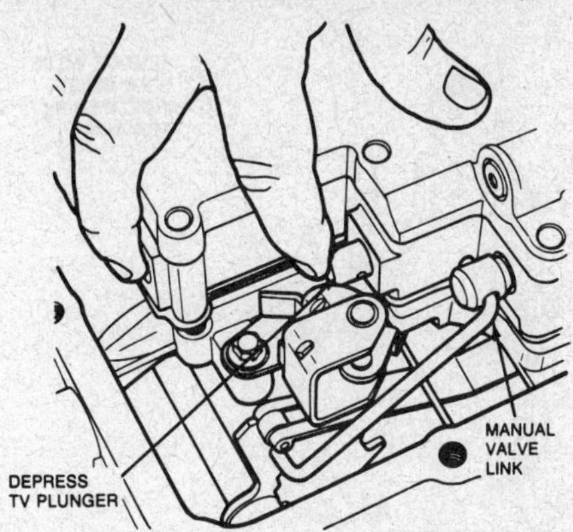


**Fig. 8 Disconnecting manual valve link. AXOD**

well socket on the crankshaft pulley to complete engagement of the pump shaft to pump.

b. Remove manual valve from valve body, then rotate assembly as necessary to allow full engagement of pump shaft to pump.

5. Using valve body alignment pin tool No. T86P-70100-C or equivalent to position valve body, install pump and valve body attaching bolts. **Torque** attaching bolts to 7-9 ft. lbs. in the sequence shown in **Fig. 9. Use caution not to use attaching bolts to draw pump and valve body into position.**
6. Install pump, valve body cover and new gasket. **Torque** cover attaching bolts to 10-12 ft. lbs.
7. Install lefthand engine mounts and supports, then remove engine and transaxle supporting jack and lower vehicle.
8. Reconnect all hoses and electrical connectors, then install air cleaner, battery and battery tray.
9. Fill transaxle with suitable oil, then start engine and ensure transaxle operates properly.

## AXOD-E

### Removal

1. Disconnect battery ground cable, then remove battery and battery tray.
2. Disconnect electrical connectors from engine.
3. Position all hoses, vacuum lines and wiring away from pump and valve body cover.
4. Remove shift lever, then two bolts attaching manual lever shift position sensor.
5. Remove splash shield cover from ABS, if equipped.
6. Remove brake reservoir hose from ABS, then cap ends to prevent contaimination.
7. Remove EGR bracket retaining bolt and install lifting eye. **Do not remove two bolts that retain oil pump and valve body assembly together.**
8. Remove throttle body bracket retaining bolt, then install lifting eye.
9. Remove righthand transaxle mount and radiator sight shield.
10. Remove transaxle side pan upper retaining bolts, then remove rear transaxle mount bolt.
11. Raise and support vehicle, then remove left front wheel and tire assembly.
12. Disconnect ride height sensor, then remove attaching bolt from sensor bracket.
13. Remove inner fender cover and position aside.
14. Loosen lefthand subframe retaining bolts, then remove two engine support mount bolts.
15. Remove lefthand engine mounts and supports.
16. Remove transaxle side pan bolts and drain transaxle fluid, then remove pan.
17. Using a screwdriver, position manual shift shaft in park position.
18. Disconnect upper bulkhead connector wiring retainer clip from valve body.
19. Disconnect electrical connectors, then remove valve body attaching bolts, **Fig. 10.**
20. Disengage linkage and remove valve body. **Do not remove oil pump cover bolts.**

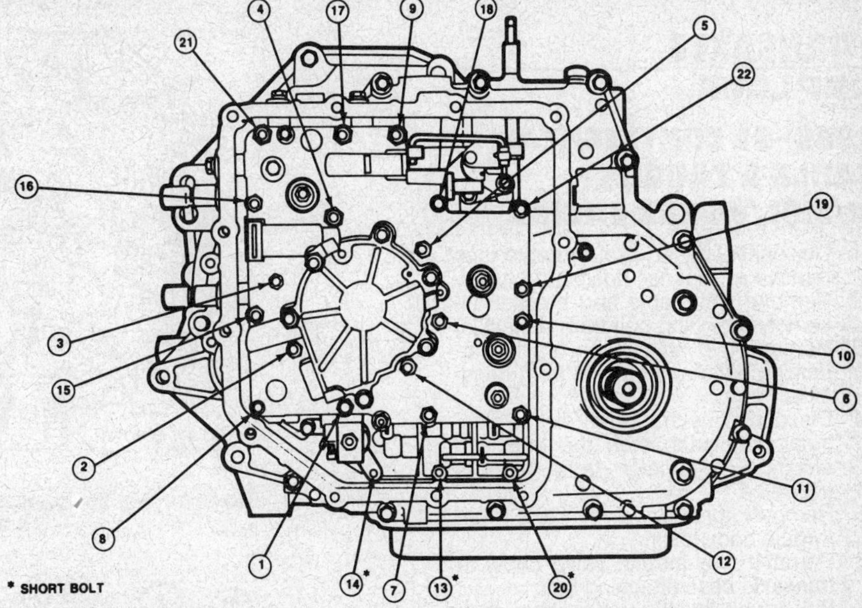


**Fig. 9 Installing oil pump & valve body attaching bolts. AXOD**

### Installation

1. Install new pump and valve body to chain cover gasket.
2. Slide pump and valve body assembly into oil pump shaft.
3. Rotate pump and valve body assembly toward dash panel, then engage manual valve link with manual valve.
4. Rotate or jiggle pump and valve body assembly to engage spline on oil pump shaft with splines on oil pump rotor. Valve body should slide flush onto chain cover without force. On vehicles without anti-skid brakes. If full engagement of the pump and valve body is not obtained, perform one of the two following methods:

a. Rotate engine using 7/8 inch deep well socket on the crankshaft pulley to complete engagement of the pump shaft to pump.

b. Remove manual valve from valve body, then rotate assembly as necessary to allow full engagement of pump shaft to pump.

5. Using valve body alignment pin tool No. T86P-70100-C or equivalent to position valve body, install pump and valve body attaching bolts. **Torque** attaching bolts to 7-9 ft. lbs. in the sequence shown in **Fig. 11. Use caution not to use attaching bolts to draw pump and valve body into position.**
6. Install new gasket, then connect upper bulkhead connector wiring to valve body.
7. Carefully install side pan, then loosely install two upper pan bolts.
8. Ensure gasket in proper position, then install remaining pan bolts. **Torque** to 14-16 ft. lbs.
9. Install lefthand engine mounts and supports.
10. **Torque** lefthand subframe bolts to 40-50 ft. lbs.
11. Connect ride height sensor, then install inner fender cover.
12. Install lefthand wheel and tire assembly, then remove engine and transaxle assembly supporting jack and lower vehicle.
13. Install radiator sight shield, then remove lifting eyes.
14. Install throttle body bracket and EGR bracket.
15. Reconnect all hoses and electrical connectors, then install manual lever position sensor.
16. Install air cleaner, battery and battery tray.
17. Fill transaxle with suitable oil, then start engine and ensure transaxle operates properly.

# TRANSAXLE REPLACE

## 1989–91 CONTINENTAL, SABLE & TAURUS w/3.0L/V6-182 ENGINE

1. Disconnect battery ground cable, then remove air cleaner, hoses and tubes.
2. Remove shift cable and bracket assembly attaching bolt from transaxle.
3. Remove two shift cable bracket attaching bolts and bracket from transaxle.
4. Disconnect neutral safety switch electrical connector, then the bulkhead electrical connector from rear of transaxle.
5. Remove throttle valve cable from throttle body lever.
6. Remove one throttle valve cable to transaxle case attaching bolt.
7. Pull up on throttle valve cable, then disconnect cable from link. **Use care to avoid bending internal throttle valve bracket.**
8. Remove lefthand engine support strut attaching bolt, if equipped, then the four torque converter housing attaching bolts from top of transaxle.
9. Install suitable engine support fixture to three engine lift points, then raise engine slightly to relieve weight from engine mounts.
10. Raise and support vehicle, then remove both front wheels.
11. Remove each tie rod end from its spindle.
12. Remove both lower ball joint attaching bolts, then the lower ball joint.
13. Remove lower control arms from each spindle, then the stabilizer bar attaching nuts.
14. Remove two rack and pinion to sub-frame attaching bolts.
15. Remove two engine mount attaching bolts, then disconnect exhaust gas oxygen (EGO) sensor.
16. Remove exhaust Y-pipe from engine and rear portion of exhaust system.
17. Remove four bolts from sub-frame attaching points, then two bolts from lefthand engine support mount. Lower sub-frame from vehicle.
18. Position suitable jack under transaxle oil pan, then remove vehicle speed sensor from transaxle. Vehicles with electronic instrument clusters do not use a speedometer cable.
19. Remove two transaxle mount attaching bolts.
20. Remove four lefthand engine support attaching bolts, then the support.
21. Remove separator plate attaching bolts.
22. Remove two starter attaching bolts and position starter aside.
23. Remove separator plate.
24. Rotate engine with a 1/2 inch drive socket and a 7/8 inch deep well socket on crankshaft pulley bolt to align torque converter bolts with starter drive hole.

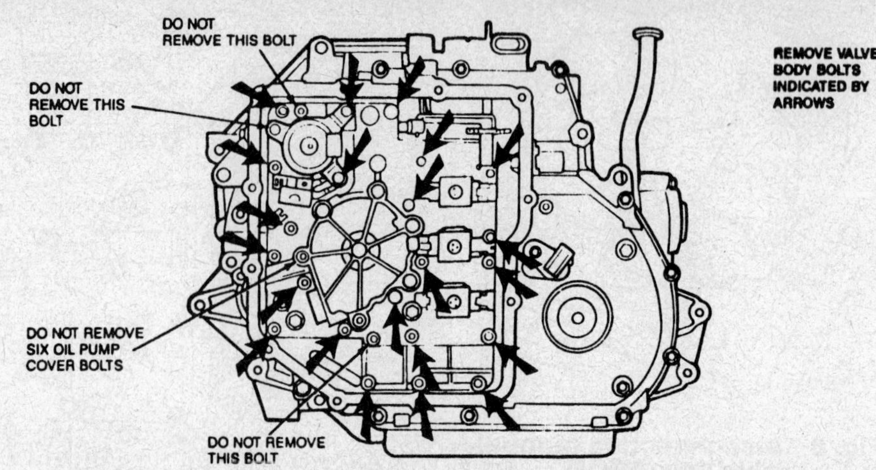


**Fig. 10 Removing oil pump & valve body attaching bolts. AXOD-E**

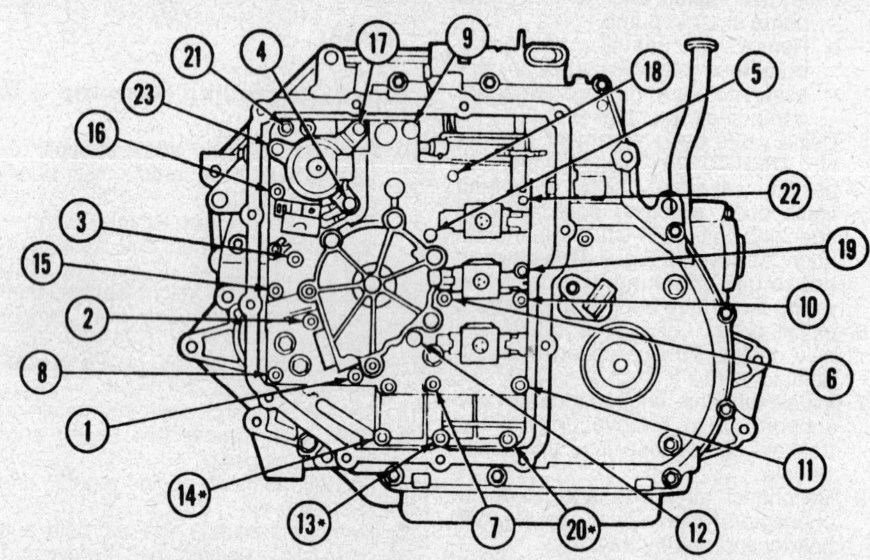


**Fig. 11 Installing oil pump & valve body attaching bolts. AXOD-E**

25. Remove four torque converter to flywheel attaching nuts, then disconnect transaxle cooler lines.
26. Remove half shafts as follows:
    a. Screw extension tool No. T86P-3514-A2 or equivalent into CV joint puller tool No. T86P-3514-A1 or equivalent and install slide hammer tool No. D79P-100-A or equivalent into extension.
    b. Position puller behind CV joint and remove joint.
27. Remove two remaining torque converter housing attaching bolts.
28. Separate transaxle from engine, then lower transaxle from vehicle.
29. Reverse procedure to install.

## SABLE, TAURUS & 1990–91 CONTINENTAL w/3.8L/V6-232 ENGINE

1. Disconnect battery ground cable.
2. Remove air cleaner assembly.
3. Disconnect neutral start switch electrical connector.
4. Remove retaining bolts from transaxle selector bracket and position bracket aside.
5. Remove oil level indicator, then disconnect throttle valve control cable.
6. Remove Thermactor exhaust air supply pump, then install engine lifting eye.
7. Disconnect power steering pump pressure and return line bracket.
8. Remove transmission support assembly, then install engine support fixture.
9. Raise and support vehicle. **On models equipped with air suspension, ensure battery ground cable is disconnected or turn off switch in luggage compartment.**
10. Remove front wheel and tire assemblies.
11. Remove engine drive belts.
12. Disconnect lefthand outer tie rod end.
13. Remove suspension height sensor, then disconnect brake line support

brackets.
14. Remove retaining bolts from front stabilizer bar assembly.
15. Remove brake sensors.
16. Disconnect both side lower arm assemblies.
17. Remove retaining nuts from steering gear assembly and secure aside in vehicle.
18. Disconnect exhaust gas oxygen (EGO) sensor electrical connector.
19. Remove single inlet converter assembly and mounting bracket.
20. Remove both side engine front insulator supports.
21. Position suitable sub-frame removal tool, then remove power steering gear and insulator to sub-frame.
22. Remove sub-frame-to-body retaining bolts, then lower sub-frame from vehicle.
23. Remove starter motor, then the converter housing cover.
24. Disconnect transaxle brace.
25. Disconnect transaxle oil cooler lines, then remove oil cooler from sub-frame.
26. Remove manual control lever bracket and speedometer sensor heat shield.
27. Position transmission jack under transaxle.
28. Remove torque converter-to-flex plate attaching nuts.
29. Remove half shafts as follows:
    a. Screw extension tool No. T86P-3514-A2 or equivalent into CV joint puller tool No. T86P-3514-A1 or equivalent and install slide hammer tool No. D79P-100-A or equivalent into extension.
    b. Position puller behind CV joint and remove joint.
30. Remove engine-to-transaxle attaching bolts.
31. Separate transaxle from engine, then lower transaxle from vehicle.
32. Reverse procedure to install.

## TIGHTENING SPECIFICATIONS

| Component | Torque/Ft. Lbs. |
|---|---|
| Bracket Tubes To Case | 7-9 |
| Brake Hose Routing Clip | 8 |
| Case To Chain Cover (10 mm) | 7-9 |
| Case To Chain Cover (13 mm) | 24-26 |
| Case To Reverse Clutch Nut | 25-35 |
| Case To Reverse Clutch Screw | 7-9 |
| Case To Stator Support | 7-9 |
| Chain Cover To Case (10 mm) | 7-9 |
| Chain Cover To Case (13 mm) | 20-22 |
| Chain Cover To Front Support (7 mm) | 25-35 |
| Chain Cover To Front Support (13 mm) | 20-22 |
| Control Arm To Knuckle | 36-44 |
| Detent Spring To Chain Cover | 7-9 |
| Differential Brace To Case | 26-37 |
| Dust Cover To Case | 7-9 |
| Dust Cover | 15-21 |
| Engine To Case | 41-50 |
| Filler Tube To Case | 7-9 |
| Governor Cover To Case | 7-9 |
| Insulator Bracket To Frame | 40-50 |
| Insulator Mount To Transmission | 25-33 |
| Insulator To Bracket | 55-70 |
| Low/Intermediate Servo Cover To Case | 7-9 |
| Main Control Cover To Chain Cover | 10-12 |
| Manual Cable Bracket | 10-20 |
| Manual Lever To Manual Shaft | 12-16 |
| Neutral Start Switch To Case | 7-9 |
| Oil Pan To Case | 10-12 |
| Oil Pump Assembly To Main Control | 7-9 |
| Overdrive Servo Cover To Case | 7-9 |
| Park Abutment To case | 20-22 |
| Pressure Switch To Pump Body | 9-13 |
| Pressure Tap plug For Chain Cover & Pump Body | 9-13 |
| Pump Body To Chain Cover | 7-9 |
| Pump Cover To Pump Body | 7-9 |
| Seperator Plate To Main Control | 7-9 |
| Seperator Plate To Pump Body | 7-9 |
| Solenoid To Main Control | 7-9 |

## TIGHTENING SPECIFICATIONS—Continued

| Component | Torque/Ft. Lbs. |
|---|---|
| Stabilizer To Control Arm | 98–125 |
| Stabilizer U-Clamp To Bracket | 60–70 |
| Starter | 30–40 |
| TV Cable To Case | 9–13 |
| Tie Rod To Knuckle | 23–35① |
| Torque Converter To Flywheel | 23–39 |
| Transaxle To Engine | 41–50 |
| TV Control Lever To Chain Cover | 7–9 |
| Valve Body/Solenoid To Chain Cover | 7–9 |

①—Tighten to minimum specified torque, continue tightening to nearest cotter pin slot.

# Ford Festiva & 1989 Mercury Tracer Automatic Transaxle

## INDEX



## DESCRIPTION

This automatic transaxle combines an automatic transmission and differential into a single powertrain unit. This unit is designed specifically for front-wheel drive applications. The transaxle housing is made of a lightweight aluminum alloy and is mounted transversely to the engine.

## TROUBLESHOOTING

### NO DRIVE IN ANY RANGE

1. Loose valve body.
2. Valve body sticking.
3. Worn or damaged rear clutch.
4. Internal leakage.
5. Damaged pump or turbine shaft.

### NO DRIVE IN D

1. Manual linkage adjustment.
2. Improper oil pressure control system operation.
3. Sticking valve body.
4. Worn or damaged one-way clutch.

### NO DRIVE IN D, 2 OR 1

1. Valve body sticking.
2. Worn or damaged rear clutch.
3. Improper oil pressure control system operation.

### NO DRIVE IN R

1. Improper oil pressure control system operation.
2. Sticking valve body.
3. Worn or damaged rear clutch.

### NO SHIFT OUT OF 1ST GEAR IN D

1. Sticking valve body.
2. Worn or damaged governor.
3. Improper oil pressure control system operation.

### NO 2–3 SHIFT IN D

1. Sticking valve body.
2. Faulty governor valve.
3. Improper oil pressure control system operation.

### SHIFTS FROM 1–3 IN D

1. Improper fluid level.
2. Sticking valve body.
3. Faulty governor valve.
4. Faulty band servo.
5. Worn or damaged band or drum.

### SLIPS ON 2–3 SHIFT

1. Improper fluid level.
2. Faulty vacuum diaphragm or vacuum line.
3. Faulty governor valve.
4. Improper front clutch application.
5. Worn or damaged front clutch.
6. Improper oil pressure control system operation.

### SLIPS ON 1–2 SHIFT

1. Improper fluid level.
2. Sticking valve body.
3. Improper oil pressure control system operation.
4. Faulty vacuum diaphragm or vacuum line.
5. Faulty band servo.
6. Worn or damaged band or drum.

### IMPROPER SHIFT POINTS

1. Defective kickdown switch, solenoid or wiring.
2. Faulty vacuum diaphragm or vacuum line.
3. Worn or damaged governor.
4. Improper band or clutch application.
5. Improper oil pressure control system operation.

### NO FORCED DOWNSHIFT IN D

1. Improper oil control system operation.
2. Improper band application.
3. Sticking valve body.
4. Sticking governor valve.
5. Faulty vacuum diaphragm or vacuum line.
6. Defective kickdown switch, solenoid or wiring.

### NO 3–2 SHIFT ON MANUAL D TO 2 OR 1 SHIFT

1. Sticking valve body.
2. Improper oil pressure control system operation.
3. Faulty band servo.
4. Worn or damaged band or drum.

### DOWNSHIFT AT SPEEDS ABOVE KICKDOWN LIMIT

1. Faulty vacuum diaphragm or vacuum line.
2. Sticking valve body.
3. Improper front clutch application.
4. Improper oil pressure control system operation.

### SLIPS ON 3–2 DOWNSHIFT

1. Improper fluid level.
2. Improper band application.
3. Improper oil pressure control system operation.
4. Faulty band servo.
5. Worn or damaged band or drum.

### NO ENGINE BRAKING IN 1

1. Improper fluid level.
2. Improperly adjusted manual linkage.
3. Improper oil pressure control system operation.
4. Sticking valve body.
5. Worn or damaged low reverse brake.

### SLOW INITIAL ENGAGEMENT

1. Improper fluid level.
2. Contaminated fluid.
3. Sticking valve body.
4. Improper clutch application.
5. Improper oil pressure control system operation.

### HARSH INITIAL ENGAGEMENT

1. Improper engine idle speed.
2. Worn half shaft constant velocity joints.
3. Damaged or loose engine mounts.
4. Faulty vacuum diaphragm or vacuum line.
5. Improper rear clutch application.
6. Improper oil pressure control system operation.
7. Sticking valve body.

### HARSH 1–2 SHIFT

1. Sticking valve body.
2. Faulty vacuum diaphragm or vacuum line.
3. Improper band application.
4. Improper oil pressure control system operation.
5. Improper engine performance.

### HARSH 2–3 SHIFT

1. Sticking valve body.
2. Improper front clutch application.
3. Improper oil pressure control circuit operation.
4. Faulty band servo.
5. Worn or damaged brake band.

### VEHICLE BRAKED WHEN SHIFTED FROM 1 TO 2

1. Sticking valve body.
2. Improper front clutch application.
3. Improper oil control circuit system operation.
4. Worn or damaged low reverse brake.
5. Seized one-way clutch.

### VEHICLE BRAKED WHEN SHIFTED FROM 2 TO D

1. Sticking valve body.
2. Improper operation of brake band or servo.

### SLIPS OR CHATTERS IN D

1. Improper fluid level.
2. Worn or damaged rear clutch.
3. Improper oil pressure control system operation.

### SLIPS OR CHATTERS IN 2ND GEAR IN D

1. Improper fluid level.
2. Internal leakage.
3. Sticking valve body.
4. Improper rear clutch application.
5. Improper oil pressure control system operation.
6. Faulty band servo.
7. Worn or damaged band or drum.

### NOISY DURING ACCELERATION OR DECELERATION

1. Improperly routed speedometer cable.
2. Improperly routed shift cable.
3. Defective engine mounts.

### NOISY IN P OR N

1. Loose flywheel bolts.
2. Damaged oil pump.
3. Faulty torque converter.

### NOISY IN ALL RANGES

1. Worn or damaged drive gear set.
2. Worn or damaged speedometer gears.
3. Worn or damaged bearings.

### NOISY IN LOW

1. Worn damaged planetary gear set.

### NOISY IN D RANGES OR R

1. Improper fluid level.
2. Improper fluid control pressure.
3. Worn or damaged rear clutch.
4. Worn or damaged oil pump.
5. Worn or damaged one-way clutch.
6. Worn or damaged planetary gears.

### TRANSAXLE NOISY

1. Improper fluid level.
2. Improper band or clutch operation.
3. Improper oil pressure control system operation.
4. Improperly routed oil cooler lines.
5. Sticking valve body.
6. Internal leakage.
7. Oil pump cavitation.

### TRANSAXLE OVERHEATS

1. Improper fluid level.
2. Improper engine performance.
3. Improper clutch or band application.
4. Improper oil pressure control operation.
5. Restricted oil cooler lines.
6. Sticking valve body.
7. Seized one-way clutch.

## MAINTENANCE

### OIL LEVEL CHECK

With vehicle on a level surface, start engine and operate at fast idle for several minutes. With engine at curb idle speed and brakes applied, move selector lever through all gear positions, then return lever to P. With engine still operating at curb idle speed, clean area around transaxle dipstick, then remove dipstick and check fluid level. Fluid level should be between the L and F marks. Add Dexron Type II fluid, as necessary, to bring fluid level between L and F marks. After completing fluid level check, ensure transaxle dipstick is properly seated in dipstick tube.

### CHANGING FLUID

Under normal operating circumstances, changing of transaxle fluid is not required. Under severe conditions, such as continuous stop and go driving or accumulation of 5000 miles or more per month, the transaxle fluid should be changed every 30,000 miles.

1. Raise and support front of vehicle, then remove underbody covers to gain access to transaxle drain plug.
2. Position a drain pan under transaxle, then remove drain plug and allow transaxle to drain. The transaxle drain plug is located under the final drive housing.
3. Remove transaxle oil pan attaching bolts and carefully remove oil pan.

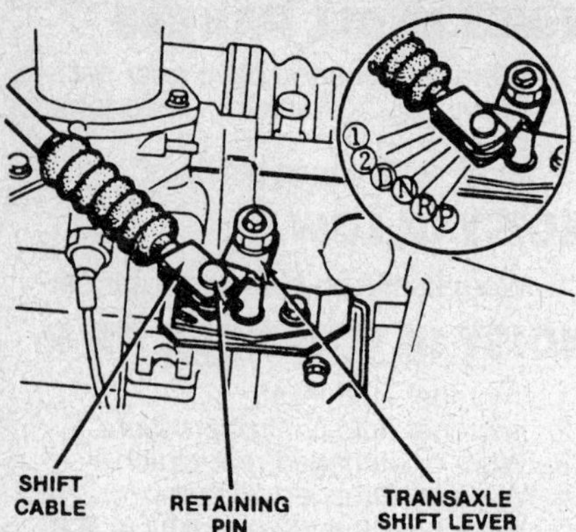


**Fig. 1 Shift cable to transaxle shift lever attachment**

4. Clean oil pan and screen. If necessary, replace screen.
5. Install oil pan drain plug and **torque** to 29-40 ft. lbs.
6. Position gasket to transaxle oil pan, then install oil pan on transaxle. **Torque** oil pan-to-transaxle attaching screws to 4-6 ft. lbs. **Do not use any sealer on transaxle oil pan gasket.**
7. Install underbody covers, then lower vehicle.
8. Remove transaxle dipstick and add 3 quarts of Dexron Type II fluid to transaxle through dipstick tube.
9. Start engine and allow to reach operating temperature, then check fluid level as outlined under "Oil Level Check."

# IN-VEHICLE ADJUSTMENTS

## SHIFT CONTROL CABLE, ADJUST

### Tracer

1. Place gear shift lever in N position.
2. Remove clip and pin retaining shift cable to transaxle lever, **Fig. 1.**
3. Rotate transaxle lever fully counterclockwise to P position, then rotate lever two detents clockwise to N position.
4. If hole in shift lever aligns with holes in trunnion, shift cable is properly adjusted. If holes do not align proceed to step 5.
5. Remove shift lever quadrant bezel attaching screw, then lift upward on bezel to disengage from console.
6. Remove shift quadrant attaching screws, the rotate quadrant to provide access to shift cable adjusting nuts.
7. Position gear shift lever in P and check position of detent spring roller. If roller is not centered in park detent, loosen attaching screws and move detent spring as necessary to center, then install quadrant attaching screws.
8. Position gear shift lever in N, then adjust cable adjusting nuts to as necessary to align transaxle shift lever and cable trunnion holes, **Fig. 2.**
9. After completing adjustment, **torque** cable adjusting nuts to 69-95 inch lbs.
10. Position shift cable trunnion to transaxle shift lever, then install pin and clip.
11. With gear shift lever in N position, press on shift interlock button and move gear shift lever forward until transaxle axle gear shift lever just begins to move and note distance.
12. With gear shift lever in N position, press on shift interlock button and move gear shift lever rearward until transaxle axle gear shift lever just begins to move and note distance.
13. If necessary, rotate shift cable adjusting nuts slightly, until forward and rearward movement of gear shift are equal. After completing adjustment, **torque** adjusting nuts to 69-95 inch lbs.
14. Install shift quadrant bezel, then check for proper operation of gear shift linkage and neutral safety switch.

### Festiva

1. Engage parking brake, then remove the shift quadrant bezel.
2. Remove shift quadrant, then loosen adjuster nuts on shift cable.
3. Shift selector lever to N and ensure detent spring roller is in the N position.
4. Move transaxle shift lever into the N position.
5. Tighten lower adjuster nut by hand until it contacts the T-joint, then loosen nut one-half turn. **Tighten** upper adjuster nut to 69-95 inch lbs.
6. Press selector interlock button, then push selector lever toward R with 4.4 lbs. of force. Measure distance selector lever has moved. This distance should be no more than .31 inch.
7. Repeat step 6 toward the D position.
8. If the distance toward R is greater than toward D, tighten lower adjusting nut until distance is equal. If the distance toward D is greater, loosen lower adjusting nut until distance is equal.
9. Check operation of manual linkage. If shift is not smooth, place selector lever in P. Loosen attaching screws on detent spring and roller assembly, then adjust position of detent spring roller. If this adjustment is made, repeat steps 6 through 9. **Ensure linkage adjustment has not affected operation of neutral safety switch. Engine must crank in P and N positions only.**
10. Install shift quadrant, then the shift quadrant bezel.

# IN-VEHICLE REPAIRS

## VALVE BODY, REPLACE

### Removal

1. Disconnect battery ground cable.
2. Raise and support front of vehicle, then remove body undercovers.
3. Remove transaxle drain plug and allow fluid to drain.
4. Remove transaxle oil pan attaching screws and oil pan.

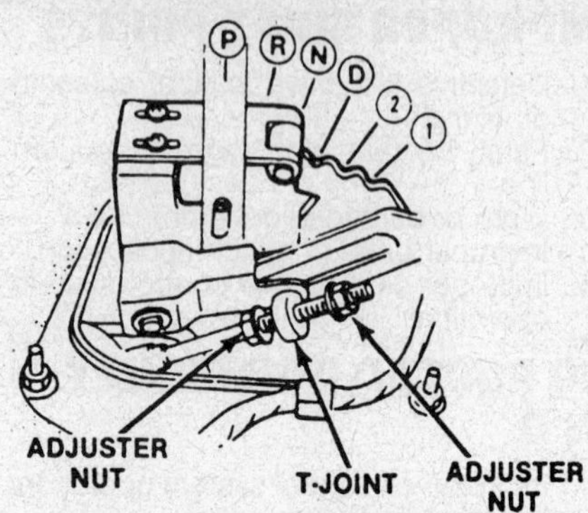


**Fig. 2 Shift cable adjustment**

5. Remove valve body attaching bolts, **Fig. 3,** then carefully remove valve, using care not to loosen vacuum diaphragm rod or ball and spring for converter relief valve.

### Installation

1. Position vacuum diaphragm rod to hole in case, **Fig. 4.**
2. Install check ball and spring into case bore, **Fig. 4.** Use petroleum jelly to hold ball and spring in position.
3. Position groove in manual valve with drive pin of shift rod, then index dowel in transaxle case to valve body holes, **Fig. 5.** Install valve body attaching bolts and **torque** to 70-95 inch lbs.
4. Install oil pan and gasket. **Torque** oil pan attaching bolts to 43-69 inch lbs. **Do not use any sealer on oil pan gasket.**
5. Install underbody covers, then lower vehicle.
6. Add three quarts of Dexron Type II fluid to transaxle, then start engine and check fluid level as outlined under "Oil Level Check."

## SERVO PISTON, REPLACE

1. Raise and support front of vehicle, then drain transaxle fluid.
2. Remove valve body as outlined under "Valve Body, Replace."
3. Remove left front wheel and tire assembly.
4. **On Festiva models,** remove stabilizer bar mounting nuts and brackets.
5. **On all models,** remove lefthand ball joint to steering knuckle attaching bolt, then pull lower control arm downward to separate ball joint from steering knuckle.
6. Using a suitable pry bar, separate half shaft from differential side gear, **Fig. 6.** Suspend half shaft from coil spring using wire. **When inserting pry bar use care not to damage oil seal.**
7. Loosen band anchor bolt and locknut, **Fig. 7,** then remove band strut.
8. Using a C-clamp and socket, compress servo piston, then using a screwdriver, remove servo snap ring, **Fig. 8.**
9. Carefully loosen C-clamp, then remove servo retainer, piston and spring.

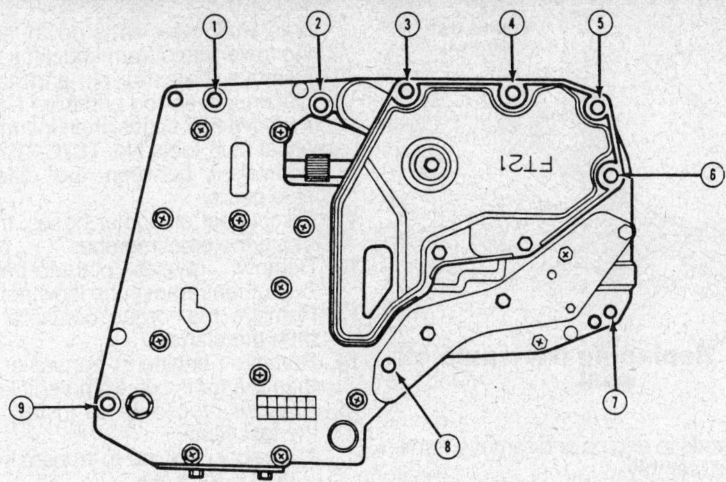


Fig. 3 Valve body attaching bolt removal sequence

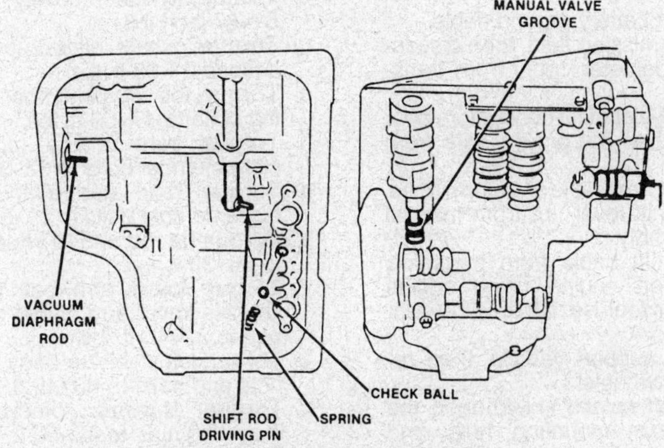


Fig. 4 Vacuum diaphragm rod, check ball & spring installation

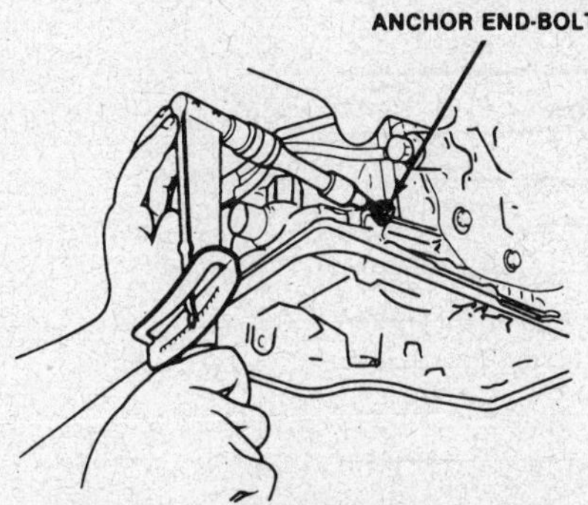


Fig. 7 Band anchor bolt location

10. Reverse procedure to install. Prior to installation, lubricate servo piston with Dexron Type II fluid. When installing band anchor end bolt, **tighten** bolt to 8.7-10.8 ft. lbs., then loosen bolt three turns. While holding anchor end bolt in position, **torque** locknut to 41-59 ft. lbs. When installing half shaft, use a new circlip. While supporting at constant velocity joint, slide half shaft into transaxle until circlip engages differential side gear groove. **Torque** lower ball joint to steering knuckle attaching bolt to 32-40 ft. lbs.

## TRANSAXLE OIL SEAL, REPLACE

1. Raise and support front of vehicle, then remove underbody covers.
2. Remove stabilizer bar to lower control arm attachment.
3. Remove wheel and tire assembly.
4. Remove ball joint to steering knuckle attaching bolt, then pull lower control arm downward to separate ball joint from steering knuckle.
5. Remove transaxle drain plug and allow transaxle to drain.
6. Using a suitable pry bar, separate half shaft from differential side gear, **Fig. 6.** Suspend half shaft from coil spring using wire. **When inserting pry bar use care not to damage oil seal.**
7. Using a suitable screwdriver, remove oil seal from case, **Fig. 9.**
8. Reverse procedure to install. Use seal installer tool No. T87C-77000-H or equivalent to install oil seal. When installing half shaft, use a new circlip. While supporting at constant velocity joint, slide half shaft into transaxle until circlip engages differential side gear groove. **Torque** lower ball joint-to-steering knuckle attaching

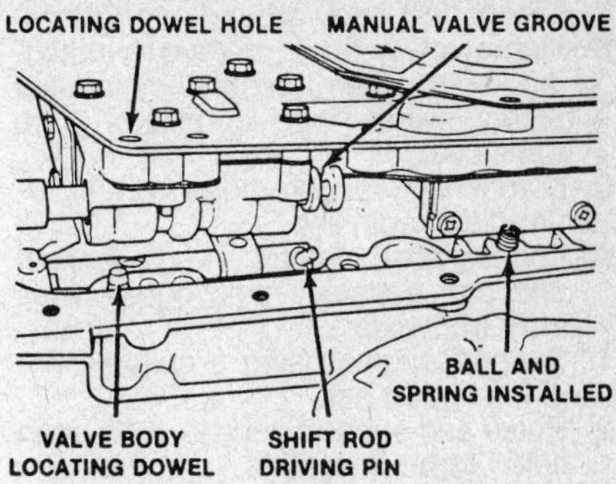


Fig. 5 Installing valve body

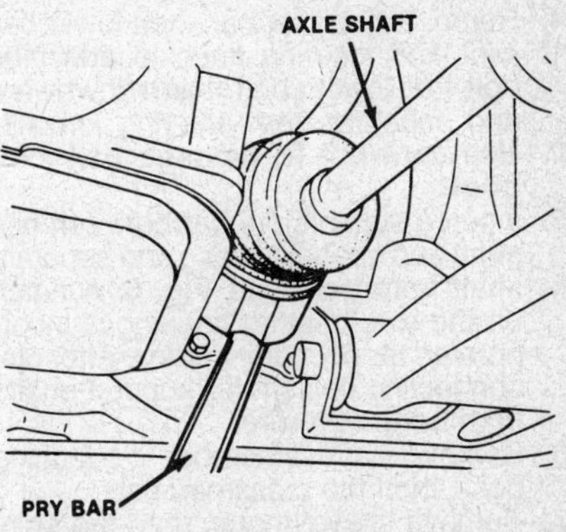


Fig. 6 Separating half shaft from transaxle

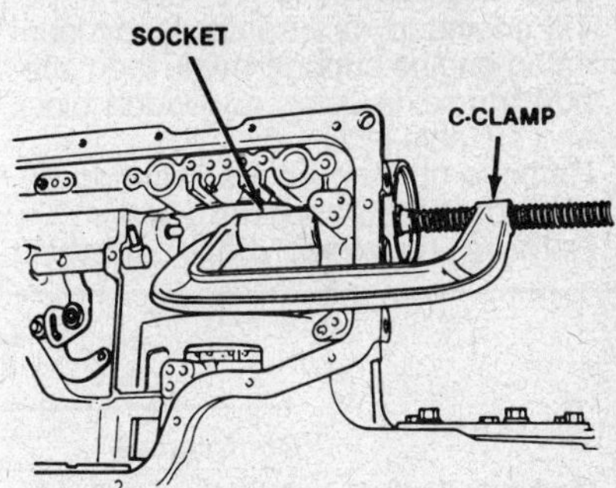


Fig. 8 Compressing servo piston spring

bolt to 32-40 ft. lbs. When installing stabilizer bar link, **tighten** nut until 7/16 inch of thread extends beyond nut.

## TRANSAXLE REPLACE

### TRACER

1. Disconnect battery ground cable.
2. Remove air cleaner.
3. Disconnect speedometer cable and shift control linkage at transaxle.
4. Disconnect engine ground cable at cylinder head, then coolant pipe bracket.
5. Remove secondary air pipe and EGR pipe bracket, then remove wiring harness clip.
6. Disconnect neutral safety switch and kick down solenoid engine compartment electrical connectors located near ignition coil.

7. Disconnect body ground connector.
8. Remove two upper transaxle attaching bolts, then disconnect neutral safety switch wire connector from transaxle.
9. Disconnect vacuum hose from vacuum diaphragm line.
10. Loosen hose clamps and disconnect and cap transaxle fluid cooler lines from transaxle.
11. Support engine using a suitable engine support bar.
12. Raise and support vehicle, then drain fluid from transaxle and remove wheel and tire assemblies.
13. Remove engine compartment under and side covers.
14. Remove stabilizer bar, then lower ball joint and steering knuckle attaching bolt. Pull lower control arm downward and separate from steering knuckle. **Use care not to damage ball joint boot.**
15. Insert a suitable pry bar between half shaft and transaxle case and separate shaft from transaxle, **Fig. 6.** A notch on the side bearing housing is incorporated for pry bar insertion. After disconnecting half shafts, support shafts from body with wire.
16. Remove crossmember attaching bolts, then the crossmember.
17. Remove starter motor, then the bolts attaching end plate to transaxle.
18. Remove torque converter-to-flex plate attaching bolts.
19. Tilt engine toward transaxle, by loosening engine support hook, then support transaxle using a wooden block and suitable jack.
20. Remove nuts and bolts securing engine mount to transaxle.
21. Remove remaining bolts attaching transaxle to engine and remove transaxle assembly.
22. Reverse procedure to install.

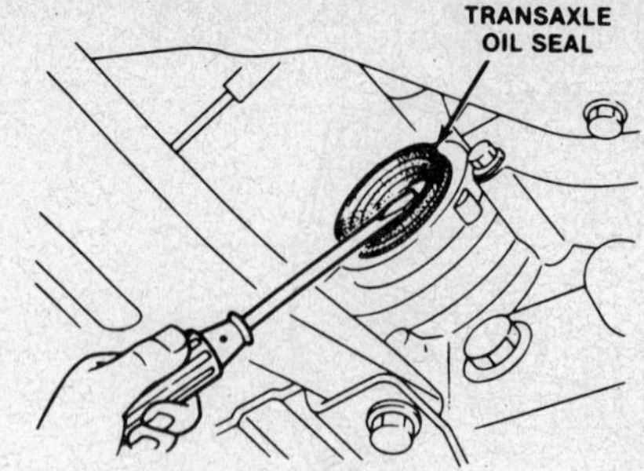


**Fig. 9 Replacing transaxle oil seal**

## FESTIVA

1. Disconnect battery ground cable.
2. Drain transmission fluid, then disconnect speedometer cable from transaxle.
3. Disconnect electrical connectors near governor, then the ground wire from transaxle.
4. Disconnect transaxle vacuum hose, then the shift lever nut from manual shaft assembly.
5. Remove shift cable from transaxle, then support engine using engine support bar tool No. D87L-6000-A or equivalent.
6. Raise and support vehicle, then remove front wheels.
7. Remove left splash shield, then the stabilizer bar mounting nuts and brackets.
8. Remove lower arm clamp bolts and nuts. Pull lower arms down, separating lower arms from knuckles.
9. Remove the cotter pin and nut, then disconnect tie rod end from knuckle.
10. Remove half shafts, then install differential plug tools No. T87C-7025-C or equivalent between the differential side gears.
11. Disconnect oil cooler hoses, then remove the crossmember.
12. Remove gusset plate-to-transaxle bolts, then remove the flywheel cover.
13. Remove the torque converter bolts, then the starter.
14. Remove engine-to-transaxle bolts, then the transaxle from vehicle.
15. Reverse procedure to install, noting the following:
    a. **Torque** engine-to-transaxle bolts to 41-59 ft. lbs.
    b. **Torque** the torque converter bolts to 26-36 ft. lbs.
    c. **Torque** flywheel cover bolts to 61-87 inch lbs.
    d. **Torque** gusset plate-to-transaxle bolts to 27-38 ft. lbs.
    e. **Torque** the crossmember attaching bolts to 47-66 ft. lbs.
    f. **Torque** front engine mount to crossmember bolts to 32-38 ft. lbs.
    g. **Torque** rear engine mount to crossmember bolts to 21-34 ft. lbs.
    h. **Torque** tie rod end to knuckle nut to 26-30 ft. lbs.
    i. **Torque** lower arm ball joint to knuckle lower arm clamp nut and bolt to 32-40 ft. lbs.
    j. **Torque** left stabilizer body bracket nuts and bolts to 40-45 ft. lbs.
    k. **Torque** stabilizer bracket and mounting nuts to 40-50 ft. lbs.
    l. **Torque** shift lever nut on manual shaft assembly to 34-57 ft. lbs.

## TIGHTENING SPECIFICATIONS

| Component | Torque/Ft. Lbs. |
|---|---|
| Adjuster Locknut | 41–59 |
| Anchor End Bolt | 104–130① |
| Anchor End Bolt Locknut | 41–59 |
| Bearing Housing | 14–19 |
| Bearing/Stator Support Bolts | 8–10 |
| Crossmember Attaching Bolts | 46–66 |
| Differential Ring Gear Bolts | 51–62 |
| Engine To Transaxle Bolts | 41–59 |
| Flywheel Cover Attaching Bolts | 61–87 |
| Front Engine Mount To Crossmember Bolts | 32–38 |
| Gasket Plate To Transaxle Bolts | 27–38 |
| Governor Cover Attaching Bolts | 69–15 |
| Idler Gear Locknut | 94–130 |
| Intermediate Band Adjuster Bolt | 9–11 |
| Lower Arm Clamp Bolt | 32–40 |
| Manual Shaft Nut | 22–29 |
| Manual Shaft Support Bolts | 43–69① |
| Neutral Safety Switch | 14–19 |
| Oil Filler Tube Retaining Bolt | 61–87① |
| Oil Pan Attaching Bolts | 43–69① |

*Continued*

## TIGHTENING SPECIFICATIONS—Continued

| Component | Torque/Ft. Lbs. |
|---|---|
| Oil Pump Cover Bolts | 95–122① |
| Oil Pump To Transaxle Bolts | 11–16 |
| Parking Paw Actuator Support Bolts | 9–12 |
| Rear Engine Mount To Crossmember Nut | 21–34 |
| Shift Linkage To Manual Shift Bolt | 34–57 |
| Speedometer Drive Gear Bolt | 69–95① |
| Stabilizer Body Bracket Nuts | 40–45 |
| Stabilizer Mounting Nuts | 40–50 |
| Tie Rod End Attaching Nut | 26–30 |
| Torque Converter Attaching Bolts | 26–36 |
| Transaxle Case To Clutch Housing Bolts | 22–34 |
| Transaxle Drain Plug | 29–40 |
| Valve Body Mounting Bolts | 69–95① |
| Valve Body Side Plate Bolts | 22–30① |
| Valve Body Retaining Bolts | 69–95① |

①—Inch lbs.

# Ford 4EAT Automatic Transaxle

## INDEX



## TRANSAXLE IDENTIFICATION

The transmission identification code is stamped on a metal tag **Fig. 1,** attached to the driver's side of the instrument panel. It is visible from outside the vehicle through the windshield.

## DESCRIPTION

The 4EAT transaxle **Fig. 2,** is an electronically controlled automatic transaxle which uses a combination of electronic and mechanical systems to control forward gear shifting and torque converter lockup. A shift mode switch provides a choice of shift patterns, plus a manual switch for slow driving on steep or slippery surfaces.

Other unique mechanical features include a single compact combination type 4-speed planetary gear instead of the usual two planetary gears used in 3-speed transaxles, making a reduction in overall size possible. Also a variable capacity oil pump is used, which provides constant oil quantity at and above medium speed and reduces power losses resulting from pumping more oil than is necessary at higher speeds.

The electronic system controls transaxle shifting in forward speeds and torque converter lockup by means of solenoid operated valves. The solenoid valves when energized (on) actuate clutches and bands to control shifting in the planetary gear. Shift timing and torque converter lockup are regulated by the control unit with programmed logic and in response to input sensors and switches to produce optimim driveability.

## TROUBLESHOOTING

### VEHICLE DOES NOT MOVE IN OVERDRIVE, D, L OR R RANGE

1. Fluid level too low or fluid contaminated.
2. Incorrectly adjusted selector lever.
3. Malfunctioning control valve(s).
4. Defective oil pump.
5. Problem in hydraulic circuit.
6. Defective torque converter.
7. Defective forward clutch.
8. Defective reverse clutch.
9. Defective one way clutch 1.
10. Defective one way clutch 2.
11. Defective parking gear.

## VEHICLE MOVES IN N RANGE

1. Incorrectly adjusted selector lever.
2. Malfunctioning control valve(s).

## EXCESSIVE CREEP

1. Incorrectly adjusted throttle cable.
2. Check idle speed and ignition timing.
3. Defective torque converter.

## NO CREEP AT ALL

1. Fluid level too low or fluid contaminated.
2. Incorrectly adjusted selector lever.
3. Incorrectly adjusted throttle cable.
4. Malfunctioning control valve(s).
5. Defective oil pump.
6. Problem in hydraulic circuit.
7. Defective forward clutch.
8. Defective reverse clutch.

## NO SHIFT

1. Defective inhibitor switch.
2. Defective hold switch.
3. Defective 1-2 solenoid.
4. Defective 2-3 solenoid.
5. Defective 3-4 solenoid.
6. Fluid level too low or fluid contaminated.
7. Incorrectly adjusted selector cable.
8. Malfunctioning control valve(s).
9. Defective oil pump.

## ABNORMAL SHIFT SEQUENCE

1. Defective inhibitor switch.
2. Defective hold switch.
3. Defective throttle sensor.
4. Defective cruise control switch.
5. Defective water temperature switch.
6. Defective pulse generator.
7. Defective 1-2 solenoid.
8. Defective 2-3 solenoid.
9. Defective 3-4 solenoid.
10. Fluid level too low or fluid contaminated.
11. Incorrectly adjusted selector lever.
12. Malfunctioning control valve(s).
13. Defective 2-4 brake band and/or servo.

## FREQUENT SHIFTING

1. Defective inhibitor switch.
2. Defective mode switch.
3. Defective throttle sensor.
4. Defective cruise control switch.
5. Defective pulse generator.
6. Defective 1-2 solenoid.
7. Defective 2-3 solenoid.
8. Defective 3-4 solenoid.
9. Defective lockup solenoid.
10. Malfunctioning control valve(s).

## EXCESSIVELY HIGH OR LOW SHIFT POINT

1. Defective inhibitor switch.
2. Defective mode switch.
3. Defective hold switch.
4. Defective idle switch.
5. Defective throttle sensor.
6. Defective throttle generator.
7. Defective 1-2 solenoid.
8. Defective 2-3 solenoid.
9. Defective 3-4 solenoid.
10. Incorrectly adjusted selector cable.
11. Malfunctioning control valve(s).

1. MONTH AND YEAR OF PRODUCTION
2. GVWR (GROSS VEHICLE WEIGHT RATING)
3. FROM GAWR (FRONT GROSS AXLE WEIGHT RATING)
4. REAR GAWR (REAR AXLE WEIGHT RATING)
5. VIN (VEHICLE IDENTIFICATION NUMBER)
6. TYPE
9. EXTERIOR PAINT COLORS
10. BODY
13. INTERIOR TRIM
15. RADIO TYPE
17. AXLE RATIO
18. TRANSMISSION
20. DSO (SPECIAL ORDER CODE)

**Fig. 1 Transaxle identification tag**

## NO LOCKUP

1. Defective brake light switch.
2. Defective throttle sensor.
3. Defective cruise control switch.
4. Defective water temperature switch.
5. Defective pulse generator.
6. Defective 1-2 solenoid.
7. Defective 2-3 solenoid.
8. Defective 3-4 solenoid.
9. Defective lockup solenoid.
10. Incorrectly adjusted selector lever.
11. Defective torque converter.

## NO KICKDOWN

1. Defective inhibitor switch.
2. Defective hold switch.
3. Defective throttle sensor.
4. Incorrectly adjusted selector lever.

## ENGINE RUNAWAY OR SLIP WHEN STARTING VEHICLE

1. Defective inhibitor switch.
2. Fluid level too low or fluid contaminated.
3. Malfunctioning control valve(s).
4. Defective oil pump.
5. Defective forward clutch.
6. Defective one way clutch 1.

## ENGINE RUNAWAY OR SLIP WHEN UPSHIFTING OR DOWNSHIFTING

1. Defective inhibitor switch.
2. Fluid level too low or fluid contaminated.
3. Malfunctioning control valve(s).
4. Defective oil pump.
5. Defective forward clutch.
6. Defective reverse clutch.
7. Defective 3-4 clutch.
8. Defective 2-4 brake band and/or servo.
9. Defective one way clutch 1.

## EXCESSIVE N TO D OR N TO R SHIFT SHOCK

1. Fluid level too low or fluid contaminated.
2. Check idle speed and ignition timing.
3. Malfunctioning control valve(s).
4. Defective accumulator(s).
5. Defective forward clutch.
6. Defective reverse clutch.

## EXCESSIVE SHIFT SHOCK WHEN UPSHIFTING OR DOWNSHIFTING

**The following procedure have been revised by a Technical Service Bulletin.**

1. Fluid level too low or fluid contaminated.
2. Incorrectly adjusted throttle cable.
3. Malfunctioning control valve(s).
4. Defective accumulator(s).
5. Defective coasting clutch.
6. Defective 3-4 clutch.
7. Defective 2-4 brake band and/or servo.
8. Weak servo return spring.

## EXCESSIVE SHIFT SHOCK WHEN CHANGING RANGES

1. Defective inhibitor switch.
2. Incorrectly adjusted selector lever.
3. Malfunctioning control valve(s).
4. Defective coasting clutch.
5. Defective low and reverse brake.

## TRANSAXLE NOISY IN N OR P RANGE

1. Fluid level too low or fluid contaminated.
2. Defective oil pump.
3. Defective torque converter.
4. Defective differential assembly.

## TRANSAXLE NOISY IN OVERDRIVE, D, L OR R RANGE

1. Fluid level too low or fluid contaminated.
2. Defective forward clutch.
3. Defective one way clutch 1.
4. Defective planetary gear.

## NO ENGINE BRAKING

1. Defective 2-3 solenoid.
2. Defective 3-4 solenoid.
3. Malfunctioning control valve(s).
4. Problem in hydraulic circuit.
5. Defective coasting clutch.
6. Defective low and reverse brake.

## NO MODE CHANGE

1. Defective inhibitor switch.
2. Defective mode switch.
3. Defective hold switch.
4. Defective throttle sensor.

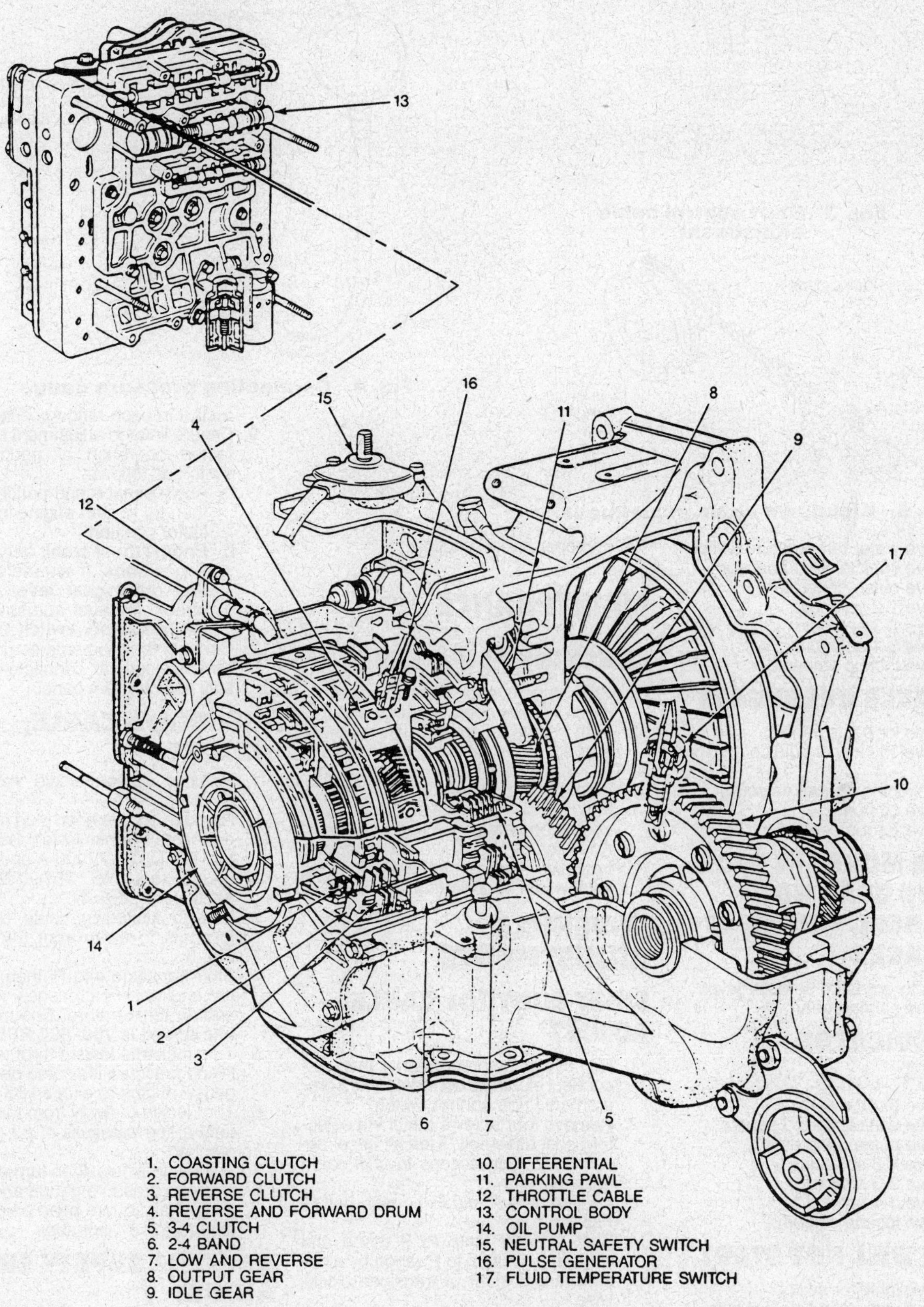


1. COASTING CLUTCH
2. FORWARD CLUTCH
3. REVERSE CLUTCH
4. REVERSE AND FORWARD DRUM
5. 3-4 CLUTCH
6. 2-4 BAND
7. LOW AND REVERSE
8. OUTPUT GEAR
9. IDLE GEAR
10. DIFFERENTIAL
11. PARKING PAWL
12. THROTTLE CABLE
13. CONTROL BODY
14. OIL PUMP
15. NEUTRAL SAFETY SWITCH
16. PULSE GENERATOR
17. FLUID TEMPERATURE SWITCH

**Fig. 2 Sectional view of Ford 4EAT automatic transaxle**

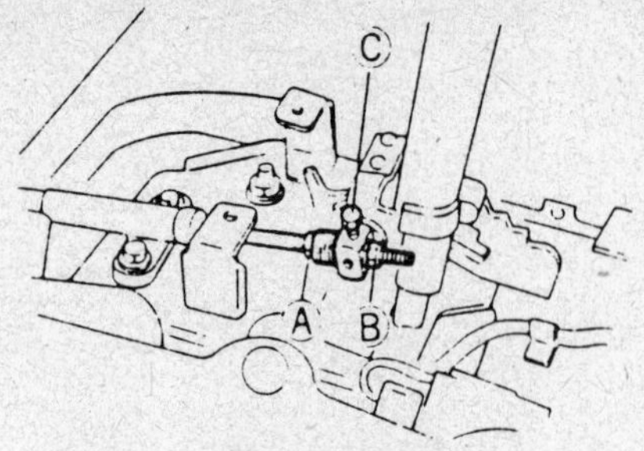


**Fig. 3 Shift control cable adjustment**

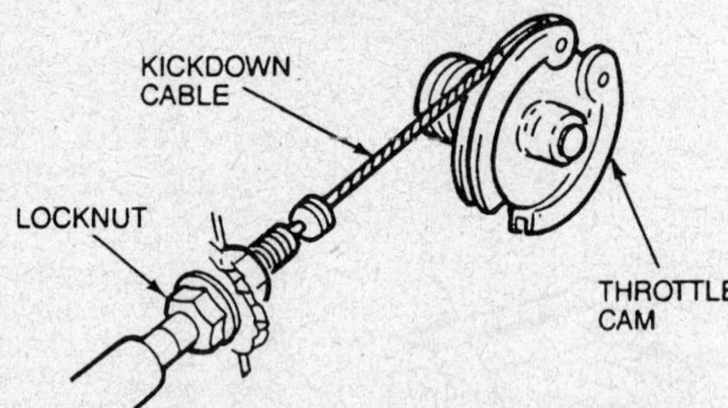


**Fig. 5 Kickdown cable adjustment**

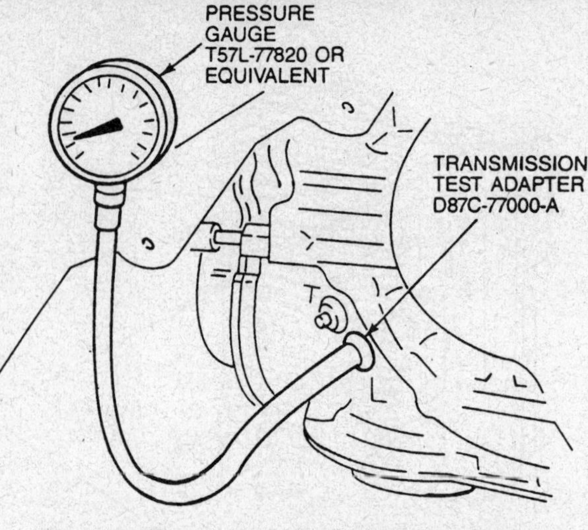


**Fig. 4 Connecting pressure gauge**

5. Defective water temperature switch.
6. Defective vehicle speed sensor.
7. Defective pulse generator.
8. Defective 1-2 solenoid.
9. Defective 2-3 solenoid.
10. Defective 3-4 solenoid.
11. Defective lockup solenoid.

## TRANSAXLE OVERHEATS

1. Defective lockup solenoid.
2. Fluid level too low or fluid contaminated.
3. Malfunctioning control valve(s).
4. Defective oil pump.
5. Defective torque converter.

## VEHICLE MOVES IN P, OR PARKING GEAR NOT DISENGAGED WHEN P IS DISENGAGED

1. Incorrectly adjusted selector lever.
2. Defective parking gear.

## HOLD INDICATOR FLASHES

1. Defective throttle sensor.
2. Defective vehicle speed sensor.
3. Defective pulse generator.
4. Defective 1-2 solenoid.
5. Defective 2-3 solenoid.
6. Defective 3-4 solenoid.
7. Defective lockup solenoid.

## ENGINE WILL NOT START

1. Defective inhibitor switch.
2. Incorrectly adjusted selector lever.

## VEHICLE DRAGS IN FORWARD & REVERSE GEARS

1. Bands improperly adjusted.
2. Improper brake function.

# MAINTENANCE

## CHECKING FLUID LEVEL

1. Start engine and allow transaxle to reach normal operating temperature.
2. With engine idling and parking brake applied, move selector lever through all ranges, then return to P position.
3. With engine idling, remove dipstick and check fluid level. Fluid level should be between F and L marks.
4. Add Mercon or equivalent automatic transaxle fluid as necessary to bring level within specifications.

# IN-VEHICLE ADJUSTMENTS

## SHIFT CONTROL CABLE, ADJUST

1. Remove selector trim panel, then disconnect electrical connector from programmed ride control switch.
2. Remove four screws attaching selector bezel assembly, then lift bezel assembly to gain access to shift cable adjuster.
3. Loosen nuts A and B. Loosen bolt C, **Fig. 3.**
4. Shift selector lever to P range and shift transmission to P range by moving manual shaft of transaxle clockwise.
5. **Torque** bolt C to 67-96 inch lbs.
6. Tighten nut A until nut touches trunion.
7. **Torque** nut B to 67-96 inch lbs. **Ensure nut B seats against spacer and not against spring.**
8. Install selector bezel. Ensure there is a click in each range position.
9. Ensure linkage adjustment has not affected operation of neutral safety switch as follows:
   a. Apply service and parking brakes, then try to start engine in each selector position.
   b. **Engine must crank only in N and P positions. If engine cranks in any other gear lever position, check linkage adjustment and neutral safety switch operation.**
10. Connect the programmed ride control switch electrical connector, then install selector trim panel.

## KICKDOWN CABLE, ADJUST

1. Remove splash shield next to left front tire.
2. Remove square head plug (marked L) and install transmission test adapter tool No. D87C-77000-A and pressure gauge tool No. T57L-77820-A or equivalents, **Fig. 4.**
3. Loosen kickdown cable by turning locknuts to away from throttle cam, **Fig. 5.**
4. Shift transaxle into P, then start and run engine until it reaches normal operating temperature. **Ensure engine idle speed is 700-800 RPM.**
5. Turn locknuts toward throttle cam until line pressure indicated on pressure gauge begins to exceed 63-66 psi.
6. Turn locknuts away from throttle cam until a line pressure of 63-66 psi. is reached.
7. Tighten locknuts, then turn engine off.
8. Remove pressure gauge and adapter and install square head plug. **Torque** plug to 43-87 inch lbs.

## NEUTRAL SAFETY SWITCH, ADJUST

1. Shift selector lever in N range, then loosen switch attaching bolts.
2. Remove switch screw, then move switch so that small hole is aligned with screw hole.
3. Adjust switch by inserting a .079 inch diameter pin through holes.

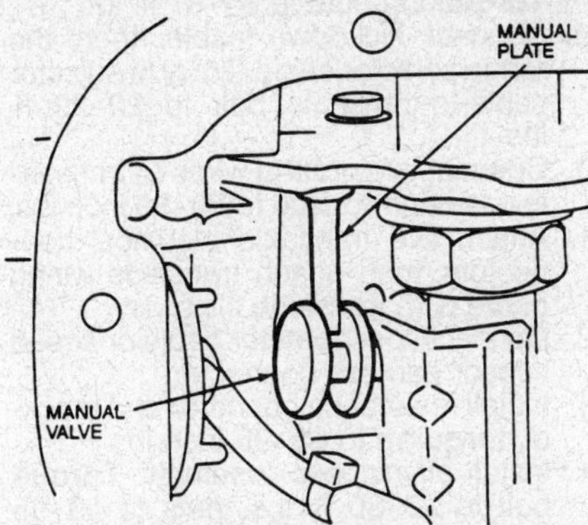


**Fig. 6 Aligning manual valve with manual plate.**

4. **Torque** switch attaching bolts to 69-95 inch lbs., then remove alignment pin and install screw.

## 2–4 BRAKE BAND, ADJUST

1. Raise and support vehicle.
2. Remove oil pan.
3. Loosen locknut and **torque** piston stem to 78-95 inch lbs.
4. Loosen piston stem 2 turns.
5. **Torque** locknut to 18-29 ft. lbs.

# IN-VEHICLE REPAIRS

## VALVE BODY, REPLACE

### Removal

1. Disconnect battery cables, then remove battery and battery carrier.
2. Disconnect main fuse block.
3. Disconnect five transaxle electrical connectors, then separate transaxle wiring harness from transaxle clips.
4. Raise and support vehicle, then drain transaxle fluid.
5. Disconnect oil cooler outlet and inlet hoses.
6. Remove valve body cover and gasket.
7. Disconnect kickdown cable from throttle cam.
8. Disconnect solenoid connector, then pinch tangs of mating connector mounted on transaxle case. Remove by pushing inward.
9. Remove valve body attaching bolts, then the valve body.

### Installation

1. Shift transaxle into R to place manual plate in correct position for installation.
2. Install valve body, using a mirror to align groove of manual valve with manual plate, **Fig. 6.**
3. **Torque** valve body attaching bolts to 95-130 inch lbs.
4. Insert solenoid connector into transaxle case hole, then attach mating connector.
5. Attach kickdown cable to throttle cam.
6. Install valve body cover using a new gasket. **Torque** cover attaching bolts to 69-95 inch lbs. **Do not use any type of sealer on cover or gasket.**
7. Connect oil cooler hoses.
8. Attach five transaxle electrical connectors, then attach transaxle wiring harness to transaxle clips.
9. Connect main fuse block, then install battery carrier and battery. Connect battery cables.
10. Add specified transaxle fluid, check for leaks and check fluid level.

## DIFFERENTIAL OIL SEALS, REPLACE

### Removal

1. Raise and support vehicle, then remove front wheel and tire assemblies.
2. Remove splash shields, then drain transaxle fluid.
3. Remove tie rod nuts and cotter pins, then disconnect both tie rod ends.
4. Remove both stabilizer link assemblies.
5. Remove bolts and nuts from both lower arm ball joints.
6. Pull lower arms down to separate from knuckles.
7. Remove righthand joint shaft bracket.
8. Remove half shafts from transaxle by prying with a bar inserted between shaft and transaxle case. Support half shafts in vehicle with wire.
9. Remove differential oil seals using a flat-tip screwdriver.

### Installation

1. Install new differential oil seals using differential seal replacer tool No. T87C-77000-H or equivalent.
2. Replace circlip on end of each half shaft, then install half shafts in transaxle.
3. Attach lower arm ball joints to knuckles.
4. Install tie rod ends and **torque** nuts to 22-33 ft. lbs. Install new cotter pins.
5. Install lower arm ball joint bolts and nuts, **torquing** to 32-40 ft. lbs.
6. Install stabilizer link assemblies. **Tighten** nuts on each assembly until one inch (25.4 mm) of bolt thread can be measured from upper nut, then secure upper nut and back off lower nut until a **torque** of 12-17 ft. lbs. is reached.
7. Install splash shields, then the front wheel and tire assemblies. **Torque** lug nuts to 65-87 ft. lbs.
8. Add specified transaxle fluid, check for leaks and check fluid level.

# TRANSAXLE REPLACE

### REMOVAL

1. Disconnect battery cables, then remove battery and battery carrier.
2. Disconnect main fuse block and distributor lead.
3. Disconnect air flow meter connector and remove air cleaner assembly.
4. Remove resonance chamber, then the resonance chamber bracket.
5. **On models with electro-mechanical dash cluster,** disconnect speedometer cable from transaxle.
6. **On models with electronic dash cluster,** disconnect speed sensor harness connector from transaxle.
7. **On all models,** disconnect five transaxle electrical connectors, then separate transaxle wiring harness from transaxle clips.
8. Disconnect two ground wires from transaxle case.
9. Disconnect range selector cable from transaxle case.
10. Disconnect kickdown cable from throttle cam.
11. Raise and support vehicle, then remove front wheel and tire assemblies.
12. Remove splash shields, then drain transaxle fluid.
13. Disconnect oil cooler inlet and outlet hoses. Insert plugs to prevent fluid leakage.
14. Remove tie rod nuts and cotter pins, then disconnect both tie rod ends.
15. Remove both stabilizer link assemblies.
16. Remove bolts and nuts from both lower arm ball joints.
17. Pull lower arms down to separate from knuckles.
18. Remove righthand joint shaft bracket.
19. Remove half shafts from transaxle by prying with a bar inserted between shaft and transaxle case. Support half shafts in vehicle with wire.
20. Install two transaxle plug tools No. T88C-7025-AH or equivalent, into differential side gears. **Failure to install transaxle plugs may allow differential side gears to become incorrectly positioned.**
21. Remove gusset plate-to-transaxle bolts.
22. Remove torque converter cover, then the torque converter nuts.
23. Remove starter motor and access brackets.
24. Install engine support bar tool No. D87L-6000-A or equivalent and attach to engine hanger.
25. Remove center transaxle mount and bracket, then the left transaxle mount.
26. Remove nut and bolt attaching right transaxle mount to frame.
27. Remove crossmember and the left lower arm as an assembly.
28. Position a transmission jack under transaxle and secure transaxle to jack.
29. Remove six engine-to-transaxle attaching bolts.
30. **Before transaxle can be lowered out of vehicle, torque converter studs must be clear of flex plate.** Insert a screwdriver between flex plate and converter, then carefully disengage studs.
31. Lower transaxle out of vehicle.

### INSTALLATION

**The following procedure has been revised by a Technical Service Bulletin.**

A pin is used to hold the throttle valve in a fixed position on new or remanufactured service replacement transaxle assemblies.

The pin is used during the assembly process to make installation of the control valve easier. When installing a new or remanufactured 4EAT transaxle, ensure to remove the pin and install a new retaining bolt. **Failure to remove pin from the throttle cam will hold the transmission throttle lever in a fixed position resulting in a shift concern.**

1. Place transaxle on transmission jack and secure.
2. Raise transaxle to proper height and mount transaxle to engine. **Align torque converter studs and flex plate holes.**
3. Install six engine-to-transaxle attaching bolts, **torquing** to 66-86 ft. lbs.
4. Install center transaxle mount and bracket. **Torque** bolts to 27-40 ft. lbs., nuts to 47-66 ft. lbs.
5. Install left transaxle mount. **Torque** transaxle-to-mount nut to 63-86 ft. lbs., mount-to-bracket nut and bolt to 49-69 ft. lbs.
6. Install crossmember and left lower arm as an assembly. **Torque** bolts to 27-40 ft. lbs., nuts to 55-69 ft. lbs.
7. Install right transaxle mount bolt and nut, **torquing** to 63-86 ft. lbs.
8. Install starter motor and access brackets.
9. Install torque converter-to-flex plate nuts, **torquing** to 32-45 ft. lbs.
10. Install torque converter cover. **Torque** attaching bolts to 69-95 inch lbs.
11. Install gusset plate-to-transaxle bolts, **torquing** to 27-38 ft. lbs.
12. Replace circlips on end of each half shaft, remove transaxle plugs, then install half shafts in transaxle.
13. Attach lower arm ball joints to knuckles.
14. Install tie rod ends and **torque** nuts to 22-33 ft. lbs. Install new cotter pins.
15. Install lower arm ball joint bolts and nuts, **torquing** to 32-40 ft. lbs.
16. Install stabilizer link assemblies. **Tighten** nuts on each assembly until one inch (25.4 mm) of bolt thread can be measured from upper nut, then secure upper nut and back off lower nut until a **torque** of 12-17 ft. lbs. is reached.
17. Connect oil cooler inlet and outlet hoses, then install splash shields.
18. Install front wheel and tire assemblies. **Torque** lug nuts to 65-87 ft. lbs.
19. Connect kickdown cable, then the range selector cable. **Torque** selector cable-to-transaxle bolt to 22-29 ft. lbs.
20. Connect two ground wires to transaxle case and **torque** to 69-95 inch lbs.
21. Attach five transaxle electrical connectors, then attach transaxle wiring harness to transaxle clips.
22. Connect speedometer cable or speed sensor harness connector.
23. Install resonance chamber and bracket, **torquing** to 69-95 inch lbs.
24. Install air cleaner assembly. **Torque** bolt to 23-30 ft. lbs., nuts to 69-95 inch. lbs.
25. Connect air flow meter electrical connector and distributor lead.
26. Connect main fuse block and **torque** to 69-95 inch. lbs.
27. Install battery carrier and battery, then connect battery cables.
28. Remove engine support bracket.
29. Add specified transaxle fluid, check for leaks and check fluid level.
30. Adjust kickdown cable as outlined under "Kickdown Cable, Adjust."

## TIGHTENING SPECIFICATIONS

| Component | Torque/Ft. Lbs. |
|---|---|
| Actuator Support | 8–10 |
| Bearing Housing | 14–19 |
| Center Transaxle Mount Bolts | 27–40 |
| Center Transaxle Mount Nuts | 47–66 |
| Converter Cover | 69–95① |
| Crossmember Bolts | 27–40 |
| Crossmember Nuts | 55–69 |
| Dipstick Tube | 61–87① |
| Drain Plug | 29–43 |
| Fluid Temperature Switch | 22–29 |
| Gusset Plate To Transaxle | 27–38 |
| Left Mount To Bracket | 49–69 |
| Line Pressure Plug | 43–87① |
| Manual Plate | 30–41 |
| Neutral Safety Switch | 69–95① |
| Oil Line Plug | 23–35 |
| Oil Pan | 69–95 |
| Oil Pump | 14–19 |
| Pulse Generator | 69–95① |
| Range Selector To Transaxle | 22–29 |
| Right Transaxle Mount | 63–86 |
| Switch Box | 12–17 |
| Throttle Cable Bracket | 14–19 |
| Throttle Cam | 61–87① |
| Torque Converter | 32–45 |
| Transaxle Case To Converter Housing | 27–38 |
| Transaxle To Engine | 66–86 |
| Transaxle To Left Mount | 63–86 |
| Valve Body | 95–130① |

①—Inch lbs.

# FRONT WHEEL DRIVE AXLES

TABLE OF CONTENTS



# Tempo, Topaz & 1989–90 Escort

INDEX



## TROUBLESHOOTING

### NOISE & VIBRATION IN TURNS

Clicking, popping or grinding noises while turning may be caused by the following:

1. Cut or damaged CV joint boots, resulting in contaminated lube in outboard or inboard CV joints.
2. Loose CV joint clamps.
3. Worn, damaged or improperly installed wheel bearings.

### VIBRATION AT HIGHWAY SPEEDS

1. Out of balance front wheels or tires.
2. Improperly seated outboard CV joint in front wheel hub.
3. Bent interconnecting shaft.
4. Front tires out of round.

### SHUDDER OR VIBRATION DURING ACCELERATION

1. Excessively worn or damaged inboard or outboard CV joint.
2. Excessively high CV joint operating angle caused by improper ride height.

### HALFSHAFT OR CV JOINT PULL-OUT

#### Engine Or Transaxle Misaligned

1. Check engine mounts for damage.

#### Front Suspension Components Worn Or Damaged

1. Check for worn bushings or bent front suspension components.

#### Improperly Installed Or Missing Retainers

1. Check for CV joint circlip missing or not properly seated in transaxle side gear.

## DRIVESHAFTS REPLACE

**If removing both right and left side halfshafts, plugs T81P-1177B or equivalent must be installed. Failure to do so may result in dislocation of differential side gears, necessitating transaxle disassembly to re-align the gears. Also, halfshaft removal and installation procedures are the same for manual and automatic transaxles except for the following: due to automatic transaxle case configuration the right side halfshaft assembly must be removed first. Tool T81P-4026A or equivalent is then inserted into transaxle to remove left side inner constant velocity joint assembly from transaxle. If only the left side halfshaft is to be removed from the vehicle, remove right side halfshaft assembly from the transaxle case only and secure to underside of vehicle, then remove left side halfshaft assembly. The hub nut and lower control arm to steering knuckle attaching bolt and nut must be discarded after removal and new nuts and bolts installed.**

Driveshaft assembly removal and installation procedures are the same for ATX/FLC (automatic transaxle) applications as for MTX (manual transaxle) applications except the ATX/FLC case configuration requires that the righthand halfshaft assembly be removed first. Differential rotator T81P-4026-A or equivalent, should then be inserted into the transaxle to drive the lefthand inboard constant velocity joint assembly from the transaxle. If only the lefthand halfshaft assembly is to be removed for service, remove the righthand halfshaft assembly from the transaxle only. After removal, support it with a length of wire, then drive the lefthand halfshaft assembly from the transaxle case. **Do not begin this removal procedure unless the following parts are known to be available, a new hub retainer nut, a new longer lower control arm to steering knuckle attaching bolt and nut and a new inboard constant velocity joint stub shaft snap ring. Once removed, these components must not be reused during the assembly procedure. Their torque holding ability or retention capability is greatly diminished during removal.**

1. Loosen hub nut without unstaking. Use of a chisel or similar tool to unstake nut may damage spindle threads.
2. Raise and support vehicle and remove wheel assemblies.
3. Remove hub nut and washer. **Discard hub attaching nut, it is a torque prevailing design and cannot be reused.**
4. Remove bolt attaching brake hose routing clip to suspension strut.
5. Remove nut from ball joint to steering knuckle attaching bolt, then drive bolt from knuckle using suitable punch and hammer. **Discard bolt and nut, they are torque prevailing design and cannot be reused.**
6. Separate ball joint from steering knuckle using pry bar, **Fig. 1. Lower ball joints fit into a pocket formed in the plastic disc brake shield. The shield must be positioned away from the ball joint while removing ball joint from steering knuckle.**
7. Remove halfshaft from differential housing using suitable pry bar. Use caution not to damage dust deflector located between shaft and case, **Fig.**

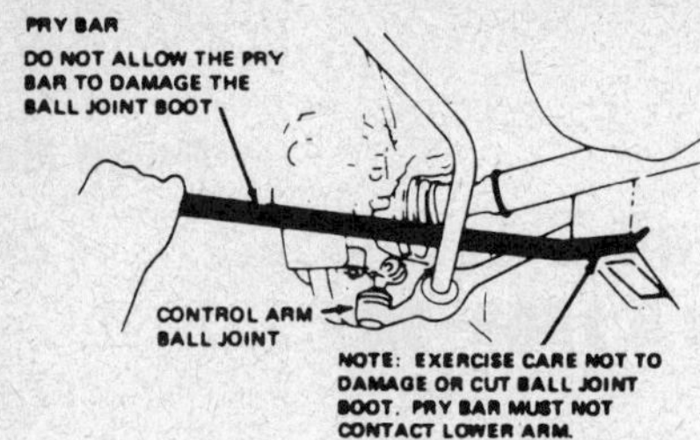


**Fig. 1 Separating ball joint from steering knuckle**

2. If an automatic transaxle halfshaft assembly cannot be removed from differential by using a pry bar, insert a large bladed screwdriver between differential pinion shaft and inboard constant velocity joint stub shaft. Sharply tap on screwdriver handle, to free halfshaft from differential. **Use caution not to damage differential oil seal, constant velocity joint boot or constant velocity joint dust deflector.**

8. Suspend shaft from suitable underbody component using suitable wire. **Do not allow shaft to hang as outboard CV joint damage may result.**
9. Separate outer constant velocity joint from hub using puller T81P-1104C or equivalent, **Fig. 3,** and adapters T81P-1104B and T81P-1104A or equivalent. **Do not use a hammer to separate outboard constant velocity joint stub shaft from hub as damage to internal components may result.**
10. Reverse procedure to install, noting the following:
    a. Install new circlip on inboard constant velocity joint stub shaft.
    b. Align splines of inboard constant velocity joint stub shaft with splines in differential.
    c. Push joint into differential until circlip seats in side gear, **Fig. 4.**
    d. **Torque** new control arm to steering knuckle nut to 40-54 ft. lbs.
    e. **Torque** brake hose routing clip to strut attaching bolt to 8 ft. lbs.
    f. **Torque** wheel lug nut to 80-105 ft. lbs.
    g. **Torque** new hub nut to 180-200 ft. lbs., during tightening, an audible click will indicate the proper ratchet function of hub attaching nut, as nut tightens, ensure one of three locking tabs on nut is aligned with CV joint shaft slot, if nut is damaged or more then one locking tab is missing, replace hub attaching nut.

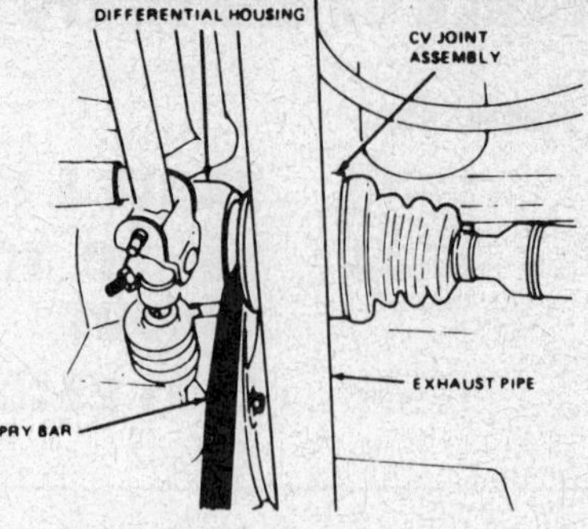


**Fig. 2 Removing halfshaft from differential housing**

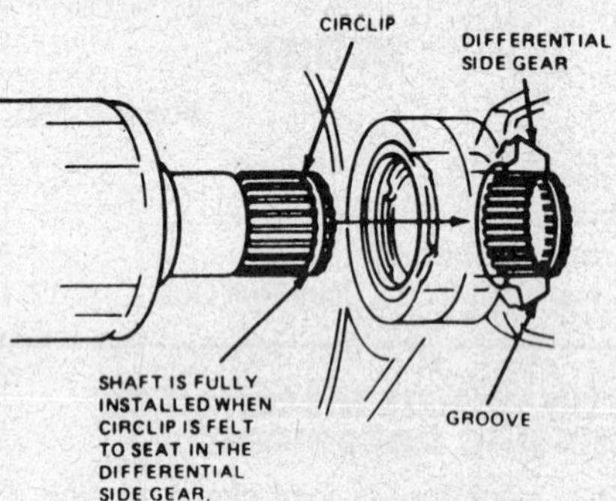


**Fig. 4 Installing inner constant velocity joint into differential side gear**

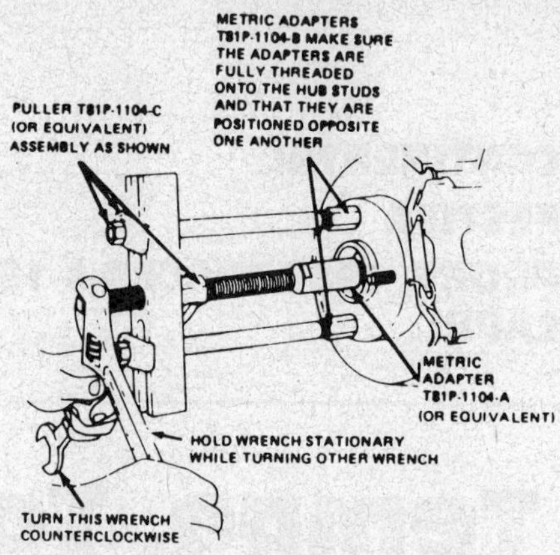


**Fig. 3 Separating outer constant velocity joint from hub**

# CONSTANT VELOCITY JOINT SERVICE

## REMOVAL

### Except 5 Speed Manual Transaxle Inboard Constant Velocity Joint & Boot

1. Place halfshaft in suitable vise. Use caution not to damage boot or clamp.
2. Cut large boot clamp and remove from boot, **Fig. 5,** then position boot upward on shaft. If boot only is being replaced due to damage, check joint grease for contamination. If joints were operating satisfactorily and grease is not contaminated, add grease and install new boot. If grease is contaminated, joint must be completely disassembled.
3. Place interconnecting shaft in a suitable vise and angle constant velocity joint so that inner bearing race is exposed, **Fig. 6.**
4. Using suitable drift and hammer, tap inner bearing race to dislodge internal circlip and separate constant velocity joint from interconnecting shaft, being careful not to drop joint.
5. Remove boot from shaft, cutting remaining clamp as necessary.
6. Remove circlip from end of shaft and discard. Inspect stop ring for damage and replace as necessary.

### Inboard Constant Velocity Joint & Boot, 5 Speed Manual Transaxle

1. Remove large boot clamp, roll boot back, and wipe away excess grease.
2. Remove wire ring bearing retainer from outer race, then remove outer race.
3. Pull inner race and bearing assembly out until it rests on circlip, then, using suitable pliers, spread stop ring and move it back on shaft.
4. Slide inner race and bearing assembly down shaft to expose circlip, then remove circlip.
5. Remove inner race and bearing assembly and, if necessary, remove boot.

## INSTALLATION

### Joints Except 5 Speed Manual Transmission Inboard Constant Velocity Joint & Boot

1. Install new stop ring, if removed. Ensure that stop ring is properly seated in groove.
2. Install new circlip in groove nearest end of shaft. To avoid over-expansion or twisting of circlip, start one end in groove and work circlip over stub shaft end and into groove. **Interconnecting shafts are different depending on application. These shafts are non-symmetrical. Outboard end is approximately 1/4 inch longer, from end of shaft to end of boot groove, than inboard end. Be careful to install inboard and outboard constant velocity joints to proper ends of shaft.**
3. Install constant velocity joint boot, if removed, ensuring that boot is seated in groove. Tighten clamp securely, but not too tight.
4. Before positioning boot over constant velocity joint, pack joint and boot as follows:
    a. **On inboard constant velocity joint,** fill boot with 45 grams of grease and pack joint with 90 grams of grease.
    b. **On outboard constant velocity joint,** fill boot with 45 grams of grease and pack joint with 45 grams of grease. **Use only lubricant E2FZ-19590-A or equivalent.**
5. Position boot upward toward end of shaft, then position constant velocity joint onto shaft and tap into position using plastic mallet. Joint is fully seated when circlip locks in groove cut

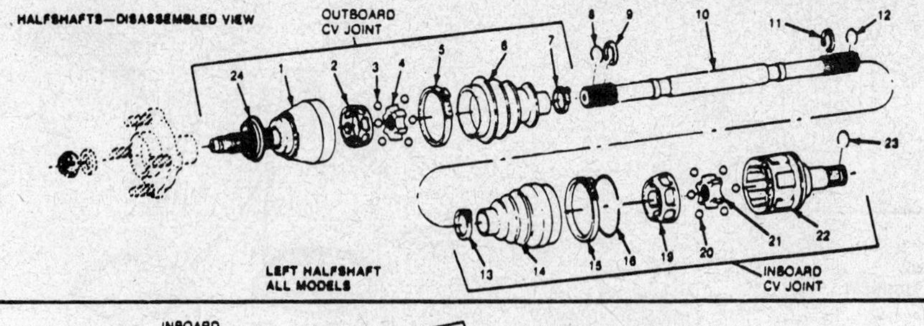


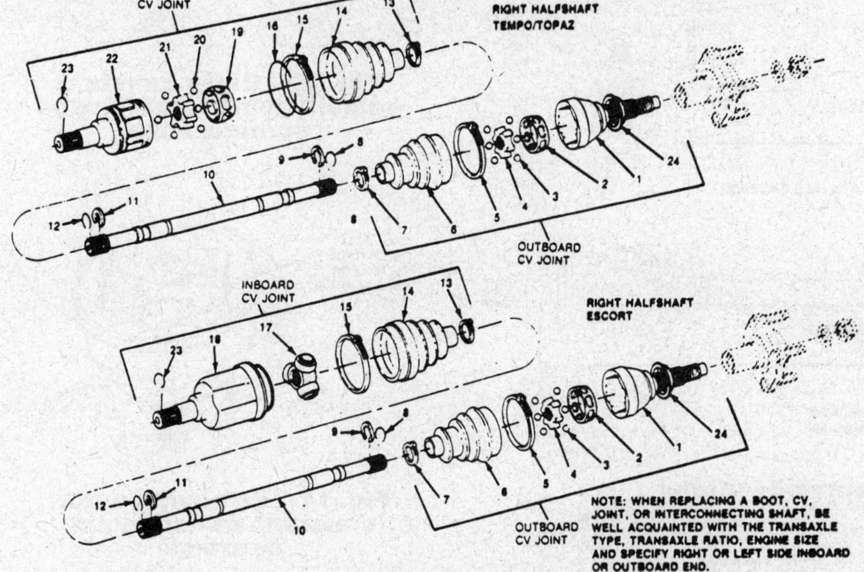


LEGEND:

| | | | |
|---|---|---|---|
| 1. | OUTBOARD JOINT OUTER RACE AND STUB SHAFT | 13. | BOOT CLAMP (SMALL) |
| 2. | BALL CAGE | 14. | BOOT |
| 3. | BALLS (SIX) | 15. | BOOT CLAMP (LARGE) |
| 4. | OUTBOARD JOINT INNER RACE | 16. | WIRE RING BALL RETAINER |
| 5. | BOOT CLAMP (LARGE) | 17. | TRIPOD ASSY |
| 6. | BOOT | 18. | TRIPOD OUTER RACE |
| 7. | BOOT CLAMP (SMALL) | 19. | BALL CAGE |
| 8. | CIRCLIP | 20. | BALLS (SIX) |
| 9. | STOP RING | 21. | INBOARD JOINT INNER RACE |
| 10. | INTERCONNECTING SHAFT | 22. | INBOARD JOINT OUTER RACE AND STUB SHAFT |
| 11. | STOP RING | 23. | CIRCLIP |
| 12. | CIRCLIP | 24. | DUST SEAL |

**Fig. 5 Halfshaft assemblies**

into joint bearing inner race. Check for proper seating by trying to pull joint from shaft.

6. Remove all excess grease from external surfaces of constant velocity joint, then position boot over constant velocity joint and move joint in or out to adjust to proper length, **Fig. 7.**
7. Before installing boot clamp, insert dulled screwdriver blade between boot and outer bearing race to allow trapped air to escape.
8. Ensure that boot is seated in groove, then install clamp securely but not too tight.

### Inboard Constant Velocity Joint & Boot, 5 Speed Manual Transmission

1. Move circlip and stop ring back into their respective grooves on shaft. **Lefthand interconnecting shaft is symmetrical and inboard and outboard constant velocity joints may be installed on either end. Righthand interconnecting shaft is non-symmetrical and care must be taken so that inboard and outboard constant velocity joints are correctly installed, Fig. 8 and 9.**
2. Install constant velocity joint boot, if removed. Ensure that boot is seated in groove, then install clamp securely but not too tight.
3. Install new circlip in groove nearest end of shaft. To avoid over-expansion or twisting of circlip, start one end in groove and work circlip over stub shaft end and into groove.
4. Fill boot with 45 grams of grease and fill outer race with 90 grams of grease. Use only lubricant E2FZ-19590-A or equivalent.
5. Push inner race and bearing assembly into outer race by hand.
6. Install ball retainer into groove inside outer race.
7. With boot positioned upward toward end of shaft, install constant velocity joint using suitable hammer. Ensure that splines are aligned before hammering constant velocity joint onto shaft.

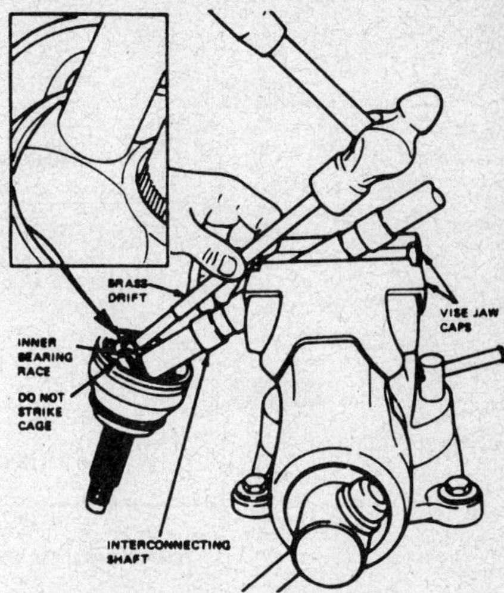


**Fig. 6 Separating constant velocity joint from shaft**

8. Remove all excess grease from external surfaces of constant velocity joint, then position boot over constant velocity joint and move joint in or out to adjust to proper length, **Fig. 7.**
9. Before installing boot clamp, insert dulled screwdriver blade between boot and outer bearing race to allow trapped air to escape.
10. Ensure that boot is seated in groove, then install clamp securely but not too tight.

## OUTER JOINT SERVICE

### Disassembly & Assembly

Different bearing cages are used on the outer joints. One type contains four equal sized windows and two elongated windows while the other type contains six windows of equal size, **Fig. 10.**

1. Position stub shaft in suitable vise with bearing facing upward.
2. Press downward on inner race until bearing can be removed, **Fig. 11.** Remove all six bearings in this manner.
3. Pivot bearing cage and inner race assembly into position shown in **Fig. 12.** Align cage windows with outer race lands while pivoting cage, **Fig. 13,** then remove from outer race.
4. To separate inner race from cage, determine cage design and proceed as follows: on cages with six equal windows rotate inner race upward and remove from cage. **On cages with two elongated windows,** pivot inner race until it is in position shown in **Fig. 12,** then align one inner race band with one elongated window and position race through the window. Rotate inner race upward and remove from cage, **Fig. 14.**
5. Reverse procedure to assemble. Refer to **Fig. 15,** for ball groove and window alignment and proper counterbore positioning.

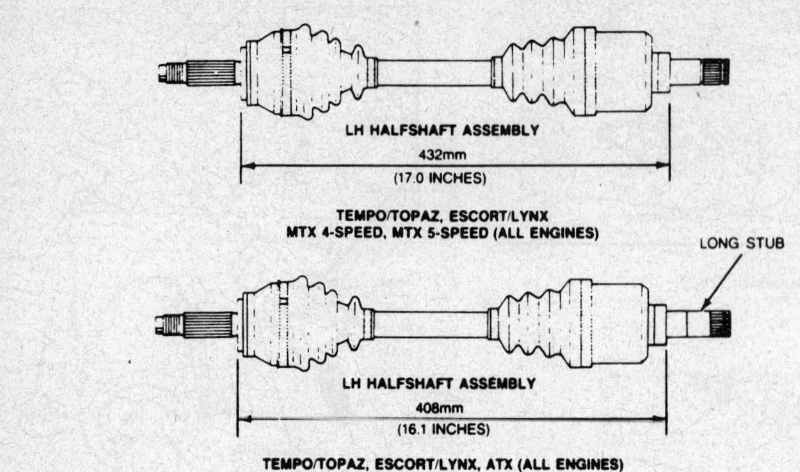


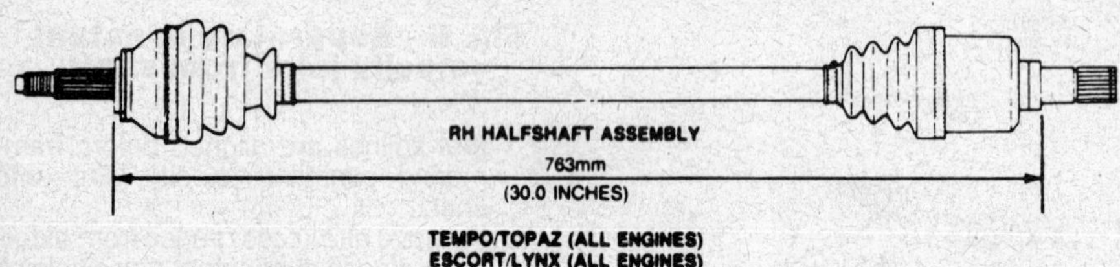


**Fig. 7 Halfshaft assembled lengths**

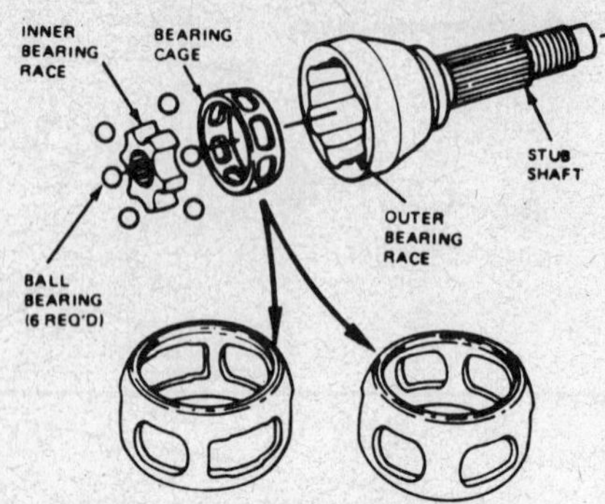


**Fig. 10 Outer constant velocity joint bearing cage configuration**

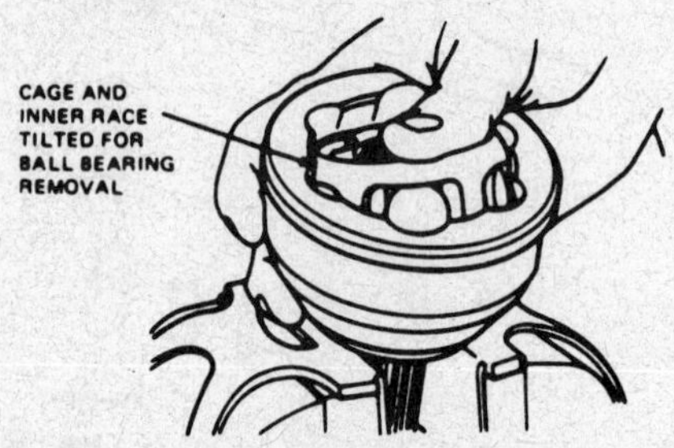


**Fig. 11 Removing outer constant velocity joint bearings**

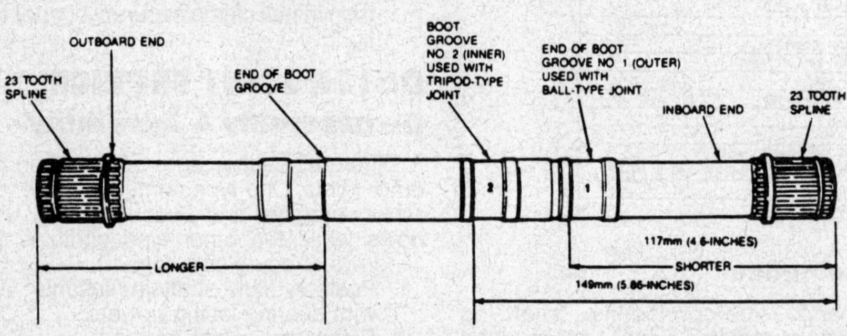


**Fig. 8 Interconnecting shaft. 1989–90**

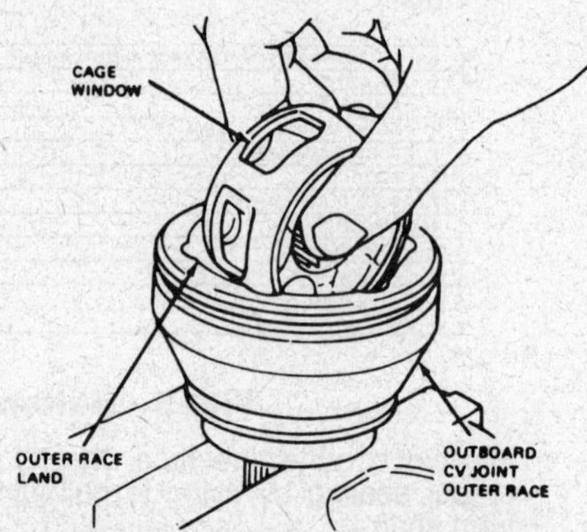


**Fig. 12 Removing bearing cage & inner race assembly from outer constant velocity joint**

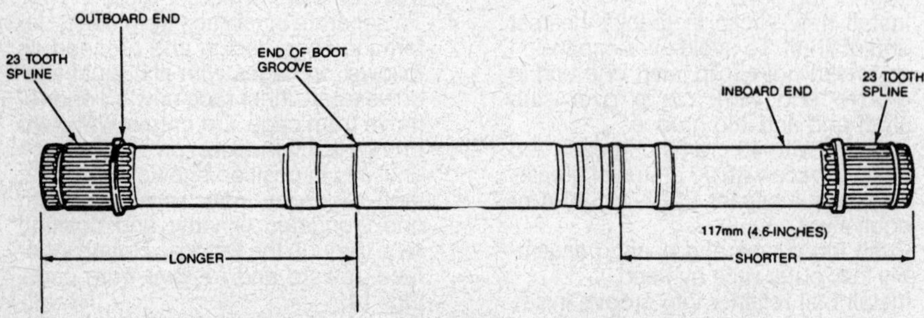


**Fig. 9 Interconnecting shaft. 1991**

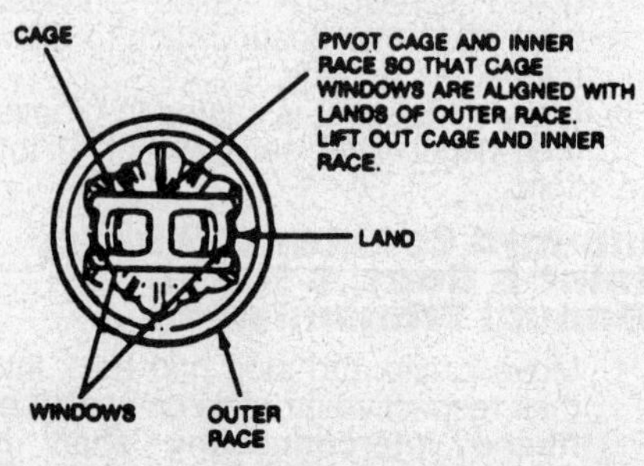


**Fig. 13 Aligning inner cage & bearing race**

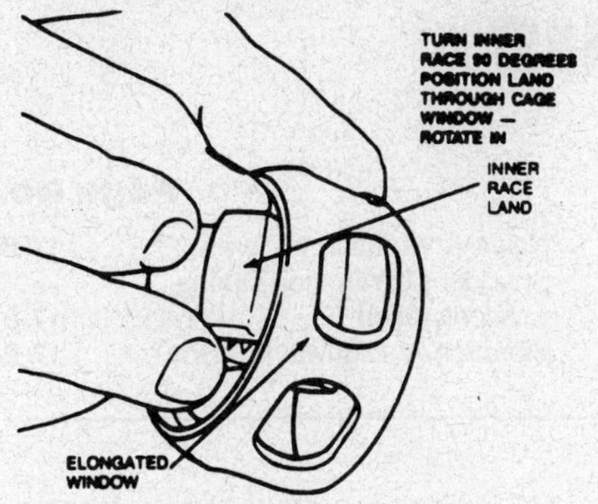


**Fig. 14 Removing inner race from bearing cage**

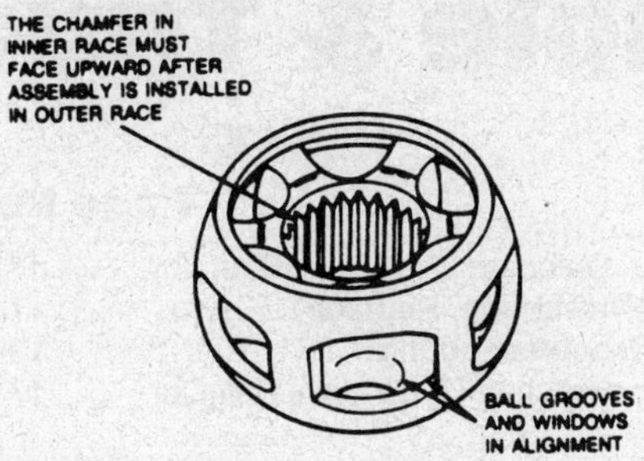

**Fig. 15 Counterbore positioning & ball groove & window alignment**

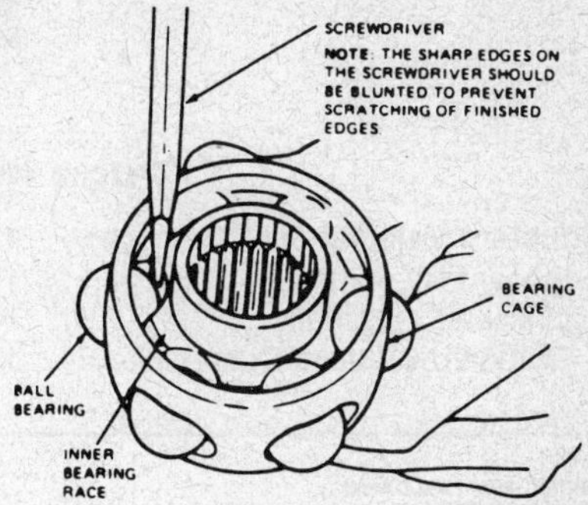

**Fig. 17 Removing bearings from cage**

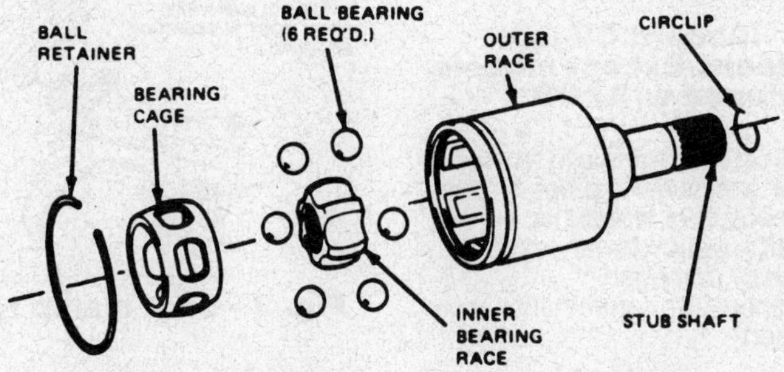

**Fig. 16 Inner constant velocity joint assembly. Wire ring ball retainer type**

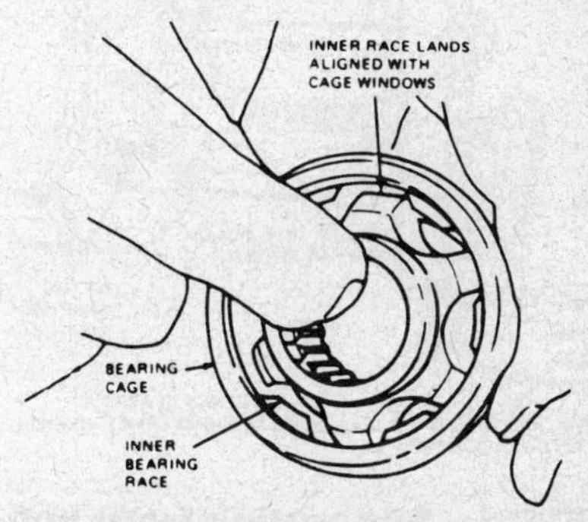


**Fig. 18 Removing inner race from bearing cage**

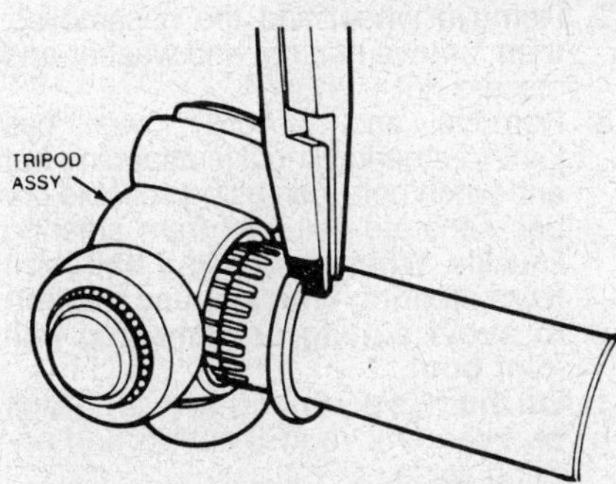


**Fig. 19 Removing snap ring from shaft**

## INNER JOINT SERVICE

### Wire Ring Ball Retainer Type

1. Remove large clamp, then slide boot back and wipe excess grease, **Fig. 16. Inspect CV joint grease for contamination by rubbing a small amount between two fingers. Any gritty feeling indicates contamination. If grease is contaminated, proceed with disassembly. If grease is not contaminated and joint was operating satisfactorily, add grease and replace boot.**
2. Using a suitable tool, remove wire ring ball retainer from race.
3. Remove outer race.
4. Pull inner race and bearing assembly out until race contacts snap ring.
5. Using suitable pliers, spread then slide snap ring back onto shaft.
6. Slide inner race and bearing assembly down the shaft to allow access to the snap ring.
7. Using a suitable screwdriver, remove snap ring.
8. Remove inner race and bearing assembly.
9. Remove bearings from cage by prying with a dulled screwdriver. Use caution not to damage or scratch any components, **Fig. 17.**
10. Rotate inner race to align lands with cage windows, then remove race from bearing cage through wider end of cage, **Fig. 18.**
11. Reverse procedure to assemble. Fill CV joint outer race with 3.2 ounces of grease and spread 1.4 ounces in CV boot. Use Ford Constant Velocity Joint Grease (High Temperature) E43Z-19590-A or equivalent.

### Tripot CV Joint, RH Side, Escort

1. Remove large clamp, then slide boot back and wipe off excess grease. **Inspect CV joint grease for contamination by rubbing a small amount between two fingers. Any gritty feeling indicates contamination. If grease is contaminated, proceed with disassembly. If grease is not contaminated and joint was operating satisfactorily, add grease and replace boot.**
2. Using suitable pliers, bend retaining tabs back and separate outer race from tripot assembly.
3. Using suitable snap ring pliers, slide snap ring back on shaft, **Fig. 19.**
4. Push tripot assembly back on shaft, to gain access to circlip, then remove circlip from shaft.
5. Remove tripot assembly from shaft, and boot if necessary.
6. Reverse procedure to install noting the following:
   a. Fill CV joint outer race with 3.5 ounces of grease and CV boot with 2.1 ounces of grease. Use Ford Constant Velocity Joint Grease/High Temperature E43Z-19590-A or equivalent.

# Sable & Taurus

## INDEX



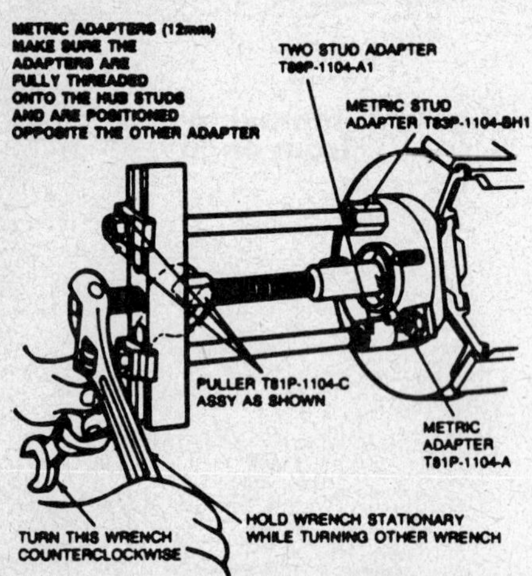


**Fig. 1 Separating front hub from outer CV joint**

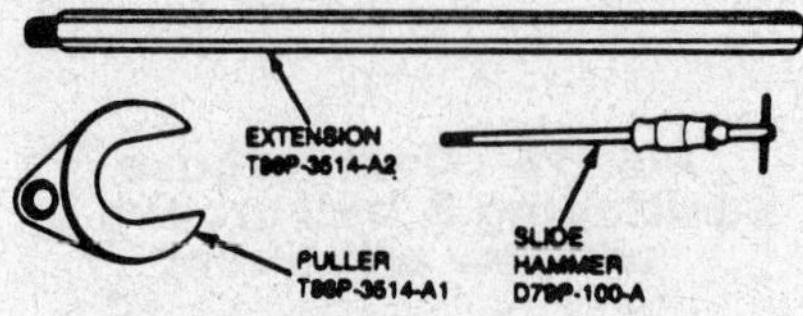


**Fig. 2 Inboard CV joint removal tools. Except models equipped w/AXOD**

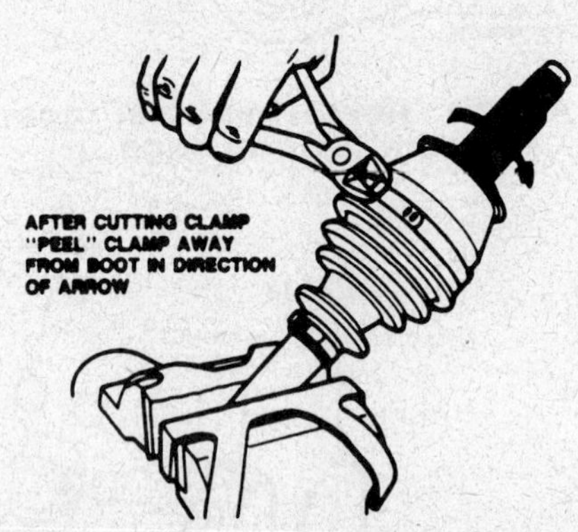


**Fig. 3 Boot clamp removal**

# TROUBLESHOOTING

## NOISE & VIBRATION IN TURNS

Clicking, popping or grinding noises while turning may be caused by the following:

1. Cut or damaged CV joint boots, resulting in contaminated lube in outboard or inboard CV joints.
2. Loose CV joint clamps.
3. Worn, damaged or improperly installed wheel bearings.
4. Foreign object contacting halfshaft assembly.

## VIBRATION AT HIGHWAY SPEEDS

1. Out of balance front wheels or tires.
2. Improperly seated outboard CV joint in front wheel hub.
3. Bent interconnecting shaft.
4. Front tires out of round.

## SHUDDER OR VIBRATION DURING ACCELERATION

1. Excessively worn or damaged inboard or outboard CV joint.
2. Excessively high CV joint operating angles caused by improper ride height.

## HALFSHAFT OR CV JOINT PULL-OUT

1. Inboard CV joint circlip missing or improperly seated in transaxle side gear.
2. Engine or transaxle improperly positioned, check engine mounts.
3. Frame rail or strut tower improperly positioned or damaged.
4. Front suspension components worn or damaged.

# DRIVESHAFTS

## REPLACE

**If removing both right and left side halfshafts, plugs T81P-1177-B or equivalent must be installed. Failure to do so may result in dislocation of differential side gears, necessitating transaxle disassembly to realign the gears. Also, halfshaft removal and installation procedures are the same for automatic and manual transaxles except for the following: due to the automatic transaxle case configuration, the right side halfshaft and linkshaft must be removed first. Tool T81P-4026-A or equivalent is then inserted into transaxle to remove left side inner Constant Velocity (CV) joint assembly from transaxle. If only the left side halfshaft is being removed from the vehicle, remove right side halfshaft assembly from the transaxle case and secure it in a horizontal position to the underside of vehicle, then remove left side halfshaft assembly.**

**Do not begin this removal procedure unless the following parts are known to be available, a new hub retainer nut, a new lower control arm to steering knuckle attaching nut and bolt, a new inboard CV joint stub shaft circlip and a new link shaft snap ring. Once removed these components must not be reused. Their torque holding ability or retention capability is greatly diminished during removal.**

**Whenever removed, the hub nut, lower control arm-to-steering knuckle attaching nut and bolt and inboard CV joint stub shaft circlip must be replaced as their torque holding ability is destroyed during removal.**

1. Loosen hub nut and lug nuts, then raise and support front of vehicle.
2. Remove wheel and tire assemblies, then remove hub nut and washer and discard nut.
3. Remove and discard lower ball joint-to-steering knuckle attaching nut and pinch bolt, then using suitable pry bar, separate ball joint from steering knuckle. **When separating ball joint from steering knuckle, use caution to avoid cutting or damaging ball joint boot.**
4. **On models equipped with anti-lock brakes,** remove ABS sensor and position aside.
5. **On all models,** remove stabilizer bar link at stabilizer bar.
6. To remove right side halfshaft and linkshaft from all models equipped with manual transaxle and Fluid Lock-up Converter (FLC), proceed as follows:
   a. Remove two bearing support-to-bracket attaching bolts, then slide link shaft out of transaxle. Support end of shaft in horizontal position with suitable wire. **Do not allow shaft to hang unsupported as damage to the outboard CV joint can result.**
   b. Separate hub assembly from outer CV joint using hub remover T81P-1104-C, adapters T83P-1104-BH, T86P-1104-A1 and T81P-1104-A or equivalent, **Fig. 1. Never use a hammer to separate hub assembly from outer CV joint as damage to the CV joint threads and internal components may result.**

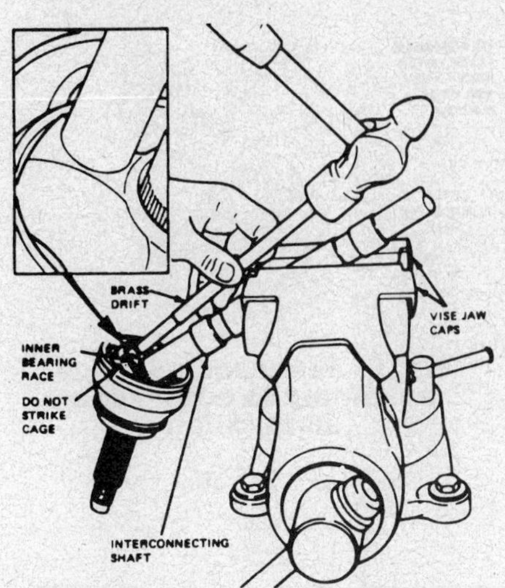


**Fig. 4 Removing internal snap ring**

c. Remove right side halfshaft and linkshaft from vehicle as an assembly.

7. To remove both halfshafts on models equipped with Automatic Overdrive Transaxle (AXOD) or left side halfshaft on models equipped with manual transaxle, proceed as follows:
   a. Turn steering hub to one side or wire and/or wire strut assembly aside.
   b. Using puller tools shown in **Fig. 2**, attached to the inboard side of the inboard CV joint, remove CV joint from transaxle.
   c. Support end of shaft in horizontal position with suitable wire. **Do not allow shaft to hang unsupported as damage to the outboard CV joint can result.**
   d. Separate hub assembly from outer CV joint using hub remover T81P-1104-C, adapters T83P-1104-BH, T86P-1104-A1 and T81P-1104-A or equivalent, **Fig. 1. Never use a hammer to separate hub assembly from outer CV joint as damage to the CV joint threads and internal components may result.**
   e. Remove halfshaft from vehicle.
8. To remove left side halfshaft from models equipped with Fluid Lockup Converter (FLC), proceed as follows. **If removing both right and left side halfshafts, plugs T81P-1177-B or equivalent must be installed. Failure to do so may result in dislocation of differential side gears, necessitating transaxle disassembly to re-align the gears.**
   a. Remove right side halfshaft assembly from the transaxle case and secure it in a horizontal position to the underside of vehicle, then remove left side halfshaft by inserting driver T81P-4026-A or equivalent into right side halfshaft opening and driving left side halfshaft and CV joint from transaxle.
   b. Support end of shaft in horizontal position with suitable wire. **Do not allow shaft to hang unsupported as damage to the outboard CV joint can result.**
   c. Separate hub assembly from outer CV joint using hub remover T81P-1104-C, adapters T83P-1104-BH, T86P-1104-A1 and T81P-1104-A or equivalent, **Fig. 1. Never use a hammer to separate hub assembly from outer CV joint as damage to the CV joint threads and internal components may result.**
   d. Remove halfshaft from vehicle.
9. Prior to installation install new circlip on inboard CV joint stub shaft and/or linkshaft. **The original circlip cannot be reused.** On models equipped with manual transaxle and FLC, **torque** linkshaft bearing to 16-23 ft. lbs.
10. Align CV joint splines with transaxle differential splines, then push CV joint into differential splines until circlip is felt to seat inside side gears. **Some force may be necessary to insert CV joints. Ensure differential oil seal is not damaged during installation. If difficulty is encountered installing CV joints, a non-metallic mallet may be used on the outside joint CV joint stub shaft.**
11. Align CV joint splines with hub splines, then install stub shaft in hub as far as possible.
12. Temporarily fasten rotor to hub with two lug nuts and suitable washers. Install steel rod between lug nuts and use to prevent rotor from turning.
13. Install hub washer and new hub nut, then manually thread nut onto CV joint stub shaft as far as possible.
14. Connect steering knuckle to lower ball joint stud, then install new nut and bolt and **torque** to 40-55 ft. lbs.

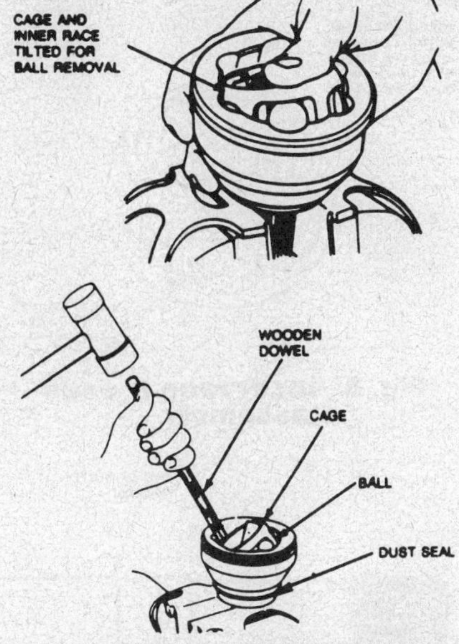


**Fig. 5 CV joint ball removal**

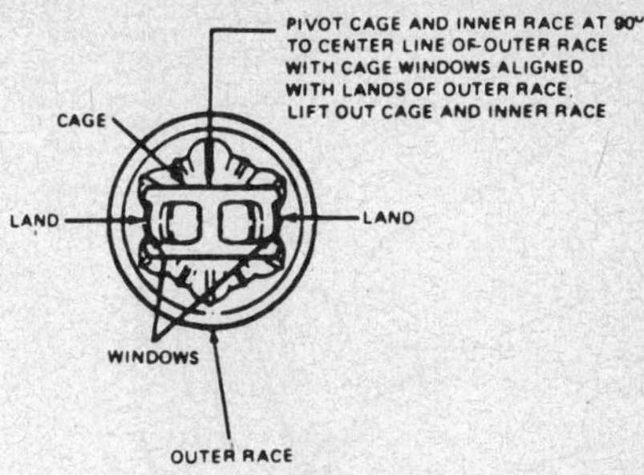


**Fig. 6 Cage & inner race removal**

15. **On models equipped with anti-lock brakes,** install ABS sensor.
16. **On all models,** connect stabilizer bar to stabilizer bar link, **torque** to 38-48 ft. lbs.
17. Install wheel and tire assembly, then lower vehicle to ground. **Torque** hub nut to 180-200 ft. lbs., **torque** wheel lug nuts to 80-105 ft. lbs.
18. Top off transaxle with lubricant using ESP-M2C185-A Mercon or equivalent.

# CONSTANT VELOCITY JOINT SERVICE

## OUTBOARD CV JOINT & BOOT

### Disassembly

During manufacture, CV joints components are matched and cannot be interchanged with components of other CV joint. If a CV joint component is defective, the entire CV joint should be replaced.

1. Install soft vise jaw caps in vise to prevent damage to halfshaft, then position halfshaft in vise. Do not allow the vise to contact the CV joint boot or clamps.
2. Using suitable side cutting pliers, cut large boot clamp and peel away from boot. Roll boot back over halfshaft, **Fig. 3.**
3. Turn halfshaft over in vise, then angle CV joint so that inner bearing race is exposed, **Fig. 4.** Using suitable brass drift and hammer, give a sharp rap to inner bearing race to dislodge internal snap ring. Separate CV joint from halfshaft. Take care not to drop the CV joint. Remove CV boot from shaft.
4. Inspect CV joint grease for contamination. If grease is contaminated, proceed with disassembly. If grease is not contaminated and joint was operating satisfactorily, add grease and replace boot.
5. Remove and discard circlip from end of shaft. Inspect stop ring located below circlip, if it is worn or damaged, replace it.
6. Clamp CV joint stub axle in vise with soft vise jaw caps. Be careful not to damage dust seal.
7. Push down on CV joint inner race until it tilts enough to allow ball removal, **Fig. 5. If inner race is tight, it can be tilted by tapping inner race with**

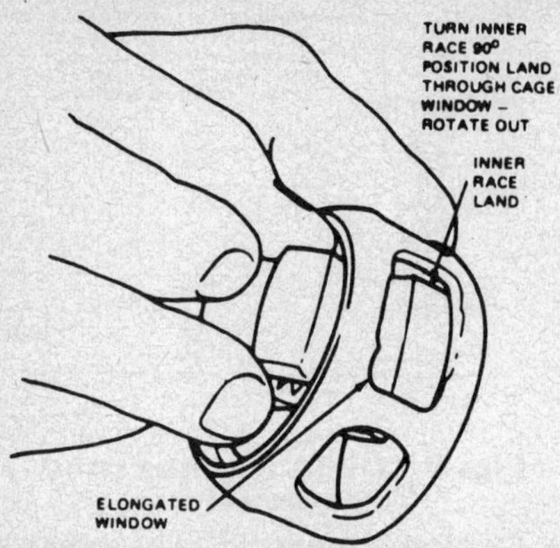


**Fig. 7 Inner race removal & installation**

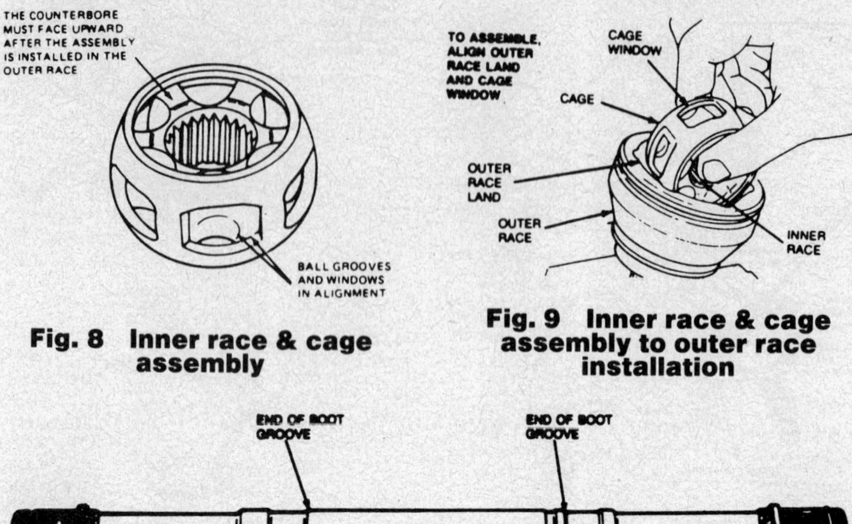


**Fig. 8 Inner race & cage assembly**

**Fig. 9 Inner race & cage assembly to outer race installation**

**wooden dowel and hammer. Do not hit cage.**

8. Remove balls from cage. If balls are tight, use blunt screwdriver to pry balls from cage.
9. Pivot cage and inner race assembly until its straight up, **Fig. 6.** Align cage windows with outer race lands while pivoting bearing cage, then lift out cage and inner race.
10. Rotate inner race up and out of cage, **Fig. 7.**

END OF BOOT GROOVE
END OF BOOT GROOVE
OUTBOARD SHORTER
INBOARD LONGER

**Fig. 10 Halfshaft end identification**

### Inspection

During manufacture, CV joints components are matched and cannot be interchanged with components of other CV joint. If a CV joint component is defective, the entire CV joint should be replaced.

Inspect all parts. If any parts are cracked, broken, severely pitted, worn or otherwise unserviceable, replace CV joint. If any parts appear polished, do not replace CV joint as this is a normal condition.

### Assembly

1. Apply light coating of Ford constant velocity joint grease No. E2FZ-19590-A or equivalent on inner and outer races, then install inner race in bearing cage, **Fig. 7.**
2. Install inner race and cage assembly in outer race land, **Fig. 8.**
3. Install CV joint assembly into outer race and pivot 90° into position, **Fig. 9.**
4. Align bearing cage and inner race with outer race, then tilt inner race and install a ball, followed by remaining five balls.
5. Determine which end of halfshaft is for outboard CV joint. The outboard joint side has a shorter end of boot groove to end of shaft dimension, **Fig. 10.**
6. Install CV joint boot and small boot clamp. If stop ring was removed, install at this time. If stop ring was not removed, ensure it is seated properly in groove.
7. Install new circlip, **Fig. 11. Do not over expand or twist the circlip during installation. To install properly, start one end in the groove and work the circlip over the stub shaft and into the circlip groove.**
8. Pack CV joint with Ford CV joint grease No. E2FZ-19590-A or equivalent. Correct quantity is 3.52 ounces on 1989 models, or 3.17 ounces on 1990 models. Any remaining grease is to be spread evenly inside CV boot.
9. With boot peeled back, position CV joint on halfshaft and tap into position with suitable plastic hammer. The CV joint is properly seated when the circlip locks into position. Check for proper retention by attempting to pull off CV joint.
10. Remove all excess grease from CV external surfaces, then position boot over CV joint. Ensure boot is seated in its groove and install clamp.

## OUTBOARD CV JOINT DUST SEAL

### Disassembly

1. With halfshaft removed, use a light duty hammer and screwdriver to tap evenly around seal until unseated and remove seal, **Fig. 12.**

### Assembly

Using spindle/axle seal tool T83T-3132-A1 and dust seal installer tool T83P-3425-AH or equivalent, install dust seal, **Fig. 13.** The dust seal flange must face outboard.

## INBOARD CV JOINT

### Disassembly

These models use two different types of inboard CV joints and boots, **Fig. 14.** The first one is of a conventional boot design that uses a crimped can on the large end. The other is a tri-lobe design CV joint that does not require a crimped can on the large end. Although both designs are similar, they are not interchangeable.

1. Cut and remove both large and small boot clamps from CV joint, then slide boot back on shaft. **All right side inboard CV joints use a re-usable low profile large boot clamp. Do not cut this clamp as it will be re-used.**
2. Slide outer race off tripot assembly. Inspect CV joint grease for contamination by rubbing a small amount between two fingers. Any gritty feeling indicates contamination. If grease is contaminated, proceed with disassembly. If grease is not contaminated and joint was operating satisfactorily, add grease and replace boot.
3. Using suitable snap ring pliers, slide stop ring back on shaft.
4. Slide tripot assembly back on shaft to provide clearance to circlip, then remove circlip, tripot assembly and boot.

### Assembly

1. Install CV boot on shaft. Ensure boot small end is seated properly in halfshaft groove, then tighten small end clamp.
2. Install tripot assembly on shaft with chamfered side toward stop ring, then install new circlip. **Circlips cannot be re-used. They must be replaced with new ones.**
3. Slide tripot assembly forward to expose stop ring groove, then slide stop ring into position. Ensure stop ring is fully seated in groove.
4. **On models with conventional design boots, Fig. 14,** fill CV joint outer race with 3.5 ounces and CV boot

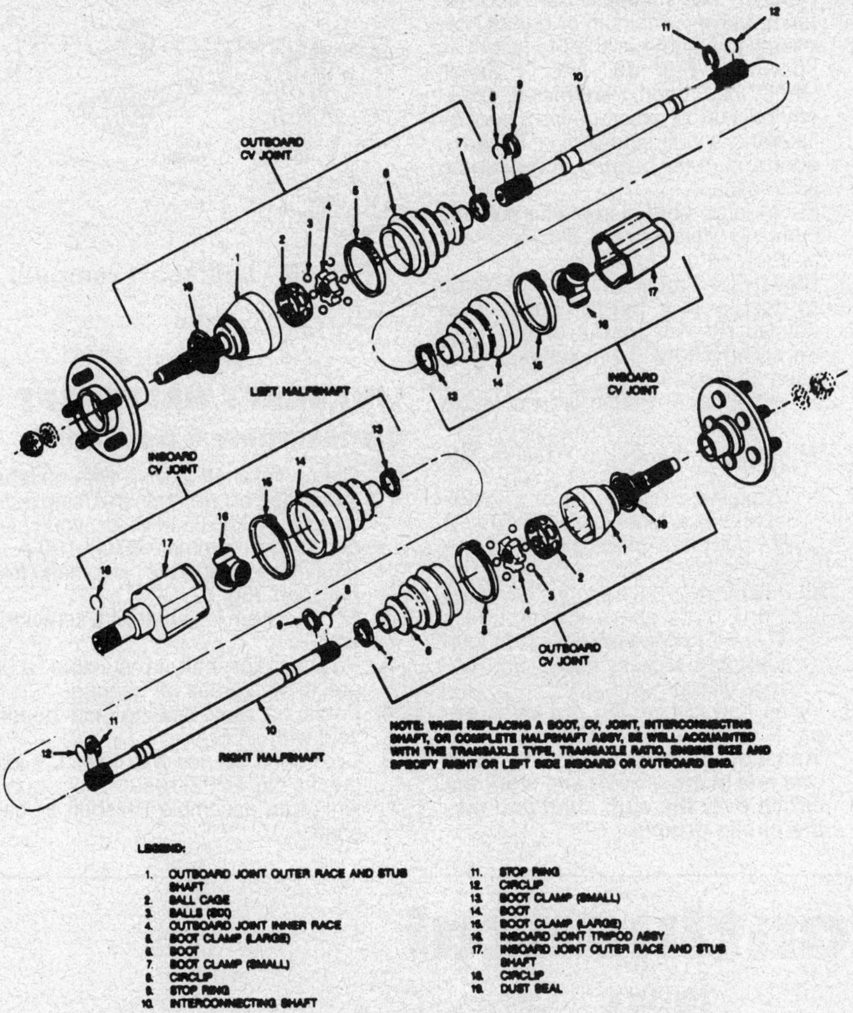

NOTE: WHEN REPLACING A BOOT, CV, JOINT, INTERCONNECTING SHAFT, OR COMPLETE HALFSHAFT ASSY, BE WELL ACQUAINTED WITH THE TRANSAXLE TYPE, TRANSAXLE RATIO, ENGINE SIZE AND SPECIFY RIGHT OR LEFT SIDE INBOARD OR OUTBOARD END.

LEGEND:

1. OUTBOARD JOINT OUTER RACE AND STUB SHAFT
2. BALL CAGE
3. BALLS (SIX)
4. OUTBOARD JOINT INNER RACE
5. BOOT CLAMP (LARGE)
6. BOOT
7. BOOT CLAMP (SMALL)
8. CIRCLIP
9. STOP RING
10. INTERCONNECTING SHAFT
11. STOP RING
12. CIRCLIP
13. BOOT CLAMP (SMALL)
14. BOOT
15. BOOT CLAMP (LARGE)
16. INBOARD JOINT TRIPOD ASSY
17. INBOARD JOINT OUTER RACE AND STUB SHAFT
18. CIRCLIP
19. DUST SEAL

**Fig. 11 Exploded view of halfshaft assemblies**

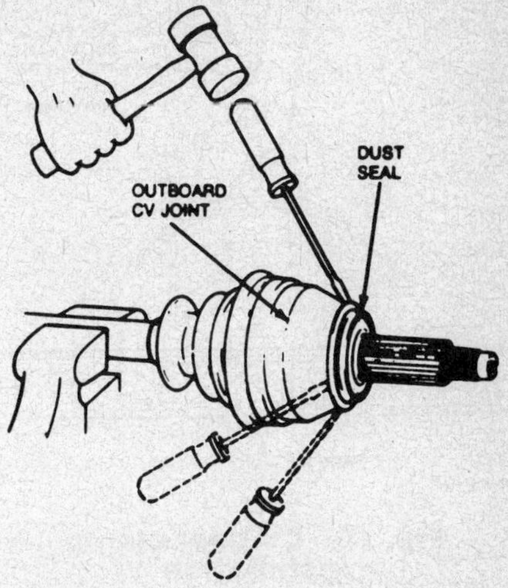

**Fig. 12 Dust seal removal**

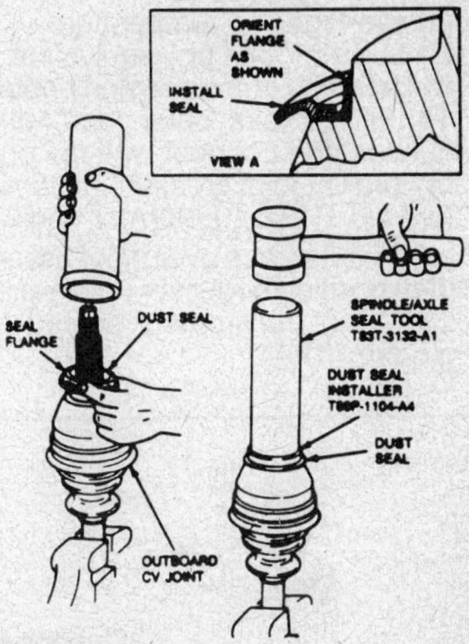

**Fig. 13 Dust seal installation**

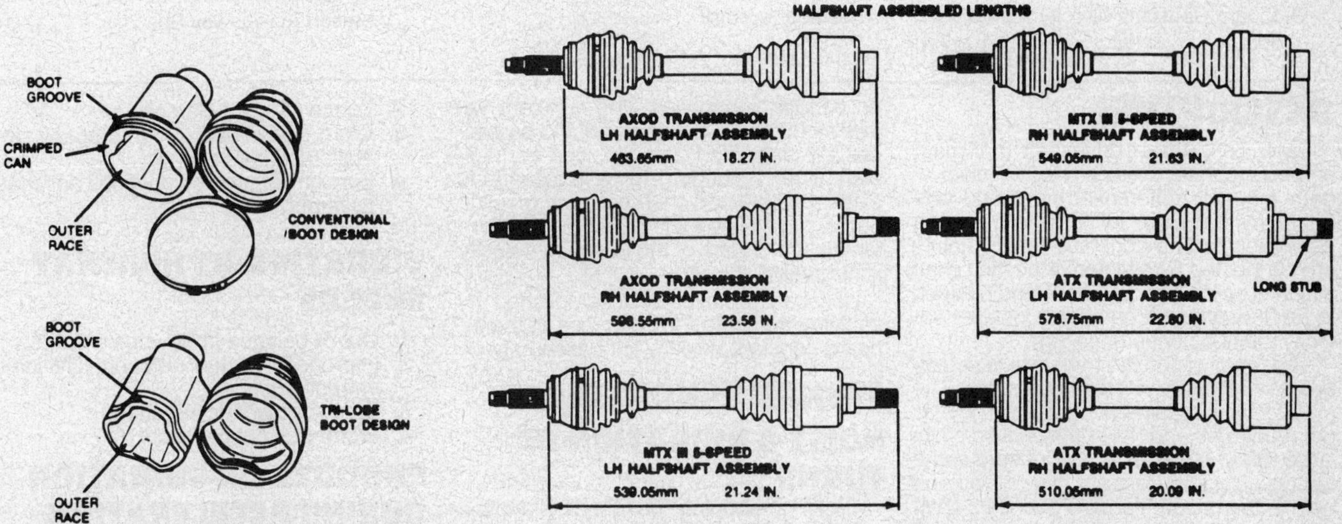


**Fig. 14 CV joint identification**

**Fig. 15 Halfshaft assembled length**

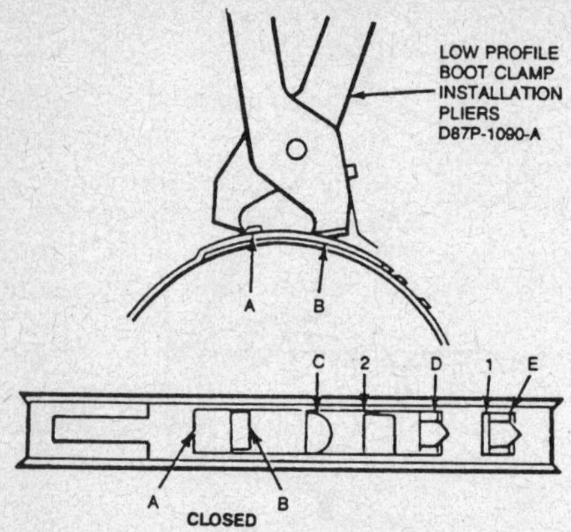


**Fig. 16 CV boot clamp installation**

with 2.5 ounces of Ford CV joint grease-high temperature No. E43Z-19590-A or equivalent. On models with tri-lobe design boots, **Fig. 14,** fill CV joint outer race with 4.4 ounces and CV boot with 4.4 ounces of Ford CV joint grease-high temperature No. E43Z-19590-A or equivalent.

5. Install outer race over tripot assembly, then position boot over outer race. Ensure boot is properly seated in its groove.
6. Remove excess grease from boot exterior. Move CV joint in or out as necessary to adjust halfshaft to length as shown in **Fig. 15.** After halfshaft length has been determined, expel any built up air pressure from boot by inserting a dull screwdriver between boot and outer bearing and allowing air to escape.
7. Install large boot clamp with suitable crimping pliers tool No. D87P-1098-A or equivalent.
8. **Right side inboard CV joints use a re-usable low profile large boot clamp. Do not install clamp with crimping pliers.** To install boot proceed as follows:
   a. With boot seated in groove, install clamp.
   b. Engage hook (C) in window, **Fig. 16.**
   c. Using low profile boot clamp installation pliers tool No. D87P-1090-A or equivalent, place pincer jaws in closing hooks (A and B).
   d. Pull closing hooks together, when 1 and 2 are above locking hooks (D and E) spring tab will press window over locking hooks and engage clamp.
9. Install new circlip. **Do not over expand or twist the circlip during installation. To install properly, start one end in the groove and work the circlip over the stub shaft and into the circlip groove.**

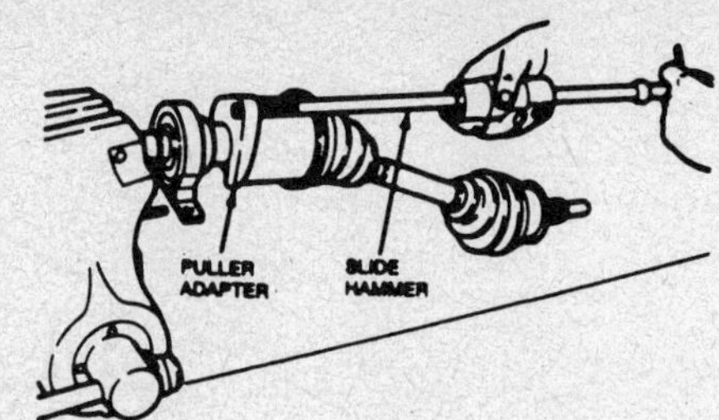


**Fig. 17 Linkshaft removal**

## LINKSHAFT/HALFSHAFT

### Disassembly & Assembly

1. Clamp linkshaft in vise with halfshaft supported on workbench. Using puller adapter T86P-3514-A or equivalent and slide hammer D79P-100-A or equivalent, separate linkshaft from halfshaft, **Fig. 17.**
2. Pry seal from linkshaft with screwdriver.
3. Position linkshaft in suitable arbor press, then press off bearing.
4. Press on new bearing and bearing seal with arbor press.
5. Coat shaft splines with Ford CV joint grease No. E2FZ-19590-A or equivalent, then assemble linkshaft to halfshaft.

# Continental

## INDEX



## DESCRIPTION

Each front wheel driveshaft (halfshaft) employs constant velocity (CV) joints at both inboard (differential side) and outboard (wheel side) for vehicle operating smoothness. The constant velocity joints are connected by an interconnecting shaft which is splined at both ends and retained in the inboard and outboard constant velocity joints by snap rings, **Fig. 1.**

The inboard constant velocity joint may be either a tripod joint or a triplan joint. The tripod joint is repairable. The triplan joint is not repairable and may be identified by its large round outer race. The inboard constant velocity joint stub shaft is splined and held in the differential side gear by a snap ring. The outboard constant velocity joint stub shaft is pressed on and secured with a prevailing torque nut. The constant velocity joints are lube-for-life with a special constant velocity joint grease and require no periodic lubrication. The constant velocity joint boots, however, should be periodically inspected and replaced immediately when damage or grease leakage is evident. Continued operation may result in constant velocity joint failure due to contamination or loss of the constant velocity joint grease.

Halfshaft removal is accomplished by applying a load to the back face of the inboard constant velocity joint assembly.

## TROUBLESHOOTING

### NOISE & VIBRATION IN TURNS

Clicking, popping or grinding noises while turning may be caused by the following:

1. Cut or damaged CV joint boots, resulting in contaminated lube in outboard or inboard CV joints.
2. Loose CV joint clamps.
3. Worn, damaged or improperly installed wheel bearings.
4. Foreign object contacting halfshaft assembly.

### VIBRATION AT HIGHWAY SPEEDS

1. Out of balance front wheels or tires.
2. Improperly seated outboard CV joint in front wheel hub.
3. Bent interconnecting shaft.
4. Front tires out of round.

### SHUDDER OR VIBRATION DURING ACCELERATION

1. Excessively worn or damaged inboard or outboard CV joint.
2. Excessively high CV joint operating angle, caused by improper ride height.

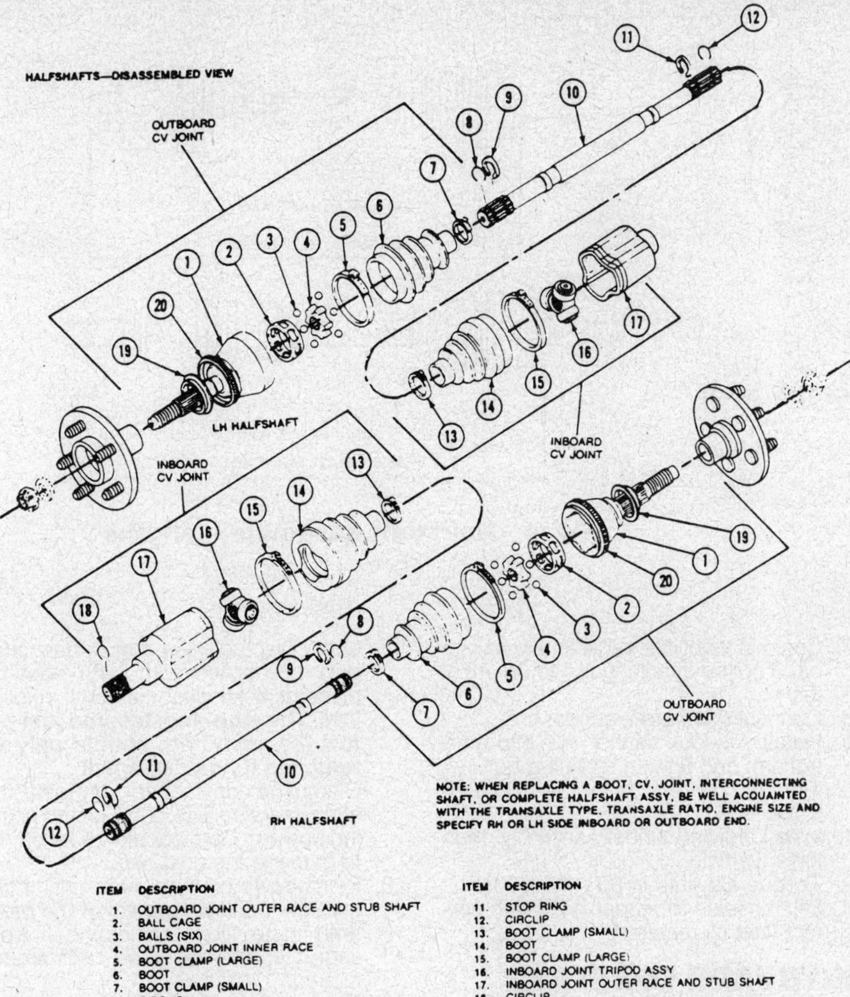


**Fig. 1 Disassembled view of halfshaft assemblies**

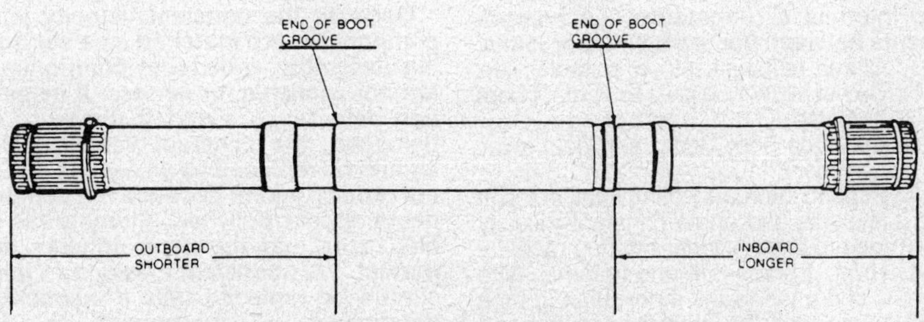


**Fig. 2 Interconnecting shaft identification**

## HALFSHAFT OR CV JOINT PULL-OUT

### Engine Or Transaxle Misaligned

1. Check engine mounts for damage.

### Front Suspension Components Worn Or Damaged

1. Check for worn bushings or bent front suspension components.

### Improperly Installed Or Missing Retainers

1. Check for CV joint circlip missing or not properly seated in transaxle side gear.

## HALFSHAFT SERVICE

### REMOVAL

**If removing both right and left side halfshafts, plugs T81P-1177B or equivalent must be installed. Failure to do so may result in dislocation of differential side gears, necessitating transaxle disassembly to re-align the gears. Should the gears become misaligned, the differential will have to be removed from the transaxle to realign the gears.**

**Do not begin this procedure unless a new hub retainer nut, a new lower control arm to steering knuckle attaching bolt and nut and a new inboard constant velocity joint stub shaft snap ring are available.**

Once removed, these components must not be reused during assembly/installation. Their torque holding ability or retention capability is diminished during removal.

1. Remove hub retainer nut and washer. Discard nut after removal.
2. Raise and support vehicle. Remove tire and wheel assemblies.
3. Remove attaching nut from ball joint to steering knuckle attaching bolt.
4. Using a suitable punch and hammer, drive bolt out of steering knuckle. **Discard bolt and nut.**
5. Remove anti-lock brake sensor from steering knuckle. Remove height sensor link at lower arm ball stud attachment.
6. Remove stabilizer bar link at stabilizer bar.
7. Separate ball joint from steering knuckle using a suitable pry bar. **Position end of pry bar outside of bushing pocket to avoid damage to the bushing.**

Tools T86P-3514-A2, T86P-3514-A1 and D79P-100-A or equivalents, must be used to perform the following steps.

8. Install tool T86P-3514-A1 or equivalent, between constant velocity joint and transaxle case. Turn steering hub and/or wire strut assembly out of the way.
9. Screw extension T86P-3514-A2 or equivalent, into constant velocity joint puller and hand tighten. Screw impact slide hammer D79P-100-A or equivalent onto extension.
10. Remove constant velocity joint from transaxle.
11. Support end of shaft by suspending it from a conventional underbody component with a length or wire. **Do not allow shaft to hang unsupported, damage to the outboard constant velocity joint may result.**
12. Separate outboard constant velocity joint from hub using front hub remover tools T81P-1104-C, T83P-1104-BH, T86P-1104-A1 and T81P-1104-A or equivalents. **Never**

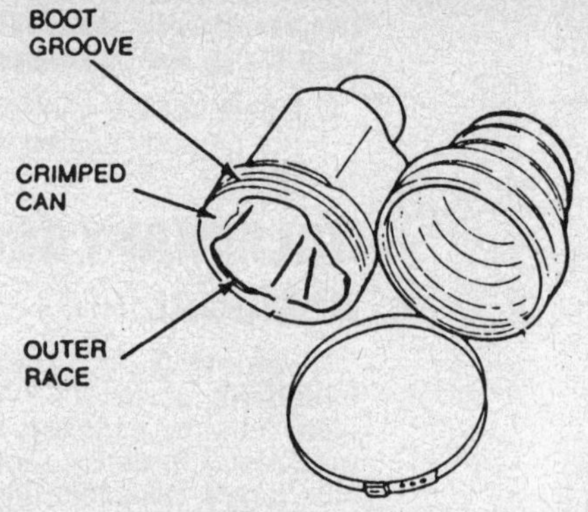


**Fig. 3 Constant velocity joint & boot**

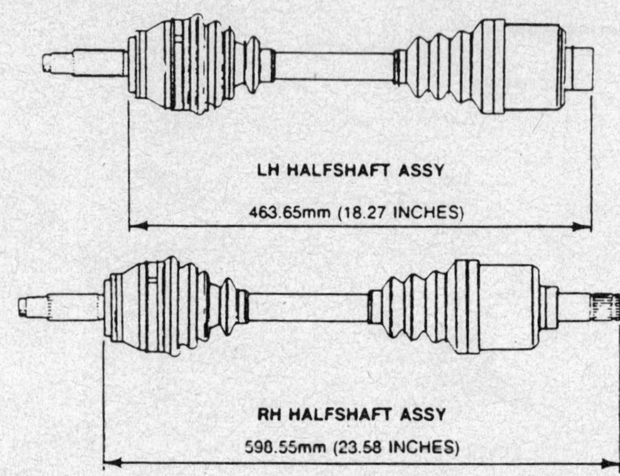


**Fig. 4 Halfshaft assembled lengths**

**use a hammer to separate the outboard constant velocity joint stub shaft from the hub. Damage to the constant velocity joint threads and internal components may result.**

13. Remove halfshaft assembly from vehicle.

## INSTALLATION

1. Install a new snap ring onto inboard constant velocity joint stub shaft and/or link shaft. **The outboard constant velocity joint stub shaft does not have a snap ring. To install the snap ring correctly, start one end in the groove and work the snap ring over the stub shaft end and into the groove. This will avoid over expanding the snap ring. The old snap ring must not be reused. A new snap ring must be installed each time the inboard constant velocity joint is installed into the transaxle differential.**
2. Carefully align splines of inboard constant velocity joint stub shaft or link shaft with splines in differential. Exerting force, push constant velocity joint into differential until snap ring seats in differential side gear. **Use care to prevent damage to the differential oil seal. A plastic hammer or equivalent, may be used to aid in seating the snap ring into the differential side gear groove.**
3. Carefully align splines of outboard constant velocity joint stub shaft with splines in hub and push the shaft into the hub as far as possible.
4. Temporarily attach rotor to hub with washers and two wheel lug nuts. Insert a steel rod into rotor and rotate clockwise to contact the steering knuckle to prevent rotor from turning during constant velocity joint installation.
5. Install hub nut washer and a new hub retainer nut. Manually thread retainer onto constant velocity joint shaft as far as possible. **A new hub retainer nut must be installed.**
6. Connect control arm to steering knuckle. Install a new nut and bolt. **Torque** nut to 40-55 ft. lbs. **A new nut and bolt must be installed.**
7. Connect stabilizer bar link to stabilizer bar. **Torque** attaching nut to 35-48 ft. lbs.
8. Connect ride height sensor link.
9. Install anti-lock sensor link into control arm and tighten retaining bolt.
10. **Torque** hub retainer nut to 180-200 ft. lbs.
11. Install tire and wheel assembly, then lower vehicle.
12. **Torque** lug nuts to 80-105 ft. lbs.
13. Fill transaxle to proper level with correct fluid as required.

## OUTBOARD CONSTANT VELOCITY JOINT & BOOT

### Disassembly

**The constant velocity joint components are matched during manufacture and cannot be interchanged with components from another constant velocity joint. Extreme care should be taken not to intermix or substitute like components between constant velocity joints.**

1. Clamp halfshaft into a suitable vise. Do not allow vise jaws to contact boot or clamp.
2. Cut large boot clamp and peel away from boot.
3. Support interconnecting shaft in a soft jaw vise and angle constant velocity joint to expose inner bearing race.
4. Using a brass drift and hammer, give a sharp tap to the inner bearing race to dislodge the internal snap ring and separate the constant velocity joint from the interconnecting shaft. The boot can now be removed from the shaft.
5. inspect constant velocity joint grease for contamination. If constant velocity joints are operating satisfactorily, and grease does not appear to be contaminated, add grease and replace boot. If lubricant appears contaminated, proceed with a complete constant velocity joint disassembly and inspection.
6. Remove snap ring located near end of shaft. Discard snap ring. A new snap ring is supplied with both boot replacement kit and constant velocity joint. **The stop ring, located just below the snap ring, should only be removed if it is damaged.**
7. Clamp the constant velocity joint stub shaft in a vise with outer facing pointing upward. Care should be taken not to damage the dust seal.
8. Press down on inner race until it tilts enough to allow removal of the ball.
9. With cage tilted, remove ball from cage. Repeat until all six balls are removed.
10. Pivot cage and inner race assembly until it is facing straight up and down in outer race. Align cage windows with the outer race lands while pivoting bearing race. With cage pivoted and aligned, lift assembly from outer race.
11. Rotate inner race up and out of cage.

### Assembly

**Because the constant velocity joint components are matched as a set during assembly, individual components are not available for service. If inspection determines a part to be worn or damaged, the constant velocity joint should be replaced as an assembly. Do not replace a joint because the components appear polished. Shiny areas in ball races and the cage spheres are normal. A constant velocity joint should be replaced only if inspection determines a component to be cracked, broken, severely pitted, worn or otherwise unserviceable.**

1. Apply a light coat of grease onto inner and outer ball races. **Use only Ford CV grease E2FZ-19590-A or equivalent.**
2. Install inner race into bearing cage.
3. Install inner race and cage assembly into outer race.
4. Install assembly vertically and pivot 90° into position.
5. Align bearing cage and inner race with outer race.

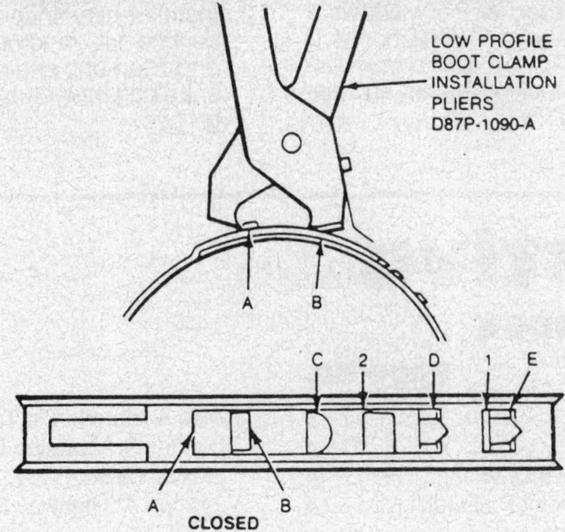


**Fig. 5 Boot clamp installation**

6. Tilt inner race and cage, then install a ball. Repeat this step until all six balls are installed.
7. The lefthand and righthand interconnecting shafts are not the same end-for-end. The outboard end is shorter from end of shaft to end of boot groove than the inboard end. Take a measurement to ensure correct inboard and outboard constant velocity joint to shaft installation, **Fig. 2.**
8. If removed, install constant velocity joint boot after removing stop ring.
9. Ensure boot is properly seated in its groove and clamp into position.
10. If removed, install stop ring. If not removed, ensure stop ring is properly seated in groove.
11. Install a new snap ring, supplied with service kit, in groove nearest end of shaft.
12. Do not over expand or twist snap ring during installation.
13. Before positioning boot over constant velocity joint, pack constant velocity joint and boot with grease supplied in service kit. Add 3.52 ounces.
14. With boot peeled back, position constant velocity joint on shaft and tap into position. **The constant velocity joint is completely seated when the snap ring locks in groove cut into constant velocity joint inner race. Check for snap ring seating by trying to pull joint from shaft.**
15. Remove all excess grease from the constant velocity joint external surfaces.
16. Position boot over constant velocity joint.
17. Ensure boot is seated in its groove and clamp in position.

## OUTBOARD CONSTANT VELOCITY JOINT DUST SEAL

### Disassembly

Using a suitable hammer, gently and uniformly tap around dust seal until unseated.

### Assembly

Using tools T83T-3132-A1 and T86P-1104-A4 or equivalents, install dust seal. The dust seal flange must face outboard.

## SPEED INDICATOR RING

### Disassembly

1. Remove outboard constant velocity joint as described previously.
2. Position tool T88P-2020-A or equivalent, onto a suitable press.
3. Position constant velocity joint onto tool.
4. With constant velocity joint position on tool, use press ram to apply pressure to the constant velocity joint and remove speed indicator ring.

### Assembly

1. With tool T88P-2020-A or equivalent, positioned on press, place sensor ring on tool.
2. Position constant velocity joint into speed indicator ring tool T88P-2020-A or equivalent. Allow constant velocity joint to rest on ring.
3. With constant velocity joint installed on tool, place a steel plate across the constant velocity joint back face. Press constant velocity joint until constant velocity joint bottoms out in tool. The ring will be properly installed when bottomed out in tool.

## INBOARD CONSTANT VELOCITY JOINT

### Disassembly

Two different types of inboard constant velocity joints and boots are used. The conventional style uses a crimped can on the large end. The tri-lobe style constant velocity joint does not require a crimped can on the large end. Although the designs are similar, there are no interchangeable components between the two designs, **Fig. 3.** The constant velocity joint tripot, outer race, boot and interconnecting shaft are unique for each style.

1. Cut and remove both boot clamps and slide boot back onto shaft. **The righthand inboard constant velocity joint requires a reuseable low profile large boot clamp. A special tool is required to remove and install the clamp.**
2. Remove clamp by using tool D87P-1090-A or equivalent. Engage jaws of tool in closing hooks and draw hooks on clamp together. Disengage windows and locking hooks, then remove the clamp.
3. Slide outer race off of the tripot.
4. When replacing a damaged constant velocity joint boot, the grease should be checked for contamination. If the constant velocity joints are operating satisfactory and grease does not appear to be contaminated, add grease and replace the boot. If grease appears contaminated, proceed with a complete constant velocity joint disassembly and inspection.
5. Using suitable pliers, move stop ring back on shaft.
6. Move tripot assembly back on shaft to allow access to snap ring.
7. Remove snap ring from shaft.
8. Remove tripot assembly from shaft. Remove boot, if necessary.

### Assembly

1. Install constant velocity joint boot on shaft, if removed during disassembly. Ensure boot is seated in boot groove on shaft. Tighten clamp using crimping pliers.
2. Install tripot assembly onto shaft with chamfered side toward stop ring.
3. Install a new snap ring.
4. Compress snap ring and slide tripot assembly forward over the snap ring to expose stop ring groove.
5. Move stop ring into groove. Ensure stop ring is completely seated in groove.
6. Fill constant velocity joint outer race and constant velocity boot with suitable grease as shown in **Fig. 3.**
7. Install outer race over tripot assembly and position boot over outer race. Ensure boot is properly seated in groove.
8. Remove all excess grease from constant velocity joint external surfaces. Position boot over constant velocity joint. Move constant velocity joint inward and outward as necessary to length shown in **Fig. 4. Before installing boot clamp, ensure that any air pressure which may have built up in boot is relieved. Insert a dulled tip screwdriver blade between boot and outer bearing race to allow trapped air to escape from boot. The air should be released from the boot only after adjusting to specified dimension.**
9. Seat boot into groove and clamp in position. Install clamp as follows:
   a. With boot seated in groove, place clamp over boot.

b. Engage hook C in window, **Fig. 5.**
c. Using tool D87P-1090-A or equivalent, place tool pincer jaws in closing hooks A and B.
d. Secure clamp by drawing closing hooks together. When windows 1 and 2 are above locking hooks D and E spring tab will press windows over locking hooks and engage clamp.

10. Install a new snap ring, supplied with service kit, in groove nearest shaft end. Start one end in groove and work snap ring over stub shaft end and into groove.

# Festiva

## INDEX



## TROUBLESHOOTING

### NOISE & VIBRATION IN TURNS

Clicking, popping or grinding noises while turning may be caused by the following:

1. Cut or damaged CV joint boots, resulting in contaminated lube in outboard or inboard CV joints.
2. Loose CV joint clamps.
3. Worn, damaged or improperly installed wheel bearings.
4. Foreign object contacting halfshaft assembly.

### VIBRATION AT HIGHWAY SPEEDS

1. Out of balance front wheels or tires.
2. Improperly seated outboard CV joint in front wheel hub.
3. Bent interconnecting shaft.
4. Front tires out of round.

### SHUDDER OR VIBRATION DURING ACCELERATION

1. Excessively worn or damaged inboard or outboard CV joint.
2. Ensure axle shaft is not twisted or cracked.
3. If equipped with vibration damper, ensure damper is not damaged or loose on shaft.

### HALFSHAFT OR CV JOINT PULL-OUT

#### Engine Or Transaxle Misaligned

1. Check engine mounts for damage.

#### Front Suspension Components Worn Or Damaged

1. Check for worn bushings or bent front suspension components.

#### Improperly Installed Or Missing Retainers

1. Check for CV joint circlip missing or not properly seated in transaxle side gear.

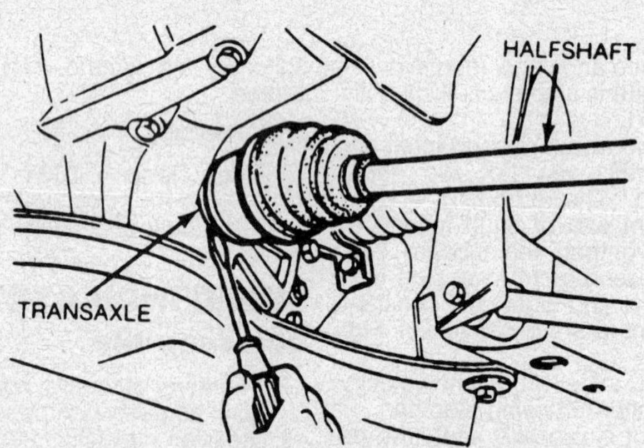


**Fig. 1 Disengaging halfshaft from transaxle**

### FAULTY OPERATION OF DRIVESHAFT

1. Check for broken ball joint, tripot joint or worn or seized joint.

## HALFSHAFT

### REPLACE

#### REMOVAL

1. Raise and support front of vehicle, then drain transaxle.
2. Remove front wheel, then the splash shield.
3. Unstake halfshaft attaching nut, apply brakes, then loosen nut. Do not remove attaching nut at this time.
4. Disconnect stabilizer bar from lower control arm.
5. Remove ball joint to steering knuckle clamp bolt and nut, then pry downward on control arm and disengage ball joint from steering knuckle. **Do not damage ball joint dust boot.**
6. Using a large screwdriver, disengage halfshaft from transaxle, **Fig. 1. Disengage halfshaft gradually to prevent damage to oil seal.**
7. Remove halfshaft attaching nut and lockwasher, then pull outward on steering knuckle and disengage halfshaft from hub. If difficulty is encountered separating hub from halfshaft, tap end of shaft with plastic mallet to facilitate removal.
8. Withdraw halfshaft from vehicle, then install differential plug T87C-7025-C or equivalent into transaxle to prevent movement of side gears.

#### INSTALLATION

1. Install new circlip on inboard end of halfshaft.
2. Lubricate inboard splines of halfshaft with grease, remove differential plug, then carefully install halfshaft into transaxle to avoid damaging oil seal.
3. Lubricate outboard splines of halfshaft with grease, then carefully install halfshaft into hub to avoid damaging oil seal.
4. Install new lockwasher and attaching nut. Do not tighten attaching nut at this time.
5. Push up on control arm, reconnect ball joint to steering knuckle, then install clamp bolt and nut. **Torque** nut to 32-40 ft. lbs.

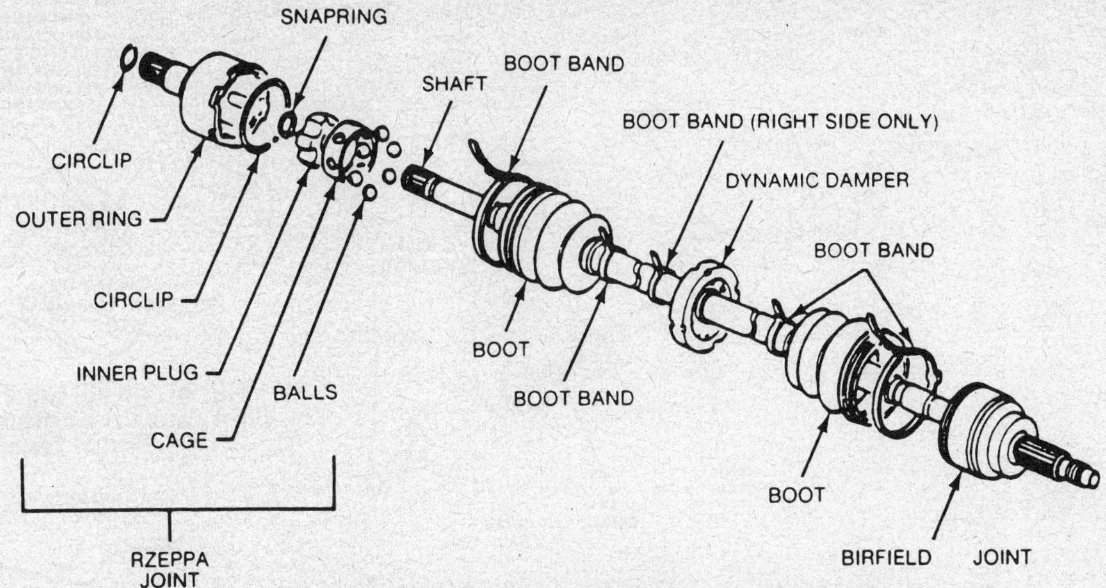


**Fig. 2 Disassembled view of halfshaft. Rzeppa type**

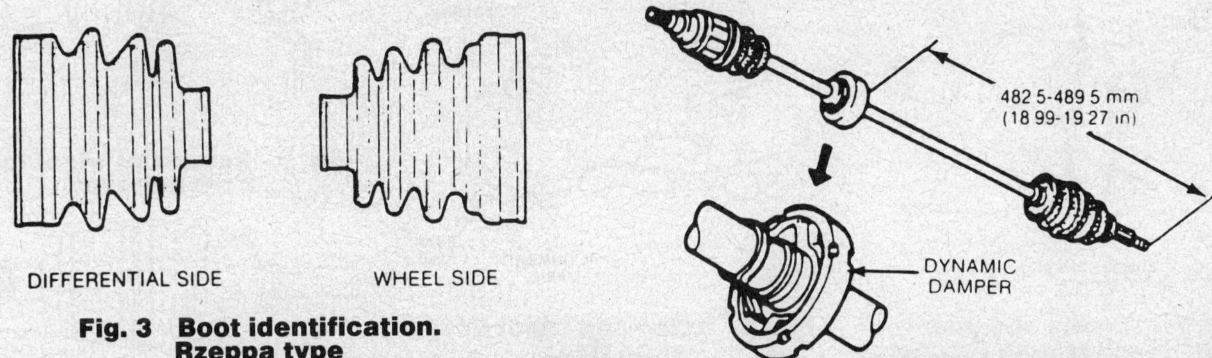


**Fig. 3 Boot identification. Rzeppa type**

**Fig. 4 Installing dynamic damper (right shaft only). Rzeppa type**

6. Apply brakes to prevent hub assembly from turning, then **torque** halfshaft attaching nut to 116-174 ft. lbs., then stake crush nut. **Do not stake crush nut with pointed tool, ensure locking tab is bent at least .16 inch into slot in crush nut to assure locking. After staking crush nut, pull rearward strongly on wheel hub ensuring halfshaft is properly installed. Turn wheel hub to ensure smooth operation.**
7. Reconnect stabilizer bar to control arm and **torque** attaching nut to 40-50 ft. lbs.
8. Install splash shield and front wheel, then lower vehicle.
9. Fill transaxle with lubricant as required.

# HALFSHAFT SERVICE

## RZEPPA TYPE

On 1989 models, two different types of CV joints are used. The inboard joints are repairable Rzeppa type joints, while the outboard joints are non-repairable Birfield joints.

### Disassembly

1. Clamp shaft assembly in soft jaw vise.
2. Using suitable screwdriver, pry up locking clips of boot bands, then cut bands off boots and discard.
3. Slide boot off Rzeppa joint, **Fig. 2**, then paint alignment marks on outer ring and shaft to aid assembly.
4. Remove large circlip retaining Rzeppa joint to outer ring. If no damage is evident, leave circlip installed.
5. Withdraw outer ring from Rzeppa joint.
6. Place punch marks on shaft and joint inner plug, then remove snap ring retaining shaft to plug and withdraw Rzeppa joint assembly from shaft.
7. Paint alignment marks on inner plug and cage to aid assembly, then position blade of screwdriver between inner plug and cage and remove balls.
8. Turn cage approximately 30°, then separate cage from inner plug.
9. Remove Rzeppa joint inner boot and dynamic damper (right shaft only) from shaft.
10. Remove Birfield joint inner boot from shaft. **Do not remove Birfield joint from shaft unless damage or excessive wear is evident. If necessary, replace complete Birfield joint assembly as required.**

### Inspection

1. Clean all metal parts in suitable solvent and dry with compressed air.
2. Check shaft for twisting and/or worn or scored splines, joint components for rust, damage or excessive wear, and boots for cracks, damage or deterioration.
3. Replace all components as necessary.

### Assembly

1. Install new Birfield joint, if necessary.
2. Place tape on shaft splines, then install wheel side boot. **Wheel side and differential side boots are not interchangeable. Refer to Fig. 3 for proper identification.**
3. If working on right halfshaft, install dynamic damper at a distance of 18.99-19.27 inches from outboard end of shaft, **Fig. 4.** Ensure outboard joint is fully engaged onto shaft before

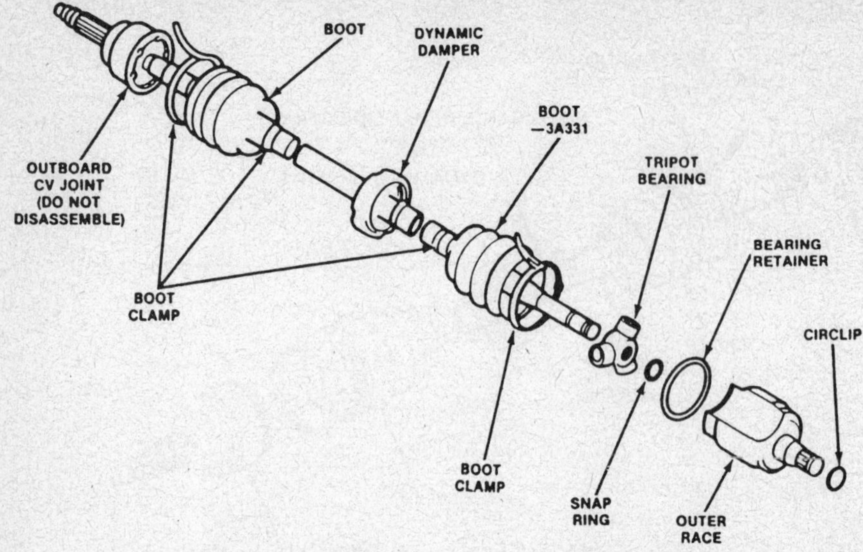


**Fig. 5 Halfshaft w/tripot type constant velocity joint**

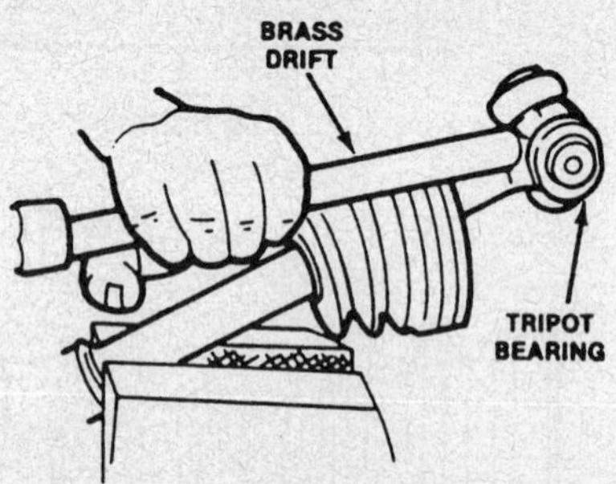


**Fig. 6 Checking CV joint lubricant for contamination. Tripot type**

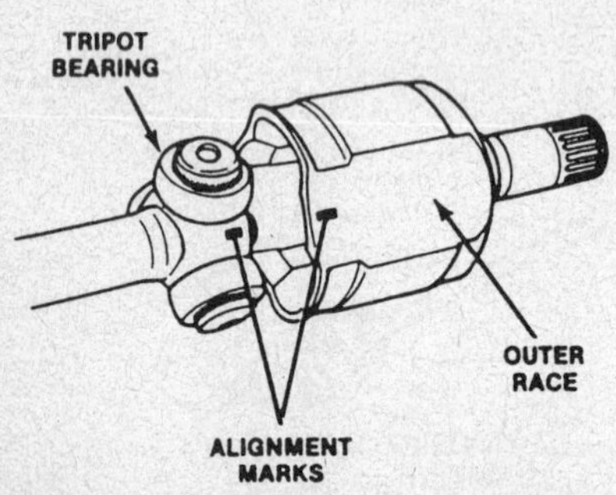


**Fig. 7 Placing alignment marks in outer race & tripot joint**

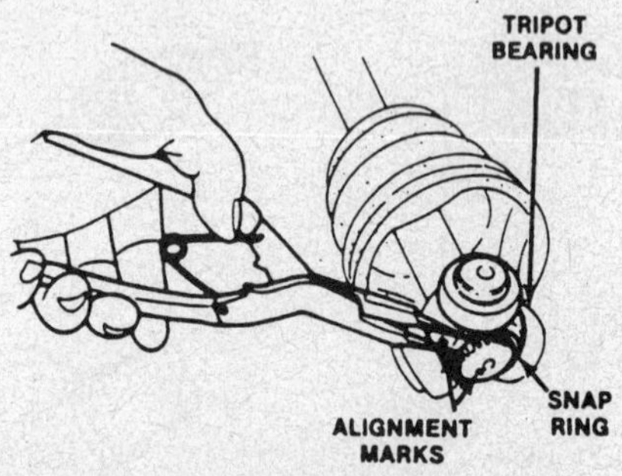


**Fig. 8 Removing tripot joint snap ring**

**Fig. 9 Removing tripot joint from halfshaft**

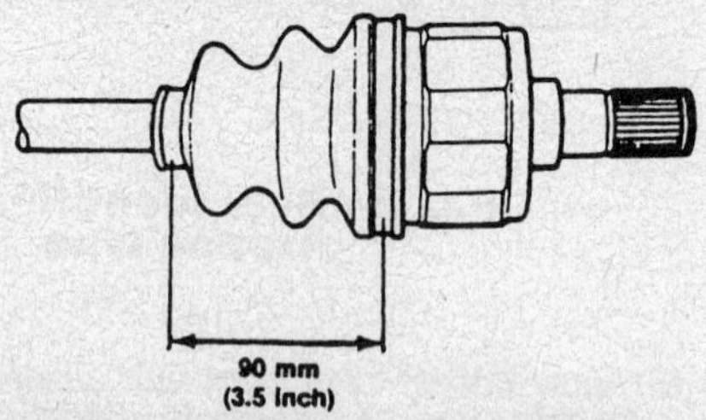


**Fig. 10 Position CV joint on halfshaft. Tripot type**

taking measurement.

4. Install differential side boot onto shaft.
5. Noting marks made during disassembly, reassemble cage, balls and inner plug. Coat all components of joint with molybdenum disulfide grease.
6. Noting marks made during disassembly, position joint onto halfshaft and retain with snap ring.
7. Again noting marks made during disassembly, install joint into outer ring. Secure joint to outer ring using new circlip.
8. Carefully fit boots in grooves on joints, then install new boot bands around boot in opposite direction of halfshaft forward rotation, using pliers to apply proper tension.
9. Bend locking tabs down to secure bands, then remove tape from shaft splines.

## TRIPOT TYPE

1990-91 models use a tripot type constant velocity joint at the transaxle end of the halfshaft and a Birfield type constant velocity joint at the hub side of the halfshaft, **Fig. 5.** The tripot type constant velocity type joint can be disassembled and serviced. The Birfield type constant velocity joint should not be disassembled and is serviced only as an assembly with the halfshaft. To service the tripot type constant velocity joint, proceed as follows:

1. Position halfshaft in a soft jawed vise.
2. Remove large boot clamp, the roll boot back over shaft, **Fig. 5.**
3. Check joint grease for contamination, **Fig. 6.** If grease is not contaminated and joint has been operating satisfactorily, add required amount of lubricant and install a replacement bolt. If grease is contaminated, then constant velocity joint must be disassembled and inspected.
4. Remove bearing retaining ring.
5. Place alignment marks on outer race and tripot joint, then remove outer race, **Fig. 7.**
6. Place alignment mark on tripot bearing and halfshaft, then remove snap ring, **Fig. 8.**
7. Using a brass drift, carefully drive tripot joint from halfshaft, **Fig. 9.**
8. If necessary, remove boot small clamp, then wrap tape around halfshaft splines and remove boot.
9. Check tripot joint for wear and damage and replace as necessary.
10. If removed, wrap halfshaft splines with tape and install boot to halfshaft groove.
11. Align marks on halfshaft and tripot joint made during removal.
12. Using a brass drift, drive tripot joint into position on halfshaft, then install snap ring.
13. Fill outer race with 3.5 ounces of lubricant E43Z-19590-A or equivalent, then position outer race over tripot joint, aligning marks made during removal.
14. Install bearing retaining ring, then position boot in groove on outer race.
15. Position joint so that distance between halfshaft boot groove and outer race groove is 3½inches, **Fig. 10.**
16. Using a screwdriver with sharp edges filled off, pry up on boot at outer race end to allow trapped air to escape.
17. Install and lock boot clamps, then check joint for smoothness of operation through its full range of travel.

# Probe, 1989 Tracer & 1991 Capri

## INDEX



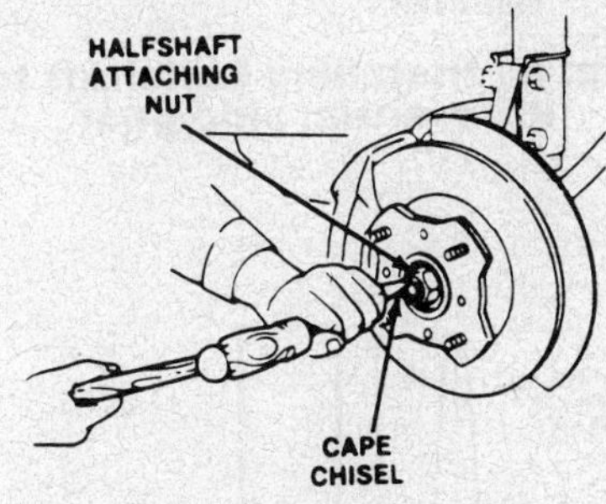


**Fig. 1 Unstaking axle nut**

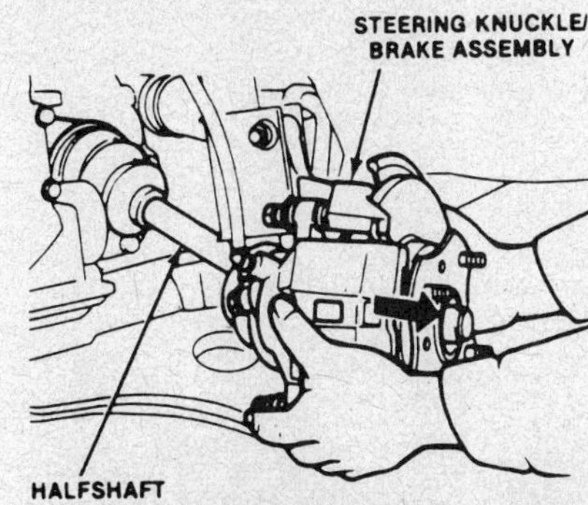


**Fig. 2 Separating halfshaft from differential side gear. Manual transaxle models**

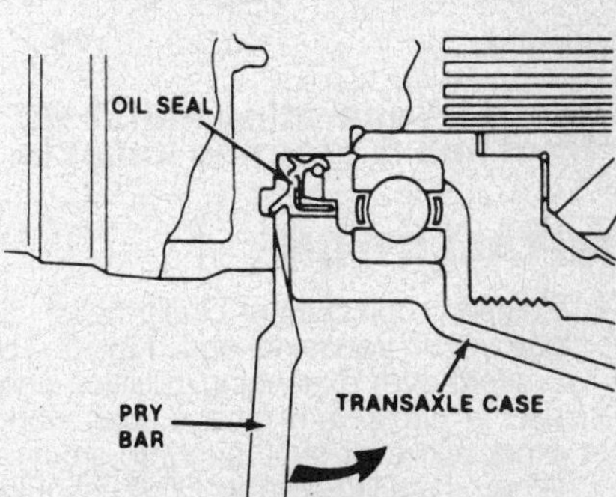


**Fig. 3 Inserting pry bar to separate halfshaft from differential side gear**

## TROUBLESHOOTING

### NOISE & VIBRATION IN TURNS

Clicking, popping or grinding noises while turning may be caused by the following:

1. Cut or damaged CV joint boots, resulting in contaminated lube in outboard or inboard CV joints.
2. Loose CV joint clamps.
3. Worn, damaged or improperly installed wheel bearings.
4. Foreign object contacting halfshaft assembly.

### VIBRATION AT HIGHWAY SPEEDS

1. Out of balance front wheels or tires.
2. Improperly seated outboard CV joint in front wheel hub.
3. Bent interconnecting shaft.
4. Front tires out of round.

### SHUDDER OR VIBRATION DURING ACCELERATION

1. Excessively worn or damaged inboard or outboard CV joint.

### HALFSHAFT OR CV JOINT PULL-OUT

#### Engine Or Transaxle Misaligned

1. Check engine mounts for damage.

#### Front Suspension Components Worn Or Damaged

1. Check for worn bushings or bent front suspension components.

#### Improperly Installed Or Missing Retainers

1. Check for CV joint circlip missing or not properly seated in transaxle side gear.

### FAULTY OPERATION OF DRIVESHAFT

1. Check for broken ball joint, tripot joint or worn or seized joint.

## HALFSHAFT REPLACE

**When removing halfshafts, differential plugs No. T87C-7025-C or equivalent must be installed to prevent oil leakage.**

### REMOVAL

1. Raise and support front of vehicle, then remove wheel and tire assembly.
2. Remove underbody covers, then remove stabilizer bar link from control arm.
3. Using a suitable chisel, raise staked portion of axle nut, then with brakes applied, loosen but do not remove nut, **Fig. 1.**
4. **On all models except Probe,** remove clamp bolt attaching lower control arm ball joint to steering knuckle, then pry downward on lower control arm to separate ball joint from steering knuckle.
5. **On Probe models,** remove lower control arm ball joint clamp bolt, then pry lower control arm downward and push inward on rotor to separate ball joint from steering knuckle. **If removing RH halfshaft, remove dynamic damper from cylinder block.**
6. **On models with manual transaxle,** pull outward on steering knuckle and hub assembly to separate halfshaft from differential side gear, **Fig. 2.** Use only enough force to loosen the halfshaft. In some cases, it may be necessary to position a pry bar between halfshaft and transaxle and light tap end of bar to loosen halfshaft from differential side gear, **Fig. 3.** When using a pry bar, use care not to damage transaxle case, oil seal or CV joint or boot. Do not pull halfshaft completely out of transaxle, as damage to oil seal may result.
7. **On models with automatic transaxle,** position pry bar between transaxle case and halfshaft, then lightly tap end of bar to loosen halfshaft from differential side gear, **Fig. 3.** Use care not damage transaxle case, oil seal or CV joint or boot.
8. **On all models,** remove axle nut and washer, then pull halfshaft from hub and steering knuckle assembly, **Fig. 4.** If binding is encountered, use puller D80L-1002-L to separate halfshaft from hub and knuckle assembly.
9. Support halfshaft and carefully slide from transaxle. Use care not to damage transaxle case oil seal when removing halfshaft.
10. Cap transaxle halfshaft openings.

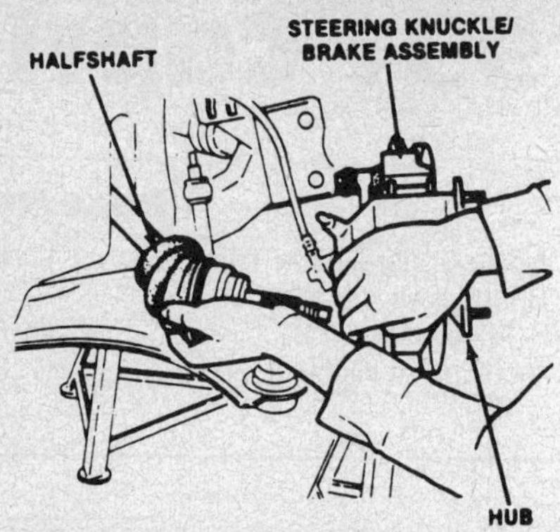


**Fig. 4 Separating halfshaft from hub & steering knuckle**

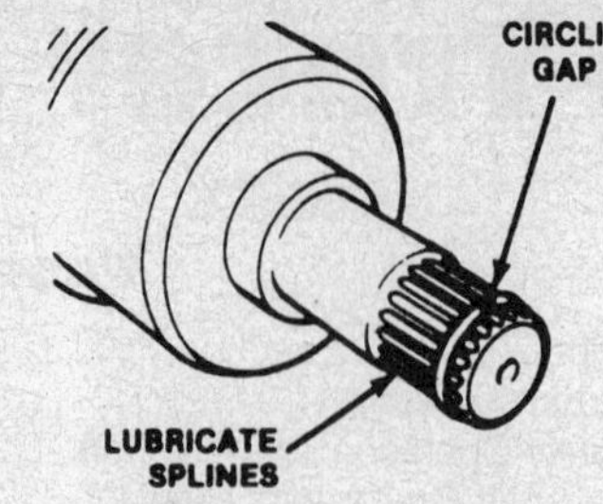


**Fig. 5 Position circlip on halfshaft spline**

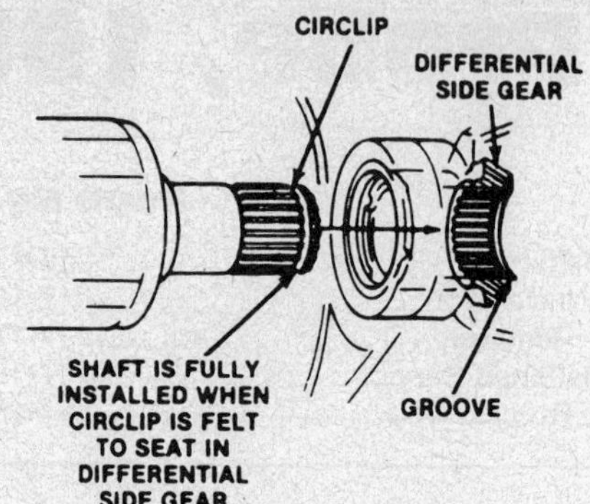


**Fig. 6 Installing halfshaft to differential side gear**

## INSTALLATION

1. Position replacement circlip halfshaft groove at transaxle end, **Fig. 5.** To prevent over expanding, position one end of circlip into groove then work other end over shaft and into groove. When installed, gap in circlip should be at top of halfshaft splines.
2. Lightly lubricate halfshaft splines with lubricant C1AZ-1959D or equivalent on Probe and Tracer models or C1AZ-19590-BA or equivalent on Capri models, then position halfshaft splines to differential side splines, **Fig. 6.**
3. Push halfshaft splines into differential until circlip snaps into differential side gear groove, **Fig. 6.**
4. Position halfshaft through hub and steering knuckle and loosely install replacement axle nut and washer, **Fig. 4.**
5. **On Probe models,** install dynamic damper, then **torque** attaching bolts to 31-46 ft. lbs.
6. **On all models,** position lower control arm ball joint to steering knuckle, then install and **torque** clamp bolt to 32-40 ft. lbs.
7. Install stabilizer bar link to lower control arm. Tighten nut until .43 inch of bolt thread extends beyond nut on Capri and Tracer models or .79 inch on Probe models.
8. Install underbody covers.
9. **Torque** axle nut to 116-174 ft. lbs., then stake nut using a suitable chisel, **Fig. 7.** If nut is damaged during staking, it must be replaced.
10. Install wheel and tire assembly, then lower vehicle.

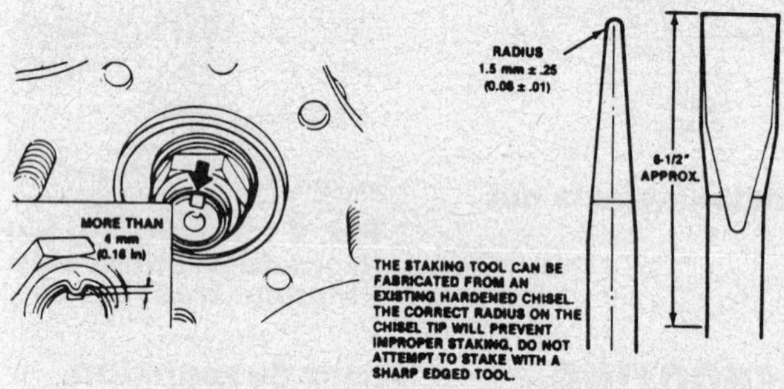


**Fig. 7 Staking axle nut**

# HALFSHAFT SERVICE

## RZEPPA TYPE

Models with manual transaxle use a Rzeppa type constant velocity joint at the transaxle end of the halfshaft and a Birfield type constant velocity joint at the hub side of the halfshaft, **Fig. 8.** The Rzeppa type constant velocity type joint can be disassembled and serviced. The Birfield type constant velocity joint should not be disassembled and is serviced only as an as-

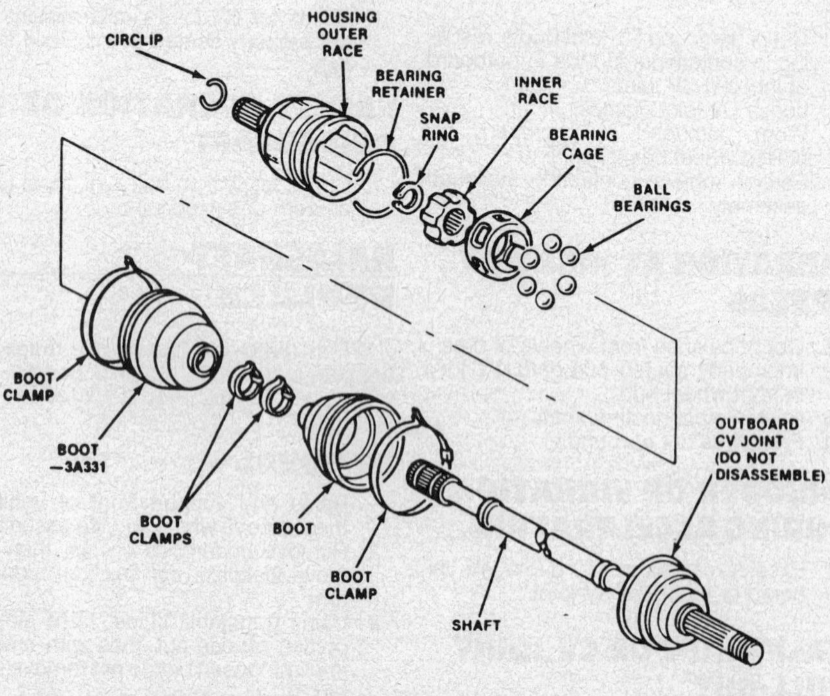

**Fig. 8 Halfshaft w/Rzeppa type constant velocity joint**

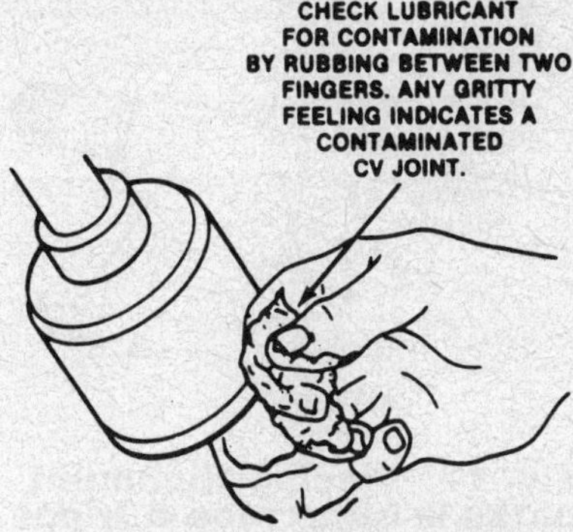


**Fig. 9 Checking constant velocity joint lubricant for contamination**

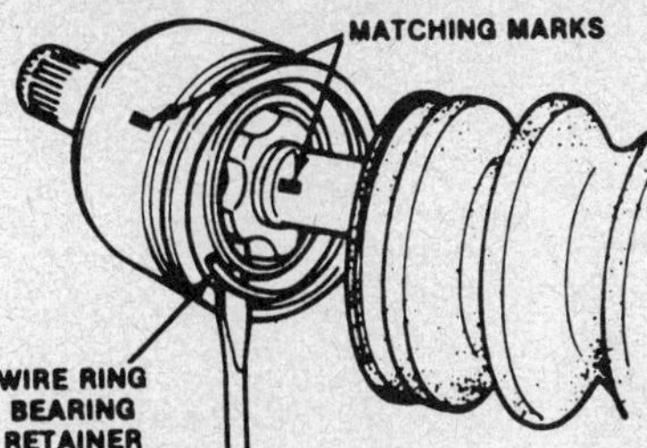


**Fig. 10 Removing bearing retaining ring**

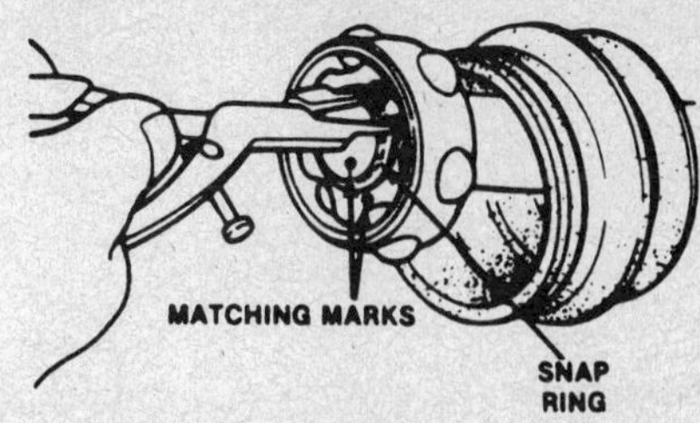


**Fig. 11 Removing inner bearing race snap ring**

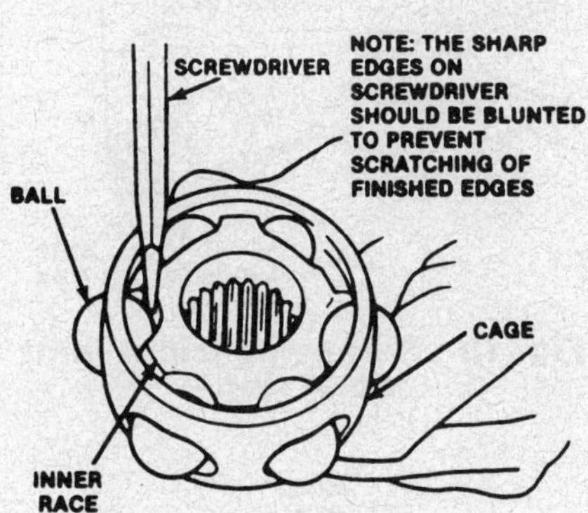


**Fig. 12 Removing ball bearings from cage**

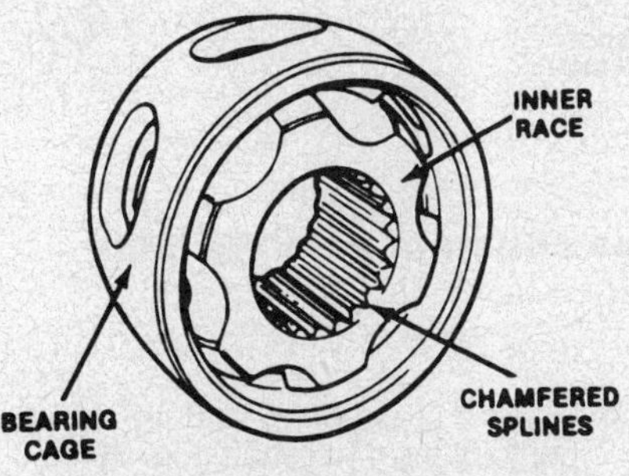


**Fig. 13 Positioning inner bearing race to cage**

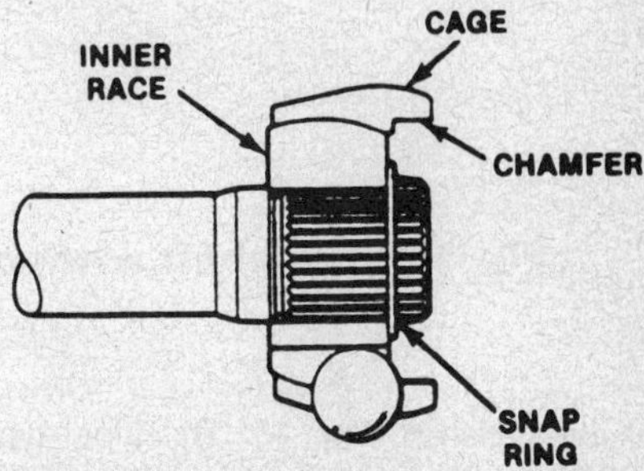


**Fig. 14 Positioning bearing cage to halfshaft**

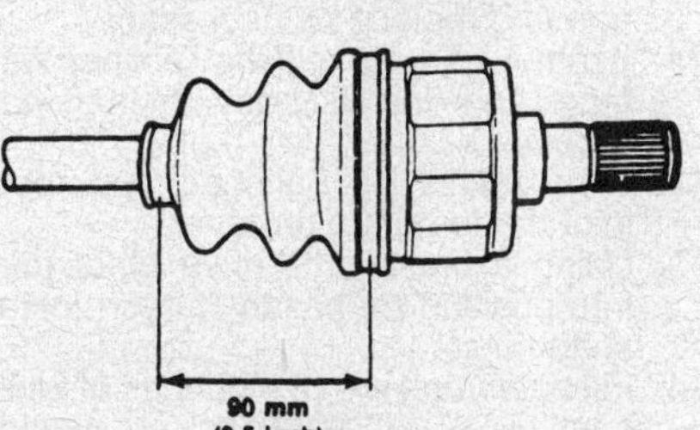


**Fig. 15 Position constant velocity joint on halfshaft**

sembly with the halfshaft. To service the Rzeppa type constant velocity joint, proceed as follows:

1. Remove halfshaft as described under "Halfshaft, Replace."
2. Position halfshaft in a soft jawed vise.
3. Remove large boot clamp, the roll boot back over shaft, **Fig. 8.**
4. Check joint grease for contamination, **Fig. 9.** If grease is not contaminated and joint has been operating satisfactorily, add required amount of lubricant and install a replacement bolt. If grease is contaminated, then constant velocity joint must be disassembled and inspected.
5. Place alignment marks on bearing outer race and halfshaft, then remove bearing retaining ring, **Fig. 10.**
6. Remove outer race.
7. Place alignment marks on bearing inner race and halfshaft, then remove snap ring, **Fig. 11.**
8. Remove inner race, bearing cage and ball bearing assembly.
9. Using a screwdriver with sharp edges filed down, pry ball bearings from cage **Fig. 12.**
10. Place alignment marks on bearing inner race and bearing cage.
11. Rotate bearing cage inner race to align bearing lands, then remove inner race through large end of cage.
12. If necessary, remove small clamp and boot from halfshaft. If boot is to be reused, wrap halfshaft splines with tape before removing.
13. Check all bearing components for wear and damage. Bearing components are matched during the manufacturing process, therefore components from another constant velocity should not be interchanged. If bearing is found to unsatisfactory, replace the constant velocity joint assembly.
14. Cover halfshaft spline with tape and install boot, if removed.
15. Lubricate inner race, bearing cage and ball bearings with lubricant E43Z-19590-A or equivalent.
16. Aligning mark made during disassembly, position inner race into bearing cage. Inner race chamfered splines should face large end of cage, **Fig. 13.**
17. Using hand pressure, press ball bearings into cage windows.
18. Aligning marks on inner race and halfshaft made during disassembly, position inner race, cage and ball bearing assembly onto halfshaft, then insert snap ring into halfshaft groove. When install bearing assembly on halfshaft, chamfered end of cage should face snap ring, **Fig. 14.**
19. Apply 1.4 to 2.1 ounces of lubricant E43Z-19590-A or equivalent to outer race, then install outer race over inner race, cage and ball bearing assembly.
20. Add approximately .7 to 1 ounce of lubricant specified in step 19 to outer race, then install outer race bearing retaining ring.
21. Seat boot in grooves on halfshaft and outer race, then extend constant velocity joint until distance between boot grooves is 3½ inches, **Fig. 15.** Keep joint at this distance until after boot clamps have been installed.
22. Using a screwdriver with sharp edges filed off, pry up on boot at outer race to allow trapped air to escape.
23. Install and lock boot clamps.
24. Check constant velocity joint for smoothness of operation through its full range of travel.
25. Install halfshaft on vehicle as described under "Halfshaft, Replace."

## TRIPOT TYPE

Models with automatic transaxle use a tripot type constant velocity joint at the transaxle end of the halfshaft and a Birfield type constant velocity joint at the hub side

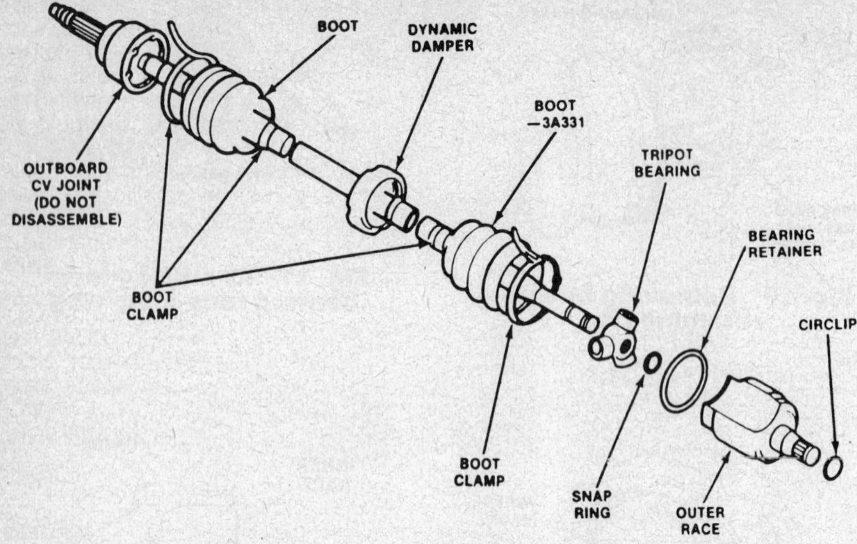


**Fig. 16 Halfshaft w/tripot type constant velocity joint**

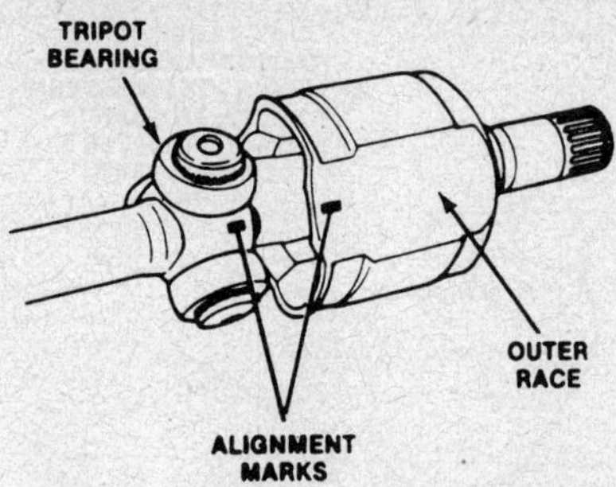


**Fig. 17 Placing alignment marks in outer race & tripot joint**

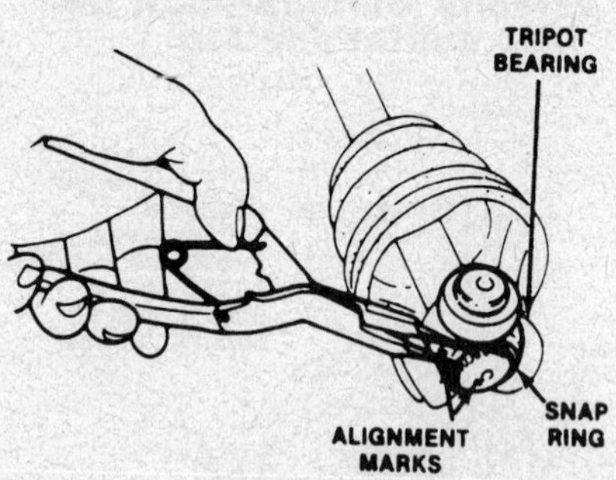


**Fig. 18 Removing tripot joint snap ring**

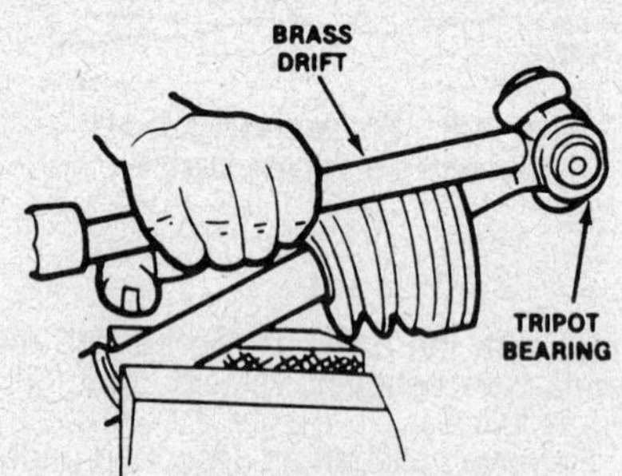


**Fig. 19 Removing tripot joint from halfshaft**

of the halfshaft, **Fig. 16.** The tripot type constant velocity type joint can be disassembled and serviced. The Birfield type constant velocity joint should not be disassembled and is serviced only as an assembly with the halfshaft. To service the tripot type constant velocity joint, proceed as follows:

1. Remove halfshaft as described under "Halfshaft, Replace."
2. Position halfshaft in a soft jawed vise.
3. Remove large boot clamp, the roll boot back over shaft, **Fig. 16.**
4. Check joint grease for contamination, **Fig. 9.** If grease is not contaminated and joint has been operating satisfactorily, add required amount of lubricant and install a replacement bolt. If grease is contaminated, then constant velocity joint must be disassembled and inspected.
5. Remove bearing retaining ring.
6. Place alignment marks on outer race and tripot joint, then remove outer race, **Fig. 17.**
7. Place alignment mark on tripot bearing and halfshaft, then remove snap ring, **Fig. 18.**
8. Using a brass drift, carefully drive tripot joint from halfshaft, **Fig. 19.**
9. If necessary, remove boot small clamp, then wrap tape around halfshaft splines and remove boot.
10. Check tripot joint for wear and damage and replace as necessary.
11. If removed, wrap halfshaft splines with tape and install boot to halfshaft groove.
12. Align marks on halfshaft and tripot joint made during removal.
13. Using a brass drift, drive tripot joint into position on halfshaft, then install snap ring.
14. Fill outer race with 3.5 ounces of lubricant E43Z-19590-A or equivalent, then position outer race over tripot joint, aligning marks made during removal.
15. Install bearing retaining ring, then position boot in groove on outer race.
16. Position joint so that distance between halfshaft boot groove and outer race groove is 3½inches, **Fig. 15.**
17. Using a screwdriver with sharp edges filled off, pry up on boot at outer race end to allow trapped air to escape.
18. Install and lock boot clamps, then check joint for smoothness of operation through its full range of travel.
19. Install halfshaft on vehicle as described under "Halfshaft, Replace."

# 1991 Escort/Tracer

## INDEX



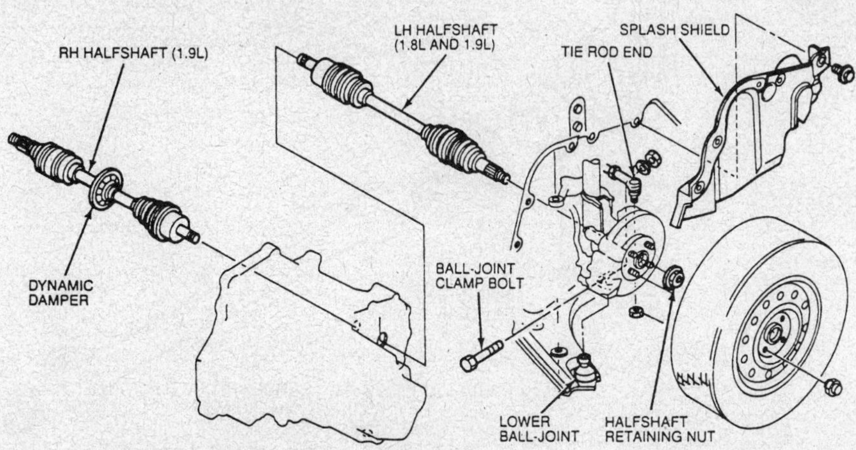


**Fig. 1 Halfshaft removal. Except 1.8L RH halfshaft**

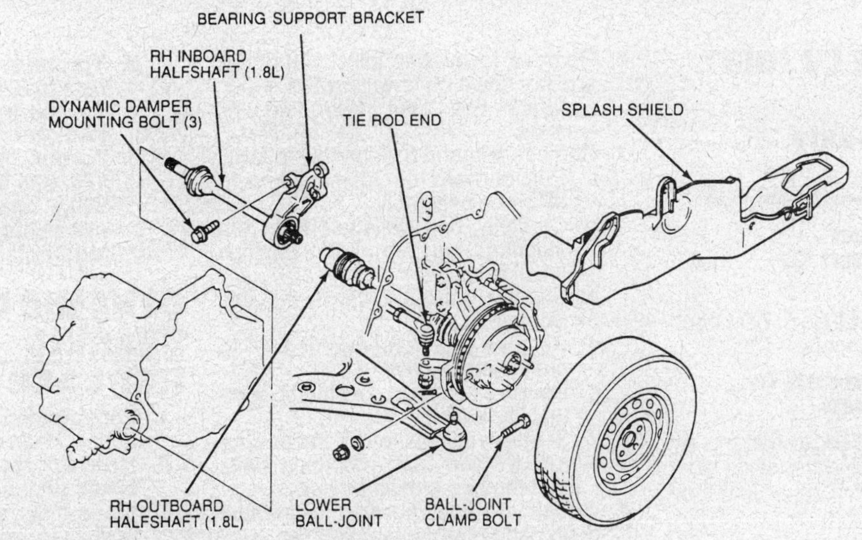


**Fig. 2 Halfshaft removal. 1.8L RH halfshaft**

## TROUBLESHOOTING

### NOISE & VIBRATION IN TURNS

Clicking, popping or grinding noises while turning may be caused by the following:

1. Cut or damaged CV joint boots, resulting in contaminated lube in outboard or inboard CV joints.
2. Loose CV joint clamps.
3. Worn, damaged or improperly installed wheel bearings.
4. Halfshaft assembly connecting component.

### VIBRATION AT HIGHWAY SPEEDS

1. Out of balance front wheels or tires.
2. Front tires out of round.

### SHUDDER OR VIBRATION DURING ACCELERATION

1. Excessively worn or damaged inboard or outboard CV joint.
2. Excessively high CV joint operating angles caused by improper ride height.

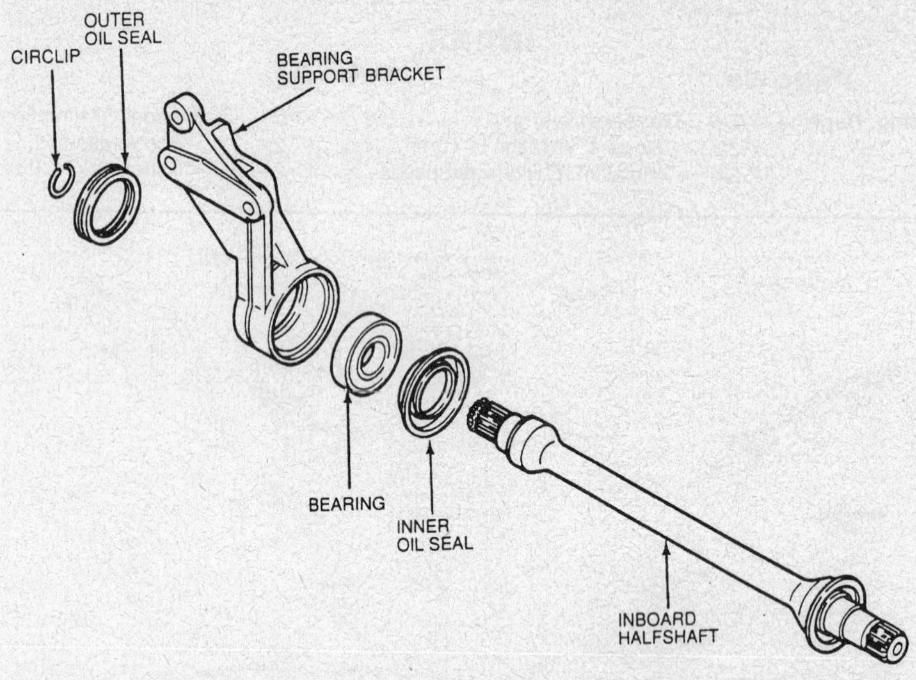


**Fig. 3 Dynamic damper bearing. 1.8L engine**

## HALFSHAFT OR CV JOINT PULL-OUT

### Engine Or Transaxle Misaligned

1. Check engine mounts for damage.

### Front Suspension Components Worn Or Damaged

1. Check for worn bushings or bent front suspension components.

### Improperly Installed Or Missing Retainers

1. Check for CV joint circlip missing or not properly seated in transaxle side gear.

## HALFSHAFTS

### REPLACE

**If removing both right and left side halfshafts, appropriate plugs must be installed. Failure to do so may result in dislocation of differential side gears, necessitating transaxle disassembly to re-align the gears.**

1. Raise and support vehicle.
2. Remove wheel and splash shield.
3. Raise staked portion of halfshaft retaining nut using suitable tool.
4. Remove retaining nut and discard.
5. Remove cotter pin from tie rod end and separate tie rod end from steering knuckle using a suitable tie rod remover tool, **Figs. 1 and 2.**
6. Remove lower ball joint clamp bolt and pry down on lower control arm to separate ball joint from steering knuckle.
7. Remove lefthand halfshaft as follows:
   a. Pull outward on steering knuckle/brake assembly.
   b. Carefully pull halfshaft from the steering knuckle and position knuckle aside.
   c. Support transaxle with a suitable jack stand.
   d. Remove four transaxle mount to crossmember nuts.
   e. Remove two rear crossmember attaching nuts.
   f. Support rear of crossmember then remove two front mounting bolts and remove crossmember.
8. **On all models,** position a suitable drain pan under transaxle.
9. **On 1.8L engine righthand side halfshaft,** remove three dynamic damper mounting bolts.
10. **On all models,** insert a pry bar between halfshaft and the transaxle case.
11. Remove halfshaft.
12. Reverse procedure to install, noting the following:
    a. Position circlip on inner CV joint spline on circlip gap is at top. Lubricate splines lightly with Motorcraft XG-1-c grease or equivalent.
    b. Position halfshaft so CV joint splines are aligned with differential side gears splines. Push halfshaft into differential.
    c. **Torque** crossmember bolts and nuts to 47-66 ft. lbs.
    d. **Torque** transaxle to crossmember nuts to 32-43 ft. lbs.
    e. **Torque** tie rod end nuts and ball joint clamp bolt to 31-42 ft. lbs.
    f. **Torque** halfshaft retaining nut to 174-235 ft. lbs.
    g. Stake retaining nut into place. **If nut splits or cracks after staking, replace with a new nut.**

## DYNAMIC DAMPER BEARING

### REPLACE

1. Perform steps 1 through 14 outlined under "Halfshafts, Replace."
2. Insert a pry bar between outboard halfshaft and bearing support bracket housing at engine block. Pry outward until outboard halfshaft is released from inboard halfshaft circlip. Remove outboard halfshaft assembly.
3. Remove three bearing support bracket bolts.
4. Insert a pry bar between the bearing support bracket and starter motor brace.
5. Pry outward until inboard halfshaft is released from differential side gear.
6. Remove inboard halfshaft/bearing support bracket assembly, **Fig. 3.**
7. Remove circlip from inboard halfshaft.
8. Using an arbor press, press inboard halfshaft from bearing support bracket.
9. Using an arbor press, press bearing and inner oil seal from bearing support bracket. Discard bearing and oil seal.

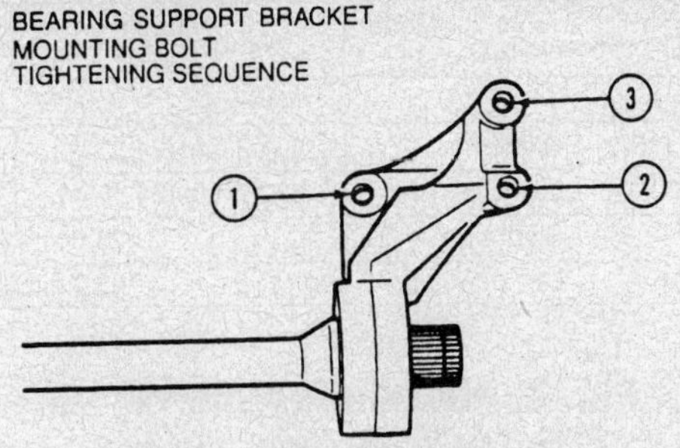


**Fig. 4 Bearing support bracket mounting bolt**

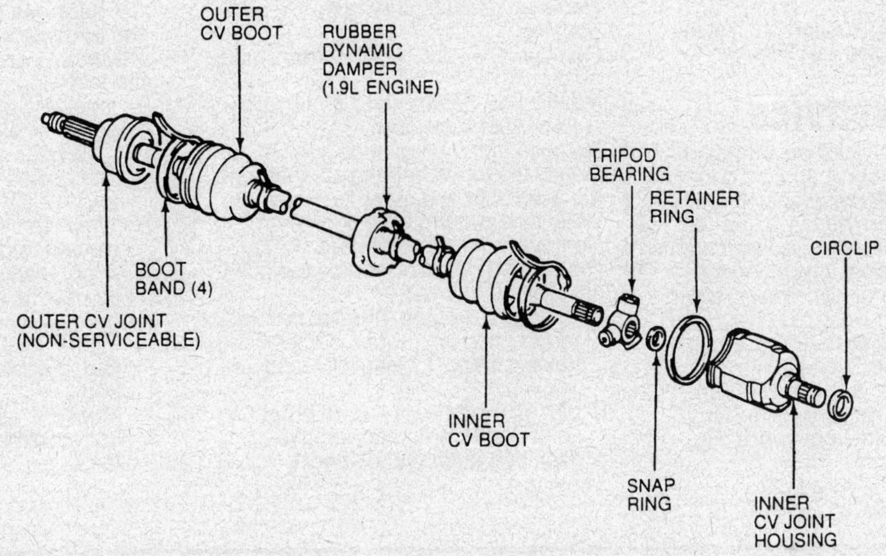


**Fig. 5 Halfshaft service**

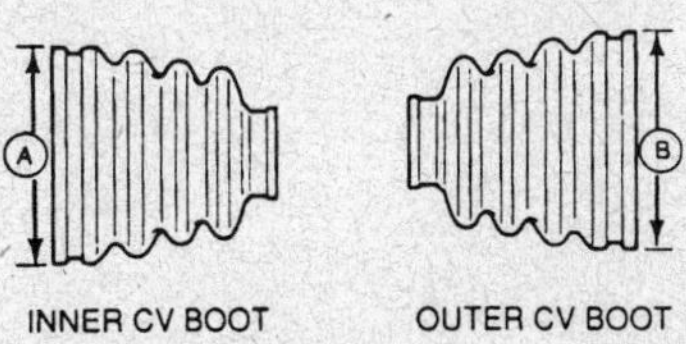


| | 1.9L Engine | | 1.8L Engine | |
|---|---|---|---|---|
| | Right Side | Left Side | Right Side | Left Side |
| Ⓐ | 84.0 mm (3.31 in) | 90.0 mm (3.54 in) | 89.9 mm (3.54 in) | |
| Ⓑ | 89.0 mm (3.50 in) | | 85.2 mm (3.35 in) | |

**Fig. 6 CV joint boots**

| Item \ Model | | 1.8L Engine | 1.9L Engine |
|---|---|---|---|
| Halfshaft | | | |
| Length of joint (between center of joint) | Right side | 631.2 mm (24.85 in) | 918.7 mm (36.16 in) |
| | Left side | 621.7 mm (24.48 in) | 640.7 mm (25.22 in) |
| Shaft diameter | Right side | 23.0 mm (0.91 in) | |
| | Left side | 23.0 mm (0.91 in) | |

**Fig. 7 Halfshaft dimensions**

10. Remove and discard outer oil seal from bearing support bracket using a suitable seal remover.
11. Reverse procedure to install, noting the following:
    a. **Torque** bearing support bracket in sequence shown in **Fig. 4** to 31-46 ft. lbs.

## HALFSHAFT SERVICE

The Birfield type CV joint on outboard end of the halfshaft is serviced as a complete CV joint/halfshaft assembly. If only the outer CV joint boot needs to be replaced, follow the applicable disassembly and assembly steps below. The tripod type inner CV joint can be disassembled and serviced.

1. Remove halfshaft as outlined under "Halfshaft, Replace."
2. Secure halfshaft in a soft jawed vise.
3. Using a screwdriver, pry up locking tabs of inner CV joint boot bands, **Fig. 5.**
4. Remove bands with pliers.
5. Slide boot back to expose CV joint.
6. Mark shaft and CV joint housing to ensure correct assembly.
7. Remove retainer ring from CV joint housing.
8. Remove CV joint housing from halfshaft.
9. Mark tripod bearing and shaft to ensure correct assembly.
10. Remove tripod snap ring.
11. Gently tap tripod bearing off shaft using a suitable soft faced hammer.
12. Wrap tape around splines of shaft.
13. Remove inner CV joint boot.
14. If outer CV joint boot is to be replaced proceed as follows:
    a. **On 1.8L engine righthand halfshaft,** pry up rubber damper retaining band locking clip and remove.
    b. **On all models,** pry up on outer CV joint band clamp and remove.
    c. Remove outer CV joint boot.
15. Inspect all CV joint grease for contamination. **A contaminated CV joint must be completely disassembled, cleaned and inspected. If the outer CV joint has contaminated grease, the assembly must be replaced.**
16. Reverse procedure to install, noting the following:
    a. Inner and outer CV joints are different in size. Failure to correctly install boot on proper end of halfshaft could lead to premature boot and /or CV joint wear, **Fig. 6.**
    b. Wrap CV joint boot clamps in a clockwise direction.
    c. Align marks made during disassembly to ensure correct assembly.
    d. Fill CV joint and boots with specified grease and "burp" air from boot.
    e. Measure assembled halfshaft for correct dimension as shown in **Fig. 7.**

# ALL WHEEL DRIVE

## INDEX



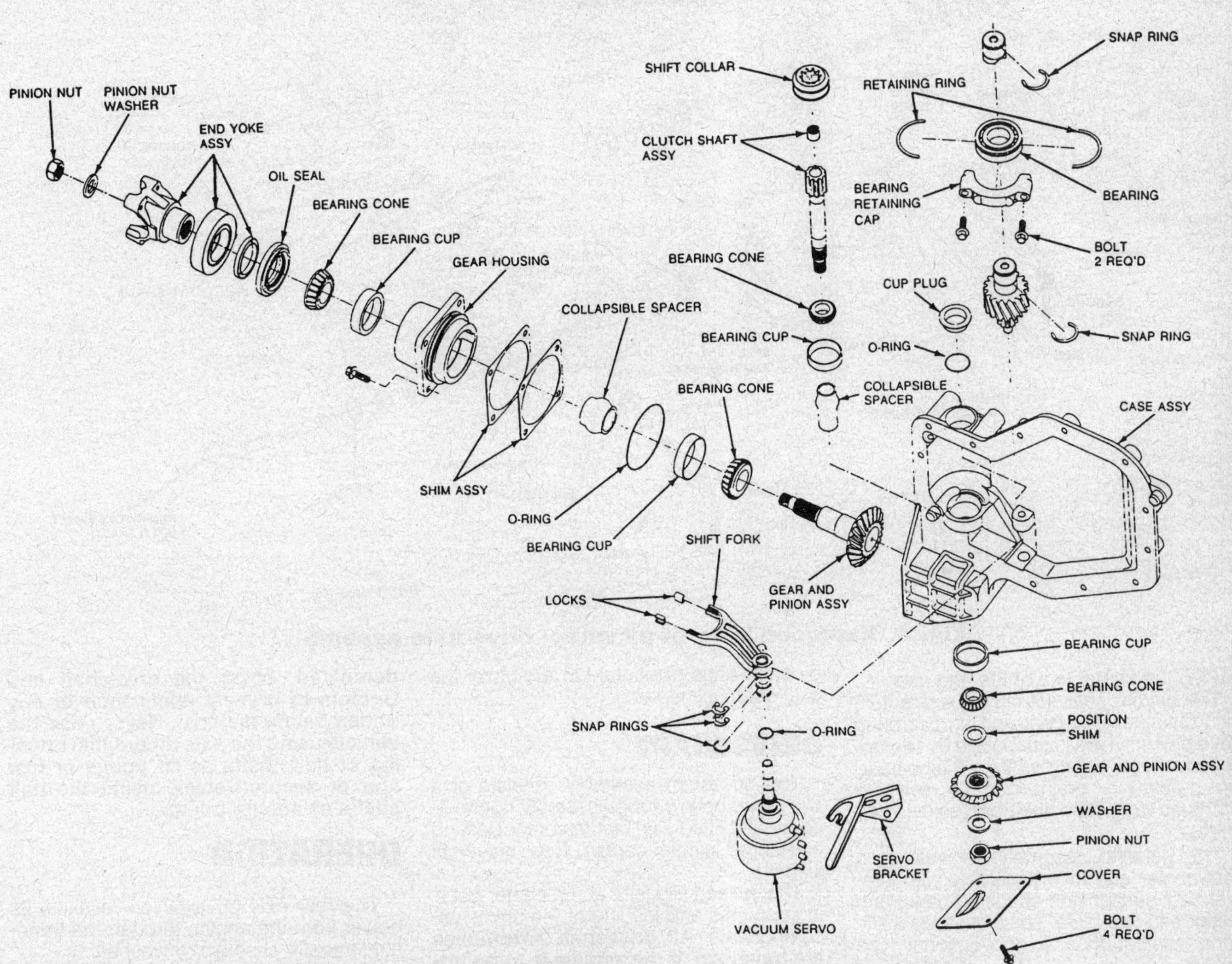


**Fig. 1 Exploded view of all wheel drive transfer case assembly**

## DESCRIPTION

The All Wheel Drive system available on Tempo and Topaz models, is intended to provide increased on the road traction and has "shift on the fly" capability. It can be shifted into or out of the all wheel drive mode at any speed as well as when the vehicle is standing still, by using an on/off toggle switch. The main components of this system are a transfer case, rear drive axle, half shafts and driveshaft assemblies.

### TRANSFER CASE

The transfer case, **Fig. 1,** is actuated by an electrically controlled vacuum servo system. When the all wheel switch is turned on, a relay activates the 4WD solenoid valve. The 4WD solenoid valve allows a vacuum to be created in the lefthand chambers of the vacuum servo. Vacuum in the lefthand chambers moves the servo rod and sliding collar into engagement with the transfer case output gears, driveshaft and rear axle. When the AWD switch is turned OFF, a relay activates the 2WD solenoid valve. The 2WD solenoid valve then allows a vacuum to be created in the righthand chambers of the vacuum servo. Vacuum in the righthand chambers then returns the servo rod and sliding collar, disengaging the transfer case, driveshaft and rear axle output gears.

### AXLE

The rear axle, **Fig. 2,** assembly is an integral type housing hypoid gear design with the center line of the pinion offset (set

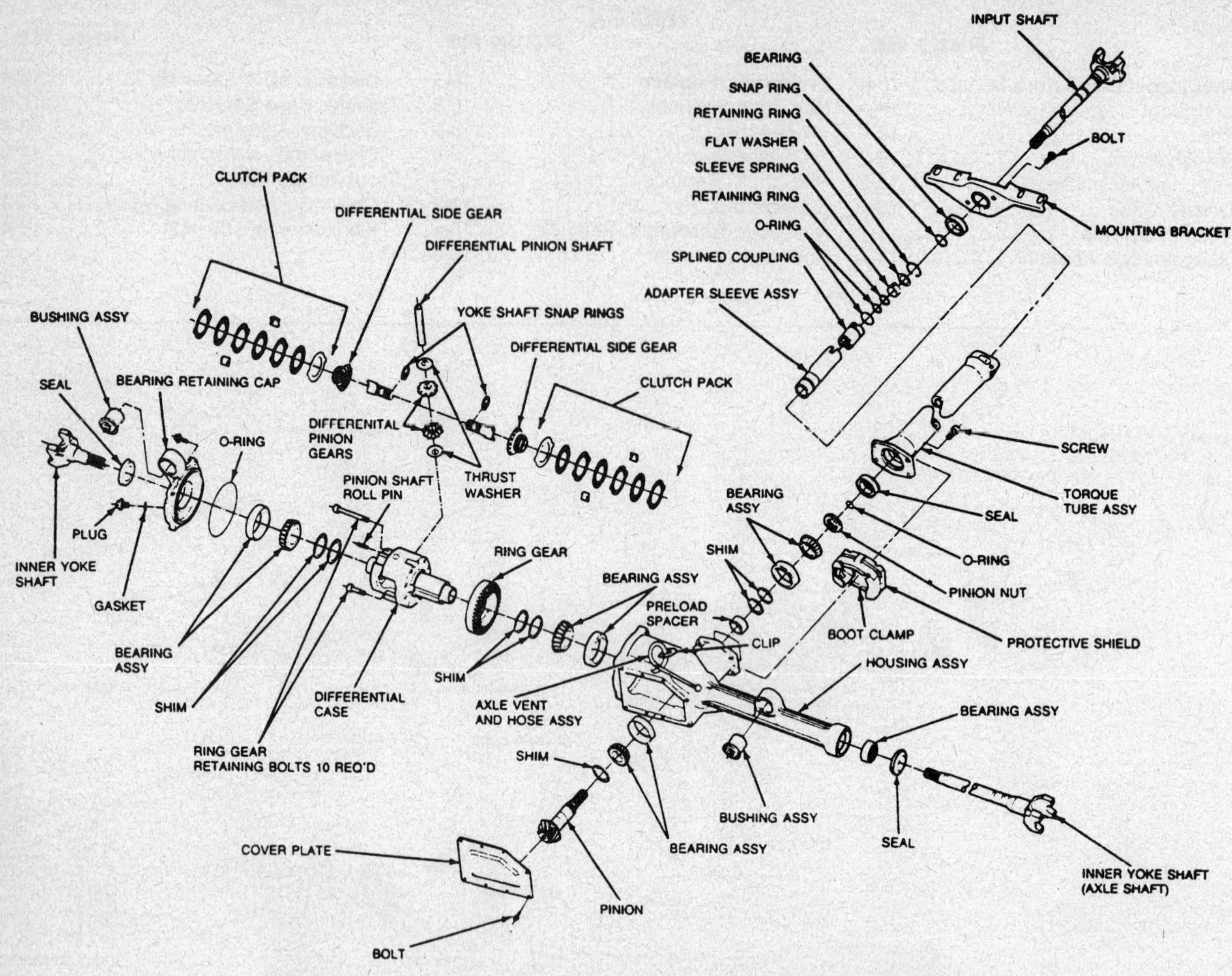


**Fig. 2 Exploded view of all wheel drive axle assembly**

below) the center line of the ring gear.

The hypoid gear set consists of a 4.75 inch diameter ring gear and an overhung drive pinion which is supported by two opposed tapered roller bearings. Pinion bearing preload is maintained by selected shims on the pinion shaft and adjusted by shims.

The housing assembly consists of a cast center and tube assembly with integral cast suspension attaching gears and a stamped rear plate. The plate uses a silicone sealant than a conventional type gasket.

The differential case is a one piece design with two openings to allow for assembly of internal components and lubricant flow. The differential pinion shaft is retained with a roll pin assembled to the case. The differential case assembly is mounted in the carrier between two opposed tapered roller bearings. The bearings are retained in the carrier by removable end caps.

Differential bearing preload and ring gear backlash is adjusted by the use of shims located between the differential bearing cone and the differential case assembly.

The axle shafts are held in the housing by snap rings positioned in a slot on the axle shaft splined end.

## DRIVESHAFT

The driveshaft assembly consists of a two piece hollow tube assembly connected by a splined slip joint, a center bearing and three single cardan type universal joints.

The splined slip joint at the center bearing prevents end loading of the driveshaft components. **All driveshaft assemblies are balanced, if the vehicle is to be undercoated, cover the driveshaft and U-joints to prevent application of any undercoating material.**

## HALF SHAFT ASSEMBLIES

The rear half shaft assemblies are used to transmit torque from the differential to the rear wheels. They have single cardan universal joints at both their inboard (axle) and outboard (wheel) ends. The universal joints are connected by interconnecting shafts which are splined at the center. This splined slip yoke is covered by a protective boot. The lefthand and righthand shafts are the same. **All driveshaft assemblies are balanced. If the vehicle is to be undercoated, cover the driveshaft and U-joints to prevent application of any undercoating material. Never raise the vehicle using the axle differential housing or half shafts as lift points or tow and/or secure vehicle using the half shafts as anchor points.**

## OPERATION

The rear axle drive pinion receives its power from the engine through the transaxle transfer case and driveshaft.

The pinion gear rotates the differential case through engagement with the ring gear which is bolted to the case outer flange.

Within the case, two differential pinion gears are mounted on the differential shaft which is pinned to the case. These pinion gears are engaged with the side gears, to which the axle shafts are splined.

As the differential components turn, it rotates the axle shafts and rear wheels. When it is necessary for one wheel and axle shaft to rotate faster than the other, the faster turning side gear causes the pinions to roll on the slower turning side gear to allow differential action between the two axle shafts.

| CONDITION | POSSIBLE SOURCE | ACTION |
|---|---|---|
| Insufficient vacuum | • Damaged or clogged manifold fitting.<br>• Damaged hoses.<br>• Damaged or worn check valve. | • Service or replace fitting.<br>• Service as required.<br>• Replace/service. |
| Reservoir not maintaining vacuum | • Worn or damaged reservoir. | • Check for leak by installing a vacuum gauge at rubber tee (input to dual solenoids). Gauge should rear 54-67 kPa (16-20 inches) vacuum. |
| Dual solenoid assembly inoperative | • Damaged or worn solenoid assembly. | • Check for vacuum at solenoids as outlined. |
| No AWD engagement | • Insufficient vacuum at vacuum servo.<br>• Damaged or worn vacuum servo. | • Disconnect vacuum harness at single to double connector and install a vacuum gauge. With engine running and AWD switch in proper position, check for vacuum.<br>• Place transaxle in NEUTRAL. Raise vehicle on a hoist and disconnect vacuum harness at single to double connector. Install a hand vacuum pump onto red tube connector and block off black connector. Apply 54-67 kPa (16-20 inches) vacuum at servo end of harness. While rotating front wheels, note that rear wheels also rotate. If rear wheels do not rotate, replace vacuum servo. |

**Fig. 3 All wheel drive vacuum system troubleshooting**

The all wheel drive is not engaged, the half shafts, rear wheels and driveshaft are driven by the moving rear wheels. **When in operation, some noise is acceptable and may be audible at certain speeds or under various driving conditions.**

# TROUBLESHOOTING

Refer to **Figs. 3 and 4** when troubleshooting system malfunctions.

## CENTER SUPPORT BEARING NOISE

A "howling" noise from the driveshaft during cold initial take-off in either two or four wheel drive mode may be caused by the driveshaft center support bearing. The noise will become less noticeable as the bearing warms up during vehicle operation. This condition can be corrected by installing a new design bearing as follows. **The bearing must be properly supported during removal and installation.**

1. Mark U-joints for assembly reference.
2. Remove front U-joint retaining bolts and straps, **Fig. 5.**
3. Slide driveshaft toward rear of vehicle, then remove rear U-joint retaining bolts and straps from the tube yoke flange.
4. Slide driveshaft toward front of vehicle, then remove center support bearing retaining bolts, **Fig. 6. Do not allow splined shafts to contact each other with excessive force.**
5. Tape U-joint bearing cups to hold them in place, then remove the driveshaft.
6. Mark front and rear driveshaft position for assembly reference.
7. Remove bearing retaining bolts and straps, then separate front and rear driveshafts.
8. Mount driveshaft with center support bearing in a soft-jawed vise, then remove driveshaft yoke.
9. Remove driveshaft yoke using a suitable two-jaw puller (part No. T70P-4221-A or equivalent).
10. Mount driveshaft in a press with the yoke nut installed flush with end of shaft.
11. Remove center support bearing using bearing removal tool (part No. D79L-4621-A or equivalent).
12. Install new center support bearing (part No. E73Z-4800-B). Engine "V" section points toward coupling shaft.
13. Mount driveshaft in a soft-jawed vise.
14. Align reference marks, then install driveshaft yoke and retaining nut. **Torque** nut to 100--120 ft. lbs.
15. Remove driveshaft from vise, then align reference marks and position driveshaft to rear yoke.
16. Apply suitable locking compound to bearing retaining bolts, then install the bearing strap and bolts. **Torque** bolts to 15-17 ft. lbs.
17. Ensure outermost ends of driveshaft assembly are positioned as shown, **Fig. 7,** then install driveshaft at rear torque tube flange, ensuring U-joint is in its original position. **If driveshaft is not in line, a low speed shudder will result.**
18. Apply suitable locking compound to bearing retainer nuts, then install the bearing straps and bolts. **Torque** bolts to 15-17 ft. lbs.
19. Position front U-joint, then apply suitable locking compound to bearing retaining bolts and install the bearing straps and bolts. **Torque** bolts to 15-17 ft. lbs.
20. Apply suitable locking compound to center support bearing retaining bolts, then install the bearing and bolts. **Torque** bolts to 23-30 ft. lbs.

AWD — ELECTRICAL DIAGNOSIS

| CONDITION | POSSIBLE SOURCE | ACTION |
|---|---|---|
| AWD system inoperative | • Blown fuse.<br>• Connector at fuse panel disengaged. | • Replace fuse.<br>• Install connector firmly into fuse panel. |
| AWD switch indicator inoperative | • Loose connection at switch.<br>• Worn or damaged switch. | • Push connector firmly into switch.<br>• Replace switch. |
| AWD relay inoperative | • Poor connection at relay.<br>• Open or short in harness.<br>• Worn or damaged relay. | • Check connection at relay.<br>• Service or replace harness as necessary.<br>• Replace relay. |
| AWD dual solenoids inoperative | • Open or short in harness. | • Service or replace harness. |

**Fig. 4 All wheel drive electrical system troubleshooting**

## VIBRATION AT 45–65 mph

Vibration at 45-65 mph transmitted to the seats, floor and/or steering column may be caused by an out-of-balance driveshaft. This condition may be corrected as follows:

1. Raise vehicle on a hoist.
2. Ensure paint marks on driveshaft and axle end yoke are properly matched. Realign if necessary. If vibration still exists, proceed to step 3.
3. Remove rear halfshaft assemblies from vehicle, then road test vehicle with AWD switch in the Off position. **The AWD feature must not be engaged while operating vehicle with the halfshafts removed while the vehicle is moving.**
4. If vibration is still present, balance the wheel and tire assemblies.
5. Install rear halfshaft assemblies.
6. With the vehicle at a complete stop, depress the AWD switch to the On position, then allow vehicle to roll forward for approximately 30 feet until the AWD system engages.
7. Road test vehicle and check for vibration. If vibration still exists, balance the driveshaft as follows:
   a. Remove wheel and tire assemblies, then reinstall all lug nuts. **Do not allow suspension to hang freely. If the CV joint is run at a very high angle, damage to the seals and joints may occur. Also, support lower control arm out as far as possible. To bring vehicle to proper ride height, the full weight of the vehicle should be supported by front floor jacks.**
   b. Mark rear of driveshaft in four equal parts, numbering them 1 through 4.
   c. Install a Whittek type hose clamp at rear of driveshaft assembly forward of the torque tube at position No. 1, then operate driveline at speed which vibration occurred.
   d. Rotate clamp to each of the other three positions and check for vibrations.
   e. If vibration is worse in all positions, proceed to step 10. If vibration is less in any one position, proceed to step 8. If vibration is less in any two position, rotate clamp screw to a mid-point between the two positions, then proceed to step 8.
   f. Install another clamp with screw in same position as first clamp, then operate vehicle at speed which vibration occurred. If vibration is not corrected, proceed to step 9.
   g. Rotate screws of clamps equally away from each other approximately 1/2 inch, then operate driveline at speed which vibration occurred.
   h. If vibration is corrected with both clamps installed, they should remain on the driveshaft assembly. If vibration is less with one clamp than with two clamps, remove one clamp and return remaining clamp to best position previously set.

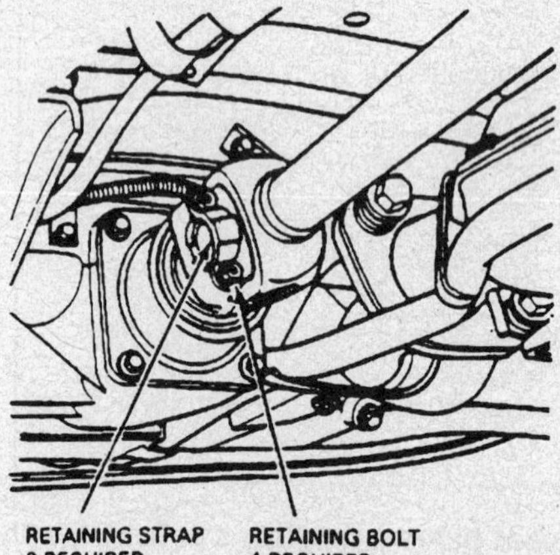


**Fig. 5 Front U-joint retaining bolts & straps**

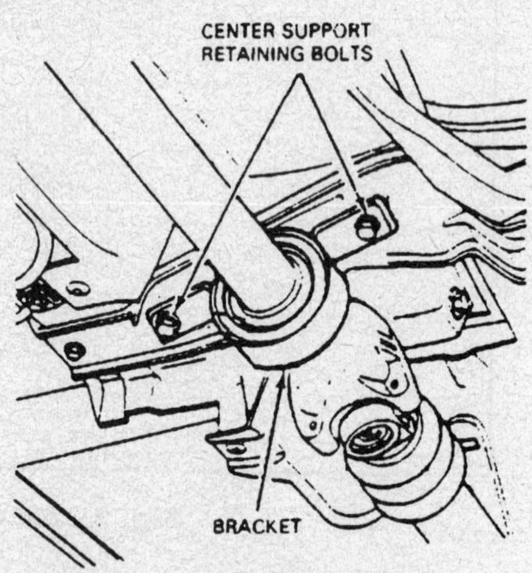


**Fig. 6 Driveshaft center support bearing retaining bolts**

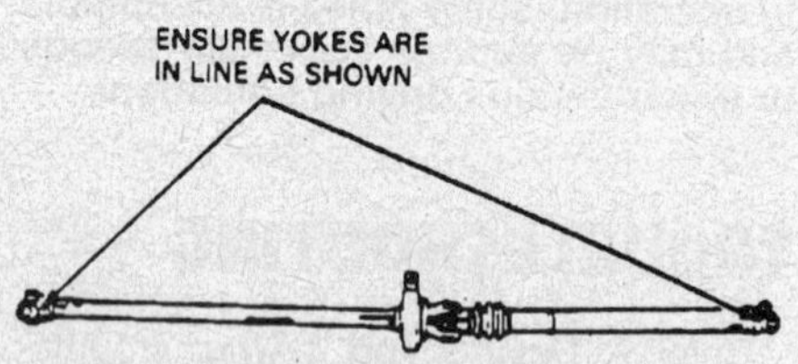


**Fig. 7 Driveshaft alignment**

## CARRIER INSPECTION BEFORE SERVICE

The differential case assemblies and drive pinion should be inspected before they are removed from the carrier casting. These inspections can locate the condition and determine the resolution needed.

1. Wipe clean lubricant from internal components, then visually inspect components for wear and/or damage.

2. Rotate gears and check if there is any roughness which would indicate worn and/or damaged bearings or gears.
3. Check ring gear teeth for signs of scoring, abnormal wear or nicks/chips.
4. Install a suitable dial indicator and check ring gear backlash and ring gear backface runout.
5. Do not check for gear tooth contact pattern. A contact pattern is not an acceptable guide to check for noise. Proper gear set assembly must be checked using specified tools.

## REAR AXLE ASSEMBLY

### REPLACE

**Remove rear axle assembly to a suitable workbench to conduct all axle repairs. Any time a U-joint attaching bolt is loosened and removed, Loctite 242 or equivalent, must be applied to the attaching bolts prior to installation.**

1. Disconnect battery ground cable.
2. Raise and support vehicle, then position safety stands under the rear axle assembly.
3. Disconnect and remove exhaust system components from catalytic converter to rear of vehicle.
4. Remove rear U-joints bolts and caps retaining driveshaft from torque tube yoke flange. Lower driveshaft.
5. Remove four attaching bolts from torque tube support bracket.
6. Remove axle attaching bolt from lefthand differential support bracket.
7. Remove axle attaching bolt from center differential support bracket.
8. Lower axle assembly and remove inboard U-joint attaching bolts and caps from each half shaft. Remove and wire half shaft assemblies aside.
9. Reverse procedure to install. **Torque** inboard U-joint cap attaching nuts to 15-17 ft. lbs. **Torque** differential housing to left hand and center differential support bracket attaching bolts to 70-80 ft. lbs. **Torque** mounting bracket and **torque** tube to crossmember attaching bolts to 28-35 ft. lbs. **Torque** driveshaft to torque tube yoke flange attaching bolts to 15-17 ft. lbs.

## HALF SHAFT

### REPLACE

**Any time a U-joint attaching bolt is loosened and removed, Loctite 242 or equivalent, must be applied to the attaching bolts prior to installation.**

1. Remove rear suspension control arm attaching bolt.
2. Remove outboard U-joint attaching bolts and caps.
3. Remove inboard U-joint attaching bolts and caps.
4. Carefully slide shafts together. Do not allow splined shafts to contact with excessive force. Remove half shafts. **Do not drop the half shafts as the impact may damage U-joint bearing cups.**
5. Remove and retain bearing cups.
6. Inspect U-joint assemblies for wear and/or damage. Replace U-joints, if necessary.
7. Reverse procedure to install, noting the following:
   a. The inboard shaft has a larger diameter than the outboard shaft.
   b. **Torque** inboard U-joint attaching bolts to 15-17 ft. lbs.
   c. **Torque** outboard U-joint attaching bolts to 15-17 ft. lbs.
   d. **Torque** rear suspension control arm attaching bolt to 60-86 ft. lbs.

## DRIVESHAFT

### REPLACE

During removal and installation, support driveshaft using a suitable jack or hoist under the center bearing assembly.

**Any time a U-joint attaching bolt is loosened and removed, Loctite 242 or equivalent, must be applied to the attaching bolts prior to installation.**

1. To maintain driveshaft balance, mark U-joints so they may be installed in their original positions. **Do not use a sharp tool to place alignment marks on any component.**
2. Remove front U-joint attaching bolts and caps.
3. Slide driveshaft toward rear of vehicle and disengage driveshaft.
4. Remove rear U-joint attaching bolts and caps attaching driveshaft, from torque tube yoke flange.
5. Slide driveshaft toward front of vehicle and disengage driveshaft. **Do not allow splined shafts to contact with excessive force.**
6. Remove center bearing attaching bolts.
7. Remove driveshaft and retain bearing cups with tape, if necessary.
8. Inspect U-joint assemblies for wear or damage. Replace, if necessary.
9. Reverse procedure to install. **Torque** U-joint retaining caps and bolts to 15-17 ft. lbs. **Torque** center bearing and attaching bolts to 23-30 ft. lbs.

## REAR AXLE SERVICE

### DISASSEMBLY & ASSEMBLY

**Eye protection must be worn when removing or installing snap rings on this unit or serious injury may result. If during the disassembly or assembly procedure on this unit, snap rings have to be removed or installed, ensure to stop at that point and wear safety goggles.**

1. Remove torque tube attaching bolts, then carefully slide torque tube from rear axle.
2. Position torque tube assembly on a suitable workbench, then remove two mounting bracket bolts.
3. Remove input shaft assembly from torque tube and place into a soft jaw vise. Using a suitable puller, remove adapter sleeve (which is press fitted) from input shaft.
4. Place torque tube assembly into a suitable vise, then remove and discard oil seal from torque tube.
5. Using a suitable a suitable tool, install a new oil seal with beveled edge facing toward torque tube. Lubricate oil seal lip with suitable grease, then remove torque tube from vise.
6. **Eye protection must be worn to perform the following procedure step.** Place yoke end of input shaft into a suitable vise, then remove and discard snap ring.
7. Install input shaft into a suitable press with yoke end facing downward. Install a suitable bearing removal tool and remove bearing and mounting bracket. **If mounting bracket is bent or damaged, if should be replace during assembly.**
8. **Eye protection must be worn to perform the following procedure step.** Position input shaft into a suitable press with yoke end facing upward, then install mounting bracket. Install a new bearing. Ensure bearing is completely seated against input shaft shoulder and snap ring groove is clear of bearing. Install new snap ring. Ensure snap ring is completely seated in groove. Assemble press fit adapter sleeve onto input shaft. Carefully pound adapter sleeve onto shaft with a suitable hammer until snap ring in adapter sleeve bottoms out against input shaft. **Avoid damaging the seal surface on the adapter sleeve.** Carefully slide input shaft and adapter sleeve into torque tube. Ensure snap ring is completely seated in groove.
9. **Torque** two mounting bracket attaching bolts to 45-50 ft. lbs.
10. Remove eight bolts attaching cover plate to rear axle assembly. Remove cover plate and drain lubricant into a suitable container.
11. **Eye protection must be worn to perform the following procedure step.** Remove inner yoke snap rings using suitable pliers. Remove inner yoke shafts.
12. Remove righthand inner yoke shaft bearing and seal.
13. Remove lefthand yoke shaft seal.
14. Wipe bearing bore clean. Install new righthand inner yoke shaft bearing with name side facing outboard.
15. Install new righthand and lefthand inner yoke shaft oil seals. Grease lip seal with suitable lubricant.
16. Remove and discard rubber mounting bushing assemblies.
17. Soap new rubber bushing assemblies and mounting holes in rear axle housing. Install new rubber bushing assemblies.
18. Remove four bolts attaching bearing retaining cap and remove bearing cap.
19. Remove and discard bearing retaining cap O-ring.
20. Remove differential case assembly from housing.
21. Place differential assembly into a suitable vise. Remove righthand and lefthand differential bearing cones from differential case. Tag bearings and

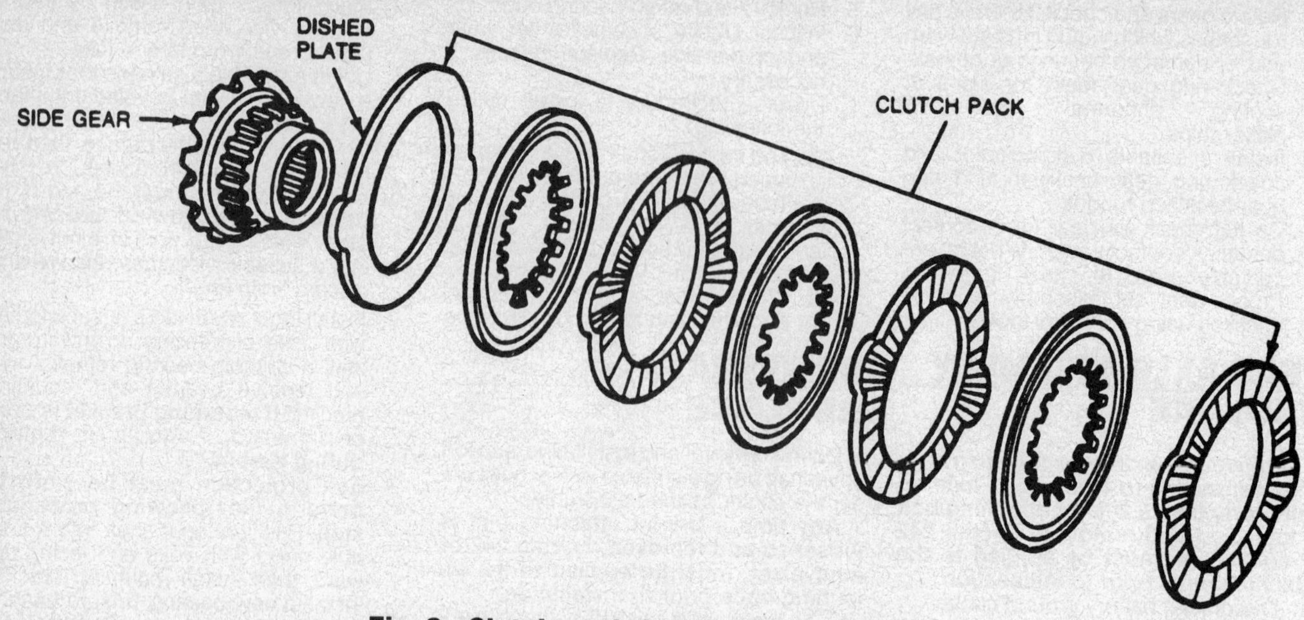


**Fig. 8 Clutch pack & side gear assembly**

shims to identify from which side they were removed. Shims are available in thicknesses of .003, .005, .010 and .030 inch. If shims are bent or damaged, replace them with new ones of the same thickness during assembly.

22. With differential case assembly in a vise, remove ring gear attaching bolts.
23. Remove differential case assembly from vise. Tap ring gear on alternate sides using a suitable hammer and drift, then remove ring gear from differential case.
24. Place short inner yoke shaft in a suitable vise, locating it on yoke end. Install differential assembly onto yoke shaft. Remove differential pinion shaft roll pin using a suitable hammer and drift.
25. Remove differential pinion shaft using a suitable hammer and drift.
26. Remove differential assembly from yoke shaft, and place onto a suitable workbench with short end of differential case down. Install tool No. D80L-630-1 or equivalent into side gear.
27. Install tool No. T87P-4205-A or equivalent into differential case.
28. Install short inner yoke shaft into a suitable vise, locating it on the yoke end. Install differential assembly onto yoke shaft. Tighten forcing screw of tool installed in step 27, until pinion gears become loose.
29. Using a suitable feeler gauge, push pinion gear thrust washers from between pinion gears and differential case. Remove thrust washers.
30. Insert tool No. T87P-4205-B or equivalent into pinion shaft bore and turn case to "walk" pinion gears out of differential case windows. Remove pinions.
31. Remove differential assembly from yoke shaft.
32. Remove tool, clutch packs and side gears, **Fig. 8.** Inspect all components for wear or damage, replace components, if necessary.
33. Lubricate clutch plates and discs with lubricant C8AZ-19B546-A or equivalent. Assemble lefthand clutch pack and side gear assembly. Install clutch pack and side gear into differential case. Ensure clutch pack retainers are aligned in the differential case.
34. Turn differential case over and assemble righthand clutch pack and side gear assembly. Install righthand side gear and clutch pack into differential case and hold in position. Ensure clutch pack retainers are aligned in the differential case.
35. Install tool No. D80L-630-1 or equivalent into lefthand side gear. Install forcing screw of tool, through differential case and install tool No. T87P-4205-A or equivalent. Position case on inner yoke shaft. Lightly tighten forcing screw.
36. Install differential assembly over yoke shaft.
37. Position pinion gears into windows of differential case so that they mesh with side gear teeth. Hold pinion gears in position. Ensure pinion gears are 180° apart so they will correctly align with pinion shaft bore.
38. Insert tool No. T87P-4205-B or equivalent into pinion shaft bore and turn differential case. This will cause pinion gears to engage side gears and "walk" into differential case. Rotate differential case until pinion mating shaft holes are aligned exactly with holes in pinion gears. **It may be necessary to tighten or loosen the forcing screw of tool. Allow pinion and side gears to rotate.**
39. Tighten forcing screw of tool, until side gears become loose. Lubricate and install differential pinion thrust washers. Ensure thrust washers align exactly with holes and remove tools.
40. Install differential pinion shaft from roll pin hole side of case. Ensure to align pin hole in shaft with roll pin hole in case.
41. Install roll pin.
42. Remove and discard pinion to adapter O-ring seal.
43. Remove pinion nut using suitable tools. Tap pinion using a suitable hammer to remove it from housing. Save bearing preload spacer and preload shim. Remove outer pinion bearing cone.
44. Remove inner pinion bearing cone.
45. Remove inner and outer pinion bearing cups, **Fig. 9.**
46. Remove ring gear side differential bearing cup.
47. Place differential bearing cap in a suitable vise. Remove bearing cap differential bearing cup.
48. Wipe clean pinion and differential bearing bores. Install inner and outer pinion bearing cups.
49. Install tools Nos. T76P-4020-A11, T80T-4020-F43, T76P-4020-A14 and T87P-4020-A or equivalents into inner pinion bearing bore of carrier.
50. Place gauge bar part of tool kit No. T87P-4020-A or equivalent into bearing bore.
51. Install bearing attaching cap with O-ring from gauge bar tool part of tool kit T87P-4020-A or equivalent in cap bore. Tighten retaining screws slightly.
52. Select the thickest feeler gauge or shim(s) that will enter between the pinion gauge block tool and gauge bar. The feeler gauge fit should be a slight drag type feeling. Ensure the feeler gauge or shim(s) is free of dirt to prevent an incorrect reading.

53. After the correct feeler gauge reading is obtained, check the reading. This is the thickness of shim(s) required providing that upon inspection of the service gear, there are no markings. If the service pinion gear is marked with a plus (+) reading this amount must be subtracted from the thickness dimension obtained in step 52.
54. If the service pinion gear is marked with a minus (−) reading, this amount must be added to the thickness dimension obtained in step 52.
55. For example, if a pinion is etched +3, it will require a selected shim .003 inch thinner than a pinion etched zero (0). If a pinion is etched +5, it will require a selected shim .005 inch thicker than a pinion marked zero (0).
56. Assemble selected shim and inner pinion bearing cone to pinion. Place in a suitable press, tools Nos. T62F-4621-A and T75L-1165-B or equivalents. Install bearing.
57. Install pinion bearing preload spacer, preload shims from disassembly and a new O-ring onto pinion.
58. Assemble pinion into carrier. Install outer pinion bearing cone and pinion nut. Tighten pinion nut using tools Nos. T87P-4850-A and T87P-4850-B or equivalents to 180-210 ft. lbs. Do not stake pinion nut at this time.
59. Using a suitable inch pound torque wrench and socket T87P-4850-A or equivalent, measure pinion rotational torque, it should be 15-35 inch lbs., with new bearings.
60. Install gauge bar tool No. PS85-167-1-1A or equivalent. Install dummy pinion gauge block tool No. PS85-167-1-3 or equivalent, between button on pinion and gauge bar tool.
61. Insert feeler gauge or shims between gauge bar and dummy pinion gauge block until a slight drag is felt.
62. The reading should be .020 inch, added, to the drive pinion etching, which could be plus (+) or minus (−) with a tolerance (plus or minus) of .002 inch.
63. For example, a drive pinion with a "−2" etching would have a .018 inch distance and a tolerance of .020 inch, would require .016-.020 inch amount of shims.
64. If the distance must be increased, remove shims from beneath the inner pinion bearing cone. If the distance must be decreased, add shims beneath the inner pinion bearing cone.
65. Install dummy bearings T87P-4222-A or equivalent, onto differential case trunnions.
66. Install differential case assembly into carrier without ring gear. Assemble bearing retaining cap and tighten attaching screws snug. Install dial indicator and adapter tool No. T75L-4201-A or equivalent, onto carrier and locate tip of indicator on machined surface of differential case. Force case assembly as far as it will go in one direction and zero dial indicator.
67. Force case assembly as far as it will go in the opposite direction and obtain total case movement within carrier. Repeat these steps until consistent readings are obtained. Record indicator reading. This amount, in shims, will be used in final assembly to establish differential bearing preload and backlash. Remove differential case assembly.

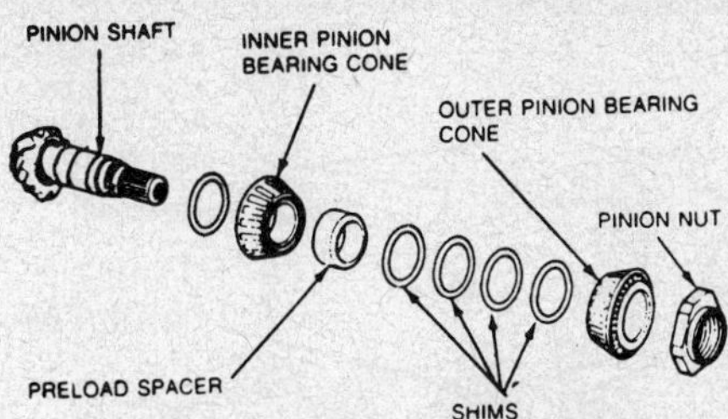


**Fig. 9 Inner & outer cone assembly**

68. Ensure flange face of case assembly is free of nicks or burrs. Install ring gear to differential case and insert attaching bolts. **Torque** bolts alternately to 28-32 ft. lbs.
69. With dummy bearings installed on case, place differential assembly into carrier. Install bearing retaining cap and "snug up" attaching screws. Place dial indicator and adapter onto machined surface of case or ring gear. Force case assembly as far as it will go in one direction. Zero (0) dial indicator.
70. Force case assembly as far as it will go in opposite direction. Repeat these steps until consistent readings are obtained. Ensure indicator returns to zero. Record this measurement.
71. Remove dial indicator and differential case assembly. Remove dummy bearings from case trunnions.
72. Subtract .010 inch from reading obtained and assemble this amount in shims onto ring gear side of differential case.
73. Install differential bearing cone using suitable tools. Ensure bearing is completely seated. Assemble shims equal to difference obtained by subtracting measurement obtained from total measurement plus an additional .005 inch onto opposite trunnion of case. Install opposite differential bearing cone.
74. For example, a total .098 inch case movement minus .058 inch movement with ring and pinion gears installed, gives a balance of .040 inch. Shim stacks for this example would be ring gear side .058 inch minus .010 inch gives .048 inch. Pinion side .040 inch plus .005 inch gives .045 inch.
75. Install ring gear side differential bearing cup into carrier.
76. Install bearing retaining cap differential bearing cup.
77. Install differential assembly into carrier. Install a new bearing retaining cap O-ring. Install bearing retaining cap. **Torque** four attaching bolts to 20-26 ft. lbs.
78. Install dial indicator and measure ring gear backlash in three equally spaced points. Backlash should be between .005-.008 inch. Using a suitable inch pound torque wrench, measure total pinion rotational torque. Total turning effort with differential case assembly installed (with new bearings) should be 4-7 inch lbs., greater than turning effort of pinion only. If backlash is excessive, it can be corrected by changing differential bearing shims from pinion side to ring gear side, moving ring gear closer to the pinion. If backlash is less than specified, it can be corrected by changing differential bearing shims from ring gear side to pinion side, moving the ring gear away from pinion. Turning effort to rotate pinion is corrected by adding shims to differential bearing shim stack. When both backlash and total turning effort are within specification, continue with assembly.
79. Use a white marking compound to obtain a gear tooth contact pattern. Contact pattern should be within primary area of ring gear tooth surface, avoiding any narrow or hard contact with outer perimeter of tooth (top to bottom, toe to heel). Pattern inspection should be on drive side of tooth. If an incorrect pattern error is detected, with a backlash of .005-.008 inch, adjust drive pinion gear shim stack. Increasing shim stack thickness of pinion gear should move contact pattern on drive side of ring gear toward toe of tooth. Reducing shims stack thickness should move contact pattern on drive side of ring gear tooth toward heel of tooth.
80. When the gear tooth contact pattern is acceptable, carefully stake pinion nut at keyway groove in pinion shaft. **Eye protection must be worn for the following step.**
81. Install yoke and snap rings.
82. Apply a bead of silicone gasket and sealant, to plate of carrier face. Install plate cover and attaching bolts. **Torque** attaching bolts to 7-12 ft. lbs.
83. Apply a bead of silicone gasket sealant to torque tube. Install torque tube assembly to rear axle. Install attaching bolts. **Torque** four attaching bolts to 40-50 ft. lbs.
84. Fill axle assembly with suitable lubricant (20.5 ounces) and friction modifier (1.5 ounces).

# DRIVESHAFT SERVICE

## DISASSEMBLY & ASSEMBLY

1. Mark front and rear driveshaft position for assembly.
2. Remove bearing retaining cap bolts and remove bearing caps. Separate front and rear half or driveshafts.
3. Mount driveshaft assembly in a suitable vise.
4. Remove driveshaft yoke attaching nut.
5. Using a suitable tool, remove driveshaft.
6. Mount driveshaft into a suitable press

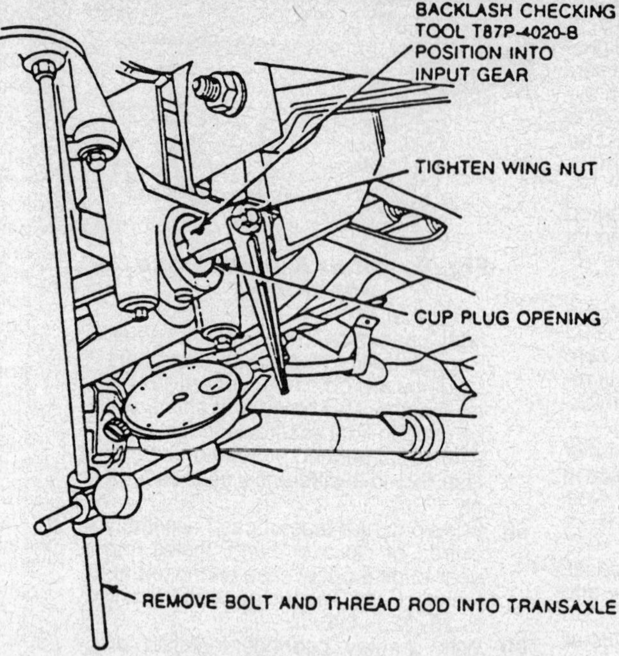


**Fig. 10 Transfer case backlash adjustment**

with yoke nut installed flush with end of shaft.

7. Check center support bearing for wear or rough action by rotating the inner race while holding outer race. If any wear or roughness is evident, replace the bearing.
8. Install center support bearing. **Support driveshaft under slinger mounting flange.**
9. Mark stub shaft and slip yoke position to ensure that they are assembled in same position.
10. Remove and discard snap rings retaining U-joint bearings in yoke.
11. Using tool No. T74P-4635-C or equivalent, remove bearing yoke. If bearing cannot be completely removed from yoke with tool, remove it using suitable pliers. Discard bearing after removal.
12. Cut boot retaining clamps using side cutters. Remove and discard clamps.
13. Separate stub shaft from slip yoke.
14. Remove rubber boot. Inspect boot for rips or tears, replace if required. Check grease for contamination. If driveshaft was operating satisfactory and grease does not appear to be contaminated, add grease as described and replace the boot. If grease appears contaminated, inspect stub shaft and yoke for wear.
15. Install rubber boot over splined stub shaft.
16. Install a new clamp.
17. Pull boot toward stub shaft and coat stub shaft splines with suitable lubricant.
18. Fill boot with approximately 10 grams of suitable lubricant.
19. Align "blind splines" on splined stub shaft to slip yoke. Push slip yoke onto stub shaft, ensuring splines are aligned properly.
20. Remove all excess grease from boot and slip yoke surfaces. Position boot over slip yoke boot groove.
21. Before installing a clamp over slip yoke, ensure that any air pressure which may have built up in the boot is relieved. Insert a dulled screwdriver between the boot and slip yoke, then allow trapped air to escape from boot.
22. Start a new U-joint bearing into yoke.
23. Position spider in yoke and press bearing 1/4 inch below surface using U-joint tool.
24. Remove tool and install a new snap ring.
25. Start a new bearing into opposite side of yoke.
26. Install a suitable U-joint tool, and press bearing until opposite bearing contacts snap ring.
27. Remove tool and install a new snap ring.
28. Mount driveshaft assembly into a suitable vise. Install yoke and retaining nut. **Torque** nut to 100-120 ft. lbs.
29. Remove driveshaft from vise.
30. Position front driveshaft assembly to rear yoke assembly. Ensure to match alignment marks during disassembly. Install bearing retaining caps and bolts. **Torque** bolts to 15-17 ft. lbs.

## HALF SHAFT SERVICE

### DISASSEMBLY

1. Place half shaft assembly on a workbench.
2. Remove and discard snap rings retaining U-joint bearings in yoke.
3. Using a suitable tool, remove bearing from yoke. Discard bearing.
4. Mark stub shaft and slip yoke position to ensure that they are assembled in the same position.
5. Cut boot retaining clamps and remove and discard clamps.
6. Separate stub shaft from slip yoke.
7. Remove rubber boot. Inspect boot for rips or tears.

### ASSEMBLY

1. Install rubber boot with smaller diameter facing splined stub shaft.
2. Install a new clamp.
3. Pull boot toward stub shaft and coat stub shaft splines with suitable grease.
4. Fill boot with approximately 10 grams of suitable lubricant.
5. Align "blind splines" on splined stub shaft to slip yoke. Push slip yoke onto stub shaft. Ensure both blind splines are matched.
6. Remove all excess grease from boot and slip yoke surfaces. Position boot over slip yoke boot groove.
7. Before installing the new large clamp, ensure that any air pressure which may have built up in the boot is relieved. Insert a dulled screwdriver between the boot and slip yoke and allow trapped air to escape from boot.
8. Start a new U-joint bearing into yoke.
9. Position spider in yoke and press bearing 1/4 inch below surface.
10. Remove tool and install a new snap ring.
11. Start a new bearing into side of yoke.
12. Install a suitable U-joint tool and press

on bearing until opposite bearing contacts snap ring.

13. Remove tool and install a new snap ring.

# TRANSFER CASE SERVICE

## BACKLASH ADJUSTMENT

A growling noise from the transaxle that gets louder as vehicle speed increases may be caused by an incorrect transfer case backlash setting.

### Models PMA-BX Through PMA-BX10 Transfer Cases

1. Remove transfer case and discard gasket.
2. Clean gasket surface, then install a new gasket (part No. E83Z-7Z168-A).
3. Install transfer case to transaxle and **torque** all 13 attaching bolts to 12-15 ft. lbs.
4. Remove cup plug and secure backlash measuring gauge through opening, **Fig. 10.** Tighten wing nut on back of tool.
5. With transaxle in Park position, remove one bolt from transfer case, then install a rod on transaxle panrail.
6. Secure dial indicator to rod, **Fig. 10,** then rotate both front wheels until park gear is wedged tightly against park pawl.
7. Position stylus of dial indicator on end of backlash measuring gauge, then push gauge upward to zero the dial indicator.
8. Push down on measuring gauge and read backlash. **Maintain load on park gear, park pawl and wheels while reading backlash.**
9. Backlash should measure .031-.066 inch.
10. Replace existing gasket with the appropriate new gasket, then recheck backlash:
    a. If backlash measures .031 inch or less, install gasket 7A191-K.
    b. If backlash measures .066 inch or greater, install gasket 7A191-I.
    c. If backlash measures .031-.066 inch, install gasket 7A191-J.

### Except Models PMA-BX Through PMA-BX10 Transfer Cases

1. Remove transfer case and discard gasket.
2. Clean gasket surface, then install a new gasket (part No. 7A191-H).
3. Install transfer case to transaxle and **torque** all 13 attaching bolts to 15-19 ft. lbs.
4. Remove cup plug and secure backlash measuring gauge through opening, **Fig. 10.** Tighten wing nut on back of tool.
5. With transaxle in Park position, remove one bolt from transfer case, then install a rod on transaxle panrail.
6. Secure dial indicator to rod, **Fig. 10,** then rotate both front wheels until park gear is wedged tightly against park pawl.
7. Position stylus of dial indicator on end of backlash measuring gauge, then push gauge upward to zero the dial indicator.
8. Push down on measuring gauge and read backlash. **Maintain load on park gear, park pawl and wheels while reading backlash.**
9. Backlash should measure .012-.047 inch.
10. Replace existing gasket with the appropriate new gasket, then recheck backlash:
    a. If backlash measures .012-.047 inch, install gasket 7A191-H.
    b. If backlash measures .048-.053 inch, install gasket 7A191-G.
    c. If backlash measures .054-.060 inch, install gasket 7A191-F.
    d. If backlash measures .061 inch or greater, install gasket 7A191-E.

## DISASSEMBLY & ASSEMBLY

1. Remove transfer case from vehicle.
2. Remove transfer case side cover attaching bolts and cover. Clean gasket material from transfer case and cover.
3. Remove gear housing attaching bolts and gear housing subassembly.
4. Remove O-ring and shims. Wire shim stack together for assembly. Discard O-ring.
5. Place gear housing subassembly in a vise. Remove pinion nut, end yoke and washer.
6. Using a suitable hammer, tap drive gear, then remove from gear housing. Remove and discard collapsible spacer.
7. Remove inner bearing cone from drive gear. **Install nut on end of drive gear to protect shaft.**
8. Clean drive gear with suitable solvent. Install a new inner bearing cone assembly.
9. Mount drive gear housing in a suitable vise.
10. Remove drive gear housing oil seal.
11. Remove inner and outer drive gear bearing cups.
12. Remove gear housing from vise. Install new inner and outer drive bearing cups.
13. Lubricate and install new outer bearing cone.
14. Install a new collapsible spacer on drive gear stem.
15. Install drive gear into gear housing.
16. Install end yoke, washer and nut.
17. Tighten pinion nut in small increments until rotational effort is 15-32 inch lbs., with new bearings. **Do not exceed this specification or a new collapsible spacer will have to be installed.**
18. **Eye protection must be worn when performing the following procedure:**
    a. Remove snap rings from vacuum servo shaft and shift fork. Remove shift motor assembly. Remove shift fork and fork clips.
    b. Remove transfer case bearing cap attaching bolts and bearing cap.
    c. Rotate bearing and remove two-piece snap ring from bearing.
    d. Using a suitable screwdriver, remove inner snap ring which positions input gear to ball bearing. Slide bearing toward input gear and remove outer snap ring.
    e. Slide input gear toward ball bearing until input gear and bearing can be lifted out of the transfer case.
    f. Remove ball bearing from input gear.
    g. Remove shift collar from clutch shaft.
    h. Remove pinion nut and washer from clutch shaft. Using suitable tools, tap clutch shaft from transfer case.
    i. Remove pinion gear, outer bearing and shims from transfer case. Wire shim(s) together and retain. Remove and discard clutch shaft collapsible spacer.
    j. Remove clutch shaft inner bearing.
    k. Place clutch shaft into a suitable vise. Remove clutch shaft needle bearing which centers input gear. Discard bearing.
19. Install a new clutch shaft needle bearing. Pack bearing with grease to maintain proper needle position.
20. Install clutch shaft inner bearing cone.
21. Place transfer case into a suitable working fixture. Install clutch shaft inner bearing cup remover T87P-7120-D or equivalent, and tighten.
22. Install tool No. T50T-100-A or equivalent, into a cup remover. Remove inner bearing cup. Remove outer bearing using the same procedure.
23. Wipe bearing boss clean. Install inner and outer bearing cups.
24. Install a new collapsible spacer onto clutch shaft.
25. Install clutch shaft into transfer case. Assemble original shim stack, removed earlier and pinion gear. Using a inch lb. torque wrench, measure torque until shaft rotational effort is 10-15 inch lbs., with new bearing installed.
26. Do not exceed specification or a new collapsible spacer will be required to obtain proper bearing preload.
27. Position shims and a new O-ring onto gear housing. Lubricate O-ring.
28. Install gear housing subassembly to transfer case. **Torque** four attaching bolts to 8-12 ft. lbs.
29. Check backlash between drive and pinion gear using a suitable dial indicator. Backlash should be .004-.006 inch.
30. Use white paint to obtain a gear contact tooth pattern. The contact pattern should be within the primary area of the drive gear tooth surface, avoiding any narrow or hard contact with outer perimeter of tooth (top to bottom, toe to heel). If a gross pattern error is detected with backlash set at .004-.006 inch, adjust drive pinion gear shim stack. Increasing shim stack thickness of the pinion gear should move the contact pattern on drive (pull) side

of drive gear toward toe of tooth. Reducing shim stack thickness should move the contact pattern on drive (pull) side of drive gear tooth toward heel of tooth. When backlash and gear contact pattern are acceptable continue with assembly.

31. Install shift collar onto clutch shaft.
32. Side ball bearing onto input gear.
33. Install input gear into transfer case. Slide small end of input gear into clutch shaft.
34. Install snap ring onto outer end of shaft.
35. Slide bearing outboard and install snap ring onto inner end of input shaft. Ensure snap rings are completely seated in groove.
36. Install two-piece snap ring into groove for ball bearing and transfer case.
37. Install bearing cap and two attaching bolts. **Torque** bolts to 18-24 ft. lbs.
38. Inspect shift fork clips and replace, if necessary. Install shift fork onto clutch collar.
39. Install a new O-ring onto vacuum servo shaft. Lubricate O-ring with clean automatic transmission fluid.
40. **Eye protection must be worn when performing the following procedure:**
    a. Install vacuum servo assembly into transfer case. Install snap ring. Ensure snap ring is completely seated in groove. Install shift fork snap rings.
    b. Install transfer case side cover. Apply a bead of silicone rubber or equivalent onto cover surface of transfer case. **Torque** attaching bolts to 7-12 ft. lbs. The bead must be continuous and not go outside the cover holes.
    c. Install transfer case and a new gasket to transaxle.
    d. Install a new O-ring onto cup plug. Install cup plug into transfer case.

# HYDRAULIC BRAKES

## INDEX

**NOTE:** On Vehicles Equipped With Anti-lock Brakes Refer To "Anti-Lock Brake" Section.



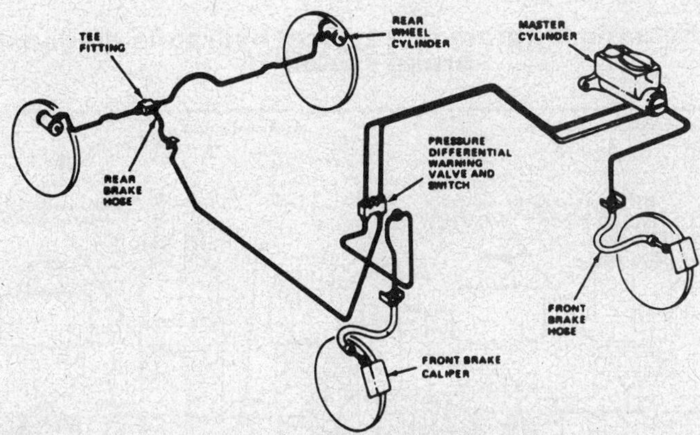


**Fig. 1 Schematic diagram of a typical hydraulic front & rear split brake system**

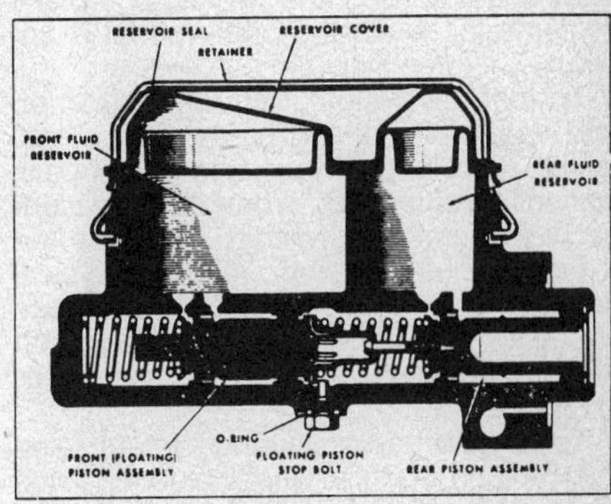


**Fig. 2 Bendix dual master cylinder (Typical)**

# DUAL MASTER CYLINDER SYSTEMS

## FRONT & REAR SPLIT SYSTEMS

When the brake pedal is depressed, both the primary (front brake) and the secondary (rear brake) master cylinder pistons are moved simultaneously to exert hydraulic fluid pressure on their respective independent hydraulic systems. The fluid displacement of the two master cylinders is proportioned to fulfill the requirements of each of the two independent hydraulic brake systems, **Figs. 1 and 2.**

If a failure of a rear (secondary) brake system should occur, initial brake pedal movement causes the unrestricted secondary piston to bottom in the master cylinder bore. Primary piston movement displaces hydraulic fluid in the primary section of the dual master cylinder to actuate the front brake system.

Should the front (primary) brake system fail, initial brake pedal movement causes the unrestricted primary piston to bottom out against the secondary piston. Continued downward movement of the brake pedal moves the secondary piston to displace hydraulic fluid in the rear brake system to actuate the rear brakes.

The increased pedal travel and the increased pedal effort required to compensate for the loss of the failed portion of the brake system provides a warning that a partial brake system failure has occurred. When the ignition switch is turned on, a brake warning light on the instrument panel provides a visual indication that one of the dual brake systems has become inoperative.

Should a failure of either the front or rear brake hydraulic system occur, the hydraulic fluid pressure differential resulting from pressure loss of the failed brake system forces the valve toward the low pressure area to light the brake warning lamp.

## DIAGONALLY SPLIT SYSTEMS

This system operates on the same principles as conventional front and rear split systems using primary and secondary master cylinders moving simultaneously to exert hydraulic pressure on their respective systems.

The hydraulic brake lines on this system, however, have been diagonally split front to rear (left front to right rear and right front to left rear) in place of separate lines to the front and rear wheels, **Fig. 3.**

In the event of a system failure this would cause the remaining good system to do all the braking on one front wheel and the opposite rear wheel, thus maintaining 50% of the total braking force. The hydraulic pressure loss would result in a pressure differential in the system and cause a warning light on the dashboard to glow as in front and rear split systems.

## BRAKE WARNING LIGHT SWITCHES

There are four basic types of brake warning light switches as shown in **Figs. 4 through 6** and usually form a common electrical circuit with the brake warning light.

When a pressure differential occurs between the front and rear brake systems, the valves will shuttle toward the side with the low pressure.

As shown in **Fig. 4**, movement of the differential valve forces the switch plunger upward over the tapered shoulder of the valve to close the switch contacts and light the dual brake warning lamp, signaling a brake system failure.

In **Fig. 5**, the valve assembly consists of two valves in a common bore that are spring loaded toward the centered position. The spring-loaded switch contact plunger rests on top of the valves in the centered position (right view). When a pressure differential occurs between the front and rear brake systems, the valves will shuttle toward the side with the low pressure. The spring-loaded switch plunger is triggered and the ground circuit for

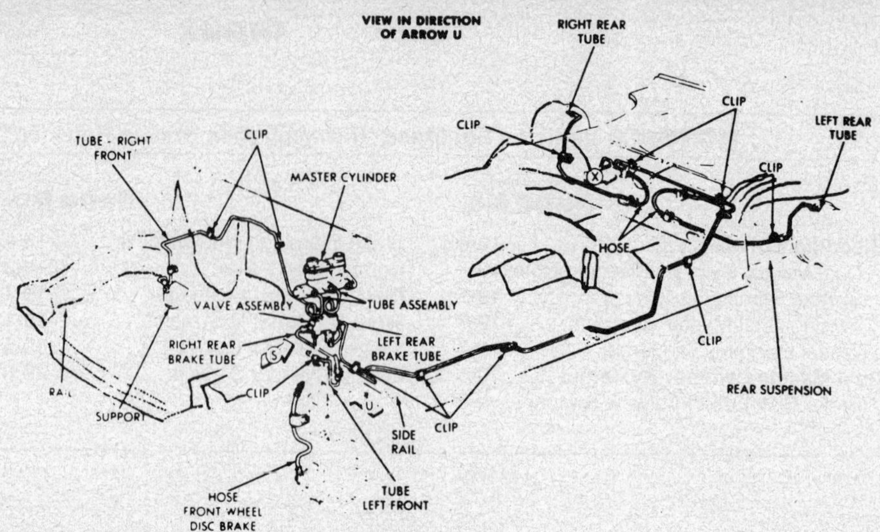


**Fig. 3 Schematic diagram of a typical hydraulic diagonally split brake system**

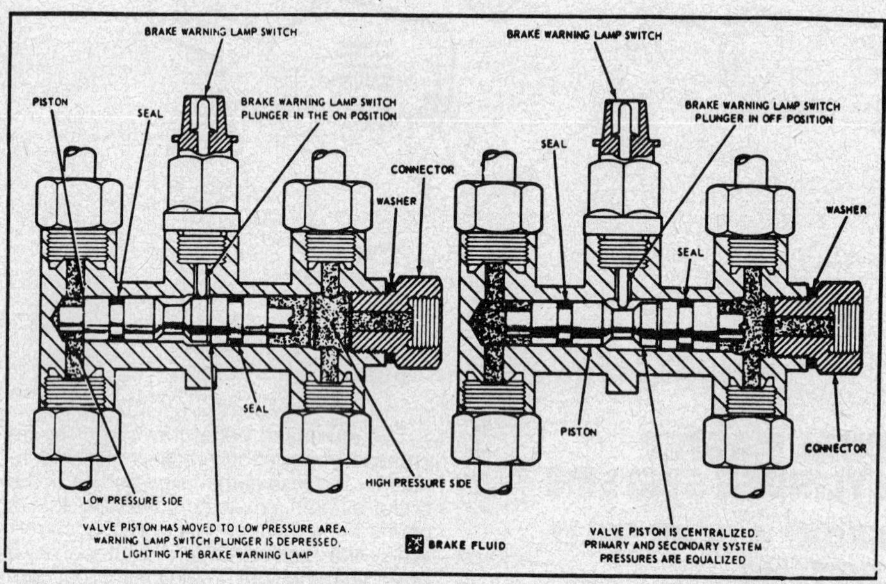


**Fig. 4 Pressure differential valve & brake warning light switch**

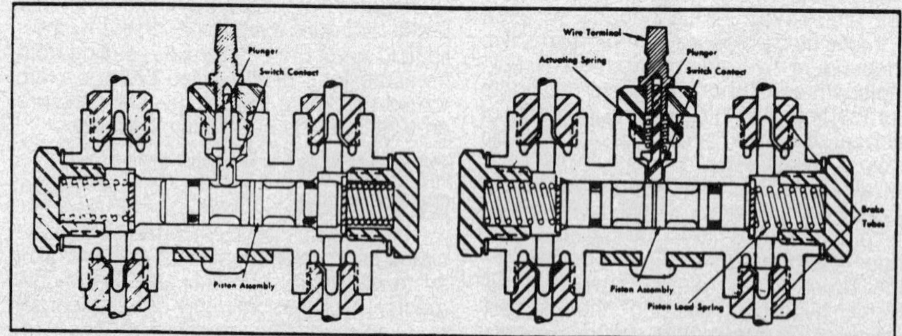


**Fig. 5 Pressure differential valve & brake warning light switch**

the warning light is completed, lighting the lamp (left view).

In **Fig. 6**, as pressure falls in one system, the other system's normal pressure forces the piston to the inoperative side, contacting the switch terminal, causing the warning light on the instrument panel to glow.

On front wheel drive models, a fluid level indicator replaces the pressure differential valve used in previous brake systems. It is contained inside the body of the master cylinder plastic reservoir and activates the brake warning light when fluid level is low.

### Testing Warning Light System

If the parking brake light is connected into the service brake warning light system, the brake warning light will flash only when the parking brake is applied with the ignition turned ON. The same light will also glow should one of the two service brake systems fail when the brake pedal is applied.

To test the system, turn the ignition on and apply the parking brake. If the lamp fails to light, inspect for a burned out bulb, disconnected socket, a broken or disconnected wire at the switch.

**Fig. 7** is an exterior view of a typical brake warning light switch. The brake warning light switch is usually mounted on the left frame side rail or on the brake pedal bracket.

To test the brake warning system, raise the car and open a wheel bleeder valve while a helper depresses the brake pedal and observes the warning light on the instrument panel. If the bulb fails to light, inspect for a burned out bulb, disconnected socket, or a broken or disconnected wire at the switch. If the bulb is not burned out, and wire continuity is proven, replace the brake warning switch.

## COMBINATION VALVE

On all models except Capri, the combination valve, **Fig. 8** is a metering valve, failure warning switch, and a proportioner in one assembly and is used on disc brake applications. The metering valve delays front disc braking until the rear drum brake shoes contact the drum. The failure warning switch is actuated in event of front or rear brake system failure, in turn activating a dash warning lamp. The proportioner balances front to rear braking action during rapid deceleration.

Combination valves used on diagonally split brake systems do not use metering valves instead two proportioning valves are used, **Fig. 9.**

### Metering Valve

When the brakes are not applied, the metering valve permits the brake fluid to flow through the valve, thus allowing the fluid to expand and contract with temperature changes.

When the brakes are initially applied, the metering valve stem moves to the left, preventing fluid to flow through the valve to the front disc brakes. This is accomplished by the smooth end of the metering valve stem contacting the metering valve seal lip at 4-30 psi, **Fig. 10.** The metering valve spring holds the retainer against the seal until a predetermined pressure is produced at the valve inlet port which overcomes the spring pressure and permits hydraulic pressure to actuate the front disc brakes, **Fig. 11.** The increased pressure into the valve is metered through the valve seal, to the front disc brakes, producing an increased force on the diaphragm. The diaphragm then pulls the pin, in turn pulling the retainer and reduces the spring pres-

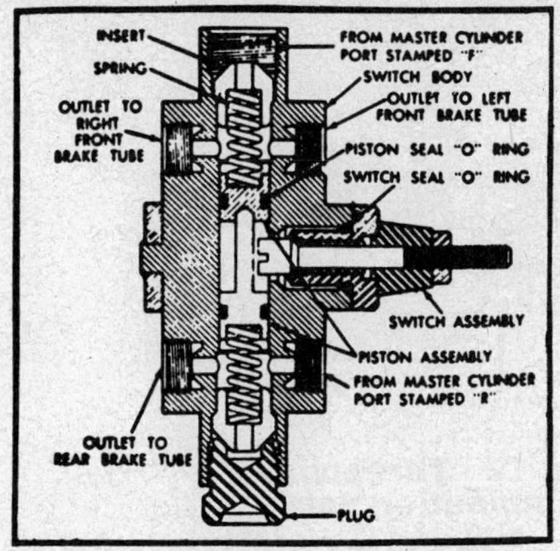


**Fig. 6 Pressure differential valve & brake warning light switch**

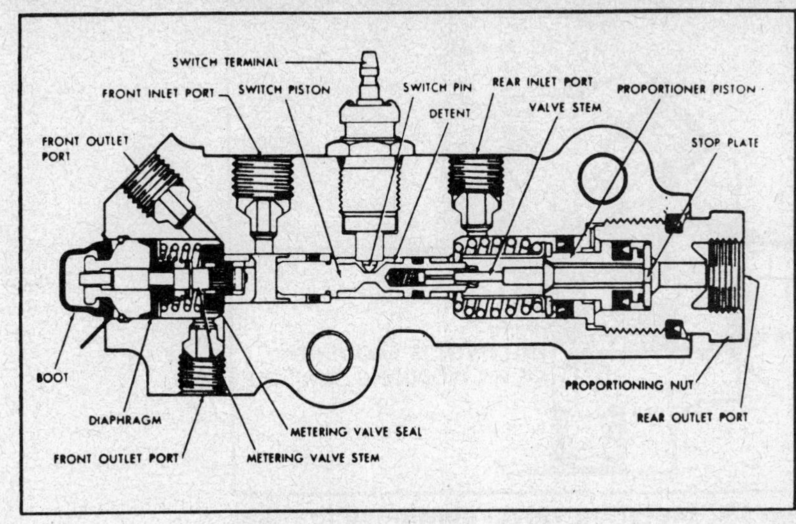


**Fig. 8 Combination valve**

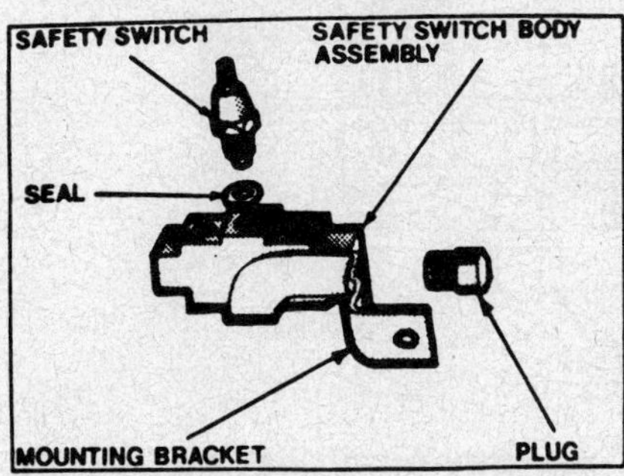


**Fig. 7 Typical pressure valve & brake warning light switch**

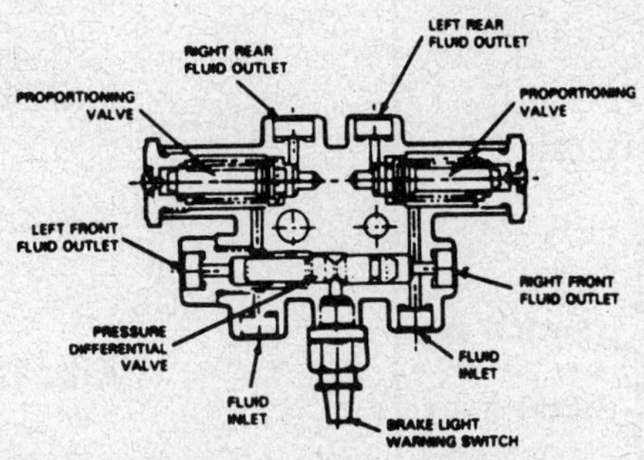

**Fig. 9 Diagonally split system combination valve**

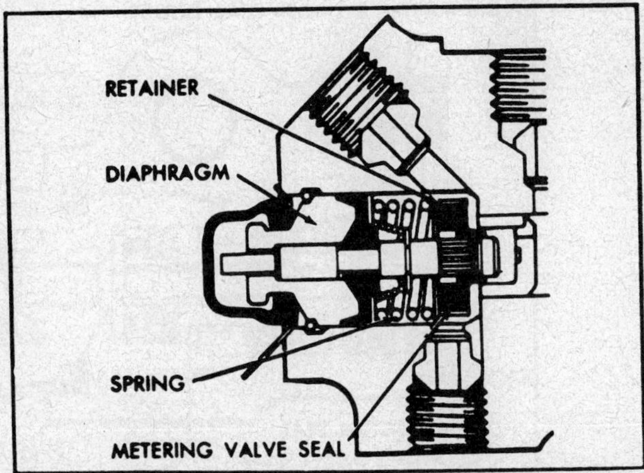


**Fig. 10 Metering valve, initial braking**

sure on the metering valve seal. Eventually, the pressure reaches a point at which the spring is pulled away by the diaphragm pin and retainer, leaving the metering valve unrestricted, permitting full pressure to pass through the metering valve.

On some applications, two-way or three-way combination valves are used. The three-way combination valve consists of a metering valve, failure warning switch and a proportioner mounted in an aluminum body, **Fig. 12.** The two-way combination valve, **Fig. 13,** consists of a failure warning switch and a proportioner. On models equipped with metering valves, the metering valve release rod must be pushed in during bleeding operations on the front wheels.

On Capri models, the proportioning valves are an integral part of the master cylinder.

## Failure Warning Switch

If the rear brake system fails, the front system pressure forces the switch piston to the right, **Fig. 14.** The switch pin is then forced up into the switch, completing the electrical circuit and activates the dash warning lamp.

When repairs are made and pressure returns to the system, the piston moves to the left, resetting the switch. The detent on the piston requires approximately 100-450 psi to permit full reset of the piston. In event of front brake system failure, the piston moves to the left and the same sequence of events is followed as for rear system failure except the piston resets to the right.

## Proportioner Or Pressure Control Valves

During rapid deceleration, a portion of vehicle weight is transferred to the front wheels. This resultant loss of weight at rear wheels must be compensated for to avoid early rear wheel skid. The proportioner or pressure control valve reduces rear brake system pressure, delaying rear wheel skid. When the proportioner or pressure control valve is incorporated in the combination valve assembly, pressure developed within the valve acts against the large end of the piston, overcoming the spring pressure, moving the piston left, **Fig. 15.** The piston then contacts the stem seat and restricts line pressure through the valve.

During normal braking operation, the proportioner or pressure control valve is not functional. Brake fluid flows into the proportioner or pressure control valve between the piston center hole and the valve stem, through the stop plate and to the rear brakes. Spring pressure loads the piston during normal braking, causing it to rest against the stop plate, **Fig. 16.**

On diagonally split brake systems, two proportioners or pressure control valves are used. One controls the left rear brake, the other the right rear brake. On front wheel drive models less power brakes, the proportioners or pressure control valves are located in the combination valve, **Fig. 9.** On front wheel drive models with power brakes, the proportioners or pressure control valves are installed in the master cylinder rear brake outlet ports, **Fig. 17.**

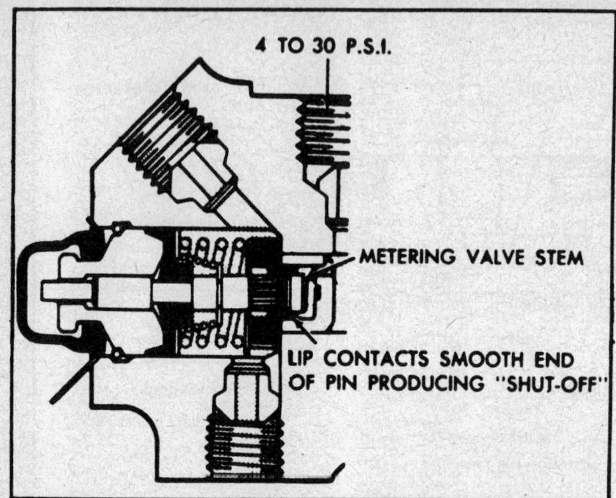


Fig. 11 Metering valve, continued braking

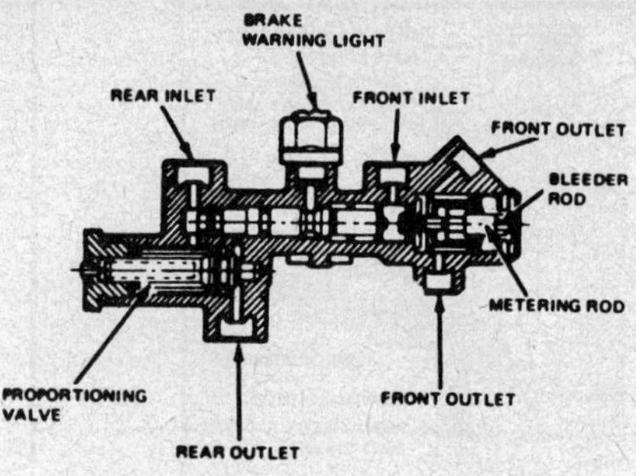


Fig. 12 Three-way combination valve

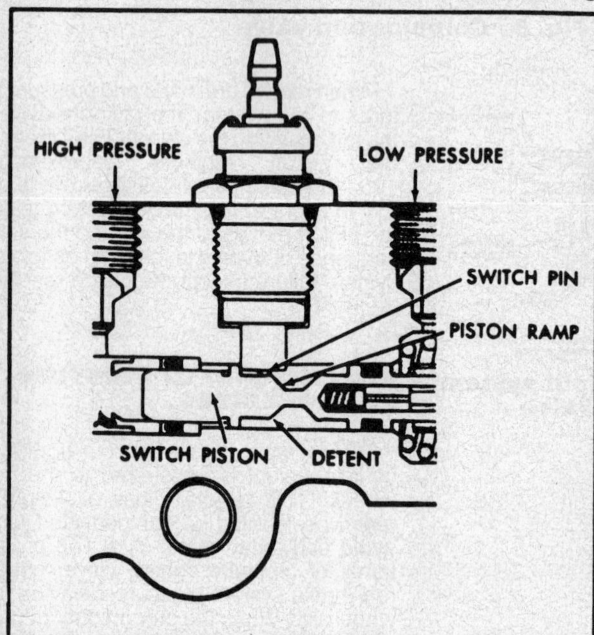


Fig. 14 Failure warning switch, rear system failure

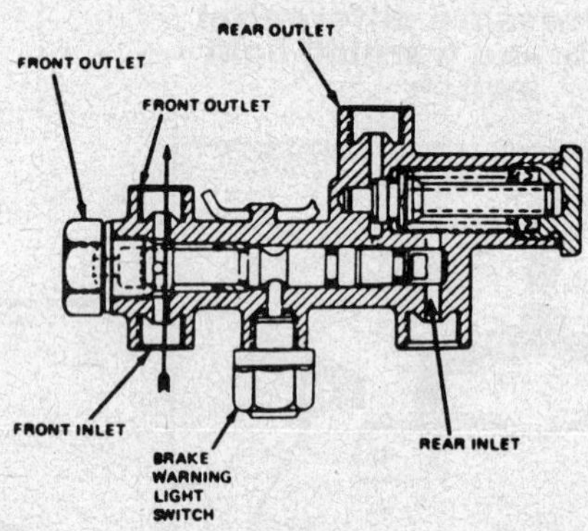


Fig. 13 Two-way combination valve

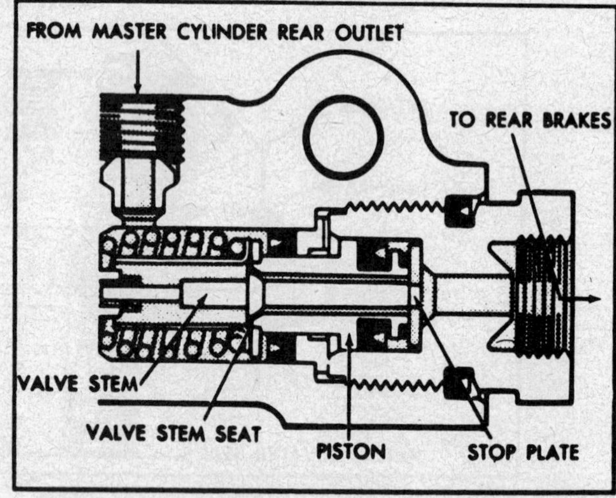


Fig. 15 Proportioner, rapid deceleration

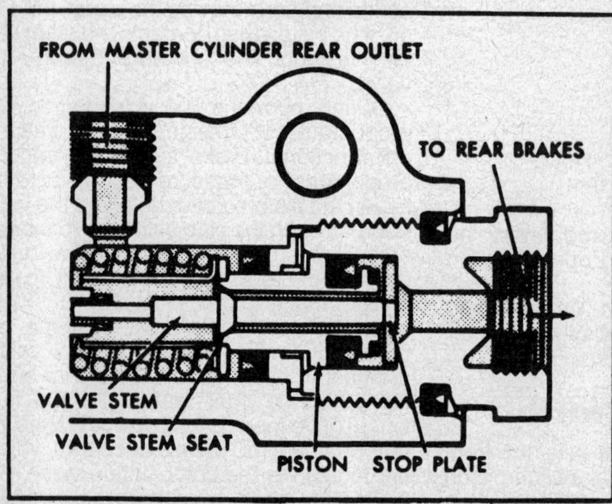


Fig. 16 Proportioner, normal braking

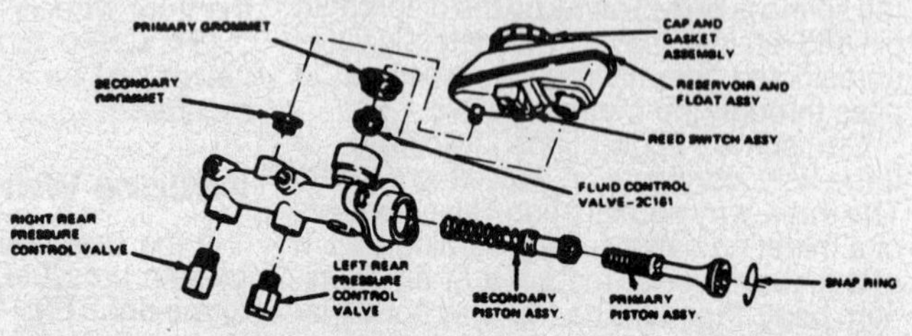


Fig. 17 Pressure control valves installed in master cylinder. Front wheel drive models

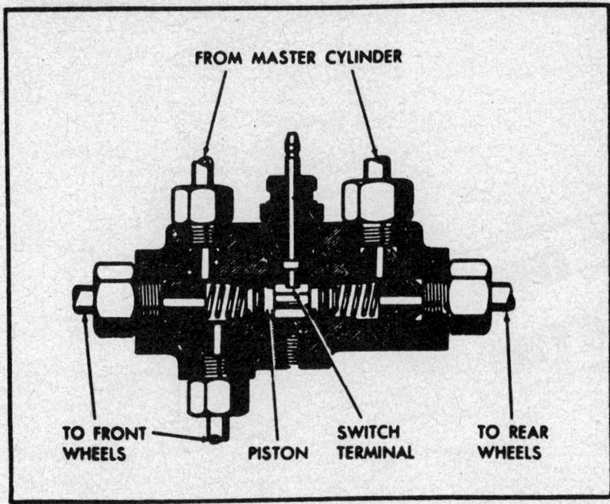


**Fig. 18 Brake distribution switch (normal)**

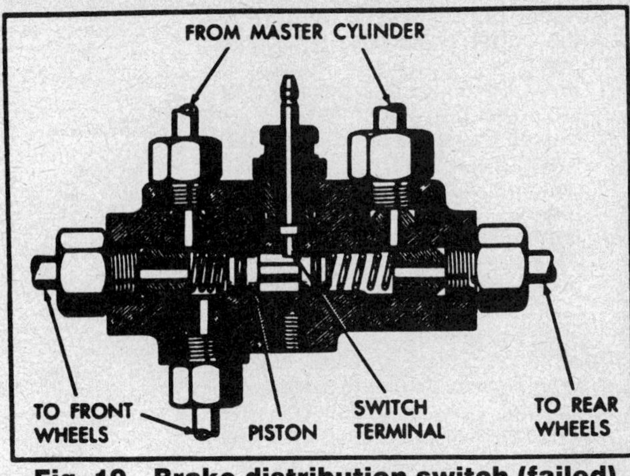


**Fig. 19 Brake distribution switch (failed)**

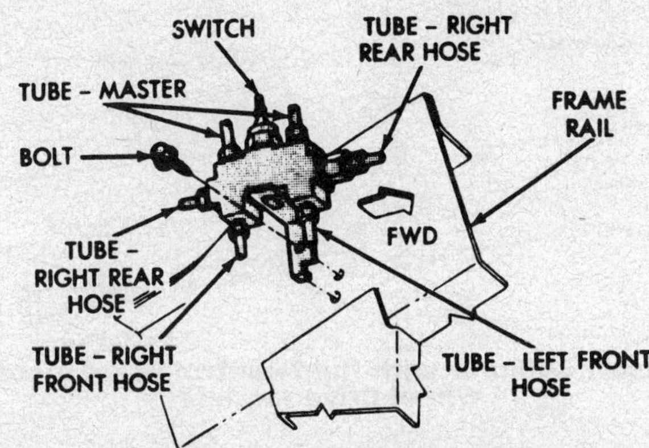


**Fig. 20 Typical brake distribution switch used in diagonally split brake systems**

## BRAKE DISTRIBUTION VALVE & SWITCH

This switch assembly which is used on some diagonally split brake systems and Corvette four wheel disc brake systems, is connected to the outlet ports of the master cylinder and also to the brake warning light that warns the driver if either the primary or secondary brake system has failed.

When hydraulic pressure is equal in both primary and secondary brake systems, the switch remains centered, **Fig. 18.** If pressure fails in one of the systems, hydraulic pressure moves the piston toward the inoperative side, **Fig. 19.** The shoulder of the piston contacts the switch terminal, providing a ground and lighting the warning lamp.

**Fig. 20** shows a brake distribution valve and switch used on some diagonally split brake system applications.

## MASTER CYLINDER, REPLACE

### Except Capri, Sable, Taurus, 1991 Escort & Tracer

1. Disconnect brake lines from master cylinder, then all necessary electrical connectors.
2. Remove nuts retaining master cylinder to brake booster.
3. Remove master cylinder.
4. Reverse procedure to install. After installation is complete, fill master cylinder with manufacturer recommended brake fluid and bleed brakes.

### Sable & Taurus

1. Remove brake tubes form primary and secondary fluid outlet ports. On wagon models, remove brake tubes from pressure control valves. **Sedan models do not use master cylinder mounted pressure control valves. Instead, a floor pan mounted brake differential control valve is used. This valve utilizes a mechanical linkage to the lower control arm to vary rear brake hydraulic pressure according to vehicle load.**
2. Disconnect brake warning light connector.
3. Remove brake booster-to-master cylinder attaching bolts, then slide master cylinder upward from vehicle.
4. Reverse procedure to install. After installation is complete, fill master cylinder with manufacturer recommended brake fluid and bleed brakes.

### Capri

Pump brake pedal several times to exhaust any vacuum in booster.

1. Disconnect brake lines from master cylinder, then cap brake lines and master cylinder ports to prevent contamination from entering system.
2. Remove vacuum valve from booster, then disconnect pressure warning switch connector.
3. Remove two nut and washer assemblies retaining master cylinder to brake booster.
4. Remove master cylinder from brake booster. **It may be necessary to insert a small pry bar between the booster and the master cylinder to free the master cylinder.**
5. Reverse Procedure to install, noting the following:
   a. **Torque** master cylinder retaining nuts to 7-12 ft. lbs.
   b. Check and if necessary, adjust stoplamp switch.

### 1991 Escort & Tracer

1. Remove the battery from vehicle.
2. Disconnect the low fluid level sensor electrical connector.
3. Loosen the brake line flare nuts, then disconnect the brake lines from the master cylinder assembly.
4. **On models with manual transaxles,** remove clamp, then pull the clutch hose from the brake/clutch fluid reservoir.
5. **On all models,** cap the lines and master cylinder ports.
6. Remove the two master cylinder retaining nuts, then master cylinder.
7. Adjust master cylinder piston to push rod clearance as follows:
   a. Position Master Cylinder Gauge tool No. T87C-2500-A or equivalent on the end of the master cylinder, loosen the set screw on end of master cylinder. Push the gauge plunger against the bottom of the primary piston.
   b. While holding the gauge in position, tighten the set screw.

  c. Apply 19.7 inches Hg vacuum to the power brake with a vacuum pump.
  d. Invert the gauge and place it over the power brake push rod.
  e. Ensure that there is no space between the end of the adjustment gauge and the power brake push rod.
  f. If there is space between the end of the adjustment gauge and the power brake push rod, loosen the push rod locknut and adjust the push rod until there is no space.
8. Reverse procedure to install master cylinder. Reactivate airbag system. After master cylinder installation, the piston to push rod clearance will be as follows:
  a. With no vacuum applied, 0.016-0.024 inches.
  b. With 19.7 inches Hg applied, 0.004-0.01 inches.

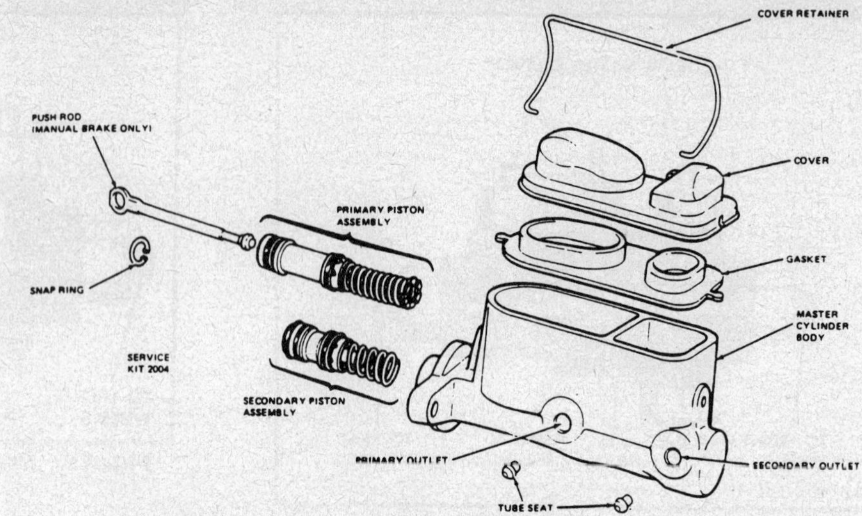


**Fig. 21 Cutaway view of Bendix dual master cylinder used with disc brakes (typical)**

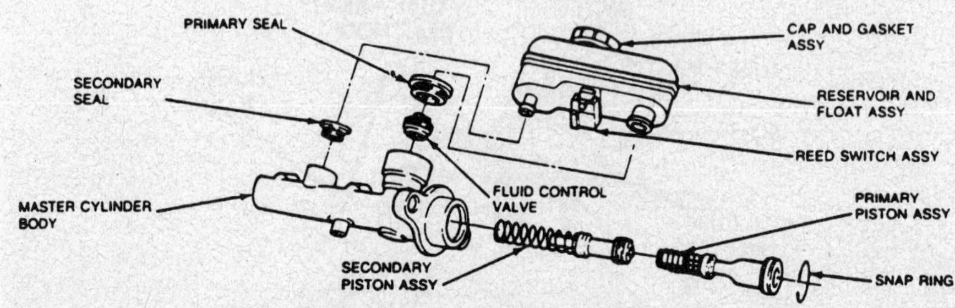


**Fig. 22 Master cylinder with fluid control valve installed. Front wheel drive models**

## DUAL MASTER CYLINDER SERVICE

### Disassemble

1. Remove cover and diaphragm then drain brake fluid from master cylinder, **Fig. 21.**
2. **On front wheel drive models,** using a screwdriver, pry up on reservoir and remove primary port from master cylinder, **Fig. 22.**
3. Rotate reservoir out of way and remove sealing grommet from master cylinder casting.
4. Using a socket, remove fluid control valve.
5. **On all models,** depress primary piston and remove snap ring from retaining groove at open end of bore.
6. Remove primary and secondary piston assemblies from master cylinder. If secondary piston does not readily come out, apply air pressure to secondary outlet port to remove.

### Inspection

When disassembled, wash all parts in clean brake fluid only. Use an air hose to blow out all passages, orifices and valve holes. Air dry and place parts on clean paper or lint-free cloth. Inspect master cylinder bore for scoring, rust, pitting or etching. Any of these conditions will require replacement of the housing. Inspect master cylinder pistons for scoring, pitting or distortion. Replace piston if any of these conditions exist.

If either master cylinder housing or piston is replaced, clean new parts with clean brake fluid and blow out all passages with air hose.

Examine reservoirs for foreign matter and check all passages for restrictions. If there is any suspicion of contamination or evidence of corrosion, completely flush hydraulic system as outlined below.

When overhauling a master cylinder, use all parts contained in repair kit. Before starting reassembly, dip all cups, seals, pistons, springs, check valves and retainers in clean brake fluid and place in a clean pan or on clean paper. Wash hands with soap and water only to prevent contamination of rubber parts from oil, kerosene or gasoline. During assembly, dip all parts in clean brake fluid.

Inspect through side outlet of dual master cylinder housing to make certain cup lips do not hang up on edge of hole or turn back, which would result in faulty operation. A piece of 3/16 inch rod with an end rounded off will be helpful in guiding cups past hole.

When overhauling aluminum master cylinders, carefully inspect master cylinder bore for corrosion. If corroded, replace master cylinder. Do not hone or use abrasives on the bore of these cylinders.

### Assembly

1. Install secondary piston assembly into bore, spring end first.
2. Install primary piston assembly, spring end first.
3. Depress primary piston and install snap ring.
4. **On front wheel drive models,** install fluid control valve and **torque** to 97-115 inch lbs.
5. Lubricate new grommet with brake fluid and install in primary port.
6. Install reservoir in new grommet.
7. **On all models,** fill and bench bleed master cylinder.
8. Install cap and diaphragm on master cylinder reservoir.

## BLEEDING BRAKES

Pressure bleeding is recommended for all hydraulic brake systems.

The bleeding operation itself is fairly well standardized. First step in all cases is cleaning the dirt from the filler cap before removing it from the master cylinder. This should be done thoroughly.

Pressure bleeding is fastest because the master cylinder doesn't have to be refilled several times, and the job can be done by one man. To prevent air from the pressure tank getting into the lines, do not shake the tank while air is being added to the tank or after it has been pressurized. Set the tank in the required location, bring the air hose to the tank, and do not move it during the bleeding operation. The tank should be kept at least one-third full.

On vehicles equipped with disc brakes and master cylinders without proportioners or pressure control valves located in the master cylinder outlet port, the brake metering valve or combination valve must be held in position using a suitable tool.

If air does get into the fluid, releasing the pressure will cause the bubbles to increase in size, rise to the top of the fluid, and escape. Pressure should not be greater than about 35 psi.

On vehicles equipped with plastic reservoirs, do not exceed 25 psi bleeding pressure.

When bleeding without pressure, open the bleed valve three-quarters of a turn, depress the pedal a full stroke, then allow

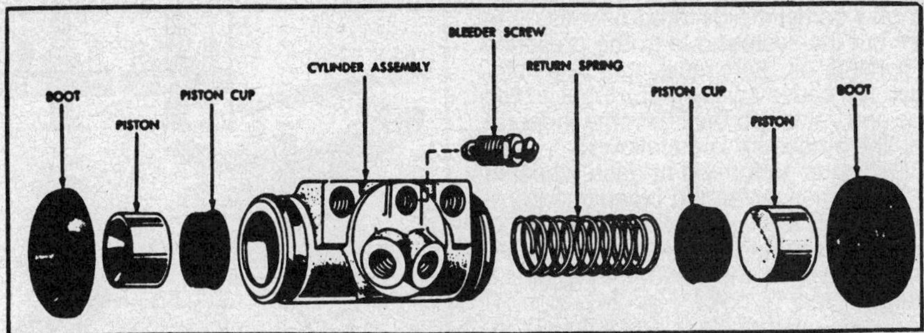


**Fig. 23 Disassembled view of typical wheel cylinder**

the pedal to return slowly to its released position. It is suggested that after the pedal has been depressed to the end of its stroke, the bleeder valve should be closed before the start of the return stroke. On models with power brakes, first reduce the vacuum in the power unit to zero by pumping the brake pedal several times with the engine off before starting to bleed the system.

Pressure bleeding, of course, eliminates the need for pedal pumping.

Discard drained or bled brake fluid. Care should be taken not to spill brake fluid, since this can damage the finish of the car.

Flushing is essential if there is water, mineral oil or other contaminants in the lines, and whenever new parts are installed in the hydraulic system. Fluid contamination is usually indicated by swollen and deteriorated cups and other rubber parts.

Wheel cylinders on disc brakes are equipped with bleeder valves, and are bled in the same manner as wheel cylinders for drum brakes.

Bleeding is necessary on all four wheels if air has entered the system because of low fluid level, or the line or lines have been disconnected. If a line is disconnected at any one wheel cylinder, that cylinder only need be bled. Of course, on brake reline jobs, bleeding is advisable to remove any air or contaminants.

Master cylinders equipped with bleeder valves should be bled first before the wheel cylinders are bled. In all cases where a master cylinder has been overhauled, it must be bled. Where there is no bleeder valve, this can be done by leaving the lines loose, actuating the brake pedal to expel the air and then tightening the lines.

After overhauling a dual master cylinder used in conjunction with disc brakes, it is advisable to bleed the cylinder before installing it on the car. The reason for this recommendation is that air may be trapped between the master cylinder pistons because there is only one residual pressure valve (check valve) used in these units.

## SYSTEM PRIMING

When a new master cylinder has been installed or the brake system emptied or partially emptied, fluid may not flow from the bleeder screws during normal bleeding. It may be necessary to prime the system using the following procedure:

1. Using a tubing wrench, remove the brake lines from the master cylinder.
2. Install short brake lines in the master cylinder and position them back into the reservoir, ensure that the short brake line ends are submerged in the reservoir brake fluid.
3. Fill the reservoir with recommended brake fluid, then cover master cylinder fluid reservoir with shop towel.
4. Pump the brakes until clear, bubble free fluid comes out of both brake lines. **If any brake fluid spills on paint, wash it off immediately with water.**
5. Remove the short brake lines, then reinstall original brake lines.
6. Bleed each brake line at the master cylinder using the following procedure:
   a. Have assistant pump brake pedal 10 times, then hold firm pressure on the pedal.
   b. Open the rearmost brake line fittings with a tubing wrench until a stream of brake fluid comes out. Have assistant maintain pressure on the brake pedal until the brake line fitting is tightened again.
   c. Repeat this operation until clear, bubble free fluid comes out from around tube fitting.
   d. Repeat this bleeding operation at the front brake line fitting.
7. If any of the brake lines or calipers have been removed, it may be helpful to prime the system by gravity bleeding. this should be done after the master cylinder is primed and bled. To prime the system using the gravity method, proceed as follows:
   a. Fill the master cylinder with manufacturer recommended brake fluid or equivalent.
   b. Loosen both rear bleeder screws and leave them open until clear brake fluid flows out. **Check reservoir fluid level frequently, do not allow fluid level to drop below half full.**
   c. Tighten rear bleeder screws.
   d. Loosen bleeder screw on front caliper, leave open until clear fluid flows out. **Bleed front calipers one side at a time.**
8. After the master cylinder has been primed, the lines bled at the master cylinder and the brake system primed, normal brake system bleeding can be resumed at each wheel.

## TESTING DUAL MASTER CYLINDERS

Ensure that the master cylinder compensates in both parts. This can be done by applying the brake pedal lightly (engine running with power brakes) and observing for brake fluid squirting up in the reservoirs. This may only occur in the front chamber. To determine if the rear compensating port is open, pump up the brakes rapidly and hold the pedal down. Have an observer watch the fluid in the rear reservoir while the pedal is raised. A disturbance in the fluid indicates that the compensating port is open.

## WHEEL BLEEDING SEQUENCE

Rear Wheel Drive......... RR-LR-RF-LF
Front Wheel Drive ........ RR-LF-LR-RF

## DUAL MASTER CYLINDER BLEEDING NOTES

The following information applies to master cylinders without proportioners or pressure control valves located in the master cylinder outlet ports.

All vehicles use a self-centering valve. After any bleeding operation, turn ignition switch to ACC or ON position and depress brake pedal. Valve will center itself.

## WHEEL CYLINDERS

1. Remove wheel, drum and brake shoes.
2. Disconnect hydraulic line at wheel cylinder. Do not pull metal line away from cylinder as the cylinder connection will bend metal line and make installation difficult. Line will separate from cylinder when cylinder is moved away from brake backing plate.
3. Remove screws holding cylinder to brake plate and remove cylinder.

## OVERHAUL

1. Referring to **Fig. 23** as a guide, remove boots, pistons, springs and cups from cylinder.
2. Place all parts, except cylinder casting in clean brake fluid. Wipe cylinder walls with clean brake fluid.
3. Examine cylinder bore. A scored bore may be honed providing the diameter is not increased more than .005 inch. Replace worn or damaged parts from the repair kit.
4. Before assembling, wash hands with soap and water only, as oil, kerosene or gasoline will contaminate rubber parts.

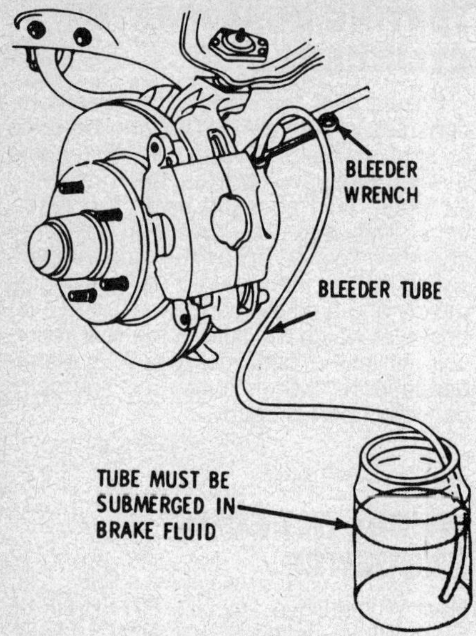


**Fig. 24 Bleeding wheel cylinder**

5. Lubricate cylinder wall and rubber cups with brake fluid.
6. Install springs, cups, pistons and boots in housing.
7. Wipe end of hydraulic line to remove any foreign matter.
8. Place hydraulic cylinder in position. Enter tubing into cylinder and start connecting fitting.
9. Secure cylinder to backing plate and then complete tightening of tubing fitting.
10. Install brake shoes, drum and wheel.
11. Bleed system as outlined previously, and adjust brakes.

## FLUSHING HYDRAULIC SYSTEM

Whenever new brake components are installed in the hydraulic system, it is recommended that the entire hydraulic system be thoroughly flushed with clean brake fluid.

It may sometime become necessary to flush out the system due to the presence of mineral oil, kerosene, gasoline, etc., which will cause swelling of rubber piston cups and valves so they become inoperative. The procedure is as follows:

Flushing is performed at each wheel in the same manner as the bleeding operation except that the bleeder valve is opened 1½ turns and the fluid is forced through the lines and bleeder valve until it emerges clear in color, **Fig. 24.** Approximately one quart of clean brake fluid is required to flush the hydraulic system. After completing the flushing operation at all bleeder valves, check to ensure the master cylinder is filled to the proper level.

## HYDRAULIC TUBING

Never use copper tubing as a replacement for steel tubing. Copper tubing is subject to fatigue cracking and corrosion which could result in brake system failure.

Steel tubing is used to conduct hydraulic pressure to the brakes. All fittings, tubing and hose should be inspected for rusted, damaged or defective flared seats. The tubing is equipped with a double flare/inverted seat or I.S.O. flare to insure more positive seating in the fitting. To repair or reflare tubing, proceed as follows:

### DOUBLE FLARE/INVERTED SEAT

1. Using the tool shown in **Fig. 25** or equivalent, cut off the damaged seat or damaged tubing.
2. Ream out any burrs or rough edges showing on inside edges of tubing. This will make the ends of the tubing square and insure better seating on the flared end. Before flaring tubing, place a compression nut on tubing.
3. Open handles of flaring tool and rotate jaws of tool until mating jaws of tubing size are centered in the area between vertical posts.

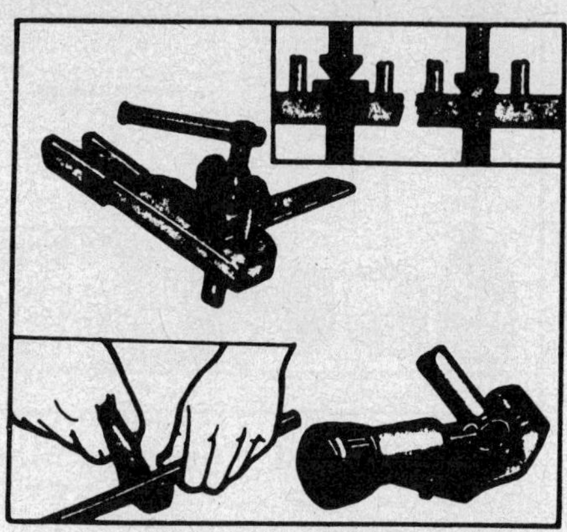

**Fig. 25 Flaring hydraulic brake tubing**

4. Slowly close handles with tubing inserted in jaws but do not apply heavy pressure to handle as this will lock tubing in place.
5. Referring to **Fig. 25,** place gauge on edge over end of tubing and push tubing through jaws until end of tubing contacts recessed notch of gauge matching size of tubing.
6. Squeeze handles of flaring tool and lock tubing in place.
7. Place proper size plug of gauge down in end of tubing. Swing compression disc over gauge and center tapered flaring screw in recess in disc.
8. Lubricate taper of flaring or screw and screw in until plug gauge has seated in jaws of flaring tool. This action has started to invert the extended end of tubing.
9. Remove gauge and apply lubricant to tapered end of flaring screw and continue to screw down until tool is firmly seated in tubing.
10. Remove tubing from flaring tool and inspect the seat. If seat is cracked, cut off cracked end and repeat flaring operation.

## HYDRAULIC BRAKE SPECIFICATIONS

| Year | Model | Master Cylinder Bore Dia. |
|---|---|---|
| **FORD & MERCURY** | | |
| 1989–90 | Cougar & Thunderbird | .940 |
| | Crown Victoria & Grand Marquis | 1.00 |
| | Escort | .780 |
| | Festiva | .750 |
| | Mustang | .830 |
| | Probe | .875 |
| | Sable & Taurus | .938 |
| | Tempo & Topaz | .780 |
| | Tracer① | .875 |

*Continued*

## HYDRAULIC BRAKE SPECIFICATIONS—Continued

| Year | Model | Master Cylinder Bore Dia. |
|---|---|---|
| **FORD & MERCURY** | | |
| 1991 | Capri | .811 |
| | Cougar & Thunderbird | .940 |
| | Crown Victoria & Grand Marquis | 1.00 |
| | Escort | .875 |
| | Festiva | .750 |
| | Mustang | .830 |
| | Probe | .875 |
| | Sable & Taurus | .938 |
| | Tempo & Topaz | .780 |
| | Tracer① | .875 |
| **LINCOLN** | | |
| 1989-91 | Mark VII & Town Car | 1.000 |
| | Continental | .940 |
| **MERKUR** | | |
| 1989 | Scorpio | .938 |
| | XR4Ti | 1.000 |

①—1989 only.

# POWER BRAKES

**NOTE:** On Vehicles Equipped With Anti-lock Brakes Refer To "Anti-Lock Brake" Section.

## INDEX



## APPLICATION

### CAPRI

1991 ........ Single Diaphragm

### COUGAR & THUNDERBIRD

1989-91① ... Bendix Single Diaphragm

### FORD & MERCURY FULLSIZE

1989-91① ... Bendix Single Diaphragm

### ESCORT

1989-90 ..... Bendix Single Diaphragm ① or Teves Single Diaphragm②
1991 ........ Single Diaphragm

### TEMPO & TOPAZ

1989-91 ..... Bendix Single Diaphragm ① or Teves Single Diaphragm②

### FESTIVA

1989-91 ..... Single Diaphragm Booster

### LINCOLN

1989-91①③ . Bendix Single Diaphragm

### MUSTANG

1989-91 2.3L Except Convertible① ..... Bendix Single Diaphragm
1989-91 5.0L & All Convertible① ...... Bendix Tandem Diaphragm

### PROBE

1989-91 ..... Single Diaphragm Booster

### SABLE & TAURUS

1989-91① ... Bendix Single Diaphragm

### TRACER

1989 ........ Single Diaphragm Booster
1991 ........ Single Diaphragm Booster

### XR4Ti

1989 ....... Double Diaphragm Booster

**①—The only service that may be performed on Bendix type brake booster is replacement of the grommet, check valve and pushrod adjustment. If any other malfunction is apparent, booster should be replaced.**
**②—The only service that may be performed on Teves type brake booster is replacement of grommet and check valve. If any other malfunction is apparent, booster should be replaced.**
**③—Town Car.**

## SYSTEM DESCRIPTION

The vacuum assist diaphragm assembly multiplies the force exerted on the master cylinder piston in order to increase the hydraulic pressure delivered to the wheel cylinders while decreasing the effort necessary to obtain acceptable stopping performance.

Vacuum assist units get their energy by opposing engine vacuum to atmospheric pressure. A piston, cylinder and flexible diaphragm utilize this energy to provide brake assistance. The diaphragm is balanced with engine vacuum until the brake pedal is depressed, allowing atmospheric pressure to unbalance the unit and apply force to the brake system.

Brakes will operate even if the power unit fails. This means the conventional brake system and the power assist system are completely separate. Troubleshooting conventional and power assist systems are exactly the same until the power unit is reached. As with conventional hydraulic brakes, a spongy pedal still means air is trapped in the hydraulic system. Power brakes give higher line pressure, making leaks more critical.

## POWER BOOSTER REPLACE

### CROWN VICTORIA, GRAND MARQUIS, TEMPO, TOPAZ & 1989–90 ESCORT

1. Disconnect battery ground cable.
2. Disconnect master cylinder from booster and position aside. **It is not necessary to disconnect brake lines, but care should be taken to avoid twisting or kinking lines.**
3. Disconnect manifold vacuum hose from booster check valve.
4. Working under instrument panel, disconnect stop lamp switch electrical connector under instrument panel.
5. Remove stop lamp switch retaining pin. Slide switch off brake pedal pin enough so outer plate of switch clears the pin, then remove switch from pin.
6. Remove booster-to-dash panel attaching screws.
7. Slide booster pushrod, nylon washers and bushing off brake pedal pin.
8. Move booster forward until booster studs clear dash panel, then remove booster.
9. Reverse procedure to install.

### COUGAR & THUNDERBIRD

#### 3.8L/V6-232 & 5.0L/V8-302 Engines

1. Disconnect battery ground cable and remove air cleaner.
2. Disconnect manifold vacuum hose from booster check valve.
3. Disconnect brake lines from primary and secondary outlet ports of master cylinder.
4. Remove master cylinder-to-booster attaching nuts and the master cylinder.
5. Working under instrument panel, disconnect electrical connector from stop lamp switch.
6. Remove hairpin type retainer. Slide stop lamp switch off brake pedal pin just far enough for the switch outer hole to clear the pin, then lower switch away from pin.
7. Remove booster-to-dash panel attaching nuts.
8. **On models equipped with speed control,** unfasten control amplifier from lower outboard booster stud and position aside.
9. **On all models,** slide booster pushrod, bushing and inner nylon washer off brake pedal pin.
10. Move booster forward in engine compartment until booster studs clear dash panel, then rotate front of booster toward engine and remove booster.
11. Reverse procedure to install.

### TOWN CAR

1. Disconnect battery ground cable.
2. Remove master cylinder from booster. Position side without disconnecting the hydraulic lines. **It is not necessary to disconnect hydraulic lines, but care should be taken so brake lines are not kinked. Kinking of brake lines can lead to tube damage.**
3. Disconnect manifold vacuum hose from booster check valve.
4. Disconnect stoplamp switch connector.
5. Remove stoplamp switch retaining pin, then slide stoplamp switch off from brake pedal pin just far enough for outer plate of stoplamp switch to clear pin, then remove stoplamp switch.
6. Remove booster to dash panel retaining nuts, then slide booster push rod, nylon washers and bushing off brake pedal pin.
7. Remove booster assembly from dash panel by sliding push rod out from engine side of dash panel.
8. Reverse procedure to install, noting the following:
   a. **Torque** booster to dash panel retaining nuts to 13-25 ft. lbs.
   b. **Torque** master cylinder to booster locking nuts to 13-25 ft. lbs.

### MUSTANG

#### 5.0L/V8-302 Engine

1. Remove stoplight switch and slide booster pushrod, bushing and inner nylon washer from brake pedal pin.
2. Remove air cleaner.
3. Disconnect accelerator cable from throttle body. Remove screws securing accelerator cable bracket to engine and rotate bracket toward engine. Disconnect inlet hose of choke water cover and position aside.
4. Disconnect vacuum hose from power brake unit.
5. Disconnect hydraulic lines from master cylinder and cap open lines and ports.
6. Remove master cylinder.
7. From inside vehicle, remove power brake unit to dash panel attaching nuts.
8. **On models with speed control,** remove control amplifier which is mounted on the lower outboard booster stud and set aside.
9. **On all models,** work from engine compartment and move booster forward until booster studs clear the dash panel, then raise front of unit and remove from vehicle.

#### 2.3L/4-140 Engine

1. Disconnect battery ground cable, then remove air cleaner.
2. Disconnect accelerator cable from throttle body.
3. Remove screw that secures accelerator cable to shaft bracket, then remove cable from bracket.
4. Remove two screws that secure accelerator shaft bracket to manifold, and rotate bracket toward engine.
5. Remove RPO horn, if equipped.
6. Release fuel system pressure, then disconnect the two manifold injector connectors located near oil dipstick retaining bracket. Disconnect two fuel lines to fuel supply manifold assembly.
7. Remove engine oil dipstick tube and bracket.
8. Remove windshield wiper motor.
9. Disconnect vacuum lines located over brake booster at dash panel vacuum tee.
10. Remove bolt securing clutch cable stand, then move bracket to side rail at fender inner panel.
11. **On models equipped with speed control,** move speed control cable to one side to clear booster.
12. **On all models,** disconnect manifold booster line from booster check valve.
13. Disconnect brake lines from master cylinder, remove master cylinder attaching nuts, then master cylinder.
14. Working under instrument panel, disconnect electrical connector from stop lamp switch.
15. Remove hairpin type retainer and outer nylon washer from brake pedal pin, then slide stop lamp switch off brake pedal pin just enough for outer arm to clear pin.
16. **On models equipped with speed control,** unfasten control amplifier from lower outboard booster stud and position aside. Slide booster pushrod, bushing, and inner nylon washer off brake pedal pin.
17. **On all models,** move booster forward in engine compartment until booster studs clear dash panel, then rotate front of booster toward engine and remove booster.
18. Reverse procedure to install.

### SABLE & TAURUS

1. Disconnect battery ground cable.
2. Remove master cylinder as outlined under " Master Cylinder, Replace."
3. Disconnect booster vacuum hose from check valve.

4. Remove stop lamp switch retaining pin and white nylon washer. Slide switch off brake pedal pin enough so outer plate of switch clears the pin, then remove switch from pin.
5. Remove brake booster-to-dash panel attaching nuts, then slide booster pushrod and pushrod bushing off brake pedal pin.
6. Remove vacuum tee attaching bolts, then position tee aside.
7. Position wiring harness aside.
8. Remove transmission shift cable and bracket.
9. Move booster assembly forwards until it clears dash panel, then remove booster.
10. Reverse procedure to install.

## CAPRI, PROBE, 1991 ESCORT & TRACER

Pump brake pedal several times to exhaust any vacuum in the booster.

1. **On Capri models,** disconnect battery cables, then remove battery from vehicle.
2. **On all models,** remove master cylinder as outlined under "Master Cylinder, Replace."
3. Disconnect rubber hose connecting intake manifold to power brake unit.
4. Remove spring clip in brake pedal clevis pin.
5. Remove brake pedal clevis pin, then brake pedal push rod from brake pedal.
6. Remove power brake unit attaching nuts, then power brake unit from vehicle.
7. Reverse procedure to install.

## XR4Ti

### Removal

1. Depress brake pedal several times to deplete vacuum reserve in power booster.
2. Depressurize EFI fuel system using hand operated vacuum pump. Connect pump hose to fuel system pressure regulator and apply at least 25 inches vacuum.
3. Disconnect fuel inlet line at pulse damper, then fuel return line.
4. Disconnect low oil level sensor electrical connector and remove oil dipstick.
5. Remove oil dipstick tube to pulse damper bracket attaching screw.
6. Remove pulse damper bracket to intake manifold attaching nuts, then disconnect pulse damper from fuel manifold and remove damper/bracket assembly.
7. Disconnect source hose from vacuum tree and remove vacuum tree attaching screws.
8. Disconnect low brake fluid warning electrical connector at master cylinder cap.
9. Pull vacuum check valve out of power booster.
10. Disconnect brake lines at master cylinder and plug brake tubes to prevent

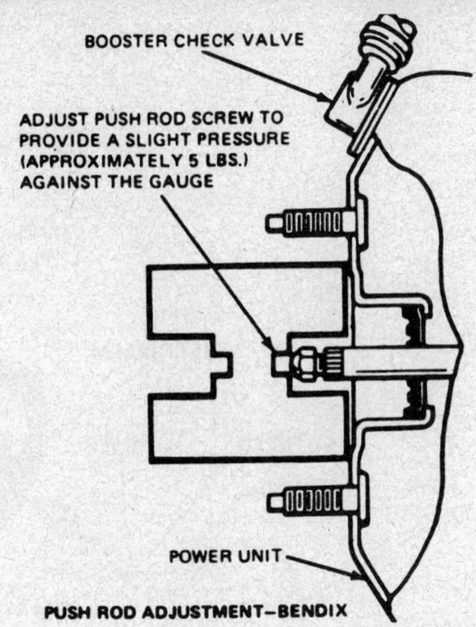
BOOSTER CHECK VALVE
ADJUST PUSH ROD SCREW TO PROVIDE A SLIGHT PRESSURE (APPROXIMATELY 5 LBS.) AGAINST THE GAUGE
POWER UNIT
PUSH ROD ADJUSTMENT—BENDIX

**Fig. 1 Master cylinder pushrod adjustment. Bendix type vacuum booster**

entry of foreign matter.

11. Remove sound insulator located under instrument panel inside passenger compartment.
12. Remove booster pushrod to brake pedal retaining clip.
13. Remove booster attaching nuts, then power booster/master cylinder from vehicle.
14. Remove master cylinder attaching nuts and separate booster from master cylinder.

### Installation

1. Install master cylinder on power booster, **torquing** attaching nuts to 16-20 ft. lbs.
2. Apply bead of caulking cord No. D6AZ-19560-A or equivalent to rear of booster where it mates to dash panel.
3. Apply light coat of lubricant on bushing, install bushing on booster pushrod and position booster in vehicle.
4. Working from inside vehicle, guide booster into position.
5. Install retaining clip on booster pushrod and install booster attaching nuts.
6. Install sound deadening panel.
7. Connect brake lines at master cylinder.
8. Position vacuum tree and install attaching screw, then connect source hose to vacuum tree.
9. Install vacuum check valve in power booster and connect electrical connector at master cylinder cap.
10. Connect pulse damper to fuel rail and position bracket on intake manifold studs.
11. Install pulse damper bracket stud nuts.
12. Install oil dipstick tube bracket attaching screw, then install dipstick and connect electrical connector at low oil level sensor.
13. Connect fuel inlet line to pulse damper and the fuel supply line to fuel rail.
14. Bleed brake system.

## FESTIVA & 1989 TRACER

1. Remove master cylinder as described under "Master Cylinder, Replace."
2. Disconnect vacuum hose from power brake unit.
3. From under instrument panel, remove brake pedal clevis pin, then detach push rod from brake pedal.
4. Remove power brake unit attaching nuts, then remove power brake unit.
5. Reverse procedure to install.

# PUSHROD ADJUST

Proper adjustment of the master cylinder pushrod is necessary to ensure proper operation of the power brake system. A pushrod that is too long will prevent the master cylinder piston from completely releasing hydraulic pressure, eventually, causing the brakes to drag. A pushrod that is too short will cause excessive brake pedal travel and cause groaning noises to come from the booster when the brakes are applied. A properly adjusted pushrod that remains assembled to the booster with which is was matched during production should not require service adjustment. However, if the booster, master cylinder or pushrod are serviced, the pushrod may require adjustment.

If the power unit pushrod requires an adjustment the Power Unit Repair Kit for the unit being serviced includes a gauge. The gauge measures from the end of the pushrod to the power unit shell.

On Capri models, push rod length is not adjustable. To ensure the master cylinder is free to return to its rest position with no residual pressure, verify stoplamp switch adjustment.

On 1991 Escort and Tracer models, refer to "Master Cylinder, Replace" in "Hydraulic Brakes" section for adjustment procedure.

## BENDIX TYPE

1. Disconnect master cylinder from booster leaving brake lines connected, and secure cylinder to prevent lines from being damaged.
2. Start engine and operate engine at idle speed.
3. With engine running, position gauge over pushrod. Gauge should bottom against booster housing with a force of approximately 5 lbs. applied to pushrod, **Fig. 1.**
4. If force required to seat gauge exceeds 5 lb., shorten length of pushrod. If force required to seat gauge is less than 5 lbs., lengthen pushrod. **Ensure that pushrod is properly seated in booster when performing gauge check.**
5. Install master cylinder, then remove reservoir cover.
6. With engine running, observe fluid surface in reservoir when brakes are applied and released rapidly. If no movement is observed on fluid surface, pushrod is adjusted too long.

## SINGLE DIAPHRAGM BOOSTER

1. Remove master cylinder as previously outlined.
2. Position master cylinder gauge T87C-2500-A or equivalent on end of master cylinder.
3. Loosen set screw and push gauge plunger against bottom of primary piston.
4. While holding gauge in position, tighten set screw.
5. Invert gauge and place over brake booster push rod, reading should be 0.
6. If clearance is not 0, loosen push rod locknut and adjust push rod.
7. Reverse procedure to install.

# CHECKING COMPLAINTS

Complaints about power brake operation should be handled as if two separate systems exist. Check for faults in the hydraulic system first. If it is satisfactory, start inspecting the power brake circuit. For a quick check of proper power unit operation, press the brake pedal firmly and then start the engine. The pedal should fall away slightly and less pressure should be needed to maintain the pedal in any position.

Another check begins with installation of a suitable pressure gauge in the brake hydraulic system. Take a reading with the engine off and the power unit not operating. Maintaining the same pedal height, start the engine and take another reading. There should be a substantial pressure increase in the second reading.

Pedal free travel and total travel are critical on cars equipped with power brakes. Pedal travel should be kept strictly to specifications.

Take a manifold vacuum reading or check operation of the external vacuum pump if the power unit isn't giving enough assistance. Remember, though, currently produced emission controlled engines, manifold vacuum readings may be less than 15 inches Hg at idle. If manifold vacuum is abnormally low, tune the engine and then try the power brakes again. Naturally, loose vacuum lines and clogged air intake filters will cut down brake efficiency. Most units have a check valve that retains some vacuum in the system when the engine is off. A vacuum gauge check of this valve will tell you when it is restricted or stuck open or closed.

Failure of the brakes to release in most instances is caused by a tight or misaligned connection between the power unit and the brake linkage. If this connection is free, look for a broken piston, diaphragm or bellows and return spring.

A simple check of the hydraulic system should be made before proceeding. Loosen the connection between the master cylinder and the brake booster. If the brakes release, the trouble is in the power unit; if the brakes still will not release, look for a restricted brake line or similar difficulties in the regular hydraulic circuit.

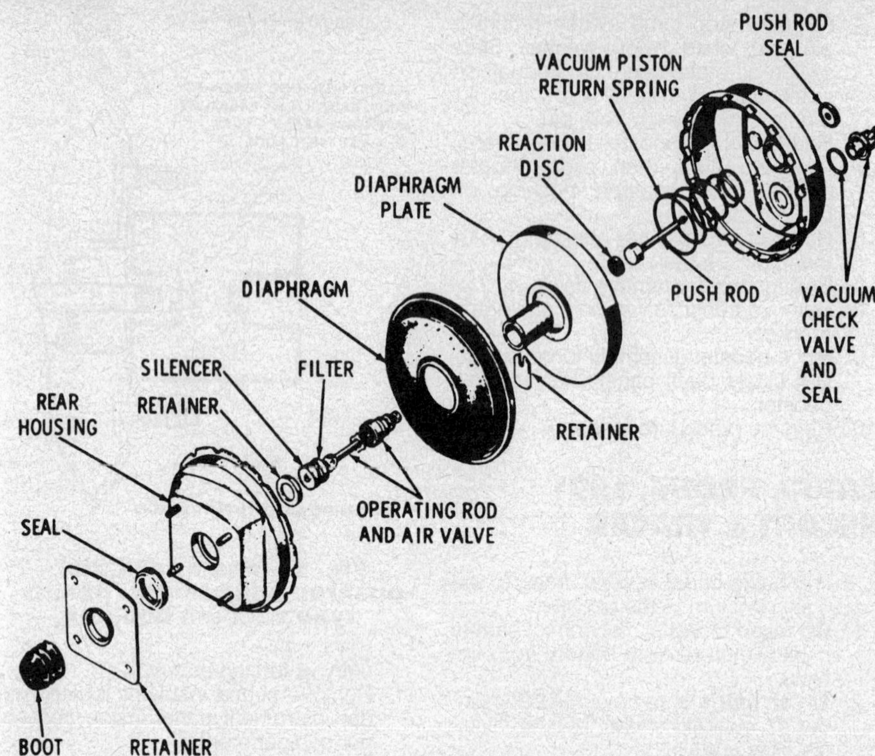


**Fig. 2 Bendix single diaphragm power brake unit**

A residual pressure check valve is usually included immediately under the brake line connection on hydraulic assist power brakes. This valve maintains a slight hydraulic pressure within the brake lines and wheel cylinders to give better pedal response. If it is sticking, the brakes may not release.

Power brakes that have a hard pedal are usually suffering from a milder form of the same ills that cause complete power unit failure. Collapsed or leaking vacuum lines or insufficient manifold vacuum, as well as punctured diaphragms or bellows and leaky piston seals, all lead to weak power unit operation. A steady hiss when the brake is held down means a vacuum leak that will cause poor power unit operation.

Do not immediately condemn the power unit if the brakes grab. First look for all the usual causes, such as greasy linings, scored rotors or drums. Then investigate the power unit. When the trouble has been traced to the power unit, check for a damaged reaction control. The reaction control is usually made up of a diaphragm, spring and valves that tends to resist pedal action. It is put in the system to give the pedal "feel."

# BENDIX DIAPHRAGM TYPES

## DESCRIPTION

These units are of the vacuum suspended type. Some units are of the single diaphragm type, **Fig. 2** while others are of the tandem diaphragm type, **Fig. 3.** Both single piston and double piston or split system type master cylinders are used.

The vacuum suspended diaphragm type units utilize engine manifold vacuum and atmospheric pressure for its power. It consists of three basic elements combined into a single power unit. The three basic elements of the single diaphragm type are:

1. A vacuum power section which includes a front and rear shell, a power diaphragm, a return spring and a pushrod.
2. A control valve, built integral with the power diaphragm and connected through a valve rod to the brake pedal, controls the degree of brake application or release in accordance with the pressure applied to the brake pedal.
3. A hydraulic master cylinder, attached to the vacuum power section which contains all the elements of the conventional brake master cylinder except for the pushrod, supplies fluid under pressure to the wheel brakes in proportion to the pressure applied to the brake pedal.

## OPERATION

Upon application of the brakes, the valve rod and plunger move to the left in the power diaphragm to close the vacuum port and open the atmospheric port to admit air through the air cleaner and valve at the rear diaphragm chamber. With vacuum present in the rear chamber, a force is developed to move the power diaphragm, hydraulic pushrod and hydraulic piston or pistons to close the compensating port or ports and force fluid under pressure through the residual check valve or valves

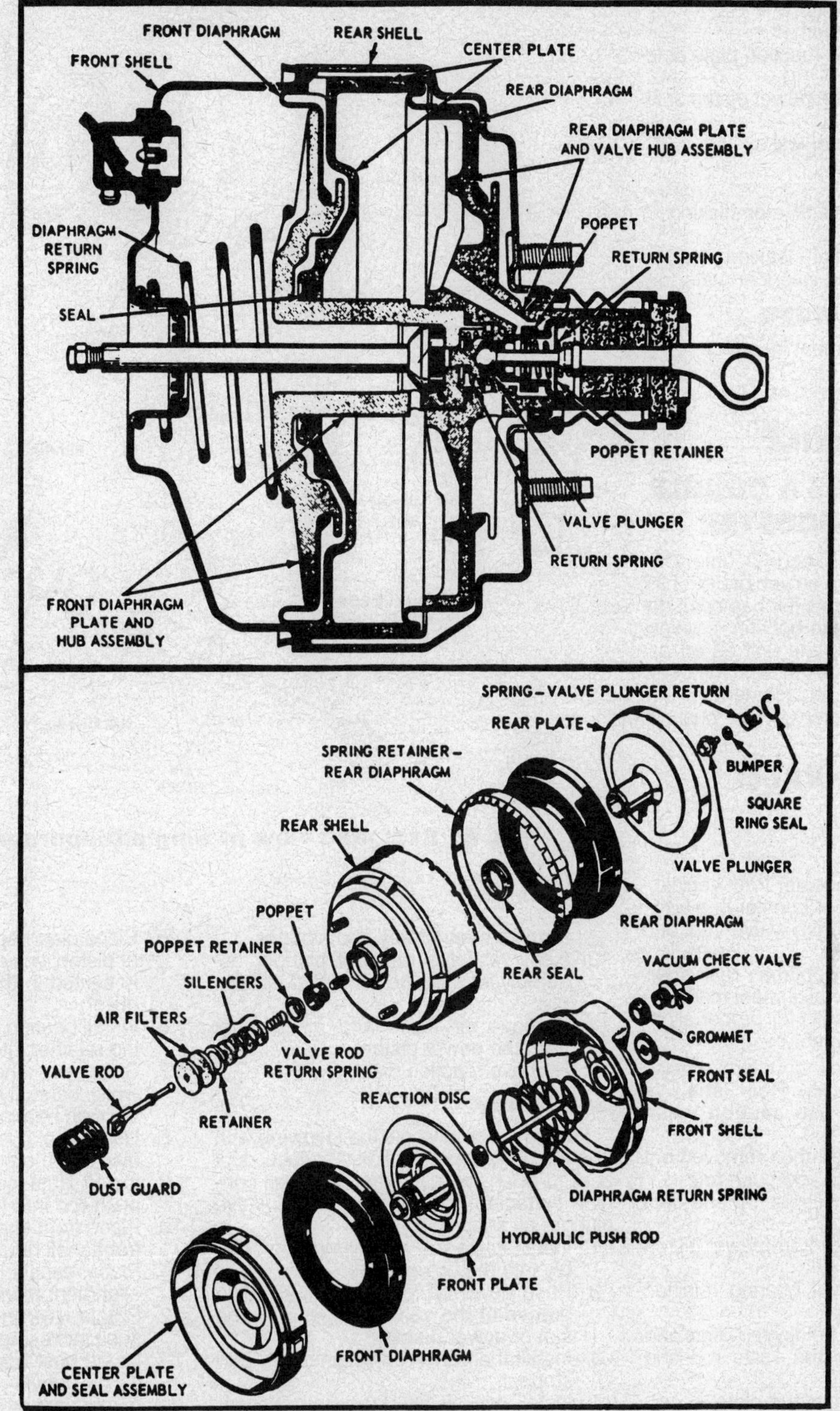


**Fig. 3 Bendix tandem diaphragm power brake (Type B-2)**

and lines into the front and rear wheel cylinders to actuate the brakes.

As pressure is developed within the master cylinder a counter force acting through the hydraulic pushrod and reaction disc against the vacuum power diaphragm and valve plunger sets up a reaction force opposing the force applied to the valve rod and plunger. This reaction force tends to close the atmospheric port and reopen the vacuum port. Since this force is in opposition to the force applied to the brake pedal by the driver it gives the driver a "feel" of the amount of brake applied. The proportion of reactive force applied to the valve plunger through the reaction disc is designed into the Master-Vac to assure maximum power consistent with maintaining pedal feel. The reaction force is in direct proportion to the hydraulic pressure developed within the brake system.

## TROUBLESHOOTING

### Hard Pedal Or No Assist

1. Air cleaner element clogged.

2. Control valve faulty.
3. Defective diaphragm.
4. Worn or distorted reaction plate or levers.
5. Cracked or broken power piston or levers.
6. Internal or external leaks.

### Brakes Grab

1. Control valve defective or sticking.
2. Bind in linkage.
3. Reaction diaphragm leaking.
4. Worn or distorted levers or plate.

### No Or Slow Release

1. Push rod adjustment incorrect.
2. Linkage binding.
3. Return spring defective.

# SYSTEM SERVICE

## BENDIX, TEVES & DOUBLE DIAPHRAGM BOOSTER

On Bendix, Teves and Double Diaphragm Booster type power brake units, overhaul is not required. If it has been determined that the brake booster is defective, replace power brake unit as an assembly. In some instances, the only service required is replacement of the check valve and grommet and pushrod adjustment.

## SINGLE DIAPHRAGM BOOSTER

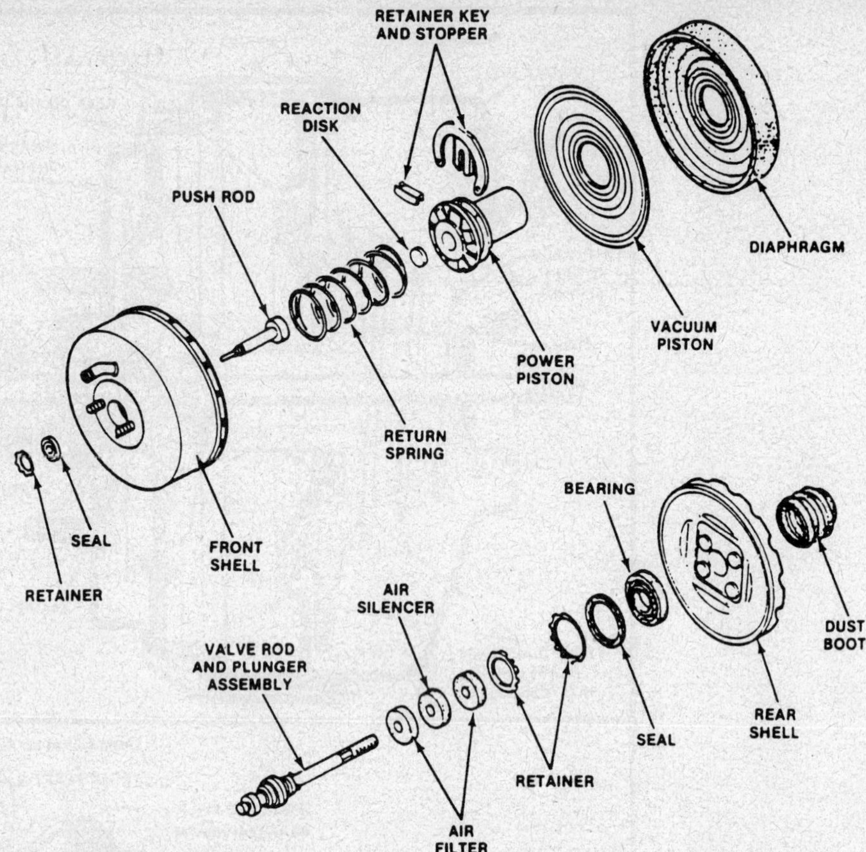


**Fig. 4 Exploded view of Single Diaphragm Booster**

### Disassembly

1. Remove brake booster from vehicle.
2. Place front shell of booster in a vise.
3. Remove clevis from valve rod and plunger assembly.
4. Remove dust boot from rear shell, **Fig. 4**, then place alignment marks on front and rear shells for proper alignment during assembly.
5. Rotate rear shell counterclockwise until shell unlocks. **Rear shell is spring loaded, use caution when removing it.**
6. Remove rear shell, then remove front shell return spring and push rod.
7. Remove front shell retainer and dust boot.
8. Remove rear shell from power piston assembly.
9. Remove rear shell bearing retainer, seal and bearing.
10. Remove retainer holding air filters and air silencer from the valve rod and plunger assembly.
11. Remove diaphragm and plate.
12. Slightly push down on valve rod and remove retainer key and stopper.
13. Remove valve rod and plunger assembly from the power piston assembly.
14. Remove air filters and air silencer from the power piston.
15. Remove reaction disc.

### Assembly

Prior to assembly coat the following with silicone grease; reaction disc surface, dust seal lip, push rod, diaphragm-to-shell contact surfaces, power piston and valve plunger oil seal.

1. Install valve rod and plunger assembly into the power piston.
2. Push down on valve rod, then align groove of the valve plunger with the slot of power piston.
3. Install the valve rod retainer key and stopper.
4. Install two air filters and air silencer into power piston.
5. Place diaphragm and plate onto power piston, ensure the diaphragm is fully seated in the groove of the power piston.
6. Install bearing, bearing seal and bearing retainer into rear shell.
7. Slide rear shell onto power piston while carefully guiding power piston through bearing seal.
8. Using the push rod, install reaction disc into the power piston.
9. Install dust seal, front retainer and push rod into front shell.
10. Place front shell in a vise, then install front shell return spring.
11. Place rear shell onto front shell noting alignment marks.
12. Rotate rear shell clockwise until rear shell locks into place with front shell.
13. Install dust boot onto rear shell then install clevis onto valve rod and plunger assembly.
14. Install master cylinder.

# ANTI-LOCK BRAKES

## TABLE OF CONTENTS



# Cougar, Mark VII, Thunderbird & 1989 Continental

**NOTE:** Wire Code Identification And Symbol Identification Located In The Front Of This Manual Can Be Used As An Aid When Using Wiring Circuits Found In This Section.

## INDEX



## DESCRIPTION

These models are equipped with a four wheel anti-lock brake system (ABS), **Fig. 1.** The system prevents lockup by automatically modulating brake system pressure during an emergency stop situation.

By controlling wheel lockup, the vehicle's operator can maintain steering control and stop the vehicle in the shortest possible distance, under most driving conditions.

The ABS system controls the front brakes separately and the rear brakes as a pair, whenever wheel lockup begins. The brake pedal application force required to engage the system function may vary with road surface conditions. A dry surface will require a higher force, while a slippery surface will require a much less force.

During system operation, the vehicle's operator will sense a slight pulsation in the brake pedal, accompanied by a rise in brake pedal height and a clicking sound.

## SYSTEM COMPONENTS

### HYDRAULIC ACTUATION UNIT

The hydraulic actuation unit, **Figs. 2 and 3,** consists of two sections, the master cylinder and brake booster, which are arranged in the conventional fore and aft sequence. The booster contains a control valve, located in a parallel bore above the master cylinder.

### ELECTRIC PUMP ASSEMBLY

This system uses high pressure brake fluid stored in a hydraulic accumulator, **Fig. 4,** for power assist as well as for rear wheel braking. The accumulator is a gas filled pressure chamber that stores brake fluid up to 2600 psi. The fluid is pressurized by an electric motor driven pump. The pump is switched on and off automatically

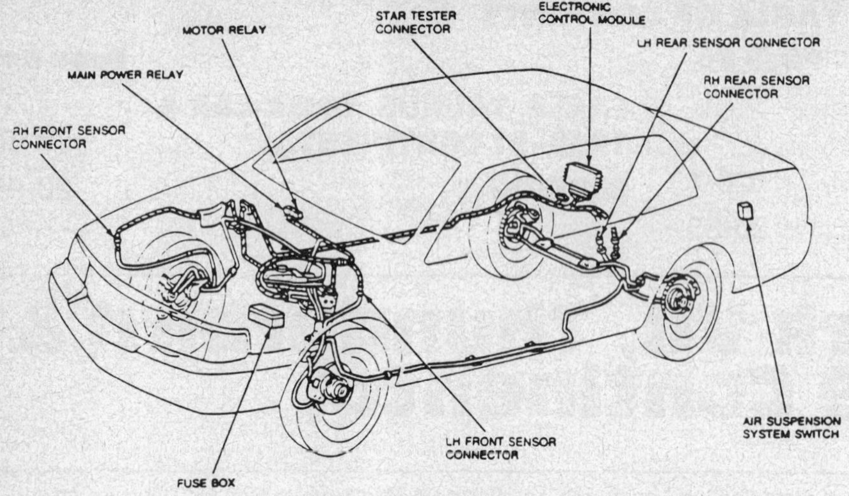


**Fig. 1 Anti-lock brake system**

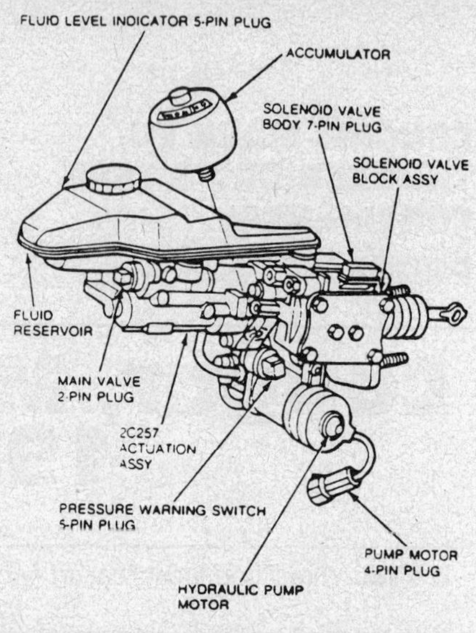


**Fig. 2 Hydraulic actuation unit. Cougar, Thunderbird & 1989 Continental**

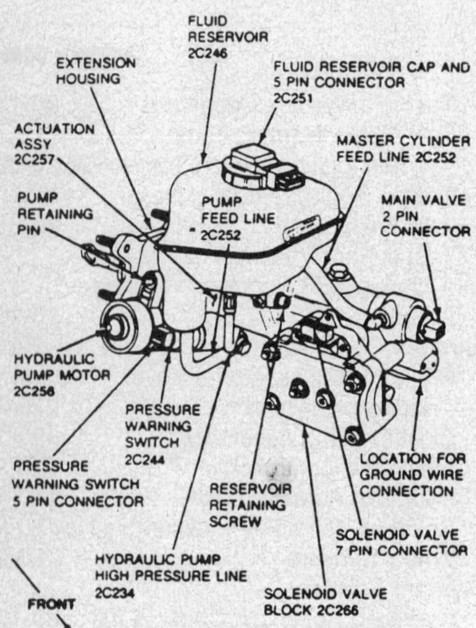


**Fig. 3 Hydraulic actuation unit. Mark VII**

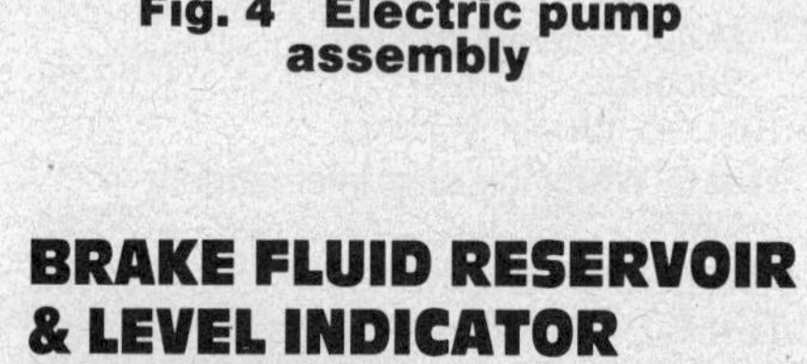


**Fig. 4 Electric pump assembly**

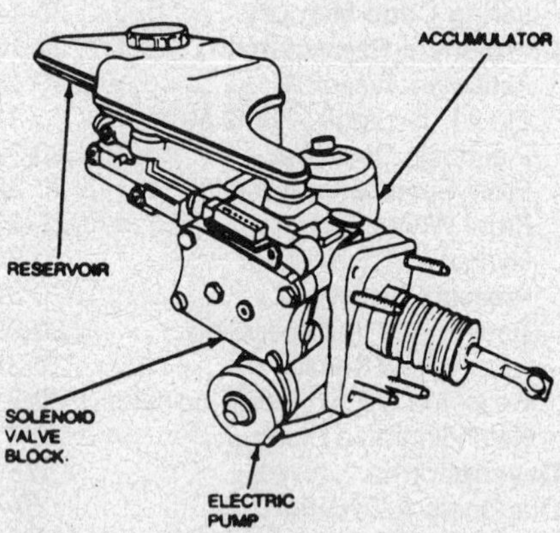


**Fig. 5 Solenoid valve block assembly**

by a pressure sensing switch through a relay circuit.

## SOLENOID VALVE BLOCK ASSEMBLY

The solenoid valve block assembly, **Fig. 5,** contains three pairs of solenoid valves, one pair for each front wheel and the third pair for both rear wheels. The paired solenoid valves are inlet and outlet valves, with the inlet valve normally open and the outlet valve normally closed. During ABS operation, the inlet and outlet valves are alternately opened and closed approximately 10 times per second to provide pressure modulation to wheel of impending lockup. The solenoid valve block is bolted to the hydraulic actuation unit, behind the lefthand shock tower.

## BRAKE FLUID RESERVOIR & LEVEL INDICATOR ASSEMBLY

The brake fluid reservoir and level indicator assembly, **Fig. 6,** is a translucent, plastic container that is mounted on the top of the hydraulic actuation unit. The reservoir is connected to the pump inlet port by a low pressure hose, and to the master cylinder by a sealed feed port.

## WHEEL SENSORS

This system, **Figs. 7 through 9,** uses four sets of variable reluctance sensors and toothed speed indicator rings to determine the rotational speed of each wheel. The sensors operate on magnetic induction principle. For example, as the teeth on the speed indicator ring rotate past the stationary sensor, a signal proportional to the speed of the rotation is generated and transmitted to the electronic control unit (ECU) through a coaxial cable.

The front sensors are attached to the

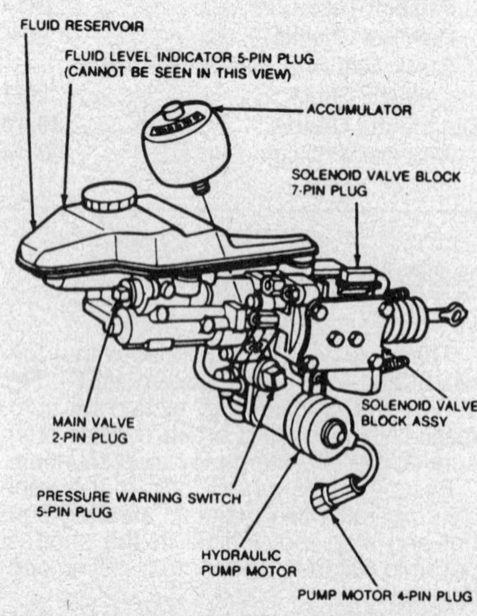


**Fig. 6 Brake fluid reservoir & level indicator assembly**

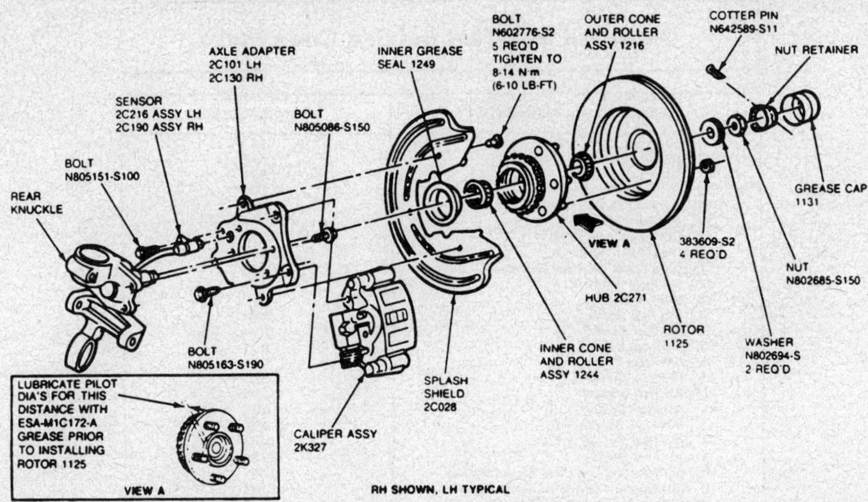


**Fig. 7 Wheel sensor assembly (righthand side shown, lefthand side similar). 1989 Continental**

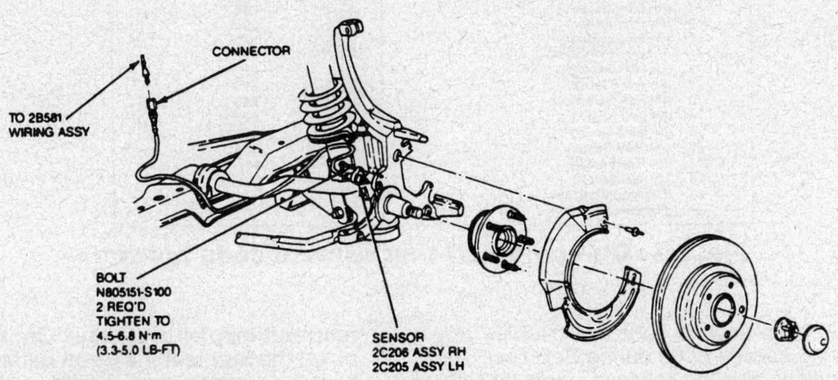


**Fig. 8 Wheel sensor assembly. Cougar & Thunderbird**

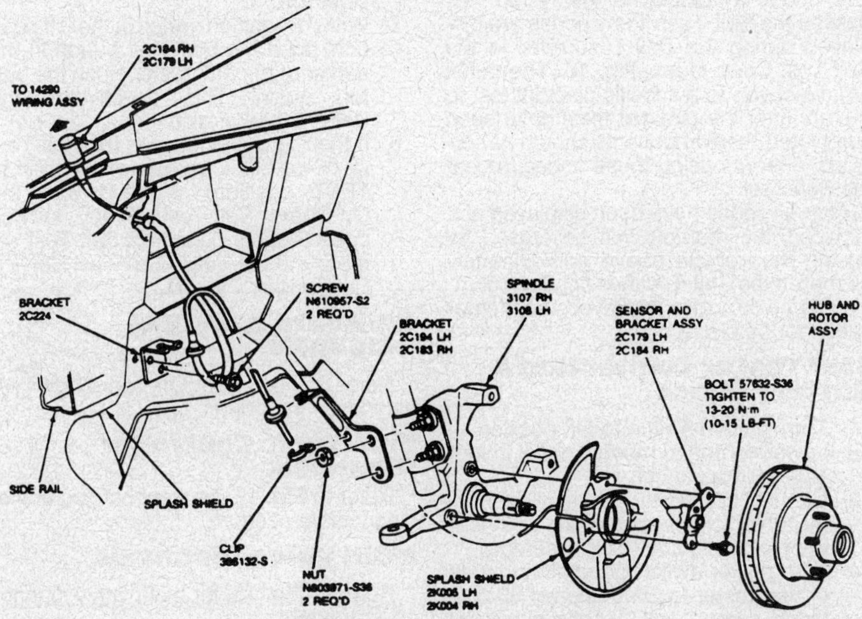


**Fig. 9 Wheel sensor assembly. Mark VII**

suspension knuckles and the speed indicator rings are pressed onto the outer constant velocity joints. The rear sensors are attached to the rear caliper anchor plate and the speed indicator rings are pressed onto the rear wheel hub assemblies. The sensors and the speed indicator rings are serviced individually.

## ELECTRONIC CONTROLLER

The electronic controller is located in the luggage compartment of the vehicle, behind the righthand side of the rear seat. It is an on-board self test non-repairable unit, consisting of two microprocessors and the necessary circuitry for their operation. These microprocessors are programmed identically and operate on the principle of two channel redundant data processing and plausibility criteria monitoring.

## SYSTEM OPERATION

The hydraulic pump maintains system pressure between approximately 2030-2610 psi, within the accumulator and is connected by a high pressure hose to the booster chamber portion of the hydraulic actuation assembly and a control valve. When the brakes are applied, a scissor lever mechanism activates the control valve and a pressure, proportional to brake pedal travel, enters the booster chamber portion of the hydraulic actuation assembly. This pressure is transmitted through the normally open solenoid valve through the proportioning valve to the rear brakes. The same pressure moves the booster piston against the master cylinder piston, shutting off the central valves in the master cylinder. This applies pressure to the front wheels through the two front normally open solenoid valves.

The electronic controller monitors the electro-mechanical components of t he system. Malfunction of the ABS system will cause the electronic controller to shut off or inhibit the ABS function, while retaining normal power assisted braking. Malfunctions are indicated by one or two warning lamps inside the vehicle.

Loss of hydraulic fluid or power boost pressure will disable the ABS syst em.

The four wheel ABS system is self monitoring. When the ignition switch is turned to the RUN position, the electronic controller will perform a preliminary self check on the ABS electrical system indicated by a three or four second illumination of the amber "Check Anti-Lock Brakes" lamp in the instrument cluster. During vehicle operation, including normal and anti-lock braking, the electronic controller monitors all electrical anti-lock functions and some hydraulic system operation.

For most malfunctions of the ABS system, the amber "Check Anti-Lock Brakes" and/or the red "Brake" lamp will be illuminated. The sequence of illumination of these warning lamps, combined with the problem symptoms, can determine the appropriate diagnostic test to perform. Most malfunctions are recorded as a coded number in the controller memory, pinpointing the exact component requiring service.

# DIAGNOSIS & TESTING

**Ensure the following diagnosis procedures are used in the sequence and step-by-step order indicated. Following the wrong sequence or bypassing steps will only lead to unnecessary replacement of system components and/or incorrect resolution of the problem. The diagnostic procedure consists of five sub-tests: Pre-test Checks, On-Board Self-Tests, Manual Quick Tests, Warning Lamp Symptom Chart and the Diagnostic Tests. As stated previously, do not attempt to bypass any procedure steps or tests.**

## PRE-TEST CHECKS

1. Verify that the parking brake is completely released. If the parking brake is applied, the "Brake" lamp will be illuminated.
2. Check brake fluid. **As the fluid level drops, the red "Brake" lamp will illuminate. If fluid level continues to fall, the amber "Check Anti-Lock Brake" lamp will illuminate and the anti-lock function will be inhibited.**
3. Verify that all of the following connectors are properly connected and in good operating condition:
   a. 7 pin connector of the solenoid valve block assembly.
   b. 2 pin connector of the main valve.
   c. 5 pin connector of the fluid level indicator.
   d. 5 pin connector of the pressure warning switch.
   e. 2 pin connector on all four sensors.
   f. 4 pin connector on the pump motor.
   g. 32 pin connector of the electronic controller.
   h. 5 pin connector of the main relay.
   i. 5 pin connector of the pump motor relay.
4. Check that the fuses and diode are not damaged.
5. Ensure all battery connections are clean and tight.
6. Check ground connections on front end of hydraulic unit in luggage compartment.

## ON-BOARD SELF-TEST & MAIN COMPONENT DIAGNOSIS

The ABS electronic control module is capable of performing a self-test using Star tester 007-00017 or Super Star tester 007-00019 or equivalents. If the Star tester is not available, the ABS Quick Check sheet can be used as described further on.

The ABS control module monitors system operation and stores up to seven different service codes in its memory. However, it cannot store two services codes with the same first digit. For example: the module cannot store a code 25 and a code 26 at the same time (it can store a code 25 and a code 35). The code 25 is stored first. It must be serviced, the memory must be cleared and the vehicle operated before the code 26 can be stored.

**On-Board Self-Test Service Code Index**

| SERVICE CODE (COMPONENT) | PINPOINT TEST STEP |
|---|---|
| 11 (Electronic Controller) | AA1 |
| 12 (Electronic Controller-Replacer) | AA2 |
| 21 (Main Valve) | BB1 |
| 22 (LH Front Inlet Valve) | CC1 |
| 23 (LH Front Outlet Valve) | CC2 |
| 24 (RH Front Inlet Valve) | CC3 |
| 25 (RH Front Outlet Valve) | CC4 |
| 26 (Rear Inlet Valve) | CC5 |
| 27 (Rear Outlet Valve and Ground) | CC6 |
| 31 (LH Front Sensor) | DD1 |
| 32 (RH Front Sensor) | DD6 |
| 33 (RH Rear Sensor) | DD11 |
| 34 (LH Rear Sensor) | DD16 |
| 35 (LH Front Sensor) | DD1 |
| 36 (RH Front Sensor) | DD6 |
| 37 (RH Rear Sensor) | DD11 |
| 38 (LH Rear Sensor) | DD16 |
| 41 (LH Front Sensor) | DD1 |
| 42 (RH Front Sensor) | DD6 |
| 43 (RH Rear Sensor) | DD11 |
| 44 (LH Rear Sensor) | DD16 |
| 45 (LH Front and One Other Sensor Signals) | DD21 |
| 46 (RH Front and One Other Sensor Signals) | DD24 |
| 47 (Missing Both Rear Sensor Signals) | DD25 |
| 48 (Missing Three of Four Sensor Signals) | DD26 |
| 51 (LH Front Outlet Valve) | EE1 |
| 52 (RH Front Outlet Valve) | EE3 |
| 53 (Rear Outlet Valve) | EE5 |
| 54 (Rear Outlet Valve) | EE7 |
| 55 (LH Front Sensor) | DD1 |
| 56 (RH Front Sensor) | DD6 |
| 57 (RH Rear Sensor) | DD11 |
| 58 (LH Rear Sensor) | DD16 |
| 61 (FLI and PWS Circuit) | FF1 |
| 71 (LH Front Sensor) | EE1 |
| 72 (RH Front Sensor) | EE3 |
| 73 (RH Rear Sensor) | EE5 |
| 74 (LH Rear Sensor) | EE7 |
| 75 (LH Front Sensor) | DD1 |
| 76 (RH Front Sensor) | DD6 |
| 77 (RH Rear Sensor) | DD11 |
| 78 (LH Rear Sensor) | DD16 |
| 88 (Electronic Controller) | AA1 |
| 99 (Electronic Controller) | AA1 |

**Fig. 10 On-board self-test service code index**

A valve service code will override any stored service code during Self-Test. The condition must be serviced before any other codes can be displayed. After the valve has been serviced, the Self-Test can be run and any stored codes will be displayed. If no codes are displayed, the system has passed the Self-Test. If any codes are displayed during the Self-Test, refer to the Self-Test Code Index, **Fig. 10.** The index will direct you to a specific pinpoint test to be run. After the pinpoint tests have been completed, the components should be serviced. After servicing these codes, repeat the Self-Test.

After all codes have been displayed and serviced, the memory will be erased by driving the vehicle above approximately 25 mph. If the Self-Test has not been completed and all codes displayed, the memory cannot be erased.

### Star Tester Connection & Battery Check

1. Turn ignition switch to Off position.
2. Lower righthand module panel in luggage compartment.
3. Connect Star tester electrical connector to vehicle connector located near the electronic controller assembly.
4. Turn power switch on righthand side of Star tester to On. A steady 00 or a blank screen will appear signifying that the tester is ready to start the Self-Test and receive service codes. **If the message LO BAT appears in the upper lefthand corner of the read-out display and stays On, replace the Star tester's 9 volt battery before continuing with the Self-Test. The message LO BAT will appear momentarily when the power switch is turned to the Off position.**
5. With the ignition switch in the Off position, push the Self-Test button in the center of the Star tester. Push the button again. This deactivates the Self-Test sequence.
6. If the Star tester passes the Self-Test (a 00 or blank screen with button in TEST position), proceed with the On-Board Self-Test. If any service codes appear during the Self-Test, refer to the On-Board Self-Test Service Code Index, **Fig. 10.**

### On-Board Self-Test Diagnosis

Refer to **Fig. 11,** for On-Board Self-Test diagnosis procedure.

### Electronic Controller Diagnosis

Refer to **Fig. 12,** for electronic controller diagnosis procedure.

### Main Valve Diagnosis

Refer to **Fig. 13,** for main valve diagnosis procedure.

### Solenoid Valve Diagnosis

Refer to **Fig. 14,** for solenoid valve diagnosis procedure.

## On-Board Self-Test

| TEST STEP | RESULT ▶ | ACTION TO TAKE |
|---|---|---|
| **1.0** CONNECT STAR TESTER | | |
| • Turn ignition switch to OFF.<br>• Connect Rotunda SUPER STAR II Tester 007-00028, 007-00041 or equivalent to Anti-Lock self-test connector.<br>• Turn tester on.<br>**NOTE: Do not move vehicle or turn steering wheel during test.**<br>• Depress SUPER STAR II Tester push-button to test position. Display should show:<br>COLON DISPLAY **: 00** COLON MUST BE DISPLAYED TO RECEIVE SERVICE CODES.<br>• Turn ignition switch to RUN position. Wait 45 seconds.<br>• Observe tester display. | Pass code ( ) displayed and warning lamps off. ▶<br><br>Pass code ( ) displayed and warning lamp turns on. ▶<br><br>Service code displayed. ▶ | Vehicle OK. RETURN vehicle to customer.<br><br>PERFORM anti-lock Quick Test.<br><br>GO to **2.0**. |
| **2.0** CHECK SERVICE CODES | | |
| • Record service code.<br>• Release, then depress SUPER STAR II Tester push-button. Wait 45 seconds.<br>**NOTE: If first displayed code indicates a valve failure (first digit is 2), service that valve. Then, repeat Step 1.0.**<br>• Observe tester display. | Service code displayed. ▶<br><br>Pass code ( ) displayed. ▶ | REPEAT Step 2.0 each time a service code is displayed. RECORD each service code as it is displayed.<br><br>SERVICE indicated fault(s). GO to **3.0** or GO to Quick Check.<br>**NOTE: Cross off each service code from list as it is serviced.** |
| **3.0** CHECK FOR OTHER FAULT CODES | | |
| • Repeat Step 1.0 to see if any other new service codes are stored in memory. | If no new service codes are displayed. ▶<br><br>Service code displayed. ▶ | GO to **4.0**.<br><br>GO to **2.0**. |

**Fig. 11 On-board self-test (Part 1 of 2)**

## On-Board Self-Test

| TEST STEP | RESULT ▶ | ACTION TO TAKE |
|---|---|---|
| **4.0** CHECK SYSTEM OPERATION | | |
| • Turn ignition to OFF position.<br>• Disconnect Super Star II Tester.<br>• Turn ignition to RUN position and check warning lamp sequence.<br>• Test drive vehicle. | "CHECK ANTI-LOCK" and "BRAKE" warning lamps Off ▶<br><br>"CHECK ANTI-LOCK" and/or "BRAKE" lamp On ▶ | RETURN vehicle to customer.<br><br>REPEAT Step **1.0**, or if there is no power brake, GO to Step **D1**. |

**Fig. 11 On-board self-test (Part 2 of 2)**

## Electronic Controller Diagnosis — Test AA

| TEST STEP | RESULT ▶ | ACTION TO TAKE |
|---|---|---|
| **AA1** SERVICE CODE 11 AND/OR 99: ELECTRICAL DISTURBANCE | | |
| • Read all service codes by releasing and pressing the Super Star II Tester push button.<br>• Allow a minimum of 45 seconds to pass after each time the push button is pressed.<br>• Write down on paper all service codes.<br>• After all service codes are read and written down, drive vehicle above 40 km/h (25 mph) to clear memory.<br>• Read again all service codes. | Service code 11 and/or 99 repeated. ▶<br><br>Memory erased or other service codes present except code 11 and/or 99. ▶ | REPLACE electronic controller.<br><br>PERFORM test step associated with service code or codes. REFER to On-Board Self-Test Service Code Index. |
| **AA2** SERVICE CODE 12: REPLACE ELECTRONIC CONTROLLER | | |
| • No test step to be performed. | (OK crossed out) ▶ | REPLACE electronic controller. |

**Fig. 12 Test AA, electronic controller diagnosis**

## Main Valve Diagnosis — Test BB

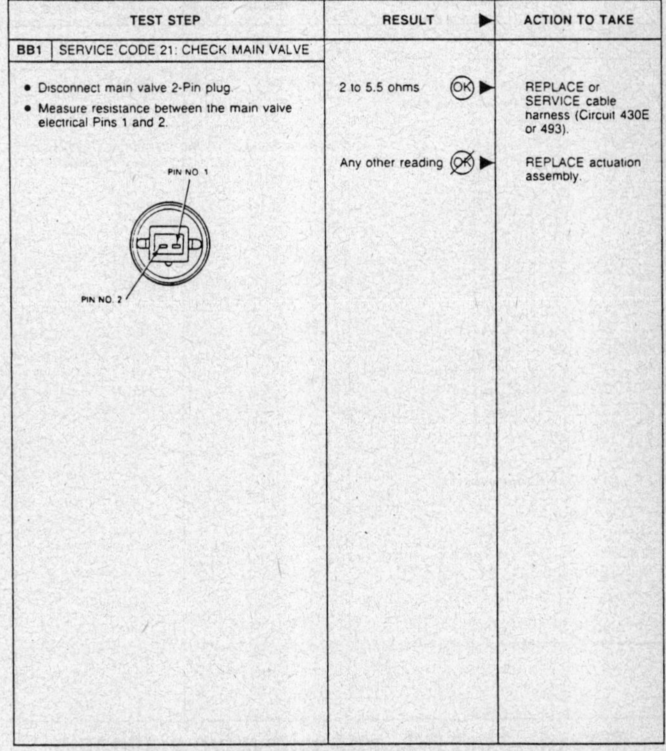

| TEST STEP | RESULT ▶ | ACTION TO TAKE |
|---|---|---|
| **BB1** SERVICE CODE 21: CHECK MAIN VALVE | | |
| • Disconnect main valve 2-Pin plug.<br>• Measure resistance between the main valve electrical Pins 1 and 2. | 2 to 5.5 ohms (OK) ▶<br><br>Any other reading (OK crossed out) ▶ | REPLACE or SERVICE cable harness (Circuit 430E or 493).<br><br>REPLACE actuation assembly. |



**Fig. 13 Test BB, main valve diagnosis**

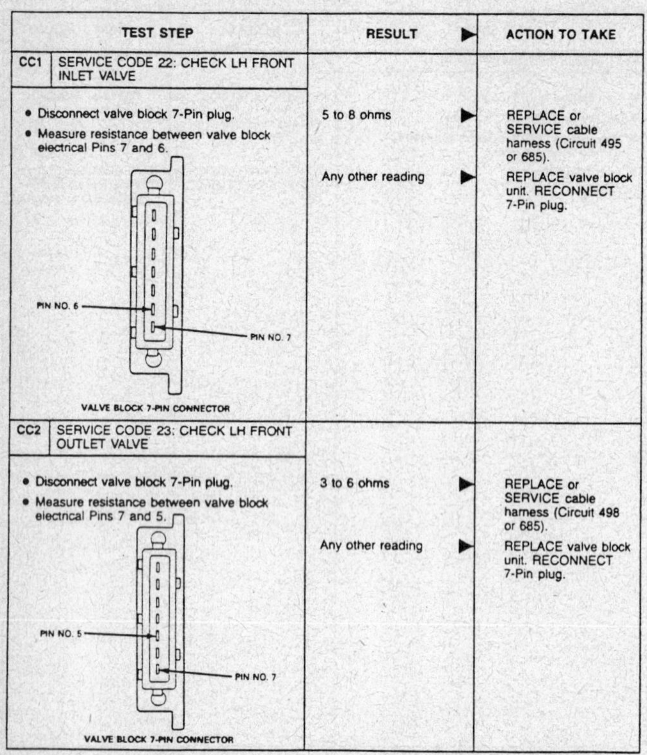

## Solenoid Valve Diagnosis — Test CC

| TEST STEP | RESULT ▶ | ACTION TO TAKE |
|---|---|---|
| **CC1** SERVICE CODE 22: CHECK LH FRONT INLET VALVE | | |
| • Disconnect valve block 7-Pin plug.<br>• Measure resistance between valve block electrical Pins 7 and 6.<br>PIN NO. 6<br>PIN NO. 7<br>VALVE BLOCK 7-PIN CONNECTOR | 5 to 8 ohms ▶<br><br>Any other reading ▶ | REPLACE or SERVICE cable harness (Circuit 495 or 685).<br><br>REPLACE valve block unit. RECONNECT 7-Pin plug. |
| **CC2** SERVICE CODE 23: CHECK LH FRONT OUTLET VALVE | | |
| • Disconnect valve block 7-Pin plug.<br>• Measure resistance between valve block electrical Pins 7 and 5.<br>PIN NO. 5<br>PIN NO. 7<br>VALVE BLOCK 7-PIN CONNECTOR | 3 to 6 ohms ▶<br><br>Any other reading ▶ | REPLACE or SERVICE cable harness (Circuit 498 or 685).<br><br>REPLACE valve block unit. RECONNECT 7-Pin plug. |

**Fig. 14 Test CC, solenoid valve diagnosis (Part 1 of 6)**

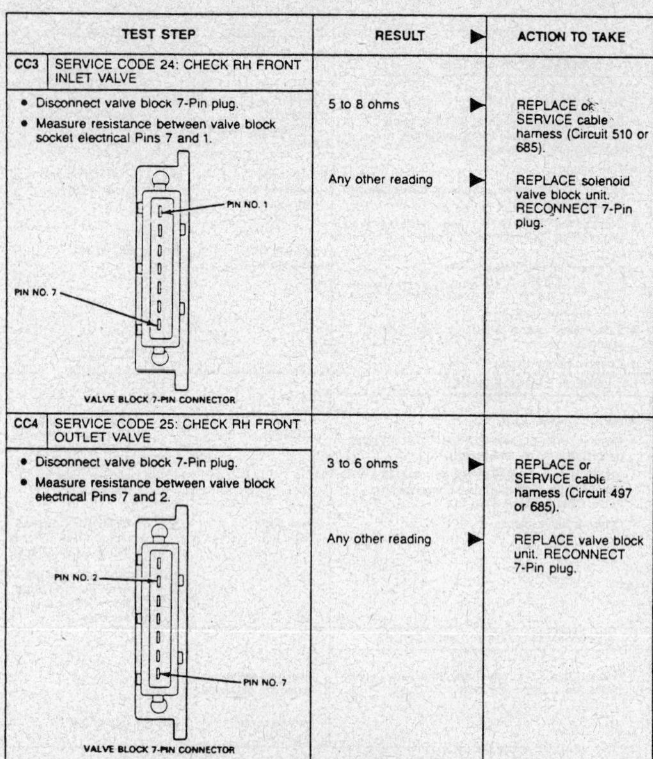

## Solenoid Valve Diagnosis — Test CC

| TEST STEP | RESULT ▶ | ACTION TO TAKE |
|---|---|---|
| **CC3** SERVICE CODE 24: CHECK RH FRONT INLET VALVE | | |
| • Disconnect valve block 7-Pin plug.<br>• Measure resistance between valve block socket electrical Pins 7 and 1.<br>PIN NO. 1<br>PIN NO. 7<br>VALVE BLOCK 7-PIN CONNECTOR | 5 to 8 ohms ▶<br><br>Any other reading ▶ | REPLACE or SERVICE cable harness (Circuit 510 or 685).<br><br>REPLACE solenoid valve block unit. RECONNECT 7-Pin plug. |
| **CC4** SERVICE CODE 25: CHECK RH FRONT OUTLET VALVE | | |
| • Disconnect valve block 7-Pin plug.<br>• Measure resistance between valve block electrical Pins 7 and 2.<br>PIN NO. 2<br>PIN NO. 7<br>VALVE BLOCK 7-PIN CONNECTOR | 3 to 6 ohms ▶<br><br>Any other reading ▶ | REPLACE or SERVICE cable harness (Circuit 497 or 685).<br><br>REPLACE valve block unit. RECONNECT 7-Pin plug. |

**Fig. 14 Test CC, solenoid valve diagnosis (Part 2 of 6)**

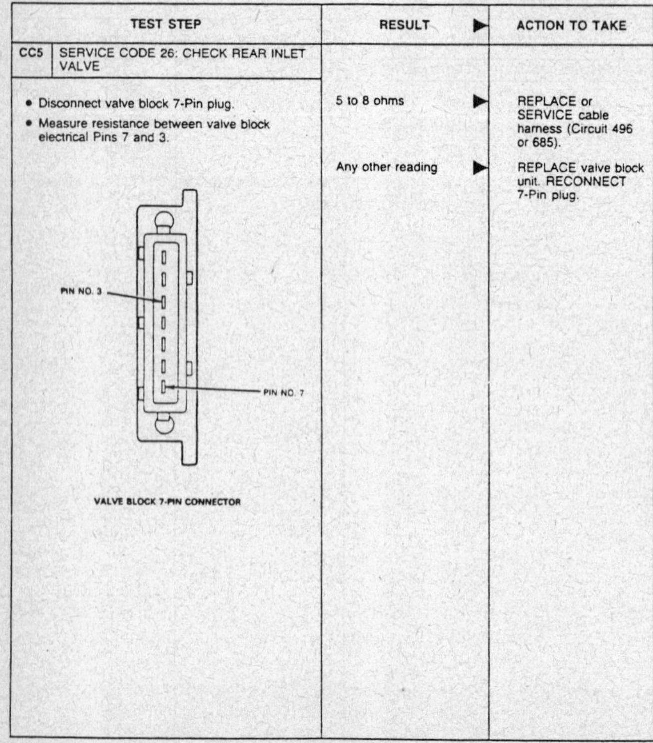

## Solenoid Valve Diagnosis — Test CC

| TEST STEP | RESULT ▶ | ACTION TO TAKE |
|---|---|---|
| **CC5** SERVICE CODE 26: CHECK REAR INLET VALVE | | |
| • Disconnect valve block 7-Pin plug.<br>• Measure resistance between valve block electrical Pins 7 and 3.<br>PIN NO. 3<br>PIN NO. 7<br>VALVE BLOCK 7-PIN CONNECTOR | 5 to 8 ohms ▶<br><br>Any other reading ▶ | REPLACE or SERVICE cable harness (Circuit 496 or 685).<br><br>REPLACE valve block unit. RECONNECT 7-Pin plug. |

**Fig. 14 Test CC, solenoid valve diagnosis (Part 3 of 6)**

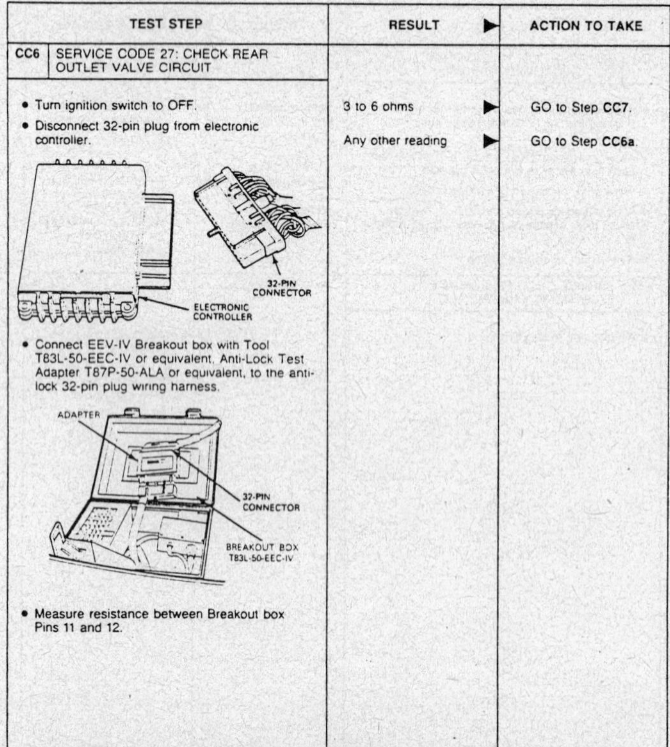

## Solenoid Valve Diagnosis — Test CC

| TEST STEP | RESULT ▶ | ACTION TO TAKE |
|---|---|---|
| **CC6** SERVICE CODE 27: CHECK REAR OUTLET VALVE CIRCUIT | | |
| • Turn ignition switch to OFF.<br>• Disconnect 32-pin plug from electronic controller.<br>32-PIN CONNECTOR<br>ELECTRONIC CONTROLLER<br>• Connect EEV-IV Breakout box with Tool T83L-50-EEC-IV or equivalent, Anti-Lock Test Adapter T87P-50-ALA or equivalent, to the anti-lock 32-pin plug wiring harness.<br>ADAPTER<br>32-PIN CONNECTOR<br>BREAKOUT BOX T83L-50-EEC-IV<br>• Measure resistance between Breakout box Pins 11 and 12. | 3 to 6 ohms ▶<br><br>Any other reading ▶ | GO to Step **CC7**.<br><br>GO to Step **CC6a**. |

**Fig. 14 Test CC, solenoid valve diagnosis (Part 4 of 6)**

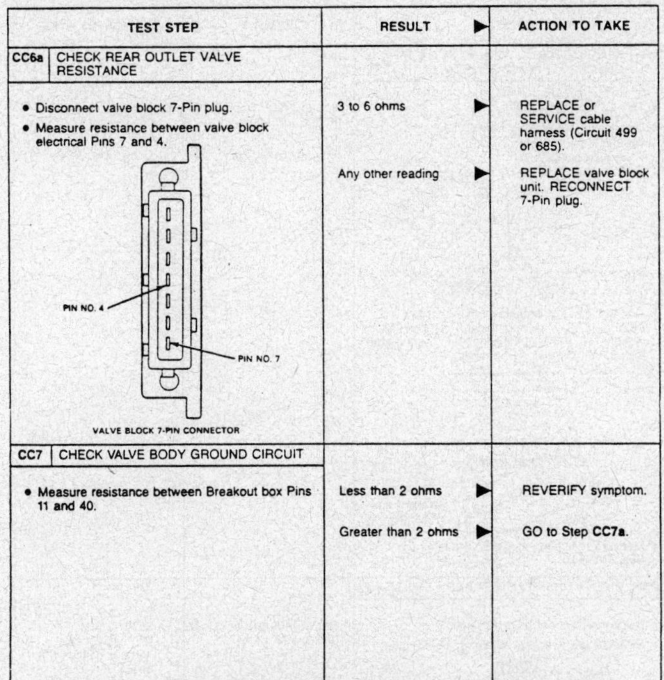

**Solenoid Valve Diagnosis** — **Test CC**

| TEST STEP | RESULT | ACTION TO TAKE |
|---|---|---|
| **CC6a** CHECK REAR OUTLET VALVE RESISTANCE | | |
| • Disconnect valve block 7-Pin plug.<br>• Measure resistance between valve block electrical Pins 7 and 4. | 3 to 6 ohms | REPLACE or SERVICE cable harness (Circuit 499 or 685). |
| | Any other reading | REPLACE valve block unit. RECONNECT 7-Pin plug. |
| **CC7** CHECK VALVE BODY GROUND CIRCUIT | | |
| • Measure resistance between Breakout box Pins 11 and 40. | Less than 2 ohms | REVERIFY symptom. |
| | Greater than 2 ohms | GO to Step **CC7a**. |



**Fig. 14 Test CC, solenoid valve diagnosis (Part 5 of 6)**

**Solenoid Valve Diagnosis** — **Test CC**

| TEST STEP | RESULT | ACTION TO TAKE |
|---|---|---|
| **CC7a** CHECK VALVE BODY GROUND | | |
| • Disconnect valve block 7-Pin plug.<br>• Measure resistance between valve block electrical Pin 7 and valve block body. | Less than 2 ohms (OK) | REPLACE or SERVICE cable harness (Circuit 685). |
| | Greater than 2 ohms (NOT OK) | GO to Step **CC7b**. |
| **CC7b** CHECK VALVE BODY GROUND WIRE | | |
| • Remove negative (−) ground strap from battery.<br>• Check for continuity between valve body and body ground. | Continuity (OK) | REPLACE valve block unit (internal ground problem). |
| | No or poor continuity (NOT OK) | SERVICE or REPLACE hydraulic unit ground strap (Circuit 430G). |

PIN NO. 7
VALVE BLOCK 7-PIN CONNECTOR

**Fig. 14 Test CC, solenoid valve diagnosis (Part 6 of 6)**

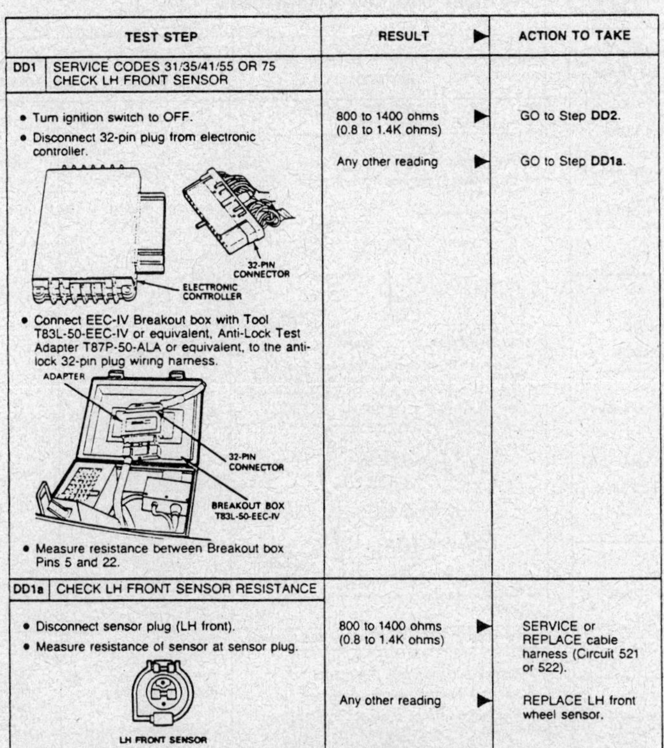

**Wheel Sensor Diagnosis** — **Test DD**

| TEST STEP | RESULT | ACTION TO TAKE |
|---|---|---|
| **DD1** SERVICE CODES 31/35/41/55 OR 75 CHECK LH FRONT SENSOR | | |
| • Turn ignition switch to OFF.<br>• Disconnect 32-pin plug from electronic controller.<br>• Connect EEC-IV Breakout box with Tool T83L-50-EEC-IV or equivalent, Anti-Lock Test Adapter T87P-50-ALA or equivalent, to the anti-lock 32-pin plug wiring harness.<br>• Measure resistance between Breakout box Pins 5 and 22. | 800 to 1400 ohms (0.8 to 1.4K ohms) | GO to Step **DD2**. |
| | Any other reading | GO to Step **DD1a**. |
| **DD1a** CHECK LH FRONT SENSOR RESISTANCE | | |
| • Disconnect sensor plug (LH front).<br>• Measure resistance of sensor at sensor plug. | 800 to 1400 ohms (0.8 to 1.4K ohms) | SERVICE or REPLACE cable harness (Circuit 521 or 522). |
| | Any other reading | REPLACE LH front wheel sensor. |



**Fig. 15 Test DD, wheel sensor diagnosis (Part 1 of 12)**

## Wheel Sensor Diagnosis

Refer to **Fig. 15,** for wheel sensor diagnosis procedure.

## Outlet Valve Diagnosis

Refer to **Fig. 16,** for outlet valve diagnosis procedure.

## Warning Circuit Diagnosis

Refer to **Fig. 17,** for warning circuit diagnosis procedure.

# QUICK TEST CHECKS & ABS QUICK CHECK SHEET

To properly conduct the Quick Test Checks an EEC-IV breakout box No. T83L-50-EEC-IV, anti-lock harness adapter No. T87P-50-ALA and a digital volt/ohmmeter (No. 007-00001), or equivalents must be used. All quick tests are performed in the vehicle's luggage compartment using the EEC-IV breakout box and the harness adapter. These group of tests will lead to specific diagnostic Pinpoint Test that will, in most cases, identify the fault/malfunction. If the fault/malfunction is not determined by the Quick Test procedure, use the following Diagnostic Lamp Symptom Chart to identify the proper diagnostic procedure to be conducted.

Refer to ABS quick check sheet **Fig. 18,** for item to be tested, ignition switch mode position, measurement taken between terminal pin numbers, tester scale/range, volt/ohm specifications and the specific pinpoint test to correct this group of malfunctions.

*Continued on page 20-14*

## Wheel Sensor Diagnosis — Test DD

| TEST STEP | RESULT ▶ | ACTION TO TAKE |
|---|---|---|
| **DD2** CHECK LH FRONT SENSOR VOLTAGE | | |
| • Turn ignition switch Off.<br>• Turn air suspension switch in luggage compartment Off, if so equipped.<br>• Place vehicle on hoist and raise wheels clear of ground. Refer to Pre-Delivery Manual, Section 50-04.<br>• Set multi-meter on voltage range (2V-AC).<br>• Measure voltage between Breakout box Pins 5 and 22 while spinning LH front wheel at approximately 1 revolution per second. | Between 0.05 and 0.70 Vac ▶<br>Less than 0.05 or more than 0.70 Vac ▶ | GO to Step **DD3**.<br>CHECK sensor mounting, air gap, or toothed wheel mounting. CORRECT as required. |
| **DD3** CHECK LH FRONT SENSOR CIRCUIT CONTINUITY | | |
| • Check continuity between Breakout box Pins 40 and 5. | No continuity ▶<br>Continuity ▶ | GO to Step **DD4**.<br>GO to Step **DD3A**. |
| **DD3A** CHECK LH FRONT SENSOR CIRCUITRY | | |
| • Disconnect wheel sensor plug (LH front).<br>• Check for continuity between each sensor plug pin (sensor side) and vehicle ground.<br>LH FRONT SENSOR | Continuity ▶<br>No continuity ▶ | REPLACE sensor, (LH front).<br>SERVICE or REPLACE cable harness. RECONNECT sensor plug. |
| **DD4** CHECK ELECTRONIC CONTROLLER TO GROUND WIRE | | |
| • Check continuity between Breakout box Pin 40 and body ground. | Continuity ▶<br>No continuity ▶ | GO to Step **DD5**.<br>SERVICE or REPLACE cable harness (Circuit 530A). |
| **DD5** CHECK LH FRONT WHEEL BEARING | | |
| • Check front wheel bearing end play.<br>• Inspect toothed sensor ring visually for damaged teeth.<br>**NOTE: Turn air suspension switch On when vehicle is off hoist, if so equipped.** | Loose or damaged parts ▶<br>Not loose or damaged ▶ | ADJUST bearings or REPLACE faulty parts.<br>REVERIFY symptom. |

**Fig. 15 Test DD, wheel sensor diagnosis (Part 2 of 12)**

## Wheel Sensor Diagnosis — Test DD

| TEST STEP | RESULT ▶ | ACTION TO TAKE |
|---|---|---|
| **DD6** SERVICE CODES 32/36/42/56 OR 76 CHECK RH FRONT SENSOR | | |
| • Turn ignition switch Off.<br>• Disconnect 32-pin plug from electronic controller.<br>32-PIN CONNECTOR; ELECTRONIC CONTROLLER<br>• Connect EEC-IV Breakout box with Tool T83L-50-EEC-IV or equivalent, Anti-Lock Test Adapter T87P-50-ALA or equivalent, to the anti-lock 32-pin plug wiring harness.<br>ADAPTER; 32-PIN CONNECTOR; BREAKOUT BOX T83L-50-EEC-IV<br>• Measure resistance between Breakout box Pins 3 and 20. | 800 to 1400 ohms (0.8 to 1.4K ohms) ▶<br>Any other reading ▶ | GO to Step **DD7**.<br>GO to Step **DD6a**. |
| **DD6a** CHECK RH FRONT SENSOR RESISTANCE | | |
| • Disconnect sensor plug (RH front).<br>• Measure resistance of sensor at sensor plug.<br>RH FRONT SENSOR | 800 to 1400 ohms (0.8 to 1.4K ohms) ▶<br>Any other reading ▶ | SERVICE or REPLACE cable harness (Circuit 514 or 516).<br>REPLACE RH front wheel sensor. |

**Fig. 15 Test DD, wheel sensor diagnosis (Part 3 of 12)**

## Wheel Sensor Diagnosis — Test DD

| TEST STEP | RESULT ▶ | ACTION TO TAKE |
|---|---|---|
| **DD7** CHECK RH FRONT SENSOR VOLTAGE | | |
| • Turn air suspension switch in luggage compartment Off, if so equipped.<br>• Place vehicle on hoist and raise wheels clear of ground. Refer to Pre-Delivery Manual, Section 50-04.<br>• Set multi-meter on voltage range (2V-AC).<br>• Measure voltage between Breakout box Pins 3 and 20 while spinning the RH front wheel at approximately 1 revolution per second. | Between 0.05 and 0.70 Vac ▶<br>Less than 0.05 or more than 0.70 Vac ▶ | GO to Step **DD8**.<br>CHECK wheel sensor mounting, air gap, or toothed wheel mounting. CORRECT as required. |
| **DD8** CHECK RH FRONT SENSOR CIRCUIT CONTINUITY | | |
| • Check continuity between Breakout box Pins 40 and 3. | Continuity ▶<br>No continuity ▶ | GO to Step **DD8a**.<br>GO to Step **DD9**. |
| **DD8a** CHECK RH FRONT SENSOR CONTINUITY | | |
| • Disconnect wheel sensor plug (RH front).<br>• Check for continuity between each sensor plug pin (sensor side) and vehicle ground.<br>RH FRONT SENSOR | Continuity ▶<br>No continuity ▶ | REPLACE right front sensor.<br>SERVICE or REPLACE cable harness. RECONNECT sensor plug. |
| **DD9** CHECK ELECTRONIC CONTROLLER TO GROUND WIRE | | |
| • Check continuity between Breakout box Pin 40 and body ground. | Continuity ▶<br>No continuity ▶ | GO to Step **DD10**.<br>SERVICE or REPLACE cable harness (Circuit 530A). |
| **DD10** CHECK RH FRONT WHEELING BEARING | | |
| • Check front wheel bearing end play.<br>• Inspect toothed sensor ring visually for damaged teeth.<br>**NOTE: Turn air suspension switch On when vehicle is off hoist, if so equipped.** | Loose or damaged parts ▶<br>Not loose or damaged ▶ | ADJUST bearings or REPLACE faulty parts.<br>REVERIFY symptom. |

**Fig. 15 Test DD, wheel sensor diagnosis (Part 4 of 12)**

## Wheel Sensor Diagnosis — Test DD

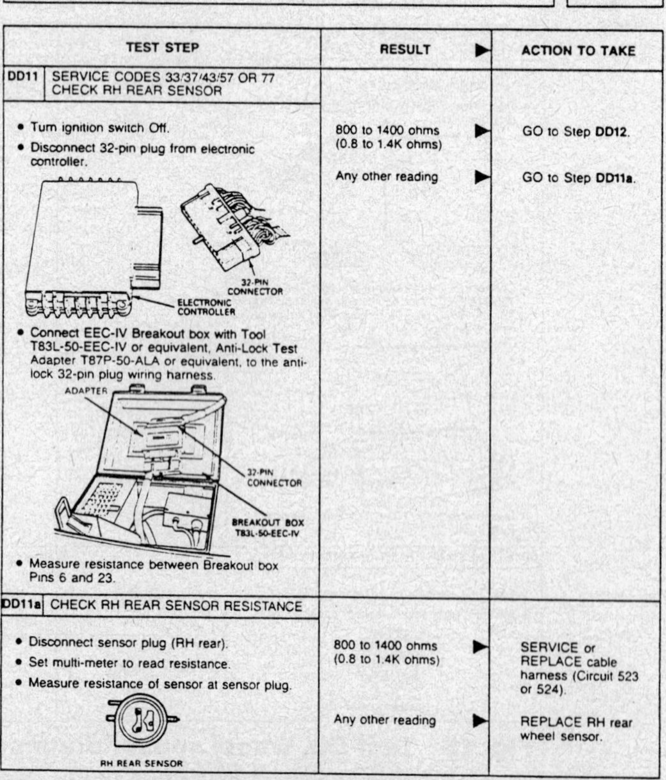

| TEST STEP | RESULT ▶ | ACTION TO TAKE |
|---|---|---|
| **DD11** SERVICE CODES 33/37/43/57 OR 77 CHECK RH REAR SENSOR | | |
| • Turn ignition switch Off.<br>• Disconnect 32-pin plug from electronic controller.<br>32-PIN CONNECTOR; ELECTRONIC CONTROLLER<br>• Connect EEC-IV Breakout box with Tool T83L-50-EEC-IV or equivalent, Anti-Lock Test Adapter T87P-50-ALA or equivalent, to the anti-lock 32-pin plug wiring harness.<br>ADAPTER; 32-PIN CONNECTOR; BREAKOUT BOX T83L-50-EEC-IV<br>• Measure resistance between Breakout box Pins 6 and 23. | 800 to 1400 ohms (0.8 to 1.4K ohms) ▶<br>Any other reading ▶ | GO to Step **DD12**.<br>GO to Step **DD11a**. |
| **DD11a** CHECK RH REAR SENSOR RESISTANCE | | |
| • Disconnect sensor plug (RH rear).<br>• Set multi-meter to read resistance.<br>• Measure resistance of sensor at sensor plug.<br>RH REAR SENSOR | 800 to 1400 ohms (0.8 to 1.4K ohms) ▶<br>Any other reading ▶ | SERVICE or REPLACE cable harness (Circuit 523 or 524).<br>REPLACE RH rear wheel sensor. |

**Fig. 15 Test DD, wheel sensor diagnosis (Part 5 of 12)**

## Wheel Sensor Diagnosis — Test DD

| TEST STEP | RESULT ▶ | ACTION TO TAKE |
|---|---|---|
| **DD12** CHECK RH REAR SENSOR VOLTAGE | | |
| • Turn air suspension switch in luggage compartment Off, if so equipped.<br>• Place vehicle on hoist and raise wheels clear of ground. Refer to Pre-Delivery Manual, Section 50-04.<br>• Set multi-meter on voltage range (2V-AC).<br>• Measure voltage between Breakout box Pins 6 and 23 while spinning the RH rear wheel at approximately 1 revolution per second. | Between 0.05 and 0.70 Vac ▶ | GO to Step **DD13**. |
| | Less than 0.05 or more than 0.70 Vac ▶ | CHECK sensor mounting, air gap, or toothed wheel mounting. CORRECT as required. |
| **DD13** CHECK RH REAR SENSOR CIRCUIT CONTINUITY | | |
| • Check continuity between Breakout box Pins 40 and 6. | No continuity ▶ | GO to Step **DD14**. |
| | Continuity ▶ | GO to Step **DD13a**. |
| **DD13a** CHECK RH REAR SENSOR CONTINUITY | | |
| • Disconnect wheel sensor plug (RH rear).<br>• Check for continuity between each sensor plug pin (sensor side) and vehicle ground.<br>RH REAR SENSOR | Continuity ▶ | REPLACE sensor (RH rear). |
| | No continuity ▶ | SERVICE or REPLACE. |
| **DD14** CHECK ELECTRONIC CONTROLLER TO GROUND WIRE | | |
| • Check continuity between Breakout box Pin 40 and body ground. | Continuity ▶ | GO to Step **DD15**. |
| | No continuity ▶ | SERVICE or REPLACE cable harness (Circuit 530A). |
| **DD15** CHECK FOR EXCESSIVE AXLE VIBRATION | | |
| • Check differential housing for excessive play.<br>• Check rear axle bearings for excessive play.<br>• Inspect toothed sensor ring visually for damaged teeth.<br>**NOTE: Turn air suspension switch On when vehicle is off hoist, if so equipped.** | Loose or damaged parts ▶ | SERVICE or REPLACE faulty parts. |
| | Not loose or damaged ▶ | REVERIFY symptom. |

**Fig. 15 Test DD, wheel sensor diagnosis (Part 6 of 12)**

## Wheel Sensor Diagnosis — Test DD

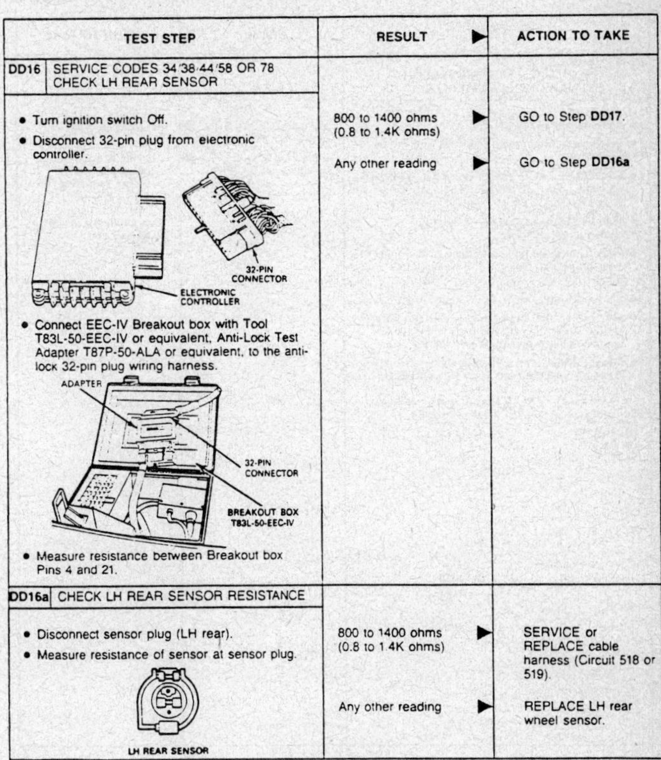

| TEST STEP | RESULT ▶ | ACTION TO TAKE |
|---|---|---|
| **DD16** SERVICE CODES 34/38/44/58 OR 78 CHECK LH REAR SENSOR | | |
| • Turn ignition switch Off.<br>• Disconnect 32-pin plug from electronic controller.<br>32-PIN CONNECTOR<br>ELECTRONIC CONTROLLER<br>• Connect EEC-IV Breakout box with Tool T83L-50-EEC-IV or equivalent, Anti-Lock Test Adapter T87P-50-ALA or equivalent, to the anti-lock 32-pin plug wiring harness.<br>ADAPTER<br>32-PIN CONNECTOR<br>BREAKOUT BOX T83L-50-EEC-IV<br>• Measure resistance between Breakout box Pins 4 and 21. | 800 to 1400 ohms (0.8 to 1.4K ohms) ▶ | GO to Step **DD17**. |
| | Any other reading ▶ | GO to Step **DD16a** |
| **DD16a** CHECK LH REAR SENSOR RESISTANCE | | |
| • Disconnect sensor plug (LH rear).<br>• Measure resistance of sensor at sensor plug.<br>LH REAR SENSOR | 800 to 1400 ohms (0.8 to 1.4K ohms) ▶ | SERVICE or REPLACE cable harness (Circuit 518 or 519). |
| | Any other reading ▶ | REPLACE LH rear wheel sensor. |

**Fig. 15 Test DD, wheel sensor diagnosis (Part 7 of 12)**

## Wheel Sensor Diagnosis — Test DD

| TEST STEP | RESULT ▶ | ACTION TO TAKE |
|---|---|---|
| **DD17** CHECK LH REAR SENSOR VOLTAGE | | |
| • Turn air suspension switch in luggage compartment Off, if so equipped.<br>• Place vehicle on hoist and raise wheels clear of ground. Refer to Pre-Delivery Manual, Section 50-04.<br>• Set multi-meter on voltage range (2V-AC).<br>• Measure voltage between Breakout box Pins 4 and 21 while spinning the LH rear wheel at approximately 1 revolution per second. | Between 0.05 and 0.70 Vac ▶ | GO to Step **DD18**. |
| | Less than 0.05 or more than 0.70 Vac ▶ | CHECK sensor mounting, air gap, or toothed wheel mounting. CORRECT as required. |
| **DD18** CHECK LH REAR SENSOR CIRCUIT CONTINUITY | | |
| • Check continuity between Breakout box Pins 40 and 4. | No continuity ▶ | GO to Step **DD19**. |
| | Continuity ▶ | GO to Step **DD18a**. |
| **DD18a** CHECK LH REAR SENSOR CONTINUITY | | |
| • Disconnect wheel sensor plug (LH front).<br>• Check for continuity between each sensor.<br>LH REAR SENSOR | Continuity ▶ | REPLACE sensor (LH front). |
| | No continuity ▶ | SERVICE or REPLACE cable harness RECONNECT sensor plug. |
| **DD19** CHECK ELECTRONIC CONTROLLER TO GROUND WIRE | | |
| • Check continuity between Breakout box Pin 40 and body ground. | Continuity ▶ | GO to Step **DD20**. |
| | No continuity ▶ | SERVICE or REPLACE cable harness (Circuit 530A). |
| **DD20** CHECK FOR EXCESSIVE AXLE VIBRATION | | |
| • Check differential housing for excessive play.<br>• Check rear axle bearings for excessive play.<br>• Inspect toothed sensor ring visually for damaged teeth.<br>**NOTE: Turn air suspension switch On when vehicle is off hoist, if so equipped.** | Loose or damaged parts ▶ | SERVICE or REPLACE faulty parts. |
| | Not loose or damaged ▶ | REVERIFY symptom. |

**Fig. 15 Test DD, wheel sensor diagnosis (Part 8 of 12)**

## Wheel Sensor Diagnosis — Test DD

| TEST STEP | RESULT ▶ | ACTION TO TAKE |
|---|---|---|
| **DD21** SERVICE CODE 45 CHECK FOR TWO MISSING SENSOR SIGNALS ONE BEING THE LH FRONT | | |
| • Turn ignition switch to OFF.<br>• Disconnect 32-pin plug from Electronic Controller.<br>• Connect EEC-IV Breakout Box T83L-50-EEC-IV with Anti-Lock Test Adapter T87P-50-ALA or equivalent to 32-pin plug wiring harness.<br>• Turn air suspension switch in luggage compartment off.<br>• Place vehicle on hoist and raise until wheels are clear of ground. Refer to Pre-Delivery manual. Section 50-04.<br>• Set multi-meter on 2V AC voltage range.<br>• Measure voltage between Breakout box Pins 5 and 22 while spinning LH front wheel at approximately 1 revolution per second.<br>• Repeat wheel sensor voltage check described in previous step for the other wheels by:<br>Spinning — Measuring A/C volts between Pins<br>RH Front — 3 and 20<br>RH Rear — 6 and 23<br>LH Rear — 4 and 21 | Voltage between 0.05 and 0.70V AC ▶ | GO to Step **DD22**. |
| | Less than 0.05 or greater than 0.70V AC ▶ | CHECK out-of-range wheel for proper sensor mounting, air gap and speed indicator ring mounting. CORRECT as required. |
| **DD22** ELECTRONIC CONTROLLER TO GROUND | | |
| • Check continuity betwe[illegible]kout box Pin 40 and body ground. | Continuity ▶ | GO to Step **DD23**. |
| | No continuity ▶ | SERVICE or REPLACE cable harness (530). |
| **DD23** CHECK WHEEL BEARINGS | | |
| • Check wheel bearing end play on all wheels.<br>• Inspect toothed sensor ring visually for damaged teeth.<br>**NOTE: Turn air suspension switch On when vehicle is off hoist.** | Loose or damaged parts ▶ | ADJUST bearings or REPLACE damaged parts. |
| | Not loose or damaged ▶ | REVERIFY symptom. |

**Fig. 15 Test DD, wheel sensor diagnosis (Part 9 of 12)**

## Wheel Sensor Diagnosis — Test DD

| TEST STEP | RESULT ▶ | ACTION TO TAKE |
|---|---|---|
| **DD24** SERVICE CODE 46<br>CHECK FOR 2 MISSING SENSOR SIGNALS ONE BEING RH FRONT | | |
| • Turn ignition switch to OFF<br>• Disconnect 32-pin plug from Electronic Controller<br>• Connect EEC-IV Breakout Box T83L-50-EEC-IV with Anti-Lock Test Adapter T87P-50-ALA or equivalent, to 32-pin plug wiring harness<br>• Turn air suspension switch in luggage compartment off<br>• Place vehicle on hoist and raise until wheels are clear of ground. Refer to Pre-Delivery manual, Section 50-04<br>• Set multi-meter on 2V AC voltage range<br>• Measure voltage between Breakout box Pins 3 and 20 while spinning RH front wheel at approximately 1 revolution per second<br>• Repeat wheel sensor voltage check described in previous step for the other two wheels by<br><br>**Spinning** / **Measuring A C volts between Pins**<br>RH Rear — 6 and 23<br>LH Rear — 4 and 21 | Voltage between 0.05 and 0.70V AC ▶<br><br>Less than 0.05 or greater than 0.70V AC ▶ | GO to Step **DD22**<br><br>CHECK out-of-range wheel for proper sensor mounting, air gap and speed indication ring mounting. CORRECT as required |

**Fig. 15 Test DD, wheel sensor diagnosis (Part 10 of 12)**

## Wheel Sensor Diagnosis — Test DD

| TEST STEP | RESULT ▶ | ACTION TO TAKE |
|---|---|---|
| **DD25** SERVICE CODE 47<br>CHECK FOR BOTH REAR WHEEL SENSOR SIGNALS MISSING | | |
| • Turn ignition switch to OFF.<br>• Disconnect 32-pin plug from Electronic Controller.<br>• Connect EEC-IV Breakout Box T83L-50-EEC-IV with Anti-Lock Test Adapter T87P-50-ALA or equivalent, to 32-pin plug wiring harness.<br>• Turn air suspension switch in luggage compartment off.<br>• Place vehicle on hoist and raise until wheels are clear of ground. Refer to Pre-Delivery manual, Section 50-04.<br>• Set multi-meter on 2V AC voltage range.<br>• Measure voltage between Breakout box Pins 6 and 23 while spinning RH rear wheel at approximately 1 revolution per second.<br>• Measure voltage between Breakout box Pins 4 and 21 while spinning LH rear wheel at approximately 1 revolution per second. | Voltage between 0.05 and 0.70V AC ▶<br><br>Less than 0.05 or greater than 0.70V AC ▶ | GO to Step **DD22**.<br><br>CHECK out-of-range wheel for proper sensor mounting, air gap and speed indication ring mounting. CORRECT as required. |

**Fig. 15 Test DD, wheel sensor diagnosis (Part 11 of 12)**

## Wheel Sensor Diagnosis — Test DD

| TEST STEP | RESULT ▶ | ACTION TO TAKE |
|---|---|---|
| **DD26** SERVICE CODE 48<br>ANY 3 OF 4 WHEEL SPEED SENSOR SIGNALS MISSING | | |
| • Turn ignition switch to OFF.<br>• Disconnect 32-pin plug from Electronic Controller.<br>• Connect EEC-IV Breakout Box T83L-50-EEC-IV with Anti-Lock Test Adapter T87P-50-ALA or equivalent, to 32 pin plug wiring harness<br>• Turn air suspension switch in luggage compartment off.<br>• Place vehicle on hoist and raise until wheels are clear of ground. Refer to Pre-Delivery manual, Section 50-04.<br>• Set multi-meter on 2V AC voltage range.<br>• Measure voltage between Breakout box pins indicated below while spinning appropriate wheel at approximately 1 revolution per second.<br><br>**Spinning** / **Measuring A/C volts between Pins**<br>LH Front — 5 and 22<br>RH Front — 3 and 20<br>RH Rear — 6 and 23<br>LH Rear — 4 and 21 | Voltage between 0.05 and 0.70V AC ▶<br><br>Less than 0.05 or greater than 0.70V AC ▶ | GO to Step **DD22**<br><br>CHECK out-of-range wheel for proper sensor mounting, air gap and speed indicator ring mounting. CORRECT as required. |

**Fig. 15 Test DD, wheel sensor diagnosis (Part 12 of 12)**

## Outlet Valve Diagnosis — Test EE

| TEST STEP | RESULT ▶ | ACTION TO TAKE |
|---|---|---|
| **EE1** SERVICE CODE 51 AND/OR 71<br>CHECK LH FRONT SENSOR CIRCUIT CONTINUITY | | |
| • Turn ignition switch Off.<br>• Disconnect 32-Pin plug from electronic controller.<br>• Connect EEC-IV Breakout box with Tool T83L-50-EEC-IV or equivalent, Anti-Lock Test Adapter T87P-50-ALA or equivalent, to the anti-lock 32-Pin plug wiring harness.<br>• Check for continuity between Breakout box Pins 40 and 5. | Continuity (OK) ▶<br><br>No continuity (OK) ▶ | GO to Step **EE1a**.<br><br>GO to Step **EE2**. |

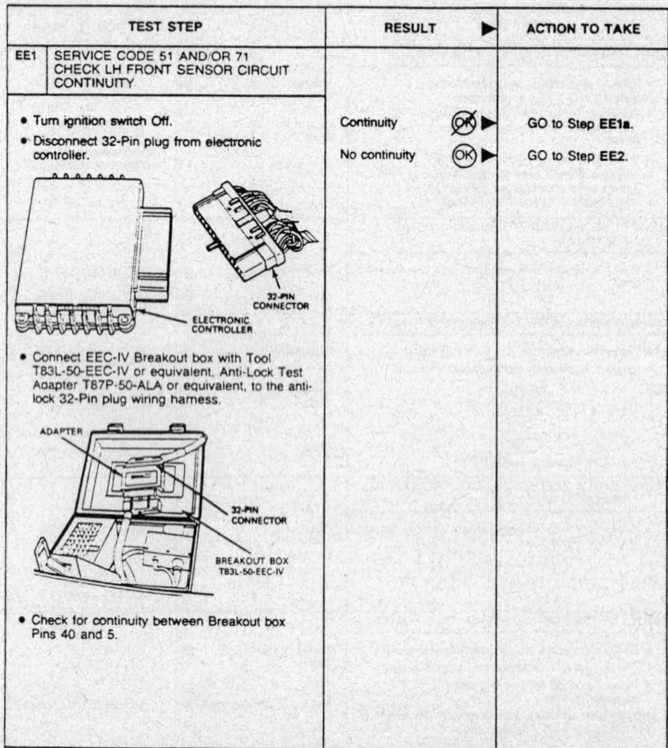


**Fig. 16 Test EE, outlet valve diagnosis (Part 1 of 8)**

## Outlet Valve Diagnosis — Test EE

| TEST STEP | RESULT ▶ | ACTION TO TAKE |
|---|---|---|
| **EE1a** CHECK LH FRONT SENSOR CONTINUITY | | |
| • Disconnect wheel sensor plug (LH front).<br>• Check for continuity between each sensor plug pin (sensor side) and vehicle ground.<br>LH FRONT SENSOR | Continuity (OK crossed) ▶<br>No continuity (OK) ▶ | REPLACE sensor (LH front).<br>SERVICE or REPLACE cable harness. RECONNECT sensor plug. |
| **EE2** CHECK ANTI-LOCK OPERATION LH FRONT WHEEL | | |
| • Turn air suspension Off, if so equipped.<br>• Lift vehicle and rotate wheels to ensure they turn freely.<br>• Short Pins 18, 14 and 31 to each other at Breakout box.<br>• Apply moderate brake pedal effort and check that LH front wheel will not turn.<br>• Check to see that LH front wheel turns freely with ignition switch On.<br>• Turn air suspension on when vehicle is off hoist, if so equipped.<br>CAUTION: DO NOT LEAVE IGNITION ON FOR MORE THAN 1 MINUTE MAXIMUM, OR SOLENOID VALVE DAMAGE MAY RESULT. | If wheel turns freely ▶<br>If wheel does not turn freely or pedal drops ▶ | REVERIFY symptom.<br>REPLACE solenoid valve block. |

**Fig. 16 Test EE, outlet valve diagnosis (Part 2 of 8)**

## Outlet Valve Diagnosis — Test EE

| TEST STEP | RESULT ▶ | ACTION TO TAKE |
|---|---|---|
| **EE3** SERVICE CODE 52 AND/OR 72 CHECK RH FRONT SENSOR CIRCUIT CONTINUITY | | |
| • Turn ignition switch Off.<br>• Disconnect 32-Pin plug from electronic controller.<br>32-PIN CONNECTOR<br>ELECTRONIC CONTROLLER<br>• Connect EEC-IV Breakout box with Tool T83L-50-EEC-IV or equivalent, Anti-Lock Test Adapter T87P-50-ALA or equivalent, to the anti-lock 32-Pin plug wiring harness.<br>ADAPTER<br>32-PIN CONNECTOR<br>BREAKOUT BOX T83L-50-EEC-IV<br>• Check for continuity between Breakout box Pins 40 and 3. | Continuity (OK crossed) ▶<br>No continuity (OK) ▶ | GO to Step EE3a.<br>GO to Step EE4. |

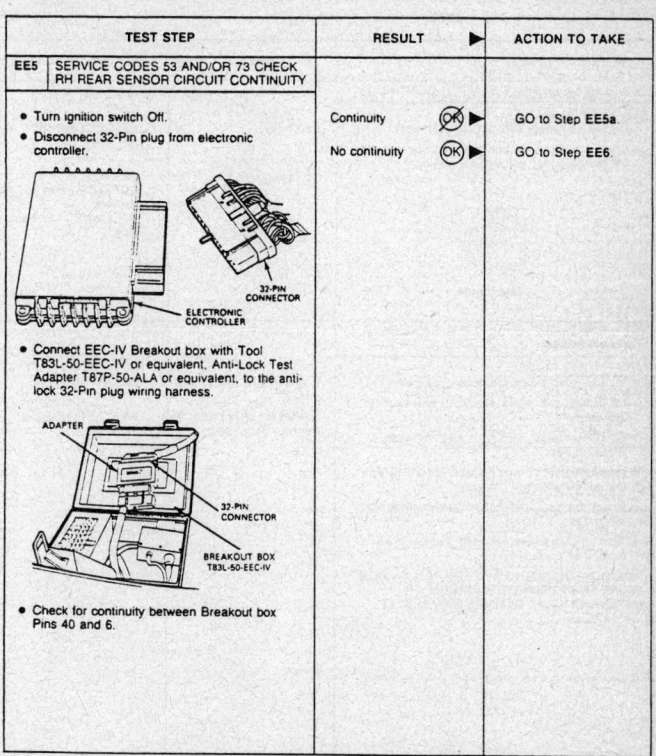

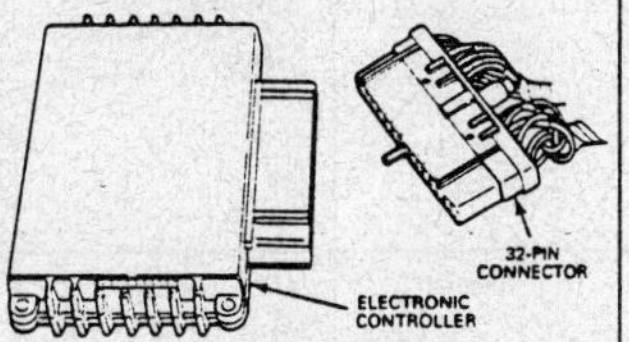

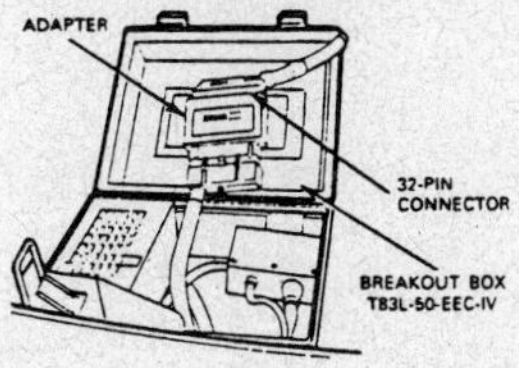

**Fig. 16 Test EE, outlet valve diagnosis (Part 3 of 8)**

## Outlet Valve Diagnosis — Test EE

| TEST STEP | RESULT ▶ | ACTION TO TAKE |
|---|---|---|
| **EE3a** CHECK RH FRONT SENSOR CONTINUITY | | |
| • Disconnect wheel sensor plug (RH front).<br>• Check for continuity between each sensor plug pin (sensor side) and vehicle ground.<br>RH FRONT SENSOR | Continuity ▶<br>No continuity ▶ | REPLACE right front sensor.<br>SERVICE or REPLACE cable harness. RECONNECT sensor plug. |
| **EE4** CHECK ANTI-LOCK OPERATION RH FRONT WHEEL | | |
| • Turn air suspension Off, if so equipped.<br>• Lift vehicle and rotate wheels to ensure they turn freely.<br>• Short Pins 18, 32 and 13 to each other at Breakout box.<br>• Apply moderate brake effort. Check that RH front wheel does not turn.<br>• Check to see that RH front wheel turns freely with ignition switch On.<br>• Turn air suspension on when vehicle is off hoist, if so equipped.<br>CAUTION: DO NOT LEAVE IGNITION ON FOR MORE THAN 1 MINUTE MAXIMUM, OR SOLENOID VALVE DAMAGE MAY RESULT. | If wheel turns freely ▶<br>If wheel does not turn freely or pedal drops ▶ | REVERIFY symptom.<br>REPLACE solenoid valve block. |

**Fig. 16 Test EE, outlet valve diagnosis (Part 4 of 8)**

## Outlet Valve Diagnosis — Test EE

| TEST STEP | RESULT ▶ | ACTION TO TAKE |
|---|---|---|
| **EE5** SERVICE CODES 53 AND/OR 73 CHECK RH REAR SENSOR CIRCUIT CONTINUITY | | |
| • Turn ignition switch Off.<br>• Disconnect 32-Pin plug from electronic controller.<br>32-PIN CONNECTOR<br>ELECTRONIC CONTROLLER<br>• Connect EEC-IV Breakout box with Tool T83L-50-EEC-IV or equivalent, Anti-Lock Test Adapter T87P-50-ALA or equivalent, to the anti-lock 32-Pin plug wiring harness.<br>ADAPTER<br>32-PIN CONNECTOR<br>BREAKOUT BOX T83L-50-EEC-IV<br>• Check for continuity between Breakout box Pins 40 and 6. | Continuity (OK crossed) ▶<br>No continuity (OK) ▶ | GO to Step EE5a.<br>GO to Step EE6. |

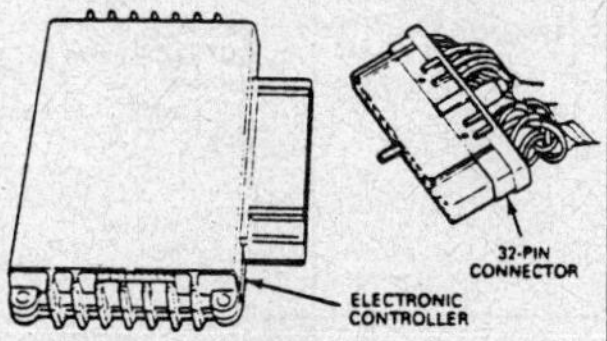

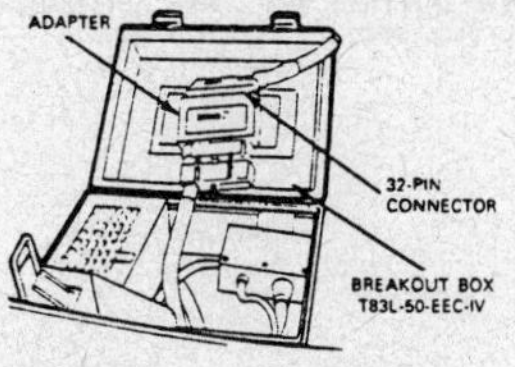

**Fig. 16 Test EE, outlet valve diagnosis (Part 5 of 8)**

## Outlet Valve Diagnosis — Test EE

| TEST STEP | RESULT ▶ | ACTION TO TAKE |
|---|---|---|
| **EE5a** CHECK RH REAR SENSOR CONTINUITY | | |
| • Disconnect wheel sensor plug (RH rear).<br>• Check for continuity between each sensor plug pin (sensor side) and vehicle ground.<br>RH REAR SENSOR | Continuity (OK crossed out) ▶<br>No continuity (OK) ▶ | REPLACE sensor (RH rear).<br>SERVICE or REPLACE cable harness. RECONNECT sensor plug. |
| **EE6** CHECK ANTI-LOCK OPERATION: REAR WHEELS | | |
| • Turn air suspension Off, if so equipped.<br>• Lift vehicle and rotate wheels to ensure they turn freely.<br>• Short Pins 18, 30 and 12 to each other at Breakout box.<br>• Apply moderate brake pedal pressure. Check that rear wheels will not turn.<br>• Check that rear wheels turn freely with ignition switch On.<br>• Turn air suspension On when vehicle is off hoist, if so equipped.<br>**CAUTION: DO NOT LEAVE IGNITION ON FOR MORE THAN 1 MINUTE MAXIMUM OR SOLENOID VALVE DAMAGE MAY RESULT.** | If wheel turns freely ▶<br>If wheel does not turn freely or pedal drops ▶ | REVERIFY symptom.<br>REPLACE solenoid valve block. |

**Fig. 16 Test EE, outlet valve diagnosis (Part 6 of 8)**

## Outlet Valve Diagnosis — Test EE

| TEST STEP | RESULT ▶ | ACTION TO TAKE |
|---|---|---|
| **EE7** SERVICE CODES 54 AND/OR 74 CHECK LH REAR SENSOR CIRCUIT CONTINUITY | | |
| • Turn ignition switch Off.<br>• Disconnect 32-pin plug from electronic controller.<br>32-PIN CONNECTOR; ELECTRONIC CONTROLLER<br>• Connect EEC-IV Breakout box with Tool T83L-50-EEC-IV or equivalent, Anti-Lock Test Adapter T87P-50-ALA or equivalent, to the anti-lock 32-pin plug wiring harness.<br>ADAPTER; 35 PIN CONNECTOR; BREAKOUT BOX T83L-50-EEC-IV<br>• Check for continuity between Breakout box Pins 40 and 4. | Continuity ▶<br>No continuity ▶ | GO to Step **Step EE7a**.<br>GO to Step **Step EE8**. |

**Fig. 16 Test EE, outlet valve diagnosis (Part 7 of 8)**

## Outlet Valve Diagnosis — Test EE

| TEST STEP | RESULT ▶ | ACTION TO TAKE |
|---|---|---|
| **EE7A** CHECK LH REAR SENSOR CONTINUITY | | |
| • Disconnect wheel sensor plug (LH rear).<br>• Check for continuity between each sensor plug pin (sensor side) and vehicle ground.<br>LH REAR SENSOR | Continuity ▶<br>No continuity ▶ | REPLACE sensor (LH rear).<br>SERVICE or REPLACE cable harness. RECONNECT sensor plug. |
| **EE8** CHECK ANTI-LOCK OPERATION: REAR WHEELS | | |
| • Turn air suspension Off, if so equipped.<br>• Lift vehicle and rotate wheels to ensure they turn freely.<br>• Short Pins 18, 30 and 12 to each other at Breakout box.<br>• Apply moderate brake pedal pressure. Check that rear wheels will not turn.<br>• Check that rear wheels turn freely with ignition switch On.<br>• Turn air suspension On when vehicle is off hoist, if so equipped.<br>**CAUTION: DO NOT LEAVE IGNITION ON FOR MORE THAN 1 MINUTE MAXIMUM OR SOLENOID VALVE DAMAGE MAY RESULT.** | If wheel turns freely ▶<br>If wheel does not turn freely or pedal drops ▶ | VERIFY symptom.<br>REPLACE solenoid valve block. |

**Fig. 16 Test EE, outlet valve diagnosis (Part 8 of 8)**

## Warning Circuit Diagnosis — Test FF

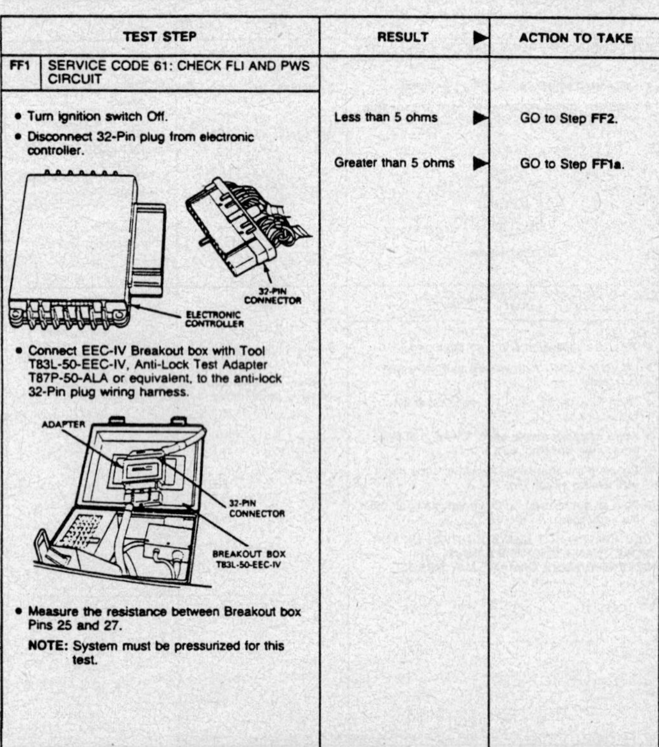

| TEST STEP | RESULT ▶ | ACTION TO TAKE |
|---|---|---|
| **FF1** SERVICE CODE 61: CHECK FLI AND PWS CIRCUIT | | |
| • Turn ignition switch Off.<br>• Disconnect 32-Pin plug from electronic controller.<br>32-PIN CONNECTOR; ELECTRONIC CONTROLLER<br>• Connect EEC-IV Breakout box with Tool T83L-50-EEC-IV, Anti-Lock Test Adapter T87P-50-ALA or equivalent, to the anti-lock 32-Pin plug wiring harness.<br>ADAPTER; 32-PIN CONNECTOR; BREAKOUT BOX T83L-50-EEC-IV<br>• Measure the resistance between Breakout box Pins 25 and 27.<br>**NOTE:** System must be pressurized for this test. | Less than 5 ohms ▶<br>Greater than 5 ohms ▶ | GO to Step **FF2**.<br>GO to Step **FF1a**. |

**Fig. 17 Test FF, warning circuit diagnosis (Part 1 of 6)**

## Warning Circuit Diagnosis — Test FF

| TEST STEP | RESULT ▶ | ACTION TO TAKE |
|---|---|---|
| **FF1a** CHECK FLI ANTI-LOCK WARNING CIRCUIT | | |
| • Disconnect 5-pin plug on reservoir fluid level indicator (FLI).<br>• Measure resistance between fluid level indicator electrical socket Pins 1 and 2 (with brake fluid level at maximum mark on reservoir).<br>PIN NO. 3, PIN NO.5, PIN NO. 1, PIN NO.4, PIN NO. 2<br>FLUID LEVEL INDICATOR | Less than 2 ohms — OK ▶ | GO to Step **FF1b**. |
| | Greater than 2 ohms — ~~OK~~ ▶ | REPLACE fluid level indicator cap. |
| **FF1b** CHECK PWS ANTI-LOCK WARNING CIRCUIT | | |
| • Disconnect 5-pin plug at pressure warning switch (PWS).<br>• Check for continuity between pressure warning switch socket Pins 3 and 5.<br>**NOTE: System must be pressurized for this test.**<br>PIN NO. 3, PIN NO. 5<br>PRESSURE WARNING SWITCH | Continuity — OK ▶ | GO to Step **FF1c**. |
| | No continuity — ~~OK~~ ▶ | REPLACE pressure warning switch. |

**Fig. 17 Test FF, warning circuit diagnosis (Part 2 of 6)**

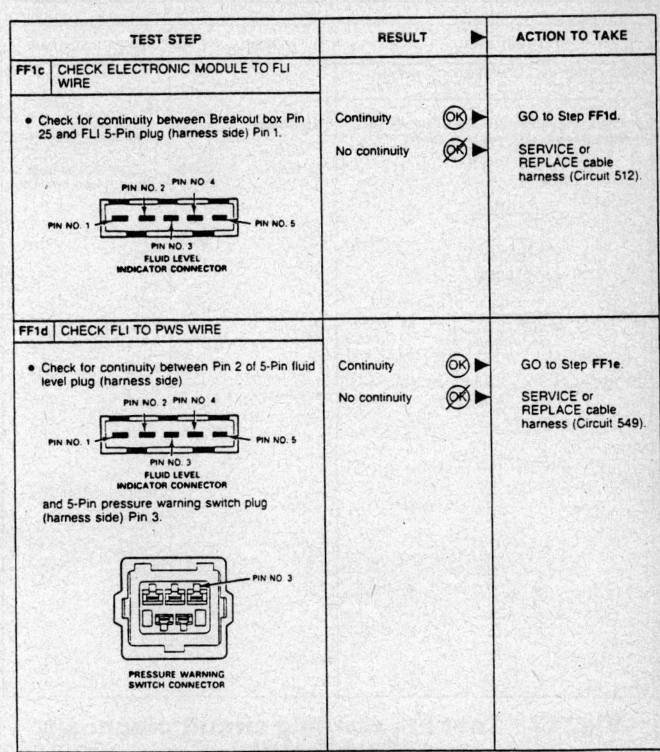

## Warning Circuit Diagnosis — Test FF

| TEST STEP | RESULT ▶ | ACTION TO TAKE |
|---|---|---|
| **FF1c** CHECK ELECTRONIC MODULE TO FLI WIRE | | |
| • Check for continuity between Breakout box Pin 25 and FLI 5-Pin plug (harness side) Pin 1.<br>PIN NO. 2, PIN NO. 4, PIN NO. 1, PIN NO. 5, PIN NO. 3<br>FLUID LEVEL INDICATOR CONNECTOR | Continuity — OK ▶ | GO to Step **FF1d**. |
| | No continuity — ~~OK~~ ▶ | SERVICE or REPLACE cable harness (Circuit 512). |
| **FF1d** CHECK FLI TO PWS WIRE | | |
| • Check for continuity between Pin 2 of 5-Pin fluid level plug (harness side)<br>PIN NO. 2, PIN NO. 4, PIN NO. 1, PIN NO. 5, PIN NO. 3<br>FLUID LEVEL INDICATOR CONNECTOR<br>and 5-Pin pressure warning switch plug (harness side) Pin 3.<br>PIN NO. 3<br>PRESSURE WARNING SWITCH CONNECTOR | Continuity — OK ▶ | GO to Step **FF1e**. |
| | No continuity — ~~OK~~ ▶ | SERVICE or REPLACE cable harness (Circuit 549). |

**Fig. 17 Test FF, warning circuit diagnosis (Part 3 of 6)**

## Warning Circuit Diagnosis — Test FF

| TEST STEP | RESULT ▶ | ACTION TO TAKE |
|---|---|---|
| **FF1e** PWS TO ELECTRONIC CONTROLLER WIRE | | |
| • Check for continuity between 5-Pin pressure warning switch plug (harness side) Pin 5<br>PIN NO. 5<br>PRESSURE WARNING SWITCH CONNECTOR<br>and Breakout box Pin 27. | Continuity — OK ▶ | TURN ignition OFF. CONNECT all electrical connections. REVERIFY symptom. |
| | No continuity — ~~OK~~ ▶ | SERVICE or REPLACE cable harness (Circuit 535). |
| **FF2** ISOLATION TEST FLI AND PWS | | |
| • Check for continuity between Breakout box Pin 25 and body ground and Pin 27 and body ground. | Continuity — ~~OK~~ ▶ | GO to Step **FF2a**. |
| | No continuity — OK ▶ | REVERIFY Symptom. |
| **FF2a** CHECK FLUID LEVEL INDICATOR PIN NO. 1 | | |
| • Check for continuity between FLI plug Pin 1 (harness side) and body ground.<br>PIN NO. 2, PIN NO. 4, PIN NO. 1, PIN NO. 5, PIN NO. 3<br>FLUID LEVEL INDICATOR | Continuity — ~~OK~~ ▶ | SERVICE or REPLACE Circuit 512. |
| | No continuity — OK ▶ | GO to Step **FF2b**. |

**Fig. 17 Test FF, warning circuit diagnosis (Part 4 of 6)**

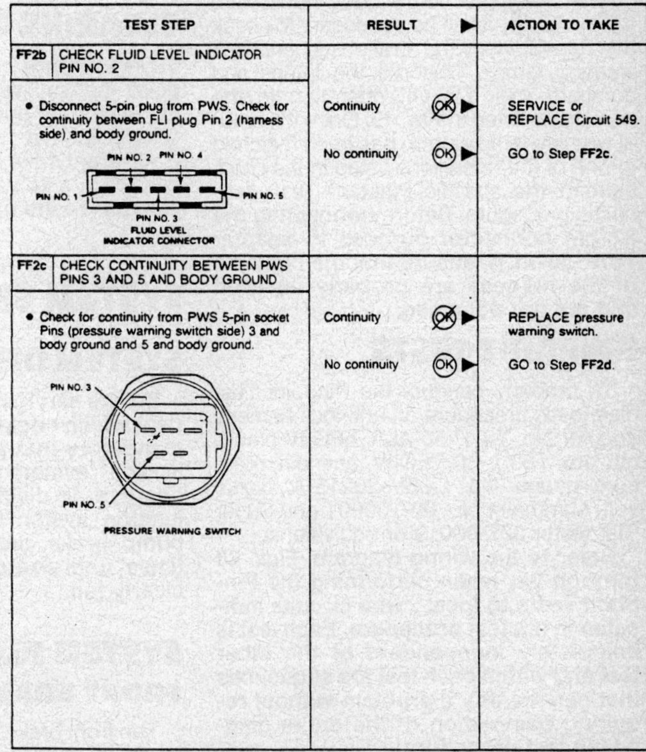

## Warning Circuit Diagnosis — Test FF

| TEST STEP | RESULT ▶ | ACTION TO TAKE |
|---|---|---|
| **FF2b** CHECK FLUID LEVEL INDICATOR PIN NO. 2 | | |
| • Disconnect 5-pin plug from PWS. Check for continuity between FLI plug Pin 2 (harness side) and body ground.<br>PIN NO. 2, PIN NO. 4, PIN NO. 1, PIN NO. 5, PIN NO. 3<br>FLUID LEVEL INDICATOR CONNECTOR | Continuity — ~~OK~~ ▶ | SERVICE or REPLACE Circuit 549. |
| | No continuity — OK ▶ | GO to Step **FF2c**. |
| **FF2c** CHECK CONTINUITY BETWEEN PWS PINS 3 AND 5 AND BODY GROUND | | |
| • Check for continuity from PWS 5-pin socket Pins (pressure warning switch side) 3 and body ground and 5 and body ground.<br>PIN NO. 3, PIN NO. 5<br>PRESSURE WARNING SWITCH | Continuity — ~~OK~~ ▶ | REPLACE pressure warning switch. |
| | No continuity — OK ▶ | GO to Step **FF2d**. |

**Fig. 17 Test FF, warning circuit diagnosis (Part 5 of 6)**

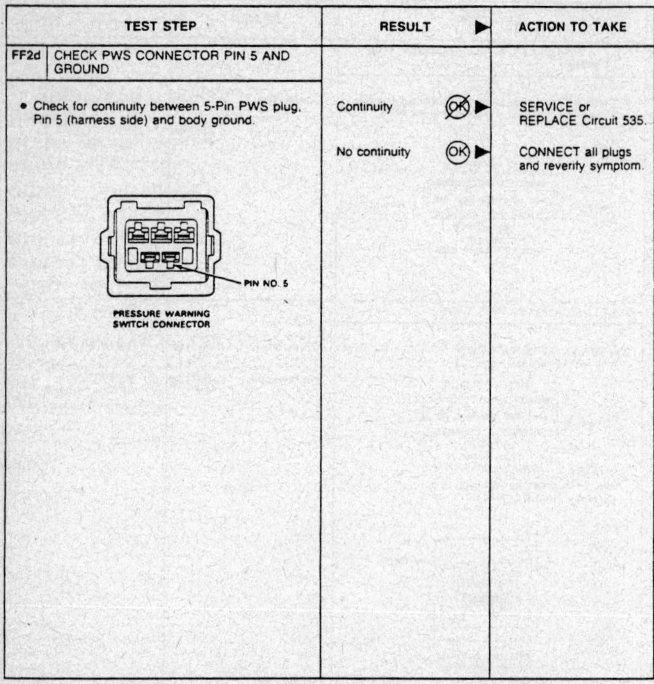

| Warning Circuit Diagnosis | Test FF |
|---|---|

| TEST STEP | | RESULT ▶ | ACTION TO TAKE |
|---|---|---|---|
| FF2d | CHECK PWS CONNECTOR PIN 5 AND GROUND | | |
| • Check for continuity between 5-Pin PWS plug, Pin 5 (harness side) and body ground. | | Continuity (OK crossed out) ▶ | SERVICE or REPLACE Circuit 535. |
| | | No continuity (OK) ▶ | CONNECT all plugs and reverify symptom. |



**Fig. 17 Test FF, warning circuit diagnosis (Part 6 of 6)**

## Anti-Lock Quick Check Sheet Using 60-Pin EEC-IV Breakout Box, Tool T83L-50-EEC-IV①

NOTE: Before performing tests below, the Pre-Test Checks must be performed as outlined.
NOTE: If fault is intermittent the tests listed below will NOT find the fault. Use controller service code or call Hot-Line if this situation occurs.

| Item to be Tested | | Ignition Mode | Measure Between Pin Numbers | Tester Scale/ Range | Specification | Test Step |
|---|---|---|---|---|---|---|
| No Boost/No Power Brakes (Hard Brake Pedal) | | — | — | — | — | D-1 |
| Battery Check | | On | 40 + 18 | Volts | 10 minimum | A-1 |
| Main Power Relay | | Off | 40 + 9 | Ohms | 45 Ohms — 105 Ohms | A-6 |
| | | | Place a jumper between pins 9 and 18 | | | |
| | | On | 40 + 16 | Volts | 10 minimum | A-7 |
| Power from Main Power Relay | | On | 40 + 15 | Volts | 10 minimum | A-3 |
| | | | Remove jumper from pins 9 and 18 | | | |
| Main Power Relay Circuit | | Off | 40 - 16 | Continuity | Continuity | A-2 |
| Main Power Relay Circuit | | Off | 15 + 40 | Continuity | Continuity | A-3a |
| Sensor Resistance | (RR) | Off | 6 - 23 | K Ohms | 800 to 1400 Ohms | A-8 |
| Sensor Resistance | (LF) | Off | 5 - 22 | K Ohms | 800 to 1400 Ohms | A-9 |
| Sensor Resistance | (LR) | Off | 4 - 21 | K Ohms | 800 to 1400 Ohms | A-10 |
| Sensor Resistance | (RF) | Off | 3 + 20 | K Ohms | 800 to 1400 Ohms | A-11 |
| Main Valve Resistance | | Off | 11 + 29 | Ohms | 2 Ohms to 5.5 Ohms | A-12 |
| Inlet & Outlet Valves | | Off | 11 + 40 | Continuity | Continuity | A-13 |
| | | Off | 11 + 32 | Ohms | 5 Ohms to 8 Ohms | A-14 |
| | | Off | 11 + 30 | Ohms | 5 Ohms to 8 Ohms | A-15 |
| | | Off | 11 + 31 | Ohms | 5 Ohms to 8 Ohms | A-16 |
| | | Off | 11 + 12 | Ohms | 3 Ohms to 6 Ohms | A-17 |
| | | Off | 11 - 14 | Ohms | 3 Ohms to 6 Ohms | A-18 |
| | | Off | 11 - 13 | Ohms | 3 Ohms to 6 Ohms | A-19 |
| Reservoir Warning | | On | 25 - 27 | Ohms | Less than 5 Ohms | A-4a |
| Lift Fluid Level Indicator from Reservoir (Float at bottom position) | | Off | 25 - 27 | Ohms | Infinite (Open Circuit) | 4-5a |
| Sensor Cable Continuity Shielding to Ground | (RR) | Off | 40 - 6 | Continuity | No Continuity | B-1a |
| | (LF) | Off | 40 - 5 | Continuity | No Continuity | B-2a |
| | (LR) | Off | 40 + 4 | Continuity | No Continuity | B-3a |
| | (RF) | Off | 40 + 3 | Continuity | No Continuity | B-4a |
| Sensor Voltage (Rotate wheels at 1 revolution per second minimum) (Shut off air suspension switch in luggage compartment with vehicle on hoist if so equipped.) | (RR) | Off② | 6 + 23 | AC Millivolts | 50-700 Millivolts | C-5 |
| | (LF) | Off② | 5 + 22 | AC Millivolts | 50-700 Millivolts | C-6 |
| | (LR) | Off② | 4 + 21 | AC Millivolts | 50-700 Millivolts | C-7 |
| | (RF) | Off② | 3 + 20 | AC Millivolts | 50-700 Millivolts | C-8 |

① If Quick Test does not isolate symptom, refer to Diagnostic Lamp Symptom Chart.
② The most accurate measurements are taken with the breakout box in back seat and an assistant is driving the vehicle 4.5-5.0 mph.

**Fig. 18 ABS quick check sheet**

## DIAGNOSTIC LAMP SYMPTOM CHART

If the quick test checks and ABS quick check sheet procedure does not isolate the symptom, it will be necessary to check the operation of the brake and anti-lock warning lamps. Observe the lamps and compare their On/Off operation to the conditions listed in **Fig. 19.** Once the actual warning lamp pattern has been matched to one of the conditions listed in the chart, perform the specific Pinpoint Test diagnostic procedure. **Before connecting the 32 pin connector harness to adapter T87P-50-ALA, ensure that the contacts of the harness are properly installed and are not damaged.**

## PINPOINT TESTS

To properly conduct the Pinpoint Test diagnostic procedure an anti-lock harness adapter No. T87P-50-ALA, EEC-IV breakout box T83 L-50-EEC-IV, anti-lock pressure gauge No. D88M-20215-A, digital volt/ohmmeter No. 007-00001 and Super Star tester 007-00019 or equivalents.

**Refer to the wiring diagram, Figs. 20 through 22, when performing the Pinpoint Tests to locate wire circuits indicated in the test procedure. Each test is completely independent of the other test and within each test are sequences that can identify a problem without requiring completion of the entire diagnostic test procedure.**

Refer to **Figs. 23 through 31,** for Pinpoint Test diagnostic procedures.

## CLEARING CODE MEMORY

Original error codes stored in the computer memory will erase automatically if the system is operating properly and the vehicle is driven above 25 mph.

All error codes must be output, all faults corrected and vehicle driven above 25 mph before the memory will clear.

# SYSTEM SERVICE

## SYSTEM DISCHARGE

**Before servicing any system component which contains high pressure, it is mandatory that the hydraulic pressure in the system be completely discharged. To discharge the system, turn ignition switch to Off position, then pump brake pedal a minimum of 20 times, until an increase in pedal force is clearly felt.**

## SYSTEM BLEEDING

### FRONT BRAKES

The front brakes can be bled in the conventional manner or with brake bleeder tool No. 104-00064 or equivalent, with or without the accumulator being charged.

#### Brake Bleeding Less Pressure Bleeder

1. Remove dust cap from the righthand caliper bleeder fitting. Attach a rubber drain tube to fitting. Ensure that the end of the tube fits snugly around the fitting.
2. Submerge free end of the tube in a suitable container, partially filled with clean brake fluid.
3. Loosen bleeder fitting approximately three-quarter turn. Push brake pedal down slowly through full travel and hold at that position.
4. Close bleeder fitting, then return pedal to full release position. Wait five seconds, then repeat operation until air bubbles cease to appear at submerged end of bleeder tube.
5. Repeat operation at the lefthand caliper.

#### Brake Bleeding w/Pressure Bleeder

1. Clean all dirt from the reservoir filler cap area. Attach pressure bleeder to reservoir cap opening.
2. Maintain approximately 35 psi pressure on the system.
3. Remove dust cap from righthand front caliper bleeder fitting.

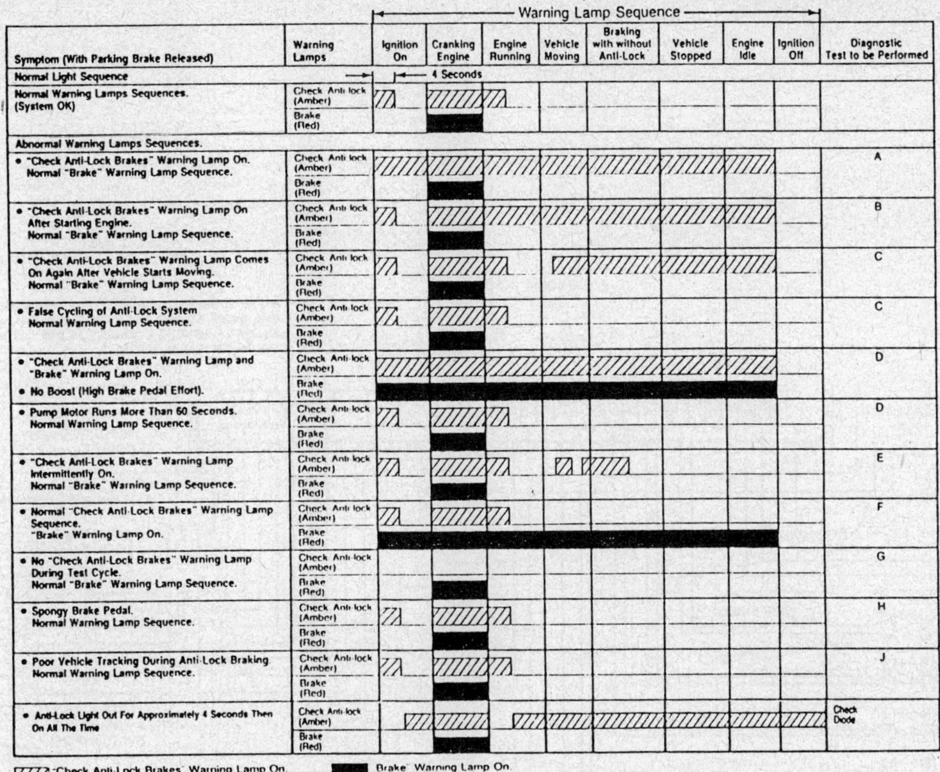


**Fig. 19 Diagnostic lamp symptom chart**

4. Attach a rubber drain tube to the fitting. Ensure that the end of the tube fits snugly around the fitting.
5. With the ignition switch in the Off position and the brake pedal in the fully released position, open the righthand front caliper bleeder fitting for 10 seconds at a time until an air free stream of brake fluid is observed from submerged end of hose.
6. Repeat procedure at lefthand caliper.

## REAR BRAKES

The rear brakes can be pressure bled using brake bleeder 104-00064, or equivalent, or through the use of a fully charged accumulator.

### Brake Bleeding w/Pressure Bleeder

1. Clean all dirt from reservoir filler cap area. Attach pressure bleeder to reservoir cap opening.
2. Maintain approximately 35 psi on the system.
3. Remove dust cap from righthand caliper bleeder fitting. Attach a rubber drain tube to the fitting. Ensure that end of tube fits snugly around fitting.
4. With ignition switch in the Off position, and brake pedal at rest, open righthand caliper bleeder fitting for 10 seconds at a time, until an air free stream of brake fluid flow is observed.
5. Repeat procedure at lefthand caliper.
6. Place ignition switch in the RUN position, then pump brake pedal several times to complete the bleeding procedure and completely charge accumulator.
7. Siphon off excess fluid in reservoir to adjust level to the MAX mark with a fully charged accumulator.

### Bleeding System Using A Fully Charged Accumulator

1. Remove dust cap from righthand caliper bleeder fitting. Attach a rubber drain tube to the fitting. Ensure that end of tube fits snugly around fitting.
2. Turn ignition switch to the RUN position. This will activate the electric pump to charge the accumulator as required.

**Before proceeding with next step, ensure care is used when opening the bleeder screws due to the high pressures available from a completely charged accumulator.**

3. Hold brake pedal in the applied position. Open the righthand caliper bleeder fitting for 10 seconds at a time until an air free stream of brake fluid is observed.
4. Repeat procedure at lefthand caliper.
5. Pump brake pedal several times to complete bleeding procedure and charge accumulator.
6. Adjust brake fluid level in reservoir to MAX mark with a completely charged accumulator. **If the pump motor is allowed to operate continuously for approximately 20 minutes, a thermal safety switch inside the motor may shut the motor off, to prevent it from overheating. If an overheat condition occurs, a 2-10 minute cool down period is required before normal operation can resume.**

## HYDRAULIC RESERVOIR, CHECK & FILL

Refer to **Fig. 6,** during the following procedure.

1. With ignition switch in the On position, pump brake pedal until the hydraulic pump motor begins to operate.
2. Wait until the hydraulic pump motor is operating, then check brake fluid level. If fluid level drops below the MAX fill level, add enough fluid to bring level to the MAX mark.
3. Do not add fluid as to bring level above MAX mark. Overfilling the reservoir may cause the brake fluid to overflow when the accumulator discharges during normal operation. **It is possible, depending on the state of the charge of the accumulator, that the fluid level could show above the MAX mark when first viewed, If so, repeat steps 1 and 2.**

# COMPONENT REPLACEMENT

## ACTUATION ASSEMBLY

Refer to **Figs. 2 and 3,** during the following procedure.

1. With hydraulic system discharged, disconnect battery ground cable.
2. Remove air cleaner housing and duct assembly, if necessary.

*Continued on page 20-31*

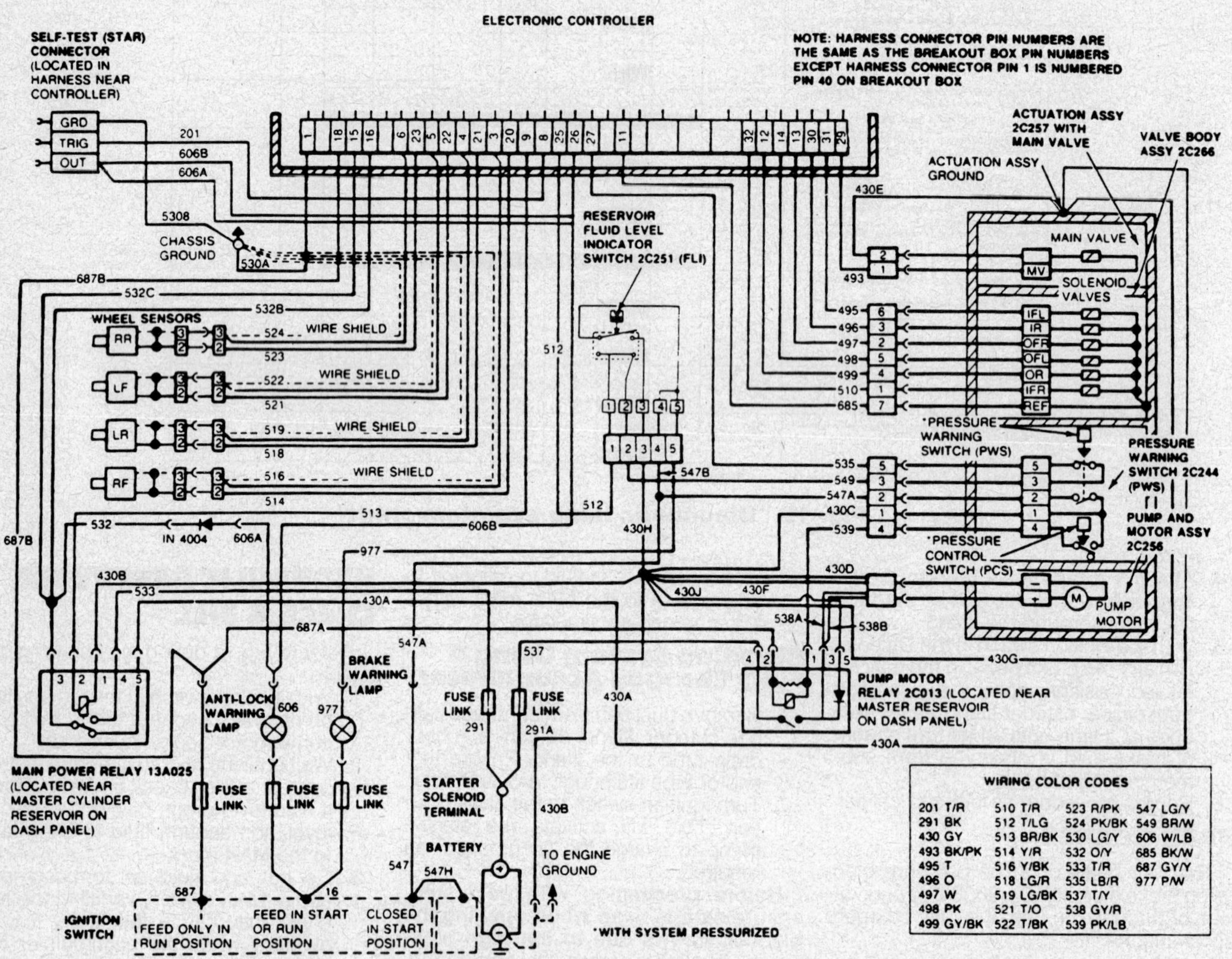


**Fig. 20 ABS wiring circuit. 1989 Continental**

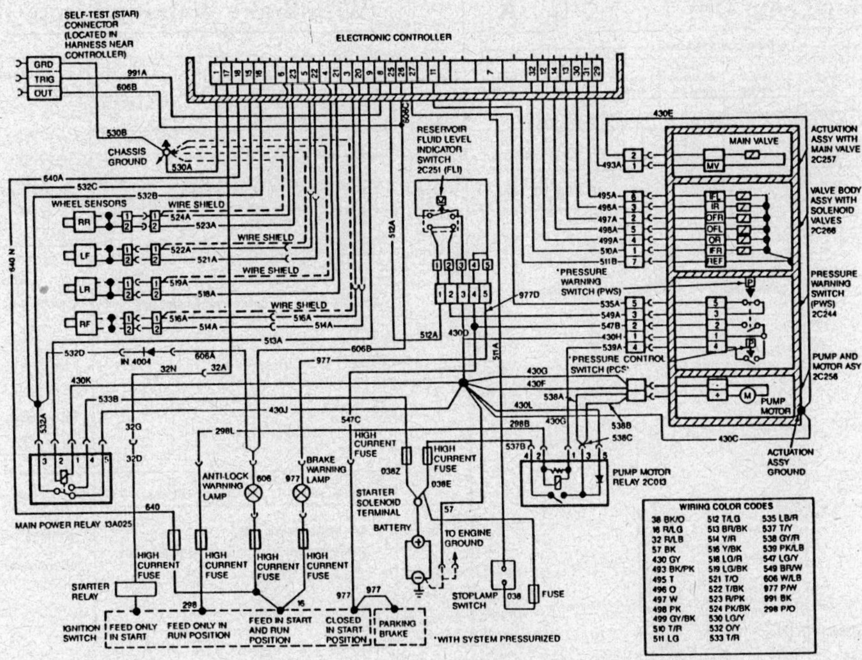


**Fig. 21 ABS wiring circuit. Cougar & Thunderbird**

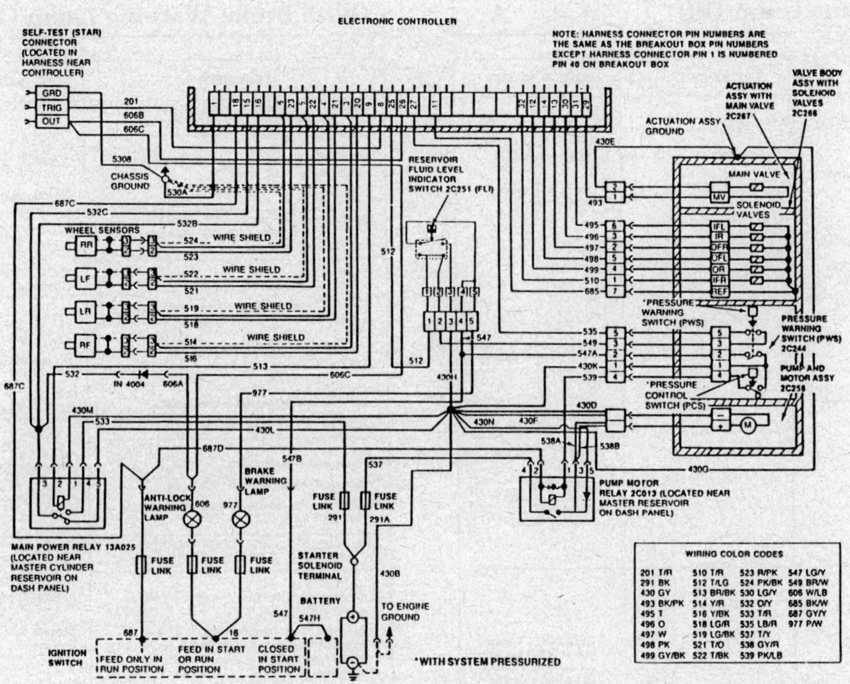


**Fig. 22 ABS wiring circuit. Mark VII**

## Anti-Lock Warning Lamp On (With Brake Warning Lamp Off) — Test A

WARNING LIGHTS SEQUENCE

| Warning Lamps | Ignition On | Cranking Engine | Engine Running | Vehicle Moving | Braking with/without Anti-Lock | Vehicle Stopped | Engine Idle | Ignition Off |
|---|---|---|---|---|---|---|---|---|
| Check Anti-Lock (Amber) | | | | | | | | |
| Brake (Red) | | | | | | | | |

| TEST STEP | RESULT ▶ | ACTION TO TAKE |
|---|---|---|
| **A1** 32 PIN PLUG TESTING | | |
| • Turn ignition switch OFF.<br>• Disconnect 32-pin Plug from electronic controller.<br>ELECTRONIC CONTROLLER; 32 PIN CONNECTOR<br>• Connect EEC-IV Breakout box Tool T83L-50-EEC-IV and anti-lock test adapter Tool T87P-50-ALA or equivalents, to the anti-lock 32-pin plug wiring harness.<br>ADAPTER; 32 PIN CONNECTOR; BREAKOUT BOX T83L-50-EEC-IV<br>• Set multi-meter to read volts DC.<br>• Turn ignition switch ON.<br>• Measure voltage between Breakout box Pins 40 and 18. | Over 10V (OK) ▶<br>Under 10V (NOT OK) ▶ | GO to Step **A2**.<br>GO to Step **A1a**. |

**Fig. 23 Test A, warning lamp On (Part 1 of 24)**

## Anti-Lock Warning Lamp On (With Brake Warning Lamp Off) — Test A

| TEST STEP | RESULT ▶ | ACTION TO TAKE |
|---|---|---|
| **A1a** CHECK ELECTRONIC CONTROLLER TO GROUND WIRE | | |
| • Check: — fuse link to anti-lock warning lamp.<br>— battery.<br>• Remove positive battery cable.<br>• Check continuity between Breakout box pin 40 and body ground. | Continuity ▶<br>No continuity ▶ | GO to Step **A1b**.<br>SERVICE or REPLACE cable harness (Circuit 530A). |
| **A1b** CHECK IGNITION TO ELECTRONIC CONTROLLER WIRE | | |
| • Check continuity between Breakout box Pin 18 and ignition switch wire 640N. | Continuity ▶<br>No continuity ▶ | RECONNECT positive battery cable. CHECK for power at ignition switch pin with switch ON. If okay, connect electronic controller and reverify symptom.<br>SERVICE or REPLACE cable harness (Circuit 640N.) |
| **A2** CHECK MAIN POWER RELAY SECONDARY CIRCUIT (NORMAL) | | |
| • Turn ignition switch OFF.<br>• Check for continuity between Breakout box Pins 40 and 16. | Continuity ▶<br>No continuity ▶ | GO to **A3**.<br>GO to **A2a**. |

**Fig. 23 Test A, warning lamp On (Part 2 of 24)**

## Anti-Lock Warning Lamp On (With Brake Warning Lamp Off) — Test A

| TEST STEP | RESULT ▶ | ACTION TO TAKE |
|---|---|---|
| **A2a** CHECK MAIN POWER RELAY SECONDARY CIRCUIT (NORMAL) | | |
| • Disconnect main relay from socket.<br>• Check for continuity between main power relay socket Pins 3 and 5.<br>PIN NO. 3; PIN NO. 5; MAIN POWER RELAY | Continuity ▶<br>No continuity ▶ | GO to Step **A2b**.<br>REPLACE main power relay. |
| **A2b** CHECK MAIN POWER RELAY SECONDARY CIRCUIT WIRING HARNESS | | |
| • Disconnect positive battery cable.<br>• Check for continuity between main power relay socket Pin 3 and Breakout box Pin 16.<br>PIN NO. 3; MAIN POWER RELAY CONNECTOR | Continuity ▶<br>No continuity ▶ | GO to Step **A2c**.<br>SERVICE or REPLACE cable harness (Circuit 532A, 532B or 532D). |
| **A2c** CHECK MAIN POWER RELAY SECONDARY CIRCUIT WIRING HARNESS | | |
| • Check for continuity between main power relay socket Pin 5 and body ground.<br>PIN NO. 5; MAIN POWER RELAY CONNECTOR | Continuity ▶<br>No continuity ▶ | RECONNECT main power relay, electronic controller and battery cable and reverify symptom.<br>SERVICE or REPLACE cable harness (Circuit 430J). |

**Fig. 23 Test A, warning lamp On (Part 3 of 24)**

## With Anti-Lock Warning Lamp On (With Brake Warning Lamp Off) — Test A

| TEST STEP | RESULT ▶ | ACTION TO TAKE |
|---|---|---|
| **A3** CHECK MAIN POWER RELAY SECONDARY CIRCUIT (NORMAL) | | |
| • Check for continuity between Breakout box Pins 40 and 15. | Continuity ▶<br>No continuity ▶ | GO to Step **A4**.<br>GO to Step **A3a**. |
| **A3a** CHECK MAIN POWER RELAY SECONDARY CIRCUIT WIRING HARNESS | | |
| • Remove main power relay.<br>• Check for continuity between main power relay socket Pin 3 and Breakout box Pin 15.<br>PIN NO. 3; MAIN POWER RELAY CONNECTOR | Continuity ▶<br>No continuity ▶ | CONNECT main power relay and electronic controller and reverify symptom.<br>SERVICE or REPLACE cable harness (Circuit 532A, 532C or 532D). |
| **A4** CHECK FLI AND PWS CIRCUIT | | |
| • Turn ignition switch ON.<br>• Set multi-meter to read resistance.<br>• Measure the resistance between Breakout box Pins 25 and 27. | Less than 5 ohms ▶<br>Greater than 5 ohms ▶ | GO to Step **A5**.<br>GO to Step **A4a**. |
| **A4a** CHECK FLI ANTI-LOCK WARNING CIRCUIT | | |
| • Disconnect 5-Pin plug on reservoir Fluid Level Indicator (FLI).<br>• Measure resistance between fluid level indicator electrical socket Pins 1 and 2 (with brake fluid level at maximum mark on reservoir).<br>PIN NO. 5; PIN NO. 1; PIN NO. 4; PIN NO. 2; PIN NO. 3; 5-PIN FLUID LEVEL INDICATOR | Less than 2 ohms ▶<br>Greater than 2 ohms ▶ | GO to Step **A4b**.<br>REPLACE fluid level indicator. |

**Fig. 23 Test A, warning lamp On (Part 4 of 24)**

## Anti-Lock Warning Lamp On (With Brake Warning Lamp Off) — Test A

| TEST STEP | RESULT ▶ | ACTION TO TAKE |
|---|---|---|
| **A4b** CHECK PWS ANTI-LOCK WARNING CIRCUIT | | |
| • Disconnect 5-Pin plug at pressure warning switch (PWS).<br>• Check for continuity between pressure warning switch socket Pins 3 and 5.<br>**NOTE: Systems must be pressurized during this test.**<br>PIN NO. 3 / PIN NO. 5 / PRESSURE WARNING SWITCH | Continuity ▶ | GO to Step **A4c**. |
| | No continuity ▶ | REPLACE pressure warning switch. |
| **A4c** CHECK ELECTRONIC MODULE TO FLI WIRE | | |
| • Check for continuity between Breakout box Pin 25 and FLI 5-Pin plug (harness side) Pin 1.<br>PIN NO. 1 / PIN NO. 2 / PIN NO. 3 / PIN NO. 4 / PIN NO. 5 / FLUID LEVEL INDICATOR CONNECTOR | Continuity ▶ | GO to Step **A4d**. |
| | No continuity ▶ | SERVICE or REPLACE cable harness (Circuit 512A). |

**Fig. 23 Test A, warning lamp On (Part 5 of 24)**

## Anti-Lock Warning Lamp On (With Brake Warning Lamp Off) — Test A

| TEST STEP | RESULT ▶ | ACTION TO TAKE |
|---|---|---|
| **A4d** CHECK FLI TO PWS WIRE | | |
| • Check for continuity between Pin 2 of 5-Pin fluid level plug (harness side)<br>PIN NO. 1 / PIN NO. 2 / PIN NO. 3 / PIN NO. 4 / PIN NO. 5 / FLUID LEVEL INDICATOR CONNECTOR<br>and 5-Pin pressure warning switch plug (harness side) Pin 3.<br>PIN NO. 3 / PRESSURE WARNING SWITCH CONNECTOR | Continuity (OK) ▶ | GO to Step **A4e**. |
| | No continuity (~~OK~~) ▶ | SERVICE or REPLACE cable harness (Circuit 549). |
| **A4e** PWS TO ELECTRONIC CONTROLLER WIRE | | |
| • Check for continuity between 5-Pin pressure warning switch plug (harness side) Pin 5<br>PIN NO. 5 / PRESSURE WARNING SWITCH CONNECTOR<br>and Breakout box Pin 27. | Continuity (OK) ▶ | TURN ignition OFF. CONNECT all electrical connections. Reverify symptom. |
| | No continuity (~~OK~~) ▶ | SERVICE or REPLACE cable harness (Circuit 535). |
| **A5** ISOLATION TEST FLI AND PWS | | |
| • Check for continuity between Breakout box Pin 25 and body ground. | Continuity (~~OK~~) ▶ | GO to Step **A5a**. |
| | No continuity (OK) ▶ | GO to Step **A6**. |

**Fig. 23 Test A, warning lamp On (Part 6 of 24)**

## Anti-Lock Warning Lamp On (With Brake Warning Lamp Off) — Test A

| TEST STEP | RESULT ▶ | ACTION TO TAKE |
|---|---|---|
| **A5a** CHECK FLUID LEVEL INDICATOR PIN NO. 2 | | |
| • Disconnect FLI 5-Pin plug and check for continuity between FLI socket Pin 2 and body ground and Pin 1 and body ground.<br>NOTE: Ensure that brake fluid is at max level.<br>PIN NO. 1 / PIN NO. 2 / PIN NO. 3 / PIN NO. 4 / PIN NO. 5 / 5-PIN FLUID LEVEL INDICATOR | Continuity (~~OK~~) ▶ | REPLACE FLI. |
| | No continuity (OK) ▶ | GO to Step **A5b**. |
| **A5b** CHECK FLUID LEVEL INDICATOR PIN NO. 1 | | |
| • Check for continuity between FLI plug Pin 1 (harness side) and body ground.<br>PIN NO. 1 / PIN NO. 2 / PIN NO. 3 / PIN NO. 4 / PIN NO. 5 / FLUID LEVER INDICATOR CONNECTOR | Continuity (~~OK~~) ▶ | SERVICE or REPLACE Circuit 512. |
| | No continuity (OK) ▶ | GO to Step **A5c**. |
| **A5c** CHECK FLUID LEVEL INDICATOR PIN NO. 2 | | |
| • Disconnect 5-Pin plug from PWS. Check for continuity between FLI plug Pin 2 (harness side) and body ground.<br>PIN NO. 1 / PIN NO. 2 / PIN NO. 3 / PIN NO. 4 / PIN NO. 5 / FLUID LEVER INDICATOR CONNECTOR | Continuity (~~OK~~) ▶ | SERVICE or REPLACE Circuit 549. |
| | No continuity (OK) ▶ | GO to Step **A5d**. |

**Fig. 23 Test A, warning lamp On (Part 7 of 24)**

## Anti-Lock Warning Lamp On (With Brake Warning Lamp Off) — Test A

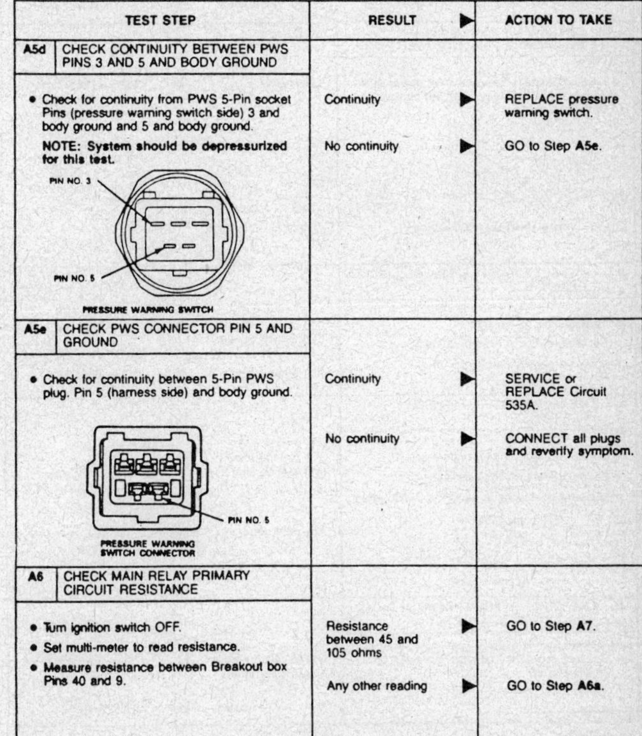

| TEST STEP | RESULT ▶ | ACTION TO TAKE |
|---|---|---|
| **A5d** CHECK CONTINUITY BETWEEN PWS PINS 3 AND 5 AND BODY GROUND | | |
| • Check for continuity from PWS 5-Pin socket Pins (pressure warning switch side) 3 and body ground and 5 and body ground.<br>**NOTE: System should be depressurized for this test.**<br>PIN NO. 3 / PIN NO. 5 / PRESSURE WARNING SWITCH | Continuity ▶ | REPLACE pressure warning switch. |
| | No continuity ▶ | GO to Step **A5e**. |
| **A5e** CHECK PWS CONNECTOR PIN 5 AND GROUND | | |
| • Check for continuity between 5-Pin PWS plug. Pin 5 (harness side) and body ground.<br>PIN NO. 5 / PRESSURE WARNING SWITCH CONNECTOR | Continuity ▶ | SERVICE or REPLACE Circuit 535A. |
| | No continuity ▶ | CONNECT all plugs and reverify symptom. |
| **A6** CHECK MAIN RELAY PRIMARY CIRCUIT RESISTANCE | | |
| • Turn ignition switch OFF.<br>• Set multi-meter to read resistance.<br>• Measure resistance between Breakout box Pins 40 and 9. | Resistance between 45 and 105 ohms ▶ | GO to Step **A7**. |
| | Any other reading ▶ | GO to Step **A6a**. |

**Fig. 23 Test A, warning lamp On (Part 8 of 24)**

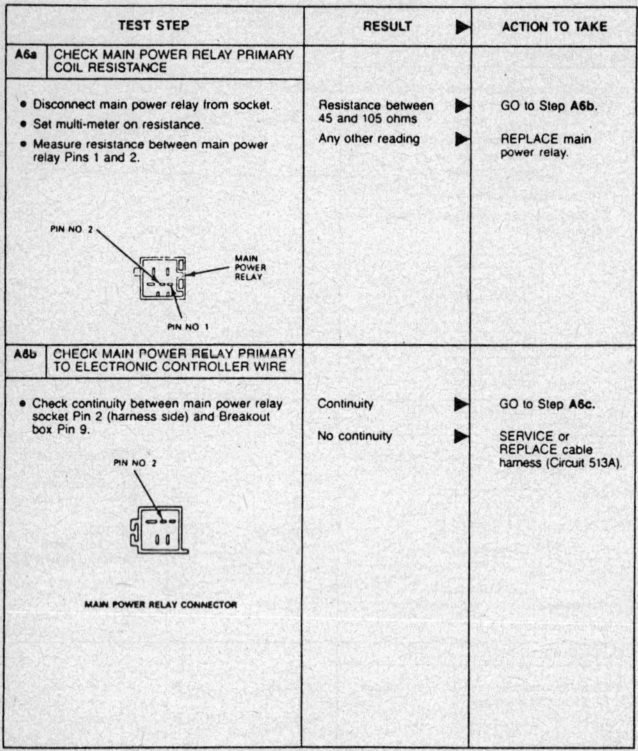

## Anti-Lock Warning Lamp On (With Brake Warning Lamp Off) — Test A

| TEST STEP | RESULT ▶ | ACTION TO TAKE |
|---|---|---|
| **A6a** CHECK MAIN POWER RELAY PRIMARY COIL RESISTANCE | | |
| • Disconnect main power relay from socket.<br>• Set multi-meter on resistance.<br>• Measure resistance between main power relay Pins 1 and 2.<br>PIN NO 2<br>MAIN POWER RELAY<br>PIN NO 1 | Resistance between 45 and 105 ohms ▶<br>Any other reading ▶ | GO to Step **A6b**.<br>REPLACE main power relay. |
| **A6b** CHECK MAIN POWER RELAY PRIMARY TO ELECTRONIC CONTROLLER WIRE | | |
| • Check continuity between main power relay socket Pin 2 (harness side) and Breakout box Pin 9.<br>PIN NO 2<br>MAIN POWER RELAY CONNECTOR | Continuity ▶<br>No continuity ▶ | GO to Step **A6c**.<br>SERVICE or REPLACE cable harness (Circuit 513A). |

**Fig. 23 Test A, warning lamp On (Part 9 of 24)**

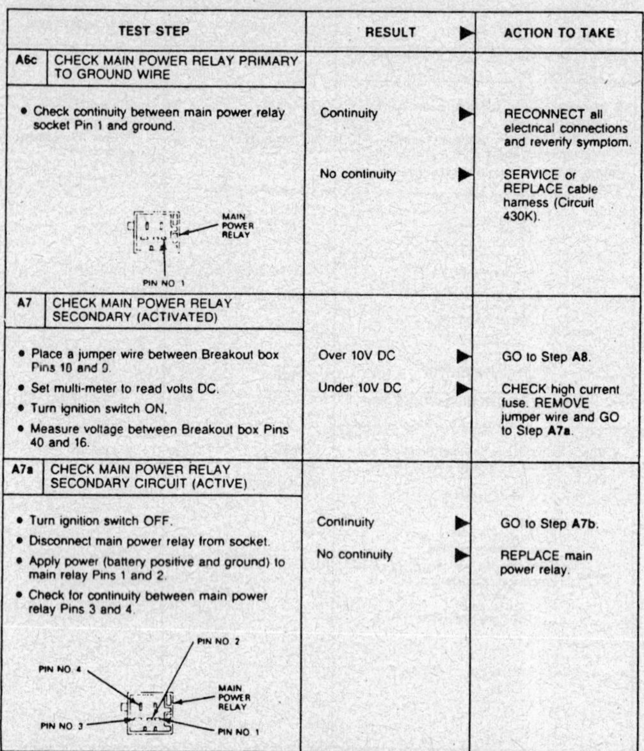

## Anti-Lock Warning Lamp On (With Brake Warning Lamp Off) — Test A

| TEST STEP | RESULT ▶ | ACTION TO TAKE |
|---|---|---|
| **A6c** CHECK MAIN POWER RELAY PRIMARY TO GROUND WIRE | | |
| • Check continuity between main power relay socket Pin 1 and ground.<br>MAIN POWER RELAY<br>PIN NO 1 | Continuity ▶<br>No continuity ▶ | RECONNECT all electrical connections and reverify symptom.<br>SERVICE or REPLACE cable harness (Circuit 430K). |
| **A7** CHECK MAIN POWER RELAY SECONDARY (ACTIVATED) | | |
| • Place a jumper wire between Breakout box Pins 10 and 9.<br>• Set multi-meter to read volts DC.<br>• Turn ignition switch ON.<br>• Measure voltage between Breakout box Pins 40 and 16. | Over 10V DC ▶<br>Under 10V DC ▶ | GO to Step **A8**.<br>CHECK high current fuse. REMOVE jumper wire and GO to Step **A7a**. |
| **A7a** CHECK MAIN POWER RELAY SECONDARY CIRCUIT (ACTIVE) | | |
| • Turn ignition switch OFF.<br>• Disconnect main power relay from socket.<br>• Apply power (battery positive and ground) to main relay Pins 1 and 2.<br>• Check for continuity between main power relay Pins 3 and 4.<br>PIN NO 2<br>PIN NO 4<br>MAIN POWER RELAY<br>PIN NO 3<br>PIN NO 1 | Continuity ▶<br>No continuity ▶ | GO to Step **A7b**.<br>REPLACE main power relay. |

**Fig. 23 Test A, warning lamp On (Part 10 of 24)**

## Anti-Lock Warning Lamp On (With Brake Warning Lamp Off) — Test A

| TEST STEP | RESULT ▶ | ACTION TO TAKE |
|---|---|---|
| **A7b** CHECK MAIN POWER RELAY SECONDARY CIRCUIT POWER WIRE | | |
| • Check continuity between main power relay socket Pin 4 (harness side) and positive battery terminal.<br>PIN NO 4<br>MAIN POWER RELAY CONNECTOR | Continuity ▶<br>No continuity ▶ | RECONNECT main power relay and reverify symptom.<br>SERVICE or REPLACE cable harness (Circuit 533C) or high current fuse (Circuit 038Z). |
| **A8** MEASURE RH REAR SENSOR CIRCUIT RESISTANCE | | |
| • Turn ignition switch OFF.<br>• Set multi-meter to read resistance.<br>• Measure resistance between Breakout box Pin 6 and 23. | 800 to 1400 ohms (0.8 to 1.4K ohms) ▶<br>Any other reading ▶ | GO to Step **A9**.<br>GO to Step **A8a**. |
| **A8a** MEASURE RH REAR SENSOR RESISTANCE | | |
| • Disconnect sensor plug (right rear).<br>• Set multi-meter to read resistance.<br>• Measure resistance of sensor at sensor plug.<br>RH REAR SENSOR | 800 to 1400 ohms (0.8 to 1.4K ohms) ▶<br>Any other reading ▶ | SERVICE or REPLACE cable harness (Circuit 523 or 524).<br>REPLACE right rear wheel sensor. |
| **A9** MEASURE LH FRONT SENSOR CIRCUIT RESISTANCE | | |
| • Measure resistance between Breakout box Pins 5 and 22. | 800 to 1400 ohms (0.8 to 1.4K ohms) ▶<br>Any other reading ▶ | GO to Step **A10**.<br>GO to Step **A9a**. |

**Fig. 23 Test A, warning lamp On (Part 11 of 24)**

## Anti-Lock Warning Lamp On (With Brake Warning Lamp Off) — Test A

| TEST STEP | RESULT ▶ | ACTION TO TAKE |
|---|---|---|
| **A9a** MEASURE LH FRONT SENSOR RESISTANCE | | |
| • Disconnect sensor plug (left front).<br>• Measure resistance of sensor at sensor plug.<br>LH FRONT SENSOR | 800 to 1400 ohms (0.8 to 1.4K ohms) ▶<br>Any other reading ▶ | SERVICE or REPLACE cable harness (Circuit 521 or 522).<br>REPLACE left front wheel sensor. |
| **A10** MEASURE LH REAR SENSOR CIRCUIT RESISTANCE | | |
| • Measure resistance between Breakout box Pins 4 and 21. | 800 to 1400 ohms (0.8 to 1.4K ohms) ▶<br>Any other reading ▶ | GO to Step **A11**.<br>GO to Step **A10a**. |
| **A10a** MEASURE LH REAR SENSOR RESISTANCE | | |
| • Disconnect sensor plug (left rear).<br>• Measure resistance of sensor at left rear sensor plug.<br>LH REAR SENSOR | 800 to 1400 ohms (0.8 to 1.4K ohms) ▶<br>Any other reading ▶ | SERVICE or REPLACE cable harness (Circuit 518 or 519).<br>REPLACE left rear wheel sensor. |
| **A11** MEASURE RH FRONT SENSOR CIRCUIT RESISTANCE | | |
| • Measure resistance between Breakout box Pins 3 and 20. | 800 to 1400 ohms (0.8 to 1.4K ohms) ▶<br>Any other reading ▶ | GO to Step **A12**.<br>GO to Step **A11a**. |

**Fig. 23 Test A, warning lamp On (Part 12 of 24)**

## Anti-Lock Warning Lamp On (With Brake Warning Lamp Off) — Test A

| TEST STEP | RESULT ▶ | ACTION TO TAKE |
|---|---|---|
| **A11a** MEASURE RH FRONT SENSOR RESISTANCE | | |
| • Disconnect sensor plug (RH front).<br>• Measure resistance of sensor at sensor plug.<br>RH FRONT SENSOR | 800 to 1400 ohms (0.8 to 1.4K ohms) ▶ | SERVICE or REPLACE cable harness (Circuit 514 or 516). |
| | Any other reading ▶ | REPLACE RH front wheel sensor. |
| **A12** MEASURE MAIN VALVE CIRCUIT RESISTANCE | | |
| • Turn ignition switch OFF.<br>• Set multi-meter to read resistance.<br>• Measure the resistance between Breakout box Pins 11 and 29. | 2 to 5 ohms ▶ | GO to Step **A13**. |
| | Any other reading ▶ | GO to Step **A12a**. |
| **A12a** MEASURE MAIN VALVE RESISTANCE | | |
| • Disconnect main valve 2-Pin plug.<br>• Measure resistance between the main valve electrical Pins 1 and 2.<br>PIN NO. 2 PIN NO. 1 | 2 to 5.5 ohms ▶ | REPLACE or SERVICE cable harness (Circuit 430E or 493A). |
| | Any other reading ▶ | REPLACE actuation assembly. |
| **A13** CHECK VALVE BLOCK GROUND CIRCUIT | | |
| • Measure resistance between Breakout box Pins 11 and 40. | Less than 2 ohms ▶ | GO to Step **A14**. |
| | Greater than 2 ohms ▶ | GO to Step **A13a**. |

**Fig. 23 Test A, warning lamp On (Part 13 of 24)**

## Anti-Lock Warning Lamp On (With Brake Warning Lamp Off) — Test A

| TEST STEP | RESULT ▶ | ACTION TO TAKE |
|---|---|---|
| **A13a** TEST VALVE PLUG PIN NO. 7 | | |
| • Disconnect valve block 7-Pin plug.<br>• Measure resistance between valve block electrical Pin 7 and valve block body.<br>PIN NO. 7<br>VALVE BLOCK 7-PIN CONNECTOR | Less than 2 ohms ▶ | SERVICE or REPLACE cable harness (Circuit 511B). |
| | Greater than 2 ohms ▶ | GO to Step **A13b**. |
| **A13b** CHECK ACTUATION ASSEMBLY GROUND WIRE | | |
| • Remove negative (−) ground strap from battery.<br>• Check for continuity between actuation assembly and body ground. | Continuity ▶ | Go to Step **A14**. |
| | No or Poor continuity ▶ | SERVICE or REPLACE actuation assembly ground strap (Circuit 430C). |
| **A14** MEASURE RH FRONT INLET VALVE CIRCUIT RESISTANCE | | |
| • Measure resistance between Breakout box Pins 11 and 32. | 5 to 8 ohms ▶ | GO to Step **A15**. |
| | Any other reading ▶ | GO to Step **A14a**. |

**Fig. 23 Test A, warning lamp On (Part 14 of 24)**

## Anti-Lock Warning Lamp On (With Brake Warning Lamp Off) — Test A

| TEST STEP | RESULT ▶ | ACTION TO TAKE |
|---|---|---|
| **A14a** MEASURE RH FRONT INLET VALVE RESISTANCE | | |
| • Disconnect valve block 7-Pin plug.<br>• Measure resistance between valve block electrical Pin 7 and 1.<br>PIN NO 1<br>PIN NO 7<br>VALVE BLOCK 7-PIN CONNECTOR | 5 to 8 ohms ▶ | SERVICE or REPLACE cable harness (Circuit 510A). |
| | Any other reading ▶ | REPlACE solenoid valve block unit. CONNECT 7-Pin plug. |
| **A15** MEASURE REAR INLET VALVE CIRCUIT RESISTANCE | | |
| • Measure resistance between Breakout box Pins 11 and 30. | 5 to 8 ohms ▶ | GO to Step **A16**. |
| | Any other reading ▶ | GO to Step **A15a**. |

**Fig. 23 Test A, warning lamp On (Part 15 of 24)**

## Anti-Lock Warning Lamp On (With Brake Warning Lamp Off) — Test A

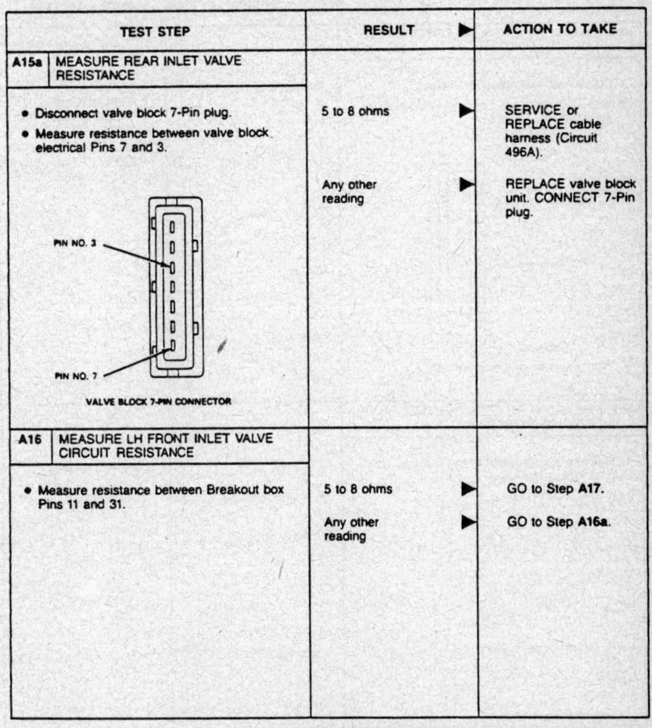

| TEST STEP | RESULT ▶ | ACTION TO TAKE |
|---|---|---|
| **A15a** MEASURE REAR INLET VALVE RESISTANCE | | |
| • Disconnect valve block 7-Pin plug.<br>• Measure resistance between valve block electrical Pins 7 and 3.<br>PIN NO. 3<br>PIN NO. 7<br>VALVE BLOCK 7-PIN CONNECTOR | 5 to 8 ohms ▶ | SERVICE or REPLACE cable harness (Circuit 496A). |
| | Any other reading ▶ | REPLACE valve block unit. CONNECT 7-Pin plug. |
| **A16** MEASURE LH FRONT INLET VALVE CIRCUIT RESISTANCE | | |
| • Measure resistance between Breakout box Pins 11 and 31. | 5 to 8 ohms ▶ | GO to Step **A17**. |
| | Any other reading ▶ | GO to Step **A16a**. |

**Fig. 23 Test A, warning lamp On (Part 16 of 24)**

## Anti-Lock Warning Lamp On (With Brake Warning Lamp Off) — Test A

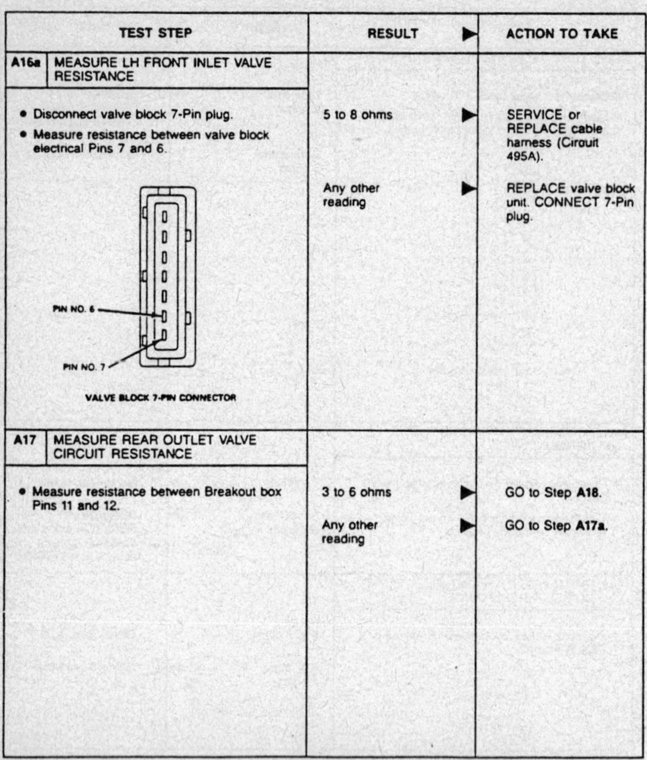

| TEST STEP | RESULT ▶ | ACTION TO TAKE |
|---|---|---|
| **A16a** MEASURE LH FRONT INLET VALVE RESISTANCE | | |
| • Disconnect valve block 7-Pin plug.<br>• Measure resistance between valve block electrical Pins 7 and 6. | 5 to 8 ohms ▶ | SERVICE or REPLACE cable harness (Circuit 495A). |
| | Any other reading ▶ | REPLACE valve block unit. CONNECT 7-Pin plug. |
| **A17** MEASURE REAR OUTLET VALVE CIRCUIT RESISTANCE | | |
| • Measure resistance between Breakout box Pins 11 and 12. | 3 to 6 ohms ▶ | GO to Step **A18**. |
| | Any other reading ▶ | GO to Step **A17a**. |



**Fig. 23 Test A, warning lamp On (Part 17 of 24)**

## Anti-Lock Warning Lamp On (With Brake Warning Lamp Off) — Test A

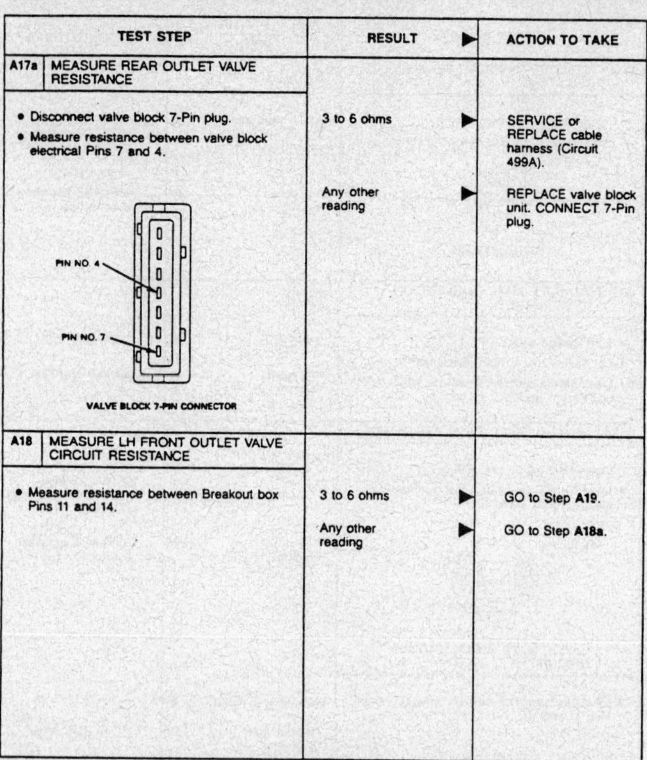

| TEST STEP | RESULT ▶ | ACTION TO TAKE |
|---|---|---|
| **A17a** MEASURE REAR OUTLET VALVE RESISTANCE | | |
| • Disconnect valve block 7-Pin plug.<br>• Measure resistance between valve block electrical Pins 7 and 4. | 3 to 6 ohms ▶ | SERVICE or REPLACE cable harness (Circuit 499A). |
| | Any other reading ▶ | REPLACE valve block unit. CONNECT 7-Pin plug. |
| **A18** MEASURE LH FRONT OUTLET VALVE CIRCUIT RESISTANCE | | |
| • Measure resistance between Breakout box Pins 11 and 14. | 3 to 6 ohms ▶ | GO to Step **A19**. |
| | Any other reading ▶ | GO to Step **A18a**. |



**Fig. 23 Test A, warning lamp On (Part 18 of 24)**

## Anti-Lock Warning Lamp On (With Brake Warning Lamp Off) — Test A

| TEST STEP | RESULT ▶ | ACTION TO TAKE |
|---|---|---|
| **A18a** MEASURE LH FRONT OUTLET VALVE RESISTANCE | | |
| • Disconnect valve block 7-Pin plug.<br>• Measure resistance between valve block electrical Pin 7 and 5. | 3 to 6 ohms ▶ | SERVICE or REPLACE cable harness (Circuit 498A). |
| | Any other reading ▶ | REPLACE valve block unit. CONNECT 7-Pin plug. |
| PIN NO. 5<br>PIN NO. 7<br>VALVE BLOCK 7-PIN CONNECTOR | | |
| **A19** MEASURE RH FRONT OUTLET VALVE CIRCUIT RESISTANCE | | |
| • Measure resistance between Breakout box Pins 11 and 13. | 3 to 6 ohms ▶ | GO to Step **A20**. |
| | Any other reading ▶ | GO to Step **A19a**. |

**Fig. 23 Test A, warning lamp On (Part 19 of 24)**

## Anti-Lock Warning Lamp On (With Brake Warning Lamp Off) — Test A

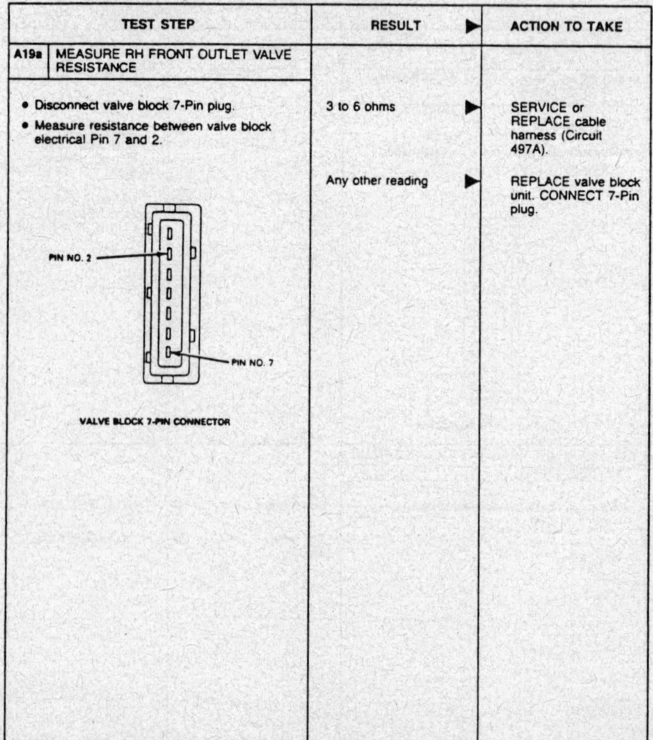

| TEST STEP | RESULT ▶ | ACTION TO TAKE |
|---|---|---|
| **A19a** MEASURE RH FRONT OUTLET VALVE RESISTANCE | | |
| • Disconnect valve block 7-Pin plug.<br>• Measure resistance between valve block electrical Pin 7 and 2. | 3 to 6 ohms ▶ | SERVICE or REPLACE cable harness (Circuit 497A). |
| | Any other reading ▶ | REPLACE valve block unit. CONNECT 7-Pin plug. |



**Fig. 23 Test A, warning lamp On (Part 20 of 24)**

## Anti-Lock Warning Lamp On (With Brake Warning Lamp Off) — Test A

| TEST STEP | RESULT ▶ | ACTION TO TAKE |
|---|---|---|
| **A20** CHECK PWS BRAKELAMP CIRCUIT (WITH SYSTEM PRESSURE) | | |
| • Vehicle must be cooled to room temperature.<br>• Discharge the brake system as follows:<br>a. Turn ignition switch to OFF.<br>b. Pump brake pedal at least 20 times until you feel the pedal become hard.<br>• Disconnect pressure warning switch 5-pin plug<br>• Check continuity between pressure warning switch electrical Pins 1 and 2. | Continuity (OK) ▶<br>No continuity (NOT OK) ▶ | GO to Step **A21**.<br>REPLACE pressure warning switch and pump motor relay. |

PIN NO. 1
PIN NO. 2
PRESSURE WARNING SWITCH

**Fig. 23 Test A, warning lamp On (Part 21 of 24)**

## Anti-Lock Warning Lamp On (With Brake Warning Lamp Off) — Test A

| TEST STEP | RESULT ▶ | ACTION TO TAKE |
|---|---|---|
| **A21** CHECK PWS BRAKELAMP CIRCUIT (WITH SYSTEM PRESSURE) | | |
| • Reconnect pressure warning switch 5-pin plug.<br>• Turn ignition switch to ON.<br>When pump motor stops, turn ignition switch to OFF.<br>• Disconnect pressure warning switch 5-pin plug again.<br>• Check for continuity between pressure warning switch electrical Pins 1 and 2. | Continuity (NOT OK) ▶<br>No continuity (OK) ▶ | REPLACE pressure warning switch and pump motor relay.<br>GO to Step **A22**. |

PIN NO. 1
PIN NO. 2
PRESSURE WARNING SWITCH

**Fig. 23 Test A, warning lamp On (Part 22 of 24)**

## Anti-Lock Warning Lamp On (With Brake Warning Lamp Off) — Test A

| TEST STEP | RESULT ▶ | ACTION TO TAKE |
|---|---|---|
| **A22** CHECK PWS BRAKE LAMP CIRCUIT THRESHOLD | | |
| **WARNING: BEFORE DISCONNECTING ANY HYDRAULIC LINES, YOU MUST ENSURE THAT THE PRESSURE SYSTEM IS DISCHARGED.**<br>• Discharge the brake system as follows:<br>a. Turn ignition switch OFF.<br>b. Pump brake pedal at least 20 times until you feel the pedal become hard.<br>• Remove accumulator.<br>• Install Pressure Gauge Adapter T88P-20215-AH or equivalent.<br>NOTE: Be sure sealing washers are installed correctly.<br>• Install accumulator.<br>• Connect Anti-Lock High Pressure Gauge to gauge nipple.<br>**WARNING: DO NOT DISCONNECT ANTI-LOCK HIGH PRESSURE GAUGE WHILE SYSTEM IS UNDER PRESSURE.**<br>• Reconnect pressure warning switch (PWS) 5-Pin connector.<br>• Turn ignition switch to ON.<br>• When pump motor stops, disconnect pressure warning switch (PWS) 5-pin plug.<br>• Lower hydraulic accumulator pressure by slowly pumping the brake pedal until you have continuity between pressure warning switch electrical Pins 1 and 2.<br>• Observe the hydraulic pressure gauge when continuity is reached.<br>• If you missed the reading or want to reverify the reading:<br>— Reconnect the 5-pin plug.<br>— Turn the ignition switch on until the pump stops.<br>— Disconnect the 5-pin plug and reverify the readings. | 100-110 Bar (1,450-1,595 psi) ▶<br>Any other reading ▶ | GO to Step **A23**.<br>REPLACE pressure warning switch and pump motor relay. |

PIN NO. 1
PIN NO. 2
PRESSURE WARNING SWITCH

**Fig. 23 Test A, warning lamp On (Part 23 of 24)**

## Anti-Lock Warning Lamp On (With Brake Warning Lamp Off) — Test A

| TEST STEP | RESULT ▶ | ACTION TO TAKE |
|---|---|---|
| **A23** CHECK PWS HARNESS GROUND | | |
| • Check for continuity between pressure warning switch 5-pin plug Pin 1 and body ground (harness side). | Continuity ▶<br>No continuity ▶ | GO to Step **A24**.<br>SERVICE or REPLACE cable harness (Circuit 430H). |
| **A24** REVERIFY SYSTEM SYMPTOM | | |
| • Reconnect all electrical connections.<br>• Remove Pressure Gauge Adaptor.<br>• Install accumulator.<br>**WARNING: Before disconnecting any hydraulic lines, you must ensure that the brake hydraulic pressure system is discharged.**<br>• Discharge the brake system as follows:<br>a. Turn ignition switch to OFF.<br>b. Pump brake pedal at least 20 times until you feel the pedal become hard.<br>• Reverify symptom. | Symptom not present ▶<br>Symptom still present ▶ | FAULT may have been a loose electrical connection.<br>REPLACE electronic control module. |

PIN NO. 1
PRESSURE WARNING SWITCH HARNESS CONNECTOR

**Fig. 23 Test A, warning lamp On (Part 24 of 24)**

## Anti-Lock Lamp On After Engine Starts (Brake Warning Lamp Off) — Test B

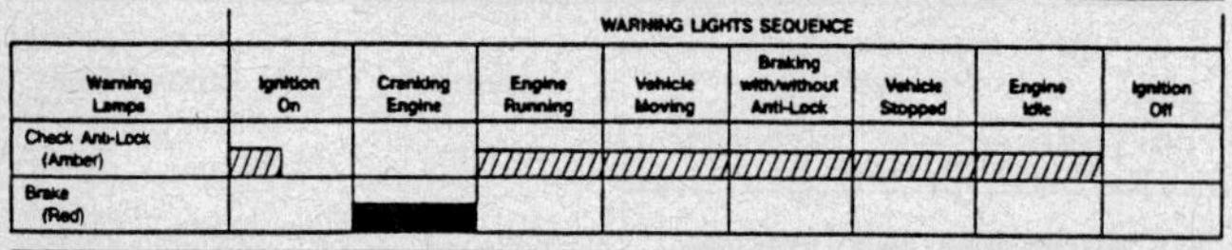

| Warning Lamps | Ignition On | Cranking Engine | Engine Running | Vehicle Moving | Braking with/without Anti-Lock | Vehicle Stopped | Engine Idle | Ignition Off |
|---|---|---|---|---|---|---|---|---|
| | WARNING LIGHTS SEQUENCE | | | | | | | |
| Check Anti-Lock (Amber) | | | | | | | | |
| Brake (Red) | | | | | | | | |

| TEST STEP | RESULT ▶ | ACTION TO TAKE |
|---|---|---|
| **B1** CHECK CONTINUITY OF CIRCUIT 523 AND 524 | | |
| • Ignition switch Off.<br>• Disconnect 32-pin plug from controller.<br>• Connect EEC-IV Breakout box T83L-50-EEC-IV with Anti-Lock Test Adapter T87P-50-ALA to the Anti-Lock 32-pin plug wiring harness.<br>• Check continuity between Breakout box Pins 40 and 6. | Continuity ▶<br>No continuity ▶ | GO to Step **B1a**.<br>GO to Step **B2**. |
| **B1a** CHECK CONTINUITY OF RH REAR SENSOR | | |
| • Disconnect wheel sensor plug (RH rear).<br>• Check for continuity between each sensor plug pin (sensor side) and vehicle ground. <br>RH REAR SENSOR | Continuity ▶<br>No continuity ▶ | REPLACE sensor (RH rear).<br>REPLACE or SERVICE cable harness (523 or 524). RECONNECT sensor plug. |
| **B2** CHECK CONTINUITY OF CIRCUIT 521 AND 522 | | |
| • Check for continuity between Breakout box Pins 40 and 5. | Continuity ▶<br>No continuity ▶ | GO to Step **B2a**.<br>GO to Step **B3**. |

**Fig. 24 Test B, ABS lamp On after engine starts (Part 1 of 3)**

## Anti-Lock Lamp On After Engine Starts (Brake Warning Lamp Off) — Test B

| TEST STEP | RESULT ▶ | ACTION TO TAKE |
|---|---|---|
| **B2a** CHECK CONTINUITY OF LH FRONT SENSOR | | |
| • Disconnect wheel sensor plug (LH front).<br>• Check for continuity between each sensor plug pin (sensor side) and vehicle ground. <br>LH FRONT SENSOR | Continuity ▶<br>No continuity ▶ | REPLACE sensor (LH front).<br>REPLACE or SERVICE cable harness. (521 or 522) CONNECT sensor plug. |
| **B3** CHECK CONTINUITY OF CIRCUIT 518 AND 519 | | |
| • Check for continuity between Breakout box Pins 40 and 4. | Continuity ▶<br>No continuity ▶ | GO to Step **B3a**.<br>GO to Step **B4**. |
| **B3a** CHECK CONTINUITY OF LH REAR SENSOR | | |
| • Disconnect sensor plug (LH rear).<br>• Check for continuity between each sensor plug pin (sensor side) and vehicle ground. <br>LH REAR SENSOR | Continuity ▶<br>No continuity ▶ | REPLACE sensor (LH rear).<br>REPLACE or SERVICE cable harness. (518 or 519) CONNECT sensor plug. |

**Fig. 24 Test B, ABS lamp On after engine starts (Part 2 of 3)**

## Anti-Lock Lamp On After Engine Starts (Brake Warning Lamp Off) — Test B

| TEST STEP | RESULT ▶ | ACTION TO TAKE |
|---|---|---|
| **B4** CHECK CONTINUITY OF CIRCUIT 514 AND 516 | | |
| • Check for continuity between Breakout box Pins 40 and 3. | Continuity ▶<br>No continuity ▶ | GO to Step **B4a**.<br>Test complete. If Anti-Lock lamp pattern remains, REPEAT Test B. |
| **B4a** CHECK CONTINUITY OF RH FRONT SENSOR | | |
| • Disconnect wheel sensor plug (RH front).<br>• Check for continuity between each sensor plug pin (sensor side) and vehicle ground. <br>RH FRONT SENSOR | Continuity ▶<br>No Continuity ▶ | REPLACE RH front sensor.<br>REPLACE or SERVICE cable harness. (514 or 516) CONNECT sensor plug. |

**Fig. 24 Test B, ABS lamp On after engine starts (Part 3 of 3)**

## Anti-Lock Warning Lamp On After Vehicle Starts To Move Or False Cycling Of Anti-Lock System — Test C

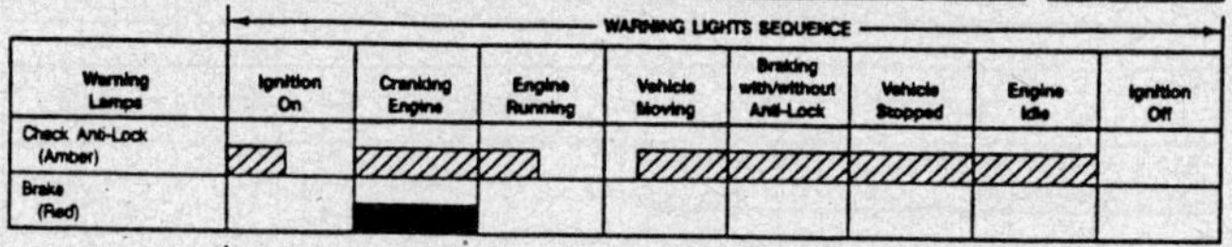

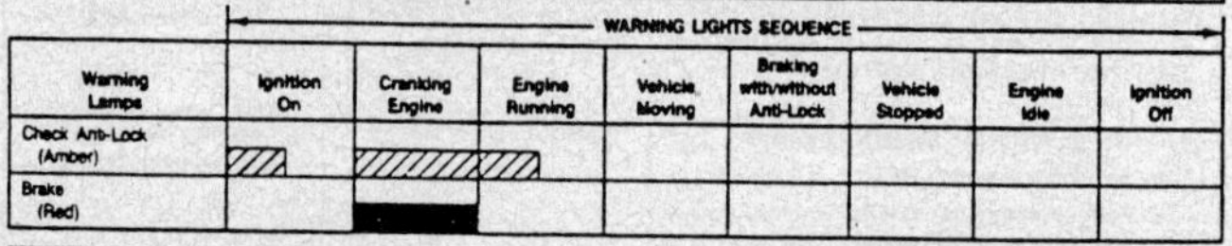

| Warning Lamps | Ignition On | Cranking Engine | Engine Running | Vehicle Moving | Braking with/without Anti-Lock | Vehicle Stopped | Engine Idle | Ignition Off |
|---|---|---|---|---|---|---|---|---|
| | WARNING LIGHTS SEQUENCE | | | | | | | |
| Check Anti-Lock (Amber) | | | | | | | | |
| Brake (Red) | | | | | | | | |

| Warning Lamps | Ignition On | Cranking Engine | Engine Running | Vehicle Moving | Braking with/without Anti-Lock | Vehicle Stopped | Engine Idle | Ignition Off |
|---|---|---|---|---|---|---|---|---|
| | WARNING LIGHTS SEQUENCE | | | | | | | |
| Check Anti-Lock (Amber) | | | | | | | | |
| Brake (Red) | | | | | | | | |

| TEST STEP | RESULT ▶ | ACTION TO TAKE |
|---|---|---|
| **C1** MEASURE RH REAR SENSOR CIRCUIT RESISTANCE | | |
| • Turn ignition switch OFF.<br>• Disconnect 32-Pin plug from electronic controller.<br>• Connect EEC-IV Breakout Box Tool T83L-50-EEC-IV and Anti-Lock Test Adapter Tool T87P-50-ALA or equivalent to anti-lock 32-Pin connector.<br>• Set multi-meter to read resistance.<br>• Measure resistance between Breakout box Pins 6 and 23. | 800 to 1400 ohms (0.8 to 1.4K ohms) ▶<br>Any other reading ▶ | GO to Step **C2**.<br>GO to Step **C1a**. |
| **C1a** MEASURE RH REAR SENSOR RESISTANCE | | |
| • Disconnect sensor plug (RH rear).<br>• Set multi-meter to read resistance.<br>• Measure resistance of sensor at sensor plug. <br>RH REAR SENSOR | 800 to 1400 ohms (0.8 to 1.4K ohms) ▶<br>Any other reading ▶ | SERVICE or REPLACE cable harness (Circuit 523 or 524).<br>REPLACE RH rear wheel sensor. |

**Fig. 25 Test C, warning lamp On after vehicle moves/or false cycling of system (Part 1 of 5)**

| Anti-Lock Warning Lamp On After Vehicle Starts To Move Or False Cycling Of Anti-Lock System | Test C |
|---|---|

| TEST STEP | RESULT ▶ | ACTION TO TAKE |
|---|---|---|
| **C2** MEASURE LH FRONT SENSOR CIRCUIT RESISTANCE | | |
| • Measure resistance between Breakout box Pins 5 and 22. | 800 to 1400 ohms (0.8 to 1.4K ohms) (OK) ▶ | GO to Step **C3**. |
| | Any other reading ~~(OK)~~ ▶ | GO to Step **C2a**. |
| **C2a** MEASURE LH FRONT SENSOR RESISTANCE | | |
| • Disconnect wheel sensor plug (LH rear).<br>• Measure resistance of sensor at sensor plug.<br>LH FRONT SENSOR | 800 to 1400 ohms (0.8 to 1.4K ohms) (OK) ▶ | SERVICE or REPLACE cable harness (Circuit 521 or 522). |
| | Any other reading ~~(OK)~~ ▶ | REPLACE LH front wheel sensor. |
| **C3** MEASURE LH REAR SENSOR CIRCUIT RESISTANCE | | |
| • Measure resistance between Breakout box Pins 4 and 21. | 800 to 1400 ohms (0.8 to 1.4K ohms) (OK) ▶ | GO to Step **C4**. |
| | Any other reading ~~(OK)~~ ▶ | GO to Step **C3a**. |

**Fig. 25 Test C, warning lamp On after vehicle moves/or false cycling of system (Part 2 of 5)**

| Anti-Lock Warning Lamp On After Vehicle Starts To Move Or False Cycling Of Anti-Lock System | Test C |
|---|---|

| TEST STEP | RESULT ▶ | ACTION TO TAKE |
|---|---|---|
| **C3a** MEASURE LH REAR SENSOR RESISTANCE | | |
| • Disconnect sensor plug (LH rear).<br>• Measure resistance of sensor at left rear sensor plug.<br>LH REAR SENSOR | 800 to 1400 ohms (0.8 to 1.4K ohms) ▶ | SERVICE or REPLACE cable harness (Circuit 518 or 519). |
| | Any other reading ▶ | REPLACE LH rear wheel sensor. |
| **C4** MEASURE RH FRONT SENSOR CIRCUIT RESISTANCE | | |
| • Measure resistance between Breakout box Pins 3 and 20. | 800 to 1400 ohms (0.8 to 1.4K ohms) ▶ | GO to Step **C5**. |
| | Any other reading ▶ | GO to Step **C4a**. |
| **C4a** MEASURE RH FRONT SENSOR RESISTANCE | | |
| • Disconnect sensor plug (RH front).<br>• Measure resistance of sensor at sensor plug.<br>RH FRONT SENSOR | 800 to 1400 ohms (0.8 to 1.4K ohms) ▶ | SERVICE or REPLACE cable harness (Circuit 514 or 516). |
| | Any other reading ▶ | REPLACE RH front wheel sensor. |

**Fig. 25 Test C, warning lamp On after vehicle moves/or false cycling of system (Part 3 of 5)**

| Anti-Lock Warning Lamp On After Vehicle Starts To Move Or False Cycling Of Anti-Lock System | Test C |
|---|---|

| TEST STEP | RESULT ▶ | ACTION TO TAKE |
|---|---|---|
| **C5** CHECK RH REAR SENSOR | | |
| • Turn ignition switch OFF.<br>• Turn air suspension switch in luggage compartment OFF, if so equipped.<br>• Place vehicle on hoist and raise wheels clear of ground. Refer to Pre-Delivery Manual Section 50-04.<br>• Set multi-meter on voltage range (2V-AC).<br>• Measure voltage between Breakout box Pins 6 and 23 while spinning RH rear wheel at approximately 1 revolution per second. | Between 0.05 and 0.70 Vac (OK) ▶ | GO to Step **C6**. |
| | Less than 0.05 or more than 0.70 Vac ~~(OK)~~ ▶ | CHECK sensor mounting, air gap, or toothed wheel mounting. CORRECT as required. |
| **C6** CHECK LH FRONT SENSOR | | |
| • Measure voltage between Breakout box Pins 5 and 22 while spinning LH front wheel at approximately 1 revolution per second. | Between 0.05 and 0.70 Vac ▶ | GO to Step **C7**. |
| | Less than 0.05 or more than 0.70 Vac ▶ | CHECK sensor mounting, air gap, or toothed wheel mounting. CORRECT as required. |
| **C7** CHECK LH REAR SENSOR | | |
| • Measure voltage between Breakout box Pins 4 and 21 while spinning LH rear wheel at approximately 1 revolution per second. | Between 0.05 and 0.70 Vac ▶ | GO to Step **C8**. |
| | Less than 0.05 or more than 0.07 Vac ▶ | CHECK wheel sensor mounting, air gap, or toothed wheel mounting. CORRECT as required. |

**Fig. 25 Test C, warning lamp On after vehicle moves/or false cycling of system (Part 4 of 5)**

| Anti-Lock Warning Lamp on After Vehicle Starts to Move or False Cycling of Anti-Lock System | Test C |
|---|---|

| TEST STEP | RESULT ▶ | ACTION TO TAKE |
|---|---|---|
| **C8** CHECK RH FRONT SENSOR | | |
| • Measure voltage between Breakout box Pins 3 and 20 while spinning RH front wheel at approximately 1 revolution per second. | Between 0.05 and 0.70 Vac ▶ | GO to Step **C9**. |
| | Less than 0.05 or more than 0.70 Vac ▶ | CHECK wheel sensor mounting, air gap, or toothed wheel mounting. CORRECT as required. |
| **C9** CHECK FRONT WHEEL BEARINGS | | |
| • Check front wheel bearing end play.<br>• Inspect each toothed sensor ring visually for damaged teeth.<br>NOTE: Turn air suspension switch ON when vehicle is off hoist. | Loose or damaged parts ▶ | ADJUST bearings or REPLACE faulty parts. |
| | Not loose or damaged ▶ | REVERIFY symptom. |

**Fig. 25 Test C, warning lamp On after vehicle moves/or false cycling of system (Part 5 of 5)**

| Anti-Lock Warning Lamp And Brake Warning Lamp On And/Or Pump Motor Runs More Than 60 Seconds | Test D |
|---|---|

WARNING LIGHTS SEQUENCE

| Warning Lamps | Ignition On | Cranking Engine | Engine Running | Vehicle Moving | Braking with/without Anti-Lock | Vehicle Stopped | Engine Idle | Ignition Off |
|---|---|---|---|---|---|---|---|---|
| Check Anti-Lock (Amber) | | | | | | | | |
| Brake (Red) | | | | | | | | |

WARNING LIGHTS SEQUENCE

| Warning Lamps | Ignition On | Cranking Engine | Engine Running | Vehicle Moving | Braking with without Anti-Lock | Vehicle Stopped | Engine Idle | Ignition Off |
|---|---|---|---|---|---|---|---|---|
| Check Anti-Lock (Amber) | | | | | | | | |
| Brake (Red) | | | | | | | | |

| TEST STEP | RESULT ▶ | ACTION TO TAKE |
|---|---|---|
| **D1** CHECK PUMP MOTOR OPERATION | | |
| • Turn ignition OFF.<br>• Pump brake pedal at least 20 times until it becomes hard.<br>• Turn ignition switch ON.<br>• Pump motor should run.<br>**NOTE: If pump motor is allowed to run continuously for approximately 20 minutes, a thermal safety switch (inside motor) will shut off motor. A 2-to-10 minute cool-down period is typical before normal operation can resume.** | OK ▶<br>Not OK ▶ | GO to **D2**.<br>GO to **D1a**. |

**Fig. 26 Test D, warning lamp & brake warning lamp On and/or pump motor runs more than 60 seconds (Part 1 of 10)**

| Anti-Lock Warning Lamp And Brake Warning Lamp On And/Or Pump Motor Runs More Than 60 Seconds | Test D |
|---|---|

| TEST STEP | RESULT ▶ | ACTION TO TAKE |
|---|---|---|
| **D1a** PUMP MOTOR UNIT | | |
| • Disconnect 4-pin plug on pump motor unit.<br>• Turn ignition switch ON.<br>• Set multi-meter on 20 Volt DC.<br>• Connect meter to the 4-pin plug on the harness side. (Use one negative and one positive pin).<br>• Observe voltmeter.<br>POSITIVE PIN / NEGATIVE PIN / NEGATIVE PIN / POSITIVE PIN<br>4-PIN MOTOR CONNECTOR | More than 10V DC ▶<br>Less than 10V DC ▶ | GO to D2.<br>GO to D1b. |
| **D1b** CHECK CONTINUITY CIRCUITS 538A, 538B AND 538C | | |
| • Disconnect pump motor relay.<br>• Check for continuity between motor relay socket Pin 3 (harness side) and each positive pin of the 4-pin motor connector (harness side).<br>PIN NO. 3<br>MOTOR RELAY CONNECTOR<br>POSITIVE PIN / POSITIVE PIN<br>4-PIN MOTOR CONNECTOR | OK ▶<br>Not OK ▶ | GO to **D1c**.<br>SERVICE Circuits 538A, 538B and 538C. |

**Fig. 26 Test D, warning lamp & brake warning lamp On and/or pump motor runs more than 60 seconds (Part 2 of 10)**

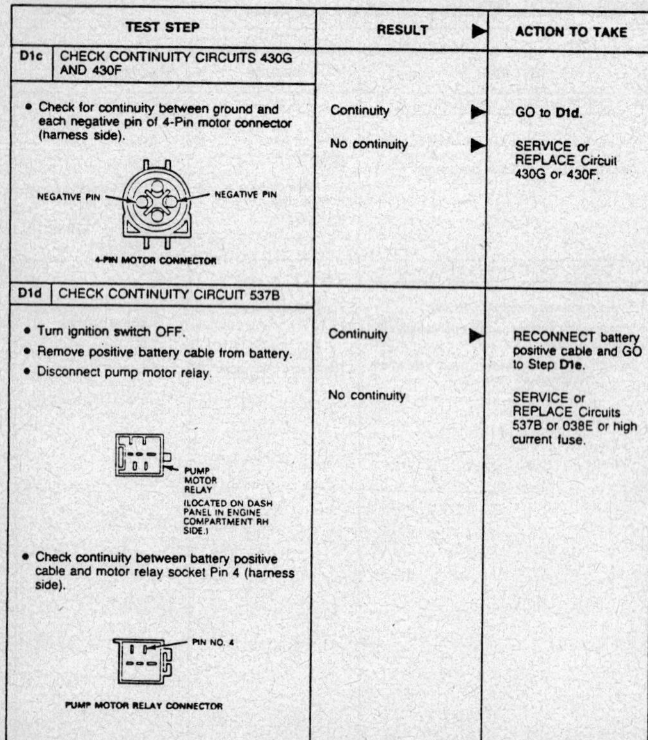

| Anti-Lock Warning Lamp And Brake Warning Lamp On And/Or Pump Motor Runs More Than 60 Seconds | Test D |
|---|---|

| TEST STEP | RESULT ▶ | ACTION TO TAKE |
|---|---|---|
| **D1c** CHECK CONTINUITY CIRCUITS 430G AND 430F | | |
| • Check for continuity between ground and each negative pin of 4-Pin motor connector (harness side).<br>NEGATIVE PIN / NEGATIVE PIN<br>4-PIN MOTOR CONNECTOR | Continuity ▶<br>No continuity ▶ | GO to **D1d**.<br>SERVICE or REPLACE Circuit 430G or 430F. |
| **D1d** CHECK CONTINUITY CIRCUIT 537B | | |
| • Turn ignition switch OFF.<br>• Remove positive battery cable from battery.<br>• Disconnect pump motor relay.<br>PUMP MOTOR RELAY (LOCATED ON DASH PANEL IN ENGINE COMPARTMENT RH SIDE.)<br>• Check continuity between battery positive cable and motor relay socket Pin 4 (harness side).<br>PIN NO. 4<br>PUMP MOTOR RELAY CONNECTOR | Continuity ▶<br>No continuity | RECONNECT battery positive cable and GO to Step **D1e**.<br>SERVICE or REPLACE Circuits 537B or 038E or high current fuse. |

**Fig. 26 Test D, warning lamp & brake warning lamp On and/or pump motor runs more than 60 seconds (Part 3 of 10)**

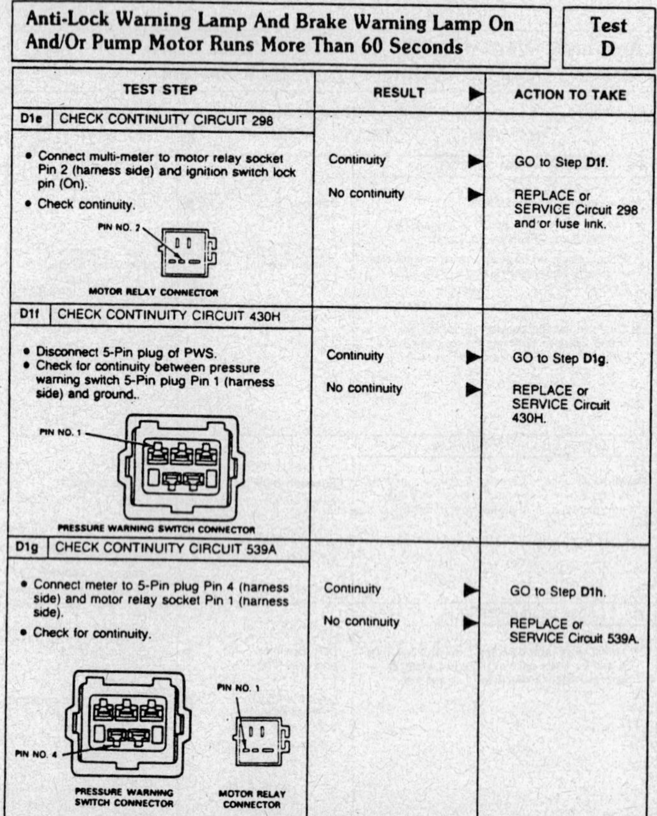

| Anti-Lock Warning Lamp And Brake Warning Lamp On And/Or Pump Motor Runs More Than 60 Seconds | Test D |
|---|---|

| TEST STEP | RESULT ▶ | ACTION TO TAKE |
|---|---|---|
| **D1e** CHECK CONTINUITY CIRCUIT 298 | | |
| • Connect multi-meter to motor relay socket Pin 2 (harness side) and ignition switch lock pin (On).<br>• Check continuity.<br>PIN NO. 2<br>MOTOR RELAY CONNECTOR | Continuity ▶<br>No continuity ▶ | GO to Step **D1f**.<br>REPLACE or SERVICE Circuit 298 and/or fuse link. |
| **D1f** CHECK CONTINUITY CIRCUIT 430H | | |
| • Disconnect 5-Pin plug of PWS.<br>• Check for continuity between pressure warning switch 5-Pin plug Pin 1 (harness side) and ground.<br>PIN NO. 1<br>PRESSURE WARNING SWITCH CONNECTOR | Continuity ▶<br>No continuity ▶ | GO to Step **D1g**.<br>REPLACE or SERVICE Circuit 430H. |
| **D1g** CHECK CONTINUITY CIRCUIT 539A | | |
| • Connect meter to 5-Pin plug Pin 4 (harness side) and motor relay socket Pin 1 (harness side).<br>• Check for continuity.<br>PIN NO. 1<br>PIN NO. 4<br>PRESSURE WARNING SWITCH CONNECTOR<br>MOTOR RELAY CONNECTOR | Continuity ▶<br>No continuity ▶ | GO to Step **D1h**.<br>REPLACE or SERVICE Circuit 539A. |

**Fig. 26 Test D, warning lamp & brake warning lamp On and/or pump motor runs more than 60 seconds (Part 4 of 10)**

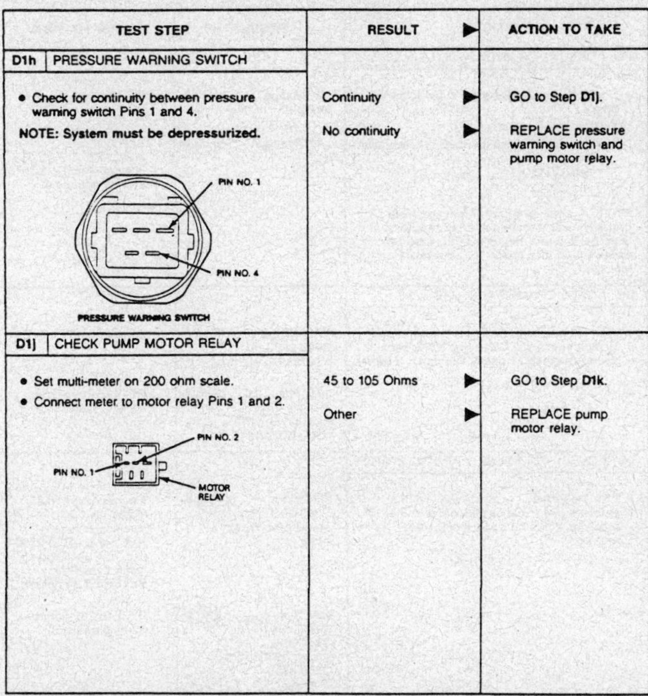

| Anti-Lock Warning Lamp And Brake Warning Lamp On And/Or Pump Motor Runs More Than 60 Seconds | Test D |
|---|---|

| TEST STEP | RESULT ▶ | ACTION TO TAKE |
|---|---|---|
| **D1h** PRESSURE WARNING SWITCH | | |
| • Check for continuity between pressure warning switch Pins 1 and 4.<br>**NOTE: System must be depressurized.**<br>PIN NO. 1 / PIN NO. 4 / PRESSURE WARNING SWITCH | Continuity ▶ | GO to Step **D1j**. |
| | No continuity ▶ | REPLACE pressure warning switch and pump motor relay. |
| **D1j** CHECK PUMP MOTOR RELAY | | |
| • Set multi-meter on 200 ohm scale.<br>• Connect meter to motor relay Pins 1 and 2.<br>PIN NO. 2 / PIN NO. 1 / MOTOR RELAY | 45 to 105 Ohms ▶ | GO to Step **D1k**. |
| | Other ▶ | REPLACE pump motor relay. |

**Fig. 26 Test D, warning lamp & brake warning lamp On and/or pump motor runs more than 60 seconds (Part 5 of 10)**

| Anti-Lock Warning Lamp And Brake Warning Lamp On And/Or Pump Motor Runs More Than 60 Seconds | Test D |
|---|---|

| TEST STEP | RESULT ▶ | ACTION TO TAKE |
|---|---|---|
| **D1p** CHECK PUMP MOTOR | | |
| • Apply 12 volts to 4-pin plug of motor (use one negative and one positive pin).<br>• Pump motor should run.<br>POSITIVE PIN / NEGATIVE PIN / NEGATIVE PIN / POSITIVE PIN / 4-PIN MOTOR CONNECTOR | Pump runs ▶ | End of test. CONNECT all electrical plugs and relay. REVERIFY symptom. |
| | Pump does not operate ▶ | REPLACE pump/motor assembly. |
| **D2** CHECK PUMP MOTOR UNIT | | |
| • Turn ignition switch OFF.<br>• Pump brake pedal 20 times to discharge system.<br>• Connect ammeter between battery positive cable and battery positive terminal.<br>• Turn Off any electrical components.<br>• Connect 4-pin motor plug.<br>• Turn ignition switch ON.<br>• Measure pump motor current. | Current more than 25 amps ▶ | REPLACE pump motor unit. |
| | Current less than 25 amps ▶ | GO to Step **D2a**. |
| **D2a** CHECK PUMP MOTOR | | |
| • Turn ignition switch OFF.<br>• Pump brake pedal at least 20 times, until brake pedal becomes hard.<br>• Turn ignition switch ON.<br>• Measure time pump takes to shut OFF. | Under 60 seconds ▶ | GO to Step **D2b**. |
| | Over 60 seconds (or motor never turns on) ▶ | CHECK for corroded connections at:<br>• Motor 4-pin plug.<br>• Body ground (Circuit 430F and D).<br>• Motor relay Pin 4 socket (Circuit 537).<br>• Battery to Pin 4.<br>GO to Step **D2b**. |

**Fig. 26 Test D, warning lamp & brake warning lamp On and/or pump motor runs more than 60 seconds (Part 7 of 10)**

| Anti-Lock Warning Lamp And Brake Warning Lamp On And/Or Pump Motor Runs More Than 60 Seconds | Test D |
|---|---|

| TEST STEP | RESULT ▶ | ACTION TO TAKE |
|---|---|---|
| **D1k** CHECK PUMP MOTOR RELAY (CONTINUED) | | |
| • Connect meter and check continuity between motor relay Pins 3 and 4.<br>PIN NO. 3 / PIN NO. 4 / MOTOR RELAY | No continuity ▶ | GO to Step **D1m**. |
| | Continuity ▶ | REPLACE pump motor relay. |
| **D1m** CHECK PUMP MOTOR RELAY (CONTINUED) | | |
| • Connect battery to motor relay terminals 1 and 2.<br>• Check continuity between relay Pins 3 and 4 with multi-meter.<br>PIN NO. 2 / PIN NO. 1 / PIN NO. 3 / PIN NO. 5 / PIN NO. 4 | Continuity ▶ | GO to Step **D1n**. |
| | No continuity ▶ | REPLACE pump motor relay. |
| **D1n** CHECK MOTOR RELAY DIODE | | |
| • Set multi-meter to check a diode (approx. 2000 Ohm scale). Check between relay Pins 3 and 5 in both directions by reversing leads. | Diode blocks (high resistance) in one direction and conducts (low resistance) in other direction. ▶ | GO to Step **D1p**. |
| | Diode blocks in both directions. Diode conducts in both directions. ▶ | REPLACE pump motor relay. |

**Fig. 26 Test D, warning lamp & brake warning lamp On and/or pump motor runs more than 60 seconds (Part 6 of 10)**

| Anti-Lock Warning Lamp And Brake Warning Lamp On And/Or Pump Motor Runs More Than 60 Seconds | Test D |
|---|---|

| TEST STEP | RESULT ▶ | ACTION TO TAKE |
|---|---|---|
| **D2b** CHECK LOW PRESSURE FLOW | | |
| • Turn ignition switch OFF.<br>• Disconnect low pressure hose from pump and allow fluid to flow into a suitable container.<br>**NOTE: Discard fluid after test.** | Free fluid flow ▶ | CONNECT low pressure hose. FILL reservoir to MAX. GO to D2c. |
| | Restricted flow ▶ | SERVICE or REPLACE reservoir and or low pressure hose as required. |
| **D2c** CHECK VOLTAGE TO PUMP MOTOR | | |
| • Turn ignition switch OFF.<br>• Pump brake pedal to discharge pressure system.<br>• Set meter to 20 Volts DC range.<br>• Connect voltmeter in parallel at 4-Pin motor plug.<br>• Turn ignition switch ON.<br>POSITIVE PIN / POSITIVE PIN / NEGATIVE PIN / NEGATIVE PIN / 4-PIN MOTOR CONNECTOR | With pump running: ▶<br>Voltage over 8 Volts DC | GO to Step **D3**. |
| | Voltage under 8 Volts DC ▶ | CHECK Circuits 430G, 430F, 538A, 538B, Pin 4 to battery and relay Pins 3 and 4 for voltage drop. SERVICE or REPLACE as necessary. |

**Fig. 26 Test D, warning lamp & brake warning lamp On and/or pump motor runs more than 60 seconds (Part 8 of 10)**

## Anti-Lock Warning Lamp And Brake Warning Lamp On And/Or Pump Motor Runs More Than 60 Seconds — Test D

| TEST STEP | RESULT ▶ | ACTION TO TAKE |
|---|---|---|
| **D3** ACCUMULATOR: PRE-CHARGE | | |
| • Vehicle must be cooled to room temperature.<br>**WARNING: BEFORE DISCONNECTING ANY HYDRAULIC LINES, YOU MUST ENSURE THAT THE PRESSURE SYSTEM IS DISCHARGED.**<br>• To discharge hydraulic accumulator pressure, turn ignition OFF, pump brake pedal at least 20 times until you feel it become hard.<br>• Remove accumulator.<br>• Install Pressure Gauge Adaptor T88P-20215-AH or equivalent.<br>• Install accumulator.<br>• Install Anti-Lock Pressure Gauge Tool T85P-20215-A or equivalent.<br>• Turn ignition switch on and read accumulator precharge pressure. (Gauge needle will spring to this point).<br>**Note: Gauge needle reading should spring to 40-90 bar (600-1325 psi) and climb to 16,203-19,306 kPa bar (2350-2800 psi).**<br>• If reading was missed, discharge accumulator as described and repeat ignition ON sequence. | 4137-9135 kPa (600-1325 psi) ▶<br><br>Under 4137 kPa (600 psi) ▶<br><br>Over 9135 kPa (1325 psi) ▶ | GO to Step **D4**.<br><br>REPLACE accumulator.<br>**Note: Measure nipple length to determine correct service replacement accumulator.**<br><br>REPLACE accumulator.<br>**Note: Measure nipple length to determine correct service replacement accumulator.** |
| **D4** CHECK HYDRAULIC ACTUATION UNIT | | |
| • Turn ignition switch ON; wait until pump motor stops. Wait 3 more minutes to stabilize gauge pressure.<br>• Read pressure gauge.<br>• Wait 5 minutes and read pressure gauge again to determine the pressure loss over those 5 minutes. | Pressure loss less than 10 bar (140 psi) on gauge ▶<br><br>More than 10 bar (140 psi) ▶ | GO to Step **D5**.<br><br>CHECK for external leakage at actuation assembly and SERVICE. If no external leakage is found, GO to Step **D4a**. |

**Fig. 26 Test D, warning lamp & brake warning lamp On and/or pump motor runs more than 60 seconds (Part 9 of 10)**

## Anti-Lock Warning Lamp And Brake Warning Lamp On And/Or Pump Motor Runs More Than 60 Seconds — Test D

| TEST STEP | RESULT ▶ | ACTION TO TAKE |
|---|---|---|
| **D4a** CHECK FOR HYDRAULIC LEAKS | | |
| • Check for brake fluid leaks in the following areas:<br>a. Brake lines and calipers.<br>b. High and low pressure hoses on actuation assembly.<br>c. Reservoir seals and seams.<br>d. Accumulator.<br>**NOTE: A small amount of leakage from pressure warning switch is allowable. If any leakage is found below switch, wipe off excess fluid and check for excessive leakage.** | No leakage found (OK) ▶<br><br>Leakage found (NOT OK) ▶ | GO to **D5**.<br><br>SERVICE or REPLACE components. CHECK system operation. |
| **D5** CHECK PUMP PRESSURE | | |
| • With the pressure gauge still attached and ignition switch still ON, pump brake pedal to decrease pressure until pump motor restarts. | 13100-15169 kPa (1900-2200 psi) when pump starts (OK) ▶<br><br>Less than or more than 13100-15169 kPa (1900-2200 psi) (NOT OK) ▶ | GO to Step **D6**.<br><br>REPLACE pressure warning switch. |
| **D6** CHECK PRESSURE WARNING SWITCH | | |
| • With the ignition switch still ON and the pressure gauge connected, observe the pressure when the pump motor stops running. | 16203 kPa (2350-2800 psi) when pump motor stops (OK) ▶<br><br>Less than 16203 kPa (2350 psi) or over 19306 kPa (2800 psi) (NOT OK) ▶ | If pump motor takes longer than 60 seconds to reach 16203 kPa (2350-2800 psi), REPLACE pump/motor assembly. REVERIFY symptom.<br><br>REPLACE pressure warning switch. |

**Fig. 26 Test D, warning lamp & brake warning lamp On and/or pump motor runs more than 60 seconds (Part 10 of 10)**

## Anti-Lock Warning Lamp Intermittently On — Test E

WARNING LIGHTS SEQUENCE

| Warning Lamps | Ignition On | Cranking Engine | Engine Running | Vehicle Moving | Braking with/without Anti-Lock | Vehicle Stopped | Engine Idle | Ignition Off |
|---|---|---|---|---|---|---|---|---|
| Check Anti-Lock (Amber) | | | | | | | | |
| Brake (Red) | | | | | | | | |

| TEST STEP | RESULT ▶ | ACTION TO TAKE |
|---|---|---|
| **E1** CHECK FLI AND PWS CIRCUIT | | |
| • Disconnect 32-Pin plug from electronic controller.<br>• Connect EEC-IV Breakout box, T83L-50-EEC-IV with Anti-Lock Test Adapter T87P-50-ALA or equivalent to the Anti-Lock 32-Pin plug wiring harness.<br>• Turn ignition switch ON.<br>• Set multi-meter to read resistance.<br>• Measure the resistance between Breakout box Pins 25 and 27. | Less than 5 ohms (OK) ▶<br><br>Greater than 5 ohms (NOT OK) ▶ | GO to Step **E2**.<br><br>GO to Step **E1a**. |
| **E1a** CHECK FLI ANTI-LOCK WARNING CIRCUIT | | |
| • Disconnect 5-Pin plug on reservoir fluid level indicator (FLI).<br>• Measure resistance between fluid level indicator electrical Pins 1 and 2 (with brake fluid at maximum fluid level).<br><br>PIN NO. 2, PIN NO. 4, PIN NO. 1, PIN NO. 5, PIN NO. 3<br>FLUID LEVEL INDICATOR ON RESERVOIR CONNECTOR | Less than 2 ohms (OK) ▶<br><br>Greater than 2 ohms (NOT OK) ▶ | GO to Step **E1b**.<br><br>REPLACE fluid reservoir. |

**Fig. 27 Test E, warning lamp intermittently On (Part 1 of 5)**

## Anti-Lock Warning Lamp Intermittently On — Test E

| TEST STEP | RESULT ▶ | ACTION TO TAKE |
|---|---|---|
| **E1b** CHECK PWS ANTI-LOCK WARNING CIRCUIT (NO SYSTEM PRESSURE) | | |
| • Turn ignition switch OFF.<br>• Pump brake pedal to discharge pressure system.<br>• Disconnect 5-Pin plug at pressure warning switch (PWS).<br>• Check for continuity between pressure warning switch Pins 3 and 5.<br><br>PIN NO. 3, PIN NO. 5<br>PRESSURE WARNING SWITCH | No Continuity ▶<br><br>Continuity ▶ | GO to Step **E1c**.<br><br>REPLACE pressure warning switch. |
| **E1c** CHECK ELECTRONIC MODULE TO FLI WIRE | | |
| • Check for continuity between Breakout box Pin 25 and FLI 5-Pin plug Pin 1 (harness side).<br><br>PIN NO. 2, PIN NO. 4, PIN NO. 1, PIN NO. 5, PIN NO. 3<br>FLUID LEVEL INDICATOR CONNECTOR | Continuity ▶<br><br>No continuity ▶ | GO to Step **E1d**.<br><br>REPLACE or SERVICE cable harness (Circuit 512A). |

**Fig. 27 Test E, warning lamp intermittently On (Part 2 of 5)**

## Anti-Lock Warning Lamp Intermittently On — Test E

| TEST STEP | RESULT ▶ | ACTION TO TAKE |
|---|---|---|
| **E1d** CHECK FLI TO PWS WIRE | | |
| • Check for continuity between 5-Pin fluid level plug Pin 2 (harness side)<br>PIN NO. 2 PIN NO. 4 PIN NO. 1 PIN NO. 5 PIN NO. 3<br>FLUID LEVEL INDICATOR CONNECTOR<br>and 5-Pin pressure warning switch plug Pin 3 (harness side).<br>PIN NO. 3<br>PRESSURE WARNING SWITCH CONNECTOR | Continuity ▶<br>No continuity ▶ | GO to Step **E1e**.<br>SERVICE or REPLACE cable harness (Circuit 549A). |
| **E1e** CHECK PWS TO ELECTRONIC CONTROLLER WIRE | | |
| • Check for continuity between 5-Pin pressure warning switch plug Pin 5 (harness side) and Breakout box Pin 27.<br>PIN NO. 5<br>PRESSURE WARNING SWITCH CONNECTOR | Continuity ▶<br>No continuity ▶ | TURN ignition OFF. CONNECT all electrical connections. REVERIFY symptom.<br>SERVICE or REPLACE cable harness (Circuit 535A). |

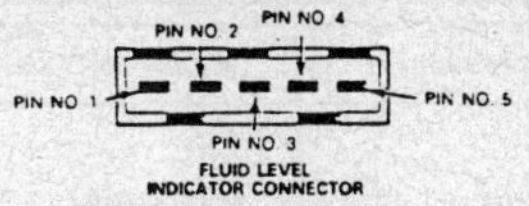

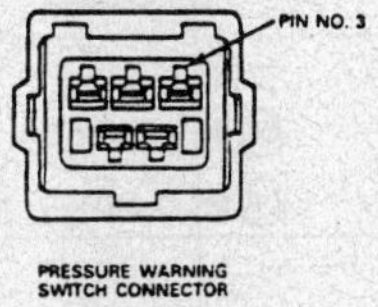

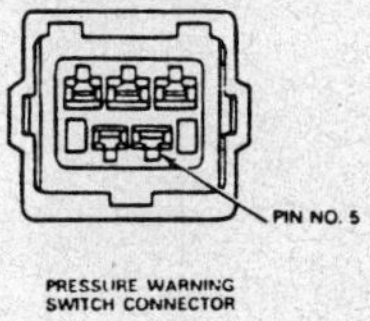

**Fig. 27 Test E, warning lamp intermittently On (Part 3 of 5)**

## Anti-Lock Warning Lamp Intermittently On — Test E

| TEST STEP | RESULT ▶ | ACTION TO TAKE |
|---|---|---|
| **E2** CHECK ISOLATION TEST FLI AND PWS | | |
| • Check for continuity between Breakout box Pin 25 and body ground. | Continuity ▶<br>No continuity ▶ | GO to Step **E2a**.<br>REVERIFY symptom. |
| **E2a** CHECK CONTINUITY OF FLI SWITCH | | |
| • Disconnect FLI plug and check for continuity between socket Pin 1 and Pins 3, 4, and 5 and Pin 2 and Pins 3, 4, and 5.<br>PIN NO. 5 PIN NO. 1 PIN NO. 4 PIN NO. 2 PIN NO. 3<br>FLUID LEVEL INDICATOR | Continuity ▶<br>No continuity ▶ | REPLACE FLI.<br>GO to Step **E2b**. |
| **E2b** CHECK CONTINUITY CIRCUIT 512A | | |
| • Check for continuity between FLI plug Pin 1 (harness side) and body ground.<br>PIN NO. 2 PIN NO. 4 PIN NO. 1 PIN NO. 5 PIN NO. 3<br>FLUID LEVEL INDICATOR CONNECTOR | Continuity ▶<br>No continuity ▶ | SERVICE or REPLACE Circuit 512A.<br>GO to Step **E2c**. |
| **E2c** CHECK CONTINUITY CIRCUIT 549A | | |
| • Disconnect 5-Pin plug from PWS. Check for continuity between FLI plug Pin 2 (harness side) and body ground.<br>PIN NO. 2 PIN NO. 4 PIN NO. 1 PIN NO. 5 PIN NO. 3<br>FLUID LEVEL INDICATOR CONNECTOR | Continuity ▶<br>No continuity ▶ | SERVICE or REPLACE Circuit 549A.<br>GO to Step **E2d**. |

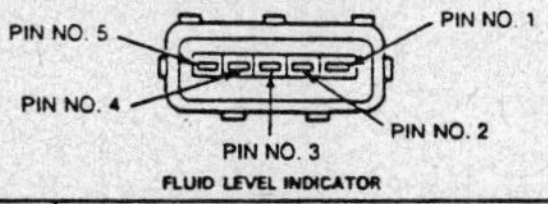

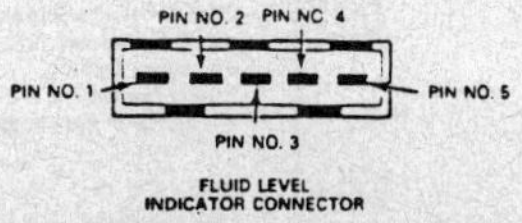

**Fig. 27 Test E, warning lamp intermittently On (Part 4 of 5)**

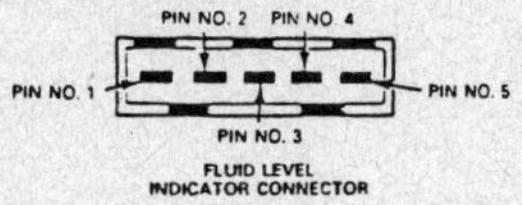

## Anti-Lock Warning Lamp Intermittently On — Test E

| TEST STEP | RESULT ▶ | ACTION TO TAKE |
|---|---|---|
| **E2d** CHECK CONTINUITY OF PWS | | |
| • Check for continuity from PWS 5-Pin socket Pin 3 to body ground, and from Pin 5 to body ground.<br>PIN NO. 3 PIN NO. 5<br>PRESSURE WARNING SWITCH | Continuity ▶<br>No continuity ▶ | REPLACE pressure warning switch.<br>GO to Step **E2e**. |
| **E2e** CHECK CONTINUITY CIRCUIT 535A | | |
| • Check for continuity between 5-Pin PWS plug (harness side) Pin 5 and body ground.<br>PIN NO. 5<br>PRESSURE WARNING SWITCH CONNECTOR | Continuity ▶<br>No continuity ▶ | SERVICE or REPLACE Circuit 535A.<br>CONNECT all plugs and REVERIFY symptom. |

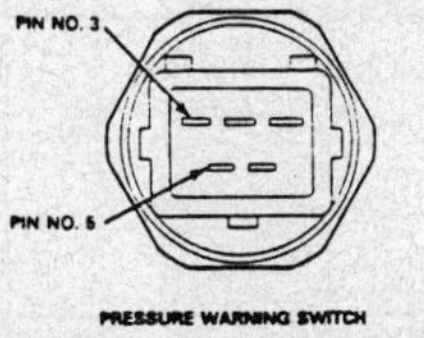

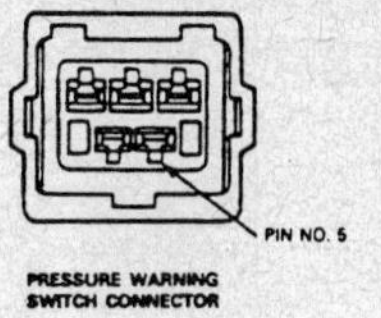

**Fig. 27 Test E, warning lamp intermittently On (Part 5 of 5)**

## Brake Warning Lamp On (With Anti-Lock Lamp Off, Parking Brake Released And Brake Lining Wear Checked) — Test F

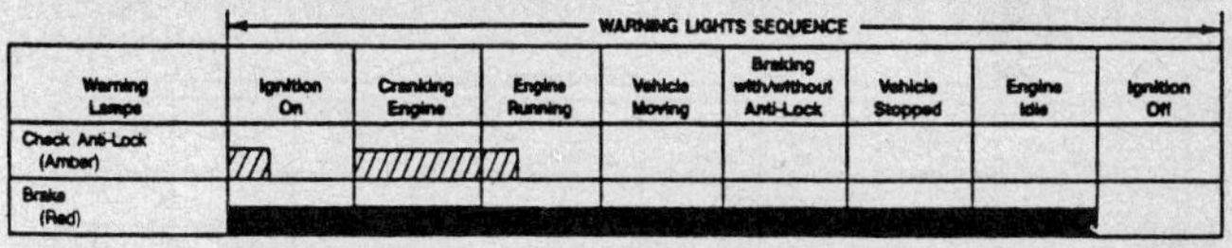

WARNING LIGHTS SEQUENCE

| Warning Lamps | Ignition On | Cranking Engine | Engine Running | Vehicle Moving | Braking with/without Anti-Lock | Vehicle Stopped | Engine Idle | Ignition Off |
|---|---|---|---|---|---|---|---|---|
| Check Anti-Lock (Amber) | | | | | | | | |
| Brake (Red) | | | | | | | | |

| TEST STEP | RESULT ▶ | ACTION TO TAKE |
|---|---|---|
| **F1** CHECK BRAKE FLUID LEVEL | | |
| • Turn ignition switch ON.<br>• Pump brake pedal until pump motor starts.<br>• When pump motor stops check brake fluid level. | Low (OK) ▶<br>Normal (Ø) ▶ | CHECK system for external leaks. SERVICE as required.<br>GO to Step **F2**. |
| **F2** CHECK CONTINUITY FLI SWITCH | | |
| • Disconnect 5-Pin plug on fluid reservoir.<br>• Set multi-meter to measure continuity. Connect to reservoir Pins 3 and 4.<br>PIN NO. 3 PIN NO. 5 PIN NO. 1 PIN NO. 4 PIN NO. 2<br>FLUID RESERVOIR CAP | No continuity (OK) ▶<br>Continuity (Ø) ▶ | GO to Step **F3**.<br>REPLACE fluid reservoir. |

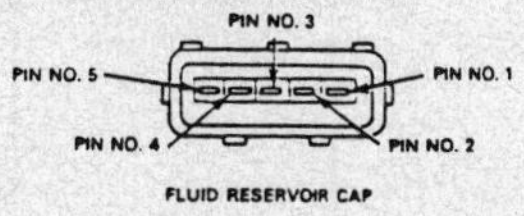

**Fig. 28 Test F, brake warning lamp On w/ABS lamp Off, parking brake released & lining wear checked (Part 1 of 2)**

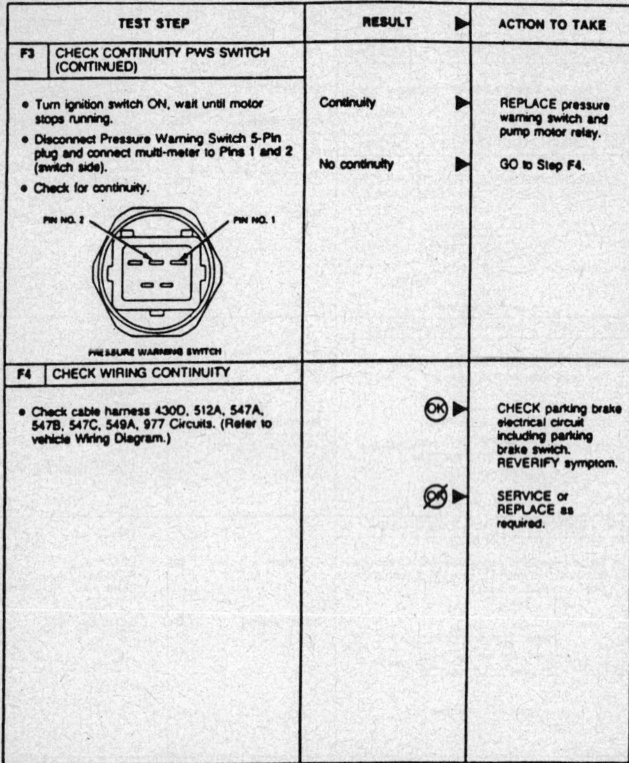

| Brake Warning Lamp On (With Anti-Lock Lamp Off, Parking Brake Released And Brake Lining Wear Checked) | Test F |
|---|---|

| TEST STEP | RESULT ▶ | ACTION TO TAKE |
|---|---|---|
| **F3 CHECK CONTINUITY PWS SWITCH (CONTINUED)** | | |
| • Turn ignition switch ON, wait until motor stops running.<br>• Disconnect Pressure Warning Switch 5-Pin plug and connect multi-meter to Pins 1 and 2 (switch side).<br>• Check for continuity. | Continuity ▶ | REPLACE pressure warning switch and pump motor relay. |
| | No continuity ▶ | GO to Step F4. |
| **F4 CHECK WIRING CONTINUITY** | | |
| • Check cable harness 430D, 512A, 547A, 547B, 547C, 549A, 977 Circuits. (Refer to vehicle Wiring Diagram.) | OK ▶ | CHECK parking brake electrical circuit including parking brake switch. REVERIFY symptom. |
| | NOT OK ▶ | SERVICE or REPLACE as required. |



**Fig. 28 Test F, brake warning lamp On w/ABS lamp Off, parking brake released & lining wear checked (Part 2 of 2)**

| No Anti-Lock Warning Lamp On When Ignition Switch Turned On | Test G |
|---|---|

| Warning Lamps | Ignition On | Cranking Engine | Engine Running | Vehicle Moving | Braking with/without Anti-Lock | Vehicle Stopped | Engine Idle | Ignition Off |
|---|---|---|---|---|---|---|---|---|
| | WARNING LIGHTS SEQUENCE | | | | | | | |
| Check Anti-Lock (Amber) | | | | | | | | |
| Brake (Red) | | ■ | | | | | | |

| TEST STEP | RESULT ▶ | ACTION TO TAKE |
|---|---|---|
| **G1 CHECK FUSE AND FUSE LINKS** | | |
| • Check in-line fuse links with ignition turned ON. | Fuse Links OK ▶ | GO to Step G2. |
| | Fuse Links NOT OK ▶ | SERVICE or REPLACE as required. |
| **G2 CHECK WARNING LAMP BULB** | | |
| • Check warning lamp bulb. | OK ▶ | GO to Step G3. |
| | NOT OK ▶ | REPLACE bulb. |
| **G3 CHECK WARNING LAMP OPERATION** | | |
| • Turn ignition switch ON.<br>• Disconnect 32-Pin connector from control module. | Anti-Lock lamp goes ON ▶ | SERVICE or REPLACE Circuit 606B. |
| | Anti-Lock lamp is not ON ▶ | SERVICE or REPLACE connector to 14401 wire harness. |

**Fig. 29 Test G, no warning lamp On when ignition switch turned On**

| Spongy Brake Pedal With/Without Anti-Lock Function (No Warning Lamp) | Test H |
|---|---|

| Warning Lamps | Ignition On | Cranking Engine | Engine Running | Vehicle Moving | Braking with without Anti-Lock | Vehicle Stopped | Engine Idle | Ignition Off |
|---|---|---|---|---|---|---|---|---|
| | WARNING LIGHTS SEQUENCE | | | | | | | |
| Check Anti-Lock (Amber) | ▨ | ▨ | ▨ | | | | | |
| Brake (Red) | | ■ | | | | | | |

| TEST STEP | RESULT ▶ | ACTION TO TAKE |
|---|---|---|
| **H1 CHECK COMPONENT MOUNTING** | | |
| • Check for proper brake pedal and hydraulic unit attachment.<br>• Bleed brakes as outlined. | Pedal still spongy NOT OK ▶ | GO to Step H2. |
| | Pedal feels normal OK ▶ | Condition corrected. |
| **H2 BLEED BRAKE SYSTEM** | | |
| • Turn off air suspension switch in luggage compartment if so equipped.<br>• Rebleed brake system.<br>• Turn on air suspension switch when vehicle is off hoist if so equipped. | Pedal still spongy NOT OK ▶ | REPLACE actuation assembly. |
| | Pedal feels normal OK ▶ | Condition corrected. |

**Fig. 30 Test H, spongy pedal & no warning lamp**

| Poor Vehicle Tracking During Anti-Lock Function (Warning Lamp Off) | Test J |
|---|---|

| Warning Lamps | Ignition On | Cranking Engine | Engine Running | Vehicle Moving | Braking with/without Anti-Lock | Vehicle Stopped | Engine Idle | Ignition Off |
|---|---|---|---|---|---|---|---|---|
| | WARNING LIGHTS SEQUENCE | | | | | | | |
| Check Anti-Lock (Amber) | ▨ | ▨ | ▨ | | | | | |
| Brake (Red) | | ■ | | | | | | |

| TEST STEP | RESULT ▶ | ACTION TO TAKE |
|---|---|---|
| **J1 VERIFY CONDITION** | | |
| • Verify condition exists as reported.<br>• Turn air suspension off if so equipped.<br>• Bleed brake system per shop manual for Anti-Lock brake system.<br>• Turn air suspension on when vehicle is off hoist. | Vehicle tracks properly ▶ | Condition corrected. |
| | Vehicle still tracks poorly ▶ | GO to J2. |
| **J2 CHECK ANTI-LOCK OPERATION — LH FRONT WHEEL** | | |
| • Turn air suspension off if so equipped.<br>• Lift vehicle and rotate wheels to assure they turn freely.<br>• Turn ignition switch OFF.<br>• Disconnect 32-Pin plug from electronic controller.<br>• Connect EEC-IV Breakout box, Tool T83L-50-EEC-IV with Anti-Lock test adapter, Tool T87P-50-ALA to the Anti-Lock 32-Pin plug wiring harness.<br>• Short Pins 18, 14 and 31 to each other at Breakout box.<br>• Apply moderate brake pedal effort and check that LH front wheel will not turn.<br>• Check to see that LH front wheel turns freely with ignition switch ON.<br>• Turn air suspension on when vehicle is off hoist if so equipped.<br>CAUTION: DO NOT LEAVE IGNITION ON FOR MORE THAN 1 MINUTE MAXIMUM, OR SOLENOID VALVE DAMAGE MAY RESULT. | If wheel turns freely ▶ | TURN ignition switch Off. DISCONNECT wire leads. Go to Step J3. |
| | If wheel does not turn freely or pedal drops ▶ | REPLACE solenoid valve block. |

**Fig. 31 Test J, poor vehicle tracking during ABS function, warning lamp Off (Part 1 of 2)**

| Poor Vehicle Tracking During Anti-Lock Function (Warning Lamp Off) | Test J |
|---|---|

| TEST STEP | RESULT ▶ | ACTION TO TAKE |
|---|---|---|
| **J3** CHECK ANTI-LOCK OPERATION — RH FRONT WHEEL | | |
| • Turn air suspension off.<br>• Short Pins 18, 32 and 13 to each other at Breakout box.<br>• Apply moderate brake effort. Check that RH front wheel does not turn.<br>• Check that RH front wheel turns freely with ignition switch ON.<br>CAUTION: DO NOT LEAVE IGNITION ON MORE THAN 1 MINUTE MAXIMUM OR SOLENOID VALVE DAMAGE MAY RESULT. | Wheel turns freely ▶<br><br>Wheel does not turn freely or brake pedal drops ▶ | TURN ignition switch OFF. DISCONNECT wire leads. GO to Step J4.<br><br>REPLACE solenoid valve block. |
| **J4** CHECK ANTI-LOCK OPERATION — REAR WHEELS | | |
| • Turn air suspension off if so equipped.<br>• Short Pins 18, 30 and 12 to each other at Breakout box.<br>• Apply moderate brake pedal pressure. Check that rear wheels will not turn.<br>• Check that rear wheels turn freely with ignition switch ON.<br>• Turn air suspension on when vehicle is off hoist if so equipped.<br>CAUTION: DO NOT LEAVE IGNITION ON MORE THAN 1 MINUTE MAXIMUM OR SOLENOID VALVE DAMAGE MAY RESULT. | Wheels turn freely ▶<br><br>Wheels do not turn freely or brake pedal drops ▶ | TURN ignition switch OFF. DISCONNECT wire lead and Breakout box. LOWER vehicle. REVERIFY symptom.<br><br>REPLACE solenoid valve block. |

**Fig. 31 Test J, poor vehicle tracking during ABS function, warning lamp Off (Part 2 of 2)**

3. Label, then disconnect electrical connectors from fluid level indicator, main valve, solenoid valve block, pressure warning switch, hydraulic pump motor and ground connector from master cylinder portion of actuation assembly.
4. Disconnect and plug brake tube fittings. Do not allow brake fluid to come in contact with any electrical connectors.
5. Remove trim panel under steering column. Disconnect actuation assembly push rod from brake pedal. Slide switch, push rod and plastic bushings off pedal pin.
6. Remove four retaining nuts, securing actuation assembly to brake pedal support bracket.
7. Remove actuation assembly from engine compartment.
8. Reverse procedure to install. **Torque** the four hydraulic unit to pedal support nuts to 13-25 ft. lbs. and brake tube nuts to 10-18 ft. lbs.

## HYDRAULIC ACCUMULATOR

1. With hydraulic system discharged, disconnect battery ground cable and electrical connector at hydraulic pump motor.
2. Using a 8 mm hex wrench, loosen and completely unscrew accumulator. Ensure contaminants do not fall into open port.
3. Remove O-ring.
4. Reverse procedure to install. Install and **torque** accumulator to 30-34 ft. lbs. Turn ignition switch to On position and check that the red "Brake" warning lamp and the amber "Anti-Lock" warning lamp both go out after approximately 1 minute. Top off brake fluid reservoir if necessary.

## ELECTRIC HYDRAULIC PUMP MOTOR

Refer to **Fig. 4,** during the following procedure.

1. With hydraulic system discharged, disconnect battery ground cable.
2. Drain as much brake fluid as possible from reservoir.
3. Disconnect suction line between reservoir and pump.
4. Remove accumulator and banjo bolt attaching high pressure line to pump housing.
5. Disconnect low pressure line between fluid reservoir and pump suction port.
6. Raise and support vehicle, then disconnect electrical connector from pump motor and pressure switch. It may be necessary to disconnect the lefthand tie-rod from the steering knuckle to gain access to the pressure warning switch electrical connector.
7. Remove bolt and spacer attaching pump and motor assembly to hydraulic actuation unit. Slide pump and motor assembly toward driver's side to clear attaching pin. Remove pump and motor assembly.
8. Reverse procedure to install. **Torque** Allen head bolt to 5-7 ft. lbs. There must be a gap of .06-.13 inch between washer on Allen head bolt and isolator bushing retainer cap. **Torque** banjo bolt to 12-15 ft. lbs.

## RESERVOIR & FLUID LEVEL INDICATOR

Refer to **Fig. 6,** during the following procedure.

1. With hydraulic system discharged, disconnect battery ground cable.
2. Disconnect electrical connector from fluid level indicator.
3. Empty reservoir of as mush brake fluid as possible.
4. Remove suction line between pump and reservoir, from reservoir by rotating and pulling hose from fitting.
5. Remove reservoir by placing a flat blade screwdriver between push-in outlet and push-in stud/grommet, then prying up gently. Ensure short sleeve and O-ring are removed from booster grommet hole.
6. Reverse procedure to install.

## SOLENOID VALVE BLOCK

### Cougar & Thunderbird

1. Discharge system and disconnect battery ground cable.
2. Remove LH cowl vent screen and disconnect electrical connector from valve block.
3. Disconnect and plug brake lines at solenoid valve block.
4. Remove solenoid valve block.
5. Reverse procedure to install. Use new O-rings and **torque** solenoid valve block mounting bolts to 15-21 ft. lbs.

### Mark VII

1. Discharge system and disconnect battery ground cable.
2. Disconnect electrical connectors from fluid reservoir cap, main valve, solenoid valve block, pressure warning switch, hydraulic pump motor and ground connector from actuation assembly.
3. Disconnect brake tubes from solenoid valve block one at a time. Immediately plug each threaded tube opening in valve body to prevent fluid loss. **Do not allow brake fluid to contact any electrical connectors.**
4. Using an 8mm hex wrench, loosen and completely remove accumulator.
5. Working inside passenger compartment, disconnect actuation assembly push rod from brake pedal as follows:
   a. Disconnect stoplamp switch wires at connector on brake pedal.
   b. Remove hairpin connector at stoplamp switch on brake pedal and slide switch off of pedal pin far enough for switch outer hole to clear pin.
   c. Remove switch using a twisting motion, using caution not to damage switch.
   d. Remove four retaining nuts at dash

panel.
6. Inside engine compartment, remove actuation assembly from dash panel.
7. Gently clamp off reservoir to actuation assembly brake fluid supply hose to prevent loss of reservoir fluid.
8. Using a 13mm hex socket, remove three nuts holding valve block to actuation assembly.
9. Slide valve block away from actuation assembly until it clears three mounting studs and remove from actuation assembly.
10. Reverse procedure to install, noting the following:
    a. Use new O-rings, lubricated with brake fluid, in four ports of valve block mounting face.
    b. **Torque** valve block mounting nuts to 15-21 ft. lbs.
    c. **Torque** four actuation assembly locknuts to 13-25 ft. lbs.
    d. Following installation, turn ignition to Run position. Wait until Brake and ABS indicators go out, the apply brake pedal with medium force and hold for 15-30 seconds and release. Repeat three times.
    e. Check for leaks at valve block tube seats and mating surface.

## ELECTRONIC CONTROLLER

1. Disconnect battery ground cable.
2. Remove trim panel in luggage compartment (located behind back seat), to expose the electronic control module.
3. Disconnect the 32 pin electrical connector from the electronic controller.
4. Remove attaching bolts, then the electronic controller.
5. Reverse procedure to install. **Torque** retaining bolt to 28-48 inch lbs.

## PRESSURE SWITCH

**Before removing pressure warning switch, ensure hydraulic system pressure is completely discharged. Whenever the pressure warning switch assembly is replaced, the pump motor relay assembly should also be replaced.**

1. Disconnect battery ground cable.
2. Raise and support vehicle.
3. Disconnect electrical connector from pressure warning switch. **It may be necessary to remove the lefthand front tie-rod at the steering knuckle to gain access to the switch.**
4. Using socket tool T85P-20215-B, or equivalent, 1/2 to 3/8 inch adapter and a 3/8 inch ratchet, remove pressure warning switch.
5. Reverse procedure to install. **Torque** pressure warning switch to 15-25 ft. lbs.

## FRONT WHEEL SENSOR

### 1989 Continental

1. Disconnect battery ground cable.
2. Disconnect sensor connector from engine compartment.
3. For the righthand front sensor, remove two plastic push studs to loosen the front section of splash shield in the wheelwell. For the lefthand front sensor, remove two plastic studs to loosen the rear section of the splash shield.
4. Thread sensor wire through holes in fender apron. For the righthand front sensor, remove two attaching clips behind the splash shield.
5. Raise and support vehicle.
6. Remove wheel and tire assembly.
7. Disconnect sensor wire grommets at height sensor bracket and from retainer clip at shock tower.
8. Loosen sensor retainer screw and remove sensor assembly from front knuckle.
9. Reverse procedure to install. **Torque** sensor attaching screw to 40-60 inch lbs.

### Mark VII

1. Disconnect battery ground cable.
2. Disconnect sensor electrical connector.
3. Raise and support vehicle, disengage wire grommet from shock tower, then pull sensor cable connector through hole. Use care not to damage connector.
4. Remove sensor wire from bracket on shock strut and side rail.
5. Loosen 5 mm set screw retaining sensor to sensor bracket post. Remove sensor through hole in disc brake splash shield.
6. Reverse procedure to install, noting the following:
    a. If sensor is to be reused or adjusted, ensure sensor face is clean and free of foreign material. Carefully scrape pole face with a dull knife. Glue a new front paper spacer on pole face (spacer is marked with a "F" and is .051 inch thick). Steel sleeve around post bolt must be rotated to provide a new surface for setscrew to indent and lock into.
    b. Install sensor through brake shield onto sensor bracket post. Ensure paper spacer remains in place throughout installation.
    c. Push sensor toward toothed sensor ring, until new paper spacer contacts the ring. Holding sensor against ring, **torque** 5 mm setscrew to 21-26 inch lbs.

### Cougar & Thunderbird

1. Disconnect battery ground cable.
2. Disconnect sensor electrical connector, located near radiator support.
3. Remove routing clips along wiring harness.
4. Remove Torx head screw securing sensor to spindle.
5. Reverse procedure to install. **Torque** Torx head screw to 40-60 inch lbs.

## REAR WHEEL SENSOR

### 1989 Continental

1. Disconnect sensor electrical connector in luggage compartment.
2. Push rubber grommet through sheet metal floor pan.
3. Turn air suspension switch in luggage compartment to the Off position. Raise and support vehicle and remove retainer clips for sensor wire, then the wire from routing.
4. Loosen sensor attaching screw at caliper anchor plate.
5. Install tool T88P-5310-A or equivalent onto the front suspension arm. Using suitable breaker bar, lower the arm to provide clearance for the sensor wire connector to pass through. Remove sensor.
6. Reverse procedure to install. **Torque** sensor attaching screw to 40-60 inch lbs.

### Cougar, Mark VII & Thunderbird

1. Disconnect battery ground cable.
2. Disconnect wheel sensor electrical connector, located behind wheelwell, under carpeting, inside luggage compartment.
3. Push sensor wire grommet through hole in luggage compartment floor.
4. Raise and support vehicle, then remove sensor wire from routing clips.
5. **On Cougar and Thunderbird models,** remove sensor retaining bolt with a 1/2 inch socket.
6. **On Mark VII models,** proceed as follows:
    a. Remove wheel and tire assembly, then caliper and rotor assemblies.
    b. Remove Torx head retaining bolt, then slip grommet out of rear brake splash shield and pull sensor out through the hole.
7. **On all models,** reverse procedure to install, noting the following:
    a. **On Cougar and Thunderbird models,** align sensor locating tab and bolt hole to axle, then push into position.
    b. **Torque** retaining bolt to 14-20 ft. lbs.
    c. **On Mark VII models,** loosen 5 mm setscrew on sensor and ensure sensor slides freely on sensor bracket post.
    d. If sensor is to be reused or adjusted, ensure sensor face is clean and free of foreign material. Carefully scrape pole face with a dull knife. Glue a new front paper spacer on pole face (spacer is marked with a "R" and is .043 inch thick). Steel sleeve around post bolt must be rotated to provide a new surface for setscrew to indent and lock into.
    e. **Torque** Torx head screw to 40-60 inch lbs.
    f. Push sensor toward toothed ring, until new paper sensor contacts sensor ring. Hold sensor, then **torque** 5 mm setscrew to 21-26 inch lbs.

## FRONT SPEED INDICATOR RING

### 1989 Continental

1. With outboard constant velocity joint removed from vehicle, position speed

indicator ring removal/installer tool T88P-20202-A or equivalent on a suitable press. Position constant velocity joint onto tool.
2. With constant velocity joint properly positioned on tool, use press ram to apply pressure to constant velocity joint and remove speed indicator ring.
3. Reverse procedure to install.

### Cougar & Thunderbird

1. Remove wheel and tire assembly.
2. Remove caliper, rotor and hub assemblies.
3. Remove indicator ring from hub, using a three-jawed puller.
4. Support center of hub so wheel studs do not rest on work surface.
5. Position sensor ring on hub, place a flat plate on top of ring, then press until flush with top of hub.
6. Install hub, rotor and caliper assemblies, then tire and wheel assembly.

### Mark VII

1. Remove wheel and tire assembly.
2. Remove caliper and assembly.
3. Position rotor assembly on an arbor press with studs facing up. Press each stud individually and carefully, only until they contact surface of sensor ring.
4. Position anti-lock sensing ring remover T85P-20202-A, or equivalent, on top of studs, then press all four studs and sensor ring out of rotor assembly together.
5. Install studs into rotor one at a time.
6. Position sensor ring on rotor, then press sensor ring onto rotor, using anti-lock sensing ring replacer T87P-20202-A, or equivalent, until sensor ring is seated. Ensure ring is pressed on straight.
7. Install rotor and caliper assemblies, then wheel and tire assembly.

## REAR SPEED INDICATOR RING

### 1989 Continental

1. With air suspension switch in the Off position, raise and support vehicle.
2. Remove wheel and tire assembly.
3. Remove caliper, rotor and rear hub assemblies.
4. Remove rear sensor ring spring retainer.
5. Position hub assembly in a suitable press and press hub out of speed sensor ring.
6. Reverse procedure to install.

### Mark VII

1. Remove rear axle shaft, as described elsewhere in this manual.
2. Install pinion bearing cone remover T71P-4621-B, or equivalent, between axle shaft flange and sensor ring.
3. Position axle in arbor press, then press axle from sensor ring.
4. To install, position sensor ring with recessed side facing inboard on axle, then install piston bearing cone remover T71P-4621-B, or equivalent, on axle shaft.
5. Place bar stock on top of axle flange, then press sensor ring onto axle shaft, until a gap of 2.48-2.55 inches remains between face of sensor ring and face of flange.
6. Install axle shaft.

# Probe

**NOTE:** Wire Code Identification And Symbol Identification Located In The Front Of This Manual Can Be Used As An Aid When Using Wiring Circuits Found In This Section.

## INDEX



## DESCRIPTION

The Anti-Lock Brake System (ABS) functions by releasing and applying fluid pressure to wheel cylinders during braking, **Fig. 1.** During normal driving conditions the system does not function and has no effect on front to rear brake proportioning. When one or more wheels approaches a slip condition. The ABS automatically senses the slip and activates the pressure control function.

Through pre-programming, the control unit decides which wheel or wheel's brakes pressures need modulation. The control unit sends appropriate signals to solenoid valves located in the actuation assembly. The control valves then modulate fluid pressure which results in a pressure reduction at wheel cylinder to prevent further lock up.

## SYSTEM COMPONENTS

### Master Cylinder

The master cylinder is attached to the brake pedal lever and provides brake pressure to wheel cylinders during braking.

### Actuation Assembly

The actuation assembly, **Fig. 2.** contains the solenoid valves, control valves, accumulator, pump motor and fluid reservoir. It provides pressure modulation of master cylinder brake pressure during ABS operation. The actuation assembly is mounted below master cylinder on the firewall.

### Accumulator

The accumulator is part of the actuation assembly and accumulates hydraulic pressure for use in ABS control.

### Solenoid Valves

The solenoid valves are located inside the actuation assembly. It provides pressure modulation to all wheel cylinders during ABS operation.

### Fluid Reservoir

The fluid reservoir is part of the actua-

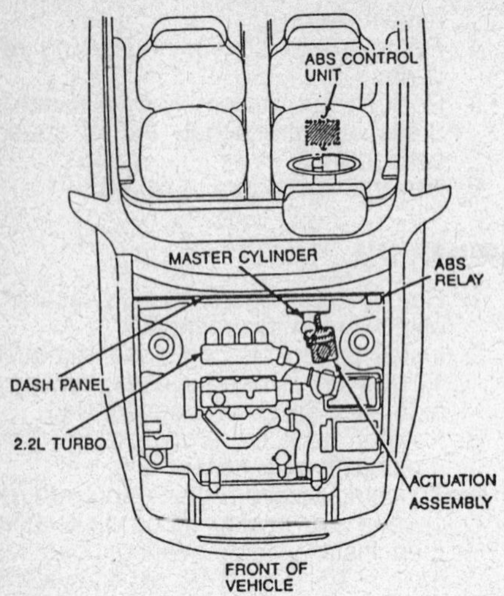


**Fig. 1 Anti-Lock brake system**

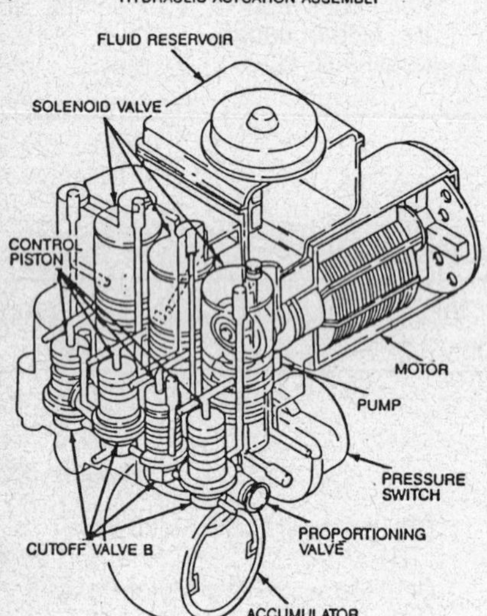


**Fig. 2 Hydraulic actuation assembly**

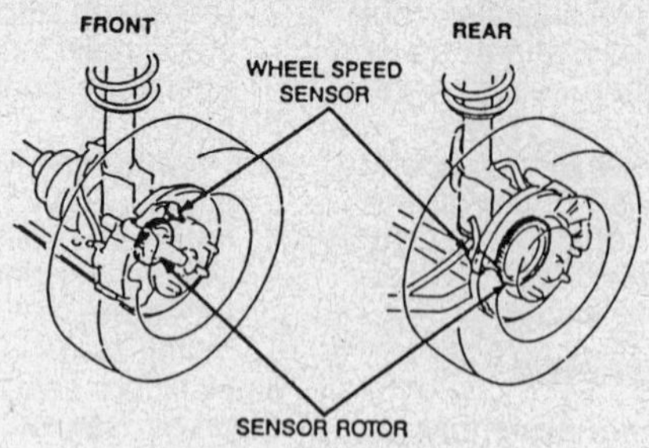


**Fig. 3 Wheel speed sensors**

| ELECTRICAL | MECHANICAL |
|---|---|
| • Blown fuses (10, 15, 20, 60 and 80 AMP)<br>• Blown ABS Warning Bulb<br>• Shorted Wires<br>• Poor Connections<br>• Corroded Connectors<br>• Poor Insulation<br>• Damaged Wheel Speed Sensors<br>• Damaged ABS Relays<br>• Damaged Hydraulic Actuation Assembly Solenoids, Motor or Pressure Switches<br>• Damaged Brake On/Off Switch<br>• Damaged ABS Control Module | • Insufficient ABS Hydraulic Fluid<br>• Damaged Wheel Speed Sensor Rotors<br>• Damaged Hydraulic Actuation Assembly |

**Fig. 4 Visual inspection chart**

| CONDITION | POSSIBLE SOURCE | ACTION |
|---|---|---|
| • ABS Warning Light Always ON | • Blown fuse (10 AMP).<br>• ABS Electrical Circuit Failure.<br>• ABS Warning Light Circuit Shorted.<br>• ABS Wheel Sensor Failure.<br>• ABS Relay(s) Failure<br>• Hydraulic Actuation Unit Failure<br>• ABS Control Module Failure.<br>• Low Alternator Voltage Output. | • GO to ABS Quick Test. |
| • ABS Warning Light Flashes | • Intermittent ABS Electrical Circuit Failure.<br>• ABS Control Module Malfunction.<br>• Intermittent ABS Relay(s) Failure.<br>• Intermittent Hydraulic Actuation Unit Failure. | • GO to ABS Quick Test. |
| • Noisy Hydraulic Actuation Unit | • ABS Electrical Circuit Failure.<br>• Hydraulic Actuation Unit Failure. | • GO to ABS Quick Test. |

| CONDITION | POSSIBLE SOURCE | ACTION |
|---|---|---|
| • ABS Warning Light Always Off | • Blown Fuse (15 AMP).<br>• Blown Warning Light Bulb<br>• ABS Warning Light Circuit Failure.<br>• ABS Control Module Failure. | • GO to ABS Quick Test. |
| • ABS Inoperative | • Blown Fuse(s).<br>• Insufficient ABS Hydraulic Fluid.<br>• ABS Electrical Circuit Failure.<br>• Inoperative ABS Relay(s).<br>• Hydraulic Actuation Unit Malfunction.<br>• Damaged Wheel Speed Sensor(s).<br>• Inoperative ABS Control Module. | • GO to ABS Quick Test. |
| • All Other Symptoms | • All Other Symptoms are Common to All Brake Systems. | |

**Fig. 5 Symptom chart**

tion assembly. It stores hydraulic fluid for use by the ABS actuation system.

### Control Unit

The control unit is located under the driver's seat. Its a digital control unit which receives inputs from wheel sensors and provides program output to the actuation assembly.

### Wheel Sensors

The wheel sensors are located at each wheel hub, **Fig. 3**.. It sends a signal to the control unit in proportion with vehicle speed.

# DIAGNOSIS & TESTING

## VISUAL INSPECTION

Refer to **Fig. 4.** for ABS visual component inspection.

The hydraulic actuation assembly is non-serviceable and cannot be pressure checked. If any of its components fail, it must be replaced as a complete unit. Problems in other areas that may effect ABS system include suspension and steering components, tire wear and air pressure, wheel bearings and brake components. If inspection is satisfactory, refer to the symptom chart, **Fig. 5.**

## QUICK TEST

The Quick test consists of two sub-tests: Key On Engine Running Test and Continuous Test. Prior to performing either test, an inspection of ABS warning light is required to verify that a fault has been detected by ABS control unit or if system is operating normally. When ABS system is operating normally, the ABS warning light will illuminate during Key On Engine Off and go off after engine has started.

If ABS warning light should stay on after engine starts, this indicates a present failure. Any time ABS warning light flashes, this indicates either a present or past (intermittent) failure. All failures are stored in ABS control unit. ABS service codes are retrieved by identifying voltage fluctuations of a voltmeter connected to ABS test connector.

Service codes may indicate different failures and parting from Quick Test may result in code identification error. It is recommended that the Quick Test procedure be followed completely. ABS warning light mode inspection and ABS service codes retrieval are covered in Quick Test.

### Key On Engine Running Test

This test when activated checks ABS

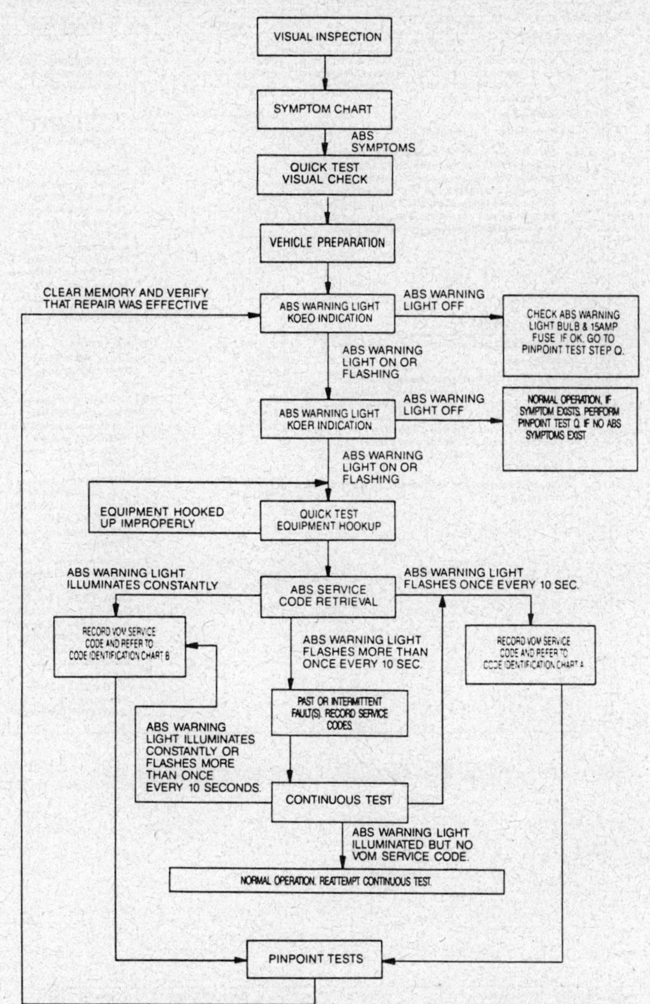


**Fig. 6 Quick test (Part 1 of 4)**

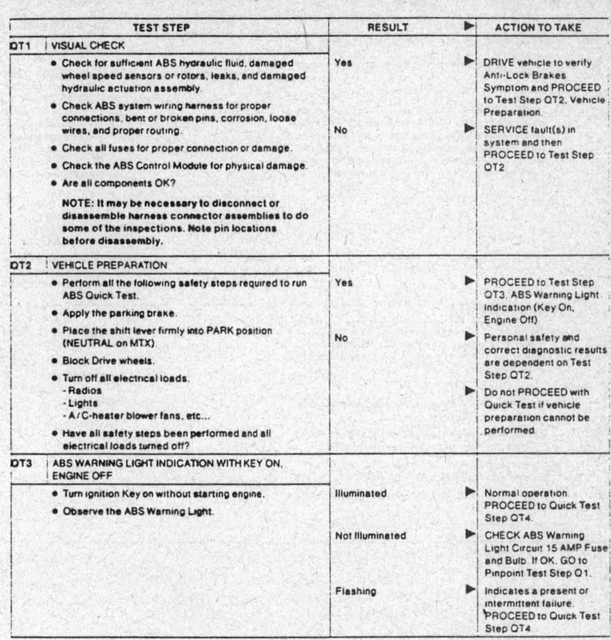

| | TEST STEP | RESULT | ▶ ACTION TO TAKE |
|---|---|---|---|
| QT1 | VISUAL CHECK | | |
| | • Check for sufficient ABS hydraulic fluid, damaged wheel speed sensors or rotors, leaks, and damaged hydraulic actuation assembly.<br>• Check ABS system wiring harness for proper connections, bent or broken pins, corrosion, loose wires, and proper routing.<br>• Check all fuses for proper connection or damage.<br>• Check the ABS Control Module for physical damage.<br>• Are all components OK?<br>**NOTE: It may be necessary to disconnect or disassemble harness connector assemblies to do some of the inspections. Note pin locations before disassembly.** | Yes<br><br>No | ▶ DRIVE vehicle to verify Anti-Lock Brakes Symptom and PROCEED to Test Step QT2, Vehicle Preparation.<br>▶ SERVICE fault(s) in system and then PROCEED to Test Step QT2 |
| QT2 | VEHICLE PREPARATION | | |
| | • Perform all the following safety steps required to run ABS Quick Test.<br>• Apply the parking brake.<br>• Place the shift lever firmly into PARK position (NEUTRAL on MTX).<br>• Block Drive wheels.<br>• Turn off all electrical loads.<br>- Radios<br>- Lights<br>- A/C-heater blower fans, etc...<br>• Have all safety steps been performed and all electrical loads turned off? | Yes<br><br>No | ▶ PROCEED to Test Step QT3, ABS Warning Light Indication (Key On, Engine Off)<br>▶ Personal safety and correct diagnostic results are dependent on Test Step QT2.<br>▶ Do not PROCEED with Quick Test if vehicle preparation cannot be performed. |
| QT3 | ABS WARNING LIGHT INDICATION WITH KEY ON, ENGINE OFF | | |
| | • Turn ignition Key on without starting engine.<br>• Observe the ABS Warning Light. | Illuminated<br><br>Not Illuminated<br><br>Flashing | ▶ Normal operation. PROCEED to Quick Test Step QT4.<br>▶ CHECK ABS Warning Light Circuit 15 AMP Fuse and Bulb. If OK, GO to Pinpoint Test Step Q1.<br>▶ Indicates a present or intermittent failure. PROCEED to Quick Test Step QT4 |

**Fig. 6 Quick test (Part 2 of 4)**

control unit and system circuitry by testing its integrity and processing capability, then verifies that the various sensors and actuators are connected and operating properly. Code patterns will be indicated through ABS test connector and ABS warning light will indicate type of failure.

### Continuous Test

This test is intended as an aid in diagnosing intermittent failures in the ABS system. It is identical to Key On Engine Running Test, but also allows the technician to enter this mode of test and to attempt to recreate the intermittent failure by tapping, moving and wiggling the harness and/or suspected sensor. If voltmeter indicates a fault, the corresponding code pattern will be indicated. Remember to observe the voltmeter/ohmmeter and ABS warning light for any change which will indicate intermittent is located. Anytime a repair is made, erase ABS control unit memory and repeat quick test to to ensure repair was effective. If all phases of quick test result in a pass it is likely the problem is non-electronic related. For quick test, refer to **Fig. 6.** For ABS warning light code indication charts, refer to **Figs. 7 and 8.**

## CLEARING MEMORY CODES

To clear memory codes, refer to **Fig. 9.**

## PINPOINT TEST

Do not perform any of the following pinpoint tests unless instructed to so by the Quick Test. Each pinpoint test assumes that a fault (malfunction) has been detected in the system with direction to enter a specific repair routine. Conducting any pinpoint test without direction from the quick test procedures may produce incorrect results and replacement of satisfactory components. Correct test results for quick test are dependent on the proper operation of related components/systems. Do not replace any component unless the test result indicates replacement. When more than one service code is received always start service with the first code received. Refer to wiring circuit, **Fig. 10.** when performing the Pinpoint Tests to locate wire circuits indicated in the test procedure. For Pinpoint Tests, refer to **Figs. 11 through 25.**

## COMPONENT REPLACEMENT

### HYDRAULIC ACTUATION UNIT

1. Remove fuel and air filter assembly.
2. Remove coil assembly, then disconnect wiring harness from bottom of coil and fuel filter mounting bracket.
3. Remove coil and fuel filter mounting brackets.
4. Disconnect three electrical connectors, then remove two banjo bolts and washers from brake lines at hydraulic actuation unit.
5. Remove banjo bolts and washers from master cylinder, then disconnect brake lines between master cylinder and hydraulic actuation unit. **Note routing of brake lines to ensure proper installation.**
6. Remove routing clip from brake lines. Using a six inch extension and 6 point, 10mm crowfoot wrench, disconnect four brake lines at hydraulic actuation unit, **Fig. 26.**
7. Remove mounting nuts, lockwashers and washers, then carefully lift hydraulic actuation assembly.
8. Remove mounting bushings from hydraulic actuation assembly.
9. Remove attaching bolts and hydraulic unit mounting bracket.
10. Reverse procedure to install, noting the following:
    a. Do not remove reservoir shipping cap until hydraulic unit is installed to prevent leaking.
    b. **Torque** banjo bolts to 14-23 ft. lbs.
    c. **Torque** coil and fuel filter mounting bracket to 34-46 ft. lbs.
    d. Bleed brake system.

*Continued on page 20-45*

| TEST STEP | RESULT | ACTION TO TAKE |
|---|---|---|
| **QT4 ABS WARNING LIGHT INDICATION WITH ENGINE RUNNING** | | |
| • Start engine.<br>• Drive vehicle if no light, if necessary<br>**NOTE: Certain ABS faults require that the vehicle be driven in order for the warning light to come on. Other faults will cause the light to turn on each time the engine is started. If a service code is in ABS Control Module Memory, the warning light will flash once each time the vehicle is started.**<br>• Observe the ABS Warning Light | Not Illuminated | ▶ Normal operation. If ABS symptom exists or light was flashing in Test Step QT3, PERFORM Pinpoint Test Q. If no ABS symptoms exist and light was illuminated in Test Step QT3, ABS system is operating normally. |
| | Illuminated | ▶ Indicated a presend failure. PROCEED to Quick Test Step QT5. |
| | Flashing | ▶ indicated a presend or intermittent failure. PROCEED to Quick Test Step QT5. |
| **QT5 EQUIPMENT HOOKUP** | | |
| • Verify that a failure has been detected in the ABS System. (An illuminated or flashing ABS Warning Light in the "Key On Engine Running" mode indicates a failure.)<br>• Turn ignition key OFF.<br>• Remove the driver's seat to access the ABS Control Module.<br>• Connect a jumper wire at the test connector from the "GN/BK" to "BK" terminals. (see illustration.)<br>• Connect an Analog VOM between the "GN/R" terminal and engine ground (see illustration.)<br>• Set the VOM on a DC Voltage Range to read from 0 to 20 Volts.<br>• Is the jumper wire and VOM hooked up properly as shown in illustration? | Yes | ▶ PROCEED to QT6, ABS Service Code Retrieval. |
| | No | ▶ RE-ATTEMPT Step QT5, Equipment Hookup. SERVICE any faults if necessary. |

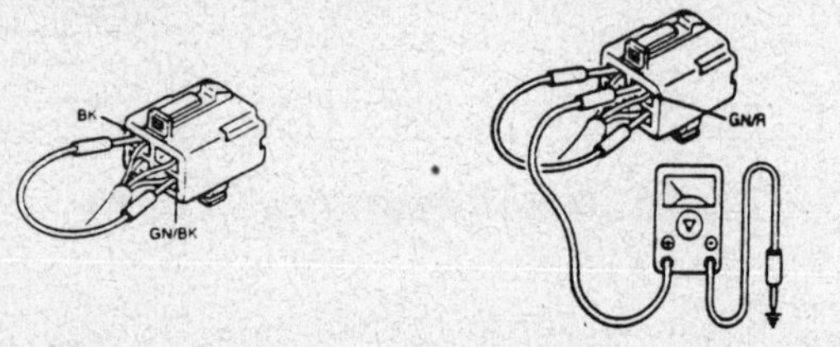

**Fig. 6 Quick test (Part 3 of 4)**

| TEST STEP | RESULT | ACTION TO TAKE |
|---|---|---|
| **QT6 ABS SERVICE CODE RETRIEVAL** | | |
| • Verify that the ABS Warning Light illuminated (Prior to equipment hookup) in the Key On Engine Off Test and illuminated or flashed in the Key On Engine Running Test before continuing.<br>• Start engine.<br>• Observe ABS Warning Light.<br>**NOTE: When a Service Code is reported on the Analog VOM, it will represent itself as a pulsing or sweeping movement of the Voltmeter's needle across the dial face. Code 1 will be represented by one pulse every 10 seconds and Code 2 by two pulses every 10 seconds and so on. Codes will be repeated after all memory codes have been displayed once.** | Flashes once every 10 seconds | ▶ RECORD VOM Service Codes and REFER to Code Identification Chart A. |
| | Illuminated constantly | ▶ RECORD VOM Service Codes and REFER to Code Identification Chart B. |
| | Flashes more than once every 10 seconds | ▶ Indicates past or intermittent fault(s). Be sure to RECORD the service codes before erasing each fault (REFER to Code Identification Chart B). ERASE fault incidents from the memory one at a time as explained in Clearing Memory Codes, then PROCEED to QT7. |
| **QT7 CONTINUOUS TEST** | | |
| • Hookup VOM and jumper wire as in Test Step QT5.<br>• Start engine.<br>• You are now in the Engine Running Continuous Monitor Mode. Tap, move and wiggle suspect sensor and/or harness working with short sections from the sensor to Dash Panel and to ABS Control Module. It is necessary to drive the vehicle each time this is done in order to recreate the intermittent failure and to allow the Control Module to sense and record a Service Code.<br>• Keep your eyes on the ABS Warning Light and VOM for any indication. | Flashes more than once every 10 seconds | ▶ RECORD VOM Service Codes, and REFER to Code Identification Chart B. |
| | Flashes once every 10 seconds | ▶ RECORD VOM Service Codes and REFER to Code Identification Chart A. SERVICE only the codes recreated in this Test Step. |
| | Illuminated constantly | ▶ RECORD VOM Service Codes and REFER to Code Identification Chart B. SERVICE only the Codes recreated in this Test Step. |
| | Illuminated but no VOM Service Code | ▶ Normal operation. If intermittent fault cannot be recreated, disconnect suspect Sensor and Control Unit from harness very carefully. Visually INSPECT all terminals for corrosion, bad crimps, improperly seated terminals, etc. RECONNECT harness connectors and RE-ATTEMPT Continuous Test. |

**Fig. 6 Quick test (Part 4 of 4)**

| ABS Warning Light Indication | VOM Indication | Service Code | Action To Take |
|---|---|---|---|
| Flashes Once Every 10 Seconds | 12 V / 10 SECONDS / 0 V | 01 | GO to Pinpoint Test AFR |
| | 12 V / 10 SECONDS / 0 V | 02 | GO to Pinpoint Test AFL |
| | 12 V / 10 SECONDS / 0 V | 03 | GO to Pinpoint Test ARW |
| | 12 V / 10 SECONDS / 0 V | 04 | GO to Pinpoint Test BFR |
| | 12 V / 10 SECONDS / 0 V | 05 | GO to Pinpoint Test BFL |
| | 12 V / 10 SECONDS / 0 V | 06 | GO to Pinpoint Test BRR |
| | 12 V / 10 SECONDS / 0 V | 07 | GO to Pinpoint Test BRL |
| | 0 V | No Codes | GO to Pinpoint Test Q |
| Flashes Continuously | Pulses With ABS Warning Light | No Codes | GO to Pinpoint Test P |

NOTE: For any service codes retrieved that are not listed go to Pinpoint Test Q.

**Fig. 7 Code identification chart A**

| ABS Warning Light Indication | VOM Indication | Service Code | Action To Take |
|---|---|---|---|
| • Illuminated Constantly For Present Failure.<br>• Flashes Four Times Every 10 Seconds For Past Failure. | 12 V / 10 SECONDS / 0 V | 01 | GO to Pinpoint Test CA |
| • Illuminated Constantly For Present Failure.<br>• Flashes Six Times Every 10 Seconds For Past Failure. | 12 V / 10 SECONDS / 0 V | 02 | GO to Pinpoint Test DB |
| | 12 V / 10 SECONDS / 0 V | 03 | GO to Pinpoint Test DC |
| | 12 V / 10 SECONDS / 0 V | 04 | GO to Pinpoint Test DE |
| | 12 V / 10 SECONDS / 0 V | 05 | GO to Pinpoint Test FA |
| | 12 V / 10 SECONDS / 0 V | 06 | GO to Pinpoint Test HUC |
| Illuminated Constantly. | 0 V | No Codes | GO to Pinpoint Test Q |

NOTE: For any service codes retrieved that are not listed go to Pinpoint Test Q.

**Fig. 8 Code identification chart B**

ABS CONTROL MODULE (LOCATED UNDER DRIVER'S SEAT)

STEP A:

GN/R

CONNECTED

GN/BK

JUMPER WIRE

STEP B:

JUMPER WIRE

OPEN

**HOW TO CLEAR CODES IN MEMORY.**

**Step A:**
1. Connect a and b terminals with a jumper wire.
2. Turn the ignition switch ON.
3. Check that warning light is illuminated, and wait 1—2 seconds.
4. Turn the ignition switch OFF.

**Step B:**
5. Disconnect the jumper wire from terminal a.
6. Start the engine and wait for the warning lamp to go OFF.
7. Turn the ignition switch OFF after 30 seconds.
8. Remove the jumper wire.

**NOTE:**
1. One failure condition is erased each time steps 1—7 are taken. Since the memory has the capacity of storing 32 failures, repeat the process if the warning light flashes after repairs have been made.
2. Repeat the steps until all memories have been cancelled.
3. The memory in the control unit is not cancelled when the battery is disconnected.

**Fig. 9 Clearing memory codes**

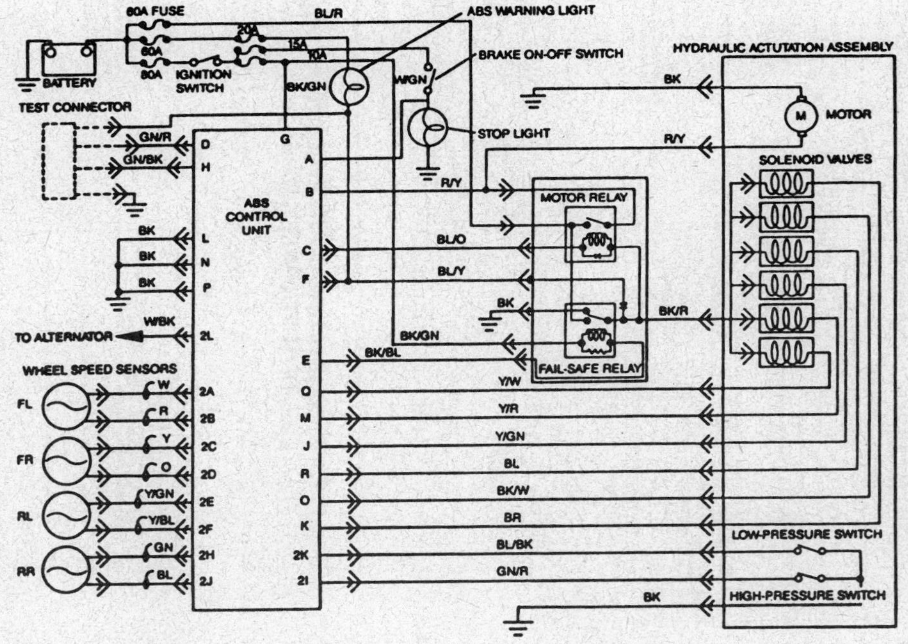


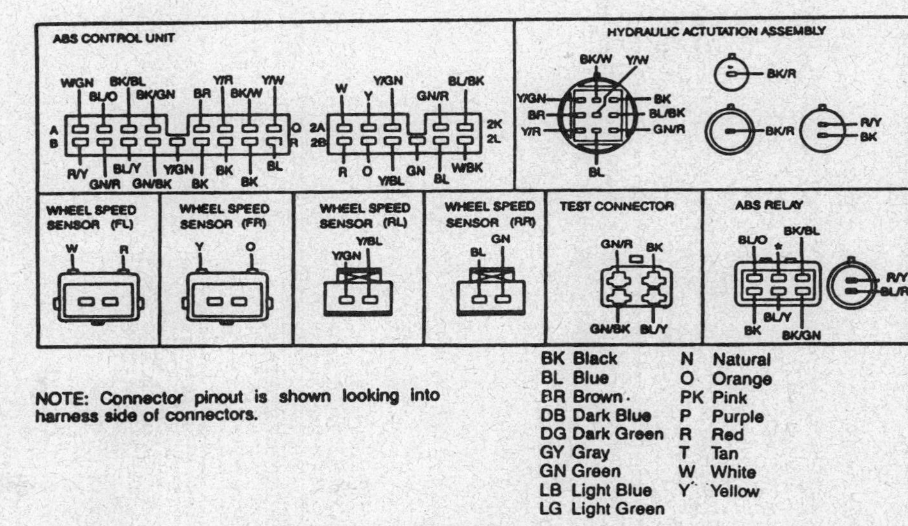


NOTE: Connector pinout is shown looking into harness side of connectors.

| | | | |
|---|---|---|---|
| BK | Black | N | Natural |
| BL | Blue | O | Orange |
| BR | Brown | PK | Pink |
| DB | Dark Blue | P | Purple |
| DG | Dark Green | R | Red |
| GY | Gray | T | Tan |
| GN | Green | W | White |
| LB | Light Blue | Y | Yellow |
| LG | Light Green | | |

**Fig. 10 ABS wiring circuit**

| TEST STEP | | RESULT | ▶ | ACTION TO TAKE |
|---|---|---|---|---|
| AFR1 | INTEGRITY | | | |
| | • Visually inspect all wiring, wiring harness, connectors, brake lines and components for evidence of overheating, insulation damage, looseness, shorting or other damage.<br>• Is there any cause for concern? | Yes<br>No | ▶<br>▶ | SERVICE as required.<br>GO to AFR2. |

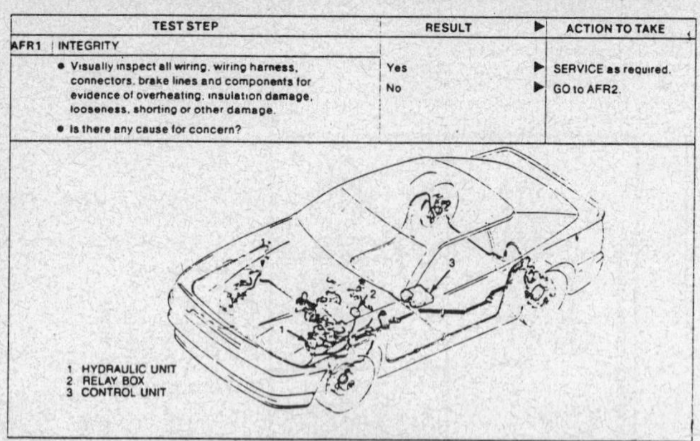


**Fig. 11 Pinpoint test AFR. Front right wheel sensor (Part 1 of 4)**

| TEST STEP | | RESULT | ▶ | ACTION TO TAKE |
|---|---|---|---|---|
| AFR2 | SHORT TO GROUND CHECK | | | |
| | • Key OFF.<br>• ABS module disconnected.<br>• VOM 200K ohm scale.<br>• Measure resistance between ABS module connector "Y" wire and ground.<br>• Is resistance above 10K ohms? | Yes<br>No | ▶<br>▶ | GO to AFR3.<br>REPAIR short to ground "Y" and/or "O" wire(s) from speed sensor to unit. |
| AFR3 | RESISTANCE AT ABS MODULE CONNECTOR | | | |
| | • Key OFF.<br>• ABS Module disconnected.<br>• VOM 2000 ohm scale.<br>• Measure resistance between "V" wire and "O" wire at the ABS module connector leading to the wheel sensor.<br>• Is resistance reading 800-1200 ohms? | Yes<br>No | ▶<br>▶ | GO to AFR5.<br>GO to AFR4. |
| AFR4 | RESISTANCE AT SENSOR | | | |
| | • Disconnect right front sensor.<br>• VOM 2000 ohm scale.<br>• Measure resistance between right front sensor pins ("Y" and "O" wires).<br>• Is resistance reading 800-1200 ohms? | Yes<br>No | ▶<br>▶ | REPAIR "Y" and/or "O" wire(s) from sensor to unit.<br>REPLACE right front wheel speed sensor. |

FRONT
WHEEL SPEED SENSOR
SENSOR ROTOR
OHMMETER
FRONT

**Fig. 11 Pinpoint test AFR. Front right wheel sensor (Part 2 of 4)**

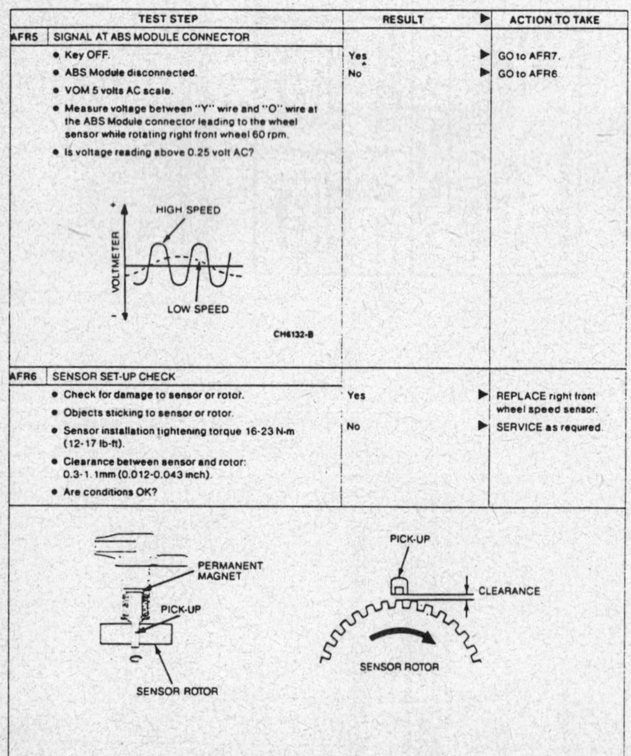

| TEST STEP | | RESULT | ▶ | ACTION TO TAKE |
|---|---|---|---|---|
| AFR5 | SIGNAL AT ABS MODULE CONNECTOR | | | |
| | • Key OFF.<br>• ABS Module disconnected.<br>• VOM 5 volts AC scale.<br>• Measure voltage between "Y" wire and "O" wire at the ABS Module connector leading to the wheel sensor while rotating right front wheel 60 rpm.<br>• Is voltage reading above 0.25 volt AC? | Yes<br>No | ▶<br>▶ | GO to AFR7.<br>GO to AFR6. |
| AFR6 | SENSOR SET-UP CHECK | | | |
| | • Check for damage to sensor or rotor.<br>• Objects sticking to sensor or rotor.<br>• Sensor installation tightening torque 16-23 N-m (12-17 lb-ft).<br>• Clearance between sensor and rotor: 0.3-1.1mm (0.012-0.043 inch).<br>• Are conditions OK? | Yes<br>No | ▶<br>▶ | REPLACE right front wheel speed sensor.<br>SERVICE as required. |



**Fig. 11 Pinpoint test AFR. Front right wheel sensor (Part 3 of 4)**

| TEST STEP | | RESULT | ▶ | ACTION TO TAKE |
|---|---|---|---|---|
| AFR7 | ABS UNIT CHECK | | | |
| | • Connect check connector "GN/BK" and "BK" terminals with jumper wire.<br>• Start engine.<br>• Verify ABS warning light remains illuminated.<br>• Drive vehicle at 15 km/h (9 mph).<br>• Does ABS warning light flash 0.25 seconds on/off? | Yes<br>No | ▶<br>▶ | CHECK brake lines to right front wheel; if OK, REPLACE hydraulic unit.<br>REPLACE ABS module. |

BK
GN/BK

**Fig. 11 Pinpoint test AFR. Front right wheel sensor (Part 4 of 4)**

| TEST STEP | | RESULT | ▶ | ACTION TO TAKE |
|---|---|---|---|---|
| AFL1 | INTEGRITY | | | |
| | • Visually inspect all wiring, wiring harness, connectors, brake lines and components for evidence of overheating, insulation damage, looseness, shorting or other damage.<br>• Is there any cause for concern? See illustration in TEST STEP AFR1. | Yes<br>No | ▶<br>▶ | SERVICE as required.<br>GO to AFL2. |
| AFL2 | SHORT TO GROUND CHECK | | | |
| | • Key OFF.<br>• ABS module disconnected.<br>• VOM 200K ohm scale.<br>• Measure resistance between ABS module connector "W" wire and ground.<br>• Is resistance above 10K ohms? | Yes<br>No | ▶<br>▶ | GO to AFL3.<br>REPAIR short to ground "W" and/or "R" wire(s) from sensor to unit. |

**Fig. 12 Pinpoint test AFL. Front left wheel sensor (Part 1 of 3)**

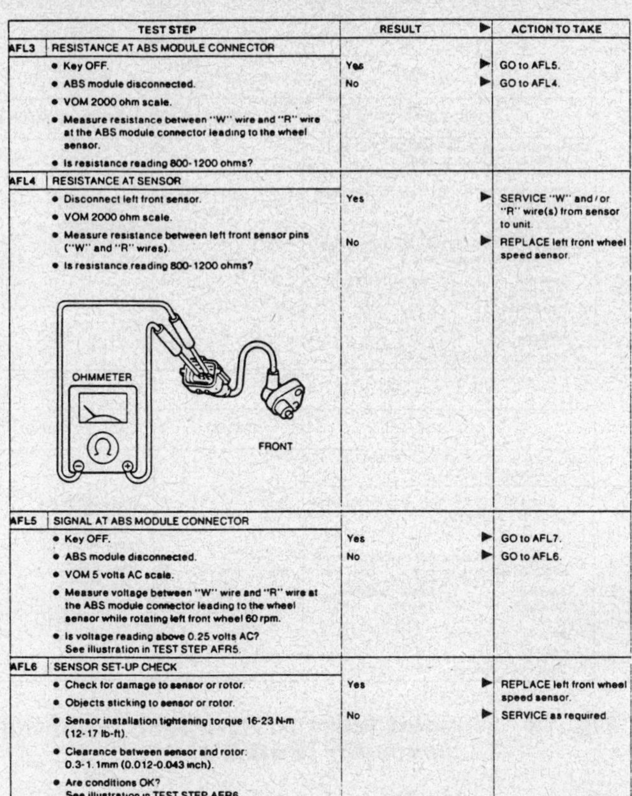

| TEST STEP | RESULT | ACTION TO TAKE |
|---|---|---|
| **AFL3 RESISTANCE AT ABS MODULE CONNECTOR** | | |
| • Key OFF.<br>• ABS module disconnected.<br>• VOM 2000 ohm scale.<br>• Measure resistance between "W" wire and "R" wire at the ABS module connector leading to the wheel sensor.<br>• Is resistance reading 800-1200 ohms? | Yes<br>No | ▶ GO to AFL5.<br>▶ GO to AFL4. |
| **AFL4 RESISTANCE AT SENSOR** | | |
| • Disconnect left front sensor.<br>• VOM 2000 ohm scale.<br>• Measure resistance between left front sensor pins ("W" and "R" wires).<br>• Is resistance reading 800-1200 ohms? | Yes<br>No | ▶ SERVICE "W" and/or "R" wire(s) from sensor to unit.<br>▶ REPLACE left front wheel speed sensor. |
| OHMMETER<br>FRONT | | |
| **AFL5 SIGNAL AT ABS MODULE CONNECTOR** | | |
| • Key OFF.<br>• ABS module disconnected.<br>• VOM 5 volts AC scale.<br>• Measure voltage between "W" wire and "R" wire at the ABS module connector leading to the wheel sensor while rotating left front wheel 60 rpm.<br>• Is voltage reading above 0.25 volts AC?<br>See illustration in TEST STEP AFR5. | Yes<br>No | ▶ GO to AFL7.<br>▶ GO to AFL6. |
| **AFL6 SENSOR SET-UP CHECK** | | |
| • Check for damage to sensor or rotor.<br>• Objects sticking to sensor or rotor.<br>• Sensor installation tightening torque 16-23 N-m (12-17 lb-ft).<br>• Clearance between sensor and rotor: 0.3-1.1mm (0.012-0.043 inch).<br>• Are conditions OK?<br>See illustration in TEST STEP AFR6. | Yes<br>No | ▶ REPLACE left front wheel speed sensor.<br>▶ SERVICE as required. |

**Fig. 12 Pinpoint test AFL. Front left wheel sensor (Part 2 of 3)**

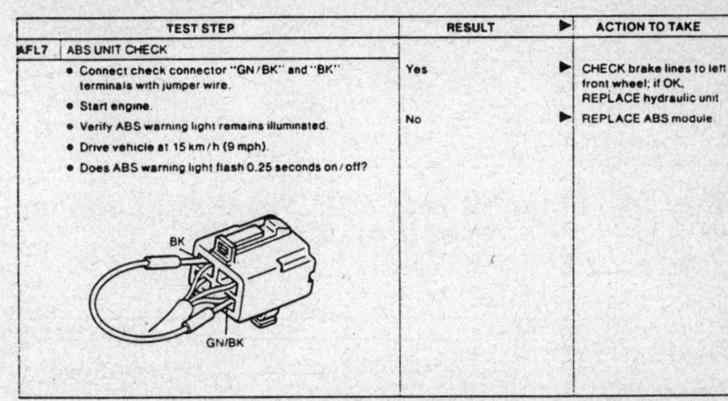

| TEST STEP | RESULT | ACTION TO TAKE |
|---|---|---|
| **AFL7 ABS UNIT CHECK** | | |
| • Connect check connector "GN/BK" and "BK" terminals with jumper wire.<br>• Start engine.<br>• Verify ABS warning light remains illuminated.<br>• Drive vehicle at 15 km/h (9 mph).<br>• Does ABS warning light flash 0.25 seconds on/off? | Yes<br>No | ▶ CHECK brake lines to left front wheel; if OK, REPLACE hydraulic unit.<br>▶ REPLACE ABS module. |
| BK<br>GN/BK | | |

**Fig. 12 Pinpoint test AFL. Front left wheel sensor (Part 3 of 3)**

| TEST STEP | RESULT | ACTION TO TAKE |
|---|---|---|
| **ARW1 INTEGRITY** | | |
| • Visually inspect all wiring, wiring harness, connectors, brake lines and components for evidence of overheating, insulation damage, looseness, shorting or other damage.<br>• Is there any cause for concern?<br>See illustration in TEST STEP AFR1. | Yes<br>No | ▶ SERVICE as required.<br>▶ GO to ARW2. |
| **ARW2 SHORT TO GROUND CHECK** | | |
| • Key OFF.<br>• ABS module disconnected.<br>• VOM 200K ohm scale.<br>• Measure resistance between ABS module connector "Y/GN" wire and ground, ABS module connector "GN" wire and ground.<br>• Is resistance above 10K ohms? | Yes<br>No | ▶ GO to ARW3.<br>▶ SERVICE short to ground from sensor(s) to ABS module. |

**Fig. 13 Pinpoint test ARW. Rear wheel speed sensor (Part 1 of 3)**

| TEST STEP | RESULT | ACTION TO TAKE |
|---|---|---|
| **ARW3 RESISTANCE AT ABS MODULE CONNECTOR** | | |
| • Key OFF.<br>• ABS module disconnected.<br>• VOM 2000 ohm scale.<br>• Measure resistance between "GN" wire and "BL" wire of the ABS module connector leading to the right rear wheel sensor.<br>• Measure resistance between "Y/GN" wire and "Y/BL" wire of the ABS module connector leading to the left rear wheel sensor.<br>• Is resistance reading 800-1200 ohms? | Yes<br>No | ▶ GO to ARW5.<br>▶ GO to ARW4. |
| **ARW4 RESISTANCE AT SENSOR** | | |
| • Disconnect rear sensor(s).<br>• VOM 2000 ohm scale.<br>• Measure resistance between right rear sensor pins ("GN" and "BL" wires), left rear sensor pins ("Y/GN" and "Y/BL" wires).<br>• Is resistance reading 800-1200 ohms? | Yes<br>No | ▶ SERVICE open in wire(s) from sensor(s) to ABS unit.<br>▶ REPLACE rear wheel speed sensor(s). |
| REAR | | |
| **ARW5 SIGNAL AT ABS MODULE CONNECTOR** | | |
| • Key OFF.<br>• VOM 5 volts AC scale.<br>• Measure voltage between "GN" wire and "BL" wire of the ABS module connector leading to the right rear wheel sensor while rotating right rear wheel 60 rpm.<br>• Measure voltage between "Y/GN" wire and "Y/BL" wire of the ABS module connector leading to the left rear wheel sensor while rotating left rear wheel 60 rpm.<br>• Is voltage reading above 0.25 volts AC?<br>See illustration in TEST STEP AFR5. | Yes<br>No | ▶ GO to ARW7.<br>▶ GO to ARW6. |

**Fig. 13 Pinpoint test ARW. Rear wheel speed sensor (Part 2 of 3)**

| TEST STEP | RESULT | ACTION TO TAKE |
|---|---|---|
| **ARW6 SENSOR SET-UP CHECK** | | |
| • Check for damage to sensor or rotor.<br>• Objects sticking to sensor or rotor.<br>• Sensor installation tightening torque 16-23 N-m (12-17 lb-ft).<br>• Clearance between sensor and rotor: 0.3-1.1mm (0.012-0.043 inch).<br>• Are conditions OK?<br>See illustration in TEST STEP AFR6. | Yes<br>No | ▶ REPLACE rear wheel speed sensor(s).<br>▶ SERVICE as required. |
| **ARW7 ABS MODULE CHECK** | | |
| • Connect check connector "GN/BK" and "BK" terminals with jumper wire.<br>• Start engine.<br>• Verify ABS warning light remains illuminated.<br>• Drive vehicle at 15 km/h (9 mph).<br>• Does ABS warning light flash 0.25 seconds on/off? | Yes<br>No | ▶ CHECK brake lines to rear wheel(s), if OK; REPLACE hydraulic actuation assembly.<br>▶ REPLACE ABS module. |
| BK<br>GN/BK | | |

**Fig. 13 Pinpoint test ARW. Rear wheel speed sensor (Part 3 of 3)**

| TEST STEP | RESULT | ACTION TO TAKE |
|---|---|---|
| **BFR1 CHECK ROTOR TEETH FOR DAMAGE** | | |
| • Visually inspect right front rotor for any signs of damage, such as broken, worn or chipped teeth, or objects sticking to rotor. Also, check related wiring, wiring harness, connectors and components for any evidence of damage.<br>• Are any concerns present?<br>See illustration in TEST STEP AFR6. | Yes<br>No | ▶ SERVICE as required.<br>▶ GO to BFR2. |

**Fig. 14 Pinpoint test BFR. Front right sensor rotor (Part 1 of 2)**

| TEST STEP | RESULT | ACTION TO TAKE |
|---|---|---|
| **BFR2** CHECK SENSOR INSTALLATION | | |
| • Sensor tightening torque: 16-23 N-m (12-17 lb-ft).<br>• Clearance between sensor and rotor: 0.3-1.1mm (0.012-0.043 inch).<br>• Are readings OK? See illustration in TEST STEP AFR6. | Yes<br>No | ► CHECK for intermittent problem from sensor to ABS control module.<br>► SERVICE as required. |

**Fig. 14 Pinpoint test BFR. Front right sensor rotor (Part 2 of 2)**

| TEST STEP | RESULT | ACTION TO TAKE |
|---|---|---|
| **BFL1** CHECK ROTOR TEETH FOR DAMAGE | | |
| • Visually inspect left front rotor for any signs of damage, such as broken, worn or chipped teeth, or objects sticking to rotor. Also, check related wiring, wiring harness, connectors and components for any evidence of damage.<br>• Are any concerns present? See illustrations in TEST STEPS AFR1 and AFR6. | Yes<br>No | ► SERVICE as required.<br>► GO to BFL2. |
| **BFL2** CHECK SENSOR INSTALLATION | | |
| • Sensor tightening torque: 16-23 N-m (12-17 lb-ft).<br>• Clearance between sensor and rotor: 0.3-1.1mm (0.012-0.043 inch).<br>• Are readings OK? See illustration in TEST STEP AFR6. | Yes<br>No | ► CHECK for intermittent problem from sensor to ABS control module.<br>► SERVICE as required. |

**Fig. 15 Pinpoint test BFL. Front left sensor rotor**

| TEST STEP | RESULT | ACTION TO TAKE |
|---|---|---|
| **BRR1** CHECK ROTOR TEETH FOR DAMAGE | | |
| • Visually inspect right rear rotor for any signs of damage, such as broken, worn or chipped teeth, or objects sticking to rotor. Also, check related wiring, wiring harness, connectors and components for any evidence of damage.<br>• Are any concerns present? See illustrations in TEST STEPS AFR1 and AFR6. | Yes<br>No | ► SERVICE as required.<br>► GO to BRR2. |
| **BRR2** CHECK SENSOR INSTALLATION | | |
| • Sensor tightening torque 16-23 N-m (12-17 lb-ft).<br>• Clearance between sensor and rotor: 0.3-1.1mm (0.012-0.043 inch).<br>• Are readings OK? See illustration in TEST STEP AFR6. | Yes<br>No | ► CHECK for intermittent problem from sensor to ABS control module.<br>► SERVICE as required. |

**Fig. 16 Pinpoint test BRR. Rear right sensor rotor**

| TEST STEP | RESULT | ACTION TO TAKE |
|---|---|---|
| **BRL1** CHECK ROTOR TEETH FOR DAMAGE | | |
| • Visually inspect left rear rotor for any signs of damage, such as broken, worn or chipped teeth, or objects sticking to rotor. Also, check related wiring, wiring harness, connectors and components for any evidence of damage.<br>• Are any concerns present? See illustrations in TEST STEPS AFR1 AND AFR6. | Yes<br>No | ► SERVICE as required.<br>► GO to BRL2. |
| **BRL2** CHECK SENSOR INSTALLATION | | |
| • Sensor tightening torque: 16-23 N-m (12-17 lb-ft).<br>• Clearance between sensor and rotor: 0.3-1.1mm (0.012-0.043 inch).<br>• Are readings OK? See illustration in TEST STEP AFR6. | Yes<br>No | ► CHECK for intermittent problem from sensor to ABS control module.<br>► SERVICE as required. |

**Fig. 17 Pinpoint test BRL. Rear left sensor rotor**

| TEST STEP | RESULT | ACTION TO TAKE |
|---|---|---|
| **CA1** INTEGRITY CHECK | | |
| • Visually inspect all wiring, wiring harness, connectors, brake lines and components for evidence of overheating, insulation damage, looseness, shorting or other damage.<br>• Is there any cause for concern? | Yes<br>No | ► SERVICE as required.<br>► GO to CA2. |

1 HYDRAULIC UNIT
2 RELAY BOX
3 CONTROL UNIT

**Fig. 18 Pinpoint test CA. Hydraulic actuation assembly (Part 1 of 4)**

| TEST STEP | RESULT | ACTION TO TAKE |
|---|---|---|
| **CA2** HYDRAULIC PUMP MOTOR CHECK FROM HYDRAULIC UNIT | | |
| • Disconnect only the "BK" wire from hydraulic unit connector.<br>• Start engine.<br>• Connect the following hydraulic unit terminals to ground with jumper wire.<br>**Terminal** — **Motor Operation**<br>"BL/BK" and "GN/R" — Off<br>"GN/R" only — On<br>"BL/BK" only — Off<br>Neither — Off<br>• Does motor operate properly? | Yes<br>No | ► GO to CA7.<br>► GO to CA3. |

| TEST STEP | RESULT | ACTION TO TAKE |
|---|---|---|
| **CA3** HYDRAULIC PUMP MOTOR CHECK FROM ABS MODULE | | |
| • Disconnect only the "BK" wire from hydraulic unit (C185 connector).<br>• Start engine.<br>• Connect the following ABS module terminals to ground with jumper wire.<br>**Terminal** — **Motor Operation**<br>2K and 2I — Off<br>2I only — On<br>2K only — Off<br>Neither — Off<br>• Does motor operate properly? | Yes<br>No | ► SERVICE "BL/BK" and/or "GN/R" wire(s) from ABS module to hydraulic unit.<br>► GO to CA4. |

**Fig. 18 Pinpoint test CA. Hydraulic actuation assembly (Part 2 of 4)**

| TEST STEP | RESULT | ACTION TO TAKE |
|---|---|---|
| **CA4** ABS OUTPUT CHECK | | |
| • Disconnect only the "BK" wire from hydraulic unit (C185 connector).<br>• Start engine.<br>• VOM 20 volt scale.<br>• Measure voltage between ABS module "BL/O" (C) and ground when:<br>• Connect the following ABS module terminals to ground with jumper wire.<br>**Terminal** — **Output at (C)**<br>2K and 2I — above 10v<br>2I only — below 2.0v<br>2K only — above 10v<br>Neither — above 10v<br>• Is output of ABS module OK? | Yes<br>No | ► GO to CA5.<br>► REPLACE ABS module. |

| TEST STEP | RESULT | ACTION TO TAKE |
|---|---|---|
| **CA5** PUMP OPERATION CHECK | | |
| • Key off.<br>• Connect 12 volts to hydraulic unit "R/Y" wire with jumper wire.<br>• Does motor operate? | Yes<br>No | ► SERVICE "R/Y" wire from hydraulic unit to hydraulic pump motor relay.<br>► GO to CA6. |

| TEST STEP | RESULT | ACTION TO TAKE |
|---|---|---|
| **CA6** HYDRAULIC UNIT GROUND CHECK | | |
| • Key off.<br>• VOM 200 ohm scale.<br>• Measure resistance between hydraulic unit "BK" wire (C196 connector) and ground.<br>• Is resistance below 5 ohms? | Yes<br>No | ► REPLACE hydraulic unit.<br>► SERVICE "BK" wire to ground. |

**Fig. 18 Pinpoint test CA. Hydraulic actuation assembly (Part 3 of 4)**

| TEST STEP | RESULT ► | ACTION TO TAKE |
|---|---|---|
| **CA7** PRESSURE SWITCH(ES) OPERATION | | |
| • Key off.<br>• VOM 200 ohm scale.<br>• Measure resistance between hydraulic unit "GN/R" wire and ground hydraulic unit "BL/BK" wire and ground.<br>• Depress brake pedal several times.<br>• Connect 12 volts to hydraulic unit "Y/W," "Y/R," and "Y/GN" for 30 seconds each; (to relieve pressure in hydraulic unit).<br>• Connect 12 volts to hydraulic unit pump motor "R/Y" wire for 30 seconds; (to increase pressure).<br>Resistance<br>Pressure — "GN/R" — "BL/BK"<br>Low — Open — Open<br>Normal — 0 ohms — Open<br>High — 0 ohms — 0 ohms<br>• Are conditions OK? | Yes ►<br><br>No ► | REPAIR "BK" wire to ground (C185 connector).<br><br>REPLACE hydraulic actuation assembly. |

**Fig. 18 Pinpoint test CA. Hydraulic actuation assembly (Part 4 of 4)**

| TEST STEP | RESULT ► | ACTION TO TAKE |
|---|---|---|
| **DB1** INTEGRITY | | |
| • Visually inspect all wiring, wiring harness, connectors, brake lines, and components for evidence of overheating, insulation damage, looseness, shorting or other damage.<br>• Is there any cause for concern?<br>See illustration in TEST CA1 | Yes ►<br>No ► | SERVICE as required.<br>GO to DB2 |

**Fig. 19 Pinpoint test DB. Hydraulic pump motor relay B (Part 1 of 4)**

| TEST STEP | RESULT ► | ACTION TO TAKE |
|---|---|---|
| **DB2** VOLTAGE AT ABS MODULE (C) | | |
| • Disconnect ABS module.<br>• Connect relay "BK/BL" wire to ground with jumper wire.<br>• VOM 20 volt scale.<br>• Measure voltage between ABS module "BL/O" wire and ground.<br>Key off .............................. 0v<br>Key on ...................... above 10v<br>• Are voltage readings OK? | Yes ►<br>No ► | GO to DB3.<br>GO to DB8. |

| TEST STEP | RESULT ► | ACTION TO TAKE |
|---|---|---|
| **DB3** VOLTAGE AT ABS MODULE (B) | | |
| • Disconnect ABS module.<br>• Key on.<br>• VOM on 20 volt scale.<br>• Measure voltage between ABS module B ("R/Y" wire) and ground.<br>• Is voltage below 1.5 volts? | Yes ►<br>No ► | GO to DB5.<br>GO to DB4. |

| TEST STEP | RESULT ► | ACTION TO TAKE |
|---|---|---|
| **DB4** VOLTAGE (B) WITHOUT RELAY | | |
| • Disconnect relay, ABS module.<br>• Key on.<br>• VOM 20 volt scale.<br>• Measure voltage between ABS module "R/Y" wire and ground.<br>• Is voltage below 1.5 volts? | Yes ►<br>No ► | REPLACE relay.<br>REPAIR "R/Y" wire. |

**Fig. 19 Pinpoint test DB. Hydraulic pump motor relay B (Part 2 of 4)**

| TEST STEP | RESULT ► | ACTION TO TAKE |
|---|---|---|
| **DB5** CONTINUITY TO GROUND AT (B) | | |
| • Key off.<br>• VOM 200 ohm scale.<br>• Measure resistance between ABS module "R/Y" wire and ground.<br>• Is resistance below 100 ohms? | Yes ►<br>No ► | REPLACE ABS control module.<br>GO to DB6 |

| TEST STEP | RESULT ► | ACTION TO TAKE |
|---|---|---|
| **DB6** CONTINUITY TO HYDRAULIC ACTUATION ASSEMBLY | | |
| • Key off.<br>• VOM 200 ohm scale.<br>• Measure resistance between ABS module "R/Y" and hydraulic actuation assembly "R/Y."<br>• Is resistance below 5 ohms? | Yes ►<br>No ► | GO to DB7.<br>REPAIR "R/Y" wire. |

| TEST STEP | RESULT ► | ACTION TO TAKE |
|---|---|---|
| **DB7** HYDRAULIC GROUND CHECK | | |
| • Key off.<br>• VOM 200 ohm scale.<br>• Measure resistance between hydraulic actuation assembly "BK" wire and ground.<br>• Is resistance below 5 ohms? | Yes ►<br><br>No ► | REPLACE hydraulic actuation assembly.<br>NOTE: Check hydraulic pump motor operation.<br>REPAIR "BK" ground wire. |

**Fig. 19 Pinpoint test DB. Hydraulic pump motor relay B (Part 3 of 4)**

| TEST STEP | RESULT ► | ACTION TO TAKE |
|---|---|---|
| **DB8** VOLTAGE AT RELAY | | |
| • Disconnect ABS module.<br>• Connect relay "BK/BL" wire to ground with jumper wire.<br>• VOM 20v scale.<br>• Measure voltage between relay "BL/O" wire and ground.<br>Key off .............................. 0v<br>Key on ...................... above 10v<br>• Are voltage readings OK? | Yes ►<br><br>No ► | REPAIR "BL/O" wire from relay to ABS module.<br>GO to Pinpoint Test Q. |

**Fig. 19 Pinpoint test DB. Hydraulic pump motor relay B (Part 4 of 4)**

| TEST STEP | RESULT ► | ACTION TO TAKE |
|---|---|---|
| **DC1** INTEGRITY | | |
| • Visually inspect all wiring, wiring harness, connectors, brake lines, and components for evidence of overheating, insulation damage, looseness, shorting or other damage.<br>• Is there any cause for concern?<br>See illustration in TEST STEP CA1 | Yes ►<br>No ► | SERVICE as required.<br>GO to DC2. |

**Fig. 20 Pinpoint test DC. Hydraulic pump motor relay C (Part 1 of 3)**

| TEST STEP | RESULT ► | ACTION TO TAKE |
|---|---|---|
| DC2 VOLTAGE AT ABS MODULE (C) | | |
| • Disconnect ABS module.<br>• Connect relay "BK/BL" wire to ground with jumper wire.<br>• VOM 20 volt scale.<br>• Measure voltage between ABS module "BL/O" wire and ground.<br>Key off .......... 0v<br>Key on .......... above 10v<br>• Are voltage readings OK? | Yes ►<br>No ► | GO to DC3.<br>GO to DC5. |

| TEST STEP | RESULT ► | ACTION TO TAKE |
|---|---|---|
| DC3 VOLTAGE AT ABS MODULE (E) | | |
| • Disconnect ABS module.<br>• VOM 20 volt scale.<br>• Measure voltage between ABS module "BK/BL" wire and ground<br>Key off .......... 0v<br>Key on .......... above 10v<br>• Are voltage readings OK? | Yes ►<br>No ► | REPLACE ABS module.<br>GO to DC4. |

| TEST STEP | RESULT ► | ACTION TO TAKE |
|---|---|---|
| DC4 VOLTAGE FROM RELAY | | |
| • Disconnect ABS module.<br>• VOM 20 volt scale.<br>• Measure voltage between relay "BK/BL" wire and ground<br>Key off .......... 0v<br>Key on .......... above 10v<br>• Are voltage readings OK? | Yes ►<br>No ► | REPAIR "BK/BL" wire from relay to ABS module.<br>GO to Pinpoint Test Q. |

**Fig. 20 Pinpoint test DC. Hydraulic pump motor relay C (Part 2 of 3)**

| TEST STEP | RESULT ► | ACTION TO TAKE |
|---|---|---|
| DC5 VOLTAGE AT RELAY ("BL/O") | | |
| • Disconnect ABS module.<br>• Connect relay "BK/BL" wire to ground with jumper wire.<br>• VOM 20 volt scale.<br>• Measure voltage between relay "BL/O" wire and ground<br>Key off .......... 0v<br>Key on .......... above 10v<br>• Are voltage readings OK? | Yes ►<br>No ► | REPAIR "BL/O" wire from relay to ABS module.<br>GO to Pinpoint Test Q. |

**Fig. 20 Pinpoint test DC. Hydraulic pump motor relay C (Part 3 of 3)**

| TEST STEP | RESULT ► | ACTION TO TAKE |
|---|---|---|
| DE1 INTEGRITY | | |
| • Visually inspect all wiring, wiring harness, connectors, brake lines, and components for evidence of overheating, insulation damage, looseness, shorting or other damage.<br>• Is there any cause for concern?<br>See illustration in TEST CA1 | Yes ►<br>No ► | SERVICE as required.<br>GO to DE2. |

**Fig. 21 Pinpoint test DE. Hydraulic motor pump relay E (Part 1 of 4)**

| TEST STEP | RESULT ► | ACTION TO TAKE |
|---|---|---|
| DE2 VOLTAGE AT HYDRAULIC ACTUATION ASSEMBLY | | |
| • Disconnect ABS module.<br>• Connect relay "BK/BL" wire to ground with jumper wire.<br>• VOM 20 volt scale.<br>• Measure voltage between hydraulic actuation assembly "BK/R" wire and ground.<br>Key off .......... 0v<br>Key on .......... above 10v<br>• Are voltage readings OK? | Yes ►<br>No ► | GO to DE3.<br>GO to Pinpoint Test Q. |

| TEST STEP | RESULT ► | ACTION TO TAKE |
|---|---|---|
| DE3 VOLTAGE AT ABS MODULE TERMINAL (E) | | |
| • Disconnect ABS module.<br>• VOM 20 volt scale.<br>• Measure voltage between ABS module "BK/BL" wire and ground.<br>Key off .......... 0v<br>Key on .......... above 10v<br>• Are voltage readings OK? | Yes ►<br>No ► | GO to DE4.<br>REPAIR "BK/BL" wire from relay to ABS module. |

| TEST STEP | RESULT ► | ACTION TO TAKE |
|---|---|---|
| DE4 RELAY DIODE CHECK AT ABS MODULE | | |
| • Disconnect ABS module.<br>• Key off.<br>• VOM 200 ohm scale<br>• Measure resistance between ABS module "BL/O" wire (+) and relay "BK" wire (–).<br>• Change (+) and (–) leads.<br>• Does resistance increase when leads are changed? | Yes ►<br>No ► | GO to DE6.<br>GO to DE5. |

**Fig. 21 Pinpoint test DE. Hydraulic motor pump relay E (Part 2 of 4)**

| TEST STEP | RESULT ► | ACTION TO TAKE |
|---|---|---|
| DE5 RELAY DIODE CHECK AT RELAY | | |
| • Disconnect relay.<br>• Key off.<br>• VOM 200 ohm scale<br>• Measure resistance between relay "BL/O" (+) and "BK" (–) terminals.<br>• Change (+) and (–) leads.<br>• Does resistance increase when leads are changed? | Yes ►<br>No ► | REPAIR "BL/O" wire from relay to ABS module.<br>REPLACE relay. |

| TEST STEP | RESULT ► | ACTION TO TAKE |
|---|---|---|
| DE6 VOLTAGE AT ABS MODULE TERMINAL (B) | | |
| • Disconnect ABS module.<br>• Connect relay "BL/O" wire to ground with jumper wire.<br>• VOM 20 volt scale.<br>• Measure voltage between ABS module "R/Y" wire and ground.<br>Key off .......... 0v<br>Key on .......... above 10v<br>• Are voltage readings OK? | Yes ►<br>No ► | REPLACE ABS control module.<br>GO to DE7. |

| TEST STEP | RESULT ► | ACTION TO TAKE |
|---|---|---|
| DE7 VOLTAGE AT ABS MODULE TERMINAL (B) WITHOUT MOTOR | | |
| • Disconnect ABS module and hydraulic actuation assembly.<br>• Connect relay "BL/O" wire to ground with jumper wire.<br>• Measure voltage between ABS module "R/Y" wire and ground<br>Key off .......... 0v<br>Key on .......... above 10v<br>• Are voltage readings OK? | Yes ►<br>No ► | REPLACE hydraulic actuation assembly.<br>GO to DE8. |

**Fig. 21 Pinpoint test DE. Hydraulic motor pump relay E (Part 3 of 4)**

| TEST STEP | RESULT ► | ACTION TO TAKE |
|---|---|---|
| DE8 VOLTAGE FROM RELAY | | |
| • Disconnect ABS module.<br>• Connect relay "BL/O" wire to ground with jumper wire.<br>• VOM 20 volt scale.<br>• Measure voltage between relay "R/Y" wire and ground.<br>Key off ............................ 0v<br>Key on ..................... above 10v<br>• Are voltage readings OK? | Yes ►<br>No ► | SERVICE "R/Y" wire from relay to ABS module.<br>GO to Pinpoint Test Q. |

**Fig. 21 Pinpoint test DE. Hydraulic motor pump relay E (Part 4 of 4)**

| TEST STEP | RESULT ► | ACTION TO TAKE |
|---|---|---|
| FA1 INTEGRITY | | |
| • Visually inspect all wiring, wiring harness, connectors, brake lines, and components for evidence of overheating, insulation damage, looseness, shorting or other damage.<br>• Is there any cause for concern?<br>See illustration in TEST CA1 | Yes ►<br>No ► | SERVICE as required.<br>GO to FA2. |

**Fig. 22 Pinpoint test FA. Solenoid control valve (Part 1 of 3)**

| TEST STEP | RESULT ► | ACTION TO TAKE |
|---|---|---|
| FA2 SOLENOID SIGNAL CHECK | | |
| • Disconnect hydraulic actuation assembly.<br>• VOM 20 volt scale.<br>• Measure voltage between hydraulic motor relay "BK/R" and ground.<br>Condition — Voltage<br>Key off — 0v<br>Key on — Above 10v<br>• Are voltage readings OK? | Yes ►<br>No ► | GO to FA3.<br>GO to FA5. |

| TEST STEP | RESULT ► | ACTION TO TAKE |
|---|---|---|
| FA3 SOLENOID CHECK AT ABS MODULE | | |
| • Key off.<br>• Disconnect ABS module.<br>• VOM 200 ohm scale.<br>• Measure resistance between: | Yes ►<br>No ► | REPLACE ABS control module.<br>Service wire in question, if all OK, GO to FA4. |

| ABS Module | Hydraulic Actuation Assembly | Resistance (OHMs) |
|---|---|---|
| Y/W | BK & R/Y | Over 10,000 |
| | BK/R | 0-4 |
| Y/R | BK & R/Y | Over 10,000 |
| | BK/R | 0-4 |
| Y/GN | BK & R/Y | Over 10,000 |
| | BK/R | 0-4 |
| BL | BK & R/Y | Over 10,000 |
| | BK/R | 0-4 |
| BK/W | BK & R/Y | Over 10,000 |
| | BK/R | 0-4 |
| BR | BK & R/Y | Over 10,000 |
| | BK/R | 0-4 |

• Are all resistance readings OK?

**Fig. 22 Pinpoint test FA. Solenoid control valve (Part 2 of 3)**

| TEST STEP | RESULT ► | ACTION TO TAKE |
|---|---|---|
| FA4 SOLENOID CHECK AT HYDRAULIC ACTUATION ASSEMBLY | | |
| • Key off.<br>• VOM 200 ohm scale.<br>• Measure resistance between:<br>Hydraulic Actuation Assembly Terminal: "Y/W", "Y/R", "Y/GN", "BL", "BK/W", "BR"<br>Hydraulic Actuation Assembly Terminal: "BK/R"<br>Resistance: Between 2 and and 4 ohms<br>• Are all resistance readings OK? | Yes ►<br>No ► | SERVICE wire(s) in question.<br>REPLACE hydraulic Act. Asy. |

| TEST STEP | RESULT ► | ACTION TO TAKE |
|---|---|---|
| FA5 RELAY OPERATION | | |
| • VOM 20 volt scale.<br>• Measure voltage between hydraulic relay "BK/R" and ground.<br>Condition — Voltage<br>Key off — 0V<br>Key on — Above 10V<br>• Are voltage readings OK? | Yes ►<br>No ► | SERVICE "BK/R" wire from relay to hydraulic actuator assembly.<br>GO to Pinpoint Test Q1. |

**Fig. 22 Pinpoint test FA. Solenoid control valve (Part 3 of 3)**

| TEST STEP | RESULT ► | ACTION TO TAKE |
|---|---|---|
| HUC1 INTEGRITY | | |
| • Visually inspect all wiring, wiring harness, connectors, brake lines and components for evidence of overheating, insulation damage, looseness, shorting or other damage.<br>• Is there any cause for concern?<br>See illustration in TEST STEP AFR1. | Yes ►<br>No ► | SERVICE as required.<br>GO to HUC2. |

| TEST STEP | RESULT ► | ACTION TO TAKE |
|---|---|---|
| HUC2 POWER TO ABS MODULE | | |
| • VOM 20 volt scale.<br>• Measure voltage between: ABS module terminal G ("BK/GN" wire) and ground.<br>Condition — Voltage<br>Key Off — 0v<br>Key On — Above 10v<br>Engine Running — Above 10v<br>ABS module terminal 2L ("W/BK" wire) and ground.<br>Condition — Voltage<br>Key Off — 0v–3v<br>Key On — 0v–3v<br>Engine Running — Above 12v<br>• Are voltage readings OK? | Yes ►<br>No ► | GO to HUC3.<br>GO to Pinpoint Test Q1. |

**Fig. 23 Pinpoint test HUC. Control module (Part 1 of 2)**

| TEST STEP | RESULT ► | ACTION TO TAKE |
|---|---|---|
| HUC3 ABS MODULE GROUND CHECK | | |
| • Key off.<br>• VOM 200 ohm scale.<br>• Measure resistance between:<br>ABS Module Terminal: L ("BK"), N ("BK"), P ("BK")<br>And: Ground<br>Resistance: Below 5 ohms<br>• Are resistance readings OK? | Yes ►<br>No ► | REPLACE ABS electronic control module.<br>SERVICE "BK" wire(s) to ground. |

**Fig. 23 Pinpoint test HUC. Control module (Part 2 of 2)**

| TEST STEP | RESULT ► | ACTION TO TAKE |
|---|---|---|
| **P1 CHECK FOR SHORT** | | |
| • Key OFF.<br>• Disconnect Battery.<br>• Disconnect ABS Module.<br>• Disconnect Hydraulic Actuation Assembly.<br>• Measure resistance between: | Yes ►<br>No ► | RECONNECT Battery. GO to P2.<br>SERVICE wire in question. |

| Hydraulic Actuation Assembly | ABS Module | Resistance (OHMs) |
|---|---|---|
| Y/W | BK/GN | Over 10,000 |
| | BK | Over 10,000 |
| | BL/O | Over 10,000 |
| Y/R | BK/GN | Over 10,000 |
| | BK | Over 10,000 |
| | BL/O | Over 10,000 |
| Y/GN | BK/GN | Over 10,000 |
| | BK | Over 10,000 |
| | BL/O | Over 10,000 |
| BL | BK/GN | Over 10,000 |
| | BK | Over 10,000 |
| | BL/O | Over 10,000 |
| BK/W | BK/GN | Over 10,000 |
| | BK | Over 10,000 |
| | BL/O | Over 10,000 |
| BR | BK/GN | Over 10,000 |
| | BK | Over 10,000 |
| | BL/O | Over 10,000 |

• Are all resistances OK?

| TEST STEP | RESULT ► | ACTION TO TAKE |
|---|---|---|
| **P2 CHECK FOR SHORT TO POWER** | | |
| • Key ON<br>• Disconnect ABS Module.<br>• Disconnect Hydraulic Actuation Assembly.<br>• Measure voltage at ABS Module Connector "Y / W", "Y / R", "Y / GN", "BL", "BK / W" and "BR" terminals.<br>• Are any voltages greater than 10V? | Yes ►<br>No ► | SERVICE wire in question for short to power.<br>RECONNECT ABS Module. GO to P3. |

**Fig. 24 Pinpoint test P (Part 1 of 2)**

| TEST STEP | RESULT ► | ACTION TO TAKE |
|---|---|---|
| **P3 CHECK ABS MODULE** | | |
| • Disconnect Hydraulic Actuator Assembly.<br>• Key ON.<br>• Measure voltage at ABS Module "Y / W", "Y / R", "Y / GN", "BL", "BK / W" and "BR" terminals.<br>• Are any voltages greater than 10V? | Yes ►<br>No ► | REPLACE ABS Module.<br>REPLACE Hydraulic Actuation Assembly. |

**Fig. 24 Pinpoint test P (Part 2 of 2)**

| TEST STEP | RESULT ► | ACTION TO TAKE |
|---|---|---|
| **Q1 BOO SWITCH CHECK** | | |
| • Key on.<br>• Measure voltage at ABS Module 1A (W/GN) terminal.<br>• Is voltage 0V with brake pedal released and 10-12V with brake pedal depressed? | Yes ►<br>No ► | GO to Q2.<br>Service W/GN wire or Brake on-off switch as required. |

| TEST STEP | RESULT ► | ACTION TO TAKE |
|---|---|---|
| **Q2 ALTERNATOR OUTPUT** | | |
| • VOM 20 volt scale.<br>• Measure voltage between ABS module "W/BK" wire and "BK" wire.<br>**Condition** — **Voltage**<br>Key Off — 0V–3V<br>Key On — 0V–3V<br>Engine Running — Above 12V<br>• Is alternator output OK? | Yes ►<br>No ► | GO to Q3.<br>SERVICE "W/BK" wire to alternator. |

**Fig. 25 Pinpoint test Q (Part 1 of 5)**

| TEST STEP | RESULT ► | ACTION TO TAKE |
|---|---|---|
| **Q3 POWER TO SYSTEM** | | |
| • VOM 20 volt scale.<br>• Measure voltage between: ABS Relay "BL/R" wire and ground<br>**Condition** — **Voltage**<br>Key Off — Above 10v<br>Key On — Above 10v<br>Engine Running — 10-14v<br>• Are voltage readings OK? | Yes ►<br>No ► | GO to Q4.<br>SERVICE wire(s) in question. |

| TEST STEP | RESULT ► | ACTION TO TAKE |
|---|---|---|
| **Q4 KEY POWER CHECK** | | |
| • Key on.<br>• Measure voltage at ABS Module E (BK/BL) and C (BL/O) terminals.<br>• Are both voltages greater than 10V? | Yes ►<br>No ► | GO to Q7.<br>GO to Q5. |

| TEST STEP | RESULT ► | ACTION TO TAKE |
|---|---|---|
| **Q5 POWER FROM IGNITION SWITCH** | | |
| • Key on.<br>• VOM 20 volt scale.<br>• Measure voltage between:<br>ABS relay "BK/GN" wire and ground<br>ABS warning light "BL/Y" wire and ground<br>ABS module "BK/GN" wire and ground<br>**Condition** — **Voltage**<br>Key Off — 0v<br>Key On — Above 10v<br>Engine Running — Above 10v<br>• Are voltage readings OK? | Yes ►<br>No ► | GO to Q6.<br>SERVICE fuse(s) or wire(s) in question. |

**Fig. 25 Pinpoint test Q (Part 2 of 5)**

| TEST STEP | RESULT ► | ACTION TO TAKE |
|---|---|---|
| **Q6 RELAY OPERATION** | | |
| • VOM 20 volt scale.<br>• Connect hydraulic relay "BK/BL" and "BL/O" wires to ground with jumper wire(s).<br>• Measure voltage between:<br>Hydraulic Act. Assy. "R/Y" wire and ground<br>ABS Module "R/Y" wire and ground<br>Hydraulic Act. Assy. "BK/R" wire and ground<br>**Condition** — **Voltage**<br>Key Off — 0v<br>Key On — Above 10v<br>Engine Running — Above 10v<br>• Are voltage readings OK? | Yes ►<br>No ► | Service BL/O or BK/BL wires from ABS Relay to ABS Module.<br>Service R/Y or BK/R wires. If all OK, replace Relay. |

| TEST STEP | RESULT ► | ACTION TO TAKE |
|---|---|---|
| **Q7 GROUND CHECK** | | |
| • Key off.<br>• VOM 200 ohm scale.<br>• Measure resistance between:<br>—ABS relay "BK" wire and ground<br>—ABS module terminal(s) L ("BK"), N ("BK"), P ("BK") wire(s) and ground<br>—ABS Hydraulic Act. Assy. BK terminals (2) and ground.<br>• Self-Test connector "BK" wire and ground.<br>• Are resistance readings below 5 ohm? | Yes ►<br>No ► | GO to Q8.<br>SERVICE "BK" wire(s) to ground. |

**Fig. 25 Pinpoint test Q (Part 3 of 5)**

| TEST STEP | RESULT | ACTION TO TAKE |
|---|---|---|
| **Q8** PRESSURE SWITCH CHECK | | |
| • Key off.<br>• Disconnect ABS Module.<br>• Disconnect Hydraulic Actuation Assembly.<br>• Measure resistance between: | Yes<br>No | GO to **Q9**.<br>SERVICE wire in question. |

| ABS Module Terminal | Hydraulic Actuation Assembly Terminal | Resistance (OHMs) |
|---|---|---|
| BL/BK | BL/BK | 0-4 |
| | BK | Over 10,000 |
| GN/R | GN/R | 0-4 |
| | BK | Over 10,000 |

• Are resistances OK?

| TEST STEP | RESULT | ACTION TO TAKE |
|---|---|---|
| **Q9** CHECK FOR SHORT TO POWER | | |
| • Key on.<br>• Disconnect ABS Module.<br>• Disconnect Hydraulic Actuation Assembly.<br>• Measure voltage at ABS module connector GN/BK and GN/R terminals.<br>• Are any voltages greater than 10V? | Yes<br>No | Service wire in question for short to power.<br>GO to **Q10** |

**Fig. 25 Pinpoint test Q (Part 4 of 5)**

| TEST STEP | RESULT | ACTION TO TAKE |
|---|---|---|
| **Q10** SELF-TEST CONNECTOR (STC) CONTINUITY | | |
| • Key off.<br>• VOM 200 ohm scale.<br>• Measure resistance between:<br>STC "GN/R" wire and ABS module terminal D ("GN/R" wire)<br>STC "GN/BK" wire and ABS module terminal H ("GN/BK" wire)<br>STC "BL/Y" wire and ABS module terminal F ("BL/Y" wire)<br>STC "BL/Y" wire and ABS warning light "BL/Y" wire<br>STC "BL/Y" wire and ABS relay "BL/Y" wire<br>• Are all resistance readings below 5 ohms? | Yes<br>No | REPLACE ABS electronic control module.<br>SERVICE wire(s) in question. |

**Fig. 25 Pinpoint test Q (Part 5 of 5)**

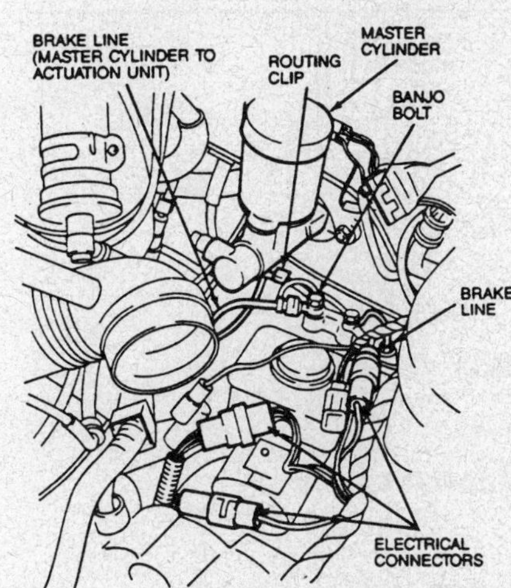


**Fig. 26 Hydraulic actuation unit replacement**

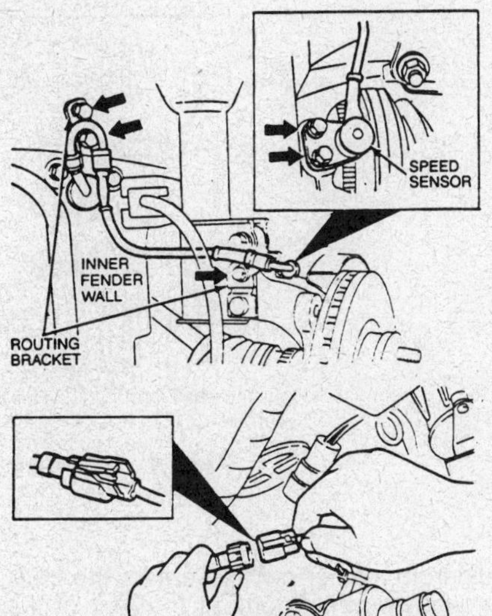


**Fig. 27 Front speed sensor replacement**

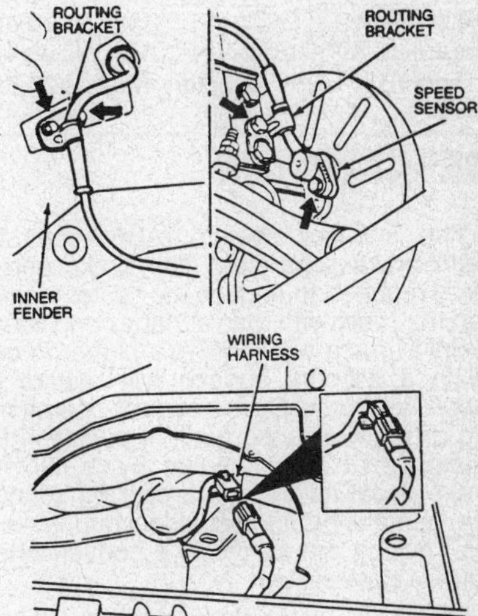


**Fig. 28 Rear speed sensor replacement**

## FRONT WHEEL SENSOR ROTOR

1. Remove wheel and tire assembly.
2. Remove halfshaft.
3. Using a soft faced drift, tap sensor rotor from outboard CV joint.
4. Reverse procedure to install.

## REAR WHEEL SENSOR ROTOR

1. Remove wheel and tire assembly.
2. Remove caliper, anchor bracket and rotor
3. Using a two jawed puller and center plate, remove sensor rotor.
4. Reverse procedure to install.

## FRONT SPEED SENSOR

1. Remove wheel and tire assembly.
2. Remove two retaining bolts, then remove speed sensor from knuckle.
3. Remove routing bracket from strut assembly, **Fig. 27.**
4. Disconnect wiring harness, then remove speed sensor.
5. Reverse procedure to install, noting the following:
   a. Left and right speed sensors are not interchangeable.
   b. **Torque** routing bracket and speed sensor to 12-17 ft. lbs.

## REAR SPEED SENSOR

1. Remove wheel and tire assembly.
2. Remove retaining bolt and speed sensor from knuckle.
3. Remove routing bracket from inner fenderwell, **Fig. 28.**
4. Remove interior panels as necessary to gain access to wiring harness
5. Disconnect wiring harness, then remove speed sensor.
6. Reverse procedure to install, noting the following:
   a. Left and right speed sensors are not interchangeable.
   b. **Torque** routing bracket to 12-17 ft. lbs.
   c. **Torque** speed sensor to 8-19 ft. lbs.

# Sable, Taurus, Town Car & 1990–91 Continental

**NOTE:** Wire Code Identification And Symbol Identification Located In The Front Of This Manual Can Be Used As An Aid When Using Wiring Circuits Found In This Section.

## INDEX



## DESCRIPTION

The anti-lock system (ABS) controls each brake separately. The brake pedal force required to engage the system function may vary with road surface conditions. A dry surface will require a higher force, while a slippery surface will require a much less force. During system operation, the driver will sense a slight pulsation in brake pedal accompanied by a rise in brake pedal height and a clicking sound. The pedal effort and pedal feel during normal braking are similar to a conventional power brake system.

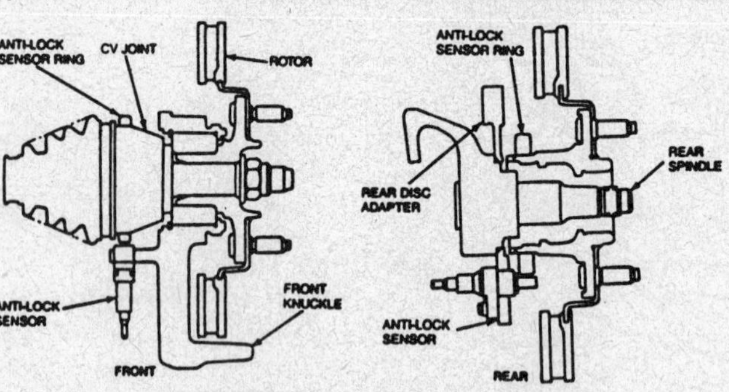


**Fig. 1 Wheel sensor assembly**

## SYSTEM COMPONENTS

### VACUUM BOOSTER

The diaphragm type brake booster is self-contained and is mounted on the left side of engine compartment. The vacuum brake booster uses engine intake manifold vacuum and atmospheric pressure for power.

### MASTER CYLINDER

This unit is a tandem master cylinder. The primary (rear) circuit feeds right front and left rear brakes. The secondary circuit (front) feeds left front and right rear brakes. The reservoir is a clear translucent plastic container. An integral fluid level switch is part of reservoir cap assembly, with one electrical connector pointing rearward for wire harness connection.

### HYDRAULIC CONTROL UNIT

The hydraulic control unit (HCU) is located on the front lefthand side of the engine compartment. It consists of a valve body assembly, pump, motor assembly and brake fluid reservoir with fluid lever indicator assembly. During normal braking, fluid from master cylinder enters the HCU through two inlet ports at the rear of the HCU. The fluid passes through four normally open inlet valves, one to each wheel. When electronic control unit (ECU) senses wheel lock conditions, the ECU produces a pulse to appropriate inlet valve which closes that valve. This prevents any more fluid from entering affected brake. The ECU senses the wheel again, if the wheel is still decelerating the ECU then pulses open the normally closed valve which decreases pressure trapped in line.

### ELECTRONIC CONTROL UNIT

The electronic control unit (ECU) is located in the engine compartment. This unit is a self-test non-repairable unit consisting of two micro-processors which are programmed identically. The ECU monitors system operation during normal driving as well as during anti-lock braking. Under normal driving conditions, the micro-processors transmit short test pulses to solenoid valves to check electrical system. Under wheel lock conditions, the ECU produces signals to open and close the appropriate solenoid valve. This results in moderate pulsations in brake pedal. During anti-lock braking, moderate pulsation in the brake pedal are accompanied by a change in pedal height. This rise in pedal height will continue until the pedal travel switch closes and pump will shut off. During normal braking, the brake pedal feel will be identical to a standard brake system.

### WHEEL SENSORS

This system uses four sets of variable resistance sensors and toothed speed indicator rings to determined the rotational speed of each wheel, **Fig. 1.** The sensors operate on magnetic induction principle. For example, as the teeth on speed indicator ring rotate past a stationary sensor, a signal proportional to speed sensor rotation is generated and transmitted to the electronic control unit (ECU) through a coaxial cable.

The front sensors are attached to suspension knuckles and the front speed indicators are pressed onto the outer constant velocity joints. The rear sensors are at-

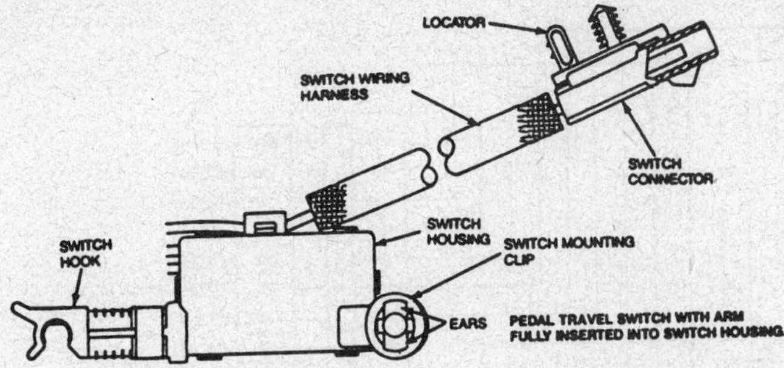


**Fig. 2 Pedal travel switch adjustment**

tached to rear caliper adapter plates, and the rear speed indicator rings are pressed onto the rear hub assemblies.

## PEDAL TRAVEL SWITCH

This system uses a pedal travel switch which monitors brake pedal travel and sends information to electronic control unit (ECU) through the wiring harness. Switch adjustment is critical to pedal feel during ABS cycling. The switch is mounted on the right side of brake pedal support near the dump valve adapter bracket.

The switch is normally closed. When brake pedal travel exceeds the switch setting during an anti-lock stop, the electronic controller senses the switch is open and grounds the pump motor relay coil. This energizes the relay and turns the pump motor on. When the pump motor is running, the master cylinder is filled with high pressure brake fluid and the brake pedal will be pushed up until the switch closes. When the switch closes, the pump is turned off and pedal will drop with each ABS control cycle until travel switch opens again and pump is turned on again. This minimizes pedal feedback during ABS cycling.

If pedal travel switch is not adjusted properly or is not electrically connected, it will result in an incorrect pedal feel during ABS stops. Some problems with the switch or its installation will result in the pump running during entire ABS stop. The pedal will become very firm, pushing the driver's foot up to an very high position.

## PEDAL TRAVEL SWITCH ADJUST

1. Push switch plunger completely into switch housing, this zeros out switch adjustment so it can automatically reset to correct dimension, **Fig. 2.**
2. Slowly pull arm back, out of switch housing past detent point. **At this point it should be impossible to reattach arm to pin unless brake pedal is forced down.**
3. Depress brake pedal until switch hook can be snapped onto pin. Snap hook onto pin and pull brake pedal back up to its normal position. This automatically sets switch to proper adjustment. When switch is unhooked from pin, the above resetting procedure should be performed to ensure correct switch adjustment.

## OPERATION

When brakes are applied, fluid is forced from the master cylinder outlet ports to the hydraulic control unit (HCU) inlet ports. This pressure is transmitted through four normally open solenoid valves contained inside the HCU, then through outlet ports of the HCU to each wheel. The primary (rear) circuit of the master cylinder feeds the right front and left rear brakes. The secondary (front) circuit feeds the left front and right rear brakes.

When the electronic control unit ECU senses wheel lock conditions, based on wheel speed sensor data, it pulses the normally open solenoid valve closed for that circuit. This prevents any more fluid from entering that circuit. The ECU senses the wheel again, if the wheel is still decelerating the ECU then pulses open the normally closed valve which decreases pressure trapped in line.

The ECU monitors the electro-mechanical components of the system. Malfunction of the anti-lock brake system will cause the ECU to shut off or inhibit the anti-lock function, while retaining normal power assisted braking. Malfunctions are indicated by one or two warning lamps inside the vehicle.

Loss of hydraulic fluid in the HCU reservoir will disable the anti-lock brake system.

The four wheel anti-lock brake system is self monitoring. When the ignition switch is turned to the RUN position, the ECU will perform a preliminary self check on the anti-lock electrical system indicated by a three or four second illumination of the amber "Check Anti-Lock Brakes" lamp on the instrument cluster. During vehicle operation, including normal and anti-lock braking, the ECU monitors all electrical anti-lock functions and some hydraulic system operation.

For most malfunctions of the anti-lock brake system, the amber "Check Anti-Lock Brakes" and/or the red "Brake" lamp will be illuminated. The sequence of illumination of these warning lamps, combined with the problem symptoms, can determine the appropriate diagnostic test to perform. Most malfunctions are recorded as a coded number in the controller memory, pinpointing the exact component requiring service.

# DIAGNOSIS & TESTING

**Ensure the following diagnosis procedures are used in the sequence and step-by-step order indicated. Following the wrong sequence or bypassing steps will only lead to unnecessary replacement of system components and/or incorrect resolution of the problem. The diagnostic procedure consists of five sub-tests: Pre-test Checks, On-Board Self-Tests, Manual Quick Tests, Warning Lamp Symptom Chart and the Diagnostic Tests.**

Refer to the ABS wiring circuits, **Figs. 3 through 8** when performing following diagnostic procedures.

## PRE-TEST CHECKS

1. Verify that the parking brake is completely released. If the parking brake is applied, the "Brake" lamp will be illuminated.
2. Check brake fluid. **As the fluid level drops, the red "Brake" lamp will illuminate. If fluid level continues to fall, the amber "Check Anti-Lock Brake" lamp will illuminate and the anti-lock function will be inhibited.**
3. Verify that all of the following connectors are properly connected and in good operating condition:
   a. 55 pin connector of the computer module.
   b. 19 pin connector of HCU valve body.
   c. 4 and 7 pin connectors of pump motor relay.
   d. 3 pin connector of master cylinder reservoir.
   e. 2 pin connector of HCU reservoir.
   f. 5 pin connector of main power relay.
   g. 2 pin connector of each wheel sensor.
   h. 2 pin connector of pedal travel switch.
   i. 2 pin connector of stoplamp switch.
4. Check that the fuses and diode are not damaged.
5. Ensure all battery connections are clean and tight.
6. Check ground connections for anti-lock system located near computer module and pump motor relay.

## ON-BOARD SELF-TEST

The anti-lock brake electronic control module is capable of performing a self-test using Rotunda Super Star II tester 007-00041 or equivalent. If the Super Star tester is not available, the anti-lock Quick Check sheet can be used as described.

The anti-lock control module monitors system operation and stores up all defined service codes in its memory. It is important to understand that the control module Cannot recognize some failures therefore is a problem exists and no service codes are stored by the control module, other diagnostic steps must be followed. The module cannot store a service code if there is no power to the module. This fault code can be found by using Quick-Check

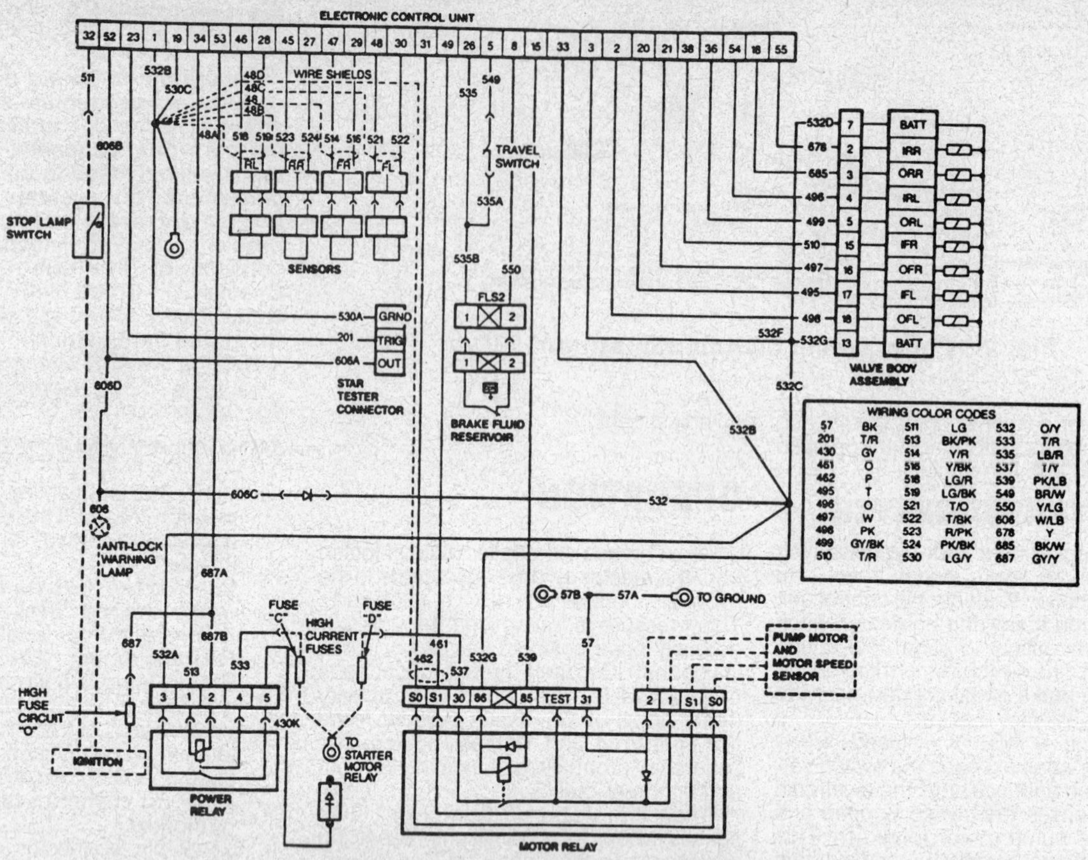


WIRING COLOR CODES

| | | | | | |
|---|---|---|---|---|---|
| 57 | BK | 511 | LG | 532 | O/Y |
| 201 | T/R | 513 | BK/PK | 533 | T/R |
| 430 | GY | 514 | Y/R | 535 | LB/R |
| 461 | O | 516 | Y/BK | 537 | T/Y |
| 462 | P | 518 | LG/R | 539 | PK/LB |
| 495 | T | 519 | LG/BK | 549 | BR/W |
| 496 | O | 521 | T/O | 550 | Y/LG |
| 497 | W | 522 | T/BK | 606 | W/LB |
| 498 | PK | 523 | R/PK | 678 | Y |
| 499 | GY/BK | 524 | PK/BK | 685 | BK/W |
| 510 | T/R | 530 | LG/Y | 687 | GY/Y |

**Fig. 3 ABS wiring circuit. 1990–91 Continental**

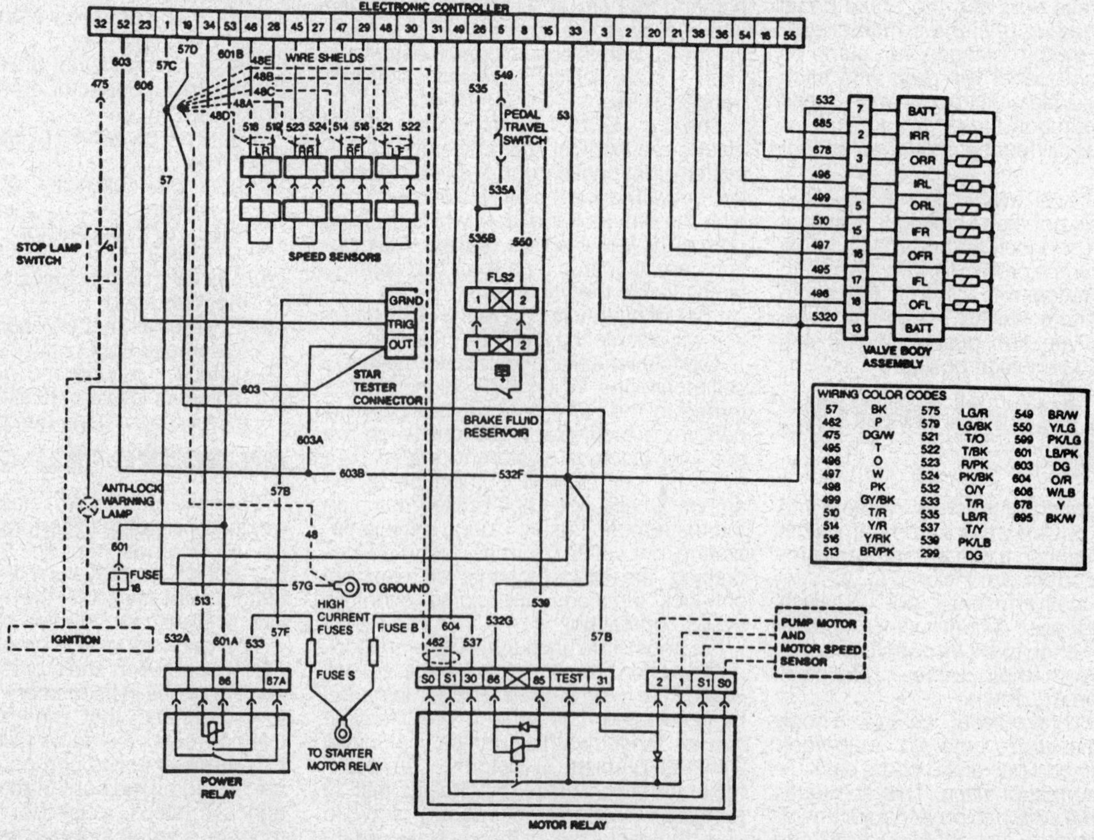


WIRING COLOR CODES

| | | | | | |
|---|---|---|---|---|---|
| 57 | BK | 575 | LG/R | 549 | BR/W |
| 462 | P | 579 | LG/BK | 550 | Y/LG |
| 475 | DG/W | 521 | T/O | 599 | PK/LG |
| 495 | T | 522 | T/BK | 601 | LB/PK |
| 496 | O | 523 | R/PK | 603 | DG |
| 497 | W | 524 | PK/BK | 604 | O/R |
| 498 | PK | 532 | O/Y | 606 | W/LB |
| 499 | GY/BK | 533 | T/R | 678 | Y |
| 510 | T/R | 535 | LB/R | 695 | BK/W |
| 514 | Y/R | 537 | T/Y | | |
| 516 | Y/RK | 539 | PK/LB | | |
| 513 | BR/PK | 299 | DG | | |

**Fig. 4 ABS wiring circuit. 1990 Town Car**

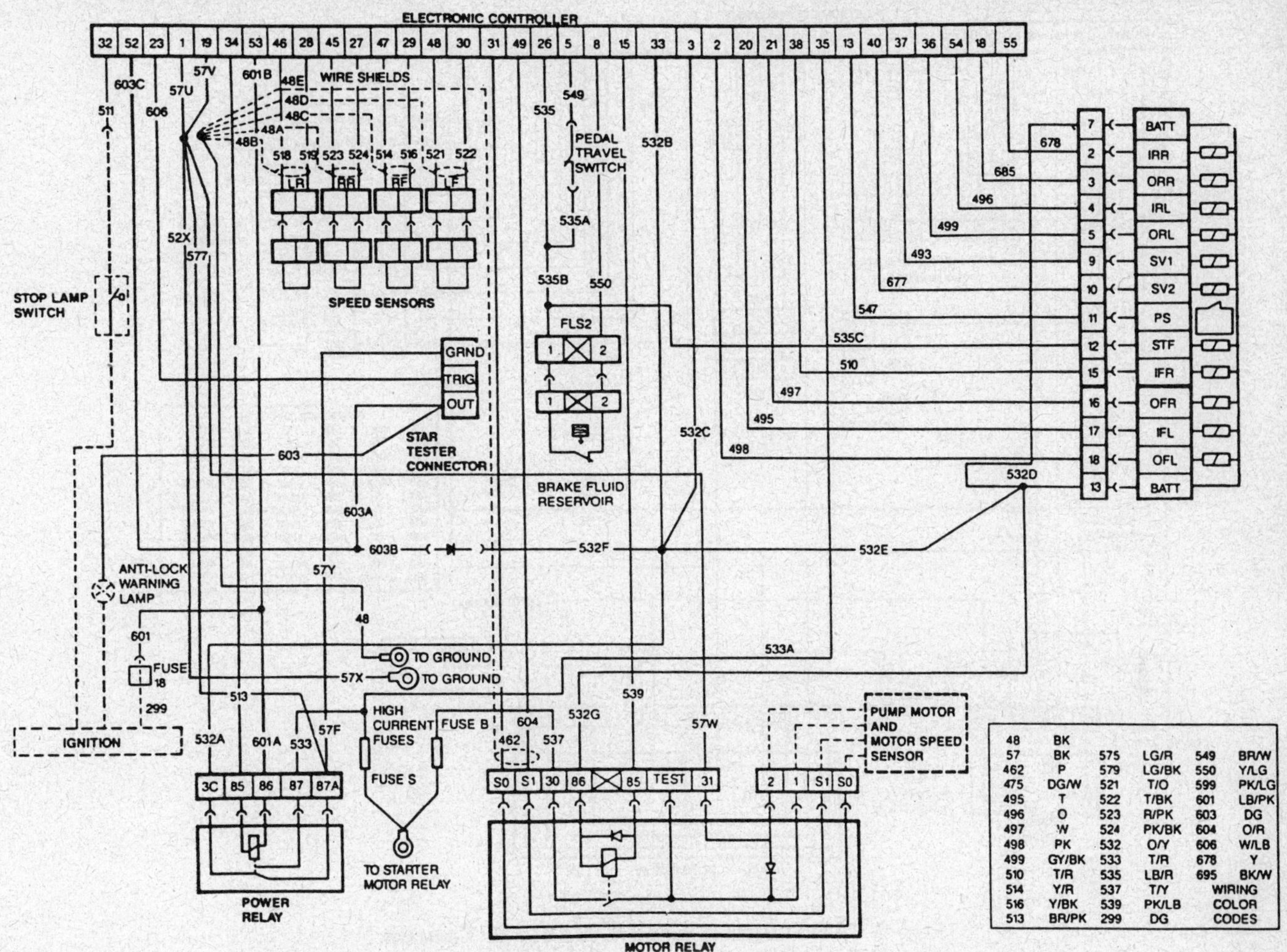


**Fig. 5 ABS wiring circuit. 1991 Town Car**

Tests.

A 20 series code will override any other stored code and will not allow other codes to be output if failure exists while the Self-Test is being run. If failure is intermittent or if code was left in the computer due to improper erasing procedures, the code will be output during Self-Test but the next code will also be output.

## Star Tester Connection & Battery Check

1. Turn ignition switch to OFF position.
2. Locate Star tester connector on engine compartment right shock tower.
3. Connect Super Star tester electrical connector to vehicle connector. **One multi-pin connector is used.**
4. Turn power switch on righthand side of Super Star tester to On. A steady 00 or a blank screen will appear signifying that the tester is ready to start the Self-Test and receive service codes. **If the message LO BAT appears in the upper lefthand corner of the read-out display and stays On, replace the Super Star tester's 9 volt battery before continuing with the Self-Test. The message LO BAT will appear momentarily when the power switch is turned to the Off.**
5. With the ignition switch in the Off position, push the Self-Test button in the center of the Super Star II tester. Push the button again. This deactivates the Self-Test sequence.
6. If the Super Star tester passes the Self-Test (a 00 or blank screen with button in TEST position), proceed with the On-Board Self-Test. If any service codes appear during the Self-Test, refer to the On-Board Self-Test Service Code Index, **Figs. 9 and 10.**

## On Board Self-Test Procedure

The anti-lock brake system is capable of self-diagnostic, however the module as received from manufacturing is equipped with a stored error code 61. This will affect service procedure.

The error codes can be retrieved from the computer as follows:

1. Connect Super Star II tester to connector located in engine compartment.
2. Turn on Super Star II tester and latch button down in Test position.
3. Turn ignition switch to Run position.
4. Read first code output. After approximately 15 seconds the next code will be output. Leave button latched until all codes are output. **Ensure all codes are written down.**

If check Anti-Lock Brake warning lamp is on or intermittently comes on, refer to "Warning Lamp Diagnosis." The diagnostic procedure is as follows:

1. If first code received is in the 20's and no other code is received, service the indicated fault. No other codes can output if a code 20's fault exists. After servicing the indicated 20's code, repeat procedure for retrieving error codes.
2. If there are more codes stored in the computer's memory, no codes will erase until all codes have been output by the Super Star Tester II, all faults have been serviced and the vehicle is driven about 25 mph. This means if a 20's code originally existed and was serviced, it can be ignored when running the Self-Test the second time.
3. If Code 61 is received with any other code, ignore code 61 and service other indicated faults. If after correcting all other indicated the Check

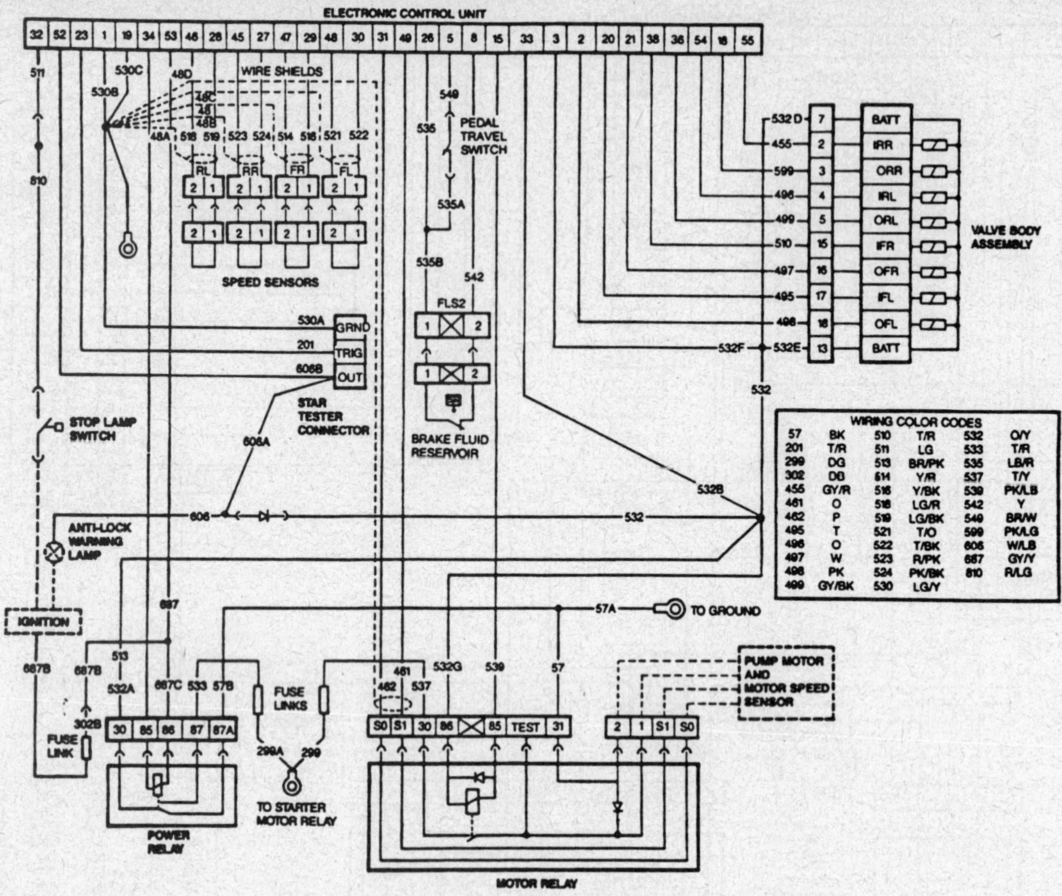


**Fig. 6 ABS wiring circuit. Sable & Taurus**

Anti-Lock Brake lamp is still on, service indicated Code 61 fault.

4. If no code, or only a Code 10 is received, use the Anti-Lock Quick Tests Checks since some faults are not recognized and retained in the computer memory.

### Memory Erasing

The original error codes in the computer from the assembly plant will erase automatically is everything is in working order and vehicle is driven about (25 mph). All error codes must be output, all fault corrected (anti-lock lamp off), and vehicle driven (25 mph) before memory will clear.

### Electronic Controller

Refer to **Fig. 11,** for electronic controller diagnosis procedure.

### Solenoid Valve

Refer to **Figs. 12 through 31,** for solenoid valve diagnosis procedure.

### Wheel Sensor

Refer to **Figs. 32 through 53,** for wheel sensor diagnosis procedure.

### Fluid Level Indicator, Pedal Travel Switch & Pump Motor

Refer to **Figs. 54 through 81,** for fluid lever indicator, pedal travel switch/pump motor diagnosis procedure.

## QUICK TEST CHECKS

To properly conduct Quick Test Checks an EEC-IV breakout box No. T83L-50-EEC-IV, anti-lock harness adapter No. T90P-50-ALA or equivalent and a digital volt/ohmmeter tool No. 007-00001 or equivalent must be used. This group of tests will lead to specific diagnostic Pinpoint Test that will, in most cases, identify the fault/malfunction. If fault/malfunction is not determined by the Quick Test procedure, use the following Diagnostic Lamp Symptom Chart to a identify the proper diagnostic procedure to be conducted.

Refer to anti-lock quick check **Figs. 82 and 83,** for item to be tested, ignition switch mode position, measurement taken between terminal pin numbers, tester scale/range, volt/ohm specifications and the specific pinpoint test to correct the malfunction.

## DIAGNOSTIC LAMP SYMPTOM CHART

If quick test checks and anti-lock quick check sheet procedure does not isolate the symptom, it will be necessary to check operation of the brake and anti-lock warning lamps. Observe lamps and compare their On/Off operation to conditions listed in **Figs. 84 and 85.** Once actual warning lamp pattern has been matched to one of conditions listed in chart, perform the specific Pinpoint Test diagnostic procedure.

## PINPOINT TESTS

To properly conduct the Pinpoint Test diagnostic procedure an anti-lock harness adapter No. T90P-50-ALA, EEC-IV breakout box T83L-50-EEC-IV, digital volt/ohmmeter No. 007-00001 and Super Star Tester II 007-00028 or equivalents.

**Refer to wiring diagrams, Figs. 3 through 8,** when performing Pinpoint Tests to locate wire circuits indicated in test procedure. Each test is completely independent of the other test and within each test are sequences that can identify a problem without requiring completion of entire diagnostic test procedure.

Refer to **Figs. 86 through 149,** for Pinpoint Test diagnostic procedures.

## SYSTEM BLEEDING

1. Disconnect 55-pin plug from electronic control unit, then attach Anti-Lock Breakout Box/Bleeding Adapter tool No. T90P-50-ALA or equivalent to wiring harness 55-pin plug.
2. Place bleed/harness switch in bleed position.
3. Turn ignition to On position, the red Off light should turn on.
4. Push motor button on adapter down

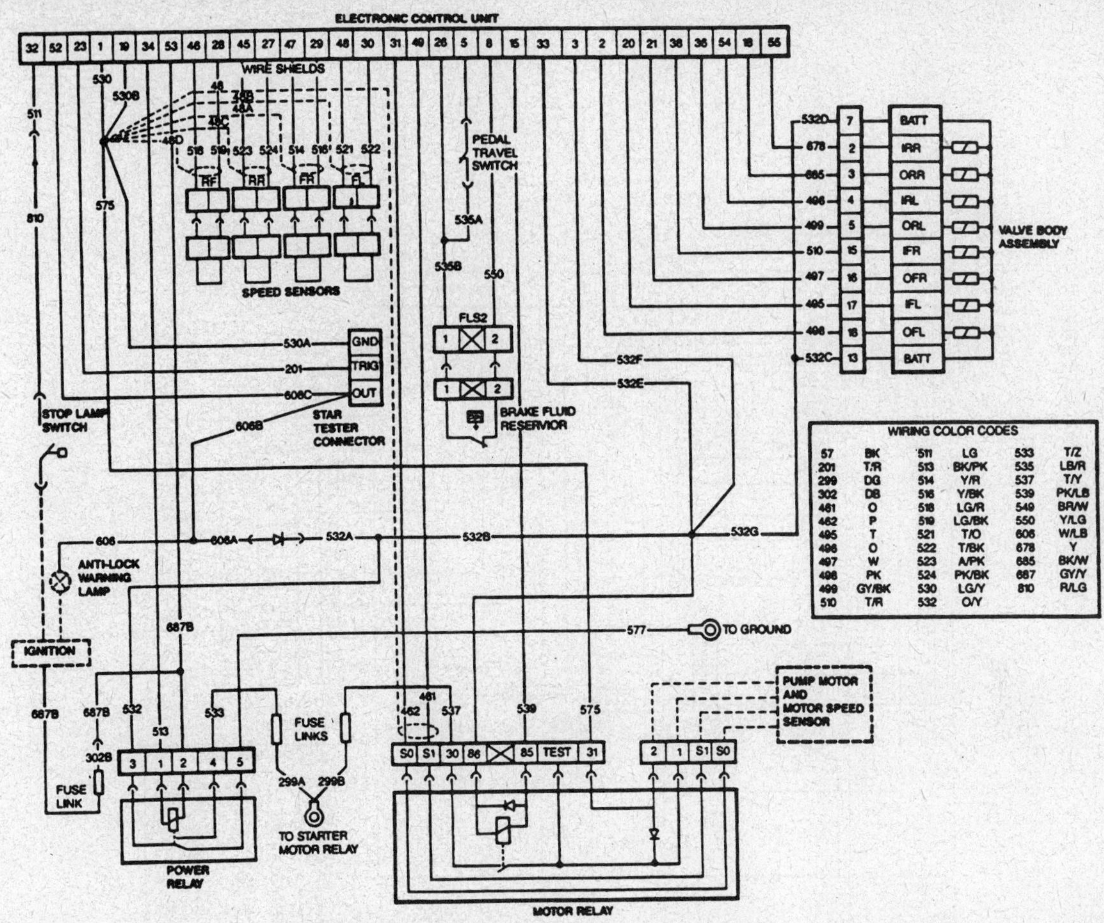


**Fig. 7 ABS wiring circuit. 1990 Taurus SHO**

to start pump motor. The Red Off light will turn off and green On light will turn on. The pump motor will run for 60 seconds once motor button is pushed.

5. If pump motor is turns off before 60 seconds has elapsed, push abort button and pump motor will turn off.
6. After 20 seconds of operation, push and hold valve button down. Hold valve button for 20 seconds, then release.
7. Pump motor will continue to run an additional 20 seconds after valve button is released.
8. Brake lines can be bled in a conventional manner in the following sequence:
   a. Right rear.
   b. Left front.
   c. Left rear.
   d. Right front.

# COMPONENT REPLACEMENT

## HYDRAULIC CONTROL UNIT, REPLACE

1. **On Taurus SHO models,** disconnect battery ground cable, then remove ECU and mounting bracket from hydraulic control unit (HCU).
2. **On all models except Taurus SHO,** disconnect battery cables and remove battery and tray.
3. Remove plastic pushpins holding acid shield to HCU mounting bracket, then remove acid shield, **Fig. 150.**
4. **On all models,** disconnect 19-pin connector from HCU wiring harness, then disconnect 4-pin connector from HCU motor pump relay.
5. Remove two tubes from inlet ports and four tubes from outlet ports of HCU, then plug each port to prevent spilling.
6. Remove relay mounting bracket attaching nut.
7. Remove attaching nuts retaining HCU assembly to mounting bracket, then remove assembly.
8. Reverse procedure to install. **Torque** mounting brackets nuts to 16-24 ft. lbs.

## ELECTRONIC CONTROL UNIT

### Except Town Car

1. Disconnect battery ground cable.
2. Remove trim panel in luggage compartment, located behind back seat to expose the electronic control module.
3. Disconnect the 55-pin connector by pulling up lever completely, then move connector away from electronic control unit until all terminals are clear.
4. Remove attaching screws, then the electronic control unit.
5. Reverse procedure to install.

### Town Car

1. Disconnect battery ground cable.
2. Locate ECU at RH front side of radiator support. Disconnect 55 pin electrical connector.
3. Unlock connector by pulling up lever completely. Move to of connector away from ECU until terminals are clear, then pull connector up out of slots in ECU.
4. Remove three mounting screws attaching ECU to mounting bracket.
5. Reverse procedure to install, noting the following:
   a. Align ECU with bracket so lever is facing up and side with two mounting holes is flat against bracket top.
   B. **Torque** mounting screws to 40-60 inch lbs.

## FRONT WHEEL SENSOR, REPLACE

### Except Town Car

1. Disconnect wheel sensor electrical connector, located in engine compartment.
2. When removing right side sensor, re-

Continued on page 22-95

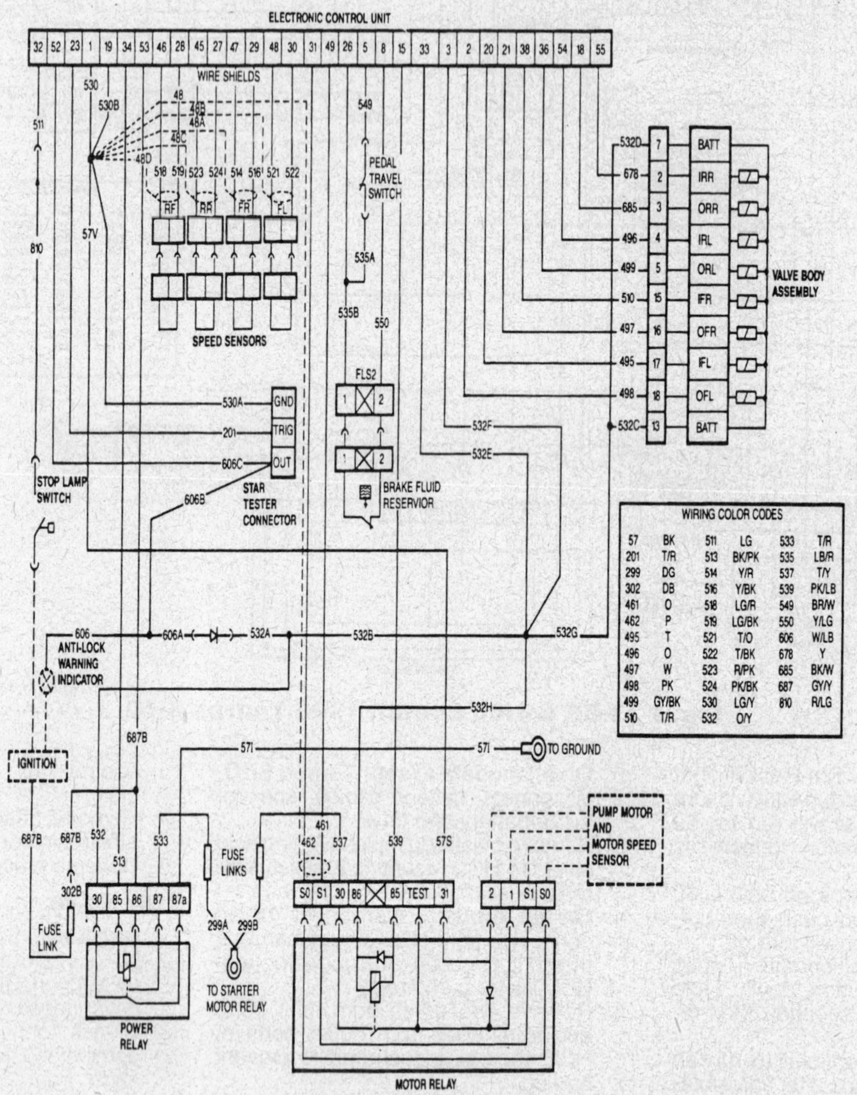


| | | | | | |
|---|---|---|---|---|---|
| 57 | BK | 511 | LG | 533 | T/R |
| 201 | T/R | 513 | BK/PK | 535 | LB/R |
| 299 | DG | 514 | Y/R | 537 | T/Y |
| 302 | DB | 516 | Y/BK | 539 | PK/LB |
| 461 | O | 518 | LG/R | 549 | BR/W |
| 462 | P | 519 | LG/BK | 550 | Y/LG |
| 495 | T | 521 | T/O | 606 | W/LB |
| 496 | O | 522 | T/BK | 678 | Y |
| 497 | W | 523 | R/PK | 685 | BK/W |
| 498 | PK | 524 | PK/BK | 687 | GY/Y |
| 499 | GY/BK | 530 | LG/Y | 810 | R/LG |
| 510 | T/R | 532 | O/Y | | |

**Fig. 8 ABS wiring circuit. 1991 Taurus SHO**

# DIAGNOSTIC TEST CHART INDEX

| Test Chart | Description | Year | Page No. | Fig. No. |
|---|---|---|---|---|
| **TOWN CAR** | | | | |
| | ABS Quick Check Sheet | 1990 | 20-77 | 82 |
| | ABS Quick Check Sheet | 1991 | 20-77 | 83 |
| | Diagnostic Warning Lamp Symptom Chart | 1990 | 20-78 | 84 |
| | Diagnostic Warning Lamp Symptom Chart | 1991 | 20-78 | 85 |
| | On-Board Self Test Service Code Index | 1990 | 20-59 | 9 |
| | On-Board Self Test Service Code Index | 1991 | 20-59 | 10 |
| A1, A1a, A1b & A1c | ABS Lamp On | 1990 | 20-79 | 88 |
| A1, A1a, A1b & A1c | ABS Lamp On | 1991 | 20-79 | 89 |
| A2, A3, A3a & A3b | ABS Lamp On | 1990–91 | 20-80 | 90 |
| A3c & A3d | ABS Lamp On | 1990–91 | 20-80 | 93 |
| A3e & A3f | ABS Lamp On | 1990–91 | 20-81 | 96 |
| A4 & A5 | ABS Lamp On | 1990 | 20-82 | 99 |
| A4 & A5 | ABS Lamp On | 1991 | 20-82 | 100 |
| A6, A6a & A7 | ABS Lamp On | 1990–91 | 20-82 | 101 |
| AA | Electronic Controller | 1990–91 | 20-59 | 11 |
| B1 | ABS Lamp On After Engine Starts | 1990–91 | 20-83 | 102 |
| B1a, B2 & B2a | ABS Lamp On After Engine Starts | 1990–91 | 20-83 | 103 |
| B3, B3a & B4 | ABS Lamp On After Engine Starts | 1990–91 | 20-83 | 104 |
| B4a | ABS Lamp On After Engine Starts | 1990–91 | 20-83 | 105 |
| BB1 | Solenoid Valve | 1990 | 20-61 | 18 |
| BB1 | Solenoid Valve | 1991 | 20-61 | 19 |
| BB2, BB2a & BB3 | Solenoid Valve | 1990–91 | 20-61 | 20 |
| BB3a, BB4, BB4a & BB5 | Solenoid Valve | 1990–91 | 20-62 | 21 |
| BB5a, BB6, BB6a & BB7 | Solenoid Valve | 1990–91 | 20-62 | 22 |
| BB7a, BB8, BB8a & BB9 | Solenoid Valve | 1990–91 | 20-62 | 23 |
| BB9a, BB10 & BB10a | Solenoid Valve | 1990–91 | 20-62 | 24 |
| BB11, BB11a, BB12 & BB12a | Solenoid Valve | 1991 | 20-63 | 25 |
| C1 | ABS Lamp ON After Vehicle Starts | 1990–91 | 20-84 | 106 |
| C1, C1a & C2 | ABS Lamp ON After Vehicle Starts | 1990–91 | 20-84 | 107 |
| C2a, C3 & C3a | ABS Lamp ON After Vehicle Starts | 1990–91 | 20-84 | 108 |
| C4, C4a, C5 & C5a | ABS Lamp ON After Vehicle Starts | 1990–91 | 20-84 | 109 |
| C6, C6a, C7, C7a & C8 | ABS Lamp ON After Vehicle Starts | 1990–91 | 20-85 | 110 |
| C8a, C9, C10 & C11 | ABS Lamp ON After Vehicle Starts | 1990–91 | 20-85 | 111 |
| C12, C13 & C13a | ABS Lamp ON After Vehicle Starts | 1990–91 | 20-85 | 112 |
| C13b, C13c & C13d | ABS Lamp ON After Vehicle Starts | 1990–91 | 20-85 | 113 |
| C13e, C14, C14a, C14b & C14c | ABS Lamp ON After Vehicle Starts | 1990–91 | 20-86 | 115 |
| C15, C15a, C15b, C15c & C16 | ABS Lamp ON After Vehicle Starts | 1990–91 | 20-86 | 116 |
| C16a & C16b | ABS Lamp ON After Vehicle Starts | 1990–91 | 20-86 | 117 |
| C16c & C16d | ABS Lamp ON After Vehicle Starts | 1990–91 | 20-87 | 118 |
| C16e, C16f, C16g & C16h | ABS Lamp ON After Vehicle Starts | 1990 | 20-87 | 119 |
| C16e, C16f, C16g & C16h | ABS Lamp ON After Vehicle Starts | 1991 | 20-87 | 120 |
| CC1 | Wheel Sensor | 1990–91 | 20-64 | 32 |
| CC1a, CC2 & CC3 | Wheel Sensor | 1990–91 | 20-65 | 33 |
| CC3a, CC4 & CC5 | Wheel Sensor | 1990–91 | 20-65 | 34 |
| CC6 | Wheel Sensor | 1990–91 | 20-65 | 35 |
| CC6a, CC7 & CC8 | Wheel Sensor | 1990–91 | 20-65 | 36 |
| CC8a, CC9 & CC10 | Wheel Sensor | 1990–91 | 20-66 | 37 |
| CC11 | Wheel Sensor | 1990–91 | 20-66 | 38 |
| CC11a, CC12 & CC13 | Wheel Sensor | 1990–91 | 20-66 | 39 |

*Continued*

## DIAGNOSTIC TEST CHART INDEX—Continued

| Test Chart | Description | Year | Page No. | Fig. No. |
|---|---|---|---|---|
| **TOWN CAR–Continued** | | | | |
| CC13a, CC14 & CC15 | Wheel Sensor | 1990–91 | 20-66 | 40 |
| CC16 | Wheel Sensor | 1990–91 | 20-67 | 41 |
| CC16a, CC17 & CC18 | Wheel Sensor | 1990–91 | 20-67 | 42 |
| CC18a, CC19 & CC20 | Wheel Sensor | 1990–91 | 20-67 | 43 |
| D1 | Warning Sequence Normal/Brake Pedal Rises Or Drops Excessively During ABS Cycling | 1991 | 20-88 | 124 |
| D1, D1a, D2, D2a & D3 | Warning Sequence Normal/Brake Pedal Rises Or Drops Excessively During ABS Cycling | 1990 | 20-88 | 122 |
| D1, D1a, D2, D2a & D3 | Warning Sequence Normal/Brake Pedal Rises Or Drops Excessively During ABS Cycling | 1991 | 20-88 | 125 |
| D1 | Warning Sequence Normal/Brake Pedal Rises Or Drops Excessively During ABS Cycling | 1990 | 20-87 | 121 |
| DD1 | Wheel Sensor | 1990–91 | 20-67 | 44 |
| DD1a, DD2 & DD3 | Wheel Sensor | 1990–91 | 20-68 | 45 |
| DD4 | Wheel Sensor | 1990–91 | 20-68 | 46 |
| DD4a, DD5 & DD6 | Wheel Sensor | 1990 | 20-68 | 47 |
| DD4a, DD5 & DD6 | Wheel Sensor | 1991 | 20-68 | 48 |
| DD7 | Wheel Sensor | 1990–91 | 20-69 | 49 |
| DD7a, DD8 & DD9 | Wheel Sensor | 1990–91 | 20-69 | 50 |
| DD10 | Wheel Sensor | 1990–91 | 20-69 | 51 |
| DD10a, DD11 & DD12 | Wheel Sensor | 1990 | 20-69 | 52 |
| DD10a, DD11 & DD12 | Wheel Sensor | 1991 | 20-70 | 53 |
| E1 & E2 | Warning Sequence Normal/ABS Pump Motor Run Continuously | 1990 | 20-89 | 126 |
| E1 & E2 | Warning Sequence Normal/ABS Pump Motor Run Continuously | 1991 | 20-89 | 127 |
| E3 | Warning Sequence Normal/ABS Pump Motor Run Continuously | 1990–91 | 20-89 | 128 |
| E3a & E4 | Warning Sequence Normal/ABS Pump Motor Run Continuously | 1990–91 | 20-89 | 129 |
| EE1 | Fluid Level Indicator, Pedal Travel Switch & Pump Motor | 1991 | 20-70 | 56 |
| EE1 | Fluid Level Indicator, Pedal Travel Switch & Pump Motor | 1990–91 | 20-70 | 54 |
| EE1a, EE2 & EE2a | Fluid Level Indicator/Pedal Travel Switch/Pump Motor | 1990 | 20-71 | 57 |
| EE1a, EE2 & EE2a | Fluid Level Indicator/Pedal Travel Switch/Pump Motor | 1991 | 20-71 | 58 |
| EE3 | Fluid Level Indicator/Pedal Travel Switch/Pump Motor | 1990–91 | 20-71 | 59 |
| EE3, EE3a & EE4 | Fluid Level Indicator/Pedal Travel Switch/Pump Motor | 1991 | 20-72 | 61 |
| EE3a, EE4 & EE4a | Fluid Level Indicator/Pedal Travel Switch/Pump Motor | 1990 | 20-72 | 62 |
| EE4a | Fluid Level Indicator/Pedal Travel Switch/Pump Motor | 1991 | 20-72 | 63 |
| EE5 | Fluid Level Indicator/Pedal Travel Switch/Pump Motor | 1990 | 20-72 | 64 |
| EE5, EE5a, EE6 & EE6a | Fluid Level Indicator/Pedal Travel Switch/Pump Motor | 1991 | 20-73 | 65 |
| EE5a, EE5b & EE5c | Fluid Level Indicator/Pedal Travel Switch/Pump Motor | 1990 | 20-73 | 66 |
| EE5d, EE5e, EE6, EE6a & EE6b | Fluid Level Indicator/Pedal Travel Switch/Pump Motor | 1990–91 | 20-73 | 67 |
| EE6c, EE7, EE7a, EE7b, EE7c & EE8 | Fluid Level Indicator/Pedal Travel Switch/Pump Motor | 1990–91 | 20-74 | 69 |
| EE7 | Fluid Level Indicator/Pedal Travel Switch/Pump Motor | 1991 | 20-74 | 71 |
| EE7a, EE7b & EE7c | Fluid Level Indicator/Pedal Travel Switch/Pump Motor | 1991 | 20-74 | 72 |
| EE7d, EE7e, EE8, EE8a & EE8b | Fluid Level Indicator/Pedal Travel Switch/Pump Motor | 1991 | 20-75 | 73 |
| EE8a & EE8b | Fluid Level Indicator/Pedal Travel Switch/Pump Motor | 1990 | 20-75 | 74 |
| EE8c, EE8d & EE8e | Fluid Level Indicator/Pedal Travel Switch/Pump Motor | 1990 | 20-75 | 75 |
| EE8c, EE9 & EE9a, EE9b, EE9c & EE10 | Fluid Level Indicator/Pedal Travel Switch/Pump Motor | 1991 | 20-76 | 78 |
| EE8f, EE8g & EE8h | Fluid Level Indicator/Pedal Travel Switch/Pump Motor | 1990 | 20-75 | 76 |
| EE9 | Fluid Level Indicator/Pedal Travel Switch/Pump Motor | 1990 | 20-76 | 77 |
| EE10a & EE10b | Fluid Level Indicator/PeDal Travel Switch/Pump Motor | 1991 | 20-76 | 79 |
| EE10c, EE10d & EE10e | Fluid Level Indicator/Pedal Travel Switch/Pump Motor | 1991 | 20-76 | 80 |
| EE10f, EE10g, EE10h | Fluid Level Indicator/Pedal Travel Switch/Pump Motor | 1991 | 20-77 | 81 |

*Continued*

## DIAGNOSTIC TEST CHART INDEX—Continued

| Test Chart | Description | Year | Page No. | Fig. No. |
|---|---|---|---|---|
| **TOWN CAR–Continued** | | | | |
| F1 & F2 | Brake Lamp ON w/ABS Lamp OFF, Parking Brake Released & Lining Wear Checked | 1990 | 20-90 | 130 |
| F1 & F2 | Brake Lamp ON w/ABS Lamp OFF, Parking Brake Released & Lining Wear Checked | 1991 | 20-90 | 131 |
| F3 | Brake Warning Lamp ON w/ABS Lamp OFF, Parking Brake Released & Lining Wear Checked | 1990–91 | 20-90 | 132 |
| G1, G2 & G3 | No Warning Lamp ON When Ignition Switch Turned ON | 1990 | 20-90 | 133 |
| G1, G2, G3 & G4 | No Warning Lamp ON When Ignition Switch Turned ON | 1991 | 20-91 | 134 |
| H1 & H2 | Spongy Pedal, No Warning Lamp | 1990 | 20-91 | 136 |
| H1 & H2 | Spongy Pedal, No Warning Lamp | 1991 | 20-91 | 137 |
| J1 & J2 | Poor Vehicle Tracking During ABS Function | 1990 | 20-92 | 138 |
| J1 & J2 | Poor Vehicle Tracking During ABS Function | 1991 | 20-92 | 139 |
| J2 | Poor Vehicle Tracking During ABS Function | 1990 | 20-92 | 140 |
| J2 | Poor Vehicle Tracking During ABS Function | 1991 | 20-92 | 141 |
| J3 & J4 | Poor Vehicle Tracking During ABS Function | 1990 | 20-93 | 142 |
| J3 & J4 | Poor Vehicle Tracking During ABS Function | 1991 | 20-93 | 143 |
| J3 & J4 | Poor Vehicle Tracking During ABS Function | 1991 | 20-93 | 144 |
| J5 | Poor Vehicle Tracking During ABS Function | 1990 | 20-93 | 145 |
| J5 | Poor Vehicle Tracking During ABS Function | 1991 | 20-94 | 147 |
| K1, K2, K3, K3a & K4 | ABS Indicator Sequence Normal, False Cycling Of Traction Assist | 1991 | 20-94 | 148 |
| L1 | ABS Indicator Sequence Normal, False Cycling Of Traction Assist | 1991 | 20-94 | 149 |
| **CONTINENTAL** | | | | |
| | ABS Quick Check Sheet | 1990–91 | 20-77 | 82 |
| | Diagnostic Warning Lamp Symptom Chart | 1990–91 | 20-78 | 84 |
| | On-Board Self Test Service Code Index | 1999–91 | 20-59 | 9 |
| A1 | ABS Lamp ON | 1990–91 | 20-79 | 86 |
| A1a, A1b, A2 & A3 | ABS Lamp ON | 1990–91 | 20-79 | 87 |
| A3a, A3b, A3c | ABS Lamp ON | 1990–91 | 20-80 | 91 |
| A3d & A3e | ABS Lamp ON | 1990–91 | 20-81 | 94 |
| A3f, A4 & A5 | ABS Lamp ON | 1990–91 | 20-81 | 97 |
| A6, A6a & A7 | ABS Lamp ON | 1990–91 | 20-82 | 101 |
| AA1 | Electronic Controller | — | 20-59 | 11 |
| B1 | ABS Lamp ON After Engine Starts | 1990–91 | 20-83 | 102 |
| B1a, B2 & B2a | ABS Lamp ON After Engine Starts | 1990–91 | 20-83 | 103 |
| B3, B3a & B4 | ABS Lamp On After Engine Starts | 1990–91 | 20-83 | 104 |
| B4a | ABS Lamp On After Engine Starts | 1990–91 | 20-83 | 105 |
| BB1 | Solenoid Valve | 1990–91 | 20-59 | 12 |
| BB2, BB2a & BB3 | Solenoid Valve | 1990–91 | 20-60 | 13 |
| BB3a, BB4, BB4a & BB5 | Solenoid Valve | 1990–91 | 20-60 | 14 |
| BB5a, BB6, BB6a & BB7 | Solenoid Valve | 1990–91 | 20-60 | 15 |
| BB7a, BB8, BB8a & BB9 | Solenoid Valve | 1990–91 | 20-60 | 16 |
| BB9a, BB10 & BB10a | Solenoid Valve | 1990–91 | 20-61 | 17 |
| C1 | ABS Lamp ON After Vehicle Starts | 1990–91 | 20-84 | 106 |
| C1, C1a & C2 | ABS Lamp ON After Vehicle Starts | 1990–91 | 20-84 | 107 |
| C2a, C3 & C3a | ABS Lamp ON After Vehicle Starts | 1990–91 | 20-84 | 108 |
| C4, C4a, C5 & C5a | ABS Lamp ON After Vehicle Starts | 1990–91 | 20-84 | 109 |
| C6, C6a, C7, C7a & C8 | ABS Lamp ON After Vehicle Starts | 1990–91 | 20-85 | 110 |
| C8a, C9, C10 & C11 | ABS Lamp ON After Vehicle Starts | 1990–91 | 20-85 | 111 |
| C12, C13 & C13a | ABS Lamp ON After Vehicle Starts | 1990–91 | 20-85 | 112 |
| C13b, C13c & C13d | ABS Lamp ON After Vehicle Starts | 1990–91 | 20-85 | 113 |

## DIAGNOSTIC TEST CHART INDEX—Continued

| Test Chart | Description | Year | Page No. | Fig. No. |
|---|---|---|---|---|
| **CONTINENTAL–Continued** | | | | |
| C13e, C14, C14a, C14b & C14c | ABS Lamp ON After Vehicle Starts | 1990–91 | 20-86 | 114 |
| C15, C15a, C15b, C15c & C16 | ABS Lamp ON After Vehicle Starts | 1990–91 | 20-86 | 116 |
| C16a & C16b | ABS Lamp ON After Vehicle Starts | 1990–91 | 20-86 | 117 |
| C16c & C16d | ABS Lamp ON After Vehicle Starts | 1990–91 | 20-87 | 118 |
| C16e, C16f, C16g & C16h | ABS Lamp ON After Vehicle Starts | 1990–91 | 20-87 | 119 |
| CC1 | Wheel Sensor | 1990–91 | 20-64 | 32 |
| CC1a, CC2 & CC3 | Wheel Sensor | 1990–91 | 20-65 | 33 |
| CC3a, CC4 & CC5 | Wheel Sensor | 1990–91 | 20-65 | 34 |
| CC6 | Wheel Sensor | 1990–91 | 20-65 | 35 |
| CC6a, CC7 & CC8 | Wheel Sensor | 1990–91 | 20-65 | 36 |
| CC8a, CC9 & CC10 | Wheel Sensor | 1990–91 | 20-66 | 37 |
| CC11 | Wheel Sensor | 1990–91 | 20-66 | 38 |
| CC11a, CC12 & CC13 | Wheel Sensor | 1990–91 | 20-66 | 39 |
| CC13a, CC14 & CC15 | Wheel Sensor | 1990–91 | 20-66 | 40 |
| CC16 | Wheel Sensor | 1990–91 | 20-67 | 41 |
| CC16a, CC17 & CC18 | Wheel Sensor | 1990–91 | 20-67 | 42 |
| CC18a, CC19 & CC20 | Wheel Sensor | 1990–91 | 20-67 | 43 |
| D1, D1a, D2, D2a & D3 | Warning Sequence Normal/Brake Pedal Rises Or Drops Excessively During ABS Cycling | 1990–91 | 20-88 | 122 |
| D1 | Warning Sequence Normal/Brake Pedal Rises Or Drops Excessively During ABS Cycling | 1990–91 | 20-87 | 121 |
| DD1 | Wheel Sensor | 1990–91 | 20-67 | 44 |
| DD1a, DD2 & DD3 | Wheel Sensor | 1990–91 | 20-68 | 45 |
| DD4 | Wheel Sensor | 1990–91 | 20-68 | 46 |
| DD4a, DD5 & DD6 | Wheel Sensor | 1990–91 | 20-68 | 47 |
| DD7 | Wheel Sensor | 1990–91 | 20-69 | 49 |
| DD7a, DD8 & DD9 | Wheel Sensor | 1990–91 | 20-69 | 50 |
| DD10 | Wheel Sensor | 1990–91 | 20-69 | 51 |
| DD10a, DD11 & DD12 | Wheel Sensor | 1990–91 | 20-69 | 52 |
| E1 & E2 | Warning Sequence Normal/ABS Pump Motor Run Continuously | 1990–91 | 20-89 | 126 |
| E3 | Warning Sequence Normal/ABS Pump Motor Run Continuously | 1990–91 | 20-89 | 128 |
| E3a & E4 | Warning Sequence Normal/ABS Pump Motor Run Continuously | 1990–91 | 20-89 | 129 |
| EE1 | Fluid Level Indicator, Pedal Travel Switch & Pump Motor | 1990 | 20-70 | 54 |
| EE1 | Fluid Level Indicator, Pedal Travel Switch & Pump Motor | 1991 | 20-70 | 55 |
| EE1a, EE2 & EE2a | Fluid Level Indicator/Pedal Travel Switch/Pump Motor | 1990–91 | 20-71 | 57 |
| EE3 | Fluid Level Indicator/Pedal Travel Switch/Pump Motor | 1990 | 20-71 | 59 |
| EE3 | Fluid Level Indicator/Pedal Travel Switch/Pump Motor | 1991 | 20-71 | 60 |
| EE3a, EE4 & EE4a | Fluid Level Indicator/Pedal Travel Switch/Pump Motor | 1990–91 | 20-72 | 62 |
| EE5 | Fluid Level Indicator/Pedal Travel Switch/Pump Motor | 1990–91 | 20-72 | 64 |
| EE5a, EE5b & EE5c | Fluid Level Indicator/Pedal Travel Switch/Pump Motor | 1990–91 | 20-73 | 66 |
| EE5d, EE5e, EE6, EE6a & EE6b | Fluid Level Indicator/Pedal Travel Switch/Pump Motor | 1990 | 20-73 | 67 |
| EE5d, EE5e, EE6, EE6a & EE6b | Fluid Level Indicator/Pedal Travel Switch/Pump Motor | 1991 | 20-73 | 68 |
| EE6c, EE7, EE7a, EE7b, EE7c & EE8 | Fluid Level Indicator/Pedal Travel Switch/Pump Motor | 1990 | 20-74 | 69 |
| EE6c, EE7, EE7a, EE7b, EE7c & EE8 | Fluid Level Indicator/Pedal TrAvel Switch/Pump Motor | 1991 | 20-74 | 70 |
| EE8a & EE8b | Fluid Level Indicator/Pedal Travel Switch/Pump Motor | 1990–91 | 20-75 | 74 |
| EE8c, EE8d & EE8e | Fluid Level Indicator/Pedal Travel Switch/Pump Motor | 1990–91 | 20-75 | 75 |
| EE8f, EE8g & EE8h | Fluid Level Indicator/Pedal Travel Switch/Pump Motor | 1990–91 | 20-75 | 76 |
| EE9 | Fluid Level Indicator/Pedal Travel Switch/Pump Motor | 1990–91 | 20-76 | 77 |

*Continued*

## DIAGNOSTIC TEST CHART INDEX —Continued



*Continued*

## DIAGNOSTIC TEST INDEX—Continued

| Test Chart | Description | Year | Page No. | Fig. No. |
|---|---|---|---|---|
| **SABLE & TAURUS—Continued** | | | | |
| CC8a, CC9 & CC10 | Wheel Sensor | 1990–91 | 20-66 | 37 |
| CC11 | Wheel Sensor | 1990–91 | 20-66 | 38 |
| CC11a, CC12 & CC13 | Wheel Sensor | 1990–91 | 20-66 | 39 |
| CC13a, CC14 & CC15 | Wheel Sensor | 1990–91 | 20-66 | 40 |
| CC16 | Wheel Sensor | 1990–91 | 20-67 | 41 |
| CC16a, CC17 & CC18 | Wheel Sensor | 1990–91 | 20-67 | 42 |
| CC18a, CC19 & CC20 | Wheel Sensor | 1990–91 | 20-67 | 43 |
| D1, D1a, D2, D2a & D3 | Warning Sequence Normal/Brake Pedal Rises Or Drops Excessively During ABS Cycling | 1990 | 20-88 | 122 |
| D1, D1a, D2, D2a & D3 | Warning Sequence Normal/Brake Pedal Rises Or Drops Excessively During ABS Cycling | 1991 | 20-88 | 123 |
| D1 | Warning Sequence Normal/Brake Pedal Rises Or Drops Excessively During ABS Cycling | 1990–91 | 20-87 | 121 |
| DD1 | Wheel Sensor | 1990–91 | 20-67 | 44 |
| DD1a, DD2 & DD3 | Wheel Sensor | 1990–91 | 20-68 | 45 |
| DD4 | Wheel Sensor | 1990–91 | 20-68 | 46 |
| DD4a, DD5 & DD6 | Wheel Sensor | 1990–91 | 20-68 | 47 |
| DD7 | Wheel Sensor | 1990–91 | 20-69 | 49 |
| DD7a, DD8 & DD9 | Wheel Sensor | 1990–91 | 20-69 | 50 |
| DD10 | Wheel Sensor | 1990–91 | 20-69 | 51 |
| DD10a, DD11 & DD12 | Wheel Sensor | 1990–91 | 20-69 | 52 |
| E1 & E2 | Warning Sequence Normal/ABS Pump Motor Run Continuously | 1990–91 | 20-89 | 126 |
| E3 | Warning Sequence Normal/ABS Pump Motor Run Continuously | 1990–91 | 20-89 | 128 |
| E3a & E4 | Warning Sequence Normal/ABS Pump Motor Run Continuously | 1990–91 | 20-89 | 129 |
| EE1 | Fluid Level Indicator, Pedal Travel Switch & Pump Motor | 1990 | 20-70 | 54 |
| EE1 | Fluid Level Indicator, Pedal Travel Switch & Pump Motor | 1991 | 20-70 | 55 |
| EE1a, EE2 & EE2a | Fluid Level Indicator/Pedal Travel Switch/Pump Motor | 1990–91 | 20-71 | 57 |
| EE3 | Fluid Level Indicator/Pedal Travel Switch/Pump Motor | 1990 | 20-71 | 59 |
| EE3 | Fluid Level Indicator/Pedal Travel Switch/Pump Motor | 1991 | 20-71 | 60 |
| EE3a, EE4 & EE4a | Fluid Level Indicator/Pedal Travel Switch/Pump Motor | 1990–91 | 20-72 | 62 |
| EE5 | Fluid Level Indicator/Pedal Travel Switch/Pump Motor | 1990–91 | 20-72 | 64 |
| EE5a, EE5b & EE5c | Fluid Level Indicator/Pedal Travel Switch/Pump Motor | 1990–91 | 20-73 | 66 |
| EE5d, EE5e, EE6, EE6a & EE6b | Fluid Level Indicator/Pedal Travel Switch/Pump Motor | 1990–91 | 20-73 | 68 |
| EE6c, EE7, EE7a, EE7b, EE7c & EE8 | Fluid Level Indicator/Pedal Travel Switch/Pump Motor | 1990–91 | 20-74 | 70 |
| EE8a & EE8b | Fluid Level Indicator/Pedal Travel Switch/Pump Motor | 1990–91 | 20-75 | 74 |
| EE8c, EE8d & EE8e | Fluid Level Indicator/Pedal Travel Switch/Pump Motor | 1990–91 | 20-75 | 75 |
| EE8f, EE8g & EE8h | Fluid Level Indicator/Pedal Travel Switch/Pump Motor | 1990–91 | 20-75 | 76 |
| EE9 | Fluid Level Indicator/Pedal Travel Switch/Pump Motor | 1990–91 | 20-76 | 77 |
| F1 & F2 | Brake Lamp ON w/ABS Lamp OFF, Parking Brake Released & Lining Wear Checked | 1990–91 | 20-90 | 130 |
| F3 | Brake Warning Lamp ON w/ABS Lamp OFF, Parking Brake Released & Lining Wear Checked | 1990–91 | 20-90 | 132 |
| G1, G2 & G3 | No Warning Lamp ON When Ignition Switch Turned ON | 1990–91 | 20-91 | 135 |
| H1 & H2 | Spongy Pedal, No Warning Lamp | 1990–91 | 20-91 | 136 |
| J1 & J2 | Poor Vehicle Tracking During ABS Function | 1990–91 | 20-92 | 138 |
| J2 | Poor Vehicle Tracking During ABS Function | 1990–91 | 20-92 | 140 |
| J3 & J4 | Poor Vehicle Tracking During ABS Function | 1990 | 20-93 | 142 |
| J3 & J4 | Poor Vehicle Tracking During ABS Function | 1991 | 20-93 | 143 |
| J5 | Poor Vehicle Tracking During ABS Function | 1990 | 20-93 | 145 |
| J5 | Poor Vehicle Tracking During ABS Function | 1991 | 20-94 | 146 |

## On-Board Self-Test Service Code Index

| SERVICE CODE (COMPONENT) | PINPOINT TEST STEP |
|---|---|
| 11 (Electronic Controller) | AA1 |
| 22 (Ref. Voltage of IFL) | BB1 |
| 23 (LH Front Outlet Valve) | BB3 |
| 24 (RH Front Inlet Valve) | BB4 |
| 25 (RH Front Outlet Valve) | BB5 |
| 26 (RH Rear Inlet Valve) | BB6 |
| 27 (RH Rear Outlet Valve) | BB7 |
| 28 (LH Rear Inlet Valve) | BB8 |
| 29 (LH Rear Outlet Valve) | BB9 |
| 31 (LH Front Sensor) | CC1 |
| 32 (RH Front Sensor) | CC6 |
| 33 (RH Rear Sensor) | CC11 |
| 34 (LH Rear Sensor) | CC16 |
| 35 (LH Front Sensor) | CC1 |
| 36 (RH Front Sensor) | CC6 |
| 37 (RH Rear Sensor) | CC11 |
| 38 (LH Rear Sensor) | CC16 |
| 41 (LH Front Sensor) | CC1 |
| 42 (RH Front Sensor) | CC6 |
| 43 (RH Rear Sensor) | CC11 |
| 44 (LH Rear Sensor) | CC16 |
| 51 (LH Front Outlet Valve) | DD1 |
| 52 (RH Front Outlet Valve) | DD3 |
| 53 (RH Rear Outlet Valve) | DD5 |
| 54 (LH Rear Outlet Valve) | DD7 |
| 55 (LH Front Sensor) | CC1 |
| 56 (RH Front Sensor) | CC6 |
| 57 (RH Rear Sensor) | CC11 |
| 58 (LH Rear Sensor) | CC16 |
| 61 (FLI Circuits) | EE1 |
| 62 (Travel Switch) | EE3 |
| 63 (Pump Motor Speed Sensor) | EE5 |
| 64 (Pump Motor Pressure) | EE8 |
| 71 (LH Front Sensor) | CC1 |
| 72 (RH Front Sensor) | CC6 |
| 73 (RH Rear Sensor) | CC11 |
| 74 (LH Rear Sensor) | CC16 |
| 75 (LH Front Sensor) | CC1 |
| 76 (RH Front Sensor) | CC6 |
| 77 (RH Rear Sensor) | CC11 |
| 78 (LH Rear Sensor) | CC16 |

**Fig. 9 On-board self test service code index. Except 1991 Town Car**

## On-Board Self-Test Service Code Index

| SERVICE CODE (COMPONENT) | PINPOINT TEST STEP |
|---|---|
| 11 (Electronic Controller) | AA1 |
| 17 (Reference Voltage)* | BB1 |
| 18 (Isolation Valve No. 1)* | BB11 |
| 19 (Isolation Valve No. 2)* | BB12 |
| 22 (Ref. Voltage of IFL) | BB1 |
| 23 (LH Front Outlet Valve) | BB3 |
| 24 (RH Front Inlet Valve) | BB4 |
| 25 (RH Front Outlet Valve) | BB5 |
| 26 (RH Rear Inlet Valve) | BB6 |
| 27 (RH Rear Outlet Valve) | BB7 |
| 28 (LH Rear Inlet Valve) | BB8 |
| 29 (LH Rear Outlet Valve) | BB9 |
| 31 (LH Front Sensor) | CC1 |
| 32 (RH Front Sensor) | CC6 |
| 33 (RH Rear Sensor) | CC11 |
| 34 (LH Rear Sensor) | CC16 |
| 35 (LH Front Sensor) | CC1 |
| 36 (RH Front Sensor) | CC6 |
| 37 (RH Rear Sensor) | CC11 |
| 38 (LH Rear Sensor) | CC16 |
| 41 (LH Front Sensor) | CC1 |
| 42 (RH Front Sensor) | CC6 |
| 43 (RH Rear Sensor) | CC11 |
| 44 (LH Rear Sensor) | CC16 |
| 51 (LH Front Outlet Valve) | DD1 |
| 52 (RH Front Outlet Valve) | DD3 |
| 53 (RH Rear Outlet Valve) | DD5 |
| 54 (LH Rear Outlet Valve) | DD7 |
| 55 (LH Front Sensor) | CC1 |
| 56 (RH Front Sensor) | CC6 |
| 57 (RH Rear Sensor) | CC11 |
| 58 (LH Rear Sensor) | CC16 |
| 61 (FLI Circuits) | EE1 |
| 62 (Travel Switch) | EE3 |
| 63 (Pump Motor Speed Sensor) | EE7 |
| 64 (Pump Motor Pressure) | EE8 |
| 66 (Pressure Switch) | EE1 |
| 67 (Pump Motor Relay)* | |
| 71 (LH Front Sensor) | CC1 |
| 72 (RH Front Sensor) | CC6 |
| 73 (RH Rear Sensor) | CC11 |
| 74 (LH Rear Sensor) | CC16 |
| 75 (LH Front Sensor) | CC1 |
| 76 (RH Front Sensor) | CC6 |
| 77 (RH Rear Sensor) | CC11 |
| 78 (LH Rear Sensor) | CC16 |

*Traction Assist Codes

**Fig. 10 On-board self test service code index. 1991 Town Car**

## Electronic Controller Diagnosis — Test AA

| TEST STEP | RESULT ▶ | ACTION TO TAKE |
|---|---|---|
| **AA1** SERVICE CODE 11: ELECTRICAL DISTURBANCE | | |
| • Read all service codes and record.<br>• After all service codes are read and written down, drive vehicle above 40 km/h (25 mph) to clear memory.<br>• Read all service codes again | Service code 11 repeated ▶ | REPLACE electronic controller. |
| | Memory erased or other service codes present except code 11 ▶ | PERFORM test step associated with service code or codes. REFER to On-Board Self-Test service code index, and SERVICE next code. |

**Fig. 11 Test AA1, electronic controller**

## Solenoid Valve Diagnosis — Test BB

| TEST STEP | RESULT ▶ | ACTION TO TAKE |
|---|---|---|
| **BB1** SERVICE CODE 22: NO REFERENCE VOLTAGE OR LH FRONT INLET VALVE | | |
| • Disconnect 55-pin plug from electronic controller.<br>ELECTRONIC CONTROLLER<br>55 PIN CONNECTOR<br>• Connect EEC-IV Breakout Box T83L-50-EEC-IV, with Anti-Lock Test Adapter T90P-50-ALA, or equivalent, to the anti-lock 55-pin plug wiring harness.<br>ANTI-LOCK HARNESS ADAPTER T90P-50-ALA<br>55 PIN CONNECTOR<br>EEC-IV BREAKOUT BOX T83L-50-EEC-IV<br>• With ignition switch ON, measure voltage between breakout box pins 3 and 60. | 10 volts minimum ▶ | GO to Step BB2. |
| | Less than 10 volts ▶ | REPLACE or SERVICE cable harness Circuit 532, 532C, 532D, 532E, 532F, 606, or 606C. |

**Fig. 12 Test BB1 (solenoid valve). 1990–91 Continental**

## Solenoid Valve Diagnosis — Test BB

| TEST STEP | RESULT ▶ | ACTION TO TAKE |
|---|---|---|
| **BB2** CHECK LH FRONT INLET VALVE AND CIRCUITRY | | |
| • Measure resistance between breakout box Pins 3 and 20. | 5 to 8 ohms ▶ | REVERIFY code 22. NOTE: If other codes are output, ignore code 22 and service next code. |
| | Any other reading ▶ | GO to Step BB2a. |
| **BB2a** CHECK LH FRONT INLET VALVE | | |
| • Disconnect valve body 19-pin connector.<br>• Measure resistance between Pins 17 and 7. | 5 to 8 ohms ▶ | REPLACE or SERVICE cable harness Circuit 495. |
| | Any other reading ▶ | REPLACE valve body. |
| **BB3** SERVICE CODE 23: CHECK LH FRONT OUTLET VALVE AND CIRCUIT | | |
| • Measure resistance between breakout box Pins 3 and 2. | 3 to 6 ohms ▶ | GO to Step BB4. |
| | Any other reading ▶ | GO to Step BB3a. |

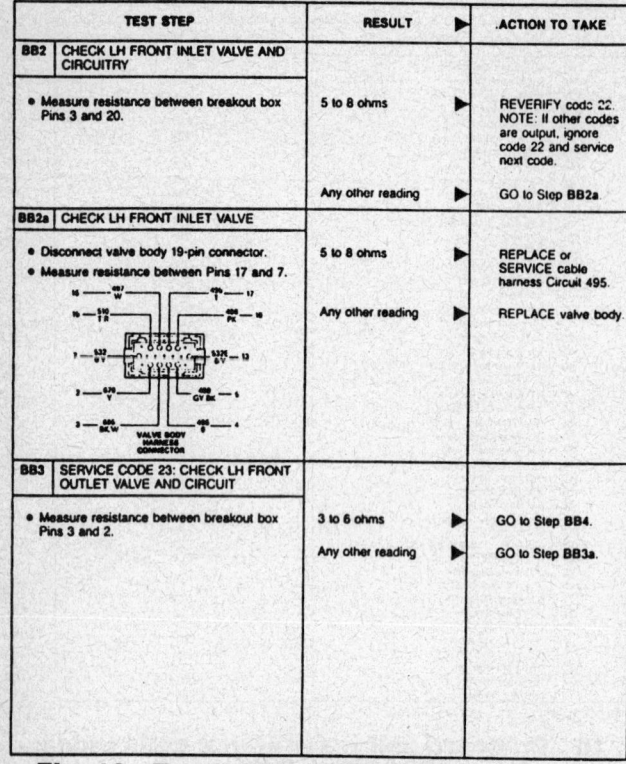

**Fig. 13 Tests BB2, BB2a & BB3 (solenoid valve). 1990–91 Continental**

## Solenoid Valve Diagnosis — Test BB

| TEST STEP | RESULT ▶ | ACTION TO TAKE |
|---|---|---|
| **BB3a** CHECK LH FRONT OUTLET VALVE | | |
| • Disconnect valve body 19-pin connector.<br>• Measure resistance between Pins 18 and 7. | 3 to 6 ohms ▶ | REPLACE or SERVICE cable harness Circuit 496. |
| | Any other reading ▶ | REPLACE valve body. |
| **BB4** SERVICE CODE 24: CHECK RH FRONT INLET VALVE AND CIRCUIT | | |
| • Measure resistance between Breakout Box Pins 3 and 38. | 5 to 8 ohms ▶ | GO to Step BB5. |
| | Any other reading ▶ | GO to Step BB4a. |
| **BB4a** CHECK RH FRONT INLET VALVE | | |
| • Disconnect valve body 19-pin connector.<br>• Measure resistance between Pins 15 and 7. | 5 to 8 ohms ▶ | REPLACE or SERVICE cable harness Circuit 510. |
| | Any other reading ▶ | REPLACE valve body. |
| **BB5** SERVICE CODE 25: CHECK RH FRONT OUTLET VALVE AND CIRCUIT | | |
| • Measure resistance between Breakout Box Pins 3 and 21. | 3 to 6 ohms ▶ | GO to Step BB6. |
| | Any other reading ▶ | GO to Step BB5a. |

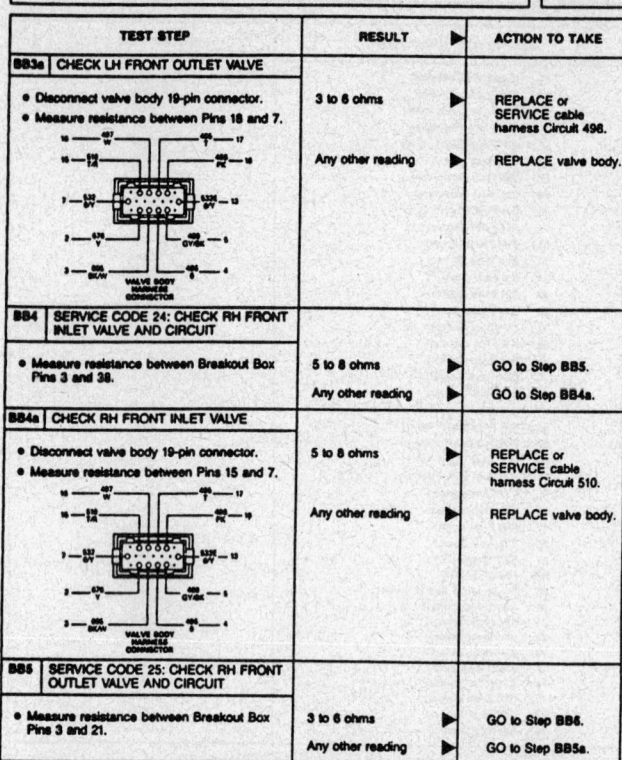

**Fig. 14 Tests BB3a, BB4, BB4a & BB5 (solenoid valve). 1990–91 Continental**

## Solenoid Valve Diagnosis — Test BB

| TEST STEP | RESULT ▶ | ACTION TO TAKE |
|---|---|---|
| **BB5a** CHECK RH FRONT OUTLET VALVE | | |
| • Disconnect valve body 19-pin connector.<br>• Measure resistance between Pins 16 and 7. | 3 to 6 ohms ▶ | REPLACE or SERVICE cable harness Circuit 497. |
| | Any other reading ▶ | REPLACE valve body. |
| **BB6** SERVICE CODE 26: CHECK RH REAR INLET VALVE AND CIRCUIT | | |
| • Measure resistance between Breakout Box Pins 3 and 55. | 5 to 8 ohms ▶ | GO to Step BB7. |
| | Any other reading ▶ | GO to Step BB6a. |
| **BB6a** CHECK RH REAR INLET VALVE | | |
| • Disconnect valve body 19-pin connector.<br>• Measure resistance between Pins 2 and 7. | 5 to 8 ohms ▶ | REPLACE or SERVICE cable harness Circuit 678. |
| | Any other reading ▶ | REPLACE valve body. |
| **BB7** SERVICE CODE 27: CHECK RH REAR OUTLET VALVE AND CIRCUIT | | |
| • Measure resistance between Breakout Box Pins 3 and 18. | 3 to 6 ohms ▶ | GO to Step BB8. |
| | Any other reading ▶ | GO to Step BB7a. |

**Fig. 15 Tests BB5a, BB6, BB6a & BB7 (solenoid valve). 1990–91 Continental**

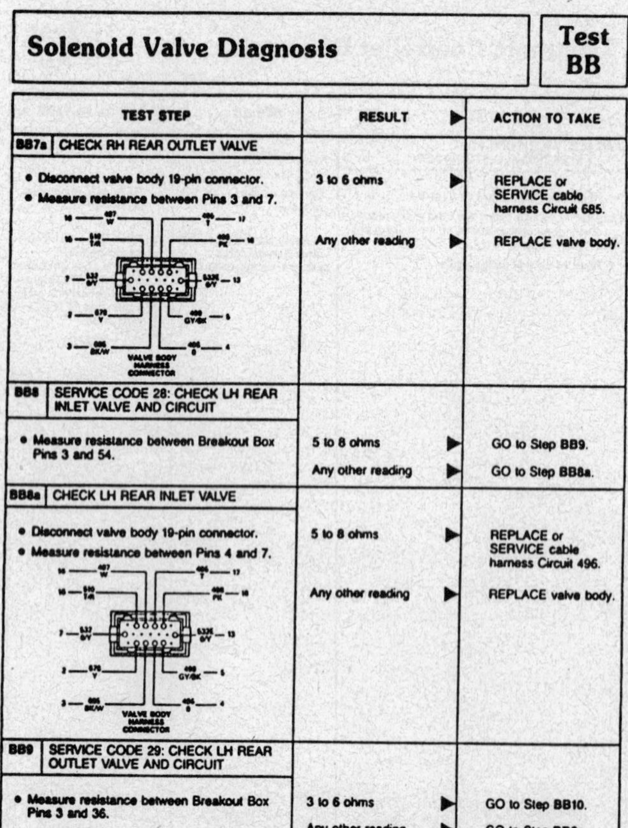

## Solenoid Valve Diagnosis — Test BB

| TEST STEP | RESULT ▶ | ACTION TO TAKE |
|---|---|---|
| **BB7a** CHECK RH REAR OUTLET VALVE | | |
| • Disconnect valve body 19-pin connector.<br>• Measure resistance between Pins 3 and 7. | 3 to 6 ohms ▶ | REPLACE or SERVICE cable harness Circuit 685. |
| | Any other reading ▶ | REPLACE valve body. |
| **BB8** SERVICE CODE 28: CHECK LH REAR INLET VALVE AND CIRCUIT | | |
| • Measure resistance between Breakout Box Pins 3 and 54. | 5 to 8 ohms ▶ | GO to Step BB9. |
| | Any other reading ▶ | GO to Step BB8a. |
| **BB8a** CHECK LH REAR INLET VALVE | | |
| • Disconnect valve body 19-pin connector.<br>• Measure resistance between Pins 4 and 7. | 5 to 8 ohms ▶ | REPLACE or SERVICE cable harness Circuit 496. |
| | Any other reading ▶ | REPLACE valve body. |
| **BB9** SERVICE CODE 29: CHECK LH REAR OUTLET VALVE AND CIRCUIT | | |
| • Measure resistance between Breakout Box Pins 3 and 36. | 3 to 6 ohms ▶ | GO to Step BB10. |
| | Any other reading ▶ | GO to Step BB9a. |

**Fig. 16 Tests BB7a, BB8, BB8a & BB9 (solenoid valve). 1990–91 Continental**

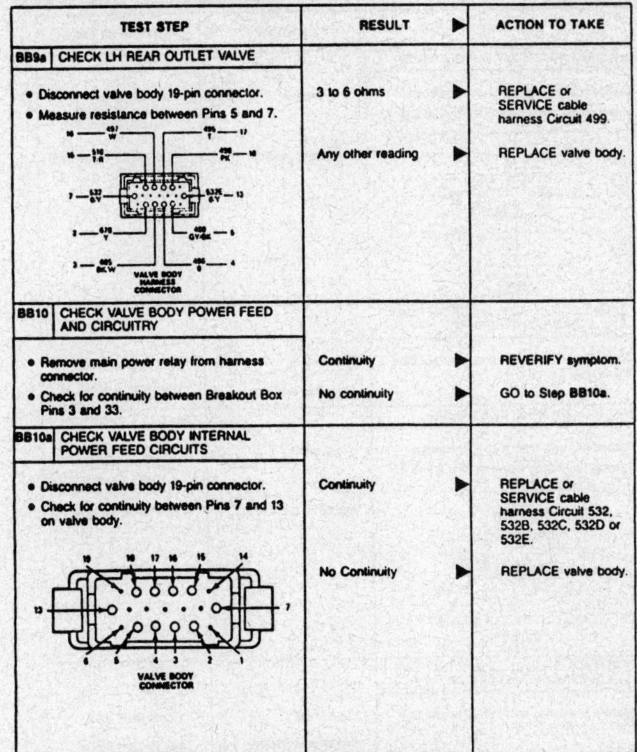

**Solenoid Valve Diagnosis** — Test BB

| TEST STEP | RESULT ▶ | ACTION TO TAKE |
|---|---|---|
| **BB9a** CHECK LH REAR OUTLET VALVE | | |
| • Disconnect valve body 19-pin connector.<br>• Measure resistance between Pins 5 and 7. | 3 to 6 ohms ▶<br>Any other reading ▶ | REPLACE or SERVICE cable harness Circuit 499.<br>REPLACE valve body. |
| **BB10** CHECK VALVE BODY POWER FEED AND CIRCUITRY | | |
| • Remove main power relay from harness connector.<br>• Check for continuity between Breakout Box Pins 3 and 33. | Continuity ▶<br>No continuity ▶ | REVERIFY symptom.<br>GO to Step BB10a. |
| **BB10a** CHECK VALVE BODY INTERNAL POWER FEED CIRCUITS | | |
| • Disconnect valve body 19-pin connector.<br>• Check for continuity between Pins 7 and 13 on valve body. | Continuity ▶<br>No Continuity ▶ | REPLACE or SERVICE cable harness Circuit 532, 532B, 532C, 532D or 532E.<br>REPLACE valve body. |



**Fig. 17 Tests BB9a, BB10 & BB10a (solenoid valve). 1990–91 Continental**

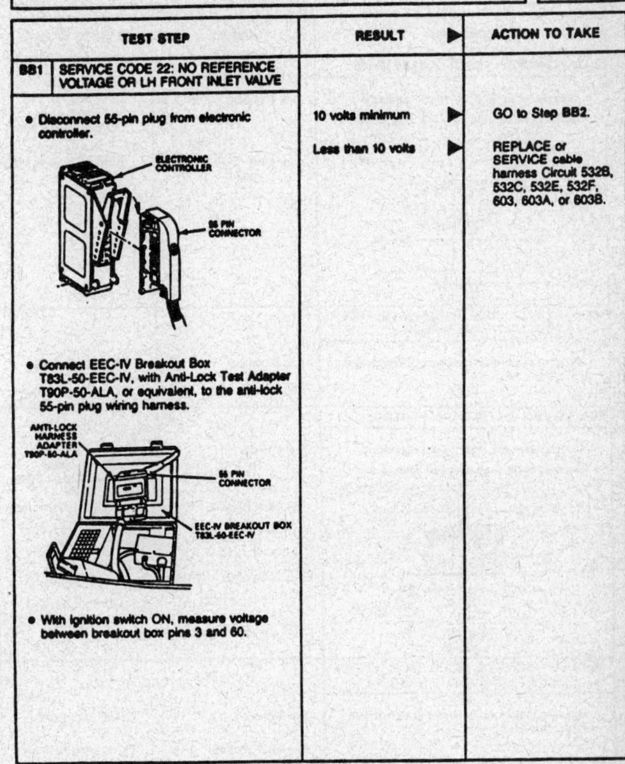

**Solenoid Valve Diagnosis** — Test BB

| TEST STEP | RESULT ▶ | ACTION TO TAKE |
|---|---|---|
| **BB1** SERVICE CODE 22: NO REFERENCE VOLTAGE OR LH FRONT INLET VALVE | | |
| • Disconnect 55-pin plug from electronic controller.<br>• Connect EEC-IV Breakout Box T83L-50-EEC-IV, with Anti-Lock Test Adapter T90P-50-ALA, or equivalent, to the anti-lock 55-pin plug wiring harness.<br>• With ignition switch ON, measure voltage between breakout box pins 3 and 60. | 10 volts minimum ▶<br>Less than 10 volts ▶ | GO to Step BB2.<br>REPLACE or SERVICE cable harness Circuit 532B, 532C, 532E, 532F, 603, 603A, or 603B. |



**Fig. 18 Test BB1 (solenoid valve). 1990 Town Car**

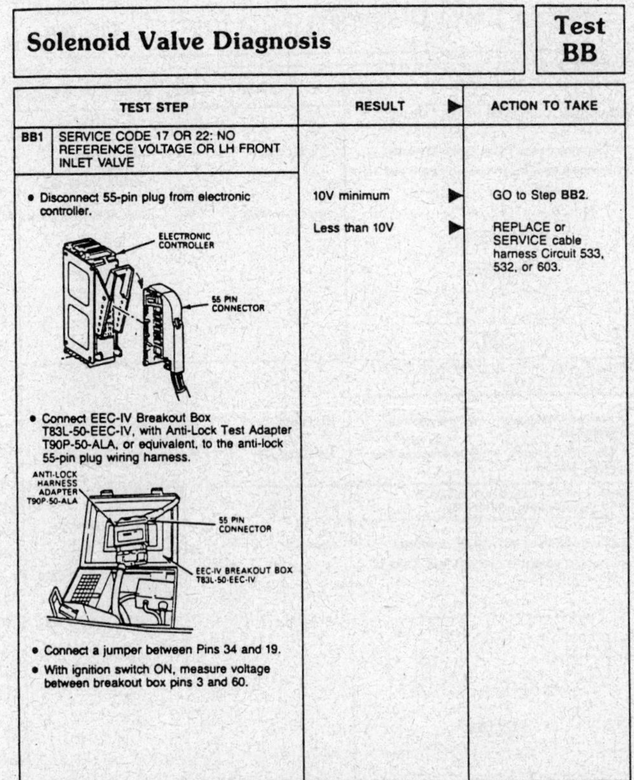

**Solenoid Valve Diagnosis** — Test BB

| TEST STEP | RESULT ▶ | ACTION TO TAKE |
|---|---|---|
| **BB1** SERVICE CODE 17 OR 22: NO REFERENCE VOLTAGE OR LH FRONT INLET VALVE | | |
| • Disconnect 55-pin plug from electronic controller.<br>• Connect EEC-IV Breakout Box T83L-50-EEC-IV, with Anti-Lock Test Adapter T90P-50-ALA, or equivalent, to the anti-lock 55-pin plug wiring harness.<br>• Connect a jumper between Pins 34 and 19.<br>• With ignition switch ON, measure voltage between breakout box pins 3 and 60. | 10V minimum ▶<br>Less than 10V ▶ | GO to Step BB2.<br>REPLACE or SERVICE cable harness Circuit 533, 532, or 603. |



**Fig. 19 Test BB1 (solenoid valve). 1991 Town Car**

**Solenoid Valve Diagnosis** — Test BB

| TEST STEP | RESULT ▶ | ACTION TO TAKE |
|---|---|---|
| **BB2** CHECK LH FRONT INLET VALVE AND CIRCUITRY | | |
| • Measure resistance between breakout box Pins 3 and 20. | 5 to 8 ohms ▶<br>Any other reading ▶ | REVERIFY code 22. NOTE: If other codes are output, ignore code 22 and service next code.<br>GO to Step BB2a. |
| **BB2a** CHECK LH FRONT INLET VALVE | | |
| • Disconnect valve body 19-pin connector.<br>• Measure resistance between Pins 17 and 7.<br>VALVE BODY HARNESS CONNECTOR | 5 to 8 ohms ▶<br>Any other reading ▶ | REPLACE or SERVICE cable harness Circuit 495.<br>REPLACE valve body. |
| **BB3** SERVICE CODE 23: CHECK LH FRONT OUTLET VALVE AND CIRCUIT | | |
| • Measure resistance between breakout box Pins 3 and 2. | 3 to 6 ohms ▶<br>Any other reading ▶ | GO to Step BB4.<br>GO to Step BB3a. |

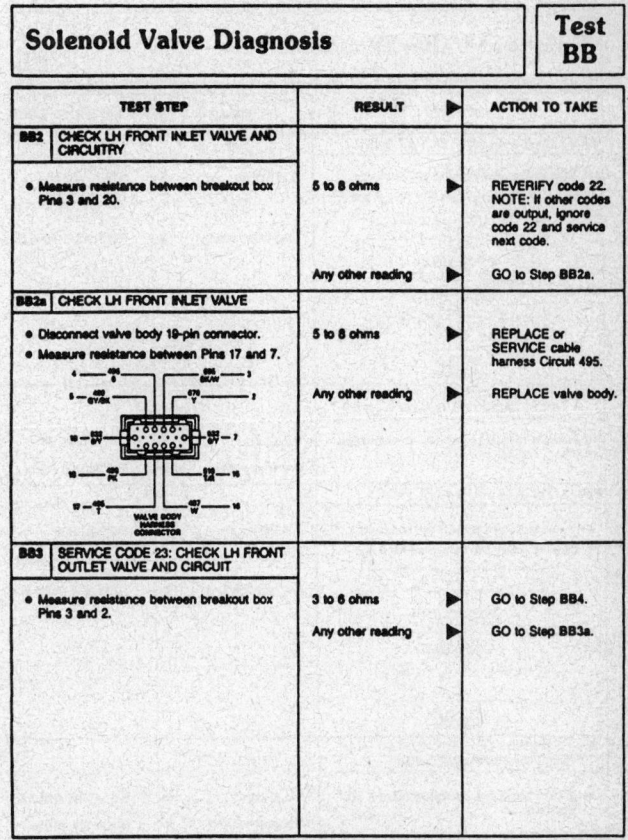

**Fig. 20 Tests BB@, BB2a & BB3 (solenoid valve). Town Car**

## Solenoid Valve Diagnosis — Test BB

| TEST STEP | RESULT ▶ | ACTION TO TAKE |
|---|---|---|
| **BB3a** CHECK LH FRONT OUTLET VALVE | | |
| • Disconnect valve body 19-pin connector. • Measure resistance between Pins 18 and 7. | 3 to 6 ohms ▶ | REPLACE or SERVICE cable harness Circuit 498. |
| | Any other reading ▶ | REPLACE valve body. |
| **BB4** SERVICE CODE 24: CHECK RH FRONT INLET VALVE AND CIRCUIT | | |
| • Measure resistance between Breakout Box Pins 3 and 38. | 5 to 8 ohms ▶ | GO to Step BB5. |
| | Any other reading ▶ | GO to Step BB4a. |
| **BB4a** CHECK RH FRONT INLET VALVE | | |
| • Disconnect valve body 19-pin connector. • Measure resistance between Pins 15 and 7. | 5 to 8 ohms ▶ | REPLACE or SERVICE cable harness Circuit 510. |
| | Any other reading ▶ | REPLACE valve body. |
| **BB5** SERVICE CODE 25: CHECK RH FRONT OUTLET VALVE AND CIRCUIT | | |
| • Measure resistance between Breakout Box Pins 3 and 21. | 3 to 6 ohms ▶ | GO to Step BB6. |
| | Any other reading ▶ | GO to Step BB5a. |

**Fig. 21 Tests BB3a, BB4, BB4a & BB5 (solenoid valve). Town Car**

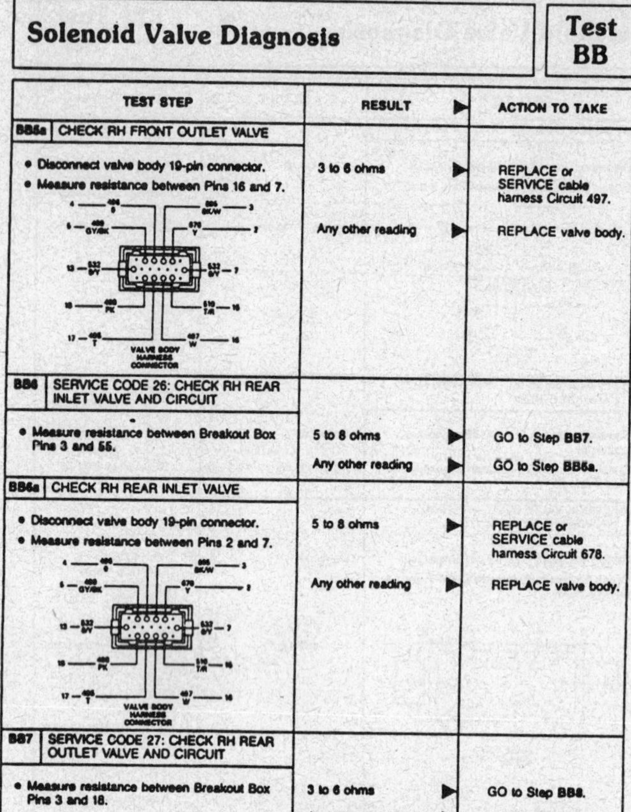

## Solenoid Valve Diagnosis — Test BB

| TEST STEP | RESULT ▶ | ACTION TO TAKE |
|---|---|---|
| **BB5a** CHECK RH FRONT OUTLET VALVE | | |
| • Disconnect valve body 19-pin connector. • Measure resistance between Pins 16 and 7. | 3 to 6 ohms ▶ | REPLACE or SERVICE cable harness Circuit 497. |
| | Any other reading ▶ | REPLACE valve body. |
| **BB6** SERVICE CODE 26: CHECK RH REAR INLET VALVE AND CIRCUIT | | |
| • Measure resistance between Breakout Box Pins 3 and 55. | 5 to 8 ohms ▶ | GO to Step BB7. |
| | Any other reading ▶ | GO to Step BB6a. |
| **BB6a** CHECK RH REAR INLET VALVE | | |
| • Disconnect valve body 19-pin connector. • Measure resistance between Pins 2 and 7. | 5 to 8 ohms ▶ | REPLACE or SERVICE cable harness Circuit 678. |
| | Any other reading ▶ | REPLACE valve body. |
| **BB7** SERVICE CODE 27: CHECK RH REAR OUTLET VALVE AND CIRCUIT | | |
| • Measure resistance between Breakout Box Pins 3 and 18. | 3 to 6 ohms ▶ | GO to Step BB8. |
| | Any other reading ▶ | GO to Step BB7a. |

**Fig. 22 Tests BB5a, BB6, BB6a & BB7 (solenoid valve). Town Car**

## Solenoid Valve Diagnosis — Test BB

| TEST STEP | RESULT ▶ | ACTION TO TAKE |
|---|---|---|
| **BB7a** CHECK RH REAR OUTLET VALVE | | |
| • Disconnect valve body 19-pin connector. • Measure resistance between Pins 3 and 7. | 3 to 6 ohms ▶ | REPLACE or SERVICE cable harness Circuit 685. |
| | Any other reading ▶ | REPLACE valve body. |
| **BB8** SERVICE CODE 28: CHECK LH REAR INLET VALVE AND CIRCUIT | | |
| • Measure resistance between Breakout Box Pins 3 and 54. | 5 to 8 ohms ▶ | GO to Step BB9. |
| | Any other reading ▶ | GO to Step BB8a. |
| **BB8a** CHECK LH REAR INLET VALVE | | |
| • Disconnect valve body 19-pin connector. • Measure resistance between Pins 4 and 7. | 5 to 8 ohms ▶ | REPLACE or SERVICE cable harness Circuit 496. |
| | Any other reading ▶ | REPLACE valve body. |
| **BB9** SERVICE CODE 29: CHECK LH REAR OUTLET VALVE AND CIRCUIT | | |
| • Measure resistance between Breakout Box Pins 3 and 36. | 3 to 6 ohms ▶ | GO to Step BB10. |
| | Any other reading ▶ | GO to Step BB9a. |

**Fig. 23 Tests BB7a, BB8, BB8a & BB9 (solenoid valve). Town Car**

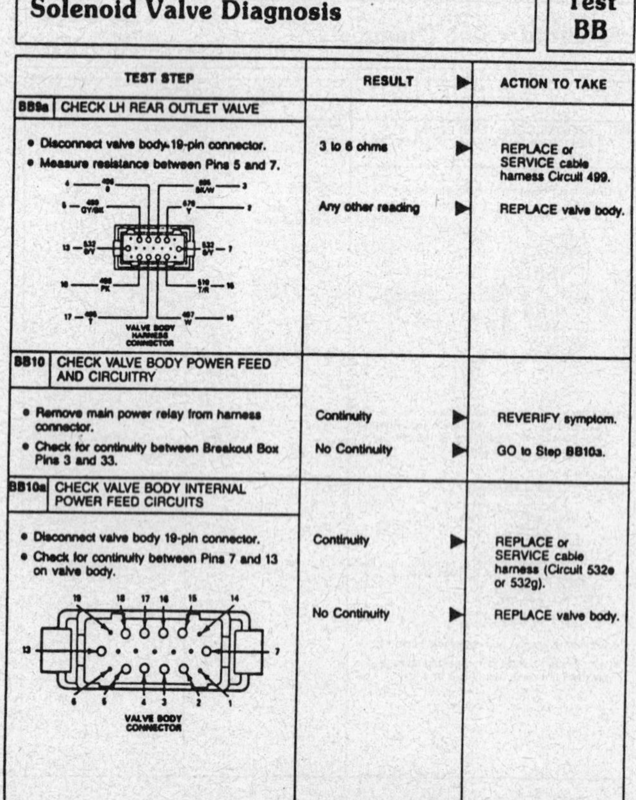

## Solenoid Valve Diagnosis — Test BB

| TEST STEP | RESULT ▶ | ACTION TO TAKE |
|---|---|---|
| **BB9a** CHECK LH REAR OUTLET VALVE | | |
| • Disconnect valve body 19-pin connector. • Measure resistance between Pins 5 and 7. | 3 to 6 ohms ▶ | REPLACE or SERVICE cable harness Circuit 499. |
| | Any other reading ▶ | REPLACE valve body. |
| **BB10** CHECK VALVE BODY POWER FEED AND CIRCUITRY | | |
| • Remove main power relay from harness connector. • Check for continuity between Breakout Box Pins 3 and 33. | Continuity ▶ | REVERIFY symptom. |
| | No Continuity ▶ | GO to Step BB10a. |
| **BB10a** CHECK VALVE BODY INTERNAL POWER FEED CIRCUITS | | |
| • Disconnect valve body 19-pin connector. • Check for continuity between Pins 7 and 13 on valve body. | Continuity ▶ | REPLACE or SERVICE cable harness (Circuit 532e or 532g). |
| | No Continuity ▶ | REPLACE valve body. |

**Fig. 24 Tests BB9a, BB10 & BB10a (solenoid valve). Town Car**

**Solenoid Valve Diagnosis** — **Test BB**

| TEST STEP | RESULT ▶ | ACTION TO TAKE |
|---|---|---|
| **BB11** SERVICE CODE 18 ISOLATION VALVE 1 | | |
| • Measure resistance between breakout box Pins 3 and 37. | 5 to 8 ohms ▶ | GO to Step **BB12**. |
| | Any other reading ▶ | GO to Step **BB11a**. |
| **BB11a** CHECK ISOLATION VALVE 1 | | |
| • Disconnect valve body 19-pin connector. • Measure resistance between Pins 7 and 9. (VALVE BODY CONNECTOR) | 5 to 8 ohms ▶ | SERVICE or REPLACE cable harness Circuit 493. |
| | Any other reading ▶ | REPLACE valve body. |
| **BB12** SERVICE CODE 19 ISOLATION VALVE 2 | | |
| • Measure resistance between breakout box Pins 3 and 40. | 5 to 8 ohms ▶ | VERIFY code 19. |
| | Any other reading ▶ | GO to Step **BB12a**. |
| **BB12a** CHECK ISOLATION VALVE 2 | | |
| • Disconnect valve body 19-pin connector. • Measure resistance between Pins 7 and 10. (VALVE BODY CONNECTOR) | 5 to 8 ohms ▶ | SERVICE or REPLACE cable harness Circuit 677. |
| | Any other reading ▶ | REPLACE valve body. |

**Fig. 25 Tests BB11, BB11a, BB12 & BB12a (solenoid valve). 1991 Town Car**

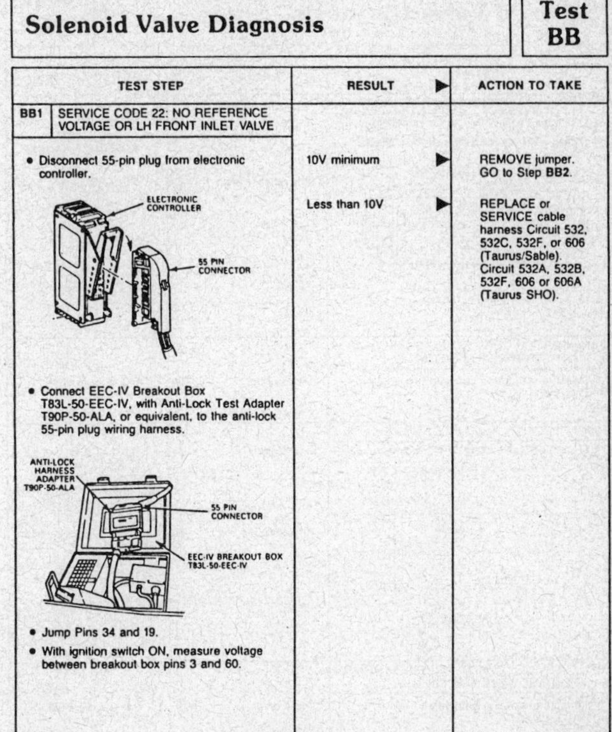

**Solenoid Valve Diagnosis** — **Test BB**

| TEST STEP | RESULT ▶ | ACTION TO TAKE |
|---|---|---|
| **BB1** SERVICE CODE 22: NO REFERENCE VOLTAGE OR LH FRONT INLET VALVE | | |
| • Disconnect 55-pin plug from electronic controller. (ELECTRONIC CONTROLLER; 55 PIN CONNECTOR) • Connect EEC-IV Breakout Box T83L-50-EEC-IV, with Anti-Lock Test Adapter T90P-50-ALA, or equivalent, to the anti-lock 55-pin plug wiring harness. (ANTI-LOCK HARNESS ADAPTER T90P-50-ALA; 55 PIN CONNECTOR; EEC-IV BREAKOUT BOX T83L-50-EEC-IV) • Jump Pins 34 and 19. • With ignition switch ON, measure voltage between breakout box pins 3 and 60. | 10V minimum ▶ | REMOVE jumper. GO to Step BB2. |
| | Less than 10V ▶ | REPLACE or SERVICE cable harness Circuit 532, 532C, 532F, or 606 (Taurus/Sable). Circuit 532A, 532B, 532F, 606 or 606A (Taurus SHO). |

**Fig. 26 Test BB1 (solenoid valve). Sable & Taurus**

**Solenoid Valve Diagnosis** — **Test BB**

| TEST STEP | RESULT ▶ | ACTION TO TAKE |
|---|---|---|
| **BB2** CHECK LH FRONT INLET VALVE AND CIRCUITRY | | |
| • Measure resistance between breakout box Pins 3 and 20. | 5 to 8 ohms ▶ | REVERIFY code 22. NOTE: If other codes are output, ignore code 22 and service next code. |
| | Any other reading ▶ | GO to Step **BB2a**. |
| **BB2a** CHECK LH FRONT INLET VALVE | | |
| • Disconnect valve body 19-pin connector. • Measure resistance between Pins 17 and 7. (VALVE BODY CONNECTOR) | 5 to 8 ohms ▶ | REPLACE or SERVICE cable harness Circuit 495, 532C, 532D or 532E (Taurus/Sable). Circuit 495, 532C, 532D or 532G (Taurus SHO). |
| | Any other reading ▶ | REPLACE valve body. |
| **BB3** SERVICE CODE 23: CHECK LH FRONT OUTLET VALVE AND CIRCUIT | | |
| • Measure resistance between breakout box Pins 3 and 2. | 3 to 6 ohms ▶ | GO to Step BB4. |
| | Any other reading ▶ | GO to Step **BB3a**. |

**Fig. 27 Tests BB2, BB2a & BB3 (solenoid valve). Sable & Taurus**

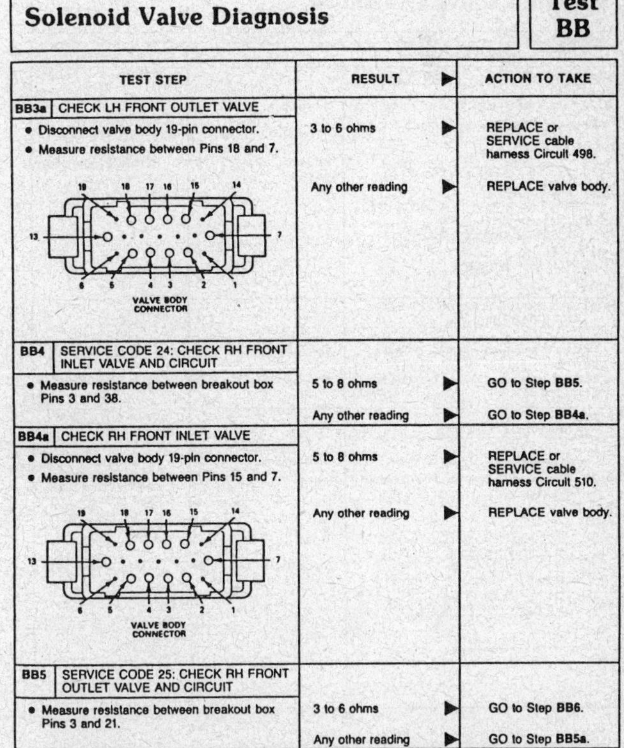

**Solenoid Valve Diagnosis** — **Test BB**

| TEST STEP | RESULT ▶ | ACTION TO TAKE |
|---|---|---|
| **BB3a** CHECK LH FRONT OUTLET VALVE | | |
| • Disconnect valve body 19-pin connector. • Measure resistance between Pins 18 and 7. (VALVE BODY CONNECTOR) | 3 to 6 ohms ▶ | REPLACE or SERVICE cable harness Circuit 498. |
| | Any other reading ▶ | REPLACE valve body. |
| **BB4** SERVICE CODE 24: CHECK RH FRONT INLET VALVE AND CIRCUIT | | |
| • Measure resistance between breakout box Pins 3 and 38. | 5 to 8 ohms ▶ | GO to Step **BB5**. |
| | Any other reading ▶ | GO to Step **BB4a**. |
| **BB4a** CHECK RH FRONT INLET VALVE | | |
| • Disconnect valve body 19-pin connector. • Measure resistance between Pins 15 and 7. (VALVE BODY CONNECTOR) | 5 to 8 ohms ▶ | REPLACE or SERVICE cable harness Circuit 510. |
| | Any other reading ▶ | REPLACE valve body. |
| **BB5** SERVICE CODE 25: CHECK RH FRONT OUTLET VALVE AND CIRCUIT | | |
| • Measure resistance between breakout box Pins 3 and 21. | 3 to 6 ohms ▶ | GO to Step **BB6**. |
| | Any other reading ▶ | GO to Step **BB5a**. |

**Fig. 28 Tests BB3a, BB4, BB4a & BB5 (solenoid valve). Sable & Taurus**

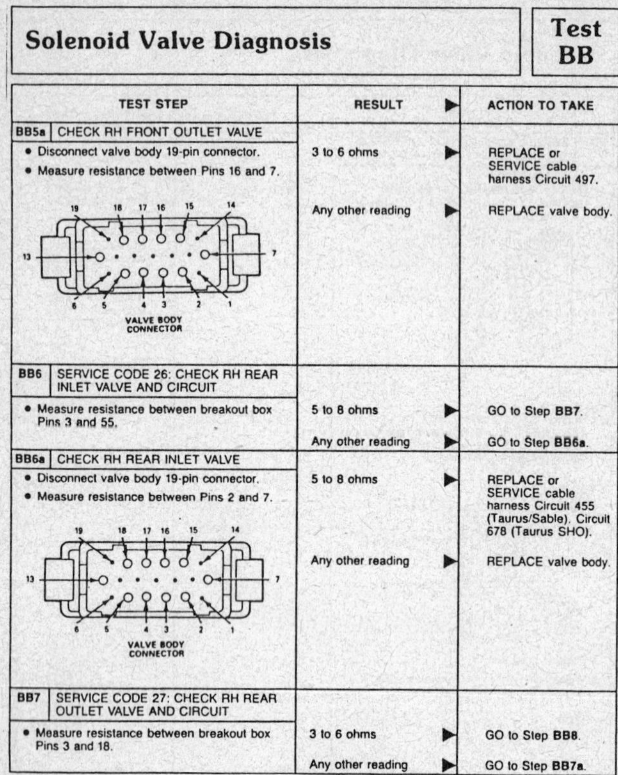

## Solenoid Valve Diagnosis — Test BB

| TEST STEP | RESULT ▶ | ACTION TO TAKE |
|---|---|---|
| **BB5a** CHECK RH FRONT OUTLET VALVE | | |
| • Disconnect valve body 19-pin connector.<br>• Measure resistance between Pins 16 and 7. | 3 to 6 ohms ▶ | REPLACE or SERVICE cable harness Circuit 497. |
| | Any other reading ▶ | REPLACE valve body. |
| **BB6** SERVICE CODE 26: CHECK RH REAR INLET VALVE AND CIRCUIT | | |
| • Measure resistance between breakout box Pins 3 and 55. | 5 to 8 ohms ▶ | GO to Step **BB7**. |
| | Any other reading ▶ | GO to Step **BB6a**. |
| **BB6a** CHECK RH REAR INLET VALVE | | |
| • Disconnect valve body 19-pin connector.<br>• Measure resistance between Pins 2 and 7. | 5 to 8 ohms ▶ | REPLACE or SERVICE cable harness Circuit 455 (Taurus/Sable). Circuit 678 (Taurus SHO). |
| | Any other reading ▶ | REPLACE valve body. |
| **BB7** SERVICE CODE 27: CHECK RH REAR OUTLET VALVE AND CIRCUIT | | |
| • Measure resistance between breakout box Pins 3 and 18. | 3 to 6 ohms ▶ | GO to Step **BB8**. |
| | Any other reading ▶ | GO to Step **BB7a**. |



**Fig. 29 Tests BB5a, BB6, BB6a & BB7 (solenoid valve). Sable & Taurus**

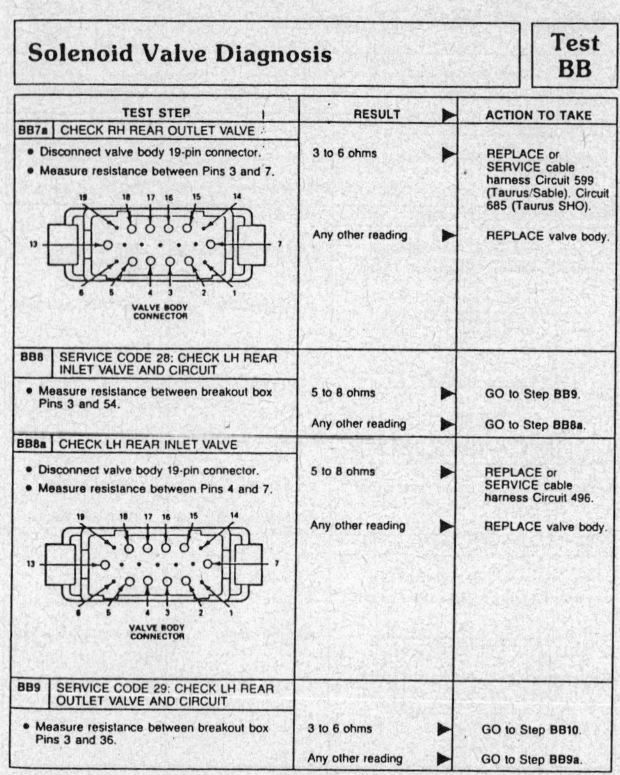

## Solenoid Valve Diagnosis — Test BB

| TEST STEP | RESULT ▶ | ACTION TO TAKE |
|---|---|---|
| **BB7a** CHECK RH REAR OUTLET VALVE | | |
| • Disconnect valve body 19-pin connector.<br>• Measure resistance between Pins 3 and 7. | 3 to 6 ohms ▶ | REPLACE or SERVICE cable harness Circuit 599 (Taurus/Sable). Circuit 685 (Taurus SHO). |
| | Any other reading ▶ | REPLACE valve body. |
| **BB8** SERVICE CODE 28: CHECK LH REAR INLET VALVE AND CIRCUIT | | |
| • Measure resistance between breakout box Pins 3 and 54. | 5 to 8 ohms ▶ | GO to Step **BB9**. |
| | Any other reading ▶ | GO to Step **BB8a**. |
| **BB8a** CHECK LH REAR INLET VALVE | | |
| • Disconnect valve body 19-pin connector.<br>• Measure resistance between Pins 4 and 7. | 5 to 8 ohms ▶ | REPLACE or SERVICE cable harness Circuit 496. |
| | Any other reading ▶ | REPLACE valve body. |
| **BB9** SERVICE CODE 29: CHECK LH REAR OUTLET VALVE AND CIRCUIT | | |
| • Measure resistance between breakout box Pins 3 and 36. | 3 to 6 ohms ▶ | GO to Step **BB10**. |
| | Any other reading ▶ | GO to Step **BB9a**. |



**Fig. 30 Tests BB7a, BB8, BB8a & BB9 (solenoid valve). Sable & Taurus**

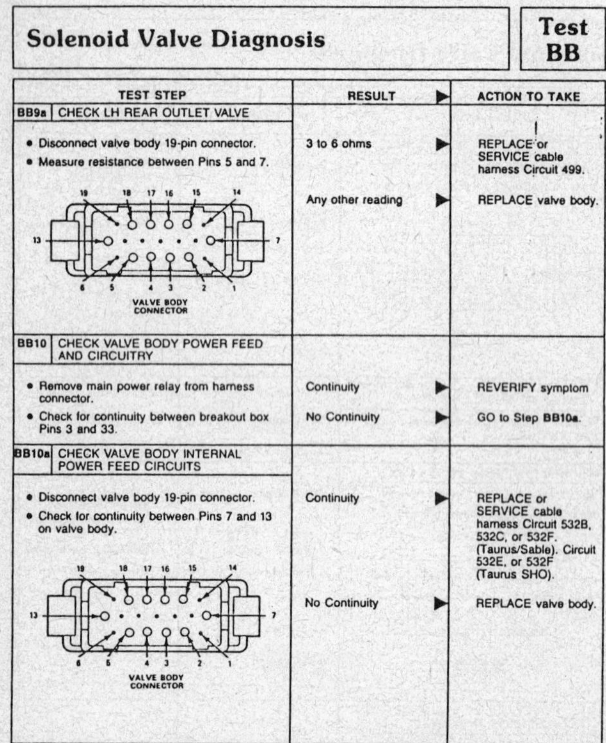

## Solenoid Valve Diagnosis — Test BB

| TEST STEP | RESULT ▶ | ACTION TO TAKE |
|---|---|---|
| **BB9a** CHECK LH REAR OUTLET VALVE | | |
| • Disconnect valve body 19-pin connector.<br>• Measure resistance between Pins 5 and 7. | 3 to 6 ohms ▶ | REPLACE or SERVICE cable harness Circuit 499. |
| | Any other reading ▶ | REPLACE valve body. |
| **BB10** CHECK VALVE BODY POWER FEED AND CIRCUITRY | | |
| • Remove main power relay from harness connector.<br>• Check for continuity between breakout box Pins 3 and 33. | Continuity ▶ | REVERIFY symptom |
| | No Continuity ▶ | GO to Step **BB10a**. |
| **BB10a** CHECK VALVE BODY INTERNAL POWER FEED CIRCUITS | | |
| • Disconnect valve body 19-pin connector.<br>• Check for continuity between Pins 7 and 13 on valve body. | Continuity ▶ | REPLACE or SERVICE cable harness Circuit 532B, 532C, or 532F. (Taurus/Sable). Circuit 532E, or 532F (Taurus SHO). |
| | No Continuity ▶ | REPLACE valve body. |



**Fig. 31 Tests BB9a, BB10 & BB10a (solenoid valve). Sable & Taurus**

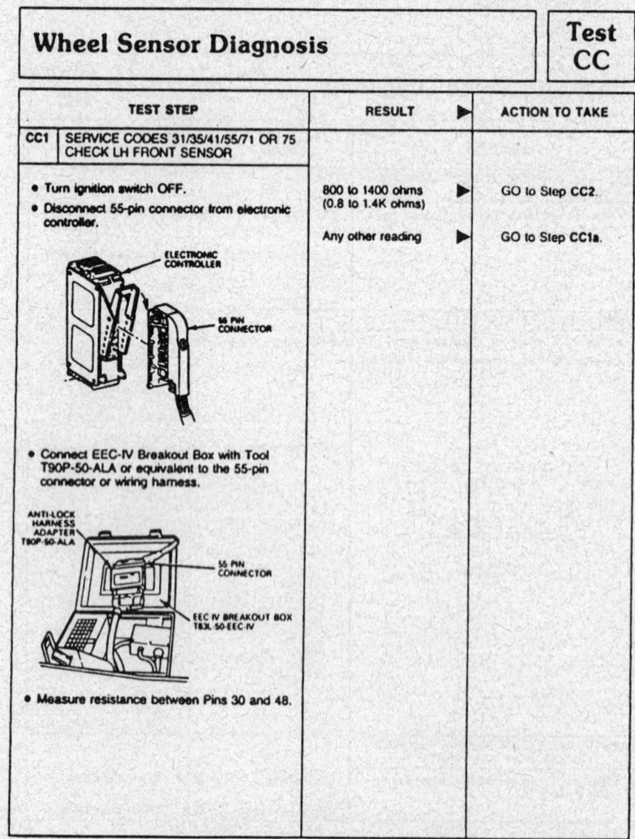

## Wheel Sensor Diagnosis — Test CC

| TEST STEP | RESULT ▶ | ACTION TO TAKE |
|---|---|---|
| **CC1** SERVICE CODES 31/35/41/55/71 OR 75 CHECK LH FRONT SENSOR | | |
| • Turn ignition switch OFF.<br>• Disconnect 55-pin connector from electronic controller.<br>• Connect EEC-IV Breakout Box with Tool T90P-50-ALA or equivalent to the 55-pin connector or wiring harness.<br>• Measure resistance between Pins 30 and 48. | 800 to 1400 ohms (0.8 to 1.4K ohms) ▶ | GO to Step **CC2**. |
| | Any other reading ▶ | GO to Step **CC1a**. |



**Fig. 32 Test CC1 (wheel sensor)**

## Wheel Sensor Diagnosis — Test CC

| TEST STEP | RESULT ▶ | ACTION TO TAKE |
|---|---|---|
| **CC1a** CHECK LH FRONT SENSOR RESISTANCE | | |
| • Disconnect LH front wheel sensor plug.<br>• Measure resistance of sensor at sensor plug.<br>LH FRONT SENSOR | 800 to 1400 ohms (0.8 to 1.4K ohms) ▶ | SERVICE or REPLACE cable harness Circuit |
| | Any other reading ▶ | REPLACE LH front sensor. |
| **CC2** CHECK LH FRONT SENSOR VOLTAGE | | |
| • Turn ignition switch OFF<br>• Turn air suspension switch OFF, if so equipped.<br>• Place vehicle on hoist and raise wheels clear of ground.<br>• Set multi-meter to voltage range (2 volt-AC).<br>• Measure voltage between Pins 30 and 48 at Breakout Box while spinning LH front at approximately 1 revolution per second. | Between 0.10 and 1.40 volts AC ▶ | GO to Step **CC3**. |
| | Less than 0.10 or more than 1.40 volts AC ▶ | CHECK sensor mounting, air gap or toothed wheel mounting. CORRECT as required. |
| **CC3** CHECK LH FRONT SENSOR CIRCUIT CONTINUITY TO GROUND | | |
| • Check continuity between Breakout Box Pins 30 and 60. | No Continuity ▶ | GO to Step **CC4**. |
| | Continuity ▶ | GO to Step **CC3a**. |

**Fig. 33 Tests CC1a, CC2 & CC3 (wheel sensor)**

## Wheel Sensor Diagnosis — Test CC

| TEST STEP | RESULT ▶ | ACTION TO TAKE |
|---|---|---|
| **CC3a** CHECK LH FRONT SENSOR TO GROUND | | |
| • Disconnect LH front wheel sensor plug.<br>• Check for continuity between each sensor plug pin (sensor side) and vehicle ground.<br>LH FRONT SENSOR | Continuity ▶ | REPLACE LH front sensor. |
| | No Continuity ▶ | SERVICE or REPLACE cable harness Circuit RECONNECT sensor plug. |
| **CC4** CHECK ELECTRONIC CONTROLLER TO GROUND WIRE | | |
| • Check continuity between Breakout Box Pin 60 and body ground. | Continuity ▶ | GO to Step **CC5**. |
| | No Continuity ▶ | SERVICE or REPLACE cable harness Circuit |
| **CC5** CHECK LH FRONT WHEEL BEARING | | |
| • Check front wheel bearing end play.<br>• Inspect toothed sensor ring visually for damaged teeth.<br>NOTE: Turn air suspension switch ON when vehicle is off hoist, if so equipped. | Loose or damaged parts ▶ | REPLACE damaged parts. |
| | Not loose or damaged ▶ | REVERIFY symptom |

**Fig. 34 Tests CC3a, CC4 & CC5 (wheel sensor)**

## Wheel Sensor Diagnosis — Test CC

| TEST STEP | RESULT ▶ | ACTION TO TAKE |
|---|---|---|
| **CC6** SERVICE CODES 32/36/42/56/72 OR 76 CHECK RH FRONT SENSOR | | |
| • Turn ignition switch OFF.<br>• Disconnect 55-pin connector from electronic controller.<br>ELECTRONIC CONTROLLER<br>55 PIN CONNECTOR<br>• Connect EEC-IV Breakout Box with Tool T90P-50-ALA or equivalent to the 55-pin connector on wiring harness.<br>ANTI-LOCK HARNESS ADAPTER T90P-50-ALA<br>55 PIN CONNECTOR<br>EEC-IV BREAKOUT BOX T83L-50-EEC-IV<br>• Measure resistance between Pins 29 and 47. | 800 to 1400 ohms (0.8 to 1.4K ohms) ▶ | GO to Step **CC7**. |
| | Any other reading ▶ | GO to Step **CC6a**. |

**Fig. 35 Tests CC6 (wheel sensor)**

## Wheel Sensor Diagnosis — Test CC

| TEST STEP | RESULT ▶ | ACTION TO TAKE |
|---|---|---|
| **CC6a** CHECK RH FRONT SENSOR RESISTANCE | | |
| • Disconnect RH front sensor plug.<br>• Measure resistance of sensor at sensor plug.<br>RH FRONT SENSOR | 800 to 1400 ohms (0.8 to 1.4K ohms) ▶ | SERVICE or REPLACE cable harness Circuit |
| | Any other reading ▶ | REPLACE RH front sensor. |
| **CC7** CHECK RH FRONT SENSOR VOLTAGE | | |
| • Turn ignition switch OFF.<br>• Turn air suspension switch OFF, if so equipped.<br>• Place vehicle on hoist and raise wheels clear of ground.<br>• Set multi-meter to voltage range (2 volt-AC).<br>• Measure voltage between Pins 29 and 47 at Breakout Box while spinning RH front at approximately 1 revolution per second. | Between 0.10 and 1.40 volts AC ▶ | GO to Step **CC8**. |
| | Less than 0.10 or more than 1.40 volts AC ▶ | CHECK sensor mounting, air gap or toothed wheel mounting. CORRECT as required. |
| **CC8** CHECK RH FRONT SENSOR CIRCUIT CONTINUITY TO GROUND | | |
| • Check continuity between Breakout Box Pins 29 and 60. | No Continuity ▶ | GO to Step **CC9**. |
| | Continuity ▶ | GO to Step **CC8a**. |

**Fig. 36 Tests CC6a, CC7 & CC8 (wheel sensor)**

## Wheel Sensor Diagnosis — Test CC

| TEST STEP | RESULT | ACTION TO TAKE |
|---|---|---|
| **CC8a** CHECK RH FRONT SENSOR TO GROUND | | |
| • Disconnect RH front wheel sensor plug.<br>• Check for continuity between each sensor plug pin (sensor side) and vehicle ground. <br>RH FRONT SENSOR | Continuity ▶ | REPLACE RH front sensor. |
| | No Continuity ▶ | SERVICE or REPLACE cable harness Circuit RECONNECT sensor plug. |
| **CC9** CHECK ELECTRONIC CONTROLLER TO GROUND WIRE | | |
| • Check continuity between Breakout Box Pin 60 and body ground. | Continuity ▶ | GO to Step CC10. |
| | No Continiuty ▶ | SERVICE or REPLACE cable harness Circuit |
| **CC10** CHECK RH FRONT WHEEL BEARING | | |
| • Check front wheel bearing end play.<br>• Inspect toothed sensor ring visually for damaged teeth.<br>NOTE: Turn air suspension switch ON when vehicle is off hoist, if so equipped. | Loose or damaged parts ▶ | REPLACE faulty parts. |
| | Not loose or damaged ▶ | REVERIFY symptom |

**Fig. 37 Tests CC8a, CC9 & CC10 (wheel sensor)**

## Wheel Sensor Diagnosis — Test CC

| TEST STEP | RESULT | ACTION TO TAKE |
|---|---|---|
| **CC11** SERVICE CODES 33/37/43/57/73 OR 77 CHECK RH REAR SENSOR | | |
| • Turn ignition switch OFF.<br>• Disconnect 55-pin connector from electronic controller. 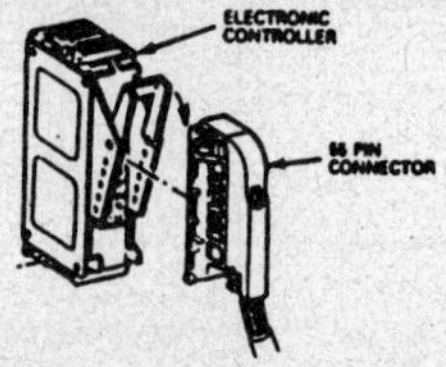<br>ELECTRONIC CONTROLLER<br>55 PIN CONNECTOR<br>• Connect EEC-IV Breakout Box with Tool T90P-50-ALA or equivalent to the 55-pin connector on wiring harness. 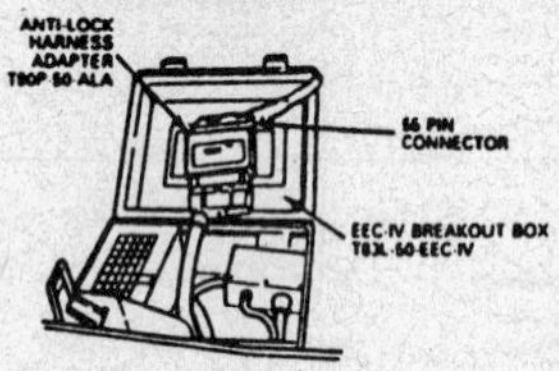<br>ANTI-LOCK HARNESS ADAPTER T90P 50 ALA<br>55 PIN CONNECTOR<br>EEC-IV BREAKOUT BOX T83L-50-EEC-IV<br>• Measure resistance between Pins 27 and 45. | 800 to 1400 ohms (0.8 to 1.4K ohms) ▶ | GO to Step CC12. |
| | Any other reading ▶ | GO to Step CC11a. |

**Fig. 38 Test CC11 (wheel sensor)**

## Wheel Sensor Diagnosis — Test CC

| TEST STEP | RESULT | ACTION TO TAKE |
|---|---|---|
| **CC11a** CHECK RH REAR SENSOR RESISTANCE | | |
| • Disconnect RH rear sensor plug.<br>• Measure resistance of sensor at sensor plug. <br>RH REAR SENSOR | 800 to 1400 ohms (0.8 to 1.4K ohms) ▶ | SERVICE or REPLACE cable harness Circuit |
| | Any other reading ▶ | REPLACE RH rear sensor. |
| **CC12** CHECK RH REAR SENSOR VOLTAGE | | |
| • Turn ignition switch OFF.<br>• Turn air suspension switch OFF, if so equipped.<br>• Place vehicle on hoist and raise wheels clear of ground.<br>• Set multi-meter to voltage range (2 volt-AC).<br>• Measure voltage between Pins 27 and 45 at Breakout Box while spinning RH rear at approximately 1 revolution per second. | Between 0.10 and 1.40 volts AC ▶ | GO to Step CC13. |
| | Less than 0.10 or more than 1.40 volts AC ▶ | CHECK sensor mounting, air gap or toothed wheel mounting. CORRECT as required. |
| **CC13** CHECK RH REAR SENSOR CIRCUIT CONTINUITY TO GROUND | | |
| • Check continuity between Breakout Box Pins 27 and 60. | No Continuity ▶ | GO to Step CC14. |
| | Continuity ▶ | GO to Step CC13a. |

**Fig. 39 Tests CC11a, CC12 & CC13 (wheel sensor)**

## Wheel Sensor Diagnosis — Test CC

| TEST STEP | RESULT | ACTION TO TAKE |
|---|---|---|
| **CC13a** CHECK RH REAR SENSOR TO GROUND | | |
| • Disconnect RH rear wheel sensor plug.<br>• Check for continuity between each sensor plug pin (sensor side) and vehicle ground. <br>RH REAR SENSOR | Continuity ▶ | REPLACE RH rear sensor. |
| | No Continuity ▶ | SERVICE or REPLACE cable harness Circuit RECONNECT sensor plug. |
| **CC14** CHECK ELECTRONIC CONTROLLER TO GROUND WIRE | | |
| • Check continuity between Breakout Box Pin 60 and body ground. | Continuity ▶ | GO to Step CC15. |
| | No Continuity ▶ | SERVICE or REPLACE cable harness Circuit |
| **CC15** CHECK FOR EXCESSIVE AXLE VIBRATION | | |
| • Check differential housing for excessive play.<br>• Check rear axle bearings for excessive play.<br>• Inspect toothed sensor ring for damaged teeth.<br>NOTE: Turn air suspension switch ON when vehicle is off hoist, if so equipped. | Loose or damaged parts ▶ | SERVICE or REPLACE damaged parts. |
| | Not loose or damaged ▶ | REVERIFY symptom. |

**Fig. 40 Tests CC13a, CC14 & CC15 (wheel sensor)**

**Wheel Sensor Diagnosis** — Test CC

| TEST STEP | RESULT ▶ | ACTION TO TAKE |
|---|---|---|
| **CC16** SERVICE CODES 34/38/44/58/74 OR 78 CHECK LH REAR SENSOR | | |
| • Turn ignition switch OFF.<br>• Disconnect 55-pin connector from electronic controller. 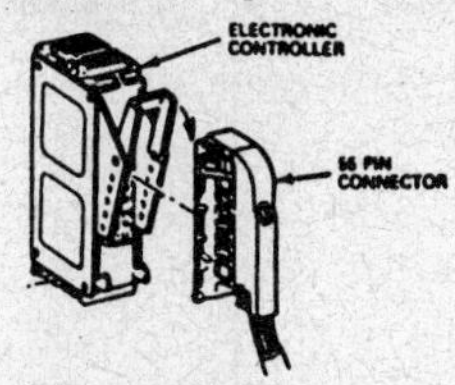<br>ELECTRONIC CONTROLLER<br>55 PIN CONNECTOR<br>• Connect EEC-IV Breakout Box with Tool T90P-50-ALA or equivalent to the 55-pin connector on wiring harness. 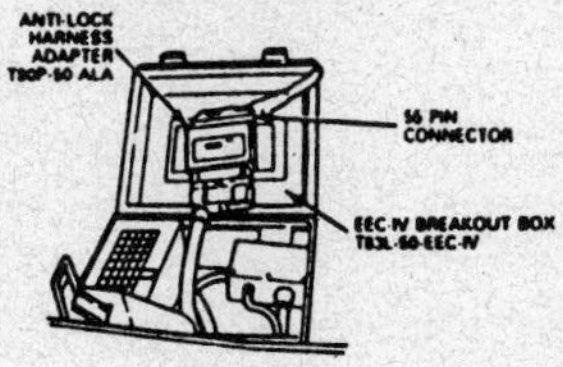<br>ANTI-LOCK HARNESS ADAPTER T90P-50 ALA<br>55 PIN CONNECTOR<br>EEC-IV BREAKOUT BOX T83L-50-EEC-IV<br>• Measure resistance between Pins 28 and 46. | 800 to 1400 ohms (0.8 to 1.4K ohms) ▶<br>Any other reading ▶ | GO to Step CC17.<br>GO to Step CC16a. |

Fig. 41 Test CC16 (wheel sensor)

**Wheel Sensor Diagnosis** — Test CC

| TEST STEP | RESULT ▶ | ACTION TO TAKE |
|---|---|---|
| **CC16a** CHECK LH REAR SENSOR RESISTANCE | | |
| • Disconnect LH rear sensor plug.<br>• Measure resistance of sensor at sensor plug. <br>LH REAR SENSOR | 800 to 1400 ohms (0.8 to 1.4K ohms) ▶<br>Any other reading ▶ | SERVICE or REPLACE cable harness Circuit<br>REPLACE LH rear sensor. |
| **CC17** CHECK LH REAR SENSOR VOLTAGE | | |
| • Turn ignition switch OFF.<br>• Turn air suspension switch OFF, if so equipped.<br>• Place vehicle on hoist and raise wheels clear of ground.<br>• Set multi-meter to voltage range (2 volt-AC).<br>• Measure voltage between Pins 28 and 46 at Breakout Box while spinning RH rear at approximately 1 revolution per second. | Between 0.10 and 1.40 volts AC ▶<br>Less than 0.10 or more than 1.40 volts AC ▶ | GO to Step CC18.<br>CHECK sensor mounting, air gap or toothed wheel mounting. CORRECT as required. |
| **CC18** CHECK LH REAR SENSOR CIRCUIT CONTINUITY TO GROUND | | |
| • Check continuity between Breakout Box Pins 28 and 60. | No Continuity ▶<br>Continuity ▶ | GO to Step CC19.<br>GO to Step CC18a. |

Fig. 42 Tests CC16a, CC17 & CC18 (wheel sensor)

**Wheel Sensor Diagnosis** — Test CC

| TEST STEP | RESULT ▶ | ACTION TO TAKE |
|---|---|---|
| **CC18a** CHECK LH REAR SENSOR TO GROUND | | |
| • Disconnect LH rear wheel sensor plug.<br>• Check for continuity between each sensor plug pin (sensor side) and vehicle ground. <br>LH REAR SENSOR | Continuity ▶<br>No Continuity ▶ | REPLACE LH rear sensor.<br>SERVICE or REPLACE cable harness Circuit RECONNECT sensor plug. |
| **CC19** CHECK ELECTRONIC CONTROLLER TO GROUND WIRE | | |
| • Check continuity between Breakout Box Pin 60 and body ground. | Continuity ▶<br>No Continuity ▶ | GO to Step CC20.<br>SERVICE or REPLACE cable harness Circuit |
| **CC20** CHECK FOR EXCESSIVE AXLE VIBRATION | | |
| • Check differential housing for excessive play.<br>• Check rear axle bearings for excessive play.<br>• Inspect toothed sensor ring for damaged teeth.<br>NOTE: Turn air suspension switch ON when vehicle is off hoist, if so equipped. | Loose or damaged parts ▶<br>Not loose or damaged ▶ | SERVICE or REPLACE damaged parts.<br>REVERIFY symptom. |

Fig. 43 Tests CC18a, CC19 & CC20 (wheel sensor)

**Wheel Sensor Diagnosis** — Test DD

| TEST STEP | RESULT ▶ | ACTION TO TAKE |
|---|---|---|
| **DD1** SERVICE CODE 51 AND/OR 71 CHECK LH FRONT SENSOR CIRCUIT CONTINUITY | | |
| • Turn ignition switch OFF.<br>• Disconnect 55-pin plug from electronic controller. 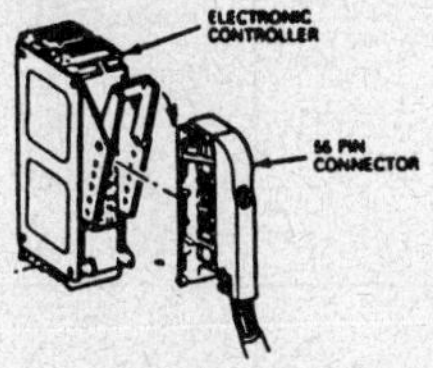<br>ELECTRONIC CONTROLLER<br>55 PIN CONNECTOR<br>• Connect EEC-IV Breakout Box, T83L-50-EEC-IV, with Anti-Lock Test Adapter, T90P-50-ALA or equivalent, to the anti-lock 55-pin plug harness. 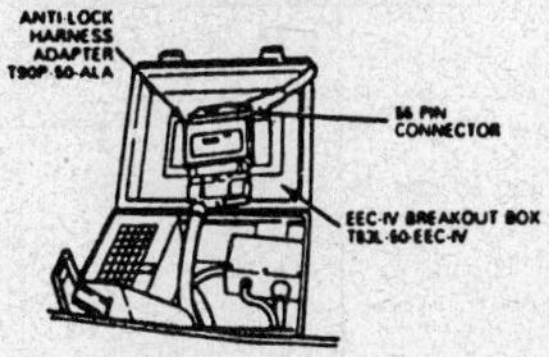<br>ANTI-LOCK HARNESS ADAPTER T90P-50-ALA<br>55 PIN CONNECTOR<br>EEC-IV BREAKOUT BOX T83L-50-EEC-IV<br>• Check for continuity between Breakout Box Pins 60 and 30. | Continuity ▶<br>No Continuity ▶ | GO to Step DD1a.<br>GO to Step DD2. |

Fig. 44 Test DD1 (wheel sensor)

## Wheel Sensor Diagnosis — Test DD

| TEST STEP | RESULT ▶ | ACTION TO TAKE |
|---|---|---|
| **DD1a** CHECK LH FRONT SENSOR CONTINUITY | | |
| • Disconnect wheel sensor plug (LH Front).<br>• Check for continuity between each sensor plug pin (sensor side) and vehicle ground.<br>LH FRONT SENSOR | Continuity ▶ | REPLACE LH front sensor. |
| | No Continuity ▶ | SERVICE or REPLACE cable harness Circuit RECONNECT sensor plug. |
| **DD2** CHECK ELECTRONIC CONTROLLER TO GROUND WIRE | | |
| • Check continuity between Breakout Box Pin 60 and body ground. | Continuity ▶ | GO to Step DD3. |
| | No Continuity ▶ | SERVICE or REPLACE cable harness Circuit |
| **DD3** CHECK ANTI-LOCK OPERATION LH FRONT WHEEL | | |
| • Turn air suspension OFF, if so equipped.<br>• Lift vehicle and rotate wheels to ensure they turn freely.<br>• Apply moderate brake pedal effort and check that LH front wheel will not turn.<br>• Short Pins 2, 20 and 60 to each other at Breakout Box.<br>• Check that LH front wheel turns freely with ignition switch ON.<br>**CAUTION: Do not leave ignition on for more than 1 minute, or valve damage may result.**<br>• Turn air suspension on when vehicle is off hoist, if so equipped. | If wheel turns freely ▶ | REVERIFY symptom. |
| | If wheel does not turn freely or pedal drops ▶ | REPLACE solenoid valve body. |

**Fig. 45 Tests DD1a, DD2 & DD3 (wheel sensor)**

## Wheel Sensor Diagnosis — Test DD

| TEST STEP | RESULT ▶ | ACTION TO TAKE |
|---|---|---|
| **DD4** SERVICE CODE 52 AND/OR 72 CHECK RH FRONT SENSOR CIRCUIT CONTINUITY | | |
| • Turn ignition switch OFF.<br>• Disconnect 55-pin plug from electronic controller.<br>ELECTRONIC CONTROLLER<br>55 PIN CONNECTOR<br>• Connect EEC-IV Breakout Box, T83L-50-EEC-IV, with Anti-Lock Test Adapter, T90P-50-ALA, or equivalent, to the anti-lock 55-pin plug wiring harness.<br>ANTI-LOCK HARNESS ADAPTER T90P-50-ALA<br>55 PIN CONNECTOR<br>EEC-IV BREAKOUT BOX T83L-50-EEC-IV<br>• Check for continuity between Breakout Box Pins 60 and 29. | Continuity ▶ | GO to Step DD4a. |
| | No Continuity ▶ | GO to Step DD5. |

**Fig. 46 Test DD4 (wheel sensor)**

## Wheel Sensor Diagnosis — Test DD

| TEST STEP | RESULT ▶ | ACTION TO TAKE |
|---|---|---|
| **DD4a** CHECK RH FRONT SENSOR CONTINUITY | | |
| • Disconnect RH front wheel sensor.<br>• Check for continuity between each sensor plug pin (sensor side) and vehicle ground.<br>RH FRONT SENSOR | Continuity ▶ | REPLACE RH front sensor. |
| | No Continuity ▶ | SERVICE or REPLACE cable harness Circuit RECONNECT sensor plug. |
| **DD5** CHECK ELECTRONIC CONTROLLER TO GROUND WIRE | | |
| • Check continuity between Breakout Box Pin 60 and body ground. | Continuity ▶ | GO to Step DD6. |
| | No Continuity ▶ | SERVICE or REPLACE cable harness Circuit |
| **DD6** CHECK ANTI-LOCK OPERATION RH FRONT WHEEL | | |
| • Turn air suspension OFF, if so equipped.<br>• Lift vehicle and rotate wheels to ensure they turn freely.<br>• Apply moderate brake pedal effort and check that RH front wheel will not turn.<br>• Short Pins 21, 38 and 60 to each other at Breakout Box.<br>• Check that RH front wheel turns freely with ignition switch ON.<br>• Turn air suspension ON when vehicle is off hoist, if so equipped. | If wheel turns freely ▶ | REVERIFY symptom. |
| | If wheel does not turn freely or pedal drops ▶ | REPLACE solenoid valve body. |

**Fig. 47 Tests DD4a, DD5 & DD6 (wheel sensor). Except 1991 Town Car**

## Wheel Sensor Diagnosis — Test DD

| TEST STEP | RESULT ▶ | ACTION TO TAKE |
|---|---|---|
| **DD4a** CHECK RH FRONT SENSOR CONTINUITY | | |
| • Disconnect RH front wheel sensor.<br>• Check for continuity between each sensor plug pin (sensor side) and vehicle ground.<br>RH FRONT SENSOR | Continuity ▶ | REPLACE RH front sensor. |
| | No Continuity ▶ | SERVICE or REPLACE cable harness Circuit 514 or 516. RECONNECT sensor plug. |
| **DD5** CHECK ELECTRONIC CONTROLLER TO GROUND WIRE | | |
| • Check continuity between Breakout Box Pin 60 and body ground. | Continuity ▶ | GO to Step DD6. |
| | No Continuity ▶ | SERVICE or REPLACE cable harness Circuit 57. |
| **DD6** CHECK ANTI-LOCK OPERATION RH FRONT WHEEL | | |
| • Turn air suspension OFF, if so equipped.<br>• Lift vehicle and rotate wheels to ensure they turn freely.<br>• Apply moderate brake pedal effort and check that RH front wheel will not turn.<br>• Jump Pins 34 and 19.<br>• Short Pins 21, 38 and 60 to each other at Breakout Box.<br>• Check that RH front wheel turns freely with ignition switch ON.<br>• Turn air suspension ON when vehicle is off hoist, if so equipped. | If wheel turns freely ▶ | REVERIFY symptom. |
| | If wheel does not turn freely or pedal drops ▶ | REPLACE solenoid valve body. |

**Fig. 48 Tests DD4a, DD5 & DD6 (wheel sensor). 1991 Town Car**

## Wheel Sensor Diagnosis — Test DD

| TEST STEP | RESULT ▶ | ACTION TO TAKE |
|---|---|---|
| **DD7** SERVICE CODE 53 AND/OR 73 CHECK RH REAR SENSOR CIRCUIT CONTINUITY | | |
| • Turn ignition switch OFF.<br>• Disconnect 55-pin plug from electronic controller. | Continuity ▶<br>No Continuity ▶ | GO to Step **DD7a**.<br>GO to Step **DD8**. |
| • Connect EEC-IV Breakout Box, T83L-50-EEC-IV, with Anti-Lock Test Adapter, T90P-50-ALA, or equivalent, to the anti-lock 55-pin plug wiring harness. | | |
| • Check for continuity between Breakout Box Pins 60 and 27. | | |

**Fig. 49 Test DD7 (wheel sensor)**

## Wheel Sensor Diagnosis — Test DD

| TEST STEP | RESULT ▶ | ACTION TO TAKE |
|---|---|---|
| **DD7a** CHECK RH REAR SENSOR CONTINUITY | | |
| • Disconnect wheel sensor plug (RH Rear).<br>• Check for continuity between each sensor plug pin (sensor side) and vehicle ground. | Continuity ▶<br>No Continuity ▶ | REPLACE RH rear sensor.<br>SERVICE or REPLACE cable harness Circuit RECONNECT sensor plug. |
| **DD8** CHECK ELECTRONIC CONTROLLER TO GROUND WIRE | | |
| • Check continuity between Breakout Box Pin 60 and body ground. | Continuity ▶<br>No Continuity ▶ | GO to Step **DD9**.<br>SERVICE or REPLACE cable harness Circuit |
| **DD9** CHECK ANTI-LOCK OPERATION RH REAR WHEEL | | |
| • Turn air suspension OFF, if so equipped.<br>• Lift vehicle and rotate wheels to ensure they turn freely.<br>• Apply moderate brake pedal effort and check that RH rear wheel will not turn.<br>• Short Pins 18, 55 and 60 to each other at Breakout Box.<br>• Check that RH rear wheel turns freely with ignition switch ON.<br>• Turn air suspension ON when vehicle is off hoist, if so equipped. | If wheel turns freely ▶<br>If wheel does not turn freely or pedal drops ▶ | REVERIFY symptom.<br>REPLACE solenoid valve body. |

**Fig. 50 Tests DD7a, DD8 & DD9 (wheel sensor)**

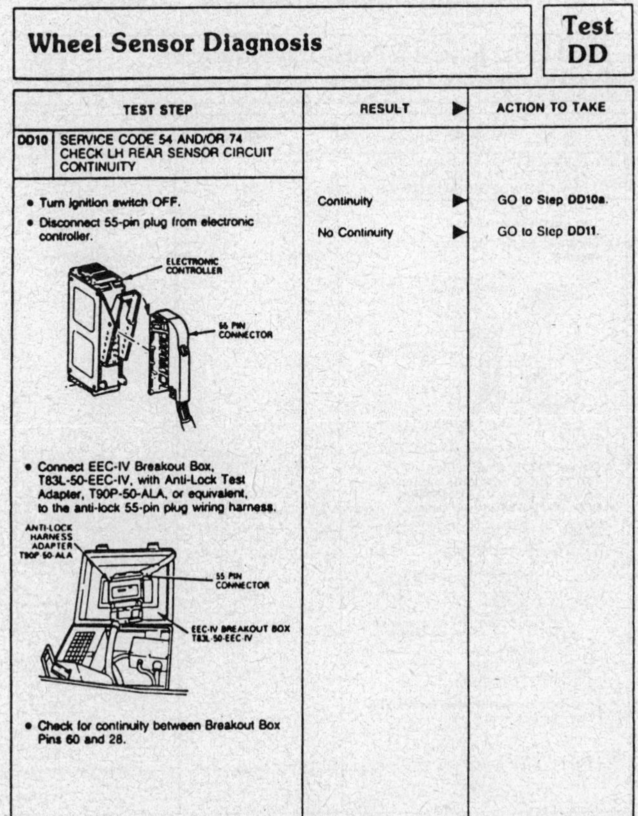

## Wheel Sensor Diagnosis — Test DD

| TEST STEP | RESULT ▶ | ACTION TO TAKE |
|---|---|---|
| **DD10** SERVICE CODE 54 AND/OR 74 CHECK LH REAR SENSOR CIRCUIT CONTINUITY | | |
| • Turn ignition switch OFF.<br>• Disconnect 55-pin plug from electronic controller. | Continuity ▶<br>No Continuity ▶ | GO to Step **DD10a**.<br>GO to Step **DD11**. |
| • Connect EEC-IV Breakout Box, T83L-50-EEC-IV, with Anti-Lock Test Adapter, T90P-50-ALA, or equivalent, to the anti-lock 55-pin plug wiring harness. | | |
| • Check for continuity between Breakout Box Pins 60 and 28. | | |

**Fig. 51 Test DD10 (wheel sensor)**

## Wheel Sensor Diagnosis — Test DD

| TEST STEP | RESULT ▶ | ACTION TO TAKE |
|---|---|---|
| **DD10a** CHECK LH REAR SENSOR CONTINUITY | | |
| • Disconnect wheel sensor plug (LH Rear).<br>• Check for continuity between each sensor plug pin (sensor side) and vehicle ground. | Continuity ▶<br>No Continuity ▶ | REPLACE LH rear sensor.<br>SERVICE or REPLACE cable harness Circuit RECONNECT sensor plug. |
| **DD11** CHECK ELECTRONIC CONTROLLER TO GROUND WIRE | | |
| • Check continuity between Breakout Box Pin 60 and body ground. | Continuity ▶<br>No Continuity ▶ | GO to Step **DD12**.<br>SERVICE or REPLACE cable harness Circuit |
| **DD12** CHECK ANTI-LOCK OPERATION LH REAR WHEEL | | |
| • Turn air suspension OFF, if so equipped.<br>• Lift vehicle and rotate wheels to ensure they turn freely.<br>• Apply moderate brake pedal effort and check that LH rear wheel will not turn.<br>• Short Pins 36, 54 and 60 to each other at Breakout Box.<br>• Check that LH rear wheel turns freely with ignition switch ON.<br>**CAUTION: Do not leave ignition on for more than 1 minute, or valve damage may result.**<br>• Turn air suspension ON when vehicle is off hoist, if so equipped. | If wheel turns freely ▶<br>If wheel does not turn freely or pedal drops ▶ | REVERIFY symptom.<br>REPLACE solenoid valve body. |

**Fig. 52 Tests DD10a, DD11 & DD12 (wheel sensor). Except 1991 Town Car**

## Wheel Sensor Diagnosis — Test DD

| TEST STEP | RESULT ▶ | ACTION TO TAKE |
|---|---|---|
| **DD10a** CHECK LH REAR SENSOR CONTINUITY | | |
| • Disconnect wheel sensor plug (LH Rear).<br>• Check for continuity between each sensor plug pin (sensor side) and vehicle ground.  | Continuity ▶ | REPLACE LH rear sensor. |
| | No Continuity ▶ | SERVICE or REPLACE cable harness Circuit 518 or 519. RECONNECT sensor plug. |
| **DD11** CHECK ELECTRONIC CONTROLLER TO GROUND WIRE | | |
| • Check continuity between Breakout Box Pin 60 and body ground. | Continuity ▶ | GO to Step DD12. |
| | No Continuity ▶ | SERVICE or REPLACE cable harness Circuit 57. |
| **DD12** CHECK ANTI-LOCK OPERATION LH REAR WHEEL | | |
| • Turn air suspension OFF, if so equipped.<br>• Lift vehicle and rotate wheels to ensure they turn freely.<br>• Apply moderate brake pedal effort and check that LH rear wheel will not turn.<br>• Jump Pins 34 and 19.<br>• Short Pins 36, 54 and 60 to each other at Breakout Box.<br>• Check that LH rear wheel turns freely with ignition switch ON.<br>**CAUTION: Do not leave ignition on for more than 1 minute, or valve damage may result.**<br>• Turn air suspension ON when vehicle is off hoist, if so equipped. | If wheel turns freely ▶ | REVERIFY symptom. |
| | If wheel does not turn freely or pedal drops ▶ | REPLACE solenoid valve body. |

**Fig. 53 Tests DD10a, DD11 & DD12 (wheel sensor). 1991 Town Car**

## Fluid Level Indicator/Pedal Travel Switch/Pump Motor Diagnosis — Test EE

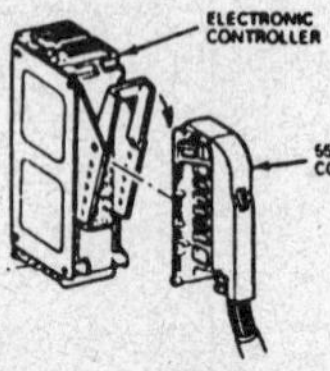

| TEST STEP | RESULT ▶ | ACTION TO TAKE |
|---|---|---|
| **EE1** SERVICE CODE 61: CHECK FLS #2 CIRCUIT | | |
| • Turn ignition switch OFF.<br>• Disconnect 55-pin plug from electronic controller.<br>• Connect EEC-IV Breakout Box, T83L-50-EEC-IV, with Anti-Lock Test Adapter, T90P-50-ALA or equivalent, to the anti-lock 55-pin plug harness.<br>• Check for continuity between Breakout Box Pins 8 and 60. | No Continuity ▶ | GO to Step **EE2**. |
| | Continuity ▶ | GO to Step **EE1a**. |

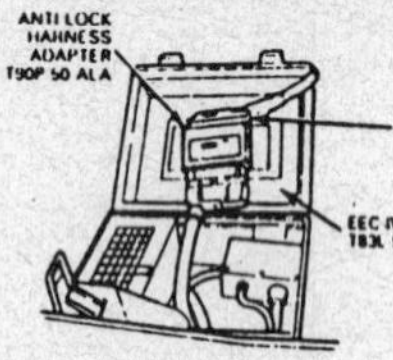

**Fig. 54 Test EE1 (Fluid level indicator, pedal travel switch & pump motor). 1990 Continental, Sable, Taurus & Town Car**

## Fluid Level Indicator/Pedal Travel Switch/Pump Motor Diagnosis — Test EE

| TEST STEP | RESULT ▶ | ACTION TO TAKE |
|---|---|---|
| **EE1** SERVICE CODE 61 AND/OR 62: CHECK FLS #2 CIRCUIT AND PEDAL TRAVEL SWITCH | | |
| • Turn ignition switch to OFF position.<br>• Disconnect 55-pin plug from electronic controller.<br>• Connect EEC-IV Breakout Box, T83L-50-EEC-IV, with Anti-Lock Test Adapter, T90P-50-ALA or equivalent, to the anti-lock 55-pin plug harness.<br>• Check for continuity between Breakout Box Pins 8 and 60. | No Continuity ▶ | GO to Step **EE2**. |
| | Continuity ▶ | GO to Step **EE1a**. |

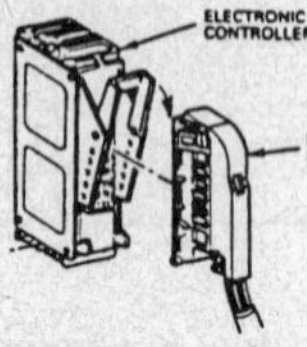

**Fig. 55 Test EE1 (Fluid level indicator, pedal travel switch & pump motor). 1991 Continental, Sable & Taurus**

## Fluid Level Indicator/Pedal Travel Switch/Pressure Switch Diagnosis — Test EE

| TEST STEP | RESULT ▶ | ACTION TO TAKE |
|---|---|---|
| **EE1** SERVICE CODE 61, 62 AND/OR 66: CHECK FLS #2, PEDAL TRAVEL SWITCH AND PRESSURE SWITCH | | |
| • Turn ignition switch OFF.<br>• Disconnect 55-pin plug from electronic controller.<br>• Connect EEC-IV Breakout Box, T83L-50-EEC-IV, with Anti-Lock Test Adapter, T90P-50-ALA or equivalent, to the anti-lock 55-pin plug harness.<br>• Check for continuity between Breakout Box Pins 8 and 60. | No Continuity ▶ | GO to Step **EE2**. |
| | Continuity ▶ | GO to Step **EE1a**. |

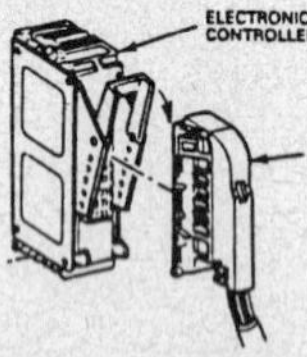

**Fig. 56 Test EE1 (Fluid level indicator, pedal travel switch & pump motor). 1991 Town Car**

### Fluid Level Indicator/Pedal Travel Switch/ Pump Motor Diagnosis — Test EE

| TEST STEP | RESULT ▶ | ACTION TO TAKE |
|---|---|---|
| **EE1a** CHECK FLI #2 SWITCH | | |
| • Disconnect 2-pin plug on FLI located on small reservoir on Hydraulic Control Unit.<br>2 PIN CONNECTOR ON SMALL RESERVOIR ON HCU<br>• Check for continuity between each pin and body ground. | Continuity ▶<br>No Continuity ▶ | REPLACE HCU reservoir.<br>SERVICE OR REPLACE cable harness Circuit |
| **EE2** CHECK FOR VOLTAGE ON FLS #2 SWITCH AND CIRCUITRY | | |
| • Turn ignition switch ON.<br>• Measure voltage between Breakout Box Pins 8 and 60. | No voltage ▶<br>12 volts ▶ | REVERIFY code 61.<br>GO to Step EE2a. |
| **EE2a** CHECK FOR VOLTAGE ON FLS #2 | | |
| • Disconnect 2-pin plug on FLI located on small reservoir on hydraulic control unit.<br>2 PIN CONNECTOR ON SMALL RESERVOIR ON HCU<br>• Measure voltage between each pin and body ground. | 12 volts ▶<br>No voltage ▶ | REPLACE HCU reservoir.<br>SERVICE OR REPLACE cable harness Circuit |

**Fig. 57 Tests EE1a, EE2 & EE2a (Fluid level indicator/pedal travel switch/pump motor). Except 1991 Town Car**

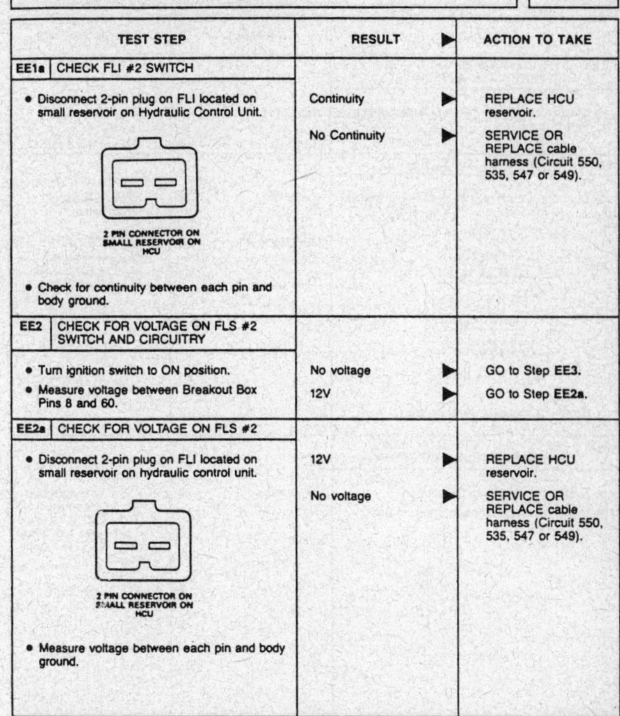

### Fluid Level Indicator/Pedal Travel Switch/ Pressure Switch Diagnosis — Test EE

| TEST STEP | RESULT ▶ | ACTION TO TAKE |
|---|---|---|
| **EE1a** CHECK FLI #2 SWITCH | | |
| • Disconnect 2-pin plug on FLI located on small reservoir on Hydraulic Control Unit.<br>2 PIN CONNECTOR ON SMALL RESERVOIR ON HCU<br>• Check for continuity between each pin and body ground. | Continuity ▶<br>No Continuity ▶ | REPLACE HCU reservoir.<br>SERVICE OR REPLACE cable harness (Circuit 550, 535, 547 or 549). |
| **EE2** CHECK FOR VOLTAGE ON FLS #2 SWITCH AND CIRCUITRY | | |
| • Turn ignition switch to ON position.<br>• Measure voltage between Breakout Box Pins 8 and 60. | No voltage ▶<br>12V ▶ | GO to Step EE3.<br>GO to Step EE2a. |
| **EE2a** CHECK FOR VOLTAGE ON FLS #2 | | |
| • Disconnect 2-pin plug on FLI located on small reservoir on hydraulic control unit.<br>2 PIN CONNECTOR ON SMALL RESERVOIR ON HCU<br>• Measure voltage between each pin and body ground. | 12V ▶<br>No voltage ▶ | REPLACE HCU reservoir.<br>SERVICE OR REPLACE cable harness (Circuit 550, 535, 547 or 549). |

**Fig. 58 Tests EE1a, EE2 & EE2a (Fluid level indicator/pedal travel switch/pump motor). 1991 Town Car**

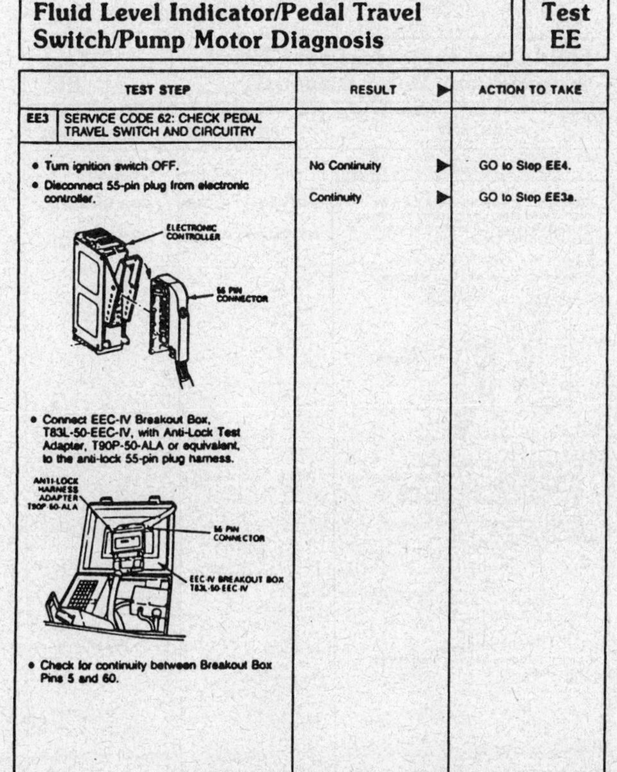

### Fluid Level Indicator/Pedal Travel Switch/Pump Motor Diagnosis — Test EE

| TEST STEP | RESULT ▶ | ACTION TO TAKE |
|---|---|---|
| **EE3** SERVICE CODE 62: CHECK PEDAL TRAVEL SWITCH AND CIRCUITRY | | |
| • Turn ignition switch OFF.<br>• Disconnect 55-pin plug from electronic controller.<br>ELECTRONIC CONTROLLER / 55 PIN CONNECTOR<br>• Connect EEC-IV Breakout Box, T83L-50-EEC-IV, with Anti-Lock Test Adapter, T90P-50-ALA or equivalent, to the anti-lock 55-pin plug harness.<br>ANTI-LOCK HARNESS ADAPTER T90P 50-ALA / 55 PIN CONNECTOR / EEC-IV BREAKOUT BOX T83L-50-EEC-IV<br>• Check for continuity between Breakout Box Pins 5 and 60. | No Continuity ▶<br>Continuity ▶ | GO to Step EE4.<br>GO to Step EE3a. |

**Fig. 59 Test EE3 (Fluid level indicator/pedal travel switch/pump motor). 1990 Continental, Sable, Taurus & Town Car**

### Fluid Level Indicator/Pedal Travel Switch/Pump Motor Diagnosis — Test EE

| TEST STEP | RESULT ▶ | ACTION TO TAKE |
|---|---|---|
| **EE3** CHECK PEDAL TRAVEL SWITCH AND CIRCUITRY | | |
| • Turn ignition switch OFF.<br>• Disconnect 55-pin plug from electronic controller.<br>ELECTRONIC CONTROLLER / 55 PIN CONNECTOR<br>• Connect EEC-IV Breakout Box, T83L-50-EEC-IV, with Anti-Lock Test Adapter, T90P-50-ALA or equivalent, to the anti-lock 55-pin plug harness.<br>ANTI-LOCK HARNESS ADAPTER T90P-50-ALA / 55 PIN CONNECTOR / EEC-IV BREAKOUT BOX T83L-50-EEC-IV<br>• Check for continuity between Breakout Box Pins 5 and 60. | No Continuity ▶<br>Continuity ▶ | GO to Step EE4.<br>GO to Step EE3a. |

**Fig. 60 Test EE3 (Fluid level indicator/pedal travel switch/pump motor). 1991 Continental, Sable & Taurus**

## Fluid Level Indicator/Pedal Travel Switch/ Pressure Switch Diagnosis — Test EE

| TEST STEP | RESULT ▶ | ACTION TO TAKE |
|---|---|---|
| **EE3** SERVICE CODE 62: CHECK PEDAL TRAVEL SWITCH AND CIRCUITRY | | |
| • Check for continuity between Breakout Box Pins 5 and 60. | No Continuity ▶ | GO to Step EE4. |
| | Continuity ▶ | GO to Step EE3a. |
| **EE3a** CHECK PEDAL TRAVEL SWITCH | | |
| • Disconnect 2-pin plug on pedal travel switch. (2 PIN BRAKE PEDAL POSITION SWITCH) • Check for continuity between each pin and body ground. | Continuity ▶ | REPLACE pedal travel switch. |
| | No Continuity ▶ | SERVICE OR REPLACE cable harness (Circuit 535, 547, 549 or 550). |
| **EE4** CHECK FOR VOLTAGE ON PEDAL TRAVEL SWITCH AND CIRCUITRY | | |
| • Turn ignition switch to ON position. • Measure voltage between Breakout Box Pins 5 and 60. | No voltage ▶ | If vehicle is equipped with traction assist: Go to EE5. If vehicle is equipped with ABS only: REVERIFY code 61 and/or 62. |
| | 12V ▶ | GO to Step EE4a. |

**Fig. 61 Tests EE3, EE3a & EE4 (Fluid level indicator/pedal travel switch/pump motor). 1991 Town Car**

## Fluid Level Indicator/Pedal Travel Switch/ Pump Motor Diagnosis — Test EE

| TEST STEP | RESULT ▶ | ACTION TO TAKE |
|---|---|---|
| **EE3a** CHECK PEDAL TRAVEL SWITCH | | |
| • Disconnect 2-pin plug on pedal travel switch. (2 PIN BRAKE PEDAL POSITION SWITCH) • Check for continuity between each pin and body ground. | Continuity ▶ | REPLACE pedal travel switch. |
| | No Continuity ▶ | SERVICE OR REPLACE cable harness Circuit |
| **EE4** CHECK FOR VOLTAGE ON PEDAL TRAVEL SWITCH AND CIRCUITRY | | |
| • Turn ignition switch ON. • Measure voltage between Breakout Box Pins 5 and 60. | No voltage ▶ | REVERIFY code 62. |
| | 12 volts ▶ | GO to Step EE4a |
| **EE4a** CHECK FOR VOLTAGE ON PEDAL TRAVEL SWITCH | | |
| • Disconnect 2-pin plug on pedal travel switch. (2 PIN BRAKE PEDAL POSITION SWITCH) • Measure voltage between each pin and body ground. | 12 volts ▶ | REPLACE pedal travel switch. |
| | No voltage ▶ | SERVICE OR REPLACE cable harness Circuit |

**Fig. 62 Tests EE3a, EE4 & EE4a (Fluid level indicator/pedal travel switch/pump motor). Except 1991 Town Car**

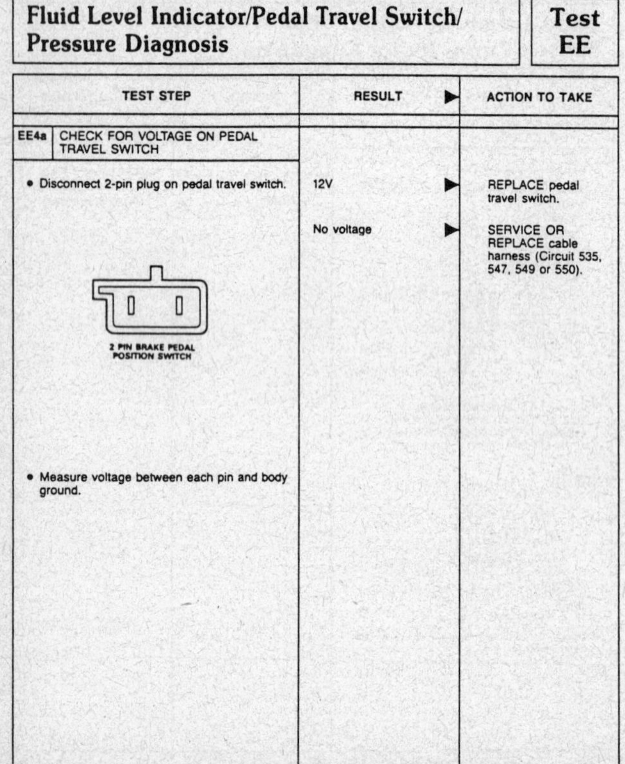

## Fluid Level Indicator/Pedal Travel Switch/ Pressure Diagnosis — Test EE

| TEST STEP | RESULT ▶ | ACTION TO TAKE |
|---|---|---|
| **EE4a** CHECK FOR VOLTAGE ON PEDAL TRAVEL SWITCH | | |
| • Disconnect 2-pin plug on pedal travel switch. (2 PIN BRAKE PEDAL POSITION SWITCH) • Measure voltage between each pin and body ground. | 12V ▶ | REPLACE pedal travel switch. |
| | No voltage ▶ | SERVICE OR REPLACE cable harness (Circuit 535, 547, 549 or 550). |

**Fig. 63 Test EE4a (Fluid level indicator/pedal travel switch/pump motor). 1991 Town Car**

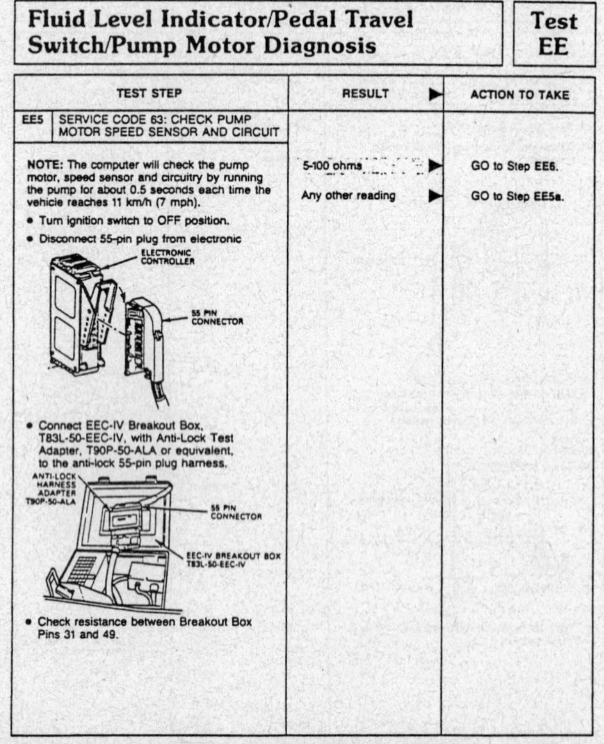

## Fluid Level Indicator/Pedal Travel Switch/Pump Motor Diagnosis — Test EE

| TEST STEP | RESULT ▶ | ACTION TO TAKE |
|---|---|---|
| **EE5** SERVICE CODE 63: CHECK PUMP MOTOR SPEED SENSOR AND CIRCUIT | | |
| NOTE: The computer will check the pump motor, speed sensor and circuitry by running the pump for about 0.5 seconds each time the vehicle reaches 11 km/h (7 mph). • Turn ignition switch to OFF position. • Disconnect 55-pin plug from electronic (ELECTRONIC CONTROLLER; 55 PIN CONNECTOR) • Connect EEC-IV Breakout Box, T83L-50-EEC-IV, with Anti-Lock Test Adapter, T90P-50-ALA or equivalent, to the anti-lock 55-pin plug harness. (ANTI-LOCK HARNESS ADAPTER T90P-50-ALA; 55 PIN CONNECTOR; EEC-IV BREAKOUT BOX T83L-50-EEC-IV) • Check resistance between Breakout Box Pins 31 and 49. | 5-100 ohms ▶ | GO to Step EE6. |
| | Any other reading ▶ | GO to Step EE5a. |

**Fig. 64 Test EE5 (Fluid level indicator/pedal travel switch/pump motor). Except 1991 Town Car**

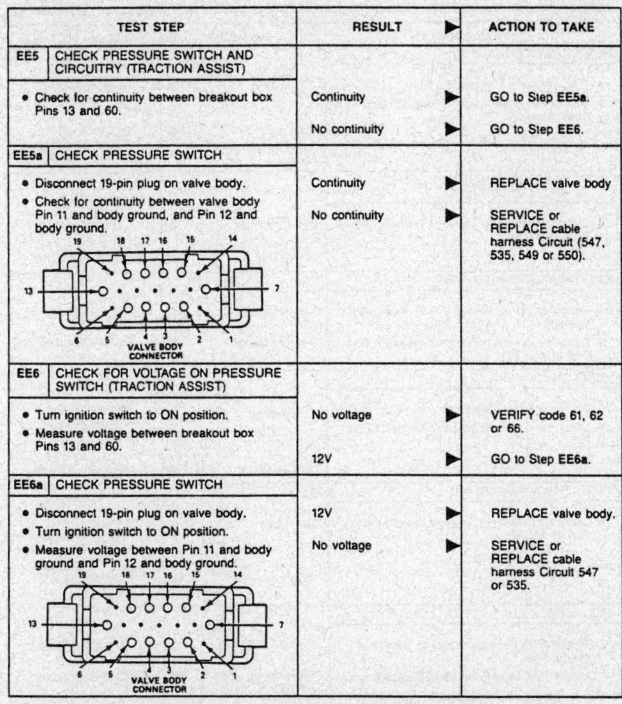

**Fluid Level Indicator/Pedal Travel Switch/Pressure Switch Diagnosis** — Test EE

| TEST STEP | RESULT ▶ | ACTION TO TAKE |
|---|---|---|
| **EE5** CHECK PRESSURE SWITCH AND CIRCUITRY (TRACTION ASSIST) | | |
| • Check for continuity between breakout box Pins 13 and 60. | Continuity ▶ | GO to Step **EE5a**. |
| | No continuity ▶ | GO to Step **EE6**. |
| **EE5a** CHECK PRESSURE SWITCH | | |
| • Disconnect 19-pin plug on valve body.<br>• Check for continuity between valve body Pin 11 and body ground, and Pin 12 and body ground.<br>VALVE BODY CONNECTOR | Continuity ▶ | REPLACE valve body |
| | No continuity ▶ | SERVICE or REPLACE cable harness Circuit (547, 535, 549 or 550). |
| **EE6** CHECK FOR VOLTAGE ON PRESSURE SWITCH (TRACTION ASSIST) | | |
| • Turn ignition switch to ON position.<br>• Measure voltage between breakout box Pins 13 and 60. | No voltage ▶ | VERIFY code 61, 62 or 66. |
| | 12V ▶ | GO to Step **EE6a**. |
| **EE6a** CHECK PRESSURE SWITCH | | |
| • Disconnect 19-pin plug on valve body.<br>• Turn ignition switch to ON position.<br>• Measure voltage between Pin 11 and body ground and Pin 12 and body ground.<br>VALVE BODY CONNECTOR | 12V ▶ | REPLACE valve body. |
| | No voltage ▶ | SERVICE or REPLACE cable harness Circuit 547 or 535. |

**Fig. 65 Tests EE5, EE5a, EE6 & EE6a (Fluid level indicator/pedal travel switch/pump motor). 1991 Town Car**

**Fluid Level Indicator/Pedal Travel Switch/Pump Motor Diagnosis** — Test EE

| TEST STEP | RESULT ▶ | ACTION TO TAKE |
|---|---|---|
| **EE5d** CHECK CIRCUIT 462 | | |
| • Check continuity between Breakout Box Pin 31 and Pin S0 on pump motor connector 7-pin plug (harness side).<br>7 PIN PUMP MOTOR RELAY CONNECTOR HARNESS SIDE | Continuity ▶ | GO to Step **EE5e**. |
| | No Continuity ▶ | SERVICE or REPLACE cable harness Circuit |
| **EE5e** CHECK CIRCUIT 604 | | |
| • Check continuity between Breakout Box Pin 49 and Pin S1 on pump motor connector 7-pin plug (harness side). | Continuity ▶ | REVERIFY reading at EE5. |
| | No Continuity ▶ | SERVICE or REPLACE cable harness Circuit |
| **EE6** CHECK MOTOR SPEED SENSOR SHORT TO BATTERY + | | |
| • Turn ignition switch to ON.<br>• Measure voltage between Breakout Box Pins 31 and 60. | No voltage ▶ | GO to Step **EE7**. |
| | 12 volts ▶ | GO to Step **EE6a**. |
| **EE6a** CHECK PUMP MOTOR | | |
| • Disconnect pump motor to relay 4-pin plug connector.<br>• Turn ignition switch to ON.<br>• Measure voltage between Breakout Box Pins 31 and 60. | No voltage ▶ | REPLACE pump and motor. |
| | 12 volts ▶ | GO to Step **EE6b**. |
| **EE6b** CHECK CIRCUIT 462 | | |
| • Disconnect wire harness to relay 7-pin plug.<br>• Turn ignition switch to ON.<br>• Measure voltage between Breakout Box Pins 31 and 60. | No voltage ▶ | GO to Step **EE6c**. |
| | 12 volts ▶ | SERVICE or REPLACE cable harness Circuit |

**Fig. 67 Tests EE5d, EE5e, EE6, EE6a & EE6b (Fluid level indicator/pedal travel switch/pump motor). 1990 Continental & Town Car**

**Fluid Level Indicator/Pedal Travel Switch/Pump Motor Diagnosis** — Test EE

| TEST STEP | RESULT ▶ | ACTION TO TAKE |
|---|---|---|
| **EE5a** CHECK PUMP MOTOR SPEED SENSOR | | |
| • Disconnect 4-pin plug on pump motor.<br>• Measure resistance between Pins S0 and S1 on pump motor.<br>4 PIN PUMP MOTOR CONNECTOR HARNESS SIDE | 5-100 ohms ▶ | GO to Step EE5b. |
| | Any other reading ▶ | REPLACE pump and motor. |
| **EE5b** CHECK PUMP MOTOR RELAY | | |
| • Disconnect 7-pin plug on pump motor relay and remove relay.<br>• Check continuity from Pin S0 on 7-pin side to Pin S0 on 4-pin side of relay.<br>PUMP MOTOR RELAY | Continuity ▶ | GO to Step EE5c. |
| | No Continuity ▶ | REPLACE pump motor relay. |
| **EE5c** CHECK PUMP MOTOR RELAY | | |
| • Check continuity from Pin S1 on 7-pin side to Pin S1 on 4-pin side of relay. | Continuity ▶ | GO to Step EE5d. |
| | No Continuity ▶ | REPLACE pump motor relay. |

**Fig. 66 Tests EE5a, EE5b & EE5c (Fluid level indicator/pedal travel switch/pump motor). Except 1991 Town Car**

**Fluid Level Indicator/Pedal Travel Switch/Pump Motor Diagnosis** — Test EE

| TEST STEP | RESULT ▶ | ACTION TO TAKE |
|---|---|---|
| **EE5d** CHECK CIRCUIT 462 | | |
| • Check continuity between Breakout Box Pin 31 and Pin S0 on pump motor connector 7-pin plug (harness side).<br>7 PIN PUMP MOTOR RELAY CONNECTOR HARNESS SIDE | Continuity ▶ | GO to Step **EE5e**. |
| | No Continuity ▶ | SERVICE or REPLACE cable harness Circuit 462. |
| **EE5e** CHECK CIRCUIT 461 | | |
| • Check continuity between Breakout Box Pin 49 and Pin S1 on pump motor connector 7-pin plug (harness side). | Continuity ▶ | REVERIFY reading at EE5. |
| | No Continuity ▶ | SERVICE or REPLACE cable harness Circuit 461. |
| **EE6** CHECK MOTOR SPEED SENSOR SHORT TO BATTERY + | | |
| • Turn ignition switch to ON position.<br>• Measure voltage between Breakout Box Pins 31 and 60. | No voltage ▶ | GO to Step **EE7**. |
| | 12V ▶ | GO to Step **EE6a**. |
| **EE6a** CHECK PUMP MOTOR | | |
| • Disconnect pump motor to relay 4-pin plug connector.<br>• Turn ignition switch to ON position.<br>• Measure voltage between Breakout Box Pins 31 and 60. | No voltage ▶ | REPLACE pump and motor. |
| | 12V ▶ | GO to Step **EE6b**. |
| **EE6b** CHECK CIRCUIT 462 | | |
| • Disconnect wire harness to relay 7-pin plug.<br>• Turn ignition switch to ON position.<br>• Measure voltage between Breakout Box Pins 31 and 60. | No voltage ▶ | GO to Step **EE6c**. |
| | 12V ▶ | SERVICE or REPLACE cable harness Circuit 462. |

**Fig. 68 Tests EE5d, EE5e, EE6, EE6a & EE6b (Fluid level indicator/pedal travel switch/pump motor). Sable, Taurus & 1991 Continental**

## Fluid Level Indicator/Pedal Travel Switch/ Pump Motor Diagnosis — Test EE

| TEST STEP | RESULT ▶ | ACTION TO TAKE |
|---|---|---|
| **EE6c** CHECK CIRCUIT 604 | | |
| • Turn ignition switch to ON. • Measure voltage between Breakout Box Pins 49 and 60. | No voltage ▶ | REPLACE pump motor relay. |
| | 12 volts ▶ | SERVICE or REPLACE cable harness Circuit |
| **EE7** CHECK MOTOR SPEED SENSOR SHORT TO GROUND | | |
| • Check for continuity between Breakout Box Pins 31 and 60. | No Continuity ▶ | GO to Step **EE8**. |
| | Continuity ▶ | GO to Step **EE7a**. |
| **EE7a** CHECK PUMP MOTOR | | |
| • Disconnect pump to motor relay 4-pin plug connector. • Check for continuity between Breakout Box Pins 31 and 60. | Continuity ▶ | GO to Step **EE7b**. |
| | No Continuity ▶ | REPLACE pump and motor. |
| **EE7b** CHECK CIRCUIT 462 | | |
| • Disconnect wire harness to relay 7-pin plug. • Check for continuity between Breakout Box Pins 31 and 60. | Continuity ▶ | SERVICE or REPLACE cable harness Circuit |
| | No Continuity ▶ | GO to Step **EE7c**. |
| **EE7c** CHECK CIRCUIT 604 | | |
| • Check for continuity between Breakout Box Pins 49 and 60. | Continuity ▶ | SERVICE or REPLACE cable harness Circuit |
| | No Continuity ▶ | REPLACE pump motor relay. |
| **EE8** CHECK PUMP MOTOR OPERATION | | |
| • Reconnect pump motor relay to pump and wire harness. • Jumper Pins 15, 34 and 60 at Breakout Box. • Turn ignition to ON position. | Pump motor runs ▶ | GO to Step **EE9**. |
| | Pump motor does not run ▶ | GO to Step **EE8a**. |

**Fig. 69 Tests EE6c, EE7, EE7a, EE7b, EE7c & EE8 (Fluid level indicator/pedal travel switch/pump motor). 1990 Continental & Town Car**

## Fluid Level Indicator/Pedal Travel Switch/Pump Motor Diagnosis — Test EE

| TEST STEP | RESULT ▶ | ACTION TO TAKE |
|---|---|---|
| **EE6c** CHECK CIRCUIT 461 | | |
| • Turn ignition switch to ON. • Measure voltage between Breakout Box Pins 49 and 60. | No voltage ▶ | REPLACE pump motor relay. |
| | 12V ▶ | SERVICE or REPLACE cable harness Circuit 461. |
| **EE7** CHECK MOTOR SPEED SENSOR SHORT TO GROUND | | |
| • Check for continuity between Breakout Box Pins 31 and 60. | No Continuity ▶ | GO to Step **EE8**. |
| | Continuity ▶ | GO to Step **EE7a**. |
| **EE7a** CHECK PUMP MOTOR | | |
| • Disconnect pump to motor relay 4-pin plug connector. • Check for continuity between Breakout Box Pins 31 and 60. | Continuity ▶ | GO to Step **EE7b**. |
| | No Continuity ▶ | REPLACE pump and motor. |
| **EE7b** CHECK CIRCUIT 462 | | |
| • Disconnect wire harness to relay 7-pin plug. • Check for continuity between Breakout Box Pins 31 and 60. | Continuity ▶ | SERVICE or REPLACE cable harness Circuit 462. |
| | No Continuity ▶ | GO to Step **EE7c**. |
| **EE7c** CHECK CIRCUIT 461 | | |
| • Check for continuity between Breakout Box Pins 49 and 60. | Continuity ▶ | SERVICE or REPLACE cable harness Circuit 461. |
| | No Continuity ▶ | REPLACE pump motor relay. |
| **EE8** CHECK PUMP MOTOR OPERATION | | |
| • Reconnect pump motor relay to pump and wire harness. • Jumper Pins 15, 34 and 60 at Breakout Box. • Turn ignition to ON position. | Pump motor runs ▶ | VERIFY code 62. |
| | Pump motor does not run ▶ | GO to Step **EE8a**. |

**Fig. 70 Tests EE6c, EE7, EE7a, EE7b, EE7c & EE8 (Fluid level indicator/pedal travel switch/pump motor). Sable, Taurus & 1991 Continental**

## Fluid Level Indicator/Pedal Travel Switch/ Pressure Switch Diagnosis — Test EE

| TEST STEP | RESULT ▶ | ACTION TO TAKE |
|---|---|---|
| **EE7** SERVICE CODE 63: CHECK PUMP MOTOR SPEED SENSOR AND CIRCUIT | | |
| • Turn ignition switch OFF. • Disconnect 55-pin plug from electronic controller. | 5 to 100 ohms ▶ | GO to Step EE8. |
| (ELECTRONIC CONTROLLER; 55 PIN CONNECTOR) | Any other reading ▶ | GO to Step EE7a. |
| • Connect EEC-IV Breakout Box, T83L-50-EEC-IV, with Anti-Lock Test Adapter, T90P-50-ALA or equivalent, to the anti-lock 55-pin plug harness. (ANTI-LOCK HARNESS ADAPTER T90P-50-ALA; 55 PIN CONNECTOR; EEC IV BREAKOUT BOX T83L-50-EEC-IV) | | |
| • Check resistance between Breakout Box Pins 31 and 49. | | |

**Fig. 71 Test EE7 (Fluid level indicator/pedal travel switch/pump motor). 1991 Town Car**

## Fluid Level Indicator/Pedal Travel Switch/ Pressure Switch Diagnosis — Test EE

| TEST STEP | RESULT ▶ | ACTION TO TAKE |
|---|---|---|
| **EE7a** CHECK PUMP MOTOR SPEED SENSOR | | |
| • Disconnect 4-pin plug on pump motor. • Measure resistance between Pins S0 and S1 on pump motor. | 5 to 100 ohms ▶ | GO to Step EE7b. |
| (S0; MOTOR (-) 1; MOTOR (+) 2; S1; 4 PIN PUMP MOTOR CONNECTOR HARNESS SIDE) | Any other reading ▶ | REPLACE pump and motor. |
| **EE7b** CHECK PUMP MOTOR RELAY | | |
| • Disconnect 7-pin plug on pump motor relay and remove relay. • Check continuity from Pin S0 on 7-pin side to Pin S0 on 4-pin side of relay. | Continuity ▶ | GO to Step EE7c. |
| (1; 31; S0; 86; TEST; S0; 30; 2; S1; S1; 85; PUMP MOTOR RELAY) | No Continuity ▶ | REPLACE pump motor relay. |
| **EE7c** CHECK PUMP MOTOR RELAY | | |
| • Check continuity from Pin S1 on 7-pin side to Pin S1 on 4-pin side of relay. | Continuity ▶ | GO to Step EE7d. |
| | No Continuity ▶ | REPLACE pump motor relay. |

**Fig. 72 Tests EE7a, EE7b & EE7c (Fluid level indicator/pedal travel switch/pump motor). 1991 Town Car**

## Fluid Level Indicator/Pedal Travel Switch/ Pressure Switch Diagnosis — Test EE

| TEST STEP | RESULT ▶ | ACTION TO TAKE |
|---|---|---|
| **EE7d** CHECK CIRCUIT 462 | | |
| • Check continuity between Breakout Box Pin 31 and Pin S0 on pump motor connector 7-pin plug (harness side). 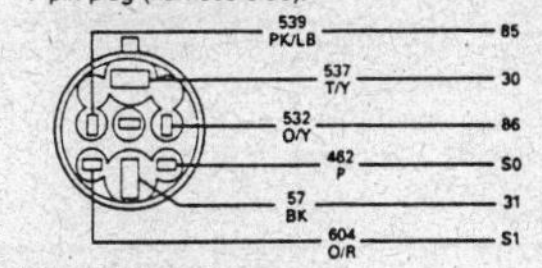<br>539 PK/LB — 85; 537 T/Y — 30; 532 O/Y — 86; 462 P — S0; 57 BK — 31; 604 O/R — S1<br>7 PIN PUMP MOTOR RELAY CONNECTOR HARNESS SIDE | Continuity ▶<br>No Continuity ▶ | GO to Step EE7e.<br>SERVICE or REPLACE cable harness Circuit 462. |
| **EE7e** CHECK CIRCUIT 604 | | |
| • Check continuity between Breakout Box Pin 49 and Pin S1 on pump motor connector 7-pin plug (harness side). | Continuity ▶<br>No Continuity ▶ | REVERIFY reading at EE7.<br>SERVICE or REPLACE cable harness Circuit 604. |
| **EE8** CHECK MOTOR SPEED SENSOR SHORT TO BATTERY + | | |
| • Turn ignition switch to ON.<br>• Measure voltage between Breakout Box Pins 31 and 60. | No voltage ▶<br>12V ▶ | GO to Step EE9.<br>GO to Step EE8a. |
| **EE8a** CHECK PUMP MOTOR | | |
| • Disconnect pump motor to relay 4-pin plug connector.<br>• Turn ignition switch to ON.<br>• Measure voltage between Breakout Box Pins 31 and 60. | No voltage ▶<br>12V ▶ | REPLACE pump and motor.<br>GO to Step EE8b. |
| **EE8b** CHECK CIRCUIT 462 | | |
| • Disconnect wire harness to relay 7-pin plug.<br>• Turn ignition switch to ON.<br>• Measure voltage between Breakout Box Pins 31 and 60. | No voltage ▶<br>12V ▶ | GO to Step EE8c.<br>SERVICE or REPLACE cable harness Circuit 462. |

**Fig. 73 Tests EE7d, EE7e, EE8, EE8a & EE8b (Fluid level indicator/pedal travel switch/pump motor). 1991 Town Car**

## Fluid Level Indicator/Pedal Travel Switch/ Pump Motor Diagnosis — Test EE

| TEST STEP | RESULT ▶ | ACTION TO TAKE |
|---|---|---|
| **EE8a** CHECK PUMP MOTOR OPERATION | | |
| • Disconnect pump motor relay from pump motor.<br>• Ground Pin 2 and apply 12 volts to Pin 1 of pump motor connector. 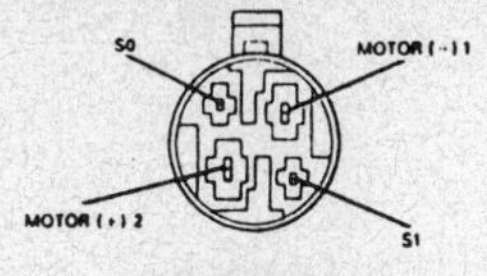<br>S0; MOTOR (−) 1; MOTOR (+) 2; S1<br>4 PIN PUMP MOTOR CONNECTOR HARNESS SIDE | Pump motor runs ▶<br>Pump motor does not run ▶ | GO to Step EE8b.<br>REPLACE pump motor. |
| **EE8b** CHECK POWER TO RELAY | | |
| • Disconnect wire harness from pump motor relay.<br>• Check voltage between Pin 30 on wire harness to pump motor relay connector and ground. 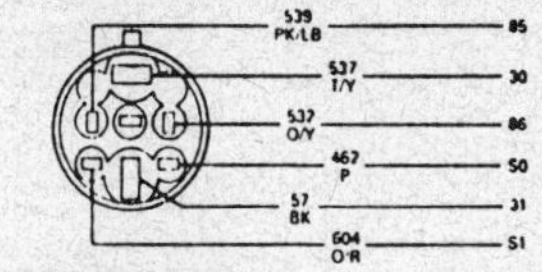<br>539 PK/LB — 85; 537 T/Y — 30; 537 O/Y — 86; 462 P — S0; 57 BK — 31; 604 O/R — S1<br>7 PIN PUMP MOTOR RELAY CONNECTOR HARNESS SIDE | Over 10 volts ▶<br>Less than 10 volts ▶ | GO to Step EE8c.<br>SERVICE or REPLACE battery, fuse or Circuit |

**Fig. 74 Tests EE8a & EE8b (Fluid level indicator/pedal travel switch/pump motor). Except 1991 Town Car**

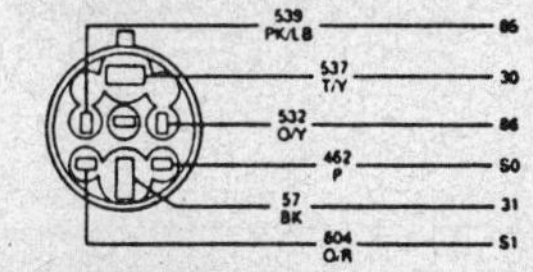

## Fluid Level Indicator/Pedal Travel Switch/ Pump Motor Diagnosis — Test EE

| TEST STEP | RESULT ▶ | ACTION TO TAKE |
|---|---|---|
| **EE8c** CHECK POWER TO RELAY COIL | | |
| • Jumper Pins 34 and 60 at Breakout Box.<br>• Turn ignition to ON position.<br>• Measure voltage between Pins 86 and ground.<br>539 PK/LB — 86; 537 T/Y — 30; 532 O/Y — 86; 462 P — S0; 57 BK — 31; 604 O/R — S1<br>7 PIN PUMP MOTOR RELAY CONNECTOR HARNESS SIDE | Over 10 volts ▶<br>Less than 10 volts ▶ | GO to Step EE8d.<br>SERVICE or REPLACE cable harnoss Circuit |
| **EE8d** CHECK PUMP MOTOR RELAY COIL | | |
| • Measure resistance between Pins 85 and 86 on pump motor relay.<br>1; 31; S0; 86; TEST; S0; 30; 2; S1; S1; 85<br>PUMP MOTOR RELAY | 45 to 105 ohms ▶<br>Any other reading ▶ | GO to Step EE8e.<br>REPLACE pump motor relay. |
| **EE8e** CHECK CIRCUIT 539 | | |
| • Check for continuity between Breakout Box Pin 15 and Pin 85 on wire harnoss to pump motor relay connector.<br>539 PK/LB — 86; 537 T/Y — 30; 532 O/Y — 86; 462 P — S0; 57 BK — 31; 604 O/R — S1<br>7 PIN PUMP MOTOR RELAY CONNECTOR HARNESS SIDE | Continuity ▶<br>No Continuity ▶ | GO to Step EE8f.<br>SERVICE or REPLACE cable harness Circuit |

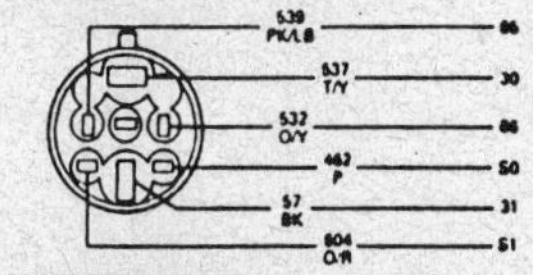

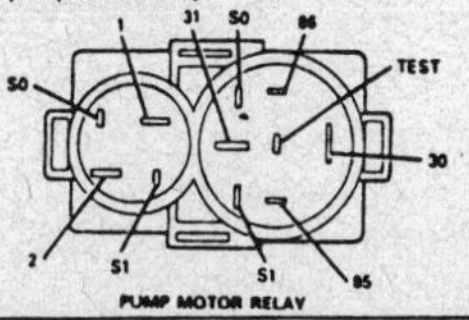

**Fig. 75 Tests EE8c, EE8d & EE8e (Fluid level indicator/pedal travel switch/pump motor). Except 1991 Town Car**

## Fluid Level Indicator/Pedal Travel Switch/ Pump Motor Diagnosis — Test EE

| TEST STEP | RESULT ▶ | ACTION TO TAKE |
|---|---|---|
| **EE8f** CHECK CIRCUIT 57e | | |
| • Check for continuity between wire harness to pump motor relay connector Pin 31 and ground. | Continuity ▶<br>No Continuity ▶ | GO to Step EE8g.<br>SERVICE or REPLACE cable harness Circuit |
| **EE8g** CHECK PUMP MOTOR RELAY | | |
| • Connect battery + to Pin 86 and battery − to Pin 85 of pump motor relay.<br>• Check for continuity between Pin 30 and Pin 1 on relay. | Continuity ▶<br>No Continuity ▶ | GO to Step EE8h.<br>REPLACE pump motor relay. |
| **EE8h** CHECK PUMP MOTOR RELAY | | |
| • Check continuity between Pins 2 and 31 on pump motor relay. 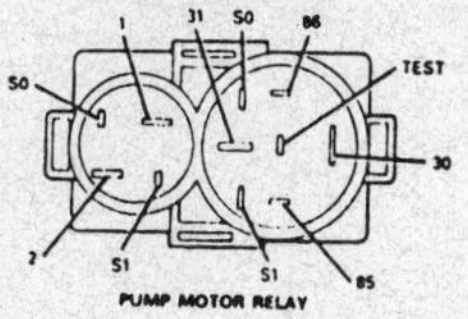<br>1; 31; S0; 86; TEST; S0; 30; 2; S1; S1; 85<br>PUMP MOTOR RELAY | Continuity ▶<br>No Continuity ▶ | REPLACE computer module.<br>REPLACE pump motor relay. |

**Fig. 76 Tests EE8f, EE8g & EE8h (Fluid level indicator/pedal travel switch/pump motor). Except 1991 Town Car**

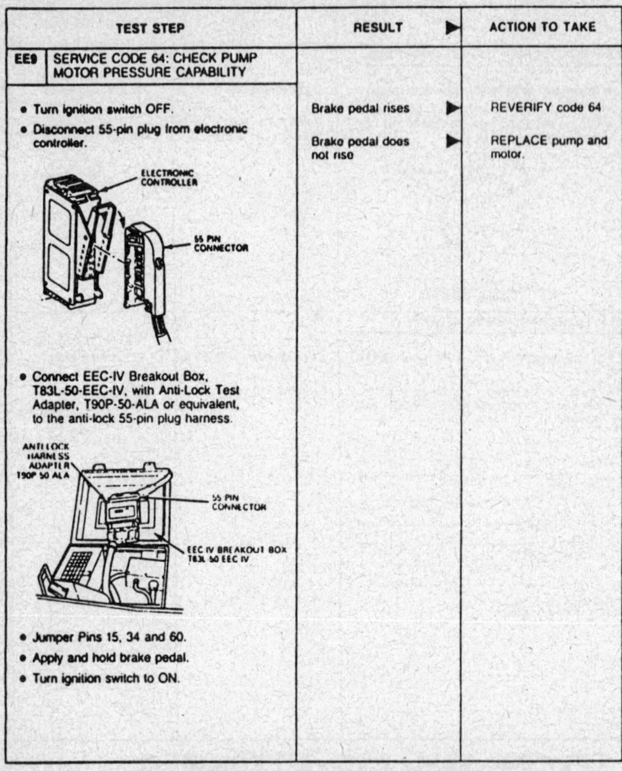

**Fluid Level Indicator/Pedal Travel Switch/ Pump Motor Diagnosis** — Test EE

| TEST STEP | RESULT ▶ | ACTION TO TAKE |
|---|---|---|
| **EE9** SERVICE CODE 64: CHECK PUMP MOTOR PRESSURE CAPABILITY | | |
| • Turn ignition switch OFF.<br>• Disconnect 55-pin plug from electronic controller.<br>• Connect EEC-IV Breakout Box, T83L-50-EEC-IV, with Anti-Lock Test Adapter, T90P-50-ALA or equivalent, to the anti-lock 55-pin plug harness.<br>• Jumper Pins 15, 34 and 60.<br>• Apply and hold brake pedal.<br>• Turn ignition switch to ON. | Brake pedal rises ▶<br>Brake pedal does not rise ▶ | REVERIFY code 64<br>REPLACE pump and motor. |



**Fig. 77 Tests EE9 (Fluid level indicator/pedal travel switch/pump motor). Except 1991 Town Car**

**Fluid Level Indicator/Pedal Travel Switch/ Pressure Switch Diagnosis** — Test EE

| TEST STEP | RESULT ▶ | ACTION TO TAKE |
|---|---|---|
| **EE8c** CHECK CIRCUIT 604 | | |
| • Turn ignition switch to ON.<br>• Measure voltage between Breakout Box Pins 49 and 60. | No voltage ▶<br>12V ▶ | REPLACE pump motor relay.<br>SERVICE or REPLACE cable harness Circuit 604. |
| **EE9** CHECK MOTOR SPEED SENSOR SHORT TO GROUND | | |
| • Check for continuity between Breakout Box Pins 31 and 60. | No Continuity ▶<br>Continuity ▶ | GO to Step **EE10.**<br>GO to Step **EE9a.** |
| **EE9a** CHECK PUMP MOTOR | | |
| • Disconnect pump to motor relay 4-pin plug connector.<br>• Check for continuity between Breakout Box Pins 31 and 60. | Continuity ▶<br>No Continuity ▶ | GO to Step **EE9b.**<br>REPLACE pump and motor. |
| **EE9b** CHECK CIRCUIT 462 | | |
| • Disconnect wire harness to relay 7-pin plug.<br>• Check for continuity between Breakout Box Pins 31 and 60. | Continuity ▶<br>No Continuity ▶ | SERVICE or REPLACE cable harness Circuit 462.<br>GO to Step **EE9c.** |
| **EE9c** CHECK CIRCUIT 604 | | |
| • Check for continuity between Breakout Box Pins 49 and 60. | Continuity ▶<br>No Continuity ▶ | SERVICE or REPLACE cable harness Circuit 604.<br>REPLACE pump motor relay. |
| **EE10** CHECK PUMP MOTOR OPERATION | | |
| • Reconnect pump motor relay to pump and wire harness.<br>• Jumper Pins 15, 34 and 60 at Breakout Box.<br>• Turn ignition to ON position. | Pump motor runs ▶<br>Pump motor does not run ▶ | GO to Step **EE11.**<br>GO to Step **EE10a.** |

**Fig. 78 Tests EE8c, EE9 & EE9a, EE9b, EE9c & EE10 (Fluid level indicator/pedal travel switch/pump motor). 1991 Town Car**

**Fluid Level Indicator/Pedal Travel Switch/ Pressure Switch Diagnosis** — Test EE

| TEST STEP | RESULT ▶ | ACTION TO TAKE |
|---|---|---|
| **EE10a** CHECK PUMP MOTOR OPERATION | | |
| • Disconnect pump motor relay from pump motor.<br>• Ground Pin 2 and apply 12 volts to Pin 1 of pump motor connector.<br>S0 / MOTOR (−) 1 / MOTOR (+) 2 / S1<br>4 PIN PUMP MOTOR CONNECTOR HARNESS SIDE | Pump motor runs ▶<br>Pump motor does not run ▶ | GO to Step **EE10b.**<br>REPLACE pump motor. |
| **EE10b** CHECK POWER TO RELAY | | |
| • Disconnect wire harness from pump motor relay.<br>• Check voltage between Pin 30 on wire harness to pump motor relay connector and ground.<br>539 PK/LB — 85; 537 T/Y — 30; 532 O/Y — 86; 462 P — S0; 57 BK — 31; 604 O/R — S1<br>7 PIN PUMP MOTOR RELAY CONNECTOR HARNESS SIDE | Over 10V ▶<br>Less than 10V ▶ | GO to Step **EE10c.**<br>SERVICE or REPLACE battery, fuse or Circuit 537. |

**Fig. 79 Tests EE10a & EE10b (Fluid level indicator/pedal travel switch/pump motor). 1991 Town Car**

**Fluid Level Indicator/Pedal Travel Switch/ Pressure Switch Diagnosis** — Test EE

| TEST STEP | RESULT ▶ | ACTION TO TAKE |
|---|---|---|
| **EE10c** CHECK POWER TO RELAY COIL | | |
| • Jumper Pins 34 and 60 at Breakout Box.<br>• Turn ignition to ON position.<br>• Measure voltage between Pins 86 and ground.<br>539 PK/LB — 85; 537 T/Y — 30; 532 O/Y — 86; 462 P — S0; 57 BK — 31; 604 O/R — S1<br>7 PIN PUMP MOTOR RELAY CONNECTOR HARNESS SIDE | Over 10V ▶<br>Less than 10V ▶ | GO to Step **EE10d.**<br>SERVICE or REPLACE cable harness Circuit 532g. |
| **EE10d** CHECK PUMP MOTOR RELAY COIL | | |
| • Measure resistance between Pins 85 and 86 on pump motor relay.<br>1, 31, S0, 86, TEST, 30, 85, S1, S1, 2<br>PUMP MOTOR RELAY | 45 to 105 ohms ▶<br>Any other reading ▶ | GO to Step **EE10e.**<br>REPLACE pump motor relay. |
| **EE10e** CHECK CIRCUIT 539 | | |
| • Check for continuity between Breakout Box Pin 15 and Pin 85 on wire harness to pump motor relay connector.<br>539 PK/LB — 85; 537 T/Y — 30; 532 O/Y — 86; 462 P — S0; 57 BK — 31; 604 O/R — S1<br>7 PIN PUMP MOTOR RELAY CONNECTOR HARNESS SIDE | Continuity ▶<br>No Continuity ▶ | GO to Step **EE10f.**<br>SERVICE or REPLACE cable harness Circuit 539. |

**Fig. 80 Tests EE10c, EE10d & EE10e (Fluid level indicator/pedal travel switch/pump motor). 1991 Town Car**

## Fluid Level Indicator/Pedal Travel Switch/ Pressure Switch Diagnosis — Test EE

| TEST STEP | RESULT | ACTION TO TAKE |
|---|---|---|
| **EE10f** CHECK CIRCUIT 57e | | |
| • Check for continuity between wire harness to pump motor relay connector Pin 31 and ground. | Continuity ▶ | GO to Step EE10g. |
| | No Continuity ▶ | SERVICE or REPLACE cable harness Circuit 57w. |
| **EE10g** CHECK PUMP MOTOR RELAY | | |
| • Connect battery + to Pin 86 and battery – to Pin 85 of pump motor relay. | Continuity ▶ | GO to Step EE10h. |
| • Check for continuity between Pin 30 and Pin 1 on relay. | No Continuity ▶ | REPLACE pump motor relay. |
| **EE10h** CHECK PUMP MOTOR RELAY | | |
| • Check continuity between Pins 2 and 31 on pump motor relay. | Continuity ▶ | REPLACE computer module. |
| | No Continuity ▶ | REPLACE pump motor relay. |

1 31 S0 86
S0 TEST
30
2 S1 S1 85
PUMP MOTOR RELAY

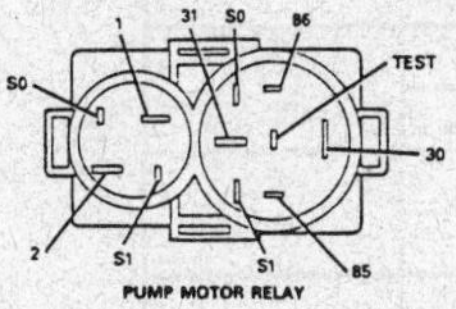

**Fig. 81 Tests EE10f, EE10g, EE10h (Fluid level indicator/pedal travel switch/pump motor). 1991 Town Car**

## Anti-Lock Quick Check Sheet Using 60-Pin EEC-IV Breakout Box, Tool T83L-50-EEC-IV①

**NOTE: Before performing tests below, the Pre-Test Checks must be performed as outlined.**

**NOTE: If fault is intermittent the tests listed below will NOT find the fault. Use controller service code or call Hot-Line if this situation occurs.**

| Item to be Tested | Ignition Mode | Measure Between Pin Numbers | Tester Scale/Range | Specification | Test Step |
|---|---|---|---|---|---|
| Battery Check | ON | 60 + 53 | VOLTS | 10 minimum | A1 |
| Main Relay Coil | OFF | 53 + 34 | OHMS | 45 to 90 ohms | A3a |
| Jumper pins 60 + 34 | | | | | |
| Power from Main Relay | ON | 19 + 33 | VOLTS | 10 minimum | A2 |
| | Remove jumper from pins 60 + 34 | | | | |
| Main Relay Circuit | OFF | 60 + 33 | CONTINUITY | continuity | A4 |
| Sensor Resistance (RR) | OFF | 27 + 45 | K OHMS | 0.8-1.4 Kohms | C3 |
| Sensor Resistance (LF) | OFF | 30 + 48 | K OHMS | 0.8-1.4 Kohms | C1 |
| Sensor Resistance (LR) | OFF | 28 + 46 | K OHMS | 0.8-1.4 Kohms | C4 |
| Sensor Resistance (RF) | OFF | 29 + 47 | K OHMS | 0.8-1.4 Kohms | C2 |
| Valve Resistance (IFL) | OFF | 3 + 20 | OHMS | 5-8 ohms | BB2 |
| Valve Resistance (IFR) | OFF | 3 + 38 | OHMS | 5-8 ohms | BB4 |
| Valve Resistance (IRL) | OFF | 3 + 54 | OHMS | 5-8 ohms | BB8 |
| Valve Resistance (IRR) | OFF | 3 + 55 | OHMS | 5-8 ohms | BB6 |
| Valve Resistance (OFL) | OFF | 3 + 2 | OHMS | 3-6 ohms | BB3 |
| Valve Resistance (OFR) | OFF | 3 + 21 | OHMS | 3-6 ohms | BB5 |
| Valve Resistance (ORR) | OFF | 3 + 18 | OHMS | 3-6 ohms | BB7 |
| Valve Resistance (ORL) | OFF | 3 + 36 | OHMS | 3-6 ohms | BB9 |
| Pump Motor Speed Sensor Resistance | OFF | 31 + 94 | OHMS | 5-100 ohms | EE5 |
| Reservoir Warning (FLS #2) | OFF | 8 + 26 | OHMS | LESS THAN 5 OHMS | A6 |
| Pedal Travel Switch: Pedal NOT Applied | OFF | 5 + 26 | CONTINUITY | continuity | D1 |
| With Minimum 3 Inch Apply | OFF | 5 + 26 | CONTINUITY | no continuity | D2 |
| Sensor Cable Continuity Wiring to Ground (RR) | OFF | 27 + 60 | CONTINUITY | no continuity | B2 |
| (LF) | OFF | 30 + 60 | CONTINUITY | no continuity | B4 |
| (LR) | OFF | 28 + 60 | CONTINUITY | no continuity | B1 |
| (RF) | OFF | 29 + 60 | CONTINUITY | no continuity | B3 |
| Sensor Voltage: Rotate wheels @ 1 revolution per second. (RR) | OFF | 27 + 45 | AC MVOLTS | 100-1400 mvolts | C11 |
| (LF) | OFF | 30 + 48 | AC MVOLTS | 100-1400 mvolts | C9 |
| (LR) | OFF | 28 + 46 | AC MVOLTS | 100-1400 mvolts | C12 |
| (RF) | OFF | 29 + 47 | AC MVOLTS | 100-1400 mvolts | C10 |

① If Quick Test does not isolate symptom, refer to Diagnostic Indicator Symptom Chart.

**Fig. 82 Anti-lock quick check sheet. Except 1991 Town Car**

## Anti-Lock Quick Check Sheet Using 60-Pin EEC-IV Breakout Box, Tool T83L-50-EEC-IV①

**NOTE: Before performing tests below, the Pre-Test Checks must be performed as outlined.**

| Item to be Tested | Ignition Mode | Measure Between Pin Numbers | Tester Scale/Range | Specification | Test Step |
|---|---|---|---|---|---|
| Battery Check | ON | 60 + 53 | VOLTS | 10 minimum | A1 |
| Main Relay Coil | OFF | 53 + 34 | OHMS | 45 to 90 ohms | A3a |
| Jumper pins 60 + 34 | | | | | |
| Power from Main Relay | ON | 19 + 33 | VOLTS | 10 minimum | A2 |
| | Remove jumper from pins 60 + 34 | | | | |
| Main Relay Circuit | OFF | 60 + 33 | CONTINUITY | continuity | A4 |
| Sensor Resistance (RR) | OFF | 27 + 45 | K OHMS | 0.8-1.4 Kohms | C3 |
| Sensor Resistance (LF) | OFF | 30 + 48 | K OHMS | 0.8-1.4 Kohms | C1 |
| Sensor Resistance (LR) | OFF | 28 + 46 | K OHMS | 0.8-1.4 Kohms | C4 |
| Sensor Resistance (RF) | OFF | 29 + 47 | K OHMS | 0.8-1.4 Kohms | C2 |
| Valve Resistance (IFL) | OFF | 3 + 20 | OHMS | 5-8 ohms | BB2 |
| Valve Resistance (IFR) | OFF | 3 + 38 | OHMS | 5-8 ohms | BB4 |
| Valve Resistance (IRL) | OFF | 3 + 54 | OHMS | 5-8 ohms | BB8 |
| Valve Resistance (IRR) | OFF | 3 + 55 | OHMS | 5-8 ohms | BB6 |
| Valve Resistance (OFL) | OFF | 3 + 2 | OHMS | 3-6 ohms | BB3 |
| Valve Resistance (OFR) | OFF | 3 + 21 | OHMS | 3-6 ohms | BB5 |
| Valve Resistance (ORR) | OFF | 3 + 18 | OHMS | 3-6 ohms | BB7 |
| Valve Resistance (ORL) | OFF | 3 + 36 | OHMS | 3-6 ohms | BB9 |
| Reservoir Warning (FLS #2) | OFF | 8 + 26 | OHMS | LESS THAN 5 OHMS | A6 |
| Pedal Travel Switch: Pedal NOT Applied | OFF | 5 + 26 | CONTINUITY | continuity | D1 |
| With Minimum 3 Inch Apply | OFF | 5 + 26 | CONTINUITY | no continuity | D2 |
| Sensor Cable Continuity Wiring to Ground (RR) | OFF | 27 + 60 | CONTINUITY | no continuity | B2 |
| (LF) | OFF | 30 + 60 | CONTINUITY | no continuity | B4 |
| (LR) | OFF | 28 + 60 | CONTINUITY | no continuity | B1 |
| (RF) | OFF | 29 + 60 | CONTINUITY | no continuity | B3 |
| Sensor Voltage: Rotate wheels @ 1 revolution per second. (RR) | OFF | 27 + 45 | AC MVOLTS | 100-1400 mvolts | C11 |
| (LF) | OFF | 30 + 48 | AC MVOLTS | 100-1400 mvolts | C9 |
| (LR) | OFF | 28 + 46 | AC MVOLTS | 100-1400 mvolts | C12 |
| (RF) | OFF | 29 + 47 | AC MVOLTS | 100-1400 mvolts | C10 |
| Pump Motor Speed Sensor Resistance | OFF | 31 + 49 | OHMS | 5-100 ohms | EE7 |
| Additional Tests for Traction — Assist Only | | | | | |
| Valve Resistance (SV1) | OFF | 3 + 37 | OHMS | 5-8 ohms | BB11 |
| Valve Resistance (SV2) | OFF | 3 + 40 | OHMS | 5-8 ohms | BB12 |
| Pressure Switch (Brake Pedal Not Applied) | OFF | 13 + 26 | CONTINUITY | Continuity | K3 |

**Fig. 83 Anti-lock quick check sheet. 1991 Town Car**

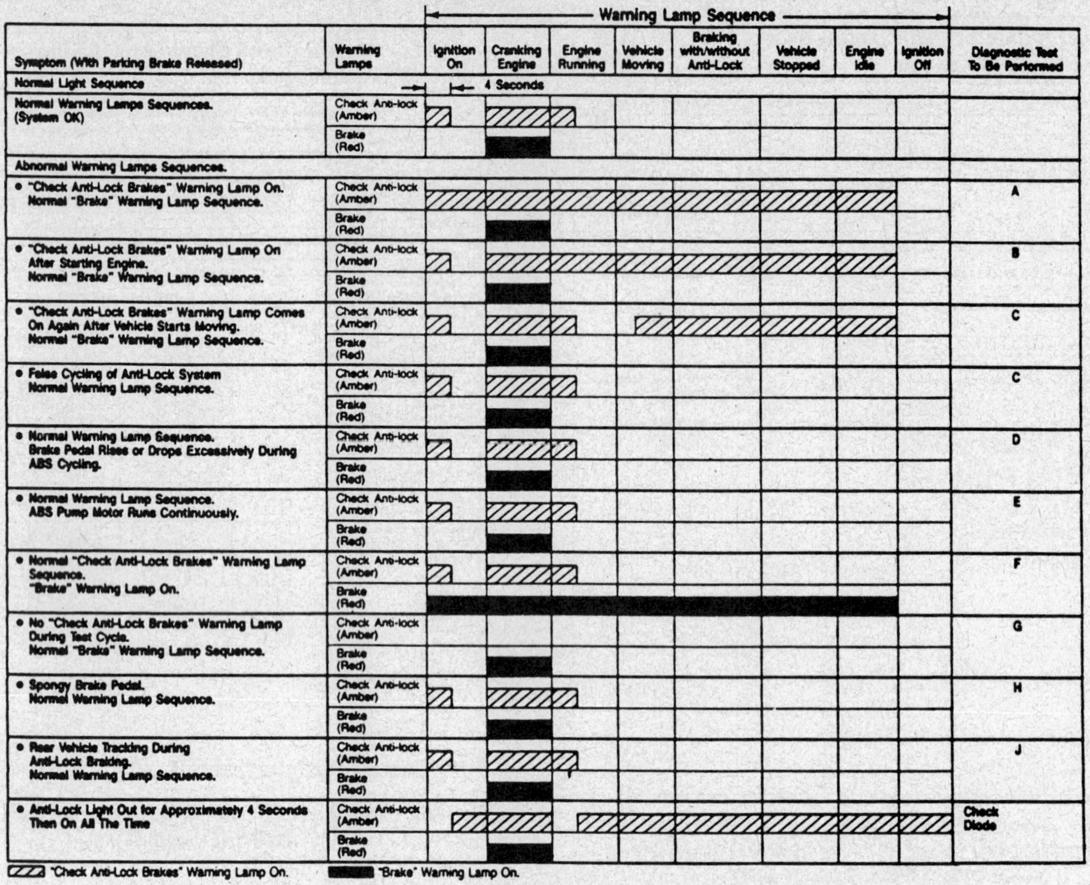

| Symptom (With Parking Brake Released) | Warning Lamps | Warning Lamp Sequence: Ignition On | Cranking Engine | Engine Running | Vehicle Moving | Braking with/without Anti-Lock | Vehicle Stopped | Engine Idle | Ignition Off | Diagnostic Test To Be Performed |
|---|---|---|---|---|---|---|---|---|---|---|
| Normal Light Sequence | | ← 4 Seconds | | | | | | | | |
| Normal Warning Lamps Sequences. (System OK) | Check Anti-lock (Amber) | | | | | | | | | |
| | Brake (Red) | | | | | | | | | |
| Abnormal Warning Lamps Sequences. | | | | | | | | | | |
| • "Check Anti-Lock Brakes" Warning Lamp On. Normal "Brake" Warning Lamp Sequence. | Check Anti-lock (Amber) | | | | | | | | | A |
| | Brake (Red) | | | | | | | | | |
| • "Check Anti-Lock Brakes" Warning Lamp On After Starting Engine. Normal "Brake" Warning Lamp Sequence. | Check Anti-lock (Amber) | | | | | | | | | B |
| | Brake (Red) | | | | | | | | | |
| • "Check Anti-Lock Brakes" Warning Lamp Comes On Again After Vehicle Starts Moving. Normal "Brake" Warning Lamp Sequence. | Check Anti-lock (Amber) | | | | | | | | | C |
| | Brake (Red) | | | | | | | | | |
| • False Cycling of Anti-Lock System Normal Warning Lamp Sequence. | Check Anti-lock (Amber) | | | | | | | | | C |
| | Brake (Red) | | | | | | | | | |
| • Normal Warning Lamp Sequence. Brake Pedal Rises or Drops Excessively During ABS Cycling. | Check Anti-lock (Amber) | | | | | | | | | D |
| | Brake (Red) | | | | | | | | | |
| • Normal Warning Lamp Sequence. ABS Pump Motor Runs Continuously. | Check Anti-lock (Amber) | | | | | | | | | E |
| | Brake (Red) | | | | | | | | | |
| • Normal "Check Anti-Lock Brakes" Warning Lamp Sequence. "Brake" Warning Lamp On. | Check Anti-lock (Amber) | | | | | | | | | F |
| | Brake (Red) | | | | | | | | | |
| • No "Check Anti-Lock Brakes" Warning Lamp During Test Cycle. Normal "Brake" Warning Lamp Sequence. | Check Anti-lock (Amber) | | | | | | | | | G |
| | Brake (Red) | | | | | | | | | |
| • Spongy Brake Pedal. Normal Warning Lamp Sequence. | Check Anti-lock (Amber) | | | | | | | | | H |
| | Brake (Red) | | | | | | | | | |
| • Rear Vehicle Tracking During Anti-Lock Braking. Normal Warning Lamp Sequence. | Check Anti-lock (Amber) | | | | | | | | | J |
| | Brake (Red) | | | | | | | | | |
| • Anti-Lock Light Out for Approximately 4 Seconds Then On All The Time | Check Anti-lock (Amber) | | | | | | | | | Check Diode |
| | Brake (Red) | | | | | | | | | |

"Check Anti-Lock Brakes" Warning Lamp On. "Brake" Warning Lamp On.

**Fig. 84 Diagnostic warning lamp symptom chart. Except 1991 Town Car**

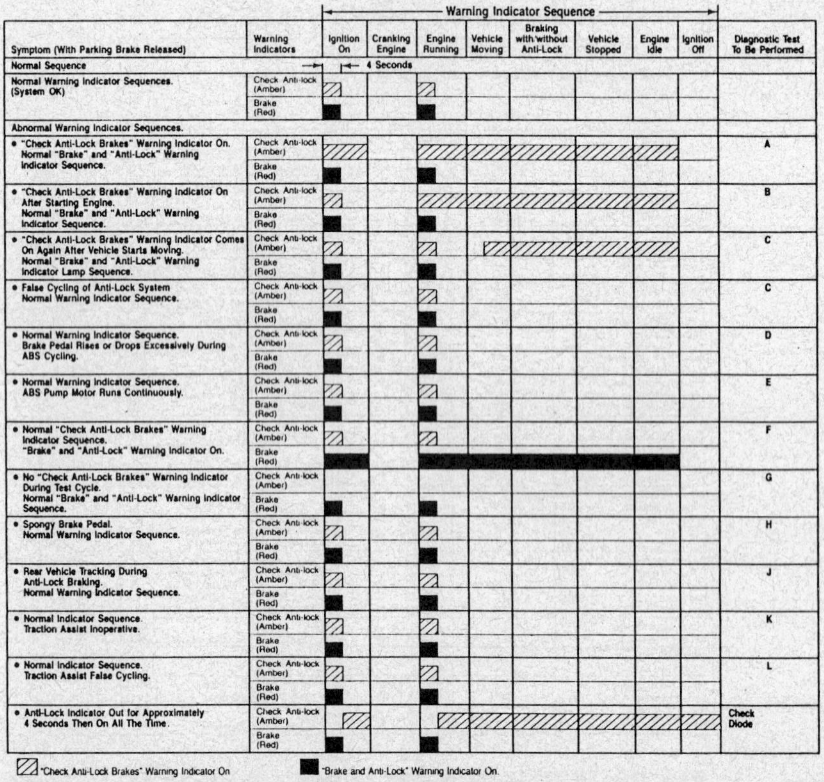

| Symptom (With Parking Brake Released) | Warning Indicators | Warning Indicator Sequence: Ignition On | Cranking Engine | Engine Running | Vehicle Moving | Braking with/without Anti-Lock | Vehicle Stopped | Engine Idle | Ignition Off | Diagnostic Test To Be Performed |
|---|---|---|---|---|---|---|---|---|---|---|
| Normal Sequence | | ← 4 Seconds | | | | | | | | |
| Normal Warning Indicator Sequences. (System OK) | Check Anti-lock (Amber) | | | | | | | | | |
| | Brake (Red) | | | | | | | | | |
| Abnormal Warning Indicator Sequences. | | | | | | | | | | |
| • "Check Anti-Lock Brakes" Warning Indicator On. Normal "Brake" and "Anti-Lock" Warning Indicator Sequence. | Check Anti-lock (Amber) | | | | | | | | | A |
| | Brake (Red) | | | | | | | | | |
| • "Check Anti-Lock Brakes" Warning Indicator On After Starting Engine. Normal "Brake" and "Anti-Lock" Warning Indicator Sequence. | Check Anti-lock (Amber) | | | | | | | | | B |
| | Brake (Red) | | | | | | | | | |
| • "Check Anti-Lock Brakes" Warning Indicator Comes On Again After Vehicle Starts Moving. Normal "Brake" and "Anti-Lock" Warning Indicator Lamp Sequence. | Check Anti-lock (Amber) | | | | | | | | | C |
| | Brake (Red) | | | | | | | | | |
| • False Cycling of Anti-Lock System Normal Warning Indicator Sequence. | Check Anti-lock (Amber) | | | | | | | | | C |
| | Brake (Red) | | | | | | | | | |
| • Normal Warning Indicator Sequence. Brake Pedal Rises or Drops Excessively During ABS Cycling. | Check Anti-lock (Amber) | | | | | | | | | D |
| | Brake (Red) | | | | | | | | | |
| • Normal Warning Indicator Sequence. ABS Pump Motor Runs Continuously. | Check Anti-lock (Amber) | | | | | | | | | E |
| | Brake (Red) | | | | | | | | | |
| • Normal "Check Anti-Lock Brakes" Warning Indicator Sequence. "Brake" and "Anti-Lock" Warning Indicator On. | Check Anti-lock (Amber) | | | | | | | | | F |
| | Brake (Red) | | | | | | | | | |
| • No "Check Anti-Lock Brakes" Warning Indicator During Test Cycle. Normal "Brake" and "Anti-Lock" Warning Indicator Sequence. | Check Anti-lock (Amber) | | | | | | | | | G |
| | Brake (Red) | | | | | | | | | |
| • Spongy Brake Pedal. Normal Warning Indicator Sequence. | Check Anti-lock (Amber) | | | | | | | | | H |
| | Brake (Red) | | | | | | | | | |
| • Rear Vehicle Tracking During Anti-Lock Braking. Normal Warning Indicator Sequence. | Check Anti-lock (Amber) | | | | | | | | | J |
| | Brake (Red) | | | | | | | | | |
| • Normal Indicator Sequence. Traction Assist Inoperative. | Check Anti-lock (Amber) | | | | | | | | | K |
| | Brake (Red) | | | | | | | | | |
| • Normal Indicator Sequence. Traction Assist False Cycling. | Check Anti-lock (Amber) | | | | | | | | | L |
| | Brake (Red) | | | | | | | | | |
| • Anti-Lock Indicator Out for Approximately 4 Seconds Then On All The Time. | Check Anti-lock (Amber) | | | | | | | | | Check Diode |
| | Brake (Red) | | | | | | | | | |

"Check Anti-Lock Brakes" Warning Indicator On. "Brake and Anti-Lock" Warning Indicator On.

**Fig. 85 Diagnostic warning lamp symptom chart. 1991 Town Car**

## Anti-Lock Warning Lamp On (With Brake Warning Lamp Off) — Test A

WARNING LIGHTS SEQUENCE

| Warning Lamps | Ignition On | Cranking Engine | Engine Running | Vehicle Moving | Braking with/without Anti-Lock | Vehicle Stopped | Engine Idle | Ignition Off |
|---|---|---|---|---|---|---|---|---|
| Check Anti-Lock (Amber) | | | | | | | | |
| Brake (Red) | | | | | | | | |

| TEST STEP | RESULT ▶ | ACTION TO TAKE |
|---|---|---|
| **A1** CHECK POWER TO CONTROLLER | | |
| • Disconnect 55-pin plug from electronic controller.<br>ELECTRONIC CONTROLLER<br>55 PIN CONNECTOR<br>• Connect EEC-IV Breakout Box, T83L-50-EEC-IV with Anti-Lock Test Adapter T90P-50-ALA or equivalent to the Anti-Lock 55-pin plug wiring harness.<br>ANTI-LOCK HARNESS ADAPTER T90P-50-ALA<br>55 PIN CONNECTOR<br>EEC-IV BREAKOUT BOX T83L-50-EEC-IV<br>• Set multi-meter to read volts DC.<br>• Turn ignition switch ON.<br>• Measure voltage between breakout box Pins 53 and 60. | Over 10 volts ▶<br>Under 10 volts ▶ | GO to Step A2.<br>GO to Step A1a. |

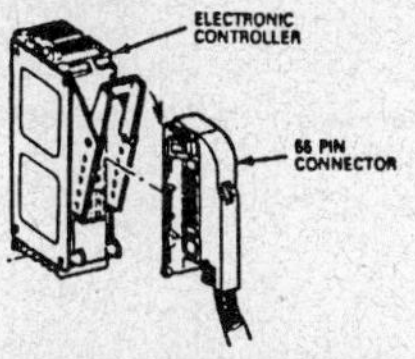

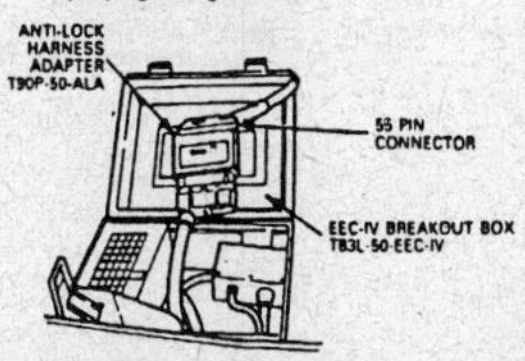

**Fig. 86 Test A1 (ABS lamp On). Sable, Taurus & 1990–91 Continental**

## Anti-Lock Warning Lamp On (With Brake Warning Lamp Off) — Test A

| TEST STEP | RESULT ▶ | ACTION TO TAKE |
|---|---|---|
| **A1a** CHECK ELECTRONIC CONTROLLER TO GROUND WIRE | | |
| • Check continuity between breakout box Pin 60 and body ground. | Continuity ▶<br>No Continuity ▶ | GO to Step A1b.<br>SERVICE or REPLACE cable harness Circuit |
| **A1b** CHECK IGNITION TO ELECTRONIC CONTROLLER WIRE | | |
| • Check for continuity between breakout box Pin 53 and ignition switch wire 687B. | Continuity ▶<br>No Continuity ▶ | CHECK ignition switch.<br>SERVICE or REPLACE cable harness circuit |
| **A2** CHECK GROUND | | |
| • Check for continuity between breakout box Pins 19 and 60. | Continuity ▶<br>No Continuity ▶ | GO to Step A3.<br>SERVICE or REPLACE cable harness circuit |
| **A3** CHECK MAIN RELAY OPERATION | | |
| • Jumper pins 34 and 60 at breakout box.<br>• Turn ignition to ON.<br>• Measure voltage between breakout box Pins 33 and 19. | Over 10 volts DC ▶<br>Under 10 volts DC ▶ | GO to Step A4.<br>GO to Step A3a. |

**Fig. 87 Tests A1a, A1b, A2 & A3 (ABS lamp On). Sable, Taurus & 1990–91 Continental**

## Anti-Lock Warning Lamp On (With Brake Warning Lamp Off) — Test A

WARNING LIGHTS SEQUENCE

| Warning Lamps | Ignition On | Cranking Engine | Engine Running | Vehicle Moving | Braking with/without Anti-Lock | Vehicle Stopped | Engine Idle | Ignition Off |
|---|---|---|---|---|---|---|---|---|
| Check Anti-Lock (Amber) | | | | | | | | |
| Brake (Red) | | | | | | | | |

| TEST STEP | RESULT ▶ | ACTION TO TAKE |
|---|---|---|
| **A1** CHECK POWER TO CONTROLLER | | |
| • Disconnect 55-pin plug from electronic controller.<br>• Connect EEC-IV Breakout Box, T83L-50-EEC-IV with Anti-Lock Test Adapter T90P-50-ALA or equivalent to the Anti-Lock 55-pin plug wiring harness.<br>• Set multi-meter to read volts DC.<br>• Turn ignition switch ON.<br>• Measure voltage between breakout box Pins 53 and 60. | Over 10 volts ▶<br>Under 10 volts ▶ | GO to Step A2.<br>GO to Step A1a. |
| **A1a** CHECK ELECTRONIC CONTROLLER TO GROUND WIRE | | |
| • Check continuity between breakout box Pin 60 and body ground. | Continuity ▶<br>No Continuity ▶ | GO to Step A1b.<br>SERVICE or REPLACE cable harness circuit |
| **A1b** CHECK IGNITION TO ELECTRONIC CONTROLLER WIRE | | |
| • Check for continuity between breakout box Pin 53 and ignition switch | Continuity ▶<br>No Continuity ▶ | GO to Step A1c.<br>SERVICE or REPLACE cable harness circuit |
| **A1c** CHECK FUSE 18 | | |
| • Check fuse 18. | Fuse good ▶<br>Fuse bad ▶ | CHECK ignition switch.<br>REPLACE fuse. |

**Fig. 88 Tests A1, A1a, A1b & A1c (ABS lamp On). 1990 Town Car**

## Anti-Lock Warning Indicator On (With Brake Warning Indicator Off) — Test A

WARNING INDICATORS SEQUENCE

| Warning Indicators | Ignition On | Cranking Engine | Engine Running | Vehicle Moving | Braking with/without Anti-Lock | Vehicle Stopped | Engine Idle | Ignition Off |
|---|---|---|---|---|---|---|---|---|
| Check Anti-Lock (Amber) | | | | | | | | |
| Brake (Red) | | | | | | | | |

| TEST STEP | RESULT ▶ | ACTION TO TAKE |
|---|---|---|
| **A1** CHECK POWER TO CONTROLLER | | |
| • Disconnect 55-pin plug from electronic controller.<br>• Connect EEC-IV Breakout Box, T83L-50-EEC-IV with Anti-Lock Test Adapter T90P-50-ALA or equivalent to the Anti-Lock 55-pin plug wiring harness.<br>• Set multi-meter to read volts DC.<br>• Turn ignition switch ON.<br>• Measure voltage between breakout box Pins 53 and 60. | Over 10V ▶<br>Under 10V ▶ | GO to Step A2.<br>GO to Step A1a. |
| **A1a** CHECK ELECTRONIC CONTROLLER TO GROUND WIRE | | |
| • Check continuity between breakout box Pin 60 and body ground. | Continuity ▶<br>No Continuity ▶ | GO to Step A1b.<br>SERVICE or REPLACE cable harness Circuit 57V, or 57X. |
| **A1b** CHECK IGNITION TO ELECTRONIC CONTROLLER WIRE | | |
| • Check for continuity between breakout box Pin 53 and ignition switch wire 299. | Continuity ▶<br>No Continuity ▶ | GO to Step A1c.<br>SERVICE or REPLACE cable harness Circuit 299, 601 or 601b. |
| **A1c** CHECK FUSE 18 | | |
| • Check fuse 18. | Fuse good ▶<br>Fuse bad ▶ | CHECK ignition switch.<br>REPLACE fuse. |

**Fig. 89 Tests A1, A1a, A1b & A1c (ABS lamp On). 1991 Town Car**

| Anti-Lock Warning Indicator On (With Brake Warning Indicator Off) | Test A |
|---|---|

| TEST STEP | RESULT ▶ | ACTION TO TAKE |
|---|---|---|
| **A2** CHECK GROUND | | |
| • Check for continuity between breakout box Pins 19 and 60. | Continuity ▶<br>No Continuity ▶ | GO TO Step **A3**.<br>SERVICE or REPLACE cable harness Circuit 57 |
| **A3** CHECK MAIN RELAY OPERATION | | |
| • Jumper Pins 34 and 60 at breakout box.<br>• Turn ignition to ON.<br>• Measure voltage between breakout box Pins 33 and 19. | Over 10V DC ▶<br>Under 10V DC ▶ | GO TO Step **A4**.<br>GO TO Step **A3a**. |
| **A3a** CHECK MAIN RELAY COIL | | |
| • Turn ignition to OFF.<br>• Remove jumper from breakout box Pins 34 and 60.<br>• Measure resistance between breakout box Pins 53 and 34. | 45 to 90 ohms ▶<br>Any other reading ▶ | GO TO Step **A3c**.<br>GO TO Step **A3b**. |
| **A3b** CHECK MAIN RELAY COIL | | |
| • Remove main power relay.<br>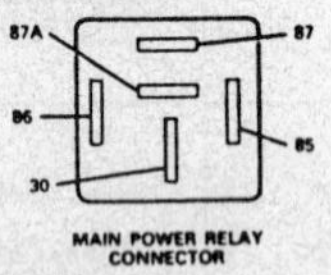<br>• Measure resistance between main relay Pins 85 and 86. | 45 to 90 ohms ▶<br>Any other reading ▶ | SERVICE or REPLACE cable harness Circuit 513, 601a or 601b.<br>REPLACE main relay. |

**Fig. 90 Tests A2, A3, A3a & A3b (ABS lamp On). Town Car**

| Anti-Lock Warning Lamp On (With Brake Warning Lamp Off) | Test A |
|---|---|

| TEST STEP | RESULT ▶ | ACTION TO TAKE |
|---|---|---|
| **A3a** CHECK MAIN RELAY COIL | | |
| • Turn ignition to OFF.<br>• Remove jumper from breakout box Pins 34 and 60.<br>• Measure resistance between breakout box Pins 53 and 34. | 45 to 90 ohms ▶<br>Any other reading ▶ | GO to Step **A3c**.<br>GO to Step **A3b**. |
| **A3b** CHECK MAIN RELAY COIL | | |
| • Remove main power relay.<br>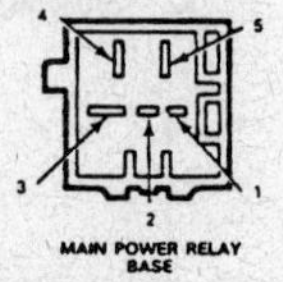<br>• Measure resistance between main relay pins 1 and 2. | 45 to 90 ohms ▶<br>Any other reading ▶ | SERVICE or REPLACE cable harness circuit 513 or 687a or 687b.<br>REPLACE main relay. |
| **A3c** CHECK CIRCUIT 687b | | |
| • Turn ignition ON.<br>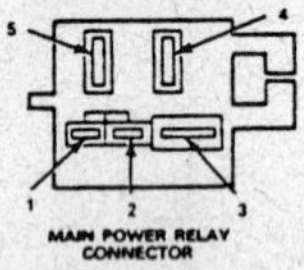<br>• Measure voltage between main relay connector Pin 2 and ground. | Over 10 volts DC ▶<br>Under 10 volts DC ▶ | GO to Step **A3d**.<br>SERVICE cable harness circuit 687b. |

**Fig. 91 Tests A3a, A3b, A3c (ABS lamp On). 1990–91 Continental**

| Anti-Lock Warning Indicator On (With Brake Warning Indicator Off) | Test A |
|---|---|

| TEST STEP | RESULT ▶ | ACTION TO TAKE |
|---|---|---|
| **A3a** CHECK MAIN RELAY COIL | | |
| • Turn ignition to OFF position.<br>• Remove jumper from breakout box Pins 34 and 60.<br>• Measure resistance between breakout box Pins 53 and 34. | 45 to 90 ohms ▶<br>Any other reading ▶ | GO to Step **A3c**.<br>GO to Step **A3b**. |
| **A3b** CHECK MAIN RELAY COIL | | |
| • Remove main power relay.<br>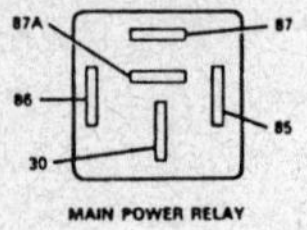<br>• Measure resistance between main relay Pins 85 and 86. | 45 to 90 ohms ▶<br>Any other reading ▶ | SERVICE or REPLACE cable harness Circuit<br>REPLACE main relay. |
| **A3c** CHECK CIRCUIT 687c | | |
| • Turn ignition ON.<br>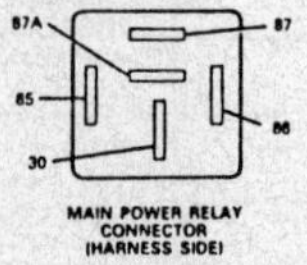<br>• Measure voltage between main relay connector Pin 86 and ground. | Over 10V DC ▶<br>Under 10V DC ▶ | GO to Step **A3d**.<br>SERVICE cable harness Circuit |

**Fig. 92 Tests A3a, A3b, A3c (ABS lamp On). Sable & Taurus**

| Anti-Lock Warning Lamp On (With Brake Warning Lamp Off) | Test A |
|---|---|

| TEST STEP | RESULT ▶ | ACTION TO TAKE |
|---|---|---|
| **A3c** CHECK CIRCUIT 601a | | |
| • Turn ignition ON.<br>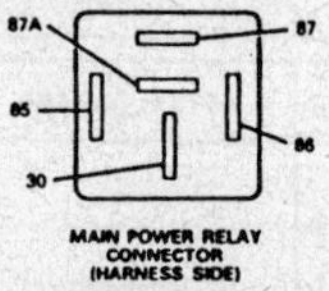<br>• Measure voltage between main relay connector Pin 86 and ground. | Over 10 volts DC ▶<br>Under 10 volts DC ▶ | GO to Step **A3d**.<br>SERVICE cable harness circuit 601a. |
| **A3d** CHECK POWER TO RELAY | | |
| • Turn ignition ON.<br>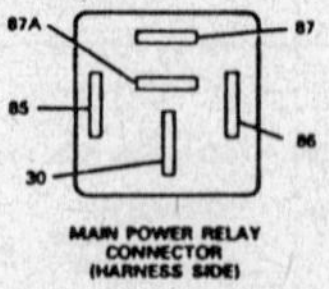<br>• Measure voltage between main relay connector Pin 87 and ground. | Over 10 volts DC ▶<br>Under 10 volts DC ▶ | GO to Step **A3e**.<br>SERVICE cable harness circuit 533 or Fuse S. |

**Fig. 93 Tests A3c & A3d (ABS lamp On). Town Car**

## Anti-Lock Warning Lamp On (With Brake Warning Lamp Off) — Test A

| TEST STEP | RESULT ▶ | ACTION TO TAKE |
|---|---|---|
| **A3d** CHECK POWER TO RELAY | | |
| • Turn ignition ON. 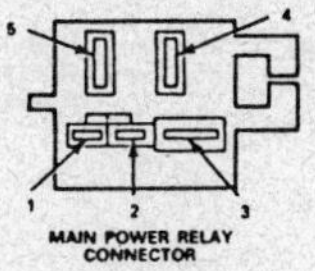 (MAIN POWER RELAY CONNECTOR: pins 1, 2, 3, 4, 5) • Measure voltage between main relay connector Pin 4 and ground. | Over 10 volts DC ▶<br>Under 10 volts DC ▶ | GO to Step **A3e**.<br>SERVICE cable harness circuit 533 or Fuse C. |
| **A3e** CHECK CIRCUIT 532a | | |
| • Turn ignition OFF. 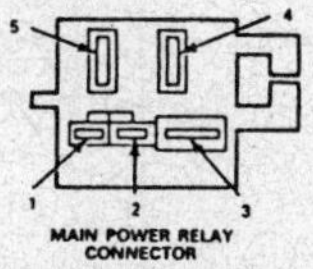 (MAIN POWER RELAY CONNECTOR: pins 1, 2, 3, 4, 5) • Check for continuity between main relay connector pin 3 and breakout box Pin 33. | Continuity ▶<br>No Continuity ▶ | GO to Step **A3f**.<br>SERVICE or REPLACE cable harness circuit 532a or 532b. |

**Fig. 94 Tests A3d & A3e (ABS lamp On). 1990–91 Continental**

## Anti-Lock Warning Lamp On (With Brake Warning Lamp Off) — Test A

| TEST STEP | RESULT ▶ | ACTION TO TAKE |
|---|---|---|
| **A3d** CHECK POWER TO RELAY | | |
| • Turn ignition ON. 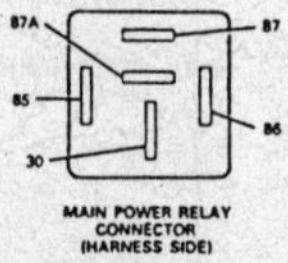 (MAIN POWER RELAY CONNECTOR (HARNESS SIDE): pins 87A, 87, 85, 86, 30) • Measure voltage between main relay connector Pin 87 and ground. | Over 10 volts DC ▶<br>Under 10 volts DC ▶ | GO to Step **A3e**.<br>SERVICE cable harness circuit 533, 299A Fuse Link. |
| **A3e** CHECK CIRCUIT 532A & 532B | | |
| • Turn ignition OFF. 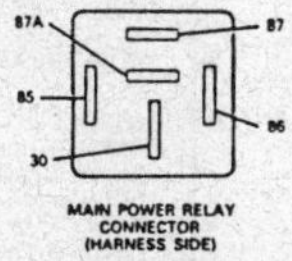 (MAIN POWER RELAY CONNECTOR (HARNESS SIDE): pins 87A, 87, 85, 86, 30) • Check for continuity between main relay connector pin 30 and breakout box Pin 33. | Continuity ▶<br>No Continuity ▶ | GO to Step **A3f**.<br>SERVICE or REPLACE cable harness circuit 532A or 532B. |

**Fig. 95 Tests A3d & A3e (ABS lamp On). Sable & Taurus**

## Anti-Lock Warning Indicator On (With Brake Warning Indicator Off) — Test A

| TEST STEP | RESULT ▶ | ACTION TO TAKE |
|---|---|---|
| **A3e** CHECK CIRCUIT 532 | | |
| • Turn ignition OFF. 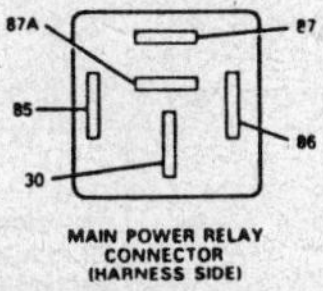 (MAIN POWER RELAY CONNECTOR (HARNESS SIDE): pins 87A, 87, 85, 86, 30) • Check for continuity between main relay connector Pin 30 and breakout box Pin 33. | Continuity ▶<br>No Continuity ▶ | GO to Step **A3f**.<br>SERVICE or REPLACE cable harness Circuit 532a or 532b. |
| **A3f** CHECK RELAY OPERATION | | |
| • With main power relay removed from connector. • Apply Battery + to Pin 86 and Battery − to Pin 85 on relay. • Check continuity between relay Pins 30 and 87. 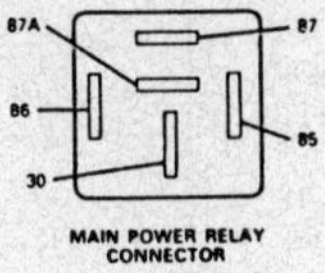 (MAIN POWER RELAY CONNECTOR: pins 87A, 87, 86, 85, 30) | Continuity ▶<br>No Continuity ▶ | REVERIFY reading at test A3.<br>REPLACE main power relay. |

**Fig. 96 Tests A3e & A3f (ABS lamp On). Town Car**

## Anti-Lock Warning Lamp On (With Brake Warning Lamp Off) — Test A

| TEST STEP | RESULT ▶ | ACTION TO TAKE |
|---|---|---|
| **A3f** CHECK RELAY OPERATION | | |
| • With main power relay removed from connector. • Apply Battery voltage to pin 2 and Battery ground to pin 1 on relay. • Check continuity between relay pins 3 and 4. 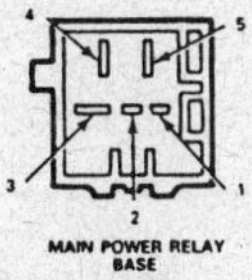 (MAIN POWER RELAY BASE: pins 1, 2, 3, 4, 5) | Continuity ▶<br>No Continuity ▶ | REVERIFY reading at test A3.<br>REPLACE main power relay. |
| **A4** CHECK CIRCUIT 430K | | |
| • Check for continuity between relay connector Pin 5 and ground. 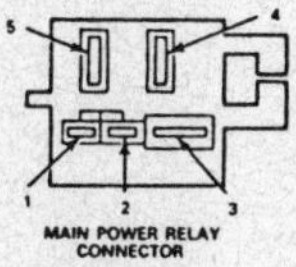 (MAIN POWER RELAY CONNECTOR: pins 1, 2, 3, 4, 5) | Continuity ▶<br>No Continuity ▶ | GO to Step **A5**.<br>SERVICE or REPLACE cable harness circuit 430K. |
| **A5** CHECK CIRCUIT 606 | | |
| • Turn ignition ON. • Check voltage between breakout box Pins 52 and 60. | Over 10 volts DC ▶<br>Under 10 volts DC ▶ | GO to Step **A6**.<br>SERVICE or REPLACE cable harness circuits 606, 606b or 606d. |

**Fig. 97 Tests A3f, A4 & A5 (ABS lamp On). 1990–91 Continental**

**Anti-Lock Warning Lamp On (With Brake Warning Lamp Off)** — **Test A**

| TEST STEP | RESULT | ACTION TO TAKE |
|---|---|---|
| **A3f** CHECK RELAY OPERATION | | |
| • With main power relay removed from connector. • Apply Battery + to Pin 86 and Battery − to Pin 85 on relay. (87A, 87, 86, 85, 30 — MAIN POWER RELAY CONNECTOR HARNESS SIDE) • Check continuity between relay Pins 30 and 87. | Continuity ▶ | REVERIFY reading at TEST A3. |
| | No Continuity ▶ | REPLACE main power relay. |
| **A4** CHECK RELAY TO GROUND | | |
| • Check for continuity between relay connector Pin 87A and ground. (87A, 87, 86, 85, 30 — MAIN POWER RELAY CONNECTOR (HARNESS SIDE)) | Continuity ▶ | GO to Step A5. |
| | No Continuity ▶ | SERVICE or REPLACE cable harness Circuit 57A or 57B (Taurus/Sable). Circuit 57T or 57R (Taurus SHO). |
| **A5** CHECK CIRCUIT 606. | | |
| • Jumper Pins 34 and 19 at breakout box. • Turn ignition ON. • Check voltage between breakout box Pins 52 and 60. | Over 10 Volts DC ▶ | GO to Step A6. |
| | Under 10 Volts DC ▶ | SERVICE or REPLACE cable harness Circuits 606, 606A or 606B (Taurus/Sable). Circuit 606, 606B or 606C (Taurus SHO). |

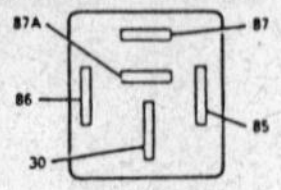

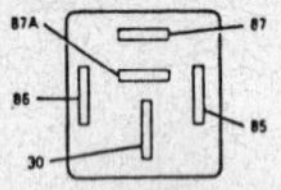

**Fig. 98 Tests A3f, A4 & A5 (ABS lamp On). Sable & Taurus**

**Anti-Lock Warning Lamp On (With Brake Warning Lamp Off)** — **Test A**

| TEST STEP | RESULT | ACTION TO TAKE |
|---|---|---|
| **A4** CHECK CIRCUIT 57I. | | |
| • Check for continuity between relay connector Pin 87a and ground. (87A, 87, 85, 86, 30 — MAIN POWER RELAY CONNECTOR (HARNESS SIDE)) | Continuity ▶ | GO to Step A5. |
| | No Continuity ▶ | SERVICE or REPLACE cable harness |
| **A5** CHECK CIRCUIT 603 | | |
| • Turn ignition ON. • Check voltage between breakout box Pins 52 and 60. | Over 10 volts DC ▶ | GO to Step A6. |
| | Under 10 volts DC ▶ | SERVICE or REPLACE cable harness circuits |

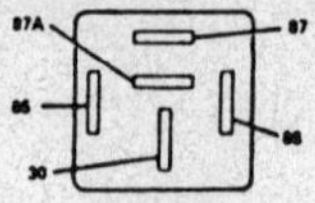

**Fig. 99 Tests A4 & A5 (ABS lamp On). 1990 Town Car**

**Anti-Lock Warning Indicator On (With Brake Warning Indicator Off)** — **Test A**

| TEST STEP | RESULT | ACTION TO TAKE |
|---|---|---|
| **A4** CHECK CIRCUIT 57T. | | |
| • Check for continuity between relay connector Pin 87a and ground. (87A, 87, 85, 86, 30 — MAIN POWER RELAY CONNECTOR (HARNESS SIDE)) | Continuity ▶ | GO to Step A5. |
| | No Continuity ▶ | SERVICE or REPLACE cable harness Circuit 57T. |
| **A5** CHECK CIRCUIT 603 | | |
| • Jumper Pins 34 and 19 at breakout box. • Turn ignition ON. • Check voltage between breakout box Pins 52 and 60. | Over 10V DC ▶ | GO to Step A6. |
| | Under 10V DC ▶ | SERVICE or REPLACE cable harness Circuits 603, 603a or 603c. |

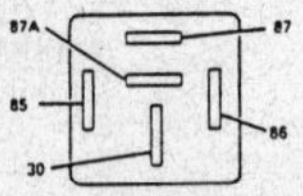

**Fig. 100 Tests A4 & A5 (ABS lamp On). 1991 Town Car**

**Anti-Lock Warning Lamp On (With Brake Warning Lamp Off)** — **Test A**

| TEST STEP | RESULT | ACTION TO TAKE |
|---|---|---|
| **A6** CHECK FLI #2 AND CIRCUITRY | | |
| • Measure resistance between breakout box Pins 8 and 26. | Less than 5 ohms ▶ | GO to Step A7. |
| | Any other reading ▶ | GO to Step A6a. |
| **A6a** CHECK FLI #2 | | |
| • Disconnect 2-pin plug from FLI #2, located on HCU reservoir. • Measure resistance between Pins 1 and 2 on HCU reservoir. | Less than 5 ohms ▶ | SERVICE or REPLACE cable harness circuit |
| | Any other reading ▶ | REPLACE HCU reservoir. |
| **A7** ELECTRONIC CONTROLLER CHECK | | |
| • If Self-Diagnostics, ABS Quick Test and Test A did not find problem. Replace Electronic Controller with a known good controller. | ABS light off. ▶ | REPLACE Controller. |
| | ABS light still on ▶ | REVERIFY that all tests have been performed. |

**Fig. 101 Tests A6, A6a & A7 (ABS lamp On)**

## Anti-Lock Lamp On After Engine Starts (Brake Warning Lamp Off) — Test B

WARNING LIGHTS SEQUENCE

| Warning Lamps | Ignition On | Cranking Engine | Engine Running | Vehicle Moving | Braking with/without Anti-Lock | Vehicle Stopped | Engine Idle | Ignition Off |
|---|---|---|---|---|---|---|---|---|
| Check Anti-Lock (Amber) | | | | | | | | |
| Brake (Red) | | | | | | | | |

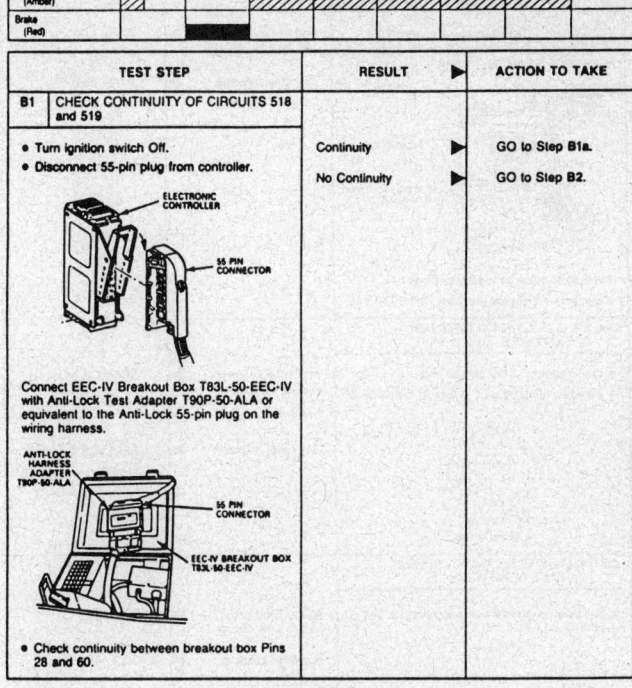

| TEST STEP | RESULT ▶ | ACTION TO TAKE |
|---|---|---|
| **B1** CHECK CONTINUITY OF CIRCUITS 518 and 519 | | |
| • Turn ignition switch Off.<br>• Disconnect 55-pin plug from controller.<br>ELECTRONIC CONTROLLER<br>55 PIN CONNECTOR<br>Connect EEC-IV Breakout Box T83L-50-EEC-IV with Anti-Lock Test Adapter T90P-50-ALA or equivalent to the Anti-Lock 55-pin plug on the wiring harness.<br>ANTI-LOCK HARNESS ADAPTER T90P-50-ALA<br>55 PIN CONNECTOR<br>EEC-IV BREAKOUT BOX T83L-50-EEC-IV<br>• Check continuity between breakout box Pins 28 and 60. | Continuity ▶<br>No Continuity ▶ | GO to Step B1a.<br>GO to Step B2. |

**Fig. 102 Test B1 (ABS lamp On after engine starts)**

## Anti-Lock Lamp On After Engine Starts (Brake Warning Lamp Off) — Test B

| TEST STEP | RESULT ▶ | ACTION TO TAKE |
|---|---|---|
| **B1a** CHECK LH REAR SENSOR TO GROUND | | |
| • Disconnect LH rear wheel sensor plug.<br>• Check for continuity between each sensor pin (sensor side) and vehicle ground.<br>LH REAR SENSOR | Continuity ▶<br>No Continuity ▶ | REPLACE LH rear sensor.<br>REPLACE or SERVICE cable harness circuit |
| **B2** CHECK CONTINUITY OF CIRCUITS 523 and 524 | | |
| • Check for continuity between breakout box Pins 27 and 60. | Continuity ▶<br>No Continuity ▶ | GO to Step B2a.<br>GO to Step B3. |
| **B2a** CHECK RH REAR SENSOR TO GROUND | | |
| • Disconnect RH rear wheel sensor plug.<br>• Check for continuity between each sensor pin (sensor side) and vehicle ground.<br>RH REAR SENSOR | Continuity ▶<br>No Continuity ▶ | REPLACE RH rear sensor.<br>REPLACE or SERVICE cable harness circuit |

**Fig. 103 Tests B1a, B2 & B2a (ABS lamp On after engine starts)**

## Anti-Lock Lamp On After Engine Starts (Brake Warning Lamp Off) — Test B

| TEST STEP | RESULT ▶ | ACTION TO TAKE |
|---|---|---|
| **B3** CHECK CONTINUITY OF CIRCUITS 514 and 516 | | |
| • Check for continuity between breakout box Pins 29 and 60. | Continuity ▶<br>No Continuity ▶ | GO to Step B3a.<br>GO to Step B4. |
| **B3a** CHECK RH FRONT SENSOR TO GROUND | | |
| • Disconnect RH front wheel sensor plug.<br>• Check for continuity between each sensor pin (sensor side) and vehicle ground.<br>RH FRONT SENSOR | Continuity ▶<br>No Continuity ▶ | REPLACE RH front sensor.<br>REPLACE or SERVICE cable harness circuit |
| **B4** CHECK CONTINUITY OF CIRCUITS 521 and 522 | | |
| • Check for continuity between breakout box Pins 30 and 60. | Continuity ▶<br>No Continuity ▶ | GO to Step B4a.<br>Test complete. If Anti-Lock lamp pattern remains, REPEAT Test B. |

**Fig. 104 Tests B3, B3a & B4 (ABS lamp On after engine starts)**

## Anti-Lock Lamp On After Engine Starts (Brake Warning Lamp Off) — Test B

| TEST STEP | RESULT ▶ | ACTION TO TAKE |
|---|---|---|
| **B4a** CHECK LH FRONT SENSOR TO GROUND | | |
| • Disconnect LH front wheel sensor plug.<br>• Check for continuity between each sensor pin (sensor side) and vehicle ground.<br>LH FRONT SENSOR | Continuity ▶<br>No Continuity ▶ | REPLACE LH front sensor.<br>REPLACE or SERVICE cable harness circuit |

**Fig. 105 Test B4a (ABS lamp On after engine starts)**

## Anti-Lock Warning Lamp On After Vehicle Starts To Move Or False Cycling Of Anti-Lock System — Test C

WARNING LIGHTS SEQUENCE

| Warning Lamps | Ignition On | Cranking Engine | Engine Running | Vehicle Moving | Braking with/without Anti-Lock | Vehicle Stopped | Engine Idle | Ignition Off |
|---|---|---|---|---|---|---|---|---|
| Check Anti-Lock (Amber) | | | | | | | | |
| Brake (Red) | | | | | | | | |

WARNING LIGHTS SEQUENCE

| Warning Lamps | Ignition On | Cranking Engine | Engine Running | Vehicle Moving | Braking with/without Anti-Lock | Vehicle Stopped | Engine Idle | Ignition Off |
|---|---|---|---|---|---|---|---|---|
| Check Anti-Lock (Amber) | | | | | | | | |
| Brake (Red) | | | | | | | | |

| TEST STEP | RESULT ▶ | ACTION TO TAKE |
|---|---|---|
| **C1** MEASURE LH FRONT SENSOR CIRCUIT RESISTANCE | | |
| • Turn ignition switch OFF.<br>• Disconnect 55-pin connector from electronic controller. | | |



**Fig. 106 Test C1 (ABS lamp ON after vehicle starts)**

## Anti-Lock Warning Lamp On After Vehicle Starts To Move Or False Cycling Of Anti-Lock System — Test C

| TEST STEP | RESULT ▶ | ACTION TO TAKE |
|---|---|---|
| **C1** MEASURE LH FRONT SENSOR CIRCUIT RESISTANCE — Continued | | |
| • Connect EEC-IV Breakout Box with Tool T90P-50-ALA or equivalent to the 55-pin connector on wiring harness. | 800 to 1400 ohms (0.8 to 1.4K ohms) ▶ | GO to Step **C2**. |
| | Any other reading ▶ | GO to Step **C1a**. |
| • Set multi-meter to read resistance.<br>• Measure resistance between Pins 30 and 48. | | |
| **C1a** CHECK LH FRONT SENSOR RESISTANCE | | |
| • Disconnect LH front sensor plug.<br>• Measure resistance of sensor at sensor plug. | 800 to 1400 ohms (0.8 to 1.4K ohms) ▶ | SERVICE or REPLACE cable harness Circuit |
| | Any other reading ▶ | REPLACE LH front sensor. |
| **C2** MEASURE RH FRONT SENSOR CIRCUIT RESISTANCE | | |
| • Measure resistance between breakout box Pins 29 and 47. | 800 to 1400 ohms (0.8 to 1.4K ohms) ▶ | GO to Step **C3**. |
| | Any other reading ▶ | GO to Step **C2a**. |



**Fig. 107 Tests C1, C1a & C2 (ABS lamp ON after vehicle starts)**

## Anti-Lock Warning Lamp On After Vehicle Starts To Move Or False Cycling Of Anti-Lock System — Test C

| TEST STEP | RESULT ▶ | ACTION TO TAKE |
|---|---|---|
| **C2a** CHECK RH FRONT SENSOR RESISTANCE | | |
| • Disconnect RH front sensor plug.<br>• Measure resistance of sensor at sensor plug. | 800 to 1400 ohms (0.8 to 1.4K ohms) ▶ | SERVICE or REPLACE cable harness Circuit |
| | Any other reading ▶ | REPLACE RH front sensor. |
| **C3** MEASURE RH REAR SENSOR CIRCUIT RESISTANCE | | |
| • Measure resistance between Breakout box Pins 27 and 45. | 800 to 1400 ohms (0.8 to 1.4K ohms) ▶ | GO to Step **C4**. |
| | Any other reading ▶ | GO to Step **C3a**. |
| **C3a** CHECK RH REAR SENSOR RESISTANCE | | |
| • Disconnect RH rear sensor plug.<br>• Measure resistance of sensor at sensor plug. | 800 to 1400 ohms (0.8 to 1.4K ohms) ▶ | SERVICE or REPLACE cable harness Circuit |
| | Any other reading ▶ | REPLACE RH rear sensor. |



**Fig. 108 Tests C2a, C3 & C3a (ABS lamp ON after vehicle starts)**

## Anti-Lock Warning Lamp On After Vehicle Starts To Move Or False Cycling Of Anti-Lock System — Test C

| TEST STEP | RESULT ▶ | ACTION TO TAKE |
|---|---|---|
| **C4** MEASURE LH REAR SENSOR CIRCUIT RESISTANCE | | |
| • Measure resistance between breakout box Pins 28 and 46. | 800 to 1400 ohms (0.8 to 1.4K ohms) ▶ | GO to Step **C5**. |
| | Any other reading ▶ | GO to Step **C4a**. |
| **C4a** CHECK LH REAR SENSOR RESISTANCE | | |
| • Disconnect LH rear sensor plug.<br>• Measure resistance of sensor at sensor plug. | 800 to 1400 ohms (0.8 to 1.4K ohms) ▶ | SERVICE or REPLACE cable harness Circuit |
| | Any other reading ▶ | REPLACE LH rear sensor. |
| **C5** CHECK LH FRONT SENSOR AND CIRCUITRY TO GROUND | | |
| • Check for continuity between breakout box Pins 30 and 60. | Continuity ▶ | GO to Step **C5a**. |
| | No Continuity ▶ | GO to Step **C6**. |
| **C5a** CHECK LH FRONT SENSOR TO GROUND | | |
| • Disconnect LH front sensor plug.<br>• Check for continuity between each sensor pin and body ground. | Continuity ▶ | REPLACE LH front sensor. |
| | No Continuity ▶ | REPAIR OR REPLACE cable harness Circuit |



**Fig. 109 Tests C4, C4a, C5 & C5a (ABS lamp ON after vehicle starts)**

| Anti-Lock Warning Lamp On After Vehicle Starts To Move Or False Cycling Of Anti-Lock System | Test C |
|---|---|

| TEST STEP | RESULT ▶ | ACTION TO TAKE |
|---|---|---|
| **C6** CHECK RH FRONT SENSOR AND CIRCUITRY TO GROUND | | |
| • Check for continuity between breakout box Pins 29 and 60. | Continuity ▶ | GO to Step C6a. |
| | No Continuity ▶ | GO to Step C7. |
| **C6a** CHECK RH FRONT SENSOR TO GROUND | | |
| • Disconnect RH front sensor plug.<br>• Check for continuity between each sensor pin and body ground. | Continuity ▶ | REPLACE RH front sensor. |
| | No Continuity ▶ | REPAIR OR REPLACE cable harness Circuit |
| **C7** CHECK RH REAR SENSOR AND CIRCUITRY TO GROUND | | |
| • Check for continuity between breakout box Pins 27 and 60. | Continuity ▶ | GO to Step C7a. |
| | No Continuity ▶ | GO to Step C8. |
| **C7a** CHECK RH REAR SENSOR TO GROUND | | |
| • Disconnect RH rear sensor plug.<br>• Check for continuity between each sensor pin and body ground. | Continuity ▶ | REPLACE RH rear sensor. |
| | No Continuity ▶ | REPAIR OR REPLACE cable harness Circuit |
| **C8** CHECK LH REAR SENSOR AND CIRCUITRY TO GROUND | | |
| • Check for continuity between breakout box Pins 28 and 60. | Continuity ▶ | GO to Step C8a. |
| | No Continuity ▶ | GO to Step C9. |

**Fig. 110 Tests C6, C6a, C7, C7a & C8 (ABS lamp ON after vehicle starts)**

| Anti-Lock Warning Lamp On After Vehicle Starts To Move Or False Cycling Of Anti-Lock System | Test C |
|---|---|

| TEST STEP | RESULT ▶ | ACTION TO TAKE |
|---|---|---|
| **C8a** CHECK LH REAR SENSOR TO GROUND | | |
| • Disconnect LH rear sensor plug.<br>• Check for continuity between each sensor pin and body ground. | Continuity ▶ | REPLACE LH rear sensor. |
| | No Continuity ▶ | REPAIR OR REPLACE cable harness Circuit |
| **C9** CHECK LH FRONT SENSOR VOLTAGE OUTPUT | | |
| • Measure voltage between breakout box Pins 30 and 48 while spinning LH front wheel at approximately 1 revolution per second. | Between 0.10 and 1.40 volts AC ▶ | GO to Step C10. |
| | Less than 0.10 or more than 1.40 volts AC ▶ | CHECK wheel sensor mounting, air gap, or toothed wheel. CORRECT as required. |
| **C10** CHECK RH FRONT SENSOR VOLTAGE OUTPUT | | |
| • Measure voltage between breakout box Pins 29 and 47 while spinning RH front wheel at approximately 1 revolution per second. | Between 0.10 and 1.40 volts AC ▶ | GO to Step C11. |
| | Less than 0.10 or more than 1.40 volts AC ▶ | CHECK wheel sensor mounting, air gap, or toothed wheel. CORRECT as required. |
| **C11** CHECK RH REAR SENSOR VOLTAGE OUTPUT | | |
| • Measure voltage between breakout box Pins 27 and 45 while spinning RH rear wheel at approximately 1 revolution per second. | Between 0.10 and 1.40 volts AC ▶ | GO to Step C12. |
| | Less than 0.10 or more than 1.40 volts AC ▶ | CHECK wheel sensor mounting, air gap, or toothed wheel. CORRECT as required. |

**Fig. 111 Tests C8a, C9, C10 & C11 (ABS lamp ON after vehicle starts)**

| Anti-Lock Warning Indicator On After Vehicle Starts To Move Or False Cycling Of Anti-Lock System | Test C |
|---|---|

| TEST STEP | RESULT ▶ | ACTION TO TAKE |
|---|---|---|
| **C12** CHECK LH REAR SENSOR VOLTAGE OUTPUT | | |
| • Measure voltage between breakout box Pins 28 and 46 while spinning LH rear wheel at approximately 1 revolution per second. | Between 0.10V and 1.40V AC ▶ | GO to Step C13. |
| | Less than 0.10V or more than 1.40V AC ▶ | CHECK wheel sensor mounting, air gap, or toothed wheel. CORRECT as required. |
| **C13** CHECK MOTOR SPEED SENSOR AND CIRCUITRY | | |
| • Measure resistance between breakout box Pins 31 and 49. | 5-100 ohms ▶ | GO to Step C14. |
| | Any other reading ▶ | GO to Step C13a. |
| **C13a** CHECK PUMP MOTOR SPEED SENSOR | | |
| • Disconnect 4-Pin plug on pump motor.<br>• Measure resistance between Pins S0 and S1 on pump motor.<br>S0 MOTOR(−)2 MOTOR(+)1 S1<br>4 PIN PUMP MOTOR CONNECTOR | 5-100 ohms ▶ | GO to Step C13b. |
| | Any other reading ▶ | REPLACE pump and motor. |

**Fig. 112 Tests C12, C13 & C13a (ABS lamp ON after vehicle starts)**

| Anti-Lock Warning Lamp On After Vehicle Starts To Move Or False Cycling Of Anti-Lock System | Test C |
|---|---|

| TEST STEP | RESULT ▶ | ACTION TO TAKE |
|---|---|---|
| **C13b** CHECK PUMP MOTOR RELAY | | |
| • Disconnect 7-pin plug on pump motor relay and remove relay.<br>• Check continuity from Pin S0 on 7-pin side to Pin S0 on 4-pin side of relay. | Continuity ▶ | GO to Step C13c. |
| PUMP MOTOR RELAY | No Continuity ▶ | REPLACE pump motor relay. |
| **C13c** CHECK PUMP MOTOR RELAY | | |
| • Check continuity from Pin S1 on 7-pin side to Pin S1 on 4-pin side of relay. | Continuity ▶ | GO to Step C13d. |
| | No Continuity ▶ | REPLACE pump motor relay. |
| **C13d** CHECK CIRCUIT 462 | | |
| • Check continuity between breakout box Pin 31 and Pin S0 on pump motor connector 7-pin plug (harness side).<br>7 PIN PUMP MOTOR RELAY CONNECTOR HARNESS SIDE | Continuity ▶ | GO to Step C13e. |
| | No Continuity ▶ | SERVICE or REPLACE cable harness Circuit 462. |

**Fig. 113 Tests C13b, C13c & C13d (ABS lamp ON after vehicle starts)**

| Anti-Lock Warning Lamp On After Vehicle Starts To Move Or False Cycling Of Anti-Lock System | Test C |
|---|---|

| TEST STEP | RESULT ▶ | ACTION TO TAKE |
|---|---|---|
| **C13e** CHECK CIRCUIT 461 | | |
| • Check continuity between breakout box Pin 49 and Pin S1 on pump motor connector 7-pin plug (harness side). | Continuity ▶ | REVERIFY reading at C13. |
| | No Continuity ▶ | SERVICE or REPLACE cable harness Circuit 461. |
| **C14** CHECK MOTOR SPEED SENSOR SHORT TO BATTERY + | | |
| • Turn ignition switch to ON.<br>• Measure voltage between breakout box Pins 31 and 60. | No voltage ▶ | GO to Step C15. |
| | 12 volts ▶ | GO to Step C14a. |
| **C14a** CHECK PUMP MOTOR | | |
| • Disconnect pump motor to relay 4-pin plug connector.<br>• Turn ignition switch to ON.<br>• Measure voltage between breakout box Pins 31 and 60. | No voltage ▶ | REPLACE pump and motor. |
| | 12 volts ▶ | GO to Step C14b. |
| **C14b** CHECK CIRCUIT 462 | | |
| • Disconnect wire harness to relay 7-pin plug.<br>• Turn ignition switch to ON.<br>• Measure voltage between breakout box Pins 31 and 60. | No voltage ▶ | GO to Step C14c. |
| | 12 volts ▶ | SERVICE or REPLACE cable harness Circuit 462. |
| **C14c** CHECK CIRCUIT 461 | | |
| • Turn ignition switch to ON.<br>• Measure voltage between breakout box Pins 49 and 60. | No voltage ▶ | REPLACE pump motor relay. |
| | 12 volts ▶ | SERVICE or REPLACE cable harness Circuit 461. |

**Fig. 114 Tests C13e, C14, C14a, C14b & C14c (ABS lamp ON after vehicle starts). Sable, Taurus & 1990–91 Continental**

| Anti-Lock Warning Lamp On After Vehicle Starts To Move Or False Cycling Of Anti-Lock System | Test C |
|---|---|

| TEST STEP | RESULT ▶ | ACTION TO TAKE |
|---|---|---|
| **C13e** CHECK CIRCUIT 604 | | |
| • Check continuity between breakout box Pin 49 and Pin S1 on pump motor connector 7-pin plug (harness side). | Continuity ▶ | REVERIFY reading at C13. |
| | No Continuity ▶ | SERVICE or REPLACE cable harness Circuit |
| **C14** CHECK MOTOR SPEED SENSOR SHORT TO BATTERY + | | |
| • Turn ignition switch to ON.<br>• Measure voltage between breakout box Pins 31 and 60. | No voltage ▶ | GO to Step C15. |
| | 12 volts ▶ | GO to Step C14a. |
| **C14a** CHECK PUMP MOTOR | | |
| • Disconnect pump motor to relay 4-pin plug connector.<br>• Turn ignition switch to ON.<br>• Measure voltage between breakout box Pins 31 and 60. | No voltage ▶ | REPLACE pump and motor. |
| | 12 volts ▶ | GO to Step C14b. |
| **C14b** CHECK CIRCUIT 462 | | |
| • Disconnect wire harness to relay 7-pin plug.<br>• Turn ignition switch to ON.<br>• Measure voltage between breakout box Pins 31 and 60. | No voltage ▶ | GO to Step C14c. |
| | 12 volts ▶ | SERVICE or REPLACE cable harness Circuit |
| **C14c** CHECK CIRCUIT 604 | | |
| • Turn ignition switch to ON.<br>• Measure voltage between breakout box Pins 49 and 60. | No voltage ▶ | REPLACE pump motor relay. |
| | 12 volts ▶ | SERVICE or REPLACE cable harness Circuit |

**Fig. 115 Tests C13e, C14, C14a, C14b & C14c (ABS lamp ON after vehicle starts). Town Car**

| Anti-Lock Warning Lamp On After Vehicle Starts To Move Or False Cycling Of Anti-Lock System | Test C |
|---|---|

| TEST STEP | RESULT ▶ | ACTION TO TAKE |
|---|---|---|
| **C15** CHECK MOTOR SPEED SENSOR SHORT TO GROUND | | |
| • Check for continuity between breakout box Pins 31 and 60. | No Continuity ▶ | GO to Step C16. |
| | Continuity ▶ | GO to Step C15a. |
| **C15a** CHECK PUMP MOTOR | | |
| • Disconnect pump to motor relay 4-pin plug connector.<br>• Check for continuity between breakout box Pins 31 and 60. | Continuity ▶ | GO to Step C15b. |
| | No Continuity ▶ | REPLACE pump and motor. |
| **C15b** CHECK CIRCUIT 462 | | |
| • Disconnect wire harness to relay 7-pin plug.<br>• Check for continuity between breakout box Pins 31 and 60. | Continuity ▶ | SERVICE or REPLACE cable harness Circuit |
| | No Continuity ▶ | GO to Step C15c. |
| **C15c** CHECK CIRCUIT 604 | | |
| • Check for continuity between breakout box Pins 49 and 60. | Continuity ▶ | SERVICE Or REPLACE cable harness Circuit |
| | No Continuity ▶ | REPLACE pump motor relay. |
| **C16** CHECK PUMP MOTOR OPERATION | | |
| • Reconnect pump motor relay to pump and wire harness.<br>• Jumper Pins 15, 34 and 60 at breakout box.<br>• Turn ignition to ON position. | Pump motor runs ▶ | GO to Step C17. |
| | Pump motor does not run ▶ | GO to Step C16a. |

**Fig. 116 Tests C15, C15a, C15b, C15c & C16 (ABS lamp ON after vehicle starts)**

| Anti-Lock Warning Lamp On After Vehicle Starts To Move Or False Cycling Of Anti-Lock System | Test C |
|---|---|

| TEST STEP | RESULT ▶ | ACTION TO TAKE |
|---|---|---|
| **C16a** CHECK PUMP MOTOR OPERATION | | |
| • Disconnect pump motor relay from pump motor.<br>• Ground Pin 2 and apply 12 volts to Pin 1 of pump motor connector.<br>50 / MOTOR (–) 2 / MOTOR (+) 1 / S1<br>4 PIN PUMP MOTOR CONNECTOR HARNESS SIDE | Pump motor runs ▶ | GO to Step C16b. |
| | Pump motor does not run ▶ | REPLACE pump motor. |
| **C16b** CHECK POWER TO RELAY | | |
| • Disconnect wire harness from pump motor relay.<br>• Check voltage between Pin 30 on wire harness to pump motor relay connector and ground.<br>539 PK/LB — 85 / 537 T/Y — 30 / 532 O/Y — 86 / 462 P — 50 / 57 BK — 31 / 604 O/R — S1<br>7 PIN PUMP MOTOR RELAY CONNECTOR HARNESS SIDE | Over 10 volts ▶ | GO to Step C16c. |
| | Less than 10 volts ▶ | SERVICE or REPLACE battery fuse or circuit |

**Fig. 117 Tests C16a & C16b (ABS lamp ON after vehicle starts)**

| Anti-Lock Warning Lamp On After Vehicle Starts To Move Or False Cycling Of Anti-Lock System | Test C |
|---|---|

| TEST STEP | RESULT ▶ | ACTION TO TAKE |
|---|---|---|
| **C16c** CHECK POWER TO RELAY COIL | | |
| • Jumper Pins 34 and 60 at breakout box.<br>• Turn ignition to ON position.<br>• Measure voltage between Pin 86 and ground.<br>539 PK/LB — 85; 537 T/Y — 30; 532 O/Y — 86; 462 P — 50; 57 BK — 31; 604 O/R — S1<br>7 PIN PUMP MOTOR RELAY CONNECTOR HARNESS SIDE | Over 10 volts ▶<br>Less than 10 volts ▶ | GO to Step C16d.<br>SERVICE or REPLACE cable harness Circuit |
| **C16d** CHECK PUMP MOTOR RELAY COIL | | |
| • Measure resistance between Pins 85 and 86 on pump motor relay.<br>1, 31, 50, 86, TEST, 30, 85, S1, S1, 2, 50<br>PUMP MOTOR RELAY | 45 to 105 ohms ▶<br>Any other reading ▶ | GO to Step C16e.<br>REPLACE pump motor relay. |

**Fig. 118 Tests C16c & C16d (ABS lamp ON after vehicle starts)**

| Anti-Lock Warning Indicator On After Vehicle Starts to Move or False Cycling of Anti-Lock System | Test C |
|---|---|

| TEST STEP | RESULT ▶ | ACTION TO TAKE |
|---|---|---|
| **C16e** CHECK CIRCUIT 539 | | |
| • Check for continuity between Breakout Box Pin 15 and Pin 85 on wire harness to pump motor relay connector.<br>539 PK/LB — 85; 537 T/Y — 30; 532 O/Y — 86; 462 P — 50; 57 BK — 31; 604 O/R — S1<br>7 PIN PUMP MOTOR RELAY CONNECTOR HARNESS SIDE | Continuity ▶<br>No Continuity ▶ | GO to Step C16f.<br>SERVICE or REPLACE cable harness Circuit 539. |
| **C16f** CHECK CIRCUIT 57w | | |
| • Check for continuity between wire harness to pump motor relay connector Pin 31 and ground. | Continuity ▶<br>No Continuity ▶ | GO to Step C16g.<br>SERVICE or REPLACE cable harness Circuit 57w. |
| **C16g** CHECK PUMP MOTOR RELAY | | |
| • Connect battery + to Pin 86 and battery − to Pin 85 of pump motor relay.<br>• Check for continuity between Pin 30 and Pin 1 on relay. | Continuity ▶<br>No Continuity ▶ | GO to Step C16h.<br>REPLACE pump motor relay. |
| **C16h** CHECK PUMP MOTOR RELAY | | |
| • Check continuity between Pins 2 and 31 on pump motor relay<br>1, 31, 50, 86, TEST, 30, 85, S1, S1, 2, 50<br>PUMP MOTOR RELAY | Continuity ▶<br>No Continuity ▶ | REPLACE computer module.<br>REPLACE pump motor relay. |

**Fig. 120 Tests C16e, C16f, C16g & C16h (ABS lamp ON after vehicle starts). 1991 Town Car**

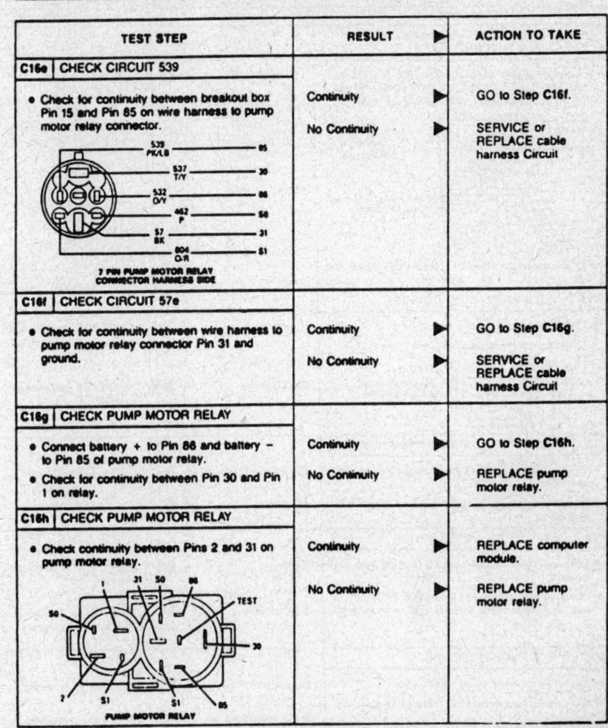

| Anti-Lock Warning Lamp On After Vehicle Starts To Move Or False Cycling Of Anti-Lock System | Test C |
|---|---|

| TEST STEP | RESULT ▶ | ACTION TO TAKE |
|---|---|---|
| **C16e** CHECK CIRCUIT 539 | | |
| • Check for continuity between breakout box Pin 15 and Pin 85 on wire harness to pump motor relay connector.<br>539 PK/LB — 85; 537 T/Y — 30; 532 O/Y — 86; 462 P — 50; 57 BK — 31; 604 O/R — S1<br>7 PIN PUMP MOTOR RELAY CONNECTOR HARNESS SIDE | Continuity ▶<br>No Continuity ▶ | GO to Step C16f.<br>SERVICE or REPLACE cable harness Circuit |
| **C16f** CHECK CIRCUIT 57e | | |
| • Check for continuity between wire harness to pump motor relay connector Pin 31 and ground. | Continuity ▶<br>No Continuity ▶ | GO to Step C16g.<br>SERVICE or REPLACE cable harness Circuit |
| **C16g** CHECK PUMP MOTOR RELAY | | |
| • Connect battery + to Pin 86 and battery − to Pin 85 of pump motor relay.<br>• Check for continuity between Pin 30 and Pin 1 on relay. | Continuity ▶<br>No Continuity ▶ | GO to Step C16h.<br>REPLACE pump motor relay. |
| **C16h** CHECK PUMP MOTOR RELAY | | |
| • Check continuity between Pins 2 and 31 on pump motor relay.<br>1, 31, 50, 86, TEST, 30, 85, S1, S1, 2, 50<br>PUMP MOTOR RELAY | Continuity ▶<br>No Continuity ▶ | REPLACE computer module.<br>REPLACE pump motor relay. |

**Fig. 119 Tests C16e, C16f, C16g & C16h (ABS lamp ON after vehicle starts). Except 1991 Town Car**

| Anti-Lock Warning Lamp Sequence Normal — Brake Pedal Rises Or Drops Excessively During ABS Cycling | Test D |
|---|---|

| Warning Lamps | Ignition On | Cranking Engine | Engine Running | Vehicle Moving | Braking with/without Anti-Lock | Vehicle Stopped | Engine Idle | Ignition Off |
|---|---|---|---|---|---|---|---|---|
| Check Anti-Lock (Amber) | | | | | | | | |
| Brake (Red) | | | | | | | | |

(WARNING LIGHTS SEQUENCE)

| TEST STEP | RESULT ▶ | ACTION TO TAKE |
|---|---|---|
| BEFORE RUNNING TEST STEP D — ADJUST PEDAL POSITION SWITCH | Pedal feel normal during ABS cycling<br>Pedal feel not normal during ABS. | Condition corrected.<br>PERFORM Test D. |
| **D1** CHECK PEDAL TRAVEL SWITCH AND CIRCUITRY | | |
| • Turn ignition switch Off.<br>• Disconnect 55-pin plug from controller. | | |

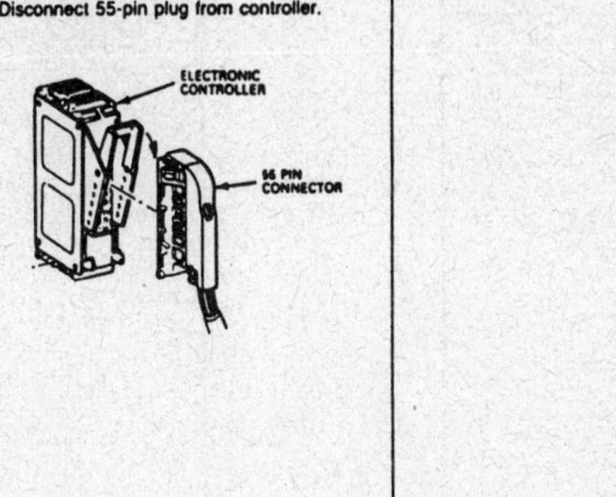


**Fig. 121 Test D1 (Warning sequence normal/brake pedal rises or drops excessively during ABS cycling). Except 1991 Town Car**

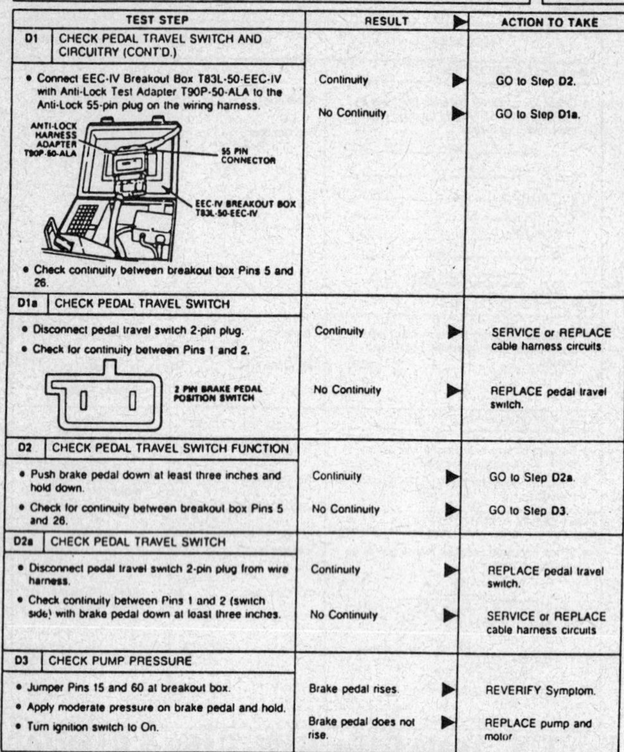

**Anti-Lock Warning Lamp Sequence Normal — Brake Pedal Rises Or Drops Excessively During ABS Cycling** | **Test D**

| TEST STEP | RESULT ▶ | ACTION TO TAKE |
|---|---|---|
| **D1** CHECK PEDAL TRAVEL SWITCH AND CIRCUITRY (CONT'D.) | | |
| • Connect EEC-IV Breakout Box T83L-50-EEC-IV with Anti-Lock Test Adapter T90P-50-ALA to the Anti-Lock 55-pin plug on the wiring harness. (ANTI-LOCK HARNESS ADAPTER T90P-50-ALA; 55 PIN CONNECTOR; EEC-IV BREAKOUT BOX T83L-50-EEC-IV) • Check continuity between breakout box Pins 5 and 26. | Continuity ▶<br>No Continuity ▶ | GO to Step D2.<br>GO to Step D1a. |
| **D1a** CHECK PEDAL TRAVEL SWITCH | | |
| • Disconnect pedal travel switch 2-pin plug. • Check for continuity between Pins 1 and 2. (2 PIN BRAKE PEDAL POSITION SWITCH) | Continuity ▶<br>No Continuity ▶ | SERVICE or REPLACE cable harness circuits<br>REPLACE pedal travel switch. |
| **D2** CHECK PEDAL TRAVEL SWITCH FUNCTION | | |
| • Push brake pedal down at least three inches and hold down. • Check for continuity between breakout box Pins 5 and 26. | Continuity ▶<br>No Continuity ▶ | GO to Step D2a.<br>GO to Step D3. |
| **D2a** CHECK PEDAL TRAVEL SWITCH | | |
| • Disconnect pedal travel switch 2-pin plug from wire harness. • Check continuity between Pins 1 and 2 (switch side) with brake pedal down at least three inches. | Continuity ▶<br>No Continuity ▶ | REPLACE pedal travel switch.<br>SERVICE or REPLACE cable harness circuits |
| **D3** CHECK PUMP PRESSURE | | |
| • Jumper Pins 15 and 60 at breakout box. • Apply moderate pressure on brake pedal and hold. • Turn ignition switch to On. | Brake pedal rises. ▶<br>Brake pedal does not rise. ▶ | REVERIFY Symptom.<br>REPLACE pump and motor |

**Fig. 122 Tests D1, D1a, D2, D2a & D3 (Warning sequence normal/brake pedal rises or drops excessively during ABS cycling). 1990–91 Continental, 1990 Sable, Taurus & Town Car**

**Anti-Lock Warning Indicator Sequence Normal — Brake Pedal Rises Or Drops Excessively During ABS Cycling** | **Test D**

WARNING INDICATORS SEQUENCE

| Warning Indicators | Ignition On | Cranking Engine | Engine Running | Vehicle Moving | Braking with/without Anti-Lock | Vehicle Stopped | Engine Idle | Ignition Off |
|---|---|---|---|---|---|---|---|---|
| Check Anti-Lock (Amber) | ▨ | | ▨ | | | | | |
| Brake (Red) | ■ | | ■ | | | | | |

| TEST STEP | RESULT ▶ | ACTION TO TAKE |
|---|---|---|
| BEFORE RUNNING TEST STEP D — ADJUST PEDAL POSITION SWITCH AS OUTLINED IN THIS SECTION. | Pedal feel normal during ABS cycling<br>Pedal feel not normal during ABS | Condition corrected.<br>PERFORM Test D. |
| **D1** CHECK PEDAL TRAVEL SWITCH AND CIRCUITRY | | |
| • Turn ignition switch to OFF position. • Disconnect 55-pin plug from controller. (ELECTRONIC CONTROLLER; 55 PIN CONNECTOR) | | |

**Fig. 124 Test D1 (Warning sequence normal/brake pedal rises or drops excessively during ABS cycling). 1991 Town Car**

**Anti-Lock Warning Indicator Sequence Normal — Brake Pedal Rises Or Drops Excessively During ABS Cycling** | **Test D**

| TEST STEP | RESULT ▶ | ACTION TO TAKE |
|---|---|---|
| **D1** CHECK PEDAL TRAVEL SWITCH AND CIRCUITRY (CONT'D.) | | |
| • Connect EEC-IV Breakout Box T83L-50-EEC-IV with Anti-Lock Test Adapter T90P-50-ALA to the Anti-Lock 55-pin plug on the wiring harness. (ANTI-LOCK HARNESS ADAPTER T90P-50-ALA; 55 PIN CONNECTOR; EEC-IV BREAKOUT BOX T83L-50-EEC-IV) • Check continuity between breakout box Pins 5 and 26. | Continuity ▶<br>No Continuity ▶ | GO to Step D2.<br>GO to Step D1a. |
| **D1a** CHECK PEDAL TRAVEL SWITCH | | |
| • Disconnect pedal travel switch 2-pin plug. • Check for continuity between Pins 1 and 2. (2 PIN BRAKE PEDAL POSITION SWITCH) | Continuity ▶<br>No Continuity ▶ | SERVICE or REPLACE cable harness Circuits 535 or 549.<br>REPLACE pedal travel switch. |
| **D2** CHECK PEDAL TRAVEL SWITCH FUNCTION | | |
| • Push brake pedal down at least three inches and hold down. • Check for continuity between breakout box Pins 5 and 26. | Continuity ▶<br>No Continuity ▶ | GO to Step D2a.<br>GO to Step D3. |
| **D2a** CHECK PEDAL TRAVEL SWITCH | | |
| • Disconnect pedal travel switch 2-pin plug from wire harness. • Check continuity between Pins 1 and 2 (switch side) with brake pedal down at least three inches. | Continuity ▶<br>No Continuity ▶ | REPLACE pedal travel switch.<br>SERVICE or REPLACE cable harness Circuits 535 or 549. |
| **D3** CHECK PUMP PRESSURE | | |
| • Jumper Pins 15, 34 and 60 at breakout box. • Apply moderate pressure on brake pedal and hold. • Turn ignition switch to ON position. | Brake pedal rises. ▶<br>Brake pedal does not rise. ▶ | REVERIFY symptom.<br>REPLACE pump and motor. |

**Fig. 123 Tests D1, D1a, D2, D2a & D3 (Warning sequence normal/brake pedal rises or drops excessively during ABS cycling). 1991 Sable & Taurus**

**Anti-Lock Warning Indicator Sequence Normal — Brake Pedal Rises Or Drops Excessively During ABS Cycling** | **Test D**

| TEST STEP | RESULT ▶ | ACTION TO TAKE |
|---|---|---|
| **D1** CHECK PEDAL TRAVEL SWITCH AND CIRCUITRY (CONT'D.) | | |
| • Connect EEC-IV Breakout Box T83L-50-EEC-IV with Anti-Lock Test Adapter T90P-50-ALA to the Anti-Lock 55-pin plug on the wiring harness. (ANTI-LOCK HARNESS ADAPTER T90P-50-ALA; 55 PIN CONNECTOR; EEC-IV BREAKOUT BOX T83L-50-EEC-IV) • Check continuity between breakout box Pins 5 and 26. | Continuity ▶<br>No Continuity ▶ | GO to Step D2.<br>GO to Step D1a. |
| **D1a** CHECK PEDAL TRAVEL SWITCH | | |
| • Disconnect pedal travel switch 2-pin plug. • Check for continuity between Pins 1 and 2. (2 PIN BRAKE PEDAL POSITION SWITCH) | Continuity ▶<br>No Continuity ▶ | SERVICE or REPLACE cable harness Circuits 535 or 549.<br>REPLACE pedal travel switch. |
| **D2** CHECK PEDAL TRAVEL SWITCH FUNCTION | | |
| • Push brake pedal down at least three inches and hold down. • Check for continuity between breakout box Pins 5 and 26. | Continuity ▶<br>No Continuity ▶ | GO to Step D2a.<br>GO to Step D3. |
| **D2a** CHECK PEDAL TRAVEL SWITCH | | |
| • Disconnect pedal travel switch 2-pin plug from wire harness. • Check continuity between Pins 1 and 2 (switch side) with brake pedal down at least three inches. | Continuity ▶<br>No Continuity ▶ | REPLACE pedal travel switch.<br>SERVICE or REPLACE cable harness Circuits 535 or 549. |
| **D3** CHECK PUMP PRESSURE | | |
| • Jumper Pins 15, 34 and 60 at breakout box. • Apply moderate pressure on brake pedal and hold. • Turn ignition switch to ON position. | Brake pedal rises. ▶<br>Brake pedal does not rise. ▶ | REVERIFY symptom.<br>REPLACE pump and motor. |

**Fig. 125 Tests D1, D1a, D2, D2a & D3 (Warning sequence normal/brake pedal rises or drops excessively during ABS cycling). 1991 Town Car**

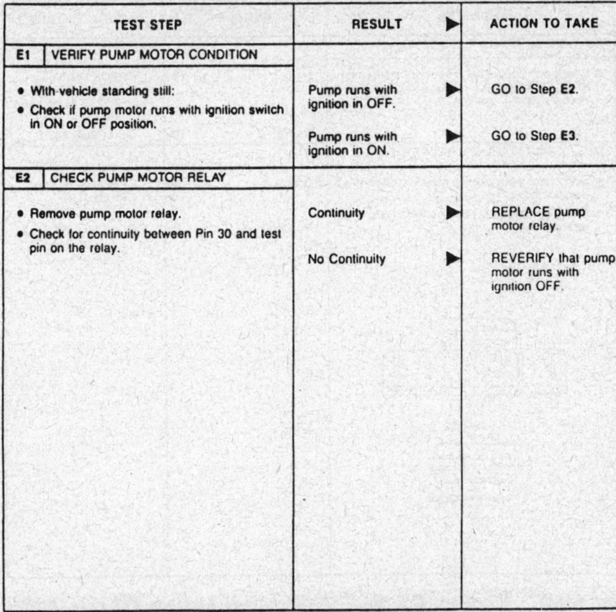

**Anti-Lock Warning Lamp Sequence Normal — ABS Pump Motor Runs Continuously (Ignition On/Ignition Off)** — **Test E**

WARNING LIGHTS SEQUENCE

| Warning Lamps | Ignition On | Cranking Engine | Engine Running | Vehicle Moving | Braking with/without Anti-Lock | Vehicle Stopped | Engine Idle | Ignition Off |
|---|---|---|---|---|---|---|---|---|
| Check Anti-Lock (Amber) | | | | | | | | |
| Brake (Red) | | | | | | | | |

| TEST STEP | RESULT ▶ | ACTION TO TAKE |
|---|---|---|
| **E1** VERIFY PUMP MOTOR CONDITION | | |
| • With vehicle standing still:<br>• Check if pump motor runs with ignition switch in ON or OFF position. | Pump runs with ignition in OFF. ▶ | GO to Step **E2**. |
| | Pump runs with ignition in ON. ▶ | GO to Step **E3**. |
| **E2** CHECK PUMP MOTOR RELAY | | |
| • Remove pump motor relay.<br>• Check for continuity between Pin 30 and test pin on the relay. | Continuity ▶ | REPLACE pump motor relay. |
| | No Continuity ▶ | REVERIFY that pump motor runs with ignition OFF. |

**Fig. 126 Tests E1 & E2 (Warning sequence normal/ABS pump motor run continuously). Except 1991 Town Car**

**Anti-Lock Warning Indicator Sequence Normal — ABS Pump Motor Runs Continuously (Ignition On/Ignition Off)** — **Test E**

WARNING INDICATORS SEQUENCE

| Warning Indicators | Ignition On | Cranking Engine | Engine Running | Vehicle Moving | Braking with/without Anti-Lock | Vehicle Stopped | Engine Idle | Ignition Off |
|---|---|---|---|---|---|---|---|---|
| Check Anti-Lock (Amber) | | | | | | | | |
| Brake (Red) | | | | | | | | |

| TEST STEP | RESULT ▶ | ACTION TO TAKE |
|---|---|---|
| **E1** VERIFY PUMP MOTOR CONDITION | | |
| • With vehicle standing still:<br>• Check if pump motor runs with ignition switch in ON or OFF position. | Pump runs with ignition in OFF position. ▶ | GO to Step E2. |
| | Pump runs with ignition in ON position. ▶ | GO to Step E3. |
| **E2** CHECK PUMP MOTOR RELAY | | |
| • Remove pump motor relay.<br>• Check for continuity between Pin 30 and test pin on the relay. | Continuity ▶ | REPLACE pump motor relay. |
| | No Continuity ▶ | REVERIFY that pump motor runs with ignition in OFF position. |

**Fig. 127 Tests E1 & E2 (Warning sequence normal/ABS pump motor run continuously). 1991 Town Car**

**Anti-Lock Warning Lamp Sequence Normal — ABS Pump Motor Runs Continuously (Ignition On/Ignition Off)** — **Test E**

| TEST STEP | RESULT ▶ | ACTION TO TAKE |
|---|---|---|
| **E3** CHECK CIRCUIT 539 TO GROUND | | |
| • Disconnect 55-pin plug from electronic controller.<br>ELECTRONIC CONTROLLER<br>55 PIN CONNECTOR<br>• Connect EEC-IV Breakout Box, T83L-50-EEC-IV with Anti-Lock Test Adapter T90P-50-ALA or equivalent to the Anti-Lock 55-pin plug wiring harness.<br>ANTI-LOCK HARNESS ADAPTER T90P-50-ALA<br>55 PIN CONNECTOR<br>EEC-IV BREAKOUT BOX T83L-50-EEC-IV<br>• Check for continuity between breakout box Pins 15 and 60. | Continuity ▶ | GO to Step **E3a**. |
| | No Continuity ▶ | GO to Step E4. |

**Fig. 128 Test E3 (Warning sequence normal/ABS pump motor run continuously)**

**Anti-Lock Warning Lamp Sequence Normal — ABS Pump Motor Runs Continuously (Ignition On/Ignition Off)** — **Test E**

| TEST STEP | RESULT ▶ | ACTION TO TAKE |
|---|---|---|
| **E3a** CHECK CIRCUIT 539 | | |
| • Disconnect pump motor relay from wire harness.<br>• Check for continuity between breakout box Pins 15 and 60. | Continuity ▶ | SERVICE or REPLACE cable harness circuit. |
| | No Continuity ▶ | REPLACE pump motor relay. |
| **E4** CHECK CONTROLLER | | |
| • Reconnect pump motor relay and electronic controller.<br>• Turn ignition to ON. | Pump motor runs ▶ | REPLACE electronic controller. |
| | Pump motor does not run. ▶ | REVERIFY symptom. |

**Fig. 129 Tests E3a & E4 (Warning sequence normal/ABS pump motor run continuously)**

**Brake Warning Lamp On (With Anti-Lock Lamp Off, Parking Brake Released And Brake Lining Wear Checked)** — **Test F**

WARNING LIGHTS SEQUENCE

| Warning Lamps | Ignition On | Cranking Engine | Engine Running | Vehicle Moving | Braking with/without Anti-Lock | Vehicle Stopped | Engine Idle | Ignition Off |
|---|---|---|---|---|---|---|---|---|
| Check Anti-Lock (Amber) | | | | | | | | |
| Brake (Red) | | | | | | | | |

| TEST STEP | RESULT ▶ | ACTION TO TAKE |
|---|---|---|
| **F1** CHECK BRAKE FLUID LEVEL | | |
| • Check that brake fluid is no more than 4mm (0.16 in.) below MAX line located on side of master cylinder reservoir. | Low ▶ | CHECK system for external leaks. SERVICE as required. |
| | Normal ▶ | GO to Step F2. |
| **F2** CHECK FLUID LEVEL SWITCH | | |
| • Disconnect 3-pin plug on master cylinder fluid reservoir cap. | Continuity ▶ | REPLACE reservoir fluid cap. |
| • Check for continuity between Pins 1 and 3 on reservoir cap. | No Continuity ▶ | GO to Step F3. |



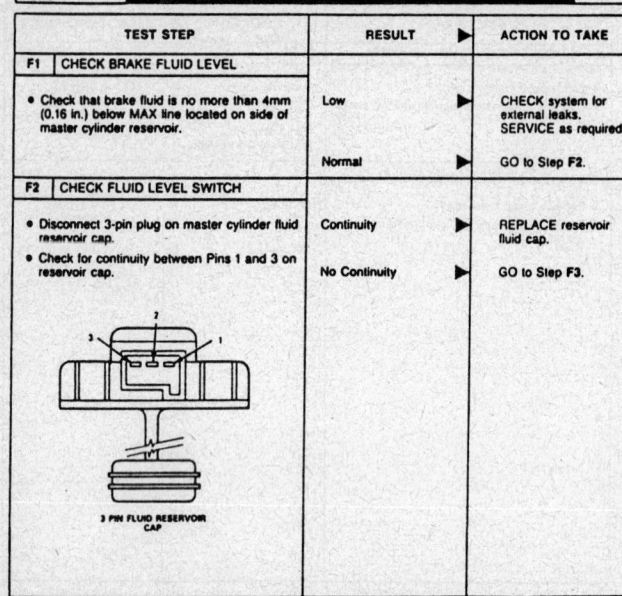

**Fig. 130 Tests F1 & F2 (Brake lamp ON w/ABS lamp OFF, parking brake released & lining wear checked). Except 1991 Town Car**

**Brake Warning Indicator On (With Anti-Lock Indicator Off, Parking Brake Released And Brake Lining Wear Checked)** — **Test F**

WARNING INDICATORS SEQUENCE

| Warning Indicators | Ignition On | Cranking Engine | Engine Running | Vehicle Moving | Braking with/without Anti-Lock | Vehicle Stopped | Engine Idle | Ignition Off |
|---|---|---|---|---|---|---|---|---|
| Check Anti-Lock (Amber) | | | | | | | | |
| Brake (Red) | | | | | | | | |

| TEST STEP | RESULT ▶ | ACTION TO TAKE |
|---|---|---|
| **F1** CHECK BRAKE FLUID LEVEL | | |
| • Check that brake fluid is no more than 4mm (0.16 in.) below MAX line located on side of master cylinder reservoir. | Low ▶ | CHECK system for external leaks. SERVICE as required. |
| | Normal ▶ | GO to Step F2. |
| **F2** CHECK FLUID LEVEL SWITCH | | |
| • Disconnect 3-pin plug on master cylinder fluid reservoir cap. | Continuity ▶ | REPLACE reservoir fluid cap. |
| • Check for continuity between Pins 1 and 3 on reservoir cap. | No Continuity ▶ | GO to Step F3. |



**Fig. 131 Tests F1 & F2 (Brake lamp ON w/ABS lamp OFF, parking brake released & lining wear checked). 1991 Town Car**

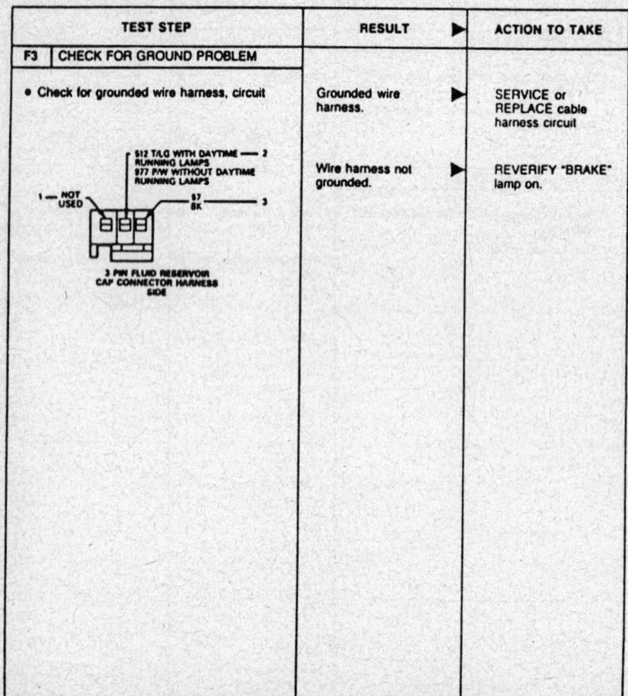

**Brake Warning Lamp On (With Anti-Lock Lamp Off, Parking Brake Released And Brake Lining Wear Checked)** — **Test F**

| TEST STEP | RESULT ▶ | ACTION TO TAKE |
|---|---|---|
| **F3** CHECK FOR GROUND PROBLEM | | |
| • Check for grounded wire harness, circuit | Grounded wire harness. ▶ | SERVICE or REPLACE cable harness circuit |
| | Wire harness not grounded. ▶ | REVERIFY "BRAKE" lamp on. |



**Fig. 132 Test F3 (Brake warning lamp ON w/anti-lock lamp OFF, parking brake released & lining wear checked)**

**No Anti-Lock Warning Lamp On When Ignition Switch Turned On** — **Test G**

WARNING LIGHTS SEQUENCE

| Warning Lamps | Ignition On | Cranking Engine | Engine Running | Vehicle Moving | Braking with/without Anti-Lock | Vehicle Stopped | Engine Idle | Ignition Off |
|---|---|---|---|---|---|---|---|---|
| Check Anti-Lock (Amber) | | | | | | | | |
| Brake (Red) | | | | | | | | |

| TEST STEP | RESULT ▶ | ACTION TO TAKE |
|---|---|---|
| **G1** CHECK IGNITION FEED AND FUSE | | |
| • Check for 12 volts to lamp socket with ignition ON. | 12 volts ▶ | GO to Step G2. |
| | No voltage ▶ | SERVICE ignition feed or fuse as required. |
| **G2** CHECK WARNING LAMP BULB | | |
| • Check warning lamp bulb | Bulb good ▶ | GO to Step G3. |
| | Bulb bad ▶ | REPLACE Bulb. |
| **G3** CHECK CIRCUIT 603 | | |
| • Check continuity between lamp socket and breakout box Pin 52 | No Continuity ▶ | SERVICE or REPLACE cable harness circuit |
| | Continuity ▶ | REVERIFY symptom. |

**Fig. 133 Tests G1, G2 & G3 (No warning lamp ON when ignition switch turned ON). 1990 Town Car**

| No Anti-Lock Warning Indicator On When Ignition Switch Turned On | Test G |
|---|---|

| Warning Indicators | Ignition On | Cranking Engine | Engine Running | Vehicle Moving | Braking with/without Anti-Lock | Vehicle Stopped | Engine Idle | Ignition Off |
|---|---|---|---|---|---|---|---|---|
| | WARNING INDICATORS SEQUENCE | | | | | | | |
| Check Anti-Lock (Amber) | | | | | | | | |
| Brake (Red) | | | | | | | | |

| TEST STEP | RESULT | ACTION TO TAKE |
|---|---|---|
| **G1 CHECK IGNITION FEED AND FUSE** | | |
| • Check for 12 volts to lamp socket with ignition ON. | 12V ▶ | GO to Step G2. |
| | No voltage ▶ | SERVICE ignition feed or fuse as required. |
| **G2 CHECK WARNING LAMP BULB** | | |
| • Check warning lamp bulb | Bulb good ▶ | GO to Step G3. |
| | Bulb bad ▶ | REPLACE Bulb. |
| **G3 CHECK CIRCUIT 603** | | |
| • Check continuity between lamp socket and breakout box Pin 52 | No Continuity ▶ | SERVICE or REPLACE cable harness Circuit 603. |
| | Continuity ▶ | GO to Step G4. |
| **G4 CHECK DIODE** | | |
| • Inspect diode for damage or loose or bad connection. | Diode good ▶ | REVERIFY symptom. |
| • Check if diode is installed backwards. | Diode damaged or installed backwards. ▶ | REPLACE diode. |

**Fig. 134 Tests G1, G2, G3 & G4 (No warning lamp ON when ignition switch turned ON). 1991 Town Car**

| No Anti-Lock Warning Lamp On When Ignition Switch Turned On | Test G |
|---|---|

| Warning Lamps | Ignition On | Cranking Engine | Engine Running | Vehicle Moving | Braking with/without Anti-Lock | Vehicle Stopped | Engine Idle | Ignition Off |
|---|---|---|---|---|---|---|---|---|
| | WARNING LIGHTS SEQUENCE | | | | | | | |
| Check Anti-Lock (Amber) | | | | | | | | |
| Brake (Red) | | | | | | | | |

| TEST STEP | RESULT | ACTION TO TAKE |
|---|---|---|
| **G1 CHECK IGNITION FEED AND FUSE** | | |
| • Check for 12 volts to lamp socket with ignition ON. | 12 volts ▶ | GO to Step G2. |
| | No voltage ▶ | SERVICE ignition feed or fuse as required. |
| **G2 CHECK WARNING LAMP BULB** | | |
| • Check warning lamp bulb. | Bulb good ▶ | GO to Step G3. |
| | Bulb bad ▶ | REPLACE Bulb. |
| **G3 CHECK CIRCUIT 606** | | |
| • Check continuity between lamp socket and breakout box Pin 52. | No Continuity ▶ | SERVICE or REPLACE cable harness Circuit 606, 606A or 606B (Taurus/Sable). Circuit 606, 606B or 606D (Taurus SHO). |
| | Continuity ▶ | REVERIFY symptom. |

**Fig. 135 Tests G1, G2 & G3 (No warning lamp ON when ignition switch turned ON). Sable, Taurus & 1990–91 Continental**

| Spongy Brake Pedal With/Without Anti-Lock Function (No Warning Lamp) | Test H |
|---|---|

| Warning Lamps | Ignition On | Cranking Engine | Engine Running | Vehicle Moving | Braking with/without Anti-Lock | Vehicle Stopped | Engine Idle | Ignition Off |
|---|---|---|---|---|---|---|---|---|
| | WARNING LIGHTS SEQUENCE | | | | | | | |
| Check Anti-Lock (Amber) | | | | | | | | |
| Brake (Red) | | | | | | | | |

| TEST STEP | RESULT | ACTION TO TAKE |
|---|---|---|
| **H1 CHECK COMPONENT MOUNTING** | | |
| • Check for proper brake pedal and booster/master cylinder attachment. | Pedal still spongy ▶ | GO to Step H2. |
| • Bleed brake system as outlined. | Pedal feels normal ▶ | Condition corrected. |
| **H2 BLEED BRAKE SYSTEM** | | |
| • Rebleed brake system. | Pedal still spongy ▶ | REPLACE master cylinder. |
| | Pedal feels normal ▶ | Condition corrected. |

**Fig. 136 Tests H1 & H2 (Spongy pedal with/without ABS function, no warning lamp). Except 1991 Town Car**

| Spongy Brake Pedal With/Without Anti-Lock Function (No Warning Indicator) | Test H |
|---|---|

| Warning Indicators | Ignition On | Cranking Engine | Engine Running | Vehicle Moving | Braking with/without Anti-Lock | Vehicle Stopped | Engine Idle | Ignition Off |
|---|---|---|---|---|---|---|---|---|
| | WARNING INDICATORS SEQUENCE | | | | | | | |
| Check Anti-Lock (Amber) | | | | | | | | |
| Brake (Red) | | | | | | | | |

| TEST STEP | RESULT | ACTION TO TAKE |
|---|---|---|
| **H1 CHECK COMPONENT MOUNTING** | | |
| • Check for proper brake pedal and booster/master cylinder attachment. | Pedal still spongy ▶ | GO to Step H2. |
| • Bleed brake system as outlined. | Pedal feels normal ▶ | Condition corrected. |
| **H2 BLEED BRAKE SYSTEM** | | |
| • Rebleed brake system. | Pedal still spongy ▶ | REPLACE master cylinder. |
| | Pedal feels normal ▶ | Condition corrected. |

**Fig. 137 Tests H1 & H2 (Spongy pedal with/without ABS function, no warning lamp). 1991 Town Car**

## Poor Vehicle Tracking During Anti-Lock Function (Warning Lamp Off) — Test J

WARNING LIGHTS SEQUENCE

| Warning Lamps | Ignition On | Cranking Engine | Engine Running | Vehicle Moving | Braking with/without Anti-Lock | Vehicle Stopped | Engine Idle | Ignition Off |
|---|---|---|---|---|---|---|---|---|
| Check Anti-Lock (Amber) | | | | | | | | |
| Brake (Red) | | | | | | | | |

| TEST STEP | RESULT ▶ | ACTION TO TAKE |
|---|---|---|
| **J1 VERIFY CONDITION** | | |
| • Verify condition exists as reported.<br>• Turn air suspension OFF if so equipped.<br>• Bleed brake system as outlined.<br>• Turn air suspension back ON when vehicle is off hoist. | Vehicle tracks properly. ▶<br><br>Vehicle still tracks poorly. ▶ | Condition corrected.<br><br>GO to Step J2. |
| **J2 CHECK ANTI-LOCK VALVE OPERATION** | | |
| • Turn air suspension OFF if so equipped.<br>• Turn ignition switch OFF.<br>• Disconnect 55-pin plug from electronic controller.<br><br>ELECTRONIC CONTROLLER<br>55 PIN CONNECTOR | | |

Fig. 138 Tests J1 & J2 (Poor vehicle tracking during ABS function). Except 1991 Town Car

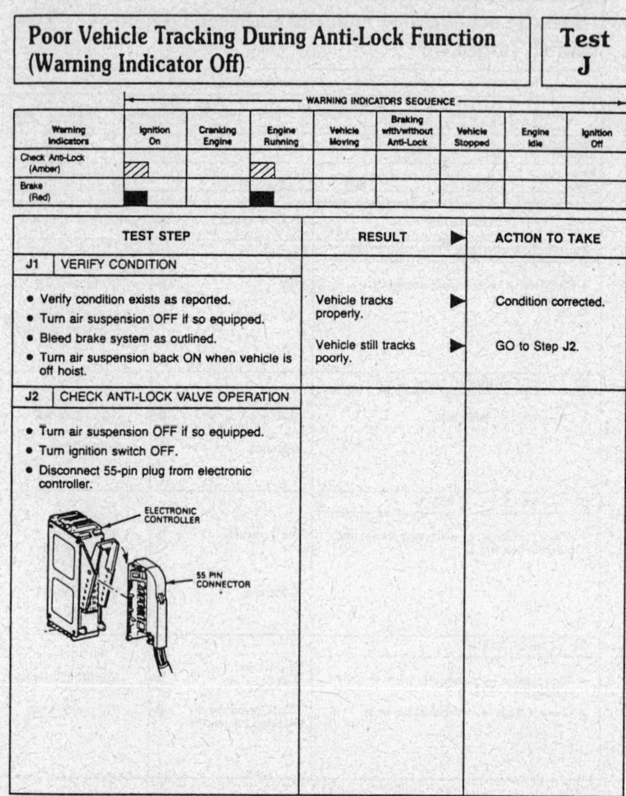

## Poor Vehicle Tracking During Anti-Lock Function (Warning Indicator Off) — Test J

WARNING INDICATORS SEQUENCE

| Warning Indicators | Ignition On | Cranking Engine | Engine Running | Vehicle Moving | Braking with/without Anti-Lock | Vehicle Stopped | Engine Idle | Ignition Off |
|---|---|---|---|---|---|---|---|---|
| Check Anti-Lock (Amber) | | | | | | | | |
| Brake (Red) | | | | | | | | |

| TEST STEP | RESULT ▶ | ACTION TO TAKE |
|---|---|---|
| **J1 VERIFY CONDITION** | | |
| • Verify condition exists as reported.<br>• Turn air suspension OFF if so equipped.<br>• Bleed brake system as outlined.<br>• Turn air suspension back ON when vehicle is off hoist. | Vehicle tracks properly. ▶<br><br>Vehicle still tracks poorly. ▶ | Condition corrected.<br><br>GO to Step J2. |
| **J2 CHECK ANTI-LOCK VALVE OPERATION** | | |
| • Turn air suspension OFF if so equipped.<br>• Turn ignition switch OFF.<br>• Disconnect 55-pin plug from electronic controller.<br><br>ELECTRONIC CONTROLLER<br>55 PIN CONNECTOR | | |

Fig. 139 Tests J1 & J2 (Poor vehicle tracking during ABS function). 1991 Town Car

## Poor Vehicle Tracking During Anti-Lock Function (Warning Lamp Off) — Test J

| TEST STEP | RESULT ▶ | ACTION TO TAKE |
|---|---|---|
| **J2 CHECK ANTI-LOCK VALVE OPERATION (Cont'd)** | | |
| • Connect EEC-IV Breakout Box, Tool T83L-50-EEC-IV with Anti-Lock test adapter, Tool T90P-50-ALA to the Anti-Lock 55-pin connector on wire harness.<br><br>ANTI-LOCK HARNESS ADAPTER T90P-50-ALA<br>55 PIN CONNECTOR<br>EEC-IV BREAKOUT BOX T83L-50-EEC-IV<br><br>• Lift vehicle and rotate wheels to assure they turn freely.<br>• Short Pins 20, 2 and 60 to each other at Breakout Box.<br>• Apply moderate brake pedal effort and check that LH front wheel will not turn.<br>• Check to see that LH front wheel turns freely when ignition switch is ON.<br>• Turn air suspension ON when vehicle is off hoist, if so equipped.<br>CAUTION: DO NOT LEAVE IGNITION ON FOR MORE THAN 1 MINUTE, OR VALVE DAMAGE MAY RESULT. | Wheel turns freely ▶<br><br>Wheel does not turn freely or pedal drops ▶ | TURN ignition switch OFF. DISCONNECT wire leads. GO to Step J3.<br><br>VERIFY correct wiring between 55-pin connector and 19-pin connector on valve block per wiring diagram.<br><br>If wiring is correct, REPLACE solenoid valve block. |

Fig. 140 Test J2 (Poor vehicle tracking during ABS function). Except 1991 Town Car

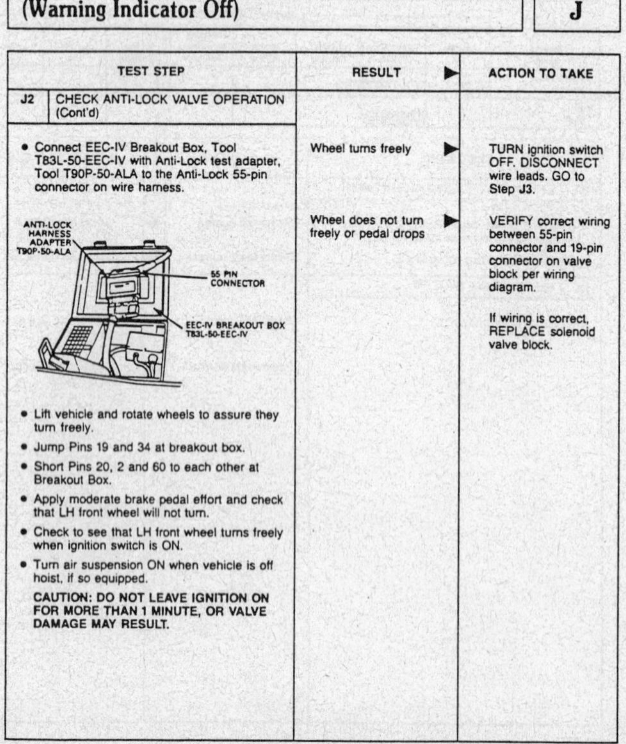

## Poor Vehicle Tracking During Anti-Lock Function (Warning Indicator Off) — Test J

| TEST STEP | RESULT ▶ | ACTION TO TAKE |
|---|---|---|
| **J2 CHECK ANTI-LOCK VALVE OPERATION (Cont'd)** | | |
| • Connect EEC-IV Breakout Box, Tool T83L-50-EEC-IV with Anti-Lock test adapter, Tool T90P-50-ALA to the Anti-Lock 55-pin connector on wire harness.<br><br>ANTI-LOCK HARNESS ADAPTER T90P-50-ALA<br>55 PIN CONNECTOR<br>EEC-IV BREAKOUT BOX T83L-50-EEC-IV<br><br>• Lift vehicle and rotate wheels to assure they turn freely.<br>• Jump Pins 19 and 34 at breakout box.<br>• Short Pins 20, 2 and 60 to each other at Breakout Box.<br>• Apply moderate brake pedal effort and check that LH front wheel will not turn.<br>• Check to see that LH front wheel turns freely when ignition switch is ON.<br>• Turn air suspension ON when vehicle is off hoist, if so equipped.<br>CAUTION: DO NOT LEAVE IGNITION ON FOR MORE THAN 1 MINUTE, OR VALVE DAMAGE MAY RESULT. | Wheel turns freely ▶<br><br>Wheel does not turn freely or pedal drops ▶ | TURN ignition switch OFF. DISCONNECT wire leads. GO to Step J3.<br><br>VERIFY correct wiring between 55-pin connector and 19-pin connector on valve block per wiring diagram.<br><br>If wiring is correct, REPLACE solenoid valve block. |

Fig. 141 Test J2 (Poor vehicle tracking during ABS function). 1991 Town Car

Poor Vehicle Tracking During Anti-Lock Function (Warning Lamp Off) — Test J

| TEST STEP | RESULT ▶ | ACTION TO TAKE |
|---|---|---|
| **J3 CHECK ANTI-LOCK OPERATION RH FRONT WHEEL** | | |
| • Short Pins 38, 21 and 60 to each other at breakout box.<br>• Apply moderate brake pedal effort. Check that RH front wheel will not turn with ignition OFF.<br>• Check that RH front wheel turns freely with ignition ON.<br>CAUTION: DO NOT LEAVE IGNITION ON FOR MORE THAN 1 MINUTE OR VALVE DAMAGE MAY RESULT. | Wheel turns freely ▶ | TURN ignition switch off. DISCONNECT wire leads. GO to Step J4. |
| | Wheel does not turn freely or pedal drops ▶ | VERIFY correct wiring between 55-pin connector and 19-pin connector on valve block per wiring diagram.<br>If wiring is correct, REPLACE solenoid valve block. |
| **J4 CHECK ANTI-LOCK OPERATION RH REAR WHEEL** | | |
| • Short Pins 55, 18 and 60 to each other at breakout box.<br>• Apply moderate brake pedal effort. Check that RH rear wheel will not turn with ignition OFF.<br>• Check that RH rear wheel turns freely with ignition ON.<br>CAUTION: DO NOT LEAVE IGNITION ON FOR MORE THAN 1 MINUTE OR VALVE DAMAGE MAY RESULT. | Wheel turns freely ▶ | TURN ignition switch off. DISCONNECT wire leads. GO to Step J5. |
| | Wheel does not turn freely or pedal drops ▶ | VERIFY correct wiring between 55-pin connector and 19-pin connector on valve block per wiring diagram.<br>If wiring is correct, REPLACE solenoid valve block. |

**Fig. 142 Tests J3 & J4 (Poor vehicle tracking during ABS function). 1990–91 Continental, 1990 Sable, Taurus & Town Car**

Poor Vehicle Tracking During Anti-Lock Function (Warning Indicator Off) — Test J

| TEST STEP | RESULT ▶ | ACTION TO TAKE |
|---|---|---|
| **J3 CHECK ANTI-LOCK OPERATION RH FRONT WHEEL** | | |
| • Jump Pins 19 and 34 at breakout box.<br>• Short Pins 38, 21 and 60 to each other at breakout box.<br>• Apply moderate brake pedal effort. Check that RH front wheel will not turn with ignition OFF.<br>• Check that RH front wheel turns freely with ignition ON.<br>CAUTION: DO NOT LEAVE IGNITION ON FOR MORE THAN 1 MINUTE OR VALVE DAMAGE MAY RESULT. | Wheel turns freely ▶ | TURN ignition switch off. DISCONNECT wire leads. GO to Step J4. |
| | Wheel does not turn freely or pedal drops ▶ | VERIFY correct wiring between 55-pin connector and 19-pin connector on valve block per wiring diagram.<br>If wiring is correct, REPLACE solenoid valve block. |
| **J4 CHECK ANTI-LOCK OPERATION RH REAR WHEEL** | | |
| • Jump Pins 19 and 34 at breakout box.<br>• Short Pins 55, 18 and 60 to each other at breakout box.<br>• Apply moderate brake pedal effort. Check that RH rear wheel will not turn with ignition OFF.<br>• Check that RH rear wheel turns freely with ignition ON.<br>CAUTION: DO NOT LEAVE IGNITION ON FOR MORE THAN 1 MINUTE OR VALVE DAMAGE MAY RESULT. | Wheel turns freely ▶ | TURN ignition switch off. DISCONNECT wire leads. GO to Step J5. |
| | Wheel does not turn freely or pedal drops ▶ | VERIFY correct wiring between 55-pin connector and 19-pin connector on valve block per wiring diagram.<br>If wiring is correct, REPLACE solenoid valve block. |

**Fig. 143 Tests J3 & J4 (Poor vehicle tracking during ABS function). 1991 Sable & Taurus**

Poor Vehicle Tracking During Anti-Lock Function (Warning Indicator Off) — Test J

| TEST STEP | RESULT ▶ | ACTION TO TAKE |
|---|---|---|
| **J3 CHECK ANTI-LOCK OPERATION RH FRONT WHEEL** | | |
| • Jump Pins 19 and 34 at breakout box.<br>• Short Pins 38, 21 and 60 to each other at breakout box.<br>• Apply moderate brake pedal effort. Check that RH front wheel will not turn with ignition OFF.<br>• Check that RH front wheel turns freely with ignition ON.<br>CAUTION: DO NOT LEAVE IGNITION ON FOR MORE THAN 1 MINUTE OR VALVE DAMAGE MAY RESULT. | Wheel turns freely ▶ | TURN ignition switch off. DISCONNECT wire leads. GO to Step J4. |
| | Wheel does not turn freely or pedal drops ▶ | VERIFY correct wiring between 55-pin connector and 19-pin connector on valve block per wiring diagram.<br>If wiring is correct, REPLACE solenoid valve block. |
| **J4 CHECK ANTI-LOCK OPERATION RH REAR WHEEL** | | |
| • Jump Pins 19 and 34 at breakout box.<br>• Short Pins 55, 18 and 60 to each other at breakout box.<br>• Apply moderate brake pedal effort. Check that RH rear wheel will not turn with ignition OFF.<br>• Check that RH rear wheel turns freely with ignition ON.<br>CAUTION: DO NOT LEAVE IGNITION ON FOR MORE THAN 1 MINUTE OR VALVE DAMAGE MAY RESULT. | Wheel turns freely ▶ | TURN ignition switch off. DISCONNECT wire leads. GO to Step J5. |
| | Wheel does not turn freely or pedal drops ▶ | VERIFY correct wiring between 55-pin connector and 19-pin connector on valve block per wiring diagram.<br>If wiring is correct, REPLACE solenoid valve block. |

**Fig. 144 Tests J3 & J4 (Poor vehicle tracking during ABS function). 1991 Town Car**

Poor Vehicle Tracking During Anti-Lock Function (Warning Lamp Off) — Test J

| TEST STEP | RESULT ▶ | ACTION TO TAKE |
|---|---|---|
| **J5 CHECK ANTI-LOCK OPERATION LH REAR WHEEL** | | |
| • Short Pins 36, 54 and 60 to each other at breakout box.<br>• Apply moderate brake pedal effort. Check that LH rear wheel will not turn with ignition OFF.<br>• Check that LH rear wheel turns freely with ignition ON.<br>CAUTION: DO NOT LEAVE IGNITION ON FOR MORE THAN 1 MINUTE OR VALVE DAMAGE MAY RESULT. | Wheel turns freely ▶ | TURN ignition switch off. DISCONNECT wire leads and Breakout Box. LOWER vehicle. REVERIFY symptom. |
| | Wheel does not turn freely or pedal drops ▶ | VERIFY correct wiring between 55-pin connector and 19-pin connector on valve block per wiring diagram.<br>If wiring is correct, REPLACE solenoid valve block. |

**Fig. 145 Test J5 (Poor vehicle tracking during ABS function). 1990–91 Continental, 1990 Sable, Taurus & Town Car**

## Poor Vehicle Tracking During Anti-Lock Function (Warning Indicator Off) — Test J

| TEST STEP | RESULT ▶ | ACTION TO TAKE |
|---|---|---|
| **J5** CHECK ANTI-LOCK OPERATION LH REAR WHEEL | | |
| • Jump Pins 19 and 34 at breakout box.<br>• Short Pins 36, 54 and 60 to each other at breakout box.<br>• Apply moderate brake pedal effort. Check that LH rear wheel will not turn with ignition OFF. | Wheel turns freely ▶ | TURN ignition switch off. DISCONNECT wire leads and Breakout Box. LOWER vehicle. REVERIFY symptom. |
| • Check that LH rear wheel turns freely with ignition ON.<br>CAUTION: DO NOT LEAVE IGNITION ON FOR MORE THAN 1 MINUTE OR VALVE DAMAGE MAY RESULT. | Wheel does not turn freely or pedal drops ▶ | VERIFY correct wiring between 55-pin connector and 19-pin connector on valve block per wiring diagram.<br>If wiring is correct, REPLACE solenoid valve block. |

**Fig. 146 Test J5 (Poor vehicle tracking during ABS function). 1991 Sable & Taurus**

## Poor Vehicle Tracking During Anti-Lock Function (Warning Indicator Off) — Test J

| TEST STEP | RESULT ▶ | ACTION TO TAKE |
|---|---|---|
| **J5** CHECK ANTI-LOCK OPERATION LH REAR WHEEL | | |
| • Jump Pins 19 and 34 at breakout box.<br>• Short Pins 36, 54 and 60 to each other at breakout box.<br>• Apply moderate brake pedal effort. Check that LH rear wheel will not turn with ignition OFF. | Wheel turns freely ▶ | TURN ignition switch off. DISCONNECT wire leads and Breakout Box. LOWER vehicle. REVERIFY symptom. |
| • Check that LH rear wheel turns freely with ignition ON.<br>CAUTION: DO NOT LEAVE IGNITION ON FOR MORE THAN 1 MINUTE OR VALVE DAMAGE MAY RESULT. | Wheel does not turn freely or pedal drops ▶ | VERIFY correct wiring between 55-pin connector and 19-pin connector on valve block per wiring diagram.<br>If wiring is correct, REPLACE solenoid valve block. |

**Fig. 147 Test J5 (Poor vehicle tracking during ABS function). 1991 Town Car**

## Anti-Lock Warning Indicator Sequence Normal — False Cycling of Traction Assist — Test K

| TEST STEP | RESULT ▶ | ACTION TO TAKE |
|---|---|---|
| **K1** VERIFY CONDITION — ONE SIDE OR BOTH SIDES | | |
| • Traction assist inoperative: | Both rear wheels ▶ | GO to Step K2. |
| | One rear wheel only ▶ | GO to Step K4. |
| **K2** CHECK BRAKELAMP SWITCH | | |
| • Connect EEC-IV Breakout Box T831-50-EEC-IV with Anti-Lock test adapter, Tool T90P-50-ALA to the Anti-Lock 55-pin connector on the wire harness.<br>• Turn ignition switch to ON position.<br>• Measure voltage between breakout box Pins 32 and 60.<br>• **NOTE: DO NOT apply brake pedal while performing this test.** | No voltage ▶<br>12V ▶ | GO to Step K3.<br>REPLACE brakelamp switch or SERVICE cable harness Circuit 511. |
| **K3** CHECK PRESSURE SWITCH AND CIRCUITRY | | |
| • Check continuity between breakout box Pins 13 and 26. | Continuity ▶ | VERIFY Symptom. |
| | No Continuity ▶ | GO to Step K3a. |
| **K3a** CHECK PRESSURE SWITCH | | |
| • Disconnect 19-pin valve body connector from harness.<br>• Check continuity between valve body Pins 11 and 12. | Continuity ▶ | SERVICE or REPLACE cable harness Circuit 535, 535c or 547. |
| | No Continuity ▶ | REPLACE valve body. |
| **K4** CHECK ABS FUNCTION | | |
| • Make an Anti-Lock stop on a slippery surface.<br>• Notice if brake pedal rises when pump comes on or if the pedal continues downward when pump comes on. | Brake pedal rises ▶<br>Brake pedal falls ▶ | REPLACE valve body.<br>REPLACE pump and motor. |

**Fig. 148 Tests K1, K2, K3, K3a & K4 (ABS indicator sequence normal, false cycling of traction assist). 1991 Town Car**

## Anti-Lock Warning Indicator Sequence Normal — False Cycling of Traction Assist — Test L

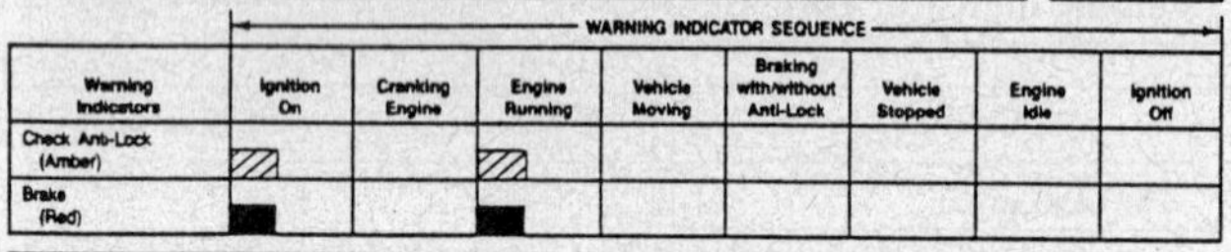

WARNING INDICATOR SEQUENCE

| Warning Indicators | Ignition On | Cranking Engine | Engine Running | Vehicle Moving | Braking with/without Anti-Lock | Vehicle Stopped | Engine Idle | Ignition Off |
|---|---|---|---|---|---|---|---|---|
| Check Anti-Lock (Amber) | | | | | | | | |
| Brake (Red) | | | | | | | | |

| TEST STEP | RESULT ▶ | ACTION TO TAKE |
|---|---|---|
| **L1** RUN SELF-TEST | | |
| • Refer to On-Board-Self-Test to run Self-Test. | Sensor code received. ▶ | REPLACE sensor for code received. |
| | No codes in E-module ▶ | VERIFY that traction assist system is false cycling. |

**Fig. 149 Test L1 (ABS indicator sequence normal, false cycling of traction assist). 1991 Town Car**

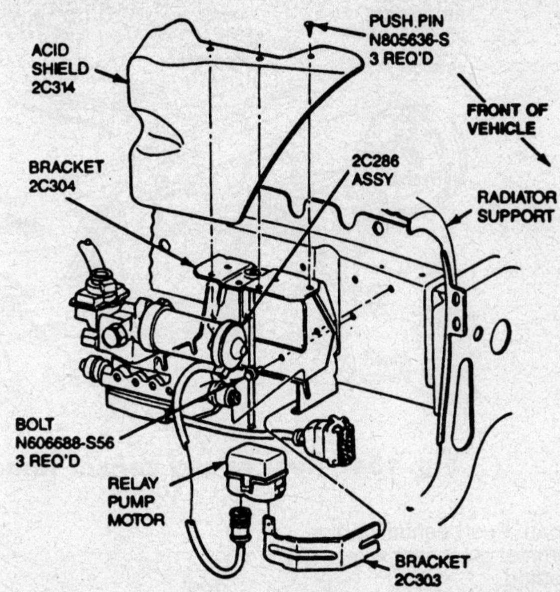


**Fig. 150 Hydraulic control unit replacement**

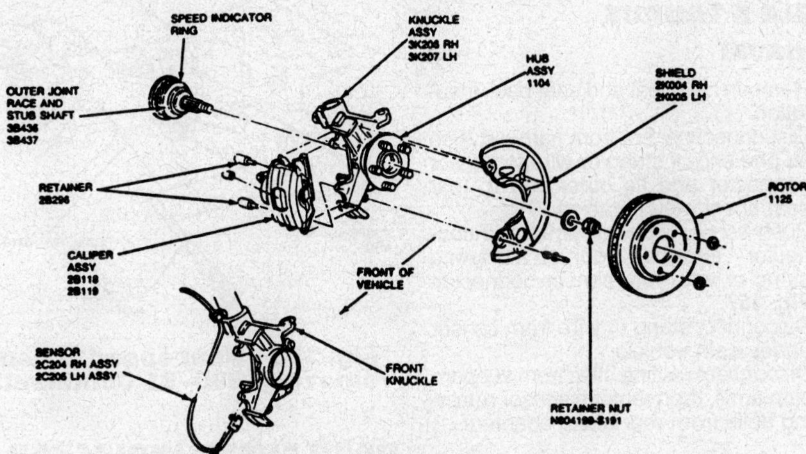


**Fig. 151 Front speed sensor removal. 1990–91 Continental**

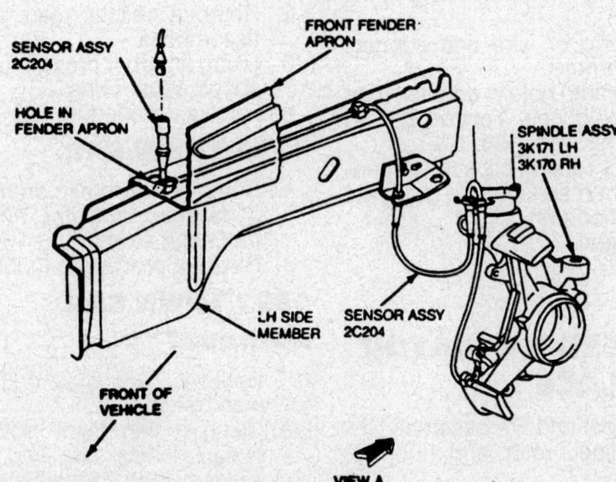


**Fig. 152 Front speed sensor removal. Sable & Taurus**

move plastic push studs and loosen front of splash shield, **Figs. 151 and 152.**

3. When removing left side sensor, remove plastic push studs and loosen rear of splash shield.
4. Thread sensor wire through holes in fender apron. On right front sensor, remove retaining clips behind splash shield.
5. Raise and support vehicle, then remove tire and wheel assembly.
6. Disconnect sensor wire grommets at height sensor bracket, and from retainer clip on shock strut.
7. Loosen screw securing sensor, then remove sensor assembly from front knuckle.
8. Reverse procedure to install. **Torque** sensor attaching screw to 40 inch lbs.

### Town Car

1. From inside engine compartment, disconnect sensor assembly two-pin connector from wiring harness.
2. When removing left sensor, remove steel routing clip attaching sensor wire to tube bundle, **Fig. 153.**
3. When removing right sensor, remove plastic routing clip attaching wire to frame.
4. Remove rubber coated steel spring clip holding sensor wire to frame.
5. Remove sensor attaching bolt from spindle, then slide sensor out of mounting hole.
6. Reverse procedure to install.

## REAR WHEEL SENSOR, REPLACE

### TOWN CAR

1. From inside luggage compartment, disconnect two-pin sensor connector from wiring harness pushing sensor wire through hole in floor.
2. From below vehicle, remove sensor wire from routing bracket located on top of rear axle carrier housing, **Fig. 154.**
3. Remove attaching screw from clip, holding sensor wire and brake tube bracket on axle.
4. **On 1990 models,** using a screwdriver, open split ring and remove sensor from bracket in rear brake backing plate.
5. Reverse procedure to install, noting the following:
   a. Ensure split ring is located in groove properly. Opening in ring should not line up with notch in tube shaped sensor retainer.
   b. Install sensor into bracket with notch correctly aligned with bracket. Push sensor until split ring locks sensor into place, **Fig. 155.**
6. **On 1991 models,** remove sensor to rear adapter retaining bolt, then remove sensor.
7. Reverse procedure to install, noting the following:
   a. **Torque** retaining bolt to 40-60 inch lbs.
   b. **Torque** sensor and brake tube to

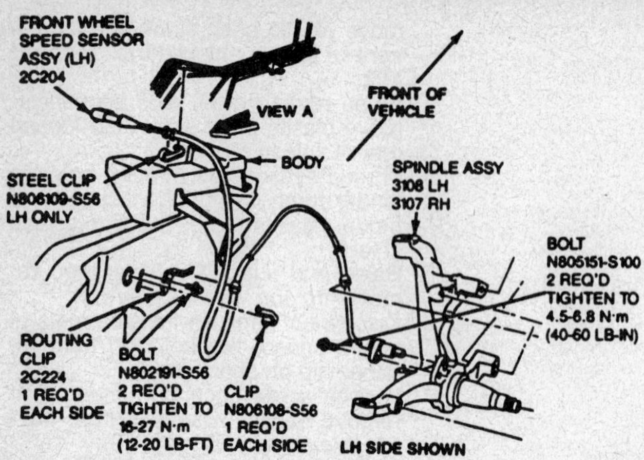


**Fig. 153 Front speed sensor removal. Town Car**

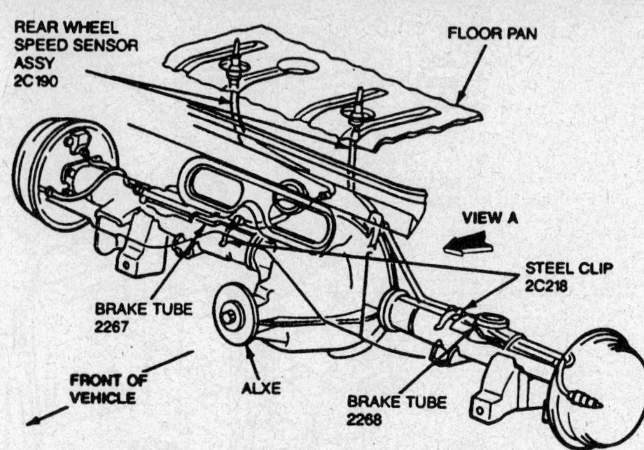


**Fig. 154 Rear speed sensor removal. Town Car**

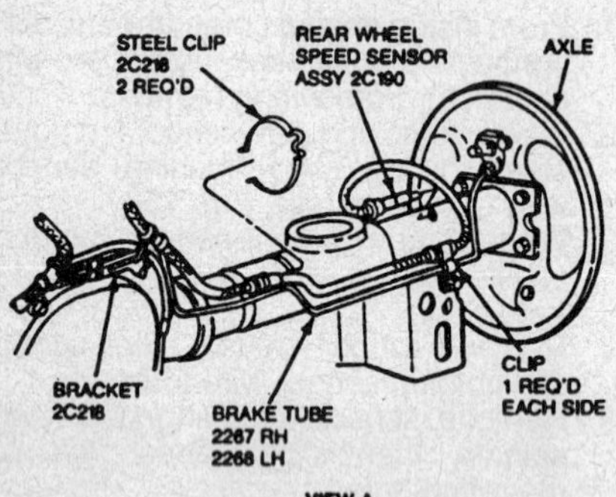


**Fig. 155 Rear speed sensor installation. Town Car**

bracket retaining screw to 40-60 inch lbs.

## 1990–91 CONTINENTAL

### Removal

1. Turn air suspension switch in luggage compartment to Off position.
2. Disconnect sensor connector in luggage compartment, then push rubber grommet through sheet metal floorpan.
3. Raise and support vehicle, then remove retaining clips for sensor wire and remove the wire from routing position.
4. Loosen sensor retaining screw at caliper anchor plate, then remove sensor.
5. Install spring replacement tool No. T88P-5310-A or equivalent on front suspension arm, then using 3/4 inch breaker bar, lower arm to provide clearance for sensor connector, **Fig. 156.**

### Installation

1. With suspension arm lowered, thread sensor wire connector through opening above arm.
2. Install front suspension arm, then align sensor with mounting holes on caliper anchor plate. **Torque** sensor retainer screw to 40-60 inch lbs.
3. Position sensor wire in routing position, then install retaining clips.
4. Thread sensor connector through hole in floorpan. Push center portion of rubber grommet on sensor wire until properly seated.
5. Connect electrical connector in luggage compartment and turn On air suspension switch.

## SABLE & TAURUS

### Removal

1. Remove rear seat and seat back insulation.
2. Disconnect sensor from harness, then tie one end of string or wire to sensor connector and tie other end to rear seat sheet metal bracket.
3. Push sensor wire grommet and connector through floorpan drawing string or wire with sensor connector, **Fig. 157.**
4. Disconnect string or wire from sensor underneath vehicle.
5. Disconnect routing clips from suspension arms, then remove sensor retaining bolts from rear brake adapters.

### Installation

1. Attach string or wire to new sensor connector, then pull sensor connector through hole in floorpan using string or wire.
2. Remove string or wire and connect sensor to harness.
3. Insert sensor into hole in adapter, then install retaining bolt. **Torque** bolt to 40-60 inch lbs, **Fig. 158.**
4. Install sensor routing clips to suspension arms, then sensor wire grommet into hole in floorpan.
5. Install rear seat.

## FRONT SPEED INDICATOR RING, REPLACE

1. Remove wheel and tire assembly.
2. Remove caliper, rotor and hub assemblies.
3. Using a three jaw puller, remove indicator ring from hub.
4. Reverse procedure to install.

**Fig. 156 Rear speed sensor removal. 1990–91 Continental**

## REAR SPEED INDICATOR RING, REPLACE

### EXCEPT TOWN CAR

1. Remove wheel and tire assembly.
2. Remove caliper, rotor and rear hub assemblies.
3. Using an arbor press, press hub out of speed sensor ring.
4. Reverse procedure to install.

### 1990 TOWN CAR

1. Remove rear brake drum.
2. Slide rear indicator ring off wheel mounting studs.
3. Reverse procedure to install.

### 1991 TOWN CAR

### Removal

1. Remove axle shaft and position on workbench.
2. Using a thin blade cold chisel between sensor ring and axle flange, strike evenly around flange, forcing indicator ring off of sensor ring journal. **Do not use a screwdriver or similar tool.** Extreme care must be taken not

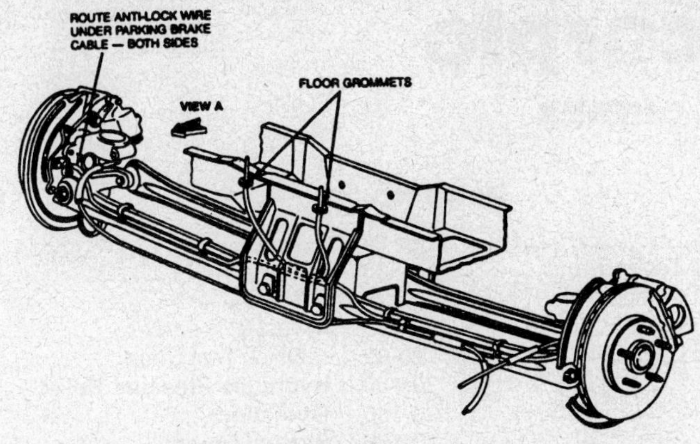


Fig. 157 Rear speed sensor removal. Sable & Taurus

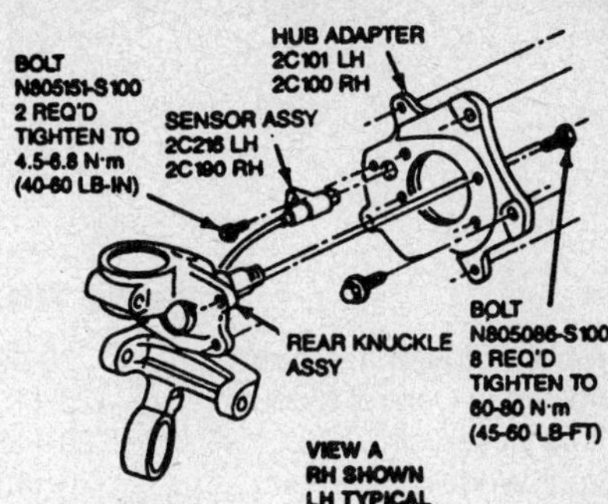


Fig. 158 Rear speed sensor installation. Sable & Taurus

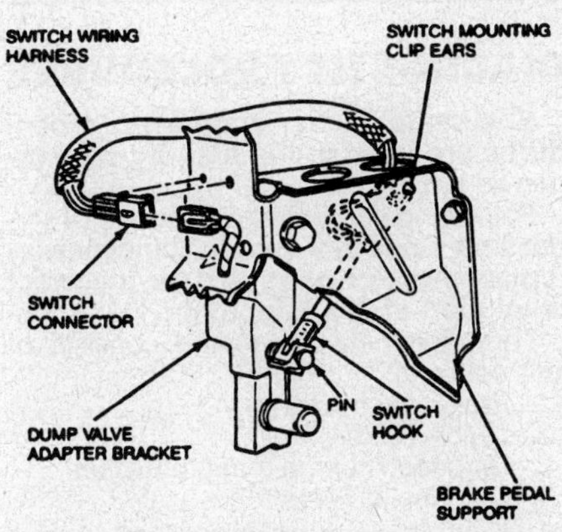


Fig. 159 Pedal travel switch replacement. Except Town Car

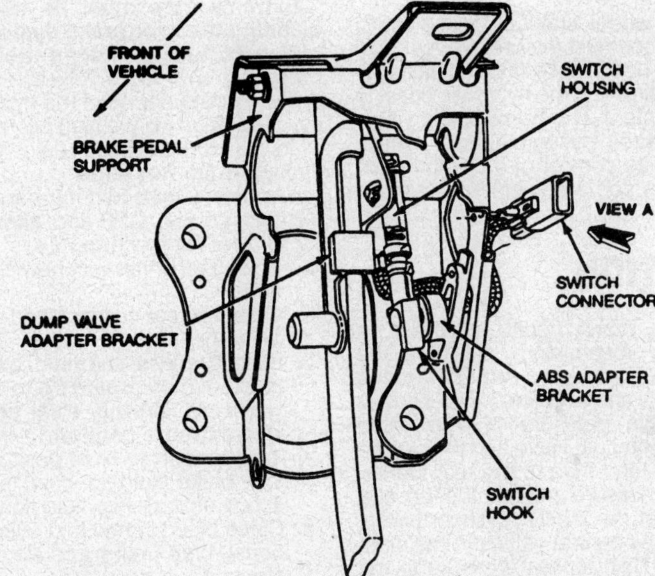


Fig. 160 Pedal travel switch replacement. Town Car

to scratch or nick wheel bearing and seal journal.

### Installation

1. Prior to installation of new ring, remove any burrs or nicks from journal.
2. Position indicator ring installation tool No. T89P-20202-A or equivalent, on press with pilot ring facing down.
3. Place new indicator ring over installation tool and insert axle shaft through tool.
4. Place spacer tool No. T85T-4616-AH or equivalent, over hub end of axle shaft.
5. Press axle shaft until it bottoms out on axle flange.
6. Install axle shaft on vehicle.

## PEDAL TRAVEL SWITCH, REPLACE

### Except Town Car

1. Disconnect battery ground cable, then the wiring harness lead at switch connector.
2. Using a screwdriver, pry connector locator from holes in brake pedal support.
3. Unsnap switch hook from pin on dump valve adapter bracket, **Fig. 159.**
4. Using needle nose pliers or equivalent, squeeze ears on switch mounting clip, then push clip through hole in brake pedal support.
5. Remove switch by feeding switch harness through hole of brake pedal support bracket.
6. Reverse procedure to install, noting the following:
   a. Rotate switch and ensure mounting clip ears are completely engaged.
   b. Adjust switch as outlined under "Pedal Travel Switch, Adjust."

### Town Car

1. Disconnect battery ground cable, then the wiring harness lead at switch connector.
2. Using a screwdriver, pry connector locator from holes in brake pedal support.
3. Unsnap switch hook from pin on ABS adapter bracket.
4. Hold brake pedal down to gain access, then using needle nose pliers, squeeze ears on switch mounting clip. Push clip through hole in dump valve adapter bracket, **Fig. 160.**
5. Remove rear attaching screw on ABS adapter bracket, then loosen second screw.
6. Rotate bracket, then remove switch and wire assembly.
7. Reverse procedure to install, noting the following:
   a. Rotate switch and ensure mounting clip ears are completely engaged.
   b. Adjust switch as outlined under in "Pedal Travel Switch, Adjust."

# Scorpio

## INDEX



## DESCRIPTION

The four wheel anti-lock brake (ABS) system is a compact integral power brake system that uses brake fluid for both the braking function and the hydraulic boost to the brake system. The brake system is divided into three system circuits. These system circuits consist of individual front brake circuits and a combined rear brake circuit.

## OPERATION

When the brake pedal is applied, a scissor-lever mechanism activates the control valve. Pressure, proportional to the pedal travel, then enters the booster chamber. This pressure is transmitted through the solenoid valve and the proportioning valve, and then to the rear brakes. The same pressure moves the booster piston against the master cylinder piston, shutting off the central valves in the master cylinder. This applies pressure to the front wheels through the two front solenoid valves.

The electronic control module monitors the electro-mechanical components of the system. Malfunction of the ABS system will cause the electronic control module to shut off or inhibit the ABS system. However, normal power-assisted braking will remain available. Malfunctions are indicated by one or two warning lamps inside the vehicle.

## SYSTEM BLEED

### FRONT

1. Top off reservoir with specified clean new brake fluid.
2. Open front LH caliper bleed screw one full turn.
3. Pump brake pedal to full travel and hold.
4. Close bleed screw and release brake pedal.
5. Repeat above steps until brake fluid flows air-free from bleed screw.
6. Check brake system for leaks.

### REAR

**Extreme care must be taken when bleeding the rear brake system, as the hydraulic fluid is under extremely high pressure.**

The running sound of the hydraulic motor will change from a high pitched buzz to a lower sound, once fluid has been through it. **Do not allow pump motor to run for more than two minutes, without turning ignition OFF and allowing motor to cool for ten minutes.**

1. Top off reservoir with new clean brake fluid.
2. Open LH rear caliper bleed screw one full turn.
3. Partially press and hold brake pedal. **System may create up to 378 psi of pressure during this procedure. Use extreme caution.**
4. Turn ignition to RUN position and allow brake fluid to flow from bleed screw until air free fluid flows.
5. Close bleed screw and release brake pedal. Wait until hydraulic pump has stopped.
6. Push brake pedal 1/2 way and hold.
7. Repeat procedure for RH rear caliper.
8. Top off reservoir with new clean brake fluid.
9. Check for correct operation of ABS warning lamps and check for leaks.

## DIAGNOSIS & TESTING

The ABS system is capable of self-diagnosis. When the ignition switch is placed in the RUN position, the electronic control module will perform a preliminary self check on the system. ABS electrical system condition is indicated by illumination of the instrument cluster mounted ANTI-LOCK lamp for up to four seconds.

In most malfunctions of the ABS system, the ANTI-LOCK and/or BRAKE lamps will be illuminated. The sequence of illumination of the warning lamps, combined with the problem symptoms, determine the appropriate diagnostic tests to perform. The diagnostic tests will then pinpoint the exact component in need of service.

## DIAGNOSTIC PROCEDURES

**Ensure following diagnostic procedures are used in the step-by-step order as indicated.**

**Following the wrong sequence or bypassing steps will lead to unnecessary replacement of parts and/or incorrect resolution of the symptom.**

This diagnostic procedure consists of four sections:

1. Pre-Test checks.
2. Quick Tests.
3. Diagnostic Lamp Symptom Chart.
4. Diagnostic Tests.

### Pre-Test Checks

1. Ensure parking brake is fully released, brake warning lamp switch is not grounded and battery has been checked.
2. Ensure contacts of 35-pin electronic control module harness connector are properly inserted and are not damaged.
3. Check 35 contacts of the electronic control module assembly. If there are any damaged contacts, replace electronic control module assembly.
4. Ensure all the following connectors or wires are connected/attached:
   a. Valve block unit 7-pin connector.
   b. Main valve 2-pin connector.
   c. Combined pressure warning switch 5-pin plug.
   d. Fluid reservoir cap 2-pin and 3-pin connector.
   e. Motor wire 2-pin connector.
   f. ABS electronic control module relay.
   g. ABS pump motor relay and power relay.
   h. Ground attachment on front of hydraulic booster assembly and ground attachment on passenger A-pillar near 35-pin control module plug.
   i. Ground attachment wire from hydraulic unit to fender sheet metal.
5. Check that all relays, diodes, fuses and fuse links are intact and/or properly inserted.
6. Check that all battery cable connections are clean and tight.

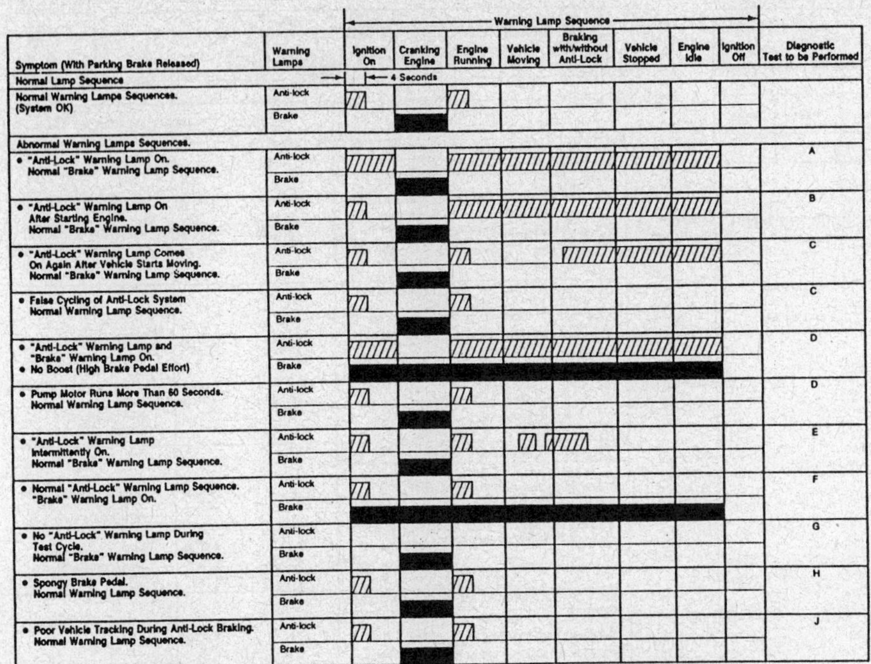


**Fig. 1 Diagnostic lamp symptom chart**

QUIK TEST

| Item To Be Tested | | Ignition Mode | Measure Between Pin Numbers | Meter Scale/ Range | Specification | Test Step |
|---|---|---|---|---|---|---|
| Battery Voltage | | Run | 40-2 | V DC | 10V Minimum | A1 |
| Main Relay Continuity | | Off | 40-3 | Ohms (1x) | Continuity | A2 |
| | | Off | 40-20 | Ohms (1x) | Continuity | A3 |
| Main Relay Resistance | | Off | 40-8 | Ohms (1x) | 50-100 Ohms | A6 |
| Main Relay Operation | | Run | 40-3① | V DC | 10V Minimum | A7 |
| | | Run | 40-20① | V DC | 10V Minimum | A3 |
| Wheel Sensor Resistance | RR | Off | 4-22 | Ohms (10x) | 800-1400 Ohms | A8 |
| | LF | Off | 5-23 | Ohms (10x) | 800-1400 Ohms | A9 |
| | LR | Off | 6-24 | Ohms (10x) | 800-1400 Ohms | A10 |
| | RF | Off | 7-25 | Ohms (10x) | 800-1400 Ohms | A11 |
| Wheel Sensor Voltage② | RR | Off | 4-22 | 2V AC | 0.15V Minimum | C5 |
| | LF | Off | 5-23 | 2V AC | 0.15V Minimum | C6 |
| | LR | Off | 6-24 | 2V AC | 0.15V Minimum | C7 |
| | RF | Off | 7-25 | 2V AC | 0.15V Minimum | C8 |
| Wheel Sensor Cable Shield | RR | Off | 40-4 | Ohms (1x) | Infinite | B1 |
| | LF | Off | 40-5 | Ohms (1x) | Infinite | B2 |
| | LR | Off | 40-6 | Ohms (1x) | Infinite | B3 |
| | RF | Off | 40-7 | Ohms (1x) | Infinite | B4 |
| Main Valve Resistance | | Off | 40-18 | Ohms (1x) | 2-5 Ohms | A12 |
| Inlet and Outlet Valve Continuity | | Off | 40-11 | Ohms (1x) | Continuity | A13 |
| | | Off | 11-15 | Ohms (1x) | 5-7 Ohms | A14 |
| | | Off | 11-17 | Ohms (1x) | 5-7 Ohms | A15 |
| | | Off | 11-35 | Ohms (1x) | 5-7 Ohms | A16 |
| | | Off | 11-33 | Ohms (1x) | 3-5 Ohms | A17 |
| | | Off | 11-16 | Ohms (1x) | 3-5 Ohms | A18 |
| | | Off | 11-34 | Ohms (1x) | 3-5 Ohms | A19 |
| Inlet and Outlet Valve Operation (Service Brakes Applied) | LF | Off | Jumper 2, 16, 35 | — | Wheel Locked | J2 |
| | | On | — | — | Wheel Rotates | |
| | RF | Off | Jumper 2, 15, 34 | — | Wheel Locked | J3 |
| | | On | . — | — | Wheel Rotates | |
| | Rear | Off | Jumper 2, 17, 33 | — | Wheels Locked | J4 |
| | | On | — | — | Wheels Rotate | |
| Fluid Level Indicator and Pressure Warning Switch Continuity③ | | Off | 9-10 | Ohms (1x) | Continuity | A4a |
| | | Off | 9-40 | Ohms (1x) | No Continuity | A4d |
| Fluid Level Indicator Operation③④ | | Off | 9-10 | Ohms (1x) | Continuity/ No Continuity | Replace Fluid Level Indicator |
| Pressure Warning Switch Operation | | Off | 9-10 | Ohms (1x) | No Continuity | A5d |

①Jumper Pins 2 and 8.
②Wheel off floor. Rotate wheel at one revolution per second.
③System charged.
④Remove reservoir cap. Move float between maximum and minimum positions.

**Fig. 2 Quick test chart**

7. Check the ground terminals of the electronic control module and the hydraulic unit.

### Quick Tests & Diagnostic Indicator Lamp Symptom Chart

The following tools and testing equipment is required to properly diagnosis the ABS system:

1. EEC-IV Breakout Box tool No. T83L-50-EEC-IV, Rotunda Breakout Box tool No. 014-00322 or equivalents.
2. ABS harness adapter tool No. T85P-50-ASA or equivalent.
3. Digital volt-ohm meter tool No. 007-00001 or equivalent.

All quick tests are performed in the passenger compartment using the EEC-IV breakout box and harness adapter. These tests lead to a specific diagnostic test that will in most cases, identify the malfunction. If the malfunction is not found by the quick test, use the diagnostic indicator lamp symptom chart, **Fig. 1,** to identify the proper diagnostic procedure.

Refer to the Quick Test chart, **Fig. 2,** and the related tests, **Figs. 3 through 11** as directed by chart.

## HYDRAULIC PRESSURE RELIEF

**Before replacing many components, it is mandatory that the hydraulic pressure be discharged from the system. The hydraulic accumulator contains brake fluid under extreme pressure.**

1. Turn ignition switch to OFF position.
2. Pump brake pedal a minimum of 20 times, until there is a noticeable increase in pedal force.

## COMPONENT REPLACEMENT

### HYDRAULIC UNIT

1. Discharge hydraulic pressure as described under "Hydraulic Pressure Relief."
2. Disconnect battery ground cable, then electrical connectors from following components:
   a. Reservoir cap.
   b. Main valve.
   c. Pressure switch.
   d. Valve block.
   e. Electric pump and ground connector.
3. Disconnect hydraulic lines from hydraulic unit valve body, one at a time. Immediately plug each line to prevent fluid loss.
4. Remove under-dash trim panel from around brake pedal.
5. Support hydraulic unit in engine compartment and remove brake pedal push rod clip from below instrument panel.
6. Lift hydraulic actuation unit from vehicle and drain reservoir. **Do not lift unit by hoses, reservoir or push rod.**
7. Remove and discard sealing gasket from hydraulic unit and dash panel.
8. Reverse procedure to install, noting the following:
   a. Do not force push rod from its natural position.
   b. **Torque** hydraulic unit mounting nuts to 30-37 ft. lbs.
   c. Bleed front and rear brakes and check for proper operation.

### HYDRAULIC ACCUMULATOR

1. Discharge hydraulic pressure as described under "Hydraulic Pressure Relief."

*Continued on page 20-113*

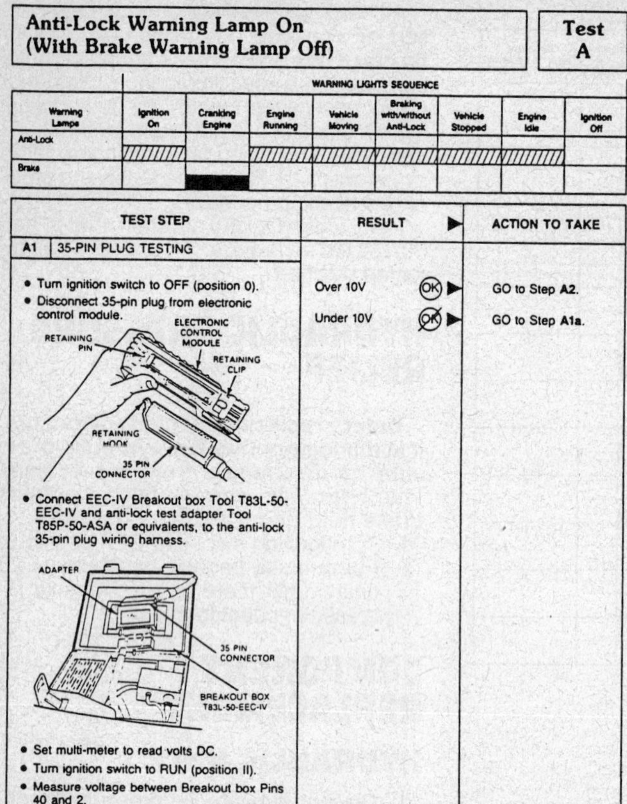

## Anti-Lock Warning Lamp On (With Brake Warning Lamp Off) — Test A

WARNING LIGHTS SEQUENCE

| Warning Lamps | Ignition On | Cranking Engine | Engine Running | Vehicle Moving | Braking with/without Anti-Lock | Vehicle Stopped | Engine Idle | Ignition Off |
|---|---|---|---|---|---|---|---|---|
| Anti-Lock | | | | | | | | |
| Brake | | | | | | | | |

| TEST STEP | RESULT ▶ | ACTION TO TAKE |
|---|---|---|
| **A1** 35-PIN PLUG TESTING | | |
| • Turn ignition switch to OFF (position 0).<br>• Disconnect 35-pin plug from electronic control module. | Over 10V (OK) ▶ | GO to Step **A2**. |
| | Under 10V (Not OK) ▶ | GO to Step **A1a**. |
| • Connect EEC-IV Breakout box Tool T83L-50-EEC-IV and anti-lock test adapter Tool T85P-50-ASA or equivalents, to the anti-lock 35-pin plug wiring harness.<br>• Set multi-meter to read volts DC.<br>• Turn ignition switch to RUN (position II).<br>• Measure voltage between Breakout box Pins 40 and 2. | | |



**Fig. 3 Test A, ABS lamp On (Part 1 of 25)**

## Anti-Lock Warning Lamp On (With Brake Warning Lamp Off) — Test A

| TEST STEP | RESULT ▶ | ACTION TO TAKE |
|---|---|---|
| **A1a** CHECK ELECTRONIC CONTROL MODULE TO GROUND WIRE | | |
| • Check: — fuse 22 to anti-lock warning lamp. — battery.<br>• Remove positive battery cable.<br>• Check continuity between Breakout box Pin 40 and body ground. | Continuity (OK) ▶ | Go to Step **A1b**. |
| | No continuity (Not OK) ▶ | SERVICE or REPLACE Circuit 31-49BR. |
| **A1b** CHECK IGNITION TO ELECTRONIC CONTROL MODULE WIRE | | |
| • Check continuity between Breakout box Pin 2 and ignition switch Circuit 75Y. | Continuity (OK) ▶ | RECONNECT positive battery cable. GO to **A1c**. |
| | No continuity (Not OK) ▶ | SERVICE or REPLACE cable Circuit 75Y. |
| **A1c** CHECK VOLTAGE CIRCUIT 75Y | | |
| • Turn ignition switch to RUN (position II).<br>• Set volt meter to 20V DC scale.<br>• Check for battery voltage at ignition switch Circuit 75Y (single connector). | (OK) ▶ | CONNECT electronic controller connector. REVERIFY symptom. |
| | (Not OK) ▶ | REPLACE ignition switch. CHECK system operation. |
| **A2** CHECK ELECTRONIC CONTROL RELAY | | |
| • Turn ignition switch to RUN (position II).<br>• Check for battery voltage between Breakout box Pins 40 and 2. | (OK) ▶ | GO to **A3**. |
| | (Not OK) ▶ | GO to **A2a**. |

**Fig. 3 Test A, ABS lamp On (Part 2 of 25)**

## Anti-Lock Warning Lamp On (With Brake Warning Lamp Off) — Test A

| TEST STEP | RESULT ▶ | ACTION TO TAKE |
|---|---|---|
| **A2a** CHECK ELECTRONIC CONTROL RELAY SECONDARY CIRCUIT | | |
| • Turn ignition switch to RUN (position II).<br>• Check for battery voltage at relay socket Pin 30. | (OK) ▶ | GO to **A2b**. |
| | (Not OK) ▶ | SERVICE open between relay and ignition switch. |
| **A2b** CHECK ELECTRONIC CONTROL RELAY SECONDARY CIRCUIT (CONTINUED) | | |
| • Turn ignition to OFF (position 0).<br>• Check continuity between relay socket Pin 87a and Breakout box Pin 2. | (OK) ▶ | REPLACE electronic control relay. |
| | (Not OK) ▶ | SERVICE open in circuit between relay and control module. |
| **A3** CHECK MAIN POWER RELAY SECONDARY CIRCUIT (NORMAL) | | |
| • Turn ignition switch to OFF (position 0).<br>• Check for continuity between Breakout box Pins 40 and 3. | Continuity (OK) ▶ | GO to **A4**. |
| | No continuity (Not OK) ▶ | GO to **A3a**. |
| **A3a** CHECK MAIN POWER RELAY SECONDARY CIRCUIT (NORMAL) | | |
| • Disconnect main power relay (green) from socket.<br>• Check for continuity between main power relay Pins 30 and 87A.<br><br>PIN NO. 30<br>PIN 87A | Continuity (OK) ▶ | Go to Step **A3b**. |
| | No continuity (Not OK) ▶ | REPLACE main power relay. |

**Fig. 3 Test A, ABS lamp On (Part 3 of 25)**

## Anti-Lock Warning Lamp On (With Brake Warning Lamp Off) — Test A

| TEST STEP | RESULT ▶ | ACTION TO TAKE |
|---|---|---|
| **A3b** CHECK MAIN POWER RELAY SECONDARY CIRCUIT WIRING HARNESS | | |
| • Disconnect positive battery cable.<br>• Check for continuity between main power relay socket Pin 30 and Breakout box Pin 3.<br><br>PIN NO. 30 | Continuity (OK) ▶ | GO to Step **A2c**. |
| | No continuity (Not OK) ▶ | SERVICE or REPLACE Circuit 32-13BL/GR. |
| **A3c** CHECK MAIN POWER RELAY SECONDARY CIRCUIT WIRING HARNESS | | |
| • Check for continuity between main power relay socket Pin 87A and body ground.<br><br>PIN NO. 87A | Continuity (OK) ▶ | CONNECT main power relay, electronic controller and battery cable. REVERIFY symptom. |
| | No continuity (Not OK) ▶ | SERVICE or REPLACE cable harness (Circuit 430M). |
| **A4** CHECK MAIN POWER RELAY SECONDARY CIRCUIT (NORMAL) | | |
| • Check for continuity between Breakout box Pins 40 and 20. | Continuity (OK) ▶ | GO to Step **A5**. |
| | No continuity (Not OK) ▶ | GO to Step **A4a**. |

**Fig. 3 Test A, ABS lamp On (Part 4 of 25)**

**Anti-Lock Warning Lamp On (With Brake Warning Lamp Off)** — **Test A**

| TEST STEP | RESULT ▶ | ACTION TO TAKE |
|---|---|---|
| **A4a** CHECK MAIN POWER RELAY SECONDARY CIRCUIT WIRING HARNESS | | |
| • Remove main power relay.<br>• Check for continuity between main power relay socket Pin 30 and Breakout box Pin 20.<br>PIN NO. 30 | Continuity OK ▶ | CONNECT main power relay and electronic controller. REVERIFY symptom. |
| | No continuity ~~OK~~ ▶ | SERVICE or REPLACE Circuit 32-13 BL/GR. |
| **A5** CHECK FLI AND PWS CIRCUIT | | |
| • Turn ignition switch to RUN (position II).<br>• Measure the resistance between Breakout box Pins 9 and 10. | Less than 5 ohms OK ▶ | GO to Step **A6**. |
| | Greater than 5 ohms ~~OK~~ ▶ | GO to Step **A5a**. |
| **A5a** CHECK FLI ANTI-LOCK WARNING CIRCUIT | | |
| • Disconnect 2-pin connector on reservoir FLI.<br>• Measure resistance between FLI socket Pins 1 and 2 (with brake fluid level at maximum mark on reservoir).<br>PIN NO. 2<br>PIN NO. 1<br>FLUID LEVEL INDICATOR | Less than 2 ohms OK ▶ | Go to Step **A5b**. |
| | Greater than 2 ohms ~~OK~~ ▶ | REPLACE FLI. |

**Fig. 3 Test A, ABS lamp On (Part 5 of 25)**

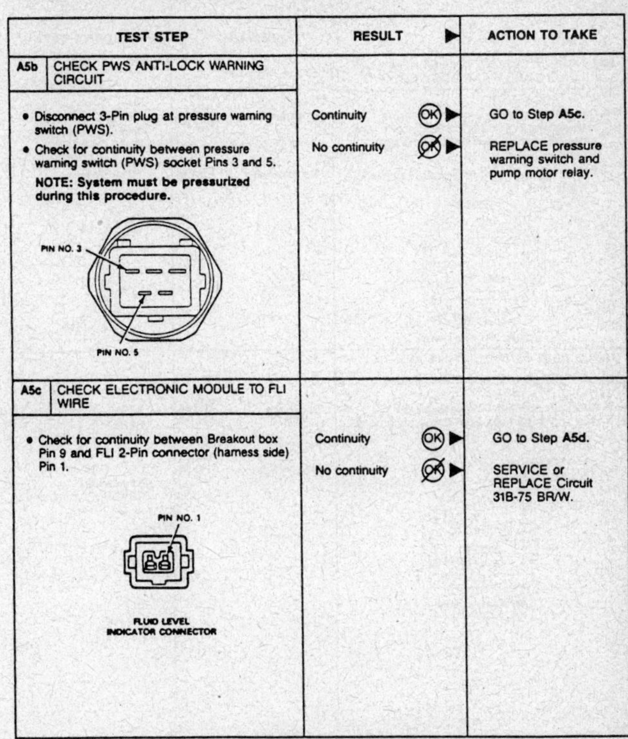

**Anti-Lock Warning Lamp On (With Brake Warning Lamp Off)** — **Test A**

| TEST STEP | RESULT ▶ | ACTION TO TAKE |
|---|---|---|
| **A5b** CHECK PWS ANTI-LOCK WARNING CIRCUIT | | |
| • Disconnect 3-Pin plug at pressure warning switch (PWS).<br>• Check for continuity between pressure warning switch (PWS) socket Pins 3 and 5.<br>**NOTE: System must be pressurized during this procedure.**<br>PIN NO. 3<br>PIN NO. 5 | Continuity OK ▶ | GO to Step **A5c**. |
| | No continuity ~~OK~~ ▶ | REPLACE pressure warning switch and pump motor relay. |
| **A5c** CHECK ELECTRONIC MODULE TO FLI WIRE | | |
| • Check for continuity between Breakout box Pin 9 and FLI 2-Pin connector (harness side) Pin 1.<br>PIN NO. 1<br>FLUID LEVEL INDICATOR CONNECTOR | Continuity OK ▶ | GO to Step **A5d**. |
| | No continuity ~~OK~~ ▶ | SERVICE or REPLACE Circuit 31B-75 BR/W. |

**Fig. 3 Test A, ABS lamp On (Part 6 of 25)**

**Anti-Lock Warning Lamp On (With Brake Warning Lamp Off)** — **Test A**

| TEST STEP | RESULT ▶ | ACTION TO TAKE |
|---|---|---|
| **A5d** CHECK FLI TO PWS WIRE | | |
| • Check for continuity between Pin 2 of 5-pin fluid level plug (harness side)<br>PIN NO. 2<br>FLUID LEVEL INDICATOR CONNECTOR<br>and 5-pin pressure warning switch plug (harness side) Pin 3.<br>PIN NO.3<br>PRESSURE WARNING SWITCH CONNECTOR | Continuity OK ▶ | GO to Step **A5e**. |
| | No continuity ~~OK~~ ▶ | SERVICE or REPLACE Circuit 31B-79 BR/W. |
| **A5e** CHECK ELECTRONIC MODULE TO PWS WIRE | | |
| • Check for continuity between PWS 5-pin pressure plug (harness side) Pin 5<br>PIN NO.5<br>PRESSURE WARNING SWITCH CONNECTOR<br>and Breakout box Pin 10. | Continuity OK ▶ | TURN ignition OFF. CONNECT all electrical connections. REVERIFY symptom. |
| | No continuity ~~OK~~ ▶ | SERVICE or REPLACE Circuit 31B-75 BR/GR. |
| **A6** ISOLATION TEST FLI AND PWS | | |
| • Check for continuity between Breakout box Pin 9 and body ground, and Pin 10 and ground. | Continuity OK ▶ | GO to Step **A6a**. |
| | No continuity ~~OK~~ ▶ | GO to Step **A7**. |

**Fig. 3 Test A, ABS lamp On (Part 7 of 25)**

**Anti-Lock Warning Lamp On (With Brake Warning Lamp Off)** — **Test A**

| TEST STEP | RESULT ▶ | ACTION TO TAKE |
|---|---|---|
| **A6a** CHECK FLI PIN NO. 1 AND NO. 2 | | |
| • Disconnect FLI 2-pin plug and check for continuity between FLI socket Pin 2 and body ground and Pin 1 and body ground.<br>**NOTE: Ensure that brake fluid is at max level.**<br>PIN NO. 1<br>PIN NO. 2 | Continuity ~~OK~~ ▶ | REPLACE FLI. |
| | No continuity OK ▶ | GO to Step **A6b**. |
| **A6b** CHECK FLI PIN NO. 1 | | |
| • Check for continuity between FLI plug Pin 1 (harness side) and body ground.<br>PIN NO. 1 | Continuity ~~OK~~ ▶ | SERVICE or REPLACE Circuit 31B-79 BR/W. |
| | No continuity OK ▶ | GO to Step **A6c**. |
| **A6c** CHECK FLI PIN NO. 2 | | |
| • Disconnect 5-pin plug from PWS. Check for continuity between FLI plug Pin 2 (harness side) and body ground.<br>PIN NO. 2 | Continuity ~~OK~~ ▶ | SERVICE or REPLACE Circuit 31B-79 BR/W. |
| | No continuity OK ▶ | GO to Step **A6d**. |

**Fig. 3 Test A, ABS lamp On (Part 8 of 25)**

## Anti-Lock Warning Lamp On (With Brake Warning Lamp Off) — Test A

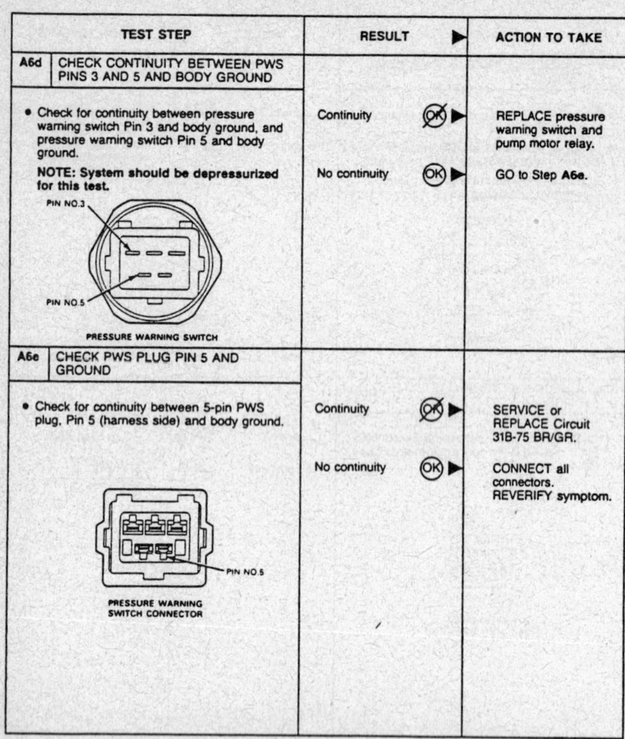

| TEST STEP | RESULT ▶ | ACTION TO TAKE |
|---|---|---|
| **A6d** CHECK CONTINUITY BETWEEN PWS PINS 3 AND 5 AND BODY GROUND | | |
| • Check for continuity between pressure warning switch Pin 3 and body ground, and pressure warning switch Pin 5 and body ground.<br>**NOTE: System should be depressurized for this test.**<br>(PIN NO.3, PIN NO.5, PRESSURE WARNING SWITCH) | Continuity ~~OK~~ ▶<br>No continuity OK ▶ | REPLACE pressure warning switch and pump motor relay.<br>GO to Step **A6e**. |
| **A6e** CHECK PWS PLUG PIN 5 AND GROUND | | |
| • Check for continuity between 5-pin PWS plug, Pin 5 (harness side) and body ground.<br>(PIN NO.5, PRESSURE WARNING SWITCH CONNECTOR) | Continuity ~~OK~~ ▶<br>No continuity OK ▶ | SERVICE or REPLACE Circuit 31B-75 BR/GR.<br>CONNECT all connectors. REVERIFY symptom. |

**Fig. 3 Test A, ABS lamp On (Part 9 of 25)**

## Anti-Lock Warning Lamp On (With Brake Warning Lamp Off) — Test A

| TEST STEP | RESULT ▶ | ACTION TO TAKE |
|---|---|---|
| **A7** CHECK MAIN POWER RELAY PRIMARY CIRCUIT RESISTANCE | | |
| • Turn ignition switch OFF.<br>• Measure resistance between Breakout box Pins 40 and 8 | Resistance between 50 and 100 ohms OK ▶<br>Any other reading ~~OK~~ ▶ | GO to Step **A8**.<br>Go to Step **A7a**. |
| **A7a** CHECK MAIN POWER RELAY PRIMARY COIL RESISTANCE | | |
| • Disconnect main power relay (green) from socket.<br>• Measure resistance between main power relay Pins 85 and 86.<br>(PIN NO. 86, PIN NO. 85, RELAY) | Resistance between 50 and 100 ohms OK ▶<br>Any other reading ~~OK~~ ▶ | GO to Step **A7b**.<br>REPLACE main power relay. |
| **A7b** CHECK MAIN POWER RELAY PRIMARY TO ELECTRONIC CONTROLLER WIRE | | |
| • Check continuity between main power relay connector Pin 86 and Breakout box Pin 8.<br>(PIN NO. 86, RELAY CONNECTOR) | Continuity OK ▶<br>No continuity ~~OK~~ ▶ | GO to Step **A7c**.<br>SERVICE or REPLACE Circuit 9-35 BL/GR. |

**Fig. 3 Test A, ABS lamp On (Part 10 of 25)**

## Anti-Lock Warning Lamp On (With Brake Warning Lamp Off) — Test A

| TEST STEP | RESULT ▶ | ACTION TO TAKE |
|---|---|---|
| **A7c** CHECK MAIN POWER RELAY PRIMARY TO GROUND WIRE | | |
| • Check continuity between main power relay connector Pin 85 and ground.<br>(PIN NO. 85, RELAY CONNECTOR) | Continuity OK ▶<br>No continuity ~~OK~~ ▶ | CONNECT all electrical connections REVERIFY symptom.<br>SERVICE or REPLACE Circuit 31-49 BR and/or 31-17 BR. |
| **A8** CHECK MAIN POWER RELAY SECONDARY (ACTIVATED) | | |
| • Place a jumper wire between Breakout box Pins 2 and 8.<br>• Set multi-meter to 20V scale.<br>• Turn ignition switch to RUN (position II).<br>• Measure voltage between Breakout box Pins 40 and 3. | Over 10 V DC OK ▶<br>Under 10 V DC ~~OK~~ ▶ | REMOVE jumper wire. GO to Step **A9**.<br>CHECK fuse 19. REMOVE jumper wire. GO to Step **A8a**. |
| **A8a** CHECK MAIN POWER RELAY SECONDARY CIRCUIT (ACTIVE) | | |
| • Turn ignition switch OFF (position 0).<br>• Disconnect main power relay from socket.<br>• Apply power (battery positive and ground) to main relay Pins 85 and 86.<br>• Check for continuity between main relay Pins 30 and 87.<br>(PIN NO 30, PIN NO. 87, PIN NO. 86, PIN NO. 85, RELAY) | Continuity OK ▶<br>No continuity ~~OK~~ ▶ | GO to Step **A8b**.<br>REPLACE main power relay. |

**Fig. 3 Test A, ABS lamp On (Part 11 of 25)**

## Anti-Lock Warning Lamp On (With Brake Warning Lamp Off) — Test A

| TEST STEP | RESULT ▶ | ACTION TO TAKE |
|---|---|---|
| **A8b** CHECK MAIN POWER RELAY SECONDARY CIRCUIT POWER WIRE | | |
| • Check continuity between main power relay socket Pin 87 and positive battery terminal.<br>(PIN NO. 87, RELAY CONNECTOR) | Continuity OK ▶<br>No continuity ~~OK~~ ▶ | CONNECT main power relay. REVERIFY symptom.<br>SERVICE or REPLACE Circuit 30-44R and/or fuse 27. |
| **A9** MEASURE RH REAR SENSOR CIRCUIT RESISTANCE | | |
| • Turn ignition switch to OFF (position 0).<br>• Measure resistance between Breakout box Pins 4 and 22. | 800 to 1400 ohms (0.8 to 1.4K ohms) OK ▶<br>Any other reading ~~OK~~ ▶ | GO to Step **A10**.<br>REPLACE damaged cable to sensor or REPLACE sensor. |
| **A10** MEASURE LH FRONT SENSOR CIRCUIT RESISTANCE | | |
| • Measure resistance between Breakout box Pins 5 and 23. | 800 to 1400 ohms (0.8 to 1.4K ohms) OK ▶<br>Any other reading ~~OK~~ ▶ | GO to Step **A11**.<br>REPLACE damaged cable to sensor or REPLACE sensor. |

**Fig. 3 Test A, ABS lamp On (Part 12 of 25)**

**Anti-Lock Warning Lamp On (With Brake Warning Lamp Off)** — **Test A**

| TEST STEP | RESULT ▶ | ACTION TO TAKE |
|---|---|---|
| **A11** MEASURE LH REAR SENSOR CIRCUIT RESISTANCE | | |
| • Measure resistance between Breakout box Pins 6 and 24. | 800 to 1400 ohms (0.8 to 1.4K ohms OK ▶ | GO to Step **A12**. |
| | Any other reading ~~OK~~ ▶ | REPLACE damaged cable to sensor or REPLACE sensor. |
| **A12** MEASURE RH FRONT SENSOR CIRCUIT RESISTANCE | | |
| • Measure resistance between Breakout box Pins 7 and 25. | 800 to 1400 ohms (0.8 to 1.4K ohms) OK ▶ | GO to Step **A13**. |
| | Any other reading ~~OK~~ ▶ | REPLACE damaged cable to sensor or REPLACE sensor. |
| **A13** MEASURE MAIN VALVE CIRCUIT RESISTANCE | | |
| • Turn ignition switch to OFF (position 0).<br>• Measure the resistance between Breakout box Pins 11 and 18. | 2 to 5 ohms OK ▶ | GO to Step **A14**. |
| | Any other reading ~~OK~~ ▶ | GO to Step **A13a**. |
| **A13a** MEASURE MAIN VALVE RESISTANCE | | |
| • Disconnect main valve 2-pin connector.<br>• Measure resistance between the main valve Pins 1 and 2.<br>PIN NO.2 PIN NO.1 | 2 to 5 ohms OK ▶ | REPLACE or SERVICE Circuit 31-17 BR or 9-34 BL/W. |
| | Any other reading ~~OK~~ ▶ | REPLACE actuation assembly. |
| **A14** CHECK VALVE BODY GROUND CIRCUIT | | |
| • Measure resistance between Breakout box Pins 11 and 40. | Less than 2 ohms OK ▶ | Go to Step **A15**. |
| | Greater than 2 ohms ~~OK~~ ▶ | Go to Step **A14a**. |

**Fig. 3 Test A, ABS lamp On (Part 13 of 25)**

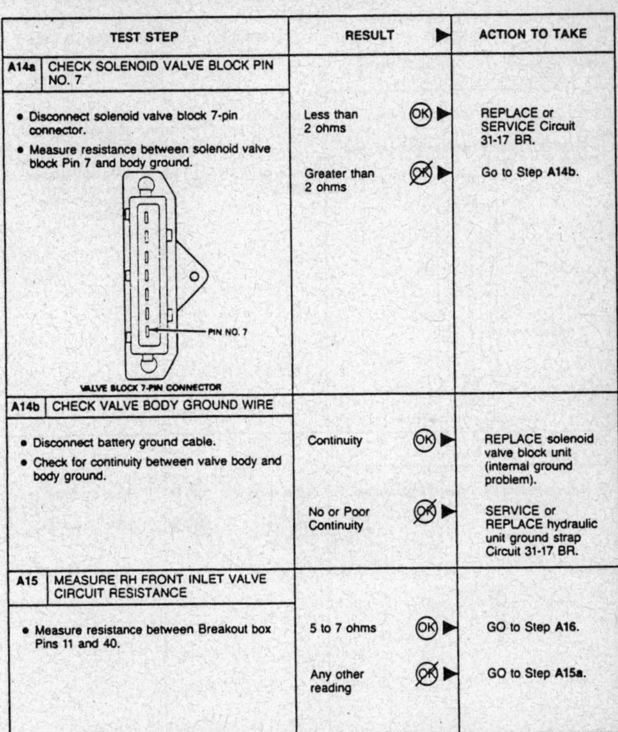

**Anti-Lock Warning Lamp On (With Brake Warning Lamp Off)** — **Test A**

| TEST STEP | RESULT ▶ | ACTION TO TAKE |
|---|---|---|
| **A14a** CHECK SOLENOID VALVE BLOCK PIN NO. 7 | | |
| • Disconnect solenoid valve block 7-pin connector.<br>• Measure resistance between solenoid valve block Pin 7 and body ground.<br>PIN NO. 7<br>VALVE BLOCK 7-PIN CONNECTOR | Less than 2 ohms OK ▶ | REPLACE or SERVICE Circuit 31-17 BR. |
| | Greater than 2 ohms ~~OK~~ ▶ | Go to Step **A14b**. |
| **A14b** CHECK VALVE BODY GROUND WIRE | | |
| • Disconnect battery ground cable.<br>• Check for continuity between valve body and body ground. | Continuity OK ▶ | REPLACE solenoid valve block unit (internal ground problem). |
| | No or Poor Continuity ~~OK~~ ▶ | SERVICE or REPLACE hydraulic unit ground strap Circuit 31-17 BR. |
| **A15** MEASURE RH FRONT INLET VALVE CIRCUIT RESISTANCE | | |
| • Measure resistance between Breakout box Pins 11 and 40. | 5 to 7 ohms OK ▶ | GO to Step **A16**. |
| | Any other reading ~~OK~~ ▶ | GO to Step **A15a**. |

**Fig. 3 Test A, ABS lamp On (Part 14 of 25)**

**Anti-Lock Warning Lamp On (With Brake Warning Lamp Off)** — **Test A**

| TEST STEP | RESULT ▶ | ACTION TO TAKE |
|---|---|---|
| **A15a** MEASURE RH FRONT INLET VALVE RESISTANCE | | |
| • Disconnect solenoid valve block 7-pin connector.<br>• Measure resistance between solenoid valve block Pins 7 and 1.<br>PIN NO. 1<br>PIN NO. 7<br>VALVE BLOCK 7-PIN CONNECTOR | 5 to 7 ohms OK ▶ | REPLACE or SERVICE Circuit 9-28 BL/W. |
| | Any other reading ~~OK~~ ▶ | REPLACE solenoid valve block unit. CONNECT 7-Pin connector. |
| **A16** MEASURE REAR INLET VALVE CIRCUIT RESISTANCE | | |
| • Measure resistance between Breakout box Pins 11 and 15. | 5 to 7 ohms OK ▶ | GO to Step **A17**. |
| | Any other reading ~~OK~~ ▶ | GO to Step **A16a**. |

**Fig. 3 Test A, ABS lamp On (Part 15 of 25)**

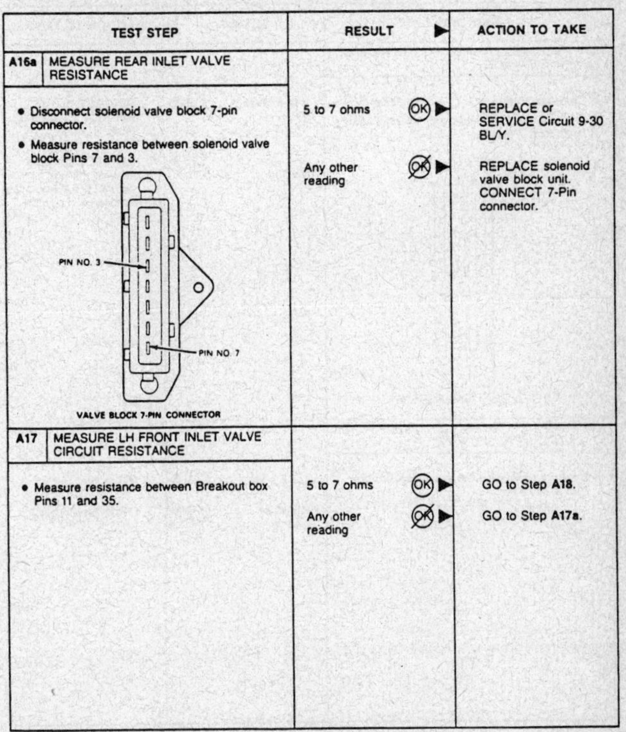

**Anti-Lock Warning Lamp On (With Brake Warning Lamp Off)** — **Test A**

| TEST STEP | RESULT ▶ | ACTION TO TAKE |
|---|---|---|
| **A16a** MEASURE REAR INLET VALVE RESISTANCE | | |
| • Disconnect solenoid valve block 7-pin connector.<br>• Measure resistance between solenoid valve block Pins 7 and 3.<br>PIN NO. 3<br>PIN NO. 7<br>VALVE BLOCK 7-PIN CONNECTOR | 5 to 7 ohms OK ▶ | REPLACE or SERVICE Circuit 9-30 BL/Y. |
| | Any other reading ~~OK~~ ▶ | REPLACE solenoid valve block unit. CONNECT 7-Pin connector. |
| **A17** MEASURE LH FRONT INLET VALVE CIRCUIT RESISTANCE | | |
| • Measure resistance between Breakout box Pins 11 and 35. | 5 to 7 ohms OK ▶ | GO to Step **A18**. |
| | Any other reading ~~OK~~ ▶ | GO to Step **A17a**. |

**Fig. 3 Test A, ABS lamp On (Part 16 of 25)**

## Anti-Lock Warning Lamp On (With Brake Warning Lamp Off) — Test A

| TEST STEP | RESULT ▶ | ACTION TO TAKE |
|---|---|---|
| **A17a** MEASURE LH FRONT INLET VALVE RESISTANCE | | |
| • Disconnect solenoid valve block 7-pin connector.<br>• Measure resistance between solenoid valve block Pins 7 and 6.<br>PIN NO. 6<br>PIN NO. 7<br>VALVE BLOCK 7-PIN CONNECTOR | 5 to 7 ohms OK ▶ | REPLACE or SERVICE Circuit 9-33 BL/BK. |
| | Any other reading ~~OK~~ ▶ | REPLACE solenoid valve block unit. CONNECT 7-Pin connector. |
| **A18** MEASURE REAR OUTLET VALVE CIRCUIT RESISTANCE | | |
| • Measure resistance between Breakout box Pins 11 and 33. | 3 to 5 ohms OK ▶ | GO to Step **A19**. |
| | Any other reading ~~OK~~ ▶ | GO to Step **A18a**. |

**Fig. 3 Test A, ABS lamp On (Part 17 of 25)**

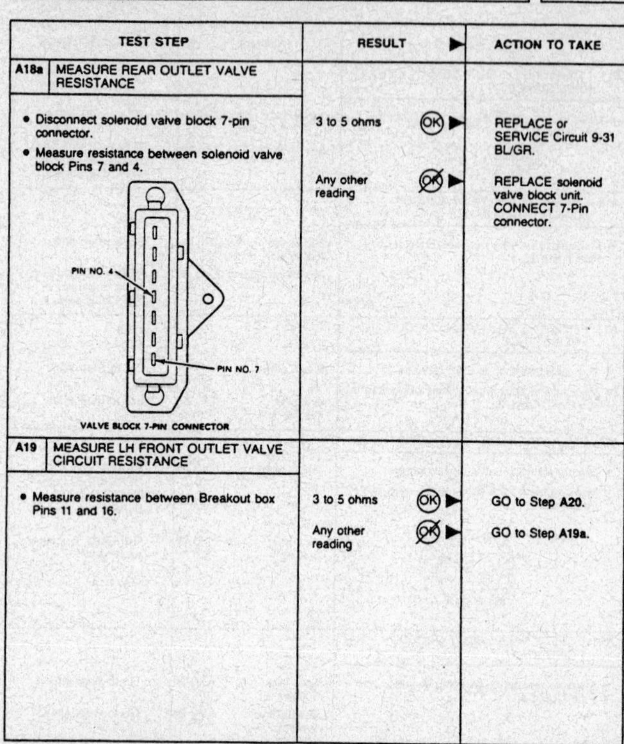

## Anti-Lock Warning Lamp On (With Brake Warning Lamp Off) — Test A

| TEST STEP | RESULT ▶ | ACTION TO TAKE |
|---|---|---|
| **A18a** MEASURE REAR OUTLET VALVE RESISTANCE | | |
| • Disconnect solenoid valve block 7-pin connector.<br>• Measure resistance between solenoid valve block Pins 7 and 4. | 3 to 5 ohms OK ▶ | REPLACE or SERVICE Circuit 9-31 BL/GR. |
| | Any other reading ~~OK~~ ▶ | REPLACE solenoid valve block unit. CONNECT 7-Pin connector. |
| **A19** MEASURE LH FRONT OUTLET VALVE CIRCUIT RESISTANCE | | |
| • Measure resistance between Breakout box Pins 11 and 16. | 3 to 5 ohms OK ▶ | GO to Step **A20**. |
| | Any other reading ~~OK~~ ▶ | GO to Step **A19a**. |



**Fig. 3 Test A, ABS lamp On (Part 18 of 25)**

## Anti-Lock Warning Lamp On (With Brake Warning Lamp Off) — Test A

| TEST STEP | RESULT ▶ | ACTION TO TAKE |
|---|---|---|
| **A19a** MEASURE LH FRONT OUTLET VALVE RESISTANCE | | |
| • Disconnect valve block 7-pin connector.<br>• Measure resistance between solenoid valve block Pins 7 and 5.<br>PIN NO. 5<br>PIN NO. 7<br>VALVE BLOCK 7-PIN CONNECTOR | 3 to 6 ohms OK ▶ | REPLACE or SERVICE Circuit 9-32 BL/R. |
| | Any other reading ~~OK~~ ▶ | REPLACE solenoid valve block unit. CONNECT 7-Pin connector. |
| **A20** MEASURE RH FRONT OUTLET VALVE CIRCUIT RESISTANCE | | |
| • Measure resistance between Breakout box Pins 11 and 34. | 3 to 6 ohms OK ▶ | GO to Step **A21**. |
| | Any other reading ~~OK~~ ▶ | GO to Step **A20a**. |

**Fig. 3 Test A, ABS lamp On (Part 19 of 25)**

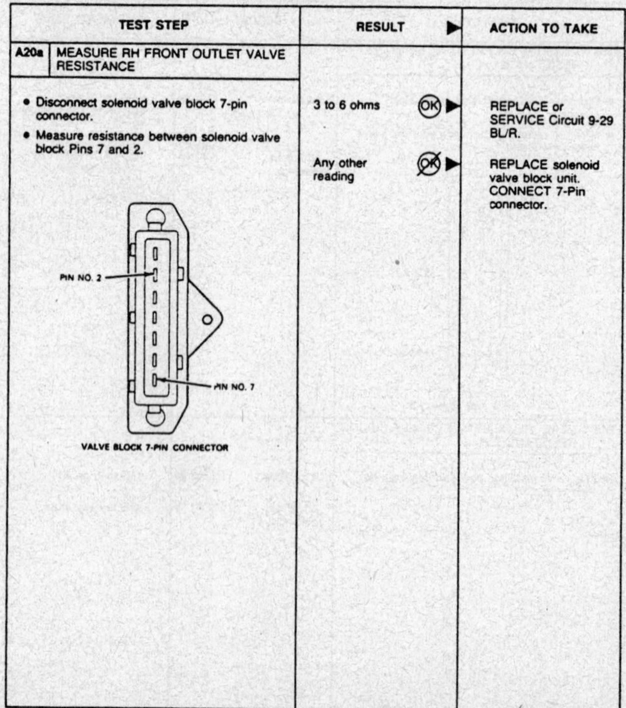

## Anti-Lock Warning Lamp On (With Brake Warning Lamp Off) — Test A

| TEST STEP | RESULT ▶ | ACTION TO TAKE |
|---|---|---|
| **A20a** MEASURE RH FRONT OUTLET VALVE RESISTANCE | | |
| • Disconnect solenoid valve block 7-pin connector.<br>• Measure resistance between solenoid valve block Pins 7 and 2. | 3 to 6 ohms OK ▶ | REPLACE or SERVICE Circuit 9-29 BL/R. |
| | Any other reading ~~OK~~ ▶ | REPLACE solenoid valve block unit. CONNECT 7-Pin connector. |



**Fig. 3 Test A, ABS lamp On (Part 20 of 25)**

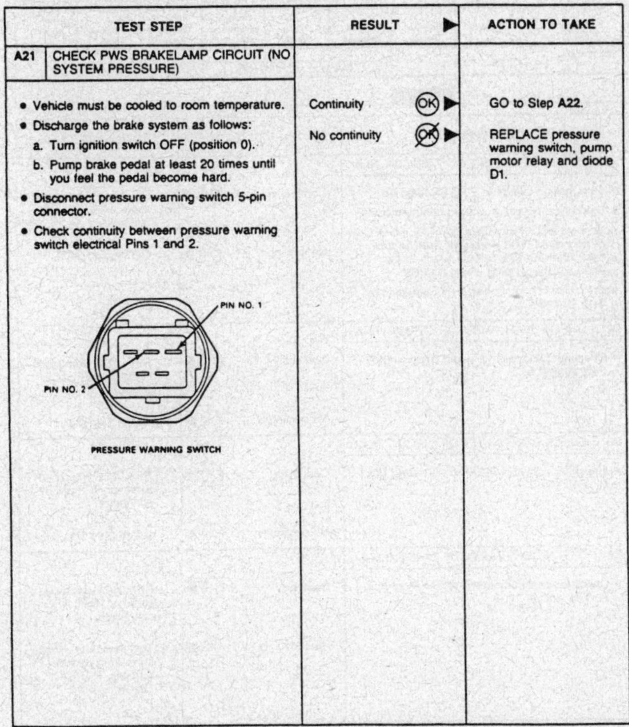

| Anti-Lock Warning Lamp On (With Brake Warning Lamp Off) | Test A |
|---|---|

| TEST STEP | RESULT ▶ | ACTION TO TAKE |
|---|---|---|
| **A21** CHECK PWS BRAKELAMP CIRCUIT (NO SYSTEM PRESSURE) | | |
| • Vehicle must be cooled to room temperature.<br>• Discharge the brake system as follows:<br>a. Turn ignition switch OFF (position 0).<br>b. Pump brake pedal at least 20 times until you feel the pedal become hard.<br>• Disconnect pressure warning switch 5-pin connector.<br>• Check continuity between pressure warning switch electrical Pins 1 and 2. | Continuity (OK) ▶<br>No continuity (NOT OK) ▶ | GO to Step **A22**.<br>REPLACE pressure warning switch, pump motor relay and diode D1. |



**Fig. 3 Test A, ABS lamp On (Part 21 of 25)**

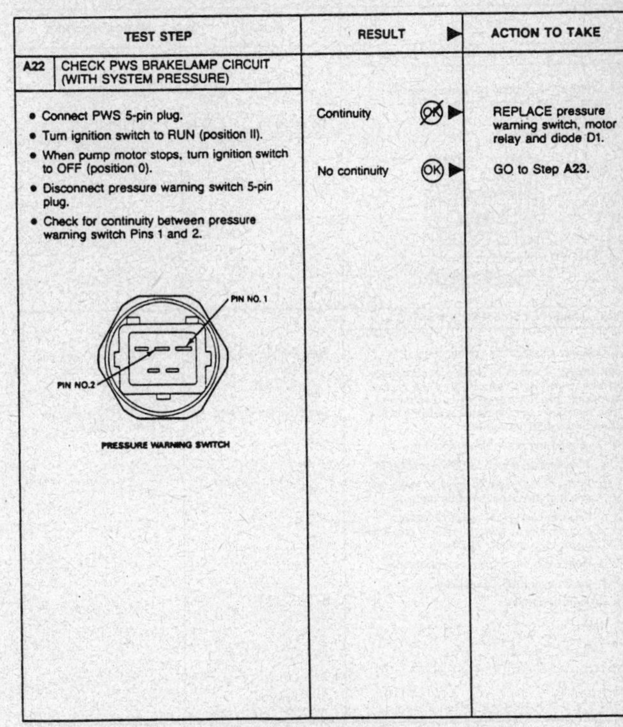

| Anti-Lock Warning Lamp On (With Brake Warning Lamp Off) | Test A |
|---|---|

| TEST STEP | RESULT ▶ | ACTION TO TAKE |
|---|---|---|
| **A22** CHECK PWS BRAKELAMP CIRCUIT (WITH SYSTEM PRESSURE) | | |
| • Connect PWS 5-pin plug.<br>• Turn ignition switch to RUN (position II).<br>• When pump motor stops, turn ignition switch to OFF (position 0).<br>• Disconnect pressure warning switch 5-pin plug.<br>• Check for continuity between pressure warning switch Pins 1 and 2. | Continuity (NOT OK) ▶<br>No continuity (OK) ▶ | REPLACE pressure warning switch, motor relay and diode D1.<br>GO to Step **A23**. |



**Fig. 3 Test A, ABS lamp On (Part 22 of 25)**

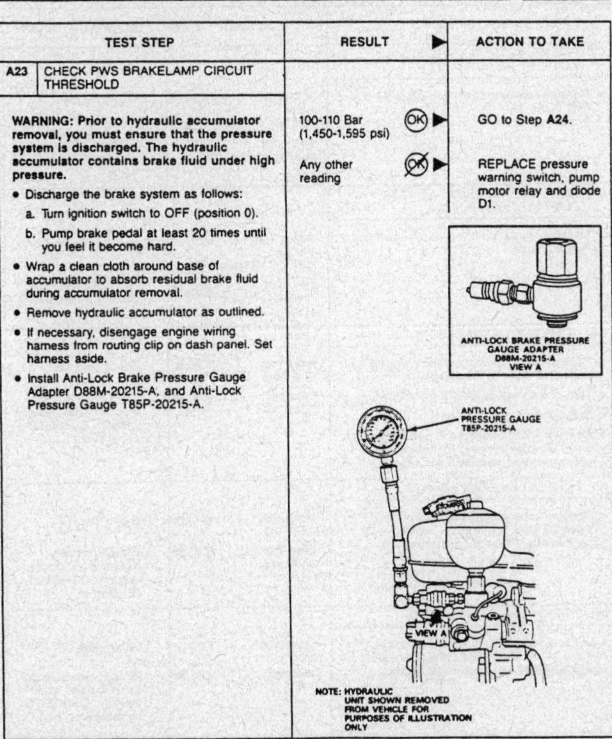

| Anti-Lock Warning Lamp On (With Brake Warning Lamp Off) | Test A |
|---|---|

| TEST STEP | RESULT ▶ | ACTION TO TAKE |
|---|---|---|
| **A23** CHECK PWS BRAKELAMP CIRCUIT THRESHOLD | | |
| **WARNING: Prior to hydraulic accumulator removal, you must ensure that the pressure system is discharged. The hydraulic accumulator contains brake fluid under high pressure.**<br>• Discharge the brake system as follows:<br>a. Turn ignition switch to OFF (position 0).<br>b. Pump brake pedal at least 20 times until you feel it become hard.<br>• Wrap a clean cloth around base of accumulator to absorb residual brake fluid during accumulator removal.<br>• Remove hydraulic accumulator as outlined.<br>• If necessary, disengage engine wiring harness from routing clip on dash panel. Set harness aside.<br>• Install Anti-Lock Brake Pressure Gauge Adapter D88M-20215-A, and Anti-Lock Pressure Gauge T85P-20215-A. | 100-110 Bar (1,450-1,595 psi) (OK) ▶<br>Any other reading (NOT OK) ▶ | GO to Step **A24**.<br>REPLACE pressure warning switch, pump motor relay and diode D1. |



**Fig. 3 Test A, ABS lamp On (Part 23 of 25)**

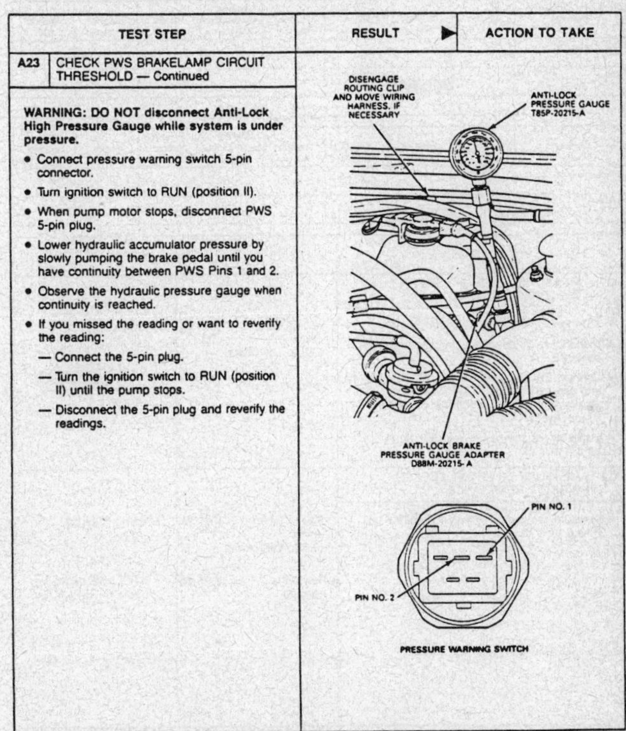

| Anti-Lock Warning Lamp On (With Brake Warning Lamp Off) | Test A |
|---|---|

| TEST STEP | RESULT ▶ | ACTION TO TAKE |
|---|---|---|
| **A23** CHECK PWS BRAKELAMP CIRCUIT THRESHOLD — Continued | | |
| **WARNING: DO NOT disconnect Anti-Lock High Pressure Gauge while system is under pressure.**<br>• Connect pressure warning switch 5-pin connector.<br>• Turn ignition switch to RUN (position II).<br>• When pump motor stops, disconnect PWS 5-pin plug.<br>• Lower hydraulic accumulator pressure by slowly pumping the brake pedal until you have continuity between PWS Pins 1 and 2.<br>• Observe the hydraulic pressure gauge when continuity is reached.<br>• If you missed the reading or want to reverify the reading:<br>— Connect the 5-pin plug.<br>— Turn the ignition switch to RUN (position II) until the pump stops.<br>— Disconnect the 5-pin plug and reverify the readings. | | |



**Fig. 3 Test A, ABS lamp On (Part 24 of 25)**

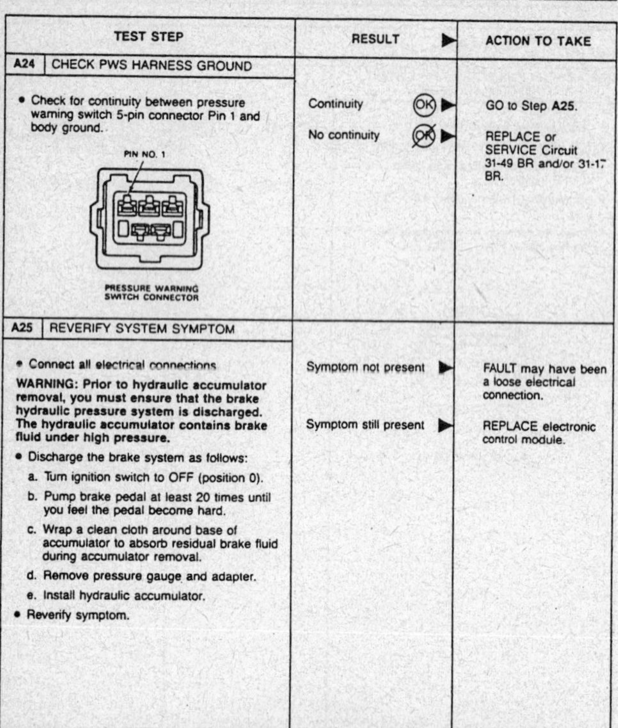

## Anti-Lock Warning Lamp On (With Brake Warning Lamp Off) — Test A

| TEST STEP | RESULT ▶ | ACTION TO TAKE |
|---|---|---|
| **A24** CHECK PWS HARNESS GROUND | | |
| • Check for continuity between pressure warning switch 5-pin connector Pin 1 and body ground. | Continuity (OK) ▶ | GO to Step **A25**. |
| | No continuity (Not OK) ▶ | REPLACE or SERVICE Circuit 31-49 BR and/or 31-17 BR. |
| **A25** REVERIFY SYSTEM SYMPTOM | | |
| • Connect all electrical connections. **WARNING: Prior to hydraulic accumulator removal, you must ensure that the brake hydraulic pressure system is discharged. The hydraulic accumulator contains brake fluid under high pressure.** • Discharge the brake system as follows: a. Turn ignition switch to OFF (position 0). b. Pump brake pedal at least 20 times until you feel the pedal become hard. c. Wrap a clean cloth around base of accumulator to absorb residual brake fluid during accumulator removal. d. Remove pressure gauge and adapter. e. Install hydraulic accumulator. • Reverify symptom. | Symptom not present ▶ | FAULT may have been a loose electrical connection. |
| | Symptom still present ▶ | REPLACE electronic control module. |



**Fig. 3 Test A, ABS lamp On (Part 25 of 25)**

## Anti-Lock Lamp On After Engine Starts (Brake Warning Lamp Off) — Test B

WARNING LIGHTS SEQUENCE

| Warning Lamps | Ignition On | Cranking Engine | Engine Running | Vehicle Moving | Braking with/without Anti-Lock | Vehicle Stopped | Engine Idle | Ignition Off |
|---|---|---|---|---|---|---|---|---|
| Check Anti-Lock | ▨ | | ▨ | ▨ | ▨ | ▨ | ▨ | |
| Brake | | ■ | | | | | | |

| TEST STEP | RESULT ▶ | ACTION TO TAKE |
|---|---|---|
| **B1** CHECK CONTINUITY OF CIRCUIT 78-8 | | |
| • Turn ignition switch to OFF (position 0). • Disconnect 35-pin plug from control module. • Connect EEC-IV Breakout box T83L-50-EEC-IV or equivalent, with Anti-Lock Test Adapter Tool T85P-50-ASA or equivalent, to the Anti-Lock 35-pin plug wiring harness. • Check for continuity between Breakout box Pins 40 and 4. | Continuity (Not OK) ▶ | REPLACE damaged cable or REPLACE connector. |
| | No continuity (OK) ▶ | GO to Step **B2**. |
| **B2** CHECK CONTINUITY OF CIRCUIT 78-2 | | |
| • Check for continuity between Breakout box Pins 40 and 5. | Continuity (Not OK) ▶ | REPLACE damaged cable or REPLACE connector. |
| | No continuity (OK) ▶ | GO to Step **B3**. |
| **B3** CHECK CONTINUITY OF CIRCUIT 78-6 | | |
| • Check for continuity between Breakout box Pins 40 and 6. | Continuity (Not OK) ▶ | REPLACE damaged cable or REPLACE connector. |
| | No continuity (OK) ▶ | GO to Step **B4**. |
| **B4** CHECK CONTINUITY OF CIRCUIT 78-4 | | |
| • Check for continuity between Breakout box Pins 40 and 7. | Continuity (Not OK) ▶ | REPLACE damaged cable or REPLACE connector. |
| | No continuity (OK) ▶ | Test complete. If Anti-Lock lamp pattern remains, REPEAT Test B. |

**Fig. 4 Test B (ABS lamp On after engine starts)**

## Anti-Lock Warning Lamp On After Vehicle Starts to Move or False Cycling of Anti-Lock System — Test C

WARNING LIGHTS SEQUENCE

| Warning Lamps | Ignition On | Cranking Engine | Engine Running | Vehicle Moving | Braking with/without Anti-Lock | Vehicle Stopped | Engine Idle | Ignition Off |
|---|---|---|---|---|---|---|---|---|
| Check Anti-Lock | ▨ | | ▨ | ▨ | ▨ | ▨ | ▨ | |
| Brake | | ■ | | | | | | |

WARNING LIGHTS SEQUENCE

| Warning Lamps | Ignition On | Cranking Engine | Engine Running | Vehicle Moving | Braking with/without Anti-Lock | Vehicle Stopped | Engine Idle | Ignition Off |
|---|---|---|---|---|---|---|---|---|
| Check Anti-Lock | ▨ | | ▨ | | | | | |
| Brake | | ■ | | | | | | |

| TEST STEP | RESULT ▶ | ACTION TO TAKE |
|---|---|---|
| **C1** MEASURE RH REAR SENSOR CIRCUIT RESISTANCE | | |
| • Turn ignition switch to OFF (position 0). • Disconnect 35-pin connector from electronic controller. • Connect EEC-IV Breakout box T83L-50-EEC-IV and anti-lock adapter T85P-50-ASA or equivalent to 35-pin electronic controller connector. • Measure resistance between Breakout box Pins 4 and 22. | 800 to 1400 ohms (0.8 to 1.4K ohms) (OK) ▶ | GO to Step **C2**. |
| | Any other reading (Not OK) ▶ | REPLACE damaged cable or REPLACE sensor. |
| **C2** MEASURE LH FRONT SENSOR CIRCUIT RESISTANCE | | |
| • Measure resistance between Breakout box Pins 5 and 23. | 800 to 1400 ohms (0.8 to 1.4K ohms) (Not OK) ▶ | GO to Step **C3**. |
| | Any other reading. (OK) ▶ | REPLACE damaged cable or REPLACE sensor. |

**Fig. 5 Test C, ABS lamp On after vehicle starts (Part 1 of 3)**

## Anti-Lock Warning Lamp On After Vehicle Starts to Move or False Cycling of Anti-Lock System — Test C

| TEST STEP | RESULT ▶ | ACTION TO TAKE |
|---|---|---|
| **C3** MEASURE LH REAR SENSOR CIRCUIT RESISTANCE | | |
| • Measure resistance between Breakout box Pins 6 and 24. | 800 to 1400 ohms (0.8 to 1.4K ohms) (OK) ▶ | GO to Step **C4**. |
| | Any other reading (Not OK) ▶ | REPLACE damaged cable or REPLACE sensor. |
| **C4** MEASURE RH FRONT SENSOR CIRCUIT RESISTANCE | | |
| • Measure resistance between Breakout box Pins 7 and 25. | 800 to 1400 ohms (0.8 to 1.4K ohms) (OK) ▶ | GO to Step **C5**. |
| | Any other reading (Not OK) ▶ | REPLACE damaged cable or REPLACE sensor. |
| **C5** CHECK RH REAR SENSOR | | |
| • Place vehicle on hoist and raise wheels clear of ground. Refer to Section 50-04. • Turn ignition switch to OFF (position 0). • Set voltmeter to 2V AC scale. • Measure voltage between Breakout box Pins 4 and 22 while spinning RH rear wheel at approximately 1 revolution per second. | More than 0.15V AC (OK) ▶ | GO to Step **C6**. |
| | Less than 0.15V AC (Not OK) ▶ | CHECK sensor mounting and cable integrity. CORRECT as required. |
| **C6** CHECK LH FRONT SENSOR | | |
| • Measure voltage between Breakout box Pins 5 and 23 while spinning LH front wheel at approximately 1 revolution per second. | More than 0.15V AC (OK) ▶ | GO to Step **C7**. |
| | Less than 0.15V AC (Not OK) ▶ | CHECK sensor mounting and cable integrity. CORRECT as required. |
| **C7** CHECK LH REAR SENSOR | | |
| • Measure voltage between Breakout box Pins 6 and 24 while spinning LH rear wheel at approximately 1 revolution per second. | More than 0.15V AC (OK) ▶ | GO to Step **C8**. |
| | Less than 0.15V AC (Not OK) ▶ | CHECK wheel sensor mounting and cable integrity. CORRECT as required. |

**Fig. 5 Test C, ABS lamp On after vehicle starts (Part 2 of 3)**

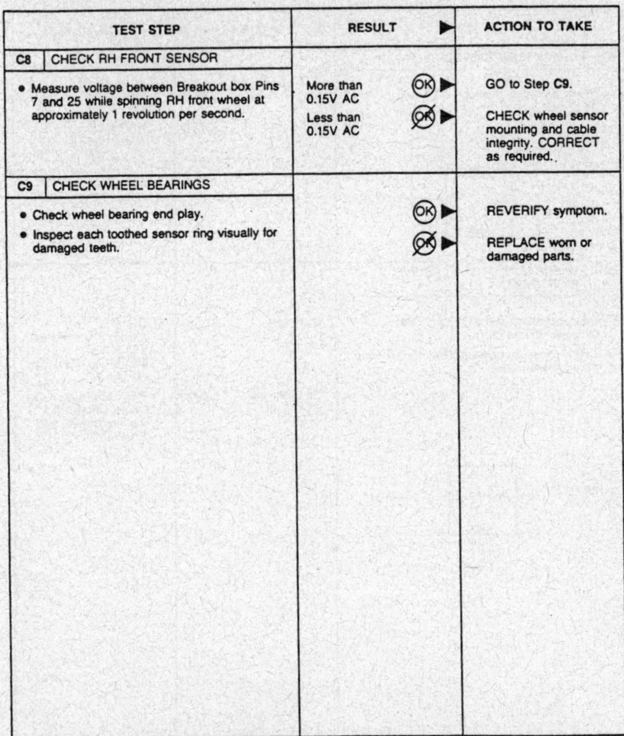

| Anti-Lock Warning Lamp On After Vehicle Starts to Move or False Cycling of Anti-Lock System | Test C |
|---|---|

| TEST STEP | RESULT ▶ | ACTION TO TAKE |
|---|---|---|
| **C8** CHECK RH FRONT SENSOR | | |
| • Measure voltage between Breakout box Pins 7 and 25 while spinning RH front wheel at approximately 1 revolution per second. | More than 0.15V AC (OK) ▶ | GO to Step **C9**. |
| | Less than 0.15V AC (NOT OK) ▶ | CHECK wheel sensor mounting and cable integrity. CORRECT as required. |
| **C9** CHECK WHEEL BEARINGS | | |
| • Check wheel bearing end play.<br>• Inspect each toothed sensor ring visually for damaged teeth. | (OK) ▶ | REVERIFY symptom. |
| | (NOT OK) ▶ | REPLACE worn or damaged parts. |

**Fig. 5 Test C, ABS lamp On after vehicle starts (Part 3 of 3)**

| Anti-Lock Warning Lamp And Brake Warning Lamp On And/Or Pump Motor Runs More Than 60 Seconds | Test D |
|---|---|

WARNING LIGHTS SEQUENCE

| Warning Lamps | Ignition On | Cranking Engine | Engine Running | Vehicle Moving | Braking with/without Anti-Lock | Vehicle Stopped | Engine Idle | Ignition Off |
|---|---|---|---|---|---|---|---|---|
| Anti-Lock | | | | | | | | |
| Brake | | | | | | | | |

WARNING LIGHTS SEQUENCE

| Warning Lamps | Ignition On | Cranking Engine | Engine Running | Vehicle Moving | Braking with/without Anti-Lock | Vehicle Stopped | Engine Idle | Ignition Off |
|---|---|---|---|---|---|---|---|---|
| Anti-Lock | | | | | | | | |
| Brake | | | | | | | | |

| TEST STEP | RESULT ▶ | ACTION TO TAKE |
|---|---|---|
| **D1** CHECK FOR HYDRAULIC LEAKS | | |
| • Check for brake fluid leaks in the following areas:<br>a. Brake lines and calipers<br>b. High and low pressure lines on hydraulic unit<br>c. Reservoir seals and seams<br>d. Accumulator<br>**NOTE: A small amount of leakage from pressure warning switch is allowable. If any leakage is found below switch, wipe off fluid and recheck for excessive leakage.** | No leakage found (OK) ▶ | Go to **D2**. |
| | Leakage found (NOT OK) ▶ | SERVICE or REPLACE leaking components. CHECK system operation. |
| **D2** CHECK PUMP MOTOR OPERATION | | |
| • Turn ignition switch to OFF (position 0).<br>• Pump brake pedal at least 20 times until it becomes hard.<br>• Turn ignition switch to RUN (position II).<br>• Pump motor should operate. | (OK) ▶ | GO to **D3**. |
| | (NOT OK) ▶ | GO to **D2a**. |

**Fig. 6 Test D, ABS & brake lamps On and/or pump motor runs more than 60 seconds (Part 1 of 9)**

| Anti-Lock Warning Lamp And Brake Warning Lamp On And/Or Pump Motor Runs More Than 60 Seconds | Test D |
|---|---|

| TEST STEP | RESULT ▶ | ACTION TO TAKE |
|---|---|---|
| **D2a** PUMP MOTOR UNIT | | |
| • Disconnect 2-pin plug on pump motor unit.<br>• Turn ignition switch to RUN (position II).<br>• Set voltmeter on 20V scale.<br>• Check for voltage at 2-pin connector Pin 1.<br>[PIN NO. 1 — 2-PIN MOTOR CONNECTOR] | More than 10V DC (OK) ▶ | GO to **D2b**. |
| | Less than 10V DC (NOT OK) ▶ | GO to **D2c**. |
| **D2b** CHECK MOTOR GROUND | | |
| • Turn ignition switch to OFF (position 0).<br>• Set ohmmeter to 1× scale.<br>• Check continuity between motor connector Pin 2 and ground.<br>[PIN NO. 2 — 2-PIN MOTOR CONNECTOR] | Continuity (OK) ▶ | CHECK brake reservoir filter and/or suction hose. REPLACE if necessary. GO to **D3**. |
| | No Continuity (NOT OK) ▶ | SERVICE open in Circuit 31-17 BR. |

**Fig. 6 Test D, ABS & brake lamps On and/or pump motor runs more than 60 seconds (Part 2 of 9)**

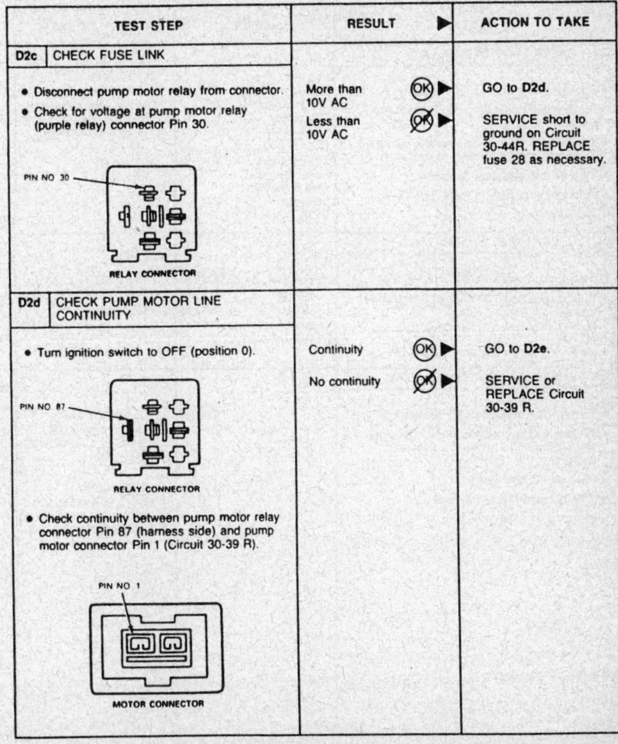

| Anti-Lock Warning Lamp And Brake Warning Lamp On And/Or Pump Motor Runs More Than 60 Seconds | Test D |
|---|---|

| TEST STEP | RESULT ▶ | ACTION TO TAKE |
|---|---|---|
| **D2c** CHECK FUSE LINK | | |
| • Disconnect pump motor relay from connector.<br>• Check for voltage at pump motor relay (purple relay) connector Pin 30.<br>[PIN NO 30 — RELAY CONNECTOR] | More than 10V AC (OK) ▶ | GO to **D2d**. |
| | Less than 10V AC (NOT OK) ▶ | SERVICE short to ground on Circuit 30-44R. REPLACE fuse 28 as necessary. |
| **D2d** CHECK PUMP MOTOR LINE CONTINUITY | | |
| • Turn ignition switch to OFF (position 0).<br>[PIN NO 87 — RELAY CONNECTOR]<br>• Check continuity between pump motor relay connector Pin 87 (harness side) and pump motor connector Pin 1 (Circuit 30-39 R).<br>[PIN NO 1 — MOTOR CONNECTOR] | Continuity (OK) ▶ | GO to **D2e**. |
| | No continuity (NOT OK) ▶ | SERVICE or REPLACE Circuit 30-39 R. |

**Fig. 6 Test D, ABS & brake lamps On and/or pump motor runs more than 60 seconds (Part 3 of 9)**

| Anti-Lock Warning Lamp And Brake Warning Lamp On And/Or Pump Motor Runs More Than 60 Seconds | Test D |
|---|---|

| TEST STEP | RESULT ▶ | ACTION TO TAKE |
|---|---|---|
| **D2e** PRESSURE WARNING SWITCH | | |
| • Turn ignition switch to OFF (position 0).<br>• Pump brake pedal at least 20 times until pedal becomes hard (pressure discharged).<br>• Disconnect pressure warning switch 5-pin plug.<br>• Check for continuity between pressure warning switch Pins 1 and 4.<br>**NOTE: System must be depressurized.**<br>PIN NO. 1<br>PIN NO. 4<br>PRESSURE WARNING SWITCH | Continuity (OK) ▶ | GO to **D2f**. |
| | No continuity (NOT OK) ▶ | REPLACE pressure warning switch diode D1, and pump motor relay. |
| **D2f** CABLE HARNESS PRESSURE WARNING SWITCH | | |
| • Check for continuity between pressure warning switch 5-pin connector Pin 1 and ground.<br>PIN NO. 1<br>PRESSURE WARNING SWITCH CONNECTOR | Continuity (OK) ▶ | GO to **D2g**. |
| | No continuity (NOT OK) ▶ | REPLACE or SERVICE Circuit 31-49 BR and/or 31-17 BR. |

**Fig. 6 Test D, ABS & brake lamps On and/or pump motor runs more than 60 seconds (Part 4 of 9)**

| Anti-Lock Warning Lamp And Brake Warning Lamp On And/Or Pump Motor Runs More Than 60 Seconds | Test D |
|---|---|

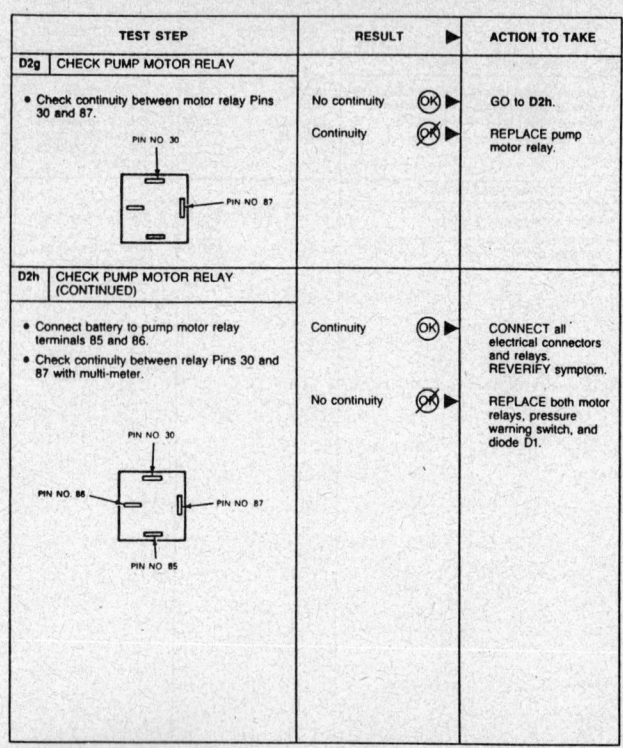

| TEST STEP | RESULT ▶ | ACTION TO TAKE |
|---|---|---|
| **D2g** CHECK PUMP MOTOR RELAY | | |
| • Check continuity between motor relay Pins 30 and 87.<br>PIN NO 30<br>PIN NO 87 | No continuity (OK) ▶ | GO to **D2h**. |
| | Continuity (NOT OK) ▶ | REPLACE pump motor relay. |
| **D2h** CHECK PUMP MOTOR RELAY (CONTINUED) | | |
| • Connect battery to pump motor relay terminals 85 and 86.<br>• Check continuity between relay Pins 30 and 87 with multi-meter.<br>PIN NO 30<br>PIN NO 86<br>PIN NO 87<br>PIN NO 85 | Continuity (OK) ▶ | CONNECT all electrical connectors and relays. REVERIFY symptom. |
| | No continuity (NOT OK) ▶ | REPLACE both motor relays, pressure warning switch, and diode D1. |

**Fig. 6 Test D, ABS & brake lamps On and/or pump motor runs more than 60 seconds (Part 5 of 9)**

| Anti-Lock Warning Lamp And Brake Warning Lamp On And/Or Pump Motor Runs More Than 60 Seconds | Test D |
|---|---|

| TEST STEP | RESULT ▶ | ACTION TO TAKE |
|---|---|---|
| **D3** CHECK PUMP MOTOR UNIT | | |
| • Turn ignition switch to OFF (position 0).<br>• Pump brake pedal 20 times to discharge system.<br>• Connect ammeter between battery positive cable and battery positive terminal.<br>• Turn off any electrical components.<br>• Turn ignition switch to RUN (position II).<br>• Measure pump motor current. | Current 0 amps or more than 25 amps (NOT OK) ▶ | REPLACE pump motor unit, pressure warning switch, motor relay and diode D1. |
| | Current less than 25 amps but more than 0 amps (OK) ▶ | GO to **D4**. |
| **D4** CHECK PUMP MOTOR | | |
| • Turn ignition switch to OFF (position 0).<br>• Pump brake pedal at least 20 times, until brake pedal becomes hard.<br>• Turn ignition switch to RUN (position II).<br>• Measure time pump takes to shut off. | Under 60 seconds (OK) ▶ | GO to **D5**. |
| | Over 60 seconds (or motor never turns on) (NOT OK) ▶ | GO to **D4a**. |
| **D4a** CHECK LOW PRESSURE FLOW | | |
| • Turn ignition switch to OFF (position 0).<br>• Disconnect low pressure hose from pump and allow fluid to flow into a suitable container.<br>• Fluid should flow freely.<br>**NOTE: Discard fluid after test.** | (OK) ▶ | CONNECT low pressure hose. FILL reservoir to MAX line. GO to **D5**. |
| | (NOT OK) ▶ | SERVICE or REPLACE reservoir and/or low pressure hose as required. |

**Fig. 6 Test D, ABS & brake lamps On and/or pump motor runs more than 60 seconds (Part 6 of 9)**

| Anti-Lock Warning Lamp And Brake Warning Lamp On And/Or Pump Motor Runs More Than 60 Seconds | Test D |
|---|---|

| TEST STEP | RESULT ▶ | ACTION TO TAKE |
|---|---|---|
| **D5** ACCUMULATOR: PRE-CHARGE | | |
| • Vehicle must be cooled to room temperature.<br>**WARNING: Prior to hydraulic accumulator removal, you must ensure that the pressure system is discharged. The hydraulic accumulator contains brake fluid under high pressure.**<br>• To discharge hydraulic accumulator pressure, turn ignition to OFF (position 0), pump brake pedal at least 20 times until you feel it become hard.<br>• Wrap a clean cloth around base of accumulator to absorb any residual brake fluid during accumulator removal.<br>• Remove hydraulic accumulator as outlined.<br>• If necessary, disengage engine wiring harness from routing clip on dash panel. Set harness aside.<br>• Install Anti-Lock Brake Pressure Gauge Adapter D88M-20215-A and Anti-Lock Pressure Gauge T85P-20215-A.<br>• Install Anti-Lock Pressure Gauge Tool T85P-20215-A or equivalent. | 4137-9135 kPa (600-1325 psi) (OK) ▶ | GO to **D6**. |
| | Under 4137 kPa (600 psi) or over 9135 kPa (1325 psi) (NOT OK) ▶ | REPLACE accumulator. |

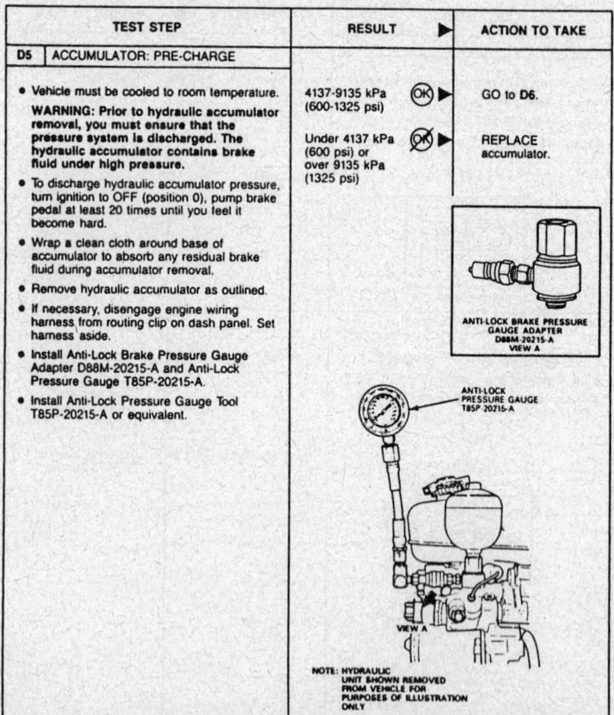


**Fig. 6 Test D, ABS & brake lamps On and/or pump motor runs more than 60 seconds (Part 7 of 9)**

**Anti-Lock Warning Lamp And Brake Warning Lamp On And/Or Pump Motor Runs More Than 60 Seconds** — **Test D**

| TEST STEP | RESULT ▶ | ACTION TO TAKE |
|---|---|---|
| **D5** ACCUMULATOR: PRE-CHARGE — Continued | | |
| • Turn ignition switch to RUN (position II) and read accumulator precharge pressure.<br>• Gauge needle reading should spring to 4137-9135 kPa (600-1325 psi).<br>**Note: If reading was missed, discharge accumulator as described and repeat Ignition ON sequence.** | 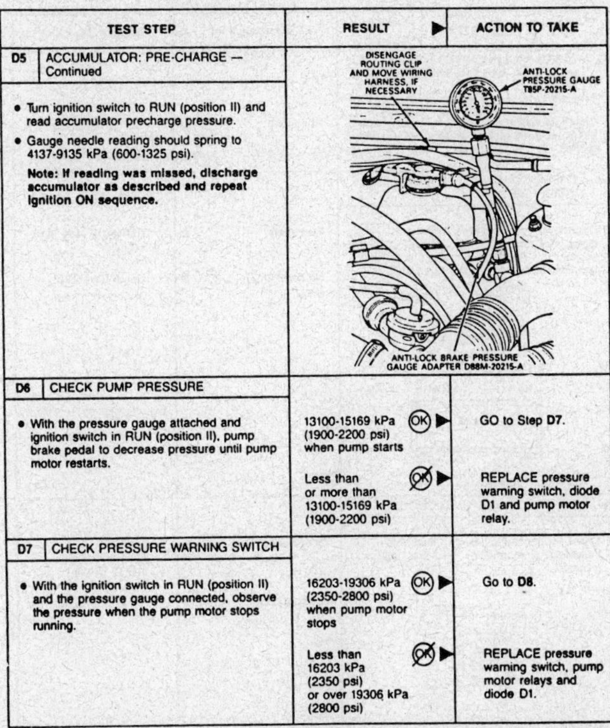<br> | |
| **D6** CHECK PUMP PRESSURE | | |
| • With the pressure gauge attached and ignition switch in RUN (position II), pump brake pedal to decrease pressure until pump motor restarts. | 13100-15169 kPa (1900-2200 psi) when pump starts (OK) ▶ | GO to Step **D7**. |
| | Less than or more than 13100-15169 kPa (1900-2200 psi) (NOT OK) ▶ | REPLACE pressure warning switch, diode D1 and pump motor relay. |
| **D7** CHECK PRESSURE WARNING SWITCH | | |
| • With the ignition switch in RUN (position II) and the pressure gauge connected, observe the pressure when the pump motor stops running. | 16203-19306 kPa (2350-2800 psi) when pump motor stops (OK) ▶ | Go to **D8**. |
| | Less than 16203 kPa (2350 psi) or over 19306 kPa (2800 psi) (NOT OK) ▶ | REPLACE pressure warning switch, pump motor relays and diode D1. |

**Fig. 6 Test D, ABS & brake lamps On and/or pump motor runs more than 60 seconds (Part 8 of 9)**

**Anti-Lock Warning Lamp And Brake Warning Lamp On And/Or Pump Motor Runs More Than 60 Seconds** — **Test D**

| TEST STEP | RESULT ▶ | ACTION TO TAKE |
|---|---|---|
| **D8** CHECK WARNING INDICATORS | | |
| • Disconnect 2-pin connector from motor.<br>• Pump brake pedal until pressure falls to 10,000-11,000 kPa (1450-1595 psi).<br>• Anit-Lock warning indicator and brake warning indicator should light. | Indicators light between 10,000-11,000 kPa (1450-1595 psi) (OK) ▶ | GO to **D9**. |
| | Indicators light above or below 10,000-11,000 kPa (1450-1595 psi) (NOT OK) ▶ | REPLACE pressure warning switch, pump relays and diode D1. |
| **D9** CHECK HYDRAULIC UNIT | | |
| • Turn ignition switch to RUN (Position II); wait until pump motor stops. Wait 3 more minutes to stabilize gauge pressure.<br>• Read pressure gauge.<br>• Wait 5 minutes and read pressure gauge again to determine the pressure loss over those 5 minutes.<br>**WARNING: When removing test equipment, ensure that brake system pressure is discharged. Wrap a clean cloth around accumulator base to absorb residual brake fluid during accumulator removal. The accumulator contains brake fluid under high pressure.** | Pressure loss less than 1000 kPa (145 psi) on gauge (OK) ▶ | REMOVE pressure gauge. PERFORM Quick Check. |
| | More than 1000 kPa (145 psi) (NOT OK) ▶ | REPLACE hydraulic unit. |

**Fig. 6 Test D, ABS & brake lamps On and/or pump motor runs more than 60 seconds (Part 9 of 9)**

**Anti-Lock Warning Lamp Intermittently On** — **Test E**

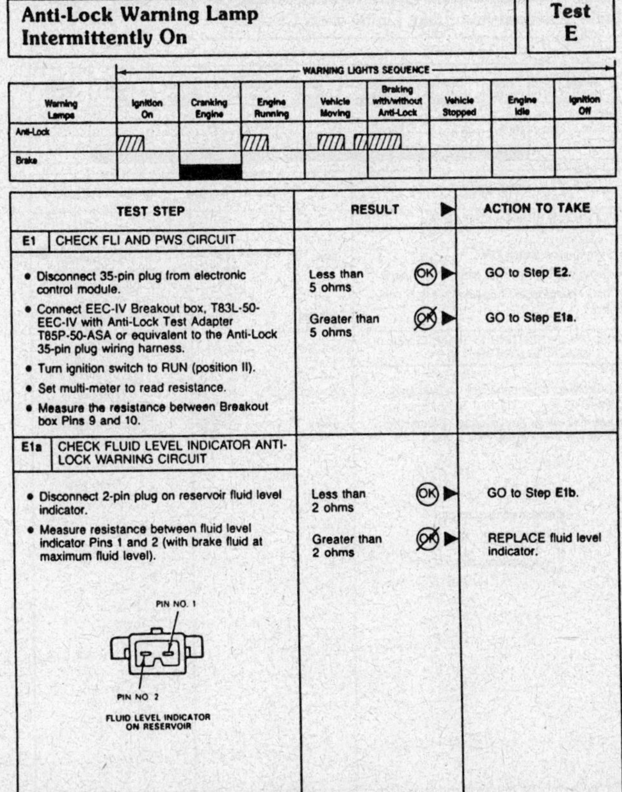

| Warning Lamps | Ignition On | Cranking Engine | Engine Running | Vehicle Moving | Braking with/without Anti-Lock | Vehicle Stopped | Engine Idle | Ignition Off |
|---|---|---|---|---|---|---|---|---|
| | WARNING LIGHTS SEQUENCE | | | | | | | |
| Anti-Lock | | | | | | | | |
| Brake | | | | | | | | |

| TEST STEP | RESULT ▶ | ACTION TO TAKE |
|---|---|---|
| **E1** CHECK FLI AND PWS CIRCUIT | | |
| • Disconnect 35-pin plug from electronic control module.<br>• Connect EEC-IV Breakout box, T83L-50-EEC-IV with Anti-Lock Test Adapter T85P-50-ASA or equivalent to the Anti-Lock 35-pin plug wiring harness.<br>• Turn ignition switch to RUN (position II).<br>• Set multi-meter to read resistance.<br>• Measure the resistance between Breakout box Pins 9 and 10. | Less than 5 ohms (OK) ▶ | GO to Step **E2**. |
| | Greater than 5 ohms (NOT OK) ▶ | GO to Step **E1a**. |
| **E1a** CHECK FLUID LEVEL INDICATOR ANTI-LOCK WARNING CIRCUIT | | |
| • Disconnect 2-pin plug on reservoir fluid level indicator.<br>• Measure resistance between fluid level indicator Pins 1 and 2 (with brake fluid at maximum fluid level).<br> | Less than 2 ohms (OK) ▶ | GO to Step **E1b**. |
| | Greater than 2 ohms (NOT OK) ▶ | REPLACE fluid level indicator. |

**Fig. 7 Test E, ABS lamp On intermittently (Part 1 of 5)**

**Anti-Lock Warning Lamp Intermittently On** — **Test E**

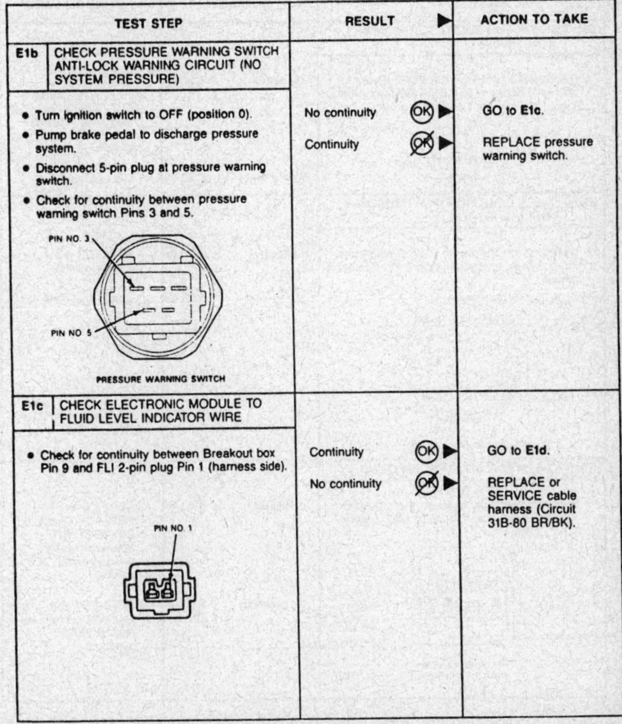

| TEST STEP | RESULT ▶ | ACTION TO TAKE |
|---|---|---|
| **E1b** CHECK PRESSURE WARNING SWITCH ANTI-LOCK WARNING CIRCUIT (NO SYSTEM PRESSURE) | | |
| • Turn ignition switch to OFF (position 0).<br>• Pump brake pedal to discharge pressure system.<br>• Disconnect 5-pin plug at pressure warning switch.<br>• Check for continuity between pressure warning switch Pins 3 and 5.<br> | No continuity (OK) ▶ | GO to **E1c**. |
| | Continuity (NOT OK) ▶ | REPLACE pressure warning switch. |
| **E1c** CHECK ELECTRONIC MODULE TO FLUID LEVEL INDICATOR WIRE | | |
| • Check for continuity between Breakout box Pin 9 and FLI 2-pin plug Pin 1 (harness side).<br> | Continuity (OK) ▶ | GO to **E1d**. |
| | No continuity (NOT OK) ▶ | REPLACE or SERVICE cable harness (Circuit 31B-80 BR/BK). |

**Fig. 7 Test E, ABS lamp On intermittently (Part 2 of 5)**

## Anti-Lock Warning Lamp Intermittently On — Test E

| TEST STEP | | RESULT ▶ | ACTION TO TAKE |
|---|---|---|---|
| E1d | CHECK FLUID LEVEL INDICATOR TO PRESSURE WARNING SWITCH WIRE | | |
| | • Check for continuity between 2-pin fluid level connector Pin 2 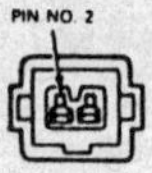<br>PIN NO. 2<br>and 5-pin pressure warning switch plug Pin 3 (harness side). 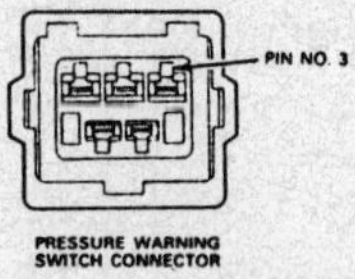<br>PIN NO. 3<br>PRESSURE WARNING SWITCH CONNECTOR | Continuity ▶ | GO to Step E1e. |
| | | No continuity ▶ | SERVICE or REPLACE cable harness (Circuit 31B-79 BR/W) between pressure warning switch and fluid level indicator. |
| E1e | CHECK PRESSURE WARNING SWITCH TO ELECTRONIC CONTROLLER WIRE | | |
| | • Check for continuity between 5-pin pressure warning switch connector Pin 5 (harness side) 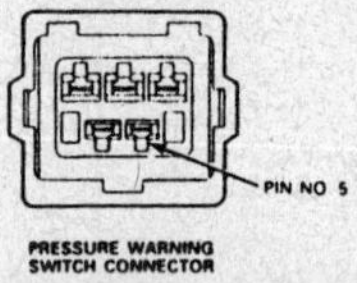<br>PIN NO. 5<br>PRESSURE WARNING SWITCH CONNECTOR<br>and Breakout box Pin 10. | Continuity ▶ | TURN Ignition OFF. CONNECT all electrical connections. REVERIFY symptom. |
| | | No continuity ▶ | SERVICE or REPLACE cable harness (Circuit 31B-75 BR/GR) between pressure warning switch and module. |

**Fig. 7 Test E, ABS lamp On intermittently (Part 3 of 5)**

## Anti-Lock Warning Lamp Intermittently On — Test E

| TEST STEP | | RESULT ▶ | ACTION TO TAKE |
|---|---|---|---|
| E2 | CHECK ISOLATION TEST FLUID LEVEL INDICATOR AND PRESSURE WARNING SWITCH | | |
| | • Check for continuity between Breakout box Pin 9 and body ground and Pin 10 and body ground. | Continuity ▶ | GO to Step E2a. |
| | | No continuity ▶ | REVERIFY symptom. |
| E2a | CHECK CONTINUITY OF FLUID LEVEL INDICATOR SWITCH | | |
| | • Disconnect both fluid level indicator connectors and check for continuity between socket Pin 1 and Pins 3, 4 and 5 and Pin 2 and Pins 3, 4, and 5 of the FLI switch. 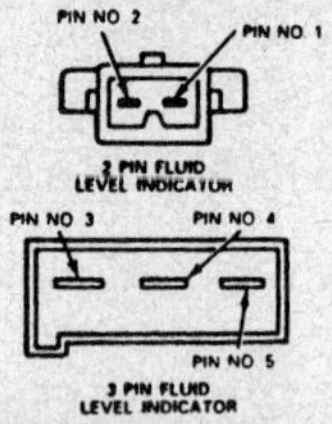<br>PIN NO. 2 — PIN NO. 1<br>2 PIN FLUID LEVEL INDICATOR<br>PIN NO. 3 — PIN NO. 4 — PIN NO. 5<br>3 PIN FLUID LEVEL INDICATOR | Continuity ▶ | REPLACE fluid level indicator. |
| | | No continuity ▶ | GO to Step E2b. |
| E2b | CHECK FOR SHORT TO GROUND | | |
| | • Check for continuity between fluid level indicator 2-pin connector Pin 1 and body ground. 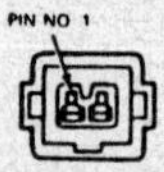<br>PIN NO. 1 | Continuity ▶ | SERVICE or REPLACE Circuit 31B-79 BR/W. |
| | | No continuity ▶ | GO to Step E2c. |

**Fig. 7 Test E, ABS lamp On intermittently (Part 4 of 5)**

## Anti-Lock Warning Lamp Intermittently On — Test E

| TEST STEP | | RESULT ▶ | ACTION TO TAKE |
|---|---|---|---|
| E2c | CHECK FOR SHORT TO GROUND (CONTINUED) | | |
| | • Disconnect 5-pin plug from PWS. Check for continuity between fluid level indicator plug Pin 2 (harness side) and body ground. 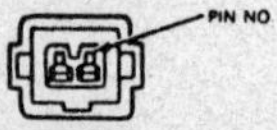<br>PIN NO. 2 | Continuity ▶ | SERVICE or REPLACE Circuit 31B-79 BR/W between fluid level indicator and pressure warning switch. |
| | | No continuity ▶ | GO to Step E2d. |
| E2d | CHECK CONTINUITY OF PRESSURE WARNING SWITCH | | |
| | • Check for continuity from PWS 5-pin socket Pin 3 to body ground, and from Pin 5 to body ground. 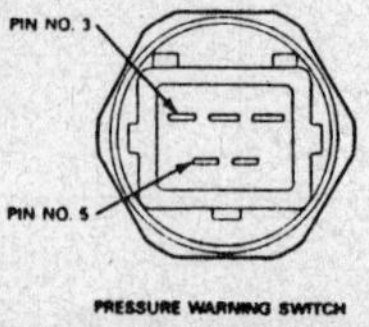<br>PIN NO. 3 — PIN NO. 5<br>PRESSURE WARNING SWITCH | Continuity ▶ | REPLACE pressure warning switch. |
| | | No continuity ▶ | GO to Step E2e. |
| E2e | CHECK FOR SHORT TO GROUND | | |
| | • Check for continuity between 5-pin pressure warning switch plug Pin 5 and body ground. 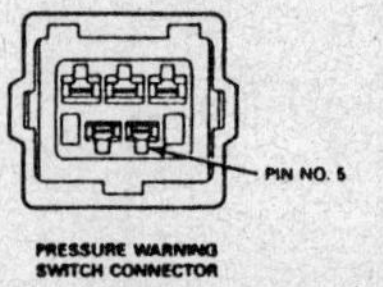<br>PIN NO. 5<br>PRESSURE WARNING SWITCH CONNECTOR | Continuity ▶ | SERVICE or REPLACE Circuit 31B-75 BR/GR between pressure warning switch and module. |
| | | No continuity ▶ | CONNECT all electrical connectors and REVERIFY symptom. |

**Fig. 7 Test E, ABS lamp On intermittently (Part 5 of 5)**

## Brake Warning Lamp On (With Anti-Lock Lamp Off, Parking Brake Released And Brake Lining Wear Checked) — Test F

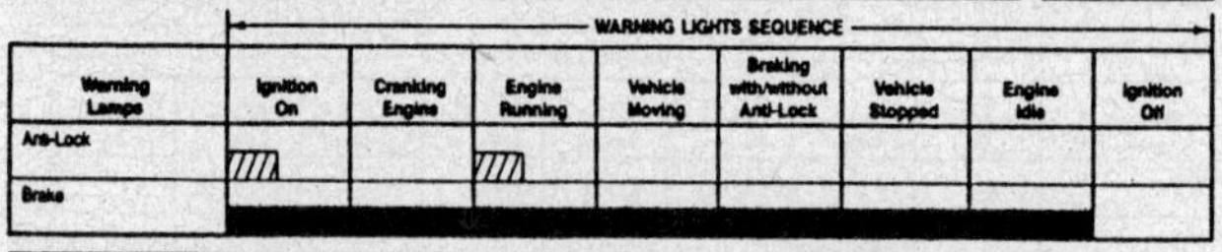

WARNING LIGHTS SEQUENCE

| Warning Lamps | Ignition On | Cranking Engine | Engine Running | Vehicle Moving | Braking with/without Anti-Lock | Vehicle Stopped | Engine Idle | Ignition Off |
|---|---|---|---|---|---|---|---|---|
| Anti-Lock | | | | | | | | |
| Brake | | | | | | | | |

| TEST STEP | | RESULT ▶ | ACTION TO TAKE |
|---|---|---|---|
| F1 | CHECK BRAKE FLUID LEVEL | | |
| | • Turn ignition switch ON.<br>• Pump brake pedal until pump motor starts.<br>• When pump motor stops check brake fluid level. | Low ▶ | CHECK system for external leaks. SERVICE as required. |
| | | Normal ▶ | GO to Step F2. |
| F2 | CHECK CONTINUITY FLUID LEVEL INDICATOR SWITCH | | |
| | • Disconnect 3-pin connector on fluid level indicator.<br>• Set multi-meter on 10x range. Connect to reservoir warning cap Pins 3 and 4. 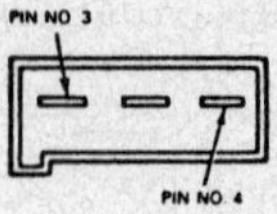<br>PIN NO. 3 — PIN NO. 4 | Above 10 ohms ▶ | GO to Step F3. |
| | | Below 10 ohms ▶ | REPLACE fluid level indicator cap. |

**Fig. 8 Test F, brake lamp On (Part 1 of 3)**

**Brake Warning Lamp On (With Anti-Lock Lamp Off, Parking Brake Released And Brake Lining Wear Checked)** — **Test F**

| TEST STEP | RESULT ▶ | ACTION TO TAKE |
|---|---|---|
| **F3** CHECK CONTINUITY PRESSURE WARNING SWITCH | | |
| • Turn ignition switch to RUN (position II), wait until motor stops running.<br>• Disconnect pressure warning switch 5-pin plug and connect multi-meter to Pins 1 and 2.<br>• Check for continuity.<br>PIN NO. 2 / PIN NO. 1 / PRESSURE WARNING SWITCH | Continuity (OK crossed) ▶ | REPLACE pressure warning switch. |
| | No continuity (OK) ▶ | GO to Step **F4**. |
| **F4** CHECK WIRING CONTINUITY | | |
| • Check for continuity between 3-pin fluid level indicator connector Pin 4 and body ground.<br>• Resistance should be 16 ohms.<br>PIN NO. 4 / PIN NO. 3 | (OK) ▶ | GO to **F5**. |
| | (OK crossed) ▶ | SERVICE or REPLACE Circuit 31B-17 BR/W as necessary. |

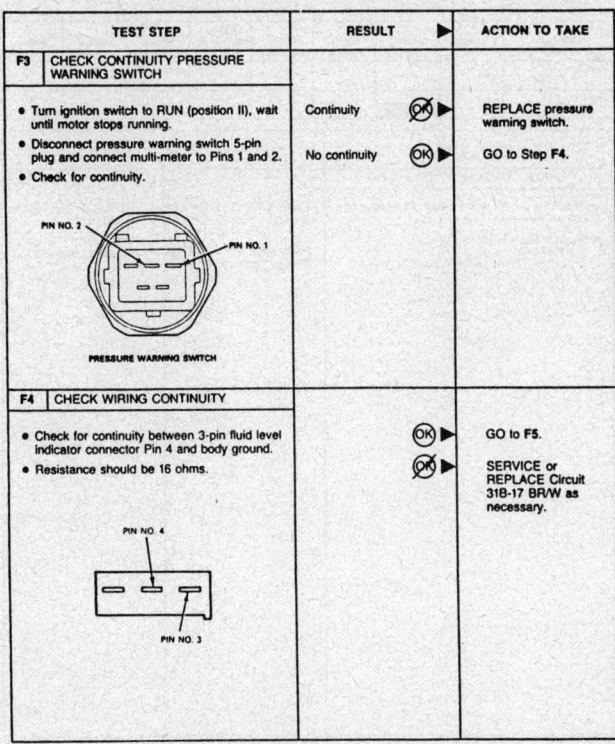

**Fig. 8 Test F, brake lamp On (Part 2 of 3)**

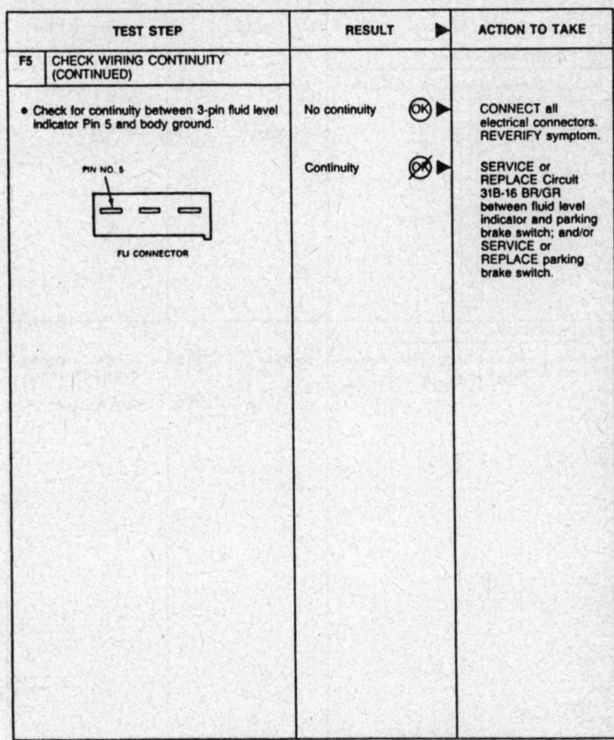

**Brake Warning Lamp On (With Anti-Lock Lamp Off, Parking Brake Released And Brake Lining Wear Checked)** — **Test F**

| TEST STEP | RESULT ▶ | ACTION TO TAKE |
|---|---|---|
| **F5** CHECK WIRING CONTINUITY (CONTINUED) | | |
| • Check for continuity between 3-pin fluid level indicator Pin 5 and body ground.<br>PIN NO. 5 / FLI CONNECTOR | No continuity (OK) ▶ | CONNECT all electrical connectors. REVERIFY symptom. |
| | Continuity (OK crossed) ▶ | SERVICE or REPLACE Circuit 31B-16 BR/GR between fluid level indicator and parking brake switch; and/or SERVICE or REPLACE parking brake switch. |

**Fig. 8 Test F, brake lamp On (Part 3 of 3)**

**No Anti-Lock Warning Lamp On When Ignition Switch Turned On** — **Test G**

WARNING LIGHTS SEQUENCE

| Warning Lamps | Ignition On | Cranking Engine | Engine Running | Vehicle Moving | Braking with/without Anti-Lock | Vehicle Stopped | Engine Idle | Ignition Off |
|---|---|---|---|---|---|---|---|---|
| Anti-Lock | | | | | | | | |
| Brake | | | | | | | | |

| TEST STEP | RESULT ▶ | ACTION TO TAKE |
|---|---|---|
| **G1** CHECK FOR VOLTAGE | | |
| • Turn ignition to RUN (position II).<br>• Apply parking brake.<br>• Check to see that parking brake warning indicator lights. | (OK) ▶ | GO to **G2**. |
| **G2** CHECK MAIN RELAY | | |
| • Turn ignition to OFF (position 0).<br>• Disconnect main power relay.<br>• Set ohmmeter to 1x scale.<br>• Check for continuity between relay Pin 30 and Pin 87a. | Continuity (OK) ▶ | GO to **G3**. |
| | No continuity (OK crossed) ▶ | REPLACE main relay. CHECK lamp operation. |
| **G3** CHECK CIRCUIT 31-49 BR | | |
| • Check for continuity between main power relay connector Pin 87a and ground. | Continuity (OK) ▶ | GO to **G4**. |
| | No continuity (OK crossed) ▶ | SERVICE open in Circuit 31-49 BR. CHECK lamp operation. |

**Fig. 9 Test G, no ABS lamp when ignition switch On (Part 1 of 3)**

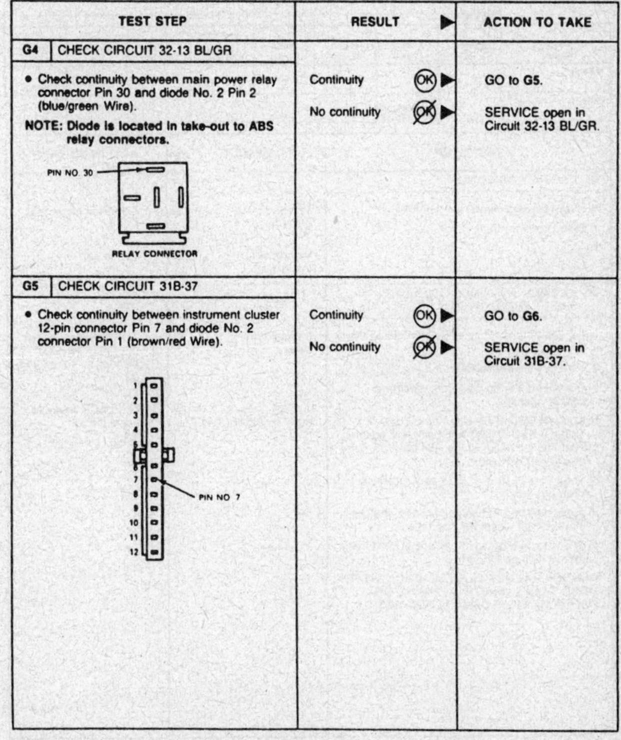

**No Anti-Lock Warning Lamp On When Ignition Switch Turned On** — **Test G**

| TEST STEP | RESULT ▶ | ACTION TO TAKE |
|---|---|---|
| **G4** CHECK CIRCUIT 32-13 BL/GR | | |
| • Check continuity between main power relay connector Pin 30 and diode No. 2 Pin 2 (blue/green Wire).<br>**NOTE: Diode is located in take-out to ABS relay connectors.**<br>PIN NO. 30 / RELAY CONNECTOR | Continuity (OK) ▶ | GO to **G5**. |
| | No continuity (OK crossed) ▶ | SERVICE open in Circuit 32-13 BL/GR. |
| **G5** CHECK CIRCUIT 31B-37 | | |
| • Check continuity between instrument cluster 12-pin connector Pin 7 and diode No. 2 connector Pin 1 (brown/red Wire).<br>1 2 3 4 5 6 7 8 9 10 11 12 / PIN NO. 7 | Continuity (OK) ▶ | GO to **G6**. |
| | No continuity (OK crossed) ▶ | SERVICE open in Circuit 31B-37. |

**Fig. 9 Test G, no ABS lamp when ignition switch On (Part 2 of 3)**

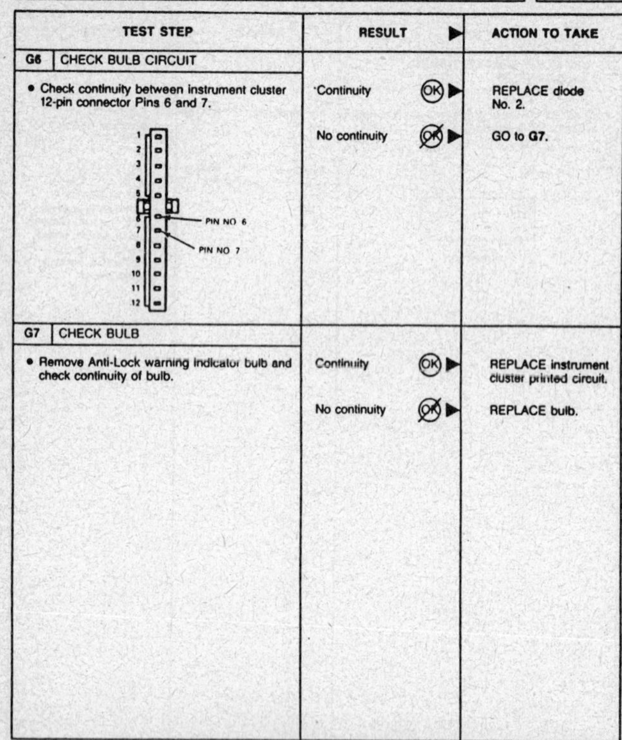

## No Anti-Lock Warning Lamp On When Ignition Switch Turned On (Cont'd) — Test G

| TEST STEP | RESULT ▶ | ACTION TO TAKE |
|---|---|---|
| **G6** CHECK BULB CIRCUIT | | |
| • Check continuity between instrument cluster 12-pin connector Pins 6 and 7. | Continuity (OK) ▶ | REPLACE diode No. 2. |
| | No continuity (NOT OK) ▶ | GO to **G7**. |
| **G7** CHECK BULB | | |
| • Remove Anti-Lock warning indicator bulb and check continuity of bulb. | Continuity (OK) ▶ | REPLACE instrument cluster printed circuit. |
| | No continuity (NOT OK) ▶ | REPLACE bulb. |



**Fig. 9 Test G, no ABS lamp when ignition switch On (Part 3 of 3)**

## Spongy Brake Pedal With/Without Anti-Lock Function (No Warning Lamp) — Test H

| Warning Lamps | Ignition On | Cranking Engine | Engine Running | Vehicle Moving | Braking with/without Anti-Lock | Vehicle Stopped | Engine Idle | Ignition Off |
|---|---|---|---|---|---|---|---|---|
| Anti-Lock | | | | | | | | |
| Brake | | | | | | | | |

(WARNING LIGHTS SEQUENCE)

| TEST STEP | RESULT ▶ | ACTION TO TAKE |
|---|---|---|
| **H1** CHECK COMPONENT MOUNTING | | |
| • Check for proper brake pedal and hydraulic unit attachment.<br>• Bleed brake system. | Pedal still spongy (NOT OK) ▶ | REPLACE hydraulic unit. |
| | Pedal feels normal (OK) ▶ | Condition corrected. |

**Fig. 10 Test H (Spongy pedal with/without ABS function)**

## Poor Vehicle Tracking During Anti-Lock Function (Warning Lamp Off) — Test J

| Warning Lamps | Ignition On | Cranking Engine | Engine Running | Vehicle Moving | Braking with/without Anti-Lock | Vehicle Stopped | Engine Idle | Ignition Off |
|---|---|---|---|---|---|---|---|---|
| Anti-Lock | | | | | | | | |
| Brake | | | | | | | | |

(WARNING LIGHTS SEQUENCE)

| TEST STEP | RESULT ▶ | ACTION TO TAKE |
|---|---|---|
| **J1** VERIFY CONDITION | | |
| • Verify condition exists as reported.<br>• Bleed brake system. | Vehicle tracks properly ▶ | Condition corrected. |
| | Vehicle still tracks poorly ▶ | GO to **J2**. |
| **J2** CHECK ANTI-LOCK OPERATION — LEFT FRONT WHEEL | | |
| • Lift vehicle and rotate wheels to assure they turn freely.<br>• Turn ignition switch OFF.<br>• Disconnect 35-Pin plug from electronic control module.<br>• Connect EEC-IV Breakout box, Tool T83L-50-EEC-IV with Anti-Lock test adapter, Tool T85P-50-ASA to the Anti-Lock 35-Pin plug wiring harness.<br>• Short Pins 2, 16 and 35 to each other at Breakout box.<br>• Apply moderate brake pedal effort and check that LH front wheel will not turn.<br>• Check to see that LH front wheel turns freely with ignition switch ON.<br>CAUTION: DO NOT LEAVE IGNITION ON FOR MORE THAN 1 MINUTE MAXIMUM, OR SOLENOID VALVE DAMAGE MAY RESULT. | If wheel turns freely ▶ | TURN ignition switch off. DISCONNECT wire leads. Go to Step J3. |
| | If wheel does not turn freely or pedal drops ▶ | REPLACE solenoid valve block. |

**Fig. 11 Test J, poor vehicle tracking during ABS function (Part 1 of 2)**

## Poor Vehicle Tracking During Anti-Lock Function (Warning Lamp Off) — Test J

| TEST STEP | RESULT ▶ | ACTION TO TAKE |
|---|---|---|
| **J3** CHECK ANTI-LOCK OPERATION — RIGHT FRONT WHEEL | | |
| • Short Pins 2, 15 and 34 to each other at Breakout box.<br>• Apply moderate brake effort. Check that RH front wheel does not turn.<br>• Check that RH front wheel turns freely with ignition switch ON.<br>CAUTION: DO NOT LEAVE IGNITION ON FOR MORE THAN 1 MINUTE MAXIMUM OR SOLENOID VALVE DAMAGE MAY RESULT. | Wheel truns freely ▶ | TURN ignition switch to OFF (position 0). DISCONNECT wire leads. GO to Step J4. |
| | Wheel does not turn freely or brake pedal drops ▶ | REPLACE solenoid valve block. |
| **J4** CHECK ANTI-LOCK OPERATION — REAR WHEELS | | |
| • Short Pins 2, 17 and 33 to each other at Breakout box.<br>• Apply moderate brake pedal pressure. Check that rear wheels will not turn.<br>• Check that rear wheels turn freely with ignition switch ON.<br>CAUTION: DO NOT LEAVE IGNITION ON MORE THAN 1 MINUTE MAXIMUM OR SOLENOID VALVE DAMAGE MAY RESULT. | Wheels turn freely ▶ | TURN ignition switch to OFF (position 0). DISCONNECT wire leads and Breakout box. LOWER vehicle. REVERIFY symptom. |
| | Wheels do not turn freely or brake pedal drops ▶ | REPLACE solenoid valve block. |

**Fig. 11 Test J, poor vehicle tracking during ABS function (Part 2 of 2)**

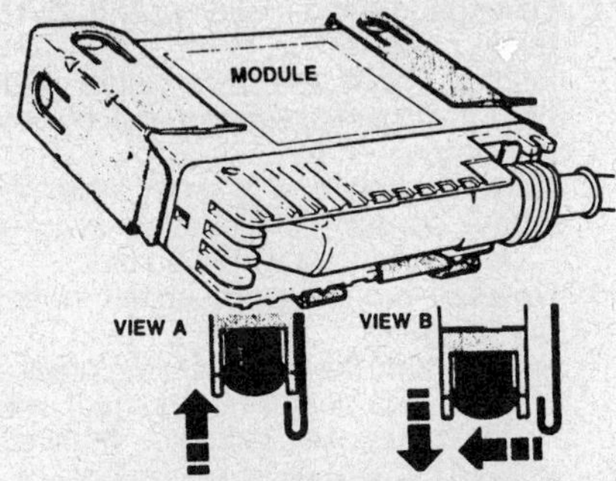


Fig. 12 Electronic control module replacement

2. Disconnect battery ground cable.
3. Wrap a clean cloth around base of accumulator to absorb residual brake fluid during removal.
4. Using an 8mm allen wrench, remove accumulator from hydraulic unit.
5. Cover base of accumulator with a clean cloth to prevent entry of contaminants.
6. Remove O-ring seal from accumulator and discard.
7. Reverse procedure to install, noting the following:
   a. **Torque** mounting bolts 25-33 ft. lbs.
   b. Check accumulator charge time by turning ignition switch to RUN position. Correct charge time is less than one minute.
   c. Bleed brake system and check for leaks. Check for proper operation of brake system.

## FLUID RESERVOIR

1. Discharge hydraulic pressure as described under "Hydraulic Pressure Relief."
2. Disconnect battery ground cable and ensure braking system pressure is fully discharged.
3. Disconnect fluid reservoir filler cap electrical connector. Remove filler cap.
4. Remove spring clip retaining low pressure hose to electrical pump.
5. Drain hydraulic fluid into container.
6. Remove allen head screw securing reservoir retaining bracket, then remove bracket.
7. Using two screwdrivers, carefully pry reservoir from hydraulic unit.
8. Remove and discard reservoir seals from hydraulic unit.
9. Remove low pressure hose from reservoir.
10. Reverse procedure to install, noting the following:
    a. Lubricate reservoir seals and connections with brake fluid.
    b. Bleed brake system as described under "System Bleed."
    c. Check brake system for proper operation.

## HYDRAULIC PUMP MOTOR

1. Discharge hydraulic pressure as described under "Hydraulic Pressure Relief."

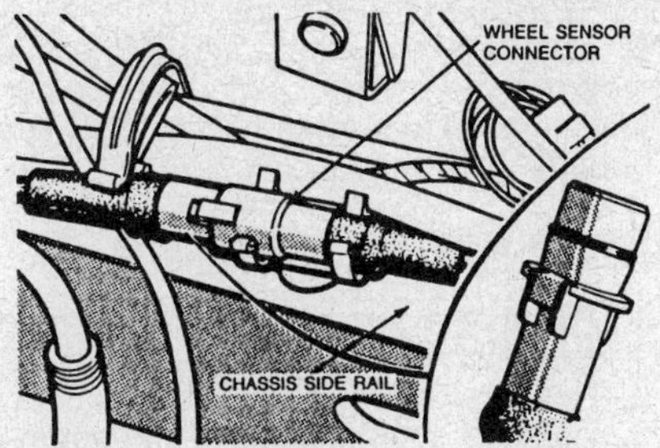


Fig. 13 Front wheel sensor removal

2. Disconnect battery ground cable.
3. Remove high-pressure line and fitting from pump body.
4. Remove accumulator as outlined above.
5. Disconnect electrical connector from pressure switch, then disconnect connector from pump motor as follows: Disconnect electrical connector from pump motor as follows:
   a. Pull back rubber boot covering connector.
   b. Pull back sleeve to release lock.
   c. Remove connector.
6. Remove pump housing to hydraulic accumulator assembly mounting bolt.
7. Remove pump housing assembly from hydraulic unit, then remove spring clip securing low-pressure hose to hydraulic pump.
8. Remove and clamp low-pressure hose, the remove pressure switch from pump housing.
9. Pry out pump mounting insulators and tubes from pump body.
10. Reverse procedure to install, noting the following:
    a. **Torque** retaining bolt to 5.2-6.6 ft. lbs.
    b. **Torque** high pressure line M10 flare fitting to 9-11 ft. lbs. and M12 flare fitting to 11-13 ft. lbs.
    c. Turn ignition switch to RUN position and check for hydraulic leaks.
    d. Allow pump to run until it shuts off, then bleed brake system and check for proper operation of ABS system.

## PRESSURE SWITCH

1. Discharge hydraulic pressure as described under "Hydraulic Pressure Relief."
2. Disconnect battery ground cable and pressure switch connector.
3. Using pressure switch socket tool No. T85P-20215-B or equivalent, remove pressure switch.
4. Remove and discard O-ring from pressure switch.
5. Reverse procedure to install, noting the following:
   a. Install new O-ring onto pressure switch.
   b. **Torque** pressure switch to 15-19 ft. lbs.
   c. Turn ignition switch to RUN position and check switch and pump operation.

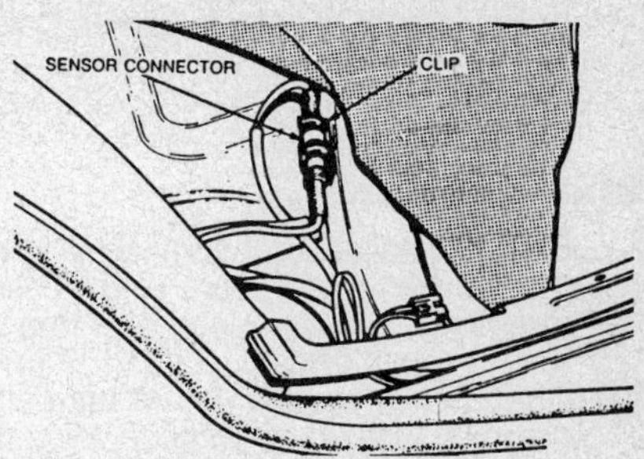


Fig. 14 Rear wheel sensor replacement

   d. Bleed brake system.

## ELECTRONIC CONTROL MODULE

1. Remove passenger side under-dash trim panel.
2. Remove module as follows:
   a. Push module upward, releasing lower catch (view A). **Fig. 12.**
   b. Swing module forward and lower from clip (view B).
3. Remove electrical connector from module by pressing in locking lever and pulling connector.
4. Reverse procedure to install.

## SENSOR RING

1. Remove hub cap.
2. Using a 40mm thin wall socket, loosen but do not remove axle stub shaft nut.
3. Remove wheel and tire assembly, then remove spring clip retaining rotor to hub.
4. Remove two caliper anchor bracket retaining bolts.
5. Remove parking brake cable from retaining bracket.
6. Remove brake pad wear sensor connector from retainer on caliper.
7. Remove caliper assembly from rotor, then remove rotor.
8. Remove six T-32 Torx head bolts securing axle stub shaft to halfshaft. Rotate halfshaft to gain access to all bolts.
9. Lift outer end of halfshaft upward and position away from stub shaft.
10. Remove axle stub shaft nut and washer.
11. Remove hub from axle stub shaft using 2-jaw puller tool No. D80L-1013-A or equivalent.
12. Remove axle stub shaft from rear carrier assembly.
13. Reverse procedure to install, noting the following:
    a. **Torque** six Torx head bolts to 28-32 ft. lbs.
    b. **Torque** axle stub shaft nut to 250-290 ft. lbs.

## FRONT WHEEL SENSOR

### Removal

1. Disconnect main wheel sensor connector. **Fig. 13.**
2. Remove bolt and washer securing

wheel sensor to spindle carrier. Carefully pull out sensor and O-ring.
3. Remove sensor loom from cable supports.

### Installation

1. Before installation, ensure wheel spindle sensor carrier bore and sensor mounting face are clean and free of rust or rough edges.
2. Coat sensor spindle carrier bore and chamfer with multi-purpose long-life lubricant C1AZ-19540-B or equivalent.
3. Install new O-ring on wheel sensor.
4. Coat sensor with multi-purpose long-life lubricant C1AZ-19540-B or equivalent. Push sensor firmly into spindle carrier bore until flush.
5. Install retaining washer and bolt. **Torque** to 6.2-8 ft. lbs.
6. Install sensor wiring into cable supports and connect sensor connector.
7. Check proper operation of ABS system.

## REAR WHEEL SENSOR

1. Raise and support vehicle, then remove wheel and tire assembly.
2. Remove rear seat cushion.
3. Remove scuff plate retaining screws, then remove scuff plate.
4. Fold back carpeting to gain access to wheel sensor plug connector.
5. Remove wheel sensor connector from clip, then disconnect connector. **Fig. 14.**
6. Pry out grommet and feed sensor wiring through floorpan.
7. Disengage hand brake cable from retaining bracket.
8. Remove front bolt from caliper slide pin. Lift front of caliper up and retain in position.
9. Remove bolt and washer retaining wheel sensor to mounting bracket. Carefully remove wheel sensor.
10. Reverse procedure to install, noting the following:
    a. Fill wheel sensor mounting bracket bore and coat wheel sensor with multi-purpose long-life lubricant C1AZ-19540-B or equivalent.
    b. **Torque** retaining bolt to 6.2-8 ft. lbs.
    c. **Torque** caliper slide pin front bolt to 23-26 ft. lbs.
    d. Ensure proper operation of ABS system.

# REAR DRIVE AXLES

## TABLE OF CONTENTS



# Except Merkur

## INDEX



## DRIVE AXLE IDENTIFICATION

**NOTE: The Plant Code Shown In Fig. 1 On The Axle Identification Tag Is Used To identify The Axle Assembly. The Plant Code Will Not Change As Long As That Particular Axle Assembly Never Undergoes An External Design Change. If An Internal Design Change Is Made To An Axle During The Production Life Of The Axle And That Internal Change Affects Service Parts Interchangeability, A Dash And Numerical Suffix Will Be Added To The Plant Code, Fig. 2**

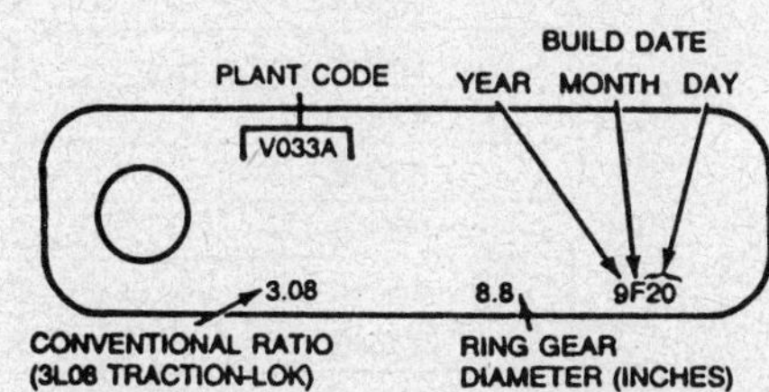


**Fig. 1 Rear axle identification tag.**

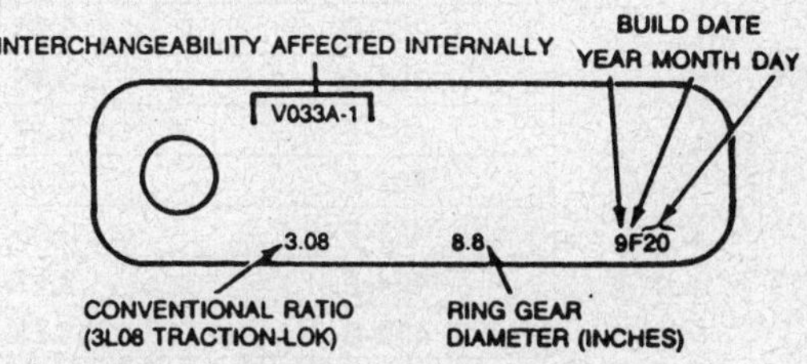


**Fig. 2 Rear axle identification tag w/internal modification.**

| Year | Axle Code | Gear Ratio |
|---|---|---|
| 1989 | 012-B | 2.73 |
| | 013-B | 2.73 |
| | 014-B | 3.08 |
| | 014-C | 3.08 |
| | 015-B | 3.08 |
| | 015-C | 3.08 |
| | 016-B | 3.27 |
| | 017-B | 3.27 |
| | 017-C | 3.27 |
| | 030-B | 2.73 |
| | 031-B | 2.73 |

| Year | Axle Code | Gear Ratio |
|---|---|---|
| 1989 (cont'd) | 033-B | 3.08 |
| | 034-B | 3.08 |
| | 037-C | 3.55 |
| | 037-B | 3.55 |
| | 038-B | 3.27 |
| | 039-A | 3.27 |
| | 201-A | 2.73 |
| | 203-F | 3.08 |
| | 205-F | 3.27 |
| | 266-D | 3.73 |
| | 281-D | 3.45 |

*Continued*

## DRIVE AXLE INDENTIFICATION—Continued

| Year | Axle Code | Gear Ratio |
|---|---|---|
| 1989 (cont'd) | 404-F | 3.08 |
| | 407-F | 3.27 |
| | 423-F | 3.08 |
| | 424-F | 3.27 |
| | 433-B | 3.73 |
| | 445-C | 3.08 |
| | 447-C | 3.08 |
| | 462-B | 3.08 |
| | 479-B | 3.08 |
| | 502-A | 3.27 |
| 1990 | 013-B | 2.73 |
| | 014-B | 3.08 |
| | 014-C | 3.08 |
| | 015-B | 3.08 |
| | 015-C | 3.08 |
| | 016-B | 3.27 |
| | 017-B | 3.27 |
| | 017-C | 3.27 |
| | 030-B | 2.73 |
| | 031-B | 2.73 |
| | 033-B | 3.08 |
| | 034-B | 3.08 |
| | 037-B | 3.55 |
| | 037-C | 3.55 |
| | 038-B | 3.27 |
| | 039-A | 3.27 |
| | 201-A | 2.73 |
| | 203-F | 3.08 |
| | 205-F | 3.27 |
| | 266-D | 3.73 |
| | 281-D | 3.45 |
| | 404-F | 3.27 |
| | 407-F | 3.27 |
| | 423-F | 3.08 |
| | 424-F | 3.27 |
| | 433-B | 3.73 |
| | 445-C | 3.08 |
| | 447-C | 3.08 |
| | 462-B | 3.08 |
| | 479-B | 3.08 |
| | 502-A | 3.27 |
| 1991 | 016-E | 3.27 |
| | 016-H | 3.27 |
| | 016-P | 3.27 |
| | 017-C | 3.27 |
| | 017-D | 3.27 |
| | 017-E | 3.27 |
| | 018-H | 3.56 |
| | 019-E | 3.55 |
| | 020-A | 3.08 |

| Year | Axle Code | Gear Ratio |
|---|---|---|
| 1991 (cont'd) | 025-A | 3.55 |
| | 030-A | 2.73 |
| | 030-B | 2.73 |
| | 030-D | 2.73 |
| | 031-A | 2.73 |
| | 031-B | 2.73 |
| | 031-D | 2.73 |
| | 033-A | 3.08 |
| | 033-B | 3.08 |
| | 033-D | 3.08 |
| | 033-E | 3.08 |
| | 033-G | 3.08 |
| | 033-GG | 3.08 |
| | 034-A | 3.08 |
| | 034-B | 3.08 |
| | 034-D | 3.08 |
| | 034-E | 3.08 |
| | 034-G | 3.08 |
| | 036-A | 3.55 |
| | 037-C | 3.55 |
| | 037-D | 3.55 |
| | 037-E | 3.55 |
| | 037-G | 3.55 |
| | 037-P | 3.55 |
| | 038-A | 3.27 |
| | 038-B | 3.27 |
| | 038-D | 3.27 |
| | 038-E | 3.27 |
| | 038-G | 3.27 |
| | 039-A | 3.27 |
| | 039-B | 3.27 |
| | 039-D | 3.27 |
| | 039-E | 3.27 |
| | 039-G | 3.27 |
| | 040-A | 3.08 |
| | 266-D | 3.73 |
| | 457-B | 2.73 |
| | 458-A | 2.73 |
| | 458-B | 2.73 |
| | 462-A | 3.08 |
| | 462-B | 3.08 |
| | 463-A | 3.08 |
| | 463-B | 3.08 |
| | 485-B | 3.27 |
| | 467-A | 3.45 |
| | 467-B | 3.45 |
| | 468-A | 3.45 |
| | 468-B | 3.45 |
| | 477-B | 2.73 |

*Continued*

## DRIVE AXLE INDENTIFICATION—Continued

| Year | Axle Code | Gear Ratio |
|---|---|---|
| 1991 (cont'd) | 478-B | 2.73 |
| | 479-B | 3.08 |
| | 480-A | 2.73 |
| | 482-B | 3.08 |
| | 485-B | 2.73 |
| | 486-B | 3.27 |
| | 487-B | 2.73 |
| | 488-B | 3.45 |

| Year | Axle Code | Gear Ratio |
|---|---|---|
| 1991 (cont'd) | 491-B | 2.73 |
| | 492-B | 3.27 |
| | 493-B | 2.73 |
| | 493-C | 3.45 |
| | 494-B | 3.08 |
| | 495-B | 3.08 |
| | 496-B | 3.27 |
| | 497-B | 3.45 |

| CONDITION | POSSIBLE SOURCE |
|---|---|
| • Noise is the same in all modes | • Road noise • Tire noise • Front wheel bearing noise • Pinion Bearings • Wheel Bearings • Axle Shaft Surface Finish |
| • Noise changes with type of road | • Road noise • Tire noise |
| • Noise tone lowers as vehicle speed is lowered | • Tire noise |
| • Noise most pronounced on turns | • Differential side and pinion gears |
| • Similar noise is produced with vehicle standing and driving | • Engine noise • Transmission noise |
| • Noise is in one or more modes (Drive, Cruise, Coast, Float) | • Ring and pinion gear |
| • Clunk on acceleration or deceleration | • Worn differential cross shaft in case |

REAR AXLE DIAGNOSIS

| CONDITION | POSSIBLE SOURCE | ACTION |
|---|---|---|
| • Excessive Rear Axle noise. | • Differential carrier | • Road test vehicle to ensure problem is rear axle noise rather than other system noise. |
| • Loud "Clunk" in the driveshaft when shifting from REVERSE to DRIVE. | • Driveshaft | • Raise vehicle, rotate driveshaft by hand to isolate problem as driveshaft or rear axle problem. Service or replace as required. |
| | • Rear axle shafts or carrier | • Remove and inspect. Service as necessary. |
| • Limited-slip or Traction-Lok axle does not work in snow, mud or on ice. | • Differential | • Perform Traction-Lok Differential Operation Check in this Section. Service as required. |
| • On turns, the rear axle has a high-pitched chattering noise (Limited-slip or Traction-Lok axles only). Slight chatter noise on slow turns after extended highway driving is considered acceptable and has no detrimental effect on the locking axle function. | • Lubricant | • Road test vehicle — Drive vehicle in tight circles — 5 clockwise and 5 counterclockwise. If chatter is still evident, flush and replace with E0AZ-19580-A Limited Slip Lubricant or equivalent — plus 4 ounces of C8AZ-19B546-A Friction Modifier or equivalent. |
| | • Differential | • Remove differential, service as required. |

**Fig. 3 Troubleshooting chart**

# TROUBLESHOOTING

Refer to troubleshooting chart **Fig. 3**, for rear axle symptoms.

# NOISE ACCEPTABILITY

A gear driven unit, especially a drive axle, will produce a certain amount of noise. Some noise is acceptable and may be audible at certain speeds or under various driving conditions such as a newly paved blacktop road. The slight noise is in no way detrimental to operation of the rear axle and may be considered normal.

With Traction-Lok limited slip differential axle, slight chatter noise on slow turns after extended highway driving is considered acceptable and has no detrimental affect on the locking axle function.

# LEAKAGE CONDITIONS

Most rear axle leakage conditions can be corrected without a teardown. However, it is important to clean the leaking area enough to identify the exact source of the leak.

A plugged or siezed jiggle cap vent will cause excessive seal lip wear due to internal pressure buildup. When a leak occurs, check cap by pressing down on it with index finger. If the cap moves up and down freely, it is working properly. If it does not move freely, it must be replaced.

Check axle lubricant level. Lubricant should be $^{9}/_{16}$ inch below bottom of filler hole.

## Drive Pinion Seal

When the drive pinion seal leaks, it is usually because of improper installation, or because of poor quality of the seal journal surface. Any damage to the seal bore (dings, dents, gouges, etc.) will distort the seal casing and allow leakage past the outer edge of the seal.

## Pinion Nut

Some models may experiance oil leakage past the threads of the pinion nut. The condition can be corrected by removing the nut and applying pipe sealant with Teflon part No. D8AZ-19554-A or equivalent on the pinion threads and nut face. **Ensure the correct procedure for setting the bearing preload is followed when the nut is installed.**

## Holes In Casting

The differential carrier may leak through small pockets in the metal. These pockets (casting leakage) are caused by gas bubbles in the casting process and are known as a porous condition or porosity.

Because there is always the danger of changing the axle's sound characteristics if torn down to replace the carrier, servicing the porosity is preferable. There are two recommended types of service procedures outlined below for this condition.

1. Peen a small amount of body lead into the hole, then seal the pocket with Epoxy Sealer Metallic Plastic part No. C6A7-A9554-A or equivalent.
2. In larger pockets, drill a shallow hole and tap it for a small setscrew. Install the setscrew and seal it over with Epoxy Sealer Metallic Plastic part No. C6A7-A9554-A or equivalent.

### Axle Vent

There have been some occurrences of lubricant leaking through the axle vent. This may be caused by a clogged or sticking axle vent cap. If this is the case, the vent assembly should be replaced, use Stud and Bearing Mount part No. EOAZ-19554-BA or equivalent on threads of vent to ensure retention.

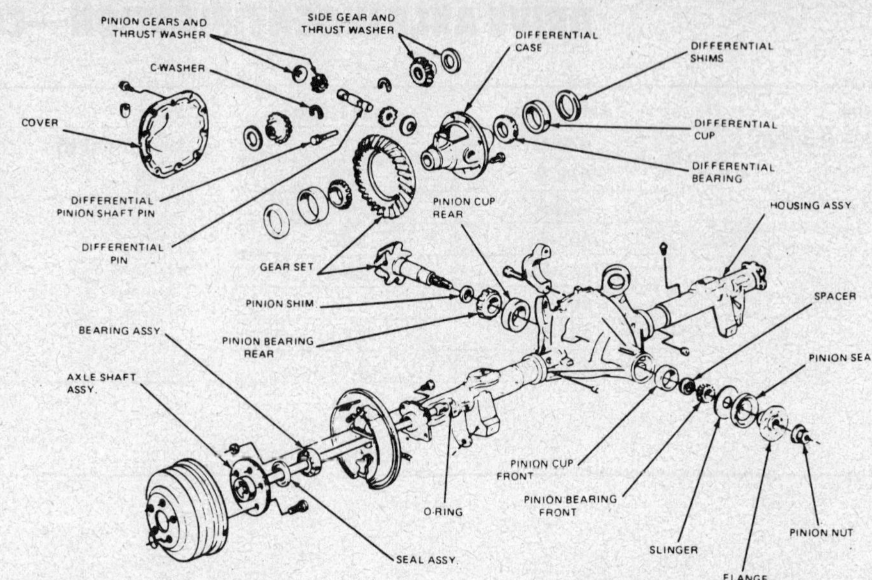


**Fig. 4 Exploded view of 7½ & 8.8 inch ring gear rear axle**

## AXLE NOISE

### Gear Noise

Gear noise is the typical "howling" or "whining" of the ring gear and pinion due to an improper gear pattern, gear damage, or improper bearing preload. It can occur at various speeds and driving conditions, or it can be continuous.

### Chuckle

Chuckle is a particular "rattling" noise that sounds like a stick against the spokes of a bicycle wheel. It occurs while decelerating from 40 mph and can be heard all the way to a stop. The frequency varies with the speed of the vehicle.

### Knock

Knock is very similar to chuckle, though it may be louder and occurs on acceleration or deceleration.

### Clunk

Clunk may be a metallic noise heard when the automatic transmission is engaged in reverse or drive, or it may occur when throttle is applied or released. It is caused by backlash somewhere in the driveline, or loose suspension components.

### Bearing Whine

Bearing whine is a high pitched sound similar to a whistle. It is usually caused by malfunctioning pinion bearings, which are operating at driveshaft speed. Bearing noise occurs at all driving speeds; this distinguishes it from gear whine, which usually comes and goes as speed changes.

### Bearing Rumble

Bearing rumble sounds like marbles being tumbled. This condition is usually caused by a malfunctioning wheel bearing. The lower pitch is because the wheel bearing turns at only about one-third of driveshaft speed. In addition, wheel bearing noise may be high pitched, similar to gear noise but will be evident in all four driving modes.

### Chatter On Cornering

Chattering noise when cornering is a condition where the whole rear end vibrates only when the vehicle is moving. The vibration is plainly felt as well as heard. In conventional axles, extra differential thrust washers cause a condition of partial lockup which creates this chatter. Chatter noise on Traction-Lok axles can usually be traced to erratic movement between adjacent clutch plates and can be corrected with a lubricant change.

### Click At Engagement

Click at engagement is a condition on axles of a slight noise, distinct from a "clunk" that happens in Reverse or Drive engagement. It can be corrected by installing a slinger between the companion flange and front pinion bearing.

## VIBRATION CONDITIONS

Few vibration conditions are caused by the axle. Most vibration in the rear end is caused by tires or driveline angle.

**Vehicles equipped with a traction-Lok differential will always have both wheels driving. If, while the vehicle is being serviced, only one wheel is raised off the floor and the rear axle is driven by the engine, the wheel on the floor could drive the vehicle off the safety stand. Ensure both rear wheels are raised off the floor.**

### Tires

**Some vehicles are equipped with directional tires (see tire rotation arrows on tire sidewall). If a directional tire is removed for service, it must be remounted in its original location.**

**Do not balance the rear wheels and tires while they are mounted on the vehicle. Possible tire disintegration and/or differential failure could result, causing personal injury and/or extensive component damage. Use off-vehicle wheel and tire balancer only.**

A vibration can sometimes be corrected by properly rotating or inflating the tires. The best tires should be placed on the rear to minimize vibration, especially on vehicles with rear coil springs.

### Driveline Angle

An incorrect driveline (pinion) angle can often be detected by the driving condition when vibration occurs.

1. A vibration during coasting from 35 to 45 mph is often caused by a high pinion angle.
2. A vibration during acceleration from 35 to 45 mph may indicate a lower than specified pinion angle.

## TRACTION-LOK DIFFERENTIAL OPERATION CHECK

A Traction-Lok differential can be checked for proper operation without removing it from the axle housing using procedure outlined below:

1. Raise and support one rear wheel, then remove the wheel cover.
2. Install adapter for Traction-Lok differential tool No. T66L-4204-A or equivalent, then connect a torque wrench of at least a 200 foot pound capacity.
3. Rotate the axle shaft. **Ensure the transmission is in Neutral, one wheel is on the floor, and the other rear wheel is raised off the floor.**

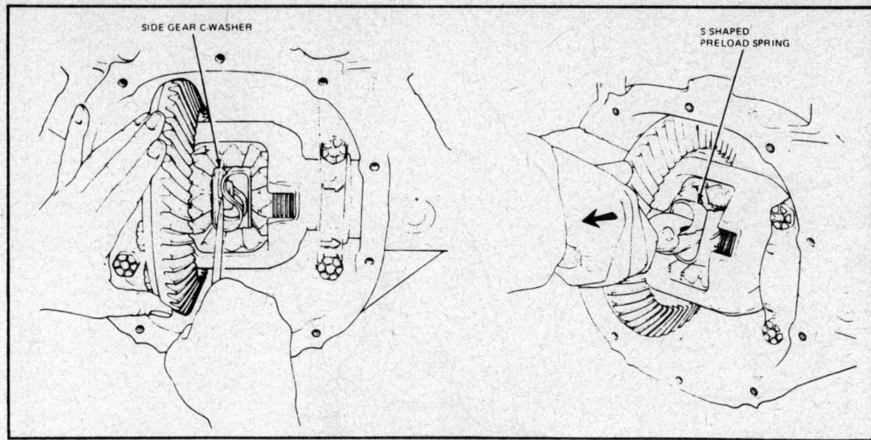


**Fig. 5 Removing C-clips and "S" shaped preload spring. Ford Traction-Lok**

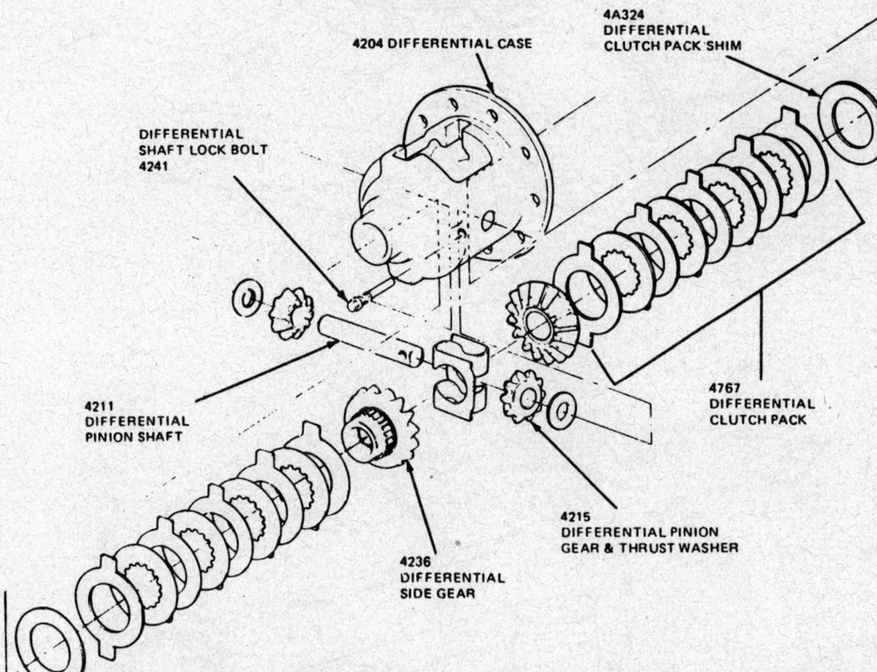


**Fig. 6 Exploded view of Ford Traction-Lok**

4. The breakaway torque required to start rotation should be at least 40 ft. lbs. The initial breakaway torque may be higher than the continuous turning torque, this is considered normal.
5. The axle shaft should turn with even pressure throughout the check without slipping or binding. If the torque reading is less than specified, check the differential for improper assembly.

# REMOVAL

## DIFFERENTIAL CASE ASSEMBLY

1. Raise and support rear of vehicle, then loosen axle housing cover bolts and allow lubricant to drain into suitable container, **Fig. 4.**
2. Remove axle housing cover, then proceed as follows:
   a. Wipe excess lubricant from inside axle housing, then visually inspect parts for wear and/or damage.
   b. Rotate gears and check for roughness, indicating damaged bearings or gears.
   c. Install suitable dial indicator on axle housing cover flange, then check and record ring gear back face run-out. Maximum back face run-out is .004 inch.
3. Remove rear axles and propeller shaft. Refer to "Rear Axle & Suspension" section for procedures.
4. Scribe reference marks on differential bearing caps for assembly reference, then loosen bearing cap bolts. **Observe and record direction the arrows are facing on the bearing caps. During installation, the arrows must face in the same direction.**
5. Using suitable tool, pry differential case, bearing cups and shims out of housing until loose in the bearing caps. Remove bearing caps, then the differential assembly. Mark which side cups and shims came from for reference during reassembly.

## DRIVE PINION

1. Scribe reference mark between drive pinion and companion flange, then hold flange with suitable tool and remove pinion nut and pinion flange.
2. Using suitable soft faced hammer, drive pinion out of front bearing cone and remove from rear of axle housing.
3. Remove oil seal and front bearing cone and roller from pinion housing.
4. Using suitable arbor press and adapters, remove rear pinion bearing.
5. Using suitable micrometer, measure and record thickness of shim which is found under rear bearing cone.
6. Remove pinion bearing cups from pinion housing with suitable brass drift. Install cups using suitable bearing cup installer. Cups are not properly installed if a .015 feeler gauge can be installed between cup and bottom of bore at any point around the cup. **If any bearing cups are replaced, the respective bearing cone and roller must be replaced.**

# DIFFERENTIAL CASE DISASSEMBLY

## EXCEPT TRACTION-LOK LIMITED SLIP DIFFERENTIAL

1. If differential bearings are to be replaced, remove and replace with suitable puller.
2. If the ring gear backlash measured during removal exceeded specifications, proceed as follows:
   a. Install differential bearing cups on cones, then install differential case in rear housing with drive pinion removed.
   b. Install a .265 inch shim on left side of case, then install bearing cap and tighten bolts finger tight. Install progressively larger shims on right side of case until the largest shim selected can be installed with a slight drag. Install bearing cap and **torque** bolts to 70-85 ft. lbs.
3. Rotate differential several turns in either direction to ensure free rotation and to seat bearings.
4. Mount suitable dial indicator to axle housing, then check ring gear back face run-out. Ring gear back face run-out should be within .004 inch. If ring gear back face run-out is now within specifications, the original reading was caused by insufficient differential bearing preload. If ring gear back face run-out is still not within

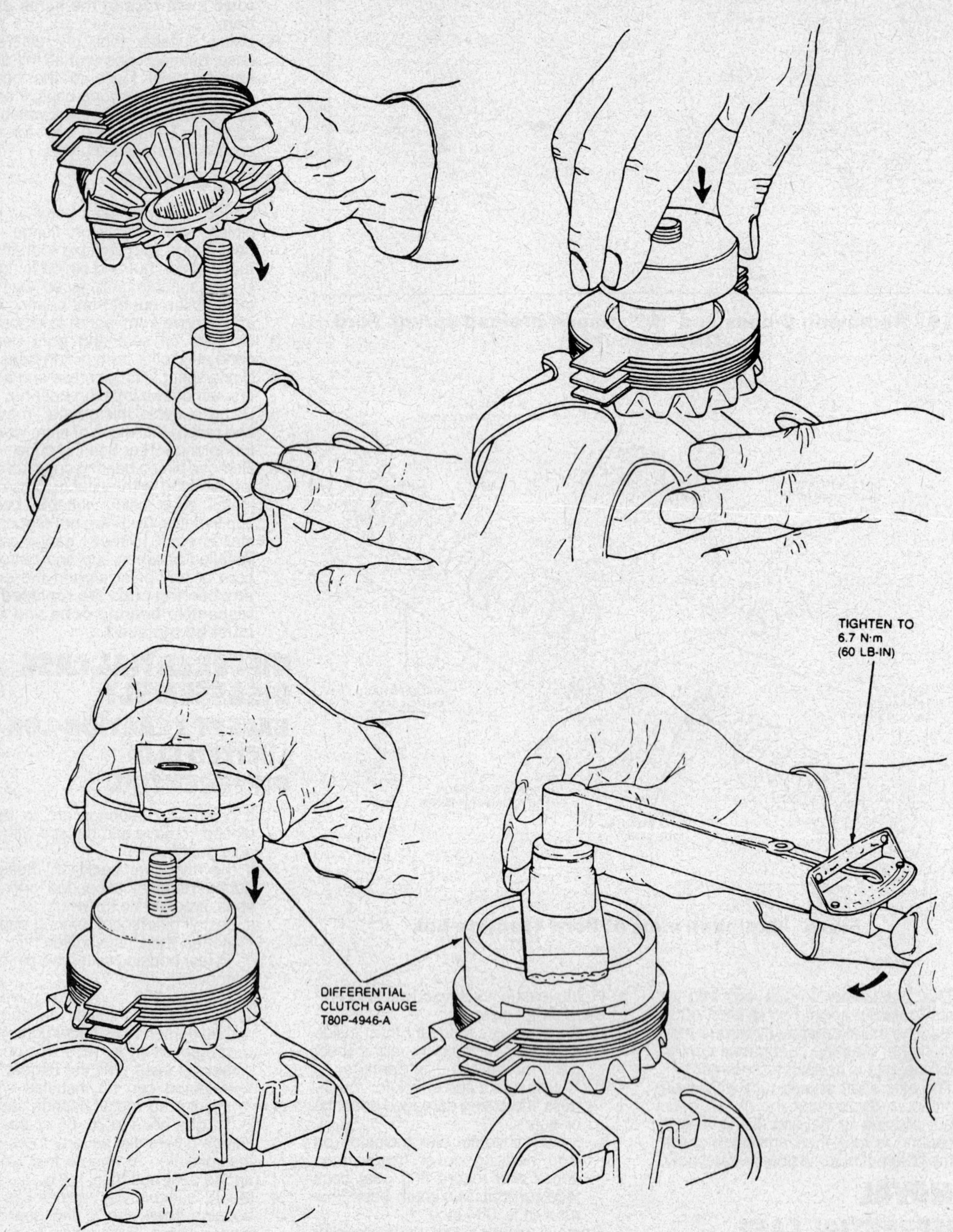


Fig. 7 Measuring shim thickness. Ford Traction-Lok

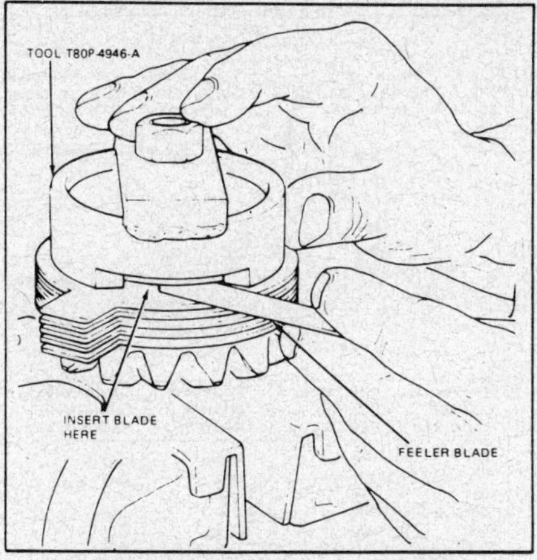


**Fig. 8 Installing tool T80P-4946-A or equivalent to measure shim thickness. Ford Traction-Lok**

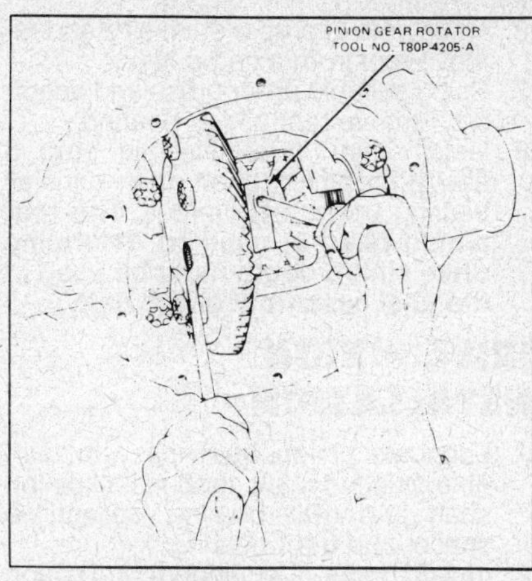


**Fig. 9 Pinion gear removal & installation. Ford Traction-Lok**

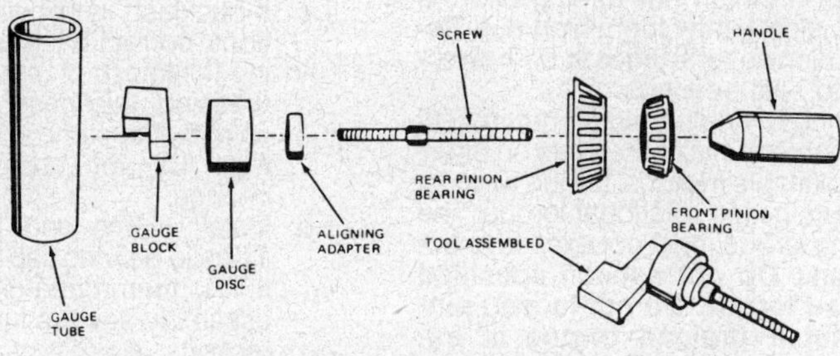


**Fig. 10 Rear axle pinion depth gauge**

specifications, proceed to step 6.

5. Remove differential case from axle housing, then remove ring gear. Install differential case less ring gear in housing following procedures given above.
6. Check differential case run-out. Run-out should be within .004 inch. If run-out is now within specifications, ring gear is out of specifications and should be replaced. If run-out is not within specifications, the differential case is damaged and should be replaced.

### TRACTION-LOK LIMITED SLIP DIFFERENTIAL

For differential case and ring gear run-out checks and differential bearing replacement, refer to "Except Traction-Lok Limited Slip Differential."

1. Remove and discard ring gear to differential case attaching bolts.
2. Tap on ring gear using a suitable mallet and remove ring gear from case.
3. Remove pinion shaft lock screw and pinion shaft.
4. Remove preloaded "S" shaped spring, **Fig. 5. Use caution when removing "S" shaped spring, since it is under tension.**
5. Rotate pinion gears and thrust washers using 12 inch socket extension inserted into pinion gear rotator T80P-4205-A or equivalent until they can be removed through access hole.
6. Remove left and right side gears, clutch packs and shims, **Fig. 6.** Note order of removal and side removed from and tag for reference during assembly.

## CLEANING & INSPECTION

### EXCEPT TRACTION-LOK LIMITED SLIP DIFFERENTIAL

Clean all parts in suitable solvent. Dry all parts except bearings with compressed air or shop towels. Allow bearings to air dry or dry with shop towels. Do not use compressed air to dry bearings, as damage may result.

Inspect differential bearings and cups for wear, pitting, galling, flat spots or cracks. Any bearing or cup showing any signs of wear or damage must be replaced. Bearings and respective cups must be replaced as an assembly only. Do not attempt to interchange bearings and cups as bearing life will be affected.

Inspect non-machined differential case surfaces for nicks and burrs which can be removed with an oil stone or fine tooth file. Inspect pinion shaft bore to ensure it is not elongated or worn. If damage is evident, differential case must be replaced. Inspect machined differential surfaces and counterbores. They must be smooth and free of nicks, gouges, cracks and other visible damage. If damage is evident, differential case must be replaced.

Inspect pinion shaft for excessive wear, scoring or galling. Ensure shaft is smooth and concentric. If any wear or damage is evident, replace shaft. Inspect pinion shaft lock pin for damage and to ensure it has a snug fit in differential case. Replace lock pin or case as necessary.

Inspect pinion and ring gears for worn or chipped teeth, cracks, damaged bearing journals or attaching bolt threads. If any of the above are evident, replace ring gear and pinion as a matched set.

Inspect pinion and side gears. Gears must exhibit a uniform contact pattern without any signs of cracks, wear, scoring or galling. If any of the above are evident, replace all the gears. Inspect thrust washers for wear and replace as necessary.

Inspect pinion and ring gears for worn or chipped teeth, cracks, damaged bearing journals or attaching bolt threads. If any of the above are evident, replace ring gear and pinion as a matched set.

Inspect axle shaft C-locks (if equipped) for signs of cracks or wear and replace as necessary.

### TRACTION-LOC LIMITED SLIP DIFFERENTIAL

The cleaning and inspection of these units is the same as for conventional differentials except that cleaning solvent should not be allowed to contact the clutch plates. The clutch plates should be wiped clean only. In addition, the following steps should be performed which apply to the Traction-Loc differential only.

Visually inspect clutch packs, side gears, pinion gears and pinion shaft for damage or wear and replace as necessary.

Place each clutch pack without shims into tool T80P-4946-A or equivalent, **Fig. 7. Torque** nut to 60 inch lbs. Using feeler gauge, determine thickness of new shims by inserting thickest blade possible between clutch pack and tool, **Fig. 8,** and note size for use during reassembly.

## ASSEMBLY & ADJUSTMENT

### DIFFERENTIAL CASE ASSEMBLY

#### EXCEPT TRACTION-LOK LIMITED SLIP DIFFERENTIAL

1. Install replacement ring gear (if removed). Apply suitable locking compound to new bolts and **torque** to 70-85 ft. lbs.

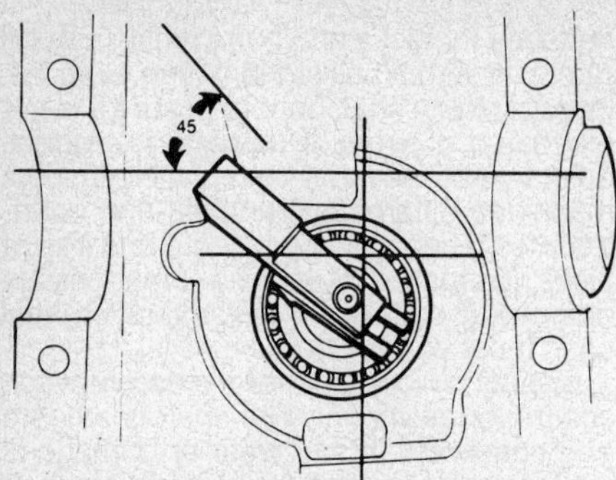


**Fig. 11 Pinion depth gauge block installation**

### TRACTION-LOK LIMITED SLIP DIFFERENTIAL

1. Apply suitable lubricant to clutch plates, then install left side gear, clutch pack and new shim into differential case. Repeat procedure for right hand side.
2. Install pinion gears and thrust washers 180° apart and in contact with side gears.
3. Align gears with pinion shaft bore, **Fig. 9**, using 12 inch socket extension inserted in pinion shaft rotator.
4. Install "S" shaped preload spring into differential using soft faced hammer.

## DETERMINING DRIVE PINION DEPTH

Prior to determining drive pinion depth, clean pinion bearing cups and differential bearing pedestals thoroughly to ensure an accurate reading. Apply only a light oil film to bearing assemblies to avoid false readings.

1. Assemble aligning adapter, gauge disc and gauge block to tool T79P-4020-A, **Fig. 10.**
2. Place rear pinion bearing over aligning adapter, then insert tool and bearing in rear pinion bearing cup in pinion housing bore. Place front pinion bearing over screw in front pinion bearing cup and assemble tool handle onto screw. **Torque** handle to 20 ft. lbs. Ensure tool is mounted securely between front and rear bearings.
3. Rotate gauge block several half turns to ensure bearings are seated properly. Rotational **torque** should be 20 ft. lbs. with new bearings. Set gauge block at an angle approximately 45° from horizontal, **Fig. 11.**
4. Install gauge tube in differential bearing mounts, then install bearing caps and bearing cap bolts.
5. Use pinion shims to determine pinion depth by inserting shims between gauge block and gauge tube. The correct shim will fit with a slight drag. Do not attempt to force a shim between block and tube. **Do not use shims that are bent, dirty, nicked or mutilated as a gauge.**
6. Make note of proper shim size and remove tool from axle housing.
7. Using suitable arbor press and adapters, remove rear pinion bearing.
8. Install shim determined in step 5 above on pinion shaft, then reinstall bearing using arbor press. **The rear pinion bearing used to determine drive pinion depth must be used in the final assembly of the axle.**

## DRIVE PINION INSTALLATION

1. Lubricate pinion bearings with suitable axle lubricant, then install pinion shaft and rear bearing, collapsible spacer and front bearing.
2. Install slinger (if equipped) and pinion oil seal, then insert pinion flange in seal and hold firmly in place against front bearing. From rear of housing, insert pinion shaft into flange.
3. Install pinion nut. While holding pinion flange, tighten nut only enough to remove bearing endplay. When an increase in pinion nut turning effort is noted, stop tightening pinion nut. Rotate pinion several times in both directions to seat bearings.
4. Continue to tighten pinion nut in very small increments, then, every so often, using suitable inch lbs. torque wrench, measure pinion rotational torque. The rotating torque must not exceed specifications. **Do not exceed specified preload torque. Do not loosen pinion nut if preload torque is exceeded. If preload torque is exceeded, remove pinion nut, yoke, oil seal, slinger (if equipped) and collapsible spacer. Replace collapsible spacer and oil seal with new ones and repeat procedure.**

## DIFFERENTIAL CASE INSTALLATION

1. Apply suitable axle lubricant to differential bearing bores.
2. Place differential bearing cups on bearings, then set differential assembly in axle housing. **If ring gear and pinion gear have punch marks, assemble ring gear in carrier so that marked tooth on pinion is indexed between the marked teeth of ring gear.**
3. Check and adjust backlash as follows:
   a. Mount suitable dial indicator on axle housing cover flange, then measure ring gear backlash. If backlash is within specifications, proceed to step f. If backlash is not within specifications, proceed to step c. If backlash is zero, proceed to step b.
   b. If backlash measured above is zero, add .020 inch (.5 mm) to right side of case and subtract .020 inch (.5 mm) from left side of case, then recheck backlash. If backlash is now within specifications, proceed to step d.
   c. If backlash is not within specifications, correct backlash by increasing thickness of one shim and decreasing thickness on the other shim by the same amount. Refer to **Fig. 12,** for approximate shim change.
   d. Install shims and bearing caps. **Torque** bearing cap bolts to 70-85 ft. lbs., then rotate differential case assembly several turns in both directions.
   e. Check backlash. If backlash is within specifications, proceed to step f. If not within specifications, repeat step c.
   f. Increase both left and right side shims by .006 inch to provide proper differential bearing preload. Ensure shims are fully seated and the case assembly turns freely.
   g. Using suitable white marking compound applied to ring gear, check tooth mesh contacting pattern. **Tooth mesh contacting pattern can be improved by installing the propeller shaft and axle assemblies and rotating both tires in the drive and coast direction.**
   h. Contacting pattern should be within the primary area of the ring gear tooth surface avoiding narrow contact with the outer perimeter of tooth. Inspect pattern on the drive (pull) side of the ring gear. If serious error is determined, recheck pinion shim selection.
4. Install axle housing cover, driveshaft and axle assemblies. Refer to "Rear Axles, Propeller Shaft & Brakes" for procedures.
5. Fill rear axle assembly with axle lubricant recommended by manufacturer. On models equipped with 7½ inch Traction-Lok differentials, subtract 4 ounces of axle lubricant and replace with 4 ounces of Friction Modifier C8AZ-19546-A or equivalent.

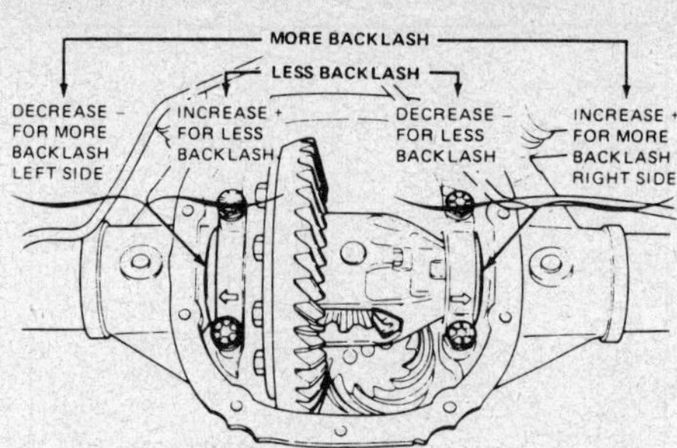


| BACKLASH CHANGE REQUIRED | THICKNESS CHANGE REQUIRED | BACKLASH CHANGE REQUIRED | THICKNESS CHANGE REQUIRED |
|---|---|---|---|
| .001 | .002 | .009 | .012 |
| .002 | .002 | .010 | .014 |
| .003 | .004 | .011 | .014 |
| .004 | .006 | .012 | .016 |
| .005 | .006 | .013 | .018 |
| .006 | .008 | .014 | .018 |
| .007 | .010 | .015 | .020 |
| .008 | .010 | | |

**Fig. 12 Rear axle backlash adjustment**

# Merkur

## INDEX



## DRIVE AXLE IDENTIFICATION

| Year | Axle Code | Gear Ratio |
|---|---|---|
| 1989 | ① | 3.36 |
| | ② | 3.64 |

①—Automatic transmission.
②—Manual transmission.

**NOISE CONDITIONS**

**Bearing Noise**
- Half Shaft CV Joint
- Pinion Bearing
- Wheel Bearing

**Chatter on Corners**
- Differential Thrust Washers

**Chuckle Noise**
- Differential Gear Clearance
- Damaged Gear Teeth

**Clunk Noise**
- Stub Shaft Spline Fit
- Stub Shaft C-Clips Missing, Worn or Wrong Fit
- Total Axle Backlash

**Gear Howl and Whine**
- Check Bearing Preload
- Check Gear Set Backlash
- Incorrect Pinion Depth
- Inspect Gear Set

**Knock Noise**
- Gear Tooth Damage
- Ring Gear Bolts

**NON-AXLE NOISES**
- Exhaust
- Grille Whistle
- Tires
- Trim Moulding Whistle

**LEAKAGE CONDITIONS**

- Axle Cover Sealant
- Stub Shaft Seals
- Axle Vent and/or Hose
- Casting Porosity (Holes in Casting)
- Drive Pinion Nut
- Drive Pinion Seal

**VIBRATION CONDITIONS**

- Half Shaft Bent
- Drive Pinion Stem and Flange
- Tires
- Universal Joint
- Center Bearing

**INOPERATIVE CONDITIONS**

- Axle Lock-Up
- Broken Axle Shaft
- Broken Gear Teeth
- Broken Pinion Stem

**Fig. 1 Troubleshooting chart**

## TROUBLESHOOTING

Refer to **Fig. 1,** for troubleshooting of rear drive axle.

## DISASSEMBLY

### AXLE ASSEMBLY

1. Mount axle assembly into holding fixture T57L-500-B or equivalent and position drain pan under axle.
2. Remove cover attaching bolts, then the cover.
3. Remove stub shaft C-clips, **Fig. 2.**
4. Remove stub shafts.
5. Mark left and right bearing carriers for assembly.
6. Remove stub shaft oil seals.
7. Remove bearing carrier lock plates.
8. Using a suitable tool, remove bearing carriers.
9. Remove and discard bearing carrier O-rings.
10. Remove differential assembly from case.
11. Remove companion flange attaching nut.
12. Using tool No. D80L-1002-L or equivalent, remove companion flange.
13. Remove pinion oil seal.
14. Remove staking from pinion nuts.
15. Remove pinion nut. **If pinion has a left hand thread, remove nut by turning the spline socket counterclockwise while holding the pinion nut socket stationary.**
16. Discard pinion nut.
17. Remove pinion and pinion inner bearing and collapsible spacer.
18. Remove spacer from pinion shaft. Discard spacer.
19. Remove pinion outer bearing from case.

### PINION BEARING CUPS

1. Remove bearing cup from case using tool D78P-1225-B or equivalent.
2. Discard pinion depth shim under inner bearing cup.

### PINION INNER BEARING

1. Remove pinion inner bearing using tool No. T71P-4621-B or equivalent.
2. Remove bearing from case.

### DIFFERENTIAL SIDE BEARING CONES

Using tools T77F-4220-B1 and T77F-4220-B2 or equivalent, remove bearing cones from differential assembly.

### DIFFERENTIAL CASE

1. Remove bolts securing ring gear to the differential case flange.
2. Using a brass drift and hammer, remove ring gear from differential case.

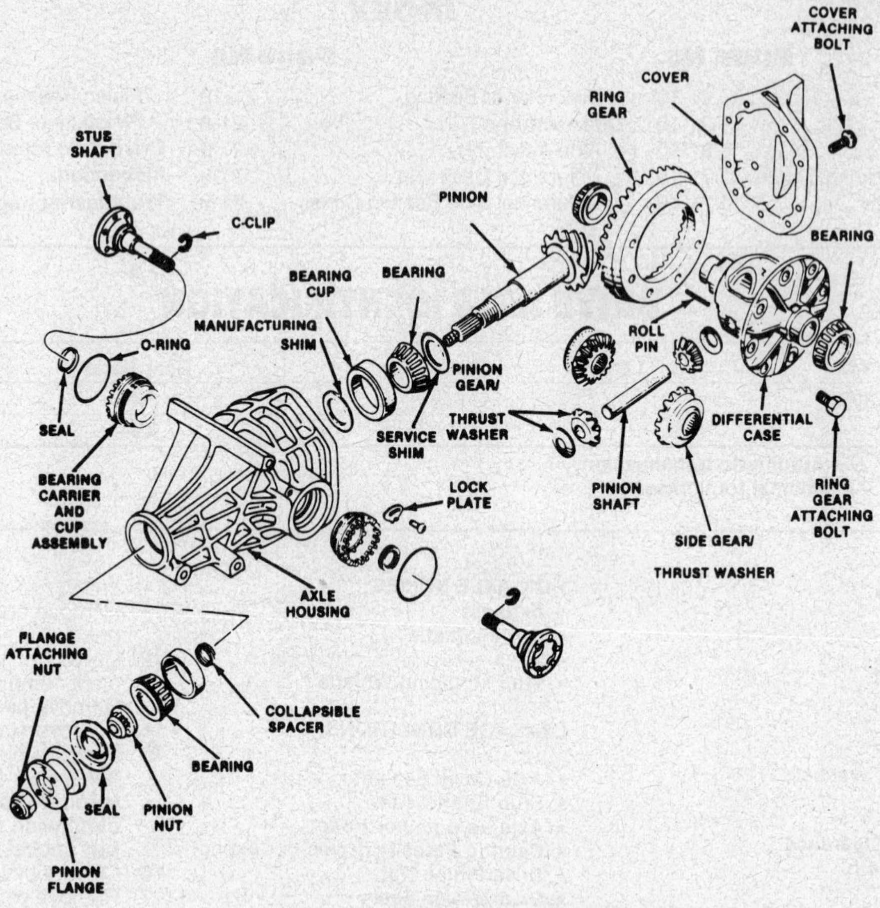


**Fig. 2 Exploded view of rear axle**

3. Drive pinion shaft roll pin out of case.
4. Drive pinion shaft from case.
5. Rotate side gears until the pinions revolve into the openings in the case.
6. Remove pinions, side gears and thrust washer.

## INSPECTION

Inspect all disassembled components for excessive wear and/or damage. Worn or damaged axle components must be replaced as necessary. Check side gear clearance. Check clearance between side gears and thrust washers. If clearance exceeds .006 inch, replace thrust washers.

## ASSEMBLY

### DIFFERENTIAL CASE

1. Install thrust washers onto side gears and position into differential case.
2. Install thrust washers onto pinions and mesh them with the side gears.
3. Rotate side gears to position the pinions in the differential case.
4. Install pinion shaft, aligning roll pin holes in shaft and case.
5. Install pinion shaft roll pin.
6. Position ring gear onto differential case and install new mounting screws. Torque screws progressively in a crisscross pattern to draw the ring gear evenly on the case. **Torque** screws to 58-62 ft. lbs. on Scorpio models, or 55-66 ft. lbs. on XR4Ti models.

### DIFFERENTIAL SIDE BEARING CONES

1. Using tool T85M-4221-A or equivalent, press new bearings onto differential case hubs.
2. Ensure bearings are completely and evenly seated in case hubs.

### PINION INNER BEARING

**Do not install a new bearing at this time. The bearing will be used with the pinion depth gauge tools during axle assembly.**

### PINION BEARING CUPS

1. Position a standard 2 mm pinion depth shim in the inner bearing cup bore.
2. Lubricate bearing cup bore.
3. Install inner bearing cup into bore using the following tools:
   a. Pinion bearing cup replacer tool T85M-4616-A. Position this tool against the inner cup.
   b. Pinion bearing cup replacer tool.
   c. Draw bolt T75T-1176-A or equivalents.

### AXLE ASSEMBLY

1. Lubricate pinion bearings with suitable grease.
2. Assemble pinion bearings and dummy pinion depth tools into rear axle case as shown in **Fig. 3**. Ensure gauge screw is tight in the gauge disc before assembling the tool.
3. Hold gauge disc stationary and gradually tighten the tool handle until a rolling **torque** of 14-18 inch lbs. is mea-

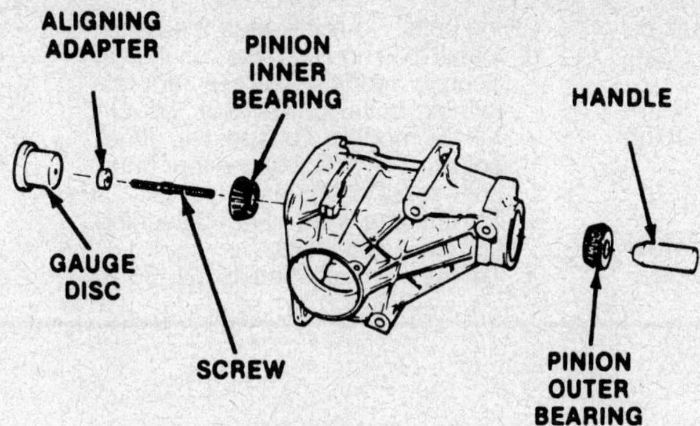


**Fig. 3 Installing depth tools**

sured at the pinion depth tool handle. **Before conducting the rolling torque check, turn tool shaft ten times to seat the bearings. Any time the tool is loosened or tightened, rotate the pinion ten times before another rotational torque check is made.**

4. Position pinion depth gauge tool tube T85M-4020-A1 or equivalent into case. Ensure tube gauging surface is aligned with gauge disc, then install bearing carriers. The bearing carriers must be installed in their original case bores and without the O-ring seals.
5. Thread the bearing carriers evenly into the case. When the carriers contact the gauge tube, snug them down to remove all endplay from the tube. The carriers are properly tightened when a moderate amount of effort is required to turn the gauge tube by hand.
6. From the available selective pinion depth shims, determine the clearance between the gauge tube and gauge disc. **The correct shim thickness has been determined when a slight drag is felt between the shim and gauging surfaces.**
7. The clearance check in step 6 has determined the pinion depth shim thickness for a nominal or zero variance pinion. To determine if this is the correct shim thickness, inspect the pinion shaft for a pinion variance marking and proceed as follows:
   a. If the pinion shaft does not have a variance marking, a pinion variance calculation is not necessary.
   b. If the pinion shaft has a minus pinion variance marking (1 to 3), measure the shim from step 6 with a micrometer to determine its thickness. From this measured thickness, add .0004 inch (.01 mm) for a minus 1 marking, .0008 inch (.02 mm) for a minus 2 marking or .0012 inch (.03 mm) for a minus 3 marking depending upon the pinion variance marking.
   c. If the pinion shaft has a positive pinion variance marking (+1 to +3), measure the shim from step 6 with a micrometer to determine its thickness. From this measured thickness, subtract .0004 inch (.01

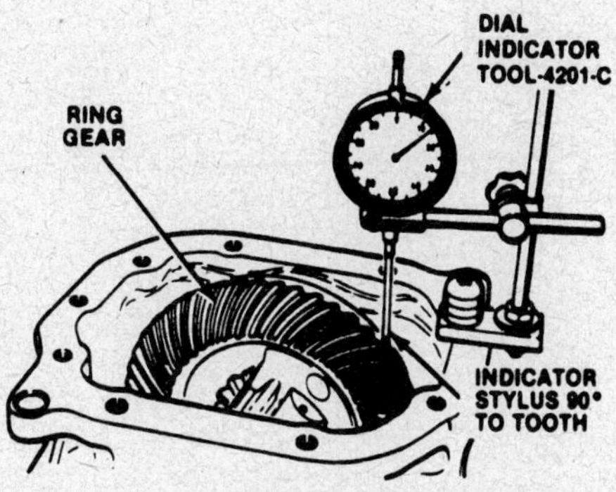


**Fig. 4 Installing dial indicator onto axle housing**

mm) for a positive 1 marking, .0008 inch (.02 mm) for a positive 2 marking or .0012 inch (.03 mm) for a positive 3 marking depending upon the pinion variance marking.

8. Install inner pinion bearing. **Ensure pinion depth shim is in position on the pinion shaft before installing the bearing.**
9. Install a new collapsible spacer onto pinion shaft.
10. Position pinion into case and install the outer bearing. Lubricate the bearings before installing the case.
11. Install the pinion nut.
12. To preload the pinion bearings, gradually tighten the pinion nut. Each time the nut is tightened, check the pinion shaft rolling torque (bearing preload), using an inch lb. torque wrench. Continue tightening the pinion nut in small increments until a rolling **torque** of 14-18 ft. lbs. is measured at the pinion shaft. **An increasing resistance will be felt as the pinion bearing preload is increased by the action of the collapsible spacer. If the nut is tightened beyond the specified rolling torque, remove pinion and install a new collapsible spacer and repeat step 12.**
13. Stake pinion nut to the pinion shaft.
14. Install pinion seal.
15. Install pinion flange and attaching nut. **Torque** attaching nut to 95-110 ft. lbs.
16. Position differential assembly into case.
17. Install new O-rings onto bearing carriers and position carriers into their original positions. Lubricate the bearing carrier threads and O-rings with the correct axle lubricant before installing case.
18. Using a suitable tool, turn bearing carriers into axle case until they lightly seat against the differential bearings. This seating action can be felt as the bearing carrier cups contact the differential bearings. **When the bearing carrier O-rings enter the case, the turning effort will increase.**
19. Mount a suitable dial indicator onto axle housing as shown in **Fig. 4**. Position indicator stylus to contact a ring gear tooth at a 90° angle.
20. Rock the ring gear forward and backward and note the reading on the dial indicator.
21. Thread the bearing carriers into the case in equal amounts until the dial indicator reads a backlash of .0004 inch (.01 mm).
22. After the minimum backlash of .0004 inch is set, tighten the bearing carrier on the differential side of the case an additional four to five teeth of the carrier to preload the bearings. **If steps 18 through 22 have been correctly done, the correct amount of backlash .004-.007 inch (.10-.17 mm) should now exist between the pinion and ring gear assembly.**
23. Install bearing carrier lock plates. **Torque** attaching bolts to 14-18 ft. lbs.
24. Install stub shafts.
25. From available selective C-clips, install the thickest possible clip in each stub shaft groove.
26. Coat axle housing to cover sealing surfaces with sealant E1FZ-19562-A, or equivalent. Install cover. **Torque** cover attaching bolts to 33-44 ft. lbs.
27. If the axle case, axle assembly or suspension crossmember has been replaced, it is necessary to determine whether a gap exists between the rear axle mounting boss and the crossmember mounting flanges. If a

gap is found, selective shims must be installed to compensate for the clearance. Proceed as follows:

a. Install rear mount onto axle housing rear cover. **Torque** attaching bolts to 37-41 ft. lbs.
b. Lift assembly into position between crossmember flanges.
c. Install the through bolt and the four axle bolts to crossmember attaching bolts. Do not tighten the bolts.
d. Install axle housing rear mount. On Scorpio models, **torque** four attaching bolts to 14-18 ft. lbs. On XR4Ti models, **torque** two inner bolts to 37-41 ft. lbs. and four outer bolts to 37-50 ft. lbs.
e. **Torque** the front lower attaching bolt to 51-66 ft. lbs.
f. **Torque** through bolt to 51-66 ft. lbs.
g. Using a feeler gauge check clearance between crossmember flanges and rear axle mounting boss.
h. Select and install appropriate shims between the crossmember and axle.
i. **Torque** attaching bolts to 51-66 ft. lbs.

# MANUAL STEERING GEARS

## TABLE OF CONTENTS



# Rack & Pinion Except Festiva, Tracer & 1991 Escort

## INDEX



## AIRBAG SYSTEM DISARMING

**The electrical circuit necessary for system deployment is powered directly from the battery and backup power supply. To avoid accidental deployment and possible personal injury, the airbag system must be deactivated prior to servicing or replacing any system components.**

A back-up power supply is included in the system to provide airbag deployment in the event the battery or battery cables are damaged in an accident before the sensors can close. The power supply is a capacitor that will retain a charge for approximately 15 minutes after the battery ground cable is disconnected. To remove and install backup power supply refer to "Component Replacement" procedure.

1. Disconnect battery ground cable.
2. Disconnect backup power supply as described under "Backup Power Supply, Replace."
3. Remove four nut and washer assemblies securing airbag module to steering wheel, then disconnect airbag electrical connector. Attach jumper wire to airbag terminals on clockspring as shown in **Fig. 1**.
4. **On models equipped with passenger-side airbag,** disconnect airbag module connector located behind glove compartment. Attach a jumper wire to airbag terminals on wiring harness side of passenger airbag module connector, as shown in **Fig. 1**.
5. **On all models,** if necessary, reconnect battery and backup power supply.
6. To reactivate, disconnect battery ground cable and backup power supply, then reverse remainder of deactivation procedure. **Torque** airbag module to steering wheel nut assemblies to 24-32 inch lbs. on Crown Victoria and Grand Marquis, or 35-53 inch lbs. on all other models.
7. Verify airbag lamp after reactivating system.

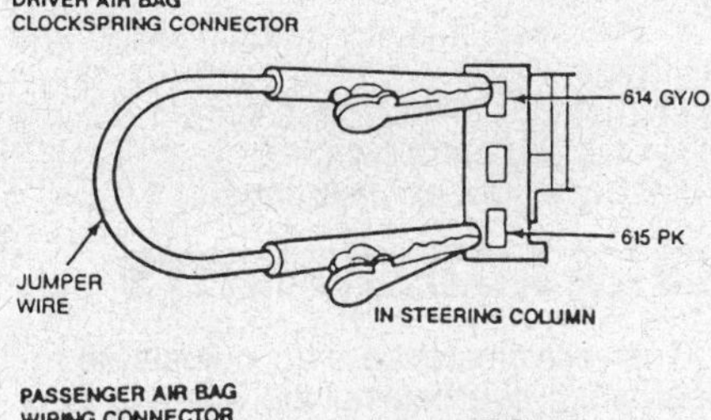


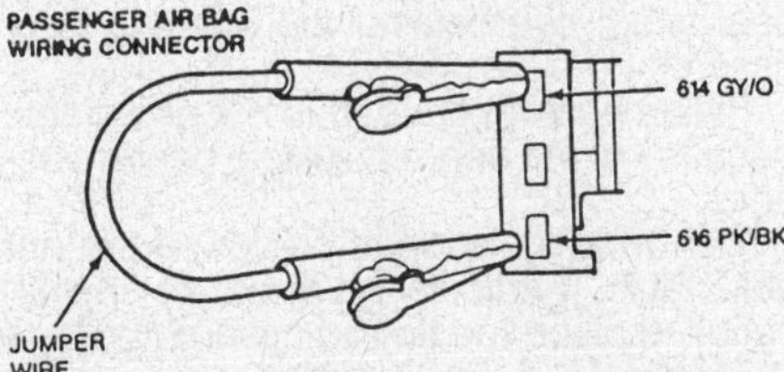


**Fig. 1 Airbag system disarming**

## DESCRIPTION

The type 5 manual steering gear is a conventional rack and pinion design. The helically machined pinion is supported by a parallel needle bearing above the pinion teeth and a non-adjustable ball bearing below the pinion teeth. Correct meshing of pinion teeth with the rack is achieved by a spring loaded yoke retained by a plug. The free end of the rack is supported by a polyurethane bushing located in the end of the rack tube. Tie rods connect the ends of the steering rack to the rear facing of the steering arms through separate tie rod ends. The inner ball joints are preset at the factory for articulation and are not adjustable.

## TROUBLESHOOTING

### STEERING FEELS HEAVY

1. Steering fluid leakage or loss.
2. Twisted or cut plastic valve ring.
3. Faulty plastic piston ring.
4. Loose rack piston.
5. Faulty rubber back-up piston O-ring.
6. Faulty rack assembly.
7. Improper belt tension.
8. Hose, cooler or pump external leakage.
9. Improper engine idle speed.
10. Faulty pulley.
11. Hose or cooler line restriction.

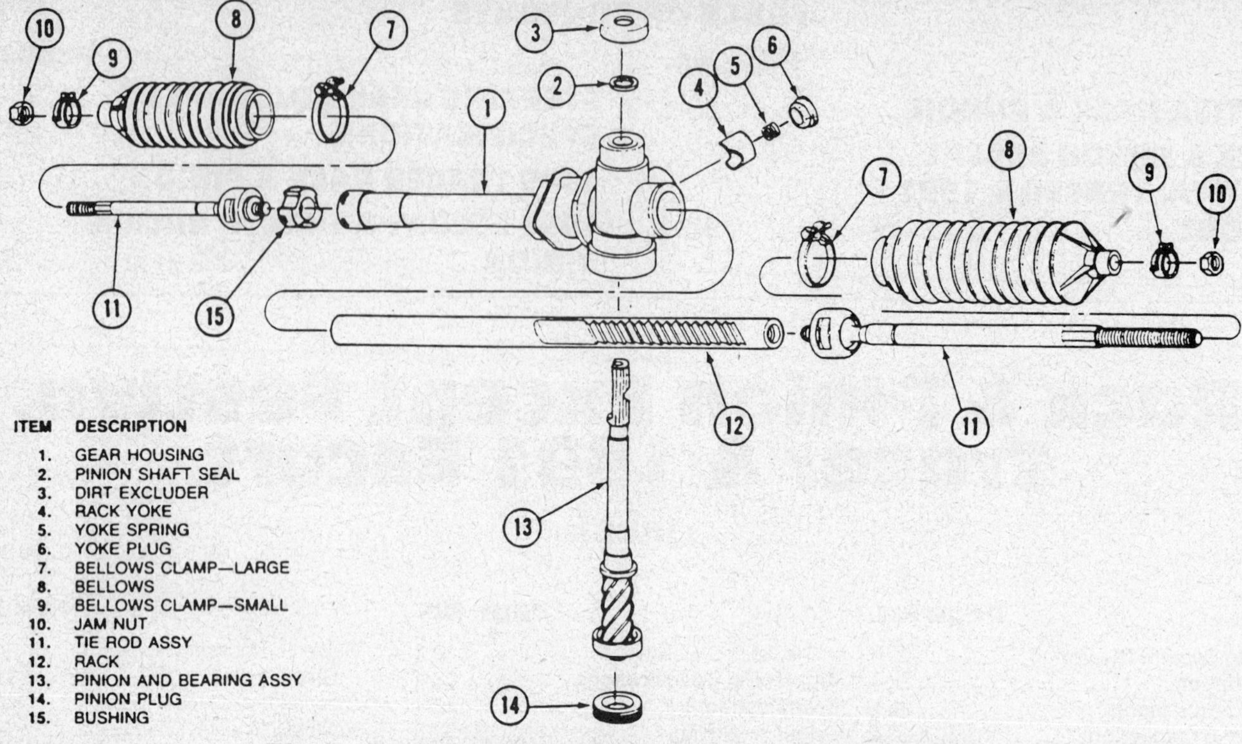


**Fig. 2 Exploded view of Ford manual steering gear**

## IMPROPER STEERING WHEEL RETURN

1. Improperly aligned steering column or flange.
2. Binding intermediate shaft.
3. Valve assembly binding.
4. Damaged sub frame or rack.
5. Binding column bearing.
6. Improper wheel alignment settings.
7. Power steering system contamination.
8. Deformed engine mounts.

## VEHICLE WANDERS

1. Loose tie rod ends.
2. Loose or worn inner ball housing.
3. Loose gear assembly mount.
4. Loose column intermediate shaft bolts.
5. Loose or worn column intermediate shaft joints.
6. Improper wheel alignment settings.

## RATTLE OR KNOCKING NOISE FROM STEERING GEAR

1. Loose column u-joints.
2. Loose tie rod ends.
3. Loose gear assembly mount.
4. Loose pinion bearing cap.
5. Loose or worn ball joint.
6. Rack piston loose or disengaged.
7. Worn steering gear yoke.
8. Loose column intermediate shaft bolts.
9. Loose struts.

## HISSING SOUND

Hissing sound is a normal characteristic of rotary steering gears and in no way affects steering.

1. Improper steering column shaft and gear.
2. Improper clearance between flexible coupling components.
3. Loose boot at dash panel.

## GEAR ADJUSTMENTS

The yoke clearance is not adjustable except when overhauling the steering gear assembly.

Pinion bearing preload is not adjustable because of the non-adjustable bearing usage.

Tie rod articulation is preset and is not adjustable. If articulation is out of specification, replace the tie rod assembly.

## REPAIR & INSPECTION

### TIE RODS & BELLOWS

#### Disassembly

1. Disable airbag system as described in "Airbag System Disarming," if equipped, then clean exterior of gear assembly.
2. Loosen jam nuts and remove tie rod ends and jam nuts,**Fig. 2.**
3. Remove bellows clamps and the small (outer) tie rod clamps. Discard bellows clamps.
4. Remove the bellows.
5. Cycle gear to full right turn to expose rack teeth. Mount rack teeth in soft jawed vise to remove either or both tie rod ends.
6. Remove tie rod ends by turning ball socket with pipe wrench.
7. Check rack for corrosion and contamination. If either is present, the gear must be completely overhauled or replaced.

#### Assembly

1. Cycle gear to full right turn to expose rack teeth. Mount rack teeth in a soft jawed vise.
2. Before installing tie rods, inspect ends of rack for flatness. If burrs are present, remove by lightly filing.
3. Install service tie rods and tighten to specifications.
4. Remove gear assembly from vise.
5. Support ball socket, and stake to rack using a stake punch. Center of stake punch should be approximately 1.5 mm (.06 inch) away from rack end. Perform visual inspection to verify displacement of metal into rack slot.
6. Replenish any grease that may have been removed with fresh grease by applying it to the rack teeth. Coat remainder of rack (both ends) with a light film of grease. Use specified steering gear lubricant.
7. Install bellows and clamps. Ensure small diameter of bellows is in the tie rod groove.
8. Install jam nuts and tie rod end, then rearm air bag system, if equipped.

### PINION, RACK & HOUSING

#### Disassembly

If pinion is removed, the entire gear must be disassembled for cleaning because the pinion plug threads must be re-tapped and cleaned.

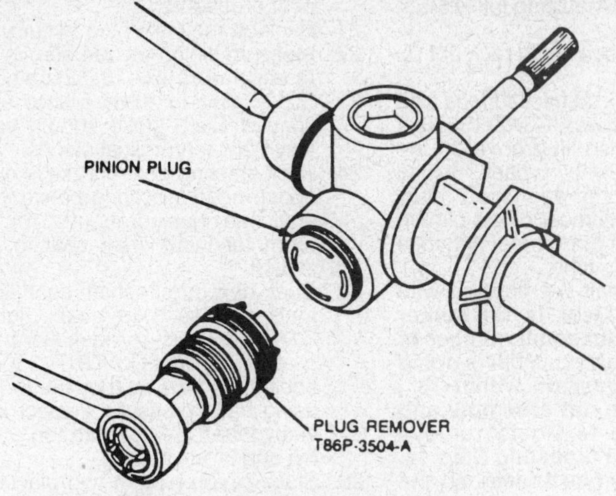


Fig. 3 Pinion plug removal

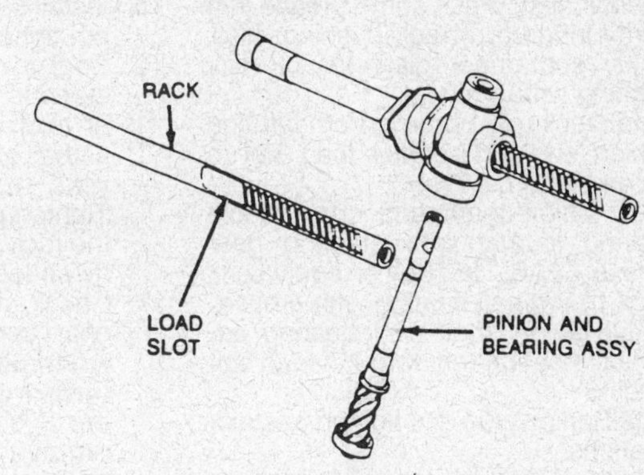


Fig. 4 Pinion & bearing assembly removal

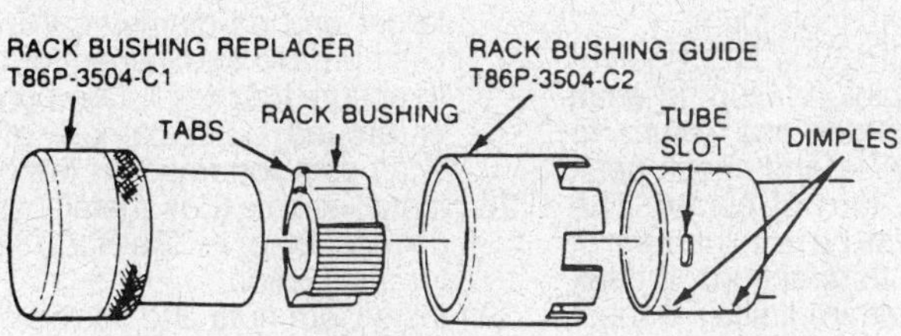


Fig. 5 Rack bushing guide alignment

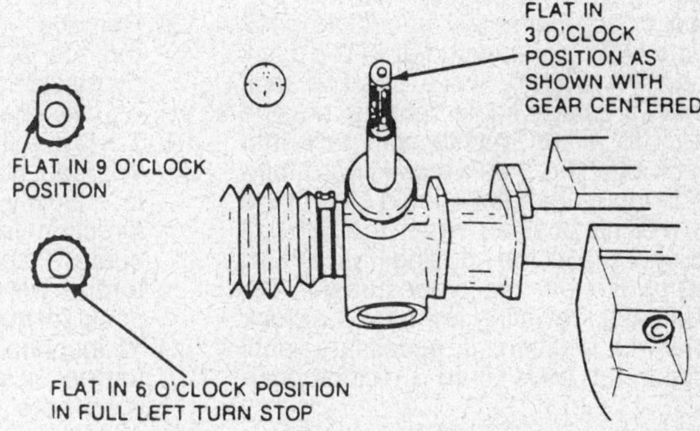


Fig. 6 Pinion flat positioning

1. Remove tie rod ends, jam nuts, bellows and tie rods. Refer to "Tie Rod & Bellows" procedures.
2. Hold gear housing in a vise, positioned as required for the following steps.
3. Twist and pull off plastic dirt extruder on pinion and discard.
4. Turn pinion to full right position so that load slot is at pinion. Pinion will rotate without moving rack teeth when it is in the load slot.
5. Remove pinion plug using tool No. T86P-3504-A or equivalent, **Fig. 3.** Discard plug.
6. Reverse tool and remove yoke plug. Discard plug.
7. Remove spring and yoke.
8. Remove pinion and bearing assembly by pushing out through the pinion plug opening, **Fig. 4.** Tap lightly with plastic mallet if necessary.
9. Remove rack from left side (pinion end).
10. Pry out pinion shaft seal with a screwdriver and discard. Take care not to damage gear housing.
11. Using tool No. T86P-3504-A or equivalent, clean up threads in the yoke plug bore and pinion plug bore.
12. Wash all parts in suitable washing solution, and dry prior to reassembly. Do not submerge right end of housing tube containing polyurethane rack bushing.
13. Clean pinion and yoke threads with solvent to remove washing solution residue.
14. Inspect rack bushing for wear or damage. If worn, remove by prying with a screwdriver, taking care not to damage gear housing rack tube.

## Inspection

1. Inspect gear housing for damage. Discard housing if yoke and pinion plug threads have previously re-staked (more than three yoke plug stakes and more than two pinion plug stakes). Check threads for damage. Examine plastic bushing for wear or damage and ensure bushing tabs are properly located in tube slots. Check needle bearing for wear and roughness. Replace housing assemble if any of its components are worn or damaged, except for the rack bushing which can be replaced.
2. Examine rack for corrosion, straightness, tooth wear or damage. Check threads in end of rack. Replace rack as required.
3. Inspect pinion rack for corrosion at seal area and below. Lightly oil the pinion ball bearing and check for bearing wear and roughness. Examine pinion shaft for straightness. Check pinion teeth for wear, cracking, scoring, pitting or breakage. Replace pinion as required.
4. Inspect end of rack for burrs. File ends lightly, if necessary, to provide a square, flat surface for tie rod sockets.

## Assembly

1. If rack bushing was not removed, proceed to Step 7.
2. Align three slots of Rack Bushing Guide T86P-3504-C2 or equivalent over dimples in rack tube, **Fig. 5.** Align extra slot exactly over one of the tube slots.
3. Lubricate new rack bushing outer diameter with steering gear grease C3AZ-19578-A or equivalent.
4. Insert new rack bushings into tool so tabs align with grooves in tool. Tabs must be up (away from rack housing).
5. Push bearing into rack tube with tool No. T86P-3504-C1 or equivalent using hand pressure until tool bottoms. Remove guide tool. Reapply hand pressure with replacer tool to fully seat tabs in slots, if necessary. **Use only enough force to fully engage tabs in slots.**
6. Inspect installation of rack bushing to ensure tabs are engaged into slots. If tabs are not properly positioned, dislocation of bushing may occur.
7. Fill rack teeth spacers with steering gear grease C3AZ-19578-A or equivalent. Coat remainder of rack with light coat of grease.

8. Pack pinion needle bearing with steering gear grease C3AZ-19578-A or equivalent. Pack some grease into cavity inboard of rack bushing. Also, lightly coat inner diameter of rack bushing with grease.
9. Install rack into housing from left end (pinion end) and center load slot in pinion bore.
10. Pack pinion teeth and coat needle bearing journal with steering gear grease C3AZ-19578-A or equivalent. Pack pinion ball bearing with grease.
11. Install pinion shaft and bearing assembly from bottom through load slot in rack.
12. Install pinion plug and tighten to specifications.
13. Install left tie rod assembly to rack. Seat it against rack but do not tighten at this time. This establishes the left turn stop position of the rack.
14. Mount gear housing in vise with pinion in approximately in-vehicle position. Hold pinion with flat in 9 o'clock position, **Fig. 6,** while pushing rack into housing. Jiggle rack to engage rack to pinion and to start rack into rack bushing. Push rack inward fully. The input shaft flat should stop in the 6 o'clock position when the left ball joint contacts the housing (full left turn stop). Repeat the procedures at the load slot, deviating from the 9 o'clock starting position, if necessary, until pinion flat ends up in 6 o'clock position with rack pushed in to full left turn stop.
15. Install tie rod assembly to rack but do not tighten.
16. Coat yoke at rack contact surface with steering gear grease C3AZ-19578-A or equivalent. Also fill groove on the same surface with grease. Install yoke, yoke spring and yoke plug. Tighten plug until most of the play in the rack is taken out. Do not set yoke mesh load at this time.
17. Check pinion shaft flat position with gear centered. **Gear is on center when pinion is an equal number of turns from each stop. If flat is not in the 3 o'clock position within 10°, remove right tie rod assembly and go back to step 14. Do not remove yoke plug when repeating Step 14. The pinion only has 4 teeth, so the flat can only be in one of 4 positions, 90° apart.**
18. Remove yoke plug and restart the threads 1/2 to 1 turn. Apply 3 drops of hydraulic sealant to plug threads equally spaced.
19. **Torque** yoke to 40 inch lbs.
20. With tool No. T86P-3504-B or equivalent, slowly turn pinion 1/2turn in each direction from center and return to center. Repeat twice and check peak torque within 1/4 turn of center. The peak **torque** must be a minimum of 15 inch lbs. in both directions. If peak torque is not within limits, inspect yoke bore threads for burrs and repeat procedure.
21. Back off the yoke plug 1/4 turn.
22. Measure pinion **torque** across center to ensure it is 4.6-13.2 inch lbs.
23. Stake plug in three places equally spaced. Each stake should be midway between original stakes.
24. Pack steering gear grease into space above needle bearing between input shaft and housing, about 2/3 full. Leave room for input shaft seal to be installed.
25. Coat new input shaft seal lip with multi-purpose long-life lubricant C1AZ-19590-B or equivalent. Press seal in with tool No. T81P-3504-Y or equivalent size washer (5/8 to 3/4 ID), using hand pressure. Inspect seal to verify that it is flush with top of housing and is not twisted.
26. Stake pinion plug in two places midway between original stakes.
27. Fill the plastic dirt extruder with long life lubricant C1AZ-19590-B or equivalent and hand install until bottomed on gear housing. Use a twisting motion to force the dirt excluder onto the larger ground diameter. Wipe off excess grease and inspect dirt extruder to ensure that it is located on the larger (ground) outer diameter of the input shaft and bottomed on the housing.
28. Install new tie rods. Install bellows and clamps. Refer to "Tie Rods & Bellows" for installation.
29. Install jam nuts and tie rod ends.

## TIGHTENING SPECIFICATIONS

| Year | Component | Torque, Ft. Lbs. |
|---|---|---|
| 1989–91 | Bellhousing To Rack | 50–60 |
| | Connecting Rod End To Inner Tie Rod Jam Nut | 35–50 |
| | Connecting Rod To Spindle Arm | 27–32① |
| | Pinion Plug | 52–73 |
| | Pinion Shaft Intermediate Shaft Bolts | 20–37 |
| | Steering Gear | 40–55 |
| | Yoke Plug | ② |

①—Tighten to specifications, then tighten to nearest cotter pin slot.
②—Refer to text.

# Festiva Rack & Pinion

INDEX



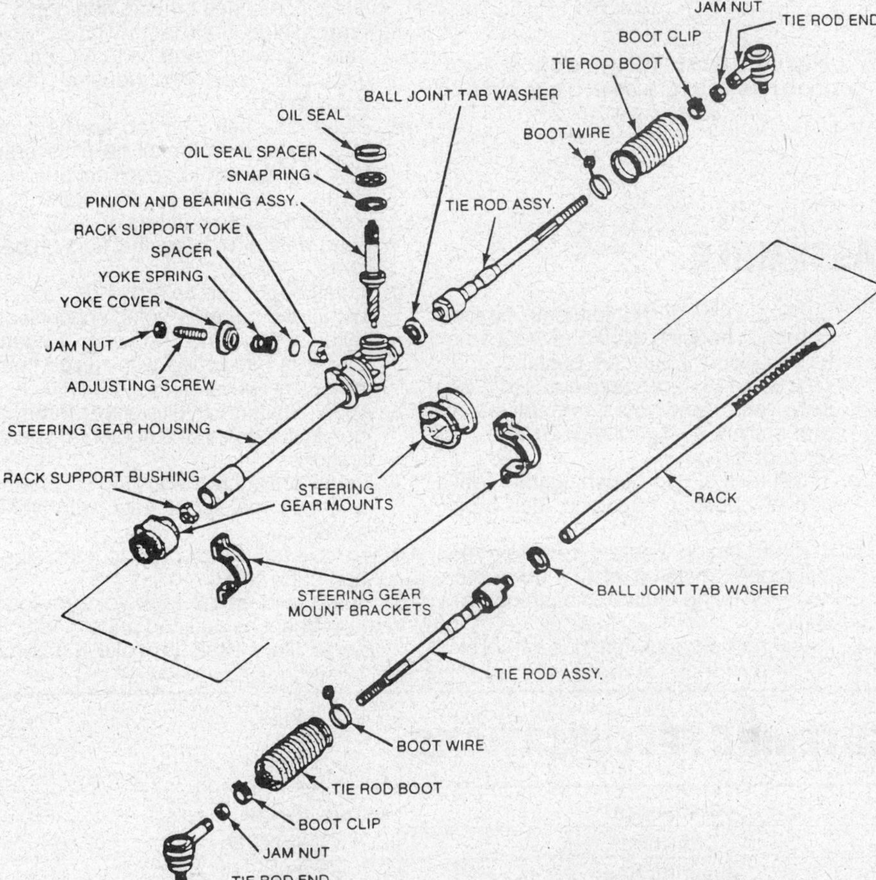


**Fig. 1 Exploded view of steering gear assembly**

## TROUBLESHOOTING

### STEERING FEELS HEAVY W/VEHICLE RAISED

1. Poor lubrication, foreign material in mechanism, damaged or binding ball joint.
2. Improper steering gear preload.
3. Faulty steering gear.
4. Faulty steering shaft joint.
5. Worn or cracked steering gear bushings.
6. Faulty suspension component.

### STEERING WHEEL PULLS

1. Faulty steering linkage.
2. Faulty wheel or tire.
3. Faulty in brake system.
4. Faulty suspension component.

### INSTABILITY WHEN DRIVING

1. Worn or damaged steering joints.
2. Improper steering gear preload.
3. Damaged steering linkage.
4. Damaged wheel or tire.
5. Faulty suspension component.

### UNSTABLE STEERING

1. Faulty steering gear.
2. Faulty steering joints.
3. Faulty steering linkage.

### EXCESSIVE STEERING WHEEL PLAY

1. Worn steering gear.
2. Worn or damaged steering joints.
3. Loose steering gear mounting bolts.

### POOR STEERING WHEEL RETURN

1. Damaged or binding steering joints.
2. Improper steering gear preload.
3. Faulty wheel or tire.
4. Faulty suspension component.

### STEERING WHEEL VIBRATES

1. Damaged steering linkage.
2. Loose steering gear mounting bolts.
3. Damaged or binding steering joints.
4. Worn or faulty front wheel bearing.
5. Faulty wheel or tire.
6. Faulty suspension component.

### ABNORMAL NOISE

1. Loose steering gear mounting bolt.
2. Faulty steering gear.
3. Obstruction near steering column.
4. Loose steering linkage.
5. Worn steering joints.

## ADJUSTMENTS

### RACK PRELOAD/SUPPORT YOKE

1. Loosen locknut.
2. Install yoke adjustment tool No. T90P-3504-JH or equivalent, **torque** yoke plug to 8.7 inch lbs, then loosen bolt 10-40°.
3. Using pinion shaft tool No. T86P-3504-K or equivalent, measure pinion torque, 9-11.5 inch lbs. should be indicated at neutral position ±90°, 14.7 inch lbs. or less should be indicated in any other position.
4. If pinion torque is not as specified, turn adjusting bolt to correct, then tighten adjusting bolt locknut.

## DISASSEMBLE

1. Remove mount brackets and rubber mounts, then position steering gear in suitable soft jaw vise.
2. Mark position of tie rod ends in relation to tie rods, then remove tie rod ends and boots.
3. Disengage tab washers from ball joints using suitable tool, extend rack from either side of housing, then remove tie rods from rack.
4. Remove rack preload adjusting screw and jam nut from yoke cover, **Fig. 1.**
5. Remove cover and yoke spring from housing, then the spacer and yoke.

6. Carefully pry pinion oil seal from housing, then remove seal spacer, snap ring and pinion and bearing assembly.
7. Remove rack from pinion side of housing. **If rack is removed through right side (bushing end) of housing, damage to bushing may result.**
8. If pinion lower bearing is to be replaced, remove it at this time using suitable slide hammer type puller.
9. Press the three rack support bushing lock tabs inward, then remove bushing from right side of housing using puller mentioned in previous step.

## INSPECTION

1. Inspect rack and pinion gear teeth for abnormal wear, and steering gear housing for cracks or damage. Replace components as necessary.
2. Position rack in V blocks, then check runout in center portion of rack using suitable dial indicator. If runout exceeds .012 inch, replace rack and pinion gear.
3. Rotate pinion bearings and check for looseness or rough operation. If upper bearing requires replacement, replace bearing and pinion gear as an assembly.
4. Check fit of rack support bushing on rack for looseness or abnormal wear. Replace bushing as necessary.
5. Check tie rod ball joints and tie rod ends for free flexing without excessive looseness. Replace joints and tie rod ends as required.
6. Check tie rods for bending and boots for cuts, nicks or abrasions. Replace parts as necessary.

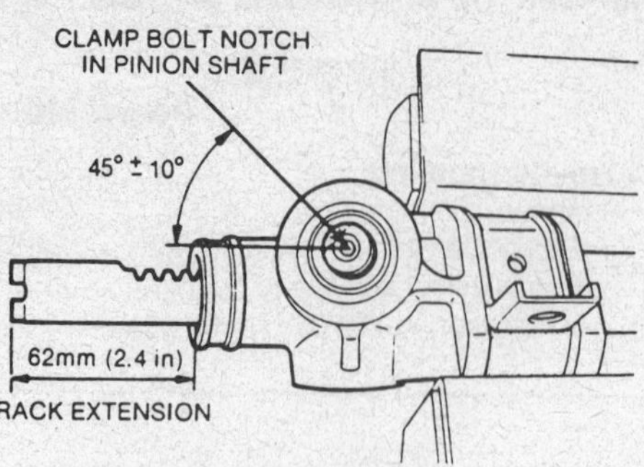


**Fig. 2 Installing rack & pinion/bearing assembly into housing**

## ASSEMBLE

1. Lubricate rack and pinion teeth, pinion bearings, housing, pinion oil seal lips, rack support yoke and bushing and rack using lithium-based greased. **Ensure rack vent holes remain open and are not clogged with grease after lubrication.**
2. Install rack support bushing into right end of housing, engaging lock tabs with housing slots.
3. If lower pinion bearing requires replacement, install it at this time into housing using suitable bushing installer.
4. Install rack through left side of housing, ensuring rack teeth face pinion bore. When properly positioned, left side of rack should extend approximately 2.4 inches from end of housing, **Fig. 2.**
5. Install pinion and upper bearing assembly into housing. When bearing is fully seated, pinion notch for steering column universal joint clamp bolt should face forward 35°-55° as seen from top end of pinion shaft when rack is centered, **Fig. 2.**
6. Install pinion bearing snap ring with beveled side facing upward, then the seal spacer tabbed side down. Ensure tab is positioned in snap ring gap.
7. Wrap pinion shaft teeth with suitable tape to prevent damage to oil seal lip, then drive seal into housing using suitable tool.
8. Place new ball joint tab washers on rack ends, then install tie rods onto rack and tighten to specifications.
9. Using a suitable punch, stake tab washer lips into notches on rack, then bend washer tabs against flats on ball joints.
10. Install boots and tie rod ends.
11. Install rack support yoke, spacer and yoke spring into housing. Ensure spacer is positioned with raised center facing outward.
12. Apply sealant to yoke cover threads, then install cover and tighten to specifications.
13. Install and tighten adjusting screw until it just makes contact with yoke spacer.
14. **Torque** adjusting screw to 9 inch lbs., then back off 10-40°.
15. Check and adjust rack yoke preload adjustment as outlined under "Adjustments, Rack Preload/Yoke Support."

## TIGHTENING SPECIFICATIONS

| Year | Component | Torque, Ft. Lbs. |
|---|---|---|
| 1989–91 | Ball Joints | 43–58 |
| | Steering Gear | 23–34 |
| | Steering Rack Support Cover | 29–43 |
| | Steering Rack Support Cover Adjusting Screw | 8.8① |
| | Support Yoke Locknut | 29–36 |
| | Tie Rod Jam Nut | 7.4–11 |
| | Tie Rod End Stud Nut | 26–30 |

①—Inch lbs.

# 1989 Tracer Rack & Pinion

## INDEX

Page No.



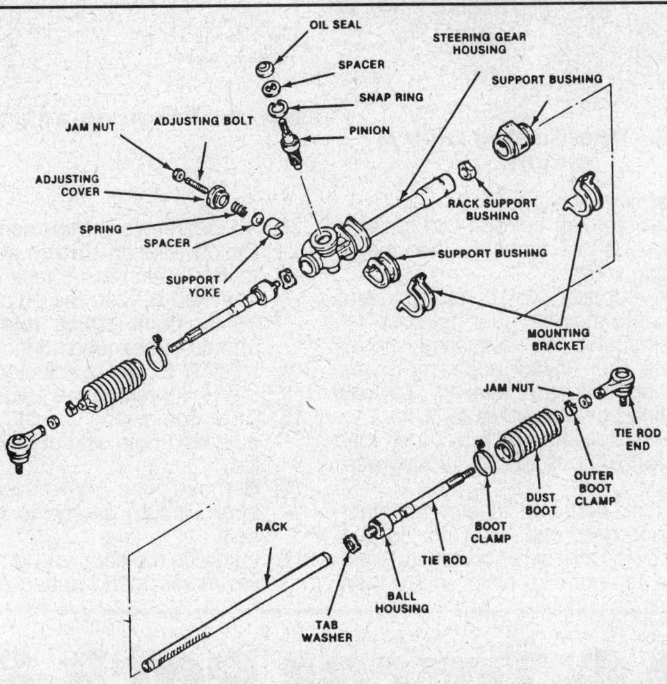


Fig. 1 Exploded view of manual rack & pinion steering gear

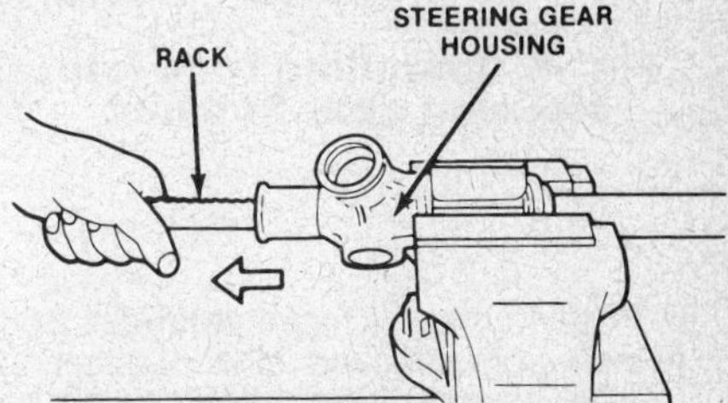


Fig. 2 Removing rack from steering gear housing

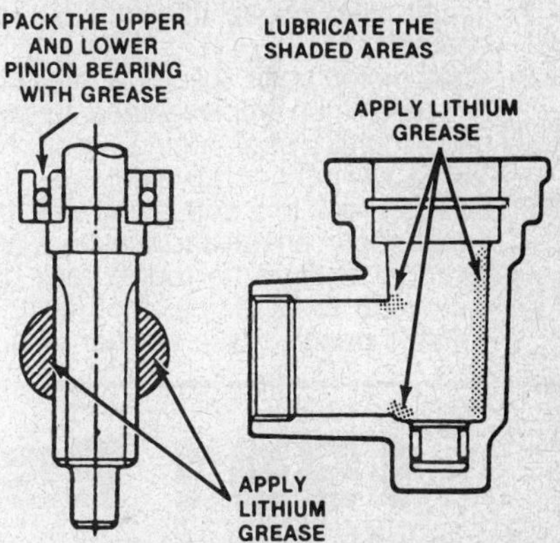


Fig. 3 Applying grease to steering gear housing

## TROUBLESHOOTING

Refer to "Festiva Rack & Pinion" for troubleshooting procedure.

## DISASSEMBLE

1. Position steering gear in a soft jawed vise, then remove mounting brackets and mounting bushings, **Fig. 1.**
2. Place alignment marks on tie rod, tie rod end and jam nut so they can be installed in the same position.
3. Remove tie rod ends and jam nuts from tie rod.
4. Remove tie rod boot from steering gear housing, then using a suitable chisel, uncrimp tabs on tie rod washer.
5. Position rack in soft jawed vise, then using a suitable wrench loosen ball housing and remove tie rod from rack. Remove tie rod from other side of rack in the same manner.
6. Remove locknut, adjusting cover and adjusting bolt from steering gear housing.
7. Using suitable pliers, remove support yoke, spring and shim from steering gear housing.
8. Mounting steering gear housing in soft jawed vise, then using a suitable screwdriver, pry pinion seal from housing. When removing seal, use care not to damage pinion shaft. It maybe necessary to remove steering gear housing from vise and shake pinion seal spacer from housing.
9. Remove pinion bearing snap ring, then pull pinion assembly out of upper bearing side of steering gear housing. If difficulty is encountered when removing pinion assembly, use tool T78P-3504-B to remove pinion assembly.
10. Pull rack out through pinion side of steering gear housing, **Fig. 2.**
11. Remove steering gear housing support bracket and bushing, the remove pinion lower bearing using tools D80L-100-L and T50T-100A or equivalent, if necessary.
12. Using a suitable screwdriver push inward on lock tabs of rack support bushing, then using tools D80L-100-R and T50T-100-R or equivalent, remove bushing from housing.
13. After bushing has been removed, clean steering gear housing.

## INSPECTION

Check rack and pinion teeth for wear and damage. Position rack in V-blocks and check run-out using a suitable dial indicator. Rack run-out should not exceed .012 inch. Check pinion bearing for looseness and wear. If rack, pinion or pinion bearings are found to be unsatisfactory, the rack and pinion must be replaced as a set.

Check steering gear housing for wear and damage. Check tie rod ball units for looseness and smoothness of operation. Check for bent tie rods or tie rod ends. Check tie rod boots for damage. If any components are found to be unsatisfactory, they should be replaced.

## ASSEMBLE

1. Apply lithium grease to rack, pinion, oil seal lips, support yoke and housing areas indicated in, **Fig. 3.** Also pack upper and lower pinion bearings with lithium grease.
2. Lubricate rack support bushing with lithium grease, position bushing to steering gear housing and push in until locking tabs engage slots in housing.
3. Install support bushings and brackets onto steering gear housing, **Fig. 1.**
4. Install lower pinion bearing using a suitable tool, if removed.
5. Slide rack into steering gear housing as far as possible, **Fig. 4.**

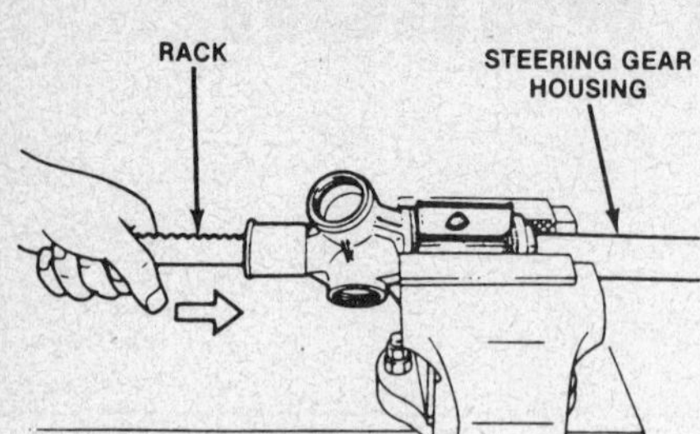


Fig. 4 Installing rack into steering gear housing

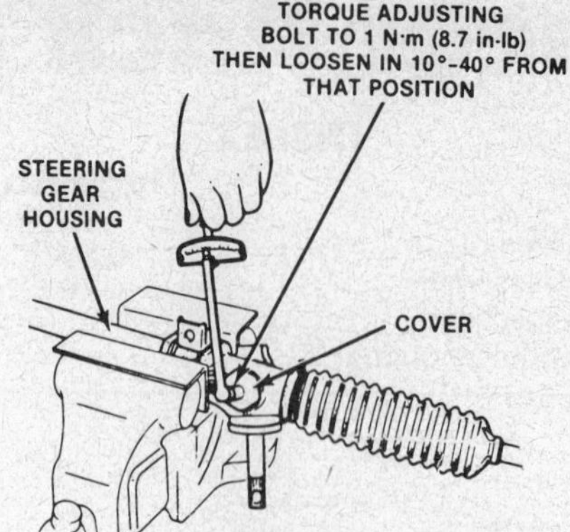


Fig. 5 Positioning rack & pinion

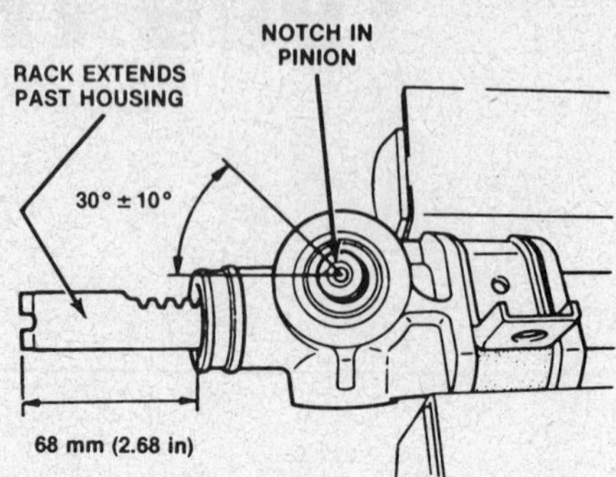


Fig. 6 Torquing adjusting bolt

6. Position rock so that it protrudes 2.68 inch from lefthand side of steering gear housing, then install pinion so that the notch on the pinion shaft is at a 30 degree angle from center line of steering gear housing, **Fig. 5.**
7. Install pinion snap ring and oil seal spacer.
8. Wrap pinion shaft splines with electrical tape, then apply grease to tape and install seal using tool No. T87C-3504-C or equivalent.
9. Position rack in a soft jawed vise, the install replacement tab washers and tie rods. **Torque** tie rod to rack ball unit to 58 to 72 ft. lbs., then using a suitable punch, stake washer tabs to rack at two locations.
10. Slide boots over tie rods and position on steering gear housing, then install retaining wires.
11. Install support yoke, spacer and spring into steering gear housing.
12. Apply sealer to adjusting cover threads, then install adjusting cover, adjusting bolt and locknut. **Torque** adjusting cover to 29 to 43 ft. lbs.
13. **Torque** adjusting bolt to 8.7 inch lbs., then loosen bolt 10 to 40 degrees, **Fig. 6.**
14. With rack centered in steering gear housing, use and inch lb. torque wrench to measure pinion rotating torque. Do not turn pinion more than 90 degrees past the center position. Pinion rotating **torque** should be 7.8 to 11.28 inch lbs. If rack needs to be checked beyond the 90 degrees from center point, pinion rotating **torque** should nut exceed 13 inch lbs. Pinion rotating torque is adjusted by loosening or tightening the adjusting bolt.
15. After completing adjustment, **torque** adjusting bolt locknut to 7.2 to 10.8 ft. lbs.
16. Remove tape from pinion shaft and apply lithium grease to area around seal.
17. Install tie rod ends and jam nuts, aligning marks made during disassembly.

# 1991 Escort & Tracer Rack & Pinion

## INDEX



## DESCRIPTION

The manual rack and pinion steering gear is sealed against entry of water and dirt by boots at each end of the steering gear housing and at the pinion shaft. The steering gear is lubricated at assembly and must be removed and disassembled if lubrication is needed. The rack is positioned and guided in the housing by a bushing at the right end, and a support yoke holding it in engagement with the pinion at the left end. The support yoke is spring loaded against the rack and a yoke plug adjusting bolt and locknut keep the rack fully engaged with the pinion under load. Rubber mounts ta each end of the steering gear housing cushion the steering gear mount to minimize vibration.

## TROUBLESHOOTING

### STEERING FEELS HEAVY W/VEHICLE RAISED

1. Poor lubrication, foreign material in mechanism, damaged or binding ball joint.
2. Improper steering gear preload.
3. Faulty steering gear.
4. Faulty steering shaft joint.
5. Worn or cracked steering gear bushings.
6. Faulty suspension component.

### STEERING WHEEL PULLS

1. Faulty steering linkage.
2. Faulty wheel or tire.
3. Faulty in brake system.
4. Faulty suspension component.

### INSTABILITY WHEN DRIVING

1. Worn or damaged steering joints.
2. Improper steering gear preload.
3. Damaged steering linkage.
4. Damaged wheel or tire.
5. Faulty suspension component.

### UNSTABLE STEERING

1. Faulty steering gear.
2. Faulty steering joints.
3. Faulty steering linkage.

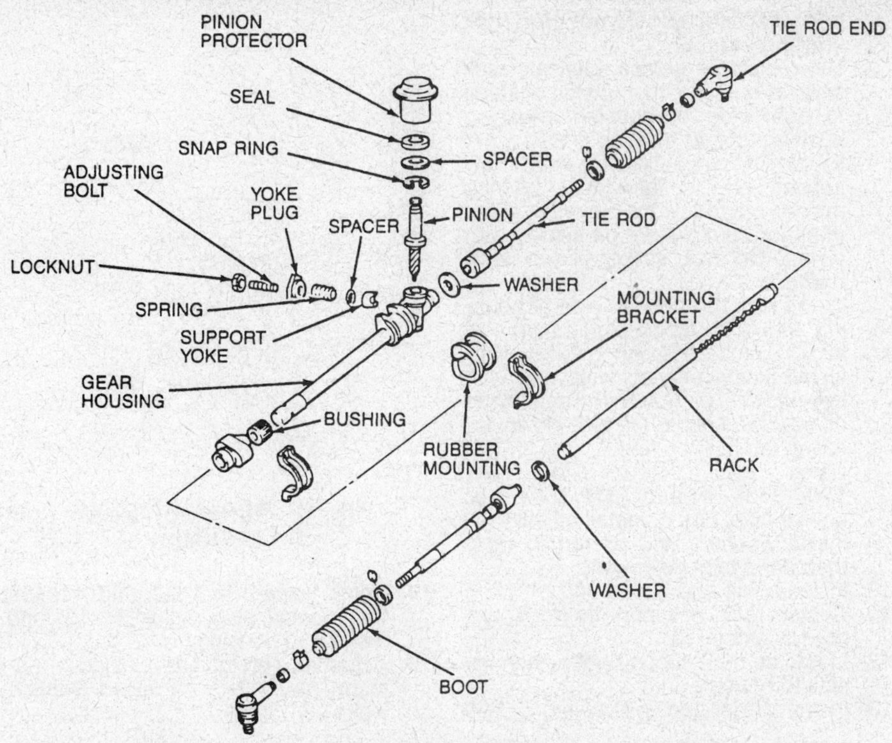


Fig. 1 Exploded view of manual rack & pinion

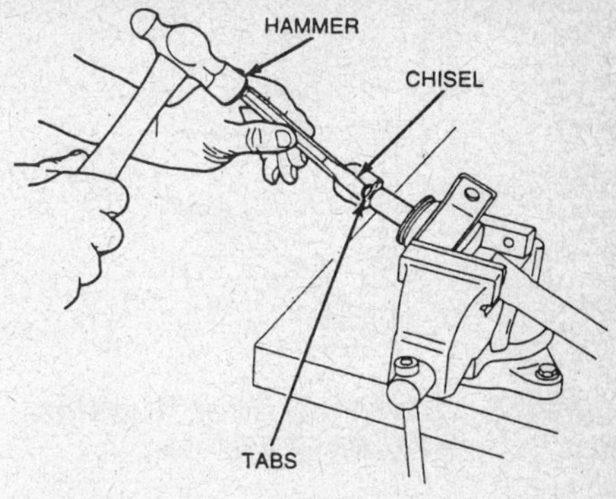


Fig. 2 Tie rod removal

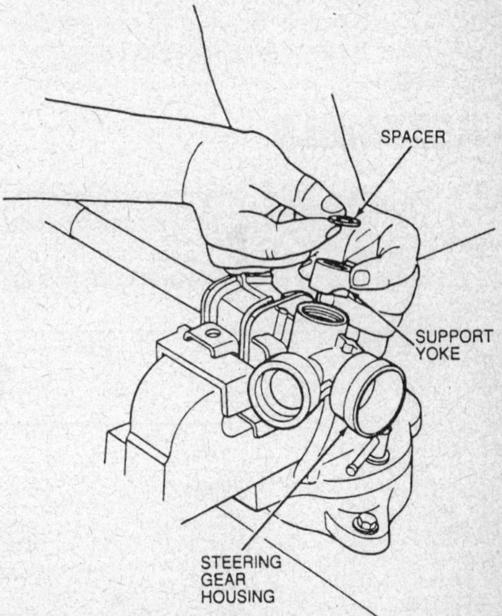


Fig. 4 Spacer & support yoke removal

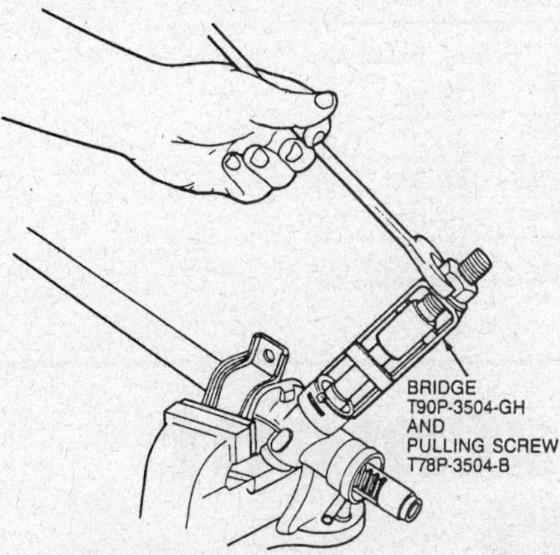


Fig. 3 Pinion & bearing removal

## EXCESSIVE STEERING WHEEL PLAY

1. Worn steering gear.
2. Worn or damaged steering joints.
3. Loose steering gear mounting bolts.

## POOR STEERING WHEEL RETURN

1. Damaged or binding steering joints.
2. Improper steering gear preload.
3. Faulty wheel or tire.
4. Faulty suspension component.

## STEERING WHEEL VIBRATES

1. Damaged steering linkage.
2. Loose steering gear mounting bolts.
3. Damaged or binding steering joints.
4. Worn or faulty front wheel bearing.
5. Faulty wheel or tire.
6. Faulty suspension component.

## ABNORMAL NOISE

1. Loose steering gear mounting bolt.
2. Faulty steering gear.
3. Obstruction near steering column.
4. Loose steering linkage.
5. Worn steering joints.

# ADJUSTMENTS

## RACK PRELOAD/SUPPORT YOKE

1. Loosen locknut.
2. Install yoke adjustment tool No. T90P-3504-JH or equivalent, **torque** yoke plug to 8.7 inch lbs, then loosen bolt 10-40°.
3. Using pinion shaft tool No. T86P-3504-K or equivalent, measure pinion torque, 9-12 inch lbs. should be indicated at neutral position ±90°, 14.7 inch lbs. or less should be indicated in any other position.
4. If pinion torque is not as specified, turn adjusting bolt to correct, then tighten adjusting bolt locknut.

# DISASSEMBLE

1. Place alignment marks on tie rod and tie rod end, then remove end.
2. Remove tie rod boot small clips **Fig. 1**, then remove boot wire at steering gear housing.
3. Slide boot off tie rods.
4. Using suitable hammer and cold chisel, **Fig. 2**, straighten tie rod to rack tabs.
5. Unscrew tie rod from rack, then remove rods and washers.
6. Remove rack mount brackets and bushings as required.
7. Remove pinion protector, then using suitable screwdriver or seal remover, remove pinion oil seal from shaft. **Do not score pinion shaft.**
8. Remove pinion oil seal spacer, then pinion bearing snap ring.
9. Using bridge tool No. T90P-3504-GH and pulling screw tool No. T78P-3504-B or equivalents, **Fig. 3**, remove pinion and bearing assembly from housing.
10. Remove locknut, adjusting bolt, yoke plug and spring.
11. Remove spacer and yoke support, **Fig. 4**.
12. Pull rack out left side of housing to remove. **If rack is remove through rack bushing at right side of housing, bushing damage may result.**

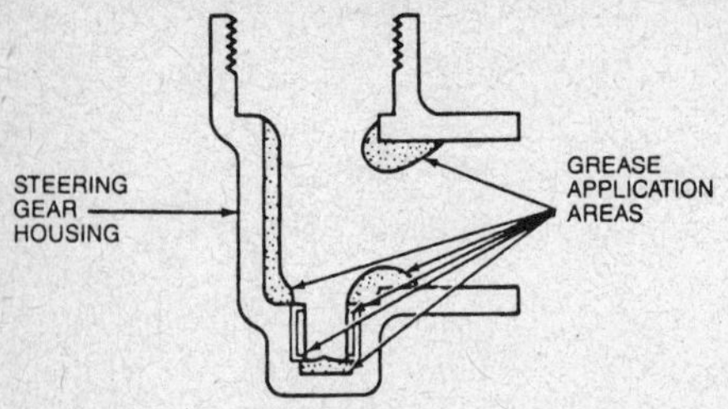


**Fig. 5 Steering gear housing lubricant points**

13. At steering gear housing, depress bushing locking tabs.
14. Remove rack support bushing from right side of steering gear.
15. Lower pinion bearing is not serviceable, if damaged, replace rack housing.

## ASSEMBLE

1. Lubricate rack teeth, pinion bearing and housing, **Fig. 5,** with appropriate grease.
2. Lubricate pinion oil seal lips, rack support yoke and rack. **Do not plug rack vent holes.**
3. Using suitable grease, lubricate rack support bushing, then install bushing to right side of housing engaging bushing tabs to housing slots.
4. If replacing pinion bearing, install new bearing with suitable tool, bearing may be started with a pinion as alignment tool but cannot be seated with pinion. **Do not strike pinion with hammer.**
5. Install rack through LH side of housing, with teeth facing pinion bore.
6. Install pinion and bearing to housing.
7. Install pinion bearing snap ring with beveled side up (toward oil seal), then oil seal tab spacer tab side down, locating tab in snap ring.
8. Using seal installer tool No. T90P-3504-HH and T81P-3504-P or equivalents, **Fig. 6,** install oil seal.
9. Install washers and tie rod to rack, then bend tabs downward.
10. Install boots and tie rod ends.
11. Center rack ensuring tie rods are equally extended.
12. Lubricate rack support yoke, then install to housing.
13. Install spacer and yoke spring.

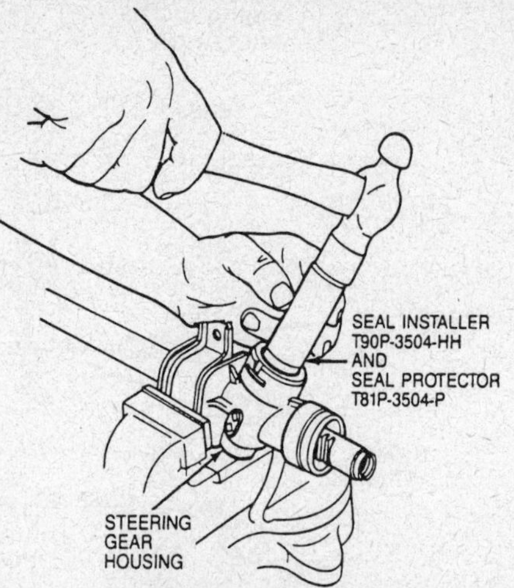


**Fig. 6 Pinion oil seal installation**

14. Apply sealant to yoke plug threads, then install plug, adjusting nut and locknut to housing.
15. Adjust rack preload as outlined in "Adjustments, Rack Preload/Support Yoke."

## TIGHTENING SPECIFICATIONS

| Year | Component | Torque, Ft. Lbs. |
|---|---|---|
| 1991 | Intermediate Shaft To Pinion Shaft Bolts | 13–20 |
| | Rack Preload/Support Yoke Adjustment Bolt | 8.7① |
| | Steering Gear Bracket Nuts | 27–38 |
| | Tie Rod End Jam Nut | 25–29 |
| | Tie Rod Stud To Steering Knuckle Nut | 31–42 |

①—Inch lbs.

# Steering Gear Adjustment Specifications

| Year & Model | Gear Type | Worm Bearing Preload | Cross Shaft Preload | Rack Preload |
|---|---|---|---|---|
| **1989–91** | | | | |
| Ford② | Rack & Pinion | ① | 4.6-13.2③ | — |
| **1989–91** | | | | |
| Ford Festiva | Rack & Pinion | — | — | 8-11.5③ |
| **1989** | | | | |
| Mercury Tracer | Rack & Pinion | — | — | 7.8-11.2③ |
| **1991** | | | | |
| Ford Escort & Mercury Tracer | Rack & Pinion | — | — | 9-12③ |

①—Not adjustable.
②—Except Ford Festiva, Mercury Tracer & 1991 Ford Escort.
③—Inch lbs.

# POWER STEERING

## TABLE OF CONTENTS



# Application Charts

## POWER STEERING PUMPS

| Year | Model | Type | Page No. |
|---|---|---|---|
| 1989 | Continental | Ford Model CII Slipper Type Pump | 22-14 |
| | Cougar & Thunderbird | Ford Model CII Slipper Type Pump | 22-14 |
| | Crown Victoria & Grand Marquis | Ford Model CII Slipper Type Pump | 22-14 |
| | Escort | Ford Model CII Slipper Type Pump | 22-14 |
| | Festiva | Festiva Steering Pump | 22-22 |
| | Mark VII | Ford Model CII Slipper Type Pump | 22-14 |
| | Mustang | Ford Model CII Slipper Type Pump | 22-14 |
| | Probe | Probe Steering Pump | 22-114 |
| | Sable & Taurus | Ford Model CII Slipper Type Pump | 22-14 |
| | Scorpio | Saginaw TC Model | 22-18 |
| | Tempo & Topaz | Ford Model CII Slipper Type Pump | 22-14 |
| | Town Car | Ford Model CII Slipper Type Pump | 22-14 |
| | Tracer | 1989 Tracer & 1991 Capri Steering Pump | 22-19 |
| | XR4TI | Ford Model CII Slipper Type Pump | 22-14 |
| 1990 | Continental | Ford Model CII Slipper Type Pump | 22-14 |
| | Cougar & Thunderbird | Ford Model CII Slipper Type Pump | 22-14 |
| | Crown Victoria & Grand Marquis | Ford Model CII Slipper Type Pump | 22-14 |
| | Escort | Ford Model CII Slipper Type Pump | 22-14 |
| | Festiva | Festiva Steering Pump | 22-22 |

*Continued*

## APPLICATION CHARTS—Continued

| Year | Model | Type | Page No. |
|---|---|---|---|
| 1990-cont'd. | Mark VII | Ford Model CII Slipper Type Pump | 22-14 |
| | Mustang | Ford Model CII Slipper Type Pump | 22-14 |
| | Probe | Probe Steering Pump | 22-114 |
| | Sable & Taurus | Ford Model CII Slipper Type Pump | 22-14 |
| | Scorpio | Saginaw TC Model | 22-18 |
| | Tempo & Topaz | Ford Model CII Slipper Type Pump | 22-14 |
| | Town Car | Ford Model CII Slipper Type Pump | 22-14 |
| 1991 | Capri | 1989 Tracer & 1991 Capri Steering Pump | 22-19 |
| | Continental | Ford Model CIII Slipper Type Pump ① | — |
| | Cougar & Thunderbird | Ford Model CII Slipper Type Pump | 22-14 |
| | Crown Victoria & Grand Marquis | Ford Model CII Slipper Type Pump | 22-14 |
| | Escort & Tracer ② | Ford Model CII Slipper Type Pump | 22-14 |
| | Festiva | Festiva Steering Pump | 22-22 |
| | Mark VII | Ford Model CII Slipper Type Pump | 22-14 |
| | Mustang | Ford Model CII Slipper Type Pump | 22-14 |
| | Probe | Probe Steering Pump | 22-114 |
| | Sable & Taurus | Ford Model CII Slipper Type Pump | 22-14 |
| | Tempo & Topaz | Ford Model CII Slipper Type Pump | 22-14 |
| | Town Car | Ford Model CII Slipper Type Pump | 22-14 |

①—Not serviceable.
②—1.9L models.

## POWER STEERING GEARS

| Year | Model | Type | Page No. |
|---|---|---|---|
| 1989 | Continental | Ford Variable Assist, Except Electronic Variable Orifice System | 22-90 |
| | Cougar & Thunderbird | Ford Variable Assist, Electronic Variable Orifice System (EVO) | 22-102 |
| | Crown Victoria & Grand Marquis | Ford Torsion Bar Power Steering | 22-24 |
| | Escort | TRW Rack & Pinion Steering | 22-77 |
| | Festiva | Rack & Pinion Steering Gear, Festiva | 22-69 |
| | Mustang | Ford Rack & Pinion Steering Gear | 22-27 |
| | Mark VII | Ford Rack & Pinion Steering Gear | 22-27 |
| | Probe | Rack & Pinion Steering Gear, Probe Less Variable Assist | 22-64 |
| | | Rack & Pinion Steering Gear, Probe w/Variable Assist | 22-39 |
| | Sable & Taurus | Ford Rack & Pinion Steering Gear | 22-27 |
| | Scorpio | ZF Rack & Pinion Steering Gear | 22-87 |
| | Tempo & Topaz | TRW Rack & Pinion Steering | 22-77 |
| | Town Car | Ford Torsion Bar Power Steering | 22-24 |
| | Tracer | 1989 Tracer & 1991 Capri Rack & Pinion Steering Gear | 22-66 |
| | XR4Ti | TRW Rack & Pinion Steering Gear | 22-77 |
| | | ZF Rack & Pinion Steering Gear | 22-87 |
| 1990 | Continental | Ford Variable Assist, Except Electronic Variable Orifice System | 22-90 |
| | Cougar & Thunderbird | Ford Variable Assist, Electronic Variable Orifice System (EVO) | 22-120 |
| | Crown Victoria & Grand Marquis | Ford Torsion Bar Power Steering | 22-24 |
| | Escort | Ford Rack & Pinion Steering Gear | 22-27 |
| | Festiva | Rack & Pinion Steering Gear, Festiva | 22-69 |
| | Mark VII | Ford Rack & Pinion Steering Gear | 22-27 |
| | Mustang | Ford Rack & Pinion Steering Gear | 22-27 |
| | Probe | Rack & Pinion Steering Gear, Probe Less Variable Assist | 22-64 |
| | | Rack & Pinion Steering Gear, Probe w/Variable Assist | 22-39 |

*Continued*

## APPLICATION CHARTS—Continued

| Year | Model | Type | Page No. |
|---|---|---|---|
| 1990-cont'd. | Sable & Taurus | Ford Rack & Pinion Steering Gear | 22-27 |
| | | Ford Variable Assist, Except Electronic Variable Orifice System | 22- 90 |
| | Scorpio | ZF Rack & Pinion Steering Gear | 22-87 |
| | Tempo & Topaz | Ford Rack & Pinion Steering Gear | 22-27 |
| | Town Car | Ford Torsion Bar Power Steering | 22-24 |
| | | Ford Variable Assist, Electronic Variable Orifice System (EVO) | 22-120 |
| 1991 | Capri | 1989 Tracer & 1991 Capri Rack & Pinion Steering Gear | 22-66 |
| | Continental | Ford Variable Assist, Except Electronic Variable Orifice System | 22-90 |
| | Cougar & Thunderbird | Ford Variable Assist, Electronic Variable Orifice System (EVO) | 22-120 |
| | Crown Victoria & Grand Marquis | Ford Torsion Bar Power Steering | 22-24 |
| | Escort & Tracer | 1991 Escort & Tracer Rack & Pinion Steering Gear | 22-71 |
| | Festiva | Rack & Pinion Steering Gear, Festiva | 22-69 |
| | Mark VII | Ford Rack & Pinion Steering Gear | 22-27 |
| | Mustang | Ford Rack & Pinion Steering Gear | 22-27 |
| | Probe | Rack & Pinion Steering Gear, Probe Less Variable Assist | 22-64 |
| | | Rack & Pinion Steering Gear, Probe w/Variable Assist | 22-39 |
| | Sable & Taurus | Ford Rack & Pinion Steering Gear | 22-27 |
| | | Ford Variable Assist, Except Electronic Variable Orifice System | 22-90 |
| | Tempo & Topaz | Ford Rack & Pinion Steering Gear | 22-27 |
| | Town Car | Ford Torsion Bar Power Steering | 22-24 |
| | | Ford Variable Assist, Electronic Variable Orifice System (EVO) | 22-102 |

# Power Steering Pressure Specifications

| Year | Engine | Vehicle | Minimum Flow ① ② | Minimum Relief Pressure, Psi | Maximum Relief Pressure, Psi | Pump Model ③ | Maximum Free Flow @ 1500 RPM① |
|---|---|---|---|---|---|---|---|
| 1989 | 1.6L | Tracer | — | 924 | — | — | — |
| | 2.3L | XR4TI | .95 | 950 | 1130 | HBC-GC | 2.2 |
| 1989–90 | 1.9L⑤ | Escort | 1.1 | 850 | 1030 | HBC-GM | 2.2 |
| | 1.9L⑥ | Escort | 1.1 | 850 | 1030 | HBC-GL | 2.2 |
| | 2.9L | Scorpio | 1.32④ | 1100 | 1200 | HBA-HC | 2.24 |
| 1989–91 | 2.3L | Tempo/Topaz | .95 | 1200 | 1380 | HBC-GJ | 2.2 |
| | 2.3L | Mustang | 1.3 | 850 | 1130 | ⑦ | 2.6 |
| | 2.5L/3.0L | Sable/Taurus | .9 | 1200 | 1480 | HBC-GF | 2.6 |
| | 3.8L | Cougar/Thunderbird⑧ | 1.25 | 1200 | 1380 | HBC-JB | 2.6 |
| | 3.8L | Cougar/Thunderbird⑨ | 1.4 | 1200 | 1380 | HBC-JA | 3.0⑩ |
| | 3.8L | Sable/Taurus | .9 | 1200 | 1480 | HBC-GE | 2.6 |
| | 3.8L | Continental | 1.5 | 1300 | 1380 | HBC-HM | 3.0 |
| | All | Probe | — | 1066 | 1138 | — | — |
| | 5.0L | Mustang⑪ | ⑫ | 950 | 1230 | ⑬ | 2.6 |
| | 5.0.L | Mustang⑭ | 1.6 | 1200 | 1480 | HBU-JD | 2.6 |
| | 5.0L | Mark VII | 1.6 | 1200 | 1480 | HBC-JG | ⑮ |
| | All | ⑯ | 1.5 | 1200 | 1380 | HBC-FV | 3.0 |
| | All | ⑰ | 1.5 | 1200 | 1380 | HBC-FU | 3.4 |
| | All | Town Car | 1.5 | 1200 | 1380 | HBC-FU | 3.4 |
| 1990–91 | 1.3L | Festiva | — | 1031 | 1138 | — | — |
| 1991 | 1.8L | Escort/Tracer | — | 1067 | — | — | — |
| | 1.9L⑤ | Escort | 1.1 | 850 | 1030 | HBC-GM | 2.2 |
| | 1.9L⑥ | Escort | 1.1 | 850 | 1030 | HBC-GL | 2.2 |

Continued

## POWER STEERING PRESSURE SPECIFICATIONS—Continued

① —Gallons per minute.
② —Flow is dependent on pump model, engine RPM and pulley ratio. Engine idle speed must be within specifications when checking minimum flow.
③ —Power steering pump identification tag is located on the reservoir body.
④ —At 49.96 psi.
⑤ —CFI.
⑥ —EFI.
⑦ —Either HBC-HX or HBC-GW pump.
⑧ —Base model.
⑨ —Super coupe or XR7.
⑩ —Measured w/vehicle not moving.
⑪ —Manual transmission.
⑫ —On models w/HBC-HX pump, 1.35 gal, w/HBC-GU pump, 1.4 gal.
⑬ —Either HBC-HX or HBC-GU pump.
⑭ —Automatic transmission.
⑮ —On LSC models, 3 gal., except LSC, 2.6 gal.
⑯ —Except police.
⑰ —Police models.

# Ford Model CII Slipper Type Pump

## INDEX



## DESCRIPTION

The Ford model CII power steering pump is a belt driven 10-slipper type pump incorporating a fiberglass filled nylon reservoir. The reservoir is attached to the rear side of the aluminum pump housing assembly. The pump body is encased within the housing and reservoir assembly. The pump design incorporates a pump pressure fitting which allows the pump pressure line to swivel. A pressure sensitive identification tag is attached to the reservoir body. This tag indicates the basic model number and the suffix.

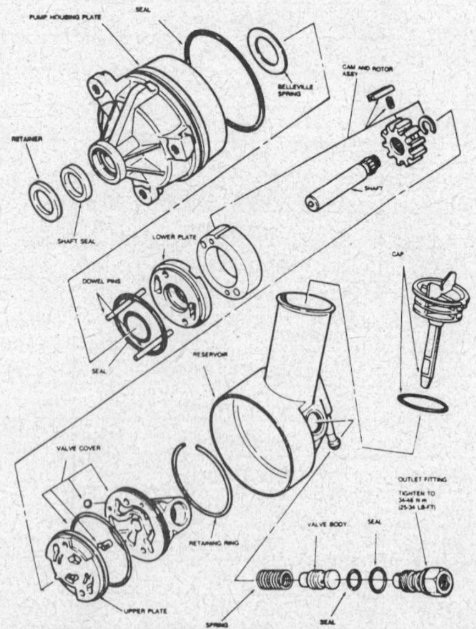


**Fig. 1 Exploded view of Ford Model CII power steering pump**

## TROUBLESHOOTING

### POWER STEERING PUMP LEAKS

1. Excessive fluid fill.
2. Dipstick missing, loose, damaged or missing O-ring.
3. Broken or cracked fluid reservoir.
4. Loose or damaged hose fittings.
5. Shaft seal not pressed flush with housing surface.
6. Shaft seal damage.
7. Rotor shaft damage, helical grooving or OD has an axial scratch.
8. Shaft bushing worn.
9. Plugged drainback hole.
10. Damaged or missing reservoir O-ring.
11. Damaged or missing outlet fitting O-rings.
12. Excessive pump assembly bracket vibration.
13. Plate and bushing reservoir seal groove damage, metal chips or foreign material in seal groove.
14. Faulty outlet fitting.

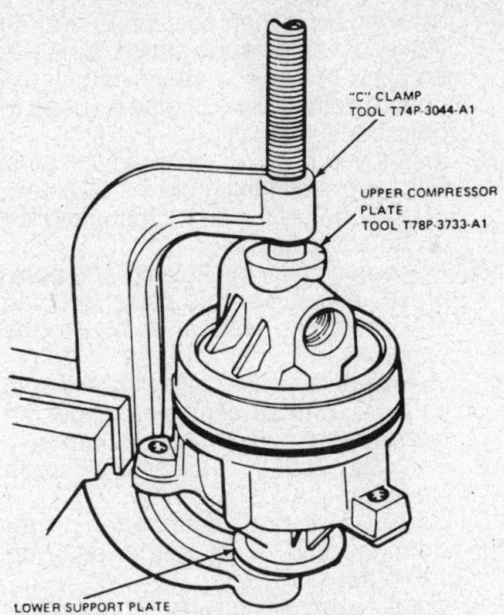


**Fig. 2 Positioning pump in C-clamp**

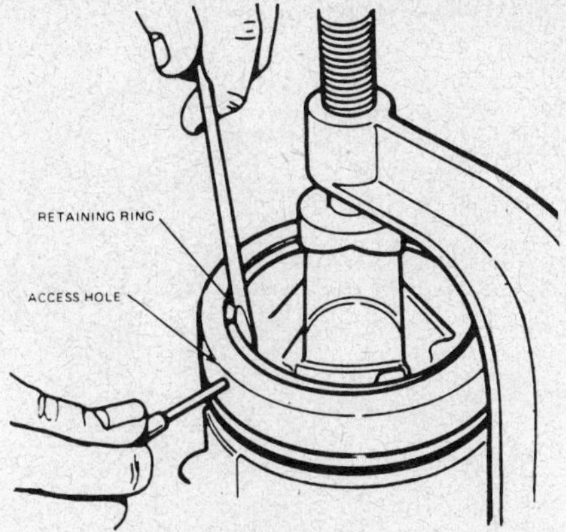


**Fig. 3 Removing valve cover retaining ring**

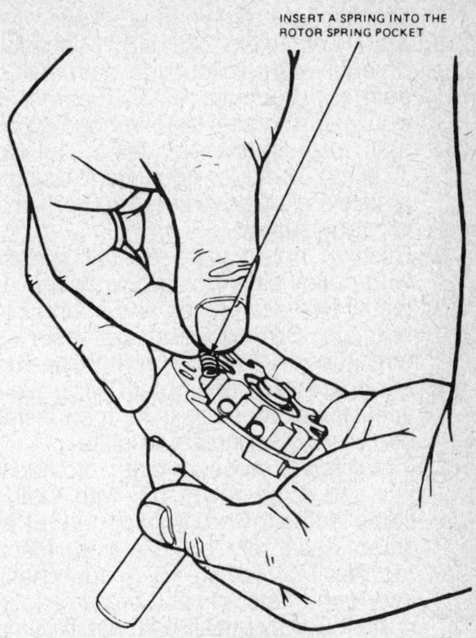


**Fig. 4 Installing slipper springs**

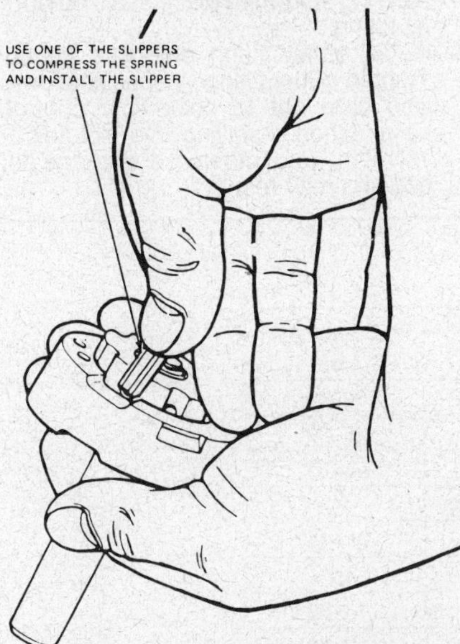


**Fig. 5 Installing slippers**

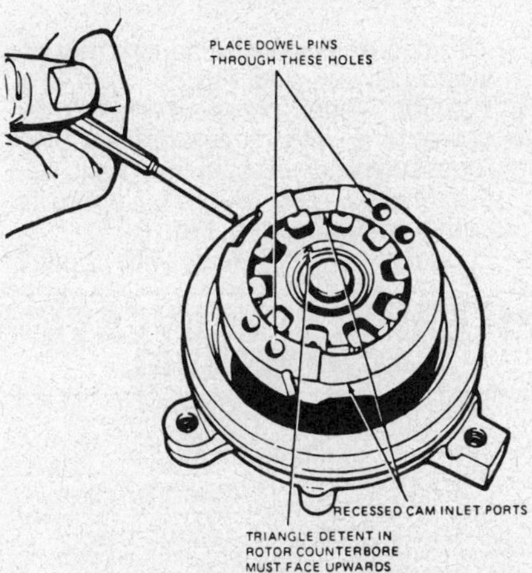


**Fig. 6 Assembling cam, slippers & rotor**

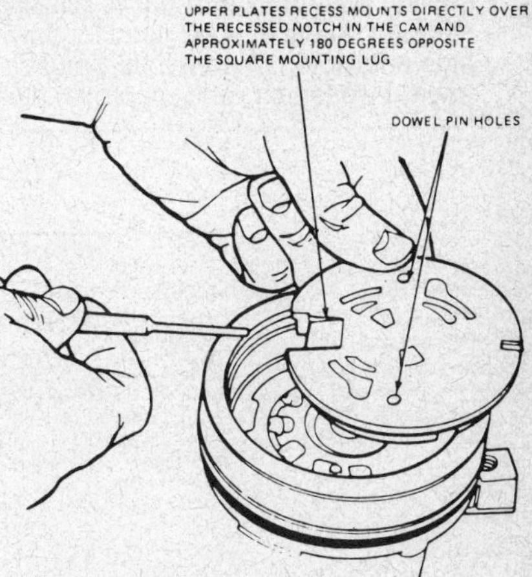


**Fig. 7 Installing upper pressure plate**

## POWER STEERING PUMP NOISE, MOAN OR WHINE

1. Fluid aeration.
2. Low fluid.
3. Hose grounded.
4. Steering column grounded.
5. Valve cover O-ring or baffle missing or damaged.
6. Interference between components in pumping elements.
7. Loose or poor bracket alignment.
8. Cam contour damaged.

## DISASSEMBLE

1. Remove pulley from pump, **Fig. 1.**
2. Remove outlet fitting, flow control valve and flow control valve spring from pump, then remove reservoir.
3. Place a suitable C-clamp in a vise.
4. Position lower support plate T78P-3733-A2, or equivalent, over pump rotor shaft.
5. Install upper compressor plate T78P-3733-A1, or equivalent, into upper portion of C-clamp.
6. While holding compressor tool, place pump assembly into C-clamp with rotor shaft facing downward, **Fig. 2.**
7. Tighten C-clamp until a slight bottoming of valve cover is observed.
8. Through small hole located on side of pump housing, insert a suitable drift and push inward on valve cover snap ring. While pushing inward on snap ring, place a screwdriver under snap ring edge and remove ring from housing, **Fig. 3.**
9. Loosen C-clamp and remove upper compressor plate T78P-3733-A2, or equivalent, then remove pump assembly.
10. Remove pump valve cover and O-ring.
11. Remove rotor shaft, upper plate, cam and rotor assembly and two dowel pins.
12. Remove lower plate and spring, by tapping housing on a flat surface.
13. Using a suitable screwdriver, remove rotor shaft seal.

## ASSEMBLE

1. Position rotor on rotor shaft splines with triangle detent on rotor counterbore facing upward, **Fig. 1.**
2. Install snap ring into groove on end of rotor shaft.
3. Position insert cam over rotor. Ensure recessed notch on insert cam is facing upward.
4. With rotor extended upward approximately half out of cam, insert spring into rotor pocket, **Fig. 4.**
5. Use a slipper to compress spring, then install slipper with groove facing cam, **Fig. 5.**
6. Perform steps 4 and 5 on slipper cavity beneath opposite inlet recess.
7. While holding cam stationary, index rotor left or right one space and install another spring and slipper until all ten rotor cavities have been filled. Use care when turning rotor that springs

and slippers remain in position.

8. Apply Loctite No. 242 or 271 adhesive or equivalent to outside diameter of seal and Locquic NF or T primer or equivalent to seal bore in housing. Install rotor shaft seal using tool No. T78P-3733-A3, or equivalent. Using a plastic mallet, drive seal into bore until properly seated.
9. Position pump plate on flat surface with pulley side facing downward.
10. Install two dowel pins and spring into housing. **Spring must be inserted with dished surface facing upward.**
11. Lubricate inner and outer O-ring seals with power steering fluid, then install seals on lower pressure plate.
12. Install lower pressure plate into housing and over dowel pin with O-ring seals facing toward front of pump. Position assembly on C-clamp. Place tool No. T78P-3733-A3, or equivalent, into rotor shaft hole and press on lower plate lightly until it bottoms in pump housing. This will seat the outer O-ring seal.
13. Install cam, rotor, rotor and slippers and rotor shaft assembly into pump housing over dowel pins. When installing assembly into pump housing, stepped holes must be used for dowel pins and notch in cam insert must be toward reservoir and approximately 180 degrees opposite square mounting lug on housing, **Fig. 6.**

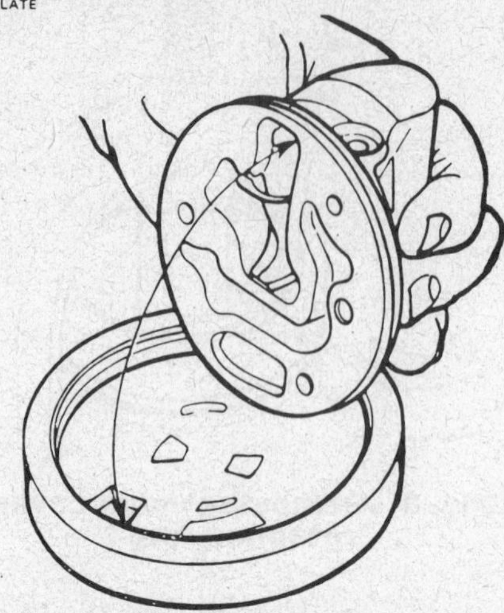
PRESSURE CHANNEL IN THE VALVE COVER FITS DIRECTLY OVER THE RECESS IN THE UPPER PLATE

**Fig. 8 Installing valve cover**

14. Position upper pressure plate over dowel pins with recess directly over recessed notch on cam insert and approximately 180 degrees opposite square mounting lug, **Fig. 7.**
15. Lubricate O-ring seal with power steering fluid, then position O-ring on valve cover. Ensure plastic baffle is securely in position on valve cover. A coat of petroleum jelly may be used to hold baffle in position.
16. Insert valve cover over dowel pins. Ensure outlet fitting hole in valve cover is aligned with square mounting lug on housing, **Fig. 8.**
17. Place assembly in C-clamp and compress valve cover into pump housing until snap ring groove on housing is exposed.
18. Install valve cover snap ring in pump housing. Ensure snap ring ends are near access hole in pump housing.
19. Remove pump assembly from C-clamp.
20. Lubricate O-ring seal with power steering fluid, then place seal on pump housing.
21. Install reservoir on pump housing.
22. Install flow control valve and spring into valve cover.
23. Lubricate O-ring seals with power steering fluid, then place seals on outlet fitting.
24. Install outlet fitting on valve cover. Tighten outlet fitting to specifications. Use care not to cock flow control valve when installing. Do not force valve forward otherwise damage to housing may result.

# TIGHTENING SPECIFICATIONS

## CONTINENTAL

| Year | Component | Torque, Ft. Lbs. |
|---|---|---|
| 1989–91 | Front Bolts To Support Bracket | 30–41 |
| | Outlet Fitting To Valve Cover① | 25–39 |
| | Pivot Bolt | 45–57 |
| | Pressure Hose Tube Nut To Pump Pressure Fitting | ② |
| | Pump To Bracket | 30–45 |
| | Return Hose To Pump (Hose Clamp) | 8–24③ |
| | Support Bracket To Cylinder Head | 15–22 |
| | Support Bracket To Engine | 15–22 |

①—1991 models.
②—1989–90 models, 10–15 ft. lbs., 1991 models, 31–39 ft. lbs.
③—Inch lbs.

## COUGAR & THUNDERBIRD

| Year | Component | Torque, Ft. Lbs. |
|---|---|---|
| 1989–91 | Front Bolts To Support Bracket | 30–45 |
| | Outlet Fitting | 25–34 |
| | Pivot Bolt | 30–45 |
| | Pressure Hose Tube Nut To Pump Pressure Fitting① | 10–25 |
| | Pump To Bracket | 30–45 |
| | Pump Bracket To Rear Support | ② |
| | Quick Connect Power Steering Fitting ③ | 20–25 |
| | Rear Support To Engine Head | 30–45 |
| | Return Hose To Pump (Hose Clamp) | 12–24④ |
| | Support Bracket To Engine | 30–45 |
| | Support Bracket To Water Pump Housing | 30–45 |

①—1989 models.
②—1989–90 models w/A/C, 18–24 ft. lbs., less A/C, 30–45 ft. lbs., 1991 models, 18–24 ft. lbs.
③—1991 models.
④—Inch lbs.

## CROWN VICTORIA, GRAND MARQUIS & TOWN CAR

| Year | Component | Torque, Ft. Lbs. |
|---|---|---|
| 1989–91 | Front Bolts To Support Bracket | 30–45 |
| | Outlet Fitting | 25–34 |
| | Pivot Bolt | 30–45 |
| | Pressure Hose Tube Nut To Pump Pressure Fitting① | 12–15 |
| | Pump To Bracket | 30–45 |
| | Quick Connect Tube Nut | ② |
| | Return Hose To Pump (Hose Clamp) | 12–24③ |
| | Support Bracket To Engine | 30–45 |
| | Support Bracket To Water Pump Housing | 30–45 |

①—1989 models.
②—1989 models, 10–25 ft. lbs., 1990–91 models, 20–25 ft. lbs.
③—Inch lbs.

## MARK VII & MUSTANG

| Year | Component | Torque, Ft. Lbs. |
|---|---|---|
| 1989–91 | Front Bolts To Support Bracket | 30–45 |
| | Outlet Fitting To Reservoir & Valve Cover① | 25–34 |
| | Pivot Bolt | 30–45 |
| | Pressure Hose Tube Nut To Pump Pressure Fitting | 10–25 |
| | Pump To Bracket | 30–45 |
| | Pump Bracket To Rear Support | ③ |
| | Quick Connect Power Steering Fitting② | 20–25 |
| | Rear Support To Engine Head | 30–45 |
| | Return Hose To Pump (Hose Clamp) | 12–24④ |
| | Support Bracket To Engine | 30–45 |
| | Support Bracket To Water Pump Housing | 30–45 |

①—1991 models.
②—1989–90 models.
③—Less A/C, 30–45 ft. lbs., w/A/C, 18–24 ft. lbs.
④—Inch lbs.

## SABLE, TAURUS, TEMPO, TOPAZ, 1989–90 ESCORT & 1991 ESCORT w/1.9L

| Year | Component | Torque, Ft. Lbs. |
|---|---|---|
| 1989–91 | Front Bolts To Support Bracket | 30–45 |
| | Outlet Fitting To Valve Cover | 25–39 |
| | Pivot Bolt | 30–45 |
| | Pressure Hose Tube Nut To Pump Pressure Fitting | ① |
| | Pulley To Pulley Hub | 15–24 |
| | Pump To Bracket | 30–45 |
| | Return Hose To Pump (Hose Clamp) | 8–24② |
| | Support Bracket To Cylinder Head | 15–24 |
| | Support Bracket To Engine | 30–45 |

①—Except 1991 Sable & Taurus, 10–15 ft. lbs., on 1991 Sable & Taurus, 31–39 ft. lbs.
②—Inch lbs.

## XR4TI

| Year | Component | Torque, Ft. Lbs. |
|---|---|---|
| 1989 | Outlet Fitting | 25–34 |
| | Power Steering Pressure Hose Tube Nut | 10–25 |
| | Pump Bolts | 30–45 |

# Saginaw TC Model Pump

## INDEX



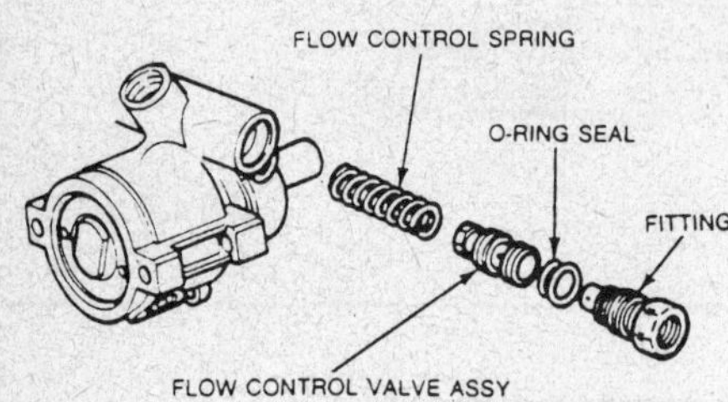


**Fig. 1 Removing fitting**

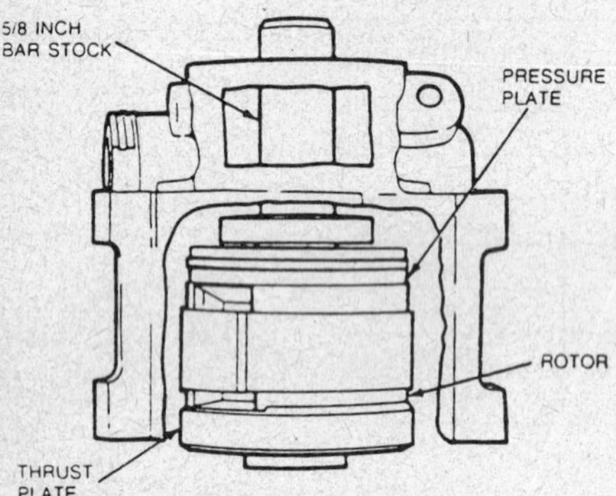


**Fig. 4 Removing thrust plate**

## DISASSEMBLE

1. Using drive flange puller tool No. T67L-3600-A, remove drive flange.
2. Remove fitting, **Fig. 1**, and discard O-rings.
3. Remove retaining ring from housing. Note that beveled edge of ring faces outward for reference during assembly.
4. Remove driveshaft and bearing from housing, **Fig. 2.**
5. Press bearing off driveshaft, if necessary.
6. Remove driveshaft seal from housing, if necessary.
7. Remove rear retaining ring, **Fig. 3.**
8. Using 5/8 inch diameter bar stock or suitable brass drift, press on pressure plate hub until thrust plate can be removed, **Fig. 4.**
9. Remove ten vanes, rotor and two dowels from pump ring, **Fig. 5.**
10. Remove O-ring from housing.
11. Remove pump ring from housing, then the pressure plate.
12. Remove and discard O-ring from pressure plate.
13. Remove spring and dowel pin from housing.

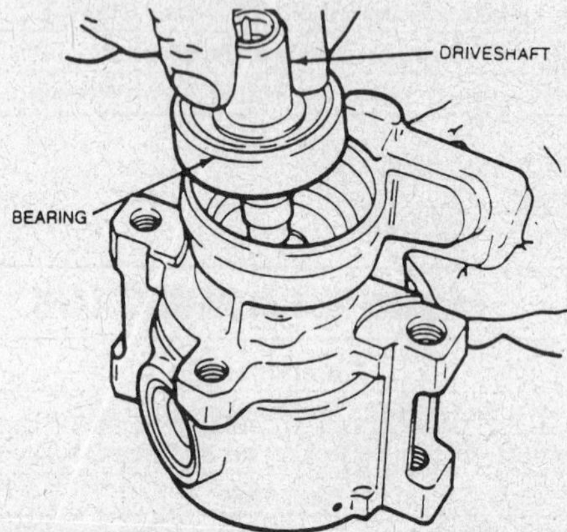


**Fig. 2 Removing driveshaft & bearing**

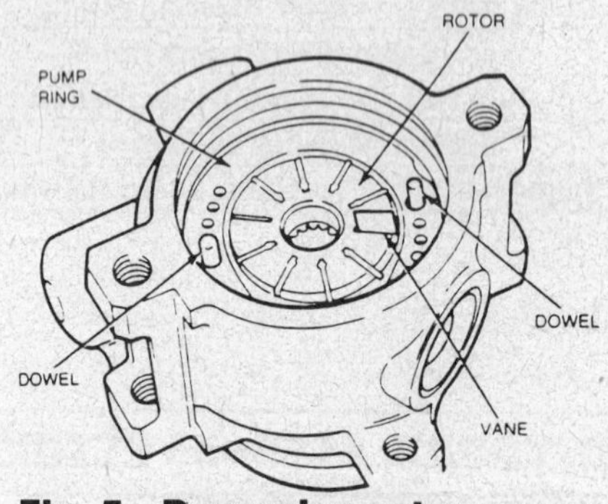


**Fig. 5 Removing rotor vanes & dowel pins**

14. Remove O-ring from sleeve.
15. Remove sleeve from housing, **Fig. 6,** if necessary.

## ASSEMBLE

Prior to assembly, lubricate all parts with type F automatic transmission fluid.

1. Using a suitable socket, press sleeve in housing, **Fig. 7.**
2. Install new O-ring in sleeve, then the dowel pin.
3. Install spring over sleeve.
4. Install new O-ring on pressure plate.
5. Place a reference mark on housing directly over dowel pin, then place a mark on pressure plate directly over dowel pin hole.
6. Align reference marks, **Fig. 8,** then install pressure plate in housing.
7. Install two dowel pins in pressure plate.
8. Install pump ring over dowel pins with identification marks on ring facing thrust plate, **Fig. 9.**
9. Install rotor in pump ring so rotor counterbore faces driveshaft and bearing assembly, then install ten vanes into rotor.
10. Install new O-ring in housing.
11. Position thrust plate in pump so dimples on plate are aligned with mounting holes, **Fig. 10.**
12. Press thrust plate into housing, then install retaining ring so opening in ring faces mounting bolt hole nearest to access hole.
13. Press bearing on driveshaft, if removed.
14. Using suitable socket install driveshaft seal into housing, if removed.

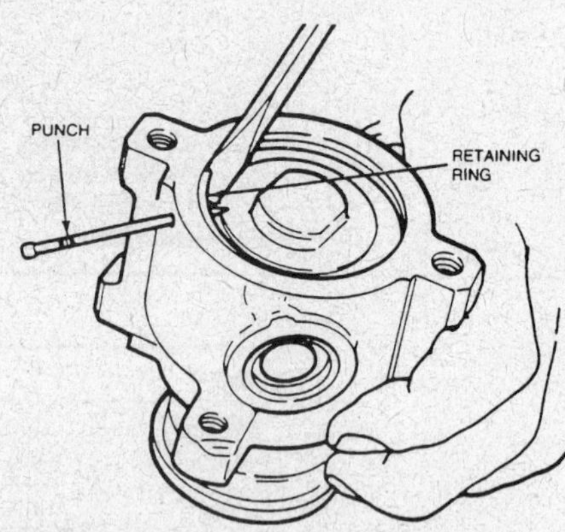


**Fig. 3 Removing retaining ring**

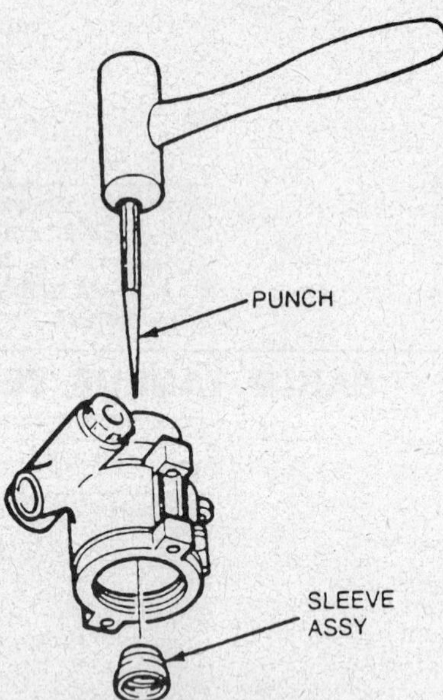


**Fig. 6 Removing sleeve assembly**

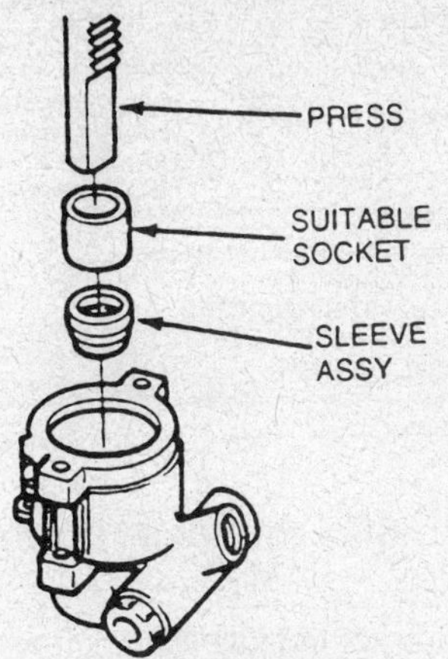


**Fig. 7 Installing sleeve assembly**

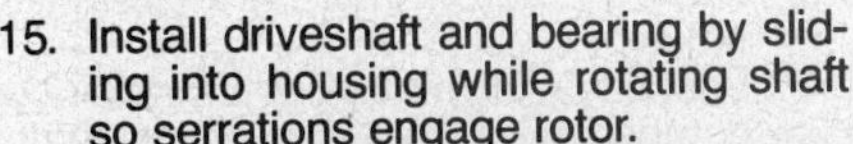

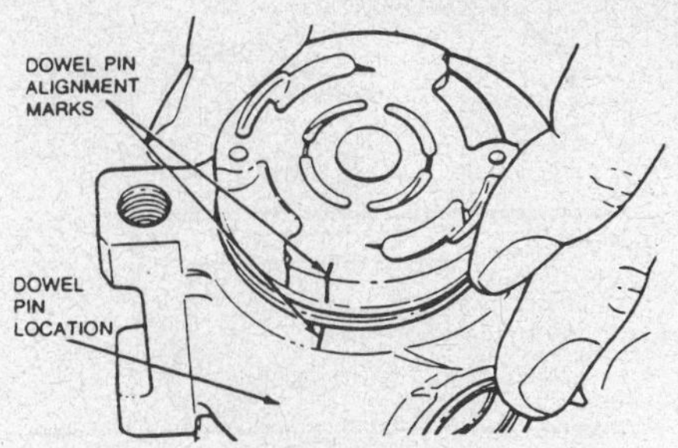


**Fig. 8 Aligning reference marks**

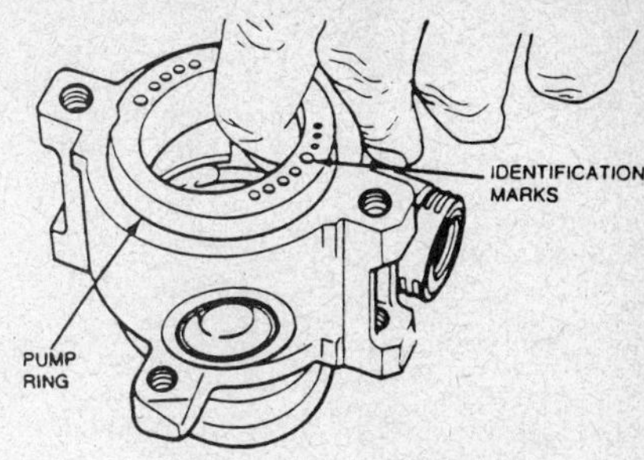


**Fig. 9 Pump ring identification marks**

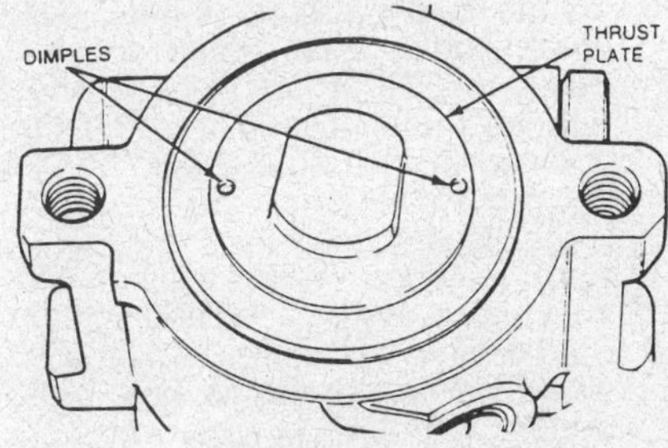


**Fig. 10 Aligning thrust plate**

15. Install driveshaft and bearing by sliding into housing while rotating shaft so serrations engage rotor.
16. Ensure shaft and bearing are bottomed in housing, then install retaining ring with beveled edge up.
17. Install spring, control valve and O-ring.
18. Install fitting and tighten to specifications.
19. Using flange installer tool No. T65P-3A733-1 or equivalent, install drive flange.

## TIGHTENING SPECIFICATIONS

| Year | Component | Torque, Ft. Lbs. |
|---|---|---|
| 1989–90 | Pressure Fitting To Housing | 37–55 |
| | Pressure Hose To Fitting | 23–30 |
| | Pump Adjust Bolt | 30–42 |
| | Pump Pivot Bolt | 30–42 |
| | Pump To Bracket | 16–18 |

# 1989 Tracer & 1991 Capri Steering Pump

## INDEX



## TROUBLESHOOTING

### HEAVY STEERING WHEEL MOVEMENT

1. Loose or damaged belt.
2. Low fluid level or air in fluid.
3. Twisted or crimped hose or pipe.
4. Fluid leakage.
5. Low hydraulic pressure.
6. Insufficient tire pressure.
7. Improperly adjusted wheel alignment.
8. Faulty ball joint linkage.
9. Binding steering shaft.

### IMPROPER STEERING WHEEL RETURN

1. Incorrect tire pressure.
2. Improperly adjusted wheel alignment.
3. Faulty ball joint linkage.
4. Restricted, over tightened or bent steering shaft.

### UNEVEN STEERING EFFORT

1. Loose belt.
2. Loose steering shaft bolt(s).
3. Rough steering linkage operation.
4. Faulty steering gear.

### STEERING WHEEL PULLS

1. Incorrect tire pressure.
2. Improper preload adjustment.
3. Faulty wheel bearing.
4. Improperly adjusted wheel alignment.
5. Faulty steering gear.

### FLUID LEAKAGE

1. Hose coupling.
2. Damaged or clogged hose.
3. Faulty reservoir tank.
4. Faulty steering pump.

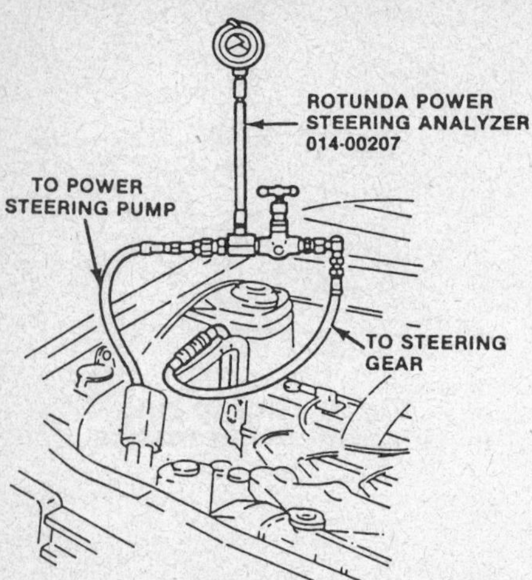


**Fig. 1 Pressure test analyzer**

5. Faulty steering gear.

## ABNORMAL NOISE

1. Loose power steering pump.
2. Loose steering gear.
3. Loose pump bracket.
4. Loose pump pulley nut.
5. Improperly adjusted belt.
6. Faulty steering gear.
7. Faulty steering pump.
8. Obstruction near steering column or pressure hose.
9. Loose steering linkage.

## POWER STEERING PRESSURE TEST

**During the following procedure, power steering pressure may exceed 1200 psi. Ensure proper tool fitment prior to performing test. Exercise extreme caution or damage or personal injury may result.**

1. Disconnect power steering pump pressure hose where it connects to tubing, Install power steering system analyzer tool No. 014-00207 and adapter tool No. 014-00454 or equivalents, **torque** fitting to 29-36 ft. lbs, **Fig. 1.**
2. Position thermometer in power steering pump reservoir. **Ensure gauge valve is set open to allow normal system function. Do not hold steering wheel against a stop for more than 10 seconds at a time.**
3. Start engine, then slowly turn steering wheel from lock to lock ten times to bleed system.
4. If required, turn steering wheel fully left and right several times to raise fluid temperature to 122-140D°F (50-60°C). **Gauge valve must be briefly closed to read operating pressures. Do not leave valve closed for more than 15 seconds.**
5. To measure pump output pressure, close gauge set valve, **Fig. 2,** then increase engine speed to 1000-1500 RPM, read pressure, then open valve. Operating pressure should be 924 psi, if pressure is low, service or replace pump.

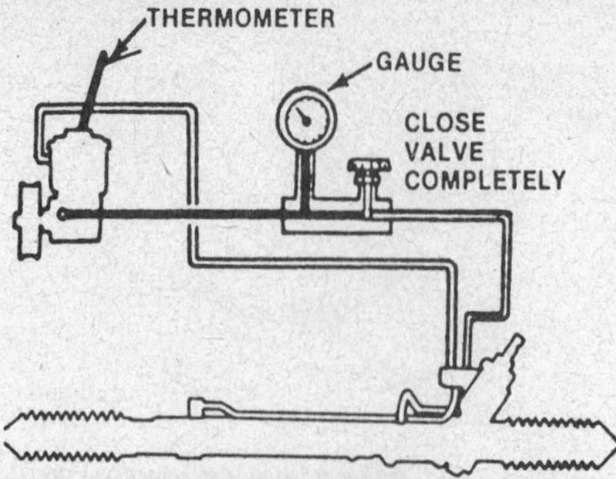


**Fig. 2 Power steering pump pressure test**

6. To measure pressure at gear, open valve, then increase engine speed to 1000-1500 RPM, turn steering wheel fully left and right, read pressure, **Fig. 3.** Operating pressure should be 924 psi, if pressure is low, service or replace steering gear.
7. Remove gauge set and adapter, connect high pressure hose and tighten.
8. Start engine, then slowly turn steering wheel lock to lock ten times to bleed system.

## POWER STEERING SYSTEM FLUSH

If the power steering pump has been serviced, flush the power steering gear and lines prior to installation.

1. Remove and flush power steering pressure hose, then reinstall.
2. Place gear fluid return line in suitable container, then plug reservoir return line at reservoir.
3. Fill reservoir using Motorcraft DEXRON II part No. ESW-M2C-138-CJ or equivalent.
4. Disconnect coil wire, then raise and support front wheels.
5. Add about two quarts of fluid while cranking engine with starter and turning steering wheel right to left.
6. When all the fluid is added, stop cranking engine.
7. Remove reservoir return line plug, then connect line to reservoir.
8. Fill reservoir to specified level.
9. Crank engine with starter and add fluid until level remains constant.
10. While cranking engine, rotate steering wheel from stop to stop. **Front wheels must be off the ground during steering wheel stop to stop rotation.**
11. Check fluid level, add as required.
12. Start engine, allow to run for several minutes.
13. Rotate steering wheel from far left to right several times.
14. Turn off engine, check fluid level add as required.

## DRIVE PULLEY REPLACE

1. Remove drive belt.
2. Disconnect ground wire from front of cylinder head.
3. Disconnect pressure switch electrical

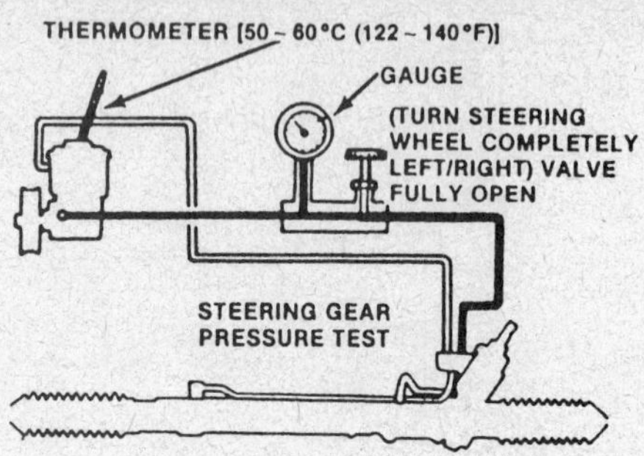


**Fig. 3 Steering gear pressure test**

connector from steering pump.
4. Remove pump adjusting bolts, block and nut.
5. Remove pump pivot bolt.
6. Remove pump and position on upper radiator support.
7. Hold pump pulley from rotating by installing a screwdriver through pulley holes.
8. Loosen pulley retaining nut until it becomes flush with end of pump shaft.
9. Hold pulley and tap on shaft until pulley loosens.
10. Remove nut and pulley.
11. Check pulley, belt and key for excessive wear or damage.
12. Reverse procedure to install.

## PUMP SERVICE

Refer to **Fig. 4**, for reference, when servicing steering pump.

### DISASSEMBLE

1. Remove pump pulley as described under "Drive Pulley, Replace."
2. Remove pulley key.
3. Remove reservoir cap and strainer, then drain fluid from pump.
4. Remove rear bracket, then front bracket.
5. Remove oil reservoir, then reservoir O-ring.
6. Remove rear cover and O-ring.
7. Remove pump center body and O-ring.
8. Remove cam ring, then shaft rear snap ring.
9. Remove vanes from rotor.
10. Remove rotor from shaft. Note position of rotor for reference during assembly.
11. Remove pump shaft from front of pump.
12. **On Capri models,** remove front bracket attaching bolts and bracket.
13. **On all models,** remove dowel pins from pump body if necessary.
14. Remove shaft oil seal.
15. Remove pressure regulator valve if necessary.
16. Remove pressure switch if necessary.

### INSPECTION

1. Inspect vanes and rotor faces for scored or chipped faces, wear or burring, replace as required.
2. Measure clearance between vane

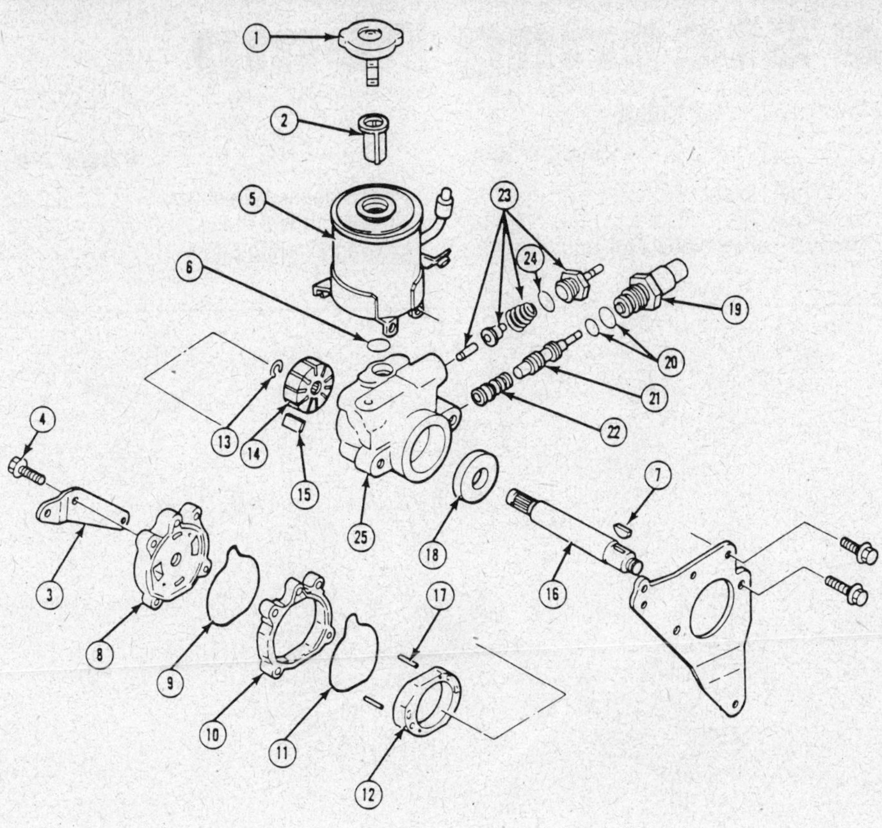


1. OIL LEVEL GAUGE
2. OIL STRAINER
3. REAR BRACKET
4. BOLT
5. OIL TANK
6. O-RING
7. KEY
8. PUMP BODY REAR
9. O-RING
10. PUMP BODY CENTER
11. O-RING
12. CAM RING
13. SNAP RING
14. ROTOR
15. VANE
16. SHAFT
17. DOWEL PIN
18. OIL SEAL
19. CONNECTOR
20. O-RINGS
21. CONTROL VALVE
22. SPRING
23. OIL PRESSURE SWITCH
24. O-RING
25. PUMP BODY

**Fig. 4 Exploded view of power steering pump**

and rotor groove, .0004-.0024 inch should be indicated.

3. Inspect rotor thrust faces, bushing diameter and shaft seal diameter for excessive wear or scoring.
4. If bushing is scored or excessively worn or O-ring grooves are damaged, replace housing. Measure clearance between bushing and shafts .001-.004 inch should be indicated.

## ASSEMBLE

Wash all parts except seals in chlorinated solvent, and dry with compressed air or allow to drip dry. Do not use cloth to dry.

1. Install pressure switch, if removed.
2. Install pressure regulator valve, if removed.
3. Install new shaft oil seal using a suitable socket. Coat seal lip with suitable lithium base grease.
4. Install dowel pins in pump body, if removed.
5. Install pump shaft, then rotor in position noted during disassembly.
6. Install rotor to shaft snap ring. Ensure snap ring is fully seated in groove.
7. Install vanes in rotor with rounded edges facing out.
8. Install cam ring onto dowel pins.
9. Install pump body center and front O-ring.
10. Install pump body rear and O-ring.
11. Install reservoir and O-ring.
12. Install short bolt into tank bracket and tighten.
13. Install rear mounting bracket and attaching bolts.
14. Install front mounting bracket and attaching bolts.
15. Install pulley key in shaft slot.
16. Install pulley as described under "Drive Pulley, Replace."
17. Rotate pulley and ensure smooth operation, if pulley does not operate smoothly, disassemble pump and check cause.

# Festiva Steering Pump

## INDEX



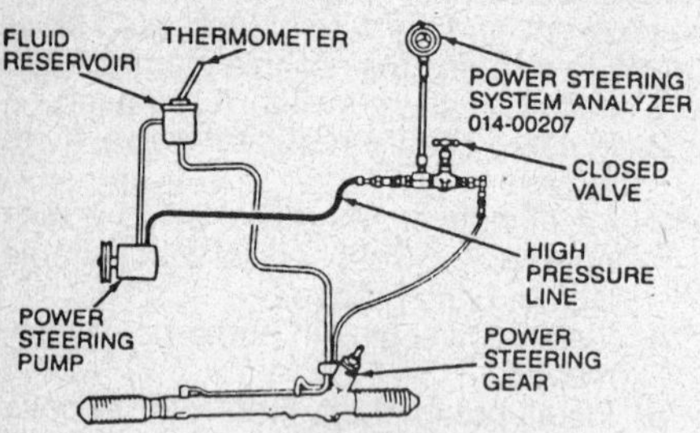


**Fig. 1 Pressure test connections**

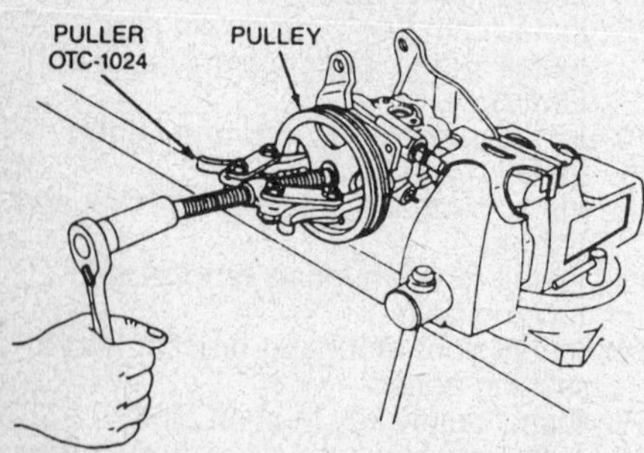


**Fig. 3 Removing pump pulley**

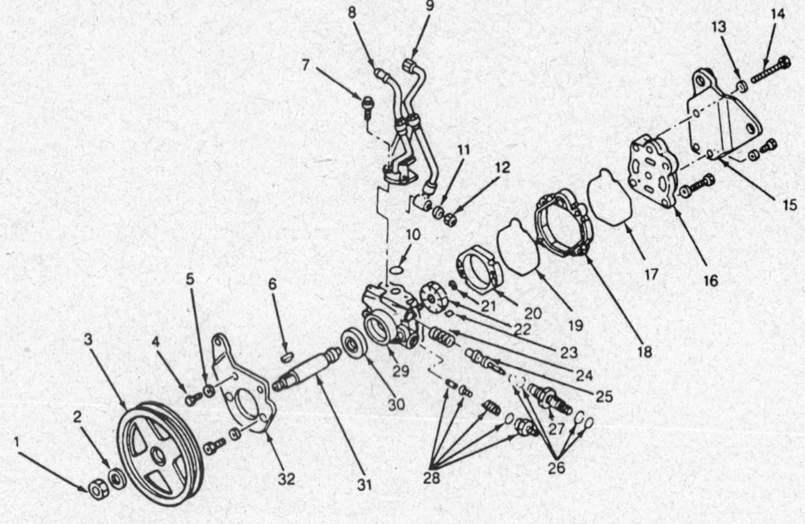


1. NUT
2. WASHER
3. PULLEY
4. BOLT
5. WASHER
6. KEY
7. BOLT
8. RETURN LINE
9. HIGH PRESSURE LINE
10. O-RING
11. WASHER
12. NUT
13. WASHER
14. BOLT
15. REAR BRACKET
16. REAR BODY
17. O-RING
18. CENTER BODY
19. O-RING
20. CAM RING
21. RETAINING RING
22. ROTOR
23. VANE
24. SPRING
25. CONTROL VALVE
26. O-RING
27. VALVE FITTING
28. PRESSURE SWITCH ASSEMBLY
29. FRONT BODY
30. SEAL
31. SHAFT
32. FRONT BRACKET

**Fig. 2 Exploded view of power steering pump**

## TROUBLESHOOTING

### HEAVY STEERING WHEEL MOVEMENT

1. Loose or damaged belt.
2. Low fluid level or air in fluid.
3. Twisted or crimped hose or pipe.
4. Fluid leakage.
5. Low hydraulic pressure.
6. Insufficient tire pressure.
7. Improperly adjusted wheel alignment.
8. Faulty ball joint linkage.
9. Binding steering shaft.

### POOR STEERING WHEEL RETURN

1. Incorrect tire pressure.
2. Improperly adjusted wheel alignment.
3. Faulty ball joint linkage.
4. Restricted, over tightened or bent steering shaft.

### UNEVEN STEERING EFFORT

1. Loose belt.
2. Loose steering shaft bolt(s).
3. Rough steering linkage operation.
4. Faulty steering gear.

### STEERING WHEEL PULLS

1. Incorrect tire pressure.
2. Improper preload adjustment.
3. Faulty wheel bearing.
4. Improperly adjusted wheel alignment.
5. Faulty steering gear.

### FLUID LEAKAGE

1. Hose coupling.
2. Damaged or clogged hose.
3. Faulty reservoir tank.
4. Faulty steering pump.
5. Faulty steering gear.

### ABNORMAL NOISE

1. Loose power steering pump.
2. Loose steering gear.
3. Loose pump bracket.
4. Loose pump pulley nut.
5. Improperly adjusted belt.
6. Faulty steering gear.
7. Faulty steering pump.
8. Obstruction near steering column or pressure hose.
9. Fluid aeration.
10. Loose steering linkage.

## POWER STEERING PRESSURE TEST

**During the following procedure, power steering pressure may exceed 1200 psi. Ensure proper tool fitment prior to performing test. Exercise extreme caution or damage or personal injury may result.**

1. Disconnect power steering pump pressure hose where it connects to tubing, Install power steering system analyzer tool No. 014-00207 and adapter tool No. 014-00454 or equivalents, **torque** fitting to 29-36 ft. lbs, **Fig. 1.**

2. Position thermometer in power steering pump reservoir. **Ensure gauge valve is open to allow normal system function. Do not hold steering wheel against a stop for more than 10 seconds at a time.**
3. Start engine, then slowly turn steering wheel from lock to lock ten times to bleed system.
4. If required, turn steering wheel fully left and right several times to raise fluid temperature to 122-140D°F (50-60°C). **Gauge valve must be briefly closed to read operating pressures. Do not leave valve closed for more than 15 seconds.**
5. To measure pump output pressure, close gauge set valve, then increase engine speed to 1000-1500 RPM, read pressure, then open valve. Operating pressure should be 1031-1138 psi, if pressure is low, repair or replace pump.
6. To measure pressure at gear, open valve, then increase engine speed to 1000-1500 RPM, turn steering wheel fully left and right, read pressure. Operating pressure should be 1031-1138 psi, if pressure is low, repair or replace steering gear.
7. Remove gauge set and adapter, connect high pressure hose and **torque** fitting to 29-36 ft. lbs.

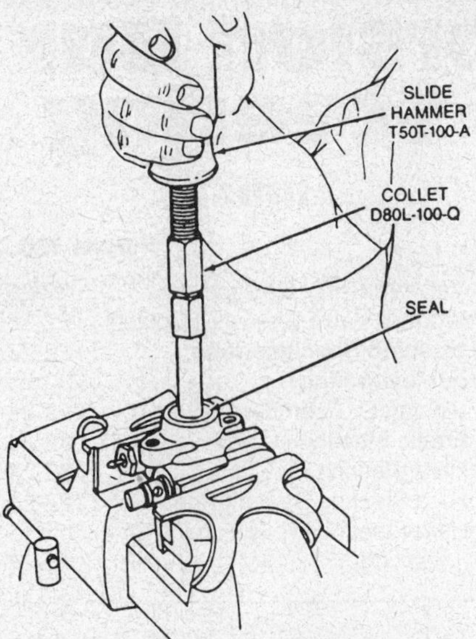


**Fig. 4 Removing dust seal**

8. Remove thermometer, then start engine, slowly turn steering wheel lock to lock ten times to bleed system.

## PUMP SERVICE

1. Secure power steering pump in a soft-jawed vise.
2. Remove both pressure and return lines from pump, **Fig. 2.**
3. Remove pulley nut, washer and O-ring.
4. Remove pump pulley and keyway using tool No. OCT-1024 or equivalent, **Fig. 3.**
5. Remove front and rear bracket bolts and washers, then the brackets.
6. Remove rear body bolts and washers, then the rear body.
7. Remove shaft and rotor by first removing shaft retaining ring.
8. Remove vanes and O-ring, then the center body.
9. Remove cam ring O-ring and cam ring.
10. Remove dust seal using tool Nos. D80L-100-Q and T50T-100-A, **Fig. 4.**
11. Remove valve fitting, then remove O-ring from valve fitting.
12. Remove control valve and spring.
13. Remove pressure switch fitting and spring.
14. Remove pressure switch spring seat and plunger.
15. Reverse procedure to assemble, noting the following:
    a. When installing vanes, rounded edge of vanes should face toward center of rotor.

## TIGHTENING SPECIFICATIONS

| Year | Component | Torque, Ft. Lbs. |
|---|---|---|
| 1989–91 | Fluid Reservoir Bolts | 60–84① |
| | High Pressure Hose Nut | 29–36 |
| | Pump Attaching Bolt | 27–40 |
| | Pump Attaching Locknut | 27–38 |

①—Inch lbs.

# Ford Torsion Bar Power Steering

## INDEX



## DESCRIPTION

The power steering unit, **Fig. 1,** is a torsion bar type of hydraulic-assisted system. This system furnishes power to reduce the amount of turning effort required at the steering wheel. It also reduces road shock and vibrations.

The unit includes a worm and one piece rack-piston which is meshed to the gear teeth on the steering sector shaft. The unit also includes a hydraulic valve, valve actuator, input shaft and torsion bar assembly which are mounted on the end of the worm shaft and operated by a twisting action of the torsion bar.

The gear unit is designed with the one piece rack-piston, worm and sector shaft in the one housing and the valve spool in an attaching housing. This makes possible internal fluid passages between valve and cylinder, thus eliminating all external lines and hoses except the pressure and return hoses between pump and gear.

The power cylinder is an integral part of the gear housing. The piston is double acting in that fluid pressure may be applied to either side of the piston.

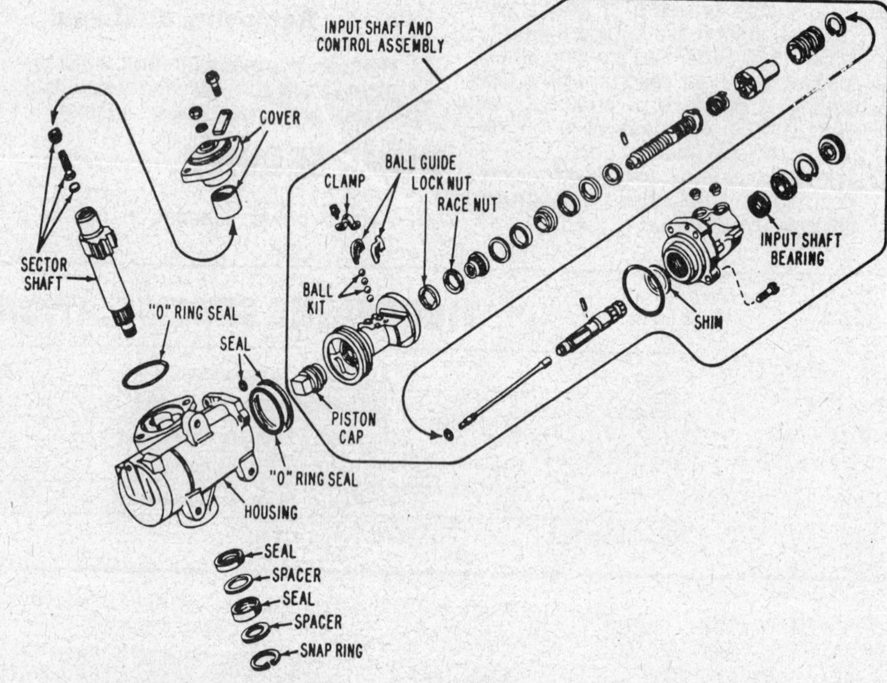


**Fig. 1 Exploded view of Ford power steering gear**

## OPERATION

The operation of the hydraulic control valve spool is governed by the twisting of a torsion bar. All effort applied to the steering wheel is transmitted directly through the input shaft and torsion bar to the worm and piston. Any resistance to the turning of the front wheels results in twisting of the bar. The twisting of the bar increases as the front wheel turning effort increases. The control valve spool, actuated by the twisting of the torsion bar, directs fluid to the side of the piston where hydraulic assistance is required.

As the torsion bar twists, its radial motion is transferred into axial motion by three helical threads. Thus, the valve is moved off center, and fluid is directed to one side of the piston or the other.

## TROUBLESHOOTING

### HARD STEERING

1. Low or uneven tire pressure.
2. Improper gear adjustment.
3. Improper wheel alignment.
4. Low fluid level.
5. Twisted or bent suspension parts, frame and linkage components.
6. Tight wheel bearings.
7. Steering spindle bent.
8. Pump belt out of adjustment.
9. Pump output low.
10. Air in system.
11. Valve spool out of adjustment.
12. Valve spool sticking.
13. Steering linkage binding.

### HARD STEERING STRAIGHT AHEAD

1. Steering adjustment too tight.
2. Steering gear shaft binding.

### HARD STEERING WHILE TURNING OR PARKING

1. Oil level low.
2. Pump pressure low.
3. Pressure loss in steering gear due to leakage past O-rings.
4. Pressure loss between valve spool and sleeve.
5. Pressure loss past piston ring or scored housing bore.

### LOOSE STEERING

1. Loose wheel bearings.
2. Loose tie rod ends or linkage.
3. Worn ball joints.
4. Worn suspension parts.
5. Insufficient mesh load.
6. Insufficient worm bearing preload.
7. Valve spool out of adjustment.

### ERRATIC STEERING

1. Oil or brake fluid on brake lining.
2. Out of round brake drums.
3. Improperly adjusted brakes.
4. Under-inflated tires.
5. Broken spring or other details in sus-

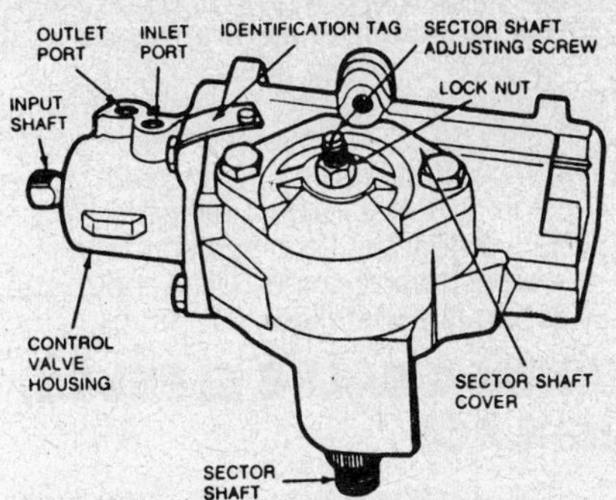


Fig. 2 Adjusting mesh load

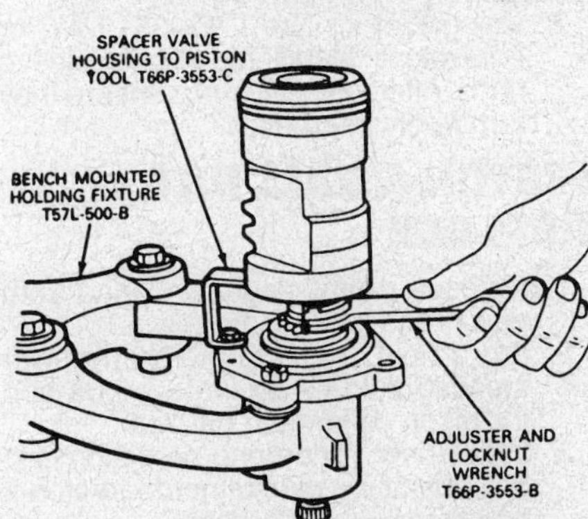


Fig. 4 Input shaft removal

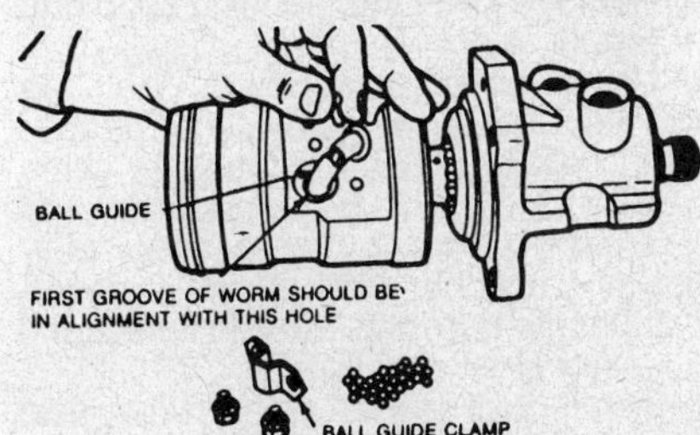


Fig. 7 Assembling piston on worm shaft

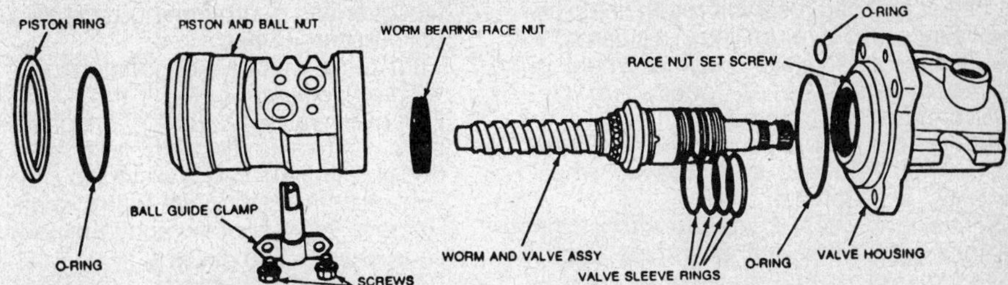


Fig. 3 Ball nut & valve housing disassembled

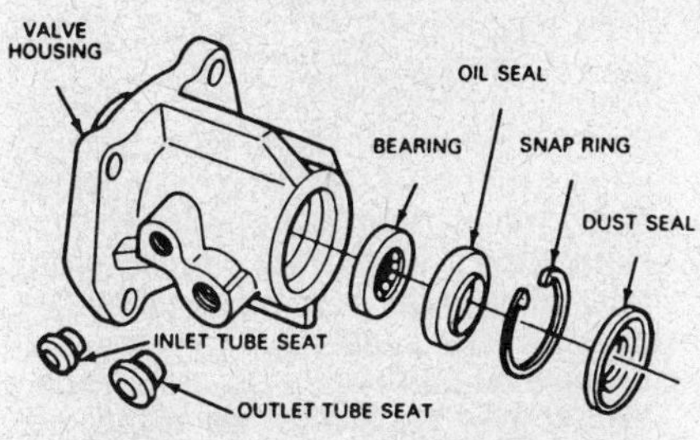


Fig. 5 Valve housing disassembled

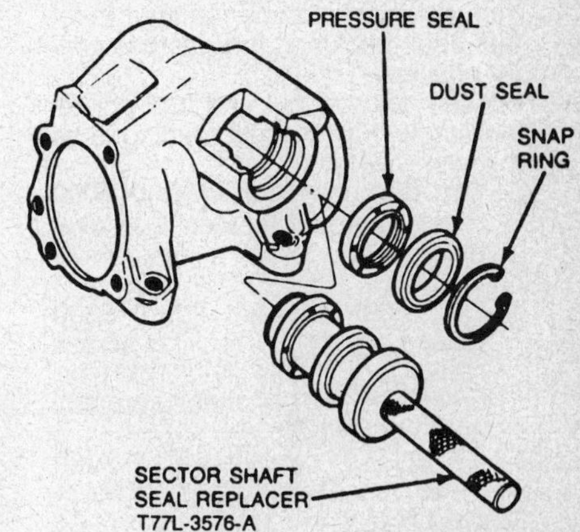


Fig. 6 Steering gear housing disassembled

pension system.
6. Improper caster adjustment.
7. Fluid level low.

## BINDING OR POOR RECOVERY

1. Steering gear shaft binding.
2. Steering gear out of adjustment.
3. Steering linkage binding.
4. Valve spool binding due to dirt or burred edges.
5. Valve spool out of adjustment.
6. Interference at sector shaft and ball stud.

## LOSS OF POWER ASSIST

1. Pump inoperative.
2. Hydraulic lines damaged.
3. Power cylinder damaged.
4. Valve spool out of adjustment.

## LOSS OF POWER ASSIST IN ONE DIRECTION

1. Valve spool out of adjustment.

## NOISY PUMP

1. Air being drawn into pump.
2. Lines touching other parts of car.
3. Oil level low.
4. Excessive backpressure caused by obstructions in lines.
5. Excessive wear of internal parts.

## POOR RETURN TO CENTER

1. Valve spool sticking.
2. Valve spool out of adjustment.
3. All items given under "Binding or Poor Recovery."

## STEERING WHEEL SURGE WHILE TURNING

1. Valve spool sticking.
2. Excessive internal leakage.
3. Belt slippage.

# IN-VEHICLE ADJUSTMENTS & REPAIRS

## VALVE SPOOL CENTERING CHECK

The "out-of-car" procedure for valve centering check is the same as for the "in-car" except the torque and simultaneous pressure reading must be made at the right and left stops instead of either side of center.

1. Install a 2000 psi pressure gauge in pressure line between pump outlet port and steering gear inlet port. Make sure that valve on gauge in is fully open position.
2. Check fluid level in reservoir and replenish as required.
3. Start engine and cycle steering wheel from stop-to-stop to bring steering lubricant up to normal operating temperature. Stop engine and recheck reservoir. Add fluid as necessary.
4. With engine running at a fast idle speed (1000 RPM) and steering wheel centered, attach an inch-pound torque wrench to steering wheel retaining nut. Apply sufficient torque to wrench in each direction (either side of center) to get a gauge reading of 250 psi.
5. The torque reading should be the same in both directions. If the difference between readings exceed 4 inch lbs., the shaft and control assemblies must be replaced.

## STEERING GEAR ADJUSTMENTS

Preload (thrust bearing adjustment) and worm-to-rack preload cannot be changed in service. The only adjustment that can be performed is the total over-center position load to eliminate excessive lash between sector and rack teeth.

1. Disconnect pitman arm from sector shaft.
2. Disconnect fluid return line at reser-

voir and cap reservoir return line pipe.

3. Place end of return line in a clean container and cycle steering wheel in both directions as required to discharge fluid from gear.
4. Remove ornamental cover from wheel hub and turn steering wheel 45° from left stop.
5. Using an inch lb. torque wrench on steering wheel nut, determine torque required to rotate shaft slowly through an approximately 1/4 turn from the 45° position.
6. Turn steering gear back to center, then determine torque required to rotate shaft back and forth across center position.
7. Loosen adjuster nut and turn adjusting screw, **Fig. 2**, until reading is as follows:
   a. **On 1989 models with 0-5000 miles,** reset if total meshload over mechanical center if not 14-29 inch lbs.
   b. **On 1989 models with 0-5000 miles,** set torque rocking across center to a values 14-20 inch lbs. greater than that measured 45° from right stop.
   c. **On 1990-91 models with 0-5000 miles,** reset if total meshload over mechanical center if not 15-24 inch lbs.
   d. **On 1990—91 models with 0-5000 miles,** set torque rocking across center to a values 11-15 inch lbs. greater than that measured 45° from right stop.
   e. **On all models with more than 5000 miles,** reset if meshload measured while rocking input shaft over center is less then 10 inch lbs. greater then the torque 45° from right stop.
   f. **On all models over 5000 miles,** set torque measured rocking across center to a value of 10-14 inch lbs. greater than measured 45° from right stop.
8. Recheck readings and replace pitman arm and steering wheel.
9. Connect fluid return line and replenish reservoir.

## STEERING GEAR REPAIRS

### DISASSEMBLE

1. Hold steering gear over drain pan in an inverted position and cycle input shaft six times to drain remaining fluid from gear.
2. Using suitable mounting pads for support, install gear in bench mounting fixture tool No. T57L-500-B or equivalent.
3. Remove locknut from adjusting screw.
4. Turn input shaft to either stop, then turn it back approximately 1 5/8 turns to center the gear. **Input shaft spline indexing flat should be facing downward.**
5. Remove two sector shaft cover bolts.
6. Tap lower end of sector shaft with a soft-faced hammer to loosen it, then lift cover and shaft from housing as a unit. Discard O-ring.
7. Turn sector shaft cover counterclockwise off adjuster screw.
8. Remove valve housing attaching bolts. Lift valve housing from gear housing while holding piston to prevent it from rotating off worm shaft. Remove valve housing and lube passage O-rings and discard.
9. Remove valve housing attaching bolts and ID tag, while holding piston separate valve housing from housing, remove and discard O-rings.
10. With piston held, remove ball clamp screws and guide clamp, **Fig. 3.**
11. With finger over ball guide opening, turn piston so ball guide faces downward over clean container, then allow guide tubes to drop to container.
12. Rotate input shaft from stop to stop, until all balls fall from piston, then remove valve assembly from piston. **Ensure all balls have been remove. Worm may no longer be removed from piston.**
13. Install valve body to bench mounting fixture tool No. T57L-500-B or equivalent, then loosen valve housing race nut lockscrew. Using adjuster locknut wrench tool No. T66P-3553-B and spacer valve housing tool No. T66P-3553-C or equivalents, remove worm bearing race.
14. Slide input shaft, worm and valve assembly from valve housing, **Fig. 4.**

## VALVE HOUSING, REPLACE

1. Using puller attachment tool No. T58L-101-B or equivalent, remove and discard dust seal, **Fig. 5.**
2. Remove snap ring from valve housing, then turn fixture so valve housing is upside down.
3. Install bearing remover tool No. T65P-3524-A2 and installer tool No. T65P-3524-A3 or equivalents to valve body opposite the oil seal, then gently tap bearing and seal from housing, discard seal. **Exercise care when inserting and removing tool to prevent damage to valve bore in housing.**
4. Remove oil inlet and outlet tube seats with tool T74P-3504-L, or equivalent, if damaged.
5. Coat tube seats with petroleum jelly and position them in housing. Install and tighten tube nuts to press seats to proper location, using brass tube seat replacer tool No. T74P-3504-M or equivalent.
6. Coat bearing and seal surface in housing with a film of petroleum jelly.
7. Install bearing with metal side that covers rollers facing downward, then using bearing installer tool No. T65P-3524-A or equivalent, seat bearing, ensuring smooth bearing operation.
8. Dip new oil seal in premium power steering fluid or equivalent, then place it in housing with metal side of seal facing outward. Drive seal into housing until outer edge of seal does not quite clear snap ring.
9. Place snap ring in housing, then drive on ring until snap ring seats in its groove to locate seal properly.
10. Apply coating of suitable multipurpose grease between seals.
11. Place dust seal in housing with dished side (rubber side) facing outward. Drive dust seal in place so that it is located behind undercut in input shaft when it is installed.

## WORM & VALVE SLEEVES, REPLACE

1. Cut valve sleeve rings from valve sleeve, then position worm end of assembly in soft jawed vice.
2. Using tool kit No. T75L-3517-A1, or equivalent, install four valve sleeve rings. After installing rings ensure they turn freely in grooves.

## PISTON & BALL NUT, REPLACE

1. Remove plastic ring and O-ring from piston and ball nut, **Fig. 3.**
2. Dip a new O-ring in premium power steering fluid or equivalent lube and install on piston and ball nut.
3. Install new Teflon ring on piston and ball nut, being careful not to stretch it any more than necessary.

## GEAR HOUSING

1. Remove lower end housing snap ring, **Fig. 6.**
2. Using puller attachment tool No. T58L-101-B or equivalent, remove and discard dust and pressure seals. **Bearing is not a serviceable and must be replaced as an assembly.**
3. Using suitable multi purpose grease, lubricate new pressure, dust seal and sector shaft seal bore.
4. Install dust seal on sector shaft seal replacer tool No. T77L-3576-A or equivalent, with seal raised lip toward tool, then install pressure seal with lip away from tool, pressure seal flat side should be against flat side of dust deal.
5. Install tool to sector shaft bore, then drive tool until seals clear snap ring grooves. **Do not bottom seal against bearing or seals will not function properly.**
6. Install snap ring in housing groove.

## ASSEMBLE

1. Install worm and valve in housing.
2. Install retaining nut in housing, then torque nut using tool No. T66P-3553-B. Because length of tool required to torque nut will affect torque wrench reading, the following formula must be used to determine torque. Torque (using tool T66P-3553-B, or equivalent) equals (length of torque wrench x 72 ft. lbs.)/(length of torque wrench + 5.5 inches).
3. Install race nut screw and tighten to specifications.
4. Place piston on bench with ball guide holes facing up. Insert worm shaft into piston so that first groove is in align-

ment with hole nearest to center of piston, **Fig. 7.**

5. Place ball guide into piston. Place balls in guide (27 minimum), turning worm clockwise (viewed from input end of shaft). If all balls have not been fed into guide upon reaching right stop, rotate input shaft in one direction and then in the other while installing balls. After balls have been installed, do not rotate input shaft or piston more than 3½ turns off the right stop to prevent balls from falling out of circuit.
6. Securing guides to ball nut with clamp and tighten to specifications.
7. Apply petroleum jelly to piston seal.
8. Place a new O-ring on valve housing.
9. Slide piston and valve into gear housing, being careful not to damage seal.
10. Align lube passage in valve housing with one in gear housing, place O-ring in gear housing oil passage hole, then identification tag and install but do not tighten attaching bolts at this time.
11. Rotate ball nut so that teeth are in same plane as sector teeth. Tighten valve housing attaching bolts.
12. Position sector shaft cover O-ring in gear housing. Turn input shaft as required to center piston.
13. Apply petroleum jelly to sector shaft journal, then position sector shaft and cover into gear housing. Install air conditioner line mounting bracket, if equipped, and two sector shaft cover bolts, then tighten to specifications.
14. Attach an inch lb. torque wrench to input shaft and adjust mesh load as outlined previously.

## TIGHTENING SPECIFICATIONS

| Year | Component | Torque, Ft. Lbs. |
|---|---|---|
| 1989–91 | Ball Return Guide Clamp Screw | 42–70① |
| | Flex Coupling To Gear Input Shaft Bolt | 20–30 |
| | Gear To Side Rail Bolts | 50–65 |
| | Hose Clamps | 1–2 |
| | Meshload Adjusting Screw Locknut | 35–45 |
| | Piston End Cap | 70–110 |
| | Pitman Arm To Sector Shaft Nut | 200–250 |
| | Pressure Hose To Gear | 16–25 |
| | Race Nut Setscrew | 15–25① |
| | Race Retaining Nut | ② |
| | Return Hose To Gear | 25–34 |
| | Sector Shaft Cover Bolts | 55–70 |
| | Valve Housing To Gear Housing | 30–45 |

①—Inch lbs.
②—Refer to text.

# Ford Rack & Pinion Steering Gear

## INDEX



## DESCRIPTION

This power rack and pinion steering gear, **Figs. 1 through 4,** are hydraulic-mechanical units, using an integral piston and rack to provide power assisted steering control. Internal valve controls pump flow and pressure as required during operation. The unit consists of a rotary hydraulic control valve connected to the input shaft and a boost cylinder integral with the rack.

## OPERATION

The rotary control valve utilizes the relative rotational motion of the input shaft and valve sleeve to control fluid flow. As the steering wheel is turned, the resistance of the wheels and weight of the vehicle cause a torsion bar to deflect, **Figs. 1 through 4.** This torsion bar deflection changes position of rotary valve and sleeve ports, thereby directing fluid under pressure to the proper end of the power cylinder. The pressure differential acting on the piston attached to the rack, provides the power assist.

The control valve is forced back to a centered position by the torsion bar when steering effort is removed. Pressure is then equalized on each side of the piston and the front wheels tend to return to a straight ahead position.

## TROUBLESHOOTING

Refer to **Fig. 5,** for troubleshooting procedure.

## POWER STEERING SYSTEM FLUSH

1. Disconnect power steering return hose.
2. Place return line in suitable container, then plug reservoir return line at reservoir.
3. Fill reservoir using Motorcraft DEXRON II part No. ESW-M2C33-F or equivalent.
4. Disconnect coil wire, then raise and support front wheels.
5. While adding about two quarts of fluid, turn ignition to start position (using ignition key), then crank engine with starter and turn steering wheel right to left.
6. When all the fluid is added, turn ignition off, and connect coil wire.
7. Remove reservoir return line plug, then connect line to reservoir.
8. Fill reservoir to specified level.
9. Lower vehicle, then start engine, slowly turn steering wheel several times lock to lock, then recheck fluid level, add as required.

## POWER STEERING SYSTEM PURGE

1. Air trapped in power steering system may be remove with power steering pump air evacuator assembly vacuum tester 021-00014 or equivalent.
2. **Do not use engine vacuum to purge power steering system.**
3. Remove reservoir cap.
4. Check and fill reservoir to cold fill mark with suitable fluid.
5. Disconnect ignition coil wire, then raise and support front wheels.
6. Crank engine with starter motor, then check fluid level. **Do not turn steering wheel.**
7. If fluid level has dropped, fill reservoir to cold fill mark, crank engine with starter motor while turning steering wheel lock to lock, then check fluid level.
8. Install air evacuator rubber stopper tightly to pump reservoir, then connect coil wire.
9. With engine at idle, apply 15 inch Hg maximum vacuum to pump reservoir for a minimum of three minutes, as air purges from system, vacuum will decrease, maintain adequate vacuum.
10. Release vacuum, then remove vacuum source, if fluid level has dropped, fill to cold fill mark.
11. With engine at idle, apply 15 inch Hg maximum vacuum to pump reservoir, turn steering wheel from lock to lock ever 30 seconds for about five minutes. **Do not hold steering wheel on stops when turning.** Maintain adequate vacuum.
12. Release vacuum, then remove vacuum equipment add power steering fluid id required, install cap.
13. Start engine, turn steering wheel, check connections for oil leaks.
14. If severe aeration is indicated, repeat steps 7 through 13.

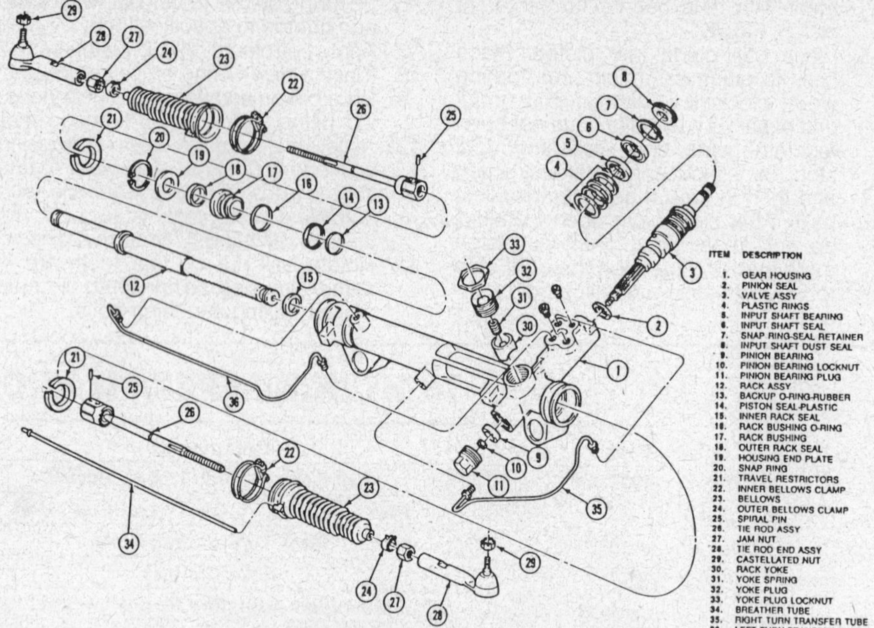


**Fig. 1 Exploded view of steering gear. Except Taurus, Sable, Tempo, Topaz & 1989–90 Escort**

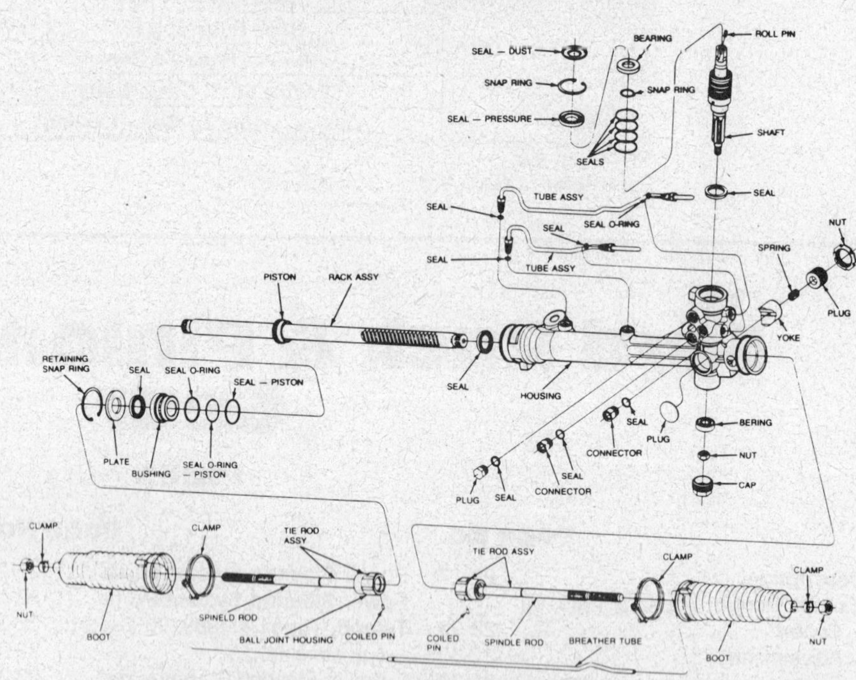


**Fig. 2 Exploded view of steering gear. Sable & Taurus, except SHO**

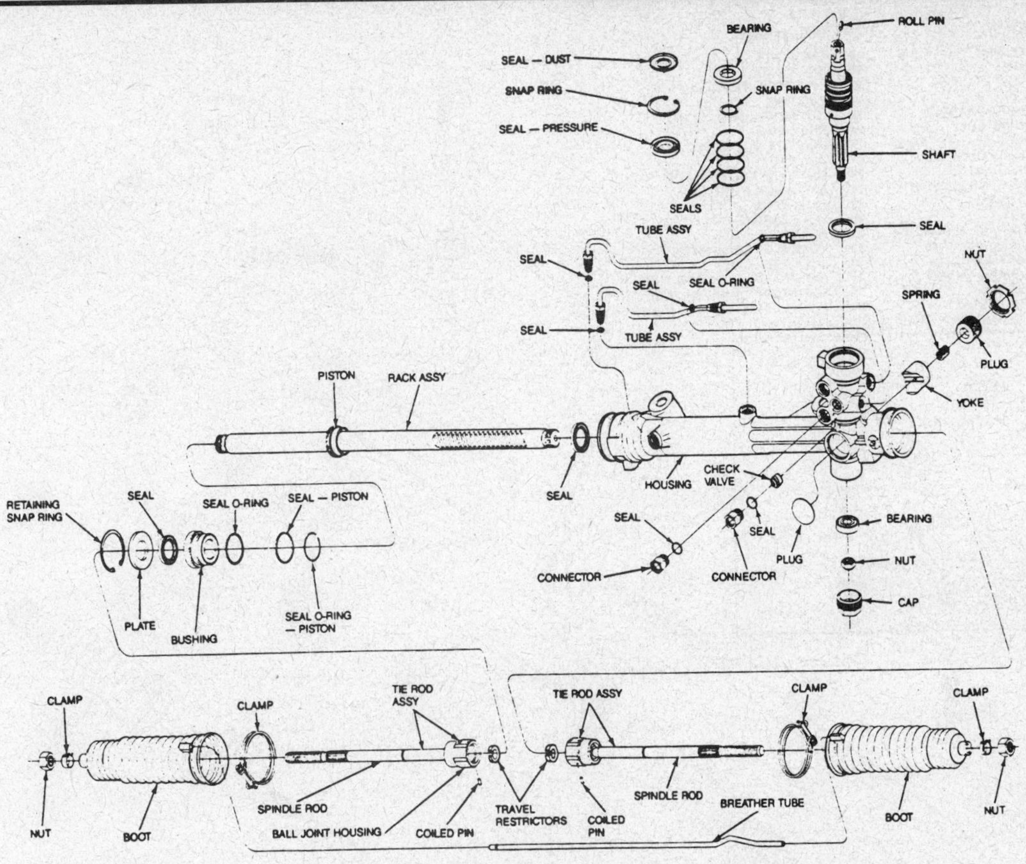


**Fig. 3 Exploded view of steering gear. Taurus SHO**

# EXCEPT TEMPO, TOPAZ & 1989–90 ESCORT

## POWER STEERING PRESSURE TEST

### Except Sable & Taurus

**During the following procedure, power steering system pressure may exceed 1200 psi. Ensure proper tool fitment prior to performing test. Exercise extreme caution or damage or personal injury may result.**

1. Prior to performing pump flow and pressure tests, ensure following conditions exist:
   a. Proper pump reservoir fluid level.
   b. Correct tire air pressure.
   c. Proper pump belt tension.
   d. Correct model and vehicle pump application.
   e. Correct size pulleys on pump and engine.
   f. Ensure system is not damaged or leaking, repair as required.
2. The following test equipment is required:
   a. Engine tachometer.
   b. Thermometer: 0-300°F (17.8-148.9°C).
   c. Power steering system analyzer tool No. 014-00207 or equivalent.
   d. Set of adapter fittings.
3. The test procedure used in conjunction with the power steering system analyzer can be used to determine:
   a. System backpressure.
   b. Pump flow.
   c. Steering gear internal leakage.
   d. Pump relief pressure.
4. The readouts from step 3 can be used to determine which of the following conditions or components may be faulty:
   a. Hose or fitting restriction.
   b. Sticking gear valve.
   c. Insufficient pump capacity.
   d. Sticking relief valve.
   e. Suspension system binding.
5. Disconnect pump high pressure line, then connect suitable analyzer hose adapter, **Fig. 6.**
6. Thread other analyzer adapter to pump.
7. Connect analyzer hose to adapters, tighten both connections to 15 ft. lbs. maximum.
8. If required, add power steering fluid, start engine and allow to run about two minutes. Ensure idle is set to specifications.
9. With engine at idle, record the following:
   a. Flow, gallons per minute at 167-177°F (76-80°C).
   b. Pressure, psi at 167-177°F (76-80°C), at idle with gate fully open.
   c. If gallon per minute flow is below specifications, pump may require service, however continue test, check flow and relief pressure.
   d. If pressure is above 150 psi check hoses for restrictions.
10. Partially close gate valve to build up 740 psi, observe and record flow at 167-177°F (76-80°C):
    a. If flow drops lower below specifications, disassemble pump and replace cam pack, if pressure plates are cracked or worn, replace.
11. Completely close and partially open gate valve three times. **Do not allow valve to remain closed for more then five seconds.** Observe and record pressure.
12. If pressure is lower than specifications, replace pump flow control valve.
13. If pressure is above specifications, pump flow control valve should be removed and cleaned or replaced.
14. Increase engine speed to about 1500 RPM, observe and record flow.
15. If flow exceeds maximum free flow per minute, pump flow control valve should be removed and cleaned or replaced.
16. If flow exceeds maximum free flow per minute, pump should be removed and cleaned or replaced.
17. Check idle speed, with engine at idle, turn steering wheel to left and right stops, record pressure and flow at stops.
18. Pressure at both stops should be about the same as maximum pump output pressure, flow should drop below 0.5 gallons per minute.
19. If pressure is not within specification,

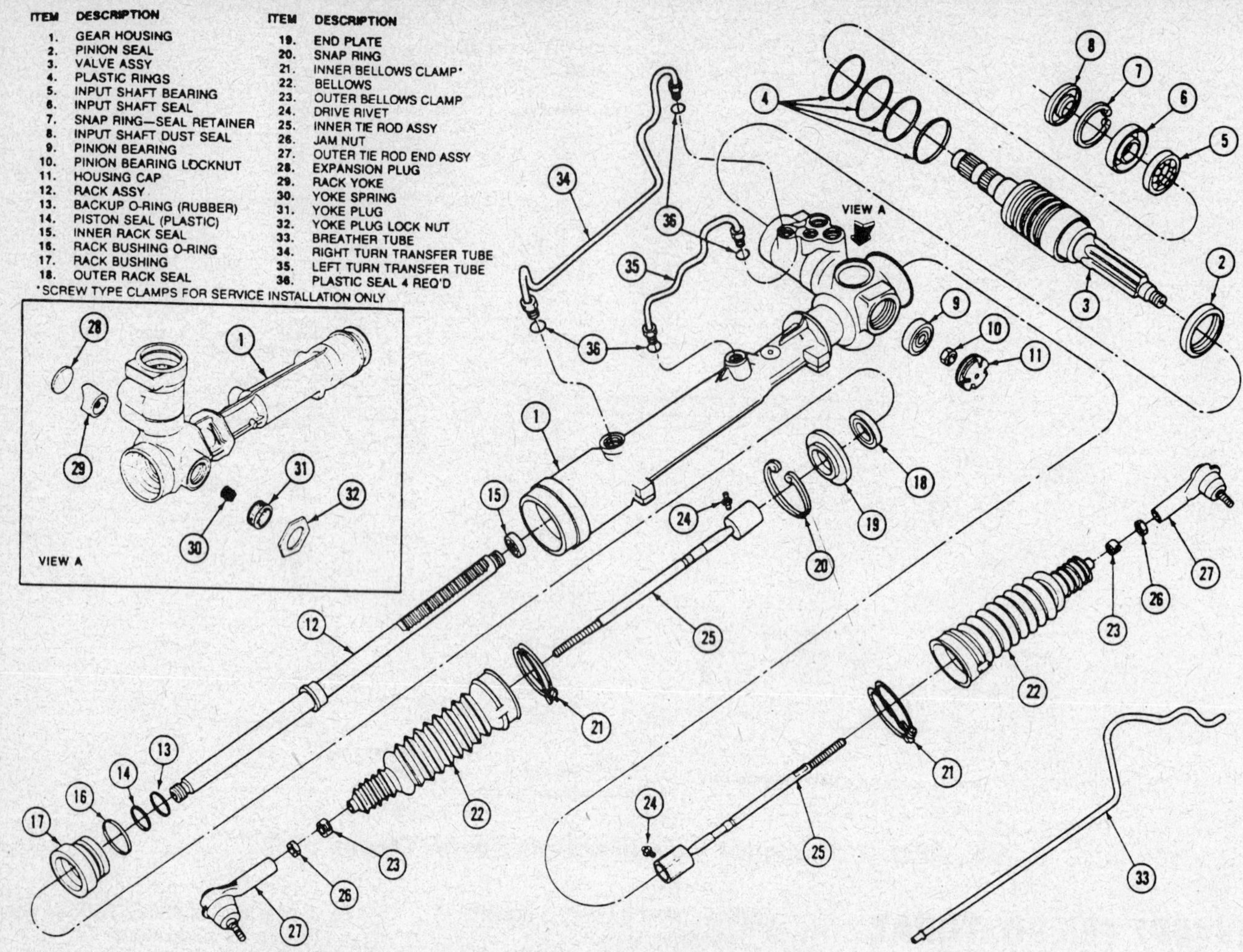


**Fig. 4 Exploded view of steering gear. Tempo, Topaz & 1989–90 Escort**

excessive internal leakage is indicated, remove and disassemble steering gear, replace worn or damaged parts and inspect rack piston and valve seals for damage.

20. While watching pressure gauge, turn steering wheel slightly in both directions and quickly release wheel, gauge needle should move from normal backpressure and snap back as the wheel is released. If needle returns slowly or sticks, the steering gear rotary valve is sticking.
21. Remove and disassemble steering as described under "Disassemble," then flush power steering hoses and pump before gear installation.
22. If problem still exists, check ball joint and linkage.
23. Disconnect and remove analyzer, then connect lines.

### Sable & Taurus

Refer to "Ford Variable Assist, Except Electronic Variable Orifice System," for pressure testing procedure.

## ADJUSTMENTS

Rack yoke bearing preload is the only service adjustment required. This adjustment is performed with the steering gear removed from the vehicle. Refer to the individual car chapters for steering gear removal.

1. Clean exterior of steering gear, then install two long bolts and washers through bushings and attach to bench fixture T57L-500-B or equivalent.
2. Do not remove external pressure lines unless damaged or leaking. Drain power steering fluid by rotating input shaft from lock to lock two times using tool No. T74P-3504-R, or equivalent (T86P-3504-K Sable & Taurus). Cover ports on valve housing with a clean shop cloth while draining gear.
3. Position an inch lb. torque wrench and tool No. T74P-3504-R, or equivalent, on input shaft splines.
4. Loosen yoke plug locknut using tool No. T78P-3504-H, or equivalent, then loosen yoke plug using a 3/4 inch socket wrench, **Fig. 7.**
5. Clean yoke plug threads, then with rack at center of travel, **torque** yoke plug to 40-50 inch lbs.
6. Back off yoke plug approximately 1/8 turn until **torque** required to rotate input shaft is 7 to 18 inch lbs.
7. While holding yoke plug in position, tighten locknut to specifications. Using tool No. T78P-3504-H, or equivalent. Recheck input shaft rotating torque after tightening locknut.
8. If the external pressure lines were removed in step two, they must be replaced with new pressure lines. Remove the copper seals from the pressure ports previous to installation of new lines.
9. Remove steering gear from holding fixture, then install external pressure lines. Tighten pump to gear and return line fittings and valve and power cylinder (gear housing) fittings to specifications.

## STEERING GEAR REPAIRS

### TIE ROD ENDS, BELLOWS & BALL JOINT SOCKETS

### Disassembly

1. Install two long bolts and washers through bushings and attach gear to holding fixture T57L-500-B, or equivalent.
2. Loosen jam nuts on outer ends of tie rods, then remove tie rod ends and jam nuts.
3. Remove four clamps attaching bellows to tie rods and gear housing.
4. Drain power steering fluid, then re-

| CONDITION | POSSIBLE SOURCE | ACTION |
|---|---|---|
| • Wander — Vehicle wander is a condition where the vehicle wanders side to side on the roadway when it is driven straight ahead while the steering wheel is held in a firm position. Evaluation should be conducted on a level road (little road crown). | • Improper wheel alignment. | • Set alignment to specification. |
| | • Loose outer tie rod ends. | • Replace outer tie rod end assemblies. |
| | • Inner tie rod ball housing loose or worn. | • Replace inner tie rod assemblies. |
| | • Gear assembly mounting loose. | • Tighten mounting bolts to specification. |
| | • Loose suspension struts or ball joints. | • Adjust or replace as required. |
| | • Column intermediate shaft connecting bolts loose. | • Tighten bolts to specification. |
| | • Loose wheel bearings. | • Service as required. |
| | • Column intermediate shaft joints loose or worn. | • Replace intermediate shaft. |
| • Feedback — (Rattle, chuckle, knocking noises in the steering gear). Feedback is a condition where roughness is felt in the steering wheel by the driver when the vehicle is driven over rough pavement. | • Column U-joints loose. | • Replace if bad. |
| | • Loose outer tie rod ends. | • Replace outer tie rod end assemblies. |
| | • Loose/worn inner tie rod ball. | • Replace inner tie rod assemblies. |
| | • Gear assembly mounting loose. | • Tighten mounting bolts to specification. |
| | • Loose pinion bearing cap. | • Tighten cap to specification. |
| | • Loose pinion bearing locknut. | • Tighten locknut to specification. |
| | • Piston disengaged or loose on rack. | • Replace rack assembly. |
| | • Steering gear yoke worn. | • Replace yoke assembly. |
| | • Column intermediate shaft connecting bolts loose. | • Tighten bolts to specification. |
| | • Loose suspension struts on ball joints. | • Adjust or replace as necessary. |

**Fig. 5 Troubleshooting (Part 1 of 3)**

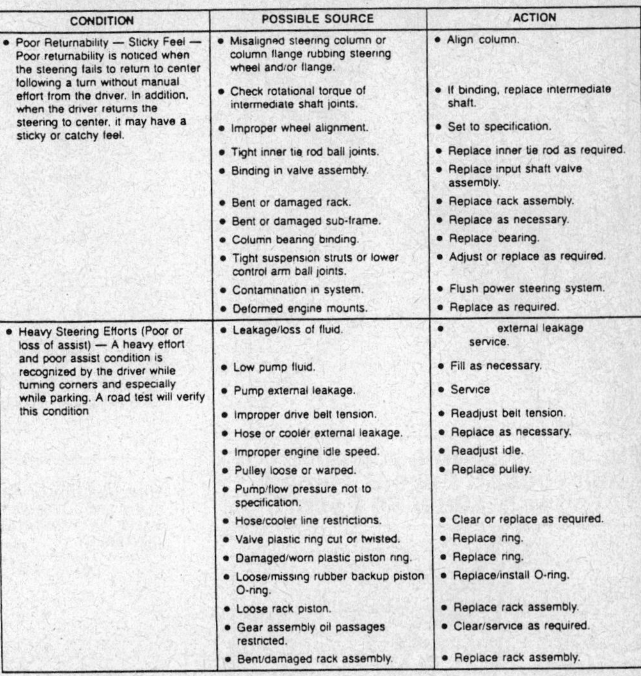

| CONDITION | POSSIBLE SOURCE | ACTION |
|---|---|---|
| • Poor Returnability — Sticky Feel — Poor returnability is noticed when the steering fails to return to center following a turn without manual effort from the driver. In addition, when the driver returns the steering to center, it may have a sticky or catchy feel. | • Misaligned steering column or column flange rubbing steering wheel and/or flange. | • Align column. |
| | • Check rotational torque of intermediate shaft joints. | • If binding, replace intermediate shaft. |
| | • Improper wheel alignment. | • Set to specification. |
| | • Tight inner tie rod ball joints. | • Replace inner tie rod as required. |
| | • Binding in valve assembly. | • Replace input shaft valve assembly. |
| | • Bent or damaged rack. | • Replace rack assembly. |
| | • Bent or damaged sub-frame. | • Replace as necessary. |
| | • Column bearing binding. | • Replace bearing. |
| | • Tight suspension struts or lower control arm ball joints. | • Adjust or replace as required. |
| | • Contamination in system. | • Flush power steering system. |
| | • Deformed engine mounts. | • Replace as required. |
| • Heavy Steering Efforts (Poor or loss of assist) — A heavy effort and poor assist condition is recognized by the driver while turning corners and especially while parking. A road test will verify this condition | • Leakage/loss of fluid. | • external leakage service. |
| | • Low pump fluid. | • Fill as necessary. |
| | • Pump external leakage. | • Service |
| | • Improper drive belt tension. | • Readjust belt tension. |
| | • Hose or cooler external leakage. | • Replace as necessary. |
| | • Improper engine idle speed. | • Readjust idle. |
| | • Pulley loose or warped. | • Replace pulley. |
| | • Pump/flow pressure not to specification. | |
| | • Hose/cooler line restrictions. | • Clear or replace as required. |
| | • Valve plastic ring cut or twisted. | • Replace ring. |
| | • Damaged/worn plastic piston ring. | • Replace ring. |
| | • Loose/missing rubber backup piston O-ring. | • Replace/install O-ring. |
| | • Loose rack piston. | • Replace rack assembly. |
| | • Gear assembly oil passages restricted. | • Clear/service as required. |
| | • Bent/damaged rack assembly. | • Replace rack assembly. |

**Fig. 5 Troubleshooting (Part 2 of 3)**

| CONDITION | POSSIBLE SOURCE | ACTION |
|---|---|---|
| • Hissing Sound<br>There is some noise in all power steering systems. One of the most common is a hissing sound most evident at standstill parking. There is no relationship between this noise and the performance of the steering gear.<br>**CAUTION: Do not hold steering wheel at full lock more than five seconds, as damage to power steering pump may result.** | • Hiss may be expected when the steering wheel is at the end of travel or when turning at standstill. | • Hiss is a normal characteristic of rotary steering gears and in no way affects steering. Do not replace the rack assembly unless the hiss is extremely objectionable. A replacement rack will also exhibit a slight noise and is not always a cure for the condition. Investigate for a grounded column or a loose boot at the dash panel. Any metal-to-metal contact will transmit valve hiss into the passenger compartment through the steering column. Verify clearance between flexible coupling components. Ensure steering column shaft and gear are aligned so flexible coupling rotates in a flat plane and is not distorted as shaft rotates. |

**Fig. 5 Troubleshooting (Part 3 of 3)**

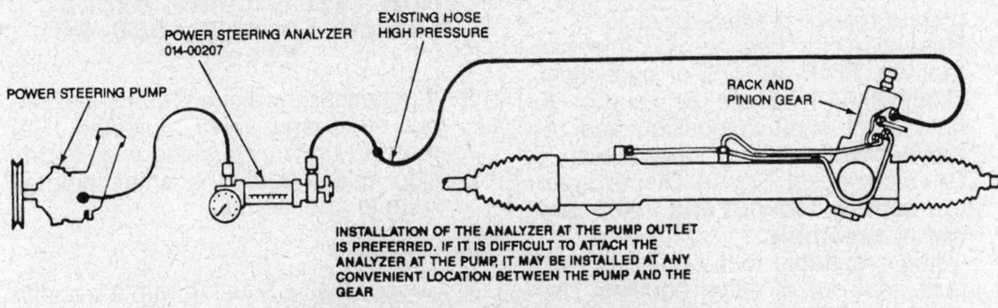
EXISTING HOSE
HIGH PRESSURE
POWER STEERING ANALYZER
014-00207
POWER STEERING PUMP
RACK AND
PINION GEAR
INSTALLATION OF THE ANALYZER AT THE PUMP OUTLET IS PREFERRED. IF IT IS DIFFICULT TO ATTACH THE ANALYZER AT THE PUMP, IT MAY BE INSTALLED AT ANY CONVENIENT LOCATION BETWEEN THE PUMP AND THE GEAR

**Fig. 6 Pressure test connections. Except Sable & Taurus**

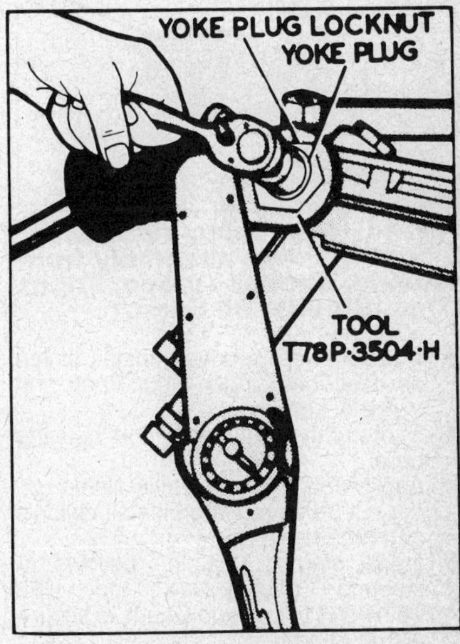
YOKE PLUG LOCKNUT
YOKE PLUG
TOOL
T78P-3504-H

**Fig. 7 Loosening yoke plug locknut. Except Tempo, Topaz & 1989–90 Escort**

move bellows with breather tube. Use care not to damage bellows.

5. If pinion is to be removed, remove pinion before proceeding as described under Input Shaft & Valve Assembly.
6. Thread point of roll pin remover T78P-3504-N into roll pin on ball socket and tighten tool finger tight, then remove roll pins, **Fig. 8.**
7. If pinion was not removed, remove gear housing from holding fixture and place on bench to prevent damage to gear teeth.
8. Position rack so that several teeth are exposed. Hold rack using an adjustable wrench on end teeth while loosening ball sockets with tool No. T74P-3504-U, or equivalent, **Fig. 9.**

## Assembly

1. Install tie rod and ball socket assemblies onto rack. Hold one ball socket with 1 5/16 inch wrench while tightening other ball socket to specifications, using tool No. T74P-3504-U, or equivalent. Both ball socket assemblies will be torqued simultaneously using this method. **If pinion was not removed from housing, this step must be performed with the steering gear removed from the holding fixture and positioned on bench to prevent damage to gear teeth.**
2. Support ball housing using a wooden block, then install roll pins by tapping lightly with a plastic mallet.

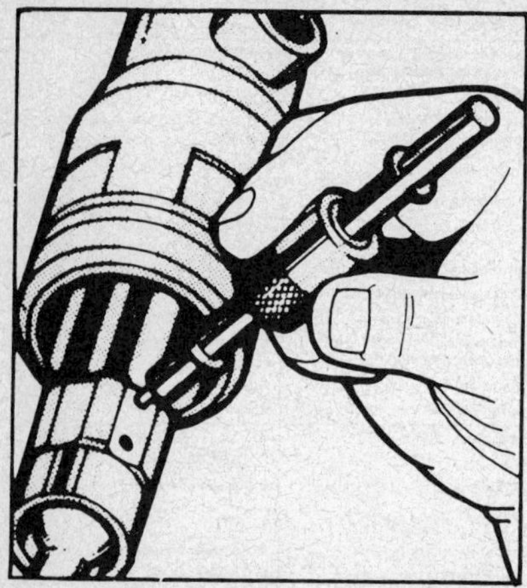

Fig. 8 Removing roll pin from ball socket. Except Tempo, Topaz & 1989–90 Escort

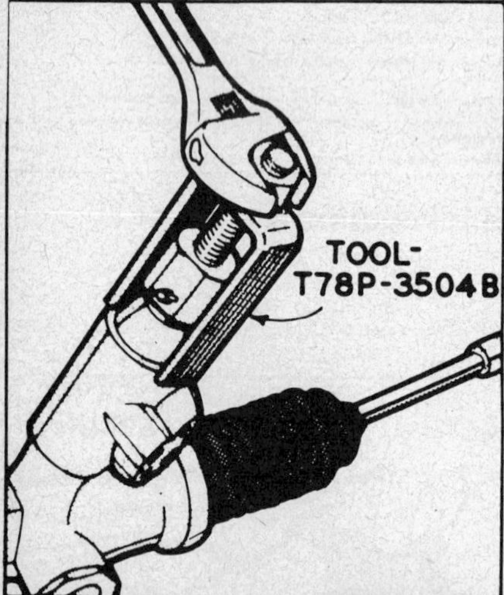


Fig. 11 Removing input shaft & control valve assembly from housing. Except Tempo, Topaz & 1989–90 Escort

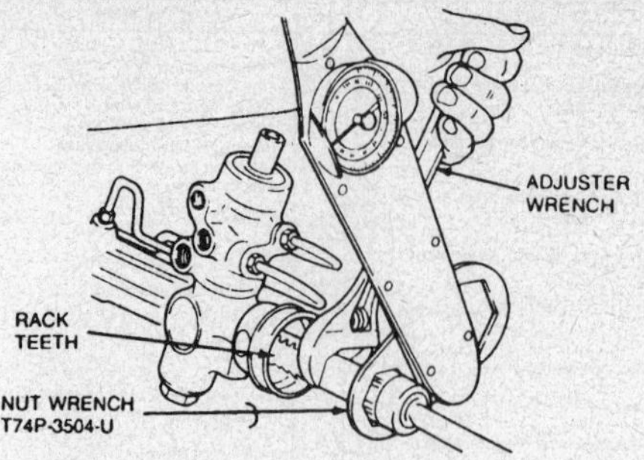


Fig. 9 Removing tie rod & ball socket assembly. Except Tempo, Topaz & 1989–90 Escort

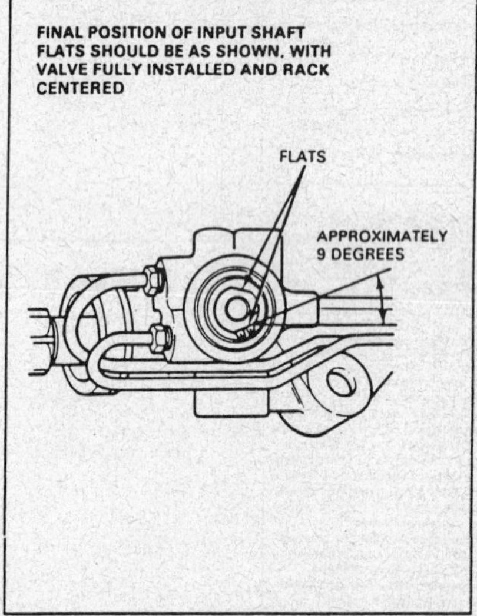


Fig. 12 Aligning input shaft. Taurus & Sable

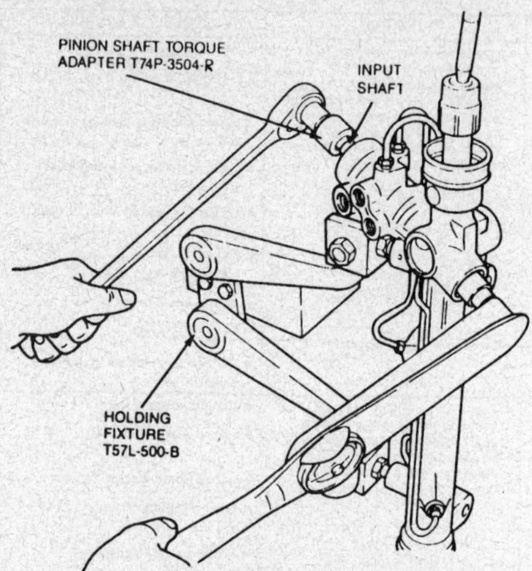


Fig. 10 Removing pinion bearing locknut. Except Tempo, Topaz & 1989–90 Escort

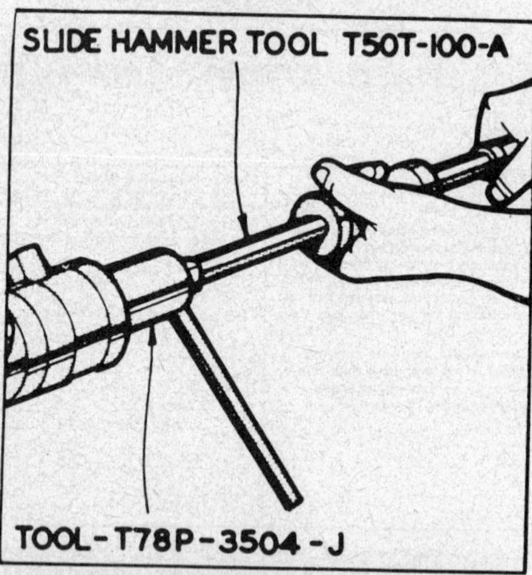


Fig. 13 Removing rack seal from gear housing. Except Tempo, Topaz & 1989–90 Escort

3. If pinion was removed, install pinion as described under Input Shaft and Valve Assembly.
4. Thoroughly clean rack and housing bore.
5. Apply lubricant to bellows clamp under cut on tie rod, then install bellows and breather tube.
6. Install clamps retaining bellows to steering gear. Use tool No. T63P-9171-A, or equivalent, to secure clamp to gear.
7. Install clamps retaining bellows to tie rods, then install jam nuts and tie rod end.

## INPUT SHAFT & VALVE ASSEMBLY

**The following procedure has been revised by a Technical Service Bulletin.**

### Disassembly

1. Thoroughly clean steering gear housing, then mount gear in holding fixture T57L-500-B or equivalent.
2. Do not remove the external pressure lines unless damaged or leaking. Loosen yoke plug locknut and yoke plug to relieve preload on rack.
3. Remove pinion bearing plug, then use tool No. T74P-3504-R, or equivalent, (T86P-3504-K Sable & Taurus) to hold input shaft in position and remove pinion bearing locknut with a 11/16 inch socket, **Fig. 10. Discard pinion bearing locknut and use a new nut at assembly.**
4. Using a suitable tool, pry input shaft dust seal out of valve housing. Use care not to damage valve housing.
5. Remove snap ring from valve housing.
6. Attach puller T78P-3504-B, or equivalent, to input shaft and remove input shaft seal and bearing and valve body, **Fig. 11.**. On Sable & Taurus, attach valve body puller (bridge) T86P-3504-B and valve body puller (screw) T78P-3504-B and remove input shaft seal, input shaft and and valve body.
7. Use tool No. T78P-3504-E, or equivalent, and a suitable slide hammer to remove lower pinion shaft seal.
8. Remove pinion bearing from gear housing using tool No. T58L-101-A, or equivalent, and a suitable slide hammer.
9. If necessary, remove O-rings from input shaft and valve assembly. Remove O-rings by pushing rings to one side and inserting a small pointed knife to cut ring off.

### Assembly

1. Support valve housing with a wooden block, then using tool No. T78P-3504-G, or equivalent, install pinion bearing in gear bore. Seat bearing against shoulder in bore.
2. Apply grease to pinion oil seal, then position seal on tool No. T78P-3504-F, or equivalent, (T86P-3504-G on Sable & Taurus) with seal lip facing towards tool. Install seal in valve bore, seating seal against shoulder.
3. Position pinion end of valve assembly in a soft jawed vise.
4. Install mandrel T75L-3517-A1, or equivalent, over sleeve, then slide one valve sleeve ring over mandrel.
5. Slide tool No. T75L-3517-A2, or equivalent, over mandrel, then rapidly push down on tool to force ring down

**Fig. 14 Removing rack seat from rack bushing. Except Tempo, Topaz & 1989–90 Escort**

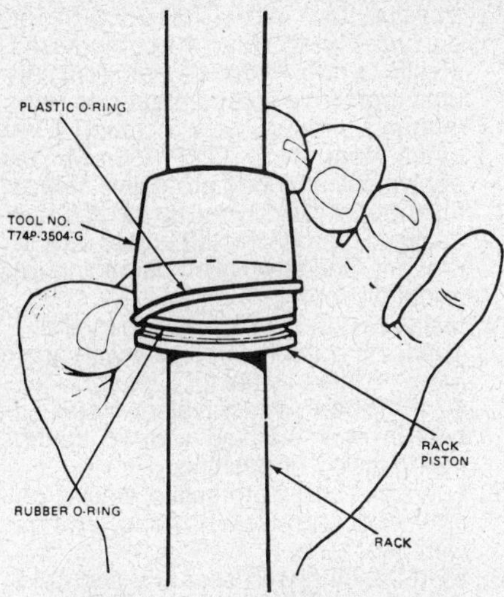


**Fig. 15 Installing plastic O-ring on rack piston. Except Tempo, Topaz & 1989–90 Escort**

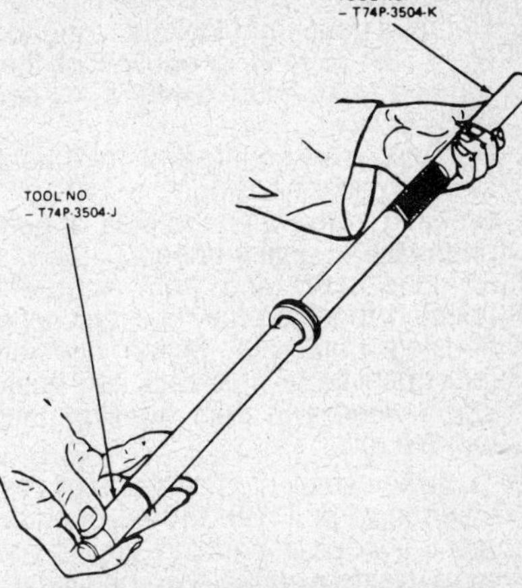


**Fig. 16 Positioning sleeve protector on rack. Except Tempo, Topaz & 1989–90 Escort**

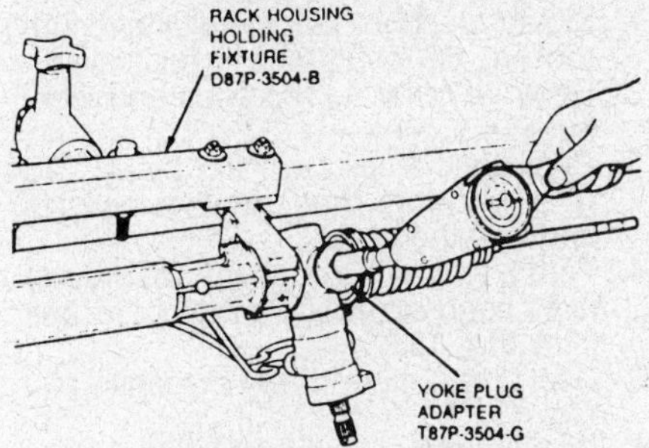


**Fig. 17 Adjusting rack yoke plug preload. Tempo, Topaz & 1989–90 Escort**

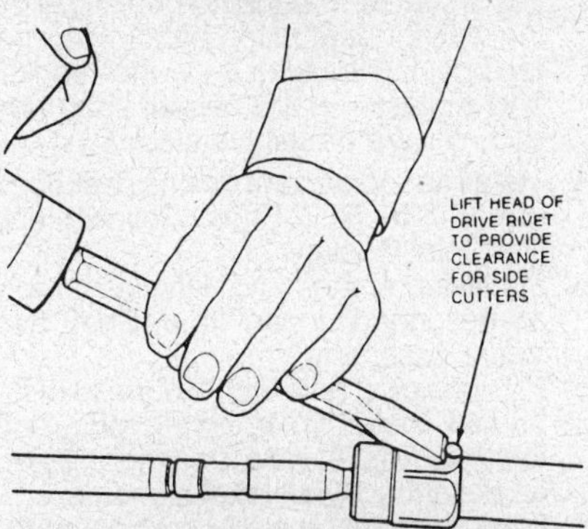


**Fig. 18 Loosening tie rod retaining rivet. Tempo, Topaz & 1989–90 Escort**

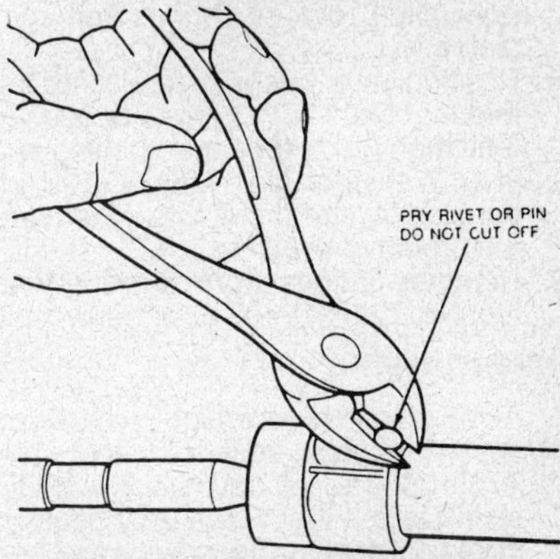


**Fig. 19 Removing tie rod retaining rivet. Tempo, Topaz & 1989–90 Escort**

into fourth groove of valve sleeve. Add one spacer of tool No. T75L-3517-A3, or equivalent, under mandrel, to align mandrel with the next groove on the valve sleeve. Repeat procedure until all sleeve rings have been installed.

6. Apply a light coat of power steering fluid to sleeve and sleeve rings.
7. Install one spacer over input shaft, then slowly install tool No. T75L-3517-A4, or equivalent, over sleeve valve end of input shaft onto valve sleeve rings.
8. Remove tool No. T75L-3517-A4, or equivalent, and check condition of sleeve rings. Ensure that rings turn freely in grooves.
9. If rack is removed, position rack so that mark made during disassembly is centered in valve bore. If rack was not removed, position rack in housing so that three teeth protrude from lefthand end of housing.
10. **On all models except Sable and Taurus,** align blocked tooth of input shaft with center of yoke plug hole and insert valve assembly into bore. The blocked tooth must face straight up when gear is installed in vehicle with gear in straight ahead position. Rotate input shaft assembly from side to side if necessary to mesh with rack teeth. Push valve assembly in by hand until fully seated.
11. **On Sable and Taurus models,** align input shaft flats as shown in **Fig. 12.**
12. **On all models,** using tool No. T74P-3504-R, or equivalent, (T86P-3504-K Sable & Taurus), to turn input shaft, count number of turns from center to each stop which should be approximately 1½ turns. If number of turns is unequal, pull valve assembly out of housing far enough to free pinion teeth. Rotate input shaft 60 degrees, one tooth, in direction which required less fewer turns from center to stop. Reinstall valve assembly and check if gear is centered.
13. While holding input shaft with tool No. T74P-3504-R, or equivalent, install a new pinion bearing locknut on pinion end of valve assembly. Tighten pinion bearing locknut to specifications. The rack must be away from stops when installing locknut.
14. Lubricate input shaft bearing, then install bearing into valve bore and seat with tool No. T78P-3504-D, or equivalent.
15. Lubricate input shaft seal, then install seal with seal lip facing valve assembly.
16. Install snap ring into valve bore.
17. Coat input shaft in area of dust seal with lubriplate or equivalent, then install dust seal and seat seal with tool No. T78P-3504-D, or equivalent.
18. Install steering gear housing cap.
19. Fill yoke housing with 2 ounces of lubricant, then install yoke. The yoke must seat against the rack with finger pressure, if not check for burrs in yoke housing.
20. Install yoke spring and yoke plug. Adjust yoke bearing preload as described under Adjustments.
21. Install yoke plug locknut and tighten to specifications.
22. If the external pressure lines were removed in step two, they must be replaced with new pressure lines. Remove the copper seals from the pressure ports previous to installation of new lines. Tighten pump to gear pressure line fitting and return line fitting and pressure line fittings at valve and power cylinder to specifications.

## GEAR HOUSING & RACK ASSEMBLY

### Disassembly

1. Remove tie rod and socket assemblies and input shaft and valve as-

sembly as described previously.

2. Remove yoke plug locknut using tool No. T78P-3504-H, or equivalent, then remove yoke plug using a 3/4 inch socket.
3. Remove yoke spring and yoke bearing from gear housing.
4. Working from righthand side of gear, push rack in until it bottoms.
5. Remove snap ring from right end housing, then carefully pull rack out of housing until rack piston contacts rack bushings. Pull on rack until bushing is withdrawn from housing, then remove rack.
6. To remove rack high pressure oil seal, insert tool No. T78P-3504-J, or equivalent, into gear housing until it bottoms. Using a suitable wrench tighten tool until expander is fully tightened, then attach a suitable slide hammer to tool and remove seal, **Fig. 13.**
7. Using tool No. T71P-19703-C, or equivalent, remove O-rings from rack piston.
8. Position rack bushing, seal end first into tool No. T78P-3504-L, or equivalent, then place tool and bushing in a vise. With tool No. T78P-3504-J, or equivalent, and a suitable slide hammer, remove seal, **Fig. 14.**
9. Remove O-rings from bushing with tool No. T71P-19703-C, or equivalent.

#### Assembly

1. Apply grease to rack high pressure oil seal, position seal on tool No. T78P-3504-K, or equivalent, with lip spring facing tool. Place gear housing in vertical position, then place tool into right side of housing. Tap on tool handle until seal is seated. **Use care not to cock handle of tool when installing seal.**
2. Mark center tooth of rack so that it will be visible through valve bore.
3. Install rubber O-ring into groove on rack piston.
4. Position plastic O-ring on tool No. T74P-3504-G, or equivalent, then slide tool and O-ring onto rack until they are adjacent to the rack piston. Slide plastic O-ring off tool and into piston groove over rubber O-ring, **Fig. 15.**
5. Apply lubricant ESB-M1C119-A, or equivalent, to rack teeth. Also apply a light coating of lubricant opposite rack teeth in yoke bearing contact area.
6. Install protective sleeve T74P-3504-K, or equivalent, over rack gear teeth to prevent damage to integral oil seal in gear housing. Also thread sleeve protector T74P-3504-J, or equivalent, over rack threads, **Fig. 16.**
7. Lubricate plastic O-ring and protective sleeves with power steering fluid.
8. Position small diameter end of tool No. T78P-3504-M, or equivalent, into righthand side opening of gear housing.
9. Place rack toothed end first, into tool No. T78P-3504-M, or equivalent, then carefully push rack into housing until leading end engages internal oil seal. Position tool No. T78P-3504-M, or equivalent, so that it compresses plastic O-ring. Push rack into housing until protective sleeve protrudes from lefthand side of gear housing. Remove tool No. T78P-3504-M, or equivalent, and long protective sleeve from end of rack. Install tie rod and ball socket assembly on left end of rack to prevent rack teeth from damaging internal oil seal.
10. Install two O-rings on rack bushing.
11. Lubricate outer rack oil seal with gear lube, then using tool No. T74P-3504-F, or equivalent, install oil seal in rack bushing with lip spring facing inside of bushing.
12. Lubricate short protective sleeve on rack end and rack bushing O-rings with gear lube.
13. Start bushing with seal end first onto rack. Position bushing and seal over protective sleeve and into housing bore. Using tool No. T78P-3504-M, or equivalent, apply hand pressure to end plate and rack bushing until bushing is seated in housing bore. If bushing will not seat using hand pressure, tap bushing in using a 1 1/8 inch socket and a plastic mallet. Install snap ring and remove protective sleeve.
14. Install tie rod assemblies as described under "Tie Rod Ends, Bellows and Ball Joint Sockets."
15. Install input shaft and valve assembly as described under "Input Shaft and Valve Assembly."
16. Fill yoke plug hole with 2 ounces of lubricant. Install yoke, spring, plug and locknut. Adjust yoke bearing preload as described under Adjustments.
17. If the external pressure lines were removed, they must be replaced with new pressure lines. Remove the copper seals from the pressure ports previous to installation of new lines. Tighten pump to gear pressure line and return line fittings and pressure line fittings at valve and power cylinder to specifications.
18. Apply lubricant under cuts in tie rod, then install bellows, equalizer tube, clamps, jam nuts and tie rod ends.

# TEMPO, TOPAZ & 1989–90 ESCORT

## POWER STEERING PRESSURE TEST

Refer to "TRW Rack & Pinion Steering" for procedures.

## ADJUSTMENTS

### Rack Yoke Plug Preload

1. Clean exterior of steering gear thoroughly.
2. Mount gear in holding fixture tool No. D87P-3504-B or equivalent. **Do not hold gear in vise.**
3. Do not remove external pressure lines unless they are leaking.
4. Drain gear by rotating input shaft from lock to lock with input shaft torque adapter tool No. T81P-3504-R or equivalent.
5. Loosen yoke plug locknut and yoke plug with yoke locknut wrench tool No. T81P-3504-G or equivalent.
6. With rack in center position, **torque** yoke plug to 44-50 inch lbs. Clean threads of yoke plug prior to tightening, **Fig. 17.**
7. Install yoke plug adapter tool No. T78P-3504-G or equivalent. Mark location of 0° on housing. Back off adjuster so 48° mark lines up with 0° mark.
8. While holding yoke plug, tighten yoke plug locknut to specifications.
9. Check input shaft torque after tightening locknut.

## STEERING GEAR REPAIRS

### INNER TIE ROD & BELLOWS

#### Disassembly

1. Mount steering gear in holding fixture tool No. D87P-3504-B or equivalent.
2. Remove outer tie rod ends and locknuts.
3. Remove clamps retaining bellows to gear housing, then remove bellows and breather tube.
4. With a sharp chisel, gently tap around rivet head so it lifts away from ball joint, **Fig. 18.**
5. Use side cutters to pry out drive pin, **Fig. 19.**
6. Position rack so several teeth are exposed. Hold hack with an adjustable wrench on end teeth only, while loosening ball joints nuts with yoke locknut tool No. T81P-3504-G or equivalent.

#### Assembly

1. With several rack teeth exposed, hold rack with an adjustable wrench and tighten each tie rod ball joint assembly to specifications using yoke locknut tool T81P-3504-G or equivalent.
2. Install a new rivet in tie rod ball housing until pin is flush with rivet head, **Fig. 20.**
3. Install bellows and breather tube.
4. Install tie rod outer ends.

### INPUT SHAFT & VALVE ASSEMBLY

#### Disassembly

The only serviceable component of the input shaft and valve assembly are the four plastic O-rings.

1. Clean exterior of steering gear thoroughly.
2. Mount gear in holding fixture tool No. D87P-3504-B or equivalent. **Do not hold gear in vise.**
3. Do not remove external pressure lines unless they are leaking.
4. Loosen yoke plug locknut to relieve preload on rack.
5. Remove pinion bearing plug using pinion plug spanner tool No. T83P-3504-AH or equivalent.
6. While holding input shaft, remove and discard pinion bearing locknut, **Fig. 21.**
7. Pry out input shaft dust seal using an

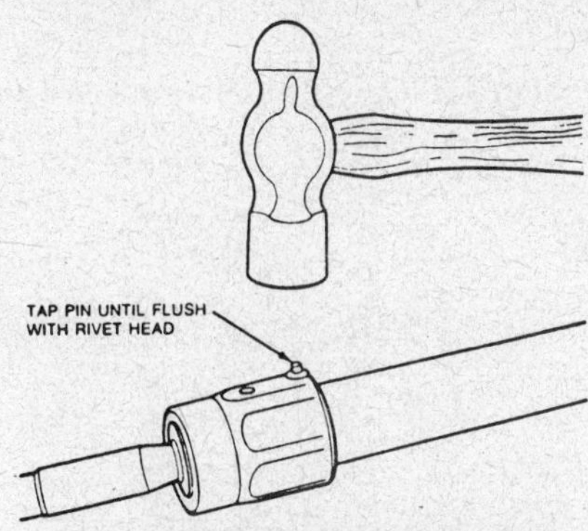


**Fig. 20 Installing tie rod retaining rivet. Tempo, Topaz & 1989–90 Escort**

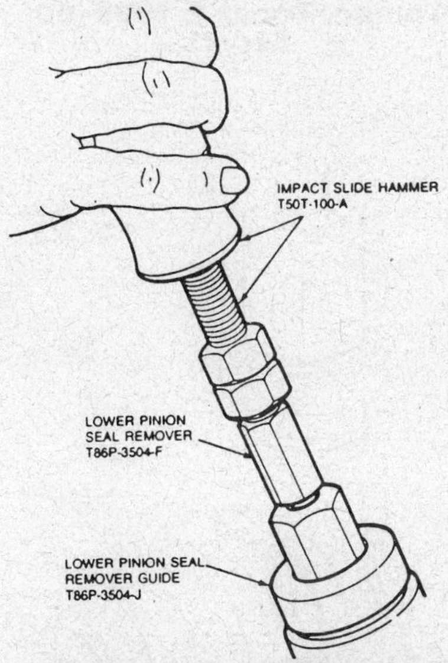


**Fig. 23 Lower pinion seal removal tool. Tempo, Topaz & 1989–90 Escort**

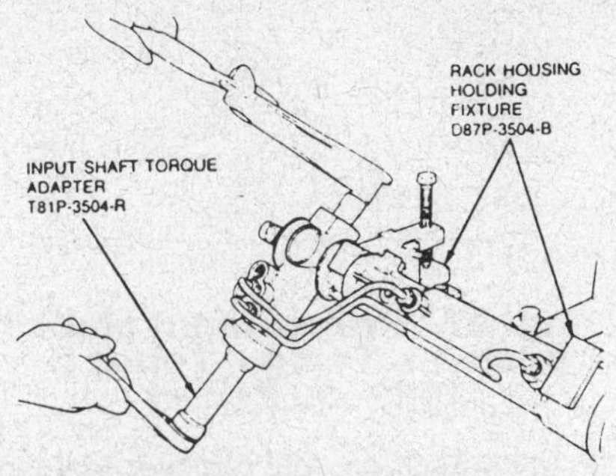


**Fig. 21 Removing pinion bearing locknut. Tempo, Topaz & 1989–90 Escort**

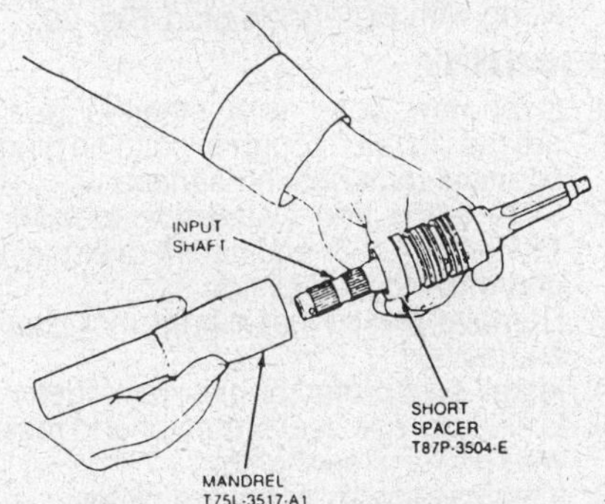


**Fig. 24 Installing plastic valve rings. Tempo, Topaz & 1989–90 Escort**

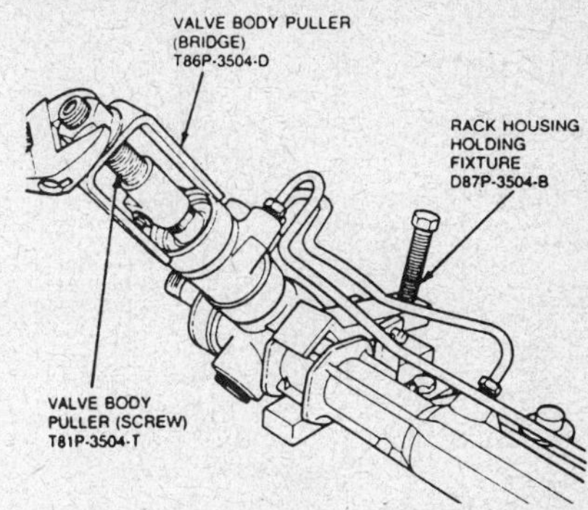


**Fig. 22 Valve body puller tool. Tempo, Topaz & 1989–90 Escort**

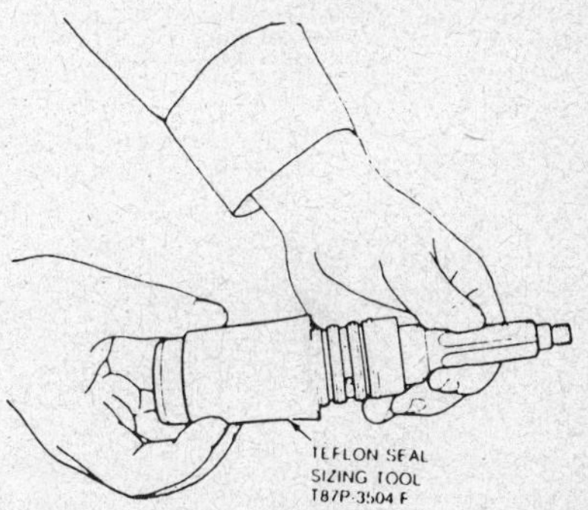


**Fig. 25 Installing seal sizing tool. Tempo, Topaz & 1989–90 Escort**

appropriate tool.

8. Remove snap ring, located under dust seal, from housing.
9. Attach valve body puller tool No. T86P-3504-D and valve body puller tool No. T81P-3504-T or equivalent to input shaft, **Fig. 22.**
10. Turn nut to remove valve. Input shaft seal and bearing will come out with valve body.
11. Remove lower pinion shaft seal using seal removal tool Nos. T86P-3504-F, T86P-3504-J and T50T-100-A or equivalent, **Fig. 23.**
12. Remove pinion bearing from gear housing using puller tool No. T58L-101-B or equivalent.
13. Remove O-rings by pushing rings to one side, then inserting small pointed tool under each ring, and cutting ring off.

## Assembly

1. Install steering gear pinion bearing in gear housing using lower pinion bearing replacer tool No. T81P-3504-H or equivalent. Seat bearing against shoulder in boar. **Support valve housing when seating pinion bearing.**
2. Apply Steering gear grease No. C3AZ-19578-A or equivalent to pinion seal and place it on lower pinion seal replacer tool No. T87P-3504-C or equivalent with seal lip toward tool.
3. Install short spacer over input shaft of valve assembly, **Fig. 24.**Install mandral part of valve seal installer tool No. T75L-3517-A or equivalent over shaft and spacer. Mandrel will line up with second groove from input shaft.
4. Lubricate mandrel with power steering fluid. Place one valve sleeve over mandrel. Rapidly push ring down with pusher tool. Ring will drop into proper groove.
5. Install long spacer over input shaft. Mandral will line up with first groove on input shaft. Repeat step 4.
6. Repeat steps 3 through 5 sliding mandrel over the pinion end of valve.
7. After four valve sleeves are installed, apply a light coat of steering gear grease to sleeve and rings.
8. Slowly install Teflon seal sizing tool No. T87P-3504-F or equivalent over valve sleeve rings, **Fig. 25. Ensure that rings are not being bent over or out of grooves as tube is slid over them.**
9. Continue sliding sizing tool over rings until it has passed over rings and comes off other end. Ensure rings turn freely in the grooves.
10. Position rack in housing so four complete tooth spaces protrude from left-hand end of housing, then move rack slightly, as necessary, to center tooth visible in valve bore, **Fig. 26.**
11. Position Teflon seal sizing tool in valve housing bore.
12. Position D-flat on input shaft at the 3 o'clock position and insert valve assembly into bore. **The D-flat surface must be at the 3 o'clock position in the vehicle with the gear on center position. Rotate input shaft slightly, if necessary, to mesh the pinion with the rack teeth.**
13. Push valve assembly in by hand until seated properly, then remove sizing tool.
14. Using input shaft torque adjuster tool No. T81P-3504-R or equivalent count total turns, stop to stop. From one stop, back off half the total of turns. D-flat should be ad shown in **Fig. 27.** If not, repeat steps 11 through 13.
15. Install bearing assembly in valve bore and seat with input shaft and seal installer tool No. T78P-3504-D or equivalent.
16. Install input shaft protector tool No. T81P-3504-P or equivalent over input shaft and install input shaft seal with lip spring toward valve.
17. Remove seal protector and seat seal.
18. Install retaining snap ring in valve bore.
19. Apply a generous amount of grease over top of input shaft pressure seal around input shaft.
20. Install dust seal and seat with seal installer tool No. T78P-3504-D or equivalent.
21. Install nut on pinion end of valve assembly. Holding input shaft tighten

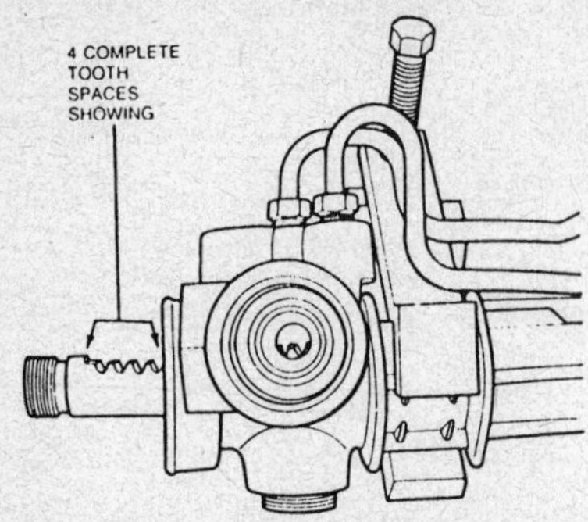


**Fig. 26 Positioning rack in housing. Tempo, Topaz & 1989–90 Escort**

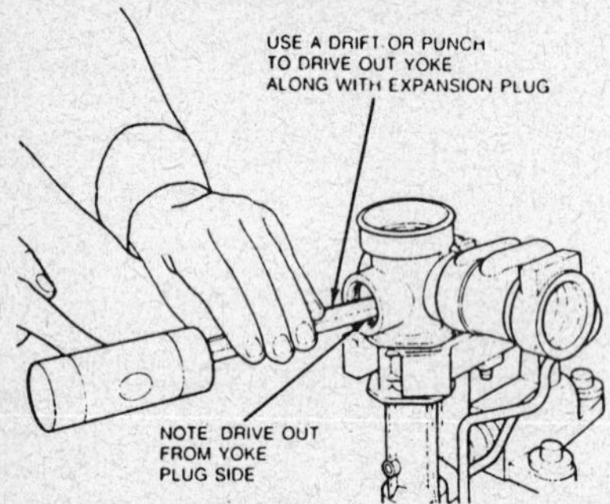


**Fig. 29 Removing yoke & expansion plug. Tempo, Topaz & 1989–90 Escort**

nut to specifications. **Rack must be in center position when tightening.**

22. Install steering gear pinion bearing cap, then tighten to specifications.
23. Set rack preload as outlined under "Adjustments, Rack Yoke Plug Preload."

## GEAR HOUSING, RACK YOKE PLUG, RACK ASSEMBLY, RACK BUSHING & OIL SEAL

### Disassembly

1. Remove tie rods and socket assemblies from both ends of rack, also remove input shaft and valve assembly from gear housing as described previously.
2. Remove yoke plug and spring. **Yoke cannot be removed at this time.**
3. Working from righthand side of gear, push rack in just far enough to enable removal of snap ring, **Fig. 28.**
4. Slowly pull rack out of righthand side of housing until rack position contacts aluminum rack bushing. Apply pulling effort and remove rack from housing. **Do not hammer on rack until bushing is withdrawn from housing.**
5. Using rack oil seal remover tool No. T87P-3504-A or equivalent, remove internal high pressure oil seal.
6. Remove plastic O-ring and rubber O-ring from rack piston.
7. Insert rack bushing into rack bushing holder tool No. T78P-3504-L or equivalent, seal end first. Place tool and bushing into vice.

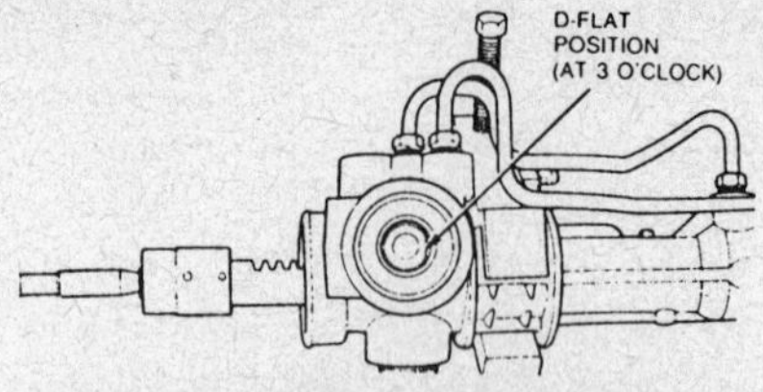


**Fig. 27 Proper input shaft position. Tempo, Topaz & 1989–90 Escort**

8. Using rack oil seal remover tool No. T87P-3504-A, remove seal.
9. Remove rubber O-ring from rack bushing.
10. Use a drift or punch to knock out yoke, along with expansion plug, **Fig. 29.**

### Assembly

1. Coat new yoke with steering gear grease. Install through expansion plug opening, rack bearing surface up.
2. Slide teflon ring installation tool No. T81P-3504-L or equivalent over plain end of rack up to piston.
3. Remove plastic insert from rack seal and save.
4. Install seal protector over rack teeth.
5. Lubricate rack seal protector and rack with power steering fluid.
6. Install seal with lip toward piston.
7. Install plastic insert in rack seal. Remove seal protector.
8. Apply steering gear lubricant to rack teeth and power steering fluid to the piston seal and rack seal outside diameter.
9. Install Teflon seal sizing tool No. T87P-3504-F or equivalent into end of gear housing.
10. Ensure yoke in positioned correctly then install rack, ensuring not to scratch housing piston bore.
11. Carefully push piston through sizing tool. Continue pushing on rack until it bottoms. Remove sizing tool.
12. Seat rack seal with rack by driving end of rack with a drift and plastic mallet.
13. Install lefthand tie rod hand tight to prevent potential inner seal damage due to excessive rack travel.
14. Center rack in housing.
15. Install rubber O-ring on aluminum rack bushing.
16. Apply power steering fluid to outer rack seal and install seal in rack bushing. Seal lip spring must face inside of bushing, **Fig. 30.**
17. Install rack seal protector tool No. T81P-3504-N or equivalent over threads on righthand side of rack. apply power steering fluid to protective sleeve.
18. Start bushing, seal side out, on rack. Position bushing into housing. Place end plate against rack bushing.Apply hand pressure to end plate and rack bushing until bushing seats in gear housing. If rack bushing will not seat with hand pressure, a 1 1/8 inch deep socket and a plastic mallet may be used to tap bushing in place.
19. Install retaining ring and remove protective sleeve.

**Fig. 28 Snap ring removal. Tempo, Topaz & 1989–90 Escort**

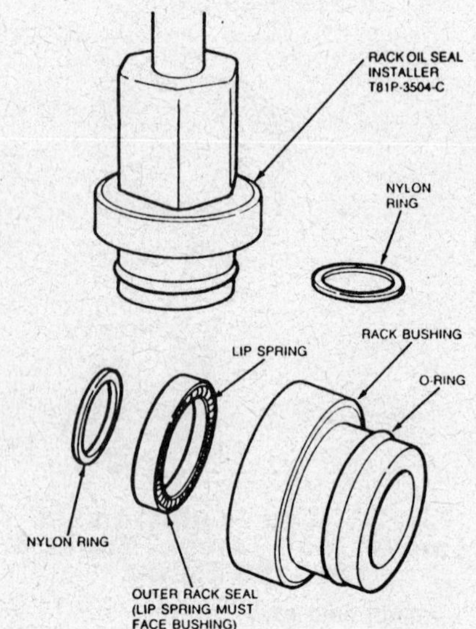


**Fig. 30 Rack bushing and seal. Tempo, Topaz & 1989–90 Escort**

20. Install tie rod assemblies as previously described.
21. Install input shaft and valve assembly.
22. Support gear on wood block at yoke plug opening. Using a 1 1/4 bar with a flat end, flatten expansion plug until flat portion is approximately 1/2 to 3/4 of total plug diameter. **Do not flatten plug completely or it may fall out.**
23. Install spring, plug and locknut. Adjust yoke plug preload as previous described.
24. Fully extend lefthand end of rack. Apply two ounces gear lubricant to pack rack teeth. Place any remaining grease into lefthand end of gear housing.
25. Install bellows, breather tube and bellows clamps.
26. Install jam nuts and tie rod ends on tie rods.

# TIGHTENING SPECIFICATIONS

## COUGAR & THUNDERBIRD

| Year | Component | Torque, Ft. Lbs. |
|---|---|---|
| 1989–91 | Bellows Clamp Screw | 20–30 ⑤ |
| | External Transfer Tubes | 22–28 |
| | Gear Hose Fittings | ② |
| | Gear To Crossmember | ① |
| | Pinion Bearing Cap | ③ |
| | Pinion Bearing Locknut | 30–40 |
| | Pump Pressure Hose Fitting | 10–15 |
| | Steering Flex Coupling Bolt | 20–30 |
| | Tie Rod End Jam Nut | 35–50 |
| | Tie Rod End To Spindle Arm | 39–54 |
| | Tie Rod Socket Assembly To Rack | 55–65 |
| | Yoke Plug | ④ |
| | Yoke Plug Locknut | 44–66 |

①—1989–90 models, 175–230 ft. lbs., 1991, 100–144 ft. lbs.
②—1989–90 models, 15–25 ft. lbs., 1991, 20–25 ft. lbs.
③—1989–90 models, 40–60 ft. lbs., 1991, 40–50 ft. lbs.
④—Refer to text.
⑤—Inch lbs.

## MARK VII & MUSTANG

| Year | Component | Torque, Ft. Lbs. |
|---|---|---|
| 1989–91 | Bellows Clamp Screw | 20–30 ① |
| | External Transfer Tubes | ② |
| | Gear Hose Fittings | ③ |
| | Gear To Crossmember | 30–40 |
| | Pinion Bearing Cap | 40–50 |
| | Pinion Bearing Locknut | 30–40 |
| | Pump Pressure Hose Fitting | 10–15 |
| | Steering Flex Coupling Bolt | 20–30 |
| | Tie Rod End Jam Nut | 35–50 |
| | Tie Rod End To Spindle Arm | 35–47 |
| | Tie Rod Socket Assembly To Rack | 55–65 |
| | Yoke Plug | ④ |
| | Yoke Plug Locknut | 44–66 |

①—Inch lbs.
②—1989–90 models, 22–28 ft. lbs., 1991, 15–25 ft. lbs.
③—1989–90 models, 15–25 ft. lbs., 1991, 20–25 ft. lbs.
④—Refer to text.

## SABLE & TAURUS

| Year | Component | Torque, Ft. Lbs. |
|---|---|---|
| 1989–91 | Bellows Clamp Screw | 20–30① |
| | External Transfer Tubes② | 10–20 |
| | Gear Hose Fittings | 15–25 |
| | Gear Housing Return Line② | 20–25 |
| | Gear To Crossmember | 85–100 |
| | Intermediate Shaft To Steering Column | 15–25 |
| | Intermediate Shaft To Steering Gear | 30–38 |
| | Pinion Bearing Cap | 40–50 |
| | Pinion Bearing Locknut | 30–40 |
| | Pressure Line Fitting To Actuator Banjo Bolt② | 22–28 |
| | Pressure Line Fittings At Power Cylinder③ | 22–28 |
| | Pump Pressure Line Fitting | 10—15 |
| | Tie Rod Ball Socket To Rack | 55–65 |
| | Tie Rod End Jam Nut | 35–50 |
| | Tie Rod End To Spindle Arm | 35–47 |
| | VAPS Actuator② | 20–25 |
| | Yoke Plug | ④ |
| | Yoke Plug Locknut | 40–50 |

①—Inch lbs.
②—1990–91 models.
③—1989 models.
④—Refer to text.

## TEMPO, TOPAZ & 1989–90 ESCORT

| Year | Component | Torque, Ft. Lbs. |
|---|---|---|
| 1989–91 | Flex Coupling To Gear Input Shaft Clamp Bolt | 20–30 |
| | Steering Gear | 40–55 |
| | Pinion Cap | 35–45 |
| | Pinion Locknut | 20–35 |
| | Pressure & Return Lines | 20–25 |
| | Tie Rod Ball Housing | 40–50 |
| | Tie Rod End Jam Nut | 42–50 |
| | Tie Rod End To Spindle Arm | 27–32① |
| | Transfer Lines | 15–20 |
| | Yoke Plug Locknut | 40–50 |

①—Tighten to specifications, then tighten to nearest cotter pin slot.

# Rack & Pinion Steering Gear, Probe w/Variable Assist

INDEX



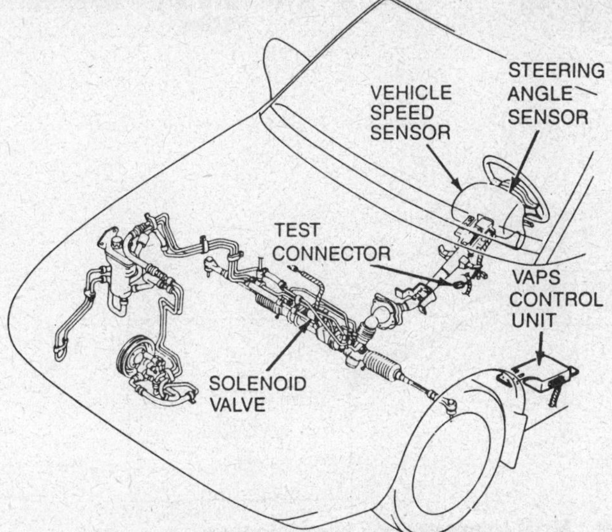


**Fig. 1 Electronic power steering system**

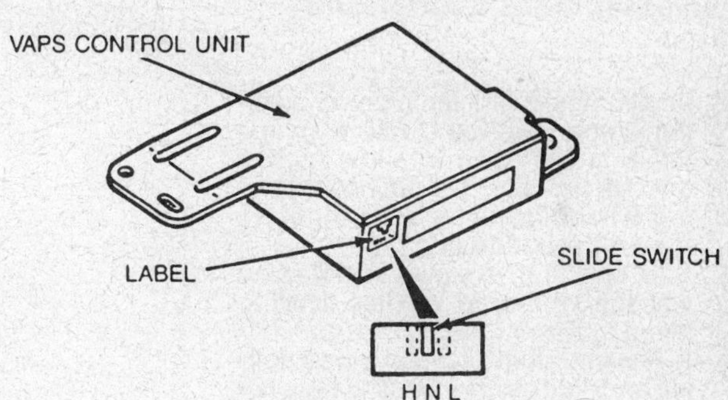


**Fig. 2 Electronic control module**

## DESCRIPTION

The Variable Assist Power Steering System (VAPS) automatically adjusts power steering pressure to provide light steering effort during low speed operation and parking, and high steering effort during high speeds to provide for better road feel.

The VAPS system uses a steering angle sensor and vehicle speed sensor, **Fig. 1**, to provide the control unit with input information, the control unit then adjusts the solenoid valve according to the inputs.

The control unit is equipped with a slide switch, **Fig. 2,** enabling a selection of normal operation or a 10% lighter or harder steering effort.

## TROUBLESHOOTING

### EXCESSIVE STEERING EFFORT

1. Insufficient tire pressure.
2. Loose or damaged belt.
3. Low fluid level or fluid aeration.
4. Crimped or twisted hoses or pipes.
5. Low hydraulic pressure.
6. Improperly adjusted wheel alignment.
7. Rough ball joint linkage operation.
8. Binding or bent steering shaft.

### POOR STEERING WHEEL RETURN

1. Incorrect tire pressure.
2. Improperly adjusted wheel alignment.
3. Faulty ball joint linkage.
4. Restricted, over tightened or bent steering shaft.

### UNEVEN STEERING EFFORT

1. Loose belt.
2. Loose steering shaft bolt(s).
3. Rough steering linkage operation.
4. Faulty steering gear.

### STEERING WHEEL PULLS

1. Incorrect tire pressure.
2. Improper preload adjustment.
3. Faulty wheel bearing.
4. Improperly adjusted wheel alignment.
5. Faulty steering gear.

### FLUID LEAKAGE

1. Hose coupling.
2. Damaged or clogged hose.
3. Faulty reservoir tank.
4. Faulty steering pump.
5. Faulty steering gear.

### ABNORMAL NOISE

1. Loose power steering pump.
2. Loose steering gear.
3. Loose pump bracket.
4. Loose pump pulley nut.
5. Improperly adjusted belt.
6. Faulty steering gear.
7. Faulty steering pump.
8. Obstruction near steering column or pressure hose.
9. Loose steering linkage.

## DIAGNOSIS & TESTING

### POWER STEERING PRESSURE TEST

**During the following procedure, power steering pressure may exceed 1200 psi. Ensure proper tool fitment prior to performing test. Exercise extreme caution or damage or personal injury may result.**

1. Disconnect power steering pump pressure hose where it connects to tubing, Install power steering system analyzer tool No. 014-00207 and adapter tool No. 014-00454 or equivalents, **torque** fitting to 29-36 ft. lbs, **Fig. 3.**

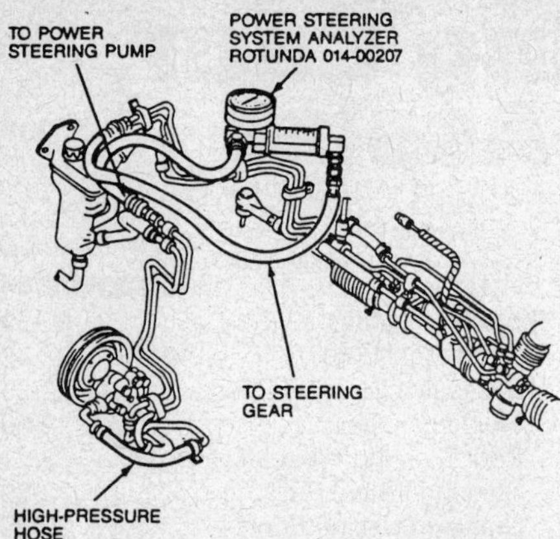


**Fig. 3 Pressure test equipment connection**

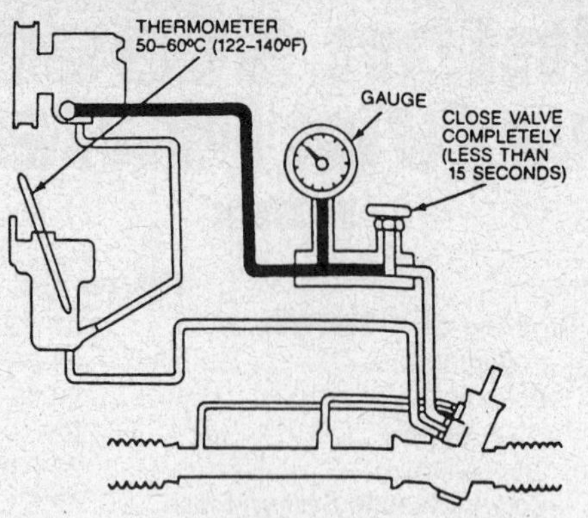


**Fig. 4 Steering pump pressure test**

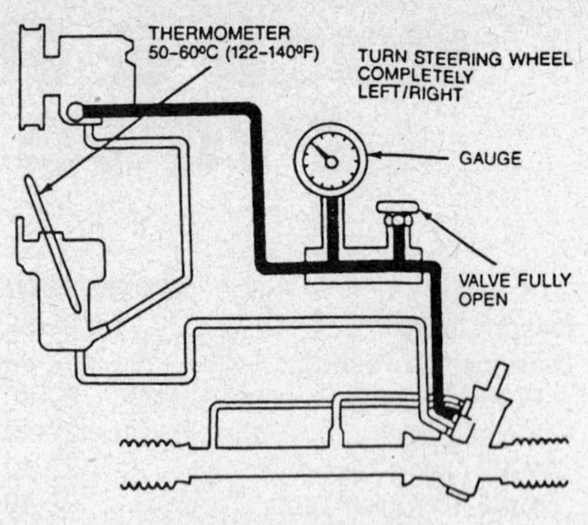


**Fig. 5 Steering gear pressure test**

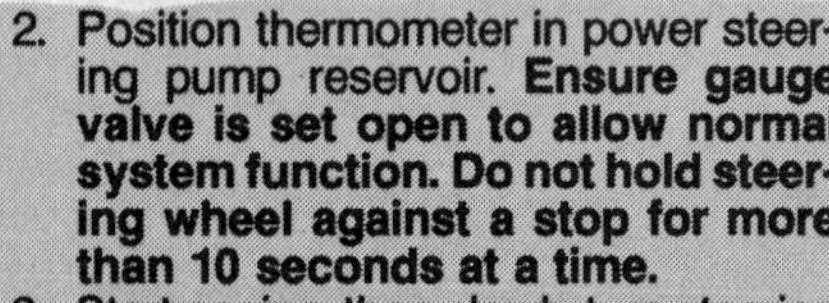

2. Position thermometer in power steering pump reservoir. **Ensure gauge valve is set open to allow normal system function. Do not hold steering wheel against a stop for more than 10 seconds at a time.**
3. Start engine, then slowly turn steering wheel from lock to lock ten times to bleed system.
4. If required, turn steering wheel fully left and right several times to raise fluid temperature to 122-140D°F (50-60°C). **Gauge valve must be briefly closed to read operating pressures. Do not leave valve closed for more than 15 seconds.**
5. To measure pump output pressure, close gauge set valve, **Fig. 4**, then increase engine speed to 1000-1500 RPM, read pressure, then open valve. Operating pressure should be 1066-1138 psi, if pressure is low, repair or replace pump.
6. To measure pressure at gear, open valve, then increase engine speed to 1000-1500 RPM, turn steering wheel fully left and right, read pressure, **Fig. 5.** Operating pressure should be 1066-1138 psi, if pressure is low, repair or replace steering gear.
7. Remove gauge set and adapter, connect high pressure hose and tighten.
8. Start engine, then slowly turn steering wheel lock to lock ten times to bleed system.

## VISUAL CHECK

1. Check steering gear and linkage for damage, leaks, cracks and proper mounting.
2. Check VAPS system wiring harness for proper connections, bent or broken pins, corrosion, loose wires and proper routing.
3. Check the control unit, sensors and solenoid for physical damage.
4. Check tires for proper pressure.

## 1989 QUICK TEST

Prior to performing the following tests, a suitable analog volt/ohm meter should be installed on the vehicle as shown, **Fig 6.**

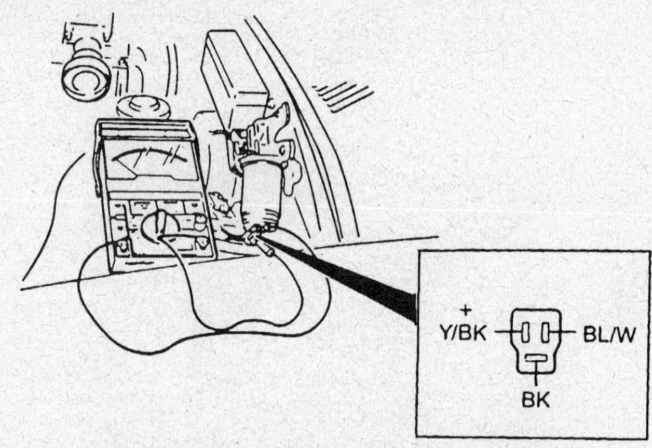


**Fig. 6 Volt/ohmmeter installation**

## KEY ON ENGINE RUNNING TEST

### Step A

1. Turn ignition key Off to reset control unit.
2. Ensure visual check of system was performed.
3. Start engine and run at idle.
4. Turn steering wheel to straight ahead position.
5. Activate self-test by turning volt/ohmmeter On.
6. Record all service codes displayed, **Fig. 7,** then refer to pinpoint tests, **Figs. 8 through 12,** as indicated.

### Step B

1. Turn ignition key Off to reset control unit.
2. Start engine and run at idle.
3. Turn steering wheel 45° left and right of center with engine idling.
4. Record all service codes displayed, **Fig. 13,** then refer to pinpoint tests, **Figs. 8 through 12,** as indicated.

### Step C

1. Turn ignition key Off to reset control unit.
2. Raise and support vehicle.
3. Start engine and run at idle.
4. Drive front wheels at a speed above 6.2 mph.
5. Record all service codes displayed, **Fig. 14,** then refer to pinpoint tests, **Figs. 8 through 12,** as indicated.

## CONTINUOUS TEST

1. Ensure a pass code was indicated in all steps of "Key On Engine Running Test."
2. With volt/ohmmeter installed, **Fig. 6,** start engine and run at idle.
3. Tap, move and wiggle sensor connectors and wiring harness while observing volt/ohmmeter, if a fault code is indicated, **Figs. 7, 13 and 14, refer to appropriate pinpoint test Figs. 8 through 12.**
4. If no fault code is indicated, reconnect all sensor connectors and terminals.

## 1990–91 QUICK TEST

The quick test procedure should only be used when diagnosing variable assist power steering symptoms.

Quick test is divided into two specialized tests; "Key On Engine Running" and " Continuous Test."

Refer to **Figs. 15 through 20,** for quick test procedures.

*Continued on page 22-63*

| TEST STEP | CODE PATTERN | ACTION TO TAKE |
|---|---|---|
| A<br>(Set steering wheel in straight ahead position with engine idling) | 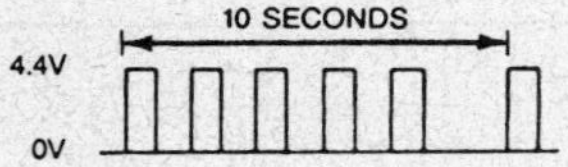 10 SECONDS<br>4.4V<br>0V | Go to Pinpoint Test A |
| |  4.4V<br>0V | Go to Pinpoint Test B |
| |  4.4V<br>0V | Go to Pinpoint Test C |
| | 4.4V<br>0V | Pass Code |
| |  0V | Go to Pinpoint Test Q |

**Fig. 7 Quick test (Step A). 1989 models**

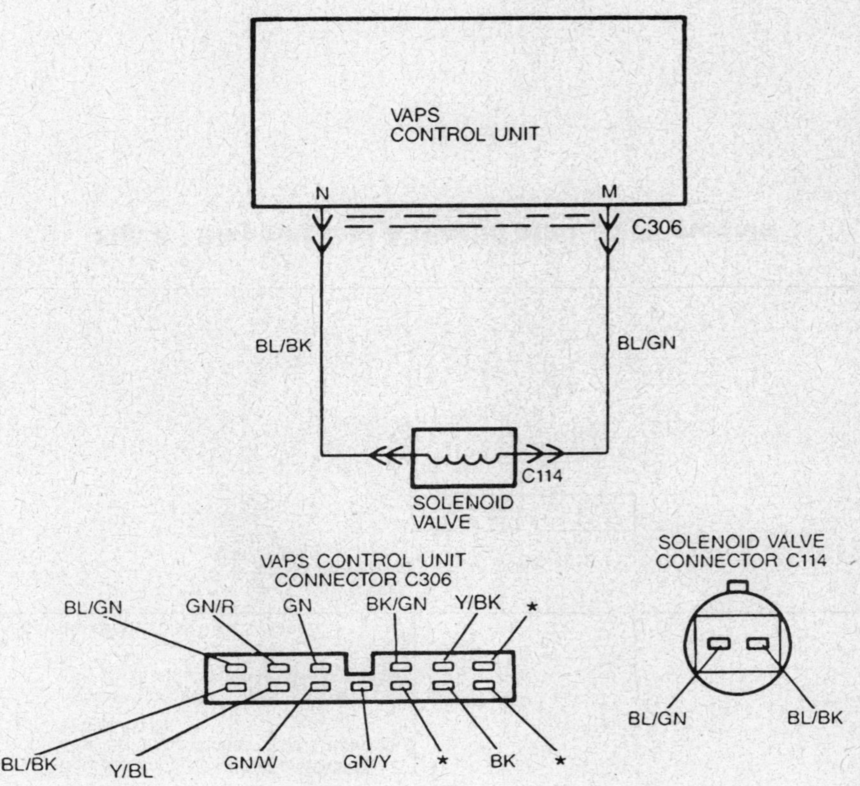


**Fig. 8 Pinpoint test A (Part 1 of 6). 1989 models**

| TEST STEP | RESULT ► | ACTION TO TAKE |
|---|---|---|
| A1 SYSTEM INTEGRITY CHECK | | |
| • Visually inspect all wiring, wiring harness, connectors and components for evidence of overheating, insulation damage, looseness, shorting or other damage.<br>• Is there any cause for concern? | Yes ►<br>No ► | SERVICE as required.<br>GO to A2 . |

**Fig. 8 Pinpoint test A (Part 2 of 6). 1989 models**

| TEST STEP | RESULT ► | ACTION TO TAKE |
|---|---|---|
| **A2** SOLENOID FUNCTION CHECK | | |
| • Disconnect solenoid valve connector C114.<br>• Apply 12 volts and ground to terminals as shown and listen for actuation sound.<br>• Is clicking sound heard when applying 12 volts? | Yes ►<br>No ► | GO to A3.<br>REPLACE solenoid. |

Fig. 8 Pinpoint test A (Part 3 of 6). 1989 models

| TEST STEP | RESULT ► | ACTION TO TAKE |
|---|---|---|
| **A3** SOLENOID RESISTANCE CHECK | | |
| • VOM on 200 ohm scale.<br>• Measure resistance between solenoid terminals.<br>• Is resistance between 3.4 and 6.9 ohms? | Yes ►<br>No ► | GO to A4.<br>REPLACE solenoid. |

Fig. 8 Pinpoint test A (Part 4 of 6). 1989 models

| TEST STEP | RESULT ► | ACTION TO TAKE |
|---|---|---|
| **A4** SOLENOID CIRCUIT RESISTANCE CHECK | | |
| • Disconnect VAPS control unit (connector C306) and solenoid (connector C114).<br>• Key off.<br>• VOM on 200 ohm scale.<br>• Measure resistance between the following terminals.<br>(1) Between connector C306 terminal M ("BL/GN") and connector C114 terminal M ("BL/GN").<br>(2) Between connector C306 terminal N ("BL/BK") and connector C114 terminal N ("BL/BK").<br>• Are resistances less than 5 ohms? | Yes ►<br>No ► | GO to A5.<br>REPAIR wire in question for opens. |

Fig. 8 Pinpoint test A (Part 5 of 6). 1989 models

| TEST STEP | RESULT ► | ACTION TO TAKE |
|---|---|---|
| **A5** SOLENOID CIRCUIT SHORT TO GROUND AND VPWR CHECK | | |
| • Leave VAPS control unit (connector C306) and solenoid (connector C114) disconnected.<br>• Disconnect battery.<br>• VOM on 200K ohm scale.<br>• Measure resistance as follows:<br>(1) Between connector C306 terminal M ("BL/GN") and chassis ground.<br>(2) Between connector C306 terminal M ("BL/GN") and terminal E ("BK/GN").<br>(3) Between connector C306 terminal N ("BL/BK") and chassis ground.<br>(4) Between connector C306 terminal N ("BL/BK") and terminal E ("BK/GN").<br>• Are all resistances greater than 10,000 ohms? | Yes ►<br>No ► | GO to Pinpoint Test Q.<br>REPAIR wires in question between VAPS control unit and solenoid for shorts to ground or VPWR. |

Fig. 8 Pinpoint test A (Part 6 of 6). 1989 models

| TEST STEP | RESULT ► | ACTION TO TAKE |
|---|---|---|
| **B1** SYSTEM INTEGRITY CHECK | | |
| • Visually inspect all wiring, wiring harness, connectors and components for evidence of overheating, insulation damage, looseness, shorting or other damage.<br>• Is there any cause for concern? | Yes ►<br>No ► | SERVICE as required.<br>GO to B2 . |

Fig. 9 Pinpoint test B (Part 2 of 5). 1989 models

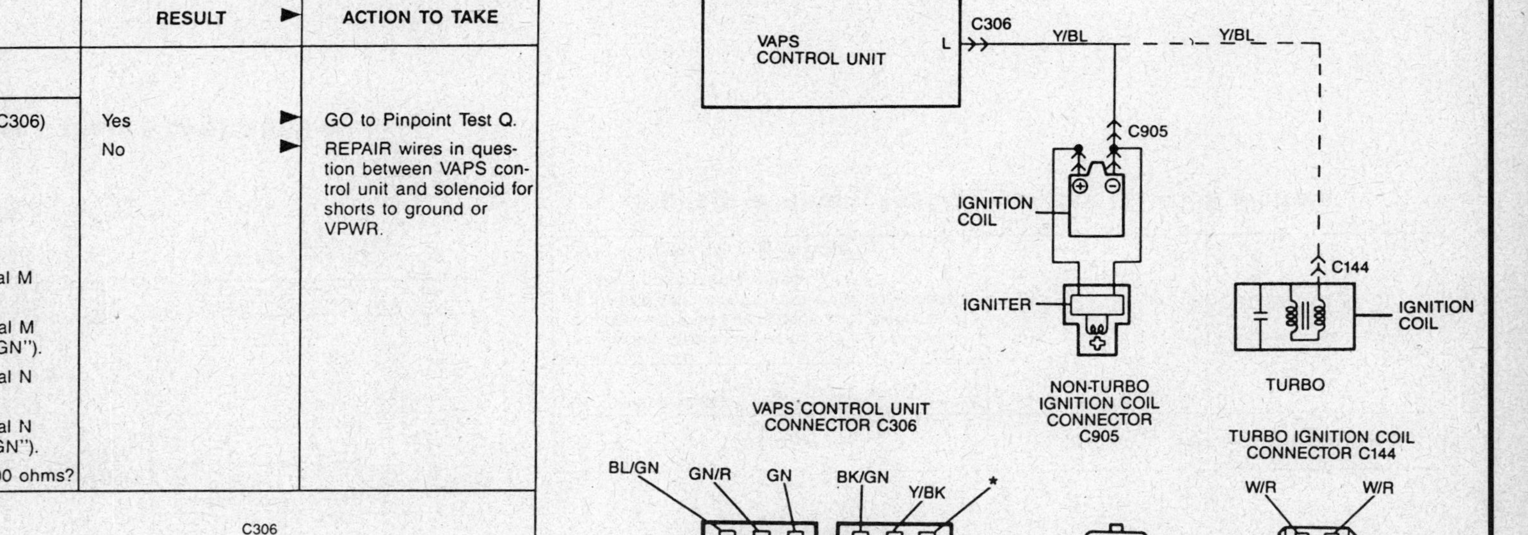


Fig. 9 Pinpoint test B (Part 1 of 5). 1989 models

| TEST STEP | RESULT ► | ACTION TO TAKE |
|---|---|---|
| **B2** IGNITION COIL CIRCUIT VOLTAGE CHECK | | |
| • Disconnect VAPS control unit (connector C306).<br>• Key on; engine running.<br>• Measure voltage at connector C306 between terminal L ("Y/BL") and chassis ground.<br>• Is voltage above 10 volts? | Yes ►<br>No ► | GO to Pinpoint Test Q.<br>GO to B3 . |

Fig. 9 Pinpoint test B (Part 3 of 5). 1989 models

| TEST STEP | RESULT ► | ACTION TO TAKE |
|---|---|---|
| **B3** CIRCUIT CONTINUITY CHECK | | |
| • Leave VAPS control unit connector C306 disconnected.<br>• Disconnect ignition coil connector (C905 non-turbo) or (C144 turbo).<br>• VOM on 200 ohm scale.<br>• Measure resistance between ignition coil ("Y/BL") wire and connector C306 terminal L ("Y/BL").<br>• Is resistance less than 5 ohms? | Yes ►<br>No ► | GO to B4 .<br>SERVICE ("Y/BL") wire between ignition coil and VAPS control unit for opens. |

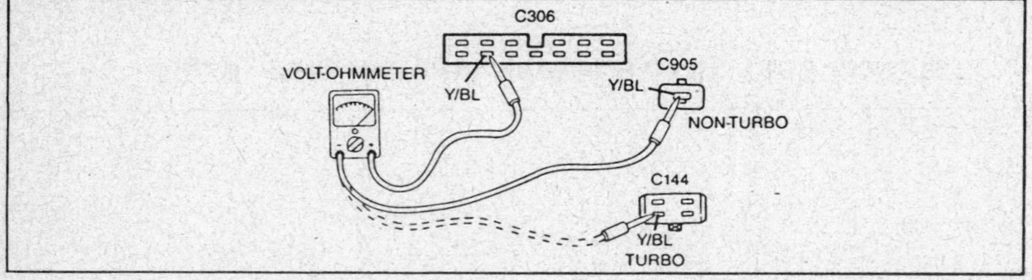

Fig. 9 Pinpoint test B (Part 4 of 5). 1989 models

| TEST STEP | RESULT ► | ACTION TO TAKE |
|---|---|---|
| **B4** CIRCUIT SHORT TO GROUND AND VPWR CHECK | | |
| • Leave VAPS control unit connector C306 disconnected.<br>• Disconnect battery.<br>• VOM on 200K ohm scale.<br>• Measure resistance between connector C306 terminal L ("Y/BL") and chassis ground and between terminal L ("Y/BL") and terminal E ("BK/GN").<br>• Are resistances greater than 10,000 ohms? | Yes ►<br>No ► | GO to Pinpoint Test Q.<br>REPAIR ("Y/BL") wire between ingition coil and VAPS control module for short to ground or VPWR. |

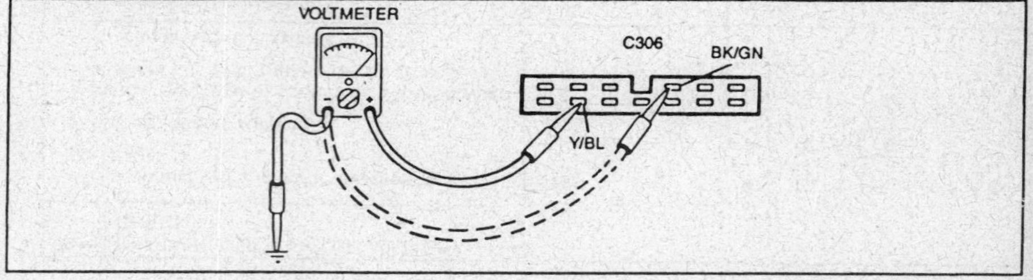

Fig. 9 Pinpoint test B (Part 5 of 5). 1989 models

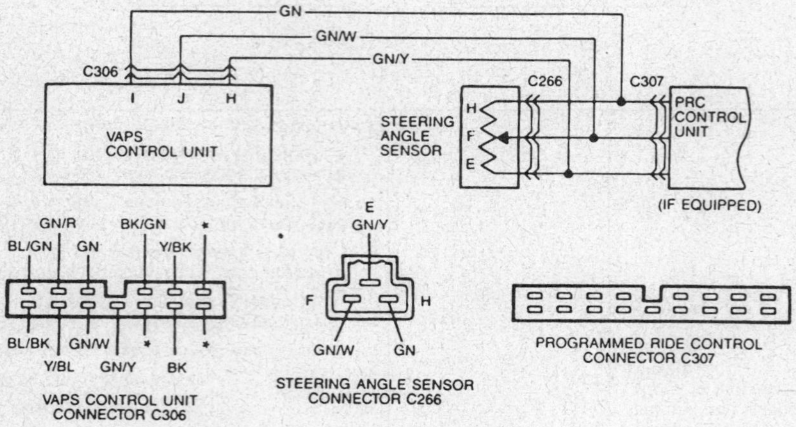

Fig. 10 Pinpoint test C (Part 1 of 8). 1989 models

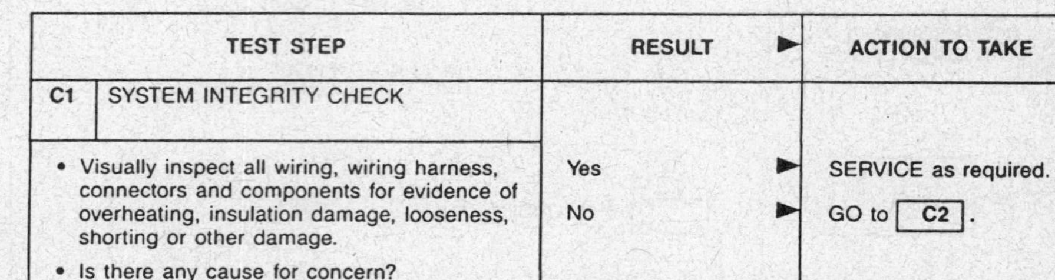

| TEST STEP | RESULT ► | ACTION TO TAKE |
|---|---|---|
| **C1** SYSTEM INTEGRITY CHECK | | |
| • Visually inspect all wiring, wiring harness, connectors and components for evidence of overheating, insulation damage, looseness, shorting or other damage.<br>• Is there any cause for concern? | Yes ►<br>No ► | SERVICE as required.<br>GO to C2 . |

Fig. 10 Pinpoint test C (Part 2 of 8). 1989 models

| TEST STEP | RESULT | ► | ACTION TO TAKE |
|---|---|---|---|
| **C2** STEERING ANGLE SENSOR RESISTANCE CHECK | | | |
| • Key off.<br>• Remove steering column cover and disconnect steering angle sensor (connector C266).<br>• Set the steering wheel so wheels are in a straight ahead position.<br>• Measure the resistance between the following steering angle sensor terminals:<br>**Terminal** / **Resistance**<br>1. H ("GN") – F ("GN/W") 20–30K ohms<br>2. H ("GN") – E ("GN/Y") 40–60K ohms<br>3. E ("GN/Y") – F ("GN/W") 20–30K ohms<br>• Are all resistances within specification? | Yes<br>No | ►<br>► | GO to **C3**.<br>REPLACE steering angle sensor. |



**Fig. 10 Pinpoint test C (Part 3 of 8). 1989 models**

| TEST STEP | RESULT | ► | ACTION TO TAKE |
|---|---|---|---|
| **C3** STEERING ANGLE SENSOR CHECK | | | |
| • Steering angle sensor (connector C266) disconnected.<br>• Set the steering wheel in the straight ahead position.<br>• VOM on 200K ohms scale.<br>• Measure the resistance as decribed in the table below.<br>• Are all resistances within specification? | Yes<br>No | ►<br>► | GO to **C4**.<br>REPLACE steering angle sensor. |

| Terminal | Steering Wheel Position | Resistance Value |
|---|---|---|
| F–H | Turn the wheel a little at a time from the straight ahead position 180 degrees to the right. | Increase from approximately 25K ohms to approximately 50K ohms. |
| F–H | Straight ahead position. | 20–30K ohms. |



**Fig. 10 Pinpoint test C (Part 4 of 8). 1989 models**

| TEST STEP | RESULT ► | ACTION TO TAKE |
|---|---|---|
| **C4** STEERING ANGLE SENSOR CHECK | | |
| • Steering angle sensor (connector C266) disconnected.<br>• Set the steering wheel in a straight ahead position.<br>• VOM on 200K ohms scale.<br>• Measure the resistance as decribed in the table below.<br>• Are all resistances within specification? | Yes ►<br>No ► | GO to C5 .<br>REPLACE steering angle sensor. |

| Terminal | Steering Wheel Position | Resistance Value |
|---|---|---|
| F–H | Turn the wheel a little at a time from the straight ahead position 180 degrees to the left. | Increase from approximately 25K ohms to approximately 200K ohms. |
| E–H | Straight ahead position. | 40–60K ohms. |

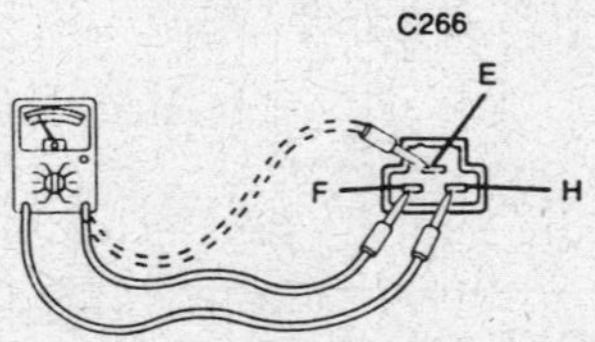

**Fig. 10 Pinpoint test C (Part 5 of 8). 1989 models**

| TEST STEP | RESULT ► | ACTION TO TAKE |
|---|---|---|
| **C5** CIRCUIT CONTINUITY CHECK | | |
| • Steering angle sensor (connector C266) disconnected.<br>• Disconnect VAPS control unit (connector C306).<br>• VOM on 200 ohms scale.<br>• Measure resistance between connectors C306 and C266 as follows:<br>1. C306 terminal I ("GN") and C266 terminal H ("GN")<br>2. C306 terminal J ("GN/W") and C266 terminal F ("GN/W")<br>3. C306 terminal H ("GN/Y") and C266 terminal E ("GN/Y").<br>• Are all resistance readings less than 5 ohms? | Yes ►<br>No ► | GO to C6 .<br>SERVICE wire in question for opens. |

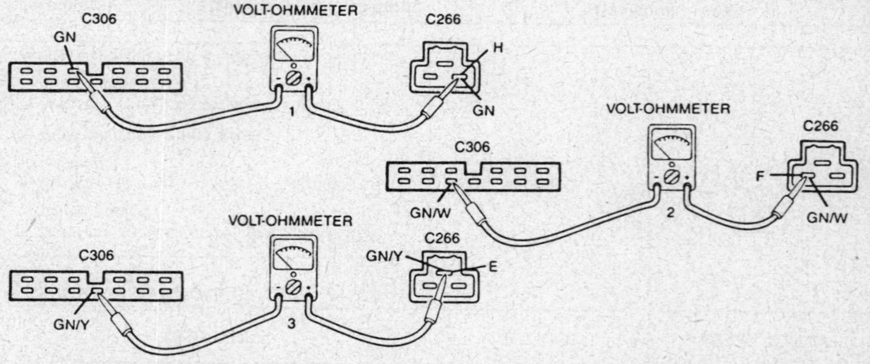

**Fig. 10 Pinpoint test C (Part 6 of 8). 1989 models**

| TEST STEP | RESULT ► | ACTION TO TAKE |
|---|---|---|
| **C6** SHORT TO VPWR CHECK | | |
| • Disconnect VAPS control unit (connector C306) and steering angle sensor (connector C266).<br>• Programmed Ride Control unit (connector C307) disconnected (if equipped).<br>• Key on; engine off.<br>• VOM on 20 volt scale.<br>• Measure voltage at connector C306 as follows:<br>Between terminal I ("GN") and ground<br>Between terminal J ("GN/W") and ground<br>Between terminal H ("GN/Y") and ground.<br>• Are any voltages above 0 volts?<br>See illustration in TEST STEP C7 | Yes ►<br>No ► | SERVICE wire in question for shorts to VPWR.<br>GO to C7 . |

**Fig. 10 Pinpoint test C (Part 7 of 8). 1989 models**

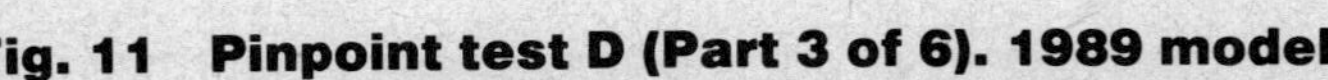

| TEST STEP | RESULT ► | ACTION TO TAKE |
|---|---|---|
| **C7** SHORT TO GROUND CHECK | | |
| • Key off.<br>• VAPS control unit (connector C306) disconnected.<br>• Programmed ride control unit (connector C307) disconnected (if equipped).<br>• VOM on 200K ohm scale.<br>• Measure resistance between connector C306 and ground as follows:<br>1. C306 terminal I ("GN") and ground<br>2. C306 terminal J ("GN/W") and ground<br>3. C306 terminal H ("GN/Y") and ground.<br>• Are all resistance readings greater than 10,000 ohms? | Yes ►<br>No ► | GO to Pinpoint Test Q.<br>SERVICE wire in question for shorts to ground. |

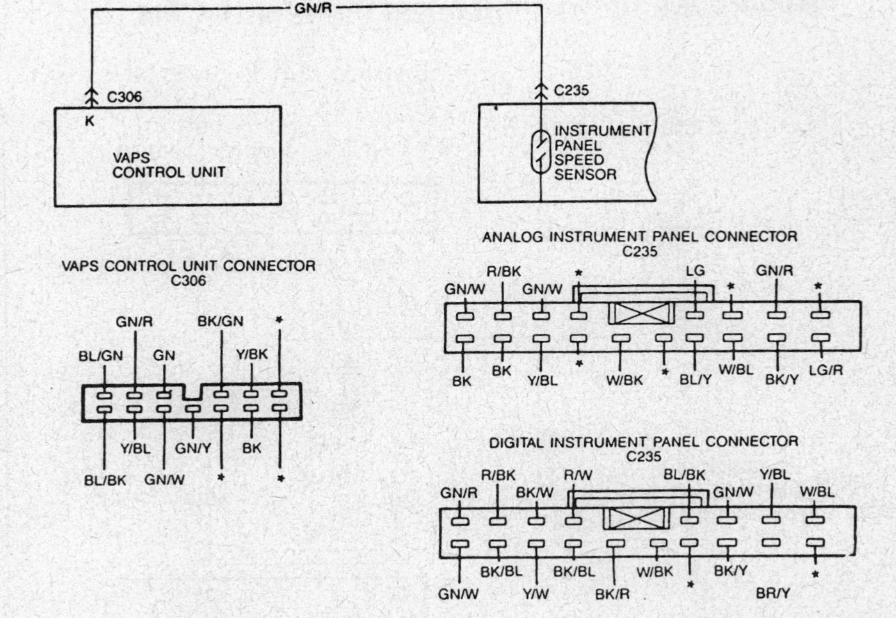


**Fig. 10 Pinpoint test C (Part 8 of 8). 1989 models**

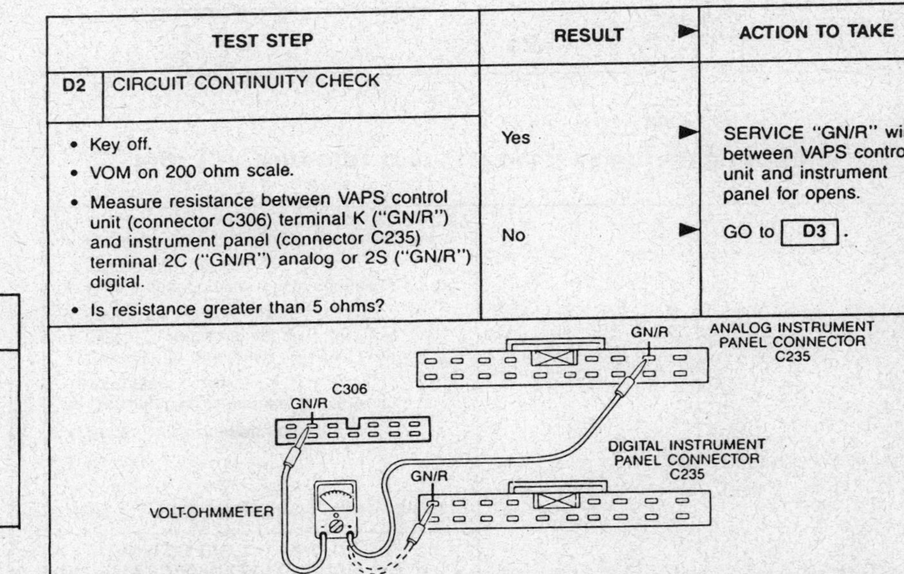


**Fig. 11 Pinpoint test D (Part 1 of 6). 1989 models**

| TEST STEP | RESULT ► | ACTION TO TAKE |
|---|---|---|
| **D1** SYSTEM INTEGRITY CHECK | | |
| • Visually inspect all wiring, wiring harness, connectors and components for evidence of overheating, insulation damage, looseness, shorting or other damage.<br>• Is there any cause for concern? | Yes ►<br>No ► | SERVICE as required.<br>GO to D2. |

**Fig. 11 Pinpoint test D (Part 2 of 6). 1989 models**

| TEST STEP | RESULT ► | ACTION TO TAKE |
|---|---|---|
| **D2** CIRCUIT CONTINUITY CHECK | | |
| • Key off.<br>• VOM on 200 ohm scale.<br>• Measure resistance between VAPS control unit (connector C306) terminal K ("GN/R") and instrument panel (connector C235) terminal 2C ("GN/R") analog or 2S ("GN/R") digital.<br>• Is resistance greater than 5 ohms? | Yes ►<br>No ► | SERVICE "GN/R" wire between VAPS control unit and instrument panel for opens.<br>GO to D3. |

ANALOG INSTRUMENT PANEL CONNECTOR C235 · GN/R · C306 · GN/R · DIGITAL INSTRUMENT PANEL CONNECTOR C235 · GN/R · VOLT-OHMMETER

**Fig. 11 Pinpoint test D (Part 3 of 6). 1989 models**

| TEST STEP | RESULT ► | ACTION TO TAKE |
|---|---|---|
| **D3** SHORT TO VPWR CHECK | | |
| • VAPS control unit (connector C306) and instrument cluster (connector C235) disconnected.<br>• Programmed ride control unit (connector C306) disconnected (if equipped).<br>• Key on; engine off.<br>• VOM on 20 volt scale.<br>• Measure voltage between VAPS control unit (connector C306) terminal K ("GN/R") and ground.<br>• Is voltage reading above 0 volts?<br>See illustration in TEST STEP D5 | Yes ►<br>No ► | SERVICE "GN/R" wire for short to VPWR.<br>(Analog Instrument Panel) GO to D4.<br>(Digital Instrument Panel) GO to Speed Sensor Diagnosis. |

**Fig. 11 Pinpoint test D (Part 4 of 6). 1989 models**

| TEST STEP | RESULT ► | ACTION TO TAKE |
|---|---|---|
| **D5** SHORT TO GROUND CHECK | | |
| • Disconnect VAPS control unit (connector C306) and instrument panel (connector C235).<br>• VOM on 200K ohm scale.<br>• Measure resistance between VAPS control unit (connector C306) terminal K ("GN/R") and ground.<br>• Is resistance less than 10,000 ohms? | Yes ►<br>No ► | SERVICE "GN/R" wire between VAPS control unit and instrument panel for shorts to ground.<br>GO to Pinpoint Test Q. |

VOLT-OHMMETER C306 GN/R

**Fig. 11 Pinpoint test D (Part 6 of 6). 1989 models**

| TEST STEP | RESULT ► | ACTION TO TAKE |
|---|---|---|
| **D4** SPEED SENSOR FUNCTION CHECK (ANALOG DISPLAY ONLY) | | |
| NOTE: This test is for Analog Display only.<br>• Key off.<br>• Remove instrumment cluster.<br>• Disconnect speedometer cable from instrument cluster.<br>• Connect an ohmmeter between terminal 2C ("GN/R") and terminal 2R ("BK") of connector C235.<br>• Rotate speedometer cable connector on the instrument cluster.<br>• Are there four continuity interruptions per rotation of the speedometer cable connector? | Yes ►<br>No ► | GO to D5.<br>REPLACE speed sensor. |

**Fig. 11 Pinpoint test D (Part 5 of 6). 1989 models**

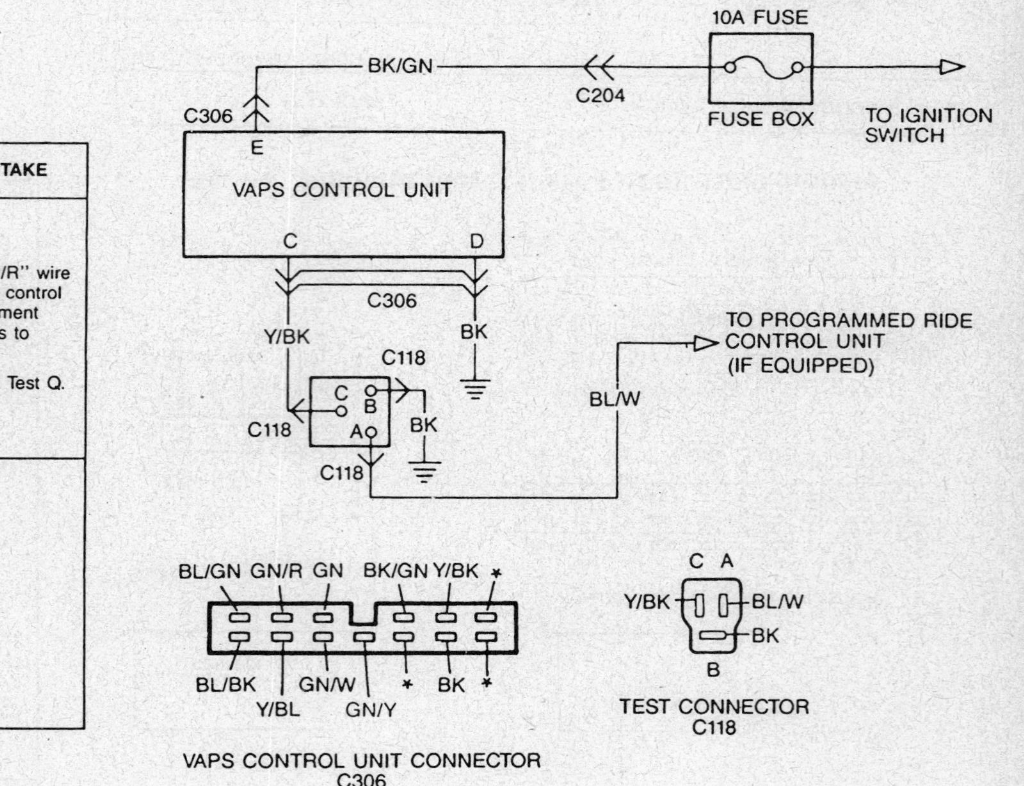


**Fig. 12 Pinpoint test Q (Part 1 of 8). 1989 models**

| TEST STEP | RESULT ► | ACTION TO TAKE |
|---|---|---|
| **Q1** SYSTEM INTEGRITY CHECK | | |
| • Visually inspect all wiring, wiring harness, connectors and components for evidence of overheating, insulation damage, looseness, shorting or other damage.<br>• Is there any cause for concern? | Yes ►<br>No ► | SERVICE as required.<br>GO to Q2 . |

**Fig. 12 Pinpoint test Q (Part 2 of 8). 1989 models**

| TEST STEP | RESULT ► | ACTION TO TAKE |
|---|---|---|
| **Q2** CHECK POWER TO VAPS CONTROL UNIT | | |
| • Disconnect VAPS control unit (connector C306).<br>• Key on; engine off.<br>• VOM on 20 volt scale.<br>• Measure voltage between terminal E ("BK/GN") and ground.<br>• Is voltage above 10 volts? | Yes ►<br>No ► | GO to Q3 .<br>REPLACE 10A fuse or REPAIR "BK/GN" wire between VAPS control unit and fuse box. |

**Fig. 12 Pinpoint test Q (Part 3 of 8). 1989 models**

| TEST STEP | RESULT ► | ACTION TO TAKE |
|---|---|---|
| **Q3** CHECK VAPS CONTROL UNIT GROUND | | |
| • Leave VAPS control unit (connector C306) disconnected.<br>• VOM on 200 ohm scale.<br>• Measure resistance between D ("BK") and ground.<br>• Is resistance less than 5 ohms? | Yes ►<br>No ► | GO to Q4 .<br>REPAIR "BK" wire between VAPS control unit and chassis ground for opens. |

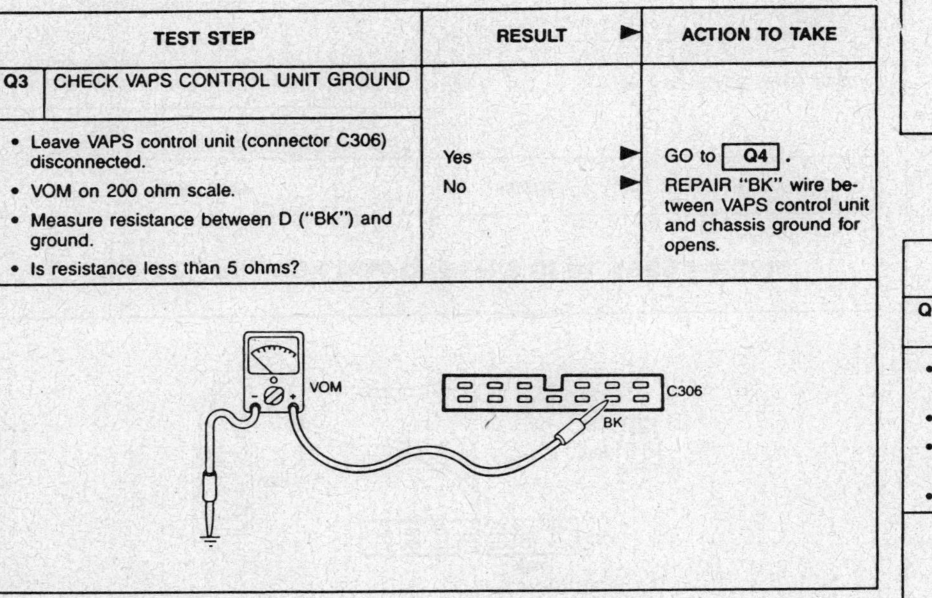


**Fig. 12 Pinpoint test Q (Part 4 of 8). 1989 models**

| TEST STEP | RESULT ► | ACTION TO TAKE |
|---|---|---|
| **Q4** CHECK TEST CONNECTOR GROUND | | |
| • Disconnect test connector C118 from mounting.<br>• VOM on 200 ohm scale.<br>• Measure resistance between terminal B ("BK") and ground.<br>• Is resistance reading less than 5 ohms? | Yes ►<br>No ► | GO to Q5 .<br>REPAIR "BK" wire between test connector and chassis ground. |

**Fig. 12 Pinpoint test Q (Part 5 of 8). 1989 models**

| TEST STEP | RESULT ▶ | ACTION TO TAKE |
|---|---|---|
| **Q5** CHECK CONTINUITY BETWEEN VAPS CONTROL UNIT AND TEST CONNECTOR | | |
| • Disconnect VAPS control unit (connector C306).<br>• VOM on 200 ohm scale.<br>• Measure resistance between connector C306 terminal C ("Y/BK") and test connector C118 terminal C ("Y/BK").<br>• Is resistance less than 5 ohms? | Yes ▶<br><br>No ▶ | GO to Q6 .<br><br>REPAIR ("Y/BK") wire between VAPS control unit and test connector for opens. |

VOM
Y/BK
C306
C
Y/BK
C118

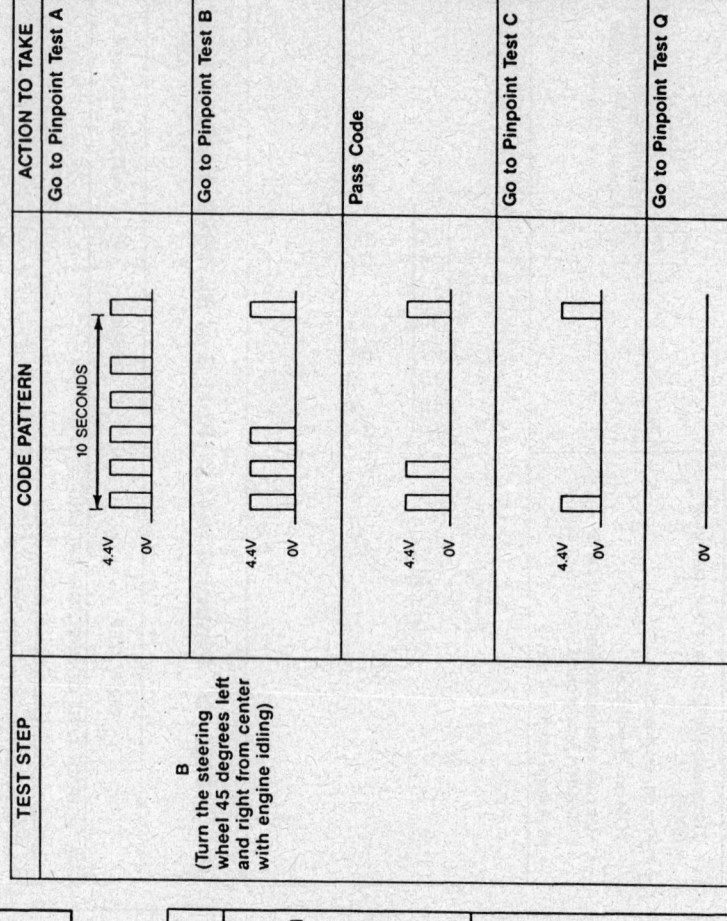

**Fig. 12 Pinpoint test Q (Part 6 of 8). 1989 models**

| TEST STEP | RESULT ▶ | ACTION TO TAKE |
|---|---|---|
| **Q7** CHECK TEST CONNECTOR FOR SHORT TO GROUND | | |
| • Leave VAPS control unit (connector C306) disconnected.<br>• Key off.<br>• VOM on 200K ohm scale.<br>• Measure resistance between connector C306 terminal C ("Y/BK") and ground.<br>• Is resistance greater than 10,000 ohms? | Yes ▶<br><br>No ▶ | REPLACE VAPS control unit.<br><br>REPAIR ("Y/BK") wire between VAPS control unit and test connector for short to ground. |

VOM
Y/BK
C306

**Fig. 12 Pinpoint test Q (Part 8 of 8). 1989 models**

| TEST STEP | RESULT ▶ | ACTION TO TAKE |
|---|---|---|
| **Q6** CHECK TEST CONNECTOR CIRCUIT FOR SHORT TO VPWR | | |
| • Leave VAPS control unit (connector C306) disconnected.<br>• Key on; engine off.<br>• VOM on 20 volt scale.<br>• Measure voltage between connector C306 terminal C ("Y/BK") and ground.<br>• Is voltage reading above 0 volts?<br>See illustration in TEST STEP Q7 | Yes ▶<br><br>No ▶ | REPAIR "Y/BK" wire between VAPS control unit and test connector for shorts to VPWR.<br><br>GO to Q7 . |

**Fig. 12 Pinpoint test Q (Part 7 of 8). 1989 models**

| TEST STEP | CODE PATTERN | ACTION TO TAKE |
|---|---|---|
| B<br>(Turn the steering wheel 45 degrees left and right from center with engine idling) | 10 SECONDS; 4.4V; 0V | Go to Pinpoint Test A |
| | 4.4V; 0V | Go to Pinpoint Test B |
| | 4.4V; 0V | Pass Code |
| | 4.4V; 0V | Go to Pinpoint Test C |
| | 0V | Go to Pinpoint Test Q |

**Fig. 13 Quick test (Step B). 1989 models**

| TEST STEP | CODE PATTERN | ACTION TO TAKE |
|---|---|---|
| C (Jack up the vehicle, and drive the front wheels at more than 10 km/h [6.2 mph]) | 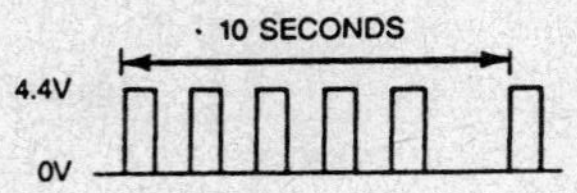 10 SECONDS 4.4V 0V | Go to Pinpoint Test A |
| | 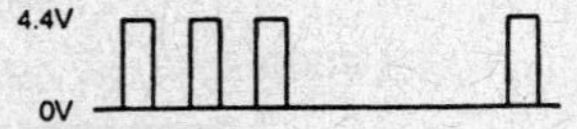 4.4V 0V | Go to Pinpoint Test B |
| | 4.4V 0V | Go to Pinpoint Test C |
| | 4.4V 0V | Go to Pinpoint Test D |
| |  4.4V 0V | Go to Pinpoint Test C<br>If fault is not found within steering angle sensor or circuit, Do Not proceed to Pinpoint Test Q as directed in STEP C7. |
| | 0V | Go to Pinpoint Test Q |

Fig. 14 Quick test (Step C). 1989 models

| TEST STEP | RESULT | ACTION TO TAKE |
|---|---|---|
| QT1 VISUAL CHECK | | |
| Check steering gear and linkage for damage, leaks, cracks, and proper mounting.<br>Check VAPS system wiring harness for proper connections, bent or broken pins, corrosion, loose wires, and proper routing.<br>Check the VAPS control unit, sensors, and solenoid for physical damage.<br>Are a VAPS system components ok?<br>**Note:** It may be necessary to disconnect or disassemble harness connector assemblies to do some of the inspections. Note pin locations before disassembly. | Yes ►<br>No ► | PROCEEED to QT2 vehicle preparation.<br>SERVICE fault(s) in system and then proceed to test step QT2 . |

Fig. 15 Quick test (Part 1 of 9). 1990–91 models

| TEST STEP | RESULT | ACTION TO TAKE |
|---|---|---|
| QT2 VISUAL PREPARATION | | |
| Perform all the following safety steps required to run VAPS Quick Test.<br>Apply the parking brake.<br>Place the shift lever firmly into the park position (neutral on MTX).<br>Turn off all electrical loads.<br>Radios<br>Lights<br>A/C-Heater Blower Fans, etc...<br>Have all safety steps been performed and all electrical loads turned off? | Yes ►<br>No ► | PROCEED to QT3 equipment hookup.<br>Personal safety and correct diagnostic results are dependant on test step QT2 .<br>Do not proceed with quick test if vehicle preparation cannot be performed. |

Fig. 15 Quick test (Part 2 of 9). 1990–91 models

| TEST STEP | RESULT | ACTION TO TAKE |
|---|---|---|
| **QT3 EQUIPMENT HOOKUP** | | |
| Turn ignition key off.<br>Set the VOM on a DC voltage range to read from 0 to 15 volts.<br>Connect the VOM positive lead to the Y/BK and negative lead to the BK terminals of the suspension test connector. | Yes ► | PROCEED to QT4. Key On Engine Running Test. |
| | No ► | RE-ATTEMPT step QT3 Equipment hookup. |
| Y/BK BL/W BK | | |
| **Note:** For correct reading of service codes use only an analog VOM.<br>Is analog VOM hooked up properly? | | |

**Fig. 15 Quick test (Part 3 of 9). 1990–91 models**

| TEST STEP | RESULT | ACTION TO TAKE |
|---|---|---|
| **QT5 KEY ON ENGINE RUNNING TEST** | | |
| Turn ignition key off to reset processor.<br>Set steering wheel in the straight ahead position.<br>Key on, Engine running at idle.<br>Turn VOM on.<br>Turn the steering wheel 45 degrees left and right from center.<br>Record any service codes. | CODE 1 | PERFORM Pinpoint Test C. |
| | CODE 2 | Indicates a pass code. PROCEED to QT6. |
| | CODE 3 | PERFORM Pinpoint Test B. |
| | CODE 5 | PERFORM Pinpoint Test A. |
| | NO CODES | PERFORM Pinpoint Test Q. |
| | CODE UNLISTED | PERFORM Pinpoint Test Q. |

**Fig. 15 Quick test (Part 5 of 9). 1990–91 models**

| TEST STEP | RESULT | ACTION TO TAKE |
|---|---|---|
| **QT4 KEY ON ENGINE RUNNING** | | |
| Turn ignition key off.<br>Verify that the vehicle has been properly prepared per Quick Test steps QT2 and QT3.<br>Key on, Engine running at idle.<br>Set steering wheel in the straight ahead position.<br>Activate self-test by turning analog VOM on.<br>Record any service codes.<br>**Note:** When a service code is reported on the analog VOM, it will represent itself as a pulsing or sweeping movement of the voltmeter's needle across the dial face. Code 1 will be represented by one pulse and code 2 by two pulses and so on. | CODE 1 | Indicates a pass code. PROCEED to QT5. |
| | CODE 2 | PERFORM Pinpoint Test C. |
| | CODE 3 | PERFORM Pinpoint Test B. |
| | CODE 5 | PERFORM Pinpoint Test A. |
| | NO CODES | PERFORM Pinpoint Test Q. |
| | CODE UNLISTED | PERFORM Pinpoint Test Q. |

**Fig. 15 Quick test (Part 4 of 9). 1990–91 models**

| TEST STEP | RESULT | ACTION TO TAKE |
|---|---|---|
| **QT6 KEY ON ENGINE RUNNING TEST** | | |
| Turn ignition key to reset processor.<br>Set steering wheel in the straight ahead position.<br>Key on, Engine running at idle.<br>Turn VOM on.<br>Hoist vehicle and rotate front wheels at above 10km/h (6.2 MPH).<br>Record any service codes. | CODE 1 | PERFORM Pinpoint Test D. |
| | CODE 2 | PERFORM Pinpoint Test C. |
| | CODE 3 | PERFORM Pinpoint Test B. |
| | CODE 5 | PERFROM Pinpoint Test A. |
| | CONSTANT 4.4 VOLTS | Pass Code. PERFORM Pinpoint Test C to verify steering angle sensor VREF and SIGRTN circuits are ok. For intermittent symptoms PROCEED to QT7. |
| | NO CODES | PERFORM Pinpoint Test Q. |
| | CODE UNLISTED | PERFORM Pinpoint Test Q. |

**Fig. 15 Quick test (Part 6 of 9). 1990–91 models**

| TEST STEP | RESULT | ACTION TO TAKE |
|---|---|---|
| **QT7** CONTINUOUS TEST | | |
| Verify that a pass code was indicated in all steps of the Key On Engine Running Test. | CODE 1 | Indicates a pass code. PROCEED to QT8. |
| Verify that the vehicle has been properly prepared per Quick Test steps QT2 and QT3. | CODE 2 | PERFORM Pinpoint Test C. |
| Key on, Engine running at idle.<br>Activate self-test by turning analog VOM on. | CODE 3 | PERFORM Pinpoint Test B. |
| While steering wheel is in the straight ahead position, tap, move and wiggle VAPS components and harness while observing for any service code indentification on the VOM. | CODE 5 | PERFORM Pinpoint Test A. |
| | NO CODES | PERFORM Pinpoint Test Q. |
| Record any service codes. | CODE UNLISTED | PERFORM Pinpoint Test Q. |

**Fig. 15 Quick test (Part 7 of 9). 1990–91 models**

| TEST STEP | RESULT | ACTION TO TAKE |
|---|---|---|
| **QT8** CONTINUOUS TEST | | |
| Turn ignition key off to reset processor. | CODE 1 | PERFORM Pinpoint Test C. |
| Set steering wheel in the straignt ahead position.<br>Key on, Engine running at idle. | CODE 2 | Indicates a pass code. PROCEED to QT9. |
| Turn VOM on. | CODE 3 | PERFORM Pinpoint Test B. |
| While turning the steering wheel 45 degrees left and right from center, tap, move and wiggle VAPS components and harness while observing for any service code indication on the VOM. | CODE 5 | PERFORM Pinpoint Test A. |
| | NO CODES | PERFORM Pinpoint Test Q. |
| Record any Service Codes. | CODE UNLISTED | PERFORM Pinpoint Test Q. |

**Fig. 15 Quick test (Part 8 of 9). 1990–91 models**

| TEST STEP | RESULT | ACTION TO TAKE |
|---|---|---|
| **QT9** CONTINUOUS TEST | | |
| Turn ignition key off to reset processor. | CODE 1 | PERFORM Pinpoint Test D. |
| Set steering wheel in the straignt ahead position. | CODE 2 | PEFORM Pinpoint Test C. |
| Key on, Engine running at idle.<br>Turn VOM on. | CODE 3 | PERFORM Pinpoint Test B. |
| Hoist vehicle. | CODE 5 | PERFORM Pinpoint Test A. |
| While rotating front wheels at above 10km/h (6.2MPH), tap, move and wiggle VAPS components and harness while observing for any service code indication on the VOM. | CONSTANT 4.4 VOLTS | Indicates a pass code. PERFORM Pinpoint Test Q to verify that the VAPS control module and circuitry are OK. |
| Record any service codes. | NO CODES | PERFORM Pinpoint Test Q. |
| | CODE UNLISTED | PERFORM Pinpoint Test Q. |

**Fig. 15 Quick test (Part 9 of 9). 1990–91 models**

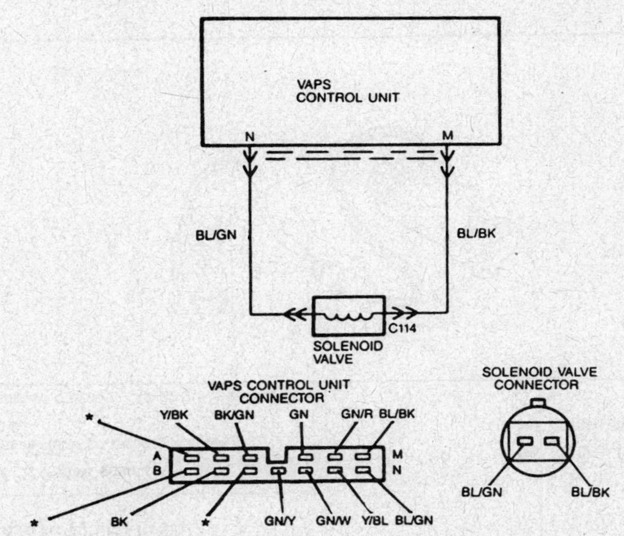


**Fig. 16 Pinpoint test A (Part 1 of 4). 1990–91 models**

| TEST STEP | RESULT ► | ACTION TO TAKE |
|---|---|---|
| **A1** SYSTEM INTEGRITY CHECK | | |
| • Visually inspect all wiring, wiring harness, connectors and components for evidence of overheating, insulation damage, looseness, shorting or other damage.<br>• Is there any cause for concern? | Yes ►<br>No ► | SERVICE as required.<br>GO to A2 |

| TEST STEP | RESULT ► | ACTION TO TAKE |
|---|---|---|
| **A2** SOLENOID FUNCTION CHECK | | |
| • Disconnect solenoid valve connector.<br>• Apply 12 volts and ground to terminals as shown and listen for actuation sound.<br>• Is clicking sound heard when applying 12 volts? | Yes ►<br>No ► | GO to A3 .<br>REPLACE solenoid. |



**Fig. 16 Pinpoint test A (Part 2 of 4). 1990–91 models**

| TEST STEP | RESULT ► | ACTION TO TAKE |
|---|---|---|
| **A3** SOLENOID RESISTANCE CHECK | | |
| • VOM on 200 ohm scale.<br>• Measure resistance between solenoid terminals.<br>• Is resistance between 3.4 and 6.9 ohms? | Yes ►<br>No ► | GO to A4 .<br>REPLACE solenoid. |

| TEST STEP | RESULT ► | ACTION TO TAKE |
|---|---|---|
| **A4** SOLENOID CIRCUIT RESISTANCE CHECK | | |
| • Disconnect VAPS control unit connector and solenoid connector.<br>• Key off.<br>• VOM on 200 ohm scale.<br>• Measure resistance between the following terminals.<br>1 Between VAPS Control Unit connector terminal M ("BL/BK") and solenoid valve connector "BL/BK" wire.<br>2 Between VAPS Control Unit connector terminal N ("BL/GN") and solenoid valve connector "BL/GN" wire.<br>• Are resistances less than 5 ohms? | Yes ►<br>No ► | GO to A5 .<br>REPAIR wire in question for opens. |

**Fig. 16 Pinpoint test A (Part 3 of 4). 1990–91 models**

| TEST STEP | RESULT ► | ACTION TO TAKE |
|---|---|---|
| **A5** SOLENOID CIRCUIT SHORT TO GROUND AND VPWR CHECK | | |
| • Leave VAPS control unit connector and solenoid connector disconnected.<br>• Disconnect battery.<br>• VOM on 200K ohm scale.<br>• Measure resistance as follows:<br>1 Between VAPS control unit connector terminal M ("BL/BK") and chassis ground.<br>2 Between VAPS Control Unit terminal M ("BL/BK") and terminal E ("BK/GN").<br>3 Between VAPS Control Unit connector terminal N ("BL/GN") and chassis ground.<br>4 Between VAPS Control Unit connector terminal N ("BL/GN") and terminal E ("BK/GN").<br>• Are all resistances greater than 10,000 ohms? | Yes ►<br>No ► | GO to Pinpoint Test Q.<br>REPAIR wires in question between VAPS control unit and solenoid for shorts to ground or VPWR. |

**Fig. 16 Pinpoint test A (Part 4 of 4). 1990–91 models**

| TEST STEP | RESULT ► | ACTION TO TAKE |
|---|---|---|
| **B1** SYSTEM INTEGRITY CHECK | | |
| • Visually inspect all wiring, wiring harness, connectors and components for evidence of overheating, insulation damage, looseness, shorting or other damage.<br>• Is there any cause for concern? | Yes ►<br>No ► | SERVICE as required.<br>GO to B2 . |

**Fig. 17 Pinpoint test B (Part 2 of 3). 1990–91 models**

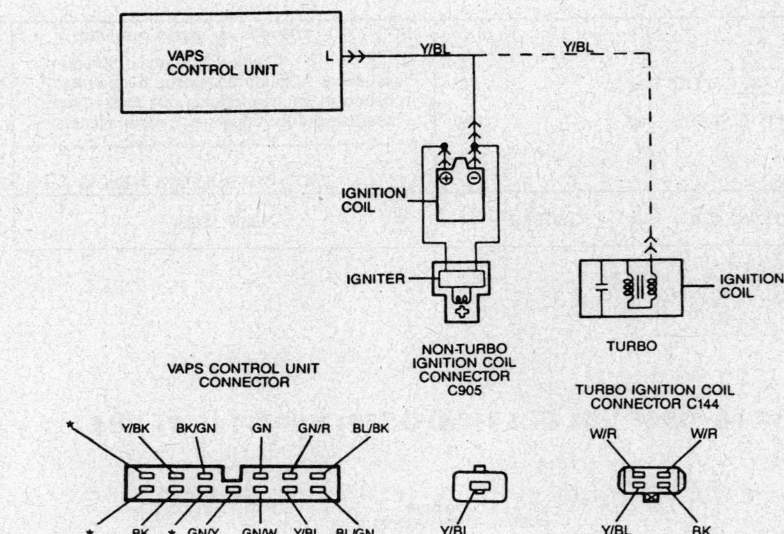


**Fig. 17 Pinpoint test B (Part 1 of 3). 1990–91 models**

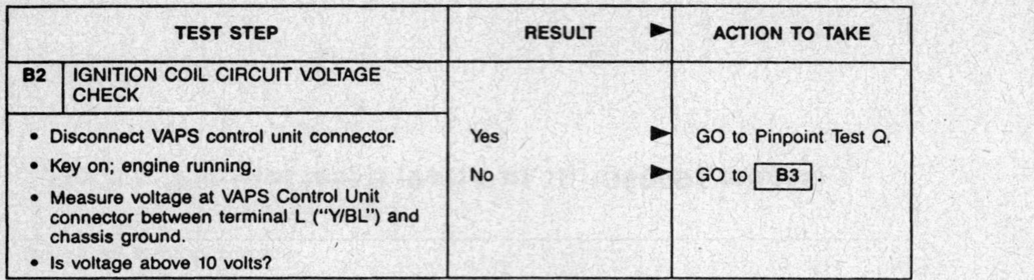

| TEST STEP | RESULT ► | ACTION TO TAKE |
|---|---|---|
| **B2** IGNITION COIL CIRCUIT VOLTAGE CHECK | | |
| • Disconnect VAPS control unit connector.<br>• Key on; engine running.<br>• Measure voltage at VAPS Control Unit connector between terminal L ("Y/BL") and chassis ground.<br>• Is voltage above 10 volts? | Yes ►<br>No ► | GO to Pinpoint Test Q.<br>GO to B3 . |

| TEST STEP | RESULT ► | ACTION TO TAKE |
|---|---|---|
| **B3** CIRCUIT CONTINUITY CHECK | | |
| • Leave VAPS control unit connector disconnected.<br>• Disconnect ignition coil connector.<br>• VOM on 200 ohm scale.<br>• Measure resistance between ignition coil ("Y/BL") wire and VAPS Control Unit connector terminal L ("Y/BL").<br>• Is resistance less than 5 ohms? | Yes ►<br>No ► | GO to B4 .<br>SERVICE ("Y/BL") wire between ignition coil and VAPS control unit for opens. |

| TEST STEP | RESULT ► | ACTION TO TAKE |
|---|---|---|
| **B4** CIRCUIT SHORT TO GROUND AND VPWR CHECK | | |
| • Leave VAPS control unit connector disconnected.<br>• Disconnect battery.<br>• VOM on 200K ohm scale.<br>• Measure resistance between VAPS Control Unit connector terminal L ("Y/BL") and chassis ground and between terminal L ("Y/BL") and terminal E ("BK/GN").<br>• Are resistances greater than 10,000 ohms? | Yes ►<br>No ► | GO to Pinpoint Test Q.<br>REPAIR ("Y/BL") wire between ignition coil and VAPS control unit for short to ground or VPWR. |

**Fig. 17 Pinpoint test B (Part 3 of 3). 1990–91 models**

**Fig. 18 Pinpoint test C (Part 1 of 12). 1990–91 models**

| TEST STEP | RESULT ► | ACTION TO TAKE |
|---|---|---|
| **C1** SYSTEM INTEGRITY CHECK | | |
| • Visually inspect all wiring, wiring harness, connectors and components for evidence of overheating, insulation damage, looseness, shorting or other damage.<br>• Is there any cause for concern? | Yes ►<br>No ► | SERVICE as required.<br>GO to C2 . |

**Fig. 18 Pinpoint test C (Part 2 of 12). 1990–91 models**

| TEST STEP | RESULT ► | ACTION TO TAKE |
|---|---|---|
| **C2** STEERING ANGLE SENSOR RESISTANCE CHECK | | |
| • Key off.<br>• Remove steering column cover and disconnect steering angle sensor connector.<br>• Set the steering wheel so wheels are in a straight ahead position.<br>• Measure the resistance between the following steering angle sensor terminals:<br>**Terminal** — **Resistance**<br>1. ("GN") – ("GN/W") — 20–30K ohms<br>2. ("GN") – ("GN/Y") — 40–60K ohms<br>3. ("GN/Y") – ("GN/W") — 20–30K ohms<br>• Are all resistances within specification? | Yes ►<br>No ► | GO to C3.<br>REPLACE steering angle sensor. |

1 GN GN/W 2 GN GN/Y 3 GN/Y GN/W

**Fig. 18 Pinpoint test C (Part 3 of 12). 1990 models**

| TEST STEP | RESULT ► | ACTION TO TAKE |
|---|---|---|
| **C3** STEERING ANGLE SENSOR CHECK | | |
| • Steering angle sensor connector disconnected.<br>• Set the steering wheel in the straight ahead position.<br>• VOM on 200K ohms scale.<br>• Measure the resistance as decribed in the table below.<br>• Are all resistances within specification? | Yes ►<br>No ► | GO to C4.<br>REPLACE steering angle sensor. |

| Terminal | Steering Wheel Position | Resistance Value |
|---|---|---|
| GN-GN/W | Turn the wheel a little at a time from the straight ahead position 180 degrees to the right. | Increase from approximately 25K ohms to approximately 50K ohms. |
| | Straight ahead position. | 20–30K ohms. |

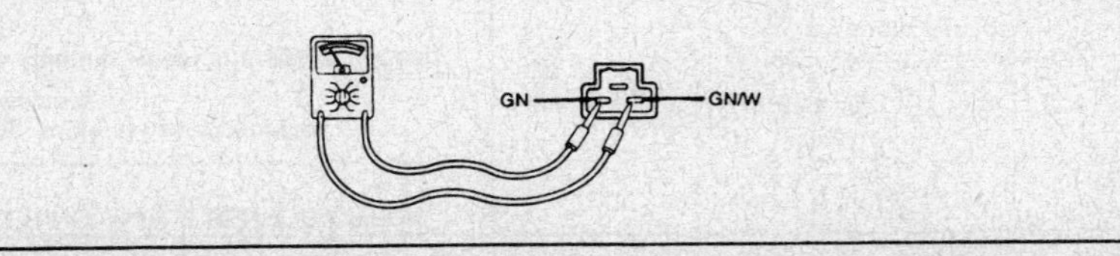


**Fig. 18 Pinpoint test C (Part 5 of 12). 1990 models**

| TEST STEP | RESULT ► | ACTION TO TAKE |
|---|---|---|
| **C2** STEERING ANGLE SENSOR RESISTANCE CHECK | | |
| • Key off.<br>• Remove steering column cover and disconnect steering angle sensor connector.<br>• Set the steering wheel so wheels are in a straight ahead position.<br>• Measure the resistance between the following steering angle sensor terminals with the VOM meter set on the 200K scale:<br>**Terminal** — **Resistance**<br>1. ("GN") – ("GN/W") — 0–15K ohms<br>2. ("GN") – ("GN/Y") — 40–60K ohms<br>3. ("GN/Y") – ("GN/W") — 30–50K ohms<br>• Are all resistances within specification? | Yes ►<br>No ► | GO to C3.<br>REPLACE steering angle sensor. |

1 GN GN/W 2 GN GN/Y 3 GN/Y GN/W

**Fig. 18 Pinpoint Test C (Part 4 of 12). 1991 models**

| TEST STEP | RESULT ► | ACTION TO TAKE |
|---|---|---|
| **C3** STEERING ANGLE SENSOR CHECK | | |
| • Steering angle sensor connector disconnected.<br>• Set the steering wheel in the straight ahead position.<br>• VOM on 200K ohms scale.<br>• Measure the resistance as decribed in the table below.<br>• Are all resistances within specification? | Yes ►<br>No ► | GO to C4.<br>REPLACE steering angle sensor. |

| Terminal | Steering Wheel Position | Resistance Value |
|---|---|---|
| GN-GN/W | Turn the wheel a little at a time from the straight ahead position 180 degrees to the right. | Increases approximately 20K ohms from the straight ahead value. |
| GN-GN/W | Straight ahead position. | 0–15K ohms. |

GN GN/W

**Fig. 18 Pinpoint Test C (Part 6 of 12). 1991 models**

| TEST STEP | RESULT ► | ACTION TO TAKE |
|---|---|---|
| **C4 STEERING ANGLE SENSOR CHECK** | | |
| • Steering angle sensor connector disconnected.<br>• Set the steering wheel in a straight ahead position.<br>• VOM on 200K ohms scale.<br>• Measure the resistance as decribed in the table below.<br>• Are all resistances within specification? | Yes ►<br>No ► | GO to C5 .<br>REPLACE steering angle sensor. |

| Terminal | Steering Wheel Position | Resistance Value |
|---|---|---|
| GN–GN/W | Turn the wheel a little at a time from the straight ahead position 180 degrees to the left. | Increase from approximately 25K ohms to approximately 200K ohms. |
| GN/Y–GN/W | Straight ahead position. | 40–60K ohms. |



Fig. 18 Pinpoint test C (Part 7 of 12). 1990 models

| TEST STEP | RESULT ► | ACTION TO TAKE |
|---|---|---|
| **C4 STEERING ANGLE SENSOR CHECK** | | |
| • Steering angle sensor connector disconnected.<br>• Set the steering wheel in a straight ahead position.<br>• VOM on 200K ohms scale.<br>• Measure the resistance as decribed in the table below.<br>• At the straight ahead position, observe the ohmmeter reading. This is your base reading. As you turn the wheel to your left, the reading will decrease to O ohms. The reading will then change to 45K ohms and continue to decrease from that value.<br>• Are all resistances within specification? | Yes ►<br>No ► | GO to C5 .<br>REPLACE steering angle sensor. |

| Terminal | Steering Wheel Position | Resistance Value |
|---|---|---|
| GN–GN/W | Turn the wheel a little at a time from the straight ahead position 180 degrees to the left. | Decreases approximately 20K ohms from the straight ahead value. |
| GN–GN/W | Straight ahead position. | 0–15K ohms. |



Fig. 18 Pinpoint Test C (Part 8 of 12). 1991 models

| TEST STEP | RESULT ► | ACTION TO TAKE |
|---|---|---|
| **C5 CIRCUIT CONTINUITY CHECK** | | |
| • Steering angle sensor connector disconnected.<br>• Disconnect VAPS control unit connector.<br>• VOM on 200 ohms scale.<br>• Measure resistance between connectors as follows:<br>**VAPS Control Unit Steering Angle Sensor**<br>Terminal I GN Wire — GN Wire<br>Terminal J GN/W Wire — GN/W Wire<br>Terminal H GN/Y Wire — GN/Y Wire<br>• Are all resistance readings less than 5 ohms? | Yes ►<br>No ► | GO to C6 .<br>SERVICE wire in question for opens. |

Fig. 18 Pinpoint test C (Part 9 of 12). 1990–91 models

| TEST STEP | RESULT ► | ACTION TO TAKE |
|---|---|---|
| **C6 SHORT TO VPWR CHECK** | | |
| • Disconnect VAPS control unit connector and steering angle sensor connector.<br>• Programmed Ride Control unit connector disconnected (if equipped).<br>• Key on; engine off.<br>• VOM on 20 volt scale.<br>• Measure voltage at VAPS control unit as follows:<br>Between terminal I ("GN") and ground.<br>Between terminal J ("GN/W") and ground.<br>Between terminal H ("GN/Y") and ground.<br>• Are any voltages above 0 volts? | Yes ►<br>No ► | SERVICE wire in question for shorts to VPWR.<br>GO to C7 . |

Fig. 18 Pinpoint test C (Part 10 of 12). 1990 models

| TEST STEP | RESULT ► | ACTION TO TAKE |
|---|---|---|
| **C6** SHORT TO VPWR CHECK | | |
| • Disconnect VAPS control unit connector and steering angle sensor connector.<br>• Programmed Ride Control unit connector disconnected (if equipped).<br>• Key on; engine off.<br>• VOM on 20 volt scale.<br>• Measure voltage at VAPS control unit as follows:<br>Between terminal I ("GN") and ground.<br>Between terminal J ("GN/W") and ground.<br>Between terminal H ("GN/Y") and ground.<br>• Do all measurements read 0 volts? | Yes ►<br><br>No ► | GO to C7<br><br>SERVICE wire in question for shorts to VPWR. |

**Fig. 18 Pinpoint Test C (Part 11 of 12). 1991 models**

| TEST STEP | RESULT ► | ACTION TO TAKE |
|---|---|---|
| **C7** SHORT TO GROUND CHECK | | |
| • Key off.<br>• VAPS control unit connector disconnected.<br>• Programmed ride control unit connector disconnected (if equipped).<br>• VOM on 200K ohm scale.<br>• Measure resistance between VAPS control unit connector and ground as follows:<br>1. Terminal I ("GN") and ground.<br>2. Terminal J ("GN/W") and ground.<br>3. Terminal H ("GN/Y") and ground.<br>• Are all resistance readings greater than 10,000 ohms? | Yes ►<br>No ► | GO to Pinpoint Test Q.<br>SERVICE wire in question for shorts to ground. |

**Fig. 18 Pinpoint test C (Part 12 of 12). 1990–91 models**

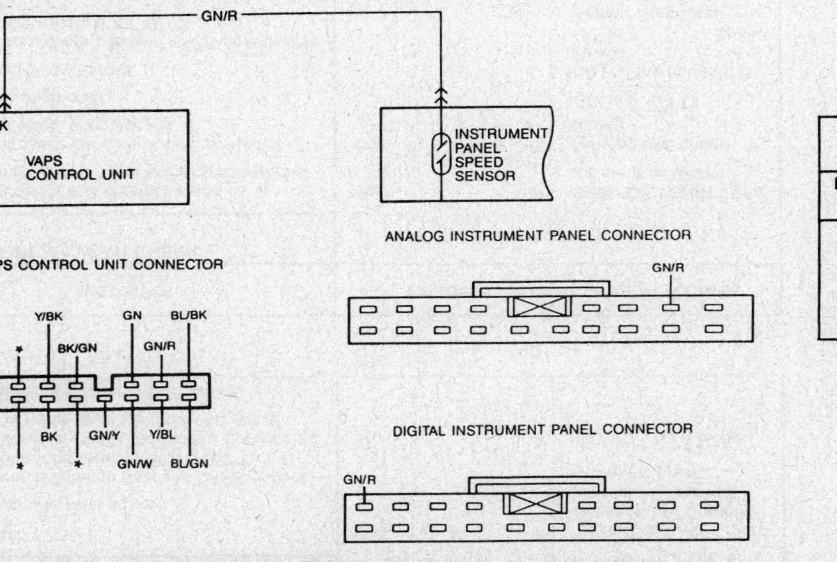


**Fig. 19 Pinpoint test D (Part 1 of 6). 1990–91 models**

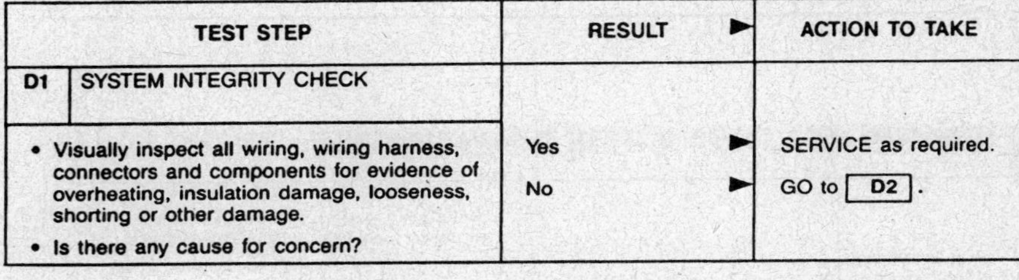

| TEST STEP | RESULT ► | ACTION TO TAKE |
|---|---|---|
| **D1** SYSTEM INTEGRITY CHECK | | |
| • Visually inspect all wiring, wiring harness, connectors and components for evidence of overheating, insulation damage, looseness, shorting or other damage.<br>• Is there any cause for concern? | Yes ►<br>No ► | SERVICE as required.<br>GO to D2 . |

**Fig. 19 Pinpoint test D (Part 2 of 6). 1990 models**

| TEST STEP | RESULT ▶ | ACTION TO TAKE |
|---|---|---|
| **D2 CIRCUIT CONTINUITY CHECK** | | |
| • Key off.<br>• VOM on 200 ohm scale.<br>• Measure resistance between VAPS control unit connector terminal K ("GN/R") and instrument panel connector terminal 2C ("GN/R") analog or 2S ("GN/R") digital.<br>• Is resistance greater than 5 ohms? | Yes ▶<br>No ▶ | SERVICE "GN/R" wire between VAPS control unit and instrument panel for opens.<br>GO to D3. |

| TEST STEP | RESULT ▶ | ACTION TO TAKE |
|---|---|---|
| **D3 SHORT TO VPWR CHECK** | | |
| • VAPS control unit connector and instrument cluster connector disconnected.<br>• Programmed ride control unit connector disconnected (if equipped).<br>• Key on; engine off.<br>• VOM on 20 volt scale.<br>• Measure voltage between VAPS control unit connector terminal K ("GN/R") and ground.<br>• Is voltage reading above 0 volts? | Yes ▶<br>No ▶ | SERVICE "GN/R" wire for short to VPWR.<br>(Analog Instrument Panel) GO to D4.<br>(Digital Instrument Panel) GO to Speed Sensor Diagnosis. |

**Fig. 19 Pinpoint test D (Part 3 of 6). 1990 models**

| TEST STEP | RESULT ▶ | ACTION TO TAKE |
|---|---|---|
| **D2 CIRCUIT CONTINUITY CHECK** | | |
| • Key OFF.<br>• VOM on 200 ohm scale.<br>• Measure resistance between VAPS control unit connector terminal K ("GN/R") and instrument panel connector terminal 2C ("GN/R") analog or 2S ("GN/R") digital.<br>• Is resistance greater than than 5 ohms? | Yes ▶<br>No ▶ | SERVICE "GN/R" wire between VAPS control unit and instrument panel for opens.<br>GO to D3. |
| **D3 SHORT TO VPWR CHECK** | | |
| • VAPS control unit connector and instrument cluster connector disconnected.<br>• Programmed ride control unit connector disconnected (if equipped).<br>• Key ON; engine OFF.<br>• VOM on 20 volt scale.<br>• Measure voltage between VAPS control unit connector terminal K ("GN/R") and ground.<br>• Is voltage reading below 6 volts? | Yes ▶<br>No ▶ | (Analog Instrument Panel) GO to D4.<br>(Digital Instrument Panel) Speed Sensor Diagnosis.<br>SERVICE "GN/R" wire for short to VPWR. |

**Fig. 19 Pinpoint test D (Part 4 of 6). 1991 models**

| TEST STEP | RESULT ▶ | ACTION TO TAKE |
|---|---|---|
| **D4 SPEED SENSOR FUNCTION CHECK (ANALOG DISPLAY ONLY)** | | |
| NOTE: This test is for Analog Display only.<br>• Key off.<br>• Remove instrumment cluster.<br>• Disconnect speedometer cable from instrument cluster.<br>• Connect an ohmmeter between terminal 2C ("GN/R") and terminal 2R ("BK") of cluster connector.<br>• Rotate speedometer cable connector on the instrument cluster.<br>• Are there four continuity interruptions per rotation of the speedometer cable connector? | Yes ▶<br>No ▶ | GO to D5.<br>REPLACE speed sensor. |

| TEST STEP | RESULT ▶ | ACTION TO TAKE |
|---|---|---|
| **D5 SHORT TO GROUND CHECK** | | |
| • Disconnect VAPS control unit connector and instrument panel connector.<br>• VOM on 200K ohm scale.<br>• Measure resistance between VAPS control unit connector terminal K ("GN/R") and ground.<br>• Is resistance less than 10,000 ohms? | Yes ▶<br>No ▶ | SERVICE "GN/R" wire between VAPS control unit and instrument panel for shorts to ground.<br>GO to Pinpoint Test Q. |

**Fig. 19 Pinpoint test D (Part 5 of 6). 1990 models**

| TEST STEP | RESULT ▶ | ACTION TO TAKE |
|---|---|---|
| **D4 SPEED SENSOR FUNCTION CHECK (ANALOG DISPLAY ONLY)** | | |
| NOTE: This test is for Analog Display only.<br>• Key OFF.<br>• Remove instrument cluster.<br>• Disconnect speedometer cable from instrument cluster.<br>• Connect an ohmmeter between terminal 2C ("GN/R") and terminal 2R ("BK") of cluster connector.<br>• Rotate speedometer cable connector on the instrument cluster.<br>• Are there four continuity interruptions per rotation of the speedometer cable connector? | Yes ▶<br>No ▶ | GO to D5.<br>REPLACE speed sensor. |
| **D5 SHORT TO GROUND CHECK** | | |
| • Disconnect VAPS control unit connector and instrument panel connector.<br>• VOM on 200K ohm scale.<br>• Measure resistance between VAPS control unit connector terminal K ("GN/R") and ground.<br>• Is resistance greater than 10,000 ohm? | Yes ▶<br>No ▶ | GO to Pinpoint Test Q.<br>SERVICE "GN/R" wire between VAPS control unit and instrument panel for shorts to ground. |

**Fig. 19 Pinpoint test D (Part 6 of 6). 1991 models**

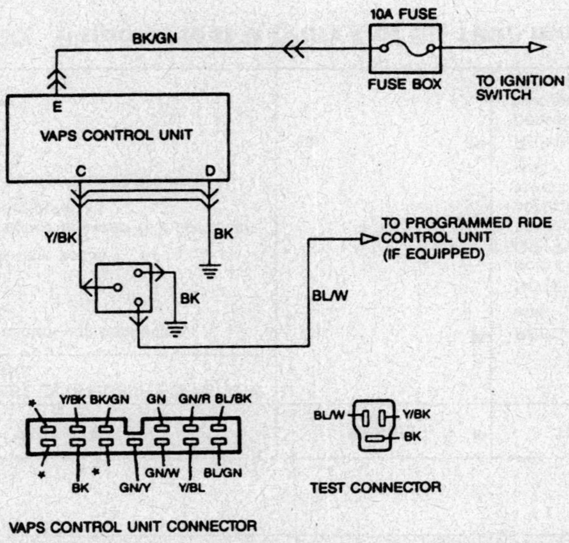

BK/GN
10A FUSE
FUSE BOX
TO IGNITION SWITCH
E
VAPS CONTROL UNIT
C
D
Y/BK
BK
BK
TO PROGRAMMED RIDE CONTROL UNIT (IF EQUIPPED)
BL/W
Y/BK BK/GN GN GN/R BL/BK
BK GN/Y GN/W Y/BL BL/GN
VAPS CONTROL UNIT CONNECTOR
BL/W Y/BK BK
TEST CONNECTOR

**Fig. 20 Pinpoint test Q (Part 1 of 5). 1990–91 models**

| TEST STEP | RESULT ► | ACTION TO TAKE |
|---|---|---|
| **Q1** SYSTEM INTEGRITY CHECK | | |
| • Visually inspect all wiring, wiring harness, connectors and components for evidence of overheating, insulation damage, looseness, shorting or other damage.<br>• Is there any cause for concern? | Yes ►<br>No ► | SERVICE as required.<br>GO to Q2. |

**Fig. 20 Pinpoint test Q (Part 2 of 5). 1990–91 models**

| TEST STEP | RESULT ► | ACTION TO TAKE |
|---|---|---|
| **Q2** CHECK POWER TO VAPS CONTROL UNIT | | |
| • Disconnect VAPS control unit connector.<br>• Key on; engine off.<br>• VOM on 20 volt scale.<br>• Measure voltage between terminal E ("BK/GN") and ground.<br>• Is voltage above 10 volts? | Yes ►<br>No ► | GO to Q3.<br>REPLACE 10A fuse or REPAIR "BK/GN" wire between VAPS control unit and fuse box. |

| TEST STEP | RESULT ► | ACTION TO TAKE |
|---|---|---|
| **Q3** CHECK VAPS CONTROL UNIT GROUND | | |
| • Leave VAPS control unit connector disconnected.<br>• VOM on 200 ohm scale.<br>• Measure resistance between D ("BK") and ground.<br>• Is resistance less than 5 ohms? | Yes ►<br>No ► | GO to Q4.<br>REPAIR "BK" wire between VAPS control unit and chassis ground for opens. |

| TEST STEP | RESULT ► | ACTION TO TAKE |
|---|---|---|
| **Q4** CHECK TEST CONNECTOR GROUND | | |
| • Disconnect test connector from mounting.<br>• VOM on 200 ohm scale.<br>• Measure resistance between BK wire and ground.<br>• Is resistance reading less than 5 ohms? | Yes ►<br>No ► | GO to Q5.<br>REPAIR "BK" wire between test connector and chassis ground. |

**Fig. 20 Pinpoint test Q (Part 3 of 5). 1990 models**

| TEST STEP | RESULT ▶ | ACTION TO TAKE |
|---|---|---|
| **Q5** CHECK CONTINUITY BETWEEN VAPS CONTROL UNIT AND TEST CONNECTOR | | |
| • Disconnect VAPS control unit connector.<br>• VOM on 200 ohm scale.<br>• Measure resistance between VAPS control unit connector terminal C ("Y/BK") and test connector terminal C "Y/BK" wire.<br>• Is resistance less than 5 ohms? | Yes ▶<br>No ▶ | GO to Q6.<br>REPAIR ("Y/BK") wire between VAPS control unit and test connector for opens. |

| TEST STEP | RESULT ▶ | ACTION TO TAKE |
|---|---|---|
| **Q6** CHECK TEST CONNECTOR CIRCUIT FOR SHORT TO VPWR | | |
| • Leave VAPS control unit connector disconnected.<br>• Key on; engine off.<br>• VOM on 20 volt scale.<br>• Measure voltage between Test connector Y/BK wire and ground.<br>• Is voltage reading above 0 volts? | Yes ▶<br>No ▶ | REPAIR "Y/BK" wire between VAPS control unit and test connector for shorts to VPWR.<br>GO to Q7. |

| TEST STEP | RESULT ▶ | ACTION TO TAKE |
|---|---|---|
| **Q7** CHECK TEST CONNECTOR FOR SHORT TO GROUND | | |
| • Leave VAPS control unit connector disconnected.<br>• Key off.<br>• VOM on 200K ohm scale.<br>• Measure resistance between Test connector Y/BK wire and ground.<br>• Is resistance greater than 10,000 ohms? | Yes ▶<br><br>No ▶ | REPLACE VAPS control unit.<br>**NOTE:** If directed here from Quick Test Step Q9 "PASS CODE" do not replace VAPS control unit. Re-attempt to recreate intermittent fault.<br>REPAIR ("Y/BK") wire between VAPS control unit and test connector for short to ground. |

**Fig. 20 Pinpoint test Q (Part 4 of 5). 1990 models**

| TEST STEP | RESULT ▶ | ACTION TO TAKE |
|---|---|---|
| **Q2** CHECK POWER TO VAPS CONTROL UNIT | | |
| • Disconnect VAPS control unit connector.<br>• Key ON; engine OFF.<br>• VOM on 20 volt scale.<br>• Measure voltage between terminal E ("BK/GN") and ground.<br>• Is voltage above 10 volts? | Yes ▶<br>No ▶ | GO to Q3.<br>REPLACE 10A fuse or REPAIR "BK/GN" wire between VAPS control unit and fuse box. |
| **Q3** CHECK VAPS CONTROL UNIT GROUND | | |
| • Leave VAPS control unit connector disconnected.<br>• VOM on 200 ohm scale.<br>• Measure resistance between D ("BK") and ground.<br>• Is resistance less than 5 ohms? | Yes ▶<br>No ▶ | GO to Q4.<br>REPAIR "BK" wire between VAPS control unit and chassis ground for opens. |
| **Q4** CHECK TEST CONNECTOR GROUND | | |
| • Disconnect test connector from mounting.<br>• VOM on 200 ohm scale.<br>• Measure resistance between "BK" wire and ground.<br>• Is resistance reading less than 5 ohms? | Yes ▶<br>No ▶ | GO to Q5.<br>REPAIR "BK" wire between test connector and chassis ground. |
| **Q5** CHECK CONTINUITY BETWEEN VAPS CONTROL UNIT AND TEST CONNECTOR | | |
| • Disconnect VAPS control unit connector.<br>• VOM on 200 ohm scale.<br>• Measure resistance between VAPS control unit connector terminal C ("Y/BK") and test connector terminal C "Y/BK" wire.<br>• Is resistance less than 5 ohms? | Yes ▶<br>No ▶ | GO to Q6.<br>REPAIR "Y/BK" wire between VAPS control unit and test connector for opens. |
| **Q6** CHECK TEST CONNECTOR CIRCUIT FOR SHORT TO VPWR | | |
| • Leave VAPS control unit connector disconnected.<br>• Key ON; engine OFF.<br>• VOM on 20 volt scale.<br>• Measure voltage between Test connector "Y/BK" wire and ground.<br>• Is voltage reading 0 volts? | Yes ▶<br>No ▶ | GO to Q7.<br>REPAIR "Y/BK" wire between VAPS control unit and test connector for shorts to VPWR. |
| **Q7** CHECK TEST CONNECTOR FOR SHORT TO GROUND | | |
| • Leave VAPS control unit connector disconnected.<br>• Key OFF.<br>• VOM on 200K ohm scale.<br>• Measure resistance between Test connector "Y/BK" wire and ground.<br>• Is resistance greater than 10,000 ohms? | Yes ▶<br><br>No ▶ | REPLACE VAPS control unit.<br>**NOTE: If directed here from Quick Test Step Q9 "PASS Code" do not replace VAPS control unit. Re-attempt to recreate intermittent fault.**<br>REPAIR "Y/BK" wire between VAPS control unit and test connector for short to ground. |

**Fig. 20 Pinpoint test Q (Part 5 of 5). 1991 models**

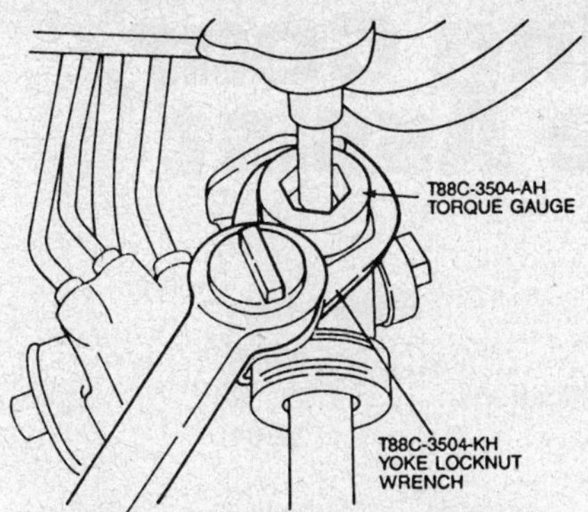


**Fig. 21 Adjusting yoke locknut. 1990–91 models**

# STEERING GEAR SERVICE

## POWER STEERING SYSTEM FLUSH

If the power steering pump has been serviced, flush the power steering gear and lines prior to installation.

1. Remove and flush power steering pressure hose, then reinstall.
2. Place gear fluid return line in suitable container, then plug reservoir return line at reservoir.
3. Fill reservoir using Motorcraft DEXRON II part No. ESW-M2C-138-CJ or equivalent.
4. Disconnect coil wire, then raise and support front wheels.
5. Add about two quarts of fluid while cranking engine with starter and turning steering wheel right to left.
6. When all the fluid is added, stop cranking engine.
7. Remove reservoir return line plug, then connect line to reservoir.
8. Fill reservoir to specified level.
9. Crank engine with starter and add fluid until level remains constant.
10. While cranking engine, rotate steering wheel from stop to stop. **Front wheels must be off the ground during steering wheel stop to stop rotation.**
11. Check fluid level, add as required.
12. Start engine, allow to run for several minutes.
13. Rotate steering wheel from far left to right several times.
14. Turn off engine, check fluid level add as required.
15. Disconnect battery ground cable.
16. Depress brake pedal for at least five seconds.
17. Connect battery ground cable.

## ADJUSTMENT

### RACK YOKE PRELOAD

### 1990–91

1. With rack out of vehicle, measure pinion torque using an inch lb. torque wrench and pinion adapter tool No. T88C-3504-BH. **Torque** should be 88.5-123.9 inch lbs.

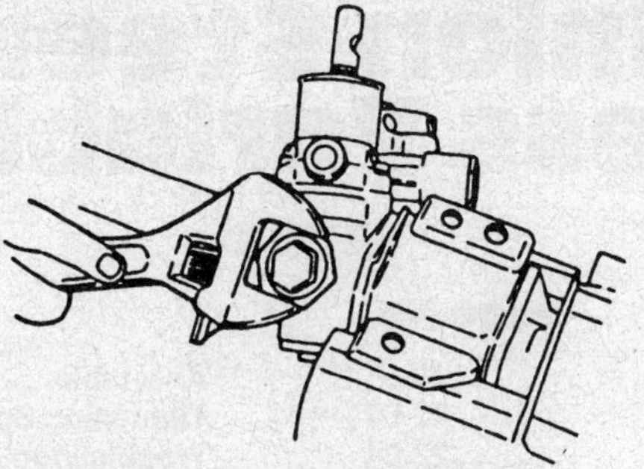

**Fig. 22 Removing adjust cover locknut**

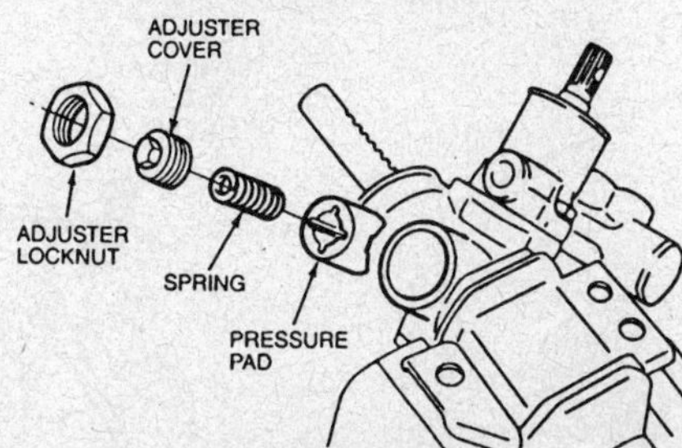


**Fig. 24 Installing pressure pad & spring**

2. If pinion torque is not within specification, loosen pinion locknut.
3. Using torque gauge tool No. T88C-3504-AH or equivalent, **torque** adjusting cover to 39-48 inch lbs. then loosen it 35°, **Fig. 21.**
4. Using yoke locknut wrench tool No. T88C-3504-KH, **torque** locknut to 29-36 ft. lbs.

## DISASSEMBLE

1. Mount steering gear in a suitable vise equipped with soft jaws.
2. Remove external hydraulic lines connecting valve body to steering gear housing.
3. Remove solenoid valve from left mounting bracket.
4. Remove mounting brackets and rubber bushings from steering gear.
5. Scribe alignment marks on tie rods and tie rod ends, then remove tie rod ends.
6. Using a suitable chisel, uncrimp tie rod assembly lockwasher.
7. Using a 30mm crowfoot wrench, remove tie rod from steering gear.
8. Remove adjust cover locknut, **Fig. 22.**
9. Using yoke torque gauge tool No. T88C-3504-AH, remove adjust cover, spring and pressure pad.
10. Using outer torque box adapter tool No. T88C-3504-CH, remove outer box assembly.
11. Using a screwdriver, remove pinion shaft oil seal.

## INSPECTION

1. Check bearings for looseness, abnormal noise or poor operation. **If pinion bearing requires replacement, replace entire steering gear assembly.**

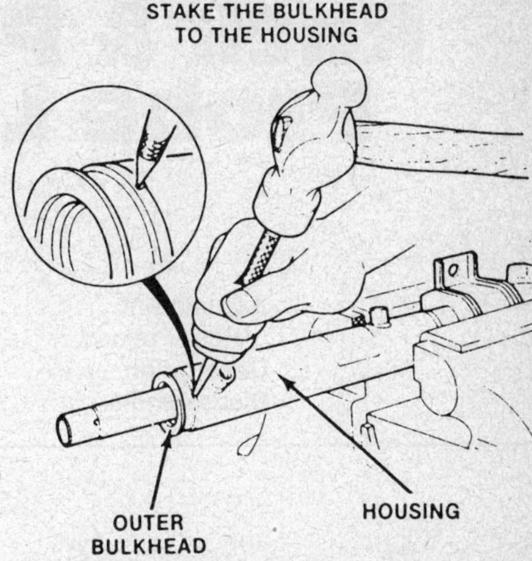


**Fig. 23 Staking the bulkhead**

2. Check for looseness or lack of smoothness in tie rod ball housings.
3. Check for bent tie rods or tie rod ends.
4. Check outer bulkhead bushing for wear.
5. Check tie rod boot for cracking, damage or deterioration.

## ASSEMBLE

1. Lubricate outer box assembly with automatic transmission fluid.
2. Using outer torque adapter tool No. T88C-3504-CH, install outer box assembly.
3. Stake the outer box assembly to the rack housing using a punch, **Fig. 23.**
4. Apply a thin coat of grease to lips of pinion seal, then install pinion seal using seal installer tool No. T88C-3504-BH.
5. Install pressure pad and spring into gear housing, **Fig 24.**
6. Apply thread sealer to adjust cover.
7. Using torque gauge tool No. T88C-3504-AH, install adjust cover and **torque** to 29-36 inch lbs.
8. Loosen adjust cover 35°.
9. Using pinion adapter tool No. T88C-3504-BH, measure pinion torque, **torque** should be 88.5-123.9 inch lbs.
10. Install adjust cover locknut and **torque** to 28.9-36.2 ft. lbs.
11. Install washer and tie rod. **Torque** tie rod to 43.4-57.9 ft .lbs.
12. Bend washer tang to lock tie rod in place.
13. Slide tie rod boot over tie rod and position it on steering gear.
14. Wrap a new piece of mechanics wire around the boot twice, then around a Phillips screwdriver. Twist the wire four or five times with the screwdriver. **Ensure boot is not dented or twisted.**
15. Install outer boot clamp.
16. Install tie rod ends, ensuring index marks are aligned.
17. Install rubber mounting bushings and mounting brackets.
18. Install solenoid valve on mounting bracket.
19. Install external hydraulic lines connecting valve body to gear. Use new copper washers at each banjo fitting.

# Rack & Pinion Steering Gear, Probe Less Variable Assist

## INDEX



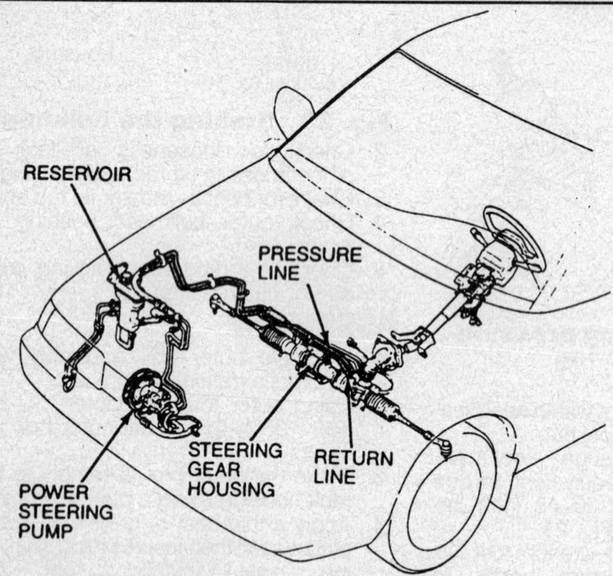


**Fig. 1 Power steering system**

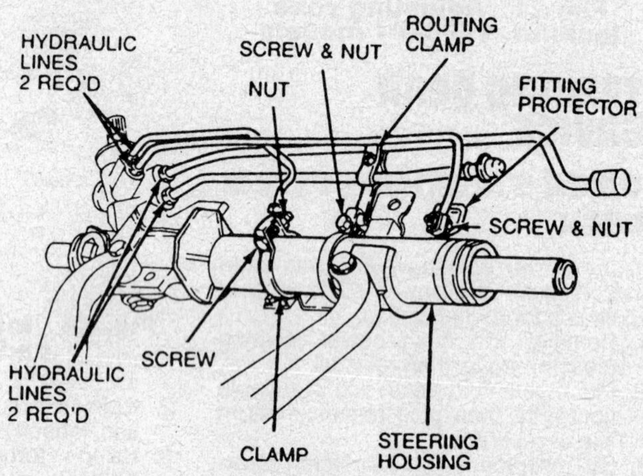


**Fig. 2 Steering rack assembly**

## DESCRIPTION

This power rack and pinion steering gear has a integral valving and power assist system, **Fig. 1.**

The valve body is an integral part of the steering gear housing. A pressure line and return line attach the pump to the gear, while a rotary valve directs high pressure hydraulic fluid through external oil lines to the correct side of the rack piston.

## TROUBLESHOOTING

Refer to "Rack & Pinion Steering Gear, Probe w/Variable Assist" for troubleshooting procedure.

## ADJUSTMENT

### RACK PRELOAD

1. Removed rack from vehicle and mount in holding fixture tool No. T57L-500-B, or equivalent.
2. Measure pinion torque using an inch lb. torque wrench and pinion adapter tool No. T88C-3504-BH or equivalent. **Torque** should be 88.5-123.9 inch lbs.
3. In pinion torque is not within specifications, loosen pinion locknut.
4. Using torque gauge tool No. T88C-3504-AH or equivalent, **torque** adjust cover to 7.2 ft. lbs. then loosen it.
5. **Torque** adjust cover again to 3.6 ft. lbs. then loosen the adjusting cover 45°.
6. Using yoke locknut wrench tool No. T88C-3504-KH or equivalent, then tighten to specifications.

## DISASSEMBLE

1. Mount steering gear in holding fixture tool No. T57L-500-B.
2. Remove screw and nut from clamp, then the clamp from steering housing.
3. Note position of hydraulic lines for reference during assembly, then remove screw and nut from routing clamp and spread clamp, **Fig. 2.**
4. Remove two hydraulic lines and routing clamp from steering gear housing.
5. Remove screw and nut from fitting protector, then spread protector and remove, **Fig. 2.**
6. Remove two remaining hydraulic lines.
7. Using roll pin remover tool No. T78P-3504-N, remove roll pin, **Fig. 3.**
8. Using a 30mm crowfoot wrench, remove tie rod assembly from rack.
9. Using torque gauge tool No. T88C-3504-AH and yoke locknut wrench tool No. T88C-3504-KH, remove adjuster cover, locknut, spring and pressure pad.
10. Drill out the staked area, then remove the housing cover.
11. Remove snap ring from upper pinion bearing.
12. Using tool No. T88C-3504-BH, hold pinion and remove pinion locknut.
13. Using puller bridge tool No. T86P-3504-D, puller tool No. T78P-3504-B and spacer tool No. T78P-3733-A2, remove pinion and upper bearing from steering gear housing.
14. Remove lower bearing from steering housing.
15. **On 1989 models,** drill out staked area of rack bushing, **Fig. 4.**
16. **On all models,** using adapter tool No. T88C-3504-CH, remove rack bushing assembly.
17. Using slide hammer tool No. D79P-100-A and adapter tool No. T88C-3504-OH, remove the rack from the pinion side of the steering housing, **Fig. 5.**
18. Using seal remover tool No. T78P-3504-J and slide hammer tool No. D79P-100-A, remove inner rack seal and washer from the tube side of the steering housing.

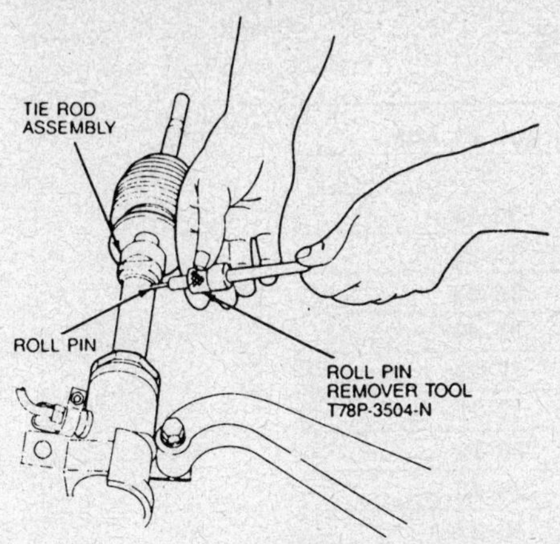


Fig. 3 Removing roll pin

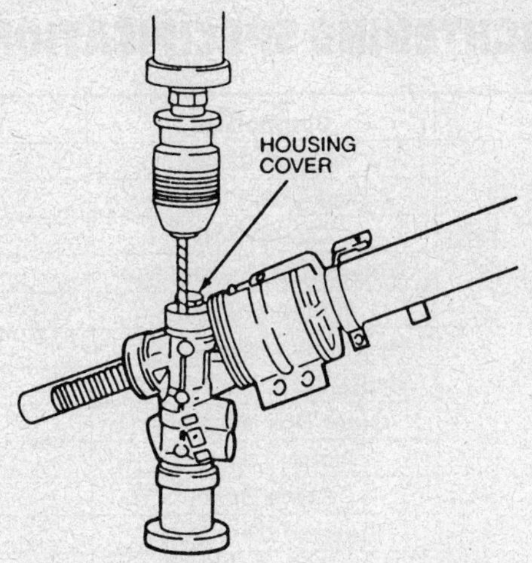


Fig. 4 Drilling out staked area

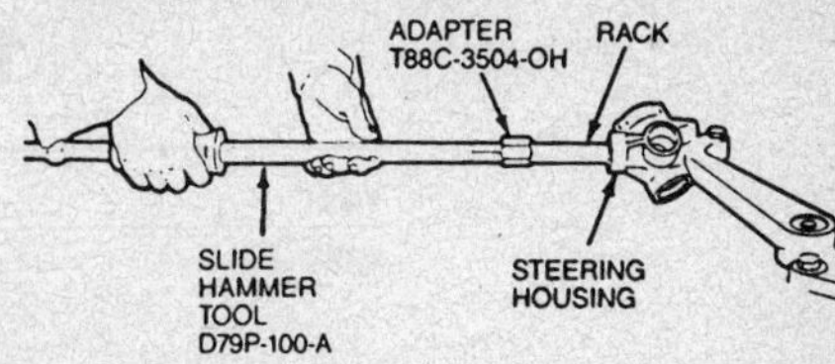


Fig. 5 Removing rack from housing

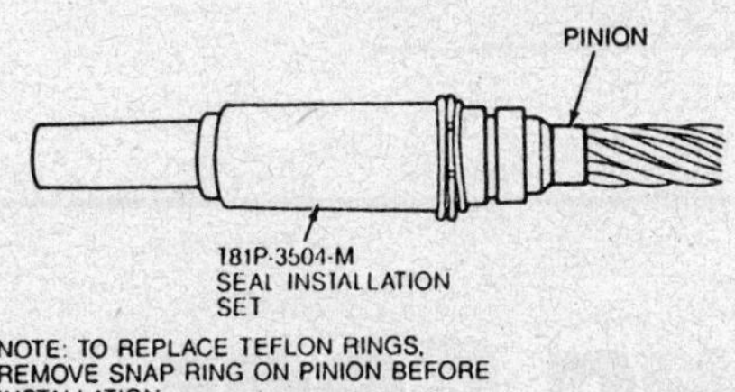


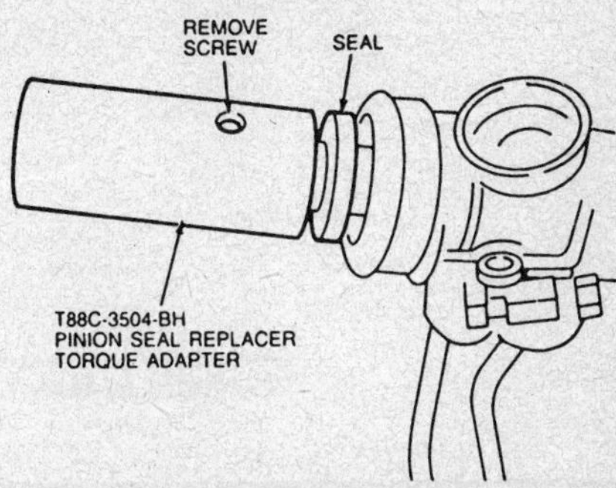


Fig. 7 Installing upper seal

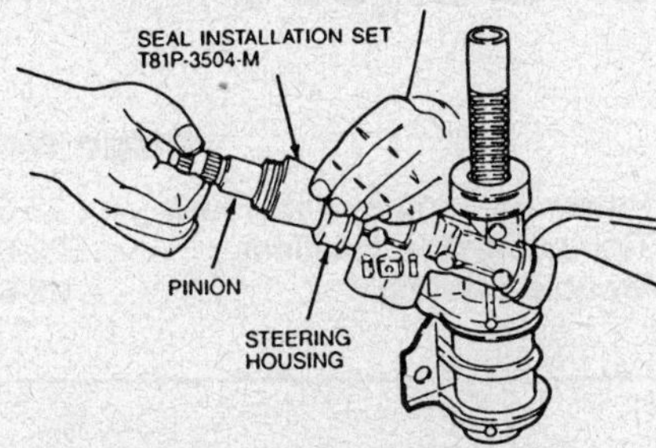


Fig. 6 Installing seals and pinion into housing

## ASSEMBLY

1. Using seal installer tool No. T88C-3504-DH, install inner rack seal and washer.
2. Using seal installer tool No. T88C-3504-EH, Install teflon seal ring and O-ring onto rack.
3. Install protective sleeve tool No. T85L-3504-B onto the rack, then position ring sizer tool No. T88C-3504-FH on steering housing and install rack into steering housing. Leave protective sleeve in place.
4. With protective sleeve still in place, slide outer box seal into steering housing.
5. Using outer box torque adapter tool No. T88C-3504-CH, install outer box assembly. Tighten outer box assembly to specifications, then stake box assembly in place.
6. Using installer tool No. T88C-3504-HH, install intermediate bearing.
7. Using installer tool T87M-3504-E, install lower pinion bearing.
8. Using seal installer tool No. T88C-3504-MH, install inner pinion seal.
9. Using seal installation set No. T81P-3504-M, install three teflon seals onto the pinion, **Fig. 6.**
10. Using set No. T81P-3504-M, install pinion into steering housing.
11. Install upper pinion bearing.
12. Install input shaft seal protector tool No. T81P-3504-P, then install upper pinion seal into steering housing.
13. Remove screw from torque adapter tool No. T88C-3504-BH, then use tool to seat upper seal, **Fig. 7.**
14. Install pinion snap ring. Ensure snap ring is fully seated in groove.
15. Using tool No. T88C-3504-BH to hold pinion, install pinion locknut and tighten to specifications.
16. Apply suitable thread sealer to housing cover, then install housing cover and tighten to specifications.
17. Using a suitable center punch, stake housing cover in place.
18. Install pressure pad, spring and adjust cover.
19. Using yoke torque gauge tool No. T88C-3504-AH, **torque** adjust cover to 7.2 ft. lbs., then loosen adjust cover and **torque** to 3.6 ft. lbs., loosen adjust cover 45°.
20. Using pinion torque adapter tool No. T88C-3504-BH and a suitable inch lb. torque wrench, measure pinion torque. Pinion **torque** should measure 88.5-123.9 inch lbs., if torque is not within specifications repeat step 19 as necessary.
21. Install adjust cover locknut.
22. Using yoke locknut wrench tool No. T88C-3504-KH, tighten locknut to specifications.
23. Using a 30mm crowfoot wrench, install tie rod assembly into steering rack and tighten to specifications.
24. Install roll pin.
25. Install two hydraulic lines and routing clamp, then install clamp screw and tighten securely.
26. Install two remaining hydraulic lines, fitting protector and remaining clamp on steering housing.

## TIGHTENING SPECIFICATIONS

| Year | Component | Torque, Ft. Lbs. |
|---|---|---|
| 1989-91 | Adjust Cover | ① |
| | Adjust Cover Locknut | 36-43 |
| | Clamp Bolt | 13-20 |
| | Differential Bearing Nut | 36-43 |
| | Housing Cover | 30-40 |
| | Hydraulic Lines (Large) | 25-33 |
| | Hydraulic Lines (Small) | 18-22 |
| | Outer Box Assembly | 65-72 |
| | Pinion Locknut | 29-36 |
| | Pump Bolts | 15-22 |
| | Steering Gear Bolts | 27-40 |
| | Tie Rod | 91-105 |
| | Tie Rod End Locknut | 51-72 |

①—Refer to text.

# Rack & Pinion Steering Gear, 1989 Tracer & 1991 Capri

## INDEX



## TROUBLESHOOTING

Refer to "1989 Tracer & 1991 Capri Steering Pump" for troubleshooting power steering system.

## POWER STEERING PRESSURE TEST

Refer to "1989 Tracer & 1991 Capri Steering Pump" for power steering system pressure test.

## POWER STEERING SYSTEM FLUSH

Refer to "1989 Tracer & 1991 Capri Steering Pump" for power steering flush procedure.

## ADJUSTMENTS

### RACK YOKE PRELOAD

1. Remove steering gear, the position in suitable soft-jawed vise.
2. Measure pinion torque using a suitable inch lb. wrench and adapter tool No. T87C-3504-C or equivalent, **torque** should be 5.3-13.3 inch lbs.
3. If not as indicated, readjust pinion torque by tightening or loosening adjusting plug.

## DISASSEMBLE

1. Position steering gear in a soft jawed vise.
2. Disconnect valve body to steering gear hydraulic tubes, **Fig. 1.**
3. Remove steering gear mounting brackets and bushings.
4. Using two screwdrivers and a self tapping screw, remove brass tubing seats from steering gear housing, **Fig. 2.**
5. Using a suitable cold chisel, remove pinion shaft dust boot.
6. Using a No. 40 Torx bit, remove valve body attaching bolts and valve body.
7. Wrap cloth around valve body, then position valve body in vise.
8. Remove valve body end plug, then remove pivot lever collar, **Fig. 3.**
9. Using a suitable punch in pivot lever hole, slide spool valve part way out of valve body.
10. Carefully remove spool valve from valve body, then remove spool valve O-ring.
11. Place alignment marks on on tie rods, jam nuts and tie rod ends so they can be installed in the same position.
12. Remove tie rod ends and jam nuts from tie rods.
13. Remove tie rod boots from from steering gear housing.
14. Using a suitable cold chisel, uncrimp tie rod washer tabs.
15. Position rack in a soft jawed vise, then using a suitable wrench, remove tie rods from rack.
16. Loosen locknut, then remove adjusting plug, spring and yoke from steering gear.
17. Protect outer bulkhead with a cloth, then remove outer bulkhead using a pipe wrench.
18. Remove O-ring from outer bulkhead and discard.
19. Pull pinion shaft assembly out through lower bearing side of steering gear housing.
20. Using a wooden dowel, drive upper pinion bearing out of housing.
21. Remove rack from steering gear housing in direction indicated in **Fig. 4.**
22. Using tool No. T87C-3504-A, remove remove rack inner guide and seal.

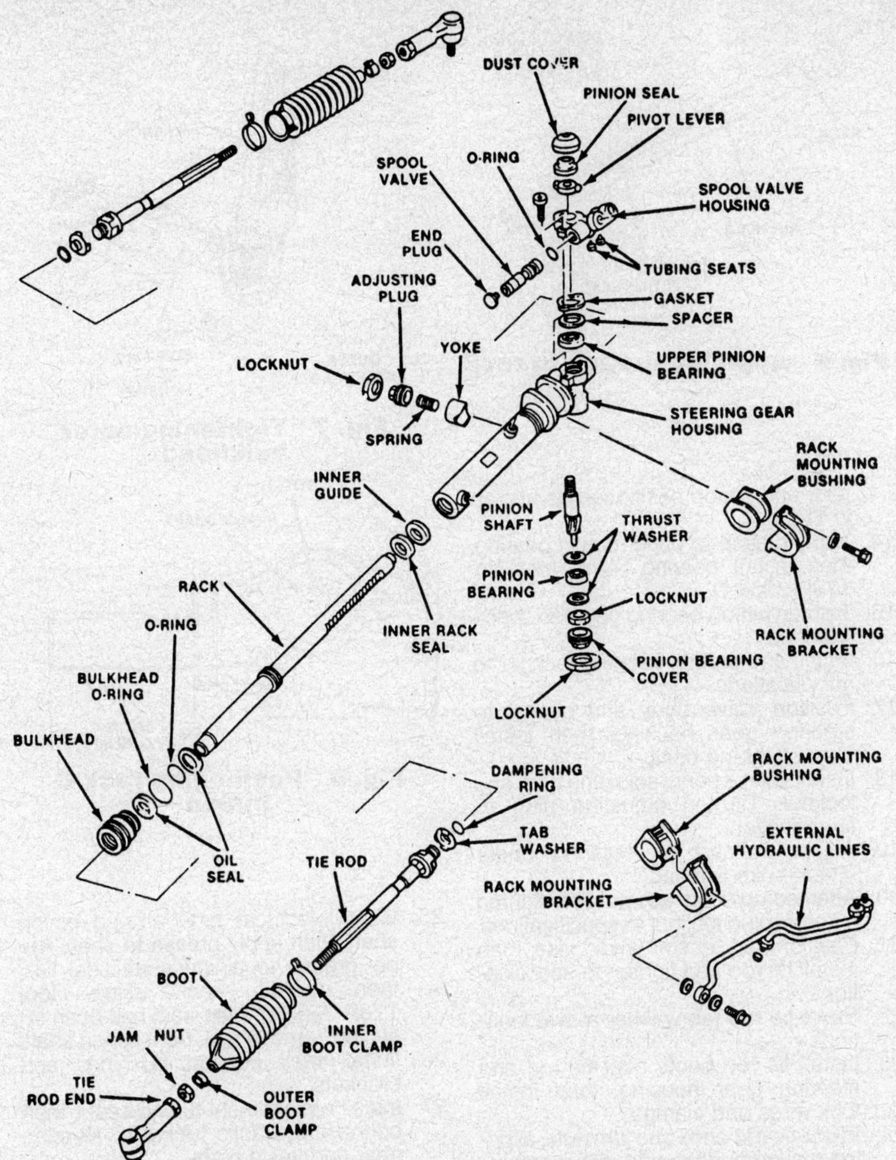


**Fig. 1 Exploded view of rack & pinion steering gear**

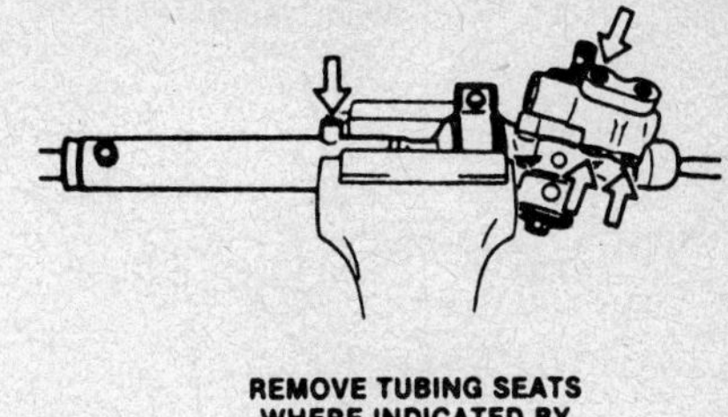


**Fig. 2 Tubing seat locations**

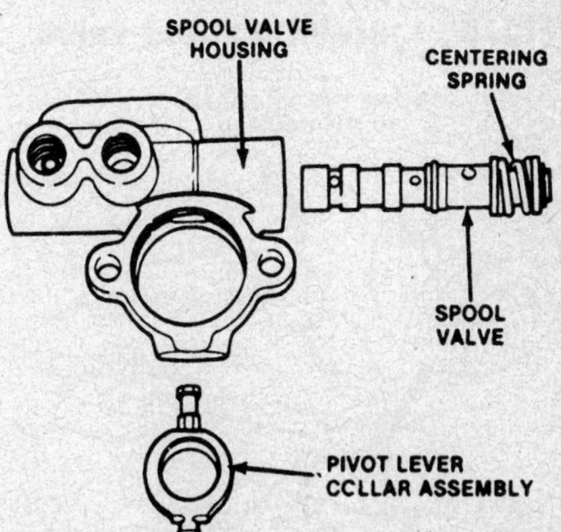


**Fig. 3 Exploded view of valve body**

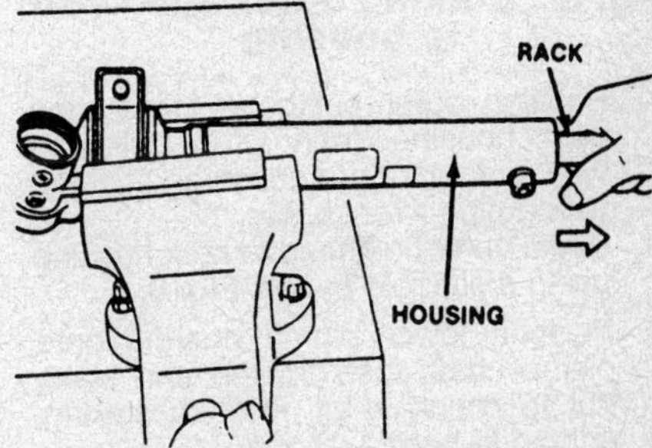


**Fig. 4 Removing rack from steering gear housing**

## INSPECTION

Check rack and pinion teeth for wear and damage. Position rack in V-blocks and check run-out using a suitable dial indicator. Rack run-out should not exceed .012 inch. Check pinion bearing for looseness and wear. If rack, pinion or pinion bearings are found to be unsatisfactory, the rack and pinion must be replaced as a set.

Check steering gear housing for wear and damage. Check tie rod ball units for looseness and smoothness of operation. Check for bent tie rods or tie rod ends. Check tie rod boots for damage. If any components are found to be unsatisfactory, they should be replaced.

Check rack bushing located inside steering gear housing for wear. The bushing and steering gear housing must be replaced as an assembly. Check yoke sliding surface for wear and replace as necessary. Check outer bulkhead bushing for wear and replace as necessary.

Check pivot lever collar for wear and damage and replace as necessary. Also check spool valve for wear and damage and polish with crocus cloth as necessary.

## ASSEMBLE

1. Install replacement O-rings on spool valve. Apply molybdenum disulfide grease to spool valve pivot lever hole. Lubricate remainder of spool valve with automatic transmission fluid.
2. Position spool valve into valve body, **Fig. 5.**
3. Apply molybdenum disulfide grease to pivot lever hose in valve body and to ends of pivot lever collar and bushing, install pivot lever into valve housing, ensuring spherical ends are properly seated.
4. Install valve body end plug, **Fig. 1.**
5. Lubricate inner rack guide and seal with automatic transmission fluid, then install guide and seal using tool No. T87C-3504-A or equivalent. Push guide and seal into housing until fully seated.
6. Apply grease to rack teeth, then position rack seal protector D83P-3504-K or equivalent over rack teeth. When applying grease teeth, do not cover rack air hole, **Fig. 6.**
7. Using tool T81P-3504, install rack piston seal.
8. Lubricate rack piston and housing cylinder bore with automatic transmission fluid, then slide rack into housing until fully seated. Remove rack seal protector from rack teeth.
9. Using tool T81P-3504-Y or equivalent, install replacement bushing into outer bulkhead. Also install replacement sealing ring, O-rings and oil seal on outer bulkhead. Prior to installation, lubricate bushing and seals with automatic transmission fluid.

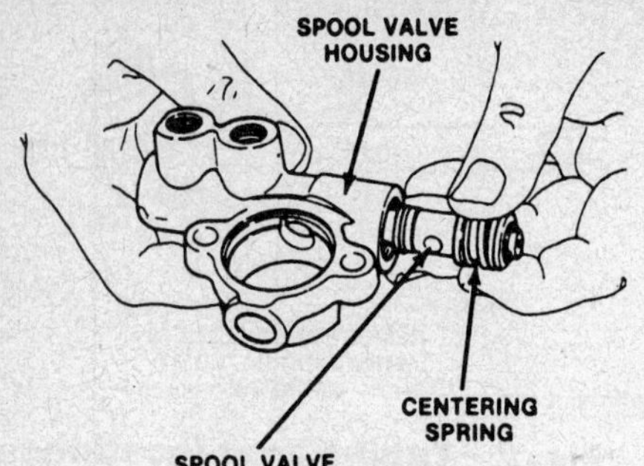


**Fig. 5 Installing spool valve**

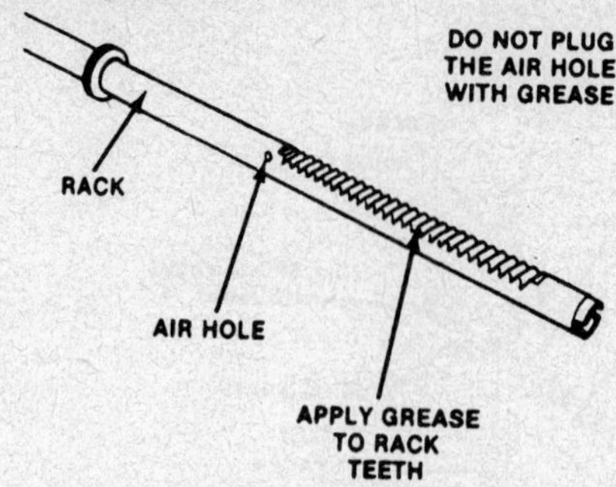


**Fig. 6 Applying grease to rack**

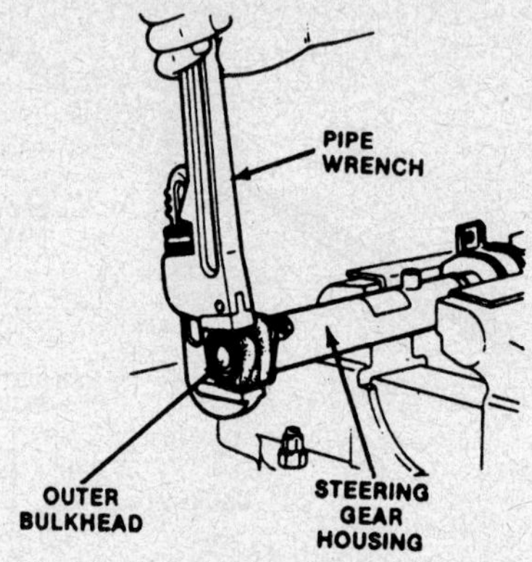


**Fig. 7 Tightening outer bulkhead**

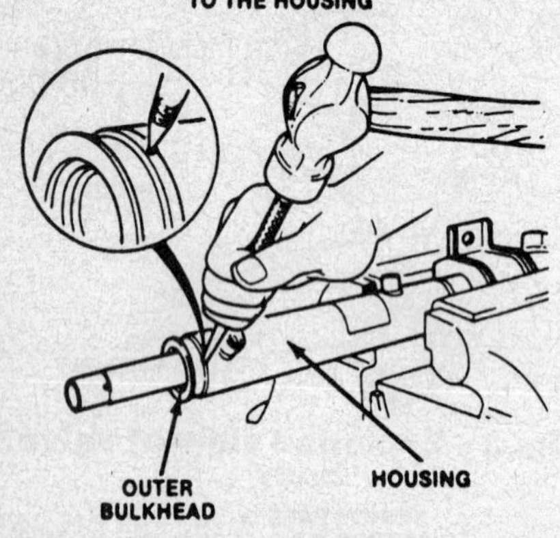


**Fig. 8 Staking outer bulkhead to housing**

10. Position outer bulkhead to steering gear housing, then wrap bulkhead with a cloth for protection and tighten with a pipe wrench, **Fig. 7.**
11. Stake outer bulkhead to rack housing using a suitable punch, **Fig. 8.**
12. Position lower pinion bearing onto pinion shaft, then tighten and stake nut to pinion shaft. Prior to staking, tighten to specifications.
13. Install pinion shaft assembly, with rack and pinion positioned as shown in **Fig. 9.**
14. Apply grease to upper pinion bearing, then install bearing using tool No. T78P-3504-D.
15. Tighten pinion bearing cover to specifications.
16. Install and tighten housing locknut to specifications.
17. Position valve body and gasket to steering gear housing, then install Torx attaching bolts.
18. Install yoke, spring, adjusting plug and locknut. Tighten adjusting plug to specifications.
19. Adjust preload as outlined under "Rack Yoke Preload."
20. After completing adjustment, tighten adjuster plug locknut to specifications.
21. Position rack in soft jawed vise, then install tie rod and tighten to specifications.
22. Stake tie rod tab washer at two locations.
23. Install tie rod boots over tie rod and steering gear housing, then install lock wires and clamps.
24. Install tie rod ends and jam nuts, aligning marks made during disassembly.

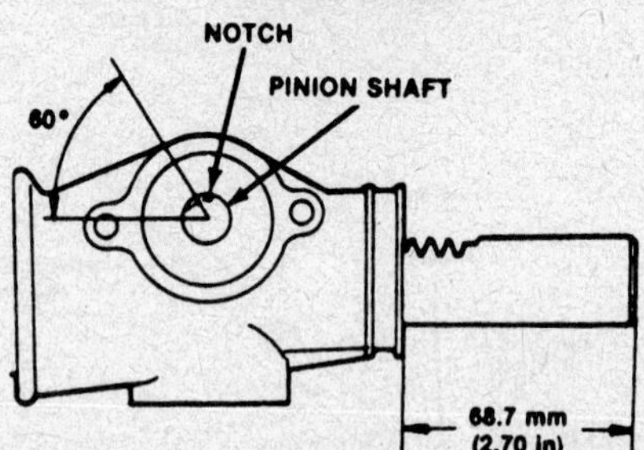


**Fig. 9 Positioning rack & pinion**

25. Wrap electrical tape around pinion shaft, then apply grease to shaft. Apply grease to pinion shaft seal lips, then install seal using tool T78P-3504-D. After seal has been installed, remove tape from pinion shaft.
26. Install rack support bushings and brackets.
27. Install replacement tubing seats, then connect hydraulic tubing to steering gear and valve body.

## TIGHTENING SPECIFICATIONS

| Year | Component | Torque, Ft. lbs. |
|---|---|---|
| 1989 & 1991 | Pinion Bearing Cover | 39.1–47.1① |
| | Pinion Bearing Housing Locknut | 28.9–36.2 |
| | Pinion Cover | 28.9–36.2 |
| | Pinion Shaft Nut | 28.9–36.2 |
| | Tie Rod End | 26–29 |
| | Tie Rod To Rack | 43.4–57.9 |
| | Wheel Lug Nuts | 67–88 |

①—Inch lbs.

# Rack & Pinion Steering Gear, Festiva

## INDEX



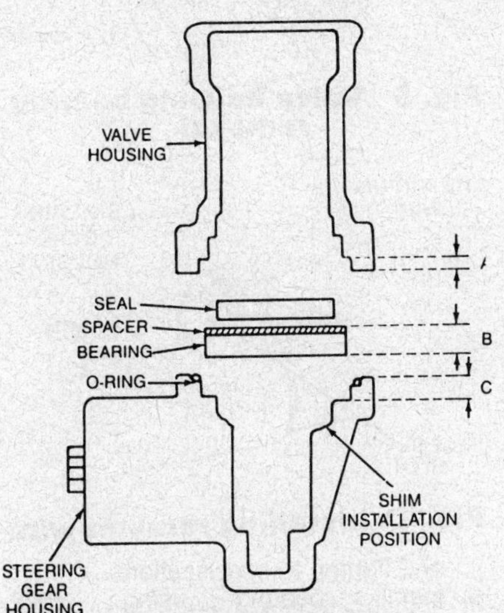


**Fig. 1 Selecting proper valve housing shims**

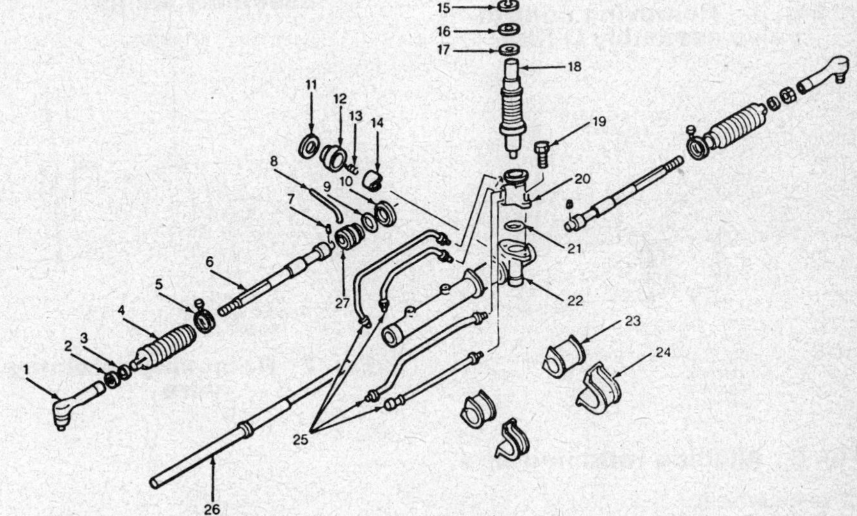


**Fig. 2 Steering rack exploded view**

## TROUBLESHOOTING

Refer to "Festiva Steering Pump" for troubleshooting procedures.

## POWER STEERING PRESSURE TEST

Refer to "Festiva Steering Pump" for power steering pressure test procedure.

## ADJUSTMENTS

### VALVE HOUSING

Perform this adjustment if the valve housing, steering gear housing or pinion control valve assembly have been replaced.

1. Measure valve housing, lower bearing and spacer and steering gear housing as shown in **Fig. 1.**
2. To determine proper thickness of shim needed, use this formula, T = A + C − B. Where T is shim thickness needed.
3. Shims are available in .0020 inch only. Determine number of shims using this formula, N = T / .0020 inch. Where N is number of shims needed. Round up or down to the closest full number.

## DISASSEMBLE

Refer to **Fig. 2** when performing the following procedure:

1. Secure steering gear on a soft jawed vise.
2. Remove fluid lines.
3. Place alignment marks on lefthand tie rod to ease installation.
4. Loosen jam nut and remove left tie rod end.
5. Remove boot clamps then the boot.
6. Using lockpin tool No. T78P-3504-N or equivalent, remove tie rod lockpins.
7. Remove tie rods from rack assembly.
8. Using locknut tool No. T90C-3504-BH or equivalent, remove yoke plug locknut.
9. Remove yoke plug, spring and support yoke.
10. Remove pinion and control valve assembly retaining snap ring.
11. Remove seal using locknut pin remover tool No. T78P-3504-N or equivalent, **Fig. 3.**
12. Remove valve housing attaching bolts, then valve housing, pinion and control valve assembly.
13. If present, remove shim(s) from steering gear housing, **Fig. 4.**
14. Remove steering gear O-ring.
15. Remove pinion and control valve assembly from valve housing by lightly tapping with a rubber mallet.
16. Press bearing out of valve housing using pinion seal replacer tool No. T88P-3504-MH and handle tool No. Y87P-3504-D or equivalent, **Fig. 5.**
17. Using outer box torque adapter tool No. T88C-3504-CH, rotate rack bushing until hooked end of retaining wire is aligned with slot in steering gear housing, **Fig. 6.**
18. Pry retaining wire from bushing hole.
19. Rotate bushing and remove retaining wire, **Fig. 7.**
20. Remove rack from right side of steering gear.
21. Remove O-ring and seal using rack inner seal remover tool T87C-3504-A

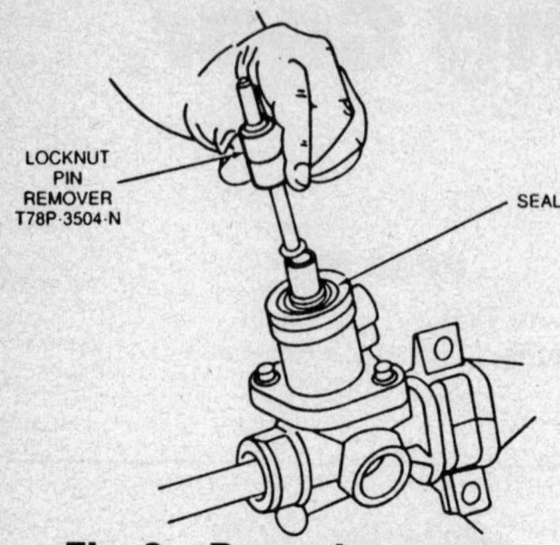


**Fig. 3. Removing control valve assembly O-ring**



**Fig. 6 Aligning retaining wire.**

or equivalent.

## ASSEMBLE

1. Install a new seal and O-ring using a suitable seal and Teflon ring expander installer.
2. Install rack into steering gear.
3. Insert retaining wire through slot and into bushing hole, **Fig. 8.**
4. Install retaining wire using outer box torque adapter tool No. T88C-3504-CH.
5. If valve housing, steering gear housing or pinion and control valve assembly has been replaced, perform valve housing adjustment procedure as outlined under "Adjustments, Valve Housing" in this section.
6. Insert pinion and control valve assem-

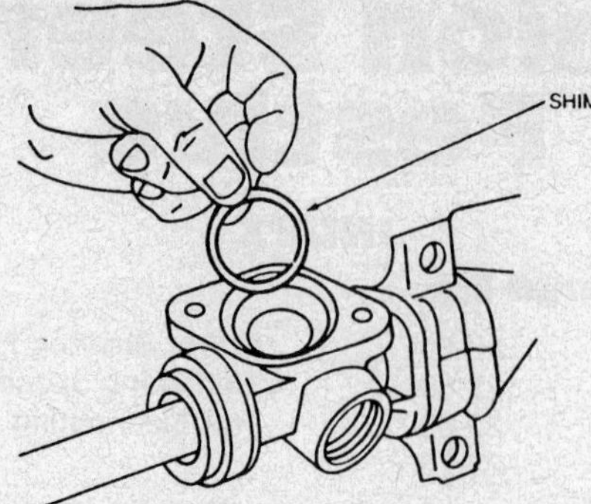


**Fig. 4 Removing control valve assembly shims**

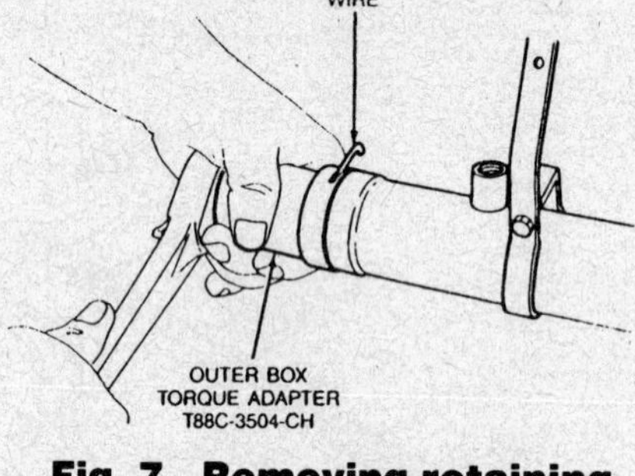


**Fig. 7 Removing retaining wire**

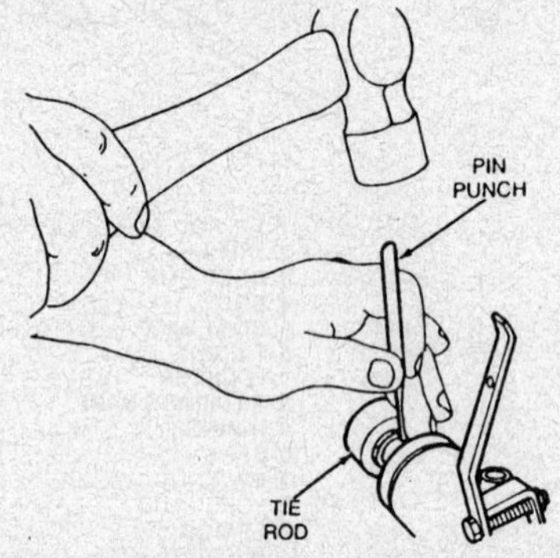


**Fig. 9 Installing pinion seal**

bly into valve housing, ensuring that it seats properly.

7. Install a new O-ring.
8. Install valve housing, pinion and control valve assembly into steering gear

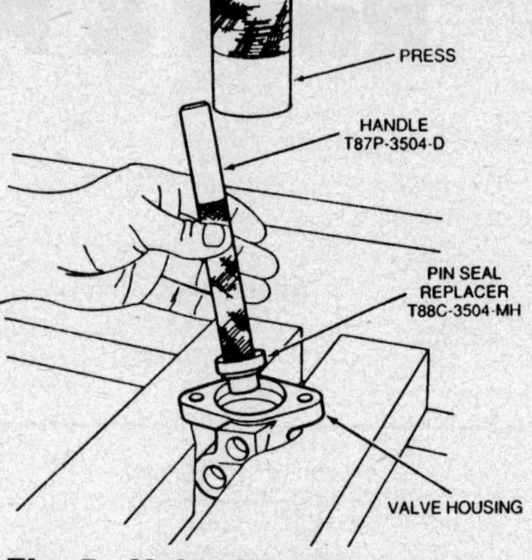


**Fig. 5 Valve housing bearing removal**

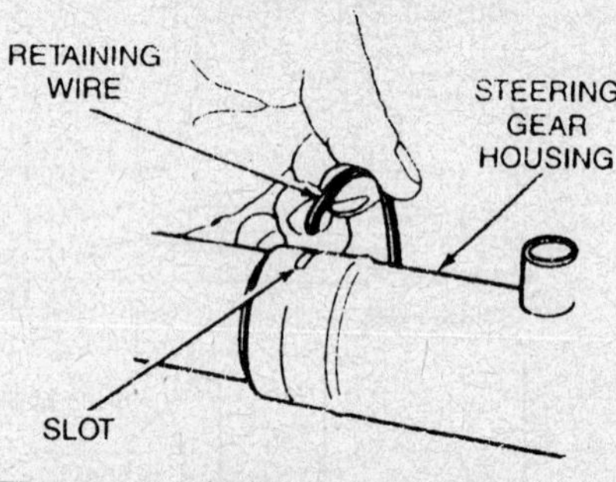


**Fig. 8 Installing retainer wire**

and tighten to specifications.

9. Install bearing using pinion seal/torque adapter tool No. T88C-3504-BH or equivalent.
10. Install seal using same tool, **Fig. 9.**
11. Install snap ring, support yoke, spring and yoke plug.
12. **Torque** yoke plug to 7.2 ft. lbs. then loosen it.
13. **Torque** yoke to 38-48 inch lbs. then loosen it 45°.
14. Apply sealant to exposed threads of yoke plug.
15. Install yoke plug locknut and tighten to specifications.
16. Install tie rods using a suitable pin punch on lockpins.
17. Install boots, boot wires and clips.
18. Install left tie rod end and jam nut.
19. Install fluid lines.

## TIGHTENING SPECIFICATIONS

| Year | Component | Torque, Ft. Lbs. |
|---|---|---|
| 1989–91 | Control Valve Assembly | 15–19 |
| | Fluid Reservoir Bolts | 60–84① |
| | High Pressure Hose Nut | 29–36 |
| | Intermediate Shaft Clamp Bolt | 13–20 |
| | Steering Gear Attaching Bolts | 23–34 |
| | Yoke Plug | ② |
| | Yoke Plug Locknut | 36–43 |

①—Inch lbs.
②—Refer to text.

# Rack & Pinion Steering Gear, 1991 Escort & Tracer

## INDEX



## DESCRIPTION

The power steering system consists of a rack and pinion steering gear, a power steering pump, a fluid reservoir and interconnecting hydraulic lines. The power steering system uses hydraulic pressure generated by the power steering pump to reduce the effort required to turn the steering wheel.

The rack and pinion gear is held in place by two mounting brackets and moulded rubber grommets. The gear is a hydraulic mechanical unit that uses and intergral piston and rack design to provide power assisted steering control.

**On models equipped with 1.9L engine, the middle bearing is not ser viceable and should not be removed from the steering gear housing. If the bearing is worn or damaged, replace short rack assembly.**

## 1.8L MODELS

### TROUBLESHOOTING

#### Steering Feels Heavy

1. Poor lubrication.
2. Foreign material in mechanism.
3. Faulty ball joint.
4. Improper steering gear preload.
5. Faulty steering gear.
6. Faulty steering shaft joint.
7. Power steering fluid leakage.
8. Low fluid level or air in system.
9. Faulty power steering oil pump or drive belt.
10. Clogged lines.
11. Faulty wheel or tire.
12. Faulty suspension component.

#### Steering Wheel Pulls

1. Faulty steering linkage.
2. Faulty wheel or tire.
3. Fault in brake system.
4. Faulty suspension component.

#### General Instability

1. Faulty steering ball joint.
2. Improper steering pinion preload.
3. Faulty steering linkage.
4. Faulty wheel or tire.

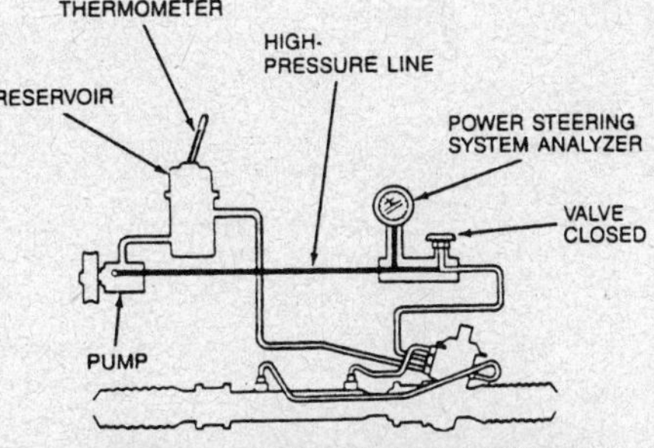


**Fig. 1 Power steering pressure test connections. 1.8L**

5. Faulty suspension component.

#### Steering Feels Unstable

1. Faulty power steering drive belt.
2. Faulty steering gear.
3. Faulty ball joint.
4. Faulty steering linkage.

#### Excessive Steering Wheel Play

1. Faulty steering gear.
2. Faulty ball joint.
3. Loose steering gear mounting bolts.

#### Improper Steering Wheel Return

1. Faulty ball joint.
2. Improper steering pinion preload.
3. Faulty wheel or tire.
4. Faulty suspension component.

#### Steering Wheel Vibrates

1. Faulty steering linkage.
2. Loose steering gear mounting bolts.
3. Faulty ball joint.
4. Faulty front wheel bearing.
5. Faulty wheel or tire.
6. Faulty suspension component.

#### Steering System Noise

1. Loose steering gear mounting bolts.
2. Faulty steering gear.
3. Steering column obstruction.
4. Faulty steering linkage.
5. Faulty ball joint.
6. Faulty power steering pump drive belt.
7. Loose power steering pump bracket.
8. Air in power steering system.
9. Faulty power steering pump.

### POWER STEERING PRESSURE TEST

**During the following procedure, power steering system pressure may exceed 1200 psi. Ensure proper tool fitment prior to performing test. Exercise extreme caution or damage or personal injury may result.**

1. Disconnect high pressure line, install power steering system analyzer 014-00207 or equivalent, using appropriate adapters, **Fig. 1. Torque** adapters to 12-17 ft. lbs.
2. Install thermometer to power steering fluid reservoir.
3. **Ensure analyzer valve is open to allow system to function properly.**
4. **Do not hold steering wheel against a stop of more the 10 seconds at a time.**
5. Start engine, then bleed system by turning steering wheel lock to lock 10 times.
6. Check power steering fluid temperature, if fluid id not 122-140°F, turn steering wheel lock to lock until temperature is reached.
7. **The valve on the analyzer must be closed briefly to read operating pressure. Do not leave valve closed for more than 15 seconds.**
8. Measure power steering pump output pressure by closing analyzer valve and increasing engine speed to 1000-1500 RPM, 1067 psi should be indicated, if so, proceed to step 9, if pressure is low, replace power steering pump.
9. With analyzer valve open, increase engine speed to 1000-1500 RPM.
10. Turn steering wheel fully to left or right, then read measured pressure, 1067 psi should be indicated, if pressure is low, replace steering gear.
11. Remove analyzer and adapters.
12. Reconnect high pressure line, then **torque** fitting to 12-17 ft. lbs.
13. Remove thermometer, then bleed system by starting engine and slowly turning steering wheel from lock to lock 10 times.

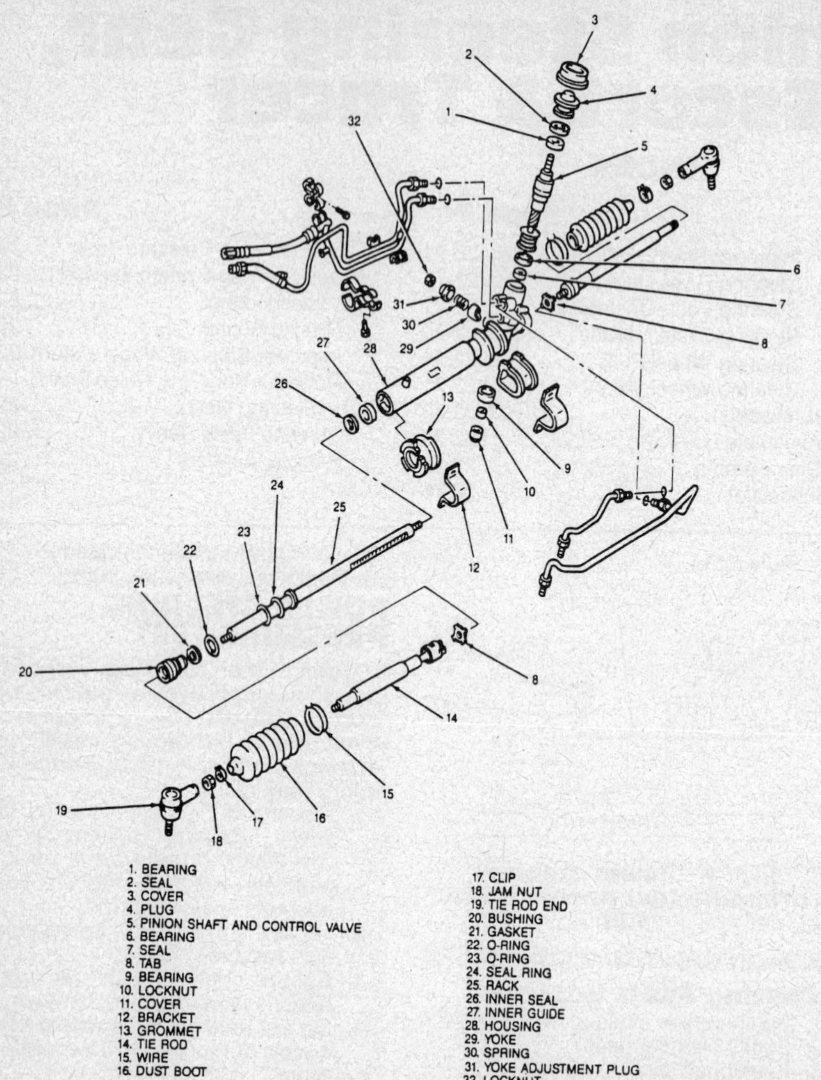


**Fig. 2 Exploded view of steering gear. 1.8L**

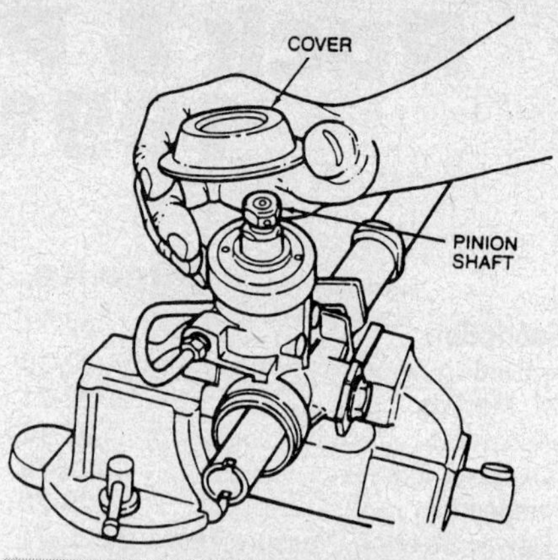


**Fig. 3 Lower bearing & seal removal. 1.8L**

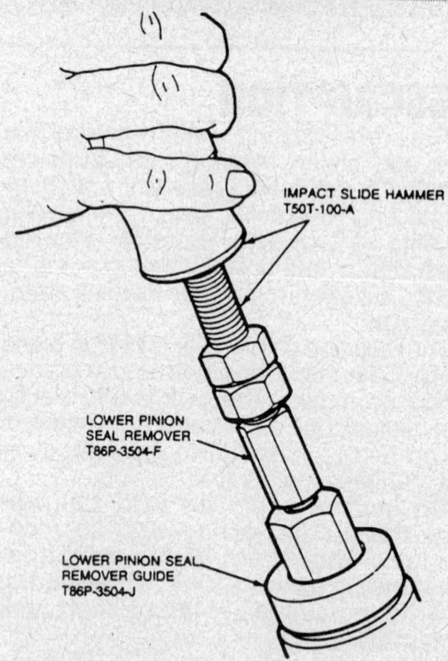


**Fig. 4 Pinion shaft inner seal removal. 1.8L**

## DISASSEMBLE

1. Place installation alignment marks on tie rod end, jam nut and tie rod.
2. Remove tie rod ends and jam nuts, **Fig. 2.**
3. Remove each dust boot clamp, then boot wire and discard, then remove boots.
4. Position steering gear in suitable soft jawed vise.
5. Using suitable chisel, uncrimp tie rod tabs, then remove tie rods and discard tabs.
6. Remove pinion shaft cover.
7. Using pinion torque adapter tool No. T90P-3504-KH or equivalent, remove pinion shaft plug.
8. Using pinion seal replacer tool No. T86P-3504-G or equivalent, remove plug bearing and seal, **Fig. 3.**
9. Remove pinion shaft locknut cover.
10. Using pinion torque adapter T86-3504-K or equivalent, hold pinion shaft, then remove shaft locknut.
11. Using torque gauge tool No. T90P-3504-LH or equivalent, remove yoke adjustment plug locknut, then remove adjusting plug.
12. Remove spring, support yoke, pinion shaft and control valve from gear housing.
13. Using suitable seal remover, remove control valve seal ring.
14. Press bearing from pinion shaft.
15. Using outer box torque adapter tool No. T90P-3504-MH or equivalent, remove steering gear bushing.
16. Remove rack from RH side of housing, then remove rack piston seal ring and discard.
17. Using rack inner seal remover tool No. T87P-3504-A or equivalent, remove inner steering gear seal and discard, then remove guide from housing.
18. Using lower pinion seal remover tool No. T86P-3504-F, remover tool No. T86P-3504-J and slide hammer tool No. T50T-100-A or equivalents, **Fig. 4,** remove pinion shaft inner seal.
19. Using puller attachment T58L-101-B and slide hammer tool No. T50T-100-A or equivalents, remove pinion bearing from housing.
20. Remove steering gear attaching brackets and grommets.

## INSPECTION

1. Inspect pinion shaft teeth and bearing for damage.
2. Inspect control valve seal for damage or abnormal wear.
3. Inspect steering rack for cracks or damaged teeth.
4. Inspect steering rack piston seal ring for abnormal wear or damage.

## ASSEMBLE

1. Install grommets and mounting brackets.
2. Using pinion bearing installer tool No. T90P-3504-OH and handle tool No. T80T-4000-W or equivalents, install pinion bearing to housing.
3. Using pinion seal installer tool No. T90P-3504-PH and handle T87P-3504-D or equivalents, install pinion shaft inner seal.
4. Lubricate new seal ring using Teflon ring expander tool No. T90P-3504-QH or equivalent, then install to steering rack piston. Ensure seal ring is properly seated. Size seal

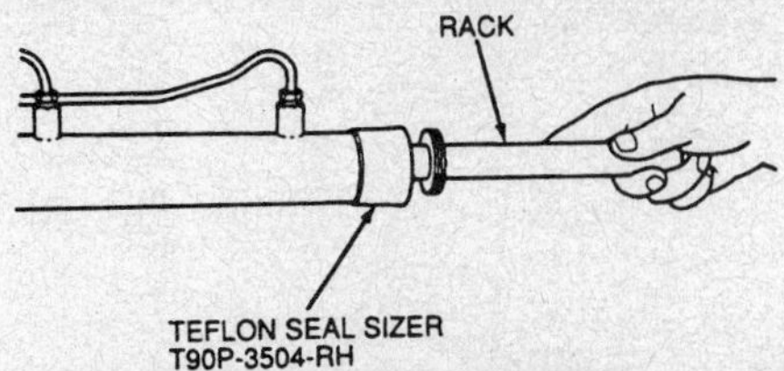


Fig. 5 Steering rack replacement. 1.8L

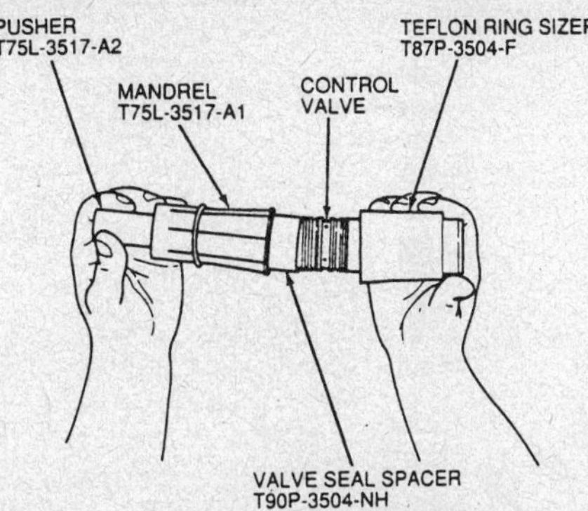


Fig. 6 Control valve seal replacement. 1.8L

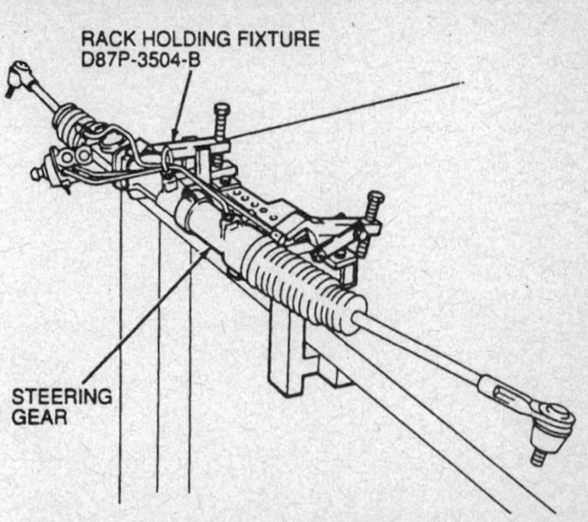


Fig. 7 Steering gear holding fixture. 1.9L

ring using Teflon seal sizer tool No. T90P-3504-RH.

5. Lubricate inner guide, then slide onto rack.
6. Lubricate inner seal, then using rack seal protector tool No. T87P-3504-H or equivalent, slide seal on rack, then remove protector.
7. Position Teflon seal sizer tool No. T90P-3504-RH or equivalent, on rack, then slide steering rack onto housing until inner seal is fully seated, **Fig. 5.**
8. Install steering gear busing using outer box torque adapter tool No. T90P-3504-MH or equivalent.
9. Using suitable vacuum pump, apply 400 mm-Hg to steering gear housing, ensuring vacuum is maintained for 30 seconds, if vacuum is not maintained, replace inner seal.
10. Using Mandrel tool No. T75L-3517-A1, pusher tool No. T75L-3517-A2, Teflon ring sizer tool No. T87P-3504-F and valve seal spacer tool No. T90P-3504-NH or equivalents, install control valve seal ring, **Fig. 6.**
11. Center rack in housing, then using Teflon ring sizer tool No. T87P-3504-F or equivalent, install pinion shaft and control valve to housing.
12. Using pinion torque adapter tool No. T86P-3504-K or equivalent, hold pinion shaft, then install pinion shaft locknut and tighten to specifications.
13. Install pinion shaft locknut cover, then tighten to specifications.
14. Apply suitable sealant to pinion shaft locknut cover, then using gear bushing adapter tool No. T80L-77209-A or equivalent, install pinion shaft plug seal.
15. Install bearing to pinion shaft plug, then apply suitable grease to plug seal, then using pinion cover torque adapter tool No. T90P-3504-KH or equivalent, install plug.
16. Install pinion shaft cover, support yoke and spring.
17. Apply sealant to yoke adjustment locknut, install adjustment plug and tighten to specifications.
18. Using torque gauge tool No. T90P-3504-H or equivalent, install yoke adjustment locknut, then tighten to specifications.
19. Using pinion torque adapter tool No. T86K-3504-K or equivalent, measure pinion torque, 8.7-10 inch lbs. within a pinion rotation angle of ± 90° from rack center position should be indicated, if not as specified, repeat steps 17 and 18.
20. Install tie rods, then using suitable chisel install tie rod tabs.
21. Install dust boots with wire and clips, then tie rod end jam nut.
22. Install tie rod ends, aligning installation marks, then tighten tie rod end jam nuts to specifications.

# 1.9L MODELS

## TROUBLESHOOTING

### Steering Feels Heavy

1. Steering fluid leakage or loss.
2. Twisted or cut plastic valve ring.
3. Faulty plastic piston ring.
4. Loose rack piston.
5. Faulty rubber back-up piston O-ring.
6. Faulty rack assembly.
7. Improper belt tension.
8. Hose, cooler or pump external leakage.
9. Improper engine idle speed.
10. Faulty pulley.
11. Hose or cooler line restriction.

### Improper Steering Wheel Return

1. Improperly aligned steering column or flange.
2. Binding intermediate shaft.
3. Valve assembly binding.
4. Damaged sub frame or rack.
5. Binding column bearing.
6. Improper wheel alignment settings.
7. Power steering system contamination.
8. Deformed engine mounts.

### Vehicle Wanders

1. Loose tie rod ends.
2. Loose or worn inner ball housing.
3. Loose gear assembly mount.
4. Loose column intermediate shaft bolts.
5. Loose or worn column intermediate shaft joints.
6. Improper wheel alignment settings.

### Rattle Or Knocking Noise From Steering Gear

1. Loose column u-joints.
2. Loose tie rod ends.
3. Loose gear assembly mount.
4. Loose pinion bearing cap.
5. Loose or worn ball joint.
6. Rack piston loose or disengaged.
7. Worn steering gear yoke.
8. Loose column intermediate shaft bolts.
9. Loose struts.

### Hissing Sound

Hissing sound is a normal characteristic of rotary steering gears and in no way affects steering.

1. Improper steering column shaft and gear.
2. Improper clearance between flexible coupling components.
3. Loose boot at dash panel.

## POWER STEERING PRESSURE TEST

**During the following procedure, power steering system pressure may exceed 1200 psi. Ensure proper tool fitment prior to performing test. Exercise extreme caution or damage or personal injury may result.**

1. Prior to performing pump flow and pressure tests, ensure following conditions exist:
   a. Proper pump reservoir fluid level.
   b. Correct tire air pressure.
   c. Proper pump belt tension.
   d. Correct model and vehicle pump application.
   e. Correct size pulleys on pump and engine.
   f. Ensure system is not damaged or leaking, repair as required.
2. The following test equipment is required:
   a. Engine tachometer.
   b. Thermometer: 0-300°F (17.8-148.9°C).
   c. Power steering system analyzer tool No. 014-00207 or equivalent.
   d. Set of adapter fittings.
3. The test procedure used in conjunction with the power steering system

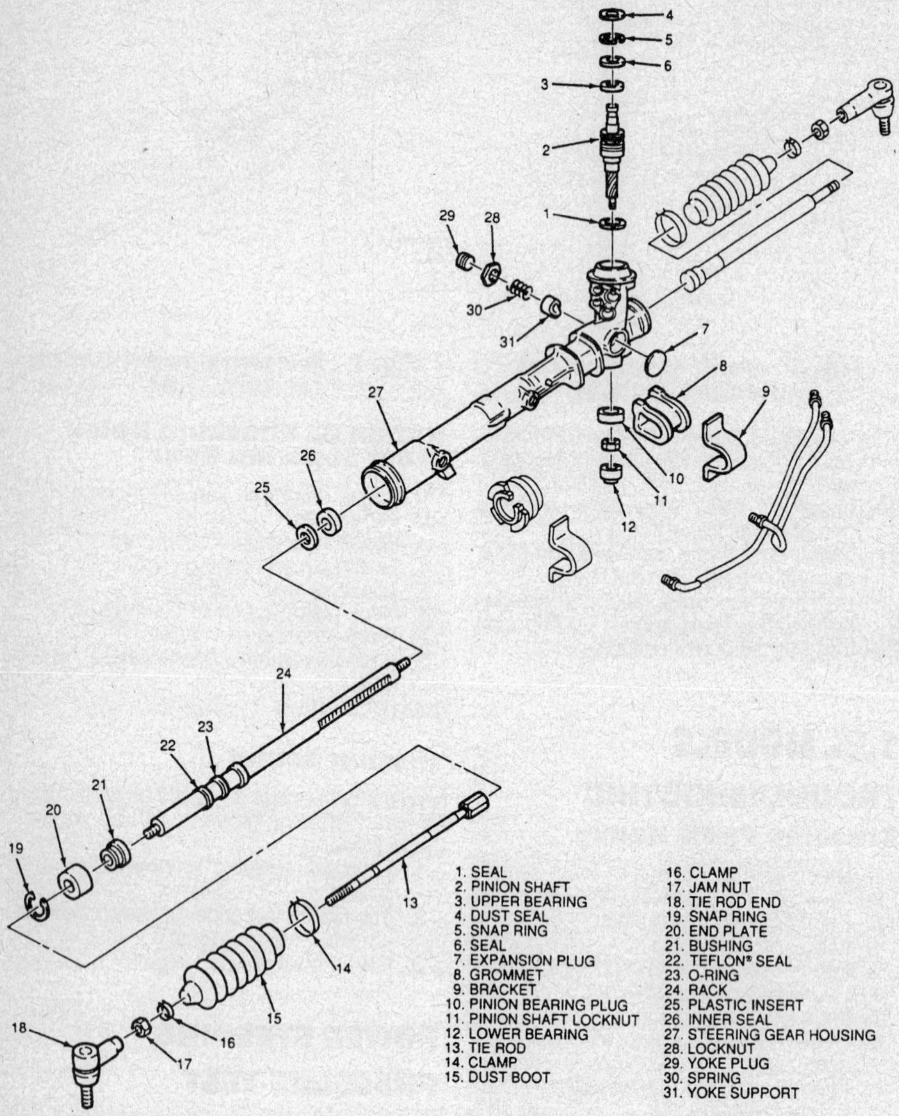

1. SEAL
2. PINION SHAFT
3. UPPER BEARING
4. DUST SEAL
5. SNAP RING
6. SEAL
7. EXPANSION PLUG
8. GROMMET
9. BRACKET
10. PINION BEARING PLUG
11. PINION SHAFT LOCKNUT
12. LOWER BEARING
13. TIE ROD
14. CLAMP
15. DUST BOOT
16. CLAMP
17. JAM NUT
18. TIE ROD END
19. SNAP RING
20. END PLATE
21. BUSHING
22. TEFLON® SEAL
23. O-RING
24. RACK
25. PLASTIC INSERT
26. INNER SEAL
27. STEERING GEAR HOUSING
28. LOCKNUT
29. YOKE PLUG
30. SPRING
31. YOKE SUPPORT

**Fig. 8 Exploded view of steering gear. 1.9L**

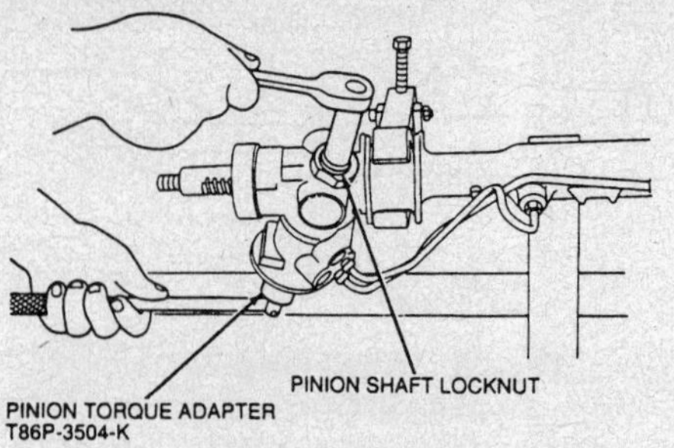

PINION SHAFT LOCKNUT
PINION TORQUE ADAPTER
T86P-3504-K

**Fig. 9 Pinion shaft locknut removal. 1.9L**

IMPACT SLIDE HAMMER
T50T-100-A
LOWER PINION
SEAL REMOVER
T86P-3504-F
LOWER PINION SEAL
REMOVER GUIDE
T86P-3504-J

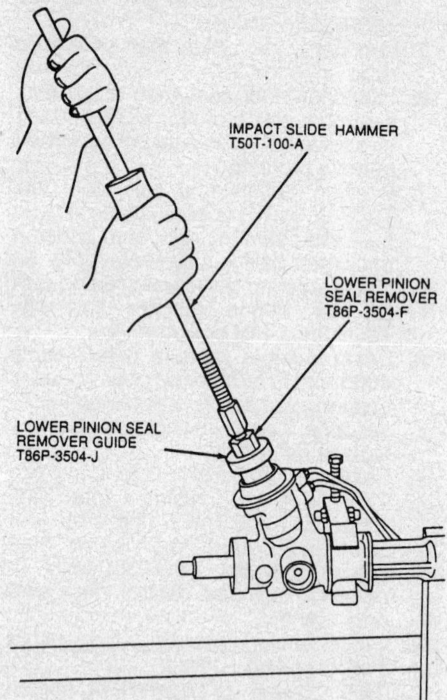

**Fig. 10 Pinion seal removal. 1.9L**

analyzer can be used to determine:
   a. System backpressure.
   b. Pump flow.
   c. Steering gear internal leakage.
   d. Pump relief pressure.
4. The readouts from step 3 can be used to determine which of the following conditions or components may be faulty:
   a. Hose or fitting restriction.
   b. Sticking gear valve.
   c. Insufficient pump capacity.
   d. Sticking relief valve.
   e. Suspension system binding.
5. Remove pump high pressure line, then connect suitable analyzer hose adapter.
6. Thread other analyzer adapter to pump. **Do not hook analyzer to gear intermediate fitting.**
7. Connect analyzer hose to adapters, tighten both connections to 15 ft. lbs. maximum.
8. If required, add power steering fluid, start engine and allow to run about two minutes.
9. With engine at idle, record the following:
   a. Flow, gallons per minute at 167-177°F (76-80°C).
   b. Pressure, psi at 167-177°F (76-80°C), at idle with gate fully open.
   c. If flow is below 1.5 gallons per minute, pump may require service, however continue test, check flow and relief pressure.
   d. If pressure is above 150 psi check hoses for restrictions.
10. Partially close gate valve to build up 740 psi, observe and record flow:
   a. If flow drops lower than .85 gallons per minute, disassemble pump and replace cam pack, if pressure plates are cracked or worn, replace.
11. Completely close and partially open gate valve three times. **Do not allow valve to remain closed for more then five seconds.** Observe and record pressure.
12. If pressure is lower than 1100 psi, replace pump check valve.
13. If pressure is above 1200 psi, pump check valve should be removed and cleaned or replaced.
14. Increase engine speed to about 1500 RPM, observe and record flow.
15. If flow exceeds 2.2 gallons per minute, pump flow control valve should be removed and cleaned or replaced.
16. Check idle speed, with engine at idle, turn steering wheel to left and right stops, record pressure and flow at stops.
17. Pressure at both stops should be about 1200 psi, flow should drop below 0.5 gallons per minute.
18. If pressure is not within specification,

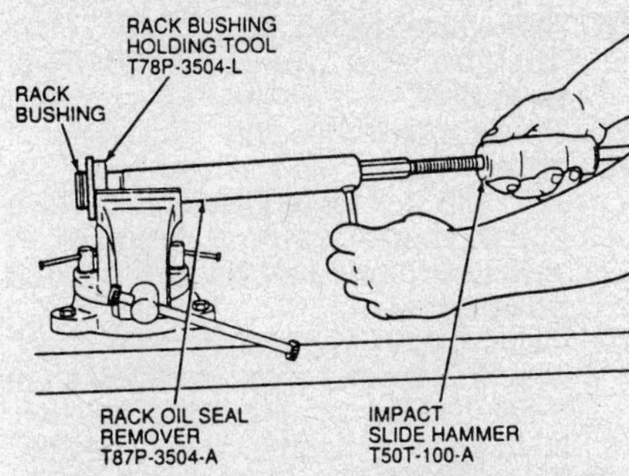


**Fig. 11 Rack bushing seal removal. 1.9L**

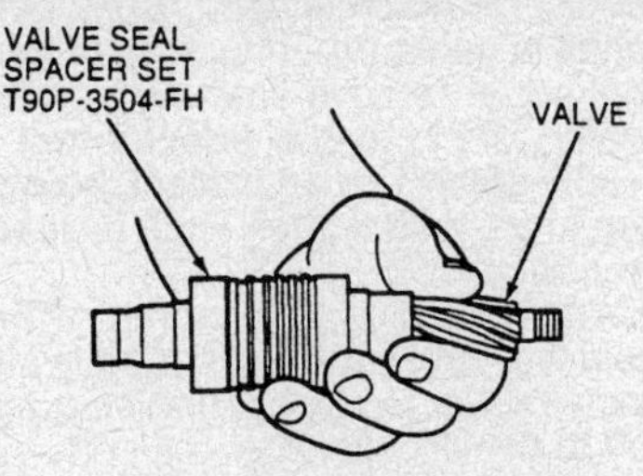


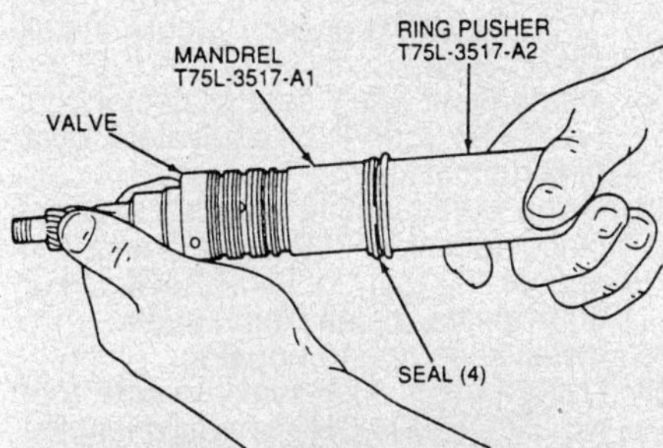


**Fig. 14 Valve seal installation. 1.9L**

excessive internal leakage is indicated, remove and disassemble steering gear, replace worn or damaged parts and inspect rack piston and valve seals for damage.

19. While watching pressure gauge, turn steering wheel slightly in both directions and quickly release wheel, gauge needle should move from normal backpressure and snap back as the wheel is released. If needle returns slowly or sticks, the steering gear rotary valve is sticking.
20. Remove and disassemble steering as described under "Disassemble," then flush power steering hoses and pump before gear installation.
21. If problem still exists, check ball joint and linkage.
22. Disconnect and remove analyzer, then connect lines.

# POWER STEERING SYSTEM SERVICE

## Air Bleed

If air bubbles are present in power steering system, bleed system.

1. Fill power steering reservoir.
2. Run engine until fluid reaches normal operating temperature 165-175°F (74-79°C).

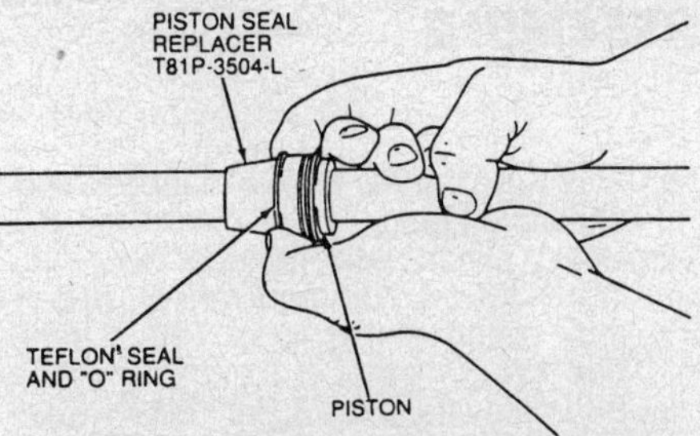


**Fig. 12 Rack piston O-ring & seal installation. 1.9L**

3. Turn steering wheel lock to lock several times. **Do not hold steering wheel in far right or left position.**
4. Check fluid level.
5. If air bubble are still present purge system as outlined under "Power Steering System Purge."

## Power Steering System Purge

1. Air trapped in power steering system may be remove with power steering pump air evacuator assembly vacuum tester 021-00014 or equivalent.
2. **Do not use engine vacuum to purge power steering system.**
3. Remove reservoir cap.
4. Check and fill reservoir to "F" mark with suitable fluid.
5. Disconnect EDIS coil pack electrical connector, then raise and support front wheels.
6. Crank engine with starter motor, then check fluid level. **Do not turn steering wheel.**
7. If fluid level has dropped, fill reservoir to "F" mark, crank engine with starter motor while turning steering wheel lock to lock, then check fluid level.
8. Install air evacuator rubber stopper tightly to pump reservoir, then connect EDIS coil pack electrical connector.
9. With engine at idle, apply 15 inch Hg maximum vacuum to pump reservoir for a minimum of three minutes, as air purges from system, vacuum will decrease, maintain adequate vacuum.
10. Release vacuum, then remove vacuum source, if fluid level has dropped, fill to "F" mark.
11. With engine at idle, apply 15 inch Hg maximum vacuum to pump reservoir, turn steering wheel from lock to lock ever 30 seconds for about five minutes. **Do not hold steering wheel on stops when turning.** Maintain adequate vacuum.
12. Release vacuum, then remove vacuum equipment add power steering fluid id required, install cap.
13. Start engine, turn steering wheel, check connections for oil leaks.
14. If severe aeration is indicated, repeat steps 7 through 13.
15. Lower vehicle.

# DISASSEMBLE

1. Install steering gear to rack holding fixture tool No. D87P-3504-B or equivalent, **Fig. 7.**
2. Place installation alignment marks on tie rod end, jam nut and tie rod.

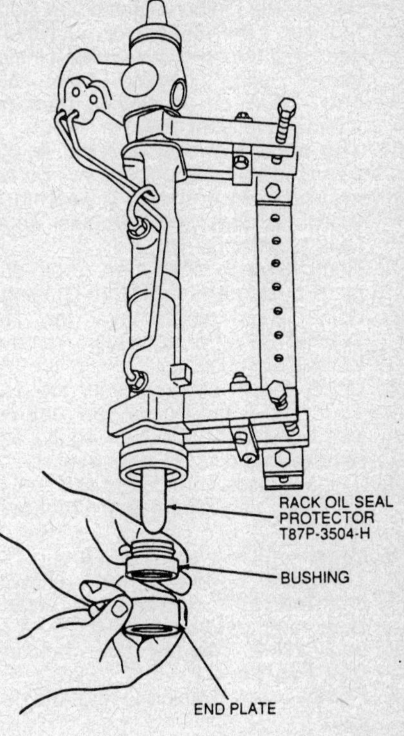


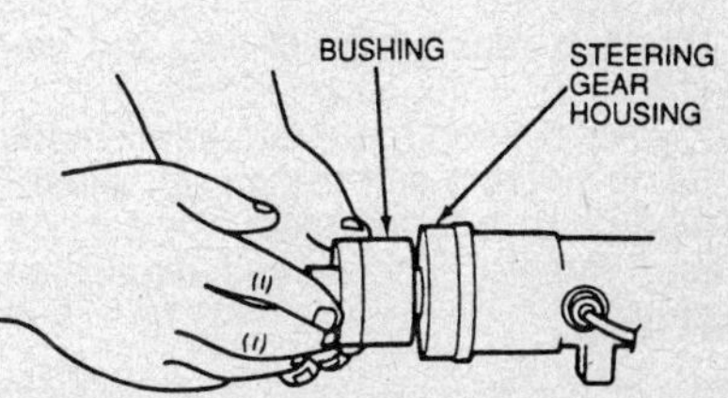


**Fig. 13 Rack bushing & end plate installation. 1.9L**

3. Remove tire rod ends and jam nuts, **Fig. 8.**
4. Remove boot clamps, the remove boots.
5. Remove tie rods, then pinion shaft dust seal.
6. Remove pinion shaft snap ring, then using yoke locknut wrench tool No. T81P-3504-G or equivalent, remove yoke plug locknut.
7. Using yoke plug adapter tool No. T87P-3504-G or equivalent, remove yoke plug.
8. Remove spring, then using pinion plug spanner wrench tool No. T90P-3504-AH or equivalent, remove lower pinion bearing plug.
9. Using pinion torque adapter tool No. T86P-3504-K or equivalent, to hold pinion shaft, remove pinion shaft locknut, **Fig. 9.**
10. Using valve body puller bridge tool No. T86P-3504-D and spool valve puller tool No. T81P-3504-T or equivalents, remove pinion shaft seal, bearing and shaft from housing.
11. Remove four valve Teflon O-rings and discard.
12. Expand lower pinion seal remover tool No. T86P-3504-F or equivalent to 1.08-1.13 inch (27.4-28.7 mm), then

using lower pinion seal remover guide tool No. T86P-3504-J or equivalent, seat seal remover to seal, then install impact slide hammer tool No. T50T-100A or equivalent, then remove pinion seal, **Fig. 10.**

13. **The middle pinion bearing is not serviceable, and should not be removed from housing. If bearing is worn or damaged, replace short rack assembly.**
14. Remove rack snap ring, rack end plate, busing and rack from housing.
15. Using piston pin remover tool No. T68P-6135-A7 or equivalent, remove lower pinion bearing.
16. Using impact slide hammer tool No. T50T-100-A and rack oil seal remover tool No. T87P-3504-A or equivalent, remove and discard inner seal.
17. If plastic insert is removed and seal is left in housing, repeat step 17 for seal removal.
18. Using rack bushing tool No. T87P-3504-L, rack oil seal remover tool No. T87P-3504-A and impact slide hammer tool No. T50T-100-A or equivalents, remove rack bushing seal, **Fig. 11.**
19. Remove rack bushing O-ring and discard.
20. Remove rack piston Teflon seal and discard.
21. Remove rack piston O-ring and discard.
22. If yoke support requires replacement, using suitable drift, punch out expansion plug, then remove yoke support and discard support and expansion plug.

## INSPECTION

1. Inspect pinion shaft bearing for fit on shaft.
2. Check fluid passages for obstruction or leakage.
3. Inspect housing for cracks and stripped threads.
4. Check mating surfaces for burrs.
5. Inspect valve and piston bores for scoring.
6. Ensure pinion shaft rotates freely.
7. Inspect piston rack and pinion shaft teeth for nicks and burrs.

## ASSEMBLE

1. If required, install yoke support and expansion plug.
2. Using piston seal replacer tool No. T81P-3504-L or equivalent, install rack piston O-ring, then Teflon seal, **Fig. 12.**
3. Separate steering gear inner seal plastic insert and save for later installation.
4. Install rack oil seal protector tool No. T87P-3504-H or equivalent, over rack, then install plastic insert and inner seal to piston, then remove seal protector.
5. Snap plastic insert into inner seal.
6. Using suitable steering gear lubricant, pack steering rack teeth, then apply light lubricant to rack yoke contact area.
7. Using suitable power steering fluid, lubricate piston seal and gear inner seal outer edge.
8. Install rack piston seal sizer tool No. T81P-3504-K or equivalent, to end of steering gear housing, then install rack.
9. Using suitable punch and plastic hammer, drive end of rack to seat inner seal.
10. Install rack bushing O-ring, then using rack oil seal replacer tool No. T81P-3504-C or equivalent, install rack bushing seal.
11. Using rack oil seal protector tool No. T87P-3504-H or equivalent, over rack, install rack bushing and end plate, **Fig. 13.**
12. Install rack attaching snap ring to housing.
13. Using pinion bearing replacer tool No. T90P-3504-BH and driver handle tool No. T80T-4000-W or equivalents, install lower pinion bearing.
14. Using lower pinion seal replacer tool No. T87P-3504-C and handle T87P-3504-D or equivalents, install pinion seal.
15. Install valve seal spacer set tool No. T90P-3504-FH or equivalent, then using mandrel tool No. T75L-3517-A1 and ring pusher tool No. T75L-3517-A2 or equivalents, install valve Teflon seal, **Fig. 14.**
16. Size valve Teflon seals with Teflon ring sizer tool No. T87P-3504-F or equivalent.
17. Center rack in housing.
18. Install Teflon ring sizer tool No. T87P-3504-F or equivalent, ti valve housing bore. **Center of pinion shaft V-flat surface must be in 9 o'clock position.**
19. Install pinion shaft until teeth mech with rack teeth, center of pinion shaft V-flat will be in 9 o'clock position, push shaft by hand until fully seated.
20. Using pinion torque adapter tool No. T86P-3504-K or equivalent, turn pinion shaft, count number of turns from center to each stop, ensure pinion shaft is centered, is number of turn is not equal, remove shaft and reinstall.
21. Using pinion torque adapter tool No. T86P-3504-K or equivalent, hold pinion shaft, then tighten shaft locknut to specifications.
22. Using pinion plug spanner wrench tool No. T90P-3504-AH or equivalent, install lower pinion bearing plug, tighten to specifications.
23. Using upper pinion bearing/seal replacer tool No. T78P-3504-D and bearing spacer ring tool No. T90P-3504-CH or equivalents, install pinion shaft bearing.
24. Install input shaft seal protector tool No. T81P-3504-P or equivalent, over pinion shaft.
25. Using upper pinion bearing/seal replacer tool No. T78P-3504-D and seal spacer ring tool No. T90P-3504-DH or equivalents, install pinion shaft.
26. Install snap ring to housing.
27. Using pinion dust seal replacer tool No. T85T-3504-CH1 or equivalent, install pinion shaft dust seal.
28. Install yoke plug bore spring, then using yoke plug adapter too No. T87P-3504-G or equivalent, install yoke plug then tighten to specifications.
29. Using yoke locknut wrench tool No. T81P-3504-G or equivalent, tighten yoke plug locknut to specifications.
30. Apply ESE-MAG203-A2 to tie rods, then install to rack and tighten to specifications.
31. Install and clamp boots.
32. Install jam nuts, then tie rod ends and tighten to specifications.

## TIGHTENING SPECIFICATIONS

| Year | Component | Torque, Ft. Lbs. |
|---|---|---|
| **1.8L Engine** | | |
| 1991 | Intermediate Shaft To Pinion Shaft Bolt | 13-20 |
| | Pinion Shaft Locknut | 29-36 |
| | Pinion Shaft Locknut Cover | 29-36 |
| | Pressure Line Flare Nut At Gear | 22-28 |
| | Pressure Line Flare Nut At Pump | 12-17 |
| | Pump High Pressure line Fitting | 12-17 |
| | Pump Mounting Bolts | 27-38 |
| | Pump Bracket Bolt | 27-40 |
| | Return Line Flare Nut At Gear | 22-28 |

*Continued*

## TIGHTENING SPECIFICATIONS —Continued

| Year | Component | Torque, Ft. Lbs. |
|---|---|---|
| | Steering Gear Bracket Nuts | 27–38 |
| | Tensioner To Pump Bracket Nut & Bolt | 23–34 |
| | Tensioner To Pump Nut & Bolt | 14–19 |
| | Tie Rod End Attaching Nuts | 31–42 |
| | Tie Rod End Jam Nuts | 26–86① |
| | Yoke Adjustment Nut | ② |
| | Yoke Plug Locknut | 29–36 |
| **1.9L Engine** | | |
| 1991 | A/C Compressor | 30–40 |
| | High Pressure Line To Housing Flare Nut | 21–25 |
| | Lower Pinion Bearing Plug | 22–28 |
| | Pinion Shaft Locknut | 20–35 |
| | Return Line To Housing Flare Nut | 21–25 |
| | Tie Rod End Jam Nuts | 25–37 |
| | Tie Rod To Rack | 40–50 |
| | Valve Outlet Fittings | 25–40 |
| | Yoke Plug | ③ |
| | Yoke Plug Locknut | 40–50 |

①—Inch lbs.
②—Tighten to 43 inch lbs., then loosen ⅛ turn (45°).
③—Tighten to 42–44 inch lbs., then loosen 44–52°, then tighten.

# TRW Rack & Pinion Steering

## INDEX



## 1989 ESCORT, TEMPO & TOPAZ

### TROUBLESHOOTING

#### Front End Wanders

1. Improper tire pressure or size.
2. Vehicle over or unevenly loaded.
3. Loose column intermediate shaft connecting bolts.
4. Gear assembly loose on body bracket.
5. Faulty wheel bearing.
6. Improper wheel alignment adjustment.
7. Faulty front or rear suspension component(s).

#### Steering Wheel Pulls

1. Improper tire pressure or size.
2. Vehicle over or unevenly loaded.
3. Improper wheel alignment adjustment.
4. Faulty front or rear suspension component(s).

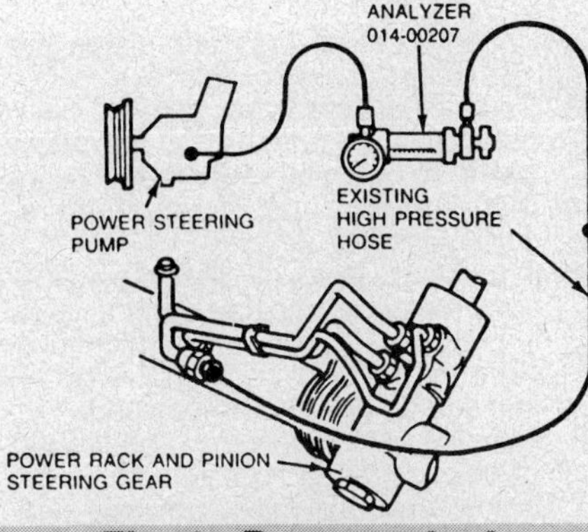


**Fig. 1 Pressure test connections**

5. Faulty steering gear valve.
6. Faulty front or rear brake operation.
7. Faulty wheel bearing.

#### Steering Gear Rattle, Squeak Or Knock

1. Improper yoke preload adjustment.
2. Loosen suspension component(s).
3. Loose column intermediate shaft connecting bolts.
4. Gear assembly loose on body bracket.
5. Loose or worn column intermediate shaft universal joints.

#### Poor Steering Wheel Return

1. Improper tire pressure.
2. Improper tire size or type.
3. Column flange rubbing steering wheel.
4. Binding column intermediate shaft universal joints.
5. Improper toe adjustment.
6. Binding column bearing.
7. System contamination.
8. Improper yoke preload.

### POWER STEERING PRESSURE TEST

During the following procedure, power steering system pressure may

**exceed 1200 psi. Ensure proper tool fitment prior to performing test. Exercise extreme caution or damage or personal injury may result.**

1. Prior to performing pump flow and pressure tests, ensure following conditions exist:
   a. Proper pump reservoir fluid level.
   b. Correct tire air pressure.
   c. Proper pump belt tension.
   d. Correct model and vehicle pump application.
   e. Correct size pulleys on pump and engine.
   f. Ensure system is not damaged or leaking, repair as required.
2. The following test equipment is required:
   a. Engine tachometer.
   b. Thermometer: 0-300°F (17.8-148.9°C).
   c. Power steering system analyzer tool No. 014-00207 or equivalent.
   d. Set of adapter fittings.
3. The test procedure used in conjunction with the power steering system analyzer can be used to determine:
   a. System backpressure.
   b. Pump flow.
   c. Steering gear internal leakage.
   d. Pump relief pressure.
4. The readouts from step 3 can be used to determine which of the following conditions or components may be faulty:
   a. Hose or fitting restriction.
   b. Sticking gear valve.
   c. Insufficient pump capacity.
   d. Sticking relief valve.
   e. Suspension system binding.
5. Remove air pump, then position belt away from power steering pulley.
6. **On Tempo and Topaz models,** loosen pressure line brackets at engine oil filter and above transmission.
7. **On all models,** disconnect pump high pressure line, then connect suitable analyzer hose adapter, **Fig. 1.**
8. Thread other analyzer adapter to pump.
9. Connect analyzer hose to adapters, tighten both connections to 15 ft. lbs. maximum. **Do not hook up analyzer at gear intermediate fitting.**
10. If required, add power steering fluid, start engine and allow to run about two minutes. Ensure idle is set to specifications.
11. With engine at idle, record the following:
    a. Flow, gallons per minute at 167-177°F (76-80°C).
    b. Pressure, psi at 167-177°F (76-80°C), at idle with gate fully open.
    c. If flow is below 1.5 gallons per minute, pump may require service, however continue test, check flow and relief pressure.
    d. If pressure is above 150 psi check hoses for restrictions.
12. Partially close gate valve to build up 740 psi, observe and record flow at 167-177°F (76-80°C):
    a. If flow drops below specifications, disassemble pump and replace cam pack, if pressure plates are cracked or worn, replace.
13. Completely close and partially open gate valve three times. **Do not allow valve to remain closed for more then five seconds.** Observe and record pressure.
14. If pressure is lower than specifications, replace pump flow control valve.
15. If pressure is above specifications, pump flow control valve should be removed and cleaned or replaced.
16. Increase engine speed to about 1500 RPM, observe and record flow.
17. If flow exceeds maximum free flow per minute, pump flow control valve should be removed and cleaned or replaced.
18. Check idle speed, with engine at idle, turn steering wheel to left and right stops, record pressure and flow at stops.
19. Pressure at both stops should be about the same as maximum pump output pressure, flow should drop below 0.5 gallons per minute.
20. If pressure is not within specification, excessive internal leakage is indicated, remove and disassemble steering gear, replace worn or damaged parts and inspect rack piston and valve seals for damage.
21. While watching pressure gauge, turn steering wheel slightly in both directions and quickly release wheel, gauge needle should move from normal backpressure and snap back as the wheel is released. If needle returns slowly or sticks, the steering gear rotary valve is sticking.
22. Remove and disassemble steering as described under "Disassemble," then flush power steering hoses and pump before gear installation.
23. If problem still exists, check ball joint and linkage.

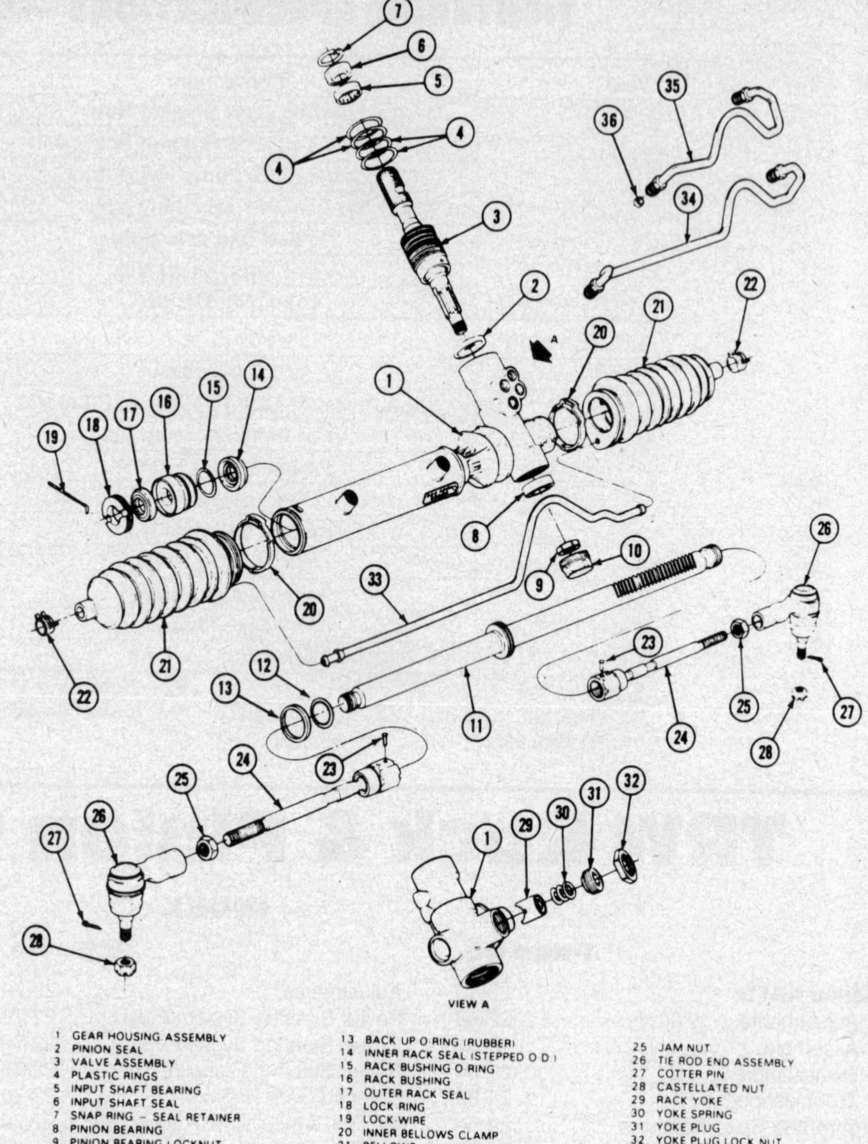


1 GEAR HOUSING ASSEMBLY
2 PINION SEAL
3 VALVE ASSEMBLY
4 PLASTIC RINGS
5 INPUT SHAFT BEARING
6 INPUT SHAFT SEAL
7 SNAP RING – SEAL RETAINER
8 PINION BEARING
9 PINION BEARING LOCKNUT
10 HOUSING CAP
11 RACK ASSEMBLY
12 PISTON SEAL (PLASTIC)
13 BACK UP O-RING (RUBBER)
14 INNER RACK SEAL (STEPPED O.D.)
15 RACK BUSHING O-RING
16 RACK BUSHING
17 OUTER RACK SEAL
18 LOCK RING
19 LOCK WIRE
20 INNER BELLOWS CLAMP
21 BELLOWS
22 OUTER BELLOWS CLAMP
23 SPIRAL PIN
24 TIE ROD ASSEMBLY
25 JAM NUT
26 TIE ROD END ASSEMBLY
27 COTTER PIN
28 CASTELLATED NUT
29 RACK YOKE
30 YOKE SPRING
31 YOKE PLUG
32 YOKE PLUG LOCK NUT
33 BREATHER TUBE
34 RIGHT TURN TRANSFER TUBE
35 LEFT TURN TRANSFER TUBE
36 COPPER SEAL (4 REQ D)

**Fig. 2 Exploded view of TRW power rack & pinion steering gear**

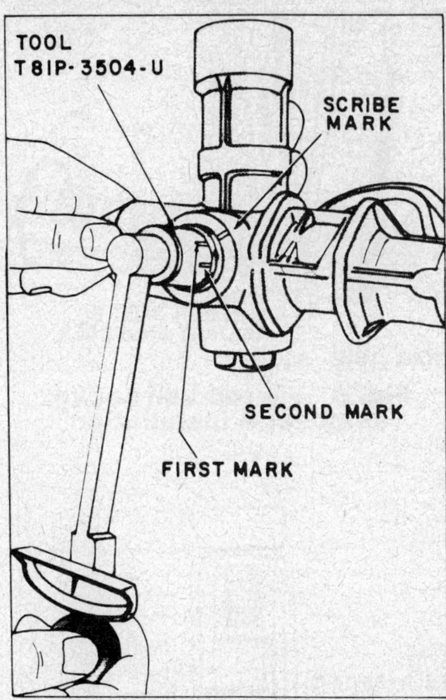


**Fig. 3 Adjusting yoke plug**

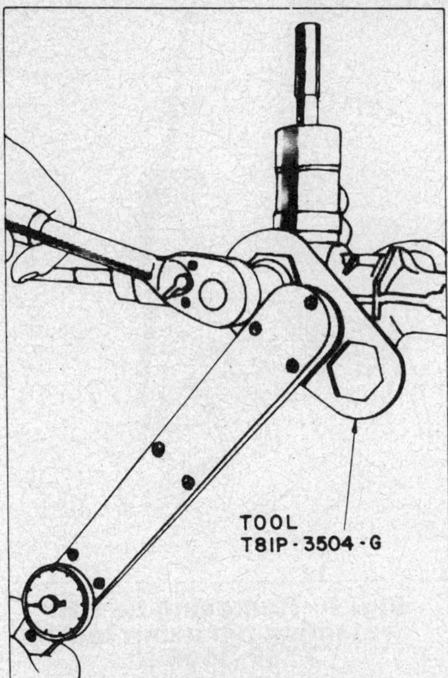


**Fig. 4 Yoke plug locknut removal & installation**

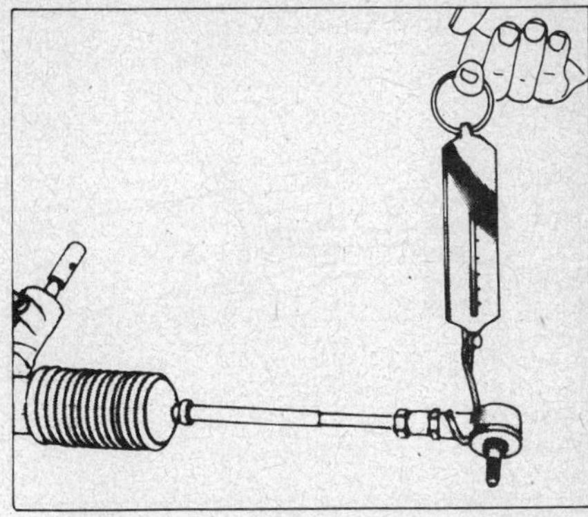

**Fig. 5 Tie rod articulation torque check**

24. Disconnect and remove analyzer, then connect lines.
25. **On Tempo and Topaz models,** install pressure line brackets.

## POWER STEERING SYSTEM PURGE

1. Air trapped in power steering system may be remove with power steering pump air evacuator assembly vacuum tester 021-00014 or equivalent.
2. **Do not use engine vacuum to purge power steering system.**
3. Remove pump filler neck adapter and dipstick or dipstick cap assembly.
4. Check and fill reservoir to cold fill mark with suitable fluid.
5. Disconnect ignition coil wire, then raise and support front wheels.
6. Crank engine with starter motor, then check fluid level. **Do not turn steering wheel.**
7. If fluid level has dropped, fill reservoir to cold fill mark, crank engine with starter motor while turning steering wheel lock to lock, then check fluid level.
8. Install air evacuator rubber stopper tightly to pump reservoir, then connect coil wire.
9. With engine at idle, apply 15 inch Hg maximum vacuum to pump reservoir for a minimum of three minutes, as air purges from system, vacuum will decrease, maintain adequate vacuum.
10. Release vacuum, then remove vacuum source, if fluid level has dropped, fill to cold fill mark.
11. With engine at idle, apply 15 inch Hg maximum vacuum to pump reservoir, turn steering wheel from lock to lock ever 30 seconds for about five minutes. **Do not hold steering wheel on stops when turning.** Maintain adequate vacuum.
12. Release vacuum, then remove vacuum equipment add power steering fluid id required, install cap.
13. Start engine, turn steering wheel, check connections for oil leaks.
14. If severe aeration is indicated, repeat steps 7 through 13.
15. Lower vehicle.

## POWER STEERING SYSTEM FLUSH

1. Install pump but do not attach return hose.
2. Place return line in suitable container, then plug reservoir return line at reservoir.
3. Fill reservoir using Motorcraft DEXRON II part No. ESW-M2C33-F or equivalent.
4. Disconnect coil wire, then raise and support front wheels.
5. While adding about two quarts of fluid, turn ignition to start position (using ignition key), then crank engine with starter and turn steering wheel right to left.
6. When all the fluid is added, turn ignition off, and connect coil wire.
7. Remove reservoir return line plug, then connect line to reservoir.
8. Fill reservoir to specified level.
9. Lower vehicle, then start engine, slowly turn steering wheel several times lock to lock, then recheck fluid level, add as required.

## ADJUSTMENTS

### Rack Yoke Preload

The steering gear must be removed from the vehicle to perform this adjustment.

1. Clean exterior of the rack and pinion assembly, drain power steering fluid out of the pressure and return ports, **Fig. 2.** Do not remove external pressure lines unless they are leaking or damaged.
2. Loosen and remove yoke plug locknut.
3. Loosen yoke plug one turn.
4. Using a 100 inch-pound capacity torque wrench, **torque** yoke plug to 45 inch pounds, **Fig. 3.**
5. Using "O" mark on tool as a reference point, make an index mark on the gear housing, **Fig. 3.**
6. Loosen yoke plug just enough until the second mark aligns with the mark previously made on the gear housing, **Fig. 3.**
7. Holding plug, install and tighten to specifications, **Fig. 4.**

## TIE ROD ARTICULATION TORQUE CHECK

This check can be done in the car or on the bench.

1. Remove tie rod end from steering knuckle.
2. Hook end of a spring scale to tie rod end and measure force necessary to move the tie rod, **Fig. 5.**
3. If the force required to move the tie rod is not between 1 and 9 lbs., replace tie rod.

## STEERING GEAR REPAIRS

### TIE ROD BALL SOCKETS

#### Disassembly

1. Mount power steering in a vise, clamping only by the steel tube section between the rack pressure ports.
2. Remove tie rod ends and jam nuts, **Fig. 2.** Mark position of tie rod ends on tie rod for reassembly.
3. Remove bellow clamps, bellows and breather tube. Use care not to damage bellows.
4. Using an easy-out, **Fig. 6,** or tool No. T78P-3504-N, **Fig. 7,** remove spiral pin which locks each tie rod socket to the rack.
5. The following tools must be used to remove the socket, tool No. T81P-3504-G, or equivalent, a torque wrench and an adjustable wrench to hold the rack from rotating, **Fig. 8.**

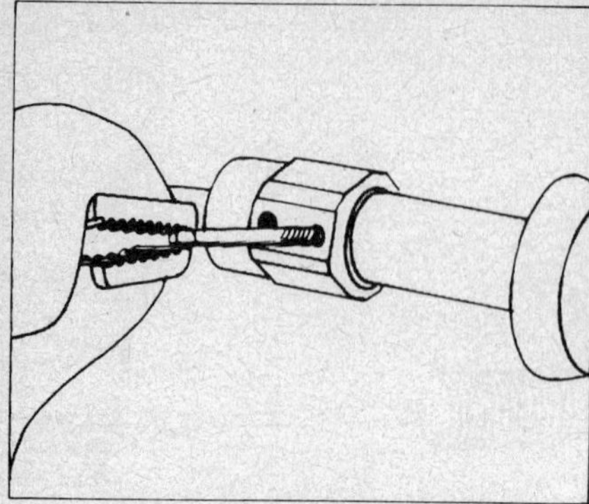

Fig. 6 Removing tie ball socket retaining pin w/easy-out

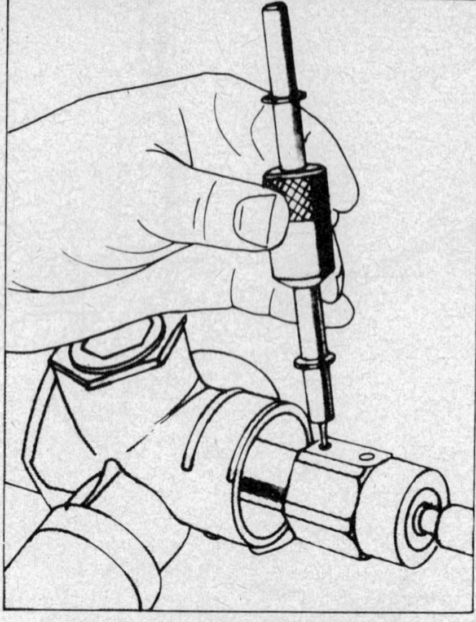

Fig. 7 Removing tie ball retaining pin using tool T78P-3504-N

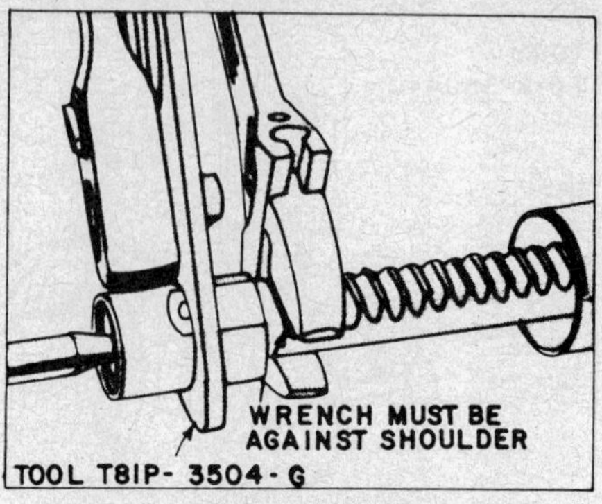


Fig. 8 Tie rod ball socket removal & installation

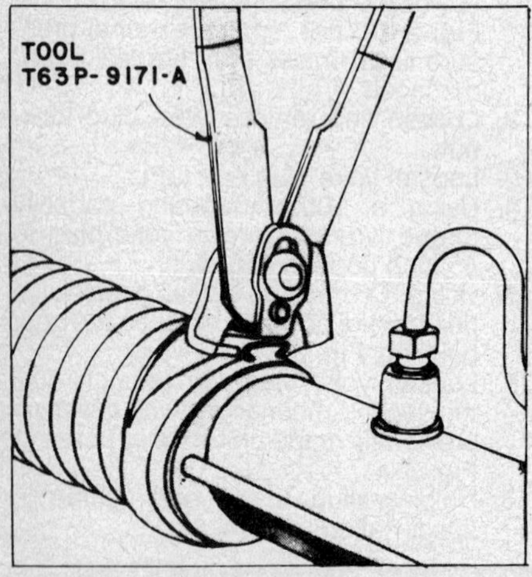


Fig. 9 Installing power rack & pinion bellows

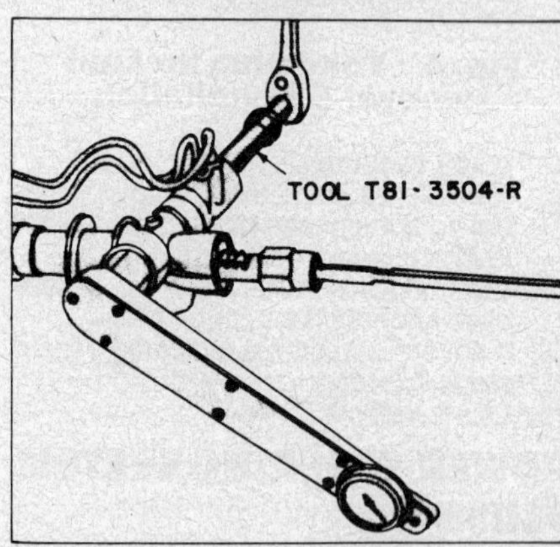


Fig. 10 Removing & installing pinion bearing locknut

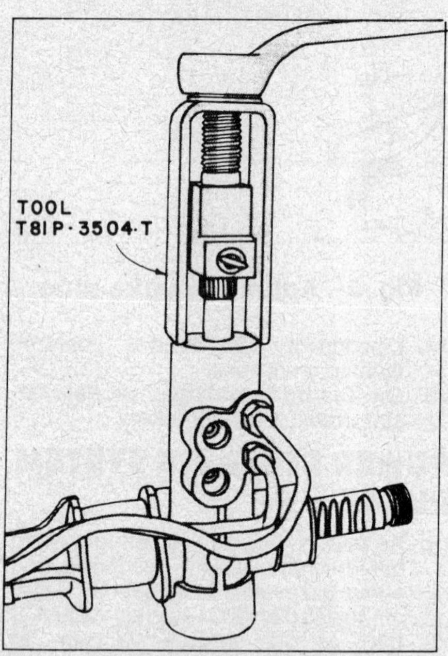


Fig. 11 Removing valve, input shaft seal & bearing

## Assembly

1. Install and tighten tie rod ball sockets hand tight.
2. Using an adjustable wrench to prevent rack from rotating, tighten lefthand ball socket to specifications using tool No. T81P-3504-G, or equivalent, **Fig. 8.** If rack is not restrained from rotating, damage to rack or pinion teeth may result.
3. Install spiral pin for lefthand socket using a pair of pliers and a small hammer.
4. Restrain lefthand tie ball socket from turning while tightening righthand socket to specifications, then install spiral pin.
5. Install bellows, breather tube and clamps. Using tool No. T63P-9171-A or equivalent, secure clamps properly, **Fig. 9.**
6. Install tie rod ends and jam nuts.

## INPUT SHAFT & VALVE ASSEMBLY

### Disassembly

1. Thoroughly clean rack and pinion assembly and mount in a vise, clamping only by the steel tube section between the rack pressure ports.
2. Do not remove the external pressure lines unless damaged or leaking. If the lines are removed the copper seals must be replaced.
3. Using tool No. T81P-3504-G, or equivalent, loosen yoke plug locknut, **Fig. 4,** remove yoke plug with tool No. T81P-3504-U, or equivalent, **Fig. 3,** lift out spring and yoke.
4. Remove power steering gear housing cap.
5. Position tool No. T81P-3504-R, or equivalent, on input shaft. While holding input shaft, remove pinion bearing locknut using a suitable 17 mm socket, **Fig. 10.** Discard locknut.
6. Remove input shaft seal snap ring.
7. Position input shaft and valve body puller tool No. T81P-3504-T, or equivalent, on input shaft, **Fig. 11.** Using a suitable wrench, turn nut to remove input shaft, valve body, input shaft seal and bearing.
8. Remove the lower pinion shaft seal using protective sleeve tool T78P-3504-E, or equivalent. Insert the tools into the gear housing. Using a plastic mallet, tap the tool lightly to seat it, **Fig. 12.** Activate the tool expander, **Fig. 13.**
9. Using a slide hammer tool No. T50T-100-A, or equivalent, remove seal, then tools, **Fig. 14.**
10. Position a suitable expanding type puller over the gear housing and remove pinion bearing. **Remove the pinion bearing only if damaged.**
11. If the valve assembly plastic seal rings are to be replaced use a sharp pocket knife to cut them off. Use care not to scratch or nick the valve sleeve.

### Assembly

1. Support the valve housing on a clean flat surface. Using tool No. T81P-3504-H, or equivalent, install new pinion bearing, **Fig. 15.**
2. With the valve housing supported as in step 1, apply grease to a new pinion oil seal. Using a suitable seal installer, position the pinion oil seal on the installer with seal lip towards tool and install in valve housing, seating seal against shoulder.
3. Install four valve sleeve rings, refer to **Fig. 16 A-F, (substeps A through F appear within Fig. 16)** and the following steps:

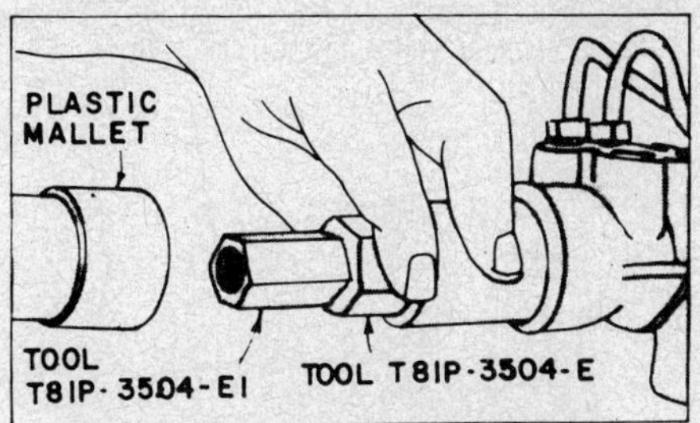


**Fig. 12 Positioning lower pinion shaft seal remover**

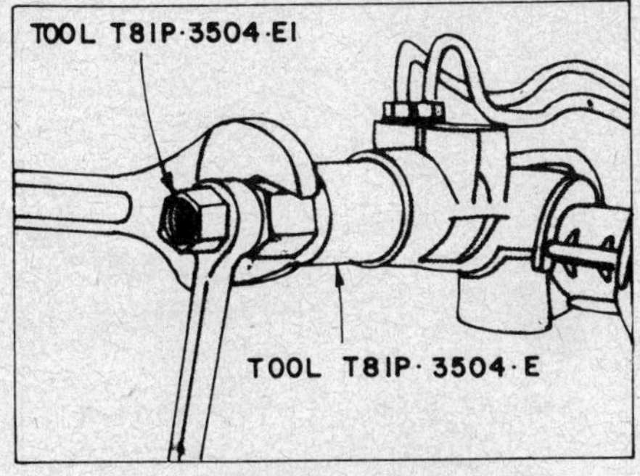


**Fig. 13 Activating tool expander**

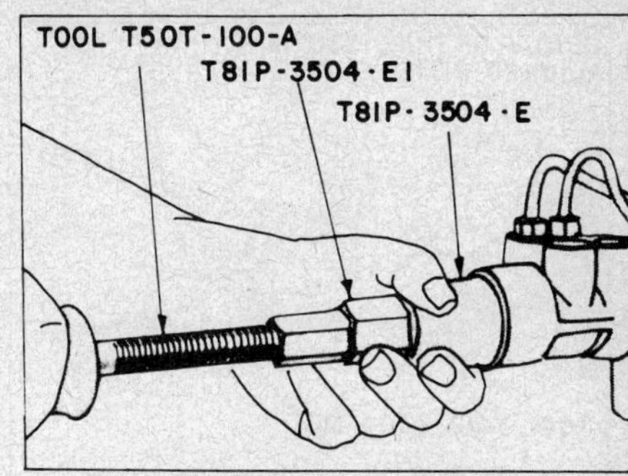


**Fig. 14 Removing lower pinion shaft seal**

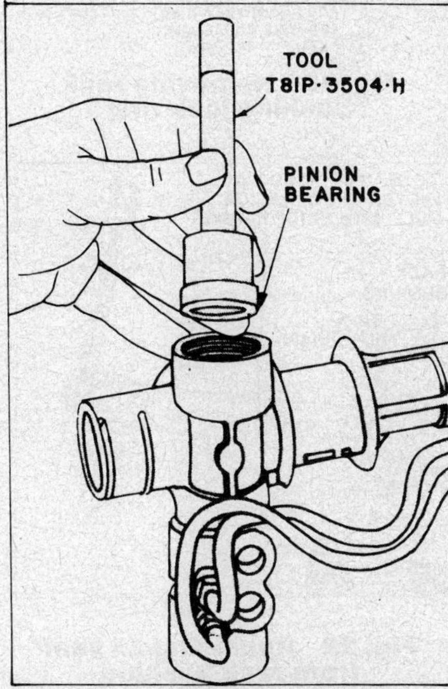


**Fig. 15 Pinion bearing installation**

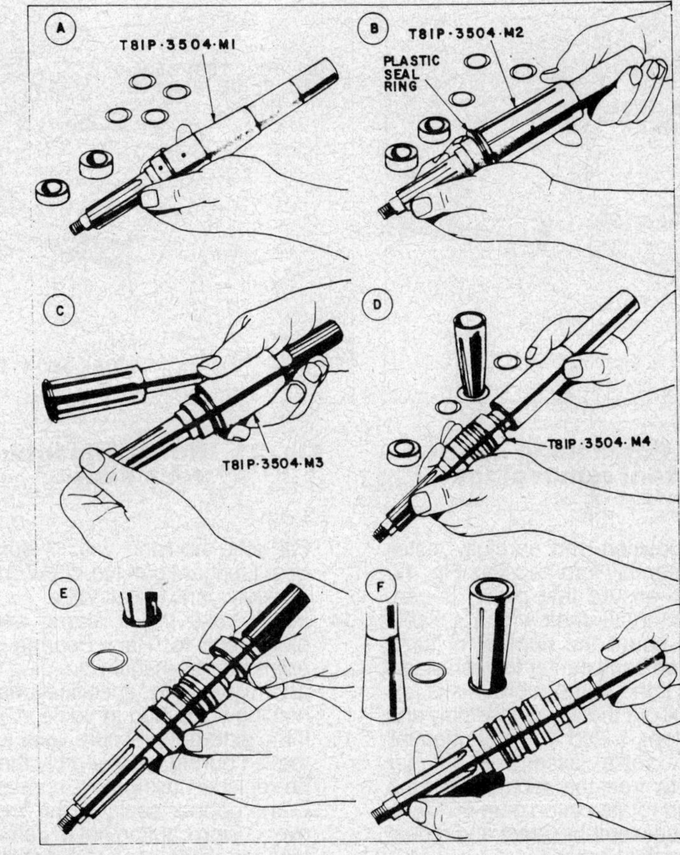


**Fig. 16 Valve assembly sleeve ring installation sequence**

a. Lubricate sleeve tool No. T81P-3504-M1, or equivalent, with automatic transmission fluid type F or equivalent, position tool over valve assembly, **Fig. 16 (substep A).**
b. Place valve sleeve ring over tool, quickly push down on pusher tool No. T81P-3504-M2, or equivalent, sliding the ring down into the fourth groove, **Fig. 16 (substep B).**
c. Using automatic transmission fluid type F, lubricate inside of sizing tool T81P-3504-M3, or equivalent, slowly work the tool over the installed ring to seat it. Take care not to deform the ring. Repeat this step after each ring is installed, **Fig. 16 (substep C).**
d. Position spacer tool No. T81P-3504-M4, or equivalent, over input shaft with the thin lip toward the input shaft splines. This aligns the sleeve tool No. T81P-3504-M1, or equivalent, with the third groove, **Fig. 16 (substep D),** repeat substeps A, B and C.
e. Position the second spacer tool with the lip toward the input shaft splines, **Fig. 16 (substep E).** Repeat steps A, B and C.
f. Remove the second spacer and turn it over so the thin lip of the second spacer contacts the thin lip of the first spacer, **Fig. 16 (substep F).** Repeat steps A, B and C.

4. Remove tools from input shaft and valve assembly, carefully inspect sleeve rings to ensure they are seated correctly and turn freely in their grooves.
5. Position rack in rack housing with three rack teeth protruding from left side of housing. Carefully observe rack while looking through valve housing bore and center the visible rack tooth in the valve bore.
6. Insert sizing tool No. T81P-3504-M3, or equivalent, into valve housing. Position "D" flat on input shaft at the 3

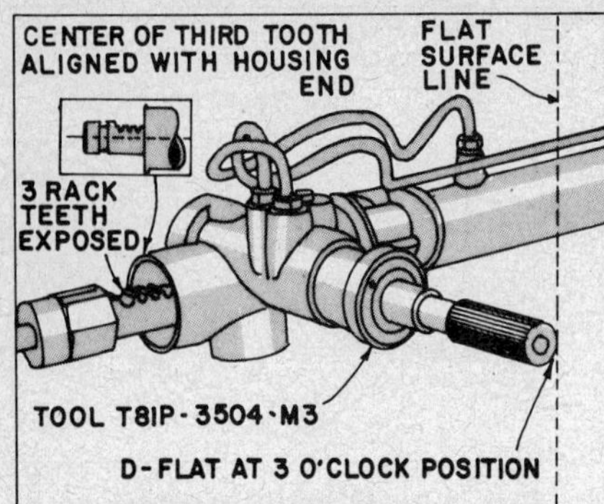


**Fig. 17 Installing valve assembly**

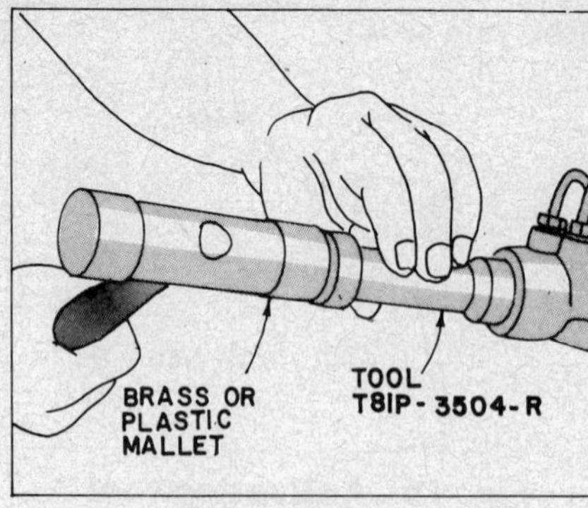


**Fig. 18 Installing input shaft bearing**

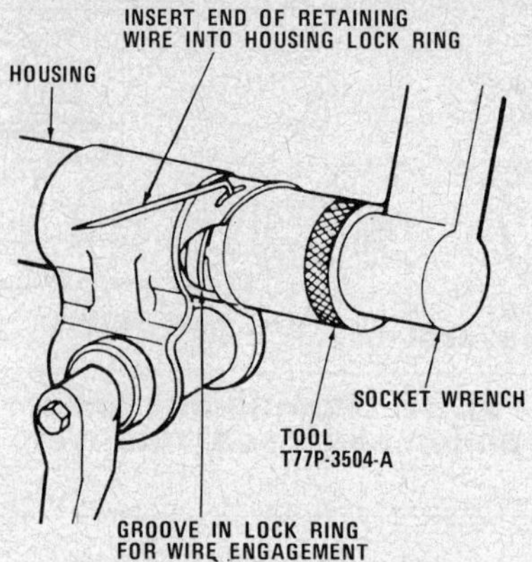


**Fig. 19 Removing rack bushing lock ring**

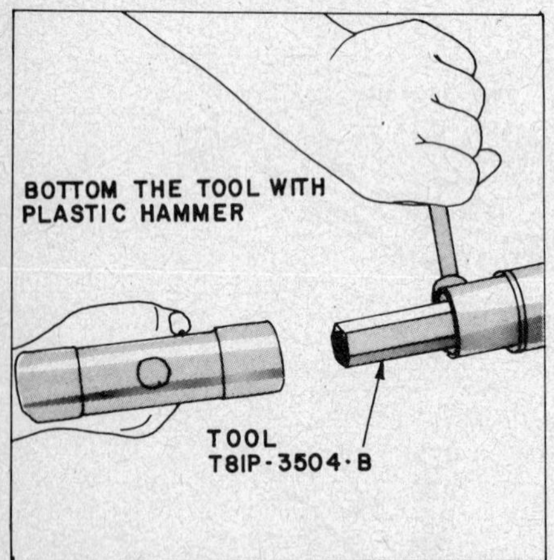


**Fig. 20 Positioning internal rack seal removal tool**

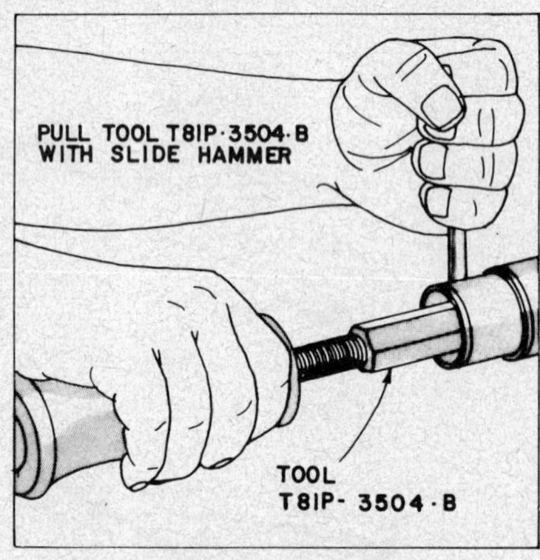


**Fig. 21 Removing internal rack seal**

**Fig. 22 Removing oil seal from rack bushing**

o'clock position and carefully install valve assembly into housing, **Fig. 17.**

7. Check to ensure that pinion is centered, turn input shaft with a suitable tool and count the number of turns from pinion shaft center to each steering stop. If the number of turns is unequal, pull out the valve assembly and repeat steps 5 and 6. If still unequal, pull the valve assembly out far enough to free the rack and pinion gears and rotate pinion gear 60° (one tooth). Reassemble, retest and repeat procedure if necessary.
8. Using tool No. T81P-3504-R, or equivalent, install input shaft bearing, wide face up in valve bore, **Fig. 18.**
9. Holding input shaft with a suitable tool install a new locknut on pinion end, tighten locknut to specifications, **Fig. 10.** This operation must be performed with the rack near center position.
10. Install input shaft seal protector tool No. T81P-3504-P, or equivalent, over input shaft, apply a film of gear lube part No. C3AZ-19578-A or equivalent to the input shaft seal and install seal with lip spring facing valve assembly.
11. Install input shaft seal retaining snap ring.
12. Install power steering gear housing cover, then tighten to specifications.
13. Fill yoke housing with 2 ounces of gear lubricant part No. C3AZ-19578-A or equivalent, install yoke.
14. Install yoke thrust spring and yoke plug. Refer to "Rack Bearing Preload Adjustment." Install yoke plug locknut and tighten to specifications while holding yoke plug in position, **Fig. 4.**
15. If the external pressure lines were removed during disassembly they must be replaced using new copper seals. Crimp copper seals to the lines with pliers using caution not to damage the exterior of the seals. Do not drop the seals into pressure ports as they may misalign.

## GEAR HOUSING, RACK YOKE BEARING, RACK ASSEMBLY, RACK BUSHING & OIL SEALS

### Disassembly

1. Remove tie rods and sockets from both ends of rack, also remove input shaft, valve assembly and rack yoke as described previously.
2. Working from the right side of gear, push in rack until it bottoms. Position rack bushing lock ring tool No. T77P-3504-A, or equivalent, over exposed end of rack and engage socket drive tabs in end plate slots, rotate tool clockwise until the end of the retainer wire is visible in the tube slot, turn tool counterclockwise and using an ice pick or similar tool, start the retainer wire out of the slot and remove, **Fig. 19.**
3. Pull the rack, end plate, rack bushing and rack piston out the right side of housing. **If rack, end plate, rack bushing and rack bushing assembly are difficult to remove, install tie rod hand tight on rack assembly, then install slide hammer weight over tie rod. Install a nut on tie rod to slide weight against, and use the weight and tie rod assembly as a slide hammer to remove rack assembly.**
4. Insert internal rack seal remover tool No. T81P-3504-B, or equivalent, into housing bore, tap tool with plastic mallet until it bottoms, **Fig. 20.** Using a suitable wrench, tighten tool until fully expanded. Attach slide hammer and remove seal and nylon back-up ring, **Fig. 21.**
5. Cut off rack piston seal ring and remove back-up O-ring with a small pointed tool.
6. Insert rack bushing in holding tool

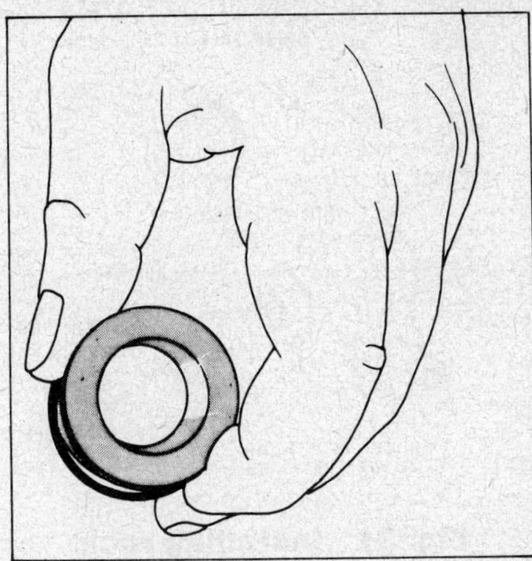

Fig. 23 Rack bushing O-ring removal

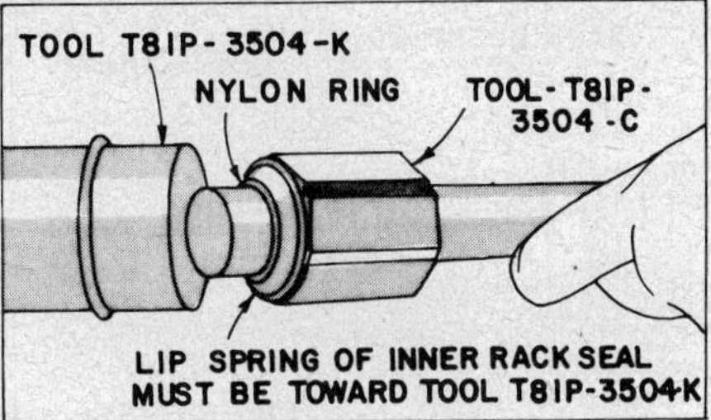


Fig. 24 Rack bushing seal installation

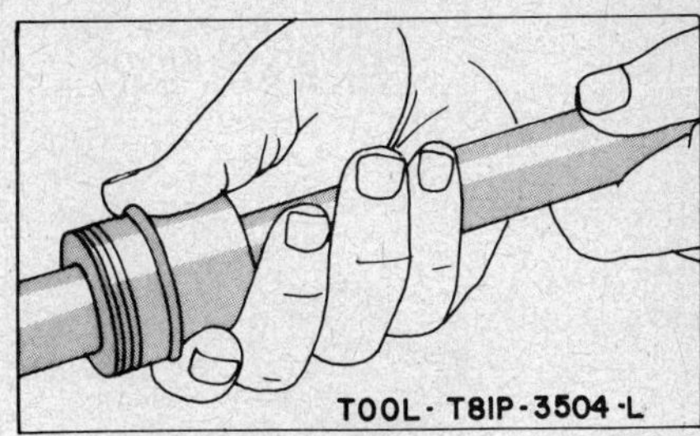


Fig. 25 Rack piston, seal & O-ring installation

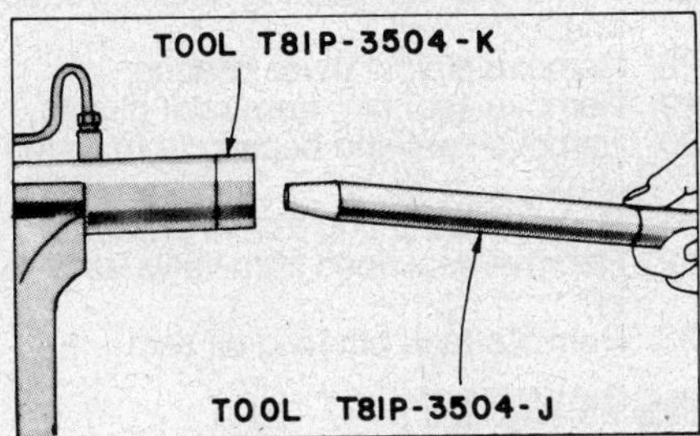


Fig. 26 Protective sleeve installed on rack

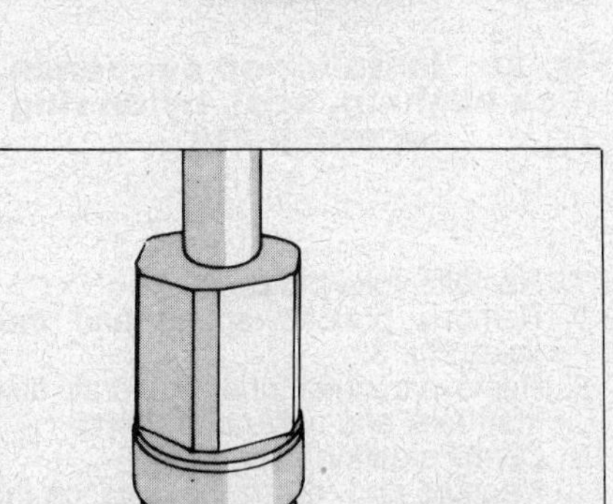

Fig. 27 Outer rack oil seal installation

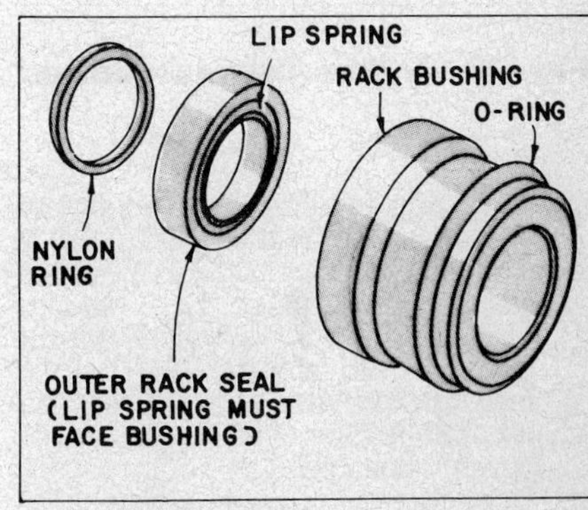


Fig. 28 Outer rack oil seal & bushing, disassembled

T81P-3504-D, or equivalent, seal end first. Place tool and bushing in a vise, using tool T81P-3504-A, or equivalent, and a suitable slide hammer remove seal, **Fig. 22.**

7. Remove rack bushing O-ring by pushing it to one side with fingertips, then roll the O-ring over and remove, **Fig. 23.**

## Assembly

1. Using rack oil seal replacer tool No. T81P-3504-C, or equivalent, apply power steering fluid to inner rack seal and position seal on tool, seal lip facing tool, **Fig. 24.** Insert sizing tool T81P-3504-K, or equivalent, in end of rack tube, position seal replacer in sizing tool and carefully push in by hand until bottomed, tap the tool with a plastic hammer to seat the seal, leaving sizing tool installed in rack.
2. Position rack piston seal installer tool No. T81P-3504-L, or equivalent, on rack as shown in **Fig. 25,** slide rubber O-ring over the tool into piston groove then slide plastic seal ring over tool into piston groove on top of the O-ring.
3. Apply fluid grease C3AZ-19578-A, or equivalent to rack teeth and position long protective sleeve tool No. T81P-3504-J, or equivalent, over the rack gear teeth, **Fig. 26.**
4. Lubricate piston seal ring and protective sleeve tool with power steering fluid.
5. Position rack in rack sizing tool, carefully push rack into the housing and through rack internal oil seal. Ensure the sizing tool is properly positioned to compress and guide the plastic seal ring into housing bore. Push rack in until the protective sleeve protrudes from left side of gear, remove tools and install lefthand tie rod assembly hand tight.
6. Apply gear lube to outer rack oil seal, install oil seal in rack bushing with outer rack oil seal replacer, **Fig. 27.** Lip spring must face the inside of the bushing, **Fig. 28.** Install nylon ring in oil seal, **Fig. 29.**
7. Install outer rack bushing O-ring.
8. Position short protective sleeve tool No. T81P-3504-N, or equivalent, over right side tie ball socket threads, apply automatic transmission fluid to protective sleeve tool and rack bushing O-ring.
9. Position rack bushing with seal and nylon ring facing out on protective sleeve, **Fig. 30.** Slide the rack bushing over the sleeve into housing bore, place end plate against the rack bushing with drive slots facing out. Remove protective sleeve.
10. Using lock ring wrench tool No. T77P-3504-A, or equivalent, with drive tabs engaged in the end plate slots, push in end plate until end plate retainer wire groove is visible through the rack cylinder slot. Rotate end plate to line up the retainer wire hole with the cylinder slot, insert bent end of the retainer wire in the wire hole and rotate end plate clockwise until the retainer wire is fully engaged. Turn an additional 180 degrees, **Fig. 31.**
11. Install tie rod ball sockets as described previously.
12. Install input shaft and valve assembly as described previously.
13. Install yoke bearing, spring, plug and locknut. Prior to torquing locknut, adjust yoke bearing preload as described under "Rack Yoke Bearing Preload Adjustment."
14. Install bellows and tie rod ends.

# MERKUR XR4Ti

## TROUBLESHOOTING

Refer to "ZF Rack & Pinion Steering Gear" for troubleshooting procedures.

## ADJUSTMENTS

### Rack Yoke Preload

1. Position rack in straight ahead position, then using yoke plug hex adapter tool No. T85M-3504-C or equivalent, remove yoke plug.

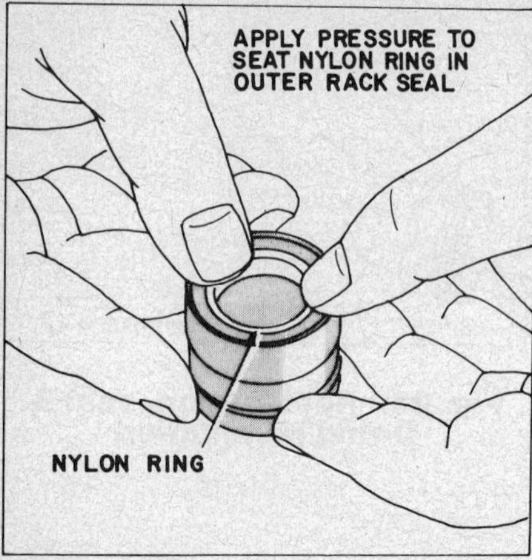


**Fig. 29 Nylon ring installation**

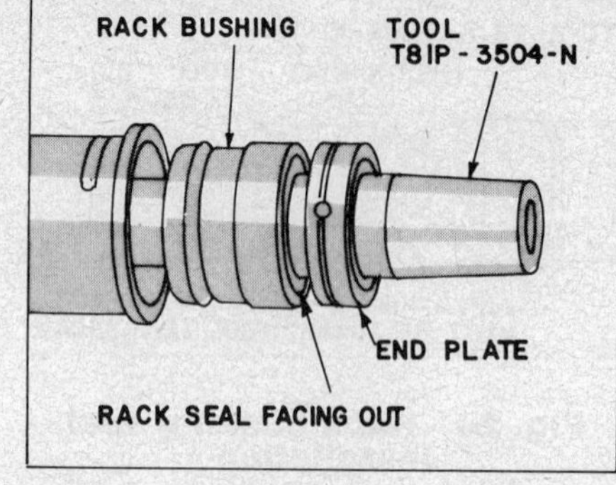


**Fig. 30 Installation sequence, rack bushing, seal, nylon ring & end plate**

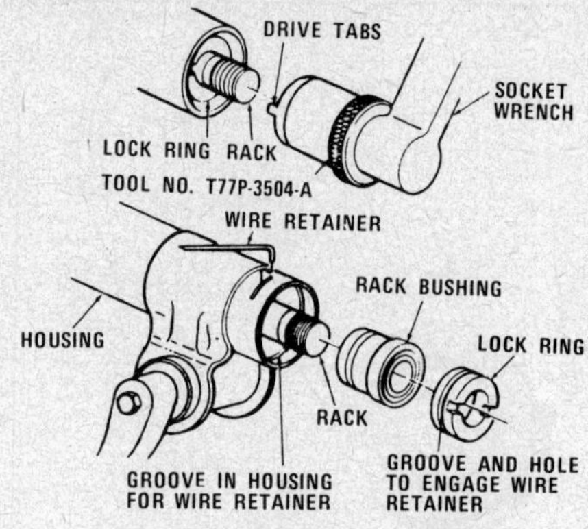


**Fig. 31 Installing rack bushing lock ring**

2. Apply Loctite activator or equivalent, on yoke plug threads, then install to gear.
3. Using yoke plug hex adapter T85K-3504-C or equivalent, **torque** plug to 30-35 inch lbs.
4. Install pinion shaft seal replacer tool No. T85M-3504-B or equivalent, on pinion shaft, position tool ensuring lock screws engage pinion shaft splines.
5. Turn pinion in one direction then in opposite direction until rack has moved twice from stop to stop.
6. Return rack to straight ahead position, then check yoke plug torque, readjust as required.
7. Using pinion shaft seal replacer tool No. T85M-3504-B or equivalent and suitable inch lb. torque wrench, measure pinion shaft turning effort, less then 12 inch lbs. should be indicated, if less repeat step 6.
8. **Rack cylinder should be horizontal position when checking pinion torque to prevent rack weight from affecting measurement.**
9. If pinion shaft is within specification, back off yoke plug 22-27°.
10. Check pinion shaft rotation again, less the 15 inch lbs. should be indicated.
11. If torque exceeds 15 inch lbs, back off cover 5° maximum.
12. Apply suitable penetrating grade anerobic sealant on yoke cover threads.
13. Stake steering gear housing in three places around yoke plug. **Do not use original stake positions.**
14. Install steering gear.

## DISASSEMBLE

1. Mount steering gear into a suitable holding fixture.
2. Remove tie rod ends and locknuts.
3. Cut, then remove dust boot clamps.
4. Remove dust boots.
5. Remove tie rod ball joints.
6. Apply Loctite activator N(764) or equivalent, on the yoke plug threads to loosen the Loctite sealant applied during assembly of the gear.
7. Remove yoke plug.
8. Remove preload spring and rack yoke, **Fig. 32.**
9. Remove transfer tubes and drain fluid from rack and valve body ports.
10. Center steering gear.
11. Measure and record the distance the rack extends from the pinion end of the housing. Take measurement from the edge of the housing to the end of the rack.
12. Mark housing in line with the blind spline on the input shaft.
13. Remove pinion shaft dust cap.
14. Remove pinion lower bearing bore plug.
15. Remove pinion bearing locknuts.
16. Remove pinion upper bearing and seal retaining snap ring.
17. Drive end of pinion shaft out of lower bearing.
18. Pull input shaft/pinion assembly out of the housing upper end.
19. Push rack toward the pinion end of the housing until it bottoms in the housing.
20. Turn rack bushing clockwise until free end of the lock wire is visible through the slot in the housing.
21. While holding the lock wire, turn the rack bushing counterclockwise to start the wire through the slot.
22. Continue turning the bushing to remove the lock wire through the housing slot.
23. Pull rack from housing.
24. If rack bushing is stuck in the housing, proceed as follows:
    a. Install a tie rod and ball joint assembly.
    b. Install the weight from slide hammer T50T-100-A onto the tie rod.
    c. Install a flat washer and tie rod end locknut.
    d. Using the slide hammer weight against the washer and locknut, pull rack bushing out of the housing.
25. To remove rack inner seal and support ring modify a drift approximately 1.03 inch in diameter. A socket wrench and long extension will work. Drive the ring and seal out of the rack bushing end of the cylinder.
26. Remove pinion lower seal and bushing.
27. Remove pinion bearing retaining snap ring.
28. Remove pinion lower bearing.
29. Remove seal ring from rack piston.
30. Remove seal and bearing from pinion shaft.
31. Remove snap ring from input shaft.
32. Remove seal rings from valve assembly.
33. Remove rack bushing oil seal.

## ASSEMBLE

1. Lubricate rack piston with automatic transmission fluid or power steering fluid.
2. Install piston seal onto piston.
3. Lubricate, then install seals onto valve assembly. Install mandrel T81P-3504-M1 or equivalent over the valve assembly. Lubricate and install seals onto mandrel. Slide ring pusher T81P-3504-M2 or equivalent over the mandrel and push down rapidly to force the seal over the mandrel ramp into the seal groove. Remove mandrel.
4. Ensure seals are properly seated in their grooves.
5. Lubricate the inside of sizing tube T81P-3504-M3 or equivalent, and slowly work the tool over the seal using a rotating motion.
6. Install spacer T81P-3504-M4 or equivalent. The spacer will align the mandrel with the second seal groove. Repeat steps 3 through 6.
7. Install a second spacer T81P-3504-M4 or equivalent, against the first spacer, these spacers will align the mandrel with the third seal groove. Repeat steps 3 through 6.
8. Remove the second spacer, turn it over and install on the shaft, opposing the first spacer. The spacers will now align the mandrel with the fourth seal groove. Repeat steps 3 through 6. Remove mandrel and spacers.
9. Install double-wrap snap ring into input shaft groove.
10. Install rack bushing seal using a suitable tool with seal lip and spring facing the tool.

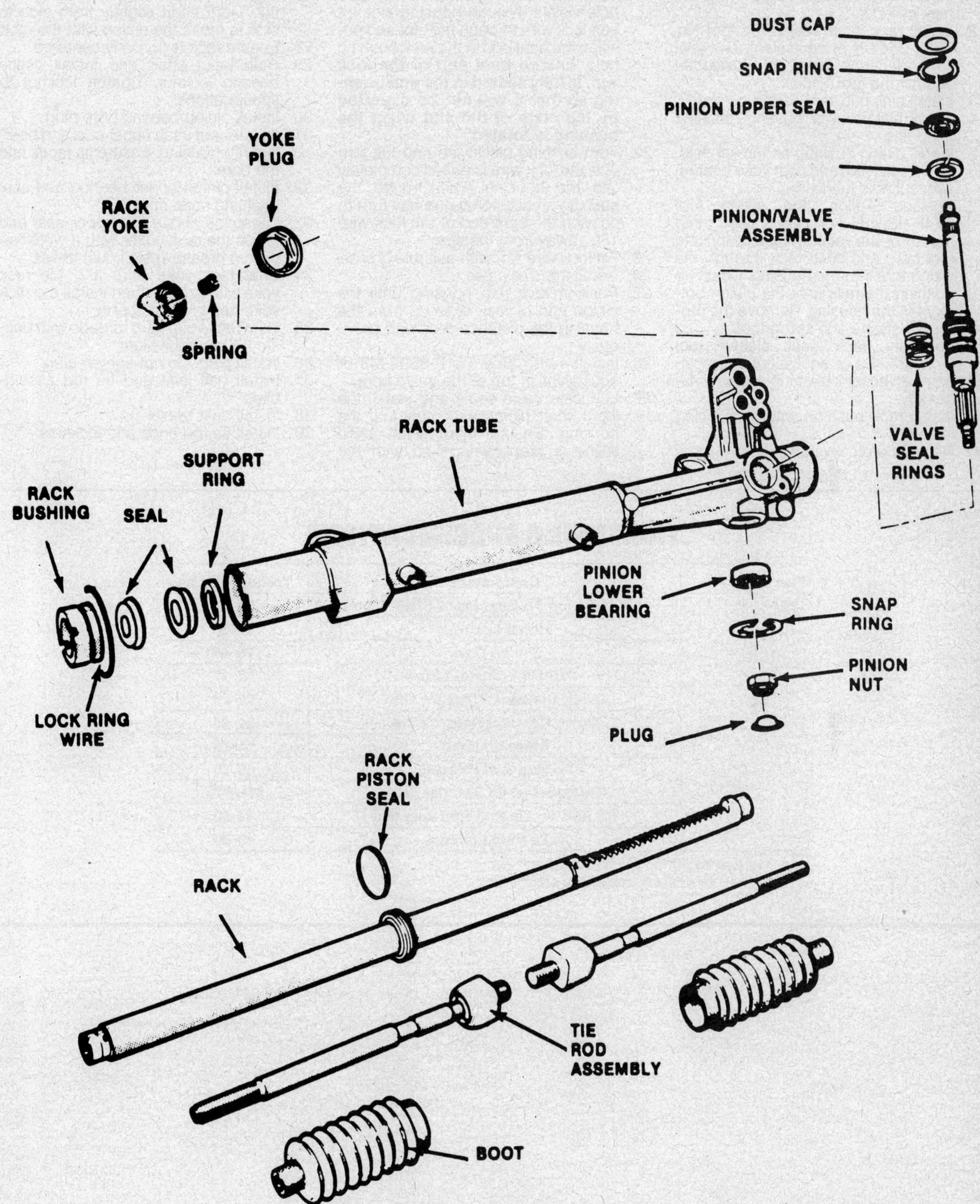


**Fig. 32 Exploded view of TRW steering gear. Merkur**

11. Install rack inner seal support ring into rack cylinder.
12. Install rack inner seal using tool No. T78P-3504-K or equivalent. The seal lip and spring must be positioned against the tool.
13. Install pinion lower bearing.
14. Install pinion lower bearing retaining snap ring.
15. Install pinion bushing and lower seal.
16. Pack rack teeth and coat yoke bearing with suitable lubricant.
17. Position Teflon ring sizing tool T74P-3504-H or equivalent, into mouth of the rack cylinder. Lubricate tool bore and push rack through the sizing tool into the housing. Continue pushing the rack until the piston bottoms in the housing. Remove the protective sleeve and sizing tool.
18. Lubricate rack seal sleeve tool T74P-3504-J or equivalent and position it in the rack bushing and seal assembly.
19. Install rack bushing with seal facing inward.
20. Remove protective sleeve.
21. Turn rack bushing until the lock wire hole visible through housing slot. Insert lock wire through the slot and position the bent end in the rack bushing hole. **Ensure bent end of the lock wire is fully seated in the end bushing so that it will not be distorted by the edge of the slot when the bushing is rotated.**
22. Turn bushing clockwise one full turn until the lock wire is pulled completely into the housing. Then rotate the bushing an additional one-half turn to position the bent end of the lock wire 180° away from the slot.
23. Fill lock wire slot with suitable grease.
24. Install transfer tubes.
25. Position rack into housing until the pinion end of rack extends from the housing the distance recorded previously.
26. Install sizing tube T81P-3504-M3 or equivalent, in top of the valve bore.
27. Lubricate valve seals and install the input shaft/pinion assembly into the housing. Ensure input shaft blind spline is properly indexed with the alignment mark on the housing. Rotate input shaft slightly from side to side to mesh the pinion with the rack.
28. Ensure rack is properly centered.
29. Hold input shaft and install pinion bearing locknut. Tighten locknut to specifications.
30. Install pinion bearing bore plug.
31. Install input shaft upper seal and bearing into housing. Ensure lip faces into the bore.
32. Install pinion upper bearing and seal retaining snap ring.
33. Fill space above the upper seal and inside the dust cover with a water repellent grease. Install dust cover.
34. Coat rack yoke bore and the rack yoke with grease, then install the rack yoke and preload spring.
35. Coat rack yoke plug threads with Loctite 290 or equivalent.
36. Install plug. Do not tighten plug.
37. Install ball joint and tie rod assemblies.
38. Install dust boots.
39. Install tie rod ends and locknuts.

## TIGHTENING SPECIFICATIONS

| Year | Component | Torque, Ft. Lbs. |
|---|---|---|
| 1989 | Flex Coupling To Gear Input Shaft Clamp | 20–30 |
| | Pinion Locknut | 20–35 |
| | Pinion Cap | 35–45 |
| | P/S Oil Transfer Line | 12–17 |
| | Quick Connect Pressure Line | 20–25 |
| | Quick Connect Return Line | 20–25 |
| | Steering Gear | 54–75 |
| | Tie Rod Ball Housing | 40–50 |
| | Tie Rod End To Spindle Arm | 27–32① |
| | Tie Rod To Tie Rod End Jam Nut | 42–50 |
| | Yoke Plug Locknut | 40–50 |

①—Tighten to minimum torque, then tighten to nearest cotter pin slot.

# ZF Rack & Pinion Steering Gear

INDEX



## TROUBLESHOOTING

### GEAR LEAKAGE

1. Pressure or return line fittings.
2. Rack piston tube fitting.
3. Loose hose clamp at secondary cooler.
4. Faulty input shaft seal.
5. Damaged cooler tubes.

### RATTLE OR KNOCK IN STEERING GEAR

1. Loose or worn steering column intermediate shaft joints.
2. Loose tie rod ends or tie rod inner ball joints.
3. Loose or damaged steering gear mounting insulators.
4. Loose steering column intermediate shaft connecting bolts.

### RATTLE OR NOISE IN STEERING COLUMN

1. Loose bolts ot brackets.
2. Insufficient lube.
3. Loose ball bearings.
4. Compressed or extended flex coupling.

### SQUEAK OR CRACKS IN STEERING COLUMN

1. Loose or improperly positioned shrouds.
2. Improperly positioned upper or lower bearing.

### POOR STEERING WHEEL RETURN

1. Incorrect tire pressure or other tire problem.
2. Binding column intermediate shaft universal joints.
3. Torn boot(s).
4. Binding or damaged tie rod ends or ball joints.
5. Incorrect wheel alignment.
6. Binding steering column bearing.
7. System contamination.

### EXCESSIVE STEERING EFFORT

1. Steering fluid aeration.
2. Low pump fluid.
3. External or internal gear leakage.
4. External pump leakage.
5. Loose or worn drive belts.
6. External hose or cooler leakage.
7. Improper engine idle speed.
8. Loose, warped or improperly aligned pulley.
9. Restricted or kinked hose or cooler line.
10. System contamination.

### PULLS TO ONE SIDE

1. Tire related problem.
2. Vehicle over or unevenly loaded.
3. Improper wheel alignment.
4. Faulty front or rear suspension components.
5. Out of balance steering gear valve effort.
6. Improper front and/or rear brake operation.

### VEHICLE WANDERS

1. Tire related problem.
2. Vehicle over or unevenly loaded.
3. Loose or worn tie rod ends or ball socket.
4. Steering gear mount insulators and/or attachment bolt loose or damaged.
5. Loose struts.
6. Loose column intermediate shaft.
7. Loose or worn column intermediate shaft universal joints.
8. Improper wheel alignment.
9. Improper steering gear rack yoke adjustment.

## ADJUSTMENTS

### RACK YOKE PRELOAD

**The rack yoke preload adjustment is not a service adjustment. It is only to be done as part of a complete overhaul of the steering gear to maintain accurate steering gear operation.**

1. Position rack in the straight-ahead position and remove yoke plug using tool T85M-3504-C or equivalent.
2. Apply Loctite Activator N(764) or equivalent, on yoke plug threads and install into steering gear.
3. Using tool T85M-3504-C or equivalent and a suitable torque wrench, **torque** plug to 30-35 inch lbs.
4. Install pinion shaft seal replacer/torque adapter tool onto pinion shaft. Position the tool so lock screws engage pinion shaft splines. Using the tool, turn pinion in one direction and then in the opposite direction until rack has moved twice from stop-to-stop.
5. Return rack to straight-ahead position.
6. Check yoke plug torque. If necessary, **torque** again to 30-35 inch lbs.
7. Using tool T85M-3504-8 or equivalent and a suitable torque wrench, check pinion shaft turning effort. Turning effort as indicated by the torque wrench should be no less than 12 inch lbs. If turning effort reading obtained is less then 12 inch. lbs., repeat step 6. **The rack cylinder should be in the horizontal position when checking pinion torque to prevent rack weight from affecting the reading.**
8. With pinion shaft rotation **torque** at 12 inch lbs. Back off yoke plug 22-27°.
9. Check pinion shaft rotation again. Now, it should not exceed 15 inch lbs.
10. If **torque** exceeds 15 inch lbs., back off yoke cover a maximum of 5°.
11. Apply Loctite 290 sealant or equivalent, onto yoke cover threads.
12. Stake steering gear housing in three places around the yoke plug. Do not use the original staking positions.

## DISASSEMBLE

1. Mount steering gear in a suitable holding fixture.
2. Remove tie rod end locknuts and the tie rod ends.
3. Remove bellows clamps, then the bellows, **Fig. 1.**
4. Slowly turn steering rack from lock to lock and drain fluid from pressure and return ports into a suitable container. **If rack is allowed to turn, pinion damage could result during ball joint removal.**
5. Secure flat surface of rack in a suitable vise, then remove ball joint and tie rod assemblies.
6. Turn steering rack clockwise to left-hand lock position, then remove housing cap from lower pinion valve housing. Remove locknut and washer.
7. Center steering gear, then measure and record the distance rack extends from pinion end of housing, **Fig. 2.** Also, mark relationship between pinion spline and housing for assembly reference.
8. Remove yoke cover attaching bolts, then the yoke cover, shims and spring.
9. Remove dust cap, then the upper bearing circlip from pinion housing.
10. Remove pinion shaft and valve assembly from housing using a pulling and twisting motion. **Use care to avoid contaminants from entering**

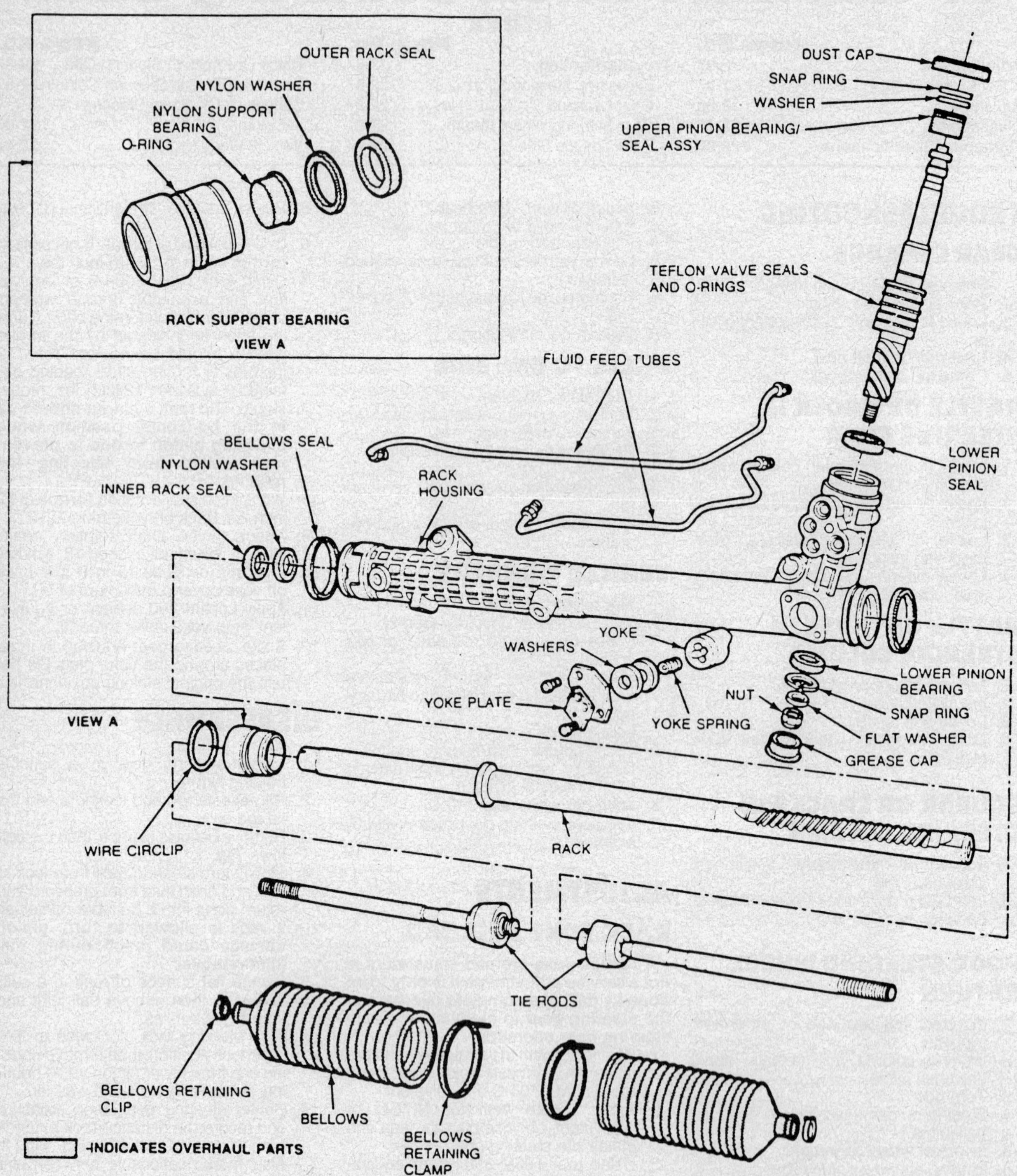

OUTER RACK SEAL
NYLON WASHER
NYLON SUPPORT BEARING
O-RING
RACK SUPPORT BEARING
VIEW A
DUST CAP
SNAP RING
WASHER
UPPER PINION BEARING/ SEAL ASSY
TEFLON VALVE SEALS AND O-RINGS
FLUID FEED TUBES
LOWER PINION SEAL
BELLOWS SEAL
NYLON WASHER
INNER RACK SEAL
RACK HOUSING
YOKE
WASHERS
LOWER PINION BEARING
NUT
SNAP RING
YOKE PLATE
YOKE SPRING
FLAT WASHER
VIEW A
GREASE CAP
WIRE CIRCLIP
RACK
TIE RODS
BELLOWS RETAINING CLIP
BELLOWS
BELLOWS RETAINING CLAMP
-INDICATES OVERHAUL PARTS

**Fig. 1 Exploded view of ZF steering gear**

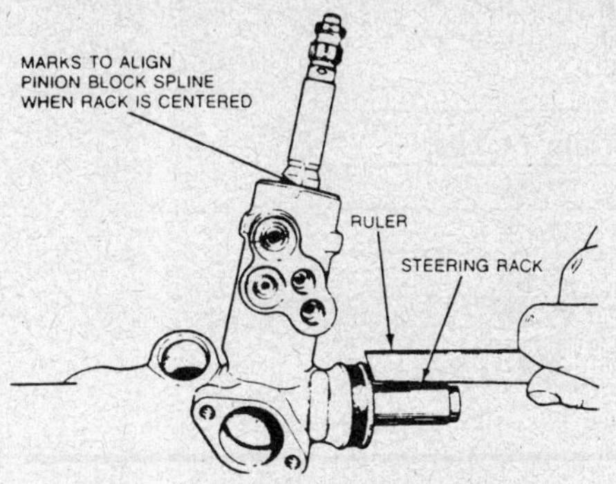


**Fig. 2 Rack projection measurement**

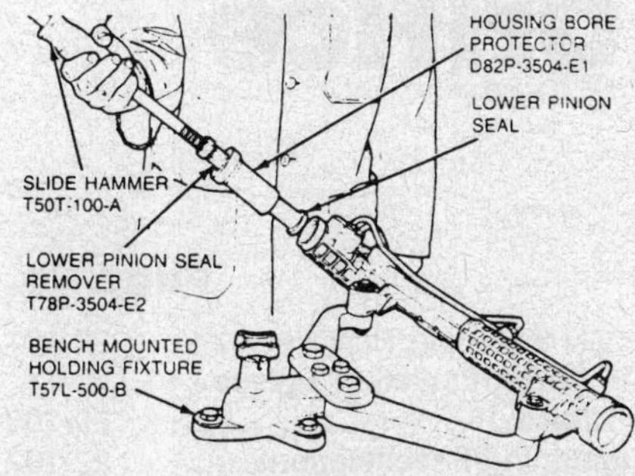


**Fig. 3 Lower pinion valve seal removal**

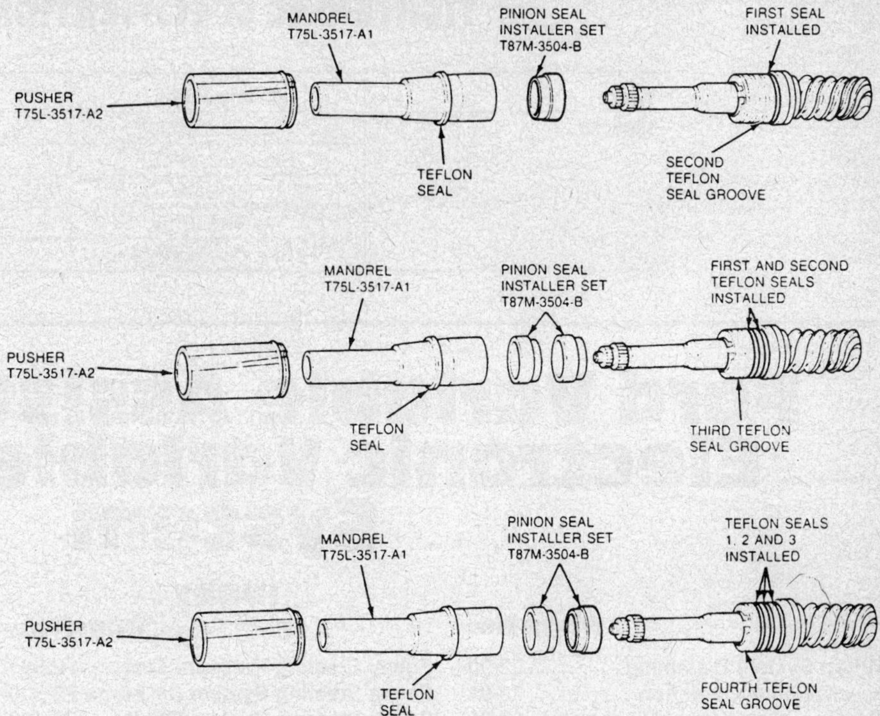


**Fig. 4 Pinion/valve assembly seal installation**

**the valve body or sleeve valve.**

11. Remove oil seal and upper pinion bearing from input shaft. **The valve and pinion assembly must not be disassembled.**
12. Remove and discard all Teflon seals and the O-ring seal tensioners under the seals.
13. Retract rack, then remove circlip retaining rack support bearing and seal.
14. Remove steering rack with rack support bearing and seal from rack tube.
15. Remove Teflon ring and O-ring from rack assembly using tool No. T71P-19703-C or equivalent.
16. Remove lower pinion bearing circlip, then drive bearing out using a soft punch.
17. Install housing bore protector, then remove lower pinion valve seal from pinion housing using tools shown in **Fig. 3.**
18. Remove yoke from valve housing.
19. Carefully drive inner rack seal and nylon washer from steering rack using a 3/4 inch socket with an 18 inch extension.

## ASSEMBLE

1. Install new lower pinion seal into housing using tools T87P-3504-D and T87M-3504-F or equivalents. Ensure seal lip faces control valve.
2. Install lower pinion bearing into piston housing using tools T87P-3504-D and T87M-3504-E or equivalents. Install retaining clip to secure bearing.
3. Apply clean power steering fluid to rack tube, then install new O-ring onto rack.
4. Install rack piston Teflon seal on rack using tools T87M-3504-C and T75L-3517-A2 or equivalents.
5. Install inner rack seal and nylon washer into steering rack housing bore using tool No. T81P-3504-C or equivalent.
6. Position ring sizing tool No. T87M-3504-D or equivalent in end of rack housing to protect bore and size Teflon rack seal during rack installation.
7. Position seal protector tool No. T87P-3504-H or equivalent on rack.
8. Apply clean power steering fluid to rack, then insert rack into housing. **Ensure rack teeth are properly aligned for pinion installation.**
9. Remove tools, then install rack support bushing into housing and secure with wire clip.
10. Install pinion valve O-rings.
11. Secure end of pinion valve in a suitable soft-jawed vise.
12. Apply clean power steering fluid to tool No. T57L-3517-A1 or equivalent, then position tool over pinion and valve assembly.
13. Install new Teflon seals as shown in **Fig. 4.** Note proper positioning of spacers for installation of each seal.
14. Size Teflon seals using tool No. T87M-3504-G or equivalent. Leave tool in position for one full minute to allow seal to settle fully.
15. Center steering rack, then install pinion assembly into housing with tool No. T87M-3504-H or equivalent used as a bore protector. **Align reference marks made during disassembly.**
16. Install upper pinion bearing and seal assembly onto pinion input shaft.
17. Install upper washer, then the retaining circlip and dust cap onto input shaft.
18. Position new O-ring on yoke, then install yoke, spring and original shims in pinion housing.
19. Apply suitable sealant to yoke cover plate, then install the plate and tighten to specifications.
20. Install pinion washer and locknut, then tighten to specifications.
21. Fill dust cap and locknut area with suitable grease, then install dust cap on pinion housing.
22. Install tie rod and ball joint assemblies and tighten to specifications, while holding flat of rack to prevent from turning.
23. Apply clean power steering fluid to rack teeth.
24. Apply suitable grease to rack bellows, then slide bellows over toe rods and rack housing and secure with retaining clamps.
25. Install tie rod ends and locknuts, then tighten to specifications.

## TIGHTENING SPECIFICATIONS

| Year | Component | Torque, Ft. Lbs. |
|---|---|---|
| 1989–90 | Ball Joint | 52–56 |
| | Pinion Locknut | 11–15 |
| | Tie Rod | 52–56 |
| | Tie Rod Ends | 42–50 |
| | Yoke Cover Plate | 5–6 |

# Ford Variable Assist, Except Electronic Variable Orifice System

## INDEX



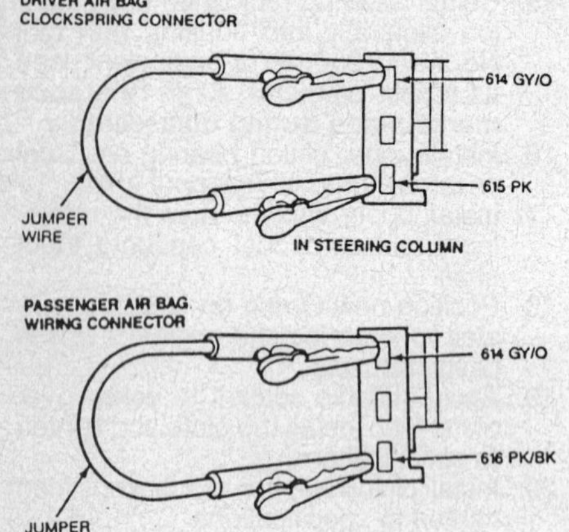


**Fig. 1 Airbag system disarming**

**Fig. 2 VAPS system**

## AIRBAG SYSTEM DISARMING

**The electrical circuit necessary for system deployment is powered directly from the battery and backup power supply. To avoid accidental deployment and possible personal injury, the airbag system must be deactivated prior to servicing or replacing any system components.**

A back-up power supply is included in the system to provide airbag deployment in the event the battery or battery cables are damaged in an accident before the sensors can close. The power supply is a capacitor that will retain a charge for approximately 15 minutes after the battery ground cable is disconnected. To remove and install backup power supply refer to "Component Replacement" procedure.

1. Disconnect battery ground cable.
2. Disconnect backup power supply as described under "Backup Power Supply, Replace."
3. Remove four nut and washer assemblies securing airbag module to steering wheel, then disconnect airbag electrical connector. Attach jumper wire to airbag terminals on clockspring as shown in **Fig. 1.**
4. **On models equipped with passenger-side airbag,** disconnect airbag module connector located behind glove compartment. Attach a

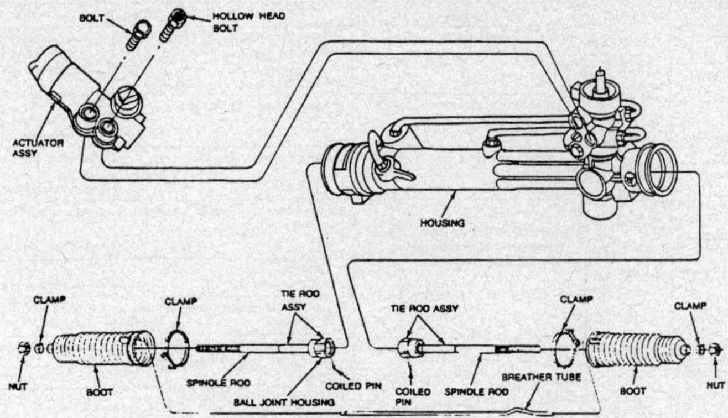


**Fig. 3 VAPS gear assembly**

jumper wire to airbag terminals on wiring harness side of passenger airbag module connector, as shown in **Fig. 1.**

5. **On all models,** if necessary, reconnect battery and backup power supply.
6. To reactivate, disconnect battery ground cable and backup power supply, then reverse remainder of deactivation procedure. **Torque** airbag module to steering wheel nut assemblies to 24-32 inch lbs. on Crown Victoria and Grand Marquis, or 35-53 inch lbs. on all other models.
7. Verify airbag lamp after reactivating system.

## DESCRIPTION & OPERATION

The variable assist power steering (VAPS) system consists of a microprocessor-based control module, a power rack and pinion gear, an actuator valve assembly, interconnecting hose assemblies and a high efficiency power steering pump, **Fig. 2.**

The VAPS system incorporates a modified rotary valve in the gear with two independent hydraulic circuits called the primary and secondary circuits. During parking and low vehicle speed operation, fluid flow from the pump is routed to the primary circuit by an electrically controlled actuator valve assembly. As vehicle speed increases, the actuator valve gradually opens, diverting the increased fluid volume to the secondary circuit.

The actuator valve assembly, **Fig. 3,** is a pressure balanced variable orifice valve, controlled by a stepper motor driven linear spool. The VAPS module receives inputs from the vehicle speed sensor and transmits signals to the stepper motor driven spool to adjust orifice opening of the actuator valve.

The VAPS module is programmed to perform a self-diagnostic check every 16 milliseconds. If a malfunction is detected, the module microprocessor deactivates its outputs allowing control assist power steering operation.

The VAPS module is programmed to perform a service diagnostic procedure when activated by a service technician.

The rotary design control valve directs fluid flow using relative rotational motion of the input shaft and valve sleeve. When the steering wheel is turned, resistance of the wheels and the weight of the vehicle will cause a torsion bar to deflect. The deflection action changes the position of the valve spool and sleeve ports, directing pressurized fluid to the appropriate end of the the power cylinder. The pressure differential acts on the piston and helps move the rack to assist in the turning effort. The piston is attached directly to the rack and the housing functions as the power cylinder. The fluid in the opposite end of the power cylinder is forced to the control valve and back into the pump reservoir. When no steering effort is applied, the valve is forced back to a centered position by the torsion bar. When this occurs, pressure is equalized on both sides of the piston and the front wheels return to a straight-ahead position.

## TROUBLESHOOTING

The following steering system troubleshooting charts provide procedures to resolve typical problems encountered with the power steering system. Follow the sequence indicated to identify the condition and the corrective action to perform.

Refer to **Fig. 4,** for steering system troubleshooting procedures.

## ELECTRICAL COMPONENT DIAGNOSIS

**The following procedure has been revised by a Technical Service Bulletin.**

This portion of the power steering diagnosis procedure, applies only to the electrical components of the VAPS system. The VAPS control module, speed sensor, actuator valve, wiring harness and electrical connectors will be tested, **Figs. 5 through 7.**

The diagnostic connector to activate the diagnostic procedure is located within the engine compartment near the brake fluid reservoir and brake booster assembly, **Fig. 8.**

Refer to **Figs. 9 and 10,** for variable assist power steering electrical component diagnostic procedures.

## POWER STEERING PRESSURE TEST

**During the following procedure, power steering system pressure may exceed 1200 psi. Ensure proper tool fitment prior to performing test. Exercise extreme caution or damage or personal injury may result.**

1. Prior to performing pump flow and pressure tests, ensure following conditions exist:
   a. Proper pump reservoir fluid level.
   b. Correct tire air pressure.
   c. Proper pump belt tension.
   d. Correct model and vehicle pump application.
   e. Correct size pulleys on pump and engine.
   f. Ensure system is not damaged or leaking, repair as required.
2. The following test equipment is required:
   a. Engine tachometer.
   b. Thermometer: 0-300°F (17.8-148.9°C).
   c. **On all models except SHO,** power steering system analyzer tool No. 014-00207 or equivalent.
   d. **On SHO models,** power steering system analyzer tool No. 014-00208 or equivalent.
   e. **On all models,** set of adapter fittings.
3. The test procedure used in conjunction with the power steering system analyzer can be used to determine:
   a. System backpressure.
   b. Pump flow.
   c. Steering gear internal leakage.
   d. Pump relief pressure.
4. The readouts from step 3 can be used to determine which of the following conditions or components may be faulty:
   a. Hose or fitting restriction.
   b. Sticking gear valve.
   c. Insufficient pump capacity.
   d. Sticking relief valve.
   e. Suspension system binding.
5. Disconnect pump high pressure line, then connect suitable analyzer hose adapter, **Figs. 11 through 13.**
6. **On all models except SHO,** thread other analyzer adapter to pump.
7. **On SHO models,** thread adapter into steering gear.
8. **On all models,** connect analyzer hose to adapters, tighten both connections to 15 ft. lbs. maximum.
9. If required, add power steering fluid, start engine and allow to run about two minutes. Ensure idle is set to specifications.
10. With engine at idle, record the following:
    a. Flow, gallons per minute at 167-177°F (76-80°C).
    b. Pressure, psi at 167-177°F (76-80°C), at idle with gate fully open.
    c. **On all models except SHO,** if flow is below 1.5 gallons per minute, pump may require service, however continue test, check flow and relief pressure.

| CONDITION | POSSIBLE SOURCE | ACTION |
|---|---|---|
| • High (Excessive) Steering Gear Efforts at All Vehicle Speeds is a condition recognized while turning corners and during low speed maneuvers and especially while parking. The assist problems may occur in both directions or only in one direction, they may be intermittent, or consistent.<br>**NOTE:** Discolored steering fluid in a rack-and-pinion steering system should not be misdiagnosed as a functional or noise problem. | • Low pump fluid. | • Fill as required and check for system leaks. |
| | • Gear assembly external or internal leakage. | • Replace steering gear assembly. |
| | • Pump external leakage. | • |
| | • Pump pressure and flow below specification. | • Perform pump flow and relief pressure tests. Repair as required. |
| | • VAPS (Variable Assist Power Steering) system malfunction. | • Refer to VAPS system diagnostic procedure |
| | • Improper drive belt tension. | • Check for proper belt tension. |
| | • Hose or cooler external leakage. | • Service or replace as necessary. |
| | • Hose or cooler line restriction. | • Clean and replace as necessary. |
| | • Pump pulley loose/warped. | • Replace pulley. |
| | • Power steering pump belt loose/glazed/broken or water on belt. | • Inspect, adjust belt tension or replace as required. |
| | • Engine idle too low. | • Adjust idle. |
| | • Tires not properly inflated. | • Inflate to specification. |
| | • Suspension bent or interference. | • Inspect service or replace as necessary. |
| | • System contamination. | • Inspect system for foreign objects, kinked hose, etc.<br>— flush system<br>— refer to power steering pump. |
| | • Plugged valve screen. | • Prior to rebuilding a pump, examine the valve screen for contamination. Replace all valves which have plugged or contaminated valve screens. |
| | • Flex coupling rubbing against housing face. | • Reposition flex coupling. |
| | • Column misaligned or binding. | • Align column assembly. |

**Fig. 4 Steering system troubleshooting (Part 1 of 8)**

| CONDITION | POSSIBLE SOURCE | ACTION |
|---|---|---|
| • Loose On Center<br>**NOTE:** This condition should be checked on center only. The loose condition can be detected with greater reliability with the engine off and steering wheel straight ahead. A very light touch on the steering wheel should be used in checking for this condition. | • Steering gear mounting bolts loose. | • Tighten attaching nuts to specification. |
| | • Column intermediate shaft connecting bolt loose. | • Tighten to specification. |
| | • Intermediate shaft spring loaded U-bolt distorted.<br>Flex coupling clamp bolt loose. | • Replace U-bolt.<br>• Tighten to specification. |
| | • Gear tie rod inner ball socket loose. | • Replace gear tie rod. |
| | • Column intermediate shaft joints loose or worn. | • Replace intermediate shaft assembly. |
| | • Steering column shaft clips missing or broken. | • Replace as required. |
| | • Flex coupling fractured. | • Replace as required. |
| | • Tie rod ends loose or worn. | • Tighten or replace as required. |
| | • Wheel bearing adjustments. | • Adjust to specification. |
| | • Loose wheel lug nuts. | • Tighten to specification. |
| • Steering Wheel Not Centered Properly.<br>**NOTE:** Groove on steel hub of steering wheel must be in line with mark on top end of steering shaft with front wheels in straight ahead position to line up steering wheel spokes properly. Steering wheel centerline should be within 10 degrees of vertical plane after toe-in is adjusted. | • Incorrect toe setting. | • Set to specification. |
| | • Flex coupling clamp bolts loose/missing. | • Replace and tighten to specification. |
| | • Pinion installed in rack off location. | • Replace gear assembly. |
| | • Improperly installed steering wheel. | • Reposition steering wheel. |
| | • Steering gear loose on frame. | • Tighten to specification. |
| | • Column intermediate shaft installed off location in column shaft V-block. | • Index shaft to correct position. |

**Fig. 4 Steering system troubleshooting (Part 3 of 8)**

| CONDITION | POSSIBLE SOURCE | ACTION |
|---|---|---|
| • Uneven Drive Efforts, Pulls or Leads to One Side is a condition recognized by the driver while turning the steering wheel in a left or right turn. This condition will reveal lighter efforts in one direction, very noticeable to the driver. Vehicle pulls or leads to one side. Keep in mind road conditions and wind. Pulls or leads refers to the tendency of a vehicle to drift consistently to one side on a reasonably flat road. It may or may not be accompanied by unequal effort requirements at the steering wheel.<br>**NOTE:** Peform the following test to determine if problem is related to steering gear or vehicle system.<br>At 15-55 mph on a flat straight surface, set vehicle in a straight line, place shift selector in NEUTRAL position and turn off ignition. If the vehicle continues to pull or drift in the same direction as the original problem, then the steering gear is not the cause. If the vehicle does not pull, but remains on a straight line this indicates a steering gear problem, and steering efforts should also be noticeably light in direction of pull. This condition is normally due to an unbalanced steering gear valve assembly. | • Radial tires (misaligned belts). | • Replace as necessary. |
| | • Front or rear end misaligned. | • Align to specification. |
| | • Steering gear valve efforts unbalanced. (Efforts will be lighter in one direction.) | • Replace gear assembly. |
| | • Front suspension components damaged. | • Replace as required. |
| | • Low tire pressure or incorrect front to rear. | • Inflate to specification. |
| | • Incorrect tire size or different type make. | • Correct as required. |
| | • Check front and rear brakes for proper operation. | • Adjust if necessary. |
| | • Check bent rear axle housing and for damaged or sagging springs in the front or rear suspension. | • Replace if necessary. |
| | • Check rear suspension for loose or worn shock absorber struts, suspension arm attaching fasteners. | • Tighten all attaching fasteners to specification. |
| | • Vehicle unevenly loaded. | • Correct as required. |
| | • Front and rear wheel bearing adjustment. | • Adjust to specification. |
| | • Steering gear attaching bolts loose or damaged. | • Tighten attachment nuts to specification. |
| | • Column misaligned or binding. | • Align column assembly. |
| | • Halfshaft or CV joint bind. | • Replace CV joints. |

**Fig. 4 Steering system troubleshooting (Part 5 of 8)**

| CONDITION | POSSIBLE SOURCE | ACTION |
|---|---|---|
| • High (Excessive) Efforts at Low Vehicle Speeds | • VAPS (Variable Assist Power Steering) system malfunction. | • Refer to VAPS system diagnostic procedure and service or replace components accordingly. |
| • Low Efforts at All Vehicle Speeds | • VAPS system malfunction. | • Refer to VAPS system diagnostic procedure and service or replace components accordingly. |
| • Low Steering Gear Efforts Above 30 mph. | • VAPS system malfunction. | • Refer to VAPS system diagnostic procedure and service or replace components accordingly. |
| • External Leakage<br>**NOTE:** Clean off the steering gear before performing any steering gear external leakage checks. | • Leaks between actuator and gear. | • Tighten actuator bolts.<br>• Replace two lower actuator seals. |
| | • Leaks between actuator and actuator bolts. | • Tighten actuator bolts.<br>• Replace two upper actuator seals. |
| | • Gear fittings loose, cross threaded or stripped. | • Inspect and tighten or replace gear assembly. |
| | • Leaks from steering gear seals (input shaft, pinion or either rack seals). | • Replace gear assembly. |
| | • Housing cracked or leaking (due to a porous condition). | • Replace gear assembly. |

**NOTE:** The only serviceable components on the steering gear are the boots, tie rods, actuator, and actuator bolts and seals. All external leaks, which cannot be repaired by tightening tube fittings, are to be repaired by installing a "short rack" assembly (Part No. 3L547)

**Fig. 4 Steering system troubleshooting (Part 2 of 8)**

| CONDITION | POSSIBLE SOURCE | ACTION |
|---|---|---|
| • Smoothness/Sticky Feeling is a condition of momentary build up, hitch, lump, or hesitation in steering efforts, usually occurring just as the turn is begun. It may occur right or left, and in rare cases, occur in both directions. It may be noticed during parking, low speed turns, or at road speeds. If this condition is detected during parking maneuvers, it may also be noticed during higher speed driving.<br>**NOTE:** Discolored steering fluid in rack-and-pinion steering system should not be misdiagnosed as a functional or noise problem. | • Loose or worn pulley belt. | • Tighten or replace. |
| | • Front lower control arm ball joint worn. | • Replace front lower control arm assembly. |
| | • Column trim rubbing steering wheel. | • Reposition trim on column. |
| | • Binding in gear control valve assembly. | • Replace gear assembly. |
| | • Water or oil on pulley belt. | • Clean or replace. |
| | • Column misaligned or binding. | • Align column assembly. |
| | • Flex coupling distorted or fractured. | • Align or replace as required. |
| | • Flex coupling rubbing against housing face. | • Align or reposition flex coupling. |
| | • Column intermediate shaft joints loose, worn or binding. | • Replace as required. |
| | • Column intermediate shaft connecting bolt loose. | • Tighten to specification. |
| | • Steering linkage, shock absorbers or struts are loose, worn or binding. | • Lubricate, adjust or replace as necessary. |
| | • Tight steering column bearings. | • Lubricate or replace as required. |
| | • Column shaft clips missing or damaged. | • Service as required. |
| | • Steering gear attaching bolts loose or damaged. | • Tighten attaching nuts to specification. |
| | • Wheel bearing adjustment. | • Adjust to specification. |
| | • Loose wheel lug nuts. | • Tighten to specification. |
| | • Bent or damaged rack assembly. | • Replace gear assembly. |
| | • Low tire pressure. | • Inflate to specification. |
| | • Improper front end alignment. | • Align front end. |

**Fig. 4 Steering system troubleshooting (Part 4 of 8)**

| CONDITION | POSSIBLE SOURCE | ACTION |
|---|---|---|
| • Poor Returnability is a condition noticed when the vehicle fails to return to a nearly straight ahead position after a corner maneuver. The wheel should return within a reasonable period of time without undue help from the driver. Returnability problems may occur from both directions or only from one direction.<br>*This condition is accompanied by poor returnability and a momentary build up, hitch, lump, or hesitation, in steering efforts usually occurring just off center either in one direction or both. Problem occurs only during driving, and not during parking maneuvers. | • Column trim rubbing steering wheel. | • Reposition trim ring in column assembly slots. |
| | • Front lower control arms worn.* | • Replace lower control arms. |
| | • Brinelled or binding upper strut bearing. | • Replace bearing. |
| | • Tight tie rod and/or tie rod end ball joints. | • Replace tie rod and/or tie rod ends. |
| | • Steering valve assembly off balance. Efforts will be light in one direction and return will be poor in light direction. | • Replace gear assembly. |
| | • Improper front end alignment. | • Align front end. |
| | • Steering linkage, shock absorbers, struts, loose, worn or binding. | • Lubricate, adjust or replace as necessary. |
| | • Tilt column bearing sideloaded by spring. | • Remove spring. If improved, replace tilt yoke, shaft or steering wheel. |
| | • Intermediate column shaft joints binding. | • Replace intermediate shaft assembly. |
| | • Bent or damaged crossmember. | • Replace as necessary. |
| | • Column bearing binding. | • Replace as necessary. |
| | • Column misaligned or binding. | • Align column assembly. |
| | • Low tire pressure or incorrect pressure front to rear. | • Inflate to specification. |
| | • Steering wheel clear vision off location. | • Adjust as required. |
| | • Incorrect tire size or different type make. | • Replace as required. |

**Fig. 4 Steering system troubleshooting (Part 6 of 8)**

| CONDITION | POSSIBLE SOURCE | ACTION |
|---|---|---|
| • Noise/Rattle Chuckle/Clicks/Pops/ Squeaks/Creaks/Clunk/Squawk/ Hiss<br>There are many systems noises which can be misdiagnosed as originating from the power steering gear. Most system noises are RPM sensitive. Therefore, turning the steering wheel will vary the RPM and consequently the noise pitch. Careful diagnosis is necessary to prevent unnecessary services. Disconnecting of belts and re-evaluation is essential in many cases, as is partially cycling the steering wheel with the engine in OFF.<br>NOTE: A common noise in the rack-and-pinion steering gear is a hissing sound. The sound is most evident at static position or during parking maneuvers. There is no relationship between this noise and performance of the steering. "Hiss" may occur at end of steering wheel travel or when slowly turning at stand still, or at a particular position. | • Column intermediate shaft connecting bolt loose. | • Tighten to specification. |
| | • Column trim rubbing steering wheel. | • Reposition trim on column. |
| | • Loose or worn pump belt. | • Adjust or replace as required. |
| | • Front lower control arm worn or binding. | • Replace control arms. |
| | • Brinelled or binding upper strut bearing. | • Replace strut bearing. |
| | • Flex coupling distorted. | • Align flex coupling. |
| | • Flex coupling clamp bolt loose. | • Tighten to specification. |
| | • Pump bracket loose or misaligned. | • Tighten and align to specification. |
| | • Lack of lubricant where horn brush contacts rub steering wheel plate. | • Lubricate or adjust as required. |
| | • Column shaft clips missing. | • Replace as required. |
| | • Column U-joints loose. | • Replace if necessary. |
| | • Loose tie rod ends or ball joints. | • Replace tie rod assembly. |
| | • Gear assembly loose on frame. | • Tighten to specification. |
| | • Loose suspension struts. | • Adjust or replace as required. |
| | • Flex coupling fractured. | • Replace as required. |
| | • Loose wheel lug nuts. | • Tighten to specification. |
| | • Pressure hose grounded against fender or vacuum canister. | • Reposition pressure hoses. |
| | • Front wheel bearing adjustment. | • Adjust to specification. |
| | • Column misaligned or lower bearing out of position. | • Correct as necessary. |
| | • Steering shaft insulators cracked or dry. | • Replace or lubricate as required. |
| | • Kinked pressure hoses. | • Reposition pressure hoses. |
| | • Steering gear or pump external leakage. | • Inspect and replace or repair as required. |
| | • Pulley loose or warped. | • Replace pulley assembly. |
| | • Aerated fluid. | • Purge and evacuate system. |
| | • Water in steering fluid. | • Purge and evacuate system. |

**Fig. 4 Steering system troubleshooting (Part 7 of 8)**

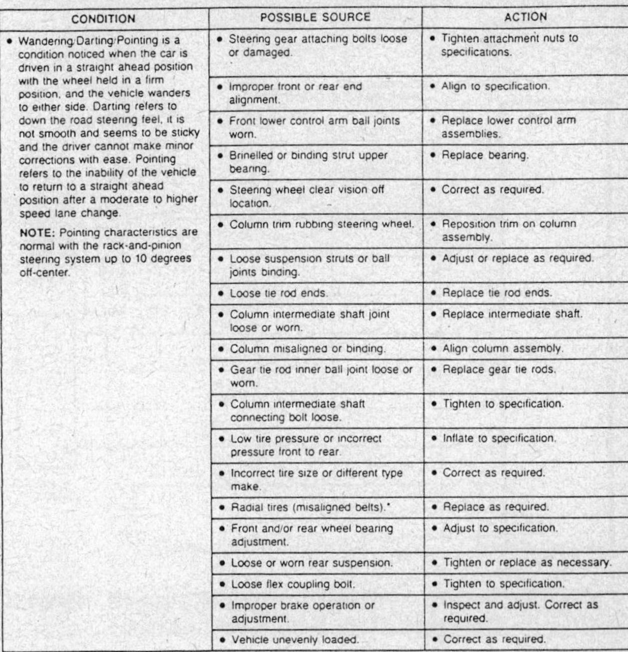

| CONDITION | POSSIBLE SOURCE | ACTION |
|---|---|---|
| • Wandering/Darting/Pointing is a condition noticed when the car is driven in a straight ahead position with the wheel held in a firm position, and the vehicle wanders to either side. Darting refers to down the road steering feel, it is not smooth and seems to be sticky and the driver cannot make minor corrections with ease. Pointing refers to the inability of the vehicle to return to a straight ahead position after a moderate to higher speed lane change.<br>NOTE: Pointing characteristics are normal with the rack-and-pinion steering system up to 10 degrees off-center. | • Steering gear attaching bolts loose or damaged. | • Tighten attachment nuts to specifications. |
| | • Improper front or rear end alignment. | • Align to specification. |
| | • Front lower control arm ball joints worn. | • Replace lower control arm assemblies. |
| | • Brinelled or binding strut upper bearing. | • Replace bearing. |
| | • Steering wheel clear vision off location. | • Correct as required. |
| | • Column trim rubbing steering wheel. | • Reposition trim on column assembly. |
| | • Loose suspension struts or ball joints binding. | • Adjust or replace as required. |
| | • Loose tie rod ends. | • Replace tie rod ends. |
| | • Column intermediate shaft joint loose or worn. | • Replace intermediate shaft. |
| | • Column misaligned or binding. | • Align column assembly. |
| | • Gear tie rod inner ball joint loose or worn. | • Replace gear tie rods. |
| | • Column intermediate shaft connecting bolt loose. | • Tighten to specification. |
| | • Low tire pressure or incorrect pressure front to rear. | • Inflate to specification. |
| | • Incorrect tire size or different type make. | • Correct as required. |
| | • Radial tires (misaligned belts).* | • Replace as required. |
| | • Front and/or rear wheel bearing adjustment. | • Adjust to specification. |
| | • Loose or worn rear suspension. | • Tighten or replace as necessary. |
| | • Loose flex coupling bolt. | • Tighten to specification. |
| | • Improper brake operation or adjustment. | • Inspect and adjust. Correct as required. |
| | • Vehicle unevenly loaded. | • Correct as required. |

**Fig. 4 Steering system troubleshooting (Part 8 of 8)**

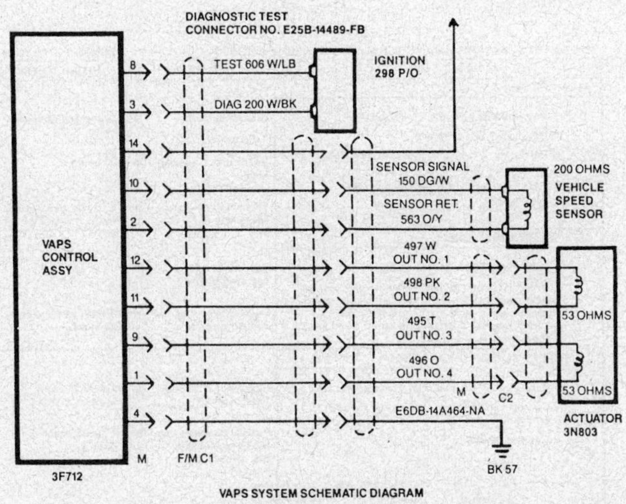


**Fig. 5 VAPS system wiring diagram. 1989 Continental**

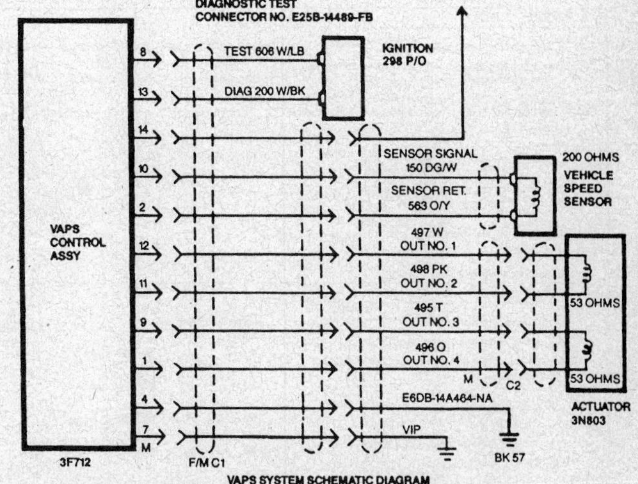


**Fig. 6 VAPS system wiring diagram. 1990 Continental, Sable & Taurus**

d. **On all SHO models,** if flow is below 2.2 gallons per minute, pump may require service, however continue test, check flow and relief pressure.

e. **On all models,** if pressure is above 150 psi check hoses for restrictions.

11. Partially close gate valve to build up 740 psi, observe and record flow at 167-177°F (76-80°C):

a. **On all models except SHO,** if flow drops lower than .9 gallons per minute, disassemble pump and replace cam pack, if pressure plates are cracked or worn, replace.

b. **On SHO models,** if flow drops lower than .9 gallons per minute, replace pump.

12. **On all models,** completely close and partially open gate valve three times. **Do not allow valve to remain closed for more then five seconds.** Observe and record pressure.

13. **On all models except SHO,** if pressure is lower than specifications, replace pump flow control valve.

14. **On SHO models,** if pressure is lower than specifications, replace pump.

15. **On all models except SHO,** if pressure is above specifications, pump flow control valve should be removed and cleaned or replaced.

16. **On SHO models,** if pressure is above specifications, pump should be removed and cleaned or replaced.

17. **On all models,** increase engine speed to about 1500 RPM, observe and record flow.

18. **On all models except SHO,** if flow exceeds maximum free flow per min-

*Continued on page 22-99*

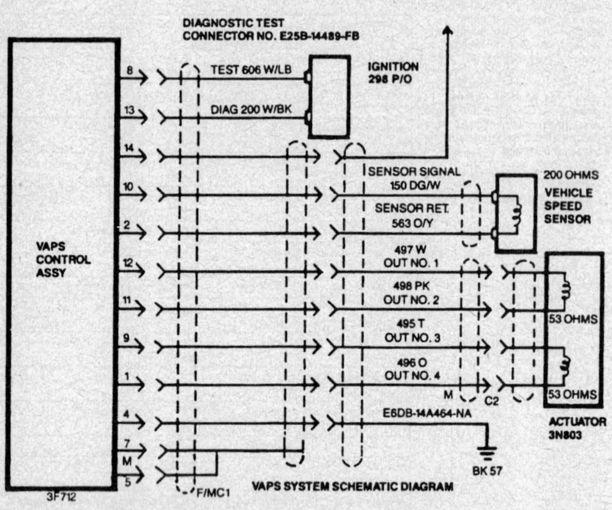


**Fig. 7 VAPS system wiring diagram. 1991 Continental, Sable & Taurus**

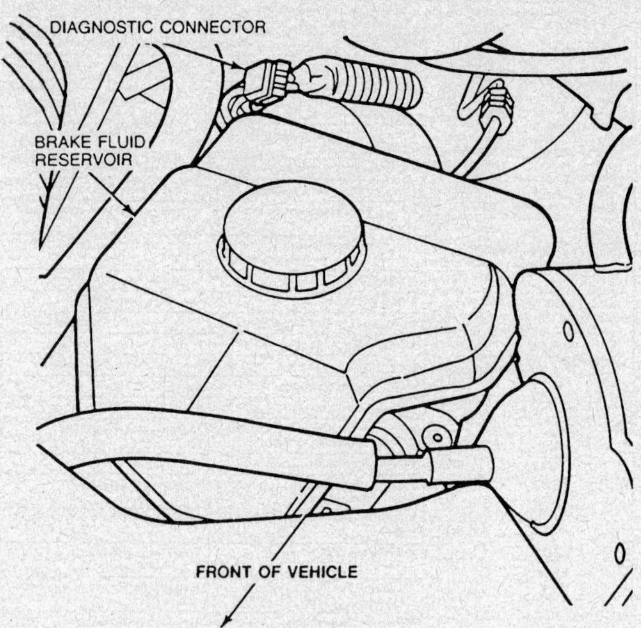


**Fig. 8 Diagnostic connector location**

PINPOINT TEST A: VARIABLE ASSIST POWER STEERING ELECTRICAL COMPONENT DIAGNOSIS

| TEST STEP | RESULT ▶ | ACTION TO TAKE |
|---|---|---|
| **A1** MODULE CHECK | | |
| • Turn ignition switch to OFF. • Locate test connector 14489 in engine compartment near brake booster. • Connect DVOM positive lead (red) to Circuit No. 606 and negative lead (black) to vehicle ground. | Voltage reads 11V-14V ▶ | GO to **A2**. |
| | Voltage reads zero ▶ | GO to **A3**. |
| • Position DVOM where it can be observed. • Start engine. • Observe voltage reading on DVOM. | | |
| **A2** MODULE CHECK | | |
| • Turn ignition switch to OFF. • Connect an analog voltmeter as in Step A1. • Use jumper wire and ground Circuit No. 200. | Efforts Change? / Number of Sweeps | |
| | Yes 4 ▶ | GO to **A4**. |
| | No 0 ▶ | GO to **A12**. |
| | No 4 ▶ | GO to **A7**. |
| | No 6 ▶ | GO to **A12**. |
| • Start engine. • Rotate steering wheel for approximately 90 seconds noting any changes in steering effort. The effort required to turn the steering wheel should vary between light and heavy in both directions. • After approximately 90 seconds, voltmeter will show a sweep pattern four times between battery voltage and zero if module proveout is OK. Six or zero sweeps if a system component is malfunctioning. After a five second pause, the sweep pattern will be repeated. | | |
| **A3** FUSE CHECK | | |
| • Inspect fuse located in fuse panel on LH side below instrument panel. | Fuse good ▶ | GO to **A16**. |
| | Fuse blown ▶ | REPLACE fuse. GO to A1. |

**Fig. 9 Electrical component diagnosis (Part 1 of 8). 1989 Continental**

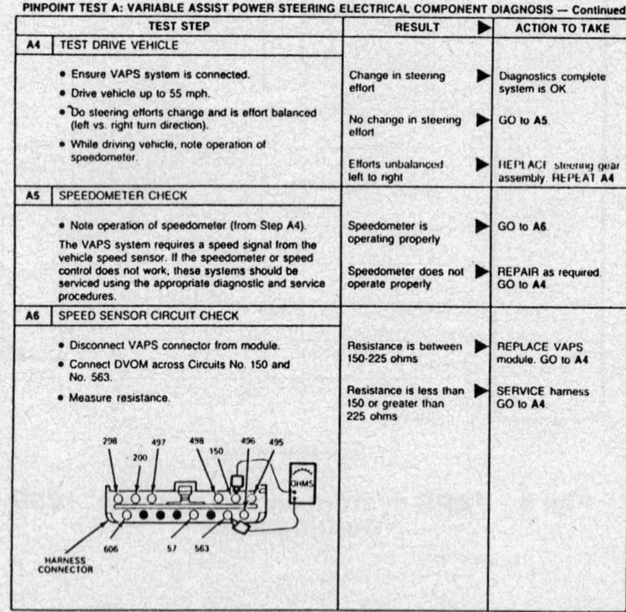

PINPOINT TEST A: VARIABLE ASSIST POWER STEERING ELECTRICAL COMPONENT DIAGNOSIS — Continued

| TEST STEP | RESULT ▶ | ACTION TO TAKE |
|---|---|---|
| **A4** TEST DRIVE VEHICLE | | |
| • Ensure VAPS system is connected. • Drive vehicle up to 55 mph. • Do steering efforts change and is effort balanced (left vs. right turn direction). • While driving vehicle, note operation of speedometer. | Change in steering effort ▶ | Diagnostics complete system is OK. |
| | No change in steering effort ▶ | GO to **A5**. |
| | Efforts unbalanced left to right ▶ | REPLACE steering gear assembly. REPEAT **A4** |
| **A5** SPEEDOMETER CHECK | | |
| • Note operation of speedometer (from Step A4). The VAPS system requires a speed signal from the vehicle speed sensor. If the speedometer or speed control does not work, these systems should be serviced using the appropriate diagnostic and service procedures. | Speedometer is operating properly ▶ | GO to **A6**. |
| | Speedometer does not operate properly ▶ | REPAIR as required. GO to **A4**. |
| **A6** SPEED SENSOR CIRCUIT CHECK | | |
| • Disconnect VAPS connector from module. • Connect DVOM across Circuits No. 150 and No. 563. • Measure resistance. | Resistance is between 150-225 ohms ▶ | REPLACE VAPS module. GO to **A4**. |
| | Resistance is less than 150 or greater than 225 ohms ▶ | SERVICE harness GO to **A4**. |

**Fig. 9 Electrical component diagnosis (Part 2 of 8). 1989 Continental**

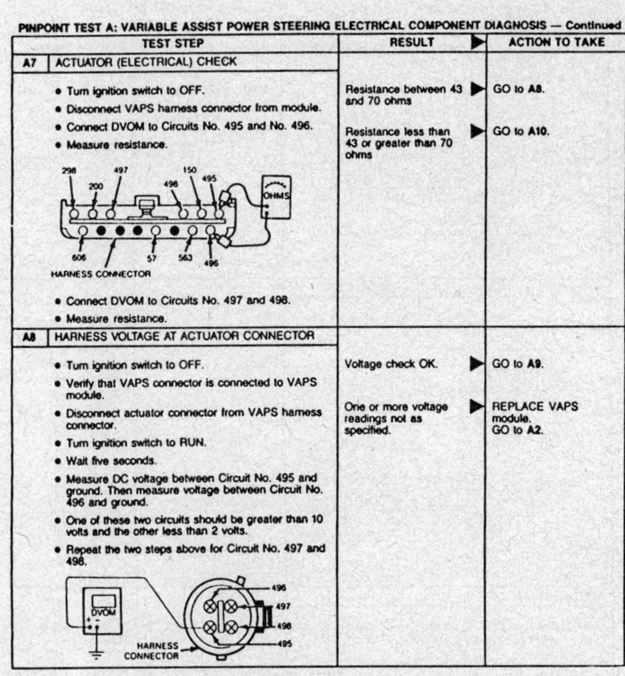

PINPOINT TEST A: VARIABLE ASSIST POWER STEERING ELECTRICAL COMPONENT DIAGNOSIS — Continued

| TEST STEP | RESULT | ACTION TO TAKE |
|---|---|---|
| **A7** ACTUATOR (ELECTRICAL) CHECK | | |
| • Turn ignition switch to OFF.<br>• Disconnect VAPS harness connector from module.<br>• Connect DVOM to Circuits No. 495 and No. 496.<br>• Measure resistance. | Resistance between 43 and 70 ohms ▶<br><br>Resistance less than 43 or greater than 70 ohms ▶ | GO to **A8**.<br><br>GO to **A10**. |
| • Connect DVOM to Circuits No. 497 and 498.<br>• Measure resistance. | | |
| **A8** HARNESS VOLTAGE AT ACTUATOR CONNECTOR | | |
| • Turn ignition switch to OFF.<br>• Verify that VAPS connector is connected to VAPS module.<br>• Disconnect actuator connector from VAPS harness connector.<br>• Turn ignition switch to RUN.<br>• Wait five seconds.<br>• Measure DC voltage between Circuit No. 495 and ground. Then measure voltage between Circuit No. 496 and ground.<br>• One of these two circuits should be greater than 10 volts and the other less than 2 volts.<br>• Repeat the two steps above for Circuit No. 497 and 498. | Voltage check OK. ▶<br><br>One or more voltage readings not as specified. ▶ | GO to **A9**.<br><br>REPLACE VAPS module.<br>GO to **A2**. |



**Fig. 9 Electrical component diagnosis (Part 3 of 8). 1989 Continental**

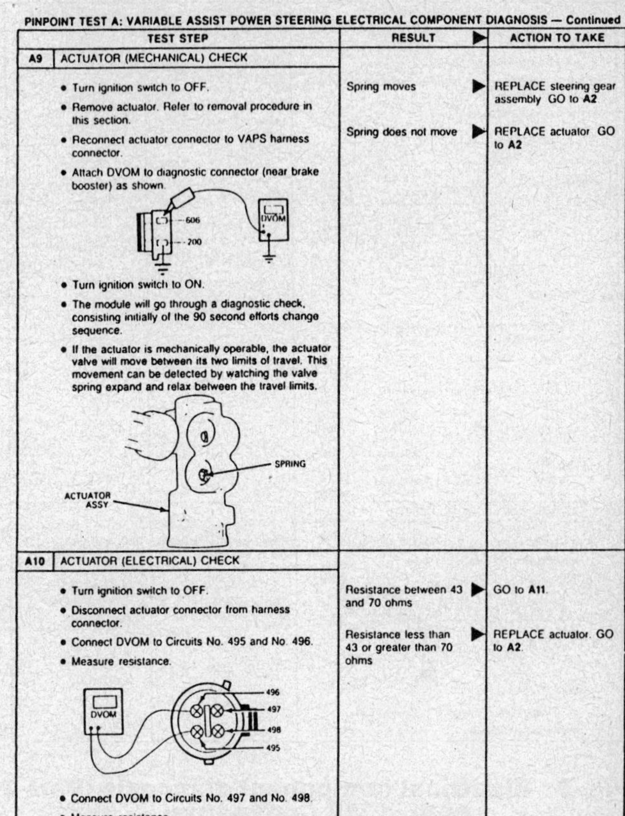

PINPOINT TEST A: VARIABLE ASSIST POWER STEERING ELECTRICAL COMPONENT DIAGNOSIS — Continued

| TEST STEP | RESULT | ACTION TO TAKE |
|---|---|---|
| **A9** ACTUATOR (MECHANICAL) CHECK | | |
| • Turn ignition switch to OFF.<br>• Remove actuator. Refer to removal procedure in this section.<br>• Reconnect actuator connector to VAPS harness connector.<br>• Attach DVOM to diagnostic connector (near brake booster) as shown.<br>• Turn ignition switch to ON.<br>• The module will go through a diagnostic check, consisting initially of the 90 second efforts change sequence.<br>• If the actuator is mechanically operable, the actuator valve will move between its two limits of travel. This movement can be detected by watching the valve spring expand and relax between the travel limits. | Spring moves ▶<br><br>Spring does not move ▶ | REPLACE steering gear assembly GO to **A2**<br><br>REPLACE actuator GO to **A2** |
| **A10** ACTUATOR (ELECTRICAL) CHECK | | |
| • Turn ignition switch to OFF.<br>• Disconnect actuator connector from harness connector.<br>• Connect DVOM to Circuits No. 495 and No. 496.<br>• Measure resistance.<br>• Connect DVOM to Circuits No. 497 and No. 498.<br>• Measure resistance. | Resistance between 43 and 70 ohms ▶<br><br>Resistance less than 43 or greater than 70 ohms ▶ | GO to **A11**.<br><br>REPLACE actuator. GO to **A2**. |



**Fig. 9 Electrical component diagnosis (Part 4 of 8). 1989 Continental**

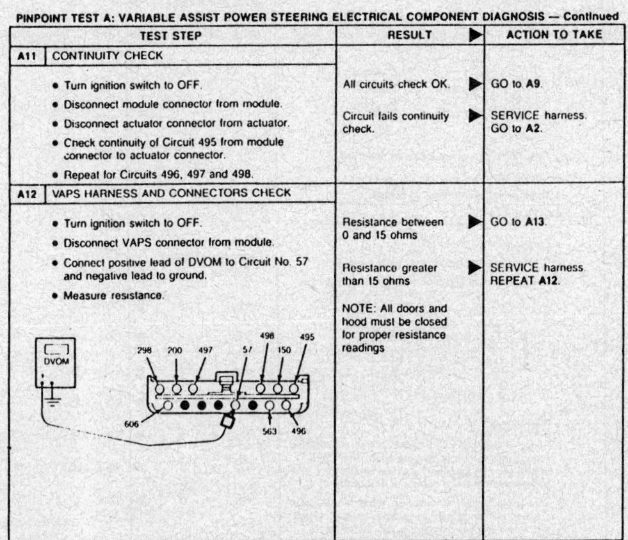

PINPOINT TEST A: VARIABLE ASSIST POWER STEERING ELECTRICAL COMPONENT DIAGNOSIS — Continued

| TEST STEP | RESULT | ACTION TO TAKE |
|---|---|---|
| **A11** CONTINUITY CHECK | | |
| • Turn ignition switch to OFF.<br>• Disconnect module connector from module.<br>• Disconnect actuator connector from actuator.<br>• Check continuity of Circuit 495 from module connector to actuator connector.<br>• Repeat for Circuits 496, 497 and 498. | All circuits check OK. ▶<br><br>Circuit fails continuity check. ▶ | GO to **A9**.<br><br>SERVICE harness. GO to **A2**. |
| **A12** VAPS HARNESS AND CONNECTORS CHECK | | |
| • Turn ignition switch to OFF.<br>• Disconnect VAPS connector from module.<br>• Connect positive lead of DVOM to Circuit No. 57 and negative lead to ground.<br>• Measure resistance. | Resistance between 0 and 15 ohms ▶<br><br>Resistance greater than 15 ohms ▶<br><br>NOTE: All doors and hood must be closed for proper resistance readings | GO to **A13**.<br><br>SERVICE harness. REPEAT **A12**. |



**Fig. 9 Electrical component diagnosis (Part 5 of 8). 1989 Continental**

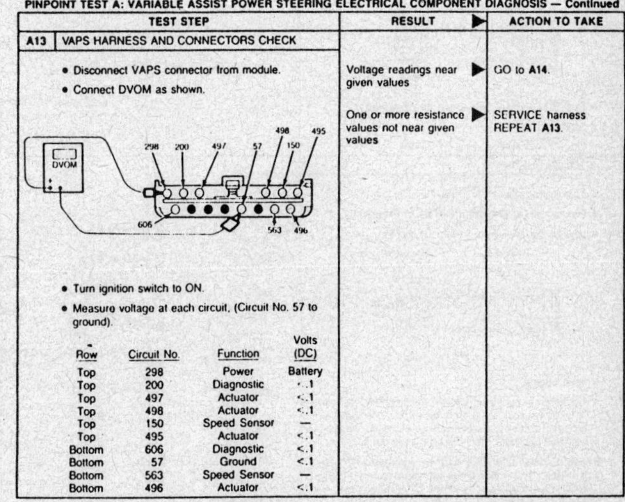

PINPOINT TEST A: VARIABLE ASSIST POWER STEERING ELECTRICAL COMPONENT DIAGNOSIS — Continued

| TEST STEP | RESULT | ACTION TO TAKE |
|---|---|---|
| **A13** VAPS HARNESS AND CONNECTORS CHECK | | |
| • Disconnect VAPS connector from module.<br>• Connect DVOM as shown.<br>• Turn ignition switch to ON.<br>• Measure voltage at each circuit, (Circuit No. 57 to ground). | Voltage readings near given values ▶<br><br>One or more resistance values not near given values ▶ | GO to **A14**.<br><br>SERVICE harness REPEAT **A13**. |



| Row | Circuit No. | Function | Volts (DC) |
|---|---|---|---|
| Top | 298 | Power | Battery |
| Top | 200 | Diagnostic | <.1 |
| Top | 497 | Actuator | <.1 |
| Top | 498 | Actuator | <.1 |
| Top | 150 | Speed Sensor | — |
| Top | 495 | Actuator | <.1 |
| Bottom | 606 | Diagnostic | <.1 |
| Bottom | 57 | Ground | <.1 |
| Bottom | 563 | Speed Sensor | — |
| Bottom | 496 | Actuator | <.1 |

**Fig. 9 Electrical component diagnosis (Part 6 of 8). 1989 Continental**

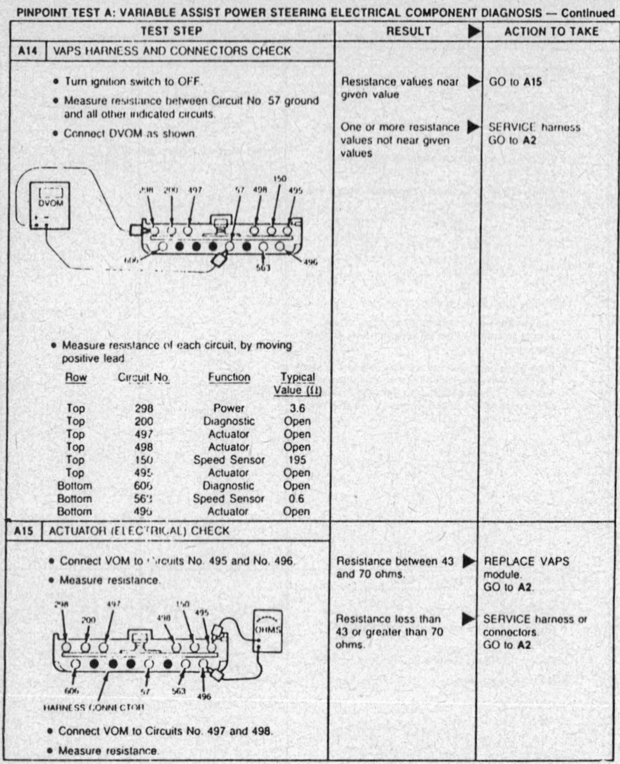

PINPOINT TEST A: VARIABLE ASSIST POWER STEERING ELECTRICAL COMPONENT DIAGNOSIS — Continued

| TEST STEP | RESULT ▶ | ACTION TO TAKE |
|---|---|---|
| **A14** VAPS HARNESS AND CONNECTORS CHECK | | |
| • Turn ignition switch to OFF.<br>• Measure resistance between Circuit No. 57 ground and all other indicated circuits.<br>• Connect DVOM as shown. | Resistance values near given value ▶ | GO to **A15** |
| | One or more resistance values not near given values ▶ | SERVICE harness<br>GO to **A2** |
| • Measure resistance of each circuit, by moving positive lead | | |

| Row | Circuit No. | Function | Typical Value (Ω) |
|---|---|---|---|
| Top | 298 | Power | 3.6 |
| Top | 200 | Diagnostic | Open |
| Top | 497 | Actuator | Open |
| Top | 498 | Actuator | Open |
| Top | 150 | Speed Sensor | 195 |
| Top | 495 | Actuator | Open |
| Bottom | 606 | Diagnostic | Open |
| Bottom | 563 | Speed Sensor | 0.6 |
| Bottom | 496 | Actuator | Open |

| TEST STEP | RESULT ▶ | ACTION TO TAKE |
|---|---|---|
| **A15** ACTUATOR (ELECTRICAL) CHECK | | |
| • Connect VOM to Circuits No. 495 and No. 496.<br>• Measure resistance. | Resistance between 43 and 70 ohms. ▶ | REPLACE VAPS module.<br>GO to **A2**. |
| | Resistance less than 43 or greater than 70 ohms. ▶ | SERVICE harness or connectors.<br>GO to **A2**. |
| • Connect VOM to Circuits No. 497 and 498.<br>• Measure resistance. | | |

Fig. 9 Electrical component diagnosis (Part 7 of 8). 1989 Continental

PINPOINT TEST A: VARIABLE ASSIST POWER STEERING ELECTRICAL COMPONENT DIAGNOSIS — Continued

| TEST STEP | RESULT ▶ | ACTION TO TAKE |
|---|---|---|
| **A16** VAPS HARNESS AND CONNECTORS CHECK | | |
| • Turn ignition switch to OFF.<br>• Disconnect VAPS connector from module<br>• Connect positive lead of DVOM to Circuit No. 57 and negative lead to ground.<br>• Measure resistance. | Resistance between 0 and 15 ohms ▶ | GO to **A17** |
| | Resistance greater than 15 ohms ▶ | SERVICE harness<br>GO to **A1** |
| | **NOTE:** All doors and hood must be closed for proper resistance readings. | |
| **A17** VAPS HARNESS AND CONNECTORS CHECK | | |
| • Connect positive lead of DVOM to Circuit No. 298 and negative lead to Circuit No. 57.<br>• Turn ignition switch to ON.<br>• Measure voltage.<br>• Turn ignition switch to OFF. | 12V ▶ | GO to **A18**. |
| | 0 volt ▶ | SERVICE harness<br>GO to **A1**. |
| **A18** CONTINUITY CHECK | | |
| • Check continuity of Circuit No. 606 from diagnostic connector to module connector. | Circuit No. 606 is OK. ▶ | REPLACE module.<br>GO to **A1**. |
| | Circuit No. 606 is BAD. ▶ | SERVICE Circuit No. 606.<br>GO to **A1**. |

Fig. 9 Electrical component diagnosis (Part 8 of 8). 1989 Continental

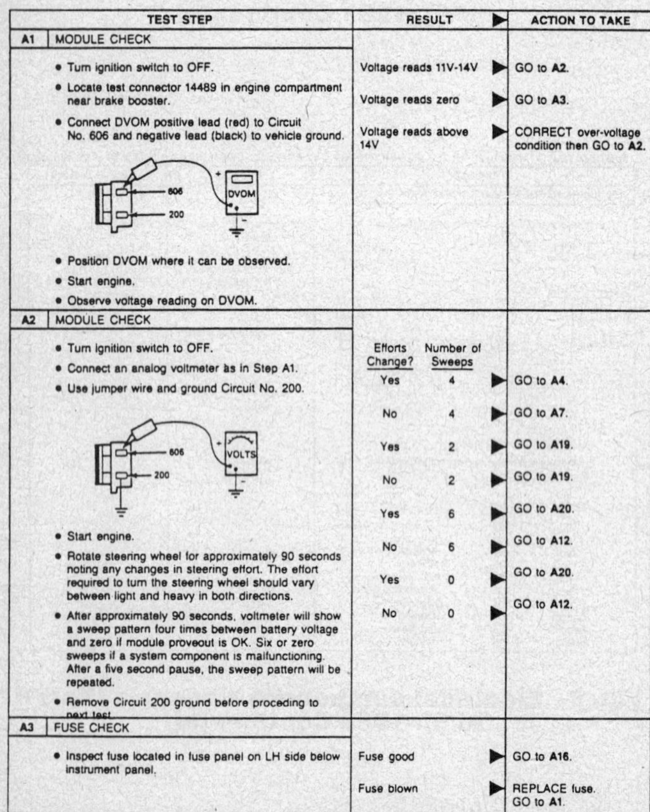

| TEST STEP | RESULT ▶ | ACTION TO TAKE |
|---|---|---|
| **A1** MODULE CHECK | | |
| • Turn ignition switch to OFF.<br>• Locate test connector 14489 in engine compartment near brake booster.<br>• Connect DVOM positive lead (red) to Circuit No. 606 and negative lead (black) to vehicle ground. | Voltage reads 11V-14V ▶ | GO to **A2**. |
| | Voltage reads zero ▶ | GO to **A3**. |
| | Voltage reads above 14V ▶ | CORRECT over-voltage condition then GO to **A2**. |
| • Position DVOM where it can be observed.<br>• Start engine.<br>• Observe voltage reading on DVOM. | | |
| **A2** MODULE CHECK | | |
| • Turn ignition switch to OFF.<br>• Connect an analog voltmeter as in Step A1.<br>• Use jumper wire and ground Circuit No. 200. | Efforts Change? / Number of Sweeps | |
| | Yes 4 ▶ | GO to A4. |
| | No 4 ▶ | GO to A7. |
| | Yes 2 ▶ | GO to A19. |
| | No 2 ▶ | GO to A19. |
| • Start engine.<br>• Rotate steering wheel for approximately 90 seconds noting any changes in steering effort. The effort required to turn the steering wheel should vary between light and heavy in both directions.<br>• After approximately 90 seconds, voltmeter will show a sweep pattern four times between battery voltage and zero if module proveout is OK. Six or zero sweeps if a system component is malfunctioning. After a five second pause, the sweep pattern will be repeated.<br>• Remove Circuit 200 ground before proceding to next test. | Yes 6 ▶ | GO to A20. |
| | No 6 ▶ | GO to A12. |
| | Yes 0 ▶ | GO to A20. |
| | No 0 ▶ | GO to A12. |
| **A3** FUSE CHECK | | |
| • Inspect fuse located in fuse panel on LH side below instrument panel. | Fuse good ▶ | GO to A16. |
| | Fuse blown ▶ | REPLACE fuse.<br>GO to A1. |

Fig. 10 Electrical component diagnosis (Part 1 of 13). 1990–91 Continental

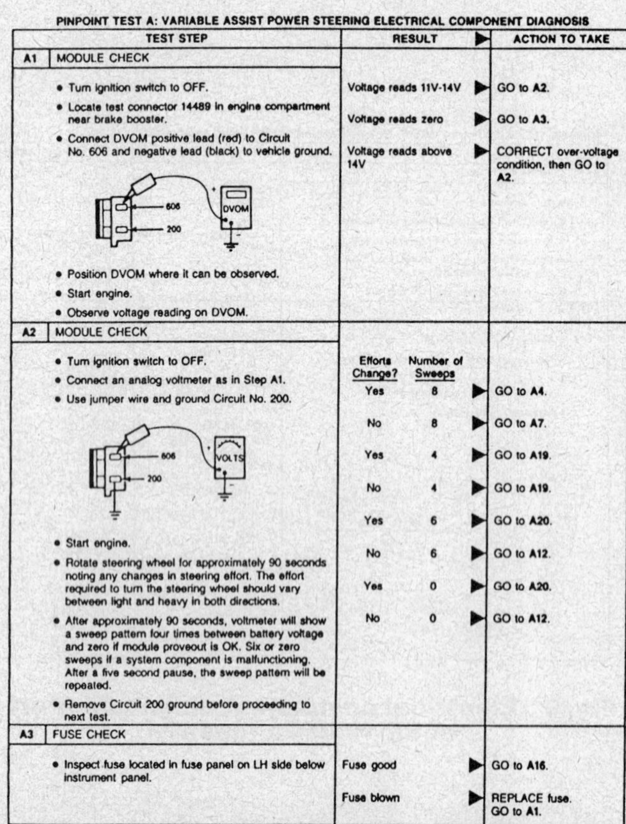

PINPOINT TEST A: VARIABLE ASSIST POWER STEERING ELECTRICAL COMPONENT DIAGNOSIS

| TEST STEP | RESULT ▶ | ACTION TO TAKE |
|---|---|---|
| **A1** MODULE CHECK | | |
| • Turn ignition switch to OFF.<br>• Locate test connector 14489 in engine compartment near brake booster.<br>• Connect DVOM positive lead (red) to Circuit No. 606 and negative lead (black) to vehicle ground. | Voltage reads 11V-14V ▶ | GO to **A2**. |
| | Voltage reads zero ▶ | GO to **A3**. |
| | Voltage reads above 14V ▶ | CORRECT over-voltage condition, then GO to **A2**. |
| • Position DVOM where it can be observed.<br>• Start engine.<br>• Observe voltage reading on DVOM. | | |
| **A2** MODULE CHECK | | |
| • Turn ignition switch to OFF.<br>• Connect an analog voltmeter as in Step A1.<br>• Use jumper wire and ground Circuit No. 200. | Efforts Change? / Number of Sweeps | |
| | Yes 8 ▶ | GO to A4. |
| | No 8 ▶ | GO to A7. |
| | Yes 4 ▶ | GO to A19. |
| | No 4 ▶ | GO to A19. |
| • Start engine.<br>• Rotate steering wheel for approximately 90 seconds noting any changes in steering effort. The effort required to turn the steering wheel should vary between light and heavy in both directions.<br>• After approximately 90 seconds, voltmeter will show a sweep pattern four times between battery voltage and zero if module proveout is OK. Six or zero sweeps if a system component is malfunctioning. After a five second pause, the sweep pattern will be repeated.<br>• Remove Circuit 200 ground before proceeding to next test. | Yes 6 ▶ | GO to A20. |
| | No 6 ▶ | GO to A12. |
| | Yes 0 ▶ | GO to A20. |
| | No 0 ▶ | GO to A12. |
| **A3** FUSE CHECK | | |
| • Inspect fuse located in fuse panel on LH side below instrument panel. | Fuse good ▶ | GO to A16. |
| | Fuse blown ▶ | REPLACE fuse.<br>GO to A1. |

Fig. 10 Electrical component diagnosis (Part 2 of 13). 1990 Sable & Taurus

| TEST STEP | RESULT ▶ | ACTION TO TAKE |
|---|---|---|
| **A1 MODULE CHECK** | | |
| • Turn ignition switch to OFF. | Voltage reads 11V-14V ▶ | GO to **A2**. |
| • Locate test connector 14489 in engine compartment near brake booster. | Voltage reads zero ▶ | GO to **A3**. |
| • Connect DVOM positive lead (red) to Circuit No. 606 and negative lead (black) to vehicle ground. | Voltage reads above 14V ▶ | CORRECT over-voltage condition, then GO to **A2**. |
| • Position DVOM where it can be observed.<br>• Start engine.<br>• Observe voltage reading on DVOM. | | |
| **A2 MODULE CHECK** | | |
| • Turn ignition switch to OFF.<br>• Connect an analog voltmeter as in Step A1.<br>• Use jumper wire and ground Circuit No. 200. | Efforts Change? / Number of Sweeps: Yes / 2 ▶ | GO to **A4**. |
| | No / 2 ▶ | GO to **A7**. |
| | Yes / 4 ▶ | GO to **A19**. |
| | No / 4 ▶ | GO to **A19**. |
| • Start engine. | Yes / 6 ▶ | GO to **A20**. |
| • Rotate steering wheel for approximately 90 seconds noting any changes in steering effort. The effort required to turn the steering wheel should vary between light and heavy in both directions. | No / 6 ▶ | GO to **A12**. |
| | Yes / 0 ▶ | GO to **A20**. |
| • After approximately 90 seconds, voltmeter will show a sweep pattern four times between battery voltage and zero if module proveout is OK. Six or zero sweeps if a system component is malfunctioning. After a five second pause, the sweep pattern will be repeated. | No / 0 ▶ | GO to **A12**. |
| • Remove Circuit 200 ground before proceeding to next test. | | |
| **A3 FUSE CHECK** | | |
| • Inspect fuse located in fuse panel on LH side below instrument panel. | Fuse good ▶ | GO to **A16**. |
| | Fuse blown ▶ | REPLACE fuse. GO to **A1**. |

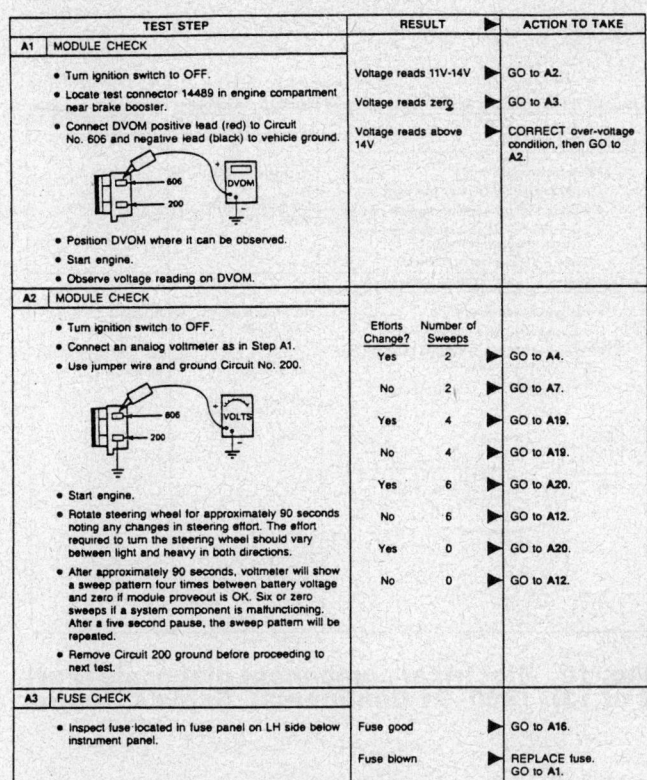

**Fig. 10 Electrical component diagnosis (Part 3 of 13). 1991 Sable & Taurus**

| TEST STEP | RESULT ▶ | ACTION TO TAKE |
|---|---|---|
| **A4 TEST DRIVE VEHICLE** | | |
| • Ensure VAPS system is connected. | Change in steering effort ▶ | Diagnostics complete system is OK. |
| • Drive vehicle up to 55 mph and set speed control.<br>• Do steering efforts change and is effort balanced (left vs. right turn direction). | Assist only at high speed ▶ | GO to **A11**. |
| • While driving vehicle, note operation of speedometer. | No change in steering effort ▶ | GO to **A5**. |
| | Efforts unbalanced left to right ▶ | REPLACE steering gear assembly. REPEAT **A4**. |
| **A5 SPEEDOMETER CHECK** | | |
| • Note operation of speedometer and speed control (from Step A4). | Speedometer and speed control is operating properly ▶ | GO to **A6**. |
| The VAPS system requires a speed signal from the vehicle speed sensor. If the speedometer or speed control does not work, these systems should be serviced using the appropriate diagnostic and service procedures. | Speedometer or speed control does not operate properly ▶ | REPAIR as required. GO to **A4**. |
| **A6 SPEED SENSOR CIRCUIT CHECK** | | |
| • Disconnect VAPS connector from module. | Resistance is between 150-225 ohms ▶ | REPLACE VAPS module. GO to **A4**. |
| • Connect DVOM across Circuits No. 150 and No. 563.<br>• Measure resistance. | Resistance is less than 150 or greater than 225 ohms ▶ | SERVICE harness. GO to **A4**. |

**Fig. 10 Electrical component diagnosis (Part 5 of 13). 1991 Continental, Sable & Taurus**

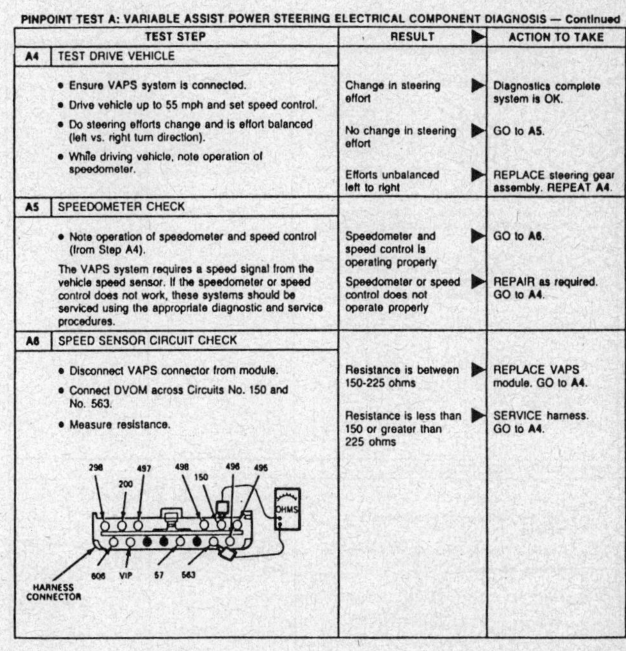

PINPOINT TEST A: VARIABLE ASSIST POWER STEERING ELECTRICAL COMPONENT DIAGNOSIS — Continued

| TEST STEP | RESULT ▶ | ACTION TO TAKE |
|---|---|---|
| **A4 TEST DRIVE VEHICLE** | | |
| • Ensure VAPS system is connected.<br>• Drive vehicle up to 55 mph and set speed control. | Change in steering effort ▶ | Diagnostics complete system is OK. |
| • Do steering efforts change and is effort balanced (left vs. right turn direction).<br>• While driving vehicle, note operation of speedometer. | No change in steering effort ▶ | GO to **A5**. |
| | Efforts unbalanced left to right ▶ | REPLACE steering gear assembly. REPEAT **A4**. |
| **A5 SPEEDOMETER CHECK** | | |
| • Note operation of speedometer and speed control (from Step A4). | Speedometer and speed control is operating properly ▶ | GO to **A6**. |
| The VAPS system requires a speed signal from the vehicle speed sensor. If the speedometer or speed control does not work, these systems should be serviced using the appropriate diagnostic and service procedures. | Speedometer or speed control does not operate properly ▶ | REPAIR as required. GO to **A4**. |
| **A6 SPEED SENSOR CIRCUIT CHECK** | | |
| • Disconnect VAPS connector from module.<br>• Connect DVOM across Circuits No. 150 and No. 563. | Resistance is between 150-225 ohms ▶ | REPLACE VAPS module. GO to **A4**. |
| • Measure resistance. | Resistance is less than 150 or greater than 225 ohms ▶ | SERVICE harness. GO to **A4**. |

**Fig. 10 Electrical component diagnosis (Part 4 of 13). 1990 Continental, Sable & Taurus**

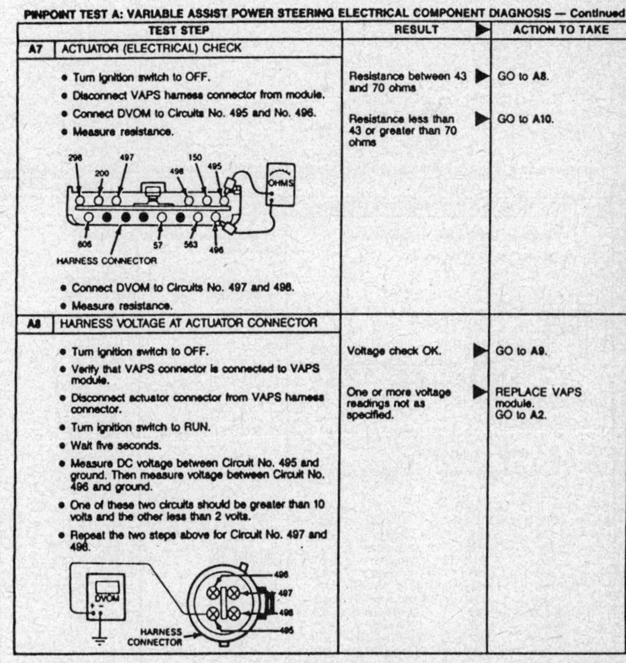

PINPOINT TEST A: VARIABLE ASSIST POWER STEERING ELECTRICAL COMPONENT DIAGNOSIS — Continued

| TEST STEP | RESULT ▶ | ACTION TO TAKE |
|---|---|---|
| **A7 ACTUATOR (ELECTRICAL) CHECK** | | |
| • Turn ignition switch to OFF.<br>• Disconnect VAPS harness connector from module. | Resistance between 43 and 70 ohms ▶ | GO to **A8**. |
| • Connect DVOM to Circuits No. 495 and No. 496.<br>• Measure resistance. | Resistance less than 43 or greater than 70 ohms ▶ | GO to **A10**. |
| • Connect DVOM to Circuits No. 497 and 498.<br>• Measure resistance. | | |
| **A8 HARNESS VOLTAGE AT ACTUATOR CONNECTOR** | | |
| • Turn ignition switch to OFF. | Voltage check OK. ▶ | GO to **A9**. |
| • Verify that VAPS connector is connected to VAPS module.<br>• Disconnect actuator connector from VAPS harness connector. | One or more voltage readings not as specified. ▶ | REPLACE VAPS module. GO to **A2**. |
| • Turn ignition switch to RUN.<br>• Wait five seconds.<br>• Measure DC voltage between Circuit No. 495 and ground. Then measure voltage between Circuit No. 496 and ground.<br>• One of these two circuits should be greater than 10 volts and the other less than 2 volts.<br>• Repeat the two steps above for Circuit No. 497 and 498. | | |

**Fig. 10 Electrical component diagnosis (Part 6 of 13). 1990–91 Continental, Sable & Taurus**

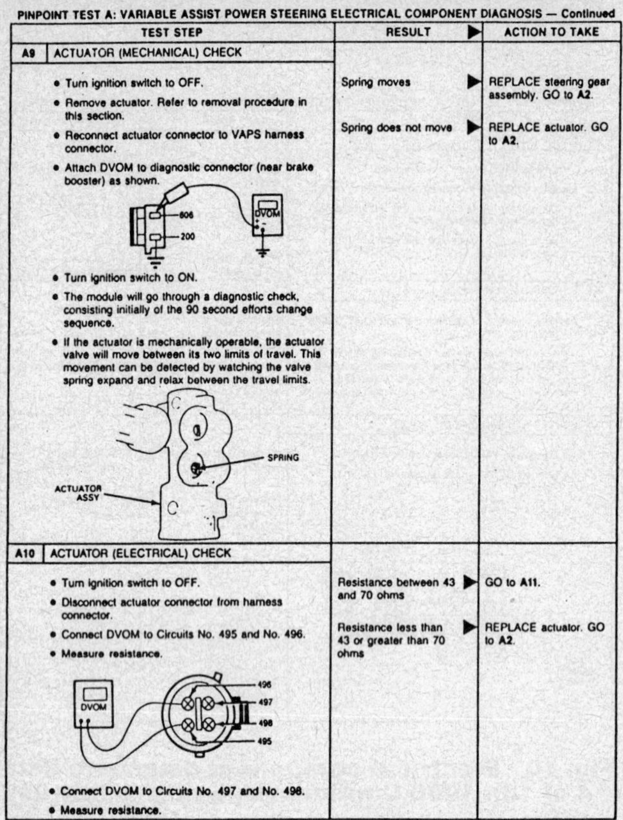

PINPOINT TEST A: VARIABLE ASSIST POWER STEERING ELECTRICAL COMPONENT DIAGNOSIS — Continued

| TEST STEP | RESULT ▶ | ACTION TO TAKE |
|---|---|---|
| **A9 ACTUATOR (MECHANICAL) CHECK** | | |
| • Turn ignition switch to OFF.<br>• Remove actuator. Refer to removal procedure in this section.<br>• Reconnect actuator connector to VAPS harness connector.<br>• Attach DVOM to diagnostic connector (near brake booster) as shown.<br>• Turn ignition switch to ON.<br>• The module will go through a diagnostic check, consisting initially of the 90 second efforts change sequence.<br>• If the actuator is mechanically operable, the actuator valve will move between its two limits of travel. This movement can be detected by watching the valve spring expand and relax between the travel limits. | Spring moves ▶ | REPLACE steering gear assembly. GO to **A2**. |
| | Spring does not move ▶ | REPLACE actuator. GO to **A2**. |
| **A10 ACTUATOR (ELECTRICAL) CHECK** | | |
| • Turn ignition switch to OFF.<br>• Disconnect actuator connector from harness connector.<br>• Connect DVOM to Circuits No. 495 and No. 496.<br>• Measure resistance.<br>• Connect DVOM to Circuits No. 497 and No. 498.<br>• Measure resistance. | Resistance between 43 and 70 ohms ▶ | GO to **A11**. |
| | Resistance less than 43 or greater than 70 ohms ▶ | REPLACE actuator. GO to **A2**. |

**Fig. 10 Electrical component diagnosis (Part 7 of 13). 1990–91 Continental, Sable & Taurus**

PINPOINT TEST A: VARIABLE ASSIST POWER STEERING ELECTRICAL COMPONENT DIAGNOSIS — Continued

| TEST STEP | RESULT ▶ | ACTION TO TAKE |
|---|---|---|
| **A11 CONTINUITY CHECK** | | |
| • Turn ignition switch to OFF.<br>• Disconnect module connector from module.<br>• Disconnect actuator connector from actuator.<br>• Check continuity of Circuit 495 from module connector to actuator connector.<br>• Repeat for Circuits 496, 497 and 498. | All circuits check OK. ▶ | GO to **A9**. |
| | Circuit fails continuity check. ▶ | SERVICE harness. GO to **A2**. |
| **A12 VAPS HARNESS AND CONNECTORS CHECK** | | |
| • Turn ignition switch to OFF.<br>• Disconnect VAPS connector from module.<br>• Connect positive lead of DVOM to Circuit No. 57 and negative lead to ground.<br>• Measure resistance. | Resistance between 0 and 15 ohms ▶ | GO to **A13**. |
| | Resistance greater than 15 ohms ▶ | SERVICE harness. REPEAT **A12**. |
| | NOTE: All doors and hood must be closed for proper resistance readings | |

**Fig. 10 Electrical component diagnosis (Part 8 of 13). 1990–91 Continental, Sable & Taurus**

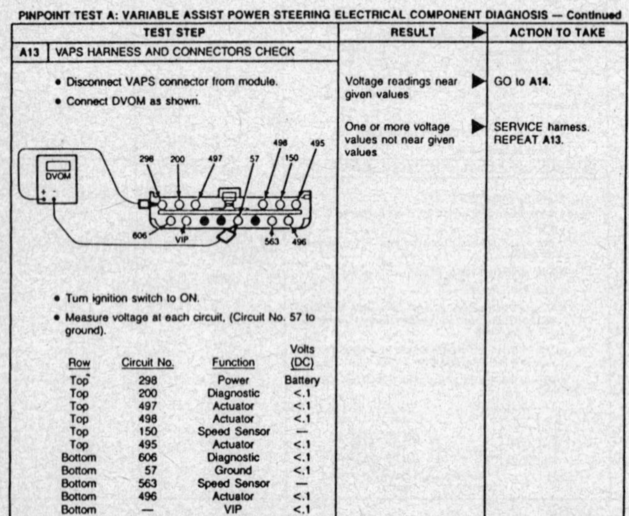

PINPOINT TEST A: VARIABLE ASSIST POWER STEERING ELECTRICAL COMPONENT DIAGNOSIS — Continued

| TEST STEP | RESULT ▶ | ACTION TO TAKE |
|---|---|---|
| **A13 VAPS HARNESS AND CONNECTORS CHECK** | | |
| • Disconnect VAPS connector from module.<br>• Connect DVOM as shown.<br>• Turn ignition switch to ON.<br>• Measure voltage at each circuit, (Circuit No. 57 to ground). | Voltage readings near given values ▶ | GO to **A14**. |
| | One or more voltage values not near given values ▶ | SERVICE harness. REPEAT **A13**. |

| Row | Circuit No. | Function | Volts (DC) |
|---|---|---|---|
| Top | 298 | Power | Battery |
| Top | 200 | Diagnostic | <.1 |
| Top | 497 | Actuator | <.1 |
| Top | 498 | Actuator | <.1 |
| Top | 150 | Speed Sensor | — |
| Top | 495 | Actuator | <.1 |
| Bottom | 606 | Diagnostic | <.1 |
| Bottom | 57 | Ground | <.1 |
| Bottom | 563 | Speed Sensor | — |
| Bottom | 496 | Actuator | <.1 |
| Bottom | — | VIP | <.1 |

**Fig. 10 Electrical component diagnosis (Part 9 of 13). 1990–91 Continental, Sable & Taurus**

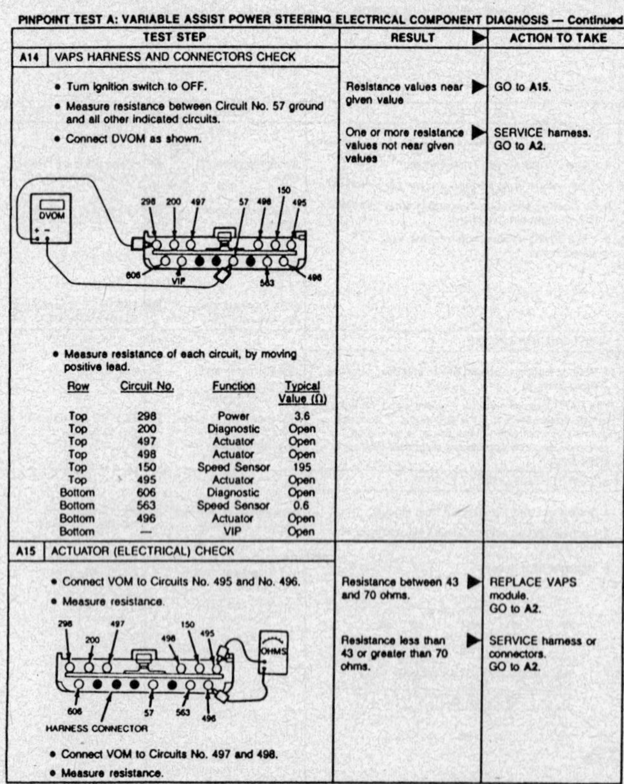

PINPOINT TEST A: VARIABLE ASSIST POWER STEERING ELECTRICAL COMPONENT DIAGNOSIS — Continued

| TEST STEP | RESULT ▶ | ACTION TO TAKE |
|---|---|---|
| **A14 VAPS HARNESS AND CONNECTORS CHECK** | | |
| • Turn ignition switch to OFF.<br>• Measure resistance between Circuit No. 57 ground and all other indicated circuits.<br>• Connect DVOM as shown.<br>• Measure resistance of each circuit, by moving positive lead. | Resistance values near given value ▶ | GO to **A15**. |
| | One or more resistance values not near given values ▶ | SERVICE harness. GO to **A2**. |

| Row | Circuit No. | Function | Typical Value (Ω) |
|---|---|---|---|
| Top | 298 | Power | 3.6 |
| Top | 200 | Diagnostic | Open |
| Top | 497 | Actuator | Open |
| Top | 498 | Actuator | Open |
| Top | 150 | Speed Sensor | 195 |
| Top | 495 | Actuator | Open |
| Bottom | 606 | Diagnostic | Open |
| Bottom | 563 | Speed Sensor | 0.6 |
| Bottom | 496 | Actuator | Open |
| Bottom | — | VIP | Open |

| TEST STEP | RESULT ▶ | ACTION TO TAKE |
|---|---|---|
| **A15 ACTUATOR (ELECTRICAL) CHECK** | | |
| • Connect VOM to Circuits No. 495 and No. 496.<br>• Measure resistance.<br>• Connect VOM to Circuits No. 497 and 498.<br>• Measure resistance. | Resistance between 43 and 70 ohms. ▶ | REPLACE VAPS module. GO to **A2**. |
| | Resistance less than 43 or greater than 70 ohms. ▶ | SERVICE harness or connectors. GO to **A2**. |

**Fig. 10 Electrical component diagnosis (Part 10 of 13). 1990–91 Continental, Sable & Taurus**

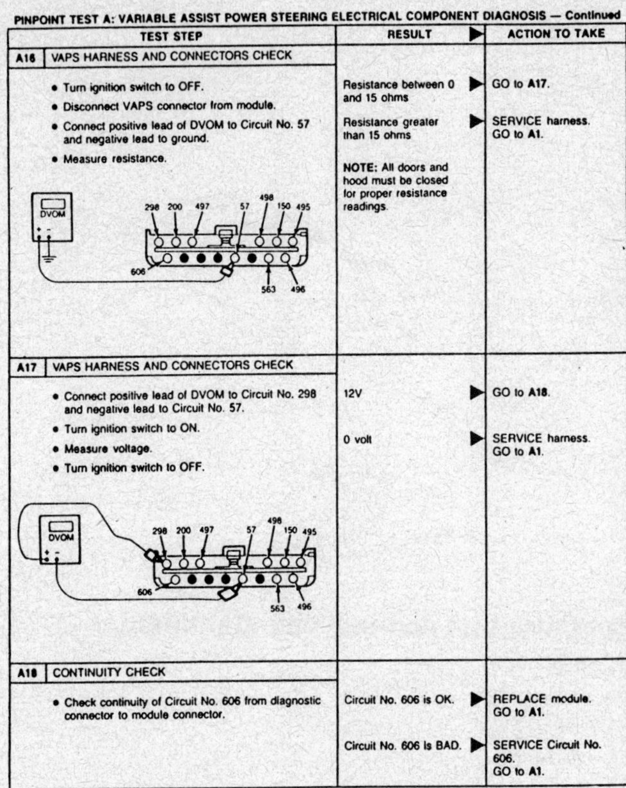

PINPOINT TEST A: VARIABLE ASSIST POWER STEERING ELECTRICAL COMPONENT DIAGNOSIS — Continued

| TEST STEP | RESULT ▶ | ACTION TO TAKE |
|---|---|---|
| **A16** VAPS HARNESS AND CONNECTORS CHECK | | |
| • Turn ignition switch to OFF.<br>• Disconnect VAPS connector from module.<br>• Connect positive lead of DVOM to Circuit No. 57 and negative lead to ground.<br>• Measure resistance. | Resistance between 0 and 15 ohms ▶ | GO to **A17**. |
| | Resistance greater than 15 ohms ▶ | SERVICE harness. GO to **A1**. |
| | **NOTE:** All doors and hood must be closed for proper resistance readings. | |
| **A17** VAPS HARNESS AND CONNECTORS CHECK | | |
| • Connect positive lead of DVOM to Circuit No. 298 and negative lead to Circuit No. 57.<br>• Turn ignition switch to ON.<br>• Measure voltage.<br>• Turn ignition switch to OFF. | 12V ▶ | GO to **A18**. |
| | 0 volt ▶ | SERVICE harness. GO to **A1**. |
| **A18** CONTINUITY CHECK | | |
| • Check continuity of Circuit No. 606 from diagnostic connector to module connector. | Circuit No. 606 is OK. ▶ | REPLACE module. GO to **A1**. |
| | Circuit No. 606 is BAD. ▶ | SERVICE Circuit No. 606. GO to **A1**. |



**Fig. 10 Electrical component diagnosis (Part 11 of 13). 1990–91 Continental, Sable & Taurus**

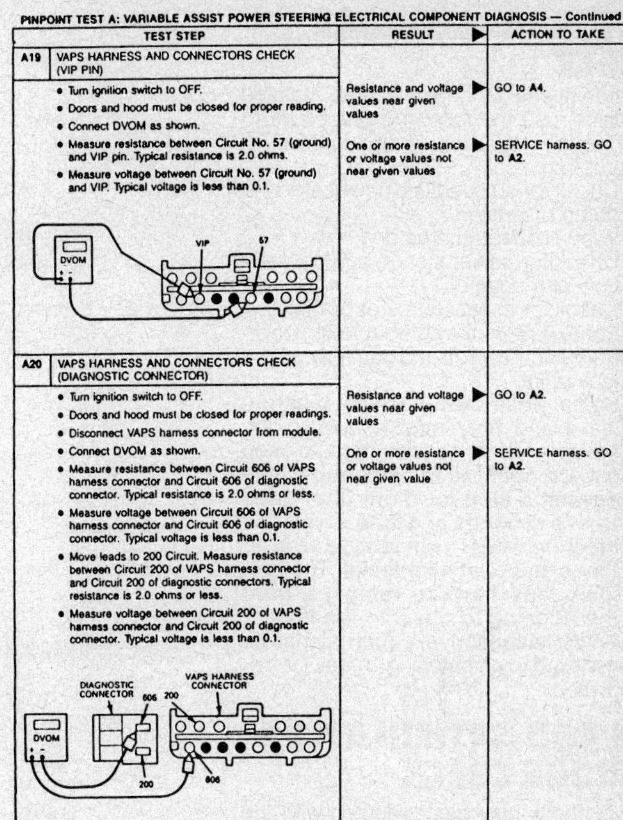

PINPOINT TEST A: VARIABLE ASSIST POWER STEERING ELECTRICAL COMPONENT DIAGNOSIS — Continued

| TEST STEP | RESULT ▶ | ACTION TO TAKE |
|---|---|---|
| **A19** VAPS HARNESS AND CONNECTORS CHECK (VIP PIN) | | |
| • Turn ignition switch to OFF.<br>• Doors and hood must be closed for proper reading.<br>• Connect DVOM as shown.<br>• Measure resistance between Circuit No. 57 (ground) and VIP pin. Typical resistance is 2.0 ohms.<br>• Measure voltage between Circuit No. 57 (ground) and VIP. Typical voltage is less than 0.1. | Resistance and voltage values near given values ▶ | GO to **A4**. |
| | One or more resistance or voltage values not near given values ▶ | SERVICE harness. GO to **A2**. |
| **A20** VAPS HARNESS AND CONNECTORS CHECK (DIAGNOSTIC CONNECTOR) | | |
| • Turn ignition switch to OFF.<br>• Doors and hood must be closed for proper readings.<br>• Disconnect VAPS harness connector from module.<br>• Connect DVOM as shown.<br>• Measure resistance between Circuit 606 of VAPS harness connector and Circuit 606 of diagnostic connector. Typical resistance is 2.0 ohms or less.<br>• Measure voltage between Circuit 606 of VAPS harness connector and Circuit 606 of diagnostic connector. Typical voltage is less than 0.1.<br>• Move leads to 200 Circuit. Measure resistance between Circuit 200 of VAPS harness connector and Circuit 200 of diagnostic connectors. Typical resistance is 2.0 ohms or less.<br>• Measure voltage between Circuit 200 of VAPS harness connector and Circuit 200 of diagnostic connector. Typical voltage is less than 0.1. | Resistance and voltage values near given values ▶ | GO to **A2**. |
| | One or more resistance or voltage values not near given value ▶ | SERVICE harness. GO to **A2**. |



**Fig. 10 Electrical component diagnosis (Part 12 of 13). 1990 Continental, Sable & Taurus**

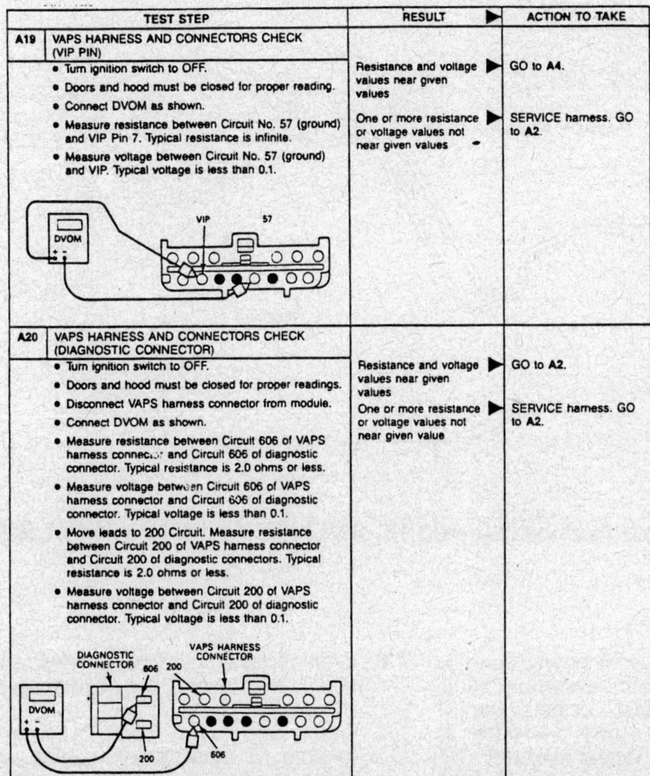

| TEST STEP | RESULT ▶ | ACTION TO TAKE |
|---|---|---|
| **A19** VAPS HARNESS AND CONNECTORS CHECK (VIP PIN) | | |
| • Turn ignition switch to OFF.<br>• Doors and hood must be closed for proper reading.<br>• Connect DVOM as shown.<br>• Measure resistance between Circuit No. 57 (ground) and VIP Pin 7. Typical resistance is infinite.<br>• Measure voltage between Circuit No. 57 (ground) and VIP. Typical voltage is less than 0.1. | Resistance and voltage values near given values ▶ | GO to **A4**. |
| | One or more resistance or voltage values not near given values ▶ | SERVICE harness. GO to **A2**. |
| **A20** VAPS HARNESS AND CONNECTORS CHECK (DIAGNOSTIC CONNECTOR) | | |
| • Turn ignition switch to OFF.<br>• Doors and hood must be closed for proper readings.<br>• Disconnect VAPS harness connector from module.<br>• Connect DVOM as shown.<br>• Measure resistance between Circuit 606 of VAPS harness connector and Circuit 606 of diagnostic connector. Typical resistance is 2.0 ohms or less.<br>• Measure voltage between Circuit 606 of VAPS harness connector and Circuit 606 of diagnostic connector. Typical voltage is less than 0.1.<br>• Move leads to 200 Circuit. Measure resistance between Circuit 200 of VAPS harness connector and Circuit 200 of diagnostic connectors. Typical resistance is 2.0 ohms or less.<br>• Measure voltage between Circuit 200 of VAPS harness connector and Circuit 200 of diagnostic connector. Typical voltage is less than 0.1. | Resistance and voltage values near given values ▶ | GO to **A2**. |
| | One or more resistance or voltage values not near given value ▶ | SERVICE harness. GO to **A2**. |



**Fig. 10 Electrical component diagnosis (Part 13 of 13). 1991 Continental, Sable & Taurus**

ute, pump flow control valve should be removed and cleaned or replaced.

19. **On SHO models,** if flow exceeds maximum free flow per minute, pump should be removed and cleaned or replaced.
20. **On all models,** check idle speed, with engine at idle, turn steering wheel to left and right stops, record pressure and flow at stops.
21. Pressure at both stops should be about the same as maximum pump output pressure, flow should drop below 0.5 gallons per minute.
22. If pressure is not within specification, excessive internal leakage is indicated, remove and disassemble steering gear, replace worn or damaged parts and inspect rack piston and valve seals for damage.
23. While watching pressure gauge, turn steering wheel slightly in both directions and quickly release wheel, gauge needle should move from normal backpressure and snap back as the wheel is released. If needle returns slowly or sticks, the steering gear rotary valve is sticking.
24. Remove and disassemble steering as described under "Disassemble," then flush power steering hoses and pump before gear installation.
25. If problem still exists, check ball joint and linkage.
26. Disconnect and remove analyzer, then connect lines.

## EXTERNAL LEAKAGE CHECK

When trying to detect a fluid leakage condition, use the following procedure to pinpoint the exact cause and location of the problem:

1. Check for an overfilled power steering pump reservoir.
2. Wipe suspected area dry.
3. Check for power steering pump overflow and aeration.
4. Check for exact source of oil leakage. For example; oil may be running down from another area and drip may not be leak point.
5. Some leaks may be high pressure leaks and may require holding the steering wheel against stops to seep out. **Do not hold the steering wheel against a stop for more than three to five seconds at a time. Cycle the steering wheel from stop to stop 10 times and check for leaks. The bellows may have to removed from the housing to observe the leak.**
6. Power steering leaks that cannot be serviced by tightening, must be replaced.

## TIE ROD ARTICULATION TORQUE CHECK

This check may be conducted with the gear on or off the vehicle.

1. Disconnect tie rod from spindle using tool T-3290-D or equivalent.
2. Install spring scale T74P-3504-Y or equivalent, over tie rod end, then measure force required to move tie rod.
3. If force required to move tie rod is not approximately 2-10 lbs., replace tie rod as required.

## POWER STEERING SYSTEM FLUSH

1. Disconnect power steering return hose.
2. Place return line in suitable container, then plug reservoir return line at reservoir.
3. Fill reservoir using Motorcraft DEXRON II part No. ESW-M2C33-F or equivalent.
4. Disconnect coil wire, then raise and support front wheels.
5. While adding about two quarts of fluid, turn ignition to start position (using ignition key), then crank engine with starter and turn steering wheel right to left.
6. When all the fluid is added, turn ignition off, and connect coil wire.
7. Remove reservoir return line plug, then connect line to reservoir.
8. Fill reservoir to specified level.
9. Lower vehicle, then start engine, slowly turn steering wheel several times lock to lock, then recheck fluid level, add as required.

## POWER STEERING SYSTEM AIR PURGE

1. Air trapped in power steering system may be remove with power steering pump air evacuator assembly vacuum tester 021-00014 or equivalent.
2. **Do not use engine vacuum to purge power steering system.**
3. Remove reservoir cap.
4. Check and fill reservoir to cold fill mark with suitable fluid.
5. Disconnect ignition coil wire, then raise and support front wheels.
6. Crank engine with starter motor, then check fluid level. **Do not turn steering wheel.**
7. If fluid level has dropped, fill reservoir to cold fill mark, crank engine with starter motor while turning steering wheel lock to lock, then check fluid level.
8. Install air evacuator rubber stopper tightly to pump reservoir, then con-

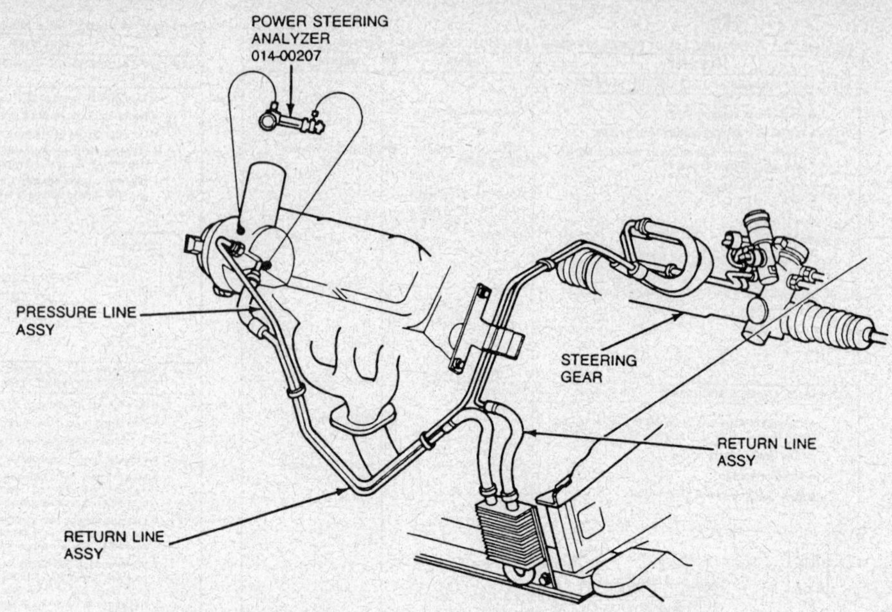


**Fig. 11 Pressure test connections. Continental**

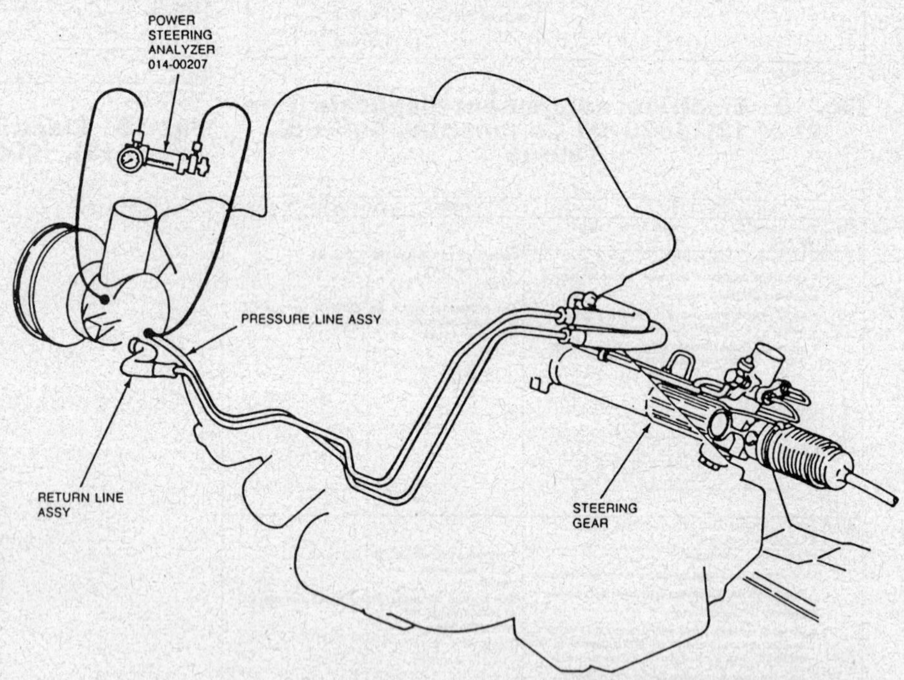


**Fig. 12 Pressure test connections. Sable & Taurus, except SHO**

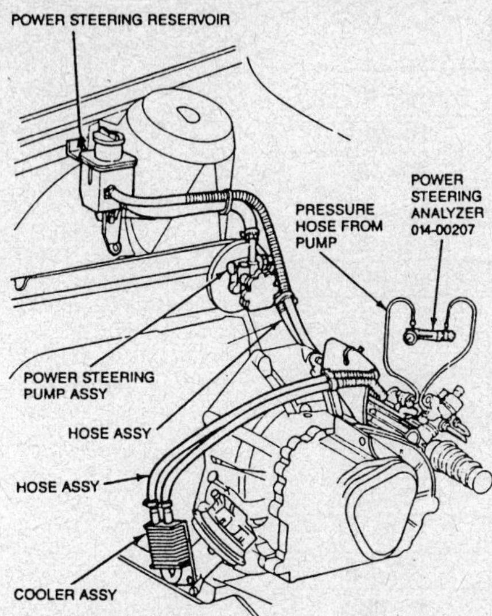


**Fig. 13 Pressure test connections. Taurus SHO**

nect coil wire.

9. With engine at idle, apply 15 inch Hg maximum vacuum to pump reservoir for a minimum of three minutes, as air purges from system, vacuum will decrease, maintain adequate vacuum.
10. Release vacuum, then remove vacuum source, if fluid level has dropped, fill to cold fill mark.
11. With engine at idle, apply 15 inch Hg maximum vacuum to pump reservoir, turn steering wheel from lock to lock ever 30 seconds for about five minutes. **Do not hold steering wheel on stops when turning.** Maintain adequate vacuum.
12. Release vacuum, then remove vacuum equipment add power steering fluid id required, install cap.
13. Start engine, turn steering wheel, check connections for oil leaks.
14. If severe aeration is indicated, repeat steps 7 through 13.
15. Lower vehicle.

# SYSTEM SERVICE

## TIE ROD END, REPLACE

The following procedure is performed with the steering gear installed on the vehicle.

1. Disable airbag system as described under "Airbag System Disarming."
2. Remove and discard cotter pin and nut from worn tie rod end ball stud.
3. Using tool T-3290-D or equivalent, disconnect tie rod end from steering spindle.
4. Hold tie rod end using a suitable wrench, then loosen tie rod jam nut.
5. Note depth to which tie rod is located, then grip tie rod with a pair of pliers and remove tie rod end assembly from tie rod.
6. Reverse procedure to install.

## STEERING GEAR ACTUATOR, REPLACE

1. Disable airbag system as described under "Airbag System Disarming."
2. Remove air inlet duct for access to actuator.
3. Disconnect VAPS electrical connector from actuator.
4. Remove pressure switch.
5. Remove two actuator to steering gear attaching bolts.
6. Lift actuator from steering gear assembly.
7. Reverse procedure to install. Tighten attaching nuts and bolts to specifications.

## VAPS MODULE, REPLACE

The VAPS module is located below the instrument panel on the righthand side of the steering column.

1. Disable airbag system as described under "Airbag System Disarming."
2. Remove four instrument panel cover attaching screws, then the cover.
3. Remove three sound package insulation push pins, then the sound package.
4. Disconnect VAPS electrical connectors.
5. Remove VAPS module.
6. Reverse procedure to install. Tighten screw to specifications.

# OVERHAUL

## TIE ROD BELLOWS

### Disassembly

1. Place steering gear assembly into holding fixture T57L-500-B or equivalent. **If necessary, drill out the mounting holes on the holding fixture to allow gear assembly mounting bolts to fit.**
2. Remove tie rod ends.
3. Remove four clamps attaching bellows to steering gear housing and tie rods.
4. Discard clamps if damaged or excessively corroded.
5. Remove bellows along with breather tube. Do not damage bellows.

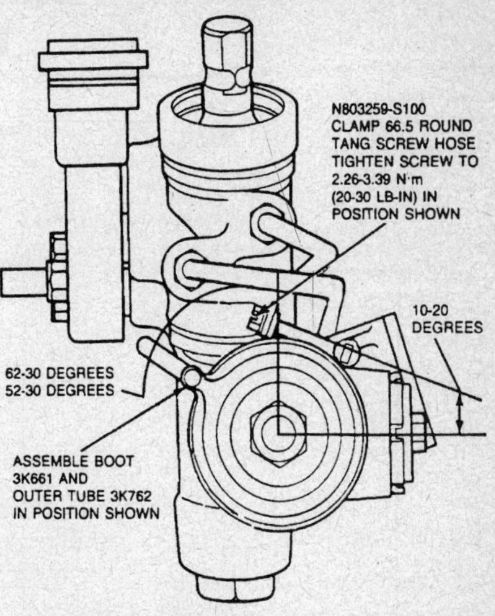


**Fig. 14 Screw axis position**

6. Using tool D81P-3504-N or equivalent, remove coiled lockpins from inner tie rod ball joints.
7. **On models equipped with rivets,** using suitable chisel, gently tap around rivet head to lift from ball joint. **Do not sheer off center pin,** then using suitable side cutters, pry out drive pin.
8. **On all models,** position rack so that several rack teeth are exposed. Hold rack with an adjustable wrench on end teeth only, while loosening ball joint nuts with tool T74P-3504-U or equivalent.

### Assembly

1. Expose several rack teeth and hold rack with an adjustable wrench.
2. Tighten each ball joint assembly separately to specifications, using nut wrench T74P-3504-U or equivalent.
3. Install new coiled pins in tie rod ball housing by tapping lightly with a suitable hammer.
4. Thoroughly clean rack and housing bore. Replenish any grease that may have been removed from rack teeth.
5. Apply grease C3AZ-19578-A or equivalent to groove in rods where bellows clamp to tie rod. This allows for toe-in adjustment without twisting bellows.
6. Install bellows and breather tube. Ensure breather tube is correctly installed.
7. Install clamps, then position screw axis, **Fig. 14.**
8. Install new clamps attaching bellows to tie rods.
9. Apply grease D7AZ-19590-A or equivalent to tie rod threads.
10. Install tie rod outer ends.

## TIGHTENING SPECIFICATIONS

| Year | Component | Torque, Ft. Lbs. |
|---|---|---|
| 1989–91 | Bellow Clamp Screw | 20–30① |
| | Gear To Subframe Bolt | 86–100 |
| | Intermediate Shaft To Steering Column Nuts | 15–25 |
| | Intermediate Shaft To Steering Gear Bolt | 30–38 |
| | Pressure Fitting At Actuator | 20–25③ |
| | Pressure Line Fitting To Actuator | 22–28⑤ |
| | Pump To Gear Pressure Line Fitting | ② |
| | Return line fitting At Valve | 15–25③ |
| | Tie Rod Ball Socket Assembly To Rack | 55–65 |
| | Tie Rod End Jam Nut | 35–50 |
| | Tie Rod End To Spindle Nut | 35–47 |
| | Transfer Tube Fitting | ④ |
| | VAPS Actuator Bolts | 20–25 |
| | VAPS Module | 35–45① |
| | Weather Boot To I/P | 4–5 |

①—Inch lbs.
②—1989–90 models, 10–15 ft. lbs., 1991 models, 20–25 ft. lbs.
③—1989 models.
④—1989–90 models, 10–15 ft. lbs., 1991 models, 100–20 ft. lbs.
⑤—1991 models.

# Ford Variable Assist, Electronic Variable Orifice System (EVO)

### INDEX



## AIRBAG SYSTEM DISARMING

**The electrical circuit necessary for system deployment is powered directly from the battery and backup power supply. To avoid accidental deployment and possible personal injury, the airbag system must be deactivated prior to servicing or replacing any system components.**

A back-up power supply is included in the system to provide airbag deployment in the event the battery or battery cables are damaged in an accident before the sensors can close. The power supply is a capacitor that will retain a charge for approximately 15 minutes after the battery ground cable is disconnected. To remove and install backup power supply refer to "Component Replacement" procedure.

1. Disconnect battery ground cable.
2. Disconnect backup power supply as described under "Backup Power Supply, Replace."

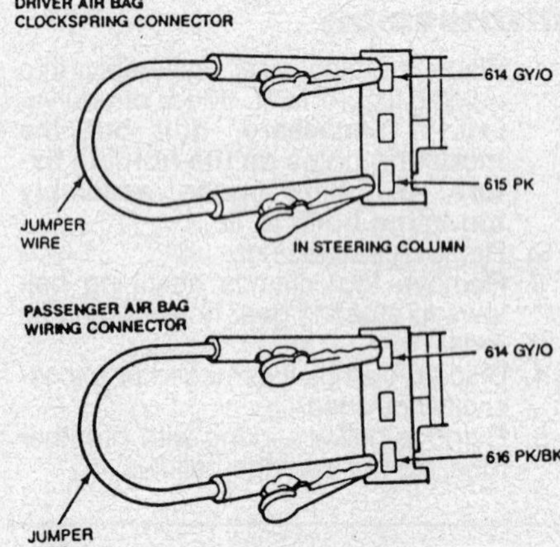


**Fig. 1 Airbag system disarming**

3. Remove four nut and washer assemblies securing airbag module to steering wheel, then disconnect airbag electrical connector. Attach jumper wire to airbag terminals on clockspring as shown in **Fig. 1.**
4. **On models equipped with passenger-side airbag,** disconnect airbag module connector located behind glove compartment. Attach a jumper wire to airbag terminals on wiring harness side of passenger airbag module connector, as shown in **Fig. 1.**
5. **On all models,** if necessary, reconnect battery and backup power supply.
6. To reactivate, disconnect battery ground cable and backup power supply, then reverse remainder of deactivation procedure. **Torque** airbag module to steering wheel nut assemblies to 24-32 inch lbs. on Crown Victoria and Grand Marquis, or 35-53 inch lbs. on all other models.
7. Verify airbag lamp after reactivating system.

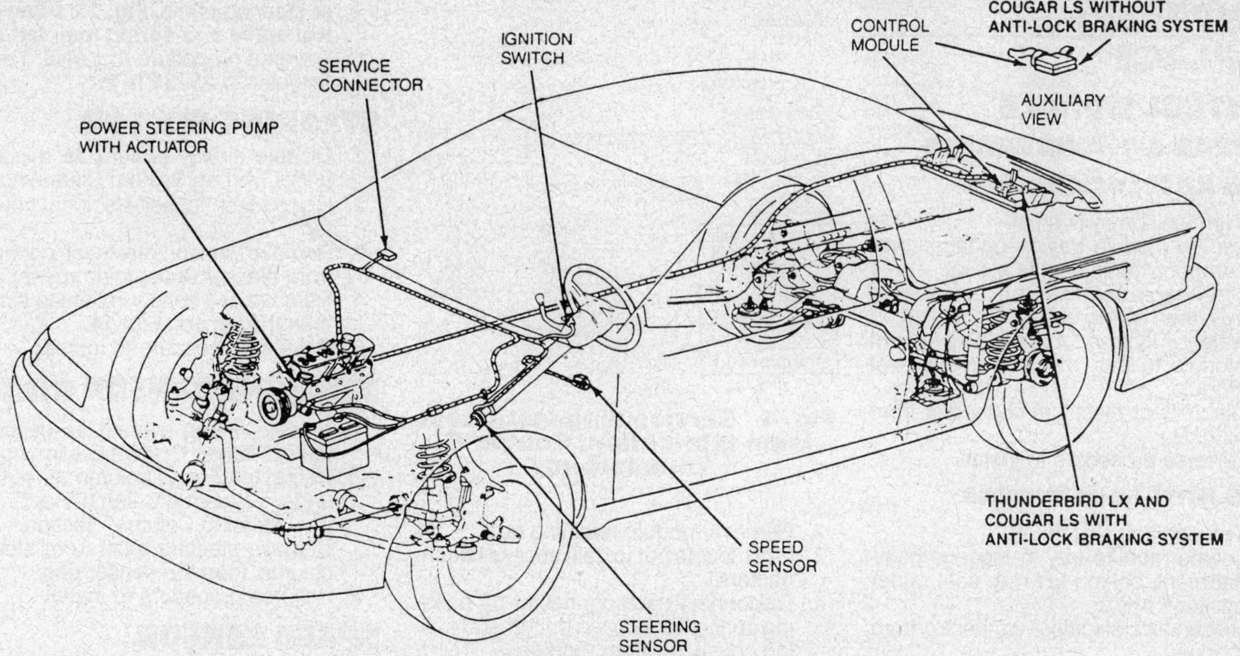


**Fig. 2 Electronic variable orifice system. Cougar & Thunderbird**

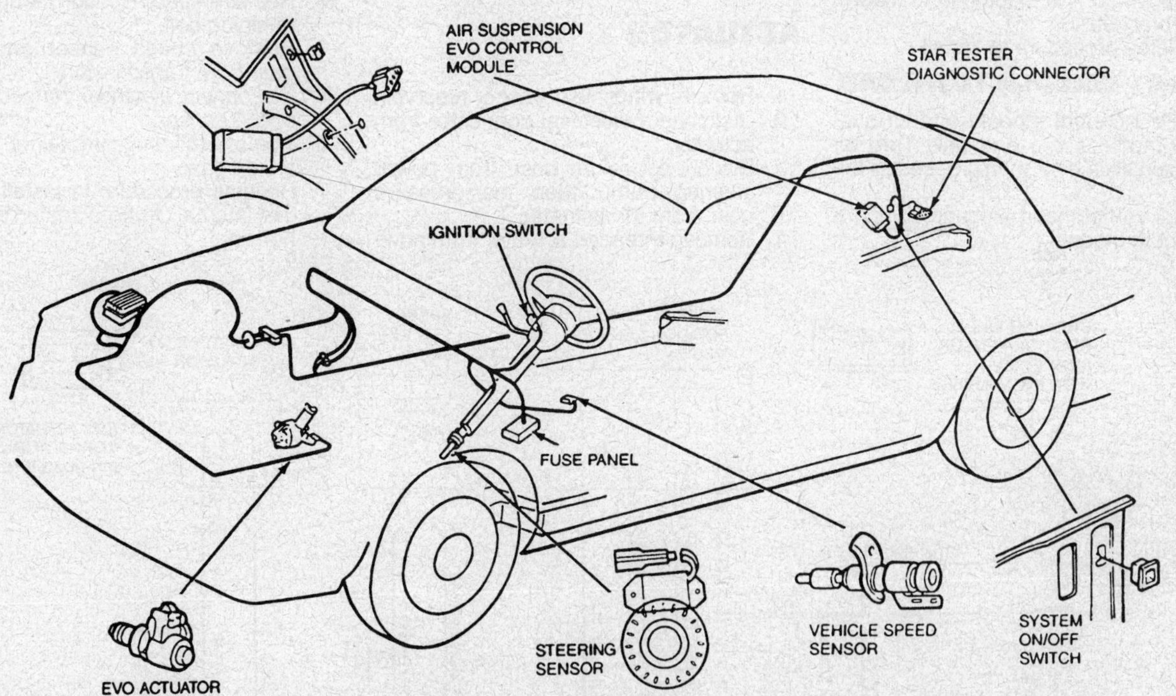


**Fig. 3 Electronic variable orifice system. 1990–91 Lincoln Town Car**

# DESCRIPTION & OPERATION

The electronic variable orifice system, **Figs. 2 and 3,** is designed to vary the flow from the power steering pump based on vehicle speed and the rate of steering wheel rotation. The system provides full assist at low speed for light parking effort and minimum assist at high speed for good road feel and directional stability. In the event of system failure, full assist is provided.

# DIAGNOSIS & TESTING

## COUGAR & THUNDERBIRD

Diagnosis and testing of system will require the fabrication of a service diagnostic test lamp, **Fig. 4.**

Refer to **Figs. 5 through 7,** for diagnosis and testing of the system.

## 1990–91 LINCOLN TOWN CAR

Diagnosis and testing requires using the Star or Super Star II hand held diagnostic tester, Rotunda model No. 007-00017 or 007-00028 or equivalent.

Refer to **Figs. 8 through 12,** for diagnosis and testing of the system.

## COMPONENT REPLACE

### CONTROL MODULE

#### COUGAR & THUNDERBIRD

#### With Anti-Lock Brakes

1. Turn ignition switch Off.
2. Locate module tray in luggage compartment, behind LH rear seat.
3. Disengage push-pin on LH side of tray, then swing tray down.
4. Release locking tabs retaining control module to tray, then remove control module.
5. Disconnect electrical connector from module.
6. Reverse procedure to install.

#### Less Anti-Lock Brakes

1. Turn ignition switch Off.
2. Locate module tray in luggage compartment, behind LH rear seat under package tray.
3. Disconnect electrical connector from module.
4. Unscrew two plastic rivets on sides of module, then pull down rivet and head assembly from module.
5. Remove control module from mounting bracket.
6. Reverse procedure to install.

#### 1990–91 LINCOLN TOWN CAR

The EVO control module and air suspension modules are one unit. Turn air suspension switch off, then proceed as follows:

1. Remove righthand luggage compartment trim panel.

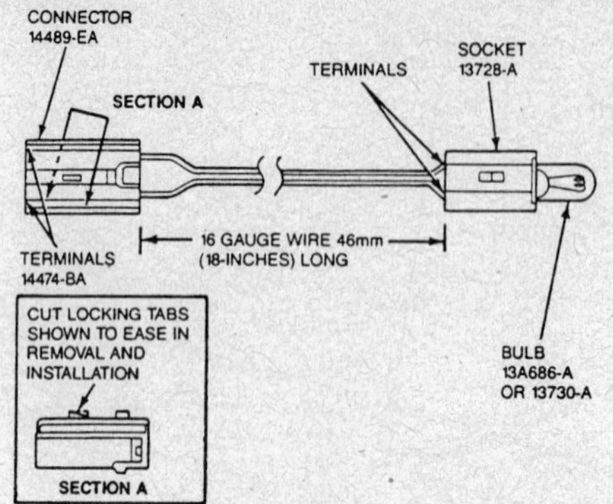


**Fig. 4 Service diagnostic test lamp fabrication. Cougar & Thunderbird**

2. Remove module retaining nuts.
3. Pull module out to gain access to connectors.
4. Disconnect each connector by pushing connector release button and pulling connector from module.
5. Reverse procedure to install. **Torque** attaching nuts to 5-7 ft. lbs.

### ACTUATOR

1. Remove windshield washer reservoir.
2. Disconnect electrical connector from actuator.
3. Disconnect return hose from power steering pump, then the pressure hose from the actuator.
4. Remove threaded actuator from power steering pump, **Fig. 13. Flow control valve and spring may fall out.**
5. Reverse procedure to install. **Torque** actuator to 25-34 ft. lbs.

### STEERING SENSOR

1. Disable airbag system as described under "Airbag System Disarming."
2. Disconnect sensor electrical connector.
3. Remove sensor electrical connector from bracket under instrument panel.
4. Remove two sensor retaining screws, then the sensor, **Fig. 14.**
5. Reverse procedure to install.

### STEERING SENSOR RING

1. Disable airbag system as described under "Airbag System Disarming."
2. Remove steering column as outlined under ""Steering Column, Replace" in the "Steering Column" section.
3. Remove steering shaft from steering column, then the sensor ring.
4. Reverse procedure to install.

### SPEED SENSOR

1. Disable airbag system as described under "Airbag System Disarming."
2. Raise and support vehicle.
3. Remove speed sensor mounting clip retaining bolt.
4. Remove speed sensor and driven gear from transmission.
5. Disconnect electrical connector from speed sensor.
6. Remove driven gear retainer, then the driven gear.
7. Reverse procedure to install. Ensure that internal O-ring is seated in sensor housing.

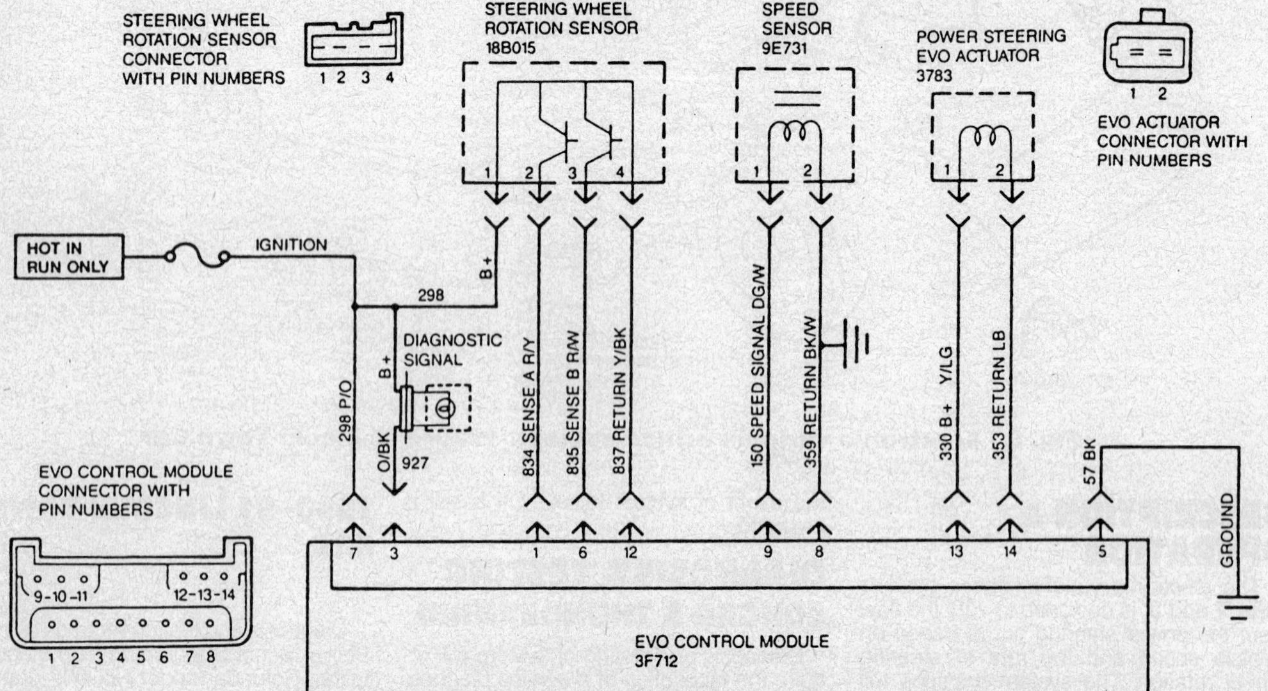


**Fig. 5 Electronic variable orifice system wiring circuit. Cougar & Thunderbird**

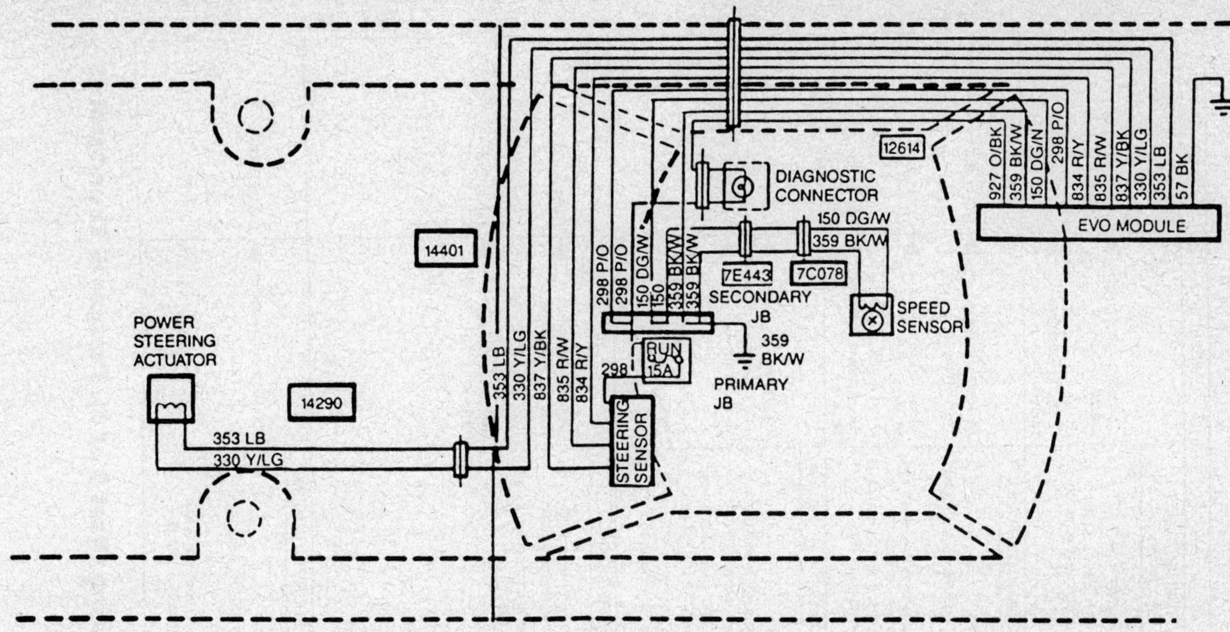


NOTE: The service diagnostic connector is located in the glove compartment.

**Fig. 6 Electronic variable orifice system component location. Cougar & Thunderbird**

| TEST STEP | | RESULT | ACTION TO TAKE |
|---|---|---|---|
| A0 | CHECK CONNECTIONS | | |
| | • Verify harness connector at EVO actuator valve on power steering pump is seated. <br> • Verify harness connector on EVO control module is seated (located in luggage compartment). <br> EVO ACTUATOR VALVE CONNECTOR | Connector was not properly seated | MAKE proper connection. GO to **A1**. |
| | | Connector properly seated | GO to **A1**. |
| A1 | CONTROL MODULE CHECK | | |
| | • Turn ignition switch to OFF position. <br> • Locate service diagnostic connector in the upper glove compartment. <br> • Connect the EVO service diagnostic lamp to the connector in the upper glove compartment. <br> • Start engine. When engine starts, the controller will turn on the diagnostic lamp for one second to indicate: <br> a) control module is functional <br> b) bulb is functional | Lamp is turned on for one second | GO to **A2**. |
| | | Lamp does NOT turn on | GO to **E1**. |
| | | Lamp flickers | GO to **E1**. |
| A2 | ACTUATOR OUTPUT CIRCUIT CHECK | | |
| | • After the one second control module check, the controller will perform the Actuator Output Test. If there is a short to ground or an open circuit, after two seconds delay, the diagnostic lamp will flash a "code 6" (on for 0.5 seconds and off for 0.5 seconds, 6 times) then delay two seconds and repeat continuously until the power is turned off. During this "failure mode" the controller output will be off and both speed and steering wheel rotation inputs will be disabled. Once this "failure mode" has occured, the controller will be inoperable until power is removed and reapplied. | Lamp flashes a "code 6" (on for 0.5 seconds and off for 0.5 seconds, 6 times) then delays two seconds and repeats | GO to **B1**. |
| | | After the two second delay lamp does not flash a " code 6" (Actuator output circuit is OK) | GO to **A3**. |

**Fig. 7 System testing (Part 1 of 8). Cougar & Thunderbird**

| | TEST STEP | RESULT ▶ | ACTION TO TAKE |
|---|---|---|---|
| A3 | STEERING WHEEL SENSOR CHECK | | |
| | • Ignition switch in RUN position.<br>• Vehicle speed: 0 km/h (MPH)<br>• Turn steering wheel from lock to lock. The steering wheel must be rotated in one direction at least 220 degrees. | Diagnostic lamp turns on for three seconds after the wheel has been sufficiently rotated ▶ | GO to **A4**. |
| | | Diagnostic lamp does not turn on ▶ | GO to **C1**. |
| A4 | VEHICLE SPEED SENSOR CHECK | | |
| | • Ignition switch in RUN position.<br>• Steering wheel rate: 0 rpm<br>• Operate vehicle on road and apply vehicle speed of greater than 24 km/h (15 mph). | Diagnostic lamp turns on for all speeds greater than 24 km/h (15 mph) ▶ | GO to **A4.1**. |
| | | Diagnostic lamp does not turn on ▶ | GO to **D1**. |
| A4.1 | VEHICLE SPEED SENSOR SWITCH CHECK (cont'd) | | |
| | • Reduce vehicle speed to below 16 km/h (10 mph) | Diagnostic lamp turns off when vehicle speed drops below 16 km/h (10 mph) ▶ | Electrical portion of system is functioning. GO to **A5**. |
| | | Diagnostic lamp does not turn off ▶ | GO to **D1**. |
| A5 | SERVICE POWER STEERING | | |
| | • Perform PUMP FLOW and Pressure Tests, and REPLACE AS REQUIRED. | | |

**Fig. 7 System testing (Part 2 of 8). Cougar & Thunderbird**

| | TEST STEP | RESULT ▶ | ACTION TO TAKE |
|---|---|---|---|
| B1 | CODE "6" ACTIVATED: EVO ACTUATOR VALVE CHECK (short to ground or an open circuit) | | |
| | • Turn ignition switch to OFF position.<br>• Verify harness connection on the EVO actuator valve on power steering pump is properly seated. | Connector not properly seated ▶ | Make proper connection, GO to **A1**. |
| | | Connector properly seated ▶ | GO to **B2**. |
| B2 | CHECK RESISTANCE ACROSS ACTUATOR VALVE | | |
| | • Ignition switch in OFF position.<br>• Locate the control module in luggage compartment. (Refer to Removal.)<br>• Using an ohmmeter, measure resistance across Pin No. 13 and Pin No. 14 of harness connector. Resistance should be 7-18 ohms. If the resistance is greater than 1000 ohms, the circuit is open. | Resistance is over 1000 ohms ▶ | GO to **B3**. |
| | | Resistance is over 18 ohms ▶ | GO to **B4**. |
| | | Resistance is less than 18 ohms ▶ | GO to **B3**. |
| B3 | CHECK CONTINUITY OF WIRING | | |
| | • Ignition switch in OFF position.<br>• Disconnect EVO harness connector from EVO actuator valve located on power steering pump.<br>• Test continuity of circuits No. 330 and No. 353 from the actuator connector to the 14 pin EVO control module connector.<br>• Refer to Component Location Schematic and System Schematic. | Continuity ▶ | GO to **B4**. |
| | | No continuity ▶ | SERVICE wires as necessary. GO to **A0**. |
| B4 | CHECK EVO ACTUATOR VALVE RESISTANCE | | |
| | • Disconnect EVO harness connector from EVO actuator valve located on power steering pump.<br>• Using an ohmmeter, measure resistance across the two actuator valve connector pins. | Resistance greater than 20 ohms or less than 5 ohms ▶ | REPLACE EVO valve. |
| | | Resistance is 5-20 ohms ▶ | GO to **B5**. |
| B5 | CHECK WIRE HARNESS FOR SHORT TO GROUND | | |
| | • Ignition switch in OFF position.<br>• EVO harness disconnected from EVO actuator valve.<br>• Disconnect EVO control module from the 14 pin connector in luggage compartment. (Refer to removal.) | Module disconnected ▶ | GO to **B5.1**. |

**Fig. 7 System testing (Part 3 of 8). Cougar & Thunderbird**

| TEST STEP | | RESULT | ACTION TO TAKE |
|---|---|---|---|
| **B5.1** | CHECK WIRE HARNESS FOR SHORT TO GROUND (Cont'd.) | | |
| | • Using on ohmmeter, measure resistance between Pin No. 5 (ground) and Pin No. 13 of harness connector. | Resistance is over 1000 ohms ▶ | GO to **B5.2**. |
| | | Resistance is less than 10 ohms ▶ | SERVICE Harness, GO to **B5.2**. |
| **B5.2** | CHECK WIRE HARNESS FOR SHORT TO GROUND (Cont'd.) | | |
| | • Using an ohmmeter, measure resistance between Pin No. 5 (ground) and Pin No. 14 of harness connector. | Resistance is less than 10 ohms ▶ | SERVICE Harness. |
| | | Resistance is over 1000 ohms ▶ | GO to **B6**. |
| **B6** | CHECK HARNESS FOR SHORT TO B + | | |
| | • Ignition switch in RUN position.<br>• EVO harness disconnected from EVO actuator valve on power steering pump. | Voltage is over 5 volts (short) ▶ | SERVICE wires, GO to **A0**. |
| | • Using a voltmeter, measure the voltage across<br>Pin No. 13 and Pin No. 5<br>Pin No. 14 and Pin No. 5 | Voltage is less than 5 volts ▶ | GO to **B7**. |
| **B7** | CHECK FOR SHORT ACROSS CIRCUITS NO. 330 AND NO. 353 | | |
| | • Ignition switch in OFF position.<br>• EVO harness disconnected from EVO actuator valve on power steering pump. | Resistance is less than 10 ohms (short) ▶ | SERVICE wires, GO to **A0**. |
| | • EVO control module disconnected from 14 pin harness connector.<br>• Using an ohmmeter, measure resistance across Pin No. 13 and Pin No. 14 on harness connector. | Resistance is over 1000 ohms ▶ | REPLACE EVO Control Module. |

**Fig. 7 System testing (Part 4 of 8). Cougar & Thunderbird**

| TEST STEP | | RESULT | ACTION TO TAKE |
|---|---|---|---|
| **C1** | CHECK STEERING WHEEL SENSOR CONNECTION | | |
| | • Verify harness connection on steering wheel rotation sensor (located on lower portion of steering column) is properly seated. | Connector is properly seated ▶ | GO to **C2**. |
| | | Connector is not properly seated ▶ | MAKE proper connection, GO to **A0**. |
| **C2** | STEERING WHEEL ROTATION SENSOR CHECK | | |
| | • Ignition switch in OFF position. | Damaged or crossed wires ▶ | SERVICE wires as necessary, GO to **A0**. |
| | • Disconnect EVO control module from 14 pin connector — located in luggage compartment. (Refer to removal.)<br>• Examine wiring harness, verify that there is no damage and<br>• Circuit No. 834 is in Pin No. 1.<br>• Circuit No. 835 is in Pin No. 6.<br>• Circuit No. 837 is in Pin No. 12. | No damage found ▶ | GO to **C3**. |
| **C3** | TEST STEERING WHEEL ROTATION SENSOR SIGNALS | | |
| | • Using a jumper, connect Pin No. 12 to Pin No. 5 (connector disconnected) of the 14 pin connector.<br>• Start engine. | Meter needle swings for both circuits. (steering wheel sensor is functioning). ▶ | SHUT off engine. REPLACE EVO Control Module. |
| | • While rotating the steering wheel slowly, and using an analog ohmmeter set to the 1K scale, measure the resistance from<br>• Pin No. 1 to Pin No. 5<br>• Pin No. 6 to Pin No. 5<br>**NOTE: The resistance values will vary between meters, but the needle on all meters should swing from a low to a higher resistance and back approximately every nine degrees of steering wheel rotation.**<br>(After this check remove jumper). | Meter needle does not swing for both circuits ▶ | GO to **C4**. |
| **C4** | STEERING WHEEL ROTATION SENSOR WIRE CHECK | | |
| | • Ignition switch in the OFF position.<br>• Unplug steering sensor (located on lower steering column). | DAMAGED or crossed wires ▶ | SERVICE wires as necessary. |
| | • Check wires at steering sensor connector for damage and/or incorrect location. | No Continuity ▶ | SERVICE wires as necessary. GO to **A0**. |
| | • Test continuity of circuits No. 834, No. 835 and No. 837 from steering sensor to 14 pin EVO control module connector. (Refer to System Schematic.) | No problems found ▶ | GO to **C5**. |

**Fig. 7 System testing (Part 5 of 8). Cougar & Thunderbird**

| TEST STEP | RESULT ▶ | ACTION TO TAKE |
|---|---|---|
| **C5** CHECK FOR SHORT ACROSS CIRCUITS 834 AND 835 | | |
| • Turn ignition switch to OFF position.<br>• Steering Sensor disconnected.<br>• Disconnect 14 pin connector. Measure resistance between<br>Pin No. 1 and Pin No. 6<br>Pin No. 1 and Pin No. 12<br>Pin No. 6 and Pin No. 12<br>of the 14 pin connector (in luggage compartment). | Resistance is over 1000 ohms ▶ | GO to **C6**. |
| | Resistance is less than 10 ohms (short) ▶ | SERVICE wires as necessary. GO to **A0**. |
| **C6** TEST STEERING SENSOR POWER | | |
| • Using a jumper, connect Pin No. 12 to Pin No. 5 of the 14 pin connector. (Connector disconnected.)<br>• Turn ignition switch to RUN position.<br>• Using a voltmeter, measure the voltage between Circuits No. 298 and No. 837 at the steering sensor connector. | 12 volts ▶ | GO to **C7**. |
| | 0 volts (short or open circuit) ▶ | SERVICE circuit 298. GO to **A0**. |
| **C7** TEST STEERING SENSOR POWER CIRCUIT | | |
| • Remove jumper from Pin 12 to Pin 5 and connect 14 pin connector.<br>• Using a voltmeter, measure voltage between circuits No. 298 and No. 837 at the steering sensor connector. | 12 volts ▶ | REPLACE steering sensor. |
| | 0 volts ▶ | REPLACE control module. |

**Fig. 7 System testing (Part 6 of 8). Cougar & Thunderbird**

| TEST STEP | RESULT ▶ | ACTION TO TAKE |
|---|---|---|
| **D1** CHECK SPEED SENSOR CONNECTION | | |
| • Ensure harness connection on speed sensor, (located on the transmission) is properly seated. | Connector is properly seated ▶ | GO to **D2**. |
| | Connector is not properly seated ▶ | MAKE proper connection. GO to **A0**. |
| **D2** SPEED SENSOR CHECK | | |
| • Turn ignition switch to the OFF position.<br>• Disconnect the 14-pin electrical connector from the EVO module (located in luggage compartment).<br>• Ensure there is no damage to harness and that:<br>• Circuit No. 150 is in Pin No. 9<br>• Circuit No. 359 is in Pin No. 8 | Damaged or crossed wires ▶ | SERVICE wires. GO to **A0**. |
| | No damage found ▶ | GO to **D3**. |
| **D3** TEST SPEED SENSOR GROUND CIRCUIT | | |
| • Test continuity of speed sensor ground circuit No. 359, from Pin No. 8 to Pin No. 5 of 14-pin connector. | Continuity ▶ | GO to **D4**. |
| | Open Circuit ▶ | SERVICE wire or ground eyelet as necessary. GO to **A0**. |
| **D4** TEST SPEED SENSOR | | |
| • Turn ignition switch to RUN position.<br>• Perform "speedometer reads 0 mph at all speeds". | Problem(s) found ▶ | SERVICE<br>GO to **A0**. |
| | No Problem(s) found ▶ | REPLACE EVO control module. |

**Fig. 7 System testing (Part 7 of 8). Cougar & Thunderbird**

| TEST STEP | RESULT ▶ | ACTION TO TAKE |
|---|---|---|
| **E1** DIAGNOSTIC LAMP CHECK | | |
| • Check bulb in EVO Service Diagnostic Lamp.<br>• Check connection of bulb in tool. | Bad bulb ▶ | REPLACE bulb. GO to **A1**. |
| | Good bulb (Lamp never turned on during step A1) ▶ | GO to **F1**. |
| | Good bulb (Lamp flickered during step A1) ▶ | GO to **E2**. |
| **E2** RE-TEST CONTROL MODULE | | |
| • Turn ignition switch to off position.<br>• Connect EVO service diagnostic lamp to connector in upper glove compartment.<br>• Start Engine. | Lamp is ON for one second ▶ | GO to **A2**. |
| | Lamp does not turn on ▶ | GO to **F1**. |
| | Lamp flickers ▶ | REPLACE EVO Module. |
| **F1** EVO CONTROL MODULE CHECK | | |
| • Turn ignition switch to OFF position.<br>• Ensure 14 pin connector is properly connected to module. (Located in luggage compartment.) | Properly Connected ▶ | GO to **F2**. |
| | Connection is not properly secured ▶ | SECURE connection. GO to **A1**. |
| **F2** CHECK POWER FEED | | |
| • Turn ignition switch to the OFF position.<br>• Disonnect EVO control module 14 pin connector. (Located in luggage compartment.)<br>• Turn ignition switch to RUN position.<br>• Using a DVOM, measure voltage from Pin No. 7 (ignition-run only) to Pin No. 5 (ground) at 14 pin connector. | 12 volts ▶ | REPLACE EVO Control Module. |
| | 0 volts ▶ | SERVICE short to ground or open in circuit No. 298 as necessary. GO to **A0**. |

**Fig. 7 System testing (Part 8 of 8). Cougar & Thunderbird**

### Drive Cycle Test

IGNITION OFF

CONNECT STAR TESTER WITH BUTTON RELEASED

WAIT A MINIMUM OF FIVE SECONDS

DEPRESS STAR TESTER BUTTON

DRIVE CYCLE CODES WILL BE DISPLAYED

- DRIVE CYCLE TEST ACCESSES ERROR CODE GENERATED IN LAST DRIVE CYCLE (IGNITION ON TO IGNITION OFF).
- WHEN IGNITION IS TURNED TO ON AGAIN, PREVIOUSLY GENERATED CODES ARE ERASED.

**Fig. 8 Drive cycle test. 1990 Lincoln Town Car**

SERVICE BAY DIAGNOSTIC PROCEDURE FLOW CHART

IGNITION

CONNECT STAR TESTER W/BUTTON RELEASED

TURN IGNITION ON

WAIT MINIMUM OF 5 SECONDS

DEPRESS STAR TESTER BUTTON

CODE 10 DISPLAYED TEST IN PROGRESS

CODE 12 OR 13 DISPLAYED END OF AUTO TEST

PERFORM MANUAL TESTS:
- OPEN AND CLOSE ALL FOUR DOORS
- TURN STEERING WHEEL

RELEASE STAR TEST BUTTON WAIT MINIMUM 5 SECONDS DEPRESS STAR TEST BUTTON

STAR TESTER WILL DISPLAY:
- CODE 11 IF SYSTEM OK
- ERROR CODES

EXIT BY IGNITION OFF

AIR SUSPENSION/EVO STAR TESTER ERROR CODES

| Code | Description |
|---|---|
| 10 | Diagnostics Entered, Auto Test in Progress |
| 11 | Vehicle Passes |
| 12 | Auto Test Passed |
| 13 | Automatic Test Failure |
| 15 | No Drive Cycle Errors Detected |
| 16 | EVO Short Circuit |
| 17 | EVO Open Circuit |
| 18 | Bad Valve |
| 23 | *Suspension Error Code, refer to Suspension Portion |
| 26 | *Suspension Error Code, refer to Suspension Portion |
| 31 | *Suspension Error Code, refer to Suspension Portion |
| 32 | *Suspension Error Code, refer to Suspension Portion |
| 33 | *Suspension Error Code, refer to Suspension Portion |
| 35 | *Suspension Error Code, refer to Suspension Portion |
| 36 | *Suspension Error Code, refer to Suspension Portion |
| 39 | *Suspension Error Code, refer to Suspension Portion |
| 42 | *Suspension Error Code, refer to Suspension Portion |
| 43 | *Suspension Error Code, refer to Suspension Portion |
| 44 | *Suspension Error Code, refer to Suspension Portion |
| 45 | *Suspension Error Code, refer to Suspension Portion |
| 46 | *Suspension Error Code, refer to Suspension Portion |
| 51 | *Suspension Error Code, refer to Suspension Portion |
| 54 | *Suspension Error Code, refer to Suspension Portion |
| 55 | Speed > 15 mph not detected (Drive Cycle Only) |
| 68 | *Suspension Error Code, refer to Suspension Portion |
| 70 | *Suspension Error Code, refer to Suspension Portion |
| 71 | *Suspension Error Code, refer to Suspension Portion |
| 72 | *Suspension Error Code, refer to Suspension Portion |
| 74 | Steering Wheel Rotation not Detected |
| 80 | Insufficient Battery Voltage to Run Diagnostics |

**Fig. 9 Error code flow chart. 1990–91 Lincoln Town Car**

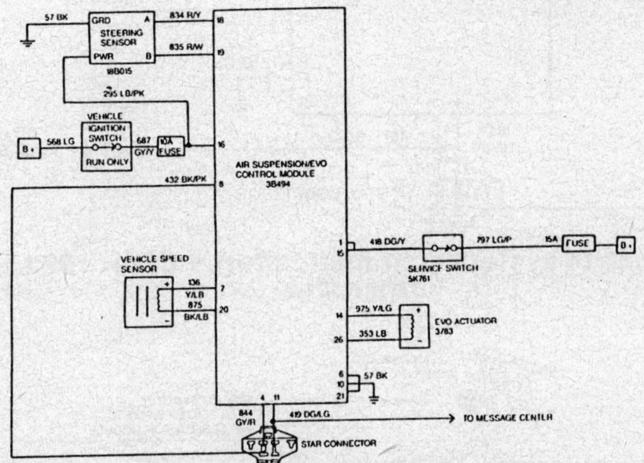


**Fig. 10 Control system schematic (Part 1 of 2). 1990 Lincoln Town Car**

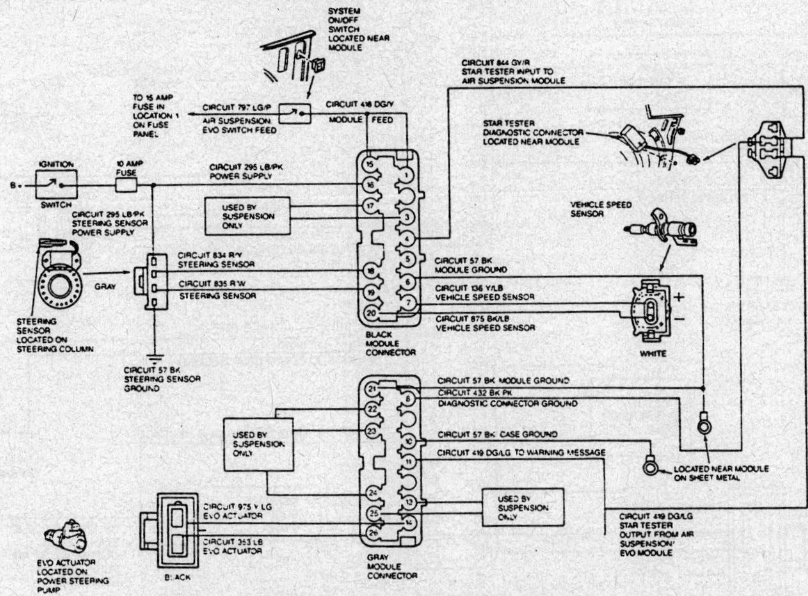


**Fig. 10 Control system schematic (Part 2 of 2). 1990 Lincoln Town Car**

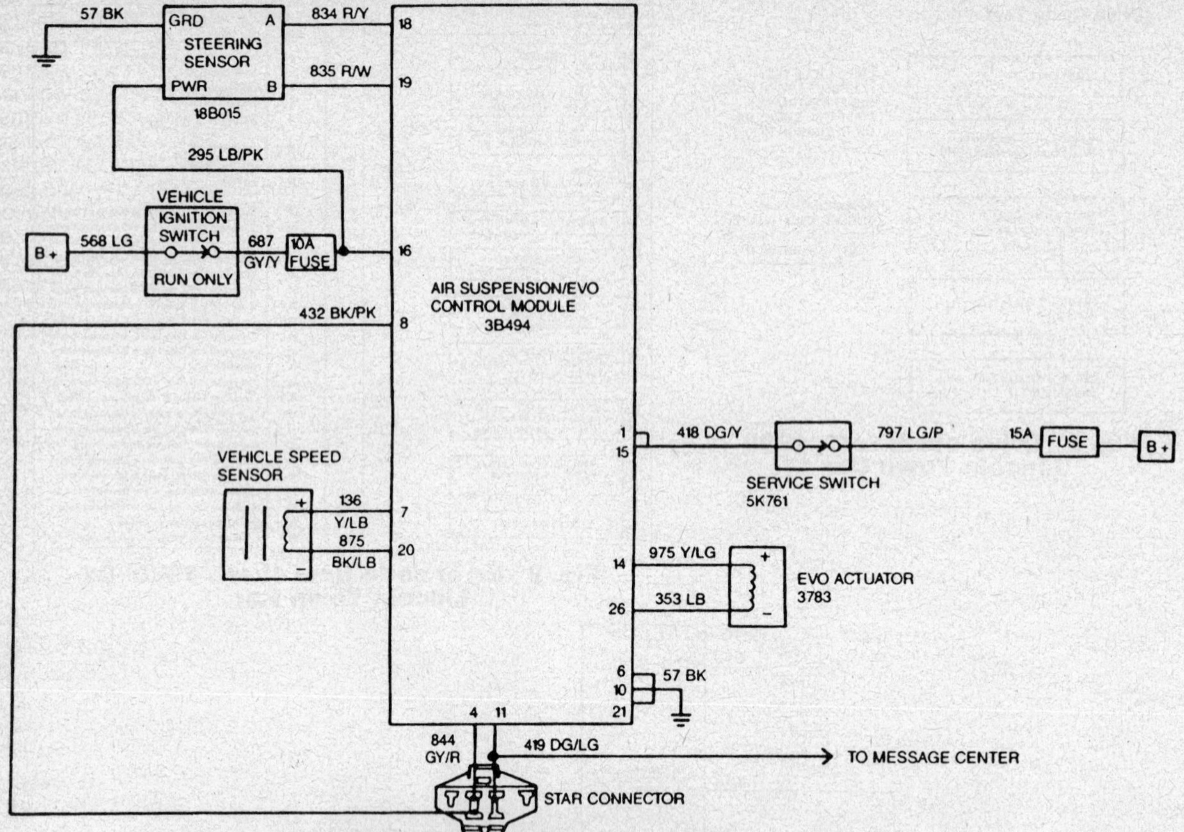


**Fig. 11 Control system schematic (Part 1 of 2). 1991 Lincoln Town Car**

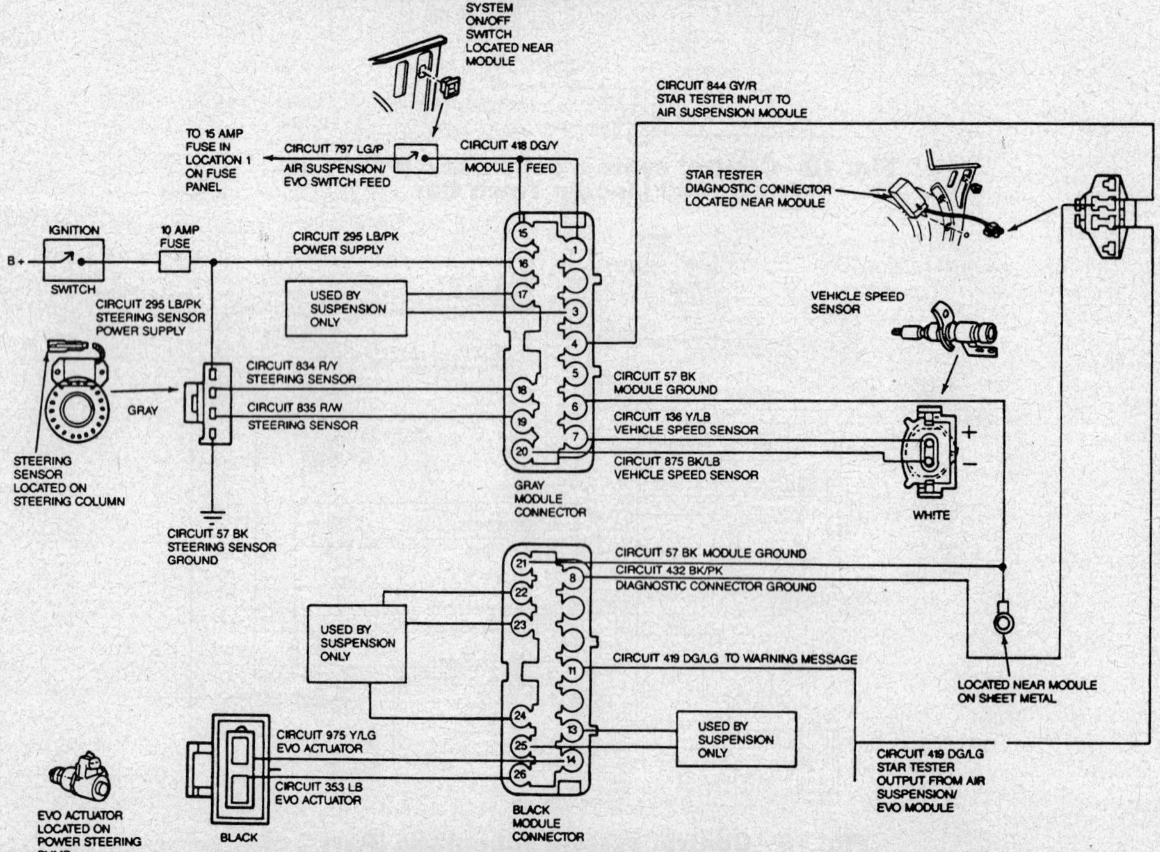


**Fig. 11 Control system schematic (Part 2 of 2). 1991 Lincoln Town Car**

| | TEST STEP | RESULT | ACTION TO TAKE |
|---|---|---|---|
| A0 | RUN DRIVE CYCLE TEST | | |
| | **NOTE: To obtain accurate results, vehicle must be driven at speeds in excess of 24 Km/h (MPH) before drive cycle test is performed.**<br>• With ignition OFF, connect star tester, with button released, to service bay diagnostic connector (located in luggage compartment).<br>• After star tester is connected, wait a minimum of five seconds and depress star tester button. | Codes will be displayed (record codes) | GO to A1. |
| A1 | PERFORM SERVICE BAY DIAGNOSTICS | | |
| | Service Bay Diagnostic procedure. | Record all codes | GO to A2. |
| A2 | DETERMINE REQUIRED TEST STEP | | |
| | • Read displayed code(s).<br>• Each code must be addressed individually. If more than one error code is detected, perform the test step required for each code.<br>**NOTE: Code 55 is only generated in drive cycle test.** | Codes 16, 17 or 18 are displayed | GO to B1. |
| | | Code 74 displayed | GO to C1. |
| | | Code 55 displayed | GO to D1. |
| | | No error codes | GO to A3. |
| A3 | SERVICE POWER STEERING | | |
| | • Perform Pump Flow and Pressure Tests and REPLACE AS REQUIRED. | | |

**Fig. 12 System testing (Part 1 of 10). 1990 Lincoln Town Car**

| | TEST STEP | RESULT | ACTION TO TAKE |
|---|---|---|---|
| A1 | PERFORM SERVICE BAY DIAGNOSTICS | | |
| | Service Bay Diagnostic procedure. | Record all codes | GO to A2. |
| A2 | DETERMINE REQUIRED TEST STEP | | |
| | • Read displayed code(s).<br>• Each code must be addressed individually. If more than one error code is detected, perform the test step required for each code.<br>**NOTE: Code 55 is only generated in drive cycle test.** | Codes 16, 17 or 18 are displayed | GO to B1. |
| | | Code 74 displayed | GO to C1. |
| | | Code 55 displayed | GO to D1. |
| | | No error codes | GO to A3. |
| | | If any other codes are displayed | REFER air suspension Diagnostic procedure. |
| A3 | SERVICE POWER STEERING | | |
| | • Perform Pump Flow and Pressure Tests and REPLACE AS REQUIRED. | | |

**Fig. 12 System testing (Part 2 of 10). 1991 Lincoln Town Car**

| | TEST STEP | RESULT | ACTION TO TAKE |
|---|---|---|---|
| B1 | CODE ACTIVATED: EVO ACTUATOR VALVE CHECK (short to ground or an open circuit) | | |
| | • Turn ignition switch to OFF position.<br>• Verify harness connection on the EVO actuator valve on power steering pump is properly seated.<br>• Read all codes. | Connector not properly seated | Make proper connection, GO to A1. |
| | | Connector properly seated | GO to B2. |
| | | Code 16 displayed | GO to B5. |
| | | Code 17 displayed | GO to B2. |
| | | Code 18 displayed | GO to B4. |
| B2 | CHECK RESISTANCE ACROSS ACTUATOR VALVE | | |
| | • Ignition switch in OFF position.<br>• Locate the control module in luggage compartment. (Refer to Removal.)<br>• Using an ohmmeter, measure resistance across Pin No. 14 and Pin No. 26 of harness connector. Resistance should be 7-18 ohms. If the resistance is greater than 1000 ohms, the circuit is open. | Resistance is over 1000 ohms | GO to B3. |
| | | Resistance is over 18 ohms | GO to B4. |
| | | Resistance is less than 18 ohms | GO to B3. |
| B3 | CHECK CONTINUITY OF WIRING | | |
| | • Ignition switch in OFF position.<br>• Disconnect EVO harness connector from EVO actuator valve located on power steering pump.<br>• Test continuity of circuits No. 975 and No. 353 from the actuator connector to the 26 pin EVO control module connector.<br>• Refer to Component Location Schematic and System Schematic. | Continuity | GO to B4. |
| | | No continuity | SERVICE wires as necessary. GO to A1. |
| B4 | CHECK EVO ACTUATOR VALVE RESISTANCE | | |
| | • Disconnect EVO harness connector from EVO actuator valve located on power steering pump.<br>• Using an ohmmeter, measure resistance across the two actuator valve connector pins. | Resistance greater than 20 ohms or less than 5 ohms | REPLACE EVO valve. |
| | | Resistance is 5-20 ohms | GO to B5. |

**Fig. 12 System testing (Part 3 of 10). 1990 Lincoln Town Car**

| | TEST STEP | RESULT | ACTION TO TAKE |
|---|---|---|---|
| B1 | CODE ACTIVATED: EVO ACTUATOR VALVE CHECK (short to ground or an open circuit) | | |
| | • Turn ignition switch to OFF position.<br>• Verify harness connection on the EVO actuator valve on power steering pump is properly seated.<br>• Read all codes. | Connector not properly seated | Make proper connection, GO to A1. |
| | | Connector properly seated | GO to B2. |
| | | Code 16 displayed | GO to B4. |
| | | Code 17 displayed | GO to B2. |
| | | Code 18 displayed | GO to B3. |
| B2 | CHECK RESISTANCE ACROSS ACTUATOR VALVE | | |
| | • Ignition switch in OFF position.<br>• Locate the control module in luggage compartment. Harness connectors can be disconnected from module without removing module.<br>• Using an ohmmeter, measure resistance across Pin No. 14 and Pin No. 26 of harness connector. Resistance should be 7-18 ohms. If the resistance is greater than 1000 ohms, the circuit is open. | Resistance is over 1000 ohms | GO to B3. |
| | | Resistance is over 18 ohms | GO to B4. |
| | | Resistance is less than 18 ohms | GO to B3. |
| B3 | CHECK CONTINUITY OF WIRING | | |
| | • Ignition switch in OFF position.<br>• Disconnect EVO harness connector from EVO actuator valve located on power steering pump.<br>• Test continuity of Circuits No. 975 and No. 353 from the actuator connector to the 26 pin EVO control module connector. | Continuity | GO to B4. |
| | | No continuity | SERVICE wires as necessary. GO to A1. |
| B4 | CHECK EVO ACTUATOR VALVE RESISTANCE | | |
| | • Disconnect EVO harness connector from EVO actuator valve located on power steering pump.<br>• Using an ohmmeter, measure resistance across the two actuator valve connector pins. | Resistance greater than 20 ohms or less than 5 ohms | REPLACE EVO valve. |
| | | Resistance is 5-20 ohms | GO to B5. |

**Fig. 12 System testing (Part 4 of 10). 1991 Lincoln Town Car**

| TEST STEP | | RESULT ▶ | ACTION TO TAKE |
|---|---|---|---|
| B5 | CHECK WIRE HARNESS FOR SHORT TO GROUND | | |
| | • Ignition switch in OFF position.<br>• EVO harness disconnected from EVO actuator valve.<br>• Disconnect EVO control module from the 26 pin connectors in luggage compartment. (Refer to removal.) | Module disconnected ▶ | GO to **B5.1** |
| B5.1 | CHECK WIRE HARNESS FOR SHORT TO GROUND (Cont'd.) | | |
| | • Using on ohmmeter, measure resistance between Pin No. 21 (ground) and Pin No. 14 of harness connector. | Resistance is over 1000 ohms ▶ | GO to **B5.2**. |
| | | Resistance is less than 10 ohms ▶ | SERVICE Harness, GO to **B5.2**. |
| B5.2 | CHECK WIRE HARNESS FOR SHORT TO GROUND (Cont'd.) | | |
| | • Using an ohmmeter, measure resistance between Pin No. 21 (ground) and Pin No. 26 of harness connector. | Resistance is less than 10 ohms ▶ | SERVICE Harness. |
| | | Resistance is over 1000 ohms ▶ | GO to **B6**. |
| B6 | CHECK HARNESS FOR SHORT TO B + | | |
| | • Ignition switch in RUN position.<br>• EVO harness disconnected from EVO actuator valve on power steering pump. | Voltage is over 5 volts (short) ▶ | SERVICE wires, GO to **A1**. |
| | • Using a voltmeter, measure the voltage across<br>Pin No. 14 and Pin No. 21<br>Pin No. 26 and Pin No. 21 | Voltage is less than 5 volts ▶ | GO to **B7**. |
| B7 | CHECK FOR SHORT ACROSS CIRCUITS NO. 975 AND NO. 353 | | |
| | • Ignition switch in OFF position.<br>• EVO harness disconnected from EVO actuator valve on power steering pump. | Resistance is less than 10 ohms (short) ▶ | SERVICE wires, GO to **A1**. |
| | • EVO control module disconnected from pin harness connector.<br>• Using an ohmmeter, measure resistance across Pin No. 14 and Pin No. 26 on harness connector. | Resistance is over 1000 ohms ▶ | REPLACE EVO Control Module. |

**Fig. 12 System testing (Part 5 of 10). 1990–91 Lincoln Town Car**

| TEST STEP | | RESULT ▶ | ACTION TO TAKE |
|---|---|---|---|
| C1 | CHECK STEERING WHEEL SENSOR CONNECTION | | |
| | • Verify harness connection on steering wheel rotation sensor (located on lower portion of steering column) is properly seated. | Connector is properly seated ▶ | GO to **C2**. |
| | | Connector is not properly seated ▶ | MAKE proper connection, GO to **A1**. |
| C2 | STEERING WHEEL ROTATION SENSOR CHECK | | |
| | • Ignition switch in OFF position.<br>• Disconnect EVO control module and leave connectors mated. | Damaged or crossed wires ▶ | SERVICE wires as necessary, GO to **A1**. |
| | • Examine wiring harness, verify that there is no damage and<br>• Circuit No. 834 is in Pin No. 18.<br>• Circuit No. 835 is in Pin No. 19.<br>• Circuit No. 57 is in Pin No. 6 (ground). | No damage found ▶ | GO to **C3**. |
| C3 | TEST STEERING WHEEL ROTATION SENSOR SIGNALS | | |
| | • Start engine.<br>• While rotating the steering wheel slowly, and using an analog ohmmeter such as, Inductive Dwell-Tach-Volt Ohmmeter 059-00010 or equivalent, set to the 1K scale, measure the resistance from | Meter needle swings for both circuits. (steering wheel sensor is functioning). ▶ | SHUT off engine. REPLACE EVO Control Module. |
| | • Pin No. 18 to Pin No. 6<br>• Pin No. 19 to Pin No. 6<br>**NOTE: The resistance values will vary between meters, but the needle on all meters should swing from a low to a higher resistance and back approximately every nine degrees of steering wheel rotation.** | Meter needle does not swing for both circuits ▶ | GO to **C4**. |
| C4 | STEERING WHEEL ROTATION SENSOR WIRE CHECK | | |
| | • Disconnect EVO control module from 26 pin connectors located in luggage compartment.<br>• Ignition switch in the OFF position. | DAMAGED or crossed wires ▶ | SERVICE wires as necessary. |
| | • Unplug steering sensor (located on lower steering column). | No Continuity ▶ | SERVICE wires as necessary. GO to **A1**. |
| | • Check wires at steering sensor connector for damage and/or incorrect location.<br>• Test continuity of Circuits No. 834, No. 835 and No. 57 from steering sensor to EVO control module connector. | No problems found ▶ | GO to **C5**. |

**Fig. 12 System testing (Part 6 of 10). 1990–91 Lincoln Town Car**

| TEST STEP | | RESULT ▶ | ACTION TO TAKE |
|---|---|---|---|
| C5 | CHECK FOR SHORT ACROSS CIRCUITS 834 AND 835 | | |
| | • Turn ignition switch to OFF position.<br>• Steering Sensor disconnected. | Resistance is over 1000 ohms ▶ | GO to **C6**. |
| | • Disconnect pin connectors. Measure resistance between<br>Pin No. 18 and Pin No. 19<br>Pin No. 18 and Pin No. 6<br>Pin No. 19 and Pin No. 6<br>of the pin connectors (in luggage compartment). | Resistance is less than 10 ohms (short) ▶ | SERVICE wires as necessary. GO to **A1**. |
| C6 | TEST STEERING SENSOR POWER | | |
| | • Turn ignition switch to RUN position. | 12 volts ▶ | GO to **C7**. |
| | • Using a voltmeter, measure the voltage between Circuits No. 295 and No. 57 at the steering sensor connector. | 0 volts (short or open circuit) ▶ | SERVICE circuit 295. GO to **A1**. |
| C7 | TEST STEERING SENSOR POWER CIRCUIT | | |
| | • Using a voltmeter, measure voltage between circuits No. 295 and No. 57 at the steering sensor connector. | 12 volts ▶ | REPLACE steering sensor. |
| | | 0 volts ▶ | REPLACE control module. |

**Fig. 12 System testing (Part 7 of 10). 1990–91 Lincoln Town Car**

| TEST STEP | | RESULT | ACTION TO TAKE |
|---|---|---|---|
| D1 | CHECK SPEED SENSOR CONNECTION | | |
| | • Ensure harness connection on speed sensor, (located on the transmission) is properly seated. | Connector is properly seated | GO to D2. |
| | | Connector is not properly seated | MAKE proper connection. GO to A0. |
| D2 | SPEED SENSOR CHECK | | |
| | • Turn ignition switch to the OFF position. • Disconnect electrical connectors from the EVO module (located in luggage compartment). • Ensure there is no damage to harness and that: • Circuit No. 136 is in Pin No. 7 • Circuit No. 875 is in Pin No. 20 | Damaged or crossed wires | SERVICE wires. GO to A0. |
| | | No damage found | GO to D3. |
| D3 | TEST SPEED SENSOR GROUND CIRCUIT | | |
| | • Test continuity of speed sensor ground circuit No. 875, from Pin No. 20 to Pin No. 6 of 26 pin connectors. | Continuity | GO to D4. |
| | | Open Circuit | SERVICE wire or ground eyelet as necessary. GO to A0. |
| D4 | TEST SPEED SENSOR | | |
| | • Turn ignition switch to RUN position. • Perform "speedometer reads 0 mph at all speeds". | Problem(s) found | SERVICE as outlined in Section 33-10. GO to A0. |
| | | No Problem(s) found | REPLACE EVO control module. |

| TEST STEP | | RESULT | ACTION TO TAKE |
|---|---|---|---|
| E1 | EVO CONTROL MODULE CHECK | | |
| | • Turn ignition switch to OFF position. • Ensure pin connectors are properly connected to module. (Located in luggage compartment.) | Properly Connected | GO to E2. |
| | | Connection is not properly secured | SECURE connection. GO to A0. |
| E2 | CHECK POWER FEED | | |
| | • Turn ignition switch to the OFF position. • Disconnect EVO control module 26 pin connectors. (Located in luggage compartment.) • Turn ignition switch to RUN position. • Using a DVOM, measure voltage from Pin No. 16 (ignition-run only) to Pin No. 6 (ground) at pin connectors. | 12 volts | REPLACE EVO Control Module. |
| | | 0 volts | SERVICE short to ground or open in circuit No. 295 as necessary. GO to A0. |

**Fig. 12 System testing (Part 8 of 10). 1990 Lincoln Town Car**

| TEST STEP | | RESULT | ACTION TO TAKE |
|---|---|---|---|
| D1 | CHECK SPEED SENSOR CONNECTION | | |
| | • Ensure harness connection on speed sensor, (located on the transmission) is properly seated. | Connector is properly seated | GO to D2. |
| | | Connector is not properly seated | MAKE proper connection. GO to A1. |
| D2 | SPEED SENSOR CHECK | | |
| | • Turn ignition switch to the OFF position. • Disconnect electrical connectors from the EVO module (located in luggage compartment). • Ensure there is no damage to harness and that: • Circuit No. 136 is in Pin No. 7 • Circuit No. 875 is in Pin No. 20 | Damaged or crossed wires | SERVICE wires. GO to A1. |
| | | No damage found | GO to D3. |
| D3 | TEST SPEED SENSOR GROUND CIRCUIT | | |
| | • Test continuity of speed sensor ground circuit No. 875, from Pin No. 20 to Pin No. 6 of 26 pin connectors. | Continuity | GO to D4. |
| | | Open Circuit | SERVICE wire or ground eyelet as necessary. GO to A1. |
| D4 | TEST SPEED SENSOR | | |
| | • Turn ignition switch to RUN position. • Perform "Speedometer Reads 0 mph at all Speeds". | Problem(s) found | SERVICE GO to A1. |
| | | No Problem(s) found | REPLACE EVO control module. |

**Fig. 12 System testing (Part 9 of 10). 1991 Lincoln Town Car**

| TEST STEP | | RESULT | ACTION TO TAKE |
|---|---|---|---|
| E1 | EVO CONTROL MODULE CHECK | | |
| | • Turn ignition switch to OFF position. • Ensure pin connectors are properly connected to module. (Located in luggage compartment.) • Check air suspension switch. | Properly Connected | GO to E2. |
| | | Connection is not properly secured Air suspension switch in luggage compartment is off | SECURE connection. GO to A1. TURN air suspension switch ON. GO to A0. |
| E2 | CHECK POWER FEED | | |
| | • Turn ignition switch to the OFF position. • Disconnect EVO control module 26 pin connectors. (Located in luggage compartment.) • Turn ignition switch to RUN position. • Using a DVOM, measure voltage from Pin No. 16 (ignition-run only) to Pin No. 6 (ground) at pin connectors. • Measure voltage from Pin No. 1 to Pin No. 6. | Both 12V | REPLACE EVO Control Module. |
| | | Zero volts from No. 295 or No. 418 | SERVICE short to ground or open in circuit No. 418 or No. 295 as necessary. GO to A1. |

**Fig. 12 System testing (Part 10 of 10). 1991 Lincoln Town Car**

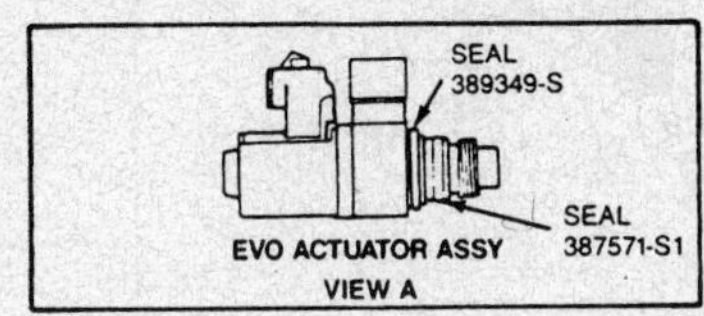


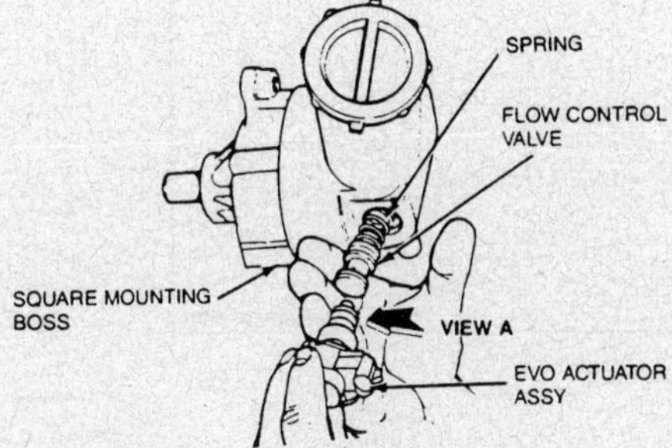


**Fig. 13 Actuator removal**

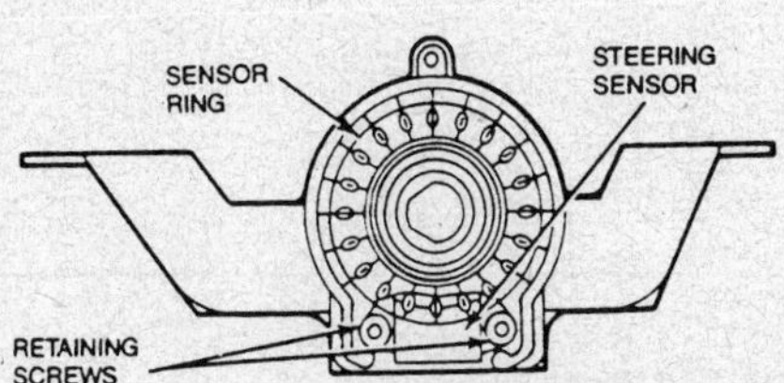


**Fig. 14 Steering sensor removal**

# Probe Steering Pump

## INDEX



## DISASSEMBLE

1. Secure pump in a suitable holding fixture.
2. Disassemble pump in numbered order, **Fig. 1.**

## INSPECTION

Check the following components for excessive wear or damage and replace as necessary:

1. Vane, cam ring, rotor and side plate.
2. Control valve.
3. Control valve installation hole.
4. Pump body.

## ASSEMBLE

Assemble pump in the reverse oder of disassembly. Ensure vanes are positioned in the rotor with rounded edges against the cam.

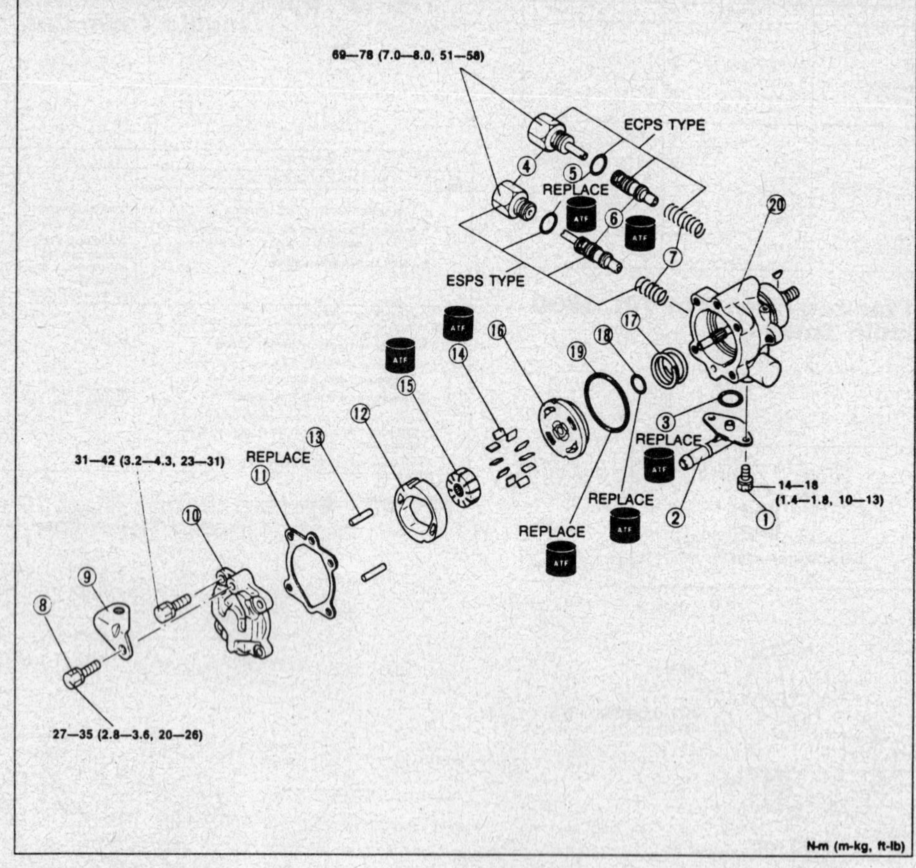


1. Bolt
2. Pipe
3. O-ring
4. Connector
5. O-ring
6. Control valve
7. Spring
8. Bolt
9. Bracket
10. Pump body (rear)
11. Gasket
12. Cam ring
13. Dowel pin
14. Vane
15. Rotor
16. Side plate
17. Spring
18. O-ring
19. O-ring
20. Pump body assembly

**Fig. 1. Exploded view of power steering pump**

# DASH PANEL SERVICE

## INDEX



---

## AIRBAG DEACTIVATION & REACTIVATION

**The electrical circuit necessary for system deployment is powered directly from the battery and a backup power supply. To avoid accidental deployment and possible personal injury, the airbag system must be deactivated prior to servicing or replacing any system components.**

A back-up power supply is included in the system to provide airbag deployment in the event the battery or battery cables are damaged in an accident before the sensors can close. The power supply is a capacitor that will retain a charge for approximately 15 minutes after the battery ground cable is disconnected. **Backup power supply must be disconnected to deactivate airbag system.** To remove backup power supply, refer to "Airbags" in the "Passive Restraint" section.

1. Disconnect battery ground cable.
2. Disconnect backup power supply.
3. Remove four nut and washer assemblies securing airbag module to steering wheel, then disconnect airbag electrical connector. Attach jumper wire to airbag terminals on clockspring terminals.
4. **On models equipped with passenger-side airbag,** disconnect airbag module connector located behind glove compartment. Attach a jumper wire to airbag terminals on wiring harness side of passenger airbag module connector terminals.
5. **On all models,** reconnect battery and backup power supply if necessary to perform repair procedure.
6. To reactivate, disconnect battery ground cable and backup power supply, then reverse remainder of deactivation procedure. **Torque** airbag module to steering wheel nut assemblies to 24-32 inch lbs. on Crown Victoria and Grand Marquis, or 35-53 inch lbs. on all other models.
7. Verify airbag lamp after reactivating system.

## CONTINENTAL

1. Disarm airbag system as described under "Airbag System Disarming."
2. Disconnect battery ground cable.
3. Remove four nut and washer assemblies attaching driver air bag module to steering wheel.
4. Disconnect driver air bag module electrical connector and remove air bag from vehicle. **Place air bag on bench with trim cover facing up.**
5. Remove right side finish moulding by pulling upward to unsnap five clips and disconnect wiring, **Fig. 1.**
6. Open glove compartment door and depress side inward and lower glove box assembly toward floor.
7. Remove four screws attaching passenger air bag module to instrument panel, **Fig. 2.**
8. Disconnect passenger air bag module electrical connector and remove air bag from vehicle. **Place air bag on bench with trim cover facing up.**
9. Remove left side finish moulding by pulling upward to unsnap two clips.
10. Remove four screws retaining lower steering column cover and remove cover.
11. Remove four screws attaching lower instrument panel steering column reinforcement and remove reinforcement.
12. Remove three screws retaining upper steering column shroud and remove shroud.
13. Remove one tilt/wheel lever retaining screw and remove lever.
14. Remove lock cylinder by pushing a small Allen wrench into groove located beneath lock cylinder. Place key into ignition and gently wiggle to work cylinder free.
15. Remove lower steering column shroud by pulling out.
16. Remove bolt retaining steering wheel and remove wheel.
17. Remove bolt attaching PRNDL cable to steering column.
18. **On 1989 models,** disconnect all steering column electrical connectors, **Fig. 3.**
19. **On 1990-91 models,** disconnect all steering column electrical connectors, **Fig. 4.**
20. **On all models,** disconnect hood and brake release cables.
21. **On 1989 models,** remove five plastic retainers, and three push on nuts holding left and right lower close-out panels in place. Remove close out panels, **Fig. 2.**
22. Remove two lower shaft universal joint retention nuts. Pull lower shaft away from steering column.
23. **On 1990-91 model,** remove four push pins holding left and right close-out panels in place. Remove close-out panels, **Fig. 5.**
24. **On all models,** remove four nuts retaining steering column, then lower column.
25. **On 1989 models,** remove one screw and clip retaining transmission shift cable.
26. Disconnect two vacuum hoses. Remove steering column from the vehicle.
27. **On all models,** remove two screws at steering column opening, retaining instrument panel to brake pedal support.
28. Remove two screws under ash receptacle, which holds instrument panel to A/C plenum case.
29. Remove headlamp switch knob.
30. Remove five screws from cluster opening finish panel and remove panel, **Fig. 1.**
31. Remove four screws retaining A/C control. Disconnect electrical connectors and one vacuum connector.
32. Remove four screws retaining cluster, then disconnect electrical connectors.
33. Remove three screws to remove glove box assembly.
34. Remove three screws located above left side of glove compartment, **Fig. 6.**
35. Remove both speaker grilles by snapping out to release. Disconnect electrical connector at right side grille.
36. Remove two screws seated in plastic push clips and remove center defrost grille.
37. Open engine compartment hood, disconnect all electrical connectors of main wire loom.

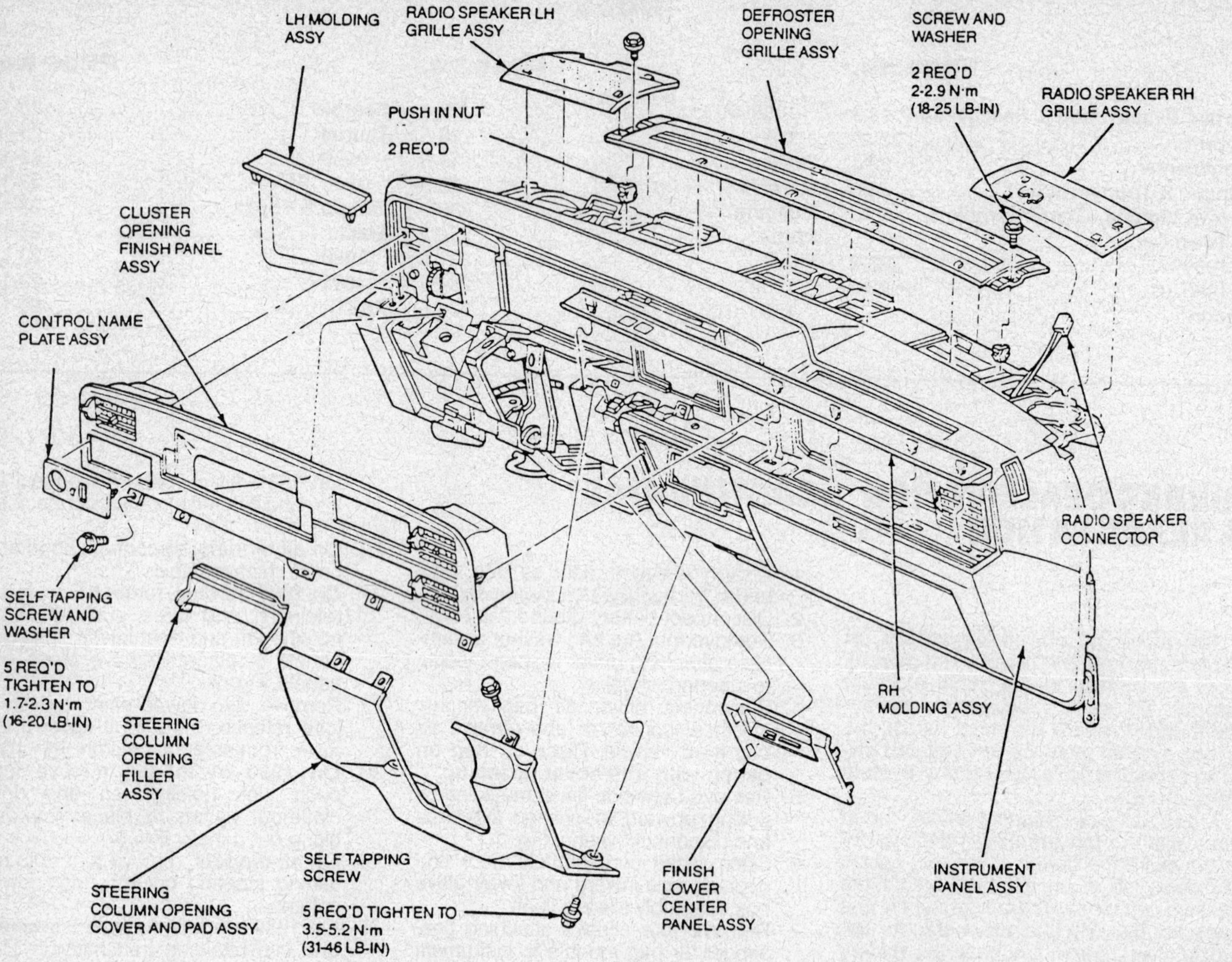

LH MOLDING ASSY
RADIO SPEAKER LH GRILLE ASSY
PUSH IN NUT
2 REQ'D
DEFROSTER OPENING GRILLE ASSY
SCREW AND WASHER
2 REQ'D
2-2.9 N·m
(18-25 LB-IN)
RADIO SPEAKER RH GRILLE ASSY
CLUSTER OPENING FINISH PANEL ASSY
CONTROL NAME PLATE ASSY
RADIO SPEAKER CONNECTOR
SELF TAPPING SCREW AND WASHER
5 REQ'D
TIGHTEN TO
1.7-2.3 N·m
(16-20 LB-IN)
STEERING COLUMN OPENING FILLER ASSY
RH MOLDING ASSY
SELF TAPPING SCREW
5 REQ'D TIGHTEN TO
3.5-5.2 N·m
(31-46 LB-IN)
STEERING COLUMN OPENING COVER AND PAD ASSY
FINISH LOWER CENTER PANEL ASSY
INSTRUMENT PANEL ASSY

**Fig. 1 Removing trim & accessory panels. Continental**

38. Disengage rubber grommet from dash panel and feed wiring and connectors through hole into instrument panel area.
39. Remove three screws at both left and right side cowl trim panels, then remove panels.
40. Remove lower two screws at instrument panel, one at each end, **Fig. 6.**
41. Remove three upper instrument panel retaining screws and carefully lower instrument panel. Disconnect all electrical and vacuum connections. Remove instrument panel from the vehicle.
42. Reverse procedure to install.
43. Reactivate airbag system as described under "Airbag System Disarming."

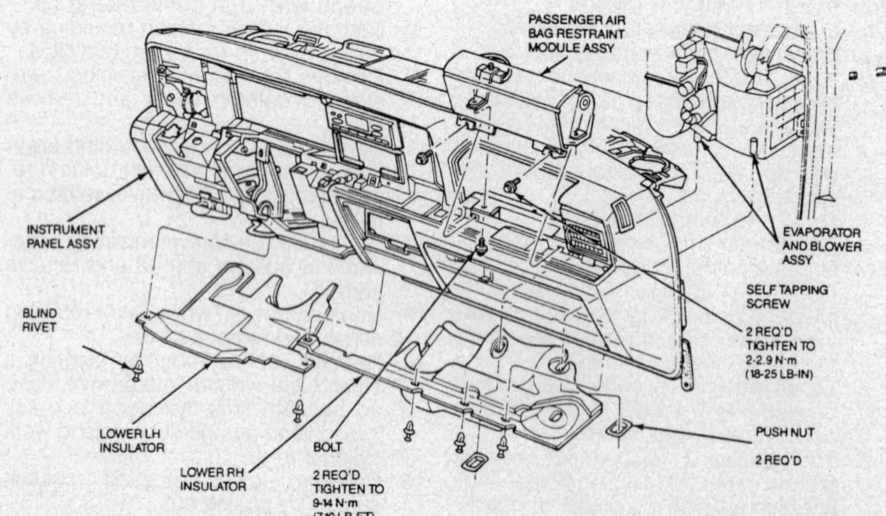


**Fig. 2 Removing passenger air bag module. 1989 Continental**

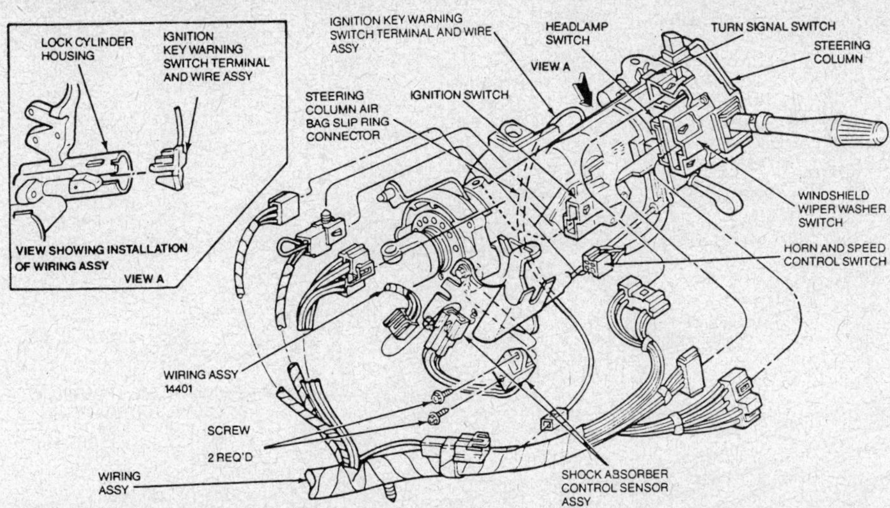


**Fig. 3 Steering column electrical connectors. 1989 Continental**

# COUGAR & THUNDERBIRD

1. Disconnect battery ground cable.
2. Disconnect all underhood wiring connectors from main wiring harness. Remove rubber grommet seal from dash panel and push wiring harness and connectors into passenger compartment.
3. Remove steering column lower trim cover, **Fig. 7.**
4. Remove six steering column lower opening reinforcement retaining screws, **Fig. 7.**
5. Remove steering column upper and lower shrouds.
6. Disconnect steering column wiring connectors, **Figs. 8 and 9.**
7. Remove shift interlock switch.
8. Disconnect steering column lower universal joint.
9. Support steering column and remove four nuts retaining column to support. Remove column from vehicle.
10. Remove one screw retaining left side of instrument panel to parking brake bracket.
11. Install lower steering column lower opening reinforcement, **Fig. 7.** Inforcement prevents instrument panel from twisting when being removed from vehicle.
12. Remove right and left side cowl trim panels, **Fig. 10.**
13. Open floor console door and remove container and mat to gain access to two console to floorpan retaining screws. Remove screws,**Fig. 11.**
14. **On models with 5 speed manual transmission,** remove gear shift knob.
15. **On all models,** remove two rear finish panel retaining screws.
16. Tilt finish panel forward and disconnect electrical connectors, then remove finish panel.
17. Remove two front console to instrument panel retaining screws and remove console.
18. Remove two nuts retaining center of instrument panel to floor.
19. Open glove compartment, squeeze sides of bin and lower to full open position.
20. From underneath instrument panel and through glove compartment opening, disconnect wiring, and heater-A/C vacuum lines and control cables.
21. Remove two retaining screws from both the left and right sides of the instrument panel, **Fig. 12.**
22. Remove right and left side upper finish panels by pulling up to disengage snap-in retainers, **Fig. 13.**
23. Remove instrument panel to cowl top attaching screws, **Figs. 14 and 15.**
24. Remove right and left roof rail trim panel panel, then remove door frame weather strip.
25. Carefully pull instrument panel away from cowl and disconnect any remaining wiring or controls.
26. Remove instrument panel from the vehicle.
27. Reverse procedure to install.

# CROWN VICTORIA, GRAND MARQUIS & TOWN CAR

## 1989

For instrument panel removal on these models refer to **Figs. 16 and 17.**

## 1990–91

1. Disarm airbag system as described under "Airbag System Disarming."
2. Position front wheels straight ahead.
3. Disconnect battery ground cable.
4. Remove instrument panel right and left moulding, **Fig. 19.**
5. Remove headlamp control knobs.
6. Remove finish panel to instrument panel attaching screws.
7. Pull finish panel from instrument panel, then disconnect electrical connectors.
8. Remove finish panel.
9. Remove right and left lower insulation panels, then remove bulb and socket assembly, **Fig. 19.**
10. Remove lower instrument panel steering column cover attaching screws.

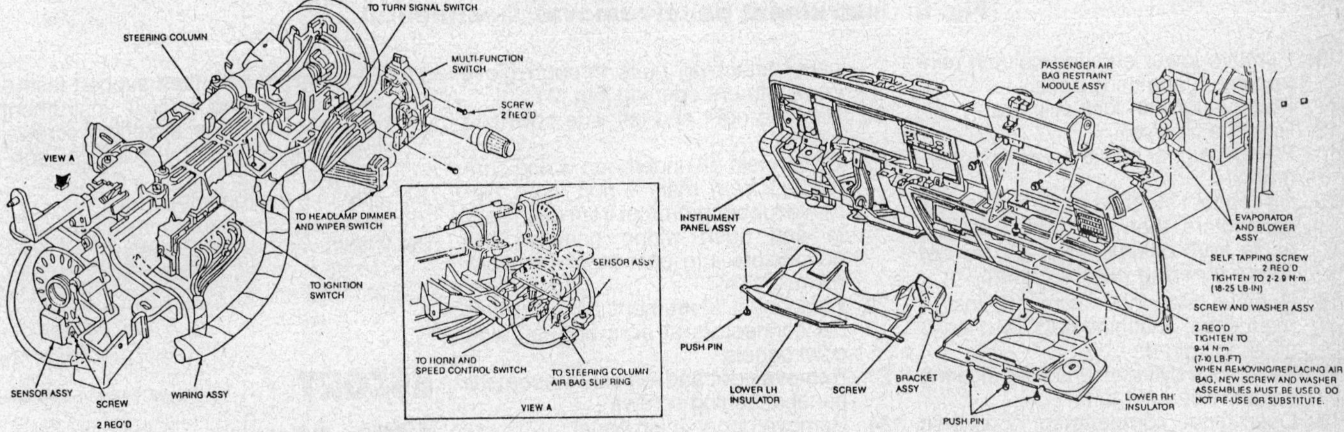


**Fig. 4 Steering column electrical connectors. 1990–91 Continental**

**Fig. 5 Close out panel removal. 1990–91 Continental**

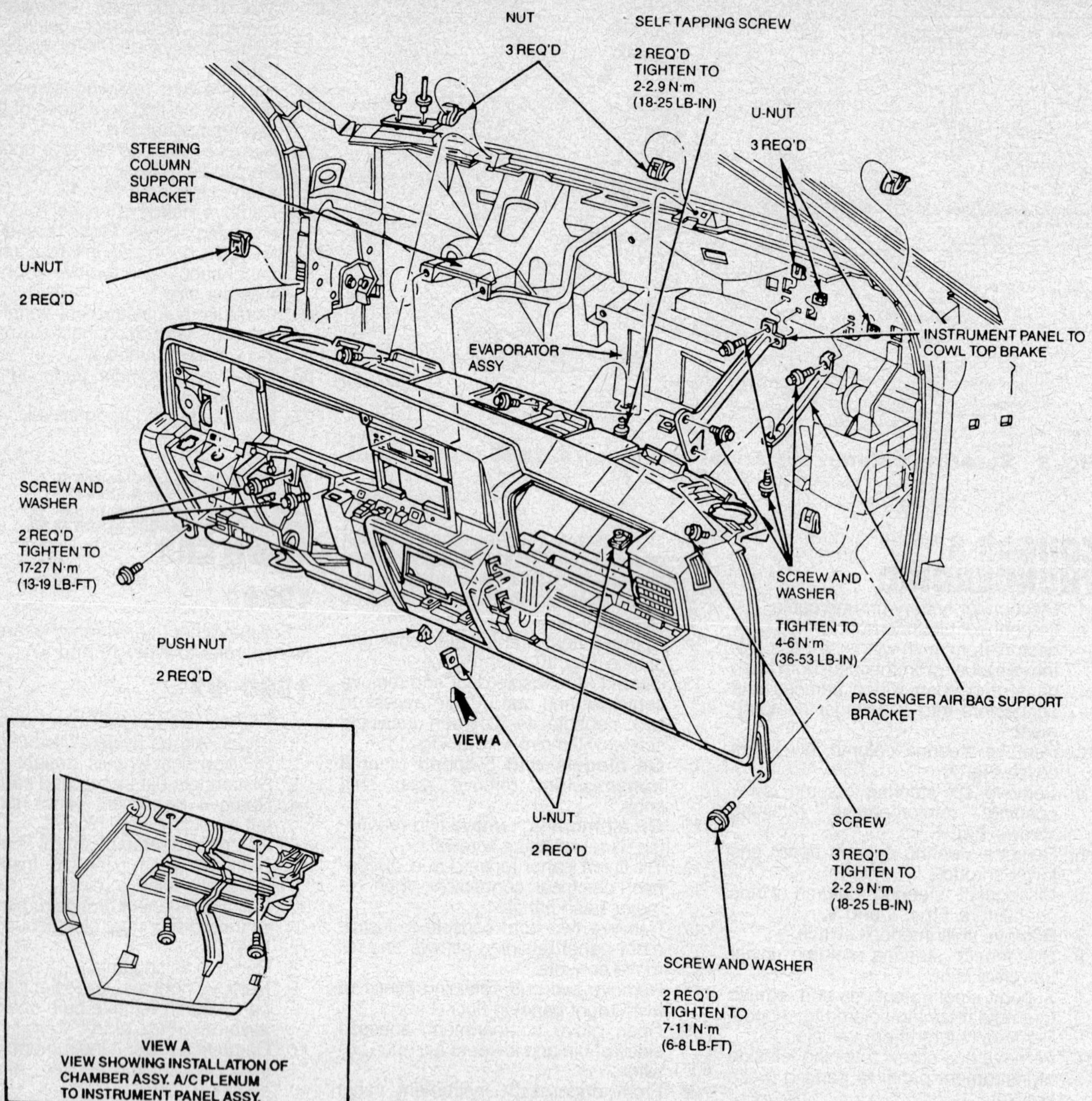


**Fig. 6 Instrument panel removal. Continental**

11. Remove lower steering column reinforcement attaching bolts.
12. Remove ignition lock cylinder.
13. Remove tilt lever.
14. Remove upper and lower steering column shrouds.
15. Disconnect steering column electrical connectors, then disconnect PRNDL cable from column, **Fig. 20. Do not rotate steering column shaft.**
16. Remove steering column to instrument panel attaching nuts, then lower steering column.
17. Install lock cylinder, ensuring steering column does not turn.
18. Open glove compartment door, then depress sides inward and lower assembly towards floor.
19. Remove instrument panel to dash panel attaching bolts through glove compartment opening, **Fig. 21.**
20. Remove right and left side cowl trim panels.
21. Disconnect all underhood wiring connectors from main wiring loom. Remove rubber grommet from dash panel and push wiring harness and connectors into passenger compartment.
22. Disconnect instrument panel electrical connectors at right and left side cowl panels.
23. Remove right and left side instrument panel attaching screws.
24. Remove upper finish panel.
25. Disconnect electrical connectors, vacuum hoses, demister hose, heater A/C vacuum lines and radio antenna.
26. Close glove box, then support instrument panel and remove instrument panel to cowl top attaching screws, then disconnect any electrical connectors.
27. Remove instrument panel.
28. Reverse procedure to install.
29. Reactivate airbag system as described under "Airbag System Disarming."

# ESCORT

## 1989–90

Refer to **Figs. 22 through 25,** when performing this procedure.

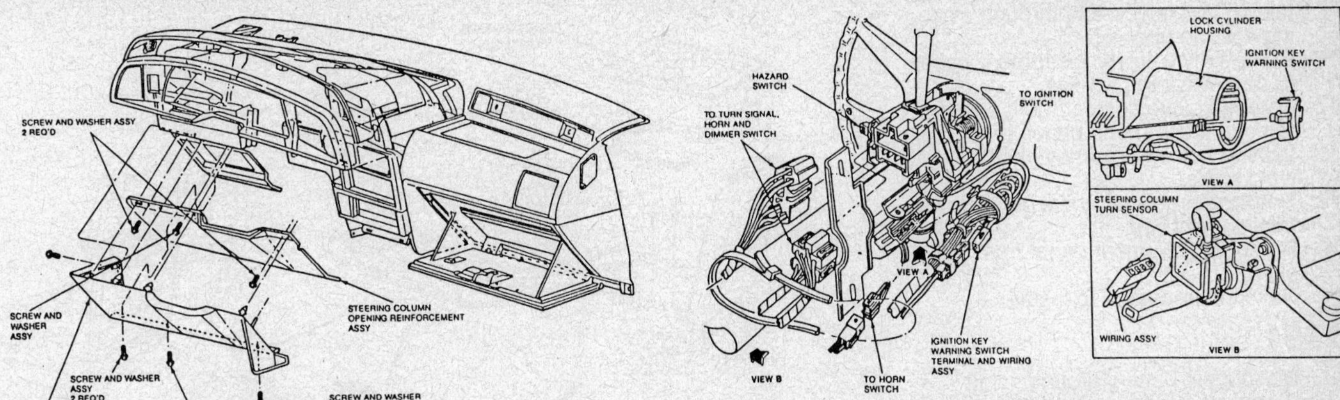


**Fig. 7 Steering column trim cover and reinforcement. 1989–90 Cougar & Thunderbird**

**Fig. 9 Steering column wiring connectors. 1990–91 Cougar & Thunderbird**

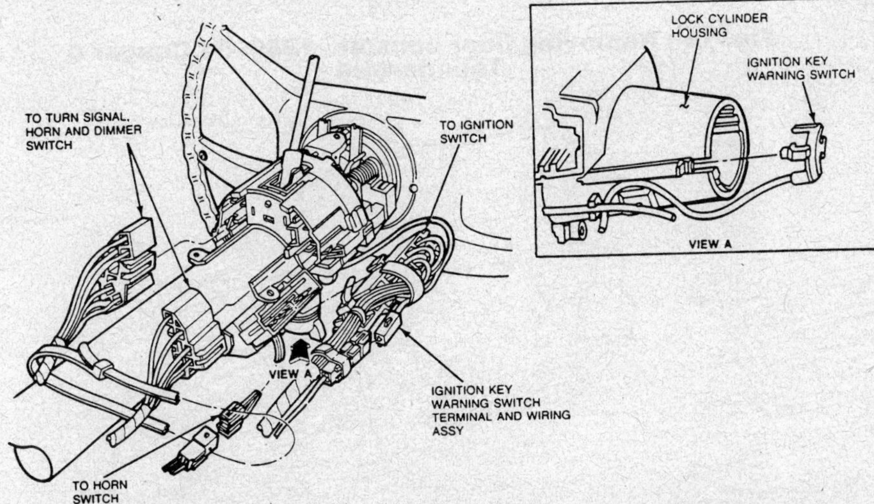


**Fig. 8 Steering column wiring connectors. 1989 Cougar & Thunderbird**

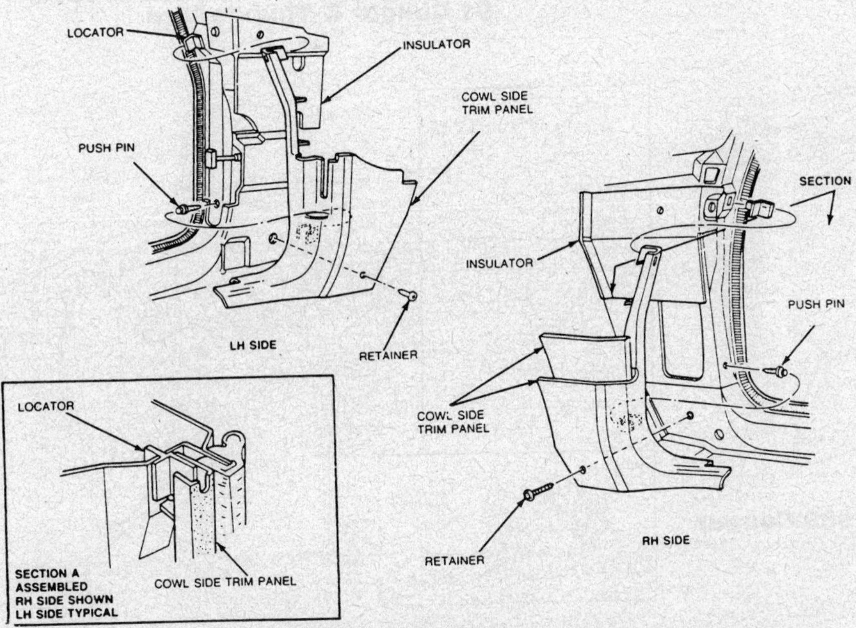


**Fig. 10 Removing cowl trim panels. 1989–91 Cougar & Thunderbird**

1. Disconnect battery ground cable.
2. Remove two steering column shroud retaining screws, then the shroud.
3. Remove two retaining screws at bottom of steering column opening cover. Disengage two clips on top of cover and remove cover.
4. Remove two steering column retaining screws and two retaining nuts from steering column support bracket. Lower steering column.
5. Disconnect all electrical connections from steering column switches.
6. Remove retaining screw from left side finish panel and carefully disengage clip on left side. Remove finish panel.
7. Remove six cluster opening finish panel retaining screws. Pull finish panel rearward, then disconnect fog lamp switch connector and remove finish panel.
8. Disconnect speedometer cable by reaching up under instrument panel and pressing on flat surface of plastic connector.
9. Remove four cluster retaining screws, then disconnect cluster wiring and remove cluster.
10. Remove four center finish panel retaining screws and remove center finish panel.
11. Remove four right side utility compartment retaining screws. Pull out bin side first and pull to left to disengage clip on right side of register.
12. Remove three glove compartment hinge attachment support screws, then remove glove compartment assembly by depressing sides of bin. **If hinge is not removed, use care when dropping glove compartment door as damage may occur.**
13. Using cluster opening, and by reaching under instrument panel, disconnect all electrical connections, vacuum hoses, heater-A/C control cables and radio antenna.
14. Disconnect all underhood electrical connectors of main wire loom. Disengage rubber grommet from dash panel and feed wire and connectors into instrument panel area.
15. Remove one instrument panel to steering column support bracket re-

taining nut, accessible through steering column opening.
16. Remove two lower instrument panel to cowl retaining screws.
17. Through glove compartment opening, remove instrument panel brace attaching nuts, then remove brace from weld studs.
18. Remove three instrument panel upper retaining screws.
19. Remove instrument panel from vehicle.
20. Reverse procedure to install.

## 1991

1. Disconnect battery ground cable.
2. If equipped with a standard column, remove four column retaining bolts and lower steering column.
3. Remove instrument cluster bezel retaining screws, **Fig. 26,** then the bezel.
4. Disconnect speedometer cable at the transaxle by pulling cable out of vehicle speed sensor.
5. Remove instrument cluster retaining screws, **Fig. 27,** then pull the cluster

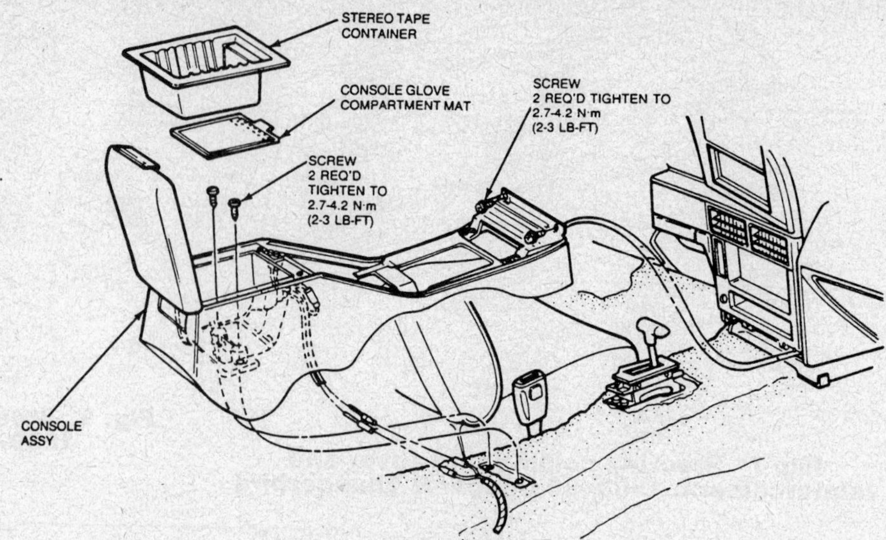


**Fig. 11 Removing floor console. 1989–91 Cougar & Thunderbird**

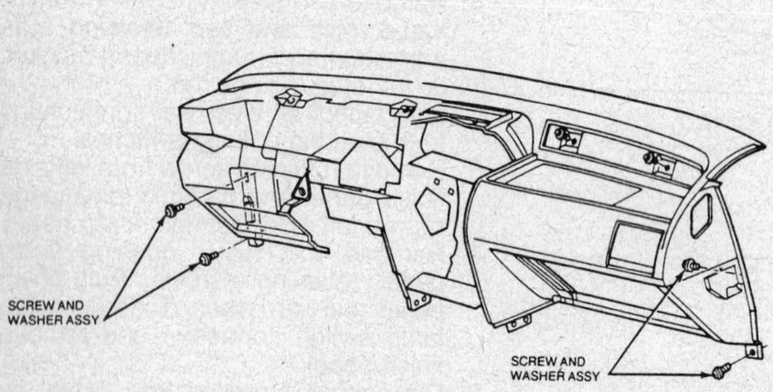


**Fig. 12 Removing I/P retaining screws. 1989–91 Cougar & Thunderbird**

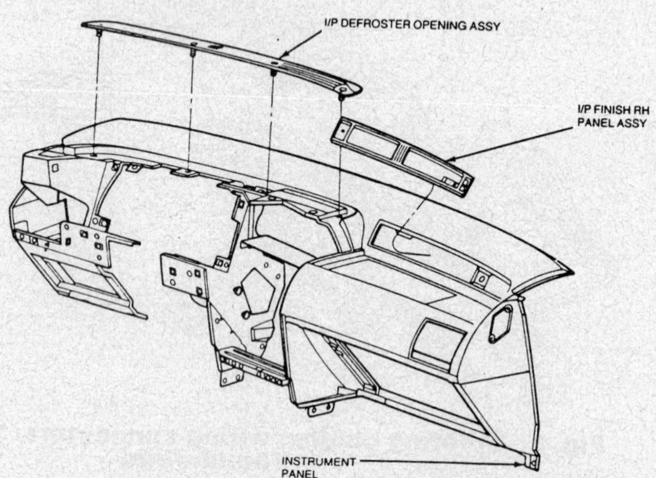


**Fig. 13 Removing upper finish panels. 1989—91 Cougar & Thunderbird**

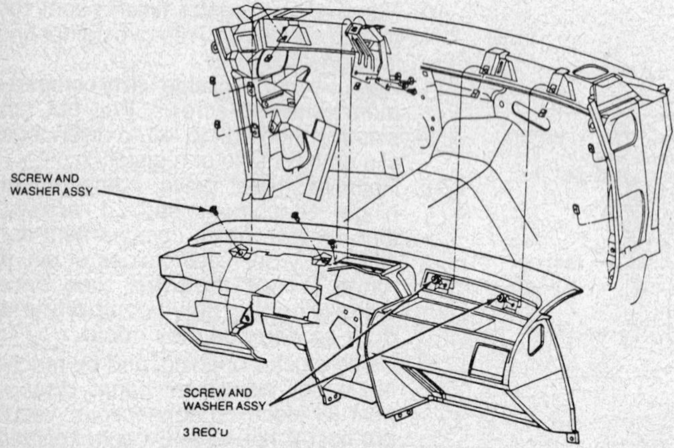


**Fig. 14 Removing I/P from cowl. 1989 Cougar & Thunderbird**

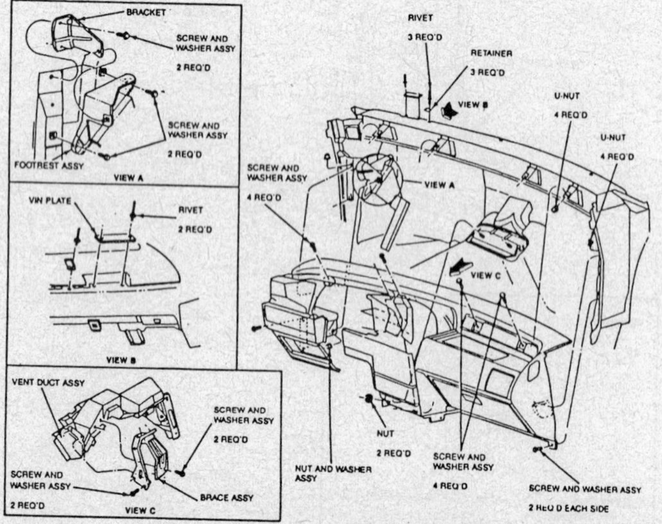


**Fig. 15 Removing I/P from cowl. 1990–91 Cougar & Thunderbird**

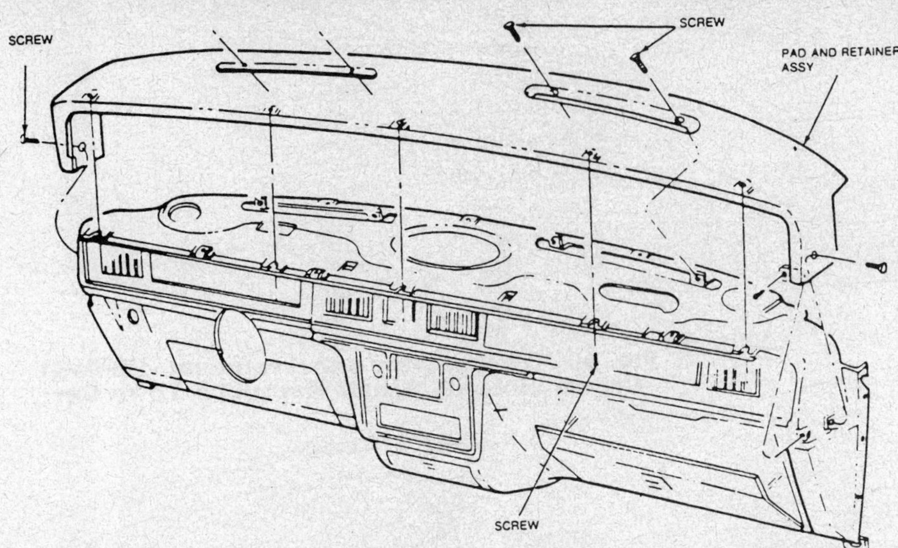


**Fig. 16 Removing I/P top pad. 1989 Crown Victoria, Grand Marquis & Town Car**

out slightly and disconnect electrical connectors.

6. Disconnect speedometer cable from back of cluster, then remove the cluster.
7. Disconnect hood release cable from LH lower dash trim panel.
8. Remove dash side panels by prying each panel away from I/P.
9. Remove four retaining screws and the left lower trim panel, then disconnect all necessary electrical connectors.
10. Remove two glove compartment hinge screws, then the compartment door.
11. Remove the climate control assembly, ashtray and seven accessory console retaining screws.
12. Disconnect the antenna, radio wire connector and cigar lighter.
13. Remove the RH lower dash trim panel retaining screws.
14. Support the steering column, then remove four retaining bolts and lower column away from I/P.
15. Disconnect amplifier wire connectors, then remove four I/P frame bolts to floor pan.

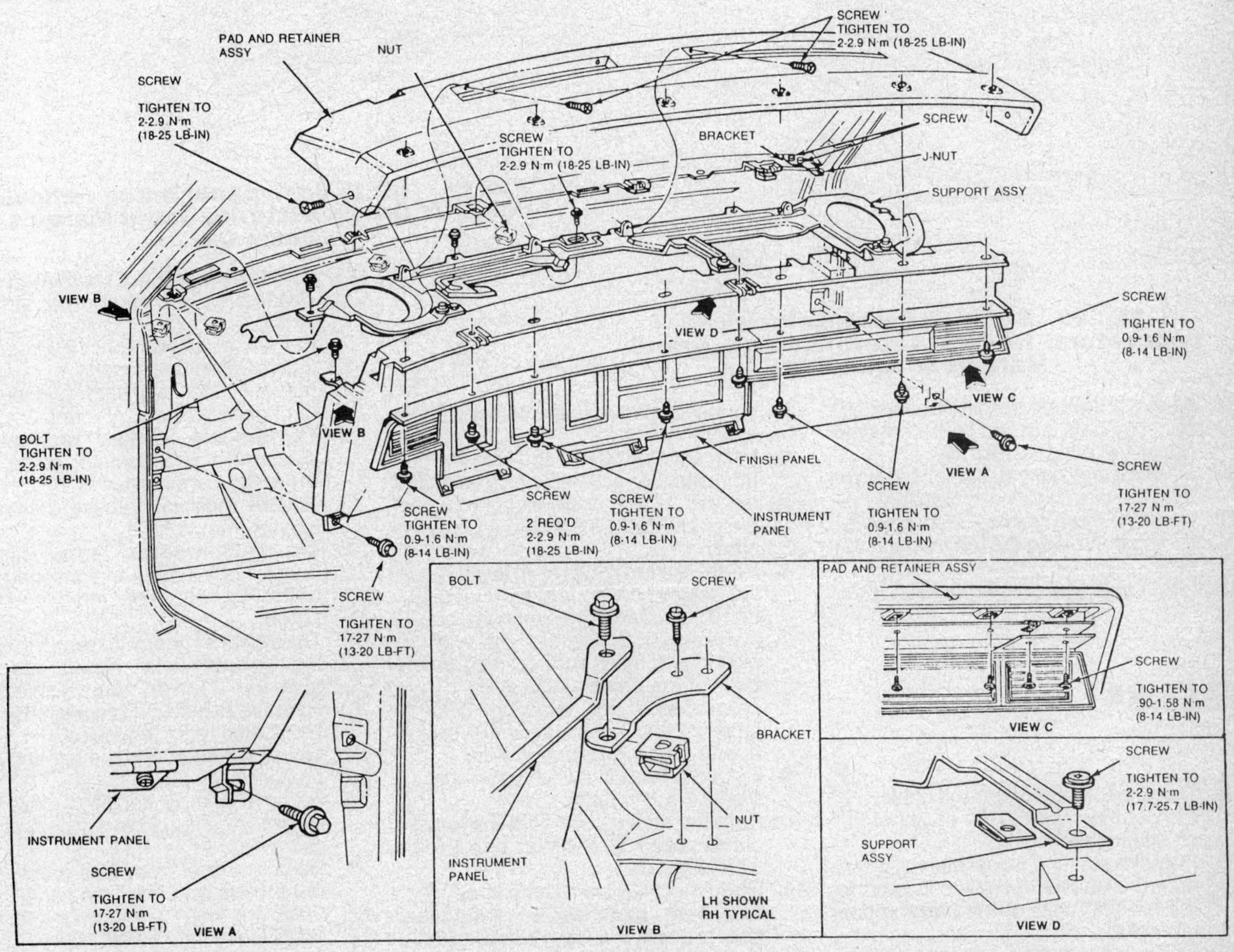

**Fig. 17 Instrument panel removal. 1989 Crown Victoria, Grand Marquis & Town Car**

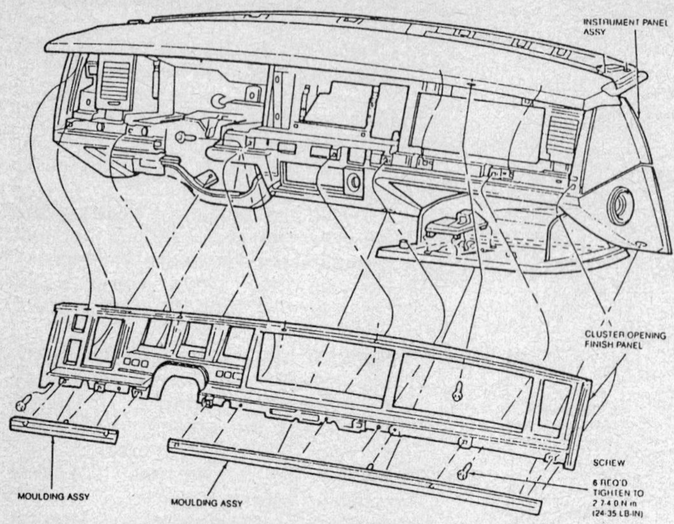


Fig. 18 I/P moulding removal. 1990–91 Crown Victoria, Grand Marquis & Town Car

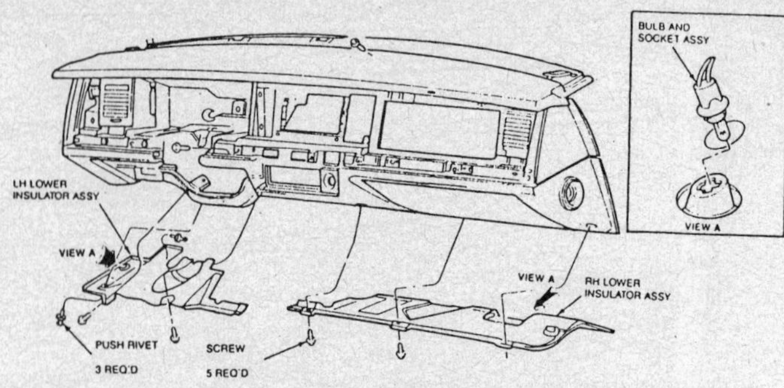


Fig. 19 I/P insulator panel removal. 1990–91 Crown Victoria, Grand Marquis & Town Car

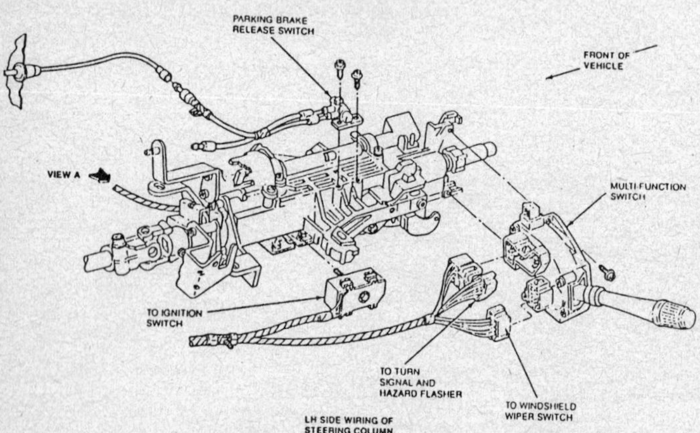


Fig. 20 Steering column electrical connectors. 1990–91 Crown Victoria, Grand Marquis & Town Car

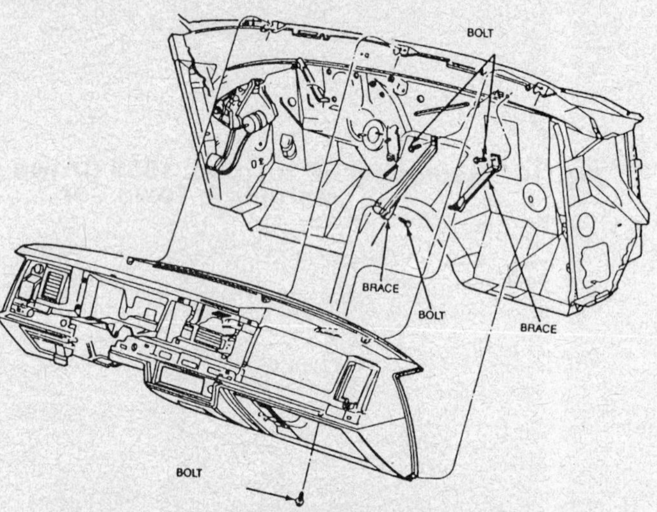


Fig. 21 I/P to dash panel brace removal. 1990–91 Crown Victoria, Grand Marquis & Town Car

16. Remove the bolt from both lower I/P panel mounts and two bolts from both upper I/P mounts, **Fig. 28.**
17. Remove the defroster duct bezel retaining screws, then the bezel.
18. Remove three upper I/P to cowl retaining bolts, then the I/P from the vehicle.
19. Reverse procedures to install.

# FESTIVA

1. Disconnect battery ground cable.
2. Pry out trim insert in the center of the steering wheel cover.
3. Remove steering wheel attaching nut, then the attaching screws located to the left and right of the steering column stud.
4. Remove two screws from the back of the steering wheel spokes, freeing steering wheel cover assembly, with cover bracket and horn buttons. Disconnect horn wire and remove cover assembly.
5. Mark steering wheel and steering column shaft for assembly reference and remove wheel with steering wheel puller tool No. T67L-3600-A or equivalent.
6. Remove five screws from lower steering column cover, and remove upper and lower steering column covers.
7. Release wiring harness clip and unplug four harness connectors from the back of the combination switch.
8. From below the steering column, loosen band clamp securing switch hub to steering column jacket.
9. Pull combination switch assembly off the steering column.
10. Remove screws securing instrument cluster bezel and move bezel rearward, **Fig. 29.**
11. Disconnect switch electrical connectors from switches on instrument cluster bezel, then remove instrument cluster bezel.
12. **On models equipped with tachometer,** disconnect tachometer at rear of instrument panel.
13. **On models without tachometer,** disconnect speedometer cable at transaxle.
14. **On all models,** remove instrument cluster attaching screws.
15. Move cluster rearward and disconnect cluster electrical wiring.
16. **On models without tachometer,** disconnect speedometer cable from the instrument cluster.
17. **On all models,** remove instrument cluster from vehicle.
18. **On 1989 models,** remove spacer brace bolts under the steering column, **Fig. 30,** then remove spacer brace.
19. **On 1990-91 models,** remove steering column inner shield attaching nuts, **Fig. 31,** then remove shield.
20. Remove two shield bracket attaching bolts, then remove bracket.
21. **On all models,** remove left and right heater ducts, **Fig. 32.**
22. Remove screws securing glove box hinges to the glove box, then the glove box.
23. Remove cover from fuse panel, then the screws securing fuse panel.
24. Push the fuse panel forward, but do not remove fuse panel.
25. Remove shift lever knob, then the console attaching screws, **Fig. 33. Remove only the three screws shown in the figure. The remaining**

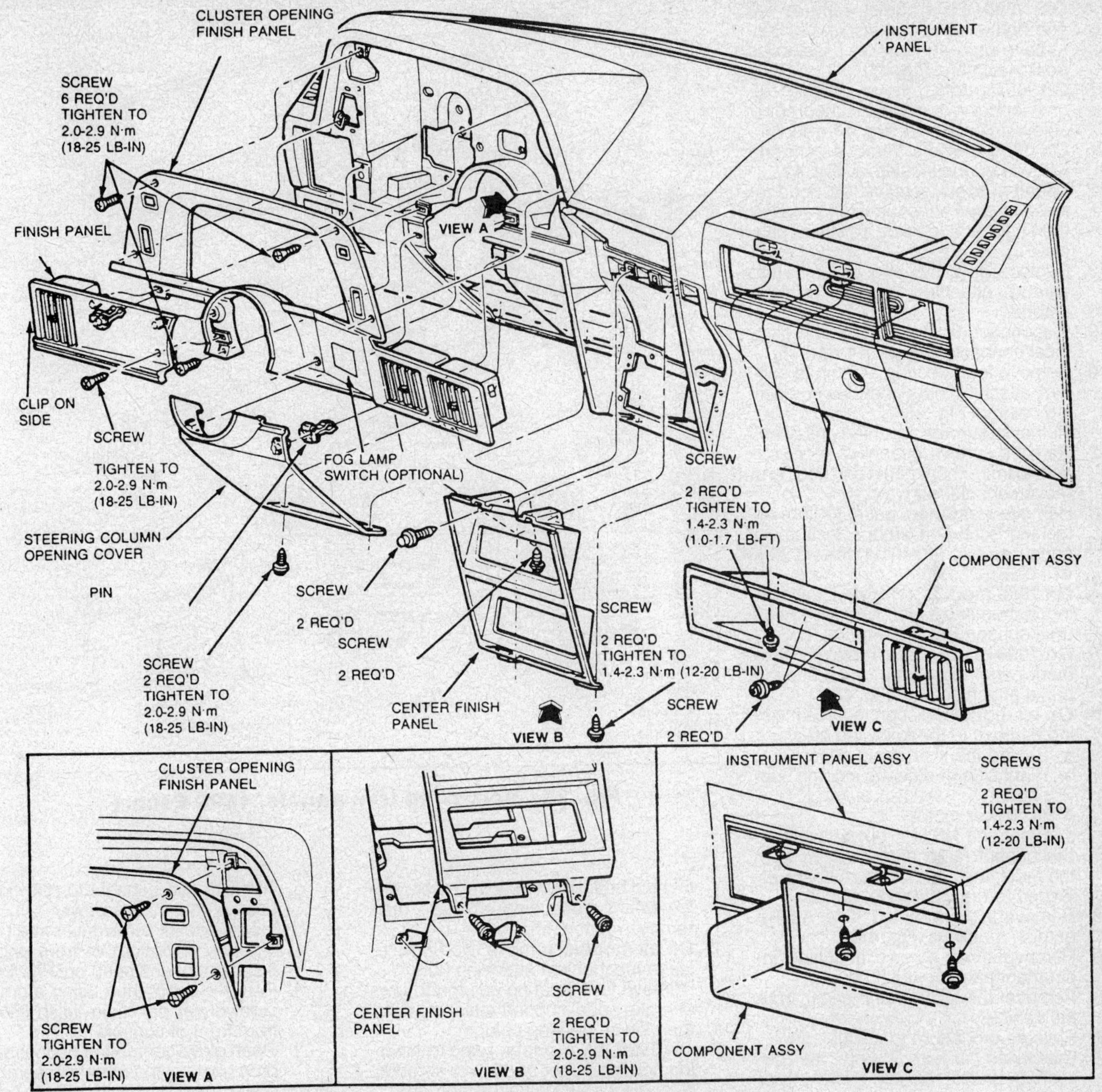


**Fig. 22 Removing trim panels. 1989 Escort**

**screw secures the console stiffener bracket.**

26. Remove the center console.
27. **On 1990-91 models,** remove support bracket attaching bolts and nut below ashtray assembly, then remove bracket.
28. **On all models,** remove radio and heater-A/C control bezel attaching screws.
29. Remove two screws securing radio to instrument panel.
30. Pull radio rearward and disconnect antenna lead and wiring connectors.
31. Remove rubber mounting insulator from the radio ground stud.
32. Remove nut and radio ground wire from ground stud.
33. Remove radio from the vehicle.
34. Remove four heater-A/C control assembly attaching screws.
35. Reaching through the glove box opening, disconnect recirc/fresh air door cable at the door operating lever, **Fig. 34.**
36. Disconnect mode selector cable at function control lever, **Fig. 35.**
37. Disconnect temperature control cable from control lever, **Fig. 36.**
38. Pull control assembly away from instrument panel, then disconnect blower motor, illumination lamp and lighter wiring connectors.
39. Remove snap in trim inserts concealing the instrument panel attaching bolts, **Fig. 37.**
40. Remove seven instrument panel attaching bolts and two attaching nuts, **Fig. 38.**
41. Disconnect any remaining electrical connectors, and remove instrument panel.
42. Reverse procedure to install.

## MARK VII

1. Disarm airbag system as described under "Airbag System Disarming."
2. Disconnect battery ground cable.
3. Disconnect all underhood wiring connectors from main wiring harness, **Figs. 39 and 40.** Remove rubber grommet seal from dash panel and push wiring harness and connectors into passenger compartment.

4. **On 1990-91 models,** remove left and right side sound insulators, then remove bulb and socket assemblies from insulators, **Fig. 41.**
5. **On all models,**remove steering column opening trim cover, then cover steel reinforcement, **Fig. 41 and 42.**
6. **On 1989 models,** remove right and left side sound insulators, **Fig. 42.**
7. **On all models,** remove two hood release to cowl panel attaching screws, then right and left side cowl trim panels, **Fig. 43.**
8. Remove five steering column trim shroud attaching screws, remove shroud.
9. Disconnect all steering column electrical connectors, **Figs. 44 and 45.**
10. Remove four steering column to support attaching nuts, then lower steering column, **Fig. 46.**
11. Remove defroster opening grill panel.
12. Remove screws attaching floor console to instrument panel and floor, and move console rearward.
13. Remove instrument panel to floor attaching screws. Remove instrument panel to cowl attaching screws, **Fig. 47.**
14. **On 1989 models,** remove nut attaching instrument panel to steering column support bracket, **Fig. 47.**
15. **On 1990-91 models,** remove instrument panel to parking brake support brake attaching bolt, **Fig. 48.**
16. **On all models,** disconnect main wiring harness in the following areas:
    a. Behind the instrument panel.
    b. Right side of steering column support.
    c. At blower motor.
    d. Right and left side cowl panels.
17. Disconnect radio antenna lead from the radio, then any vacuum hoses attached to the instrument panel.
18. Remove right and left side A-pillar garnish moldings, **Fig. 49.**
19. Remove three screws attaching instrument panel to dash panel.
20. Remove the instrument panel from the vehicle.
21. Reverse procedure to install.
22. Reactivate airbag system as described under "Airbag System Disarming."

## MUSTANG

1. Disarm airbag system as described under "Airbag System Disarming."
2. Disconnect battery ground cable.
3. Disconnect all underhood wiring connectors from main wiring harness. Remove rubber grommet seal from dash panel and push wiring harness and connectors into passenger compartment.
4. **On 1989 models,** remove two extension steering column shroud to dash attaching screws,then remove shroud, **Figs. 50 and 51.**
5. **On all models,** remove three steering column cover attaching screws.
6. **On 1990-91 models,** remove steering column opening reinforcement attaching bolts, then remove lower reinforcement attaching bolts, then remove reinforcement.

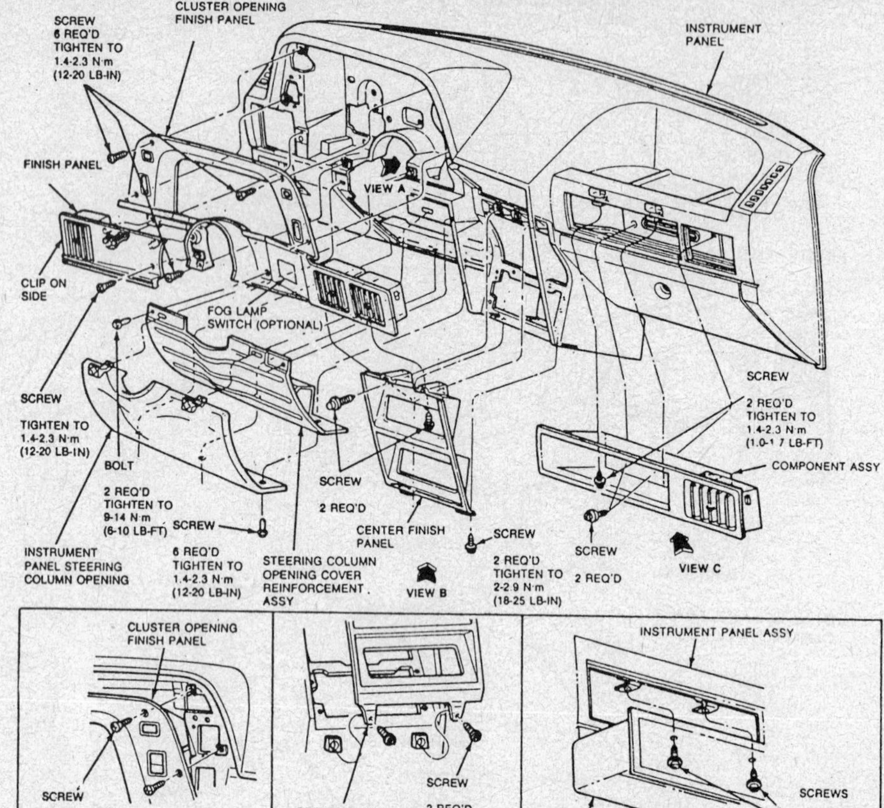


**Fig. 23 Removing trim panels. 1990 Escort**

7. **On all models,** remove two hood release mechanism attaching nuts.
8. Remove four steering column to lower brake pedal support attaching nuts, then lower steering column.
9. **On 1990-91 models,** remove steering column upper and lower shrouds, then disconnect multifunction switch electrical connectors.
10. **On all models,** remove console assembly as follows:
    a. Remove two access covers at rear of console to gain access to armrest retaining bolts.
    b. Remove four armrest to floor bracket retaining bolts and remove armrest assembly, **Fig. 52.**
    c. **On models with automatic transmission,** remove shift lever opening finish panel.
    d. **On models with manual transmission,** remove shift knob and slide boot and finish panel up shift lever to remove.
    e. **On all models,** position emergency brake lever in the up position.
    f. Remove four top finish panel retaining screws, then disconnect necessary electrical connectors and remove panel, **Fig. 53.**
    g. Remove two console to rear floor bracket attaching screws.
    h. Insert a small screwdriver into two notches at bottom of front upper finish panel and snap out,**Fig. 54.**
    i. Remove radio, then using a small screwdriver pry radio finish cover from front of console.
    j. Open glove compartment door and drop glove compartment assembly down. If equipped with remote control fuel filler door, switch must be removed. Remove two instrument panel to console retaining screws.
    k. Remove four console to bracket retaining screws.
    l. Remove console from the vehicle.
11. **On 1990-91 models,** remove brake pedal support attaching nut.
12. **On all models,** snap out defroster grille, then remove screws from speaker covers and snap out.
13. **On 1989 models,** remove four steering column brace to cowl side retaining screws.
14. **On 1990-91 models,** remove front screws attaching right and left scuff plates at cowl trim panel.
15. **On all models,** remove right and left side cowl panels.
16. Disconnect right and left side cowl panel electrical connectors, then remove cowl side retaining bolts from

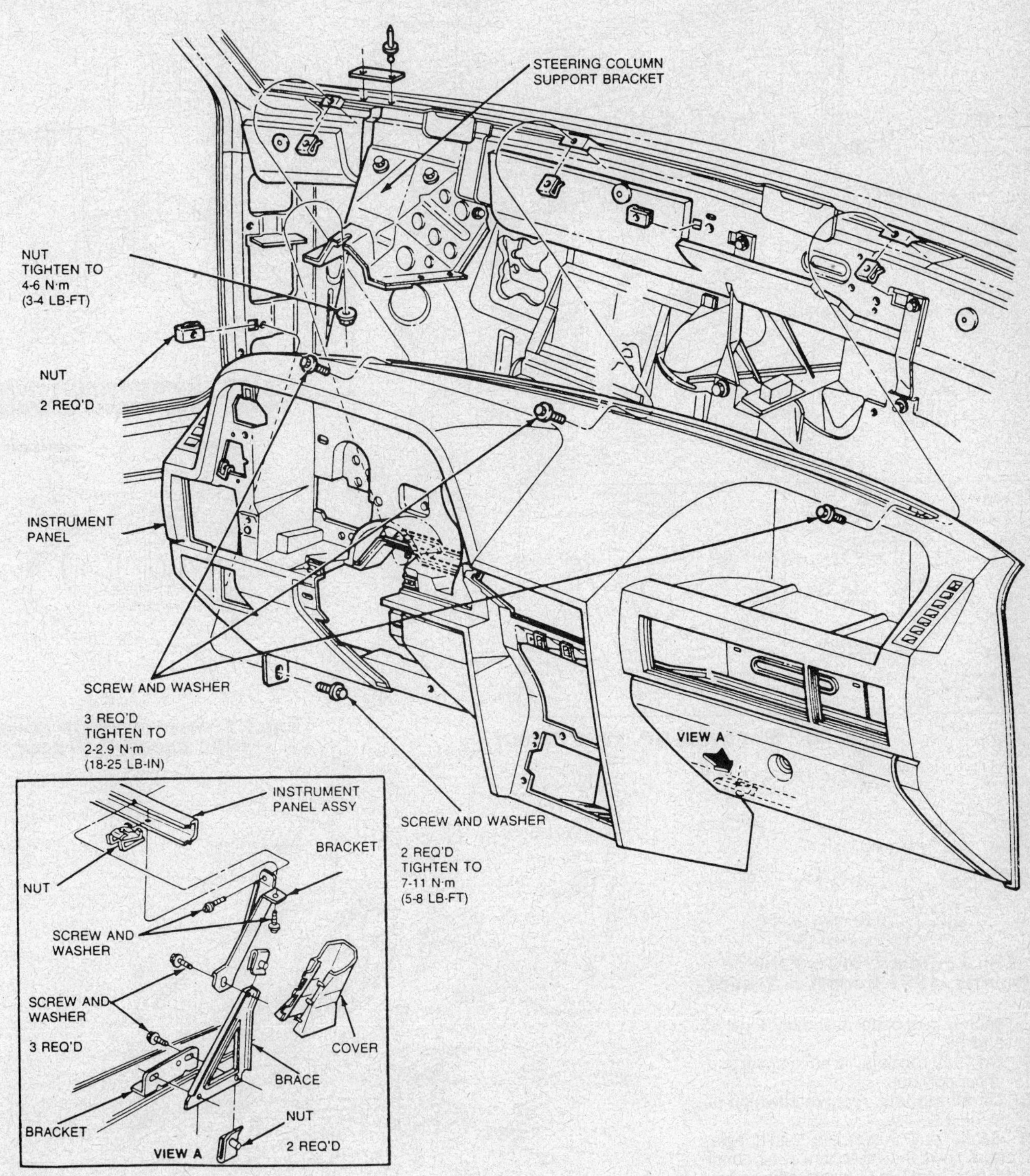


**Fig. 24 Removing I/P. 1989 Escort**

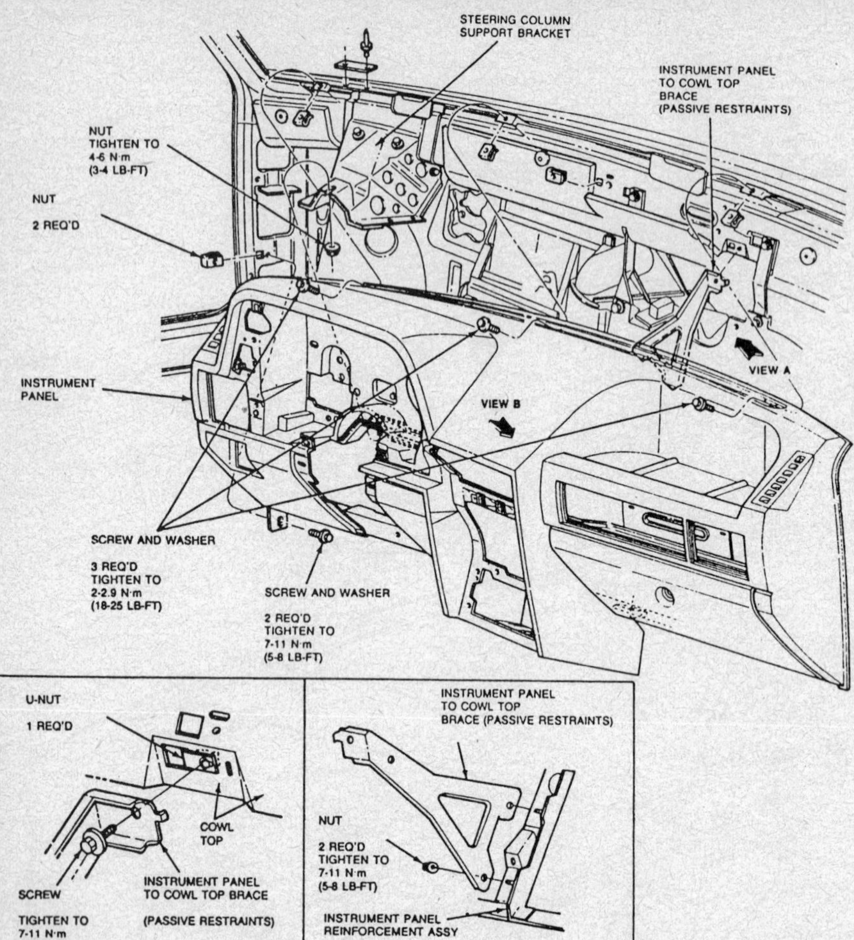

**Fig. 25 Removing I/P. 1990 Escort**

**Fig. 26 Removing I/P cluster bezel. 1991 Escort & Tracer**

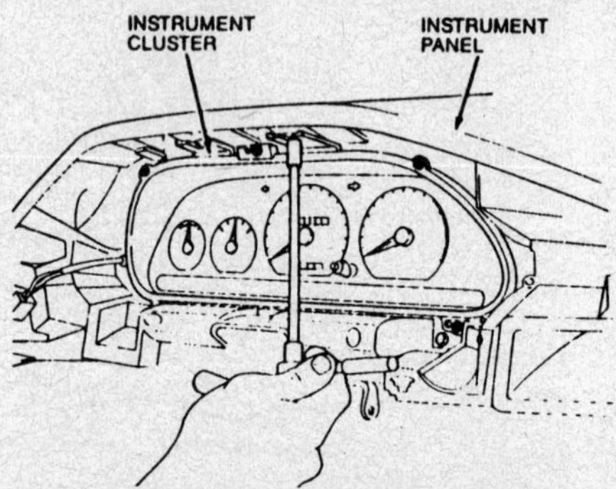


**Fig. 27 Removing I/P cluster. 1991 Escort & Tracer**

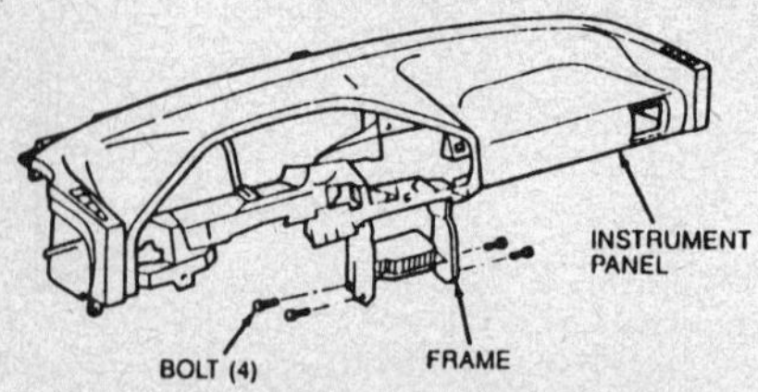


**Fig. 28 Removing I/P lower mounts. 1991 Escort & Tracer**

each side of panel assembly, **Figs. 55 and 56.**

17. **On 1989 models,** remove brake pedal support nut.
18. **On all models,** remove cowl top attaching screws.
19. Gently pull instrument panel away from cowl, then disconnect air conditioning controls and wire connectors.
20. Remove instrument panel form vehicle.
21. Reverse procedure to install.
22. Reactivate airbag system as described under "Airbag System Disarming."

## PROBE

Refer to **Fig. 57**, when performing this procedure.

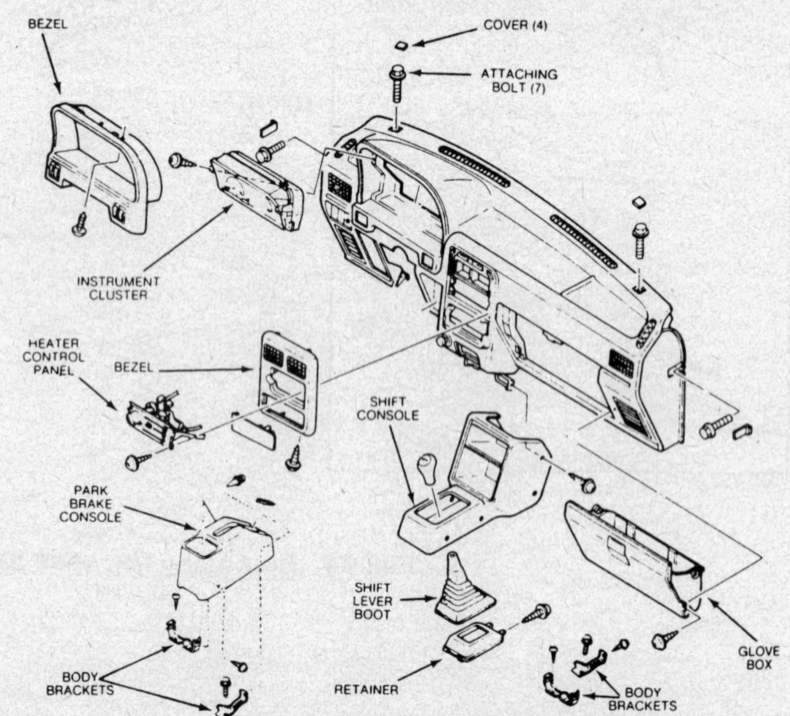


**Fig. 29 Exploded view of I/P. Festiva**

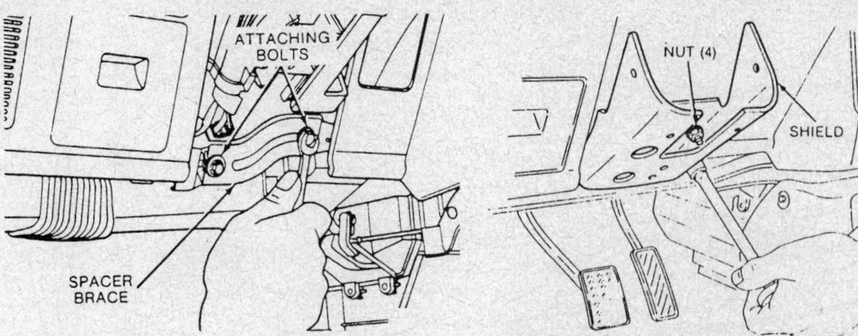


**Fig. 30 Removing steering column spacer brace. 1989 Festiva**

**Fig. 31 Removing steering column lower shield. 1990–91 Festiva**

**Fig. 32 Removing heater ducts. Festiva**

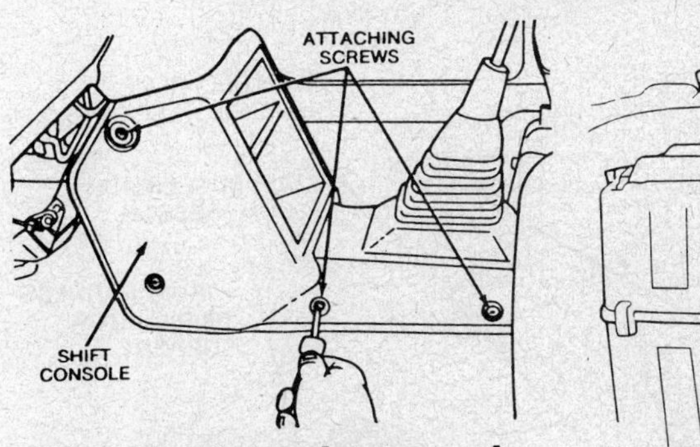


**Fig. 33 Removing console housing. Festiva**

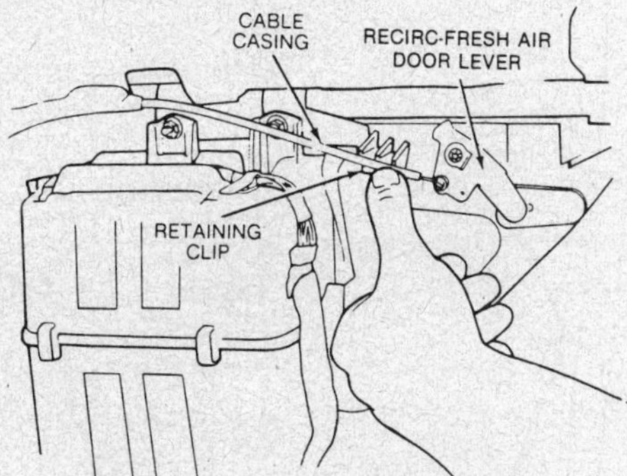


**Fig. 34 Disconnecting recirc/fresh air door cable. Festiva**

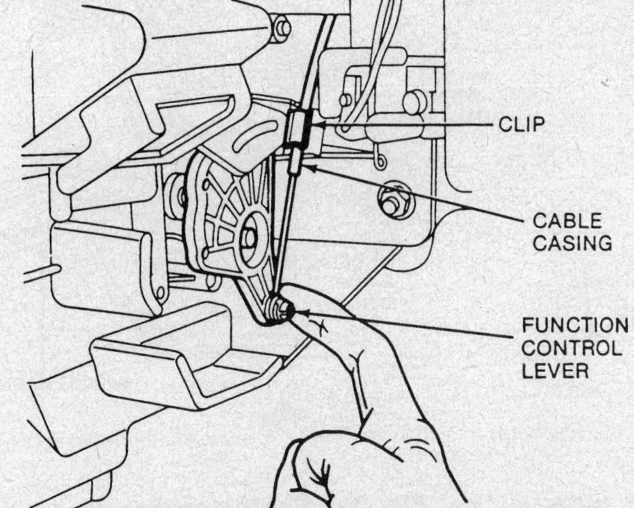


**Fig. 35 Disconnecting mode selector cable. Festiva**

1. Disconnect battery ground cable.
2. Remove steering wheel insert, then remove steering wheel attaching nut.
3. Mark steering wheel and steering column shaft for assembly reference and remove wheel with steering wheel puller tool No. T67L-3600-A or equivalent.
4. Remove two screws securing column cover, then remove cover.
5. Remove nine attaching screws from the cluster module, **Fig. 58.**
6. Carefully pull cluster module outward to gain access to the electrical connectors.
7. Disconnect seven electrical connectors and remove ignition illumination bulb.
8. Remove cluster module, then loosen two cover hinge screws, **Fig. 59.**
9. Remove six screws from the instrument cluster cover, then remove the cover.
10. Remove lower cluster cover panel, then the four attaching screws from the cluster.
11. Disconnect electrical connectors from the back of the cluster, and remove cluster.
12. **On models with automatic transmission,** remove floor console as follows:
    a. Remove two screws securing selector knob to selector lever.
    b. Remove selector trim piece.
    c. Remove four screws securing selector bezel, then lift bezel to gain access to the selector illumination bulb and the shift control switch.
    d. Disconnect illumination bulb and shift control switch electrical harness, then remove bezel.
    e. Remove front ash receptacle and cigar lighter.
    f. Remove four front mounting screws, then position front seat to gain access to the console rear access hole covers.
    g. Remove access hole covers from each side of the console, **Fig. 60 and 61.**
    h. Remove rear retaining bolts, then position front seats all the way to the rear.
    i. Lift console from the rear and disconnect electrical connectors for the mirror and ride control switches.
    j. Apply parking brake and remove console.
13. **On models with manual transmission,** remove floor console as follows:
    a. Slide shifter boot down and remove shift knob.
    b. Remove trim panel and boot.
    c. Remove front ash receptacle and cigar lighter.
    d. Remove four front console mounting screws, then position front seats to gain access to console rear access hole covers.
    e. Remove four rear retaining bolts, then position front seats all the way to the rear.
    f. Lift console from the rear and disconnect electrical connectors for

the mirror and ride control switches.
g. Apply parking brake and remove console.
14. Remove hood release handle from cable.
15. Remove right and left side console kick panels.
16. Remove left and right instrument panel dash side covers.
17. Remove bezel cover from heater-A/C control assembly face.
18. Remove four attaching screws from control assembly housing.
19. Remove left and right sound deadening panels from instrument panel.
20. Remove REC/FRESH control cable from REC/FRESH selector door assembly.
21. **On 1990-91 models,** disconnect blower switch and control assembly illumination electrical connectors.
22. **On all models,** remove temperature control cable from the temperature blend door assembly at the right side of heater case.
23. Remove function selector cable from function control doors assembly at the let side of heater case.

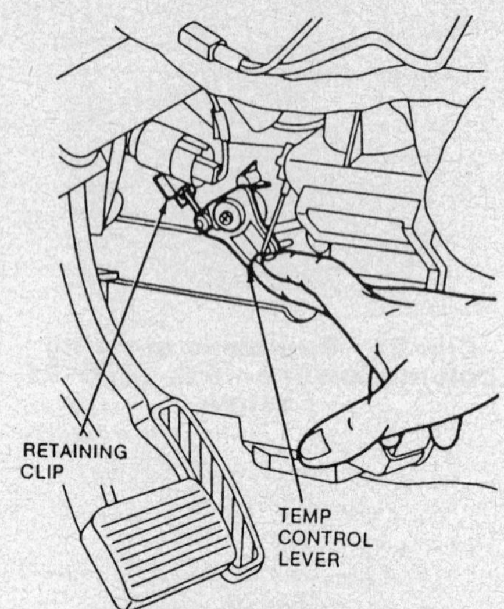


**Fig. 36 Disconnecting temperature control cable. Festiva**

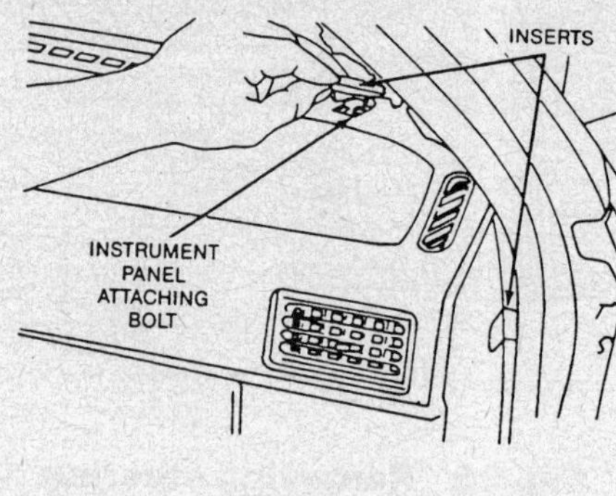


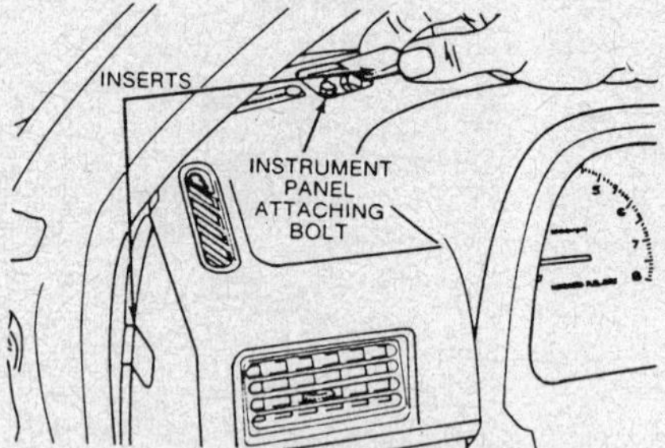


**Fig. 37 Removing trim inserts. Festiva**

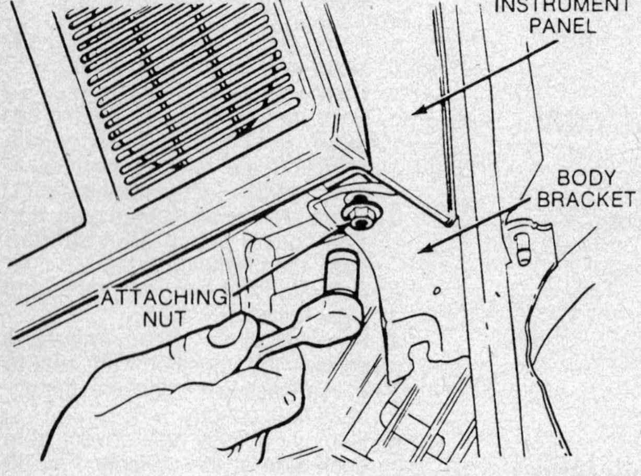


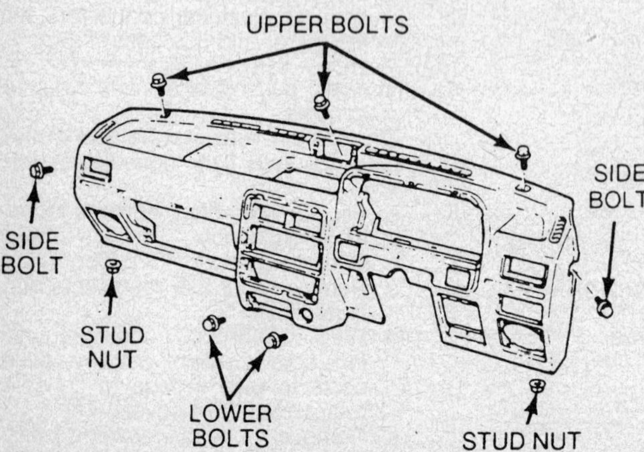


**Fig. 38 Removing I/P attaching bolts & nuts. Festiva**

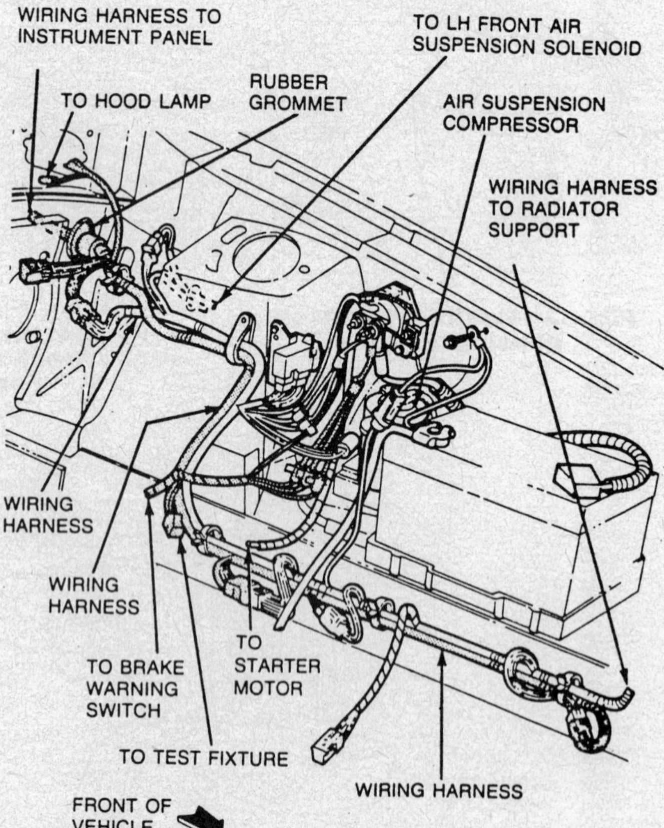


**Fig. 39 Engine compartment electrical connectors. 1989 Mark VII**

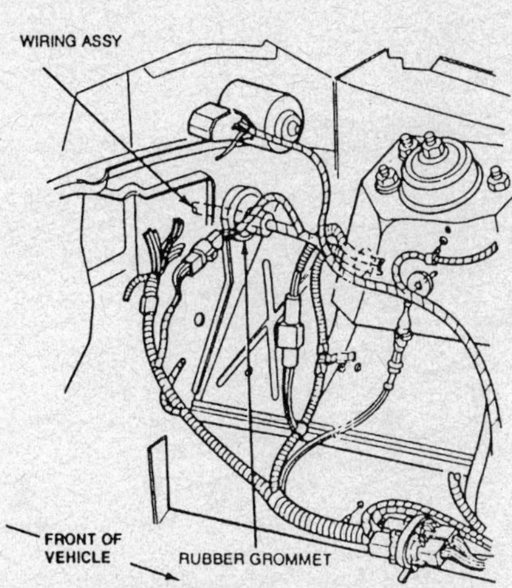


**Fig. 40 Engine compartment electrical connectors. 1990–91 Mark VII**

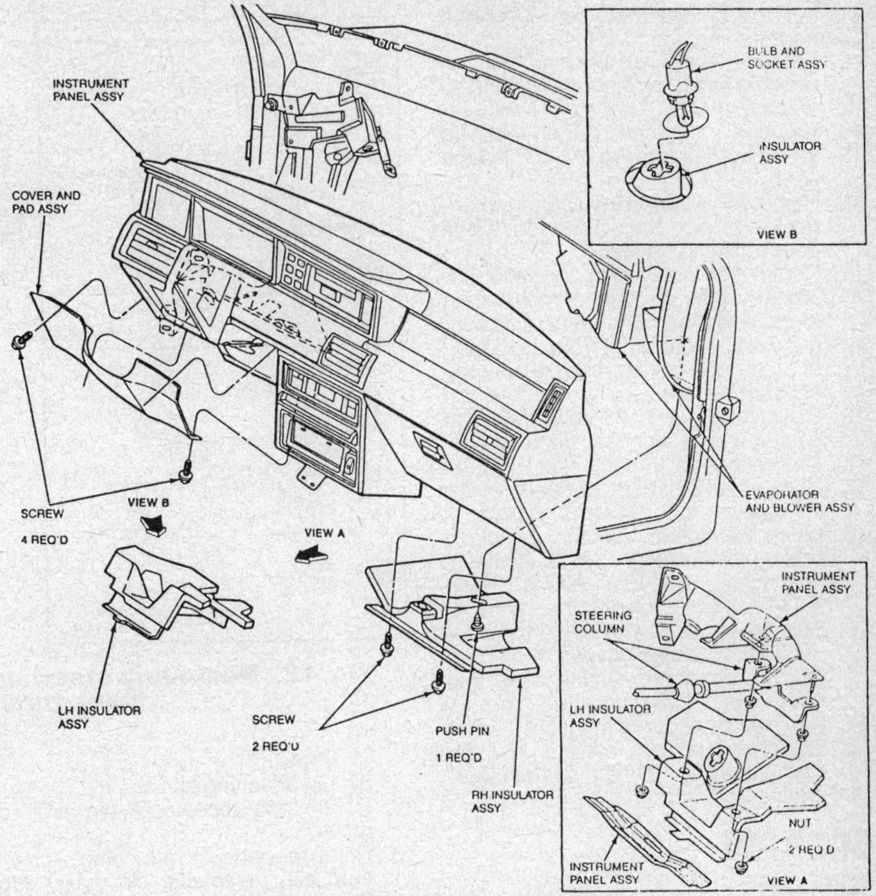


**Fig. 41 Insulator panel removal. 1990–91 Mark VII**

24. Noting position of cables for assembly reference, remove control assembly and cables as an assembly.
25. Remove two radio retaining screws, disconnect antenna and electrical connectors.
26. Remove radio and/or tape player from the vehicle.
27. Remove trip computer display cover bezel from the instrument panel, if equipped.
28. Remove two attaching screws from trip computer display housing and pull housing straight out of the dash.
29. Disconnect electrical connector from rear of trip computer display.
30. Remove dash panel access cover to gain access to center instrument panel mounting nut, then remove nut, **Fig. 62.**
31. Remove remaining instrument panel mounting bolts, then lift instrument panel toward rear of vehicle, then disconnect remaining electrical connectors.
32. Remove instrument panel from vehicle.
33. Reverse procedure to install.

# SABLE

## 1989

1. Disarm airbag system as described under "Airbag System Disarming."
2. Disconnect battery ground cable.
3. Remove four screws retaining steering column opening cover and remove cover, **Fig. 63.**
4. Remove sound insulator located under glove compartment by removing two pushnuts securing insulator to studs on climate control case.
5. Remove steering column trim shrouds, then disconnect all electrical connections from steering column switches.
6. Remove one bolt and nut at lock collar U-joint and four screws at steering column bracket to remove steering column.
7. Remove lower left side and radio finish panels by snapping out, **Fig. 64.**
8. Remove five cluster opening finish panel retaining screws, **Fig. 65.** Remove finish panel by disengaging five snap fasteners located along upper edge, and rocking upper edge outward.
9. Disconnect speedometer cable by reaching up under instrument panel and pressing on flat surface of plastic connector.
10. Release glove compartment assembly by depressing side of glove compartment bin and swinging door/bin down.
11. Using steering column, cluster and glove compartment openings, and by reaching under instrument panel, disconnect all electrical connections, vacuum hoses, heater-A/C control cables and radio antenna.
12. Disconnect all underhood electrical connectors of main wire loom. Disengage rubber grommet from dash panel and feed wire and connectors into instrument panel area.
13. Remove one instrument panel brace retaining screw located under radio.
14. Remove two lower instrument panel to cowl retaining screws, **Fig. 66.**
15. Remove right and left side speaker covers, then defroster grille, **Fig. 67.**
16. Remove three upper instrument panel retaining screws.
17. Remove instrument panel from vehicle.
18. Reverse procedure to install.
19. Reactivate airbag system as described under "Airbag System Disarming."

## 1990–91

1. Disarm airbag system as described under "Airbag System Disarming."
2. Position front wheels straight ahead.
3. Disconnect battery ground cable, then back-up power supply, **Fig. 68,** behind glove compartment. Open glove box, past its stops.
4. Remove four finish panel retaining screws on cluster, **Fig. 69,** then the instrument cluster.
5. Remove tilt lever, if equipped, **Fig. 70,** then two bolts and reinforcement from under steering column.
6. Remove four nuts and cover plate from under steering column. Do not rotate steering column shaft, **Fig. 71.**
7. Disconnect parking brake release cable and wiring connector.
8. Remove four steering column retaining nuts to instrument panel, then lower column to the seat. Install lock cyl-

inder to ensure the steering column from turning.

9. Remove screw at steering column opening attaching instrument panel to brace, **Fig. 71.**
10. Remove instrument panel retaining screw from brace, **Fig. 72,** behind the radio.
11. Remove RH sound insulator from under glove box, then three glove box door retaining screws.
12. Remove air cleaner, battery and battery tray, then disconnect main wiring loom in engine compartment. Disengage rubber grommet from dash panel and feed wiring into passenger compartment.
13. Remove LH and RH cowl side trim panels, then disconnect wires from instrument panel at each side.
14. Remove one instrument panel retaining screw from both sides of panel.
15. Using the steering column and glove box opening, disconnect all electrical connectors, vacuum hoses, heater/AC control cables and antenna.
16. Support panel, then remove three instrument retaining screws from cowl top. Disconnect remaining wires and remove panel from vehicle.
17. Reverse procedures to install.
18. Reactivate airbag system as described under "Airbag System Disarming."

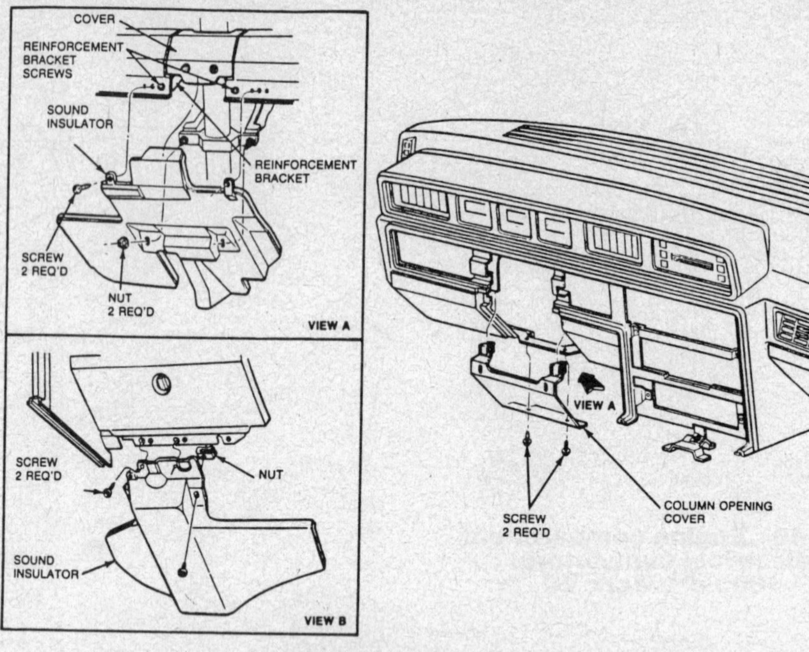


**Fig. 42 Removing steering column cover & I/P trim sound insulators. 1989 Mark VII**

## SCORPIO

1. Disconnect battery ground cable.
2. Ensure steering wheel is in straight ahead position.
3. Remove clamp bolt securing upper universal joint to steering column shaft. The clamp is located above the universal joint nearest the dash panel. Swing the clamp plate to one side and allow to hang free.
4. Remove screws retaining upper and lower steering column shrouds, **Fig. 73.**
5. To remove upper shroud, lower steering column height adjuster.
6. Remove lower shroud, then hood release lever from column tube housing, **Fig. 74.**
7. Lower steering column.
8. Remove heater louver panels by carefully prying from each side of lower instrument panel pad.
9. Remove four instrument cluster trim panel retaining screws, then the panel, **Fig. 75.**
10. Remove eight screws securing front and side surfaces of instrument panel pad.
11. Remove four clips securing instrument panel pad to frame.
12. Remove left side footwell lamp, and disconnect electrical connector.
13. Remove two left side trim panel outboard attaching screws.
14. Remove inboard attaching screws, then left side trim panel.
15. Remove six attaching screws at top and side of right side lower trim panel, **Fig. 76.**
16. Remove ash receptacle, and receptacle bin attaching screws.
17. Rotate ash receptacle bin and remove.
18. Remove console attaching screws from ash receptacle bin cavity, **Fig. 77.**
19. Pull center finish trim from edge of radio, amplifier and ash receptacle.
20. Remove lamp and cigar lighter electrical connectors from back of center finish trim.
21. Remove fuse holders from auxiliary fuse panel door, mounted inside glove compartment cavity, **Fig. 78.**
22. Remove two screws securing glove compartment switch assembly. Disconnect electrical connector from switch.
23. Remove right side footwell lamp and disconnect electrical connectors.
24. Remove two attaching nuts from glove compartment cavity.
25. Remove vent control knob from rear console panel, **Fig. 79.**
26. Remove two screws retaining rear control panel to console.
27. Remove rear control panel from console, disconnect cigar lighter and lamp connectors.
28. Remove two heater control attaching screws, then heater control.
29. Open armrest door to gain and remove two switch panel retaining screws.
30. Remove rear power window switches from floor console to center panel.
31. Remove rear power cutoff switch from floor console center panel.
32. Remove fuel filler door switch from switch console.
33. Remove floor console center panel by lifting rear edge and moving center panel backward to disengage from console, **Fig. 80.**
34. Remove floor console center panel (with parking brake boot) from parking brake.
35. Remove ash receptacle, then two front console attaching screws.
36. Lift carpet at each side of console to expose attaching screws, then remove screws.
37. Remove two attaching screws inside cassette storage bin.
38. Remove gear selector knob, then the console.
39. Remove gear selector lamp from selector lever guide bracket.
40. Remove four gear selector attaching bolts, then raise gear selector and remove shift rod retaining clip, **Fig. 81.**
41. Remove shift mechanism and control linkage.
42. Remove clip at edge of lower trim panel near steering column.
43. Pull trim panel forward and lift to release.
44. Reverse procedure to install.

## TAURUS

### 1989

1. Disarm airbag system as described under "Airbag System Disarming."
2. Disconnect battery ground cable.
3. Remove four screws retaining steering column opening cover and remove cover, **Fig. 82.**
4. Remove sound insulator located under glove compartment by removing two pushnuts securing insulator to studs on climate control case.
5. Remove steering column trim shrouds, then disconnect all electrical connections from steering column switches.
6. Remove four screws at steering col-

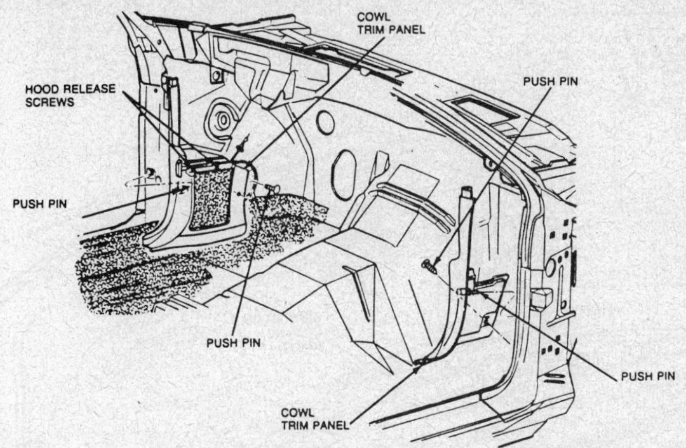


**Fig. 43 Removing hood release cable. Mark VII**

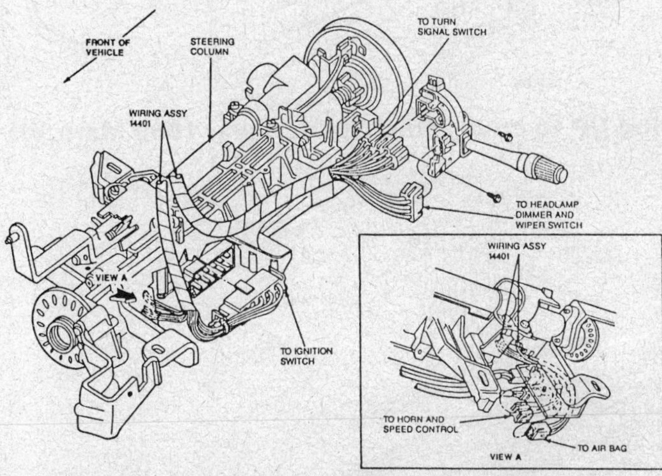


**Fig. 45 Steering column electrical connectors. 1990–91 Mark VII**

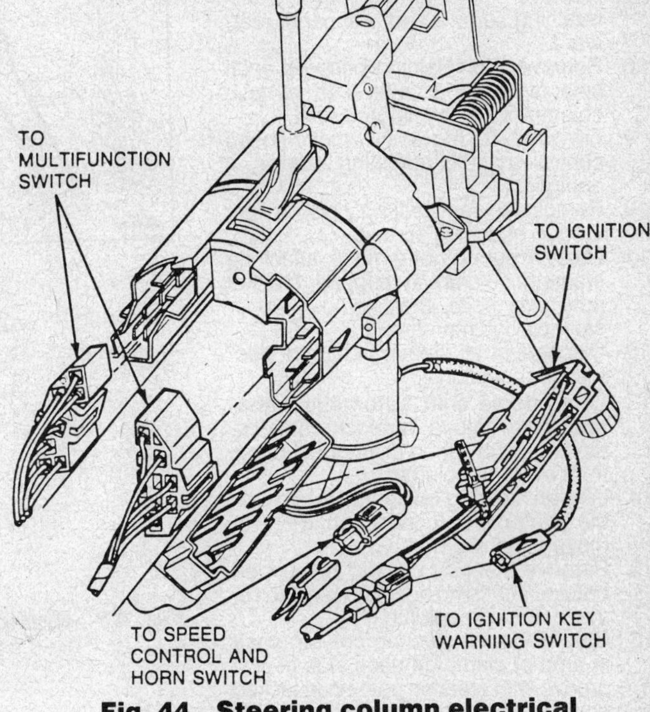


**Fig. 44 Steering column electrical connectors. 1989 Mark VII**

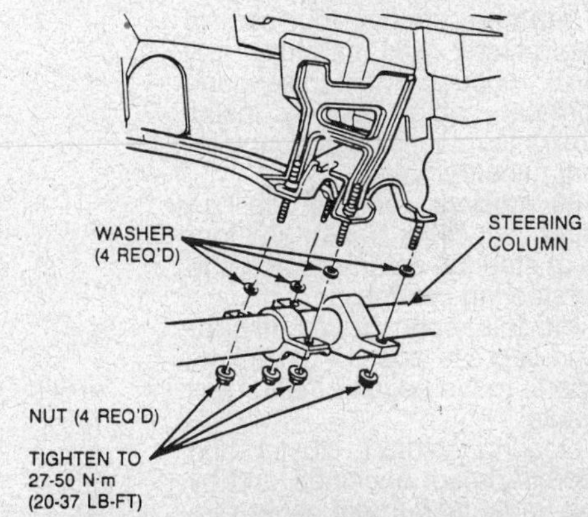


**Fig. 46 Removing steering column support. Mark VII**

umn bracket to remove steering column.

7. Remove screws retaining lower left side and radio finish panels, **Fig. 83.** Remove panels by snapping out.
8. Remove seven cluster opening finish panel retaining screws, **Fig. 84.**
9. Remove one jam nut behind headlamp switch, and one screw behind clock.
10. Remove finish panel by rocking upper edge toward driver.
11. Disconnect speedometer cable by reaching up under instrument panel and pressing on flat surface of plastic connector.
12. Release glove compartment assembly by depressing side of glove compartment bin and swinging door/bin down.
13. Using steering column, cluster and glove compartment openings, and by reaching under instrument panel, disconnect all electrical connections, vacuum hoses, heater-A/C control cables and radio antenna.
14. Remove right and left speaker opening covers, **Fig. 85.**
15. Remove two lower instrument panel to cowl retaining screws, **Fig. 66.**
16. Remove one instrument panel brace retaining screw located under radio.
17. Remove three upper instrument panel retaining screws.
18. Remove instrument panel from vehicle.
19. Reverse procedure to install.
20. Reactivate airbag system as described under "Airbag System Disarming."

## 1990–91

Refer to "1990-91 Sable" for dash panel replacement procedure.

## TEMPO & TOPAZ

**On models with airbags, whenever the steering column is being separated from the I/P, the steering column must be locked to prevent the column from rotating. Turn ignition switch to lock position and rotate steering wheel about 16° counterclockwise until locked into position. This will prevent any damage to the airbag clockspring.**

1. Disarm airbag system as described under "Airbag System Disarming."
2. Disconnect battery ground cable.
3. Disconnect speedometer cable at transaxle.
4. Remove two retaining screws at bottom of steering column opening and snap column cover out, **Fig. 86.**
5. **On 1989 models,** remove steering column trim shrouds, then disconnect all electrical connections from steering column switches.
6. **On all models,** remove snap-in lower cluster finish panels to expose two

screws and two bolts.
7. Remove cluster opening finish panel retaining screws and pull panel rearward.
8. Remove two retaining bolts on each side of steering column to remove column opening reinforcement.
9. **On 1990-91 models,** remove speed control module attaching screws, if equipped.
10. Remove lower steering column trim shroud attaching screws.
11. Loosen, but do not remove, attaching steering column to support bracket nuts and bolts, then remove upper steering column shroud.
12. Disconnect all steering column electrical connections.
13. **On console shift automatic transmission,** remove interlock cable attaching screw, then disconnect cable from steering column.
14. Loosen steering column to intermediate shaft clamp connection, then remove attaching bolt.
15. Remove steering column to support bracket attaching nuts and bolts to remove steering column.
16. Carefully open steering column shaft in area of clamp on each side of bolt groove with steering column in locked position. **Do not use excessive force, damage may result.**
17. Inspect two steering column bracket clips, if bent or distorted, replace.
18. **On all models,** remove four screws retaining cluster and carefully pull rearward enough to disengage speedometer cable. Loosely install two screws to retain cluster during instrument panel removal.
19. **On 1989 models,** remove one bolt and nut at lock collar U-joint and four screws at steering column bracket to remove steering column.
20. **On all models,** open glove compartment and depress sides of bin, allowing stops to move beyond instrument panel walls.
21. Using steering column, cluster and glove compartment openings, and by reaching under instrument panel, disconnect all electrical connections, vacuum hoses, heater-A/C control cables and radio antenna.
22. Disconnect all underhood electrical connectors of main wire loom. Disengage rubber grommet from dash panel and feed wire and connectors into instrument panel area.
23. Remove one instrument panel to steering column support bracket retaining nut, accessible through steering column opening.
24. Remove two lower instrument panel to cowl side retaining screws, **Fig. 87.**
25. Remove two instrument panel vertical brace retaining screws.
26. Remove four instrument panel cowl top retaining screws.
27. Remove instrument panel from the vehicle.
28. Reverse procedure to install.
29. Reactivate airbag system as described under "Airbag System Disarming."

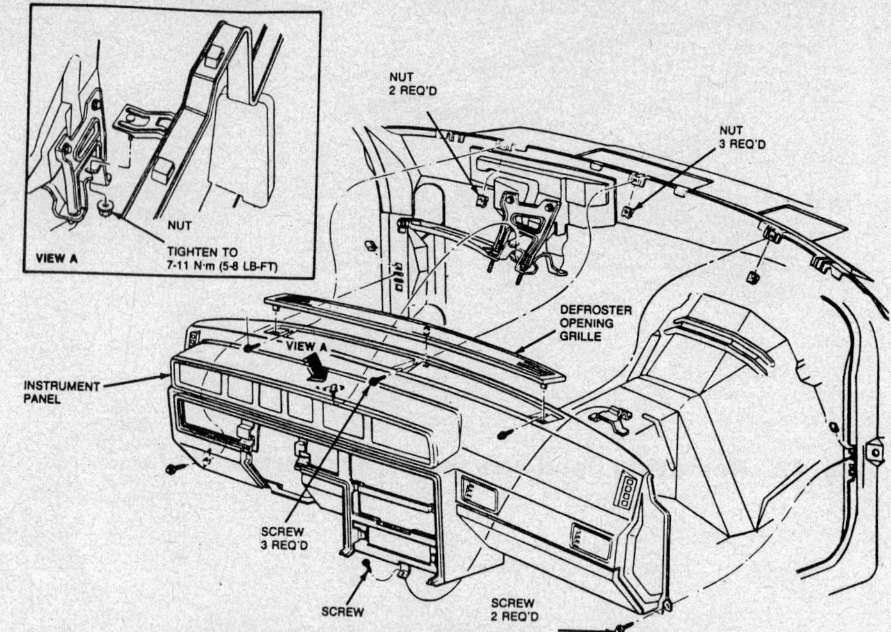


**Fig. 47 Removing I/P to cowl attaching screws. 1989 Mark VII**

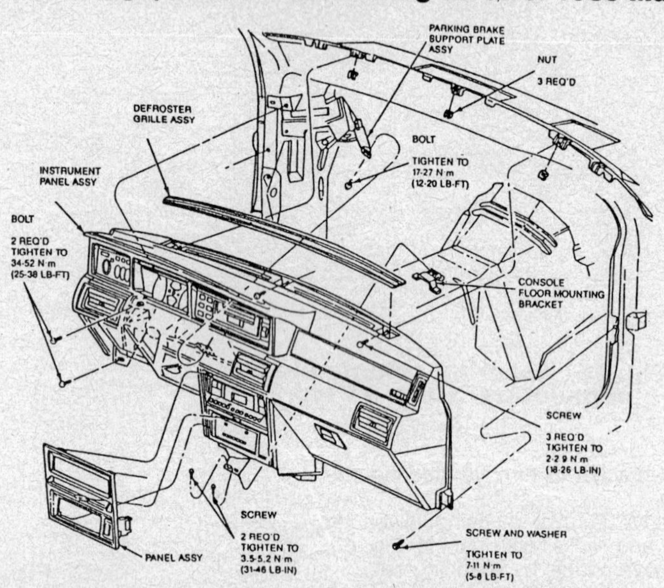


**Fig. 48 Removing I/P to cowl attaching screws. 1990–91 Mark VII**

## TRACER

## 1989

1. Disconnect battery ground cable.
2. Remove left and right side sound deadening panels, **Fig. 88.**
3. Remove two screws attaching lap duct register panel and remove panel.
4. Remove heater control cable ends at three air control doors, located at blower case and at either side of heater case.
5. Reach behind instrument cluster, depress lock tab and pull speedometer cable out from instrument cluster.
6. Reach behind instrument cluster and disconnect three electrical connectors by pushing the lock tab and pulling connector from instrument cluster.

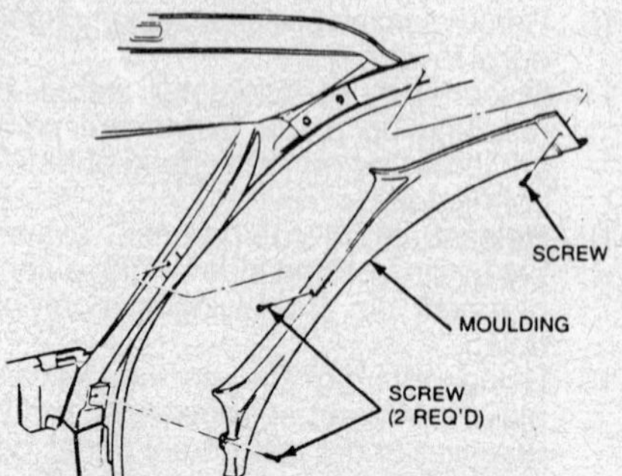


**Fig. 49 Removing A-pillar molding. Mark VII**

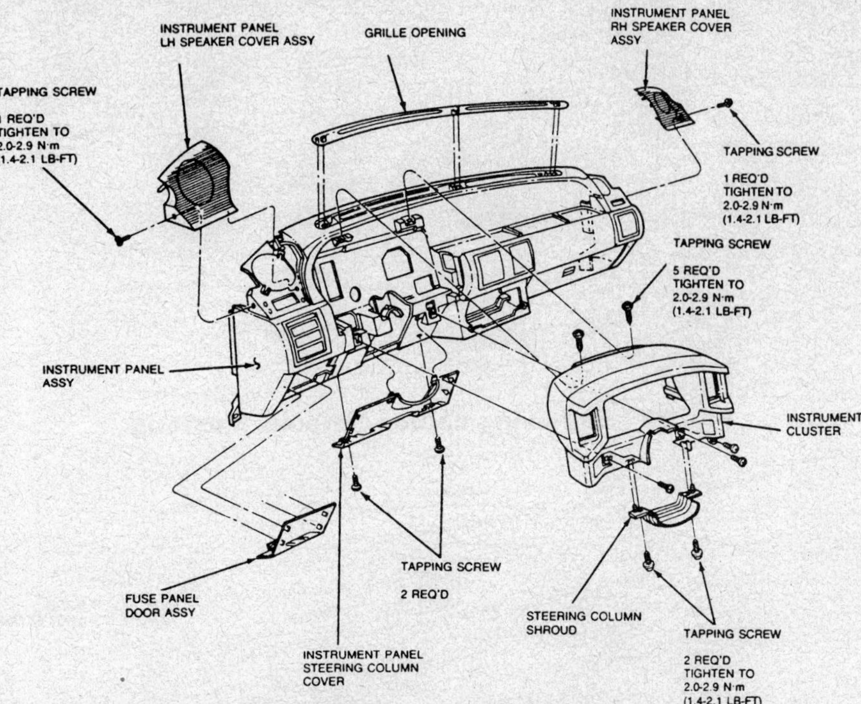


**Fig. 50 Exploded view of I/P. 1989 Mustang**

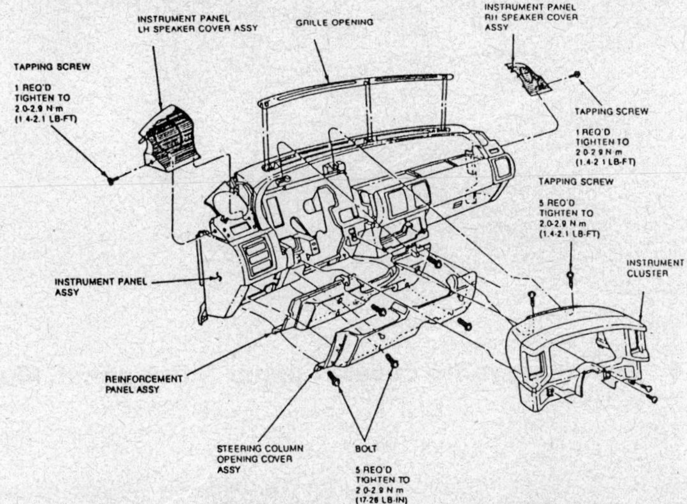


**Fig. 51 Exploded view of I/P. 1990–91 Mustang**

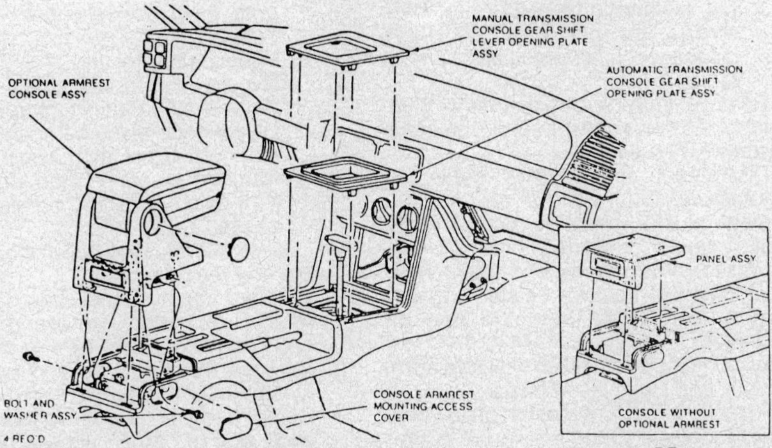


**Fig. 52 Removing console trim plates & armrest. Mustang**

7. Remove three screws attaching brace below lap duct, **Fig. 89.**
8. Remove lap duct and left side demister tube.
9. Remove five screws attaching steering column lower cover and remove cover, **Fig. 90.**
10. Remove four steering column mount bolts and lower steering column.
11. Remove two screws attaching glove box and remove glove box.
12. Loosen nut securing hood release cable to instrument panel and move to one side.
13. Slide front seats all the way forward, then remove two screws securing rear of rear console.
14. Slide front seats all the way rearward, then remove two screws securing rear console to front console.
15. Remove shifter knob, then four screws securing front console to mounting bracket.
16. Remove console sidewalls, front console and shifter boot.
17. Remove five instrument panel mounting bolt covers, **Fig. 91.**
18. Remove nine instrument panel mounting bolts and two mounting nuts.
19. Lift up on instrument panel and pull out slightly.
20. Disconnect blower motor electrical connector and radio antenna at back of radio.
21. Disconnect three instrument panel harness connectors at lower left corner of instrument panel.
22. Remove instrument panel assembly.
23. Reverse procedure to install.

## 1991

Refer to "1991 Escort" for instrument panel service procedures.

## XR4Ti

1. Disconnect battery ground cable.
2. Remove cowl side trim panel attaching screws, **Fig. 92.**
3. Pull cowl side trim panel away from the body, disconnect courtesy light wires and remove the panel.
4. Remove upper and lower steering column shrouds.
5. Remove five screws and detach left side lower instrument panel pad, **Fig. 93.**
6. Disconnect speaker wires and remove left side lower instrument panel.
7. Remove three screws retaining front section of floor console to console base.
8. Disconnect power window switch and remove front section. It may be necessary to pinch console at the "arrows" indicated in **Fig. 94,** to dislodge internal tangs.
9. Remove five screws retaining storage compartment to console base, then disconnect cigarette lighter wires and remove storage compartment, **Fig. 95.**
10. Pull off combination fan/air conditioning rotary switch and bezel, **Fig. 96.**

11. Remove eight screws retaining lower right side instrument panel.
12. Disconnect speaker wires and glove box lamp, ashtray lamp, blower switch harness connector, cigarette lighter and radio connections. Remove lower right side instrument panel.
13. Remove instrument panel illumination control and intermittent wiper control rheostats.
14. Remove four instrument cluster bezel retaining screws and remove bezel.
15. Remove four screws retaining instrument cluster and pull cluster towards steering wheel.
16. Disconnect speedometer cable, harness connector, and turbo boost gauge vacuum line from rear of cluster assembly and remove cluster.
17. Remove message center fascia and its retaining screw.
18. Remove screw from graphic display module retainer, then remove retainer and pull to remove graphic display module.
19. Using a thin bladed screwdriver, pry out graphic display module electrical connector, then disconnect from module.
20. Remove three heater control retaining screws.
21. Disconnect auxiliary warning harness connector from instrument panel.
22. Remove fog lamp, and heated rear window switches by prying out from the bottom rear wiper/washer of the switch with a flat bladed screwdriver and disconnecting the harness connectors.
23. Remove five upper instrument panel retaining screws, **Fig. 97.**
24. Disconnect all heater-A/C vent hoses and remove upper instrument panel.
25. Reverse procedure to install.

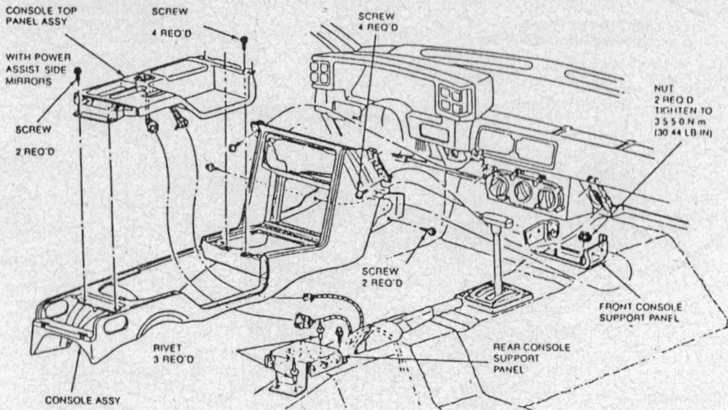


**Fig. 53 Removing center console. Mustang**

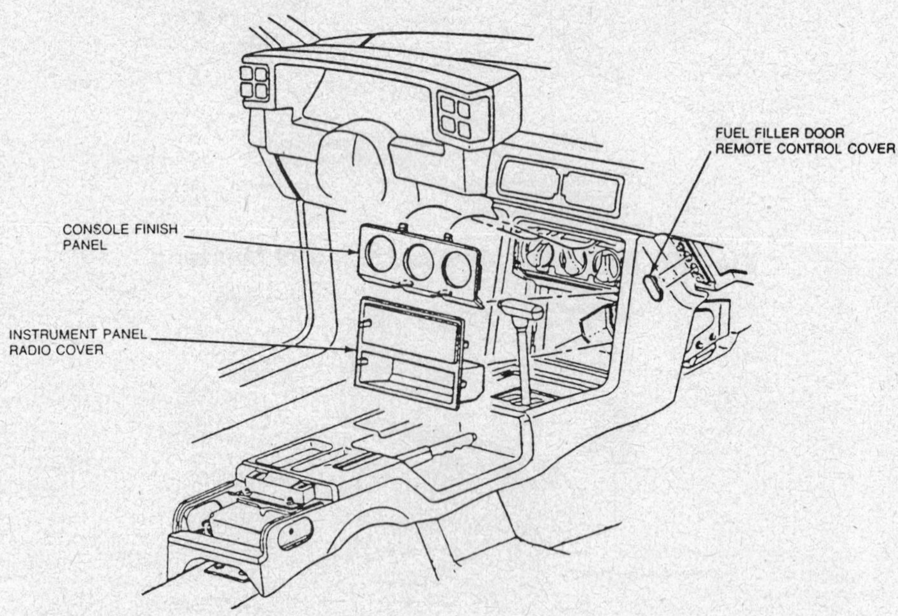


**Fig. 54 Removing radio cover & upper finish panel. Mustang**

# CAPRI

## 1991

1. Disarm airbag system as described under "Airbag System Disarming."
2. Disconnect battery ground cable.
3. Remove both lower cowl trim panels by pulling back door opening weatherstrip and removing push pin and screw.
4. Remove front and rear floor consoles as follows:
   a. Slide front seat completely rearward and remove screws retaining rear console to front console.
   b. Raise parking lever maximum distance.
   c. Raise rear console and pull backwards to remove.
   d. **On automatic models,** remove shift handle.
   e. **On all models,** raise ash tray and disconnect wiring on bottom, then remove center carpet panels and brackets if necessary.
   f. **On manual transaxle,** remove screws retaining manual shift lever boot to bottom of front console.
   g. Remove screws and front console leaving shift knob and boot on shift lever.
   h. Unscrew shift knob with boot and remove from shift lever if necessary.
   i. **On automatic transaxle,** remove screws and shift quadrant, then disconnect quadrant lamp connector.
5. Remove storage compartment, then four heater/radio bezel retaining screws, **Fig. 98.**
6. Disconnect speedometer cable at transaxle, then remove four instrument cluster retaining screws and slide cluster outward.
7. Press lock tab to release speedometer cable at back of cluster and remove connectors from the rear of cluster.
8. Disconnect electrical connectors from clock and switches in bezel.
9. Remove trim cover located on LH and RH Side of steering column, then remove steering column as follows:
   a. Remove access panel and trim cover, then the defroster duct connecting hose and lower shroud.
   b. Loosen column lower retaining nuts, then remove upper retaining bolts.
   c. With column resting on I/P brace, remove ignition lock shield and ignition switch retaining screw.
   d. Disconnect electrical connectors from turn signal and hazard switch.
   e. Remove steering shaft universal joint pinch bolts and carefully pull column out of I/P.
10. Loosen nut retaining hood release cable and remove radio.
11. Remove control panel, then tag and remove all wiring harness retainers and connectors from I/P.
12. Remove three screws and washers located near base of windshield.
13. Remove two bolts and washers from each side of I/P, an access panel is provided for upper bolts.

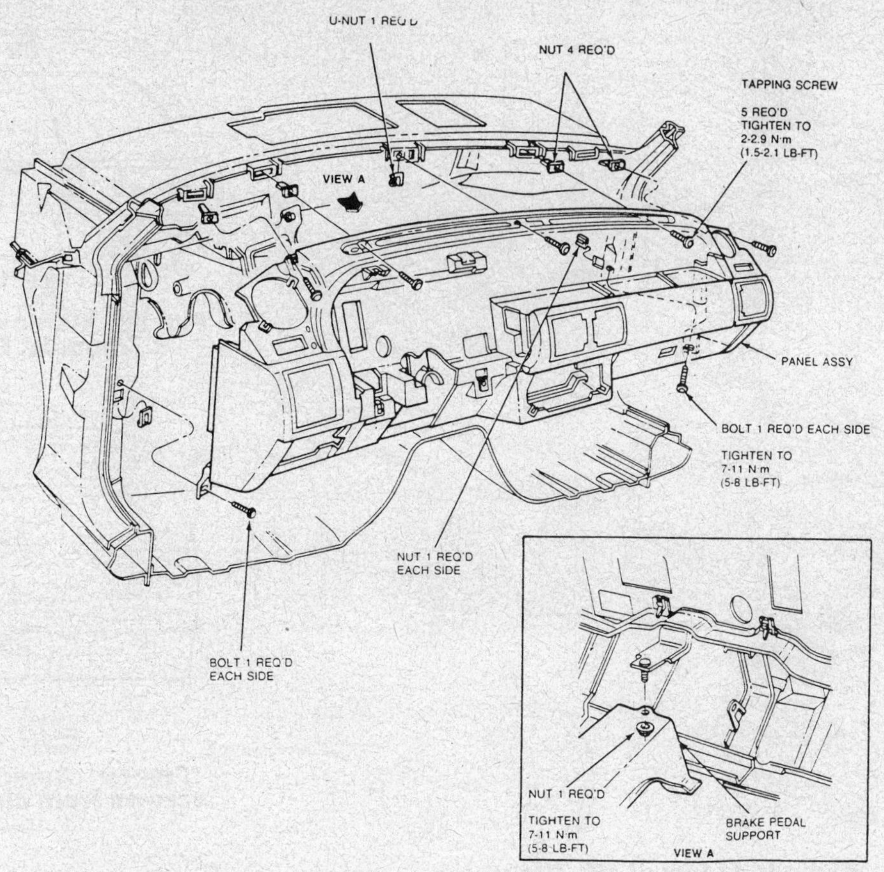


**Fig. 55 Removing I/P mounting bolts & nuts. 1989 Mustang**

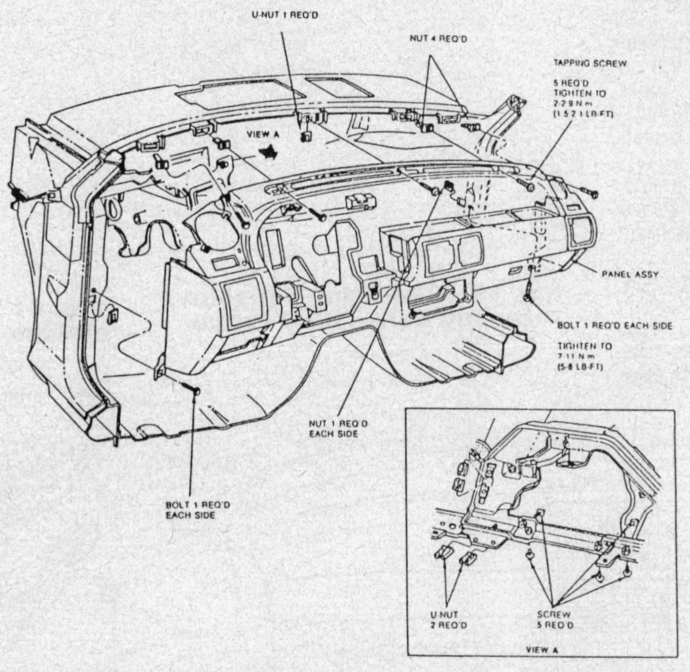


**Fig. 56 Removing I/P mounting bolts & nuts. 1990–91 Mustang**

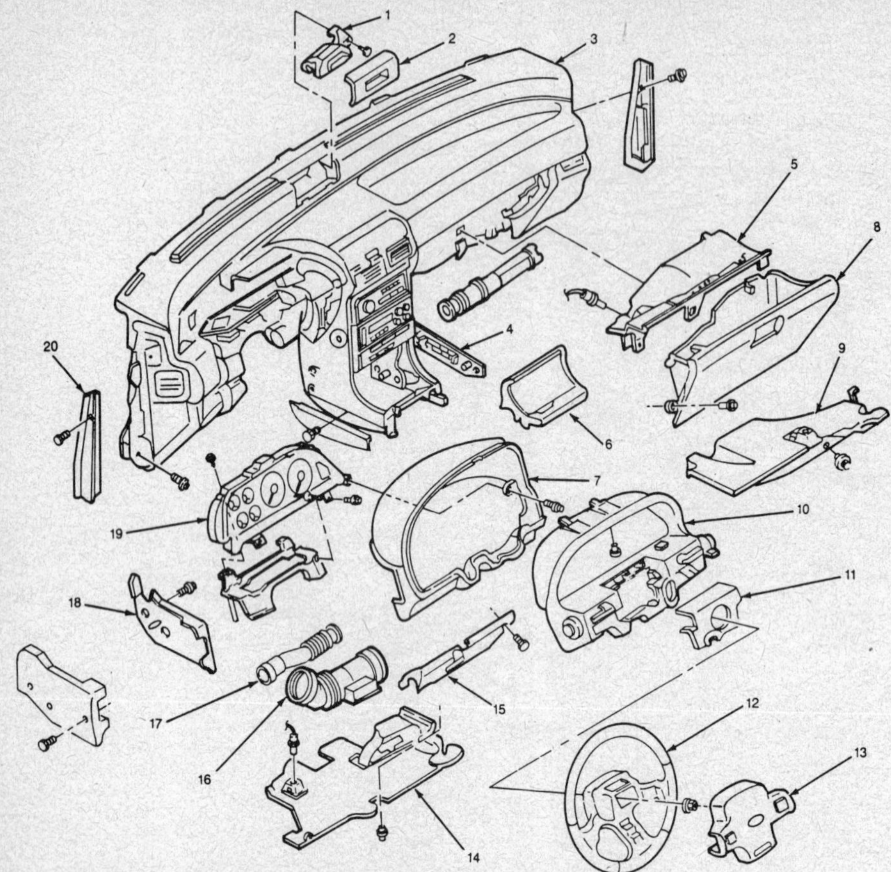
Fig. 57 Exploded view of I/P. Probe

14. Remove two screws and washers retaining I/P to center floor bracket, then two screws retaining I/P to column support.
15. Carefully slide I/P outward and disconnect ducts and wiring, **Fig. 99.**
16. Remove lamps, screws and upper glove compartment support bracket.
17. Remove screws, radio support bracket and defroster grilles.
18. Remove two screws above instrument cluster, three screws above glove compartment and two screws from underside of I/P.
19. Remove I/P panel pad and passenger side register from pad.
20. Reverse procedure to install.
21. Reactivate airbag system as described under "Airbag System Disarming."

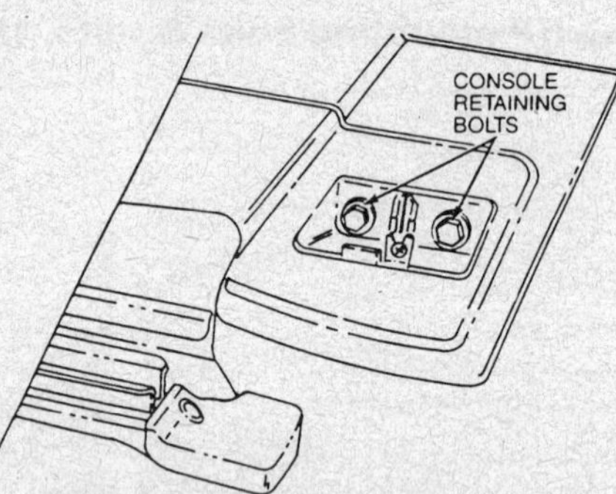

Fig. 60 Removing console retaining bolts. 1989 Probe

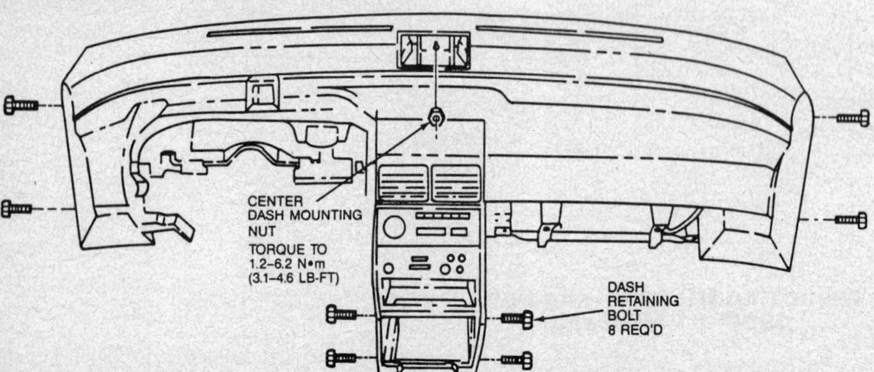

Fig. 62 Removing I/P attaching bolts & nuts. Probe

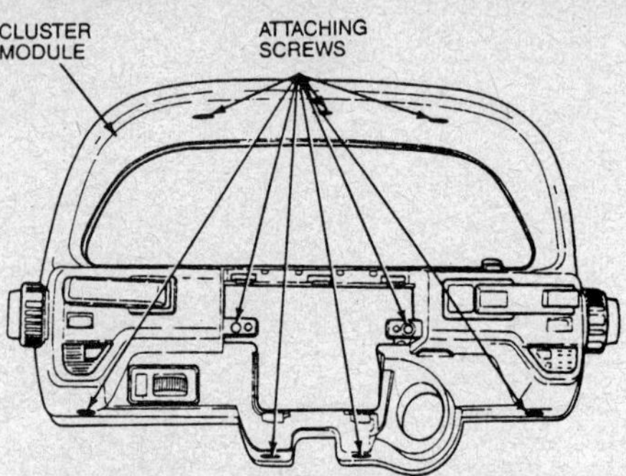

Fig. 58 Removing cluster module. Probe

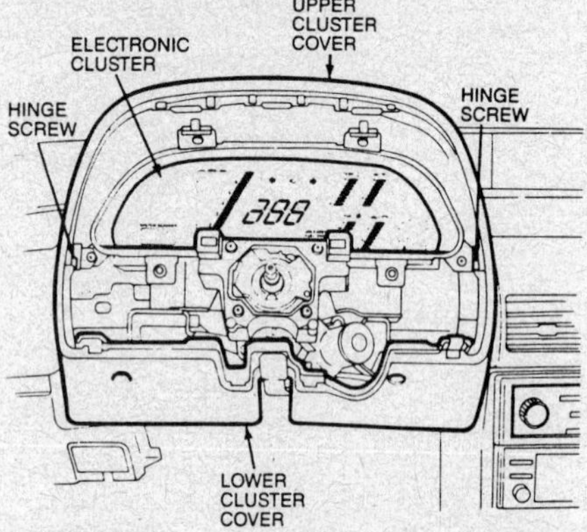

Fig. 59 Removing hinge screws from cluster. Probe

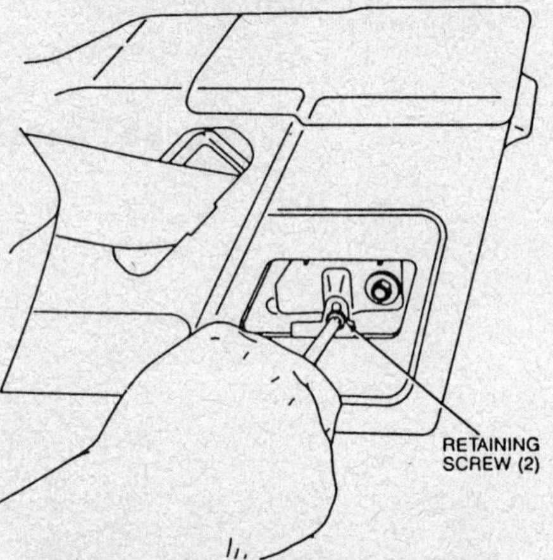

Fig. 61 Removing console retaining bolt. 1990–91 Probe

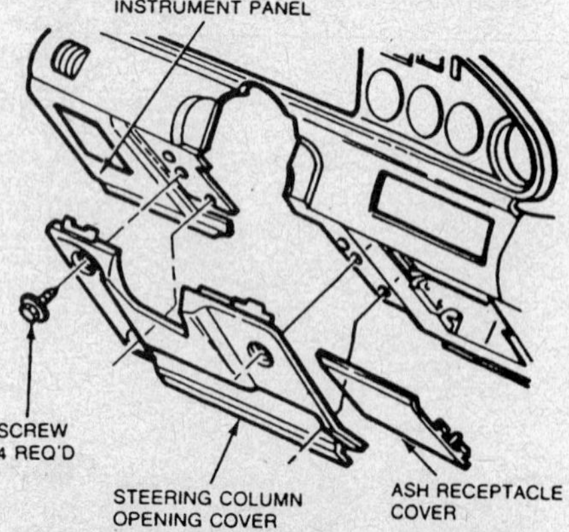

Fig. 63 Removing steering column opening cover. 1989 Sable

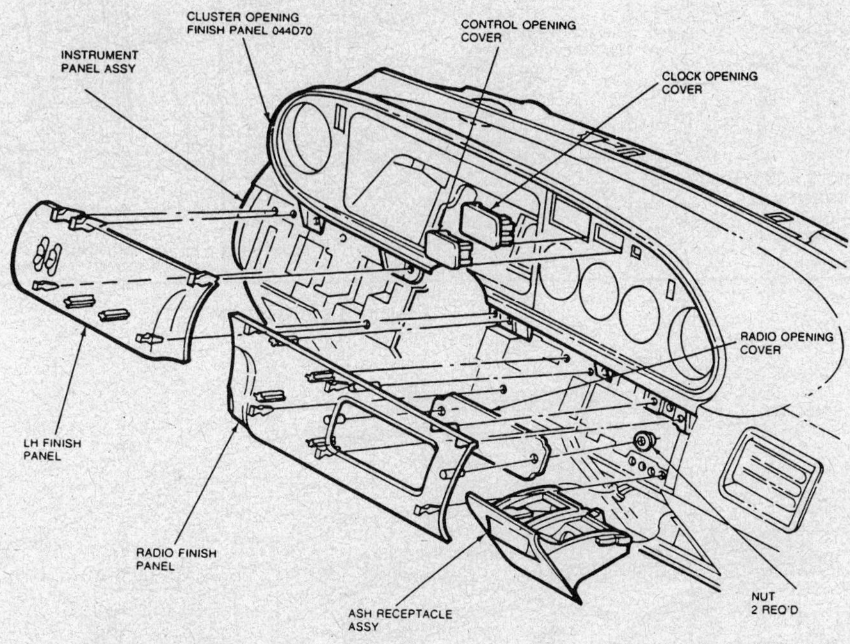


**Fig. 64 Removing I/P finish panels. 1989 Sable**

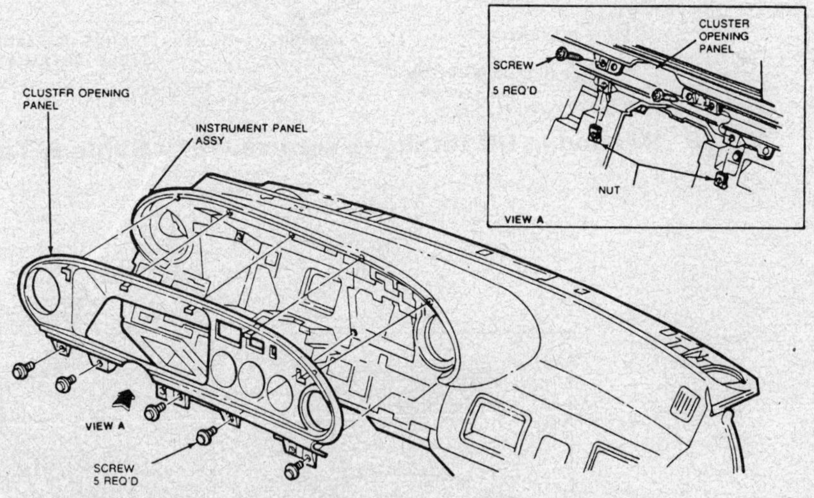


**Fig. 65 Removing cluster opening finish panel. 1989 Sable**

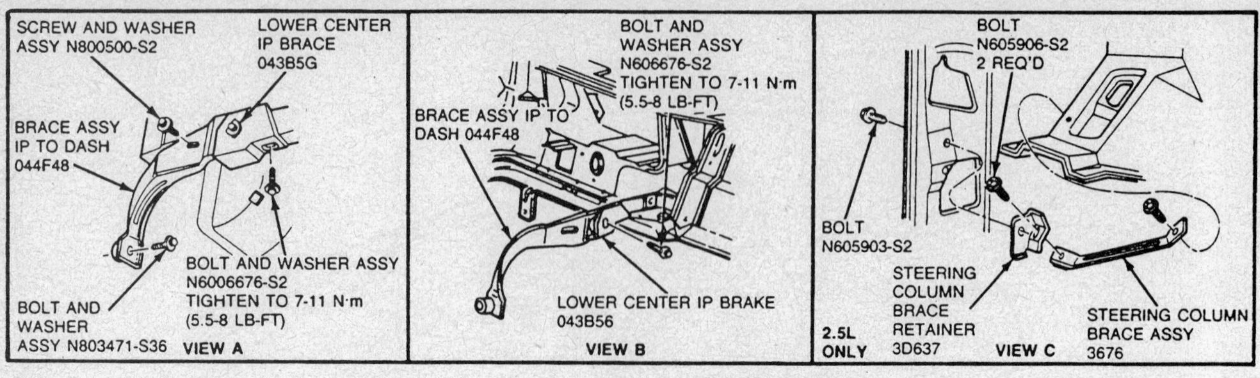


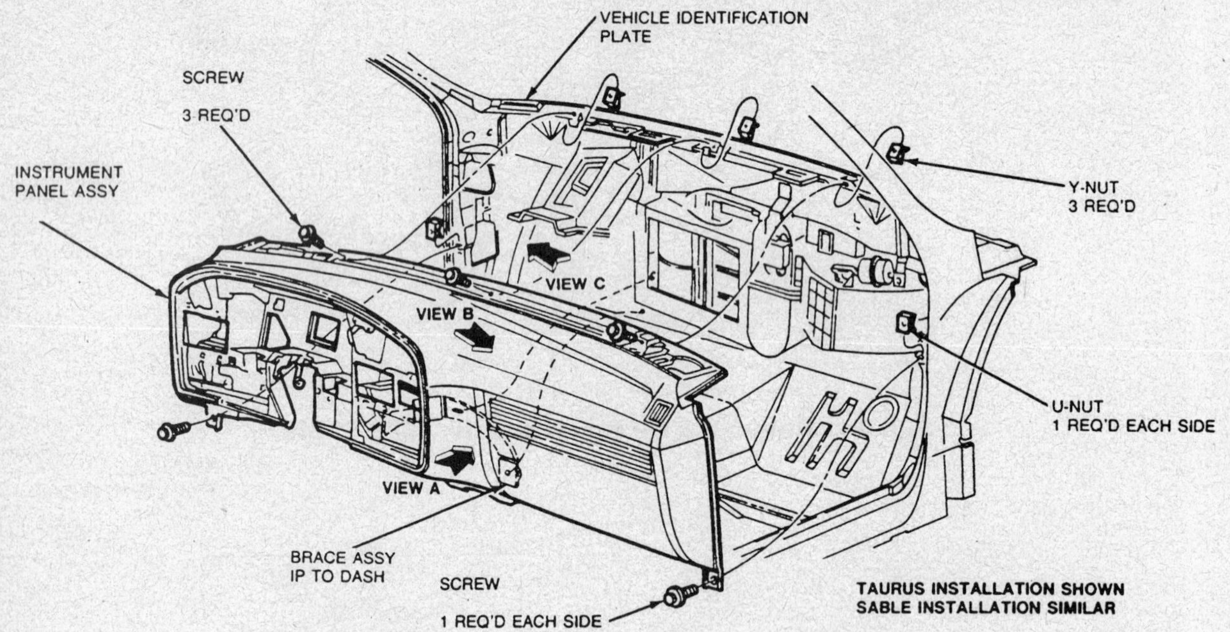


Fig. 66 Removing I/P retaining screws. 1989 Sable & Taurus

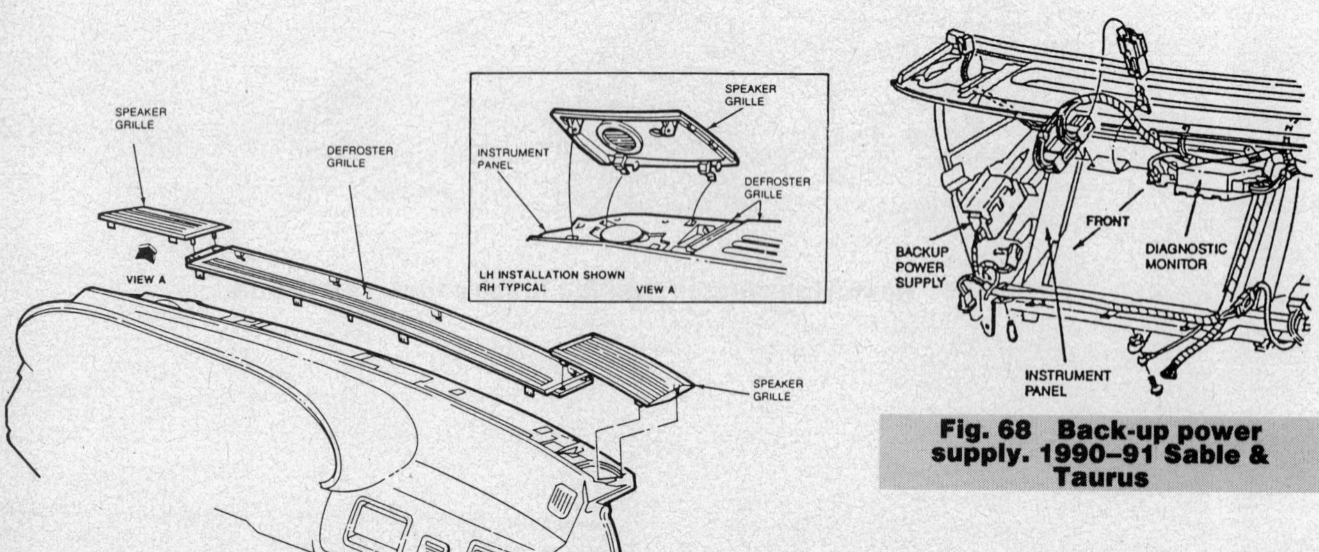


Fig. 68 Back-up power supply. 1990–91 Sable & Taurus

Fig. 67 Removing defroster & speaker grilles. Sable & Taurus

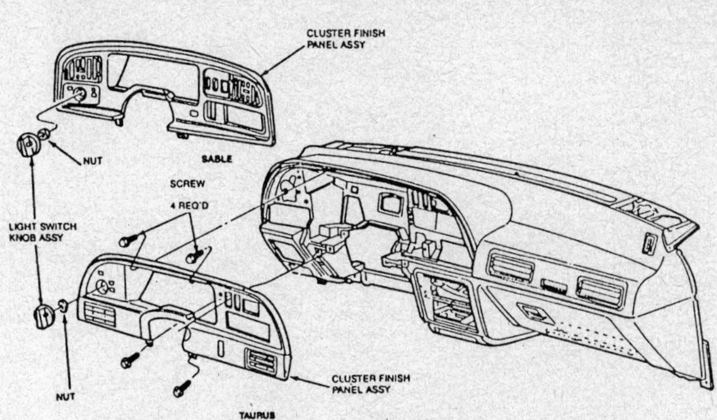


**Fig. 69 Steering column electrical connectors. 1990–91 Sable & Taurus**

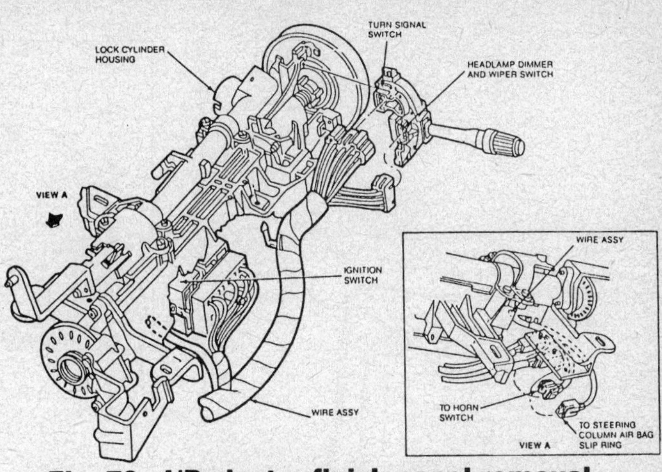


**Fig. 70 I/P cluster finish panel removal. 1990–91 Sable & Taurus**

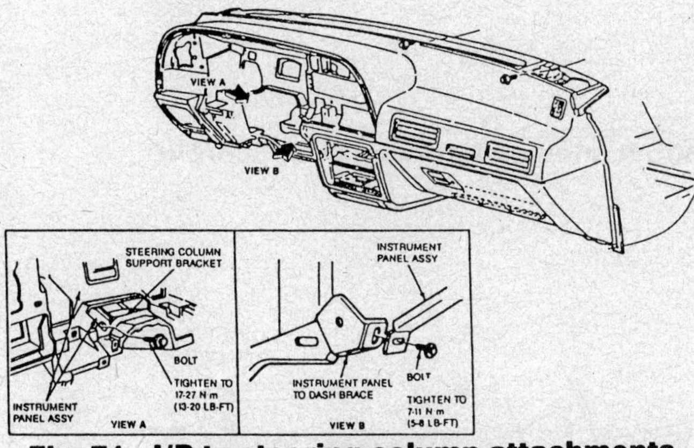


**Fig. 71 I/P to steering column attachments. 1990–91 Sable & Taurus**

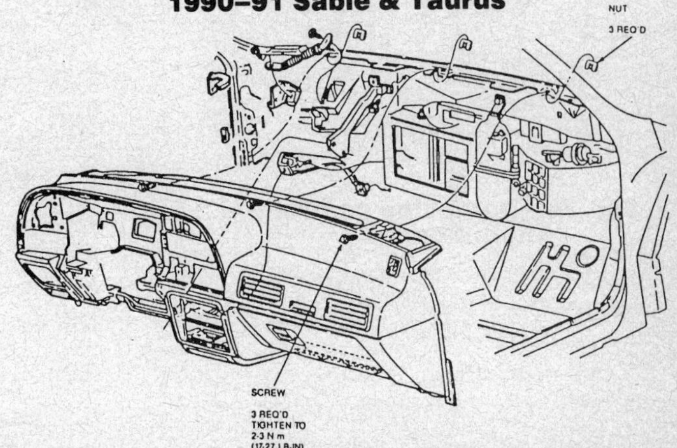


**Fig. 72 I/P to dash brace removal. 1990–91 Sable & Taurus**

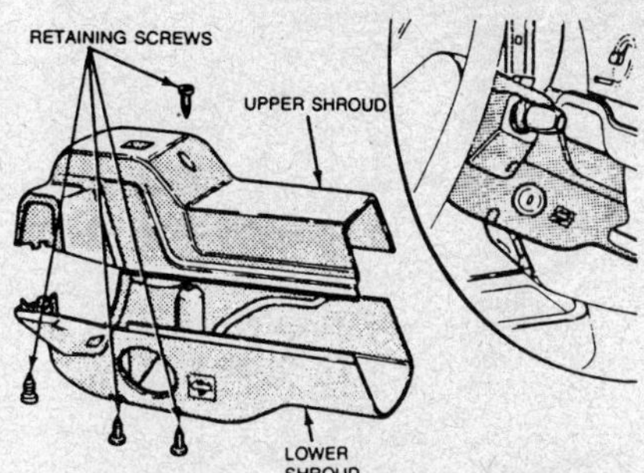


**Fig. 73 Removing steering column upper & lower shrouds. Scorpio**

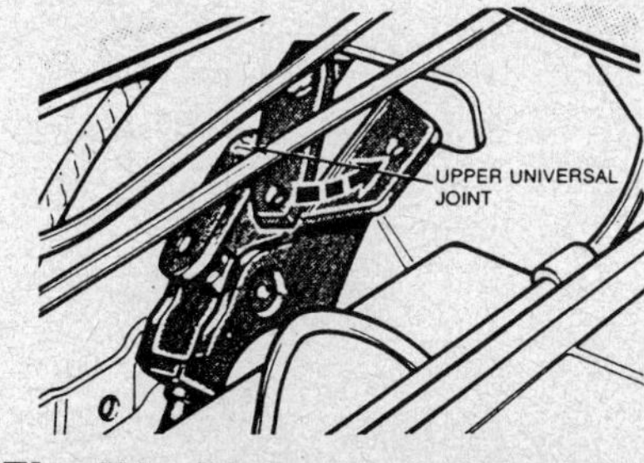


**Fig. 74 Disconnecting hood release cable. Scorpio**

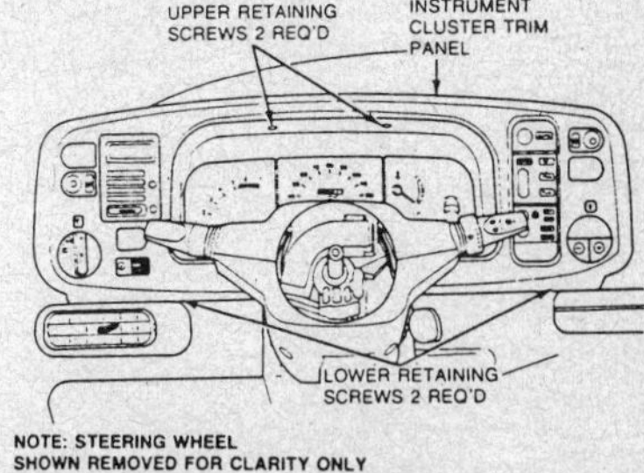


**Fig. 75 Removing instrument cluster retaining screws. Scorpio**

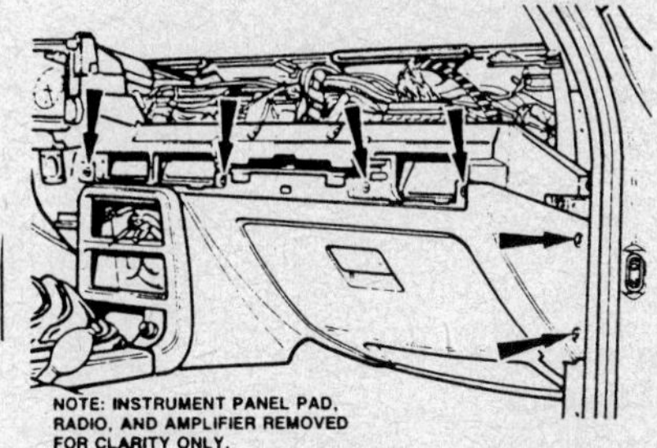


**Fig. 76 Removing right side lower trim panel. Scorpio**

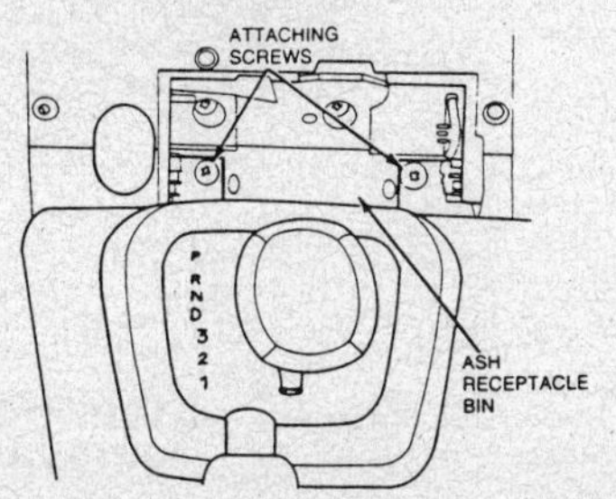


**Fig. 77 Removing console attaching bolts. Scorpio**

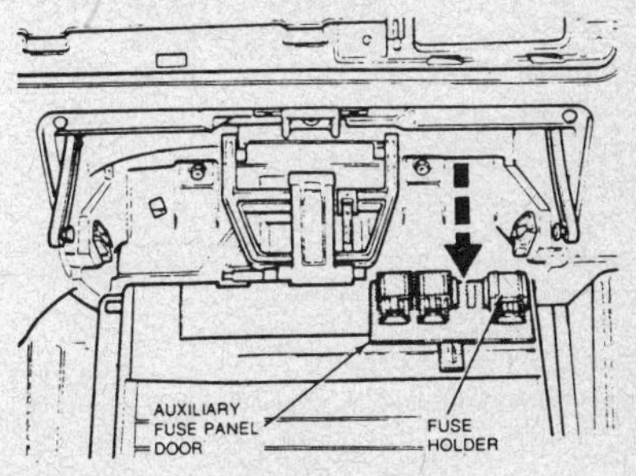


**Fig. 78 Auxiliary fuse panel. Scorpio**

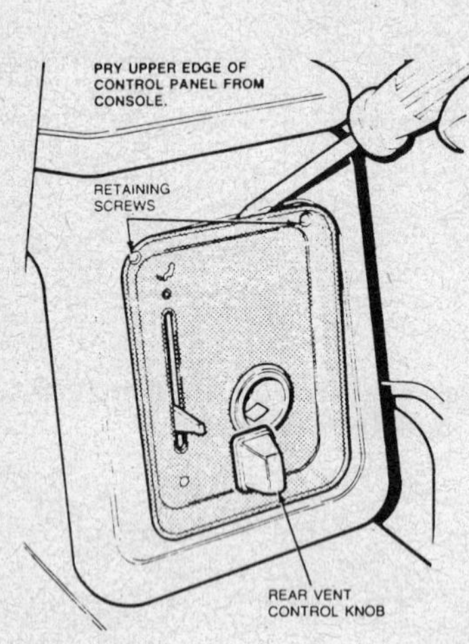


**Fig. 79 Removing control knob. Scorpio**

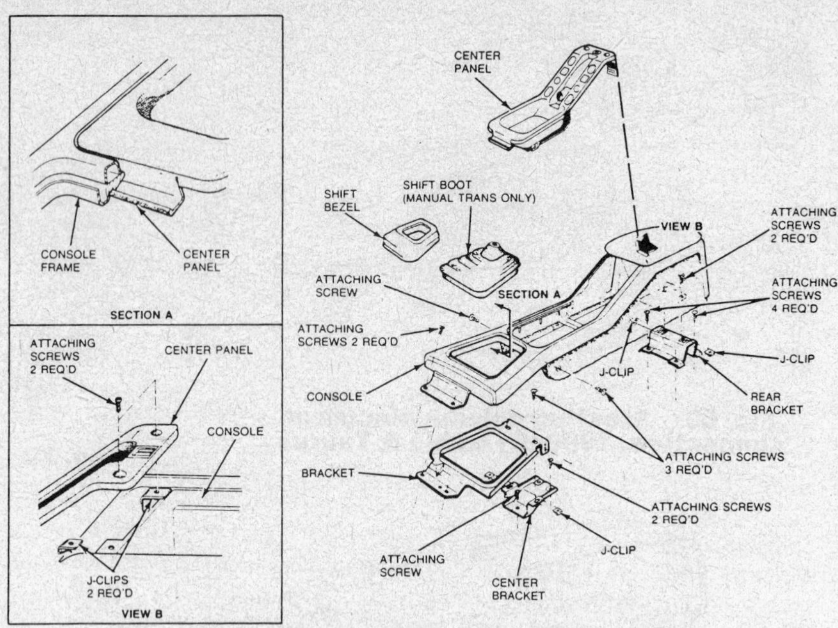


**Fig. 80 Removing floor console. Scorpio**

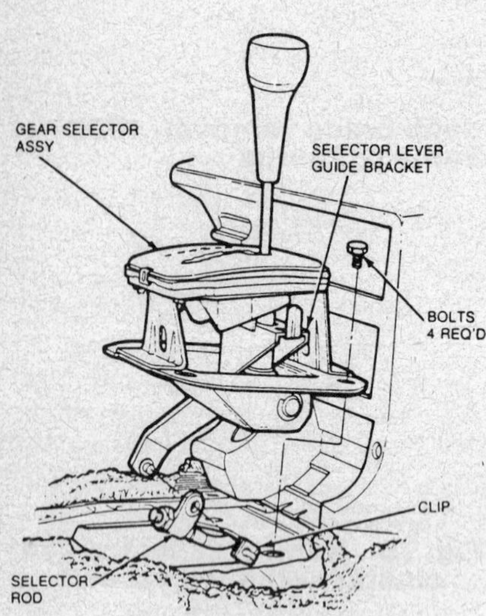


**Fig. 81 Removing gear selector. Scorpio**

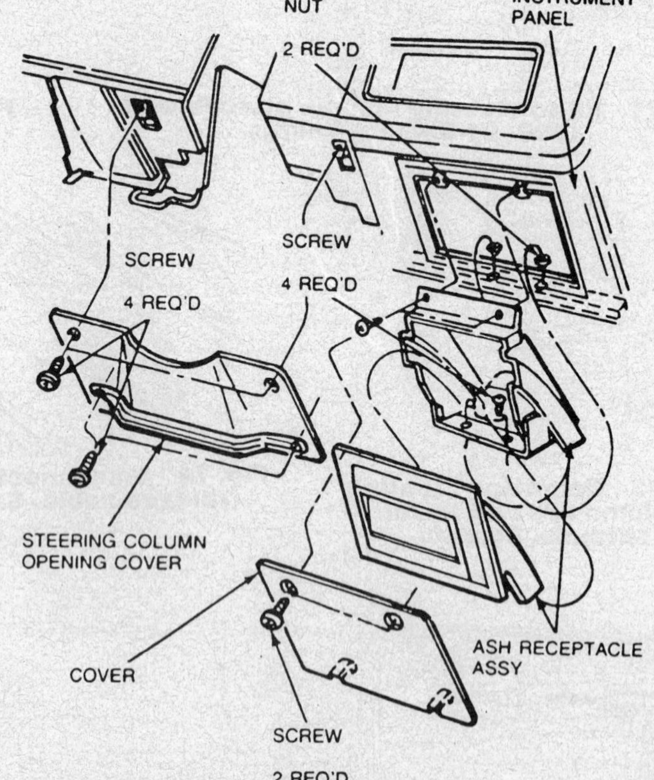


**Fig. 82 Steering column opening cover removal. 1989 Taurus**

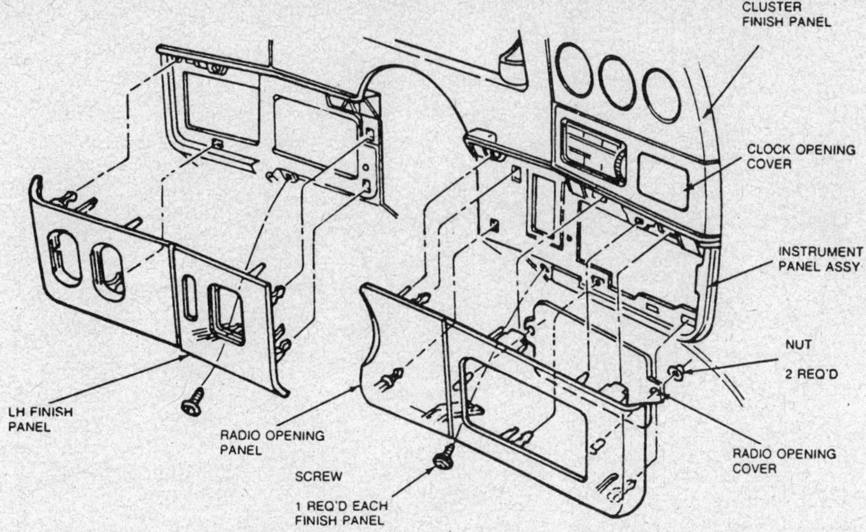


**Fig. 83 Removing finish panels. 1989 Taurus**

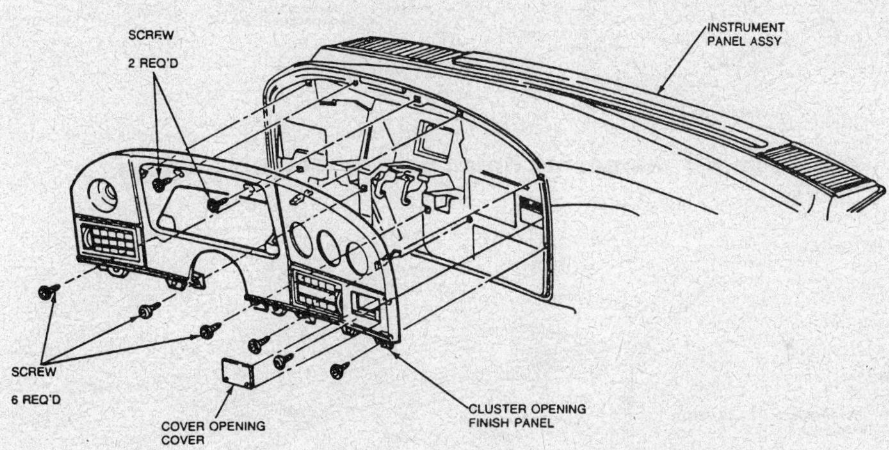


**Fig. 84 Removing cluster finish panel. 1989 Taurus**

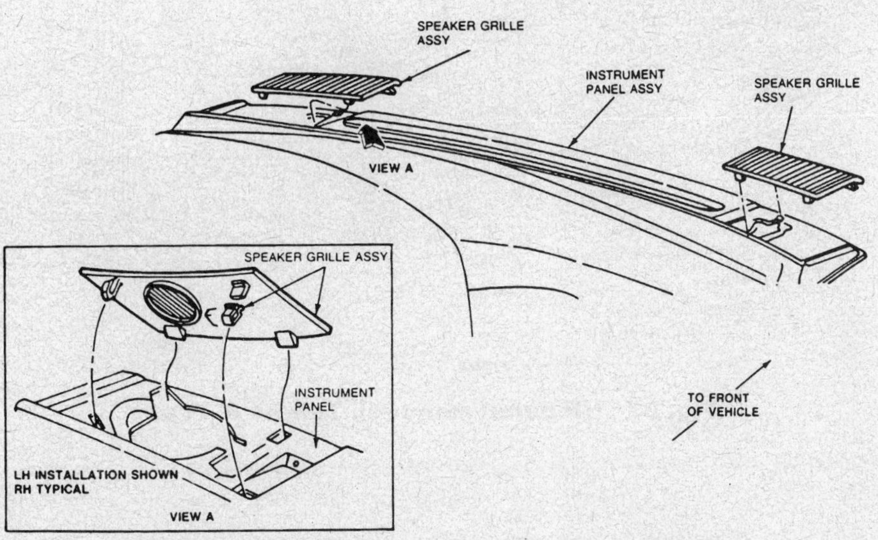


**Fig. 85 Removing speaker covers. Taurus**

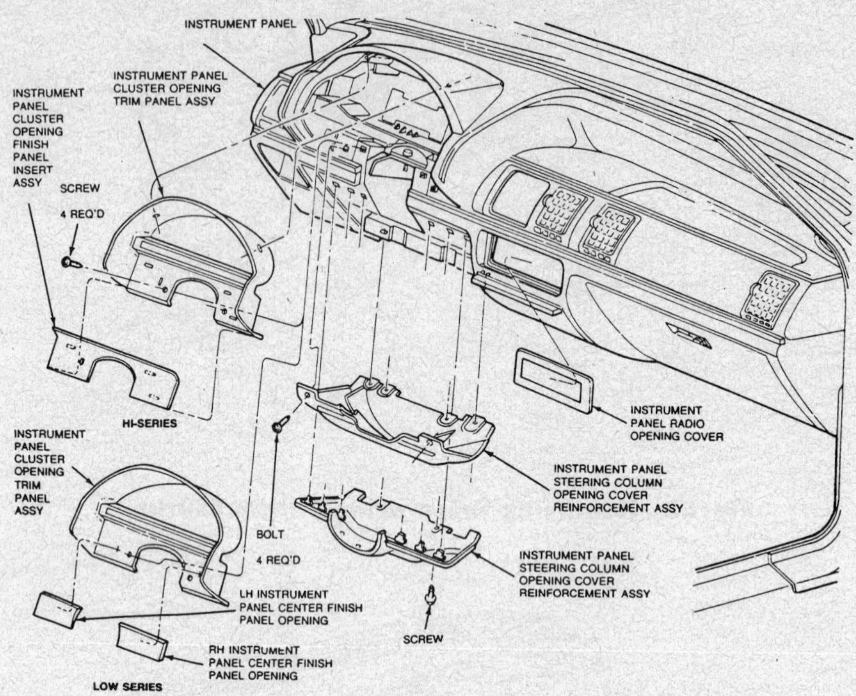


**Fig. 86 Removing finish panels. Tempo & Topaz**

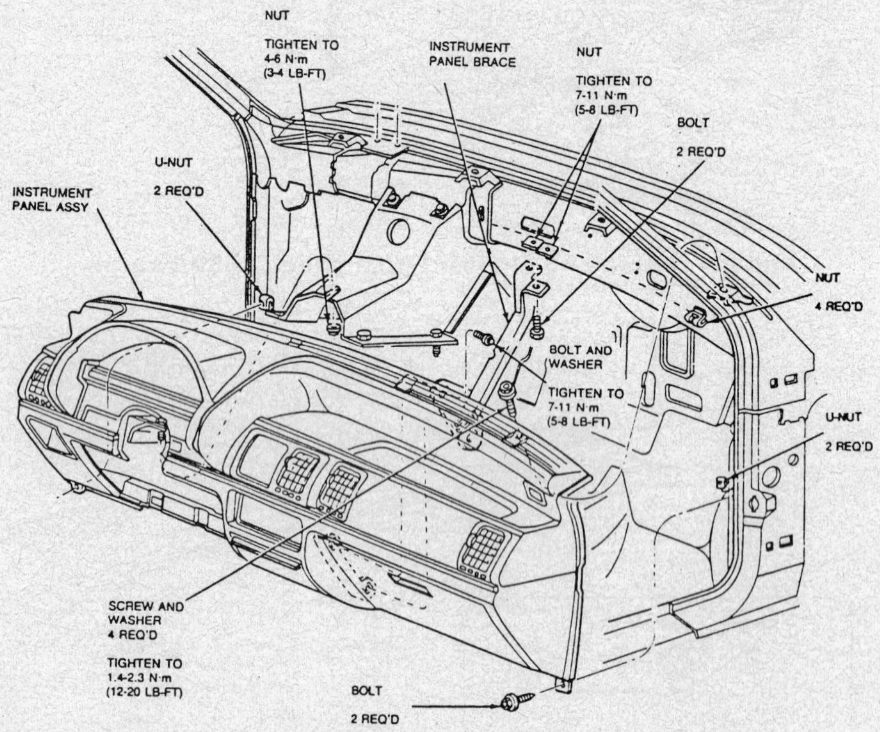


**Fig. 87 I/P panel removal. Tempo & Topaz**

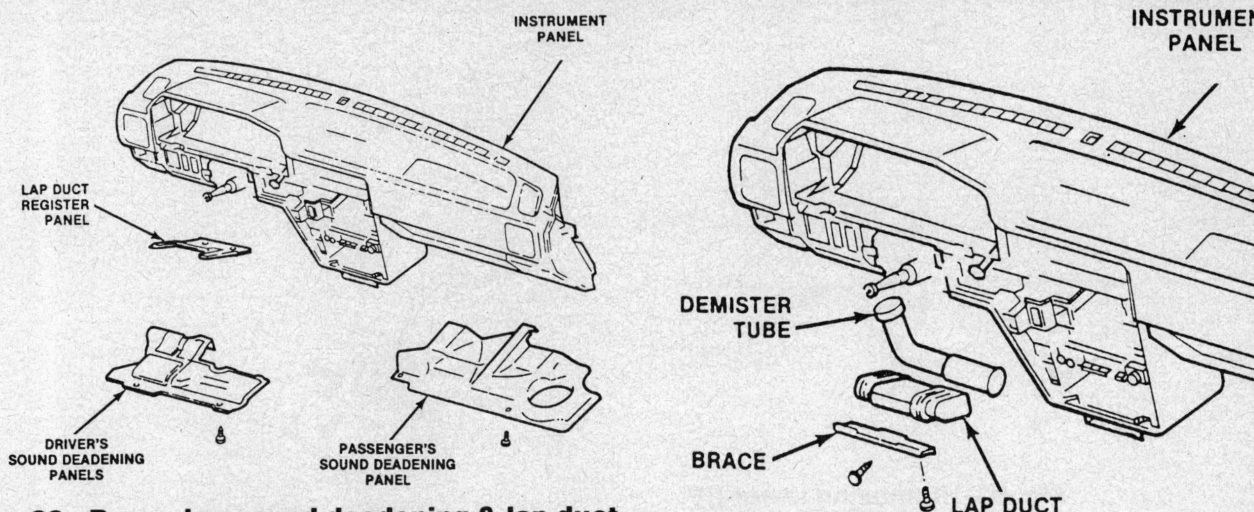


**Fig. 88 Removing sound deadening & lap duct panels. Tracer**

**Fig. 89 Removing lap duct & demister tube. Tracer**

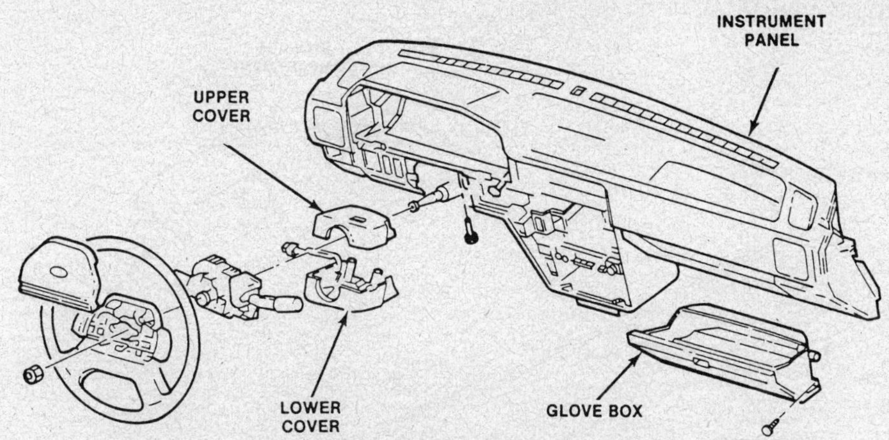


**Fig. 90 Removing steering column covers. Tracer**

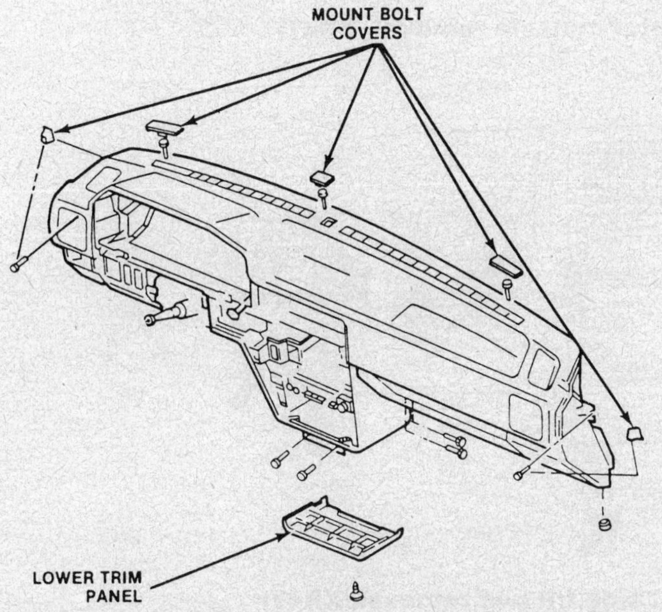


**Fig. 91 Mounting bolt cover locations. Tracer**

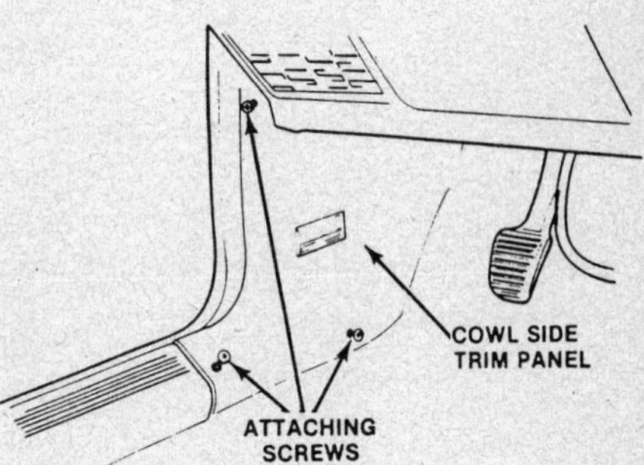


**Fig. 92 Mounting bolt cover locations. XR4Ti**

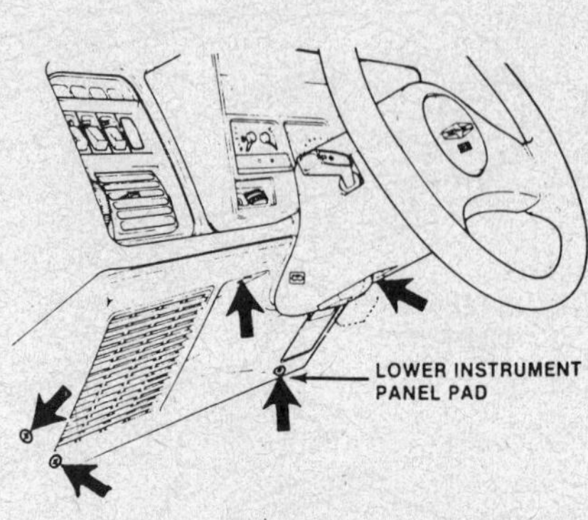


**Fig. 93 Removing lower I/P pad. XR4Ti**

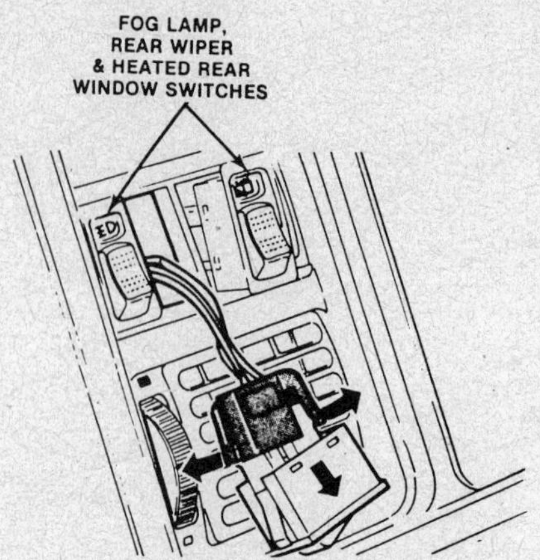


**Fig. 94 Removing center console switches. XR4Ti**

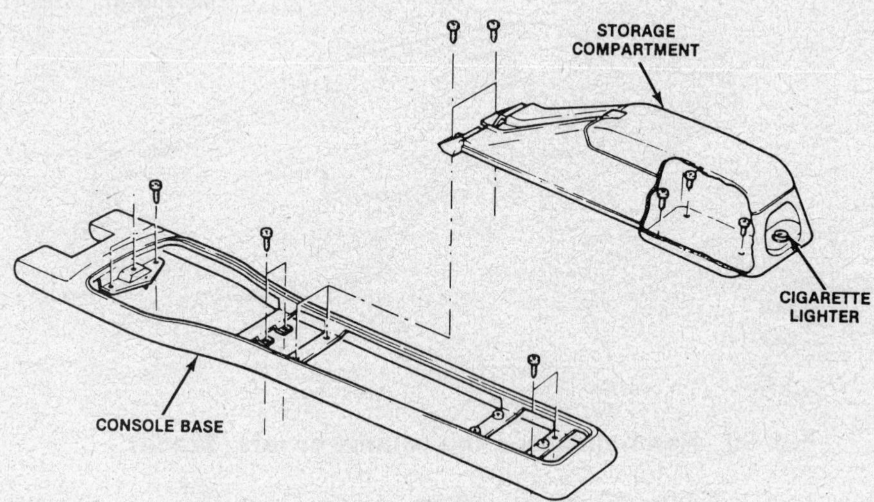


**Fig. 95 Center console removal. XR4Ti**

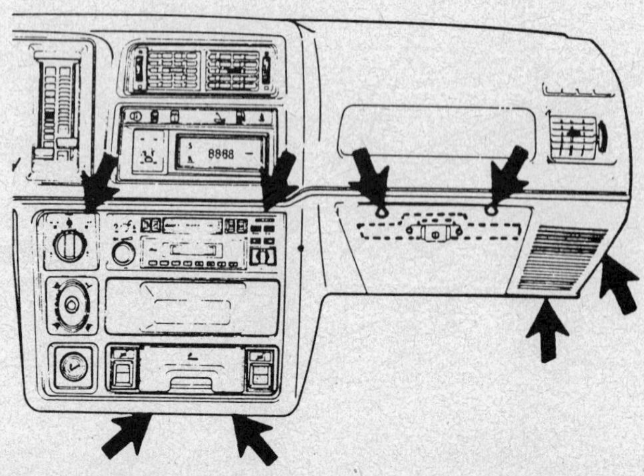

**Fig. 96 Right side I/P pad removal. XR4Ti**

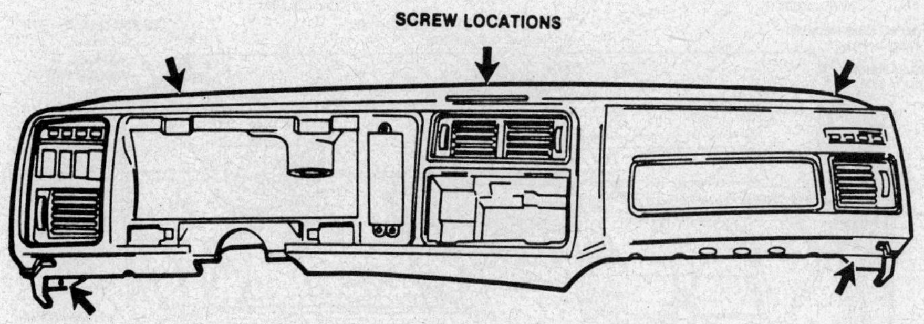


**Fig. 97 Upper I/P removal. XR4Ti**

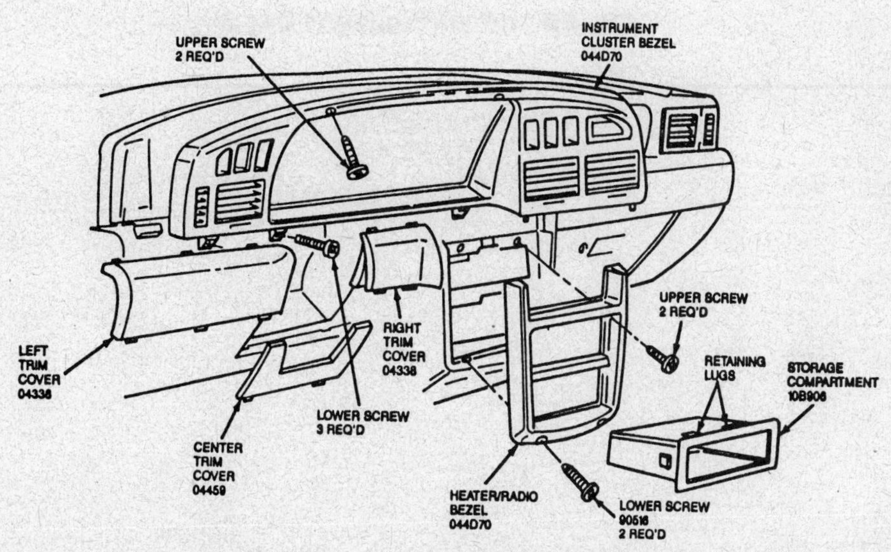


**Fig. 98 Removing I/P. 1991 Capri**

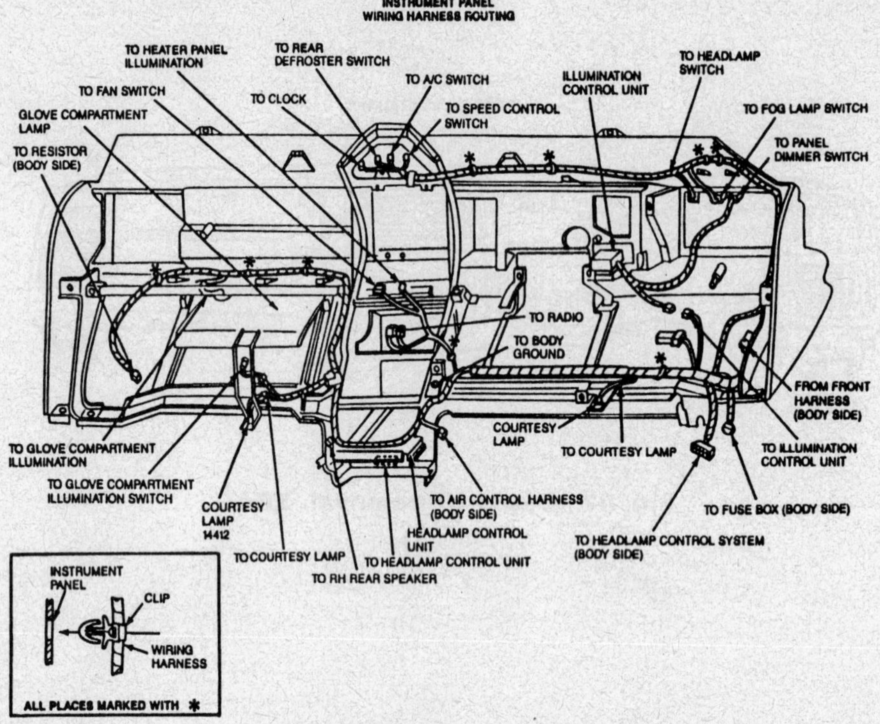
INSTRUMENT PANEL
WIRING HARNESS ROUTING
TO HEATER PANEL
ILLUMINATION
TO REAR
DEFROSTER SWITCH
TO A/C SWITCH
ILLUMINATION
CONTROL UNIT
TO HEADLAMP
SWITCH
TO FAN SWITCH
TO CLOCK
TO SPEED CONTROL
SWITCH
TO FOG LAMP SWITCH
GLOVE COMPARTMENT
LAMP
TO PANEL
DIMMER SWITCH
TO RESISTOR
(BODY SIDE)
TO RADIO
TO BODY
GROUND
FROM FRONT
HARNESS
(BODY SIDE)
COURTESY
LAMP
TO COURTESY LAMP
TO ILLUMINATION
CONTROL UNIT
TO GLOVE COMPARTMENT
ILLUMINATION
TO GLOVE COMPARTMENT
ILLUMINATION SWITCH
COURTESY
LAMP
14412
TO AIR CONTROL HARNESS
(BODY SIDE)
TO FUSE BOX (BODY SIDE)
HEADLAMP CONTROL
UNIT
TO HEADLAMP CONTROL SYSTEM
(BODY SIDE)
TO COURTESY LAMP
TO HEADLAMP CONTROL UNIT
TO RH REAR SPEAKER
INSTRUMENT
PANEL
CLIP
WIRING
HARNESS
ALL PLACES MARKED WITH *

**Fig. 99 I/P wiring. 1991 Capri**

# STEERING COLUMNS

**NOTE: Models Equipped With "Automatic Ride Control System," Utilize A Steering Sensor Located On The Steering Column Assembly. For Replacement Of Sensor, Refer To "Automatic Ride Control System" In The "Active Suspension" Section.**

TABLE OF CONTENTS



# Vehicles Less Airbag System

## INDEX



## STEERING COLUMN REPLACE

**When servicing collapsible steering columns, care should be exercised since they are extremely susceptible to damage. Dropping of or leaning on column or striking sharp blows on end of steering shaft or shift levers could loosen or shear plastic fasteners which maintain column rigidity. It is important that only the specified screws, bolts and nuts be used during the mandatory reassembly sequence and torqued to specifications to insure proper breakaway action of column under impact. Avoid using excessively long bolts as they may prevent a portion of the steering column from collapsing under impact. When removing or installing, steering wheel, ignition switch or lock, turn signal switch, adjusting transmission linkage, or installing and adjusting neutral-start or back-up light switch, refer to appropriate car chapter. If a shift tube shows a sheared plastic injection, a new shift tube must be installed. If a steering shaft shows a sheared plastic, or if the steering column has been collapsed a complete new column must be installed. On some models, the attaching brackets will shear under impact and must also be replaced.**

### CROWN VICTORIA, GRAND MARQUIS & TOWN CAR

Refer to **Figs. 1 and 2** for steering column component identification.

#### Removal

1. Disconnect battery ground cable.
2. Remove steering wheel from steering shaft.
3. Remove bolt attaching steering column shaft to lower steering shaft assembly, then disengage safety strap and bolt assembly from flexible coupling.
4. Disconnect transmission shift rod from control lever. **The old grommet must be replaced with a new one using tool No. T67P-7341A, or equivalent.**
5. Remove steering column trim shrouds. Also remove steering column cover and hood release mechanism from under steering column.
6. Disconnect wire connectors from turn signal, windshield wiper/washer, ignition, horn and headlight dimmer switches.
7. Loosen four steering column to brake pedal support attaching nuts and lower steering column to gain access to PRND21 lever and cable assembly. **Use care not to lower column so far that lever or cable become damaged due to weight of column.**
8. Reach between steering column and instrument panel and lift cable off PRND21 lever cleat, then remove cable clamp from steering column tube.
9. Remove four dust boot to dash panel attaching screws.
10. Remove four nuts attaching steering column to brake pedal support, then lower steering column to clear the four mounting bolts and remove column assembly from vehicle.

#### Installation

1. Insert U-joint assembly through opening in dash panel.
2. Align four bolts on brake pedal support with bolt holes on column collar and bracket, then loosely install attaching nuts so that there is clearance between column and instrument panel.
3. Loosely assemble PRND21 cable clamp to steering column outer tube,

then reach between instrument panel and column and attach cable to cleat on lever.
4. **Torque** four nuts attaching steering column to brake pedal support to 20 to 37 ft. lbs.
5. Place transmission selector lever into Drive position, then rotate PRND21 bracket until pointer on instrument cluster aligns with D and tighten bracket nut.
6. Connect wire connectors to ignition, turn signal, windshield wiper/washer, horn and headlight dimmer switches.
7. Slide lower steering shaft assembly into steering column shaft, then install nut and bolt and **torque** to 35 to 45 ft. lbs. **Pry lower shaft back and forth to obtain a ± 1/8 inch coupling insulator flatness.**
8. Connect shift rod to shift lever using tool No. T67P-7341A, or equivalent, then adjust transmission shift linkage as described elsewhere in this manual.
9. Engage dust boot at end of steering column to dash panel opening, then install four dust boot attaching screws.
10. Install steering column trim shrouds.
11. Install hood release mechanism and steering column cover.
12. Install steering wheel on steering shaft.
13. Connect battery ground cable and check steering column operation.

## MARK VII

Refer to **Fig. 3** for steering column component identification.

### Removal

1. Disconnect battery ground cable.
2. Remove two nuts retaining flexible coupling to flange on steering input shaft, then disengage safety strap and bolt assembly from flexible coupling.
3. **On column shift automatic transmission models,** disconnect transmission shift rod from transmission control selector lever. **The old grommet must be replaced with a new one using tool T67P-7341-A or equivalent.**
4. Remove steering wheel.
5. Remove steering column trim shrouds by loosening screws, then remove steering column cover and hood release mechanism from under column.
6. Disconnect all electrical connectors from steering column switches.
7. **On column shift automatic transmission models,** loosen four nuts retaining column to brake pedal support, then lower column to allow access to PRND21 lever and cable assembly. Reach between steering column and instrument panel and carefully lift PRND21 cable off cleat on lever, then remove PRND21 cable clamp from steering column tube. **Use care to assure that column is not lowered too far so that plastic lever or cable is damaged due to weight of column.**
8. Remove four screws attaching dust

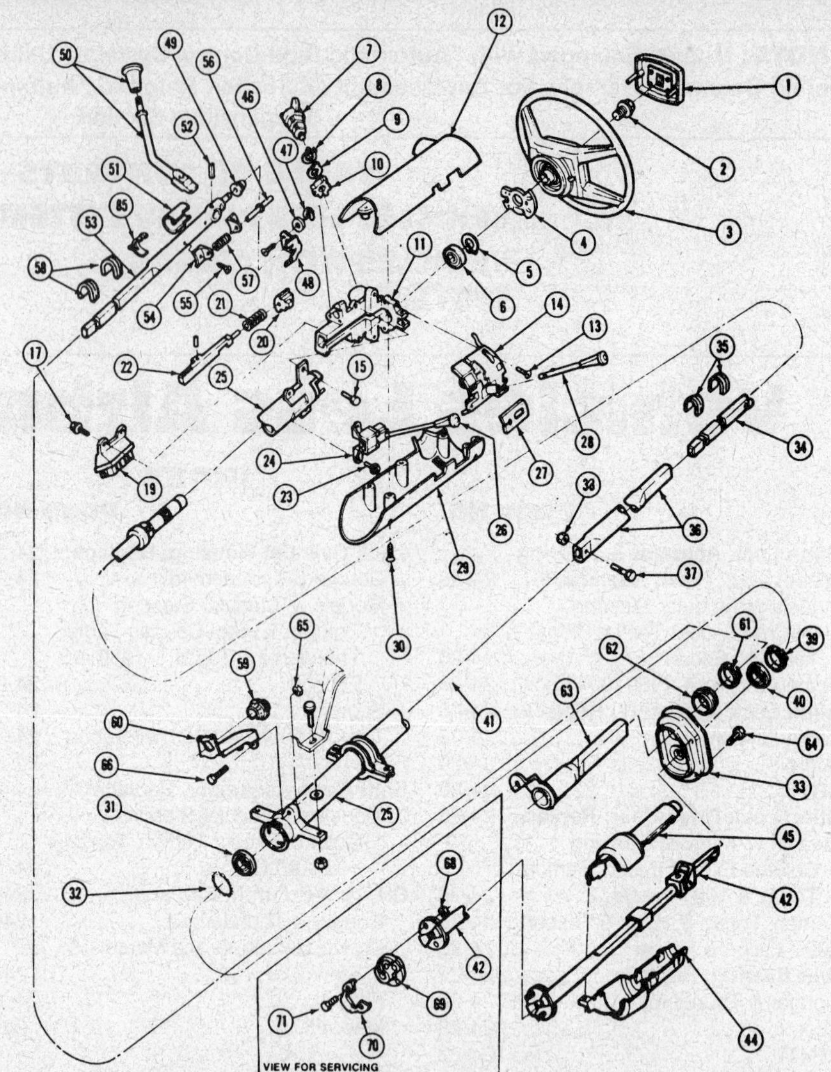


**Fig. 1 Fixed steering column installation (Part 1 of 2). Crown Victoria, Grand Marquis, & Town Car**

| ITEM | PART NO. | DESCRIPTION | ITEM | PART NO. | DESCRIPTION |
|---|---|---|---|---|---|
| 1. | 3A515 | Emblem Assy. | 36. | 3E628 | Shaft — Strng. Gear Lower |
| 2. | N804217 | Bolt — M10 × 1.50 × 17.0 Hex | 37. | 58655-S2 | Bolt — 7/16-14 × 1-1/2 Hex. |
| 3. | 3600 | Wheel Assy. | 38. | 388795-S100 | Nut — 7/16 × 14 Hex. Lock |
| 4. | 3L525 | Plate — Strng. Col. Clip Retainer | 39. | 3507 | Retainer Bearing |
| 5. | 97476-S100 | Ring — 3/4 Retaining Type | 40. | 3E733 | Bearing |
| 6. | 3517 | Bearing Assy. — Strng. Col. Upper | 42. | 3C662 | Shaft Assy. — Strng. Col. Lower |
| 7. | | Lock Cyl. — Body | 44. | 3F540 | Stone Shield Lower |
| 8. | N800205-S100 | Ring — 24 × 1.07 Retaining Type for Zinc Lock Hsg. (Silver Color) or 3F579 Retainer for Magnesium Lock Hsg. (Gold Color) | 45. | 3F540 | Stone Shield Upper |
| | | | 46. | 388021-S2 | Ring — 5/16 Retainer |
| | | | 47. | N800178-S2 | Washer — 8.23 Flat |
| 9. | 3E700 | Bearing | 48. | 7A216 | Insert — Trans. Control |
| 10. | 3E717 | Gear — Steering Column Lock | 49. | 7225 | Bearing — Trans. Gear Shift Lever Socket |
| 11. | 3E643 | Housing — Strng. Col. Lock Cyl. | 50. | 7202 | Lever Assy. — Trans. Control Selector |
| 12. | 3530 | Shroud — Upper | 51. | 7C369 | Cover — Trans. Control Selector Lever Opening |
| 13. | 52794-S2 | Screw — No. 8 × 18 × .62 Pan Head (2 Req'd.) | 52. | N100198 | Pin — 5mm Spring Coiled |
| 14. | 13B302 | Switch Assy. — Turn & Emergency | 53. | 7212 | Tube Assy. — Trans. Control Selector |
| 15. | N605531-S2 | Bolt — M8 × 1.25 Hex. Hd. (2 Req'd.) | 54. | 3E543 | Retainer — Strng. Col. Lever (2 Req'd.) |
| 17. | N804855-S100 | Bolt (2 Req'd.) | 55. | N800210-S2 | Screw — 4mm 0.7 × 12.7 Type "D" Oval (2 Req'd.) |
| 19. | 11572 | Switch Assy. — Ignition | 56. | 7361 | Plunger — Trans. Control Selector Lever |
| 20. | 3E691 | Pawl — Strng. Col. Lock | 57. | 7B071 | Spring — Trans. Control Selector Lever Return |
| 21. | 3E696 | Spring — Strng. Col. Lock | 58. | 3E629 | Anti-Rattle Clip (2 Req'd.) |
| 22. | 3E723 | Actuator Assy. — Strng. Col. Lock | 59. | 7K189 | Bushing — Trans. Gear Shift Shaft |
| 23. | | Screws — Wash/Wipe Switch (Body) | 60. | 7K730 | Brkt. — Trans. Gear Shift Support |
| 24. | | Wash/Wipe Switch (Body) | 61. | 3507 | Retainer Bearing |
| 25. | 3A617 | Tube Assy. — Col. Outer | 62. | 3E733 | Bearing |
| 26. | | Handle & Shank Assy. — Wash/Wipe (Body) | 63. | 7212 | Tube Assy. — Trans. Control Selector |
| 27. | 13B365 | Foam Cover — Turn Sig. & W/W Switch | 64. | 388489-S9 | Screw — No. 8 × .75 Hex. Washer Head — Tapping |
| 28. | 13305 | Handle & Shank Assy. — Turn Sig. Switch | | | |
| 29. | 3530 | Shroud — Strng. Col. Lower | 65. | 34976-S2 | Nut — 5/16-18 Hex. P.T. |
| 30. | 55931-S2 | Screw — No. 8-18 × 1.50 Pan Hd. Tap (5 Req'd.) | 66. | 56724-S2 | Bolt — 5/16-18 × 1.50 Hex. Flange Head |
| 31. | 3E733 | Bearing Assy. — Strng. Gear Shaft Lower | 67. | 3C686 | Spacer Clip |
| 32. | 3F543 | Ring — Strng. Gear Shaft Lower Bearing Retainer | 68. | 34976-S100 | Nut — 5/16-18 Hex. Lock |
| 33. | 3E735 | Boot Assy. — Strng. Col. | 69. | 3A525 | Flange and Insulator Assy. |
| 34. | 3A526 | Shaft Assy. — Strng. Col. Upper | 70. | 3B629 | Reinforcement |
| 35. | 3E744 | Anti-Rattle Clip (2 Req'd.) | 71. | 383177-S100 | Bolt — 5/16-18 × 1.00 Hex. Shoulder |

**Fig. 1 Fixed steering column installation (Part 2 of 2). Crown Victoria, Grand Marquis, & Town Car**

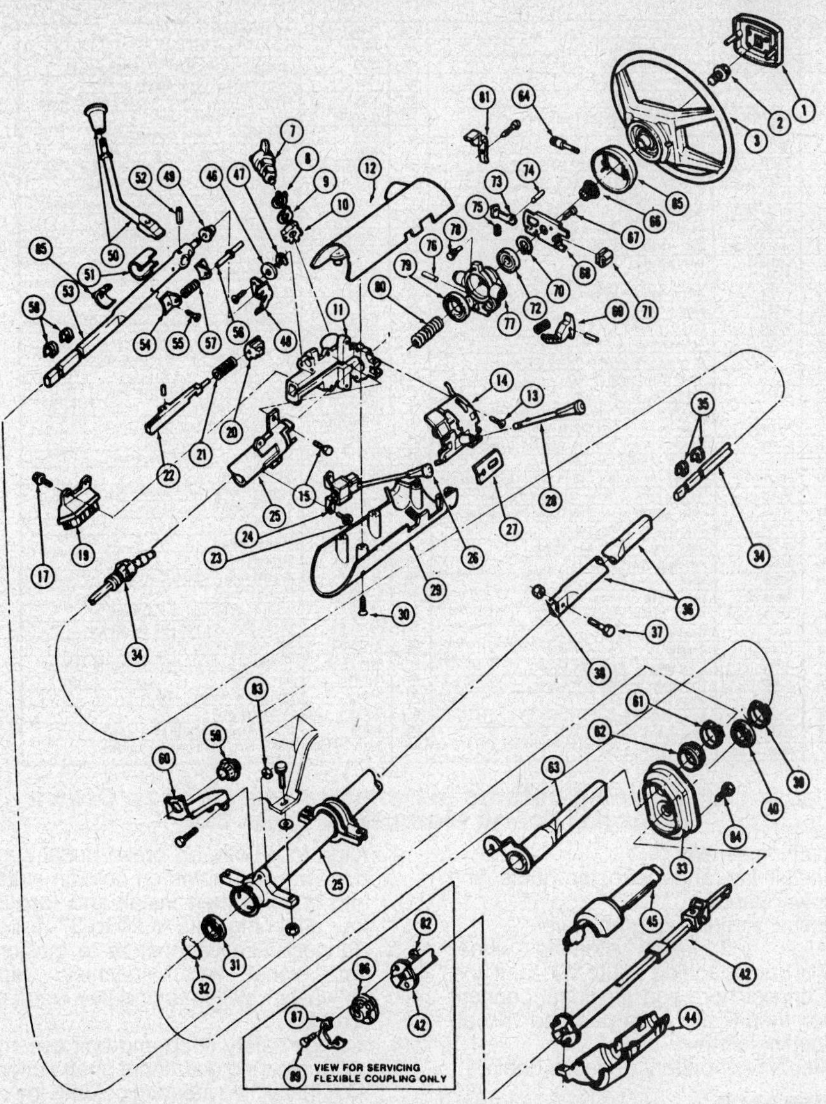


**Fig. 2 Tilt steering column installation (Part 1 of 2). Crown Victoria, Grand Marquis, & Town Car**

boot to dash panel and four nuts holding column to brake pedal support. Lower column to clear four mounting bolts and pull column so that U-joint assembly passes through clearance hole in dash panel.

### Installation

1. Install steering column by inserting U-joint assembly and lower shift cane through dash panel opening.
2. Align four bolts on brake pedal support with mounting holes on column collar and bracket. Install nuts loosely so that column is supported with clearance between column and instrument panel.
3. Loosely assemble PRND21 cable clamp onto steering column outer tube, then reach between steering column and instrument panel and attach PRND21 cable onto lever by slipping loop on cable over cleat on lever.
4. **Torque** four nuts retaining column to brake pedal support to 20-37 ft. lbs.
5. Move shift selector into Drive position against drive stop on insert plate. Then rotate PRND21 bracket located about midpoint on steering column outer tube clockwise or counterclockwise until PRND21 pointer in instrument cluster aligns with D. Tighten nut on bracket.
6. Connect ignition switch, turn signal switch and washer/wiper switch connectors.
7. Engage safety strap and bolt assembly with flange on steering gear input shaft. Then install two nuts attaching steering column lower shaft and U-joint assembly to flange on steering gear input shaft and **torque** nuts to 20-37 ft. lbs. **The safety strap must be properly positioned to prevent metal to metal contact after torquing the nuts. Also, flexible coupling must not be distorted when nuts are torqued. Pry steering shaft up or down with a pry bar to obtain ±1/8 inch coupling insulator flatness.**
8. Connect shift rod to shift lever at lower end of steering column using tool T67P-7341-A or equivalent. Make sure that a new grommet has been installed.
9. Loosen adjustment nut on transmission shift rod, then move manual lever to Drive position by rotating it rearward until it stops and then rotating forward two detent positions. Make sure shift lever handle on steering column is in Drive position. Apply a load of six pounds maximum on shift selector lever to assure that lever is located firmly against drive detent, then tighten nut on transmission shift rod.
10. Install dust boot, trim shrouds, hood release mechanism, steering column cover and steering wheel.
11. Reconnect battery ground cable and check steering column for proper operation.

## COUGAR & THUNDERBIRD

Refer to **Figs. 4 and 5** for steering column component identification.

1. Disconnect battery ground cable.
2. Separate horn pad and cover assembly from steering wheel. Disconnect horn electrical connector from contact plate terminal. If equipped, disconnect speed control electrical connector.
3. Remove and discard steering wheel attaching bolt.
4. Using a suitable puller, separate steering wheel from steering shaft. **To prevent damage to steering shaft bearing, never hit steering wheel attaching bolt or use a knock-off type steering wheel puller.**
5. Remove bolts retaining lower right-hand finish panel. Carefully separate finish panel from retaining clips.
6. Remove bolts retaining lower right-hand reinforcement panel, then the panel.
7. Remove screws retaining lower and upper steering column shrouds, then the shrouds.
8. Disconnect ignition key courtesy light, cruise control, ignition switch, multi-function switch and steering shock absorber sensor electrical connectors.
9. Remove pinch bolt from steering shaft U-joint.
10. Remove nuts retaining steering column.
11. Disconnect hazard warning electrical connector.
12. Remove screw retaining starter interlock switch, then the switch.
13. Remove steering column from vehicle.
14. Reverse procedure to install noting the following:
    a. **Torque** U-joint pinch bolt to 30-42 ft. lbs.
    b. **Torque** new steering wheel attaching bolt to 23-33 ft. lbs.

## PROBE

Refer to **Fig. 6**, for steering column component identification.

### Removal

1. Disconnect battery ground cable.

2. Working from back side of steering wheel, remove two horn pad attaching screws. Carefully separate horn pad from steering wheel, disconnect electrical connector, then place pad aside.
3. Remove steering wheel attaching nut.
4. **On 1989-90 models,** use a suitable puller, separate steering wheel from steering shaft.
5. **On 1991 models, do not use a steering wheel puller, using a puller will collapse the steering shaft.** Paint an aligning stripe on steering wheel and shaft, then pull steering wheel off.
6. **On all models,** remove two steering column cover attaching screws, then the cover.
7. Remove nine instrument cover attaching screws, then carefully pull instrument cover outward and remove ignition illumination bulb. Disconnect electrical connectors and remove cover.
8. Loosen two instrument cluster cover hinge screws.
9. Remove six instrument cluster cover attaching screws, then the cover.
10. Remove lower panel.
11. Remove lap and defroster ducts.
12. Disconnect four electrical connectors from turn signal switch assembly.
13. Remove U-joint cinch bolt from lower end of steering shaft.
14. Remove hinge bracket mounting nuts.
15. Remove four cluster support nuts.
16. Remove four nuts and two bolts from upper steering column bracket, then the steering shaft assembly.
17. Raise dust boot covering intermediate shaft U-joint at steering rack, then remove cinch bolt from U-joint.
18. Remove four intermediate shaft dust cover assembly attaching nuts, then the intermediate shaft assembly.

### Installation

1. Guide lower U-joint onto steering rack pinion while an assistant holds intermediate shaft and dust cover assembly. Install and **torque** cinch bolt to 13-20 ft. lbs.
2. Install dust cover assembly with retaining nuts.
3. Guide steering column into upper intermediate U-joint while an assistant holds the column. Do not install cinch bolt at this time.
4. Install hinge bracket nuts. Do not tighten at this time.
5. Install four upper column bracket bolts.
6. **Torque** hinge bracket nuts to 12-17 ft. lbs and upper bracket bolts to 12-17 ft. lbs.
7. Install and **torque** support nuts and cluster support nuts to 6.5-10 ft. lbs.
8. Connect ignition switch electrical connectors.
9. Install instrument cluster cover. Tighten attaching screws and two hinge screws.
10. Connect seven instrument cluster electrical connectors.
11. Install ignition illumination bulb.
12. Install instrument cover with nine attaching screws.
13. Install lap and defroster ducts and lower panel.
14. Install steering column cover.
15. Align and install steering wheel. **Torque** attaching nut to 29-36 ft. lbs.
16. Connect horn pad electrical connector, then install horn pad and two attaching screws.
17. Reconnect battery negative cable.

| ITEM | PART NO. | DESCRIPTION |
|---|---|---|
| 1. | 3A515 | Emblem Assy. |
| 2. | N804217 | Bolt - M10 × 1.50 × 17.0 Hex |
| 3. | 3600 | Wheel Assy. |
| 7. | | Lock Cyl. — Body |
| 8. | N800205-S100 | Ring — 24 × 1.07 Retaining Type |
| 9. | 3E700 | Bearing |
| 10. | 3E717 | Gear — Steering Column Lock |
| 11. | 3E643 | Housing — Strng. Col. Lock Cyl. |
| 12. | 3530 | Shroud — Upper |
| 13. | 52794-S2 | Screw — No. 8 × 18 × .62 Pan Head (2 Req'd.) |
| 14. | 13B302 | Switch Assy. — Turn & Emergency |
| 15. | N605531-S2 | Bolt — M8 × 1.25 Hex. Hd. (2 Req'd.) |
| 17. | N804855-S100 | Bolt (2 Req'd.) |
| 19. | 11572 | Switch Assy. — Ignifion |
| 20. | 3E691 | Pawl — Strng. Col. Lock |
| 21. | 3E696 | Spring — Strng. Col. Lock |
| 22. | 3E723 | Actuator Assy. — Strng. Col. Lock |
| 23. | | Screws — Wash/Wipe Switch (Body) |
| 24. | | Wash/Wipe Switch (Body) |
| 25. | 3A617 | Tube Assy. — Col. Outer |
| 26. | | Handle & Shank Assy. — Wash/Wipe (Body) |
| 27. | 13B365 | Foam Cover — Turn Sig. & W/W Switch |
| 28. | 13305 | Handle & Shank Assy. — Turn Sig. Switch |
| 29. | 3530 | Shroud — Strng. Col. Lower |
| 30. | 55931-S2 | Screw — No. 8-18 × 1.50 Pan Hd. Tap (5 Req'd.) |
| 31. | 3E733 | Bearing Assy. — Strng. Gear Shaft Lower |
| 32. | 3F543 | Ring — Strng. Gear Shaft Lower Bearing Retainer |
| 33. | 3E735 | Boot Assy. — Strng. Col. |
| 34. | 3A526 | Shaft Assy. — Strng. Col. Upper |
| 35. | 3E744 | Anti-Rattle Clip (2 Req'd.) |
| 36. | 3E628 | Shaft — Strng. Gear Lower |
| 37. | 58655-S2 | Bolt — 7/16 × 14 Hex. |
| 38. | 388795-S100 | Nut — 7/16-14 × 1.50 |
| 39. | 3507 | Retainer Bearing |
| 40. | 3E733 | Bearing |
| 41. | 3C662 | Shaft Assy. — Strng. Col. Lower |
| 42. | 3C662 | Shaft Assy. — Strng. Col. Lower |
| 44. | 3F540 | Stone Shield Lower |
| 45. | 3F540 | Stone Shield Upper |
| 46. | 388021-S2 | Ring — 5/16 Retainer |
| 47. | N800178-S2 | Washer — 8.23 Flat |
| 48. | 7A216 | Insert — Trans. Control |
| 49. | 7225 | Bearing — Trans. Gear Shift Lever Socket |
| 50. | 7202 | Lever Assy. — Trans. Control Selector |
| 51. | 7C369 | Cover — Trans. Control Selector Lever Opening |
| 52. | N100198 | Pin — 5mm Spring Coiled |
| 53. | 7212 | Tube Assy. — Trans. Control Selector |
| 54. | 3E543 | Retainer — Strng. Col. Lever (2 Req'd.) |
| 55. | N800210-S2 | Screw — 4mm 0.7 × 12.7 Type "D" Oval (2 Req'd.) |
| 56. | 7361 | Plunger — Trans. Control Selector Lever |
| 57. | 7B071 | Spring — Trans. Control Selector Lever Return |
| 58. | 3E629 | Anti-Rattle Clip (2 Req'd.) |
| 59. | 7K189 | Bushing — Trans. Gear Shift Shaft |
| 60. | 7K730 | Brkt. — Trans. Gear Shift Support |
| 61. | 3507 | Retainer Bearing |
| 62. | 3E733 | Bearing |
| 63. | 7212 | Tube Assy. — Trans. Control Selector |
| 64. | 3F609 | Tilt Strng. Wheel Lever — Handle & Shank Assy. |
| 65. | 3R564 | Extension — Strng. Wheel Shroud |
| 66. | 3520 | Spring — Strng. Col. Upper Bearing |
| 67. | 52794-S2 | Screw (2 Req'd.) |
| 68. | 3L525 | Plate — Strng. Col. Clip Retainer |
| 69. | 3B662 | Lever — Strng. Col. Lock |
| 70. | 97476-S100 | Ring — 3/4 Retaining Type |
| 71. | 3K712 | Clip — Strng. Col. Shroud |
| 72. | 3517 | Bearing Assy. — Strng. Col. Upper |
| 73. | 3D544 | Release Lever |
| 74. | 3C732 | Spring — Strng. Col. Release Lever |
| 75. | N800329 | Pin — 4mm × 5.75 |
| 76. | 3D739 | Pivot Pin |
| 77. | 3511 | Flange Casting |
| 78. | 3D656 | Bumpers |
| 79. | 3517 | Bearing Assy. — Strng. Col. Upper |
| 80. | 3D655 | Position Spring |
| 81. | 3E745 | Cover — Strng. Col. Lock Actuator |
| 82. | 56724-S2 | Bolt — 5/16-18 × 1.50 Hex. Hd. Flange |
| 83. | 34976-S2 | Nut — 5/16-18 Hex. P.T. |
| 84. | 388489-S9 | Screw — No. 8 × .75 Hex. Washer Hd. Tapping |
| 85. | 3C686 | Spacer Clip |
| 86. | 3A525 | Flange and Insulator Assy. |
| 87. | 3B629 | Reinforcement |
| 88. | 34976 | S100 — Nut — 5/16-18 Hex. Lock |
| 89. | 383177-S100 | Bolt — 5/16-18 × 1.00 Hex. Shoulder |

**Fig. 2 Tilt steering column installation (Part 2 of 2). Crown Victoria, Grand Marquis, & Town Car**

## MUSTANG

Refer to **Figs. 7 and 8,** for component identification.

### Removal

1. Disconnect battery ground cable.
2. Remove steering wheel from steering shaft.
3. Remove two flexible coupling to steering gear input shaft attaching nuts, then disengage safety strap and bolt assembly from flexible coupling.
4. Remove steering column trim shrouds.
5. Remove steering column cover and hood release mechanism located under steering column.
6. Disconnect wire connectors from turn signal, windshield wiper/washer and ignition switches and key warning buzzer.
7. Remove four screws attaching dust boot to dash panel.
8. Remove four nuts attaching steering column to brake pedal support, then lower column assembly to clear four mounting bolts and remove column assembly from vehicle.

### Installation

1. Insert U-joint assembly through opening in dash panel.
2. Align four bolts on brake pedal support with bolt holes on column collar and bracket, then install and **torque** four attaching nuts to 20 to 37 ft. lbs.
3. Connect wire connectors to ignition, turn signal and windshield wiper/washer switches and key warning buzzer.
4. Engage safety strap and bolt assembly to steering gear input shaft flange, then install two steering column lower shaft and U-joint assembly to input shaft flange attaching nuts. **Torque** nuts to 20 to 37 ft. lbs. **The safety strap must be properly positioned to prevent metal to metal contact. Also, the flexible coupling must not be distorted when nuts are torqued. Pry steering haft upward or downward to obtain ±1/8 inch coupling insulator flatness.**
5. Engage dust boot at end of steering column to dash panel opening, then install four dust boot attaching screws.
6. Install steering wheel on steering shaft.
7. Install steering column trim shrouds.
8. Install hood release mechanism and steering column cover.
9. Connect battery ground cable and check steering column for proper operation.

## TEMPO, TOPAZ & 1989–90 ESCORT

Refer to **Figs. 9 through 11** for steering column component identification.

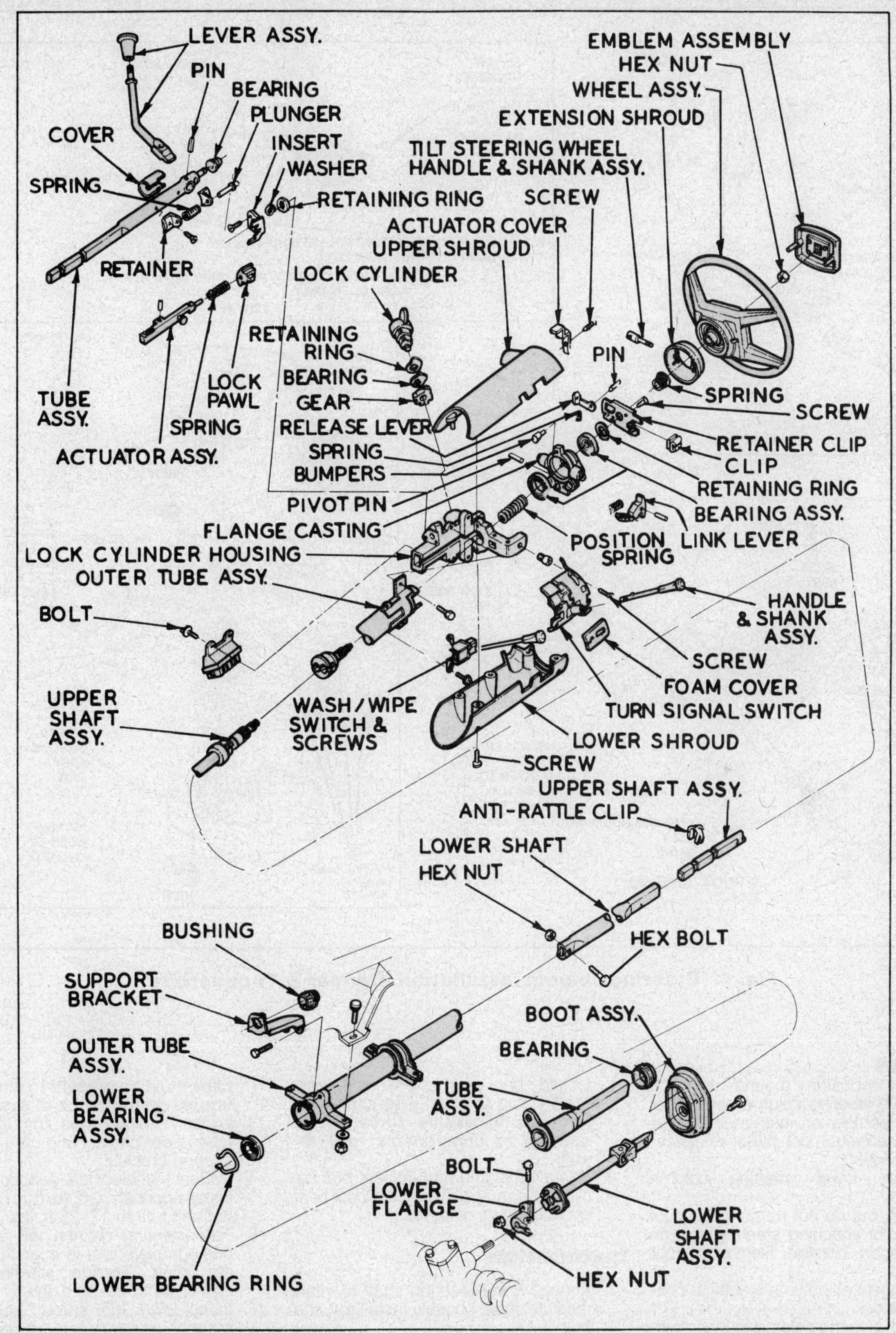


**Fig. 3 Tilt steering column w/column shift exploded view. Mark VII**

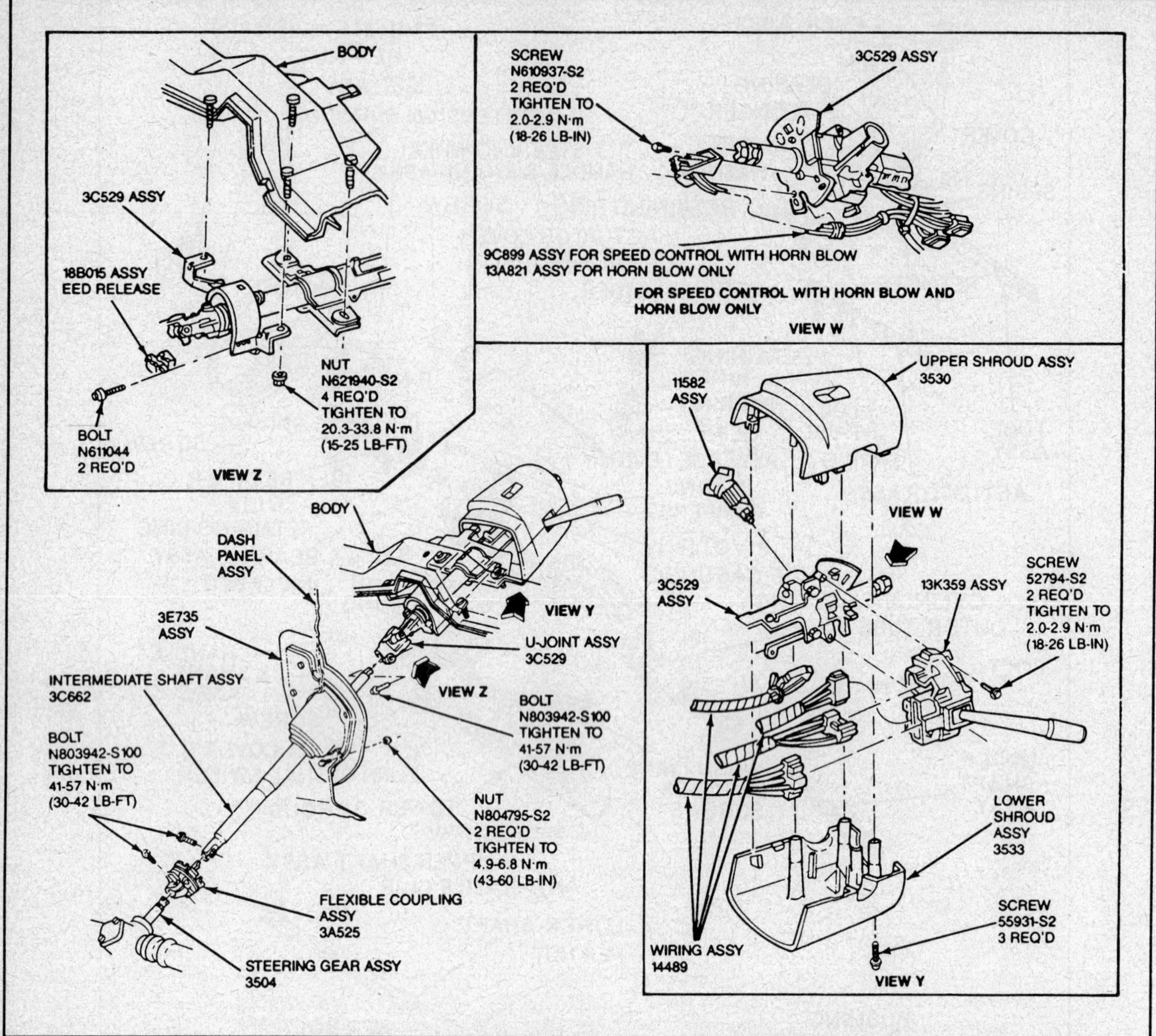


**Fig. 4 Steering column installation. Cougar & Thunderbird**

## Removal

1. Disconnect battery ground cable.
2. Remove steering column cover from lower portion of instrument panel, then the instrument panel reinforcement section.
3. Remove lower steering column shroud.
4. Loosen, but do not remove two nuts and bolts attaching steering column to support bracket. Remove upper shroud.
5. Disconnect all column electrical connectors.
6. Loosen steering column to intermediate shaft clamp and remove nut or bolt.
7. Remove two nuts and bolts attaching column to support bracket and lower column to floor. With steering column locked, pry open steering column shaft clamp to disengage shafts. **Do not use excessive force, since damage to components may result.**
8. Remove column and inspect bracket clips for damage. Replace clips if bent or excessively distorted.

## Installation

1. Engage lower steering shaft to intermediate shaft. Loosely install nut and bolt.
2. Place steering column under instrument panel, align bolts of support bracket with outer tube and loosely install two nuts. Check for presence of two clips on outer bracket. **These clips must be present to ensure adequate performance of system.**
3. Loosely install bolts through outer tube upper bracket and clips and into support bracket.
4. Connect all electrical connectors and install upper shroud, **torque** mounting nut and bolt to 17-25 ft. lbs.
5. Turn steering column left and right one complete turn to align intermediate shaft. **Torque** steering shaft clamp nut to 20-30 ft. lbs.
6. Install lower trim shroud and instrument panel reinforcement section.
7. Install steering column cover on instrument panel.
8. Connect battery ground cable and check steering column for proper operation.

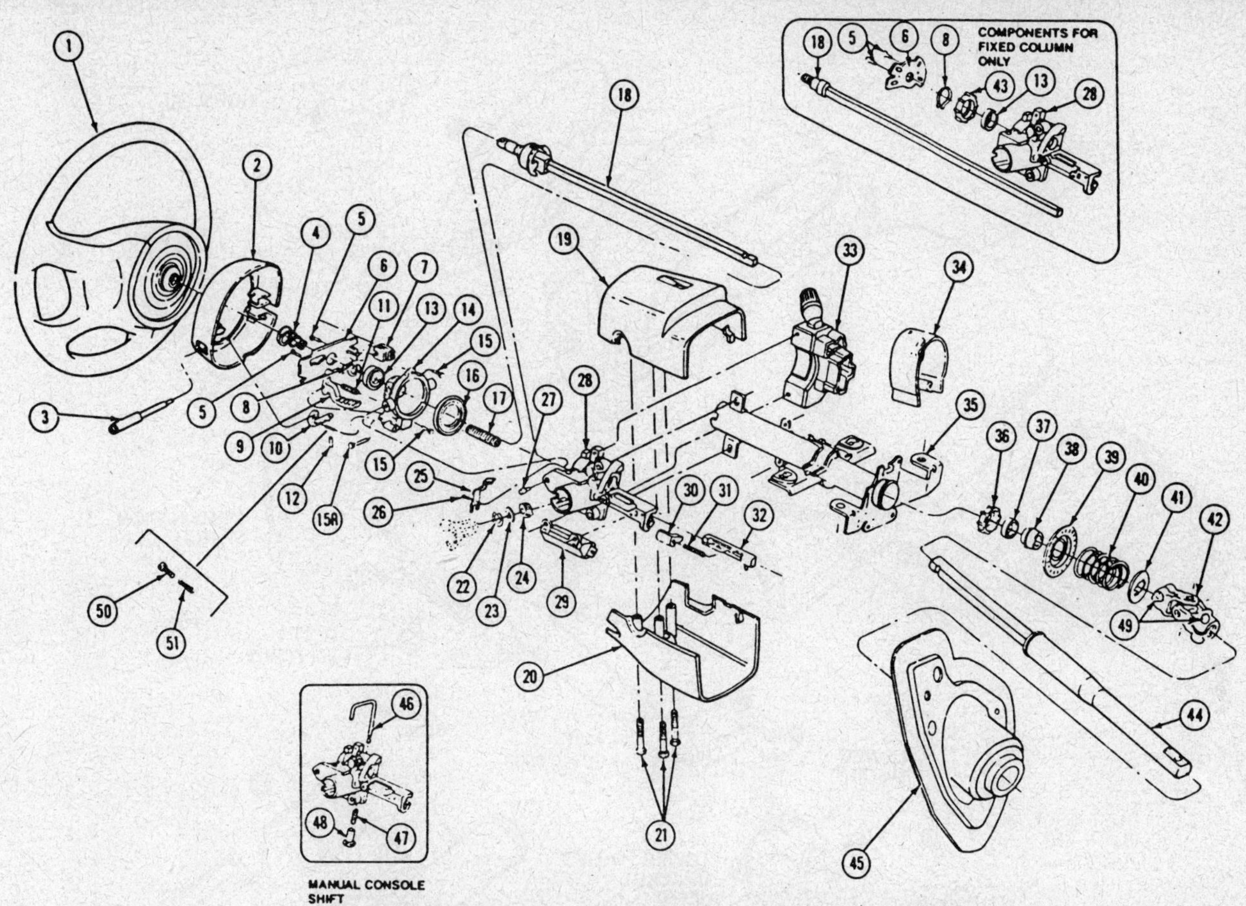


| Item | Part Number | Description | Item | Part Number | Description |
|---|---|---|---|---|---|
| 1 | 3600 | Steering Wheel Assembly | 26 | 390345-S36 | Screw |
| 2 | 3R564 | Steering Column Shroud Extension | 27 | 3D739 | Pivot Pin |
| 3 | 3F609 | Tilt Wheel Handle and Shank Assembly | 28 | 3F643 (Fixed), 3F642 (Tilt) | Lock Cylinder Housing |
| 4 | 3520 | Upper Bearing Spring | 29 | 11572 | Ignition Switch Assembly |
| 5 | 390345-S36 | Retainer Plate Screws | 30 | 3E691 | Steering Column Lock Pawl |
| 6 | 3C610 (Fixed), 3L525 (Tilt) | Steering Column Clip Retainer Plate | 31 | 3E696 | Steering Column Lock Spring |
| 7 | 3K712 | Shroud Clip | 32 | 3E723 | Steering Column Lock Actuator Assembly |
| 8 | 3C610 (Fixed), 97476-S9M (Tilt) | Retaining Clip | 33 | 13K359 | Multi-Function Switch Assembly |
| 9 | 3B662 | Steering Column Lever Link | 34 | 3F724 | Shield |
| 10 | 3D544 | Release Lever | 35 | 3514 | Steering Column Tube Assembly |
| 11 | 3B768 | Position Lock Spring | 36 | 3518 | Lower Bearing Sleeve |
| 12 | N801012-S | Pin | 37 | 3517 | Lower Column Shaft Bearing |
| 13 | 3517 | Upper Bearing Assembly | 38 | 3C664 | Sleeve |
| 14 | 3511 | Flange Housing | 39 | 3C131 | Sensor Ring |
| 15 | 3D656 | Rubber Bumpers | 40 | 3C674 | Sensor Ring Spring |
| 15A | — | Pin | 41 | 3D682 | Spring Retainer Ring |
| 16 | 3517 | Bearing Assembly | 42 | 3N725 | Lower Column Shaft Assembly |
| 17 | 3D655 | Position Spring | 43 | 3518 | Upper Bearing |
| 18 | 3A526 (Fixed), 3D657 (Tilt) | Shaft Assembly | 44 | 3C662 | Intermediate Shaft |
| 19 | 3530 | Upper Shroud | 45 | 3E735 | Lower Column Boot Assembly |
| 20 | 3533 | Lower Shroud | 46 | 3F528 | Lock Actuator Lever (Manual Trans. Only) |
| 21 | 55921-S2 | Screws | 47 | 3E696 | Lock Actuator Spring |
| 22 | 3F579 | Retainer | 48 | 3F531 | Lock Actuator Knob |
| 23 | 3E700 | Bearing | 49 | N803942-S100 | Bolt |
| 24 | 3E717 | Lock Gear | 50 | 3E518 | Cap |
| 25 | 3E745 | Lock Actuator Cover | 51 | 3C732 | Spring |

**Fig. 5 Steering column exploded view. Cougar & Thunderbird**

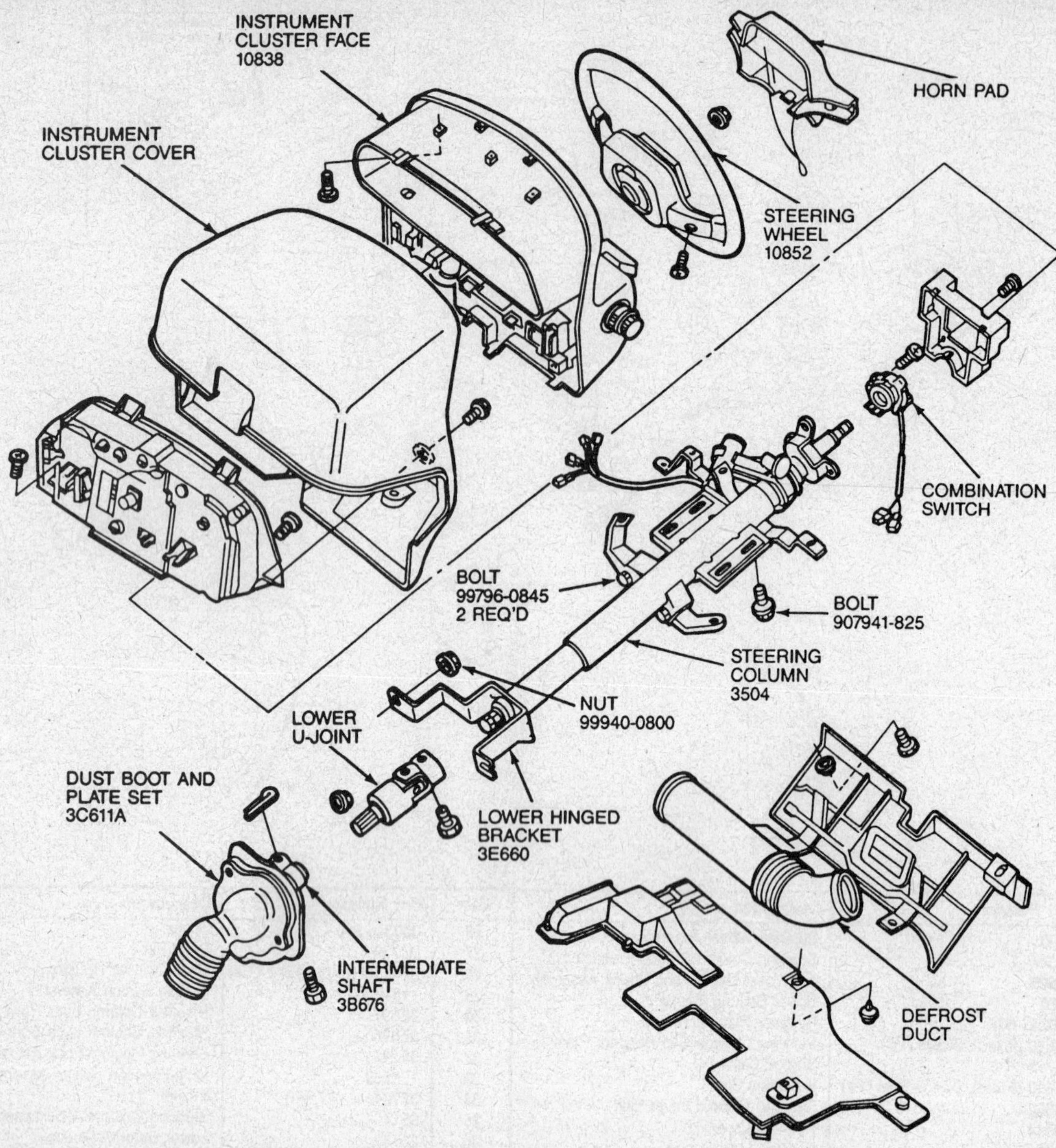


**Fig. 6 Steering column installation. Probe**

## 1991 ESCORT & TRACER

### Removal

1. Disconnect battery ground cable.
2. Remove steering wheel cover retaining screws from back side of steering wheel, then the cover.
3. Lift pad cover slightly at bottom, then slide it upward until center tab clears slots in steering wheel. Disconnect horn connector and speed control connectors, if equipped. Lift cover away from steering wheel.
4. Remove steering wheel retaining nut, then using a puller, T67L-3600-A or equivalent, remove steering wheel. Do not use or attempt to use a hammer to remove a steering wheel.
5. Remove four steering column lower cover attaching, then the lower cover.
6. Remove upper cover and disconnect three multi-function switch connectors.
7. Remove multi-function switch retaining screw, then pull electrical connectors from bracket and remove switch.
8. Disconnect ignition switch electrical connector, then remove shift-lock cable mounting bracket bolt, place bracket and cable aside.
9. Remove four steering column upper mounting bracket bolts and lower column.
10. Remove five set plate mounting nuts, then the set plate.
11. Remove intermediate shaft to pinion shaft bolt, two steering column lower mounting bracket nuts, then the column.

### Installation

1. Position steering column and install two lower mounting bracket nuts, then the intermediate shaft to pinion shaft bolts. **Torque** bolts 30-36 ft. lbs.
2. Position set plate, then install five mounting nuts.
3. Install four steering column upper mounting bracket bolts, **torquing** to 80-123 ft. lbs.
4. Position shift lock cable mounting bracket and install bolt, **torque** bolt to 37-55 inch lbs.
5. Connect ignition switch electrical connectors and install multi-function switch.
6. Position steering wheel, then install retaining nut. **Torque** nut to 29-36 ft. lbs.
7. Connect horn electrical connectors and speed control connectors, if equipped.
8. Position steering wheel cover and install retaining screws.

## SABLE, TAURUS & CONTINENTAL

Refer to **Figs. 12 and 13** for steering column component identification.

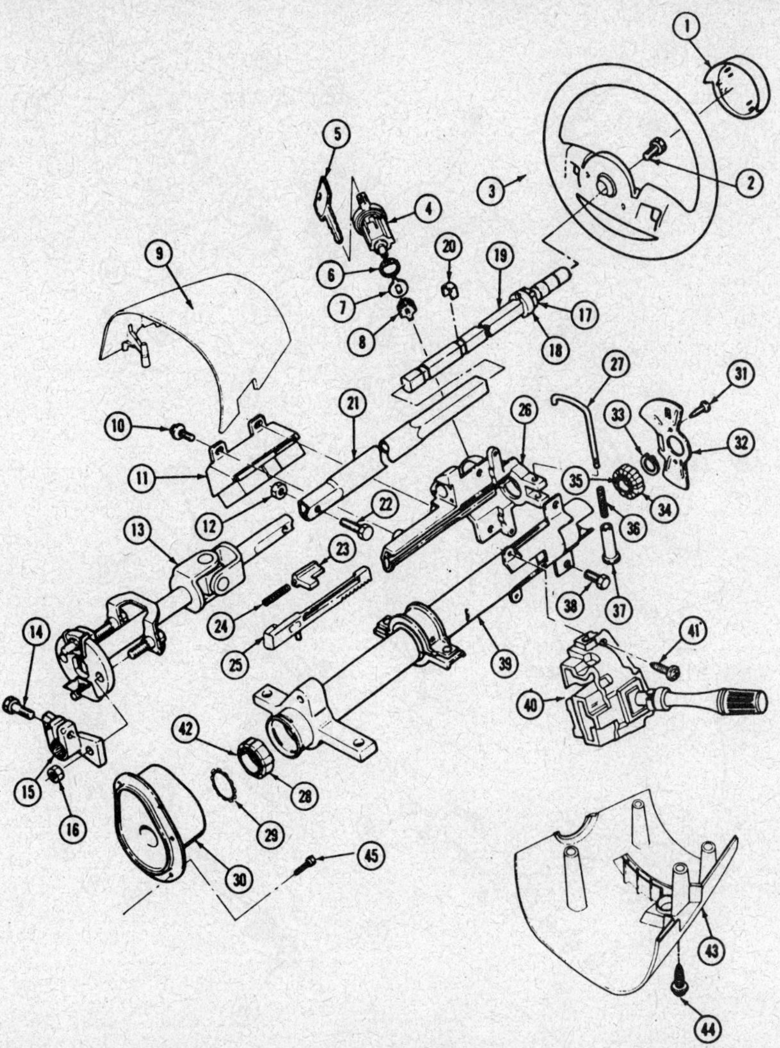


**Fig. 7 Fixed steering column exploded view (Part 1 of 2). . Mustang**

| ITEM | PART NO. | DESCRIPTION | ITEM | PART NO. | DESCRIPTION |
|---|---|---|---|---|---|
| 1. | 13K802 | Emblem Assy. | 24. | 3E696 | Spring — Stng. Col. Lock |
| 2. | N804385 | Bolt | 25. | 3E723 | Actuator Assy. — Stng. Col. Lock |
| 3. | 3600 | Wheel Assy. — Stng. | 26. | 3F643 | Housing — Stng. Col. Lock Cyl. |
| 4. | 11582 | Lock Cyl. | 27. | 3F528 | Lever — Stng. Col. Lock Actuator |
| 5. | | Key (Body) | 28. | 3E733 | Bearing Assy. — Stng. Gear Shaft Lower |
| 6. | 3F579 | Retainer | 29. | 3F543 | Ring — Stng. Gear Shaft Lower Bearing Retainer |
| 7. | 3E700 | Bearing | 30. | 3E735 | Boot Assy. — Stng. Col. |
| 8. | 3E717 | Gear — Stng. Col. Lock | 31. | 390345 | Screw — No. 8-18 × .62 Pan Hd. Tap (2 Req'd.) |
| 9. | 3530 | Shroud — Upper | 32. | 3610 | Retainer — Stng. Col. Upper Bearing |
| 10. | N804855-S100 | Bolt (2 Req'd.) | 33. | 3C610 | Retainer — Stng. Col. Upper Bearing |
| 11. | 11572 | Switch Assy. — Ignition | 34. | 3518 | Sleeve — Stng. Col. Upper Bearing |
| 12. | 388795-S100 | Nut — 7/16-14 Hex Lock | 35. | 3517 | Bearing Assy. — Stng. Col. Upper |
| 13. | 3C662 | Shaft Assy. — Stng. Col. Lower | 36. | 3E696 | Spring — Stng. Col. Lock |
| 14. | 385970-S100 | Bolt — 3/8-24 × 1.22 | 37. | | Knob — Stng. Col. Lock Actuator |
| 15. | 3459 | Flange — Stng. Shaft Lower | 38. | N605531-S2 | Bolt — M8 × 1.25 Hex Hd. (2 Req'd.) |
| 16. | 34977-S2 | Nut — 3/8-16 Hex Lock | 39. | 3A617 | Tube Assy. Col. Outer |
| 17. | 13318 | Cam — Turn Sig. Turn Off | 40. | 13K759 | Multi-Function Switch |
| 18. | 3B767 | Lock — Stng. Col. Position | 41. | 52794-S2 | Screw — No. 8-18 × .62 Pan Hd. Tap (2 Req'd.) |
| 19. | 3A527 | Shaft — Stng. Gear Upper | 42. | 3A649 | Sleeve — Steering Column Lower Bearing |
| 20. | 3E629 | Anti-Rattle Clips (2 Req'd.) | 43. | 3530 | Shroud — Stng. Col. Lower |
| 21. | 3E628 | Shaft — Stng. Gear Lower | 44. | 55931-S2 | Screw — No. 8-18 × 1.50 Pan Hd. Tap (5 Req'd.) |
| 22. | 58655-S2 | Bolt — 7/16-14 × 1.50 Hex | | | |
| 23. | 3E691 | Pawl — Stng. Col. Lock | 45. | 388489-S2 | Screw (4 Req'd.) |

**Fig. 7 Fixed steering column exploded view (Part 2 of 2). . Mustang**

## Removal

1. Disconnect battery ground cable.
2. Remove steering column cover from lower portion of instrument panel by taking out self-tapping screws.
3. **On models equipped with tilt column,** remove tilt release lever by removing one retaining screw.
4. **On all models,** remove ignition lock cylinder.
5. Remove three self tapping screws from bottom of lower shroud, then the shroud.
6. Remove horn pad and steering wheel assembly.
7. **On models equipped with column shift,** proceed as follows:
    a. Disconnect PRNDL cable from lock cylinder housing by removing retaining screw.
    b. Disconnect PRNDL cable from shift socket.
    c. Remove PRNDL cable from retaining hook on bottom of lock cylinder housing.
8. **On all models,** disconnect speed control/horn brush wiring connector from main wiring harness.
9. Remove multi-function switch wiring harness retainer from lock cylinder housing by squeezing end of retainer and pushing out.
10. Disconnect multi-function switch connector from switch and remove switch from lock cylinder housing by removing two self tapping screws.
11. Disconnect key warning buzzer switch electrical connector from main wiring harness.
12. Disconnect electrical connector from ignition switch.
13. Disconnect steering shaft from intermediate shaft by removing two nuts and one U-clamp.
14. **On models equipped with column shift,** proceed as follows:
    a. Remove shift cable plastic terminal from column selector lever pivot ball using a screwdriver and prying between plastic terminal and selector lever. Be careful not to damage cable during or after assembly.
    b. Remove shift cable bracket (with shift cable still attached) from lock cylinder housing by taking out two retaining screws.
15. **On models equipped with automatic parking brake release mechanism,** remove vacuum hose from parking brake release switch.
16. **On models equipped with tilt column,** remove tilt return spring.
17. **On all models,** unbolt column assembly from mounting bracket by removing bolt or nuts.
18. While supporting column assembly, unbolt column assembly from steering column support bracket by removing two bolts or nuts.
19. Rotate column assembly so that intermediate bracket mounting flanges will pass through instrument panel opening and slowly pull column assembly through instrument panel.

## Installation

1. Rotate column assembly so that inter-

mediate bracket mounting flanges will pass through instrument panel opening and slowly slide column assembly forward while feeding steering shaft universal joint tongue over forward mounting bracket.

2. Rotate column assembly clockwise and hand start two retaining bolts that attach column assembly to column support bracket.
3. Hand start one TORX head bolt that attaches column assembly to intermediate mounting bracket.
4. Center column assembly in instrument opening. **Tighten** TORX head bolt or nuts to 15-25 ft. lbs.
5. **Torque** two retaining bolts or nuts to 15-25 ft. lbs.
6. **On models equipped with tilt column,** attach tilt return spring.
7. **On models equipped with automatic parking brake release mechanism,** install vacuum hose on parking brake release switch.
8. **On models equipped with column shift,** proceed as follows:
   a. Attach shift cable bracket (with shift cable attached) to lock cylinder housing with two retaining screws. **Torque** to 30-60 inch lbs.
   b. Snap transmission shift cable terminal to selector lever pivot ball on steering column.
9. **On all models,** connect steering shaft to intermediate shaft with one U-clamp and two hex nuts. **Torque** to 15-25 ft. lbs. Tilt column must be in middle position before nuts are tightened.
10. Reconnect ignition switch electrical connector.
11. Reconnect key warning buzzer switch electrical connector.
12. Install multi-function switch to lock cylinder housing with two self tapping screws.
13. Install multi-function switch wiring harness retainer over shroud mounting boss and snap it into the slot in lock cylinder housing.
14. Reconnect speed control/horn brush electrical connector to main wiring harness.
15. **On models equipped with column shift,** proceed as follows:
   a. Install PRNDL cable into retaining hook on lock cylinder housing.
   b. Connect PRNDL cable to shift socket.
   c. Loosely install PRNDL cable onto lock cylinder housing with one retaining screw.
   d. To adjust PRNDL cable, place shift lever in Drive position with CLC transmission or in Overdrive position with AXOD transmission. Adjust PRNDL cable until pointer is centered on D for CLC transmission or OD on AXOD transmission. Tighten hex head screw. Cycle shift lever through all positions and ensure PRNDL pointer is centered over proper letter or number in each position.
16. Install steering wheel, horn pad and shrouds.
17. **On tilt columns,** install tilt release le-

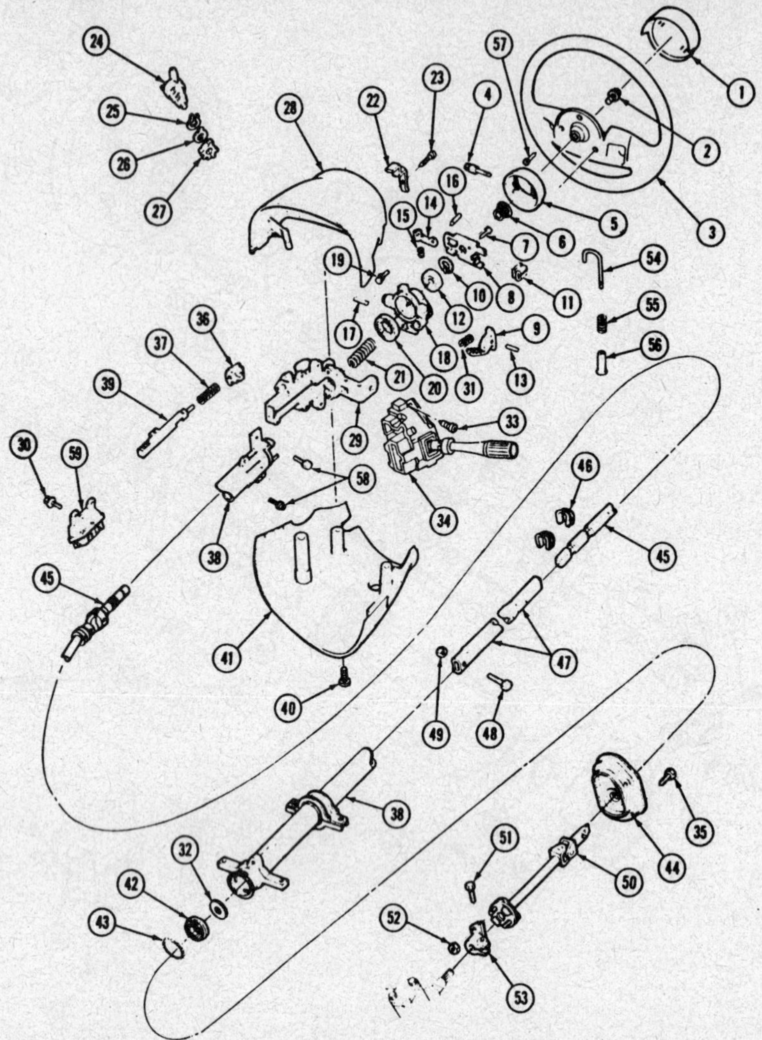

**Fig. 8 Tilt steering column exploded view (Part 1 of 2). Mustang**

| ITEM | PART NO. | DESCRIPTION | ITEM | PART NO. | DESCRIPTION |
|---|---|---|---|---|---|
| 1. | 13K802 | Emblem Assy. | 31. | 3B768 | Spring — Steering Column Position Lock |
| 2. | N804385 | Bolt | 32. | 3A649 | Sleeve — Steering Column Lower Bearing |
| 3. | 3600 | Wheel Assy. — Strng. | 33. | 52794-S2 | Screw No. 8-18 x .62 Pan Head Tap (2 Req'd.) |
| 4. | 3F609 | Handle & Shank Assy. — Tilt Strng. Wheel Lever | 34. | 13K759 | Multi-Function Switch |
| 5. | 3R564 | Extension — Strng. Col. Shroud | 35. | 388489 | Screw |
| 6. | 3520 | Spring — Strng. Col. Upper Bearing | 36. | 3E691 | Pawl — Strng. Col. Lock |
| 7. | 390345 | Screw | 37. | 3E696 | Spring — Strng. Col. Lock |
| 8. | 3L525 | Plate Strng. Col. Clip Retainer | 38. | 3A617 | Tube Assy. Col. Outer |
| 9. | 3B662 | Lever Strng. Col. Lock | 39. | 3E723 | Actuator Assy. — Strng. Col. Lock |
| 10. | 97476-S100 | Ring 3/4 Retaining Type | 40. | 55931-S2 | Screw No. 8-18 x 1.50 Pan Head Tap (5 Req'd.) |
| 11. | 3K712 | Clip — Strng. Col. Shroud | 41. | 3530 | Shroud — Strng. Col. Lower |
| 12. | 3517 | Bearing Assy. — Strng. Col. Upper | 42. | 3E733 | Bearing Assy. — Strng. Gear Shaft Lower |
| 13. | N800328-S | Pin 4mm x 25.6 Straight Round End | 43. | 3F543 | Ring — Strng. Gear Shaft Lower Bearing Retainer |
| 14. | 3D544 | Release Lever | 44. | 3E735 | Boot Assy. — Strng. Col. |
| 15. | 3C732 | Spring — Strng. Col. Release Lever | 45. | 3A526 | Shaft Assy. — Strng. Col. Upper |
| 16. | N801012 | Pin — 4mm x 5.75 | 46. | 3E629 | Anti-Rattle Clips (2 Req'd.) |
| 17. | 3D739 | Pivot Pin | 47. | 3E628 | Shaft — Strng. Gear Lower |
| 18. | 3511 | Flange Casting | 48. | 58655-S2 | Bolt 7/16-14 x 1.50 Hex |
| 19. | 3D656 | Bumpers | 49. | 388795-S100 | Nut 7/16-14 Hex Lock |
| 20. | 3517 | Bearing Assy. — Strng. Col. Upper | 50. | 3C662 | Shaft Assy. — Strng. Col. Lower |
| 21. | 3D655 | Position Spring | 51. | 385970-S100 | Bolt — 3/8-24 x 1.22 |
| 22. | 3E745 | Cover — Strng. Col. Lock Actuator | 52. | 34977-S2 | Nut 3/8-16 Hex Lock |
| 23. | 390345 | Screw | 53. | 3459 | Flange — Strng. Shaft Lower |
| 24. | 11582 | Lock Cyl. | 54. | 3F528 | Lever — Strng. Col. Lock Actuator |
| 25. | N800205-S100 | Ring 24 x 1.07 Retainer Type | 55. | 3E696 | Spring — Strng. Col. Lock |
| 26. | 3E700 | Bearing | 56. | 3F531 | Knob — Strng. Col. Lock Actuator |
| 27. | 3E717 | Gear — Strng. Col. Lock | 57. | 56903-S2 | Screw — Strng. Wheel |
| 28. | 3530 | Shroud — Upper | 58. | N605531 | Bolt |
| 29. | 3F642 | Housing — Strng. Col. Lock Cyl. | 59. | 11572 | Ignition Switch |
| 30. | N804855-S100 | Bolt | | | |

**Fig. 8 Tilt steering column exploded view (Part 2 of 2). Mustang**

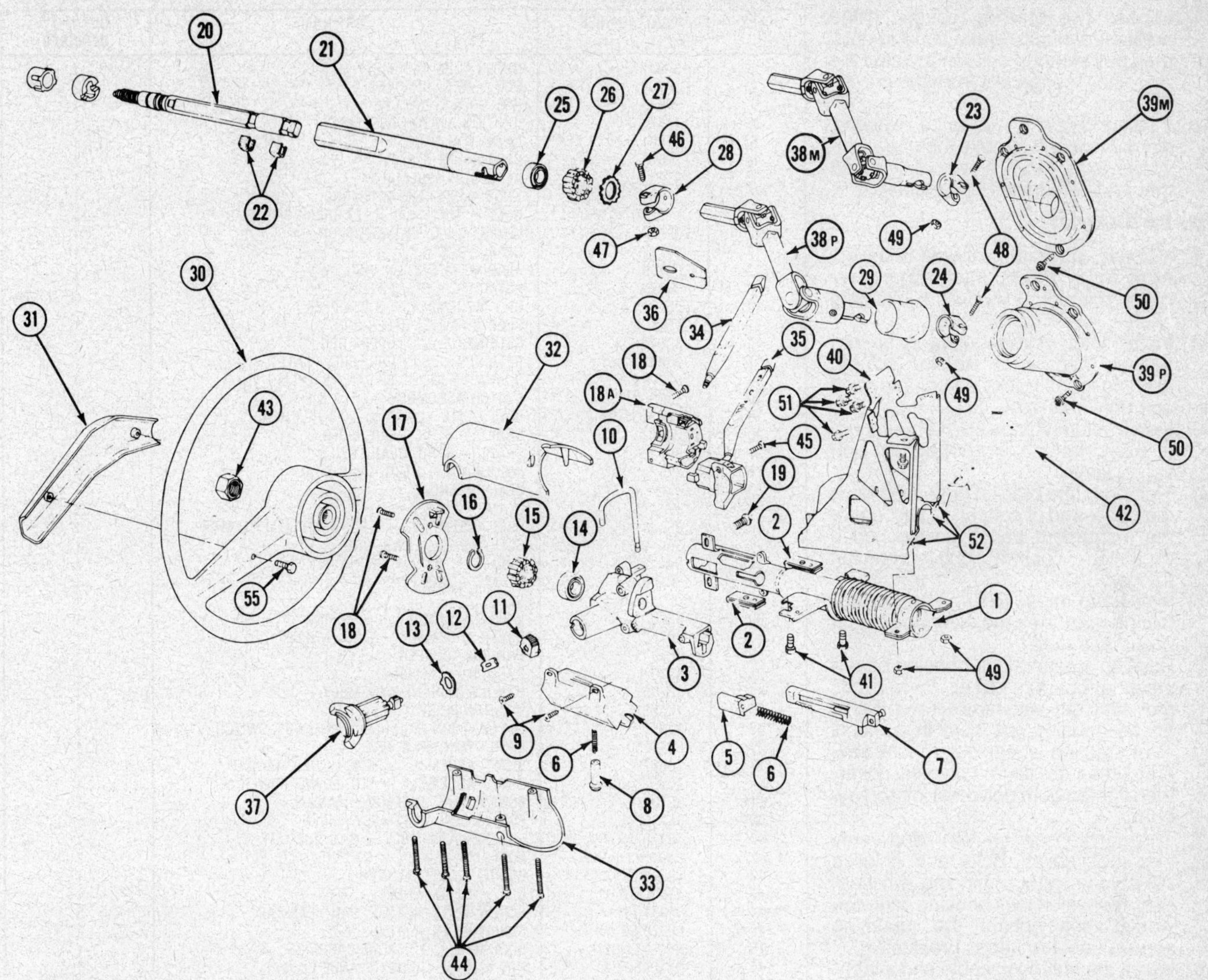


**Fig. 9 Fixed steering column exploded view (Part 1 Of 2). Tempo, Topaz & 1989–90 Escort**

ver.

18. Install ignition lock cylinder and steering column cover.
19. Connect battery ground cable and ensure all steering column functions operate properly.

## FESTIVA
### 1989–90

Disassembly of the steering column, **Fig. 14,** involves removal of the steering wheel, combination switch, ignition switch, ignition lock and tilt mechanism, if equipped. Beyond this, the basic steering column consisting of shaft, jacket, bearings and lower hinge bracket is serviced as an assembly.

To disassemble and assemble the tilt mechanism, proceed as follows:

1. Remove lock lever screw and lock lever, then the adjusting nut and tilt clamp bolt.
2. Separate column upper mount bracket from column assembly, **Fig. 14.**
3. Position upper bracket on column, then install clamp bolt from left side, engaging lands under bolt head with slot in bracket.
4. Install adjusting nut and **torque** to 7-11 ft. lbs.
5. Install lock lever on adjusting nut, position lever against stop, then **torque** lever screw to 13-19 ft. lbs.
6. Check tilt mechanism for proper operation.

### 1991
#### Removal

1. Disconnect battery negative cable, then set front wheels in straight line.
2. Remove two steering wheel cover retaining screws, then disconnect horn wire and remove cover.
3. Remove steering wheel nut, then mark steering wheel and column shaft for assembly reference.
4. Remove steering wheel using a steering wheel puller T67L-3600-A or equivalent.
5. Remove combination switch and ignition switch.
6. Remove shift lock cable attaching bolt, then disconnect cable from lock housing.
7. Using slim-nose locking pliers, remove round-head mounting screws securing steering lock housing and cap to steering column jacket. Remove the lock housing.
8. Remove four shield nuts, then the column shield.
9. Remove two upper steering column to instrument panel mounting nuts, then lower upper end of column to gain access to intermediate shaft universal joint.
10. Make an index mark at juncture of steering shaft and intermediate shaft upper universal joint for proper alignment during installation. Remove universal joint clamp screw.

11. Loosen two steering column hinge bracket to clutch/brake support nuts, then pull steering column towards the rear and disengage it from the universal joint.
12. If steering gear needs to be removed, index mark and remove the upper universal joint. Mark universal joint, so that ends are installed correctly.

### Installation

1. If upper universal joint was removed, align index marks made during removal procedure and install joint onto shaft.
2. Install joint clamp bolt, but do not tighten, then install steering column aligning index marks on column shaft and universal joint.
3. Install column hinge bracket with pedal support studs. Do not tighten universal joint.
4. Tighten hinge bracket nuts, then raise the upper end of column to seat under the instrument panel, position shim clips on column upper bracket flanges.
5. Install two upper steering column retaining nuts, then the steering column shield and nuts.
6. Position steering lock housing on the steering column jacket, then install mounting cap with new screws. Tighten so housing will hold in position. Turn steering wheel lock to lock several times to align universal joints, then tighten both universal joint clamp bolts.
7. Turn ignition switch "On" and verify that mechanism locks and unlocks the column without binding. If necessary, reposition lock housing until lock works. then tighten the mounting screws until the heads break off.
8. Install the shift-lock cable and attaching bolt. **torque** bolt to 37-54 inch lbs.
9. Install ignition switch/combination switch, then align the index marks and install the steering wheel. **Torque** steering wheel nut to 29-36 ft. lbs.
10. With the steering wheel cover bracket and horn button installed in the cover, connect horn electrical connector to horn button leads.
11. Position steering wheel cover, then install screws.

| KEY | PART NUMBER | PART NAME | QUANTITY REQUIRED |
|---|---|---|---|
| 1 | 3A617 | OUTER TUBE ASSEMBLY — S.C. | 1 |
| 2 | 3A504 | CLIP — S.C. BRACKET | 2 |
| 3 | 3F643 | HSE. — S.C. LK. CYL. | 1 |
| 4 | 11572 | IGNITION SWITCH ASSEMBLY | 1 |
| 5 | 3E691 | PAWL — S.C. LOCK | 1 |
| 6 | 3E696 | SPRING — S.C. LK. | 2 |
| 7 | 3E723 | ACTUATOR ASSEMBLY | 1 |
| 8 | 3F531 | KNOB — S.C. LK. ACTUATOR | 1 |
| 9 | N800207-S100 | BOLT — M6 — 1.0 × 10 BREAK-OFF HEAD | 2 |
| 10 | 3F528 | LEVER — S.C. LK. ACTUATOR | 1 |
| 11 | 3E717 | GEAR — S.C. LK. | 1 |
| 12 | 3E700 | BEARING — S.C. LK. HSG. | 1 |
| 13 | 3F579 | RETAINER — S.C. LK. GR. | 1 |
| 14 | 3517 | BRG. ASSEMBLY — S.C. UPPER | 1 |
| 15 | 3518 | SLEEVE — S.C. UPPER BRG. | 1 |
| 16 | 3C610 | RETAINER — S.C. UPPER BRG. | 1 |
| 17 | 3C610 | RETAINER — S.C. UPR. BRG. PLATE | 1 |
| 18 | 52794-S2 | SCREW #8-18 × .62 PAN HEAD TAPPING | 4 |
| 18A | 13B302 | SWITCH ASSEMBLY — T/S & E | 1 |
| 19 | N605531-S2 | BOLT — M8 — 1.25 × 20.0 HEX HEAD | 2 |
| 20 | 3A527 | SHAFT — STRG. GEAR UPPER | 1 |
| 21 | 3E628 | SHAFT — STRG. GEAR LOWER | 1 |
| 22 | 3E629 | INSULATOR — STRG. GEAR SHAFT | 2 |
| 23 | | CLAMP MANUAL | 1 |
| 24 | | CLAMP POWER | 1 |
| 25 | 3E733 | BRG. ASSEMBLY — STRG. GEAR SHAFT LOWER | 1 |
| 26 | 3A649 | SLEEVE — S.C. LWR. BRG. | 1 |
| 27 | N801520-S | RING — 41.22 MM, PRONG RET. INT. | 1 |
| 28 | 3R548 | CLAMP — S.C. LWR. | 1 |
| 29 | | SEAL | 1 |
| 30 | 3600 | WHEEL ASSEMBLY — STEERING | 1 |
| 31 | 3D752 | COVER ASSEMBLY —STRG. WHEEL | 1 |
| 32 | 3530 | SHROUD — UPPER | 1 |
| 33 | 3530 | SHROUD — LOWER | 1 |
| 34 | 13305 | HANDLE & SHANK ASSEMBLY — T/S | 1 |
| 35 | 17A553 | WASH/WIPE SWITCH | 1 |
| 36 | 13B365 | COVER, TURN SIGNAL & WASH/WIPE SWITCH | 1 |
| 37 | 6122050 | LOCK CYLINDER & KEY | 1 |
| 38M | 3C662 | SHAFT ASSEMBLY — S.C. LOWER MANUAL | 1 |
| 38P | 3C662 | SHAFT ASSEMBLY — S.C. LOWER POWER | 1 |
| 39M | 3E735 | BOOT & SEAL ASSEMBLY MANUAL | 1 |
| 39P | 3E735 | BOOT & SEAL ASSEMBLY POWER | 1 |
| 40 | 3B139 | BRACKET ASSEMBLY — S.C. SUPPORT | 1 |
| 41 | N801571 | BOLT, M8 × 1.25 × 23.0 HEX FLG. PLT. | 2 |
| 42 | 3B743 | BRACE — LATERAL/NVH | 1 |
| 43 | 33850-S2 | NUT — STRG. WHEEL | 1 |
| 44 | 55931-S2 | SCREW #8-18 × 1.50'' PAN HEAD TAP | 5 |
| 45 | 56920-S2 | SCREW #8-18 × 1.50'' | 2 |
| 46 | N606331-S2 | BOLT M10 × 1.5 × 45 CARRIAGE | 1 |
| 47 | N620482-S2 | NUT M10 × 1.5 HEX FLANGE LK. P/T | 1 |
| 48 | N606325-S2 | BOLT M8 × 1.25 × 40 CARRIAGE | 1 |
| 49 | N620481-S2 | NUT M8 × 1.25 HEX FLANGE LK. P/T | 4 |
| 50 | 388489-S9 | SCREW | 4 |
| 51 | N605905-S2 | BOLT M8 × 1.25 × 20 FLANGE HEAD | 6 |
| 52 | N801490 | BOLT M8 × 1.25 × 35 CARRIAGE (PIA-E1EC-3B139) | 3 |
| 55 | 56902-S2 | SCREW #8-18 × 1/2'' | 2 |

**Fig. 9 Fixed steering column exploded view (Part 2 Of 2). Tempo, Topaz & 1989–90 Escort**

## XR4TI

Refer to **Fig. 15** for steering column component identification.

### STEERING WHEEL
### Removal

1. Disconnect battery ground cable.
2. Center steering wheel and remove center hub cover from steering wheel.
3. Loosen steering wheel attaching nut, then turn ignition switch to Run position.
4. Pull outward on steering wheel to release it from steering shaft taper.
5. Remove steering wheel attaching nut, then the steering wheel.

### Installation

1. Ensure turn signal switch cancelling lever and turn signal cam are aligned, **Fig. 16.**
2. Install steering wheel. Ensure slot on underside of steering wheel is aligned with turn signal cancelling cam tab, **Fig. 17.**
3. Install and **torque** steering wheel attaching nut to 33-40 ft. lbs.
4. Remove ignition key and ensure wheel lock operation is proper.
5. Install steering wheel center hub cover.
6. Reconnect battery ground cable.

### STEERING COLUMN
### Removal

1. Disconnect battery ground cable.
2. Raise and support vehicle.
3. Loosen steering shaft U-joint clamp bolt, then lower the vehicle.
4. Remove screws retaining upper and lower steering column trim covers, then the covers.
5. Remove screw retaining hood release bracket.
6. Working from below the instrument panel, remove screws retaining sound deadening panel, then the panel.
7. Remove screws retaining cowl side trim panel. Carefully pull trim panel outward, disconnect courtesy lamp, then place panel aside.
8. Remove screws retaining left lower instrument panel, then carefully lower panel, disconnect speaker wires and place panel aside.
9. Remove steering column mounting bracket nuts and washers.
10. Disconnect turn signal, headlight, wiper/washer, horn, ignition switch gang and ignition switch bullet electrical connectors.
11. Pull outward on the steering wheel to disengage steering shaft from universal joint clamp.

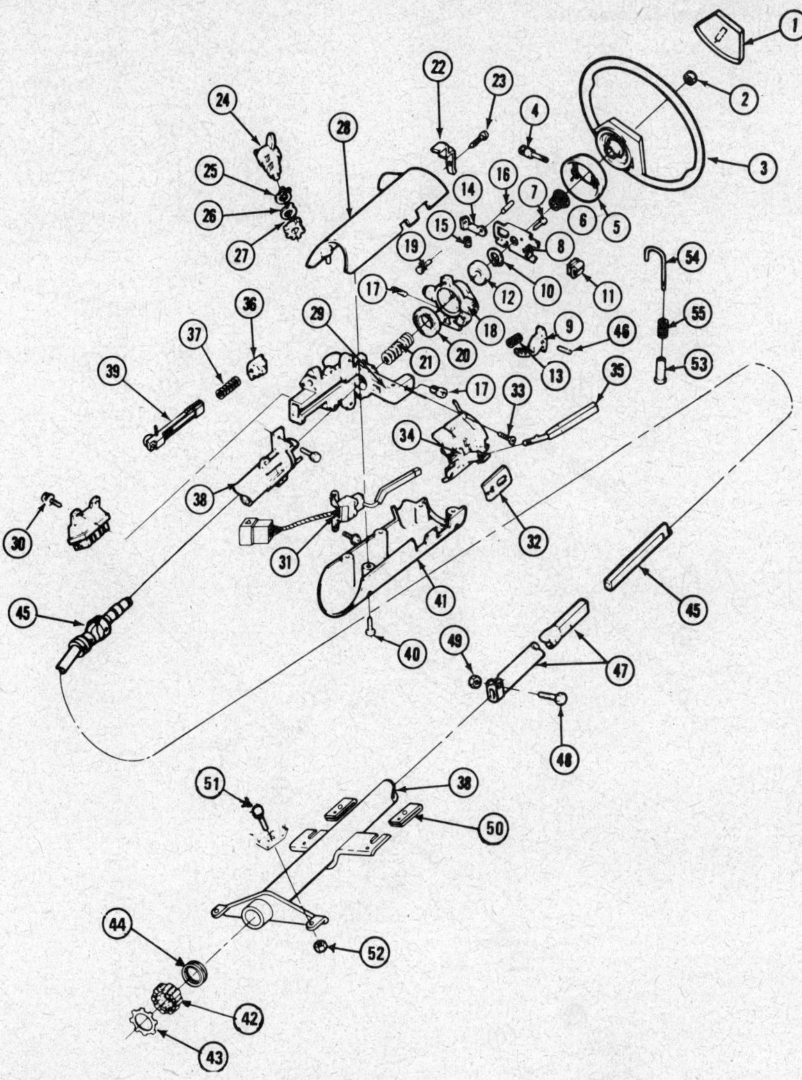

1. EMBLEM ASSEMBLY
2. NUT
3. STEERING WHEEL
4. TILT WHEEL LEVER HANDLE & SHANK ASSEMBLY
5. SHROUD EXTENSION
6. UPPER BEARING SPRING
7. SCREW
8. CLIP RETAINER PLATE
9. LINK LEVER
10. RETAINING RING
11. COLUMN SHROUD CLIP
12. UPPER BEARING ASSEMBLY
13. POSITION LOCK SPRING
14. RELEASE LEVER
15. RELEASE SPRING
16. PIN
17. PIVOT PIN
18. FLANGE CASTING
19. BUMPERS
20. UPPER BEARING ASSEMBLY
21. POSITION SPRING
22. LOCK ACTUATOR COVER
23. SCREW
24. LOCK CYLINDER
25. RETAINER RING
26. BEARING
27. LOCK GEAR
28. UPPER SHROUD
29. LOCK CYLINDER HOUSING
30. BOLT
31. WASH WIPE SWITCH & SCREWS
32. TURN SIGNAL & WASH WIPE SWITCH FOAM COVER
33. SCREW
34. TURN SIGNAL SWITCH
35. TURN SIGNAL SWITCH HANDLE & SIGNAL ASSEMBLY
36. PAWL
37. SPRING
38. OUTER TUBE ASSEMBLY
39. LOCK ACTUATOR ASSEMBLY
40. SCREW
41. LOWER SHROUD
42. STEERING GEAR SHAFT LOWER BEARING ASSEMBLY
43. STEERING GEAR SHAFT LOWER BEARING RETAINER RING
44. BOOT ASSEMBLY
45. SHAFT ASSEMBLY
46. PIN
47. LOWER SHAFT ASSEMBLY
48. BOLT
49. NUT
50. SPRING CLIPS
51. BOLT
52. NUT
53. LOCK ACTUATOR KNOB
54. LOCK ACTUATOR LEVER
55. LOCK SPRING

**Fig. 10 Tilt steering column exploded view. 1989 Tempo & Topaz**

12. Remove steering column from vehicle.

### Installation

1. Position steering column in vehicle.
2. Raise and support vehicle.
3. Install steering column. While centering the steering wheel have an assistant align U-joint clamp with the steering shaft.
4. Lower the vehicle.
5. Reconnect turn signal, headlight, wiper/washer, horn, ignition switch gang and ignition switch bullet electrical connectors.
6. Install mounting bracket with retaining washers and nuts. **Torque** nuts to 13-16 ft. lbs.
7. Reconnect cowl side trim panel courtesy lamp, then install the trim panel.
8. Reconnect left lower instrument panel speaker wires, then install the instrument panel.
9. Install sound deadening panel and hood release bracket.
10. Install steering column lower and upper trim covers.
11. Raise and support vehicle, then **torque** steering shaft universal joint clamp bolt to 14-19 ft. lbs.
12. Lower vehicle and reconnect battery ground cable.

## SCORPIO

Refer to **Fig. 18** for steering column component identification.

### STEERING WHEEL
### Removal

1. Disconnect battery ground cable.
2. Center steering wheel and remove steering wheel horn pad.
3. Remove steering wheel attaching nut.
4. Turn ignition switch to ACC position, then remove steering wheel.

### Installation

1. With ignition switch in the ACC position, align and install steering wheel.
2. Install and **torque** steering wheel attaching nut to 33-40 ft. lbs.
3. Install steering wheel horn pad.
4. Reconnect battery ground cable.

### STEERING COLUMN
### Removal

1. Disconnect battery ground cable.
2. Center the steering wheel.
3. Remove upper universal joint-to-steering column shaft clamp bolt. Position clamp plate to the side and allow it to hang.
4. Remove upper and lower shroud retaining screws, then the shrouds. Steering column height adjuster may have to be lowered to remove upper shroud.
5. Remove hood release lever from column tube housing. Separate cable end from hood release lever. Remove outer cable casing from tube housing guide.
6. Disconnect horn switch, multi-function switch and ignition switch electrical connectors.
7. Remove lefthand vent register.
8. Remove lefthand instrument panel sound insulator.
9. Remove lefthand instrument panel trim panel retaining screws and clips, then the panel.
10. Separate auxiliary warning system module from trim panel.
11. Remove three column height adjuster mounting bracket-to-body retaining nuts.
12. Remove steering column from vehicle.

### Installation

1. Set steering shaft to minimum length.
2. Position steering column in vehicle. Install three column height adjuster mounting bracket-to-body retaining nuts.
3. Set steering wheel column adjustment to maximum down and forward position.

4. Secure universal joint-to-steering column shaft with retaining clamp.
5. Install auxiliary warning system module to trim panel.
6. Install instrument panel trim panel.
7. Install lefthand instrument panel sound insulator.
8. Install lefthand vent register.
9. Reconnect horn switch, multi-function switch and ignition switch electrical connectors.
10. Install cable end to hood release lever, hood release lever to column tube housing, then the outer cable casing to tube housing guide.
11. Adjust column height to lowest position, then install upper and lower shrouds.
12. Install universal joint-to-steering column shaft clamp bolt, then ensure steering wheel is centered and **torque** clamp bolt to 15-22 ft. lbs.
13. Reconnect battery ground cable.

## 1989 TRACER

Refer to **Fig. 19** for steering column component identification.

### Steering Wheel

1. Disconnect battery ground cable.
2. Working from back side of steering wheel, remove two screws retaining cover pad and separate cover pad from steering wheel.
3. Remove steering wheel attaching nut.
4. Remove two cover pad mounting bracket attaching screws, then the bracket.
5. Using a suitable puller, separate steering wheel from steering shaft.
6. Reverse procedure to install.

### Steering Column

1. Disconnect battery ground cable.
2. Remove two lap duct register panel retaining screws.
3. Remove three lap duct-to-brace retaining screws, then the lap duct and brace.
4. Remove five combination switch lower cover retaining screws.
5. Remove lower steering column attaching nuts.
6. Remove lower steering column U-joint mounting bolt.
7. Remove four upper steering column retaining bolts, then lower the steering column.
8. Disconnect five wiring harness plugs from steering column and remove steering column from vehicle.
9. Reverse procedure to install.

# STEERING COLUMN SERVICE

## XR4TI

Refer to **Fig. 15** for steering column component identification.

### TUBE/SWITCH

#### Removal

1. Remove steering wheel as previously described.

Tilt Column—Exploded View

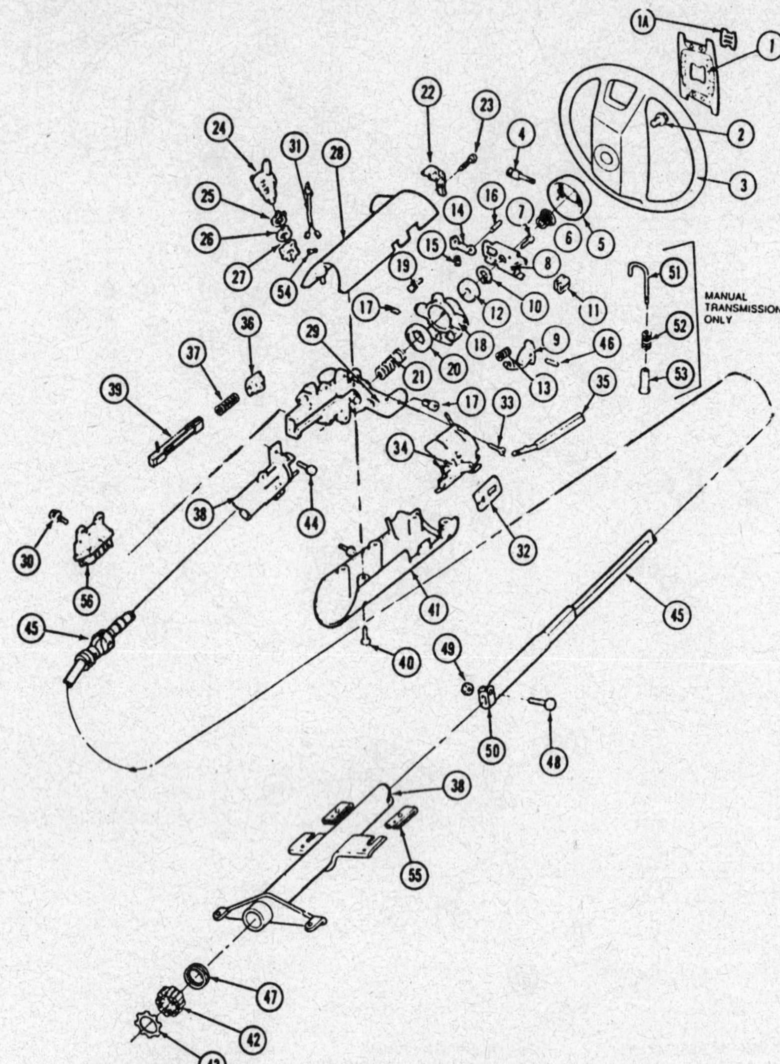


| ITEM | DESCRIPTION | ITEM | DESCRIPTION |
|---|---|---|---|
| 1 | Cover Assembly — Steering Wheel | 29 | Housing — Steering Column Lock Cylinder |
| 1A | Emblem Assembly — Steering Wheel | 30 | Bolt (Break Off Head) |
| 2 | Bolt — Steering Wheel | 31 | Brush Assembly — Horn/Speed Control |
| 3 | Wheel Assembly — Steering | 32 | Foam Cover — Turn Signal & Wash/Wipe Switch |
| 4 | Handle & Shank Assy. — Tilt Steering Wheel Lever | 33 | Screw |
| 5 | Extension — Steering Column Shroud | 34 | Turn Signal Switch |
| 6 | Spring — Steering Column Upper Bearing | 35 | Handle & Signal Assembly — Turn Signal Switch |
| 7 | Screw | 36 | Pawl — Steering Column Lock |
| 8 | Plate Steering Column Clip Retainer | 37 | Spring — Steering Column Lock |
| 9 | Lever Steering Column Link | 38 | Tube Assembly Column Outer |
| 10 | Ring — 3/4 Retaining Type | 39 | Actuator Assembly — Steering Column Lock |
| 11 | Clip — Steering Column Shroud | 40 | Screw |
| 12 | Bearing Assembly — Steering Column Upper | 41 | Shroud — Steering Column Lower |
| 13 | Spring — Steering Column Position Lock | 42 | Bearing Assembly — Steering Gear Shaft Lower |
| 14 | Release Lever | 43 | Ring — Steering Gear Shaft Lower Bearing Retainer |
| 15 | Spring — Steering Column Release | 44 | Bolt |
| 16 | Pin | 45 | Shaft Assembly — Steering Column |
| 17 | Pivot Pin | 46 | Pin |
| 18 | Flange Casting | 47 | Sleeve — Steering Column Lower Bearing |
| 19 | Bumpers | 48 | Bolt |
| 20 | Bearing Assembly — Steering Column Upper | 49 | Nut |
| 21 | Position Spring | 50 | Clamp — Steering Column Lower |
| 22 | Cover — Steering Column Lock Actuator | 51 | Lever — Steering Column Lock Actuator |
| 23 | Screw | 52 | Spring — Steering Column Lock |
| 24 | Lock Cylinder | 53 | Knob — Steering Column Lock Actuator |
| 25 | Ring | 54 | Screw — Hex Washer Head Tapping |
| 26 | Bearing | 55 | Clip — Steering Column Bracket |
| 27 | Gear — Steering Column Lock | 56 | Ignition Switch Assembly |
| 28 | Shroud — Upper | | |

**Fig. 11 Tilt steering column exploded view. 1990 Escort & 1990–91 Tempo & Topaz**

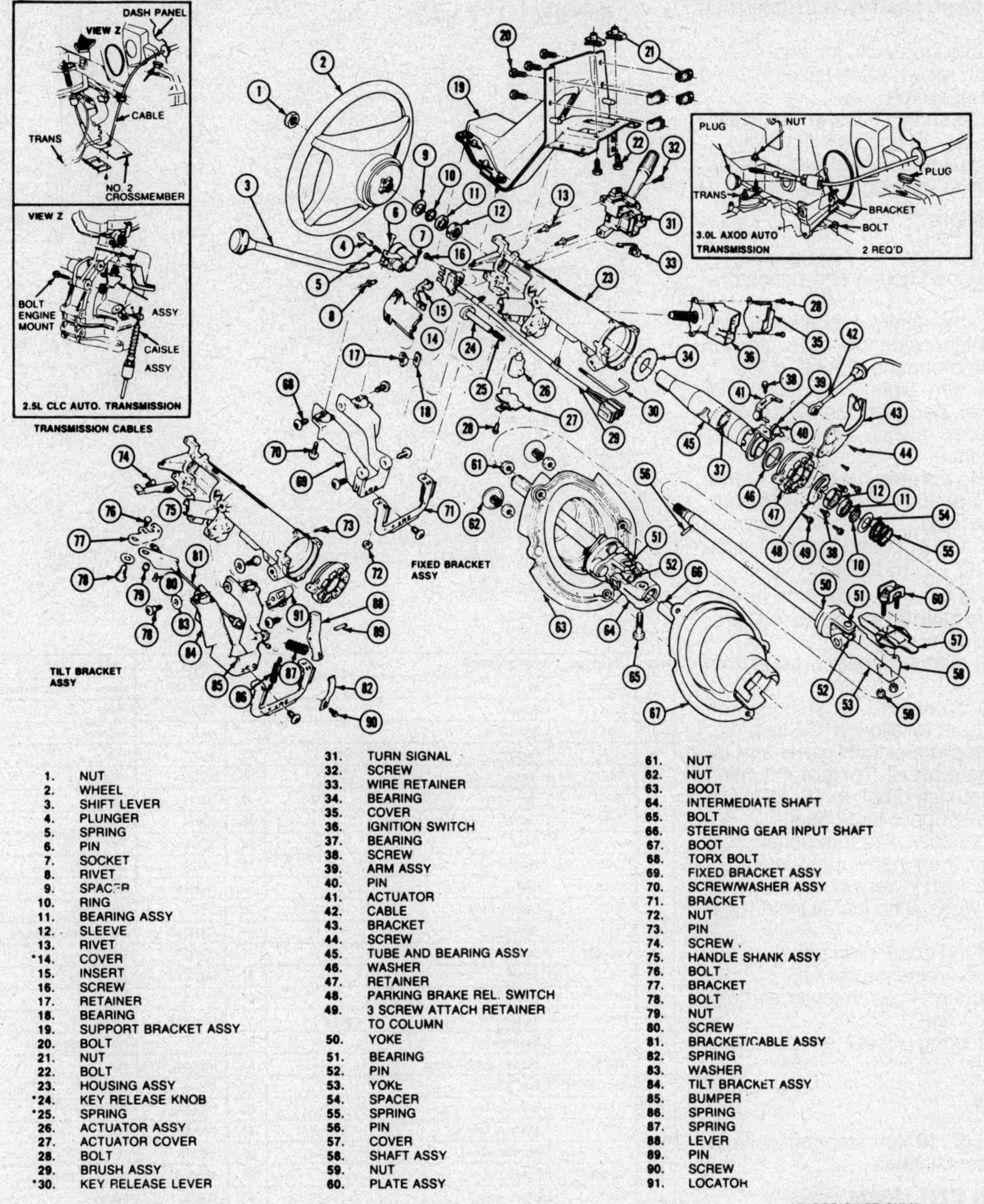


**Fig. 12 Fixed steering column exploded view. Sable & Taurus**

2. Remove screws retaining upper and lower steering column trim covers, then the covers.
3. Remove hood release bracket attaching screw.
4. Working from below the instrument panel, remove screws retaining sound deadening panel, then the panel.
5. Remove screws retaining cowl side trim panel, then carefully pull trim panel outward, disconnect courtesy lamp and place panel aside.
6. Remove screws retaining left lower instrument panel, then carefully lower panel, disconnect speaker wires and place panel aside.
7. Remove nuts and washers retaining steering tube mounting bracket.
8. Disconnect turn signal, headlight, wiper/washer, horn, ignition switch gang and ignition switch bullet electrical connectors.
9. Pull steering column tube outward and away from shaft. When tube/switch assembly is free from shaft remove upper bearing tolerance ring and turn signal cancelling cam.
10. Remove preload spring and lower bearing tolerance ring from steering shaft.

## Disassembly

1. Using a screwdriver and hammer, remove lower bearing.
2. Using a suitable wrench, remove steering column mounting bracket.
3. Remove turn signal switch and headlight/wiper switch retaining screws, then the switches.
4. Using a screwdriver, pry out horn contacts and upper bearing.
5. Remove ignition switch retaining screws, then the switch.
6. Using ignition key, turn ignition switch to position I.
7. Using a screwdriver, depress lock cylinder clip and pull lock cylinder out from housing.

## Assembly

1. Using ignition key, turn ignition switch to position I, then install lock cylinder into housing and remove ignition key.
2. Using a suitable socket and hammer,

install upper bearing with tolerance ring.
3. Install horn contacts, ignition switch, headlight/wiper switch assembly and turn signal switch.
4. Install steering column mounting bracket. Do not tighten pinch bolts.
5. Using a suitable socket and hammer, install lower bearing.

### Installation

1. Install turn signal cancelling cam.
2. Install preload spring and bearing retainer.
3. Install mounting bracket and tube/switch assembly onto steering shaft and mounting bracket studs.
4. Connect turn signal, headlight, wiper/washer, horn, ignition switch gang and ignition switch bullet electrical connectors.
5. **If steering column mounting bracket was not loosened or removed,** install mounting bracket with retaining washers and nuts and **torque** retaining nuts to 13-16 ft. lbs.
6. **If steering column mounting bracket was loosened or removed,** proceed as follows:
   a. Install steering column upper trim panel.
   b. Press downward on steering column tube to allow a 3/16 inch gap between upper trim panel and instrument panel. **Torque** mounting bracket clamp bolt to 15-19 ft. lbs.
   c. Remove upper trim panel.
7. Reconnect cowl side trim panel courtesy lamp, then install trim panel.
8. Reconnect left lower instrument panel speaker wires, then install instrument panel.
9. Install sound deadening panel.
10. Install hood release bracket.
11. Install steering column lower and upper trim covers.
12. Install steering wheel as described previously.

## SCORPIO

Refer to **Fig. 18** for steering column component identification.

### STEERING COLUMN

### Disassembly

1. Remove steering wheel and steering column as described previously.
2. Remove plastic upper bearing tolerance ring.
3. Loosen height adjuster pinch bolt. Insert a flathead screwdriver into height adjuster slit, **Fig. 20,** then twist screwdriver to widen slit, then remove lower bearing.
4. Separate steering column and shaft assembly.
5. Remove and discard lower column spire washer from steering shaft.
6. Remove bearing, tolerance washer and spring from steering shaft.
7. Remove four multi-function switch and wiper/washer switch retaining screws, then the switches.
8. Turn ignition switch to ACC position, depress lock barrel locking plunger as

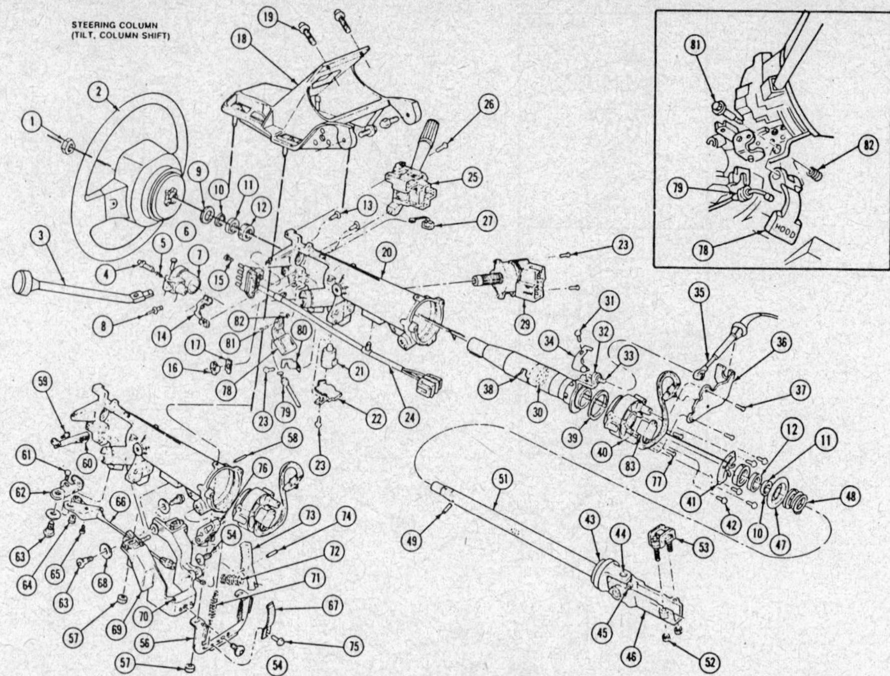


| ITEM | PART NO. | DESCRIPTION | ITEM | PART NO. | DESCRIPTION |
|---|---|---|---|---|---|
| 1. | N803843 | Nut | 42. | N804130 | Screw — Attach Retainer to Col., 3 Req'd. |
| 2. | 3600 | Wheel | 43. | 3B250 | Yoke |
| 3. | 7202 | Shift Lever | 44. | 4869 | Bearing |
| 4. | 7361 | Plunger | 45. | 3D661 | Pin |
| 5. | 7B071 | Spring | 46. | 3A325 | Yoke |
| 6. | 7G357 | Pin | 47. | 3C131 | Ring |
| 7. | 7228 | Socket | 48. | 3C674 | Spring |
| 8. | 380098 | Rivet | 49. | 3E718 | Pin |
| 9. | 3D640 | Spacer | 51. | 3E729 | Shaft Assy. |
| 10. | 3L539 | Ring | 52. | N620467 | Nut, 2 Req'd. |
| 11. | 3517 | Bearing Assy. | 53. | 3C088 | Plate Assy |
| 12. | 3518 | Sleeve | 54. | N804086 | TORX® Bolt, 2 Req'd. |
| 13. | N804096 | Rivet, 2 Req'd. | 56. | 3B632 | Bracket |
| 14. | 7A216 | Insert | 57. | N802811 | Nut, 4 Req'd. |
| 15. | N804445 | Screw | 58. | 3E718 | Pin |
| 16. | 3F579 | Retainer | 59. | N802953 | Screw |
| 17. | 3E700 | Bearing | 60. | 3F609 | Handle Shank Assy. |
| 18. | 3B139 | Support Bracket Assy. | 61. | N804087 | Bolt |
| 19. | N801662 | Bolt, 4 Req'd. | 62. | 3D544 | Bracket |
| 20. | 3F643 | Housing Assy. | 63. | N804088 | Bolt, 2 Req'd. |
| 21. | 3E723 | Actuator Assy. | 64. | N804084 | Nut |
| 22. | 3E745 | Actuator Cover | 65. | 390345 | Screw |
| 23. | N804089 | Bolt, 4 Req'd. | 66. | 3F700 | Bracket Cable Assy. |
| 24. | 9C899 | Brush Assy. | 67. | 3D655 | Spring |
| 25. | 13K359 | Turn Signal | 68. | N804085 | Washer, 3 Req'd. |
| 26. | 52794 | Screw, 2 Req'd. | 69. | 3B140 | Tilt Bracket Assy. |
| 27. | 14A163 | Wire Retainer | 70. | 3D656 | Bumper |
| 29. | 11572 | Ignition Switch Assy. | 71. | 3D655 | Spring |
| 30. | 3K618 | Bearing | 72. | 3D655 | Spring |
| 31. | N611133 | Screw, 3 Req'd. | 73. | 3B662 | Lever |
| 32. | 7302 | Arm Assy. | 74. | N804090 | Pin |
| 33. | 7F031 | Pin | 75. | N804409 | Screw, 7 Req'd. |
| 34. | 2B624 | Actuator | 76. | 3F716 | Locator |
| 35. | 7E395 | Cable | 77. | N611133 | Screw, 2 Req'd. |
| 36. | 7E364 | Bracket | 78. | 16B974 | Hood Release Handle |
| 37. | N605771 | Screw, 2 Req'd. | 79. | 16C656 | Hood Release Cable Assy. |
| 38. | 3K521 | Tube and Bearing Assy. | 80. | 16C730 | Hood Release Cable Bracket |
| 39. | 3C708 | Washer | 81. | N804924 | Shoulder Bolt |
| 40. | 3E738 | Retainer | 82. | N-800354 | Nut |
| 41. | 2B623 | Parking Brake Rel. Sw. | 83. | 18B015 | Sensor Assy. |

**Fig. 13 Tilt steering column exploded view. Continental**

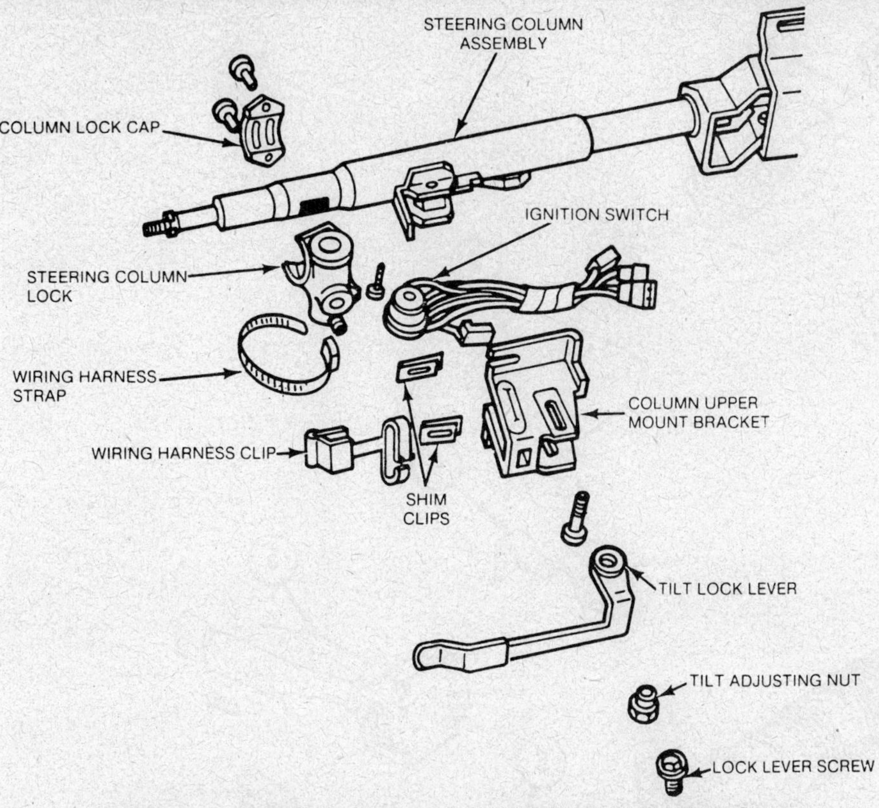


**Fig. 14 Steering column exploded view. Festiva**

shown in **Fig. 21,** then pull ignition lock barrel from housing.

9. Using a suitable screwdriver, depress and unclip ignition switch harness and plate assembly.
10. Disconnect and remove horn pickup electrical connector as shown in **Fig. 22.**
11. Remove and discard height adjuster pivot nut and bolt, then the height adjuster and steering column mounting bracket from column tube.
12. Disengage height adjuster from steering column mounting bracket, then remove spring, plastic sides and washer.
13. Remove upper bearing as shown in **Fig. 23.**

### Assembly

1. Install height adjuster and plastic sides to column tube mounting bracket, then the new pivot bolt, lever and cam plates.
2. Install height adjuster spring. **Ensure spring seats properly in locating clips.**
3. Set height adjuster to column lock position, then apply Loctite compound to pivot bolt thread and **torque** pivot bolt to 8-10 ft. lbs.
4. Insert a flathead screwdriver into height adjuster slit, **Fig. 20,** then twist screwdriver to widen slit. Install lower bearing, then remove the screwdriver. Install and **torque** pinch bolt to 16-18 ft. lbs.
5. Install new upper bearing as shown in **Fig. 24.**
6. Reconnect horn pickup electrical connector and install it into column housing.
7. Install ignition switch harness and plate assembly to column housing.
8. Ensure ignition switch is in the RUN position, then while depressing lock plunger, press ignition lock barrel into housing. **Ensure lock plunger engages into access hole.**
9. Install multi-function and wiper/washer switches.
10. Install plastic bushing and retaining clip onto triangular end of steering shaft as shown in **Fig. 25.**
11. Loosely install spring tolerance ring and lower bearing onto steering shaft.
12. Install new spire washer 11.29 inches from upper end of shaft.
13. Install steering shaft through column tube and adjuster assembly.
14. Install plastic upper bearing tolerance ring.
15. Install steering column and steering wheel as outlined previously.
16. Align shroud and switches to instrument panel, then **torque** height adjuster pinch bolt to 16-18 ft. lbs.

## SHIFT CANE ASSEMBLY REPLACE

### MODELS W/MODULAR STEERING COLUMN EXCEPT TEMPO, TOPAZ & 1989–90 ESCORT

Refer to **Figs. 1, 2, and 3** for component identification.

### Removal & Disassembly

1. Remove steering column from vehicle as described previously.
2. Remove two nuts and bolts which connect transmission gear shift shaft support bracket to steering column collar.
3. Remove C-clip retainer from upper end of shift cane assembly, then pull assembly down and out of bearing and washer located in lock cylinder housing and detent plate.
4. Inspect bearing, if damaged or excessively worn, replace using tool T67L-7341-A, or equivalent.
5. Pull plastic transmission control selector lever opening cover from upper shaft and allow it to hang on shift selector lever.
6. Using a small drift, remove roll pin which connects gear shift selector lever to shift cane upper shaft.
7. If shift selector lever spring and plunger assembly is damaged or excessively worn, replace by removing two screws on upper shift cane shaft.
8. If PRND21 lever is damaged or excessively worn, replace by removing one screw on upper shift cane assembly.
9. Scribe a mark on both the upper and lower shafts, where the shafts form a joint. **Scribe marks on one side only to ensure that the two shafts will not be reassembled 180 degrees out of position.**
10. Separate upper and lower shift cane sections, then slide lower shift cane support bracket off lower shaft. Replace bushing if damaged or excessively worn.
11. Remove and discard two steel anti-rattle clips.

### Assembly & Installation

1. Install two new steel anti-rattle clips so that they face in the same direction as grooves on shift cane upper shaft. With bushing installed on lower shift cane support bracket, install bracket onto lower shaft.
2. Using chassis grease, liberally lubricate lower six inches of the shift cane upper shaft, then place lower shift cane shaft in a vise and install the upper shaft into lower shaft to mark scribed on during disassembly procedure. **Use care not to damage upper end of shaft cane during assembly of the lower shaft. Check scribed marks on upper and lower shafts made during disassembly to ensure that two shaft sections are not installed 180 degrees out of position.**
3. Loosely install plastic transmission control selector lever opening cover on shift selector lever, then insert selector lever through slot in upper shaft and install new roll pin. **The tip of the selector lever should protrude through the upper shaft on the side of the plunger and spring assembly.**

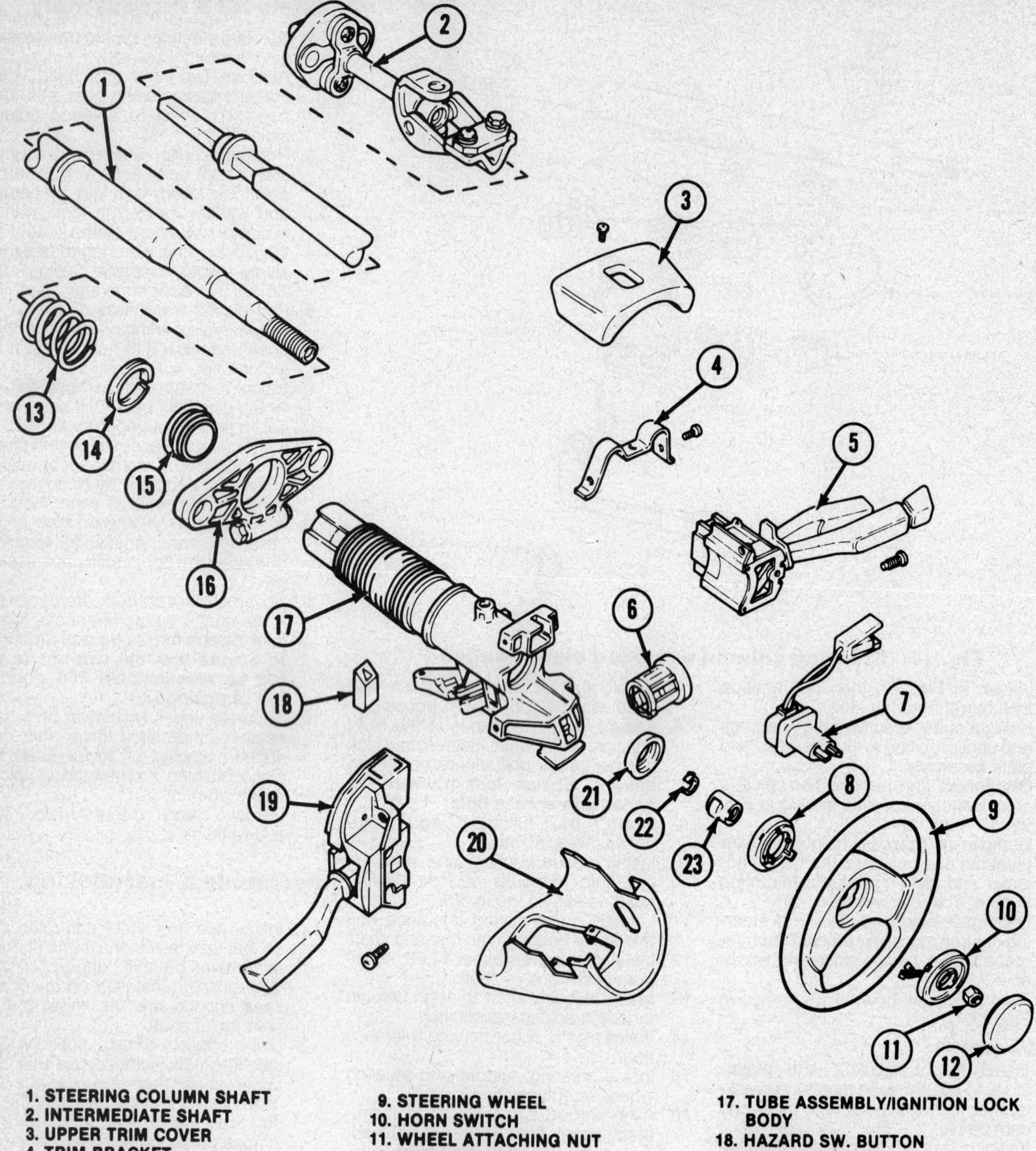


1. STEERING COLUMN SHAFT
2. INTERMEDIATE SHAFT
3. UPPER TRIM COVER
4. TRIM BRACKET
5. HEADLIGHT/WIPER SW.
6. LOCK CYLINDER
7. HORN CONTACTS
8. HORN RING
9. STEERING WHEEL
10. HORN SWITCH
11. WHEEL ATTACHING NUT
12. HUB COVER
13. PRELOAD SPRING
14. TOLERANCE RING
15. LOWER BEARING
16. MOUNTING BRACKET
17. TUBE ASSEMBLY/IGNITION LOCK BODY
18. HAZARD SW. BUTTON
19. TURN SIGNAL SW.
20. LOWER TRIM COVER
21. UPPER BEARING
22. TOLERANCE RING
23. CANCELLING CAM

**Fig. 15 Steering column exploded view. XR4TI**

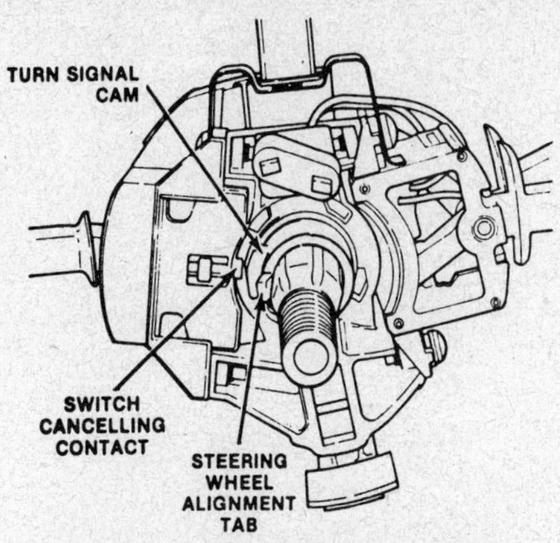


**Fig. 16 Turn signal switch cancelling lever-to-turn signal cam alignment. XR4Ti**

4. Install plastic transmission control selector lever opening cover on upper shaft, then insert upper end of shift cane into bearing and washer in lock cylinder housing and install C-clip retainer. **Ensure shift selector lever mates correctly with detent plate on lock cylinder housing.**
5. Align lower support bracket with two holes in steering column collar, then install two nuts and bolts and **torque** to 15-22 ft. lbs.
6. Check shift cane for smooth operation. Lubricate selector lever, plunger, spring and detent plate with chassis lubricant.
7. Install steering column as described previously.

# UPPER BEARING REPLACE

## MODELS w/MODULAR STEERING COLUMN, EXCEPT COUGAR & THUNDERBIRD

Refer to **Figs. 1, 2, 3, 9 through 11** for component identification.

### Removal

1. Remove steering wheel, then the two trim shroud halves and upper bearing retainer plate.
2. Remove nuts which attach steering column lower shaft and U-joint assembly to flange on steering gear input shaft.
3. Remove snap ring which retains upper bearing onto steering shaft.
4. Pull outward on steering shaft about $1/4$ inch, then insert blades of two screwdrivers under bearing by using two ramps provided in casting for this purpose. Gently pry bearing off knurl on steering shaft.

### Installation

1. Using a punch, upset serrated portion of upper shaft sufficiently to ensure an interference fit between bearing inner race and steering column upper shaft.
2. Place bearing and insulator on steering column upper shaft and work bearing and insulator as far down as possible. Place a piece of pipe ($3/4$ inch dia. X $1\,1/2$ inch long) over end of upper shaft, then install steering wheel nut and tighten nut until bearing is seated firmly on steering shaft.
3. Remove steering wheel nut and pipe, then install snap ring above bearing and bearing retainer plate.
4. **On all except Ford & Mercury full size,** engage safety strap and bolt assembly onto steering gear input shaft, then install two nuts and **torque** to 20-37 ft. lbs. **The safety strap must be properly positioned to prevent metal to metal contact after torquing the nuts. Also, pry steering shaft up or down with a pry bar to obtain $\pm 1/8$ inch coupling insulator flatness.**
5. **On all models,** install trim shrouds and steering wheel, then check steering column for proper operation.

## COUGAR & THUNDERBIRD

Refer to **Figs. 4 and 5** for replacement procedure.

### FIXED COLUMN

### Removal

1. Remove steering column as described previously.
2. Separate lower steering column U-joint assembly from steering shaft.
3. Remove two screws retaining multi-function switch, then the switch.
4. Remove two screws retaining upper bearing retainer plate, then the plate.
5. Remove upper bearing snap ring.
6. Remove two lock cylinder housing assembly-to-column tube retaining bolts, then the housing assembly.
7. If equipped remove sensor ring shield, two sensor switch retaining screws, then the switch.
8. Remove and discard spring retainer.
9. Remove spring and sensor ring.
10. Using a suitable tool, remove shaft bearing sleeve.
11. Remove shaft and lock cylinder housing assembly from column tube.
12. Using a soft hammer, separate shaft from bearing as shown **Fig. 26.**

### Installation

1. Position lock cylinder housing assembly on shaft assembly and install assemblies into column tube.
2. Install and **torque** two lock cylinder housing retaining bolts to 12-21 ft. lbs.
3. Position upper steering shaft bearing and sleeve on shaft. Install sleeve and shaft assembly into lock cylinder housing bearing bore.
4. Install new bearing snap ring as follows:
   a. Position a pipe spacer ($3/4$ inch ID X $3\,1/2$ inch long) over end of upper shaft.
   b. Install steering wheel attaching bolt through pipe spacer and into steering shaft.

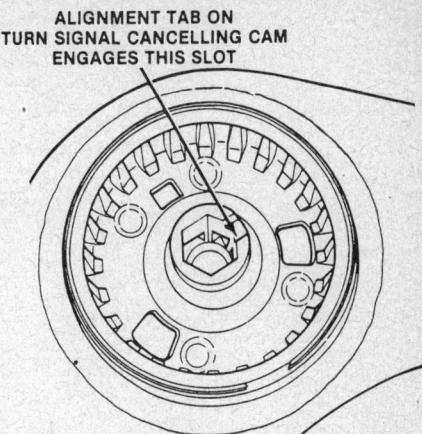

ALIGNMENT TAB ON
TURN SIGNAL CANCELLING CAM
ENGAGES THIS SLOT

**Fig. 17 Turn signal cancelling cam tab-to-steering wheel slot alignment. XR4Ti**

   c. Tighten bolt until there is enough room to allow installation of a new bearing snap ring.
   d. Install new snap ring in shaft groove, then remove steering wheel attaching bolt and pipe spacer.
5. Install multi-function switch.
6. Install lower bearing sleeve, sensor ring, spring and new spring retainer.
7. If equipped, install sensor switch and sensor ring shield.
8. Install U-joint assembly. **Torque** attaching bolt to 30-42 ft. lbs.
9. Install steering column as described previously.

### TILT COLUMN

### Removal

1. Disconnect battery ground cable.
2. Separate horn pad and cover assembly from steering wheel, then disconnect horn electrical connector from contact plate terminal. If equipped disconnect speed control electrical connector.
3. Remove and discard steering wheel attaching bolt.
4. Using a suitable puller, separate steering wheel from steering shaft. **To prevent damage to steering shaft bearing, never hit steering wheel attaching bolt or use a knock-off type steering wheel puller.**
5. Unsnap upper extension shroud from retainer clips at the 9 o'clock position.
6. Remove three screws retaining upper and lower shrouds, then the shrouds.
7. Remove conical coil spring and upper bearing retainer plate.
8. Remove shaft C-clip at top of bearing.
9. Set tilt casting in the upper position.
10. Using Pivot Pin Remover Handle tool No. T67P-3D739-C and Pivot Pin Remover tools No. T67P-3D739-B or equivalent, carefully remove pivot pins. **Use caution when removing pivot pins, they are under pressure and will expand with force.**
11. Remove tilt casting assembly and tilt spring from the column.

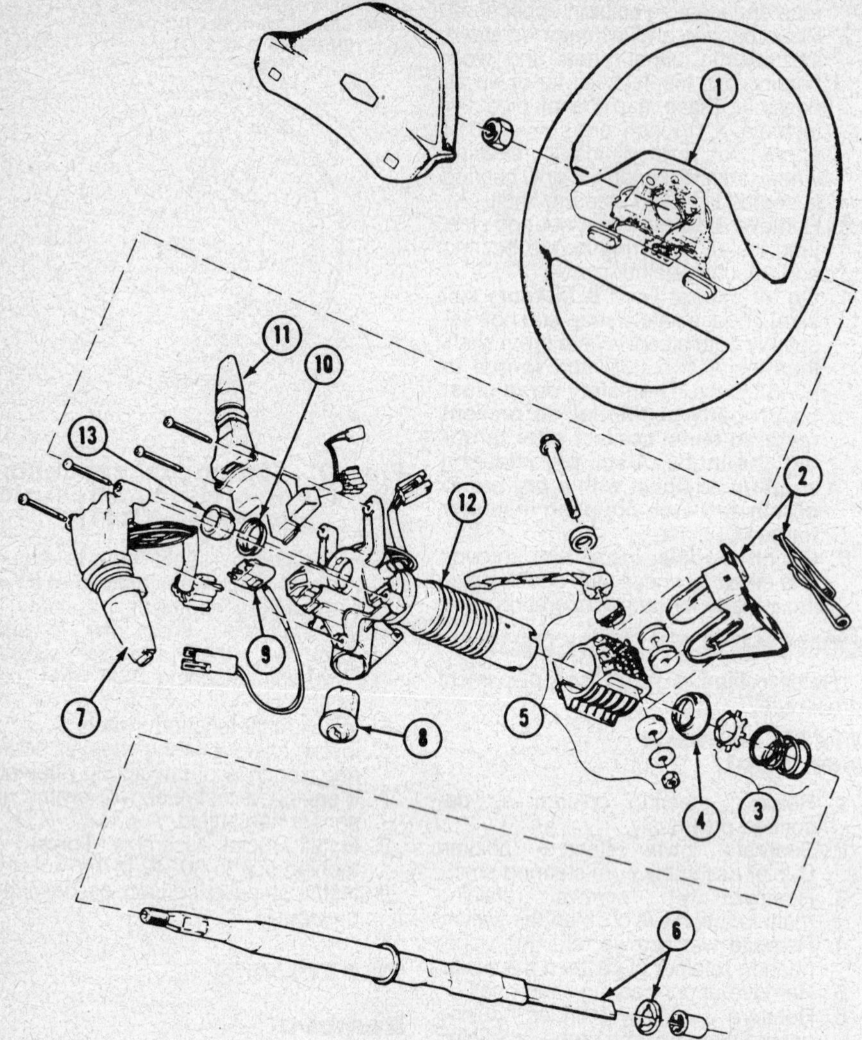


LEGEND:
1. STEERING WHEEL
2. COLUMN BRACKET AND SPRING
3. TOLERANCE RING (LOWER) AND SPRING
4. LOWER BEARING
5. HEIGHT ADJUSTER ASSY
6. COLUMN SHAFT AND LOWER BEARING
7. MULTI-FUNCTION SWITCH
8. IGNITION LOCK BARREL
9. HORN PICKUP
10. UPPER BEARING
11. MULTI-FUNCTION SWITCH
12. COLUMN LOCK TUBE ASSY
13. TOLERANCE RING (UPPER)

**Fig. 18 Steering column exploded view. Scorpio**

12. Working from bottom side of tilt casting, use a suitable drift and a hammer to remove upper bearing.
13. Working from tilt casting side-to-side relief areas, use a suitable drift and hammer to remove the lower bearing.

### Installation

1. Press fit new bearings into tilt casting. Use caution not to press on inner race.
2. Install tilt spring between upper and lower tilt castings. Latch tilt release lever in upper position.
3. Align the tilt castings, then using a C-clamp install two pivot pins until flush with casting surface.
4. Install upper bearing snap ring and retainer plate.
5. Install conical coil spring by snapping it into shaft groove.
6. Install upper, lower and extension shrouds.
7. Align and install steering wheel. **Torque** new steering wheel attaching bolt to 23-33 ft. lbs.
8. Reconnect horn electrical connector and if equipped the speed control electrical connector, to the contact plate terminal. Install horn pad and cover assembly to the steering wheel.
9. Reconnect battery ground cable.
10. Ensure steering column tilt operation is proper.

## SABLE & TAURUS

### Removal

1. Disconnect battery ground, then remove steering column cover from lower portion of instrument panel
2. Remove ignition lock cylinder.
3. **On models equipped with tilt column,** remove tilt release lever.
4. **On all models,** remove shrouds, multi-function switch, horn pad and steering wheel.
5. Fabricate tool from piece of tubing as shown in **Fig. 27.**
6. Install tool on steering shaft, aligning clearance slot over shaft retaining pin.
7. Install steering wheel nut, **Fig. 28,** and relieve spring pressure on shaft retaining pin.
8. Remove retaining pin from steering shaft using a suitable drift.
9. Remove steering wheel nut and tool.
10. Remove steering shaft retaining washer and upper alignment wedge from steering shaft.
11. Insert a small screwdriver between inner and outer race of bearing and gently pry bearing and bearing sleeve out of lock cylinder housing bearing pocket.

### Installation

1. Slip bearing sleeve over upper bearing.
2. Install upper bearing into lock housing bearing pocket.
3. Install alignment wedge and retaining washer over steering shaft.
4. Fabricate a tool from a piece of tubing as shown in **Fig. 27.**
5. Install tool on shaft, aligning pin clearance slot with shaft retaining pin hole.
6. Install steering wheel nut. Tighten nut to compress steering shaft preload spring enough to provide adequate clearance to shaft retaining pin hole.
7. Install shaft retaining pin, then remove steering wheel nut and tool.
8. Install steering wheel, multi-function switch, horn pad and shrouds.
9. **On models equipped with tilt column,** install tilt release lever.
10. **On all models,** install ignition lock cylinder, steering column covers and

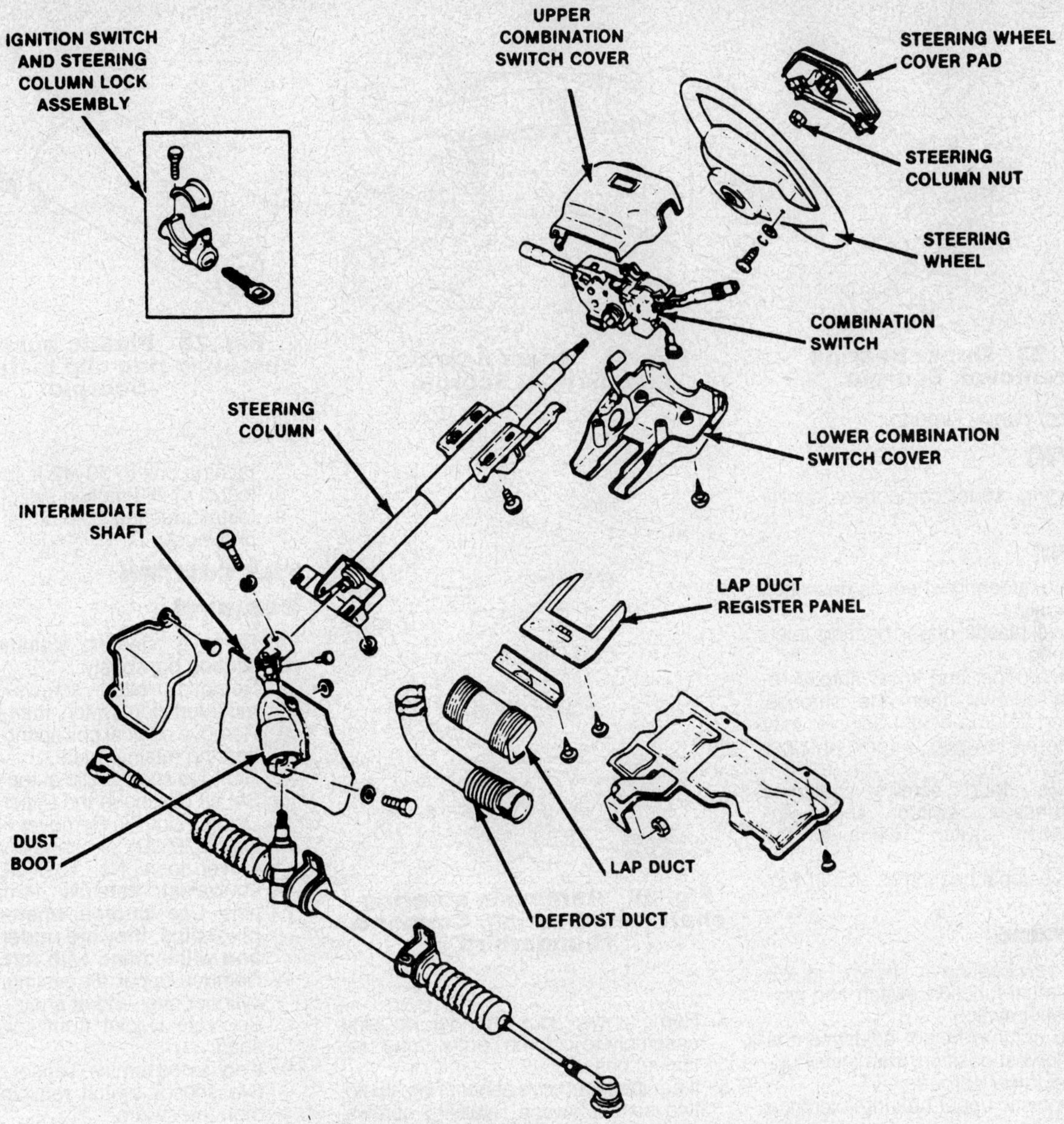

IGNITION SWITCH
AND STEERING
COLUMN LOCK
ASSEMBLY
UPPER
COMBINATION
SWITCH COVER
STEERING WHEEL
COVER PAD
STEERING
COLUMN NUT
STEERING
WHEEL
COMBINATION
SWITCH
STEERING
COLUMN
LOWER COMBINATION
SWITCH COVER
INTERMEDIATE
SHAFT
LAP DUCT
REGISTER PANEL
DUST
BOOT
LAP DUCT
DEFROST DUCT

**Fig. 19 Steering column installation. Tracer**

LOWER
BEARING
SPLIT

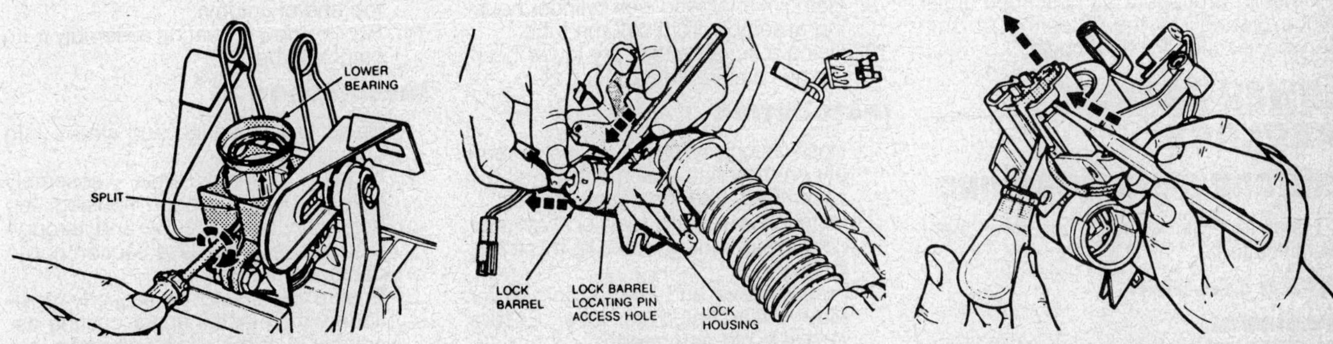

**Fig. 20 Widening height adjuster assembly slot. Scorpio**

LOCK
BARREL
LOCK BARREL
LOCATING PIN
ACCESS HOLE
LOCK
HOUSING

**Fig. 21 Ignition lock barrel removal. Scorpio**

**Fig. 22 Horn pickup electrical connector removal. Scorpio**

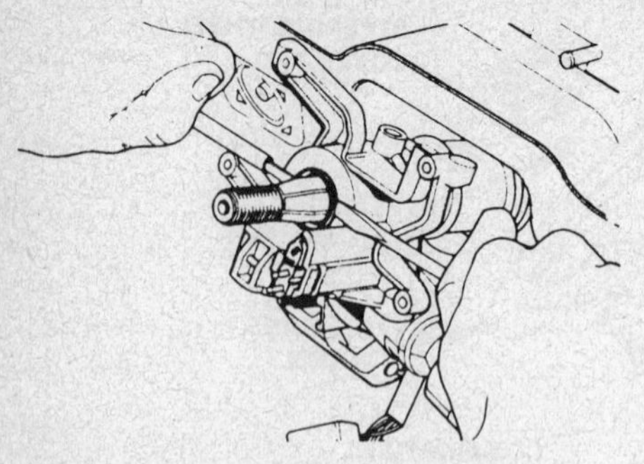

Fig. 23 Upper bearing removal. Scorpio

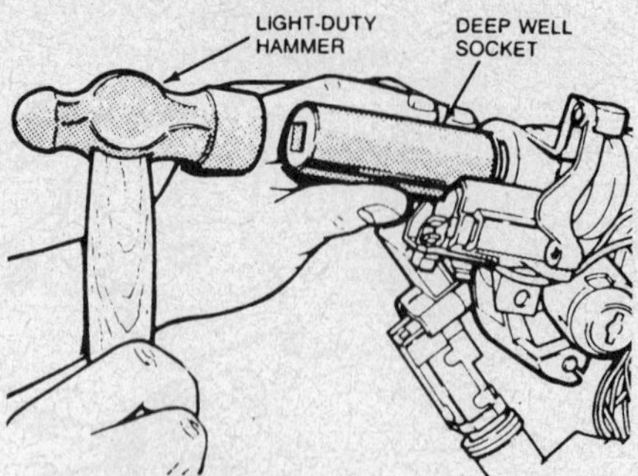


Fig. 24 Upper bearing installation. Scorpio

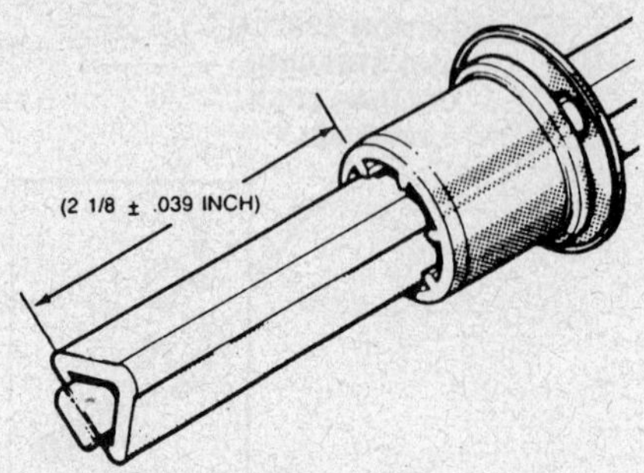


Fig. 25 Plastic bushing & retaining ring clip installation. Scorpio

connect battery ground.

## SCORPIO

Refer to **Fig. 18** for component identification.

### Removal

1. Remove steering wheel as described previously.
2. Remove plastic upper bearing tolerance ring.
3. Remove upper and lower shroud retaining screws, then the shrouds. Steering column height adjuster may have to be lowered to remove upper shroud.
4. Remove four screws retaining multi-function switch and wiper/washer switch. Remove the switches.
5. Remove upper bearing as shown, **Fig. 23.**

### Installation

1. Install new bearing as shown, **Fig. 24.**
2. Install multi-function switch and wiper/washer switch.
3. Ensure column height adjustment is in the lowest position, then install upper and lower shrouds.
4. Install plastic upper bearing tolerance ring.
5. Install steering wheel as described previously.

## XR4TI

Refer to procedure as described under "Tube/Switch" in the "Steering Column Service" section for this model.

# LOWER BEARING REPLACE

## COUGAR & THUNDERBIRD

Refer to **Figs. 4 and 5** for component identification.

### FIXED COLUMN

### Removal

1. Remove steering column as described previously.
2. Separate lower steering column U-joint assembly from steering shaft.
3. Remove two screws retaining multi-function switch, then the switch.

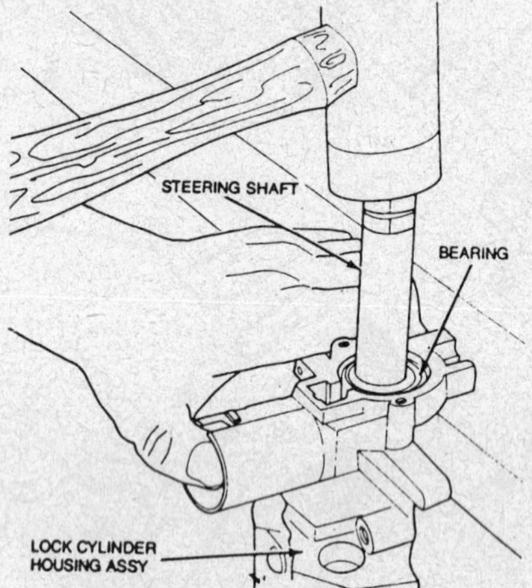


Fig. 26 Removing steering shaft from bearing. Cougar & Thunderbird

4. Remove two lock cylinder housing assembly-to-column outer tube retaining bolts.
5. If equipped remove sensor ring shield, two sensor switch retaining screws, then the switch.
6. Remove and discard spring retainer.
7. Remove spring and sensor ring.
8. Using a suitable tool, remove shaft bearing sleeve.
9. Remove shaft and lock cylinder housing assembly from column tube.
10. Using a suitable tool, pry lower bearing and sleeve from outer tube.

### Installation

1. Position lock cylinder housing assembly on the shaft assembly. Install the assemblies into the column tube.
2. Install and **torque** two lock cylinder housing retaining bolts to 12-21 ft. lbs.
3. Press sleeve and bearing into outer tube until seated to tabs. Ensure sleeve is not deformed.
4. Press shaft sleeve into lower bearing.
5. Install sensor ring, spring and new spring retainer.
6. If equipped, install sensor switch and sensor ring shield.
7. Install U-joint assembly. **Torque** attaching bolt to 30-42 ft. lbs.
8. Install multi-function switch.
9. Install steering column as described previously.

### TILT COLUMN

### Removal

1. Remove steering column as described previously.
2. Remove two screws retaining multi-function switch, then the switch.
3. Remove conical coil spring and upper bearing retainer plate.
4. Remove shaft C-clip at top of bearing.
5. Set tilt casting in the upper position.
6. Using Pivot Pin Remover Handle tool No. T67P-3D739-C and Pivot Pin Remover tools No. T67P-3D739-B or equivalent, carefully remove pivot pins. **Use caution when removing pivot pins, they are under pressure and will expand with force.**
7. Remove upper tilt casting from lock cylinder over end of shaft.
8. Separate U-joint from lower end of shaft.
9. If equipped remove sensor ring shield, two sensor switch retaining screws, then the switch.
10. Remove and discard spring retainer.
11. Remove spring and sensor ring.
12. Using a suitable tool, remove shaft bearing sleeve.
13. Remove steering shaft assembly from top end of column.
14. Remove lower bearing assembly from column tube.

### Installation

1. Press lower bearing and sleeve into column tube.
2. Install steering shaft assembly through lock cylinder housing top hole, into column tube and through the lower bearing. Use caution not to damage the bearing.
3. Ensure tilt spring is properly positioned, then install upper casting assembly over the shaft and down into lock cylinder housing ears. Ensure lock lever is latched in the top tilt position.
4. Align the tilt castings, then using a C-clamp install two pivot pins until flush with casting surface.

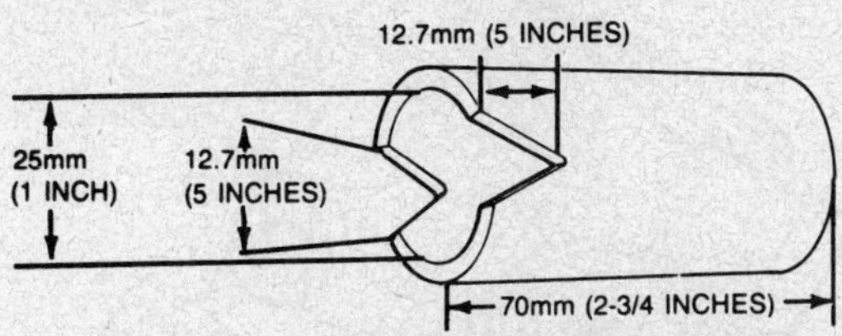


**Fig. 27 Steering column tool**

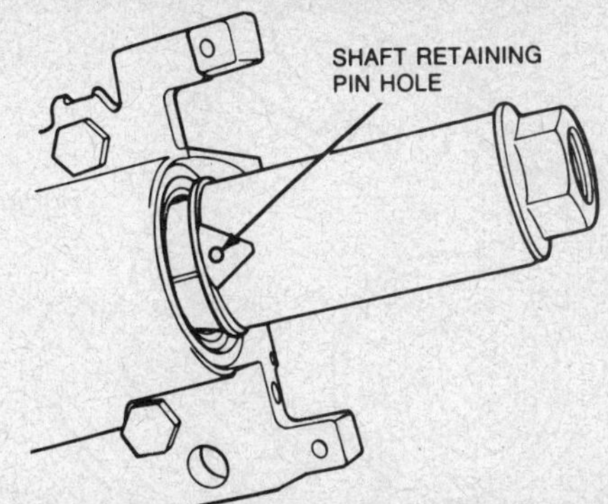


**Fig. 28 Steering column tool positioning**

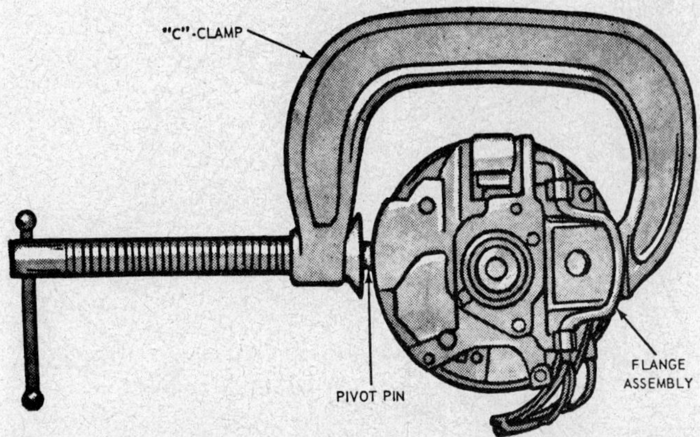


**Fig. 29 Installing flange assembly pivot pins**

5. Install upper bearing snap ring and retainer plate.
6. Install conical coil spring by snapping it into shaft groove.
7. Install multi-function switch.
8. Install lower bearing sleeve, sensor ring, spring and new spring retainer.
9. If equipped, install sensor switch and sensor ring shield.
10. Install U-joint assembly. **Torque** attaching bolt to 30-42 ft. lbs.
11. Install steering column as described previously.

## SCORPIO

Refer to procedure as described under "Steering Column Service" for this model.

## XR4TI

Refer to procedure as described under "Tube/Switch" in the "Steering Column Service" section for this model.

# LOCK CYLINDER HOUSING

## REPLACE

### MODELS w/MODULAR STEERING COLUMN, EXCEPT COUGAR, TEMPO, THUNDERBIRD, TOPAZ & 1989–90 ESCORT

#### FIXED COLUMN

Refer to **Fig. 1** for component identification.

#### Removal

1. Remove steering column assembly.
2. **On column shift models,** remove shift cane assembly as described previously.
3. Remove turn signal switch and wash/wipe switch.
4. Remove upper steering shaft bearing as described previously.
5. Remove two bolts which connect lock cylinder housing to outer tube flange bracket, then rotate ignition key to start position and pull actuator interlock nut out of clearance hole in tube. Lift casting off upper steering shaft.
6. **On column shift models,** replace shift selector detent plate if damaged or excessively worn.

#### Installation

1. Install upper steering shaft bearing and sleeve in lock cylinder housing and install upper bearing retainer plate.
2. Using a punch, upset serrated portion of upper shaft sufficiently to assure an interference fit between the bearing inner race and the steering column upper shaft. Place lock cylinder housing on steering column flange bracket with upper steering shaft protruding through upper bearing. Turn ignition key to Start position to locate actuator interlock through the clearance hole in outer tube. Install the two lock cylinder housing bolts and **torque** to 12-21 ft. lbs.
3. Place a piece of pipe (3/4 inch inside dia. x 1 1/2 inch long) over end of steering column upper shaft and install steering wheel nut. Tighten steering wheel nut until steering shaft is drawn up into bearing enough to allow installation of snap ring in groove on shaft. Remove nut and pipe.
4. Install snap ring, turn signal switch and washer/wiper switch.
5. **On column shift models,** install shift cane as described previously.
6. Install steering column as described previously.

#### TILT COLUMN

Refer to **Figs. 2 and 3** for component identification.

#### Removal

1. Remove steering column assembly as described under "Steering Column, Replace."
2. **On models with column shift,** remove shift cane assembly.
3. Remove windshield wiper/washer switch, then remove steering wheel.
4. Remove upper conical spring, bearing plate and C-clip ring.
5. Move tilt column to the uppermost position to unload spring.
6. Using tool No. T67P-3D739B, or equivalent, remove tilt pivot pins. **Use care when removing pivot pins, the tilt spring is still under pressure.**
7. Remove upper casting from lock cylinder housing.
8. **On all except Ford & Mercury full size,** remove bolt and nut attaching lower U-joint shaft assembly to steering column shaft.
9. **On all models,** remove steering shaft assembly from steering column.
10. Remove two bolts attaching lock cylinder housing to outer tube flange bracket, then rotate ignition key to Start position and pull actuator interlock out of clearance hole in tube.
11. Remove ignition lock drive gear and actuator.

#### Installation

1. Position lock cylinder housing on upper steering column flange bracket. Place key in Start position to locate actuator interlock through clearance hole in outer tube. Install and **torque** two bolts attaching lock cylinder housing to bracket to 12 to 20 ft. lbs.
2. Install steering shaft assembly into steering column tube.
3. Install upper casting assembly with tilt spring in position, over end of shaft and down into lock cylinder ears making certain lock lever is latched into the top tilt position.
4. Install tilt pivot pins through lower

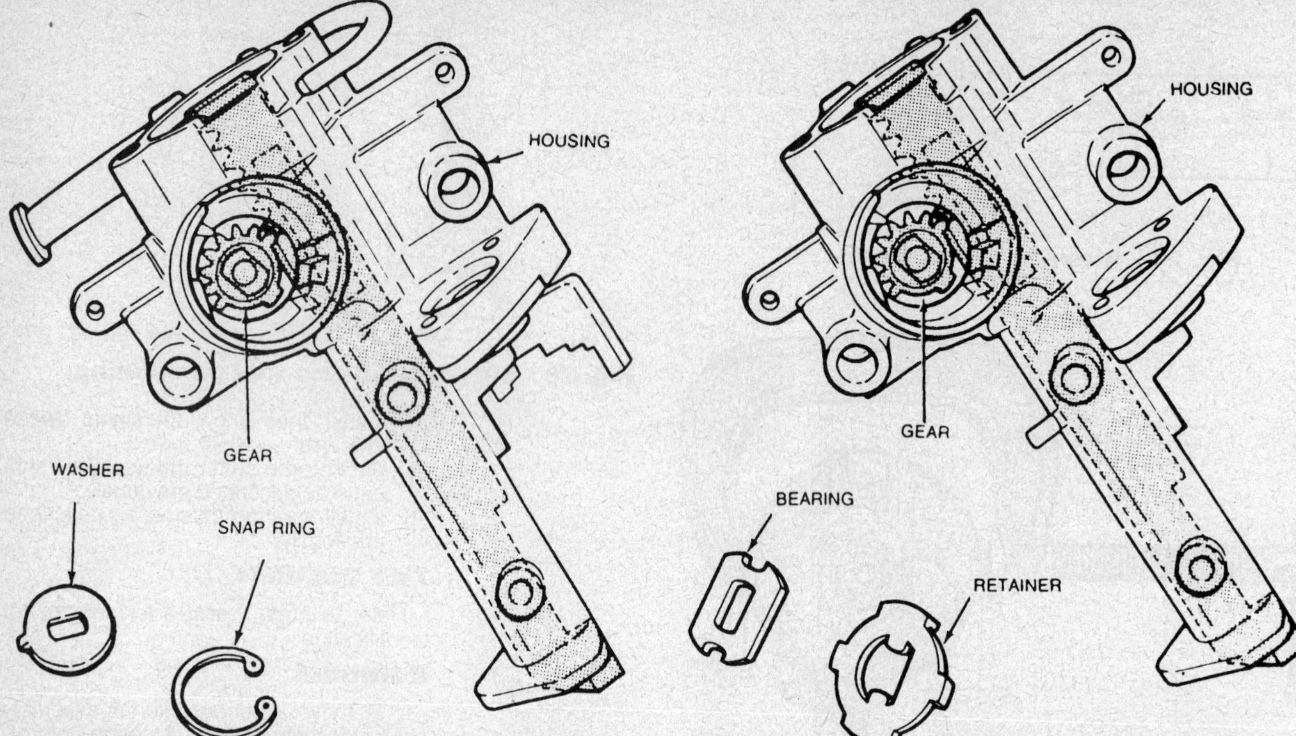


**Fig. 30 Ignition lock drive gear removal & installation. Models w/modular steering columns & silver lock cylinder**

**Fig. 31 Ignition lock drive gear removal & installation. Models w/modular steering columns & gold lock cylinder**

casting holes and into upper casting using a C-clamp, **Fig. 29.** Pivot pins must be flush with outer casing surface.

5. Install C-clip ring on upper shaft groove above bearing.
6. Install upper bearing plate and conical spring. Press spring onto upper shaft until spring snaps into groove.
7. Install turn signal switch and windshield wiper/washer switch.
8. **On column shift models,** install shift cane assembly.
9. **On all except Ford & Mercury full size,** install lower U-joint shaft assembly into lower steering shaft. Install attaching bolt with bolt head against concave portion of tube. **Torque** nut and bolt to 35 to 45 ft. lbs.
10. **On all models,** install steering column, then install steering wheel.

## TEMPO, TOPAZ & 1989–90 ESCORT

### FIXED COLUMN

#### Removal

1. Remove steering column assembly.
2. Remove turn signal switch attaching screws, then the switch.
3. Remove upper shaft bearing as described previously.
4. Remove bolts securing lock cylinder housing to outer tube flange bracket, then rotate ignition switch to start position and pull actuator interlock out of clearance hole in tube. Lift casting off upper steering shaft.
5. Remove ignition lock drive gear.

#### Installation

1. Install ignition lock drive gear and actuator.
2. Using a suitable punch, upset the serrated portion of the upper shaft sufficiently to assure an interference fit between the bearing inner race and the steering column upper shaft. Place lock cylinder housing on steering column flange bracket with upper steering shaft protruding through upper bearing. Turn ignition switch to start position to locate actuator interlock through the clearance hole in outer tube. Install lock cylinder housing bolts and **torque** to 12-21 ft. lbs.
3. Install upper shaft bearing and sleeve over end of steering shaft.
4. Place a piece of pipe (3/4 inch inside dia. x 1 1/2 inch long) over end of steering column upper shaft, then install steering wheel nut. Tighten steering wheel nut until steering shaft is drawn up into bearing enough to allow installation of snap ring in groove on shaft. Remove nut and pipe.
5. Install snap ring, turn signal switch and steering column.

### TILT COLUMN

#### Removal

1. Remove steering column assembly.
2. Remove turn signal switch attaching screws, then the switch.
3. Remove steering wheel, then upper conical spring, bearing plate and C-clip ring, **Figs. 10 & 11.**
4. Move tilt column to uppermost position to unload spring, then using tool T70P-3D739-A or equivalent, remove tilt pins. **Use care when removing pivot pins as the tilt spring is still under tension.**
5. Remove upper casting from lock cylinder housing.
6. Remove clamp from lower end of steering shaft, then pull steering shaft from end of column.
7. Remove lock cylinder housing to outer tube flange bracket attaching bolts, then rotate ignition switch to start position and pull actuator interlock out of clearance hole in tube.
8. Remove ignition lock drive gear and actuator.

#### Installation

1. Position lock cylinder housing on upper steering column flange bracket. Place ignition switch in start position to locate actuator interlock through clearance hole in outer tube. Install lock cylinder housing bolts and **torque** to 12-20 ft. lbs.
2. Install steering shaft assembly into steering column tube. Use care not to damage lower bearing.
3. Install upper casting assembly with tilt spring in position, over end of shaft and down onto lock cylinder ears making certain lock lever is latched into top tilt position.
4. Install tilt pivot pins through lower casting holes and into upper casting using a suitable C-clamp. Pivot pins must be flush with outer casting surface.

5. Install C-clip ring on upper shaft groove above bearing.
6. Install upper bearing plate and conical spring. Press conical spring onto upper shaft until spring snaps into upper groove.
7. Install turn signal switch, then lower column clamp, ensuring locating nib is in hole in shaft. Install steering column and steering wheel.

## COUGAR & THUNDERBIRD

Refer to **Figs. 4 and 5** replacement procedure.

### FIXED COLUMN

#### Removal

1. Remove steering column as described previously.
2. Remove two screws retaining multi-function switch, then the switch.
3. Remove two lock cylinder housing-to-outer tube flange bracket retaining bolts.
4. Remove two screws retaining upper bearing retainer plate.
5. Remove upper bearing snap ring.
6. If equipped remove sensor ring shield, two sensor switch retaining screws, then the switch.
7. Remove and discard spring retainer.
8. Remove spring and sensor ring.
9. Using a suitable tool, remove shaft bearing sleeve.
10. Remove shaft and lock cylinder housing assembly from column tube.
11. Using a soft hammer, separate shaft from the bearing as shown **Fig. 26.**
12. Remove shaft from the tube, then the lock cylinder housing from the shaft.
13. Remove bearing from lock cylinder housing.

#### Installation

1. Hand press upper steering shaft bearing and sleeve into lock cylinder housing bearing bore.
2. Position lock cylinder housing assembly onto the shaft assembly. Install the assemblies into the column tube.
3. Install and **torque** two lock cylinder housing retaining bolts to 12-21 ft. lbs.
4. Install new bearing snap ring as follows:
   a. Position a pipe spacer (3/4 inch ID X 3 1/2 inch long) over end of the upper shaft.
   b. Install steering wheel attaching bolt through the pipe spacer and into the steering shaft.
   c. Tighten the bolt until there is enough room to allow installation of a new bearing snap ring.
   d. Install new snap ring in shaft groove, then remove steering wheel attaching bolt and pipe spacer.
5. Install multi-function switch.
6. Install lower bearing sleeve, sensor ring, spring and new spring retainer.
7. If equipped, install sensor switch and sensor ring shield.
8. Install U-joint assembly. **Torque** attaching bolt to 30-42 ft. lbs.
9. Install steering column as described previously.

### TILT COLUMN

#### Removal

1. Remove steering column as described previously.
2. Remove two screws retaining multi-function switch, then the switch.
3. Remove conical coil spring and upper bearing retainer plate.
4. Remove shaft C-clip at top of bearing.
5. Set tilt casting in the upper position.
6. Using Pivot Pin Remover Handle tool No. T67P-3D739-C and Pivot Pin Remover tools No. T67P-3D739-B or equivalent, carefully remove pivot pins. **Use caution when removing pivot pins, they are under pressure and will expand with force.**
7. Remove upper tilt casting from lock cylinder over end of shaft.
8. Separate U-joint from lower end of shaft.
9. If equipped remove sensor ring shield, two sensor switch retaining screws, then the switch.
10. Remove and discard spring retainer.
11. Remove spring and sensor ring.
12. Using a suitable tool, remove shaft bearing sleeve.
13. Remove steering shaft assembly from top end of column.
14. Remove two lock cylinder housing-to-outer tube retaining bolts.

#### Installation

1. Position lock cylinder housing onto upper steering flange bracket. Install and **torque** two lock cylinder housing-to-bracket retaining bolts to 12-20 ft. lbs.
2. Install steering shaft assembly through lock cylinder housing top hole, into column tube and through the lower bearing. Use caution not to damage the bearing.
3. Ensure tilt spring is properly positioned, then install upper casting assembly over the shaft and down into lock cylinder housing ears. Ensure lock lever is latched in the top tilt position.
4. Align the tilt castings, then using a C-clamp install two pivot pins until flush with casting surface.
5. Install upper bearing snap ring and retainer plate.
6. Install conical coil spring by snapping it into shaft groove.
7. Install multi-function switch.
8. Install lower bearing sleeve, sensor ring, spring and new spring retainer.
9. If equipped, install sensor switch and sensor ring shield.
10. Install U-joint assembly. **Torque** attaching bolt to 30-42 ft. lbs.
11. Install steering column as described previously.

## SCORPIO

Refer to procedure as described under "Steering Column Service" for this model.

## XR4TI

Refer to procedure as described under "Tube/Switch" in the "Steering Column Section" section for this model.

# IGNITION LOCK DRIVE GEAR

# REPLACE

## MODELS w/MODULAR STEERING COLUMN EXCEPT TEMPO, TOPAZ & 1989–90 ESCORT

Refer to **Figs. 1, 2, 4 and 5** for component identification.

### SILVER COLORED LOCK CYLINDER

#### Removal

1. Remove lock cylinder assembly.
2. Insert a flat screwdriver into recess of drive gear at bottom of lock cylinder housing and turn drive gear three notches counterclockwise.
3. Remove snap ring, washer and lock driver gear from lock cylinder housing. **Carefully note relationship of lock drive gear to position of rack teeth, Fig. 30.**

#### Installation

1. Place lock drive gear in base of lock cylinder housing in same position as that noted during removal. The position of lock drive gear will be correct if the last tooth on the drive gear is meshed with the last tooth on the rack, **Fig. 30.**
2. Install washer and snap ring, then insert a flat screwdriver into recess of lock drive gear at bottom of lock cylinder housing and turn drive gear three notches in a clockwise direction.
3. Install lock cylinder assembly.

### GOLD COLORED LOCK CYLINDER

#### Removal

1. Remove lock cylinder assembly.
2. Note position of bearing retainer. Remove plastic bearing retainer by inserting tool with 90 degree bend on tip between bearing retainer and bearing, then prying upward.
3. Note position of lock drive gear to position of rack teeth, **Fig. 31.** Insert tip of screwdriver into double D slot in bearing and rotate 1/4 turn. Remove bearing and lock drive gear.

#### Installation

1. Install lock drive gear in lock cylinder housing as shown in **Fig. 31.** Position of lock drive gear is correct if last tooth on drive gear is meshed with last tooth on rack.
2. Install bearing retainer in lock cylinder housing. Insert tip of screwdriver into double D slot of bearing and turn 1/4 turn.
3. Press plastic bearing retainer into housing in original position.
4. Pull down on column lock actuator to line up flats of drive gear with flats on washer. Install lock cylinder assembly.

## TEMPO, TOPAZ & 1989–90 ESCORT

### Removal

1. Remove lock cylinder assembly.
2. Remove plastic retainer, washer and lock drive gear from lock cylinder housing. Note location of lock drive gear in relation to rack teeth.

### Installation

1. Install lock drive gear in the same position as removed from. **The lock drive gear is installed correctly when the last tooth of the drive gear is meshed with the last tooth on the rack.**
2. Install washer and plastic retainer.
3. Align drive gear flats with washer flats by pulling downward on column lock actuator.
4. Install lock cylinder assembly.

## 1991 ESCORT & TRACER

### Removal

1. Remove steering wheel, refer to "Steering Column" replace.
2. Remove Multi-function switch, refer to "Electrical Section".
3. Remove shift lock cable mounting bracket bolt and position bracket and cable aside.
4. Remove four steering column upper mounting bracket bolts and lower the column.
5. Using a hammer and chisel, make a groove in each bolt head of column lock mounting bracket, then using a screwdriver, remove and discard the bolts.
6. Remove steering column lock and mounting bracket.

### Installation

1. Replace steering column lock and mounting bracket, using two new bolts. Tighten only so column lock stays in position.
2. Place key in ignition switch and verify that column lock works properly. If not, reposition column lock until it operates properly.
3. **Torque** mounting bracket bolts until the bolt head breaks off, then position steering column and install four upper mounting bracket bolts. **Torque** bolts to 80-123 inch lbs.
4. **On tilt column,** remove upper mounting bracket retaining pin and position shift lock cable mounting bracket and install bolt. **Torque** to 37-55 inch lbs.
5. Connect ignition switch electrical connectors, then install the multi-function switch.
6. Install steering wheel, **Torquing** nut to 29-36 ft. lbs.

# IGNITION LOCK ASSEMBLY REPLACE

## SABLE & TAURUS

### Removal

1. Disconnect battery ground cable.
2. Unsnap upper extension shroud from retainer clips at the 9 o'clock position.
3. Remove three screws retaining upper and lower shrouds, then the shrouds.
4. Disconnect key warning buzzer electrical connector.
5. Turn ignition key to RUN position.
6. Place a 1/8 inch diameter piece of wire in hole in trim shroud under lock cylinder. Depress retaining pin while pulling out on lock cylinder to remove it from column housing.

### Installation

1. Install lock cylinder by turning it to RUN position and depressing retaining pin. Insert lock cylinder into lock cylinder housing. Ensure cylinder is fully seated and aligned in interlocking washer before turning it.
2. Reconnect key warning buzzer electrical connector, then install upper and lower shrouds.
3. Reconnect battery ground cable.

## SCORPIO

Refer to procedure as described under "Steering Column Service" for this model.

## XR4TI

Refer to procedure as described under "Tube/Switch" in the "Steering Column Service" section for this model.

# IGNITION LOCK ACTUATOR & STEERING WHEEL LOCK PAWL REPLACE

## MODELS W/MODULAR STEERING COLUMN EXCEPT TEMPO, TOPAZ & 1989–90 ESCORT

Refer to **Figs. 1, 2, 3, 4 and 5** for component identification.

### Removal

1. Remove lock cylinder housing, ignition lock switch, lock cylinder assembly and lock drive gear as described previously.
2. Slide actuator assembly out of the rear of the track in the lock cylinder housing.
3. Remove lock pawl and spring.

### Installation

1. Install lock pawl and spring on actuator assembly.
2. Install actuator assembly into track on lock cylinder housing and install the lock drive gear and lock cylinder assembly.
3. Install ignition switch and lock cylinder housing.

## TEMPO, TOPAZ & 1989–90 ESCORT

### Removal

1. Remove lock cylinder housing assembly, **Figs. 9 through 11,** as previously described.
2. Remove ignition switch, lock cylinder and drive gear from housing as outlined.
3. Remove actuator assembly from housing.
4. Remove lock pawl and spring.

### Installation

1. Assemble lock actuator spring and lock pawl so that spring engages locating rod of actuator and depression in lock pawl.
2. Install actuator assembly into lock cylinder housing, then install lock gear, new retainer and lock cylinder.
3. Install ignition switch.
4. Install lock cylinder housing assembly to outer tube.

# Vehicles With Airbag System

## INDEX



## AIRBAG DEACTIVATION & REACTIVATION

**The electrical circuit necessary for system deployment is powered directly from the battery and a backup power supply. To avoid accidental deployment and possible personal injury, the airbag system must be deactivated prior to servicing or replacing any system components.**

A back-up power supply is included in the system to provide airbag deployment in the event the battery or battery cables are damaged in an accident before the sensors can close. The power supply is a capacitor that will retain a charge for approximately 15 minutes after the battery ground cable is disconnected. **Backup power supply must be disconnected to deactivate airbag system.** To remove backup power supply, refer to "Airbags" in the "Passive Restraint" section.

1. Disconnect battery ground cable.
2. Disconnect backup power supply.
3. Remove four nut and washer assemblies securing airbag module to steering wheel, then disconnect airbag electrical connector. Attach jumper wire to airbag terminals on clockspring terminals.
4. **On models equipped with passenger-side airbag,** disconnect airbag module connector located behind glove compartment. Attach a jumper wire to airbag terminals on wiring harness side of passenger airbag module connector terminals.
5. **On all models,** reconnect battery and backup power supply if necessary to perform repair procedure.
6. To reactivate, disconnect battery ground cable and backup power supply, then reverse remainder of deactivation procedure. **Torque** airbag module to steering wheel nut assemblies to 24-32 inch lbs. on Crown Victoria and Grand Marquis, or 35-53 inch lbs. on all other models.
7. Verify airbag lamp after reactivating system.

## DESCRIPTION

**The steering column used on vehicles equipped with airbags is of a modular construction and features easy to service electrical switches. The washer/wiper switch and the combination turn signal/hazard/horn/flash-to-pass dimmer switch are attached with self-tapping screws.**

**The vehicle is equipped with either a brush type slip ring or a clockspring type slip ring. Removal and installation procedures for the two types are the same except where noted.**

**Fasteners used on steering column components must be replaced after removal. The fasteners are coated with a epoxy adhesive making them non-reusable.**

**Whenever the steering column is removed from the vehicle, or is separated from the steering gear, the steering column must be in locked position to prevent the steering wheel from being rotated accidentally and damaging the airbag slip ring.**

## STEERING COLUMN REPLACE

### TEMPO & TOPAZ

#### Removal

1. Disarm airbag system as described under "Airbag Deactivation & Reactivation."
2. Park vehicle with wheels in straight ahead position, then turn ignition switch to Lock position and rotate steering wheel approximately 16° counterclockwise until locked into position.
3. Deactivate airbag system.
4. Remove steering column cover on lower portion of instrument panel to expose instrument panel reinforcement section.
5. Remove lower steering column shroud, **Fig. 1.**
6. Loosen but do not remove two nuts and two bolts retaining steering column to support bracket and remove upper shroud.
7. Disconnect all steering column electrical connections.
8. Loosen steering column to intermediate shaft clamp connection and remove bolt or nut.
9. Remove two nuts and two bolts attaching steering column to support bracket.
10. Pry open steering column shaft in area of clamp on each side of bolt groove with steering column locked, opening enough to be able to disengage shafts with minimal effort. **Do not use excessive force.**
11. Inspect two steering column bracket clips for damage. If clips have been bent or excessively distorted, they must be replaced.

#### Installation

1. Engage lower steering shaft to intermediate shaft and hand start clamp and bolt nut.
2. Align two bolts on steering column support bracket assembly with outer tube mounting holes and hand start two nuts. Check for presence of two clips on outer bracket. The clips must be present to ensure adequate performance of vital parts and systems. Hand start two bolts through outer tube upper bracket and clip into support bracket nuts.
3. Connect all electrical connectors at steering column.
4. Install upper shroud.
5. **Torque** steering column mounting nut and bolts to 15-25 ft. lbs.
6. Unlock steering column and cycle steering wheel one turn left and one turn right to align intermediate shaft into column shaft. **Engine must be running during step 6 on vehicles equipped with power steering.**
7. **Torque** steering shaft clamp nut to 20-30 Ft. lbs.
8. Install lower trim shroud with five attaching screws.
9. Install steering column cover on instrument panel.
10. Connect battery grounds cable and check steering column for proper operation.
11. Rearm airbag system as described under "Airbag Deactivation & Reacti vation."

### CONTINENTAL

#### Removal

Refer to **Fig. 2,** for component identification.

1. Disarm airbag system as described under "Airbag Deactivation & Reactivation."
2. Disconnect battery ground cable.
3. Remove steering column cover from lower portion of instrument panel, by

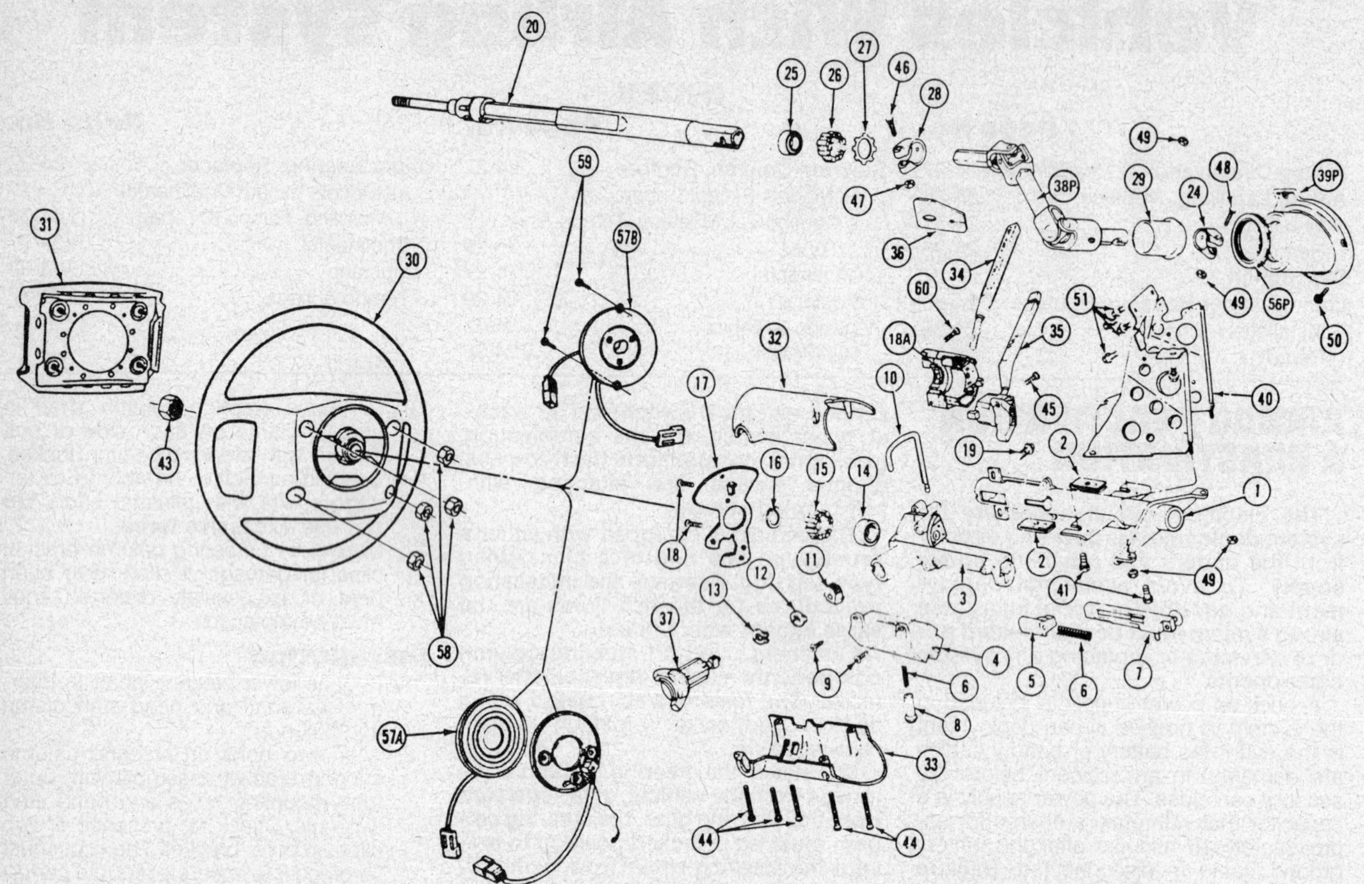


**Fig. 1 Exploded view of steering column (Part 1 of 2). Tempo & Topaz**

removing four self-tapping screws.

4. Remove tilt release lever, then the ignition lock cylinder.
5. Remove column shrouds by removing three self-tapping screws from bottom of lower shroud.
6. Remove horn pad and steering wheel assembly.
7. Remove column shift as follows:
   a. Disconnect PRNDL cable from lock cylinder housing by removing retaining screw. Remove cable from shift socket.
   b. Remove PRNDL cable from retaining hook on bottom of lock cylinder housing.
   c. Using suitable punch, remove shift lever retaining pin. Remove shift lever.
8. Disconnect speed control/horn brush wiring connector from main wiring harness.
9. Remove multi-function switch electrical connector and retaining clip from lock cylinder housing by removing two screws.
10. Disconnect warning buzzer, ignition switch from electrical connector.
11. Disconnect steering column angular speed sensor wire connector at cable bracket.
12. Disconnect steering shaft from intermediate shaft. Wire lower end of steering shaft to column housing to prevent rotation of steering shaft.
13. Remove shift cable plastic terminal from column selector lever pivot ball using a screwdriver and prying between plastic terminal and selector lever. Remove shift cable bracket (with shift cable still attached) from lock cylinder housing.
14. Remove vacuum hoses from parking brake release switch. Remove hood release cable grommet from column bracket.
15. While supporting column assembly, unbolt column assembly from steering column support bracket.
16. After removal of four nuts, column should be supported on the rear two studs by push-on clips and must be lowered by forcing the column downward. These clips are assembly aids and do not need to be replaced. **When forcing downward, care should be taken to avoid damaging safety slip-clips on steering column.**
17. Remove steering column assembly from vehicle.

## Installation

1. Carefully raise steering column assembly into position. Push column up on bolts.
2. Hand start column retaining nuts, center column assembly in instrument panel opening and **torque** four nuts to 20 ft. lbs.
3. Install vacuum hoses on parking brake release switch.
4. Install shift cable bracket (with shift cable attached) to lock cylinder housing and **torque** attaching nuts to 6 ft. lbs. Snap transmission shift cable terminal to selector lever pivot ball on steering column.
5. Liberally grease to vee-shaped steering shaft yoke. Connect steering shaft to intermediate shaft using retainer assembly and two nuts. Ensure vee-angle of intermediate shaft fits correctly in steering column yoke. **Torque** nuts to 20 ft. lbs.
6. Install ignition switch, key warning buzzer, steering sensor electrical connectors.
7. Install multi-function switch to lock cylinder housing and **torque** attaching screws to 22 inch lbs.
8. Connect speed control/horn brush electrical connector.
9. Install cable as follows:
   a. Install PRNDL cable into retaining hook on lock cylinder housing and shift socket.

| Key No. | Part Number | Part Name | Quantity |
|---|---|---|---|
| 1 | 3A517-3514 | Outer Tube Assembly — Steering Column | 1 |
| 2 | 3A504 | Clip — Steering Column Bracket | 2 |
| 3 | 3F643 | Housing — Steering Column Lock Cylinder | 1 |
| 4 | 11572 | Ignition Switch Assembly | 1 |
| 5 | 3E691 | Pawl — Steering Column Lock | 1 |
| 6 | 3E696 | Spring — Steering Column Lock | 2 |
| 7 | 3E723 | Actuator Assembly | 1 |
| 8 | 3F531 | Knob — Steering Column Lock Actuator | 1 |
| 9 | N800207-S100 | Bolt — M8 — 1.0 x 10 Break Off Head | 2 |
| 10 | 3F528 | Lever — Steering Column Lock Actuator | 1 |
| 11 | 3E717 | Gear — Steering Column Lock | 1 |
| 12 | 3E700 | Bearing — Steering Column Lock Housing | 1 |
| 13 | 3F579 | Retainer — Steering Column Lock Gear | 1 |
| 14 | 3517 | Bearing Assembly — Steering Column Upper | 1 |
| 15 | 3518 | Sleeve — Steering Column Upper Bearing | 1 |
| 16 | 3C610 | Retainer — Steering Column Upper Bearing | 1 |
| 17 | 3C610 | Retainer — Steering Column Upper Bearing Plate | 1 |
| 18 | 52794-S2 | Screw No. 8-18 x .62 Pan Head Tapping | 2 |
| 18A | 13B302 | Switch Assemble — T/S & E (with Horn) | 1 |
| 19 | N605531-S2 | Bolt — M8 — 1.25 x 20.0 Hex Head | 2 |
| 20 | 3E729 | Shaft Assembly — Steering Column | 1 |
| 24 | 3D699 | Clamp — Power | 1 |
| 25 | 3E733 | Bearing Assembly — Steering Gear Shaft Lower | 1 |
| 26 | 3A649 | Sleeve — Steering Gear Lower Bearing | 1 |
| 27 | 3F543 | Steering Gear Shaft Lower Bearing Retainer | 1 |
| 28 | 3R548 | Clamp — Steering Column Lower | 1 |
| 29 | 3C612 | Seal | 1 |
| 30 | 3600 | Wheel Assembly — Steering | 1 |
| 31 | | Module — Air Bag | 1 |
| 32 | 3530 | Shroud — Upper | 1 |
| 33 | 3530 | Shroud — Lower | 1 |
| 34 | 13305 | Handle & Shank Assembly — T/S | 1 |
| 35 | 17A553 | Wash/Wipe Switch | 1 |
| 36 | 13B365 | Cover, Turn Signal & Wash/Wipe Switch | 1 |
| 37 | 6122050 | Lock Cylinder & Key | 1 |
| 38P | 3C662 | Shaft Assembly — Steering Col. Lower — Power | 1 |
| 39P | 3E735 | Boot — Power | 1 |
| 40 | 3B139 | Bracket Assembly — Steering Column Support | 1 |
| 41 | N801571-S100 | Bolt — M8 x 1.25 x 23.0 Hex Flange Plt. | 2 |
| 42 | 3B743 | Brace — Lateral/NVH | 1 |
| 43 | 33850-S2 | Nut — Steering Wheel | 1 |
| 44 | 55931-S2 | Screw No. 8-18 x 1.50 Pan Head Tapping | 5 |
| 45 | 56920-S2 | Screw No. 8-18 x 1.50 | 2 |
| 46 | N606331-S2 | Bolt — M10 x 1.50 x 45 Carriage | 1 |
| 47 | N620482-S2 | Nut — M10 x 1.50 Hex Flange Lock P/T | 1 |
| 48 | N606325-S2 | Bolt — M8 x 1.25 x 40 Carriage | 1 |
| 49 | N802811-S2 | Nut — M8 x 1.25 Hex Flange Lock P/T | 2 |
| 50 | 389487-S2 | Screw | 4 |
| 51 | N605905-S2 | Bolt — M8 x 1.25 x 20 Flange Head | 6 |
| 55 | 56902-S2 | Screw No. 8-18 x .50 | 2 |
| 56P | 3A510 | Boot Seal — Power Steering | 1 |
| 57A | | Slip Ring Brush Type — Air Bag | 1 |
| 57B | | Slip Ring, Clock Spring Type — Air Bag | 1 |
| 58 | | Nut | 4 |
| 59 | | Screw | 2 |
| 60 | | Screw | 2 |

**Fig. 1 Exploded view of steering column (Part 2 of 2). Tempo & Topaz**

   b. Loosely install PRNDL cable onto lock cylinder housing.
10. Adjust PRNDL cable as follows:
   a. **On AXOD transmissions,** place shift lever in overdrive. A weight of 8 lbs. should be hung on shift selector lever to ensure lever is located firmly against detent.
   b. **On AXOD transmissions,** adjust PRNDL cable until PRNDL indicator completely covers overdrive. then **torque** hex-head screw to 25 ft. lbs.
   c. Cycle shift lever through all positions and check that PRNDL indicator completely covers the proper letter or number.
   d. Install shift lever using new lever retaining pin.
11. Install steering wheel and horn pad. Ensure multi-function switch is in neutral before installing steering wheel.
12. Install shrouds with retaining screws and **torque** to 8 inch lbs.
13. Install tilt release lever with one socket-head capscrew and **torque** to 8 ft. lbs.
14. Install ignition lock cylinder.
15. Install lower steering column cover with four screws.
16. Reconnect battery ground cable.
17. Rearm airbag system as described under "Airbag Deactivation & Reactivation."

## MUSTANG

### Removal

Refer to **Fig. 3,** for component identification.

1. Disarm airbag system as described under "Airbag Deactivation & Reactivation."
2. Disconnect battery ground cable.
3. Remove two nuts retaining flexible coupling to flange on steering input shaft.
4. Disengage safety strap and bolt assembly from flexible coupling.
5. Remove steering column trim shrouds.
6. Remove steering column cover and hood release mechanism directly under column.
7. Disconnect all electrical connectors from column switches (turn signal, wash/wipe, ignition and key warning buzzer connecting wire).
8. Remove four screws retaining dust boot to dash panel.
9. Remove four nuts retaining column to brake pedal support.
10. Lower column to clear the four mounting bolts, then pull column out, so that U-joint assembly passes through clearance hole in dash panel.

### Installation

1. Install steering column by inserting U-joint assembly through opening in dash panel.
2. Align the four bolts on brake pedal support with mounting holes on column collar and bracket. Install nuts and **torque** to 20-37 ft. lbs.
3. Connect ignition switch, turn signal, key warning buzzer connector wire and wash/wipe switch connectors.
4. Engage safety strap and bolt assembly to flange on steering gear input shaft. Install the two nuts retaining steering column lower shaft and U-joint assembly to flange on steering gear input shaft. **Torque** nuts to 20-37 ft. lbs. **The safety strap must be properly positioned to prevent metal to metal contact after tightening nuts. The flexible coupling must not be distorted when the nuts are tightened. Pry steering shaft up or down with a suitable pry bar to achieve plus or minus 1/8 inch coupling insulator flatness.**
5. Engage dust boot at base of steering column to dash panel opening.
6. Install four screws retaining dust boot to dash panel.
7. Install hood release mechanism and steering column cover below column.
8. Connect battery ground cable.
9. Ensure smooth operation of steering column.
10. Rearm airbag system as described under "Airbag Deactivation & Reactivation."

## ALL MODELS EXCEPT CAPRI, CONTINENTAL, MUSTANG, TEMPO & TOPAZ

### Removal

Refer to **Figs. 4 through 7,** for component identification.

1. Disarm airbag system as described under "Airbag Deactivation & Reactivation."
2. Ensure vehicle wheels are in the straight-ahead position.
3. Disconnect battery ground cable.
4. Remove four airbag module retaining nuts, then lift module off steering wheel.
5. Disconnect speed control wire har-

Continued on page 24-36

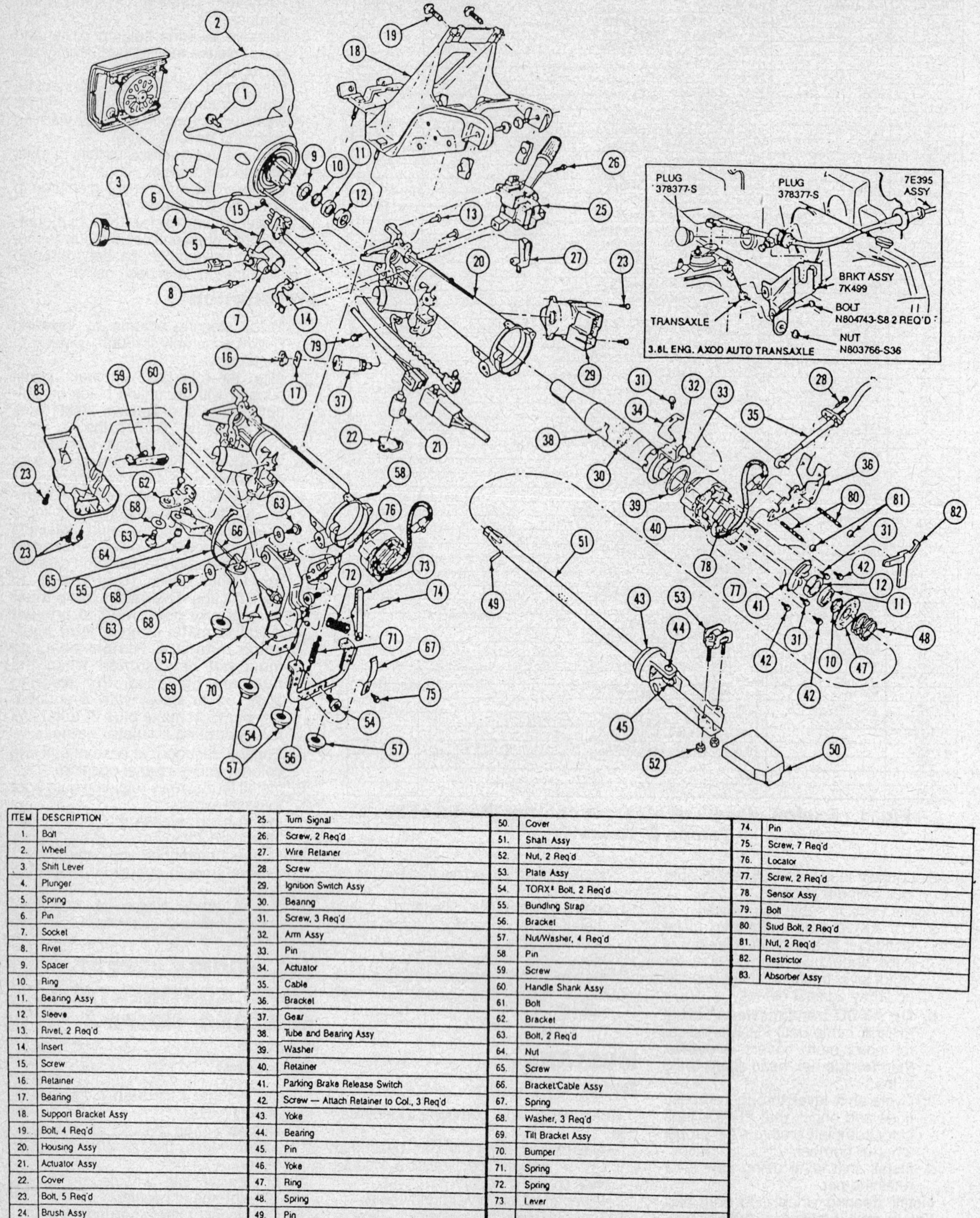


| ITEM | DESCRIPTION |
|---|---|
| 1. | Bolt |
| 2. | Wheel |
| 3. | Shift Lever |
| 4. | Plunger |
| 5. | Spring |
| 6. | Pin |
| 7. | Socket |
| 8. | Rivet |
| 9. | Spacer |
| 10. | Ring |
| 11. | Bearing Assy |
| 12. | Sleeve |
| 13. | Rivet, 2 Req'd |
| 14. | Insert |
| 15. | Screw |
| 16. | Retainer |
| 17. | Bearing |
| 18. | Support Bracket Assy |
| 19. | Bolt, 4 Req'd |
| 20. | Housing Assy |
| 21. | Actuator Assy |
| 22. | Cover |
| 23. | Bolt, 5 Req'd |
| 24. | Brush Assy |
| 25. | Turn Signal |
| 26. | Screw, 2 Req'd |
| 27. | Wire Retainer |
| 28. | Screw |
| 29. | Ignition Switch Assy |
| 30. | Bearing |
| 31. | Screw, 3 Req'd |
| 32. | Arm Assy |
| 33. | Pin |
| 34. | Actuator |
| 35. | Cable |
| 36. | Bracket |
| 37. | Gear |
| 38. | Tube and Bearing Assy |
| 39. | Washer |
| 40. | Retainer |
| 41. | Parking Brake Release Switch |
| 42. | Screw — Attach Retainer to Col., 3 Req'd |
| 43. | Yoke |
| 44. | Bearing |
| 45. | Pin |
| 46. | Yoke |
| 47. | Ring |
| 48. | Spring |
| 49. | Pin |
| 50. | Cover |
| 51. | Shaft Assy |
| 52. | Nut, 2 Req'd |
| 53. | Plate Assy |
| 54. | TORX® Bolt, 2 Req'd |
| 55. | Bundling Strap |
| 56. | Bracket |
| 57. | Nut/Washer, 4 Req'd |
| 58 | Pin |
| 59. | Screw |
| 60. | Handle Shank Assy |
| 61. | Bolt |
| 62. | Bracket |
| 63. | Bolt, 2 Req'd |
| 64. | Nut |
| 65. | Screw |
| 66. | Bracket/Cable Assy |
| 67. | Spring |
| 68. | Washer, 3 Req'd |
| 69. | Tilt Bracket Assy |
| 70. | Bumper |
| 71. | Spring |
| 72. | Spring |
| 73 | Lever |
| 74. | Pin |
| 75. | Screw, 7 Req'd |
| 76. | Locator |
| 77. | Screw, 2 Req'd |
| 78. | Sensor Assy |
| 79. | Bolt |
| 80 | Stud Bolt, 2 Req'd |
| 81. | Nut, 2 Req'd |
| 82. | Restrictor |
| 83. | Absorber Assy |

**Fig. 2 Exploded view of steering column. Continental**

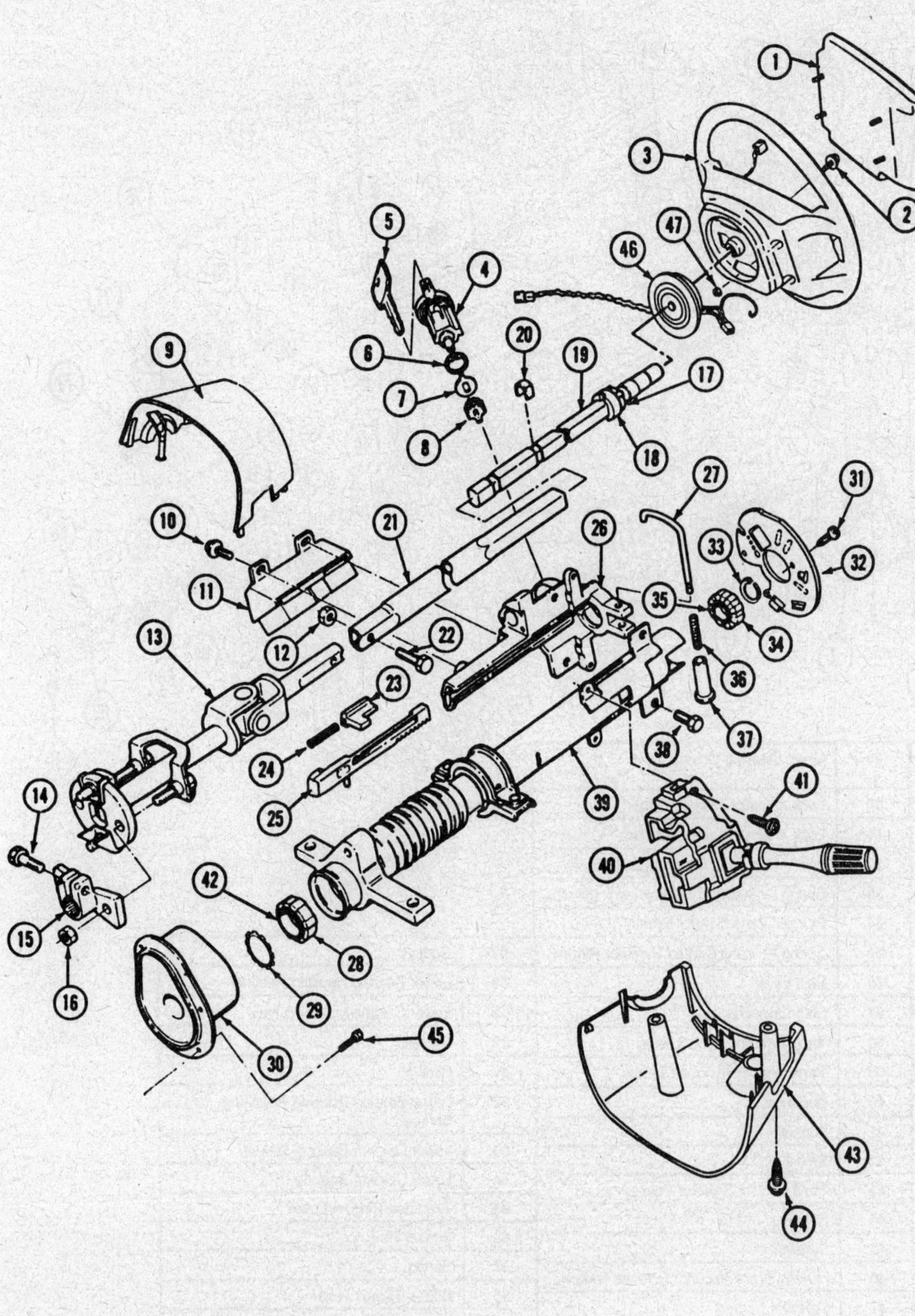

| ITEM | DESCRIPTION |
|---|---|
| 1. | Air Bag Module Assy |
| 2. | Bolt |
| 3. | Wheel Assy. — Stng. |
| 4. | Lock Cyl. |
| 5. | Key (Body) |
| 6. | Retainer |
| 7. | Bearing |
| 8. | Gear — Stng. Col. Lock |
| 9. | Shroud — Upper |
| 10. | Bolt (2 Req'd) |
| 11. | Switch Assy. — Ignition |
| 12. | Nut — 7/16-14 Hex Lock |
| 13. | Shaft Assy. — Stng. Col. Lower |
| 14. | Bolt — 3/8-24 x 1.22 |
| 15. | Flange — Stng. Shaft Lower |
| 16. | Nut — 3/8-16 Hex Lock |
| 17. | Cam — Turn Sig. Turn Off |
| 18. | Lock — Stng. Col. Position |
| 19. | Shaft — Stng. Gear Upper |
| 20. | Anti-Rattle Clips (2 Req'd.) |
| 21. | Shaft — Stng. Gear Lower |
| 22. | Bolt — 7/16-14 x 1.50 Hex |
| 23. | Pawl — Stng. Col. Lock |
| 24. | Spring — Stng. Col. Lock |
| 25. | Actuator Assy. — Stng. Col. Lock |
| 26. | Housing — Stng. Col. Lock Cyl. |
| 27. | Lever — Stng. Col. Lock Actuator |
| 28. | Bearing Assy. — Stng. Gear Shaft Lower |
| 29. | Ring — Stng. Gear Shaft Lower Bearing Retainer |
| 30. | Boot Assy. — Stng. Col. |
| 31. | Screw — No. 8-18 x .62 Pan Hd. Tap (2 Req'd.) |
| 32. | Retainer — Stng. Col. Upper Bearing |
| 33. | Snap Ring |
| 34. | Sleeve — Stng. Col. Upper Bearing |
| 35. | Bearing Assy. — Stng. Col. Upper |
| 36. | Spring — Stng. Col. Lock |
| 37. | Knob — Stng. Col. Lock Actuator |
| 38. | Bolt — M8 x 1.25 Hex Hd. (2 Req'd.) |
| 39. | Tube Assy. Col. Outer |
| 40. | Multi-Function Switch |
| 41. | Screw — No. 8-18 x .62 Pan Hd. Tap (2 Req'd.) |
| 42. | Sleeve — Steering Column Lower Bearing |
| 43. | Shroud — Stng. Col. Lower |
| 44. | Screw — No. 8-18 x 1.50 Pan Hd. Tap (5 Req'd.) |
| 45. | Screw (4 Req'd.) |
| 46. | Contact Ring |
| 47. | Nut and Washer Assy. |

**Fig. 3 Exploded view of steering column. Mustang**

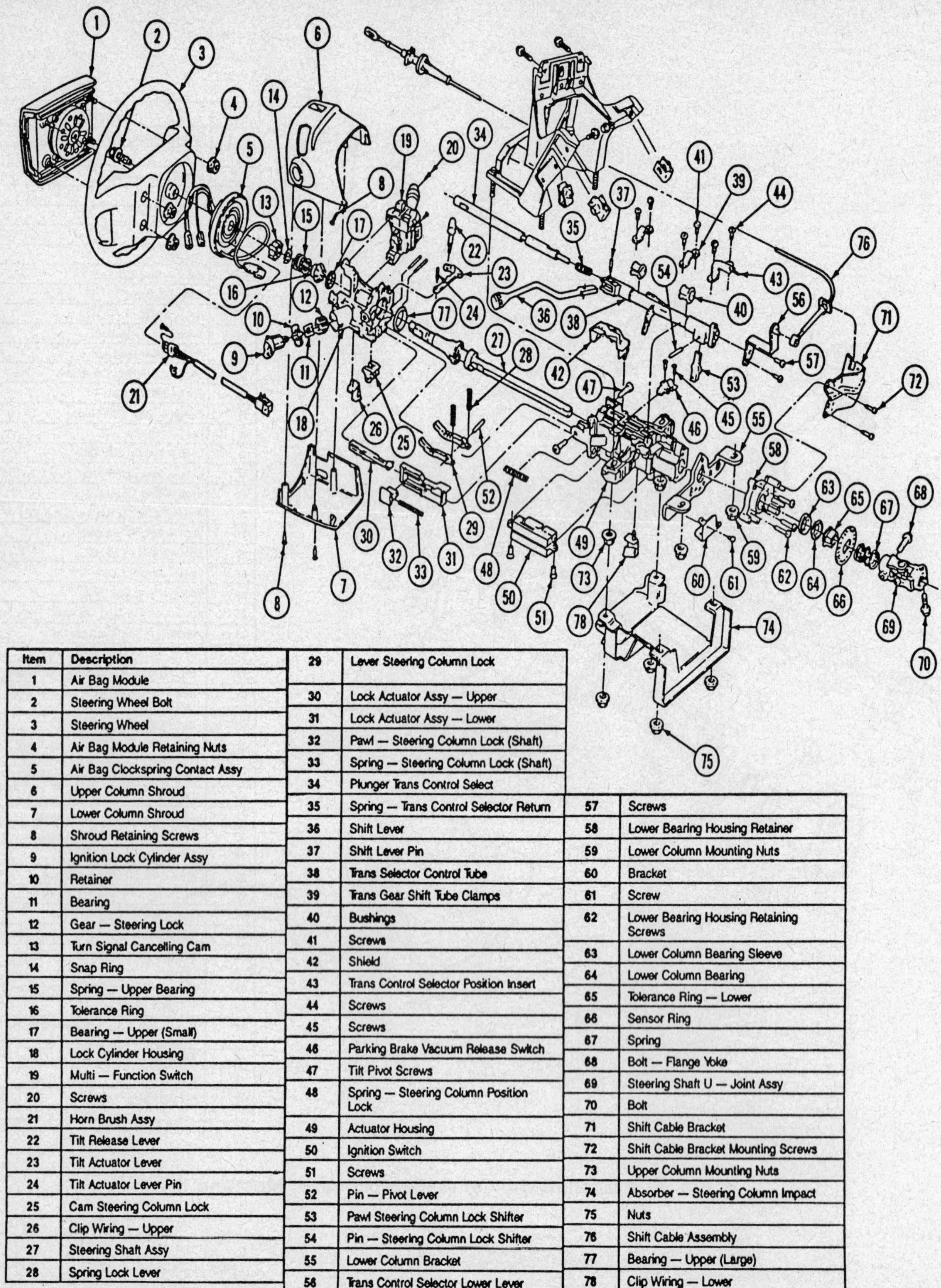

| Item | Description |
|---|---|
| 1 | Air Bag Module |
| 2 | Steering Wheel Bolt |
| 3 | Steering Wheel |
| 4 | Air Bag Module Retaining Nuts |
| 5 | Air Bag Clockspring Contact Assy |
| 6 | Upper Column Shroud |
| 7 | Lower Column Shroud |
| 8 | Shroud Retaining Screws |
| 9 | Ignition Lock Cylinder Assy |
| 10 | Retainer |
| 11 | Bearing |
| 12 | Gear — Steering Lock |
| 13 | Turn Signal Cancelling Cam |
| 14 | Snap Ring |
| 15 | Spring — Upper Bearing |
| 16 | Tolerance Ring |
| 17 | Bearing — Upper (Small) |
| 18 | Lock Cylinder Housing |
| 19 | Multi — Function Switch |
| 20 | Screws |
| 21 | Horn Brush Assy |
| 22 | Tilt Release Lever |
| 23 | Tilt Actuator Lever |
| 24 | Tilt Actuator Lever Pin |
| 25 | Cam Steering Column Lock |
| 26 | Clip Wiring — Upper |
| 27 | Steering Shaft Assy |
| 28 | Spring Lock Lever |
| 29 | Lever Steering Column Lock |
| 30 | Lock Actuator Assy — Upper |
| 31 | Lock Actuator Assy — Lower |
| 32 | Pawl — Steering Column Lock (Shaft) |
| 33 | Spring — Steering Column Lock (Shaft) |
| 34 | Plunger Trans Control Select |
| 35 | Spring — Trans Control Selector Return |
| 36 | Shift Lever |
| 37 | Shift Lever Pin |
| 38 | Trans Selector Control Tube |
| 39 | Trans Gear Shift Tube Clamps |
| 40 | Bushings |
| 41 | Screws |
| 42 | Shield |
| 43 | Trans Control Selector Position Insert |
| 44 | Screws |
| 45 | Screws |
| 46 | Parking Brake Vacuum Release Switch |
| 47 | Tilt Pivot Screws |
| 48 | Spring — Steering Column Position Lock |
| 49 | Actuator Housing |
| 50 | Ignition Switch |
| 51 | Screws |
| 52 | Pin — Pivot Lever |
| 53 | Pawl Steering Column Lock Shifter |
| 54 | Pin — Steering Column Lock Shifter |
| 55 | Lower Column Bracket |
| 56 | Trans Control Selector Lower Lever |
| 57 | Screws |
| 58 | Lower Bearing Housing Retainer |
| 59 | Lower Column Mounting Nuts |
| 60 | Bracket |
| 61 | Screw |
| 62 | Lower Bearing Housing Retaining Screws |
| 63 | Lower Column Bearing Sleeve |
| 64 | Lower Column Bearing |
| 65 | Tolerance Ring — Lower |
| 66 | Sensor Ring |
| 67 | Spring |
| 68 | Bolt — Flange Yoke |
| 69 | Steering Shaft U — Joint Assy |
| 70 | Bolt |
| 71 | Shift Cable Bracket |
| 72 | Shift Cable Bracket Mounting Screws |
| 73 | Upper Column Mounting Nuts |
| 74 | Absorber — Steering Column Impact |
| 75 | Nuts |
| 76 | Shift Cable Assembly |
| 77 | Bearing — Upper (Large) |
| 78 | Clip Wiring — Lower |

**Fig. 4 Exploded view of steering column. Sable & Taurus w/column shift**

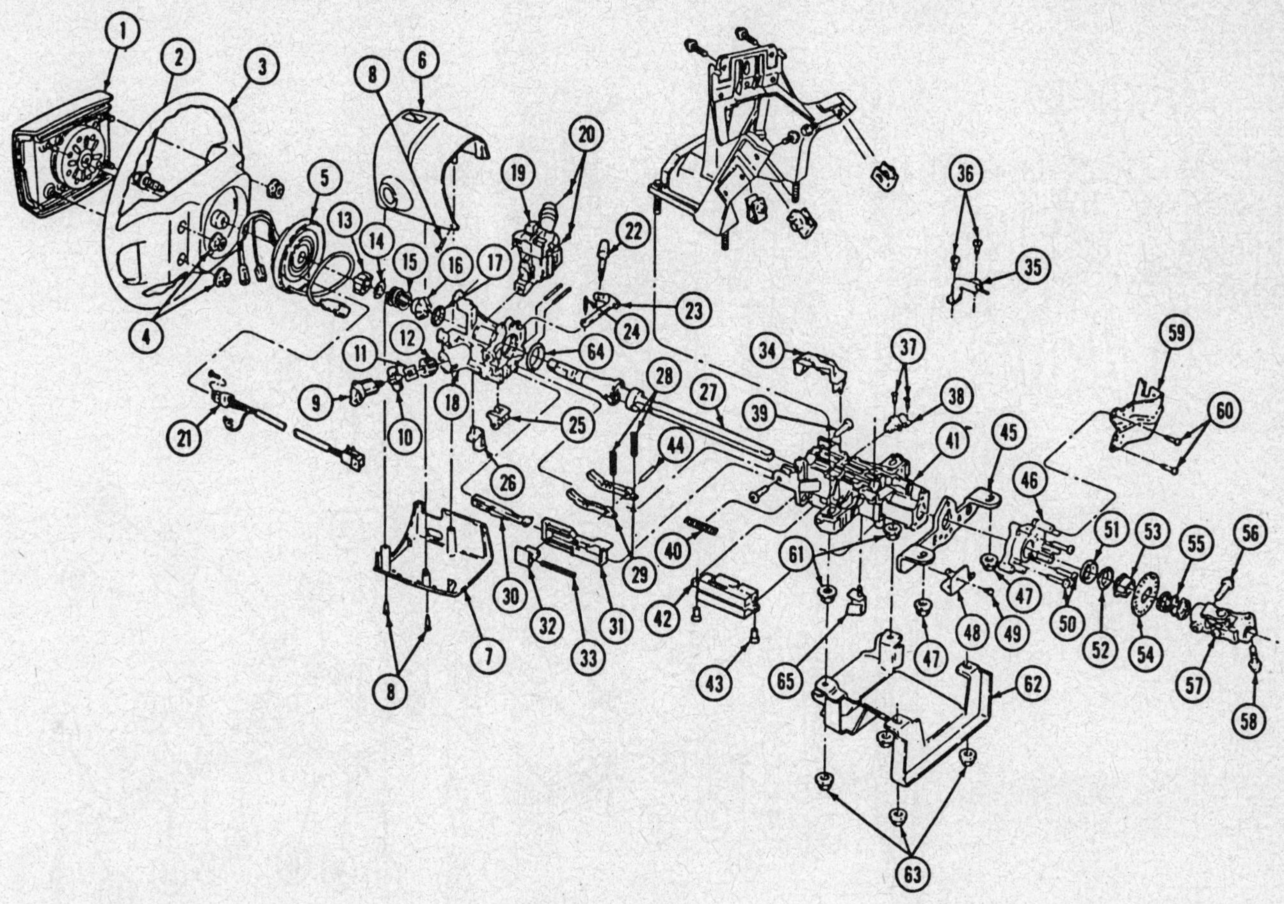

| Item | Description |
|---|---|
| 1 | Air Bag Module |
| 2 | Steering Wheel Bolt |
| 3 | Steering Wheel |
| 4 | Air Bag Module Retaining Nuts |
| 5 | Air Bag Clockspring Contact Assy |
| 6 | Upper Column Shroud |
| 7 | Lower Column Shroud |
| 8 | Shroud Retaining Screws |
| 9 | Ignition Lock Cylinder Assy |
| 10 | Retainer |
| 11 | Bearing |
| 12 | Gear — Steering Lock |
| 13 | Turn Signal Cancelling Cam |
| 14 | Snap Ring |
| 15 | Spring — Upper Bearing |
| 16 | Tolerance Ring |
| 17 | Bearing — Upper (Small) |
| 18 | Lock Cylinder Housing |
| 19 | Multi-Function Switch |
| 20 | Screws |
| 21 | Horn Brush Assy |
| 22 | Tilt Release Lever |
| 23 | Tilt Actuator Lever |
| 24 | Tilt Actuator Lever Pin |
| 25 | Cam Steering Column Lock |
| 26 | Clip Wiring — Upper |
| 27 | Steering Shaft Assy |
| 28 | Spring Lock Lever |
| 29 | Lever Steering Column Lock |
| 30 | Lock Actuator Assy — Upper |
| 31 | Lock Actuator Assy — Lower |
| 32 | Pawl — Steering Column Lock (Shaft) |
| 33 | Spring — Steering Column Lock (Shaft) |
| 34 | Shield |
| 35 | Trans Control Selector Position Insert |
| 36 | Screws |
| 37 | Screws |
| 38 | Parking Brake Vacuum Release Switch |
| 39 | Tilt Pivot Screws |
| 40 | Spring — Steering Column Position Lock |
| 41 | Actuator Housing |
| 42 | Ignition Switch |
| 43 | Screws |
| 44 | Pin — Pivot Lever |
| 45 | Lower Column Bracket |
| 46 | Lower Bearing Housing Retainer |
| 47 | Lower Column Mounting Nuts |
| 48 | Bracket |
| 49 | Screw |
| 50 | Lower Bearing Housing Retaining Screws |
| 51 | Lower Column Bearing Sleeve |
| 52 | Lower Column Bearing |
| 53 | Tolerance Ring — Lower |
| 54 | Sensor Ring |
| 55 | Spring |
| 56 | Bolt — Flange Yoke |
| 57 | Steering Shaft U — Joint Assy |
| 58 | Bolt |
| 59 | Shift Cable Bracket |
| 60 | Shift Cable Bracket Mounting Screws |
| 61 | Upper Column Mounting Nuts |
| 62 | Absorber — Steering Column Impact |
| 63 | Nuts |
| 64 | Bearing — Upper (Large) |
| 65 | Clip Wiring — Lower |

**Fig. 5 Exploded view of steering column. Sable & Taurus w/console shift**

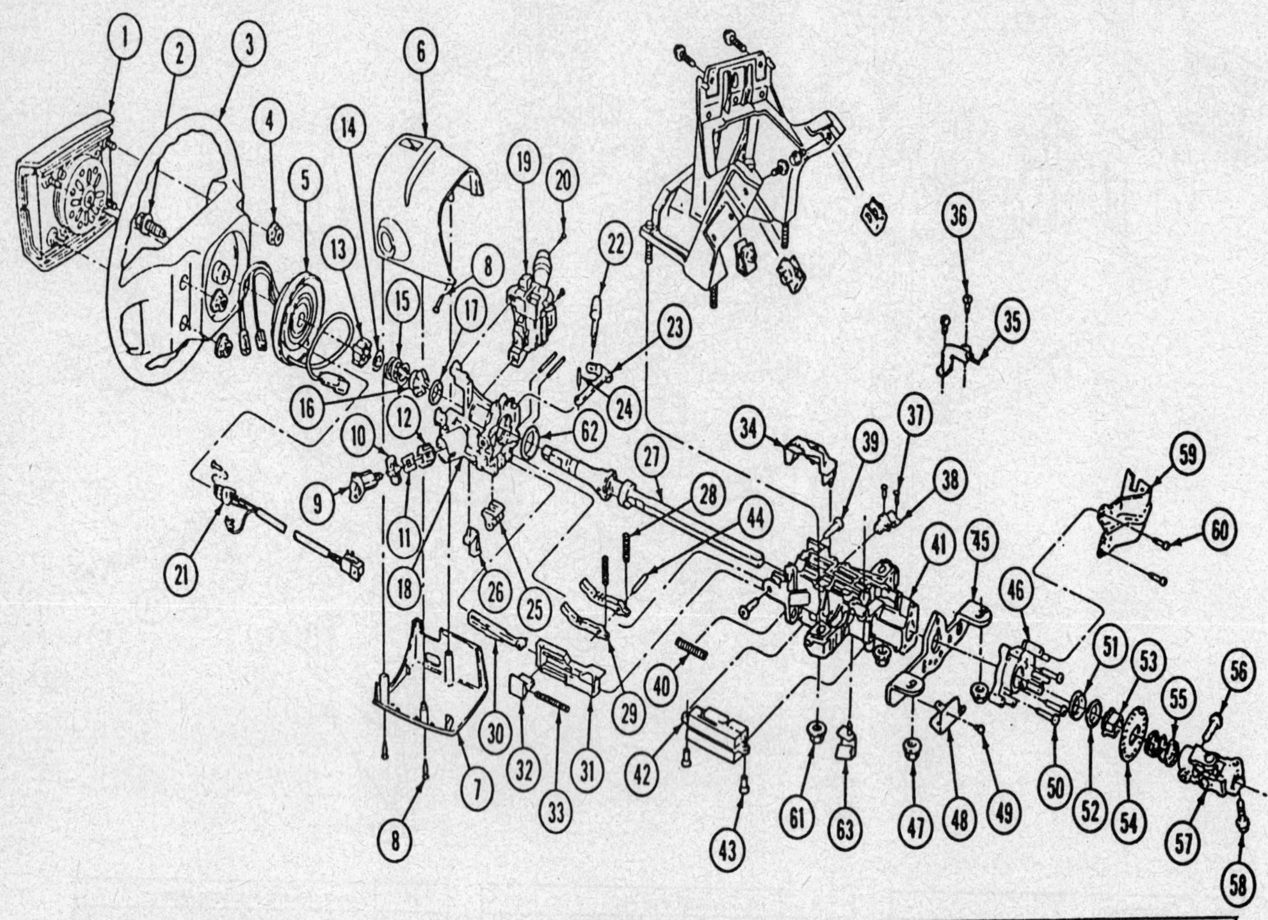

| Item | Description |
|---|---|
| 1 | Air Bag Module |
| 2 | Steering Wheel Bolt |
| 3 | Steering Wheel |
| 4 | Air Bag Module Retaining Nuts |
| 5 | Air Bag Clockspring Contact Assy |
| 6 | Upper Column Shroud |
| 7 | Lower Column Shroud |
| 8 | Shroud Retaining Screws |
| 9 | Ignition Lock Cylinder Assy |
| 10 | Retainer |
| 11 | Bearing |
| 12 | Gear — Steering Lock |
| 13 | Turn Signal Cancelling Cam |
| 14 | Snap Ring |
| 15 | Spring — Upper Bearing |
| 16 | Tolerance Ring |
| 17 | Bearing — Upper (Small) |
| 18 | Lock Cylinder Housing |
| 19 | Multi-Function Switch |
| 20 | Screws |
| 21 | Horn Brush Assy |
| 22 | Tilt Release Lever |
| 23 | Tilt Actuator Lever |
| 24 | Tilt Actuator Lever Pin |
| 25 | Cam Steering Column Lock |
| 26 | Clip Wiring — Upper |
| 27 | Steering Shaft Assy |
| 28 | Spring Lock Lever |
| 29 | Lever Steering Column Lock |
| 30 | Lock Actuator Assy — Upper |
| 31 | Lock Actuator Assy — Lower |
| 32 | Pawl — Steering Column Lock (Shaft) |
| 33 | Spring — Steering Column Lock (Shaft) |
| 34 | Shield |
| 35 | Trans Control Selector Position Insert |
| 36 | Screws |
| 37 | Screws |
| 38 | Parking Brake Vacuum Release Switch |
| 39 | Tilt Pivot Screws |
| 40 | Spring — Steering Column Position Lock |
| 41 | Actuator Housing |
| 42 | Ignition Switch |
| 43 | Screws |
| 44 | Pin — Pivot Lever |
| 45 | Lower Column Bracket |
| 46 | Lower Bearing Housing Retainer |
| 47 | Lower Column Mounting Nuts |
| 48 | Bracket |
| 49 | Screw |
| 50 | Lower Bearing Housing Retaining Screws |
| 51 | Lower Column Bearing Sleeve |
| 52 | Lower Column Bearing |
| 53 | Tolerance Ring — Lower |
| 54 | Sensor Ring |
| 55 | Spring |
| 56 | Bolt — Flange Yoke |
| 57 | Steering Shaft U — Joint Assy |
| 58 | Bolt |
| 59 | Shift Cable Bracket |
| 60 | Shift Cable Bracket Mounting Screws |
| 61 | Upper Column Mounting Nuts |
| 62 | Bearing — Upper (Large) |
| 63 | Clip Wiring — Lower |

**Fig. 6 Exploded view of steering column. Mark VII**

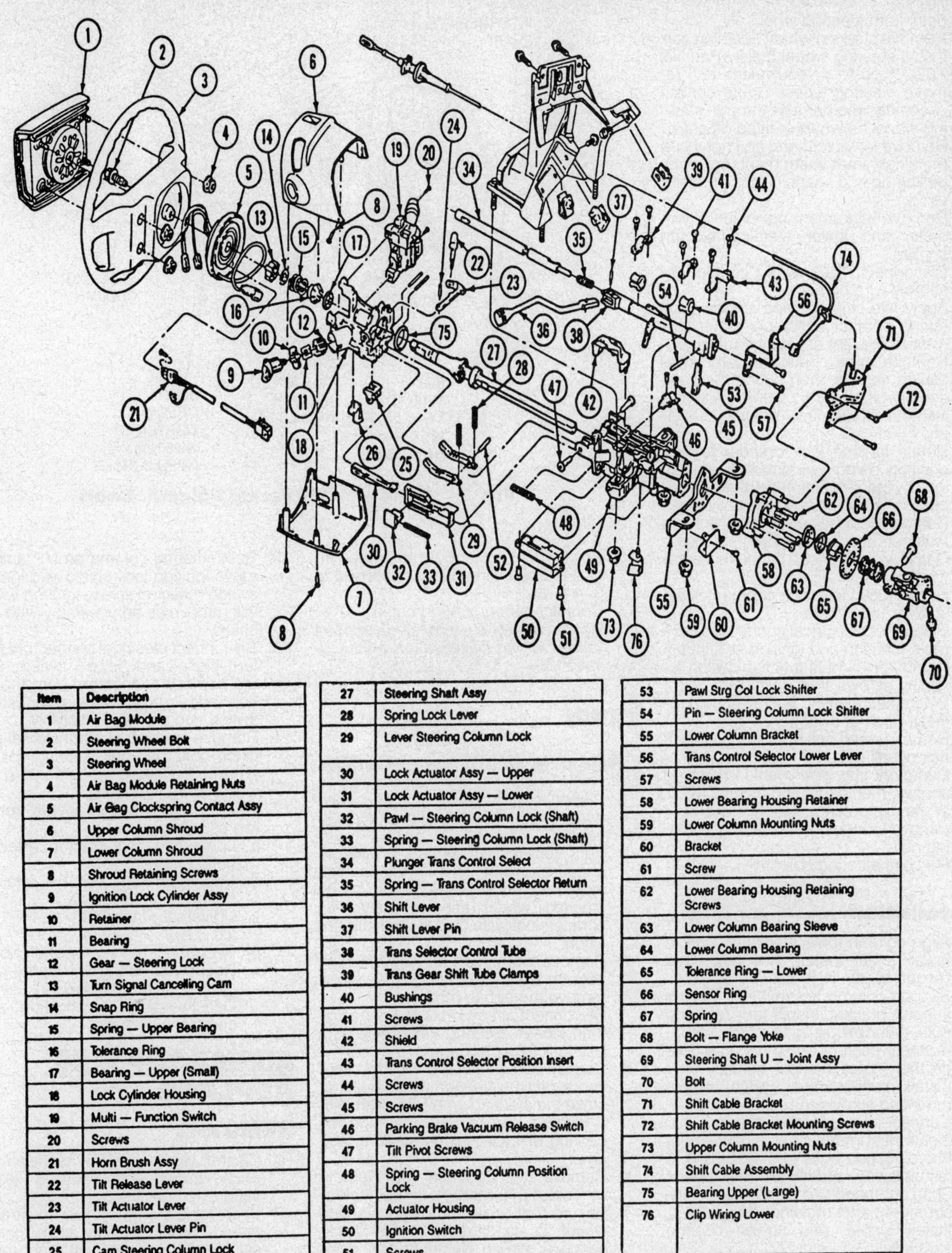

| Item | Description |
|---|---|
| 1 | Air Bag Module |
| 2 | Steering Wheel Bolt |
| 3 | Steering Wheel |
| 4 | Air Bag Module Retaining Nuts |
| 5 | Air Bag Clockspring Contact Assy |
| 6 | Upper Column Shroud |
| 7 | Lower Column Shroud |
| 8 | Shroud Retaining Screws |
| 9 | Ignition Lock Cylinder Assy |
| 10 | Retainer |
| 11 | Bearing |
| 12 | Gear — Steering Lock |
| 13 | Turn Signal Cancelling Cam |
| 14 | Snap Ring |
| 15 | Spring — Upper Bearing |
| 16 | Tolerance Ring |
| 17 | Bearing — Upper (Small) |
| 18 | Lock Cylinder Housing |
| 19 | Multi — Function Switch |
| 20 | Screws |
| 21 | Horn Brush Assy |
| 22 | Tilt Release Lever |
| 23 | Tilt Actuator Lever |
| 24 | Tilt Actuator Lever Pin |
| 25 | Cam Steering Column Lock |
| 26 | Clip Wiring — Upper |
| 27 | Steering Shaft Assy |
| 28 | Spring Lock Lever |
| 29 | Lever Steering Column Lock |
| 30 | Lock Actuator Assy — Upper |
| 31 | Lock Actuator Assy — Lower |
| 32 | Pawl — Steering Column Lock (Shaft) |
| 33 | Spring — Steering Column Lock (Shaft) |
| 34 | Plunger Trans Control Select |
| 35 | Spring — Trans Control Selector Return |
| 36 | Shift Lever |
| 37 | Shift Lever Pin |
| 38 | Trans Selector Control Tube |
| 39 | Trans Gear Shift Tube Clamps |
| 40 | Bushings |
| 41 | Screws |
| 42 | Shield |
| 43 | Trans Control Selector Position Insert |
| 44 | Screws |
| 45 | Screws |
| 46 | Parking Brake Vacuum Release Switch |
| 47 | Tilt Pivot Screws |
| 48 | Spring — Steering Column Position Lock |
| 49 | Actuator Housing |
| 50 | Ignition Switch |
| 51 | Screws |
| 52 | Pin — Pivot Lever |
| 53 | Pawl Strg Col Lock Shifter |
| 54 | Pin — Steering Column Lock Shifter |
| 55 | Lower Column Bracket |
| 56 | Trans Control Selector Lower Lever |
| 57 | Screws |
| 58 | Lower Bearing Housing Retainer |
| 59 | Lower Column Mounting Nuts |
| 60 | Bracket |
| 61 | Screw |
| 62 | Lower Bearing Housing Retaining Screws |
| 63 | Lower Column Bearing Sleeve |
| 64 | Lower Column Bearing |
| 65 | Tolerance Ring — Lower |
| 66 | Sensor Ring |
| 67 | Spring |
| 68 | Bolt — Flange Yoke |
| 69 | Steering Shaft U — Joint Assy |
| 70 | Bolt |
| 71 | Shift Cable Bracket |
| 72 | Shift Cable Bracket Mounting Screws |
| 73 | Upper Column Mounting Nuts |
| 74 | Shift Cable Assembly |
| 75 | Bearing Upper (Large) |
| 76 | Clip Wiring Lower |

**Fig. 7 Exploded view of steering column. Crown Victoria, Grand Marquis & Town Car**

ness from steering wheel.
6. Remove steering wheel retaining bolt.
7. Install steering wheel puller (Part No. T67L-3600-A) or equivalent, and remove steering wheel. Route contact assembly wire harness through steering wheel as wheel is lifted off shaft.
8. Remove lower lefthand and righthand moldings from instrument panel by pulling up and snapping out of retainer.
9. Remove instrument panel lower trim panel and lower steering column shroud.
10. Disconnect clock spring contact assembly wire harness.
11. Apply two strips of tape across clock spring contact assembly stator and rotor to prevent accidental rotation.
12. Remove three contact assembly retaining screws, then pull contact assembly off steering column shaft.
13. Remove tilt lever from column assembly.
14. Rotate ignition lock cylinder to Run position. Using a 1/8 inch drift, depress lock cylinder retaining pin through access hole and remove lock cylinder.
15. Remove four retaining screws from lower shroud, then column shrouds.
16. Remove instrument panel reinforcement.
17. Remove two interlock cable retaining screws, then cable.
18. Disconnect electrical connectors from multi-function and ignition switches.
19. Remove two multi-function switch retaining screws, then switch.
20. Disconnect parking brake vacuum release hose at switch.
21. Remove pinch bolt from steering shaft flex coupling.
22. Remove interlock cable retaining screws, then cable end assembly.
23. While supporting column assembly, remove four column assembly retaining nuts.
24. Remove steering column.

### Installation

1. Align column lower universal joint to lower shaft. Install one bolt, then **torque** to 29-41 ft. lbs.
2. Support column assembly to column support bracket. Install four retaining nuts, then **torque** to 15-25 ft. lbs.
3. Connect parking brake vacuum hoses, then install interlock cable.
4. Install multi-function switch **torque** mounting screws to 5-8 ft. lbs.
5. Connect all electrical connectors.
6. Install instrument panel reinforcement brace, **torque** bolts to 5-8 ft. lbs.
7. Install lower instrument panel cover.
8. Snap righthand and lefthand lower instrument panel moldings into place.
9. Install upper and lower column shrouds.
10. Install lock cylinder assembly, then tilt lever.
11. Install airbag clock spring contact assembly.
12. Install steering wheel, then **torque** new steering wheel retaining bolt to 23-33 ft. lbs.

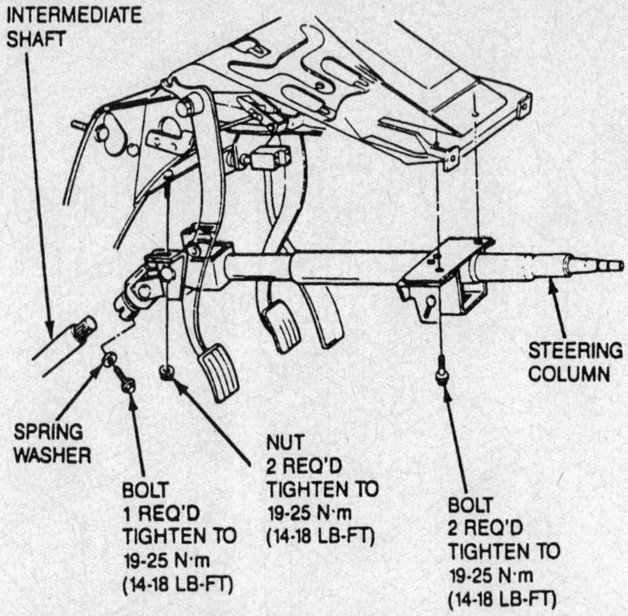


**Fig. 8 Removal of steering column. Capri**

13. Position airbag module to wheel, install four retaining nuts and **torque** to 3-4 ft. lbs.
14. Connect battery ground cable.
15. Rearm airbag system as described under "Airbag Deactivation & Reactivation."

## CAPRI

Refer to **Fig. 8,** for component identification.

1. Disarm airbag system as described under "Airbag Deactivation & Reactivation."
2. Park vehicle with wheels in straight ahead position, then turn ignition switch to Lock position and rotate steering wheel approximately 16° counterclockwise until locked into position.
3. Remove four airbag module retaining nuts on back of steering wheel, then remove the airbag module.
4. Disconnect airbag module connector, then loosen steering wheel retaining bolt four to six turns.
5. Caution should be taken not to use a knock-off type steering wheel puller or strike the steering wheel or shaft with a hammer. These could damage the bearing or collapse the steering column.
6. Remove steering wheel with Remover Tool T67L-3600-A or equivalent. Ensure that while removing steering wheel so no damage to the clockspring or airbag electrical connector happens.
7. Remove defroster duct connecting hose and steering column lower shroud.
8. Loosen steering column lower retaining nuts, then remove the upper retaining nuts.
9. Rest steering column on I/P and remove ignition lock shield and ignition switch retaining screw. Ignition switch will remove as an assembly with lock shield.
10. Disconnect electrical connectors from turn signal and hazard switch, then the harness connectors from the airbag module, key warning, windshield switch and slip ring assembly.
11. Remove steering shaft universal joint pinch bolt, then pull steering column out of I/P. Ensure no damage to any wiring or components.
12. Reverse procedure to install, **torquing** as follows:
    a. Lower steering column retaining bolts to 14-18 ft. lbs.
    b. Upper steering column retaining bolts to 14-18 ft. lbs.
    c. Universal Pinch bolts to 14-18 ft. lbs.
13. Reconnect battery ground cable.
14. Reactivate airbag and verify lamp operation as described in "Airbag Deactivation & Reactivation" after completing repairs.

## AIRBAG SLIP RING REPLACE

### REMOVAL

1. Disarm airbag system as described under "Airbag Deactivation & Reactivation."
2. Park vehicle with wheels in straight ahead position, then turn ignition switch to Lock position and rotate steering wheel approximately 16° counterclockwise until locked into position.
3. Remove steering wheel as follows:
    a. Working from rear of steering wheel, remove four nuts attaching airbag module to wheel.

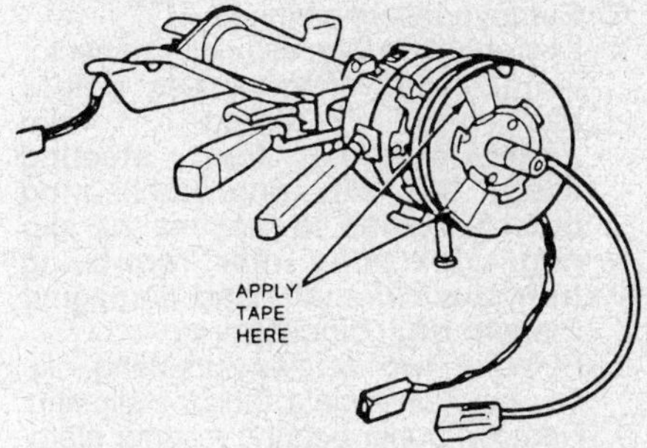


Fig. 9 Taping clockspring

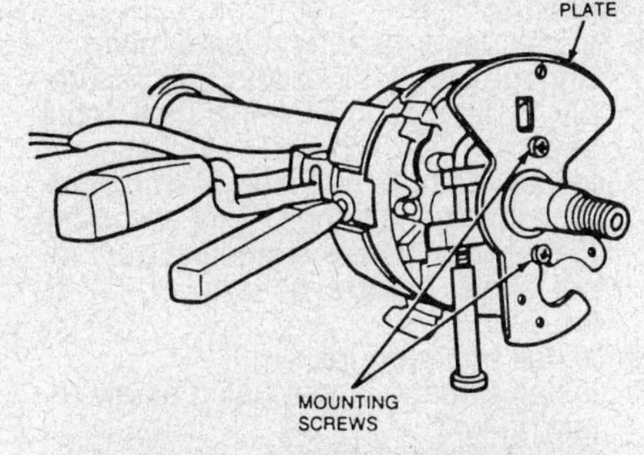


Fig. 10 Removing upper bearing retainer plate

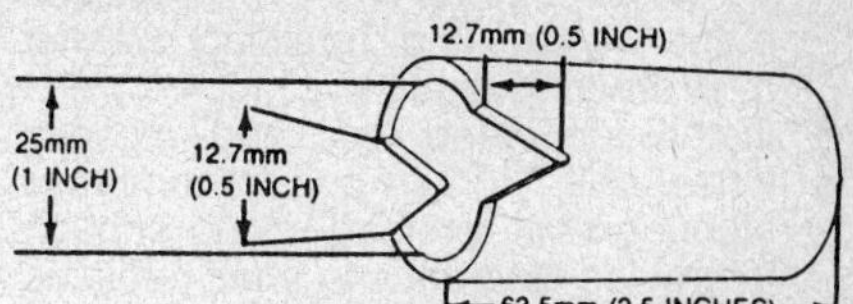


Fig. 11 Fabricated tool. Continental

b. Lift airbag module from wheel and disconnect airbag module to slip ring clockspring connector.
c. Remove and discard steering wheel attaching bolt.
d. Remove steering wheel from upper shaft using steering wheel remover No. T67L-3600-A or equivalent. Do not use a knock-off type steering wheel puller or strike end of steering column upper shaft with a hammer, otherwise, damage will occur to bearing of collapsible steering column.

4. Remove upper and lower shrouds.
5. Disconnect airbag slip ring connector from column harness. **Before removing airbag clockspring type slip ring from steering shaft, clockspring must be taped, Fig. 9, to prevent clockspring rotor from being turned accidentally and damaging clockspring.**
6. Remove two retaining screws and the slip ring.

## INSTALLATION

Service replacement slip ring will contain a red colored locking insert to prevent rotation. This insert should not be removed until slip ring is installed on column.

1. Place airbag slip ring onto steering shaft and install two retaining screws that attach slip ring to retainer plate, ensuring ground wire pigtail is secured with lower retaining screw.
2. Remove locking insert.
3. Connect slip ring wire to column harness.
4. Install upper and lower shrouds.
5. Install steering wheel as follows:
   a. Position steering wheel on end of steering wheel shaft, aligning mark on steering wheel with mark on shaft to ensure that straight ahead steering wheel position corresponds to straight ahead position of front wheels.
   b. Install new steering wheel attaching nut. **Torque** to 30-40 ft. lbs.
   c. Connect airbag module wire to slip ring connector and place module on steering wheel, then install four retaining nuts. **Torque** to 35-53 inch lbs.
6. Connect battery ground cable.
7. Rearm airbag system as described under "Airbag Deactivation & Reactivation."

# UPPER BEARING REPLACE

## TEMPO & TOPAZ

### Removal

1. Disarm airbag system as described under "Airbag Deactivation & Reactivation."
2. Park vehicle with wheels in straight ahead position, then turn ignition switch to Lock position and rotate steering wheel approximately 16° counterclockwise until locked into position.
3. Remove steering wheel and the upper and lower shrouds.
4. Disconnect airbag slip ring connector from column wiring harness. **Before removing airbag clockspring type slip ring from steering shaft, clockspring must be taped, Fig. 9, to prevent clockspring rotor from being turned accidentally and damaging clockspring.**
5. Remove two screws that attach slip ring to retaining plate, then the slip ring.
6. Remove upper bearing retaining plate, **Fig. 10.**
7. Remove and discard upper bearing retainer snap ring.
8. Insert two screwdrivers under bearing, using two ramps provided in casting, and carefully pry upper bearing and sleeve from steering shaft. Discard sleeve.

### Installation

1. Prick punch steering column upper shaft serration diameter enough to ensure an interference fit between bearing inner race and steering column upper shaft.
2. Position bearing and insulator on steering column upper shaft. Work bearing and insulator as far down steering column upper shaft as possible, then place a piece of pipe 3/4 inch diameter by 1 1/2 inches long over end of steering column upper shaft and install steering wheel attaching nut.
3. Tighten steering wheel attaching nut until bearing is seated on steering shaft.
4. Remove steering wheel attaching nut and piece of pipe from steering column upper shaft.
5. Install new snap ring in groove at top of steering column upper shaft above bearing.
6. Install upper bearing retaining plate.
7. Place airbag slip ring on steering shaft and install two retainer screws that attach slip ring to retainer plate, ensuring ground wire pigtail is secured with lower retainer screw, then remove tape from slip ring.
8. Connect slip ring wire to column wiring harness.
9. Install steering wheel and the upper and lower shrouds.
10. Connect airbag module wire to slip ring connector and place airbag module on steering wheel, then install four module attaching nuts. **Torque** to 35-53 inch lbs.
11. Connect battery ground cable.
12. Rearm airbag system as described under "Airbag Deactivation & Reactivation."

## CONTINENTAL

### Removal

1. Disarm airbag system as described under "Airbag Deactivation & Reactivation."
2. Remove steering column cover from lower portion of instrument panel.
3. Remove ignition lock cylinder and tilt release lever.
4. Remove upper and lower shrouds.
5. Remove multi-function switch and steering wheel.
6. Fabricate tool from a piece of tubing 1 inch X 2 1/2 inch **Fig. 11.**
7. Install fabricated tool on steering shaft, aligning clearance slot over shaft retaining pin. Then install steering wheel bolt, tighten bolt enough to relieve spring pressure on shaft retaining pin.
8. Using a 5/32 diameter drift punch, tap retaining pin out of steering shaft, discard pin.
9. Remove steering wheel bolt, fabricated tool, retaining washer, and alignment wedge from steering shaft.
10. Insert suitable screwdriver between inner and outer race of bearing, gently pry bearing assembly out of housing pocket.

### Installation

1. Install bearing and sleeve into housing pocket. Then install upper align-

ment wedge and retaining washer over steering shaft.
2. Install fabricated tool and steering wheel bolt. Tighten bolt to compress steering shaft preload spring enough to provide clearance to shaft retaining pin hole.
3. Install shaft retaining pin by tapping it into hole until same amount of pin extends from either side of shaft.
4. Remove steering wheel bolt and fabricated tool.
5. Install multi-function switch, and steering wheel.
6. Install airbag module.
7. Install upper and lower shrouds using three screws and **torque** to 8 inch lbs.
8. Install tilt release lever using one capscrew and **torque** to 8 ft. lbs.
9. Install ignition lock cylinder.
10. Install steering column cover from lower portion of instrument panel.
11. Reconnect battery ground cable.
12. Rearm airbag system as described under "Airbag Deactivation & Reactivation."

## MUSTANG

### Removal

1. Disarm airbag system as described under "Airbag Deactivation & Reactivation."
2. Remove steering wheel from column.
3. Remove column trim shrouds.
4. Remove upper bearing retainer plate.
5. Remove two nuts retaining steering column lower shaft and U-joint assembly to flange on steering gear input shaft.
6. Using snap ring pliers, remove snap ring holding upper bearing onto steering shaft.
7. Pull outward on steering shaft. Shaft will move approximately 1/4 inch, carrying upper bearing and sleeve with it. This movement of the bearing will allow the blades of two screwdrivers or similar tools to be inserted under the bearing by using the two ramps in the casting provided for this purpose.
8. With blades of screwdrivers under bearing, pry gently off shaft.

### Installation

1. Prick punch steering column upper shaft serration diameter sufficiently to ensure an interface fit between bearing inner race and steering column upper shaft.
2. Position bearing and insulator on steering column upper shaft. Work bearing and insulator as far down the steering column upper shaft as possible.
3. Place a piece of 3/4 inch inside diameter pipe at least 4 inches long over end of steering column upper shaft, then install steering wheel attaching bolt.
4. Tighten steering wheel retaining bolt until bearing is seated on steering shaft.
5. Install snap ring in groove at top of steering column upper shaft above bearing.
6. Install upper bearing retainer plate.
7. Engage safety strap and bolt assembly to flange on steering gear input shaft.
8. Install two nuts retaining steering column lower shaft and U-joint assembly to flange on steering steering gear input shaft. **Torque** bolts to 20-37 ft. lbs.
9. Install trim shrouds.
10. Install steering wheel, using a new retaining bolt.
11. Rearm airbag system as described under "Airbag Deactivation & Reactivation."

## ALL MODELS EXCEPT CONTINENTAL, MUSTANG, TEMPO & TOPAZ

### Removal

1. Disarm airbag system as described under "Airbag Deactivation & Reactivation."
2. Remove steering column from vehicle.
3. Remove lock cylinder housing from column.
4. Support housing, then tap out small bearing with appropriate drift and plastic hammer.

### Installation

1. Support housing. Position small bearing so that opening between races is "up." Tap into place with plastic hammer and bushing driver installer or socket the same size as outer race of bearing.
2. Install lock housing on steering column.
3. Install steering column.
4. Rearm airbag system as described under "Airbag Deactivation & Reactivation."

# LOCK CYLINDER HOUSING REPLACE

## REMOVAL

1. Disarm airbag system as described under "Airbag Deactivation & Reactivation."
2. Remove upper and lower column shrouds.
3. Peel back foam switch cover from turn signal switch.
4. Disconnect two switch electrical connectors.
5. Remove two self tapping screws that secure switch to lock cylinder housing and disengage switch from housing.
6. Remove steering wheel.
7. Disconnect airbag slip ring connector from column wiring harness. **Before removing airbag slip ring/clockspring from steering shaft, the slip ring/clockspring must be taped to prevent the slip ring/clockspring rotor from being turned accidentally and damaging the slip ring/clockspring.**
8. Remove two screws attaching slip ring to retainer plate, then the slip ring.
9. Remove upper bearing retainer plate.
10. Remove and discard upper bearing retainer snap ring.
11. Remove upper steering shaft bearing.
12. Remove two bolts retaining lock cylinder housing to outer tube flange bracket, then rotate ignition key to Start position and pull actuator interlock out of clearance hole in tube, lifting casting off upper steering shaft.
13. Remove ignition lock drive gear.

## INSTALLATION

1. Install ignition lock drive gear and the actuator.
2. Prick punch steering column upper shaft serration diameter enough to ensure an interference fit between bearing inner race and steering column upper shaft.
3. Place lock cylinder housing onto steering column flange bracket with upper steering shaft protruding through upper bearing.
4. Turn ignition key to Start position to locate actuator interlock through clearance hole in outer tube, then install two bolts attaching lock cylinder housing to bracket. **Torque** to 12-21 ft. lbs.
5. Install upper steering shaft bearing.
6. Install new snap ring in groove on upper shaft.
7. Install bearing retainer plate.
8. Align switch mounting holes with corresponding holes in lock cylinder housing, then install two self tapping screws.
9. Stick foam switch cover to switch.
10. Install two switch electrical connectors to full engagement.
11. Place airbag slip ring onto steering shift and install two retaining screws that attach slip ring to retainer plate, ensuring ground wire pigtail is secured with lower retaining screw. Remove tape from slip ring.
12. Connect slip ring/clockspring wire connector to column wiring harness.
13. Install upper and lower shrouds and the steering wheel.
14. Connect airbag module wire connector to slip ring connector and place airbag module on steering wheel, then install four attaching nuts. **Torque** to 35-53 inch lbs.
15. Connect battery ground cable.
16. Rearm airbag system as described under "Airbag Deactivation & Reactivation."

# PASSIVE RESTRAINT SYSTEM (Supplemental Restraint System)

TABLE OF CONTENTS



# Airbag System

**NOTE:** Prior to performing any testing or servicing of the airbag system, the system must be deactivated. Refer to "Airbag Deactivation & Reactivation" in this section.

## INDEX



## AIRBAG DEACTIVATION & REACTIVATION

**The electrical circuit necessary for system deployment is powered directly from the battery and a backup power supply. To avoid accidental deployment and possible personal injury, the airbag system must be deactivated prior to servicing or replacing any system components.**

A back-up power supply is included in the system to provide airbag deployment in the event the battery or battery cables are damaged in an accident before the sensors can close. The power supply is a capacitor that will retain a charge for approximately 15 minutes after the battery ground cable is disconnected. **Backup power supply must be disconnected to deactivate airbag system.** To remove backup power supply, refer to "Component Replacement" procedures.

1. Disconnect battery ground cable.
2. Disconnect backup power supply as described under "Backup Power Supply, Replace."

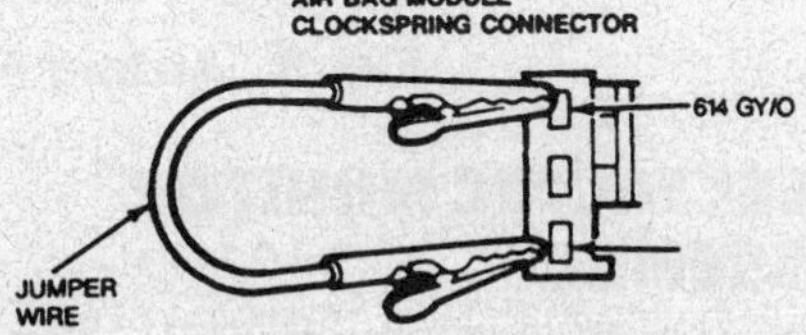


**Fig. 1 Jumper wire connections**

3. Remove four nut and washer assemblies securing airbag module to steering wheel, then disconnect airbag electrical connector. Attach jumper wire to airbag terminals on clockspring as shown in **Fig. 1.**
4. **On models equipped with passenger-side airbag,** disconnect airbag module connector located behind glove compartment. Attach a jumper wire to airbag terminals on wiring harness side of passenger airbag module connector, as shown in **Fig. 1.**
5. **On all models,** reconnect battery and backup power supply if necessary to perform repair procedure.
6. To reactivate, disconnect battery ground cable and backup power supply, then reverse remainder of deactivation procedure. **Torque** airbag module to steering wheel nut assemblies to 24-32 inch lbs. on Crown Victoria and Grand Marquis, or 35-53 inch lbs. on all other models.
7. Verify airbag lamp after reactivating system.

## DESCRIPTION & OPERATION

### AIRBAG SYSTEM

The Supplemental Airbag Restraint System consists of two basic subsystems, the driver and passenger airbags if equipped, and the electrical system; including impact sensors, electronic diagnostic monitor and a backup power supply.

### DRIVER AIRBAG MODULE

The driver airbag module is mounted in the center of the steering wheel. The module consists of an igniter assembly, inflator, mounting plate and retainer ring, the bag assembly and the liner and steering wheel trim cover, **Fig. 2.**

## PASSENGER AIRBAG MODULE

The passenger airbag module is mounted in the righthand side of the instrument panel above the glove compartment. The module consists of an igniter assembly, inflator, reaction housing. This unit may not be serviced.

## IGNITER & INFLATOR ASSEMBLY

The igniter assembly is an integral part of the inflator assembly and is not a serviceable item. When the airbag monitor assembly signals the igniter, the igniter assembly converts the electrical signal to thermal energy, causing the ignition of the inflator gas generant. This ignition reaction will combust the sodium azide/copper oxide generant in the inflator, to produce nitrogen gas, causing the airbag to inflate.

## AIRBAG ASSEMBLY

The airbag, constructed of neoprene coated nylon, is 28 inches in diameter. The airbag fills to a volume of approximately 2.3 cubic feet in approximately 40 milliseconds. The airbag is not a serviceable item.

## MOUNTING PLATE & RETAINER RING

The mounting plate and retainer ring attaches and seals the bag assembly to the inflator. The mounting bracket is also used to attach the trim cover and to mount the entire module to the wheel. These items are components of the airbag module and cannot be serviced.

## LINER & STEERING WHEEL TRIM COVER

The liner is an injection molded plastic component which encases the airbag assembly and provides support for the steering wheel trim cover assembly. When the airbag is activated, fail seams molded into the liner and steering wheel trim cover separate to allow inflation of the airbag assembly. The liner is a component of the airbag module and is not a serviceable item.

## ELECTRICAL SYSTEM

The airbag is powered directly from the battery and back-up power supply. The system can function with the ignition switch in any position, including off and lock. The system can also function when no one is sitting in the driver's seat. The electrical system performs three main functions; it detects an impact, switches electric power to the igniter assembly and monitors the system to determine readiness.

The electrical system components include an electronic monitor assembly, airbag system readiness indicator lamp, wiring harness, sensors and an igniter assembly, **Fig. 3.**

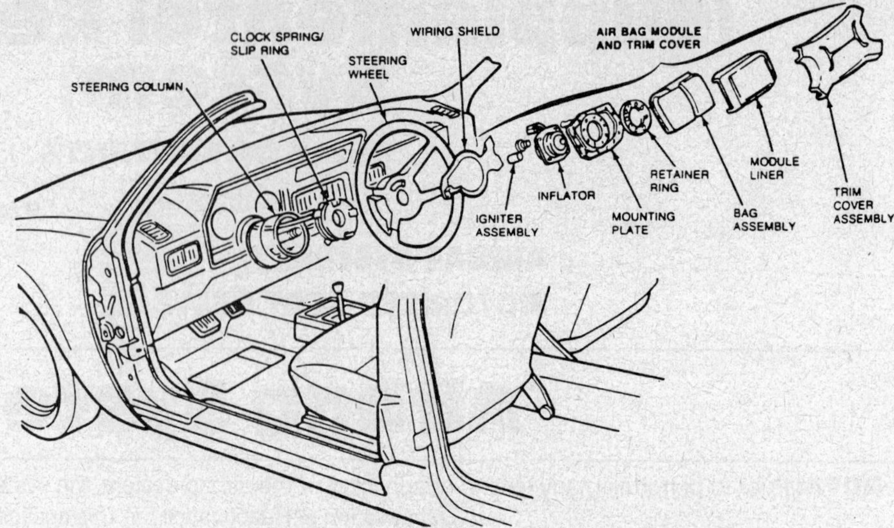


**Fig. 2 Driver airbag module exploded view**

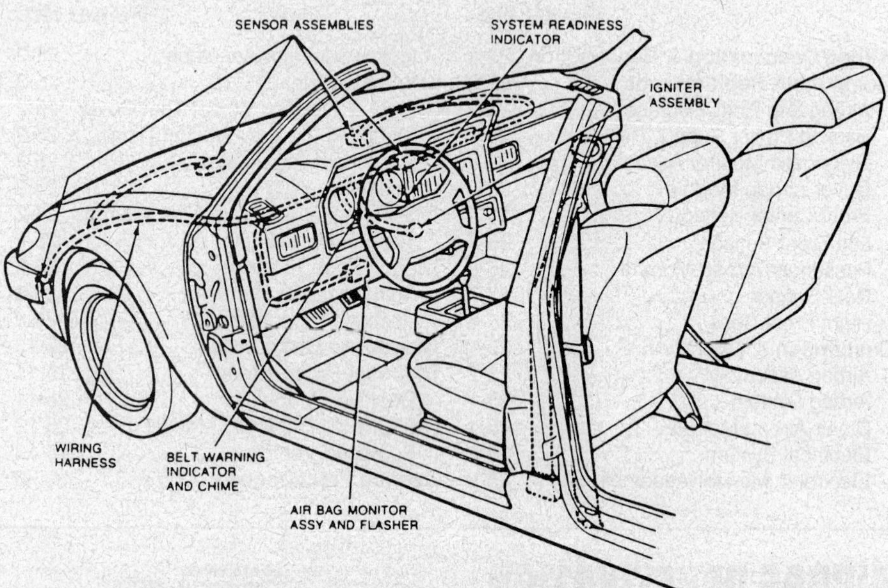


**Fig. 3 Airbag electrical system**

## ELECTRONIC MONITOR ASSEMBLY

The electronic monitor assembly contains a microcomputer that monitors the electrical system components and connections. The assembly performs a self check of the microcomputer internal circuits and energizes the system readiness indicator lamp during prove out and whenever a fault occurs. System faults can be detected and translated into a coded lamp display. If certain faults occur, the system will be disarmed by a firing disarm device built into the monitor assembly.

## SYSTEM READINESS INDICATOR LAMP

The system readiness indicator is an instrument cluster mounted lamp that will momentarily light whenever the ignition switch is turned from off to run if the airbag system is working properly. If the system is not functioning properly, the lamp will fail to light, stay on continuously or light in a flashing mode, if a system fault exists and the lamp is malfunctioning an audible tone will be heard. If a fault occurs after the prove out, the lamp will light either continuously or in a coded flashing mode.

## TONE GENERATOR

A series of five sets of five tones will be heard if the readiness lamp is out and a fault occurs in the system. The tone pattern will repeat periodically until the fault and lamp outage are serviced.

## SENSORS

The sensor assembly is an electrical switch which reacts to impacts according to direction and force. It discriminates between impacts that require airbag inflation and impacts that do not require airbag inflation. When an impact occurs that re-

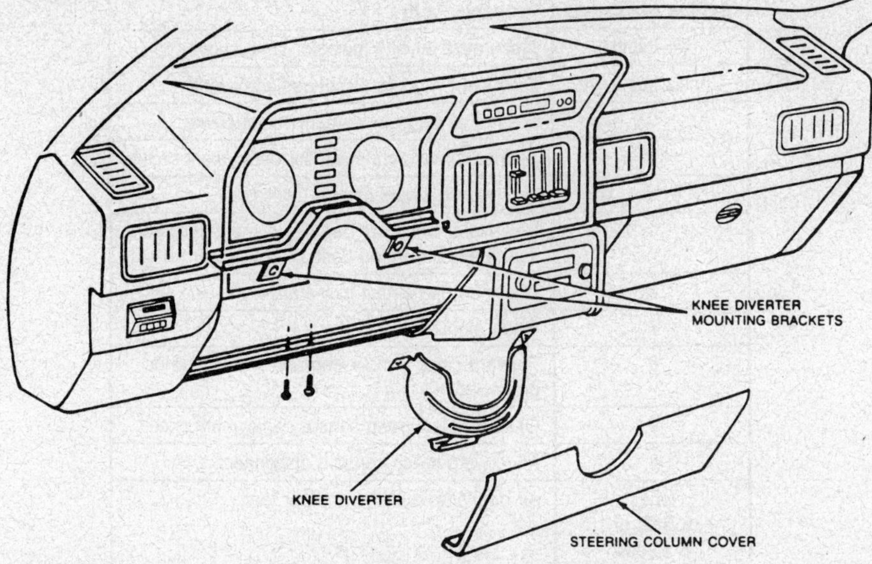


**Fig. 4 Knee diverter removal**

quires airbag inflation, the sensor contacts close, completing the electrical circuit necessary for system operation.

Five sensor assemblies are used on the vehicle. They are located on the radiator support in front of the radiator, on the left and right fender aprons and on the cowl in the passenger compartment. At least two sensors must be activated to inflate airbag.

## KNEE DIVERTER

The knee diverter is located under the steering column behind the steering column opening trim panel, **Fig. 4.** It is designed to divert some of the impact when contacted by the driver's knees. It also protects the driver's knees during impact.

# SERVICE PRECAUTIONS

**The electrical circuit necessary for system deployment is powered directly from the battery and backup power supply. To avoid accidental deployment and possible personal injury, the airbag system must be deactivated prior to servicing or replacing any system components.**

Safe handling of airbag modules requires following the procedures described below for both live and deployed airbags.

Always wear safety glasses when servicing an airbag vehicle and when handling an airbag module.

When carrying a live airbag module, ensure that bag and trim cover are pointed away from your body. In the unlikely event of an accidental deployment, the bag will then deploy with minimal chance of injury. In addition, when placing a live airbag module on a bench or other surface, always place bag and trim cover face up, away from the surface. This will reduce the motion of the module if it is accidentally deployed.

Safety precautions must also be observed when handling a deployed module. After deployment, the airbag surface may contain deposits of sodium hydroxide, a product of the gas generant combustion that is irritating to the skin. Always wear gloves and safety glasses when handling a deployed airbag module, and wash your hands with mild soap and water afterward.

Because of the critical operating requirements of the system, do not attempt to repair sensor assemblies, the slip ring/clockspring assembly, the monitor assembly or the airbag module. Corrections are made by replacement only.

Never probe the connectors on the airbag module. Doing so may result in airbag deployment which could result in personal injury.

All part replacements and wiring repairs must be made with airbag system deactivated.

The instruction Disconnect always refers to a connector. Never detach a part from vehicle when instructed to Disconnect.

If a vehicle equipped with an airbag system is involved in a crash where the fenders or grille area have been damaged, the sensors in the area of damage must be replaced whether or not the airbag deployed.

# DIAGNOSIS & TESTING

## TESTING PRECAUTIONS

Disconnect does not imply removal. A disconnected part should not be reconnected until specific reconnect instruction is given.

A voltmeter, an ohmmeter and a jumper wire will be needed the following testing procedures.

Attach positive lead to circuit voltage and negative lead to specified ground. If a digital voltmeter is used on circuits 608 and 609 with the monitor disconnected, the correct voltage will not be indicated.

All resistance checks must be made with negative lead of ohmmeter at vehicle ground, not battery ground, unless specifically directed otherwise. Three places are recommended; metal bracket of starter relay, ignition lock cylinder on the steering column or the ground wire from harness under righthand side of instrument panel.

## SELF-DIAGNOSIS

The airbag monitor assembly has a coded flashing indicator lamp feature which assists in isolating a system malfunction or fault. The coding is accomplished by a series of airbag lamp flashes. Each flash is on for approximately 1/2 second and off for approximately 1/2 second. The number of flashes in each series is based on the type of malfunction being detected. The code is repeated when the ignition switch is in the Run position and a fault exists. The trouble code feature is top priority such that if two or more different malfunctions occur at the same time, the highest priority trouble code will dominate until corrected.

If a system malfunction exists and the lamp is inoperative, an audible tone will be heard indicating the need for service. The tone produced is a series of five sets of five beeps. The number of beeps does not indicate the fault code; it means the lamp is out and a fault is present.

The most probable malfunctions and associated trouble codes are listed in the trouble code priority chart, **Fig. 5,** in the order that they are ranked from top to bottom. A similar listing not indicating priority is contained on the monitor assembly housing. These listings are for information only and should not be used for system diagnosis or troubleshooting. The following diagnostic guides and associated deactivation procedure should be used to pinpoint the specific fault and to safely diagnose and repair the system. However, if after using the diagnostic guides, the fault is not located, proceed to the diagnostic charts to perform additional diagnostic checks to determine and correct uncommon faults.

Refer to fault code priority chart, **Fig. 5,** airbag system wiring circuits, **Figs. 6 through 19,** for electrical testing procedures.

**Refer to the "Diagnostic Chart Index,"** along with the diagnostic charts, **Figs. 20 through 64,** for diagnosis and testing procedures.

"Verify Airbag Lamp" means to turn the ignition switch to Run and count the flashes only after code has cycled twice. If airbag lamp comes on continuously for 4 to 8 seconds and then goes out, the system is functioning properly and all faults have been repaired.

# COMPONENT REPLACEMENT

**The electrical circuit necessary for system deployment is powered directly from battery and back-up power supply. To avoid accidental deployment and possible personal injury, the airbag system must be deactivated prior to repairing or replacing any system components.**

Fasteners used on airbag components must be replaced after removal. The fasteners are coated with an epoxy adhesive making them non-reusable.

## BACKUP POWER SUPPLY, REPLACE

### Tempo & Topaz

1. Disconnect battery ground cable and allow backup power supply to discharge. **Backup power supply will discharge in 15 minutes if battery ground cable is disconnected, or one minute if battery positive cable is disconnected.**
2. Remove lower steering column covers.
3. Disconnect blue backup power supply connector, located below steering column.
4. Depress retaining tabs and remove backup power supply.
5. Reverse procedure to install. Ensure proper operation of airbag indicator lamp.

### Capri, Continental, Mark VII, Mustang, Sable & Taurus

1. Disconnect battery ground cable and allow backup power supply to discharge. **Backup power supply will discharge in 15 minutes if battery ground cable is disconnected, or one minute if battery positive cable is disconnected.**
2. Open glove box past stops, press in sides.
3. Remove power supply (blue box, one connector) retaining screws.
4. Disconnect connector from power supply unit.
5. Reverse procedure to install, ensure proper operation of airbag indicator lamp.

### Town Car, Grand Marquis & Crown Victoria

1. Disconnect battery ground cable and allow backup power supply to discharge. **Backup power supply will discharge in 15 minutes if battery ground cable is disconnected, or one minute if battery positive cable is disconnected.**
2. Remove headlamp switch knob and retaining nut.
3. Remove lefthand and righthand instrument panel moldings.
4. Remove 12 upper and lower instrument panel finish panel retaining screws, then finish panel.
5. Remove two bolts attaching steering column opening cover and pad assembly to instrument panel, then remove cover.
6. Remove two screws and pushpin retaining instrument panel insulator, then insulator.
7. Disconnect diagnostic monitor backup power supply electrical wiring connector, mounted to EEC module bracket.
8. Remove screws attaching EEC module bracket assembly, then the bracket assembly.
9. Remove power supply by depressing retaining tabs to bracket.
10. Reverse procedure to install, verify airbag indicator lamp.

| Number of Flashes | Probable Fault |
|---|---|
| No Lamp | Inoperative air bag indicator lamp circuit. |
| Continuous Light | Diagnostic module disconnected or faulty. |
| 3 | Loss of air bag deployment circuit power. |
| 5 | Shorted forward crash sensor deployment circuit. |
| 10 | Faulty firing circuit disarm device. |
| 4 | Potential short in air bag deployment circuit or improperly grounded dash panel sensor. |
| 6 | Driver air bag circuit inoperative. |
| 7 | Open monitor wiring circuit. |
| 8 | Forward crash sensor improperly attached or grounded. |
| 9 | Open forward crash sensor deployment circuit. |
| 2 | All forward crash sensors disconnect. |
| Tones 5 Sets of 5 Beeps | Air bag lamp out and another fault. |

**Fig. 5 Trouble code priorities chart**

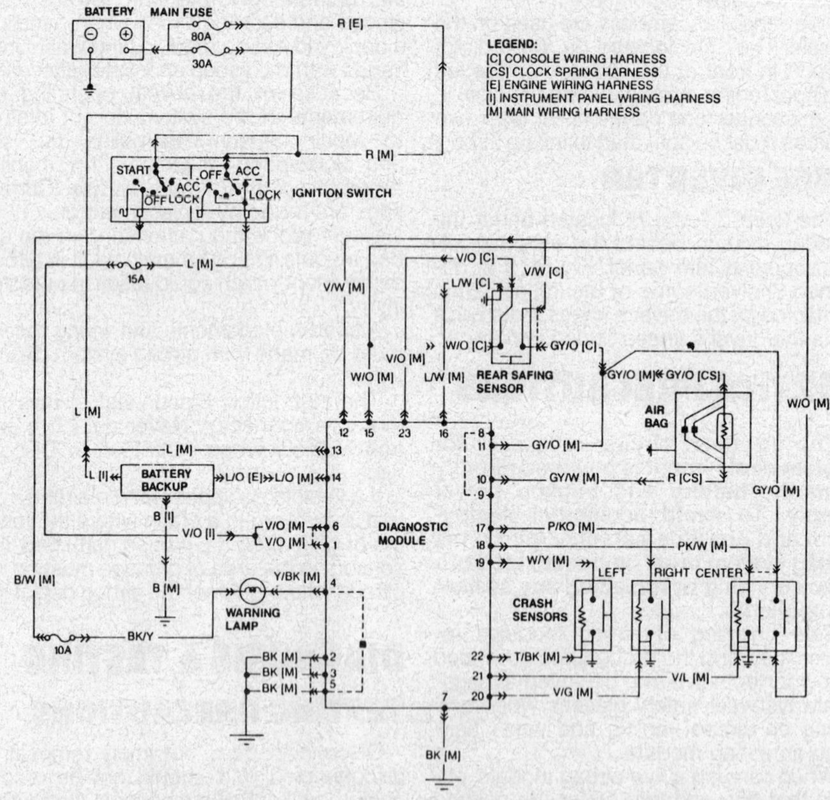


**Fig. 6 Airbag system wiring circuit. Capri**

## FRONT CENTER SENSOR

### Town Car, Crown Victoria & Grand Marquis

1. Deactivate airbag system as described under "Airbag Deactivation & Reactivation."

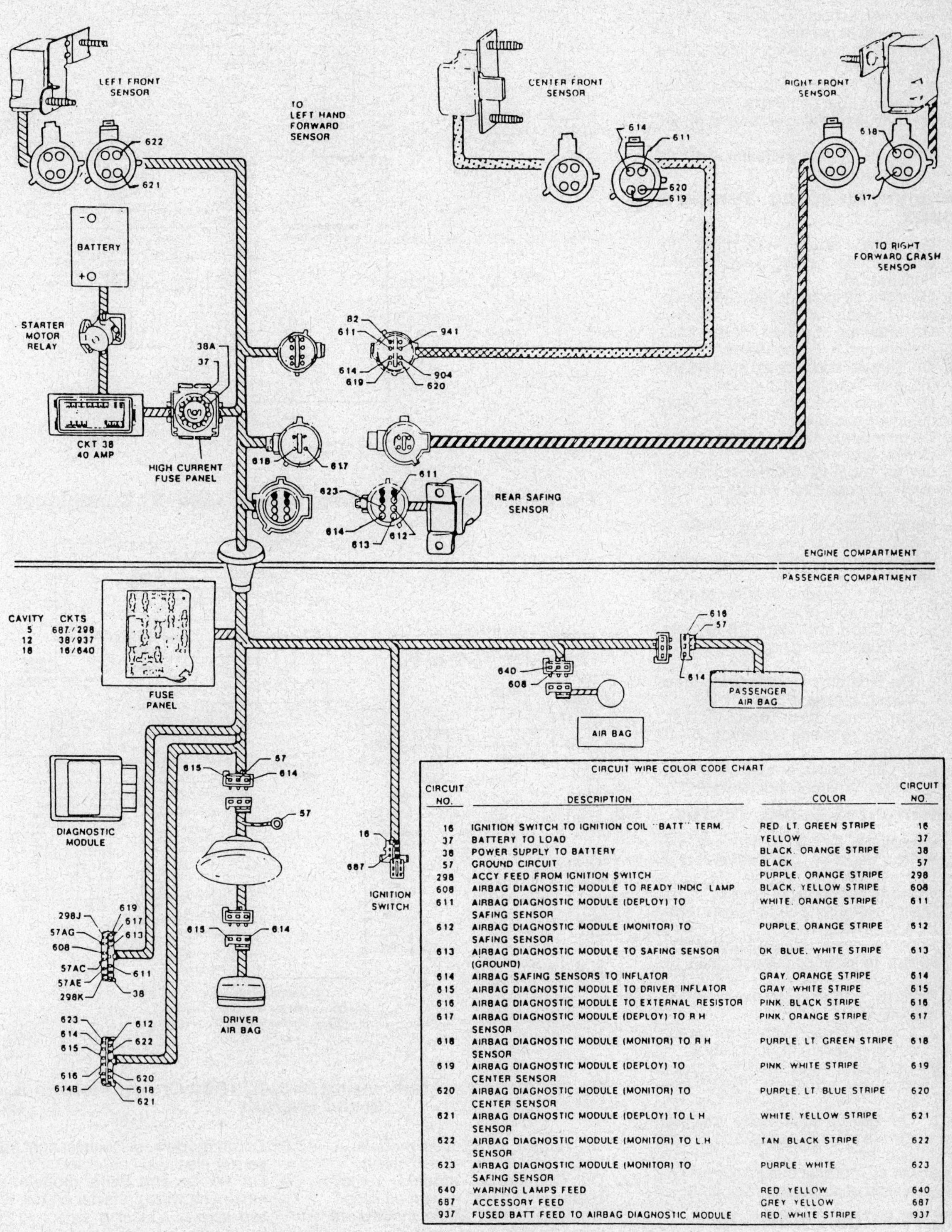


CIRCUIT WIRE COLOR CODE CHART

| CIRCUIT NO. | DESCRIPTION | COLOR | CIRCUIT NO. |
|---|---|---|---|
| 16 | IGNITION SWITCH TO IGNITION COIL "BATT" TERM. | RED, LT. GREEN STRIPE | 16 |
| 37 | BATTERY TO LOAD | YELLOW | 37 |
| 38 | POWER SUPPLY TO BATTERY | BLACK, ORANGE STRIPE | 38 |
| 57 | GROUND CIRCUIT | BLACK | 57 |
| 298 | ACCY FEED FROM IGNITION SWITCH | PURPLE, ORANGE STRIPE | 298 |
| 608 | AIRBAG DIAGNOSTIC MODULE TO READY INDIC LAMP | BLACK, YELLOW STRIPE | 608 |
| 611 | AIRBAG DIAGNOSTIC MODULE (DEPLOY) TO SAFING SENSOR | WHITE, ORANGE STRIPE | 611 |
| 612 | AIRBAG DIAGNOSTIC MODULE (MONITOR) TO SAFING SENSOR | PURPLE, ORANGE STRIPE | 612 |
| 613 | AIRBAG DIAGNOSTIC MODULE TO SAFING SENSOR (GROUND) | DK. BLUE, WHITE STRIPE | 613 |
| 614 | AIRBAG SAFING SENSORS TO INFLATOR | GRAY, ORANGE STRIPE | 614 |
| 615 | AIRBAG DIAGNOSTIC MODULE TO DRIVER INFLATOR | GRAY, WHITE STRIPE | 615 |
| 616 | AIRBAG DIAGNOSTIC MODULE TO EXTERNAL RESISTOR | PINK, BLACK STRIPE | 616 |
| 617 | AIRBAG DIAGNOSTIC MODULE (DEPLOY) TO R H SENSOR | PINK, ORANGE STRIPE | 617 |
| 618 | AIRBAG DIAGNOSTIC MODULE (MONITOR) TO R H SENSOR | PURPLE, LT. GREEN STRIPE | 618 |
| 619 | AIRBAG DIAGNOSTIC MODULE (DEPLOY) TO CENTER SENSOR | PINK, WHITE STRIPE | 619 |
| 620 | AIRBAG DIAGNOSTIC MODULE (MONITOR) TO CENTER SENSOR | PURPLE, LT. BLUE STRIPE | 620 |
| 621 | AIRBAG DIAGNOSTIC MODULE (DEPLOY) TO L H SENSOR | WHITE, YELLOW STRIPE | 621 |
| 622 | AIRBAG DIAGNOSTIC MODULE (MONITOR) TO L H SENSOR | TAN, BLACK STRIPE | 622 |
| 623 | AIRBAG DIAGNOSTIC MODULE (MONITOR) TO SAFING SENSOR | PURPLE, WHITE | 623 |
| 640 | WARNING LAMPS FEED | RED, YELLOW | 640 |
| 687 | ACCESSORY FEED | GREY, YELLOW | 687 |
| 937 | FUSED BATT FEED TO AIRBAG DIAGNOSTIC MODULE | RED, WHITE STRIPE | 937 |

**Fig. 7 Airbag system wiring circuit. 1989 Continental**

2. Disconnect sensor electrical connectors.
3. Remove sensor retaining screws, then remove sensor.
4. Reverse procedure to install, noting the following:
   a. Position sensor with arrow on top toward front of vehicle.
   b. **Torque** retaining screws to 68-92 inch lbs.
   c. Ensure correct operation of airbag indicator lamp.

### Mark VII, Mustang, Tempo & Topaz

1. Deactivate airbag system as described under "Airbag Deactivation & Reactivation."
2. **On Mark VII models,** remove or loosen RH radiator clamp.
3. **On Mustang models,** loosen facia, radiator and A/C condenser.
4. **On Tempo and Topaz models,** remove air induction resonator.
5. **On Capri models,** remove front bumper assembly.
6. **On all models except Capri,** remove air filter assembly.
7. **On all models,** disconnect sensor electrical connector and wiring locator.
8. Remove screws retaining sensor to bracket, then remove sensor.
9. Reverse procedure to install, noting the following:
   a. Position sensor with arrow pointing toward front of vehicle.
   b. **On Capri and Mark VII models, torque** retaining screws to 7-10 ft. lbs.
   c. **On Mustang models, torque** retaining screws to 5.1-9 ft. lbs.
   d. **On Tempo and Topaz models, torque** retaining screws to 29-40 inch lbs.
   e. **On all models,** ensure correct operation of airbag indicator lamp.

### Continental, Sable, Taurus

1. Deactivate airbag system as described under "Airbag Deactivation & Reactivation."
2. Remove radiator sight shield.
3. Disconnect center front sensor electrical connector.
4. Remove screws retaining center front sensor to radiator support, then remove sensor.
5. Reverse procedure to install, noting the following.
   a. Position sensor with arrow on top pointing toward front of vehicle.
   b. **On Continental models, torque** attaching screws to 29-40 inch lbs.
   c. **On Taurus and Sable models, torque** retaining screws to 62-88 inch lbs.
   d. **On all models,** ensure correct operation of airbag indicator lamp.

## RIGHT FRONT SENSOR

1. Deactivate airbag system as described under "Airbag Deactivation & Reactivation."
2. **On Capri models,** raise headlamps.

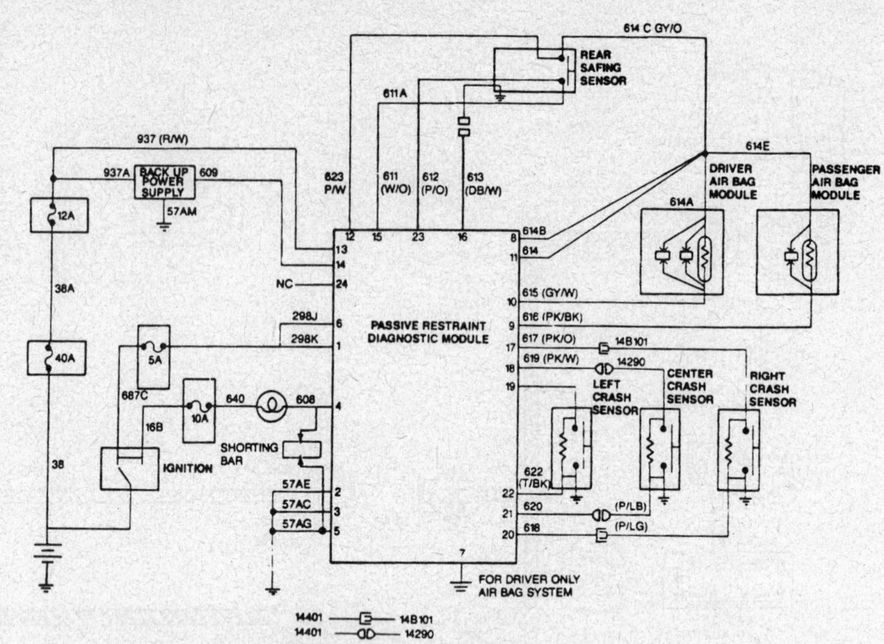


Fig. 8 Airbag system wiring circuit. 1990–91 Continental

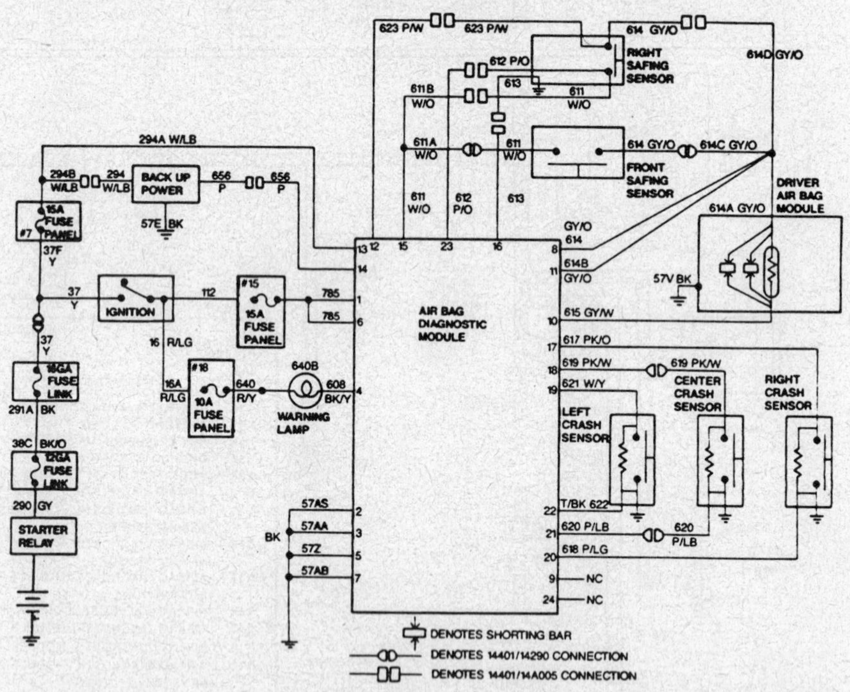


Fig. 9 Airbag system wiring circuit. 1990 Crown Victoria & Grand Marquis

3. **On Tempo and Topaz models,** remove inner fender splash shield.
4. **On Continental models,** remove heated windshield relay, if equipped.
5. **On Taurus and Sable models,** remove front bumper assembly.
6. **On Mark VII and Mustang models,** remove air cleaner assembly.
7. **On Town Car, Crown Victoria and Grand Marquis,** remove battery.
8. **On all models,** disconnect right front sensor electrical connector.
9. **On Taurus and Sable models,** remove one wiring retainer on rail, and two screws attaching sensor to RH lower outer radiator support.
10. **On Mark VII and Mustang models,** remove screws attaching sensor to radiator support, then remove sensor.
11. **On all other models,** remove screws

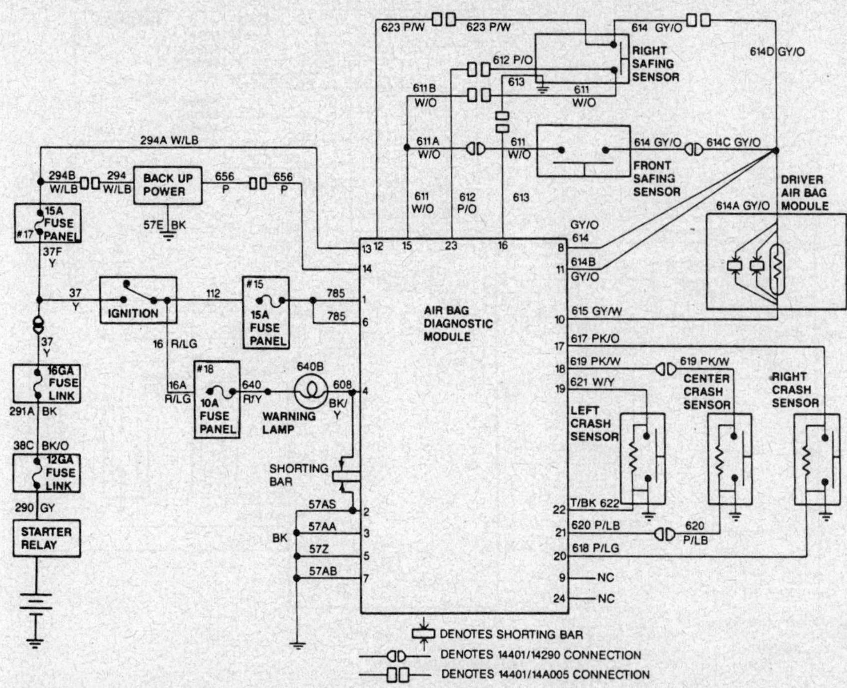


**Fig. 10 Airbag system wiring circuit. 1991 Crown Victoria & Grand Marquis**

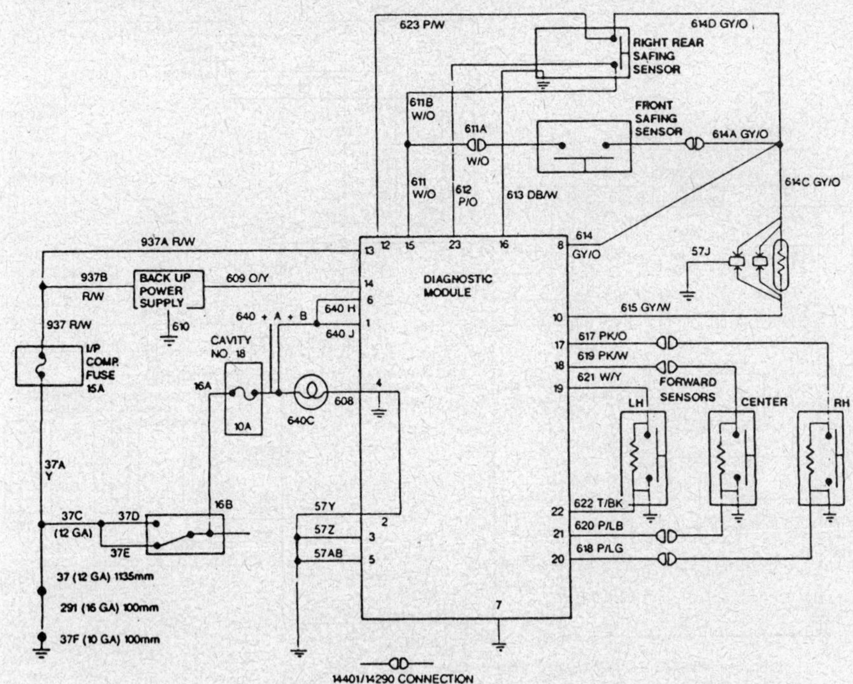


**Fig. 11 Airbag system wiring circuit. 1990 Mark VII**

attaching sensor to RH fender apron, then remove sensor.

12. Reverse procedure to install, noting the following:
    a. Position sensor with arrow toward front of vehicle.
    b. **On all models except Capri, torque** attaching screws to 7-10 ft. lbs.
    c. **On Capri models, torque** attaching screws to 15-18 ft. lbs.
    d. Ensure correct operation of airbag indicator lamp.

## LEFT FRONT SENSOR

1. Deactivate airbag system as described under "Airbag Deactivation & Reactivation."
2. **On Tempo and Topaz models,** remove inner fender splash shield.
3. **On Capri models,** raise headlamps and remove LH headlamp bezel and splash shield, then remove electrical connector retaining clip from the apron below headlamp.
4. **On Taurus and Sable models,** remove front bumper, then the inner fender splash shield.
5. **On Mark VII models,** remove battery and battery tray.
6. **On Mustang models,** remove battery, then plastic wiring shield.
7. **On Crown Victoria, Grand Marquis and Town Car models,** remove washer fluid reservoir.
8. **On all models,** disconnect left front sensor electrical connector.
9. **On Mustang models,** remove LH sensor support bracket.
10. **On Mark VII and Mustang models,** remove sensor retaining screws, then remove sensor from LH radiator support.
11. **On Capri models,** remove two screws retaining sensor to two bracket, then remove the sensor.
12. **On all other models,** remove screws attaching sensor to LH fender apron, then remove sensor.
13. Reverse procedure to install, noting the following:
    a. **On Mark VII models, torque** retaining screws to 62-88 inch lbs.
    b. **On Capri models, torque** retaining screws to 15-18 ft. lbs.
    c. **On all other models, torque** attaching screws to 7-10 ft. lbs.
    d. Ensure correct operation of airbag indicator lamp.

## REAR SENSOR

### Continental, Mustang, Tempo & Topaz

1. Deactivate airbag system as described under "Airbag Deactivation & Reactivation."
2. **On 1989-90 Tempo and Topaz models,** cut off plastic locator pin between sensor mounting nuts.
3. **On Mustang models,** remove rear seat cushion and quarter trim panel, then remove two screws retaining rear sensor to B-pillar.
4. **On all models except Mustang,** remove two nuts attaching rear sensor to dash panel in engine compartment.
5. **On all models,** disconnect sensor electrical connector and remove sensor.
6. Reverse procedure to install, noting the following:
    a. **On Continental models, torque** retaining screws to 29-40 inch lbs.
    b. **On Mustang models, torque** retaining screws to 7-10 ft. lbs.
    c. **On Tempo and Topaz models, torque** attaching nuts to 31-44 inch lbs.

### Crown Victoria, Grand Marquis, Mark VII, Sable, Taurus & Town Car

1. Deactivate airbag system as described under "Airbag Deactivation & Reactivation."
2. **On Mark VII models,** remove hood release handle and parking brake as-

sembly.

3. **On all models,** remove LH kick panel.
4. **On Crown Victoria, Grand Marquis and Town Car models,** remove connector bracket.
5. **On all models,** disconnect rear sensor wiring connector from wiring assembly connector.
6. Remove two screws retaining rear sensor to LH kick panel, then remove sensor.
7. Reverse procedure to install, noting the following;
   a. **On Crown Victoria, Grand Marquis and Town Car models, torque** retaining screws to 35-53 inch lbs.
   b. **On Mark VII models, torque** retaining screws to 30-39 inch lbs.
   c. **On Sable and Taurus models, torque** retaining screws to 7-10 ft. lbs.
   d. **On all models,** ensure proper operation of airbag indicator lamp.

### Capri

1. Deactivate airbag system as described under "Airbag Deactivation & Reactivation."
2. Remove center console.
3. Remove sensor retaining bolt and screw.
4. Disconnect sensor lead from wiring harness connector and remove sensor.
5. Reverse procedure to install, noting the following;
   a. Position sensor with arrow on top toward front of vehicle.
   b. **Torque** sensor retaining bolt to 17-22 ft. lbs.
   c. **Torque** sensor retaining screw to 26-35 ft. lbs.
   d. Ensure proper operation of airbag indicator lamp.

## DIAGNOSTIC MONITOR ASSEMBLY

### Continental, Tempo & Topaz

1. Deactivate airbag system as described under "Airbag Deactivation & Reactivation."
2. Remove screws attaching steering column opening cover to instrument panel, then cover.
3. Remove four bolts attaching bolster, then the bolster.
4. Disconnect diagnostic monitor electrical wiring connectors.
5. Remove screws attaching diagnostic monitor and bracket assembly to instrument panel brace, then remove assembly.
6. **On Continental models,** remove two screws attaching monitor to bracket.
7. **On Tempo & Topaz models,** depress tabs and remove monitor from bracket.
8. **On all models,** reverse procedure to install, ensure correct operat ion of airbag indicator lamp.

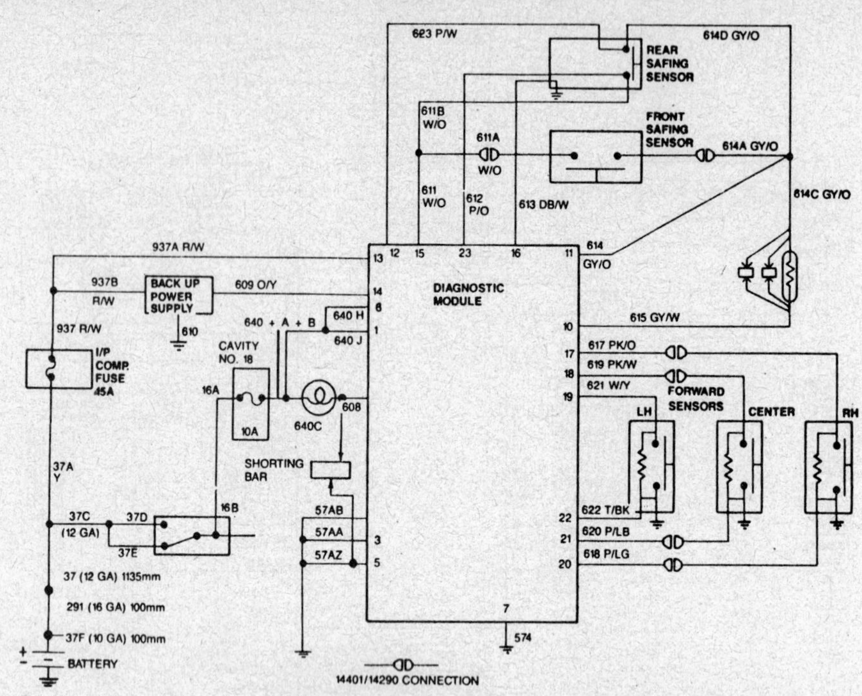


**Fig. 12 Airbag system wiring circuit. 1991 Mark VII**

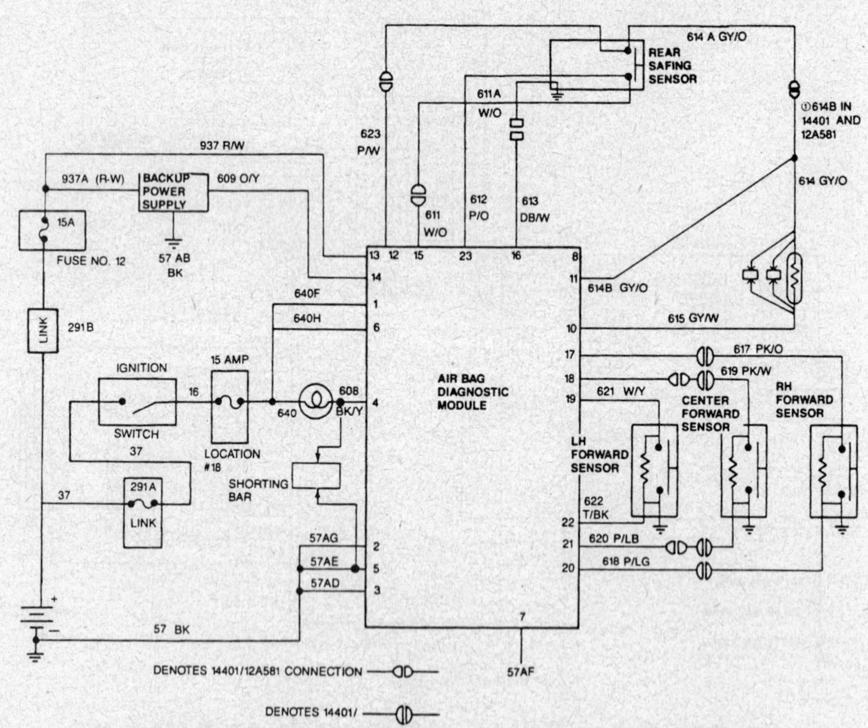


**Fig. 13 Airbag system wiring circuit. Mustang**

### Mark VII, Sable & Taurus

1. Deactivate airbag system as described under "Airbag Deactivation & Reactivation."
2. Open glove box compartment past stops.
3. **On Mark VII models,** remove heater duct above glove compartment.
4. **On all models,** disconnect two monitor connectors, then remove monitor.
5. Reverse procedure to install, ensure correct operation of airbag indicator lamp.

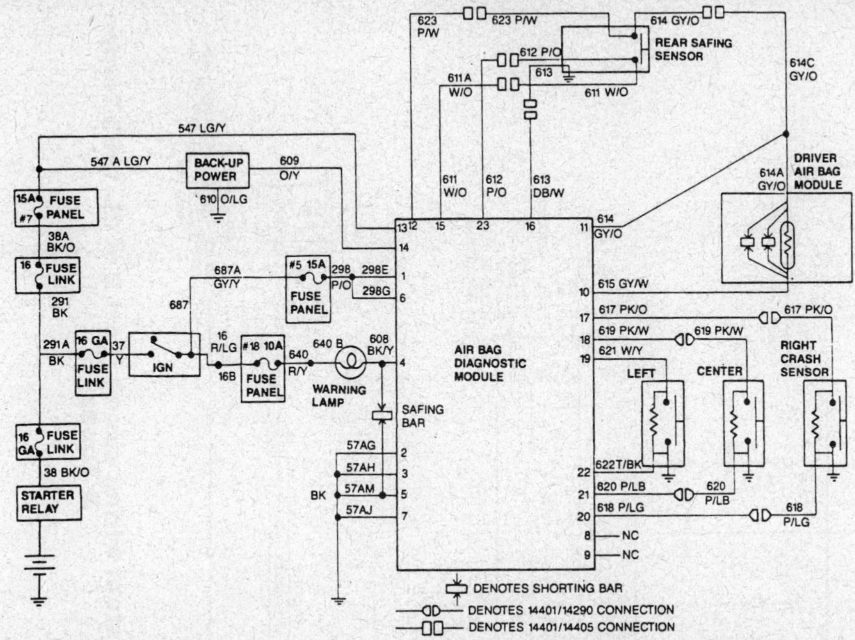


**Fig. 14 Airbag system wiring circuit. Sable & Taurus**

### Mustang

1. Deactivate airbag system as described under "Airbag Deactivation & Reactivation."
2. Remove radio, then disconnect diagnostic monitor (blue box with two connectors mounted below climate control head).
3. Remove screws attaching diagnostic monitor and bracket on instrument panel brace and remove assembly.
4. Reverse procedure to install, ensure correct operation of airbag indicator lamp.

### Crown Victoria, Grand Marquis & Town Car

1. Deactivate airbag system as described under "Airbag Deactivation & Reactivation."
2. Remove headlamp switch knob and retaining nut.
3. Remove LH and RH instrument panel moldings.
4. Remove 12 upper and lower instrument panel finish panel retaining screws, then the finish panel.
5. Remove two bolts retaining steering column opening cover and pad assembly to instrument panel and remove cover.
6. Remove two screws and push pin retaining instrument panel insulator and remove insulator.
7. Disconnect diagnostic monitor electrical wiring connectors.
8. Remove two screws attaching monitor and bracket assembly, then remove assembly.
9. Remove screws attaching monitor to bracket.
10. Reverse procedure to install, ensure operation of airbag lamp.

### Capri

1. Deactivate airbag system as described under "Airbag Deactivation & Reactivation."
2. Locate diagnostic monitor assembly (blue box) mounted behind fuse panel.
3. Depress two tabs and disengage monitor.
4. Disconnect electrical connectors and remove monitor.
5. Reverse procedure to install. Ensure correct operation of airbag indicator lamp.

## AIRBAG SLIP RING, REPLACE

### Removal

1. Park vehicle with wheels in straight ahead position, then turn ignition switch to Lock position and rotate steering wheel approximately 16° counterclockwise until locked into position.
2. Deactivate airbag system as described under "Airbag Deactivation & Reactivation."
3. Remove steering wheel as follows:
   a. Working from rear of steering wheel, remove four nuts attaching airbag module to wheel.
   b. Lift airbag module from wheel and disconnect airbag module to slip ring clockspring connector.
   c. Remove and discard steering wheel attaching bolt.
   d. Remove steering wheel from upper shaft using steering wheel remover No. T67L-3600-A or equivalent. Do not use a knock-off type steering wheel puller or strike end of steering column upper shaft with a hammer, otherwise, damage will occur to bearing of collapsible steering column.
4. Remove upper and lower shrouds.
5. Disconnect airbag slip ring connector from column harness. **Before removing airbag clockspring type slip ring from steering shaft, clockspring must be taped, Fig. 65, to prevent clockspring rotor from being turned accidentally and damaging clockspring.**
6. Remove two retaining screws and the slip ring.

### Installation

Service replacement slip ring will contain a red colored locking insert to prevent rotation. This insert should not be removed until slip ring is installed on column.

1. Place airbag slip ring onto steering shaft and install two retaining screws that attach slip ring to retainer plate, ensuring ground wire pigtail is secured with lower retaining screw.
2. Remove locking insert.
3. Connect slip ring wire to column harness.
4. Install upper and lower shrouds.
5. Install steering wheel as follows:
   a. Position steering wheel on end of steering wheel shaft, aligning mark on steering wheel with mark on shaft to ensure that straight ahead steering wheel position corresponds to straight ahead position of front wheels.
   b. Install new steering wheel attaching nut. **Torque** to 30-40 ft. lbs.
   c. Connect airbag module wire to slip ring connector and place module on steering wheel, then install four retaining nuts. **Torque** to 35-53 inch lbs.
6. Connect battery ground cable and activate airbag system as described under "Airbag Deactivation & Reactivation."

## DRIVER AIRBAG MODULE

1. Deactivate airbag system as described under "Airbag Deactivation & Reactivation."
2. Remove four nut and washer assemblies retaining airbag module to steering wheel.
3. Disconnect airbag electrical connector from slip ring/clockspring connectors and remove airbag assembly.
4. Reverse procedure to install, noting the following:
   a. **On Capri models, torque** mounting nut and washer assemblies to 17-26 inch lbs.
   b. **On Mustang models, torque** mounting nut and washer assemblies to 23-32 inch lbs.
   c. **On all other models, torque** mounting nut and washer assemblies to 35-53 inch lbs.

## PASSENGER AIRBAG MODULE

### Continental

1. Deactivate airbag system as described under "Airbag Deactivation & Reactivation."

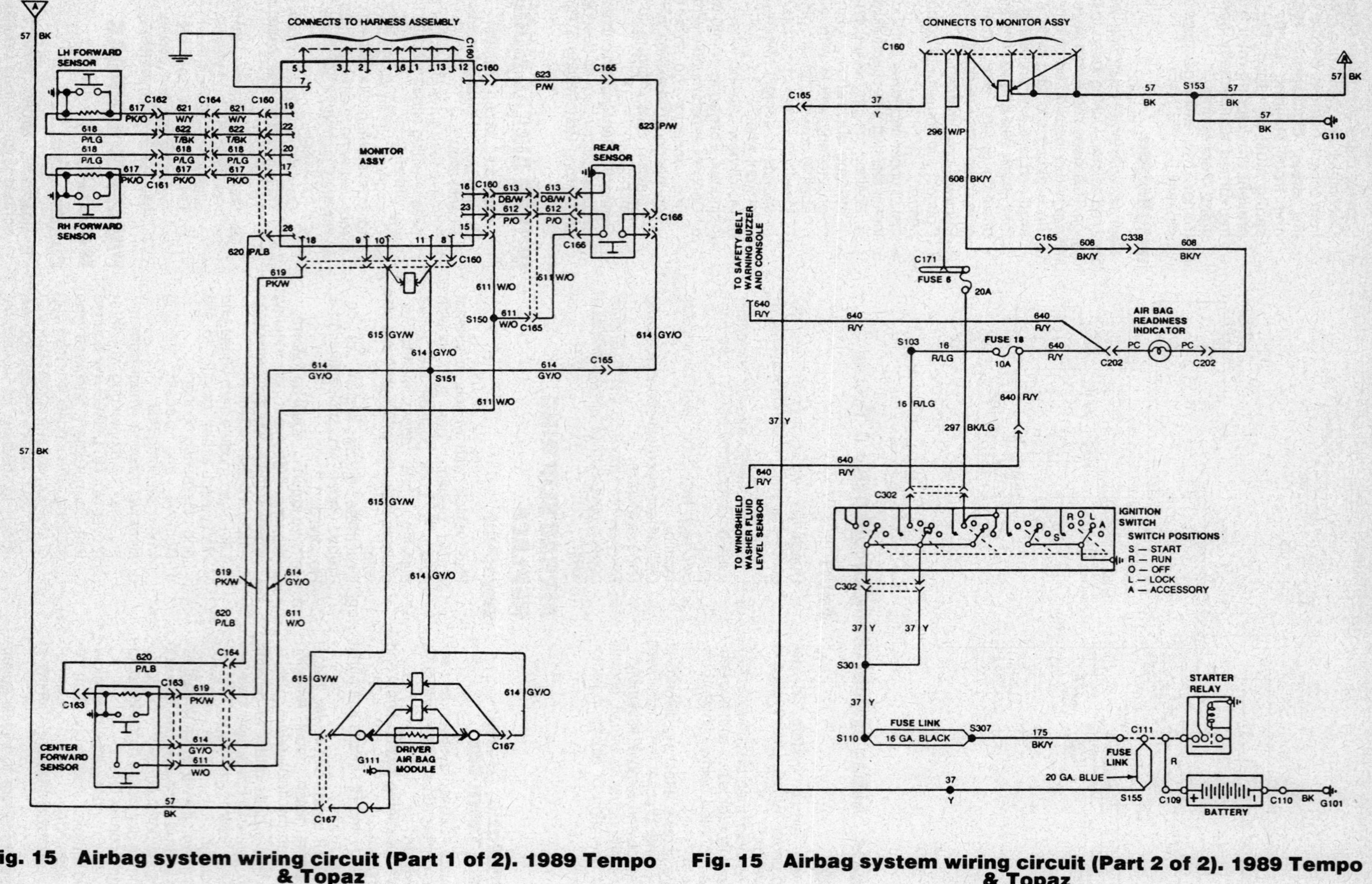


Fig. 15 Airbag system wiring circuit (Part 1 of 2). 1989 Tempo & Topaz

Fig. 15 Airbag system wiring circuit (Part 2 of 2). 1989 Tempo & Topaz

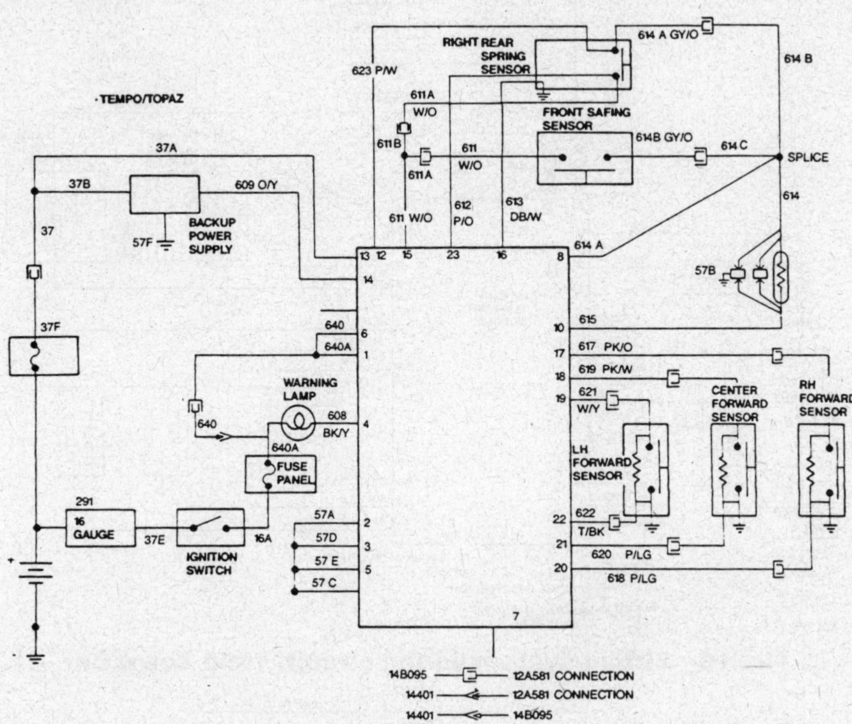


**Fig. 16 Airbag system wiring circuit. 1990 Tempo & Topaz**

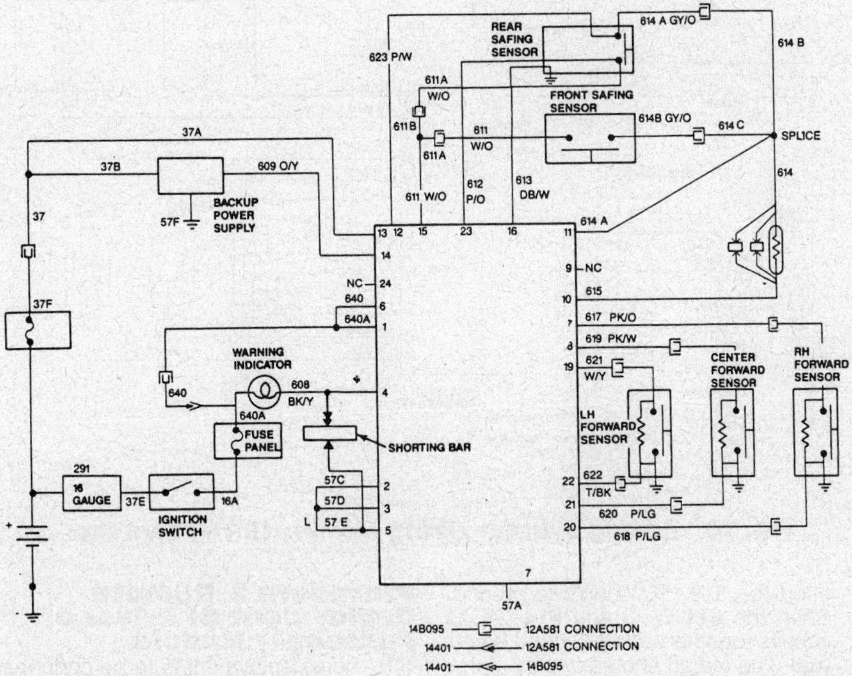


**Fig. 17 Airbag system wiring circuit. 1991 Tempo & Topaz**

2. Open glove compartment and rotate past stops.
3. Disconnect passenger airbag electrical connector.
4. Remove two bolts securing lower passenger airbag mounting bracket to instrument panel.
5. Remove instrument panel shelf molding.
6. Remove two screws securing front of airbag to instrument panel.
7. Remove passenger airbag by pushing on airbag assembly from inside panel. **Do not handle airbag by grabbing edges of deployment doors.**
8. Reverse procedure to install, noting the following:
   a. **Torque** two bolts securing lower passenger airbag mounting bracket to instrument panel to 7-10 ft. lbs.
   b. **Torque** rod and tab attaching screws to 18-25 inch. lbs.
   c. Ensure correct operation of airbag indicator lamp.

### Town Car

1. Deactivate airbag system as described under "Airbag Deactivation & Reactivation."
2. Remove righthand instrument panel.
3. Remove instrument panel finish panel retaining screws, then remove the panel.
4. Open glove compartment, press sides in and pivot glove compartment to floor.
5. Remove two lower airbag module retaining bolts, through glove compartment opening.
6. Remove four remaining airbag module retaining screws, disconnect electrical connector and remove airbag module.
7. Reverse procedure to install, noting the following:
   a. **Torque** two lower securing bolts to 6-8 ft. lbs.
   b. **Torque** four upper retaining bolts to 4-8 inch lbs.
   c. Ensure correct operation of airbag indicator lamp.

## DISPOSAL PROCEDURES

Several situations may arise when some form of disposal action must be undertaken; scrapping a vehicle containing a deployed airbag, scrapping a vehicle with a live airbag, disposal of a live but electrically inoperative airbag module and scrapping a deployed airbag, etc. These situations and the disposal recommendations are shown in the airbag disposal recommendations chart, **Fig. 66.**

## DEPLOYED MODULE

To repair a vehicle in which the airbag has deployed, the deployed driver module must be replaced with an all new module. The deployed module can be disposed of in the same manner as any part to be scrapped.

## FAULTY UN-DEPLOYED MODULE

In the event that a faulty driver airbag module is diagnosed, the faulty module must be replaced by a new module. The faulty module cannot be disposed of in the usual manner, and must be returned to the Ford Motor Company for proper disposal.

The module must be packaged and shipped according to the U. S. Department of Transportation regulations. For proper shipping instructions contact the local Ford Motor Company District Service office.

## SCRAPPED VEHICLE

Some vehicles may be damaged or inoperable to the point that repairs cannot be made, but still contain an undeployed airbag. This condition could occur by side or rear impact, or rollover, etc. The airbag should be deployed prior to vehicle disposal, per procedures 1 or 2 described below under "Airbag Disposal."

## AIRBAG DISPOSAL

### Procedure 1, Electronic Deployment With Intact Wiring

This procedure is to be used in the event that a vehicle with a live airbag inflator is to be scrapped. Disposal may be required due to severe damage in a non-airbag deployable accident, or at the end of the vehicle's useful life. This procedure assumes that the airbag wiring remains intact; that is, no fault codes are indicated by the readiness indicator, that the system proves out correctly and that the vehicles's battery is still in place. This procedure is to be performed outdoors away from other personnel, since the deploying airbag makes a loud report during actuation.

1. Check and clear the front seat of all loose objects.
2. Do not permit any occupants to remain inside the vehicle.
3. Open the hood and check for operational vehicle battery. If no battery is found, supply one and connect it in the usual manner.
4. Turn ignition switch to Run position and observe the airbag readiness indicator. If the lamp illuminates for four to eight seconds and then stops, the system is intact and may be deployed. Continue with procedure 1. If a series of fault codes appear, use procedure 2 to deploy unit.
5. Locate the center airbag sensor at the top center of the radiator support, beneath the radiator sight shield. Locate the white connector 8 inches from the sensor, toward the battery.
6. Pull the white submersible connector apart and examine the wiring harness end of the connector. Identify circuits 619 PK/W, 620 P/LB, 611 W/O and 614 GY/O, **Figs. 6 through 19.**
7. Using a 6 inch length of bared wire, short the 619 PK/W wire to ground. Short the 611 W/O and 614 GY/O circuits together with a second bared wire. The airbag should deploy. If the airbag does not deploy, proceed to procedure 2.
8. If successful, a loud report will be heard and the bag material will be visible in the center of the steering wheel. Allow at least 10 minutes before approaching the airbag to allow for cooling of the module and dissipation of the effluents.

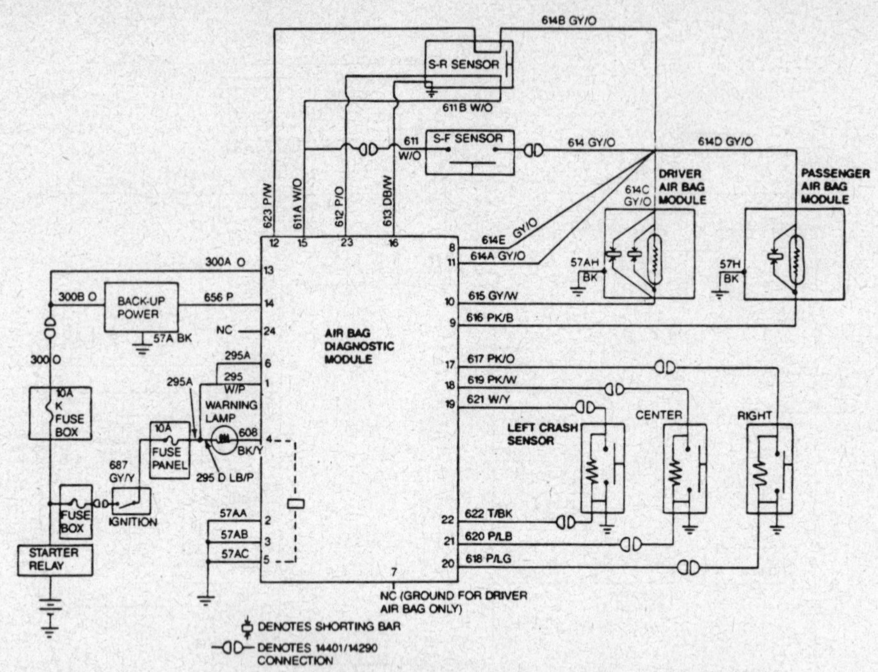


**Fig. 18 Airbag system wiring circuit. 1990 Town Car**

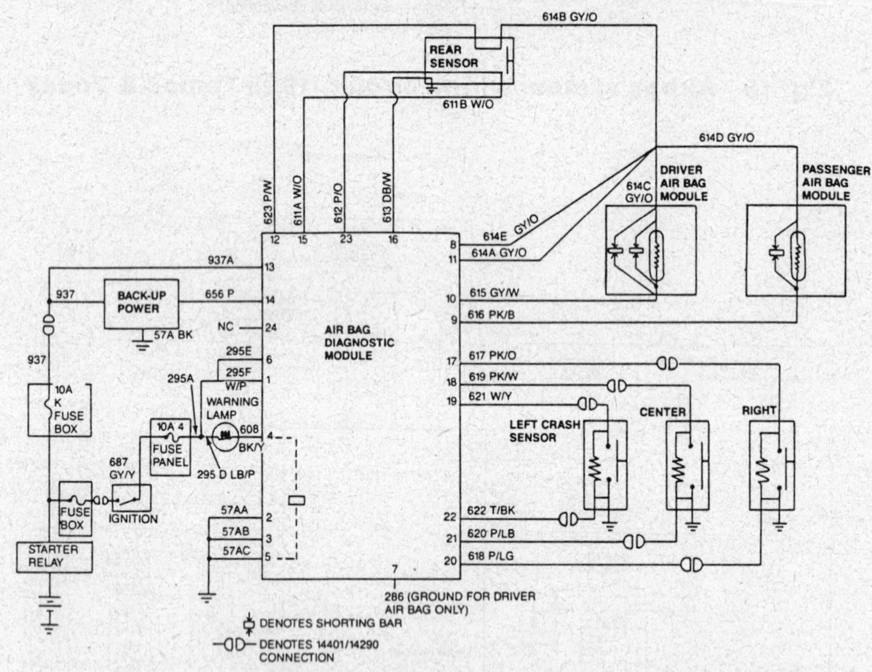


**Fig. 19 Airbag system wiring circuit. 1991 Town Car**

### Procedure 2, Remote Deployment Of Driver Or Passenger Module

Remote deployment is to be performed outdoors with all personnel at least 20 feet away to ensure personnel safety and due to loud report which occurs when an airbag is deployed.

This procedure is to be used in the event that a vehicle with a live airbag module is to be scrapped, but the vehicle does not contain an intact wiring harness or certain system components are inoperative. This procedure can also be used if step 7 of procedure 1 was unsuccessful.

1. Remove driver airbag module from steering wheel.
2. Cut the two module connector wires and strip 1 inch of insulation from the ends. Obtain two wires at least 20 feet long. Connect one end of each wire to each of the airbag module wires.
3. Place the module with the black trim cover facing upward on a flat surface in a remote area such as a parking lot or field. **Do not place the module with the trim cover facing down, as the forces of the deploying airbag may cause the module to ricochet and cause personal injury.**
4. Remaining at least 20 feet away from the module, deploy the airbag by touching the other ends of the two wires to the terminals of a 12 volt vehicle battery.
5. If successful, a loud report will be heard and the airbag material will be visible coming from the top of the module. Allow at least 10 minutes before approaching the airbag to allow for cooling of the module and dissipation of the effluents.

## DIAGNOSTIC CHART INDEX

| No. Of Flashes | Year | Possible Fault | Fig. No. | Page No. |
|---|---|---|---|---|
| **CAPRI** | | | | |
| ① | 1991 | Inoperative Airbag Lamp Circuit | 20 | 25-15 |
| ② | 1991 | Diagnostic Monitor Faulty | 28 | 25-24 |
| 2 | 1991 | All Forward Crash Sensors Disconnected | 29 | 25-25 |
| 3 | 1991 | Loss Of Airbag Circuit | 31 | 25-25 |
| 4 | 1991 | Potential Short In Circuit | 41 | 25-33 |
| 5 | 1991 | Forward Crash Sensor Or Igniter Circuit Shorted To Ground | 45 | 25-37 |
| 6 | 1991 | Driver Airbag Circuit Inoperative | 50 | 25-43 |
| 7 | 1991 | Module Wiring Circuit Inoperative | 54 | 25-44 |
| 8 | 1991 | Forward Crash Sensor Improperly Attached Or Ground | 57 | 25-46 |
| 9 | 1991 | Open Forward Crash Sensor Deployment Circuit | 60 | 25-47 |
| 10 | 1991 | — | 64 | 25-49 |
| **CONTINENTAL** | | | | |
| ① | 1989–91 | Inoperative Airbag lamp Circuit | 21 | 25-16 |
| ② | 1989–91 | Diagnostic Monitor Faulty | 28 | 25-24 |
| 2 | 1989–91 | All Forward Crash Sensors Disconnected | 30 | 25-25 |
| 3 | 1989 | Loss Of Airbag Circuit | 32 | 25-26 |
| | 1990–91 | Loss Of Airbag Circuit | 33 | 25-27 |
| 4 | 1989 | Potential Short In Circuit | 42 | 25-34 |
| | 1990–91 | Potential Short In Circuit | 44 | 25-36 |
| 5 | 1989–91 | Forward Crash Sensor Or Igniter Circuit Shorted To Ground | 46 | 25-38 |
| 6 | 1989 | Driver Airbag Circuit Inoperative | 51 | 25-43 |
| | 1990–91 | Driver Airbag Circuit Inoperative | 52 | 25-44 |
| 7 | 1989–91 | Passenger Airbag Circuit Inoperative | 55 | 25-45 |
| 8 | 1989–91 | Forward Crash Sensor Improperly Attached Or Ground | 59 | 25-47 |
| 9 | 1989 | Open Forward Crash Sensor Deployment Circuit | 61 | 25-47 |
| | 1990–91 | Open Forward Crash Sensor Deployment Circuit | 62 | 25-48 |
| 10 | 1989 | Malfunctioning Front Sensor | 63 | 25-48 |
| | 1990–91 | — | 64 | 25-49 |
| **CROWN VICTORIA & GRAND MARQUIS** | | | | |
| ① | 1990–91 | Inoperative Airbag Lamp Circuit | 22 | 25-17 |
| ② | 1990–91 | Diagnostic Monitor Faulty | 28 | 25-24 |
| 2 | 1990–91 | All Forward Crash Sensors Disconnected | 30 | 25-25 |
| 3 | 1990–91 | Loss Of Airbag Circuit | 34 | 25-28 |
| 4 | 1990–91 | Potential Short In Circuit | 44 | 25-36 |
| 5 | 1990 | Forward Crash Sensor Or Igniter Circuit Shorted To Ground | 47 | 25-40 |
| | 1991 | Forward Crash Sensor Or Igniter Circuit Shorted To Ground | 48 | 25-41 |
| 6 | 1990–91 | Driver Airbag Circuit Inoperative | 53 | 25-44 |
| 7 | 1990–91 | Monitor Wiring Circuit Inoperative | 56 | 25-45 |
| 8 | 1990–91 | Forward Crash Sensor Improperly Attached Or Ground | 59 | 25-47 |
| 9 | 1990–91 | Open Forward Crash Sensor Deployment Circuit | 62 | 25-48 |
| 10 | 1990–91 | — | 64 | 25-48 |

*Continued*

## DIAGNOSTIC CHART INDEX–CONTINUED

| No. Of Flashes | Year | Possible Fault | Fig. No. | Page No. |
|---|---|---|---|---|
| **MARK VII** | | | | |
| ① | 1990–91 | Inoperative Airbag Lamp Circuit | 23 | 25-18 |
| ② | 1990–91 | Diagnostic Monitor Faulty | 28 | 25-24 |
| 2 | 1990–91 | All Forward Crash Sensors Disconnected | 30 | 25-25 |
| 3 | 1990–91 | Loss Of Airbag Circuit | 35 | 25-28 |
| 4 | 1990–91 | Potential Short In Circuit | 44 | 25-36 |
| 5 | 1990–91 | Forward Crash Sensor Or Igniter Circuit Shorted To Ground | 49 | 25-41 |
| 6 | 1990–91 | Driver Airbag Circuit Inoperative | 53 | 25-44 |
| 7 | 1990–91 | Monitor Wiring Circuit Inoperative | 56 | 25-45 |
| 8 | 1990–91 | Forward Crash Sensor Improperly Attached Or Ground | 59 | 25-47 |
| 9 | 1990–91 | Open Forward Crash Sensor Deployment Circuit | 62 | 25-48 |
| 10 | 1990–91 | — | 64 | 25-48 |
| **MUSTANG** | | | | |
| ① | 1990–91 | Inoperative Airbag Lamp Circuit | 25 | 25-21 |
| ② | 1990–91 | Diagnostic Monitor Faulty | 28 | 25-24 |
| 2 | 1990–91 | All Forward Crash Sensors Disconnected | 30 | 25-25 |
| 3 | 1990–91 | Loss Of Airbag Circuit | 35 | 25-28 |
| 4 | 1990–91 | Potential Short In Circuit | 44 | 25-36 |
| 5 | 1990–91 | Forward Crash Sensor Or Igniter Circuit Shorted To Ground | 49 | 25-42 |
| 6 | 1990–91 | Driver Airbag Circuit Inoperative | 53 | 25-44 |
| 7 | 1990–91 | Monitor Wiring Circuit Inoperative | 56 | 25-45 |
| 8 | 1990–91 | Forward Crash Sensor Improperly Attached Or Ground | 59 | 25-47 |
| 9 | 1990–91 | Open Forward Crash Sensor Deployment Circuit | 62 | 25-48 |
| 10 | 1990–91 | — | 64 | 25-48 |
| **SABLE & TAURUS** | | | | |
| ① | 1990–91 | Inoperative Airbag Lamp Circuit | 21 | 25-16 |
| ② | 1990–91 | Diagnostic Monitor Faulty | 28 | 25-24 |
| 2 | 1990–91 | All Forward Crash Sensors Disconnected | 30 | 25-25 |
| 3 | 1990–91 | Loss Of Airbag Circuit | 36 | 25-29 |
| 4 | 1990–91 | Potential Short In Circuit | 44 | 25-36 |
| 5 | 1990–91 | Forward Crash Sensor Or Igniter Circuit Shorted To Ground | 49 | 25-42 |
| 6 | 1990–91 | Driver Airbag Circuit Inoperative | 53 | 25-44 |
| 7 | 1990–91 | Monitor Wiring Circuit Inoperative | 56 | 25-45 |
| 8 | 1990–91 | Forward Crash Sensor Improperly Attached Or Ground | 59 | 25-47 |
| 9 | 1990–91 | Open Forward Crash Sensor Deployment Circuit | 62 | 25-48 |
| 10 | 1990–91 | — | 64 | 25-48 |
| **TEMPO & TOPAZ** | | | | |
| ① | 1989 | Inoperative Airbag Lamp Circuit | 26 | 25-22 |
| ① | 1990–91 | Inoperative Airbag Lamp Circuit | 27 | 25-23 |
| ② | 1989–91 | Diagnostic Monitor Faulty | 28 | 25-24 |
| 2 | 1989–91 | All Forward Crash Sensors Disconnected | 30 | 25-25 |
| 3 | 1989 | Loss Of Airbag Circuit | 37 | 25-30 |
| | 1990–91 | Loss Of Airbag Circuit | 38 | 25-31 |
| 4 | 1989 | Potential Short In Circuit | 43 | 25-35 |
| | 1990–91 | Potential Short In Circuit | 44 | 25-36 |
| 5 | 1989–91 | Forward Crash Sensor Or Igniter Circuit Shorted To Ground | 49 | 25-42 |
| 6 | 1989–91 | Driver Airbag Circuit Inoperative | 53 | 25-44 |
| 7 | 1989–91 | Monitor Wiring Circuit Inoperative | 56 | 25-45 |
| 8 | 1989 | Forward Crash Sensor Improperly Attached Or Ground | 58 | 25-46 |
| | 1990–91 | Forward Crash Sensor Improperly Attached Or Ground | 59 | 25-47 |
| 9 | 1989 | Open Forward Crash Sensor Deployment Circuit | 61 | 25-47 |
| | 1990–91 | Open Forward Crash Sensor Deployment Circuit | 62 | 25-48 |
| 10 | 1989 | Malfunctioning Front Sensor | 63 | 25-48 |
| | 1990–91 | — | 64 | 25-48 |

*Continued*

## DIAGNOSTIC CHART INDEX—CONTINUED

| No. Of Flashes | Year | Possible Fault | Fig. No. | Page No. |
|---|---|---|---|---|
| **TOWN CAR** | | | | |
| ① | 1990–91 | Inoperative Airbag Lamp Circuit | 24 | 25-20 |
| ② | 1990–91 | Diagnostic Monitor Faulty | 28 | 25-24 |
| 2 | 1990–91 | All Forward Crash Sensors Disconnected | 30 | 25-25 |
| 3 | 1990 | Loss Of Airbag Circuit | 39 | 25-31 |
| | 1991 | Loss Of Airbag Circuit | 40 | 25-32 |
| 4 | 1990–91 | Potential Short In Circuit | 44 | 25-36 |
| | 1990 | Forward Crash Sensor Or Igniter Circuit Shorted To Ground | 47 | 25-40 |
| 5 | 1991 | Forward Crash Sensor Or Igniter Circuit Shorted To Ground | 46 | 25-38 |
| 6 | 1990–91 | Driver Airbag Circuit Inoperative | 52 | 25-44 |
| 7 | 1990–91 | Passenger Airbag Circuit Inoperative | 55 | 25-45 |
| 8 | 1990–91 | Forward Crash Sensor Improperly Attached Or Ground | 59 | 25-49 |
| 9 | 1990–91 | Open Forward Crash Sensor Deployment Circuit | 62 | 25-48 |
| 10 | 1990–91 | — | 64 | 25-48 |

①—Airbag lamp does not light.
②—Airbag lamp stays on continuously.

**Fault Indication—Air Bag Lamp**
**Does Not Light**
**Probable Fault—Inoperative Air Bag Lamp Circuit**

| | TEST STEP | RESULT | ► ACTION TO TAKE |
|---|---|---|---|
| A1 | DURING SYSTEM PROVE-OUT AIR BAG INDICATOR LAMP DID NOT LIGHT | | |
| A2 | CHECK WARNING LAMPS | | |
| | • Turn ignition switch from OFF to RUN.<br>• Warning lamps should light.<br>• Do engine and safety belt warning lamps light? | Yes<br>No | ► GO to A7.<br>► GO to A3. |
| A3 | CHECK FUSE | | |
| | • Turn ignition switch to OFF.<br>• Check meter fuse.<br>• Is fuse blown? | Yes<br>No | ► GO to A4.<br>► GO to A5. |
| A4 | REPLACE FUSE | | |
| | • Install new fuse into fuse panel.<br>• Turn ignition switch to RUN.<br>• Did fuse blow again? | No<br>Yes | ► VERIFY engine, safety belt and air bag warning lamps.<br>► TURN ignition switch to OFF. DEACTIVATE air bag system. TRACE BK / Y wire from cluster connector to fuse panel to find short to ground and SERVICE. REACTIVATE system and VERIFY warning lamps. |
| A5 | RECHECK WARNING LAMPS | | |
| | • Remove cluster connector to fuse panel, then reconnect connector.<br>• Turn ignition switch from OFF to RUN.<br>• Verify engine and safety belt warning lamps.<br>• Do engine and safety belt warning lamps light? | No<br>Yes | ► GO to A6.<br>► VERIFY engine, safety belt and air bag warning lamps. |
| A6 | CHECK FOR OPEN AIR BAG LAMP CIRCUIT | | |
| | • Turn ignition switch to OFF.<br>• Deactivite air bag system.<br>• Remove meter fuse.<br>• Attach ohmmeter to BK / Y wire at fuse panel and cluster wiring connector.<br>• Is resistance less than 1 ohm? | Yes<br>No | ► REPLACE bulbs and / or cluster printed circuit as required. REACTIVATE system and VERIFY warning lamps.<br>► TRACE BK / Y wire from cluster connector to fuse panel to find open in circuit, and REPAIR. REACTIVATE air bag system and VERIFY warning lamps. |

**Fig. 20 Inoperative airbag lamp circuit (Part 1 of 3). Capri**

**Fault Indication—Air Bag Lamp**
**Does Not Light**
**Probable Fault—Inoperative Air Bag Lamp Circuit (Continued)**

| | TEST STEP | RESULT | ► ACTION TO TAKE |
|---|---|---|---|
| A7 | CHECK THAT MODULE CONNECTOR IS PROPERLY CONNECTED | | |
| | • Are the diagnostic module connectors properly connected? | Yes<br>No | ► GO to A8.<br>► Properly connect diagnostic module connectors. VERIFY air bag lamp. If air bag lamp does not light GO to A9. |
| A8 | CHECK LAMP WITH MODULE CONNECTOR DISCONNECTED | | |
| | • Turn ignition switch to OFF.<br>• Remove module from bracket.<br>• Disconnect diagnostic module wiring gray connector from module assembly.<br>• Turn ignition switch to RUN.<br>• Is the air bag lamp continuously on? | No<br>Yes | ► GO to A9.<br>► GO to A10. |
| A9 | CHECK MODULE CONNECTOR | | |
| | • Turn ignition switch to OFF.<br>• Deactivate air bag system.<br>• Visually inspect the module connector to be sure Pin 5 (BK wire) and Pin 4 (Y / BK wire) on the gray connector are touching each other.<br>• Turn ignition switch to RUN.<br>• Does air bag lamp flash continuously? | Yes<br>No | ► GO to A10.<br>► GO to A11. |
| A10 | CHECK AIR BAG LAMP CIRCUIT VOLTAGE | | |
| | • Turn ignition switch to OFF.<br>• Deactivate air bag system.<br>• Attach voltmeter to Pin 6 (V / O wire) on gray module wiring connector and to ground.<br>• Turn ignition switch to RUN.<br>• Is voltage greater than 10 volts? | Yes<br>No | ► TURN ignition switch to OFF. REPLACE diagnostic module. RE\CTIVATE air bag system. TURN ignition switch to RUN. VERIFY air bag warning lamp.<br>► TURN ignition switch to OFF. CHECK audio fuse (15 amp). REPLACE fuse if blown and / or trace V / O wire from gray module wiring connector Pin 6 to fuse panel to find open and / or short to ground, and REPAIR. REACTIVATE air bag system. Turn ignition to RUN. VERIFY air bag warning lamp. |

**Fig. 20 Inoperative airbag lamp circuit (Part 2 of 3). Capri**

**Fault Indication—Air Bag Lamp Does Not Light**
**Probable Fault—Inoperative Air Bag Lamp Circuit (Continued)**

| TEST STEP | | RESULT ▶ | ACTION TO TAKE |
|---|---|---|---|
| A11 | CHECK AIR BAG CIRCUIT GROUND | | |
| | • Reconnect diagnostic module assembly connectors. | Yes ▶ | TURN ignition to OFF. REMOVE jumper wire. SERVICE ground circuit. REACTIVATE air bag system. TURN ignition key to RUN. VERIFY air bag warning lamp. |
| | • Attach a jumper wire to Pin 5 (BK wire) through back of module wiring connector and to ground.<br>• Does air bag lamp light? | No ▶ | GO to A12. |
| A12 | INSPECT CLUSTER PRINTED CIRCUIT | | |
| | • Turn ignition switch to OFF. | Yes ▶ | REPLACE printed circuit, connector and/or bulb as required. ACTIVATE air bag system. TURN ignition switch to RUN. VERIFY air bag warning lamp. |
| | • Remove jumper wire from Pin 5 and ground.<br>• Disconnect cluster connector.<br>• Visually inspect cluster printed circuit and air bag lamp.<br>• Does printed circuit or connector have any defects and/or is air bag lamp burnt out? | No ▶ | TRACE BK/Y wires from cluster to the Y/BK wire at module connector to find open and SERVICE. REACTIVATE air bag system. TURN ignition to RUN. VERIFY air bag warning lamp. |

**Fig. 20 Inoperative airbag lamp circuit (Part 3 of 3). Capri**

**Fault Indication — Air Bag Indicator Does Not Light**
**Probable Fault — Inoperative Air Bag Lamp Circuit**

| TEST STEP | | RESULT ▶ | ACTION TO TAKE |
|---|---|---|---|
| A5 | CHECK CIRCUIT 640 (R/Y) FOR OPEN CIRCUIT | | |
| | • Turn ignition switch to OFF.<br>• Deactivate air bag system.<br>• Remove warning indicator fuse.<br>• Attach ohmmeter to Circuit 640 (R/Y) at fuse panel and air bag indicator wiring connector.<br>• Is resistance less than 1 ohm? | Yes ▶ | REPLACE bulbs as required.<br>REACTIVATE system and VERIFY warning indicators. |
| | | No ▶ | TRACE Circuit 640 (R/Y) from air bag indicator connector to fuse panel to find open in circuit, and REPAIR.<br>REACTIVATE air bag system and VERIFY warning lamps. |
| A6 | CHECK THAT MONITOR CONNECTOR IS PROPERLY CONNECTED | | |
| | • Are the diagnostic monitor connectors properly connected?<br>AIR BAG DIAGNOSTIC MODULE CONNECTORS WIRING HARNESS SIDE | Yes ▶ | GO to A7. |
| | | No ▶ | Properly connect diagnostic monitor connectors. VERIFY air bag indicator. If air bag indicator does not light GO to A8. |

**Fig. 21 Inoperative airbag lamp circuit (Part 2 of 5). Continental, Sable & Taurus**

**Fault Indication — Air Bag Lamp Does Not Light**
**Probable Fault — Inoperative Air Bag Lamp Circuit**

| TEST STEP | | RESULT ▶ | ACTION TO TAKE |
|---|---|---|---|
| A0 | DURING SYSTEM PROVE-OUT AIR BAG INDICATOR LAMP DID NOT LIGHT | | |
| A1 | CHECK WARNING LAMPS | | |
| | • Turn ignition switch from OFF to RUN.<br>• Warning lamps should light.<br>• Do engine and safety belt warning lamps light? | Yes ▶ | GO to A6. |
| | | No ▶ | GO to A2. |
| A2 | CHECK FUSE | | |
| | • Turn ignition switch to OFF.<br>• Check warning lamps fuse.<br>• Is fuse blown? | Yes ▶ | GO to A3. |
| | | No ▶ | GO to A4. |
| A3 | REPLACE FUSE | | |
| | • Install new fuse into fuse panel.<br>• Turn ignition switch to RUN.<br>• Did fuse blow again? | No ▶ | VERIFY engine, safety belt and Air Bag warning lamps. |
| | | Yes ▶ | TURN ignition switch to OFF. DEACTIVATE Air Bag system. TRACE Circuit 640 (R/Y) from IP shelf moulding connector to fuse panel, to find short to ground and SERVICE. REACTIVATE system and VERIFY warning lamps. |
| A4 | RECHECK WARNING LAMPS | | |
| | • Remove cluster connector, then reconnect connector.<br>• Turn ignition switch from OFF to RUN.<br>• Verify engine and safety belt warning lamps.<br>• Do engine and safety belt warning lamps light? | No ▶ | GO to A5. |
| | | Yes ▶ | VERIFY engine, safety belt and Air Bag warning lamps. |

**Fig. 21 Inoperative airbag lamp circuit (Part 1 of 5). Continental, Sable & Taurus**

**Fault Indication — Air Bag Lamp Does Not Light**
**Probable Fault — Inoperative Air Bag Lamp Circuit**

| TEST STEP | | RESULT ▶ | ACTION TO TAKE |
|---|---|---|---|
| A7 | CHECK LAMP WITH MONITOR CONNECTOR DISCONNECTED | | |
| | • Turn ignition switch to OFF.<br>• Disconnect diagnostic monitor wiring from monitor assembly.<br>• Turn ignition to RUN.<br>• Is the Air Bag lamp lit continuously? | No ▶ | GO to A8. |
| | | Yes ▶ | GO to A9. |
| A8 | CHECK MONITOR CONNECTOR | | |
| | • Turn ignition switch to OFF.<br>• Deactivate Air Bag system.<br>• Visually inspect the monitor wiring connector to be sure Pin 5 (Circuit 57, BK) and Pin 4 (Circuit 608, BK/Y) are touching each other.<br>• Turn ignition to RUN.<br>• Does Air Bag lamp light continuously? | Yes ▶ | GO to A9. |
| | | No ▶ | GO to A10. |

**Fig. 21 Inoperative airbag lamp circuit (Part 3 of 5). Continental, Sable & Taurus**

## Fault Indication — Air Bag Lamp Does Not Light
## Probable Fault — Inoperative Air Bag Lamp Circuit

| TEST STEP | RESULT ▶ | ACTION TO TAKE |
|---|---|---|
| **A9** CHECK CIRCUIT 298 (P/O) | | |
| • Turn ignition switch to OFF.<br>• Deactivate air bag system.<br>• Attach voltmeter to Pin 6 (Circuit 298, P-O) on monitor wiring connector and to ground.<br>• Turn ignition switch to RUN.<br>• Is voltage greater than 10 volts? | Yes ▶ | TURN ignition switch to OFF. REPLACE diagnostic monitor.<br><br>REACTIVATE air bag system.<br><br>TURN ignition switch to RUN. VERIFY Air Bag warning lamp. |
| | No ▶ | TURN ignition switch to OFF. CHECK fuse No. 5 (15 amp). REPLACE fuse if blown and/or trace Circuit 298 (P/O) from monitor wiring connector Pin 6 to fuse panel to find open and/or short to ground, and SERVICE.<br><br>REACTIVATE air bag system. Turn ignition to RUN. VERIFY Air Bag warning lamp. |
| **A10** JUMP CIRCUIT 57 (BK) | | |
| • Reconnect diagnostic monitor assembly connector.<br>• Attach a jumper wire to Pin 5 (Circuit 57, BK) through back of monitor wiring connector and to ground.<br>• Does Air Bag lamp light? | Yes ▶ | TURN ignition to OFF. REMOVE jumper wire. SERVICE ground circuit. REACTIVATE air bag system. TURN ignition switch to RUN.<br><br>VERIFY Air Bag warning lamp. |
| | No ▶ | GO to **A11**. |

**Fig. 21 Inoperative airbag lamp circuit (Part 4 of 5). Continental, Sable & Taurus**

## Fault Indication — Air Bag Lamp Does Not Light
## Probable Fault — Inoperative Air Bag Lamp Circuit

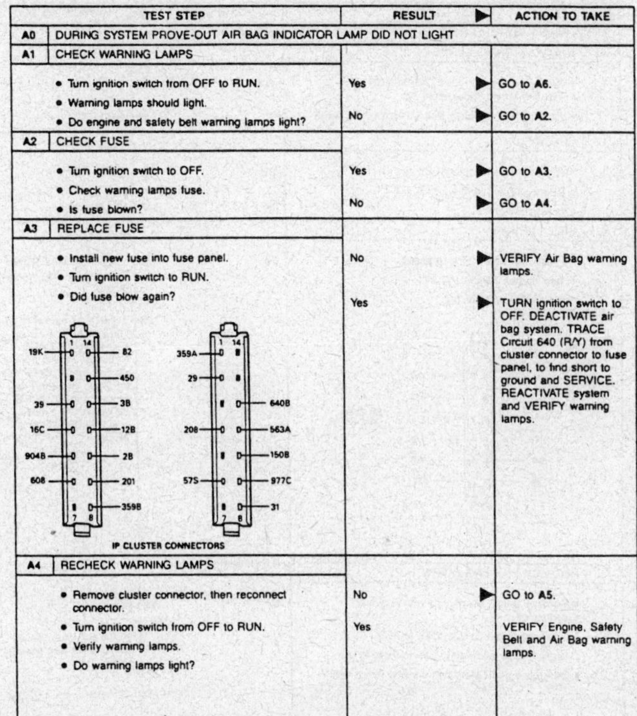


| TEST STEP | RESULT ▶ | ACTION TO TAKE |
|---|---|---|
| **A0** DURING SYSTEM PROVE-OUT AIR BAG INDICATOR LAMP DID NOT LIGHT | | |
| **A1** CHECK WARNING LAMPS | | |
| • Turn ignition switch from OFF to RUN.<br>• Warning lamps should light.<br>• Do engine and safety belt warning lamps light? | Yes ▶ | GO to **A6**. |
| | No ▶ | GO to **A2**. |
| **A2** CHECK FUSE | | |
| • Turn ignition switch to OFF.<br>• Check warning lamps fuse.<br>• Is fuse blown? | Yes ▶ | GO to **A3**. |
| | No ▶ | GO to **A4**. |
| **A3** REPLACE FUSE | | |
| • Install new fuse into fuse panel.<br>• Turn ignition switch to RUN.<br>• Did fuse blow again? | No ▶ | VERIFY Air Bag warning lamps. |
| | Yes ▶ | TURN ignition switch to OFF. DEACTIVATE air bag system. TRACE Circuit 640 (R/Y) from cluster connector to fuse panel, to find short to ground and SERVICE. REACTIVATE system and VERIFY warning lamps. |
| **A4** RECHECK WARNING LAMPS | | |
| • Remove cluster connector, then reconnect connector.<br>• Turn ignition switch from OFF to RUN.<br>• Verify warning lamps.<br>• Do warning lamps light? | No ▶ | GO to **A5**. |
| | Yes | VERIFY Engine, Safety Belt and Air Bag warning lamps. |

**Fig. 22 Inoperative airbag lamp circuit (Part 1 of 5). Crown Victoria & Grand Marquis**

## Fault Indication — Air Bag Lamp Does Not Light
## Probable Fault — Inoperative Air Bag Lamp Circuit

| TEST STEP | RESULT ▶ | ACTION TO TAKE |
|---|---|---|
| **A11** INSPECT AIR BAG WARNING LIGHT | | |
| • Turn ignition switch to OFF.<br>• Remove jumper wire.<br>• Disconnect Air Bag lamp.<br>• Visually inspect connector, wire and Air Bag lamp.<br>• Does circuit or connector have any defects and/or is Air Bag lamp burnt out? | Yes ▶ | REPLACE connector and/or lamp as required. ACTIVATE air bag system. TURN ignition switch to RUN. VERIFY Air Bag warning lamp. |
| | No ▶ | TRACE Circuit 608 (BK/Y) from indicator to monitor to find open and SERVICE. REACTIVATE air bag system. TURN ignition to RUN. VERIFY air bag warning lamp. |

**Fig. 21 Inoperative airbag lamp circuit (Part 5 of 5). Continental, Sable & Taurus**

## Fault Indication — Air Bag Lamp Does Not Light
## Probable Fault — Inoperative Air Bag Lamp Circuit

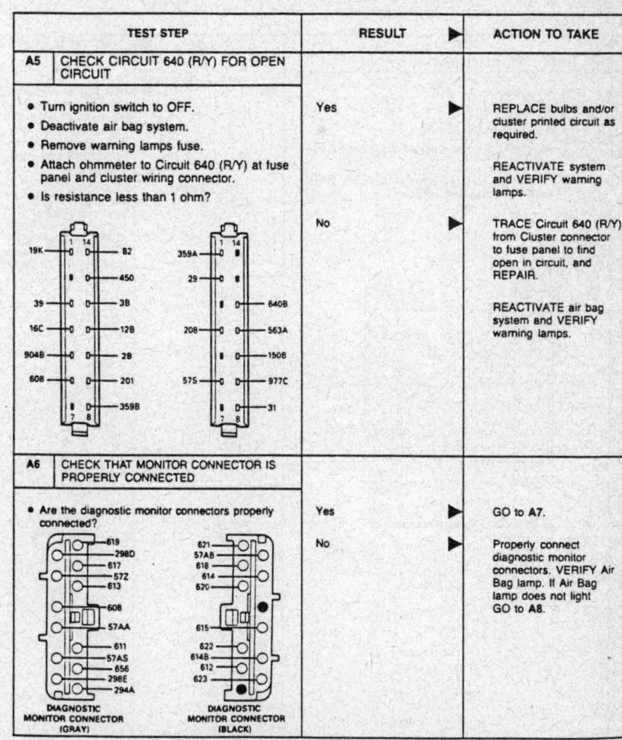


| TEST STEP | RESULT ▶ | ACTION TO TAKE |
|---|---|---|
| **A5** CHECK CIRCUIT 640 (R/Y) FOR OPEN CIRCUIT | | |
| • Turn ignition switch to OFF.<br>• Deactivate air bag system.<br>• Remove warning lamps fuse.<br>• Attach ohmmeter to Circuit 640 (R/Y) at fuse panel and cluster wiring connector.<br>• Is resistance less than 1 ohm? | Yes ▶ | REPLACE bulbs and/or cluster printed circuit as required.<br><br>REACTIVATE system and VERIFY warning lamps. |
| | No ▶ | TRACE Circuit 640 (R/Y) from Cluster connector to fuse panel to find open in circuit, and REPAIR.<br><br>REACTIVATE air bag system and VERIFY warning lamps. |
| **A6** CHECK THAT MONITOR CONNECTOR IS PROPERLY CONNECTED | | |
| • Are the diagnostic monitor connectors properly connected? | Yes ▶ | GO to A7. |
| | No ▶ | Properly connect diagnostic monitor connectors. VERIFY Air Bag lamp. If Air Bag lamp does not light GO to **A8**. |

**Fig. 22 Inoperative airbag lamp circuit (Part 2 of 5). Crown Victoria & Grand Marquis**

**Fault Indication — Air Bag Lamp Does Not Light**
**Probable Fault — Inoperative Air Bag Lamp Circuit**

| TEST STEP | RESULT ▶ | ACTION TO TAKE |
|---|---|---|
| **A7** CHECK LAMP WITH MONITOR CONNECTOR DISCONNECTED | | |
| • Turn ignition switch to OFF.<br>• Disconnect diagnostic monitor wiring from monitor assembly.<br>• Turn ignition switch to RUN.<br>• Is the air bag lamp continuously on? | No ▶<br>Yes ▶ | GO to **A8**.<br>GO to **A9**. |
| **A8** CHECK MONITOR CONNECTOR | | |
| • Turn ignition switch to OFF.<br>• Deactivate air bag system.<br>• Visually inspect the monitor connector to be sure Pin 5 (Circuit 57, BK) and Pin 4 (Circuit 608, BK/Y) are touching each other.<br>• Turn ignition switch to RUN.<br>• Does air bag lamp flash continuously? | Yes ▶<br>No ▶ | GO to **A9**.<br>GO to **A10**. |

**Fig. 22 Inoperative airbag lamp circuit (Part 3 of 5). Crown Victoria & Grand Marquis**

**Fault Indication — Air Bag Lamp Does Not Light**
**Probable Fault — Inoperative Air Bag Lamp Circuit**

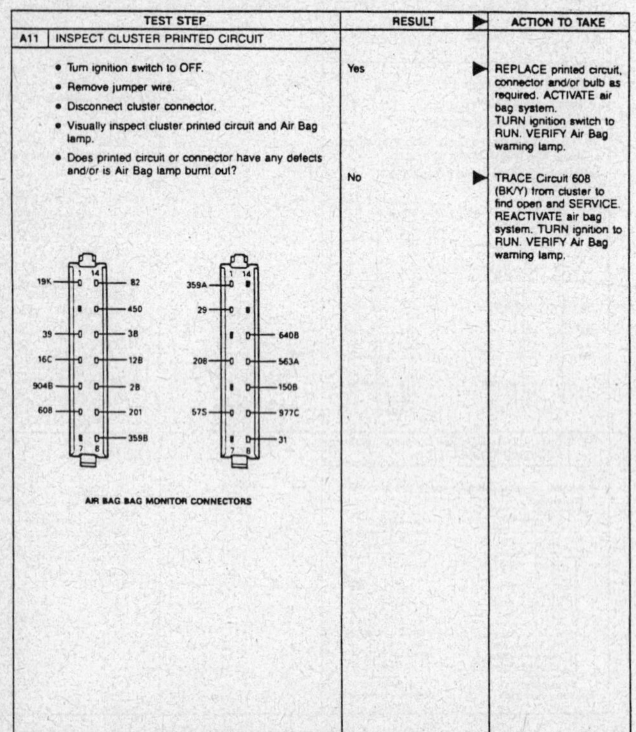

| TEST STEP | RESULT ▶ | ACTION TO TAKE |
|---|---|---|
| **A11** INSPECT CLUSTER PRINTED CIRCUIT | | |
| • Turn ignition switch to OFF.<br>• Remove jumper wire.<br>• Disconnect cluster connector.<br>• Visually inspect cluster printed circuit and Air Bag lamp.<br>• Does printed circuit or connector have any defects and/or is Air Bag lamp burnt out? | Yes ▶ | REPLACE printed circuit, connector and/or bulb as required. ACTIVATE air bag system. TURN ignition switch to RUN. VERIFY Air Bag warning lamp. |
| | No ▶ | TRACE Circuit 608 (BK/Y) from cluster to find open and SERVICE. REACTIVATE air bag system. TURN ignition to RUN. VERIFY Air Bag warning lamp. |



**Fig. 22 Inoperative airbag lamp circuit (Part 5 of 5). Crown Victoria & Grand Marquis**

**Fault Indication — Air Bag Lamp Does Not Light**
**Probable Fault — Inoperative Air Bag Lamp Circuit**

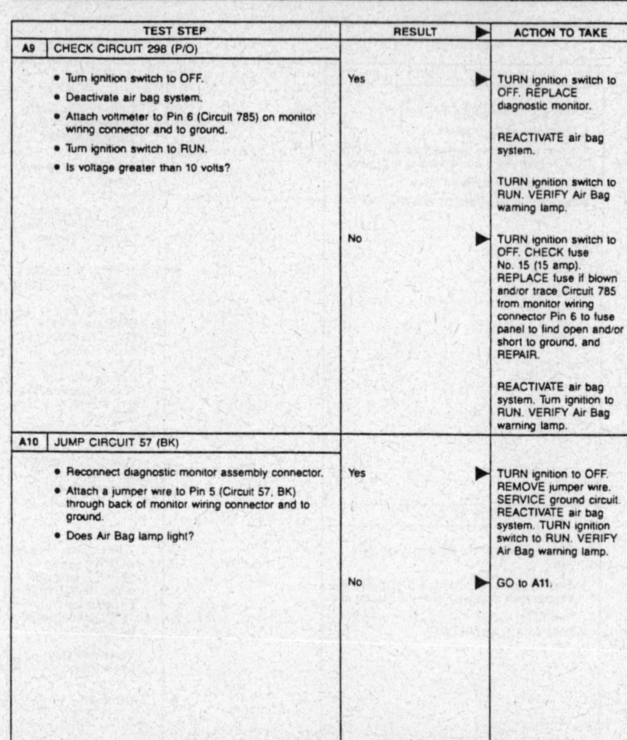

| TEST STEP | RESULT ▶ | ACTION TO TAKE |
|---|---|---|
| **A9** CHECK CIRCUIT 298 (P/O) | | |
| • Turn ignition switch to OFF.<br>• Deactivate air bag system.<br>• Attach voltmeter to Pin 6 (Circuit 785) on monitor wiring connector and to ground.<br>• Turn ignition switch to RUN.<br>• Is voltage greater than 10 volts? | Yes ▶ | TURN ignition switch to OFF. REPLACE diagnostic monitor.<br>REACTIVATE air bag system.<br>TURN ignition switch to RUN. VERIFY Air Bag warning lamp. |
| | No ▶ | TURN ignition switch to OFF. CHECK fuse No. 15 (15 amp). REPLACE fuse if blown and/or trace Circuit 785 from monitor wiring connector Pin 6 to fuse panel to find open and/or short to ground, and REPAIR.<br>REACTIVATE air bag system. Turn ignition to RUN. VERIFY Air Bag warning lamp. |
| **A10** JUMP CIRCUIT 57 (BK) | | |
| • Reconnect diagnostic monitor assembly connector.<br>• Attach a jumper wire to Pin 5 (Circuit 57, BK) through back of monitor wiring connector and to ground.<br>• Does Air Bag lamp light? | Yes ▶ | TURN ignition to OFF. REMOVE jumper wire. SERVICE ground circuit. REACTIVATE air bag system. TURN ignition switch to RUN. VERIFY Air Bag warning lamp. |
| | No ▶ | GO to A11. |

**Fig. 22 Inoperative airbag lamp circuit (Part 4 of 5). Crown Victoria & Grand Marquis**

**Fault Indication — Air Bag Lamp Does Not Light**
**Probable Fault — Inoperative Air Bag Lamp Circuit**

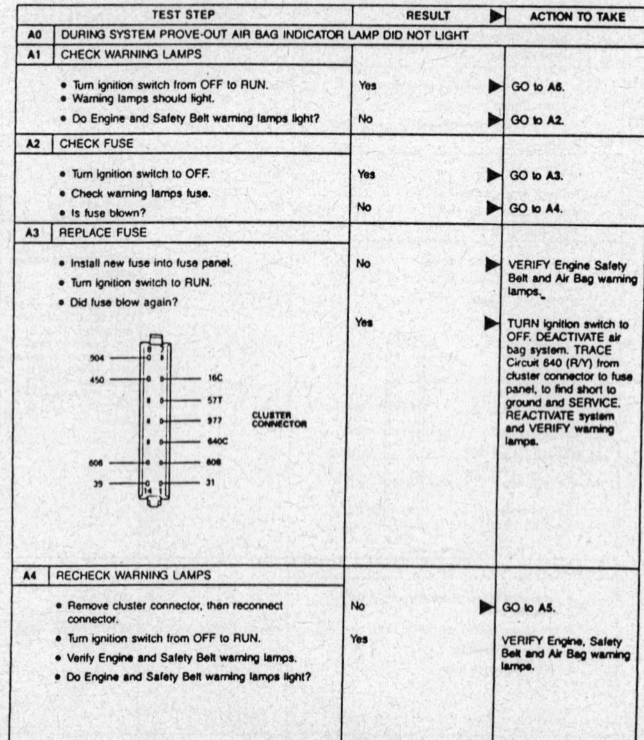

| TEST STEP | RESULT ▶ | ACTION TO TAKE |
|---|---|---|
| **A0** DURING SYSTEM PROVE-OUT AIR BAG INDICATOR LAMP DID NOT LIGHT | | |
| **A1** CHECK WARNING LAMPS | | |
| • Turn ignition switch from OFF to RUN.<br>• Warning lamps should light.<br>• Do Engine and Safety Belt warning lamps light? | Yes ▶<br>No ▶ | GO to A6.<br>GO to A2. |
| **A2** CHECK FUSE | | |
| • Turn ignition switch to OFF.<br>• Check warning lamps fuse.<br>• Is fuse blown? | Yes ▶<br>No ▶ | GO to A3.<br>GO to A4. |
| **A3** REPLACE FUSE | | |
| • Install new fuse into fuse panel.<br>• Turn ignition switch to RUN.<br>• Did fuse blow again? | No ▶ | VERIFY Engine Safety Belt and Air Bag warning lamps. |
| | Yes ▶ | TURN ignition switch to OFF. DEACTIVATE air bag system. TRACE Circuit 640 (R/Y) from cluster connector to fuse panel, to find short to ground and SERVICE. REACTIVATE system and VERIFY warning lamps. |
| **A4** RECHECK WARNING LAMPS | | |
| • Remove cluster connector, then reconnect connector.<br>• Turn ignition switch from OFF to RUN.<br>• Verify Engine and Safety Belt warning lamps.<br>• Do Engine and Safety Belt warning lamps light? | No ▶<br>Yes | GO to A5.<br>VERIFY Engine, Safety Belt and Air Bag warning lamps. |



**Fig. 23 Inoperative airbag lamp circuit (Part 1 of 5). Mark VII**

**Fault Indication — Air Bag Lamp Does Not Light**
**Probable Fault — Inoperative Air Bag Lamp Circuit**

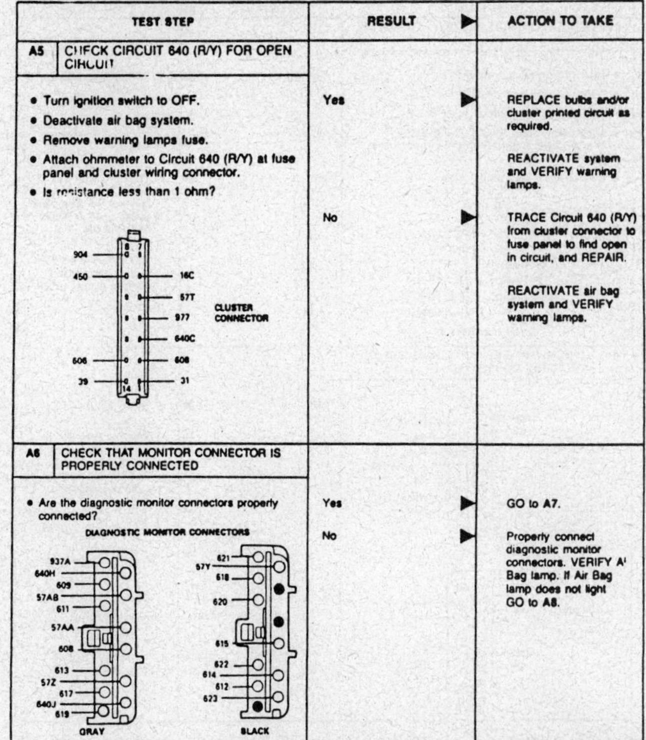

| TEST STEP | RESULT ▶ | ACTION TO TAKE |
|---|---|---|
| **A5** CHECK CIRCUIT 640 (R/Y) FOR OPEN CIRCUIT | | |
| • Turn ignition switch to OFF.<br>• Deactivate air bag system.<br>• Remove warning lamps fuse.<br>• Attach ohmmeter to Circuit 640 (R/Y) at fuse panel and cluster wiring connector.<br>• Is resistance less than 1 ohm? | Yes ▶ | REPLACE bulbs and/or cluster printed circuit as required.<br>REACTIVATE system and VERIFY warning lamps. |
| | No ▶ | TRACE Circuit 640 (R/Y) from cluster connector to fuse panel to find open in circuit, and REPAIR.<br>REACTIVATE air bag system and VERIFY warning lamps. |
| **A6** CHECK THAT MONITOR CONNECTOR IS PROPERLY CONNECTED | | |
| • Are the diagnostic monitor connectors properly connected? | Yes ▶ | GO to A7. |
| | No ▶ | Properly connect diagnostic monitor connectors. VERIFY Air Bag lamp. If Air Bag lamp does not light GO to A8. |



**Fig. 23 Inoperative airbag lamp circuit (Part 2 of 5). Mark VII**

**Fault Indication — Air Bag Lamp Does Not Light**
**Probable Fault — Inoperative Air Bag Lamp Circuit**

| TEST STEP | RESULT ▶ | ACTION TO TAKE |
|---|---|---|
| **A7** CHECK LAMP WITH MONITOR CONNECTOR DISCONNECTED | | |
| • Turn ignition switch to OFF.<br>• Disconnect diagnostic monitor wiring from monitor assembly.<br>• Turn ignition switch to RUN.<br>• Is the air bag lamp continuously on? | No ▶<br>Yes ▶ | GO to A8.<br>GO to A9. |
| **A8** CHECK MONITOR CONNECTOR | | |
| • Turn ignition switch to OFF.<br>• Deactivate air bag system.<br>• Visually inspect the monitor connector to be sure Pin 5 (Circuit 57, BK) and Pin 4 (Circuit 608, BK/Y) are touching each other.<br>• Turn ignition switch to RUN.<br>• Does air bag lamp flash continuously? | Yes ▶<br>No ▶ | GO to A9.<br>GO to A10. |

**Fig. 23 Inoperative airbag lamp circuit (Part 3 of 5). Mark VII**

**Fault Indication — Air Bag Lamp Does Not Light**
**Probable Fault — Inoperative Air Bag Lamp Circuit**

| TEST STEP | RESULT ▶ | ACTION TO TAKE |
|---|---|---|
| **A9** CHECK CIRCUIT 640 (R/Y) | | |
| • Turn ignition switch to OFF.<br>• Deactivate air bag system.<br>• Attach voltmeter to Pin 6 (Circuit 640, (R/Y) on monitor wiring connector and to ground.<br>• Turn ignition switch to RUN.<br>• Is voltage greater than 10 volts? | Yes ▶ | TURN ignition switch to OFF. REPLACE diagnostic monitor.<br>REACTIVATE air bag system.<br>TURN ignition switch to RUN. VERIFY Air Bag warning lamp. |
| | No ▶ | TURN ignition switch to OFF. CHECK fuse No. 18 (10 amp). REPLACE fuse if blown and/or trace Circuit 640 (R/Y) from monitor wiring connector Pin 6 to fuse panel to find open and/or short to ground, and REPAIR.<br>REACTIVATE air bag system. Turn ignition to RUN. VERIFY Air Bag warning lamp. |
| **A10** JUMP CIRCUIT 57 (BK) | | |
| • Reconnect diagnostic monitor assembly connector.<br>• Attach a jumper wire to Pin 5 (Circuit 57, BK) through back of monitor wiring connector and to ground.<br>• Does Air Bag lamp light? | Yes ▶ | TURN ignition to OFF. REMOVE jumper wire. SERVICE ground circuit. REACTIVATE air bag system. TURN ignition switch to RUN.<br>VERIFY Air Bag warning lamp. |
| | No ▶ | GO to A11. |

**Fig. 23 Inoperative airbag lamp circuit (Part 4 of 5). Mark VII**

**Fault Indication — Air Bag Lamp Does Not Light**
**Probable Fault — Inoperative Air Bag Lamp Circuit**

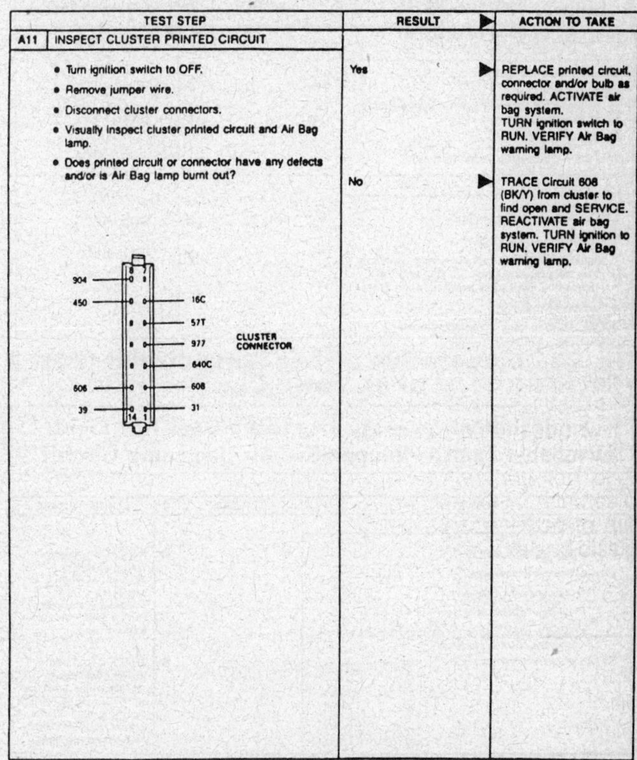

| TEST STEP | RESULT ▶ | ACTION TO TAKE |
|---|---|---|
| **A11** INSPECT CLUSTER PRINTED CIRCUIT | | |
| • Turn ignition switch to OFF.<br>• Remove jumper wire.<br>• Disconnect cluster connectors.<br>• Visually inspect cluster printed circuit and Air Bag lamp.<br>• Does printed circuit or connector have any defects and/or is Air Bag lamp burnt out? | Yes ▶ | REPLACE printed circuit, connector and/or bulb as required. ACTIVATE air bag system. TURN ignition switch to RUN. VERIFY Air Bag warning lamp. |
| | No ▶ | TRACE Circuit 608 (BK/Y) from cluster to find open and SERVICE. REACTIVATE air bag system. TURN ignition to RUN. VERIFY Air Bag warning lamp. |



**Fig. 23 Inoperative airbag lamp circuit (Part 5 of 5). Mark VII**

## Fault Indication — Air Bag Lamp Does Not Light
## Probable Fault — Inoperative Air Bag Lamp Circuit

| TEST STEP | RESULT ▶ | ACTION TO TAKE |
|---|---|---|
| **A0** DURING SYSTEM PROVE-OUT AIR BAG INDICATOR LAMP DID NOT LIGHT | | |
| **A1** CHECK WARNING LAMPS | | |
| • Turn ignition switch from OFF to RUN.<br>• Warning lamps should light.<br>• Do Engine and Safety Belt warning lamps light? | Yes ▶<br>No ▶ | GO to **A6**.<br>GO to **A2**. |
| **A2** CHECK FUSE | | |
| • Turn ignition switch to OFF.<br>• Check warning lamps fuse.<br>• Is fuse blown? | Yes ▶<br>No ▶ | GO to **A3**.<br>GO to **A4**. |
| **A3** REPLACE FUSE | | |
| • Install new fuse into fuse panel.<br>• Turn ignition switch to RUN.<br>• Did fuse blow again?<br>CLUSTER CONNECTOR (12, 6, 7, 1; 608, 450, 904, 201, 31, 977A; 3A, 2A, 12C, 19F, 295D, 875B) | No ▶<br>Yes ▶ | VERIFY Engine Safety Belt and Air Bag warning lamps.<br>TURN ignition switch to OFF. DEACTIVATE air bag system. TRACE Circuit 295 (LB/P) from IP shelf moulding connector to fuse panel, to find short to ground and SERVICE. REACTIVATE system and VERIFY warning lamps. |
| **A4** RECHECK WARNING LAMPS | | |
| • Remove cluster connector, then reconnect connector.<br>• Turn ignition switch from OFF to RUN.<br>• Verify Engine and Safety Belt warning lamps.<br>• Do Engine and Safety Belt warning lamps light? | No ▶<br>Yes ▶ | GO to **A5**.<br>VERIFY Engine, Safety Belt and Air Bag warning lamps. |

**Fig. 24 Inoperative airbag lamp circuit (Part 1 of 5). Town Car**

## Fault Indication — Air Bag Lamp Does Not Light
## Probable Fault — Inoperative Air Bag Lamp Circuit

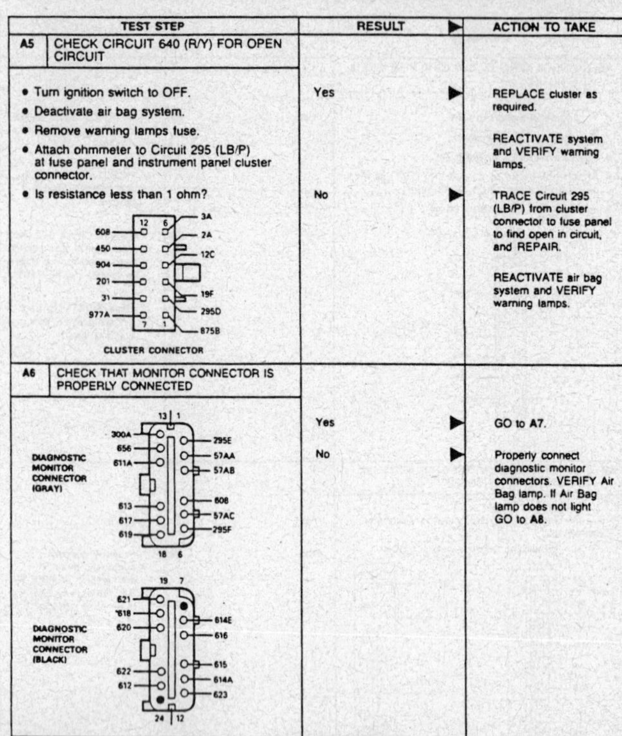

| TEST STEP | RESULT ▶ | ACTION TO TAKE |
|---|---|---|
| **A5** CHECK CIRCUIT 640 (R/Y) FOR OPEN CIRCUIT | | |
| • Turn ignition switch to OFF.<br>• Deactivate air bag system.<br>• Remove warning lamps fuse.<br>• Attach ohmmeter to Circuit 295 (LB/P) at fuse panel and instrument panel cluster connector.<br>• Is resistance less than 1 ohm?<br>CLUSTER CONNECTOR (12, 6, 7, 1; 608, 450, 904, 201, 31, 977A; 3A, 2A, 12C, 19F, 295D, 875B) | Yes ▶<br>No ▶ | REPLACE cluster as required.<br>REACTIVATE system and VERIFY warning lamps.<br>TRACE Circuit 295 (LB/P) from cluster connector to fuse panel to find open in circuit, and REPAIR.<br>REACTIVATE air bag system and VERIFY warning lamps. |
| **A6** CHECK THAT MONITOR CONNECTOR IS PROPERLY CONNECTED | | |
| DIAGNOSTIC MONITOR CONNECTOR (GRAY) (13, 1, 18, 6; 300A, 656, 611A, 613, 617, 619; 295E, 57AA, 57AB, 608, 57AC, 295F)<br>DIAGNOSTIC MONITOR CONNECTOR (BLACK) (19, 7, 24, 12; 621, 618, 620, 622, 612; 614E, 616, 615, 614A, 623) | Yes ▶<br>No ▶ | GO to **A7**.<br>Properly connect diagnostic monitor connectors. VERIFY Air Bag lamp. If Air Bag lamp does not light GO to **A8**. |

**Fig. 24 Inoperative airbag lamp circuit (Part 2 of 5). Town Car**

## Fault Indication — Air Bag Lamp Does Not Light
## Probable Fault — Inoperative Air Bag Lamp Circuit

| TEST STEP | RESULT ▶ | ACTION TO TAKE |
|---|---|---|
| **A7** CHECK LAMP WITH MONITOR CONNECTOR DISCONNECTED | | |
| • Turn ignition switch to OFF.<br>• Disconnect diagnostic monitor wiring from monitor assembly.<br>• Turn ignition to RUN.<br>• Is the Air Bag lamp lit continuously? | No ▶<br>Yes ▶ | GO to **A8**.<br>GO to **A9**. |
| **A8** CHECK MONITOR CONNECTOR | | |
| • Turn ignition switch to OFF.<br>• Deactivate Air Bag system.<br>• Visually inspect the monitor wiring connector to be sure Pin 5 (Circuit 57, BK) and Pin 4 (Circuit 608, BK/Y) are touching each other.<br>• Turn ignition to RUN.<br>• Does Air Bag lamp light continuously? | Yes ▶<br>No ▶ | GO to **A9**.<br>GO to **A10**. |

**Fig. 24 Inoperative airbag lamp circuit (Part 3 of 5). Town Car**

## Fault Indication — Air Bag Lamp Does Not Light
## Probable Fault — Inoperative Air Bag Lamp Circuit

| TEST STEP | RESULT ▶ | ACTION TO TAKE |
|---|---|---|
| **A9** CHECK CIRCUIT 295 (LB/PK) | | |
| • Turn ignition switch to OFF.<br>• Deactivate Air Bag system.<br>• Attach voltmeter to Pin 6 (Circuit 295, LB/PK) on monitor wiring connector and to ground.<br>• Turn ignition switch to RUN.<br>• Is voltage greater than 10 volts? | Yes ▶<br>No ▶ | TURN ignition switch to OFF. REPLACE diagnostic monitor.<br>REACTIVATE air bag system.<br>TURN ignition switch to RUN. VERIFY Air Bag warning lamp.<br>TURN ignition switch to OFF. CHECK fuse No. 4 (10 amp). REPLACE fuse if blown and/or trace Circuit 295 (LB/PK) from monitor wiring connector Pin 6 to fuse panel to find open and/or short to ground, and SERVICE.<br>REACTIVATE air bag system. Turn ignition to RUN. VERIFY Air Bag warning lamp. |
| **A10** JUMP CIRCUIT 57 (BK) | | |
| • Reconnect diagnostic monitor assembly connector.<br>• Attach a jumper wire to Pin 5 (Circuit 57, BK) through back of monitor wiring connector and to ground.<br>• Does Air Bag lamp light? | Yes ▶<br>No ▶ | TURN ignition to OFF. REMOVE jumper wire. SERVICE ground circuit. REACTIVATE air bag system. TURN ignition switch to RUN.<br>VERIFY Air Bag warning lamp.<br>GO to **A11**. |

**Fig. 24 Inoperative airbag lamp circuit (Part 4 of 5). Town Car**

## Fault Indication — Air Bag Lamp Does Not Light
## Probable Fault — Inoperative Air Bag Lamp Circuit

| TEST STEP | RESULT ▶ | ACTION TO TAKE |
|---|---|---|
| **A11** INSPECT CLUSTER PRINTED CIRCUIT | | |
| • Turn ignition switch to OFF.<br>• Remove jumper wire.<br>• Disconnect Air Bag lamp.<br>• Visually inspect connector, wire and Air Bag lamp.<br>• Does circuit or connector have any defects and/or is indicator operating properly? | Yes ▶<br>No ▶ | REPLACE connector and/or cluster as required. ACTIVATE air bag system. TURN ignition switch to RUN. VERIFY Air Bag warning lamp.<br>TRACE Circuit 608 (BK/Y) from lamp to monitor to find open and SERVICE. REACTIVATE air bag system. TURN ignition to RUN. VERIFY Air Bag warning lamp. |

**Fig. 24 Inoperative airbag lamp circuit (Part 5 of 5). Town Car**

**Fault Indication — Air Bag Lamp Does Not Light**
**Probable Fault — Inoperative Air Bag Lamp Circuit**

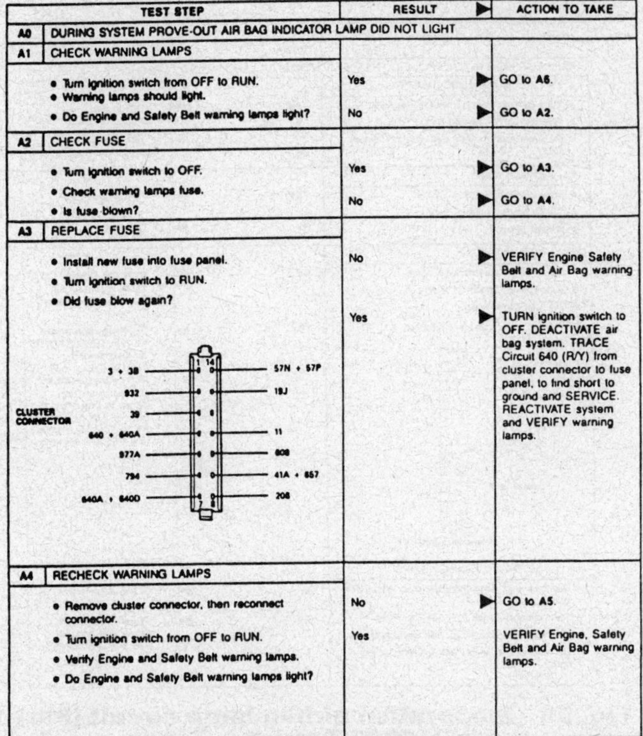

| TEST STEP | RESULT | ACTION TO TAKE |
|---|---|---|
| **A0** DURING SYSTEM PROVE-OUT AIR BAG INDICATOR LAMP DID NOT LIGHT | | |
| **A1** CHECK WARNING LAMPS | | |
| • Turn ignition switch from OFF to RUN. • Warning lamps should light. • Do Engine and Safety Belt warning lamps light? | Yes ▶ | GO to A6. |
| | No ▶ | GO to A2. |
| **A2** CHECK FUSE | | |
| • Turn ignition switch to OFF. • Check warning lamps fuse. • Is fuse blown? | Yes ▶ | GO to A3. |
| | No ▶ | GO to A4. |
| **A3** REPLACE FUSE | | |
| • Install new fuse into fuse panel. • Turn ignition switch to RUN. • Did fuse blow again? | No ▶ | VERIFY Engine Safety Belt and Air Bag warning lamps. |
| | Yes ▶ | TURN ignition switch to OFF. DEACTIVATE air bag system. TRACE Circuit 640 (R/Y) from cluster connector to fuse panel, to find short to ground and SERVICE. REACTIVATE system and VERIFY warning lamps. |
| **A4** RECHECK WARNING LAMPS | | |
| • Remove cluster connector, then reconnect connector. • Turn ignition switch from OFF to RUN. • Verify Engine and Safety Belt warning lamps. • Do Engine and Safety Belt warning lamps light? | No ▶ | GO to A5. |
| | Yes | VERIFY Engine, Safety Belt and Air Bag warning lamps. |

**Fig. 25 Inoperative airbag lamp circuit (Part 1 of 5). Mustang**

**Fault Indication — Air Bag Lamp Does Not Light**
**Probable Fault — Inoperative Air Bag Lamp Circuit**

| TEST STEP | RESULT | ACTION TO TAKE |
|---|---|---|
| **A5** CHECK CIRCUIT 640 (R/Y) FOR OPEN CIRCUIT | | |
| • Turn ignition switch to OFF. • Deactivate air bag system. • Remove warning lamps fuse. • Attach ohmmeter to Circuit 640 (R/Y) at fuse panel and cluster wiring connector. • Is resistance less than 1 ohm? | Yes ▶ | REPLACE bulbs and/or cluster printed circuit as required. REACTIVATE system and VERIFY warning lamps. |
| | No ▶ | TRACE Circuit 640 (R/Y) from light bar connector to fuse panel to find open in circuit, and REPAIR. REACTIVATE air bag system and VERIFY warning lamps. |
| **A6** CHECK THAT MONITOR CONNECTOR IS PROPERLY CONNECTED | | |
| • Are the diagnostic monitor connectors properly connected? | Yes ▶ | GO to A7. |
| | No ▶ | Properly connect diagnostic monitor connectors. VERIFY Air Bag lamp. If Air Bag lamp does not light GO to A8. |

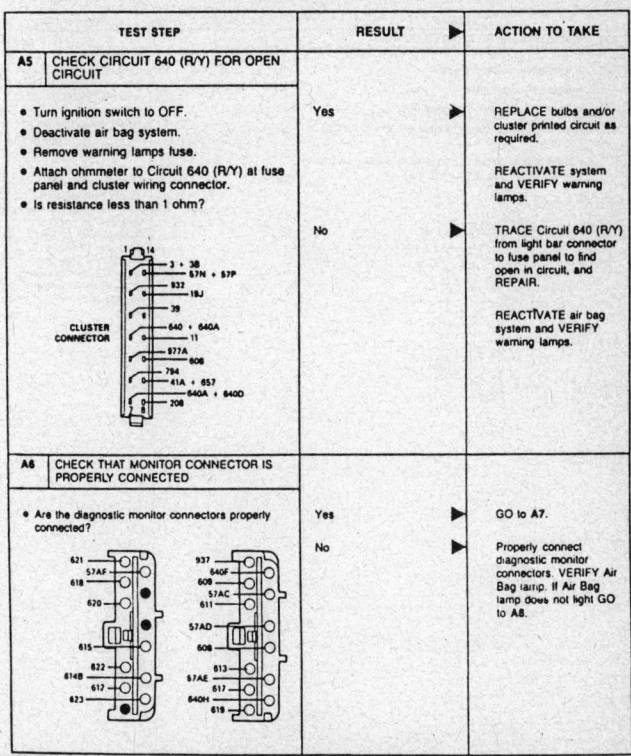

**Fig. 25 Inoperative airbag lamp circuit (Part 2 of 5). Mustang**

**Fault Indication — Air Bag Lamp Does Not Light**
**Probable Fault — Inoperative Air Bag Lamp Circuit**

| TEST STEP | RESULT | ACTION TO TAKE |
|---|---|---|
| **A7** CHECK LAMP WITH MONITOR CONNECTOR DISCONNECTED | | |
| • Turn ignition switch to OFF. • Disconnect diagnostic monitor wiring from monitor assembly. • Turn ignition switch to RUN. • Is the air bag lamp continuously on? | No ▶ | GO to A8. |
| | Yes ▶ | GO to A9. |
| **A8** CHECK MONITOR CONNECTOR | | |
| • Turn ignition switch to OFF. • Deactivate air bag system. • Visually inspect the monitor connector to be sure Pin 5 (Circuit 57, BK) and Pin 4 (Circuit 608, BK/Y) are touching each other. • Turn ignition switch to RUN. • Does air bag lamp flash continuously? | Yes ▶ | GO to A9. |
| | No ▶ | GO to A10. |

**Fig. 25 Inoperative airbag lamp circuit (Part 3 of 5). Mustang**

**Fault Indication — Air Bag Lamp Does Not Light**
**Probable Fault — Inoperative Air Bag Lamp Circuit**

| TEST STEP | RESULT | ACTION TO TAKE |
|---|---|---|
| **A9** CHECK CIRCUIT 640 (R/Y) | | |
| • Turn ignition switch to OFF. • Deactivate air bag system. • Attach voltmeter to Pin 6 (Circuit 640, (R/Y)) on monitor wiring connector and to ground. • Turn ignition switch to RUN. • Is voltage greater than 10 volts? | Yes ▶ | TURN ignition switch to OFF. REPLACE diagnostic monitor. REACTIVATE air bag system. TURN ignition switch to RUN. VERIFY Air Bag warning lamp. |
| | No ▶ | TURN ignition switch to OFF. CHECK fuse No. 18 (15 amp). REPLACE fuse if blown and/or trace Circuit 640 (R/Y) from monitor wiring connector Pin 6 to fuse panel to find open and/or short to ground, and REPAIR. REACTIVATE air bag system. Turn ignition to RUN. VERIFY Air Bag warning lamp. |
| **A10** JUMP CIRCUIT 57 (BK) | | |
| • Reconnect diagnostic monitor assembly connector. • Attach a jumper wire to Pin 5 (Circuit 57, BK) through back of monitor wiring connector and to ground. • Does Air Bag lamp light? | Yes ▶ | TURN ignition to OFF. REMOVE jumper wire. SERVICE ground circuit. REACTIVATE air bag system. TURN ignition key to RUN. VERIFY Air Bag warning lamp. |
| | No ▶ | GO to A11. |

**Fig. 25 Inoperative airbag lamp circuit (Part 4 of 5). Mustang**

**Fault Indication — Air Bag Lamp Does Not Light**
**Probable Fault — Inoperative Air Bag Lamp Circuit**

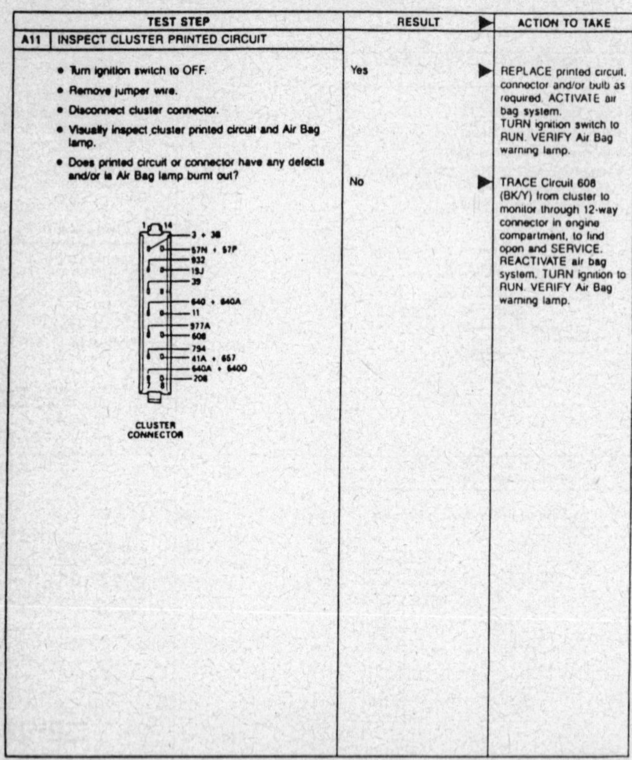

| TEST STEP | RESULT ▶ | ACTION TO TAKE |
|---|---|---|
| **A11** INSPECT CLUSTER PRINTED CIRCUIT | | |
| • Turn ignition switch to OFF.<br>• Remove jumper wire.<br>• Disconnect cluster connector.<br>• Visually inspect cluster printed circuit and Air Bag lamp.<br>• Does printed circuit or connector have any defects and/or is Air Bag lamp burnt out? | Yes ▶ | REPLACE printed circuit, connector and/or bulb as required. ACTIVATE air bag system. TURN ignition switch to RUN. VERIFY Air Bag warning lamp. |
| | No ▶ | TRACE Circuit 608 (BK/Y) from cluster to monitor through 12-way connector in engine compartment, to find open and SERVICE. REACTIVATE air bag system. TURN ignition to RUN. VERIFY Air Bag warning lamp. |



**Fig. 25 Inoperative airbag lamp circuit (Part 5 of 5). Mustang**

**Fault Indication — Air Bag Lamp Does Not Light**
**Probable Fault — Inoperative Air Bag Lamp Circuit**

| TEST STEP | RESULT ▶ | ACTION TO TAKE |
|---|---|---|
| **A0** DURING SYSTEM PROVE-OUT AIR BAG INDICATOR LAMP DID NOT LIGHT | | |
| **A1** CHECK WARNING LAMPS | | |
| • Turn ignition switch from OFF to RUN.<br>• Warning lamps should light.<br>• Do engine and safety belt warning lamps light? | Yes ▶ | GO to **A6**. |
| | No ▶ | GO to **A2**. |
| **A2** CHECK FUSE | | |
| • Turn ignition switch to OFF.<br>• Check warning lamps fuse.<br>• Is fuse blown? | Yes ▶ | GO to **A3**. |
| | No ▶ | GO to **A4**. |
| **A3** REPLACE FUSE | | |
| • Install new fuse into fuse panel.<br>• Turn ignition switch to RUN.<br>• Did fuse blow again?<br><br>LIGHT BAR CONNECTOR<br>608 (BK, Y)<br>640 (R, Y)<br>BEHIND I/P CLUSTER | No ▶ | VERIFY engine, safety belt and Air Bag warning lamps. |
| | Yes ▶ | TURN ignition switch to OFF. DEACTIVATE Air Bag system. TRACE Circuit 640 (R/Y) from Light Bar connector to fuse panel, to find short to ground and SERVICE. REACTIVATE system and VERIFY warning lamps. |
| **A4** RECHECK WARNING LAMPS | | |
| • Remove light bar connector, then reconnect connector.<br>• Turn ignition switch from OFF to RUN.<br>• Verify engine and safety belt warning lamps.<br>• Do engine and safety belt warning lamps light? | No ▶ | GO to **A5**. |
| | Yes ▶ | VERIFY engine, safety belt and Air Bag warning lamps. |

**Fig. 26 Inoperative airbag lamp circuit (Part 1 of 5). 1989 Tempo & Topaz**

**Fault Indication — Air Bag Lamp Does Not Light**
**Probable Fault — Inoperative Air Bag Lamp Circuit**

| TEST STEP | RESULT ▶ | ACTION TO TAKE |
|---|---|---|
| **A5** CHECK CIRCUIT 640 (R/Y) FOR OPEN CIRCUIT | | |
| • Turn ignition switch to OFF.<br>• Deactivate Air Bag system.<br>• Remove warning lamps fuse.<br>• Attach ohmmeter to Circuit 640 (R/Y) at fuse panel and light bar wiring connector.<br>• Is resistance less than 1 ohm?<br><br>LIGHT BAR CONNECTOR<br>608 (BK, Y)<br>640 (R, Y) | Yes ▶ | REPLACE bulbs and/or cluster printed circuit as required.<br><br>REACTIVATE system and VERIFY warning lamps. |
| | No ▶ | TRACE Circuit 640 (R/Y) from Light Bar connector to fuse panel to find open in circuit, and REPAIR.<br><br>REACTIVATE Air Bag system and VERIFY warning lamps. |

**Fig. 26 Inoperative airbag lamp circuit (Part 2 of 5). 1989 Tempo & Topaz**

**Fault Indication — Air Bag Lamp Does Not Light**
**Probable Fault — Inoperative Air Bag Lamp Circuit**

| TEST STEP | RESULT ▶ | ACTION TO TAKE |
|---|---|---|
| **A6** CHECK THAT MONITOR AND FUSE PANEL CONNECTOR ARE PROPERLY CONNECTED | | |
| • Are the diagnostic monitor connector and 8-way connector (on fuse panel) properly connected? | Yes ▶ | GO to **A7**. |
| | No ▶ | Properly connect diagnostic monitor and/or 8-way connectors. VERIFY Air Bag lamp. If Air Bag lamp does not light GO to **A8**. |

| TEST STEP | RESULT ▶ | ACTION TO TAKE |
|---|---|---|
| **A7** CHECK LAMP WITH MONITOR CONNECTOR DISCONNECTED | | |
| • Turn ignition switch to OFF<br>• Disconnect diagnostic monitor wiring from monitor assembly<br>• Turn ignition to RUN.<br>• Is the Air Bag lamp continuously flashing? | No ▶ | GO to **A8**. |
| | Yes ▶ | GO to **A9**. |
| **A8** CHECK MONITOR CONNECTOR | | |
| • Turn ignition switch to OFF<br>• Deactivate Air Bag system<br>• Visually inspect the monitor connector to be sure Pin 5 (Circuit 57, BK) and Pin 4 (Circuit 608, BK/Y) are touching each other.<br>• Turn ignition to RUN<br>• Does Air Bag lamp flash continuously? | Yes ▶ | GO to **A9** |
| | No ▶ | GO to **A10** |

**Fig. 26 Inoperative airbag lamp circuit (Part 3 of 5). 1989 Tempo & Topaz**

**Fault Indication — Air Bag Lamp Does Not Light**
**Probable Fault — Inoperative Air Bag Lamp Circuit**

| TEST STEP | RESULT ▶ | ACTION TO TAKE |
|---|---|---|
| **A9** CHECK CIRCUIT 296 (W/P) | | |
| • Turn ignition switch to OFF.<br>• Deactivate Air Bag system.<br>• Attach voltmeter to Pin 5 (Circuit 296, W/P) on monitor wiring connector and to ground.<br>• Turn ignition to RUN.<br>• Is voltage greater than 10 volts? | Yes ▶ | TURN ignition switch to OFF. REPLACE diagnostic monitor.<br><br>REACTIVATE Air Bag system.<br><br>TURN ignition switch to RUN. VERIFY Air Bag warning lamp. |
| | No ▶ | TURN ignition switch to OFF. CHECK fuse No. 6 (20 amp). REPLACE fuse if blown and/or trace Circuit 296 (W/P) from monitor wiring connector Pin 5 to fuse panel to find open and/or short to ground, and REPAIR.<br><br>REACTIVATE Air Bag system. Turn ignition to RUN. VERIFY Air Bag warning lamp. |
| **A10** JUMP CIRCUIT 57 (BK) | | |
| • Reconnect diagnostic monitor assembly connector.<br>• Attach a jumper wire to Pin 5 (Circuit 57, BK) through back of monitor wiring connector and to ground.<br>• Does Air Bag lamp light? | Yes ▶ | TURN ignition to OFF. REMOVE Jumper wire. SERVICE ground circuit. REACTIVATE Air Bag system. TURN ignition key to RUN.<br>VERIFY Air Bag warning lamp. |
| | No ▶ | GO to **A11**. |

**Fig. 26 Inoperative airbag lamp circuit (Part 4 of 5). 1989 Tempo & Topaz**

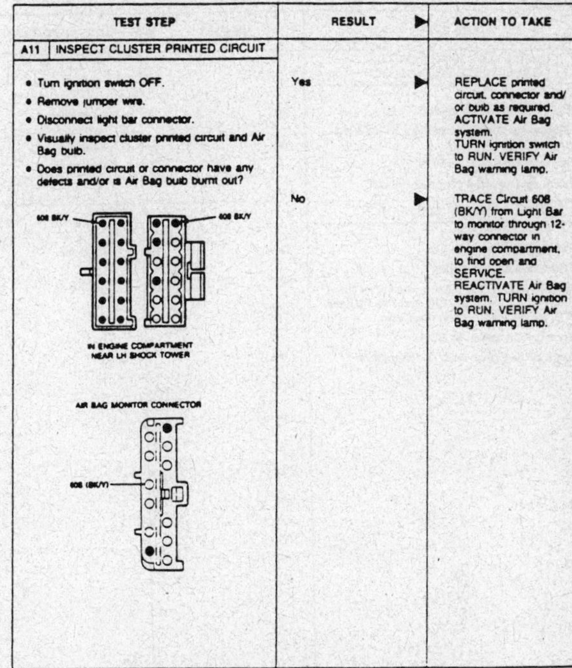

**Fault Indication — Air Bag Lamp Does Not Light**
**Probable Fault — Inoperative Air Bag Lamp Circuit**

| TEST STEP | RESULT ▶ | ACTION TO TAKE |
|---|---|---|
| **A11** INSPECT CLUSTER PRINTED CIRCUIT | | |
| • Turn ignition switch OFF.<br>• Remove jumper wire.<br>• Disconnect light bar connector.<br>• Visually inspect cluster printed circuit and Air Bag bulb.<br>• Does printed circuit or connector have any defects and/or is Air Bag bulb burnt out?<br><br>608 BK/Y — 608 BK/Y<br>IN ENGINE COMPARTMENT NEAR LH SHOCK TOWER<br><br>AIR BAG MONITOR CONNECTOR<br>608 (BK/Y) | Yes ▶ | REPLACE printed circuit, connector and/or bulb as required. ACTIVATE Air Bag system.<br>TURN ignition switch to RUN. VERIFY Air Bag warning lamp. |
| | No ▶ | TRACE Circuit 608 (BK/Y) from Light Bar to monitor through 12-way connector in engine compartment, to find open and SERVICE. REACTIVATE Air Bag system. TURN ignition to RUN. VERIFY Air Bag warning lamp. |

**Fig. 26 Inoperative airbag lamp circuit (Part 5 of 5). 1989 Tempo & Topaz**

**Fault Indication — Air Bag Lamp Does Not Light**
**Probable Fault — Inoperative Air Bag Lamp Circuit**

| TEST STEP | RESULT ▶ | ACTION TO TAKE |
|---|---|---|
| **A0** DURING SYSTEM PROVE-OUT AIR BAG INDICATOR LAMP DID NOT LIGHT | | |
| **A1** CHECK WARNING LAMPS | | |
| • Turn ignition switch from OFF to RUN.<br>• Warning lamps should light.<br>• Do engine and safety belt warning lamps light? | Yes ▶<br>No ▶ | GO to **A6**.<br>GO to **A2**. |
| **A2** CHECK FUSE | | |
| • Turn ignition switch to OFF.<br>• Check warning lamps fuse.<br>• Is fuse blown? | Yes ▶<br>No ▶ | GO to **A3**.<br>GO to **A4**. |
| **A3** REPLACE FUSE | | |
| • Install new fuse into fuse panel.<br>• Turn ignition switch to RUN.<br>• Did fuse blow again? | No ▶ | VERIFY engine, safety belt and Air Bag warning lamps. |
| LIGHT BAR CONNECTOR<br>608 (BK, Y)<br>640 (R, Y)<br>BEHIND I/P CLUSTER | Yes ▶ | TURN ignition switch to OFF. DEACTIVATE Air Bag system. TRACE Circuit 640 (R/Y) from Light Bar connector to fuse panel, to find short to ground and SERVICE. REACTIVATE system and VERIFY warning lamps. |
| **A4** RECHECK WARNING LAMPS | | |
| • Remove light bar connector, then reconnect connector.<br>• Turn ignition switch from OFF to RUN.<br>• Verify engine and safety belt warning lamps.<br>• Do engine and safety belt warning lamps light? | No ▶<br>Yes ▶ | GO to **A5**.<br>VERIFY engine, safety belt and Air Bag warning lamps. |

**Fig. 27 Inoperative airbag lamp circuit (Part 1 of 5). 1990–91 Tempo & Topaz**

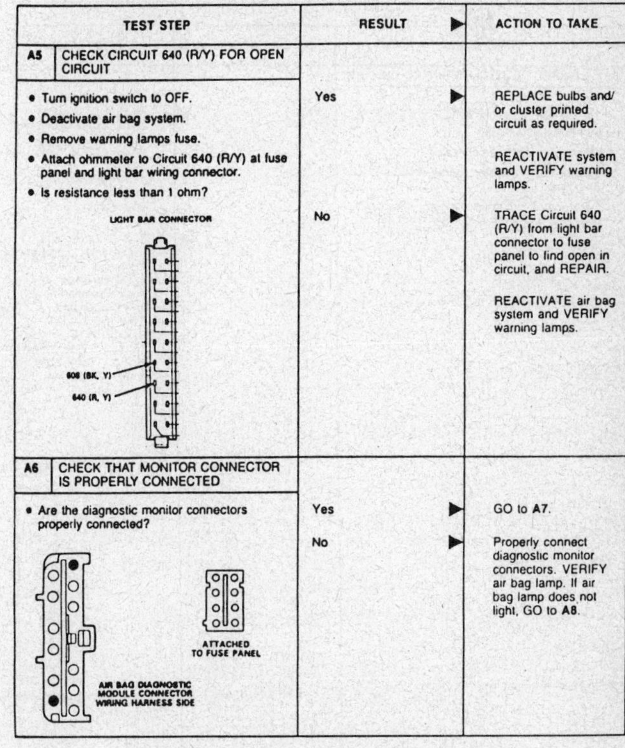

**Fault Indication — Air Bag Lamp Does Not Light**
**Probable Fault — Inoperative Air Bag Lamp Circuit**

| TEST STEP | RESULT ▶ | ACTION TO TAKE |
|---|---|---|
| **A5** CHECK CIRCUIT 640 (R/Y) FOR OPEN CIRCUIT | | |
| • Turn ignition switch to OFF.<br>• Deactivate air bag system.<br>• Remove warning lamps fuse.<br>• Attach ohmmeter to Circuit 640 (R/Y) at fuse panel and light bar wiring connector.<br>• Is resistance less than 1 ohm? | Yes ▶ | REPLACE bulbs and/or cluster printed circuit as required.<br><br>REACTIVATE system and VERIFY warning lamps. |
| LIGHT BAR CONNECTOR<br>608 (BK, Y)<br>640 (R, Y) | No ▶ | TRACE Circuit 640 (R/Y) from light bar connector to fuse panel to find open in circuit, and REPAIR.<br><br>REACTIVATE air bag system and VERIFY warning lamps. |
| **A6** CHECK THAT MONITOR CONNECTOR IS PROPERLY CONNECTED | | |
| • Are the diagnostic monitor connectors properly connected?<br><br>ATTACHED TO FUSE PANEL<br>AIR BAG DIAGNOSTIC MODULE CONNECTOR WIRING HARNESS SIDE | Yes ▶<br>No ▶ | GO to **A7**.<br>Properly connect diagnostic monitor connectors. VERIFY air bag lamp. If air bag lamp does not light, GO to **A8**. |

**Fig. 27 Inoperative airbag lamp circuit (Part 2 of 5). 1990–91 Tempo & Topaz**

**Fault Indication — Air Bag Lamp Does Not Light**
**Probable Fault — Inoperative Air Bag Lamp Circuit**

| TEST STEP | RESULT ▶ | ACTION TO TAKE |
|---|---|---|
| **A7** CHECK LAMP WITH MONITOR CONNECTOR DISCONNECTED | | |
| • Turn ignition switch to OFF.<br>• Disconnect diagnostic monitor wiring from monitor assembly.<br>• Turn ignition switch to RUN.<br>• Is the air bag lamp continuously on? | No ▶<br>Yes ▶ | GO to **A8.**<br>GO to **A9.** |
| **A8** CHECK MONITOR CONNECTOR | | |
| • Turn ignition switch to OFF.<br>• Deactivate air bag system.<br>• Visually inspect the monitor connector to be sure Pin 5 (Circuit 57, BK) and Pin 4 (Circuit 608, BK/Y) are touching each other.<br>• Turn ignition switch to RUN.<br>• Does air bag lamp flash continuously? | Yes ▶<br>No ▶ | GO to **A9.**<br>GO to **A10.** |

**Fig. 27 Inoperative airbag lamp circuit (Part 3 of 5). 1990–91 Tempo & Topaz**

**Fault Indication — Air Bag Lamp Does Not Light**
**Probable Fault — Inoperative Air Bag Lamp Circuit**

| TEST STEP | RESULT ▶ | ACTION TO TAKE |
|---|---|---|
| **A9** CHECK CIRCUIT 640 (R/Y) | | |
| • Turn ignition switch to OFF.<br>• Deactivate Air Bag system.<br>• Attach voltmeter to Pin 6 (Circuit 640, R/Y) on monitor wiring connector and to ground.<br>• Turn ignition switch to RUN.<br>• Is voltage greater than 10 volts? | Yes ▶ | TURN ignition switch to OFF. REPLACE diagnostic monitor.<br>REACTIVATE air bag system.<br>TURN ignition switch to RUN. VERIFY Air Bag warning lamp. |
| | No ▶ | TURN ignition switch to OFF. CHECK fuse. REPLACE fuse if blown and/or trace Circuit 640 (R/Y) from monitor wiring connector Pin 5 to fuse panel to find open and/or short to ground, and REPAIR.<br>REACTIVATE air bag system. Turn ignition to RUN. VERIFY Air Bag warning lamp. |
| **A10** JUMP CIRCUIT 57 (BK) | | |
| • Reconnect diagnostic monitor assembly connector.<br>• Attach a jumper wire to Pin 5 (Circuit 57, BK) through back of monitor wiring connector and to ground.<br>• Does Air Bag lamp light? | Yes ▶ | TURN ignition to OFF. REMOVE jumper wire. SERVICE ground circuit. REACTIVATE air bag system. TURN ignition switch to RUN.<br>VERIFY Air Bag warning lamp. |
| | No ▶ | GO to **A11.** |

**Fig. 27 Inoperative airbag lamp circuit (Part 4 of 5). 1990–91 Tempo & Topaz**

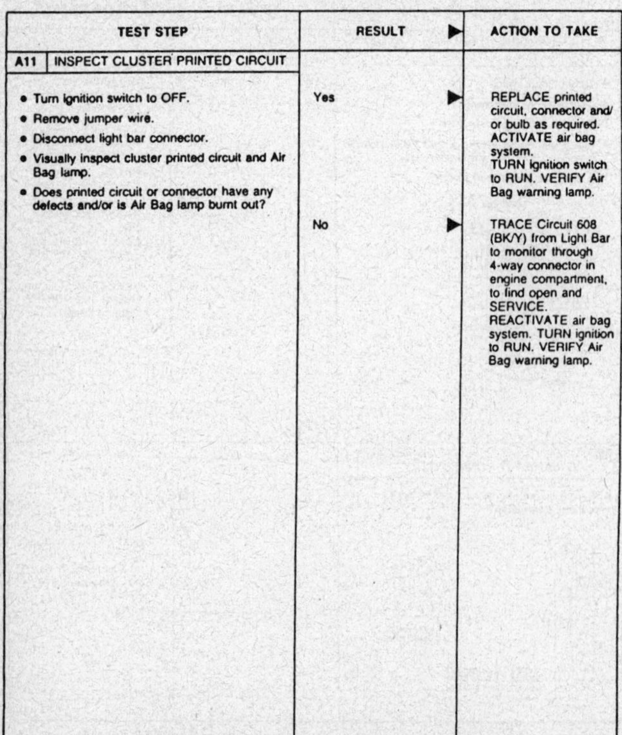

**Fault Indication — Air Bag Lamp Does Not Light**
**Probable Fault — Inoperative Air Bag Lamp Circuit**

| TEST STEP | RESULT ▶ | ACTION TO TAKE |
|---|---|---|
| **A11** INSPECT CLUSTER PRINTED CIRCUIT | | |
| • Turn ignition switch to OFF.<br>• Remove jumper wire.<br>• Disconnect light bar connector.<br>• Visually inspect cluster printed circuit and Air Bag lamp.<br>• Does printed circuit or connector have any defects and/or is Air Bag lamp burnt out? | Yes ▶ | REPLACE printed circuit, connector and/ or bulb as required. ACTIVATE air bag system. TURN ignition switch to RUN. VERIFY Air Bag warning lamp. |
| | No ▶ | TRACE Circuit 608 (BK/Y) from Light Bar to monitor through 4-way connector in engine compartment, to find open and SERVICE. REACTIVATE air bag system. TURN ignition to RUN. VERIFY Air Bag warning lamp. |

**Fig. 27 Inoperative airbag lamp circuit (Part 5 of 5). 1990–91 Tempo & Topaz**

**Fault Indication — Air Bag Lamp Stays On**
**Probable Fault — Diagnostic Monitor Disconnected or Faulty**

| TEST STEP | RESULT ▶ | ACTION TO TAKE |
|---|---|---|
| **B0** DURING SYSTEM PROVE-OUT AIR BAG LAMP STAYS ON | | |
| **B1** CHECK DIAGNOSTIC MONITOR | | |
| • Visually inspect diagnostic monitor for proper connection to monitor wiring connector.<br>• Is monitor properly connected? | Yes ▶<br>No ▶ | GO to **B2.**<br>MAKE connection. VERIFY light. |
| **B2** CHECKING DIAGNOSTIC MONITOR — CONTINUED | | |
| • Disconnect diagnostic monitor.<br>• Insert toothpick or other non-conducting object to wiring connector between Pins 4 and 5, to depress shorting bar between the two terminals.<br>• Verify Air Bag lamp.<br>• Is Air Bag lamp still on continuously? | No ▶ | REPLACE diagnostic monitor. REMOVE object. RECONNECT system. VERIFY Air Bag lamp. |
| | Yes ▶ | TRACE Circuit 608 (BK/Y) from diagnostic monitor to find contact to ground and SERVICE.<br>RECONNECT system. VERIFY Air Bag lamp. |

**Fig. 28 Lamp on continuously**

### Fault Indication — Air Bag Lamp Flashes Two Times
### Probable Fault — All Forward Crash Sensors Disconnected

| | TEST STEP | RESULT ▶ | ACTION TO TAKE |
|---|---|---|---|
| C1 | DURING SYSTEM PROVE-OUT AIR BAG LAMP PROVIDES A FAULT INDICATION OF 2 FLASHES | | |
| C2 | INSPECT FRONT SENSORS | | |
| | • Visually inspect all three front sensor assembly connections and the monitor connectors. | All three sensors are properly connected. ▶ | GO to C3. |
| | | One or all sensors are not properly connected. ▶ | Properly connect the sensor(s) or monitor connectors. VERIFY Air Bag lamp. |
| C3 | INSPECT WIRING CONNECTORS | | |
| | • Deactivate Air Bag system.<br>• Remove monitor from bracket.<br>• Disconnect diagnostic monitor.<br>• Visually inspect monitor wiring connector for proper connection at<br>Pin numbers: 17 (PK/O)<br>18 (PK/W)<br>19 (W/Y)<br>20 (V/G)<br>21 (V/L)<br>22 (T/BK)<br>• Are all connections made? | Yes ▶ | GO to C4. |
| | | No ▶ | SERVICE monitor connections. RECONNECT system. VERIFY Air Bag lamp. REACTIVATE system. |
| C4 | CHECK RESISTANCE IN DIAGNOSTIC MONITOR CIRCUITS | | |
| | • Perform all of the following circuit tests with monitor disconnected.<br>• Attach the lead of the ohmmeter to each set of pins indicated on the diagnostic monitor wiring connector to check the resistance between them. | Yes ▶ | REPLACE diagnostic monitor. VERIFY Air Bag lamp. REACTIVATE system. |
| | | Resistance is NOT between 1000-1300 ohms on one or more of the tests. ▶ | TRACE appropriate circuit(s) and find open and SERVICE. CONNECT diagnostic monitor. VERIFY Air Bag lamp. REACTIVATE system. |

| Pin A | Pin B | Corresponding Sensor | Circuit Wires |
|---|---|---|---|
| 17 | 20 | Right | PK/O<br>V/G |
| 18 | 21 | Center | PK/W<br>V/L |
| 19 | 22 | Left | W/Y<br>T/BK |

• Is resistance between 1000-1300 ohms for each sensor?

**Fig. 29 Lamp flashes 2 times (All forward crash sensors disconnected). Capri**

### Fault Indication — Air Bag Lamp Flashes Two Times
### Probable Fault — All Forward Crash Sensors Disconnected

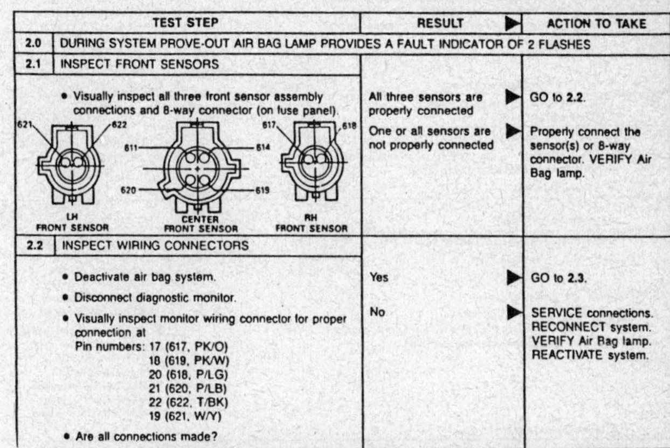


| | TEST STEP | RESULT ▶ | ACTION TO TAKE |
|---|---|---|---|
| 2.0 | DURING SYSTEM PROVE-OUT AIR BAG LAMP PROVIDES A FAULT INDICATOR OF 2 FLASHES | | |
| 2.1 | INSPECT FRONT SENSORS | | |
| | • Visually inspect all three front sensor assembly connections and 8-way connector (on fuse panel). | All three sensors are properly connected ▶ | GO to **2.2**. |
| | | One or all sensors are not properly connected ▶ | Properly connect the sensor(s) or 8-way connector. VERIFY Air Bag lamp. |
| 2.2 | INSPECT WIRING CONNECTORS | | |
| | • Deactivate air bag system.<br>• Disconnect diagnostic monitor.<br>• Visually inspect monitor wiring connector for proper connection at<br>Pin numbers: 17 (617, PK/O)<br>18 (619, PK/W)<br>20 (618, P/LG)<br>21 (620, P/LB)<br>22 (622, T/BK)<br>19 (621, W/Y)<br>• Are all connections made? | Yes ▶ | GO to **2.3**. |
| | | No ▶ | SERVICE connections. RECONNECT system. VERIFY Air Bag lamp. REACTIVATE system. |

**Fig. 30 Lamp flashes 2 times (All forward crash sensors disconnected, part 1 of 2). Except Capri**

### Fault Indication — Air Bag Lamp Flashes Two Times
### Probable Fault — All Forward Crash Sensors Disconnected

| | TEST STEP | RESULT ▶ | ACTION TO TAKE |
|---|---|---|---|
| 2.3 | CHECK RESISTANCE IN DIAGNOSTIC MONITOR CIRCUITS | | |
| | • Perform all of the following circuit tests with monitor disconnected.<br>• Attach the lead of the ohmmeter to each set of pins indicated on the diagnostic monitor wiring connector to check the resistance between them. | Yes ▶ | REPLACE diagnostic monitor. VERIFY Air Bag lamp. REACTIVATE system. |
| | | Resistance is NOT between 1000-1300 ohms on one or more of the tests. ▶ | TRACE appropriate circuit(s) and find open and SERVICE. CONNECT diagnostic monitor. VERIFY Air Bag lamp. REACTIVATE system. |

| Pin A | Pin B | Corresponding Sensor | Circuits |
|---|---|---|---|
| 17 | 20 | Right | 617 (PK/O)/<br>618 (P/LG) |
| 19 | 22 | Left | 621 (W/Y)/<br>622 (T/BK) |
| 18 | 21 | Center | 619 (PK/W)/<br>620 (P/LB) |

• Is the resistance between 1000-1300 ohms for each test?

**Fig. 30 Lamp flashes 2 times (All forward crash sensors disconnected, part 2 of 2). Except Capri**

#### Fault Indication—Air Bag Lamp Flashes Three Times
#### Probable Fault—Loss of Air Bag Circuit Deployment Power or Backup Power Supply Disconnected

| | TEST STEP | RESULT ▶ | ACTION TO TAKE |
|---|---|---|---|
| D1 | DURING SYSTEM PROVE-OUT AIR BAG LAMP PROVIDES A FAULT INDICATION OF 3 FLASHES | | |
| D2 | VISUAL INSPECTION OF FUSE IN L WIRE CIRCUIT | | |
| | • Visually inspect 30 amp fuse in L wire circuit for damage. | Yes ▶ | DISCONNECT battery ground cable and backup power supply. TRACE L wire to find short to ground and SERVICE. REPLACE 30 amp fuse. RECONNECT backup power supply and battery ground cable. VERIFY air bag lamp. |
| | • Is the fuse open (blown)? | No ▶ | GO to D3. |
| D3 | VISUAL INSPECTION OF FUSES IN V / O WIRE CIRCUIT | | |
| | • Visually inspect 15 amp audio fuse in V / O wire circuit for damage. | Yes ▶ | DISCONNECT battery negative cable and backup power supply. TRACE V / O wire to find short to ground and SERVICE. REPLACE 15 amp audio fuse. RECONNECT backup power supply and battery negative cable. VERIFY air bag lamp. |
| | • Is the fuse open (blown)? | No ▶ | GO to D4. |
| D4 | CHECK POWER SUPPLY VOLTAGE | | |
| | • Deactivate air bag system. | No ▶ | DISCONNECT battery negative cable and backup power supply. TRACE V / O wire from diagnostic module gray connector to find open circuit and SERVICE. RECONNECT backup power supply and battery negative cable. VERIFY air bag lamp. REACTIVATE system. |
| | • Remove module from bracket.<br>• Disconnect diagnostic module.<br>• Attach a voltmeter to Pin 13 (L wire) on diagnostic module gray wiring connector and to ground.<br>• Is voltage greater than 10 volts? | Yes ▶ | GO to D5. |

**Fig. 31 Lamp flashes 3 times (Loss of airbag circuit, part 1 of 3). Capri**

**Fault Indication—Air Bag Lamp Flashes Three Times**
**Probable Fault—Loss of Air Bag Circuit Deployment Power or Backup Power Supply Disconnected (Continued)**

| TEST STEP | | RESULT ▶ | ACTION TO TAKE |
|---|---|---|---|
| D5 | CHECK BACKUP POWER SUPPLY | | |
| | • Attach voltmeter to Pin 14, L/O wire on diagnostic wiring gray connector at module and to ground. | No ▶ | CHECK for backup power supply connections. SERVICE as required. If OK, CHECK L/O and V/O wires. REPAIR as required. RECONNECT and REACTIVATE system. VERIFY air bag lamp. |
| | • Is voltage greater than 10 volts? | Yes ▶ | GO to D6. |
| D6 | CHECK RESISTANCE IN W/O WIRE CIRCUIT | | |
| | • Using an ohmmeter find resistance in Pin 15 (W/O wire) on diagnostic module gray wiring connector and to ground. | No ▶ | REPLACE diagnostic module. RECONNECT system. VERIFY air bag lamp. REACTIVATE system. |
| | • Is resistance less than 1 ohm? | Yes ▶ | GO to D7. |
| D7 | CHECK RESISTANCE IN W/O WIRE CIRCUIT—CONTINUED | | |
| | • Disconnect rear safing sensor. | No ▶ | GO to D9. |
| | • Attach ohmmeter to Pin 15 (W/O wire) on diagnostic module wiring connector and to ground. | Yes ▶ | GO to D8. |
| | • Is resistance less than 1 ohm? | | |
| D8 | CHECK RESISTANCE IN W/O WIRE CIRCUIT—CONTINUED | | |
| | • Disconnect center front sensor. | No ▶ | REPLACE center front sensor. REPLACE diagnostic module. RECONNECT system. VERIFY air bag lamp. REACTIVATE system. |
| | • Attach ohmmeter to Pin 15 (W/O wire) on diagnostic module wiring connector and to ground. | Yes ▶ | TRACE W/O wire to find contact to ground and SERVICE. REPLACE diagnostic module. RECONNECT system. VERIFY air bag lamp. REACTIVATE system. |
| | • Is resistance less than 1 ohm? | | |

**Fig. 31 Lamp flashes 3 times (Loss of airbag circuit, part 2 of 3). Capri**

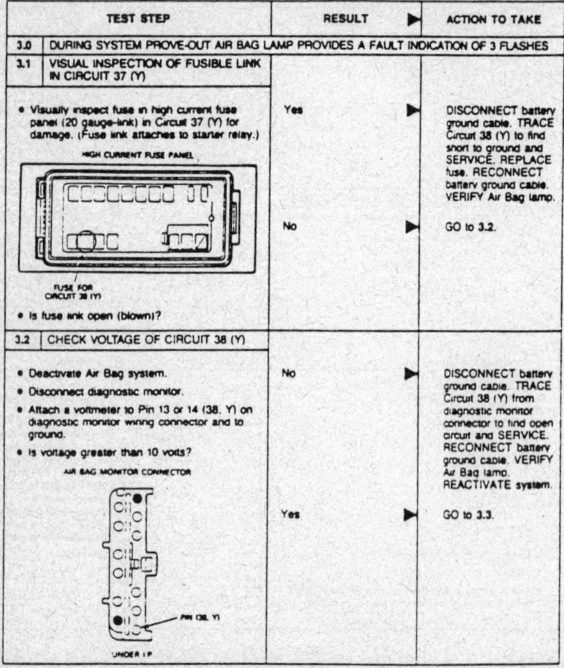


**Fault Indication — Air Bag Lamp Flashes Three Times**
**Probable Fault — Loss of Air Bag Circuit Deployment Power**

| TEST STEP | | RESULT ▶ | ACTION TO TAKE |
|---|---|---|---|
| 3.0 | DURING SYSTEM PROVE-OUT AIR BAG LAMP PROVIDES A FAULT INDICATION OF 3 FLASHES | | |
| 3.1 | VISUAL INSPECTION OF FUSIBLE LINK IN CIRCUIT 37 (Y) | | |
| | • Visually inspect fuse in high current fuse panel (20 gauge-link) in Circuit 37 (Y) for damage. (Fuse link attaches to starter relay.) | Yes ▶ | DISCONNECT battery ground cable. TRACE Circuit 38 (Y) to find short to ground and SERVICE. REPLACE fuse. RECONNECT battery ground cable. VERIFY Air Bag lamp. |
| | • Is fuse link open (blown)? | No ▶ | GO to 3.2. |
| 3.2 | CHECK VOLTAGE OF CIRCUIT 38 (Y) | | |
| | • Deactivate Air Bag system.<br>• Disconnect diagnostic monitor.<br>• Attach a voltmeter to Pin 13 or 14 (38, Y) on diagnostic monitor wiring connector and to ground.<br>• Is voltage greater than 10 volts? | No ▶ | DISCONNECT battery ground cable. TRACE Circuit 38 (Y) from diagnostic monitor connector to find open circuit and SERVICE. RECONNECT battery ground cable. VERIFY Air Bag lamp. REACTIVATE system. |
| | | Yes ▶ | GO to 3.3. |

**Fig. 32 Lamp flashes 3 times (Loss of airbag circuit, part 1 of 3). 1989 Continental**

**Fault Indication—Air Bag Lamp Flashes Three Times**
**Probable Fault—Loss of Air Bag Circuit Deployment Power or Backup Power Supply Disconnected (Continued)**

| TEST STEP | | RESULT ▶ | ACTION TO TAKE |
|---|---|---|---|
| D9 | CHECK RESISTANCE V/O WIRE CIRCUIT | | |
| | • Attach ohmmeter to V/O wire circuit on rear safing sensor wiring connector and to ground. | No ▶ | REPLACE safing sensor. REPLACE diagnostic module. RECONNECT system. VERIFY air bag lamp. REACTIVATE system. |
| | • Is resistance less than 1 ohm? | Yes ▶ | TRACE V/O wire from rear safing sensor to find contact to ground and SERVICE. REPLACE diagnostic module. RECONNECT system. VERIFY air bag lamp. REACTIVATE system. |

**Fig. 31 Lamp flashes 3 times (Loss of airbag circuit, part 3 of 3). Capri**

**Fault Indication — Air Bag Lamp Flashes Three Times**
**Probable Fault — Loss of Air Bag Circuit Deployment Power**

| TEST STEP | | RESULT ▶ | ACTION TO TAKE |
|---|---|---|---|
| 3.3 | CHECK RESISTANCE IN CIRCUIT 611 (W/O) | | |
| | • Using an ohmmeter find resistance in Pin 15 Circuit 611 (W/O) on diagnostic monitor wiring connector and to ground<br>• Is resistance less than 1 ohm? | No ▶ | REPLACE diagnostic monitor RECONNECT system. VERIFY Air Bag lamp. REACTIVATE system. |
| | | Yes ▶ | GO to 3.4. |
| 3.4 | CHECK RESISTANCE IN CIRCUIT 611 (W/O) — CONTINUED | | |
| | • Disconnect dash panel sensor. | No ▶ | GO to 3.6. |
| | • Attach ohmmeter to Pin 15 (Circuit 611, W/O) on diagnostic monitor wiring connector and to ground.<br>• Is resistance less than 1 ohm? | Yes ▶ | GO to 3.5. |
| 3.5 | CHECK RESISTANCE IN CIRCUIT 611 (W/O) — CONTINUED | | |
| | • Disconnect center front sensor.<br>• Attach ohmmeter to Pin 15 (611 W/O) on diagnostic monitor wiring connector and to ground.<br>• Is resistance less than 1 ohm? | No ▶ | REPLACE center front sensor. REPLACE diagnostic monitor. RECONNECT system. VERIFY Air Bag lamp. REACTIVATE system. |
| | | Yes ▶ | TRACE Circuit 611 (W/O) to find contact to ground and SERVICE. REPLACE diagnostic monitor. RECONNECT system. VERIFY Air Bag lamp. REACTIVATE system. |

**Fig. 32 Lamp flashes 3 times (Loss of airbag circuit, part 2 of 3). 1989 Continental**

**Fault Indication — Air Bag Lamp Flashes Three Times**
**Probable Fault — Loss of Air Bag Circuit Deployment Power**

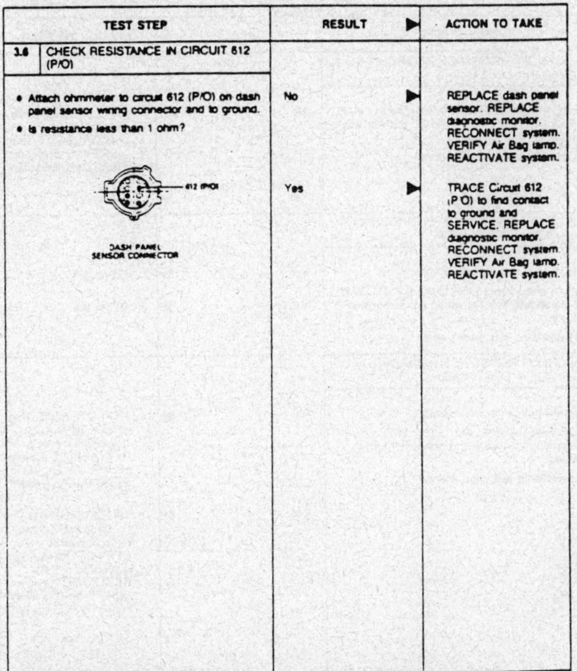

| TEST STEP | RESULT ▶ | ACTION TO TAKE |
|---|---|---|
| **3.6** CHECK RESISTANCE IN CIRCUIT 612 (P/O) | | |
| • Attach ohmmeter to circuit 612 (P/O) on dash panel sensor wiring connector and to ground.<br>• Is resistance less than 1 ohm?<br>612 (P/O)<br>DASH PANEL SENSOR CONNECTOR | No ▶ | REPLACE dash panel sensor. REPLACE diagnostic monitor. RECONNECT system. VERIFY Air Bag lamp. REACTIVATE system. |
| | Yes ▶ | TRACE Circuit 612 (P/O) to find contact to ground and SERVICE. REPLACE diagnostic monitor. RECONNECT system. VERIFY Air Bag lamp. REACTIVATE system. |

**Fig. 32 Lamp flashes 3 times (Loss of airbag circuit, part 3 of 3). 1989 Continental**

**Fault Indication — Air Bag Lamp Flashes Three Times**
**Probable Fault — Loss of Air Bag Circuit Deployment Power and/or Backup Power Supply Disconnected**

| TEST STEP | RESULT ▶ | ACTION TO TAKE |
|---|---|---|
| **3.3** CHECK BACKUP POWER SUPPLY | | |
| • Attach a voltmeter to Pin 14, Circuit 609 (O/Y) on diagnostic harness connector and ground.<br>• Is voltage greater than 10 volts? | Yes ▶ | GO to 3.4. |
| | No ▶ | CHECK backup power supply. SERVICE as required. If OK, CHECK Circuit 609 (O/Y) and Circuit 937 (R/W) for opens. SERVICE as required. RECONNECT battery ground cable and backup power supply. VERIFY air bag lamp. REACTIVATE system. |

**Fig. 33 Lamp flashes 3 times (Loss of airbag circuit, part 2 of 4). 1990–91 Continental**

**Fault Indication — Air Bag Indicator Flashes Three Times**
**Probable Fault — Loss of Air Bag Circuit Deployment Power or Backup Power Supply Disconnected**

| TEST STEP | RESULT ▶ | ACTION TO TAKE |
|---|---|---|
| **3.6** CHECK RESISTANCE IN CIRCUIT 612 (P/O) | | |
| • Attach ohmmeter to Circuit 612 (P/O) on rear safing sensor wiring connector and to ground.<br>• Is resistance less than 1 ohm?<br>623, 614, 613, 612, 611<br>REAR SAFING SENSOR CONNECTOR | No ▶ | REPLACE rear safing sensor. REPLACE diagnostic monitor. RECONNECT system. VERIFY air bag indicator. REACTIVATE system. |
| | Yes ▶ | TRACE Circuit 612 (P/O) to find contact to ground and SERVICE. REPLACE diagnostic monitor. RECONNECT system. VERIFY air bag indicator. REACTIVATE system. |

**Fig. 33 Lamp flashes 3 times (Loss of airbag circuit, part 4 of 4). 1990–91 Continental**

**Fault Indication — Air Bag Lamp Flashes Three Times**
**Probable Fault — Loss of Air Bag Circuit Deployment Power and/or Backup Power Supply Disconnected**

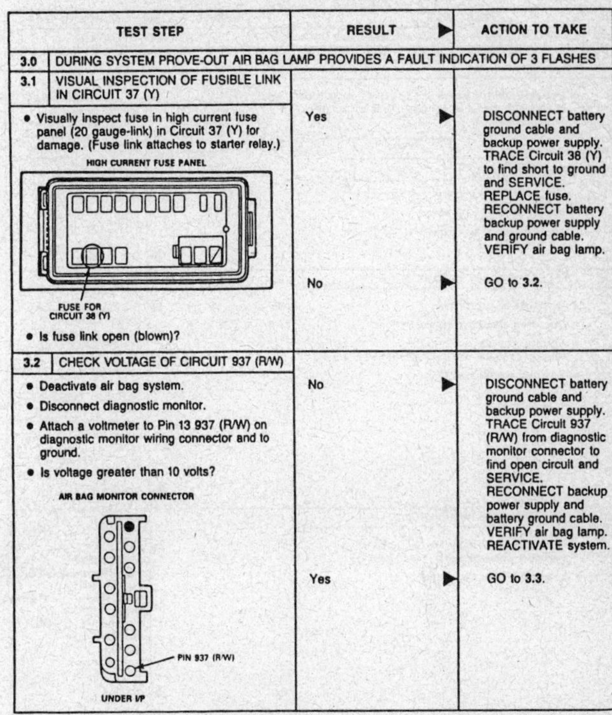

| TEST STEP | RESULT ▶ | ACTION TO TAKE |
|---|---|---|
| **3.0** DURING SYSTEM PROVE-OUT AIR BAG LAMP PROVIDES A FAULT INDICATION OF 3 FLASHES | | |
| **3.1** VISUAL INSPECTION OF FUSIBLE LINK IN CIRCUIT 37 (Y) | | |
| • Visually inspect fuse in high current fuse panel (20 gauge-link) in Circuit 37 (Y) for damage. (Fuse link attaches to starter relay.)<br>HIGH CURRENT FUSE PANEL<br>FUSE FOR CIRCUIT 38 (Y)<br>• Is fuse link open (blown)? | Yes ▶ | DISCONNECT battery ground cable and backup power supply. TRACE Circuit 38 (Y) to find short to ground and SERVICE. REPLACE fuse. RECONNECT battery backup power supply and ground cable. VERIFY air bag lamp. |
| | No ▶ | GO to 3.2. |
| **3.2** CHECK VOLTAGE OF CIRCUIT 937 (R/W) | | |
| • Deactivate air bag system.<br>• Disconnect diagnostic monitor.<br>• Attach a voltmeter to Pin 13 937 (R/W) on diagnostic monitor wiring connector and to ground.<br>• Is voltage greater than 10 volts?<br>AIR BAG MONITOR CONNECTOR<br>PIN 937 (R/W)<br>UNDER I/P | No ▶ | DISCONNECT battery ground cable and backup power supply. TRACE Circuit 937 (R/W) from diagnostic monitor connector to find open circuit and SERVICE. RECONNECT backup power supply and battery ground cable. VERIFY air bag lamp. REACTIVATE system. |
| | Yes ▶ | GO to 3.3. |

**Fig. 33 Lamp flashes 3 times (Loss of airbag circuit, part 1 of 4). 1990–91 Continental**

**Fault Indication — Air Bag Lamp Flashes Three Times**
**Probable Fault — Loss of Air Bag Circuit Deployment Power and/or Backup Power Supply Disconnected**

| TEST STEP | RESULT ▶ | ACTION TO TAKE |
|---|---|---|
| **3.4** CHECK RESISTANCE IN CIRCUIT 611 (W/O) | | |
| • Using an ohmmeter find resistance in Pin 15 Circuit 611 (W/O) on diagnostic monitor wiring connector and to ground.<br>• Is resistance less than 1 ohm? | No ▶ | REPLACE diagnostic monitor. RECONNECT system. VERIFY Air Bag lamp. REACTIVATE system. |
| | Yes ▶ | GO to 3.5. |
| **3.5** CHECK RESISTANCE IN CIRCUIT 611 (W/O) — CONTINUED | | |
| • Disconnect rear safing sensor.<br>• Attach ohmmeter to Pin 15 (Circuit 611, W/O) on diagnostic monitor wiring connector and to ground.<br>• Is resistance less than 1 ohm? | No ▶ | GO to 3.6. |
| | Yes ▶ | TRACE Circuit 611 (W/O) to find contact to ground and SERVICE. REPLACE diagnostic monitor. RECONNECT system. VERIFY air bag indicator. REACTIVATE system. |

**Fig. 33 Lamp flashes 3 times (Loss of airbag circuit, part 3 of 4). 1990–91 Continental**

**Fault Indication — Air Bag Lamp Flashes Three Times**
**Probable Fault — Loss of Air Bag Circuit Deployment Power or Backup Power Supply Disconnected**

| | TEST STEP | RESULT ▶ | ACTION TO TAKE |
|---|---|---|---|
| 3.0 | DURING SYSTEM PROVE-OUT AIR BAG LAMP PROVIDES A FAULT INDICATION OF 3 FLASHES | | |
| 3.1 | VISUAL INSPECTION OF FUSIBLE LINK IN CIRCUIT 38 (BK/O) | | |
| | • Visually inspect 16 gauge and 12 gauge fusible links in Circuit 38 (BK/O) for damage. (Fuse link attaches to starter relay). 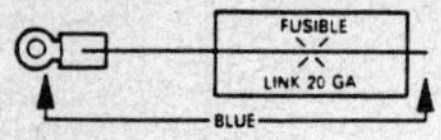  • Inspect No. 7 fuse (15 amp) • Are fuse links or fuse blows? | Yes ▶ | DISCONNECT battery ground cable and backup power supply. TRACE Circuit 38 (BK/O) to find short to ground and SERVICE. REPLACE fusible link. RECONNECT backup power supply and battery ground cable. VERIFY Air Bag lamp. |
| | | No ▶ | GO to 3.2. |
| 3.2 | CHECK VOLTAGE OF CIRCUIT 294 (W/LB) | | |
| | • Deactivate air bag system. • Disconnect diagnostic monitor. • Attach a voltmeter to Pin 13 Circuit 294 (W/LB) on diagnostic monitor wiring connector and to ground. • Is voltage greater than 10 volts? | No ▶ | DISCONNECT battery ground cable and backup power supply. TRACE Circuit 294 (W/LB) from diagnostic monitor connector to find open circuit and SERVICE. RECONNECT backup power supply and battery ground cable. VERIFY Air Bag lamp. REACTIVATE system. |
| | | Yes ▶ | GO to 3.3. |
| 3.3 | CHECK BACKUP POWER SUPPLY | | |
| | • Attach a voltmeter to Pin 14, Circuit 656 (P) on diagnostic wiring connector and to ground. • Is voltage greater than 10 volts? | No ▶ | CHECK for backup power supply connections. SERVICE as required. If OK, CHECK 656 (P) and 294 (W/LB). REPAIR as required. RECONNECT and REACTIVATE SYSTEM. VERIFY Air Bag lamp. |
| | | Yes ▶ | GO to 3.4 |

Fig. 34 Lamp flashes 3 times (Loss of airbag circuit, part 1 of 3). Crown Victoria & Grand Marquis

**Fault Indication — Air Bag Lamp Flashes Three Times**
**Probable Fault — Loss of Air Bag Circuit Deployment Power and/or Backup Power Supply Disconnected**

| | TEST STEP | RESULT ▶ | ACTION TO TAKE |
|---|---|---|---|
| 3.4 | CHECK RESISTANCE IN CIRCUIT 611 (W/O) | | |
| | • Using an ohmmeter find resistance in Pin 15 Circuit 611 (W/O) on diagnostic monitor wiring connector and to ground. • Is resistance less than 1 ohm? | No ▶ | REPLACE diagnostic monitor. RECONNECT system. VERIFY Air Bag lamp. REACTIVATE system. |
| | | Yes ▶ | GO to 3.5. |
| 3.5 | CHECK RESISTANCE IN CIRCUIT 611 (W/O) — CONTINUED | | |
| | • Disconnect rear safing sensor. • Attach ohmmeter to Pin 15 (Circuit 611, W/O) on diagnostic monitor wiring connector and to ground. • Is resistance less than 1 ohm? | No ▶ | GO to 3.7. |
| | | Yes ▶ | GO to 3.6. |
| 3.6 | CHECK RESISTANCE IN CIRCUIT 611 (W/O) — CONTINUED | | |
| | • Disconnect center front sensor. • Attach ohmmeter to Pin 15 (611 W/O) on diagnostic monitor wiring connector and to ground. • Is resistance less than 1 ohm? | No ▶ | REPLACE center front sensor. REPLACE diagnostic monitor. RECONNECT system. VERIFY Air Bag lamp. REACTIVATE system. |
| | | Yes ▶ | TRACE Circuit 611 (W/O) to find contact to ground and SERVICE. REPLACE diagnostic monitor. RECONNECT system. VERIFY Air Bag lamp. REACTIVATE system. |

Fig. 34 Lamp flashes 3 times (Loss of airbag circuit, part 2 of 3). Crown Victoria & Grand Marquis

**Fault Indication — Air Bag Lamp Flashes Three Times**
**Probable Fault — Loss of Air Bag Circuit Deployment Power or Backup Power Supply Disconnected**

| | TEST STEP | RESULT ▶ | ACTION TO TAKE |
|---|---|---|---|
| 3.7 | CHECK RESISTANCE IN CIRCUIT 612 (P/O) | | |
| | • Attach ohmmeter to Circuit 612 (P/O) on rear safing sensor wiring connector and to ground. • Is resistance less than 1 ohm? 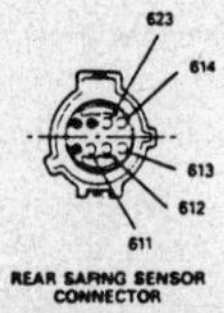  | No ▶ | REPLACE rear safing sensor. REPLACE diagnostic monitor. RECONNECT system. VERIFY Air Bag lamp. REACTIVATE system. |
| | | Yes ▶ | TRACE Circuit 612 (P/O) to find contact to ground and SERVICE. REPLACE diagnostic monitor. RECONNECT system. VERIFY Air Bag lamp. REACTIVATE system. |

Fig. 34 Lamp flashes 3 times (Loss of airbag circuit, part 3 of 3). Crown Victoria & Grand Marquis

**Fault Indication — Air Bag Lamp Flashes Three Times**
**Probable Fault — Loss of Air Bag Circuit Deployment Power or Backup Power Supply Disconnected**

| | TEST STEP | RESULT ▶ | ACTION TO TAKE |
|---|---|---|---|
| 3.0 | DURING SYSTEM PROVE-OUT AIR BAG LAMP PROVIDES A FAULT INDICATION OF 3 FLASHES | | |
| 3.1 | VISUAL INSPECTION OF FUSES IN CIRCUIT 37 (Y) | | |
| | • Visually inspect fuses in Circuit 37 (Y) for damage. • Are fuses blown? | Yes ▶ | DISCONNECT battery ground cable and backup power supply. TRACE Circuit 37 (Y) to find short to ground and SERVICE. REPLACE fuseible link per procedure in Group 34. RECONNECT backup power supply and battery ground cable. VERIFY Air Bag lamp. |
| | | No ▶ | GO to 3.2. |
| 3.2 | CHECK VOLTAGE OF CIRCUIT 937 (R/W) | | |
| | • Deactivate air bag system. • Disconnect diagnostic monitor. • Attach a voltmeter to Pin 13, Circuit 937 (R/W) on diagnostic monitor wiring connector and to ground. • Is voltage greater than 10 volts? | No ▶ | DISCONNECT battery ground cable and backup power supply. TRACE Circuit 937 (R/W) diagnostic monitor connector to find open circuit and SERVICE. RECONNECT backup power supply and battery ground cable. VERIFY Air Bag lamp. REACTIVATE system. |
| | | Yes ▶ | GO to 3.3. |
| 3.3 | CHECK BACKUP POWER SUPPLY | | |
| | • Attach voltmeter to Pin 14, Circuit 609 (O/Y) on diagnostic wiring connector and to ground. • Is voltage greator than 10 volts? | No ▶ | CHECK for backup power supply connections. SERVICE as required. If OK, CHECK Circuits 609 (O/Y) and 37 (Y). REPAIR as required. RECONNECT and REACTIVATE system. VERIFY Air Bag lamp. |
| | | Yes ▶ | GO to 3.4. |

Fig. 35 Lamp flashes 3 times (Loss of airbag circuit, part 1 of 3). Mark VII and Mustang

**Fault Indication — Air Bag Lamp Flashes Three Times**
**Probable Fault — Loss of Air Bag Circuit Deployment Power and/or Backup Power Supply Disconnected**

| TEST STEP | RESULT ▶ | ACTION TO TAKE |
|---|---|---|
| **3.4** CHECK RESISTANCE IN CIRCUIT 611 (W/O) | | |
| • Using an ohmmeter find resistance in Pin 15 Circuit 611 (W/O) on diagnostic monitor wiring connector and to ground.<br>• Is resistance less than 1 ohm? | No ▶ | REPLACE diagnostic monitor. RECONNECT system. VERIFY Air Bag lamp. REACTIVATE system. |
| | Yes ▶ | GO to 3.5. |
| **3.5** CHECK RESISTANCE IN CIRCUIT 611 (W/O) — CONTINUED | | |
| • Disconnect rear safing sensor.<br>• Attach ohmmeter to Pin 15 (Circuit 611, W/O) on diagnostic monitor wiring connector and to ground.<br>• Is resistance less than 1 ohm? | No ▶ | GO to 3.7. |
| | Yes ▶ | GO to 3.6. |
| **3.6** CHECK RESISTANCE IN CIRCUIT 611 (W/O) — CONTINUED | | |
| • Disconnect center front sensor.<br>• Attach ohmmeter to Pin 15 (611 W/O) on diagnostic monitor wiring connector and to ground.<br>• Is resistance less than 1 ohm? | No ▶ | REPLACE center front sensor. REPLACE diagnostic monitor. RECONNECT system. VERIFY Air Bag lamp. REACTIVATE system. |
| | Yes ▶ | TRACE Circuit 611 (W/O) to find contact to ground and SERVICE. REPLACE diagnostic monitor. RECONNECT system. VERIFY Air Bag lamp. REACTIVATE system. |

**Fig. 35 Lamp flashes 3 times (Loss of airbag circuit, part 2 of 3). Mark VII and Mustang**

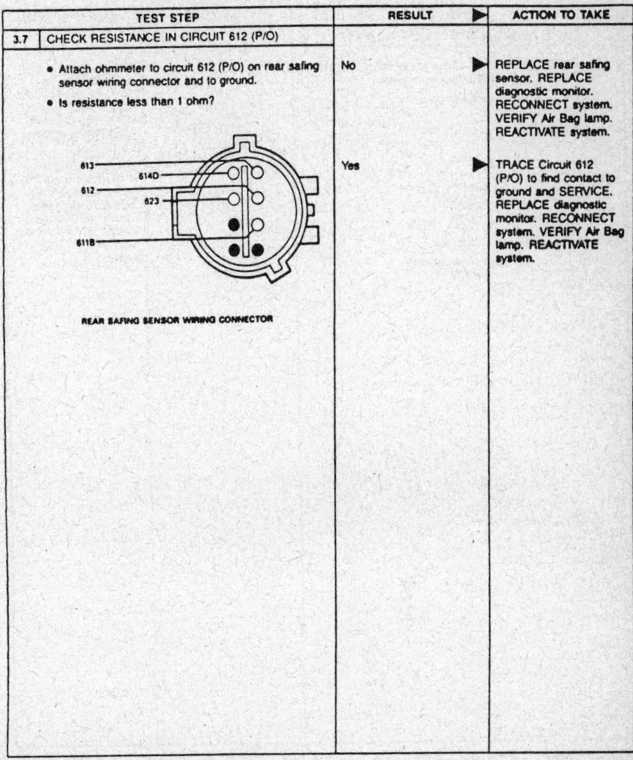

**Fault Indication — Air Bag Lamp Flashes Three Times**
**Probable Fault — Loss of Air Bag Circuit Deployment Power or Backup Power Supply Disconnected**

| TEST STEP | RESULT ▶ | ACTION TO TAKE |
|---|---|---|
| **3.7** CHECK RESISTANCE IN CIRCUIT 612 (P/O) | | |
| • Attach ohmmeter to circuit 612 (P/O) on rear safing sensor wiring connector and to ground.<br>• Is resistance less than 1 ohm? | No ▶ | REPLACE rear safing sensor. REPLACE diagnostic monitor. RECONNECT system. VERIFY Air Bag lamp. REACTIVATE system. |
| | Yes ▶ | TRACE Circuit 612 (P/O) to find contact to ground and SERVICE. REPLACE diagnostic monitor. RECONNECT system. VERIFY Air Bag lamp. REACTIVATE system. |



**Fig. 35 Lamp flashes 3 times (Loss of airbag circuit, part 3 of 3). Mark VII and Mustang**

**Fault Indication — Air Bag Lamp Flashes Three Times**
**Probable Fault — Loss Of Air Bag Circuit Deployment Power Or Backup Power Supply Disconnected**

| TEST STEP | RESULT ▶ | ACTION TO TAKE |
|---|---|---|
| **3.0** DURING SYSTEM PROVE-OUT AIR BAG LAMP PROVIDES A FAULT INDICATION OF 3 FLASHES | | |
| **3.1** VISUAL INSPECTION OF FUSIBLE LINKS IN CIRCUIT 38 (BK/O) | | |
| • Visually inspect 16 gauge fusible links in Circuit 38 (BK/O) for damage. (Fuse link attaches to starter relay).<br>• Check fuse 7 (15 amp).<br>FUSIBLE LINK 20 GA. — BLUE<br>• Are fuse links or fuse blows? | Yes ▶ | DISCONNECT battery ground cable and backup power supply. TRACE Circuit 38 (BK/O) to find short to ground and SERVICE. REPLACE fusible link<br>RECONNECT backup power supply and battery ground cable. VERIFY Air Bag lamp. |
| | No ▶ | GO to 3.2. |
| **3.2** CHECK VOLTAGE OF CIRCUIT 547 (LG/Y) | | |
| • Deactivate air bag system.<br>• Disconnect diagnostic monitor.<br>• Attach a voltmeter to Pin 13, 547 (LG/Y) on diagnostic monitor wiring connector and to ground.<br>• Is voltage greater than 10 volts? | No ▶ | DISCONNECT battery ground cable and backup power supply. TRACE Circuit 547 (LG/Y) diagnostic monitor connector to find open circuit and SERVICE. RECONNECT backup power supply and battery ground cable. VERIFY Air Bag lamp. REACTIVATE system. |
| | Yes ▶ | GO to 3.3. |
| **3.3** CHECK BACKUP POWER SUPPLY | | |
| • Attach voltmeter to Pin 14, Circuit 609 (O/Y) on diagnostic wiring connector and to ground.<br>• Is voltage greater than 10 volts? | No ▶ | CHECK for backup power supply connections. SERVICE as required. If OK, CHECK 609 (O/Y) and 547 (LG/Y). REPAIR as required. RECONNECT and REACTIVATE SYSTEM. VERIFY Air Bag lamp. |
| | Yes ▶ | GO to 3.4. |

**Fig. 36 Lamp flashes 3 times (Loss of airbag circuit, part 1 of 3). Sable & Taurus**

**Fault Indication — Air Bag Lamp Flashes Three Times**
**Probable Fault — Loss of Air Bag Circuit Deployment Power and/or Backup Power Supply Disconnected**

| TEST STEP | RESULT ▶ | ACTION TO TAKE |
|---|---|---|
| **3.4** CHECK RESISTANCE IN CIRCUIT 611 (W/O) | | |
| • Using an ohmmeter find resistance in Pin 15 Circuit 611 (W/O) on diagnostic monitor wiring connector and to ground.<br>• Is resistance less than 1 ohm? | No ▶ | REPLACE diagnostic monitor. RECONNECT system. VERIFY Air Bag lamp. REACTIVATE system. |
| | Yes ▶ | GO to 3.5. |
| **3.5** CHECK RESISTANCE IN CIRCUIT 611 (W/O) — CONTINUED | | |
| • Disconnect rear safing sensor.<br>• Attach ohmmeter to Pin 15 (Circuit 611, W/O) on diagnostic monitor wiring connector and to ground.<br>• Is resistance less than 1 ohm? | No ▶ | GO to 3.7. |
| | Yes ▶ | GO to 3.6. |
| **3.6** CHECK RESISTANCE IN CIRCUIT 611 (W/O) — CONTINUED | | |
| • Disconnect center front sensor.<br>• Attach ohmmeter to Pin 15 (611 W/O) on diagnostic monitor wiring connector and to ground.<br>• Is resistance less than 1 ohm? | No ▶ | REPLACE center front sensor. REPLACE diagnostic monitor. RECONNECT system. VERIFY Air Bag lamp. REACTIVATE system. |
| | Yes ▶ | TRACE Circuit 611 (W/O) to find contact to ground and SERVICE. REPLACE diagnostic monitor. RECONNECT system. VERIFY Air Bag lamp. REACTIVATE system |

**Fig. 36 Lamp flashes 3 times (Loss of airbag circuit, part 2 of 3). Sable & Taurus**

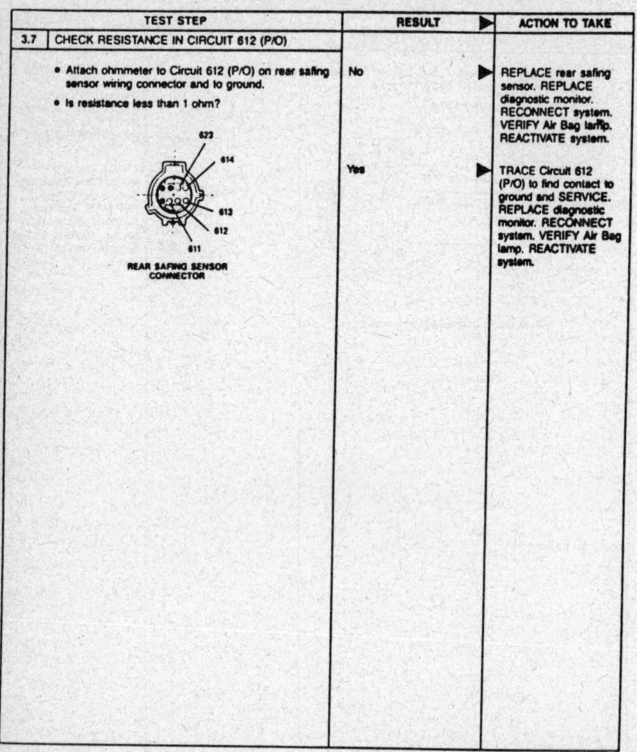


**Fault Indication — Air Bag Lamp Flashes Three Times**
**Probable Fault — Loss of Air Bag Circuit Deployment Power or Backup Power Supply Disconnected**

| TEST STEP | RESULT ▶ | ACTION TO TAKE |
|---|---|---|
| **3.7** CHECK RESISTANCE IN CIRCUIT 612 (P/O) | | |
| • Attach ohmmeter to Circuit 612 (P/O) on rear safing sensor wiring connector and to ground.<br>• Is resistance less than 1 ohm? | No ▶ | REPLACE rear safing sensor. REPLACE diagnostic monitor. RECONNECT system. VERIFY Air Bag lamp. REACTIVATE system. |
| | Yes ▶ | TRACE Circuit 612 (P/O) to find contact to ground and SERVICE. REPLACE diagnostic monitor. RECONNECT system. VERIFY Air Bag lamp. REACTIVATE system. |

**Fig. 36 Lamp flashes 3 times (Loss of airbag circuit, part 3 of 3). Sable & Taurus**

**Fault Indication — Air Bag Lamp Flashes Three Times**
**Probable Fault — Loss of Air Bag Circuit Deployment Power**

| TEST STEP | RESULT ▶ | ACTION TO TAKE |
|---|---|---|
| **3.3** CHECK RESISTANCE IN CIRCUIT 611 (W/O) | | |
| • Using an ohmmeter find resistance in Pin 15 Circuit 611 (W/O) on diagnostic monitor wiring connector and to ground.<br>• Is resistance less than 1 ohm? | No ▶ | REPLACE diagnostic monitor. RECONNECT system. VERIFY Air Bag lamp. REACTIVATE system. |
| | Yes ▶ | GO to **3.4** |
| **3.4** CHECK RESISTANCE IN CIRCUIT 611 (W/O) — CONTINUED | | |
| • Disconnect dash panel sensor.<br>• Attach ohmmeter to Pin 15 (Circuit 611, W/O) on diagnostic monitor wiring connector and to ground.<br>• Is resistance less than 1 ohm? | No ▶ | GO to **3.6** |
| | Yes ▶ | GO to **3.5** |
| **3.5** CHECK RESISTANCE IN CIRCUIT 611 (W/O) — CONTINUED | | |
| • Disconnect center front sensor.<br>• Attach ohmmeter to Pin 15 (611 W/O) on diagnostic monitor wiring connector and to ground.<br>• Is resistance less than 1 ohm? | No ▶ | REPLACE center front sensor. REPLACE diagnostic monitor. RECONNECT system. VERIFY Air Bag lamp. REACTIVATE system. |
| | Yes ▶ | TRACE Circuit 611 (W/O) to find contact to ground and SERVICE. REPLACE diagnostic monitor. RECONNECT system. VERIFY Air Bag lamp. REACTIVATE system. |

**Fig. 37 Lamp flashes 3 times (Loss of airbag circuit, part 2 of 3). 1989 Tempo & Topaz**

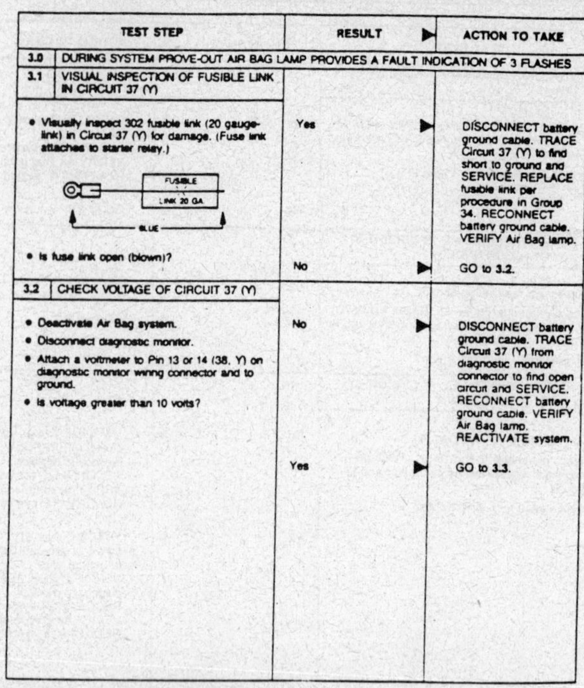


**Fault Indication — Air Bag Lamp Flashes Three Times**
**Probable Fault — Loss of Air Bag Circuit Deployment Power**

| TEST STEP | RESULT ▶ | ACTION TO TAKE |
|---|---|---|
| **3.0** DURING SYSTEM PROVE-OUT AIR BAG LAMP PROVIDES A FAULT INDICATION OF 3 FLASHES | | |
| **3.1** VISUAL INSPECTION OF FUSIBLE LINK IN CIRCUIT 37 (Y) | | |
| • Visually inspect 302 fusible link (20 gauge-link) in Circuit 37 (Y) for damage. (Fuse link attaches to starter relay.)<br>• Is fuse link open (blown)? | Yes ▶ | DISCONNECT battery ground cable. TRACE Circuit 37 (Y) to find short to ground and SERVICE. REPLACE fusible link per procedure in Group 34. RECONNECT battery ground cable. VERIFY Air Bag lamp. |
| | No ▶ | GO to **3.2.** |
| **3.2** CHECK VOLTAGE OF CIRCUIT 37 (Y) | | |
| • Deactivate Air Bag system.<br>• Disconnect diagnostic monitor.<br>• Attach a voltmeter to Pin 13 or 14 (38, Y) on diagnostic monitor wiring connector and to ground.<br>• Is voltage greater than 10 volts? | No ▶ | DISCONNECT battery ground cable. TRACE Circuit 37 (Y) from diagnostic monitor connector to find open circuit and SERVICE. RECONNECT battery ground cable. VERIFY Air Bag lamp. REACTIVATE system. |
| | Yes ▶ | GO to **3.3.** |

**Fig. 37 Lamp flashes 3 times (Loss of airbag circuit, part 1 of 3). 1989 Tempo & Topaz**

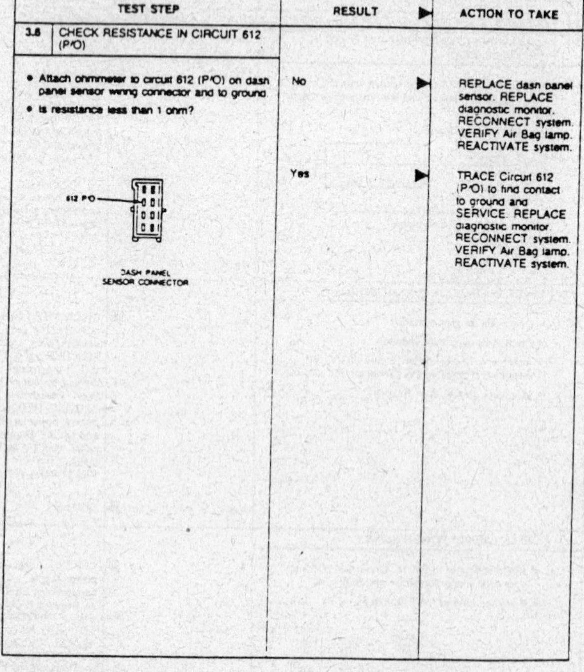


**Fault Indication — Air Bag Lamp Flashes Three Times**
**Probable Fault — Loss of Air Bag Circuit Deployment Power**

| TEST STEP | RESULT ▶ | ACTION TO TAKE |
|---|---|---|
| **3.6** CHECK RESISTANCE IN CIRCUIT 612 (P/O) | | |
| • Attach ohmmeter to circuit 612 (P/O) on dash panel sensor wiring connector and to ground.<br>• Is resistance less than 1 ohm? | No ▶ | REPLACE dash panel sensor. REPLACE diagnostic monitor. RECONNECT system. VERIFY Air Bag lamp. REACTIVATE system. |
| | Yes ▶ | TRACE Circuit 612 (P/O) to find contact to ground and SERVICE. REPLACE diagnostic monitor. RECONNECT system. VERIFY Air Bag lamp. REACTIVATE system. |

**Fig. 37 Lamp flashes 3 times (Loss of airbag circuit, part 3 of 3). 1989 Tempo & Topaz**

**Fault Indication — Air Bag Lamp Flashes Three Times**
**Probable Fault — Loss of Air Bag Circuit Deployment Power or Backup Power Supply Disconnected**

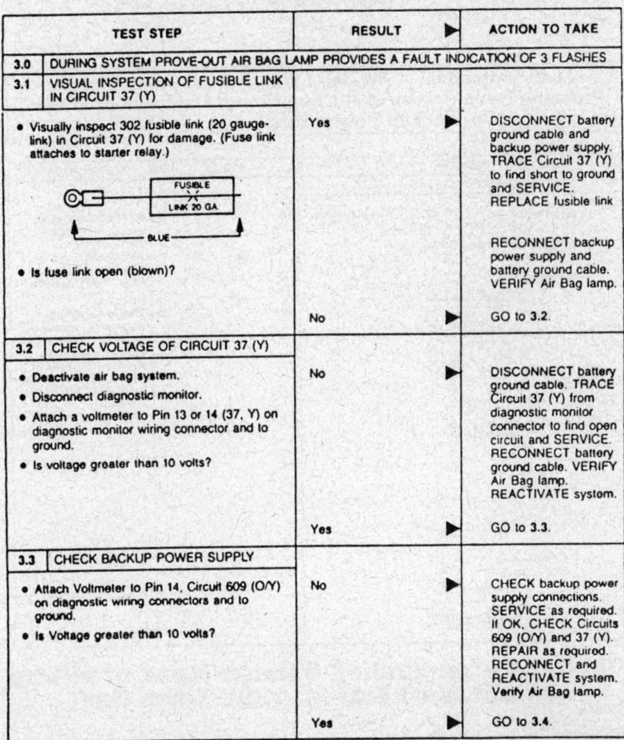

| TEST STEP | RESULT ▶ | ACTION TO TAKE |
|---|---|---|
| **3.0** DURING SYSTEM PROVE-OUT AIR BAG LAMP PROVIDES A FAULT INDICATION OF 3 FLASHES | | |
| **3.1** VISUAL INSPECTION OF FUSIBLE LINK IN CIRCUIT 37 (Y) | | |
| • Visually inspect 302 fusible link (20 gauge-link) in Circuit 37 (Y) for damage. (Fuse link attaches to starter relay.) [FUSIBLE LINK 20 GA. — BLUE] • Is fuse link open (blown)? | Yes ▶ | DISCONNECT battery ground cable and backup power supply. TRACE Circuit 37 (Y) to find short to ground and SERVICE. REPLACE fusible link RECONNECT backup power supply and battery ground cable. VERIFY Air Bag lamp. |
| | No ▶ | GO to 3.2. |
| **3.2** CHECK VOLTAGE OF CIRCUIT 37 (Y) | | |
| • Deactivate air bag system. • Disconnect diagnostic monitor. • Attach a voltmeter to Pin 13 or 14 (37, Y) on diagnostic monitor wiring connector and to ground. • Is voltage greater than 10 volts? | No ▶ | DISCONNECT battery ground cable. TRACE Circuit 37 (Y) from diagnostic monitor connector to find open circuit and SERVICE. RECONNECT battery ground cable. VERIFY Air Bag lamp. REACTIVATE system. |
| | Yes ▶ | GO to 3.3. |
| **3.3** CHECK BACKUP POWER SUPPLY | | |
| • Attach Voltmeter to Pin 14, Circuit 609 (O/Y) on diagnostic wiring connectors and to ground. • Is Voltage greater than 10 volts? | No ▶ | CHECK backup power supply connections. SERVICE as required. If OK, CHECK Circuits 609 (O/Y) and 37 (Y). REPAIR as required. RECONNECT and REACTIVATE system. Verify Air Bag lamp. |
| | Yes ▶ | GO to 3.4. |

**Fig. 38 Lamp flashes 3 times (Loss of airbag circuit, part 1 of 3). 1990–91 Tempo & Topaz**

**Fault Indication — Air Bag Lamp Flashes Three Times**
**Probable Fault — Loss of Air Bag Circuit Deployment Power and/or Backup Power Supply Disconnected**

| TEST STEP | RESULT ▶ | ACTION TO TAKE |
|---|---|---|
| **3.4** CHECK RESISTANCE IN CIRCUIT 611 (W/O) | | |
| • Using an ohmmeter find resistance in Pin 15 Circuit 611 (W/O) on diagnostic monitor wiring connector and to ground. • Is resistance less than 1 ohm? | No ▶ | REPLACE diagnostic monitor. RECONNECT system. VERIFY Air Bag lamp. REACTIVATE system. |
| | Yes ▶ | GO to 3.5. |
| **3.5** CHECK RESISTANCE IN CIRCUIT 611 (W/O) — CONTINUED | | |
| • Disconnect rear safing sensor. • Attach ohmmeter to Pin 15 (Circuit 611, W/O) on diagnostic monitor wiring connector and to ground. • Is resistance less than 1 ohm? | No ▶ | GO to 3.7. |
| | Yes ▶ | GO to 3.6. |
| **3.6** CHECK RESISTANCE IN CIRCUIT 611 (W/O) — CONTINUED | | |
| • Disconnect center front sensor. • Attach ohmmeter to Pin 15 (611 W/O) on diagnostic monitor wiring connector and to ground. • Is resistance less than 1 ohm? | No ▶ | REPLACE center front sensor. REPLACE diagnostic monitor. RECONNECT system. VERIFY Air Bag lamp. REACTIVATE system. |
| | Yes ▶ | TRACE Circuit 611 (W/O) to find contact to ground and SERVICE. REPLACE diagnostic monitor. RECONNECT system. VERIFY Air Bag lamp. REACTIVATE system. |

**Fig. 38 Lamp flashes 3 times (Loss of airbag circuit, part 2 of 3). 1990–91 Tempo & Topaz**

**Fault Indication — Air Bag Lamp Flashes Three Times**
**Probable Fault — Loss of Air Bag Circuit Deployment Power or Backup Power Supply Disconnected**

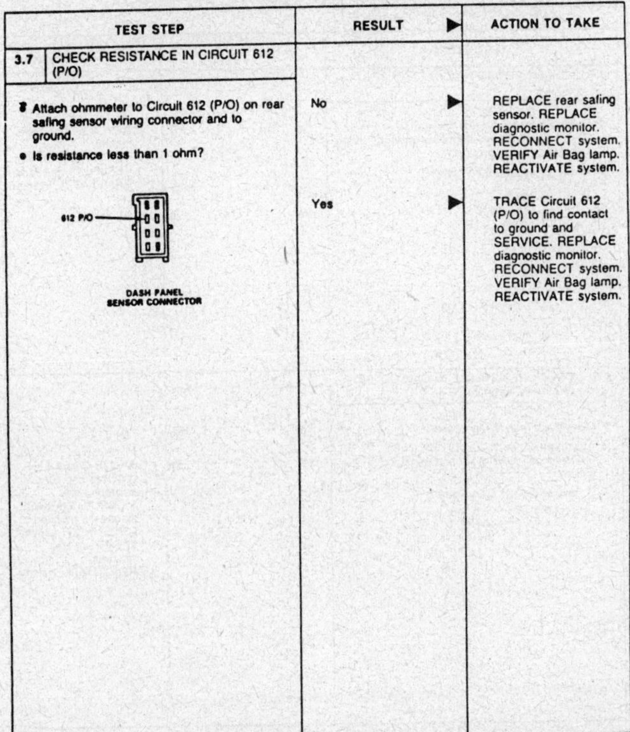

| TEST STEP | RESULT ▶ | ACTION TO TAKE |
|---|---|---|
| **3.7** CHECK RESISTANCE IN CIRCUIT 612 (P/O) | | |
| • Attach ohmmeter to Circuit 612 (P/O) on rear safing sensor wiring connector and to ground. • Is resistance less than 1 ohm? [612 P/O — DASH PANEL SENSOR CONNECTOR] | No ▶ | REPLACE rear safing sensor. REPLACE diagnostic monitor. RECONNECT system. VERIFY Air Bag lamp. REACTIVATE system. |
| | Yes ▶ | TRACE Circuit 612 (P/O) to find contact to ground and SERVICE. REPLACE diagnostic monitor. RECONNECT system. VERIFY Air Bag lamp. REACTIVATE system. |

**Fig. 38 Lamp flashes 3 times (Loss of airbag circuit, part 3 of 3). 1990–91 Tempo & Topaz**

**Fault Indication — Air Bag Lamp Flashes Three Times**
**Probable Fault — Loss of Air Bag Circuit Deployment Power and/or Backup Power Supply Disconnected**

| TEST STEP | RESULT ▶ | ACTION TO TAKE |
|---|---|---|
| **3.0** DURING SYSTEM PROVE-OUT AIR BAG LAMP PROVIDES A FAULT INDICATION OF 3 FLASHES | | |
| **3.1** VISUAL INSPECTION OF FUSIBLE LINK IN CIRCUIT 37 (Y) | | |
| • Visually inspect fuse in fuse panel (10 amp position K), for damage. • Is fuse link open (blown)? | Yes ▶ | DISCONNECT battery ground cable and backup power supply. TRACE Circuit to find short to ground and SERVICE. REPLACE fuse. RECONNECT battery backup power supply and ground cable. VERIFY Air Bag lamp. |
| | No ▶ | GO to 3.2. |
| **3.2** CHECK VOLTAGE OF CIRCUIT 300 (O) | | |
| • Deactivate air bag system. • Disconnect diagnostic monitor. • Attach a voltmeter to Pin 13, Circuit 300 (O) on diagnostic monitor wiring connector and to ground. • Is voltage greater than 10 volts? [AIR BAG MONITOR CONNECTOR — PIN 13 CIRCUIT 300 (O) — UNDER I/P] | No ▶ | DISCONNECT battery ground cable and backup power supply. TRACE Circuit 300 (O) from diagnostic monitor connector to find open circuit and SERVICE. RECONNECT backup power supply and battery ground cable. VERIFY Air Bag lamp. REACTIVATE system. |
| | Yes ▶ | GO to 3.3. |
| **3.3** CHECK BACKUP POWER SUPPLY | | |
| • Attach a voltmeter to Pin 14, Circuit 656 (P) on diagnostic wiring connector and ground. • Is voltage greater than 10 volts? | Yes ▶ | GO to 3.4. |
| | No ▶ | CHECK backup power supply. SERVICE as required. If OK, CHECK Circuit 656 (P) and Circuit 300 (O) for opens. SERVICE as required. RECONNECT battery ground cable and backup power supply. VERIFY Air Bag lamp. REACTIVATE system. |

**Fig. 39 Lamp flashes 3 times (Loss of airbag circuit, part 1 of 3). 1990 Town Car**

**Fault Indication — Air Bag Lamp Flashes Three Times**
**Probable Fault — Loss of Air Bag Circuit Deployment Power and/or Backup Power Supply Disconnected**

| TEST STEP | | RESULT ▶ | ACTION TO TAKE |
|---|---|---|---|
| 3.4 | CHECK RESISTANCE IN CIRCUIT 611 (W/O) | | |
| | • Using an ohmmeter find resistance in Pin 15 Circuit 611 (W/O) on diagnostic monitor wiring connector and to ground.<br>• Is resistance less than 1 ohm? | No ▶ | REPLACE diagnostic monitor. RECONNECT system. VERIFY Air Bag lamp. REACTIVATE system. |
| | | Yes ▶ | GO to 3.5. |
| 3.5 | CHECK RESISTANCE IN CIRCUIT 611 (W/O) — CONTINUED | | |
| | • Disconnect rear safing sensor.<br>• Attach ohmmeter to Pin 15 (Circuit 611, W/O) on diagnostic monitor wiring connector and to ground.<br>• Is resistance less than 1 ohm? | No ▶ | GO to 3.7. |
| | | Yes ▶ | GO to 3.6. |
| 3.6 | CHECK RESISTANCE IN CIRCUIT 611 (W/O) — CONTINUED | | |
| | • Disconnect center front sensor.<br>• Attach ohmmeter to Pin 15 (611 W/O) on diagnostic monitor wiring connector and to ground.<br>• Is resistance less than 1 ohm? | No ▶ | REPLACE center front sensor. REPLACE diagnostic monitor. RECONNECT system. VERIFY Air Bag lamp. REACTIVATE system. |
| | | Yes ▶ | TRACE Circuit 611 (W/O) to find contact to ground and SERVICE. REPLACE diagnostic monitor. RECONNECT system. VERIFY Air Bag lamp. REACTIVATE system. |

**Fig. 39 Lamp flashes 3 times (Loss of airbag circuit, part 2 of 3). 1990 Town Car**

**Fault Indication — Air Bag Lamp Flashes Three Times**
**Probable Fault — Loss of Air Bag Circuit Deployment Power and/or Backup Power Supply Disconnected**

| TEST STEP | | RESULT ▶ | ACTION TO TAKE |
|---|---|---|---|
| 3.7 | CHECK RESISTANCE IN CIRCUIT 612 (P/O) | | |
| | • Attach ohmmeter to Circuit 612 (P/O) on rear safing sensor wiring connector and to ground.<br>• Is resistance less than 1 ohm?<br>623 (P/W), 614B (GY/O), 613 (DB/W), 611 (W/O), 612 (P/O)<br>REAR SAFING SENSOR CONNECTOR<br>614B (GY/O), 623 (P/W), 611B (W/O), 613 (DB/W), 612 (P/O)<br>REAR SAFING SENSOR HARNESS CONNECTOR | No ▶ | REPLACE rear safing sensor. REPLACE diagnostic monitor. RECONNECT system. VERIFY Air Bag lamp. REACTIVATE system. |
| | | Yes ▶ | TRACE Circuit 612 (P/O) to find contact to ground and SERVICE. REPLACE diagnostic monitor. RECONNECT system. VERIFY Air Bag lamp. REACTIVATE system. |

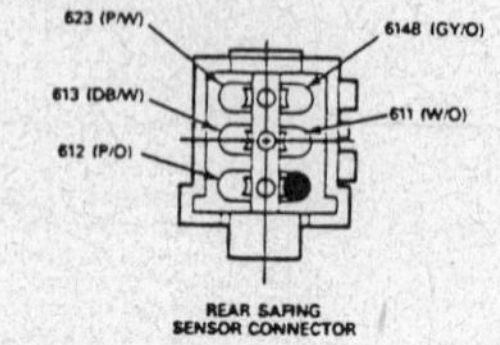

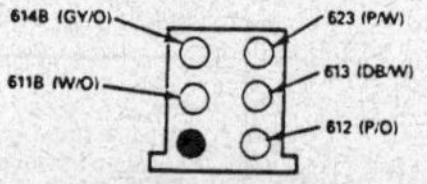

**Fig. 39 Lamp flashes 3 times (Loss of airbag circuit, part 3 of 3). 1990 Town Car**

**Fault Indication — Air Bag Indicator Flashes Three Times**
**Probable Fault — Loss of Air Bag Circuit Deployment Power and/or Backup Power Supply Disconnected**

| TEST STEP | | RESULT ▶ | ACTION TO TAKE |
|---|---|---|---|
| 3.0 | DURING SYSTEM PROVE-OUT AIR BAG INDICATOR PROVIDES A FAULT INDICATION OF 3 FLASHES | | |
| 3.1 | VISUAL INSPECTION OF FUSIBLE LINK IN CIRCUIT 37 (Y) | | |
| | • Visually inspect fuse in fuse panel (10 amp position K) for damage.<br>• Is fuse link open (blown)? | Yes ▶ | DISCONNECT battery ground cable and backup power supply. TRACE Circuit to find short to ground and SERVICE. REPLACE fuse. RECONNECT battery backup power supply and ground cable. VERIFY air bag indicator. |
| | | No ▶ | GO to 3.2. |
| 3.2 | CHECK VOLTAGE OF CIRCUIT 937A (BK/O) | | |
| | • Deactivate air bag system.<br>• Disconnect diagnostic monitor.<br>• Attach a voltmeter to Pin 13, Circuit 937A (BK/O) on diagnostic monitor wiring connector and to ground.<br>• Is voltage greater than 10 volts?<br>AIR BAG MONITOR CONNECTOR<br>PIN 13 CIRCUIT 937A (BK/O)<br>UNDER I/P | No ▶ | DISCONNECT battery ground cable and backup power supply. TRACE Circuit 937A (BK/O) from diagnostic monitor connector to find open circuit and SERVICE. RECONNECT backup power supply and battery ground cable. VERIFY air bag indicator. REACTIVATE system. |
| | | Yes ▶ | GO to 3.3. |
| 3.3 | CHECK BACKUP POWER SUPPLY | | |
| | • Attach a voltmeter to Pin 14, Circuit 656 (P) on diagnostic wiring connector and ground.<br>• Is voltage greater than 10 volts? | Yes ▶ | GO to 3.4. |
| | | No ▶ | CHECK backup power supply. SERVICE as required. If OK, CHECK Circuit 656 (P) and Circuit 937A (BK/O) for opens. SERVICE as required. RECONNECT battery ground cable and backup power supply. VERIFY air bag indicator. REACTIVATE system. |

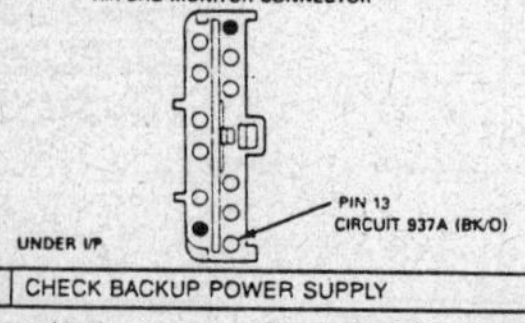

**Fig. 40 Lamp flashes 3 times (Loss of airbag circuit, part 1 of 3). 1991 Town Car**

**Fault Indication — Air Bag Lamp Flashes Three Times**
**Probable Fault — Loss of Air Bag Circuit Deployment Power and/or Backup Power Supply Disconnected**

| TEST STEP | | RESULT ▶ | ACTION TO TAKE |
|---|---|---|---|
| 3.4 | CHECK RESISTANCE IN CIRCUIT 611 (W/O) | | |
| | • Using an ohmmeter find resistance in Pin 15 Circuit 611 (W/O) on diagnostic monitor wiring connector and to ground.<br>• Is resistance less than 1 ohm? | No ▶ | REPLACE diagnostic monitor. RECONNECT system. VERIFY Air Bag lamp. REACTIVATE system. |
| | | Yes ▶ | GO to 3.5. |
| 3.5 | CHECK RESISTANCE IN CIRCUIT 611 (W/O) — CONTINUED | | |
| | • Disconnect rear safing sensor.<br>• Attach ohmmeter to Pin 15 (Circuit 611, W/O) on diagnostic monitor wiring connector and to ground.<br>• Is resistance less than 1 ohm? | No ▶ | GO to 3.6. |
| | | Yes ▶ | TRACE Circuit 611 (W/O) to find contact to ground and SERVICE. REPLACE diagnostic monitor. RECONNECT system. VERIFY air bag indicator. REACTIVATE system. |

**Fig. 40 Lamp flashes 3 times (Loss of airbag circuit, part 2 of 3). 1991 Town Car**

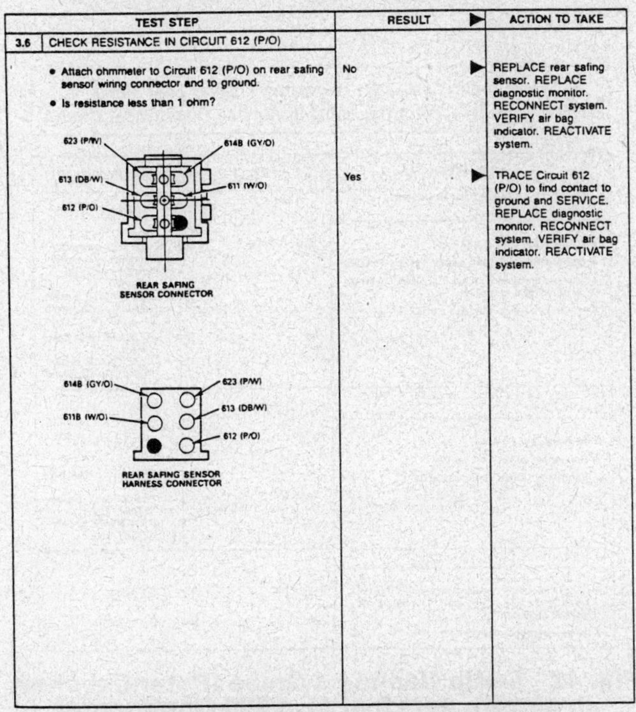

**Fault Indication — Air Bag Indicator Flashes Three Times**
**Probable Fault — Loss of Air Bag Circuit Deployment Power and/or Backup Power Supply Disconnected**

| TEST STEP | | RESULT | ACTION TO TAKE |
|---|---|---|---|
| 3.6 | CHECK RESISTANCE IN CIRCUIT 612 (P/O) | | |
| | • Attach ohmmeter to Circuit 612 (P/O) on rear safing sensor wiring connector and to ground.<br>• Is resistance less than 1 ohm? | No | ▶ REPLACE rear safing sensor. REPLACE diagnostic monitor. RECONNECT system. VERIFY air bag indicator. REACTIVATE system. |
| | | Yes | ▶ TRACE Circuit 612 (P/O) to find contact to ground and SERVICE. REPLACE diagnostic monitor. RECONNECT system. VERIFY air bag indicator. REACTIVATE system. |



**Fig. 40 Lamp flashes 3 times (Loss of airbag circuit, part 3 of 3). 1991 Town Car**

Fault Indication—Air Bag
Flashes Four Times
Probable Fault—Potential Short in Air Bag
Deployment Circuit

| TEST STEP | | RESULT | ACTION TO TAKE |
|---|---|---|---|
| E1 | DURING SYSTEM PROVE-OUT AIR BAG LAMP PROVIDES A FAULT INDICATION OF 4 FLASHES | | |
| E2 | CHECK REAR SAFING SENSOR GROUND | | |
| | • Deactivate system.<br>• Place jumper wire on the rear safing sensor L/W wire and to ground.<br>• Verify lamp. Does air bag lamp flash code 4? | Yes<br>No | ▶ GO to E5.<br>▶ GO to E3. |
| E3 | CONTINUE REAR SAFING SENSOR CHECK | | |
| | • Remove jumper wire from rear safing sensor L/W wire.<br>• Loosen and tighten rear safing sensor attaching screws.<br>• Turn ignition switch to RUN.<br>• Does air bag lamp flash code 4? | Yes<br>No | ▶ GO to E4.<br>▶ VERIFY air bag lamp. |
| E4 | CHECK SAFING SENSOR GROUND CIRCUIT | | |
| | • Turn ignition switch to OFF.<br>• Disconnect rear safing sensor wiring connector.<br>• Attach ohmmeter to L/W wire in sensor connector and to ground.<br>• Is resistance less than 1 ohm? | Yes | ▶ INSPECT connector terminals and wires and SERVICE as required. REACTIVATE system. VERIFY air bag lamp. |
| | | No | ▶ REPLACE rear safing sensor. REACTIVATE system. VERIFY air bag lamp. |

**Fig. 41 Lamp flashes 4 times (Potential short in circuit, part 1 of 4). Capri**

Fault Indication—Air Bag
Flashes Four Times
Probable Fault—Potential Short in Air Bag
Deployment Circuit (Continued)

| TEST STEP | | RESULT | ACTION TO TAKE |
|---|---|---|---|
| E5 | CHECK W/O WIRE CIRCUIT IN CENTER FRONT SENSOR | | |
| | • Remove jumper wire from rear safing sensor L/W wire.<br>• Disconnect center front sensor.<br>• Verify lamp. Does lamp flash code 4? | Yes | ▶ GO to E6. |
| | | No | ▶ REPLACE center front sensor. RECONNECT system. VERIFY lamp. REACTIVATE system. VERIFY lamp. |
| E6 | CONTINUE W/O WIRE CIRCUIT CHECK | | |
| | • Check resistance between Pin 15 (W/O wire in the gray connector) and Pin 23 (V/O wire in the black connector) at the back of the diagnostic module connectors.<br>• Is resistance less than 1 ohm? | Yes<br>No | ▶ GO to E8.<br>▶ GO to E7. |
| E7 | CHECK REAR SAFING SENSOR RESISTANCE | | |
| | • Disconnect rear safing sensor.<br>• Check resistance between W/O and V/O wires.<br>• Is resistance less than 1 ohm? | Yes | ▶ TRACE wires W/O and V/O back to diagnostic module for open circuit and SERVICE (check connectors and terminals to confirm proper connections). If no open circuit exists, REPLACE diagnostic module. RECONNECT system. REACTIVATE system. VERIFY air bag lamp. |
| | | No | ▶ REPLACE rear safing sensor. RECONNECT system. REACTIVATE system. VERIFY air bag lamp. |

**Fig. 41 Lamp flashes 4 times (Potential short in circuit, part 2 of 4). Capri**

Fault Indication—Air Bag
Flashes Four Times
Probable Fault—Potential Short in Air Bag
Deployment Circuit (Continued)

| TEST STEP | | RESULT | ACTION TO TAKE |
|---|---|---|---|
| E8 | CHECK FOR REAR SAFING SENSOR SHORT OR FORWARD CRASH SENSOR INPUT SHORT | | |
| | • Check voltage at back of diagnostic module gray connector Pin 17 (PK/O wire) and to ground.<br>• Is voltage less than 1 volt? | Yes | ▶ GO to E9. |
| | | No | ▶ A short to B+ (Battery Positive) exists in the forward crash sensor input wires GY/O, PK/O, PK/W or W/Y wires. DISCONNECT diagnostic module and CHECK for voltage on these circuits. If no short to B+ exists, REPLACE diagnostic module. RECONNECT system. REACTIVATE system. VERIFY air bag lamp. |
| E9 | CHECK V/W WIRE CIRCUIT VOLTAGE | | |
| | • Disconnect rear safing sensor.<br>• With voltmeter, probe wiring connector V/W wire to ground.<br>• Is V/W wire at battery voltage? | Yes<br>No | ▶ GO to E11.<br>▶ GO to E10. |
| E10 | CHECK V/W WIRE CIRCUIT FOR OPEN | | |
| | • With voltmeter, check voltage at back of diagnostic module black connector, Pin 12 (V/W wire).<br>• Is V/W wire at battery voltage? | Yes | ▶ SERVICE open in V/W wire between diagnostic module and rear sensor. RECONNECT system. REACTIVATE system. VERIFY lamp. |
| | | No | ▶ REPLACE diagnostic module. |
| E11 | CHECK SHORT TO BATTERY POSITIVE (B+) | | |
| | • Remove diagnostic module from bracket.<br>• With voltmeter, check rear safing sensor wiring connector between V/W wire and ground.<br>• Is V/W wire still at battery voltage? | Yes | ▶ Short to B+ exists in V/W wire between diagnostic module and rear safing sensor. TRACE circuit and SERVICE. If no short exists, REPLACE diagnostic module. RECONNECT system. VERIFY air bag lamp. REACTIVATE system. VERIFY air bag lamp. |
| | | No | ▶ RECONNECT diagnostic module. GO to E12. |

**Fig. 41 Lamp flashes 4 times (Potential short in circuit, part 3 of 4). Capri**

Fault Indication—Air Bag
Flashes Four Times
Probable Fault—Potential Short in Air Bag
Deployment Circuit (Continued)

| TEST STEP | | RESULT | ACTION TO TAKE |
|---|---|---|---|
| E12 | CHECK REAR SAFING SENSOR | | |
| | • With diagnostic module reconnected check rear safing sensor resistance between V/W and GY/O wires.<br>• Is resistance less than 1 ohm? | Yes | ▶ GO to E13. |
| | | No | ▶ REPLACE rear safing sensor. RECONNECT system. REACTIVATE system. VERIFY air bag lamp. |
| E13 | REAR SAFING SENSOR CHECKS—CONTINUED | | |
| | • Check rear safing sensor resistance between V/W wire and W/O, V/O and L/W wires.<br>• Are all paths open circuits (off scale)? | Yes | ▶ An open exists in GY/O wire between the rear safing sensor and the diagnostic module, Pin 11. FIND open and SERVICE. If no open exists, REPLACE diagnostic module. RECONNECT system. REACTIVATE system. VERIFY air bag lamp. |
| | | No | ▶ REPLACE rear safing sensor. RECONNECT system. REACTIVATE system. VERIFY air bag lamp. |

**Fig. 41 Lamp flashes 4 times (Potential short in circuit, part 4 of 4). Capri**

**Fault Indication — Air Bag Lamp Flashes Four Times**
**Probable Fault — Potential Short in Air Bag Deployment Circuit**

| TEST STEP | RESULT ▶ | ACTION TO TAKE |
|---|---|---|
| **4.0** DURING SYSTEM PROVE-OUT AIR BAG LAMP PROVIDES A FAULT INDICATION OF 4 FLASHES | | |
| **4.1** CHECK AIR BAGS | | |
| • Turn ignition OFF.<br>• Deactivate system.<br>• Verify lamp. Does Air Bag lamp flash 4 times? | Yes ▶ | GO to **4.3**. |
| | No ▶ | GO to **4.2**. |
| **4.2** ISOLATE AIR BAG | | |
| • Remove battery ground.<br>• Connect Driver Air Bag<br>• Reconnect battery ground.<br>• Verify lamp. Does Air Bag lamp flash code 4? | Yes ▶ | REPLACE driver air bag<br>REACTIVATE entire Air Bag system<br>VERIFY Air Bag lamp |
| | No ▶ | REPLACE passenger Air Bag<br>REACTIVATE entire system<br>VERIFY Air Bag lamp. |
| **4.3** CHECK REAR SAFING SENSOR GROUND | | |
| • Place jumper wire on dash panel sensor circuit 613 (DBW) and to ground.<br>• Verify lamp. Does Air Bag lamp flash code 4? | Yes ▶ | GO to **4.6**. |
| | No ▶ | GO to **4.4**. |
| **4.4** CONTINUE REAR SAFING SENSOR CHECK | | |
| • Remove jumper wire.<br>• Loosen and tighten rear safing sensor attaching nuts.<br>• Turn ignition to run.<br>• Does Air Bag lamp flash code 4? | Yes ▶ | GO to **4.5**. |
| | No ▶ | TURN ignition OFF<br>REACTIVATE system.<br>VERIFY air bag lamp. |

**Fig. 42 Lamp flashes 4 times (Potential short in circuit, part 1 of 6). 1989 Continental**

**Fault Indication — Air Bag Lamp Flashes Four Times**
**Probable Fault — Potential Short in Air Bag Deployment Circuit**

| TEST STEP | RESULT ▶ | ACTION TO TAKE |
|---|---|---|
| **4.5** CHECK SAFING SENSOR GROUND CIRCUIT | | |
| • Turn ignition OFF<br>• Disconnect dash panel sensor wiring connector.<br>• Attach ohmmeter to circuit 613 (DBW) in sensor connector and to ground.<br>• Is resistance less than one ohm? | Yes ▶ | INSPECT connector terminals and wires and SERVICE as required.<br>REACTIVATE system.<br>VERIFY Air Bag lamp. |
| | No ▶ | REPLACE dash panel sensor.<br>REACTIVATE system.<br>VERIFY Air Bag lamp. |
| **4.6** CHECK 611 CIRCUIT IN CENTER FRONT SENSOR | | |
| • Remove jumper wire.<br>• Disconnect center front sensor.<br>• Verify lamp. Does lamp flash code 4? | Yes ▶ | GO to **4.7**. |
| | No ▶ | REPLACE center front sensor.<br>RECONNECT system.<br>VERIFY lamp.<br>REACTIVATE system.<br>VERIFY lamp. |
| **4.7** CONTINUE CIRCUIT 611 CHECK | | |
| • Check resistance between circuit 611 (Pin 15) and 612 (Pin 23) at the back of the diagnostic monitor connector.<br>• Is resistance less than one ohm? | Yes ▶ | GO to **4.9**. |
| | No ▶ | GO to **4.8**. |

**Fig. 42 Lamp flashes 4 times (Potential short in circuit, part 2 of 6). 1989 Continental**

**Fault Indication — Air Bag Lamp Flashes Four Times**
**Probable Fault — Potential Short in Air Bag Deployment Circuit**

| TEST STEP | RESULT ▶ | ACTION TO TAKE |
|---|---|---|
| **4.8** CHECK 611 IN REAR SAFING SENSOR | | |
| • Disconnect rear safing sensor.<br>• Check resistance between circuits 611 (W/O) and 612 (P/O).<br>• Is resistance less than one ohm? | Yes ▶ | TRACE circuits 611 and 612 back to diagnostic monitor for open circuit and SERVICE (check connectors and terminals to confirm proper connections). If no open circuit exists, REPLACE diagnostic monitor.<br>RECONNECT system.<br>REACTIVATE system.<br>VERIFY Air Bag lamp. |
| | No ▶ | REPLACE rear safing sensor. RECONNECT system. REACTIVATE system. VERIFY Air Bag lamp. |
| **4.9** CHECK CIRCUITS 611 AND 616 (AIR BAG RETURN LINES) | | |
| • Disconnect battery ground.<br>• Remove jumpers in wiring connector to driver and passenger air bags.<br>• Reconnect battery ground.<br>• Verify lamp. Does Air Bag lamp flash code 4? | Yes ▶ | GO to **4.12**. |
| | No ▶ | GO to **4.10**. |
| **4.10** ISOLATE AIR BAG RETURN CIRCUIT | | |
| • Short is in Circuits 615 (GY/W) or 616 (PK/BK).<br>• Put jumper in wiring connector to Passenger Air Bag Circuit 616 (PK/BK) and 614 (GY/O).<br>• Does air bag lamp still flash code 4? | Yes ▶ | GO to **4.11**. |
| | No ▶ | SHORT to ground in Circuit 616 (PK/BK) between Passenger Air Bag and diagnostic monitor. TRACE and SERVICE circuit.<br>RECONNECT system.<br>REACTIVATE system.<br>VERIFY Air Bag lamp. |

**Fig. 42 Lamp flashes 4 times (Potential short in circuit, part 3 of 6). 1989 Continental**

**Fault Indication — Air Bag Lamp Flashes Four Times**
**Probable Fault — Potential Short in Air Bag Deployment Circuit**

| TEST STEP | RESULT ▶ | ACTION TO TAKE |
|---|---|---|
| **4.11** CHECK CLOCKSPRING | | |
| • Short to ground in Circuit 615 (GY/W) between driver air bag and diagnostic monitor.<br>• Disconnect clockspring connector to 14401 at base of column.<br>• Jumper wiring connector Circuits 614 (GY/O) and 615 (GY/W).<br>• Verify lamp. Does lamp flash code 4? | Yes ▶ | TRACE and SERVICE short to ground between clockspring and diagnostic monitor. If no short exists, REPLACE diagnostic module. |
| | No<br>lamp goes out ▶ | REPLACE clockspring.<br>RECONNECT system.<br>REACTIVATE system.<br>VERIFY Air Bag lamp. |
| **4.12** CHECK FOR REAR SAFING SENSOR SHORT OR FORWARD CRASH SENSOR INPUT SHORT | | |
| • Check voltage at back of diagnostic monitor connector Circuit 617 (Pin 17, PK/O) and to ground.<br>• Is voltage less than one volt? | Yes ▶ | GO to 4.13. |
| | No ▶ | A short to B+ exits in the forward crash sensor input Circuits 615 (GY/W), 616 (PK/BK), 617 (PK/O), 619 (PK/W), or 621 (W/Y). DISCONNECT diagnostic monitor and CHECK for voltage on these circuits. If no short to B+ exists, REPLACE diagnostic monitor.<br>RECONNECT system.<br>REACTIVATE system.<br>VERIFY Air Bag lamp. |
| **4.13** CHECK CIRCUIT 623 (P/W) | | |
| • Disconnect rear safing sensor.<br>• With voltmeter, probe wiring connector Circuit 623 (P/W) to ground.<br>• Is 623 at battery voltage? | Yes ▶ | GO to 4.17. |
| | No ▶ | GO to 4.14. |

**Fig. 42 Lamp flashes 4 times (Potential short in circuit, part 4 of 6). 1989 Continental**

**Fault Indication — Air Bag Lamp Flashes Four Times**
**Probable Fault — Potential Short in Air Bag Deployment Circuit**

| TEST STEP | RESULT ▶ | ACTION TO TAKE |
|---|---|---|
| **4.14** CHECK 623 OPEN OR SHORT TO GROUND | | |
| • With voltmeter, check wiring harness side of connector to diagnostic monitor, Circuit 623 (Pin 12, P W)<br>• Is 623 at battery voltage? | Yes ▶ | SERVICE open in Circuit 623 (P W) between diagnostic monitor and rear sensor. RECONNECT system. REACTIVATE system. VERIFY lamp. |
| | No ▶ | GO to **4.15** |
| **4.15** CHECK 623 SHORT TO GROUND OR DIAGNOSTIC MONITOR | | |
| • Disconnect diagnostic monitor.<br>• With ohmmeter, check harness side of connector to Circuit 623 (Pin 12, P/W) and to ground.<br>• Is resistance less than one ohm? | Yes ▶ | SERVICE Circuit 623 short to ground. RECONNECT system. REACTIVATE system. VERIFY Air Bag lamp. |
| | No ▶ | REPLACE diagnostic monitor. RECONNECT system. REACTIVATE system. VERIFY Air Bag lamp. |
| **4.16** CHECK CIRCUIT 623 SHORT TO BATTERY POSITIVE (B−) | | |
| • Disconnect diagnostic monitor.<br>• With voltmeter, check rear safing sensor wiring connector Circuit 623 (P W) and to ground.<br>• Is 623 still at battery voltage? | Yes ▶ | Short to B− exists in Circuit 623 between diagnostic monitor and rear safing sensor. TRACE circuit and SERVICE. If no short exists, REPLACE diagnostic monitor. RECONNECT system. REACTIVATE system. VERIFY Air Bag lamp. |
| | No ▶ | RECONNECT diagnostic monitor. GO to **4.17**. |

**Fig. 42 Lamp flashes 4 times (Potential short in circuit, part 5 of 6). 1989 Continental**

**Fault Indication — Air Bag Lamp Flashes Four Times**
**Probable Fault — Potential Short in Air Bag Deployment Circuit**

| TEST STEP | RESULT ▶ | ACTION TO TAKE |
|---|---|---|
| **4.17** CHECK REAR SAFING SENSOR OR CIRCUIT 614 | | |
| • With diagnostic module reconnected, check rear safing sensor resistance between Circuits 623 (P/W) and 614 (BY/O).<br>• Is resistance less than one ohm? | Yes ▶ | GO to **4.19**. |
| | No ▶ | REPLACE rear safing sensor. RECONNECT system. REACTIVATE system. VERIFY Air Bag lamp. |
| **4.18** CONTINUE REAR SAFING SENSOR CHECKS | | |
| • Check rear safing sensor resistance between Circuit 623 (P/W) and Circuits 611 (W/O), 612 (P/O), and 613 (DB/W).<br>• Are all paths open circuits (off scale)? | Yes ▶ | GO to **4.19**. |
| | No ▶ | REPLACE rear safing sensor. RECONNECT system. REACTIVATE system. VERIFY Air Bag lamp. |
| **4.19** CHECK 614 | | |
| • Check Circuit 614 (GY O) in wiring side connector to rear safing sensor and to ground.<br>• Is resistance less than one ohm? | Yes ▶ | GO to **4.20**. |
| | No ▶ | An open exists in 614 (GY O) between the rear safing sensor and the diagnostic module, Pins 8 or 11. FIND open and SERVICE. If no open exists, REPLACE diagnostic module. RECONNECT system. REACTIVATE system. VERIFY Air Bag lamp. |
| **4.20** 614 SHORTED TO GROUND | | |
| • A short to ground exists in Circuit 614 (GY/O) between safing sensors, air bags, and Pin 11 of diagnostic monitor.<br>• Disconnect diagnostic monitor and check resistance between Pin 11 of harness connector (GY/O) and to ground.<br>• Is resistance less than one ohm? | Yes ▶ | TRACE short to ground in Circuit 614 (GY/O) and SERVICE. RECONNECT system. REACTIVATE system. VERIFY Air Bag lamp. |
| | No ▶ | REPLACE diagnostic monitor. RECONNECT system. REACTIVATE system. VERIFY Air Bag lamp. |

**Fig. 42 Lamp flashes 4 times (Potential short in circuit, part 6 of 6). 1989 Continental**

**Fault Indication — Air Bag Lamp Flashes Four Times**
**Probable Fault — Potential Short in Air Bag Deployment Circuit**

| TEST STEP | RESULT ▶ | ACTION TO TAKE |
|---|---|---|
| **4.0** DURING SYSTEM PROVE-OUT AIR BAG LAMP PROVIDES A FAULT INDICATION OF 4 FLASHES | | |
| **4.1** CHECK AIR BAGS | | |
| • Turn ignition OFF.<br>• Deactivate system.<br>• Verify lamp.<br>• Does Air Bag lamp flash 4 times? | Yes ▶ | INSPECT connections at driver air bag and REPAIR as required. If connections okay, GO to 4.2. |
| | No ▶ | REPLACE driver air bag. REACTIVATE entire Air Bag system. VERIFY Air Bag lamp. |
| **4.2** CHECK REAR SAFING SENSOR GROUND | | |
| • Place jumper wire on dash panel sensor circuit 613 (DB W) and to ground.<br>• Verify lamp. Does Air Bag lamp flash code 4? | Yes ▶ | GO to 4.5. |
| | No ▶ | GO to 4.3. |
| **4.3** CONTINUE REAR SAFING SENSOR CHECK | | |
| • Remove jumper wire.<br>• Loosen and tighten rear safing sensor attaching nuts.<br>• Turn ignition to RUN.<br>• Does Air Bag lamp flash code 4? | Yes ▶ | GO to 4.4 |
| | No ▶ | TURN ignition OFF. REACTIVATE system. VERIFY air bag lamp. |
| **4.4** CHECK SAFING SENSOR GROUND CIRCUIT | | |
| • Turn ignition OFF.<br>• Disconnect dash panel sensor wiring connector.<br>• Attach ohmmeter to circuit 613 (DB W) in sensor connector and to ground.<br>• Is resistance less than one ohm? | Yes ▶ | INSPECT connector terminals and wires and SERVICE as required. RECONNECT sensors. REACTIVATE system. VERIFY Air Bag lamp. |
| | No ▶ | REPLACE dash panel sensor. REACTIVATE system. VERIFY Air Bag lamp. |

**Fig. 43 Lamp flashes 4 times (Potential short in circuit, part 1 of 5). 1989 Tempo & Topaz**

**Fault Indication — Air Bag Lamp Flashes Four Times**
**Probable Fault — Potential Short in Air Bag Deployment Circuit**

| TEST STEP | RESULT ▶ | ACTION TO TAKE |
|---|---|---|
| **4.5** CHECK 61L CIRCUIT IN CENTER FRONT SENSOR | | |
| • Remove jumper wire.<br>• Disconnect center front sensor.<br>• Verify lamp.<br>• Does lamp flash code 4? | Yes ▶ | Go to 4.6. |
| | No ▶ | REPLACE center front sensor. RECONNECT system. VERIFY lamp. REACTIVATE system. VERIFY lamp. |
| **4.6** CONTINUE CIRCUIT 611 CHECK | | |
| • Check resistance between circuit 611 (W/O, Pin 15) and 612 (P/O, Pin 23) at the back of the diagnostic monitor connector.<br>• Is resistance less than one ohm? | Yes ▶ | Go to 4.8. |
| | No ▶ | Go to 4.7. |
| **4.7** CHECK 611 IN REAR SAFING SENSOR | | |
| • Disconnect rear safing sensor.<br>• Check resistance between circuits 611 (W/O) and 612 (P/O).<br>• Is resistance less than one ohm? | Yes ▶ | TRACE circuits 611 and 612 back to diagnostic monitor for open circuit and SERVICE (check connectors and terminals to confirm proper connections). If no open circuit exists, REPLACE diagnostic monitor. RECONNECT system. REACTIVATE system. VERIFY Air Bag lamp. |
| | No ▶ | REPLACE rear safing sensor. RECONNECT system. REACTIVATE system. VERIFY Air Bag lamp. |

**Fig. 43 Lamp flashes 4 times (Potential short in circuit, part 2 of 5). 1989 Tempo & Topaz**

**Fault Indication — Air Bag Lamp Flashes Four Times**
**Probable Fault — Potential Short in Air Bag Deployment Circuit**

| TEST STEP | RESULT ▶ | ACTION TO TAKE |
|---|---|---|
| **4.8** CHECK CIRCUIT 615 (AIR BAG RETURN LINE) | | |
| • Disconnect battery ground.<br>• Remove jumpers in wiring connector to driver air bag.<br>• Reconnect battery ground.<br>• Verify lamp.<br>• Does Air Bag lamp flash code 4? | Yes ▶<br>No ▶ | Go to 4.10.<br>Go to 4.9 |
| **4.9** CHECK CLOCKSPRING | | |
| • Short to ground in Circuit 615 (GY/W) between driver air bag and diagnostic monitor.<br>• Disconnect clockspring connector to 14401 at base of column.<br>• Jumper wiring connector Circuits 614 (GY/O) and 615 (GY/W).<br>• Verify lamp. Does lamp flash code 4? | Yes ▶ | TRACE and SERVICE Circuit 615 short to ground between clockspring and diagnostic monitor. If no short exists, REPLACE diagnostic monitor. |
| | No lamp goes out ▶ | REPLACE clockspring RECONNECT system. VERIFY Air Bag lamp. |
| **4.10** CHECK FOR REAR SAFING SENSOR SHORT OR FORWARD CRASH SENSOR INPUT SHORT | | |
| • Check voltage at back of diagnostic module connector Circuit 617 (Pin 17, PK/O) and to ground.<br>• Is voltage less than one volt? | Yes ▶ | GO to 4.11. |
| | No ▶ | A short to B+ exists in the forward crash sensor input Circuits 615 (GY/W), 616 (PK/BK), 617 (PK/O), 619 (PK/W), or 621 (W/Y). Disconnect diagnostic module and CHECK for voltage on these circuits. If no short to B+ exists, REPLACE diagnostic module. RECONNECT system. REACTIVATE system. VERIFY Air Bag lamp. |

**Fig. 43 Lamp flashes 4 times (Potential short in circuit, part 3 of 5). 1989 Tempo & Topaz**

**Fault Indication — Air Bag Lamp Flashes Four Times**
**Probable Fault — Potential Short in Air Bag Deployment Circuit**

| TEST STEP | RESULT ▶ | ACTION TO TAKE |
|---|---|---|
| **4.14** CHECK CIRCUIT 623 SHORT TO BATTERY POSITIVE (B+) | | |
| • Disconnect diagnostic monitor<br>• With voltmeter, check rear safing sensor wiring connector Circuit 623 (P/W) and to ground.<br>• Is 623 still at battery voltage? | Yes ▶ | Short to B+ exists in Circuit 623 between diagnostic monitor and rear safing sensor TRACE circuit and SERVICE. If no short exists, REPLACE diagnostic monitor RECONNECT system VERIFY Air Bag lamp REACTIVATE system VERIFY Air Bag lamp |
| | No ▶ | RECONNECT diagnostic monitor. Go to 4.15 |
| **4.15** CHECK REAR SAFING SENSOR OR CIRCUIT 614 | | |
| • With diagnostic monitor reconnected check rear safing sensor resistance between Circuits 623 (P/W) and 614 (BY/O)<br>• Is resistance less than one ohm? | Yes ▶<br>No ▶ | Go to 4.16<br>REPLACE rear safing sensor. RECONNECT system. REACTIVATE system. VERIFY Air Bag lamp |
| **4.16** CONTINUE REAR SAFING SENSOR CHECKS | | |
| • Check rear safing sensor resistance between Circuit 623 (P/W) and Circuits 611 (W/O), 612 (P/O), and 613 (DB/W)<br>• Are all paths open circuits (off scale)? | Yes ▶<br>No ▶ | Go to 4.17<br>REPLACE rear safing sensor. RECONNECT system. REACTIVATE system. VERIFY Air Bag lamp |
| **4.17** CHECK 614 | | |
| • Check Circuit 614 (GY/O) in wiring side connector to rear safing sensor and to ground.<br>• Is resistance less than one ohm? | Yes ▶<br>No ▶ | Go to 4.18.<br>An open exists in 614 (GY/O) between the rear safing sensor and the diagnostic module, Pins 8 or 11. FIND open and SERVICE. If no open exists, REPLACE diagnostic module. RECONNECT system. VERIFY Air Bag lamp. |
| **4.18** 614 SHORTED TO GROUND | | |
| • A short to ground exists in Circuit 614 (GY/O) between safing sensors, air bags, and Pin 11 of diagnostic monitor.<br>• Disconnect diagnostic monitor and check resistance between Pin 11 of harness connector (GY/O) and to ground.<br>• Is resistance less than one ohm? | Yes ▶ | TRACE short to ground in Circuit 614 (GY/O) and SERVICE. RECONNECT system. REACTIVATE system. VERIFY Air Bag lamp. |
| | No ▶ | REPLACE diagnostic monitor. RECONNECT system. REACTIVATE system. VERIFY Air Bag lamp. |

**Fig. 43 Lamp flashes 4 times (Potential short in circuit, part 5 of 5). 1989 Tempo & Topaz**

**Fault Indication — Air Bag Lamp Flashes Four Times**
**Probable Fault — Potential Short in Air Bag Deployment Circuit**

| TEST STEP | RESULT ▶ | ACTION TO TAKE |
|---|---|---|
| **4.11** CHECK CIRCUIT 623 (P/W) | | |
| • Disconnect rear safing sensor.<br>• With voltmeter, probe wiring connector Circuit 623 (P/W) to ground.<br>• Is 623 at battery voltage? | Yes ▶<br>No ▶ | Go to 4.14.<br>Go to 4.12. |
| **4.12** CHECK 623 OPEN OR SHORT TO GROUND | | |
| • With voltmeter check voltage at back of diagnostic monitor connector, Circuit 623 (Pin 12, P/W)<br>• Is 623 at battery voltage? | Yes ▶ | SERVICE open in Circuit 623 (P/W) between diagnostic monitor and rear sensor. RECONNECT system. REACTIVATE system. VERIFY lamp. |
| | No ▶ | Go to 4.13 |
| **4.13** CHECK 623 SHORT TO GROUND OR DIAGNOSTIC MONITOR | | |
| • Disconnect diagnostic monitor.<br>• With ohmmeter, check harness side of connector to Circuit 623 (Pin 12, P/W) and to ground.<br>• Is resistance less than one ohm? | Yes ▶ | SERVICE Circuit 623 short to ground. RECONNECT system. REACTIVATE system. VERIFY Air Bag lamp. |
| | No ▶ | REPLACE diagnostic monitor. RECONNECT system. REACTIVATE system. VERIFY Air Bag lamp. |

**Fig. 43 Lamp flashes 4 times (Potential short in circuit, part 4 of 5). 1989 Tempo & Topaz**

**Fault Indication — Air Bag Lamp Flashes Four Times**
**Probable Fault — Potential Short in Air Bag Deployment Circuit**

| TEST STEP | RESULT ▶ | ACTION TO TAKE |
|---|---|---|
| **4.0** DURING SYSTEM PROVE-OUT AIR BAG LAMP PROVIDES A FAULT INDICATION OF 4 FLASHES | | |
| **4.1** CHECK REAR SAFING SENSOR GROUND | | |
| • Deactivate system.<br>• Place jumper wire on dash panel sensor Circuit 613 (DBW) and to ground.<br>• Verify lamp. Does Air Bag lamp flash code 4? | Yes ▶<br>No ▶ | GO to 4.4.<br>GO to 4.2. |
| **4.2** CONTINUE REAR SAFING SENSOR CHECK | | |
| • Remove jumper wire.<br>• Loosen and tighten rear safing sensor attaching screws.<br>• Turn ignition switch to RUN.<br>• Does Air Bag lamp flash code 4? | Yes ▶<br>No ▶ | GO to 4.3.<br>VERIFY air bag lamp. |
| **4.3** CHECK SAFING SENSOR GROUND CIRCUIT | | |
| • Turn ignition switch to OFF.<br>• Disconnect rear safing sensor wiring connector.<br>• Attach ohmmeter to Circuit 613 (DBW) in sensor connector and to ground.<br>• Is resistance less than one ohm? | Yes ▶ | INSPECT connector terminals and wires and SERVICE as required. REACTIVATE system. VERIFY Air Bag lamp. |
| | No ▶ | REPLACE rear safing sensor. REACTIVATE system. VERIFY Air Bag lamp. |
| **4.4** CHECK 611 CIRCUIT IN CENTER FRONT SENSOR | | |
| • Remove jumper wire.<br>• Disconnect center front sensor.<br>• Verify lamp. Does lamp flash code 4? | Yes ▶<br>No ▶ | GO to 4.5.<br>REPLACE center front sensor. RECONNECT system. VERIFY lamp. REACTIVATE system. VERIFY lamp. |
| **4.5** CONTINUE CIRCUIT 611 CHECK | | |
| • Check resistance between Circuit 611 (Pin 15) and 612 (Pin 23) at the back of the diagnostic monitor connector.<br>• Is resistance less than one ohm? | Yes ▶<br>No ▶ | GO to 4.7.<br>GO to 4.6. |

**Fig. 44 Lamp flashes 4 times (Potential short in circuit, part 1 of 4). Crown Victoria, Grand Marquis, Mark VII, Mustang, Sable, Taurus, Town Car & 1990–91 Continental, Tempo & Topaz**

**Fault Indication — Air Bag Lamp Flashes Four Times**
**Probable Fault — Potential Short in Air Bag Deployment Circuit**

| TEST STEP | RESULT | ACTION TO TAKE |
|---|---|---|
| **4.6 CHECK 611 IN REAR SAFING SENSOR** | | |
| • Disconnect rear safing sensor. • Check resistance between Circuits 611 (W/O) and 612 (P/O). • Is resistance less than one ohm? | Yes ▶ | TRACE Circuits 611 and 612 back to diagnostic monitor for open circuit and SERVICE (check connectors and terminals to confirm proper connections). If no open circuit exists, REPLACE diagnostic monitor. RECONNECT system. REACTIVATE system. VERIFY Air Bag lamp. |
| | No ▶ | REPLACE rear safing sensor. RECONNECT system. REACTIVATE system. VERIFY Air Bag lamp. |
| **4.7 CHECK FOR REAR SAFING SENSOR SHORT OR FORWARD CRASH SENSOR INPUT SHORT** | | |
| • Check voltage at back of diagnostic monitor connector Circuit 617 (Pin 17, PK/O) and to ground. • Is voltage less than one volt? | Yes ▶ | GO to 4.8. |
| | No ▶ | A short to B + exits in the forward crash sensor input Circuits 615 (GY/W), 616 (PK/BK), 617 (PK/O), 619 (PK/W), or 621 (W/Y). DISCONNECT diagnostic monitor and CHECK for voltage on these circuits. If no short to B + exists, REPLACE diagnostic monitor. RECONNECT system. REACTIVATE system. VERIFY Air Bag lamp. |

**Fig. 44 Lamp flashes 4 times (Potential short in circuit, part 2 of 4). Crown Victoria, Grand Marquis, Mark VII, Mustang, Sable, Taurus, Town Car & 1990–91 Continental, Tempo & Topaz**

**Fault Indication — Air Bag Lamp Flashes Four Times**
**Probable Fault — Potential Short in Air Bag Deployment Circuit**

| TEST STEP | RESULT | ACTION TO TAKE |
|---|---|---|
| **4.12 CONTINUE REAR SAFING SENSOR CHECKS** | | |
| • Check rear safing sensor resistance between Circuit 623 (P/W) and Circuits 611 (W/O), 612 (P/O), and 613 (DB/W). • Are all paths open circuits (off scale)? | Yes ▶ | An open exists in 614 (GY/O) between the rear safing sensor and the diagnostic monitor Pins 8 or 11. FIND open and SERVICE. If no open exists, REPLACE diagnostic monitor. RECONNECT system. REACTIVATE system. VERIFY Air Bag lamp. |
| | No ▶ | REPLACE rear safing sensor. RECONNECT system. REACTIVATE system. VERIFY Air Bag lamp. |

**Fig. 44 Lamp flashes 4 times (Potential short in circuit, part 4 of 4). Crown Victoria, Grand Marquis, Mark VII, Mustang, Sable, Taurus, Town Car & 1990–91 Continental, Tempo & Topaz**

**Fault Indication — Air Bag Lamp Flashes Four Times**
**Probable Fault — Potential Short in Air Bag Deployment Circuit**

| TEST STEP | RESULT | ACTION TO TAKE |
|---|---|---|
| **4.8 CHECK CIRCUIT 623 (P/W)** | | |
| • Disconnect rear safing sensor. • With voltmeter, probe wiring connector Circuit 623 (P/W) to ground. • Is 623 at battery voltage? | Yes ▶ | GO to 4.10. |
| | No ▶ | GO to 4.9. |
| **4.9 CHECK 623 OPEN** | | |
| • With voltmeter, check wiring harness side of connector to diagnostic monitor, Circuit 623 (Pin 12, P/W). • Is 623 at battery voltage? | Yes ▶ | SERVICE open in Circuit 623 (P/W) between diagnostic monitor and rear sensor. RECONNECT system. REACTIVATE system. VERIFY lamp. |
| | No ▶ | REPLACE diagnostic monitor. |
| **4.10 CHECK CIRCUIT 623 SHORT TO BATTERY POSITIVE (B+)** | | |
| • Disconnect diagnostic monitor. • With voltmeter, check rear safing sensor wiring connector Circuit 623 (P/W) and to ground. • Is 623 still at battery voltage? | Yes ▶ | Short to B+ exists in Circuit 623 between diagnostic monitor and rear safing sensor. TRACE circuit and SERVICE. If no short exists, REPLACE diagnostic monitor. RECONNECT system. REACTIVATE system. VERIFY Air Bag lamp. |
| | No ▶ | RECONNECT diagnostic monitor. GO to 4.11. |
| **4.11 CHECK REAR SAFING SENSOR OR CIRCUIT 614** | | |
| • With diagnostic module reconnected, check rear safing sensor resistance between Circuits 623 (P/W) and 614 (BY/O). • Is resistance less than one ohm? | Yes ▶ | GO to 4.12. |
| | No ▶ | REPLACE rear safing sensor. RECONNECT system. REACTIVATE system. VERIFY Air Bag lamp. |

**Fig. 44 Lamp flashes 4 times (Potential short in circuit, part 3 of 4). Crown Victoria, Grand Marquis, Mark VII, Mustang, Sable, Taurus, Town Car & 1990–91 Continental, Tempo & Topaz**

**Fault Indication — Air Bag Lamp Flashes Five Times**
**Probable Fault — Forward Crash Sensor Or Igniter Circuit Shorted To Ground**

| TEST STEP | RESULT | ACTION TO TAKE |
|---|---|---|
| **F1 DURING SYSTEM PROVE-OUT AIR BAG LAMP PROVIDES A FAULT INDICATION OF 5 FLASHES** | | |
| **F2 CHECK AIR BAG** | | |
| • Turn ignition OFF. • Deactivate system. • Verify lamp. Does Air Bag lamp flash 5 times? | Yes ▶ | GO to F3. |
| | No ▶ | Disconnect battery ground and backup power supply. REPLACE driver air bag. RECONNECT and REACTIVATE system. VERIFY Air Bag lamp. If code 10 is present, REPLACE diagnostic monitor. |
| **F3 VERIFY LAMP WITH ALL THREE FRONT SENSORS DISCONNECTED** | | |
| • Deactivate system. • Disconnect all front sensors (Left, Right and Center). • Verify Air Bag lamp. | Air Bag lamp flashes fault code 5 ▶ | GO to F4. |
| | Air Bag lamp flashes fault code 10 ▶ | GO to F5. |
| | Air Bag lamp does not flash either fault 5 or 10 ▶ | REPLACE diagnostic monitor. RECONNECT system. VERIFY Air Bag lamp. REACTIVATE system. |
| **F4 CHECK RESISTANCE OF THE FRONT SENSORS** | | |
| • Check for intermittent short in Pins 17 (PK/O), 18 (PK/W) and 19 (W/Y). • Perform all three of the following tests. • Attach ohmmeter to ground and to appropriate pin on each front sensor connector. | Yes ▶ | REPLACE diagnostic monitor. RECONNECT system. VERIFY Air Bag lamp. REACTIVATE system. |
| (see sensor table below) • Is resistance between 1000-1300 ohms for each sensor? | Resistance is NOT between 1000-1300 ohms for one or all sensors ▶ | REPLACE sensor(s). VERIFY Air Bag lamp. If lamp flashes fault code 10, INSTALL a new diagnostic monitor. REACTIVATE system. VERIFY Air Bag lamp. |

| Sensor | Pin | Wire Color |
|---|---|---|
| Right | 17 | PK/O |
| Center | 18 | PK/W |
| Left | 19 | W/Y |

**Fig. 45 Lamp flashes 5 times (Forward crash sensor or igniter circuit shorted to ground, part 1 of 4). Capri**

Fault Indication — Air Bag Lamp Flashes Five Times
Probable Fault — Shorted Forward Crash Sensor Deployment Circuit

| | TEST STEP | RESULT | ACTION TO TAKE |
|---|---|---|---|
| F5 | CHECK RESISTANCE IN THE FORWARD CRASH SENSOR DEPLOYMENT CIRCUIT | | |
| | • Remove monitor from bracket.<br>• Disconnect diagnostic monitor.<br>• Perform all three of the following tests.<br>• Attach ohmmeter to ground and to appropriate pin on the diagnostic monitor wiring connector. | Yes ▶ | TRACE appropriate circuit(s) to find contact to ground and SERVICE. RECONNECT system. VERIFY Air Bag lamp. If lamp flashes fault code 10, INSTALL a new diagnostic monitor. REACTIVATE system. VERIFY Air Bag lamp. |
| | Pin No. / Wire Color:<br>17 — PK/O<br>18 — PK/W<br>19 — W/Y<br>• Is resistance less than 1 ohm for any test? | Resistance is 1 ohm or greater ▶ | GO to F6. |
| F6 | CHECK GY/W WIRE BETWEEN MONITOR BLACK CONNECTOR AND DRIVER AIR BAG | | |
| | • Remove jumper in wiring connector to driver air bag. Leave open.<br>• Fault code should change to Code 4 or Code 6. | Code 6 ▶ | GO to F7. |
| | | Code 4 ▶ | GO to F8. |

Fig. 45 Lamp flashes 5 times (Forward crash sensor or igniter circuit shorted to ground, part 2 of 4). Capri

Fault Indication — Air Bag Lamp Flashes Five Times
Probable Fault — Forward Crash Sensor Or Igniter Circuit Shorted To Ground

| | TEST STEP | RESULT | ACTION TO TAKE |
|---|---|---|---|
| F7 | CHECK CLOCKSPRING | | |
| | • Short to ground in GY/W wire between driver air bag and diagnostic monitor black connector.<br>• Disconnect clockspring connector from main harness at base of column.<br>• Place jumper wire between GY/O and GY/W wires of main harness.<br>• Verify lamp. Does lamp flash code 6? | Yes ▶ | TRACE and SERVICE GY/W wire short to ground between clockspring and diagnostic monitor black connector. If code 10 is present, or no short exists, REPLACE diagnostic monitor. |
| | | No lamp goes out ▶ | REPLACE clockspring. RECONNECT system. If code 10 is present, REPLACE monitor. VERIFY Air Bag lamp. |
| F8 | CHECK FOR IGNITER CIRCUIT SHORTED TO GROUND | | |
| | • Disconnect rear safing sensor.<br>• With an ohmmeter, check GY/O wire to ground.<br>• Is resistance less than 1 ohm? | Yes ▶ | A short to ground exists in GY/O wire between safing sensors, air bag, and Pin 11 of diagnostic monitor. TRACE short to ground. REPAIR as required. RECONNECT and REACTIVATE system. VERIFY lamp. If no short is found, or code 10 is present, replace diagnostic module. |
| | | No ▶ | GO to F9. |

Fig. 45 Lamp flashes 5 times (Forward crash sensor or igniter circuit shorted to ground, part 3 of 4). Capri

Fault Indication — Air Bag Lamp Flashes Five Times
Probable Fault — Forward Crash Sensor Or Igniter Circuit Shorted To Ground

| | TEST STEP | RESULT | ACTION TO TAKE |
|---|---|---|---|
| F9 | CHECK FOR IGNITER CIRCUIT SHORTED TO GROUND — CONTINUED | | |
| | • With an ohmmeter, check V/W wire at Pin 12 and ground.<br>• Is resistance less than 1 ohm? | Yes ▶ | TRACE short to ground in V/W wire. REPAIR as required. RECONNECT and REACTIVATE system. VERIFY lamp. If code 10 exists, REPLACE monitor. |
| | | No ▶ | GO to F10. |
| F10 | CHECK REAR SAFING SENSOR | | |
| | • With an ohmmeter, check V/W wire in sensor connector and ground (with sensor attached to vehicle).<br>• Is resistance less than 1 ohm? | Yes ▶ | REPLACE rear safing sensor. If code 10 exists, REPLACE diagnostic monitor. RECONNECT and REACTIVATE system. VERIFY Air Bag lamp. |
| | | No ▶ | REPLACE diagnostic monitor. RECONNECT and REACTIVATE system. VERIFY Air Bag lamp. |

Fig. 45 Lamp flashes 5 times (Forward crash sensor or igniter circuit shorted to ground, part 4 of 4). Capri

**Fault Indication — Air Bag Indicator Flashes Five Times**
**Probable Fault — Forward Crash Sensor Or Igniter Circuit Shorted To Ground**

NOTE: Do not replace diagnostic monitor with a fault code 5 unless instructed to do so.

| | TEST STEP | RESULT | ACTION TO TAKE |
|---|---|---|---|
| 5.0 | DURING SYSTEM PROVE-OUT AIR BAG INDICATOR PROVIDES A FAULT INDICATION OF 5 FLASHES | | |
| 5.1 | DEACTIVATE SYSTEM | | |
| | • Turn ignition OFF.<br>• Deactivate system.<br>• Verify indicator. Does air bag indicator flash 5 times? | Yes ▶ | GO to 5.3. |
| | | No ▶ | GO to 5.2. |
| 5.2 | CHECK AIR BAGS | | |
| | • Measure resistance between any air bag connector pin and metal case on rear of air bag. (If equipped with passenger air bag, test both.) | Resistance is less than 10 ohms ▶ | REPLACE air bag(s). RECONNECT system. VERIFY air bag indicator. If fault code 10 is present, REPLACE diagnostic monitor. REACTIVATE system. VERIFY air bag indicator. |
| | | Resistance is 10 ohms or more ▶ | REPLACE clockspring. RECONNECT system. If fault code 10 is present, REPLACE diagnostic monitor. REACTIVATE system. |
| 5.3 | CHECK CLOCKSPRING | | |
| | • Disconnect gray 3-wire connector at base of steering column.<br>• Connect a jumper between Circuits 614 (GY/O) and 615 (GY/W) at harness connector.<br>• Does air bag indicator flash 5 times? | Yes ▶ | GO to 5.4. |
| | | No ▶ | REPLACE clockspring. RECONNECT system. VERIFY air bag indicator. If lamp flashes fault code 10, INSTALL a new diagnostic monitor. REACTIVATE system. VERIFY air bag indicator. |

Fig. 46 Lamp flashes 5 times (Forward crash sensor or igniter circuit shorted to ground, part 1 of 5). Continental & 1991 Town Car

**Fault Indication — Air Bag Indicator Flashes Five Times**
**Probable Fault — Shorted Forward Crash Sensor Deployment Circuit**

| TEST STEP | RESULT ▶ | ACTION TO TAKE |
|---|---|---|
| **5.4** REMOVE JUMPER FROM COLUMN CONNECTOR | | |
| • Remove jumper wire from between Circuits 614 and 615.<br>• Verify air bag indicator. Does indicator flash 5 times? | Yes ▶<br>No ▶ | GO to **5.5**.<br>GO to **5.9**. |
| **5.5** CHECK RESISTANCE IN CIRCUIT 615 (GY/W) | | |
| • Disconnect diagnostic module.<br>• Measure resistance between Pin 10 (615 GY/W) and ground.<br>• Is resistance less than 10 ohms?<br>DIAGNOSTIC MONITOR CONNECTOR GRAY<br>DIAGNOSTIC MONITOR CONNECTOR BLACK | Yes ▶ | LOCATE and SERVICE short in Circuit 615. RECONNECT system. VERIFY air bag warning indicator. If fault code 10 is present, REPLACE diagnostic monitor. REACTIVATE system. |
| | No ▶ | GO to **5.6**. |
| **5.6** CHECK FRONT SENSOR CIRCUITS | | |
| • Measure resistance between the following diagnostic monitor connector, pins and ground: | | |

| Pin No. | Circuit | Wire Color |
|---|---|---|
| 17 | 617 | PK/O |
| 18 | 619 | PK/W |
| 19 | 621 | W/Y |

| TEST STEP | RESULT ▶ | ACTION TO TAKE |
|---|---|---|
| • Is resistance less than 1150 ohms for any sensor? | Yes ▶ | GO to **5.7**. |
| | No ▶ | REPLACE diagnostic monitor. VERIFY air bag indicator. REACTIVATE system. |

**Fig. 46 Lamp flashes 5 times (Forward crash sensor or igniter circuit shorted to ground, part 2 of 5). Continental & 1991 Town Car**

**Fault Indication — Air Bag Indicator Flashes Five Times**
**Probable Fault — Forward Crash Sensor or Igniter Shorted to Ground**

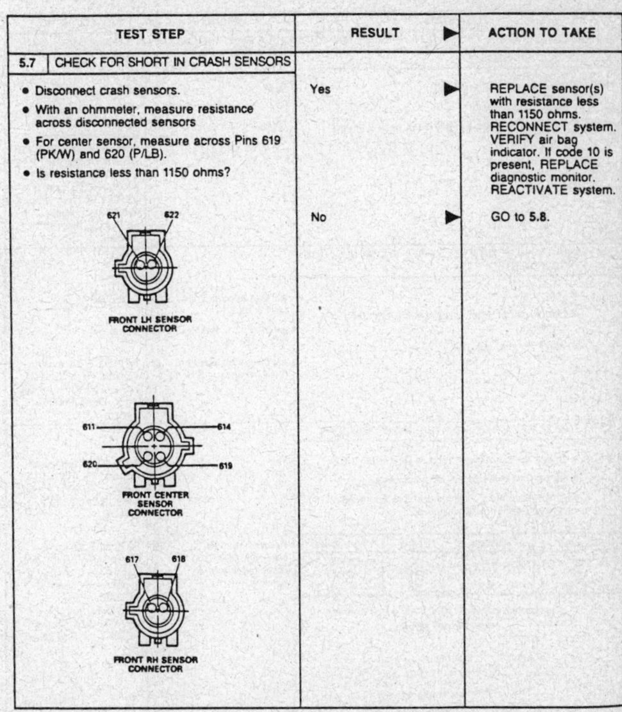

| TEST STEP | RESULT ▶ | ACTION TO TAKE |
|---|---|---|
| **5.7** CHECK FOR SHORT IN CRASH SENSORS | | |
| • Disconnect crash sensors.<br>• With an ohmmeter, measure resistance across disconnected sensors<br>• For center sensor, measure across Pins 619 (PK/W) and 620 (P/LB).<br>• Is resistance less than 1150 ohms? | Yes ▶ | REPLACE sensor(s) with resistance less than 1150 ohms. RECONNECT system. VERIFY air bag indicator. If code 10 is present, REPLACE diagnostic monitor. REACTIVATE system. |
| FRONT LH SENSOR CONNECTOR<br>FRONT CENTER SENSOR CONNECTOR<br>FRONT RH SENSOR CONNECTOR | No ▶ | GO to **5.8**. |

**Fig. 46 Lamp flashes 5 times (Forward crash sensor or igniter circuit shorted to ground, part 3 of 5). Continental & 1991 Town Car**

**Fault Indication — Air Bag Indicator Flashes Five Times**
**Probable Fault — Forward Crash Sensor or Igniter Shorted to Ground**

| TEST STEP | RESULT ▶ | ACTION TO TAKE |
|---|---|---|
| **5.8** INSPECT CONNECTORS FOR CROSSED WIRES | | |
| • Inspect sensor(s) and diagnostic monitor connectors for crossed wires. | Wires crossed ▶ | SERVICE wiring. RECONNECT system. VERIFY air bag indicator. If fault code 10 is present, REPLACE diagnostic monitor. REACTIVATE system. |
| | Wires not crossed ▶ | LOCATE and SERVICE short-to-ground in Circuit 617, 618 or 619. RECONNECT system. VERIFY air bag indicator. If fault 10 code is present, REPLACE diagnostic monitor, REACTIVATE system. |
| **5.9** CHECK REAR SAFING SENSOR CIRCUIT | | |
| • Reinstall jumper at steering column connector.<br>• Disconnect rear safing sensor.<br>• Verify air bag indicator.<br>• Does indicator flash five times? | Yes ▶ | LOCATE and SERVICE short in Circuit 614. RECONNECT system. VERIFY air bag indicator. If fault 10 is present, REPLACE diagnostic monitor. REACTIVATE system. |
| | No ▶ | GO to **5.10**. |

**Fig. 46 Lamp flashes 5 times (Forward crash sensor or igniter circuit shorted to ground, part 4 of 5). Continental & 1991 Town Car**

**Fault Indication — Air Bag Indicator Flashes Five Times**
**Probable Fault — Forward Crash Sensor or Igniter Circuit Shorted to Ground**

| TEST STEP | RESULT ▶ | ACTION TO TAKE |
|---|---|---|
| **5.10** VERIFY SHORT TO GROUND AT REAR SAFING SENSOR | | |
| • Measure resistance of sensor wiring Circuit 614 GY/O to ground.<br>• Is resistance less than 10 ohms? | Yes ▶ | REPLACE rear safing sensor. RECONNECT system. VERIFY air bag indicator. If fault 10 code is present. REPLACE diagnostic monitor. REACTIVATE system. |
| REAR SAFING SENSOR CONNECTOR | No ▶ | Go to **5.11**. |
| **5.11** VERIFY SHORT TO GROUND IN WIRING HARNESS | | |
| • Measure resistance from diagnostic monitor Pin 12 (P/W) to ground.<br>• Is resistance less than 10 ohms? | Yes ▶ | LOCATE and SERVICE short to ground in Circuit 623. RECONNECT system. VERIFY air bag indicator. If code 10 is present, REPLACE diagnostic monitor. REACTIVATE system. |
| | No ▶ | CHECK for crossed wires at sensor and diagnostic monitor. SERVICE as required. VERIFY air bag indicator. If code 10 is present, REPLACE diagnostic monitor. REACTIVATE system. |

**Fig. 46 Lamp flashes 5 times (Forward crash sensor or igniter circuit shorted to ground, part 5 of 5). Continental & 1991 Town Car**

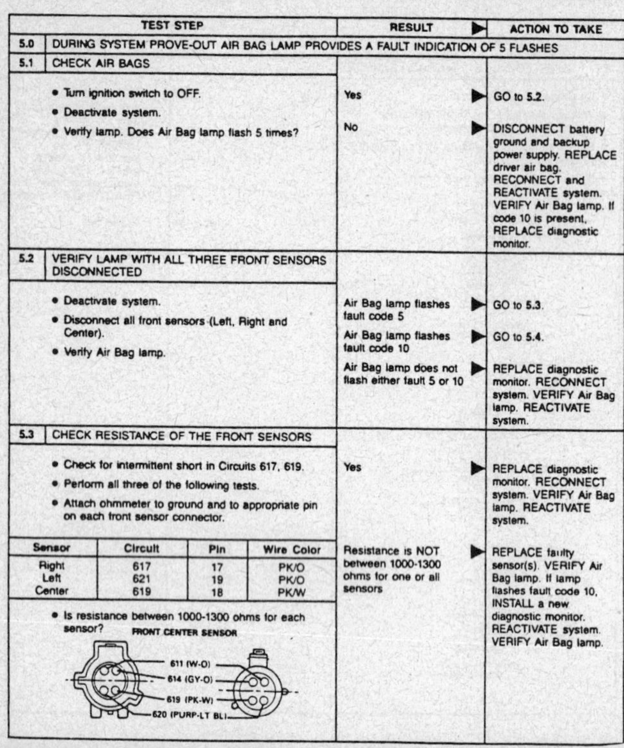

**Fault Indication — Air Bag Lamp Flashes Five Times**
**Probable Fault — Forward Crash Sensor Or Ignition Circuit Shorted to Ground**

| | TEST STEP | RESULT | ACTION TO TAKE |
|---|---|---|---|
| 5.0 | DURING SYSTEM PROVE-OUT AIR BAG LAMP PROVIDES A FAULT INDICATION OF 5 FLASHES | | |
| 5.1 | CHECK AIR BAGS | | |
| | • Turn ignition switch to OFF.<br>• Deactivate system.<br>• Verify lamp. Does Air Bag lamp flash 5 times? | Yes | GO to 5.2. |
| | | No | DISCONNECT battery ground and backup power supply. REPLACE driver air bag. RECONNECT and REACTIVATE system. VERIFY Air Bag lamp. If code 10 is present, REPLACE diagnostic monitor. |
| 5.2 | VERIFY LAMP WITH ALL THREE FRONT SENSORS DISCONNECTED | | |
| | • Deactivate system.<br>• Disconnect all front sensors (Left, Right and Center).<br>• Verify Air Bag lamp. | Air Bag lamp flashes fault code 5 | GO to 5.3. |
| | | Air Bag lamp flashes fault code 10 | GO to 5.4. |
| | | Air Bag lamp does not flash either fault 5 or 10 | REPLACE diagnostic monitor. RECONNECT system. VERIFY Air Bag lamp. REACTIVATE system. |
| 5.3 | CHECK RESISTANCE OF THE FRONT SENSORS | | |
| | • Check for intermittent short in Circuits 617, 619.<br>• Perform all three of the following tests.<br>• Attach ohmmeter to ground and to appropriate pin on each front sensor connector. | Yes | REPLACE diagnostic monitor. RECONNECT system. VERIFY Air Bag lamp. REACTIVATE system. |
| | (see sensor table below)<br>• Is resistance between 1000-1300 ohms for each sensor? | Resistance is NOT between 1000-1300 ohms for one or all sensors | REPLACE faulty sensor(s). VERIFY Air Bag lamp. If lamp flashes fault code 10, INSTALL a new diagnostic monitor. REACTIVATE system. VERIFY Air Bag lamp. |

| Sensor | Circuit | Pin | Wire Color |
|---|---|---|---|
| Right | 617 | 17 | PK/O |
| Left | 621 | 19 | PK/O |
| Center | 619 | 18 | PK/W |



**Fig. 47 Lamp flashes 5 times (Forward crash sensor or igniter shorted to ground, part 1 of 4). 1990 Crown Victoria, Grand Marquis & Town Car**

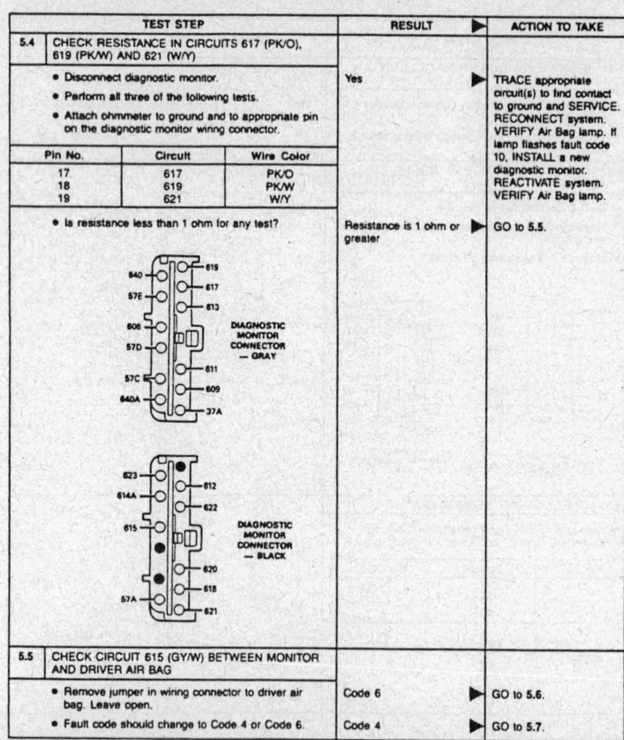

**Fault Indication — Air Bag Lamp Flashes Five Times**
**Probable Fault — Shorted Forward Crash Sensor Deployment Circuit**

| | TEST STEP | RESULT | ACTION TO TAKE |
|---|---|---|---|
| 5.4 | CHECK RESISTANCE IN CIRCUITS 617 (PK/O), 619 (PK/W) AND 621 (W/Y) | | |
| | • Disconnect diagnostic monitor.<br>• Perform all three of the following tests.<br>• Attach ohmmeter to ground and to appropriate pin on the diagnostic monitor wiring connector. | Yes | TRACE appropriate circuit(s) to find contact to ground and SERVICE. RECONNECT system. VERIFY Air Bag lamp. If lamp flashes fault code 10, INSTALL a new diagnostic monitor. REACTIVATE system. VERIFY Air Bag lamp. |
| | (see pin table below)<br>• Is resistance less than 1 ohm for any test? | Resistance is 1 ohm or greater | GO to 5.5. |
| 5.5 | CHECK CIRCUIT 615 (GY/W) BETWEEN MONITOR AND DRIVER AIR BAG | | |
| | • Remove jumper in wiring connector to driver air bag. Leave open.<br>• Fault code should change to Code 4 or Code 6. | Code 6 | GO to 5.6. |
| | | Code 4 | GO to 5.7. |

| Pin No. | Circuit | Wire Color |
|---|---|---|
| 17 | 617 | PK/O |
| 18 | 619 | PK/W |
| 19 | 621 | W/Y |



**Fig. 47 Lamp flashes 5 times (Forward crash sensor or igniter shorted to ground, part 2 of 4). 1990 Crown Victoria, Grand Marquis & Town Car**

**Fault Indication — Air Bag Lamp Flashes Five Times**
**Probable Fault — Forward Crash Sensor or Igniter Circuit Shorted to Ground**

| | TEST STEP | RESULT | ACTION TO TAKE |
|---|---|---|---|
| 5.6 | CHECK CLOCKSPRING | | |
| | • Short to ground in Circuit 615 (GY/W) between driver air bag and diagnostic monitor.<br>• Disconnect clockspring connector to 14401 at base of column.<br>• Jumper wiring connector Circuits 614 (GY/O) and 615 (GY/W).<br>• Verify lamp. Does lamp flash code 6? | Yes | TRACE and SERVICE Circuit 615 short to ground between clockspring and diagnostic monitor. If code 10 is present, or no short exists, REPLACE diagnostic monitor. |
| | | No lamp goes out | REPLACE clockspring. RECONNECT system. If code 10 is present, REPLACE monitor. VERIFY Air Bag lamp. |
| 5.7 | SHORT IN CIRCUIT 614 (GY/O) OR 623 (P/W) CHECK CIRCUIT 614 (GY/O) | | |
| | • Disconnect rear safing sensor.<br>• With an ohmmeter, check Circuit 614 (GY/O) Pin 11 and ground.<br>• Is resistance less than 1 ohm? | Yes | A short to ground exists in Circuit 614 (GY/O) between safing sensors, air bag and Pin 11 of diagnostic monitor. TRACE short to ground. REPAIR as required. RECONNECT and REACTIVATE system. VERIFY lamp. If no short is found, or code 10 is present, replace diagnostic module. |
| | | No | GO to 5.8. |
| 5.8 | CHECK CIRCUIT 623 (P/W) PIN 12 | | |
| | • With an ohmmeter check Circuit 623 (P/W) Pin 12 and ground.<br>• Is resistance less than 1 ohm? | Yes | TRACE short to ground in Circuit 623 (P/W). REPAIR as required. RECONNECT and REACTIVATE system. VERIFY lamp. If code 10 exists, REPLACE monitor. |
| | | No | GO to 5.9. |

**Fig. 47 Lamp flashes 5 times (Forward crash sensor or igniter shorted to ground, part 3 of 4). 1990 Crown Victoria, Grand Marquis & Town Car**

**Fault Indication — Air Bag Lamp Flashes Five Times**
**Probable Fault — Forward Crash Sensor or Igniter Circuit Shorted to Ground**

| | TEST STEP | RESULT | ACTION TO TAKE |
|---|---|---|---|
| 5.9 | CHECK REAR SAFING SENSOR | | |
| | • With an ohmmeter, check Circuit 623 (P/W) in sensor connector and ground. (With sensor attached to vehicle.)<br>• Is resistance less than 1 ohm? | Yes | REPLACE rear safing sensor. If code 10 exists, REPLACE diagnostic monitor. RECONNECT and REACTIVATE system. VERIFY Air Bag lamp. |
| | | No | REPLACE diagnostic monitor. RECONNECT and REACTIVATE system. VERIFY Air Bag lamp. |

**Fig. 47 Lamp flashes 5 times (Forward crash sensor or igniter shorted to ground, part 4 of 4). 1990 Crown Victoria, Grand Marquis & Town Car**

**Fault Indication — Air Bag Indicator Flashes Five Times**
**Probable Fault — Forward Crash Sensor Or Igniter Circuit Shorted To Ground**

NOTE: Do not replace diagnostic monitor with a fault code 5 unless instructed to do so.

| TEST STEP | RESULT ▶ | ACTION TO TAKE |
|---|---|---|
| **5.0** DURING SYSTEM PROVE-OUT AIR BAG INDICATOR PROVIDES A FAULT INDICATION OF 5 FLASHES | | |
| **5.1** DEACTIVATE SYSTEM | | |
| • Turn ignition OFF.<br>• Deactivate system.<br>• Verify indicator. Does air bag indicator flash 5 times? | Yes ▶ | GO to **5.3**. |
| | No ▶ | GO to **5.2**. |
| **5.2** CHECK AIR BAGS | | |
| • Measure resistance between any air bag connector pin and metal case on rear of air bag. (If equipped with passenger air bag, test both.) | Resistance is less than 10 ohms ▶ | REPLACE air bag(s). RECONNECT system. VERIFY air bag indicator. If fault code 10 is present, REPLACE diagnostic monitor. REACTIVATE system. VERIFY air bag indicator. |
| | Resistance is 10 ohms or more ▶ | REPLACE clockspring. RECONNECT system. If fault code 10 is present, REPLACE diagnostic monitor. REACTIVATE system. |
| **5.3** CHECK CLOCKSPRING | | |
| • Disconnect gray 3-wire connector at base of steering column.<br>• Connect a jumper between Circuits 614 (GY/O) and 615 (GY/W) at harness connector.<br>• Does air bag indicator flash 5 times? | Yes ▶ | GO to **5.4**. |
| | No ▶ | REPLACE clockspring. RECONNECT system. VERIFY air bag indicator. If lamp flashes fault code 10, INSTALL a new diagnostic monitor. REACTIVATE system. VERIFY air bag indicator. |

**Fig. 48 Lamp flashes 5 times (Forward crash sensor or igniter circuit shorted to ground, Part 1 of 5). 1991 Crown Victoria & Grand Marquis**

**Fault Indication — Air Bag Indicator Flashes Five Times**
**Probable Fault — Shorted Forward Crash Sensor Deployment Circuit**

| TEST STEP | RESULT ▶ | ACTION TO TAKE |
|---|---|---|
| **5.4** CHECK CIRCUITS 614. REMOVE JUMPER FROM COLUMN CONNECTOR | | |
| • Remove jumper wire from between Circuits 614 and 615.<br>• Verify air bag indicator. Does indicator flash 5 times? | Yes ▶ | GO to **5.5**. |
| | No ▶ | GO to **5.9**. |
| **5.5** CHECK RESISTANCE IN CIRCUIT 615 | | |
| • Disconnect diagnostic monitor.<br>• Measure resistance of Pin 10 to ground (Circuit 615, GY/Y).<br>• Is resistance less than 10 ohms?<br>619, 298D, 617, 572, 613, 606, 57AA, 611, 57AS, 656, 298E, 294A<br>DIAGNOSTIC MONITOR CONNECTOR (GRAY)<br>621, 57AB, 618, 614, 620, 615, 622, 614B, 612, 623<br>DIAGNOSTIC MONITOR CONNECTOR (BLACK) | Yes ▶ | LOCATE and SERVICE short to ground in Circuit 615. RECONNECT system. VERIFY air bag indicator. If fault code 10 is present, REPLACE diagnostic monitor. REACTIVATE system. |
| 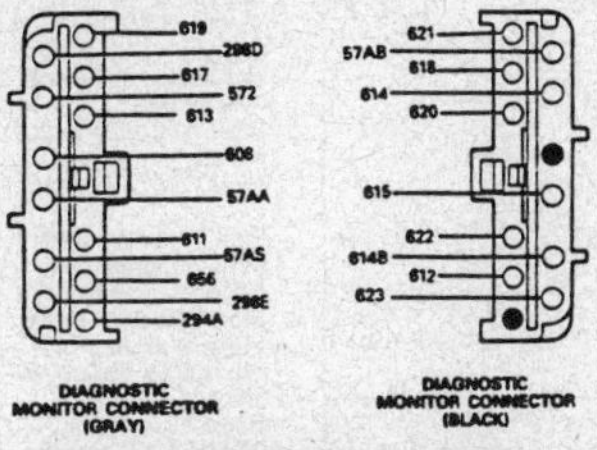 | No ▶ | GO to **5.6**. |
| **5.6** CHECK FRONT SENSOR CIRCUITS | | |
| • Measure resistance between the following diagnostic monitor connector, pins and ground: | | |

| Pin No. | Circuit | Wire Color |
|---|---|---|
| 17 | 617 | PK/O |
| 18 | 619 | PK/W |
| 19 | 621 | W/Y |

| TEST STEP | RESULT ▶ | ACTION TO TAKE |
|---|---|---|
| • Is resistance less than 1150 ohms for any sensor? | Yes ▶ | GO to **5.7**. |
| | No ▶ | REPLACE diagnostic monitor. VERIFY air bag indicator. REACTIVATE system. |

**Fig. 48 Lamp flashes 5 times (Forward crash sensor or igniter circuit shorted to ground, Part 2 of 5). 1991 Crown Victoria & Grand Marquis**

**Fault Indication — Air Bag Indicator Flashes Five Times**
**Probable Fault — Forward Crash Sensor or Igniter Circuit Shorted to Ground**

| TEST STEP | RESULT ▶ | ACTION TO TAKE |
|---|---|---|
| **5.7** CHECK FOR SHORT IN CRASH SENSORS | | |
| • Disconnect crash sensors.<br>• With an ohmmeter, measure resistance across disconnected sensors.<br>• For center sensor, measure across Pins 619 (PK/W) and 620 (P/LB).<br>• Is resistance less than 1150 ohms?<br>621, 622 FRONT LH SENSOR CONNECTOR<br>611, 614, 620, 619 FRONT CENTER SENSOR CONNECTOR<br>617, 618 FRONT RH SENSOR CONNECTOR | Yes ▶ | REPLACE sensor(s) with resistance less than 1150 ohms. RECONNECT system. VERIFY air bag indicator. If code 10 is present, REPLACE diagnostic monitor. REACTIVATE system. |
| 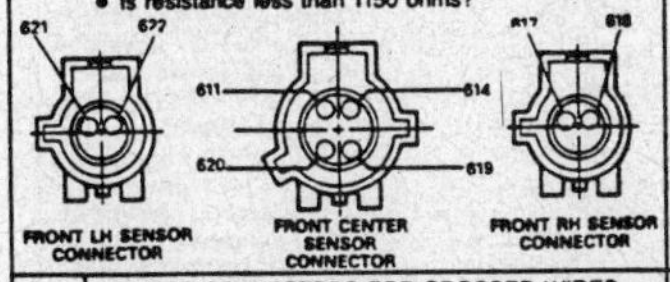 | No ▶ | GO to **5.8**. |
| **5.8** INSPECT CONNECTORS FOR CROSSED WIRES | | |
| • Inspect sensor(s) and diagnostic monitor connectors for crossed wires. | Wires crossed ▶ | SERVICE wiring. RECONNECT system. VERIFY air bag indicator. If fault code 10 is present, REPLACE diagnostic monitor. REACTIVATE system. |
| | Wires not crossed ▶ | LOCATE and SERVICE short to ground in Circuit 617, 618 or 619. RECONNECT system. VERIFY air bag indicator. If fault 10 code is present, REPLACE diagnostic monitor. REACTIVATE system. |
| **5.9** CHECK REAR SAFING SENSOR CIRCUIT | | |
| • Reinstall jumper at steering column connector.<br>• Disconnect rear safing sensor.<br>• Verify air bag indicator.<br>• Does indicator flash five times? | Yes ▶ | GO to **5.10**. |
| | No ▶ | GO to **5.11**. |

**Fig. 48 Lamp flashes 5 times (Forward crash sensor or igniter circuit shorted to ground, Part 3 of 5). 1991 Crown Victoria & Grand Marquis**

**Fault Indication — Air Bag Indicator Flashes Five Times**
**Probable Fault — Forward Crash Sensor or Igniter Circuit Shorted to Ground**

| TEST STEP | RESULT ▶ | ACTION TO TAKE |
|---|---|---|
| **5.10** CHECK CENTER SENSOR | | |
| • Disconnect center sensor.<br>• Verify air bag indicator.<br>• Does indicator flash five times? | Yes ▶ | LOCATE and SERVICE short to ground in Circuit 614. RECONNECT system. VERIFY air bag indicator. If fault 10 code is present, REPLACE diagnostic monitor. REACTIVATE system. |
| | No ▶ | Go to **5.13**. |
| **5.11** VERIFY SHORT TO GROUND AT REAR SAFING SENSOR | | |
| • Measure resistance of sensor wiring Circuit 614 GY/O to ground.<br>• Is resistance less than 10 ohms?<br>REAR SAFING SENSOR CONNECTOR<br>623, 614, 613, 612, 611 | Yes ▶ | REPLACE rear safing sensor. RECONNECT system. VERIFY air bag indicator. If fault 10 code is present, REPLACE diagnostic monitor. REACTIVATE system. |
| 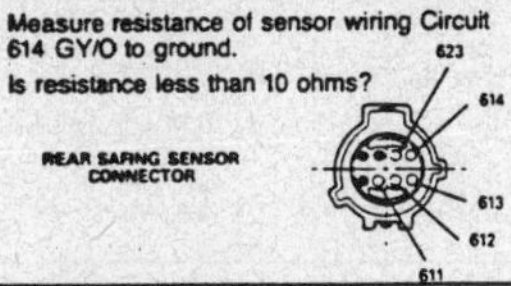 | No ▶ | Go to **5.12**. |
| **5.12** VERIFY SHORT TO GROUND IN WIRING HARNESS | | |
| • Measure resistance from sensor Circuit 614. GY/O to ground.<br>• Is resistance less than 10 ohms? | Yes ▶ | LOCATE and SERVICE short to ground in Circuit 623. RECONNECT system. VERIFY airbag indicator. If code 10 is present, REPLACE diagnostic monitor. REACTIVATE system. |
| | No ▶ | CHECK for crossed wires at sensor and diagnostic monitor. SERVICE as required. VERIFY airbag indicator. If code 10 is present, REPLACE diagnostic monitor. REACTIVATE system. |

**Fig. 48 Lamp flashes 5 times (Forward crash sensor or igniter circuit shorted to ground, Part 4 of 5). 1991 Crown Victoria & Grand Marquis**

**Fault Indication — Air Bag Indicator Flashes Five Times**
**Probable Fault — Forward Crash Sensor or Igniter Circuit Shorted to Ground**

| TEST STEP | | RESULT | ACTION TO TAKE |
|---|---|---|---|
| 5.13 | VERIFY SHORT TO GROUND AT CENTER CRASH SENSOR | | |
| | • Measure resistance from sensor Circuit 614, GY/O to ground.<br>• Is resistance less than 10 ohms? | Yes | REPLACE center sensor. RECONNECT system. VERIFY air bag indicator. If code 10 is present, REPLACE diagnostic monitor. REACTIVATE system. |
| | | No | CHECK for crossed wires at sensor and diagnostic monitor. SERVICE as required. VERIFY air bag indicator. If code 10 is present, REPLACE diagnostic monitor. REACTIVATE system. |

**Fig. 48 Lamp flashes 5 times (Forward crash sensor or igniter circuit shorted to ground, Part 5 of 5). 1991 Crown Victoria & Grand Marquis**

**Fault Indication - Air Bag Lamp Flashes Five Times**
**Probable Fault - Forward Crash Sensor Or Ignitor Circuit Shorted to Ground**

| TEST STEP | | RESULT | ACTION TO TAKE |
|---|---|---|---|
| 5.5 | CHECK RESISTANCE IN AIRBAG CIRCUIT 615 | | |
| | • Disconnect diagnostic monitor.<br>• Measure resistance of pin 10 (615, GY/W) to ground.<br>• Is resistance less than 10 ohms?<br>DIAGNOSTIC MONITOR CONNECTOR BLACK<br>DIAGNOSTIC MONITOR CONNECTOR GRAY | Yes | LOCATE and REPAIR short to ground in circuit 615 (GY/W). RECONNECT system. VERIFY air bag lamp. If fault code 10 is present, REPLACE diagnostic monitor. REACTIVATE system. |
| | | No | GO to 5.6 |
| 5.6 | CHECK RESISTANCE IN FORWARD CRASH SENSOR CIRCUITS | | |
| | • Measure resistance at diagnostic monitor connector pin #'s (circuit) #'s to ground:<br>17 (617, PK/O)<br>18 (619, PK/W)<br>19 (621, W/Y).<br>• Is resistance less than 1160 ohms for any sensor? | Yes | GO to 5.7 |
| | | No | REPLACE diagnostic monitor. VERIFY air bag lamp. REACTIVATE system. |
| 5.7 | VERIFY SHORT TO GROUND IN CRASH SENSORS | | |
| | • Disconnect sensor(s) with resistance less than 1160 ohms.<br>• Measure resistance across disconnected sensor(s). (For multi-pin center sensor, measure across 619, PK/W and 620, P/LB.)<br>• Is resistance less than 1160 ohms?<br>FRONT LH SENSOR CONNECTOR<br>FRONT CENTER CONNECTOR<br>FRONT RH SENSOR CONNECTOR | Yes | REPLACE sensor(s) with resistance less than 1160 ohms. RECONNECT system. VERIFY air bag lamp. If fault code 10 is present, REPLACE diagnostic monitor. REACTIVATE system. |
| | | No | GO to 5.8 |

**Fig. 49 Lamp flashes 5 times (Forward crash sensor or igniter circuit shorted to ground, part 2 of 4). Mark VII, Mustang, Sable, Taurus, Tempo & Topaz**

**Fault Indication - Air Bag Lamp Flashes Five Times**
**Probable Fault - Forward Crash Sensor Or Ignitor Circuit Shorted to Ground**

NOTE NEVER ATTEMPT TO REPLACE A DIAGNOSTIC MONITOR WITH A FAULT CODE 5 PRESENT UNLESS OTHERWISE INSTRUCTED TO DO SO.

| TEST STEP | | RESULT | ACTION TO TAKE |
|---|---|---|---|
| 5.0 | DURING SYSTEM PROVE-OUT, AIR BAG LAMP PROVIDES A FAULT CODE INDICATION OF 5 FLASHES. | Yes | GO to 5.1 |
| | | No | REFER to applicable fault code information |
| 5.1 | DEACTIVATE SYSTEM | | |
| | • Turn ignition switch to off.<br>• Deactivate system.<br>• Verify lamp. Does air bag lamp flash 5 times? | Yes | GO to 5.3 |
| | | No | GO to 5.2 |
| 5.2 | CHECK AIR BAG(S) | | |
| | • Examine air bag(s) and mating connectors for pinched or damaged wiring.<br>• Are any wires pinched or damaged? | Yes | REPLACE component with damaged wiring or connectors. RECONNECT system. VERIFY air bag lamp. If fault code 10 is present. REPLACE diagnostic monitor. REACTIVATE system. |
| | | No | REPLACE clockspring. RECONNECT system. VERIFY air bag lamp. If fault code 10 is present. REPLACE diagnostic monitor. REACTIVATE system. |
| 5.3 | JUMPER AT BASE OF STEERING COLUMN | | |
| | • Disconnect gray 3-wire connector at base of steering column.<br>• Jumper circuits 614 (GY/O) and 615 (GY/W) on vehicle harness side.<br>• Verify lamp. Does air bag lamp flash 5 times? | Yes | GO to 5.4 |
| | | No | REPLACE clockspring. RECONNECT system. VERIFY air bag lamp. If fault code 10 is present. REPLACE diagnostic monitor. REACTIVATE system. |
| 5.4 | REMOVE JUMPER FROM BASE OF STEERING COLUMN | | |
| | • Remove jumper from 614 and 615 circuits at base of steering column.<br>• Verify lamp. Does air bag lamp flash 5 times? | Yes | GO to 5.5 |
| | | No | GO to 5.9 |

**Fig. 49 Lamp flashes 5 times (Forward crash sensor or igniter circuit shorted to ground, part 1 of 4). Mark VII, Mustang, Sable, Taurus, Tempo & Topaz**

**Fault Indication - Air Bag Lamp Flashes Five Times**
**Probable Fault - Forward Crash Sensor Or Ignitor Circuit Shorted to Ground**

| TEST STEP | | RESULT | ACTION TO TAKE |
|---|---|---|---|
| 5.8 | INSPECT CONNECTORS FOR CROSSED WIRES | | |
| | • Inspect sensor(s) and diagnostic monitor connectors for crossed wires.<br>• Are wires crossed? | Yes | REPAIR wiring. RECONNECT system. VERIFY air bag lamp. If fault code 10 is present. REPLACE diagnostic monitor. REACTIVATE system. |
| | | No | LOCATE and REPAIR short to ground in appropriate circuits (617, 618 or 619). RECONNECT system. VERIFY air bag lamp. If fault code 10 is present. REPLACE diagnostic monitor. REACTIVATE system. |
| 5.9 | CHECK REAR SAFING SENSOR CIRCUIT | | |
| | • Reinstall jumper at base of steering column.<br>• Verify lamp. Does air bag lamp flash 5 times? | Yes | GO to 5.10 |
| | | No | GO to 5.11 |
| 5.10 | CHECK CENTER SENSOR | | |
| | • Disconnect center sensor.<br>• Verify lamp. Does air bag lamp flash 5 times? | Yes | LOCATE and REPAIR short to ground in circuit 614. RECONNECT system. VERIFY air bag lamp. If fault code 10 is present. REPLACE diagnostic monitor. REACTIVATE system. |
| | | No | GO to 5.13 |
| 5.11 | VERIFY SHORT TO GROUND IN REAR SAFING SENSOR | | |
| | • Measure resistance of sensor wiring 614, GY/O to ground.<br>• Is resistance less than 10 ohms?<br>REAR SAFING SENSOR CONNECTOR | Yes | REPLACE rear safing sensor. RECONNECT system. VERIFY air bag lamp. If fault code 10 is present, REPLACE diagnostic monitor. REACTIVATE system. |
| | | No | GO to 5.12 |

**Fig. 49 Lamp flashes 5 times (Forward crash sensor or igniter circuit shorted to ground, part 3 of 4). Mark VII, Mustang, Sable, Taurus, Tempo & Topaz**

**Fault Indication – Air Bag Lamp Flashes Five Times**
**Probable Fault – Forward Crash Sensor Or Ignition Circuit Shorted to Ground**

| | TEST STEP | RESULT ▶ | ACTION TO TAKE |
|---|---|---|---|
| 5.12 | VERIFY SHORT TO GROUND IN WIRING HARNESS | | |
| | • Measure resistance of diagnostic monitor connector pin 12 (623, P/W) to ground.<br>• Is resistance less than 10 ohms? | Yes ▶ | LOCATE and REPAIR short to ground in circuit 623. RECONNECT system. VERIFY air bag lamp. If fault code 10 is present, REPLACE diagnostic monitor. REACTIVATE system. |
| | | No ▶ | CHECK for crossed wires at sensor and diagnostic monitor connectors. REPAIR wiring. RECONNECT system. VERIFY air bag lamp. If fault code 10 is present, REPLACE diagnostic monitor. REACTIVATE system. |
| 5.13 | VERIFY SHORT TO GROUND IN CENTER SENSOR | | |
| | • Measure resistance of sensor wiring 614, GY/O to ground.<br>• Is resistance less than 10 ohms? | Yes ▶ | REPLACE center sensor. RECONNECT system. VERIFY air bag lamp. If fault code 10 is present, REPLACE diagnostic monitor. REACTIVATE system. |
| | | No ▶ | CHECK for crossed wires at sensor and diagnostic monitor connectors. REPAIR wiring. RECONNECT system. VERIFY air bag lamp. If fault code 10 is present, REPLACE diagnostic monitor. REACTIVATE system. |

**Fig. 49 Lamp flashes 5 times (Forward crash sensor or igniter circuit shorted to ground, part 4 of 4). Mark VII, Mustang, Sable, Taurus, Tempo & Topaz**

**Fault Indication—Air Bag Lamp Flashes Six Times**
**Probable Fault—Driver Air Bag Circuit Inoperative**

| | TEST STEP | RESULT ▶ | ACTION TO TAKE |
|---|---|---|---|
| G1 | DURING SYSTEM PROVE-OUT AIR BAG LAMP PROVIDES A FAULT CODE OF 6 FLASHES | | |
| G2 | CHECK CLOCKSPRING | | |
| | • Deactivate air bag system.<br>• Verify air bag lamp while slowly rotating the steering wheel assembly.<br>• Does the air bag lamp still flash fault code 6 and/or flash intermittently? | Yes ▶ | GO to G3. |
| | | No ▶ | DISCONNECT battery negative cable and backup power supply. REMOVE jumper wire. INSTALL a new driver air bag. RECONNECT system. VERIFY air bag lamp. |
| G3 | CHECK CLOCKSPRING—CONTINUED | | |
| | • Disconnect clockspring wiring connector at base of steering column.<br>• Place a jumper wire across the GY/O and GY/W wires of the clockspring main harness wire connector.<br>• Verify air bag lamp.<br>• Does the air bag lamp still flash fault code 6? | Yes ▶ | GO to G4. |
| | | No ▶ | DISCONNECT battery negative cable and backup power supply. REMOVE jumper wire from air bag clockspring wiring connector. INSTALL new clockspring. RECONNECT system. VERIFY air bag lamp. REACTIVATE system. |

**Fig. 50 Lamp flashes 6 times (Driver airbag circuit inoperative, part 1 of 2). Capri**

**Fault Indication—Air Bag Lamp Flashes Six Times**
**Probable Fault—Driver Air Bag Circuit Inoperative (Continued)**

| | TEST STEP | RESULT ▶ | ACTION TO TAKE |
|---|---|---|---|
| G4 | CHECK AIR BAG DIAGNOSTIC MODULE CONNECTORS | | |
| | • Remove jumper wire from clockspring main harness wiring connector.<br>• Remove diagnostic module from bracket.<br>• Disconnect diagnostic module connectors.<br>• Before continuing, visually inspect black connector to ensure that the GY/O wire and GY/W wire are touching.<br>• Attach ohmmeter to the GY/O wire on the black module wiring connector and GY/O wire on the clockspring wiring connector.<br>• Is resistance less than 1 ohm? | Yes ▶ | GO to G5. |
| | | No ▶ | TRACE GY/O wire from clockspring wiring connector to diagnostic module connector to locate and SERVICE open circuit. RECONNECT system. REACTIVATE air bag system. VERIFY air bag lamp. |
| G5 | CHECK RESISTANCE IN CIRCUITS | | |
| | • Attach ohmmeter to GY/W wire on diagnostic module black wiring connector and to GY/W wire on the clockspring connector.<br>• Is resistance less than 1 ohm? | Yes ▶ | INSTALL a new diagnostic module. RECONNECT system. REACTIVATE system. VERIFY air bag lamp. |
| | | No ▶ | TRACE GY/W wire from clockspring connector to diagnostic module to find open and SERVICE. RECONNECT system. REACTIVATE system. VERIFY air bag lamp. |

**Fig. 50 Lamp flashes 6 times (Driver airbag circuit inoperative, part 2 of 2). Capri**

**Fault Indication — Air Bag Lamp Flashes Six Times**
**Probable Fault — Driver Air Bag Circuit Inoperative**

| | TEST STEP | RESULT ▶ | ACTION TO TAKE |
|---|---|---|---|
| 6.0 | DURING SYSTEM PROVE-OUT AIR BAG LAMP PROVIDES A FAULT CODE OF 6 FLASHES | | |
| 6.1 | CHECK CLOCKSPRING | | |
| | • Verify Air Bag lamp while slowly rotating the steering wheel assembly.<br>• Does the Air Bag lamp still flash fault code 6 and/or flash intermittently? | Yes ▶ | GO to 6.2. |
| | | No ▶ | DISCONNECT battery ground cable. REMOVE jumper wire. INSTALL a new driver Air Bag. RECONNECT system. VERIFY Air Bag lamp. |
| 6.2 | CHECK CLOCKSPRING — CONTINUED | | |
| | • Disconnect Air Bag clockspring wiring connector.<br>• Place a jumper wire across Circuits 614 (GY O) and 615 (GY W) of the clockspring connector.<br>• Verify Air Bag lamp.<br>• Does the Air Bag lamp still flash fault code 6? | Yes ▶ | GO to 6.3 |
| | | No ▶ | DISCONNECT battery ground cable. REMOVE jumper wire from Air Bag clockspring wiring connector. INSTALL new clockspring. RECONNECT system. VERIFY Air Bag lamp. REACTIVATE system. |
| 6.3 | CHECK AIR BAG DIAGNOSTIC MONITOR CONNECTOR | | |
| | • Remove jumper wire from Air Bag clockspring wiring connector.<br>• Disconnect diagnostic monitor connector.<br>• Before continuing, visually inspect connector to ensure that Pin 11, Circuit 614 (GY O) and Pin 10, Circuit 615 (GY W) are touching.<br>• Attach ohmmeter to Pin 11, Circuit 614 (GY O) on the diagnostic monitor wiring connector and to Circuit 614 (GY O) clockspring wiring connector.<br>• Is resistance less than 1 ohm? | Yes ▶ | GO to 6.4 |
| | | No ▶ | TRACE circuit 614 (GY O) from clockspring wiring connector to diagnostic monitor connector to locate and SERVICE open circuit. RECONNECT system. REACTIVATE Air Bag system. VERIFY Air Bag lamp. |
| 6.4 | CHECK RESISTANCE IN CIRCUITS | | |
| | • Attach ohmmeter to Pin 10, Circuit 615 (GY W) on diagnostic monitor wiring connector and to Circuit 615 (GY W) on the clockspring connector.<br>• Is resistance less than 1 ohm? | Yes ▶ | INSPECT connector for properly seated pins. If okay, INSTALL a new diagnostic monitor. RECONNECT system. REACTIVATE system. VERIFY Air Bag lamp. |
| | | No ▶ | TRACE Circuit 615 (GY W) from clockspring connector to diagnostic monitor assembly to find open and SERVICE. RECONNECT system. REACTIVATE system. VERIFY Air Bag lamp. |

**Fig. 51 Lamp flashes 6 times (Driver airbag circuit inoperative). 1989 Continental**

**Fault Indication — Air Bag Lamp Flashes Six Times**
**Probable Fault — Driver Air Bag Circuit Inoperative**

| TEST STEP | RESULT ▶ | ACTION TO TAKE |
|---|---|---|
| **6.0** DURING SYSTEM PROVE-OUT AIR BAG LAMP PROVIDES A FAULT CODE OF 6 FLASHES | | |
| **6.1** CHECK DRIVER AIR BAG | | |
| • Deactivate air bag system. • Verify Air Bag lamp while slowly rotating the steering wheel assembly. • Does the Air Bag lamp still flash fault code 6 and/or flash intermittently? | Yes ▶ | GO to 6.2. |
| | No ▶ | DISCONNECT battery ground cable and power supply. REMOVE jumper wire. INSTALL a new driver air bag. RECONNECT system. VERIFY Air Bag lamp. |
| **6.2** CHECK CLOCKSPRING | | |
| • Disconnect Air Bag clockspring wiring connector at base of column. • Place a jumper wire across Circuits 614 (GY/O) and 615 (PK) of the wiring connector. • Verify Air Bag lamp. • Does the Air Bag lamp still flash fault code 6? | Yes ▶ | GO to 6.3. |
| | No ▶ | DISCONNECT battery ground cable and power supply. REMOVE jumper wire from air bag clockspring wiring connector. INSTALL new clockspring. RECONNECT system. VERIFY Air Bag lamp. REACTIVATE system. |
| **6.3** CHECK AIR BAG DIAGNOSTIC MONITOR CONNECTORS | | |
| • Remove jumper wire from air bag clockspring wiring connector. • Disconnect diagnostic monitor connectors. • Before continuing, visually inspect connector to ensure that Pin 11, Circuit 614 (GY/O) and Pin 10, Circuit 615 (PK) are touching. • Attach ohmmeter to Pin 11. Circuit 614 (GY/O) on the diagnostic monitor wiring connector and to Circuit 614 (PK) clockspring wiring connector. • Is resistance less than 1 ohm? | Yes ▶ | GO to 6.4. |
| | No ▶ | TRACE Circuit 614 (GY/O) from clockspring wiring connector to diagnostic monitor connector to locate and SERVICE open circuit. RECONNECT system. REACTIVATE air bag system. VERIFY Air Bag lamp. |

**Fig. 52 Lamp flashes 6 times (Driver airbag circuit inoperative, part 1 of 2). 1990–91 Continental & Town Car**

**Fault Indication — Air Bag Lamp Flashes Six Times**
**Probable Fault — Driver Air Bag Circuit Inoperative**

| TEST STEP | RESULT ▶ | ACTION TO TAKE |
|---|---|---|
| **6.0** DURING SYSTEM PROVE-OUT AIR BAG LAMP PROVIDES A FAULT CODE OF 6 FLASHES | | |
| **6.1** CHECK CLOCKSPRING | | |
| • Deactivate air bag system. • Verify air bag lamp while slowly rotating the steering wheel assembly. • Does the air bag lamp still flash fault code 6 and/or flash intermittently? | Yes ▶ | GO to 6.2. |
| | No ▶ | DISCONNECT battery ground cable and backup power supply. REMOVE jumper wire. INSTALL a new driver air bag. RECONNECT system. VERIFY air bag lamp. |
| **6.2** CHECK SLIP RING — CONTINUED | | |
| • Disconnect air bag clockspring wiring connector at base of steering column. • Place a jumper wire across Circuits 614 (GY O) and 615 (PK) of the clockspring connector. • Verify air bag lamp. • Does the air bag lamp still flash fault code 6? | Yes ▶ | GO to 6.3. |
| | No ▶ | DISCONNECT battery ground cable and backup power supply. REMOVE jumper wire from air bag clockspring wiring connector. INSTALL new clockspring. RECONNECT system. VERIFY air bag lamp. REACTIVATE system. |
| **6.3** CHECK AIR BAG DIAGNOSTIC MONITOR CONNECTORS | | |
| • Remove jumper wire from air bag clockspring wiring connector. • Disconnect diagnostic monitor connectors. • Before continuing, visually inspect connector to ensure that Pin 11, Circuit 614 (GY/O) and Pin 10, Circuit 615 (GY/W) are touching. • Attach ohmmeter to Pin 11, Circuit 614 (GY/O) on the monitor wiring connector and to Circuit 614 (GY/O) clockspring wiring connector. • Is resistance less than 1 ohm? | Yes ▶ | GO to 6.4. |
| | No ▶ | TRACE circuit 614 (GY/O) from clockspring wiring connector to diagnostic monitor connector to locate and SERVICE open circuit. RECONNECT system. REACTIVATE air bag system. VERIFY air bag lamp. |

**Fig. 53 Lamp flashes 6 times (Driver airbag circuit inoperative, part 1 of 2). Crown Victoria, Grand Marquis, Mark VII, Mustang, Sable, Taurus, Tempo & Topaz**

**Fault Indication — Air Bag Lamp Flashes Six Times**
**Probable Fault — Driver Air Bag Circuit Inoperative**

| TEST STEP | RESULT ▶ | ACTION TO TAKE |
|---|---|---|
| **6.4** CHECK RESISTANCE IN CIRCUITS | | |
| • Attach ohmmeter to Pin 10. Circuit 615 (GY/N) on diagnostic monitor wiring connector and to Circuit 615 (PK) on the clockspring connector. • Is resistance less than 1 ohm? | Yes ▶ | INSPECT connector for properly seated pins. If okay, INSTALL a new diagnostic monitor. RECONNECT system. REACTIVATE system. VERIFY Air Bag lamp. |
| | No ▶ | TRACE Circuit 615 (GY/W) from clockspring connector to diagnostic monitor assembly to find open and SERVICE. RECONNECT system. REACTIVATE system. VERIFY Air Bag lamp. |

**Fig. 52 Lamp flashes 6 times (Driver airbag circuit inoperative, part 2 of 2). 1990–91 Continental & Town Car**

**Fault Indication — Air Bag Lamp Flashes Six Times**
**Probable Fault — Driver Air Bag Circuit Inoperative**

| TEST STEP | RESULT ▶ | ACTION TO TAKE |
|---|---|---|
| **6.4** CHECK RESISTANCE IN CIRCUITS | | |
| • Attach ohmmeter to Pin 11, Circuit 614 (GY/O) on diagnostic monitor wiring connector and to Circuit 615 (GY/W) on the clockspring connector. • Is resistance less than 1 ohm? | Yes ▶ | INSTALL a new diagnostic monitor. RECONNECT system. REACTIVATE system. VERIFY Air Bag lamp. |
| | No ▶ | TRACE Circuit 615 (GY/W) from clockspring connector to diagnostic monitor to find open and SERVICE. RECONNECT system. REACTIVATE system. VERIFY Air Bag lamp. |

**Fig. 53 Lamp flashes 6 times (Driver airbag circuit inoperative, part 2 of 2). Crown Victoria, Grand Marquis, Mark VII, Mustang, Sable, Taurus, Tempo & Topaz**

**Fault Indication—Air Bag Lamp Flashes Seven Times**
**Probable Fault—Module Wiring Circuit Inoperative**

| TEST STEP | RESULT ▶ | ACTION TO TAKE |
|---|---|---|
| **H1** DURING SYSTEM PROVE-OUT AIR BAG LAMP PROVIDES A FAULT INDICATION OF 7 FLASHES | | |
| **H2** VERIFY AIR BAG LAMP | | |
| • Deactivate air bag system. • Remove diagnostic module from bracket. • Disconnect and visually inspect diagnostic module wiring connectors. • Reconnect diagnostic module wiring connector. • Does air bag lamp flash code 7? | Yes ▶ | GO to H3. |
| | No ▶ | REACTIVATE system. TURN ignition switch to RUN. VERIFY air bag lamp. |

**Fig. 54 Lamp flashes 7 times (Module wiring circuit inoperative, part 1 of 2). Capri**

**Fault Indication—Air Bag Lamp Flashes Seven Times**
**Probable Fault—Module Wiring Circuit Inoperative (Continued)**

| TEST STEP | RESULT ▶ | ACTION TO TAKE |
|---|---|---|
| **H3** INSPECT DIAGNOSTIC MODULE PIN 7 | | |
| • Disconnect diagnostic module. • Inspect BK wire in black wiring connector for good connection to module Pin 7. • Is BK wire properly seated to Pin 7 and good contact made? | Yes ▶ | GO to H4. |
| | No ▶ | SERVICE terminal and / or connector. RECONNECT diagnostic module. VERIFY air bag lamp. |
| **H4** INSPECT MODULE WIRING CIRCUIT GROUND | | |
| • Disconnect diagnostic module. • With ohmmeter, measure resistance from BK wire in black connector to ground. • Is resistance less than 1 ohm? | Yes ▶ | REPLACE diagnostic module. RECONNECT system. VERIFY air bag lamp. |
| | No ▶ | FIND open circuit and SERVICE. RECONNECT system. VERIFY air bag lamp. |

**Fig. 54 Lamp flashes 7 times (Module wiring circuit inoperative, part 2 of 2). Capri**

**Fault Indication — Air Bag Lamp Flashes Seven Times**
**Probable Fault — Passenger Air Bag Circuit Inoperative**

| TEST STEP | RESULT ▶ | ACTION TO TAKE |
|---|---|---|
| 7.0 DURING SYSTEM PROVE OUT AIR BAG LAMP PROVIDES A FAULT INDICATION OF 7 FLASHES. | | |
| 7.1 VERIFY AIR BAG LAMP | | |
| • Deactivate passenger air bag.<br>• Verify Air Bag lamp. | Air Bag lamp still flashes fault code 7 ▶ | GO to 7.2. |
| | Air Bag lamp does not flash fault code 7 ▶ | DISCONNECT battery ground cable and power supply. REMOVE jumper wire used in deactivation of passenger air bag. REPLACE passenger air bag. RECONNECT system. REACTIVATE system. VERIFY Air Bag lamp. |
| 7.2 CHECK DIAGNOSTIC MONITOR CONNECTOR | | |
| • Deactivate driver air bag.<br>• Remove jumper wire from passenger air bag wiring connector.<br>• Disconnect diagnostic monitor.<br>• Visually inspect the monitor wiring connector to be sure Pin 8 Circuit 614 (GY-O) and Pin 9 Circuit 616 (PK/BK) are touching. | Pins are not touching ▶ | SERVICE or REPLACE connector as required. RECONNECT system. REACTIVATE Air Bag system (passenger and driver). VERIFY Air Bag lamp. |
| | Pins are touching as required ▶ | GO to 7.3. |
| 7.3 CHECK RESISTANCE IN CIRCUIT 614 (GY/O) | | |
| • Using an ohmmeter, attach a lead to Pin 8 Circuit 614 (GY/O) on the monitor wiring connector and the other lead to Circuit 614 (GY/O) on the passenger air bag wiring connector to find the resistance. | Resistance is less than one ohm ▶ | GO to 7.4. |
| | Resistance is one ohm or greater ▶ | TRACE Circuit 614 (GY/O) from passenger air bag wiring connector to LOCATE and SERVICE open circuit. RECONNECT system. REACTIVATE air bag system (passenger and driver). VERIFY Air Bag lamp. |

**Fig. 55 Lamp flashes 7 times (Passenger airbag circuit inoperative, part 1 of 3). Continental & Town Car**

**Fault Indication — Air Bag Lamp Flashes Seven Times**
**Probable Fault — Monitor Wiring Circuit Inoperative**

| TEST STEP | RESULT ▶ | ACTION TO TAKE |
|---|---|---|
| 7.5 VERIFY AIR BAG LAMP | | |
| • Deactivate air bag system.<br>• Visually inspect diagnostic monitor wiring connector.<br>• Reconnect diagnostic monitor wiring connector.<br>• Does the Air Bag indicator flash code 7? | Yes ▶ | GO to 7.6. |
| | No ▶ | REACTIVATE system. TURN ignition switch to RUN. VERIFY Air Bag indicator. |
| 7.6 INSPECT DIAGNOSTIC MONITOR PIN 7, CIRCUIT 57 | | |
| • Disconnect diagnostic monitor.<br>• Inspect Pin 7, Circuit 57 (BK) in wiring connector for good connection to monitor.<br>• Is Pin 7 properly seated and good contact made? | Yes ▶ | GO to 7.7. |
| | No ▶ | SERVICE terminal and/or connector. RECONNECT diagnostic monitor. VERIFY Air Bag indicator. |
| 7.7 INSPECT CIRCUIT 57 | | |
| • With ohmmeter, measure resistance from Pin 7, Circuit 57 (BK) to ground.<br>• Is resistance less than one ohm? | Yes ▶ | REPLACE diagnostic monitor. RECONNECT system. VERIFY Air Bag indicator. |
| | No ▶ | LOCATE open circuit and SERVICE. RECONNECT system. VERIFY Air Bag indicator. |

**Fig. 55 Lamp flashes 7 times (Passenger airbag circuit inoperative, part 3 of 3). Continental & Town Car**

**Fault Indication — Air Bag Lamp Flashes Seven Times**
**Probable Fault — Passenger Air Bag Circuit Inoperative**

| TEST STEP | RESULT ▶ | ACTION TO TAKE |
|---|---|---|
| 7.4 CHECK RESISTANCE IN CIRCUIT 616 (PK/BK) | | |
| • Using an ohmmeter, attach a lead to Pin 9 Circuit 614 (BY/O) on the monitor wiring connector and the other lead to Circuit 616 (PK/BK) on the Passenger Air Bag wiring connector to find resistance. | Resistance is less than one ohm ▶ | REPLACE diagnostic monitor. RECONNECT system. REACTIVATE Air Bag system (Passenger and Driver). VERIFY Air Bag lamp. |
| | Resistance is one ohm or greater ▶ | TRACE Circuit 616 (PK/BK) from Passenger Air Bag wiring connector to monitor wiring connector to LOCATE and SERVICE open circuit. RECONNECT system. REACTIVATE Air Bag system (Passenger and Driver). VERIFY Air Bag lamp. |

**Fig. 55 Lamp flashes 7 times (Passenger airbag circuit inoperative, part 2 of 3). Continental & Town Car**

**Fault Indication — Air Bag Lamp Flashes Seven Times**
**Probable Fault — Monitor Wiring Circuit Inoperative**

| TEST STEP | RESULT ▶ | ACTION TO TAKE |
|---|---|---|
| 7.0 DURING SYSTEM PROVE-OUT AIR BAG LAMP PROVIDES A FAULT INDICATION OF 7 FLASHES | | |
| 7.1 VERIFY AIR BAG LAMP | | |
| • Deactivate air bag system.<br>• Visually inspect diagnostic monitor wiring connector.<br>• Reconnect diagnostic monitor wiring connector.<br>• Does the Air Bag lamp flash code 7? | Yes ▶ | GO to 7.2. |
| | No ▶ | REACTIVATE system. TURN ignition switch to RUN. VERIFY Air Bag lamp. |
| 7.2 INSPECT DIAGNOSTIC MONITOR PIN 7, CIRCUIT 57 | | |
| • Disconnect diagnostic monitor.<br>• Inspect Pin 7, Circuit 57 (BK) in wiring connector for good connection to monitor.<br>• Is Pin 7 properly seated and good contact made? | Yes ▶ | GO to 7.3. |
| | No ▶ | SERVICE terminal and/or connector. RECONNECT diagnostic monitor. VERIFY Air Bag lamp. |
| 7.3 INSPECT CIRCUIT 57 | | |
| • With ohmmeter, measure resistance from Pin 7, Circuit 57 (BK) to ground.<br>• Is resistance less than one ohm? | Yes ▶ | REPLACE diagnostic monitor. RECONNECT system. VERIFY Air Bag lamp. |
| | No ▶ | FIND open circuit and SERVICE. RECONNECT system. VERIFY Air Bag lamp. |

**Fig. 56 Lamp flashes 7 times (Monitor wiring circuit inoperative). Crown Victoria, Grand Marquis, Mark VII, Mustang, Sable, Taurus, Tempo, Topaz**

**Fault Indication — Air Bag Lamp Flashes Eight Times**
**Probable Fault — Forward Crash Sensor Improperly Attached or Grounded**

| | TEST STEP | RESULT ▶ | ACTION TO TAKE |
|---|---|---|---|
| 8.0 | DURING SYSTEM PROVE-OUT AIR BAG LAMP PROVIDES A FAULT INDICATION OF 8 FLASHES | | |
| 8.1 | INSPECT FRONT SENSORS | | |
| | • Visually inspect each front sensor to ensure they are bolted (properly grounded) to the vehicle.<br>• Are all sensors properly bolted to vehicle? | Yes ▶<br>No ▶ | GO to 8.2.<br>ATTACH sensor(s) properly. VERIFY Air Bag lamp. |
| 8.2 | INSPECT EACH SENSOR'S WIRING CONNECTORS | | |
| | • Visually check each front sensor connector for proper connection to the vehicle wiring.<br>• Are all sensors properly connected? | Yes ▶<br>No ▶ | GO to 8.3.<br>CONNECT sensor(s) properly. VERIFY Air Bag lamp. |
| 8.3 | CHECK FOR RESISTANCE IN FRONT SENSORS | | |
| | • Disconnect battery ground cable.<br>• Disconnect all front sensors.<br>• Perform the following tests.<br>• Attach an ohmmeter to ground and to appropriate pin on each front sensor connector. | Yes ▶<br>No ▶ | GO to 8.4.<br>REPLACE faulty sensor(s). VERIFY Air Bag lamp. |

| Sensor | Circuit | Wire Color |
|---|---|---|
| Right | 618 | P/LG |
| Left | 618 | P/LG |
| Center | 620 | P/LB |

• Is resistance less than 1 ohm for each test?

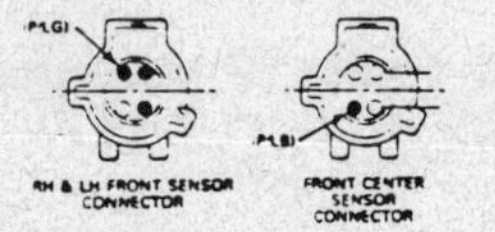

(P/LG) (P/LB)
RH & LH FRONT SENSOR CONNECTOR
FRONT CENTER SENSOR CONNECTOR

**Fig. 57 Lamp flashes 8 times (Forward crash sensor improperly attached or ground, part 1 of 2). Capri**

**Fault Indication — Air Bag Lamp Flashes Eight Times**
**Probable Fault — Forward Crash Sensor Improperly Attached or Grounded**

| | TEST STEP | RESULT ▶ | ACTION TO TAKE |
|---|---|---|---|
| 8.4 | CHECK FOR RESISTANCE IN CIRCUITS 618 (P/LG), 620 (P/LB) AND 622 (T/BK) | | |
| | • Reconnect all front sensors.<br>• Perform all three of the following tests.<br>• Attach ohmmeter to ground and to appropriate pin on diagnostic monitor connector. Probe back of connector. | Yes ▶ | INSPECT terminals in diagnostic monitor connector and SERVICE as required. If terminals and connections are OK, INSTALL a new diagnostic monitor. RECONNECT system. VERIFY Air Bag lamp. |
| | • Is the resistance less than 1 ohm for each test? | No ▶ | TRACE appropriate circuit(s) to find open(s) and SERVICE. RECONNECT system. VERIFY Air Bag lamp. |

| Pin No. | Circuit | Wire Color |
|---|---|---|
| 20 | 618 | P/LG |
| 21 | 620 | P/LB |
| 22 | 622 | T/BK |

**Fig. 57 Lamp flashes 8 times (Forward crash sensor improperly attached or ground, part 2 of 2). Capri**

**Fault Indication — Air Bag Lamp Flashes Eight Times**
**Probable Fault — Forward Crash Sensor Improperly Attached or Grounded**

| | TEST STEP | RESULT ▶ | ACTION TO TAKE |
|---|---|---|---|
| I1 | DURING SYSTEM PROVE-OUT AIR BAG LAMP PROVIDES A FAULT INDICATION OF 8 FLASHES | | |
| I2 | INSPECT FRONT SENSORS | | |
| | • Visually inspect each front sensor to ensure they are installed properly (grounded) to the vehicle.<br>• Are all sensors properly installed to vehicle? | Yes ▶<br>No ▶ | GO to I3.<br>INSTALL sensor(s) properly. VERIFY Air Bag lamp. |
| I3 | INSPECT EACH SENSOR'S WIRING CONNECTORS | | |
| | • Visually check each front sensor connector for proper connection to vehicle wiring.<br>• Are all sensors properly connected? | Yes ▶<br>No ▶ | GO to I4.<br>CONNECT sensor(s) properly. VERIFY Air Bag lamp. |
| I4 | CHECK FOR RESISTANCE IN FRONT SENSORS | | |
| | • Disconnect battery ground cable and power supply.<br>• Disconnect all front sensors.<br>• Perform the following tests.<br>• Attach an ohmmeter to ground and to appropriate wire connector on each front sensor connector. | Yes ▶<br>No ▶ | GO to I5.<br>REPLACE sensor(s). VERIFY Air Bag lamp. |

| Sensor | Wire Color |
|---|---|
| Right | V/G |
| Left | T/BK |
| Center | V/L |

• Is resistance less than 1 ohm for each test?

**Fig. 58 Lamp flashes 8 times (Forward crash sensor improperly attached or ground, part 1 of 2). 1989 Tempo & Topaz**

**Fault Indication — Air Bag Lamp Flashes Eight Times**
**Probable Fault — Forward Crash Sensor Improperly Attached or Grounded**

| | TEST STEP | RESULT ▶ | ACTION TO TAKE |
|---|---|---|---|
| I5 | CHECK FOR RESISTANCE IN FORWARD CRASH SENSOR WIRE CIRCUITS | | |
| | • Reconnect all front sensors.<br>• Remove monitor from bracket.<br>• Perform all three of the following tests.<br>• Attach ohmmeter to ground and to appropriate pin on diagnostic monitor black connector. Probe back of connector. | Yes ▶ | INSPECT terminals in diagnostic monitor connector and SERVICE as required. If terminals and connections are OK, INSTALL a new diagnostic monitor. RECONNECT system. VERIFY Air Bag lamp. |
| | • Is resistance less than 1 ohm for each test? | No ▶ | TRACE appropriate circuit(s) to find open(s) and SERVICE. RECONNECT system. VERIFY Air Bag lamp. |

| Pin No. | Wire Color |
|---|---|
| 20 | V/G |
| 21 | V/L |
| 22 | T/BK |

**Fig. 58 Lamp flashes 8 times (Forward crash sensor improperly attached or ground, part 2 of 2). 1989 Tempo & Topaz**

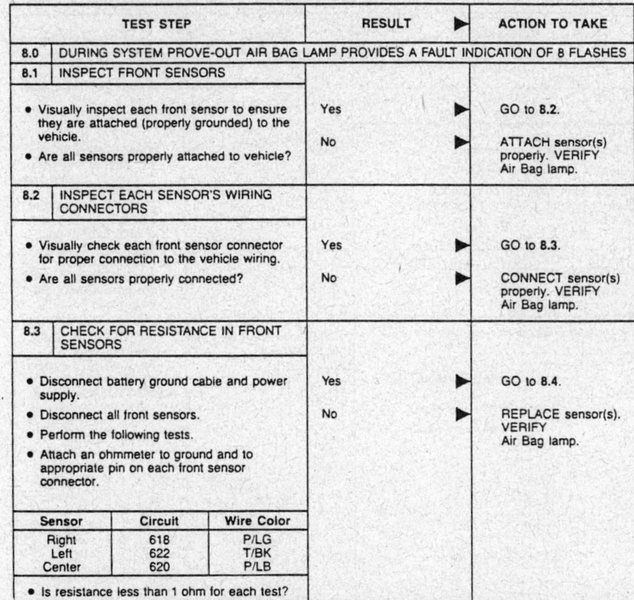

**Fault Indication — Air Bag Lamp Flashes Eight Times**
**Probable Fault — Forward Crash Sensor Improperly Attached or Grounded**

| TEST STEP | RESULT ▶ | ACTION TO TAKE |
|---|---|---|
| 8.0 DURING SYSTEM PROVE-OUT AIR BAG LAMP PROVIDES A FAULT INDICATION OF 8 FLASHES | | |
| 8.1 INSPECT FRONT SENSORS | | |
| • Visually inspect each front sensor to ensure they are attached (properly grounded) to the vehicle.<br>• Are all sensors properly attached to vehicle? | Yes ▶<br>No ▶ | GO to 8.2.<br>ATTACH sensor(s) properly. VERIFY Air Bag lamp. |
| 8.2 INSPECT EACH SENSOR'S WIRING CONNECTORS | | |
| • Visually check each front sensor connector for proper connection to the vehicle wiring.<br>• Are all sensors properly connected? | Yes ▶<br>No ▶ | GO to 8.3.<br>CONNECT sensor(s) properly. VERIFY Air Bag lamp. |
| 8.3 CHECK FOR RESISTANCE IN FRONT SENSORS | | |
| • Disconnect battery ground cable and power supply.<br>• Disconnect all front sensors.<br>• Perform the following tests.<br>• Attach an ohmmeter to ground and to appropriate pin on each front sensor connector.<br>• Is resistance less than 1 ohm for each test? | Yes ▶<br>No ▶ | GO to 8.4.<br>REPLACE sensor(s). VERIFY Air Bag lamp. |

| Sensor | Circuit | Wire Color |
|---|---|---|
| Right | 618 | P/LG |
| Left | 622 | T/BK |
| Center | 620 | P/LB |

**Fig. 59 Lamp flashes 8 times (Forward crash sensor improperly attached or ground, part 1 of 2). Continental, Crown Victoria, Grand Marquis, Mark VII, Mustang, Sable, Taurus, Town Car & 1990–91 Tempo & Topaz**

**Fault Indication — Air Bag Lamp Flashes Eight Times**
**Probable Fault — Forward Crash Sensor Improperly Attached or Grounded**

| TEST STEP | RESULT ▶ | ACTION TO TAKE |
|---|---|---|
| 8.4 CHECK FOR RESISTANCE IN CIRCUITS 618 (P/LG), 620 (P/LB) AND 622 (T/BK) | | |
| • Reconnect all front sensors.<br>• Perform all three of the following tests.<br>• Attach ohmmeter to ground and to appropriate pin on diagnostic monitor connector. Probe back of connector.<br>• Is the resistance less than 1 ohm for each test? | Yes ▶<br>No ▶ | INSPECT terminals in diagnostic monitor connector and SERVICE as required. If terminals and connections are OK, INSTALL a new diagnostic monitor. RECONNECT system. VERIFY Air Bag lamp.<br>TRACE appropriate circuit(s) to find open(s) and SERVICE. RECONNECT system. VERIFY Air Bag lamp. |

| Pin No. | Circuit | Wire Color |
|---|---|---|
| 20 | 618 | P/LG |
| 21 | 620 | P/LB |
| 22 | 622 | T/BK |

**Fig. 59 Lamp flashes 8 times (Forward crash sensor improperly attached or ground, part 2 of 2). Continental, Crown Victoria, Grand Marquis, Mark VII, Mustang, Sable, Taurus, Town Car & 1990–91 Tempo & Topaz**

**Fault Indication — Air Bag Lamp Flashes Nine Times**
**Probable Fault — Open Forward Crash Sensor Deployment Circuit**

| TEST STEP | RESULT ▶ | ACTION TO TAKE |
|---|---|---|
| J1 DURING SYSTEM PROVE-OUT AIR BAG LAMP PROVIDES A FAULT INDICATION OF 9 FLASHES | | |
| J2 INSPECT EACH FRONT SENSOR CONNECTOR TO VEHICLE WIRING | | |
| • Visually inspect each front sensor, left, right, and center for a proper connection to the vehicle wiring.<br>• Are all sensors properly connected? | Yes ▶<br>No ▶ | GO to J3.<br>CONNECT sensor(s) properly. VERIFY Air Bag lamp. |
| J3 CHECK RESISTANCE OF EACH FRONT SENSOR | | |
| • Disconnect battery ground cable and power supply.<br>• Disconnect all front sensors.<br>• Perform all three of the following tests on all three of the front sensors.<br>• Attach ohmmeter to ground and to appropriate wire on front sensor connector.<br>• Is resistance of each sensor between 1000-1300 ohms for each test? | Yes ▶<br>No ▶ | GO to J4.<br>REPLACE those sensors that did not have a resistance between 1000-1300 ohms. RECONNECT system. VERIFY Air Bag lamp. |

| Sensor | Wire Color |
|---|---|
| Right | PK/O |
| Center | PK/W |
| Left | W/Y |

| TEST STEP | RESULT ▶ | ACTION TO TAKE |
|---|---|---|
| J4 CHECK RESISTANCE OF FORWARD CRASH SENSOR DEPLOYMENT CIRCUIT WIRES | | |
| • Reconnect front sensors.<br>• Deactivate system.<br>• Perform all three of the following tests.<br>• Disconnect diagnostic monitor and attach ohmmeter to ground and to appropriate wires on diagnostic monitor wiring connectors.<br>• Is resistance between 1000-1300 ohms for each test? | Yes ▶<br>No ▶ | REPLACE diagnostic monitor. RECONNECT system. VERIFY Air Bag lamp. REACTIVATE system.<br>TRACE appropriate circuits to locate opens and SERVICE. RECONNECT system. VERIFY Air Bag lamp. REACTIVATE system. |

| Connector No. | Wire Color |
|---|---|
| 17 | PK/O |
| 18 | PK/W |
| 19 | W/Y |

**Fig. 60 Lamp flashes 9 times (Open forward crash sensor deployment circuit). Capri**

**Fault Indication — Air Bag Lamp Flashes Nine Times**
**Probable Fault — Open Forward Crash Sensor Deployment Circuit**

| TEST STEP | RESULT ▶ | ACTION TO TAKE |
|---|---|---|
| 9.0 DURING SYSTEM PROVE-OUT AIR BAG LAMP PROVIDES A FAULT INDICATION OF 9 FLASHES | | |
| 9.1 INSPECT EACH FRONT SENSOR CONNECTOR TO VEHICLE WIRING | | |
| • Visually inspect each front sensor, left, right, and center for a proper connection to the vehicle wiring.<br>• Are all sensors properly connected? | Yes ▶<br>No ▶ | GO to 9.2.<br>CONNECT sensor(s) properly. VERIFY Air Bag lamp. |
| 9.2 CHECK RESISTANCE OF EACH FRONT SENSOR | | |
| • Disconnect battery ground cable.<br>• Disconnect all front sensors.<br>• Perform all three of the following tests on all three of the front sensors.<br>• Attach ohmmeter to ground and to appropriate pin on front sensor connector.<br>• Is resistance of each sensor between 1000-1300 ohms for each test? | Yes ▶<br>No ▶ | GO to 9.3.<br>REPLACE those sensors that did not have a resistance between 1000-1300 ohms. RECONNECT system. VERIFY Air Bag lamp. |

| Sensor | Circuit | Wire Color |
|---|---|---|
| Right | 617 | PK/O |
| Center | 619 | PK/W |
| Left | 617 | PK/O |

| TEST STEP | RESULT ▶ | ACTION TO TAKE |
|---|---|---|
| 9.3 CHECK RESISTANCE OF CIRCUITS 617 (PK/O), 619 (PK/W) AND 621 (W/Y) | | |
| • Reconnect front sensors.<br>• Deactivate system.<br>• Perform all three of the following tests.<br>• Disconnect diagnostic monitor and attach ohmmeter to ground and to appropriate pin on diagnostic monitor wiring connector.<br>• Is the resistance between 1000-1300 ohms for each test? | Yes ▶<br>No ▶ | REPLACE diagnostic monitor. RECONNECT system. VERIFY Air Bag lamp. REACTIVATE system.<br>TRACE appropriate circuits to locate opens and SERVICE. RECONNECT system. VERIFY Air Bag lamp. REACTIVATE system. |

| Pin No. | Circuit | Wire Color |
|---|---|---|
| 17 | 617 | PK/O |
| 18 | 619 | PK/W |
| 19 | 621 | W/Y |

**Fig. 61 Lamp flashes 9 times (Open forward crash sensor deployment circuit). 1989 Continental, Tempo & Topaz**

**Fault Indication — Air Bag Lamp Flashes Nine Times**
**Probable Fault — Open Forward Crash Sensor Deployment Circuit**

| TEST STEP | RESULT ▶ | ACTION TO TAKE |
|---|---|---|
| **9.0** DURING SYSTEM PROVE-OUT AIR BAG LAMP PROVIDES A FAULT INDICATION OF 9 FLASHES | | |
| **9.1** INSPECT EACH FRONT SENSOR CONNECTOR TO VEHICLE WIRING | | |
| • Visually inspect each front sensor, left, right, and center for a proper connection to the vehicle wiring.<br>• Are all sensors properly connected? | Yes ▶<br>No ▶ | GO to **9.2**.<br>CONNECT sensor(s) properly. VERIFY air bag lamp. |
| **9.2** CHECK RESISTANCE OF EACH FRONT SENSOR | | |
| • Disconnect battery ground cable and power supply.<br>• Disconnect all front sensors.<br>• Perform all three of the following tests on all three of the front sensors.<br>• Attach ohmmeter to ground and to appropriate pin on front sensor connector.<br>Sensor / Circuit / Wire Color:<br>Right / 617 / PK/O<br>Center / 619 / PK/W<br>Left / 621 / W/Y<br>• Is resistance of each sensor between 1000-1300 ohms for each test? | Yes ▶<br>No ▶ | GO to **9.3**.<br>REPLACE those sensors that did not have a resistance between 1000-1300 ohms. RECONNECT system. VERIFY air bag lamp. |
| **9.3** CHECK RESISTANCE OF CIRCUITS 617 (PK/O), 619 (PK/W) AND 621 (W/Y) | | |
| • Reconnect front sensors.<br>• Deactivate system.<br>• Perform all three of the following tests.<br>• Disconnect diagnostic monitor and attach ohmmeter to ground and to appropriate pin on diagnostic monitor wiring connector.<br>Pin No. / Circuit / Wire Color:<br>17 / 617 / PK/O<br>18 / 619 / PK/W<br>19 / 621 / W/Y<br>• Is the resistance between 1000-1300 ohms for each test? | Yes ▶<br>No ▶ | REPLACE diagnostic monitor. RECONNECT system. VERIFY air bag lamp. REACTIVATE system.<br>TRACE appropriate circuits to locate opens and SERVICE. RECONNECT system. VERIFY air bag lamp. REACTIVATE system. |

**Fig. 62 Lamp flashes 9 times (Open forward crash sensor deployment circuit). Crown Victoria, Grand Marquis, Mark VII, Mustang, Sable, Taurus, Town Car & 1990–91 Continental, Tempo & Topaz**

**Fault Indication — Air Bag Lamp Flashes Ten Times**
**Probable Fault — Malfunctioning Front Sensor**

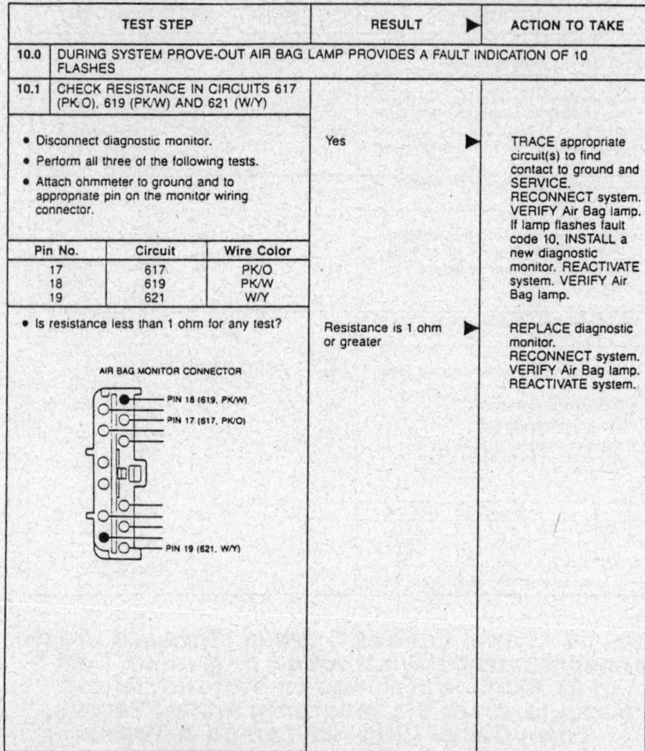

| TEST STEP | RESULT ▶ | ACTION TO TAKE |
|---|---|---|
| **10.0** DURING SYSTEM PROVE-OUT AIR BAG LAMP PROVIDES A FAULT INDICATION OF 10 FLASHES | | |
| **10.1** CHECK RESISTANCE IN CIRCUITS 617 (PK/O), 619 (PK/W) AND 621 (W/Y) | | |
| • Disconnect diagnostic monitor.<br>• Perform all three of the following tests.<br>• Attach ohmmeter to ground and to appropriate pin on the monitor wiring connector.<br>Pin No. / Circuit / Wire Color:<br>17 / 617 / PK/O<br>18 / 619 / PK/W<br>19 / 621 / W/Y | Yes ▶ | TRACE appropriate circuit(s) to find contact to ground and SERVICE. RECONNECT system. VERIFY Air Bag lamp. If lamp flashes fault code 10, INSTALL a new diagnostic monitor. REACTIVATE system. VERIFY Air Bag lamp. |
| • Is resistance less than 1 ohm for any test? | Resistance is 1 ohm or greater ▶ | REPLACE diagnostic monitor. RECONNECT system. VERIFY Air Bag lamp. REACTIVATE system. |



**Fig. 63 Lamp flashes 10 times (Malfunctioning front sensor, part 1 of 2). 1989 Continental, Tempo & Topaz**

**Fault Indication — Air Bag Lamp Flashes Ten Times**
**Probable Fault — Malfunctioning Front Sensor**

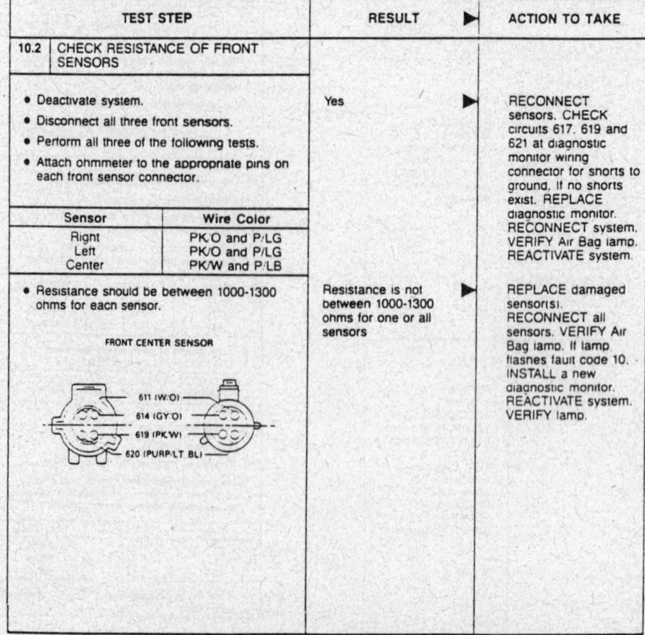

| TEST STEP | RESULT ▶ | ACTION TO TAKE |
|---|---|---|
| **10.2** CHECK RESISTANCE OF FRONT SENSORS | | |
| • Deactivate system.<br>• Disconnect all three front sensors.<br>• Perform all three of the following tests.<br>• Attach ohmmeter to the appropriate pins on each front sensor connector.<br>Sensor / Wire Color:<br>Right / PK/O and P/LG<br>Left / PK/O and P/LG<br>Center / PK/W and P/LB | Yes ▶ | RECONNECT sensors. CHECK circuits 617, 619 and 621 at diagnostic monitor wiring connector for shorts to ground. If no shorts exist, REPLACE diagnostic monitor. RECONNECT system. VERIFY Air Bag lamp. REACTIVATE system. |
| • Resistance should be between 1000-1300 ohms for each sensor. | Resistance is not between 1000-1300 ohms for one or all sensors ▶ | REPLACE damaged sensor(s). RECONNECT all sensors. VERIFY Air Bag lamp. If lamp flashes fault code 10, INSTALL a new diagnostic monitor. REACTIVATE system. VERIFY lamp. |



**Fig. 63 Lamp flashes 10 times (Malfunctioning front sensor, part 2 of 2). 1989 Continental, Tempo & Topaz**

**Fault Indication—Air Bag Lamp Flashes 10 Times**

Probable Fault:

- Firing circuit disarm device blown due to deployment circuit shorted to ground.

NOTE: A thermal fuse is built into the diagnostic monitor that opens the battery and power supply circuit to the air bag should a short occur in the air bag deployment circuit without a safing sensor being closed. This prevents unwanted air bag deployment due to damaged vehicle wiring.

The Code 10 is a result of a short to ground, as described in the diagnosis for a Code 5. Code 10 is normally found after repair of a Code 5 condition. If the Code 5 is intermittent, just the Code 10 may be showing. Always look for shorts before repairing the Code 10, (replacing the diagnostic monitor. **Since the thermal fuse is built into the diagnostic monitor, the monitor must be replaced to repair a Code 10. Refer to Code 5 diagnosis.**

**Fig. 64 Lamp flashes 10 times. Crown Victoria, Grand Marquis, Mark VII, Mustang, Sable, Taurus, Town Car & 1990–91 Continental, Tempo & Topaz**

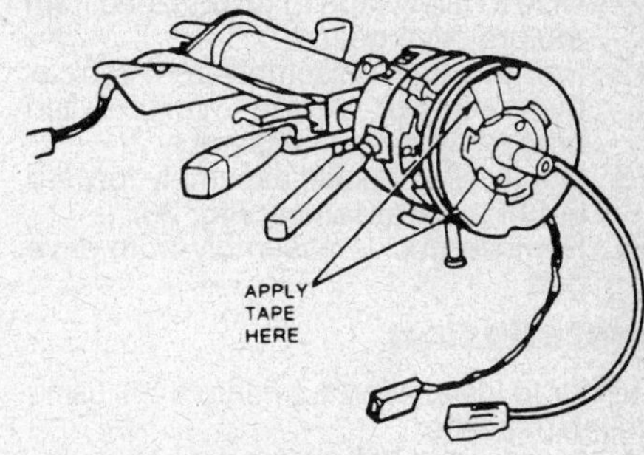


**Fig. 65 Clockspring removal**

| CONDITION | INSTRUCTIONS |
|---|---|
| 1. Vehicle to be Scrapped; Live Airbag. | Electrically Deploy Using Procedures 1 or 2 as Required. |
| 2. Vehicle to be Scrapped; Deployed Airbag. | Scrap Vehicle in the Usual Manner. |
| 3. Module Replaced; Faulty but Live Airbag. | Package and Label Properly. Return to Ford. |
| 4. Module Replaced; Deployed Airbag. | Scrap Module in the Usual Manner. |

**Fig. 66 Airbag disposal recommendations chart**

# Motorized Seat Belts

## INDEX



## DESCRIPTION & OPERATION

The motorized seat belt, which operates electrically, restrains the driver and front seat passenger in the vehicle through the use of an automatic shoulder belt.

After entering the vehicle and closing the door, turn ignition switch to On position. A motor will cause the shoulder belt to slide along a drive belt track, starting at the front body A-pillar and ending at the center B-pillar. The shoulder belt will automatically adjust itself and will lock tight only on extremely hard braking, or impacts of 5 mph or more. When the ignition is in any position and the door is opened or ajar, the shoulder belt will move forward to the A-pillar.

If the shoulder belt should stall before it reaches the B-pillar, the indicator lamp will begin to flash after nine seconds and will continue flashing until the shoulder belt is in its locked position. If indicator lamp continues to flash, refer to "Manual Override System."

On Cougar and Thunderbird models, ensure shoulder belt is latched to emergency release buckle at the A-pillar.

### EMERGENCY RELEASE

1. **On Tempo, Topaz and 1989-90 Escort models,** emergency release levers are located in the center console above emergency brake lever.
2. **On Cougar & Thunderbird models,** emergency release buttons are located on shoulder belt upper anchor

### MANUAL OVERRIDE SYSTEM

If shoulder belt does not move or stops before reaching the B-pillar position, perform the following steps before driving vehicle.

1. With ignition off, open and close doors. Ensure doors are fully closed.
2. Using a screwdriver remove access cover at lower end of B-pillar interior trim panel and turn override knob clockwise to move shoulder belt manually until it stops at B-pillar position.
3. If shoulder belt still does not move to B-pillar, drive belt may be broken, or motor drive gear stripped. Grasp belt and pull toward B-pillar while turning override knob clockwise.

## TROUBLESHOOTING

Refer to **Fig. 1,** for troubleshooting procedures.

## DIAGNOSIS & TESTING

### COUGAR, TEMPO, THUNDERBIRD, TOPAZ & 1989–90 ESCORT

Refer to the system diagnostic chart, **Fig. 2,** and related pinpoint charts, **Figs. 3 through 14** for diagnosis procedures.

Refer to **Figs. 15 and 16** for restraint system wiring circuits.

### FESTIVA, PROBE, 1991 ESCORT & TRACER

Refer to the system diagnostic charts, **Figs. 17 through 21** for diagnostic charts.

Refer to **Figs. 22 through 24** for restraint system wiring circuits.

## COMPONENT REPLACEMENT

### DRIVE BELT

#### COUGAR & THUNDERBIRD

##### Removal

1. Cycle shoulder belt to full forward position. Disengage shoulder belt from mini buckle.
2. Remove rear seat back and cushion.
3. Remove A-pillar and quarter panel trim.
4. Disconnect electrical connectors from A- and B-pillars limit switches.
5. Remove upper bolt used to retain vertical belt guide to inner quarter panel.
6. Using release tab, disengage vertical belt guide from B-pillar bracket **Fig. 25.**
7. Remove two bolts retaining track assembly to B-pillar.
8. Remove A-pillar limit switch bracket attaching screws.
9. While holding track assembly securely, remove two bolts retaining track assembly to roof rail.
10. Rotate track assembly downward at rear to disengage A-pillar limit switch bracket from A-pillar.

11. While holding track assembly, rotate thumb wheel on motor counterclockwise to allow tape to disengaged from motors drive gear.
12. Remove track assembly from vehicle, then remove A-pillar limit switch bracket from track assembly.
13. Gently slide buckle assembly forward out of track assembly **Fig. 26.**
14. Remove buckle assembly from drive belt.

### Installation

Prior to installation, lubricate track using suitable grease.

1. Insert drive belt at front of track assembly, then install buckle assembly into large slot at front end of drive belt **Fig. 27.**
2. Slide drive belt and buckle assembly into track assembly far enough to allow installation of A-pillar limit switch and bracket assembly, then secure switch and bracket.
3. Install drive belt into vertical guide.
4. Rotate thumb wheel on motor clockwise to feed drive belt through motor guide and into lower guide.
5. Rotate track assembly downward at rear and position retaining tab on A-pillar limit switch bracket into forward hole in A-pillar. Then rotate track assembly upward.
6. Engage vertical guide retaining tab into B-pillar bracket. Install but do not tighten screw and bolts used to secure track assembly to roof rail and A-pillar.
7. Secure B-pillar bracket to B-pillar and **torque** attaching bolts to 21 ft. lbs.
8. **Torque** A-pillar limit switch attachment to 25 inch lbs.
9. Install and **torque** bolt retaining vertical guide to inner quarter panel sheet metal to 50 inch lbs.
10. Reconnect electrical connectors at A- and B-pillars limit switches.
11. Install quarter trim panel and A-pillar moldings.
12. Cycle mini buckle to B-pillar position.
13. Insert tongue of shoulder belt into mini buckle. Ensure there is no twist in belt.
14. Ensure proper operation of restraint system.

| CONDITION | POSSIBLE SOURCE | ACTION |
|---|---|---|
| • Belt Appears to Run Fine But Motor Stalls at A-pillar, Motor Could Get Warm | • "A" limit switch wire shorted to ground. "A" limit switch not opening. | • Check for pinched wire along A-pillar, or behind LH or RH side cowl panel. Check that carrier reaches "A" limit switch. |
| • Fasten Belt Indicator (IP) Remains Lit After 7-10 Seconds of Running to B-pillar, Belt Appears to Run Fine But Motor Stalls at B-pillar, Motor Could Get Warm | • "B" limit switch wire is shorted to ground. | • Check for pinched wire under guide attachment screws. |
| | • Obstruction. | • Check for trim screw, obstruction in track or track seal that prevents the carrier from reaching the "B" limit switch. |
| • Belt Will Not Run, Module May Be Burned | • Motor wire shorted to ground. | • Check for short to ground on the motor circuit breaker terminals. |
| • Belt Will Not Run | • Inertia switch tripped. | • Reset (depress) fuel pump inertia switch button. |
| | • Motor wire not connected. | • Check for unconnected connectors on the motor, or behind LH and RH side cowl panels. |
| • Belt Runs to A-pillar Only, Belt Will Not Run Back to B-pillar | • Door switch wire shorted to ground. | • Check for pinched wire behind door trim panel. |
| | • "B" limit switch wire not connected. | • Check for unconnected connectors near motor, behind LH and RH side cowl panel, or on "B" limit switch. |
| | • "B" limit switch plunger stuck in depressed position. | • Correct jammed switch or replace "B" limit switch. |
| • Belt Runs to B-pillar Only, Belt Will Not Run Forward to A-pillar. | • Door switch wire not connected. | • Check for unconnected connectors on door latch switch, or behind LH and RH side cowl panel. |
| | • "A" limit switch wire not connected. | • Check for unconnected connectors behind LH and RH side cowl panel, or on "A" limit switch. |
| | • Obstruction. | • Check for a trim screw, track seal or jammed track locking pawl that prevents the carrier from reaching the "A" limit switch. |
| • Opening/Closing Door Causes Both Belts to Move | • Damaged Door Ajar lamp assembly. | • Replace Door Ajar lamp assembly. |
| • Turning Ignition Off Causes Belt to Move to A-pillar | • Damaged Door Ajar lamp assembly. | • Replace Door Ajar lamp assembly. |
| • Fasten Belt Indicator Remains On, Chime Sounds for Four to Eight Seconds | • Connector to shoulder emergency release retractor switches not connected. | • Check for unconnected connectors in console near shoulder strap connector. |
| • Excessive Noise While Motor is Running | • Motor adjustment knob on top of motor hits body. | • Loosen motor, slide motor downward, then tighten motor. |

**Fig. 1 Troubleshooting chart**

## 1989–90 ESCORT

### Removal

Refer to **Fig. 28,** for the following procedure.

1. Remove A-pillar and B-pillar interior trim moldings, then cycle shoulder belt to A-pillar.
2. Remove shoulder belt anchor plug button and bolt **Fig. 29.**
3. Remove two screws retaining drive belt track to motor **Fig. 30.**
4. Remove screw adjacent to motor, retaining drive belt vertical guide.
5. **On Escort three-door models,** remove screw retaining drive belt lower guide.
6. **On all models,** carefully disconnect drive belt track from motor allowing belt to bypass gear teeth without engagement.
7. Remove A-pillar limit switch from bracket and bracket from track assembly.
8. Gently slide shoulder belt retainer forward off track. **Drive belt should slide out of track with shoulder belt retainer.**
9. Remove shoulder belt retainer from drive belt.

### Installation

Prior to installation, lubricate track using suitable grease.

1. Insert drive belt at front of track to A-pillar.
2. Install retainer into large slot at front end of tape **Fig. 31.**
3. Slide drive belt in track rearward until end is located 1/2 inch in upper track slot.
4. Align sprocket holes in drive belt with sprocket teeth.
5. Engage track locator on switch bracket, then install into slot in A-pillar. Attach A-pillar track switch to A-pillar and track assembly.
6. Install limit switch.
7. Return belt anchor to position at B-pillar.
8. Pull webbing out of retractor at console. Allow belt webbing to lay flat on seat with no twist.
9. Locate and align anchor notch and install retaining bolt.
10. Install belt attaching shoulder belt.

## TEMPO & TOPAZ

### Removal

Refer to **Fig. 28,** for the following procedure.

1. Remove track as described under "Track Assembly, Removal."
2. Remove two screws retaining front A-pillar switch bracket to track assembly.
3. Carefully slide shoulder belt retainer forward off of track, **Fig. 29. Drive belt should slide out of track with shoulder belt retainer.**
4. Remove shoulder belt retainer from drive belt.

### Installation

1. Lubricate track assembly with Emralon 329, or equivalent.

Continued on page 25-65
MOTORIZED SEAT BELTS

| CONDITION | POSSIBLE SOURCE | ACTION |
|---|---|---|
| • Belt Transport Motors Will Not Operate | • Battery.<br>• Inertia switch.<br>• Wiring.<br>• Door switch.<br>• Function control module.<br>• Motor. | • Test battery, replace if necessary.<br>• Reset switch. If system is still not operating Go to Pinpoint Test F.<br>• Go to Pinpoint Test E.<br>• Go to Pinpoint Test C.<br>• Go to Pinpoint Test J.<br>• Go to Pinpoint Test G. |
| • Belt Transport Motors Only Move Belt to A-pillar. Warning Chimes and Warning Indicators Do Not Function. Inertia Switch Not Activated | • Wiring.<br>• Function control module.<br>• B-pillar limit switch. | • Go to Pinpoint Test F.<br>• Go to Pinpoint Test J.<br>• Go to Pinpoint Test B. |
| • Belt Transport Motors Not Operating. Warning Chimes and Indicators Do Not Function | • Battery.<br>• Inertia switch.<br>• Limit switches.<br>• Function control module.<br>• Wiring | • Test battery, replace if necessary.<br>• Reset switch. If system is still not operating. Go to Pinpoint Test F.<br>• Go to Pinpoint Tests A and B.<br>• Go to Pinpoint Test J.<br>• Go to Pinpoint Test E. |
| • Driver Belt Transport Always Remains at B-pillar. Once Positioned at B-pillar. Driver Must Lift Emergency Release | • Wiring.<br>• Driver front "A" limit switch.<br>• Door switch. | • Go to Pinpoint Test E.<br>• Go to Pinpoint Test A.<br>• Go to Pinpoint Test C. |
| • Driver Belt Transport Motors Operate As Logic Demands. Driver Motor Stalls After Reaching A-pillar Position. Motor Will Shut Off By Module After Six Seconds of Operation | • Pin 5 shorted.<br>• Driver front "A" limit switch. | • Go to Pinpoint Test A.<br>• Go to Pinpoint Test A. |
| • Driver Belt Transport Always Remains at A-pillar | • Pin 18 always open.<br>• Driver rear "B" limit switch. | • Go to Pinpoint Test B.<br>• Go to Pinpoint Test B. |
| • Passenger Belt Transport Always Remains at B-pillar Once it Has Been Positioned at B-pillar, Passenger Will Have to Activate Emergency Release Lever to Release Belt | • Wiring.<br>• Passenger front "A" limit switch. | • Go to Pinpoint Test C.<br>• Go to Pinpoint Test A. |
| • Passenger Belt Transport Always Remains at A-pillar. When Door Switch and Ignition Logic Try to Send Belt Transport to B-pillar, the Fasten Belt Indicator Will Begin Flashing, Indicating Belt is Not Properly Positioned at B-pillar | • Wiring.<br>• Passenger rear "B" limit switch. | • Go to Pinpoint Test F.<br>• Go to Pinpoint Test B. |

**Fig. 2 System diagnostic chart (Part 1 of 6). Cougar, Tempo, Thunderbird, Topaz & 1989–90 Escort,**

| CONDITION | POSSIBLE SOURCE | ACTION |
|---|---|---|
| • Crash situation, module locks belts in current location depending on logic input determination, when ignition is removed belts move to A-pillar position when logic so dictates, and remain there | • Wiring.<br>• Inertia switch always open. | • Go to Pinpoint Test E.<br>• Go to Pinpoint Test F. |
| • Normal operation; module functions as logic dictates, module will not be able to detect a "crash" situation, therefore belt transport motors will be activated by door switch and ignition signals as specified by logic. | • Wiring.<br>• Inertia switch always shorted. | • Go to Pinpoint Test E.<br>• Go to Pinpoint Test F. |
| • Fasten belts indicator does not turn ON | • Wiring.<br>• Bulb burnt. | • Go to Pinpoint Test H.<br>• Check bulb. Replace if necessary. |
| • Fasten belts indicator stays ON | • Wiring.<br>• Bulb shorted to battery positive. | • Go to Pinpoint Test H.<br>• Check bulb. Replace if necessary. |
| • Driver belt remains at B-Pillar, does not move to A-pillar | • Wiring.<br>• Driver door switch always open circuit. | • Go to Pinpoint Test A.<br>• Go to Pinpoint Test C. |
| • Driver belt remains at A-pillar, does not move to B-pillar | • Wiring.<br>• Driver door switch always shorted to ground. | • Go to Pinpoint Test B.<br>• Go to Pinpoint Test C. |
| • Passenger belt remains at B-pillar, does not move to A-pillar | • Wiring.<br>• Passenger door switch always open circuit | • Go to Pinpoint Test A.<br>• Go to Pinpoint Test C. |
| • Passenger belt remains at A-pillar, does not move to B-pillar | • Wiring.<br>• Passenger door switch always shorted to ground. | • Go to Pinpoint Test B.<br>• Go to Pinpoint Test C. |
| • Release lever warning indicator never turns ON | • Wiring.<br>• Bulb burnt. | • Go to Pinpoint Test H.<br>• Check bulb. Replace if necessary. |
| • Release lever warning indicator remains ON | • Wiring.<br>• Bulb shorted to battery positive. | • Go to Pinpoint Test H.<br>• Check bulb. Replace if necessary. |
| • Excessive pressure on occupant during normal wear | • Retractor spring wound too tightly. | • Replace |
| • Transport system does not move belt forward | • Anchor tab trim binds with track and/or vertical trim.<br>• Electrical failure. | • Adjust<br>• Go to Pinpoint Test A. |
| • Transport system does not move rearward | • Anchor tab trim binds with track and/or vertical trim.<br>• Electrical failure. | • Adjust<br>• Go to Pinpoint Test B. |

**Fig. 2 System diagnostic chart (Part 2 of 6). 1989–90 Escort, Tempo & Topaz**

| CONDITION | POSSIBLE SOURCE | ACTION |
|---|---|---|
| • Belts will never move with ignition ON. Belts will move to A-pillar only with ignition OFF. | • Wiring.<br>• Inertia switch always open. | • Go to Pinpoint Test E.<br>• Go to Pinpoint Test F. |
| • Belt transport motors will be activated by door switch and ignition signals as specified by logic in a "crash" situation. | • Wiring.<br>• Inertia switch always shorted. | • Go to Pinpoint Test E.<br>• Go to Pinpoint Test F. |
| • Fasten belts indicator does not turn ON | • Wiring.<br>• Bulb burnt. | • Go to Pinpoint Test H.<br>• Check bulb. Replace if necessary. |
| • Fasten belts indicator stays ON | • Wiring.<br>• Bulb shorted to battery positive | • Go to Pinpoint Test H.<br>• Check bulb. Replace if necessary. |
| • Driver belt remains at B-pillar, does not move to A-pillar | • Wiring<br>• Driver door switch always open circuit | • Go to Pinpoint Test A.<br>• Go to Pinpoint Test C. |
| • Driver belt remains at A-pillar, does not move to B-pillar | • Wiring.<br>• Driver door switch always shorted to ground. | • Go to Pinpoint Test B.<br>• Go to Pinpoint Test C. |
| • Passenger belt remains at B-pillar, does not move to A-pillar | • Wiring<br>• Passenger door switch always open circuit | • Go to Pinpoint Test A.<br>• Go to Pinpoint Test C. |
| • Passenger belt remains at A-pillar, does not move to B-pillar | • Wiring<br>• Passenger door switch always shorted to ground | • Go to Pinpoint Test B<br>• Go to Pinpoint Test C |
| • Excessive pressure on occupant during normal wear | • Retractor spring wound too tightly | • Replace |
| • Transport system does not move belt forward | • Anchor tab trim binds with track and/or vertical trim<br>• Electrical failure. | • Adjust<br>• Go to Pinpoint Test A. |
| • Transport system does not move rearward | • Anchor tab trim binds with track and/or vertical trim.<br>• Electrical failure. | • Adjust<br>• Go to Pinpoint Test B. |
| • Transport system moves too slowly | • Anchor tab cover binds with track and or trim.<br>• Low battery voltage.<br>• Transport motor.<br>• Tape distorted.<br>• Gear stripped. | • Adjust.<br>• Lubricate track.<br>• Check, replace if necessary.<br>• Go to Pinpoint Test G.<br>• Check, replace if necessary.<br>• Check, replace if necessary. |

**Fig. 2 System diagnostic chart (Part 3 of 6). Cougar & Thunderbird**

| CONDITION | POSSIBLE SOURCE | ACTION |
|---|---|---|
| • Transport system moves too slowly | • Anchor tab cover binds with track and or trim.<br>• Low battery voltage.<br>• Transport motor.<br>• Tape distorted.<br>• Gear stripped. | • Adjust.<br>• Lubricate Track.<br>• Check, replace if necessary.<br>• Go to Pinpoint Test G.<br>• Check, replace if necessary.<br>• Check, replace if necessary |
| • Excessive slack in webbing | • Broken rewind spring.<br>• Webbing interfering with console bezel. | • Check, replace retractor unit if necessary.<br>• Adjust console, or bezel not installed properly. |
| • Shoulder belt will not move rearward past top of B-pillar or forward | • Insufficient strength.<br>**NOTE: System might be distorted through occupant use of belt as assist handle.**<br>• Foreign material or object in track assembly.<br>• Drive tape broken.<br>• Dust seal ragged. | • Install new track<br><br>• Clean track and lubricate with Emralon 329® ESB-M99C71-A or equivalent.<br>• Check, replace if necessary.<br>• Check, replace if necessary. |
| • Lap belt retractor webbing protrudes into door opening | • Retractor assembly blocked. Foreign material in retractor.<br>• Insufficient strength from rewind spring | • Check, replace if necessary<br>• Check, replace if necessary. |
| • Webbing cannot be extracted | • Retractor blocked internally.<br>• Foreign material in retractor.<br>• Excessive spring load | • Check, replace retractor unit if necessary.<br>• Check, replace if necessary<br>• Check, replace retractor unit if necessary. |
| • Shoulder belt webbing does not retract | • Insufficient spring load.<br>• Retractor blocked internally.<br>• Foreign material in retractor.<br>• Bezel not located properly. | • Check, replace retractor unit if necessary.<br>• Check, replace retractor unit if necessary.<br>• Clean, replace if necessary.<br>• Locate properly. |
| • Shoulder belt webbing twisted | • Belt installed improperly. | • Check, correct orientation. |
| • Shoulder belt webbing frayed | • Excessive wear, or sharp object cutting belt. | • Check retractor unit, replace if necessary. |
| • Release levers do not release | • Release levers do not have sufficient travel.<br>• Levers bind on console. | • Replace if necessary.<br>• Align levers. |

**Fig. 2 System diagnostic chart (Part 4 of 6). 1989–90 Escort, Tempo & Topaz**

| CONDITION | POSSIBLE SOURCE | ACTION |
|---|---|---|
| • Excessive slack in webbing | • Broken rewind spring. | • Check, replace retractor unit if necessary. |
| | • Webbing interfering with console bezel. | • Adjust console, or bezel not installed properly. |
| • Shoulder belt will not move rearward past top of B-pillar or forward | • Insufficient strength. **NOTE: System might be distorted through occupant use of belt as assist handle.** | • Install new track |
| | • Foreign material or object in track assembly. | • Clean track and lubricate with Emraion 329® ESB-M99C71-A or equivalent. |
| | • Drive tape broken. | • Check, replace if necessary. |
| | • Dust seal ragged. | • Check, replace if necessary. |
| • Lap belt retractor webbing protrudes into door opening | • Retractor assembly blocked. Foreign material in retractor. | • Check, replace if necessary. |
| | • Insufficient strength from rewind spring. | • Check, replace if necessary. |
| • Webbing cannot be extracted | • Retractor blocked internally. | • Check, replace retractor unit if necessary. |
| | • Foreign material in retractor. | • Check, replace if necessary. |
| | • Excessive spring load. | • Check, replace retractor unit if necessary. |
| • Shoulder belt webbing does not retract | • Insufficient spring load. | • Check, replace retractor unit if necessary. |
| | • Retractor blocked internally. | • Check, replace retractor unit if necessary. |
| | • Foreign material in retractor. | • Clean, replace if necessary. |
| | • Bezel not located properly. | • Locate properly. |
| • Shoulder belt webbing twisted | • Belt installed improperly. | • Check, correct orientation. |
| • Shoulder belt webbing frayed | • Excessive wear, or sharp object cutting belt. | • Check retractor unit, replace if necessary. |

**Fig. 2 System diagnostic chart (Part 5 of 6). Cougar & Thunderbird**

| CONDITION | POSSIBLE SOURCE | ACTION |
|---|---|---|
| • Lap belt system will not release | • Internal component failure. | • Check, and replace if necessary. |
| | • Foreign material in buckle. | • Clean and replace if necessary. |
| | • Buckle cannot be felt or seen. | • Locate or install buckle assembly. |
| | • Buckle falls down between seat and console. | • Install grommet. |
| • Lap belt retractor locks prior to tongue engaging into buckle | • Customer does not use continuous motion to connect tongue into buckle. | • Refer to Owner's Guide. |
| • Tongue does not reach buckle | • Webbing too short for occupant. | • Obtain belt service extender. |
| • Lap belt does not go around child seat | • Webbing too short for child seat design. | • Obtain belt service extender. |
| • Excessive pressure on occupant during normal wearing | • Excessive retraction efforts. | • Check, replace retractor unit if necessary. |
| | • Webbing too short to accommodate occupant. | • Obtain belt service extender. |

**Fig. 2 System diagnostic chart (Part 6 of 6). Cougar, Tempo, Thunderbird, Topaz & 1989–90 Escort**

| TEST STEP | | RESULT ▶ | ACTION TO TAKE |
|---|---|---|---|
| A1 | CHECK HARNESS AND "A" LIMIT SWITCH CLOSED POSITION | | |
| | • Remove access cover over the motor of the side to be checked. | Less than 10 ohms ▶ | GO to **A2**. |
| | • Rotate the motor by hand so that the transport is somewhere in between both ends of track but at least 3 inches from either end of track. | More than 10 ohms ▶ | GO to **A3**. |
| | • Remove passive restraint module to gain access to mating connector. | | |
| | • Digital Volt-ohmmeter on 200 ohm scale, use Rotunda Digital Volt Ohm Meter 007-00001 or equivalent. | | |
| | • Measure resistance between pins of mating connector for the passive restraint module: Driver side between Pins 5 and 24. Passenger side between Pins 23 and 24. | | |
| A2 | CHECK HARNESS AND "A" LIMIT SWITCH OPEN POSITION | | |
| | • Rotate the motor by hand so that the transport is at the A-pillar. | Less than 500 K ohms ▶ | GO to **A4**. |
| | • Measure resistance between pins of mating connector for the passive restraint module: Driver side between Pins 5 and 24. Passenger side between Pins 23 and 24. | More than 500 K ohms ▶ | Switch and wiring OK. |
| A3 | CHECK "A" LIMIT SWITCH CLOSED POSITION | | |
| | • Remove the trim over the track and the "A" limit switch. | Less than 10 ohms ▶ | GO to **A5**. |
| | • Disconnect the connector from the limit switch. | More than 10 ohms ▶ | REPLACE switch. INSTALL original passive restraint module. |
| | • Measure resistance between pins of the limit switch. | | |
| A4 | CHECK "A" LIMIT SWITCH OPEN POSITION | | |
| | • Remove the trim over the track and the "A" limit switch. | Less than 500 K ohms ▶ | REPLACE switch. INSTALL original passive restraint module. |
| | • Make sure carrier fully depresses plunger of limit switch. | | |
| | • Disconnect the connector from the limit switch. | More than 500 K ohms ▶ | GO to **A5**. |
| | • Measure resistance between pins of the limit switch. | | |
| A5 | CHECK HARNESS FROM MODULE MATING CONNECTOR TO LIMIT SWITCH | | |
| | • Measure resistance from pins of the limit switch harness to pins of the Passive Restraint Module mating connector: Driver side — one limit switch pin to Pin 24 (ground), other limit switch pin to Pin 5. Passenger side — one limit switch pin to Pin 24 (ground), other limit switch pin to Pin 23. | Continuity ▶ | Wiring OK. |
| | | No continuity ▶ | CORRECT wiring. INSTALL original passive restraint module. |

**Fig. 3 Pinpoint Test A. Cougar, Tempo, Thunderbird, Topaz & 1989–90 Escort**

| TEST STEP | | RESULT ▶ | ACTION TO TAKE |
|---|---|---|---|
| B1 | CHECK HARNESS AND "B" LIMIT SWITCH CLOSED POSITION | | |
| | • Remove access cover over the motor of the side to be checked. | Less than 10 ohms ▶ | GO to **B2**. |
| | • Rotate the motor by hand so that the transport is somewhere in between both ends of track but at least 3 inches from either end of track. | More than 10 ohms ▶ | GO to **B3**. |
| | • Remove passive restraint module to gain access to mating connector. | | |
| | • Digital Volt-ohmmeter on 200 scale, use Rotunda Digital Volt Ohm Meter 007-00001 or equivalent. | | |
| | • Measure resistance between pins of mating connector for the Passive Restraint Module: Driver side between Pins 18 and 24. Passenger side between Pins 21 and 24. | | |
| B2 | CHECK HARNESS AND "B" LIMIT SWITCH OPEN POSITION | | |
| | • Rotate the motor by hand so that the transport is at the B-pillar. | Less than 500 K ohms ▶ | GO to **B4**. |
| | • Measure resistance between pins of mating connector for the passive restraint module: Driver side between Pins 18 and 24. Passenger side between Pins 21 and 24. | More than 500 K ohms ▶ | Switch and wiring OK. |
| B3 | CHECK "B" LIMIT SWITCH CLOSED POSITION | | |
| | • Remove the trim over the track and the "B" limit switch. | Less than 10 ohms ▶ | GO to **B5**. |
| | • Disconnect the connector from the limit switch. | More than 10 ohms ▶ | REPLACE switch. INSTALL original passive restraint module. |
| | • Measure resistance between pins of the limit switch. | | |
| B4 | CHECK "B" LIMIT SWITCH OPEN POSITION | | |
| | • Remove the trim over the track and the "B" limit switch. | Less than 500 K ohms ▶ | REPLACE switch. INSTALL original passive restraint module. |
| | • Make sure carrier fully depresses plunger of limit switch. | | |
| | • Disconnect the connector from the limit switch. | More than 500 K ohms ▶ | GO to **B5**. |
| | • Measure resistance between pins of the limit switch. | | |
| B5 | CHECK HARNESS FROM MODULE MATING CONNECTOR TO LIMIT SWITCH | | |
| | • Measure resistance from pins of the limit switch harness to pins of the passive restraint module mating connector: Driver side — one limit switch pin to Pin 24 (ground), other limit switch pin to Pin 18. Passenger side — one limit switch pin to Pin 24 (ground), other limit switch pin to Pin 21. | Continuity ▶ | Wiring OK. |
| | | No continuity ▶ | CORRECT wiring. INSTALL original passive restraint module. |

**Fig. 4 Pinpoint Test B. Cougar, Tempo, Thunderbird, Topaz & 1989–90 Escort**

| | TEST STEP | RESULT ▶ | ACTION TO TAKE |
|---|---|---|---|
| C1 | CHECK HARNESS AND DOOR LATCH SWITCH | | |
| | • Turn ignition to OFF (position 0).<br>• Remove passive restraint module to gain access to mating connector.<br>• Digital Volt-ohmmeter on 20,000 ohm scale, use Rotunda Digital Volt Ohm Meter 007-00001 or equivalent.<br>• Measure resistance between pins of mating connector for the Passive Restraint Module: Driver side between Pins 13 and 24. Passenger side between Pins 8 and 24.<br>• Fully close door. | Less than 500 K ohms ▶<br>More than 500 K ohms ▶ | GO to **C3**.<br>GO to **C2**. |
| C2 | CHECK HARNESS AND DOOR LATCH SWITCH (CONTINUED) | | |
| | • With door open measure resistance. | Less than 10 ohms ▶<br>More than 10 ohms ▶ | Switch and wiring OK.<br>GO to **C3**. |
| C3 | CHECK DOOR AJAR (LATCH) SWITCH | | |
| | • Remove door trim panel.<br>• Disconnect wiring harness from door latch switch.<br>• Measure resistance between switch terminal and ground (latch).<br>• Fully close door. | Less than 500 K ohms ▶<br>More than 500 K ohms ▶ | REPLACE switch. INSTALL original passive restraint module.<br>GO to **C4**. |
| C4 | CHECK DOOR AJAR (LATCH) SWITCH (CONTINUED) | | |
| | • With door open measure resistance. | Less than 10 ohms ▶<br>More than 10 ohms ▶ | GO to **C5**.<br>REPLACE switch. INSTALL original passive restraint module. |
| C5 | CHECK HARNESS FOR DOOR AJAR (LATCH) SWITCH | | |
| | • Measure resistance from pins of the door latch switch harness to pins of the passive restraint module mating connector: Driver side — door switch harness to Pin 13. Passenger side — door switch harness to Pin 8. | Continuity ▶<br>No continuity ▶ | Switch and wiring OK.<br>CORRECT wiring problem. INSTALL original passive restraint module. |

**Fig. 5 Pinpoint Test C. Cougar, Tempo, Thunderbird, Topaz & 1989–90 Escort**

| | TEST STEP | RESULT ▶ | ACTION TO TAKE |
|---|---|---|---|
| D1 | CHECK SPOOL RELEASE SWITCH | | |
| | • Disconnect both switches connected in series, located at retractor release mechanism.<br>• Digital Volt Ohm Meter on 200 ohm scale, use Rotunda Digital Volt Ohm Meter 007-00001 or an equivalent.<br>• Measure resistance across switch terminals. | Less than 10 ohms ▶<br>More than 10 ohms ▶ | GO to **D2**.<br>REPLACE switch. |
| D2 | CHECK RELEASE MECHANISM | | |
| | • When one or both release mechanism levers are in UP position, switch should be open. | Less than 10 ohms ▶<br>More than 10 ohms ▶ | REPLACE switch.<br>Switch is OK. Connect harness to switch. |

**Fig. 7 Pinpoint Test D. Tempo, Topaz & 1989–90 Escort**

| | TEST STEP | RESULT ▶ | ACTION TO TAKE |
|---|---|---|---|
| G1 | BELT TO A-PILLAR | | |
| | • Remove module to gain access to passive restraint module mating connector.<br>• Install jumpers in passive restraint module mating connector. Motors will run while jumpers are connected.<br>Driver — Pin 2 to Pin 6 or Pin 17 to Pin 19. Pin 3 to Pin 7 or Pin 4 to Pin 20<br>Passenger — Pin 9 to Pin 6 or Pin 22 to Pin 19 Pin 10 to Pin 7 or Pin 11 to Pin 20 | Motor directs drive belt toward A-pillar ▶<br>Motor does not run ▶ | GO to **G2**.<br>CHECK fuse. CHECK motor circuit breaker. CHECK wiring to motor. INSTALL original passive restraint module. |
| G2 | BELT TO B-PILLAR | | |
| | • Install jumpers in mating connector. Motors will run while jumpers are connected.<br>Driver — Pin 3 to Pin 6 or Pin 4 to Pin 19 Pin 2 to Pin 7 or Pin 17 to Pin 20<br>Passenger — Pin 10 to Pin 6 or Pin 11 to Pin 19 Pin 9 to Pin 7 or Pin 22 to Pin 20 | Motor runs toward B-pillar ▶<br>Motor does not run ▶ | System OK.<br>CHECK fuse. CHECK motor circuit breaker. CHECK wiring to motor. INSTALL original passive restraint module. |

**Fig. 10 Pinpoint Test G. Cougar & Thunderbird**

| | TEST STEP | RESULT ▶ | ACTION TO TAKE |
|---|---|---|---|
| D1 | CHECK SHOULDER BELT RETRACTOR SWITCH (BUCKLE ENGAGED) | | |
| | • Disconnect switch at connector attached to bracket on inboard side of seat track.<br>• Set Digital Volt Ohm Meter 007-00001 or equivalent on 200 ohm scale.<br>• Probe across switch connector terminals with shoulder belt tongue and buckle engaged. | Switch Closed ▶<br>Switch Open ▶ | GO to **D2**.<br>Malfunctioning switch. REPLACE retractor assembly. |
| D2 | CHECK SHOULDER BELT RETRACTOR SWITCH (BUCKLE DISENGAGED) | | |
| | • Repeat procedure described in Step D1, except with shoulder belt tongue and buckle DISENGAGED and shoulder belt retracted in excess of 305mm (12 inches) from engaged position. | Switch Closed ▶<br>Switch Open ▶ | Malfunctioning switch. REPLACE retractor assembly.<br>Switch OK. CONNECT harness to switch. |

**Fig. 6 Pinpoint Test D. Cougar & Thunderbird**

| | TEST STEP | RESULT ▶ | ACTION TO TAKE |
|---|---|---|---|
| E1 | CHECK LOGIC GROUND | | |
| | • Remove passive restraint module to gain access to mating connector.<br>• Digital Volt-ohmmeter on 200 ohm scale, use Rotunda Digital Volt Ohm Meter 007-00001 or equivalent.<br>• Measure resistance between Pin 24 of mating connector for the passive restraint module to chassis ground. | Continuity ▶<br>No continuity ▶ | GO to **E2**.<br>CORRECT wiring problem. INSTALL original passive restraint module. |
| E2 | CHECK MOTOR POWER GROUND | | |
| | • Measure resistance between Pin 6 of mating connector for the passive restraint module to chassis ground. | Continuity ▶<br>No continuity ▶ | GO to **E3**.<br>CORRECT wiring. INSTALL original passive restraint module. |
| E3 | CHECK SECOND MOTOR POWER GROUND | | |
| | • Measure resistance between Pin 19 of mating connector for the passive restraint module to chassis ground. | Continuity ▶<br>No continuity ▶ | Grounds OK.<br>CORRECT wiring. INSTALL original passive restraint module. |

**Fig. 8 Pinpoint Test E. Cougar, Tempo, Thunderbird, Topaz & 1989–90 Escort**

| | TEST STEP | RESULT ▶ | ACTION TO TAKE |
|---|---|---|---|
| F1 | CHECK B+ CONNECTION | | |
| | • Remove passive restraint module to gain access to passive restraint module mating connector.<br>• Using a Digital Volt-ohmmeter on 20V scale, measure voltage on passive restraint mating connector Pin 7 to Pin 24. | Battery voltage present ▶<br>No battery voltage present ▶ | GO to **F2**.<br>CHECK fuse. CORRECT wiring. CHECK ground. INSTALL original passive restraint module. |
| F2 | CHECK B+ CONNECTION | | |
| | • Measure voltage on passive restraint mating connector Pin 20 to Pin 24. | Battery voltage present ▶<br>No battery voltage present ▶ | GO to **F3**.<br>CHECK fuse. CORRECT wiring. CHECK ground. INSTALL original passive restraint module. |
| F3 | CHECK RUN/START CONNECTION — IGNITION OFF | | |
| | • Measure voltage on passive restraint mating connector Pin 25 to Pin 24 with ignition switch in OFF position. | Battery voltage present ▶<br>No battery voltage present ▶ | CORRECT wiring. INSTALL original passive restraint module.<br>GO to **F4**. |
| F4 | CHECK RUN/START CONNECTION — IGNITION ON | | |
| | • Measure voltage on passive restraint mating connector Pin 25 to Pin 24 with ignition switch in RUN position. | Battery voltage present ▶<br>No battery voltage present ▶ | GO to **F5**.<br>CHECK fuse. CORRECT wiring. CHECK ground. INSTALL original passive restraint module. |
| F5 | CHECK INERTIA SWITCH | | |
| | • Measure voltage on passive restraint mating connector Pin 12 to Pin 24 with ignition switch in OFF position. | Battery voltage present ▶<br>No battery voltage present ▶ | CORRECT wiring. INSTALL original passive restraint module.<br>GO to **F6**. |
| F6 | MEASURE VOLTAGE | | |
| | • Using Rotunda Digital Volt Ohm Meter 007-00001 or an equivalent measure voltage between Pin 12 and Pin 24 with ignition switch in RUN position. | Battery voltage present ▶<br>No battery voltage present ▶ | System OK.<br>RESET fuel pump inertia switch and RECHECK. CHECK fuse. CORRECT wiring. CHECK ground. INSTALL original passive restraint module. |

**Fig. 9 Pinpoint Test F. Cougar, Tempo, Thunderbird, Topaz & 1989–90 Escort**

| TEST STEP | RESULT ▶ | ACTION TO TAKE |
|---|---|---|
| **G1** BELT TO A-PILLAR | | |
| • Remove module to gain access to passive restraint module mating connector.<br>• Install jumpers in passive restraint module mating connector.<br>Driver — Pin 2 to Pin 6 and Pin 17 to Pin 19.<br>Passenger — Pin 9 to Pin 6 and Pin 22 to Pin 19<br>• Install temporary jumpers (motor will run while jumpers are connected)<br>Driver — Pin 3 to Pin 7 or Pin 4 to Pin 20<br>Passenger — Pin 10 to Pin 7 or Pin 11 to Pin 20 | Motor directs drive belt toward A-pillar ▶ | GO to G2. |
| | Motor does not run ▶ | CHECK fuse. CHECK motor circuit breaker. CHECK wiring to motor. INSTALL original passive restraint module. |
| **G2** BELT TO B-PILLAR | | |
| • Install jumpers in mating connector.<br>Driver — Pin 3 to Pin 6 and Pin 4 to Pin 19<br>Passenger — Pin 10 to Pin 6 and Pin 11 to Pin 19<br>• Install temporary jumpers (motor runs while jumpers are connected).<br>Driver — Pin 2 to Pin 7 or Pin 17 to Pin 20<br>Passenger — Pin 9 to Pin 7 or Pin 22 to Pin 20 | Motor runs toward B-pillar ▶ | System OK. |
| | Motor does not run ▶ | CHECK fuse. CHECK motor circuit breaker. CHECK wiring to motor. INSTALL original passive restraint module. GO to G3. |
| **G3** MOTOR RESISTANCE CHECK | | |
| • Using Rotunda Digital Volt Ohm Meter 007-00001 or equivalent, measure resistance between transport motor pins. Resistance should be 0.9 to 1.5 Ohms.<br>Driver side — Pins 2 and 3.<br>Passenger — Pins 9 and 10. | Within Specification ▶ | Motor OK. |
| | Out of Specification ▶ | REPLACE motor. |

**Fig. 11 Pinpoint Test G. Tempo, Topaz & 1989–90 Escort**

| TEST STEP | RESULT ▶ | ACTION TO TAKE |
|---|---|---|
| **H1** CHECK FASTEN BELT INDICATOR | | |
| • Remove module to gain access to mating connector.<br>• Install jumper in mating connector to connect Pin 16 to Pin 7. | Fasten belt indicator in instrument panel lights ▶ | System OK. |
| | Fasten belt indicator in instrument panel does not light ▶ | CHECK fuse. CHECK bulb. INSTALL original passive restraint module. |
| **H2** CHECK CHIME WARNING | | |
| • Place ignition key in ignition.<br>• Install jumper in mating connector to connect Pin 1 to Pin 7. | Chime sounds from 4 to 8 seconds ▶ | System OK. |
| | Chime does not sound ▶ | CHECK fuse. CHECK chime module. INSTALL original passive restraint module. |

**Fig. 12 Pinpoint Test H. Cougar & Thunderbird**

| TEST STEP | RESULT ▶ | ACTION TO TAKE |
|---|---|---|
| **H1** CHECK FASTEN BELT INDICATOR | | |
| • Remove module to gain access to mating connector<br>• Install jumper in mating connector to connect Pin 16 to Pin 7. | Fasten belt indicator in instrument panel lights ▶ | System OK. |
| | Fasten belt indicator in instrument panel does not light ▶ | CHECK fuse. CHECK bulb. INSTALL original passive restraint module. |
| **H2** CHECK CHIME WARNING | | |
| • Place ignition key in ignition.<br>• Install jumper in mating connector to connect Pin 1 to Pin 7. | Chime sounds ▶ | System OK. |
| | Chime does not sound ▶ | CHECK fuse. CHECK chime module. INSTALL original passive restraint module. |
| **H3** CHECK "PUSH LEVER DOWN" INDICATOR | | |
| • Install jumper in mating connector to connect Pin 26 to Pin 7. | "Push lever down" indicator lights ▶ | System OK. |
| | "Push lever down" indicator does not light ▶ | CHECK fuse. CHECK bulb. INSTALL original passive restraint module. |

**Fig. 13 Pinpoint Test H. Tempo, Topaz & 1989–90 Escort**

| TEST STEP | RESULT ▶ | ACTION TO TAKE |
|---|---|---|
| **J1** CHECK SYSTEM | | |
| • All system switches, grounds, voltages and wiring must be correct prior to checking module. | System OK ▶ | GO to J2. |
| | System failure ▶ | CORRECT problem. GO to J2. |
| **J2** CHECK BELT FUNCTION | | |
| • Operate system per driver and Passenger Operational Logic Chart. | Function agrees with chart ▶ | GO to J3. |
| | Function does not agree with chart ▶ | REPLACE module. |
| **J3** CHECK WARNING FUNCTION | | |
| • Operate warnings per the Function Table — Warnings located in this Section. | Function agrees with chart ▶ | System OK. |
| | Function does not agree with chart ▶ | REPLACE module. |

**Fig. 14 Pinpoint Test J. (Part 1 of 3) Cougar, Tempo, Thunderbird, Topaz & 1989–90 Escort**

| ACTION | RESULT |
|---|---|
| Ignition OFF — Close Door | Belt Stays at A-Pillar |
| Ignition ON — Before Door is Closed | Belt Stays at A-Pillar |
| Ignition ON — Close Door | Belt Moves From A to B-Pillar |
| Ignition ON — Open Door | Belt Moves From B to A-Pillar |
| Ignition OFF — Open Door | Belt Moves From B to A-Pillar |
| Ignition ON — Open Door, Inertia Switch OPEN | Belt Stays at B-Pillar |
| Ignition OFF — Open Door, Inertia Switch OPEN | Belt Moves From B to A-Pillar |

**Fig. 14 Pinpoint Test J (Part 2 of 3, operational logic chart). Cougar, Tempo, Thunderbird, Topaz & 1989-90 Escort**

| Action | Result |
|---|---|
| Belt doesn't properly reach B-pillar; after approximately 7.5 seconds | Fasten belt indicator (IP) remains lit, chime sounds after 16 seconds |
| Emergency shoulder belt release buckle disengaged; one or both shoulder belts retracted Ignition ON | 1. Fasten belt indicator (IP) remains lit<br>2. Chime sounds for 4 to 8 seconds |

**Fig. 14 Pinpoint Test J (Part 3 of 3, function table). Cougar, Tempo, Thunderbird, Topaz & 1989-90 Escort**

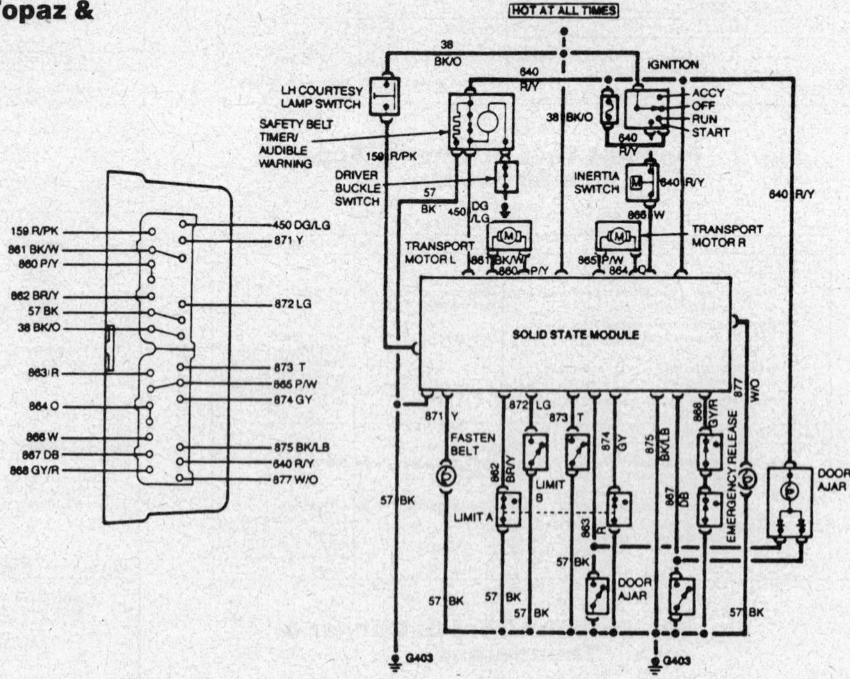


**Fig. 15 Restraint system wiring circuit. Tempo & Topaz**

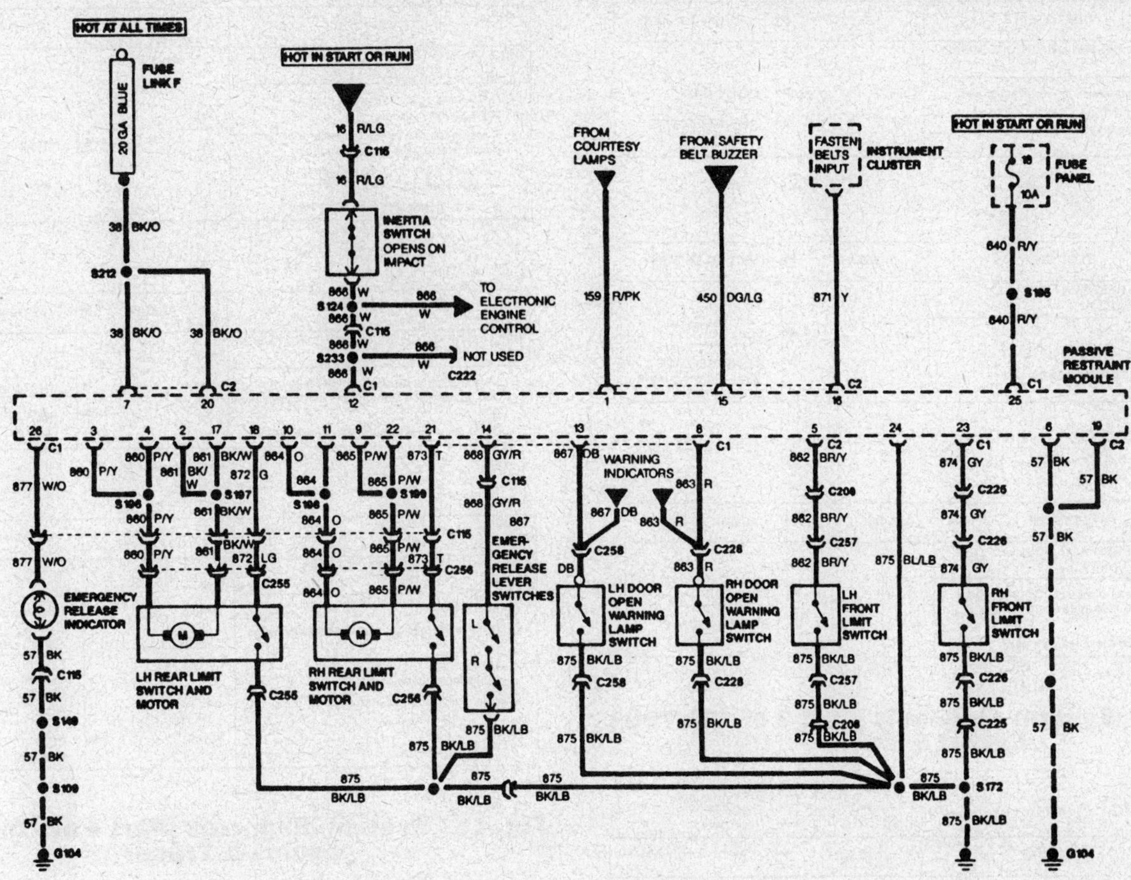


**Fig. 16 Restraint system wiring circuit. 1989–90 Escort**

| CONDITION | POSSIBLE SOURCE | ACTION |
|---|---|---|
| • Passive Restraint Does Not Work | • Passive restraint control module.<br>• Passive restraint circuit.<br>• Electrical system. | • GO to OR1. |
| • Belt Transport Will Not Move to "B" Pillar | • Door catch switch.<br>• Rear limit switch.<br>• Passive restraint control module.<br>• Track and motor assembly.<br>• Passive restraint circuit. | • GO to OR7. |
| • Belt Transport Will Not Move to "A" Pillar | • Door catch switch.<br>• Front limit switch.<br>• Passive restraint control module.<br>• Track and motor assembly.<br>• Passive restraint circuit. | • GO to OR7. |
| • Passive Restraint Stops at "A" Pillar | • Front limit switch. | • REPLACE switch. |
| • Passive Restraint Carrier Stops at "B" Pillar, Fasten Belts Indicator remains On | • Track and motor assembly. | • REPLACE track and motor assembly. |
| • Passive Restraint Carrier Stops at "B" Pillar, Motor Continues to Run. Noise is heard from the motor and/or module | • Track and motor assembly (rear limit switch). | • REPLACE track and motor assembly. |
| • Seat Belt Light and Chime Turn On Intermittently | • Seat belt retractor assembly (shoulder belts). | • GO to OR20. |
| • Both Belts will not Leave the "B" Pillar | • Inertia switch.<br>• Wire between module and inertia switch. | • GO to OR21. |

**Fig. 17 System diagnosis (Part 1 of 10). 1991 Escort & Tracer**

| TEST STEP | RESULT ► | ACTION TO TAKE |
|---|---|---|
| **OR1** OCCUPANT RESTRAINT FUSE CHECK | | |
| • Access the interior fuse panel.<br>• Check the 30 amp "belt" fuse and 15 amp "meter" fuse.<br>• Are the fuses OK? | Yes ►<br>No ► | GO to OR4.<br>Go to OR2. |

| TEST STEP | RESULT ► | ACTION TO TAKE |
|---|---|---|
| **OR2** CHECK SYSTEM | | |
| • Replace the fuse.<br>• Key ON.<br>• Did the fuse(s) blow again? | Yes ►<br>No ► | GO to OR3.<br>GO to OR4. |

| TEST STEP | RESULT ► | ACTION TO TAKE |
|---|---|---|
| **OR3** CHECK FOR SHORT TO GROUND | | |
| • Replace the blown fuse(s).<br>• Disconnect the "Y" and "BK/Y" wires at the fuse panel and the passive restraint module.<br>• Measure the resistance of each wire to ground.<br>• Is either resistance less than 5 ohms? | Yes ►<br>No ► | SERVICE wire in question.<br>REPAIR/REPLACE passive restraint control module. |

**Fig. 17 System diagnosis (Part 2 of 10). 1991 Escort & Tracer**

| TEST STEP | RESULT ► | ACTION TO TAKE |
|---|---|---|
| OR4 PASSIVE RESTRAINT MODULE SUPPLY CHECK | | |
| • Measure voltage on "Y" wires at passive restraint module. • Is the voltage greater than 10 volts? | Yes ►<br>No ► | GO to OR5 .<br>REPAIR/REPLACE wires. |

| TEST STEP | RESULT ► | ACTION TO TAKE |
|---|---|---|
| OR5 PASSIVE RESTRAINT MODULE SUPPLY CHECK | | |
| • Ignition ON. • Measure the voltage on the "BK/Y" wire. • Is the voltage greater than 10 volts? | Yes ►<br>No ► | GO to OR6 .<br>REPAIR/REPLACE "BK/Y" wire to passive restraint module. |

| TEST STEP | RESULT ► | ACTION TO TAKE |
|---|---|---|
| OR6 PASSIVE RESTRAINT MODULE GROUND CHECK | | |
| • Measure the resistance of "BK" wires from passive restraint module connector to ground. • Is the resistance less than 5 ohms? | Yes ►<br>No ► | GO to OR7 .<br>REPAIR/REPLACE "BK" wire. |

**Fig. 17 System diagnosis (Part 3 of 10). 1991 Escort & Tracer**

| TEST STEP | RESULT ► | ACTION TO TAKE |
|---|---|---|
| OR7 DOOR CATCH SWITCH SUPPLY CHECK | | |
| • Disconnect passive restraint module connections. • Measure the resistance between door catch switch and passive restraint module.<br>—driver's side - "BL/Y" wire<br>—passenger's side - "BL/O" wire<br>• Is the resistance less than 5 ohms? | Yes ►<br>No ► | GO to OR8 .<br>REPAIR/REPLACE wires as necessary. |

| TEST STEP | RESULT ► | ACTION TO TAKE |
|---|---|---|
| OR8 DOOR CATCH SWITCH GROUND CHECK | | |
| • Measure the resistance of "BK" wire (driver's and passenger's side) at door catch switch to ground. • Is the resistance less than 5 ohms? | Yes ►<br>No ► | GO to OR9 .<br>REPAIR/REPLACE "BK" wire. |

| TEST STEP | RESULT ► | ACTION TO TAKE |
|---|---|---|
| OR9 CHECK DOOR CATCH SWITCH | | |
| • Open the door. • Measure the resistance of the following wires to ground:<br>—driver's side - "BL/Y" wire<br>—passenger's side - "BL/O" wire<br>• Is the resistance less than 5 ohms? | Yes ► | Belt will not move to Pillar B - GO to OR10 .<br>Belt will not move to Pillar A - GO to OR15 . |
| | No ► | REPAIR/REPLACE door catch switch. |

**Fig. 17 System diagnosis (Part 4 of 10). 1991 Escort & Tracer**

| TEST STEP | RESULT ► | ACTION TO TAKE |
|---|---|---|
| OR10 REAR LIMIT SWITCH SUPPLY CHECK | | |
| • Measure the resistance of rear limit switch circuit between passive restraint module and passive restraint motor.<br>—driver's side - "Y/R" wire<br>—passenger's side - "W" wire<br>• Is the resistance less than 5 ohms? | Yes ►<br>No ► | GO to OR11 .<br>REPAIR/REPLACE wire. |

| TEST STEP | RESULT ► | ACTION TO TAKE |
|---|---|---|
| OR11 REAR LIMIT SWITCH GROUND CHECK | | |
| • Measure the resistance of "BK" wire (driver's and passenger's side) between passive restraint motor and ground. • Is the resistance less than 5 ohms? | Yes ►<br>No ► | GO to OR12 .<br>REPAIR/REPLACE "BK" wire. |

| TEST STEP | RESULT ► | ACTION TO TAKE |
|---|---|---|
| OR12 REAR LIMIT SWITCH CHECK | | |
| • Key ON. • Door closed. • Measure resistance of the following wires to ground:<br>—driver's side - "Y/R" wire<br>—passenger's side - "W" wire<br>• Is the resistance less than 5 ohms? | Yes ►<br>No ► | GO to OR13 .<br>REPLACE motor and track assembly. |

**Fig. 17 System diagnosis (Part 5 of 10). 1991 Escort & Tracer**

| TEST STEP | RESULT ► | ACTION TO TAKE |
|---|---|---|
| OR13 PASSIVE RESTRAINT MOTOR SUPPLY CHECK | | |
| • Measure the resistance of passive restraint motor supply between passive restraint module and passive restraint motor.<br>—driver's side - "BL/GN" wire<br>"BR" wire<br>—passenger's side - "Y/GN" wire<br>"W/BK" wire<br>• Is the resistance less than 5 ohms? | Yes ►<br>No ► | GO to OR14 .<br>REPAIR/REPLACE wires as necessary. |

**Fig. 17 System diagnosis (Part 6 of 10). 1991 Escort & Tracer**

| TEST STEP | | RESULT ► | ACTION TO TAKE |
|---|---|---|---|
| OR14 | PASSIVE RESTRAINT MOTOR FEED CHECK | | |
| | • Key ON, door open. Belt at "A" pillar.<br>• Close door. Belt is traveling to "B" pillar.<br>• Measure the voltage on the following wires at the passive restraint motor. | Yes ►<br>No ► | REPLACE track and motor assembly.<br>REPLACE passive restraint control module |

| Vehicle Side | Wire Color | Voltage |
|---|---|---|
| Driver | "BL/GN" | greater than 10 volts |
| | "BR" | less than 1 volt |
| Passenger | "W/BK" | greater than 10 volts |
| | "Y/GN" | less than 1 volt |

• Open door. Belt is traveling to the "A" pillar.
• Measure the voltage on the following wires at the passive restraint motor.

| Vehicle Side | Wire Color | Voltage |
|---|---|---|
| Driver | "BR" | greater than 10 volts |
| | "BL/GN" | less than 1 volt |
| Passenger | "Y/GN" | greater than 10 volts |
| | "W/BK" | less than 1 volt |

• Are the voltage readings OK?

| TEST STEP | | RESULT ► | ACTION TO TAKE |
|---|---|---|---|
| OR15 | FRONT LIMIT SWITCH SUPPLY CHECK | | |
| | • Measure resistance of the front limit switch circuit between passive restraint control module and passive restraint motor.<br>—driver's side - "Y/BL" wire<br>—passenger's side - "BL/W wire<br>• Is the resistance less than 5 ohms? | Yes ►<br>No ► | GO to OR16.<br>REPAIR/REPLACE wires as necessary. |

**Fig. 17 System diagnosis (Part 7 of 10). 1991 Escort & Tracer**

| TEST STEP | | RESULT ► | ACTION TO TAKE |
|---|---|---|---|
| OR16 | FRONT LIMIT SWITCH GROUND CHECK | | |
| | • Measure the resistance of "BK" wire (driver's and passenger's side) between passive restraint motor and ground.<br>• Is the resistance less than 5 ohms? | Yes ►<br>No ► | GO to OR17.<br>REPAIR/REPLACE wire. |

| TEST STEP | | RESULT ► | ACTION TO TAKE |
|---|---|---|---|
| OR17 | FRONT LIMIT SWITCH CHECK | | |
| | • Key ON.<br>• Open door.<br>• Measure the resistance of the following wires from the passive restraint module to ground.<br>—driver's side - "Y/BL" wire<br>—passenger's side - "BL/W" wire<br>• Is the resistance less than 5 ohms? | Yes ►<br>No ► | GO to OR18.<br>REPLACE front limit switch. |

| TEST STEP | | RESULT ► | ACTION TO TAKE |
|---|---|---|---|
| OR18 | PASSIVE RESTRAINT MOTOR SUPPLY CHECK | | |
| | • Measure the resistance of supply wires between passive restraint control module and passive restraint motor.<br>—driver's side - "BL/GN" wire<br>"BR" wire<br>—passenger's side - "Y/GN" wire<br>"W/BK" wire<br>• Is the resistance less than 5 ohms? | Yes ►<br>No ► | GO to OR19.<br>REPAIR/REPLACE wires as necessary. |

**Fig. 17 System diagnosis (Part 8 of 10). 1991 Escort & Tracer**

| TEST STEP | | RESULT ► | ACTION TO TAKE |
|---|---|---|---|
| OR19 | PASSIVE RESTRAINT MOTOR FEED CHECK | | |
| | • Key ON, door open. Belt at "A" pillar.<br>• Close door. Belt is traveling to "B" pillar.<br>• Measure the voltage on the following wires at the passive restraint motor. | Yes ►<br>No ► | REPLACE track and motor assembly.<br>REPLACE passive restraint control module |

| Vehicle Side | Wire Color | Voltage |
|---|---|---|
| Driver | "BL/GN" | greater than 10 volts |
| | "BR" | less than 1 volt |
| Passenger | "W/BK" | greater than 10 volts |
| | "Y/GN" | less than 1 volt |

• Open door. Belt is traveling to the "A" pillar.
• Measure the voltage on the following wires at the passive restraint motor.

| Vehicle Side | Wire Color | Voltage |
|---|---|---|
| Driver | "BR" | greater than 10 volts |
| | "BL/GN" | less than 1 volt |
| Passenger | "Y/GN" | greater than 10 volts |
| | "W/BK" | less than 1 volt |

• Are the voltage readings OK?

**Fig. 17 System diagnosis (Part 9 of 10). 1991 Escort & Tracer**

| TEST STEP | | RESULT ► | ACTION TO TAKE |
|---|---|---|---|
| OR20 | SEAT BELT RETRACTOR SWITCHES (BUCKLE SWITCHES) | | |
| | • Key ON.<br>• Both carries at "B" pillar and belts buckled.<br>• Measure the voltage on the following wires at the passive restraint module. | Yes ►<br>No ► | GO to OR9.<br>REPLACE the retractor assembly. |

| Vehicle Side | Wire Color | Voltage |
|---|---|---|
| Driver | "O/GN" | less than .75 volt |
| Passenger | "P" | less than .75 volt |

• Are the voltage readings OK?

| TEST STEP | | RESULT ► | ACTION TO TAKE |
|---|---|---|---|
| OR21 | INERTIA INPUT TO PASSIVE RESTRAINT CONTROL MODULE | | |
| | • Disconnect both passive restraint control module connectors.<br>• Measure the voltage between passive restraint module "GN/R" wire and passive restraint module "BK" wire.<br>• Is the voltage reading above 10V? | Yes ►<br>No ► | GO to OR4.<br>RESET the fuel pump interia switch. If OK, CHECK the "GN/R" wire for short. |

**Fig. 17 System diagnosis (Part 10 of 10). 1991 Escort & Tracer**

| TEST STEP | RESULT ► | ACTION TO TAKE |
|---|---|---|
| **PR1** SYMPTOM ANALYSIS | | |
| • Check the proper operation of passive restraint system:<br>**— Key On, Door Closed**<br>• Shoulder belt carrier moves to the "ON" position.<br>• "Belts" warning indicator lamp and buzzer are on; four to eight seconds when the shoulder belt is latched to the carrier and continuously when unlatched.<br>**— Key On, Door Open:**<br>• Shoulder belt carrier moves to the "OFF" position.<br>• Buzzer is on continuously.<br>**— Key Off, Door Closed:**<br>• Shoulder belt carrier does not move.<br>**— Key Off, Door Open:**<br>• Shoulder belt carrier moves to the "OFF" position.<br>**Note:** Inertia switch open, there is no operation. | No operation ►<br>Carrier inoperative ►<br>Warning indicator lamp or buzzer inoperative ► | GO to PR2 .<br>GO to PR5 .<br>GO to PR17 . |

| TEST STEP | RESULT ► | ACTION TO TAKE |
|---|---|---|
| **PR2** CHECK POWER TO PASSIVE RESTRAINT CONTROL MODULE | | |
| • Disconnect Passive Restraint Control Module connector.<br>• Measure voltage between Passive Restraint Control Module (Y) wire and ground.<br>Key Off Above 10V<br>Key On Above 10V<br>• Measure voltage between Passive Restraint Control Module (BK/Y) wire and ground.<br>Key Off 0V<br>Key On Above 10V<br>• Are voltage readings as specified? | Yes ►<br>No ► | GO to PR3 .<br>GO to PR4 . |

**Fig. 18 System diagnosis (Part 1 of 8). 1990 Festiva**

| TEST STEP | RESULT ► | ACTION TO TAKE |
|---|---|---|
| **PR6** CHECK PASSIVE RESTRAINT CONTROL MODULE OUTPUT TO MOTOR | | |
| • Disconnect Passive Restraint Control Module wires (driver side: (BK/R) and (BL/GN); passenger side: (W/BK) and (Y/GN)) and reconnect connector.<br>• Key Off<br>• Measure voltage between Passive Restraint Control Module terminals (driver side: +(U) and −(V); passenger side: +(B) and −(C)), where the disconnected wires were.<br>Key off/door closed 0V<br>Key on/door closed Above 10V<br>• Turn key off.<br>• Reverse voltmeter leads.<br>Key off/door closed 0V<br>Key off/door open Above 10V<br>• Are voltage readings as specified? | Yes ►<br>No ► | Reconnect Passive Restraint Control Module (BK/R) and (BL/GN) or (W/BK) and (Y/GN) wires.<br>GO to PR7 .<br>Reconnect Passive Restraint Control Module (BK/R) and (BL/GN) or (W/BK) and (Y/GN) wires.<br>GO to PR8 . |

| TEST STEP | RESULT ► | ACTION TO TAKE |
|---|---|---|
| **PR7** CHECK POWER TO PASSIVE RESTRAINT MOTOR | | |
| • Access Passive Restraint motor.<br>• Disconnect Passive Restraint motor connector.<br>• Key Off<br>• Measure voltage between Passive Restraint motor wires (driver side: +(BK/R) and −(BL/GN); passenger side: +(W/BK) and −(Y/GN)).<br>Key off/door closed 0V<br>Key on/door closed Above 10V<br>• Turn key off.<br>• Reverse voltmeter leads.<br>Key off/door closed 0V<br>Key off/door open Above 10V<br>• Are voltage readings as specified? | Yes ►<br>No ► | REPLACE Passive Restraint motor.<br>SERVICE Passive Restraint motor (BK/R), (BL/GN) and/or (W/BK), (Y/GN) wires to Passive Restraint control module. |

**Fig. 18 System diagnosis (Part 3 of 8). 1990 Festiva**

| TEST STEP | RESULT ► | ACTION TO TAKE |
|---|---|---|
| **PR3** CHECK GROUND AT PASSIVE RESTRAINT CONTROL MODULE | | |
| • Disconnect Passive Restraint Control Module to connector.<br>• Measure voltage between Passive Restraint Control Module (Y) wire and Passive Restraint Control Module (BK) wire(s).<br>• Are voltage readings above 10V for both (BK) wires? | Yes ►<br>No ► | GO to PR5 .<br>SERVICE (BK) wire to ground. |

| TEST STEP | RESULT ► | ACTION TO TAKE |
|---|---|---|
| **PR4** CHECK POWER TO FUSE PANEL | | |
| • Disconnect fuse panel "Belt" fuse and "Meter" fuse.<br>• Measure voltage between fuse panel (W) wire and ground.<br>Key Off Above 10V<br>Key On Above 10V<br>• Measure voltage between fuse panel (BK/W) wire and ground.<br>Key Off 0V<br>Key On Above 10V<br>• Are voltage readings as specified? | Yes ►<br>No ► | SERVICE fuse panel (Y) and/or (BK/Y) wires to Passive Restraint Control Module.<br>**Note:** REPLACE fuse(s) as required.<br>SERVICE fuse panel (W) wire to main fuse and/or (BK/W) wire to ignition switch. |

| TEST STEP | RESULT ► | ACTION TO TAKE |
|---|---|---|
| **PR5** CHECK INERTIA INPUT TO PASSIVE RESTRAINT CONTROL MODULE | | |
| • Disconnect Passive Restraint Control Module connector.<br>• Measure voltage between Passive Restraint Control Module (Y) wire and Passive Restraint Control Module (R) wire.<br>• Is voltage reading above 10V? | Yes ►<br>No ► | GO to PR6 .<br>RESET inertia switch. If OK, SERVICE Passive Restraint Control Module (R) wire to inertia switch. |

**Fig. 18 System diagnosis (Part 2 of 8). 1990 Festiva**

| TEST STEP | RESULT ► | ACTION TO TAKE |
|---|---|---|
| **PR8** CHECK DOOR INPUT TO PASSIVE RESTRAINT CONTROL MODULE | | |
| • Disconnect Passive Restraint Control Module connector.<br>• Measure voltage between Passive Restraint Control Module (Y) wire and Passive Restraint Control Module (driver side: (LG/R); passenger side: (BL/O)) wire.<br>Door closed 0V<br>Door open Above 10V<br>• Are voltage readings as specified? | Yes ►<br>No ► | GO to PR11 .<br>GO to PR9 . |

| TEST STEP | RESULT ► | ACTION TO TAKE |
|---|---|---|
| **PR9** CHECK DOOR SWITCH GROUND | | |
| • Access door switch.<br>• Disconnect door switch connector.<br>• Measure voltage between Passive Restraint Control Module (Y) wire and door switch (BK) wire.<br>• Is voltage reading above 10V? | Yes ►<br>No ► | GO to PR11 .<br>SERVICE (BK) wire to ground. |

| TEST STEP | RESULT ► | ACTION TO TAKE |
|---|---|---|
| **PR11** CHECK FRONT LIMIT SWITCH INPUT TO PASSIVE RESTRAINT CONTROL MODULE | | |
| • Disconnect Passive Restraint Control Module connector.<br>• Measure voltage between Passive Restraint Control Module (Y) wire and Passive Restraint Control Module (driver side: (Y/BL); passenger side: (BL/BK)) wire.<br>• Manually, move the shoulder belt carrier along its track.<br>Carrier in Forward A Pillar Position Above 10V<br>All other positions 0V<br>• Are voltage readings as specified? | Yes ►<br>No ► | GO to PR14 .<br>GO to PR12 . |

**Fig. 18 System diagnosis (Part 4 of 8). 1990 Festiva**

| TEST STEP | RESULT ► | ACTION TO TAKE |
|---|---|---|
| **PR12** CHECK FRONT LIMIT SWITCH GROUND | | |
| • Access Front Limit switch.<br>• Disconnect Front Limit switch connector.<br>• Measure voltage between Passive Restraint Control Module (Y) wire and Front Limit switch (BK) wire.<br>• Is voltage reading above 10V? | Yes ►<br>No ► | GO to PR13.<br>SERVICE (BK) wire to ground. |

| TEST STEP | RESULT ► | ACTION TO TAKE |
|---|---|---|
| **PR13** CHECK FRONT LIMIT SWITCH OPERATION | | |
| • Disconnect Front Limit switch connector.<br>• Measure resistance between Front Limit switch terminals (A) and (B).<br>• Manually, move the shoulder belt carrier.<br>Carrier in Forward A Pillar position — 0 OHMs<br>Any other position — Above 10K OHMs<br>• Are resistance readings as specified? | Yes ►<br>No ► | SERVICE Front Limit switch (driver side: (Y/BL); passenger side: (BL/BK)) wire to Passive Restraint Control Module.<br>REPLACE Front Limit switch. |

| TEST STEP | RESULT ► | ACTION TO TAKE |
|---|---|---|
| **PR14** CHECK REAR LIMIT INPUT TO PASSIVE RESTRAINT CONTROL MODULE | | |
| • Disconnect Passive Restraint Control Module connector.<br>• Measure voltage between Passive Restraint Control Module (Y) wire and Passive Restraint Control Module (driver side: (Y/R); passenger side: (W) wire.<br>• Manually, move shoulder belt carrier.<br>Carrier in Rear B Pillar position — Above 10V<br>Any other position — 0V<br>• Are voltage readings as specified? | Yes ►<br>No ► | REPLACE Passive Restraint Control Module.<br>GO to PR15. |

**Fig. 18 System diagnosis (Part 5 of 8). 1990 Festiva**

| TEST STEP | RESULT ► | ACTION TO TAKE |
|---|---|---|
| **PR15** CHECK REAR LIMIT SWITCH GROUND | | |
| • Access Rear Limit switch.<br>• Disconnect Rear Limit switch connector.<br>• Measure voltage between Passive Restraint Control Module (Y) wire and Rear Limit switch (BK) wire.<br>• Is voltage reading above 10V? | Yes ►<br>No ► | GO to PR16.<br>SERVICE (BK) wire to ground. |

| TEST STEP | RESULT ► | ACTION TO TAKE |
|---|---|---|
| **PR16** CHECK REAR LIMIT SWITCH OPERATION | | |
| • Disconnect Rear Limit switch connector.<br>• Measure resistance between Rear Limit switch terminals (driver side: (C) and (D); passenger side: (B) and (D)).<br>• Manually, move shoulder belt carrier.<br>Carrier in Rear B Pillar — 0 OHMs<br>Any other position — Above 10K OHMs<br>• Are resistance readings as specified? | Yes ►<br>No ► | SERVICE Rear Limit switch (driver side: (Y/R); passenger side: (W)) wire to Passive Restraint Control Module.<br>REPLACE Rear Limit switch. |

**Fig. 18 System diagnosis (Part 6 of 8). 1990 Festiva**

| TEST STEP | RESULT ► | ACTION TO TAKE |
|---|---|---|
| **PR17** CHECK PASSIVE RESTRAINT CONTROL MODULE WARNING OUTPUT | | |
| • Disconnect Passive Restraint Control Module (LG/Y) and (BR) wires and reconnect connector.<br>• Key on.<br>• Measure voltage between Passive Restraint Control Module (Y) wire and Passive Restraint Control Module (lamp: (LG/Y); Buzzer: (BR)) wire, where the disconnected wires were.<br>Condition / Voltage for: Lamp / Buzzer<br>Both shoulder belts latched — Lamp: 10V (4 - 8 Seconds); Buzzer: 10V (4 - 8 Seconds)<br>Either shoulder belt unlatched — Lamp: 10V; Buzzer: 10V<br>• Are voltage readings as specified? | Yes ►<br>No ► | Warning and Indicator Lamps.<br>GO to PR18. |

| TEST STEP | RESULT ► | ACTION TO TAKE |
|---|---|---|
| **PR18** CHECK WARNING INPUT TO PASSIVE RESTRAINT CONTROL MODULE | | |
| • Disconnect Passive Restraint Control Module connector.<br>• Measure voltage between Passive Restraint Control Module (Y) wire and Passive Restraint Control Module (driver side: (O/GN); passenger side: (PK)) wire.<br>Shoulder belt latched — 0V<br>Shoulder belt unlatched — Above 10V<br>• Repeat for both driver and passenger side.<br>• Are voltage readings as specified? | Yes ►<br>No ► | REPLACE Passive Restraint Control Module.<br>GO to PR19 |

**Fig. 18 System diagnosis (Part 7 of 8). 1990 Festiva**

| TEST STEP | RESULT ► | ACTION TO TAKE |
|---|---|---|
| **PR19** CHECK WARNING SWITCH GROUND | | |
| • Access warning switch.<br>• Disconnect warning switch connector.<br>• Measure voltage between Passive Restraint Control Module (Y) wire and warning switch (BK) wire.<br>• Repeat for both driver and passenger side.<br>• Are voltage readings above 10V? | Yes ►<br>No ► | GO to PR20.<br>SERVICE (BK) wire to ground. |

| TEST STEP | RESULT ► | ACTION TO TAKE |
|---|---|---|
| **PR20** CHECK WARNING SWITCH OPERATION | | |
| • Disconnect warning switch connector.<br>• Measure resistance between warning switch terminals (B) and (C).<br>Shoulder belt latched — 0 OHMs<br>Shoulder belt unlatched — Above 10K OHMs<br>• Repeat for both driver and passenger side.<br>• Are resistance readings as specified? | Yes ►<br>No ► | SERVICE warning switch (driver side; (O/GN); passenger side: (PK)) wire to Passive Restraint Control Module.<br>REPLACE warning switch. |

**Fig. 18 System diagnosis (Part 8 of 8). 1990 Festiva**

| CONDITION | POSSIBLE SOURCE | ACTION |
|---|---|---|
| • Passive Restraint System Does Not Operate | • Blown fuse(s).<br>• Passive restraint module.<br>• Circuit open / shorted.<br>• Inertia switch. | • GO to PR1.<br>• RESET inertia switch. If set, GO to PR7. |
| • Passive Restraint System Operates on One Side Only | • Passive restraint motor.<br>• Limit switches.<br>• Door switches.<br>• Circuit open / shorted. | • GO to PR9. |
| • Passive Restraint Motor Stays On All the Time | • Passive restraint motor.<br>• Limit Switches.<br>• Circuit open / shorted.<br>• Track assembly. | • GO to PR4.<br>• CHECK track assembly. |
| • Seatbelt Warning Indicator Does Not Operate Correctly | • Warning switch.<br>• Passive restraint module.<br>• Circuit open / shorted.<br>• Timer / buzzer unit.<br>• Track assembly. | • GO to PR18.<br>• CHECK track assembly. |
| • Seatbelt Warning Buzzer Does Not Operate Correctly | • Warning switch.<br>• Passive restraint module.<br>• Circuit open / shorted.<br>• Ignition key reminder switch.<br>• Timer / buzzer unit. | • GO to PR18.<br>• |

| | TEST STEP | RESULT | ▶ ACTION TO TAKE |
|---|---|---|---|
| PR1 | CHECK FUSE(S) | | |
| | • Check Inertia Switch / Tripped.<br>• Locate the Interior Fuse Panel.<br>• Check the 30A belt and 10A Meter fuses.<br>• Are the fuses good? | Yes<br>No | ▶ GO to PR4.<br>▶ GO to PR2. |
| PR2 | CHECK SYSTEM | | |
| | • Replace the blown fuse(s).<br>• Key ON.<br>• Did the fuse(s) blow again? | Yes<br>No | ▶ GO to PR3.<br>▶ GO to PR4. |
| PR3 | CHECK FOR SHORT TO GROUND | | |
| | • Key OFF.<br>• Disconnect the "Y" and "BK/Y" wires from the Interior Fuse Panel.<br>• Measure the resistance of the wire in question to ground.<br>• Are the resistance(s) less than 5 ohms? | Yes<br>No | ▶ SERVICE the wire(s) in question.<br>▶ GO to PR4. |
| PR4 | CHECK POWER SUPPLY TO THE PASSIVE RESTRAINT MODULE | | |
| | • Key OFF.<br>• Disconnect the Passive Restraint Module connector.<br>• Measure the voltage on the "Y" wire at the connector.<br>• Is the voltage greater than 10 volts? | Yes<br>No | ▶ GO to PR5.<br>▶ SERVICE the "Y" wire. |

**Fig. 19 System diagnosis (Part 1 of 6). 1991 Festiva**

| | TEST STEP | RESULT | ▶ ACTION TO TAKE |
|---|---|---|---|
| PR5 | CHECK POWER SUPPLY TO PASSIVE RESTRAINT MODULE | | |
| | • Measure the voltage on the "BK/Y" wire at the connector. | Yes<br>No | ▶ GO to PR6.<br>▶ SERVICE the "BK/Y" wire. |

| CONDITION | VOLTAGE |
|---|---|
| Key OFF | OV |
| Key ON | Above 10V |

| | TEST STEP | RESULT | ▶ ACTION TO TAKE |
|---|---|---|---|
| | • Are the voltages within specifications? | | |
| PR6 | CHECK PASSIVE RESTRAINT MODULE GROUNDS | | |
| | • Key OFF.<br>• Disconnect the Passive Restraint Module connector.<br>• Measure the resistance of the "BK" wires at pin M/N of the connector to ground.<br>• Is the resistance less than 5 ohms? | Yes<br>No | ▶ GO to PR7.<br>▶ SERVICE the "BK" wire. |
| PR7 | CHECK INERTIA SWITCH | | |
| | • Locate the inertia Switch.<br>• Measure the resistance of the "GN/BK" wire at the Inertia Switch connector to ground in the following conditions: | Yes<br>No | ▶ GO to PR8.<br>▶ REPLACE the Inertia Switch. |

| CONDITION | RESISTANCE |
|---|---|
| Tripped (Switch not depressed) | Less than 5 ohms |
| Not tripped (Switch depressed) | Greater than 10,000 ohms |

| | TEST STEP | RESULT | ▶ ACTION TO TAKE |
|---|---|---|---|
| | • Are the resistances within specifications? | | |
| PR8 | CHECK THE LEAD BETWEEN THE INERTIA SWITCH TO THE PASSIVE RESTRAINT MODULE | | |
| | • Disconnect the Passive Restraint Module connector.<br>• Measure the resistance of the "R" wire between the Passive Restraint Module and Inertia Switch.<br>• Is the resistance less than 5 ohms? | Yes<br>No | ▶ GO to PR9.<br>▶ SERVICE the "R" wire. |
| PR9 | CHECK DOOR SWITCH GROUND | | |
| | • Locate the driver's and passenger's door switch connectors.<br>• Measure the resistance of the "BK" wire at the connector in the respective door to ground.<br>• Are the resistances less than 5 ohms? | Yes<br>No | ▶ GO to PR10.<br>▶ SERVICE the "BK" wire in question. |

**Fig. 19 System diagnosis (Part 2 of 6). 1991 Festiva**

| | TEST STEP | RESULT | ▶ ACTION TO TAKE |
|---|---|---|---|
| PR10 | CHECK DOOR SWITCHES | | |
| | • Measure the resistance on the "LG/R" (Driver's side door) and the "GN/R" (Passenger's side door) at the connector to ground. | Yes<br>No | ▶ GO to PR11.<br>▶ REPLACE the track and motor assembly. |

| CONDITION | RESISTANCE |
|---|---|
| Door open | Less than 5 ohms |
| Door closed | Greater than 10,000 ohms |

| | TEST STEP | RESULT | ▶ ACTION TO TAKE |
|---|---|---|---|
| | • Are the resistances within specifications? | | |
| PR11 | CHECK THE LEAD BETWEEN THE DOOR SWITCH AND THE PASSIVE RESTRAINT MODULE | | |
| | • Disconnect the Passive Restraint Module connectors and both door switch connectors.<br>• Measure the resistance of the following wires between the door switch and the module. | Yes<br>No | ▶ GO to PR12.<br>▶ SERVICE the wire in question. |

| CONDITION | RESISTANCE |
|---|---|
| LH door switch "LG/R" and module "LG/R" | less than 5 ohms |
| RH door switch "LG/R" and module "BL/O" | less than 5 ohms |

| | TEST STEP | RESULT | ▶ ACTION TO TAKE |
|---|---|---|---|
| | • Are the resistances within specifications? | | |
| PR12 | CHECK THE "A" PILLAR LIMIT SWITCH GROUND | | |
| | • Locate the "A" pillar limit switches (driver and passenger side).<br>• Measure the resistance of the "BK" wires to ground.<br>• Are the resistances less than 5 ohms? | Yes<br>No | ▶ GO to PR13.<br>▶ SERVICE the "BK" wire in question. |
| PR13 | CHECK THE "A" PILLAR LIMIT SWITCHES | | |
| | • Measure the voltage on the "Y/BL" (Driver's side) and the "BL/BK" (Passenger's side) at the limit switch connector. | Yes<br>No | ▶ GO to PR14.<br>▶ REPLACE the track assembly. |

| | |
|---|---|
| Belt in motion toward "A" pillar | Above 10V |
| Everywhere else | OV |

| | TEST STEP | RESULT | ▶ ACTION TO TAKE |
|---|---|---|---|
| | • Are the voltages within specifications? | | |
| PR14 | CHECK THE "B" PILLAR LIMIT SWITCH GROUND | | |
| | • Locate the "B" pillar limit switches (driver's and passenger's side).<br>• Measure the resistance of the "BK" wires to ground.<br>• Are the resistances less than 5 ohms? | Yes<br>No | ▶ GO to PR15.<br>▶ SERVICE the "BK" wire in question. |

**Fig. 19 System diagnosis (Part 3 of 6). 1991 Festiva**

| | TEST STEP | RESULT | ▶ ACTION TO TAKE |
|---|---|---|---|
| PR15 | CHECK THE "B" PILLAR LIMIT SWITCHES | | |
| | • Measure the voltage on the "Y/R" (Driver's side) and the "W" (Passenger's side) at the limit switch connector. | Yes<br>No | ▶ GO to PR16.<br>▶ REPLACE the track and motor assembly in question. |

| | |
|---|---|
| Belt in "B" pillar position | OV |
| Everywhere else | Above 4.5V |

| | TEST STEP | RESULT | ▶ ACTION TO TAKE |
|---|---|---|---|
| | • Are the voltages within specifications? | | |
| PR16 | CHECK PASSIVE RESTRAINT MOTOR | | |
| | • Key ON, door open.<br>• Disconnect the Passive Restraint Motor connector.<br>• Ground the "BK/R" (U) (Driver's side) or the "Y/GN" (A) (Passenger's side) wire at the motor connector.<br>• Apply 12 volts to either the "BL/GN" (V) (Driver's side) or the "W/BK" (B) (Passenger's side) wire at the connector.<br>• Does the belt move from pillar "A" to pillar "B"?<br>• Reverse the power and ground leads.<br>• Does the belt move from pillar "B" to pillar "A"? | Yes<br>No | ▶ GO to PR17.<br>▶ REPLACE the track and motor assembly. |
| PR17 | CHECK LEADS BETWEEN THE PASSIVE RESTRAINT MODULE AND THE MOTOR | | |
| | • Key OFF.<br>• Disconnect the Passive Restraint Module connectors.<br>• Measure the resistance of the following wires between the module and the motor. | Yes<br>No | ▶ REPLACE the Passive Restraint Module.<br>▶ SERVICE the wire(s) in question. |

| Driver Side Connector | Passenger Side Connector |
|---|---|
| "BL/GN" (V) | "Y/GN" (A) |
| "BK/R" (U) | "W/BK" (B) |

| | TEST STEP | RESULT | ▶ ACTION TO TAKE |
|---|---|---|---|
| | • Are the resistances less than 5 ohms? | | |
| PR18 | CHECK WARNING SWITCH GROUND | | |
| | • Disconnect the warning switch connector located in center console between seatbelt retractors.<br>• Measure the resistance of both "BK" wires to ground.<br>• Are the resistances less than 5 ohms? | Yes<br>No | ▶ GO to PR19.<br>▶ SERVICE the "BK" wire(s). |

**Fig. 19 System diagnosis (Part 4 of 6). 1991 Festiva**

| TEST STEP | RESULT | ACTION TO TAKE |
|---|---|---|
| **PR19** CHECK WARNING SWITCH OPERATION | | |
| • Reconnect the warning switch.<br>• Measure the resistance of the "P" (Passenger's side) and "O/GN" (Driver's side) between the switch and ground. | Yes<br>No | ► GO to PR20.<br>► REPLACE the center console spool and belt assembly. |

| | |
|---|---|
| Shoulder belt latched | Less than 5 ohms |
| Shoulder belt unlatched | Greater than 10,000 ohms |

• Are the resistances within specifications?

| TEST STEP | RESULT | ACTION TO TAKE |
|---|---|---|
| **PR20** CHECK LEADS BETWEEN WARNING SWITCH AND PASSIVE RESTRAINT MODULE | | |
| • Disconnect the warning switch connector and both module connectors.<br>• Measure the resistance of the following wires between the warning switch and the module. | Yes<br>No | ► GO to PR21.<br>► SERVICE the wire in question. |

| Driver Side | Resistance |
|---|---|
| "O/GN" | Less than 5 ohms |
| **Passenger Side** | **Resistance** |
| "P" | Less than 5 ohms |

• Are the resistances within specifications?

| TEST STEP | RESULT | ACTION TO TAKE |
|---|---|---|
| **PR21** CHECK THE PASSIVE RESTRAINT MODULES SEAT BELT WARNING OUTPUT | | |
| • Reconnect the connectors.<br>• Measure voltage on the "LG/Y" and "BR" wires at the module under the following conditions.<br>• Turn key off and then on for each measurement. | Yes<br>No | ► GO to PR22.<br>► REPLACE the Passive Restraint Module. |

| Condition | "LG/Y" | "BR" |
|---|---|---|
| Both shoulder belts latched | <2V for 4-8 sec Then 10V | <2V for 4-8 sec then 10V |
| Either shoulder belt unlatched | <2V | <2V for 4-8 sec then 10V |

• Are the voltages within specifications?

**Fig. 19 System diagnosis (Part 5 of 6). 1991 Festiva**

| TEST STEP | RESULT | ACTION TO TAKE |
|---|---|---|
| **PR22** CHECK LEADS BETWEEN MODULE AND WARNING LAMP/BUZZER | | |
| • Key OFF<br>• Measure the resistance of the "LG/Y" wire between the Passive Restraint Module and the Instrument Cluster.<br>• Measure the resistance of the "BR" wire between the module and the warning chime (CPU).<br>• Are the resistances less than 5 ohms? | Yes "LG/Y"<br>No "BR" | ► SERVICE the wire in question. |

**Fig. 19 System diagnosis (Part 6 of 6). 1991 Festiva**

| TEST STEP | RESULT | ACTION TO TAKE |
|---|---|---|
| **PR1** SYMPTOM ANALYSIS | | |
| • Check the proper operation of passive restraint system:<br>— **Key On, Door Closed:**<br>• Shoulder belt carrier moves to the "ON" position.<br>• "Belts" warning indicator lamp and buzzer are on; four to eight seconds when the shoulder belt is latched to the carrier and continuously when unlatched.<br>— **Key On, Door Open:**<br>• Shoulder belt carrier moves to the "OFF" position.<br>• Buzzer is on continuously.<br>— **Key Off, Door Closed:**<br>• Shoulder belt carrier does not move.<br>— **Key Off, Door Open:**<br>• Shoulder belt carrier moves to the "OFF" position.<br>**Note:** Inertia switch open, there is no operation. | No operation<br>Carrier inoperative<br>Warning indicator lamp or buzzer inoperative | ► GO to PR2 .<br>► GO to PR5 .<br>► GO to PR17 . |

| TEST STEP | RESULT | ACTION TO TAKE |
|---|---|---|
| **PR2** CHECK POWER TO PASSIVE RESTRAINT CONTROL MODULE | | |
| • Disconnect both Passive Restraint Control Module connectors.<br>• Measure voltage between Passive Restraint Control Module connector (BR) wire and ground.<br>Key Off Above 10V<br>Key On Above 10V<br>• Repeat for both (BR) wires.<br>• Measure voltage between Passive Restraint Control Module (BK/Y) wire and ground.<br>Key Off 0V<br>Key On Above 10V<br>• Are voltage readings as specified? | Yes<br>No | ► GO to PR3 .<br>► GO to PR4 . |

**Fig. 20 System diagnosis (Part 1 of 8). 1990 Probe**

| TEST STEP | RESULT | ACTION TO TAKE |
|---|---|---|
| **PR3** CHECK GROUND AT PASSIVE RESTRAINT CONTROL MODULE | | |
| • Disconnect both Passive Restraint Control Module to connectors.<br>• Measure voltage between Passive Restraint Control Module connector (BR) wire and Passive Restraint Control Module (BK) wire(s).<br>• Repeat for all (BK) wires.<br>• Are voltage readings above 10V for both (BK) wires? | Yes<br>No | ► GO to PR5 .<br>► SERVICE (BK) wire to ground. |

| TEST STEP | RESULT | ACTION TO TAKE |
|---|---|---|
| **PR4** CHECK POWER TO FUSE PANEL | | |
| • Disconnect fuse panel "Belt" fuse and "Meter" fuse.<br>• Measure voltage between fuse panel (W) wire and ground.<br>Key Off Above 10V<br>Key On Above 10V | Yes | ► SERVICE fuse panel (BR) and/or (BK/Y) wires to Passive Restraint Control Module.<br>**Note:** REPLACE fuse(s) as required. |
| • Measure voltage between fuse panel (BK/W) wire and ground.<br>Key Off 0V<br>Key On Above 10V<br>• Are voltage readings as specified? | No | ► SERVICE fuse panel (W) wire to main fuse and/or (BK/W) wire to ignition switch. |

| TEST STEP | RESULT | ACTION TO TAKE |
|---|---|---|
| **PR5** CHECK INERTIA INPUT TO PASSIVE RESTRAINT CONTROL MODULE | | |
| • Disconnect both Passive Restraint Control Module connectors.<br>• Measure voltage between Passive Restraint Control Module (BK/Y) wire and Passive Restraint Control Module (GN/BK) wire.<br>• Is voltage reading above 10V? | Yes<br>No | ► GO to PR6 .<br>► RESET Fuel Pump inertia switch. If OK, SERVICE Passive Restraint Control Module (GN/BK) wire to inertia switch. |

**Fig. 20 System diagnosis (Part 2 of 8). 1990 Probe**

| TEST STEP | RESULT | ACTION TO TAKE |
|---|---|---|
| **PR6** CHECK PASSIVE RESTRAINT CONTROL MODULE OUTPUT TO MOTOR | | |
| • Remove Passive Restraint Control Module wires (driver side: (BL) and (Y); passenger side: (GN) and (R) and reconnect both connectors.<br>• Key Off<br>• Measure voltage between Passive Restraint Control Module terminals (driver side: +(1L/1K) and −(1J/1H); passenger side: +(2L/2M) and −(2J/2H) ) where the disconnected wires were.<br>Key off/door closed 0V<br>Key on/door closed Above 10V<br>• Turn key off.<br>• Reverse voltmeter leads.<br>Key off/door closed 0V,<br>Key off/door open Above 10V<br>• Are voltage readings as specified? | Yes ►<br><br>No ► | Reconnect Passive Restraint Control Module (BL) and (Y) or (GN) and (R) wires. GO to PR7 .<br><br>Reconnect Passive Restraint Control Module (BL) and (Y) or (GN) and (R) wires. GO to PR8 . |

| TEST STEP | RESULT | ACTION TO TAKE |
|---|---|---|
| **PR7** CHECK POWER TO PASSIVE RESTRAINT MOTOR | | |
| • Access Passive Restraint motor.<br>• Disconnect Passive Restraint motor connector.<br>• Key off.<br>• Measure voltage between Passive Restraint motor wires (driver side: +(BL) and −(Y); passenger side: +(GN) and −(R)).<br>Key off/door closed 0V<br>Key on/door closed Above 10V<br>• Turn key off.<br>• Reverse voltmeter leads.<br>Key off/door closed 0V<br>Key off/door open Above 10V<br>• Are voltage readings as specified? | Yes ►<br><br>No ► | REPLACE Passive Restraint motor.<br><br>SERVICE Passive Restraint motor (BL), (Y) and/or (GN), (R) wires to Passive Restraint Control Module. |

Fig. 20 System diagnosis (Part 3 of 8). 1990 Probe

| TEST STEP | RESULT | ACTION TO TAKE |
|---|---|---|
| **PR8** CHECK DOOR INPUT TO PASSIVE RESTRAINT CONTROL MODULE | | |
| • Disconnect both Passive Restraint Control Module connectors.<br>• Measure voltage between Control Module connector (BR) wire and Passive Restraint Control Module (driver side: (GN/R); passenger side: (Y/GN) ) wire.<br>Door closed 0V<br>Door open Above 10V<br>• Are voltage readings as specified? | Yes ►<br>No ► | GO to PR11 .<br>GO to PR9 . |

| TEST STEP | RESULT | ACTION TO TAKE |
|---|---|---|
| **PR9** CHECK DOOR SWITCH GROUND | | |
| • Access door switch.<br>• Disconnect door switch connector.<br>• Measure voltage between Passive Restraint Control Module (BR) wire and door switch (BK) wire.<br>• Is voltage reading above 10V? | Yes ►<br>No ► | GO to PR10 .<br>SERVICE (BK) wire to ground. |

| TEST STEP | RESULT | ACTION TO TAKE |
|---|---|---|
| **PR10** CHECK DOOR SWITCH OPERATION | | |
| • Disconnect door switch connector.<br>• Measure resistance between door switch terminals (A) and (B).<br>Door closed Above 10K OHMS<br>Door open 0 OHMS<br>• Are resistance readings as specified? | Yes ►<br><br>No ► | SERVICE door switch (driver side: (GN/R); passenger side: (Y/GN) ) wire to Passive Restraint Control Module.<br><br>REPLACE door switch. |

Fig. 20 System diagnosis (Part 4 of 8). 1990 Probe

| TEST STEP | RESULT | ACTION TO TAKE |
|---|---|---|
| **PR11** CHECK "OFF" INPUT TO PASSIVE RESTRAINT CONTROL MODULE | | |
| • Disconnect both Passive Restraint Control Module connectors.<br>• Measure voltage between Passive Restraint Control Module (BR) wire and Passive Restraint Control Module (driver side: (Y/BL); passenger side: (GN/BL)) wire.<br>• Manually, move the shoulder belt carrier along its track.<br>Carrier in "OFF" position Above 10V<br>All other positions 0V<br>• Are voltage readings as specified? | Yes ►<br>No ► | GO to PR14 .<br>GO to PR12 . |

| TEST STEP | RESULT | ACTION TO TAKE |
|---|---|---|
| **PR12** CHECK "OFF" SWITCH GROUND | | |
| • Access "OFF" switch.<br>• Disconnect "OFF" switch connector.<br>• Measure voltage between Passive Restraint Control Module (BR) wire and "OFF" switch (BK) wire.<br>• Is voltage reading above 10V? | Yes ►<br>No ► | GO to PR13 .<br>SERVICE (BK) wire to ground. |

| TEST STEP | RESULT | ACTION TO TAKE |
|---|---|---|
| **PR13** CHECK "OFF" SWITCH OPERATION | | |
| • Disconnect "OFF" switch connector.<br>• Measure resistance between "OFF" switch terminals (A) and (B).<br>• Manually, move the shoulder belt carrier.<br>Carrier in "OFF" position 0 OHMs<br>Any other position Above 10K OHMs<br>• Are resistance readings as specified? | Yes ►<br><br>No ► | SERVICE "OFF" switch (driver side: (Y/BL); passenger side: (GN/BL) ) wire to Passive Restraint Control Module.<br><br>REPLACE "OFF" switch. |

Fig. 20 System diagnosis (Part 5 of 8). 1990 Probe

| TEST STEP | RESULT | ACTION TO TAKE |
|---|---|---|
| **PR14** CHECK "ON" INPUT TO PASSIVE RESTRAINT CONTROL MODULE | | |
| • Disconnect both Passive Restraint Control Module connectors.<br>• Measure voltage between Passive Restraint Control Module (BR) wire and Passive Restraint Control Module (driver side: (BL/W); passenger side: (BL/Y)) wire.<br>• Manually, move shoulder belt carrier.<br>Carrier in "ON" position Above 10V<br>Any other position 0V<br>• Are voltage readings as specified? | Yes ►<br><br>No ► | REPLACE Passive Restraint Control Module.<br><br>GO to PR15 . |

| TEST STEP | RESULT | ACTION TO TAKE |
|---|---|---|
| **PR15** CHECK "ON" SWITCH GROUND | | |
| • Access "ON" switch.<br>• Disconnect "ON" switch connector.<br>• Measure voltage between Passive Restraint Control Module (BR) wire and "ON" switch (BK) wire.<br>• Is voltage reading above 10V? | Yes ►<br>No ► | GO to PR16 .<br>SERVICE (BK) wire to ground. |

| TEST STEP | RESULT | ACTION TO TAKE |
|---|---|---|
| **PR16** CHECK "ON" SWITCH OPERATION | | |
| • Disconnect "ON" switch connector.<br>• Measure resistance between "ON" switch terminals (C) and (D).<br>• Manually, move shoulder belt carrier.<br>Carrier in "ON" position 0 OHMs<br>Any other position Above 10K OHMs<br>• Are resistance readings as specified? | Yes ►<br><br>No ► | SERVICE "ON" switch (driver side: (BL/W); passenger side: (BL/Y)) wire to Passive Restraint Control Module.<br><br>REPLACE "ON" switch. |

Fig. 20 System diagnosis (Part 6 of 8). 1990 Probe

| TEST STEP | | RESULT ► | ACTION TO TAKE |
|---|---|---|---|
| PR17 | CHECK PASSIVE RESTRAINT CONTROL MODULE WARNING OUTPUT | | |
| | • Remove Passive Restraint Control Module (BR/BK) and (BK/BL) wires from connectors and reconnect both connectors.<br>• Key on.<br>• Measure voltage between Passive Restraint Control Module (BR) wire and Passive Restraint Control Module warning (lamp: BR/BK) and Warning Buzzer: (BK/BL) terminals where the disconnected wires were.<br><br>Voltage for:<br>Condition — Lamp — Buzzer<br>Both shoulder belts latched — 10V (4 - 8 Seconds — 10V (4 - 8 Seconds)<br>Either shoulder belt unlatched — 10V — 10V<br><br>• Are voltage readings as specified? | Yes ►<br>No ► | Warning and Indicator Lamps.<br>GO to PR18 . |

| TEST STEP | | RESULT ► | ACTION TO TAKE |
|---|---|---|---|
| PR18 | CHECK WARNING INPUT TO PASSIVE RESTRAINT CONTROL MODULE | | |
| | • Disconnect both Passive Restraint Control Module connectors.<br>• Measure voltage between Passive Restraint Control Module (BR) wire and Passive Restraint Control Module (driver side: (BL/R); passenger side: (LG/BK)) wire.<br>Shoulder belt latched — 0V<br>Shoulder belt unlatched — Above 10V<br>• Repeat for both driver and passenger side.<br>• Are voltage readings as specified? | Yes ►<br>No ► | REPLACE Passive Restraint Control Module.<br>GO to PR19 . |

**Fig. 20 System diagnosis (Part 7 of 8). 1990 Probe**

| TEST STEP | | RESULT ► | ACTION TO TAKE |
|---|---|---|---|
| PR19 | CHECK WARNING SWITCH GROUND | | |
| | • Access warning switch.<br>• Disconnect warning switch connector.<br>• Measure voltage between Passive Restraint Control Module (BR) wire and warning switch (BK) wire.<br>• Repeat for both (BK) wires.<br>• Are voltage readings above 10V? | Yes ►<br>No ► | GO to PR20 .<br>SERVICE (BK) wire to ground. |

| TEST STEP | | RESULT ► | ACTION TO TAKE |
|---|---|---|---|
| PR20 | CHECK WARNING SWITCH OPERATION | | |
| | • Disconnect warning switch connector.<br>• Measure resistance between warning switch passenger side terminals (A) and (B).<br>Shoulder belt latched — 0 OHMs<br>Shoulder belt unlatched — Above 10K OHMs<br>• Repeat for driver side terminals (C) and (D).<br>• Are resistance readings as specified? | Yes ►<br>No ► | SERVICE warning switch (driver side: (BL/R); passenger side: (LG/BK)) wire to Passive Restraint Control Module.<br>REPLACE warning switch. |

**Fig. 20 System diagnosis (Part 8 of 8). 1990 Probe**

| CONDITION | POSSIBLE SOURCE | ACTION |
|---|---|---|
| • Passive Restraint System does not Operate | • Blown fuse(s).<br>• Passive restraint module.<br>• Circuit.<br>• Inertia switch. | • GO to PR1.<br>• GO to PR7. |
| • Passive Restraint System Operates on One Side Only | • Passive restraint motor.<br>• Limit switches.<br>• Door switches.<br>• Circuit. | • GO to PR9. |
| • Passive Restraint Motor Stays on All the Time | • Passive restraint motor.<br>• Limit switches.<br>• Circuit.<br>• Track assembly. | • GO to PR4.<br>• CHECK the track assembly. |
| • Seatbelt Warning Indicator does not Operate Correctly | • Warning switch.<br>• Passive restraint module.<br>• Circuit.<br>• Timer / buzzer unit.<br>• Track assembly. | • GO to PR18.<br>• CHECK the track assembly. |
| • Seatbelt Warning Buzzer does not Operate Correctly | • Warning switch.<br>• Passive restraint module.<br>• Circuit.<br>• Ignition key reminder switch.<br>• Timer / buzzer unit. | • GO to PR18. |

| TEST STEP | | RESULT ► | ACTION TO TAKE |
|---|---|---|---|
| PR1 | CHECK FUSE(S) | | |
| | • Locate the Interior Fuse Panel.<br>• Check the 30A belt and 10A Meter Fuses.<br>• Are the fuses good? | Yes ►<br>No ► | GO to PR4.<br>GO to PR2. |
| PR2 | CHECK SYSTEM | | |
| | • Replace the blown fuse(s).<br>• Key ON.<br>• Did the fuse(s) blow again? | Yes ►<br>No ► | GO to PR3.<br>GO to PR4. |
| PR3 | CHECK FOR SHORT TO GROUND | | |
| | • Key OFF.<br>• Disconnect the "BR" and "BK / Y" wires from the Interior Fuse Panel.<br>• Measure the resistance of the wire in question to ground.<br>• Are the resistance(s) less than 5 ohms? | Yes ►<br>No ► | SERVICE the wire(s) in question.<br>GO to PR4. |
| PR4 | CHECK POWER SUPPLY TO THE PASSIVE RESTRAINT MODULE | | |
| | • Key OFF.<br>• Disconnect the Passive Restraint Module connector # 1.<br>• Measure the voltage on the "BR" wire at the connector.<br>• Is the voltage greater than 10 volts? | Yes ►<br>No ► | GO to PR5.<br>SERVICE the "BR" wire. |

**Fig. 21 System diagnosis (Part 1 of 7). 1991 Probe**

| TEST STEP | | RESULT ► | ACTION TO TAKE |
|---|---|---|---|
| PR5 | CHECK POWER SUPPLY TO PASSIVE RESTRAINT MODULE | | |
| | • Measure the voltage on the "BK / Y" wire at the connector.<br><br>Key OFF — OV<br>Key ON — Above 10V<br><br>• Are the voltages verified? | Yes ►<br>No ► | GO to PR6.<br>SERVICE the "BK / Y" wire. |
| PR6 | CHECK PASSIVE RESTRAINT MODULE GROUNDS | | |
| | • Key OFF.<br>• Disconnect the Passive Restraint Module Connector # 1<br>• Measure the resistance of the "BK" wires at pin 1C / 1D of the connector to ground.<br>• Is the resistance less than 5 ohms? | Yes ►<br>No ► | GO to PR7.<br>SERVICE the "BK / Y" wire. |
| PR7 | CHECK INERTIA SWITCH | | |
| | • Key off.<br>• Disconnect and remove the Fuel Pump Inertia Switch from the vehicle.<br>• Inspect the switch and connector for corrosion or damage.<br>• Sharply shake the Fuel Pump Inertia Switch to verify that the switch "trips".<br>• Measure resistance between the switch terminals that connect to the "W / R" and "BK" wires under the following conditions:<br><br>Switch Position — Resistance<br>Open ("tripped") — Greater than 10,000 ohms<br>Closed (set) — Less than 5 ohms<br><br>• Is the resistance OK and does the switch "trip" when shaken sharply? | Yes ►<br>No ► | GO to PR8.<br>REPLACE the Fuel Pump Inertia Switch |
| PR8 | CHECK THE LEAD BETWEEN THE FUEL PUMP INERTIA SWITCH TO THE PASSIVE RESTRAINT MODULE | | |
| | • Disconnect the Passive Restraint Module connector # 2.<br>• Measure the resistance of the "GN / BK" wire between the Passive Restraint Module and Fuel Pump Inertia Switch.<br>• Is the resistance less than 5 ohms? | Yes ►<br>No ► | GO to PR9.<br>SERVICE the "GN / BK" wire. |

**Fig. 21 System diagnosis (Part 2 of 7). 1991 Probe**

| TEST STEP | | RESULT ▶ | ACTION TO TAKE |
|---|---|---|---|
| PR9 | CHECK DOOR SWITCH GROUND | | |
| | • Locate the Driver's and Passenger's door switch connectors (inside the door).<br>• Measure the resistance of the "BK" wire at the connector in respective door to ground.<br>• Are the resistances less than 5 ohms? | Yes ▶<br>No ▶ | GO to PR10.<br>SERVICE the "BK" wire in question. |
| PR10 | CHECK DOOR SWITCHES | | |
| | • Measure the resistance on the "BR/W" (Driver's side door) and the "Y/GN" (Passenger's side door) at the connector to ground.<br>(see table below)<br>• Are the resistances verified? | Yes ▶<br>No ▶ | GO to PR11.<br>REPLACE the door latch assembly. |
| PR11 | CHECK THE LEAD BETWEEN THE DOOR SWITCH AND THE PASSIVE RESTRAINT MODULE | | |
| | • Disconnect both Passive Restraint Module connectors and both door switch connectors.<br>• Measure the resistance of the following wires between the door switch and the module connectors.<br>(see table below)<br>• Are the resistances verified? | Yes ▶<br>No ▶ | GO to PR12.<br>SERVICE the wire in question. |
| PR12 | CHECK THE A PILLAR LIMIT SWITCH GROUND | | |
| | • Locate the "A" pillar limit switches (Driver's and Passenger's side).<br>• Measure the resistance of the "BK" wires to ground.<br>• Are the resistance less than 5 ohms? | Yes ▶<br>No ▶ | GO to PR13.<br>SERVICE the "BK" wire in question. |

PR10:

| | |
|---|---|
| Door open | Less than 5 ohms |
| Door closed | Greater than 10,000 ohms |

PR11:

| | |
|---|---|
| LH door switch "BR/W" and module "GN/O" | Less than 5 ohms |
| RH door switch "BR/W" and module "Y/GN" | Less than 5 ohms |

**Fig. 21 System diagnosis (Part 3 of 7). 1991 Probe**

| TEST STEP | | RESULT ▶ | ACTION TO TAKE |
|---|---|---|---|
| PR13 | CHECK THE A PILLAR LIMIT SWITCHES | | |
| | • Measure the voltage on the "Y/BL" wire (Driver's side) and the "GN/BL" (Passenger's side) at the limit switch connector under the following conditions.<br>(see table below)<br>• Are the voltages verified? | Yes ▶<br>No ▶ | GO to PR14.<br>REPLACE the track and motor assembly. |
| PR14 | CHECK THE B PILLAR LIMIT SWITCH GROUND | | |
| | • Locate the "B" pillar limit switches (Driver's and Passenger's sides).<br>• Measure the resistance of the "BK" wires to ground.<br>• Are the resistances less than 5 ohms? | Yes ▶<br>No ▶ | GO to PR15.<br>SERVICE the "BK" wire in question. |

PR13:

| | | |
|---|---|---|
| Key OFF, Door closed | Belt in "A" pillar position | 0V |
| Key ON | Belt in motion toward "B" pillar | 0V |
| | Belt in "B" pillar position | 0V |
| Key ON, Door open | Belt in motion toward "A" pillar | Above 4.5V |
| | Belt in "A" pillar position | 0V |

**Fig. 21 System diagnosis (Part 4 of 7). 1991 Probe**

| TEST STEP | | RESULT ▶ | ACTION TO TAKE |
|---|---|---|---|
| PR15 | CHECK THE "B" PILLAR LIMIT SWITCHES | | |
| | • Measure the voltage on the "BL/W" wire (Driver's side) and the "BL/Y" wire (Passenger's side) at the limit switch connector under the following conditions:<br>(see table below)<br>• Are the voltages verified? | Yes ▶<br>No ▶ | GO to PR16.<br>REPLACE the track and motor assembly. |
| PR16 | CHECK PASSIVE RESTRAINT MOTOR | | |
| | • Key ON, door open.<br>• Disconnect the Passive Restraint Motor connector.<br>• Ground the "Y" (1J/1H) (Driver's side) or the "R" (2J/2H) (Passenger's side) wire at the motor connector.<br>• Apply 12 volts to either the "BL" (1L/1K) (Driver's side) or the "GN" (2L/2D) (Passenger's side) wire at the connector.<br>• Does the belt move from pillar "A" to pillar "B"?<br>• Reverse the power and ground leads.<br>• Does the belt move from pillar "B" to pillar "A"? | Yes ▶<br>No ▶ | GO to PR17.<br>REPLACE the track and motor unit. |

PR15:

| | | |
|---|---|---|
| Key OFF, Door closed | Belt in "A" pillar position | 0V |
| Key ON | Belt in motion toward "B" pillar | Above 4.5V |
| | Belt in "B" pillar position | 0V |
| Key ON, Door open | Belt in motion toward "A" pillar | Above 4.5V |
| | Belt in "A" pillar position | Above 4.5V |

**Fig. 21 System diagnosis (Part 5 of 7). 1991 Probe**

| TEST STEP | | RESULT ▶ | ACTION TO TAKE |
|---|---|---|---|
| PR17 | CHECK LEADS BETWEEN THE PASSIVE RESTRAINT MODULE AND THE MOTOR | | |
| | • Key OFF.<br>• Disconnect the Passive Restraint Module connectors.<br>• Measure the resistance of the following wires between the module and the motor.<br>(see table below)<br>• Are the resistances less than 5 ohms? | Yes ▶<br>No ▶ | REPLACE the Passive Restraint module.<br>SERVICE the wire(s) in question. |
| PR18 | CHECK WARNING SWITCH GROUND | | |
| | • Disconnect the warning switch connector located in the center console between the seatbelt retractors.<br>• Measure the resistance of both "BK" wires to ground.<br>• Are the resistances less than 5 ohms. | Yes ▶<br>No ▶ | GO to PR19.<br>SERVICE the "BK" wire(s). |
| PR19 | CHECK WARNING SWITCH OPERATION | | |
| | • Reconnect the warning switch.<br>• Measure the resistance of the "LG/BK" (Passenger's side) and "BL/R" (Drivers side) wires between the switch and ground.<br>(see table below)<br>• Are the resistances verified? | Yes ▶<br>No ▶ | GO to PR20.<br>REPLACE the center console spool and belt assembly. |

PR17:

| Driver Side Connector | Passenger Side Connector |
|---|---|
| Both "BL" ("1L/1K") wires | Both "GN" wires ("2L/2D") |
| Both "Y" ("1J/1H") wires | Both "R" wires ("2J/2H") |

PR19:

| | |
|---|---|
| Shoulder Belt Latched | Less than 5 ohms |
| Shoulder belt Unlatched (and belt allowed to retract into the console) | Greater than 10,000 ohms |

**Fig. 21 System diagnosis (Part 6 of 7). 1991 Probe**

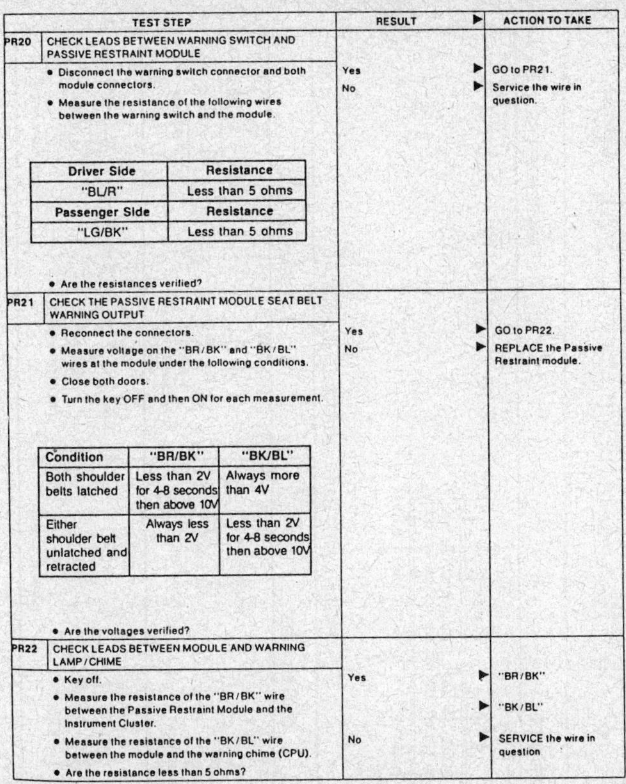

| TEST STEP | | RESULT ► | ACTION TO TAKE |
|---|---|---|---|
| PR20 | CHECK LEADS BETWEEN WARNING SWITCH AND PASSIVE RESTRAINT MODULE | | |
| | • Disconnect the warning switch connector and both module connectors.<br>• Measure the resistance of the following wires between the warning switch and the module.<br>• Are the resistances verified? | Yes ►<br>No ► | GO to PR21.<br>Service the wire in question. |
| PR21 | CHECK THE PASSIVE RESTRAINT MODULE SEAT BELT WARNING OUTPUT | | |
| | • Reconnect the connectors.<br>• Measure voltage on the "BR / BK" and "BK / BL" wires at the module under the following conditions.<br>• Close both doors.<br>• Turn the key OFF and then ON for each measurement.<br>• Are the voltages verified? | Yes ►<br>No ► | GO to PR22.<br>REPLACE the Passive Restraint module. |
| PR22 | CHECK LEADS BETWEEN MODULE AND WARNING LAMP / CHIME | | |
| | • Key off.<br>• Measure the resistance of the "BR / BK" wire between the Passive Restraint Module and the Instrument Cluster.<br>• Measure the resistance of the "BK / BL" wire between the module and the warning chime (CPU).<br>• Are the resistance less than 5 ohms? | Yes ►<br>►<br>No ► | "BR / BK"<br>"BK / BL"<br>SERVICE the wire in question |

| Driver Side | Resistance |
|---|---|
| "BL/R" | Less than 5 ohms |
| Passenger Side | Resistance |
| "LG/BK" | Less than 5 ohms |

| Condition | "BR/BK" | "BK/BL" |
|---|---|---|
| Both shoulder belts latched | Less than 2V for 4-8 seconds then above 10V | Always more than 4V |
| Either shoulder belt unlatched and retracted | Always less than 2V | Less than 2V for 4-8 seconds then above 10V |

**Fig. 21 System diagnosis (Part 7 of 7). 1991 Probe**

2. Insert drive belt at front of track A-pillar.
3. Install retainer into large slot at front end of tape.
4. Slide drive belt at rear of track until end is approximately 1/2 inch in the upper track slot.
5. Install limit switch and track assembly.

## TRACK ASSEMBLY

### COUGAR & THUNDERBIRD

### Removal

1. Cycle shoulder belt to the full forward position, then disengage shoulder belt from mini buckle.
2. Remove rear seat back and cushion.
3. Remove A-pillar and quarter panel trim.
4. Disconnect electrical connectors from A-pillar limit switch and motor assembly.
5. Remove two bolts used to retain vertical belt guide to inner quarter panel.
6. Remove three bolts retaining lower belt guide to quarter inner panel.
7. Remove two bolts retaining motor assembly to quarter panel inner panel.
8. Disengage vertical belt guide at B-pillar bracket.
9. Remove bolts retaining track assembly to B-pillar.
10. Remove screw holding A-pillar limit switch bracket to A-pillar **Fig. 26.**
11. While holding track assembly securely, remove bolts holding track assembly to roof rail **Fig. 32.**
12. Rotate track assembly downward at rear to disengage A-pillar limit switch bracket from A-pillar.
13. Remove track and motor assembly from vehicle.

### Installation

1. Position retaining tab on A-pillar limit switch bracket into forward hole in A-pillar, then rotate track assembly upward **Fig. 26.**
2. Loosely install screws and bolts used to secure track assembly to roof rail and A-pillar.
3. Secure B-pillar bracket to B-pillar and **torque** to 21 ft. lbs.
4. **Torque** A-pillar limit switch attaching bolts to 25 inch lbs.
5. **Torque** two bolts holding track assembly to roof rail to 40-62 inch lbs.
6. Engage locating tab on motor bracket into slot in quarter panel inner sheet metal, then install two motor attaching bolts and **torque** to 40-62 inch lbs.
7. Engage vertical guide retaining tab into B-pillar bracket, then secure guide to quarter panel inner sheet metal. **Torque** attaching bolts to 40-62 inch lbs.
8. Secure lower belt guide to quarter inner panel and **torque** attaching bolts to 40-62 inch lbs.
9. Connect electrical connectors at A-pillar limit switch and motor.
10. Install quarter trim panel and A-pillar moldings.
11. Cycle mini buckle to B-pillar position, then insert tongue of shoulder belt into mini buckle.
12. Cycle system to ensure proper operation.

### 1989–90 ESCORT, TEMPO & TOPAZ

### Removal

Refer to **Figs. 28 and 33,** for the following procedure.

1. Remove A and B-pillar moldings, then cycle shoulder belt retainer fully forward.
2. Disconnect A- and B-pillar electrical switch connectors.
3. Remove plug from shoulder belt anchor cover and remove retaining screw from belt anchor to shoulder belt retainer. Disconnect shoulder belt anchor.
4. Remove two screws retaining drive belt track to motor **Fig. 34.**
5. Remove screw adjacent to motor retaining vertical drive belt guide.
6. **On three-door models,** remove screw retaining lower drive belt guide.
7. Carefully disconnect drive belt track from motor, allowing belt to pass by gear teeth without engagement.
8. Remove screw from A-pillar bracket to A-pillar, then remove B-pillar bracket support plate.
9. Remove Torx bolt at B-pillar **Fig. 35.**
10. Remove screws from overhead track retaining clips.
11. Disengage vertical guide release tab at B-pillar bracket **Fig. 36.**
12. Rotate track inward to remove track limit switch retaining tab from slot in A-pillar.
13. Slide drive belt out of vertical guide.

### Installation

1. Insert drive belt in vertical guide.
2. Rotate retaining tab on limit switch bracket into slot in A-pillar.
3. Engage vertical guide retaining tab into B-pillar bracket.
4. Install Torx bolt at B-pillar.
5. Install screws in B-pillar bracket support plate, then install screws in overhead track attaching clips.
6. Install screw retaining A-pillar switch bracket to A-pillar.
7. Position drive belt guide at motor. Align drive belt and guides as required to ensure no binding prior to installing two screws.
8. **On three-door models,** install screw adjacent to motor retaining lower drive belt guide.
9. Connect electrical connectors.
10. Check system operation, then install moldings.

### 1991 ESCORT & TRACER

### Removal

1. Disconnect battery ground cable.
2. Disconnect shoulder belt from carrier, then cycle carrier to retracted position (B-pillar).
3. Remove A-B pillar trim panel and B-pillar trim panel.
4. Disconnect front limit switch electrical connector.
5. Disconnect two motor electrical connectors.

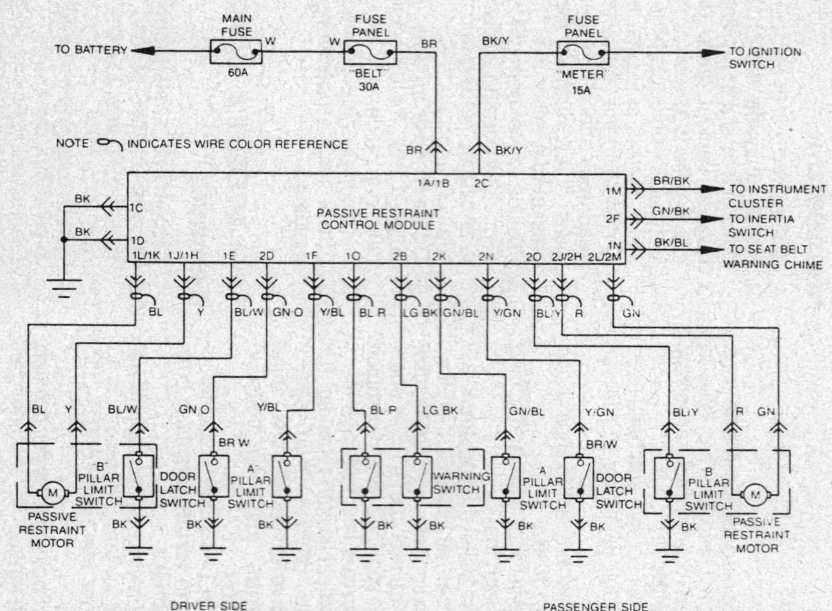

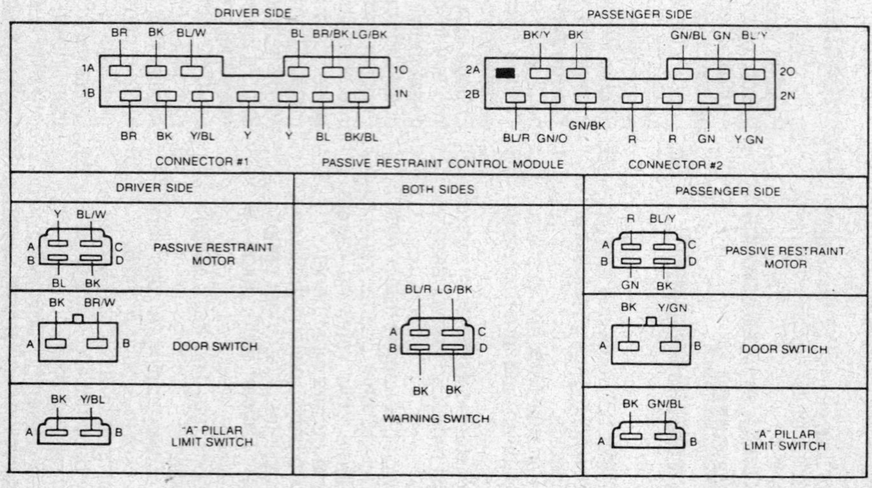

**Fig. 22 Restraint system wiring circuit. Probe**

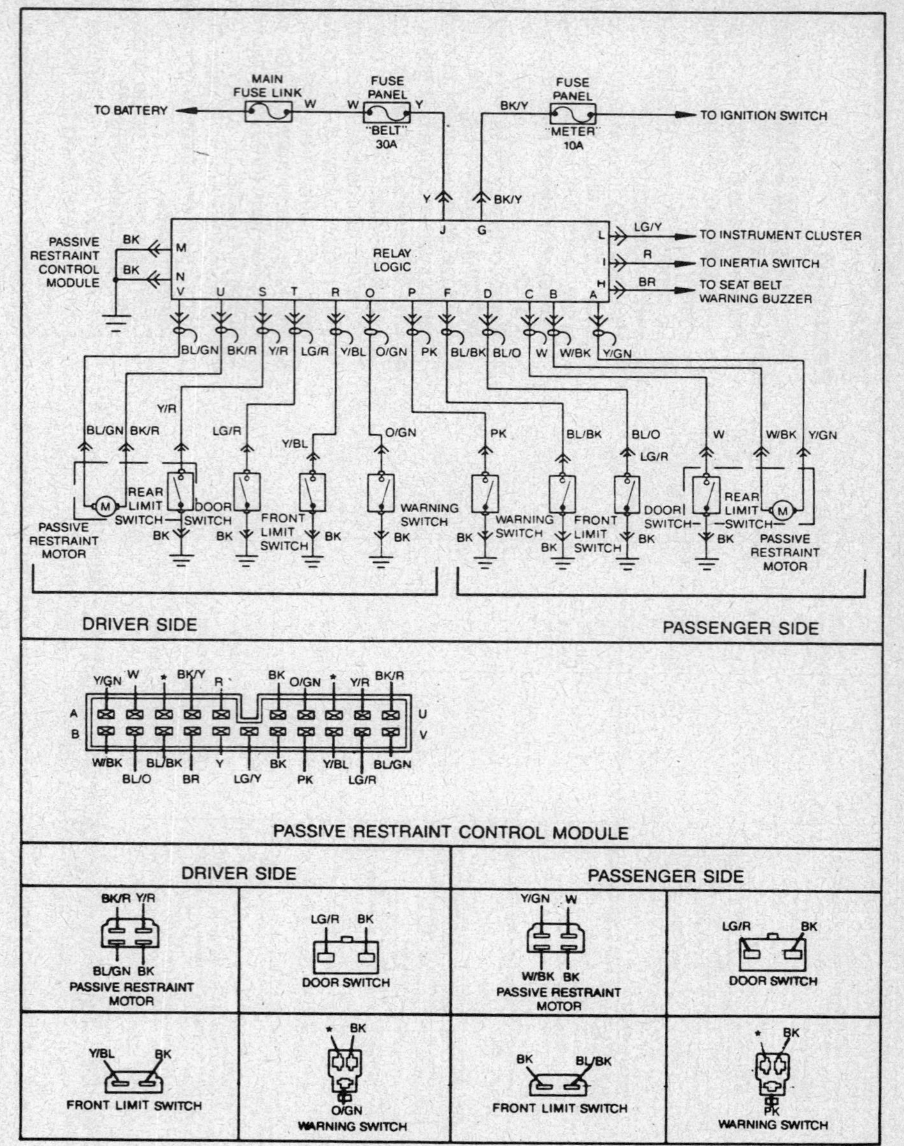

**Fig. 23 Restraint system wiring circuit. Festiva**

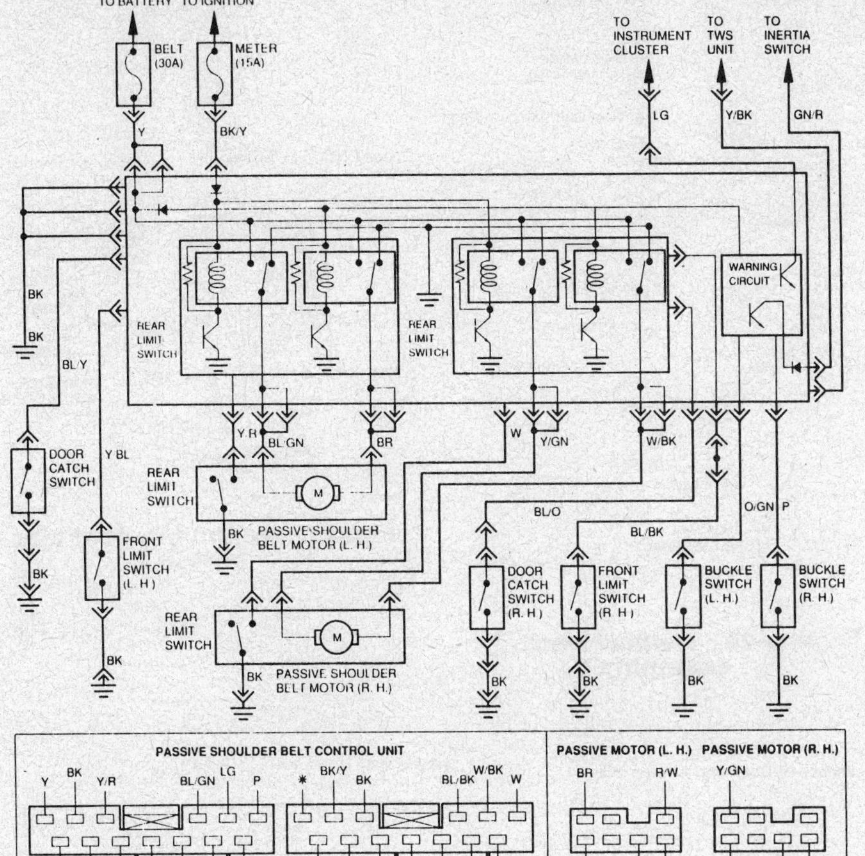


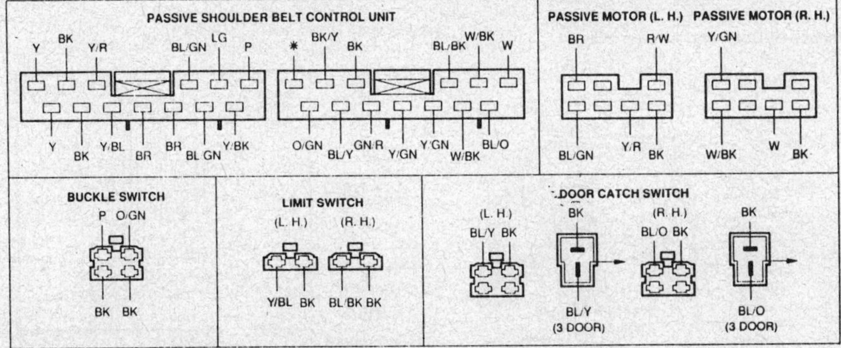


**Fig. 24 Restraint system wiring circuit. 1991 Escort & Tracer**

6. Remove all track and motor assembly mounting bolts and capscrews.
7. Remove track and motor assembly.

## Installation

1. Position track and motor assembly into position and install one track mounting bolt to hold in position.
2. Connect two motor electrical connectors.
3. Install motor mounting bolts.
   a. **On hatchback models, torque** bolts to 28-58 ft. lbs.
   b. **On all other models, torque** bolts to 69-104 inch lbs.
4. Install two track mounting bolts at rear limit switch and **torque** to 13-19 ft. lbs.
5. Install track mounting capscrews at B-pillar. **Torque** to 17-32.7 inch lbs.
6. Install all remaining track mounting bolts and capscrews. **Torque** to 69-104 inch lbs.
7. Reverse remaining removal procedure to complete installation.
8. Ensure proper operation of restraint system.

## FESTIVA

### Removal

1. Unbuckle shoulder belt from carrier.
2. Remove A-B pillar trim.
3. Cycle carrier to "B" pillar (retracted position).
4. Disconnect battery ground cable.
5. Disconnect electrical connector from front limit switch.
6. Remove two headliner clips.
7. Remove three track mounting bolts.
8. Remove screw which attaches track to rear limit switch, then remove track.

### Installation

1. Position track, then install and **torque** mounting bolts to 6-8 ft. lbs.
2. Install track to switch screw.
3. Connect front limit switch electrical connector.
4. Install A-B pillar trim.
5. Buckle shoulder belt to carrier, then connect battery ground cable.

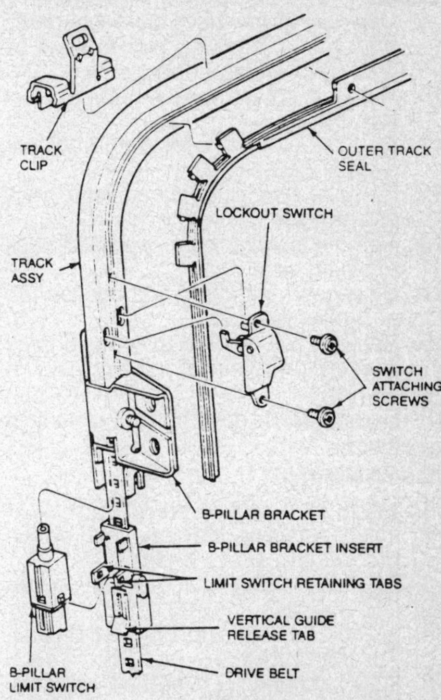


**Fig. 25 Disengaging vertical drive belt**

## PROBE

1. Unbuckle shoulder belt from carrier.
2. Cycle carrier to retracted position (retracted position).
3. Disconnect battery ground cable.
4. Remove A-B pillar trim panel and quarter trim panel.
5. Disconnect electrical connector from front limit switch.
6. Remove upper track mounting screw and bolts.
7. Remove two side track mounting bolts. **Fig. 37.**
8. Remove four cable retaining cap screws and three motor mounting bolts.
9. Disconnect electrical connector from motor.
10. Remove motor and track as an assembly.
11. Reverse procedure to install, noting the following:
    a. **Torque** track and motor mounting bolts to 28-58 ft. lbs.
    b. Ensure proper operation of restraint system.

## 1991 TEMPO & TOPAZ

1. Remove A-pillar and B-pillar moldings.
2. **On two door models,** remove rear seat.
3. **On all models,** cycle shoulder belt retainer completely forward.
4. Disconnect electrical connectors at A and B-pillars.
5. Remove plug button from shoulder belt anchor cover.
6. Remove torx screw retaining shoulder belt anchor to shoulder belt retainer and disconnect anchor.
7. Remove two screws retaining drive belt track to motor.
8. Remove screw retaining vertical drive belt guide, **Fig. 31.**

9. Carefully disconnect drive belt track from motor, allowing belt to pass by gear teeth without engagement.
10. Remove screw from A-pillar bracket to A-pillar.
11. Remove two bolts securing track assembly to B-pillar.
12. Remove two screws retaining track assembly to inner roof rail.
13. Remove screws from overhead track retaining clips.
14. Disengage vertical guide release tab at B-pillar bracket.
15. Rotate track inboard to remove track limit switch retaining tab from slot in A-pillar.
16. Carefully slide drive belt out of vertical guide.

### Installation

1. Insert drive belt in vertical track.
2. Insert retaining tab on limit switch bracket into slot in A-pillar.
3. Engage vertical guide retaining tab into B-pillar.
4. Install two retaining bolts at B-pillar. **Torque** bolts to 16-24 ft. lbs.
5. Install screws in overhead track retaining clips, then install screw retaining A-pillar switch bracket to A-pillar.
6. Position drive belt guide at motor.
7. Align drive belt and guides. Ensure no belt does not bind, then install two screws.
8. Install shoulder belt bolt. **Torque** bolt to 8-12 ft. lbs.
9. Install plug button and connect electrical connectors.
10. Ensure proper operation of restraint system, then install garnish moldings.
11. Install front seat shoulder belt track to track assembly as follows:
    a. Return shoulder belt track carrier to retracted position (B-pillar).
    b. Pull belt from retractor on the console. Allow belt to lay flat across seatback, without twisting.
    c. Install shoulder belt to track assembly by inserting anti-rotation pin in strap carrier and aligning it with notch in belt anchor.
    d. Install torx head retaining bolt. **Torque** to 8-12 ft. lbs.
12. Ensure proper operation of restraint system.
13. Install quarter trim panel.

## RETRACTOR ASSEMBLY

### COUGAR & THUNDERBIRD

### Removal

1. Cycle shoulder straps to A-pillar position.
2. Disconnect shoulder belt from emergency release buckle of motor and track carrier assembly, allowing safety straps to retract into retractor.
3. Disconnect seat wiring at floor, then remove front seat and seat track assembly.
4. Remove support assembly with belt/retractor assembly and lap belt buckle/strap assembly still attached. **Fig. 38.**
5. Remove front retaining nut and bolt.
6. Remove rear torx head bolt retaining support assembly to seat track.

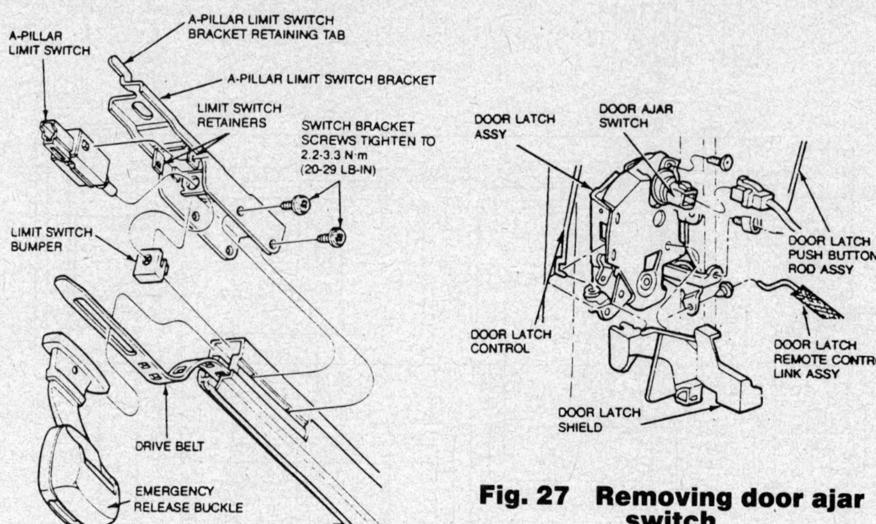


**Fig. 26 A-pillar track assembly**

**Fig. 27 Removing door ajar switch**

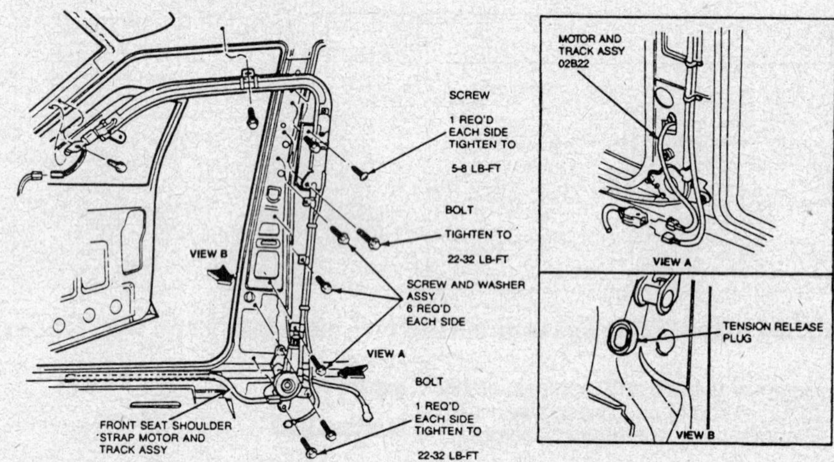


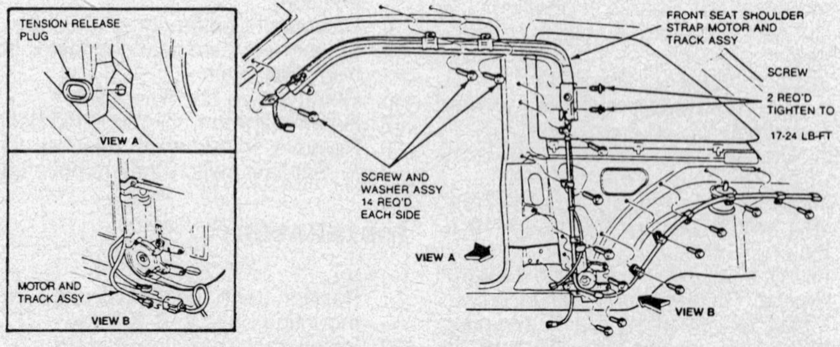


**Fig. 28 Motorized seat belt system. 1989–90 Escort**

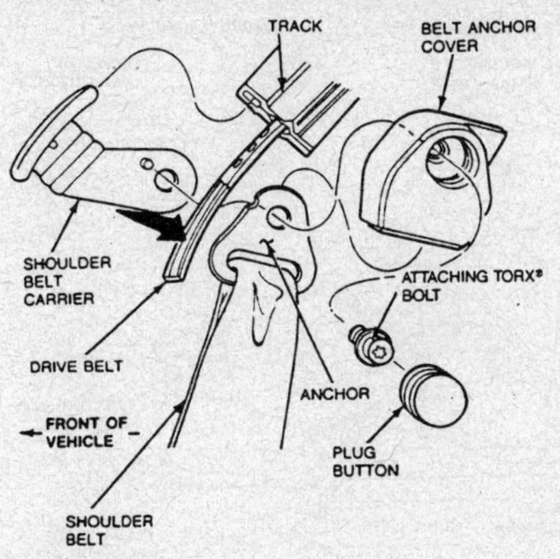


**Fig. 29 Shoulder belt upper anchor assembly**

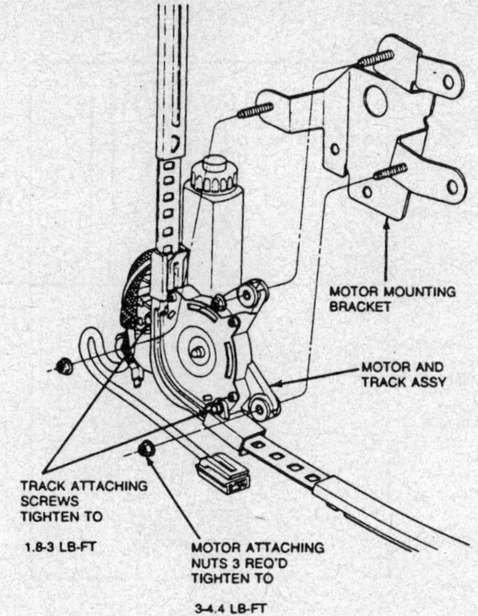


**Fig. 30 Removing drive belt**

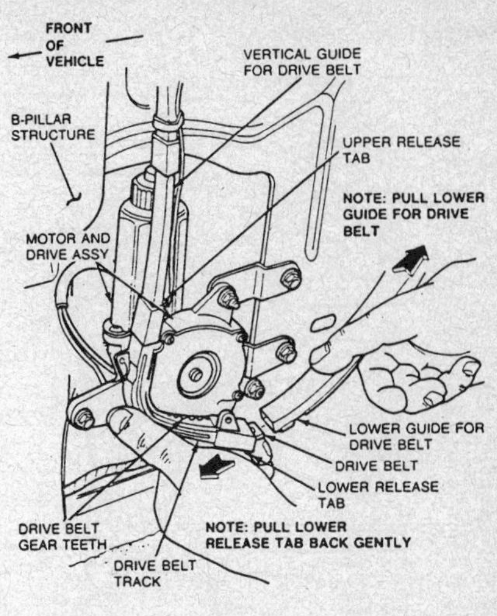


**Fig. 31 Installing drive belt**

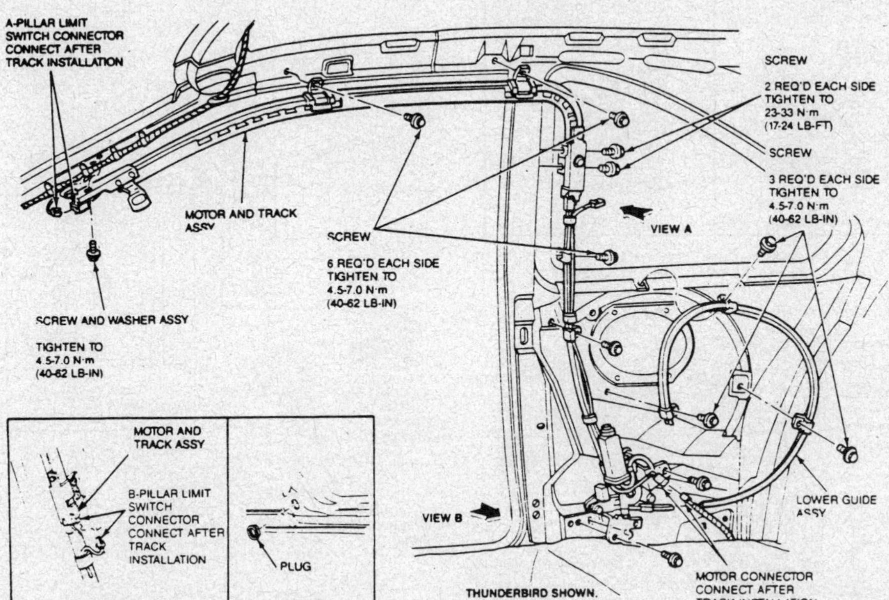


**Fig. 32 Motorized seat belt system. Cougar & Thunderbird**

7. Remove support assembly.
8. Remove torx head bolt retaining lap belt buckle assembly to support assembly. Remove buckle assembly.
9. Remove nut and washer retaining shoulder strap retractor assembly to shoulder strap support.
10. Rotate retractor up and away from support assembly until hooks disengage.
11. Remove retractor from support assembly by pulling stud out of hole.

## Installation

1. Insert retractor mounting stud into hole in support assembly.
2. With retractor pivoted up approximately 45°, loosely install retaining nut and washer.
3. Rotate retractor down toward support assembly. Ensure both retractor housing locking hooks engage into support assembly and retractor attachment bracket is on opposite side of support assembly.
4. Position lap belt buckle and strap assembly to indexing tabs on belt and retractor assembly mounting strap.
5. Ensure mounting holes are aligned and install torx head bolt to support assembly.
6. Position support assembly with belt/retractor assembly and lap belt buckle strap assembly attached, to seat and track assembly.
7. Ensure safety belt wire and connectors are properly routed between seat frame and seat track.
8. Install retaining nut and bolts. **Rubber washer must be installed between the support assembly and seat track at rear attachment.** Refer to **Fig. 38.**
9. Secure safety belt wiring connectors to metal connector mounting bracket on seat track.
10. Install front seat and seat track assembly. Connect wiring to floor harness.
11. Connect shoulder safety strap to emergency release buckle.
12. Ensure proper operation of restraint system.

## 1991 Escort & Tracer

1. Disconnect battery ground cable.
2. Remove parking brake console mounting screws, then lift console and remove shoulder belts.
3. Remove parking brake console.
4. Disconnect electrical connector from retractor, then slide seat forward and remove retractor.
5. Reverse procedure to install. **Torque** retractor mounting bolts to 28-58 ft. lbs.
6. Ensure proper operation of the restraint system.

## Festiva

1. Disconnect shoulder belt from carrier.
2. Remove retractor cover and disconnect electrical connector.
3. Remove retractor mounting bolt.
4. Remove retractor assembly.
5. Reverse procedure to install, noting the following:
   a. **Torque** retractor mounting bolt to 23-34 ft. lbs.
   b. Ensure proper operation of restraint system.

## Probe

1. Disconnect both shoulder belts from carriers.
2. Remove floor console.
3. Remove two retractor assembly mounting bolts.
4. Disconnect electrical connector and remove retractor assembly.
5. Reverse procedure to install.

Tempo/Topaz—4-Door

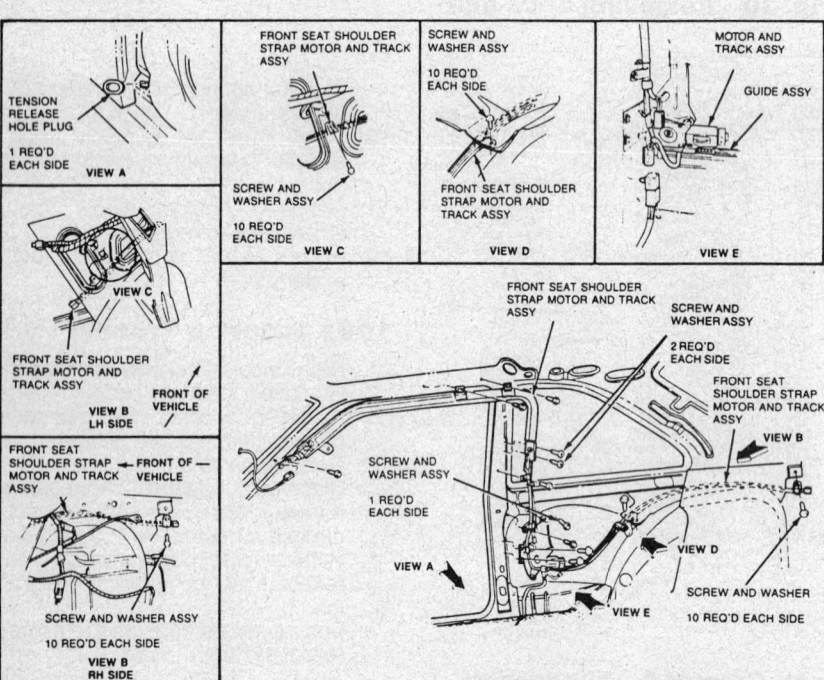

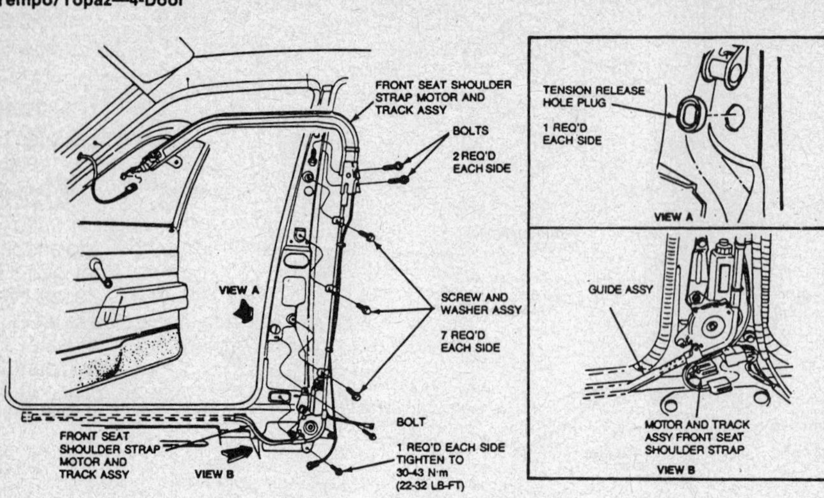


**Fig. 33 Motorized seat belt system. Tempo & Topaz**

NOTE: PASSENGER SIDE SHOWN—DRIVER'S SIDE TYPICAL

B-PILLAR STRUCTURE
FRONT OF VEHICLE
VERTICAL GUIDE FOR DRIVE BELT
MOTOR AND DRIVE ASSY
QUARTER SIDE STRUCTURE
DRIVE BELT TRACK
CIRCUIT BREAKER
LOWER GUIDE FOR DRIVE BELT
CIRCUIT BREAKER RETAINING SCREW
RETAINING SCREW

**Fig. 34 Removing drive belt track**

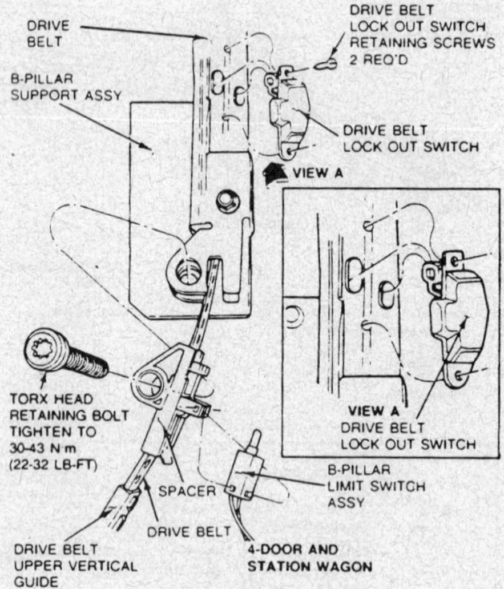


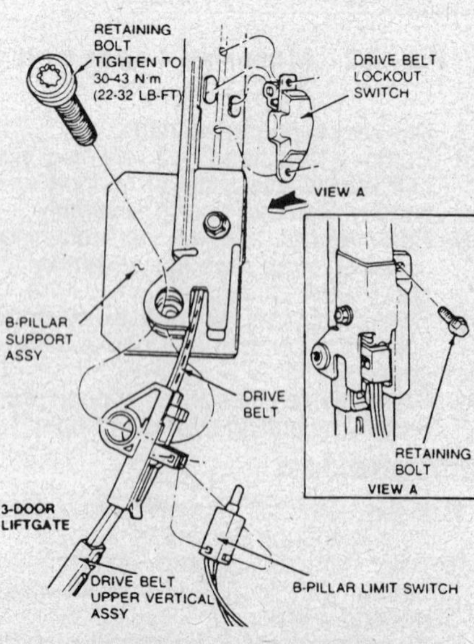


**Fig. 35 Removing Torx from limit switch bracket**

## Tempo, Topaz & 1989–90 Escort

1. Remove plug at shoulder belt retainer anchor cover, then disconnect belt anchor at retainer.
2. Remove console attaching screws, then armrest, if equipped.
3. Disengage shoulder harness opening bezel from console **Fig. 39.**
4. Remove shoulder belt retractor.
5. Reverse procedure to install, noting the following:
   a. Cycle shoulder belts to B-pillar prior to reinstalling belt anchor to belt retainer.
   b. **Torque** shoulder belt retaining bolts to 21 ft. lbs.
   c. **Torque** retractor to floor brace retaining bolts to 28 ft. lbs.

# MOTOR

## Cougar & Thunderbird

1. Remove rear seat back and cushion.
2. Remove A-pillar and quarter panel trim.
3. Remove lower bolt holding vertical guide to quarter panel inner sheet metal **Fig. 40.**
4. Disengage lower guide from motor guide.
5. Disconnect electrical connector at motor.
6. Remove two bolts holding motor to quarter panel inner sheet metal.
7. Disengage vertical guide from motor guide **Fig. 41.**
8. Rotate thumb wheel on motor counterclockwise to disengage drive belt from motor drive gear.

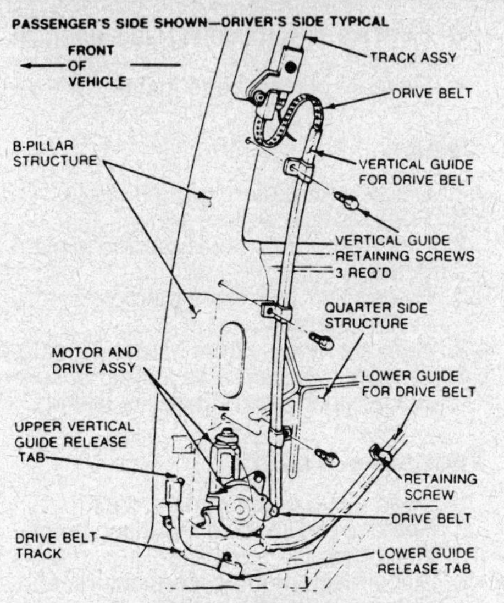


**Fig. 36 Disengaging vertical release tab**

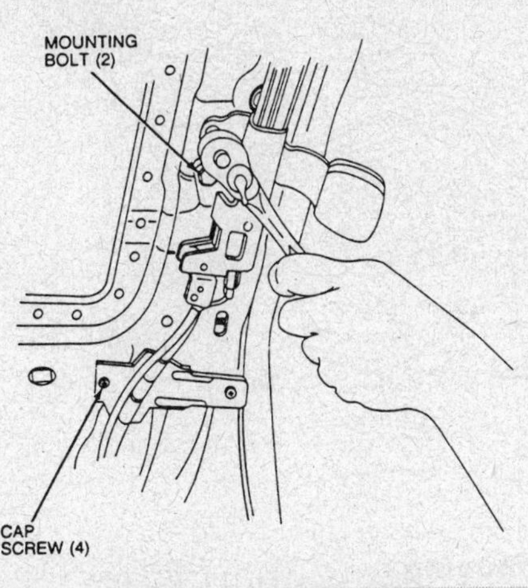


**Fig. 37 Side track removal.Probe**

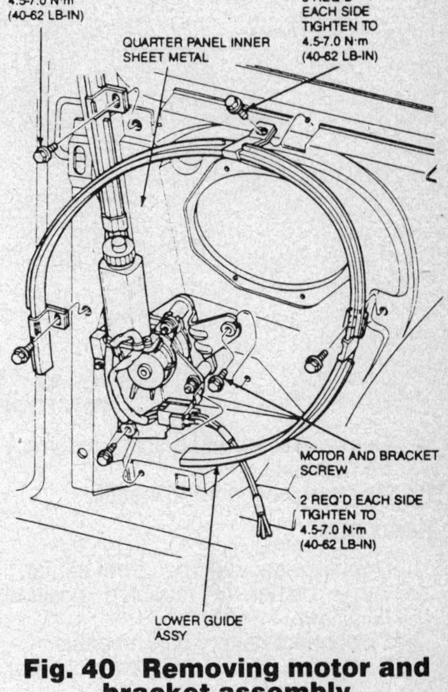


**Fig. 40 Removing motor and bracket assembly**

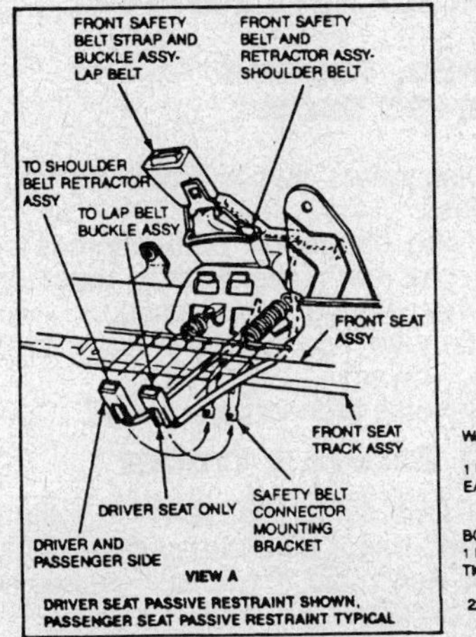


**Fig. 38 Retractor assembly removal. Cougar & Thunderbird**

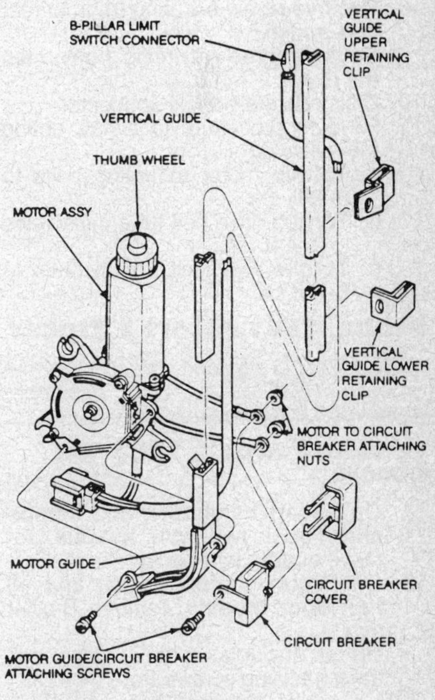


**Fig. 41 Disengaging vertical guide**

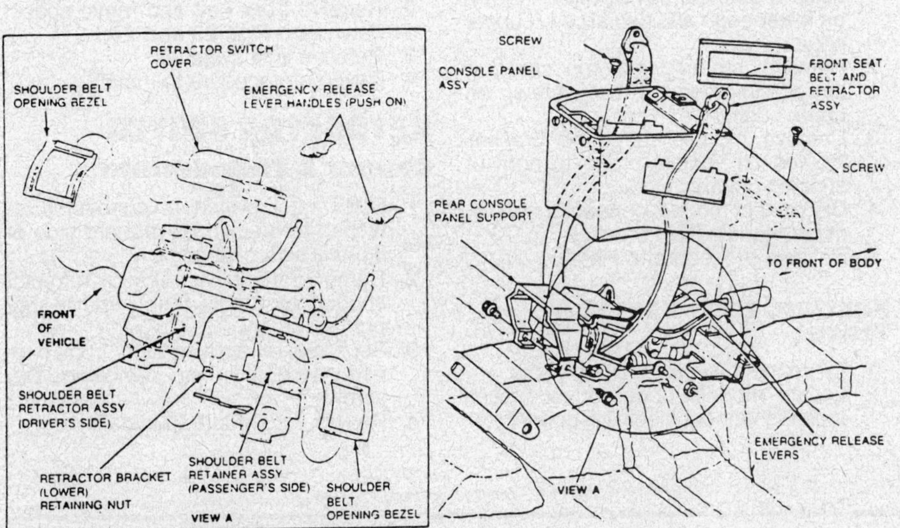


**Fig. 39 Disengaging shoulder harness**

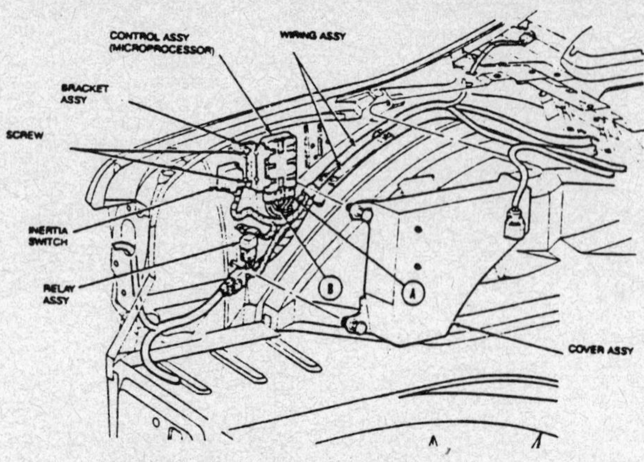


**Fig. 42 Removing microprocessor**

9. Remove motor and bracket assembly from vehicle.
10. Reverse procedure to install.

### Festiva

1. Unbuckle shoulder belt from carrier.
2. Cycle carrier to retracted position (B-pillar).
3. Disconnect battery ground cable.
4. Remove A-B pillar trim and fold rear seat forward.
5. Loosen side shelf screws to access rear quarter trim panel.
6. Remove rear quarter trim panel.
7. Remove two limit switch bolts and two capscrews retaining drive belt tube.
8. Remove screw securing track to rear limit switch.
9. Remove three mounting bolts, then the motor.
10. Disconnect electrical connector.
11. Reverse procedure to install, noting the following:
    a. **Torque** motor mounting bolts to 6-8 ft. lbs.
    b. **Torque** drive belt tube capscrews to 3-4 ft. lbs.
    c. **Torque** rear limit switch bolts to 6-8 ft.lbs.

### Probe, 1991 Escort & Tracer

The motor is serviced with the track as an assembly. Refer to "Track Assembly, Removal" for replacement procedures.

### Tempo, Topaz & 1989–90 Escort

1. **On Escort hatchback and Tempo and Topaz two-door models,** remove quarter trim panel.
2. **On Escort station wagon and all four-door models,** remove B-pillar trim.
3. **On all models,** remove drive belt track retaining screws from motor.
4. Remove screw from vertical drive belt guide adjacent to motor. Slide drive belt track down and out of the way for motor removal.
5. Disconnect electrical connectors.
6. Remove hex nuts from motor mounting bracket studs.
7. Reverse procedure to install.

## PASSIVE RESTRAINT MODULE

### Cougar & Thunderbird

1. Remove lefthand luggage compartment trim panel.
2. Disengage two cover retaining push pins and remove cover **Fig. 42.**
3. Remove processor assembly from bracket, processor snaps on bracket.
4. Disconnect electrical connectors and remove processor.
5. Reverse procedure to install.

### 1989–90 Escort

1. Remove instrument panel steering column opening cover, three screws on lower edge and two slips on upper edge.
2. Remove steering column opening cover reinforcement, two screws on upper edge.
3. Remove module mounting bracket, located on vertical brace to right of steering column.
4. Disconnect module connector and remove module from bracket.
5. Reverse procedure to install.

### Festiva, 1991 Escort & Tracer

1. Disconnect Battery ground cable.
2. Locate module under driver's seat, then disconnect electrical connector.
3. Remove two mounting screws, then module.
4. Reverse procedure to install.

### Probe

1. Disconnect battery ground cable.
2. Remove quarter trim panel.
3. Remove three module mounting plate bolts.
4. Disconnect two electrical connectors from module.
5. Remove module from mounting plate.
6. Reverse procedure to install. Ensure proper operation of restraint system.

### Tempo & Topaz

1. Open glove compartment door.
2. Remove two module mounting bracket screws.
3. Disconnect module connectors and slide module off bracket.
4. Reverse procedure to install.

## TRACK LIMIT SWITCH

### Tempo, Topaz & 1989–90 Escort

1. Disconnect switch from wiring harness.
2. Using ohmmeter probe across connector terminals. Switch must open when plunger is depressed.
3. Remove Torx bolt and move spacer downward.
4. Reverse procedure to install.

### 1991 Escort & Tracer

The limit switch is serviced with the track and motor as an assembly. Refer to "Track Assembly, Removal" for replacement procedure.

### Cougar & Thunderbird

1. Disconnect switch from wiring harness.
2. Remove Torx bolt and move spacer downward **Figs 25 and 26.**
3. Remove limit switches.
4. Reverse procedure to install.

## RETRACTOR SWITCH

### Cougar & Thunderbird

1. Disconnect switch at connector attached to bracket on inboard side of driver's side seat track.
2. Remove attaching bolts on retractor support assembly, then remove support assembly.
3. Separate retractor switch from support assembly, by removing two screws.
4. Reverse procedure to install.

# AIR SUSPENSION

## TABLE OF CONTENTS



# Mark VII

## INDEX



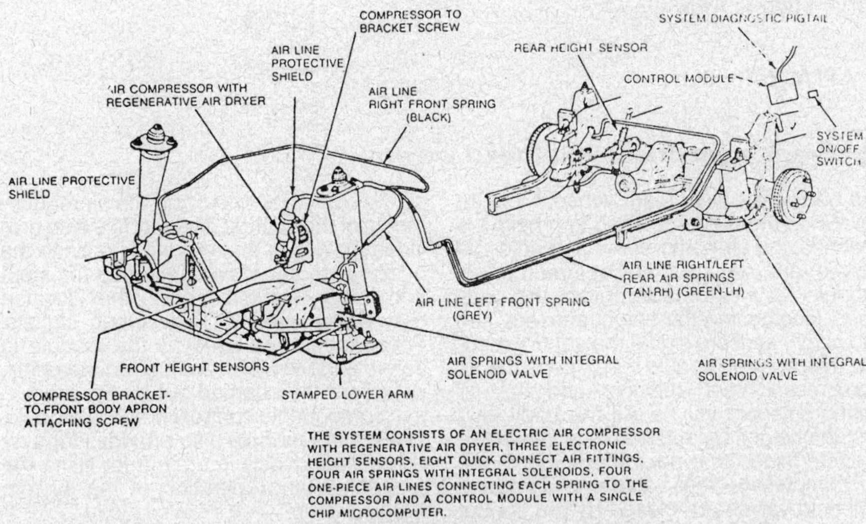


**Fig. 1 Air suspension system**

## DESCRIPTION

**The compressor relay, compressor vent solenoid and all air spring solenoids incorporate internal diodes for electrical noise suppression and are polarity sensitive. Care must be taken when servicing these components not to switch the battery feed and ground circuits or components damage will result. The electrical power supply to the air suspension system must be shut off prior to hoisting, jacking or towing vehicle. This can be accomplished by disconnecting the battery or turning off the power switch located in the luggage compartment. Failure to do so may result in unexpected inflation or deflation of the air springs which may result in shifting of the vehicle during service procedures. Do not attempt to install or inflate any air spring that has become unfolded. Any spring which has unfolded must be refolded prior to being installed in a vehicle. The air spring refolding procedure should only be used to service an air spring which has never supported the vehicle's weight while in the improperly folded position. Do not attempt to inflate any spring which has been collapsed while uninflated from the rebound (hanging) position to the jounce stop. When installing a new air spring, care must be taken not to apply a load to the suspension until springs have been inflated using air spring fill procedure. When front air springs are replaced, the height sensor must be checked and replaced if damaged. After inflating an air spring in hanging position, it must be inspected for proper shape. Failure to follow the above information may result in a sudden failure of the air spring or suspension system.**

Used on Mark VII models, the Air Suspension System, **Fig. 1,** is an air operated, microprocessor controlled suspension which replaces conventional coil springs with air springs, providing automatic front and rear load leveling.

The front air springs, **Fig. 2,** are mounted to the upper spring pocket in the crossmember and on the lower suspension arms as in conventional suspension systems. The rear springs, **Fig. 3,** are mounted ahead of the rear axle, outboard of the body side members and on the lower suspension arm.

A piston type electrically operated air compressor, attached to the left fender apron, supplies the air pressure necessary

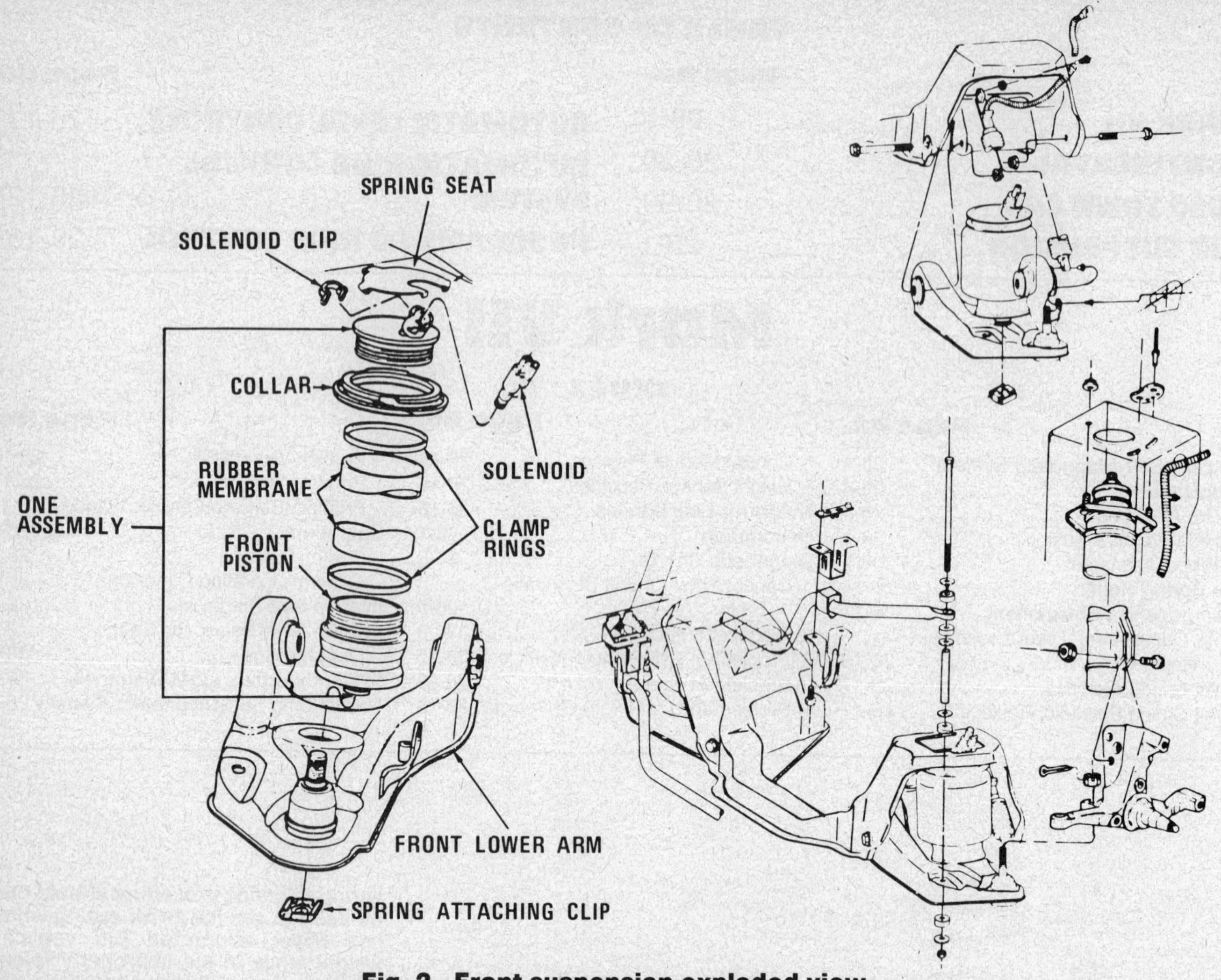


**Fig. 2 Front suspension exploded view**

for system operation. All air passing through the system is filtered through a regenerative type dryer, located on the compressor manifold. A vent solenoid, also located on the manifold, controls exhaust air.

Air flow through the entire system is controlled by the interaction of the air compressor, solenoids, height sensors and the control module.

## OPERATION

System operation is maintained by the addition or removal of air to or from the air springs, resulting in a predetermined front and rear suspension height. This predetermined height is known as the vehicle trim height. The trim height is controlled by three height sensors, two of which are located at the front wheels and a third at the rear suspension, **Fig. 1.** The height sensors are attached to the body and suspension arms and will lengthen or shorten, depending on the amount of suspension travel. As weight is added to the vehicle, the body settles, shortening the height sensors. The height sensors signal the control module, which then activates the air compressor through a relay, and signals the air spring solenoids to open. As the body rises, the height sensors lengthen. When the predetermined trim height is reached, the air compressor and solenoid valves are de-activated by the control module. As weight is removed, the body rises, lengthening the height sensors, and the height sensors signal the control module. The control module then opens the air compressor vent solenoid and the air spring solenoid valves. As the body lowers, the height sensors shorten. When the predetermined trim height is reached, the air compressor vent valve and air spring solenoid valves are closed by the control module.

The air required for leveling the vehicle is distributed from the air compressor to each spring by four nylon air lines which start at the dryer and end at the individual springs. Each air line is color coded to identify the spring to which they belong. The dryer is used to dry the air before it is delivered to each spring. The air required for compression and the vent air enter and exit through a common port on the compressor head. Vented air is controlled by a solenoid valve in the compressor head.

Electrical power to operate the system is distributed by the main body harness. The control module controls the air compressor relay, vent solenoid and the four air spring solenoids to provide the air requirements of the springs. The module also provides the power and ground circuits to the height sensors, while monitoring the input from the sensors and the Ignition Run/Brake and On/Door Open circuits. These inputs are used by the module in determining vehicle leveling requirements, which are then carried out by the air system components controlled by the module. The control module also provides for system self diagnosis, a routine for filling the air springs and operation of the system warning lamp.

## CONTROL LOGIC

### Ignition Off

When the ignition switch is turned off, the system will continue to operate for approximately one hour. During this time, the system will service requests to lower the vehicle as required, provided no sensor was reading high at the time the ignition switch was turned off. Vent time is limited to 10 seconds for the rear springs and 3 seconds for the front. Approximately 1 hour after the ignition switch is turned off, the system will correct for a low vehicle height by activating the air compressor.

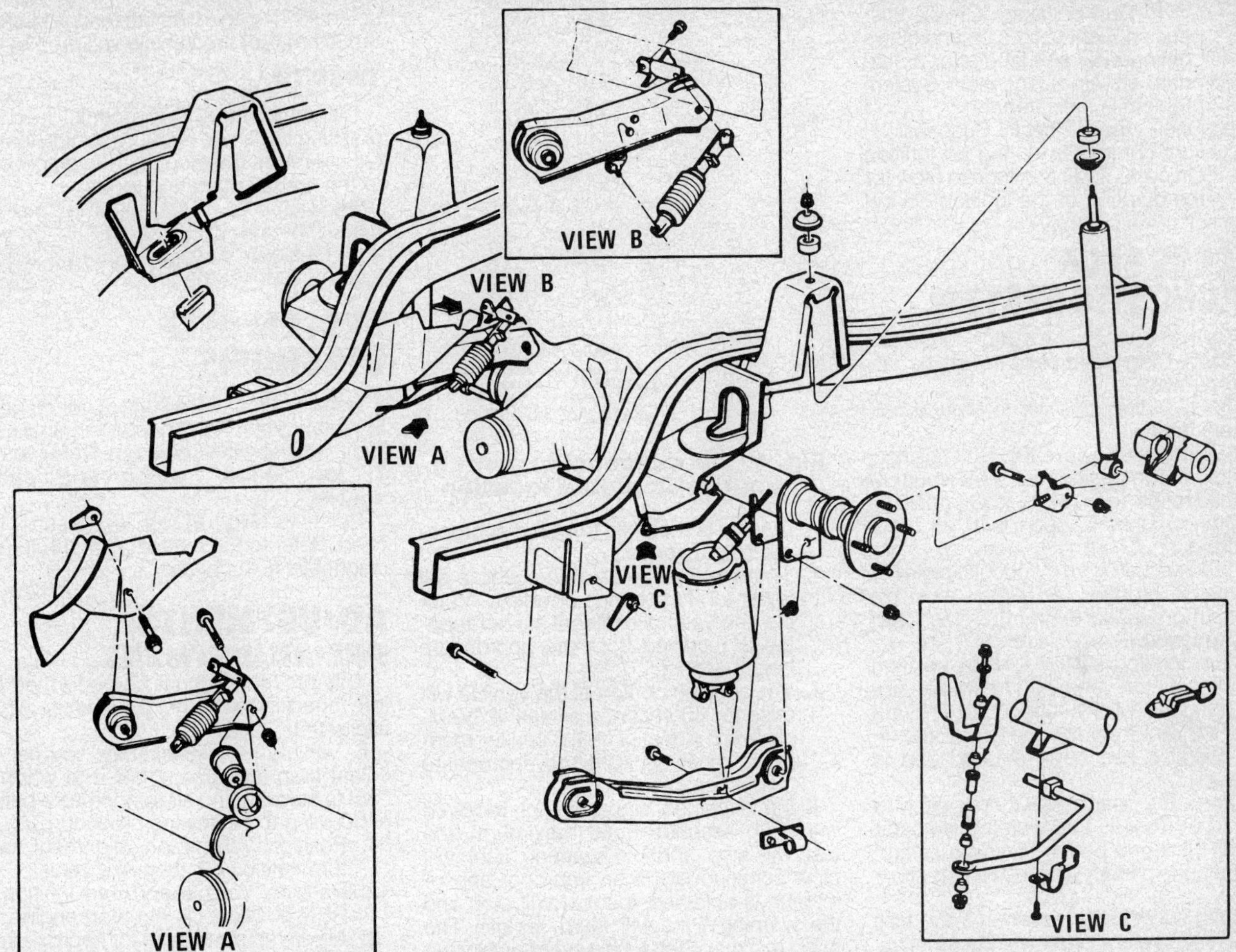


**Fig. 3 Rear suspension exploded view**

Compressor run time is limited to 15 seconds for the rear springs and 30 seconds for the front.

### Ignition In Run

When the ignition switch is first turned to the RUN position, the system will raise the vehicle as necessary. No down requests will be serviced for approximately 45 seconds. After the 45 second period, up and down requests will be serviced provided no door is open. If any door is open, no down requests will be serviced until the door is closed. However, if the brakes are applied with the doors closed, neither up nor down requests will be serviced except for a rear up request already in progress.

## GENERAL OPERATING CONDITIONS

1. Requests are serviced in the following Order: Rear Up, Front Up, Rear Down, Front Down.
2. With ignition in RUN, failure to service any request within 3 minutes will result in the activation of the warning lamp. The lamp will stay on during that complete ignition cycle. However, only the request that was being serviced will be affected. The control module will continue to service all other requests as usual.
3. The rear spring solenoids will always be operated in tandem, while the front solenoids may operate independently.
4. Front and rear requests are never serviced at the same time.
5. Turning the ignition from RUN to OFF will clear all memory in the control module, and the warning lamp may not indicate failure when the ignition is returned to the ON position. **When charging the battery, ensure ignition switch is off, as damage to the compressor or compressor relay may result.**

## SYSTEM WARNING LIGHT DIAGNOSIS

The "Check Suspension" warning light, located in the overhead console, serves the following diagnostic functions:

1. During normal operation with the ignition switch in the Run position and the "Check Suspension" light glowing, a possible air suspension problem is indicated.
2. During self diagnosis testing, the "Check Suspension" light blinks 1.8 times per second to indicate the diagnostic routine has been entered, then blinks the test number being run during the test sequence.
3. During "Air Spring Refill" procedure, the "Check Suspension" light blinks once every 2 seconds to indicate the air spring fill routine has been entered.
4. Observing the "Check Suspension" light during normal operation with the ignition switch On can aid in detecting the following Air Suspension System problems:
   a. During normal operation, the "Check Suspension" light will glow for approximately one second and go out when ignition switch is turned from Off to Run position. The lamp does not operate with the ignition in the Off or Start position.
   b. If "Check Suspension" light fails to go out after turning ignition switch from Off to Run position, no battery 12 volt power to the module is indicated.
   c. If after turning ignition switch from Off to Run position, "Check Suspension" light glows for approximately one-half second, goes out and then glows continuously after five to eight seconds, a height sensor or harness problem is indicated.
   d. If after turning ignition switch from

Off to Run position, "Check Suspension" light comes on and glows continuously any time after 8 seconds, an Air Suspension System problem is indicated.

e. Once the "Check Suspension" light comes On during an ignition On cycle, it will continue to glow for the duration of the ignition On cycle.

## ACCESS SELF DIAGNOSTIC SYSTEM

1. Turn air suspension switch to On position. Diagnostic pigtail must be ungrounded.
2. Install battery charger to reduce battery drain.
3. Cycle ignition from Off to Run position, hold in run position for a minimum of 5 seconds, then return to Off position. Driver's door is open with all other doors shut.
4. Attach a lead from diagnostic pigtail to vehicle ground. The pigtail must remain grounded during the diagnostic sequence.
5. Turn ignition switch to Run position (Do not start vehicle). The warning indicator will blink continuously at a rate of 1.8 blinks per second to indicate diagnostics has been entered and is ready.
6. Close, the open driver's door once to initiate Test 1. The warning indicator will blink one, pause, blink, pause and continue pattern until next test is started.
7. Each successive transition from door closed to door open will cause module to advance to next step in test sequence. The warning indicator will blink the current test number.

## TERMINATING SELF DIAGNOSTIC SYSTEM

Diagnostics may be terminated and the module returned to normal operational mode at any time by cycling the ignition, actuating the brake or ungrounding the diagnostic pigtail.

## SYSTEM SELF DIAGNOSTIC TEST DESCRIPTIONS

### Test 1

Test 1 is used in checking the rear suspension.

### Test 2

Test 2 is used in checking the right front suspension.

### Test 3

Test 3 is used in checking the left front suspension.

During tests 1 through 3, the following steps occur:

1. The affected portion of the vehicle will raise for 15 seconds, then continue raising an additional 15 seconds (30 seconds total maximum) or until a "Vehicle High" signal or illegal sensor reading is received from the appropriate height sensor.
2. The affected portion of the vehicle will lower for 30 seconds or until a "Vehicle Low" signal or illegal sensor reading is received from the appropriate height sensor.
3. The affected portion of the vehicle will raise for 30 seconds or until a "Vehicle Trim" signal or illegal sensor reading is received from the appropriate height sensor.

If the expected signal is not received within 30 seconds (total maximum), the test will stop and the warning light will glow continuously. If an improper sensor reading is obtained, the test will stop and the warning light will flash rapidly. The failed test may then be repeated by closing or opening the car door, or the next test may be started by opening and closing the car door twice within 15 seconds.

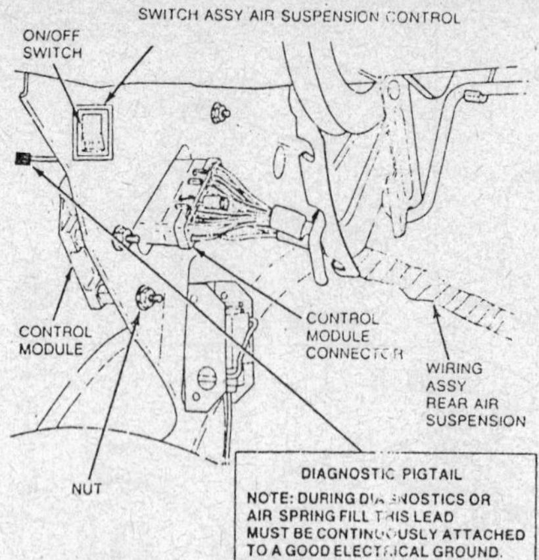


**Fig. 4 Air suspension switch & diagnostic pigtail location**

### Test 4

During test 4, the compressor is cycled On and Off at .25 Hz. The compressor is limited to a maximum of 50 cycles.

### Test 5

The compressor vent solenoid is cycled (open and closed) at 1 Hz.

### Test 6

Left front solenoid is cycled (open and closed) at 1 Hz and the compressor vent solenoid is opened. As the test progresses, the left front of the vehicle will drop slowly.

### Test 7

Right front solenoid is cycled (open and closed) at 1 Hz and the compressor vent solenoid is opened. As the test progresses, the right front of the vehicle will drop slowly.

### Test 8

Right rear solenoid is cycled (open and closed) at 1 Hz and the compressor vent solenoid is opened. As the test progresses, the right rear of the vehicle will drop slowly.

### Test 9

Left rear solenoid is cycled (open and closed) at 1 Hz and the compressor vent solenoid is opened. As the test progresses, the left rear of the vehicle will drop slowly.

### Test 10

Disconnecting the diagnostic lead, depressing the brake pedal or turning ignition Off will return the module from diagnostics to the normal operating mode.

Allow time for vehicle to return to proper height, the turn ignition switch to Off position. Remove diagnostic ground lead in luggage compartment.

## SYSTEM SELF DIAGNOSIS

Refer to **Figs. 4 through 6,** for diagnostic pigtail location, connector terminal identification and wiring diagram. **Refer to Fig. 7, for "Quick" wiring and circuit checks.**

Refer to **Fig. 8,** for troubleshooting chart. Refer to **Figs. 9 through 16,** for self diagnostic flow charts.

## ADJUSTMENTS

### PRE-ADJUSTMENT

This procedure must be performed before checking ride height and/or wheel alignment.

If vehicle is significantly warmer or colder than test area, allow it to warm or cool to surrounding air temperature before performing the following procedure.

1. Position vehicle on alignment rack, turn ignition off, then exit vehicle.
2. Re-enter vehicle and turn ignition to RUN position. Do not start engine.
3. Allow vehicle to level for approximately one minute, then push trunk release to open trunk area.
4. Turn ignition OFF and exit vehicle.
5. Allow vehicle to vent to trim height (approximately 20 seconds), then close all doors and turn off air suspension switch in trunk, **Fig. 4.**

## RIDE HEIGHT, ADJUST

All doors must be closed when adjusting ride height.

### Front Suspension

The front suspension ride height or "C" dimension, **Fig. 17,** is adjusted by moving the front left and/or right lower sensor attaching stud to one of the three adjustment positions as shown, **Fig. 18.** Loosen the attaching screw and adjust up or down as required. Changing the sensor attachment point one position will result in a .50 inch change in the "C" dimension. The "C" dimension should be indicated at .24 inches.

### Rear Suspension

The rear suspension ride height or "D" dimension, **Fig. 17,** is adjusted by moving the rear sensor attaching bracket up or down in relation to the right rear upper control arm, **Fig. 19.** Loosen the attaching nut and position up or down as required. A change to the sensor attaching point by one index mark will result in a .250 inch change to the "D" dimension. The "D" dimension should be indicated at 5.06 inches.

*Continued on page 26-17*

| Component (Harness Number) | Harness Side Connector | Pin Number | Function | Wire Harness Circuit | Wire Harness Color | Wire Harness Gauge | Circuit End Point |
|---|---|---|---|---|---|---|---|
| Compressor (1) (14290) | | 1 | Solenoid Feed | 175 | BK/Y | 14 | Starter Relay |
| | | 2 | Motor Feed | 417 | P/O | 14 | Compressor Relay |
| | | 3 | Motor Ground | 430 | GY | 14 | Battery Ground Cable |
| | | 4 | Solenoid Control | 578 | LB/PK | 18 | Module Pin No. 23 |
| Spring Solenoid (4) (14290 LF/RF) (12614 LR/RR) | | 1 | Control — LR | 429 | P/LG | 18 | Module Pin No. 9 |
| | | | Control — RR | 416 | LB/BK | 18 | Module Pin No. 10 |
| | | | Control — LF | 415 | LG/O | 18 | Module Pin No. 11 |
| | | | Control — RF | 414 | O/R | 18 | Module Pin No. 12 |
| | | 2 | Feed | 175 | BK/Y | 16 | Starter Relay |
| Front Height Sensor (2) (14290) | | 1 | Ground | 432 | BK/PK | 18 | Module Pin No. 14 |
| | | 2 | Feed — LF (RF) | 431 | PK/W | 18 | Module Pin No. 4 |
| | | 3 | Logic Line B — RF | 425 | BR/PK | 18 | Module Pin No. 16 |
| | | | Logic Line B — LF | 423 | P LG | 18 | Module Pin No. 17 |
| | | 4 | Logic Line A — RF | 424 | T | 18 | Module Pin No. 5 |
| | | | Logic Line A — LF | 422 | PK/BK | 18 | Module Pin No. 6 |
| Rear Height Sensor (1) (12614) | | 1 | Ground | 432 | BK/PK | 18 | Module Pin No. 14 |
| | | 2 | Feed | 426 | R/BK | 18 | Module Pin No. 3 |
| | | 3 | Logic Line B | 428 | O/BK | 18 | Module Pin No. 18 |
| | | 4 | Logic Line A | 427 | PK/BK | 18 | Module Pin No. 13 |
| Compressor Relay (1) (14290) | | 1 | Control | 420 | DB/Y | 18 | Module Pin No. 22 |
| | | 2 | Feed (Coil) | 175 | BK/Y | 18 | Starter Relay |
| | | 3 | Feed (Contacts) | 175 | BK/Y | 12 | Starter Relay |
| | | 4 | Compressor Motor Feed | 417 | P/O | 14 | Compressor |
| | | 5 | Compressor Motor Ground | 430 | GY | 12 | Battery Ground Cable |
| On/Off Switch (1) (12614) | | 1 | Feed to Module | 418 | DG/Y | 14 | Module Pin No. 20 |
| | | 2 | Feed to Switch | 175 | BK/Y | 14 | Starter Relay |
| Warning Lamp (1) (14A005) | | 8 | Control | 419 | DG/LG | 20 | Module Pin No. 21 |
| | | 6 | Feed | 640 | R/Y | 20 | Fuse Panel |
| Battery Ground Cable (14290) | — | — | System Ground | 577 | LG/RD | 12 | Module Pin No. 1 and 24 |
| Diagnostic Pigtail | — | — | Access to System Diagnostics and Air Fill | 606 | W/LB | 18 | Module Pin No. 2 |
| Ignition Switch (14401) | Branch of Existing Circuit | — | Ignition Sense | 687 | GY/Y | 12 | Module Pin No. 7 |
| Stoplamp Switch (14A005) | Branch of Existing Circuit | — | Brake Sense | 511 | LG | 18 | Module Pin No. 15 |
| Courtesy Lamp Door Switch (14488) | Branch of Existing Circuit | — | Door Sense | 24 | DB/O | 20 | Module Pin No. 19 |
| Module (1) (12614) | 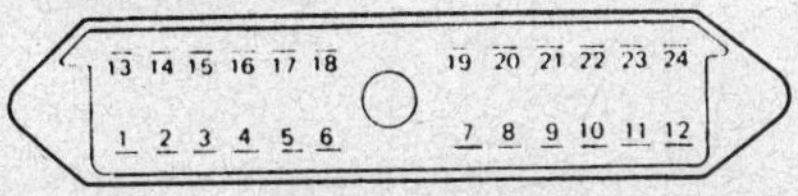 | | | | | | |

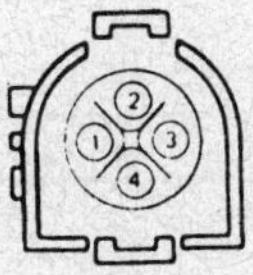

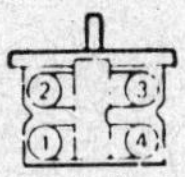

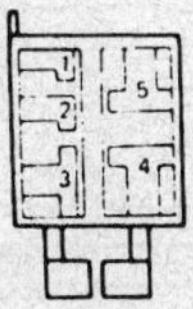

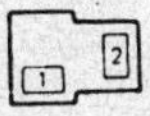

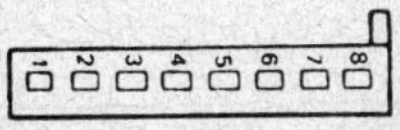

**Fig. 5 Air suspension system circuit identification**

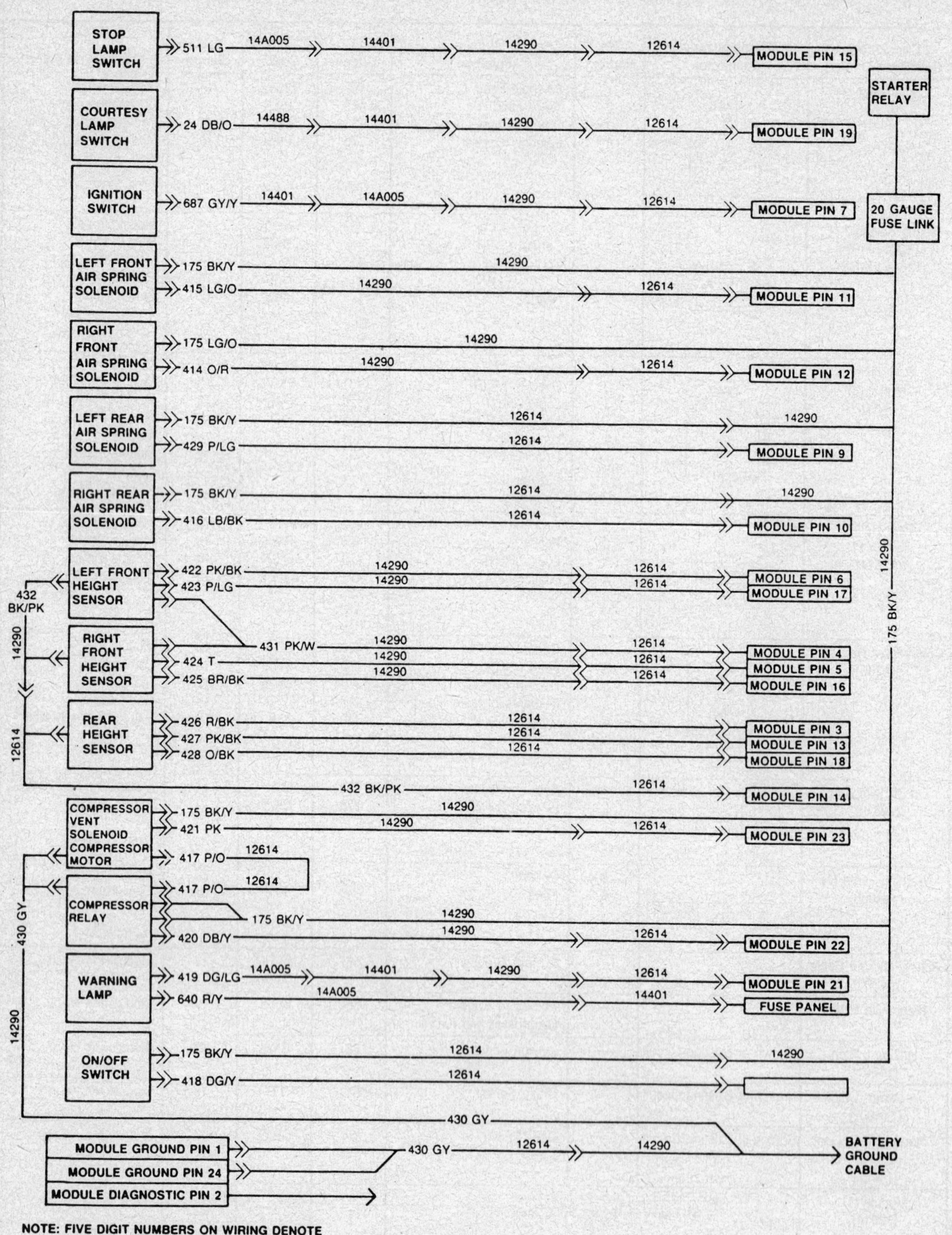


**Fig. 6 Air suspension wiring diagram**

AIR SUSPENSION "QUICK" WIRING AND CIRCUIT CHECKS

The following circuit measurements are made with the air suspension switch "On" and the module removed. The pins referred to below are on the harness connector for the module. Use an analog meter with 20,000 ohms per volt to perform the following tests.

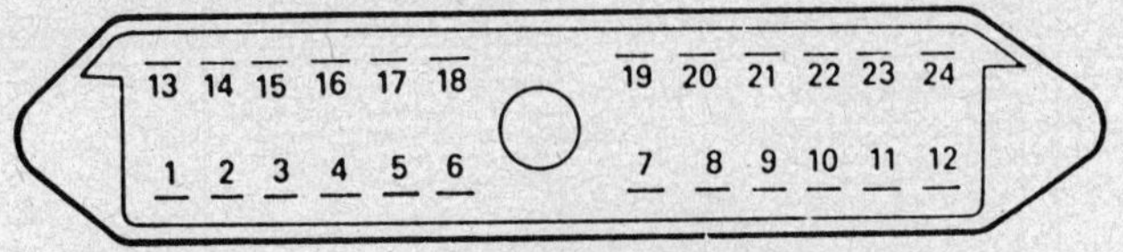


MODULE CONNECTOR

| Circuit | Pin Number | Meter Reading |
|---|---|---|
| Module Circuit | 20 (+) and 1 | Battery Voltage |
| | 20 (+) and 24 | Battery Voltage |
| | 7 (+) and 1 | Ignition Switch in RUN — Battery Voltage<br>Ignition Switch OFF — Zero Volts |
| | 15 (+) and 1 | Brake Switch On — Battery Voltage<br>Brake Switch Off — Zero Volts |
| | 19 (+) and 1 | Door Open — Battery Voltage<br>All Doors Closed — Zero Volts |
| Air Spring Solenoid Valve Circuit | 20 and 9 | (Left Rear) — Approx. 15-16 ohms (No. 20 is Positive Lead)* |
| | 20 and 10 | (Right Rear) — Approx. 15-16 ohms (No. 20 is Positive Lead)* |
| | 20 and 11 | (Left Front) — Approx. 15-16 ohms (No. 20 is Positive Lead)* |
| | 20 and 12 | (Right Front) — Approx. 15-16 ohms (No. 20 is Positive Lead)* |
| Compressor Relay Coil Circuit | 20 and 22 | Approx. 60-70 ohms* |
| Vent Solenoid Circuit | 20 and 23 | Approx. 30 ohms |

*To verify suppression diode across the coil of solenoid is good, ohmmeter will read as stated above with one meter polarity and less with the reverse polarity.

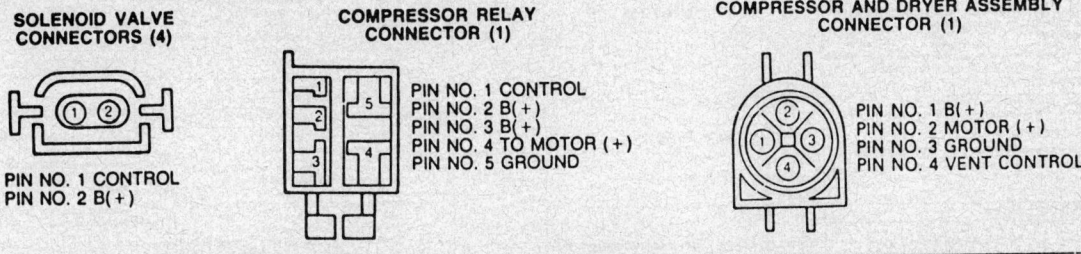

SOLENOID VALVE CONNECTORS (4)

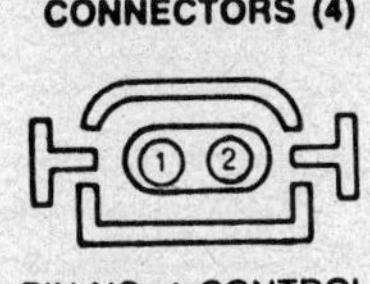


PIN NO. 1 CONTROL
PIN NO. 2 B(+)

COMPRESSOR RELAY CONNECTOR (1)

PIN NO. 1 CONTROL
PIN NO. 2 B(+)
PIN NO. 3 B(+)
PIN NO. 4 TO MOTOR (+)
PIN NO. 5 GROUND

COMPRESSOR AND DRYER ASSEMBLY CONNECTOR (1)

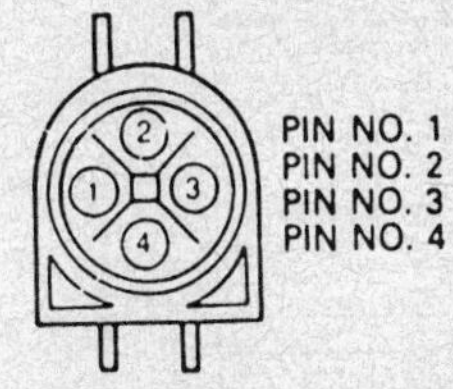


PIN NO. 1 B(+)
PIN NO. 2 MOTOR (+)
PIN NO. 3 GROUND
PIN NO. 4 VENT CONTROL

The following voltage measurements are made at the harness connector (for each sensor) with the sensor disconnected and the ignition switch in RUN and the air suspension switch on.

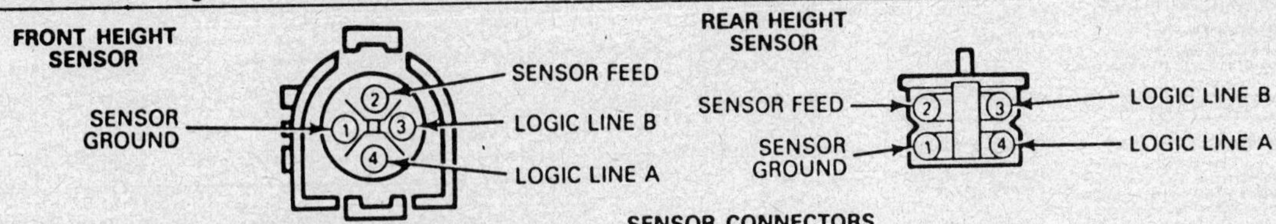


SENSOR CONNECTORS

| Circuit | Pin Number | Meter Reading |
|---|---|---|
| Height Sensor Circuits | 1 and 2 | 2-3 Volts |
| | 1 and 3 | Approx. 5 Volts |
| | 1 and 4 | Approx. 5 Volts |

**Fig. 7 Air suspension "Quick" wiring & circuit checks**

AIR SUSPENSION TROUBLESHOOTING HINTS

| Normal Air Suspension Check Light Operation is: When ignition switch is turned ON, light comes on for five seconds, turns OFF and stays off (IP light check). | | |
|---|---|---|
| **CONDITION** | **CAUSAL FACTOR** | **SUGGESTED ACTION** |
| Suspension check light REMAINS on during normal operation. | No power to module (O VDC between Pins 20 and 1). | • See if system switch in luggage compartment is on.<br>• Check switch, connector, and wiring in luggage compartment.<br>• Check system ground and feed wires near battery. |
| Suspension check light COMES BACK ON 10 SECONDS AFTER normal light check. | Module detects improper condition in sensor circuit. | • Run Steps 1, 2 and 3 of Air Suspension Diagnostic Procedure (Self-Test) to find which sensor circuit has fault — check for loose or damaged connectors and harness wiring.<br>• Swap sensor with another sensor. |
| Suspension check light COMES BACK ON AFTER a minimum of THREE MINUTES and stays on. | Module detects excessive correction time. | • Run Steps 1, 2 and 3 of Diagnostic Procedure and check for compressor and vent solenoid operation to locate fault — if any or all three fail, check for leaks.<br>• Run Steps 6, 7, 8 and 9 of Diagnostic Procedure to check for restricted air line or non-functioning air spring solenoid valve circuit. |
| Suspension check light COMES BACK ON while driving and may STAY ON or may TURN OFF | Module detects sensor system faulty signal or there is a interruption in the module ground, ignition sensing or module B+ voltage (24 pin connector, Pins 1 and 24, Pins 7, 20). | • Check for loose connections and damaged wiring or faulty wire crimps to terminals.<br>• Rapid blinking suspension check light on Steps 1, 2 or 3 of Diagnostic Procedure means fault in sensor system of wiring harness for that side of the vehicle. |
| Front down or all corners down and system cannot pump-up. | Compressor does not run. | • Run Step 4 of Diagnostic Procedure if no response, check wiring and connector at compressor.<br>• Check compressor relay, wiring and connector. |
| | Compressor does not run with voltage at compressor connector. | • Disconnect relay, wait five minutes to reset compressor internal circuit breaker. Install new compressor relay. Run Step 4 of Diagnostic Procedure to verify compressor operation. If compressor fails, check wiring harness and connectors. |
| Front down and cannot pump up (compressor operates). | Severe air leak at dryer air line fittings | • Check dryer fittings for severe leaks, replace dryer if needed; look for other air line leaks if fault remains. (Measured air pressure must be 90 psi or greater). |
| | Air line leak | • Check front air lines by disconnecting rear air lines at dryer, seal both fittings by inserting an 8-inch length of tubing and disconnect electrical connectors at the rear solenoid valves. Verify if the front will raise when air suspension is activated. If so, leak is in rear line. |

**Fig. 8 Troubleshooting air suspension (Part 1 of 2)**

AIR SUSPENSION TROUBLESHOOTING HINTS — Continued

| Normal Air Suspension Check Light Operation is: When ignition switch is turned ON, light comes on for five seconds, turns OFF and stays off (IP light check). | | |
|---|---|---|
| **CONDITION** | **CASUAL FACTOR** | **SUGGESTED ACTION** |
| Rear raises very high and then levels during otherwise normal operation.<br>One or more air springs leaks down overnight, but system will trim itself when system is operated (temperature sensitive). | Front solenoid valves fail to open to service a front corner leveling request. | • Run Steps 6 and 7 of Diagnostic Procedure to check solenoid valve operation. Inspect for loose or damaged connectors and wiring in solenoid circuits and replace solenoid valve if necessary. Check circuit resistance in both directions, as outlined in Air Suspension Quick Wiring and Circuit Checks. |
| | Compressor relay sticking or welded (can be intermittent). | • Replace relay after checking for damaged wiring. |
| | Leaking dual nose O-rings on one or more air spring solenoid valves (temperature sensitive). | • Replace leaking nose O-rings or solenoid valve. |
| **NOTE: In Diagnostic Procedure a failed test can be repeated by operating door switch. Operating door switch twice in 15 seconds advances tests to next Step.** | | |

**Fig. 8 Troubleshooting air suspension (Part 2 of 2)**

DIAGNOSTIC TEST

| | TEST STEP | RESULT ▶ | ACTION TO TAKE |
|---|---|---|---|
| A1 | CHECK VEHICLE LOAD | | |
| | • Check vehicle passenger compartment and luggage compartment for overloading, and unload as necessary.<br>• Allow the vehicle to sit with the ignition switch in the RUN position for five minutes minimum (door closed, brake off). | ▶ | GO to **A2**. |
| A2 | LEVEL VEHICLE, INITIALIZE SYSTEM | | |
| | • Turn the ignition switch to the OFF position.<br>• Turn the ignition switch to the RUN position and observe the air suspension warning lamp. | Warning lamp blinks or turns on ▶ | GO to **A3**. |
| | | Warning lamp does not blink or turn on ▶ | GO to **B1**. |
| A3 | ENTER DIAGNOSTICS | | |
| | • Before entering diagnostics, connect a battery charger to the vehicle and leave on, until completion of diagnostics.<br>• After diagnostics are entered do not open the door, depress the brake pedal, or start the engine unless you are specifically asked to do so.<br>• Turn the ignition switch to the OFF position.<br>• Ground the diagnostic pigtail.<br>• Turn the ignition switch to the RUN position. Do not start the engine, open the door, or depress the brake. | Warning lamp blinks continuously ▶ | Diagnostics entered. GO to **A4**. |
| | | The warning lamp blinks once ▶ | Diagnostics not entered. GO to **B10**. |
| | | Warning lamp stays on ▶ | Warning lamp not functioning properly. GO to **B13**. |
| A4 | RUN TEST NO. 1 — REAR SUSPENSION | | |
| | • To start Test No. 1 open and close the door.<br>• After Test No. 1 has been entered, a properly operating vehicle will raise the rear evenly for 15 to 30 seconds. When a vehicle high is received from the rear sensor, the rear will be lowered for a maximum of 30 seconds. When a rear low is received at the module, the rear of the vehicle will raise for a maximum of 30 seconds or until a rear trim signal is received at the module. Test 1 is now completed. The warning lamp will flash test No. 1 at a constant rate during the whole test. Maximum test time is 90 seconds.<br>• After 90 seconds observe the warning lamp.<br>• Record the test results for future reference. | Warning lamp flashes rapidly (approx. four blinks per second), or warning lamp on ▶ | Rear failed test. GO to **A5**. |
| | | Warning lamp flashes the test number ▶ | Rear passed test. GO to **A5**. |
| | | Warning lamp does not flash the test number, flash rapidly, or turn on ▶ | GO to **B22**. |

**Fig. 9 Air suspension diagnosis (Diagnostic test, part 1 of 5)**

DIAGNOSTIC TEST — Continued

| | TEST STEP | RESULT ▶ | ACTION TO TAKE |
|---|---|---|---|
| A5 | RUN TEST NO. 2 — RIGHT FRONT SUSPENSION | | |
| | • To start Test No. 2 open and close the door. If Test No. 1 failed, open and close the door twice.<br>• After Test No. 2 has been entered, a properly operating vehicle will raise the right front for 15 to 30 seconds. When a vehicle high is received from the right front sensor, the right front will be lowered for a maximum of 30 seconds. When a right front low is received at the module, the right front of the vehicle will raise for a maximum of 30 seconds or until a right front trim signal is received at the module. Test 2 is now completed. The warning lamp will flash test No. 2 at a constant rate during the whole test. Maximum test time is 90 seconds.<br>• After 90 seconds observe the warning lamp.<br>• Record the test results for future reference. | Warning lamp flashes rapidly (approx. four blinks per second), or warning lamp is on ▶ | Right front failed test. GO to **A6**. |
| | | Warning lamp flashes the test number ▶ | Right front passed test. GO to **A6**. |
| A6 | RUN TEST NO. 3 — LEFT FRONT SUSPENSION | | |
| | • To start Test No. 3 open and close the door. If Test No. 2 failed, open and close the door twice.<br>• After Test No. 3 has been entered a properly operating vehicle will raise the left front for 15 to 30 seconds. When a vehicle high is received from the left front sensor, the left front of the vehicle will raise for a maximum of 30 seconds or until a left front trim signal is received at the module. Test No. 3 is now completed. The warning lamp will flash Test No. 3 at a constant rate during the test. Maximum test time is 90 seconds.<br>• After 90 seconds observe the warning lamp.<br>• Record the test results for future reference. | Warning lamp flashes rapidly (approx. four blinks per second) or warning lamp is on steady ▶ | Left front failed test. GO to **A7**. |
| | | Warning lamp flashes the test number ▶ | Left front passed test. GO to **A7**. |
| A7 | RUN TEST NO. 4 — COMPRESSOR | | |
| | • To start Test No. 4 open and close the door. If Test No. 3 failed, open and close the door twice.<br>• During Test No. 4 the compressor is cycled on and off. The warning lamp will continuously blink Test No. 4. The compressor will only cycle 50 times.<br>• Lift the hood and listen for the compressor to cycle.<br>• Record the test results for future reference.<br>**NOTE: The rear of the vehicle may raise during this test.** | Compressor does not cycle, (runs continuously or does not run at all) ▶ | Compressor failed test. GO to **A8**. |
| | | Compressor cycles ▶ | Compressor passed test. GO to **A8**. |
| A8 | RUN TEST NO. 5 — VENT SOLENOID | | |
| | • To start Test No. 5, open and close the door to cycle the vent solenoid (part of compressor assembly).<br>• During Test No. 5, vent solenoid is cycled on and off, and the warning lamp will continuously blink Test No. 5.<br>• Lift the hood and listen for the vent solenoid to cycle.<br>• Record the test results for future reference. | Vent solenoid does not cycle ▶ | Vent solenoid failed test. GO to **A9**. |
| | | Vent solenoid cycles ▶ | Vent solenoid passed test. GO to **A9**. |

**Fig. 9 Air suspension diagnosis (Diagnostic test, part 2 of 5)**

DIAGNOSTIC TEST — Continued

| TEST STEP | RESULT ▶ | ACTION TO TAKE |
|---|---|---|
| **A9** RUN TEST NO. 6 — LEFT FRONT AIR SPRING SOLENOID | | |
| • Open and close the door to cycle the left front air spring solenoid.<br>• Listen for air escaping from the vent solenoid.<br>• Listen for the solenoid to cycle at the left front wheel well opening.<br>• Record the test results for future reference.<br>**NOTE: The left front corner of the vehicle will drop during this test.** | Left front air spring solenoid does not cycle, or air is not escaping from the vent solenoid ▶ | Left front air spring system failed test. GO to **A10**. |
| | Left front air spring solenoid cycles, and air is escaping from the vent solenoid ▶ | Left front air spring system passes test. GO to **A10**. |
| **A10** RUN TEST NO. 7 — RIGHT FRONT AIR SPRING SOLENOID | | |
| • Open and close the door to cycle the right front air spring solenoid.<br>• Listen for air escaping from the vent solenoid.<br>• Listen for the solenoid to cycle at the right front wheel well opening.<br>• Record the test results for future reference.<br>**NOTE: The right front corner of the vehicle will drop during this test.** | Right front air spring solenoid does not cycle, or air is not escaping from the vent solenoid ▶ | Right front air spring system failed test. GO to **A11**. |
| | Right front air spring solenoid cycles, and air is escaping from the vent solenoid ▶ | Right front air spring system passed test. GO to **A11**. |
| **A11** RUN TEST NO. 8 — RIGHT REAR AIR SPRING SOLENOID | | |
| • Open and close the door to cycle the right rear air spring solenoid.<br>• Listen for air escaping from the vent solenoid.<br>• Listen for the solenoid to cycle at the right rear wheel well opening.<br>• Record the test results for future reference.<br>**NOTE: The right rear corner of the vehicle will drop during this test.** | Right rear air spring solenoid does not cycle, or air is not escaping from the vent solenoid ▶ | Right rear air spring system failed test. GO to **A12**. |
| | Right rear air spring solenoid cycles, and air is escaping from the vent solenoid ▶ | Right rear air spring system passed test. GO to **A12**. |
| **A12** RUN TEST NO. 9 — LEFT REAR AIR SPRING SOLENOID | | |
| • Open and close the door to cycle the left rear air spring solenoid.<br>• Listen for air escaping from the vent solenoid.<br>• Listen for the solenoid to cycle at the left rear wheel well opening.<br>• Record the test results for future reference.<br>**NOTE: The left rear corner of the vehicle will drop during this test.** | Left rear air spring solenoid does not cycle, or air is not escaping from the vent solenoid ▶ | Left rear air spring system failed test. GO to **A13**. |
| | Left rear air spring solenoid cycles, and air is escaping from the vent solenoid ▶ | Left rear air spring system passed test. GO to **A13**. |

**Fig. 9 Air suspension diagnosis (Diagnostic test, part 3 of 5)**

DIAGNOSTIC TEST — Continued

| TEST STEP | RESULT ▶ | ACTION TO TAKE |
|---|---|---|
| **A13** RUN TEST NO. 10 — BRAKE CIRCUIT | | |
| • Open the door and sit in the driver's seat.<br>• Depress the brake pedal and observe the warning lamp. | Warning lamp continues to blink ▶ | Brake circuit fails test. GO to **B30**. |
| | Warning lamp stops blinking ▶ | Brake circuit passes test. Diagnostic sequence completed. Unground the diagnostic pigtail. GO to **A14**. |
| **A14** ANY FAILURES? | | |
| • Have any failures occured during diagnostics? | Yes ▶ | GO to **A15**. |
| | No ▶ | Air spring suspension system OK. No further diagnostics required. |
| • To perform pinpoint tests, the following special equipment will be required:<br>1) A test lamp using a No. 194 bulb with test pointed probes.<br>2) A volt/ohm meter (Rotunda DVOM 007-00001 or equivalent).<br>3) A pressure gauge capable of indicating 1034 kPa (150 psi). | | |
| **A15** | | |
| • Did the warning lamp flash rapidly for any of the first three tests? | Yes ▶ | The module read the sensor incorrectly. GO to **C1**. |
| | No ▶ | Sensors OK. GO to **A16**. |
| **A16** | | |
| • Did the warning lamp stay on after the completion of Test No. 1? | Yes ▶ | CHECK rear of vehicle. GO to **D1**. |
| | No ▶ | GO to **A17**. |
| **A17** | | |
| • Did the warning lamp stay on after the completion of Test No. 2? | Yes ▶ | CHECK right front. GO to **E1**. |
| | No ▶ | Right front OK. GO to **A18**. |
| **A18** | | |
| • Did the warning lamp stay on after the completion of Test No. 3? | Yes ▶ | CHECK left front. GO to **F1**. |
| | No ▶ | Left front OK. GO to **A19**. |

**Fig. 9 Air suspension diagnosis (Diagnostic test, part 4 of 5)**

DIAGNOSTIC TEST — Continued

| TEST STEP | RESULT ▶ | ACTION TO TAKE |
|---|---|---|
| **A19** | | |
| • Did the left front solenoid cycle during Test No. 6? | Yes ▶ | Left front solenoid OK. GO to **A20**. |
| | No ▶ | GO to **F1**. |
| **A20** | | |
| • Did the right front solenoid cycle during Test No. 7? | Yes ▶ | Right front solenoid OK. GO to **A21**. |
| | No ▶ | GO to **E1**. |
| **A21** | | |
| • Did the right rear solenoid cycle and air escape from the vent solenoid during Test No. 8? | Yes ▶ | Right rear solenoid OK. GO to **A20**. |
| | No ▶ | Check right rear solenoid system. GO to **D1**. |
| **A22** | | |
| • Did the left rear solenoid cycle and air escape from the vent solenoid during Test No. 9? | Yes ▶ | Left rear solenoid OK. GO to **A1**. |
| | No ▶ | Check left rear solenoid system. GO to **D1**. |

**Fig. 9 Air suspension diagnosis (Diagnostic test, part 5 of 5)**

CANNOT ENTER, SEQUENCE OR EXIT DIAGNOSTIC TEST

| TEST STEP | RESULT ▶ | ACTION TO TAKE |
|---|---|---|
| Will not initialize or enter diagnostics. | | |
| **B1** CHECK BULB | | |
| • Is air suspension warning lamp bulb burned out? | Yes ▶ | REPLACE bulb. REPEAT Diagnostic Test. |
| | No ▶ | GO to **B2**. |
| **B2** MAKE A TEST LAMP | | |
| • Attach two test leads, with pointed probes, to a No. 194 lamp for use as a test lamp. Any other lamp will cause damage to the air suspension system. | ▶ | GO to **B3**. |
| **B3** CHECK IGNITION CIRCUIT | | |
| • Turn the air suspension on/off switch to the OFF position.<br>• Turn ignition switch to the OFF position. | Warning lamp on ▶ | SERVICE short to battery on ignition Circuit No. 687 or the ignition switch. Turn air suspension On/Off switch to the ON position. REPEAT Diagnostic Test. |
| | Warning lamp off ▶ | GO to **B4**. |
| **B4** CHECK IGNITION CIRCUIT | | |
| • Attach one lead of the test lamp to ignition Circuit No. 640 at the warning lamp. Attach the other lead to ground.<br>• Turn the ignition switch to RUN and observe the test lamp. | Test lamp on ▶ | GO to **B6**. |
| | Test lamp off ▶ | GO to **B5**. |
| **B5** CHECK FUSE | | |
| • Check fuse in ignition Circuit No. 640. | Fuse OK ▶ | SERVICE open in ignition Circuit No. 640. REPEAT Diagnostic Test. |
| | Fuse blown ▶ | REPLACE fuse. SERVICE short in ignition Circuit No. 640, if second fuse fails. REPEAT Diagnostic Test. |
| **B6** CHECK IGNITION CIRCUIT | | |
| • Attach one test lamp lead to ignition Circuit No. 687 Pin 7 of the module connector.<br>• Attach the other test lamp lead to a good ground.<br>• Turn the ignition switch to RUN and observe the test lamp. | Test lamp on ▶ | Ignition circuit OK. GO to **B7**. |
| | Test lamp off ▶ | SERVICE open or short in ignition Circuit No. 687. Turn air suspension On/Off switch to ON position. REPEAT Diagnostic Test. |

**Fig. 10 Air suspension diagnosis (Cannot enter or exit diagnostic test, part 1 of 6)**

CANNOT ENTER, SEQUENCE, OR EXIT DIAGNOSTIC TEST —Continued

| TEST STEP | RESULT ▶ | ACTION TO TAKE |
|---|---|---|
| **B7** CHECK MODULE GROUND CIRCUIT | | |
| • Attach one test lamp lead to ignition Circuit No. 687 Pin 7 of the module connector.<br>• Turn the ignition switch to RUN and observe the test lamp.<br>• Attach the other test lamp to ground Circuit No. 430 Pin 1 of the module connector.<br>• Move the test lamp lead attached to Pin 1 of the module connector to Pin 24. | Test lamp on ▶<br><br>Test lamp off ▶ | Ground circuit OK. GO to B8.<br><br>SERVICE open in Circuit No. 430. REPEAT Diagnostic Test. |
| **B8** CHECK WARNING LAMP CIRCUIT | | |
| • Set up a volt meter to read 12 volts DC.<br>• Attach the negative (black) test lead to a good ground.<br>• Attach the positive (red) test lead to the warning lamp Circuit No. 419 Pin 21 of the module connector.<br>• Turn the ignition switch to the RUN position. | Voltage greater than 5V ▶<br><br>Voltage less than or equal to 5V ▶ | Warning lamp circuit OK. GO to B9.<br><br>SERVICE open in the warning lamp Circuit No. 419 from the module connector to the warning lamp connector. Turn air suspension on/off switch to the ON position. REPEAT Diagnostic Test. |
| **B9** CHECK BATTERY VOLTAGE | | |
| • Attach the negative (black) test lead to ground Circuit No. 430 Pin 24 of the module connector.<br>• Attach the positive (red) test lead to battery Circuit No. 418 Pin 20 at the module connector.<br>• Measure DC Voltage. | Less than 11V ▶<br><br>Greater than 11V ▶ | SERVICE low voltage condition due to a damaged connection, low battery, etc. REPEAT Diagnostic Test.<br><br>REPLACE air suspension module. REPEAT Quick Test. |
| **B10** | | |
| • Repeat Steps A2 and A3 and ensure the diagnostic pigtail is grounded to a good ground.<br>**NOTE: Steps A2 and A3 must be performed exactly as indicated to enter diagnostics.** | Warning lamp blinks once ▶<br><br>Warning lamp blinks ▶ | GO to B11.<br><br>REPEAT Diagnostic Test |
| **B11** MAKE A TEST LAMP | | |
| • Attach two test leads, with probes, to a No. 194 lamp for use as a test lamp. Any other lamp will cause damage to the air suspension lamp. | ▶ | GO to B12. |

**Fig. 10 Air suspension diagnosis (Cannot enter or exit diagnostic test, part 2 of 6)**

CANNOT ENTER, SEQUENCE, OR EXIT DIAGNOSTIC TEST — Continued

| TEST STEP | RESULT ▶ | ACTION TO TAKE |
|---|---|---|
| **B12** CHECK PIGTAIL | | |
| Attach one test lamp lead to diagnostic Circuit No. 606 Pin 2 at the module connector.<br>• Attach the other test lamp lead to ignition Circuit No. 687 Pin 7 at the module connector.<br>• Turn ignition switch to RUN.<br>• Ground and then unground the pigtail. | Test lamp on then off ▶<br><br>Test lamp on or off ▶ | Pigtail OK, GO to B9.<br><br>SERVICE open or short to ground in the diagnostic pigtail Circuit No. 606. REPEAT Diagnostic Test. |
| **B13** CHECK FOR SYSTEM IN DIAGNOSTIC | | |
| • Open and close the door and observe the compressor. | Compressor starts running ▶<br><br>Compressor is already running or does not start running ▶ | In diagnostics. GO to B20.<br><br>Not in diagnostics. GO to B14. |
| **B14** MAKE A TEST LAMP | | |
| • Attach two test leads, with pointed probes, to a No. 194 lamp for use as a test lamp. Any other lamp will cause damage to the air suspension system. | ▶ | GO to B15. |
| **B15** CHECK BATTERY CIRCUIT | | |
| • Attach one test lamp lead to battery Circuit No. 418 Pin 20 at the module connector.<br>• Attach the other test lamp lead to a good ground. | Test lamp on ▶<br><br>Test lamp off ▶ | GO to B21.<br><br>GO to B16. |
| **B16** CHECK FUSE LINK | | |
| • Check the fuse link in battery Circuit No. 175. | Fuse link OK ▶<br><br>Fuse link blown ▶ | GO to B17.<br><br>REPLACE fuse link. REPEAT Diagnostic Test. |
| **B17** | | |
| • Verify that the air suspension on/off switch is in the ON position. | Switch in ON position ▶<br><br>Switch in OFF position ▶ | GO to B18.<br><br>PLACE switch in ON position. REPEAT Diagnostic Test. |
| **B18** CHECK BATTERY CIRCUIT | | |
| • Attach one test lamp lead to battery Circuit No. 175 at the air suspension on/off switch Pin 2 (battery side). | Test lamp on ▶<br><br>Test lamp off ▶ | GO to B19.<br><br>SERVICE the open or short in battery Circuit No. 175 from the air suspension on/off switch Pin 2 to the battery. REPEAT Diagnostic Test. |

**Fig. 10 Air suspension diagnosis (Cannot enter or exit diagnostic test, part 3 of 6)**

CANNOT ENTER, SEQUENCE, OR EXIT DIAGNOSTIC TEST — Continued

| TEST STEP | RESULT ▶ | ACTION TO TAKE |
|---|---|---|
| **B19** CHECK ON/OFF SWITCH | | |
| • Attach one test lamp lead to battery Circuit No. 418 at the air suspension on/off switch Pin 1 (module side).<br>• Attach the other test lead to a good ground. | Test lamp on ▶<br><br>Test lamp off ▶ | SERVICE the open or short in battery Circuit No. 418 from the air suspension on/off switch Pin 1 to the battery. REPEAT Diagnostic Test.<br><br>REPLACE the air suspension on/off switch. REPEAT Diagnostic Test. |
| **B20** CHECK WARNING LAMP CIRCUIT | | |
| • Disconnect the module connector and observe the warning lamp. | Warning lamp on ▶<br><br>Warning lamp off ▶ | SERVICE short to ground in the warning lamp Circuit No. 419 from the module connector to the warning lamp.<br>RECONNECT the module connector. REPEAT Diagnostic Test.<br><br>Warning lamp circuit OK. GO to B21. |
| **B21** CHECK BATTERY VOLTAGE | | |
| • Attach the negative (black) test lead to ground Circuit No. 430 Pin 24 of the module connector.<br>• Attach the positive (red) test lead to battery Circuit No. 418 Pin 20 at the module connector.<br>• Measure DC voltage. | Less than 11 V ▶<br><br>Greater than 11 V ▶ | SERVICE low voltage condition due to a damaged connection, low battery, etc. RECONNECT connectors as required. REPEAT Diagnostic Test.<br><br>REPLACE the air suspension module. RECONNECT connectors as required. REPEAT Diagnostic Test. |
| **B22** MAKE A TEST LAMP | | |
| • Attach two test leads with pointed probes to a No. 194 lamp for use as a test lamp. Any other lamp will damage the air suspension system. | ▶ | GO to B23. |

**Fig. 10 Air suspension diagnosis (Cannot enter or exit diagnostic test, part 4 of 6)**

CANNOT ENTER, SEQUENCE, OR EXIT DIAGNOSTIC TEST — Continued

| TEST STEP | RESULT ▶ | ACTION TO TAKE |
|---|---|---|
| **B23** CHECK DOOR CIRCUIT | | |
| • Attach one test lamp lead to door Circuit No. 24 Pin 19 at the module connector.<br>• Attach the other test lamp lead to a good ground.<br>• Close the door. | Test lamp on ▶<br><br>Test lamp off ▶ | SERVICE short to battery or ignition in door Circuit No. 24 or damaged door switch. REPEAT Diagnostic Test.<br><br>GO to B24. |
| **B24** CHECK DOOR CIRCUIT | | |
| • Open the door. | Test lamp on ▶<br><br>Test lamp off ▶ | Door circuit OK. GO to B25.<br><br>SERVICE open or short in door Circuit No. 24 or malfunctioning door switch. REPEAT Diagnostic Test. |
| **B25** CHECK BRAKE CIRCUIT | | |
| • Depress and release the brake pedal. Observe the rear brake lamps. | Brake lamps operate properly ▶<br><br>Brake lamps do not operate properly ▶ | Brake circuit OK. GO to B26.<br><br>SERVICE as necessary. REPEAT Diagnostic Test |
| **B26** CHECK COMPRESSOR CIRCUIT | | |
| • Disconnect the compressor relay electrical connector.<br>• Perform Steps A2-A4.<br>• Observe the warning lamp. | Warning lamp flashes rapidly, flashes the test number or stays on ▶<br><br>Warning lamp does something else ▶ | GO to B27.<br><br>Compressor circuit OK. GO to B21. |
| **B27** CHECK COMPRESSOR CIRCUIT | | |
| • Do not reconnect the compressor relay connector.<br>• Attach the negative (black) lead of volt-ohm meter to ground.<br>• Attach the positive (red) lead to compressor Circuit No. 417 Pin 2 on the harness side of the compressor connector.<br>• Measure resistance. | Greater than 1000 Ohms ▶<br><br>Less than 1000 Ohms ▶ | GO to B28.<br><br>SERVICE short to ground on compressor Circuit No. 417. REPEAT Diagnostic Test. |

**Fig. 10 Air suspension diagnosis (Cannot enter or exit diagnostic test, part 5 of 6)**

CANNOT ENTER, SEQUENCE, OR EXIT DIAGNOSTIC TEST — Continued

| TEST STEP | RESULT | ACTION TO TAKE |
|---|---|---|
| **B28** CHECK COMPRESSOR CURRENT | | |
| • Disconnect compressor connector. • Connect a jumper (14 ga. wire minimum) between compressor connector (compressor side) Pin 3 and a good ground. • Attach the negative (black) lead of an ammeter to Pin 3 at the compressor connector (compressor side). The ammeter must be capable of measuring 40 amps minimum. • Attach the positive (red) lead to battery positive (+) terminal. • Measure current after the compressor has run for 10 seconds. Do not allow the compressor to run more than 60 seconds. | Greater than 35 amps | REPLACE and RECONNECT a new compressor assembly. REPEAT Diagnostic Test. |
| | Less than 35 amps | GO to B29. |
| **B29** CHECK COMPRESSOR VOLTAGE | | |
| • Perform Step B28 except measure the battery voltage while the compressor is running. | Greater than 11 volts | REPLACE the air suspension module. RECONNECT connectors as required. REPEAT Diagnostic Test. |
| | Less than 11 volts | CHARGE battery. REPEAT Diagnostic Test. |
| **B30** MAKE A TEST LAMP | | |
| • Attach two test leads, with pointed probes, to a No. 194 lamp for use as a test lamp. Any other lamp will damage the air suspension system. | | GO to B31. |
| **B31** CHECK BRAKE CIRCUIT | | |
| • Depress and release the brake pedal and verify the rear brake lamps operate properly. | Brake lamps operate properly | GO to B32. |
| | Brake lamps do not operate properly | SERVICE as necessary. REPEAT Diagnostic Test. |
| **B32** CHECK BRAKE CIRCUIT | | |
| • Attach one lead of the test lamp to brake Circuit No. 511 Pin 15 at the module connector. • Attach the other test lead to a good ground. • Depress the brake pedal and observe the test lamp. | Test lamp on | REPLACE the air suspension module. RECONNECT connectors as required. REPEAT Diagnostic Test. |
| | Test lamp off | SERVICE open or short in the brake Circuit No. 511. REPEAT Diagnostic Test. |

**Fig. 10 Air suspension diagnosis (Cannot enter or exit diagnostic test, part 6 of 6)**

PROBLEM SENSING VEHICLE ATTITUDE

| TEST STEP | RESULT | ACTION TO TAKE |
|---|---|---|
| **C1** | | |
| • Did the warning lamp flash for all three tests? (Test No. 1, 2 and 3). | Yes | GO to C2. |
| | No | GO to C11. |
| **C2** CHECK SENSOR GROUND CIRCUIT | | |
| • Attach one lead of the test lamp to sensor ground Circuit No. 432 Pin 1 at the left front sensor connector. • Attach the other test lamp lead to the battery positive (+) terminal. • Observe the test lamp. | Test lamp on | Sensor ground circuit OK. GO to C5. |
| | Test lamp off | GO to C3. |
| **C3** CHECK SENSOR GROUND CIRCUIT | | |
| • Attach one lead of the test lamp to sensor ground Circuit No. 432 Pin 14 at the module connector (do not disconnect the module connector). • Attach the other test lamp lead to battery Pin No. 20 at the module connector (do not disconnect the module connector). | Test lamp on | SERVICE open in sensor ground Circuit No. 432. REPEAT Quick Test. |
| | Test lamp off | GO to C4. |
| **C4** | | |
| Disconnect the module connector and inspect sensor ground Pin 14, module ground Pins 1 and 24 for corrosion and or damage. | Corrosion or damage found | SERVICE as necessary. REPEAT Quick Test. |
| | No corrosion or damage found | REPLACE the air suspension module. REPEAT Quick Test. |
| **C5** | | |
| • Set up a voltmeter to read 3 volts DC. • Attach the negative (black) test lead to sensor ground Circuit No. 432 Pin 14 of the module connector. • Attach the positive (red) test lead to sensor power Circuit No. 431 Pin 4 of the module connector. • Turn ignition to RUN and observe the voltmeter. | Voltage less than 1V and steady | GO to C6. |
| | Voltage erratic or greater than 1V but less than 5V | SERVICE open in sensor power Circuit No. 426 or 431 between the module and the sensors. REPEAT Quick Test. |
| | Voltage greater than 5V and steady | REPLACE air suspension module. . REPEAT Quick Test. |
| **C6** CHECK LEFT FRONT SENSOR | | |
| • Electrically disconnect the left front sensor and observe the voltmeter. | Voltage less than 1V and steady | Left front sensor OK. GO to C7. |
| | Voltage erratic or greater than 1V | REPLACE and connect the left front sensor. REPEAT Quick Test. |

**Fig. 11 Air suspension diagnosis (Problem sensing vehicle attitude, part 1 of 9)**

PROBLEM SENSING VEHICLE ATTITUDE — Continued

| TEST STEP | RESULT | ACTION TO TAKE |
|---|---|---|
| **C7** CHECK RIGHT FRONT SENSOR | | |
| • Do not reconnect the left front sensor. • Electrically disconnect the right front sensor and observe the voltmeter. | Voltage less than 1V and steady | Right front sensor OK. GO to C8. |
| | Voltage erratic or greater than 1V | REPLACE and connect the right front sensor. RECONNECT the left front sensor. REPEAT Quick Test. |
| **C8** CHECK THE REAR SENSOR | | |
| • Do not reconnect the right front sensor. • Electrically disconnect the rear sensor and observe the voltmeter. | Voltage less than 1V and steady | Rear sensor OK. GO to C9. |
| | Voltage erratic or greater than 1V | REPLACE and connect the rear sensor. RECONNECT the left front and right front sensors. REPEAT Quick Test. |
| **C9** CHECK SENSOR POWER CIRCUIT | | |
| • Do not reconnect the rear sensor. • Disconnect the air suspension module. • Attach the negative (black) test lead of a volt-ohm meter to module ground Circuit No. 430 Pin 1 of the module connector. • Attach the positive (red) test lead to sensor power Circuit No. 426 Pin 3 at the module connector. • Measure resistance. | Greater than 1000 Ohms | GO to C10. |
| | Less than 1000 Ohms | SERVICE short to ground in sensor power Circuit No. 426. RECONNECT right front sensors left front sensor, rear sensor and control module. REPEAT Quick Test. |
| **C10** CHECK SENSOR POWER CIRCUIT | | |
| • Move the positive (red) test lead to sensor power Circuit No. 431 Pin 4 at module connector. • Measure resistance. | Greater than 1000 Ohms | REPLACE the air suspension control module. REPEAT Quick Test. |
| | Less than 1000 Ohms | SERVICE short to ground in sensor power Circuit No. 431. RECONNECT right front sensor, left front sensor, rear sensor and control module. REPEAT Quick Test. |
| **C11** | | |
| • Did the warning lamp flash rapidly for Test No. 1? | Yes | GO to C12. |
| | No | GO to C23. |

**Fig. 11 Air suspension diagnosis (Problem sensing vehicle attitude, part 2 of 9)**

PROBLEM SENSING VEHICLE ATTITUDE — Continued

| TEST STEP | RESULT | ACTION TO TAKE |
|---|---|---|
| **C12** CHECK SENSOR GROUND CIRCUIT | | |
| • Turn the air suspension on/off switch to the OFF position. • Attach the positive (red) test lead of a volt-ohm meter to sensor ground Circuit No. 432 Pin 1 at the rear sensor. • Attach the negative (black) test lead to a good ground. • Measure resistance. | Greater than 5 Ohms | SERVICE the open in sensor ground Circuit No. 432 between the module connector and the rear sensor. REPEAT Quick Test. |
| | Less than 5 Ohms | GO to C13. |
| **C13** CHECK SENSOR POWER CIRCUIT | | |
| • Place the air suspension ON/OFF switch in the ON position. • Attach the negative (black) test lead of a volt-ohm meter to sensor ground Pin 1 Circuit No. 432 at the rear sensor connector. • Attach the positive (red) test lead to sensor power Pin 2 Circuit No. 426 at the rear sensor connector. • Turn ignition to the RUN position. • Measure resistance. | Voltage less than 1V and steady | SERVICE open in sensor power Circuit No. 426 from the rear sensor to the module. REPEAT Quick Test. |
| | Voltage erratic or greater than 1V | Sensor power circuit OK. GO to C14. |
| **C14** CHECK REAR SENSOR A CIRCUIT | | |
| • Move the positive (red) test lead to rear sensor A Circuit No. 427 Pin 4 at the rear sensor connector. • Measure DC voltage. | Greater than 1.5V or erratic | Rear sensor A Circuit OK. GO to C18. |
| | Less than 1.5V | GO to C15. |
| **C15** CHECK REAR SENSOR | | |
| • Disconnect the rear sensor connector. • Measure DC voltage. | Greater than 1.5V | REPLACE the rear sensor. REPEAT Quick Test. |
| | Less than 1.5V | GO to C16. |
| **C16** CHECK REAR SENSOR A CIRCUIT | | |
| • Do not reconnect the rear sensor. • Attach the negative (black) test lead of a volt-ohm meter to sensor ground Pin 14 Circuit No. 432 at the module connector. • Attach the positive (red) test lead to rear sensor A Circuit No. 427 Pin 13 at the module connector. • Measure DC voltage. | Greater than 1.5V | SERVICE open in rear sensor A Circuit No. 427 between the module and the sensor. RECONNECT the rear sensor connector. REPEAT Quick Test. |
| | Less than 1.5V | GO to C17. |

**Fig. 11 Air suspension diagnosis (Problem sensing vehicle attitude, part 3 of 9)**

PROBLEM SENSING VEHICLE ATTITUDE — Continued

| TEST STEP | RESULT ▶ | ACTION TO TAKE |
|---|---|---|
| **C17 CHECK REAR SENSOR A CIRCUIT** | | |
| • Disconnect the module. • Attach the negative (black) test lead of a volt-ohm meter to module ground Pin 1 Circuit No. 430 at the module connector. • Attach the positive (red) test lead to rear sensor A Circuit No. 427 Pin 13 at the module connector. • Measure resistance. | Greater than 1000 Ohms ▶ | REPLACE the air suspension module. RECONNECT the rear sensor. REPEAT Quick Test. |
| | Less than 1000 Ohms ▶ | SERVICE short to ground on rear sensor A Circuit No. 427 between the module and the rear sensor. RECONNECT the rear sensor. REPEAT Quick Test. |
| **C18 CHECK REAR B SENSOR CIRCUIT** | | |
| • Move the positive (red) test lead to rear sensor B Circuit No. 428 Pin 3 at the rear sensor connector. • Measure the DC voltage. | Greater than 1.5V or erratic ▶ | Rear Sensor B Circuit OK. GO to C19. |
| | Less than 1.5V ▶ | REPEAT Quick Test. GO to C20. |
| **C19 CHECK FOR MODULE DAMAGE** | | |
| • Rerun diagnostics test No. 1 by performing Steps A2-A4. | Warning lamp flashing rapidly ▶ | REPLACE the air suspension control module. REPEAT Quick Test. |
| | Warning lamp not flashing rapidly ▶ | REPEAT Quick Test. |
| **C20 CHECK REAR SENSOR** | | |
| • Disconnect the rear sensor connector. • Measure the DC voltage. | Greater than 1.5V ▶ | INSTALL a new rear sensor. REPEAT Quick Test. |
| | Less than 1.5V ▶ | Rear sensor OK. GO to C21. |
| **C21 CHECK REAR SENSOR B CIRCUIT** | | |
| • Do not reconnect the rear sensor. • Attach the negative (black) test lead of a volt-ohm meter to sensor ground Pin 14 Circuit No. 432 at the module connector. • Attach the positive (red) test lead to rear sensor B Circuit No. 428 Pin 18 at the module connector. • Measure DC voltage. | Greater than 1.5V ▶ | SERVICE open in rear sensor B Circuit No. 428 between the module and the sensor. RECONNECT the rear sensor connector. REPEAT Quick Test. |
| | Less than 1.5V ▶ | GO to C22. |

**Fig. 11 Air suspension diagnosis (Problem sensing vehicle attitude, part 4 of 9)**

PROBLEM SENSING VEHICLE ATTITUDE — Continued

| TEST STEP | RESULT ▶ | ACTION TO TAKE |
|---|---|---|
| **C22 CHECK REAR SENSOR B CIRCUIT** | | |
| • Disconnect the module. • Attach the negative (black) test lead of a volt-ohm meter to module ground Pin 1 Circuit No. 430 at the module connector. • Attach the positive (red) test lead to rear sensor B Circuit No. 428 Pin 18 at the module connector. • Measure resistance. | Greater than 1000 Ohms ▶ | REPLACE the air suspension module. RECONNECT the rear sensor. REPEAT Quick Test. |
| | Less than 1000 ohms ▶ | SERVICE short to ground on rear sensor B Circuit No. 428 between the module and the rear sensor. REPEAT Quick Test. |
| **C23** | | |
| • Did the warning lamp flash rapidly for Test No. 2? | Yes ▶ | GO to C24. |
| | No ▶ | GO to C35. |
| **C24 CHECK SENSOR GROUND CIRCUIT** | | |
| • Attach one test lamp lead to sensor ground Circuit No. 432 Pin 1 at the right front sensor. • Attach the other test lamp lead to the battery positive (+) terminal. • Observe the test lamp. | Test lamp on ▶ | Sensor ground circuit OK. GO to C25. |
| | Test lamp off ▶ | SERVICE the open in sensor ground Circuit No. 432 between the module connector and the right front sensor. REPEAT Quick Test. |
| **C25 CHECK SENSOR POWER CIRCUIT** | | |
| • Attach the negative (black) test lead of a volt-ohm meter to sensor ground Pin 1 Circuit No. 432 at the right front sensor connector. • Attach the positive (red) test lead to sensor power Pin 2 Circuit No. 431 at the right front sensor connector. • Turn ignition to the RUN position. • Measure DC voltage. | Voltage less than 1V and steady ▶ | SERVICE open in sensor power Circuit No. 431 from the right front sensor to the module. REPEAT Quick Test. |
| | Voltage erratic or greater than 1V ▶ | Sensor power OK. GO to C26. |
| **C26 CHECK RIGHT FRONT SENSOR A CIRCUIT** | | |
| • Move the positive (red) test lead to right front sensor A Circuit No. 424 Pin 4 at the right front sensor connector. • Measure DC voltage. | Greater than 1.5V or erratic ▶ | Right front sensor A Circuit OK. GO to C30. |
| | Less than 1.5V ▶ | OK. GO to C27. |
| **C27 CHECK RIGHT FRONT SENSOR** | | |
| • Disconnect the right front sensor connector. • Measure DC voltage. | Greater than 1.5V ▶ | REPLACE the right front sensor. REPEAT Quick Test. |
| | Less than 1.5V ▶ | Right front sensor OK. GO to C28. |

**Fig. 11 Air suspension diagnosis (Problem sensing vehicle attitude, part 5 of 9)**

PROBLEM SENSING VEHICLE ATTITUDE — Continued

| TEST STEP | RESULT ▶ | ACTION TO TAKE |
|---|---|---|
| **C28 CHECK RIGHT FRONT SENSOR A CIRCUIT** | | |
| • Do not reconnect the right front sensor. • Attach the negative (black) test lead of a volt-ohm meter to sensor ground Pin 14 Circuit No. 432 at the module connector. • Attach the positive (red) test lead to right front Sensor A Circuit No. 424 Pin 5 at the module connector. • Measure DC voltage. | Greater than 1.5V ▶ | SERVICE open in right front Sensor A Circuit No. 424 between the module and the sensor. RECONNECT the right front sensor connector. REPEAT Quick Test. |
| | Less than 1.5V ▶ | GO to C29. |
| **C29 CHECK RIGHT FRONT SENSOR A CIRCUIT** | | |
| • Disconnect the module. • Attach the negative (black) test lead of a volt-ohm meter to module ground Pin 1 Circuit No. 430 at the module connector. • Attach the positive (red) test lead to right front Sensor A Circuit No. 424 Pin 5 at the module connector. • Measure resistance. | Greater than 1000 Ohms ▶ | REPLACE the air suspension module. RECONNECT the right front sensor. REPEAT Quick Test. |
| | Less than 1000 Ohms ▶ | SERVICE short to ground on right front Sensor A Circuit No. 424 between the module and the right front sensor. RECONNECT the right front sensor. REPEAT Quick Test. |
| **C30 CHECK RIGHT FRONT SENSOR B CIRCUIT** | | |
| • Move the positive (red) test lead to right front Sensor B Circuit No. 425 Pin 3 at the right front sensor connector. • Measure the DC voltage. | Greater than 1.5V or erratic ▶ | REPLACE right front sensor. GO to C31. |
| | Less than 1.5V ▶ | GO to C32. |
| **C31 CHECK MODULE FOR DAMAGE** | | |
| • RERUN diagnostics test No. 2 by performing Steps A2-A5. | Warning light flashing rapidly during test No. 2 ▶ | REPLACE the air suspension control module. REPEAT Quick Test. |
| | Warning light not flashing rapidly during test No. 2 ▶ | REPEAT Quick Test. |
| **C32 CHECK RIGHT FRONT SENSOR** | | |
| • Disconnect the right front sensor connector. • Measure DC voltage. | Greater than 1.5V or erratic ▶ | INSTALL a new right front sensor. REPEAT Quick Test. |
| | Less than 1.5V ▶ | GO to C33. |

**Fig. 11 Air suspension diagnosis (Problem sensing vehicle attitude, part 6 of 9)**

PROBLEM SENSING VEHICLE ATTITUDE — Continued

| TEST STEP | RESULT ▶ | ACTION TO TAKE |
|---|---|---|
| **C33 CHECK RIGHT FRONT SENSOR B CIRCUIT** | | |
| • Do not reconnect the right front sensor. • Attach the negative (black) test lead of a volt-ohm meter to sensor ground Pin 14 Circuit No. 432 at the module connector. • Attach the positive (red) test lead to right front Sensor B Circuit No. 425 Pin 16. • Measure DC voltage. | Greater than 1.5V ▶ | SERVICE open in right front Sensor B Circuit No. 425 between the module and the sensor. RECONNECT the right front sensor connector. REPEAT Quick Test. |
| | Less than 1.5V ▶ | GO to C34. |
| **C34 CHECK RIGHT FRONT SENSOR B CIRCUIT** | | |
| • Disconnect the module. • Attach the negative (black) test lead of a volt-ohm meter to module ground Pin 1 Circuit No. 430 at the module connector. • Attach the positive (red) test lead to right front Sensor B Circuit No. 425 Pin 16 at the module connector. • Measure resistance. | Greater than 1000 ohms ▶ | REPLACE the air suspension module. RECONNECT the right front sensor. REPEAT Quick Test. |
| | Less than 1000 Ohms ▶ | SERVICE short to ground on right front Sensor B Circuit No. 425 between the module and the right front sensor. REPEAT Quick Test. |
| **C35 CHECK SENSOR GROUND CIRCUIT** | | |
| • Attach one test lamp lead to sensor ground Circuit No.432 Pin 1 at the left front sensor circuits. • Attach the other test lamp lead to the battery positive (+) terminal. • Observe the test lamp. | Test lamp on ▶ | Sensor ground OK. GO to C36. |
| | Test lamp off ▶ | SERVICE the open in sensor ground Circuit No. 432 between the module connector and the left front sensor. REPEAT Quick Test. |
| **C36 CHECK SENSOR POWER CIRCUIT** | | |
| • Attach the negative (black) test lead of a volt-ohm meter to sensor ground Pin 1 Circuit No.432 at the left front sensor connector. • Attach the positive (red) test lead to sensor power Pin 2 Circuit No. 431 at the left front sensor connector. • Turn ignition to the RUN position. • Measure DC voltage. | Voltage less than 1V and steady ▶ | SERVICE open in sensor power Circuit No. 431 from the left front sensor to the module. REPEAT Quick Test. |
| | Voltage erratic or greater than 1V ▶ | Sensor power circuit OK. GO to C37. |
| **C37 CHECK LEFT FRONT SENSOR A CIRCUIT** | | |
| • Move the positive (red) test lead to left front Sensor A Circuit No. 422 Pin 4 at the left front sensor connector. • Measure DC voltage. | Greater than 1.5V or erratic ▶ | Left front sensor A Circuit OK. GO to C41. |
| | Less than 1.5V ▶ | GO to C38. |

**Fig. 11 Air suspension diagnosis (Problem sensing vehicle attitude, part 7 of 9)**

PROBLEM SENSING VEHICLE ATTITUDE — Continued

| TEST STEP | RESULT ▶ | ACTION TO TAKE |
|---|---|---|
| **C38** CHECK LEFT FRONT SENSOR | | |
| • Disconnect the left front sensor connector.<br>• Measure DC voltage. | Greater than 1.5V ▶ | REPLACE the front left sensor. REPEAT Quick Test. |
| | Less than 1.5V ▶ | Left front sensor OK. GO to C39. |
| **C39** CHECK LEFT FRONT SENSOR A CIRCUIT | | |
| • Do not reconnect the left front sensor.<br>• Attach the negative (black) test lead of a volt-ohm meter to sensor ground Pin 14 Circuit No. 432 at the module connector.<br>• Attach the positive (red) test lead to right front Sensor A Circuit No. 422 Pin 6 at the module connector.<br>• Measure DC voltage. | Greater than 1.5V ▶ | SERVICE open in left Sensor A Circuit No. 422 between the module and the sensor. RECONNECT the sensor connector. REPEAT Quick Test. |
| | Less than 1.5V ▶ | GO to C40. |
| **C40** CHECK LEFT FRONT SENSOR A CIRCUIT | | |
| • Disconnect the module.<br>• Attach the negative (black) test lead of a volt-ohm meter to module ground Pin 1 Circuit No. 430 at the module connector.<br>• Attach the positive (red) test lead to left front Sensor A Circuit No. 422 Pin 6 at the module connector.<br>• Measure resistance. | Greater than 1000 Ohms ▶ | REPLACE the air suspension module. RECONNECT the left front sensor. REPEAT Quick Test. |
| | Less than 1000 Ohms ▶ | SERVICE short to ground on left front Sensor A Circuit No. 422 between the module and the left front sensor. RECONNECT the left front sensor. REPEAT Quick Test. |
| **C41** CHECK LEFT FRONT SENSOR B CIRCUIT | | |
| • Move the positive (red) test lead to left front Sensor B Circuit No. 423 Pin 3 at the left front sensor connector.<br>• Measure the DC voltage. | Greater than 1.5V or erratic ▶ | REPLACE left front sensor. GO to C42. |
| | Less than 1.5V ▶ | GO to C43. |
| **C42** CHECK MODULE FOR DAMAGE | | |
| • Rerun diagnostics test No. 3 by performing steps A2-A6. | Warning lamp flashing rapidly during test No. 3 ▶ | REPLACE the air suspension control module. REPEAT Quick Test. |
| | Warning lamp not flashing rapidly during test No. 3 ▶ | REPEAT Quick Test. |

**Fig. 11 Air suspension diagnosis (Problem sensing vehicle attitude, part 8 of 9)**

PROBLEM SENSING VEHICLE ATTITUDE — Continued

| TEST STEP | RESULT ▶ | ACTION TO TAKE |
|---|---|---|
| **C43** CHECK THE LEFT FRONT SENSOR | | |
| • Disconnect the left front sensor connector.<br>• Measure the DC voltage. | Greater than 1.5V or erratic ▶ | INSTALL a new left front sensor. REPEAT Quick Test. |
| | Less than 1.5V ▶ | Left front sensor OK. GO to C44. |
| **C44** CHECK LEFT FRONT SENSOR B CIRCUIT | | |
| • Do not reconnect the left front sensor.<br>• Attach the negative (black) test lead of a volt-ohm meter to sensor ground Pin 14 Circuit No. 432 at the module connector.<br>• Attach the positive (red) test lead to left front Sensor B Circuit No. 423 Pin 17 at the module connector.<br>• Measure DC voltage. | Greater than 1.5V ▶ | SERVICE open in left front Sensor B Circuit No. 423 between the module and the sensor. RECONNECT the left front sensor connector. REPEAT Quick Test. |
| | Less than 1.5V ▶ | GO to C45. |
| **C45** CHECK LEFT FRONT SENSOR B CIRCUIT | | |
| • Disconnect the module.<br>• Attach the negative (black) test lead of a volt-ohm meter to module ground Pin 1 Circuit No. 430 at the module connector.<br>• Attach the positive (red) test lead to left front Sensor B Circuit No. 423 Pin 17 at the module connector.<br>• Measure resistance. | Greater than 1000 Ohms ▶ | REPLACE the air suspension module. RECONNECT the left front sensor. REPEAT Quick Test. |
| | Less than 1000 Ohms ▶ | SERVICE short to ground on left front Sensor B Circuit No. 423 between the module and the left front sensor. REPEAT Quick Test. |

**Fig. 11 Air suspension diagnosis (Problem sensing vehicle attitude, part 9 of 9)**

PROBLEM AT REAR OF VEHICLE

| TEST STEP | RESULT ▶ | ACTION TO TAKE |
|---|---|---|
| **D1** | | |
| • Did the compressor cycle during test No. 4? | Yes ▶ | GO to D2. |
| | No ▶ | GO to G1. |
| **D2** | | |
| • Did the right rear solenoid cycle during test No. 8? | Yes ▶ | GO to D3. |
| | No ▶ | GO to D12. |
| **D3** | | |
| • Did the left front rear solenoid cycle during test No. 9? | Yes ▶ | GO to D4. |
| | No ▶ | GO to D23. |
| **D4** | | |
| • Did the vent solenoid cycle during test No. 5? | Yes ▶ | GO to D5. |
| | No ▶ | GO to H1. |
| **D5** CHECK COMPRESSOR | | |
| • Perform Steps A2-A3.<br>• Disconnect all the air lines at the compressor.<br>• Plug three of the four air line fittings at the compressor.<br>• Attach a pressure gauge capable of reading 1034 kPa (150 psi) to the remaining fitting at the compressor.<br>• Open and close the door and observe the pressure gauge. | Pressure greater than 827 kPa (120 psi) ▶ | Compressor OK. GO to D6. |
| | Pressure less than 827 kPa (120 psi) ▶ | INSTALL a new compressor. RECONNECT all the air lines at the compressor. REPEAT Diagnostic Test. |
| **D6** CHECK REAR SENSOR CONNECTION | | |
| • Check the rear sensor, ball studs, and bracket for secure mechanical connection. | Securely connected ▶ | GO to D7. |
| | Not securely connected ▶ | SECURE rear sensor as necessary. REPEAT Diagnostic Test. |
| **D7** CHECK IN REAR AIR SYSTEM | | |
| • Disconnect the air lines going to the right and left rear air spring at the compressor.<br>• Perform Steps A2-A3.<br>• Open and close a door and verify that air is escaping from the air lines. | Air escaping from both air lines ▶ | GO to D8. |
| | Air not escaping from one rear air line ▶ | GO to D10. |
| | Air not escaping from either air line because of no air in either air spring ▶ | GO to D8. |

**Fig. 12 Air suspension diagnosis (Problem at rear of vehicle, part 1 of 6)**

PROBLEM AT REAR OF VEHICLE — Continued

| TEST STEP | RESULT ▶ | ACTION TO TAKE |
|---|---|---|
| **D8** | | |
| • Did vehicle fail tests 2 and 3? | Yes ▶ | GO to D9. |
| | No ▶ | LOCATE and SERVICE leak in left or right spring and solenoid assembly. |
| **D9** | | |
| • Is rear of vehicle at rebound (high)? | Yes ▶ | REPLACE the compressor assembly. REPEAT Diagnostic Test. |
| | No ▶ | SERVICE leaking air line or fitting. Any of the four air lines or eight fittings may be leaking. RECONNECT all air lines. REPEAT Diagnostic Test. |
| **D10** CHECK FOR RESTRICTION IN REAR SOLENOID | | |
| • Reconnect the air lines to the rear air spring at the compressor.<br>• Perform Steps A2-A3.<br>• Disconnect the air line going to the affected rear air spring at the air spring solenoid.<br>• Open and close a door and verify that air is escaping from the affected rear air spring.<br>NOTE: The rear of the vehicle may fall during this test. | Air escaping from rear solenoid ▶ | SERVICE leak or obstruction in the affected air line or fitting. RECONNECT all air lines. REPEAT Diagnostic Test. |
| | Air is not escaping from the rear solenoid ▶ | GO to D11. |
| **D11** | | |
| • Check for leaks at affected air spring and solenoid assembly. | No leaks ▶ | REPLACE the solenoid at the affected air spring. REPEAT Diagnostic Test. |
| | Leaks found ▶ | SERVICE or REPLACE leaky air spring or solenoid. REPEAT Diagnostic Test. |
| **D12** CYCLE RIGHT REAR SOLENOID | | |
| • Perform Steps A2-A3.<br>• Open and close the door until the warning lamp blinks test No. 8. | ▶ | GO to D13. |
| **D13** CHECK RIGHT REAR SOLENOID CIRCUIT | | |
| • Attach one lead of the test lamp to right rear solenoid Circuit No. 416 at the right rear solenoid connector.<br>• Attach the other test lamp lead to battery Circuit No. 175 at the right rear solenoid connector.<br>• Observe the test lamp. | Test lamp blinking ▶ | REPLACE right rear solenoid. REPEAT Diagnostic Test. |
| | Test lamp off ▶ | GO to D14. |
| | Test lamp on ▶ | GO to D21. |

**Fig. 12 Air suspension diagnosis (Problem at rear of vehicle, part 2 of 6)**

PROBLEM AT REAR OF VEHICLE — Continued

| TEST STEP | RESULT | ACTION TO TAKE |
|---|---|---|
| **D14** CHECK FOR CONNECTOR POLARITY | | |
| • Attach one lead of test lamp to the right rear solenoid connector Pin 2. • Attach the other lead of test lamp to a good ground. | Test lamp on ▶ | GO to D17. |
| | Test lamp off ▶ | GO to D15. |
| **D15** | | |
| • Attach one lead of test lamp to the right rear solenoid connector Pin 1. • Attach the other lead of test lamp to a good ground. | Test lamp off ▶ | GO to D17. |
| | Test lamp on ▶ | REPAIR crossed wires in the solenoid connector and repeat D16. |
| **D16** CHECK BATTERY CIRCUIT | | |
| • Move the test lead connected to right rear solenoid Circuit No. 416 to a good ground. • Observe the test lamp. | Test lamp on ▶ | Battery circuit OK. GO to D17. |
| | Test lamp off ▶ | SERVICE open in Circuit No. 175 between the right rear solenoid and fuse link. REPEAT Diagnostic Test. |
| **D17** CHECK CONTROL MODULE | | |
| • Attach one test lamp lead to right rear solenoid Circuit No. 416 Pin 10 at the module connector. • Attach the other test lamp lead to battery Circuit No. 418 Pin 20 at the module connector. • Observe the test lamp. **NOTE: Test must be performed without disconnecting harness connector at module.** | Test lamp blinking ▶ | SERVICE open in Circuit No. 416 between the module and the right rear solenoid. REPEAT Diagnostic Test. |
| | Test lamp off ▶ | GO to D18. |
| **D18** | | |
| • Is the warning lamp blinking test No. 8? | Yes ▶ | GO to D19. |
| | No ▶ | GO to D12. |
| **D19** CHECK MODULE CONNECTOR PINS | | |
| • Disconnect module connector and inspect pins. | Pins OK ▶ | GO to D20. |
| | Problem found ▶ | SERVICE connector at the air suspension module. REPEAT Diagnostic Test. |

**Fig. 12 Air suspension diagnosis (Problem at rear of vehicle, part 3 of 6)**

PROBLEM AT REAR OF VEHICLE — Continued

| TEST STEP | RESULT | ACTION TO TAKE |
|---|---|---|
| **D20** CHECK RIGHT REAR SOLENOID | | |
| • Attach the negative (black) test lead of a volt-ohm meter to connector Pin 1 of the right rear solenoid. • Attach the positive (red) test lead to connector Pin 2 at the right rear solenoid. • Measure the resistance. | Greater than 13 ohms ▶ | REPLACE air suspension control module. REPEAT Diagnostic Test. |
| | Less than 13 Ohms ▶ | REPLACE right rear solenoid and air suspension module. REPEAT Diagnostic Test. |
| **D21** | | |
| • Is the warning lamp blinking test No. 8? | Yes ▶ | GO to D22. |
| | No ▶ | GO to D12. |
| **D22** CHECK RIGHT REAR SOLENOID CIRCUIT | | |
| • Disconnect the module connector. • Observe the test lamp. | Test lamp on ▶ | SERVICE short to ground on right rear solenoid Circuit No. 416 between the module connector and the right rear solenoid. REPEAT Diagnostic Test. |
| | Test lamp off ▶ | REPLACE the air suspension module. REPEAT Diagnostic Test. |
| **D23** CYCLE THE LEFT REAR SOLENOID | | |
| • Perform Steps A2-A3. • Open and close the door until the warning lamp blinks test No. 9. | ▶ | GO to D24. |
| **D24** CHECK LEFT REAR SOLENOID CIRCUIT | | |
| • Attach one lead of the test lamp to left rear solenoid Circuit No. 429 at the left rear solenoid connector. • Attach the other test lamp lead to battery Circuit No. 175 at the left rear solenoid connector. • Observe the test lamp. | Test lamp blinking ▶ | REPLACE the left rear solenoid. REPEAT Diagnostic Test. |
| | Test lamp off ▶ | GO to D25. |
| | Test lamp on ▶ | GO to D32. |
| **D25** CHECK FOR CONNECTOR POLARITY | | |
| • Attach one lead of test lamp to the left rear solenoid connector Pin 2. • Attach the other lead of test lamp to a good ground. | Test lamp on ▶ | GO to D28. |
| | Test lamp off ▶ | GO to D26. |

**Fig. 12 Air suspension diagnosis (Problem at rear of vehicle, part 4 of 6)**

PROBLEM AT REAR OF VEHICLE — Continued

| TEST STEP | RESULT | ACTION TO TAKE |
|---|---|---|
| **D26** | | |
| • Attach one lead of test lamp to the left rear solenoid connector Pin 1. • Attach the other lead of test lamp to a good ground. | Test lamp off ▶ | GO to D28. |
| | Test lamp on ▶ | SERVICE crossed wires in solenoid connector and REPEAT D27. |
| **D27** CHECK BATTERY CIRCUIT | | |
| • Move the test lead connected to the left rear solenoid Circuit No. 429 to a good ground. • Observe the test lamp. | Test lamp on ▶ | Battery circuit OK. GO to D28. |
| | Test lamp off ▶ | SERVICE open or short to ground in Circuit No. 418 between the air suspension system On/Off switch and the right rear solenoid. REPEAT Diagnostic Test. |
| **D28** CHECK CONTROL MODULE | | |
| • Attach one test lamp lead to left rear solenoid Circuit No. 429 Pin 9 at the module connector. • Attach the other test lamp lead to battery Circuit No. 418 Pin 20 at the module connector. **NOTE: Test must be performed without disconnecting harness connector of module.** | Test lamp blinking ▶ | SERVICE open in Circuit No. 429 between the module and the left rear solenoid. REPEAT Diagnostic Test. |
| | Test lamp off ▶ | GO to D29. |
| **D29** | | |
| • Is the warning lamp blinking test No. 9? | Yes ▶ | GO to D30. |
| | No ▶ | GO to D23. |
| **D30** CHECK MODULE CONNECTOR PINS | | |
| • Disconnect module connector and inspect pins. | Pins OK ▶ | GO to D31. |
| | Problem found ▶ | SERVICE connector at the air suspension module. REPEAT Diagnostic Test. |

**Fig. 12 Air suspension diagnosis (Problem at rear of vehicle, part 5 of 6)**

PROBLEM AT REAR OF VEHICLE — Continued

| TEST STEP | RESULT | ACTION TO TAKE |
|---|---|---|
| **D31** CHECK LEFT REAR SOLENOID | | |
| • Attach the negative (black) test lead of a volt-ohm meter to connector Pin 1 of the left rear solenoid. • Attach the positive (red) lead to connector Pin 2 of the left rear solenoid. • Measure the resistance. | Greater than 13 Ohms ▶ | REPLACE the air suspension control module. REPEAT Diagnostic Test. |
| | Less than 13 Ohms ▶ | REPLACE the left rear solenoid and air suspension module. REPEAT Diagnostic Test. |
| **D32** | | |
| • Is the warning lamp blinking test No. 9? | Yes ▶ | GO to D33. |
| | No ▶ | GO to D23. |
| **D33** CHECK LEFT REAR SOLENOID CIRCUIT | | |
| • Disconnect the module connector. • Observe the test lamp. | Test lamp on ▶ | SERVICE short to ground on the left rear solenoid Circuit No. 429 between the module connector and the left rear solenoid. REPEAT Diagnostic Test. |
| | Test lamp off ▶ | REPLACE the air suspension module. REPEAT Diagnostic Test. |

**Fig. 12 Air suspension diagnosis (Problem at rear of vehicle, part 6 of 6)**

PROBLEM AT RIGHT FRONT OF VEHICLE

| TEST STEP | RESULT | ACTION TO TAKE |
|---|---|---|
| **E1** | | |
| • Did vehicle pass test No. 1? | Yes | GO to E2. |
| | No | GO to D1. |
| **E2** | | |
| • Did the right front solenoid pass test No. 7? | Yes | GO to E3. |
| | Does not pass air | GO to E4. |
| | Passes air but does not click | GO to E16. |
| **E3** CHECK RIGHT FRONT SENSOR | | |
| • Check the right front sensor and ball studs for a secure mechanical connection. | Securely connected | GO to E6. |
| | Not securely connected | SECURE the right front sensor. REPEAT Diagnostic Test. |
| **E4** CHECK RIGHT FRONT SOLENOID CIRCUIT | | |
| • Perform Steps A2-A3.<br>• Open and close the door until the warning lamp blinks test No. 7.<br>• Attach one lead of the test lamp to the right front solenoid Circuit No. 414 at the right front solenoid connector.<br>• Attach the other test lamp lead to battery Circuit No. 175 at the right front solenoid connector.<br>• Observe the test lamp. | Test lamp blinking | Electrical system OK. GO to E5. |
| | Test lamp off | GO to E7. |
| | Test lamp on | GO to E14. |
| **E5** CHECK FOR RESTRICTION IN RIGHT FRONT AIR LINE | | |
| • Perform Steps A2-A3.<br>• Disconnect the air lines at the right front air spring solenoid.<br>• Open and close the door twice and verify that air is escaping from the spring solenoid line.<br>**NOTE: The right front of the vehicle will drop during this test.** | Air escaping from the air spring solenoid | SERVICE kink or obstruction in the right front air line. RECONNECT air lines. REPEAT Diagnostic Test. |
| | Air is not escaping from the air spring solenoid | GO to E6. |
| **E6** CHECK FOR SOLENOID OR AIR SPRING LEAKS | | |
| • Reconnect air lines.<br>• Perform Steps A2-A3.<br>• Open and close the door twice and verify that air is not leaking from the right front air spring or solenoid. | Air not leaking from the air spring or solenoid | SERVICE or REPLACE right front air spring solenoid due to an obstruction. REPEAT Diagnostic Test. |
| | Air leaking from the air spring or solenoid | SERVICE or REPLACE leaky right front air spring or solenoid. REPEAT Diagnostic Test. |

**Fig. 13 Air suspension diagnosis (Problem at right front of vehicle, part 1 of 3)**

PROBLEM AT RIGHT FRONT OF VEHICLE — Continued

| TEST STEP | RESULT | ACTION TO TAKE |
|---|---|---|
| **E7** CHECK FOR CONNECTOR POLARITY | | |
| • Attach one lead of test lamp to right front solenoid connector Pin 2.<br>• Attach the other lead of test lamp to a good ground. | Test lamp on | GO to E10. |
| | Test lamp off | GO to E8. |
| **E8** | | |
| • Attach one lead of test lamp to the right front solenoid connector Pin 1.<br>• Attach the other lead of test lamp to a good ground. | Test lamp off | GO to E10. |
| | Test lamp on | SERVICE crossed wires in solenoid connector and REPEAT E9. |
| **E9** CHECK BATTERY CIRCUIT | | |
| • Move the test lead connected to the right front solenoid Circuit No. 414 to a good ground.<br>• Observe the test lamp. | Test lamp on | Battery circuit OK. GO to E10. |
| | Test lamp off | SERVICE open or short to ground in battery Circuit No. 175 between the battery and the right front solenoid. REPEAT Diagnostic Test. |
| **E10** CHECK MODULE | | |
| • Attach one test lamp lead to right front solenoid Circuit No. 414 Pin 12 at the module connector.<br>• Attach the other test lamp lead to battery Circuit No. 418 Pin 20 at the module connector.<br>• Observe the test lamp.<br>**NOTE: Test must be performed without disconnecting the harness connector at the module.** | Test lamp blinking | SERVICE open in right front solenoid Circuit No. 414 between the module and the right front solenoid. REPEAT Diagnostic Test. |
| | Test lamp off | GO to E11. |
| **E11** | | |
| • Is the warning lamp blinking test No. 7? | Yes | GO to E12. |
| | No | GO to E4. |
| **E12** CHECK MODULE CONNECTOR | | |
| • Disconnect module connector and inspect pins. | Pins OK | GO to E13. |
| | Problem found | SERVICE connector at the air suspension module. REPEAT Diagnostic Test. |

**Fig. 13 Air suspension diagnosis (Problem at right front of vehicle, part 2 of 3)**

PROBLEM AT RIGHT FRONT OF VEHICLE — Continued

| TEST STEP | RESULT | ACTION TO TAKE |
|---|---|---|
| **E13** CHECK RIGHT FRONT SOLENOID | | |
| • Disconnect the right front solenoid connector.<br>• Attach the negative (black) test lead of a volt-ohm meter to connector Pin 1 of the right front solenoid connector.<br>• Attach the positive (red) test lead to connector Pin 2 of the right front solenoid connector.<br>• Measure resistance. | Greater than 13 Ohms | REPLACE the air suspension control module. REPEAT Diagnostic Test. |
| | Less than 13 Ohms | REPLACE the right front solenoid and air suspension module. REPEAT Diagnostic Test. |
| **E14** | | |
| • Is the warning lamp blinking test No. 7? | Yes | GO to E15. |
| | No | GO to E4. |
| **E15** | | |
| • Disconnect the module connector, leaving test lamp connected across Circuits No. 414 and No. 175.<br>• Observe the test lamp. | Test lamp on | SERVICE short to ground or right front solenoid Circuit No. 414 between the module connector and the right front solenoid. REPEAT Diagnostic Test. |
| | Test lamp off | REPLACE the air suspension module. REPEAT Diagnostic Test. |
| **E16** | | |
| • Disconnect the right front solenoid connector.<br>• Attach one lead of the test lamp to the right front solenoid Circuit No. 414 on the harness side of the connector.<br>• Attach the other lead to battery Circuit No. 175 on the harness side of the connector.<br>• Observe the test lamp. | Test lamp on | SERVICE short to ground in solenoid control Circuit No. 414. REPEAT Diagnostic Test. |
| | Test lamp off | REPLACE solenoid. REPEAT Diagnostic Test. |

**Fig. 13 Air suspension diagnosis (Problem at right front of vehicle, part 3 of 3)**

PROBLEM AT LEFT FRONT OF VEHICLE

| TEST STEP | RESULT | ACTION TO TAKE |
|---|---|---|
| **F1** | | |
| • Did vehicle pass test No. 1? | Yes | GO to F2. |
| | No | GO to D1. |
| **F2** | | |
| • Did the left front solenoid pass test No. 6? | Yes | GO to F3. |
| | Does not pass air | GO to F4. |
| | Passes air but does not click | GO to F16. |
| **F3** CHECK LEFT FRONT SENSOR | | |
| • Check the left front sensor and ball stud for a secure mechanical connection. | Left front sensor securely connected | GO to F6. |
| | Left front sensor not securely connected | SECURE the left front sensor. REPEAT Diagnostic Test. |
| **F4** CHECK LEFT FRONT SOLENOID CIRCUIT | | |
| • Perform Steps A2-A3.<br>• Open and close the door until the warning lamp blinks test No. 6.<br>• Attach one lead of the test lamp to the left front solenoid Circuit No. 415 at the left front solenoid connector.<br>• Attach the other test lamp lead to battery Circuit No. 175 at the left front solenoid connector.<br>• Observe the test lamp. | Test lamp blinking | Electrical system OK. GO to F5. |
| | Test lamp off | GO to F7. |
| | Test lamp on | GO to F14. |
| **F5** CHECK FOR RESTRICTIONS IN LEFT FRONT AIR LINE | | |
| • Perform Steps A2-A3.<br>• Disconnect the air lines at the left front air spring solenoid.<br>• Open and close the door three times and verify that air is escaping the spring solenoid.<br>**NOTE: The left front of the vehicle will drop during this test.** | Air escaping from the air spring solenoid | SERVICE kink or obstruction in the left front air line. RECONNECT air lines. REPEAT Diagnostic Test. |
| | Air is not escaping from the air spring solenoid | GO to F6. |

**Fig. 14 Air suspension diagnosis (Problem at left front of vehicle, part 1 of 3)**

PROBLEM AT LEFT FRONT OF VEHICLE — Continued

| TEST STEP | RESULT ▶ | ACTION TO TAKE |
|---|---|---|
| **F6** CHECK FOR SOLENOID OR AIR SPRING LEAKS | | |
| • Reconnect air lines.<br>• Perform Steps A2-A3.<br>• Open and close the door three times and verify that air is not leaking from the left front air spring or solenoid. | Air is not leaking from the air spring or solenoid ▶ | SERVICE or REPLACE left front air spring solenoid due to obstruction. REPEAT Diagnostic Test. |
| | Air is leaking from the air spring or solenoid ▶ | SERVICE or REPLACE leaky left front air spring or solenoid. REPEAT Diagnostic Test. |
| **F7** CHECK FOR CONNECTOR POLARITY | | |
| • Attach one lead of test lamp to left front solenoid connector Pin 2.<br>• Attach the other lead of test lamp to a good ground. | Test lamp on ▶ | GO to **F10**. |
| | Test lamp off ▶ | GO to **F8**. |
| **F8** | | |
| • Attach one lead of test lamp to right front solenoid connector Pin 1.<br>• Attach the other lead of test lamp to a good ground. | Test lamp off ▶ | GO to **F10**. |
| | Test lamp on ▶ | SERVICE crossed wires in solenoid connector and REPEAT F9. |
| **F9** CHECK BATTERY CIRCUIT | | |
| • Move the test lead connected to the left front solenoid Circuit No. 415 to a good ground.<br>• Observe the test lamp. | Test lamp on ▶ | Battery circuit OK. Go to **F10**. |
| | Test lamp off ▶ | SERVICE open or short to ground in battery Circuit No. 175 between the battery and the left front solenoid. REPEAT Diagnostic Test. |
| **F10** CHECK MODULE | | |
| • Attach one test lamp lead to left front solenoid Circuit No. 415 Pin 11 at the module connector.<br>• Attach the other test lamp lead to battery Circuit No. 418 Pin 20 at the module connector.<br>• Observe the test lamp.<br>**NOTE: Test must be performed without disconnecting connector at module.** | Test lamp blinking ▶ | SERVICE open in left front solenoid Circuit No. 415 between the module and the left front solenoid. REPEAT Diagnostic Test. |
| | Test lamp off ▶ | GO to **F11**. |
| **F11** | | |
| • Is the warning lamp blinking test No. 6? | Yes ▶ | GO to **F12**. |
| | No ▶ | GO to **F4**. |

**Fig. 14 Air suspension diagnosis (Problem at left front of vehicle, part 2 of 3)**

PROBLEM AT LEFT FRONT OF VEHICLE — Continued

| TEST STEP | RESULT ▶ | ACTION TO TAKE |
|---|---|---|
| **F12** | | |
| • Disconnect module connector and inspect pins. | Pins OK ▶ | GO to **F13**. |
| | Problem found ▶ | SERVICE connector at the air suspension module. REPEAT Diagnostic Test. |
| **F13** | | |
| • Disconnect the left front solenoid connector.<br>• Attach the negative (black) test lead of a volt-ohm meter to connector Pin 1 of the left front solenoid connector.<br>• Attach the positive (red) test lead to connector Pin 2 of the left front solenoid connector.<br>• Measure resistance. | Greater than 13 Ohms ▶ | REPLACE the air suspension control module. REPEAT Diagnostic Test. |
| | Less than 13 Ohms ▶ | REPLACE the left front solenoid and air suspension module. REPEAT Diagnostic Test. |
| **F14** | | |
| • Is the warning lamp blinking test No. 6? | Yes ▶ | GO to **F15**. |
| | No ▶ | GO to **F4**. |
| **F15** | | |
| • Disconnect the module connector leaving test lamp connected across Circuits No. 415 and No. 175.<br>• Observe the test lamp. | Test lamp on ▶ | SERVICE short to ground on left front solenoid Circuit No. 415 between the module connector and the left front solenoid. REPEAT Diagnostic Test. |
| | Test lamp off ▶ | REPLACE the air suspension module. REPEAT Diagnostic Test. |
| **F16** | | |
| • Disconnect the left front solenoid connector.<br>• Attach one lead of the test lamp to the left front solenoid Circuit No. 415 on the harness side of the connector.<br>• Attach the other lead to battery Circuit No. 175 on the harness side of the connector.<br>• Observe the test lamp. | Test lamp on ▶ | SERVICE short to ground in solenoid control Circuit No. 415. REPEAT Diagnostic Test. |
| | Test lamp off ▶ | REPLACE solenoid. REPEAT Diagnostic Test. |

**Fig. 14 Air suspension diagnosis (Problem at left front of vehicle, part 3 of 3)**

PROBLEM DURING FILL

| TEST STEP | RESULT ▶ | ACTION TO TAKE |
|---|---|---|
| **G1** CHECK THE COMPRESSOR RELAY | | |
| • Perform Steps A2-A3.<br>• Open and close the door until the warning lamp blinks test No. 4.<br>• The compressor circuit will only be cycled 50 times during test No. 4 (approximately three minutes). At the end of 50 cycles the compressor will turn off and not cycle until test No. 4 is reentered.<br>• Verify that the compressor relay is cycling.<br>**NOTE: The rear of the vehicle may raise during test No. 4.** | Compressor relay cycling ▶ | GO to **G2**. |
| | Compressor relay is not cycling ▶ | GO to **G5**. |
| **G2** CHECK COMPRESSOR CIRCUIT | | |
| • Disconnect the compressor connector.<br>• Attach one lead of the test lamp to compressor Circuit No. 417 at the compressor connector (harness side).<br>• Attach the other test lamp lead to good ground.<br>• Observe the test lamp. | Test lamp blinking ▶ | Compressor circuit OK. GO to G3. |
| | Test lamp on ▶ | REPLACE the compressor relay. RECONNECT the compressor connector. REPEAT Quick Test. |
| | Test lamp off ▶ | GO to G4. |
| **G3** CHECK COMPRESSOR GROUND CIRCUIT | | |
| • Move the test lamp attached to battery ground, to ground Circuit No. 430 at the compressor connector (harness side).<br>• Observe the test lamp. | Test lamp blinking ▶ | INSTALL a new compressor. RECONNECT compressor. REPEAT Quick Test. |
| | Test lamp off ▶ | SERVICE open in ground Circuit No. 430 between the compressor and the battery. RECONNECT compressor connector. REPEAT Quick Test. |
| **G4** CHECK COMPRESSOR CIRCUIT | | |
| • Reconnect the compressor connector.<br>• Perform Step G1.<br>• Attach one lead of the test lamp to compressor Circuit No. 417 at the compressor relay.<br>• Attach the other test lamp lead to a good ground.<br>• Observe test lamp. | Test lamp blinking ▶ | SERVICE open or short to ground on Circuit No. 417 between the compressor and the compressor relay. REPEAT Quick Test. |
| | Test lamp off ▶ | REPLACE the compressor relay. RECONNECT the compressor connector. REPEAT Quick Test. |

**Fig. 15 Air suspension diagnosis (Problem during fill, part 1 of 3)**

PROBLEM DURING FILL — Continued

| TEST STEP | RESULT ▶ | ACTION TO TAKE |
|---|---|---|
| **G5** CHECK COMPRESSOR RELAY CIRCUIT | | |
| • Attach one lead of the test lamp to compressor relay Circuit No.420 at the compressor relay.<br>• Attach the other test lamp lead to the battery positive (+) terminal.<br>• Observe the test lamp. | Test lamp blinks ▶ | Module relay circuit OK. GO to **G6**. |
| | Test lamp on ▶ | GO to **G8**. |
| | Test lamp off ▶ | GO to **G9**. |
| **G6** CHECK JUMPER CIRCUIT | | |
| • Attach one test lamp lead to jumper Circuit No.175A at the compressor relay Pin 2.<br>• Attach the other lead to a good ground.<br>• Observe the test lamp. | Test lamp on ▶ | REPLACE compressor relay. RECONNECT compressor connector. REPEAT Quick Test. |
| | Test lamp off ▶ | GO to **G7**. |
| **G7** CHECK BATTERY CIRCUIT | | |
| • Attach one test lamp lead to battery Circuit No.175 at the compressor relay Pin 3.<br>• Attach the other test lamp lead to a good ground.<br>• Observe the test lamp. | Test lamp on ▶ | SERVICE open or short to ground in jumper Circuit 175A. REPEAT Quick Test. |
| | Test lamp off ▶ | SERVICE open or short to ground on battery Circuit No. 175 between the compressor relay and the battery. REPEAT Quick Test. |
| **G8** CHECK MODULE | | |
| • Disconnect the module connector and observe the test lamp. | Test lamp on ▶ | SERVICE compressor relay Circuit No.420 for a short to ground. REPEAT Quick Test. |
| | Test lamp off ▶ | REPLACE the air suspension control module. REPEAT Quick Test. |
| **G9** CHECK COMPRESSOR RELAY | | |
| • Disconnect the compressor relay connector.<br>• Attach the negative (black) test lead of a volt-ohm meter to connect Pin 2 at the compressor relay connector.<br>• Attach the positive (red) test lead to connector Pin 1 at the compressor relay connector.<br>• Measure resistance. | Greater than 54 Ohms ▶ | Compressor relay OK. GO to **G10**. |
| | Less than 54 Ohms ▶ | REPLACE the compressor relay. REPEAT Quick Test.<br>**NOTE: This failure may have damaged the air suspension control module.** |

**Fig. 15 Air suspension diagnosis (Problem during fill, part 2 of 3)**

PROBLEM DURING FILL — Continued

| | TEST STEP | RESULT | ▶ | ACTION TO TAKE |
|---|---|---|---|---|
| G10 | CHECK MODULE | | | |
| | • Perform Step G1.<br>• Attach one test lamp lead to compressor relay Circuit No. 420 Pin 22 at the module connector.<br>• Attach the other test lamp lead to battery Circuit No. 418 Pin 20 at the module connector.<br>• Observe the test lamp.<br>**NOTE: This test must be performed without disconnecting module harness connector.** | Test lamp blinking | ▶ | SERVICE open in compressor relay Circuit No. 420 between the compressor relay and the module. REPEAT Quick Test. |
| | | Test lamp off | ▶ | REPLACE air suspension control module. REPEAT Quick Test. |

**Fig. 15 Air suspension diagnosis (Problem during fill, part 3 of 3)**

PROBLEM DURING VENT — Continued

| | TEST STEP | RESULT | ▶ | ACTION TO TAKE |
|---|---|---|---|---|
| H6 | CHECK VENT SOLENOID | | | |
| | • Disconnect the connector at the compressor assembly.<br>• Attach the negative (black) test lead of a volt-ohm meter to connector Pin 4 at the compressor assembly.<br>• Attach the positive (red) test lead to connector Pin 1 at the compressor assembly.<br>• Measure the resistance. | Greater than 27 Ohms | ▶ | REPLACE the air suspension control module. REPEAT Quick Test. |
| | | Less than 27 Ohms | ▶ | REPLACE the compressor assembly and air suspension control module. REPEAT Quick Test. |

**Fig. 16 Air suspension diagnosis (Problem during vent, part 2 of 2)**

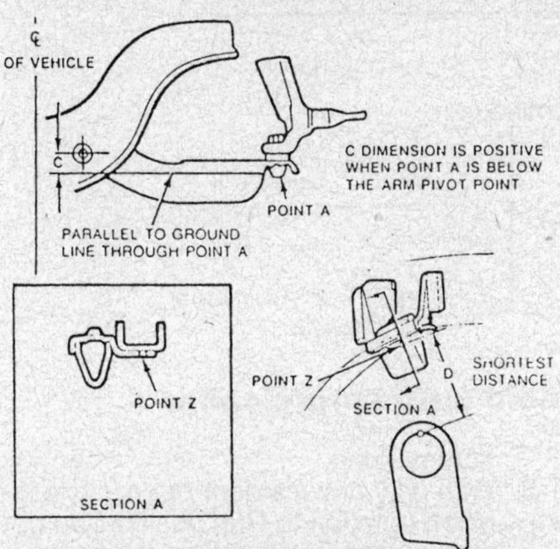


**Fig. 17 Ride height "C" and "D" dimensions**

## WHEEL ALIGNMENT

Refer to "Front Suspension & Steering Section" chapter for procedures.

# COMPONENT REPLACEMENT

## AIR SPRING SOLENOID, REPLACE

1. Turn air suspension switch off, then raise and support vehicle at body.
2. Remove wheel assembly.
3. Disconnect electrical connector and air line from air spring solenoid, then remove solenoid retaining clip.
4. Rotate solenoid counterclockwise to first stop, then pull outward to second stop and allow air to bleed from system as shown, **Fig. 20. Failure to allow air to fully bleed from system may result in personal injury.**
5. Rotate solenoid counterclockwise to third stop and remove from air spring assembly.
6. Reverse procedure to install.

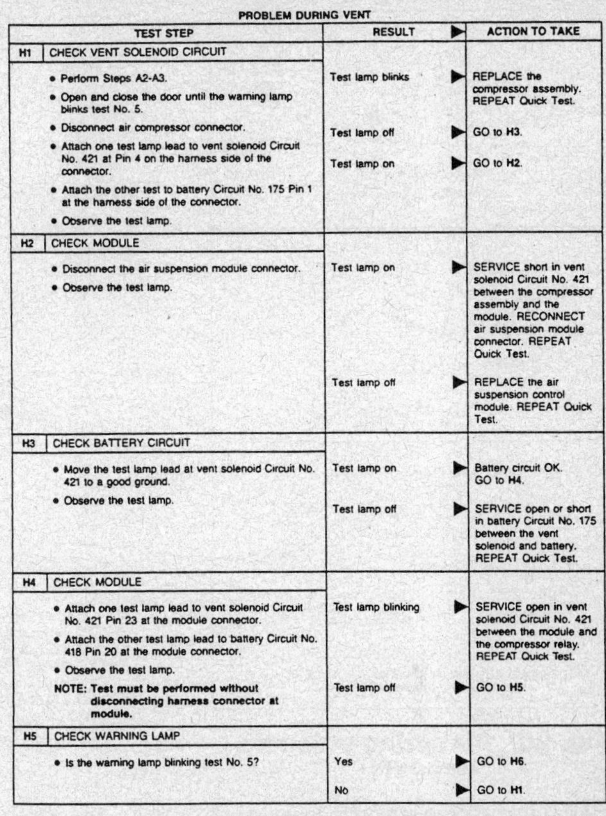

PROBLEM DURING VENT

| | TEST STEP | RESULT | ▶ | ACTION TO TAKE |
|---|---|---|---|---|
| H1 | CHECK VENT SOLENOID CIRCUIT | | | |
| | • Perform Steps A2-A3.<br>• Open and close the door until the warning lamp blinks test No. 5.<br>• Disconnect air compressor connector.<br>• Attach one test lamp lead to vent solenoid Circuit No. 421 at Pin 4 on the harness side of the connector.<br>• Attach the other test to battery Circuit No. 175 Pin 1 at the harness side of the connector.<br>• Observe the test lamp. | Test lamp blinks | ▶ | REPLACE the compressor assembly. REPEAT Quick Test. |
| | | Test lamp off | ▶ | GO to **H3**. |
| | | Test lamp on | ▶ | GO to **H2**. |
| H2 | CHECK MODULE | | | |
| | • Disconnect the air suspension module connector.<br>• Observe the test lamp. | Test lamp on | ▶ | SERVICE short in vent solenoid Circuit No. 421 between the compressor assembly and the module. RECONNECT air suspension module connector. REPEAT Quick Test. |
| | | Test lamp off | ▶ | REPLACE the air suspension control module. REPEAT Quick Test. |
| H3 | CHECK BATTERY CIRCUIT | | | |
| | • Move the test lamp lead at vent solenoid Circuit No. 421 to a good ground.<br>• Observe the test lamp. | Test lamp on | ▶ | Battery circuit OK. GO to **H4**. |
| | | Test lamp off | ▶ | SERVICE open or short in battery Circuit No. 175 between the vent solenoid and battery. REPEAT Quick Test. |
| H4 | CHECK MODULE | | | |
| | • Attach one test lamp lead to vent solenoid Circuit No. 421 Pin 23 at the module connector.<br>• Attach the other test lamp lead to battery Circuit No. 418 Pin 20 at the module connector.<br>• Observe the test lamp.<br>**NOTE: Test must be performed without disconnecting harness connector at module.** | Test lamp blinking | ▶ | SERVICE open in vent solenoid Circuit No. 421 between the module and the compressor relay. REPEAT Quick Test. |
| | | Test lamp off | ▶ | GO to **H5**. |
| H5 | CHECK WARNING LAMP | | | |
| | • Is the warning lamp blinking test No. 5? | Yes | ▶ | GO to **H6**. |
| | | No | ▶ | GO to **H1**. |

**Fig. 16 Air suspension diagnosis (Problem during vent, part 1 of 2)**

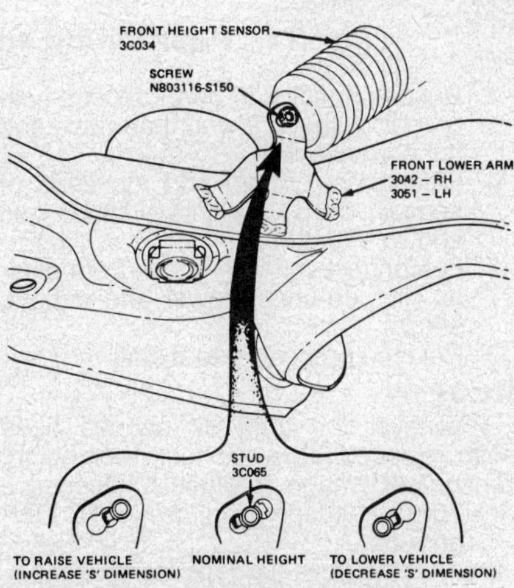


**Fig. 18 Front suspension ride height adjustment**

## AIR SPRING, REPLACE

### Removal

1. Remove air spring solenoid as outlined previously.
2. If replacing front spring, remove spring to lower control arm retaining clip. If replacing rear spring, remove retaining clip and/or bolts.
3. Push down on air spring collar spring clip, then rotate collar counterclockwise until spring releases from body spring seat.
4. Remove spring from vehicle.

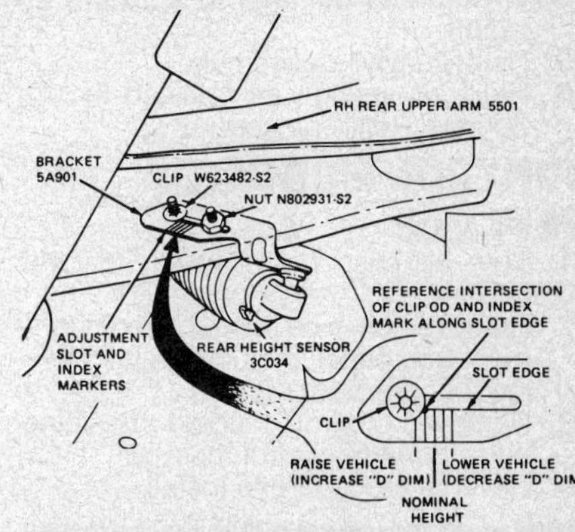


**Fig. 19 Rear suspension ride height adjustment**

### Installation

1. Install air spring solenoid. If left side spring is being replaced, position solenoid so notch on spring collar is in line with center line of solenoid. If right side spring is being replaced, position solenoid so flat on collar is in line with center line of solenoid. Refer to **Fig. 21**, for correct positioning. **Do not attempt to install or inflate any air spring which has become unfolded. If any spring has been unfolded, refold spring as shown in Fig. 22, before installing into vehicle.**
2. Install air spring into body spring seat, then rotate spring collar until spring clip snaps into position, **Fig. 21.**
3. Connect air line and electrical connector to solenoid.

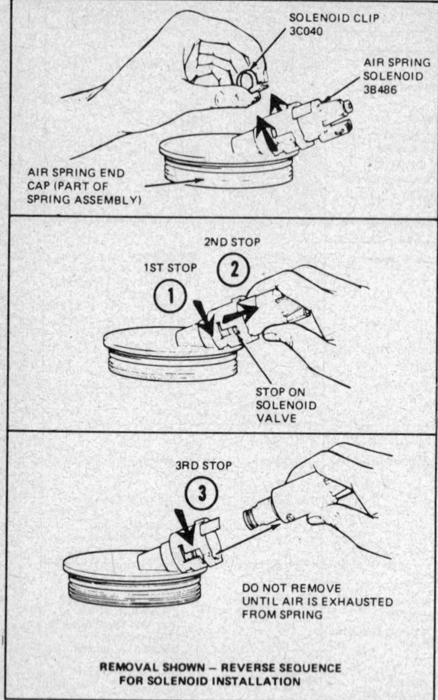


**Fig. 20 Air spring solenoid removal**

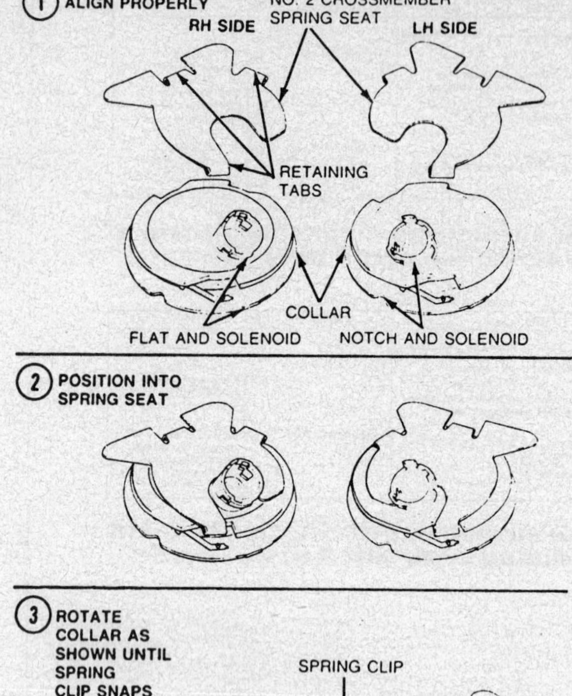


**Fig. 21 Positioning solenoid onto spring collar**

4. Align and secure spring to lower control arm. **The suspension must be at its full travel when replacing the springs, as damage to spring may result.**
5. Replace wheel assembly.
6. Refill air springs as outlined in "Air Springs, Refill" procedure.

## CONTROL MODULE, REPLACE

1. Turn air suspension switch to OFF position.
2. Remove left side luggage compartment trim panel, then disconnect wiring harness from module.
3. Remove control module retaining nuts, then the control module.
4. Reverse procedure to install.

## AIR COMPRESSOR/DRYER ASSEMBLY, REPLACE

1. Turn air suspension switch to OFF position.
2. Disconnect compressor electrical connector.
3. Remove air line protector cap from dryer by releasing the 2 pins located at bottom of cap.
4. Disconnect air lines from dryer.
5. Remove air compressor/dryer assembly to mounting bracket retaining screws, then the assembly.
6. Reverse procedure to install.

## HEIGHT SENSOR, REPLACE

### Front

1. Turn air suspension switch to OFF position.
2. Working from engine compartment, disconnect sensor electrical connector.
3. Push connector through access hole at rear of shock tower, then raise and support vehicle.
4. Disconnect bottom and top ends of sensor from attaching studs as shown, **Fig. 23.**
5. Disconnect wiring harness from plastic clips on shock tower and remove sensor.
6. Reverse procedure to install.

### Rear

Whenever the front air springs have been replaced, always check rear height sensor for damage. Replace, if necessary.

1. Turn air suspension switch to OFF position.
2. Working from luggage compartment, disconnect sensor electrical connector. Pull luggage compartment carpet back to gain access to sensor sealing grommet.
3. Raise and support vehicle, then disconnect bottom and top ends of sensor from the attaching studs, **Fig. 23.**
4. Pushing upwards, unseat sensor from grommet, then push sensor through floor pan into luggage compartment.
5. Reverse procedure to install.

## AIR SPRING REFILL

1. With suspension unloaded, turn air suspension switch to ON position, ensuring diagnostic pigtail is ungrounded. **Lower vehicle, ensuring no load on the suspension.**
2. Install battery charger to minimize battery drain.
3. With only driver's door open, cycle ignition from Off to Run position, do not start engine. Hold in Run for approximately 5 seconds, then return ignition to Off.
4. Ground the diagnostic pigtail, **Fig. 4,** then with driver's door open and brakes applied, turn ignition to Run position. The warning lamp will blink continuously, indicating the spring refill sequence has been entered.
5. To fill the rear spring(s), close, then open the driver's door once. After a 6 second delay, the spring(s) will be filled for approximately 1 minute.
6. To fill the front spring(s), close and open the driver's door twice. After a 6 second delay, the spring(s) will be filled for 1 minute.
7. If both front and rear springs are to be filled, fill the rear springs first, then open and close the driver's door once to initiate front spring filling.
8. To terminate the fill procedure, turn the ignition switch off, apply the brakes or disconnect the diagnostic pigtail.
9. Lower vehicle and start engine with all doors closed to allow vehicle to level to trim height.

## NYLON AIR LINE SERVICE

If a leak is detected in an air line, it can be serviced by carefully cutting the line

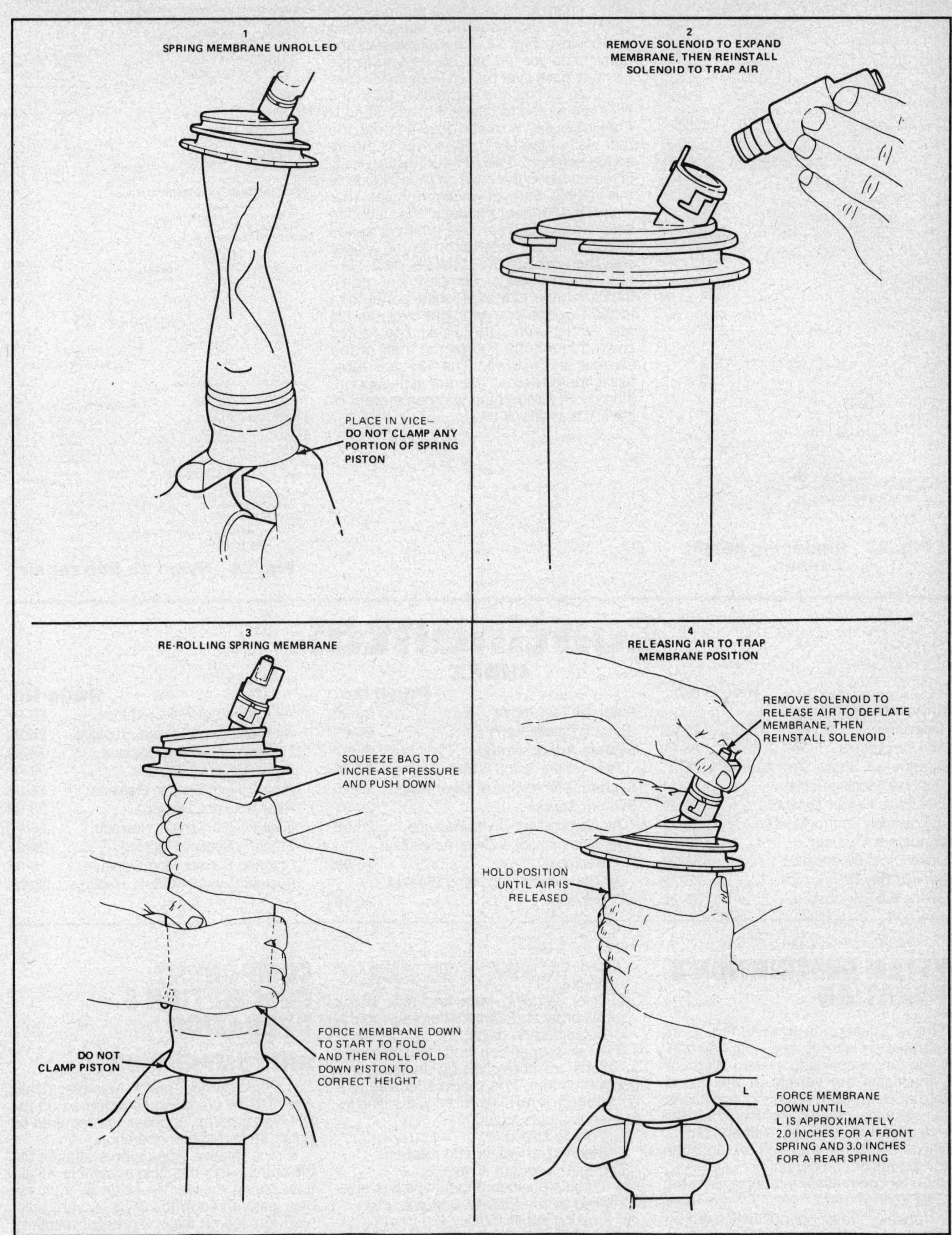
1
SPRING MEMBRANE UNROLLED
PLACE IN VICE–
DO NOT CLAMP ANY
PORTION OF SPRING
PISTON
2
REMOVE SOLENOID TO EXPAND
MEMBRANE, THEN REINSTALL
SOLENOID TO TRAP AIR
3
RE-ROLLING SPRING MEMBRANE
SQUEEZE BAG TO
INCREASE PRESSURE
AND PUSH DOWN
DO NOT
CLAMP PISTON
FORCE MEMBRANE DOWN
TO START TO FOLD
AND THEN ROLL FOLD
DOWN PISTON TO
CORRECT HEIGHT
4
RELEASING AIR TO TRAP
MEMBRANE POSITION
REMOVE SOLENOID TO
RELEASE AIR TO DEFLATE
MEMBRANE, THEN
REINSTALL SOLENOID
HOLD POSITION
UNTIL AIR IS
RELEASED
L
FORCE MEMBRANE
DOWN UNTIL
L IS APPROXIMATELY
2.0 INCHES FOR A FRONT
SPRING AND 3.0 INCHES
FOR A REAR SPRING

**Fig. 22 Refolding air spring**

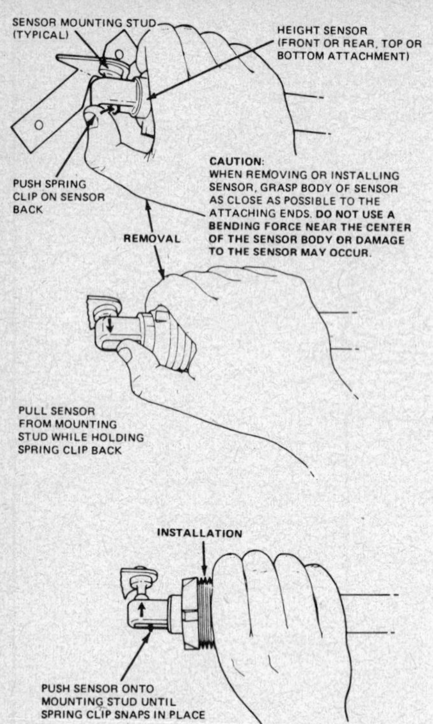


SENSOR MOUNTING STUD (TYPICAL)
HEIGHT SENSOR (FRONT OR REAR, TOP OR BOTTOM ATTACHMENT)
CAUTION:
WHEN REMOVING OR INSTALLING SENSOR, GRASP BODY OF SENSOR AS CLOSE AS POSSIBLE TO THE ATTACHING ENDS. DO NOT USE A BENDING FORCE NEAR THE CENTER OF THE SENSOR BODY OR DAMAGE TO THE SENSOR MAY OCCUR.
PUSH SPRING CLIP ON SENSOR BACK
REMOVAL
PULL SENSOR FROM MOUNTING STUD WHILE HOLDING SPRING CLIP BACK
INSTALLATION
PUSH SENSOR ONTO MOUNTING STUD UNTIL SPRING CLIP SNAPS IN PLACE

**Fig. 23 Replacing height sensor**

with a sharp knife to ensure a good, clean straight cut and installing a service fitting as shown in, **Fig. 24.** A protective cap and convoluted line protect air lines from the air dryer back over the left front shock tower. After exiting the protective tube the lines are routed to different areas. The LH front tube, gray, is routed down through the rear wall of the LH shock tower to the air spring solenoid. The RH front tube, black, is routed along the cowl on the RH side of the vehicle, then down through the rear wall of the RH shock tower to the sir spring solenoid. The LH rear tube, green, is routed through the LH side apron to the fender well, then through the LH upper dash panel to the passenger compartment, down the dash panel to the LH rocker panel, then to the luggage compartment over the LH rear fender well. The LH air line routes down through the floorpan in front of the LH rear shock tower. The RH rear tube, tan, is routed across the rear seat support, then down through the floorpan in front of the RH rear shock tower.

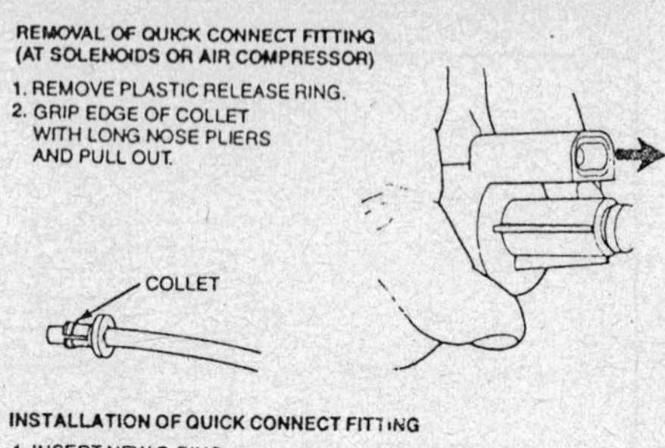


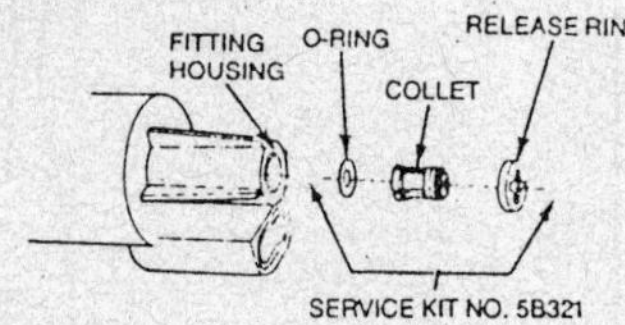


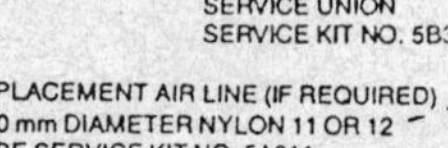


REMOVAL OF QUICK CONNECT FITTING
(AT SOLENOIDS OR AIR COMPRESSOR)
1. REMOVE PLASTIC RELEASE RING.
2. GRIP EDGE OF COLLET WITH LONG NOSE PLIERS AND PULL OUT.
COLLET

INSTALLATION OF QUICK CONNECT FITTING
1. INSERT NEW O-RING
2. PUSH NEW COLLET INTO FITTING HOUSING BY HAND
3. PUSH ON NEW RELEASE RING
FITTING HOUSING
O-RING
RELEASE RING
COLLET
SERVICE KIT NO. 5B321

SERVICE OF LEAKS IN AIR LINE
1. CLEAN CUT BOTH SIDES OF DAMAGED LINE
2. INSERT ENDS OF LINES INTO SERVICE UNION
3. WRAP WITH ELECTRICAL TAPE
X-ACTO KNIFE
SERVICE UNION
SERVICE KIT NO. 5B322
REPLACEMENT AIR LINE (IF REQUIRED)
4.70 mm DIAMETER NYLON 11 OR 12
TUBE SERVICE KIT NO. 5A911
TO SEAT, PUSH IN APPROXIMATELY 15 mm (0.59 INCH)

**Fig. 24 Nylon air line repair**

# Continental

## INDEX



## SYSTEM DESCRIPTION & OPERATION

The air suspension system, **Fig. 1,** incorporates air leveling and dual ride control into one suspension system. Air leveling maintains the vehicle at the proper level under varying operating conditions. Dual damping ride control switches the shock absorbers between soft and firm.

The air suspension system includes the following major components:

1. An air compressor to supply air to the air springs.
2. Variable rate air springs which are integral with the shock absorber struts at each corner of the vehicle.
3. Three rotary height sensors; one rear and two front height sensors to maintain the vehicle at the proper ride height.
4. Dual damping front and rear shock absorber struts with externally mounted actuators/drivers.

The air suspension and dual damping functions are controlled by an electronic control module. This module receives inputs from several different sources. The information inputs include:

1. Vehicle speed.
2. Steering wheel turning rotation.
3. Engine vacuum level.
4. Throttle position angle (which is supplied by the EEC-IV system).
5. Braking applications.
6. Ignition switch position.
7. Shock absorber damping position.
8. Door switch position.
9. Height sensor position.

## COMPONENT DESCRIPTION & OPERATION

### AIR COMPRESSOR

A single cylinder piston type electrically operated air compressor, mounted on the RH fender apron, supplies the required air pressure for system operation.

A regenerative type dryer is attached to the compressor manifold assembly. All airflow during the compression or vent cycles, pass through the dryer. A vent solenoid, located on the compressor manifold, controls air exhaustion.

Air required for leveling the vehicle is distributed from the air compressor to each air spring by four nylon air lines

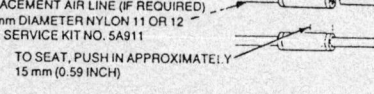

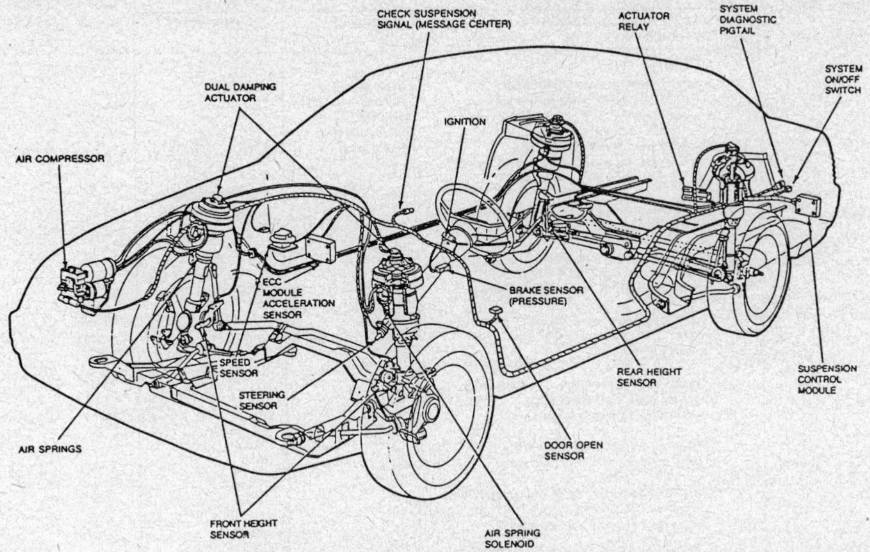


**Fig. 1 Air suspension system**

| STEP 1 of 1 | DRIVE CYCLE DIAGNOSTICS ENTRANCE PROCEDURE | RESULT | ACTION TO TAKE |
|---|---|---|---|
| | In order to enter/activate DRIVE CYCLE DIAGNOSTICS the following actions are required:<br>• After driving the vehicle for at least four minutes above a speed of 15 mph turn the ignition switch to the "OFF" position. | Within twenty seconds the STAR tester will continuously display one of the following code sets: | |
| | • Turn off headlights to battery voltage.<br>• Open trunk lid and verify that the air suspension "ON/OFF" switch is in the "ON" position. (NOTE: If this switch was turned "OFF" while the ignition was also "OFF" DRIVE CYCLE DIAGNOSTICS can not be entered.) | "15" ▶ | DRIVE CYCLE DIAGNOSTICS is completed and NO faults were detected. Disconnect the "STAR" tester to exit DRIVE CYCLE DIAGNOSTICS. |
| | • Release the "STAR" test button so that it remains in the up "HOLD" position and turn the "STAR" tester "ON".<br>• Connect the "STAR" tester to the air suspension diagnostic connector and turn "STAR" tester on. After waiting a minimum of 5 seconds depress the "STAR" test button so that it remains down in the "TEST" position. | "40" to "71" ▶ | DRIVE CYCLE DIAGNOSTICS is completed and system faults were detected. Write down the complete list of system faults only after they have been displayed at least two times. Then run SERVICE BAY DIAGNOSTICS. |
| | NOTE: Drive Cycle faults will be saved for up to 55 minutes after the ignition is turned to the "OFF" (NON-RUN) position. Any time the ignition switch is turned to the "ON" position the air suspension control module will erase all fault codes that were detected. | ALL OTHER CODES ▶ | GO TO AA1 |

**Fig. 2 Drive cycle diagnostic procedure**

which start at the compressor dryer and terminate at the individual air springs. The dryer is a common pressure manifold for all four air lines. The air lines are color coded to identify to which air spring they are attached. **The compressor relay, compressor vent solenoid and all air spring solenoids incorporate internal diodes for electrical noise suppression and are polarity sensitive. Care must be taken when servicing these components not to switch the battery positive and ground cables or system/component damage will result. When charging the battery, the ignition switch must be in the OFF position if the air suspension switch is in the ON position or damage to the air compressor relay or motor may occur.**

## AIR SPRING & SHOCK STRUT ASSEMBLY

The front and rear suspension system incorporate MacPherson type strut assemblies with integral air springs and two stage (dual) dampening mechanisms. The two stage dampening is achieved by varying the piston orifice area with an externally mounted electronic rotary actuator. The front struts are mounted to the body through a precision ball bearing and rubber mount system. The ball bearing provides a smooth and durable pivot point for the strut/wheel assembly.

The rear struts incorporate a dual path mount which separates the strut and air spring mounting surfaces to provide for maximum isolation.

## SUSPENSION CONTROL MODULE

The control module responds to signals from the various sensors in the vehicle to maintain the desired ride height while the vehicle is either moving or stopped. It accomplishes this by opening and closing the air spring valves. It also turns on the compressor through the compressor relay or opens the vent solenoid in response to signal inputs from the height sensors.

## ELECTRONIC HEIGHT SENSOR

The electronic height sensor is a rotary style design that uses an internal hall effect device to determine ride height. These sensors will indicate conditions of above trim, trim and below trim to the control module. The three sensors are located at the LH front, RH front and RH rear of the vehicle. Each one of the sensors measures the actual difference between known reference points so that the control module can respond to variations in ride height. In the parking mode, additional height positions allow the system to accurately determine if an obstruction was encountered during a parking maneuver. In the driving mode, variations in road surfaces are sensed by checking road wheel vertical speed and vertical travel. If the average wheel speed and travel is above a predetermined level, the shock absorbers are switched to the firm position. This reduces the chance of grounding out of the subframe when traveling over bumpy road surfaces.

## DUAL DAMPENING SYSTEM

The function of the dual dampening system is to automatically switch the shock strut settings from soft to firm when driving conditions require it. The system monitors vehicle accelerations, decelerations, up and down road wheel travel and also steering wheel position and steering wheel turning rates before responding to individual sensor inputs.

## DIAGNOSIS & TESTING

To properly diagnose and test this system requires the use of Rotunda Star Tester model 007-00004 or Super Star II tester 007-00019 or equivalents. Follow tool manufacturer's instructions for installation and operation of the tool.

## DRIVE CYCLE DIAGNOSTICS

On models built after 12/1/90, the suspension module will not erase system fault codes stored in memory when the ignition switch is cycled to the Run position within an hour of turning ignition switch Off. To erase fault codes, turn ignition switch Off and allow vehicle to sit for more than one hour or switch module power Off at trunk mounted suspension system switch.

The drive cycle diagnostics will illuminate the "Ride Control" warning lamp in the message center when a fault code is detected while driving the vehicle. Up to 32 fault codes will remain stored in memory for one hour after ignition switch is turned Off. The air suspension switch in luggage compartment must remain On. If the vehicle has not been driven in over an hour or the ignition switch has been turned to Run and the air suspension switch has been turned Off, vehicle must be driven to duplicate faults, refer to **Fig. 2.**

## SERVICE BAY DIAGNOSTICS

Refer to **Fig. 3.** to perform service bay diagnostic procedures.

### Auto/Manual Diagnostic Check

This test is a self diagnostic check which monitors system operation and components. After performing this check, the Star Tester will display a code 12 indicating the system is okay, proceed to manual checks or a code 13 indicating faults have been detected, proceed to manual checks. The manual input checks should be performed at this time.

### Fault Code Display

Fault codes can be displayed using the Star Tester. Each fault code detected will be displayed for about 15 seconds. Codes should be recorded at this time, refer to diagnostic code priorities chart, **Fig. 4.**

### Pinpoint Tests

Each fault code has it own pinpoint test. These tests have priorities assigned with "1" being the highest priority and "7" being the lowest. One fault may cause other fault codes to be displayed. Perform pinpoint tests in order of priority starting with the highest. For Diagnostic Codes, refer to **Fig. 4.**. For Connector Terminal Identification, refer to **Figs. 5 through 24.** For Pinpoint tests, refer to **Fig. 25 through 61.**

## SPRING FILL DIAGNOSTICS

Refer to **Fig. 62.** to perform spring fill diagnostic procedures.

*Continued on page 26-97*

| STEP 1 of 4 | SERVICE BAY DIAGNOSTICS ENTRANCE PROCEDURE | RESULT | ACTION TO TAKE |
|---|---|---|---|
| | In order to enter/activate SERVICE BAY DIAGNOSTICS the following actions are required:<br>• Connect a battery charger to the vehicle's battery and leave connected for the duration of the test sequence.<br>• If required release the STAR test button so that it remains in "HOLD" up position.<br>• Open trunk lid and connect the STAR tester to the air suspension diagnostic connector and turn the STAR tester "ON".<br>• Turn the air suspension "ON/OFF" switch to the "OFF" position and then back to the "ON" position.<br>• Check vehicle passenger compartment and trunk for loads. Remove all loads; vehicle must be at curb weight.<br>• Make sure the ignition switch is in the "OFF" position and wait ten seconds.<br>• With the brake pedal NOT depressed turn the ignition switch to the "ON/RUN" position (not necessary to start engine).<br>• Verify that the headlights, heater fan, windshield wipers, ..., etc. are turned off.<br>• Wait a minimum of 5 seconds and then depress the STAR test button so that it remains down in the "TEST" position. | Within twenty seconds the STAR tester will display one of the following codes: | |
| | | "10" ▶ | GO TO SERVICE BAY DIAGNOSTICS "STEP 2 of 4". |
| | | "21" to "28" ▶ | GO TO BB1 |
| | | "80" ▶ | GO TO DA1 |
| | | SOMETHING ELSE ▶ | GO TO BA1 |

**Fig. 3 Service bay diagnostic procedure (Part 1 of 4)**

| STEP 2 of 4 | SERVICE BAY DIAGNOSTICS AUTOMATIC MODE TESTING | RESULT | ACTION TO TAKE |
|---|---|---|---|
| | The STAR tester is displaying a code "10". The air suspension control module has completed a self check of itself and is now conducting the automatic portion of diagnostics. Do not touch or lean on the vehicle while automatic testing is being conducted (STAR code "10") . This test will take approximately three to four minutes to complete if there are no air leveling problems. IF THERE ARE AIR LEVELING PROBLEMS THIS TEST MAY TAKE FOURTEEN MINUTES. At the end of the test the STAR tester will display a code "12" or "13". | STAR tester is displaying a code: | |
| | | "12" ▶ | No system faults were detected in the automatic mode. Go to SERVICE BAY DIAGNOSTICS "STEP 3 of 4". |
| | | "13" ▶ | System faults were detected in the automatic mode. Go to SERVICE BAY DIAGNOSTICS "STEP 3 of 4". |

**Fig. 3 Service bay diagnostic procedure (Part 2 of 4)**

| STEP 3 of 4 | SERVICE BAY DIAGNOSTICS TESTING COMPLETED | RESULT | ACTION TO TAKE |
|---|---|---|---|
| | The air suspension control module has completed its automatic checks and is now waiting for the service technician to perform the following manual operations: | The STAR tester is displaying one of the following codes: | |
| | • Open the driver's door and be seated in the vehicle leaving the driver's door open.<br>• Depress the accelerator pedal to the floor and then release it.<br>• Depress the brake pedal hard and then release it. | "11" ▶ | Service Bay Diagnostics is completed and NO faults were detected. Go to SERVICE BAY DIAGNOSTICS "STEP 4 of 4". |
| | • Turn the steering wheel a minimum of a 1/4 turn in both directions.<br>• Exit the vehicle and shut the driver's door. Then open and shut the other three vehicle doors one at a time.<br>• After completing the above release the STAR test button to the "HOLD" position. After five seconds depress the STAR test button again so that it remains in the down "TEST" position.<br><br>NOTE: The detected system fault codes will be displayed in a numerical order one at a time. After the last detected system fault code is displayed the list will be repeated. This scrolling manner will continue as long as the STAR test button remains in the up "TEST" position. | "40" to "79" ▶ | Service Bay Diagnostics is completed and faults were detected. Write down the complete list of system faults only after they have been displayed at least two times. Go to SERVICE BAY DIAGNOSTICS "STEP 4 of 4". |

Fig. 3 Service bay diagnostic procedure (Part 3 of 4)

| STEP 4 of 4 | SERVICE BAY DIAGNOSTICS DETECTED SYSTEM FAULTS | RESULT | ACTION TO TAKE |
|---|---|---|---|
| | If the "DRIVE CYCLE DIAGNOSTICS" fault list included STAR code "55" add it to the "SERVICE BAY DIAGNOSTICS" detected faults list just generated. | In DRIVE CYCLE or SERVICE BAY DIAGNOSTICS system faults were detected: | |
| | Those "DRIVE CYCLE DIAGNOSTIC" detected faults that are not repeated in "SERVICE BAY DIAGNOSTICS" are to be handled as an intermittent fault. | YES ▶ | |
| | In order to minimize the time and labor involved in fixing a detected system fault the fault codes have been grouped.<br><br>NOTE: The detected system fault codes will be displayed in a numerical order one at a time. After the last detected system fault code is displayed the list will be repeated. This scrolling manner will continue as long as the STAR test button remains in the "TEST" position. | NO ▶ | To exit SERVICE BAY DIAGNOSTICS turn the ignition switch to the "OFF" position. |

Fig. 3 Service bay diagnostic procedure (Part 4 of 4)

| STAR CODE | PINPOINT PROCEDURE | DESCRIPTION | SERVICE PRIORITY |
|---|---|---|---|
| 10 | | Service Bay Diagnostics Entered | |
| 11 | | System Checked out okay | |
| 12 | | Automatic Test Completed — No Faults Detected Perform Manual Inputs | |
| 13 | | Automatic Test Completed — Faults Detected Perform Manual Inputs | |
| 15 | | No Faults Detected | |
| 21 | | Vent Right Front Air Spring | |
| 22 | | Vent Left Front Air Spring | |
| 23 | | Vent Right Rear Air Spring | |
| 24 | | Inflate Right Front Air Spring | |
| 25 | | Inflate Left Front Air Spring | |
| 26 | | Inflate Right Rear Air Spring | |
| 27 | | Vent Left Rear Air Spring | |
| 28 | | Inflate Left Rear Air Spring | |
| 31 | | Air Compressor Toggle | |
| 32 | | Vent Solenoid Valve Toggle | |
| 33 | | Air Spring Solenoid Valve Toggle | |
| 34 | | Shock Actuator Toggle (Firm/Soft) | |
| 35 | | Door Open & Door Closed Detection | |
| 40 | EA | Short — Left Frt. Air Spring Solenoid Valve Circuit | 2nd |
| 41 | EB | Short — Right Frt. Air Spring Solenoid Valve Circuit | 2nd |
| 42 | EC | Short — Left Rear Air Spring Solenoid Valve Circuit | 2nd |
| 43 | ED | Short —Right Rear Air Spring Solenoid Valve Circuit | 2nd |
| 44 | EE | Short — Vent Solenoid Valve Circuit | 2nd |
| 45 | EF | Short — Air Compressor Relay Circuit | 2nd |
| 46 | EG | Short — Height Sensor Power Supply Circuit | 2nd |
| 47 | EH | Short — Soft Shock Actuator Relay Circuit | 2nd |
| 48 | EI | Short — Firm Shock Actuator Relay Circuit | 2nd |
| 49 | HA | Unable to Detect Lowering of Right Front Corner | 5th |

**NOTE: System faults have been prioritized for repair. Start with those codes identified with a service priority of: 1st, then 2nd, then 3rd, ...and finally 7th.**

Fig. 4 Diagnostic codes, (Part 1 of 2)

| STAR CODE | PINPOINT PROCEDURE | DESCRIPTION | SERVICE PRIORITY |
|---|---|---|---|
| 50 | HB | Unable to Detect Lowering of Left Front Corner | 5th |
| 51* | HC | Unable to Detect Lowering of Right Rear Corner | 5th |
| 51* | | Unable to Detect Lowering of Rear of Vehicle | 5th |
| 52 | IA | Unable to Detect Raising of Right Front Corner | 6th |
| 53 | IB | Unable to Detect Raising of Left Front Corner | 6th |
| 54* | IC | Unable to Detect Raising of Right Rear Corner | 6th |
| 54* | | Unable to Detect Raising of Rear of Vehicle | 6th |
| 55 | JA | Speed Greater Than 15 mph Not Detected | 7th |
| 56 | GA | Soft Not Detected — Left Rear Shock Actuator Circuit | 4th |
| 57 | GB | Soft Not Detected — Right Frt. Shock Actuator Circuit | 4th |
| 58 | GC | Soft Not Detected — Left Frt. Shock Actuator Circuit | 4th |
| 59 | GD | Soft Not Detected — Right Rear Shock Actuator Circuit | 4th |
| 60 | GA | Firm Not Detected — Left Rear Shock Actuator Circuit | 4th |
| 61 | GB | Firm Not Detected — Right Frt. Shock Actuator Circuit | 4th |
| 62 | GC | Firm Not Detected — Left Frt. Shock Actuator Circuit | 4th |
| 63 | GD | Firm Not Detected — Right Rear Shock Actuator Circuit | 4th |
| 64 | GE | Soft Not Detected — All Shock Actuator Circuits | 4th |
| 65 | GE | Firm Not Detected — All Shock Actuator Circuits | 4th |
| 66 | EJ | Short — Right Front Height Sensor Circuit | 2nd |
| 67 | EK | Short — Left Front Height Sensor Circuit | 2nd |
| 68 | EL | Short — Rear Height Sensor Circuit | 2nd |
| 69 | FA | Open — Right Front Height Sensor Circuit | 3rd |
| 70 | FB | Open — Left Front Height Sensor Circuit | 3rd |
| 71 | FC | Open — Rear Height Sensor Circuit | 3rd |
| 72 | JB | At Least Four Open & Closed Door Signals Not Detected | 7th |
| 73 | JC | Brake Pressure Switch Activation Not Detected | 7th |
| 74 | JD | Steering Wheel Rotations Not Detected | 7th |
| 75 | JE | Acceleration Signal Not Detected | 7th |
| 78 | HD | Unable to Detect Lowering of Left Rear Corner | 5th |
| 79 | ID | Unable to Detect Raising of Left Rear Corner | 6th |
| 80 | DA | Insufficient Battery Voltage to Run Diagnostics | 1st |

**NOTE: System faults have been prioritized for repair. Start with those codes identified with a service priority of: 1st, then 2nd, then 3rd, ...and finally 7th.**

**Fig. 4 Diagnostic codes, (Part 2 of 2)**

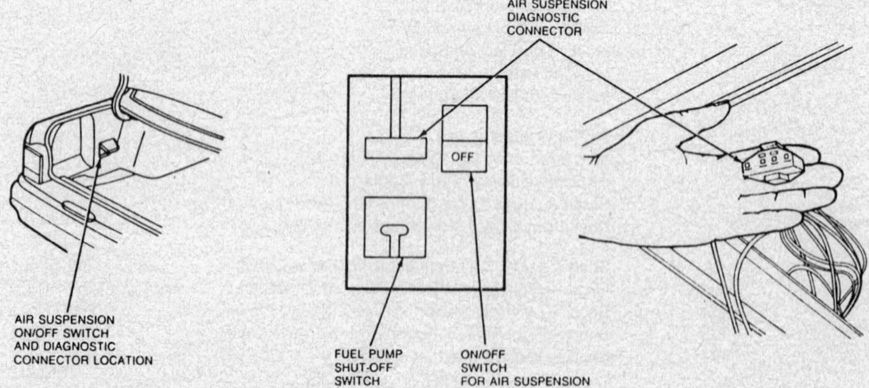


**Fig. 5 Air suspension diagnostic connector location (Part 1 of 2)**

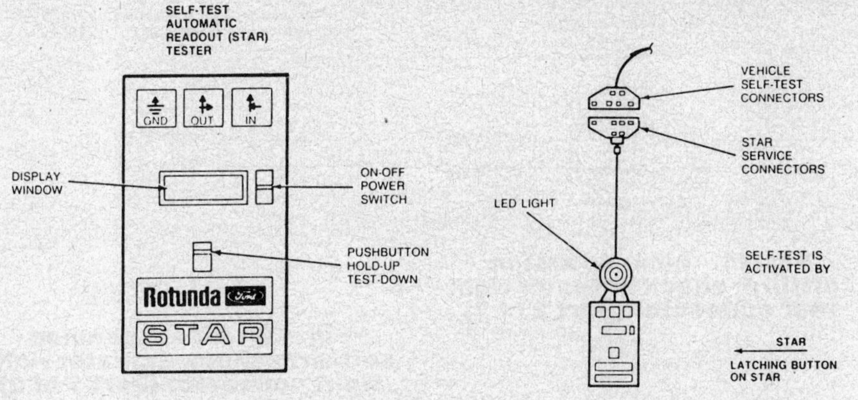


**Fig. 5 Air suspension diagnostic connector location (Part 2 of 2)**

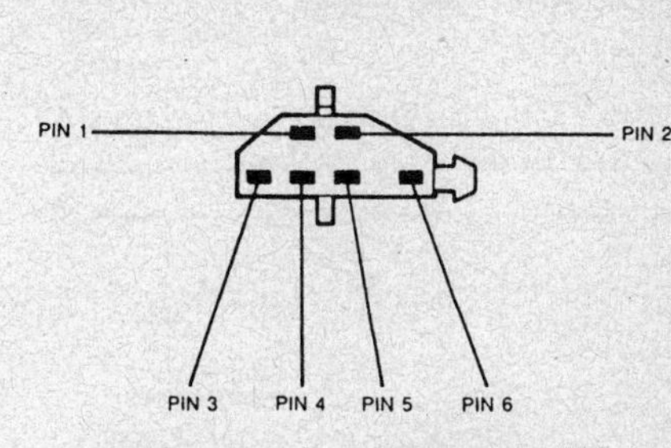


**Fig. 6 Air suspension diagnostic pigtail connector (Part 1 of 2)**

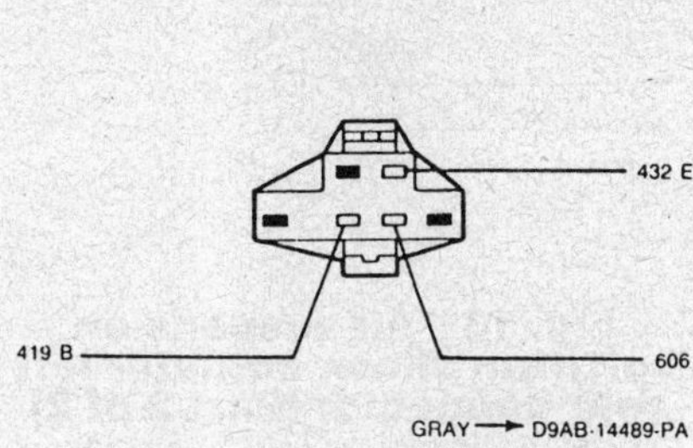


**Fig. 6 Air suspension diagnostic pigtail connector (Part 2 of 2)**

ON/OFF SWITCH CONNECTOR
VEHICLE WIRING HARNESS
175C
418
WHITE → E3EB-14489-JA

**Fig. 7 Air suspension on/off switch connector (Part 1 of 2)**

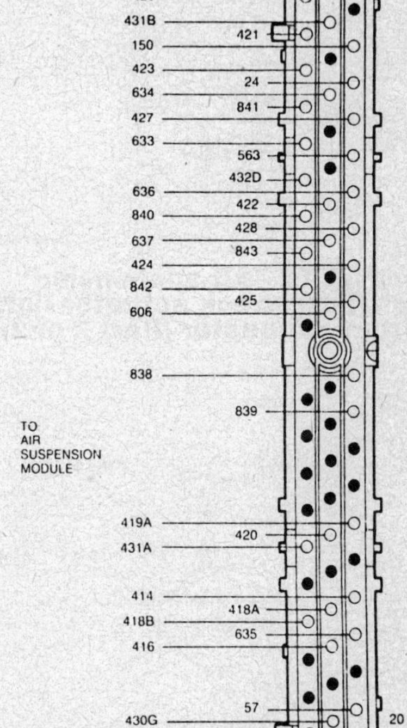


**Fig. 7 Air suspension on/off switch connector (Part 2 of 2)**

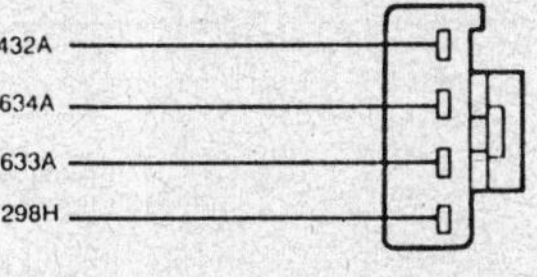


**Fig. 8 Air suspension steering wheel sensor rate/rotation connector (Part 1 of 2)**

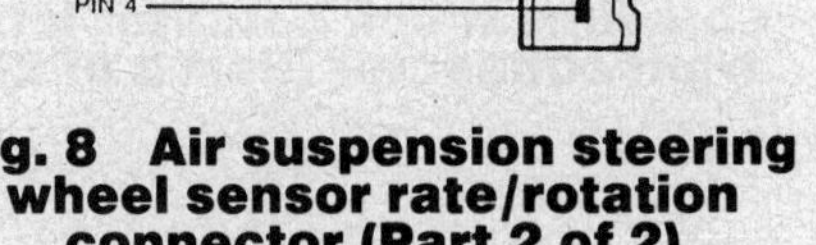


**Fig. 8 Air suspension steering wheel sensor rate/rotation connector (Part 2 of 2)**

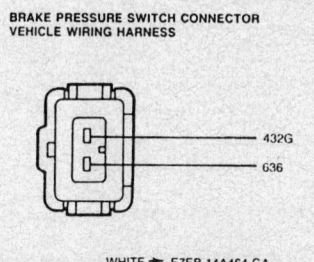

BRAKE PRESSURE SWITCH CONNECTOR
VEHICLE WIRING HARNESS
432G
636
WHITE → E7EB-14A464-GA
E7EB-14A468A-EA

**Fig. 9 Air suspension brake pressure switch connector**

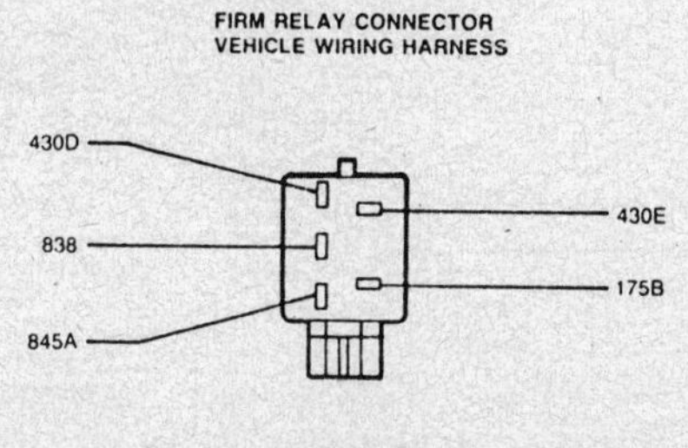


**Fig. 10 Air suspension shock actuator relay firm connector (Part 1 of 2)**

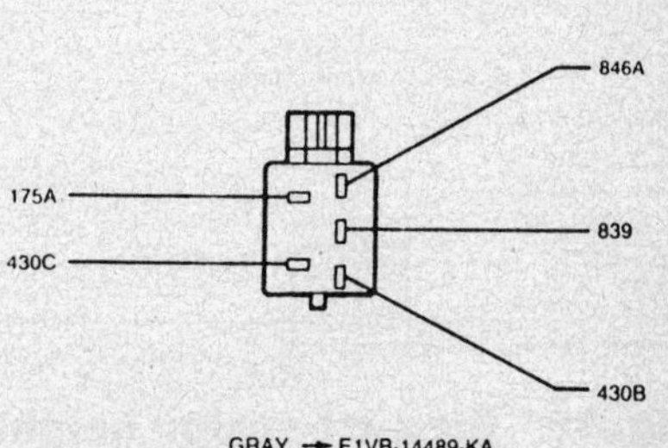


**Fig. 10 Air suspension shock actuator relay soft connector (Part 2 of 2)**

RH REAR SHOCK ACTUATOR CONNECTOR
VEHICLE WIRING HARNESS

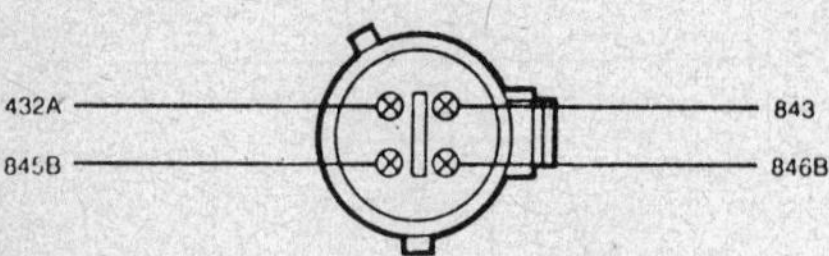


BLACK → E6DB-14A624-AB
E6DB-14A468-BB

**Fig. 11 Air suspension soft/firm shock actuator right rear connector (Part 1 of 2)**

RH REAR SHOCK ACTUATOR

**Fig. 11 Air suspension soft/firm shock actuator right rear connector (Part 2 of 2)**

RH FRONT SHOCK ACTUATOR CONNECTOR
VEHICLE WIRING HARNESS

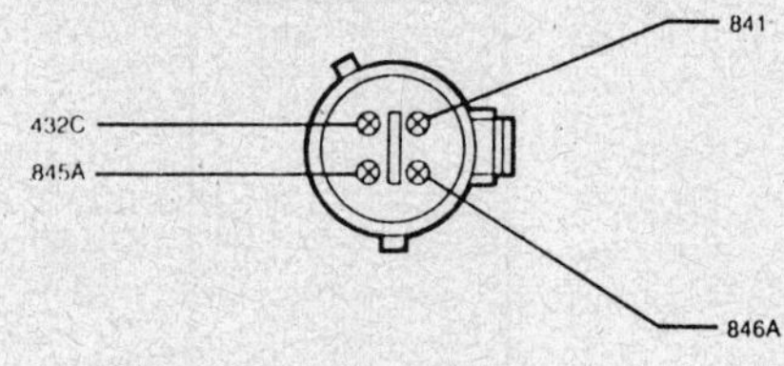


BLACK → E6DB-14A624-AB
E6DB-14A468-BB

**Fig. 12 Air suspension soft/firm shock actuator right front connector (Part 1 of 2)**

RH FRONT SHOCK ACTUATOR

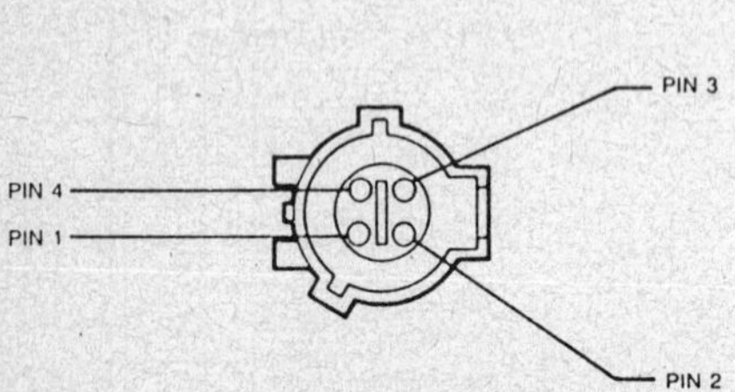


**Fig. 12 Air suspension soft/firm shock actuator right front connector (Part 2 of 2)**

LH REAR SHOCK ACTUATOR CONNECTOR
VEHICLE WIRING HARNESS

842
432C
845C
846C

BLACK → E6DB-14A624-AB
E6DB-14A468-BB

**Fig. 13 Air suspension soft/firm shock actuator left rear connector (Part 1 of 2)**

LH REAR SHOCK ACTUATOR

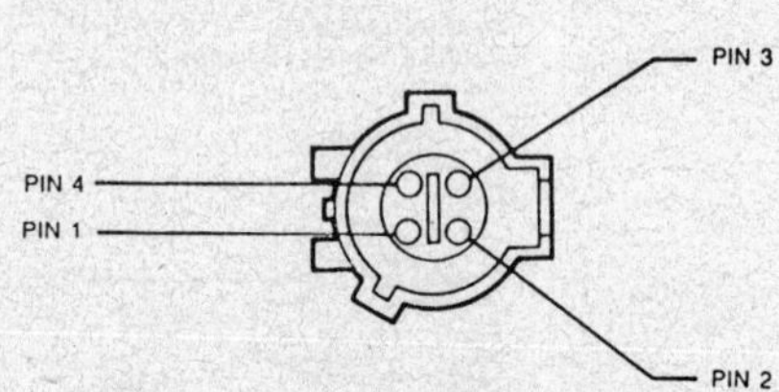


**Fig. 13 Air suspension soft/firm shock actuator left rear connector (Part 2 of 2)**

LH FRONT SHOCK ACTUATOR CONNECTOR
VEHICLE WIRING HARNESS

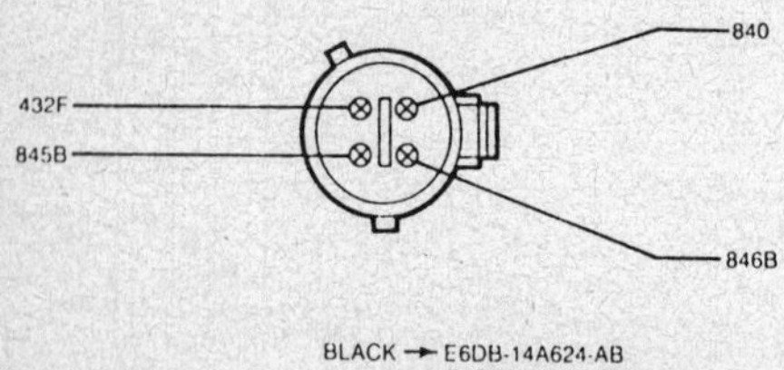


BLACK → E6DB-14A624-AB
E6DB-14A468-BB

**Fig. 14 Air suspension soft/firm shock actuator left front connector (Part 1 of 2)**

LH FRONT SHOCK ACTUATOR

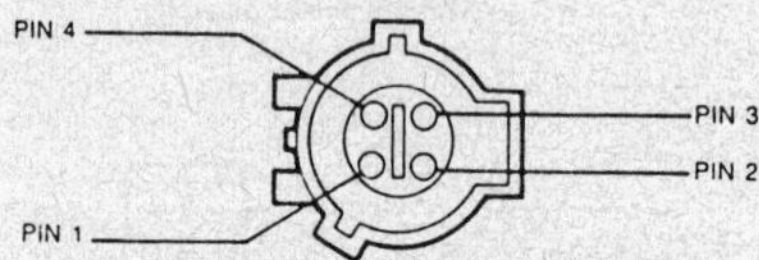


**Fig. 14 Air suspension soft/firm shock actuator left front connector (Part 2 of 2)**

REAR HEIGHT SENSOR CONNECTOR
VEHICLE WIRING HARNESS

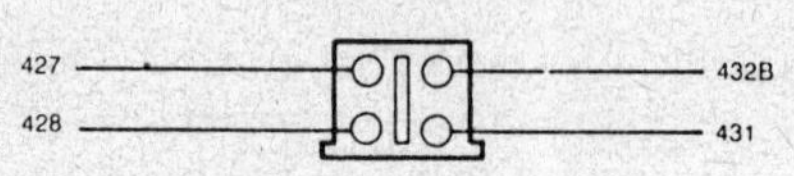


GRAY → D4AB-14489-DB
D4AB-14A468-DB

**Fig. 15 Air suspension height sensor right rear connector (Part 1 of 2)**

REAR HEIGHT SENSOR

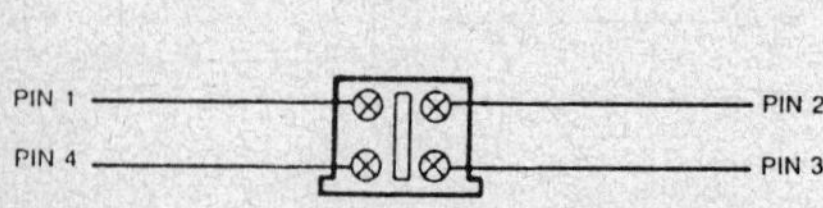


**Fig. 15 Air suspension height sensor right rear connector (Part 2 of 2)**

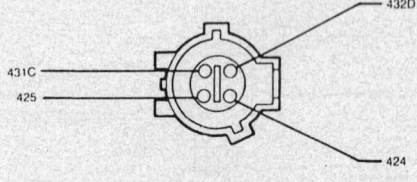

RH FRONT HEIGHT SENSOR CONNECTOR
VEHICLE WIRING HARNESS

432D
431C
425
424

GRAY → E6DB-14A464-NA
E6DB-14A468-AA

**Fig. 16 Air suspension height sensor right front connector (Part 1 of 2)**

RH FRONT HEIGHT SENSOR

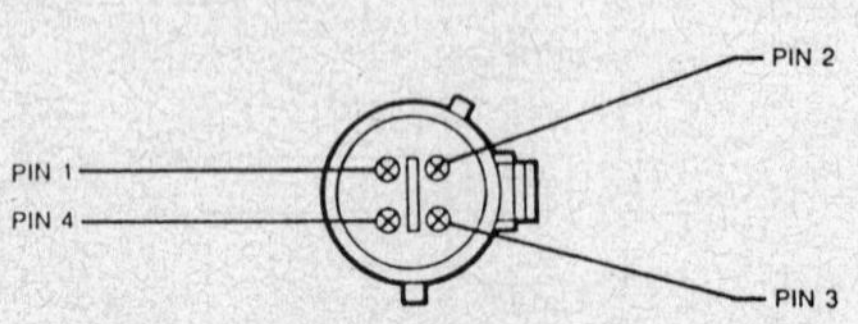


**Fig. 16 Air suspension height sensor right front connector (Part 2 of 2)**

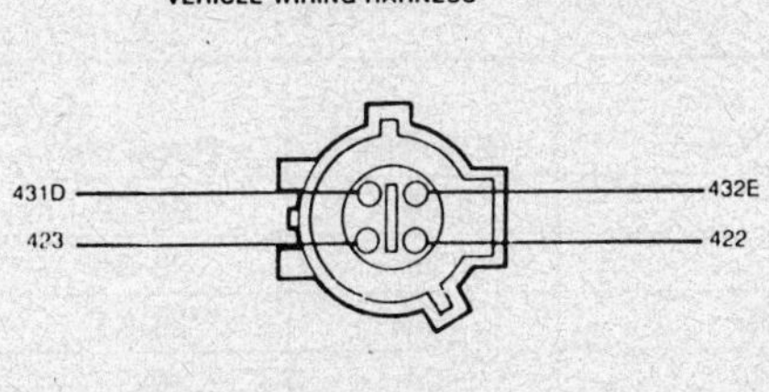


**Fig. 17 Air suspension height sensor left front connector (Part 1 of 2)**

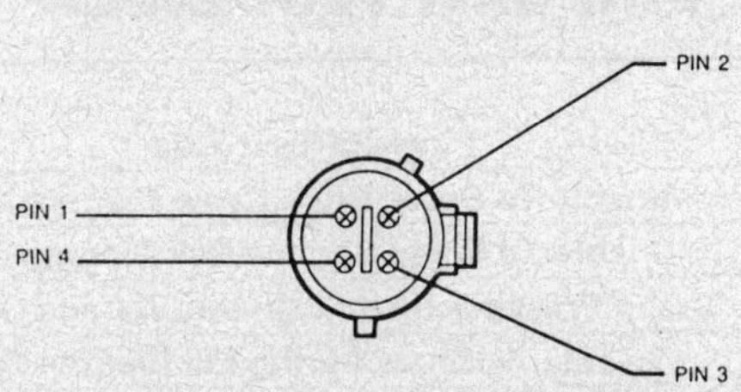


**Fig. 17 Air suspension height sensor left front connector (Part 2 of 2)**

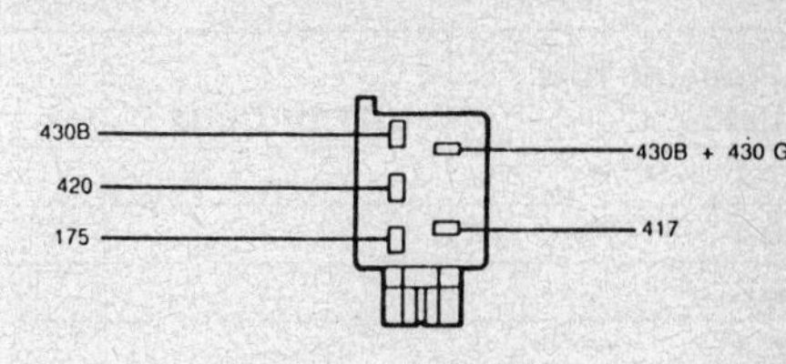


**Fig. 18 Air compressor relay connector**

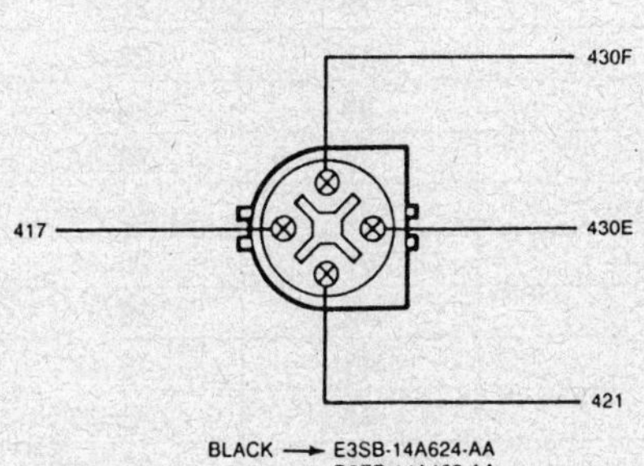


**Fig. 19 Air compressor assembly connector (Part 1 of 2)**

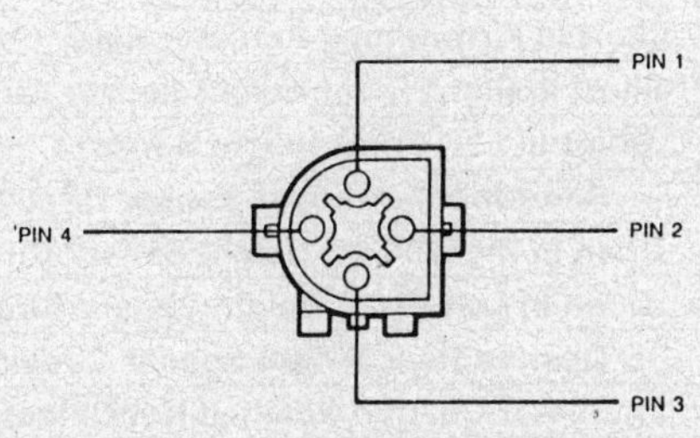


**Fig. 19 Air compressor assembly connector (Part 2 of 2)**

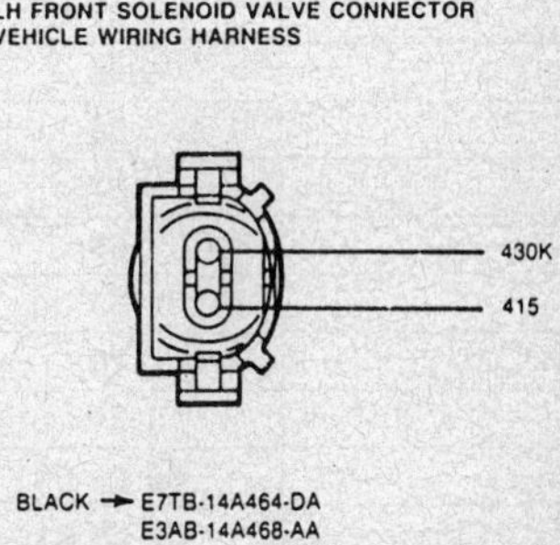


**Fig. 20 Air spring solenoid valve left front connector**

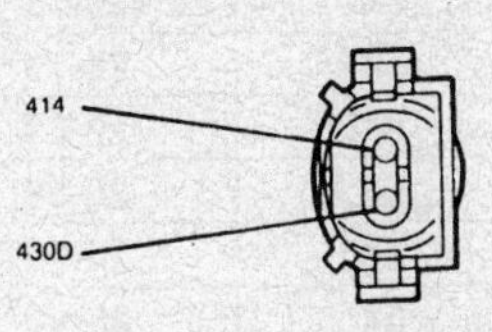


**Fig. 21 Air spring solenoid valve right front connector (Part 1 of 2)**

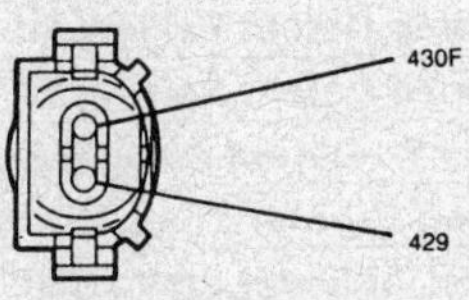


**Fig. 21 Air spring solenoid valve left rear connector (Part 2 of 2)**

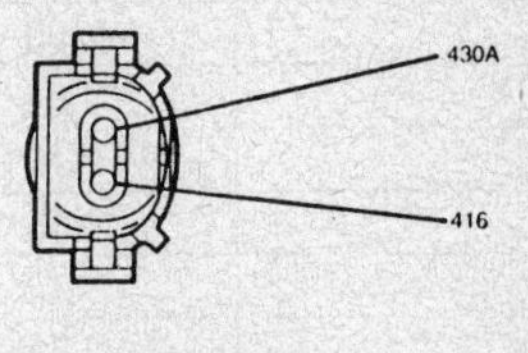


**Fig. 22 Air spring solenoid valve right rear connector**

**Fig. 23 Vehicle speed sensor connector (Part 1 of 2). 1988–89**

**Fig. 23 Vehicle speed sensor connector (Part 2 of 2). 1988–89**

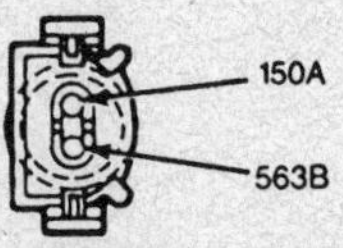


**Fig. 24 Vehicle speed sensor connector. 1990–91**

# PINPOINT TEST INDEX

| Pinpoint Test Letter | STAR Code | Pinpoint Test Title | Fig. No. | Page No |
|---|---|---|---|---|
| AA | — | Unable To Enter Drive Cycle Diagnostics | 25 | 26-29 |
| BA | — | Unable To Enter Service Bay Diagnostics | 26 | 26-30 |
| BB | — | Brake Pressure Switch Circuit Voltage Check | 26A | 26-31 |
| CA | — | Unable To Enter Spring Fill Diagnostics | 27 | 26-32 |
| DA | 80 | Low Power Supply Voltage | 28 | 26-33 |
| EA | 40 | Short In Left Front Air Spring Solenoid Valve Circuit | 29 | 26-34 |
| EB | 41 | Short In Right Front Air Spring Solenoid Valve Circuit | 30 | 26-35 |
| EC | 42 | Short In Left Rear Air Spring Solenoid Valve Circuit | 31 | 26-36 |
| ED | 43 | Short In Right Rear Air Spring Solenoid Valve Circuit | 32 | 26-37 |
| EE | 44 | Short In Vent Solenoid Valve Circuit | 33 | 26-38 |
| EF | 45 | Short In Air Compressor Relay Circuit | 34 | 26-39 |
| EG | 46 | Short In Height Sensor Power Supply Circuit | 35 | 26-40 |
| EH | 47 | Short In Soft Shock Actuator Relay Circuit | 36 | 26-41 |
| EI | 48 | Short In Firm Shock Actuator Relay Circuit | 37 | 26-42 |
| EJ | 66 | Short In Right Front Height Sensor Circuit | 38 | 26-44 |
| EK | 67 | Short In Left Front Height Sensor Circuit | 39 | 26-44 |
| EL | 68 | Short In Rear Height Sensor Circuit | 40 | 26-45 |
| FA | 69 | Open In Right Front Height Sensor Circuit | 41 | 26-46 |
| FB | 70 | Open In Left Front Height Sensor Circuit | 42 | 26-47 |
| FC | 71 | Open In Rear Height Sensor Circuit | 43 | 26-48 |
| GA | 56 Or 60 | Actuator Desired Position Not Detected | 44 | 26-50 |
| GB | 57 Or 61 | Actuator Desired Position Not Detected | 45 | 26-51 |
| GC | 58 Or 62 | Actuator Desired Position Not Detected | 46 | 26-53 |
| GD | 59 Or 63 | Actuator Desired Position Not Detected | 47 | 26-54 |
| GE | 64 Or 65 | All Shock Actuators Not In The Desired Position | 48 | 26-56 |
| HA | 49 | Unable To Detect Lowering Of Right Front Corner | 49 | 26-58 |
| HB | 50 | Unable To Detect Lowering Of Left Front Corner | 50 | 26-62 |
| HC | 51 | Unable To Detect Lowering Of Right Rear Corner | 51 | 26-66 |
| HD | 78 | Unable To Detect Lowering of Left Rear Corner | 52 | 26-70 |
| IA | 52 | Unable To Detect Raising Of Right Front Corner | 53 | 26-75 |
| IB | 53 | Unable to Detect Raising Of Left Front Corner | 54 | 26-79 |
| IC | 54 | Unable To Detect Raising Of Right Rear Corner | 55 | 26-83 |
| ID | 79 | Unable To Detect Raising Of Left Rear Corner | 56 | 26-86 |
| JA | 55 | Speed Greater Than 15 mph Not Detected | 57 | 26-90 |
| JB | 72 | Did Not Detect At Least Four Open And Close Door Signals | 58 | 26-90 |
| JC | 73 | Brake Pressure Switch Activation Not Detected | 59 | 26-94 |
| JD | 74 | Steering Wheel Rotation in Both Directions Not Detected | 60 | 26-95 |
| JE | 75 | Acceleration Signal Not Detected | 61 | 26-96 |

| | UNABLE TO ENTER DRIVE CYCLE DIAGNOSTICS | RESULT | ACTION TO TAKE |
|---|---|---|---|
| AA1 | DRIVE CYCLE DIAGNOSTICS has not been entered. There are five possible causes which are listed below:<br>• The STAR tester is defective.<br>• B+ power supply circuit is defective.<br>• The ignition switch circuit is defective.<br>• The STI circuit is defective<br>• The STO circuit is defective. | ▶ | GO TO AA2 |
| AA2 | **STAR TESTER CHECK** | | |
| | DRIVE CYCLE DIAGNOSTICS has not been entered possibly due to a defective STAR tester. To determine if this is the case the following actions are required:<br>• Disconnect the STAR tester and get another STAR tester if possible.<br>• On the new STAR tester release the STAR test button if required so that it remains in the up "HOLD" position.<br>• Connect the new STAR tester to the air suspension diagnostic connector and turn it "ON".<br>• After waiting a minimum of 5 seconds depress the STAR test button so that it remains down in the "TEST" position.<br>NOTE: Drive Cycle faults will be saved for up to 55 minutes after the ignition is turned to the "OFF" (NON-RUN) position. Any time the ignition switch is turned to the "ON" position the air suspension control module will erase all fault codes that were detected. | Within twenty seconds the STAR tester will display one of the following codes: | |
| | | "15" ▶ | DRIVE CYCLE DIAGNOSTICS is completed and NO faults were detected. Disconnect the STAR tester to exit DRIVE CYCLE DIAGNOSTICS. |
| | | "40" to "71" ▶ | DRIVE CYCLE DIAGNOSTICS is completed and system faults were detected. Write down the complete list of system faults only after they have been displayed at least two times. Then run SERVICE BAY DIAGNOSTICS. |
| | | ALL OTHER CODES ▶ | GO TO AA3 |

**Fig. 25 Pinpoint test, AA (Part 1 of 5)**

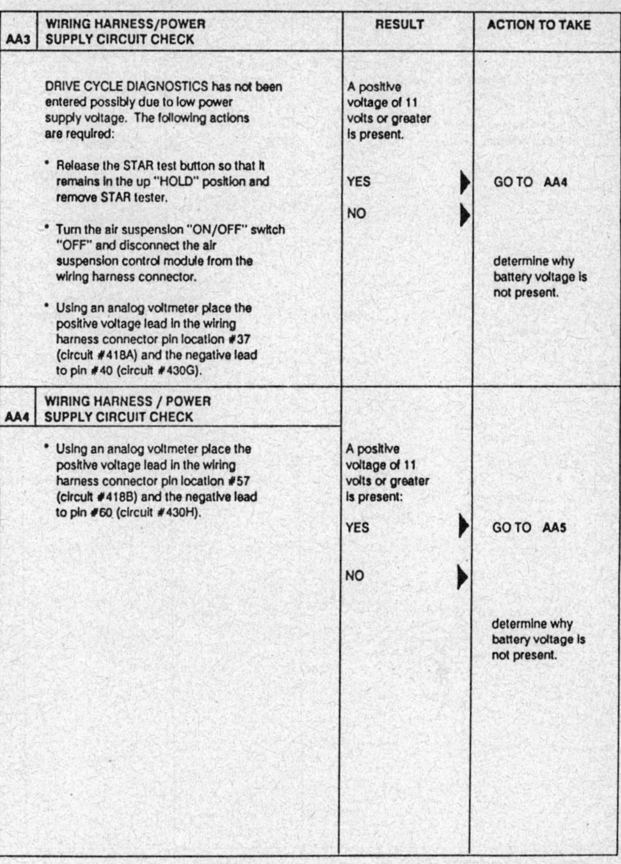

| | WIRING HARNESS/POWER SUPPLY CIRCUIT CHECK | RESULT | ACTION TO TAKE |
|---|---|---|---|
| AA3 | DRIVE CYCLE DIAGNOSTICS has not been entered possibly due to low power supply voltage. The following actions are required:<br>• Release the STAR test button so that it remains in the up "HOLD" position and remove STAR tester.<br>• Turn the air suspension "ON/OFF" switch "OFF" and disconnect the air suspension control module from the wiring harness connector.<br>• Using an analog voltmeter place the positive voltage lead in the wiring harness connector pin location #37 (circuit #418A) and the negative lead to pin #40 (circuit #430G). | A positive voltage of 11 volts or greater is present. | |
| | | YES ▶ | GO TO AA4 |
| | | NO ▶ | determine why battery voltage is not present. |
| AA4 | **WIRING HARNESS / POWER SUPPLY CIRCUIT CHECK** | | |
| | • Using an analog voltmeter place the positive voltage lead in the wiring harness connector pin location #57 (circuit #418B) and the negative lead to pin #60 (circuit #430H). | A positive voltage of 11 volts or greater is present: | |
| | | YES ▶ | GO TO AA5 |
| | | NO ▶ | determine why battery voltage is not present. |

**Fig. 25 Pinpoint test, AA (Part 2 of 5)**

| | WIRING HARNESS / CHECK IGNITION SWITCH CIRCUIT | RESULT | ACTION TO TAKE |
|---|---|---|---|
| AA5 | • Turn the ignition switch in the "OFF" position.<br>• Using an analog voltmeter place the positive voltage lead in the wiring harness connector (for the control module) pin location #1 (circuit #298) and the negative lead to pin #40 (circuit #430G). | Zero voltage is present. | |
| | | YES ▶ | GO TO AA6 |
| | | NO ▶ | determine why voltage is present. |
| AA6 | **WIRING HARNESS / CHECK IGNITION SWITCH CIRCUIT** | | |
| | • Turn the ignition switch to the "ON" position.<br>• Using an analog voltmeter place the positive voltage lead in the wiring harness connector (for the control module) pin location #1 (circuit #298) and the negative lead to pin #40 (circuit #430G). | A positive voltage of 11 volts or greater is present: | |
| | | YES ▶ | GO TO AA7 |
| | | NO ▶ | determine why a positive 11 volts is not present. |
| AA7 | **WIRING HARNESS / STI SHORT TO GROUND CHECK** | | |
| | • Using an analog ohmmeter place one lead in the wiring harness connector (for the control module) pin location #30 (circuit #606) and the other to pin location #40 (circuit #430G) | Ohmmeter reading is greater than 10,000 ohms: | |
| | | YES ▶ | GO TO AA8 |
| | | NO ▶ | The STI circuit #606 is shorted to ground. |

**Fig. 25 Pinpoint test, AA (Part 3 of 5)**

| | WIRING HARNESS STI OPEN CHECK | RESULT | ACTION TO TAKE |
|---|---|---|---|
| AA8 | • Using an analog ohmmeter place one lead in the wiring harness connector (for the air control module) pin location #30 (circuit #606) and the other to the wiring harness connector (for the STAR tester) pin location #2 (circuit #432E). | Ohmmeter reading is less than 5.0 ohms. | |
| | | YES ▶ | GO TO AA9 |
| | | NO ▶ | The STI circuit #606/432E has an open in it. |
| AA9 | **WIRING HARNESS /STO SHORT TO GROUND CHECK** | | |
| | • Using an analog ohmmeter place one lead in the wiring harness connector (for the air control module) pin location #15 (circuit #419A) and the other to pin location #40 (circuit #430G). | Ohmmeter reading is greater than 10,000 ohms: | |
| | | YES ▶ | GO TO AA10 |
| | | NO ▶ | The STO circuit #419A is shorted to ground. |

**Fig. 25 Pinpoint test, AA (Part 4 of 5)**

| AA10 WIRING HARNESS / STO OPEN CIRCUIT CHECK | RESULT | ACTION TO TAKE |
|---|---|---|
| • Using an analog ohmmeter place one lead in the wiring harness connector (for the air control module) pin location #15 (circuit #419A) and the other to the wiring harness connector (for the STAR tester) pin location #4 (circuit #419B). | Ohmmeter reading is less than 5.0 ohms: | |
| | YES ▶ | Turn the air suspension "ON/OFF" switch to the "OFF" position and replace air suspension control module and connect to vehicle wiring harness. |
| | NO ▶ | The STO circuit #419A/419B has an open in it. run SERVICE BAY DIAGNOSTICS after repair is made. |

**Fig. 25 Pinpoint test, AA (Part 5 of 5)**

| BA1 UNABLE TO ENTER SERVICE BAY DIAGNOSTICS | RESULT | ACTION TO TAKE |
|---|---|---|
| SERVICE BAY DIAGNOSTICS has not been entered. There are five possible causes which are listed below:<br>• The STAR tester is defective.<br>• B+ power supply circuit is defective.<br>• The ignition switch circuit is defective.<br>• The STI circuit is defective.<br>• The STO circuit is defective. | ▶ | GO TO BA2 |
| **BA2 STAR TESTER CHECK** | | |
| SERVICE BAY DIAGNOSTICS has not been entered possibly due to a defective STAR tester. To determine if this is the case the following actions are required:<br>• Disconnect the STAR tester and get another STAR tester if possible.<br>• On the new STAR tester release the STAR test button if required so that it remains in the up "HOLD" position.<br>• Connect the new STAR tester to the air suspension diagnostic connector and turn it "ON".<br>• Turn the ignition switch to the "OFF" position and wait ten seconds. After that turn the ignition switch back to the "ON/RUN" position and leave there.<br>• After waiting a minimum of 5 seconds depress the STAR test button so that it remains down in the "TEST" position. | Within twenty seconds the STAR tester will display one of the following codes: | |
| | "10" ▶ | SERVICE BAY DIAGNOSTICS has been entered. Proceed to "Step 2 of 4" of SERVICE BAY DIAGNOSTICS. |
| | "21" to "28" ▶ | GO TO BB1 |
| | ALL OTHER CODES ▶ | GO TO BA3 |

**Fig. 26 Pinpoint test, BA (Part 1 of 5)**

| BA3 WIRING HARNESS/POWER SUPPLY CIRCUIT CHECK | RESULT | ACTION TO TAKE |
|---|---|---|
| SERVICE BAY DIAGNOSTICS has not been entered possibly due to low power supply voltage. The following actions are required:<br>• Release the STAR test button so that it remains in the up "HOLD" position.<br>• Turn the air suspension "ON/OFF" switch "OFF" and disconnect the air suspension control module from the wiring harness connector.<br>• Now turn the air suspension "ON/OFF switch back to the "ON" position.<br>• Using an analog voltmeter place the positive voltage lead in the wiring harness connector pin location #37 (circuit #418A) and the negative lead to pin #40 (circuit #430G). | A positive voltage of 11 volts or greater is present: | |
| | YES ▶ | GO TO BA4 |
| | NO ▶ | determine why battery voltage is not present. |
| **BA4 WIRING HARNESS / POWER SUPPLY CIRCUIT CHECK** | | |
| • Using an analog voltmeter place the positive voltage lead in the wiring harness connector pin location #57 (circuit #418B) and the negative lead to pin #60 (circuit #430H). | A positive voltage of 11 volts or greater is present. | |
| | YES ▶ | GO TO BA5 |
| | NO ▶ | determine why battery voltage is not present. |

**Fig. 26 Pinpoint test, BA (Part 2 of 5)**

| BA5 WIRING HARNESS / CHECK IGNITION SWITCH CIRCUIT | RESULT | ACTION TO TAKE |
|---|---|---|
| • Turn the ignition switch in the "OFF" position.<br>• Using an analog voltmeter place the positive voltage lead in the wiring harness connector (for the control module) pin location #1 (circuit #298) and the negative lead to pin #40 (circuit #430G). | Zero voltage is present. | |
| | YES ▶ | GO TO BA6 |
| | NO ▶ | determine why voltage is present. |
| **BA6 WIRING HARNESS / CHECK IGNITION SWITCH CIRCUIT** | | |
| • Turn the ignition switch to the "ON/RUN" position.<br>• Using an analog voltmeter place the positive voltage lead in the wiring harness connector (for the control module) pin location #1 (circuit #298) and the negative lead to pin #40 (circuit #430G). | A positive voltage of 11 volts or greater is present or the test light is lit with no dimming present. | |
| | YES ▶ | GO TO BA7 |
| | NO ▶ | determine why a positive 11 volts is not present. |
| **BA7 WIRING HARNESS / STI SHORT TO GROUND CHECK** | | |
| • Using an ohmmeter place one lead in the wiring harness connector (for the control module) pin location #30 (circuit #606) and the other to pin location #40 (circuit #430G). | Ohmmeter reading is greater than 10,000 ohms: | |
| | YES ▶ | GO TO BA8 |
| | NO ▶ | The STI circuit #606 is shorted to ground. |

**Fig. 26 Pinpoint test, BA (Part 3 of 5)**

| BA8 | WIRING HARNESS STI OPEN CHECK | RESULT | | ACTION TO TAKE |
|---|---|---|---|---|
| | • Using an ohmmeter place one lead in the wiring harness connector (for the air control module) pin location #30 (circuit #606) and the other to the STAR tester vehicle wiring harness connector circuit #432E. | Ohmmeter reading is less than 5.0 ohms. | | |
| | | YES | ▶ | GO TO BA9 |
| | | NO | ▶ | The STI circuit #606/432E has an open in it. |
| BA9 | WIRING HARNESS / STO SHORT TO GROUND CHECK | | | |
| | • Using an ohmmeter place one lead in the wiring harness connector (for the control module) pin location #15 (circuit #419A) and the other to pin location #40 (circuit #430G). | Ohmmeter reading is greater than 10,000 ohms: | | |
| | | YES | ▶ | GO TO BA10 |
| | | NO | ▶ | The STO circuit #419A is shorted to ground. |

**Fig. 26 Pinpoint test, BA (Part 4 of 5)**

| BA10 | WIRING HARNESS / STO OPEN CIRCUIT CHECK | RESULT | | ACTION TO TAKE |
|---|---|---|---|---|
| | • Using an ohmmeter place one lead in the wiring harness connector (for the air control module) pin location #15 (circuit #419A) and the other to the STAR tester vehicle wiring harness connector circuit #419B. | Ohmmeter reading is less than 5.0 ohms. | | |
| | | YES | ▶ | Turn the air suspension "ON/OFF" switch to the "OFF" position, replace the suspension control module with a new one and connect it to the vehicle wiring harness. |
| | | NO | ▶ | The STO circuit #419A/419B has an open in it. |

**Fig. 26 Pinpoint test, BA (Part 5 of 5)**

| BB1 | BRAKE PRESSURE SWITCH CIRCUIT VOLTAGE CHECK | RESULT | | ACTION TO TAKE |
|---|---|---|---|---|
| | SERVICE BAY DIAGNOSTICS has not been entered but SPRING FILL was. The following actions are required if SERVICE BAY DIAGNOSTICS is desired: | Any voltage present: | | |
| | • Release the STAR test button so that it remains in the up "HOLD" position. • Turn the air suspension "ON/OFF" switch to the "OFF" position. Disconnect the air suspension control module from the wiring harness connector. | YES | ▶ | There should never be voltage on this circuit. |
| | • Using an analog voltmeter place the positive voltage lead in the wiring harness connector pin location #7 (circuit #636) and the negative lead to pin #40 (circuit #430G). | NO | ▶ | GO TO BB2 |
| BB2 | BRAKE PRESSURE SWITCH CIRCUIT RESISTANCE CHECK | | | |
| | • Using an ohmmeter measure the resistance from pin location #7 (circuit #636) and pin location #40 (circuit #430G). | Ohmmeter reading is greater than 10,000 ohms: | | |
| | | YES | ▶ | Replace air suspension control module with a new one and connect to vehicle wiring harness. Run SERVICE BAY DIAGNOSTICS after repair is made. |
| | | NO | ▶ | GO TO BB3 |

**Fig. 26A Pinpoint test, BB (Part 1 of 2)**

| BB3 | BRAKE PRESSURE SWITCH CHECK | RESULT | | ACTION TO TAKE |
|---|---|---|---|---|
| | • Disconnect the brake pressure switch from the vehicle wiring harness. | Ohmmeter reading is greater than 10,000 ohms: | | |
| | • Using an analog ohmmeter place one lead in the air suspension control module wiring harness connector pin location #7 and (circuit #636) and the other lead to pin #46 (circuit #432D). | YES | ▶ | replace the brake pressure switch. Connect the air suspension control module to the vehicle wiring harness and run SERVICE BAY DIAGNOSTICS after repair is made. |
| | | NO | ▶ | This circuit #636 has a short<br><br>After repair is made run SERVICE BAY DIAGNOSTICS. |

**Fig. 26A Pinpoint test, BB (Part 2 of 2)**

| CA1 UNABLE TO ENTER SPRING FILL DIAGNOSTICS | RESULT | ACTION TO TAKE |
|---|---|---|
| SPRING FILL DIAGNOSTICS has not been entered. There are six possible causes which are listed below:<br>• The STAR tester is defective.<br>• Brake switch circuit is defective.<br>• B+ power supply circuit is defective.<br>• The ignition switch circuit is defective.<br>• The STI circuit is defective.<br>• The STO circuit is defective. | ▶ | GO TO CA2 |
| **CA2 STAR TESTER CHECK** | | |
| SPRING FILL DIAGNOSTICS has not been entered possibly due to a defective STAR tester. To determine if this is the case the following actions are required:<br>• Disconnect the STAR tester and get another STAR tester if possible.<br>• On the new STAR tester release the STAR test button if required so that it remains in the up "HOLD" position.<br>• Connect the new STAR tester to the air suspension diagnostic connector and turn it "ON".<br>• Turn the ignition switch to the "OFF" position and wait ten seconds. After that turn the ignition switch back to the "ON/RUN" position and leave there.<br>• After waiting a minimum of 5 seconds depress the STAR test button so that it remains down in the "TEST" position. | Within twenty seconds the STAR tester will display one of the following codes: | |
| | "21" to "28" ▶ | SPRING FILL DIAGNOSTICS has been entered. Refer to SPRING FILL DIAGNOSTIC for instructions. |
| | ALL OTHER CODES ▶ | GO TO CA3 |

**Fig. 27 Pinpoint test, CA (Part 1 of 6)**

| CA3 BRAKE PRESSURE SWITCH CIRCUIT VOLTAGE CHECK | RESULT | ACTION TO TAKE |
|---|---|---|
| • Release the STAR test button so that it remains in the up "HOLD" up position.<br>• Turn the air suspension "ON/OFF" switch to the "OFF" position. Disconnect the air suspension control module from the wiring harness connector.<br>• Now turn the air suspension "ON/OFF" switch back to the "ON" position.<br>• Using an analog voltmeter place the positive voltage lead in the wiring harness connector pin location #7 (circuit #636) and the negative lead to pin #40 (circuit #430G). | Any voltage present: | |
| | YES ▶ | There should never be voltage on this circuit. |
| | NO ▶ | GO TO CA[illegible] |
| **CA4 BRAKE PRESSURE SWITCH CIRCUIT RESISTANCE CHECK** | | |
| • Using an ohmmeter measure the resistance from pin location #7 (circuit #636) and pin location #40 (circuit #430G). | Ohmmeter reading is greater than 10,000 ohms: | |
| | YES ▶ | GO TO CA6 |
| | NO ▶ | GO TO CA5 |

**Fig. 27 Pinpoint test, CA (Part 2 of 6)**

| CA5 BRAKE PRESSURE SWITCH CHECK | RESULT | ACTION TO TAKE |
|---|---|---|
| • Disconnect the brake pressure switch from the vehicle wiring harness.<br>• Using an analog ohmmeter place one lead in the wiring harness connector pin location #7 (circuit #636) and the other lead to pin #46 (circuit #432D). | Ohmmeter reading is greater than 10,000 ohms: | |
| | YES ▶ | replace the brake pressure switch. Connect the air suspension control module to the vehicle wiring harness and run SPRING FILL DIAGNOSTICS after repair is made. |
| | NO ▶ | This circuit #636 has a short<br>After repair is made run SPRING FILL DIAGNOSTICS. |
| **CA6 WIRING HARNESS / POWER SUPPLY CIRCUIT CHECK** | | |
| SPRING FILL DIAGNOSTICS has not been entered possibly due to low power supply voltage. The following actions are required:<br>• Release the STAR test button so that it remains in the up "HOLD" up position.<br>• Using an analog voltmeter place the positive voltage lead in the wiring harness connector pin location #37 (circuit #418A) and the negative lead to pin #40 (circuit #430G). | A positive voltage of 11 volts or greater is present: | |
| | YES ▶ | GO TO CA7 |
| | NO ▶ | determine why battery voltage is not present. |

**Fig. 27 Pinpoint test, CA (Part 3 of 6)**

| CA7 WIRING HARNESS / POWER SUPPLY CIRCUIT CHECK | RESULT | ACTION TO TAKE |
|---|---|---|
| • Using an analog voltmeter place the positive voltage lead in the wiring harness connector pin location #57 (circuit #418B) and the negative lead to pin #60 (circuit #430H). | A positive voltage of 11 volts or greater is present: | |
| | YES ▶ | GO TO CA8 |
| | NO ▶ | determine why battery voltage is not present. |
| **CA8 WIRING HARNESS / CHECK IGNITION SWITCH CIRCUIT** | | |
| • Turn the ignition switch in the "OFF" position.<br>• Using an analog voltmeter place the positive voltage lead in the wiring harness connector (for the control module) pin location #1 (circuit #298) and the negative lead to pin #40 (circuit #430G). | Zero voltage is present. | |
| | YES ▶ | GO TO CA9 |
| | NO ▶ | determine why voltage is present. |
| **CA9 WIRING HARNESS / CHECK IGNITION SWITCH CIRCUIT** | | |
| • Turn the ignition switch to the "ON/RUN" position.<br>• Using an analog voltmeter place the positive voltage lead in the wiring harness connector (for the control module) pin location #1 (circuit #298) negative lead to pin #40 (circuit #430G). | A positive voltage of 11 volts or greater is present: | |
| | YES ▶ | GO TO CA10 |
| | NO ▶ | determine why a positive 11 volts is not present. |

**Fig. 27 Pinpoint test, CA (Part 4 of 6)**

| CA10 | WIRING HARNESS / STI SHORT TO GROUND CHECK | RESULT | | ACTION TO TAKE |
|---|---|---|---|---|
| | • Using an ohmmeter place one lead in the wiring harness connector (for the control module) pin location #30 (circuit #606) and the other to pin location #40 (circuit #430G). | Ohmmeter reading is greater than 10,000 ohms: | | |
| | | YES | ▶ | GO TO CA11 |
| | | NO | ▶ | The STI circuit #606 is shorted to ground. |
| **CA11** | **WIRING HARNESS STI OPEN CHECK** | | | |
| | • Using an ohmmeter place one lead in the wiring harness connector (for the air control module) pin location #30 (circuit #606) and the other to the vehicle wiring harness connector (for the STAR tester) pin location #2 (circuit #432E). | Ohmmeter reading is less than 5.0 ohms: | | |
| | | YES | ▶ | GO TO CA12 |
| | | NO | ▶ | The STI circuit #606/432E has an open in it. |
| **CA12** | **WIRING HARNESS / STO SHORT TO GROUND CHECK** | | | |
| | • Using an ohmmeter place one lead in the wiring harness connector (for the control module) pin location #15 (circuit #419A) and the other to pin location #40 (circuit #430G). | Ohmmeter reading is greater than 10,000 ohms: | | |
| | | YES | ▶ | GO TO CA13 |
| | | NO | ▶ | The STO circuit #419A is shorted to ground. |

**Fig. 27 Pinpoint test, CA (Part 5 of 6)**

| CA13 | WIRING HARNESS / STO OPEN CIRCUIT CHECK | RESULT | | ACTION TO TAKE |
|---|---|---|---|---|
| | • Using an ohmmeter place one lead in the wiring harness connector (for the air control module) pin location #15 (circuit #419A) and the other to the vehicle wiring harness connector for the STAR tester circuit #419B. | Ohmmeter reading is less than 5.0 ohms: | | |
| | | YES | ▶ | Turn the air suspension "ON/OFF" switch to the "OFF" position and replace air suspension control module with a new one and connect to vehicle wiring harness. |
| | | NO | ▶ | The STO circuit #419A/419B has an open in it. |

**Fig. 27 Pinpoint test, CA (Part 6 of 6)**

| DA1 | STAR CODE: 80 LOW POWER SUPPLY VOLTAGE | RESULT | | ACTION TO TAKE |
|---|---|---|---|---|
| | The air suspension control module has detected a low power supply voltage. The following actions are required: | A positive voltage of 11 volts or greater is present: | | |
| | • Release the "STAR" test button so that it remains in the up "HOLD" position. | YES | ▶ | GO TO DA2 |
| | • Turn the air suspension "ON/OFF" switch to "OFF" and disconnect the air suspension control module from the wiring harness connector. | NO | ▶ | determine why a positive 11 volts is not present. Run SERVICE BAY DIAGNOSTICS after repair is made. |
| | • Now turn the air suspension "ON/OFF" switch back to the "ON" position. | | | |
| | • Using an analog voltmeter place the positive voltage lead in the wiring harness connector pin location #37 (circuit #418A) and the negative lead to pin #40 (circuit #430G). | | | |
| **DA2** | **WIRING HARNESS / POWER SUPPLY CIRCUIT CHECK** | | | |
| | • Using an analog voltmeter place the positive voltage lead in the wiring harness connector (for the control module) pin location #57 (circuit #418B) and the negative lead to pin #60 (circuit #430H) | A positive voltage of 11 volts or greater is present: | | |
| | | YES | ▶ | GO TO DA3 |
| | | NO | ▶ | determine why a positive 11 volts is not present. Run SERVICE BAY DIAGNOSTICS after repair is made. |

**Fig. 28 Pinpoint test, DA (Part 1 of 2)**

| DA3 | WIRING HARNESS / POWER SUPPLY CIRCUIT CHECK | RESULT | | ACTION TO TAKE |
|---|---|---|---|---|
| | • Turn the ignition key to the "OFF" position.<br>• Using an analog voltmeter place the positive voltage lead in the wiring harness connector (for the control module) pin location #1 (circuit #299) and the negative lead to pin #60 (circuit #430H). | A voltage of 1.0 volts or less is present: | | |
| | | YES | ▶ | Turn the air suspension "ON/OFF" switch to the "OFF" position and replace the air suspension control module with a new one and connect to the vehicle wiring harness. Run SERVICE BAY DIAGNOSTICS after repair is made. |
| | | NO | ▶ | reconnect the air suspension control module to the vehicle wiring harness. Then run SERVICE BAY DIAGNOSTICS. |

**Fig. 28 Pinpoint test, DA (Part 2 of 2)**

| EA1 STAR CODE: 40 SHORT IN LEFT FRONT AIR SPRING SOLENOID VALVE CIRCUIT | RESULT | ACTION TO TAKE |
|---|---|---|
| The air suspension control module has detected a short in the circuit used to activate the left front air spring solenoid valve. There are four possible causes of this short which are listed below:<br>• B+ power supply circuit is shorted to ground.<br>• The vehicle wiring harness has the B+ power supply and ground return circuit to the solenoid valve reversed.<br>• Air spring solenoid valve is defective.<br>• The air suspension control module is defective.<br>The left front air spring solenoid valve has a diode in it. When current is applied in the reverse direction this diode will act like a short. Because all ohmmeters do not have the same positive and negative polarity the following test procedures are being used to locate the cause of the short. | ▶ | GO TO EA2 |
| EA2 | | |
| • Turn the air suspension "ON/OFF" switch to the "OFF" position.<br>• Disconnect air suspension control module connector. | ▶ | GO TO EA3 |

Fig. 29 Pinpoint test, EA (Part 1 of 4)

| EA3 CHECKING WIRING HARNESS | RESULT | ACTION TO TAKE |
|---|---|---|
| Using an analog ohmmeter measure and record the following:<br>• Connect the positive lead of the ohmmeter to the wiring harness connector pin location #21 (circuit #415) and the negative lead to pin location #40 (circuit #430G).<br>• Now connect the positive lead of the ohmmeter to the wiring harness connector pin location #40 (circuit #430G) and the negative lead to pin location #21 (circuit #415). | At least one of the two ohmmeter readings is greater than 8.0 ohms:<br>YES ▶<br>NO ▶ | <br>GO TO EA5<br>GO TO EA4 |
| EA4 CHECKING WIRING HARNESS | | |
| • Disconnect the left front air spring solenoid valve from the vehicle wiring harness.<br>• Using an analog ohmmeter connect one lead to the wiring harness connector pin location #21 (circuit #415) and other to pin location #40 (circuit #430G). | Ohmmeter reading is greater than 10,000 ohms:<br>YES ▶<br>NO ▶ | <br>The left front air spring solenoid valve has an internal short circuit. Install a new air spring solenoid valve and rerun SERVICE BAY DIAGNOSTICS.<br>A short has been detected in the wiring harness circuit #415/430G. Rerun SERVICE BAY DIAGNOSTICS after repair is made. |

Fig. 29 Pinpoint test, EA (Part 2 of 4)

| EA5 CHECKING WIRING HARNESS | RESULT | ACTION TO TAKE |
|---|---|---|
| • Disconnect the left front air spring solenoid valve from the vehicle wiring harness.<br>• Using an analog ohmmeter connect one lead to the left front air spring solenoid valve vehicle wiring harness connector circuit #430K and other to a known good chassis ground. | Ohmmeter reading is less than 2.0 ohms:<br>YES ▶<br>NO ▶ | <br>GO TO EA7<br>GO TO EA6 |
| EA6 CHECKING WIRING HARNESS | | |
| In order to determine if the vehicle wiring harness has the air spring solenoid valve circuits in the proper location the following test is required:<br>• Using an analog ohmmeter connect one lead to the left front air spring solenoid valve vehicle wiring harness connector circuit #415 and other to a known good chassis ground. | Ohmmeter reading is less than 2.0 ohms:<br>YES ▶<br>NO ▶ | <br>The air spring solenoid power circuit (#415) and ground circuit (#430K) are reversed. Relocate these circuits to the proper location, reconnect the air spring solenoid valve and air suspension control module. Rerun SERVICE BAY DIAGNOSTICS after repairs are made.<br>The left front air spring solenoid valve's ground circuit (#430K) has a resistance to chassis ground that is above acceptable limits. The resistance to ground should always be less than 2.0 ohms. Rerun SERVICE BAY DIAGNOSTICS after repairs are made. |

Fig. 29 Pinpoint test, EA (Part 3 of 4)

| EA7 COMPONENT CHECK | RESULT | ACTION TO TAKE |
|---|---|---|
| The previous steps have verified that the vehicle wiring harness is not the cause of the short. There are two possible causes that must now be checked (solenoid valve or control module). In order to determine which one is causing the short the following is required:<br>• Turn the air suspension "ON/OFF" switch to the "OFF" position.<br>• Reconnect the air suspension control module to the vehicle wiring harness.<br>• Turn the air suspension "ON/OFF" switch to the "ON" position.<br>• Rerun SERVICE BAY DIAGNOSTICS without reconnecting the left front air spring solenoid valve connected to the vehicle wiring harness.<br>NOTE: This test procedure will generate extra error codes because the left front air spring solenoid valve is not connected to the vehicle wiring harness. | The STAR tester displayed code "40" again.<br>YES ▶<br>NO ▶ | <br>Turn the air suspension "ON/OFF" switch to the "OFF" position. Remove the air suspension control module and install a new one. Rerun SERVICE BAY DIAGNOSTICS afterwards.<br>Remove the left front air spring solenoid valve and install a new one. Rerun SERVICE BAY DIAGNOSTICS afterwards. |

Fig. 29 Pinpoint test, EA (Part 4 of 4)

| EB1 | STAR CODE: 41 SHORT IN RIGHT FRONT AIR SPRING SOLENOID VALVE CIRCUIT | RESULT | ACTION TO TAKE |
|---|---|---|---|
| | The air suspension control module has detected a short in the circuit used to activate the right front air spring solenoid valve. There are four possible causes of this short which are listed below:<br>• B+ power supply circuit is shorted to ground.<br>• The vehicle wiring harness has the B+ power supply and ground return circuit to the solenoid valve are reversed.<br>• Air spring solenoid valve is defective.<br>• The air suspension control module is defective.<br>The right front air spring solenoid valve has a diode in it. When current is applied in the reverse direction this diode will act like a short. Because all ohmmeters do not have the same positive and negative polarity the following test procedures are being used to locate the cause of the short. | | ▶ GO TO EB2 |
| EB2 | CHECKING WIRING HARNESS | | |
| | • Turn the air suspension "ON/OFF" switch to the "OFF" position.<br>• Disconnect air suspension control module connector. | | ▶ GO TO EB3 |

Fig. 30 Pinpoint test, EB (Part 1 of 4)

| EB3 | CHECKING WIRING HARNESS | RESULT | ACTION TO TAKE |
|---|---|---|---|
| | Using an analog ohmmeter measure and record the following:<br>• Connect the positive lead of the ohmmeter to the wiring harness connector pin location #17 (circuit #414) and the negative lead to pin location #40 (circuit #430G).<br>• Now connect the positive lead of the ohmmeter to the wiring harness connector pin location #40 (circuit #430G) and the negative lead to pin location #17 (circuit #414). | At least one of the two ohmmeter readings is greater than 8.0 ohms:<br>YES<br>NO | <br><br>▶ GO TO EB5<br>▶ GO TO EB4 |
| EB4 | CHECKING WIRING HARNESS | | |
| | • Disconnect the right front air spring solenoid valve from the vehicle wiring harness.<br>• Using an analog ohmmeter connect one lead to the wiring harness connector pin location #17 (circuit #414) and other pin location #40 (circuit #430G). | Ohmmeter reading is greater than 10,000 ohms:<br>YES<br>NO | <br><br>▶ The right front air spring solenoid valve has an internal short circuit. Install a new air spring solenoid valve and rerun SERVICE BAY DIAGNOSTICS.<br>▶ A short has been detected in the wiring harness circuit #414/430G. Rerun SERVICE BAY DIAGNOSTICS after repair is made. |

Fig. 30 Pinpoint test, EB (Part 2 of 4)

| EB5 | CHECKING WIRING HARNESS | RESULT | ACTION TO TAKE |
|---|---|---|---|
| | • Disconnect the right front air spring solenoid valve from the vehicle wiring harness.<br>• Using an analog ohmmeter connect one lead to the right front air spring solenoid valve vehicle wiring harness connector circuit #430D and other to a known good chassis ground. | Ohmmeter reading is less than 2.0 ohms:<br>YES<br>NO | <br><br>▶ GO TO EB7<br>▶ GO TO EB6 |
| EB6 | CHECKING WIRING HARNESS | | |
| | In order to determine if the vehicle wiring harness has the air spring solenoid valve circuits in the proper location the following test is required:<br>• Using an analog ohmmeter connect one lead to the right front air spring solenoid valve vehicle wiring harness connector circuit #414 and other to a known good chassis ground. | Ohmmeter reading is less than 2.0 ohms:<br>YES<br>NO | <br><br>▶ The air spring solenoid power circuit (#414) and ground circuit (#430D) are reversed. Relocate these circuits to the proper location, reconnect the air spring solenoid valve and air suspension control module. Rerun SERVICE BAY DIAGNOSTICS after repairs are made.<br>▶ The right front air spring solenoid valve's ground circuit (#430D) has a resistance to chassis ground that is above acceptable limits. The resistance to ground should always be less than 2.0 ohms. Rerun SERVICE BAY DIAGNOSTICS after repairs are made. |

Fig. 30 Pinpoint test, EB (Part 3 of 4)

| EB7 | COMPONENT CHECK | RESULT | ACTION TO TAKE |
|---|---|---|---|
| | The previous steps have verified that the vehicle wiring harness is not the cause of the short. There are two possible causes that must now be checked (solenoid valve or control module). In order to determine which one is causing the short the following is required:<br>• Turn the air suspension "ON/OFF" switch to the "OFF" position.<br>• Reconnect the air suspension control module to the vehicle wiring harness.<br>• Turn the air suspension "ON/OFF" switch to the "ON" position.<br>• Rerun SERVICE BAY DIAGNOSTICS without reconnecting the right front air spring solenoid value connected to the vehicle wiring harness.<br>NOTE: This test procedure will generate extra error codes because the right front air spring solenoid valve is not connected to the vehicle wiring harness. | The STAR tester displayed code "41" again.<br>YES<br>NO | <br><br>▶ Turn the air suspension "ON/OFF" switch to the "OFF" position. Remove the air suspension control module and install a new one. Rerun SERVICE BAY DIAGNOSTICS afterwards.<br>▶ Remove the right front air spring solenoid valve and install a new one. Rerun SERVICE BAY DIAGNOSTICS afterwards. |

Fig. 30 Pinpoint test, EB (Part 4 of 4)

| EC1 | STAR CODE: 42 SHORT IN LEFT REAR AIR SPRING SOLENOID VALVE CIRCUIT | RESULT | ACTION TO TAKE |
|---|---|---|---|
| | The air suspension control module has detected a short in the circuit used to activate the left rear air spring solenoid valve. There are four possible causes of this short which are listed below:<br>• B+ power supply circuit is shorted to ground.<br>• The vehicle wiring harness has the B+ power supply and ground return circuit to the solenoid valve reversed.<br>• Air spring solenoid valve is defective.<br>• The air suspension control module is defective.<br>The left rear air spring solenoid valve has a diode in it. When current is applied in the reverse direction this diode will act like a short. Because all ohmmeters do not have the same positive and negative polarity the following test procedures are being used to locate the cause of the short. | ▶ | GO TO EC2 |
| EC2 | | | |
| | • Turn the air suspension "ON/OFF" switch to the "OFF" position.<br>• Disconnect air suspension control module connector. | ▶ | GO TO EC3 |

Fig. 31 Pinpoint test, EC (Part 1 of 4)

| EC3 | CHECKING WIRING HARNESS | RESULT | ACTION TO TAKE |
|---|---|---|---|
| | Using an analog ohmmeter measure and record the following:<br>• Connect the positive lead of the ohmmeter to the wiring harness connector pin location #41 (circuit #429) and the negative lead to pin location #40 (circuit #430G).<br>• Now connect the positive lead of the ohmmeter to the wiring harness connector pin location #40 (circuit #430G) and the negative lead to pin location #41 (circuit #429). | At least one of the two ohmmeter readings is greater than 8.0 ohms: | |
| | | YES ▶ | GO TO EC5 |
| | | NO ▶ | GO TO EC4 |
| EC4 | CHECKING WIRING HARNESS | | |
| | • Disconnect the left rear air spring solenoid valve from the vehicle wiring harness.<br>• Using an analog ohmmeter connect one lead to the wiring harness connector pin location #41 (circuit #429) and other to pin location #40 (circuit #430G). | Ohmmeter reading is greater than 10,000 ohms: | |
| | | YES ▶ | The left rear air spring solenoid valve has an internal short circuit. Install a new air spring solenoid valve and rerun SERVICE BAY DIAGNOSTICS |
| | | NO ▶ | A short has been detected in the wiring harness circuit #429/430G. Rerun SERVICE BAY DIAGNOSTICS after repair is made. |

Fig. 31 Pinpoint test, EC (Part 2 of 4)

| EC5 | CHECKING WIRING HARNESS | RESULT | ACTION TO TAKE |
|---|---|---|---|
| | • Disconnect the left rear air spring solenoid valve from vehicle wiring harness.<br>• Using an analog ohmmeter connect one lead to the left rear air spring solenoid valve vehicle wiring harness connector circuit #430F and other to a known good chassis ground. | Ohmmeter reading is less than 2.0 ohms: | |
| | | YES ▶ | GO TO EC7 |
| | | NO ▶ | GO TO EC6 |
| EC6 | CHECKING WIRING HARNESS | | |
| | In order to determine if the vehicle wiring harness has the air spring solenoid valve circuits in the proper location the following test is required:<br>• Using an analog ohmmeter connect one lead to the left rear air spring solenoid valve vehicle wiring harness connector circuit #429 and other to a known good chassis ground. | Ohmmeter reading is less than 2.0 ohms: | |
| | | YES ▶ | The air spring solenoid power circuit (#429) and ground circuit (#430F) are reversed. Relocate these circuits to the proper location, reconnect the air spring solenoid valve and air suspension control module. Rerun SERVICE BAY DIAGNOSTICS after repairs are made. |
| | | NO ▶ | The left rear air spring solenoid valve's ground circuit(#430F) has a resistance to chassis ground that is above acceptable limits. The resistance to ground should always be less than 2..0 ohms. Rerun SERVICE BAY DIAGNOSTICS after repairs are made. |

Fig. 31 Pinpoint test, EC (Part 3 of 4)

| EC7 | COMPONENT CHECK | RESULT | ACTION TO TAKE |
|---|---|---|---|
| | The previous steps have verified that the vehicle wiring harness is not the cause of the short. There are two possible causes that must now be checked (solenoid valve or control module). In order to determine which one is causing the short the following is required:<br>• Turn the air suspension "ON/OFF" switch to the "OFF" position.<br>• Reconnect the air suspension control module to the vehicle wiring harness.<br>• Turn the air suspension "ON/OFF" switch to the "ON" position.<br>• Rerun SERVICE BAY DIAGNOSTICS without reconnecting the left rear air spring solenoid valve connected to the vehicle wiring harness.<br>NOTE: This test procedure will generate extra error codes because the left rear air spring solenoid valve is not connected to the vehicle wiring harness. | The STAR tester displayed code "42" again. | |
| | | YES ▶ | Turn the air suspension "ON/OFF" switch to the "OFF" position. Remove the air suspension control module and install a new one. Rerun SERVICE BAY DIAGNOSTICS afterwards. |
| | | NO ▶ | Remove the left rear air spring solenoid valve (refer to shop manual for procedure) and install a new one. Rerun SERVICE BAY DIAGNOSTICS AFTERWARDS. |

Fig. 31 Pinpoint test, EC (Part 4 of 4).

| ED1 | STAR CODE: 43 SHORT IN RIGHT REAR AIR SPRING SOLENOID VALVE CIRCUIT | RESULT | ACTION TO TAKE |
|---|---|---|---|
| | The air suspension control module has detected a short in the circuit used to activate the right rear air spring solenoid valve. There are four possible causes of this short which are listed below:<br>• B+ power supply circuit is shorted to ground.<br>• The vehicle wiring harness has the B+ power supply and ground return circuit to the solenoid valve are reversed.<br>• Air spring solenoid valve is defective.<br>• The air suspension control module is defective.<br>The right rear air spring solenoid valve has a diode in it. When current is applied in the reverse direction this diode will act like a short. Because all ohmmeters do not have the same positive and negative polarity the following test procedures are being used to locate the cause of the short. | | ▶ GO TO ED2 |
| ED2 | • Turn the air suspension "ON/OFF" switch to the "OFF" position.<br>• Disconnect air suspension control module connector. | | ▶ GO TO ED3 |

Fig. 32 Pinpoint test, ED (Part 1 of 5)

| ED3 | CHECKING WIRING HARNESS | RESULT | ACTION TO TAKE |
|---|---|---|---|
| | Using an analog ohmmeter measure and record the following:<br>• Connect the positive lead of the ohmmeter to the wiring harness connector pin location #38 (circuit #416) and the negative lead to pin location #40 (circuit #430G).<br>• Now connect the positive lead of the ohmmeter to the wiring harness connector pin location #40 (circuit #430G) and the negative lead to pin location #38 (circuit #416). | At least one of the two ohmmeter readings is greater than 8.0 ohms:<br>YES<br>NO | <br><br>▶ GO TO ED5<br>▶ GO TO ED4 |
| ED4 | CHECKING WIRING HARNESS | | |
| | • Disconnect the right rear air spring solenoid valve from the vehicle wiring harness.<br>• Using an analog ohmmeter connect one lead to the wiring harness connector pin location #38 (circuit #416) and other to pin location #40 (circuit #430G). | Ohmmeter reading is greater than 10,000 ohms:<br>YES | <br>▶ The right rear air spring solenoid valve has an internal short circuit. Install a new air spring solenoid valve and rerun SERVICE BAY DIAGNOSTICS. |
| | | NO | ▶ A short has been detected in the wiring harness circuit #416/430G. Rerun SERVICE BAY DIAGNOSTICS after repair is made. |

Fig. 32 Pinpoint test, ED (Part 2 of 5)

| ED5 | CHECKING WIRING HARNESS | RESULT | ACTION TO TAKE |
|---|---|---|---|
| | • Disconnect the right rear air spring solenoid valve from the vehicle wiring harness.<br>• Using an analog ohmmeter connect one lead to the right rear air spring solenoid valve vehicle wiring harness connector circuit #430A and other to a known good chassis ground. | Ohmmeter reading is less than 2.0 ohms:<br>YES<br>NO | <br>▶ GO TO ED7<br>▶ GO TO ED6 |

Fig. 32 Pinpoint test, ED (Part 3 of 5)

| ED6 | CHECKING WIRING HARNESS | RESULT | ACTION TO TAKE |
|---|---|---|---|
| | In order to determine if the vehicle wiring harness has the air spring solenoid valve circuits in the proper location the following test is required:<br>• Using an analog ohmmeter connect one lead to the right rear air spring solenoid valve vehicle wiring harness connector circuit #416 and other to a known good chassis ground. | Ohmmeter reading is less than 2.0 ohms:<br>YES | <br>▶ The air spring solenoid power circuit (#416) and ground circuit (#430A) are reversed. Relocate these circuits to the proper location, reconnect the air spring solenoid valve and air suspension control module. Rerun SERVICE BAY DIAGNOSTICS after repairs are made. |
| | | NO | ▶ The right rear air spring solenoid valve's ground circuit (#430A) has a resistance to chassis ground that is above acceptable limits. The resistance to ground should always be less than 2.0 ohms. Rerun SERVICE BAY DIAGNOSTICS after repairs are made. |

Fig. 32 Pinpoint test, ED (Part 4 of 5)

| ED7 COMPONENT CHECK | RESULT | ACTION TO TAKE |
|---|---|---|
| The previous steps have verified that the vehicle wiring harness is not the cause of the short. There are two possible causes that must now be checked (solenoid valve or control module). In order to determine which one is causing the short the the following is required:<br><br>• Turn the air suspension "ON/OFF" switch to the "OFF" position.<br><br>• Reconnect the air suspension control module to the vehicle wiring harness.<br><br>• Turn the air suspension "ON/OFF" switch to the "ON" position.<br><br>• Rerun SERVICE BAY DIAGNOSTICS without reconnecting the right rear air spring solenoid valve connected to the vehicle wiring harness.<br><br>NOTE: This test procedure will generate extra error codes because the right rear air spring solenoid valve is not connected to the vehicle wiring harness. | The STAR tester displayed code "43" again:<br><br>YES ▶ | Turn the air suspension "ON/OFF" switch to the "OFF" position. Remove the air suspension control module and install a new one. Rerun SERVICE BAY DIAGNOSTICS afterwards. |
| | NO ▶ | Remove the right rear air spring solenoid valve and install a new one. Rerun SERVICE BAY DIAGNOSTICS afterwards. |

Fig. 32 Pinpoint test, ED (Part 5 of 5)

| EE1 STAR CODE: 44 SHORT IN VENT SOLENOID VALVE CIRCUIT | RESULT | ACTION TO TAKE |
|---|---|---|
| The air suspension control module has detected a short in the circuit used to activate the vent solenoid valve. There are four possible causes of this short which are listed below:<br><br>• B+ power supply circuit is shorted to ground.<br><br>• The vehicle wiring harness has the B+ power supply circuit and ground return circuit in the wrong location.<br><br>• Vent solenoid valve is defective.<br><br>• The air suspension control module is defective.<br><br>The vent solenoid valve has a diode in it. When current is applied in the reverse direction this diode will act like a short. Because all ohmmeters do not have the same positive and negative polarity the following test procedures are being used to locate the cause of the short. | ▶ | GO TO EE2 |
| **EE2** | | |
| • Turn the air suspension "ON/OFF" switch to the "OFF" position.<br><br>• Disconnect air suspension control module connector. | ▶ | GO TO EE3 |

Fig. 33 Pinpoint test, EE (Part 1 of 4)

| EE3 CHECKING WIRING HARNESS | RESULT | ACTION TO TAKE |
|---|---|---|
| Using an analog ohmmeter measure and record the following:<br><br>• Connect the positive lead of the ohmmeter to the wiring harness connector pin location #42 (circuit #421) and the negative lead to pin location #40 (circuit #430G).<br><br>• Now connect the positive lead of the ohmmeter to the wiring harness connector pin location #40 (circuit #430G) and the negative lead to pin location #42 (circuit #421). | At least one of the two ohmmeter readings is greater than 20 ohms:<br><br>YES ▶ | GO TO EE5 |
| | NO ▶ | GO TO EE4 |
| **EE4 CHECKING WIRING HARNESS** | | |
| • Disconnect the air compressor assembly from the vehicle wiring harness.<br><br>• Using an analog ohmmeter connect one lead to the wiring harness connector pin location #42 (circuit #421) and other to pin location #40 (circuit #430G). | Ohmmeter reading is greater than 10,000 ohms:<br><br>YES ▶ | The vent solenoid valve has an internal short ircuit. Install a new air compressor assembly and rerun SERVICE BAY DIAGNOSTICS. |
| | NO ▶ | A short has been detected in the wiring harness circuit #421/430G. Rerun SERVICE BAY DIAGNOSTICS after repair is made. |

Fig. 33 Pinpoint test, EE (Part 2 of 4)

| EE5 CHECKING WIRING HARNESS | RESULT | ACTION TO TAKE |
|---|---|---|
| • Disconnect the air compressor assembly from the vehicle wiring harness.<br><br>• Using an analog ohmmeter connect one lead to the vent solenoid valve vehicle wiring harness connector circuit #430E and other to a known good chassis ground. | Ohmmeter reading is less than 2.0 ohms:<br><br>YES ▶ | GO TO EE7 |
| | NO ▶ | GO TO EE6 |
| **EE6 CHECKING WIRING HARNESS** | | |
| In order to determine if the vehicle wiring harness has the vent solenoid valve circuits in the proper location the following test is required:<br><br>• Using an analog ohmmeter connect one lead to the vent solenoid valve vehicle wiring harness connector circuit #421 and other to a known good chassis ground. | Ohmmeter reading is less than 2.0 ohms:<br><br>YES ▶ | The vent solenoid power circuit (#421) and ground circuit (#430E) are reversed. Relocate these circuits to the proper location, reconnect the air compressor assembly and air suspension control module. Rerun SERVICE BAY DIAGNOSTICS after repairs are made. |
| | NO ▶ | The vent solenoid valve's ground circuit (#430E) has a resistance to chassis ground that is above acceptable limits. The resistance to ground should always be less than 2.0 ohms. Rerun SERVICE BAY DIAGNOSTICS after repairs are made. |

Fig. 33 Pinpoint test, EE (Part 3 of 4)

| EE7 COMPONENT CHECK | RESULT | ACTION TO TAKE |
|---|---|---|
| The previous steps have verified that the vehicle wiring harness is not the cause of the short. There are two possible causes that must now be checked (vent solenoid valve or control module). In order to determine which one is causing the short the following is required:<br>• Turn the air suspension "ON/OFF" switch to the "OFF" position.<br>• Reconnect the air suspension control module to the vehicle wiring harness.<br>• Turn the air suspension "ON/OFF" switch to the "ON" position.<br>• Rerun SERVICE BAY DIAGNOSTICS without the air compressor assembly connected to the vehicle wiring harness.<br>NOTE: This test procedure will generate extra error codes because the air compressor assembly is not connected to the vehicle wiring harness. | The STAR tester displayed code "40" again: | |
| | YES ▶ | Turn the air suspension "ON/OFF" switch to the "OFF" position. Remove the air suspension control module and install a new one. Rerun SERVICE BAY DIAGNOSTICS afterwards. |
| | NO ▶ | Remove the air compressor assembly and install a new one. Rerun SERVICE BAY DIAGNOSTICS afterwards. |

Fig. 33 Pinpoint test, EE (Part 4 of 4)

| EF1 STAR CODE: 45 SHORT IN AIR COMPRESSOR RELAY CIRCUIT | RESULT | ACTION TO TAKE |
|---|---|---|
| The air suspension control module has detected a short in the circuit used to activate the air compressor relay. There are four possible causes of this short which are listed below:<br>• B+ power supply circuit is shorted to ground.<br>• The vehicle wiring harness has the B+ power supply circuit and ground return circuit in the wrong location.<br>• Air compressor relay is defective.<br>• The air suspension control module is defective.<br>The air compressor relay has a diode in it. When current is applied in the reverse direction this diode will act like a short. Because all ohmmeters do not have the same positive and negative polarity the following test procedures are being used to locate the cause of the short. | ▶ | GO TO EF2 |
| **EF2** | | |
| • Turn the air suspension "ON/OFF" switch to the "OFF" position.<br>• Disconnect air suspension control module connector. | ▶ | GO TO EF3 |
| **EF3 CHECKING WIRING HARNESS** | | |
| Using an analog ohmmeter measure and record the following:<br>• Connect the positive lead of the ohmmeter to the wiring harness connector pin location #35 (circuit #420) and the negative lead to pin location #40 (circuit #430G).<br>• Now connect the positive lead of the ohmmeter to the wiring harness connector pin location #40 (circuit #430G) and the negative lead to pin location #35 (circuit #420). | At least one of the two ohmmeter readings is greater than 40 ohms: | |
| | YES ▶ | GO TO EF5 |
| | NO ▶ | GO TO EF4 |

Fig. 34 Pinpoint test, EF (Part 1 of 5)

| EF4 CHECKING WIRING HARNESS | RESULT | ACTION TO TAKE |
|---|---|---|
| • Disconnect the air compressor relay from the vehicle wiring harness.<br>• Using an analog ohmmeter connect one lead to the wiring harness connector pin location #35 (circuit #420) and other to pin location #40 (circuit #430G). | Ohmmeter reading is greater than 10,000 ohms: | |
| | YES ▶ | The air compressor relay has an internal short circuit. Install a new air compressor relay and rerun SERVICE BAY DIAGNOSTICS. |
| | NO ▶ | A short has been detected in the wiring harness circuit #420/430G. Rerun SERVICE BAY DIAGNOSTICS after repair is made. |
| **EF5 CHECKING WIRING HARNESS** | | |
| • Disconnect the air compressor relay from the vehicle wiring harness.<br>• Using an analog ohmmeter connect one lead to the air compressor relay vehicle wiring harness connector circuit #430B and other to a known good chassis ground. | Ohmmeter reading is less than 2.0 ohms: | |
| | YES ▶ | GO TO EF8 |
| | NO ▶ | GO TO EF6 |

Fig. 34 Pinpoint test, EF (Part 2 of 5)

| EF6 CHECKING WIRING HARNESS | RESULT | ACTION TO TAKE |
|---|---|---|
| In order to determine if the vehicle wiring harness has the air compressor relay circuits in the proper location the following test is required:<br>• Using an analog ohmmeter connect one lead to the air compressor relay vehicle wiring harness connector circuit #420 and other to a known good chassis ground. | Ohmmeter reading is less than 2.0 ohms: | |
| | YES ▶ | The air compressor relay power circuit (#420) and ground circuit (#430B) are reversed. Relocate these circuits to the proper location, reconnect the air compressor relay and air suspension control module. Rerun SERVICE BAY DIAGNOSTICS after repairs are made. |
| | NO ▶ | GO TO EF7 |

Fig. 34 Pinpoint test, EF (Part 3 of 5)

| EF7 | CHECKING WIRING HARNESS | RESULT | ACTION TO TAKE |
|---|---|---|---|
| | • Verify that all the wires going to the air compressor relay are in the proper location. | All wires are in the proper location: | |
| | | YES | The air compressor relay ground circuit (#430B) has a resistance to chassis ground that is above acceptable limits. The resistance to ground should always be less than 2.0 ohms. Rerun SERVICE BAY DIAGNOSTICS after repairs are made. |
| | | NO | Relocate wires to the proper location, reconnect the air compressor relay and air suspension control module. Rerun SERVICE BAY DIAGNOSTICS after repairs are made. |

**Fig. 34 Pinpoint test, EF (Part 4 of 5)**

| EF8 | COMPONENT CHECK | RESULT | ACTION TO TAKE |
|---|---|---|---|
| | The previous steps have verified that the vehicle wiring harness is not the cause of the short. There are two possible causes that must now be checked (air compressor relay or control module). In order to determine which one is causing the short the following is required:<br>• Turn the air suspension "ON/OFF" switch to the "OFF" position.<br>• Reconnect the air suspension control module to the vehicle wiring harness.<br>• Turn the air suspension "ON/OFF" switch to the "ON" position.<br>• Rerun SERVICE BAY DIAGNOSTICS without reconnecting the air compressor relay connected to the vehicle wiring harness.<br>NOTE: This test procedure will generate extra error codes because the air compressor relay is not connected to the vehicle wiring harness. | The STAR tester displayed code "45" again: | |
| | | YES | Turn the air suspension "ON/OFF" switch to the "OFF" position. Remove the air suspension control module and install a new one. Rerun SERVICE BAY DIAGNOSTICS afterwards. |
| | | NO | Remove the air compressor relay and install a new one. Rerun SERVICE BAY DIAGNOSTICS afterwards. |

**Fig. 34 Pinpoint test, EF (Part 5 of 5)**

| EG1 | STAR CODE: 46<br>SHORT IN HEIGHT SENSOR POWER SUPPLY CIRCUIT | RESULT | ACTION TO TAKE |
|---|---|---|---|
| | The air suspension control module has detected a short in circuit used to provide power to the air suspension height sensors. There are six possible causes of this short which are listed below:<br>• B+ power supply circuit is shorted to ground.<br>• The vehicle wiring harness has the B+ power supply circuit and ground return circuit in the wrong location.<br>• The left front height sensor is defective.<br>• The right front height sensor is defective.<br>• The rear height sensor is defective.<br>• The air suspension control module is defective.<br>The three height sensors on the vehicle have a common B+ power supply circuit coming out of the air suspension control module. For this reason the following test procedure will be used to locate the cause of the short: | | GO TO EG2 |
| EG2 | ENTERING DRIVE CYCLE DIAGNOSTICS<br>In order to determine where the short is located a modified DRIVE CYCLE DIAGNOSTICS will be utilized. In order to do this the following preliminary actions are required:<br>• Release the STAR test button to the "HOLD" position.<br>• Disconnect the left front height sensor from the vehicle wiring harness.<br>• With the ignition switch in the "ON/RUN" position turn the air suspension "ON/OFF" switch to the "ON" position and wait 15 seconds. | | GO TO EG3 |

**Fig. 35 Pinpoint test, EG (Part 1 of 5)**

| EG3 | COMPONENT CHECK | RESULT | ACTION TO TAKE |
|---|---|---|---|
| | • Turn the ignition switch to the "OFF" position.<br>• Depress the STAR test button so that it remains down in the "TEST" position.<br>NOTE: This type of DRIVE CYCLE DIAGNOSTIC test will cause code "55" to be displayed, since a vehicle speed of 15mph or greater was not detected. | The STAR tester is displaying code "46" again: | |
| | | YES | GO TO EG4 |
| | | NO | Remove the left front height sensor and replace it with a new one. Rerun SERVICE BAY DIAGNOSTICS after repair is made. |
| EG4 | ENTERING DRIVE CYCLE DIAGNOSTICS<br>Again the modified DRIVE CYCLE DIAGNOSTICS will be used to help locate the cause of the short.<br>• Release the STAR test button to the "HOLD" position.<br>• Turn the air suspension "ON/OFF" switch to the "OFF" position.<br>• Disconnect the right front height sensor also from the vehicle wiring harness.<br>• With the ignition switch in the "ON/RUN" position turn the air suspension "ON/OFF" switch to the "ON" position and wait 15 seconds. | | GO TO EG5 |

**Fig. 35 Pinpoint test, EG (Part 2 of 5)**

| EG5 | COMPONENT CHECK | RESULT | ACTION TO TAKE |
|---|---|---|---|
| | • Turn the ignition switch to the "OFF" position. • Depress the STAR test button so that it remains down in the "TEST" position. NOTE: This type of DRIVE CYCLE DIAGNOSTIC test will cause code "55" to be displayed, since a vehicle speed of 15mph or greater was not detected. | The STAR tester is displaying code "46" again: | |
| | | YES ▶ | GO TO EG6 |
| | | NO ▶ | Remove the right front height sensor, replace it with a new one and reconnect the left front height sensor to the vehicle wiring harness. Rerun SERVICE BAY DIAGNOSTICS after repair is made. |
| EG6 | ENTERING DRIVE CYCLE DIAGNOSTICS | | |
| | Again the modified DRIVE CYCLE DIAGNOSTICS will be used to help locate the cause of the short. • Release the STAR test button to the "HOLD" position. • Turn the air suspension "ON/OFF" switch to the "OFF" position. • Disconnect the rear height sensor also from the vehicle wiring harness. • With the ignition switch in the "ON/RUN" position turn the air suspension "ON/OFF" switch to the "ON" position and wait 15 seconds. | ▶ | GO TO EG7 |

Fig. 35 Pinpoint test, EG (Part 3 of 5)

| EG7 | COMPONENT CHECK | RESULT | ACTION TO TAKE |
|---|---|---|---|
| | • Turn the ignition switch to the "OFF" position. • Depress the STAR test button so that it remains down in the "TEST" position. NOTE: This type of DRIVE CYCLE DIAGNOSTIC test will cause code "55" to be displayed, since a vehicle speed of 15mph or greater was not detected. | The STAR tester is displaying code "46" again: | |
| | | YES ▶ | GO TO EG8 |
| | | NO ▶ | Remove the rear height sensor, replace it with a new one and reconnect the left and right front height sensors to the vehicle wiring harness. Rerun SERVICE BAY DIAGNOSTICS after repair is made. |
| EG8 | CHECKING WIRING HARNESS | | |
| | The air suspension control module has detected a short in the circuit which is used to provide power to the air suspension height sensors even with all three height sensors removed from the circuit. This leaves just two possible causes of the short (vehicle wiring harness or air suspension control module). In order to determine which one is the the cause of the short the following actions are required: • Disconnect air suspension control module connector. • Turn the air suspension "ON/OFF" switch to the "ON" position. • Using an analog ohmmeter connect one lead to the wiring harness connector pin location #22 (circuit #431B) and other to pin location #40 (circuit #430G). | Ohmmeter reading is greater than 10,000 ohms: | |
| | | YES ▶ | GO TO EG8 |
| | | NO ▶ | A short has been detected in the wiring harness circuit #431B. rerun SERVICE BAY DIAGNOSTICS after repair is made. |

Fig. 35 Pinpoint test, EG (Part 4 of 5)

| EG9 | CHECKING WIRING HARNESS | RESULT | ACTION TO TAKE |
|---|---|---|---|
| | • Using an analog ohmmeter (20,000 ohms is recommended) connect one lead to the wiring harness connector pin location #55 (circuit #431A) and other to pin location #60 (circuit #430H). | Ohmmeter reading is greater than 10,000 ohms: | |
| | | YES ▶ | Remove the air suspension control module and install a new one. Reconnect all three height sensors to the vehicle wiring harness and rerun SERVICE BAY DIAGNOSTICS afterwards. |
| | | NO ▶ | A short has been detected in the wiring harness circuit #431B. rerun SERVICE BAY DIAGNOSTICS after repair is made. |

Fig. 35 Pinpoint test, EG (Part 5 of 5)

| EH1 | STAR CODE: 47 SHORT IN SOFT SHOCK ACTUATOR RELAY CIRCUIT | RESULT | ACTION TO TAKE |
|---|---|---|---|
| | The air suspension control module has detected a short in the circuit used to activate the soft shock position relay. There are four possible causes of this short which are listed below: • B+ power supply circuit is shorted to ground. • The vehicle wiring harness has the B+ power supply circuit and ground return circuit in the wrong location. • Soft shock relay is defective. • The air suspension control module is defective. The soft shock position relay has a diode in it. When current is applied in the reverse direction this diode will act like a short. Because all ohmmeters do not have the same positive and negative polarity the following test procedures are being used to locate the cause of the short. | ▶ | GO TO EH2 |
| EH2 | | | |
| | • Turn the air suspension "ON/OFF" switch to the "OFF" position. • Disconnect air suspension control module connector. | ▶ | GO TO EH3 |
| EH3 | CHECKING WIRING HARNESS | | |
| | Using an analog ohmmeter measure and record the following: • Connect the positive lead of the ohmmeter to the wiring harness connector pin location #12 (circuit #839) and the negative lead to pin location #40 (circuit #430G). • Now connect the positive lead of the ohmmeter to the wiring harness connector pin location #40 (circuit #430G) and the negative lead to pin location #12 (circuit #839). | At least one of the two ohmmeter readings is greater than 40 ohms: | |
| | | YES ▶ | GO TO EH5 |
| | | NO ▶ | GO TO EH4 |

Fig. 36 Pinpoint test, EH (Part 1 of 4)

| EH4 CHECKING WIRING HARNESS | RESULT | ACTION TO TAKE |
|---|---|---|
| • Disconnect the soft shock relay from the vehicle wiring harness.<br>• Using an analog ohmmeter connect one lead to the wiring harness connector pin location #12 (circuit #839) and other to pin location #40 (circuit #430G). | Ohmmeter reading is greater than 10,000 ohms: | |
| | YES | The soft shock relay has an internal short circuit. Install a new one and rerun SERVICE BAY DIAGNOSTICS. |
| | NO | A short has been detected in the wiring harness circuit #839/430G. Rerun SERVICE BAY DIAGNOSTICS after repair is made. |
| **EH5 CHECKING WIRING HARNESS** | | |
| • Disconnect the soft shock relay from the vehicle wiring harness.<br>• Using an analog ohmmeter connect one lead to the soft shock relay vehicle wiring harness connector circuit #430B and other to a known good chassis ground. | Ohmmeter reading is less than 2.0 ohms: | |
| | YES | GO TO EH8 |
| | NO | GO TO EH6 |

**Fig. 36 Pinpoint test, EH (Part 2 of 4)**

| EH6 CHECKING WIRING HARNESS | RESULT | ACTION TO TAKE |
|---|---|---|
| In order to determine if the vehicle wiring harness has the soft shock relay circuits in the proper location the following test is required:<br>• Using an analog ohmmeter connect one lead to the soft shock relay vehicle wiring harness connector circuit #839 and other to a known good chassis ground. | Ohmmeter reading is less than 2.0 ohms: | |
| | YES | The soft shock relay power circuit (#839) and ground circuit (#430B) are reversed. Relocate these circuits to the proper location, reconnect the soft shock relay and air suspension control module. Rerun SERVICE BAY DIAGNOSTICS after repairs are made. |
| | NO | GO TO EH7 |
| **EH7 CHECKING WIRING HARNESS** | | |
| • Verify that all the wires going to the soft shock relay are in the proper location. | All wires are in the proper location: | |
| | YES | The soft shock relay ground circuit (#430B) has a resistance to chassis ground that is above acceptable limits. The resistance to ground should always be less than 2..0 ohms. Rerun SERVICE BAY DIAGNOSTICS after repairs are made. |
| | NO | Relocate wires to the proper location, reconnect the soft shock relay and air suspension control. Rerun SERVICE BAY DIAGNOSTICS after repairs are made. |

**Fig. 36 Pinpoint test, EH (Part 3 of 4)**

| EH8 COMPONENT CHECK | RESULT | ACTION TO TAKE |
|---|---|---|
| The previous steps have verified that the vehicle wiring harness is not the cause of the short. There are two possible causes that must now be checked (soft shock relay or control module). In order to determine which one is causing the short the following is required:<br>• Turn the air suspension "ON/OFF" switch to the "OFF" position.<br>• Reconnect the air suspension control module to the vehicle wiring harness.<br>• Turn the air suspension "ON/OFF" switch to the "ON" position.<br>• Rerun SERVICE BAY DIAGNOSTICS without the soft shock relay connected to the vehicle wiring harness.<br>NOTE: This test procedure will generate extra error codes because the soft shock relay is not connected to the vehicle wiring harness. | The STAR tester displayed code "47" again: | |
| | YES | Turn the air suspension "ON/OFF" switch to the "OFF" position. Remove the air suspension control module and install a new one. Rerun SERVICE BAY DIAGNOSTICS afterwards. |
| | NO | Remove the soft shock relay and install a new one. Rerun SERVICE BAY DIAGNOSTICS afterwards. |

**Fig. 36 Pinpoint test, EH (Part 4 of 4)**

| EI1 STAR CODE: 48 SHORT IN FIRM SHOCK ACTUATOR RELAY CIRCUIT | RESULT | ACTION TO TAKE |
|---|---|---|
| The air suspension control module has detected a short in the circuit used to activate the firm shock position relay. There are four possible causes of this short which are listed below:<br>• B+ power supply circuit is shorted to ground.<br>• The vehicle wiring harness has the B+ power supply circuit and ground return circuit in the wrong location.<br>• Firm shock relay is defective.<br>• The air suspension control module is defective.<br>The firm shock position relay has a diode in it. When current is applied in the reverse direction this diode will act like a short. Because all ohmmeters do not have the same positive and negative polarity the following test procedures are being used to locate the cause of the short. | | GO TO EI2 |
| **EI2** | | |
| • Turn the air suspension "ON/OFF" switch to the "OFF" position.<br>• Disconnect air suspension control module connector. | | GO TO EI3 |
| **EI3 CHECKING WIRING HARNESS** | | |
| Using an analog ohmmeter measure and record the following:<br>• Connect the positive lead of the ohmmeter to the wiring harness connector pin location #11 (circuit #838) and the negative lead to pin location #40 (circuit #430G).<br>• Now connect the positive lead of the ohmmeter to the wiring harness connector pin location #40 (circuit #430G) and the negative lead to pin location #11 (circuit#838). | At least one of the two ohmmeter readings is greater than 40 ohms: | |
| | YES | GO TO EI5 |
| | NO | GO TO EI4 |

**Fig. 37 Pinpoint test, EI (Part 1 of 5)**

| EI4 | CHECKING WIRING HARNESS | RESULT | ACTION TO TAKE |
|---|---|---|---|
| | • Disconnect the firm shock relay from the vehicle wiring harness.<br>• Using an analog ohmmeter connect one lead to the wiring harness connector pin location #11 (circuit #838) and other to pin location #40 (circuit #430G). | Ohmmeter reading is greater than 10,000 ohms: | |
| | | YES ▶ | The firm shock relay has an internal short circuit. Install a new one and rerun SERVICE BAY DIAGNOSTICS. |
| | | NO ▶ | A short has been detected in the wiring harness circuit #838/430G. Rerun SERVICE BAY DIAGNOSTICS after repair is made. |
| EI5 | CHECKING WIRING HARNESS | | |
| | • Disconnect the firm shock relay from the vehicle wiring harness.<br>• Using an analog ohmmeter connect one lead to the soft shock relay vehicle wiring harness connector circuit #430D and other to a known good chassis ground. | Ohmmeter reading is less than 2.0 ohms: | |
| | | YES ▶ | GO TO EI8 |
| | | NO ▶ | GO TO EI6 |

Fig. 37 Pinpoint test, EI (Part 2 of 5)

| EI8 | CHECKING WIRING HARNESS | RESULT | ACTION TO TAKE |
|---|---|---|---|
| | In order to determine if the vehicle wiring harness has the firm shock relay circuits in the proper location the following test is required:<br>• Using an analog ohmmeter connect one lead to the soft shock relay vehicle wiring harness connector circuit #838 and other to a known good chassis ground. | Ohmmeter reading is less than 2.0 ohms: | |
| | | YES ▶ | The firm shock relay power circuit (#838) and ground circuit (#430D) are reversed. Relocate these circuits to the proper location, reconnect the firm shock relay and air suspension control module. Rerun SERVICE BAY DIAGNOSTICS after repairs are made. |
| | | NO ▶ | GO TO EI7 |

Fig. 37 Pinpoint test, EI (Part 3 of 5)

| EI7 | CHECKING WIRING HARNESS | RESULT | ACTION TO TAKE |
|---|---|---|---|
| | • Verify that all the wires going to the firm shock relay are in the proper location. | All wires are in the proper location: | |
| | | YES ▶ | The firm shock relay ground circuit (#430D) has a resistance to chassis ground that is above acceptable limits. The resistance to ground should always be less than 2.0 ohms. Rerun SERVICE BAY DIAGNOSTICS after repairs are made. |
| | | NO ▶ | Relocate wires to the proper location, reconnect the firm shock relay and air suspension control. Rerun SERVICE BAY DIAGNOSTICS after repairs are made. |

Fig. 37 Pinpoint test, EI (Part 4 of 5)

| EI8 | COMPONENT CHECK | RESULT | ACTION TO TAKE |
|---|---|---|---|
| | The previous steps have verified that the vehicle wiring harness is not the cause of the short. There are two possible causes that must now be checked (firm shock relay or control module). In order to determine which one is causing the short the following is required:<br>• Turn the air suspension "ON/OFF" switch to the "OFF" position.<br>• Reconnect the air suspension control module to the vehicle wiring harness.<br>• Turn the air suspension "ON/OFF" switch to the "ON" position.<br>• Rerun SERVICE BAY DIAGNOSTICS without the firm shock relay being connected to the vehicle wiring harness.<br>NOTE: This test procedure will generate extra error codes because the firm shock relay is not connected to the vehicle wiring harness. | The STAR tester displayed code "48" again: | |
| | | YES ▶ | Turn the air suspension "ON/OFF" switch to the "OFF" position. Remove the air suspension control module and install a new one. Rerun SERVICE BAY DIAGNOSTICS afterwards. |
| | | NO ▶ | Remove the firm shock relay and install a new one. Rerun SERVICE BAY DIAGNOSTICS afterwards. |

Fig. 37 Pinpoint test, EI (Part 5 of 5)

| EJ1 | STAR CODE: 66<br>SHORT IN RIGHT FRONT<br>HEIGHT SENSOR CIRCUIT | RESULT | ACTION TO TAKE |
|---|---|---|---|
| | The air suspension control module has detected a short in the circuit used to receive signals from the right front height sensor. There are four possible causes of this short which are listed below:<br>• Channel "A" signal return circuit is shorted to ground.<br>• Channel "B" signal return circuit is shorted to ground.<br>• The right front height sensor is defective.<br>• The air suspension control module is defective. | ▶ | GO TO EJ2 |
| EJ2 | | | |
| | In order to determine where the short is located a modified DRIVE CYCLE DIAGNOSTICS will be utilized. In order to do this the following preliminary actions are required:<br>• Turn the air suspension "ON/OFF" switch to the "OFF" position.<br>• Disconnect the right front height sensor from the vehicle wiring harness.<br>• With the ignition switch in the "ON/RUN" position turn the air suspension "ON/OFF" switch to the "ON" position and wait 15 seconds. | ▶ | GO TO EJ3 |

Fig. 38 Pinpoint test, EJ (Part 1 of 3)

| EJ3 | COMPONENT CHECK | RESULT | ACTION TO TAKE |
|---|---|---|---|
| | • Turn the ignition switch to the "OFF" position.<br>• Depress the STAR test button so that it remains down in the "TEST" position.<br>NOTE: This type of DRIVE CYCLE DIAGNOSTIC test will cause code "55" to be displayed, since a vehicle speed of 15 mph or greater was not detected. | The STAR tester is displaying code "66" again:<br>YES ▶<br>NO ▶ | GO TO EJ4<br>Remove the right front height sensor and replace it with a new one. Rerun SERVICE BAY DIAGNOSTICS after repair is made. |
| EJ4 | WIRING HARNESS CHECK | | |
| | • Turn the air suspension "ON/OFF" switch to the "OFF" position.<br>• Disconnect air suspension control module connector.<br>• Using an analog ohmmeter connect one lead to the air suspension control module wiring harness connector pin location #9 (circuit #424) and other to a known good chassis ground. | Ohmmeter reading is greater than 10,000 ohms:<br>YES ▶<br>NO ▶ | GO TO EJ5<br>A short to ground has been detected in the wiring harness circuit #424.<br>Reconnect the right front height sensor, air suspension control module and rerun SERVICE BAY DIAGNOSTICS after repair is made. |

Fig. 38 Pinpoint test, EJ (Part 2 of 3)

| EJ5 | WIRING HARNESS CHECK | RESULT | ACTION TO TAKE |
|---|---|---|---|
| | • Using an analog ohmmeter connect one lead to the air suspension control module wiring harness connector pin location #10 (circuit #425) and other to a known good chassis ground. | Ohmmeter reading is greater than 10,000 ohms:<br>YES ▶<br>NO ▶ | Turn the air suspension "ON/OFF" switch to the "OFF" position. Remove the air suspension control module and install a new one. Reconnect the right front height sensor and rerun SERVICE BAY DIAGNOSTICS afterwards.<br>A short to ground has been detected in the wiring harness circuit #425.<br>Reconnect the right front height sensor, air suspension control module and rerun SERVICE BAY DIAGNOSTICS after repair is made. |

Fig. 38 Pinpoint test, EJ (Part 3 of 3)

| EK1 | STAR CODE: 67<br>SHORT IN LEFT FRONT<br>HEIGHT SENSOR CIRCUIT | RESULT | ACTION TO TAKE |
|---|---|---|---|
| | The air suspension control module has detected a short in the circuit used to receive signals from the left front height sensor. There are four possible causes of this short which are listed below:<br>• Channel "A" signal return circuit is shorted to ground.<br>• Channel "B" signal return circuit is shorted to ground.<br>• The left front height sensor is defective.<br>• The air suspension control module is defective. | ▶ | GO TO EK2 |
| EK2 | | | |
| | In order to determine where the short is located a modified DRIVE CYCLE DIAGNOSTICS will be utilized. In order to do this the following preliminary actions are required:<br>• Turn the air suspension "ON/OFF" switch to the "OFF" position.<br>• Disconnect the left front height sensor from the vehicle wiring harness.<br>• With the ignition switch in the "ON/RUN" position turn the air suspension "ON/OFF" switch to the "ON" position and wait 15 seconds. | ▶ | GO TO EK3 |
| EK3 | COMPONENT CHECK | | |
| | • Turn the ignition switch to the "OFF" position.<br>• Depress the STAR test button so that it remains down in the "TEST" position.<br>NOTE: This type of DRIVE CYCLE DIAGNOSTIC test will cause code "55" to be displayed, since a vehicle speed of 15 mph or greater was not detected. | The STAR tester is displaying code "67" again:<br>YES ▶<br>NO ▶ | GO TO EK4<br>Remove the left front height sensor and replace it with a new one. Rerun SERVICE BAY DIAGNOSTICS after repair is made. |

Fig. 39 Pinpoint test, EK (Part 1 of 3)

| EK4 | WIRING HARNESS CHECK | RESULT | | ACTION TO TAKE |
|---|---|---|---|---|
| | • Turn the air suspension "ON/OFF" switch to the "OFF" position.<br>• Disconnect air suspension control module connector.<br>• Using an analog ohmmeter connect one lead to the air suspension control module wiring harness connector pin location #27 (circuit #422) and other to a known good chassis ground. | Ohmmeter reading is greater than 10,000 ohms: | | |
| | | YES | ▶ | GO TO EK5 |
| | | NO | ▶ | A short to ground has been detected in the wiring harness circuit #422.<br><br>Reconnect the left front height sensor, air suspension control module and rerun SERVICE BAY DIAGNOSTICS after repair is made. |

Fig. 39 Pinpoint test, EK (Part 2 of 3)

| EK5 | WIRING HARNESS CHECK | RESULT | | ACTION TO TAKE |
|---|---|---|---|---|
| | • Using an analog ohmmeter connect one lead to the air suspension control module wiring harness connector pin location #43 (circuit #423) and other to a known good chassis ground. | Ohmmeter reading is greater than 10,000 ohms: | | |
| | | YES | ▶ | Turn the air suspension "ON/OFF" switch to the "OFF" position. Remove the air suspension control module and install a new one. Reconnect the left front height sensor and rerun SERVICE BAY DIAGNOSTICS afterwards. |
| | | NO | ▶ | A short to ground has been detected in the wiring harness circuit #423.<br><br>Reconnect the left front height sensor, air suspension control module and rerun SERVICE BAY DIAGNOSTICS after repair is made. |

Fig. 39 Pinpoint test, EK (Part 3 of 3)

| EL1 | STAR CODE: 68<br>SHORT IN REAR<br>HEIGHT SENSOR CIRCUIT | RESULT | | ACTION TO TAKE |
|---|---|---|---|---|
| | The air suspension control module has detected a short in the circuit used to receive signals from the rear height sensor. There are four possible causes of this short which are listed below:<br>• Channel "A" signal return circuit is shorted to ground.<br>• Channel "B" signal return circuit is shorted to ground.<br>• The rear height sensor is defective.<br>• The air suspension control module is defective. | | ▶ | GO TO EL2 |
| EL2 | | | | |
| | In order to determine where the short is located a modified DRIVE CYCLE DIAGNOSTICS will be utilized. In order to do this the following preliminary actions are required:<br>• Turn the air suspension "ON/OFF" switch to the "OFF" position.<br>• Disconnect the rear height sensor from the vehicle wiring harness.<br>• With the ignition switch in the "ON/RUN" position turn the air suspension "ON/OFF" switch to the "ON" position and wait 15 seconds. | | ▶ | GO TO EL3 |
| EL3 | COMPONENT CHECK | | | |
| | • Turn the ignition switch to the "OFF" position.<br>• Depress the STAR test button so that it remains down in the "TEST" position.<br>NOTE: This type of DRIVE CYCLE DIAGNOSTIC test will cause code "55" to be displayed, since a vehicle speed of 15 mph or greater was not detected. | The STAR tester is displaying code "68" again: | | |
| | | YES | ▶ | GO TO EL4 |
| | | NO | ▶ | Remove the rear height sensor and replace it with a new one. Rerun SERVICE BAY DIAGNOSTICS after repair is made. |

Fig. 40 Pinpoint test, EL (Part 1 of 3)

| EL4 | WIRING HARNESS CHECK | RESULT | | ACTION TO TAKE |
|---|---|---|---|---|
| | • Turn the air suspension "ON/OFF" switch to the "OFF" position.<br>• Disconnect air suspension control module connector.<br>• Using an analog ohmmeter connect one lead to the air suspension control module wiring harness connector pin location #5 (circuit #427) and other to a known good chassis ground. | Ohmmeter reading is greater than 10,000 ohms: | | |
| | | YES | ▶ | GO TO EL5. |
| | | NO | ▶ | A short to ground has been detected in the wiring harness circuit #427.<br><br>Reconnect the rear height sensor, air suspension control module and rerun SERVICE BAY DIAGNOSTICS after repair is made. |

Fig. 40 Pinpoint test, EL (Part 2 of 3)

| EL5 WIRING HARNESS CHECK | RESULT | ACTION TO TAKE |
|---|---|---|
| • Using an analog ohmmeter connect one lead to the air suspension control module wiring harness connector pin location #8 (circuit #428) and other to a known good chassis ground. | Ohmmeter reading is greater than 10,000 ohms: | |
| | YES | ▶ Turn the air suspension "ON/OFF" switch to the "OFF" position. Remove the air suspension control module and install a new one. Reconnect the rear height sensor and rerun SERVICE BAY DIAGNOSTICS afterwards. |
| | NO | ▶ A short to ground has been detected in the wiring harness circuit #428. Reconnect the rear height sensor, air suspension control module and rerun SERVICE BAY DIAGNOSTICS after repair is made. |

**Fig. 40 Pinpoint test, EL (Part 3 of 3)**

| FA1 STAR CODE: 69 OPEN IN RIGHT FRONT HEIGHT SENSOR CIRCUIT | RESULT | ACTION TO TAKE |
|---|---|---|
| The air suspension control module has detected an open in the circuit used to receive signals from the right front height sensor. There are seven possible causes of this open which are listed below:<br>• The B+ power supply circuit to the right front height sensor has an open in it.<br>• The ground return circuit from the right front height sensor has an open in it.<br>• Channel "A" signal return circuit has an open in it.<br>• Channel "B" signal return circuit has an open in it.<br>• The right front height sensor linkage arm is not connected to the lower arm.<br>• The right front height sensor is defective.<br>• The air suspension control module is defective. | | ▶ GO TO FA2 |
| **FA2 RIGHT FRONT HEIGHT SENSOR VISUAL CHECK** | | |
| Make a visual check of the right front height sensor to ensure that linkage arm and electrical connector are connected and have no obvious damage. | Visual inspection revealed problems with the linkage or electrical connector: | |
| | YES | ▶ Make required repairs and rerun SERVICE BAY DIAGNOSTICS afterwards. |
| | NO | ▶ GO TO FA3 |

**Fig. 41 Pinpoint test, FA (Part 1 of 5)**

| FA3 B+ POWER SUPPLY CIRCUIT CHECK | RESULT | ACTION TO TAKE |
|---|---|---|
| Disconnect the right front height sensor from the vehicle wiring harness and make the following check:<br>• Using a voltmeter connect the positive lead to circuit #431C on the right front height sensor vehicle wiring harness connector and the negative lead to a known good chassis ground. | Voltage reading is greater than 4.0 volts: | |
| | YES | ▶ GO TO FA5 |
| | NO | ▶ GO TO FA4 |
| **FA4 CHECKING WIRING HARNESS** | | |
| • Turn the air suspension "ON/OFF" switch to the "OFF" position.<br>• Disconnect air suspension control module connector.<br>• Using an ohmmeter connect one lead to the air suspension control module wiring harness connector pin location #22 (circuit #431B) and other to circuit #431C of the right front height sensor vehicle wiring harness connector. | Ohmmeter reading is less than 5.0 ohms: | |
| | YES | ▶ Turn the air suspension "ON/OFF" switch to the "OFF" position and remove the air suspension control module. Install a new control module and reconnect the right front height sensor. Then rerun SERVICE BAY DIAGNOSTICS. |
| | NO | ▶ The right front height sensor power supply circuit (#431B/431C) resistance is above acceptable limits. The resistance to ground should always be less than 5.0 ohms. Reconnect the right front height sensor and rerun SERVICE BAY DIAGNOSTICS after repairs are made. |

**Fig. 41 Pinpoint test, FA (Part 2 of 5)**

| FA5 B+ POWER RETURN CIRCUIT CHECK | RESULT | ACTION TO TAKE |
|---|---|---|
| • Using an ohmmeter connect one lead to circuit #432D of the right front height sensor vehicle wiring harness connector and the other to a known good chassis ground. | Ohmmeter reading is less than 5.0 ohms: | |
| | YES | ▶ GO TO FA7 |
| | NO | ▶ GO TO FA6 |
| **FA6 CHECKING WIRING HARNESS** | | |
| • Turn the air suspension "ON/OFF" switch to the "OFF" position.<br>• Disconnect air suspension control module connector.<br>• Using an ohmmeter connect one lead to the air suspension control module wiring harness connector pin location #46 (circuit #432D) and other to circuit #432D of the right front height sensor vehicle wiring harness connector. | Ohmmeter reading is less than 5.0 ohms: | |
| | YES | ▶ Turn the air suspension "ON/OFF" switch to the "OFF" position and remove the air suspension control module. Install a new control module and reconnect the right front height sensor. Then rerun SERVICE BAY DIAGNOSTICS. |
| | NO | ▶ The right front height sensor power return circuit (#432D) resistance is above acceptable limits. The resistance to ground should always be less than 5.0 ohms. Reconnect the right front height sensor and rerun SERVICE BAY DIAGNOSTICS after repairs are made. |

**Fig. 41 Pinpoint test, FA (Part 3 of 5)**

| FA7 | HEIGHT SENSOR CHANNEL "A" CHECK | RESULT | ACTION TO TAKE |
|---|---|---|---|
| | • Using a voltmeter connect the positive lead to circuit #424 of the right front height sensor vehicle wiring harness connector and the negative lead to a known good chassis ground. | Voltage reading is greater than 4.0 volts: | |
| | | YES ▶ | GO TO FA9 |
| | | NO ▶ | GO TO FA8 |
| FA8 | CHECKING WIRING HARNESS | | |
| | • Turn the air suspension "ON/OFF" switch to the "OFF" position.<br>• Disconnect air suspension control module connector.<br>• Using an analog ohmmeter connect one lead to the air suspension control module wiring harness connector pin location #9 (circuit #424) and other to circuit #424 of the right front height sensor vehicle wiring harness connector. | Ohmmeter reading is less than 5 ohms: | |
| | | YES ▶ | Turn the air suspension "ON/OFF" switch to the "OFF" position and remove the air suspension control module. Install a new control module and reconnect the right front height sensor. Then rerun SERVICE BAY DIAGNOSTICS afterwards. |
| | | NO ▶ | The right front height sensor channel "A" circuit (#424) resistance is above acceptable limits. The resistance to ground should always be less than 5.0 ohms. Reconnect the right front height sensor and rerun SERVICE BAY DIAGNOSTICS after repairs are made. |

**Fig. 41 Pinpoint test, FA (Part 4 of 5)**

| FA9 | HEIGHT SENSOR CHANNEL "B" CHECK | RESULT | ACTION TO TAKE |
|---|---|---|---|
| | • Using a voltmeter connect the positive lead to circuit #425 of the right front height sensor vehicle wiring harness connector and the negative lead to a known good chassis ground. | Voltage reading is greater than 4.0 volts: | |
| | | YES ▶ | Remove the right front height sensor and install a new one. Rerun SERVICE BAY DIAGNOSTICS afterwards. |
| | | NO ▶ | GO TO FA10 |
| FA10 | CHECKING WIRING HARNESS | | |
| | • Turn the air suspension "ON/OFF" switch to the "OFF" position.<br>• Disconnect air suspension control module connector.<br>• Using an analog ohmmeter connect one lead to the air suspension control module wiring harness connector pin location #10 (circuit #425) and other to circuit #425 of the right front height sensor vehicle wiring harness connector. | Ohmmeter reading is less than 5 ohms: | |
| | | YES ▶ | Turn the air suspension "ON/OFF" switch to the "OFF" position and remove the air suspension control module. Install a new control module and reconnect the right front height sensor. Then rerun SERVICE BAY DIAGNOSTICS afterwards. |
| | | NO ▶ | The right front height sensor channel "B" circuit (#425) resistance is above acceptable limits. The resistance to ground should always be less than 5.0 ohms. Reconnect the right front height sensor and rerun SERVICE BAY DIAGNOSTICS after repairs are made. |

**Fig. 41 Pinpoint test, FA (Part 5 of 5)**

| FB1 | STAR CODE: 70 OPEN IN LEFT FRONT HEIGHT SENSOR CIRCUIT | RESULT | ACTION TO TAKE |
|---|---|---|---|
| | The air suspension control module has detected an open in the circuit used to receive signals from the left front height sensor. There are six possible causes of this open which are listed below:<br>• The B+ power supply circuit to the right front height sensor has an open in it.<br>• The ground return circuit from the right front height sensor has an open in it.<br>• Channel "A" signal return circuit is shorted to ground.<br>• Channel "B" signal return circuit is shorted to ground.<br>• The left front height sensor is defective.<br>• The air suspension control module is defective. | ▶ | GO TO FB2 |
| FB2 | LEFT FRONT HEIGHT SENSOR VISUAL CHECK | | |
| | Make a visual check of the left front height sensor to ensure that linkage arm and electrical connector are connected and have no obvious damage. | Visual inspection revealed problems with the linkage or electrical connector: | |
| | | YES ▶ | Make required repairs and rerun SERVICE BAY DIAGNOSTICS afterwards. |
| | | NO ▶ | GO TO FB3 |

**Fig. 42 Pinpoint test, FB (Part 1 of 5)**

| FB3 | B+ POWER SUPPLY CIRCUIT CHECK | RESULT | ACTION TO TAKE |
|---|---|---|---|
| | Disconnect the left front height sensor from the vehicle wiring harness and make the following check:<br>• Using a voltmeter connect the positive lead to circuit #431C of the left front height sensor vehicle wiring harness connector and the negative lead to a known good chassis ground. | Voltage reading is greater than 4.0 volts: | |
| | | YES ▶ | GO TO FB5 |
| | | NO ▶ | GO TO FB4 |
| FB4 | CHECKING WIRING HARNESS | | |
| | • Turn the air suspension "ON/OFF" switch to the "OFF" position.<br>• Disconnect air suspension control module connector.<br>• Using an ohmmeter connect one lead to the air suspension control module wiring harness connector pin location #22 (circuit #431B) and other to circuit #431D of the left front height sensor vehicle wiring harness connector. | Ohmmeter reading is less than 5.0 ohms: | |
| | | YES ▶ | Turn the air suspension "ON/OFF" switch to the "OFF" position and remove the air suspension control module. Install a new control module and reconnect the left front height sensor. Then rerun SERVICE BAY DIAGNOSTICS. |
| | | NO ▶ | The left front height sensor power supply circuit (#431B/431D) resistance is above acceptable limits. The resistance to ground should always be less than 5.0 ohms. Reconnect the left front height sensor and rerun SERVICE BAY DIAGNOSTICS after repairs are made. |

**Fig. 42 Pinpoint test, FB (Part 2 of 5)**

| FB5 | B+ POWER RETURN CIRCUIT CHECK | RESULT | ACTION TO TAKE |
|---|---|---|---|
| | • Using an ohmmeter connect one lead to circuit #432E of the left front height sensor vehicle wiring harness connector and the other to a known good chassis ground. | Ohmmeter reading is less than 5.0 ohms: | |
| | | YES ▶ | GO TO FB7 |
| | | NO ▶ | GO TO FB6 |
| FB6 | CHECKING WIRING HARNESS | | |
| | • Turn the air suspension "ON/OFF" switch to the "OFF" position<br>• Disconnect air suspension control module connector.<br>• Using an ohmmeter connect one lead to the air suspension control module wiring harness connector pin location #46 (circuit #432D) and other to circuit #432E of the left front circuit height sensor vehicle wiring harness connector. | Ohmmeter reading is less than 5.0 ohms: | |
| | | YES ▶ | Turn the air suspension "ON/OFF" switch to the "OFF" position and remove the air suspension control module. Install a new control module and reconnect the left front height sensor. Then rerun SERVICE BAY DIAGNOSTICS. |
| | | NO ▶ | The left front height sensor power return circuit (#432D/432E) resistance is above acceptable limits. The resistance to ground should always be less than 5.0 ohms. Reconnect the left front height sensor and rerun SERVICE BAY DIAGNOSTICS after repairs are made. |

**Fig. 42 Pinpoint test, FB (Part 3 of 5)**

| FB7 | HEIGHT SENSOR CHANNEL "A" CHECK | RESULT | ACTION TO TAKE |
|---|---|---|---|
| | • Using a voltmeter connect the ositive lead to circuit #422 of the left front height sensor vehicle wiring harness connector and the negative lead to a known good chassis ground. | Voltage reading is greater than 4.0 volts: | |
| | | YES ▶ | GO TO FB9 |
| | | NO ▶ | GO TO FB8 |
| FB8 | CHECKING WIRING HARNESS | | |
| | • Turn the air suspension "ON/OFF" switch to the "OFF" position.<br>• Disconnect air suspension control module connector.<br>• Using an analog ohmmeter (20,000 ohms per volt is recommended) connect one lead to the air suspension control module wiring harness connector pin location #27 (circuit #422) and other to circuit #422 of the left front height sensor vehicle wiring harness connector. | Ohmmeter reading is less than 5 ohms: | |
| | | YES ▶ | Turn the air suspension "ON/OFF" switch to the "OFF" position and remove the air suspension control module. Install a new control module and reconnect the left front height sensor. Then rerun SERVICE BAY DIAGNOSTICS afterwards. |
| | | NO ▶ | The left front height sensor channel "A" circuit (#422) resistance is above acceptable limits. The resistance to ground should always be less than 5.0 ohms. Reconnect the left front height sensor and rerun SERVICE BAY DIAGNOSTICS after repairs are made. |

**Fig. 42 Pinpoint test, FB (Part 4 of 5)**

| FB9 | HEIGHT SENSOR CHANNEL "B" CHECK | RESULT | ACTION TO TAKE |
|---|---|---|---|
| | • Using a voltmeter connect the positive lead to circuit #425 of the left front height sensor vehicle wiring harness connector and the negative lead to a known good chassis ground. | Voltage reading is greater than 4.0 volts: | |
| | | YES ▶ | Remove the left front height sensor and install a new one. Rerun SERVICE BAY DIAGNOSTICS afterwards. |
| | | NO ▶ | GO TO FB10 |
| FB10 | CHECKING WIRING HARNESS | | |
| | • Turn the air suspension "ON/OFF" switch to the "OFF" position.<br>• Disconnect air suspension control module connector.<br>• Using an analog ohmmeter (20,000 ohms per volt is recommended) connect one lead to the air suspension control module wiring harness connector pin location #43 (circuit #423) and other to circuit #423 of the left front height sensor vehicle wiring harness connector. | Ohmmeter reading is less than 5 ohms: | |
| | | YES ▶ | Turn the air suspension "ON/OFF" switch to the "OFF" position and remove the air suspension control module. Install a new control module and reconnect the left front height sensor. Then rerun SERVICE BAY DIAGNOSTICS afterwards. |
| | | NO ▶ | The left front height sensor channel "B" circuit (#423) resistance is above acceptable limits. The resistance to ground should always be less than 5.0 ohms. Reconnect the left front height sensor and rerun SERVICE BAY DIAGNOSTICS after repairs are made. |

**Fig. 42 Pinpoint test, FB (Part 5 of 5)**

| FC1 | STAR CODE: 71 OPEN IN REAR HEIGHT SENSOR CIRCUIT | RESULT | ACTION TO TAKE |
|---|---|---|---|
| | The air suspension control module has detected an open in the circuit used to receive signals from the rear height sensor. There are six possible causes of this open which are listed below:<br>• The B+ power supply circuit to the right front height sensor has an open in it.<br>• The ground return circuit from the right front height sensor has an open in it.<br>• Channel "A" signal return circuit is shorted to ground.<br>• Channel "B" signal return circuit is shorted to ground.<br>• The rear front height sensor is defective.<br>• The air suspension control module is defective. | ▶ | GO TO FC2 |
| FC2 | REAR HEIGHT SENSOR VISUAL CHECK | | |
| | Make a visual check of the rear height sensor to ensure that linkage arm and electrical connector are connected and have no obvious damage. | Visual inspection revealed problems with the linkage or electrical connector: | |
| | | YES ▶ | Make required repairs and rerun SERVICE BAY DIAGNOSTICS afterwards. |
| | | NO ▶ | GO TO FC3 |

**Fig. 43 Pinpoint test, FC (Part 1 of 5)**

| FC3 | B+ POWER SUPPLY CIRCUIT CHECK | RESULT | | ACTION TO TAKE |
|---|---|---|---|---|
| | Disconnect the rear height sensor from the vehicle wiring harness and make the following check:<br>• Using a voltmeter connect the positive lead to circuit #431 of the rear height sensor vehicle wiring harness connector and the negative lead to a known good chassis ground. | Voltage reading is greater than 4.0 volts:<br>YES | ▶ | GO TO FC5 |
| | | NO | ▶ | GO TO FC4 |
| FC4 | CHECKING WIRING HARNESS | | | |
| | • Turn the air suspension "ON/OFF" switch to the "OFF" position.<br>• Disconnect air suspension control module connector.<br>• Using an ohmmeter connect one lead to the air suspension control module wiring harness connector pin location #22 (circuit #431B) and other to circuit #431 of the rear height sensor vehicle wiring harness connector. | Ohmmeter reading is less than 5.0 ohms:<br>YES | ▶ | Turn the air suspension "ON/OFF" switch to the "OFF" position and remove the air suspension control module. Install a new control module and reconnect the rear height sensor. Then rerun SERVICE BAY DIAGNOSTICS. |
| | | NO | ▶ | The rear height sensor power supply circuit (#431B/431) resistance is above acceptable limits. The resistance to ground should always be less than 5.0 ohms. Reconnect the rear height sensor and rerun SERVICE BAY DIAGNOSTICS after repairs are made. |

**Fig. 43 Pinpoint test, FC (Part 2 of 5)**

| FC5 | B+ POWER RETURN CIRCUIT CHECK | RESULT | | ACTION TO TAKE |
|---|---|---|---|---|
| | • Using an ohmmeter connect one lead to circuit #432B of the rear height sensor vehicle wiring harness connector and the other to a known good chassis ground. | Ohmmeter reading is less than 5.0 ohms:<br>YES | ▶ | GO TO FC7 |
| | | NO | ▶ | GO TO FC6 |
| FC6 | CHECKING WIRING HARNESS | | | |
| | • Turn the air suspension "ON/OFF" switch to the "OFF" position.<br>• Disconnect air suspension control module connector.<br>• Using an ohmmeter connect one lead to the air suspension control module wiring harness connector pin location #46 (circuit #432D) and other to circuit #432B of the rear height sensor vehicle wiring harness connector. | Ohmmeter reading is less than 5.0 ohms:<br>YES | ▶ | Turn the air suspension "ON/OFF" switch to the "OFF" position and remove the air suspension control module. Install a new control module and reconnect the rear height sensor. Then rerun SERVICE BAY DIAGNOSTICS. |
| | | NO | ▶ | The rear height sensor power return circuit (#432B/432D) resistance is above acceptable limits. The resistance to ground should always be less than 5.0 ohms. Reconnect the rear height sensor and rerun SERVICE BAY DIAGNOSTICS after repairs are made. |

**Fig. 43 Pinpoint test, FC (Part 3 of 5)**

| FC7 | HEIGHT SENSOR CHANNEL "A" CHECK | RESULT | | ACTION TO TAKE |
|---|---|---|---|---|
| | • Using a voltmeter connect the positive lead to circuit #427 of the rear height sensor vehicle wiring harnss connector and the negative lead to a known good chassis ground. | Voltage reading is greater than 4.0 volts:<br>YES | ▶ | GO TO FC9 |
| | | NO | ▶ | GO TO FC8 |
| FC8 | CHECKING WIRING HARNESS | | | |
| | • Turn the air suspension "ON/OFF" switch to the "OFF" position.<br>• Disconnect air suspension control module connector.<br>• Using an analog ohmmeter connect one lead to the air suspension control module wiring harness connector pin location #5 (circuit #427) and other to circuit #427 of the rear height sensor vehicle wiring harness connector. | Ohmmeter reading is less than 5 ohms:<br>YES | ▶ | Turn the air suspension "ON/OFF" switch to the "OFF" position and remove the air suspension control module. Install a new control module and reconnect the rear height sensor. Then rerun SERVICE BAY DIAGNOSTICS afterwards. |
| | | NO | ▶ | The rear height sensor channel "A" circuit (#427) resistance is above acceptable limits. The resistance to ground should always be less than 5.0 ohms. Reconnect the rear height sensor and rerun SERVICE BAY DIAGNOSTICS after repairs are made. |

**Fig. 43 Pinpoint test, FC (Part 4 of 5)**

| FC9 | HEIGHT SENSOR CHANNEL "B" CHECK | RESULT | | ACTION TO TAKE |
|---|---|---|---|---|
| | • Using a voltmeter connect the positive lead to circuit #428 of the rear height sensor vehicle wiring harness connector and the negative lead to a known good chassis ground. | Voltage reading is greater than 4.0 volts:<br>YES | ▶ | Remove the rear height sensor and install a new one. Rerun SERVICE BAY DIAGNOSTICS afterwards. |
| | | NO | ▶ | GO TO FC10 |
| FC10 | CHECKING WIRING HARNESS | | | |
| | • Turn the air suspension "ON/OFF" switch to the "OFF" position.<br>• Disconnect air suspension control module connector.<br>• Using an analog ohmmeter connect one lead to the air suspension control module wiring harness connector pin location #8 (circuit #428) and other to circuit #428 of the rear height sensor vehicle wiring harness connector. | Ohmmeter reading is less than 5 ohms:<br>YES | ▶ | Turn the air suspension "ON/OFF" switch to the "OFF" position and remove the air suspension control module. Install a new control module and reconnect the rear height sensor. Then rerun SERVICE BAY DIAGNOSTICS afterwards. |
| | | NO | ▶ | The rear height sensor channel "B" circuit (#428) resistance is above acceptable limits. The resistance to ground should always be less than 5.0 ohms. Reconnect the rear height sensor and rerun SERVICE BAY DIAGNOSTICS after repairs are made. |

**Fig. 43 Pinpoint test, FC (Part 5 of 5)**

| GA1 | STAR CODE: 56 or 60 ACTUATOR DESIRED POSITION NOT DETECTED | RESULT | | ACTION TO TAKE |
|---|---|---|---|---|
| | The air suspension control module did not receive a signal that the left rear shock actuator went to the desired position when activated. There are eight possible causes of the actuator not switching to the desired position.<br>• The "SOFT" and/or "FIRM" relay is defective.<br>• The "SOFT" or "FIRM" shock relay circuit is defective.<br>• The vehicle wiring harness power supply circuit to the left rear shock actuator is shorted to ground or has an open in it.<br>• The left rear shock actuator position circuit is shorted to ground or has an open in it.<br>• The vehicle wiring harness connector for the left rear shock actuator does not have all the wires in the correct location.<br>• The left rear shock actuator is defective.<br>• The left rear shock/strut assembly on the vehicle is binding preventing the actuator from switching to the desired position.<br>• The air suspension control module is defective. | Was STAR code "64" or "65" also displayed: | | |
| | | YES | ▶ | GO TO GE1 |
| | | NO | ▶ | GO TO GA2 |
| GA2 | LEFT REAR ACTUATOR VISUAL CHECK | | | |
| | The air suspension control module did not receive a signal that the left rear shock actuator went to the desired position when activated. In order to determine why this did not happen the following actions are required:<br>• Examine the four wires of the left rear actuator connector and also those wires on the wiring harness side to ensure that there is no obvious damage and that all of the wires are in the proper location. | All wires are in the proper location with no obvious damage. | | |
| | | YES | ▶ | GO TO GA3 |
| | | NO | ▶ | Service wires as necessary and rerun SERVICE BAY DIAGNOSTICS after repair is made. |

**Fig. 44 Pinpoint test, GA (Part 1 of 7)**

| GA3 | COMPONENT CHECK LEFT REAR ACTUATOR | RESULT | | ACTION TO TAKE |
|---|---|---|---|---|
| | In order to determine if the actuator is working properly the following actions are required:<br>• Disconnect the left rear actuator from the vehicle wiring harness connector.<br>• Using an analog ohmmeter measure the resistance across the actuator pin position #1 and pin position #2. | Ohmmeter reading is: | | |
| | | 10,000 ohms or greater | ▶ | GO TO GA4 |
| | | 5 ohms or less | ▶ | GO TO GA6 |
| GA4 | COMPONENT CHECK ACTUATE TO SOFT POSITION | | | |
| | • Use a 12 volt power supply and connect the negative lead to actuator pin position #4 and the positive lead to pin position #3 for 1 to 2 seconds. This procedure should drive the actuator to the "SOFT" position. After this has been done remove power supply leads.<br>• Using an analog ohmmeter measure the resistance across the actuator pin position #1 and pin position #2. | Ohmmeter reading is: | | |
| | | 10,000 ohms or greater | ▶ | GO TO GA5 |
| | | 5 ohms or less | ▶ | GO TO GA13 |
| GA5 | COMPONENT CHECK ACTUATE TO FIRM POSITION | | | |
| | • Again use a 12 volt power supply and connect the negative lead to actuator pin position #3 and the positive lead to pin position #4 for 1 to 2 seconds. This procedure should drive the actuator to the "FIRM" position. After this has been done remove power supply leads.<br>• Using an analog ohmmeter measure the resistance across the actuator pin position #1 and pin position #2. | Ohmmeter reading is: | | |
| | | 10,000 ohms or greater | ▶ | GO TO GA8 |
| | | 5 ohms or less | ▶ | The power supply circuits (pin location #3 & #4) are reversed. Replace the left rear actuator with a new one. After repairs are made rerun SERVICE BAY DIAGNOSTICS. |

**Fig. 44 Pinpoint test, GA (Part 2 of 7)**

| GA6 | COMPONENT CHECK ACTUATE TO FIRM POSITION | RESULT | | ACTION TO TAKE |
|---|---|---|---|---|
| | • Use a 12 volt power supply and connect the negative lead to actuator pin position #3 and the positive lead to pin position #4 for 1 to 2 seconds. This procedure should drive the actuator to the "FIRM" position. After this has been done remove power supply leads.<br>• Using an analog ohmmeter measure the resistance across the actuator pin position #1 and pin position #2. | Ohmmeter reading is: | | |
| | | 10,000 ohms or greater | ▶ | GO TO GA13 |
| | | 5 ohms or less | ▶ | GO TO GA7 |
| GA7 | COMPONENT CHECK ACTUATE TO SOFT POSITION | | | |
| | • Again use a 12 volt power supply and connect the negative lead to actuator pin position #4 and the positive lead to pin position #3 for 1 to 2 seconds. This procedure should drive the actuator to the "SOFT" position. After this has been done remove power supply leads.<br>• Using an analog ohmmeter measure the resistance across the actuator pin position #1 and pin position #2. | Ohmmeter reading is: | | |
| | | 10,000 ohms or greater | ▶ | The power supply circuits (pin location #3 & #4) are reversed. Replace the left rear actuator with a new one. After repairs are made rerun SERVICE BAY DIAGNOSTICS. |
| | | 5 ohms or less | ▶ | GO TO GA8 |
| GA8 | COMPONENT CHECK POSITION CIRCUIT | | | |
| | • Remove the left rear actuator from the top of the left rear shock/strut.<br>• Use a small blade screwdriver to rotate the control tube on the bottom of the actuator to the "S" ("SOFT" position).<br>• Using an analog ohmmeter measure the resistance across pin position #1 and #2. | Ohmmeter reading is: | | |
| | | 5.0 ohms or less | ▶ | GO TO GA9 |
| | | 10,000 ohms or greater | ▶ | REPLACE the left rear actuator and rerun SERVICE BAY DIAGNOSTICS after repair is made. |

**Fig. 44 Pinpoint test, GA (Part 3 of 7)**

| GA9 | COMPONENT CHECK POSITION CIRCUIT | RESULT | | ACTION TO TAKE |
|---|---|---|---|---|
| | • Use a small blade screwdriver to rotate the control tube on the bottom of the actuator to the "H" ("FIRM" position).<br>• Using an analog ohmmeter measure the resistance across pin position #1 and #2. | Ohmmeter reading is: | | |
| | | 5.0 ohms or less | ▶ | REPLACE the left rear actuator and rerun SERVICE BAY DIAGNOSTICS after repair is made. |
| | | 10,000 ohms or greater | ▶ | GO TO GA10 |
| GA10 | COMPONENT CHECK ACTUATE TO SOFT POSITION | | | |
| | • If required use a small blade screwdriver to rotate the control tube on the bottom of the actuator to the "H" ("FIRM" position).<br>• Use a 12 volt power supply and connect the negative lead to actuator pin position #4 and the positive lead to pin position #3 for 1 to 2 seconds. This procedure should rotate the control tube on the bottom of the actuator to the "S" position. | Control tube rotated to the "S" position: | | |
| | | YES | ▶ | GO TO GA11 |
| | | NO | ▶ | REPLACE the left rear shock actuator and rerun SERVICE BAY DIAGNOSTICS after repair is made. |
| GA11 | COMPONENT CHECK ACTUATE TO FIRM POSITION | | | |
| | • If required use a small blade screwdriver to rotate the control tube on the bottom of the actuator to the "S" ("SOFT" position).<br>• Use a 12 volt power supply and connect the negative lead to actuator pin position #3 and the positive lead to pin position #4 for 1 to 2 seconds. This procedure should rotate the control tube on the bottom of the actuator to the "H" position. | Control tube rotated to the "H" position: | | |
| | | YES | ▶ | GO TO GA12 |
| | | NO | ▶ | REPLACE the left rear shock actuator and rerun SERVICE BAY DIAGNOSTICS after repair is made. |

**Fig. 44 Pinpoint test, GA (Part 4 of 7)**

| GA12 COMPONENT CHECK STRUT ASSEMBLY CHECK | RESULT | ACTION TO TAKE |
|---|---|---|
| • Remove known good right rear actuator and exchange places with the suspected left rear actuator.<br>• Install and reconnect the two shock actuators to the vehicle shocks and wiring harness.<br>• Rerun SERVICE BAY DIAGNOSTICS. | The STAR tester displayed a code 56 and/or 60: | |
| | YES ▶ | service the left rear shock/strut assembly for binding (force required to switch from "SOFT" to "FIRM"). Rerun SERVICE BAY DIAGNOSTICS after repairs are made. |
| | NO ▶ | The problem of not switching to the desired position may have been due the actuator not being properly mounted to the strut and is now corrected. |
| **GA13 WIRING HARNESS CHECK** | | |
| • Turn the air suspension "ON/OFF" switch to the "OFF" position.<br>• Release the STAR test button so that it remains in the up "HOLD" position and turn the STAR tester "OFF".<br>• Disconnect the air suspension control module from the vehicle wiring harness.<br>• Using an analog ohmmeter place one lead to the wiring harness control module connector pin location #49 (circuit #842) and the other to the left rear actuator vehicle connector circuit #842. | Ohmmeter reading is greater than 5.0 ohms (OPEN CIRCUIT): | |
| | NO ▶ | GO TO GA14 |
| | YES ▶ | There is an electrical problem in the circuit. Rerun SERVICE BAY DIAGNOSTICS after repair is made. |

**Fig. 44 Pinpoint test, GA (Part 5 of 7)**

| GA14 WIRING HARNESS CHECK | RESULT | ACTION TO TAKE |
|---|---|---|
| • Using an analog ohmmeter place one lead to the wiring harness control module connector pin location #46 (circuit #432D) and the other to the left rear actuator vehicle connector circuit #432C. | Ohmmeter reading is greater than 5.0 ohms (OPEN CIRCUIT): | |
| | NO ▶ | GO TO GA15 |
| | YES ▶ | There is an electrical problem in the circuit. Rerun SERVICE BAY DIAGNOSTICS after repair is made. |
| **GA15 WIRING HARNESS CHECK** | | |
| • Disconnect the SOFT SHOCK RELAY from the vehicle wiring harness connector.<br>• Using an analog ohmmeter place one lead to the SOFT SHOCK RELAY connector circuit #846A and the other to the left rear actuator's vehicle wiring harness connector circuit #846C. | Ohmmeter reading is greater than 5.0 ohms (OPEN CIRCUIT): | |
| | NO ▶ | GO TO GA16 |
| | YES ▶ | There is an electrical problem in the circuit. Rerun SERVICE BAY DIAGNOSTICS after repair is made. |

**Fig. 44 Pinpoint test, GA (Part 6 of 7)**

| GA16 WIRING HARNESS CHECK | RESULT | ACTION TO TAKE |
|---|---|---|
| • Disconnect the FIRM SHOCK RELAY from the vehicle wiring harness connector.<br>• Using an analog ohmmeter (20,000 ohms per volt is recommended) place one lead to the SOFT SHOCK RELAY connector circuit #845A and the other to the left rear actuator's vehicle wiring harness connector circuit #845C. | Ohmmeter reading is greater than 5.0 ohms (OPEN CIRCUIT): | |
| | NO ▶ | Rerun SERVICE BAY DIAGNOSTICS and if problem still exists replace the air suspension control module. |
| NOTE: Your ohmmeter leads may not be long enough for this test and a jumper wire may be required. | YES ▶ | There is an electrical problem in the circuit. Rerun SERVICE BAY DIAGNOSTICS after repair is made. |

**Fig. 44 Pinpoint test, GA (Part 7 of 7)**

| GB1 STAR CODE: 57 or 61 ACTUATOR DESIRED POSITION NOT DETECTED | RESULT | ACTION TO TAKE |
|---|---|---|
| The air suspension control module did not receive a signal that the right front shock actuator went to the desired position when activated. There are eight possible causes of the actuator not switching to the desired position. | Was STAR code "64" or "65" also displayed: | |
| | YES ▶ | GO TO GE1 |
| | NO ▶ | GO TO GB2 |
| • The "SOFT" and/or "FIRM" shock relay is defective.<br>• The "SOFT" or "FIRM" shock relay circuit is defective.<br>• The vehicle wiring harness power supply circuit to the right front shock actuator is shorted to ground or has an open in it.<br>• The right front shock actuator position circuit is shorted to ground or has an open in it.<br>• The vehicle wiring harness connector for the right front shock actuator does not have all the wires in the correct location.<br>• The right front shock actuator is defective.<br>• The right front shock/strut assembly on the vehicle is binding preventing the actuator from switching to the desired position.<br>• The air suspension control module is defective. | | |
| **GB2 RIGHT FRONT ACTUATOR VISUAL CHECK** | | |
| The air suspension control module did not receive a signal that the right front shock actuator went to the desired position when activated. In order to determine why this did not happen the following actions are required:<br>• Examine the four wires of the right front actuator connector and also those wires on the wiring harness side to ensure that there is no obvious damage and that all of the wires are in the proper location. | All wires are in the proper location with no obvious damage. | |
| | YES ▶ | GO TO GB3 |
| | NO ▶ | Service wires as necessary and rerun SERVICE BAY DIAGNOSTICS after repair is made. |

**Fig. 45 Pinpoint test, GB (Part 1 of 6)**

| | COMPONENT CHECK | RESULT | ACTION TO TAKE |
|---|---|---|---|
| GB3 | RIGHT FRONT ACTUATOR | | |
| | In order to determine if the actuator is working properly the following actions are required:<br>• Disconnect the right front actuator from the vehicle wiring harness connector.<br>• Using an analog ohmmeter measure the resistance across the actuator pin position #1 and pin position #2. | Ohmmeter reading is:<br>10,000 ohms or greater ▶<br>5 ohms or less ▶ | <br>GO TO GB4<br>GO TO GB6 |
| GB4 | ACTUATE TO SOFT POSITION | | |
| | • Use a 12 volt power supply and connect the negative lead to actuator pin position #4 and the positive lead to pin position #3 for 1 to 2 seconds. This procedure should drive the actuator to the "SOFT" position. After this has been done remove power supply leads.<br>• Using an analog ohmmeter measure the resistance across the actuator pin position #1 and pin position #2. | Ohmmeter reading is:<br>10,000 ohms or greater ▶<br>5 ohms or less ▶ | <br>GO TO GB5<br>GO TO GB13 |
| GB5 | ACTUATE TO FIRM POSITION | | |
| | • Again use a 12 volt power supply and connect the negative lead to actuator pin position #3 and the positive lead to pin position #4 for 1 to 2 seconds. This procedure should drive the actuator to the "FIRM" position. After this has been done remove power supply leads.<br>• Using an analog ohmmeter measure the resistance across the actuator pin position #1 and pin position #2. | Ohmmeter reading is:<br>10,000 ohms or greater ▶<br>5 ohms or less ▶ | <br>GO TO GB8<br>The power supply circuits (pin location #3 & #4) are reversed. Replace the right front actuator with a new one. After repairs are made rerun SERVICE BAY DIAGNOSTICS. |

**Fig. 45 Pinpoint test, GB (Part 2 of 6)**

| | COMPONENT CHECK | RESULT | ACTION TO TAKE |
|---|---|---|---|
| GB6 | ACTUATE TO FIRM POSITION | | |
| | • Use a 12 volt power supply and connect the negative lead to actuator pin position #3 and the positive lead to pin position #4 for 1 to 2 seconds. This procedure should drive the actuator to the "FIRM" position. After this has been done remove power supply leads.<br>• Using an analog ohmmeter measure the resistance across the actuator pin position #1 and pin position #2. | Ohmmeter reading is:<br>10,000 ohms or greater ▶<br>5 ohms or less ▶ | <br>GO TO GB13<br>GO TO GB7 |
| GB7 | ACTUATE TO SOFT POSITION | | |
| | • Again use a 12 volt power supply and connect the negative lead to actuator pin position #4 and the positive lead to pin position #3 for 1 to 2 seconds. This procedure should drive the actuator to the "SOFT" position. After this has been done remove power supply leads.<br>• Using an analog ohmmeter measure the resistance across the actuator pin position #1 and pin position #2. | Ohmmeter reading is:<br>10,000 ohms or greater ▶<br>5 ohms or less ▶ | <br>The power supply circuits (pin locations #3 & #4) are reversed. Replace the right front actuator with a new one. After repairs are made rerun SERVICE BAY DIAGNOSTICS.<br>GO TO GB8 |
| GB8 | POSITION CIRCUIT | | |
| | • Remove the right front actuator from the top of the right front shock/strut.<br>• Use a small blade screwdriver to rotate the control tube on the bottom of the actuator to the "S" ("SOFT" position).<br>• Using an analog ohmmeter measure the resistance across pin position #1 and #2. | Ohmmeter reading is:<br>5.0 ohms or less ▶<br>10,000 ohms or greater ▶ | <br>GO TO GB9<br>REPLACE the right front actuator and rerun SERVICE BAY DIAGNOSTICS after repair is made. |

**Fig. 45 Pinpoint test, GB (Part 3 of 6)**

| | COMPONENT CHECK | RESULT | ACTION TO TAKE |
|---|---|---|---|
| GB9 | POSITION CIRCUIT | | |
| | • Use a small blade screwdriver to rotate the control tube on the bottom of the actuator to the "H" ("FIRM" position).<br>• Using an analog ohmmeter measure the resistance across pin position #1 and #2. | Ohmmeter reading is:<br>5.0 ohms or less ▶<br>10,000 ohms or greater ▶ | <br>REPLACE the right front actuator and rerun SERVICE BAY DIAGNOSTICS after repair is made.<br>GO TO GB10 |
| GB10 | ACTUATE TO SOFT POSITION | | |
| | • If required use a small blade screwdriver to rotate the control tube on the bottom of the actuator to the "H" ("FIRM" position).<br>• Use a 12 volt power supply and connect the negative lead to actuator pin position #4 and the positive lead to pin position #3 for 1 to 2 seconds. This procedure should rotate the control tube on the bottom of the actuator to the "S" position. | Control tube rotated to the "S" position:<br>YES ▶<br>NO ▶ | <br>GO TO GB11<br>REPLACE the right front shock actuator and rerun SERVICE BAY DIAGNOSTICS after repair is made. |
| GB11 | ACTUATE TO FIRM POSITION | | |
| | • If required use a small blade screwdriver to rotate the control tube on the bottom of the actuator to the "S" ("SOFT" position).<br>• Use a 12 volt power supply and connect the negative lead to actuator pin position #3 and the positive lead to pin position #4 for 1 to 2 seconds. This procedure should rotate the control tube on the bottom of the actuator to the "H" position. | Control tube rotated to the "H" position:<br>YES ▶<br>NO ▶ | <br>GO TO GB12<br>REPLACE the right front shock actuator and rerun SERVICE BAY DIAGNOSTICS after repair is made. |

**Fig. 45 Pinpoint test, GB (Part 4 of 6)**

| | COMPONENT CHECK | RESULT | ACTION TO TAKE |
|---|---|---|---|
| GB12 | STRUT ASSEMBLY CHECK | | |
| | • Remove known good left front actuator and exchange places with the suspected right front actuator.<br>• Install and reconnect the two shock actuators to the vehicle shocks and wiring harness.<br>• Rerun SERVICE BAY DIAGNOSTICS. | The STAR tester displayed a code 57 and/or 61:<br>YES ▶<br>NO ▶ | <br>service the right front shock/strut assembly for binding (force required to switch from "SOFT" to "FIRM"). Rerun SERVICE BAY DIAGNOSTICS after repairs are made.<br>The problem of not switching to the desired position may have been due the actuator not being properly mounted to the strut and is now corrected. |
| GB13 | WIRING HARNESS CHECK | | |
| | • Turn the air suspension "ON/OFF" switch to the "OFF" position.<br>• Release the "STAR" test button so that it remains in the up "HOLD" position and turn the "STAR" tester "OFF".<br>• Disconnect the air suspension control module from the vehicle wiring harness.<br>• Using an analog ohmmeter place one lead to the wiring harness control module connector pin location #44 (circuit #841) and the other to the right front actuator vehicle connector circuit #841. | Ohmmeter reading is greater than 5.0 ohms (OPEN CIRCUIT):<br>NO ▶<br>YES ▶ | <br>GO TO GB14<br>There is an electrical problem in the circuit. Rerun SERVICE BAY DIAGNOSTICS after repair is made. |

**Fig. 45 Pinpoint test, GB (Part 5 of 6)**

| GB14 WIRING HARNESS CHECK | RESULT | ACTION TO TAKE |
|---|---|---|
| • Using an analog ohmmeter place one lead to the wiring harness control module connector pin location #46 (circuit #432D) and the other to the right front actuator vehicle connector circuit #432C. | Ohmmeter reading is greater than 5.0 ohms (OPEN CIRCUIT): | |
| | NO ▶ | GO TO GB15 |
| | YES ▶ | There is an electrical problem in the circuit. Rerun SERVICE BAY DIAGNOSTICS after repair is made. |
| **GB15 WIRING HARNESS CHECK** | | |
| • Disconnect the SOFT SHOCK RELAY from the vehicle wiring harness connector. • Using an analog ohmmeter place one lead to the SOFT SHOCK RELAY connector circuit #846A and the other to the right front actuator's vehicle wiring harness connector circuit #846A. | Ohmmeter reading is greater than 5.0 ohms (OPEN CIRCUIT): | |
| | NO ▶ | GO TO GB16 |
| | YES ▶ | There is an electrical problem in the circuit. Rerun SERVICE BAY DIAGNOSTICS after repair is made. |
| **GB16 WIRING HARNESS CHECK** | | |
| • Disconnect the FIRM SHOCK RELAY from the vehicle wiring harness connector. • Using an analog ohmmeter (20,000 ohms per volt is recommended) place one lead to the SOFT SHOCK RELAY connector circuit #845A and the other to the right front actuator's vehicle wiring harness connector circuit #845A. | Ohmmeter reading is greater than 5.0 ohms (OPEN CIRCUIT): | |
| | NO ▶ | Rerun SERVICE BAY DIAGNOSTICS and if problem still exists replace the air suspension control module. |
| NOTE: Your ohmmeter leads may not be long enough for this test and a jumper wire may be required. | YES ▶ | There is an electrical problem in the circuit. Rerun SERVICE BAY DIAGNOSTICS after repair is made. |

**Fig. 45 Pinpoint test, GB (Part 6 of 6)**

| GC1 STAR CODE: 58 or 62 ACTUATOR DESIRED POSITION NOT DETECTED | RESULT | ACTION TO TAKE |
|---|---|---|
| The air suspension control module did not receive a signal that the left front shock actuator went to the desired position when activated. There are eight possible causes of the actuator not switching to the desired position. | Was STAR code "64" or "65" also displayed: | |
| | YES ▶ | GO TO GE1 |
| | NO ▶ | GO TO GC2 |
| • The "SOFT" and/or "FIRM" relay is defective. • The "SOFT" or "FIRM" shock relay circuit is defective. • The vehicle wiring harness power supply circuit to the left front shock actuator is shorted to ground or has an open in it. • The left front shock actuator position circuit is shorted to ground or has an open in it. • The vehicle wiring harness connector for the left front shock actuator does not have all the wires in the correct location. • The left front shock actuator is defective. • The left front shock/strut assembly on the vehicle is binding preventing the actuator from switching to the desired position. • The air suspension control module is defective. | | |
| **GC2 LEFT FRONT ACTUATOR VISUAL CHECK** | | |
| The air suspension control module did not receive a signal that the left front shock actuator went to the desired position when activated. In order to determine why this did not happen the following actions are required: | All wires are in the proper location with no obvious damage. | |
| | YES ▶ | GO TO GC3 |
| • Examine the four wires of the left front actuator connector and also those wires on the wiring harness side to ensure that there is no obvious damage and that all of the wires are in the proper location. | NO ▶ | Service wires as necessary and rerun SERVICE BAY DIAGNOSTICS after repair is made. |

**Fig. 46 Pinpoint test, GC (Part 1 of 6)**

| GC3 COMPONENT CHECK LEFT FRONT ACTUATOR | RESULT | ACTION TO TAKE |
|---|---|---|
| In order to determine if the actuator is working properly the following actions are required: | Ohmmeter reading is: | |
| • Disconnect the left front actuator from the vehicle wiring harness connector. | 10,000 ohms or greater ▶ | GO TO GC4 |
| • Using an analog ohmmeter measure the resistance across the actuator pin position #1 and pin position #2. | 5 ohms or less ▶ | GO TO GC6 |
| **GC4 COMPONENT CHECK ACTUATE TO SOFT POSITION** | | |
| • Use a 12 volt power supply and connect the negative lead to actuator pin position #4 and the positive lead to pin position #3 for 1 to 2 seconds. This procedure should drive the actuator to the "SOFT" position. After this has been done remove power supply leads. | Ohmmeter reading is: | |
| | 10,000 ohms or greater ▶ | GO TO GC5 |
| • Using an analog ohmmeter measure the resistance across the actuator pin position #1 and pin position #2. | 5 ohms or less ▶ | GO TO GC13 |
| **GC5 COMPONENT CHECK ACTUATE TO FIRM POSITION** | | |
| • Again use a 12 volt power supply and connect the negative lead to actuator pin position #3 and the positive lead to pin position #4 for 1 to 2 seconds. This procedure should drive the actuator to the "FIRM" position. After this has been done remove power supply leads. | Ohmmeter reading is: | |
| | 10,000 ohms or greater ▶ | GO TO GC8 |
| • Using an analog ohmmeter measure the resistance across the actuator pin position #1 and pin position #2. | 5 ohms or less ▶ | The power supply circuits (pin location #3 & #4) are reversed. Replace the left front actuator with a new one. After repairs are made rerun SERVICE BAY DIAGNOSTICS. |

**Fig. 46 Pinpoint test, GC (Part 2 of 6)**

| GC6 COMPONENT CHECK ACTUATE TO FIRM POSITION | RESULT | ACTION TO TAKE |
|---|---|---|
| • Use a 12 volt power supply and connect the negative lead to actuator pin position #3 and the positive lead to pin position #4 for 1 to 2 seconds. This procedure should drive the actuator to the "FIRM" position. After this has been done remove power supply leads. | Ohmmeter reading is: | |
| | 10,000 ohms or greater ▶ | GO TO GC13 |
| | 5 ohms or less ▶ | GO TO GC7 |
| • Using an analog ohmmeter measure the resistance across the actuator pin position #1 and pin position #2. | | |
| **GC7 COMPONENT CHECK ACTUATE TO SOFT POSITION** | | |
| • Again use a 12 volt power supply and connect the negative lead to actuator pin position #4 and the positive lead to pin position #3 for 1 to 2 seconds. This procedure should drive the actuator to the "SOFT" position. After this has been done remove power supply leads. | Ohmmeter reading is: | |
| • Using an analog ohmmeter measure the resistance across the actuator pin position #1 and pin position #2. | 10,000 ohms or greater ▶ | The power supply circuits (pin location #3 & #4) are reversed. Replace the left front actuator with a new one. After repairs are made rerun SERVICE BAY DIAGNOSTICS. |
| | 5 ohms or less ▶ | GO TO GC8 |
| **GC8 COMPONENT CHECK POSITION CIRCUIT** | | |
| • Remove the left front actuator from the top of the left front shock/strut. | Ohmmeter reading is: | |
| • Use a small blade screwdriver to rotate the control tube on the bottom of the actuator to the "S" ("SOFT" position). | 5.0 ohms or less ▶ | GO TO GC9 |
| • Using an analog ohmmeter measure the resistance across pin position #1 and #2. | 10,000 ohms or greater ▶ | REPLACE the left front actuator and rerun SERVICE BAY DIAGNOSTICS after repair is made. |

**Fig. 46 Pinpoint test, GC (Part 3 of 6)**

| GC9 | COMPONENT CHECK POSITION CIRCUIT | RESULT | ACTION TO TAKE |
|---|---|---|---|
| | • Use a small blade screwdriver to rotate the control tube on the bottom of the actuator to the "H" ("FIRM" position). • Using an analog ohmmeter measure the resistance across pin position #1 and #2. | Ohmmeter reading is: | |
| | | 5.0 ohms or less ▶ | REPLACE the left front actuator and rerun SERVICE BAY DIAGNOSTICS after repair is made. |
| | | 10,000 ohms or greater ▶ | GO TO GC10 |
| **GC10** | **COMPONENT CHECK ACTUATE TO SOFT POSITION** | | |
| | • If required use a small blade screwdriver to rotate the control tube on the bottom of the actuator to the "H" ("FIRM" position). • Use a 12 volt power supply and connect the negative lead to actuator pin position #4 and the positive lead to pin position #3 for 1 to 2 seconds. This procedure should rotate the control tube on the bottom of the actuator to the "S" position. | Control tube rotated to the "S" position: | |
| | | YES ▶ | GO TO GC11 |
| | | NO ▶ | REPLACE the left front shock actuator and rerun SERVICE BAY DIAGNOSTICS after repair is made. |
| **GC11** | **COMPONENT CHECK ACTUATE TO FIRM POSITION** | | |
| | • If required use a small blade screwdriver to rotate the control tube on the bottom of the actuator to the "S" ("SOFT" position). • Use a 12 volt power supply and connect the negative lead to actuator pin position #3 and the positive lead to pin position #4 for 1 to 2 seconds. This procedure should rotate the control tube on the bottom of the actuator to the "H" position. | Control tube rotated to the "H" position: | |
| | | YES ▶ | GO TO GC12 |
| | | NO ▶ | REPLACE the left front shock actuator and rerun SERVICE BAY DIAGNOSTICS after repair is made. |

**Fig. 46 Pinpoint test, GC (Part 4 of 6)**

| GC12 | COMPONENT CHECK STRUT ASSEMBLY CHECK | RESULT | ACTION TO TAKE |
|---|---|---|---|
| | • Remove known good actuator from right front corner of the vehicle and exchange places with the suspected left front actuator. • Install and reconnect the two shock actuators to the vehicle shocks and wiring harness. • Rerun SERVICE BAY DIAGNOSTICS. | The STAR tester displayed a code 58 and/or 62: | |
| | | YES ▶ | service the left front shock/strut assembly for binding (force required to switch from "SOFT" to "FIRM"). Rerun SERVICE BAY DIAGNOSTICS after repairs are made. |
| | | NO ▶ | The problem of not switching to the desired position may have been due the actuator not being properly mounted to the strut and is now corrected. |
| **GC13** | **WIRING HARNESS CHECK** | | |
| | • Turn the air suspension "ON/OFF" switch to the "OFF" position. • Release the "STAR" test button so that it remains in the up "HOLD" position and turn the "STAR" tester "OFF". • Disconnect the air suspension control module from the vehicle wiring harness. • Using an analog ohmmeter place one lead to the wiring harness control module connector pin location #47 (circuit #840) and the other to the left rear actuator vehicle connector circuit #840. | Ohmmeter reading is greater than 5.0 ohms (OPEN CIRCUIT): | |
| | | NO ▶ | GO TO GC14 |
| | | YES ▶ | There is an electrical problem in the circuit. Rerun SERVICE BAY DIAGNOSTICS after repair is made. |

**Fig. 46 Pinpoint test, GC (Part 5 of 6)**

| GC14 | WIRING HARNESS CHECK | RESULT | ACTION TO TAKE |
|---|---|---|---|
| | • Disconnect the SOFT SHOCK RELAY from the vehicle wiring harness connector. • Using an analog ohmmeter place one lead to the SOFT SHOCK RELAY connector circuit #846A and the other to the left front actuator's vehicle wiring harness connector circuit #846B. | Ohmmeter reading is greater than 5.0 ohms (OPEN CIRCUIT): | |
| | | NO ▶ | GO TO GC15 |
| | | YES ▶ | There is an electrical problem in the circuit. Rerun SERVICE BAY DIAGNOSTICS after repair is made. |
| **GC15** | **WIRING HARNESS CHECK** | | |
| | • Disconnect the FIRM SHOCK RELAY from the vehicle wiring harness connector. • Using an analog ohmmeter place one lead to the SOFT SHOCK RELAY connector circuit #845A and the other to the left front actuator's vehicle wiring harness connector circuit #845B. | Ohmmeter reading is greater than 5.0 ohms (OPEN CIRCUIT): | |
| | | NO ▶ | Rerun SERVICE BAY DIAGNOSTICS and if problem still exists replace the air suspension control module. |
| | | YES ▶ | There is an electrical problem in the circuit. Rerun SERVICE BAY DIAGNOSTICS after repair is made. |

**Fig. 46 Pinpoint test, GC (Part 6 of 6)**

| GD1 | STAR CODE: 59 or 63 ACTUATOR DESIRED POSITION NOT DETECTED | RESULT | ACTION TO TAKE |
|---|---|---|---|
| | The air suspension control module did not receive a signal that the right rear shock actuator went to the desired position when activated. There are eight possible causes of the actuator not switching to the desired position. • The "SOFT" and/or "FIRM" relay is defective. • The "SOFT" or "FIRM" shock relay circuit is defective. • The vehicle wiring harness power supply circuit to the right rear shock actuator is shorted to ground or has an open in it. • The right rear shock actuator position circuit is shorted to ground or has an open in it. • The vehicle wiring harness connector for the right rear shock actuator does not have all the wires in the correct location. • The right rear shock actuator is defective. • The right rear shock/strut assembly on the vehicle is binding preventing the actuator from switching to the desired position. • The air suspension control module is defective. | Was STAR code "64" or "65" also displayed: | |
| | | YES ▶ | GO TO GE1 |
| | | NO ▶ | GO TO GD2 |
| **GD2** | **RIGHT REAR ACTUATOR VISUAL CHECK** | | |
| | The air suspension control module did not receive a signal that the right rear shock actuator went to the desired position when activated. In order to determine why this did not happen the following actions are required: • Examine the four wires of the right rear actuator connector and also those wires on the wiring harness side to ensure that there is no obvious damage and that all of the wires are in the proper location. | All wires are in the proper location with no obvious damage. | |
| | | YES ▶ | GO TO GD3 |
| | | NO ▶ | Service wires as necessary and rerun SERVICE BAY DIAGNOSTICS after repair is made. |

**Fig. 47 Pinpoint test, GD (Part 1 of 6)**

| COMPONENT CHECK | RESULT | ACTION TO TAKE |
|---|---|---|
| **GD3** RIGHT REAR ACTUATOR | | |
| In order to determine if the actuator is working properly the following actions are required:<br>• Disconnect the right rear actuator from the vehicle wiring harness connector.<br>• Using an analog ohmmeter measure the resistance across the actuator pin position #1 and pin position #2. | Ohmmeter reading is: | |
| | 10,000 ohms or greater | GO TO GD4 |
| | 5 ohms or less | GO TO GD6 |
| **GD4** COMPONENT CHECK ACTUATE TO SOFT POSITION | | |
| • Use a 12 volt power supply and connect the negative lead to actuator pin position #4 and the positive lead to pin position #3 for 1 to 2 seconds. This procedure should drive the actuator to the "SOFT" position. After this has been done remove power supply leads.<br>• Using an analog ohmmeter measure the resistance across the actuator pin position #1 and pin position #2. | Ohmmeter reading is: | |
| | 10,000 ohms or greater | GO TO GD5 |
| | 5 ohms or less | GO TO GD13 |
| **GD5** COMPONENT CHECK ACTUATE TO FIRM POSITION | | |
| • Again use a 12 volt power supply and connect the negative lead to actuator pin position #3 and the positive lead to pin position #4 for 1 to 2 seconds. This procedure should greater drive the actuator to the "FIRM" position. After this has been done remove power supply leads.<br>• Using an analog ohmmeter (20,000 ohms per volt is recommended) measure the resistance across the actuator pin position #1 and pin position #2. | Ohmmeter reading is: | |
| | 10,000 ohms or | GO TO GD8 |
| | 5 ohms or less | The power supply circuits (pin locations #3 & #4) are reversed. Replace the right rear actuator with a new one. After repairs are made rerun SERVICE BAY DIAGNOSTICS. |

**Fig. 47 Pinpoint test, GD (Part 2 of 6)**

| COMPONENT CHECK | RESULT | ACTION TO TAKE |
|---|---|---|
| **GD6** ACTUATE TO FIRM POSITION | | |
| • Use a 12 volt power supply and connect the negative lead to actuator pin position #3 and the positive lead to pin position #4 for 1 to 2 seconds. This procedure should drive the actuator to the "FIRM" position. After this has been done remove power supply leads.<br>• Using an analog ohmmeter measure the resistance across the actuator pin position #1 and pin position #2. | Ohmmeter reading is: | |
| | 10,000 ohms or greater | GO TO GD13 |
| | 5 ohms or less | GO TO GD7 |
| **GD7** COMPONENT CHECK ACTUATE TO SOFT POSITION | | |
| • Again use a 12 volt power supply and connect the negative lead to actuator pin position #4 and the positive lead to pin position #3 for 1 to 2 seconds. This procedure should drive the actuator to the "SOFT" position. After this has been done remove power supply leads.<br>• Using an analog ohmmeter (20,000 ohms per volt is recommended) measure the resistance across the actuator pin position #1 and pin position #2. | Ohmmeter reading is: | |
| | 10,000 ohms or greater | The power supply circuits (pin locations #3 & #4) are reversed. Replace the right rear actuator with a new one. After repairs are made rerun SERVICE BAY DIAGNOSTICS. |
| | 5 ohms or less | GO TO GD8 |
| **GD8** COMPONENT CHECK POSITION CIRCUIT | | |
| • Remove the right rear actuator from the top of the right rear shock/strut.<br>• Use a small blade screwdriver to rotate the control tube on the bottom of the actuator to the "S" ("SOFT" position).<br>• Using an analog ohmmeter measure the resistance across pin position #1 and #2. | Ohmmeter reading is: | |
| | 5.0 ohms or less | GO TO GD9 |
| | 10,000 ohms or greater | REPLACE the right rear actuator and rerun SERVICE BAY DIAGNOSTICS after repair is made. |

**Fig. 47 Pinpoint test, GD (Part 3 of 6)**

| COMPONENT CHECK | RESULT | ACTION TO TAKE |
|---|---|---|
| **GD9** POSITION CIRCUIT | | |
| • Use a small blade screwdriver to rotate the control tube on the bottom of the actuator to the "H" ("FIRM" position).<br>• Using an analog ohmmeter measure the resistance across pin position #1 and #2. | Ohmmeter reading is: | |
| | 5.0 ohms or less | REPLACE the right rear actuator and rerun SERVICE BAY DIAGNOSTICS after repair is made. |
| | 10,000 ohms or greater | GO TO GD10 |
| **GD10** COMPONENT CHECK ACTUATE TO SOFT POSITION | | |
| • If required use a small blade screwdriver to rotate the control tube on the bottom of the actuator to the "H" ("FIRM" position).<br>• Use a 12 volt power supply and connect the negative lead to actuator pin position #4 and the positive lead to pin position #3 for 1 to 2 seconds. This procedure should rotate the control tube on the bottom of the actuator to the "S" position. | Control tube rotated to the "S" position: | |
| | YES | GO TO GD11 |
| | NO | REPLACE the right rear shock actuator and rerun SERVICE BAY DIAGNOSTICS after repair is made. |
| **GD11** COMPONENT CHECK ACTUATE TO FIRM POSITION | | |
| • If required use a small blade screwdriver to rotate the control tube on the bottom of the actuator to the "S" ("SOFT" position).<br>• Use a 12 volt power supply and connect the negative lead to actuator pin position #3 and the positive lead to pin position #4 for 1 to 2 seconds. This procedure should rotate the control tube on the bottom of the actuator to the "H" position. | Control tube rotated to the "H" position: | |
| | YES | GO TO GD12 |
| | NO | REPLACE the right rear shock actuator and rerun SERVICE BAY DIAGNOSTICS after repair is made. |

**Fig. 47 Pinpoint test, GD (Part 4 of 6)**

| COMPONENT CHECK | RESULT | ACTION TO TAKE |
|---|---|---|
| **GD12** STRUT ASSEMBLY CHECK | | |
| • Remove known good left rear actuator and exchange places with the suspected right rear actuator.<br>• Install and reconnect the two shock actuators to the vehicle shocks and wiring harness.<br>• Rerun SERVICE BAY DIAGNOSTICS. | The STAR tester displayed a code 59 and/or 63: | |
| | YES | service the right rear shock/strut assembly for binding (force required to switch from "SOFT" to "FIRM"). Rerun SERVICE BAY DIAGNOSTICS after repairs are made. |
| | NO | The problem of not switching to the desired position may have been due to the actuator not being properly mounted to the strut and is now corrected. |
| **GD13** WIRING HARNESS CHECK | | |
| • Turn the air suspension "ON/OFF" switch to the "OFF" position.<br>• Release the "STAR" test button so that it remains in the up "HOLD" position and turn the STAR tester "OFF".<br>• Disconnect the air suspension control module from the vehicle wiring harness.<br>• Using an analog ohmmeter place one lead to the wiring harness control module connector pin location #48 (circuit #843) and the other to the left rear actuator vehicle connector circuit #843. | Ohmmeter reading is greater than 5.0 ohms (OPEN CIRCUIT): | |
| | NO | GO TO GD14 |
| | YES | There is an electrical problem in the circuit. Rerun SERVICE BAY DIAGNOSTICS after repair is made. |

**Fig. 47 Pinpoint test, GD (Part 5 of 6)**

| GD14 WIRING HARNESS CHECK | RESULT | ACTION TO TAKE |
|---|---|---|
| • Disconnect the SOFT SHOCK RELAY from the vehicle wiring harness connector.<br>• Using an analog ohmmeter place one lead to the SOFT SHOCK RELAY connector circuit #846A and the other to the right rear actuator's vehicle wiring harness connector circuit #846B. | Ohmmeter reading is greater than 5.0 ohms (OPEN CIRCUIT): | |
| | NO | GO TO GD15 |
| | YES | There is an electrical problem in the circuit. Rerun SERVICE BAY DIAGNOSTICS after repair is made. |
| **GD15 WIRING HARNESS CHECK** | | |
| • Disconnect the FIRM SHOCK RELAY from the vehicle wiring harness connector.<br>• Using an analog ohmmeter place one lead to the SOFT SHOCK RELAY connector circuit #845A and the other to the right rear actuator's vehicle wiring harness connector circuit #845C. | Ohmmeter reading is greater than 5.0 ohms (OPEN CIRCUIT): | |
| | NO | Rerun SERVICE BAY DIAGNOSTICS and if problem still exists replace the air suspension control module. |
| | YES | There is an electrical problem in the circuit. Rerun SERVICE BAY DIAGNOSTICS after repair is made. |

**Fig. 47 Pinpoint test, GD (Part 6 of 6)**

| GE1 STAR CODE: 64 or 65 ALL SHOCK ACTUATORS NOT IN THE DESIRED POSITION | RESULT | ACTION TO TAKE |
|---|---|---|
| The air suspension control module has detected that all shock actuators did not go to the desired position when activated. There are six possible causes of the actuator not switching to the desired position.<br>• The "SOFT" and/or "FIRM" shock relay is defective.<br>• The vehicle wiring harness power supply circuit to the shock actuator relays is shorted to ground or has an open in it.<br>• The vehicle wiring harness power supply circuit to the shock actuators is shorted to ground or has an open in it.<br>• The shock actuator position circuit is shorted to ground or has an open in it.<br>• The vehicle wiring harness connector for the "SOFT" and/or "FIRM" relay does not have all the wires in the correct location.<br>• The air suspension control module is defective. | | GO TO GE2 |
| **GE2 ENTERING FUNCTIONAL TEST MODE OF SERVICE BAY DIAG** | | |
| In order to determine why all the shock actuators did not go to the desired position when activated the following actions are required:<br>• Release the "STAR" test button to the up "HOLD" position. After five seconds depress the "STAR" test button again so that it remains in the down "TEST" position. This will allow the control module to enter the SERVICE BAY DIAGNOSTIC FUNCTIONAL TEST mode. | The "STAR" tester is displaying code: | |
| | "31", "32", "33", "34", or "35" | GO TO GE4 |
| | NO | GO TO GE3 |

**Fig. 48 Pinpoint test, GE (Part 1 of 7)**

| GE3 RETRY ENTERING FUNCTIONAL TEST MODE | RESULT | ACTION TO TAKE |
|---|---|---|
| The air suspension control module has not entered the SERVICE BAY DIAGNOSTIC FUNCTIONAL TEST mode and the following actions are required:<br>• Make sure that the "STAR" tester is still plugged into the air suspension diagnostic pigtail.<br>• Make sure that the "STAR" tester is turned "ON".<br>• Release the "STAR" test button to the up "HOLD" position. After five seconds depress the "STAR" test button again so that it remains in the down "TEST" position. This will allow the control module to enter the functional test mode. | The "STAR" tester is displaying code: | |
| | "31", "32", "33", "34", or "35" | GO TO GE4 |
| | NO | Rerun SERVICE BAY DIAGNOSTICS and if still unable to enter the functional test mode, install a new air suspension control module. |
| **GE4 CHECKING WIRING HARNESS** | | |
| It is desired to activate the "FIRM/SOFT ACTUATOR TOGGLE" test. In order to do this the following action is required:<br>• Remove the left front shock actuator from the top of the left front strut.<br>• Release the "STAR" test button so that it remains in the up "HOLD" position after the code "34" has been displayed for at least 5 seconds.<br>NOTE: As long as the "STAR" test button is in the up "HOLD" position the "FIRM/SOFT ACTUATOR TOGGLE" test will continue. | The control tube switches from "S" to "H" to "S" continuously. | |
| | YES | GO TO GE5 |
| | NO | GO TO GE6 |

**Fig. 48 Pinpoint test, GE (Part 2 of 7)**

| GE5 WIRING HARNESS CHECK | RESULT | ACTION TO TAKE |
|---|---|---|
| • Turn the "STAR" tester "ON/OFF" switch to the "OFF" position.<br>• Turn the air suspension "ON/OFF" switch to the "OFF" position and disconnect the air suspension control module.<br>• Using a small blade screwdriver rotate the control tube on the bottom of the left front actuator to the "S" position.<br>• Using an analog ohmmeter connect one lead to the control module wiring harness connector pin position #47 and the other to pin position #46. | The resistance reading is less than 5.0 ohms: | |
| | YES | Reconnect the air suspension control module and "SOFT" and "FIRM" relays. Then rerun SERVICE BAY DIAGNOSTICS. If code "64" and/or "65" is displayed again install a new air suspension control module. |
| | NO | There is an open in the actuator position signal return circuit. Rerun SERVICE BAY DIAGNOSTICS after repair is made. |
| **GE6 CHECKING WIRING HARNESS** | | |
| • Depress the "STAR" test button down so that it remains in the down "TEST" position.<br>• Remove both the "SOFT" and "FIRM" actuator relays from the vehicle.<br>• Using an analog voltmeter place the positive voltage lead on circuit #175A and the negative lead on circuit #430C (of the "SOFT" actuator relay connector). | Voltage reading is battery voltage: | |
| | YES | GO TO GE7 |
| | NO | There is an electrical problem in the vehicle wiring harness. Rerun SERVICE BAY DIAGNOSTICS after repair is made. |

**Fig. 48 Pinpoint test, GE (Part 3 of 7)**

| GE7 CHECKING WIRING HARNESS | RESULT | ACTION TO TAKE |
|---|---|---|
| • Using an analog voltmeter place the positive voltage lead on circuit #175B and the negative lead on circuit #430E (of the "FIRM" actuator relay connector). | Voltage reading is battery voltage: | |
| | YES ▶ | GO TO GE8 |
| | NO ▶ | There is an electrical problem in the vehicle wiring harness. Rerun SERVICE BAY DIAGNOSTICS after repair is made. |
| **GE8 WIRING HARNESS CHECK** | | |
| The next step is to determine if a problem exists in the actuator activation circuit. In order to do this the following actions are required: | The resistance reading is greater than 10,000 ohms: | |
| • Using an analog ohmmeter connect one lead to circuit #846A of the "SOFT" relay connector and the other lead to a known good chassis ground. | YES ▶ | GO TO GE9 |
| | NO ▶ | The actuator activation circuit has a short to ground in it. Replace both the "SOFT" and "FIRM relays with new ones and rerun SERVICE BAY DIAGNOSTICS after repair is made. |

**Fig. 48 Pinpoint test, GE (Part 4 of 7)**

| GE9 WIRING HARNESS CHECK | RESULT | ACTION TO TAKE |
|---|---|---|
| • Using an analog ohmmeter connect one lead to circuit #845A of the "FIRM" relay connector and the other lead to a known good chassis ground. | The resistance reading is greater than 10,000 ohms: | |
| | YES ▶ | GO TO GE10 |
| | NO ▶ | The actuator activation circuit has a short to ground in it. Replace both the "SOFT" and "FIRM" relays with new ones and rerun SERVICE BAY DIAGNOSTICS after repair is made. |
| **GE10 WIRING HARNESS CHECK** | | |
| • Using an analog ohmmeter connect one lead to circuit #846A of the "SOFT" relay connector and the other lead to circuit circuit #845A of the "FIRM" relay connector. | The resistance reading is less than 10 ohms: | |
| | YES ▶ | GO TO GE11 |
| | NO ▶ | The actuator activation circuit has an open in it. Rerun SERVICE BAY DIAGNOSTICS after repair is made. |

**Fig. 48 Pinpoint test, GE (Part 5 of 7)**

| GE11 WIRING HARNESS CHECK | RESULT | ACTION TO TAKE |
|---|---|---|
| The next step in determining where this problem is located is to determine if the control module signal to activate the actuator relays is reaching the relays. In order to do this the following actions are required: | The voltage reading pulses (between zero and battery voltage) continuously: | |
| • Release the "STAR" test button so that it remains in the up "HOLD" position after the code "34" been displayed for at least 5 seconds. | YES ▶ | GO TO GE13 |
| • Using a VOM place the positive lead on circuit #839 and the negative lead on circuit #430C of the "SOFT" relay connector. | NO ▶ | GO TO GE12 |
| NOTE: As long as the "STAR" test button is in the up "HOLD" position the "FIRM/SOFT ACTUATOR TEST" will continue. | | |
| **GE12 WIRING HARNESS CHECK** | | |
| • Turn the "STAR" tester "ON/OFF" switch to the "OFF" position. | The resistance reading is less than 5.0 ohms: | |
| • Turn the air suspension "ON/OFF" switch to the "OFF" position and disconnect the air suspension control module. | | |
| • Using an analog ohmmeter connect one lead to the control module wiring harness connector pin position #12 and the other lead to the "SOFT" relay connector circuit #839. | YES ▶ | Replace the air suspension control module with a new one and rerun SERVICE BAY DIAGNOSTICS. |
| | NO ▶ | There is an open in circuit #839. Rerun SERVICE BAY DIAGNOSTICS after repair is made. |

**Fig. 48 Pinpoint test, GE (Part 6 of 7)**

| GE13 WIRING HARNESS CHECK | RESULT | ACTION TO TAKE |
|---|---|---|
| • This time place the positive lead of VOM on circuit #838 and the negative lead on circuit #430E of the "SOFT" relay connector. | The voltage reading pulses (between zero and battery voltage) continuously: | |
| NOTE: As long as the "STAR" test button is in the up "HOLD" position the "FIRM/SOFT ACTUATOR TEST" will continue. | YES ▶ | Replace both the "SOFT" and "FIRM" relays with new ones and rerun SERVICE BAY DIAGNOSTICS after repairs are made. |
| | NO ▶ | GO TO GE14 |
| **GE14 WIRING HARNESS CHECK** | | |
| • Turn the "STAR" tester "ON/OFF" switch to the "OFF" position. | The resistance reading is less than 5.0 ohms: | |
| • Turn the air suspension "ON/OFF" switch to the "OFF" position and disconnect the air suspension control module. | YES ▶ | Replace the air suspension control module with a new one and rerun SERVICE BAY DIAGNOSTICS. |
| • Using an analog ohmmeter connect one lead to the control module wiring harness connector pin position #11 and the other lead to the "FIRM" relay connector circuit #838. | NO ▶ | There is an open in circuit #838. Rerun SERVICE BAY DIAGNOSTICS after repair is made. |

**Fig. 48 Pinpoint test, GE (Part 7 of 7)**

| HA1 | STAR CODE: 49 UNABLETO DETECT LOWERING OF RIGHT FRONT CORNER | RESULT | ACTION TO TAKE |
|---|---|---|---|
| | The air suspension control module has not received the signal that the right front corner of the vehicle vented during the SERVICE BAY DIAGNOSTIC check. There are ten possible causes:<br>• The height sensor linkage arm is not connected properly to the vehicle and/or height sensor.<br>• The air line for the right front air spring may be plugged.<br>• The right front air spring solenoid valve may be defective.<br>• The right front air spring B+ power supply circuit may have an open in it.<br>• The right front air spring ground return circuit may have an open in it.<br>• The vent solenoid valve may be defective.<br>• The vent solenoid B+ power supply circuit have an open in it.<br>• The vent solenoid ground return circuit may have an open in it.<br>• The air suspension control module may be defective.<br>• The left front air spring may be unable to vent. | ▶ | GO TO HA2 |

Fig. 49 Pinpoint test, HA (Part 1 of 17)

| HA2 | VISUAL COMPONENT CHECK | RESULT | ACTION TO TAKE |
|---|---|---|---|
| | • Check the right front corner of the vehicle to verify that the height sensor has no obvious damage and that the linkage is connected. | The right front height sensor is installed correctly with no obvious damage: | |
| | | YES ▶ | GO TO HA3 |
| | | NO ▶ | Make needed repairs as required and rerun SERVICE BAY DIAGNOSTICS. |
| **HA3** | **ENTERING FUNCTIONAL TEST MODE OF SERVICE BAY DIAG** | | |
| | The next step in determining why the the right front corner of the vehicle did not vent is:<br>• Release the "STAR" test button to the up "HOLD" position. After five seconds depress the "STAR" test button again so that it remains in the down "TEST" position. This will allow the control module to enter FUNCTIONAL TEST mode. | The "STAR" tester is displaying code: | |
| | | "31", "32", "33", "34", or "35" ▶ | GO TO HA5 |
| | | SOMETHING ELSE ▶ | GO TO HA4 |
| **HA4** | **RETRY FUNCTIONAL TEST ENTRANCE PROCEDURE** | | |
| | The air suspension control module has not entered the FUNCTIONAL TEST mode and the following actions are required:<br>• Make sure that the "STAR" tester is still plugged into the air suspension diagnostic pigtail.<br>• Make sure that the "STAR" tester is turned "ON".<br>• Release the "STAR" test button to the up "HOLD" position. After five seconds depress "STAR" test button again so that it remains in the down "TEST" position. This will allow the control module to enter FUNCTIONAL TEST mode. | The "STAR" tester is displaying code: | |
| | | "31", "32", "33", "34", or "35" ▶ | GO TO HA5 |
| | | SOMETHING ELSE ▶ | Rerun SERVICE BAY DIAGNOSTICS and if still unable to enter FUNCTIONAL TEST mode install a new air suspension control module and then rerun SERVICE BAY DIAGNOSTICS. |

Fig. 49 Pinpoint test, HA (Part 2 of 17)

| HA5 | VENT SOLENOID VALVE COMPONENT CHECK | RESULT | ACTION TO TAKE |
|---|---|---|---|
| | It is desired to activate the "VENT" SOLENOID VALVE TOGGLE" functional test. In order to do this the following actions are required:<br>• Raise the vehicle's hood up completely.<br>• Release the "STAR" test button so that it remains in the up "HOLD" position after the code "32" has been displayed for at least 5 seconds.<br>NOTE: As long as the "STAR" test button is in the up "HOLD" position the selected functional test will continue. The "VENT SOLENOID VALVE TOGGLE" test is used to verify that the air suspension control module can activate the vent solenoid valve by cycling it "ON" and "OFF" continuously until the "STAR" test button is depressed down again. | The air compressor assembly vent solenoid is: | |
| | | CYCLING "ON/OFF" CONTINUOUSLY ▶ | Depress the "STAR" test button so that it remains in the down "TEST" position. This action will stop the "VENT SOLENOID VALVE TOGGLE" functional test since it is no longer required. Then: GO TO HA11 |
| | | VENT SOLENOID REMAINS "OFF" ▶ | GO TO HA6 |
| **HA6** | **CHECKING WIRING HARNESS** | | |
| | Since the air suspension control module can not activate the vent solenoid valve the following actions are required:<br>• Disconnect the air compressor assembly electrical connector from the vehicle wiring harness connector.<br>• Examine both electrical connectors for damage and proper installation of wires. | Electrical connectors are good: | |
| | | YES ▶ | GO TO HA7 |
| | | NO ▶ | Make repairs as required and rerun SERVICE BAY DIAGNOSTICS. |

Fig. 49 Pinpoint test, HA (Part 3 of 17)

| HA7 | CHECKING WIRING HARNESS | RESULT | ACTION TO TAKE |
|---|---|---|---|
| | The next steps in determining why the air suspension control module could not activate the vent solenoid valve are:<br>• Turn the air suspension "ON/OFF" switch to the "OFF" position.<br>• Disconnect air suspension control module connector.<br>• Disconnect air compressor assembly electrical connector.<br>• Using an analog ohmmeter connect one lead to the air suspension control module wiring harness connector pin location #42 (circuit #421) and other to pin pin location #40 (circuit #430G). | Ohmmeter reading is greater than 10,000 ohms: | |
| | | YES ▶ | GO TO HA8 |
| | | NO ▶ | A short to ground has been detected in the wiring harness circuit #421.<br>rerun SERVICE BAY DIAGNOSTICS after repair is made. |
| **HA8** | **CHECKING WIRING HARNESS** | | |
| | • Again using an analog ohmmeter connect one lead to the air suspension control module wiring harness connector pin location #42 (circuit #421) and the other to the air compressor assembly vehicle wiring harness connector circuit #421. | Ohmmeter reading is greater than 10 ohms: | |
| | | YES ▶ | The circuit used to activate the vent solenoid valve (circuit #421) has an open in it. Rerun SERVICE BAY DIAGNOSTICS after repair is made. |
| | | NO ▶ | GO TO HA9 |
| **HA9** | **CHECKING WIRING HARNESS** | | |
| | • Again using an analog ohmmeter connect one lead to the air suspension control module wiring harness connector pin location #40 (circuit #430G) and the other to the air compressor assembly vehicle wiring harness connector circuit #430E. | Ohmmeter reading is greater than 10 ohms: | |
| | | YES ▶ | Circuit #430E has an open in it. Rerun SERVICE BAY DIAGNOSTICS after repair is made. |
| | | NO ▶ | GO TO HA10 |

Fig. 49 Pinpoint test, HA (Part 4 of 17)

| HA10 COMPONENT CHECK | RESULT | ACTION TO TAKE |
|---|---|---|
| • Using a 12 volt power supply connect the positive lead to the air compressor assembly connector pin location #1 and the negative lead to the air compressor assembly connector pin location #2 for 2 to 3 seconds. Repeat this as required. | The vent solenoid makes an audible click sound when voltage is applied: | |
| | YES ▶ | Install a new air suspension control module and rerun SERVICE BAY DIAGNOSTICS. |
| | NO ▶ | Install a new air compressor assembly and rerun SERVICE BAY DIAGNOSTICS. |
| **HA11 COMPONENT CHECK** | | |
| It is now desired to activate the "AIR SPRING SOLENOID VALVE TOGGLE" functional test. In order to do this the following action is required:<br>• Release the "STAR" test button so that it remains in the up "HOLD" position after the code "33" has been displayed for at least 5 seconds.<br>NOTE: As long as the "STAR" test button is in the up "HOLD" position the selected functional test will continue. The "AIR SPRING SOLENOID TOGGLE" test is used to verify that the air suspension control module can activate each of the air spring solenoid valves by cycling them "ON" and "OFF" continuously until the "STAR" test button is depressed down again. | The right front air spring solenoid valve is: | |
| | CYCLING "ON/OFF" CONTINUOUSLY ▶ | GO TO HA15 |
| | REMAINS "OFF" ▶ | GO TO HA12 |

**Fig. 49 Pinpoint test, HA (Part 5 of 17)**

| HA12 WIRING HARNESS CHECK | RESULT | ACTION TO TAKE |
|---|---|---|
| The air suspension control module cannot activate the right front air spring solenoid valve. In order to determine the cause of this the following actions are required:<br>• Electrically disconnect the air spring solenoid from the vehicle wiring harness connector.<br>• Using a voltmeter connect the positive lead to the air spring solenoid valve wiring harness connector circuit #414 and the negative lead to circuit #430D of the same connector.<br>NOTE: The "AIR SPRING SOLENOID VALVE TOGGLE" functional test is still being conducted. During this functional test the front ride height of the vehicle may lower and the rear ride height may raise. | The voltage reading pulses between zero and battery voltage (check is to be made over a one minute time period): | |
| | YES ▶ | Install a new right front air spring spring solenoid and then rerun SERVICE BAY DIAGNOSTICS. |
| | NO ▶ | GO TO HA13 |
| **HA13 CHECKING WIRING HARNESS** | | |
| • Turn the air suspension "ON/OFF" switch to the "OFF" position.<br>• Disconnect the air suspension control module connector.<br>• Using an analog ohmmeter connect one lead to the air suspension control module wiring harness connector pin location #17 (circuit #414) and other to the right front air spring solenoid valve wiring harness connector circuit #414. | Ohmmeter reading is greater than 10 ohms: | |
| | YES ▶ | GO TO HA14 |
| | NO ▶ | An open in circuit #414 has been detected in the wiring harness.<br>rerun SERVICE BAY DIAGNOSTICS after repair is made. |

**Fig. 49 Pinpoint test, HA (Part 6 of 17)**

| HA14 WIRING HARNESS CHECK | RESULT | ACTION TO TAKE |
|---|---|---|
| • Again using an analog ohmmeter connect one lead to the air suspension control module wiring harness connector pin location #60 (circuit #430H) and other to the right front air spring solenoid valve vehicle wiring harness connector circuit #430D. | Ohmmeter reading is less than 10 ohms: | |
| | YES ▶ | Install a new air suspension control module and rerun SERVICE BAY DIAGNOSTICS. |
| | NO ▶ | An open in circuit #430H/430D exists. Rerun SERVICE BAY DIAGNOSTICS after repair is made. |
| **HA15 ENTER SPRING FILL DIAGNOSTICS** | | |
| At this time it will be required to exit SERVICE BAY DIAGNOSTICS and enter SPRING FILL (refer to SPRING FILL DIAGNOSTIC section for instructions). | The "STAR" tester is displaying one of the following codes: | |
| | "21" to "28" ▶ | GO TO HA16 |
| | SOMETHING ELSE ▶ | Repeat SPRING FILL entrance procedure until entered. |

**Fig. 49 Pinpoint test, HA (Part 7 of 17)**

| HA16 INFLATE RIGHT FRONT AIR SPRING | RESULT | ACTION TO TAKE |
|---|---|---|
| In order to perform the right front air spring vent test we must first inflate it above the normal position. In order to do this the following action is required:<br>• Release the "STAR" test button so that it remains in the up "HOLD" position after the code "24" has been displayed for at least 5 seconds.<br>NOTE: As long as the "STAR" test button remains in the up "HOLD" position the right front air spring will continue to be inflated. When the desired amount of inflating has occurred depress the "STAR" test button so that it remains in the down "TEST" position. | The vehicle's right front air spring has been inflated so that the right front corner of the vehicle has approximately a two inch gap between the fender lip opening and the top of the tire: | |
| | YES ▶ | Depress the "STAR" test button down so that it remains in the "TEST" position. Then: GO TO HA17 |
| | NO ▶ | Continue with step "HA16" until the right front corner of the vehicle is at the desired position. If unable to the raise the vehicle look for an air line and/or air spring leak. |

**Fig. 49 Pinpoint test, HA (Part 8 of 17)**

| HA17 VENT RIGHT FRONT SPRING | RESULT | ACTION TO TAKE |
|---|---|---|
| To vent the right front air spring the following action is required:<br><br>• Release the "STAR" test button so that it remains in the up "HOLD" position after the code "21" has been displayed for at least 5 seconds.<br><br>NOTE: As long as the "STAR" test button remains in the up "HOLD" position the right front air spring will continue to vent. When the desired amount of venting has occurred depress the "STAR" test button so that it remains in the "TEST" position. | The right front corner of the vehicle has vented down to the normal ride height: | |
| | VERY SLOWLY OR NONE AT ALL ▶ | Depress the "STAR" test button down so that it remains in the "TEST" position. Then: GO TO HA18 |
| | SLOWLY OR AT A NORMAL RATE ▶ | If the left front corner of the vehicle also has leveling problems fix them first. Otherwise rerun SERVICE DIAGNOSTICS and if this problem still occurs install a new air suspension control module and then rerun SERVICE BAY DIAGNOSTICS. |

Fig. 49 Pinpoint test, HA (Part 9 of 17)

| HA18 INFLATE RIGHT FRONT AIR SPRING | RESULT | ACTION TO TAKE |
|---|---|---|
| Again it is desired to first inflate the right front corner of the vehicle above the normal position. In order to do this the following action is required:<br><br>• Release the "STAR" test button so that it remains in the up "HOLD" position after the code "24" has been displayed for at least 5 seconds.<br><br>NOTE: As long as the "STAR" test button remains in the up "HOLD" position the right front air spring will continue to be inflated. When the desired amount of inflating has occurred depress the "STAR" test button so that it remains in the down "TEST" position. | The vehicle's right front air spring has been inflated so that the right front corner of the vehicle has approximately a two inch gap between the fender lip opening and the top of the tire: | |
| | YES ▶ | Depress the "STAR" test button down so that it remains in the "TEST" position. Then: GO TO HA19 |
| | NO ▶ | Continue with step "HA18" until the right front corner of the vehicle is at the desired position. |

Fig. 49 Pinpoint test, HA (Part 10 of 17)

| HA19 VENT RIGHT FRONT SPRING | RESULT | ACTION TO TAKE |
|---|---|---|
| In order to determine why the right front corner of the vehicle is venting "VERY SLOWLY OR NONE AT ALL" the following actions are required:<br><br>• Disconnect the right front air line from the right front air spring solenoid valve.<br><br>• Release the "STAR" test button so that it remains in the "HOLD" position after the code "21" has been displayed for at least 5 seconds.<br><br>NOTE: THIS TEST STEP MAY RESULT IN A RAPID DROP IN VEHICLE RIDE HEIGHT | The right front corner of the vehicle has vented down to the normal ride height: | |
| | VERY SLOWLY OR NONE AT ALL ▶ | Depress the "STAR" test button down so that it remains in the "TEST" position. Then: GO TO HA24 |
| | AT A FAST OR NORMAL RATE ▶ | Depress the "STAR" test button down so that it remains in the "TEST" position. Then: GO TO HA20 |

Fig. 49 Pinpoint test, HA (Part 11 of 17)

| HA20 INFLATE RIGHT FRONT AIR SPRING | RESULT | ACTION TO TAKE |
|---|---|---|
| From the previous tests we have determined that the cause of the venting problem is due to a restriction in the air line or compressor assembly. In order to isolate the cause of this problem the following actions are required:<br><br>• Reconnect the air line to the right front solenoid valve.<br><br>• Inflate the right front corner of the vehicle so that the vehicle ride height is above the normal position. Then release the "STAR" test button so that it remains in the up "HOLD" position after the code "24" has been displayed for at least 5 seconds.<br><br>NOTE: As long as the "STAR" test button remains in the up "HOLD" position the right front air spring will continue to be inflated. When the desired amount of inflating has occurred depress the "STAR" test button so that it remains in the down "TEST" position. | The vehicle's right front air spring has been inflated so that the right front corner of the vehicle has approximately a two inch gap between the fender lip opening and the top of the tire: | |
| | YES ▶ | Depress the "STAR" test button down so that it remains in the "TEST" position. Then: GO TO HA21 |
| | NO ▶ | Continue with step "HA20" until the right front corner of the vehicle is at the desired position. If unable to depress the STAR test button down to the "TEST" position, wait 10 minutes and repeat step "HA20". |

Fig. 49 Pinpoint test, HA (Part 12 of 17)

| HA21 VENT RIGHT FRONT SPRING | RESULT | ACTION TO TAKE |
|---|---|---|
| In order to determine if the air line or air compressor assembly is the problem the following actions are required:<br>• Disconnect one of the air lines from the air compressor drier assembly<br>• Release the "STAR" test button so that it remains in the "HOLD" position after the "21" has been displayed for at least 5 seconds.<br>NOTE: THIS TEST STEP MAY RESULT IN A RAPID DROP IN VEHICLE RIDE HEIGHT. | The right front corner of the vehicle has vented down to a normal ride height: | |
| | VERY SLOWLY OR NONE AT ALL ▶ | Depress the "STAR" test button down so that it remains in the "TEST" position. The air line for the right front corner of the vehicle is restricted. Rerun SERVICE BAY DIAGNOSTICS after repairs are made. |
| | AT A FAST OR NORMAL RATE ▶ | Depress the "STAR" test button down so that it remains in the "TEST" position. Then: GO TO HA22 |
| **HA22 COMPONENT CHECK** | | |
| • Disconnect all of the air lines to the air compressor assembly drier.<br>• Remove the air compressor assembly from the vehicle.<br>• Remove the air compressor drier cap (air lines are inserted into this part) from the drier assembly (refer to the shop manual for instructions since it is spring loaded). | The white filter material in the air compressor drier cap is oily: | |
| | YES ▶ | GO TO HA23 |
| | NO ▶ | Install a new air compressor assembly Then rerun SERVICE BAY DIAGNOSTICS. |

**Fig. 49 Pinpoint test, HA (Part 13 of 17)**

| HA23 COMPONENT CHECK | RESULT | ACTION TO TAKE |
|---|---|---|
| One of the shock/strut assemblies on the vehicle has leaked a large amount of shock fluid into the air spring canister. Refer to the shop manual for determination and replacement procedures of the bad shock/strut. In addition to replacing the shock/strut the following components must also be replaced:<br>• All air suspension air lines.<br>• Air compressor assembly.<br>• Drier assembly.<br>• Remove all air spring solenoid valves and replace the filter located at the opposite end of where the air line attaches. | All repairs completed. ▶ | Rerun SERVICE BAY DIAGNOSTICS. |
| **HA24 COMPONENT CHECK** | | |
| From the previous tests we have determined that the cause of the venting problem is located in the air spring solenoid valve or shock/strut assembly. In order to determine which is the problem the following actions are required:<br>• Using a body hoist raise the vehicle off the floor (tire rotation height) so that no weight is on the tires.<br>• Vent the right front air spring as in step "HA19" and remove the air spring solenoid valve (refer to shop manual if required).<br>• Remove the air spring solenoid valve shock fluid mist filter. | The shock fluid mist filter is: | |
| | CLEAN OR SLIGHTLY OILY ▶ | GO TO HA25 |
| | VERY OILY ▶ | GO TO HA26 |

**Fig. 49 Pinpoint test, HA (Part 14 of 17)**

| HA25 COMPONENT CHECK | RESULT | ACTION TO TAKE |
|---|---|---|
| In order to determine if the right front air spring solenoid valve is operational the following actions are required:<br>• Make sure that the air line and vehicle electrical wiring harness connector are connected to the removed right front air spring solenoid valve.<br>• Release the "STAR" test button so that it remains in the "HOLD" position after the code "24" has been displayed for at least 5 seconds. | The right front air spring solenoid valve is passing air through it: | |
| | NO ▶ | Depress the "STAR" test button down so that it remains in the "TEST" position. Install a new right front air spring solenoid valve, reinflate the air spring before setting weight on the tire and rerun SERVICE BAY DIAGNOSTICS. |
| | YES ▶ | Depress the STAR test button down so that it remains in the "TEST" position<br>binding of the shock/strut and repair procedures. Rerun SERVICE BAY DIAGNOSTICS after repairs are made. |

**Fig. 49 Pinpoint test, HA (Part 15 of 17)**

| HA26 COMPONENT CHECK | RESULT | ACTION TO TAKE |
|---|---|---|
| In order to determine if the right front air spring solenoid valve is operational the following actions are required:<br>• Make sure that the air line and vehicle electrical wiring harness connector are connected to the removed right front air spring solenoid valve.<br>• Release the "STAR" test button so that it remains in the "HOLD" position after the code "24" has been displayed for at least 5 seconds. | The right front air spring solenoid valve is passing air through it: | |
| | NO ▶ | Depress the "STAR" test button down so that it remains in the "TEST" position. Install a new right front air spring solenoid valve, reinflate the air spring before setting weight on the tire. Then: GO TO HA27 |
| | YES ▶ | Depress the "STAR" test button down so that it remains in the "TEST" position. Then: GO TO HA27 |
| **HA27 COMPONENT CHECK** | | |
| • Disconnect all of the air lines to the air compressor assembly drier.<br>• Remove the air compressor assembly from the vehicle.<br>• Remove the air compressor drier cap (air lines are inserted into this part) from the drier assembly (refer to the shop manual for instructions since it is spring loaded). | The white filter material in the air compressor drier cap is oily: | |
| | YES ▶ | GO TO HA28 |
| | NO ▶ | Install a new right front air spring shock fluid mist filter and then rerun SERVICE BAY DIAGNOSTICS. |

**Fig. 49 Pinpoint test, HA (Part 16 of 17)**

| HA28 COMPONENT CHECK | RESULT | ACTION TO TAKE |
|---|---|---|
| The right front shock/strut assembly on the vehicle has leaked a large amount of shock fluid into the air spring canister. Refer to the shop manual for replacement procedures. In addition to replacing this shock/strut the following components must also be replaced:<br>• All air suspension air lines.<br>• Air compressor assembly.<br>• Drier assembly.<br>• Remove all air spring solenoid valves and replace the filter located at the opposite end of where the air line attaches. | All repairs completed. ▶ | Rerun SERVICE BAY DIAGNOSTICS. |

Fig. 49 Pinpoint test, HA (Part 17 of 17)

| HB1 STAR CODE: 50 / UNABLE TO DETECT LOWERING OF LEFT FRONT CORNER | RESULT | ACTION TO TAKE |
|---|---|---|
| The air suspension control module has not received the signal that the left front corner of the vehicle vented during the SERVICE BAY DIAGNOSTIC check. There are ten possible causes:<br>• The height sensor linkage arm is not connected properly to the vehicle and/or height sensor.<br>• The air line for the left front air spring may be plugged.<br>• The left front air spring solenoid valve may be defective.<br>• The left front air spring B+ power supply circuit may have an open in it.<br>• The left front air spring ground return circuit may have an open in it.<br>• The vent solenoid valve may be defective.<br>• The vent solenoid B+ power supply circuit may have an open in it.<br>• The vent solenoid ground return circuit may have an open in it.<br>• The air suspension control module may be defective.<br>• The right front air spring may be unable to vent. | ▶ | GO TO HB2 |

Fig. 50 Pinpoint test, HB (Part 1 of 17)

| HB2 VISUAL COMPONENT CHECK | RESULT | ACTION TO TAKE |
|---|---|---|
| • Check the left front corner of the vehicle to verify that the height sensor has no obvious damage and that the linkage is connected. | The left front height sensor is installed correctly with no obvious damage: | |
| | YES ▶ | GO TO HB3 |
| | NO ▶ | Make needed repairs as required and rerun SERVICE BAY DIAGNOSTICS. |
| **HB3 ENTERING FUNCTIONAL TEST MODE OF SERVICE BAY DIAG** | | |
| The next step in determining why the left front corner of the vehicle did not vent is:<br>• Release the "STAR" test button to the up "HOLD" position. After five seconds depress the "STAR" test button again so that it remains in the down "TEST" position. This will allow the control module to enter FUNCTIONAL TEST mode. | The "STAR" tester is displaying code: | |
| | "31", "32", "33", "34", or "35" ▶ | GO TO HB5 |
| | SOMETHING ELSE ▶ | GO TO HB4 |
| **HB4 RETRY FUNCTIONAL TEST ENTRANCE PROCEDURE** | | |
| The air suspension control module has not entered the FUNCTIONAL TEST mode and the following actions are required:<br>• Make sure that the "STAR" tester is still plugged into the air suspension diagnostic pigtail.<br>• Make sure that the "STAR" tester is turned "ON".<br>• Release the "STAR" test button to the up "HOLD" position. After five seconds depress the "STAR" test button again so that it remains in the down "TEST" position. This will allow the control module to enter FUNCTIONAL TEST mode. | The "STAR" tester is displaying code: | |
| | "31", "32", "33", "34", or "35" ▶ | GO TO HB5 |
| | SOMETHING ELSE ▶ | Rerun SERVICE BAY DIAGNOSTICS and if still unable to enter FUNCTIONAL TEST mode install a new air suspension control module. |

Fig. 50 Pinpoint test, HB (Part 2 of 17)

| HB5 VENT SOLENOID VALVE COMPONENT CHECK | RESULT | ACTION TO TAKE |
|---|---|---|
| It is desired to activate the "VENT SOLENOID VALVE TOGGLE" functional test. In order to do this the following action are required:<br>• Raise the vehicle's hood up completely.<br>• Release the "STAR" test button so that it remains in the up "HOLD" position after the code "32" has been displayed for at least 5 seconds.<br>NOTE: As long as the "STAR" test button is in the up "HOLD" position the selected functional test will continue. The "VENT" SOLENOID VALVE TOGGLE" test is used to verify that the air suspension control module can activate the vent solenoid valve by cycling it "ON" and "OFF" continuously until the "STAR" test button is depressed down again. | The air compressor assembly vent solenoid is: | |
| | CYCLING "ON/OFF" CONTINUOUSLY ▶ | Depress the "STAR" test button so that it remains in the down "TEST" position. This action will stop the "VENT SOLENOID VALVE TOGGLE" functional test since it is no longer required. Then: GO TO HB11 |
| | VENT SOLENOID REMAINS "OFF" ▶ | GO TO HB6 |
| **HB6 CHECKING WIRING HARNESS** | | |
| Since the air suspension control module can not activate the vent solenoid valve the following actions are required:<br>• Disconnect the air compressor assembly electrical connector from the vehicle wiring harness connector.<br>• Examine both electrical connectors for damage and proper installation of wires. | Electrical connectors are good: | |
| | YES ▶ | GO TO HB7 |
| | NO ▶ | Make repairs as required and rerun SERVICE BAY DIAGNOSTICS. |

Fig. 50 Pinpoint test, HB (Part 3 of 17)

| HB7 CHECKING WIRING HARNESS | RESULT | ACTION TO TAKE |
|---|---|---|
| The next steps in determining why the air suspension control module could not activate the vent solenoid valve are:<br>• Turn the air suspension "ON/OFF" switch to the "OFF" position.<br>• Disconnect air suspension control module connector.<br>• Disconnect the air compressor assembly electrical connector.<br>• Using an analog ohmmeter connect one lead to the air suspension control module wiring harness connector pin location #42 (circuit #421) and other to pin location #40 (circuit #430G). | Ohmmeter reading is greater than 10,000 ohms: | |
| | YES ▶ | GO TO HB8 |
| | NO ▶ | A short to ground has been detected in the wiring harness circuit #421.<br>rerun SERVICE BAY DIAGNOSTICS after repair is made. |
| **HB8 CHECKING WIRING HARNESS** | | |
| • Again using an analog ohmmeter connect one lead to the air suspension control module wiring harness connector pin location #42 (circuit #421) and the other to the air compressor assembly vehicle wiring harness connector circuit #421. | Ohmmeter reading is greater than 10 ohms: | |
| | YES ▶ | The circuit used to activate the vent solenoid valve (circuit #421) has an open in it. Rerun SERVICE BAY DIAGNOSTICS after repair is made. |
| | NO ▶ | GO TO HB9 |
| **HB9 CHECKING WIRING HARNESS** | | |
| • Again using an analog ohmmeter connect one lead to the air suspension control module wiring harness connector pin location #40 (circuit #430G) and the other to the air compressor assembly vehicle wiring harness connector circuit #430E. | Ohmmeter reading is greater than 10 ohms: | |
| | YES ▶ | Circuit #430E has an open in it. Rerun SERVICE BAY DIAGNOSTICS after repair is made. |
| | NO ▶ | GO TO HB10 |

**Fig. 50 Pinpoint test, HB (Part 4 of 17)**

| HB10 COMPONENT CHECK | RESULT | ACTION TO TAKE |
|---|---|---|
| • Using a 12 volt power supply connect the <u>positive lead</u> to the air compressor assembly connector pin location #1 and the <u>negative lead</u> to the air compressor assembly connector pin location #2 for <u>2 to 3 seconds</u>. Repeat this as required. | The vent solenoid valve makes an audible click sound when voltage is applied: | |
| | YES ▶ | Install a new air suspension control module and rerun SERVICE BAY DIAGNOSTICS. |
| | NO ▶ | Install a new air compressor assembly and rerun SERVICE BAY DIAGNOSTICS. |
| **HB11 COMPONENT CHECK** | | |
| It is now desired to activate the "AIR SPRING SOLENOID VALVE TOGGLE" functional test. In order to do this the following action is required:<br>• Release the "STAR" test button so that it remains in the up "HOLD" position after the code "33" has been displayed for at least 5 seconds. | The left front air spring solenoid valve is: | |
| | CYCLING "ON/OFF" CONTINUOUSLY ▶ | GO TO HB15 |
| | REMAINS "OFF" CONTINUOUSLY ▶ | GO TO HB12 |
| NOTE: As long as the "STAR" test button is in the up "HOLD" position the selected functional test will continue. The "AIR SPRING SOLENOID TOGGLE" test is used to verify that the air suspension control module can activate each of the air spring solenoid valves by cycling them "ON" and "OFF" continuously until the "STAR" test button is depressed down again. | | |

**Fig. 50 Pinpoint test, HB (Part 5 of 17)**

| HB12 CHECKING WIRING HARNESS | RESULT | ACTION TO TAKE |
|---|---|---|
| The air suspension control module can not activate the left front air spring solenoid valve. In order to determine the cause of this the following actions are required:<br>• Electrically disconnect the air spring solenoid from the vehicle wiring harness connector.<br>• Using a voltmeter connect the positive lead to the air spring solenoid valve wiring harness connector circuit #415 and the negative lead to circuit #430K of the same connector. | The voltage reading pulses between zero and battery voltage (check is to be made over a one minute time period): | |
| | YES ▶ | Install a new left front air spring solenoid valve and rerun SERVICE BAY DIAGNOSTICS after repair is made. |
| NOTE: The "AIR SPRING SOLENOID VALVE TOGGLE" functional test is still being conducted. During this functional test the front ride height of the vehicle may lower and the rear ride height may raise. | NO ▶ | GO TO HB13 |
| **HB13 CHECKING WIRING HARNESS** | | |
| • Turn the air suspension "ON/OFF" switch to the "OFF" position.<br>• Disconnect air suspension control module connector.<br>• Using an analog ohmmeter connect one lead to the air suspension control module wiring harness connector pin location #21 (circuit #415) and other to the left front air spring solenoid valve wiring harness connector circuit #415. | Ohmmeter reading is greater than 10 ohms: | |
| | YES ▶ | GO TO HB14 |
| | NO ▶ | An open in circuit #415 has been detected in the wiring harness.<br>rerun SERVICE BAY DIAGNOSTICS after repair is made. |

**Fig. 50 Pinpoint test, HB (Part 6 of 17)**

| HB14 WIRING HARNESS CHECK | RESULT | ACTION TO TAKE |
|---|---|---|
| • Again using an analog ohmmeter connect one lead to the air suspension control module wiring harness connector pin location #60 (circuit #430H) and other to the left front air spring solenoid valve vehicle wiring harness connector circuit #430K. | Ohmmeter reading is less than 10 ohms: | |
| | YES ▶ | Install a new air suspension control module and rerun SERVICE BAY DIAGNOSTICS. |
| | NO ▶ | An open in circuit #430H/430K exists. Rerun SERVICE BAY DIAGNOSTICS after repair is made. |
| **HB15 ENTER SPRING FILL DIAGNOSTICS** | | |
| At this time it will be required to exit SERVICE BAY DIAGNOSTICS and enter SPRING FILL (refer to SPRING FILL DIAGNOSTIC for instructions). | The STAR tester is displaying one of the following codes: | |
| | "21" to "28" ▶ | GO TO HB16 |
| | SOMETHING ELSE ▶ | Repeat SPRING FILL entrance procedure until entered. |

**Fig. 50 Pinpoint test, HB (Part 7 of 17)**

| HB16 INFLATE LEFT FRONT AIR SPRING | RESULT | ACTION TO TAKE |
|---|---|---|
| In order to perform the left front air spring vent test we must first inflate it above the normal position. In order to do that the following action is required:<br>• Release the "STAR" test button so that it remains in the up "HOLD" position after the code "25" has been displayed for at least 5 seconds.<br>NOTE: As long as the "STAR" test button remains in the up "HOLD" position the left front air spring will continue to be inflated. When the desired amount of inflating has occurred depress the "STAR" test button so that it remains in the down "TEST" position. | The vehicle's left front air spring has been inflated so that the left front corner of the vehicle has approximately a two inch gap between the fender lip opening and the top the tire: | |
| | YES ▶ | Depress the "STAR" test button down so that it remains in the "TEST" position. Then: GO TO HB16 |
| | NO ▶ | Continue with step "HB16" until the left front corner of the vehicle is at the desired position. If unable to raise the vehicle look for an air line and/or air spring leak. |

**Fig. 50 Pinpoint test, HB (Part 8 of 17)**

| HB17 VENT LEFT FRONT SPRING | RESULT | ACTION TO TAKE |
|---|---|---|
| To vent the left front air spring the following action is required:<br>• Release the "STAR" test button so that it remains in the up "HOLD" position after the code "22" has been displayed for at least 5 seconds.<br>NOTE: As long as the "STAR" test button remains in the up "HOLD" position the left front air spring will continue to vent. When the desired amount of venting has occurred depress the STAR test button so that it remains in the "TEST position. | The left front corner of the vehicle has vented down to the normal ride height: | |
| | VERY SLOWLY OR NONE AT ALL ▶ | Depress the "STAR" test button down so that it remains in the "TEST" position. Then: GO TO HB18 |
| | SLOWLY OR AT A NORMAL RATE ▶ | If the right front corner of the vehicle also has leveling problems fix them first. Otherwise rerun SERVICE BAY DIAGNOSTICS and if this problem still occurs install a new air suspension control module and then rerun SERVICE BAY DIAGNOSTICS. |

**Fig. 50 Pinpoint test, HB (Part 9 of 17)**

| HB18 INFLATE LEFT FRONT AIR SPRING | RESULT | ACTION TO TAKE |
|---|---|---|
| Again it is desired to first inflate the left front corner of the vehicle above the normal position. In order to do that the following action is required:<br>• Release the "STAR" test button so that it remains in the up "HOLD" position after the code "25" has been displayed for at least 5 seconds.<br>NOTE: As long as the "STAR" test button remains in the up "HOLD" position the left front air spring will continue to be to inflated. When the desired amount of inflating has occurred depress the "STAR" test button so that it remains in the down "TEST" position. | The vehicle's left front air spring has been inflated so that the left front corner of the vehicle has approximately a two inch gap between the fender lip opening and the top of the tire: | |
| | YES ▶ | Depress the "STAR" test button down so that it remains in the "TEST" position. Then: GO TO HB19 |
| | NO ▶ | Continue with step "HB18" until the left front corner of the vehicle is at the desired position. |

**Fig. 50 Pinpoint test, HB (Part 10 of 17)**

| HB19 VENT LEFT FRONT SPRING | RESULT | ACTION TO TAKE |
|---|---|---|
| In order to determine why the left front corner of the vehicle is venting "VERY SLOWLY OR NONE AT ALL" the following actions are required:<br>• Disconnect the left front air line from the left front air spring solenoid valve.<br>• Release the "STAR" test button so that it remains in the "HOLD" position after the code "22" has been displayed for at least 5 seconds.<br>NOTE: THIS TEST STEP MAY RESULT IN A RAPID DROP IN VEHICLE RIDE HEIGHT | The left front corner of the vehicle has vented down to the normal ride height: | |
| | VERY SLOWLY OR NONE AT ALL ▶ | Depress the "STAR" test button down so that it remains in the "TEST" position. Then: GO TO HB24 |
| | AT A FAST OR NORMAL RATE ▶ | Depress the "STAR" test button down so that it remains in the "TEST" position. Then: GO TO HB20 |

**Fig. 50 Pinpoint test, HB (Part 11 of 17)**

| HB20 | INFLATE LEFT FRONT AIR SPRING | RESULT | | ACTION TO TAKE |
|---|---|---|---|---|
| | From the previous tests we have determined that the cause of the venting problem is due to a restriction in the air line or compressor assembly. In order to isolate the cause of this problem the following actions are required:<br><br>• Reconnect the air line to the left front solenoid valve.<br><br>• Inflate the left front corner of the vehicle so that the vehicle ride height is above the normal position. Then release the "STAR" test button so that it remains in the up "HOLD" position after the code "25" has been displayed for at at least 5 seconds.<br><br>NOTE: As long as the "STAR" test button remains in the "HOLD" position the left front air spring will continue to be inflated. When the desired amount of inflating has occurred depress the "STAR" test button so that it remains in the down "TEST" position. | The vehicle's left front air spring has been inflated so that the right front corner of the vehicle has approximately a two inch gap between the fender lip opening and the top of the tire: | | |
| | | YES | ▶ | Depress the "STAR" test button down so that it remains in the "TEST" position. Then: GO TO HB21 |
| | | NO | ▶ | Continue with step "HB20" until the left front corner of the vehicle is at the desired position. |

**Fig. 50 Pinpoint test, HB (Part 12 of 17)**

| HB21 | VENT LEFT FRONT SPRING | RESULT | | ACTION TO TAKE |
|---|---|---|---|---|
| | In order to determine if the air line or air compressor assembly is the problem the following actions are required:<br><br>• Disconnect one of the air lines from the air compressor dryer assembly.<br><br>• Release the "STAR" test button so that it remains in the "HOLD" position after the code "22" has been displayed for at least 5 seconds.<br><br>NOTE: THIS TEST STEP MAY RESULT IN A <u>RAPID LOSS IN VEHICLE RIDE HEIGHT</u> | The left front corner of the vehicle has vented down to a normal ride height: | | |
| | | VERY SLOWLY OR NONE AT ALL | ▶ | Depress the "STAR" test button down so that it remains in the "TEST" position. The air line for the left front corner of the vehicle is restricted. Rerun SERVICE BAY DIAGNOSTICS after repairs are made. |
| | | AT A FAST OR NORMAL RATE | ▶ | Depress the "STAR" test button down so that it remains in the "TEST" position. Then: GO TO HB22 |
| HB22 | COMPONENT CHECK | | | |
| | • Disconnect all of the air lines to the air compressor assembly drier.<br><br>• Remove the air compressor assembly from the vehicle.<br><br>• Remove the air compressor drier cap (air lines are inserted into this part) from the drier assembly. | The white filter material in the air compressor drier cap is oily: | | |
| | | YES | ▶ | GO TO HB23 |
| | | NO | ▶ | Install a new air compressor assembly and then rerun SERVICE BAY DIAGNOSTICS. |

**Fig. 50 Pinpoint test, HB (Part 13 of 17)**

| HB23 | COMPONENT CHECK | RESULT | | ACTION TO TAKE |
|---|---|---|---|---|
| | One of the shock/strut assemblies on the vehicle has leaked a large amount of shock fluid into the air spring canister. Refer to the shop manual for determination and replacement procedures of the bad shock/strut. In addition to replacing the shock/strut the following components must also be replaced:<br><br>• All air suspension air lines.<br><br>• Air compressor assembly.<br><br>• Drier assembly.<br><br>• Remove all air spring solenoid valves and replace the filter located at the opposite end of where the air line attaches. | All repairs completed. | ▶ | Rerun SERVICE BAY DIAGNOSTICS. |
| HB24 | COMPONENT CHECK | | | |
| | From the previous tests we have determined that the cause of the venting problem is located in the air spring solenoid valve or shock/strut assembly. In order to determine which is the problem the following actions are required:<br><br>• Using a body hoist raise the vehicle off the floor (tire rotation height) so that no weight is on the tires.<br><br>• Vent the left front air spring as in step "HB19" and remove the air spring solenoid valve<br><br>• Remove the air spring solenoid valve shock fluid mist filter. | The shock fluid mist filter is: | | |
| | | CLEAN OR SLIGHTLY OILY | ▶ | GO TO HB25 |
| | | VERY OILY | ▶ | GO TO HB26 |

**Fig. 50 Pinpoint test, HB (Part 14 of 17)**

| HB25 | COMPONENT CHECK | RESULT | | ACTION TO TAKE |
|---|---|---|---|---|
| | In order to determine if the left front air spring solenoid valve is operational the following actions are required:<br><br>• Make sure that the air line and vehicle electrical wiring harness connector are connected to the removed left front air spring solenoid valve.<br><br>• Release the "STAR" test button so that it remains in the "HOLD" position after the code "25" has been displayed for at least 5 seconds. | The left front air spring solenoid valve is passing air through it: | | |
| | | NO | ▶ | Depress the "STAR" test button down so that it remains in the "TEST" position. Install a new left front air spring solenoid valve, reinflate the air spring before setting weight on the tire and rerun SERVICE BAY DIAGNOSTICS. |
| | | YES | ▶ | Depress the "STAR" test button down so that it remains in the "TEST" position. Replace the shock fluid mist filter<br><br>Rerun SERVICE BAY DIAGNOSTICS after repairs are made. |

**Fig. 50 Pinpoint test, HB (Part 15 of 17)**

| HB26 COMPONENT CHECK | RESULT | ACTION TO TAKE |
|---|---|---|
| In order to determine if the left front air spring solenoid valve is operational the following actions are required:<br>• Make sure that the air line and vehicle electrical wiring harness connector are connected to the removed left front air spring solenoid valve.<br>• Release the "STAR" test button so that it remains in the "HOLD" position after the code "25" has been displayed for at least 5 seconds. | The left front air spring solenoid valve is passing air through it: | |
| | NO | Depress the "STAR" test button down so that it remains in the test position. Install a new left front air spring solenoid valve, reinflate the air spring before setting weight on the tire. Then: GO TO HB27 |
| | YES | Depress the "STAR" test button down so that it remains in the "TEST" position. Then: GO TO HB27 |
| **HB27 COMPONENT CHECK** | | |
| • Disconnect all of the air lines to the air compressor assembly drier.<br>• Remove the air compressor assembly from the vehicle.<br>• Remove the air compressor drier cap (air lines are inserted into this part) from the drier assembly (refer to the shop manual for instructions since it is spring loaded). | The white filter material in the air compressor drier cap is oily: | |
| | YES | GO TO HB28 |
| | NO | Install a new left front air spring shock fluid mist filter and then rerun SERVICE BAY DIAGNOSTICS. |

**Fig. 50 Pinpoint test, HB (Part 16 of 17)**

| HB28 COMPONENT CHECK | RESULT | ACTION TO TAKE |
|---|---|---|
| The left front shock/strut assembly on the vehicle has leaked a large amount of shock fluid into the air spring canister. Refer to the shop manual for replacement procedures. In addition to replacing this shock/strut the following components must also be replaced:<br>• All air suspension air lines.<br>• Air compressor assembly.<br>• Drier assembly.<br>• Remove all air spring solenoid valves and replace the filter located at the opposite end of where the air line attaches. | All repairs completed | Rerun SERVICE BAY DIAGNOSTICS. |

**Fig. 50 Pinpoint test, HB (Part 17 of 17)**

| HC1 STAR CODE: 51 / UNABLE TO DETECT LOWERING OF RIGHT REAR CORNER | RESULT | ACTION TO TAKE |
|---|---|---|
| The air suspension control module has not received the signal that the right rear corner of the vehicle vented during the SERVICE BAY DIAGNOSTIC check. There are ten possible causes:<br>• The height sensor linkage arm is not connected properly to the vehicle and/or height sensor.<br>• The air line for the right rear air spring may be plugged.<br>• The right rear air spring solenoid valve may be defective.<br>• The right rear air spring B + power supply circuit may have an open in it.<br>• The right rear air spring ground return circuit may have an open in it.<br>• The vent solenoid valve may be defective.<br>• The vent solenoid B + power supply circuit may have an open in it.<br>• The vent solenoid ground return circuit may have an open in it.<br>• The air suspension control module may be defective.<br>• The left rear air spring may be unable to vent. | | GO TO HC2 |

**Fig. 51 Pinpoint test, HC (Part 1 of 17)**

| HC2 VISUAL COMPONENT CHECK | RESULT | ACTION TO TAKE |
|---|---|---|
| • Check the right rear corner of the vehicle to verify that the height sensor has no obvious damage and that the linkage is connected. | The right rear height sensor is installed correctly with no obvious damage: | |
| | YES | GO TO HC3 |
| | NO | Make needed repairs as required and rerun SERVICE BAY DIAGNOSTICS. |
| **HC3 ENTERING FUNCTIONAL TEST MODE OF SERVICE BAY DIAG** | | |
| The next step in determining why the right rear corner of the vehicle did not vent is:<br>• Release the "STAR" test button to the up "HOLD" position. After five seconds depress the "STAR" test button again so that it remains in the down "TEST" position. This will allow the control module to enter FUNCTIONAL TEST mode. | The "STAR" tester is displaying code: | |
| | "31", "32", "33", "34", or "35" | GO TO HC5 |
| | SOMETHING ELSE | GO TO HC4 |
| **HC4 RETRY FUNCTIONAL TEST ENTRANCE PROCEDURE** | | |
| The air suspension control module has not entered the PIN POINT TEST mode and the following actions are required:<br>• Make sure that the "STAR" tester is still plugged into the air suspension diagnostic pigtail.<br>• Make sure that the "STAR" tester is turned "ON".<br>• Release the "STAR" test button to the up "HOLD" position. After five seconds depress the "STAR" test button again so that it remains in the down "TEST" position. This will allow the control module to enter FUNCTIONAL TEST mode. | The "STAR" tester is displaying code: | |
| | "31", "32", "33", "34", or "35" | GO TO HC5 |
| | SOMETHING ELSE | Rerun SERVICE BAY DIAGNOSTICS and if still unable to enter FUNCTIONAL TEST mode install a new air suspension control module and then rerun SERVICE BAY DIAGNOSTICS. |

**Fig. 51 Pinpoint test, HC (Part 2 of 17)**

| HC5 VENT SOLENOID VALVE COMPONENT CHECK | RESULT | ACTION TO TAKE |
|---|---|---|
| It is desired to activate the "VENT SOLENOID VALVE TOGGLE" functional test. In order to do this the following action is required: | The air compressor assembly vent solenoid is: | |
| • Raise the vehicle's hood up completely. • Release the "STAR" test button so that it remains in the up "HOLD" position after the code "32" has been displayed for at least 5 seconds. | CYCLING "ON/OFF" CONTINUOUSLY | Depress the "STAR" test button so that it remains in the down "TEST" position. This action will stop the "VENT SOLENOID VALVE TOGGLE" functional test since it is no longer required. Then: GO TO HC11 |
| NOTE: As long as the "STAR" test button is in the up "HOLD" position the selected FUNCTIONAL TEST will continue. The "VENT SOLENOID VALVE TOGGLE" test is used to verify that the air suspension control module can activate the vent solenoid valve by cycling it "ON" and "OFF" continuously until the "STAR" test button is depressed down again. | VENT SOLENOID REMAINS "OFF" | GO TO HC6 |
| **HC6 CHECKING WIRING HARNESS** | | |
| Since the air suspension control module can not activate the vent solenoid valve the following actions are required; | Electrical connectors are good: | |
| • Disconnect the air compressor assembly electrical connector from the vehicle wiring harness connector. • Examine both electrical connectors for damage and proper installation of wires. | YES | GO TO HC7 |
| | NO | Make repairs as required and rerun SERVICE BAY DIAGNOSTICS. |

**Fig. 51 Pinpoint test, HC (Part 3 of 17)**

| HC7 CHECKING WIRING HARNESS | RESULT | ACTION TO TAKE |
|---|---|---|
| The next steps in determining why the air suspension control module could not activate the vent solenoid valve are: | Ohmmeter reading is greater than 10,000 ohms: | |
| • Turn the air suspension "ON/OFF" switch to the "OFF" position. | YES | GO TO HC8 |
| • Disconnect air suspension control module connector. • Disconnect the air compressor assembly electrical connector. • Using an analog ohmmeter connect one lead to the air suspension control module wiring harness connector pin location #42 (circuit #421) and other to pin location #40 (circuit #430G). | NO | A short to ground has been detected in the wiring harness circuit #421. and rerun SERVICE BAY DIAGNOSTICS after repair is made. |
| **HC8 CHECKING WIRING HARNESS** | | |
| • Again using an analog ohmmeter connect one lead to the air suspension control module wiring harness connector pin location #42 (circuit #421) and the the other to the air compressor assembly vehicle wiring harness connector #421. | Ohmmeter reading is greater than 10 ohms: | |
| | YES | The circuit used to activate the vent solenoid valve (circuit #421) has an open in it. Rerun SERVICE BAY DIAGNOSTICS after repair is made. |
| | NO | GO TO HC9 |
| **HC9 CHECKING WIRING HARNESS** | | |
| • Again using an analog ohmmeter connect one lead to the air suspension control module wiring harness connector pin location #40 (circuit #430G) and the other to the air compressor assembly vehicle wiring harness connector circuit #430E. | Ohmmeter reading is greater than 10 ohms: | |
| | YES | Circuit #430E has an open in it. Rerun SERVICE BAY DIAGNOSTICS after repair is made. |
| | NO | GO TO HC10 |

**Fig. 51 Pinpoint test, HC (Part 4 of 17)**

| HC10 COMPONENT CHECK | RESULT | ACTION TO TAKE |
|---|---|---|
| • Using a 12 volt power supply connect the positive lead to the air compressor assembly connector pin location #1 and the negative lead to the air compressor assembly connector pin location #2 for 2 to 3 seconds. Repeat this as required. | The vent solenoid valve is activated when the voltage is applied: | |
| | YES | Install a new air suspension control module and rerun SERVICE BAY DIAGNOSTICS. |
| | NO | Replace the air compressor assembly and rerun SERVICE BAY DIAGNOSTICS. |
| **HC11 COMPONENT CHECK** | | |
| It is now desired to activate the "AIR SPRING SOLENOID VALVE TOGGLE" functional test. In order to do this the following actions are required: | The right rear air spring solenoid valve is: | |
| • Release the "STAR" test button so that it remains in the up "HOLD" position after the code "33" has been displayed for at least 5 seconds. | CYCLING "ON/OFF" CONTINUOUSLY | GO TO HC15 |
| NOTE: As long as the "STAR" test button is in the up "HOLD" position the selected functional test will continue. The "AIR SPRING SOLENOID TOGGLE" test is used to verify that the air suspension control module can activate each of the air spring solenoid valves by cycling them "ON" and "OFF" continuously until the "STAR" test button is depressed down again. | REMAINS "OFF" | GO TO HC12 |

**Fig. 51 Pinpoint test, HC (Part 5 of 17)**

| HC12 CHECKING WIRING HARNESS | RESULT | ACTION TO TAKE |
|---|---|---|
| The air suspension control module can not activate the right rear air spring solenoid valve. In order to determine the cause of this the following actions are required: | The voltage reading pulses between zero and battery voltage (check is to be made over a one minute time period): | |
| • Electrically disconnect the air spring solenoid from the vehicle wiring harness connector. • Using a voltmeter connect the positive lead to the air spring solenoid valve wiring harness connector circuit #416 and the negative lead to circuit #430A of the same connector. | YES | Install a new right rear air spring solenoid and then rerun SERVICE BAY DIAGNOSTICS. |
| NOTE: The "AIR SPRING SOLENOID VALVE TOGGLE" functional test is still being conducted. During this functional test the front ride height of the vehicle may lower and the rear ride height may raise. | NO | GO TO HC13 |
| **HC13 CHECKING WIRING HARNESS** | | |
| • Turn the air suspension "ON/OFF" switch to the "OFF" position. • Disconnect air suspension control module connector. | Ohmmeter reading is greater than 10 ohms: | |
| | YES | GO TO HC14 |
| • Using an analog ohmmeter connect one lead to the air suspension control module wiring harness connector pin location #38 (circuit #416) and other to the right rear air spring solenoid valve wiring harness connector circuit #416. | NO | An open in circuit #416 has been detected in the wiring harness. rerun SERVICE BAY DIAGNOSTICS after repair is made. |

**Fig. 51 Pinpoint test, HC (Part 6 of 17)**

| HC14 WIRING HARNESS CHECK | RESULT | ACTION TO TAKE |
|---|---|---|
| • Again using an analog ohmmeter connect one lead to the air suspension control module wiring harness connector pin location #60 (circuit #430H) and other to the right rear air spring solenoid valve vehicle wiring harness connector circuit #430A. | Ohmmeter readings is less than 10 ohms: | |
| | YES | Install a new air suspension control module and rerun SERVICE BAY DIAGNOSTICS. |
| | NO | An open in circuit #430H/430A exists. Rerun SERVICE BAY DIAGNOSTICS after repair is made. |
| **HC15 ENTER SPRING FILL DIAGNOSTICS** | | |
| At this time it will be required to exit SERVICE BAY DIAGNOSTICS and enter SPRING FILL (refer to SPRING FILL DIAGNOSTIC for instructions). | The "STAR" tester is displaying one of the following codes: | |
| | "21" to "28" | GO TO HC16 |
| | SOMETHING ELSE | Repeat SPRING FILL entrance procedure until entered. |

Fig. 51 Pinpoint test, HC (Part 7 of 17)

| HC16 INFLATE RIGHT REAR AIR SPRING | RESULT | ACTION TO TAKE |
|---|---|---|
| In order to perform the right rear air spring vent test we must first inflate above the normal position. In order to do that the following action is required:<br>• Release the "STAR" test button so that it remains in the up "HOLD" position after the code "26" has been displayed code for at least 5 seconds.<br>NOTE: As long as the "STAR" test button remains in the up "HOLD" position the right rear air spring will continue to be inflated. When the desired amount of inflating has occurred depress the "STAR" test button so that it remains in the down "TEST" position. | The vehicle's right rear air spring has been inflated so that the right rear corner of the vehicle has approximately a two inch gap between the fender lip opening and the top of the tire: | |
| | YES | Depress the "STAR" test button down so that it remains in the "TEST" position. Then: GO TO HC17 |
| | NO | Continue with step "HC16" until the right rear corner of the vehicle is at the desired position. If unable to raise vehicle look for an air line and/or air spring leak. |

Fig. 51 Pinpoint test, HC (Part 8 of 17)

| HC17 VENT RIGHT REAR SPRING | RESULT | ACTION TO TAKE |
|---|---|---|
| To vent the right rear air spring the following action is required:<br>• Release the "STAR" test button so that it remains in the up "HOLD" position after the code "23" has been displayed for at least 5 seconds.<br>NOTE: As long as the "STAR" test button remains in the up "HOLD" position the right rear air spring will continue to vent. When the desired amount of venting has occurred depress the "STAR" test button so that it remains in the "TEST" position. | The right rear corner of the vehicle has vented down to the normal ride height: | |
| | VERY SLOWLY OR NONE AT ALL | Depress the "STAR" test button down so that it remains in the "TEST" position. Then: GO TO HC18 |
| | SLOWLY OR AT A NORMAL RATE | If the left rear corner of the vehicle also has leveling problems fix them first. Otherwise rerun SERVICE DIAGNOSTICS and if this problem still occurs install a new air suspension control module and then rerun SERVICE BAY DIAGNOSTICS. |

Fig. 51 Pinpoint test, HC (Part 9 of 17)

| HC18 INFLATE RIGHT REAR AIR SPRING | RESULT | ACTION TO TAKE |
|---|---|---|
| Again it is desired to first inflate the right rear corner of the vehicle above the normal position. In order to do this the following action is required:<br>• Release the "STAR" test button so that it remains in the up "HOLD" position after the code "26" has been displayed for at least 5 seconds.<br>NOTE: As long as the "STAR" test button remains in the up "HOLD" position the right rear air spring will continue to be to inflated. When the desired amount of inflating has occurred depress the "STAR" test button so that it remains in the down "TEST" position. | The vehicle's right rear air spring has been inflated so that the right rear corner of the vehicle has approximately a two inch gap between the fender lip opening and the top of the tire: | |
| | YES | Depress the STAR test button down so that it remains in the "TEST" Then: GO TO HC19 |
| | NO | Continue with step "HC18" until the right rear corner of the vehicle is at the desired position. |

Fig. 51 Pinpoint test, HC (Part 10 of 17)

| HC19 VENT RIGHT REAR SPRING | RESULT | ACTION TO TAKE |
|---|---|---|
| In order to determine why the right rear corner of the vehicle is venting "VERY SLOWLY OR NONE AT ALL" the following actions are required:<br>• Disconnect the right rear air line from the right rear air spring solenoid valve.<br>• Release the "STAR" test button so that it remains in the "HOLD" position after the code "23" has been displayed for at least 5 seconds.<br>NOTE: THIS TEST STEP MAY RESULT IN A RAPID LOSS OF VEHICLE RIDE HEIGHT. | The right rear corner of the vehicle has vented down to the normal ride height: | |
| | VERY SLOWLY OR NONE AT ALL ▶ | Depress the STAR test button down so that it remains in the "TEST" position. Then: GO TO **HC24** |
| | AT A FAST OR NORMAL RATE ▶ | Depress the "STAR" test button down so that it remains in the "TEST" position. Then: GO TO **HC20** |

**Fig. 51 Pinpoint test, HC (Part 11 of 17)**

| HC20 INFLATE RIGHT REAR AIR SPRING | RESULT | ACTION TO TAKE |
|---|---|---|
| From the previous tests we have determined that the cause of the venting problem is due to a restriction in the air line or compressor assembly. In order to isolate the cause of this problem the following actions are required:<br>• Reconnect the air line to the right rear solenoid valve.<br>• Inflate the right rear corner of the vehicle so that the vehicle ride height is above the normal position. Then release the "STAR" test button so that it remains in the up "HOLD" position after the code "26" has been displayed for at least 5 seconds.<br>NOTE: As long as the "STAR" test button remains in the up "HOLD" position the right rear air spring will continue to be inflated. When the desired amount of inflating has occurred depress the "STAR" test button so that it remains in the down "TEST" position. | The vehicle's right rear air spring has been inflated so that the right rear corner of the vehicle has approximately a two inch gap between the fender lip opening and the top of the tire: | |
| | YES ▶ | Depress the "STAR" test button down so that it remains in the "TEST" position. Then: GO TO **HC21**. |
| | NO ▶ | Continue with step "HC20" until the right rear corner of the vehicle is at the desired position. |

**Fig. 51 Pinpoint test, HC (Part 12 of 17)**

| HC21 VENT RIGHT REAR SPRING | RESULT | ACTION TO TAKE |
|---|---|---|
| In order to determine if the air line or air compressor assembly is the problem the following actions are required:<br>• Disconnect one of the air lines from the air compressor dryer assembly.<br>• Release the STAR test button so that it remains in the "HOLD" position after the code "23" has been displayed for at least 5 seconds.<br>NOTE: THIS TEST STEP MAY RESULT IN A RAPID LOSS OF AIR FROM THE AIR SPRING. | The right rear corner of the vehicle has vented down to a normal ride height: | |
| | VERY SLOWLY OR NONE AT ALL ▶ | Depress the "STAR" test button down so that it remains in the "TEST" position. The air line for the right rear corner of the vehicle is restricted. Rerun SERVICE BAY DIAGNOSTICS after repairs are made. |
| | AT A FAST OR NORMAL RATE ▶ | Depress the "STAR" test button down so that it remains in the "TEST" position. Then: GO TO **HC22** |
| **HC22 COMPONENT CHECK** | | |
| • Disconnect all of the air lines to the air compressor assembly drier.<br>• Remove the air compressor assembly from the vehicle.<br>• Remove the air compressor drier cap (air lines are inserted into this part) from the drier assembly (refer to the shop manual for instructions since it is spring loaded). | The white filter material in the air compressor drier cap is oily: | |
| | YES ▶ | GO TO **HC23** |
| | NO ▶ | Install a new air compressor assembly and then rerun SERVICE BAY DIAGNOSTICS. |

**Fig. 51 Pinpoint test, HC (Part 13 of 17)**

| HC23 COMPONENT CHECK | RESULT | ACTION TO TAKE |
|---|---|---|
| One of the shock/strut assemblies on the vehicle has leaked a large amount of shock fluid into the air spring canister. Refer to the shop manual for determination and replacement procedures of the bad shock/strut. In addition to replacing the shock/strut the following components must also be replaced:<br>• All air suspension air lines.<br>• Air compressor assembly.<br>• Drier assembly.<br>• Remove all air spring solenoid valves and replace the filter located at the opposite end of where the air line attaches. | All repairs completed ▶ | Rerun SERVICE BAY DIAGNOSTICS. |
| **HC24 COMPONENT CHECK** | | |
| From the previous tests we have determined that the cause of the venting problem is located in the air spring solenoid valve or shock/strut assembly. In order to determine which is the problem the the follow actions are required:<br>• Using a body hoist raise the vehicle off the floor (tire rotation height) so that no weight is on the tires.<br>• Vent the right rear air spring as in step "HC19" and remove the air spring solenoid valve (refer to shop manual if required).<br>• Remove the air spring solenoid valve shock fluid mist filter. | The shock fluid mist filter is: | |
| | CLEAN OR SLIGHTLY OILY ▶ | GO TO HC25 |
| | VERY OILY ▶ | GO TO HC26 |

**Fig. 51 Pinpoint test, HC (Part 14 of 17)**

| HC25 COMPONENT CHECK | RESULT | ACTION TO TAKE |
|---|---|---|
| In order to determine if the right rear air spring solenoid valve is operational the following actions are required:<br>• Make sure that the air line and vehicle electrical wiring harness connector are connected to the removed right rear air spring solenoid valve.<br>• Release the "STAR" test button so that it remains in the "HOLD" position after the code "26" has been displayed for at least 5 seconds. | The right rear air spring solenoid valve is passing air through it: | |
| | NO | Depress the "STAR" test button down so that it remains in the "TEST" position. Install a new right rear air spring solenoid valve, reinflate the air spring before setting weight on the tire and rerun SERVICE BAY DIAGNOSTICS. |
| | YES | Depress the "STAR" test button down so that it remains in the "TEST" position. Install a new shock fluid mist filter |
| | | Rerun SERVICE BAY DIAGNOSTICS after repairs are made. |

Fig. 51 Pinpoint test, HC (Part 15 of 17)

| HC26 COMPONENT CHECK | RESULT | ACTION TO TAKE |
|---|---|---|
| In order to determine if the right rear air spring solenoid valve is operational the following actions are required:<br>• Make sure that the air line and vehicle electrical wiring harness connector are connected to the removed right rear air spring solenoid valve.<br>• Release the "STAR" test button so that it remains in the "HOLD" position after the code "26" has been displayed for at least 5 seconds. | The right rear air spring solenoid valve is passing air through it: | |
| | NO | Depress the "STAR" test button down so that it remains in the "TEST" position. Install a new right rear air spring solenoid valve, reinflate the air spring before setting weight on the tire. Then: GO TO HC26 |
| | YES | Depress the "STAR" test button down so that it remains in the "TEST" position. Then: GO TO HC26 |
| **HC27 COMPONENT CHECK** | | |
| • Disconnect all of the air lines to the air compressor assembly drier.<br>• Remove the air compressor assembly from the vehicle.<br>• Remove the air compressor drier cap (air lines are inserted into this part) from the drier assembly | The white filter material in the air compressor drier cap is oily: | |
| | YES | GO TO HC28 |
| | NO | Install a new right rear air spring shock fluid mist filter with a new one and then rerun SERVICE BAY DIAGNOSTICS. |

Fig. 51 Pinpoint test, HC (Part 16 of 17)

| HC28 COMPONENT CHECK | RESULT | ACTION TO TAKE |
|---|---|---|
| The right rear shock/strut assembly on the vehicle has leaked a large amount of shock fluid into the air spring canister. Refer to the shop manual for replacement procedures. In addition to replacing this shock/strut the following components must also be replaced:<br>• All air suspension air lines.<br>• Air compressor assembly.<br>• Drier assembly.<br>• Remove all air spring solenoid valves and replace the filter located at the opposite end of where the air line attaches. | All repairs completed. | Rerun SERVICE BAY DIAGNOSTICS. |

Fig. 51 Pinpoint test, HC (Part 17 of 17)

| HD1 STAR CODE: 78 UNABLE TO DETECT LOWERING OF LEFT REAR CORNER | RESULT | ACTION TO TAKE |
|---|---|---|
| The air suspension control module has not received the signal that the left rear cornor of the vehicle vented during the SERVICE BAY DIAGNOSTIC check. There are ten possible causes:<br>• The height sensor linkage arm is not connected properly to the vehicle and/or height sensor.<br>• The air line for the left rear air spring may be plugged.<br>• The left rear air spring solenoid valve may be defective.<br>• The left rear air spring B+ power supply circuit may have an open in it.<br>• The left rear air spring ground return circuit may have an open in it.<br>• The vent solenoid valve may be defective.<br>• The vent solenoid B+ power supply circuit may have an open in it.<br>• The vent solenoid ground return circuit may have an open in it.<br>• The air suspension control module may be defective.<br>• The right rear air spring may be unable to vent. | | GO TO HD2 |
| **HD2 VISUAL COMPONENT CHECK** | | |
| • Check the left rear corner of the vehicle to verify that the height sensor has no obvious damage and that the linkage is connected. | The left rear height sensor is installed correctly with no obvious damage. | |
| | YES | GO TO HD3 |
| | NO | Make needed repairs as required and rerun SERVICE BAY DIAGNOSTICS. |

Fig. 52 Pinpoint test, HD (Part 1 of 17)

| HD3 | ENTERING FUNCTIONAL TEST MODE OF SERVICE BAY DIAG | RESULT | ACTION TO TAKE |
|---|---|---|---|
| | The next steps in determining why the left rear corner of the vehicle did not vent is: | The "STAR" tester is displaying code: | |
| | • Release the "STAR" test button to the up "HOLD" position. After five seconds depress the "STAR" test button again so that it remains in the down "TEST" position. This will allow the control module to enter FUNCTIONAL TEST mode. | "31", "32", "33", "34", or "35" | GO TO HD5 |
| | | SOMETHING ELSE | GO TO HD4 |
| HD4 | RETRY FUNCTIONAL TEST ENTRANCE PROCEDURE | | |
| | The air suspension control module has not entered the FUNCTIONAL TEST mode and the following actions are required: | The "STAR" tester is displaying code: | |
| | • Make sure that the "STAR" tester is still plugged into the air suspension diagnostic pigtail. | "31", "32", "33", "34", or "35" | GO TO HD5 |
| | • Make sure that the "STAR" tester is turned "ON"<br>• Release the "STAR" test button to the up "HOLD" position. After five seconds depress the "STAR" test button again so that it remains in the down "TEST" position. This will allow the control module to enter FUNCTIONAL TEST mode. | SOMETHING ELSE | Rerun SERVICE BAY DIAGNOSTICS and if still unable to enter FUNCTIONAL TEST mode install a new air suspension control module and then rerun SERVICE BAY DIAGNOSTICS. |

**Fig. 52 Pinpoint test, HD (Part 2 of 17)**

| HD5 | VENT SOLENOID VALVE COMPONENT CHECK | RESULT | ACTION TO TAKE |
|---|---|---|---|
| | It is desired to activate the "VENT SOLENOID VALVE TOGGLE" functional test. In order to do this the following action is required: | The air compressor assembly vent solenoid is: | |
| | • Raise the vehicle's hood up completely.<br>• Release the "STAR" test button so that it remains in the up "HOLD" position after the code "32" has been displayed for at least 5 seconds.<br>NOTE: As long as the "STAR" test button is in the up "HOLD" position the selected functional test will continue. The "VENT" SOLENOID VALVE TOGGLE" test is used to verify that the air suspension control module can activate the vent solenoid valve by cycling it "ON" and "OFF" continuously until the "STAR" test button is depressed down again. | CYCLING "ON" CONTINUOUSLY | Depress the "STAR" test button so that it remains in the down "TEST" position. This action will stop the "VENT SOLENOID VALVE TOGGLE" functional test since it is no longer required. Then: GO TO HD11 |
| | | VENT SOLENOID REMAINS "OFF" | GO TO HD6 |
| HD6 | CHECKING WIRING HARNESS | | |
| | Since the air suspension control module can not activate the vent solenoid valve the following actions are required: | Electrical connectors are good: | |
| | • Disconnect the air compressor assembly electrical connector from the vehicle wiring harness connector. | YES | GO TO HD7 |
| | • Examine both electrical connectors for damage and proper installation of wires. | NO | Make repairs as required and rerun SERVICE BAY DIAGNOSTICS. |

**Fig. 52 Pinpoint test, HD (Part 3 of 17)**

| HD7 | CHECKING WIRING HARNESS | RESULT | ACTION TO TAKE |
|---|---|---|---|
| | The next steps in determining why the air suspension control module could not activate the vent solenoid valve are: | Ohmmeter reading is greater than 10,000 ohms: | |
| | • Turn the air suspension "ON/OFF" switch to the "OFF" position. | YES | GO TO HD8 |
| | • Disconnect air suspension control module connector.<br>• Disconnect the air compressor assembly electrical connector.<br>• Using an analog ohmmeter connect one lead to the air suspension control module wiring harness connector pin location #42 (circuit #421) and other to pin location #40 (circuit #430G). | NO | A short to ground has been detected in the wiring harness circuit #421.<br>rerun SERVICE BAY DIAGNOSTICS after repair is made. |
| HD8 | CHECKING WIRING HARNESS | | |
| | • Again using an analog ohmmeter connect one lead to the air suspension control module wiring harness connector pin location #42 (circuit #421) and the other to the air compressor assembly vehicle wiring harness connector circuit | Ohmmeter reading is greater than 10 ohms: | |
| | | YES | The circuit used to activate the #421. vent solenoid valve (circuit #421) has an open in it. Rerun SERVICE BAY DIAGNOSTICS after repair is made. |
| | | NO | GO TO HD9 |
| HD9 | CHECKING WIRING HARNESS | | |
| | • Again using an analog ohmmeter connect one lead to the air suspension control module wiring harness connector pin location #40 (circuit #430G) and the other to the air compressor assembly vehicle wiring harness connector circuit #430E. | Ohmmeter reading is greater than 10 ohms: | |
| | | YES | Circuit #430E has an open in it. Rerun SERVICE BAY DIAGNOSTICS after repair is made. |
| | | NO | GO TO HD10 |

**Fig. 52 Pinpoint test, HD (Part 4 of 17)**

| HD10 | COMPONENT CHECK | RESULT | ACTION TO TAKE |
|---|---|---|---|
| | • Using a 12 volt power supply connect the positive lead to the air compressor assembly connector pin location #1 and the negative lead to the air compressor assembly connector pin location #2 for 2 to 3 seconds. Repeat this as required. | The vent solenoid valve is activated when the voltage is applied: | |
| | | YES | Install a new air suspension control module and rerun SERVICE BAY DIAGNOSTICS. |
| | | NO | Replace the air compressor assembly and rerun SERVICE BAY DIAGNOSTICS. |
| HD11 | COMPONENT CHECK | | |
| | It is now desired to activate the "AIR SPRING SOLENOID VALVE TOGGLE" functional test. In order to do this the following action is required: | The left rear air spring solenoid valve is: | |
| | • Release the "STAR" test button so that it remains in the up "HOLD" position after the code "33" has been displayed for at least 5 seconds. | CYCLING "ON/OFF" CONTINUOUSLY | GO TO HD15 |
| | NOTE: As long as the "STAR" test button is in the up "HOLD" position the selected functional test will continue. The "AIR SPRING SOLENOID TOGGLE" test is used to verify that the air suspension control module can activate each of the air spring solenoid valves by cycling them "ON" and "OFF" continuously until the "STAR" test button is depressed down again. | REMAINS "OFF" | GO TO HD12 |

**Fig. 52 Pinpoint test, HD (Part 5 of 17)**

| HD12 CHECKING WIRING HARNESS | RESULT | ACTION TO TAKE |
|---|---|---|
| The air suspension control module can not activate the left rear air spring solenoid valve. In order to determine the cause of this the following actions are required:<br>• Electrically disconnect the air spring solenoid from the vehicle harness connector.<br>• Using a voltmeter connect the position lead to the air spring solenoid valve wiring harness connector circuit #429 and the negative lead to circuit #430F of the same connector. | The voltage reading pulses between zero and battery voltage (check is to be made over a one minute time period): | |
| | YES ▶ | Install a new left rear air spring solenoid and then rerun SERVICE BAY DIAGNOSTICS. |
| NOTE: The "AIR SPRING SOLENOID VALVE TOGGLE" functional test is still being conducted. During this functional test the front ride height of the vehicle may lower and the rear ride height may raise. | NO ▶ | GO TO HD13 |
| **HD13 CHECKING WIRING HARNESS** | | |
| • Turn the air suspension "ON/OFF" switch to the "OFF" position.<br>• Disconnect air suspension control module connector.<br>• Using an analog ohmmeter connect one lead to the air suspension control module wiring harness connector pin location #41 (circuit #429) and other to the left rear air spring solenoid valve wiring harness connector circuit #429. | Ohmmeter reading is greater than 10 ohms: | |
| | YES ▶ | GO TO HD14 |
| | NO ▶ | An open in circuit #429 has been detected in the wiring harness.<br>rerun SERVICE BAY DIAGNOSTICS after repair is made. |

**Fig. 52 Pinpoint test, HD (Part 6 of 17)**

| HD14 WIRING HARNESS CHECK | RESULT | ACTION TO TAKE |
|---|---|---|
| • Again using an analog ohmmeter connect one lead to the air suspension control module wiring harness connector pin location #60 (circuit #430H) and other to the left rear air spring solenoid valve vehicle wiring harness connector circuit #430F. | Ohmmeter reading is less than 10 ohms: | |
| | YES ▶ | Install a new air suspension control module and rerun SERVICE BAY DIAGNOSTICS. |
| | NO ▶ | An open in circuit #430H/430F exists. Rerun SERVICE BAY DIAGNOSTICS after repair is made. |
| **HD15 ENTER SPRING FILL DIAGNOSTICS** | | |
| At this time it will be required to exit SERVICE BAY DIAGNOSTICS and enter SPRING FILL (refer to SPRING FILL DIAGNOSTIC for instructions). | The "STAR" tester is displaying one of the following codes: | |
| | "21" to "28" ▶ | GO TO HD16 |
| | SOMETHING ELSE ▶ | Repeat SPRING FILL entrance procedure until entered. |

**Fig. 52 Pinpoint test, HD (Part 7 of 17)**

| HD16 INFLATE LEFT REAR AIR SPRING | RESULT | ACTION TO TAKE |
|---|---|---|
| In order to perform the left rear air spring vent test we must first inflate it above the normal position. In order to do that the following action is required:<br>• Release the "STAR" test button so that it remains in the up "HOLD" position after the code "28" has been displayed for at least 5 seconds.<br>NOTE: As long as the "STAR" test button remains in the up "HOLD" position the left rear air spring will continue to be inflated. When the desired amount of inflating has occurred depress the "STAR" test button so that it remains in the down "TEST" position. | The vehicle's left rear air spring has been inflated so that the left rear corner of the vehicle has approximately a two inch gap between the fender lip opening and the top of the tire: | |
| | YES ▶ | Depress the "STAR" test button down so that it remains in the "TEST" position. Then: GO TO HD17 |
| | NO ▶ | Continue with step "HD16" until the left rear corner of the vehicle is at the desired position. If unable to raise vehicle look for an air line and/or air spring leak. |

**Fig. 52 Pinpoint test, HD (Part 8 of 17)**

| HD17 VENT LEFT REAR SPRING | RESULT | ACTION TO TAKE |
|---|---|---|
| To vent the left rear air spring the following action is required:<br>• Release the "STAR" test button so that it remains in the up "HOLD" position after the code "27" has been displayed for at least 5 seconds.<br>NOTE: As long as the "STAR" test button remains in the up "HOLD" position the left rear air spring will continue to vent. When the desired amount of venting has occurred depress the "STAR" test button so that it remains in the "TEST" position. | The left rear corner of the vehicle has vented down to the normal ride height: | |
| | VERY SLOWLY OR NONE AT ALL ▶ | Depress the "STAR" test button down so that it remains in the "TEST" position. Then: GO TO HD18 |
| | SLOWLY OR AT A NORMAL RATE ▶ | If the left rear corner of the vehicle also has leveling problems fix them first. Otherwise rerun SERVICE DIAGNOSTICS and if this problem still occurs install a new air suspension control module and then rerun SERVICE BAY DIAGNOSTICS. |

**Fig. 52 Pinpoint test, HD (Part 9 of 17)**

| HD18 | INFLATE LEFT REAR AIR SPRING | RESULT | ACTION TO TAKE |
|---|---|---|---|
| | Again it is desired to first inflate the left rear corner of the vehicle above the normal position. In order to do this the following action is required:<br><br>• Release the "STAR" test button so that it remains in the up "HOLD" position after the code "28" has been displayed for at least 5 seconds.<br><br>NOTE: As long as the "STAR" test button remains in the up "HOLD" position the left rear air spring will continue to be inflated. When the desired amount of inflating has occurred depress the "STAR" test button so that it remains in the down "TEST" position. | The vehicle's left rear air spring has been inflated so that the left rear corner of the vehicle has approximately a two inch gap between the fender lip opening and the top of the tire: | |
| | | YES ▶ | Depress the "STAR" test button down so that it remains in the "TEST" position. Then: GO TO HD19 |
| | | NO ▶ | Continue with step "HD18" until the left rear corner of the vehicle is at the desired position. |

Fig. 52 Pinpoint test, HD (Part 10 of 17)

| HD19 | VENT LEFT REAR SPRING | RESULT | ACTION TO TAKE |
|---|---|---|---|
| | In order to determine why the left front corner of the vehicle is venting "VERY SLOWLY OR NONE AT ALL" the following actions are required:<br><br>• Disconnect the left rear air line from the left rear air spring solenoid valve.<br><br>• Release the "STAR" test button so that it remains in the "HOLD" position after the code "27" has been displayed for at least 5 seconds.<br><br>NOTE: THIS TEST STEP MAY RESULT IN A RAPID LOSS OF VEHICLE RIDE HEIGHT | The left rear corner of the vehicle has vented down to the normal ride height: | |
| | | VERY SLOWLY OR NONE AT ALL ▶ | Depress the "STAR" test button down so that it remains in the "TEST" position. Then: GO TO HD24 |
| | | AT A FAST OR NORMAL RATE ▶ | Depress the "STAR" test button down so that it remains in the "TEST" position. Then: GO TO HD20 |

Fig. 52 Pinpoint test, HD (Part 11 of 17)

| HD20 | INFLATE LEFT REAR AIR SPRING | RESULT | ACTION TO TAKE |
|---|---|---|---|
| | From the previous tests we have determined that the cause of the venting problem is due to a restriction in the air line or compressor assembly. In order to isolate the cause of this problem the following actions are required:<br><br>• Reconnect the air line to the left rear solenoid valve.<br><br>• Inflate the left rear corner of the vehicle so that the vehicle ride height is above the normal position. Then release the "STAR" test button so that it remains in the up "HOLD" position after the code "28" has been displayed for at least 5 seconds.<br><br>NOTE: As long as the "STAR" test button remains in the up "HOLD" position the left rear air spring will continue to be inflated. When the desired amount of inflating has occurred depress the "STAR" test button so that it remains in the down "TEST" position. | The vehicle's left rear air spring has been inflated so that the left rear corner of the vehicle has approximately a two inch gap between the fender lip opening and the top of the tire: | |
| | | YES ▶ | Depress the "STAR" test button down so that it remains in the "TEST" position. Then: GO TO HD21. |
| | | NO ▶ | Continue with step "HD20" until the left rear corner of the vehicle is at the desired position. |

Fig. 52 Pinpoint test, HD (Part 12 of 17)

| HD21 | VENT LEFT REAR SPRING | RESULT | ACTION TO TAKE |
|---|---|---|---|
| | In order to determine if the air line or air compressor assembly is the problem the following actions are required:<br><br>• Disconnect one of the air lines from the air compressor drier assembly.<br><br>• Release the "STAR" test button so that it remains in the "HOLD" position after the code "27" has been displayed for at least 5 seconds.<br><br>NOTE: THIS TEST STEP MAY RESULT IN A RAPID LOSS OF VEHICLE RIDE HEIGHT | The left rear corner of the vehicle has vented down to a normal ride height: | |
| | | VERY SLOWLY OR NONE AT ALL ▶ | Depress the "STAR" test button down so that it remains in the "TEST" position. The air line for the left rear corner of the vehicle is restricted. Rerun SERVICE BAY DIAGNOSTICS after repairs are made. |
| | | AT A FAST OR NORMAL RATE ▶ | Depress the "STAR" test button down so that it remains in the "TEST" position. Then: GO TO HD22 |
| **HD22** | **COMPONENT CHECK** | | |
| | • Disconnect all of the air lines to the air compressor assembly drier.<br><br>• Remove the air compressor assembly from the vehicle.<br><br>• Remove the air compressor drier cap (air lines are inserted into this part) from the drier assembly | The white filter material in the air compressor drier cap is oily: | |
| | | YES ▶ | GO TO HD23 |
| | | NO ▶ | Install a new air compressor assembly and then rerun SERVICE BAY DIAGNOSTICS. |

Fig. 52 Pinpoint test, HD (Part 13 of 17)

| HD23 COMPONENT CHECK | RESULT | ACTION TO TAKE |
|---|---|---|
| One of the shock/strut assemblies on the vehicle has leaked a large amount of shock fluid into the air spring canister. Refer to the shop manual for determination and replacement procedures of the bad shock/strut. In addition to replacing the shock/strut the following components must also be replaced:<br>• All air suspension air lines.<br>• Air compressor assembly.<br>• Drier assembly.<br>• Remove all air spring solenoid valves and replace the filter located at the opposite end of where the air line attaches. | All repairs completed. | Rerun SERVICE BAY DIAGNOSTICS. |
| **HD24 COMPONENT CHECK** | | |
| From the previous tests we have determined that the cause of the venting problem is located in the air spring solenoid valve or shock/strut assembly. In order to determine which is the problem the following actions are required:<br>• Using a body hoist raise the vehicle off the floor (tire rotation height) so that no weight is on the tires.<br>• Vent the left rear air spring as in step "HD19" and remove the air spring solenoid valve (refer to shop manual if required).<br>• Remove the air spring solenoid valve shock fluid mist filter. | The shock fluid mist filter is:<br>CLEAN OR SLIGHTLY OILY<br>VERY OILY | <br>GO TO **HD25**<br>GO TO **HD26** |

**Fig. 52 Pinpoint test, HD (Part 14 of 17)**

| HD25 COMPONENT CHECK | RESULT | ACTION TO TAKE |
|---|---|---|
| In order to determine if the left rear air spring solenoid valve is operational the following actions are required:<br>• Make sure that the air line and vehicle electrical wiring harness connector are connected to the removed left rear air spring solenoid valve.<br>• Release the "STAR" test button so that it remains in the "HOLD" position after the code "28" has been displayed for at least 5 seconds. | The left rear air spring solenoid valve is passing air through it:<br>NO | <br>Depress the "STAR" test button down so that it remains in the "TEST" position. Install a new left rear air spring solenoid valve, reinflate the air spring before setting weight on the tire and rerun SERVICE BAY DIAGNOSTICS. |
| | YES | Depress the "STAR" test button down so that it remains in the "TEST" position. Replace the shock fluid mist filter and refer to the shop manual for detection of binding of the shock/strut and repair procedures. Rerun SERVICE BAY DIAGNOSTICS after repairs are made. |

**Fig. 52 Pinpoint test, HD (Part 15 of 17)**

| HD26 COMPONENT CHECK | RESULT | ACTION TO TAKE |
|---|---|---|
| In order to determine if the left rear air spring solenoid valve is operational the following actions are required:<br>• Make sure that the air line and vehicle electrical wiring harness connector are connected to the removed left rear air spring solenoid valve.<br>• Release the "STAR" test button so that it remains in the "HOLD" position after the code "28" has been displayed for at least 5 seconds. | The left rear air spring solenoid valve is passing air through it:<br>NO | <br>Depress the "STAR" test button down so that it remains in the "TEST" position. Install a new left rear air spring solenoid valve, reinflate the air spring before setting weight on the tire. Then: GO TO HD27 |
| | YES | Depress the "STAR" test button down so that it remains in the "TEST" position. Then: GO TO HD27 |
| **HD27 COMPONENT CHECK** | | |
| Disconnect all of the air lines to the air compressor assembly drier.<br>• Remove the air compressor assembly from the vehicle.<br>• Remove the air compressor drier cap (air lines are inserted into this part) from the drier assembly (refer to the shop manual for instructions since it is spring loaded). | The white filter material in the air compressor drier cap is oily:<br>YES | <br>GO TO HD28 |
| | NO | Install a new left rear air spring shock fluid mist filter and then rerun SERVICE BAY DIAGNOSTICS. |

**Fig. 52 Pinpoint test, HD (Part 16 of 17)**

| HD28 COMPONENT CHECK | RESULT | ACTION TO TAKE |
|---|---|---|
| The left rear shock/strut assembly on the vehicle has leaked a large amount of shock fluid into the air spring canister. Refer to the shop manual for replacement procedures. In addition to replacing this shock/strut the following components must also be replaced:<br>• All air suspension air lines.<br>• Air compressor assembly.<br>• Drier assembly.<br>• Remove all air spring solenoid valves and replace the filter located at the opposite end of where the air line attaches. | All repairs completed. | Rerun SERVICE BAY DIAGNOSTICS. |

**Fig. 52 Pinpoint test, HD (Part 17 of 17)**

| IA1 | STAR CODE: 52<br>UNABLE TO DETECT RAISING<br>OF RIGHT FRONT CORNER | RESULT | ACTION TO TAKE |
|---|---|---|---|
| | The air suspension control module has not received the signal that the right front corner of the vehicle was raised during the SERVICE BAY DIAGNOSTIC check. There are nine possible causes which are listed below:<br>• The height sensor linkage arm is not connected properly to the vehicle and/or height sensor.<br>• An air line may be defective.<br>• The right front air spring solenoid valve may be defective.<br>• The right front air spring B+ power supply circuit may have an open in it.<br>• The right front air spring ground return circuit may have an open in it.<br>• The air compressor may be defective.<br>• The air compressor B+ power supply circuit may have an open in it.<br>• The air compressor ground return circuit may have an open in it.<br>• The air suspension control module may be defective. | ▶ | GO TO IB2 |
| IA2 | VISUAL<br>COMPONENT CHECK | | |
| | • Check under the vehicle to verify that the vehicle is not hanging up on something.<br>• Check the right front corner of the vehicle to verify that the height sensor has no obvious damage and that the linkage is connected. | The right front height sensor is installed correctly with no obvious damage and under the vehicle is clear of all obstructions: | |
| | | YES ▶ | GO TO IA3 |
| | | NO ▶ | Make needed repairs as required and rerun SERVICE BAY DIAGNOSTICS. |

**Fig. 53 Pinpoint test, IA (Part 1 of 16)**

| IA3 | ENTERING FUNCTIONAL TEST<br>MODE OF SERVICE BAY DIAG | RESULT | ACTION TO TAKE |
|---|---|---|---|
| | FUNCTIONAL TEST mode will be used to determine why the right front corner of the vehicle did not raise.<br>• Release the "STAR" test button to the up "HOLD" position. After five seconds depress the "STAR" test button again so that it remains in the down "TEST" position. This will allow the control module to enter FUNCTIONAL TEST mode. | The "STAR" tester is displaying code: | |
| | | "31", "32", "33", "34", or "35" ▶ | GO TO IA5 |
| | | SOMETHING ELSE ▶ | GO TO IA4 |
| IA4 | RETRY FUNCTIONAL TEST<br>ENTRANCE PROCEDURE | | |
| | The air suspension control module has not entered the FUNCTIONAL TEST mode and the following actions are required:<br>• Make sure that the "STAR" tester is still plugged into the air suspension diagnostic pigtail.<br>• Make sure that the "STAR" tester is turned "ON".<br>• Release the "STAR" test button to the up "HOLD" position. After five seconds depress the "STAR" test button again so that it remains in the down "TEST" position. This will allow the control module to enter FUNCTIONAL TEST mode. | The "STAR" tester is displaying code: | |
| | | "31", "32", "33", "34", or "35" ▶ | GO TO IA5 |
| | | SOMETHING ELSE ▶ | Rerun SERVICE BAY DIAGNOSTICS and if still unable to enter FUNCTIONAL TEST mode install a new air suspension control module and then rerun SERVICE BAY DIAGNOSTICS. |

**Fig. 53 Pinpoint test, IA (Part 2 of 16)**

| IA5 | AIR COMPRESSOR<br>COMPONENT CHECK | RESULT | ACTION TO TAKE |
|---|---|---|---|
| | It is desired to activate the "COMPRESSOR TOGGLE" FUNCTIONAL TEST mode. In order to do this the following action is required:<br>• Raise the vehicle's hood up completely.<br>• Release the "STAR" test button so that it remains in the up "HOLD" position after the code "31" has been displayed for at least 5 seconds.<br>NOTE: As long as the "STAR" test button is in the up "HOLD" position the selected functional test will continue. The "COMPRESSOR TOGGLE" test is used to verify that the air suspension control module can activate the air compressor. This is done by cycling it "ON" AND "OFF" continuously until the "STAR" test button is depressed down again. | The air compressor is: | |
| | | CYCLING "ON/OFF" CONTINUOUSLY ▶ | Depress the STAR test button so that it remains in the "TEST" position. This action will stop the "COMPRESSOR TOGGLE" functional test since it is no longer required. Then: GO TO IA17 |
| | | AIR COMPRESSOR REMAINS "OFF" ▶ | GO TO IA6 |
| IA6 | CHECKING WIRING HARNESS | | |
| | Since the air suspension control module can not activate the air compressor the following actions are required:<br>• Depress the "STAR" test button so that it remains in the down "HOLD" position. This action will stop the "COMPRESSOR TOGGLE" functional test.<br>• Disconnect the air compressor assembly electrical connector from the vehicle wiring harness connector.<br>• Examine both electrical connectors for damage and proper installation of wires. | Electrical connectors are good: | |
| | | YES ▶ | GO TO IA7 |
| | | NO ▶ | Make repairs as required and rerun SERVICE BAY DIAGNOSTICS. |

**Fig. 53 Pinpoint test, IA (Part 3 of 16)**

| IA7 | COMPRESSOR COOL DOWN | RESULT | ACTION TO TAKE |
|---|---|---|---|
| | The air compressor has an internal thermal non-cycling circuit breaker in it that opens the B+ power supply to the air compressor armature when the internal temperature exceeds a predetermined limit. In order for this thermal circuit breaker to be reset the following two things must happen: 1) the internal temperature must drop below the predetermined limit and 2) the power to the compressor must be off. In this part of the test we will allow the compressor to cool down for 15 minutes. The air compressor thermal circuit breaker may have been tripped by repeatedly running diagnostic checks. | At least 15 minutes has elapsed since the air compressor was disconnected from the vehicle wiring harness: | |
| | | YES ▶ | GO TO IA8 |
| | | NO ▶ | Continue with step "IA7" until 15 minutes has elapsed. |
| IA8 | WIRING HARNESS CHECK | | |
| | • Reconnect the air compressor to the vehicle wiring harness. | The air compressor remains off: | |
| | | YES ▶ | GO TO IA10 |
| | | NO ▶ | GO TO IA9 |

**Fig. 53 Pinpoint test, IA (Part 4 of 16)**

| IA9 WIRING HARNESS CHECK | RESULT | ACTION TO TAKE |
|---|---|---|
| • Remove the air compressor relay from its vehicle wiring harness connector. | The air compressor stops running and remains off: | |
| | YES ▶ | Install a new air compressor relay and then rerun SERVICE BAY DIAGNOSTICS. |
| | NO ▶ | Circuit #417 has a short to B+ which is causing the air compressor to run until the air compressor's internal thermal circuit breaker is tripped. Rerun SERVICE BAY DIAGNOSTICS after repair is made and the air compressor relay has been installed again. |

**Fig. 53 Pinpoint test, IA (Part 5 of 16)**

| IA10 AIR COMPRESSOR COMPONENT CHECK | RESULT | ACTION TO TAKE |
|---|---|---|
| It is desired to activate the "COMPRESSOR TOGGLE/CYCLE" functional test mode again. In order to do this the following action is required:<br>• Release the "STAR" test button so that it remains in the up "HOLD" position after the code "31" has been displayed for at least 5 seconds.<br>NOTE: As long as the "STAR" test button is in the up "HOLD" position the selected functional test will continue. The "COMPRESSOR TOGGLE" test is used to verify that the air suspension control module can activate the air compressor. This is done by cycling it "ON" and "OFF" continuously until the STAR test button is depressed down again. | The air compressor is: | |
| | CYCLING "ON/OFF" CONTINUOUSLY ▶ | Depress the "STAR" test button so that it remains in the "TEST" position. This action will stop the "COMPRESSOR TOGGLE" functional test since it is no longer required. Rerun SERVICE BAY DIAGNOSTICS after waiting 30 minutes. |
| | AIR COMPRESSOR REMAINS "OFF" ▶ | GO TO IA11 |
| **IA11 CHECKING WIRING HARNESS** | | |
| The next step in determining why the air suspension control could not activate the air compressor is:<br>• Disconnect the air compressor assembly electrical connector from the vehicle wiring harness connector.<br>• Using a voltmeter connect the positive lead to circuit #417 of the air compressor vehicle wiring harness connector and the negative lead to circuit #430F. | The voltage reading fluctuates between zero and battery voltage (check is to be made over a one minute time period): | |
| | YES ▶ | Install a new air compressor assembly and then rerun SERVICE BAY DIAGNOSTICS after repair is made. |
| | NO ▶ | GO TO IA12 |

**Fig. 53 Pinpoint test, IA (Part 6 of 16)**

| IA12 CHECKING WIRING HARNESS | RESULT | ACTION TO TAKE |
|---|---|---|
| • Depress the "STAR" test button so that it remains in the down "TEST" position.<br>• Remove the air compressor relay from its vehicle wiring harness connector.<br>• Using an analog ohmmeter attach one lead to the air compressor relay vehicle harness connector (circuit #417) and the other lead to the air compressor vehicle wiring harness connector (circuit #417). | Ohmmeter reading is greater than 5 ohms: | |
| | YES ▶ | The circuit used to active the air compressor (circuit #417) has an open in it. Rerun SERVICE BAY DIAGNOSTICS after repair is made. |
| | NO ▶ | GO TO IA13 |
| **IA13 CHECKING WIRING HARNESS** | | |
| • Again using an analog ohmmeter connect one lead to the air compressor relay circuit #430B and the other to a known good ground. | Ohmmeter reading is greater than 5 ohms: | |
| | YES ▶ | Circuit #430B has an open in it. Rerun SERVICE BAY DIAGNOSTICS after repair is made. |
| | NO ▶ | GO TO IA14 |

**Fig. 53 Pinpoint test, IA (Part 7 of 16)**

| IA14 CHECKING WIRING HARNESS | RESULT | ACTION TO TAKE |
|---|---|---|
| • Using a voltmeter connect the positive lead to circuit #175 of the air compressor relay's wiring harness connector and the negative lead to circuit #430B. | The voltage reading is greater than 10 volts: | |
| | YES ▶ | GO TO IA15 |
| | NO ▶ | This circuit has an open or short in it. There should always be battery voltage on this circuit. Rerun SERVICE BAY DIAGNOSTICS after repairs are made. |

**Fig. 53 Pinpoint test, IA (Part 8 of 16)**

| IA15 CHECKING WIRING HARNESS | RESULT | ACTION TO TAKE |
|---|---|---|
| It is desired to activate the "COMPRESSOR TOGGLE/CYCLE" functional test again. In order to do this the following action is required:<br>• Release the "STAR" test button so that it remains in the up "HOLD" position after the code "31" has been displayed at least 5 seconds.<br>• Using a voltmeter connect the position positive lead to circuit #420 of the air compressor relay's wiring harness connector and the negative lead to circuit #430B.<br>NOTE: As long as the "STAR" test button is in the up "HOLD" position the selected functional test will continue. The "COMPRESSOR TOGGLE" test is used to verify that the air suspension control module can activate the air compressor. This is done cycling it "ON" and "OFF" continuously until the "STAR" test button is depressed down again. | The voltage reading fluctuates between zero and battery voltage (check is to be made over a one minute time period): | |
| | YES ▶ | Install a new compressor relay, reconnect the air compressor assembly to the vehicle wiring harness and then rerun SERVICE BAY DIAGNOSTICS. |
| | NO ▶ | GO TO IA16 |
| **IA16 CHECKING WIRING HARNESS** | | |
| • Turn the air suspension "ON/OFF" switch to the "OFF" position and disconnect the air suspension control module from the vehicle wiring harness.<br>• Using an analog ohmmeter connect the positive lead to circuit #420 of the air compressor relay wiring harness connector and the other lead to pin position #35 (circuit #420) of the air suspension control module wiring harness connector. | The resistance reading is less than 5.0 ohms: | |
| | YES ▶ | Install a new air suspension control module, reconnect the air compressor relay and then rerun SERVICE BAY DIAGNOSTICS. |
| | NO ▶ | The circuit (#420) used to provide B+ power to the air compressor relay has an open in it. Rerun SERVICE BAY DIAGNOSTICS after repair is made. |

Fig. 53 Pinpoint test, IA (Part 9 of 16)

| IA17 SPRING SOLENOID VALVE COMPONENT CHECK | RESULT | ACTION TO TAKE |
|---|---|---|
| It is now desired to activate the "AIR SPRING SOLENOID VALVE TOGGLE" functional test. In order to do this the following actions are required:<br>• Release the "STAR" test button so that it remains in the up "HOLD" position after the code "33" has been displayed for at least 5 seconds.<br>NOTE: As long as the "STAR" test button is in the up "HOLD" position the selected functional test will continue. The "AIR SPRING SOLENOID TOGGLE" test is used to verify that the air suspension control module can activate each of the air spring solenoid valves by cycling them "ON" and "OFF" continuously until the STAR test button is depressed down again. | The right front air spring solenoid valve is making an audible click sound: | |
| | CYCLING "ON/OFF" CONTINUOUSLY ▶ | GO TO IA21 |
| | REMAINS "OFF" ▶ | GO TO IA18 |
| **IA18 CHECKING WIRING HARNESS** | | |
| The air suspension control module can not activate the right front air spring solenoid valve. In order to determine the cause of this the following actions are required:<br>• Electrically disconnect the right front air spring solenoid from the vehicle wiring harness connector.<br>• Using a voltmeter connect the positive lead to the air spring solenoid valve wiring harness connector circuit #414 and the negative lead to circuit #430D of the same connector.<br>NOTE: The "AIR SPRING SOLENOID VALVE TOGGLE" functional test is still being conducted. During this functional test the front ride height of the vehicle may lower and the rear ride height may raise. | The voltage reading pulses between zero and battery voltage (check is to be made over a one minute time period): | |
| | YES ▶ | Install a new right front air spring solenoid and return SERVICE BAY DIAGNOSTICS. |
| | NO ▶ | GO TO IA19 |

Fig. 53 Pinpoint test, IA (Part 10 of 16)

| IA19 CHECKING WIRING HARNESS | RESULT | ACTION TO TAKE |
|---|---|---|
| • Turn the air suspension "ON/OFF" switch to the "OFF" position.<br>• Disconnect air suspension control module connector.<br>• Using an analog ohmmeter connect one lead to the air suspension control module wiring harness connector pin location #17 (circuit #414) and other to the right front air spring solenoid valve wiring harness connector circuit #414. | Ohmmeter reading is less than 10 ohms: | |
| | YES ▶ | GO TO IA20 |
| | NO ▶ | An open in circuit #414 has been detected in the wiring harness. rerun SERVICE BAY DIAGNOSTICS after repair is made. |
| **IA20 WIRING HARNESS CHECK** | | |
| • Again using an analog ohmmeter connect one lead to the air suspension control module wiring harness connector pin location #60 (circuit #430H) and other to the right front air spring solenoid valve vehicle wiring harness connector circuit #430D. | Ohmmeter reading is less than 10 ohms: | |
| | YES ▶ | Install a new air suspension control module and rerun SERVICE BAY DIAGNOSTICS. |
| | NO ▶ | An open in circuit #430H/430D exists. Rerun SERVICE BAY DIAGNOSTICS after repair is made. |
| **IA21 ENTER SPRING FILL DIAGNOSTICS** | | |
| At this time it will be required to exit SERVICE BAY DIAGNOSTICS and enter SPRING FILL (refer to SPRING FILL DIAGNOSTIC for instructions). | The "STAR" tester is displaying one of the following codes: | |
| | "21" to "28" ▶ | GO TO IA22 |
| | SOMETHING ELSE ▶ | Repeat SPRING FILL entrance procedure until entered. |

Fig. 53 Pinpoint test, IA (Part 11 of 16)

| IA22 VISUAL CHECK | RESULT | ACTION TO TAKE |
|---|---|---|
| In order to perform the right front air spring inflation test we must first determine if it is above the normal position. | The vehicle's right front corner has approximately a two inch gap or greater between the fender lip opening and the top of the tire: | |
| | YES ▶ | GO TO IA23 |
| | NO ▶ | GO TO IA24 |
| **IA23 VENT RIGHT FRONT AIR SPRING** | | |
| In order to perform the right front air spring inflation test we must first vent it below the normal position. In order to do that the following action is required:<br>• Release the "STAR" test button so that it remains in the up "HOLD" position after the code "21" has been displayed for at least 5 seconds.<br>• Continue venting the right front corner of the vehicle until the gap between the fender lip opening and the top of the tire is one inch or less.<br>NOTE: As long as the "STAR" test button remains in the up "HOLD" position the right front air spring will continue to be vented. When the desired amount of of venting has occurred depress the "STAR" test button so that it remains in the down "TEST" position. | The vehicle's right front corner has been lowered: | |
| | YES ▶ | Depress the "STAR" test button down so that it remains in the "TEST" position. Then: GO TO IA24 |
| | NO ▶ | Continue with step "IA23" until the desired height is reached. |

Fig. 53 Pinpoint test, IA (Part 12 of 16)

| I A24 INFLATE RIGHT FRONT AIR SPRING | RESULT | ACTION TO TAKE |
|---|---|---|
| To inflate the right front air spring the following action is required:<br>• Release the "STAR" test button so that it remains in the "HOLD" position after the code "25" has been displayed for at least 5 seconds.<br>NOTE: As long as the "STAR" test button remains in the up "HOLD" position the right front air spring will continue to be inflated. When the desired amount of inflating has occurred depress the "STAR" test button so that it remains in the "TEST" position. | The right front corner of the vehicle has been raised so that the gap between the fender lip tire opening and the top of the tire is approximately three inches or greater: | |
| | VERY SLOWLY OR NONE AT ALL ▶ | Depress the "STAR" test button down so that it remains in the "TEST" position. Then: GO TO IA25 |
| | SLOWLY OR AT A NORMAL RATE ▶ | Rerun SERVICE BAY DIAGNOSTICS and if this problem still occurs install a new air suspension control module and then rerun SERVICE BAY DIAGNOSTICS. |

**Fig. 53 Pinpoint test, IA (Part 13 of 16)**

| IA25 AIR LINE CHECK | RESULT | ACTION TO TAKE |
|---|---|---|
| In order to determine why the left front corner of the vehicle is inflating "VERY SLOWLY OR NONE AT ALL" the following actions are required:<br>• Disconnect the right front air line from the right front air spring solenoid valve.<br>• Disconnect the right front air spring solenoid valve electrical connector so that the solenoid valve is not connected to the vehicle wiring harness.<br>• Release the "STAR" test button so that it remains in the up "HOLD" position after the code "24" has been displayed for at least 5 seconds.<br>NOTE: As long as the "STAR" test button remains in the up "HOLD" position the air compressor assembly will continue to pump air through the air line. | Air is coming out of the air line: | |
| | VERY SLOWLY OR NONE AT ALL ▶ | GO TO IA26 |
| | AT A NORMAL RATE ▶ | GO TO IA27 |
| **IA26 AIR LINE CHECK** | | |
| From the previous tests we have determined that cause of the UNABLE TO INFLATE problem is due to a restriction in the air line or compressor assembly. In order to isolate the cause of this problem the following actions are required:<br>• Disconnect any one of the air lines that are plugged into the air compressor drier assembly.<br>NOTE: As long as the "STAR" test button remains in the up "HOLD" position the air compressor assembly will continue to pump air through the drier assembly. | The rate that the air is coming out of the drier assembly is: | |
| | SAME AS IN STEP "IA25" OR SLIGHTLY GREATER ▶ | Install a new air compressor assembly and then rerun SERVICE BAY DIAGNOSTICS. |
| | RATE IS FASTER THAN IN STEP "IA25" ▶ | There is a restriction in the left front air line. Rerun SERVICE BAY DIAGNOSTICS after repair is made. |

**Fig. 53 Pinpoint test, IA (Part 14 of 16)**

| IA27 AIR LEAK TEST | RESULT | ACTION TO TAKE |
|---|---|---|
| • Depress the "STAR" test button so that it remains in the down "TEST" position.<br>• Reconnect the air line to the air compressor drier assembly and right front air spring solenoid valve.<br>• Reconnect the vehicle wiring harness connector to the right front air spring.<br>• Take a piece of masking tape and mark a spot on the wheel lip opening. Measure and record the vertical height between wheel lip opening and the bottom of the wheel rim.<br>• Wait at least 15 minutes, remeasure and record wheel lip opening again. | The second wheel lip opening is: | |
| | APPROXIMATELY THE SAME AS THE FIRST ▶ | GO TO IA28 |
| | LESS THAN THE FIRST ▶ | GO TO IA29 |
| **IA28 AIR LEAK CHECK** | | |
| • Release the "STAR" test button so that it remains in the up "HOLD" position after the code "24" has been displayed for at least 5 seconds.<br>• Inspect the following for air leakage:<br>• air compressor / dryer assembly connection point<br>• dryer assembly / air line connection point<br>• air line / air spring solenoid valve connection point.<br>NOTE: As long as the "STAR" test button remains in the up "HOLD" position the right front air spring will continue to be inflated. When the desired amount of inflating has occurred depress the "STAR" test button so that it remains in the "TEST" position. | A leak path was detected: | |
| | YES ▶ | Make required repairs and rerun SERVICE BAY DIAGNOSTICS. |
| | NO ▶ | Install a new air suspension control module and then rerun SERVICE BAY DIAGNOSTICS. |

**Fig. 53 Pinpoint test, IA (Part 15 of 16)**

| IA29 AIR LEAK CHECK | RESULT | ACTION TO TAKE |
|---|---|---|
| • Inspect the following for air leakage on the left front air spring/strut assembly:<br>• air spring bag<br>• air spring bag / canister connection<br>• canister / mount connection<br>• air spring solenoid valve / canister connection | ▶ | Rerun SERVICE BAY DIAGNOSTICS after repairs are made. |

**Fig. 53 Pinpoint test, IA (Part 16 of 16)**

| IB1 | STAR CODE: 53<br>UNABLE TO DETECT RAISING<br>OF LEFT FRONT CORNER | RESULT | ACTION TO TAKE |
|---|---|---|---|
| | The air suspension control module has not received the signal that the left front corner of the vehicle was raised during the SERVICE BAY DIAGNOSTIC check. There are nine possible causes of this which are listed below:<br>• The height sensor linkage arm is not connected properly to the vehicle and/or height sensor.<br>• An air line may be defective.<br>• The left front air spring solenoid valve may be defective.<br>• The left front air spring B+ power supply circuit may have an open in it.<br>• The left front air spring ground return circuit may have an open in it.<br>• The air compressor may be defective.<br>• The air compressor B+ power supply circuit may have an open in it.<br>• The air compressor ground return circuit may have an open in it.<br>• The air suspension control module may be defective. | ▶ | GO TO IB2 |

Fig. 54 Pinpoint test, IB (Part 1 of 16)

| IB2 | VISUAL<br>COMPONENT CHECK | RESULT | ACTION TO TAKE |
|---|---|---|---|
| | • Check under the vehicle to verify that the vehicle is not hanging up on something.<br>• Check the left front corner of the vehicle to verify that the height sensor has no obvious damage and that the linkage is connected. | The left front height sensor is installed correctly with no obvious damage and under the vehicle is clear of all obstructions: | |
| | | YES ▶ | GO TO IB3 |
| | | NO ▶ | Make needed repairs as required and rerun SERVICE BAY DIAGNOSTICS. |
| IB3 | ENTERING FUNCTIONAL TEST MODE OF SERVICE BAY DIAG | | |
| | FUNCTIONAL TEST mode will be used to determine why the left front corner of the vehicle did not raise.<br>• Release the "STAR" test button to the up "HOLD" position. After five seconds depress the "STAR" test button again so that it remains in the down "TEST" position. This will allow the control module to enter FUNCTIONAL TEST mode. | The "STAR" tester is displaying code: | |
| | | "31", "32", "33", "34", or "35" ▶ | GO TO IB5 |
| | | SOMETHING ELSE ▶ | GO TO IB4 |
| IB4 | RETRY FUNCTIONAL TEST ENTRANCE PROCEDURE | | |
| | The air suspension control module has not entered the FUNCTIONAL TEST mode and the following actions are required:<br>• Make sure that the "STAR" tester is still plugged into the air suspension disgnostic diagnostic pigtail.<br>• Make sure that the "STAR" tester is turned "ON".<br>• Release the "STAR" test button to the up "HOLD" position. After five seconds depress the "STAR" test button again so that it remains in the down "TEST" position. This will allow the control module to enter FUNCTIONAL TEST mode. | The "STAR" tester is displaying code: | |
| | | "31", "32", "33", "34", or "35" ▶ | GO TO IB5 |
| | | SOMETHING ELSE ▶ | Rerun SERVICE BAY DIAGNOSTICS and if still unable to enter FUNCTIONAL TEST mode install a new air suspension control module and then rerun SERVICE BAY DIAGNOSTICS. |

Fig. 54 Pinpoint test, IB (Part 2 of 16)

| IB5 | AIR COMPRESSOR<br>COMPONENT CHECK | RESULT | ACTION TO TAKE |
|---|---|---|---|
| | It is desired to activate the "COMPRESSOR TOGGLE" FUNCTIONAL TEST mode. In order to do this the following action is required:<br>• Raise the vehicle's hood up completely.<br>• Release the "STAR" test button so that it remains in the up "HOLD" position after the code "31" has been displayed for at least 5 seconds.<br>NOTE: As long as the "STAR" test button is in the up "HOLD" position the selected FUNCTIONAL TEST will continue. The "COMPRESSOR TOGGLE" test is used to verify that the air suspension control module can activate the air compressor. This is done by cycling it "ON" and "OFF" continuously until the "STAR" test button is depressed down again. | The air compressor is: | |
| | | CYCLING "ON/OFF" CONTINUOUSLY ▶ | Depress the STAR test button so that it remains in the "TEST" position. This action will stop the "COMPRESSOR TOGGLE" functional test since it is no longer required. Then: GO TO IB17 |
| | | AIR COMPRESSOR REMAINS "OFF" ▶ | GO TO IB6 |
| IB6 | CHECKING WIRING HARNESS | | |
| | Since the air suspension control module can not activate the air compressor the following actions are required:<br>• Depress the "STAR" test button so that it remains in the down "HOLD" position. This action will stop the PIN POINT "COMPRESSOR TOGGLE" test.<br>• Disconnect the air compressor assembly electrical connector from the vehicle wiring harness connector.<br>• Examine both electrical connectors for damage and proper installation of wires. | Electrical connectors are good: | |
| | | YES ▶ | GO TO IB7 |
| | | NO ▶ | Make repairs as required and rerun SERVICE BAY DIAGNOSTICS. |

Fig. 54 Pinpoint test, IB (Part 3 of 16)

| IB7 | COMPRESSOR COOL DOWN | RESULT | ACTION TO TAKE |
|---|---|---|---|
| | The air compressor has an internal thermal non-cycling circuit breaker in it that opens the B+ power supply to the air compressor armature when the internal temperature exceeds a predetermined limit. In order for this thermal circuit breaker to be reset the following two things must happen: 1) the internal temperature must drop below the predetermined limit and 2) the power to the compressor must be removed. In this part of the test we will allow the compressor to cool down for 15 minutes. The air compressor thermal circuit breaker may have been tripped by repeatedly running diagnostic checks. | At least 15 minutes has elapsed since the air compressor was disconnected from the vehicle wiring harness: | |
| | | YES ▶ | GO TO IB8 |
| | | NO ▶ | Continue with step "IB7" until 15 minutes has elapsed. |
| IB8 | WIRING HARNESS CHECK | | |
| | • Reconnect the air compressor to the vehicle wiring harness. | The air compressor remains off: | |
| | | YES ▶ | GO TO IB10 |
| | | NO ▶ | GO TO IB9 |

Fig. 54 Pinpoint test, IB (Part 4 of 16)

| IB9 WIRING HARNESS CHECK | RESULT | ACTION TO TAKE |
|---|---|---|
| • Remove the air compressor relay from its vehicle wiring harness connector. | The air compressor stops running and remains off: | |
| | YES ▶ | Install a new air compressor relay and rerun SERVICE BAY DIAGNOSTICS. |
| | NO ▶ | Circuit #417 has a short to B+ which is causing the air compressor to run until the air compressor's internal thermal circuit breaker is tripped. Rerun SERVICE BAY DIAGNOSTICS after repair is made and the air compressor relay has been installed again. |

**Fig. 54 Pinpoint test, IB (Part 5 of 16)**

| IB10 AIR COMPRESSOR COMPONENT CHECK | RESULT | ACTION TO TAKE |
|---|---|---|
| It is desired to activate the "COMPRESSOR "TOGGLE functional test mode again. In order to do this the following action is required: <br> • Release the "STAR" test button so that it remains in the up "HOLD" position after the code "31" has been displayed for at least 5 seconds. <br> NOTE: As long as the "STAR" test button is in the up "HOLD" position the selected functional test will continue. The "COMPRESSOR TOGGLE" test is used to verify that the air suspension control module can activate the air compressor. This is done by cycling it "ON" and "OFF" continuously until the STAR test button is depressed down again. | The air compressor is: | |
| | CYCLING "ON/OFF" CONTINUOUSLY ▶ | Depress the STAR test button so that it remains in the "TEST" position. This action will stop the "COMPRESSOR TOGGLE" functional test since it is no longer required. Rerun SERVICE BAY DIAGNOSTICS after waiting 30 minutes. |
| | AIR COMPRESSOR REMAINS "OFF" ▶ | GO TO IB11 |

**Fig. 54 Pinpoint test, IB (Part 6 of 16)**

| IB11 CHECKING WIRING HARNESS | RESULT | ACTION TO TAKE |
|---|---|---|
| The next step in determining why the air suspension control module could not activate the air compressor is: <br> • Disconnect the air compressor assembly electrical connector from the vehicle wiring harness connector. <br> • Using a voltmeter connect the positive lead to circuit #417 of the air compressor vehicle wiring harness connector and the negative lead to circuit #430F. | The voltage reading fluctuates between zero and battery voltage (check is to be made over a one minute time period): | |
| | YES ▶ | Install a new air compressor assembly and rerun SERVICE BAY DIAGNOSTICS. |
| | NO ▶ | GO TO IB12 |
| **IB12 CHECKING WIRING HARNESS** | | |
| • Depress the "STAR" test button so that it remains in the down "TEST" position. <br> • Remove the air compressor relay from its vehicle wiring harness connector. <br> • Using an analog ohmmeter connect one lead to circuit #417 of the air compressor relay connector and the other lead to circuit #417 of the air compressor vehicle wiring harness connector. | Ohmmeter reading is greater than 5 ohms: | |
| | YES ▶ | The circuit used to activate the air compressor (circuit #417) has an open in it. Rerun SERVICE BAY DIAGNOSTICS after repair is made. |
| | NO ▶ | GO TO IB13 |
| **IB13 CHECKING WIRING HARNESS** | | |
| • Again using an analog ohmmeter connect one lead to the air compressor relay circuit #430B and the other to a known good ground. | Ohmmeter reading is greater than 5 ohms: | |
| | YES ▶ | Circuit #430B has an open in it. Rerun SERVICE BAY DIAGNOSTICS after repair is made. |
| | NO ▶ | GO TO IB14 |

**Fig. 54 Pinpoint test, IB (Part 7 of 16)**

| IB14 CHECKING WIRING HARNESS | RESULT | ACTION TO TAKE |
|---|---|---|
| • Using a voltmeter connect the positive lead to circuit #175 of the air compressor relay's wiring harness connector and the negative lead to circuit #430B. | The voltage reading is greater than 10 volts: | |
| | YES ▶ | GO TO IB15 |
| | NO ▶ | This circuit has an open or short in it. There should always be battery voltage on this circuit. Rerun SERVICE BAY DIAGNOSTICS after repairs are made. |
| **IB15 CHECKING WIRING HARNESS** | | |
| It is desired to activate the "COMPRESSOR TOGGLE" functional test mode again. In order to do this the following action is required: <br> • Release the "STAR" test button so that it remains in the up "HOLD" position after the code "31" has been displayed for at least 5 seconds. <br> • Using a voltmeter connect the positive lead to circuit #420 of the air compressor relay's wiring harness connector and the negative lead to circuit #430B. <br> NOTE: As long as the "STAR" test button is in the up "HOLD" position the selected functional test will continue. The "COMPRESSOR TOGGLE" test is used to verify that the air suspension control module can activate the air compressor. This is done by cycling it "ON" and "OFF" continuously until the STAR test button is depressed down again. | The voltage reading fluctuates between zero and battery voltage (check is to be over a one minute time period): | |
| | YES ▶ | Reconnect the air compressor assembly to the vehicle wiring harness, install a new air compressor relay and then rerun SERVICE BAY DIAGNOSTICS. |
| | NO ▶ | GO TO IB16 |

**Fig. 54 Pinpoint test, IB (Part 8 of 16)**

| IB16 CHECKING WIRING HARNESS | RESULT | ACTION TO TAKE |
|---|---|---|
| • Turn the air suspension "ON/OFF" switch to the "OFF" switch position and disconnect the air suspension control module from the vehicle wiring harness.<br>• Using an analog ohmmeter connect the positive lead to circuit #420 of the air compressor relay wiring harness connector and the other lead to pin position #35 (circuit #420) of the air suspension control module wiring harness connector. | The resistance reading is less than 5.0 ohms: | |
| | YES ▶ | Install a new air suspension control module, reconnect the air compressor relay and rerun SERVICE BAY DIAGNOSTICS. |
| | NO ▶ | The circuit (#420) used to provide B+ power to the air compressor relay has an open in it. Rerun SERVICE BAY DIAGNOSTICS after repair is made. |
| **IB17 SPRING SOLENOID VALVE COMPONENT CHECK** | | |
| It is now desired to activate the "AIR SPRING SOLENOID VALVE CYCLE" functional test. In order to do this the following actions are required:<br>• Release the "STAR" test button so that it remains in the up "HOLD" position after the code "33" has been displayed for at least 5 seconds.<br>NOTE: As long as the "STAR" test button is in the up "HOLD" position the selected functional test will continue. The "AIR SPRING SOLENOID CYCLE" test is used to verify that the air suspension control module can activate each of the air spring solenoid valves by cycling them "ON" and "OFF" continuously until the STAR test button is depressed down again. | The right front air spring solenoid makes an audible click sound when voltage is applied: | |
| | CYCLING "ON/OFF" CONTINUOUSLY ▶ | GO TO IB21 |
| | REMAINS "OFF" ▶ | GO TO IB18 |

**Fig. 54 Pinpoint test, IB (Part 9 of 16)**

| IB18 CHECKING WIRING HARNESS | RESULT | ACTION TO TAKE |
|---|---|---|
| The air suspension control module can not activate the left front air spring solenoid valve. In order to determine the cause of this the following actions are required:<br>• Electrically disconnect the left front air spring solenoid from the vehicle wiring harness connector.<br>• Using a voltmeter connect the positive lead to the air spring solenoid valve wiring harness connector circuit #415 and the negative lead to circuit #430K of the same connector.<br>NOTE: The "AIR SPRING SOLENOID VALVE CYCLE" functional test is still being conducted. During this functional test the front ride height of the vehicle may lower and the rear ride height may raise. | The voltage reading pulses between zero and battery voltage (check is to be made over a one minute time period): | |
| | YES ▶ | Install a new left front air spring solenoid and then rerun SERVICE BAY DIAGNOSTICS. |
| | NO ▶ | GO IB19 |
| **IB19 CHECKING WIRING HARNESS** | | |
| • Turn the air suspension "ON/OFF" switch to the "OFF" position.<br>• Disconnect air suspension control module connector.<br>• Using an analog ohmmeter connect one lead to the air suspension control module wiring harness connector pin location #21 (circuit # 415) and other to the left front air spring solenoid valve wiring harness connector circuit #415. | Ohmmeter reading is less than 10 ohms: | |
| | YES ▶ | GO TO IB20 |
| | NO ▶ | An open in circuit #415 has been detected in the wiring harness.<br>rerun SERVICE BAY DIAGNOSTICS after repair is made. |

**Fig. 54 Pinpoint test, IB (Part 10 of 16)**

| IB20 WIRING HARNESS CHECK | RESULT | ACTION TO TAKE |
|---|---|---|
| • Again using an analog ohmmeter connect one lead to the air suspension control module wiring harness connector pin location #60 (circuit #430H) and other to the left front air spring solenoid valve vehicle wiring harness connector circuit #430K. | Ohmmeter reading is less than 10 ohms: | |
| | YES ▶ | Install a new air suspension control module and rerun SERVICE BAY DIAGNOSTICS. |
| | NO ▶ | An open in circuit #430H/430K exists. Rerun SERVICE BAY DIAGNOSTICS after repair is made. |
| **IB21 ENTER SPRING FILL DIAGNOSTICS** | | |
| At this time it will be required to exit SERVICE BAY DIAGNOSTICS and enter SPRING FILL (refer to SPRING FILL DIAGNOSTIC section for instructions). | The STAR tester is displaying one of the following codes: | |
| | "21" to "28" ▶ | GO TO IB22 |
| | SOMETHING ELSE ▶ | Repeat SPRING FILL entrance procedure until entered. |
| **IB22 VISUAL CHECK** | | |
| In order to perform the left front air spring inflation test we must first determine if it is above the normal position. | The vehicle's left front corner has approximately a two inch gap or greater between the fender lip opening and the top of the tire: | |
| | YES ▶ | GO TO IB23 |
| | NO ▶ | GO TO IB24 |

**Fig. 54 Pinpoint test, IB (Part 11 of 16)**

| IB23 VENT LEFT FRONT AIR SPRING | RESULT | ACTION TO TAKE |
|---|---|---|
| In order to perform the left front air spring inflation test we must first vent it below the normal position. In order to do that the following action is required:<br>• Release the STAR test button so that it remains in the up "HOLD" position after the code "22" has been displayed for at least 5 seconds.<br>• Continue venting the left corner of the vehicle until gap between the fender lip opening and the top of the tire is one inch or less.<br>NOTE: As long as the "STAR" test button remains in the up "HOLD" position the left front air spring will continue to be vented. When the desired amount of venting has occurred depress the "STAR" test button so that it remains in the down "TEST" position. | The vehicle's left front corner has been lowered: | |
| | YES ▶ | Depress the STAR test button down so that it remains in in the "TEST" position. Then: GO TO IB24 |
| | NO ▶ | Continue with step "IB23" until the desired height is reached. |

**Fig. 54 Pinpoint test, IB (Part 12 of 16)**

| IB24 INFLATE LEFT FRONT AIR SPRING | RESULT | ACTION TO TAKE |
|---|---|---|
| To inflate the left front air spring the following action is required:<br>• Release the STAR test button so that it remains in the "HOLD" position after the code "25" has been displayed for at least 5 seconds.<br>NOTE: As long as the STAR test button remains in the up "HOLD" position the left front air spring will continue to be inflated. When the desired amount of inflating has occurred depress STAR test button down so that it remains in the "TEST" position. | The left front corner of the vehicle has been raised so that the gap between the fender lip opening and the top of the tire is approximately three inches or greater. | |
| | VERY SLOWLY OR NONE AT ALL ▶ | Depress the STAR test button down so that it remains in the "TEST" position. Then: GO TO IB25 |
| | SLOWLY OR AT A NORMAL RATE ▶ | Rerun SERVICE BAY DIAGNOSTICS and if this problem still occurs install a new air suspension control module and then rerun SERVICE BAY DIAGNOSTICS. |

**Fig. 54 Pinpoint test, IB (Part 13 of 16)**

| IB25 AIR LINE CHECK | RESULT | ACTION TO TAKE |
|---|---|---|
| In order to determine why the left front corner of the vehicle is inflating "VERY SLOWLY OR NONE AT ALL" the following actions are required:<br>• Disconnect the left front air line from the left front air spring solenoid valve.<br>• Disconnect the left front air spring solenoid valve electrical connector so that the solenoid valve is not connected to the vehicle wiring harness.<br>• Release the "STAR" test button so that it remains in the up "HOLD" position after the code "25" has been displayed for at least 5 seconds.<br>NOTE: As long as the "STAR" test button remains in the up "HOLD" position the air compressor assembly will continue to pump air through the air line. | Air is coming out of the air line: | |
| | VERY SLOWLY OR NONE AT ALL ▶ | GO TO IB26 |
| | AT A NORMAL RATE ▶ | GO TO IB27 |
| **IB26 AIR LINE CHECK** | | |
| From the previous tests we have determined that cause of the UNABLE TO INFLATE problem is due to a restriction in the air line or compressor assembly. In order to isolate the cause of this problem the following actions are required:<br>• Disconnect any one of the air lines that are plugged into the air compressor drier assembly.<br>NOTE: As long as the "STAR" test button remains in the up "HOLD" position the air compressor assembly will continue to pump air through the drier assembly. | The rate that the air is coming out of the drier assembly is: | |
| | SAME AS IN STEP "IB25" OR SLIGHTLY GREATER ▶ | Install a new air compressor assembly and rerun SERVICE BAY DIAGNOSTICS. |
| | RATE IS FASTER THAN IN STEP "IB25" ▶ | There is a restriction in the left front air line. Rerun SERVICE BAY DIAGNOSTICS after repair is made. |

**Fig. 54 Pinpoint test, IB (Part 14 of 16)**

| IB27 AIR LEAK TEST | RESULT | ACTION TO TAKE |
|---|---|---|
| • Depress the "STAR" test button so that it remains in the down "TEST" position.<br>• Reconnect the air line to the air compressor drier assembly and left front air spring solenoid valve.<br>• Reconnect the vehicle wiring harness connector to the left front air spring.<br>• Take a piece of masking tape and mark a spot on the wheel lip opening. Measure and record the vertical height between wheel lip opening and the bottom of the wheel rim.<br>• Wait at least 15 minutes, remeasure and record wheel lip opening again. | The second wheel lip opening is: | |
| | APPROXIMATELY THE SAME AS THE FIRST ▶ | GO TO IB28 |
| | LESS THAN THE FIRST ▶ | GO TO IB29 |
| **IB28 AIR LEAK CHECK** | | |
| • Release the STAR test button so that it remains in the up "HOLD" position after the code "25" has been displayed for at least 5 seconds.<br>• Inspect the following for air leakage:<br>• air compressor / dryer assembly connection point<br>• dryer assembly / air line connection point<br>• air line / air spring solenoid valve connection point<br>NOTE: As long as the "STAR" test button remains in the up "HOLD" position the left front air spring will continue to be inflated. When the desired amount of inflating has occurred depress the STAR test button so that it remains in the "TEST" position. | A leak path was detected: | |
| | YES ▶ | Make required repairs and rerun SERVICE BAY DIAGNOSTICS. |
| | NO ▶ | Install a new air suspension control and rerun SERVICE BAY DIAGNOSTICS. |

**Fig. 54 Pinpoint test, IB (Part 15 of 16)**

| IB29 AIR LEAK CHECK | RESULT | ACTION TO TAKE |
|---|---|---|
| • Inspect the following for air leakage on the left front air spring / strut assembly:<br>• air spring bag<br>• air spring bag / canister connection<br>• canister / mount connection<br>• air spring solenoid valve / canister connection | ▶ | Rerun SERVICE BAY DIAGNOSTICS after repairs are made. |

**Fig. 54 Pinpoint test, IB (Part 16 of 16)**

| | | RESULT | ACTION TO TAKE |
|---|---|---|---|
| IC1 | STAR CODE: 54 UNABLE TO DETECT RAISING OF RIGHT REAR CORNER | | |
| | The air suspension control module has not received the signal that the right rear corner of the vehicle was raised during the SERVICE BAY DIAGNOSTIC check. There are nine possible causes of this listed below: | | GO TO IC2 |
| | • The height sensor linkage arm is not connected properly to the vehicle and/or height sensor. | | |
| | • An air line may be defective. | | |
| | • The right rear air spring solenoid valve may be defective. | | |
| | • The right rear air spring B + power supply circuit may have an open in it. | | |
| | • The right rear air spring ground return circuit may have an open in it. | | |
| | • The air compressor may be defective. | | |
| | • The air compressor B + power supply circuit may have an open in it. | | |
| | • The air compressor ground return circuit may have an open in it. | | |
| | • The air suspension control module may be defective. | | |

**Fig. 55 Pinpoint test, IC (Part 1 of 13)**

| | | RESULT | ACTION TO TAKE |
|---|---|---|---|
| IC2 | VISUAL COMPONENT CHECK | | |
| | • Check under the vehicle to verify that the vehicle is not hanging up on something.<br>• Check the right rear corner of the vehicle to verify that the height sensor has no obvious damage and that the linkage is connected. | The right rear height sensor is installed correctly with no obvious damage and under the vehicle is clear of all obstructions: | |
| | | YES | GO TO IC3 |
| | | NO | Make needed repairs as required and rerun SERVICE BAY DIAGNOSTICS. |
| IC3 | ENTERING FUNCTIONAL TEST MODE OF SERVICE BAY DIAG | | |
| | FUNCTIONAL TEST mode will be used to determine why the right rear corner of the vehicle did not raise. | The "STAR" tester is displaying code: | |
| | • Release the "STAR" test button to the up "HOLD" position. After five seconds depress the "STAR" test button again so that it remains in the down "TEST" position. This will allow the control module to enter FUNCTIONAL TEST mode. | "31", "32", "33", "34", or "35" | GO TO IC5 |
| | | SOMETHING ELSE | GO TO IC4 |

**Fig. 55 Pinpoint test, IC (Part 2 of 13)**

| | | RESULT | ACTION TO TAKE |
|---|---|---|---|
| IC4 | RETRY FUNCTIONAL TEST ENTRANCE PROCEDURE | | |
| | The air suspension control module has not entered the FUNCTIONAL TEST mode and the following actions are required: | The "STAR" tester is displaying code: | |
| | • Make sure that the "STAR" tester is still plugged into the air suspension diagnostic pigtail. | "31", "32", "33", "34", or "35" | GO TO IC5 |
| | • Make sure that the "STAR" tester is "ON".<br>• Release the "STAR" test button to the up "HOLD" position. After five seconds depress the "STAR" test button again so that it remains in the down "TEST" position. This will allow the control module to enter FUNCTIONAL TEST mode. | SOMETHING ELSE | Rerun SERVICE BAY DIAGNOSTICS and if still unable to enter FUNCTIONAL TEST mode install new air suspension control module and then rerun SERVICE BAY DIAGNOSTICS. |
| IC5 | AIR COMPRESSOR COMPONENT CHECK | | |
| | It is desired to activate the "COMPRESSOR TOGGLE" functional test. In order to do this the following action is required: | The air compressor: | |
| | • Raise the vehicle's hood up completely.<br>• Release the "STAR" test button so that it remains in the up "HOLD" position after the code "31" has been displayed for at least 5 seconds.<br>NOTE: As long as the "STAR" test button is in the up "HOLD" position the selected functional test will continue. The "COMPRESSOR TOGGLE" test is used to verify that the air suspension control module can activate the air compressor. This is done by cycling it "ON" and "OFF" continuously until the "STAR" test button is depressed down again. | CYCLING "ON/OFF" CONTINUOUSLY | Depress the "STAR" test button so that it remains in the "TEST" position. This action will stop the "COMPRESSOR TOGGLE" functional test since it is no longer required. Then: GO TO IC17 |
| | | AIR COMPRESSOR REMAINS "OFF" CONTINUOUSLY | GO TO IC6 |

**Fig. 55 Pinpoint test, IC (Part 3 of 13)**

| | | RESULT | ACTION TO TAKE |
|---|---|---|---|
| IC6 | CHECKING WIRING HARNESS | | |
| | Since the air suspension control module can not activate the air compressor the following actions are required: | Electrical connectors are good: | |
| | • Depress the "STAR" test button so that it remains in the down "HOLD" position. This action will stop the "COMPRESSOR TOGGLE" functional test. | YES | GO TO IC7 |
| | • Disconnect the air compressor assembly electrical connector from the vehicle wiring harness connector.<br>• Examine the both electrical connectors for damage and proper installation of wires. | NO | Make repairs as required and rerun SERVICE BAY DIAGNOSTICS. |
| IC7 | COMPRESSOR COOL DOWN | | |
| | The air compressor has an internal thermal non-cycling circuit breaker in it that opens the B + power supply to the air compressor armature when the internal temperature exceeds a predetermined limit. In order for this thermal circuit breaker to be reset the following two things must happen: 1) the internal temperature must drop below the predetermined limit and 2) the power to to the compressor must be off. In this part of the test we will allow the compressor to cool down for 15 minutes. The air compressor thermal circuit breaker may have been tripped by repeatedly running diagnostic checks. | At least 15 minutes has elapsed since the air compressor was disconnected from the vehicle wiring harness: | |
| | | YES | GO TO IC8 |
| | | NO | Continue with step "IC7" until 15 minutes has elapsed. |
| IC8 | WIRING HARNESS CHECK | | |
| | • Reconnect the air compressor to the the vehicle wiring harness. | The air compressor remains off: | |
| | | YES | GO TO IC10 |
| | | NO | GO TO IC9 |

**Fig. 55 Pinpoint test, IC (Part 4 of 13)**

| IC9 WIRING HARNESS CHECK | RESULT | ACTION TO TAKE |
|---|---|---|
| • Remove the air compressor relay from its vehicle wiring harness connector. | The air compressor stops running and remains off: | |
| | YES ▶ | Install a new air compressor relay and rerun SERVICE BAY DIAGNOSTICS. |
| | NO ▶ | Circuit #417 has a short to B+ which is causing the air compressor to run until the air compressor's internal thermal circuit breaker is tripped. Rerun SERVICE BAY DIAGNOSTICS after repair is made and the air compressor relay has been installed again. |
| **IC10 AIR COMPRESSOR COMPONENT CHECK** | | |
| It is desired to activate the "COMPRESSOR TOGGLE" functional test again. In order to do this the following action is required:<br>• Release the "STAR" test button so that it remains in the up "HOLD" position after the code "31" has been displayed for at least 5 seconds.<br>NOTE: As long as the "STAR" test button is in the up "HOLD" position the selected functional test will continue. The "COMPRESSOR TOGGLE" test is used to verify that the air suspension control module can activate the air compressor. This is done by cycling it "ON" and "OFF" continuously until the "STAR" test button is depressed down again. | The air compressor is: | |
| | CYCLING "ON/OFF" CONTINUOUSLY ▶ | Depress the "STAR" test button so that it remains in the "TEST" position. This action will stop the "COMPRESSOR TOGGLE functional test since it is no longer required. Rerun SERVICE BAY DIAGNOSTICS after waiting 30 minutes. |
| | AIR COMPRESSOR REMAINS "OFF" ▶ | GO TO IC11 |

**Fig. 55 Pinpoint test, IC (Part 5 of 13)**

| IC11 CHECKING WIRING HARNESS | RESULT | ACTION TO TAKE |
|---|---|---|
| The next step in determining why the air suspension control module could not activate the air compressor is:<br>• Disconnect the air compressor assembly electrical connector from the vehicle wiring harness connector.<br>• Using a voltmeter connect the positive lead to circuit #417 of the air compressor vehicle wiring harness connector and the negative lead to circuit #430F. | The voltage reading fluctuates between zero and battery voltage (check is to be made over a one minute time period): | |
| | YES ▶ | Install a new air compressor assembly and then rerun SERVICE BAY DIAGNOSTICS. |
| | NO ▶ | GO TO IC12 |
| **IC12 CHECKING WIRING HARNESS** | | |
| • Depress the "STAR" test button so that it remains in the down "TEST" position.<br>• Remove the air compressor relay from its vehicle wiring harness connector.<br>• Using an analog ohmmeter connect one lead to circuit #417 of the air compressor relay connector and the other lead to #417 of the air compressor vehicle wiring harness connector. | Ohmmeter reading is greater than 5 ohms: | |
| | YES ▶ | The circuit used to active the air compressor (circuit #417) has an open in it. Rerun SERVICE BAY DIAGNOSTICS after repair is made. |
| | NO ▶ | GO TO IC13 |
| **IC13 CHECKING WIRING HARNESS** | | |
| • Again using an analog ohmmeter connect one lead to the air compressor relay circuit #430B and the other to a known good ground. | Ohmmeter reading is greater than 5 ohms: | |
| | YES ▶ | Circuit #430B has an open in it. Rerun SERVICE BAY DIAGNOSTICS after repair is made. |
| | NO ▶ | GO TO IC14 |

**Fig. 55 Pinpoint test, IC (Part 6 of 13)**

| IC14 CHECKING WIRING HARNESS | RESULT | ACTION TO TAKE |
|---|---|---|
| • Using a voltmeter connect the positive lead to circuit #175 of the air compressor relay's wiring harness connector and the negative lead to circuit #430B. | The voltage reading is greater than 10 volts: | |
| | YES ▶ | GO TO IC15 |
| | NO ▶ | This circuit has an open or short in it. There should always be battery voltage on this circuit. Rerun SERVICE BAY DIAGNOSTICS after repairs are made. |
| **IC15 CHECKING WIRING HARNESS** | | |
| It is desired to activate the "COMPRESSOR TOGGLE" functional test again. In order to do this the following action is required:<br>• Release the "STAR" test button so that it remains in the up "HOLD" position after after the code "31" has been displayed at least 5 seconds.<br>• Using a voltmeter connect the positive lead to circuit #420 of the air compressor relay's wiring harness connector the negative lead to circuit #430B.<br>NOTE: As long as the "STAR" test button is in the up "HOLD" position the selected functional test will continue. The "COMPRESSOR TOGGLE" test is used to verify that the air suspension control module can activate the air compressor. This is done by cycling it "ON" and "OFF" continuously until the "STAR" test button is depressed down again. | The voltage reading fluctuates between zero and battery voltage (check is to be made over a one time period): | |
| | YES ▶ | Install a new air compressor relay, reconnect the air compressor assembly and then rerun SERVICE BAY DIAGNOSTICS. |
| | NO ▶ | GO TO IC16 |

**Fig. 55 Pinpoint test, IC (Part 7 of 13)**

| IC16 CHECKING WIRING HARNESS | RESULT | ACTION TO TAKE |
|---|---|---|
| • Turn the air suspension "ON/OFF" switch to the "OFF" position and disconnect the air suspension control module from the vehicle wiring harness.<br>• Using an analog ohmmeter (20,000 ohms per volt is recommended) connect the the air compressor positive lead to circuit #420 of the air compressor relay wiring harness connector and the other lead to pin position #35 (circuit #420) of the air suspension control module wiring harness connector. | The resistance reading is less than 5.0 ohms: | |
| | YES ▶ | Install a new air suspension control module, reconnect the air compressor relay and then rerun SERVICE BAY DIAGNOSTICS. |
| | NO ▶ | The circuit (#420) used to provide B+ power to the air compressor relay has an open in it. Rerun SERVICE BAY DIAGNOSTICS after repair is made. |
| **IC17 SPRING SOLENOID VALVE COMPONENT CHECK** | | |
| It is now desired to activate the "AIR SPRING SOLENOID VALVE CYCLE" functional test. In order to do this the following actions are required:<br>• Release the "STAR" test button so that it remains in the up "HOLD" position after the code "33" has been displayed for at least 5 seconds.<br>NOTE: As long as the "STAR" test button is in the up "HOLD" position the selected functional test will continue. The "AIR SPRING SOLENOID CYCLE" test is used to verify that the air suspension control module can activate each of the air spring solenoid valves by cycling them "ON" and "OFF" continuously until the "STAR" test button is depressed down again. | The right front air spring solenoid valve is making an audible click sound: | |
| | CYCLING "ON/OFF" CONTINUOUSLY ▶ | GO TO IC21 |
| | REMAINS "OFF" ▶ | GO TO IC18 |

**Fig. 55 Pinpoint test, IC (Part 8 of 13)**

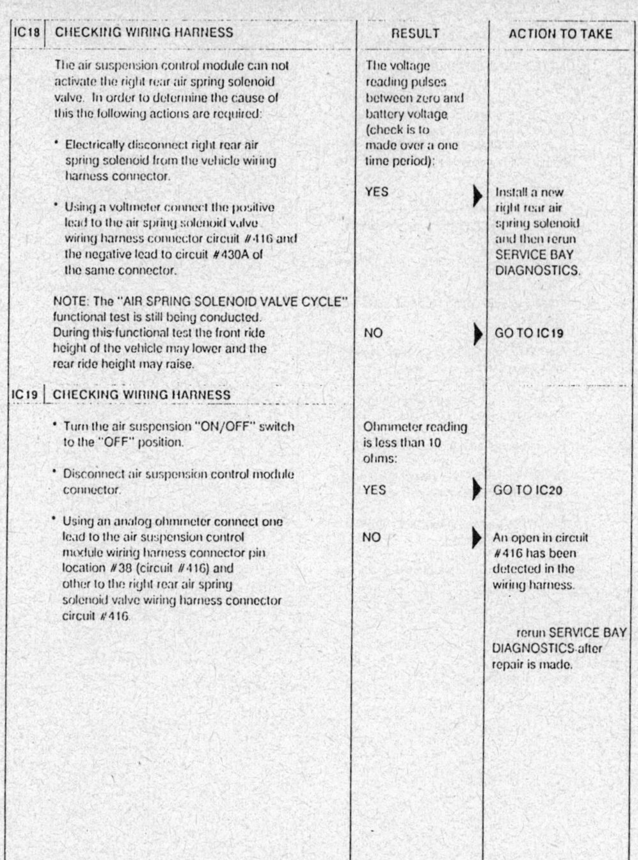

| IC18 CHECKING WIRING HARNESS | RESULT | ACTION TO TAKE |
|---|---|---|
| The air suspension control module can not activate the right rear air spring solenoid valve. In order to determine the cause of this the following actions are required:<br>• Electrically disconnect right rear air spring solenoid from the vehicle wiring harness connector.<br>• Using a voltmeter connect the positive lead to the air spring solenoid valve wiring harness connector circuit #416 and the negative lead to circuit #430A of the same connector.<br>NOTE: The "AIR SPRING SOLENOID VALVE CYCLE" functional test is still being conducted. During this functional test the front ride height of the vehicle may lower and the rear ride height may raise. | The voltage reading pulses between zero and battery voltage (check is to made over a one time period): | |
| | YES ▶ | Install a new right rear air spring solenoid and then rerun SERVICE BAY DIAGNOSTICS. |
| | NO ▶ | GO TO IC19 |
| **IC19 CHECKING WIRING HARNESS** | | |
| • Turn the air suspension "ON/OFF" switch to the "OFF" position.<br>• Disconnect air suspension control module connector.<br>• Using an analog ohmmeter connect one lead to the air suspension control module wiring harness connector pin location #38 (circuit #416) and other to the right rear air spring solenoid valve wiring harness connector circuit #416. | Ohmmeter reading is less than 10 ohms: | |
| | YES ▶ | GO TO IC20 |
| | NO ▶ | An open in circuit #416 has been detected in the wiring harness.<br>rerun SERVICE BAY DIAGNOSTICS after repair is made. |

**Fig. 55 Pinpoint test, IC (Part 9 of 13)**

| IC20 WIRING HARNESS CHECK | RESULT | ACTION TO TAKE |
|---|---|---|
| • Again using an analog ohmmeter connect one lead to the air suspension control module wiring harness connector pin location #60 (circuit #430H) and other to the right rear air spring solenoid valve vehicle wiring harness connector circuit #430A. | Ohmmeter reading is less than 10 ohms: | |
| | YES ▶ | Install a new air suspension control module and then rerun SERVICE BAY DIAGNOSTICS. |
| | NO ▶ | An open in circuit #430H/430A exists. Rerun SERVICE BAY DIAGNOSTICS after repair is made. |
| **IC21 ENTER SPRING FILL DIAGNOSTICS** | | |
| At this time it will be required to exit SERVICE BAY DIAGNOSTICS and enter SPRING FILL (refer to SPRING FILL DIAGNOSTIC for instructions). | The STAR tester is displaying one of the following codes: | |
| | "21" to "28" ▶ | GO TO IC22 |
| | SOMETHING ELSE ▶ | Repeat SPRING FILL entrance procedure until entered. |
| **IC22 VISUAL CHECK** | | |
| In order to perform the right rear air spring inflation test we must first determine if it is above the normal position. | The vehicle's right rear corner has approximately a two inch gap or greater between the fender lip opening and the top of the tire: | |
| | YES ▶ | GO TO IC23 |
| | NO ▶ | GO TO IC24 |

**Fig. 55 Pinpoint test, IC (Part 10 of 13)**

| IC23 VENT RIGHT REAR AIR SPRING | RESULT | ACTION TO TAKE |
|---|---|---|
| In order to perform the right rear air spring inflation test we must first vent it below the normal position. To do that the following action is required:<br>• Release the "STAR" test button down so that it remains in the up "HOLD" position after the code "23" has been displayed for at least 5 seconds.<br>• Continue venting the right rear corner of the vehicle until the gap between the fender lip opening and the top of the tire is one inch or less.<br>NOTE: As long as the "STAR" test button remains in the up "HOLD" position the right rear air spring will continue to be vented. When the desired amount of venting has occurred depress the "STAR" test button so that it remains in the "TEST" positiion.. | The vehicle's right rear corner has been lowered: | |
| | YES ▶ | Depress the "STAR" test button down so that it remains in the "TEST" position, then:<br>GO TO IC24 |
| | NO ▶ | Continue with step "IA23" until the desired height is reached. |
| **IC24 INFLATE RIGHT REAR AIR SPRING** | | |
| To inflate the right rear air spring the following action is required:<br>• Release the "STAR" test button so that it remains in the "HOLD" position after the code "26" has been displayed for at least 5 seconds.<br>NOTE: As long as the STAR test button remains in the up "HOLD" position the right rear air spring will continue to be inflated. When the desired amount of inflating has occurred depress the test button so that it remains in the "TEST" position. | The right rear corner of the vehicle has been raised so that the gap between the fender lip opening and the top of the tire is approximately three inches or greater. | |
| | VERY SLOWLY OR NONE AT ALL ▶ | Depress the "STAR" test button down in the "TEST" positiion Then:<br>GO TO IC25 |
| | SLOWLY OR AT A NORMAL RATE ▶ | Rerun SERVICE BAY DIAGNOSTICS. If this problem still occurs install a new suspension control module and rerun SERVICE BAY DIAGNOSTICS. |

**Fig. 55 Pinpoint test, IC (Part 11 of 13)**

| IC25 AIR LINE CHECK | RESULT | ACTION TO TAKE |
|---|---|---|
| In order to determine why the right rear corner of the vehicle is inflating "VERY SLOWLY OR NONE AT ALL" the following actions are required:<br>• Disconnect the right rear air line from the right rear air spring solenoid valve.<br>• Disconnect the right rear air spring solenoid valve electrical connector so that the solenoid valve is not connected to the vehicle wiring harness.<br>• Release the "STAR" test button so that it remains in the up "HOLD" position after the code "26" has been displayed for at least 5 seconds.<br>NOTE: As long as the "STAR" test button remains in the up "HOLD" position the air compressor assembly will continue to pump air through the air line. | Air is coming out of the air line: | |
| | VERY SLOWLY OR NONE AT ALL ▶ | GO TO IC26 |
| | AT A NORMAL RATE ▶ | GO TO IC27 |
| **IC26 AIR LINE CHECK** | | |
| From the previous tests we have determined that the cause of the UNABLE TO INFLATE problem is due to a restriction in the air line or compressor assembly. In order to isolate the cause of this problem the following actions are required:<br>• Disconnect any one of the air lines that are plugged into the air compressor drier assembly.<br>NOTE: As long as the "STAR" test button remains in the up "HOLD" position the air compressor assembly will continue to pump air through the drier assembly. | The rate that the air is coming out of the drier assembly is: | |
| | SAME AS IN STEP "IC25" OR SLIGHTLY GREATER ▶ | Install a new air compressor assembly and then rerun SERVICE BAY DIAGNOSTICS. |
| | RATE IS FASTER THEN IN STEP "IC25" ▶ | There is a restriction in the right rear air line. Rerun SERVICE BAY DIAGNOSTICS after repair is made. |

**Fig. 55 Pinpoint test, IC (Part 12 of 13)**

| IC27 AIR LEAK TEST | RESULT | ACTION TO TAKE |
|---|---|---|
| • Depress the "STAR" test button so that it remains in the down "TEST" position.<br>• Reconnect the air line to the air compressor drier assembly and right rear air spring solenoid valve.<br>• Reconnect the vehicle wiring harness connector to the right rear air spring.<br>• Take a piece of masking tape and mark a spot on the wheel lip opening. Measure and record the vertical height between wheel lip opening and the bottom of the wheel rim.<br>• Wait at least 15 minutes, remeasure and record wheel lip opening again. | The second wheel lip opening is: | |
| | APPROXIMATELY THE SAME AS THE FIRST | GO TO IC28 |
| | LESS THAN THE FIRST | GO TO IC29 |
| **IC28 AIR LEAK CHECK** | | |
| • Release the "STAR" test button so that it remains in the up "HOLD" position after the code "26" has been displayed for at least 5 seconds.<br>• Inspect the following for air leakage:<br>• air compressor / dryer assembly connection point<br>• dryer assembly / air line connection point<br>• air line / air spring solenoid valve connection point<br>NOTE: As long as the "STAR" test button remains in the up "HOLD" position the right rear air spring will continue to be inflated. When the desired amount of inflating has occurred depress the "STAR" test button so that it remains in the "TEST" position. | A leak path was detected: | |
| | YES | Make required repairs and then rerun SERVICE BAY DIAGNOSTICS. |
| | NO | Install a new air suspension control module and then rerun SERVICE BAY DIAGNOSTICS. |
| **IC29 AIR LEAK CHECK** | | |
| • Inspect the following for air leakage on the right rear air spring / strut assembly:<br>• air spring bag<br>• air spring bag / canister connection<br>• canister / mount connection<br>• air spring solenoid valve / canister connection | | Rerun SERVICE BAY DIAGNOSTICS after repairs are made. |

**Fig. 55 Pinpoint test, IC (Part 13 of 13)**

| ID1 STAR CODE: 79 UNABLE TO DETECT RAISING OF LEFT REAR CORNER | RESULT | ACTION TO TAKE |
|---|---|---|
| The air suspension control module has not received the signal that the left rear corner of the vehicle was raised during the SERVICE BAY DIAGNOSTIC check. There are nine possible causes of this which are listed below:<br>• The height sensor linkage arm is not connected properly to the vehicle and/or height sensor.<br>• An air line may be defective.<br>• The left rear air spring solenoid valve maybe defective.<br>• The left rear air spring B+ power supply circuit may have an open in it.<br>• The left rear air spring ground return circuit may have an open in it.<br>• The air compressor may be defective.<br>• The air compressor B+ power supply circuit may have an open in it.<br>• The air compressor ground return circuit may have an open in it.<br>• The air suspension control module may be defective. | | GO TO ID2 |

**Fig. 56 Pinpoint test, ID (Part 1 of 16)**

| ID2 VISUAL COMPONENT CHECK | RESULT | ACTION TO TAKE |
|---|---|---|
| • Check under the vehicle to verify that the vehicle is not hanging up on something.<br>• Check the left rear corner of the vehicle to verify that the height sensor has no obvious damage and that the linkage is connected. | The left rear height sensor is installed correctly with no obvious damage and under the vehicle is clear of all obstructions: | |
| | YES | GO TO ID3 |
| | NO | Make needed repairs as required and rerun SERVICE BAY DIAGNOSTICS. |
| **ID3 ENTERING FUNCTIONAL TEST MODE OF SERVICE BAY DIAG** | | |
| FUNCTIONAL TEST mode will be used to determine why the left rear corner of the vehicle did not raise.<br>• Release the "STAR" test button to the up "HOLD" position. After five seconds depress the "STAR" test button again so that it remains in the down "TEST" position. This will allow the control module to enter FUNCTIONAL TEST mode. | The "STAR" tester is displaying code: | |
| | "31", "32", "33", "34", or "35" | GO TO ID5 |
| | SOMETHING ELSE | GO TO ID4 |

**Fig. 56 Pinpoint test, ID (Part 2 of 16)**

| ID4 RETRY FUNCTIONAL TEST ENTRANCE PROCEDURE | RESULT | ACTION TO TAKE |
|---|---|---|
| The air suspension control module has not entered the FUNCTIONAL TEST mode and the following actions are required:<br>• Make sure that the "STAR" tester is still plugged into the air suspension diagnostic pigtail.<br>• Make sure the "STAR" tester is turned "ON"<br>• Release the "STAR" test button to the up "HOLD" position. After five seconds depress the "STAR" test button again so that it remains in the down "TEST" position. This will allow the control module to enter FUNCTIONAL TEST mode. | The "STAR" tester is displaying code: | |
| | "31", "32", "33", "34", or "35" | GO TO ID5 |
| | SOMETHING ELSE | Rerun SERVICE BAY DIAGNOSTICS and if still unable to enter FUNCTIONAL TEST model install a new air suspension control module and then rerun SERVICE BAY DIAGNOSTICS. |
| **ID5 AIR COMPRESSOR COMPONENT CHECK** | | |
| It is desired to activate the "COMPRESSOR TOGGLE" FUNCTIONAL TEST mode. In order to do this the following action is required:<br>• Raise the vehicle's hood up completely.<br>• Release the "STAR" test button so that it remains in the up "HOLD" position after the code "31" has been displayed for at least 5 seconds.<br>NOTE: As long as the "STAR" test button is in the up "HOLD" position the selected functional test will continue. The "COMPRESSOR TOGGLE" test is used to verify that the air suspension control module can activate the air compressor. This is done by cycling it "ON" and "OFF" continuously until the "STAR" test button is depressed down again. | The air compressor is: | |
| | CYCLING "ON/OFF" CONTINUOUSLY | Depress the "STAR" test button so that it remains in the "TEST" position. This action will stop the "COMPRESSOR TOGGLE" functional test since it is no longer required. Then: GO TO ID17 |
| | AIR COMPRESSOR REMAINS "OFF" | GO TO ID6 |

**Fig. 56 Pinpoint test, ID (Part 3 of 16)**

| ID6 CHECKING WIRING HARNESS | RESULT | ACTION TO TAKE |
|---|---|---|
| Since the air suspension control module can not activate the air compressor the following actions are required: | Electrical connectors are good: | |
| • Depress the "STAR" test button so that it remains in the down "HOLD" position. This action will stop the "COMPRESSOR TOGGLE" functional test. | YES ▶ | GO TO ID7 |
| • Disconnect the air compressor assembly electrical connector from the vehicle wiring harness connector. | NO ▶ | Make repairs as required and rerun SERVICE BAY DIAGNOSTICS. |
| • Examine the both electrical connectors for damage and proper installation of wires. | | |
| **ID7 COMPRESSOR COOL DOWN** | | |
| The air compressor has an internal thermal non-cycling circuit breaker in it that opens the B+ power supply to the air compressor armature when the internal temperature exceeds a predetermined limit. In order for this thermal circuit breaker to be reset the following two things must happen: 1) the internal temperature must drop below the predetermined limit and 2) the power to the compressor must be off. In this part of the test we will allow the compressor to cool down for 15 minutes. The air compressor thermal circuit breaker been tripped by repeatedly running diagnostic checks. | At least 15 minutes has elapsed since the air compressor was disconnected from the vehicle wiring harness: | |
| | YES ▶ | GO TO ID8 |
| | NO ▶ | Continue with step "ID7" until may have 15 minutes has elapsed. |
| **ID8 WIRING HARNESS CHECK** | | |
| • Reconnect the air compressor to the vehicle wiring harness. | The air compressor remains off: | |
| | YES ▶ | GO TO ID10 |
| | NO ▶ | GO TO ID9 |

**Fig. 56 Pinpoint test, ID (Part 4 of 16)**

| ID9 WIRING HARNESS CHECK | RESULT | ACTION TO TAKE |
|---|---|---|
| • Remove the air compressor relay from its vehicle wiring harness connector. | The air compressor stops running and remains off: | |
| | YES ▶ | Install a new air compressor relay and then rerun SERVICE BAY DIAGNOSTICS. |
| | NO ▶ | Circuit #417 has a short to B+ which is causing the air compressor to run until the air compressor's internal thermal circuit breaker is tripped. Rerun SERVICE BAY DIAGNOSTICS after repair is made and the air compressor relay has been installed again. |

**Fig. 56 Pinpoint test, ID (Part 5 of 16)**

| ID10 AIR COMPRESSOR COMPONENT CHECK | RESULT | ACTION TO TAKE |
|---|---|---|
| It is desired to activate the "COMPRESSOR TOGGLE" functional test again. In order to do this the following action is, required: | The air compressor is: | |
| • Release the "STAR" test button so that it remains in the up "HOLD" position after the code "31" has been displayed for at least 5 seconds.<br><br>NOTE: As long as the "STAR" test button is in the up "HOLD" position the selected functional test will continue. The "COMPRESSOR TOGGLE" test is used to verify that the air suspension control module can activate the air compressor. This is done by cycling it "ON" and "OFF" continuously until the "STAR" test button is depressed down again. | CYCLING "ON/OFF" CONTINUOUSLY ▶ | Depress the "STAR" test button so that it remains in the "TEST" position. This action will stop the "COMPRESSOR TOGGLE" functional test since it is no longer required. Rerun SERVICE BAY DIAGNOSTICS after waiting 30 minutes. |
| | AIR COMPRESSOR REMAINS "OFF" ▶ | GO TO ID11 |
| **ID11 CHECKING WIRING HARNESS** | | |
| The next step in determining why the air suspension control module could not activate the air compressor is: | The voltage reading fluctuates between zero and battery voltage (check is to be made over a one minute time period): | |
| • Disconnect the air compressor assembly electrical connector from the vehicle wiring harness connector.<br><br>• Using a voltmeter connect the positive lead to circuit #417 of the air compressor vehicle wiring harness connector and the negative lead to circuit #430F. | YES ▶ | Install a new air compressor assembly and then rerun SERVICE BAY DIAGNOSTICS. |
| | NO ▶ | GO TO ID12 |

**Fig. 56 Pinpoint test, ID (Part 6 of 16)**

| ID12 CHECKING WIRING HARNESS | RESULT | ACTION TO TAKE |
|---|---|---|
| • Depress the "STAR" test button so that it remains in the down "TEST" position. | Ohmmeter reading is greater than 5 ohms: | |
| • Remove the air compressor relay from its vehicle wiring harness connector.<br><br>• Using an analog ohmmeter connect one lead to circuit #417 of the air compressor relay connector and the other lead to circuit #417 of the air compressor vehicle wiring harness connector. | YES ▶ | The circuit used to activate the air compressor (circuit #417) has an open in it. Rerun SERVICE BAY DIAGNOSTICS after repair is made. |
| | NO ▶ | GO TO ID13 |
| **ID13 CHECKING WIRING HARNESS** | | |
| • Again using an analog ohmmeter connect one lead to the air compressor relay circuit #430B and the other to a known good ground. | Ohmmeter reading is greater than 5 ohms: | |
| | YES ▶ | Circuit #430B has an open in it. Rerun SERVICE BAY DIAGNOSTICS after repair is made. |
| | NO ▶ | GO TO ID14 |
| **ID14 CHECKING WIRING HARNESS** | | |
| • Using a voltmeter connect the positive lead to circuit #175 of the air compressor relay's wiring harness connector and the negative lead to circuit #430B. | The voltage reading is greater than 10 volts: | |
| | YES ▶ | GO TO ID15 |
| | NO ▶ | This circuit has an open or short in it. There should always be battery voltage on this circuit. Rerun SERVICE BAY DIAGNOSTICS after repairs are made. |

**Fig. 56 Pinpoint test, ID (Part 7 of 16)**

| TEST STEP | RESULT | ACTION TO TAKE |
|---|---|---|
| **ID15 CHECKING WIRING HARNESS** | | |
| It is desired to activate the "COMPRESSOR TOGGLE" functional test again. In order to do this the following action is required: | The voltage reading fluctuates between zero and battery voltage (check is to be made over a one minute time period): | |
| • Release the "STAR" test button so that it remains in the up "HOLD" position after the code "31" has been displayed for at least 5 seconds. | | |
| • Using a voltmeter connect the positive lead to circuit #420 of the air compressor relay's wiring harness connector and the negative lead to circuit #430B. | YES ▶ | Install a new air compressor relay, reconnect the air compressor assembly and then and rerun SERVICE BAY DIAGNOSTICS. |
| NOTE: As long as the "STAR" test button is in the up "HOLD" position the selected functional test will continue. The "COMPRESSOR TOGGLE" test is used to verify that the air suspension control module can activate the air compressor. This is done by cycling it "ON" and "OFF" continuously until the "STAR" test button is depressed down again. | NO ▶ | GO TO ID16 |
| **ID16 CHECKING WIRING HARNESS** | | |
| • Turn the air suspension "ON/OFF" switch to the "OFF" position and disconnect the air suspension control module from the vehicle wiring harness. | The resistance reading is less than 5.0 ohms: | |
| • Using an analog ohmmeter connect the positive lead to circuit #420 of the air compressor relay wiring harness connector and the other lead to pin position #35 (circuit #420) of the air suspension control module wiring harness connector. | YES ▶ | Install a new air suspension control module, reconnect the air compressor relay and then rerun SERVICE BAY DIAGNOSTICS. |
| | NO ▶ | The circuit (#420) used to provide B+ power to the air compressor relay has an open in it. Rerun SERVICE BAY DIAGNOSTICS after repair is made. |

**Fig. 56 Pinpoint test, ID (Part 8 of 16)**

| TEST STEP | RESULT | ACTION TO TAKE |
|---|---|---|
| **ID17 SPRING SOLENOID VALVE COMPONENT CHECK** | | |
| It is now desired to activate the "AIR SPRING SOLENOID VALVE CYCLE" functional test. In order to do this the following actions are required: | The right front air spring solenoid valve is making an audible click sound: | |
| • Release the "STAR" test button so that it remains in the up "HOLD" position after the code "33" has been displayed for at least 5 seconds. | CYCLING "ON/OFF" CONTINUOUSLY ▶ | GO TO ID21 |
| NOTE: As long as the "STAR" test button is in the up "HOLD" position the selected FUNCTIONAL TEST will continue. The "AIR SPRING SOLENOID CYCLE" test is used to verify that the air suspension control module can activate each of the air spring solenoid valves by cycling them "ON" and "OFF" continuously until the "STAR" test button is depressed down again. | REMAINS "OFF" ▶ | GO TO ID18 |
| **ID18 CHECKING WIRING HARNESS** | | |
| The air suspension control module can not activate the left rear air spring solenoid valve. In order to determine the cause of this the following actions are required: | The voltage reading pulses between zero and battery voltage (check is to made over a one minute time period): | |
| • Electrically disconnect the left rear air spring solenoid from the vehicle wiring harness connector. | | |
| • Using a voltmeter connect the positive lead to the air spring solenoid valve wiring harness connector circuit #429 and the negative lead to circuit #430F of the same connector. | YES ▶ | Install a new left rear air spring solenoid and then rerun SERVICE BAY DIAGNOSTICS. |
| | NO ▶ | GO TO ID19 |
| NOTE: The "AIR SPRING SOLENOID VALVE CYCLE" functional test is still being conducted. During this functional test the front ride height of the vehicle may lower and the rear ride height may raise. | | |

**Fig. 56 Pinpoint test, ID (Part 9 of 16)**

| TEST STEP | RESULT | ACTION TO TAKE |
|---|---|---|
| **ID19 CHECKING WIRING HARNESS** | | |
| • Turn the air suspension "ON/OFF" switch to the "OFF" position. | Ohmmeter reading is less than 10 ohms: | |
| • Disconnect air suspension control module connector. | YES ▶ | GO TO ID20 |
| • Using an analog ohmmeter (20,000 ohms per volt is recommended) connect one lead to the air suspension control module wiring harness connector pin location #41 (circuit #429) and other to the right rear air spring solenoid valve wiring harness connector circuit #429. | NO ▶ | An open in circuit #429 has been detected in the wiring harness. rerun SERVICE BAY DIAGNOSTICS after repair is made. |
| **ID20 WIRING HARNESS CHECK** | | |
| • Again using an analog ohmmeter connect one lead to the air suspension control module wiring harness connector pin location #60 (circuit #430H) and other to the left rear air spring solenoid valve vehicle wiring harness connector circuit #430F. | Ohmmeter reading is less than 10 ohms: | |
| | YES ▶ | Install a new air suspension control module and then rerun SERVICE BAY DIAGNOSTICS. |
| | NO ▶ | An open in circuit #430H/430F exists. Rerun SERVICE BAY DIAGNOSTICS after BAY DIAGNOSTICS. |

**Fig. 56 Pinpoint test, ID (Part 10 of 16)**

| TEST STEP | RESULT | ACTION TO TAKE |
|---|---|---|
| **ID21 ENTER SPRING FILL DIAGNOSTICS** | | |
| At this time it will be required to exit SERVICE BAY DIAGNOSTICS and enter SPRING FILL (refer to SPRING FILL DIAGNOSTIC for instructions). | The "STAR" tester is displaying one of the following codes: | |
| | "21" to "28" ▶ | GO TO ID22 |
| | SOMETHING ELSE ▶ | Repeat SPRING FILL entrance procedure until entered. |
| **ID22 VISUAL CHECK** | | |
| In order to perform the left rear air spring inflation test we must first determine if it is above the normal position. | The vehicle's left rear corner has approximately a two inch gap or greater between the fender lip opening and the top of the tire: | |
| | YES ▶ | GO TO ID23 |
| | NO ▶ | GO TO ID24 |

**Fig. 56 Pinpoint test, ID (Part 11 of 16)**

| ID23 VENT LEFT REAR AIR SPRING | RESULT | ACTION TO TAKE |
|---|---|---|
| In order to perform the left rear air spring inflation test we must first vent it below the normal position. In order to do that the following action is required: | The vehicle's left rear corner has been lowered: | |
| • Release the "STAR" test button so that it remains in the up "HOLD" position after the code "27" has been displayed for at least 5 seconds.<br>• Continue venting the left rear corner of vehicle until the gap between the fender lip opening and the top of the tire is one inch or less. | YES ▶ | Depress the "STAR" test button down so that it remains in the "TEST" position. Then:<br>GO TO ID24 |
| NOTE: As long as the "STAR" test button remains in the up "HOLD" position the left rear air spring will continue to be vented. When the desired amount of venting as occurred depress the "STAR" test button so that it remains in the down "TEST" position. | NO ▶ | Continue with step "ID23" until the desired height is reached. |

**Fig. 56 Pinpoint test, ID (Part 12 of 16)**

| ID24 INFLATE LEFT REAR AIR SPRING | RESULT | ACTION TO TAKE |
|---|---|---|
| To inflate the left rear air spring the following action is required:<br>• Release the "STAR" test button so that it remains in the "HOLD" position after the code "28" has been displayed for at least 5 seconds.<br>NOTE: As long as the "STAR" test button remains in the up "HOLD" position the left rear air spring will continue to be inflated. When the desired amount of inflating has occurred depress the "STAR" test button so that it remains in the "TEST" position. | The left rear corner of the vehicle has been raised so that the gap between the fender lip opening and the top of the tire is approximately three inches or greater: | |
| | VERY SLOWLY OR NONE AT ALL ▶ | Depress the "STAR" test button down so that it remains in the "TEST" position. Then: GO TO ID25 |
| | SLOWLY OR AT A NORMAL RATE ▶ | Rerun SERVICE BAY DIAGNOSTICS and if this problem still occurs install a new air suspension control module and then rerun SERVICE BAY DIAGNOSTICS. |

**Fig. 56 Pinpoint test, ID (Part 13 of 16)**

| ID25 AIR LINE CHECK | RESULT | ACTION TO TAKE |
|---|---|---|
| In order to determine why the left rear corner of the vehicle is inflating "VERY SLOWLY OR NONE AT ALL" the following actions are required: | Air is coming out of the air line: | |
| • Disconnect the left rear air line from the left rear air spring solenoid valve. | VERY SLOWLY OR NONE AT ALL ▶ | GO TO ID26 |
| • Disconnect the left rear air spring solenoid valve electrical connector so that the solenoid valve is not connected to the vehicle wiring harness.<br>• Release the "STAR" test button so that it remains in the up "HOLD" position after the code "28" has been displayed for at least 5 seconds.<br>NOTE: As long as the "STAR" test button remains in the up "HOLD" position the air compressor assembly will continue to pump air through the air line. | AT A NORMAL RATE ▶ | GO TO ID27 |
| **ID26 AIR LINE CHECK** | | |
| From the previous tests we have determined that cause of the UNABLE TO INFLATE problem is due to a restriction in the air line or compressor assembly. In order to isolate the cause of this problem the following actions are required: | The rate that the air is coming out of the drier assembly is: | |
| • Disconnect any one of the air lines that are plugged into the air compressor drier assembly. | SAME AS IN STEP "ID25" OR SLIGHTLY GREATER ▶ | Install a new air compressor assembly and then rerun SERVICE BAY DIAGNOSTICS. |
| NOTE: As long as the "STAR" test button remains in the up "HOLD" position the air compressor assembly will continue to pump air through the drier assembly. | RATE IS FASTER THAN IN STEP "ID25" ▶ | There is a restriction in the left rear air line. Rerun SERVICE BAY DIAGNOSTICS after repair is made. |

**Fig. 56 Pinpoint test, ID (Part 14 of 16)**

| ID27 AIR LEAK TEST | RESULT | ACTION TO TAKE |
|---|---|---|
| • Depress the "STAR" test button so that it remains in the down "TEST" position. | The second wheel lip opening is : | |
| • Reconnect the air line to the air compressor drier assembly and left rear air spring solenoid valve. | APPROXIMATELY THE SAME AS THE FIRST ▶ | GO TO ID28 |
| • Reconnect the vehicle wiring harness connector to the left rear air spring.<br>• Take a piece of masking tape and mark a spot on the wheel lip opening. Measure and record the vertical height between wheel lip opening and the bottom of the wheel rim.<br>• Wait at least 15 minutes, remeasure and record wheel lip opening again. | LESS THAN THE FIRST ▶ | GO TO ID29 |
| **ID28 AIR LEAK CHECK** | | |
| • Release the "STAR" test button so that it remains in the up "HOLD" position after the code "28" has been displayed for at least 5 seconds. | A leak path was detected: | |
| | YES ▶ | Make required repairs and rerun SERVICE BAY DIAGNOSTICS. |
| • Inspect the following for air leakage:<br>• air compressor / dryer assembly connection point<br>• dryer assembly / air line connection point<br>• air line / air spring solenoid valve connection point<br>NOTE: As long as the "STAR" test button remains in the up "HOLD" position the left rear air spring will continue to be inflated. When the desired amount of inflating has occurred depress the "STAR" test button so that it remains in the "TEST" position. | NO ▶ | Install a new air suspension control module and then rerun SERVICE BAY DIAGNOSTICS. |

**Fig. 56 Pinpoint test, ID (Part 15 of 16)**

| ID29 AIR LEAK CHECK | RESULT | ACTION TO TAKE |
|---|---|---|
| • Inspect the following for air leakage on the left rear air spring / strut assembly:<br>• air spring bag<br>• air spring bag / canister connection<br>• canister / mount connection<br>• air spring solenoid valve / canister connection | ▶ | Rerun SERVICE BAY DIAGNOSTICS after repairs are made. |

**Fig. 56 Pinpoint test, ID (Part 16 of 16)**

| JA1 STAR CODE: 55 SPEED GREATER THAN 15 mph NOT DETECTED | RESULT | ACTION TO TAKE |
|---|---|---|
| The air suspension control module has not received a signal the vehicle speed was above 15 mph during the DRIVE CYCLE DIAGNOSTIC test. There are five possible causes for this which are listed below:<br>• The vehicle was not driven above 15 mph during DRIVE CYCLE DIAGNOSTICS.<br>• The B+ power circuit of the speed sensor circuit has an open or short in it.<br>• The ground return circuit of the speed sensor has an open in it.<br>• The vehicle speed sensor may be defective.<br>• The air suspension control module may be defective. | The vehicle was driven above a speed of 15 mph for at least four minutes, the ignition switch has been turned to the "OFF" position and remained there. The air suspension "ON/OFF" switch has remained in the "ON" position: | |
| | YES ▶ | GO TO JA2 |
| | NO ▶ | Drive the vehicle above 15 mph for at least four minutes. |
| **JA2 SPEED SENSOR COMPONENT CHECK** | | |
| Refer to the shop manual to reverify that the vehicle speed sensor is operating properly at all speeds. | The speed sensor has been verified to operate at all speeds properly: | |
| | YES ▶ | GO TO JA3 |
| | NO ▶ | After the required repairs to the vehicle speed sensor are made rerun DRIVE CYCLE DIAGNOSTICS. |

**Fig. 57 Pinpoint test, JA (Part 1 of 2)**

| JA3 WIRING HARNESS CHECK | RESULT | ACTION TO TAKE |
|---|---|---|
| • Turn the ignition switch to the "OFF" position.<br>• Turn the air suspension "ON/OFF" switch to the "OFF" position and disconnect the air suspension control module from the vehicle wiring harness.<br>• Using an analog ohmmeter connect one lead to the air suspension control module vehicle wiring harness connector pin position #6 (circuit #563) and the other to pin position #40 (circuit #430G). | The ohmmeter reading was less than 5.0 ohms: | |
| | YES ▶ | GO TO JA4 |
| | NO ▶ | The ground circuit (#563) of the vehicle speed sensor has an open in it. Rerun DRIVE CYCLE DIAGNOSTICS after repair is made. |
| **JA4 WIRING HARNESS CHECK** | | |
| • Using an analog ohmmeter connect one lead to the air suspension control module vehicle wiring harness connector pin #3 (circuit #150) and the other to circuit #150A of the vehicle speed sensor wiring harness connector. | The ohmmeter reading is less than 5.0 ohms: | |
| | YES ▶ | Install a new air suspension control module and drive the vehicle again above 15 mph. Afterwards rerun DRIVE CYCLE DIAGNOSTICS to verify repairs. |
| | NO ▶ | An open has been detected in the speed sensor circuit (#150). Rerun DRIVE CYCLE DIAGNOSTICS after repair is made. |

**Fig. 57 Pinpoint test, JA (Part 2 of 2)**

| JB1 STAR CODE: 72 / DID NOT DETECT AT LEAST 4 OPEN AND CLOSE DOOR SIGNALS | RESULT | ACTION TO TAKE |
|---|---|---|
| The air suspension control module has not received all four door "OPEN" and "CLOSE" signals after the STAR tester displayed a code "12" or "13". There are four possible causes of the air suspension control module not detecting that all the doors were "OPEN" and "CLOSED".<br>• The door sense circuit used to detect when a door or doors are open or closed may have an open or short.<br>• The door open/close sense switch may not be installed properly.<br>• The door open/close sense switch may be defective.<br>• The air suspension control module may be defective. | After the STAR tester displayed a code "12" or "13" each of the vehicle's doors were opened and shut once: | |
| | YES ▶ | GO TO JB2 |
| | NO ▶ | Rerun SERVICE BAY DIAGNOSTICS. |
| **JB2 WIRING HARNESS CHECK** | | |
| The air suspension control module has not received all four door "OPEN" and "CLOSE" signals. In order to determine where the problem is located the following actions are required:<br>• Release the "STAR" test button to the up "HOLD" position. After five seconds depress the "STAR" test button again so that it remains in the down "TEST" position. This will allow the control module to enter FUNCTIONAL TEST mode. | The "STAR" tester is displaying code: | |
| | "31", "32", "33", "34", or "35" ▶ | GO TO JB4 |
| | NO ▶ | GO TO JB3 |

**Fig. 58 Pinpoint test, JB (Part 1 of 14)**

| JB3 CHECKING WIRING HARNESS | RESULT | ACTION TO TAKE |
|---|---|---|
| The air suspension control module has not entered the SERVICE BAY DIAGNOSTICS FUNCTIONAL TEST mode and the following actions are required:<br>• Make sure that the "STAR" tester is still plugged into the air suspension diagnostic pigtail.<br>• Make sure that the "STAR" tester is turned "ON".<br>• Release the "STAR" test button to the up "HOLD" position. After five seconds depress the "STAR" test button again so that it remains in the down "TEST" position. This will allow the control module to enter FUNCTIONAL TEST mode. | The "STAR" tester is displaying code: | |
| | "31", "32", "33", "34", or "35" | GO TO JB4 |
| | NO | Rerun SERVICE BAY DIAGNOSTICS and if still unable to enter its FUNCTIONAL TEST mode replace air suspension control module. |
| **JB4 CHECKING WIRING HARNESS** | | |
| It is desired to activate the "DOOR FUNCTIONAL TEST". In order to do this the following action is required:<br>• Raise the vehicle's hood up completely.<br>• Close all vehicle doors.<br>• Release the "STAR" test button so that it remains in the up "HOLD" position after the code "35" has been displayed for at least 5 seconds.<br>NOTE: As long as the "STAR" test button is in the up "HOLD" position the "DOOR FUNCTIONAL TEST" will continue. The "DOOR FUNCTIONAL TEST" is used to verify that the air suspension control module is receiving the door "OPEN" and "CLOSED" signals. This functional test provides the operator with two different types of audible signals. When all doors are "CLOSED" the vent solenoid located in the air compressor assembly will cycle "ON" and "OFF" continuously. If at least one door is "OPEN" then the air compressor and vent solenoid valve will cycle "ON" and "OFF" continuously. | The air compressor assembly is doing the following: | |
| | Vent solenoid cycling "ON" & "OFF" | GO TO JB5 |
| | Air compressor & vent solenoid cycling "ON" & "OFF" | GO TO JB23 |
| | Neither the air compressor or vent solenoid are cycling "ON" & "OFF" | "DOOR FUNCTIONAL TEST" was not entered. Repeat step "JB4". |

Fig. 58 Pinpoint test, JB (Part 2 of 14)

| JB5 CHECKING WIRING HARNESS | RESULT | ACTION TO TAKE |
|---|---|---|
| Since the air suspension control module has received the signal that all the doors are "CLOSED" the problem becomes simply to determine which door or doors the air suspension control module did not receive an "OPEN" door signal from. In order to do this the following action is required:<br>• Open one of the vehicle doors and leave it open. | The air compressor and vent solenoid valve are cycling together: | |
| | YES | This door circuit is operating properly. Close this door and repeat step "JB5" until all the vehicle doors have been checked. |
| | NO | The air suspension control module has not received the signal that the door was "OPEN". Record the location of this door and repeat step "JB5" until all doors have been checked. Then: GO TO JB6 |

Fig. 58 Pinpoint test, JB (Part 3 of 14)

| JB6 | RESULT | ACTION TO TAKE |
|---|---|---|
| | The following door "OPEN" circuits were recorded as having a problem in step "JB5": | |
| | LEFT REAR | GO TO JB7 |
| | RIGHT REAR | GO TO JB11 |
| | RIGHT FRONT | GO TO JB15 |
| | LEFT FRONT (This door circuit is to be repaired last due to the diode in its circuit) | GO TO JB19 |
| **JB7 VISUAL COMPONENT CHECK** | | |
| In order to determine the reason why the air suspension control module did not receive the left rear door "OPEN" signal the following action is required:<br>• Open the left rear door and examine the door "COURTESY SWITCH" for obvious damage. | The left rear door "COURTESY SWITCH" is damaged: | |
| | YES | Replace the left rear door "COURTESY SWITCH" and repeat step "JB5" to verify that the problem has been corrected. |
| | NO | GO TO JB8 |

Fig. 58 Pinpoint test, JB (Part 4 of 14)

| JB8 CHECKING WIRING HARNESS | RESULT | ACTION TO TAKE |
|---|---|---|
| • Disconnect the left rear door "COURTESY SWITCH" from the vehicle wiring harness.<br>• Using a voltmeter connect the positive lead to the "COURTESY SWITCH" wiring harness connect circuit #54H and negative lead to battery ground. | The voltage reading is greater than 10 volts: | |
| | YES | GO TO JB9 |
| | NO | The battery supply voltage circuit has an open/short. Rerun SERVICE BAY DIAGNOSTICS after repair is made. |
| **JB9 CHECKING WIRING HARNESS** | | |
| • Using a jumper wire connect the "COURTESY SWITCH" wiring harness connector circuit #54H and circuit #24B. | The air compressor and vent solenoid valve are cycling together: | |
| | YES | Replace the left rear door "COURTESY SWITCH" and rerun SERVICE BAY DIAGNOSTICS after repair is made. |
| | NO | GO TO JB10 |

Fig. 58 Pinpoint test, JB (Part 5 of 14)

| JB10 CHECKING WIRING HARNESS | RESULT | ACTION TO TAKE |
|---|---|---|
| • Turn the air suspension "ON/OFF" switch to the "OFF" position. Disconnect the air suspension control module from the wiring harness connector.<br>• Using an analog ohmmeter connect one lead to the "COURTESY SWITCH" wiring harness connector circuit #24B and the other to the air suspension control module pin location #4 (circuit #24). | The ohmmeter reading is less than 5.0 ohms: | |
| | YES ▶ | Replace the air suspension control module and rerun SERVICE BAY DIAGNOSTICS afterwards. |
| | NO ▶ | The left rear door circuit has an open in it. Rerun SERVICE BAY DIAGNOSTICS after repair is made. |
| **JB11 CHECKING WIRING HARNESS** | | |
| In order to determine the reason why the air suspension control module did not receive the right rear door "OPEN" signal the following action is required:<br>• Open the right rear door and examine the door "COURTESY SWITCH for obvious damage. | The right rear door "COURTESY SWITCH" is damaged: | |
| | YES ▶ | Replace the right rear door "COURTESY SWITCH" and repeat step "JB5" to verify that the problem has been corrected. |
| | NO ▶ | GO TO JB12 |

**Fig. 58 Pinpoint test, JB (Part 6 of 14)**

| JB12 CHECKING WIRING HARNESS | RESULT | ACTION TO TAKE |
|---|---|---|
| • Disconnect the right rear door "COURTESY SWITCH" from the vehicle wiring harness.<br>• Using a voltmeter connect the positive lead to the "COURTESY SWITCH" wiring harness connect circuit #54F and negative lead to battery ground. | The voltage reading is greater than 10 volts: | |
| | YES ▶ | GO TO JB13 |
| | NO ▶ | The battery supply voltage circuit has an open/short. Rerun SERVICE BAY DIAGNOSTICS after repair is made. |
| **JB13 CHECKING WIRING HARNESS** | | |
| • Using a jumper wire connect the "COURTESY SWITCH" wiring harness connector circuit #54F and circuit #24E. | The air compressor and vent solenoid valve are cycling together: | |
| | YES ▶ | Replace the right rear door "COURTESY SWITCH" and rerun SERVICE BAY DIAGNOSTICS after repair is made. |
| | NO ▶ | GO TO JB14 |

**Fig. 58 Pinpoint test, JB (Part 7 of 14)**

| JB14 CHECKING WIRING HARNESS | RESULT | ACTION TO TAKE |
|---|---|---|
| • Turn the air suspension "ON/OFF" switch to the "OFF" position. Disconnect the air suspension control module from the wiring harness connector.<br>• Using an analog ohmmeter connect one lead to the "COURTESY SWITCH" wiring harness connector circuit #24E and the other to the air suspension control module pin location #4 (circuit #24). | The ohmmeter reading is less than 5.0 ohms: | |
| | YES ▶ | Replace the air suspension control module and rerun SERVICE BAY DIAGNOSTICS afterwards. |
| | NO ▶ | The right rear door circuit has an open in it. Rerun SERVICE BAY DIAGNOSTICS after repair is made. |
| **JB15 CHECKING WIRING HARNESS** | | |
| In order to determine the reason why the air suspension control module did not receive the right front door "OPEN" signal the following action is required:<br>• Open the right front door and examine the door "COURTESY SWITCH" for obvious damage. | The right front door "COURTESY SWITCH" is damaged: | |
| | YES ▶ | Replace the right front door "COURTESY SWITCH" and repeat step "JB5" to verify that the problem has been corrected. |
| | NO ▶ | GO TO JB16 |

**Fig. 58 Pinpoint test, JB (Part 8 of 14)**

| JB16 CHECKING WIRING HARNESS | RESULT | ACTION TO TAKE |
|---|---|---|
| • Disconnect the right front door "COURTESY SWITCH" from the vehicle wiring harness.<br>• Using a voltmeter connect the positive lead to the "COURTESY SWITCH" wiring harness connect circuit #54G and negative lead to battery ground. | The voltage reading is greater than 10 volts: | |
| | YES ▶ | GO TO JB17 |
| | NO ▶ | The battery supply voltage circuit has an open/short. Rerun SERVICE BAY DIAGNOSTICS after repair is made. |
| **JB17 CHECKING WIRING HARNESS** | | |
| • Using a jumper wire connect the "COURTESY SWITCH" wiring harness connector circuit #54G and circuit #24F. | The air compressor and vent solenoid valve are cycling together: | |
| | YES ▶ | Replace the right front door "COURTESY SWITCH" and rerun SERVICE BAY DIAGNOSTICS after repair is made. |
| | NO ▶ | GO TO JB18 |

**Fig. 58 Pinpoint test, JB (Part 9 of 14)**

| JB18 CHECKING WIRING HARNESS | RESULT | ACTION TO TAKE |
|---|---|---|
| • Turn the air suspension "ON/OFF" switch to the "OFF" position. Disconnect the air suspension control module from the wiring harness connector.<br>• Using an analog ohmmeter connect one lead to the "COURTESY SWITCH" wiring harness connector circuit #24F and the other to the air suspension control module pin location #4 (circuit #24). | The ohmmeter reading is less than 5.0 ohms: | |
| | YES ▶ | Replace the air suspension control module and rerun SERVICE BAY DIAGNOSTICS afterwards. |
| | NO ▶ | The right front door circuit has an open in it. Rerun SERVICE BAY DIAGNOSTICS after repair is made. |
| **JB19 CHECKING WIRING HARNESS** | | |
| In order to determine the reason why the air suspension control module did not receive the left front door "OPEN" signal the following action is required:<br>• Open the left front door and examine the door "COURTESY SWITCH" for obvious damage. | The left front door "COURTESY SWITCH" is damaged: | |
| | YES ▶ | Replace the left front door "COURTESY SWITCH" and repeat step "JB5" to verify that the problem has been corrected. |
| | NO ▶ | GO TO JB20 |

**Fig. 58 Pinpoint test, JB (Part 10 of 14)**

| JB20 CHECKING WIRING HARNESS | RESULT | ACTION TO TAKE |
|---|---|---|
| • Disconnect the left front door "COURTESY SWITCH" from the vehicle wiring harness.<br>• Using a voltmeter connect the positive lead to the "COURTESY SWITCH" wiring harness connect circuit #54D and negative lead to battery ground. | The voltage reading is greater than 10 volts: | |
| | YES ▶ | GO TO JB21 |
| | NO ▶ | The battery supply voltage circuit has an open/short. Rerun SERVICE BAY DIAGNOSTICS after repair is made. |
| **JB21 CHECKING WIRING HARNESS** | | |
| • Using a jumper wire connect the "COURTESY SWITCH" wiring harness connector circuit #54D and circuit #159A. | The air compressor and vent solenoid valve are cycling together: | |
| | YES ▶ | Replace the left front door "COURTESY SWITCH" and rerun SERVICE BAY DIAGNOSTICS after repair is made. |
| | NO ▶ | GO TO JB22 |

**Fig. 58 Pinpoint test, JB (Part 11 of 14)**

| JB22 CHECKING WIRING HARNESS | RESULT | ACTION TO TAKE |
|---|---|---|
| • Turn the air suspension "ON/OFF" switch to the "OFF" position. Disconnect the suspension control module from the wiring harness connector.<br>• Using an analog ohmmeter connect one lead to the "COURTESY SWITCH" wiring harness connector circuit #159A and the other to the air suspension control module pin location #4 (circuit #24). | The ohmmeter reading is less than 5.0 ohms: | |
| | YES ▶ | Replace the air suspension control module and rerun SERVICE BAY DIAGNOSTICS afterwards. |
| | NO ▶ | The left front door circuit has an open in it. Rerun SERVICE BAY DIAGNOSTICS after repair is made. |
| **JB23 CHECKING WIRING HARNESS** | | |
| Since the air compressor and vent solenoid valve are cycling continuously the air suspension control module has not received the signal that all doors are closed. In order to minimize the work involved in locating this problem the following action is required:<br>• Select any door and open it. Then manually depress the "COURTESY SWITCH" fully. | Only the vent solenoid valve is cycling continuously: | |
| | YES ▶ | This door "COURTESY SWITCH" is not positioned correctly to detect when the door is closed. Rerun the "DOOR FUNCTIONAL TEST" after repair is made to verify that problem has been corrected. |
| | NO ▶ | Repeat step "JB23" until all doors have been checked. If the air compressor and vent solenoid valve continue to cycle continuously then: GO TO JB24 |

**Fig. 58 Pinpoint test, JB (Part 12 of 14)**

| JB24 CHECKING WIRING HARNESS | RESULT | ACTION TO TAKE |
|---|---|---|
| The next step in finding the problem requires the following action:<br>• Select any door and open it. Then disconnect the door "COURTESY SWITCH" from the vehicle wiring harness. | Only the vent solenoid valve is cycling continuously: | |
| | YES ▶ | Replace this door "COURTESY SWITCH", close the door and then rerun the "DOOR FUNCTIONAL TEST" after repair is made to verify that problem has been corrected then: GO TO JB25 |
| | NO ▶ | Repeat step "JB24" until all door "COURTESY SWITCHES" have been disconnected then: GO TO JB26 |

**Fig. 58 Pinpoint test, JB (Part 13 of 14)**

| JB25 CHECKING WIRING HARNESS | RESULT | ACTION TO TAKE |
|---|---|---|
| If more then one door "COURTESY SWITCH" was disconnected then the following is required:<br>• Reconnect one of the remaining disconnected door "COURTESY SWITCHES" and shut the door. | Only the vent solenoid valve is cycling continuously: | |
| | YES ▶ | Repeat step "JB25" until all door "COURTESY SWITCHES" have been reconnected. |
| | NO ▶ | Replace this door "COURTESY SWITCH", close the door and verify that problem was corrected. Repeat step "JB25" until all door "COURTESY SWITCHES" have been reconnected. |
| **JB26 CHECKING WIRING HARNESS** | | |
| • Turn the air suspension "ON/OFF" switch to the "OFF" position. Disconnect the air suspension control module from the wiring harness connector.<br>• Shut all vehicle doors.<br>• Using analog voltmeter connect the positive lead to the air suspension control module pin location #4 (circuit #24) and the negative lead to battery ground. | The voltage reading is greater than 1.0 volts: | |
| | YES ▶ | The door "OPEN/CLOSE" circuit is shorted to a voltage source. Rerun the "DOOR FUNCTIONAL TEST" after repair is made to verify problem has been corrected. |
| | NO ▶ | Replace the air suspension control module and rerun SERVICE BAY DIAGNOSTICS. |

**Fig. 58 Pinpoint test, JB (Part 14 of 14)**

| JC1 STAR CODE: 73 BRAKE PRESSURE SWITCH ACTIVATION NOT DETECTED | RESULT | ACTION TO TAKE |
|---|---|---|
| The air suspension control module has not received the signal that the vehicle's brake pedal was depressed hard after the STAR tester displayed a code "12" or "13". There are four possible causes of the air suspension control module not detecting that the brake pressure switch was activated by pressing down hard on the brake pedal.<br>• The brake pedal was not depressed hard at the proper time.<br>• The brake pressure switch circuit may have an open or short.<br>• The brake pressure switch may be defective.<br>• The air suspension control module may be defective. | After the STAR tester displayed a code "12" or "13" the vehicle's brake pedal was depressed hard: | |
| | YES ▶ | GO TO JC2 |
| | NO ▶ | Rerun SERVICE BAY DIAGNOSTICS. |
| **JC2 VISUAL CHECK** | | |
| The first step in trying to locate the reason why the brake pressure switch was not activated is to make a visual check. Look and make sure that there is no obvious damage and that the brake pressure switch is properly connected to the vehicle wiring harness. | Visual check revealed no obvious damage and switch is connected properly: | |
| | YES ▶ | GO TO JC3 |
| | NO ▶ | Make needed repairs and rerun SERVICE BAY DIAGNOSTICS after repairs are made. |

**Fig. 59 Pinpoint test, JC (Part 1 of 3)**

| JC3 WIRING HARNESS CHECK | RESULT | ACTION TO TAKE |
|---|---|---|
| • Release the "STAR" test button so that it remains in "HOLD" up position and turn it "OFF".<br>• Turn the air suspension "ON/OFF" switch to the "OFF" position. Disconnect the air suspension control module from the wiring harness connector.<br>• Using an analog ohmmeter (20,000 ohms per volt is recommended) connect one lead to the wiring harness connector pin location #7 (circuit #636) and the other lead to pin #40 (circuit #430G). | Ohmmeter reading is greater than 10,000 ohms: | |
| | YES ▶ | GO TO JC4 |
| | NO ▶ | There is a short to ground in brake pressure switch circuit. Rerun SERVICE BAY DIAGNOSTICS after repair is made. |
| **JC4 WIRING HARNESS CHECK** | | |
| • Using an analog ohmmeter connect one lead to the wiring harness connector pin location #7 (circuit #636) and the other lead to pin #46 (circuit #432D). | Ohmmeter reading is greater than 10,000 ohms: | |
| | YES ▶ | GO TO JC6 |
| | NO ▶ | GO TO JC5 |
| **JC5 WIRING HARNESS CHECK** | | |
| • Disconnect the vehicle's electrical wiring harness connector from the brake pressure switch.<br>• Using an analog ohmmeter again connect one lead to the wiring harness connector pin location #7 (circuit #636) and the other lead to pin #46 (circuit #432D). | Ohmmeter reading is greater than 10,000 ohms: | |
| | YES ▶ | Replace the brake pressure switch and rerun SERVICE BAY DIAGNOSTICS after repair is made. |
| | NO ▶ | The brake pressure switch circuits (#636/432D) are shorted together. Rerun SERVICE BAY DIAGNOSTICS after repair is made. |

**Fig. 59 Pinpoint test, JC (Part 2 of 3)**

| JC6 COMPONENT CHECK | RESULT | ACTION TO TAKE |
|---|---|---|
| • Using an analog ohmmeter again connect one lead to the wiring harness connector pin location #7 (circuit #636) and the other lead to pin #46 (circuit #432D).<br>• Depress the vehicle's brake pedal hard and keep it down until ohmmeter reading is completed. | Ohmmeter reading is greater than 10,000 ohms when the brake pedal was depressed: | |
| | YES ▶ | Replace the brake pressure switch and rerun SERVICE BAY DIAGNOSTICS after repair is made. |
| | NO ▶ | Replace the air suspension control module and rerun SERVICE BAY DIAGNOSTICS afterwards. |

**Fig. 59 Pinpoint test, JC (Part 3 of 3)**

| | STAR CODE: 74 / STEERING WHEEL ROTATION IN BOTH DIRECTIONS NOT DETECTED | RESULT | ACTION TO TAKE |
|---|---|---|---|
| JD1 | The air suspension control module has not received the signal that the vehicle's steering wheel was rotated in both directions after the STAR tester displayed a code "12" or "13". There are seven possible causes of the air suspension control module not detecting that the steering wheel was rotated at least a 1/4 turn in both directions. | After the STAR tester displayed a code "12" or "13" the vehicle's steering wheel was rotated 1/4 turn in both directions: | |
| | • The steering wheel was not rotated at least a 1/4 turn in both directions at the proper time. | YES | GO TO JD2 |
| | | NO | Rerun SERVICE BAY DIAGNOSTICS. |
| | • The B+ power supply circuit to the steering wheel sensor may have an open or short in it. | | |
| | • The ground return circuit may have an open in it. | | |
| | • The steering sensor channel "A" circuit may have an open or short in it. | | |
| | • The steering sensor channel "B" circuit may have an open or short in it. | | |
| | • The steering wheel sensor may be defective. | | |
| | • The air suspension control module may be defective. | | |
| JD2 | STEERING SENSOR CHECK | | |
| | The steering wheel sensor is made up of two components. One of these is the electrical sensor and the other is a metal shutter wheel. In order to determine where the problem is located the following visual inspections are required: | The steering sensor wiring has no damage and all wires are in the proper location: | |
| | • Check the wires to the steering wheel sensor located on the lower portion of the steering column to ensure that there is no obvious damage and that they are in proper location and connected to the the vehicle wiring harness. | YES | GO TO JD3 |
| | | NO | Repair wiring problems and rerun SERVICE BAY DIAGNOSTICS after repairs are made. |

**Fig. 60 Pinpoint test, JD (Part 1 of 4)**

| | STEERING SENSOR CHECK | RESULT | ACTION TO TAKE |
|---|---|---|---|
| JD3 | • Check the metal shutter wheel for damage and/or dust/grease build up in the slots. | The shutter wheel has no damage and the slots are clean: | |
| | | YES | GO TO JD4 |
| | | NO | Repair shutter wheel and rerun SERVICE BAY DIAGNOSTICS. |
| JD4 | COMPONENT CHECK | | |
| | In order to determine were the electrical problem is located the following actions are required: | The ohmmeter needle swings from a low reading to a higher resistance and to low again approximately every nine degrees of steering wheel rotation: | |
| | • Turn the "STAR" tester "ON/OFF" switch to the "OFF" position. | | |
| | • Turn the air suspension "ON/OFF" switch to the "OFF" position and disconnect the air suspension control module. | | |
| | • Using a jumper wire connect the air suspension control module wiring harness connector pin location #46 to a known good chassis ground. | YES | GO TO JD5 |
| | | NO | GO TO JD6 |
| | • Using an analog ohmmeter (set on 1K scale) connect one lead to the control module wiring harness connector pin position #45 (circuit #633) and the other to a known good chassis ground. | | |
| | • Slowly rotate the vehicle's steering wheel. | | |

**Fig. 60 Pinpoint test, JD (Part 2 of 4)**

| | COMPONENT CHECK | RESULT | ACTION TO TAKE |
|---|---|---|---|
| JD5 | • Using an analog ohmmeter (set on the 1K scale) connect one lead to the control module wiring harness connector pin position #24 (circuit #634) and the the other to a known good chassis ground. | The ohmmeter needle swings from a low reading to a higher resistance and to low again approximately every nine degrees of steering wheel rotation: | |
| | • Slowly rotate the vehicle's steering wheel. | YES | Reconnect the air suspension control module and rerun SERVICE BAY DIAGNOSTICS. If the STAR tester still displays code "74" replace the air suspension control module. |
| | | NO | GO TO JD6 |
| JD6 | WIRING HARNESS CHECK | | |
| | • Disconnect the steering wheel sensor (located on the lower portion of the steering column) from the vehicle wiring harness. | The voltage reading is battery voltage: | |
| | | YES | GO TO JD7 |
| | • Using a voltmeter connect the positive lead to the steering sensor wiring harness connector circuit #298H and the negative lead to a known good chassis ground. | NO | There is an open in circuit #298H used to supply battery voltage to the steering wheel sensor. Rerun SERVICE BAY DIAGNOSTICS after repair is made. |

**Fig. 60 Pinpoint test, JD (Part 3 of 4)**

| | WIRING HARNESS CHECK | RESULT | ACTION TO TAKE |
|---|---|---|---|
| JD7 | • Using an analog ohmmeter and jumper wire connect one lead to the control module wiring harness connector pin position #46 (circuit #432D) and the other to steering sensor wiring harness connector circuit #432A. | The ohmmeter reading is 5.0 ohms or less: | |
| | | YES | GO TO JD8 |
| | | NO | There is an open in circuit #432D/432A. Rerun SERVICE BAY DIAGNOSTICS after repair is made. |
| JD8 | WIRING HARNESS CHECK | | |
| | • Using an analog ohmmeter and jumper wire connect one lead to the control module wiring harness connector pin position #45 (circuit #633) and the other to steering sensor wiring harness connector circuit #633A. | The ohmmeter reading is 5.0 ohms or less: | |
| | | YES | GO TO JD9 |
| | | NO | There is an open in circuit #633/#633A. Rerun SERVICE BAY DIAGNOSTICS after repair is made. |
| JD9 | WIRING HARNESS CHECK | | |
| | • Using an analog ohmmeter and jumper wire connect one lead to the control module wiring harness connector pin position #24 (circuit #634) and the other to steering sensor wiring harness connector circuit #634A. | The ohmmeter reading is 5.0 ohms or less: | |
| | | YES | Replace the steering sensor and rerun SERVICE BAY DIAGNOSTICS after repair is made. |
| | | NO | There is an open in circuit #634/#634A. Rerun SERVICE BAY DIAGNOSTICS after repair is made. |

**Fig. 60 Pinpoint test, JD (Part 4 of 4)**

| JE1 STAR CODE: 75 ACCELERATION SIGNAL NOT DETECTED | RESULT | ACTION TO TAKE |
|---|---|---|
| The air suspension control module has not received the acceleration signal after the "STAR" tester displayed a code "12" or "13". There are four possible causes of the air suspension control module not receiving the acceleration signal:<br>• The accelerator pedal was not fully depressed to the floor at the proper time.<br>• The accelerator sense circuit may have an open or short in it.<br>• The EEC-IV module may be defective.<br>• The air suspension control module may be defective. | After the STAR tester displayed a code "12" or "13" the vehicle's accelerator pedal was depressed to the floor: | |
| | YES ▶ | GO TO JE2 |
| | NO ▶ | Rerun SERVICE BAY DIAGNOSTICS but this time have the engine running. |
| **JE2 WIRING HARNESS CHECK** | | |
| • Disconnect the 60 pin vehicle wiring harness connector from the engine EEC-IV control module (refer to the shop manual for EEC-IV disconnect instructions).<br>• Using a voltmeter place the positive voltage lead in the EEC-IV wiring harness connector pin location #32 (circuit #637) and the negative lead to battery ground (refer to the shop manual for EEC-IV wiring harness pin location and voltage measuring information). | The voltage reading is: | |
| | 4.0 to 6.0 volts ▶ | GO TO JE3 |
| | 0.0 to 0.5 volts ▶ | GO TO JE4 |

Fig. 61 Pinpoint test, JE (Part 1 of 2)

| JE3 CONTROL MODULE CHECK | RESULT | ACTION TO TAKE |
|---|---|---|
| The acceleration signal detection problem has been narrowed down to either the air suspension control module or the engine EEC-IV control module. In order to determine which one is causing the problem the following actions are required:<br>• Rerun the automatic portion of SERVICE BAY DIAGNOSTICS with the engine off and and the engine EEC-IV control module disconnected.<br>• When the STAR tester displays a code "12" or "13" take a jumper wire and connect one end to the EEC-IV wiring harness connector pin location #32 (circuit #637) and the other end to BATTERY GROUND for about three to four seconds. Remove the jumper wire afterwards.<br>• Perform all the other manual checks and then release the "STAR" test button to the up "HOLD" position. After waiting five seconds depress the "STAR" test button again to the down "TEST" position. | The "STAR" tester has displayed the code "72" again: | |
| | YES ▶ | Replace the air suspension control module and rerun SERVICE BAY DIAGNOSTICS. |
| | NO ▶ | The acceleration signal is not being produced by the engine EEC-IV control module. This may be due to the module itself or the components that generate the signal (vacuum level and throttle position).<br>Rerun SERVICE BAY DIAGNOSTICS after repair is made. |
| **JE4 WIRING HARNESS CHECK** | | |
| • Release the "STAR" test button so that it remains in the up "HOLD" position and turn the "STAR" tester "OFF".<br>• Turn the air suspension "ON/OFF" switch to the "OFF" position. Disconnect the suspension control module from the wiring harness connector.<br>• Using an analog ohmmeter connect one lead to the air suspension control module wiring harness connector pin location #28 (circuit #637) and the other lead to the engine EEC-iv control module wiring harness connector pin location #32 (circuit #637). | The ohmmeter reading is less than 5.0 ohms: | |
| | YES ▶ | Replace the air suspension control module and rerun SERVICE BAY DIAGNOSTICS. |
| | NO ▶ | The acceleration signal circuit #637 has an open in it. Rerun SERVICE BAY DIAGNOSTICS after repair is made. |

Fig. 61 Pinpoint test, JE (Part 2 of 2)

| STEP 1 of 2 SPRING FILL DIAGNOSTICS ENTRANCE PROCEDURE | RESULT | ACTION TO TAKE |
|---|---|---|
| In order to enter/activate SPRING FILL DIAGNOSTICS the following actions are required:<br>• Connect a battery charger to the vehicles battery and leave connected for the duration of the test sequence.<br>• If required release the STAR test button so that it remains in "HOLD" up position.<br>• Open trunk lid and connect the STAR tester to the air suspension diagnostic connector and turn the STAR tester "ON".<br>• Turn the air suspension "ON/OFF" switch to the "OFF" position and then back to the "ON" position.<br>• Check vehicle passenger compartment and trunk for loads. Remove all loads; vehicle must be at curb weight.<br>• Make sure the ignition switch is in the "OFF" position and wait ten seconds.<br>• With the brake pedal DEPRESSED HARD turn the ignition switch to the "ON/RUN" position (not necessary to start engine) and after 5 seconds release the brake pedal.<br>• Verify that the headlights, heater fan, windshield wipers, ..., etc. are turned off.<br>• Wait a minimum of 5 seconds and then depress the STAR test button so that it remains down in the "TEST" position. | Within twenty seconds the STAR tester will display one of the following codes: | |
| | "21" to "28" ▶ | GO TO SPRING FILL DIAGNOSTICS "STEP 2 of 2". |
| | SOMETHING ELSE ▶ | GO TO CA1 |

Fig. 62 Spring fill diagnostic procedure (Part 1 of 2)

| STEP 2 of 2 SPRING FILL DIAGNOSTICS ENTERED | RESULT | ACTION TO TAKE |
|---|---|---|
| SPRING FILL DIAGNOSTICS has been entered. In order to select/activate any desired SPRING FILL tests shown release the STAR test button to the up "HOLD" position after the desired code has been displayed for at least 5 seconds. The selected function will continue as long as the STAR test button remains in that position. When the desired amount of venting or inflating has occurred depress the STAR test button down so that it remains in the "TEST" position. This action will stop the test and start the scrolling of test codes again.<br>NOTE: Each of the spring fill codes to vent or inflate any corner of the vehicle will be displayed in numerical order one at a time. After the largest numerical code is displayed the list will be repeated. This scrolling manner will continue as long as the STAR test button remains in the down "TEST" position. | STAR tester is displaying the following codes:<br>"21 - Vent Right Front Air Spring"<br>"22 - Vent Left Front Air Spring"<br>"23 - Vent Right Rear Air Spring"<br>"24 - Inflate Right Front Air Spring"<br>"25 - Inflate Right Rear Air Spring"<br>"26 - Inflate Right Rear Air Spring"<br>"27 - Vent Left Rear Air Spring"<br>"28 - Inflate Left Rear Air Spring" | |
| | DESIRED TO EXIT SPRING FILL ▶ | Turn the ignition key to the "OFF" position. |

Fig. 62 Spring fill diagnostic procedure (Part 2 of 2)

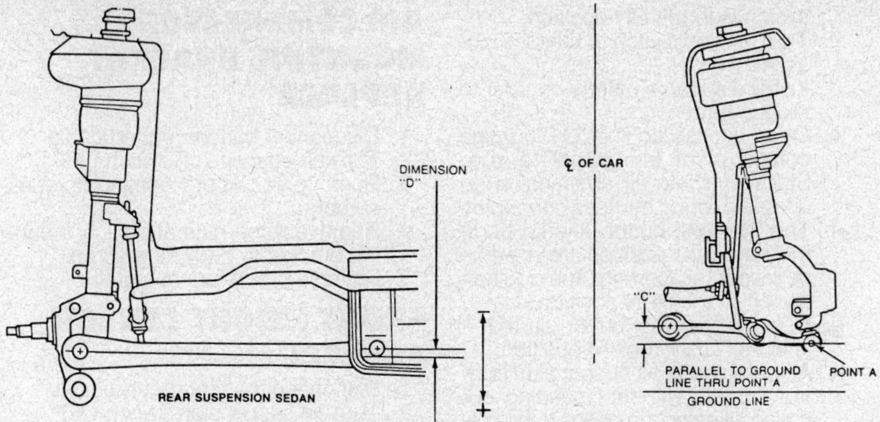


**Fig. 63 Ride height setup & measuring**

| Link Part Number | | Height Sensor Link Change | Front Ride Height Affect With Respect To The Nominal Link |
|---|---|---|---|
| LH Front | RH Front | | |
| E80F-3C111-CA | E80F-3C111-GA | Plus One (Green) | +6mm (+0.24 IN) |
| E80F-3C111-BA | E80F-3C111-FA | Minus One (Red) | -6mm (-0.24 IN) |
| E80F-3C111-JA | E80F-3C111-KA | Nominal (Blue) | -0- |
| E80F-3C111-DA | E80F-3C111-HA | Plus Two (Yellow) | +12mm (+0.47 IN) |
| E80F-3C111-AA | E80F-3C111-EA | Minus Two (White) | -12mm (-0.47 IN) |

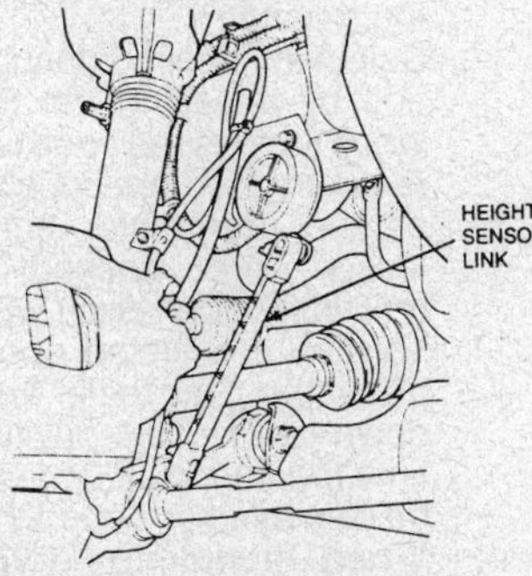


**Fig. 64 Link part No., Height sensor link change, Front ride height & height sensor link**

# SYSTEM ADJUSTMENTS

## RIDE HEIGHT SETUP & MEASUREMENT

**This adjustment must be used prior to front caster and camber alignment or ride height checking.**

1. Position vehicle on alignment rack.
2. To ensure ride heights are measured at a consistent point they should be measured only after the service bay diagnostic auto mode has successfully been completed and the Star tester displays a code 12. At this time, place the suspension power switch in the OFF position, remove the Star tester and leave the ignition switch in the RUN position.
3. At this point the vehicle is at the top of the trim band.
4. Measure the front suspension "C" dimension as shown in **Fig. 63.** The front ride height (C) is the vertical difference of the lower arm inner pivot attachment height minus the outer pivot height.
5. Measure the rear suspension "D" dimension as shown in **Fig. 63.** The rear ride height "D" is the vertical difference of the rear lower arm inner pivot attachment height minus the outer pivot height.
6. The suspension heights for the top of the trim band are:
   a. C dimension, 1.72 inch (43.6mm).
   b. D dimension, minus .36 inch (minus 9.3mm).
7. If the suspension heights are not within the listed specifications, ride height adjustment is required.
8. For reference purposes, the ride heights at the center of the trim band are approximately .35 inch (8.8mm) lower than the above suspension heights in the front and approximately .47 inch (12mm) lower in the rear.
9. If adjustment to front ride height is required, it should be performed by replacing the height sensor link according to chart, **Fig. 64.**
10. When removing a link, carefully separate it from the ball stud with a wide bladed screwdriver. Do not damage the link or ball stud. When installing a link to the sensor, support the sensor lever from behind to avoid possible damage to the sensor.
11. Rear height sensor adjustment is performed by loosening and repositioning the height sensor lever adjustment screw. For adjustment purposes, each notch on the rear height sensor lever provides approximately .60 inch (15mm) of ride height adjustment.

# SERVICE PRECAUTIONS

**When lifting the vehicle to perform service, position vehicle over hoist and turn ignition switch to OFF position. Turn air suspension switch to OFF position. The switch is located in the luggage compartment on the LH side. A body type hoist is the recommended method for lifting the vehicle. When the hoist is used, raise vehicle using standard support procedures. The suspension will be supported in the rebound by the front and rear struts after the vehicle is lifted. As stated previously, ensure to either disconnect battery ground cable or turning the the power switch located in the luggage compartment on the LH side. Failure to do so may result in unexpected inflation or deflation of the air springs which may result in shifting of the vehicle during these procedures.**

# SYSTEM SERVICE

## STEERING SENSOR, REPLACE

The steering sensor is located at the lower end of the steering column. It may be removed with the column in or out of the vehicle. The sensor and sensor ring are separate items.

1. Disconnect battery ground cable.
2. Disconnect sensor electrical connector from wiring harness.
3. Disconnect sensor electrical connector from shift control cable bracket located under instrument panel.
4. Remove two attaching screws, then the sensor.
5. Reverse procedure to install.

## STEERING SENSOR RING, REPLACE

1. Disconnect battery ground cable.
2. Remove steering column.
3. Remove steering shaft from column.
4. Remove sensor ring.
5. Reverse procedure to install.

## FRONT ACTUATOR, REPLACE

1. Disconnect battery ground cable.
2. Place vehicle on a level surface and apply parking brake.
3. Turn ignition switch to OFF or either LOCK position and raise hood.
4. Remove engine compartment covers.
5. Disconnect actuator electrical connector from wiring harness connector.
6. Remove actuator clips from upper mount attaching studs.
7. Remove two attaching screws retaining actuator to mounting bracket.
8. Remove actuator by lifting off.
9. Reverse procedure to install.

## REAR ACTUATOR, REPLACE

1. Disconnect battery ground cable.
2. Remove strut assembly from vehicle.
3. Remove actuator.
4. Reverse procedure to install.

## AIR SPRING SOLENOID, REPLACE

1. Disconnect battery ground cable.
2. Ensure air suspension service switch is in the ON position.
3. Turn ignition switch to the OFF position.

4. Install a suitable battery charger to reduce battery drain.
5. Open access door in LH luggage compartment trim panel to plug Star tester into air suspension diagnostic wiring harness connector.
6. The Star test button should be in the hold (up) position.
7. Depress Star test button so that it is in the TEST (down) position.
8. At this time the air suspension control module will start sending out spring fill selection codes to be displayed on the Star tester. These codes will be displayed in a scrolling manner. Note the following:
   a. Code 21, describes the right front vent.
   b. Code 22, describes the left front vent.
   c. Code 23, describes the right rear vent.
   d. Code 24, describes the right front compress.
   e. Code 25, describes the left front compress.
   f. Code 26, describes the right rear compress.
   g. Code 27, describes the left rear vent.
   h. Code 28, describes the left rear compress.
9. Select desired spring fill operation by releasing Star button when desired code is displayed. As long as the Star test button is released the desired operation (inflation or deflation) will continue. To stop a selected operation, depress Star button back down to Test position. At this time spring fill codes will again be displayed in a scrolling manner. **When deflating air springs, have vehicle raised off the ground.**
10. Turn the air suspension switch to the OFF position.
11. Remove wheel and tire assembly.
12. Disconnect electrical connector and then the air line.
13. Remove solenoid clip. **The air spring solenoid valve has a two stage solenoid pressure relief fitting similar to a radiator cap. A clip is first removed, and then rotation of the solenoid out of the spring releases air from the assembly before the solenoid can be removed.**
14. Rotate solenoid counterclockwise to the first stop.
15. Pull solenoid straight out slowly to second stop to bleed air from system. **Do not fully release solenoid until all air is completely bled from system.**
16. After air is bled from system, rotate solenoid counterclockwise to the third stop and remove solenoid from air spring assembly.
17. Inspect filter. If very oily, replace filter. **A very oily filter indicates a leaking air strut assembly.**
18. Reverse procedure to install. The following air spring filling procedure must be performed as follows:
   a. Disconnect battery ground cable.
   b. Ensure air suspension service switch is in the ON position.
   c. Turn ignition switch to the OFF position.
   d. Install a suitable battery charger to reduce battery drain.
   e. Open access door in LH luggage compartment trim panel to plug Star tester into air suspension diagnostic wiring harness connector.
   f. The Star test button should be in the hold (up) position. With brake pedal depressed hard, turn ignition switch to the RUN position.
   g. Depress Star test button so that it is in the TEST (down) position.
   h. At this time the air suspension control module will start sending out spring fill selection codes to be displayed on the Star tester. These codes will be displayed in a scrolling manner.
   i. Select the desired spring fill operation by releasing the Star button when the desired code is displayed (as described previously). As long as the Star tester button is released the desired operation (inflation or deflation) will continue. To stop a selected operation, depress the Star tester button back down to the Test position. At this time the spring fill codes will again be displayed in a scrolling manner. **When installing deflated are springs, lower hoist as required but do not apply a load to the suspension until after the air spring has been inflated at least 60 seconds.**
   j. After completion of operation, exit the spring fill mode by disconnecting the Star tester and turning the ignition switch to the OFF position.

## AIR COMPRESSOR & DRYER ASSEMBLY, REPLACE

1. Disconnect battery ground cable.
2. Turn air suspension switch to the OFF position.
3. Disconnect electrical connector located on the compressor.
4. Remove air line protector cap from dryer by releasing two latching pins located on bottom of the cap 180° apart.
5. Disconnect four air lines from dryer.
6. Remove three screws attaching air compressor to mounting bracket.
7. Reverse procedure to install.

## AIR COMPRESSOR DRYER, REPLACE

1. Disconnect battery ground cable.
2. Turn air suspension switch to the OFF position.
3. Remove air line protector cap from dryer by releasing two latching pins located on bottom of cap 180° apart.
4. Disconnect four air lines from dryer.
5. Remove dryer from head assembly.
6. Reverse procedure to install.

## AIR COMPRESSOR MOUNTING BRACKET, REPLACE

1. Disconnect battery ground cable.
2. Turn air suspension switch OFF.
3. Remove air compressor and dryer assembly.
4. Remove three nuts attaching mounting bracket to body side apron.
5. Reverse procedure to install.

## FRONT HEIGHT SENSOR, REPLACE

1. Disconnect battery ground cable.
2. Turn air suspension switch OFF.
3. Disconnect sensor electrical connectors. Left front sensor connector is located in the engine compartment behind the shock tower. Right front connector is located in the engine compartment, next to the air compressor.
4. Push front sensor connector through access hole in the rear of the shock tower.
5. Hoist vehicle as described previously.
6. Disconnect bottom and then top end of height sensor link from attaching studs.
7. Disconnect anti-lock wire from bracket.
8. Disconnect brake line from bracket.
9. Remove sensor attaching screws and then the sensor.
10. Reverse procedure to install. **Torque** sensor bracket attaching screw to 8-12 ft. lbs.

## REAR HEIGHT SENSOR, REPLACE

1. Disconnect battery ground cable.
2. Turn air suspension switch OFF.
3. Disconnect sensor electrical connector located in luggage compartment in front of forward trim panel. Also, pull luggage compartment carpet back for access to sensor sealing grommet located on floorpan.
4. Hoist vehicle as described previously.
5. Disconnect bottom and then top end of height sensor link from attaching studs.
6. Remove sensor attaching screws, then the sensor.
7. Reverse procedure to install. **Torque** sensor and link assembly attaching screws to 5-6.2 ft. lbs.

## SYSTEM CONTROL MODULE, REPLACE

1. Disconnect battery ground cable.
2. Turn ignition switch to the OFF position.
3. Turn air suspension switch to the OFF position.
4. Remove LH luggage compartment trim panel.
5. Disconnect wire harness from module. **Use care, harness ground wire is attached to vehicle frame.**
6. Remove upper attaching nuts and loosen two lower nuts.

7. While the module mounting bracket is held to vehicle frame by two lower attaching nuts, slip module from attaching bracket by pulling it toward rear of vehicle.
8. Reverse procedure to install. **Torque** wire harness to module attaching screw to 28-35 inch lbs.

## AIR SUSPENSION SWITCH, REPLACE

1. Disconnect battery ground cable.
2. Disconnect electrical connector.
3. Depress retaining clips attaching switch to brace, and remove switch.
4. Reverse procedure to install.

## COMPRESSOR RELAY, REPLACE

1. Disconnect battery ground cable.
2. Disconnect electrical connector.
3. Remove screw retaining relay to relay block, then the relay.
4. Reverse procedure to install.

# Town Car

## INDEX



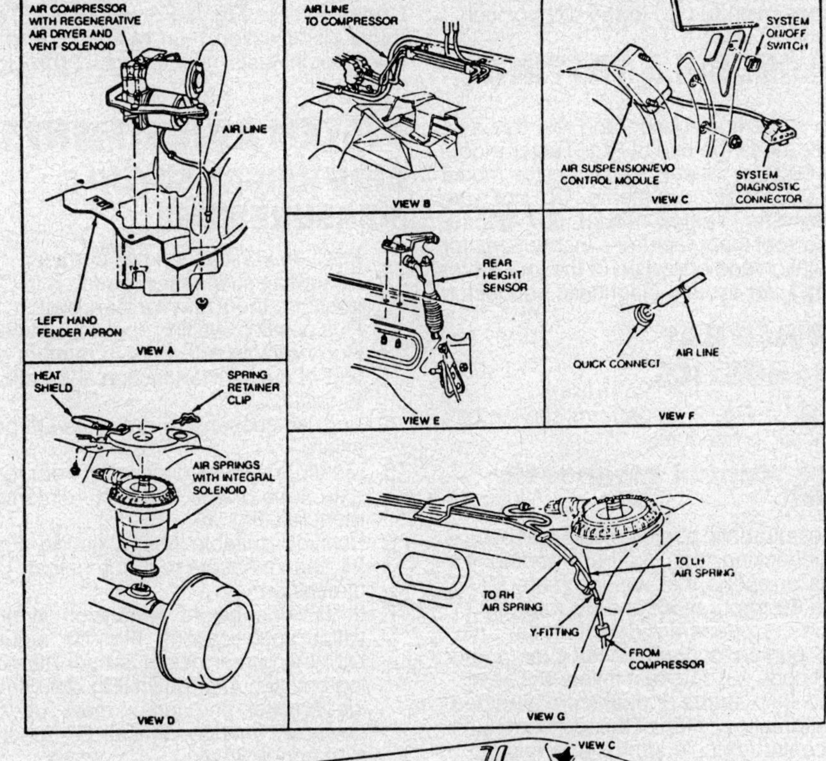


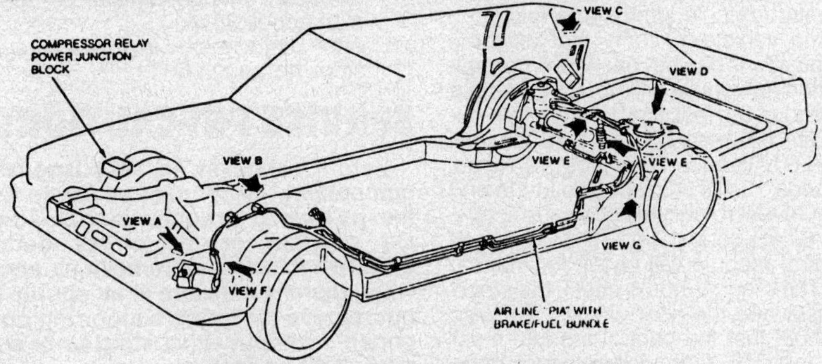


**Fig. 1 Air suspension system**

## SYSTEM DESCRIPTION & OPERATION

The rear air suspension, **Fig.1**, is an air operated microprocessor controlled, suspension system which replaces the conventional suspension. This system allows low spring rates for improved ride and automatic rear load leveling.

Two air springs replace the conventional steel springs and support the ve hicle load at the rear wheels. The air springs are mounted on the axle spring seats and to the frame upper spring seats.

The system is operational when the ignition is in the Run position and is limited for one hour after the ignition has been turned to the Off position. The air suspension switch, located on the right side of the luggage compartment, must in the Off position when the vehicle is on a hoist, being towed or jump started.

The check sir suspension warning lamp is located in the instrument panel message center, to the right of the speedometer. The warning lamp flashes five times and then stays on when the service switch is turned to the Off position or there is a system malfunction.

The rear leveling system operates by adding or removing air in the springs to maintain the level of the vehicle at a predetermined rear suspension "D" ride height dimension and is controlled by a microcomputer module.

The rear air suspension system module also controls the electronic variable orifice (EVO) steering.

The air required for the leveling is distributed from the air compressor to the air springs by a nylon air line which runs from the compressor dryer through a "Y" fitting to each individual air spring.

# COMPONENT DESCRIPTION & OPERATION

## AIR COMPRESSOR

The air compressor assembly consists of a compressor and a vent solenoid, both are non-serviceable. The compressor assembly is mounted in the engine compartment on the LH fender area below the air cleaner. The air compressor is a single single cylinder electric motor which supplies pressurized air as needed. The air compressor is powered by a relay that is controlled by the control module.

The pressurized air from the air compressor passes through the dryer assembly which contains a drying agent (silica gel). The moisture is removed from the air dryer when vented air passes out of the system during vent operation.

## VENT SOLENOID VALVE

The vent solenoid valve allows air to escape the system during venting corrections. The valve is located in the air compressor head and shares an electrical connector with the motor. The valve is enclosed in the cylinder head casting which forms an integral valve housing which allows the valve tip to enter the pressurized side of the system. Leakage is prevented by an O-ring seal.

The vent valve solenoid opens when, the rear of the vehicle is high and the control module determines lowering is necessary. When the vent solenoid valve is open pressurized air is allowed to escape. However, the vehicle will not lower unless the air spring solenoid valves are also opened to allow air to leave the springs.

**The vent solenoid valve has an internal diode for electrical noise suppression and is polarity sensitive. Do not switch battery feed and ground circuits or component damage may result.**

## AIR SPRING SOLENOID VALVE

The air spring solenoid valve allows air to enter and exit the air spring during leveling. The valve is electrically operated and is controlled by the module. The air spring solenoid valve is completely air tight, therefore the air lines are not required to be air tight. The air lines only contain pressurized air during vent and compress operations.

The valve is a two-stage pressure relief system. A clip is removed and rotation of the solenoid out of the seat will release air from the spring before the solenoid can be removed. **Never rotate an air spring solenoid valve to the release slot in the end fitting until all of the pressurized air has escaped the system.**

## COMPRESSOR RELAY

The compressor relay assists the control module in providing the necessary electrical current required to run the compressor motor.

## HEIGHT SENSOR

The height sensor sends signals to the control module. The three conditions that the control module interprets from the height sensor are that the vehicle is either at, above or below trim height.

The height sensor is attached to the frame crossmember and to the left rear upper control arm. As the rear of the vehicle moves up and down the height sensor lengthens and shortens. Magnets mounted on the lower slide portion of the sensor move relative to the to the sensor housing, generating a signal that is sent to the control module, through two small Hall effect switches that are attached to the sensor housing.

## CONTROL MODULE

The module uses approximately a 45 second averaging interval to determine when compress and vent operations are needed. Door inputs can override the 45 second averaging interval, so compress and vent operations can begin immediately. This interval is used to keep the module from making unneeded corrections. The module does not allow any vent operations for the first 45 seconds after the ignition has been turned to the ON position.

# DIAGNOSIS & TESTING

To properly diagnose and test this system requires the use of Star Tester model 007-0004 or Super Star II Tester model 007-00041 or equivalents. **Do not use Super Star Tester model 007-00019.** Follow tool manufacturer's instructions for installation and operation of the tool. Refer to **Fig.1**, for system diagnostic connector.

## SERVICE BAY DIAGNOSTICS

Refer to **Fig. 2**, to perform service bay diagnostic procedures.

### Auto/Manual Diagnostic Check

The automatic portion of this test begins with checking the control module for shorts or opens that would create STAR codes 39 through 46, and 68 through 71. If shorts or opens are detected, the automatic portion of the test is over and a STAR code 13, auto test failed, will be displayed. If no shorts or opens are detected, the automatic portion of the test continues. The control module attempts to raise and lower the vehicle to verify that all three height positions can be reached. A normally functioning vehicle will be at trim height by the end of the test. If all three height positions are not reached, the auto test will end and STAR code 13 will be displayed. STAR code 12 will be displayed at the end of the auto test if everything is satisfactory.

After STAR code 12 or 13 is displayed the control module will check for manual inputs. The manual inputs check the steering sensor and the door circuits. To pass the manual test the control module must detect that all four doors have been opened and closed, and that the steering wheel has been turned at least 1/4 turn in each direction. After the manual test, the tester must be toggled, or the control module will continue to monitor the manual test inputs indefinitely. Either STAR code 11, air suspension normal, or other STAR codes will be displayed.

### STAR Code Display

STAR codes will be automatically displayed after the "Auto/Manual Diagnostic Check" is completed. Each code detected will be displayed for about 15 seconds. Codes should be recorded at this time, refer to diagnostic code priorities chart, **Fig. 3.**

### Functional Tests

This test is run after the "Auto/Manual Diagnostic Check." Refer to **Fig. 4,** for test procedure.

### Pinpoint Tests

Each fault code has its own pinpoint test. These tests have priorities assigned with "1" being the highest priority and "4" being the lowest. One fault code may cause other fault codes to be displayed. Perform pinpoint tests in order of priority starting with the highest. For Diagnostic Codes, refer to **Fig. 3.** For Connector Terminal Identification, refer to **Figs. 5 and 6.** For Pinpoint tests, refer to **Figs. 7 through 19.**

# SYSTEM ADJUSTMENTS

## RIDE HEIGHT SETUP & MEASUREMENT

1. Position vehicle on level surface.
2. Ensure air suspension switch is in ON position, then turn ignition switch to Run position, waiting about 2 minutes.
3. Rock vehicle sideways to remove effect of suspension friction, then allow to settle.
4. Turn air suspension switch to Off position.
5. Measure vertical dimension from rear axle tube frame inboard reinforcement rail, **Fig. 20.**
6. Position suitable height gauge, **Fig. 21,** then measure rear ride height "D" dimension.
7. If "D" ride height dimension is not within specifications, **Fig. 20,** adjust by moving rear height sensor attaching bracket up or down, **Fig. 22.** Moving bracket one index mark up or down will change vertical "D" dimension about .35 inch.
8. After adjustment is made, repeat steps 4 through 6.

# SERVICE PRECAUTIONS

**Before servicing an air suspension component, disconnect power to system by turning air suspension switch to Off position or disconnect battery ground cable. Do not remove air spring when there is pressure in air spring. Do not remove air spring supporting components without exhausting air or supporting air spring.**

*Continued on page 26-114*

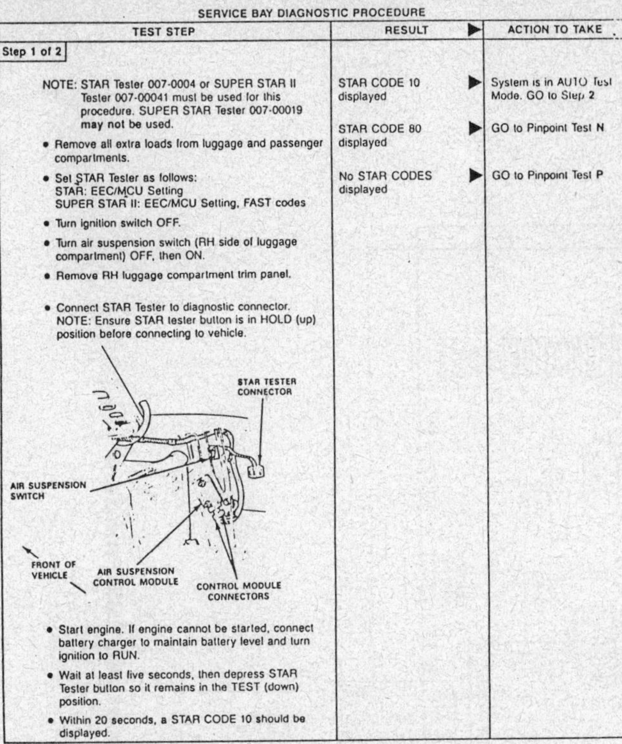


SERVICE BAY DIAGNOSTIC PROCEDURE

| TEST STEP | RESULT ▶ | ACTION TO TAKE |
|---|---|---|
| **Step 1 of 2** | | |
| NOTE: STAR Tester 007-0004 or SUPER STAR II Tester 007-00041 must be used for this procedure. SUPER STAR Tester 007-00019 may not be used.<br>• Remove all extra loads from luggage and passenger compartments.<br>• Set STAR Tester as follows:<br>STAR: EEC/MCU Setting<br>SUPER STAR II: EEC/MCU Setting, FAST codes<br>• Turn ignition switch OFF.<br>• Turn air suspension switch (RH side of luggage compartment) OFF, then ON.<br>• Remove RH luggage compartment trim panel.<br>• Connect STAR Tester to diagnostic connector. NOTE: Ensure STAR tester button is in HOLD (up) position before connecting to vehicle.<br>• Start engine. If engine cannot be started, connect battery charger to maintain battery level and turn ignition to RUN.<br>• Wait at least five seconds, then depress STAR Tester button so it remains in the TEST (down) position.<br>• Within 20 seconds, a STAR CODE 10 should be displayed. | STAR CODE 10 displayed ▶ | System is in AUTO Test Mode. GO to Step 2 |
| | STAR CODE 80 displayed ▶ | GO to Pinpoint Test N |
| | No STAR CODES displayed ▶ | GO to Pinpoint Test P |

**Fig. 2 Service Bay Diagnostic Procedure, (Part 1 of 2)**

SERVICE BAY DIAGNOSTIC PROCEDURE — Continued

| TEST STEP | RESULT ▶ | ACTION TO TAKE |
|---|---|---|
| **Step 2 of 2** | | |
| • STAR CODE 10 will be displayed for up to two minutes.<br>• **DO NOT put any weight on vehicle while STAR CODE 10 is displayed.**<br>• When Auto Test is complete a STAR CODE 12 (Auto Test passed) or STAR CODE 13 (Auto Test failed) will be displayed.<br>• With STAR CODE 12 or 13 displayed:<br>— Open all four doors.<br>— Turn steering wheel 1/4 turn in both directions<br>NOTE: The above manual inputs can be done in any sequence.<br>• Release STAR TEST button to HOLD (up) position.<br>• Wait five seconds and depress button to TEST (down) position.<br>• Within 20 seconds STAR CODES will be displayed.<br>NOTE: The STAR CODES will be displayed for about 15 seconds each. After all codes have been displayed, the codes will be repeated. The STAR CODES will continue to repeat as long as the STAR tester button is in the TEST (down) position. | STAR CODE 11 displayed ▶ | Vehicle passes. EXIT diagnostics by disconnecting STAR tester and turning ignition OFF. |
| | Any other STAR CODE ▶ | RECORD STAR CODES. REFER to Air Suspension STAR CODE chart for Pinpoint Tests for STAR CODES displayed. **DO NOT disconnect or turn off STAR tester, ignition switch or air suspension switch.** GO to Pinpoint Tests for STAR codes displayed. |

**Fig. 2 Service Bay Diagnostic Procedure, (Part 2 of 2)**

AIR SUSPENSION STAR CODES

| Star Code | Pinpoint Test | Description | Service Priority |
|---|---|---|---|
| 10 | | Diagnostics Entered, Auto Test in Progress | |
| 11 | | Vehicle Passes** | |
| 12 | | Auto Test Passed, Perform Manual Inputs | |
| 13 | | Auto Test Failed, Perform Manual Inputs | |
| 16 | — | EVO Error Code | |
| 17 | — | EVO Error Code | |
| 18 | — | EVO Error Code | |
| 23 | * | Functional Test, Vent Rear | |
| 26 | * | Functional Test, Compress Rear | |
| 31 | * | Functional Test, Air Compressor Toggle | |
| 32 | * | Functional Test, Vent Solenoid Toggle | |
| 33 | * | Functional Test, Air Spring Solenoid Toggle | |
| 39 | A | Compressor Relay Circuit Shorted to Battery | 2nd |
| 42 | B | Air Spring Solenoid Circuit Shorted to Ground | 2nd |
| 43 | C | Air Spring Solenoid Circuit Shorted to Battery | 2nd |
| 44 | D | Vent Solenoid Circuit Shorted to Battery | 2nd |
| 45 | E | Air Compressor Relay Circuit Shorted to Ground or Vent Solenoid Circuit Shorted to Ground | 2nd |
| 46 | F | Height Sensor Power Supply Circuit Shorted to Ground or Battery | 2nd |
| 51 | G | Unable to Detect Lowering of Rear | 3rd |
| 54 | H | Unable to Detect Raising of Rear | 3rd |
| 68 | J | Height Sensor Output Circuit Shorted to Ground | 2nd |
| 70 | K | Replace Air Suspension/EVO Module | 1st |
| 71 | L | Open Height Sensor Circuit | 3rd |
| 72 | M | Four Open and Closed Door Signals Not Detected | 4th |
| 74 | — | EVO Error Code | |
| 80 | N | Insufficient Battery Voltage to Run Diagnostics | 1st |
| — | P | Unable to Enter Service Bay Diagnostics | |

**Fig. 3 Diagnostic Codes & Priority Chart**

FUNCTIONAL TEST PROCEDURE

| TEST STEP | RESULT ▶ | ACTION TO TAKE |
|---|---|---|
| **Step 1 of 3** | | |
| • **Functional Tests are used in some of the STAR CODE Pinpoint Tests to aid in system diagnosis.**<br>• **The Functional Test mode can only be extended after Service Bay Diagnostics have been performed. A STAR CODE 11 or any other STAR CODES must be displayed before the Functional Test mode can be entered.** | STAR CODES displayed ▶ | GO to Step 2. |
| | No STAR CODES displayed ▶ | REPEAT Service Bay Diagnostics. If Service Bay Diagnostics cannot be entered, GO to Pinpoint Test P. |
| **Step 2 of 3** | | |
| • Release STAR Tester button to the HOLD (up) position.<br>• Wait at least 20 seconds.<br>• Depress STAR Tester button to the TEST (down) position.<br>• STAR CODE 23 should be displayed, then STAR CODES 26, 31, 32 and 33 will be displayed in order. Each STAR CODE will be displayed for about 15 seconds. After all the STAR CODES are displayed, they will repeated as long as the STAR tester button is in TEST (down) position. | Functional Test STAR CODES displayed ▶ | GO to Step 3. |
| | Functional Test STAR CODES not displayed ▶ | RELEASE STAR Tester button to HOLD (up) position. WAIT 20 seconds and depress button to TEST (down) position. If Functional Test STAR CODE are still not displayed, REPEAT Service Bay Diagnostics. |
| **Step 3 of 3** | | |
| • The following chart lists the Functional Test STAR CODES:<br>STAR CODE — DESCRIPTION<br>23 — Vent Rear<br>26 — Compress Rear<br>31 — Cycle Compressor on and off repeatedly<br>32 — Cycle vent solenoid valve on and off repeatedly<br>33 — Cycle air spring solenoid valves on and off repeatedly.<br>• Within four seconds after the desired Functional Test STAR CODE is displayed, release the STAR tester button to the HOLD (up) position.<br>NOTE: Waiting longer than four seconds will cause the next Function Test to be entered.<br>• As long as the STAR Tester button is in the HOLD (up) position, the Functional Test will continue.<br>NOTE: The STAR Tester may or may not display the STAR CODE for the Functional Test selected.<br>Example: Functional Test STAR CODE 32 is selected. STAR tester may display STAR CODE 31, even through Functional Test 32 is being run. | ▶ | RETURN to Pinpoint Test from which you were directed here. |

**Fig. 4 Functional Test, (Part 1 of 2)**

FUNCTIONAL TEST PROCEDURE (Continued)

| TEST STEP | RESULT ▶ | ACTION TO TAKE |
|---|---|---|
| **Step 3 of 3 (Continued)** | | |
| • To exit a Functional Test, depress the STAR tester button to the TEST (down) position.<br>• The Functional Test STAR CODES will be displayed. The STAR CODES will be displayed for about 15 seconds each and will be repeated over and over. The Functional Tests may be entered and exited as often as desired. | ▶ | RETURN to Pinpoint [illegible] Test from which you were directed here. |

**Fig. 4 Functional Test, (Part 2 of 2)**

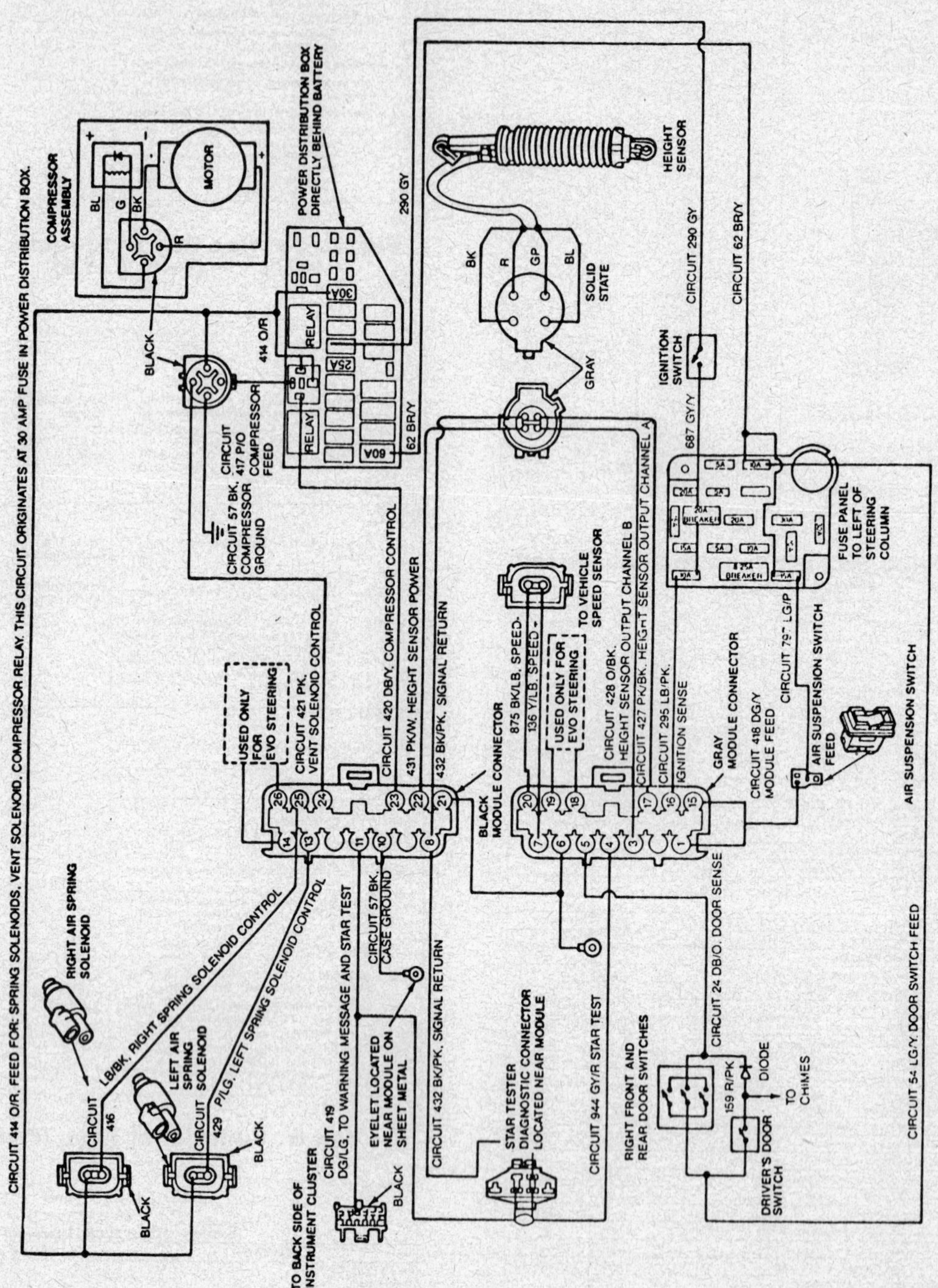


**Fig. 5 Connector Terminal Identification. 1990 models**

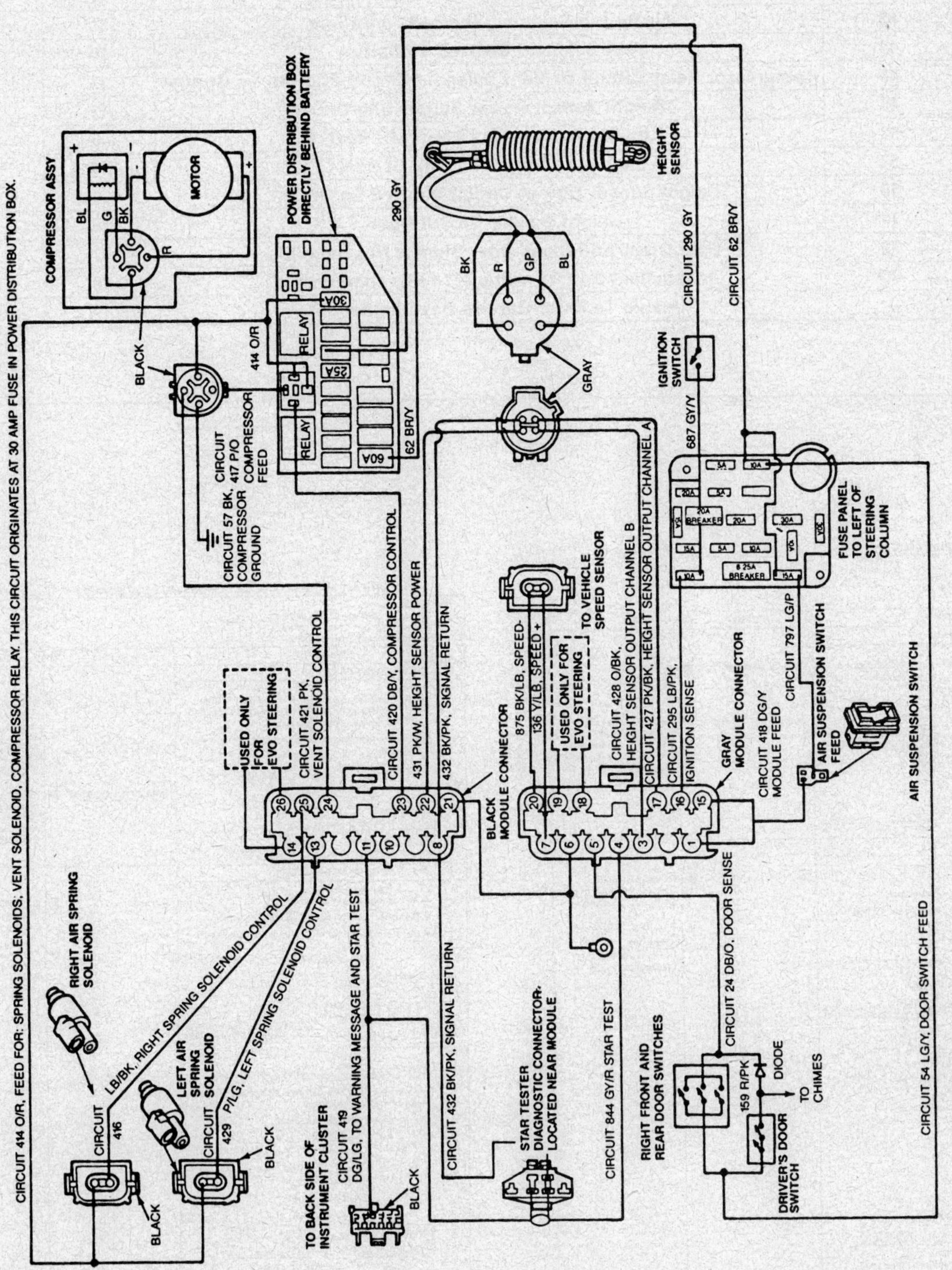


**Fig. 6 Connector Terminal Identification. 1991 models**

## PINPOINT TEST INDEX

| Pinpoint Test Letter | STAR Code | Pinpoint Test Title | Fig. No. | Page No. |
|---|---|---|---|---|
| A | 39 | Compressor Relay Circuit Shorted To Battery | 7 | 26-104 |
| B | 42 | Air Spring Solenoid Shorted To Ground | 8 | 26-105 |
| C | 43 | Air Spring Solenoid Shorted To Battery | 9 | 26-105 |
| D | 44 | Vent Solenoid Shorted To Battery | 10 | 26-106 |
| E | 45 | Compressor Relay Circuit Or Vent Solenoid Circuit Shorted To Ground | 11 | 26-106 |
| F | 46 | Height Sensor Power Supply Shorted | 12 | 26-107 |
| G | 51 | Unable To Detect Lowering Of Rear | 13 | 26-107 |
| H | 54 | Unable To Detect Raising Of Rear | 14 | 26-109 |
| J | 68 | Height Sensor Output Circuit Shorted To Ground | 15 | 26-111 |
| L | 71 | Height Sensor Circuit Open | 16 | 26-112 |
| M | 72 | Four Open And Close Door Signals Not Detected | 17 | 26-112 |
| N | 80 | Insufficient Battery Voltage To Run Diagnostics | 18 | 26-113 |
| P | — | Unable To Enter Service Bay Diagnostics. | 19 | 26-114 |

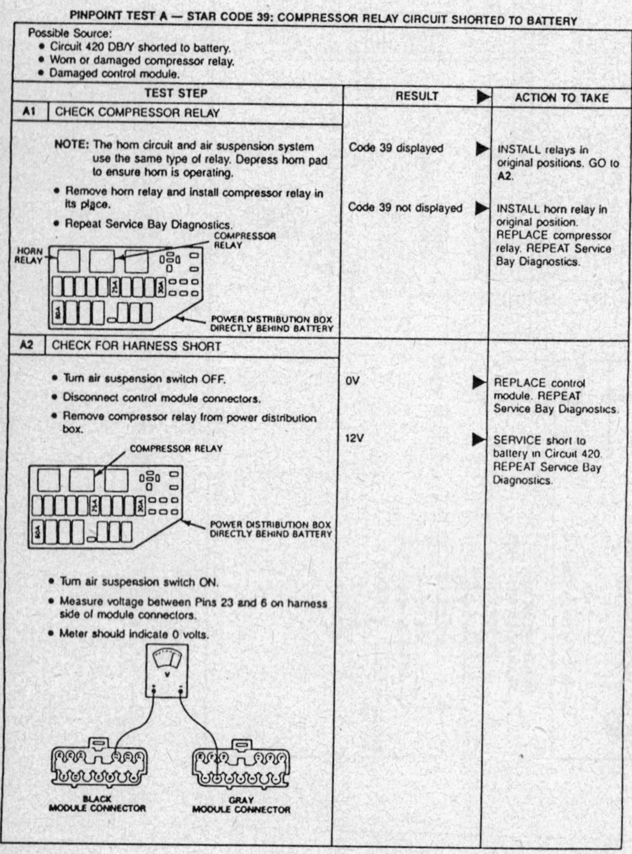

PINPOINT TEST A — STAR CODE 39: COMPRESSOR RELAY CIRCUIT SHORTED TO BATTERY

Possible Source:
- Circuit 420 DB/Y shorted to battery.
- Worn or damaged compressor relay.
- Damaged control module.

| TEST STEP | RESULT ▶ | ACTION TO TAKE |
|---|---|---|
| **A1** CHECK COMPRESSOR RELAY | | |
| NOTE: The horn circuit and air suspension system use the same type of relay. Depress horn pad to ensure horn is operating. • Remove horn relay and install compressor relay in its place. • Repeat Service Bay Diagnostics. | Code 39 displayed ▶ | INSTALL relays in original positions. GO to A2. |
| | Code 39 not displayed ▶ | INSTALL horn relay in original position. REPLACE compressor relay. REPEAT Service Bay Diagnostics. |
| **A2** CHECK FOR HARNESS SHORT | | |
| • Turn air suspension switch OFF. • Disconnect control module connectors. • Remove compressor relay from power distribution box. • Turn air suspension switch ON. • Measure voltage between Pins 23 and 6 on harness side of module connectors. • Meter should indicate 0 volts. | 0V ▶ | REPLACE control module. REPEAT Service Bay Diagnostics. |
| | 12V ▶ | SERVICE short to battery in Circuit 420. REPEAT Service Bay Diagnostics. |



**Fig. 7 Pinpoint Test, A (Part 1 of 2). 1990 models**

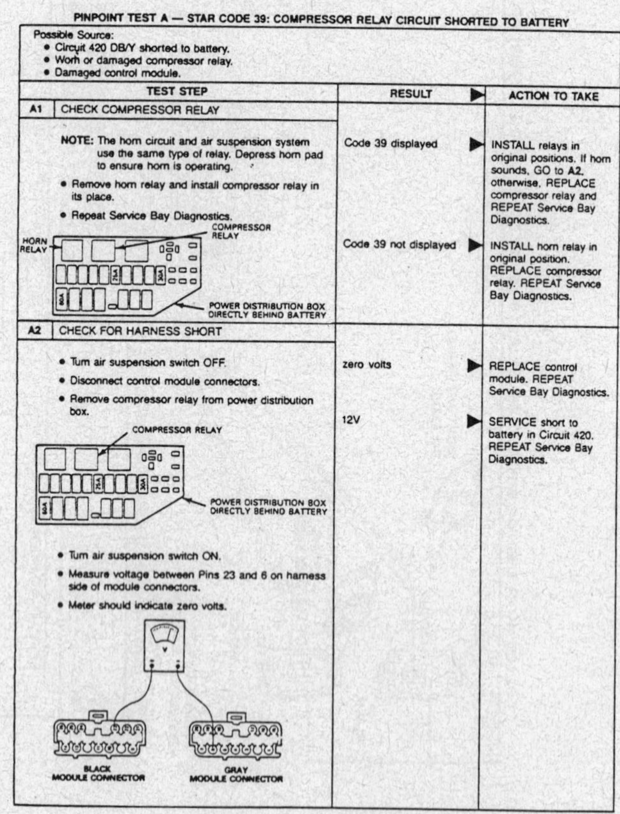

PINPOINT TEST A — STAR CODE 39: COMPRESSOR RELAY CIRCUIT SHORTED TO BATTERY

Possible Source:
- Circuit 420 DB/Y shorted to battery.
- Worn or damaged compressor relay.
- Damaged control module.

| TEST STEP | RESULT ▶ | ACTION TO TAKE |
|---|---|---|
| **A1** CHECK COMPRESSOR RELAY | | |
| NOTE: The horn circuit and air suspension system use the same type of relay. Depress horn pad to ensure horn is operating. • Remove horn relay and install compressor relay in its place. • Repeat Service Bay Diagnostics. | Code 39 displayed ▶ | INSTALL relays in original positions. If horn sounds, GO to A2, otherwise, REPLACE compressor relay and REPEAT Service Bay Diagnostics. |
| | Code 39 not displayed ▶ | INSTALL horn relay in original position. REPLACE compressor relay. REPEAT Service Bay Diagnostics. |
| **A2** CHECK FOR HARNESS SHORT | | |
| • Turn air suspension switch OFF. • Disconnect control module connectors. • Remove compressor relay from power distribution box. • Turn air suspension switch ON. • Measure voltage between Pins 23 and 6 on harness side of module connectors. • Meter should indicate zero volts. | zero volts ▶ | REPLACE control module. REPEAT Service Bay Diagnostics. |
| | 12V ▶ | SERVICE short to battery in Circuit 420. REPEAT Service Bay Diagnostics. |



**Fig. 7 Pinpoint Test, A (Part 2 of 2). 1991 models**

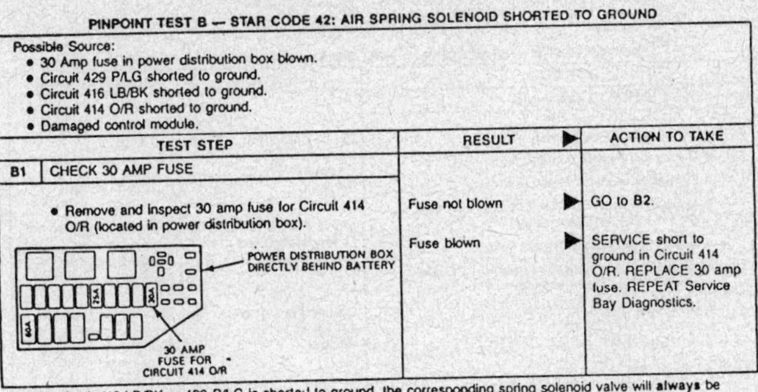

PINPOINT TEST B — STAR CODE 42: AIR SPRING SOLENOID SHORTED TO GROUND

Possible Source:
- 30 Amp fuse in power distribution box blown.
- Circuit 429 P/LG shorted to ground.
- Circuit 416 LB/BK shorted to ground.
- Circuit 414 O/R shorted to ground.
- Damaged control module.

| TEST STEP | RESULT ▶ | ACTION TO TAKE |
|---|---|---|
| **B1** CHECK 30 AMP FUSE | | |
| • Remove and inspect 30 amp fuse for Circuit 414 O/R (located in power distribution box). POWER DISTRIBUTION BOX DIRECTLY BEHIND BATTERY; 30 AMP FUSE FOR CIRCUIT 414 O/R | Fuse not blown ▶ | GO to B2. |
| | Fuse blown ▶ | SERVICE short to ground in Circuit 414 O/R. REPLACE 30 amp fuse. REPEAT Service Bay Diagnostics. |

**NOTE:** If circuit 416 LB/BK or 429 P/LG is shorted to ground, the corresponding spring solenoid valve will always be open, even with the ignition OFF.

**Fig. 8 Pinpoint Test, B (Part 1 of 2)**

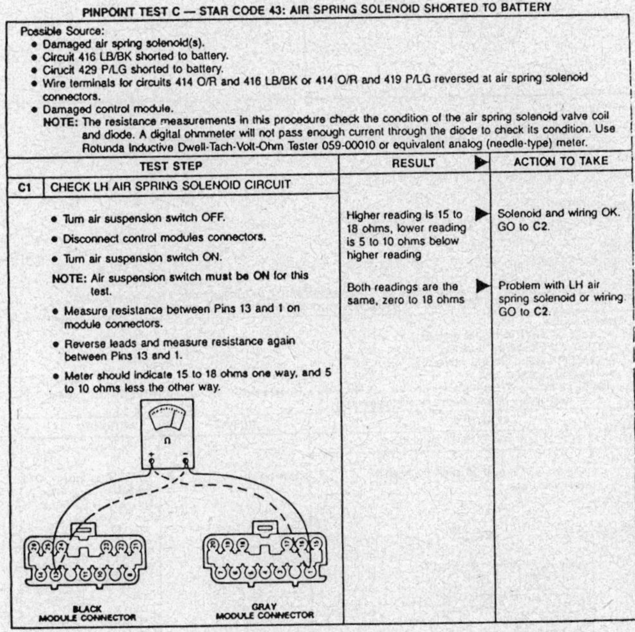

PINPOINT TEST C — STAR CODE 43: AIR SPRING SOLENOID SHORTED TO BATTERY

Possible Source:
- Damaged air spring solenoid(s).
- Circuit 416 LB/BK shorted to battery.
- Circuit 429 P/LG shorted to battery.
- Wire terminals for circuits 414 O/R and 416 LB/BK or 414 O/R and 419 P/LG reversed at air spring solenoid connectors.
- Damaged control module.

**NOTE:** The resistance measurements in this procedure check the condition of the air spring solenoid valve coil and diode. A digital ohmmeter will not pass enough current through the diode to check its condition. Use Rotunda Inductive Dwell-Tach-Volt-Ohm Tester 059-00010 or equivalent analog (needle-type) meter.

| TEST STEP | RESULT ▶ | ACTION TO TAKE |
|---|---|---|
| **C1** CHECK LH AIR SPRING SOLENOID CIRCUIT | | |
| • Turn air suspension switch OFF.<br>• Disconnect control modules connectors.<br>• Turn air suspension switch ON.<br>**NOTE:** Air suspension switch must be ON for this test.<br>• Measure resistance between Pins 13 and 1 on module connectors.<br>• Reverse leads and measure resistance again between Pins 13 and 1.<br>• Meter should indicate 15 to 18 ohms one way, and 5 to 10 ohms less the other way.<br>BLACK MODULE CONNECTOR; GRAY MODULE CONNECTOR | Higher reading is 15 to 18 ohms, lower reading is 5 to 10 ohms below higher reading ▶ | Solenoid and wiring OK. GO to C2. |
| | Both readings are the same, zero to 18 ohms ▶ | Problem with LH air spring solenoid or wiring. GO to C2. |

**Fig. 9 Pinpoint Test, C (Part 1 of 3)**

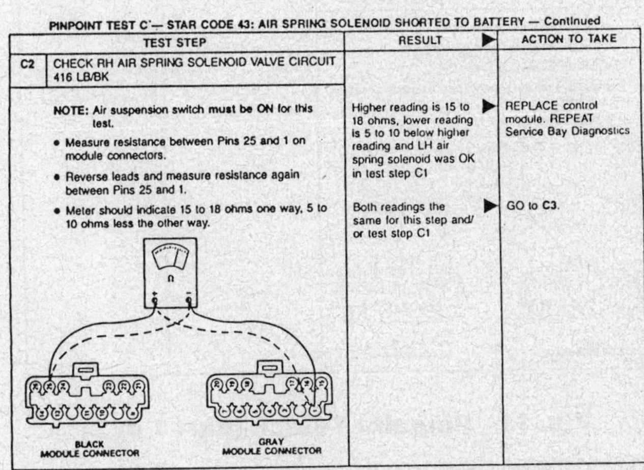

PINPOINT TEST C — STAR CODE 43: AIR SPRING SOLENOID SHORTED TO BATTERY — Continued

| TEST STEP | RESULT ▶ | ACTION TO TAKE |
|---|---|---|
| **C2** CHECK RH AIR SPRING SOLENOID VALVE CIRCUIT 416 LB/BK | | |
| **NOTE:** Air suspension switch must be ON for this test.<br>• Measure resistance between Pins 25 and 1 on module connectors.<br>• Reverse leads and measure resistance again between Pins 25 and 1.<br>• Meter should indicate 15 to 18 ohms one way, 5 to 10 ohms less the other way.<br>BLACK MODULE CONNECTOR; GRAY MODULE CONNECTOR | Higher reading is 15 to 18 ohms, lower reading is 5 to 10 below higher reading and LH air spring solenoid was OK in test step C1 ▶ | REPLACE control module. REPEAT Service Bay Diagnostics |
| | Both readings the same for this step and/ or test step C1 ▶ | GO to C3. |

**Fig. 9 Pinpoint Test, C (Part 2 of 3)**

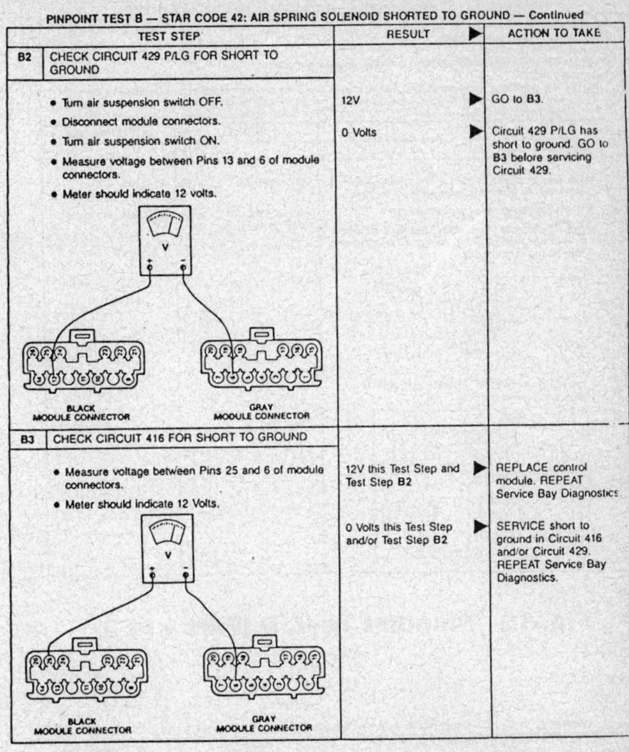

PINPOINT TEST B — STAR CODE 42: AIR SPRING SOLENOID SHORTED TO GROUND — Continued

| TEST STEP | RESULT ▶ | ACTION TO TAKE |
|---|---|---|
| **B2** CHECK CIRCUIT 429 P/LG FOR SHORT TO GROUND | | |
| • Turn air suspension switch OFF.<br>• Disconnect module connectors.<br>• Turn air suspension switch ON.<br>• Measure voltage between Pins 13 and 6 of module connectors.<br>• Meter should indicate 12 volts.<br>BLACK MODULE CONNECTOR; GRAY MODULE CONNECTOR | 12V ▶ | GO to B3. |
| | 0 Volts ▶ | Circuit 429 P/LG has short to ground. GO to B3 before servicing Circuit 429. |
| **B3** CHECK CIRCUIT 416 FOR SHORT TO GROUND | | |
| • Measure voltage between Pins 25 and 6 of module connectors.<br>• Meter should indicate 12 Volts.<br>BLACK MODULE CONNECTOR; GRAY MODULE CONNECTOR | 12V this Test Step and Test Step B2 ▶ | REPLACE control module. REPEAT Service Bay Diagnostics |
| | 0 Volts this Test Step and/or Test Step B2 ▶ | SERVICE short to ground in Circuit 416 and/or Circuit 429. REPEAT Service Bay Diagnostics. |

**Fig. 8 Pinpoint Test, B (Part 2 of 2)**

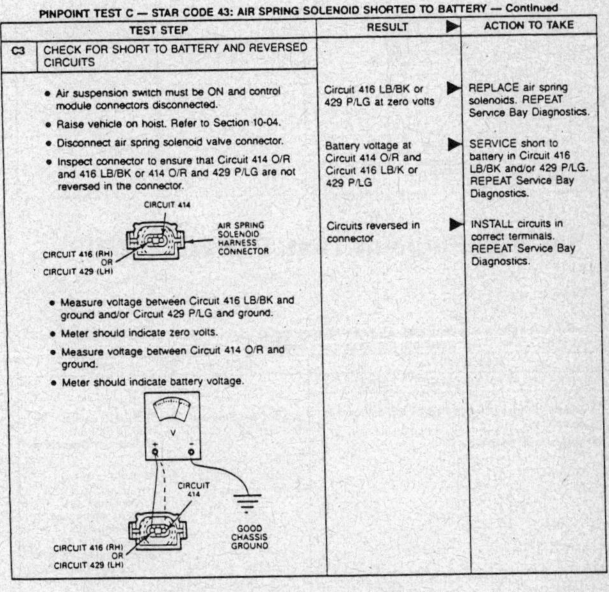

PINPOINT TEST C — STAR CODE 43: AIR SPRING SOLENOID SHORTED TO BATTERY — Continued

| TEST STEP | RESULT ▶ | ACTION TO TAKE |
|---|---|---|
| **C3** CHECK FOR SHORT TO BATTERY AND REVERSED CIRCUITS | | |
| • Air suspension switch must be ON and control module connectors disconnected.<br>• Raise vehicle on hoist. Refer to Section 10-04.<br>• Disconnect air spring solenoid valve connector.<br>• Inspect connector to ensure that Circuit 414 O/R and 416 LB/BK or 414 O/R and 429 P/LG are not reversed in the connector.<br>CIRCUIT 414; AIR SPRING SOLENOID HARNESS CONNECTOR; CIRCUIT 416 (RH) OR CIRCUIT 429 (LH)<br>• Measure voltage between Circuit 416 LB/BK and ground and/or Circuit 429 P/LG and ground.<br>• Meter should indicate zero volts.<br>• Measure voltage between Circuit 414 O/R and ground.<br>• Meter should indicate battery voltage.<br>CIRCUIT 414; GOOD CHASSIS GROUND; CIRCUIT 416 (RH) OR CIRCUIT 429 (LH) | Circuit 416 LB/BK or 429 P/LG at zero volts ▶ | REPLACE air spring solenoids. REPEAT Service Bay Diagnostics. |
| | Battery voltage at Circuit 414 O/R and Circuit 416 LB/K or 429 P/LG ▶ | SERVICE short to battery in Circuit 416 LB/BK and/or 429 P/LG. REPEAT Service Bay Diagnostics. |
| | Circuits reversed in connector ▶ | INSTALL circuits in correct terminals. REPEAT Service Bay Diagnostics. |

**Fig. 9 Pinpoint Test, C (Part 3 of 3)**

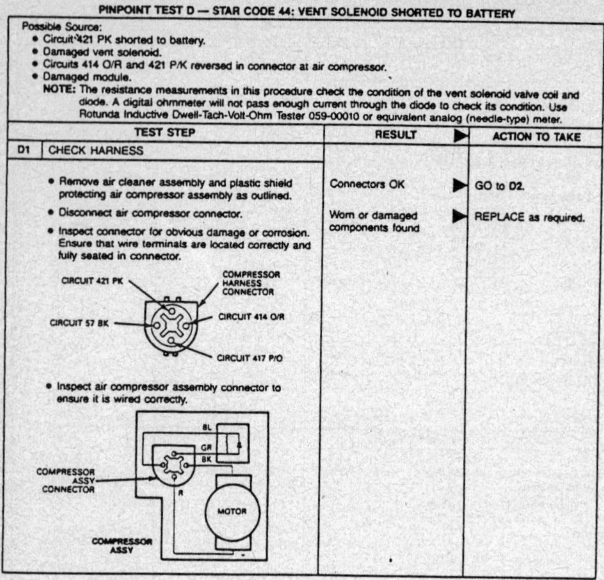

PINPOINT TEST D — STAR CODE 44: VENT SOLENOID SHORTED TO BATTERY

Possible Source:
- Circuit 421 PK shorted to battery.
- Damaged vent solenoid.
- Circuits 414 O/R and 421 P/K reversed in connector at air compressor.
- Damaged module.

NOTE: The resistance measurements in this procedure check the condition of the vent solenoid valve coil and diode. A digital ohmmeter will not pass enough current through the diode to check its condition. Use Rotunda Inductive Dwell-Tach-Volt-Ohm Tester 059-00010 or equivalent analog (needle-type) meter.

| TEST STEP | RESULT | ACTION TO TAKE |
|---|---|---|
| **D1 CHECK HARNESS** | | |
| • Remove air cleaner assembly and plastic shield protecting air compressor assembly as outlined.<br>• Disconnect air compressor connector.<br>• Inspect connector for obvious damage or corrosion. Ensure that wire terminals are located correctly and fully seated in connector.<br>• Inspect air compressor assembly connector to ensure it is wired correctly. | Connectors OK ▶ | GO to D2. |
| | Worn or damaged components found ▶ | REPLACE as required. |



Fig. 10 Pinpoint Test, D (Part 1 of 3)

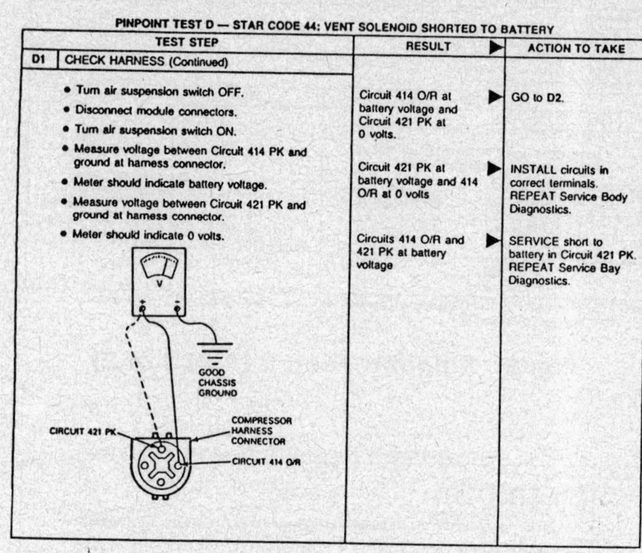

PINPOINT TEST D — STAR CODE 44: VENT SOLENOID SHORTED TO BATTERY

| TEST STEP | RESULT | ACTION TO TAKE |
|---|---|---|
| **D1 CHECK HARNESS (Continued)** | | |
| • Turn air suspension switch OFF.<br>• Disconnect module connectors.<br>• Turn air suspension switch ON.<br>• Measure voltage between Circuit 414 PK and ground at harness connector.<br>• Meter should indicate battery voltage.<br>• Measure voltage between Circuit 421 PK and ground at harness connector.<br>• Meter should indicate 0 volts. | Circuit 414 O/R at battery voltage and Circuit 421 PK at 0 volts. ▶ | GO to D2. |
| | Circuit 421 PK at battery voltage and 414 O/R at 0 volts ▶ | INSTALL circuits in correct terminals. REPEAT Service Body Diagnostics. |
| | Circuits 414 O/R and 421 PK at battery voltage ▶ | SERVICE short to battery in Circuit 421 PK. REPEAT Service Bay Diagnostics. |



Fig. 10 Pinpoint Test, D (Part 2 of 3)

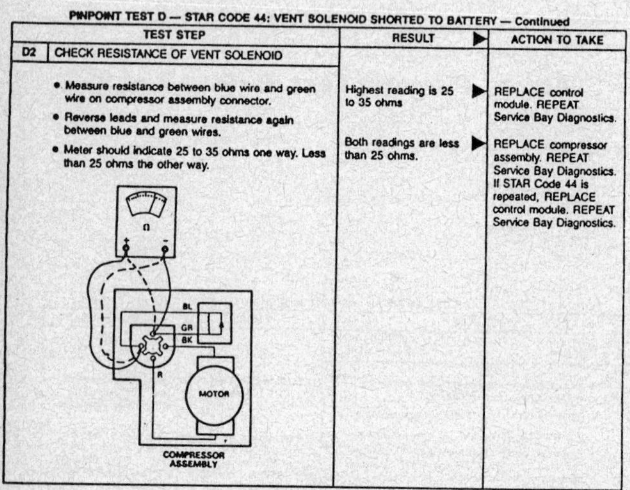

PINPOINT TEST D — STAR CODE 44: VENT SOLENOID SHORTED TO BATTERY — Continued

| TEST STEP | RESULT | ACTION TO TAKE |
|---|---|---|
| **D2 CHECK RESISTANCE OF VENT SOLENOID** | | |
| • Measure resistance between blue wire and green wire on compressor assembly connector.<br>• Reverse leads and measure resistance again between blue and green wires.<br>• Meter should indicate 25 to 35 ohms one way. Less than 25 ohms the other way. | Highest reading is 25 to 35 ohms ▶ | REPLACE control module. REPEAT Service Bay Diagnostics. |
| | Both readings are less than 25 ohms. ▶ | REPLACE compressor assembly. REPEAT Service Bay Diagnostics. If STAR Code 44 is repeated, REPLACE control module. REPEAT Service Bay Diagnostics. |



Fig. 10 Pinpoint Test, D (Part 3 of 3)

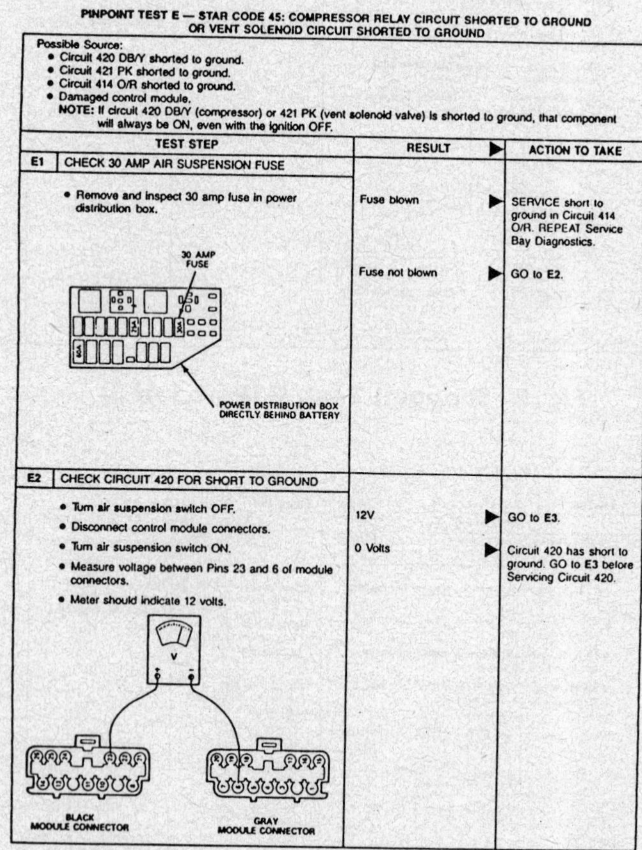

PINPOINT TEST E — STAR CODE 45: COMPRESSOR RELAY CIRCUIT SHORTED TO GROUND OR VENT SOLENOID CIRCUIT SHORTED TO GROUND

Possible Source:
- Circuit 420 DB/Y shorted to ground.
- Circuit 421 PK shorted to ground.
- Circuit 414 O/R shorted to ground.
- Damaged control module.

NOTE: If circuit 420 DB/Y (compressor) or 421 PK (vent solenoid valve) is shorted to ground, that component will always be ON, even with the ignition OFF.

| TEST STEP | RESULT | ACTION TO TAKE |
|---|---|---|
| **E1 CHECK 30 AMP AIR SUSPENSION FUSE** | | |
| • Remove and inspect 30 amp fuse in power distribution box. | Fuse blown ▶ | SERVICE short to ground in Circuit 414 O/R. REPEAT Service Bay Diagnostics. |
| | Fuse not blown ▶ | GO to E2. |
| **E2 CHECK CIRCUIT 420 FOR SHORT TO GROUND** | | |
| • Turn air suspension switch OFF.<br>• Disconnect control module connectors.<br>• Turn air suspension switch ON.<br>• Measure voltage between Pins 23 and 6 of module connectors.<br>• Meter should indicate 12 volts. | 12V ▶ | GO to E3. |
| | 0 Volts ▶ | Circuit 420 has short to ground. GO to E3 before Servicing Circuit 420. |



Fig. 11 Pinpoint Test, E (Part 1 of 2)

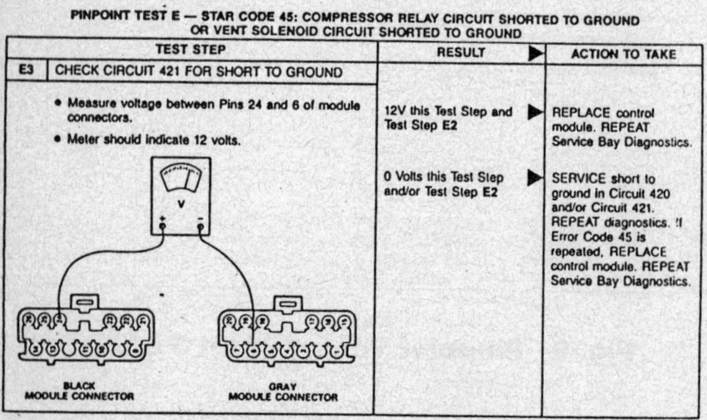

PINPOINT TEST E — STAR CODE 45: COMPRESSOR RELAY CIRCUIT SHORTED TO GROUND OR VENT SOLENOID CIRCUIT SHORTED TO GROUND

| TEST STEP | RESULT | ACTION TO TAKE |
|---|---|---|
| **E3 CHECK CIRCUIT 421 FOR SHORT TO GROUND** | | |
| • Measure voltage between Pins 24 and 6 of module connectors.<br>• Meter should indicate 12 volts. | 12V this Test Step and Test Step E2 ▶ | REPLACE control module. REPEAT Service Bay Diagnostics. |
| | 0 Volts this Test Step and/or Test Step E2 ▶ | SERVICE short to ground in Circuit 420 and/or Circuit 421. REPEAT diagnostics. If Error Code 45 is repeated, REPLACE control module. REPEAT Service Bay Diagnostics. |



Fig. 11 Pinpoint Test, E (Part 2 of 2)

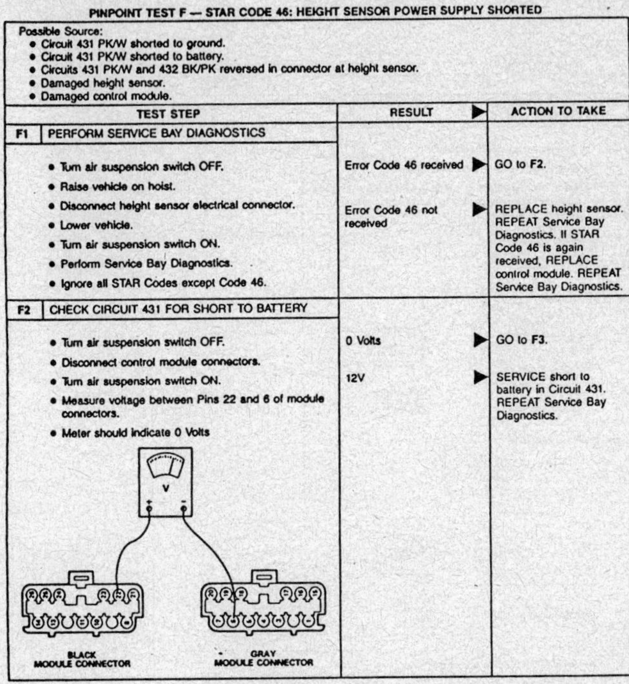

PINPOINT TEST F — STAR CODE 46: HEIGHT SENSOR POWER SUPPLY SHORTED

Possible Source:
- Circuit 431 PK/W shorted to ground.
- Circuit 431 PK/W shorted to battery.
- Circuits 431 PK/W and 432 BK/PK reversed in connector at height sensor.
- Damaged height sensor.
- Damaged control module.

| TEST STEP | RESULT ▶ | ACTION TO TAKE |
|---|---|---|
| **F1** PERFORM SERVICE BAY DIAGNOSTICS | | |
| • Turn air suspension switch OFF.<br>• Raise vehicle on hoist.<br>• Disconnect height sensor electrical connector.<br>• Lower vehicle.<br>• Turn air suspension switch ON.<br>• Perform Service Bay Diagnostics.<br>• Ignore all STAR Codes except Code 46. | Error Code 46 received ▶ | GO to F2. |
| | Error Code 46 not received ▶ | REPLACE height sensor. REPEAT Service Bay Diagnostics. If STAR Code 46 is again received, REPLACE control module. REPEAT Service Bay Diagnostics. |
| **F2** CHECK CIRCUIT 431 FOR SHORT TO BATTERY | | |
| • Turn air suspension switch OFF.<br>• Disconnect control module connectors.<br>• Turn air suspension switch ON.<br>• Measure voltage between Pins 22 and 6 of module connectors.<br>• Meter should indicate 0 Volts<br>(V meter; BLACK MODULE CONNECTOR; GRAY MODULE CONNECTOR) | 0 Volts ▶ | GO to F3. |
| | 12V ▶ | SERVICE short to battery in Circuit 431. REPEAT Service Bay Diagnostics. |

**Fig. 12 Pinpoint Test, F (Part 1 of 2)**

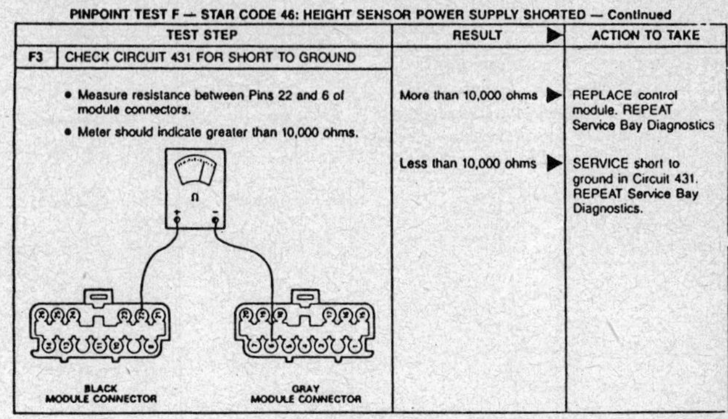

PINPOINT TEST F — STAR CODE 46: HEIGHT SENSOR POWER SUPPLY SHORTED — Continued

| TEST STEP | RESULT ▶ | ACTION TO TAKE |
|---|---|---|
| **F3** CHECK CIRCUIT 431 FOR SHORT TO GROUND | | |
| • Measure resistance between Pins 22 and 6 of module connectors.<br>• Meter should indicate greater than 10,000 ohms.<br>(Ω meter; BLACK MODULE CONNECTOR; GRAY MODULE CONNECTOR) | More than 10,000 ohms ▶ | REPLACE control module. REPEAT Service Bay Diagnostics |
| | Less than 10,000 ohms ▶ | SERVICE short to ground in Circuit 431. REPEAT Service Bay Diagnostics. |

**Fig. 12 Pinpoint Test, F (Part 2 of 2)**

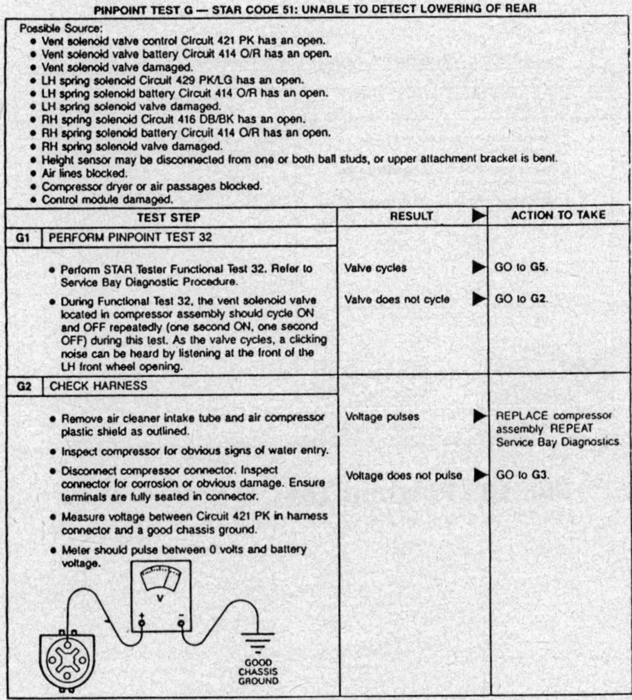

PINPOINT TEST G — STAR CODE 51: UNABLE TO DETECT LOWERING OF REAR

Possible Source:
- Vent solenoid valve control Circuit 421 PK has an open.
- Vent solenoid valve battery Circuit 414 O/R has an open.
- Vent solenoid valve damaged.
- LH spring solenoid Circuit 429 PK/LG has an open.
- LH spring solenoid battery Circuit 414 O/R has an open.
- LH spring solenoid valve damaged.
- RH spring solenoid Circuit 416 DB/BK has an open.
- RH spring solenoid battery Circuit 414 O/R has an open.
- RH spring solenoid valve damaged.
- Height sensor may be disconnected from one or both ball studs, or upper attachment bracket is bent.
- Air lines blocked.
- Compressor dryer or air passages blocked.
- Control module damaged.

| TEST STEP | RESULT ▶ | ACTION TO TAKE |
|---|---|---|
| **G1** PERFORM PINPOINT TEST 32 | | |
| • Perform STAR Tester Functional Test 32. Refer to Service Bay Diagnostic Procedure. | Valve cycles ▶ | GO to G5. |
| • During Functional Test 32, the vent solenoid valve located in compressor assembly should cycle ON and OFF repeatedly (one second ON, one second OFF) during this test. As the valve cycles, a clicking noise can be heard by listening at the front of the LH front wheel opening. | Valve does not cycle ▶ | GO to G2. |
| **G2** CHECK HARNESS | | |
| • Remove air cleaner intake tube and air compressor plastic shield as outlined.<br>• Inspect compressor for obvious signs of water entry. | Voltage pulses ▶ | REPLACE compressor assembly REPEAT Service Bay Diagnostics |
| • Disconnect compressor connector. Inspect connector for corrosion or obvious damage. Ensure terminals are fully seated in connector.<br>• Measure voltage between Circuit 421 PK in harness connector and a good chassis ground.<br>• Meter should pulse between 0 volts and battery voltage.<br>(V meter; GOOD CHASSIS GROUND) | Voltage does not pulse ▶ | GO to G3. |

**Fig. 13 Pinpoint Test, G (Part 1 of 9)**

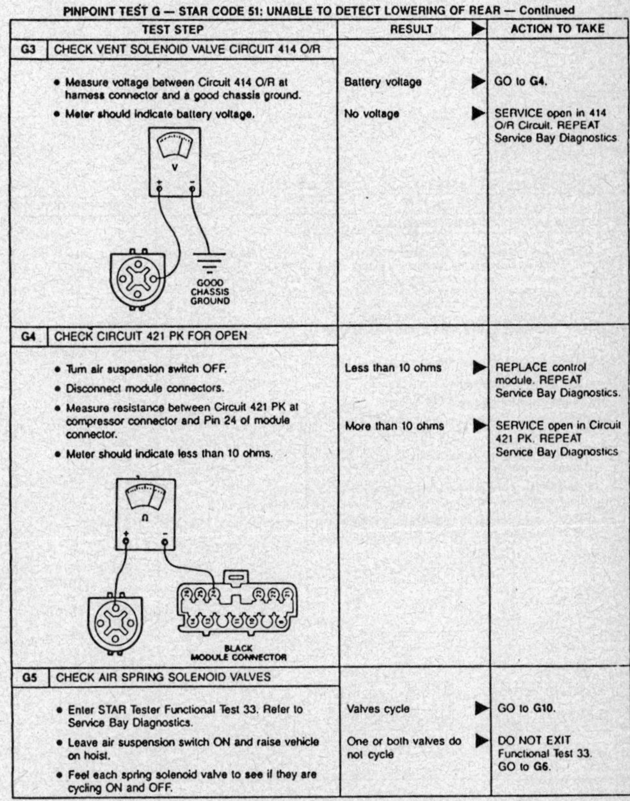

PINPOINT TEST G — STAR CODE 51: UNABLE TO DETECT LOWERING OF REAR — Continued

| TEST STEP | RESULT ▶ | ACTION TO TAKE |
|---|---|---|
| **G3** CHECK VENT SOLENOID VALVE CIRCUIT 414 O/R | | |
| • Measure voltage between Circuit 414 O/R at harness connector and a good chassis ground. | Battery voltage ▶ | GO to G4. |
| • Meter should indicate battery voltage.<br>(V meter; GOOD CHASSIS GROUND) | No voltage ▶ | SERVICE open in 414 O/R Circuit. REPEAT Service Bay Diagnostics |
| **G4** CHECK CIRCUIT 421 PK FOR OPEN | | |
| • Turn air suspension switch OFF.<br>• Disconnect module connectors. | Less than 10 ohms ▶ | REPLACE control module. REPEAT Service Bay Diagnostics. |
| • Measure resistance between Circuit 421 PK at compressor connector and Pin 24 of module connector.<br>• Meter should indicate less than 10 ohms.<br>(Ω meter; BLACK MODULE CONNECTOR) | More than 10 ohms ▶ | SERVICE open in Circuit 421 PK. REPEAT Service Bay Diagnostics |
| **G5** CHECK AIR SPRING SOLENOID VALVES | | |
| • Enter STAR Tester Functional Test 33. Refer to Service Bay Diagnostics. | Valves cycle ▶ | GO to G10. |
| • Leave air suspension switch ON and raise vehicle on hoist.<br>• Feel each spring solenoid valve to see if they are cycling ON and OFF. | One or both valves do not cycle ▶ | DO NOT EXIT Functional Test 33. GO to G6. |

**Fig. 13 Pinpoint Test, G (Part 2 of 9)**

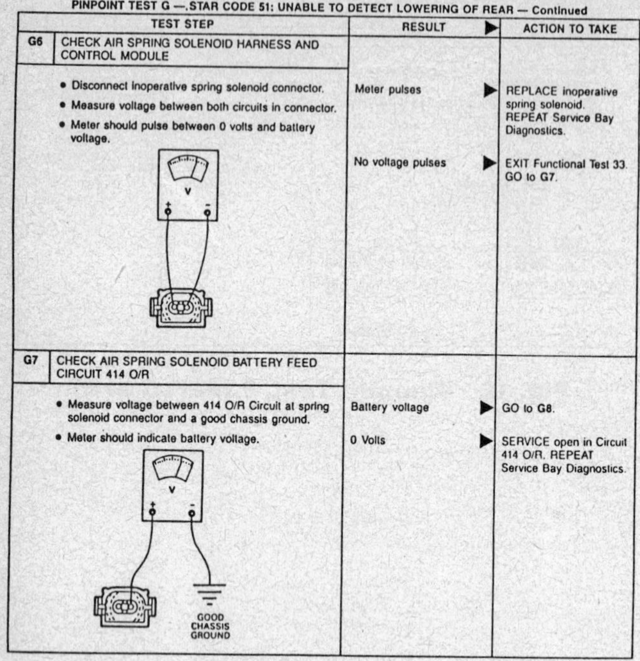

PINPOINT TEST G —.STAR CODE 51: UNABLE TO DETECT LOWERING OF REAR — Continued

| TEST STEP | | RESULT ▶ | ACTION TO TAKE |
|---|---|---|---|
| G6 | CHECK AIR SPRING SOLENOID HARNESS AND CONTROL MODULE | | |
| | • Disconnect inoperative spring solenoid connector.<br>• Measure voltage between both circuits in connector.<br>• Meter should pulse between 0 volts and battery voltage. | Meter pulses ▶ | REPLACE inoperative spring solenoid. REPEAT Service Bay Diagnostics. |
| | | No voltage pulses ▶ | EXIT Functional Test 33. GO to G7. |
| G7 | CHECK AIR SPRING SOLENOID BATTERY FEED CIRCUIT 414 O/R | | |
| | • Measure voltage between 414 O/R Circuit at spring solenoid connector and a good chassis ground.<br>• Meter should indicate battery voltage. | Battery voltage ▶ | GO to G8. |
| | | 0 Volts ▶ | SERVICE open in Circuit 414 O/R. REPEAT Service Bay Diagnostics. |



Fig. 13 Pinpoint Test, G (Part 3 of 9)

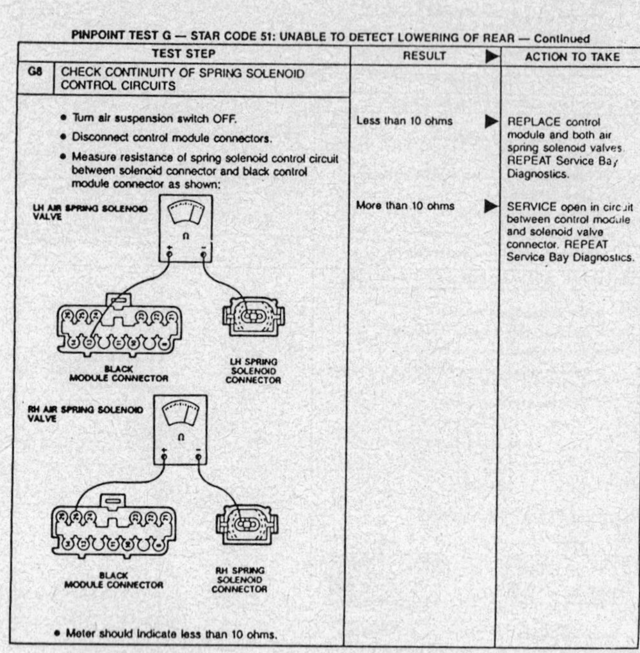

PINPOINT TEST G — STAR CODE 51: UNABLE TO DETECT LOWERING OF REAR — Continued

| TEST STEP | | RESULT ▶ | ACTION TO TAKE |
|---|---|---|---|
| G8 | CHECK CONTINUITY OF SPRING SOLENOID CONTROL CIRCUITS | | |
| | • Turn air suspension switch OFF.<br>• Disconnect control module connectors.<br>• Measure resistance of spring solenoid control circuit between solenoid connector and black control module connector as shown:<br>• Meter should indicate less than 10 ohms. | Less than 10 ohms ▶ | REPLACE control module and both air spring solenoid valves. REPEAT Service Bay Diagnostics. |
| | | More than 10 ohms ▶ | SERVICE open in circuit between control module and solenoid valve connector. REPEAT Service Bay Diagnostics. |



Fig. 13 Pinpoint Test, G (Part 4 of 9)

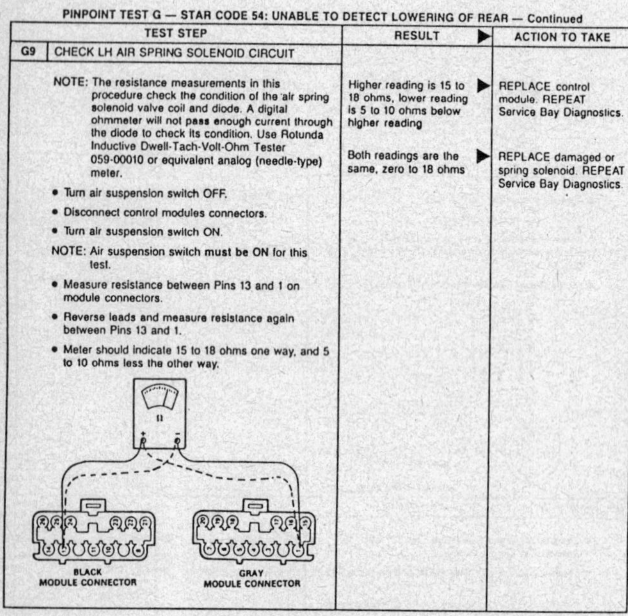

PINPOINT TEST G — STAR CODE 54: UNABLE TO DETECT LOWERING OF REAR — Continued

| TEST STEP | | RESULT ▶ | ACTION TO TAKE |
|---|---|---|---|
| G9 | CHECK LH AIR SPRING SOLENOID CIRCUIT | | |
| | NOTE: The resistance measurements in this procedure check the condition of the air spring solenoid valve coil and diode. A digital ohmmeter will not pass enough current through the diode to check its condition. Use Rotunda Inductive Dwell-Tach-Volt-Ohm Tester 059-00010 or equivalent analog (needle-type) meter.<br>• Turn air suspension switch OFF.<br>• Disconnect control modules connectors.<br>• Turn air suspension switch ON.<br>NOTE: Air suspension switch must be ON for this test.<br>• Measure resistance between Pins 13 and 1 on module connectors.<br>• Reverse leads and measure resistance again between Pins 13 and 1.<br>• Meter should indicate 15 to 18 ohms one way, and 5 to 10 ohms less the other way. | Higher reading is 15 to 18 ohms, lower reading is 5 to 10 ohms below higher reading ▶ | REPLACE control module. REPEAT Service Bay Diagnostics. |
| | | Both readings are the same, zero to 18 ohms ▶ | REPLACE damaged or spring solenoid. REPEAT Service Bay Diagnostics. |



Fig. 13 Pinpoint Test, G (Part 5 of 9)

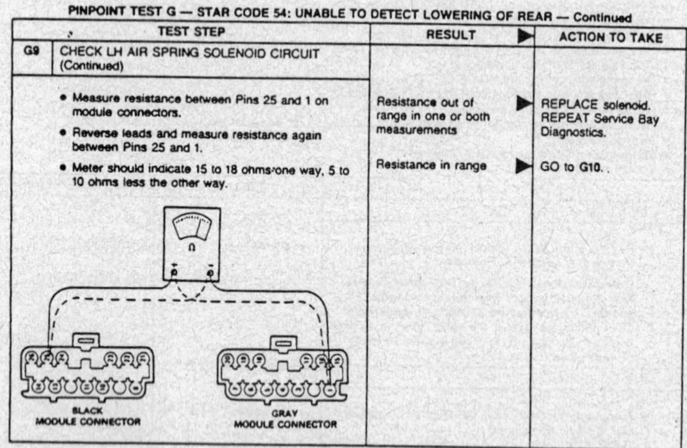

PINPOINT TEST G — STAR CODE 54: UNABLE TO DETECT LOWERING OF REAR — Continued

| TEST STEP | | RESULT ▶ | ACTION TO TAKE |
|---|---|---|---|
| G9 | CHECK LH AIR SPRING SOLENOID CIRCUIT (Continued) | | |
| | • Measure resistance between Pins 25 and 1 on module connectors.<br>• Reverse leads and measure resistance again between Pins 25 and 1.<br>• Meter should indicate 15 to 18 ohms one way, 5 to 10 ohms less the other way. | Resistance out of range in one or both measurements ▶ | REPLACE solenoid. REPEAT Service Bay Diagnostics. |
| | | Resistance in range ▶ | GO to G10. |



Fig. 13 Pinpoint Test, G (Part 6 of 9)

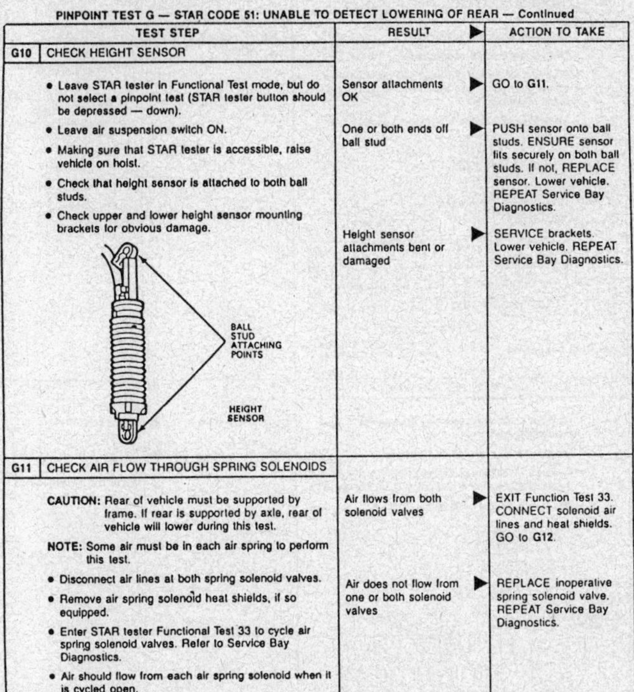

PINPOINT TEST G — STAR CODE 51: UNABLE TO DETECT LOWERING OF REAR — Continued

| TEST STEP | RESULT ▶ | ACTION TO TAKE |
|---|---|---|
| **G10** CHECK HEIGHT SENSOR | | |
| • Leave STAR tester in Functional Test mode, but do not select a pinpoint test (STAR tester button should be depressed — down).<br>• Leave air suspension switch ON.<br>• Making sure that STAR tester is accessible, raise vehicle on hoist.<br>• Check that height sensor is attached to both ball studs.<br>• Check upper and lower height sensor mounting brackets for obvious damage. | Sensor attachments OK ▶ | GO to **G11**. |
| | One or both ends off ball stud ▶ | PUSH sensor onto ball studs. ENSURE sensor fits securely on both ball studs. If not, REPLACE sensor. Lower vehicle. REPEAT Service Bay Diagnostics. |
| | Height sensor attachments bent or damaged ▶ | SERVICE brackets. Lower vehicle. REPEAT Service Bay Diagnostics. |
| **G11** CHECK AIR FLOW THROUGH SPRING SOLENOIDS | | |
| **CAUTION:** Rear of vehicle must be supported by frame. If rear is supported by axle, rear of vehicle will lower during this test.<br>**NOTE:** Some air must be in each air spring to perform this test.<br>• Disconnect air lines at both spring solenoid valves.<br>• Remove air spring solenoid heat shields, if so equipped.<br>• Enter STAR tester Functional Test 33 to cycle air spring solenoid valves. Refer to Service Bay Diagnostics.<br>• Air should flow from each air spring solenoid when it is cycled open. | Air flows from both solenoid valves ▶ | EXIT Function Test 33. CONNECT solenoid air lines and heat shields. GO to G12. |
| | Air does not flow from one or both solenoid valves ▶ | REPLACE inoperative spring solenoid valve. REPEAT Service Bay Diagnostics. |



**Fig. 13 Pinpoint Test, G (Part 7 of 9)**

PINPOINT TEST G — STAR CODE 51: UNABLE TO DETECT LOWERING OF REAR — Continued

| TEST STEP | RESULT ▶ | ACTION TO TAKE |
|---|---|---|
| **G12** CHECK FOR ADEQUATE SPRING PRESSURE | | |
| • Lower vehicle. There should be nothing supporting vehicle.<br>• Measure distance between center of lip rear wheel opening and bottom of wheel (not bottom of tire).<br>• Measurement should be a minimum of 610-635 mm (24-25 in.). This is vehicle trim height. | Vehicle higher at trim ▶ | GO to **G13**. |
| | Vehicle low ▶ | GO to G15. |
| **G13** CHECK AIR FLOW THROUGH LINES | | |
| • Remove air cleaner assembly and plastic shield from compressor assembly as outlined.<br>• Disconnect air line at compressor dryer.<br>• Enter STAR tester Functional Test 23 — vent rear. Refer to Service Bay Diagnostics. Air should flow from disconnected air line and vehicle should drop about one inch in 10-20 seconds.<br>• CAUTION: Rear of vehicle may drop rapidly once Functional Test 23 is entered. | Little or no air flow and vehicle does not lower ▶ | SERVICE air line from compressor to solenoid valves for blockage or kinks. REPEAT Service Bay Diagnostics. |
| | Air flow from air line and vehicle drops ▶ | EXIT Functional Test 23 before rear of vehicle becomes too low. GO to G14. |
| **G14** CHECK AIR FLOW THROUGH COMPRESSOR DRYER | | |
| • Remove air dryer from compressor as outlined.<br>• Connect air line to air dryer.<br>• Enter Functional Test 23 — vent rear. Refer to Service Bay Diagnostics. | Little or no air flows through air dryer ▶ | REPLACE air dryer. Install compressor assembly. REPEAT Service Bay Diagnostics |
| | Air flows through air dryer ▶ | REPLACE air compressor assembly. REPEAT Service Bay Diagnostics. |
| **G15** INFLATE REAR SPRINGS | | |
| • Enter Functional Test 26 — compress rear. Refer to Service Bay Diagnostics.<br>• Exit Functional Test 26 when rear of vehicle is raised about 50 mm (2 in.) above trim height.<br>• Distance should be about 660-685 mm (26-27 in.) from bottom of wheel (not bottom of tire) and center of rear wheel lip opening. | Rear of vehicle raises ▶ | GO to G13. |
| | Rear of vehicle does not raise, but air compressor runs ▶ | EXIT Functional Test 26. GO to G16. |
| | Rear of vehicle does not raise and air compressor does not run ▶ | GO to Pinpoint Test H. |

**Fig. 13 Pinpoint Test, G (Part 8 of 9)**

PINPOINT TEST G — STAR CODE 51: UNABLE TO DETECT LOWERING OF REAR — Continued

| TEST STEP | RESULT ▶ | ACTION TO TAKE |
|---|---|---|
| **G16** CHECK FOR AIR FLOW FROM AIR COMPRESSOR | | |
| • Raise rear of vehicle.<br>**CAUTION: Support rear of vehicle on frame. If rear of vehicle is supported by axle, air springs will be damaged during this test.**<br>• Disconnect air line from air dryer.<br>• Enter Functional Test 26 — compress rear. Refer to Service Bay Diagnostics.<br>• Air should flow from air dryer while compressor is running. | Air flows from air dryer ▶ | SERVICE blocked or kinked air line. REPEAT Service Bay Diagnostics. |
| | Little or no air flow from air dryer ▶ | EXIT Functional Test 26. GO to G17. |
| **G17** CHECK AIR FLOW WITH DRYER REMOVED | | |
| • Remove air dryer from air compressor as outlined.<br>• Enter Functional Test 26 — compress rear. Refer to Service Bay Diagnostics.<br>• Air should flow from air dryer fitting on compressor while compressor is running. | Air flows from compressor ▶ | REPLACE air dryer. REPEAT Service Bay Diagnostics. **CAUTION: Enter Functional Test 26 while in Service Bay Diagnostics and fill air springs for about 90 seconds before lowering rear of vehicle.** |
| | Little or no air flow from compressor ▶ | REPLACE compressor assembly. REPEAT Service Bay Diagnostics. **CAUTION: Enter Functional Test 26 while in Service Bay Diagnostics and fill air springs for about 90 seconds before lowering rear of vehicle.** |

**Fig. 13 Pinpoint Test, G (Part 9 of 9)**

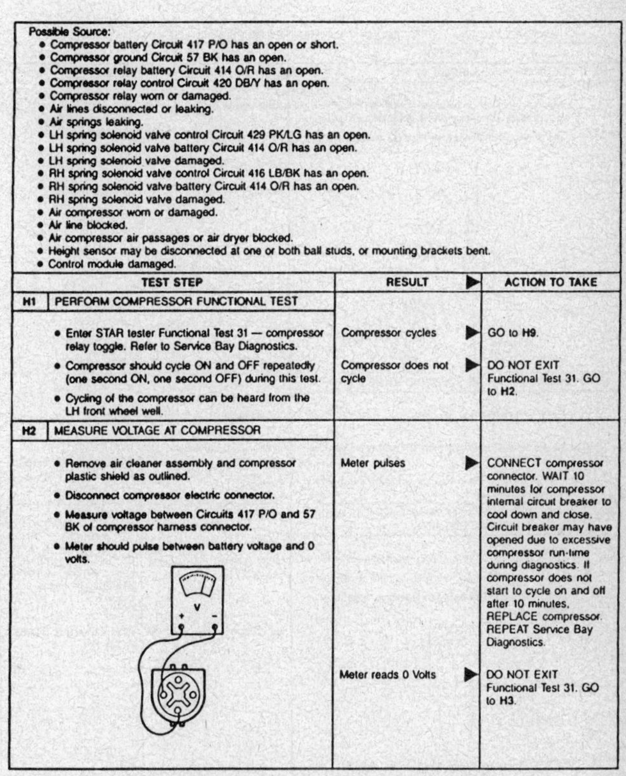

Possible Source:
- Compressor battery Circuit 417 P/O has an open or short.
- Compressor ground Circuit 57 BK has an open.
- Compressor relay battery Circuit 414 O/R has an open.
- Compressor relay control Circuit 420 DB/Y has an open.
- Compressor relay worn or damaged.
- Air lines disconnected or leaking.
- Air springs leaking.
- LH spring solenoid valve control Circuit 429 PK/LG has an open.
- LH spring solenoid valve battery Circuit 414 O/R has an open.
- LH spring solenoid valve damaged.
- RH spring solenoid valve control Circuit 416 LB/BK has an open.
- RH spring solenoid valve battery Circuit 414 O/R has an open.
- RH spring solenoid valve damaged.
- Air compressor worn or damaged.
- Air line blocked.
- Air compressor air passages or air dryer blocked.
- Height sensor may be disconnected at one or both ball studs, or mounting brackets bent.
- Control module damaged.

| TEST STEP | RESULT ▶ | ACTION TO TAKE |
|---|---|---|
| **H1** PERFORM COMPRESSOR FUNCTIONAL TEST | | |
| • Enter STAR tester Functional Test 31 — compressor relay toggle. Refer to Service Bay Diagnostics.<br>• Compressor should cycle ON and OFF repeatedly (one second ON, one second OFF) during this test.<br>• Cycling of the compressor can be heard from the LH front wheel well. | Compressor cycles ▶ | GO to **H9**. |
| | Compressor does not cycle ▶ | DO NOT EXIT Functional Test 31. GO to **H2**. |
| **H2** MEASURE VOLTAGE AT COMPRESSOR | | |
| • Remove air cleaner assembly and compressor plastic shield as outlined.<br>• Disconnect compressor electric connector.<br>• Measure voltage between Circuits 417 P/O and 57 BK of compressor harness connector.<br>• Meter should pulse between battery voltage and 0 volts. | Meter pulses ▶ | CONNECT compressor connector. WAIT 10 minutes for compressor internal circuit breaker to cool down and close. Circuit breaker may have opened due to excessive compressor run-time during diagnostics. If compressor does not start to cycle on and off after 10 minutes, REPLACE compressor. REPEAT Service Bay Diagnostics. |
| | Meter reads 0 Volts ▶ | DO NOT EXIT Functional Test 31. GO to H3. |

**Fig. 14 Pinpoint Test, H (Part 1 of 9)**

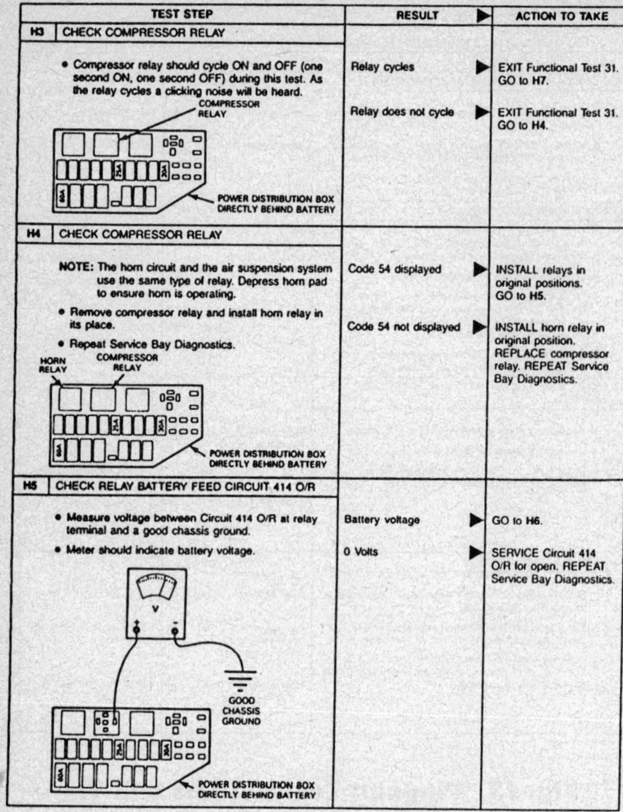

| TEST STEP | RESULT ▶ | ACTION TO TAKE |
|---|---|---|
| **H3 CHECK COMPRESSOR RELAY** | | |
| • Compressor relay should cycle ON and OFF (one second ON, one second OFF) during this test. As the relay cycles a clicking noise will be heard. (COMPRESSOR RELAY; POWER DISTRIBUTION BOX DIRECTLY BEHIND BATTERY) | Relay cycles ▶ | EXIT Functional Test 31. GO to H7. |
| | Relay does not cycle ▶ | EXIT Functional Test 31. GO to H4. |
| **H4 CHECK COMPRESSOR RELAY** | | |
| **NOTE:** The horn circuit and the air suspension system use the same type of relay. Depress horn pad to ensure horn is operating.<br>• Remove compressor relay and install horn relay in its place.<br>• Repeat Service Bay Diagnostics.<br>(HORN RELAY; COMPRESSOR RELAY; POWER DISTRIBUTION BOX DIRECTLY BEHIND BATTERY) | Code 54 displayed ▶ | INSTALL relays in original positions. GO to H5. |
| | Code 54 not displayed ▶ | INSTALL horn relay in original position. REPLACE compressor relay. REPEAT Service Bay Diagnostics. |
| **H5 CHECK RELAY BATTERY FEED CIRCUIT 414 O/R** | | |
| • Measure voltage between Circuit 414 O/R at relay terminal and a good chassis ground.<br>• Meter should indicate battery voltage.<br>(GOOD CHASSIS GROUND; POWER DISTRIBUTION BOX DIRECTLY BEHIND BATTERY) | Battery voltage ▶ | GO to H6. |
| | 0 Volts ▶ | SERVICE Circuit 414 O/R for open. REPEAT Service Bay Diagnostics. |

Fig. 14 Pinpoint Test, H (Part 2 of 9)

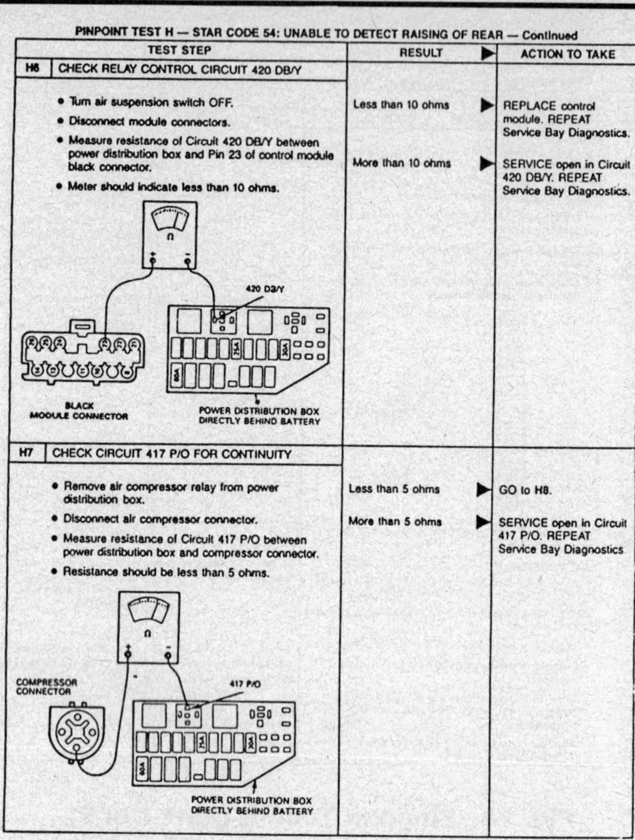

PINPOINT TEST H — STAR CODE 54: UNABLE TO DETECT RAISING OF REAR — Continued

| TEST STEP | RESULT ▶ | ACTION TO TAKE |
|---|---|---|
| **H6 CHECK RELAY CONTROL CIRCUIT 420 DB/Y** | | |
| • Turn air suspension switch OFF.<br>• Disconnect module connectors.<br>• Measure resistance of Circuit 420 DB/Y between power distribution box and Pin 23 of control module black connector.<br>• Meter should indicate less than 10 ohms.<br>(420 DB/Y; BLACK MODULE CONNECTOR; POWER DISTRIBUTION BOX DIRECTLY BEHIND BATTERY) | Less than 10 ohms ▶ | REPLACE control module. REPEAT Service Bay Diagnostics. |
| | More than 10 ohms ▶ | SERVICE open in Circuit 420 DB/Y. REPEAT Service Bay Diagnostics. |
| **H7 CHECK CIRCUIT 417 P/O FOR CONTINUITY** | | |
| • Remove air compressor relay from power distribution box.<br>• Disconnect air compressor connector.<br>• Measure resistance of Circuit 417 P/O between power distribution box and compressor connector.<br>• Resistance should be less than 5 ohms.<br>(COMPRESSOR CONNECTOR; 417 P/O; POWER DISTRIBUTION BOX DIRECTLY BEHIND BATTERY) | Less than 5 ohms ▶ | GO to H8. |
| | More than 5 ohms ▶ | SERVICE open in Circuit 417 P/O. REPEAT Service Bay Diagnostics |

Fig. 14 Pinpoint Test, H (Part 3 of 9)

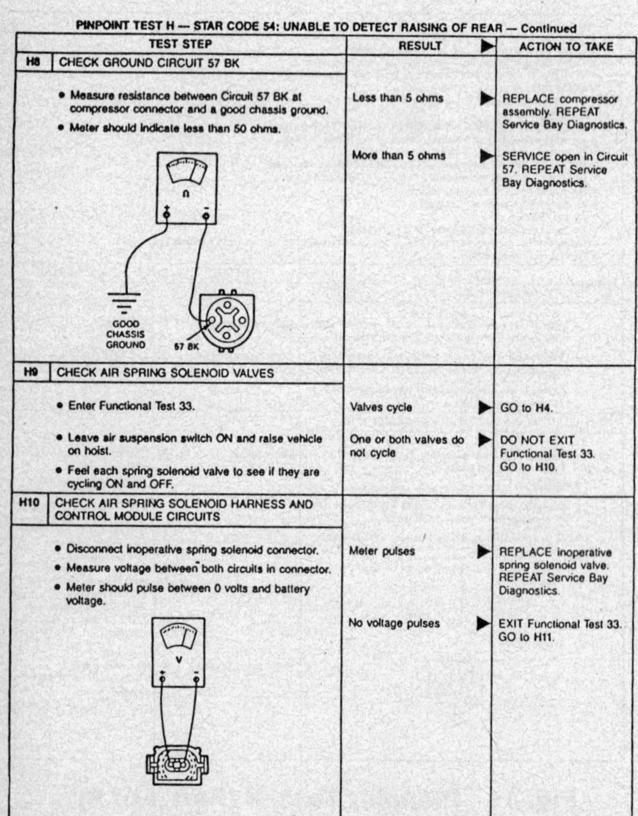

PINPOINT TEST H — STAR CODE 54: UNABLE TO DETECT RAISING OF REAR — Continued

| TEST STEP | RESULT ▶ | ACTION TO TAKE |
|---|---|---|
| **H8 CHECK GROUND CIRCUIT 57 BK** | | |
| • Measure resistance between Circuit 57 BK at compressor connector and a good chassis ground.<br>• Meter should indicate less than 50 ohms.<br>(GOOD CHASSIS GROUND; 57 BK) | Less than 5 ohms ▶ | REPLACE compressor assembly. REPEAT Service Bay Diagnostics. |
| | More than 5 ohms ▶ | SERVICE open in Circuit 57. REPEAT Service Bay Diagnostics. |
| **H9 CHECK AIR SPRING SOLENOID VALVES** | | |
| • Enter Functional Test 33. | Valves cycle ▶ | GO to H4. |
| • Leave air suspension switch ON and raise vehicle on hoist.<br>• Feel each spring solenoid valve to see if they are cycling ON and OFF. | One or both valves do not cycle ▶ | DO NOT EXIT Functional Test 33. GO to H10. |
| **H10 CHECK AIR SPRING SOLENOID HARNESS AND CONTROL MODULE CIRCUITS** | | |
| • Disconnect inoperative spring solenoid connector.<br>• Measure voltage between both circuits in connector.<br>• Meter should pulse between 0 volts and battery voltage. | Meter pulses ▶ | REPLACE inoperative spring solenoid valve. REPEAT Service Bay Diagnostics. |
| | No voltage pulses ▶ | EXIT Functional Test 33. GO to H11. |

Fig. 14 Pinpoint Test, H (Part 4 of 9)

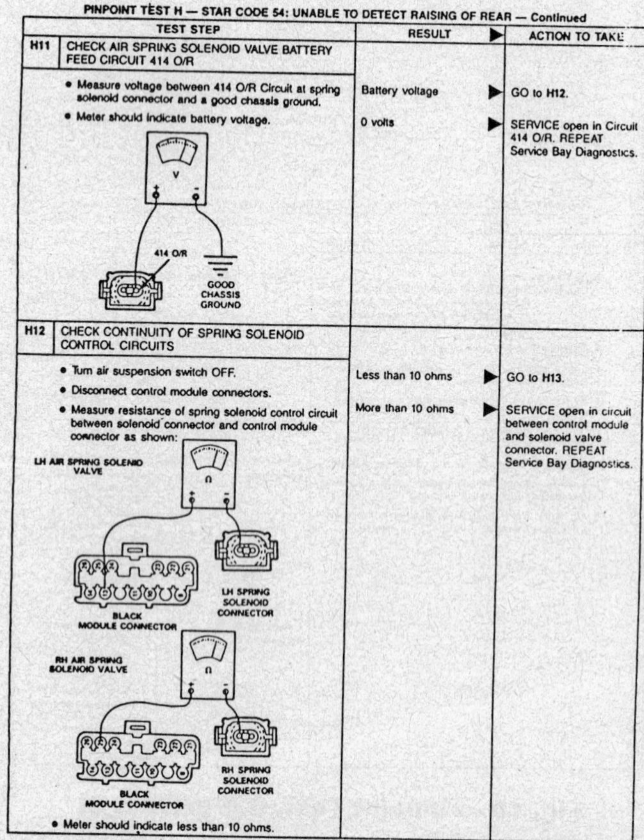

PINPOINT TEST H — STAR CODE 54: UNABLE TO DETECT RAISING OF REAR — Continued

| TEST STEP | RESULT ▶ | ACTION TO TAKE |
|---|---|---|
| **H11 CHECK AIR SPRING SOLENOID VALVE BATTERY FEED CIRCUIT 414 O/R** | | |
| • Measure voltage between 414 O/R Circuit at spring solenoid connector and a good chassis ground.<br>• Meter should indicate battery voltage.<br>(414 O/R; GOOD CHASSIS GROUND) | Battery voltage ▶ | GO to H12. |
| | 0 volts ▶ | SERVICE open in Circuit 414 O/R. REPEAT Service Bay Diagnostics. |
| **H12 CHECK CONTINUITY OF SPRING SOLENOID CONTROL CIRCUITS** | | |
| • Turn air suspension switch OFF.<br>• Disconnect control module connectors.<br>• Measure resistance of spring solenoid control circuit between solenoid connector and control module connector as shown:<br>(LH AIR SPRING SOLENOID VALVE; BLACK MODULE CONNECTOR; LH SPRING SOLENOID CONNECTOR; RH AIR SPRING SOLENOID VALVE; BLACK MODULE CONNECTOR; RH SPRING SOLENOID CONNECTOR)<br>• Meter should indicate less than 10 ohms. | Less than 10 ohms ▶ | GO to H13. |
| | More than 10 ohms ▶ | SERVICE open in circuit between control module and solenoid valve connector. REPEAT Service Bay Diagnostics. |

Fig. 14 Pinpoint Test, H (Part 5 of 9)

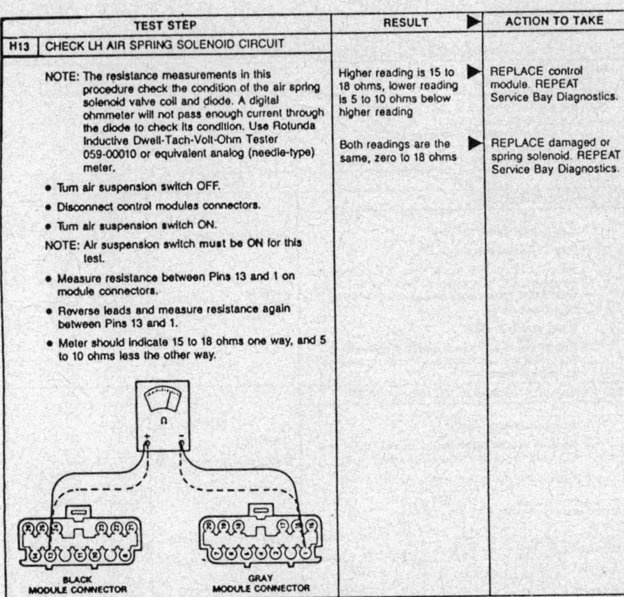

| TEST STEP | | RESULT | ▶ | ACTION TO TAKE |
|---|---|---|---|---|
| H13 | CHECK LH AIR SPRING SOLENOID CIRCUIT | | | |
| | NOTE: The resistance measurements in this procedure check the condition of the air spring solenoid valve coil and diode. A digital ohmmeter will not pass enough current through the diode to check its condition. Use Rotunda Inductive Dwell-Tach-Volt-Ohm Tester 059-00010 or equivalent analog (needle-type) meter.<br>• Turn air suspension switch OFF.<br>• Disconnect control modules connectors.<br>• Turn air suspension switch ON.<br>NOTE: Air suspension switch must be ON for this test.<br>• Measure resistance between Pins 13 and 1 on module connectors.<br>• Reverse leads and measure resistance again between Pins 13 and 1.<br>• Meter should indicate 15 to 18 ohms one way, and 5 to 10 ohms less the other way.<br>BLACK MODULE CONNECTOR<br>GRAY MODULE CONNECTOR | Higher reading is 15 to 18 ohms, lower reading is 5 to 10 ohms below higher reading | ▶ | REPLACE control module. REPEAT Service Bay Diagnostics. |
| | | Both readings are the same, zero to 18 ohms | ▶ | REPLACE damaged or spring solenoid. REPEAT Service Bay Diagnostics. |

Fig. 14 Pinpoint Test, H (Part 6 of 9)

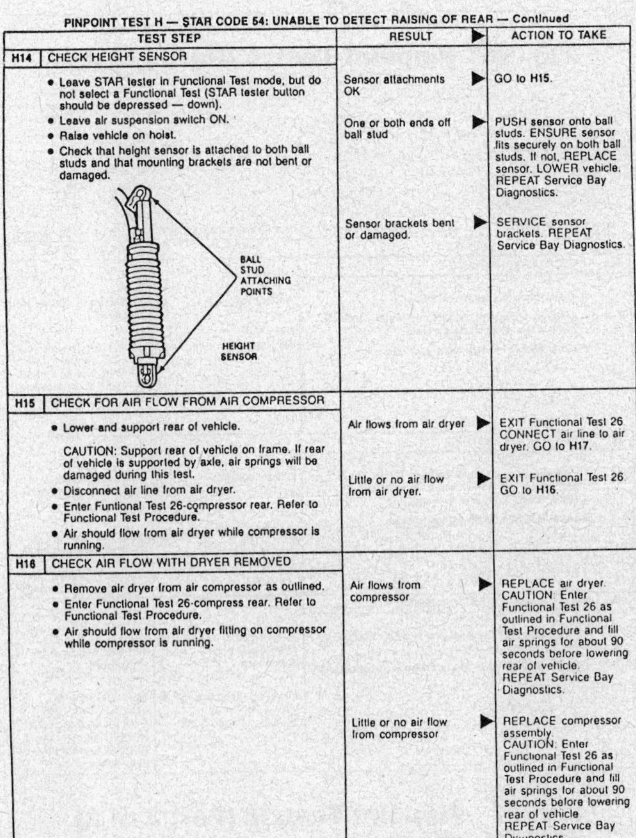

PINPOINT TEST H — STAR CODE 54: UNABLE TO DETECT RAISING OF REAR — Continued

| TEST STEP | | RESULT | ▶ | ACTION TO TAKE |
|---|---|---|---|---|
| H14 | CHECK HEIGHT SENSOR | | | |
| | • Leave STAR tester in Functional Test mode, but do not select a Functional Test (STAR tester button should be depressed — down).<br>• Leave air suspension switch ON.<br>• Raise vehicle on hoist.<br>• Check that height sensor is attached to both ball studs and that mounting brackets are not bent or damaged.<br>BALL STUD ATTACHING POINTS<br>HEIGHT SENSOR | Sensor attachments OK | ▶ | GO to H15. |
| | | One or both ends off ball stud | ▶ | PUSH sensor onto ball studs. ENSURE sensor fits securely on both ball studs. If not, REPLACE sensor. LOWER vehicle. REPEAT Service Bay Diagnostics. |
| | | Sensor brackets bent or damaged. | ▶ | SERVICE sensor brackets. REPEAT Service Bay Diagnostics. |
| H15 | CHECK FOR AIR FLOW FROM AIR COMPRESSOR | | | |
| | • Lower and support rear of vehicle.<br>CAUTION: Support rear of vehicle on frame. If rear of vehicle is supported by axle, air springs will be damaged during this test.<br>• Disconnect air line from air dryer.<br>• Enter Funtional Test 26-compressor rear. Refer to Functional Test Procedure.<br>• Air should flow from air dryer while compressor is running. | Air flows from air dryer | ▶ | EXIT Functional Test 26. CONNECT air line to air dryer. GO to H17. |
| | | Little or no air flow from air dryer. | ▶ | EXIT Functional Test 26. GO to H16. |
| H16 | CHECK AIR FLOW WITH DRYER REMOVED | | | |
| | • Remove air dryer from air compressor as outlined.<br>• Enter Functional Test 26-compress rear. Refer to Functional Test Procedure.<br>• Air should flow from air dryer fitting on compressor while compressor is running. | Air flows from compressor | ▶ | REPLACE air dryer. CAUTION: Enter Functional Test 26 as outlined in Functional Test Procedure and fill air springs for about 90 seconds before lowering rear of vehicle. REPEAT Service Bay Diagnostics. |
| | | Little or no air flow from compressor | ▶ | REPLACE compressor assembly. CAUTION: Enter Functional Test 26 as outlined in Functional Test Procedure and fill air springs for about 90 seconds before lowering rear of vehicle. REPEAT Service Bay Diagnostics. |

Fig. 14 Pinpoint Test, H (Part 8 of 9)

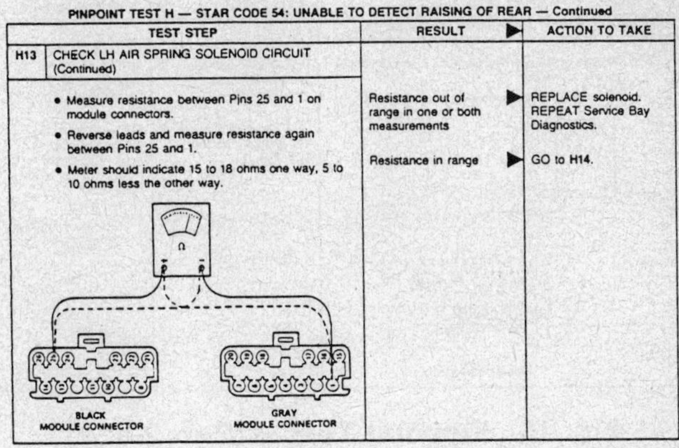

PINPOINT TEST H — STAR CODE 54: UNABLE TO DETECT RAISING OF REAR — Continued

| TEST STEP | | RESULT | ▶ | ACTION TO TAKE |
|---|---|---|---|---|
| H13 | CHECK LH AIR SPRING SOLENOID CIRCUIT (Continued) | | | |
| | • Measure resistance between Pins 25 and 1 on module connectors.<br>• Reverse leads and measure resistance again between Pins 25 and 1.<br>• Meter should indicate 15 to 18 ohms one way, 5 to 10 ohms less the other way.<br>BLACK MODULE CONNECTOR<br>GRAY MODULE CONNECTOR | Resistance out of range in one or both measurements | ▶ | REPLACE solenoid. REPEAT Service Bay Diagnostics. |
| | | Resistance in range | ▶ | GO to H14. |

Fig. 14 Pinpoint Test, H (Part 7 of 9)

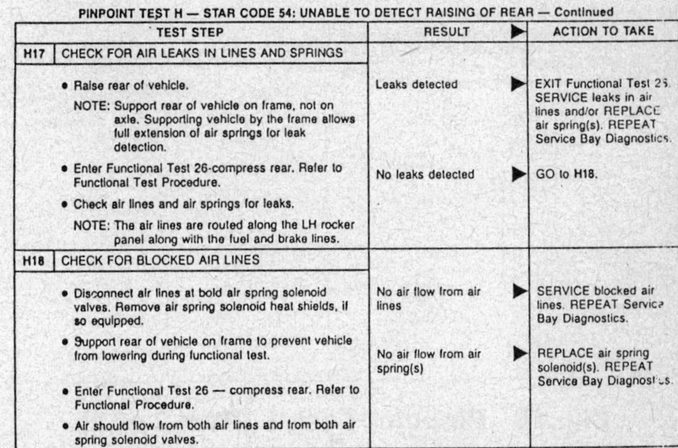

PINPOINT TEST H — STAR CODE 54: UNABLE TO DETECT RAISING OF REAR — Continued

| TEST STEP | | RESULT | ▶ | ACTION TO TAKE |
|---|---|---|---|---|
| H17 | CHECK FOR AIR LEAKS IN LINES AND SPRINGS | | | |
| | • Raise rear of vehicle.<br>NOTE: Support rear of vehicle on frame, not on axle. Supporting vehicle by the frame allows full extension of air springs for leak detection.<br>• Enter Functional Test 26-compress rear. Refer to Functional Test Procedure.<br>• Check air lines and air springs for leaks.<br>NOTE: The air lines are routed along the LH rocker panel along with the fuel and brake lines. | Leaks detected | ▶ | EXIT Functional Test 26. SERVICE leaks in air lines and/or REPLACE air spring(s). REPEAT Service Bay Diagnostics. |
| | | No leaks detected | ▶ | GO to H18. |
| H18 | CHECK FOR BLOCKED AIR LINES | | | |
| | • Disconnect air lines at bold air spring solenoid valves. Remove air spring solenoid heat shields, if so equipped.<br>• Support rear of vehicle on frame to prevent vehicle from lowering during functional test.<br>• Enter Functional Test 26 — compress rear. Refer to Functional Procedure.<br>• Air should flow from both air lines and from both air spring solenoid valves. | No air flow from air lines | ▶ | SERVICE blocked air lines. REPEAT Service Bay Diagnostics. |
| | | No air flow from air spring(s) | ▶ | REPLACE air spring solenoid(s). REPEAT Service Bay Diagnostics. |

Fig. 14 Pinpoint Test, H (Part 9 of 9)

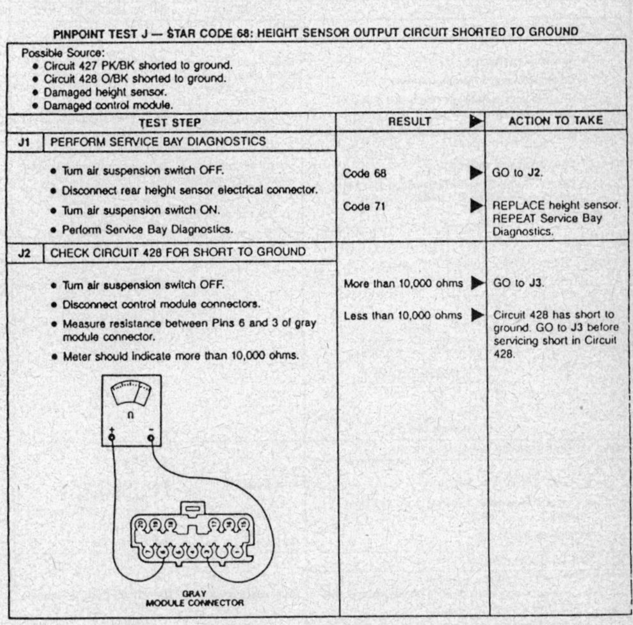

PINPOINT TEST J — STAR CODE 68: HEIGHT SENSOR OUTPUT CIRCUIT SHORTED TO GROUND

Possible Source:
- Circuit 427 PK/BK shorted to ground.
- Circuit 428 O/BK shorted to ground.
- Damaged height sensor.
- Damaged control module.

| TEST STEP | | RESULT | ▶ | ACTION TO TAKE |
|---|---|---|---|---|
| J1 | PERFORM SERVICE BAY DIAGNOSTICS | | | |
| | • Turn air suspension switch OFF.<br>• Disconnect rear height sensor electrical connector.<br>• Turn air suspension switch ON.<br>• Perform Service Bay Diagnostics. | Code 68 | ▶ | GO to J2. |
| | | Code 71 | ▶ | REPLACE height sensor. REPEAT Service Bay Diagnostics. |
| J2 | CHECK CIRCUIT 428 FOR SHORT TO GROUND | | | |
| | • Turn air suspension switch OFF.<br>• Disconnect control module connectors.<br>• Measure resistance between Pins 6 and 3 of gray module connector.<br>• Meter should indicate more than 10,000 ohms.<br>GRAY MODULE CONNECTOR | More than 10,000 ohms | ▶ | GO to J3. |
| | | Less than 10,000 ohms | ▶ | Circuit 428 has short to ground. GO to J3 before servicing short in Circuit 428. |

Fig. 15 Pinpoint Test, J (Part 1 of 2)

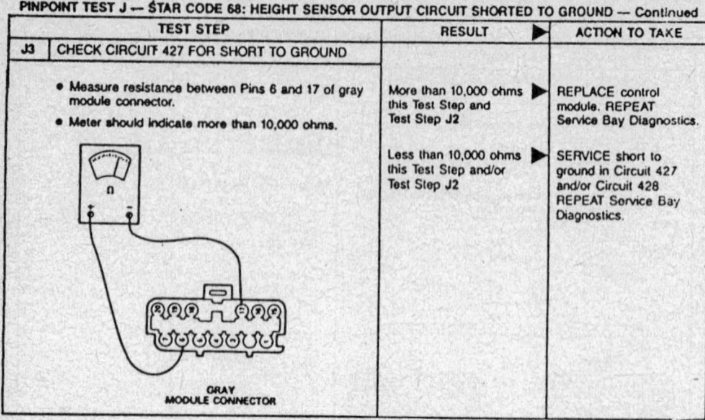

PINPOINT TEST J — STAR CODE 68: HEIGHT SENSOR OUTPUT CIRCUIT SHORTED TO GROUND — Continued

| TEST STEP | RESULT ▶ | ACTION TO TAKE |
|---|---|---|
| **J3** CHECK CIRCUIT 427 FOR SHORT TO GROUND | | |
| • Measure resistance between Pins 6 and 17 of gray module connector.<br>• Meter should indicate more than 10,000 ohms. | More than 10,000 ohms this Test Step and Test Step J2 ▶ | REPLACE control module. REPEAT Service Bay Diagnostics. |
| | Less than 10,000 ohms this Test Step and/or Test Step J2 ▶ | SERVICE short to ground in Circuit 427 and/or Circuit 428. REPEAT Service Bay Diagnostics. |



Fig. 15 Pinpoint Test, J (Part 2 of 2)

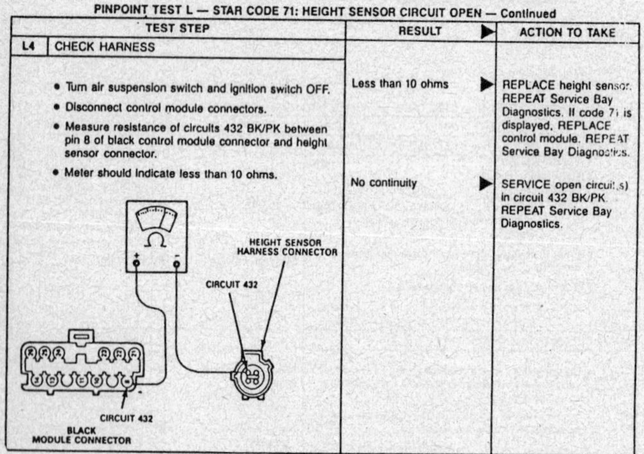

PINPOINT TEST L — STAR CODE 71: HEIGHT SENSOR CIRCUIT OPEN — Continued

| TEST STEP | RESULT ▶ | ACTION TO TAKE |
|---|---|---|
| **L4** CHECK HARNESS | | |
| • Turn air suspension switch and ignition switch OFF.<br>• Disconnect control module connectors.<br>• Measure resistance of circuits 432 BK/PK between pin 8 of black control module connector and height sensor connector.<br>• Meter should indicate less than 10 ohms. | Less than 10 ohms ▶ | REPLACE height sensor. REPEAT Service Bay Diagnostics. If code 71 is displayed, REPLACE control module. REPEAT Service Bay Diagnostics. |
| | No continuity ▶ | SERVICE open circuit(s) in circuit 432 BK/PK. REPEAT Service Bay Diagnostics. |



Fig. 16 Pinpoint Test, L (Part 2 of 2)

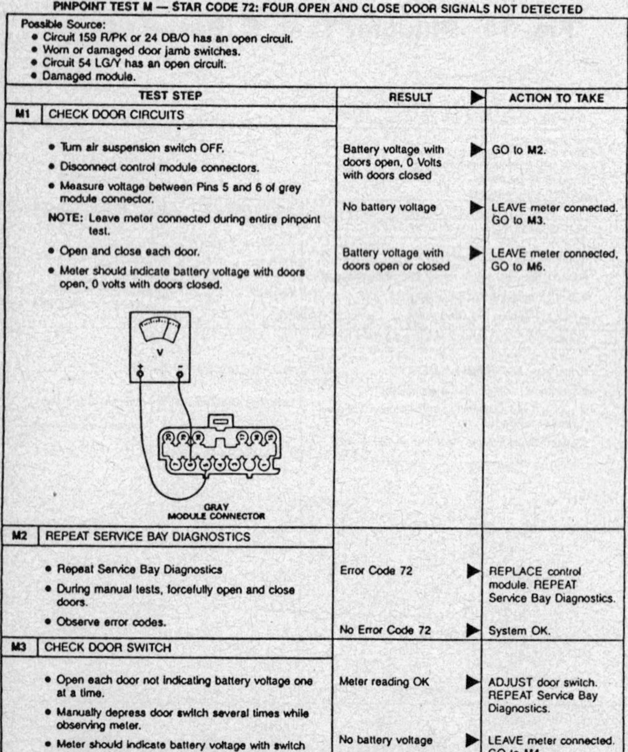

PINPOINT TEST M — STAR CODE 72: FOUR OPEN AND CLOSE DOOR SIGNALS NOT DETECTED

Possible Source:
- Circuit 159 R/PK or 24 DB/O has an open circuit.
- Worn or damaged door jamb switches.
- Circuit 54 LG/Y has an open circuit.
- Damaged module.

| TEST STEP | RESULT ▶ | ACTION TO TAKE |
|---|---|---|
| **M1** CHECK DOOR CIRCUITS | | |
| • Turn air suspension switch OFF.<br>• Disconnect control module connectors.<br>• Measure voltage between Pins 5 and 6 of grey module connector.<br>NOTE: Leave meter connected during entire pinpoint test.<br>• Open and close each door.<br>• Meter should indicate battery voltage with doors open, 0 volts with doors closed. | Battery voltage with doors open, 0 Volts with doors closed ▶ | GO to **M2**. |
| | No battery voltage ▶ | LEAVE meter connected. GO to **M3**. |
| | Battery voltage with doors open or closed ▶ | LEAVE meter connected. GO to **M6**. |
| **M2** REPEAT SERVICE BAY DIAGNOSTICS | | |
| • Repeat Service Bay Diagnostics<br>• During manual tests, forcefully open and close doors.<br>• Observe error codes. | Error Code 72 ▶ | REPLACE control module. REPEAT Service Bay Diagnostics. |
| | No Error Code 72 ▶ | System OK. |
| **M3** CHECK DOOR SWITCH | | |
| • Open each door not indicating battery voltage one at a time.<br>• Manually depress door switch several times while observing meter.<br>• Meter should indicate battery voltage with switch released, 0 volts with switch depressed. | Meter reading OK ▶ | ADJUST door switch. REPEAT Service Bay Diagnostics. |
| | No battery voltage ▶ | LEAVE meter connected. GO to **M4**. |



Fig. 17 Pinpoint Test, M (Part 1 of 2)

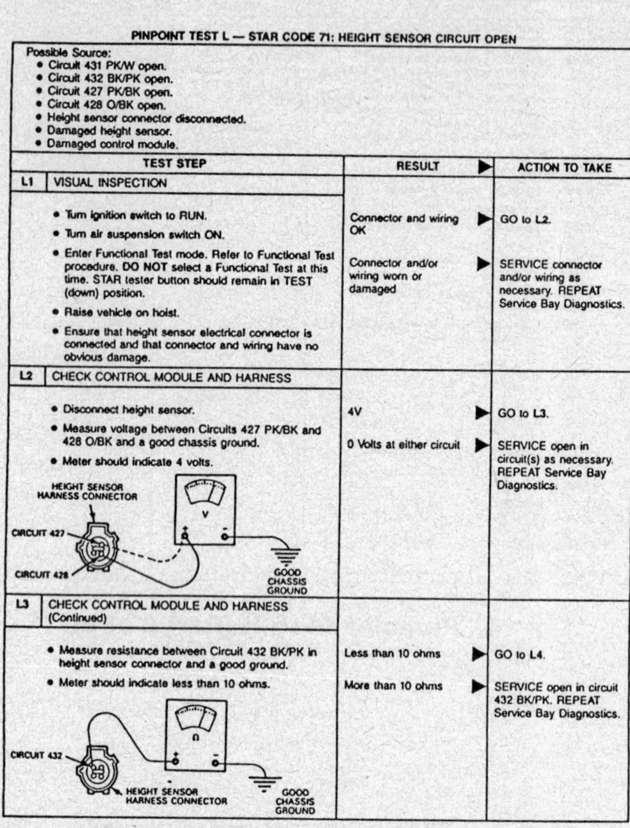

PINPOINT TEST L — STAR CODE 71: HEIGHT SENSOR CIRCUIT OPEN

Possible Source:
- Circuit 431 PK/W open.
- Circuit 432 BK/PK open.
- Circuit 427 PK/BK open.
- Circuit 428 O/BK open.
- Height sensor connector disconnected.
- Damaged height sensor.
- Damaged control module.

| TEST STEP | RESULT ▶ | ACTION TO TAKE |
|---|---|---|
| **L1** VISUAL INSPECTION | | |
| • Turn ignition switch to RUN.<br>• Turn air suspension switch ON.<br>• Enter Functional Test mode. Refer to Functional Test procedure. DO NOT select a Functional Test at this time. STAR tester button should remain in TEST (down) position.<br>• Raise vehicle on hoist.<br>• Ensure that height sensor electrical connector is connected and that connector and wiring have no obvious damage. | Connector and wiring OK ▶ | GO to L2. |
| | Connector and/or wiring worn or damaged ▶ | SERVICE connector and/or wiring as necessary. REPEAT Service Bay Diagnostics. |
| **L2** CHECK CONTROL MODULE AND HARNESS | | |
| • Disconnect height sensor.<br>• Measure voltage between Circuits 427 PK/BK and 428 O/BK and a good chassis ground.<br>• Meter should indicate 4 volts. | 4V ▶ | GO to L3. |
| | 0 Volts at either circuit ▶ | SERVICE open in circuit(s) as necessary. REPEAT Service Bay Diagnostics. |
| **L3** CHECK CONTROL MODULE AND HARNESS (Continued) | | |
| • Measure resistance between Circuit 432 BK/PK in height sensor connector and a good ground.<br>• Meter should indicate less than 10 ohms. | Less than 10 ohms ▶ | GO to L4. |
| | More than 10 ohms ▶ | SERVICE open in circuit 432 BK/PK. REPEAT Service Bay Diagnostics. |



Fig. 16 Pinpoint Test, L (Part 1 of 2)

PINPOINT TEST M — STAR CODE 72: FOUR OPEN AND CLOSE DOOR SIGNALS NOT DETECTED — Continued

| TEST STEP | RESULT ▶ | ACTION TO TAKE |
|---|---|---|
| **M4** CHECK DOOR HARNESS | | |
| • Disconnect door switch connector.<br>• Measure voltage at connector between Circuit 54 LG/Y and a good chassis ground.<br>• Meter should indicate battery voltage. | Battery voltage ▶ | LEAVE meter connected. GO to **M5**. |
| | No voltage ▶ | SERVICE open in Circuit 54 LG/Y between door switches and fuse panel. NOTE: If dome lamp works, 10 amp fuse is OK. REPEAT Service Bay Diagnostics. |
| **M5** JUMPER DOOR HARNESS | | |
| • Connect a fused jumper between Circuit 54 LG/Y and Circuit 159 R/PK (driver's door) or 24 DB/O (other doors) and observe meter.<br>• Meter should indicate battery voltage. | Battery voltage ▶ | REPLACE door switch. REPEAT Service Bay Diagnostics. |
| | No voltage ▶ | SERVICE open in Circuit 24 DB/O between door switch and control module. REPEAT Service Bay Diagnostics |
| **M6** CHECK FOR SHORT TO BATTERY | | |
| • Disconnect door switches one at a time and leave disconnected.<br>• Observe meter each time a switch is disconnected. | Meter drops to 0 Volts when a switch is disconnected ▶ | REPLACE door switch. REPEAT Service Bay Diagnostics |
| | Meter still reads battery voltage with all four switches disconnected. ▶ | SERVICE short to battery in Circuit 159 R/PK for door Circuit or 24 DB/O for other doors. REPEAT Service Bay Diagnostics. |

Fig. 17 Pinpoint Test, M (Part 2 of 2)

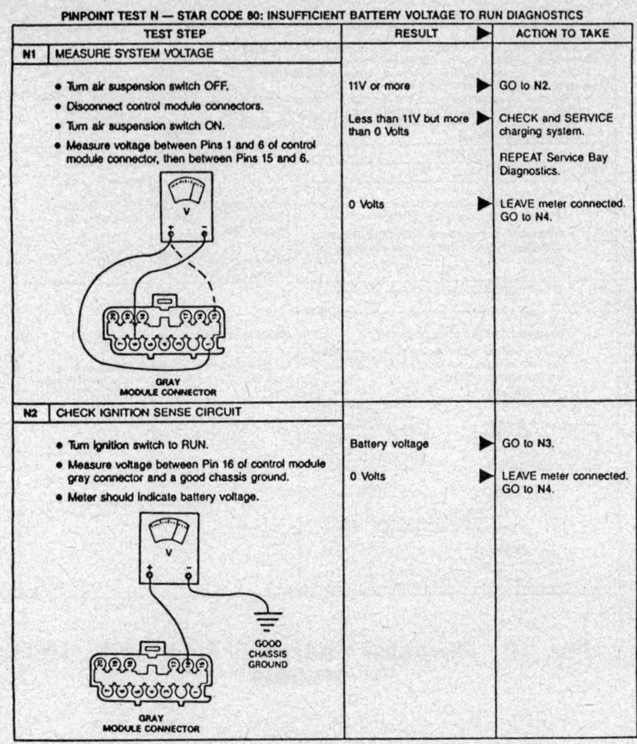

PINPOINT TEST N — STAR CODE 80: INSUFFICIENT BATTERY VOLTAGE TO RUN DIAGNOSTICS

| | TEST STEP | RESULT | ACTION TO TAKE |
|---|---|---|---|
| N1 | MEASURE SYSTEM VOLTAGE | | |
| | • Turn air suspension switch OFF.<br>• Disconnect control module connectors.<br>• Turn air suspension switch ON.<br>• Measure voltage between Pins 1 and 6 of control module connector, then between Pins 15 and 6.<br>GRAY MODULE CONNECTOR | 11V or more | GO to N2. |
| | | Less than 11V but more than 0 Volts | CHECK and SERVICE charging system.<br>REPEAT Service Bay Diagnostics. |
| | | 0 Volts | LEAVE meter connected. GO to N4. |
| N2 | CHECK IGNITION SENSE CIRCUIT | | |
| | • Turn ignition switch to RUN.<br>• Measure voltage between Pin 16 of control module gray connector and a good chassis ground.<br>• Meter should indicate battery voltage.<br>GOOD CHASSIS GROUND<br>GRAY MODULE CONNECTOR | Battery voltage | GO to N3. |
| | | 0 Volts | LEAVE meter connected. GO to N4. |

Fig. 18 Pinpoint Test, N (Part 1 of 5). All models

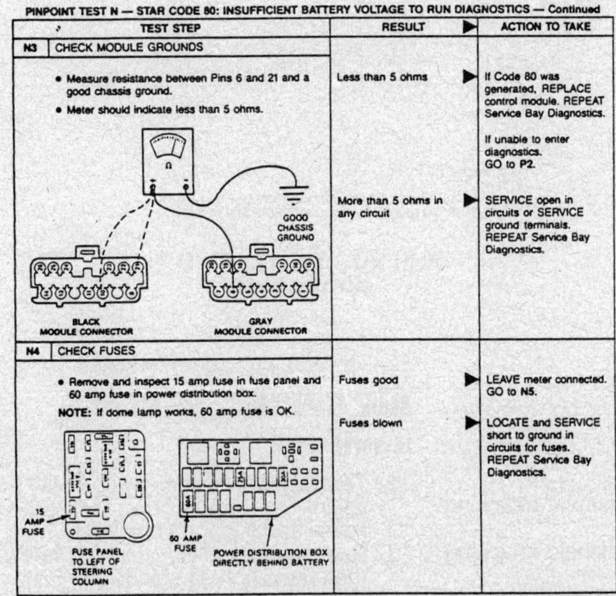

PINPOINT TEST N — STAR CODE 80: INSUFFICIENT BATTERY VOLTAGE TO RUN DIAGNOSTICS — Continued

| | TEST STEP | RESULT | ACTION TO TAKE |
|---|---|---|---|
| N3 | CHECK MODULE GROUNDS | | |
| | • Measure resistance between Pins 6 and 21 and a good chassis ground.<br>• Meter should indicate less than 5 ohms.<br>GOOD CHASSIS GROUND<br>BLACK MODULE CONNECTOR<br>GRAY MODULE CONNECTOR | Less than 5 ohms | If Code 80 was generated, REPLACE control module. REPEAT Service Bay Diagnostics.<br>If unable to enter diagnostics, GO to P2. |
| | | More than 5 ohms in any circuit | SERVICE open in circuits or SERVICE ground terminals. REPEAT Service Bay Diagnostics. |
| N4 | CHECK FUSES | | |
| | • Remove and inspect 15 amp fuse in fuse panel and 60 amp fuse in power distribution box.<br>NOTE: If dome lamp works, 60 amp fuse is OK.<br>15 AMP FUSE<br>FUSE PANEL TO LEFT OF STEERING COLUMN<br>60 AMP FUSE<br>POWER DISTRIBUTION BOX DIRECTLY BEHIND BATTERY | Fuses good | LEAVE meter connected. GO to N5. |
| | | Fuses blown | LOCATE and SERVICE short to ground in circuits for fuses. REPEAT Service Bay Diagnostics. |

Fig. 18 Pinpoint Test, N (Part 3 of 5). 1991 models

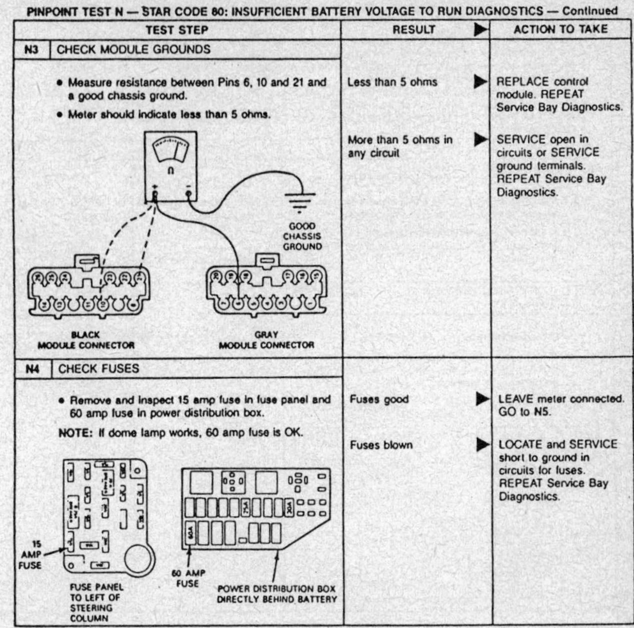

PINPOINT TEST N — STAR CODE 80: INSUFFICIENT BATTERY VOLTAGE TO RUN DIAGNOSTICS — Continued

| | TEST STEP | RESULT | ACTION TO TAKE |
|---|---|---|---|
| N3 | CHECK MODULE GROUNDS | | |
| | • Measure resistance between Pins 6, 10 and 21 and a good chassis ground.<br>• Meter should indicate less than 5 ohms.<br>GOOD CHASSIS GROUND<br>BLACK MODULE CONNECTOR<br>GRAY MODULE CONNECTOR | Less than 5 ohms | REPLACE control module. REPEAT Service Bay Diagnostics. |
| | | More than 5 ohms in any circuit | SERVICE open in circuits or SERVICE ground terminals. REPEAT Service Bay Diagnostics. |
| N4 | CHECK FUSES | | |
| | • Remove and inspect 15 amp fuse in fuse panel and 60 amp fuse in power distribution box.<br>NOTE: If dome lamp works, 60 amp fuse is OK.<br>15 AMP FUSE<br>FUSE PANEL TO LEFT OF STEERING COLUMN<br>60 AMP FUSE<br>POWER DISTRIBUTION BOX DIRECTLY BEHIND BATTERY | Fuses good | LEAVE meter connected. GO to N5. |
| | | Fuses blown | LOCATE and SERVICE short to ground in circuits for fuses. REPEAT Service Bay Diagnostics. |

Fig. 18 Pinpoint Test, N (Part 2 of 5). 1990 models

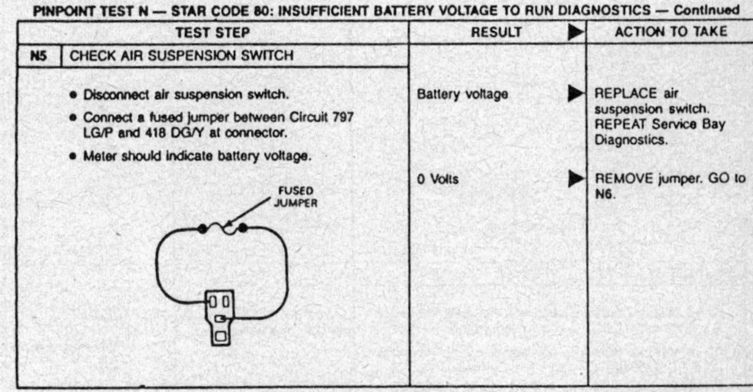

PINPOINT TEST N — STAR CODE 80: INSUFFICIENT BATTERY VOLTAGE TO RUN DIAGNOSTICS — Continued

| | TEST STEP | RESULT | ACTION TO TAKE |
|---|---|---|---|
| N5 | CHECK AIR SUSPENSION SWITCH | | |
| | • Disconnect air suspension switch.<br>• Connect a fused jumper between Circuit 797 LG/P and 418 DG/Y at connector.<br>• Meter should indicate battery voltage.<br>FUSED JUMPER | Battery voltage | REPLACE air suspension switch. REPEAT Service Bay Diagnostics. |
| | | 0 Volts | REMOVE jumper. GO to N6. |

Fig. 18 Pinpoint Test, N (Part 4 of 5). All models

PINPOINT TEST N — STAR CODE 80: INSUFFICIENT BATTERY VOLTAGE TO RUN DIAGNOSTICS — Continued

| | TEST STEP | RESULT | ACTION TO TAKE |
|---|---|---|---|
| N6 | CHECK BATTERY CIRCUIT | | |
| | • Measure voltage between Circuit 797 LG/P of air suspension switch connector and a good chassis ground.<br>• Meter should indicate battery voltage.<br>GOOD CHASSIS GROUND | Battery voltage | SERVICE open in Circuit 418 DG/Y between switch and control module. REPEAT Service Bay Diagnostics. |
| | | 0 Volts | SERVICE open in Circuit 797 LG/P between switch and fuse panel. |

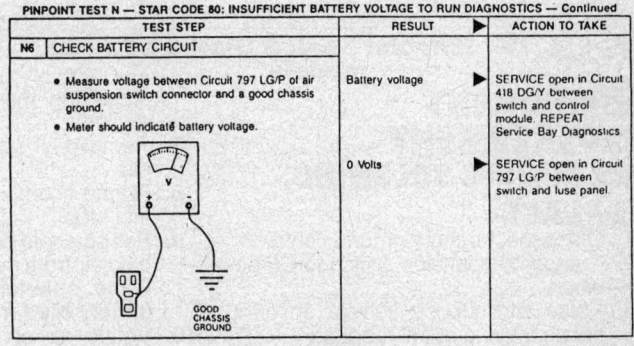

Fig. 18 Pinpoint Test, N (Part 5 of 5). All models

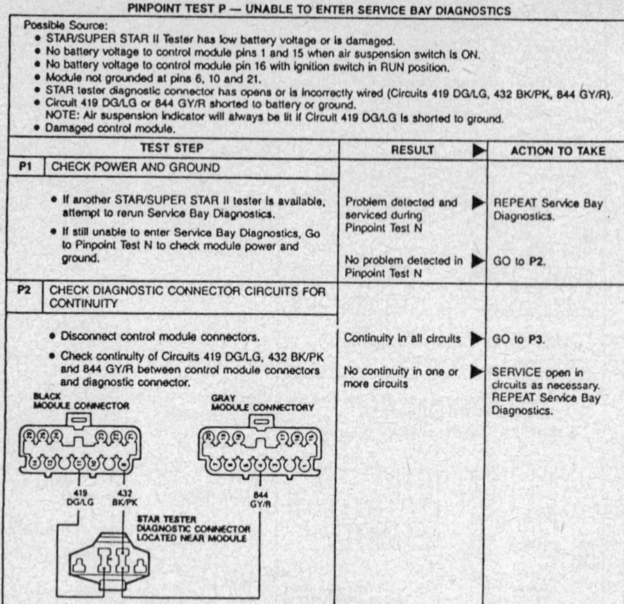

PINPOINT TEST P — UNABLE TO ENTER SERVICE BAY DIAGNOSTICS

Possible Source:
- STAR/SUPER STAR II Tester has low battery voltage or is damaged.
- No battery voltage to control module pins 1 and 15 when air suspension switch is ON.
- No battery voltage to control module pin 16 with ignition switch in RUN position.
- Module not grounded at pins 6, 10 and 21.
- STAR tester diagnostic connector has opens or is incorrectly wired (Circuits 419 DG/LG, 432 BK/PK, 844 GY/R).
- Circuit 419 DG/LG or 844 GY/R shorted to battery or ground.
NOTE: Air suspension indicator will always be lit if Circuit 419 DG/LG is shorted to ground.
- Damaged control module.

| TEST STEP | RESULT ▶ | ACTION TO TAKE |
|---|---|---|
| **P1** CHECK POWER AND GROUND | | |
| • If another STAR/SUPER STAR II tester is available, attempt to rerun Service Bay Diagnostics.<br>• If still unable to enter Service Bay Diagnostics, Go to Pinpoint Test N to check module power and ground. | Problem detected and serviced during Pinpoint Test N ▶ | REPEAT Service Bay Diagnostics. |
| | No problem detected in Pinpoint Test N ▶ | GO to P2. |
| **P2** CHECK DIAGNOSTIC CONNECTOR CIRCUITS FOR CONTINUITY | | |
| • Disconnect control module connectors.<br>• Check continuity of Circuits 419 DG/LG, 432 BK/PK and 844 GY/R between control module connectors and diagnostic connector.<br>BLACK MODULE CONNECTOR; GRAY MODULE CONNECTORY; 419 DG/LG; 432 BK/PK; 844 GY/R; STAR TESTER DIAGNOSTIC CONNECTOR LOCATED NEAR MODULE | Continuity in all circuits ▶ | GO to P3. |
| | No continuity in one or more circuits ▶ | SERVICE open in circuits as necessary. REPEAT Service Bay Diagnostics. |

Fig. 19 Pinpoint Test, P (Part 1 of 3). 1990 models

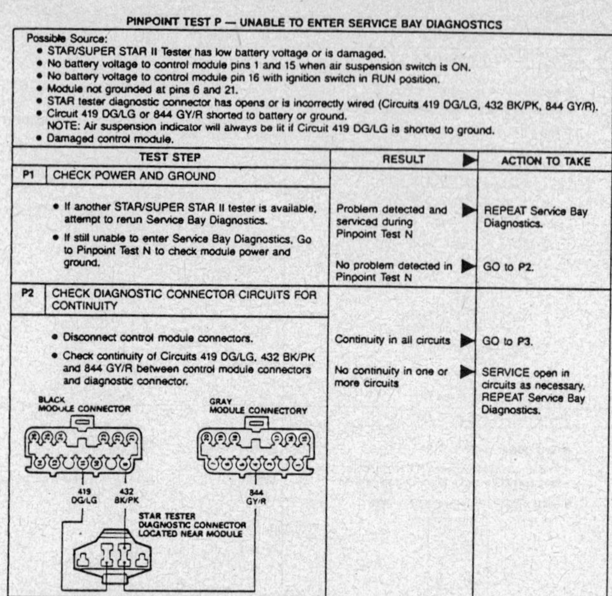

PINPOINT TEST P — UNABLE TO ENTER SERVICE BAY DIAGNOSTICS

Possible Source:
- STAR/SUPER STAR II Tester has low battery voltage or is damaged.
- No battery voltage to control module pins 1 and 15 when air suspension switch is ON.
- No battery voltage to control module pin 16 with ignition switch in RUN position.
- Module not grounded at pins 6 and 21.
- STAR tester diagnostic connector has opens or is incorrectly wired (Circuits 419 DG/LG, 432 BK/PK, 844 GY/R).
- Circuit 419 DG/LG or 844 GY/R shorted to battery or ground.
NOTE: Air suspension indicator will always be lit if Circuit 419 DG/LG is shorted to ground.
- Damaged control module.

| TEST STEP | RESULT ▶ | ACTION TO TAKE |
|---|---|---|
| **P1** CHECK POWER AND GROUND | | |
| • If another STAR/SUPER STAR II tester is available, attempt to rerun Service Bay Diagnostics.<br>• If still unable to enter Service Bay Diagnostics, Go to Pinpoint Test N to check module power and ground. | Problem detected and serviced during Pinpoint Test N ▶ | REPEAT Service Bay Diagnostics. |
| | No problem detected in Pinpoint Test N ▶ | GO to P2. |
| **P2** CHECK DIAGNOSTIC CONNECTOR CIRCUITS FOR CONTINUITY | | |
| • Disconnect control module connectors.<br>• Check continuity of Circuits 419 DG/LG, 432 BK/PK and 844 GY/R between control module connectors and diagnostic connector.<br>BLACK MODULE CONNECTOR; GRAY MODULE CONNECTORY; 419 DG/LG; 432 BK/PK; 844 GY/R; STAR TESTER DIAGNOSTIC CONNECTOR LOCATED NEAR MODULE | Continuity in all circuits ▶ | GO to P3. |
| | No continuity in one or more circuits ▶ | SERVICE open in circuits as necessary. REPEAT Service Bay Diagnostics. |

Fig. 19 Pinpoint Test, P (Part 2 of 3). 1991 models

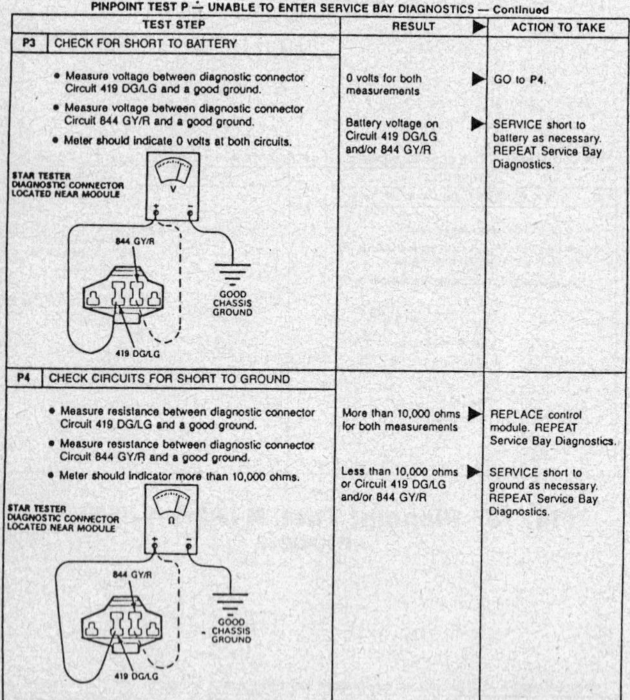

PINPOINT TEST P — UNABLE TO ENTER SERVICE BAY DIAGNOSTICS — Continued

| TEST STEP | RESULT ▶ | ACTION TO TAKE |
|---|---|---|
| **P3** CHECK FOR SHORT TO BATTERY | | |
| • Measure voltage between diagnostic connector Circuit 419 DG/LG and a good ground.<br>• Measure voltage between diagnostic connector Circuit 844 GY/R and a good ground.<br>• Meter should indicate 0 volts at both circuits.<br>STAR TESTER DIAGNOSTIC CONNECTOR LOCATED NEAR MODULE; V; 844 GY/R; GOOD CHASSIS GROUND; 419 DG/LG | 0 volts for both measurements ▶ | GO to P4. |
| | Battery voltage on Circuit 419 DG/LG and/or 844 GY/R ▶ | SERVICE short to battery as necessary. REPEAT Service Bay Diagnostics. |
| **P4** CHECK CIRCUITS FOR SHORT TO GROUND | | |
| • Measure resistance between diagnostic connector Circuit 419 DG/LG and a good ground.<br>• Measure resistance between diagnostic connector Circuit 844 GY/R and a good ground.<br>• Meter should indicator more than 10,000 ohms.<br>STAR TESTER DIAGNOSTIC CONNECTOR LOCATED NEAR MODULE; Ω; 844 GY/R; GOOD CHASSIS GROUND; 419 DG/LG | More than 10,000 ohms for both measurements ▶ | REPLACE control module. REPEAT Service Bay Diagnostics. |
| | Less than 10,000 ohms or Circuit 419 DG/LG and/or 844 GY/R ▶ | SERVICE short to ground as necessary. REPEAT Service Bay Diagnostics. |

Fig. 19 Pinpoint Test, P (Part 3 of 3). All models

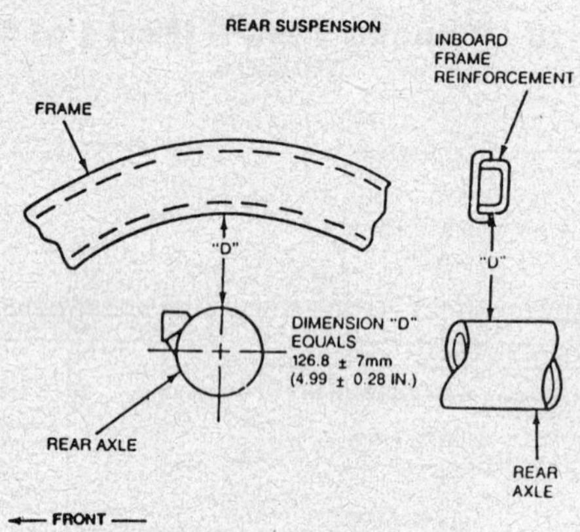


Fig. 20 Vertical "D" dimension

# COMPONENT REPLACEMENT

## AIR SPRING SOLENOID, REPLACE

1. Disconnect battery ground cable.
2. Turn air suspension switch to Off position.
3. Raise and support vehicle, ensuring suspension is at full rebound.
4. Remove heat shield, if equipped.
5. Disconnect air spring solenoid electrical connector.
6. Push down and hold air line plastic release ring, then disconnect attaching air line.
7. Remove air spring solenoid attaching clip.
8. Rotate solenoid counterclockwise to first stop.
9. Pull solenoid out to second stop, then bled air from system. **Do not fully release solenoid until air is completely bled from air spring.**
10. Rotate air spring solenoid counterclockwise to third stop, then remove solenoid from housing.
11. Remove O-ring from solenoid housing.
12. Reverse procedure to install.

## AIR SPRING, REPLACE

### Removal

1. Turn air suspension switch to Off position.
2. Raise and support vehicle.
3. Remove heat shield attaching screws, then remove heat shield.
4. Remove air spring solenoid as outlined under "Air Spring Solenoid, Replace."
5. Remove spring piston to axle spring seat as follows:
   a. Insert Air Spring Removal Tool T90P-5310-A or equivalent, between axle and spring seat on forward side of axle.
   b. Position tool so that flat end is on piston knob.

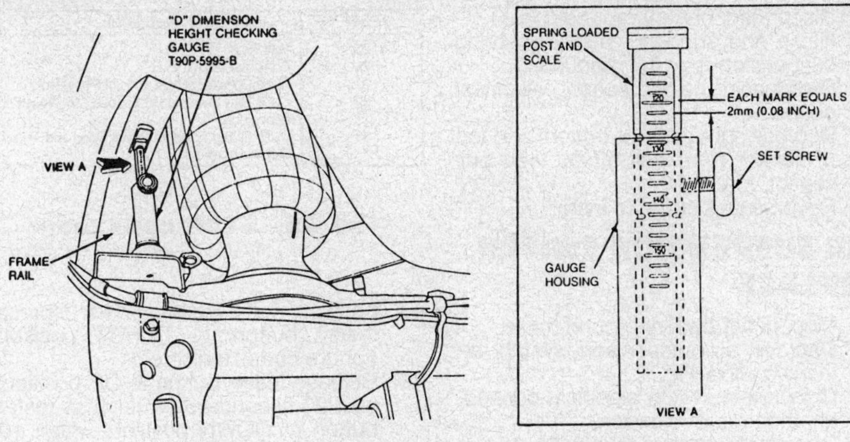


**Fig. 21 Ride height "D" dimension**

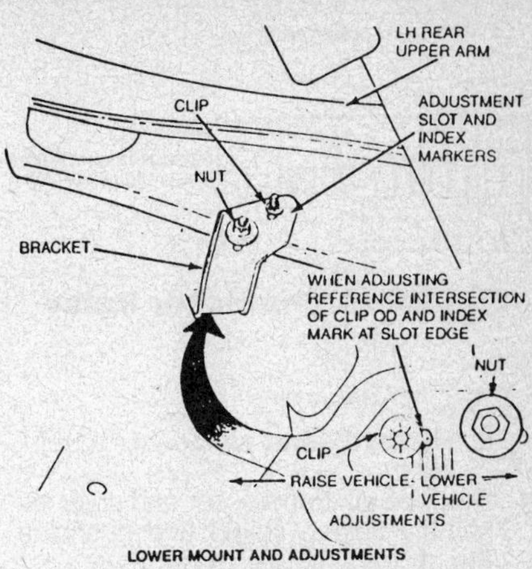


**Fig. 22 Height Sensor Adjustment**

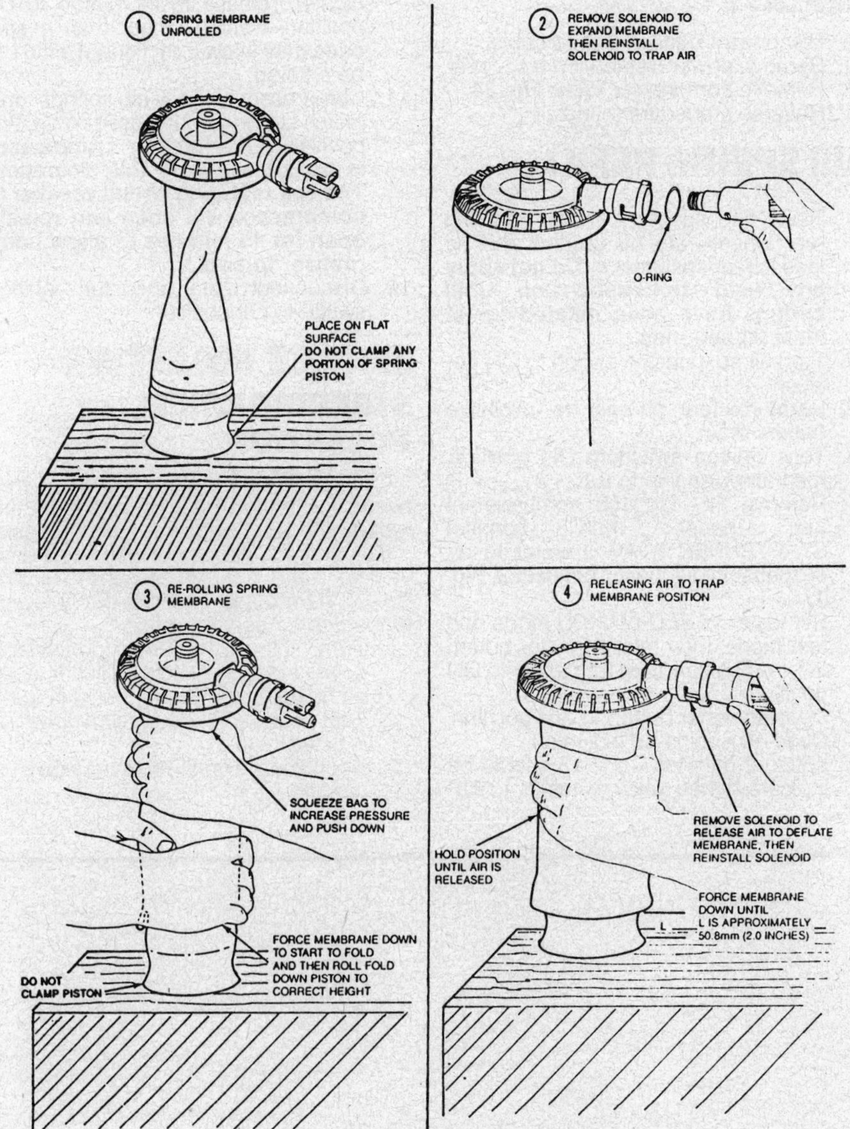


**Fig. 23 Refolding Air Spring**

c. Push downward, forcing piston and attaching clip from axle spring seat.

6. Remove air spring.

## Installation

1. Install air spring solenoid.
2. Install air spring to frame spring seat, ensuring solenoid air and electrical connectors are clean. **Do not attempt to install or inflate any air spring which has become unfolded. If any spring has been unfolded, refold spring as shown in Fig. 23, before installing unto vehicle.**
3. Install spring attaching clip to knob of spring cap at top side of frame spring seat.
4. Connect air solenoid air line and electrical connector.
5. Install heat shield.
6. Align air spring piston to axle seats. Squeeze to increase pressure and push downward on piston, then snap piston to axle seat at rebound. **Air spring may be damaged if suspension is allowed to compress before spring is inflated.**
7. Refill air springs as outlined in "Air Springs, Refill."

## SYSTEM CONTROL MODULE, REPLACE

1. Disconnect battery ground cable.
2. Turn sir suspension switch to the Off position.
3. Remove RH luggage compartment trim panel.
4. Remove control module attaching nuts, **Fig. 1.**
5. Pull module forward to gain access to electrical connectors.
6. Push control module electrical connector release button, then pull connector from module.
7. Reverse to install. **Torque** module attaching nuts to 5-7 ft. lbs.

## AIR COMPRESSOR & DRYER ASSEMBLY, REPLACE

1. Disconnect battery ground cable.
2. Turn air suspension switch to Off position.
3. Remove air cleaner housing assembly as follows:
   a. Loosen air tube to throttle body clamp, then remove air tube end.
   b. Unfasten air cleaner lid attaching clips, then remove air cleaner lid.
   c. Remove air filter element.
   d. Remove 2 outer and 1 inner lower air cleaner assembly attaching

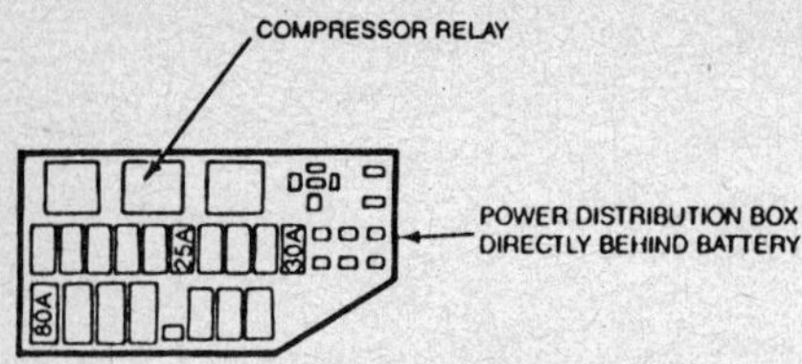


**Fig. 24 Compressor Relay**

nuts.
   e. Remove lower air cleaner assembly.
4. Remove air compressor and dryer assembly splash shield and pushpins, **Fig. 1.**
5. Push dryer air line retainer inward, then pull air line outward to remove.
6. Disconnect compressor electrical connectors.
7. Raise and support vehicle.
8. Remove compressor to fender apron attaching nuts.
9. Lower vehicle.
10. Remove compressor and dryer assembly.
11. Reverse to procedure install.

## AIR COMPRESSOR DRYER, REPLACE

1. Turn air suspension switch to the Off position.
2. Disconnect battery ground cable.
3. Remove air compressor and dryer assembly as outlined previously.
4. Remove dryer to compressor attaching screw.
5. Rotate dryer clockwise, then remove from compressor.
6. Remove O-ring seal, then discard O-ring.
7. Reverse procedure to install. **Torque** dryer to compressor attaching screw to 15-25 inch lbs.

## REAR HEIGHT SENSOR, REPLACE

1. Turn air suspension switch to Off position.
2. Disconnect battery ground cable.
3. Raise and support vehicle, ensuring suspension is at full rebound.
4. Disconnect height sensor electrical connector.
5. Depress spring clip at bottom and top of sensor from ball studs, then pull sensor, **Fig. 1.**
6. Reverse procedure to install.

## AIR SUSPENSION SWITCH, REPLACE

1. Disconnect battery ground cable.
2. Depress air suspension switch attaching clips, **Fig. 1.**
3. Disconnect switch electrical connector, then remove switch.
4. Reverse procedure to install.

## COMPRESSOR RELAY, REPLACE

1. Disconnect battery ground cable.
2. Remove power distribution box cover.
3. Remove compressor relay, **Fig. 24.**
4. Reverse procedure to install.

## AIR SPRING REFILL

1. Raise and support vehicle, ensuring rear wheels are off ground and no load to rear suspension. **Do not apply any load to suspension until springs have been inflated for at least 90 seconds.**
2. Turn air suspension switch to ON position.
3. Install battery charger to minimize battery drain.
4. Turn ignition switch to ON position, then allow engine to run.
5. Remove RH luggage compartment trim panel, then connect STAR/SUPER STAR II tester to air suspension diagnostic connector, **Fig. 1.**
6. Set tester to EEC-IV/MCU mode and fast mode, then release tester button to hold position, then turn tester to ON position.
7. Depress tester button to test position, Code 10 should be indicated.
8. Within 2 minutes Code 13 should be indicated, then release tester to UP position, wait 5 seconds, then depress tester button to DOWN position (ignore codes indicated).
9. Release tester button to UP position, wait 20 seconds, then depress tester button to DOWN position, within 10 seconds codes will be indicated in order **Fig. 25.**
10. Within 4 seconds after Code 26 is indicated release tester button to UP position, waiting longer than 4 seconds may allow Functional Test 31 to be entered.
11. Compressor will fill air springs until tester button is depressed to DOWN position. **Overheating compressor is possible during this operation. The self resetting circuit breaker in compressor will open and remain open for 15 minutes to allow compressor to cool.**
12. Disconnect tester, then turn ignition switch to Off position.

| Code | Description |
|---|---|
| 23 | Vent Rear |
| 26 | Compress Rear |
| 31 | Cycle Compressor On and Off Repeatedly |
| 32 | Cycle Vent Solenoid Valve Open and Closed Repeatedly |
| 33 | Cycle Spring Solenoid Valves Open and Closed Repeatedly |

**Fig. 25 STAR code order**

# SERVICE BULLETINS

## STEERING WHEEL PULSATION

On 1991 Town Car this condition may occur due to the RAS/EVO module fine turning the level of power steering assist.

To verify the above condition, test drive vehicle and, if necessary, replace RAS/EVO module. Refer to the following procedure for service details.

1. Turn Off air suspension/variable power steering switch. Switch is located on right rear quarter panel in trunk.
2. Test drive vehicle to confirm pulsation is gone.
3. If condition is gone, replace RAS/EVO module.

# AUTOMATIC LEVEL CONTROLS

## INDEX



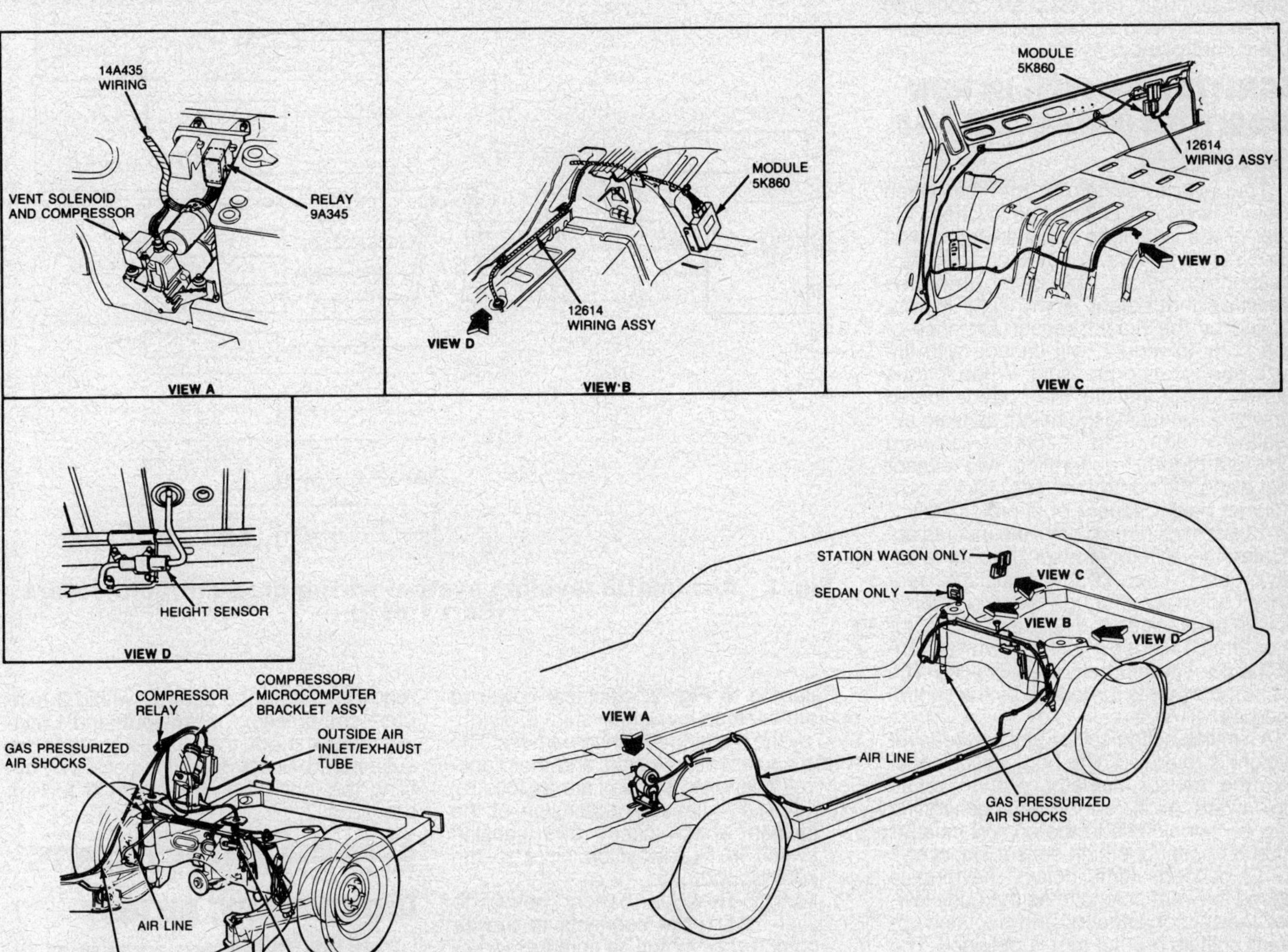


**Fig. 1 Automatic leveling system. 1989 Lincoln Town Car, 1989–91 Crown Victoria & Grand Marquis**

## SYSTEM DESCRIPTION

The automatic level control system, **Fig. 1**, is used on 1989 Lincoln Town Car, 1989-91 Crown Victoria and Grand Marquis models and is an addition to the standard rear suspension system and adjusts the vehicles trim height with varying vehicle loads automatically.

The system consists of air adjustable rear shocks, a compressor assembly, air dryer with minimum retention valve, exhaust solenoid, compressor relay, rotary height sensor, microcomputer, connecting wiring and nylon tubing.

## SYSTEM OPERATING MODES

### IGNITION SWITCH IN OFF POSITION

The system will operate for approximately 30 minutes after the ignition switch is turned from the Run to the Off position. Then, the system is inoperable through the microcomputer. The system will allow down requests only (lower vehicle) as required during the 30 minutes except that the exhaust control is suspended after continuous ON operation for one minute. Turning the ignition switch to ON position resets the operation. If the sensor arm moves to a neutral or low position, this function is also reset and normal ignition Off venting control resumes.

## IGNITION SWITCH IN RUN POSITION (LESS THAN 10 SECONDS)

The system will not allow any requests from the height sensor for the first 10 seconds, although requests are monitored continuously and stored in the microcomputer control memory.

## IGNITION SWITCH IN RUN POSITION (MORE THAN 10 SECONDS)

The leveling system is activated when weight is added to or removed from the rear of the vehicle to maintain the rear of the vehicle level at a predetermined rear suspension height. This is known as the vehicle's trim height. Trim height is controlled by the height sensor. Distance of the body to ground will change with tire size and inflation pressure. When load is added to the vehicle, the body is forced downward, causing the height sensors actuating arm to rotate upward (low-out-of-trim), generating two sensor signals to the control module. After a continuous height sensor of approximately 7 to 13 seconds (time delay), the module activates the air compressor (through a relay), sending air to the adjustable rear shock absorbers through the nylon tubing. As the body raises, the height sensor actuator arm continues rotating downward until the pre-set trim height is obtained. The air compressor is turned Off by the control module.

A similar action takes place whenever weight is removed. The body raises causing the sensor actuator arm to rotate downward (high, out-of-trim), generating two sensor signals to the control module. After a continuous high sensor signal of 7 to 13 seconds (time delay), the module opens the vent solenoid. As the body lowers, the sensor actuating arm is rotated upward until its pre-set trim is obtained. The module then closes the vent solenoid which prevents further air from escaping.

Air required for raising or lowering the vehicle is distributed from the compressor by one nylon air line which is connected between the compressor dryer and the LH air shock absorber, which has a dual port quick connect fitting. A second nylon air line starts here and connects to the RH air shock absorber. The air lines are color coded to identify which air shock they attach to. Shock-to-shock air lines are color coded, natural. Shock-to-compressor air lines are color coded blue on except station wagon models or yellow on station wagon models.

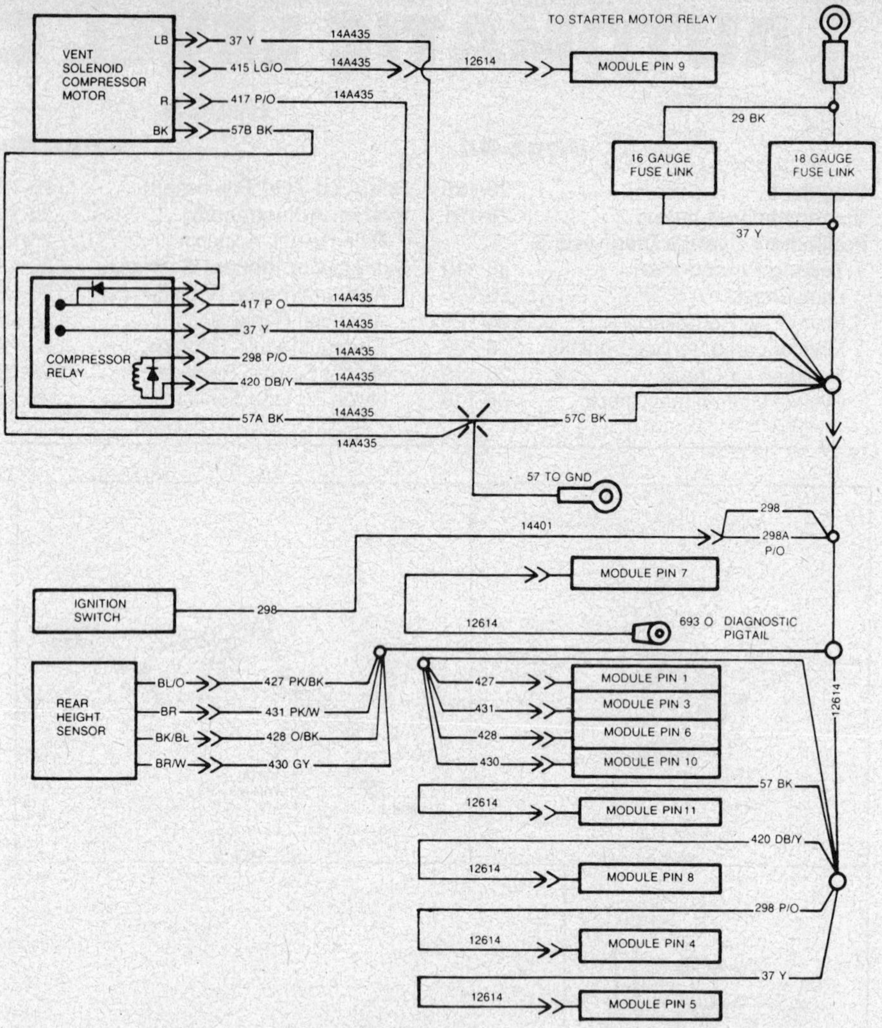

**Fig. 2 Automatic leveling system wiring diagram/connectors (Part 1 of 2)**

Referring to **Fig. 2,** electrical power to operate the load leveling system is distributed by the main body wiring harness. The wiring harnesses involved, and their function in the leveling system, are as follows:

1. 14401-Provides an extension of the ignition switch circuit 298 (ignition switch in Run position input to the control module).
2. 14A435-Supplies battery power to system. Directly connects to the air compressor motor, air compressor relay and control module.
3. 12614-Directly connects to the rotary height sensor, compressor motor, relay, vent solenoid, and the control module.

**The compressor relay and compressor vent solenoid incorporate internal diodes for electrical noise suppression and are polarity sensitive. Ensure care is taken when servicing these components as not to switch the battery feed (positive) and ground (negative) circuits or serious component and/or system damage will result.**

After turning the ignition switch to the Run position, if any upward or downward requests cannot be allowed within 2 minutes (compressor run time out) and 1 minute vent time out, the module controls are suspended. Reset operation occurs by cycling the ignition switch from Off to Run positions.

# SYSTEM ADJUSTMENTS

## RIDE HEIGHT, ADJUST

**This adjustment procedure must be performed prior to any service or diagnostic procedure. Without first adjusting vehicle's ride height and any service or diagnostic procedure is conducted, false readings and/or the replacement of satisfactory components will result.**

1. Adjust rear suspension ride height "D" dimension by moving rear sensor arm ball stud, **Fig. 3.** Three adjustments positions available.
2. Loosen attaching nut, one position change to the sensor attachment should indicate a .75 inch change (upward or downward) to rear suspension ride height "D" dimension.

| Wiring | Harness Side Connector | Pin Number | Function | Wire Harness Circuit | Wire Harness Color | Wire Harness Gauge | Circuit End Point |
|---|---|---|---|---|---|---|---|
| Front Compressor and Vent Solenoid (— 14A435 —) | | 1<br>2<br>3<br>4 | Solenoid Control<br>Motor Ground<br>Motor Feed<br>Solenoid Feed | 415<br>57B<br>417<br>37F | LG/O<br>BK<br>P/O<br>Y | 14<br>12<br>12<br>14 | Module Pin No. 9<br>Battery Ground Terminal<br>Compressor Relay<br>Starter Relay |
| Compressor Relay (1) (— 14A435 —) | | 1<br>2<br>3<br>4<br>5 | Control<br>Feed (Coil)<br>Feed (Contacts)<br>Compressor Motor Feed<br>Compressor Motor Ground | 420<br>298A<br>37C<br>417<br>57A | DB/Y<br>P/O<br>Y<br>P/O<br>BK | 18<br>18<br>12<br>12<br>12 | Module Pin No. 8<br>Compressor Relay<br>Starter Relay<br>Compressor<br>Battery Ground Terminal |
| Front/Rear Harness Connector (— 12614 —) to (— 14A435 —) | — 12614 — | 1<br>2<br>3<br>4<br>5<br>6 | Control<br>Ignition Sense<br>System Ground<br>—<br>Module Power<br>Vent Solenoid Control | 420<br>298A<br>57<br>—<br>37<br>415 | DB/Y<br>P/O<br>BK<br>—<br>Y<br>LG/O | 18<br>18<br>14<br>—<br>14<br>14 | Module Pin No. 8<br>Ignition Switch<br>Battery Ground Terminal<br>—<br>Module Pin No. 5<br>Module Pin No. 9 |
| Ignition Sense (— 12614 —) to (— 14401 —) | | | Ignition Sense | 298 and 298A | P/O<br>P/O | 18<br>18 | Module Pin No. 4<br>Compressor Relay |
| Rear Height Sensor (1) (— 12614 —) | | 1<br>2<br>3<br>4 | Logic Line B<br>Feed<br>Logic Line A<br>Ground | 428<br>431<br>427<br>430 | O/BK<br>PK/W<br>PK/BK<br>GY | 18<br>18<br>18<br>18 | Module Pin No. 6<br>Module Pin No. 3<br>Module Pin No. 1<br>Module Pin No. 10 |
| Module (1) (— 12614 —) | | | Diagnostic Monitor Lamp | 693 | O | 18 | Module Pin No. 7 |
| | | | | — 12614 — Wire Bundle | | | Control Module |

**Fig. 2 Automatic leveling system wiring diagram/connectors (Part 2 of 2)**

3. Apply static load, if vehicle does not return within .5 inch of initial "D" dimension, adjust height sensor connecting link length with load as follows:
   a. Connecting link remains attached to ball studs when link rod lengthening, **Fig. 4.**
   b. Loosen jam nuts, ensuring rod is stationary.
   c. Rotate link rod clockwise (as viewed under vehicle), one 360 degree rotation should indicate a .25 inch change in up direction to "D" dimension.
   d. Adjust link rod, up to a maximum of five times, ensuring vehicle rises within .5 inch of measurement made in step 1. **Additional turns will result in inadequate thread engagement, 3½ threads minimum, in each ball stud socket.**
   e. **Torque** jam nuts to 15-21 inch lbs.
4. Continue "System Operational Check."

# PRELIMINARY SYSTEM DIAGNOSIS & TESTING PROCEDURES

Turning the ignition switch from the Run to Off position clears all memory which is stored in the control module. Therefore, a test lamp (used during the actual diagnostic procedure) may not immediately indicate a failure when the ignition switch is returned to the Run position.

When charging the battery (battery is discharged when conducting the actual diagnostic procedure), the ignition switch must first be in the Off position or serious damage to the air compressor relay or motor may occur. However, use of a battery charger while performing the diagnostic tests (described further on in this section) is acceptable. Set the battery charger to a rate to maintain, but not damage, the vehicle battery. The following diagnostic test procedures are guides that will lead to the

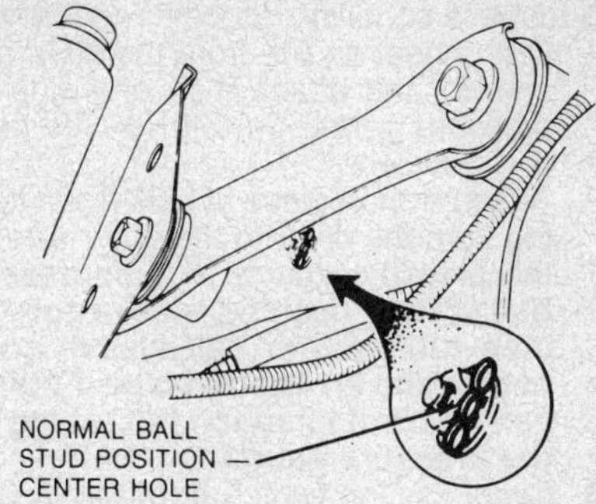


**Fig. 3 Rear sensor arm ball stud.**

most probable causes of automatic leveling system problems. It is important to accurately identify the problem or condition before selecting and using the appropriate diagnosis procedures and charts described further on. Whenever conducting diagnosis procedures, always cycle the ignition ON then Off, before starting the actual diagnosis or test procedure to ensure vent solenoid and compressor reset ON times.

## SYSTEM OPERATIONAL CHECK

1. Set vehicle trim height as described previously at recommended curb height and measure from known level floor (surface).
2. Briefly start and operate engine.
3. Apply approximately 300-350 lbs. of load to rear of vehicle and note the following:
   a. There should be a 7-13 second time delay before the compressor turns ON and rear of vehicle starts to rise.
   b. Vehicle should rise to within ½ inch of measurement taken in step 1 by the time the compressor shuts off. If vehicle does not rise, refer to diagnosis selection chart, **Fig. 5.** Failure of the vehicle to return to within ½ inch of unloaded dimension can be caused by unusual heavy loading in the luggage compartment which exceeds the system capacity. If this type of loading is encountered, remove it and repeat test.
4. Remove load applied in step 3, and note the following:
   a. There should be a 7-13 second time delay before vehicle starts to lower.
   b. Vehicle should lower to within approximately ½ inch of measurement taken in step 1 in less than one minute. If vehicle does not lower, refer to the diagnosis selection chart.

## RESIDUAL AIR CHECK

The air dryer has a valve arrangement that maintains approximately 8-24 psi in the air shocks to improve the vehicle's ride characteristics under light load conditions.

To test this condition, proceed as follows:

1. Disconnect air line from the dryer assembly and attach it to one side of pressure gauge 0-2070 (0-300 psi), or equivalent.
2. Attach a short piece of bulk nylon tubing from the dryer to the other side of the pressure gauge. **A compressor ball sleeve nut and sleeve for 3/16 inch tubing with ball sleeve connector and an internal pipe T fitting can be used to attach the tubing to the pressure gauge.**
3. Cycle ignition switch from Off to ON position.
4. Apply a load of approximately 300-350 lbs. to operate compressor and raise the vehicle.
5. Remove load applied in step 4. Allow the system to exhaust and lower the vehicle.
6. When no more air can be exhausted, the gauge should indicate 8-24 psi.
7. Remove pressure gauge. Attach the system air line to the dryer and repeat steps 3, 4 and 5 to ensure system air pressure is within the shocks.

## LEAK CHECK

1. Repeat Residual Air Check steps 1, 2, 3 and 4 and allow the system to fill, until pressure gauge reads 70-100 psi. If the compressor is permitted to operate until it reaches its maximum output pressure, the vent solenoid valve will function as the relief valve. The resulting leak down when compressor shuts off will indicate a false air leak.
2. With load still applied to the vehicle, disconnect wire harness connector from the control module and then remove applied load. Vehicle rear should rise. Cycle ignition switch to Off position.
3. Observe if pressure leaks down or holds steady (wait approximately 15 minutes) and note the following:
   a. If system will not inflate beyond 50 psi, a severe leak is indicated. Check for pinched pressure line between compressor and shocks.
   b. If pressure is maintained steady, perform the diagnosis procedures.
4. Connect wire harness connector to module.
5. Turn ignition switch from Off to Run position and allow air to exhaust (vehicle lowers).
6. After attachment of the pressure line to the dryer, repeat Residual Air Check steps 2, 3 and 4 to ensure system air pressure is within the shocks.

## MANUAL AIR REMOVAL

When compressed air enters the rear load leveling system, its only normal means of escape is through the electrically controlled air vent solenoid. To bleed air from the system manually, place a Schrader type tire valve on the air compressor. Remove the black plastic protective cap and depress the inner valve stem. When air is fully bled from the system, remove the air line from the dryer or air shocks by pushing down on the retainer and pulling the air line outward.

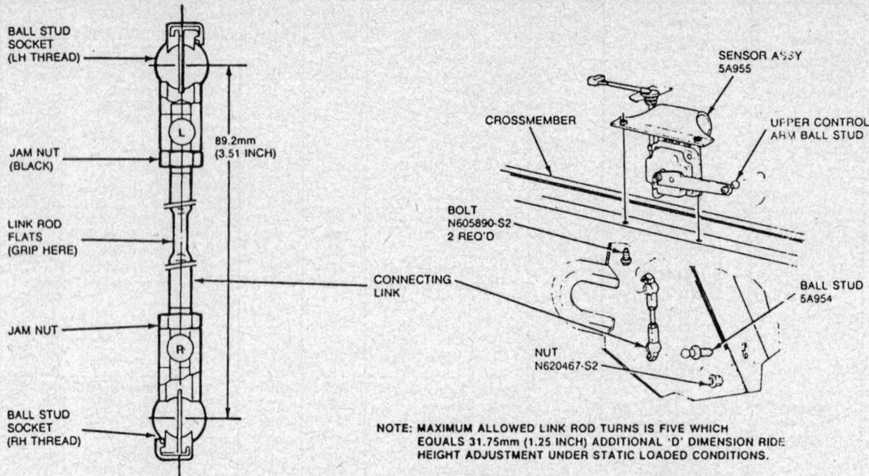


**Fig. 4 Rear suspension "D" dimension adjust**

## MONITOR LAMP SERVICE FUNCTION

1. Turning the ignition switch from Off to Run position energizes all system controls and suspends height sensor requests for 7-13 seconds, except for the service monitor lamp which is activated immediately, when the ignition switch is turned to Run position.
2. The monitor lamp blinks approximately 1.0 Hz jointly whenever the compressor relay is ON.
3. Monitor lamp is kept on at abnormal system conditions for the following Key ON operations:
   a. Disconnected rear height sensor electrical connector or any one detached line.
   b. Accumulated ON time of compressor motor relay (110-130 seconds).
   c. Continuous ON of vent solenoid for (55-65 seconds). **If the rear height lowers to or below trim position, the vent operation is reset and monitor lamp turns off, for both Key-ON and Key-Off operations.**
4. When abnormal program run is detected, the control module suspends all controls and the service monitor lamp remains ON.
5. All system functions of the control module, except compressor relay ON, are energized for 29-31 minutes after ignition switch is turned Off.
6. To reset the system, cycle the ignition switch from Off to Run position.

## REQUIRED TEST EQUIPMENT

Use only the test equipment referred to. Use of any other test tool may result in serious damage to the automatic leveling system.

To correctly perform the following diagnostic Pinpoint tests, the following test equipment is required:

1. Test lamp using bulb part No. 194 with probes. **Attach two 25-30 inch leads, one with a pointed probe and the other with a test clip, to a No. 194 bulb for use as a test lamp. Any other test lamp will cause damage to the load leveling system.**
2. Digital volt-ohmmeter tool No. 007-00001 or equivalent, with pointed probes to measure DC voltage.
3. Jumper cable with test clips.

## TESTING PROCEDURE

Connect the test lamp before cycling the ignition switch from Run to Off. When performing the tests, observe the time when the ignition switch is cycled to ensure that the module vent solenoid timer and compressor timer are operating properly. **Tests must be performed without disconnecting the harness connector at the module, unless stated to do so within the individual testing procedures (diagnostic charts). Review monitor lamp service function.**

**The compressor relay, vent solenoid and height sensor have internal diodes for electrical noise suppression, and therefore are polarity sensitive. Care must be taken when servicing these components not to switch battery feed (positive) and ground (negative) circuits or component damage will result. Specific component pinpoint diagnostic resistance checks require using an analog volt-ohmmeter only. Other type volt-ohmmeters will indicate false voltage/resistance checks.**

## DIAGNOSIS

For system diagnosis, refer to charts, **Figs. 6 through 15.** Do not conduct Pinpoint test procedures without first performing the Quick test portion of the diagnostic procedure. The Quick test portion of the diagnostic procedure will direct you to the correct Pinpoint test to perform.

# DIAGNOSTIC TEST INDEX

| Quick Test Letter | Pinpoint Test Letter | Test Title | Fig. No. | Page No. |
|---|---|---|---|---|
| — | — | Diagnosis Selection Chart | 5 | 26-121 |
| A | — | Check Vehicle Load At Curb | 6 | 26-121 |
| B | — | Power Monitor Lamp | 7 | 26-121 |
| C | — | Initialize System | 8 | 26-122 |
| — | D | Ignition Circuit | 9 | 26-122 |
| — | E | Battery Circuit | 10 | 26-122 |
| — | F | Vent Solenoid Circuit | 11 | 26-122 |
| — | G | Sensor Ground Circuit | 12 | 26-123 |
| — | H | Sensor Power Circuit | 13 | 26-123 |
| — | J | Sensor Logic Circuits | 14 | 26-123 |
| — | K | Compressor Relay/Motor Diagnosis | 15 | 26-124 |

DIAGNOSIS SELECTION CHART

| SYMPTOM | ACTION TO TAKE |
|---|---|
| • System inoperative: compressor does not run.<br>• Vehicle low or high: vehicle rises and lowers OK when load is added or removed, but normal trim height seems high or low. | • CHECK vehicle load 'D' dimension.<br>• CHECK ride height as outlined.<br>• PERFORM System Operation Check.<br>• PERFORM diagnosis procedure. |
| • Vehicles rises OK, but gradually leaks down.<br>• Compressor cycles On and Off intermittently while driving. | • REFER to Leak Checks.<br>• PERFORM diagnosis procedure.<br>• PERFORM System Operation Check. |
| • Compressor runs continuously for two minutes with ignition switch in RUN.<br>• Compressor turns Off after two minutes of accumulated operating time.<br>**NOTE: Vehicle rear may or may not rise during either situation.** | • REFER to Leak Checks.<br>• CHECK sensor link attachment.<br>• CHECK compressor relay and motor circuit for short to ground.<br>• CHECK sensor circuits — Pinpoint Tests G, H and J.<br>• PERFORM diagnosis procedure. |
| • Vehicle high or will not lower with ignition switch ON or OFF. | • CHECK vent solenoid check, Pinpoint Test F.<br>• CHECK sensor circuits — Pinpoint Tests G, H and J.<br>• CHECK ignition circuit — Pinpoint Test D.<br>• CHECK sensor link attachment and ball stud position.<br>• CHECK ride height 'D' dimension.<br>• PERFORM air check, residual.<br>• CHECK adjustments, ride height.<br>• PERFORM diagnosis procedure. |
| • Vehicle low or compressor does not run with ignition switch ON and a load applied. | • CHECK sensor link attachment.<br>• CHECK ride height 'D' dimension.<br>• CHECK ignition circuit — Pinpoint Test D.<br>• CHECK sensor circuits — Pinpoint Tests G, H and J.<br>• CHECK compressor relay and motor circuits — Pinpoint Test K.<br>• CHECK adjustments, ride height.<br>• PERFORM diagnosis procedure. |
| • Excessive bottoming in rear with load. | • CHECK ride height as outlined 'D' dimension.<br>• REFER to Leak Checks.<br>• PERFORM System Operational Check. |

**Fig. 5 Diagnosis selection chart**

QUICK TEST — A

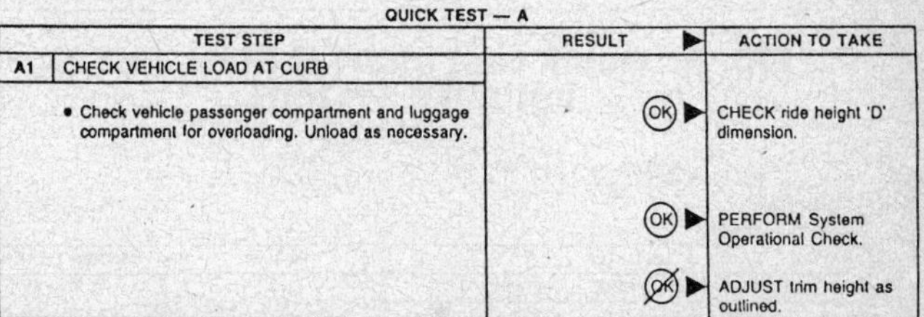

| TEST STEP | | RESULT ▶ | ACTION TO TAKE |
|---|---|---|---|
| A1 | CHECK VEHICLE LOAD AT CURB | | |
| | • Check vehicle passenger compartment and luggage compartment for overloading. Unload as necessary. | OK ▶ | CHECK ride height 'D' dimension. |
| | | OK ▶ | PERFORM System Operational Check. |
| | | NOT OK ▶ | ADJUST trim height as outlined. |

**Fig. 6 Quick test chart A, check vehicle load at curb**

| TEST STEP | | RESULT ▶ | ACTION TO TAKE |
|---|---|---|---|
| B1 | POWER MONITOR LAMP | | |
| | • Attach test lamp lead with probe to Circuit 37, Pin 5, at module connector (battery B+). | Test lamp on ▶ | GO to **B2**. |
| | • Attach test lamp lead with clip to module attaching screw or a good body ground.<br>**NOTE: Test lamp must remain connected during individual Pinpoint tests unless otherwise noted.** | Test lamp off ▶ | CHECK test clip connection. If lamp is still Off, GO to Pinpoint Test E. |
| B2 | POWER MONITOR LAMP (CONTINUED) | | |
| | • Attach test lamp lead with clip to diagnostic pig tail, Circuit 693, Pin 7; near module connector. | Test lamp off ▶ | GO to Quick Test C. |
| | | Test lamp on ▶ | RECYCLE ignition switch from RUN to OFF. If lamp remains On, REPLACE module. PERFORM System Operational Check. |

**Fig. 7 Quick test chart B, power monitor lamp**

| TEST STEP | RESULT ▶ | ACTION TO TAKE |
|---|---|---|
| **C1** INITIALIZE SYSTEM | | |
| • Before entering diagnostics, connect a battery charger to the vehicle and leave on until diagnosis is completed.<br>• With key in OFF position, power the diagnostic pigtail (Pinpoint Test B).<br>• Review monitor lamp service functions.<br>• Turn ignition switch to RUN. Observe monitor test lamp.<br>• Lamp will normally be off, then start blinking after a 7 to 13 second delay if a service request to raise the vehicle rear is indicated from the height sensor. | Lamp blinks, motor runs and vehicle rises ▶ | Normal operation. GO to **C2**. |
| | Lamp on immediately ▶ | Abnormal program run detected. GO to Pinpoint Tests G, H and J. |
| | Lamp blinks, motor runs, but vehicle does not rise ▶ | CHECK system for air leaks. CHECK sensor link attachment. NOTE: Compressor times out after two minutes of continuous running. |
| | Lamp blinks, but motor does not run and vehicle does not rise ▶ | GO to Pinpoint Tests D, E and K. |
| | Lamp does not turn On, but motor runs and vehicle rises ▶ | GO to **B1**. REINITIALIZE system. OBSERVE lamp. |
| | Lamp off, motor does not run and vehicle does not rise ▶ | Normal operation. Vehicle may be in trim or high position. CHECK for crossed harness sensor logic circuits. GO to Pinpoint Tests G, H and J. GO to **C2**. |
| | Lamp off, motor runs and vehicle does not rise ▶ | CHECK lamp. CHECK system for air leaks. PERFORM System Operational Check. |
| **C2** INITIALIZE SYSTEM (CONTINUED) | | |
| • Is lamp **off during first 60 seconds** after ignition is switched to RUN? | Lamp off, vent solenoid clicks during first 15 seconds and vehicle lowers ▶ | Normal operation. GO to **C3**. |
| | Lamp off, vent solenoid does not click during first 15 seconds and vehicle does not lower ▶ | Normal operation. GO to **C3**. |
| | Lamp on continuously ▶ | GO to Pinpoint Tests F, G, H and J. |

**Fig. 8 Quick test chart C (Part 1 of 2), initialize system**

| TEST STEP | RESULT ▶ | ACTION TO TAKE |
|---|---|---|
| **C3** INITIALIZE SYSTEM (CONTINUED) | | |
| • Is lamp **on after first 60 seconds** after ignition is switched to RUN? | Lamp on, vent solenoid clicks within first 15 seconds and vehicle does/does not lower ▶ | Normal operation. Vent solenoid timed out. GO to **C4**. |
| | Lamp off, vent solenoid does not click within first 15 seconds and vehicle does/does not lower ▶ | CHECK test lamp. Vehicle may be in trim position. GO to **C4**. |
| **C4** INITIALIZE SYSTEM (CONTINUED) | | |
| • Apply a 136 Kg (300 lb) load to rear of vehicle.<br>• Does lamp turn Off within 15 seconds?<br>**NOTE: Compressor may run after this time.**<br>**NOTE: Allow vehicle to vent and reach trim position before continuing to next Step.** | Yes (OK) ▶ | Vent time out function OK. REMOVE load. GO to **C5**. |
| | No (NOT OK) ▶ | CHECK vent solenoid. REPLACE module. CYCLE ignition Off. PERFORM System Operational Check. |
| **C5** INITIALIZE SYSTEM (CONTINUED) | | |
| • Disconnect air line at dryer as outlined.<br>**NOTE: Lamp may turn off and air may escape from removed line.**<br>• Cycle ignition switch from OFF to RUN.<br>• Apply a 136 Kg (300 lb) load to rear of vehicle.<br>• Does lamp turn On after 115-125 seconds and does compressor stop?<br>**NOTE: Time begins when compressor starts to run.** | Yes (OK) ▶ | Compressor Run timer OK. RECONNECT air line. REMOVE weight. PERFORM System Operational Check. |
| | No (NOT OK) ▶ | REPLACE module. REPEAT **C5**. PERFORM System Operational Check. |

**Fig. 8 Quick test chart C (Part 2 of 2), initialize system**

| TEST STEP | RESULT ▶ | ACTION TO TAKE |
|---|---|---|
| **D1** CHECK IGNITION CIRCUIT — IGNITION OFF | | |
| • Set volt-ohmmeter scale to read 12-volts.<br>• Attach negative (black) test lead of volt-ohmmeter to the module attaching screw.<br>• Attach positive (red) test lead to the ignition power Circuit 298, Pin 4, at module connector.<br>• Turn ignition switch OFF and remove battery charger. | Zero volts ▶ | Ignition sensor to module OK. GO to **D2**. |
| | Voltage is greater than zero ▶ | SERVICE short to module on Circuit 298 between module connector and ignition switch. REPEAT **D1**. |
| **D2** CHECK IGNITION CIRCUIT — IGNITION ON | | |
| • Cycle ignition switch to RUN.<br>**NOTE: Compressor motor may run and raise vehicle, or vent solenoid may operate and lower vehicle.** | Voltage greater than 10V ▶ | Ignition sense to module OK. GO to Pinpoint Test E. |
| | Voltage less than 10V ▶ | SERVICE open or short to ground on Circuit 298. CHECK fuse panel. SERVICE low voltage condition due to faulty connection, open fuse, low battery, etc. REPEAT **D2**. PERFORM System Operational Check. |

**Fig. 9 Pinpoint test chart D, ignition circuit diagnosis**

| TEST STEP | RESULT ▶ | ACTION TO TAKE |
|---|---|---|
| **E1** CHECK BATTERY CIRCUIT | | |
| • Cycle ignition switch OFF and remove battery charger.<br>• Set volt-ohmmeter scale to read 12-volts.<br>• Attach negative (black) test lead of the volt-ohmmeter to the module attaching screw.<br>• Attach positive (red) test lead to the module power Circuit 37, Pin 5 at the module connector.<br>**NOTE: Key OFF, 30 minute vent timer activated. Solenoid may click and vehicle may or may not lower.** | Voltage greater than 10V and steady ▶ | Battery circuit to module OK. GO to Quick Test B. |
| | Voltage less than 10V ▶ | SERVICE low voltage condition due to faulty connection, low battery, fuse link at starter relay on Circuit 37. RECONNECT connectors as required. REPEAT **E1**. |

**Fig. 10 Pinpoint test chart E, battery circuit diagnosis**

| TEST STEP | RESULT ▶ | ACTION TO TAKE |
|---|---|---|
| **F1** CHECK MONITOR LAMP SERVICE FUNCTION | | |
| • Check power monitor lamp. Remove battery charger and cycle ignition switch OFF. | Monitor lamp off ▶ | OK. GO to **F2**. |
| | Monitor lamp on 55 seconds after key off ▶ | Vent time out OK. GO to **F2**. |
| **F2** CHECK VENT SOLENOID CIRCUIT | | |
| • Set volt-ohmmeter scale to 12-volts. Attach negative (black) test lead to the module mounting screw. Attach positive (red) test lead to Circuit 415, Pin 9, at the module connector. | Voltage greater than 8.5V and steady ▶ | Vent solenoid circuit to module OK. GO to **F3**. |
| | Voltage less than 8.5V ▶ | CHECK battery voltage. GO to **F3**. |
| **F3** TEST VENT SOLENOID | | |
| • Remove positive test lead from volt-ohmmeter and touch to a good body ground or module mounting bolt. | Vent solenoid clicks ▶ | Vent solenoid and Circuit 415 to module OK. ATTACH test lead to meter. GO to **F4**. |
| | Vent solenoid does not click ▶ | ATTACH test lead to meter. GO to **F5**. |
| **F4** CHECK VENT SOLENOID TIMER | | |
| • With a floor jack, raise the rear bumper. Recycle ignition switch from RUN to OFF. | Lamp on after 55 seconds ▶ | Vent time out OK. REMOVE floor jack. |
| | Lamp off after 55 seconds ▶ | CHECK sensor circuits. REPLACE module. PERFORM System Operational Check. |
| **F5** TEST VENT SOLENOID FEED CIRCUIT | | |
| • Locate volt-ohmmeter to engine compartment LH side and attach negative test lead to a good ground.<br>• Move positive (red) test lead to solenoid feed Circuit 37 at the compressor connector.<br>**NOTE: Disregard monitor lamp.** | Voltage greater than 8.5V and steady ▶ | Solenoid feed circuit OK from battery relay. GO to **F6**. |
| | Voltage less than 8.5V and steady ▶ | SERVICE low voltage condition or open in feed Circuit 37 from starter relay to connector. REPEAT **F5**. |
| **F6** TEST VENT SOLENOID CONTROL CIRCUIT | | |
| • Move positive (red) test lead to solenoid control Circuit 415 at the compressor connector.<br>**NOTE: Disregard monitor lamp at module.** | Voltage greater than 8.5V and steady ▶ | Vent solenoid OK. GO to **F7**. |
| | Voltage less than 8.5V ▶ | Vent solenoid inoperative. REPLACE compressor assembly. REPEAT **F6**. |

**Fig. 11 Pinpoint test chart F (Part 1 of 2), vent solenoid diagnosis**

| TEST STEP | | RESULT ▶ | ACTION TO TAKE |
|---|---|---|---|
| F7 | TEST CONTROL CIRCUIT | | |
| | • Locate volt-ohmmeter to luggage compartment RH side and attach negative (black) test lead to module mounting bolt.<br>• Move positive (red) test lead to control Circuit 415, Pin 9 at the module connector.<br>**NOTE: Disregard monitor lamp.** | Voltage less than 8.5V ▶ | SERVICE open in solenoid control Circuit 415 between module connector and compressor connector. REPEAT **F7**. |
| | | Voltage greater than 8.5V ▶ | Solenoid circuit OK. GO to Pinpoint Test H. |

**Fig. 11 Pinpoint test chart F (Part 2 of 2), vent solenoid diagnosis**

| TEST STEP | | RESULT ▶ | ACTION TO TAKE |
|---|---|---|---|
| G1 | CHECK SENSOR GROUND CIRCUITS | | |
| | • Cycle ignition switch from ON to OFF. Remove battery charger.<br>• Disconnect connector from module.<br>• Set volt-ohmmeter scale to read ohms.<br>• Attach negative (black) test lead to the module mounting screw.<br>• Carefully touch the positive (red) test lead to module Pin 10.<br>**NOTE: When test step 5 is performed an analog volt/ohmmeter will be required.**<br>**NOTE: Disregard monitor lamp.** | Greater than 2 ohms ▶ | RECORD resistance measured at module. GO to **G2**. |
| | | Less than 2 ohms ▶ | Sensor ground circuit through module OK. GO to **G2**. |
| G2 | TEST GROUND CIRCUITS | | |
| | • Attach positive (red) test lead of volt-ohmmeter to Circuit 431, Pin 3, at the module connector.<br>• Move the negative (black) test lead to ground Circuit 430, Pin 10, at the module connector. | Greater than 8 ohms ▶ | GO to **G3**. |
| | | Less than 8 ohms ▶ | Sensor ground circuit OK. GO to Pinpoint Test H. |
| G3 | CHECK HARNESS SENSOR CONNECTOR | | |
| | • Disconnect rear harness sensor connector at underbody. Push harness grommet up inside luggage compartment for sedans. For station wagons, use longer test leads.<br>• Move the positive (red) test lead to ground Circuit 430 at harness sensor connector. | Greater than 2 ohms ▶ | SERVICE open in sensor ground Circuit 430 between module connector and rear sensor connector. REPEAT **G3**. |
| | | Less than 2 ohms ▶ | GO to **G4**. |
| G4 | TEST SENSOR HARNESS CIRCUIT | | |
| | • Move the positive (red) test lead to power Circuit 431 at the harness sensor connector.<br>• Move the negative (black) test lead to Circuit 431, Pin 3, at the module connector. | Greater than 2 ohms ▶ | SERVICE open in sensor Circuit 431 between module connector at the sensor connector. REPEAT **G4**. |
| | | Less than 2 ohms ▶ | Circuit 431 OK. GO to **G5**. |
| G5 | CHECK SENSOR GROUND | | |
| | • Move the positive (red) test lead to sensor connector Circuit 431 (sensor side).<br>• Move the negative (black) test lead to sensor connector Circuit 430 (sensor side). An analog type volt/ohmmeter must be used for this step. Other type meters will indicate incorrect resistance readings. | Greater than 18 ohms ▶ | REPLACE sensor. PERFORM System Operational Check. |
| | | Less than 18 ohms ▶ | GO to **G6**. |
| G6 | CHECK TOTAL RESISTANCE | | |
| | • Connect all disconnected connectors.<br>• Perform procedures outlined in G1. | Resistance less than 20 ohms ▶ | System OK. |
| | | Resistance greater than 20 ohms ▶ | REPLACE module. PERFORM System Operational Check. |

**Fig. 12 Pinpoint test chart G, sensor ground diagnosis**

| TEST STEP | | RESULT ▶ | ACTION TO TAKE |
|---|---|---|---|
| H1 | CHECK SENSOR POWER CIRCUITS | | |
| | • Connect module connector, if disconnected.<br>• Set volt-ohmmeter to read 5 volts.<br>• Attach negative (black) test lead of volt-ohmmeter to module attaching screw.<br>• Attach positive (red) test lead to sensor power Circuit 431, Pin 3, at module connector.<br>• Cycle ignition switch from RUN to OFF.<br>**NOTE: Disregard monitor lamp.**<br>**NOTE: Vent solenoid may click.**<br>• Observe voltmeter.<br>**NOTE: Voltage check must be made within 30 minutes of cycling ignition switch from RUN to OFF, or voltage will return to zero.** | Voltage is 5V and steady ▶ | Module output power OK. GO to **H2**. |
| | | Voltage is greater than 5.3V ▶ | REPLACE module. REPEAT **H1**. PERFORM System Operational Check. |
| | | Voltage is less than 4.7V ▶ | REPEAT **H1**. If still less than 4.7V, REPLACE module. PERFORM System Operational Check. |
| H2 | CHECK MODULE CIRCUIT 427 | | |
| | • Move positive (red) test lead to sensor Circuit 427, Pin 1, at module connector.<br>**NOTE: Disregard monitor lamp.** | Voltage greater than 4.1V ▶ | Module ouput power OK. GO to **H3**. |
| | | Voltage 1.3V to 4.1V ▶ | Sensor switching electrically from a low/high or high/low state. ADD approximately 136 Kg (300 lb) to rear bumper and REPEAT **H2**. |
| | | Voltage less than 1.3V but greater than zero volts ▶ | Module ouput power OK. GO to **H3**. |
| | | Zero volts ▶ | RECYCLE ignition switch to RUN, then to OFF. REPEAT **H2**. If voltage is still zero volts, GO to Pinpoint Test G. |
| H3 | CHECK MODULE CIRCUIT 428 | | |
| | • Move positive (red) test lead to sensor Circuit 428, Pin 6, at the module connector.<br>**NOTE: Disregard monitor lamp.** | Voltage greater than 4.1V or between zero volts and 1.3V ▶ | Module power circuit OK. PERFORM System Operational Check. |
| | | Voltage 1.3V to 4.1V ▶ | ADD approximately 136 Kg (300 lb) to rear bumper and REPEAT **H3**. |
| | | Zero volts ▶ | RECYCLE ignition switch to RUN, then to OFF. REPEAT **H3**. If voltage is still zero volts, GO to Pinpoint Test G. |

**Fig. 13 Pinpoint test chart H, sensor power circuit diagnosis**

| TEST STEP | | RESULT ▶ | ACTION TO TAKE |
|---|---|---|---|
| J1 | CHECK SENSOR LOGIC CIRCUITS | | |
| | • Connect module connector.<br>• Disconnect rear harness sensor connector at underbody.<br>• Cycle ignition switch to OFF. Set volt-ohmmeter scale to read 5 volts.<br>• Attach negative (black) test lead of volt-ohmmeter to the module attaching bolt.<br>• Attach positive (red) test lead to sensor Circuit A, 427, Pin 1, at module connector.<br>**NOTE: Disregard monitor lamp if connected.**<br>**NOTE: 30 minute time limit. Recycle ignition switch to OFF as required.** | Voltage greater than 4.3V ▶ | GO to **J2**. |
| | | Voltage less than 4.3V ▶ | RECYCLE ignition switch to RUN then to OFF. REPEAT **J1**. REPLACE module. RECONNECT module. PERFORM System Operational Check. |
| J2 | TEST MODULE SENSOR CIRCUIT B | | |
| | • Move positive (red) test lead to sensor Circuit B, 428, Pin 6, at module connector. | Voltage greater than 4.3V ▶ | GO to **J3**. |
| | | Voltage less than 4.3V ▶ | RECYCLE ignition switch to RUN then to OFF. REPEAT **J2**. REPLACE module. RECONNECT module. PERFORM System Operational Check. |
| J3 | CHECK SENSOR HARNESS CIRCUIT | | |
| | • Move positive (red) test lead to sensor Circuit B, 428, at rear harness sensor connector. | Voltage greater than 4.3V ▶ | Circuit B, OK. GO to **J4**. |
| | | Voltage less than 4.3V ▶ | SERVICE open in Circuit 428 between module connector and sensor harness connector. REPEAT **J3**. |
| J4 | CHECK SENSOR HARNESS CIRCUIT A | | |
| | • Move positive (red) test lead to sensor Circuit A, 427, at rear harness sensor connector. | Voltage greater than 4.3V ▶ | Circuit A, OK. GO to **J5**. |
| | | Voltage less than 4.3V ▶ | SERVICE open in Circuit 427 between module connector and sensor harness connector. REPEAT **J4**. |

**Fig. 14 Pinpoint test chart J (Part 1 of 2), sensor logic diagnosis**

| TEST STEP | | RESULT ▶ | ACTION TO TAKE |
|---|---|---|---|
| J5 | CHECK CROSSED LOGIC CIRCUITS | | |
| | • Disconnect module connector.<br>• Set volt-ohmmeter scale to read ohms.<br>• Move negative (black) test lead of volt-ohmmeter to Circuit A, 427 at module connector. | Greater than 2 ohms ▶ | Circuit 427 crossed with 428. SERVICE circuits at module or sensor harness/pin connector for correct locations. REPEAT **J5**. |
| | | Less than 2 ohms ▶ | Circuits OK. REPLACE sensor. PERFORM System Operation Check. |

**Fig. 14 Pinpoint test chart J (Part 2 of 2), sensor logic diagnosis**

# SYSTEM COMPONENT SERVICE

**Do not replace any system component without first performing the system diagnosis procedures. Replacement of satisfactory components may result.**

## AIR COMPRESSOR, REPLACE

1. Disconnect battery ground cable.
2. Disconnect air line from dryer by pushing inward on retainer and pulling out air line.
3. Remove wiring connector from air compressor by pulling up and away from bracket.
4. Disconnect electrical connectors.
5. Remove three bolts attaching compressor to mounting bracket.
6. Remove compressor assembly.
7. Reverse procedure to install. **Torque** one bolt from top side of fender apron to 6-13 ft. lbs. **Torque** compressor attaching bolts to 30-40 inch lbs.

## AIR DRYER, REPLACE

1. Disconnect battery ground cable.
2. Remove air line from dryer by pushing down on retainer and pulling air line outward.
3. Remove air compressor electrical connectors, then disconnect air dryer electrical connectors.
4. Remove air compressor at mounting bracket.
5. Remove dryer to compressor attaching screw.
6. Turn air dryer clockwise to disengage from compressor.
7. Remove air dryer and O-ring.
8. Reverse procedure to install, noting the following:
   a. Install new dryer O-ring.
   b. **Torque** dryer to compressor attaching screw to 15-25 inch lbs. **Torque** compressor to mounting bracket to 30-40 inch lbs.

## HEIGHT SENSOR, REPLACE

1. Disconnect battery ground cable.
2. Disconnect sensor electrical connector, located on sensor mounting bracket underneath luggage compartment.
3. Disconnect connecting link from upper control arm ball stud.
4. Remove two sensor mounting bolts, then the sensor.
5. Reverse procedure to install. **Torque** sensor mounting bolts to 6-13 ft. lbs.

| TEST STEP | | RESULT ▶ | ACTION TO TAKE |
|---|---|---|---|
| K1 | CHECK COMPRESSOR RELAY AND MOTOR | | |
| | • Cycle ignition switch from RUN to OFF.<br>• Set volt-ohmmeter scale to read 12-volts.<br>**NOTE: Disregard monitor lamp operation. Relay and/or vent solenoid may click.**<br>• Attach negative (black) test lead to the module mounting bolt.<br>• Attach the positive (red) test lead to Circuit 420, Pin 8 at module connector. | Voltage less than 1.0V ▶ | GO to **K2**. |
| | | Voltage greater than 1.0V ▶ | SERVICE short to module connector on Circuits 298 and 420 between ignition switch, relay and module connector. REPEAT **K1**. |
| K2 | TEST HARNESS CONNECTOR | | |
| | • Disconnect module harness connector from control module.<br>• Cycle key from OFF to RUN position.<br>• Attach positive test lead to module harness connector Circuit 420. | Voltage greater than 8.0V. ▶ | Compressor relay control Circuits 298 and 420 to module, OK. GO to **K3**. |
| | | Voltage less than 8.0V ▶ | SERVICE low voltage condition due to a faulty connection, relay, low battery, blown fuse, etc. on Circuits 298 and 420. REPEAT **K2**. |
| K3 | TEST COMPRESSOR RELAY COIL CIRCUIT | | |
| | • Remove positive (red) test lead from volt-ohmmeter and touch to the module mounting screw.<br>• Compressor relay should click.<br>**NOTE: Touch test lead several times to assure relay click can be heard from engine compartment. An assistant may be necessary at compressor relay to verify clicks.** | Compressor relay clicks ▶ | Compressor relay coil OK. ATTACH test lead to meter. GO to **K4**. |
| | | Compressor relay does not click ▶ | REPLACE relay. REPEAT **K3**. PERFORM System Operational Check. |
| K4 | CHECK COMPRESSOR MOTOR | | |
| | • Repeat procedures for Test Step **K3**. | Compressor motor cycles. ▶ | Compressor motor and ground circuits OK. ATTACH red test lead to volt-ohmmeter. GO to Pinpoint Test G. |
| | | Compressor motor does not cycle ▶ | ATTACH red test lead to volt-ohmmeter. GO to **K5**. |
| K5 | CHECK COMPRESSOR RELAY FEED CIRCUIT | | |
| | • Locate volt-ohmmeter to engine compartment LH side and attach negative (black) test lead to a good ground.<br>• Attach the positive (red) test lead to Circuit 37 at the compressor relay connector (harness side). | Voltage greater than 8.0V ▶ | Battery feed circuit to compressor relay OK. GO to **K6**. |
| | | Voltage less than 8.0V ▶ | SERVICE open or short to ground on Circuit 37 between battery and relay connector. CHECK fuse link. CHECK battery condition. REPEAT **K5**. |

**Fig. 15 Pinpoint test chart K (Part 1 of 2), compressor relay/motor diagnosis**

| TEST STEP | | RESULT ▶ | ACTION TO TAKE |
|---|---|---|---|
| K6 | CHECK RELAY CONTACTS | | |
| | • Attach one lead of a jumper cable to Circuit 420, Pin 8 at module harness connector in luggage compartment.<br>• Touch the other lead of the jumper cable to the module mounting bolt.<br>• Relay should click.<br>• Compressor motor may cycle. | OK ▶ | REMOVE jumper from mounting bolt. GO to **K7**. |
| | | ~~OK~~ ▶ | GO to **K7**. |
| K7 | CHECK VOLTAGE AT RELAY CONTACTS | | |
| | • Move positive (red) test lead to motor feed Circuit 417 at motor connector (harness side). Connect negative (black) lead to a good ground.<br>• Attach jumper lead to module mounting screw. Volt-ohmmeter should indicate more than 8.0 volts.<br>• Relay should click.<br>• Compressor motor may cycle.<br>**NOTE: An assistant may be necessary at compressor relay to verify voltage, relay clicking and compressor runs.** | OK ▶ | REMOVE jumper from mounting bolt. GO to **K8**. |
| | | ~~OK~~ ▶ | SERVICE open or short to ground on Circuit 417 between relay and motor connector or REPLACE relay as necessary. REPEAT **K7**. |
| K8 | CHECK COMPRESSOR MOTOR CIRCUIT | | |
| | • Touch jumper lead to module mounting screw. Compressor motor should cycle. | OK ▶ | Motor circuit OK. REPLACE module. PERFORM System Operational Check. |
| | | ~~OK~~ ▶ | REMOVE jumper lead from mounting bolt. GO to **K9**. |
| K9 | CHECK COMPRESSOR MOTOR RESISTANCE | | |
| | • Disconnect compressor connector.<br>• Set volt-ohmmeter to ohm scale.<br>• Attach positive (red) test lead to feed Circuit 417 at motor connector.<br>• Attach negative (black) lead to Circuit 57 at motor connector.<br>• Ohmmeter should indicate less than 2 ohms. | OK ▶ | Compressor and circuit breaker OK. GO to **K10**. |
| | | ~~OK~~ ▶ | REPLACE compressor motor. RECONNECT compressor and module connectors. PERFORM System Operational Check. |
| K10 | CHECK MOTOR HARNESS GROUND | | |
| | • Move negative (black) test lead to motor ground Circuit 57 at compressor connector (harness side).<br>• Move positive (red) test lead to motor ground Circuit 57, Pin 11, at module harness connector in luggage compartment. Then, move positive test lead to body eyelet ground Circuit 57 in engine compartment.<br>• Ohmmeter should indicate less than 2 ohms at both points.<br>**NOTE: An assistant may be necessary at compressor relay to verify voltage, relay clicking and compressor runs.** | OK ▶ | Ground circuit OK. RECONNECT motor and module connectors. PERFORM System Operational Check. |
| | | ~~OK~~ ▶ | SERVICE open in Circuit 57 between motor harness connector and ground and/or between module Pin 11 and ground. REPEAT **K10**. |

**Fig. 15 Pinpoint test chart K (Part 2 of 2), compressor relay/motor diagnosis**

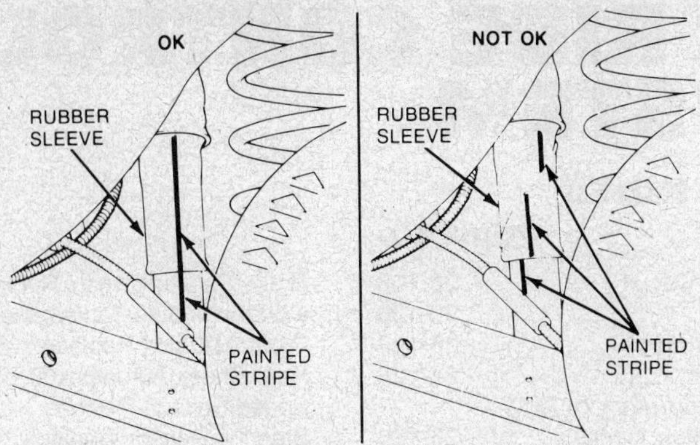


**Fig. 16 Shock absorber paint marks**

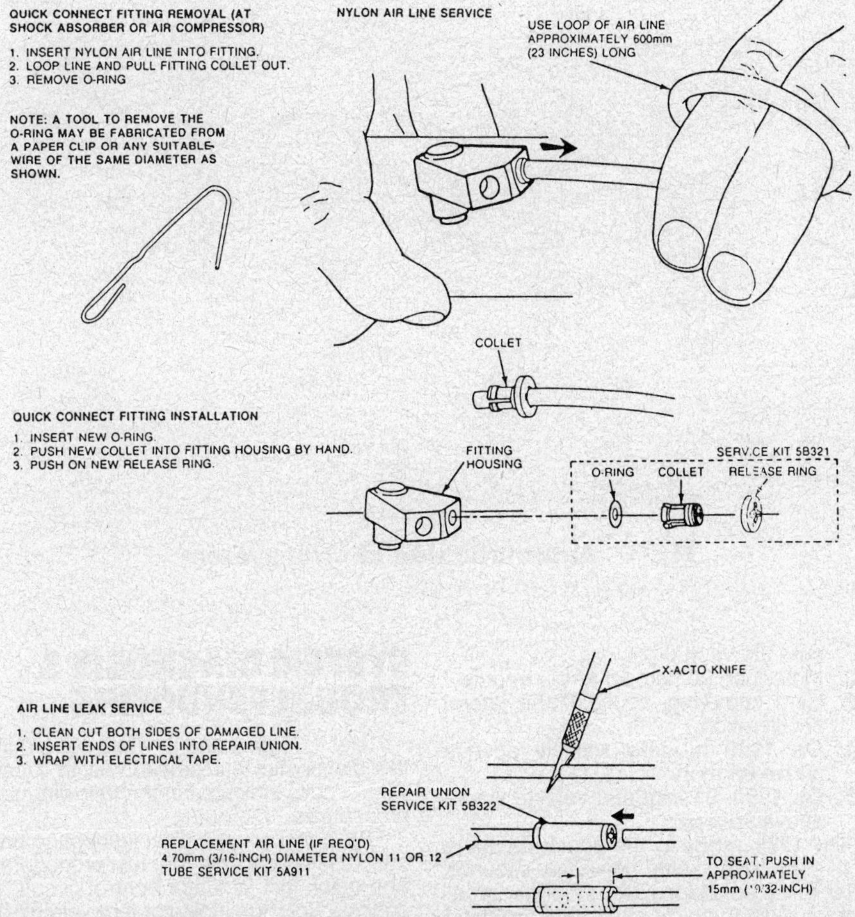


**Fig. 17 Nylon air line service**

## REAR SHOCK ABSORBER SERVICE

### Removal

**When removing and installing rear air shock absorbers, it is important that the following procedure be followed exactly. Failure to do so could result in damaged shock absorbers. Disconnect height sensor electrical connector before allowing rear axle or suspension arms to hang free. Raise vehicle on a suitable hoist so that the suspension arms hang free (full rebound) with the ignition switch in the Off position. The rear shock absorbers will vent air (hissing noise) through the compressor. When the noise stops, the air lines can be disconnected. A residual pressure of 8-24 psi will remain in the air lines. Shock absorbers need not be replaced in pairs, only replace faulty shocks.**

1. Disconnect air lines by pushing in on retainer rings and pulling lines outward.
2. Remove top attaching bolts, nuts, washers and/or bushings, if equipped.
3. Remove bottom attaching bolts, nuts, washers and/or bushings, if equipped.
4. Remove shock absorber(s).

### Installation

1. Position shock absorber(s) and install lower attaching nuts. **Torque** nuts to 52-85 ft. lbs.
2. Install top attaching nuts and **torque** to 14-26 ft. lbs. **Check rubber sleeve on shock absorber to ensure it is not wrapped up. To assist in identifying wrap up during installation, a white paint stripe has been placed on the rubber sleeve and on the shock absorber body. The stripe on the sleeve should align with the stripe on the body, Fig. 16.**
3. Connect the air line to the shock absorber by pushing in on the retainer ring and installing air line.
4. Connect height sensor connecting link.

## CONTROL MODULE, REPLACE

### Sedan Models

1. Disconnect battery ground cable.
2. Remove RH luggage compartment side trim panel.
3. Disconnect module wiring connector by pushing inward on retainer and pulling up.
4. Remove two attaching bolts.
5. Remove module.
6. Remove U-nuts from module.
7. Reverse procedure to install. **Torque** attaching bolts to 6-13 ft. lbs.

### Station Wagon Models

1. Disconnect battery ground cable.
2. Remove RH rear side trim panel (spare tire cover).
3. Disconnect module wiring connector by pushing inward on connector retainer (back side of connector) and pulling downward.
4. Remove two attaching bolts.
5. Remove module.
6. Reverse procedure to install. **Torque** attaching bolts to 6-13 ft. lbs.

## NYLON AIR LINE SERVICE

If a leak is detected in an air line, it can be serviced by carefully cutting the line with a sharp knife to ensure a good, clean straight cut and installing a service fitting as shown in, **Fig. 17.**

# AUTOMATIC RIDE CONTROL SYSTEM

## INDEX



## SYSTEM DESCRIPTION

The automatic (programmed) ride control system used on 1989-91 Thunderbird Super Coupe and 1990-91 Cougar XR7 models, provides the selection of either a firm (sport) suspension tuning or an automatic ride control.

The system is activated using a rocker switch mounted on the instrument panel to the right of the steering column. With the ride control switch in the FIRM position, the ride control computer adjusts shock absorber damping to provide a firm (sport) suspension tuning.

With the ride control switch in the AUTO position, the ride control computer adjusts shock absorber damping to provide a soft (plush) ride during normal driving conditions. The computer instantly changes suspension tuning to firm during hard braking, acceleration or cornering to provide improved handling at high speed.

A green FIRM RIDE indicator lamp is provided in the lower RH corner of the tachometer. The lamp is normally illuminated whenever the suspension is firm. This includes any time the switch is in the firm position or any time the system switches to the firm tuning in the AUTO switch position.

In the event of a system malfunction, the indicator lamp will flash ON and Off. Moving the ride control switch between positions will usually clear any false malfunction indication. If the indicator lamp continues to flash, the system should be checked for a possible malfunction.

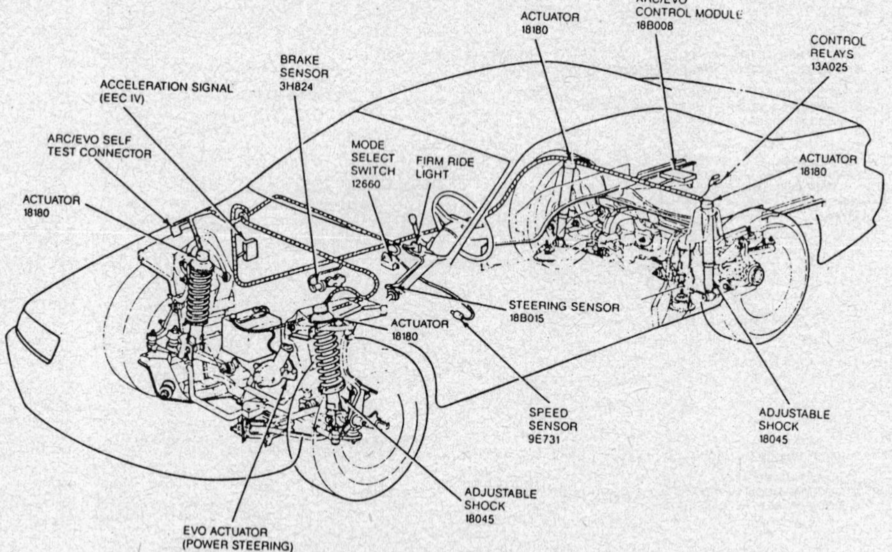


**Fig. 1 Automatic ride control system**

## SYSTEM OPERATION

The automatic ride control system, **Fig. 1,** monitors the following conditions to determine when additional shock absorber damping is required for improved handling:

1. Brake hydraulic pressure.
2. Throttle position.
3. Super charger boost.
4. Steering wheel angle.
5. Vehicle speed.

Any one of the following approximate conditions will cause the shock absorber damping to switch to FIRM:

1. Hard braking, brake hydraulic pressure above 400 psi.
2. More than 90 percent of full throttle.
3. Hard cornering, above 0.35g lateral acceleration.
4. **On 1989 models,** vehicle speeds above 83 mph.
5. **On 1990-91 models,** vehicle speed above 90 mph.

**On 1989 models,** the shock damping will return to the softer ride a few seconds after these conditions are no longer present, providing vehicle speed has dropped below 74 mph.

**On 1990-91 models,** the shock damping will return to the softer ride a few seconds after these conditions are no longer present, providing vehicle speed has dropped below 83 mph.

The automatic ride control system will not respond to hard turns during the first 80 seconds of driving. This delay allows the automatic ride control system to calculate the straight ahead steering wheel position. Severe or repeated turns in one direction could lengthen the wheel position calculation time by several minutes. All other features of the system operate normally during this period.

## SYSTEM DIAGNOSIS & TROUBLESHOOTING

Refer to **Figs. 2 and 3,** when performing the diagnostic test procedures to locate wire circuits indicated in the following test procedures.

The diagnosis and troubleshooting procedure is divided into four test procedures. The quick test, actuator control circuit diagnosis, firm ride indicator lamp circuit diagnosis and module input circuit diagnosis.

Refer to **Figs. 4 through 8,** for diagnostic test procedures.

## SYSTEM SERVICE

### AUTOMATIC (PROGRAMMED) RIDE CONTROL SWITCH, REPLACE

1. Remove console top to console base attaching screws, then disconnect top panel from console base.
2. Disconnect fog lamp switch and ride control switch electrical connectors.

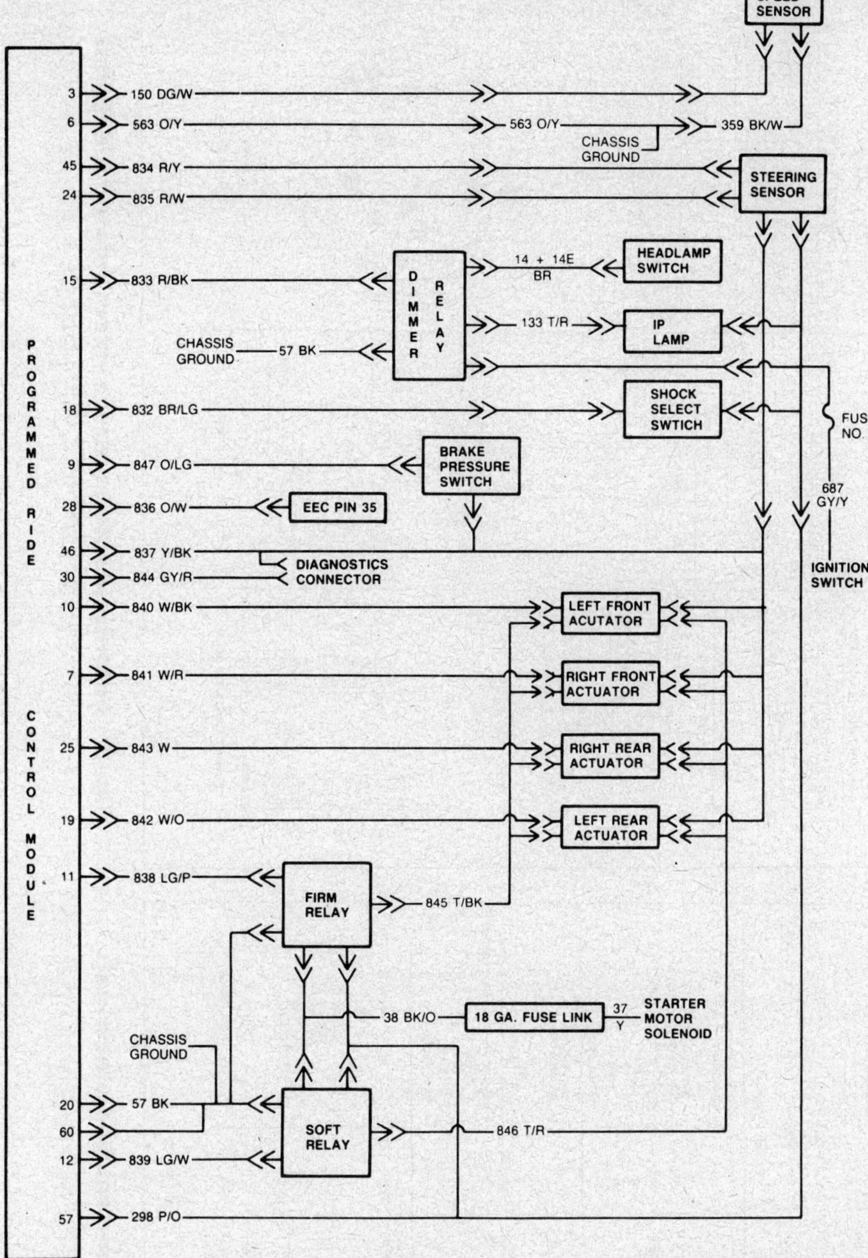


**Fig. 2 Automatic ride control system wiring diagram**

3. Remove switch attaching screws under panel.
4. Reverse procedure to install.

## FRONT ACTUATOR, REPLACE

1. Position vehicle on level surface, then apply parking brake.
2. Turn ignition switch to Off or LOCK position, then raise hood.
3. Disconnect actuator electrical connectors from wiring harness electrical connectors.
4. Unsnap actuator protective cover.
5. Remove actuator connector from protective cover by inserting small screwdriver tip between connector and white X-mas tree track, **Fig. 9.**
6. Depress actuator attaching tabs, then remove actuator.
7. Grasp shock absorber piston rod end with suitable tool, noting position of piston rod flat on thread and actuator mounting bracket.
8. Remove actuator mounting bracket to shock absorber attaching nut.
9. **On 1989 models, do not move or raise vehicle after removing bracket attaching nut. If shock absorber must be removed install nut onto shock.**
10. **On all models,** reverse procedure to install, noting the following:
    a. Ensure flat on actuator mounting bracket aligns with flat on shock absorber piston end.
    b. **On 1989 models, torque** actuator mounting bracket attaching nut to 40-48 ft. lbs.
    c. **On 1990-91 models, Torque** actuator mounting bracket attaching nut to 27-35 ft. lbs.

## BRAKE SENSOR SWITCH, REPLACE

**When servicing any component on a vehicle equipped with anti-lock brakes it is necessary to discharge the hydraulic pressure in the system. Refer to "Anti-Lock Brakes" for procedure.**

1. Disconnect battery ground cable.
2. Disconnect electrical connector from brake sensor switch.
3. Remove sensor switch from brake control valve body.
4. Reverse procedure to install. **Torque** brake sensor switch to 8-10 ft. lbs.

## SPEED SENSOR, REPLACE

1. Disconnect battery ground cable.
2. Raise and support vehicle.
3. Remove sensor and driven gear from transmission.
4. Disconnect electrical connector and speedometer cable from speed sensor. **Do not attempt to remove the spring retainer clip with the speedometer cable in the sensor.**
5. Remove driven gear retainer and remove driven gear from sensor.
6. Reverse procedure to install, ensuring internal O-ring is seated in sensor housing.

## CONTROL MODULE/RELAYS, REPLACE

1. Turn ignition switch to Off or LOCK position.
2. Working from inside luggage compartment, disconnect push pin at left side of package tray.
3. Swing tray downward.
4. Disconnect control module or relay electrical connectors, then remove control module or relays.
5. Reverse procedure to install.

## STEERING SENSOR, REPLACE

The steering sensor is located at the lower end of the steering column. It may be removed with the steering column either in or out of the vehicle.

1. Disconnect sensor electrical connectors from wiring harness.
2. Disconnect sensor electrical connectors at bracket under instrument panel.
3. Remove speed sensor attaching screws, then remove sensor.
4. Reverse procedure to install.

*Continued on page 26-134*

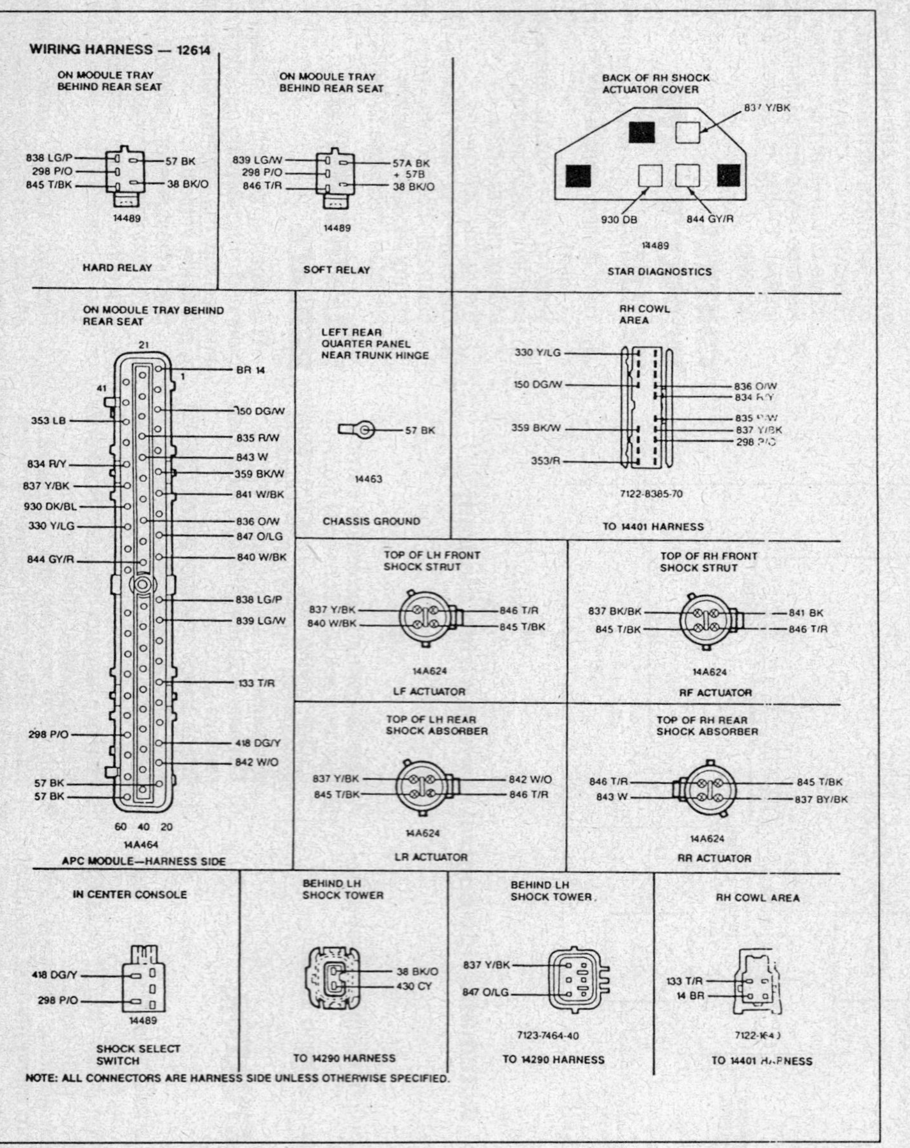


**Fig. 3 Automatic ride control system related electrical connectors (Part 1 of 4)**

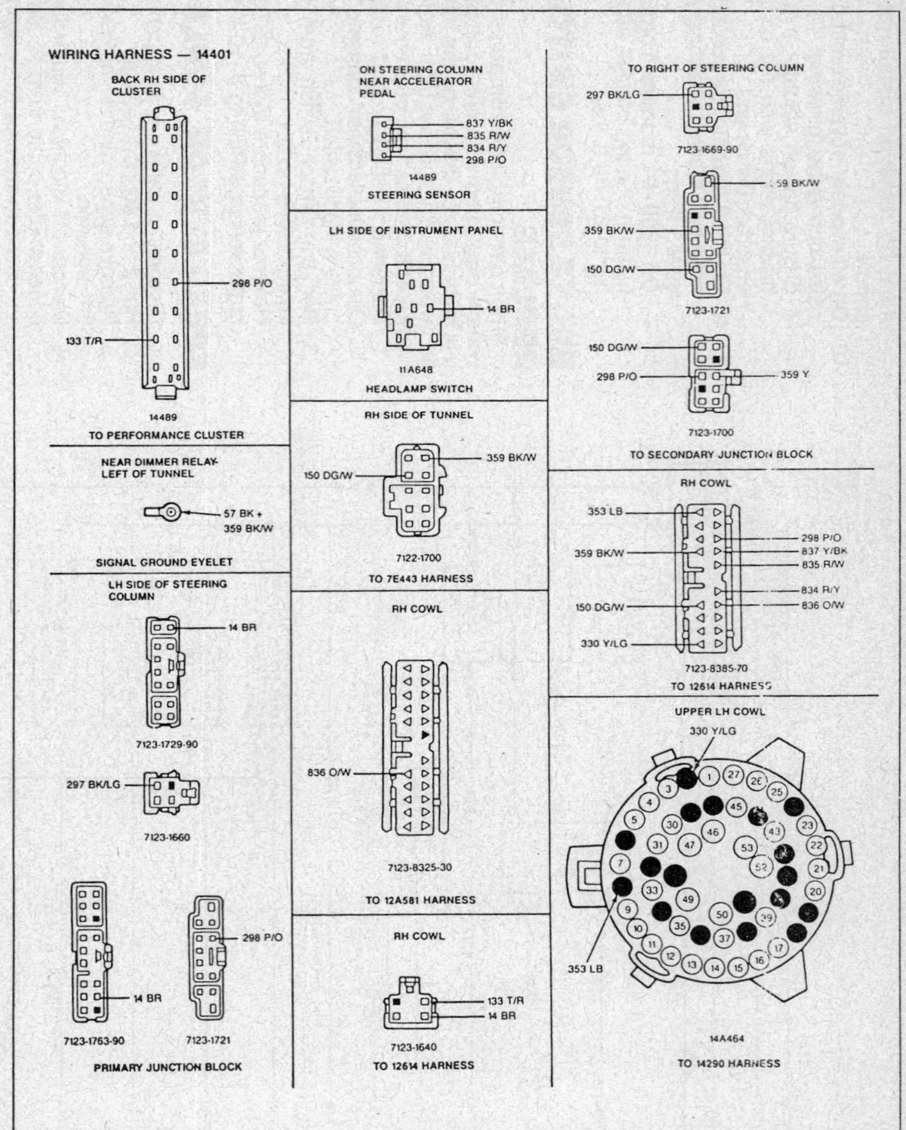


**Fig. 3 Automatic ride control system related electrical connectors (Part 2 of 4)**

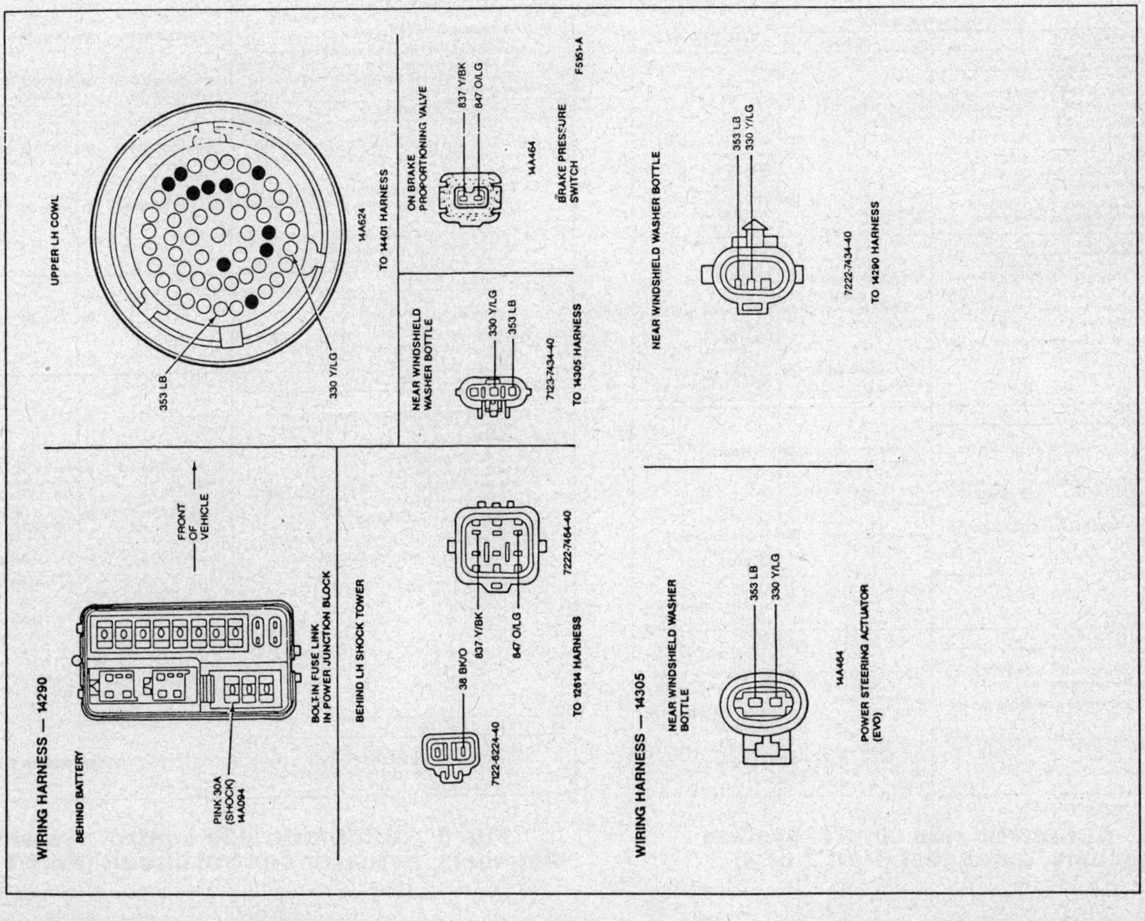

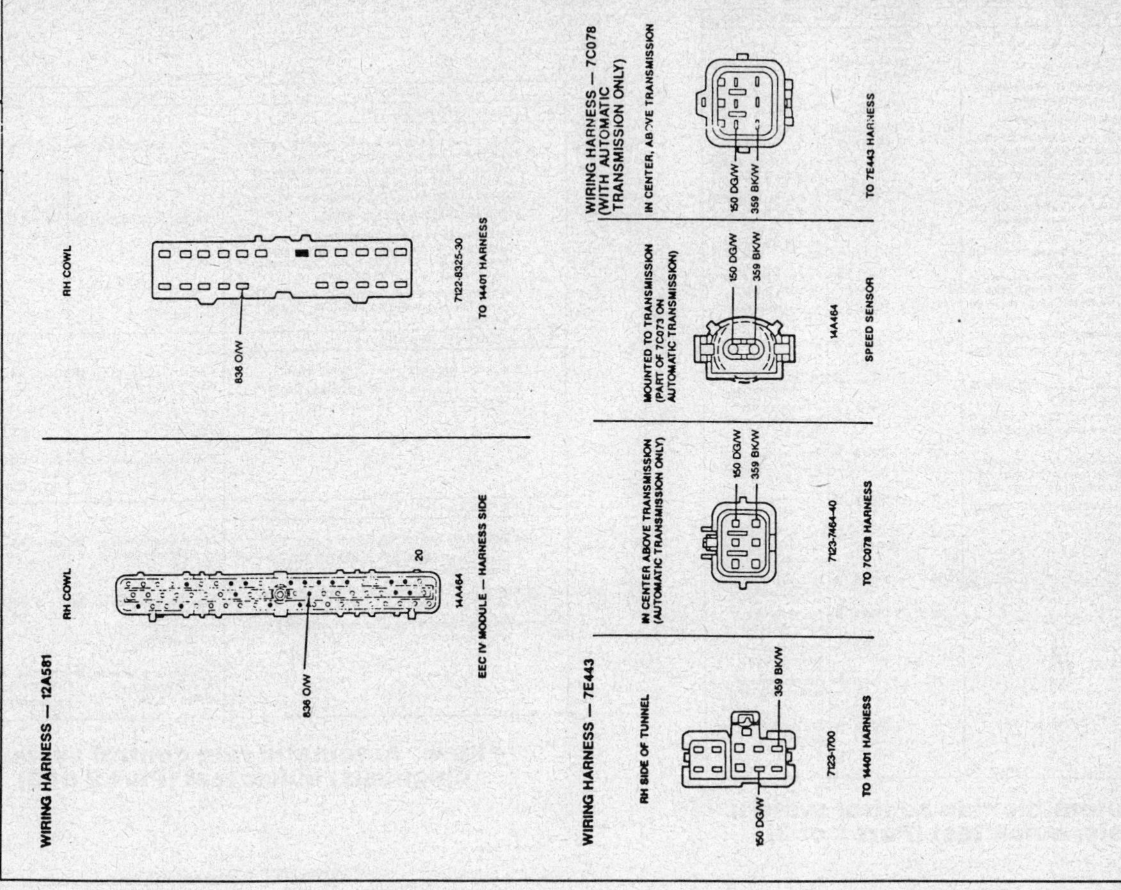


**Fig. 4 Automatic ride control system related electrical connectors (Part 4 of 4)**

WIRING HARNESS — 14290
BEHIND BATTERY
PINK 30A (SHOCK) 14A094
BOLT-IN FUSE LINK IN POWER JUNCTION BLOCK
FRONT OF VEHICLE
UPPER LH COWL
353 LB
330 Y/LG
14A624
TO 14401 HARNESS
BEHIND LH SHOCK TOWER
38 BK/O
7122-8224-40
837 Y/BK
847 O/LG
7222-7464-40
TO 12614 HARNESS
NEAR WINDSHIELD WASHER BOTTLE
330 Y/LG
353 LB
7123-7434-40
TO 14305 HARNESS
ON BRAKE PROPORTIONING VALVE
837 Y/BK
847 O/LG
14A464
BRAKE PRESSURE SWITCH
F5151-A
WIRING HARNESS — 14305
NEAR WINDSHIELD WASHER BOTTLE
353 LB
330 Y/LG
14A464
POWER STEERING ACTUATOR (EVO)
NEAR WINDSHIELD WASHER BOTTLE
353 LB
330 Y/LG
7222-7434-40
TO 14290 HARNESS

**Fig. 3 Automatic ride control system related electrical connectors (Part 3 of 4)**

**QUICK TEST**

| | TEST STEP | Star codes | Firm ride lamp blinks the following codes two times | ACTION TO TAKE |
|---|---|---|---|---|
| A1 | ENTER DIAGNOSTICS | | | |
| | • Turn ignition switch to the OFF position.<br>• Ensure headlamps, parking lamps and auto lamps are in the OFF position during the entire test.<br>• Set shock select switch to the AUTO position.<br>• Take Rotunda SUPER STAR II (Model 007-00019, 007-00028) or Star (Model 007-00017) Tester or equivalent and place in the "HOLD" up position. Format for the SUPER STAR II can be in slow or fast format for status codes.<br>• Connect SUPER STAR II or Star tester to STI connecter marked "ARC/EVO", located under hood by the passenger side shock tower.<br>• Turn the Star Tester on, and depress the Star test button to the "TEST" down position.<br>NOTE: If using a SUPER STAR II tester, make sure the mode switch is in the EEC-IV, MCU mode not the MECS mode. If in MECS mode you will get invalid error codes.<br>• Do NOT move shock select switch during test.<br>• Start engine and perform the following steps while engine is running.<br>1. The following procedure must be initiated within 20 seconds after starting the engine.<br>2. Release Star tester in the "TEST" mode to the "HOLD" mode and back to the "TEST" mode within 5 seconds.<br>3. The ARC/EVO module will run through self-test procedure and record error codes to the Star tester and also pulse out error codes to the firm ride lamp.<br>NOTE: The lamp will blink the same code two times. | 11 | 1 THEN 1 ▶ | No problem yet GO to **A2**. |
| | | NOTE: If all four actuator codes are received. | ▶ | GO to B1. |
| | | 10 | 1 ▶ | Fault in LH rear actuator circuit GO to **B8**. |
| | | 20 | 2 ▶ | Fault in RH rear actuator circuit GO to **B8**. |
| | | 30 | 3 ▶ | Fault in RH front actuator circuit GO to **B8**. |
| | | 40 | 4 ▶ | Fault in LH front actuator circuit GO to **B8**. |
| | | 50 | 5 ▶ | Short in soft relay GO to **B21**. |
| | | 60 | 6 ▶ | EVO steering open circuit GO to E1. |
| | | 70 | 7 ▶ | REPLACE automatic ride control module. |
| | | 12 | 1 then 2 ▶ | Soft relay short to ground or open circuit GO to **B21**. |
| | | 13 | 1 THEN 3 ▶ | Hard relay short to ground or open circuit GO to **B21**. |
| | | 14 | 1 THEN 4 ▶ | Fault in relay control circuit GO to **B25**. |
| | | 15 | ON ALWAYS ▶ | Firm ride lamp short to ground or open circuit GO to C9. |
| | | 16 | 1 THEN 6 ▶ | EVO steering circuit short GO to E4. |
| | | 22 | 2 THEN 2 ▶ | Soft relay short to battery GO to **B21**. |
| | | 23 | 2 THEN 3 ▶ | Hard relay short to battery GO to **B21**. |
| | | 25 | ▶ | Firm ride lamp short to battery ground GO to **C2**. |
| | | 26 | 2 THEN 6 ▶ | EVO steering valve bad GO to E4. |
| | | 00 | ▶ | GO to C1. |

**Fig. 4 Automatic ride control system diagnosis, quick test (Part 1 of 3)**

**QUICK TEST — Continued**

| | TEST STEP | RESULT ▶ | ACTION TO TAKE |
|---|---|---|---|
| A2 | CHECK STEERING SENSOR | | |
| | **NOTE: Steps A2 and A3 may be repeated as many times and in any order desired to ensure proper test results. However, once the engine is turned off or the shock select switch is moved, you must proceed to step A4 or start over at step A1.**<br>• Wait until lamp has stopped blinking.<br>• With the vehicle at rest and engine running, test the steering sensor by turning the steering wheel from lock in one direction to lock in the other direction (3 full turns) or until firm ride lamp turns on.<br>**NOTE: The lamp will usually turn on before the wheel has completed the lock turn. This is normal.** | Firm ride lamp turns on for 5 seconds, then turns off ▶ | GO to **A3**. |
| | | Firm ride lamp does not turn on ▶ | Fault in steering sensor circuit. GO to **D13**. |
| A3 | CHECK SPEED SENSOR | | |
| | • Wait until lamp has turned off from Step A2.<br>• Drive the vehicle at any desired speed above 18 mph (29 Km/h). | Firm ride lamp turns on and stays on until vehicle speed drops below 18 mph (29 Km/h) ▶ | GO to **A4**. |
| | | Firm ride lamp does not turn on ▶ | Fault in speed sensor circuit. GO to **D19**. |
| A4 | PREPARE FOR REMAINING TESTS | | |
| | • Stop vehicle and turn engine off.<br>• Move shock select switch to AUTO if it is not already there.<br>• Move the ignition switch to the RUN position, leaving the engine off.<br>• Wait until the firm ride lamp has turned off (usually after 4 seconds). | Firm ride lamp turns on for 4 seconds, then turns off ▶ | GO to **A5**. |
| | | Firm ride lamp turns on and stays on even though switch is in AUTO position ▶ | False firm signal. GO to **D6**. |
| | | Firm ride lamp turns on for 4 seconds, then flashes a code ▶ | RECORD code and REFER to Step A1 for action to take. |

**Fig. 4 Automatic ride control system diagnosis, quick test (Part 2 of 3)**

**QUICK TEST — Continued**

| | TEST STEP | RESULT ▶ | ACTION TO TAKE |
|---|---|---|---|
| A5 | CHECK SHOCK SELECT SWITCH | | |
| | **NOTE: Steps A5 through A6 may be performed in any order and as many times as desired to ensure satisfactory results.**<br>• Move the shock select switch to AUTO if it is not already there.<br>• After the firm ride lamp has turned off, move the shock select switch to the FIRM position.<br>• After the firm ride lamp has turned on, move the shock select switch back to the AUTO position. | Firm ride lamp turns on in FIRM, off in AUTO ▶ | GO to A6. |
| | | Firm ride lamp does not turn on ▶ | Fault in shock select switch circuit. GO to D23. |
| | | Firm ride lamp flashes a code ▶ | RECORD code and REFER to Step A1 for action to take. |
| A6 | CHECK BRAKE SENSOR | | |
| | • Move the shock select switch to AUTO if it is not already there.<br>• After the firm ride lamp has turned off, depress the brake pedal until the firm ride lamp turns on.<br>• After the firm ride lamp has turned on, release the brake pedal. | Firm ride lamp turns on ▶ | GO to A7. |
| | | Firm ride lamp does not turn on ▶ | Fault in brake sensor circuit. GO to D27. |
| | | Firm ride lamp flashes a code ▶ | RECORD code and REFER to Step A1 for action to take. |
| A7 | CHECK ACCELERATION SIGNAL | | |
| | • Move the shock select switch to AUTO if it is not already there.<br>• After the firm ride lamp has turned off, depress the accelerator pedal to the floor. The firm ride lamp should turn on.<br>• After the firm ride lamp has turned on, release the accelerator pedal. | Firm ride lamp turns on when pedal is pressed to the floor, off 4 seconds after the pedal is released ▶ | GO to A8. |
| | | Firm ride lamp does not turn on ▶ | Fault in acceleration signal circuit. GO to D31. |
| | | Firm ride lamp flashes a code ▶ | RECORD code and REFER to Step A1 for action to take. |
| A8 | CHECK DIMMING FUNCTION | | |
| | • Move the shock selector switch to the FIRM position to turn on instrument panel indicator.<br>• Cycle headlamps on and off while observing FIRM ride indicator. | Firm ride lamp is bright with headlamps off, dimmer with headlamps on. ▶ | If the complete test has been completed (Steps A1 through A8), then the vehicle has passed diagnostics. |
| | | Firm ride lamp does not get dimmer with headlamps on. ▶ | GO to C6. |

**Fig. 4 Automatic ride control system diagnosis, quick test (Part 3 of 3)**

**ACTUATOR CONTROL CIRCUIT DIAGNOSIS**

| | TEST STEP | RESULT ▶ | ACTION TO TAKE |
|---|---|---|---|
| B1 | CHECK CONNECTOR WIRES | | |
| | • Turn ignition to the OFF position.<br>• Examine the wires on all actuator connectors and on the wiring harness side to ensure that there is no obvious damage and that all of the wires are in the proper location. | No observed damaged ▶ | GO to B2. |
| | | Wires damaged or in wrong position ▶ | SERVICE wires as necessary. |
| B2 | SIGNAL RETURN CONTINUITY | | |
| | • Go to luggage compartment and lower the control module packaging tray behind the driver's side back seat.<br>• Disconnect the 60 pin electrical connector from the ARC module. Connect harness to 60 pin Breakout Box.<br>• Measure resistance between signal return Pin No. 46 (Circuit 837) in the wiring harness side of the actuator connector, and chassis ground. | Greater than 1000 ohms ▶ | SERVICE open circuit in signal return line (Circuit 837). |
| | | Less than 10 ohms ▶ | GO to B3. |
| B3 | ENERGIZE HARD RELAY | | |
| | • Turn the ignition to RUN position.<br>• Use a jumper wire to connect Pin No. 11 to Pin No. 60 on the wiring harness side of the 60 pin connector for 1 or 2 seconds. | ▶ | GO to B4. |
| B4 | DO POSITION SWITCHES OPEN | | |
| | • Use an ohmmeter to measure the resistance between the following pairs of wiring harness connector Pins:<br>• No. 46 and No. 19<br>• No. 46 and No. 25<br>• No. 46 and No. 7<br>• No. 46 and No. 10<br>If the measured resistance is:<br>• Greater than 1000 ohms, the switch is open.<br>• Less than 10 ohms, the switch is closed. | All four switches are open ▶ | GO to B5. |
| | | All four switches are closed ▶ | Fault in power distribution. GO to B17. |
| | | Pin No. 19 closed ▶ | Fault in LH rear actuator. GO to B7. |
| | | Pin No. 25 closed ▶ | Fault in RH rear actuator. GO to B7. |
| | | Pin No. 7 closed ▶ | Fault in RH front actuator. GO to B7. |
| | | Pin No. 10 closed ▶ | Fault in LH front actuator. GO to B7. |
| B5 | ENERGIZE SOFT RELAY | | |
| | • Use a jumper wire to connect Pin No. 12 to Pin No. 60 on the wiring harness side of the 60 pin connector for 1 or 2 seconds. | ▶ | GO to B6. |

**Fig. 5 Automatic ride control system diagnosis, actuator control circuit (Part 1 of 8)**

ACTUATOR CONTROL CIRCUIT DIAGNOSIS — Continued

| TEST STEP | | RESULT | ACTION TO TAKE |
|---|---|---|---|
| B6 | DO POSITION SWITCHES CLOSE | | |
| | • Use an ohmmeter to measure the resistance between the following pairs of wiring harness connector Pins:<br>• No. 46 and No. 19<br>• No. 46 and No. 25<br>• No. 46 and No. 7<br>• No. 46 and No. 10<br>If the measured resistance is:<br>• Greater than 1000 ohms, the switch is open.<br>• Less than 10 ohms, the switch is closed. | All four switches are closed ▶ | REPLACE ARC module |
| | | All four switches are open ▶ | Fault in power distribution. GO to **B17**. |
| | | Pin No. 19 open ▶ | Fault in LH rear actuator. GO to **B7**. |
| | | Pin No. 25 open ▶ | Fault in RH rear actuator. GO to **B7**. |
| | | Pin No. 7 open ▶ | Fault in RH front actuator. GO to **B7**. |
| | | Pin No. 10 open ▶ | REPLACE ARC module. |
| B7 | RECONNECT MODULE CONNECTOR | | |
| | • Turn ignition to the OFF position.<br>• Disconnect harness from 60 Pin Breakout Box.<br>• Reconnect the 60 pin electrical connector to the PRC module.<br>**NOTE: Do not reattach the module mounting panel at this time.** | ▶ | GO to **B8**. |
| B8 | CHECK ACTUATOR CONNECTOR WIRES | | |
| | • If the ignition is not already OFF, turn it to the OFF position.<br>• Examine the wires on the problem actuator connectors and on the wiring harness side to ensure that there is no obvious damage and that all of the wires are in the proper location. | No observed damage ▶ | GO to **B9**. |
| | | Wires damaged or in wrong position ▶ | SERVICE wires as necessary. |
| B9 | PREPARE FOR ACTUATOR ROTATION TEST | | |
| | • Disconnect all problem actuators from the top of their struts or shock absorbers.<br>**NOTE: Leave the electrical connectors plugged in.**<br>• Turn ignition to the RUN position and wait 5 seconds.<br>• Move the ride control switch to the AUTO position.<br>• Record the position (SOFT or HARD) (S or H) of the control tube on the bottom of the problem actuators. | ▶ | GO to **B10**. |

**Fig. 5 Automatic ride control system diagnosis, actuator control circuit (Part 2 of 8)**

ACTUATOR CONTROL CIRCUIT DIAGNOSIS — Continued

| TEST STEP | | RESULT | ACTION TO TAKE |
|---|---|---|---|
| B10 | DO ACTUATORS ROTATE TO HARD POSITION | | |
| | • Move the ride control switch to the FIRM position and wait 5 seconds.<br>• Observe the position (S or H) of the control tube on the bottom of the problem actuators.<br>• Did all problem actuators rotate from the S position after step B9 to the H position now? | Rotated from S to H ▶ | GO to B12. |
| | | Did not rotate (stayed in H or S position) ▶ | GO to B11. |
| | | Rotated from H to S ▶ | SERVICE crossed power feed Circuits No. 845 and No. 846 at problem actuator as necessary. |
| B11 | CAN ACTUATOR ROTATE | | |
| | • Turn ignition to OFF position.<br>• Unplug the problem actuators and plug them into the wiring harness at any position where the current actuator is functioning properly.<br>• Turn ignition to RUN position and wait 5 seconds. Move the ride control switch to the AUTO position.<br>• Are the control tubes on the bottom of the problem actuators in the S position?<br>• Move the ride control switch to the FIRM position. Do the control tubes on the bottom of the problem actuators rotate from the S to the H position? | Did not rotate ▶ | REPLACE actuator. |
| | | Rotated ▶ | SERVICE open in either Circuit No. 845 or No. 846 between relays and the original actuator connector as necessary. |
| B12 | DO ACTUATOR POSITION SWITCHES WORK | | |
| | • Disconnect the electrical connectors of the problem actuators.<br>• Use a small blade screwdriver to rotate the control tube on the bottom of the problem actuators to the S position.<br>• Use Rotunda Digital Volt Ohm-Meter 007-00001 or equivalent to measure the resistance between the position sense and signal return pins of the actuator electrical connector.<br>• Rotate the control tube on the bottom of the problem actuators to the H position. Remeasure the resistance between the position sense and signal return pins.<br>If the measured resistance is:<br>• Greater than 1000 ohms, the switch is open<br>• Less than 10 ohms, the switch is closed | Switches closed in S position and open in the H position ▶ | GO to B13. |
| | | Switches always open ▶ | REPLACE actuator. |
| | | Switches always closed ▶ | REPLACE actuator. |
| B13 | DOES ACTUATOR HAVE INTERNAL SHORT | | |
| | • Use a small blade screwdriver to rotate the control tube on the bottom of the problem actuators to the H position.<br>• Measure the resistance between the position sense and soft power pins of the actuator electrical connector. | Greater than 1000 ohms ▶ | GO to B14. |
| | | Less than 10 ohms ▶ | REPLACE actuator. |

**Fig. 5 Automatic ride control system diagnosis, actuator control circuit (Part 3 of 8)**

ACTUATOR CONTROL CIRCUIT DIAGNOSIS — Continued

| TEST STEP | | RESULT | ACTION TO TAKE |
|---|---|---|---|
| B14 | SIGNAL RETURN CONTINUITY TO GROUND | | |
| | • Measure the resistance between the signal return Pin No. 46 (Circuit 837) in the wiring harness side of the actuator connector and chassis ground. | Greater than 1000 ohms ▶ | SERVICE open circuit in signal return line (Circuit 837). |
| | | Less than 10 ohms ▶ | GO to **B15**. |
| B15 | DISCONNECT MODULE CONNECTOR | | |
| | • Turn ignition to the OFF position.<br>• Go to luggage compartment and lower the control module packaging tray behind driver's side back seat.<br>Disconnect the 60 pin electrical connector from the ARC module. Connect harness to 60 pin Breakout Box. | ▶ | GO to **B16**. |
| B16 | TEST POSITION SENSOR WIRING FOR CONTINUITY | | |
| | • Examine wire at Pin 46 for damage or mislocation.<br>• Examine the position sensors wires for the problem actuators at the 60 pin connector to ensure that there is no obvious damage and that they are in the proper location.<br>• Test the continuity of the position sensor wires for the problem actuators, and the wire at Pin 46 of the 60 pin connector to the wiring harness side of the actuator connectors. | Damaged or crossed wires or no continuity ▶ | SERVICE wires as necessary. |
| | | No wiring problems ▶ | GO to **B36**. |
| B17 | TEST RELAY POWER FEED | | |
| | • Turn ignition to the OFF position.<br>• Go to luggage compartment and unplug both ride control relays.<br>• Turn ignition to RUN position.<br>• Use Rotunda Digital Volt Ohm-Meter 007-00001 or equivalent to measure the voltage from Circuits No. 38 to No. 57 at the wiring harness side of both relay connectors. | Zero volts ▶ | GO to **B18**. |
| | | 12 volts ▶ | GO to **B19**. |
| B18 | TEST HARD POWER FEED | | |
| | • Use a voltmeter to measure the voltage from Circuit No. 38 at the wiring harness side of both relay connectors to chassis ground. | Zero volts ▶ | SERVICE short or open in Circuit No. 38 or blown fuse link as necessary. |
| | | 12 volts ▶ | SERVICE open in Circuit No. 57 as necessary. |
| B19 | TEST CONTINUITY TO ACTUATORS | | |
| | • Unplug the RH rear actuator.<br>• Test the continuity of the wiring harness power feed Circuits No. 845 and No. 846 from the relays to the actuator. | Continuity in both circuits ▶ | GO to **B20**. |
| | | Open in one or both circuits ▶ | SERVICE wires as necessary. |

**Fig. 5 Automatic ride control system diagnosis, actuator control circuit (Part 4 of 8)**

ACTUATOR CONTROL CIRCUIT DIAGNOSIS — Continued

| TEST STEP | | RESULT | ACTION TO TAKE |
|---|---|---|---|
| B20 | ARE RELAY CONTROL CIRCUITS CROSSED | | |
| | • Examine the wires on the wiring harness side of both relay electrical connectors to verify that:<br>• Circuits No. 838 and No. 845 are in the same connector.<br>• Circuits No. 839 and No. 846 are in the same connector. | Crossed wires ▶ | SERVICE wires as necessary. |
| | | No wiring problems ▶ | REPLACE firm relay. |
| B20A | | | |
| | GO to A1. Perform Quick Test. | If all four actuator codes are received again. ▶ | REPLACE soft relay. |
| B21 | DISCONNECT MODULE CONNECTOR | | |
| | • Turn ignition to the OFF position.<br>• Go to luggage compartment and lower the control module packaging tray behind driver's side back seat.<br>• Disconnect the 60 pin electrical connector from the ARC module. Connect harness to 60 pin Breakout Box. | ▶ | GO to **B22**. |
| B22 | CHECK FOR SHORT IN RELAY CONTROL CIRCUIT | | |
| | • Examine the wiring harness side of the 60 pin connector to verify that there is no obvious damage and that:<br>• Circuit No. 838 is in Pin No. 11<br>• Circuit No. 839 is in Pin No. 12<br>• Turn ignition to the RUN position.<br>• Use an ohmmeter to measure the resistance on the harness side of the 60 pin connector from:<br>• Pin No. 11 to Pin No. 60<br>• Pin No. 12 to Pin No. 60 | Both circuits greater than 1000 ohms ▶ | REPLACE ARC module. |
| | | Pin No. 11 less than 10 ohms ▶ | Fault in hard relay circuit. GO to **B23**. |
| | | Pin No. 12 less than 10 ohms ▶ | Fault in soft relay circuit GO to **B23**. |
| B23 | DISCONNECT PROBLEM RELAY | | |
| | • Disconnect problem relay. Examine the harness wires at the relay connector to ensure that there is no obvious damage and that they are in the proper location. | Damaged or crossed wires ▶ | SERVICE wires as necessary |
| | | No observed damage ▶ | GO to **B24**. |
| B24 | RETEST RELAY CONTROL CIRCUITS | | |
| | • Use an ohmmeter to measure the resistance on the harness side of the 60 pin connector from:<br>• Pin No. 11 to Pin No. 60<br>• Pin No. 12 to Pin No. 60 | Both circuits greater than 1000 ohms. ▶ | REPLACE problem relay. |
| | | Less than 10 ohms ▶ | SERVICE short in circuit as necessary. |

**Fig. 5 Automatic ride control system diagnosis, actuator control circuit (Part 5 of 8)**

ACTUATOR CONTROL CIRCUIT DIAGNOSIS — Continued

| TEST STEP | RESULT ▶ | ACTION TO TAKE |
|---|---|---|
| **B25 DISCONNECT MODULE CONNECTOR** | | |
| • Go to luggage compartment and lower the control module mounting panel on the back of the passenger side seat.<br>• Disconnect the 60 pin electrical connector from the ARC module. Connect harness to 60 pin Breakout Box. | ▶ | GO to B26. |
| **B26 ENERGIZE HARD RELAY** | | |
| • Turn the ignition to RUN position.<br>• Use a jumper wire to connect Pin No. 11 to Pin No. 60 on the wiring harness side of the 60 pin connector for 1 or 2 seconds. | ▶ | GO to B27. |
| **B27 DO POSITION SWITCHES OPEN** | | |
| • Use an ohmmeter to measure the resistance between the following pairs of wiring harness connector Pins:<br>• No. 46 and No. 19<br>• No. 46 and No. 25<br>• No. 46 and No. 7<br>• No. 46 and No. 10<br>If the measured resistance is:<br>• Greater than 1000 ohms, the switch is open<br>• Less than 10 ohms, the switch is closed | All four switches are open ▶ | GO to B28. |
| | All four switches are closed ▶ | Fault in hard relay control. GO to B30. |
| **B28 ENERGIZE SOFT RELAY** | | |
| • Use a jumper wire to connect Pin No. 12 to Pin No. 60 on the wiring harness side of the 60 pin connector for 1 or 2 seconds. | ▶ | GO to B29. |
| **B29 DO POSITION SWITCHES CLOSE** | | |
| • Use an ohmmeter to measure the resistance between the following pairs of wiring harness connector Pins:<br>• No. 46 and No. 19<br>• No. 46 and No. 25<br>• No. 46 and No. 7<br>• No. 46 and No. 10<br>If the measured resistance is:<br>• Greater than 1000 ohms, the switch is open<br>• Less than 10 ohms, the switch is closed | All four switches are closed ▶ | REPLACE ARC module. |
| | All four switches are open ▶ | Fault in soft relay control. GO to B30. |

**Fig. 5 Automatic ride control system diagnosis, actuator control circuit (Part 6 of 8)**

ACTUATOR CONTROL CIRCUIT DIAGNOSIS — Continued

| TEST STEP | RESULT ▶ | ACTION TO TAKE |
|---|---|---|
| **B30 DISCONNECT PROBLEM RELAY** | | |
| • Disconnect problem relay. Examine the harness wires at the relay connector to ensure that there is no obvious damage and that they are in the proper location. | Damaged or crossed wires ▶ | SERVICE wires as necessary. |
| | No observed damage ▶ | GO to B31. |
| **B31 TEST COIL POWER FEED** | | |
| • Use a voltmeter to measure the voltage from Circuit No. 298 at the wiring harness side of both relay connectors to chassis ground. | Zero volts ▶ | SERVICE short/open in Circuit No. 298 as necessary. |
| | 12 volts ▶ | GO to B32. |
| **B32 TEST RELAY CONTROL CIRCUIT** | | |
| • Test the continuity of the problem relay control circuit from the relay to the 60 pin connector at the ARC module as follows:<br>• Circuit No. 838 to Pin No. 11<br>• Circuit No. 839 to Pin No. 12 | Continuity ▶ | REPLACE relay. |
| | Open circuit ▶ | SERVICE wire as necessary. GO to B33. |
| **B33 ATTACH PROBLEM ACTUATOR** | | |
| • Attach problem actuator to shock absorber.<br>• Connect actuator electrical connector to wiring harness connector. | ▶ | GO to B34. |
| **B34 ENERGIZE HARD RELAY** | | |
| • Turn ignition to RUN position.<br>• Use a jumper wire to connect Pin No. 11 to Pin No. 60 on the wiring harness side of the 60 pin connector for 1 or 2 seconds. | ▶ | GO to B35. |
| **B35 DOES POSITION SWITCH OPEN?** | | |
| • Use an ohmmeter to measure the resistance of the wiring harness pins for the problem actuator as follows:<br>Problem Actuator — Harness Connector Pins<br>• LH rear — No. 46 and No. 14<br>• RH rear — No. 46 and No. 25<br>• RH front — No. 46 and No. 7<br>• LH front — No. 46 and No. 10<br>If the measured resistance is:<br>• Greater than 1000 ohms, the switch is open.<br>• Less than 10 ohms, the switch is closed. | Switch of problem actuator is open ▶ | GO to B36. |
| | Switch of problem actuator is closed ▶ | REPLACE actuator and shock absorber. (Parts are mechanically binding). |

**Fig. 5 Automatic ride control system diagnosis, actuator control circuit (Part 7 of 8)**

ACTUATOR CONTROL CIRCUIT DIAGNOSIS — Continued

| TEST STEP | RESULT ▶ | ACTION TO TAKE |
|---|---|---|
| **B36 ENERGIZE SOFT RELAY** | | |
| • Use a jumper wire to connect Pin No. 12 to Pin No. 60 on the wiring harness side of the 60 pin connector for 1 or 2 seconds. | ▶ | GO to B37. |
| **B37 DOES POSITION SWITCH CLOSE?** | | |
| • Use an ohmmeter to measure the resistance of the wiring harness pins for the problem actuator as follows:<br>Problem Actuator — Harness Connector Pins<br>• LH rear — No. 46 and No. 19<br>• RH rear — No. 46 and No. 25<br>• RH front — No. 46 and No. 7<br>• LH front — No. 46 and No. 10 | Switch of problem actuator is closed ▶ | REPLACE ARC module. |
| | Switch of problem actuator is open ▶ | REPLACE actuator and shock absorber. (Parts are mechanically binding). |

**Fig. 5 Automatic ride control system diagnosis, actuator control circuit (Part 8 of 8)**

FIRM RIDE INDICATOR LAMP CIRCUIT DIAGNOSIS

| TEST STEP | RESULT ▶ | ACTION TO TAKE |
|---|---|---|
| **C1 OBSERVE KEY ON SEQUENCE** | | |
| • Turn ignition to the OFF position.<br>• Set shock select switch to the FIRM position.<br>• Shield the firm ride lamp from bright sunlight so that you can see the lamp even if it is dim, and turn the ignition switch to RUN position. | Firm ride lamp does not turn on ▶ | REPLACE bulb. GO to C2. |
| | Firm ride lamp is dim ▶ | GO to C6. |
| | Firm ride lamp turns on ▶ | Did not enter diagnostics GO to D1. |
| **C2 DISCONNECT MODULE CONNECTOR** | | |
| • Go to luggage compartment and lower the control module packaging tray behind driver's side back seat.<br>• Disconnect the 60 pin electrical connector from the ARC module. Connect harness to 60 pin Breakout Box. | ▶ | GO to C3. |
| **C3 DOES FIRM RIDE LAMP WORK** | | |
| • Turn the ignition to RUN position.<br>• Use a jumper wire to connect Pin No. 15 to Pin No. 60 on the wiring harness side of the 60 pin connector.<br>• Observe firm ride lamp. | Firm ride lamp turns on ▶ | Fault in module power circuitry. GO to C4. |
| | Firm ride lamp does not turn on ▶ | Fault in light control circuitry. GO to C5. |
| **C4 DOES MODULE HAVE POWER** | | |
| • Use a voltmeter to measure the voltage from Pin No. 57 to Pin No. 60 on the wiring harness side or the 60 pin connector. | 0 volts ▶ | SERVICE short to ground or open in Circuit No. 298 as necessary. |
| | 12 volts ▶ | REPLACE ARC module. |
| **C5 TEST LAMP CIRCUIT** | | |
| • Locate firm ride lamp wire on instrument cluster connector. Check for continuity. | No continuity ▶ | SERVICE Circuit No. 133 as necessary. |
| | Continuity ▶ | CHECK instrument panel power, ground and bulb. |

**Fig. 6 Automatic ride control system diagnosis, firm ride indicator lamp circuit (Part 1 of 2)**

FIRM RIDE INDICATOR LAMP CIRCUIT DIAGNOSIS — Continued

| TEST STEP | | RESULT ▶ | ACTION TO TAKE |
|---|---|---|---|
| C6 | CHECK LAMP DIMMING | | |
| | • Move the shock select switch to the FIRM position to turn on FIRM ride lamp.<br>• Cycle headlamps on and off while observing FIRM ride lamp. | Firm ride lamp is bright with headlamps off, dimmer with headlamps on ▶<br>Firm ride lamp does not get dimmer with headlamps on ▶ | <br>GO to **C7**. |
| C7 | DISCONNECT MODULE CONNECTOR | | |
| | • Go to luggage compartment and lower the module packaging tray behind driver's side back seat.<br>• Disconnect the 60 pin connector from the ARC module. Connect harness to 60 pin Breakout Box. | ▶ | GO to **C8**. |
| C8 | CHECK HEADLAMP WIRING | | |
| | • Use a voltmeter to measure the voltage from Circuit No. 14 of the harness connector (Pin 1) and (Pin 60) of the harness side connector. Cycle headlamps. | 12V with headlamps on, 0V with headlamps off ▶<br>12V always or 0V always ▶ | REPLACE ARC module.<br>SERVICE fault in headlamp switch Circuit No. 14 as necessary. |
| C9 | DISCONNECT MODULE CONNECTOR | | |
| | • Turn ignition to the OFF position.<br>• Go to luggage compartment and lower the control module mounting panel on the back of the passenger side seat.<br>• Disconnect the 60 pin electrical connector from the ARC module. Connect harness to 60 pin Breakout Box. | ▶ | GO to **C10**. |
| C10 | CHECK FOR SHORT IN FIRM RIDE LAMP CIRCUIT | | |
| | • Check Circuit No. 133 at the 60 pin connector to ensure that there is no obvious damage and that it is in pin location No. 15.<br>• Use an ohmmeter to measure the resistance from Pin No. 15 to Pin No. 60 on the harness side of the 60 pin connector. | Greater than 1000 ohms ▶<br>Less than 10 ohms ▶ | REPLACE module.<br>SERVICE short to ground in Circuit No. 133 as necessary. |

**Fig. 6 Automatic ride control system diagnosis, firm ride indicator lamp circuit (Part 2 of 2)**

MODULE INPUT CIRCUIT DIAGNOSIS

| TEST STEP | | RESULT ▶ | ACTION TO TAKE |
|---|---|---|---|
| D1 | REPEAT ATTEMPT TO ENTER DIAGNOSTICS | | |
| | • Verify that diagnostic connector used in Step A1 is clean and free of corrosion.<br>• Repeat attempt to enter diagnostics (Step A1), ensuring all tester switches are in the proper position and the button is depressed at the proper time. | Second attempt successful ▶<br>Second attempt fails ▶ | CONTINUE at Step A1.<br>GO to **D2**. |
| D2 | TEST SIGNAL RETURN WIRE CONTINUITY | | |
| | • Check the signal return, diagnostic and STAR wires (Circuit Nos. 844, 837 and 930 respectively) at the star connector to ensure that there is no obvious damage.<br>• Test the continuity of Circuit No. 837 to chassis ground. | Damaged wires ▶<br>No continuity ▶<br>No problems detected ▶ | SERVICE wires as necessary.<br>SERVICE open in Circuit No. 837 as necessary.<br>GO to **D3**. |
| D3 | DISCONNECT MODULE CONNECTOR | | |
| | • Turn ignition to the OFF position.<br>• Go to luggage compartment and lower the control module packaging tray behind driver's side rear seat.<br>• Disconnect the 60 pin electrical connector from the ARC module. Connect harness to 60 pin Breakout Box. | ▶ | GO to **D4**. |
| D4 | CHECK DIAGNOSTIC CIRCUIT FOR SHORT TO GROUND | | |
| | • Examine Circuit No. 844 at the 60 pin connector to ensure that there is no obvious damage and that it is in pin location No. 30.<br>• Use an ohmmeter to measure the resistance from Pin No. 30 to Pin No. 60 on the harness side of the 60 pin connector.<br>• Use an ohmmeter to measure the resistance from Pin 47 to Pin 60 on the harness side of the 60 pin connector. | Greater than 1000 ohms ▶<br>Less than 10 ohms ▶<br>▶ | GO to **D5**.<br>SERVICE short to ground in Circuit No. 844 as necessary.<br>SERVICE short to ground in Circuit No. 930 as necessary. |
| D5 | CHECK DIAGNOSTIC CIRCUIT | | |
| | • Connect tester into diagnostic connector.<br>• Go to luggage compartment and use an ohmmeter to measure the resistance from Pin 30 to Pin 46 on the harness side of the 60 pin connector.<br>• Measure resistance with tester button depressed and not depressed. | Greater than 1000 ohms always ▶<br>Greater than 1000 ohms undepressed. Less than 10 ohms depressed ▶<br>Less than 10 ohms always ▶ | SERVICE open in Circuit No. 844 or poor contact between tester and diagnostic connector. Check tester.<br>REPLACE ARC module.<br>CHECK STAR Tester. |

**Fig. 7 Automatic ride control system diagnosis, module input circuit (Part 1 of 7)**

| TEST STEP | | RESULT ▶ | ACTION TO TAKE |
|---|---|---|---|
| D6 | CHECK SWITCH POSITIONS | | |
| | • Move switch to FIRM position. | Firm ride lamp stays on (OK) ▶<br>Firm ride lamp turns off (~~OK~~) ▶ | GO to **D7**.<br>Switch positions reversed. REPLACE switch. |
| D7 | DISCONNECT MODULE CONNECTOR | | |
| | • Turn ignition to the OFF position.<br>• Set shock select switch to the AUTO position.<br>• Go to luggage compartment and lower the control module mounting panel on the back of the passenger side seat.<br>• Disconnect the 60 pin electrical connector from the PRC module. | ▶ | GO to **D8**. |
| D8 | CHECK BRAKE SENSOR FOR SHORT TO GROUND | | |
| | • Check Circuit No. 847 at the 60 pin connector to ensure that there is no obvious damage and that it is in pin location No. 9.<br>• Use an ohmmeter to measure the resistance from Pin No. 9 to Pin No. 60 on the harness side of the 60 pin connector. | Greater than 1000 ohms (OK) ▶<br>Less than 10 ohms (~~OK~~) ▶ | GO to **D9**.<br>SERVICE short to ground in Circuit No. 847 as necessary. |
| D9 | BRAKE SENSE CIRCUIT ALWAYS CLOSED | | |
| | • Use an ohmmeter to measure the resistance from Pin No. 9 to Pin No. 46 on the harness side of the 60 pin connector. | Greater than 1000 ohms (OK) ▶<br>Less than 10 ohms (~~OK~~) ▶ | GO to **D10**.<br>REPLACE brake pressure switch. |
| D10 | SHOCK SELECT CIRCUIT ALWAYS CLOSED | | |
| | • Verify that the shock select switch is in the AUTO position.<br>• Check Circuit No. 832 at the 60 pin connector to ensure that there is no obvious damage and that it is in pin location No. 18.<br>• Use a voltmeter to measure the voltage from Pin No. 18 to Pin No. 60 on the harness side of the 60 pin connector. | 0 volts (OK) ▶<br>12 volts (~~OK~~) ▶ | GO to **D11**.<br>REPLACE shock select switch. |
| D11 | ACCELERATION SIGNAL ALWAYS CLOSED | | |
| | • Check Circuit No. 836 at the 60 pin connector to ensure that there is no obvious damage and that it is in pin location No. 28.<br>• Use an ohmmeter to measure the resistance from Pin No. 28 to Pin No. 60 on the harness side of the 60 pin connector. | Greater than 1000 ohms (~~OK~~) ▶<br>Less than 10 ohms (OK) ▶ | REPLACE defective PRC module.<br>GO to **D12**. |

**Fig. 7 Automatic ride control system diagnosis, module input circuit (Part 2 of 7)**

| TEST STEP | | RESULT ▶ | ACTION TO TAKE |
|---|---|---|---|
| D12 | ACCELERATION CIRCUIT SHORTED TO GROUND | | |
| | • Turn ignition switch to the OFF position.<br>• Unplug the EEC IV control module from the wiring harness.<br>• Return to luggage compartment and remeasure the resistance from Pin No. 28 to Pin No. 60 on the harness side of the PRC module 60 pin connector. | Greater than 1000 ohms ▶<br>Less than 10 ohms ▶ | REFER to the Engine Emissions Diagnosis Manual, Volume H Section 25 to find defective throttle position signal or EEC IV.<br>SERVICE short to ground in Circuit No. 836 as necessary. |
| D13 | DISCONNECT MODULE CONNECTOR | | |
| | • Turn ignition to the OFF position.<br>• Go to luggage compartment and lower the control module mounting panel on the back of the passenger side seat.<br>• Disconnect the 60 pin electrical connector from the PRC module. | ▶ | GO to **D14**. |
| D14 | CHECK STEERING SENSOR WIRES | | |
| | • Examine the wiring harness side of the 60 pin connector to verify that there is no obvious damage and that:<br>  • Circuit No. 834 is in Pin No. 45<br>  • Circuit No. 835 is in Pin No. 24<br>**NOTE: If these two circuits are reversed it will not affect function. Therefore, treat as no problem.** | Damaged wires (~~OK~~) ▶<br>No wiring problems (OK) ▶ | SERVICE wires as necessary.<br>GO to **D15**. |
| D15 | TEST STEERING SENSOR SIGNALS | | |
| | • Start engine.<br>• Use an analog ohmmeter on the 1k scale to measure the resistance on the harness side of the 60 pin connector from:<br>  • Pin No. 45 to Pin No. 60<br>  • Pin No. 24 to Pin No. 60<br>while rotating the steering wheel slowly.<br>**NOTE: The resistance values will vary with the meter, but the needle on all meters should swing from a low to a higher resistance and back approximately every nine degrees of steering wheel rotation.** | Meter needle does not swing for one or both circuits (OK) ▶<br>Meter needle swings for both circuits (~~OK~~) ▶ | GO to **D16**.<br>SHUT off engine. REPLACE PRC module. |

**Fig. 7 Automatic ride control system diagnosis, module input circuit (Part 3 of 7)**

| | TEST STEP | RESULT ▶ | ACTION TO TAKE |
|---|---|---|---|
| D16 | UNPLUG STEERING SENSOR | | |
| | • Turn ignition to the OFF position.<br>• Go to the lower portion of the steering column near the brake pedal and unplug steering sensor.<br>• Check the wires at the steering sensor connector to ensure that there is no obvious damage and that they are in the proper location.<br>• Test continuity of Circuits No. 834 and No. 835 from steering sensor to 60 pin PRC module connector. | Damaged/ crossed wires ~~(OK)~~ ▶<br>No continuity ~~(OK)~~ ▶<br>No wiring problems (OK) ▶ | SERVICE wires as necessary.<br>SERVICE open in Circuit No. 834 or No. 835 as necessary.<br>GO to **D17**. |
| D17 | TEST STEERING SENSOR POWER | | |
| | • Turn ignition to RUN position.<br>• Use a voltmeter to measure the voltage from Circuit No. 298 to No. 837 at the wiring harness side of the steering sensor connector. | 0 volts (OK) ▶<br>12 volts ~~(OK)~~ ▶ | GO to **D18**.<br>REPLACE steering sensor. |
| D18 | TEST STEERING SENSOR POWER CIRCUIT | | |
| | • Use a voltmeter to measure the voltage from Circuit No. 298 at the wiring harness side of the steering sensor connector. | 0 volts ▶<br>12 volts ▶ | SERVICE short/open in circuit No. 298 as necessary.<br>SERVICE open in Circuit No. 837 as necessary. |
| D19 | DISCONNECT MODULE CONNECTOR | | |
| | • Turn ignition to the OFF position.<br>• Go to luggage compartment and lower the control module mounting panel on the back of the passenger side seat.<br>• Disconnect the 60 pin electrical connector from the PRC module. | ▶ | GO to **D20**. |
| D20 | TEST SPEED SENSOR SIGNAL | | |
| | • Check the wiring harness side of the 60 pin connector to verify that there is no obvious damage and that:<br>• Circuit No. 150 is in Pin No. 3<br>• Circuit No. 563 is in Pin No. 6 | Damaged/ crossed wires ~~(OK)~~ ▶<br>No wiring problems (OK) ▶ | SERVICE wires as necessary.<br>GO to **D21**. |
| D21 | TEST SPEED SENSOR GROUND CIRCUIT | | |
| | • Test the continuity of the speed sensor ground Circuit No. 150 from Pin No. 3 to Pin No. 60 of the 60 pin connector at the PRC module. | Continuity (OK) ▶<br>Open circuit ~~(OK)~~ ▶ | GO to **D22**.<br>SERVICE wire or ground eyelet as necessary. |

**Fig. 7 Automatic ride control system diagnosis, module input circuit (Part 4 of 7)**

| | TEST STEP | RESULT ▶ | ACTION TO TAKE |
|---|---|---|---|
| D22 | TEST SPEED SENSOR | | |
| | • Turn ignition to RUN position.<br>• Perform "speedo reeds 0 mph at all speeds" | Problems encountered ▶<br>No problem ▶ | SERVICE<br>REPLACE PRC module. |
| D23 | DISCONNECT MODULE CONNECTOR | | |
| | • Turn ignition to the OFF position.<br>• Go to luggage compartment and lower the control model mounting panel on the back of the passenger side seat.<br>• Disconnect the 60 pin electrical connector from the PRC module. | ▶ | GO to **D24**. |
| D24 | DOES SWITCH SEND FIRM SIGNAL | | |
| | • Check Circuit No. 832 at the 60 pin connector to ensure that there is no obvious damage and that it is in pin location No. 18.<br>• Turn the ignition to RUN position.<br>• Set shock select switch to FIRM position.<br>• Use a voltmeter to measure the voltage from Pin No. 18 to Pin No. 60 on the harness side of the 60 pin connector. | 0 volts (OK) ▶<br>12 volts ~~(OK)~~ ▶ | GO to **D25**.<br>REPLACE PRC module. |
| D25 | DISCONNECT SHOCK SELECT SWITCH | | |
| | • Turn ignition to the OFF position.<br>• Go to the instrument panel and disconnect shock select switch.<br>• Check wires at the shock select switch connector to ensure that there is no obvious damage.<br>**NOTE: If these two circuits are reversed it will not affect function. Therefore, treat as no problem.** | Damaged wires ~~(OK)~~ ▶<br>No wiring problems (OK) ▶ | SERVICE wires as necessary.<br>GO to **D26**. |
| D26 | TEST SHOCK SELECT SWITCH POWER FEED | | |
| | • Turn ignition to RUN position.<br>• Use a voltmeter to measure the voltage from Circuit No. 298 to chassis ground at the wiring harness side of the shock select switch connector. | 0 volts ▶<br>12 volts ▶ | SERVICE open/short in Circuit No. 298 as necessary.<br>REPLACE shock select switch. |
| D27 | DISCONNECT MODULE CONNECTOR | | |
| | • Turn ignition to the OFF position.<br>• Go to luggage compartment and lower the control module mounting panel on the back of the passenger side seat.<br>• Disconnect the 60 pin electrical connector from the PRC module. | ▶ | GO to **D28**. |

**Fig. 7 Automatic ride control system diagnosis, module input circuit (Part 5 of 7)**

| | TEST STEP | RESULT ▶ | ACTION TO TAKE |
|---|---|---|---|
| D28 | DOES BRAKE SWITCH CLOSE | | |
| | • Check Circuit No. 847 at the 60 pin connector to ensure that there is no obvious damage and that it is in pin location No. 9.<br>• Start engine and press brake pedal firmly to the floor.<br>• Use an ohmmeter to measure the resistance from Pin No. 9 to Pin No. 60 on the harness side of the 60 pin connector WHILE THE BRAKE PEDAL IS DEPRESSED. | Greater than 1000 ohms (OK) ▶<br>Less than 10 ohms ~~(OK)~~ ▶ | GO to **D29**.<br>REPLACE PRC module. |
| D29 | DISCONNECT BRAKE PRESSURE SWITCH | | |
| | • Turn ignition to the OFF position.<br>• Go to the brake proportioning valve and disconnect brake pressure switch.<br>• Check the wires at the brake pressure switch connector to ensure that there is no obvious damage.<br>**NOTE: If these two circuits are reversed it will not affect function. Therefore, treat as no problem.** | Damaged wires ~~(OK)~~ ▶<br>No wiring problems (OK) ▶ | SERVICE wires as necessary.<br>GO to **D30**. |
| D30 | TEST BRAKE SWITCH GROUND CIRCUIT | | |
| | • Use an ohmmeter to measure the resistance from Circuit No. 837 to chassis ground at the wiring harness side of the brake pressure switch connector. | Greater than 1000 ohms ▶<br>Less than 10 ohms ▶ | SERVICE open/short in Circuit No. 837 as necessary.<br>REPLACE brake pressure switch. |
| D31 | DISCONNECT MODULE CONNECTOR | | |
| | • Turn ignition to the OFF position.<br>• Go to luggage compartment and lower the control module mounting panel on the back of the passenger side seat.<br>• Disconnect the 60 pin electrical connector from the PRC module. | ▶ | GO to **D32**. |
| D32 | CHECK PRC CONNECTOR | | |
| | • Examine Circuit No. 836 at the 60 pin connector to ensure that there is no obvious damage and that it is in pin location No. 28. | Damaged/ crossed wires ~~(OK)~~ ▶<br>No wiring problems (OK) ▶ | SERVICE wires as necessary.<br>GO to **D33**. |

**Fig. 7 Automatic ride control system diagnosis, module input circuit (Part 6 of 7)**

| | TEST STEP | RESULT ▶ | ACTION TO TAKE |
|---|---|---|---|
| D33 | CHECK EEC IV CONNECTOR | | |
| | • Disconnect the 60 pin electrical connector from the EEC IV module.<br>• Check Circuit No. 836 at the 60 pin connector to ensure that there is no obvious damage and that it is in pin location No. 35. | Damaged/ crossed wires. ~~(OK)~~ ▶<br>No wiring problems (OK) ▶ | SERVICE wires as necessary.<br>GO to **D34**. |
| D34 | TEST ACCELERATION CIRCUIT CONTINUITY | | |
| | Test for continuity of Circuit No. 836 from the PRC module to the EEC IV module. | No continuity ▶<br>No wiring problems ▶ | SERVICE open Circuit No. 836 as necessary.<br>REPLACE PRC module. |

**Fig. 7 Automatic ride control system diagnosis, module input circuit (Part 7 of 7)**

## REAR SHOCK ACTUATORS, REPLACE

1. Position vehicle on a level surface.
2. Turn ignition switch to Off or LOCK position.
3. Remove luggage compartment side trim panel.
4. Disconnect actuator electrical connector from harness connector.
5. Depress actuator attaching tabs, then remove actuator.
6. Grasp mounting bracket using a suitable tool.
7. While holding mounting bracket, loosen bracket attaching nut.
8. Remove mounting bracket. **Do not attempt to raise vehicle after nut is removed. If shock absorber is to be removed, install mounting bracket retaining nut.**

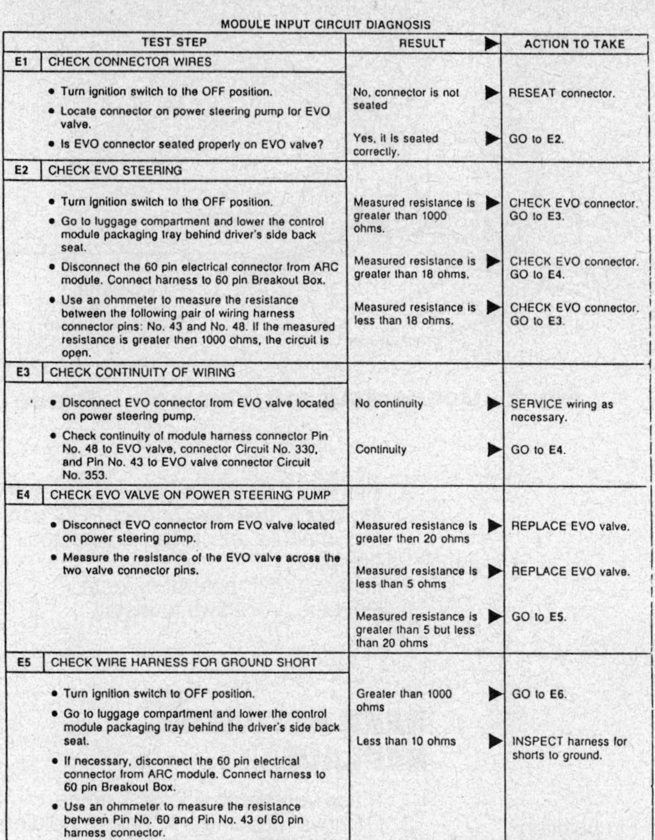

MODULE INPUT CIRCUIT DIAGNOSIS

| TEST STEP | RESULT | ACTION TO TAKE |
|---|---|---|
| **E1 CHECK CONNECTOR WIRES** | | |
| • Turn ignition switch to the OFF position.<br>• Locate connector on power steering pump for EVO valve.<br>• Is EVO connector seated properly on EVO valve? | No, connector is not seated | RESEAT connector. |
| | Yes, it is seated correctly. | GO to E2. |
| **E2 CHECK EVO STEERING** | | |
| • Turn ignition switch to the OFF position.<br>• Go to luggage compartment and lower the control module packaging tray behind driver's side back seat.<br>• Disconnect the 60 pin electrical connector from ARC module. Connect harness to 60 pin Breakout Box.<br>• Use an ohmmeter to measure the resistance between the following pair of wiring harness connector pins: No. 43 and No. 48. If the measured resistance is greater then 1000 ohms, the circuit is open. | Measured resistance is greater than 1000 ohms. | CHECK EVO connector. GO to E3. |
| | Measured resistance is greater than 18 ohms. | CHECK EVO connector. GO to E4. |
| | Measured resistance is less than 18 ohms. | CHECK EVO connector. GO to E3. |
| **E3 CHECK CONTINUITY OF WIRING** | | |
| • Disconnect EVO connector from EVO valve located on power steering pump.<br>• Check continuity of module harness connector Pin No. 48 to EVO valve, connector Circuit No. 330, and Pin No. 43 to EVO valve connector Circuit No. 353. | No continuity | SERVICE wiring as necessary. |
| | Continuity | GO to E4. |
| **E4 CHECK EVO VALVE ON POWER STEERING PUMP** | | |
| • Disconnect EVO connector from EVO valve located on power steering pump.<br>• Measure the resistance of the EVO valve across the two valve connector pins. | Measured resistance is greater then 20 ohms | REPLACE EVO valve. |
| | Measured resistance is less than 5 ohms | REPLACE EVO valve. |
| | Measured resistance is greater than 5 but less than 20 ohms | GO to E5. |
| **E5 CHECK WIRE HARNESS FOR GROUND SHORT** | | |
| • Turn ignition switch to OFF position.<br>• Go to luggage compartment and lower the control module packaging tray behind the driver's side back seat.<br>• If necessary, disconnect the 60 pin electrical connector from ARC module. Connect harness to 60 pin Breakout Box.<br>• Use an ohmmeter to measure the resistance between Pin No. 60 and Pin No. 43 of 60 pin harness connector. | Greater than 1000 ohms | GO to E6. |
| | Less than 10 ohms | INSPECT harness for shorts to ground. |

**Fig. 8 Automatic ride control system diagnosis, module input circuit (Part 1 of 2)**

| TEST STEP | RESULT | ACTION TO TAKE |
|---|---|---|
| **E6 CHECK WIRE HARNESS FOR SHORT** | | |
| • Use an ohmmeter to measure the resistance between Pin No. 60 of harness with Pin No. 48 of harness. | Greater than 1000 ohms | EVO harness OK. REPLACE ARC/EVO module. |
| | Less than 10 ohms | INSPECT harness for shorts to ground. |

**Fig. 8 Automatic ride control system diagnosis, module input circuit (Part 2 of 2)**

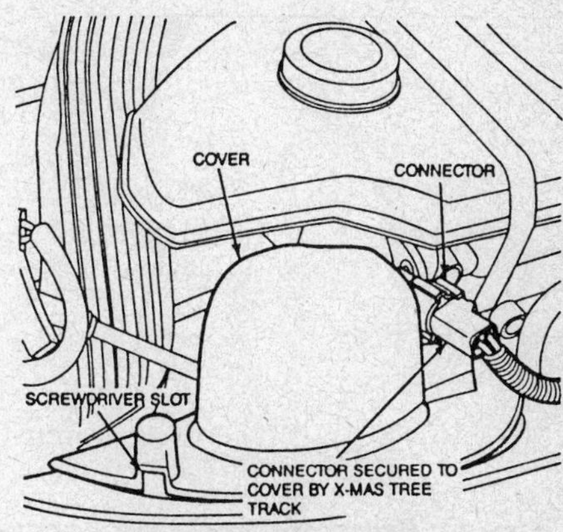


**Fig. 9 Front actuator connector removal**

9. Reverse procedure to install, ensuring flat of shock absorber piston rods aligns with mounting bracket. **Torque mounting bracket nut to 27-35 ft.lbs.**

# PROGRAMMED RIDE CONTROL

## INDEX



## DESCRIPTION

The programmed ride control system (PRC) used on Probe models, provides the selection of soft, hard, and very hard combinations of damping control from the front and rear shock absorbers. The PRC switch located in the center console allows selection for either manual or automatic control modes of the PRC suspension. With the PRC switch in SOFT position the ride control computer adjusts the shock absorber damping to provide a soft (plush) ride during normal driving conditions.

With selection of NORMAL or SPORT position this will engage the automatic adjusting suspension feature. This provides combinations of hard or very hard damping upon sensor inputs to the computer during acceleration, braking or cornering and provide improved handling at high speeds.

In the event of a system malfunction, there is no indicator lamp to alert the driver of a malfunction. The driver may or may not notice a change in driveability. The PRC system should be checked at regular service intervals for any malfunction.

## OPERATION

The programmed ride control system, **Fig. 1,** monitors the following conditions to determine when additional damping is required when the PRC switch is set in automatic modes of NORMAL OR SPORT to improved handling:

1. Vehicle speed.
2. Steering wheel angle.
3. Abrupt acceleration.
4. Hard braking.

## COMPONENTS

### Programmed Ride Control Module

The programmed ride control module is located under the passenger seat. This device receives input from various sensors and is used to switch the ride control mode based on driver input and input of the sensors.

### Vehicle Speed Sensor

The vehicle speed sensor is located within the speedometer subassembly in the analog instrument cluster. On vehicles with electronic instrument cluster the speed sensor is located on the transaxle. This is used by the PRC module for vehicle speed.

### Steering Angle Sensor

The steering angle sensor is located

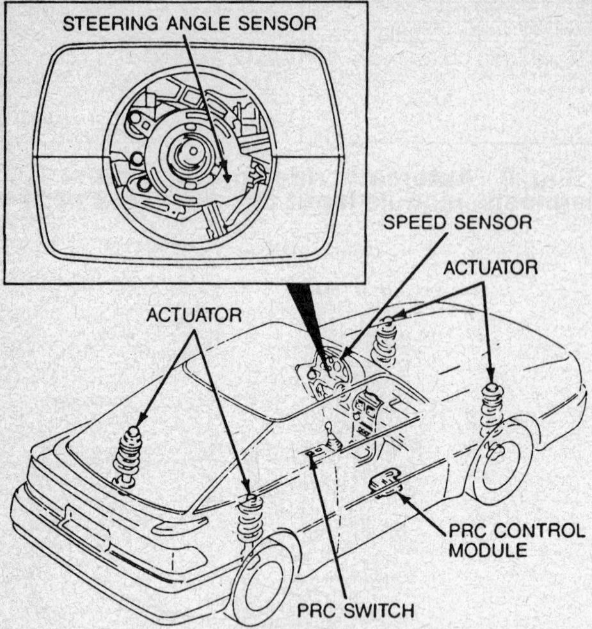


**Fig. 1 Programmed ride control system. Probe**

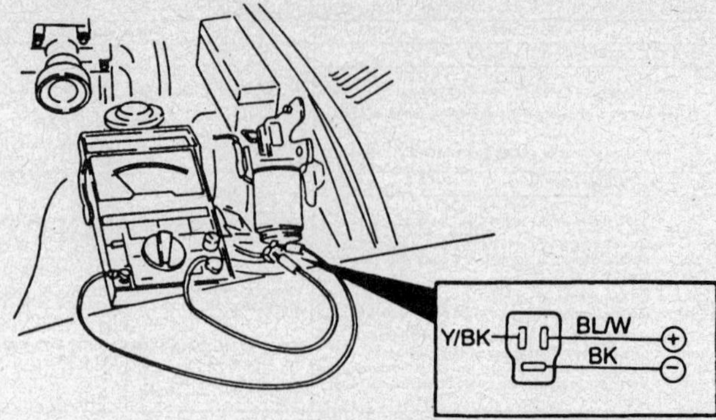


**Fig. 2 Connecting volt/ohmmeter. Probe**

within the steering column and used by the PRC module for determination of lateral forces acting on the vehicle during normal driving conditions.

### PRC Actuators

The PRC actuators are located at the top of each strut assembly. These devices are used to change the dampening of the shock absorber within each assembly.

### Adjustable Struts

The struts are located at each wheel of the vehicle, these devices are use for shock absorbing control of the vehicle.

# DIAGNOSIS & TESTING

## VEHICLE CHECK

1. Check front and rear struts for damage, leaks, cracks, and proper mounting.
2. Check PRC system wiring harness for proper connections.
3. Check control unit, sensors, and actuators for damage.
4. Check tires for proper pressure.

## KEY ON ENGINE OFF TEST

This test requires a suitable analog volt/ohmmeter meter as shown, **Fig. 2.**

1. Turn ignition key Off, then reset control unit before performing each test.
2. Perform visual check as previously described.
3. Turn ignition key to On position.
4. Activate self-test by turning voltmeter On.
5. **On 1989 models,** perform test steps in sequence, **Fig. 3.** Ensure steering wheel is in proper position and ignition key is Off prior each step test.
6. **On 1990 models,** perform quick test steps, **Fig. 4.**
7. **On all models,** record all service codes displayed, **Figs. 3 and 4.** then proceed to Pinpoint test indicated, **Figs. 5 through 10.**

# SYSTEM SERVICE

## PROGRAMMED RIDE CONTROL SWITCH, REPLACE

1. Disconnect battery ground cable.
2. Remove center console from vehicle.
3. Press on release tabs, located on each side of switch, then disconnect electrical connectors and remove switch.
4. Reverse procedure to install.

## FRONT ACTUATOR, REPLACE

1. Place vehicle on a level surface.
2. Apply parking brake, then raise hood.
3. Remove rubber cap from strut mounting block, then disconnect PRC control module electrical connector, if equipped.
4. Remove PRC control module.
5. Reverse procedure to install.

## REAR ACTUATOR, REPLACE

1. Place vehicle on a level surface.
2. Remove upper trunk side moulding and lower trim panel.
3. Disconnect PRC electrical connector, if equipped.
4. Remove PRC control module.
5. Reverse procedure to install.

## SPEED SENSOR, REPLACE

1. Disconnect battery ground cable.
2. **On models with electronic instrument cluster,** disconnect electrical connector from sensor.
3. Remove sensor attaching bolt from transaxle housing.
4. Pull sensor from transaxle housing.
5. **On models with analog instrument cluster,** remove cluster and lens assembly.
6. Remove attaching screws, then the speedometer subassembly.
7. Remove speed sensor.
8. **On all models,** reverse procedure to install.

## CONTROL MODULE, REPLACE

1. Disconnect battery ground cable.
2. Remove front passenger seat.
3. Remove attaching bolts from control module.
4. Disconnect PRC electrical connector from the control module.
5. Remove control module from vehicle.
6. Reverse procedure to install.

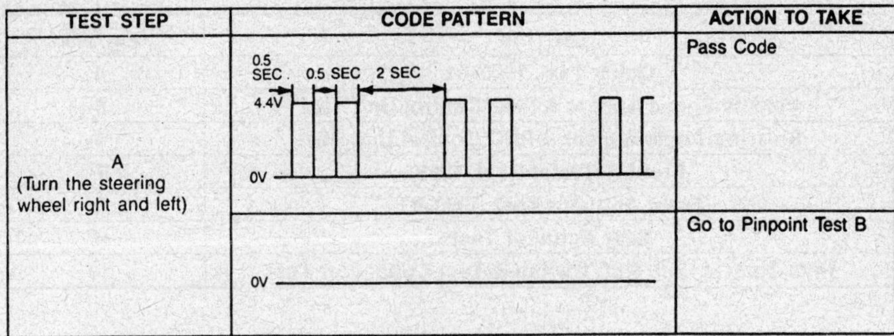

| TEST STEP | CODE PATTERN | ACTION TO TAKE |
|---|---|---|
| A (Turn the steering wheel right and left) | 0.5 SEC, 0.5 SEC, 2 SEC, 4.4V, 0V | Pass Code |
| | 0V | Go to Pinpoint Test B |

Fig. 3 Code pattern chart, (Part 1 of 3). 1989 Probe

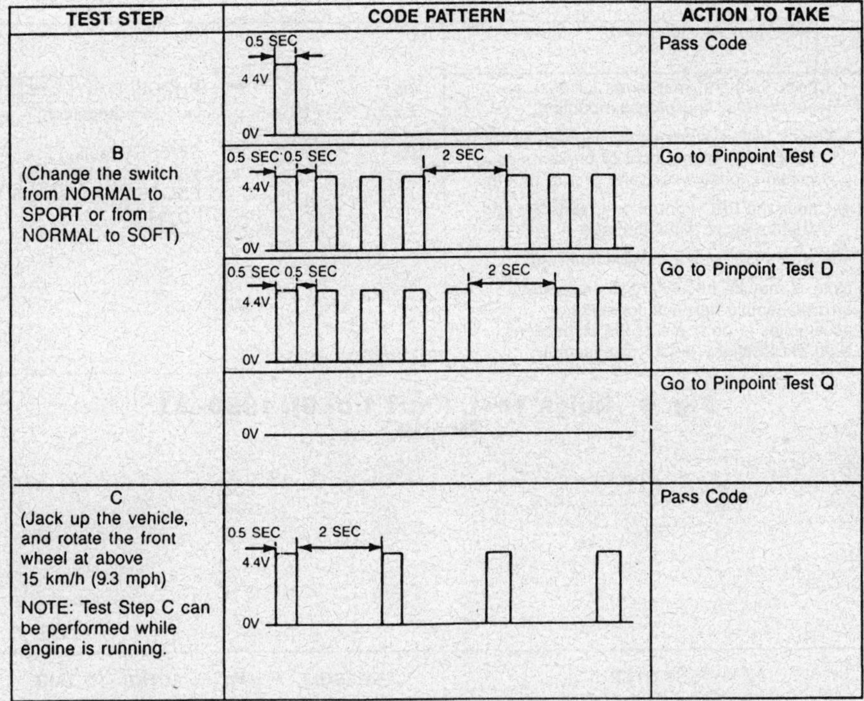

| TEST STEP | CODE PATTERN | ACTION TO TAKE |
|---|---|---|
| B (Change the switch from NORMAL to SPORT or from NORMAL to SOFT) | 0.5 SEC, 4.4V, 0V | Pass Code |
| | 0.5 SEC, 0.5 SEC, 2 SEC, 4.4V, 0V | Go to Pinpoint Test C |
| | 0.5 SEC, 0.5 SEC, 2 SEC, 4.4V, 0V | Go to Pinpoint Test D |
| | 0V | Go to Pinpoint Test Q |
| C (Jack up the vehicle, and rotate the front wheel at above 15 km/h (9.3 mph)<br>NOTE: Test Step C can be performed while engine is running. | 0.5 SEC, 2 SEC, 4.4V, 0V | Pass Code |

Fig. 3 Code pattern chart, (Part 2 of 3). 1989 Probe

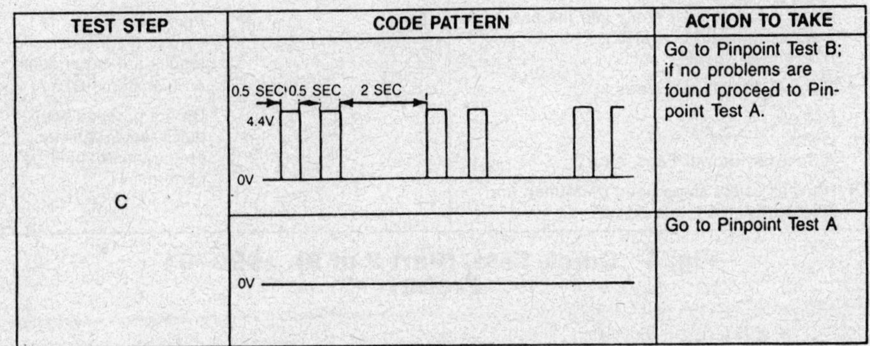

| TEST STEP | CODE PATTERN | ACTION TO TAKE |
|---|---|---|
| C | 0.5 SEC, 0.5 SEC, 2 SEC, 4.4V, 0V | Go to Pinpoint Test B; if no problems are found proceed to Pinpoint Test A. |
| | 0V | Go to Pinpoint Test A |

Fig. 3 Code pattern chart, (Part 3 of 3). 1989 Probe

# DIAGNOSTIC TEST INDEX



| TEST STEP | RESULT ► | ACTION TO TAKE |
|---|---|---|
| **QT1** VISUAL CHECK | | |
| • Check front and rear struts for damage, leaks, cracks, and proper mounting.<br>• Check PRC system wiring harness for proper connections, bent or broken pins, corrosion, loose wires, and proper routing.<br>• Check the PRC control unit, sensors, and actuators for physical damage.<br>• Are all PRC system components ok?<br>Note: It may be necessary to disconnect or disassemble harness connector assemblies to do some of the inspections. Note pin locations before disassembly. | Yes ►<br><br>No ► | PROCEED to QT2. vehicle preparation.<br><br>SERVICE fault(s) in system and then PROCEED to test step QT2. |

**Fig. 4 Quick Test, (Part 1 of 9). 1990–91 Probe**

| TEST STEP | RESULT ► | ACTION TO TAKE |
|---|---|---|
| **QT2** VEHICLE PREPARATION | | |
| • Perform all the following safety steps required to run PRC quick test.<br>Apply the parking brake<br>Place the shift lever firmly into the park position (neutral on MTX).<br>Block drive wheels.<br>• Turn off all electrical loads.<br>Radios<br>Lights<br>A/C-Heater Blower Fans, etc...<br>• Have all safety steps been performed and all electrical loads turned off? | Yes ►<br><br>No ► | PROCEED to QT3. equipment hookup.<br><br>Personal safety and correct diagnostic results are dependent on test step QT2.<br>Do not proceed with quick test if vehicle preparation cannot be performed. |

**Fig. 4 Quick Test, (Part 2 of 9). 1990–91 Probe**

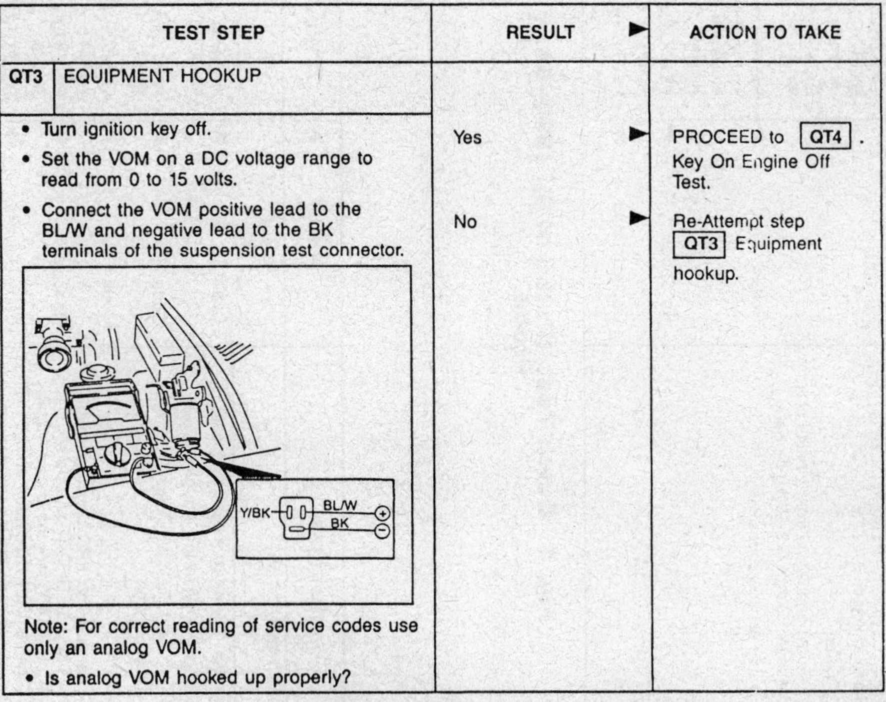


| TEST STEP | RESULT ► | ACTION TO TAKE |
|---|---|---|
| **QT3** EQUIPMENT HOOKUP | | |
| • Turn ignition key off.<br>• Set the VOM on a DC voltage range to read from 0 to 15 volts.<br>• Connect the VOM positive lead to the BL/W and negative lead to the BK terminals of the suspension test connector. | Yes ► | PROCEED to QT4. Key On Engine Off Test. |
| Note: For correct reading of service codes use only an analog VOM.<br>• Is analog VOM hooked up properly? | No ► | Re-Attempt step QT3 Equipment hookup. |

**Fig. 4 Quick Test, (Part 3 of 9). 1990–91 Probe**

| TEST STEP | RESULT ► | ACTION TO TAKE |
|---|---|---|
| **QT4** KEY ON ENGINE OFF TEST | | |
| • Turn ignition key off.<br>• Verify that the vehicle has been properly prepared per Quick Test steps QT2 and QT3.<br>• Turn ignition key on.<br>• Set steering wheel in the straight ahead position.<br>• Activate self-test by turning analog VOM on.<br>• Turn steering wheel right and left.<br>• Record any service codes.<br>Note: When a service code is reported on the analog VOM, it will represent itself as a pulsing or sweeping movement of the voltmeter's needle across the dial face. Code 1 will be represented by one pulse and code 2 by two pulses and so on. After two seconds the code will repeat itself. Refer to the code identification chart at the end of Quick Test. | Code 2 ► | Indicates a pass code. PROCEED to QT5. If Code [illegible] is also received with steering wheel straight, perform pinpoint Test B. |
| | No Codes ► | PERFORM Pinpoint Test B. |
| | Code Unlisted ► | PERFORM Pinpoint Test Q. |

**Fig. 4 Quick Test, (Part 4 of 9). 1990–91 Probe**

| TEST STEP | RESULT ► | ACTION TO TAKE |
|---|---|---|
| **QT5** KEY ON ENGINE OFF TEST | | |
| • Turn ignition key off to reset processor.<br>• Set steering wheel in the straight ahead position.<br>• Turn ignition key on.<br>• Turn VOM on.<br>• Change the PRC switch (located on center console) position from normal to sport and from normal to soft position.<br>• Record any service codes. | Code 1 ► | Indicates a pass code. PROCEED to QT6 . |
| | Code 4 ► | PERFORM Pinpoint Test C. |
| | Code 5 ► | PERFORM Pinpoint Test D. |
| | No Codes ► | PERFORM Pinpoint Test Q. |
| | Code Unlisted ► | PERFORM Pinpoint Test Q. |

**Fig. 4 Quick Test, (Part 5 of 9). 1990–91 Probe**

| TEST STEP | RESULT ► | ACTION TO TAKE |
|---|---|---|
| **QT6** KEY ON ENGINE OFF TEST | | |
| • Turn ignition key off to reset processor.<br>• Set steering wheel in the straight ahead position.<br>• Turn ignition key on.<br>• Turn VOM on.<br>• Hoise vehicle and rotate front wheels at a speed above 15km/h (9.3 MPH) by hand.<br>• Record any service codes. | Code 1 ► | Pass code PERFORM Pinpoint Test B to verify Steering Angle Sensor VREF AND SIGRTN circuits are ok. For intermittent Symptoms PROCEED to QT7 . |
| | Code 2 ► | PERFORM Pinpoint Test B. If no faults are found, proceed to Pinpoint Test A. |
| | No Codes ► | PERFORM Pinpoint Test A. |
| | Code Unlisted ► | PERFORM Pinpont Test Q. |

**Fig. 4 Quick Test, (Part 6 of 9). 1990–91 Probe**

| TEST STEP | RESULT ► | ACTION TO TAKE |
|---|---|---|
| **QT7** CONTINUOUS TEST | | |
| • Verify that a pass code was indicated in all steps of the Key On Engine Off Test.<br>• Verify that the vehicle has been properly prepared per Quick Test steps QT2 and QT3.<br>• Turn ignition key on.<br>• Activate self-test by turning analog VOM on.<br>• While turning steering wheel left and right, tap, move and wiggle steering angle sensor and/or PRC harness while observing for any service code indication on the VOM.<br>• Record any service codes. | Code 2 ► | Indicates a pass code. PROCEED to QT8 . |
| | No Codes ► | PERFORM Pinpoint Test B. |
| | Code Unlisted ► | PERFORM Pinpoint Test Q. |

**Fig. 4 Quick Test, (Part 7 of 9). 1990–91 Probe**

| TEST STEP | RESULT ► | ACTION TO TAKE |
|---|---|---|
| **QT8** CONTINUOUS TEST | | |
| • Turn ignition key off to reset processor.<br>• Set steering wheel in the straight ahead position.<br>• Turn ignition key on.<br>• Turn VOM on.<br>• While changing the PRC switch position from NORMAL to SPORT and from NORMAL to SOFT, tap, move and wiggle all PRC actuators, PRC switch and/or PRC harness while observing for any service code indication on the VOM.<br>• Record any service codes. | Code 1 ► | Indicates a pass code. PROCEED to QT9 |
| | Code 4 ► | PERFORM Pinpoint Test C. |
| | Code 5 ► | PERFORM Pinpoint Test D. |
| | No Codes ► | PERFORM Pinpoint Test Q. |
| | Code Unlisted ► | PERFORM Pinpoint Test Q. |

**Fig. 4 Quick Test, (Part 8 of 9). 1990–91 Probe**

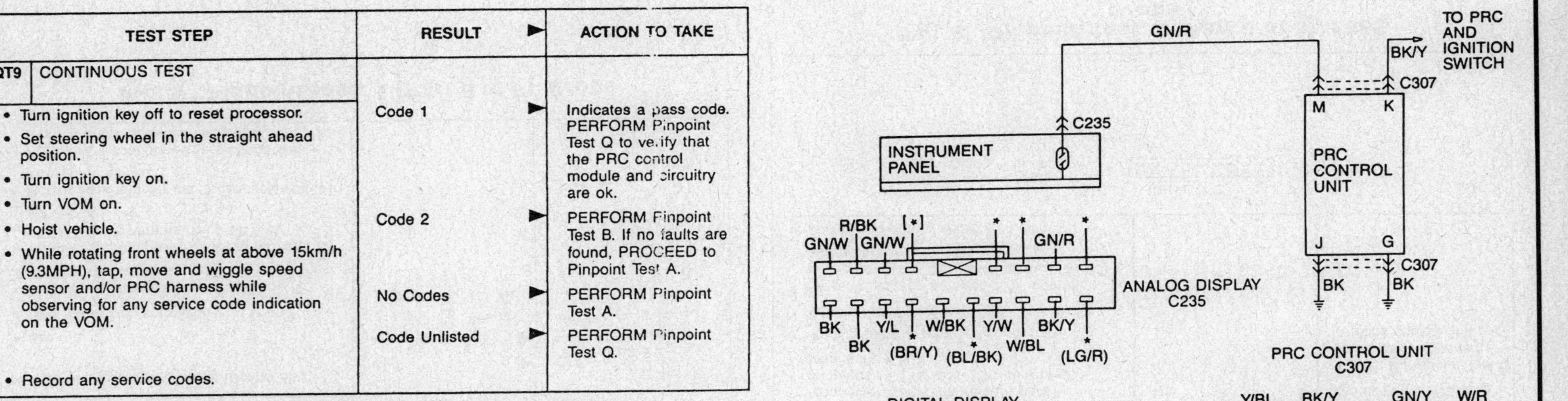

| TEST STEP | | RESULT ► | ACTION TO TAKE |
|---|---|---|---|
| QT9 | CONTINUOUS TEST | | |
| • Turn ignition key off to reset processor.<br>• Set steering wheel in the straight ahead position.<br>• Turn ignition key on.<br>• Turn VOM on.<br>• Hoist vehicle.<br>• While rotating front wheels at above 15km/h (9.3MPH), tap, move and wiggle speed sensor and/or PRC harness while observing for any service code indication on the VOM.<br>• Record any service codes. | | Code 1 ► | Indicates a pass code. PERFORM Pinpoint Test Q to verify that the PRC control module and circuitry are ok. |
| | | Code 2 ► | PERFORM Pinpoint Test B. If no faults are found, PROCEED to Pinpoint Test A. |
| | | No Codes ► | PERFORM Pinpoint Test A. |
| | | Code Unlisted ► | PERFORM Pinpoint Test Q. |

**Fig. 4 Quick Test, (Part 9 of 9). 1990–91 Probe**

GN/R
TO PRC AND IGNITION SWITCH
BK/Y
C307
C235
INSTRUMENT PANEL
PRC CONTROL UNIT
M K J G
BK BK
ANALOG DISPLAY C235
DIGITAL DISPLAY C235
PRC CONTROL UNIT C307

**Fig. 5 Pinpoint test, A (Part 1 of 6). 1989 Probe**

VEHICLE SPEED SENSOR

INSTRUMENT PANEL
ANALOG DISPLAY
DIGITAL DISPLAY
PRC CONTROL UNIT

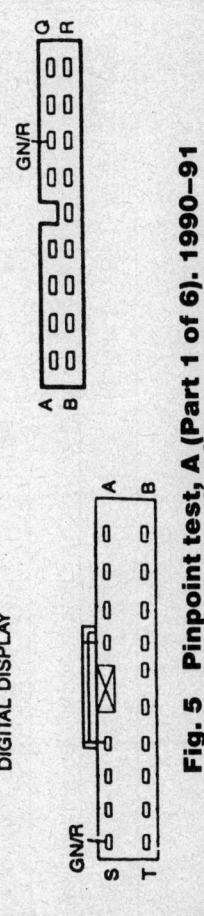

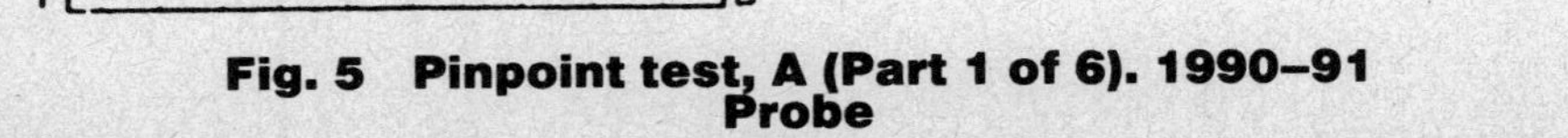

**Fig. 5 Pinpoint test, A (Part 1 of 6). 1990–91 Probe**

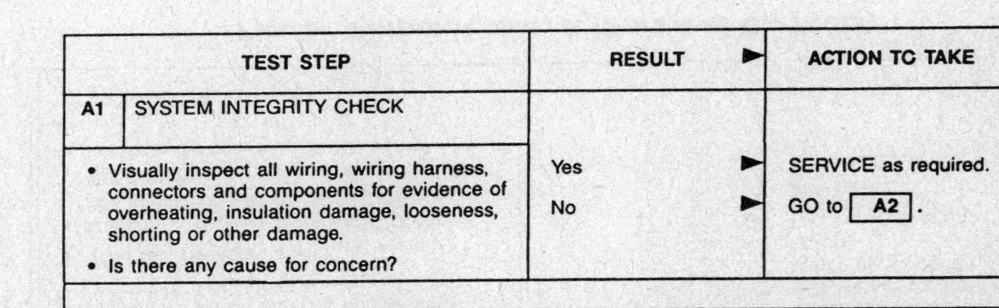

| TEST STEP | | RESULT ► | ACTION TO TAKE |
|---|---|---|---|
| A1 | SYSTEM INTEGRITY CHECK | | |
| • Visually inspect all wiring, wiring harness, connectors and components for evidence of overheating, insulation damage, looseness, shorting or other damage.<br>• Is there any cause for concern? | | Yes ► | SERVICE as required. |
| | | No ► | GO to A2. |

**Fig. 5 Pinpoint test, A (Part 2 of 6). Probe**

| TEST STEP | RESULT ► | ACTION TO TAKE |
|---|---|---|
| **A2** CIRCUIT CONTINUITY CHECK | | |
| • Key off.<br>• VOM on 200 ohm scale.<br>• Measure resistance between PRC Control Unit connector terminal M ("GN/R") and instrument panel connector terminal 2C ("GN/R") analog instrument cluster or 2S ("GN/R") digital instrument cluster.<br>• Is resistance greater than 5 ohms? | Yes ► | SERVICE "GN/R" wire between PRC control unit and instrument panel for opens. |
| | No ► | GO to A3. |

Fig. 5 Pinpoint test, A (Part 3 of 6). Probe

| TEST STEP | RESULT ► | ACTION TO TAKE |
|---|---|---|
| **A3** SHORT TO GROUND CHECK | | |
| • Disconnect PRC control unit connector.<br>• Disconnect power steering control unit connector (if equipped).<br>• VOM on 200K ohm scale.<br>• Measure resistance between PRC control unit connector terminal M ("GN/R") and ground.<br>• Is resistance less than 10,000 ohms? | Yes ► | SERVICE "GN/R" wire between PRC control unit and instrument panel for shorts to ground. |
| | No ► | (Analog instrument panel) GO to A4. |

Fig. 5 Pinpoint test, A (Part 4 of 6). Probe

| TEST STEP | RESULT ► | ACTION TO TAKE |
|---|---|---|
| **A4** SPEED SENSOR FUNCTION CHECK (ANALOG DISPLAY ONLY) | | |
| NOTE: This test is for Analog Display only.<br>• Key off.<br>• Remove instrument cluster.<br>• Disconnect speedometer cable from instrument cluster.<br>• Connect an ohmmeter between terminal 2C ("GN/R") and terminal 2R ("BK") of connector C235.<br>• Rotate speedometer cable connector on the instrument cluster.<br>• Are there 4 continuity interruptions per rotation of the speedometer cable connector? | Yes ► | GO to A5. |
| | No ► | REPLACE speed sensor. |

Fig. 5 Pinpoint test, A (Part 5 of 6). Probe

| TEST STEP | RESULT ► | ACTION TO TAKE |
|---|---|---|
| **A5** SHORT TO VPWR CHECK | | |
| • Key on; engine off.<br>• Disconnect power steering control unit (connector C306), instrument panel (connector C235) and PRC control unit (connector C301).<br>• Transmission in park.<br>• VOM on 20 volt scale.<br>• Measure voltage between PRC control unit (connector C307) terminal M ("GN/R") and ground.<br>• Is voltage reading above 0.0 volt? | Yes ► | SERVICE "GN/R" wire for shorts to VPWR. |
| | No ► | Go to Pinpoint Test Q.<br>NOTE: If Pinpoint Test Q has been performed, replace control unit. |
| GN/R C307 | | |

Fig. 5 Pinpoint test, A (Part 6 of 6). 1989 Probe

| TEST STEP | RESULT ▶ | ACTION TO TAKE |
|---|---|---|
| A5 SHORT TO VPWR CHECK | | |
| • Key on; engine off.<br>• Disconnect power steering control unit connector, instrument panel connector and PRC control unit connector.<br>• Transmission in park.<br>• VOM on 20 volt scale.<br>• Measure voltage between PRC control unit connector terminal M ("GN/R") and ground.<br>• Is voltage reading above 0.0 volt? | Yes ▶<br>No ▶ | SERVICE "GN/R" wire for shorts to VPWR.<br>GO to Pinpoint Test Q. |

**Fig. 5 Pinpoint test, A (Part 6 of 6). 1990–91 Probe**

STEERING ANGLE SENSOR

STEERING ANGLE SENSOR

GN

GN/W

GN/Y

TO PRC AND IGNITION SWITCH

K

H

F

E

PRC CONTROL UNIT

J

G

GN/Y

GN

GN/W

GN/Y

GN/W

GN

**Fig. 6 Pinpoint test, B (Part 1 of 8). 1990–91 Probe**

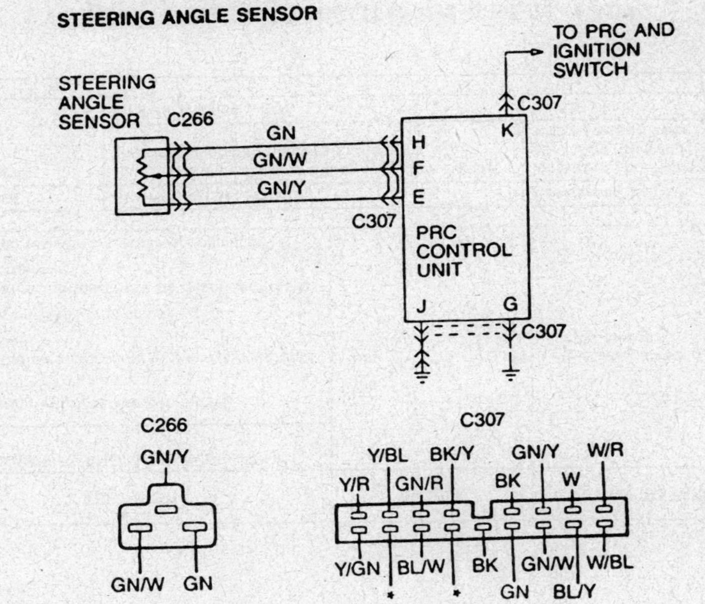


**Fig. 6 Pinpoint test, B (Part 1 of 8). 1989 Probe**

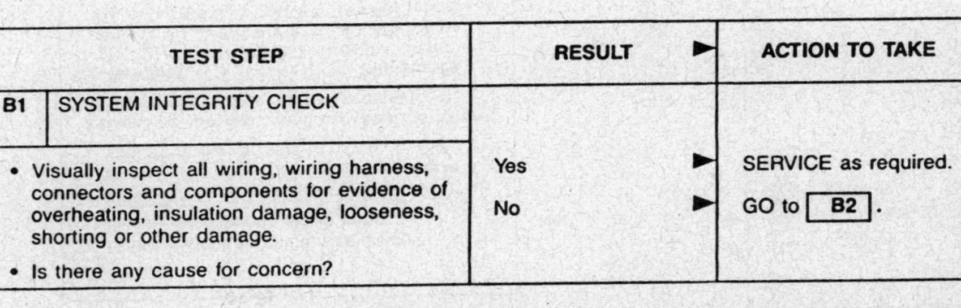

| TEST STEP | RESULT ▶ | ACTION TO TAKE |
|---|---|---|
| B1 SYSTEM INTEGRITY CHECK | | |
| • Visually inspect all wiring, wiring harness, connectors and components for evidence of overheating, insulation damage, looseness, shorting or other damage.<br>• Is there any cause for concern? | Yes ▶<br>No ▶ | SERVICE as required.<br>GO to B2 . |

**Fig. 6 Pinpoint test, B (Part 2 of 8). Probe**

| TEST STEP | RESULT ► | ACTION TO TAKE |
|---|---|---|
| **B2** STEERING ANGLE SENSOR RESISTANCE CHECK | | |
| • Key off.<br>• Remove steering column cover and disconnect steering angle sensor connector.<br>• Set the steering wheel so wheels are in a straight ahead position.<br>• Measure the resistance between the following steering angle sensor terminals.<br>**Terminal** — **Resistance**<br>① ("GN") — ("GN/W") 20–30K ohms<br>② ("GN") — ("GN/Y") 40–60K ohms<br>③ ("GN/Y") — ("GN/W") 20–30K ohms<br>• Are all resistances within specification? | Yes ►<br>No ► | GO to B3 .<br>REPLACE steering angle sensor. |

**Fig. 6 Pinpoint test, B (Part 3 of 8). 1989–90 Probe**

| TEST STEP | RESULT ► | ACTION TO TAKE |
|---|---|---|
| **B3** STEERING ANGLE SENSOR CHECK | | |
| • Steering angle sensor connector disconnected.<br>• Set the steering wheel in the straight ahead position.<br>• VOM on 200K ohm scale.<br>• Measure the resistance as described in the table below.<br>• Are all resistances within specification? | Yes ►<br>No ► | GO to B4 .<br>REPLACE steering angle sensor. |

| Terminal | Steering Wheel Position | Resistance Value |
|---|---|---|
| GN-GN/W | Turn the wheel a little at a time from the straight ahead position 180 degrees to the right. | Increases from approximately 25K ohm to approximately 50K ohm. |
| | Straight ahead position | 20–30K ohms. |

**Fig. 6 Pinpoint test, B (Part 4 of 8). 1989–90 Probe**

| TEST STEP | RESULT ► | ACTION TO TAKE |
|---|---|---|
| **B2** STEERING ANGLE SENSOR RESISTANCE CHECK | | |
| • Key off.<br>• Remove steering column cover and disconnect steering angle sensor connector.<br>• Set the steering wheel so wheels are in a straight ahead position.<br>• Measure the resistance between the following steering angle sensor terminals.<br>**Terminal** — **Resistance**<br>① ("GN") — ("GN/W") 0–15K ohms<br>② ("GN") — ("GN/Y") 40–60K ohms<br>③ ("GN/Y") — ("GN/W") 30–50K ohms<br>• Are all resistances within specification? | Yes ►<br>No ► | GO to B3 .<br>REPLACE steering angle sensor. |

**Fig. 6 Pinpoint test, B (Part 3 of 8). 1991 Probe**

| TEST STEP | RESULT ► | ACTION TO TAKE |
|---|---|---|
| **B3** STEERING ANGLE SENSOR CHECK | | |
| • Steering angle sensor connector disconnected.<br>• Set the steering wheel in the straight ahead position.<br>• VOM on 200K ohm scale.<br>• Measure the resistance as described in the table below.<br>• Are all resistances within specification? | Yes ►<br>No ► | GO to B4 .<br>REPLACE steering angle sensor. |

| Terminal | Steering Wheel Position | Resistance Value |
|---|---|---|
| GN-GN/W | Turn the wheel a little at a time from the straight ahead position 180 degrees to the right. | Increases approximately 20K ohms from the straight ahead value. |
| | Straight ahead position | 0–15K ohms |

**Fig. 6 Pinpoint test, B (Part 4 of 8). 1991 Probe**

| TEST STEP | RESULT ► | ACTION TO TAKE |
|---|---|---|
| **B4** STEERING ANGLE SENSOR CHECK | | |
| • Steering angle sensor connector disconnected.<br>• Set the steering wheel in the straight ahead position.<br>• VOM on 200K ohm scale.<br>• Measure the resistance as described in the table below.<br>• Are all resistances within specification? | Yes ►<br>No ► | GO to B5 .<br>REPLACE steering angle sensor. |

| Terminal | Steering Wheel Position | Resistance Value |
|---|---|---|
| GN-GN/W | Turn the wheel a little at a time from the straight ahead position 180 degrees to the left. | Decreases from approximately 25K ohm to approximately 200 ohm. |
| GN/Y-GN/W | Straight ahead position | 40–60K ohms. |

**Fig. 6 Pinpoint test, B (Part 5 of 8). 1989–90 Probe**

| TEST STEP | RESULT ► | ACTION TO TAKE |
|---|---|---|
| **B4** STEERING ANGLE SENSOR CHECK | | |
| • Steering angle sensor connector disconnected.<br>• Set the steering wheel in the straight ahead position.<br>• VOM on 200K ohm scale.<br>• Measure the resistance as described in the table below.<br>• At the straight ahead position, observe the ohmmeter reading. This is your base reading. As you turn the wheel to your left, the reading will decrease to 0 ohms. The reading will then change to 45K ohms and continue to decrease from that value.<br>• Are all resistances within specification? | Yes ►<br>No ► | GO to B5 .<br>REPLACE steering angle sensor. |

| Terminal | Steering Wheel Position | Resistance Value |
|---|---|---|
| GN-GN/W | Turn the wheel a little at a time from the straight ahead position 180 degrees to the left. | Decreases approximately 20K ohms from the straight ahead value. |
| GN-GN/W | Straight ahead position. | 0–15K ohms. |

**Fig. 6 Pinpoint test, B (Part 5 of 8). 1991 Probe**

| TEST STEP | RESULT ► | ACTION TO TAKE |
|---|---|---|
| **B5** CIRCUIT CONTINUITY CHECK | | |
| • Steering angle sensor connector disconnected.<br>• Disconnect PRC control unit connector.<br>• VOM on 200 ohm scale.<br>• Measure resistance between connectors as follows:<br>PRC CONTROL UNIT — STEERING ANGLE SENSOR<br>Terminal H GN Wire — GN Wire<br>Terminal F GN/W Wire — GN/W Wire<br>Terminal E GN/Y Wire — GN/Y Wire<br>• Are all resistance readings less than 5 ohms? | Yes ►<br>No ► | GO to B6<br>REPAIR wire in question for opens. |

**Fig. 6 Pinpoint test, B (Part 6 of 8). Probe**

| TEST STEP | RESULT ► | ACTION TO TAKE |
|---|---|---|
| **B6** SHORT TO GROUND CHECK | | |
| • Key off.<br>• PRC control unit connector disconnected.<br>• Power steering control unit connector disconnected (if equipped).<br>• VOM on 200K ohm scale.<br>• Measure resistance between PRC control unit connector and ground as follows:<br>Between terminal H ("GN") and ground<br>Between terminal F ("GN/W") and ground<br>Between terminal E ("GN/Y") and ground.<br>• Are all resistance readings greater than 10,000 ohms? | Yes ►<br>No ► | GO to B7 .<br>REPAIR wire in question for shorts to ground. |

**Fig. 6 Pinpoint test, B (Part 7 of 8). Probe**

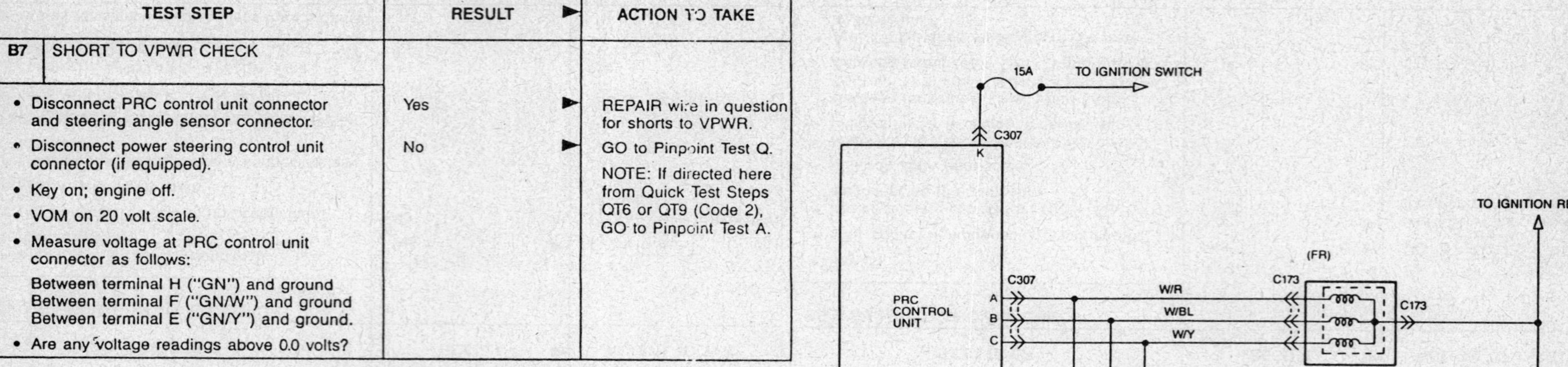

| TEST STEP | RESULT ► | ACTION TO TAKE |
|---|---|---|
| **B7** SHORT TO VPWR CHECK | | |
| • Disconnect PRC control unit connector and steering angle sensor connector.<br>• Disconnect power steering control unit connector (if equipped).<br>• Key on; engine off.<br>• VOM on 20 volt scale.<br>• Measure voltage at PRC control unit connector as follows:<br>Between terminal H ("GN") and ground<br>Between terminal F ("GN/W") and ground<br>Between terminal E ("GN/Y") and ground.<br>• Are any voltage readings above 0.0 volts? | Yes ►<br>No ► | REPAIR wire in question for shorts to VPWR.<br>GO to Pinpoint Test Q.<br>NOTE: If directed here from Quick Test Steps QT6 or QT9 (Code 2), GO to Pinpoint Test A. |

**Fig. 6 Pinpoint test, B (Part 8 of 8). Probe**



**Fig. 7 Pinpoint test, C (Part 1 of 10). 1989 Probe**

| TEST STEP | RESULT ► | ACTION TO TAKE |
|---|---|---|
| **C1** SYSTEM INTEGRITY CHECK | | |
| • Visually inspect all wiring, wiring harness, connectors and components for evidence of overheating, insulation damage, looseness, shorting or other damage.<br>• Is there any cause for concern? | Yes ►<br>No ► | SERVICE as required.<br>GO to C2. |

**Fig. 7 Pinpoint test, C (Part 2 of 10). 1989 Probe**

| TEST STEP | RESULT ► | ACTION TO TAKE |
|---|---|---|
| **C2** CHECK ACTUATOR (FR) VOLTAGE AT CONTROL UNIT | | |
| • Disconnect PRC control unit (connector C307) and (front left) actuator (connector C154).<br>• Key on; engine off.<br>• VOM on 20 volt scale.<br>• Measure voltage at connector C307 as follows:<br>Between terminal A ("W/R") and ground<br>Between terminal B ("W/BL") and ground<br>Between terminal C ("W") and ground.<br>• Are all voltages above 10 volts? | Yes ►<br>No ► | GO to C3.<br>GO to C6. |

C307 C A B

Fig. 7 Pinpoint test, C (Part 3 of 10). 1989 Probe

| TEST STEP | RESULT ► | ACTION TO TAKE |
|---|---|---|
| **C3** CHECK ACTUATOR (FL) VOLTAGE AT CONTROL UNIT | | |
| • Disconnect PRC control unit (connector C307) and (front right) actuator (connector C173).<br>• Reconnect (front left) actuator (connector C154).<br>• Key on; engine off.<br>• VOM on 20 volt scale.<br>• Measure voltage at connector C307 as follows:<br>Between terminal A ("W/R") and ground<br>Between terminal B ("W/BL") and ground<br>Between terminal C ("W") and ground.<br>• Are all voltages above 10 volts?<br>See illustration in TEST STEP C2 | Yes ►<br>No ► | GO to C4.<br>GO to C8. |

Fig. 7 Pinpoint test, C (Part 4 of 10). 1989 Probe

| TEST STEP | RESULT ► | ACTION TO TAKE |
|---|---|---|
| **C4** ACTUATOR INTEGRITY CHECK (FRONT RIGHT) | | |
| • Key off.<br>• Disconnect (front right) actuator connector C173.<br>• With a jumper wire, jump battery voltage to terminal D ("Y").<br>• With another jumper wire, ground terminal A ("W/R") then terminal B ("W/BL") then terminal C ("W/Y") and verify that the motor operates as each terminal is grounded.<br>• Does the actuator motor operate when each terminal is grounded? | Yes ►<br>No ► | GO to C5.<br>REPLACE (front right) actuator. |

C173 C A D B − +

Fig. 7 Pinpoint test, C (Part 5 of 10). 1989 Probe

| TEST STEP | RESULT ► | ACTION TO TAKE |
|---|---|---|
| **C5** ACTUATOR INTEGRITY CHECK (FRONT LEFT) | | |
| • Key off.<br>• Disconnect (front left) actuator connector C154.<br>• With a jumper wire, jump battery voltage to terminal D ("Y").<br>• With another jumper wire, ground terminal A ("W/R") then terminal B ("W/BL") then terminal C ("W") and verify that the motor operates as each terminal is grounded.<br>• Does the actuator motor operate when each terminal is grounded?<br>See illustration in TEST STEP C4 | Yes ►<br>No ► | GO to Pinpoint Test Q.<br>REPLACE (front left) actuator. |

Fig. 7 Pinpoint test, C (Part 6 of 10). 1989 Probe

| TEST STEP | RESULT ▶ | ACTION TO TAKE |
|---|---|---|
| **C6** CHECK VOLTAGE AT ACTUATOR (FRONT RIGHT) | | |
| • Leave (front left) actuator connector C154 disconnected.<br>• Key on; engine off.<br>• VOM on 20 volt scale.<br>• Probe from rear of (front right) actuator connector C173 to measure voltage as follows:<br>Between terminal A ("W/R") and ground<br>Between terminal B ("W/BL") and ground<br>Between terminal C ("W/Y") and ground.<br>• Are all voltages above 10 volts? | Yes ▶<br><br>No ▶ | REPAIR wire(s) in question between (front right) actuator and PRC control unit, including connector C222.<br><br>GO to C7 . |

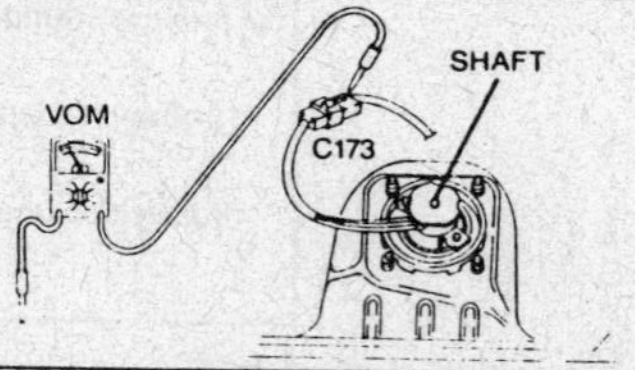

Fig. 7 Pinpoint test, C (Part 7 of 10). 1989 Probe

| TEST STEP | RESULT ▶ | ACTION TO TAKE |
|---|---|---|
| **C7** CHECK POWER TO (FRONT RIGHT) ACTUATOR | | |
| • Disconnect (front right) actuator connector C173.<br>• Key on; engine off.<br>• VOM on 20 volt scale.<br>• Measure voltage between terminal D ("Y") and ground.<br>• Is voltage above 10 volts? | Yes ▶<br><br>No ▶ | REPLACE (front right) actuator.<br><br>REPAIR "Y" wire between (front right) actuator and ignition relay. |

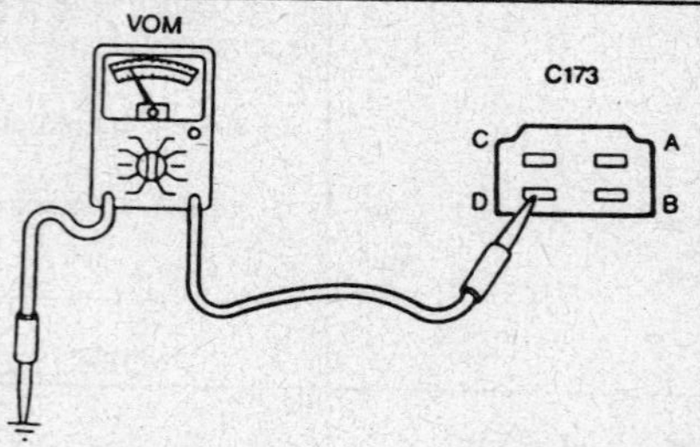

Fig. 7 Pinpoint test, C (Part 8 of 10). 1989 Probe

| TEST STEP | RESULT ▶ | ACTION TO TAKE |
|---|---|---|
| **C8** CHECK VOLTAGE AT ACTUATOR (FRONT LEFT) | | |
| • Leave (front right) connector C173 disconnected.<br>• Key on; engine off.<br>• VOM on 20 volt scale.<br>• Probe from rear of (front left) actuator connector to measure voltage as follows:<br>Between terminal A ("W/R") and ground<br>Between terminal B ("W/BL") and ground<br>Between terminal C ("W") and ground.<br>• Are all voltages above 10 volts?<br>See illustration in TEST STEP C6 | Yes ▶<br><br>No ▶ | REPAIR wire(s) in question between (front left) actuator and PRC control unit, including connector C217.<br><br>GO to C9 . |

Fig. 7 Pinpoint test, C (Part 9 of 10). 1989 Probe

| TEST STEP | RESULT ▶ | ACTION TO TAKE |
|---|---|---|
| **C9** CHECK POWER TO (FRONT LEFT) ACTUATOR | | |
| • Disconnect (front left) actuator connector C154.<br>• Key on; engine off.<br>• VOM on 20 volt scale.<br>• Measure voltage between terminal D ("Y") and ground.<br>• Is voltage above 10 volts? | Yes ▶<br><br>No ▶ | REPLACE (front left) actuator.<br><br>REPAIR "Y" wire between (front left) actuator and ignition relay. |

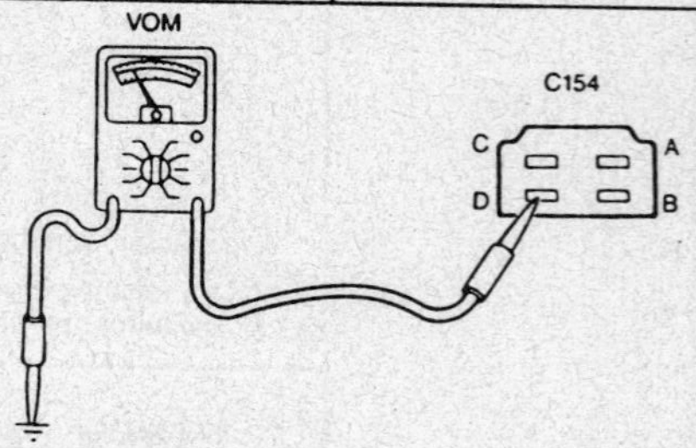

Fig. 7 Pinpoint test, C (Part 10 of 10). 1989 Probe

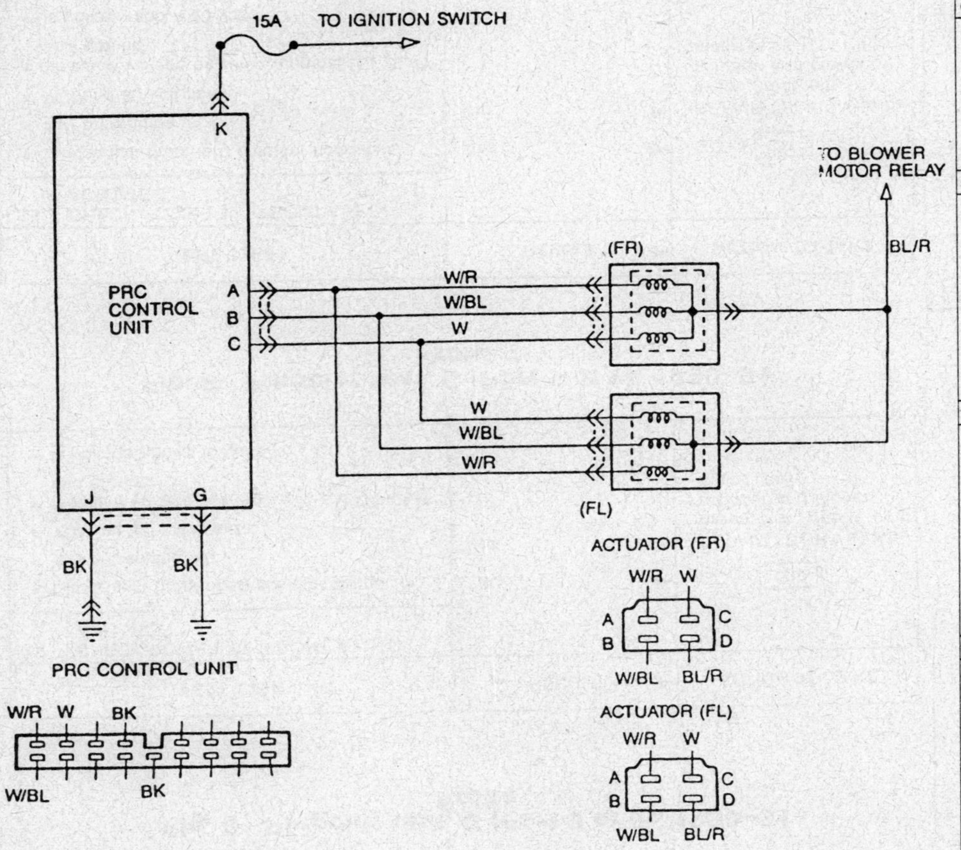

**Fig. 8 Pinpoint test, C (Part 1 of 9). 1990–91 Probe**

| | TEST STEP | RESULT | ▶ | ACTION TO TAKE |
|---|---|---|---|---|
| C1 | SYSTEM ITEGRITY CHECK | | | |
| | • Visually inspect all wiring, wiring harness, connectors and components for evidence of overheating, insulation damage, looseness, shorting or other damage.<br>• Is there any cause for concern?<br>**NOTE: Refer to the index for system component location illustration.** | Yes<br>No | ▶<br>▶ | SERVICE as required.<br>GO to C2. |
| C2 | CHECK ACTUATOR (RF) VOLTAGE AT CONTROL UNIT | | | |
| | • Disconnect PRC control unit connector and (right front) actuator connector.<br>• Key ON; engine OFF.<br>• VOM on 20 volt scale.<br>• Measure voltage at PRC control unit connector as follows:<br>- Between terminal A ("W/R") and ground<br>- Between terminal B ("W/BL") and ground<br>- Between terminal C ("W") and ground.<br>• Are all voltages above 10 volts? | Yes<br>No | ▶<br>▶ | GO to C3.<br>GO to C6. |
| C3 | CHECK ACTUATOR (LF) VOLTAGE AT CONTROL UNIT | | | |
| | • Disconnect PRC control unit connector and (left front) actuator connector.<br>• Reconnect (right front) actuator connector.<br>• Key ON; engine OFF.<br>• VOM on 20 volt scale.<br>• Measure voltage at PRC control unit as follows:<br>- Between terminal A ("W/R") and ground<br>- Between terminal B ("W/BL") and ground<br>- Between terminal C ("W") and ground.<br>• Are all voltages above 10 volts? | Yes<br>No | ▶<br>▶ | GO to C4.<br>GO to C8. |
| C4 | ACTUATOR INTEGRITY CHECK (RIGHT FRONT) | | | |
| | • Key OFF.<br>• Leave the PRC control unit disconnected.<br>• Disconnect (right front) actuator connector.<br>• With a jumper wire, jump battery voltage to terminal D ("BL/R").<br>• With another jumper wire, ground terminal A ("W/R") then terminal B ("W/BL") then terminal C ("W") and verify that the motor operates as each terminal is grounded.<br>• Does the actuator motor operate when each terminal is grounded? | Yes<br>No | ▶<br>▶ | GO to C5.<br>REPLACE (right front) actuator. |

**Fig. 8 Pinpoint test, C (Part 2 of 9). 1990–91 Probe**

| TEST STEP | RESULT ► | ACTION TO TAKE |
|---|---|---|
| **C5** ACTUATOR INTEGRITY CHECK (FRONT LEFT) | | |
| • Key off.<br>• Disconnect (front left) actuator connector.<br>• With a jumper wire, jump battery voltage to terminal D ("BL/R").<br>• With another jumper wire, ground terminal A ("W/R") then terminal B ("W/BL") then terminal C ("W") and verify that the motor operates as each terminal is grounded.<br>• Does the actuator motor operate when all terminals are grounded? | Yes ► | GO to Pinpoint Test Q. |
| | No ► | REPLACE (front left) actuator. |

**Fig. 8 Pinpoint test, C (Part 3 of 9). 1990–91 Probe**

| TEST STEP | RESULT ► | ACTION TO TAKE |
|---|---|---|
| **C6** CHECK VOLTAGE AT ACTUATOR (FRONT RIGHT) | | |
| • Leave (front left) actuator connector disconnected.<br>• Key on; engine off.<br>• VOM on 20 volt scale.<br>• Probe from rear of (front right) actuator connector to measure voltage as follows:<br>Between terminal A ("W/R") and ground<br>Between terminal B ("W/BL") and ground<br>Between terminal C ("W") and ground.<br>• Are all voltages above 10 volts? | Yes ► | REPAIR wire(s) in question between (front right) actuator and PRC control unit. |
| | No ► | GO to C7. |

**Fig. 8 Pinpoint test, C (Part 4 of 9). 1990–91 Probe**

| TEST STEP | RESULT ► | ACTION TO TAKE |
|---|---|---|
| **C7** CHECK POWER TO (FRONT RIGHT) ACTUATOR | | |
| • Disconnect (front right) actuator connector.<br>• Key on; engine off.<br>• VOM on 20 volt scale.<br>• Measure voltage between terminal D ("BL/R") and ground.<br>• Is voltage above 10 volts? | Yes ► | GO to C10. |
| | No ► | REPAIR "BL/R" wire between (front right) actuator and blower motor relay. |

**Fig. 8 Pinpoint test, C (Part 5 of 9). 1990–91 Probe**

| TEST STEP | RESULT ► | ACTION TO TAKE |
|---|---|---|
| **C8** CHECK VOLTAGE AT ACTUATOR (FRONT LEFT) | | |
| • Leave (front right) connector disconnected.<br>• Key on; engine off.<br>• VOM on 20 volt scale.<br>• Probe from rear of (front left) actuator connector to measure voltage as follows:<br>Between terminal A ("W/R") and ground<br>Between terminal B ("W/BL") and ground<br>Between terminal C ("W") and ground.<br>• Are all voltages above 10 volts? | Yes ► | REPAIR wire(s) in question between (front left) actuator and PRC control unit. |
| | No ► | GO to C9. |

**Fig. 8 Pinpoint test, C (Part 6 of 9). 1990–91 Probe**

| TEST STEP | RESULT ► | ACTION TO TAKE |
|---|---|---|
| **C9** CHECK POWER TO (FRONT LEFT) ACTUATOR | | |
| • Disconnect (front left) actuator connector.<br>• Key on; engine off.<br>• VOM on 20 volt scale.<br>• Measure voltage between terminal D ("BL/R") and ground.<br>• Is voltage above 10 volts? | Yes ► | GO to C11. |
| | No ► | REPAIR "BL/R" wire between (front left) actuator and blower motor relay. |

**Fig. 8 Pinpoint test, C (Part 7 of 9). 1990–91 Probe**

| TEST STEP | RESULT ► | ACTION TO TAKE |
|---|---|---|
| **C10** SHORT TO GROUND CHECK AT (FRONT RIGHT) ACTUATOR | | |
| • Leave PRC Control Unit Connector disconnected.<br>• Key off.<br>• Measure resistance between FR Actuator terminals and ground as follows:<br>W/R terminal and ground<br>W/BL terminal and ground<br>W terminal and ground.<br>• Are all resistance readings greater than 10,000 OHMs? | Yes ►<br>No ► | REPLACE FR Actuator.<br>SERVICE wire(s) in question between front and PRC Control Unit for short to ground. |

**Fig. 8 Pinpoint test, C (Part 8 of 9). 1990–91 Probe**

| TEST STEP | RESULT ► | ACTION TO TAKE |
|---|---|---|
| **C11** SHORT TO GROUND CHECK AT (FRONT LEFT) ACTUATOR | | |
| • Leave PRC Control Unit Connector disconnected.<br>• Key off.<br>• Measure resistance between FL Actuator terminals and ground as follows:<br>W/R terminal and ground<br>W/BL terminal and ground<br>W terminal and ground.<br>• Are all resistance readings greater than 10,000 OHMs? | Yes ►<br>No ► | REPLACE FL Actuator.<br>SERVICE wire(s) in question between front actuators and PRC Control Unit for short to ground. |

**Fig. 8 Pinpoint test, C (Part 9 of 9). 1990–91 Probe**

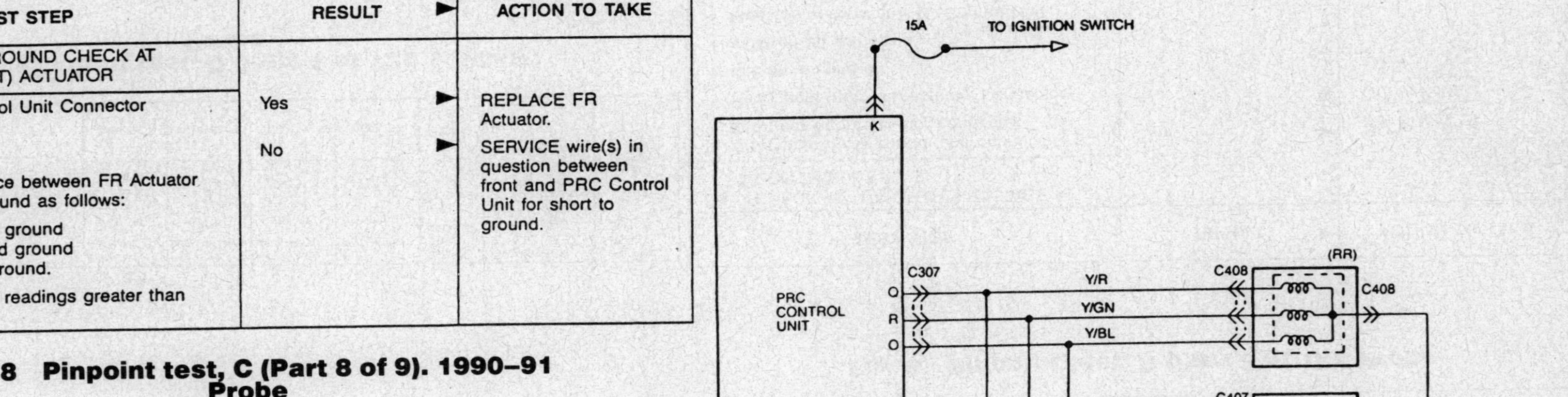

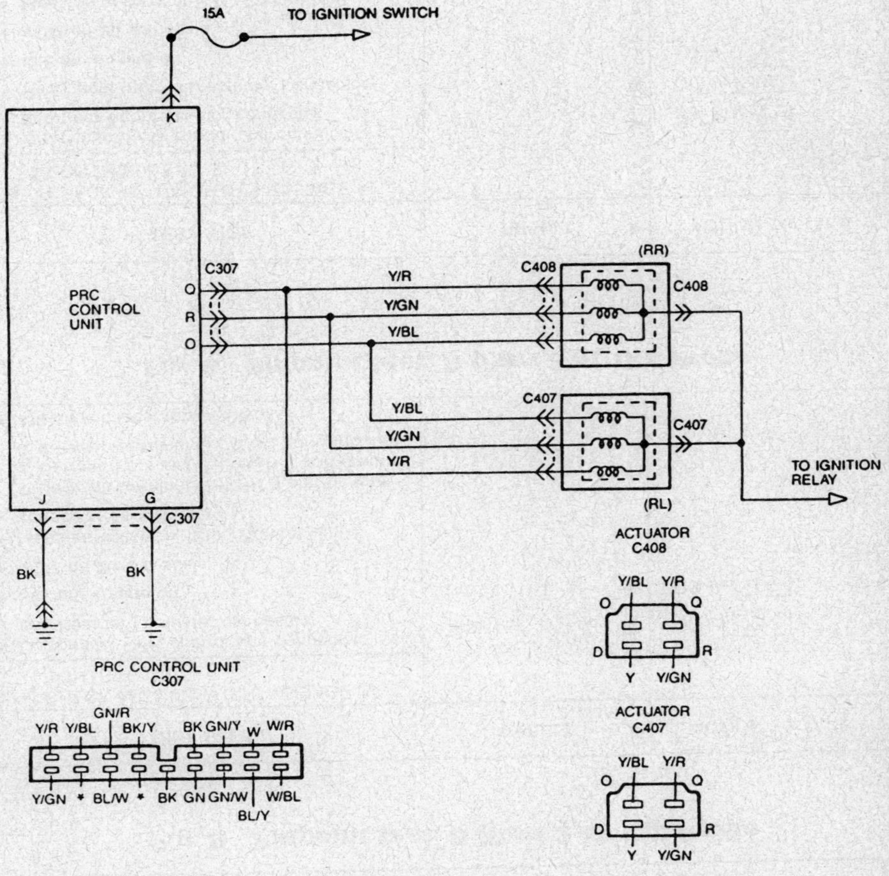

**Fig. 9 Pinpoint test, D (Part 1 of 12). 1989 Probe**

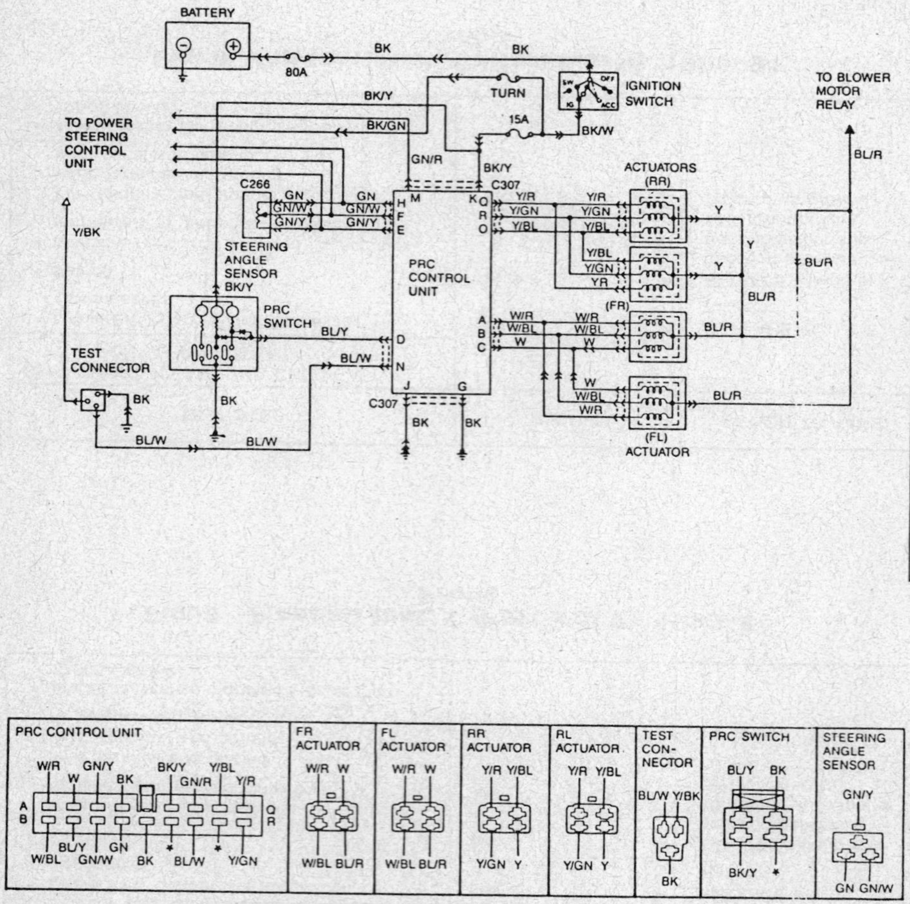

Fig. 9 Pinpoint test, D (Part 1 of 12). 1990–91 Probe

| TEST STEP | RESULT ► | ACTION TO TAKE |
|---|---|---|
| **D1** SYSTEM INTEGRITY CHECK | | |
| • Visually inspect all wiring, wiring harness, connectors and components for evidence of overheating, insulation damage, looseness, shorting or other damage.<br>• Is there any cause for concern? | Yes ►<br>No ► | SERVICE as required.<br>GO to D2 . |

Fig. 9 Pinpoint test, D (Part 2 of 12). Probe

| TEST STEP | RESULT ► | ACTION TO TAKE |
|---|---|---|
| **D2** CHECK ACTUATOR (RR) VOLTAGE AT CONTROL UNIT | | |
| • Disconnect PRC control unit connector and (rear left) actuator connector.<br>• Key on; engine off.<br>• VOM on 20 volt scale.<br>• Measure voltage at PRC Control Unit connector as follows:<br>1. Between terminal Q ("Y/R") and ground<br>2. Between terminal R ("Y/GN") and ground<br>3. Between terminal O ("Y/BL") and ground.<br>• Are all voltages above 10 volts? | Yes ►<br>No ► | GO to D3 .<br>GO to D5 . |

Fig. 9 Pinpoint test, D (Part 3 of 12). Probe

| TEST STEP | RESULT ► | ACTION TO TAKE |
|---|---|---|
| **D3** CHECK ACTUATOR (RL) VOLTAGE AT CONTROL UNIT | | |
| • Disconnect PRC control unit connector and (rear right) actuator connector.<br>• Reconnect (rear left) actuator connector.<br>• Key on; engine off.<br>• VOM on 20 volt scale.<br>• Measure voltage at PRC Control Unit connector as follows:<br>Between terminal Q ("Y/R") and ground<br>Between terminal R ("Y/GN") and ground<br>Between terminal O ("Y/BL") and ground.<br>• Are all voltages above 10 volts? | Yes ►<br>No ► | GO to D4 .<br>GO to D8 . |

Fig. 9 Pinpoint test, D (Part 4 of 12). Probe

| TEST STEP | RESULT ► | ACTION TO TAKE |
|---|---|---|
| **D4** ACTUATOR INTEGRITY CHECK (REAR RIGHT) | | |
| • Key off.<br>• Disconnect (rear right) actuator connector.<br>• With a jumper wire, jump battery voltage to terminal D ("Y").<br>• With another jumper wire, ground terminal Q ("Y/R") then terminal R ("Y/GN") then terminal O ("Y/BL") and verify that the motor operates as each terminal is grounded.<br>• Does the actuator motor operate when each terminal is grounded? | Yes ►<br>No ► | GO to D5.<br>REPLACE (rear right) actuator. |

**Fig. 9 Pinpoint test, D (Part 5 of 12). Probe**

| TEST STEP | RESULT ► | ACTION TO TAKE |
|---|---|---|
| **D5** ACTUATOR INTEGRITY CHECK (REAR LEFT) | | |
| • Key off.<br>• Disconnect (rear left) actuator connector.<br>• With a jumper wire, jump battery voltage to terminal D ("Y").<br>• With another jumper wire, ground terminal Q ("Y/R") then terminal R ("Y/GN") then terminal O ("Y/BL") and verify that the motor operates as each terminal is grounded.<br>• Does the actuator motor operate when each terminal is grounded? | Yes ►<br>No ► | GO to Pinpoint Test Q.<br>REPLACE (rear left) actuator. |

**Fig. 9 Pinpoint test, D (Part 6 of 12). Probe**

| TEST STEP | RESULT ► | ACTION TO TAKE |
|---|---|---|
| **D6** CHECK VOLTAGE AT ACTUATOR (REAR RIGHT) | | |
| • Leave (rear left) actuator connector C407 disconnected.<br>• Key on; engine off.<br>• VOM on 20 volt scale.<br>• Probe from rear of (rear right) actuator (connector C408) to measure voltages as follows:<br>Between terminal Q ("Y/R") and ground<br>Between terminal R ("Y/GN") and ground<br>Between terminal O ("Y/GN") and ground.<br>• Are all voltages above 10 volts? | Yes ►<br><br>No ► | REPAIR wire(s) in question between (rear right) actuator and PRC control unit.<br>GO to D7. |

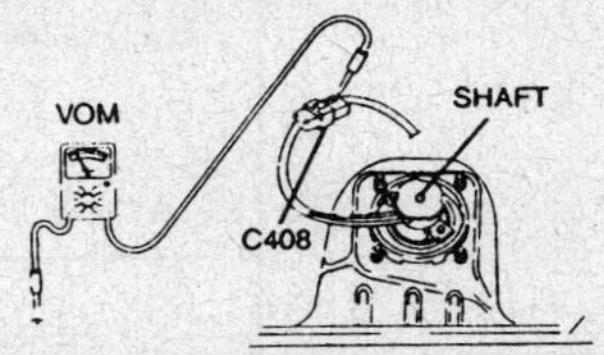

VOM
SHAFT
C408

**Fig. 9 Pinpoint test, D (Part 7 of 12). Probe**

| TEST STEP | RESULT ► | ACTION TO TAKE |
|---|---|---|
| **D7** CHECK POWER TO (REAR RIGHT) ACTUATOR | | |
| • Disconnect (rear right) actuator (connector C408).<br>• Key on; engine off.<br>• VOM on 20 volt scale.<br>• Measure voltage between terminal D ("Y") and ground.<br>• Is voltage above 10 volts? | Yes ►<br>No ► | REPLACE (rear right) actuator.<br>REPAIR "Y" wire between (rear right) actuator and ignition relay. |

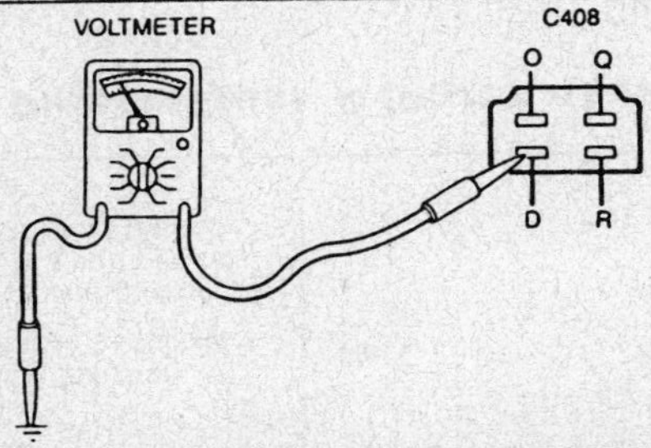

VOLTMETER
C408
O Q
D R

**Fig. 9 Pinpoint test, D (Part 8 of 12). 1989 Probe**

| TEST STEP | RESULT ► | ACTION TO TAKE |
|---|---|---|
| **D7** CHECK POWER TO (REAR RIGHT) ACTUATOR | | |
| • Disconnect (rear right) actuator connector.<br>• Key on; engine off.<br>• VOM on 20 volt scale.<br>• Measure voltage between terminal D ("Y") and ground.<br>• Is voltage above 10 volts? | Yes ► | GO to D10 . |
| | No ► | REPAIR "Y" wire between (rear right) actuator and blower motor relay. |

**Fig. 9 Pinpoint test, D (Part 8 of 12). 1990–91 Probe**

| TEST STEP | RESULT ► | ACTION TO TAKE |
|---|---|---|
| **D8** CHECK VOLTAGE AT ACTUATOR (REAR LEFT) | | |
| • Leave (rear right) connector disconnected.<br>• Key on; engine off.<br>• VOM on 20 volt scale.<br>• Probe from rear of (rear left) actuator connector to measure voltages as follows:<br>Between terminal Q ("Y/R") and ground<br>Between terminal R ("Y/GN") and ground<br>Between terminal O ("Y/BL") and ground.<br>• Are voltages above 10 volts? | Yes ► | REPAIR wire(s) in question between (rear left) actuator and PRC control unit. |
| | No ► | GO to D9 . |

**Fig. 9 Pinpoint test, D (Part 9 of 12). Probe**

| TEST STEP | RESULT ► | ACTION TO TAKE |
|---|---|---|
| **D9** CHECK POWER TO (REAR LEFT) ACTUATOR | | |
| • Disconnect (rear left) actuator (connector C407).<br>• Key on; engine off.<br>• VOM on 20 volt scale.<br>• Measure voltage between terminal D ("Y") and ground.<br>• Is voltage above 10 volts? | Yes ► | REPLACE (rear left) actuator. |
| | No ► | REPAIR "Y" wire between (rear left) actuator and ignition relay. |



**Fig. 9 Pinpoint test, D (Part 10 of 12). 1989 Probe**

| TEST STEP | RESULT ► | ACTION TO TAKE |
|---|---|---|
| **D9** CHECK POWER TO (REAR LEFT) ACTUATOR | | |
| • Disconnect (rear left) actuator connector.<br>• Key on; engine off.<br>• VOM on 20 volt scale.<br>• Measure voltage between terminal D ("Y") and ground.<br>• Is voltage above 10 volts? | Yes ► | GO to D11 . |
| | No ► | REPAIR "Y" wire between (rear left) actuator and blower motor relay. |

**Fig. 9 Pinpoint test, D (Part 10 of 12). 1990–91 Probe**

| TEST STEP | RESULT ► | ACTION TO TAKE |
|---|---|---|
| **D10** SHORT TO GROUND CHECK AT (REAR RIGHT) ACTUATOR | | |
| • Leave PRC Control Unit Connector disconnected.<br>• Key off.<br>• Measure resistance between RR Actuator terminals and ground as follows:<br>Y/R terminal and ground<br>Y/GN terminal and ground<br>Y/BL terminal and ground.<br>• Are all resistance readings greater than 10,000 OHMs? | Yes ► | REPLACE RR Actuator. |
| | No ► | SERVICE wire(s) in question between rear actuators and PRC Control Unit for short to ground. |

**Fig. 9 Pinpoint test, D (Part 11 of 12). 1990–91 Probe**

| TEST STEP | RESULT ► | ACTION TO TAKE |
|---|---|---|
| **D11** SHORT TO GROUND CHECK AT (REAR LEFT) ACTUATOR | | |
| • Leave PRC Control Unit Connector disconnected.<br>• Key off.<br>• Measure resistance between RL Actuator terminals and ground as follows:<br>Y/R terminal and ground<br>Y/GN terminal and ground<br>Y/BL terminal and ground.<br>• Are all resistance readings greater than 10,000 OHMs? | Yes ►<br><br>No ► | REPLACE RL Actuator.<br><br>SERVICE wire(s) in question between rear actuators and PRC Control Unit for short to ground. |

**Fig. 9 Pinpoint test, D (Part 12 of 12). 1990–91 Probe**

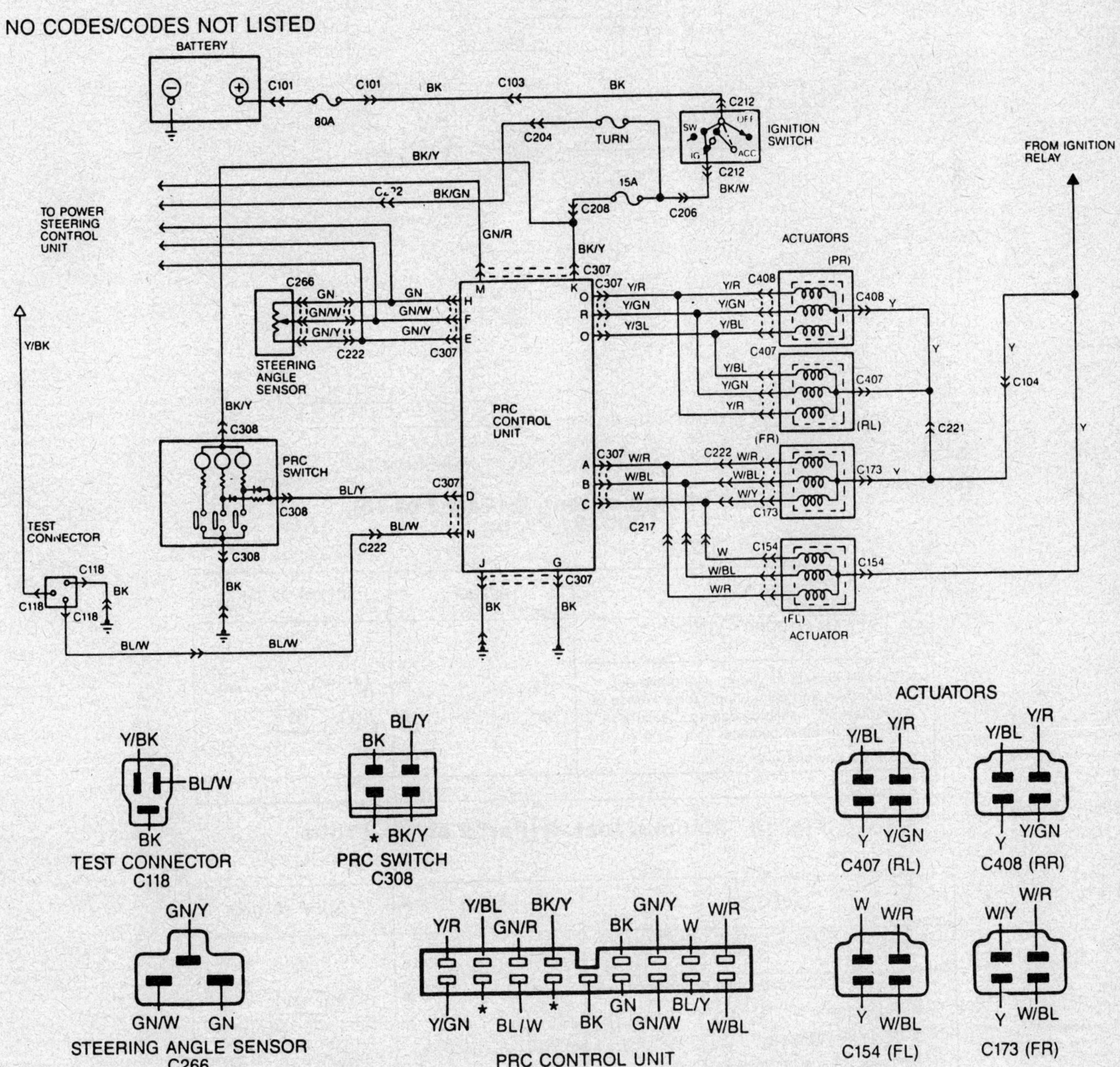


**Fig. 10 Pinpoint test, Q (Part 1 of 13). 1989 Probe**

NO CODES/CODES NOT LISTED

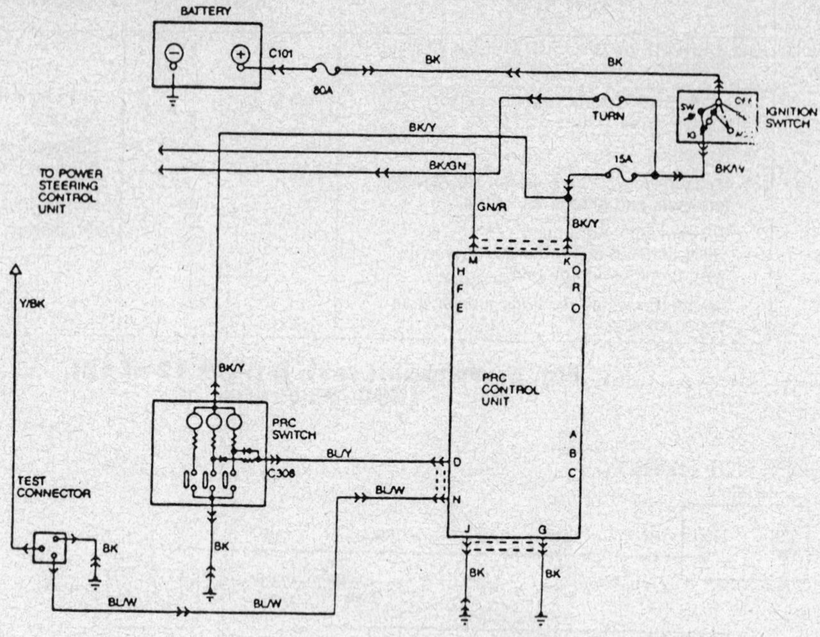


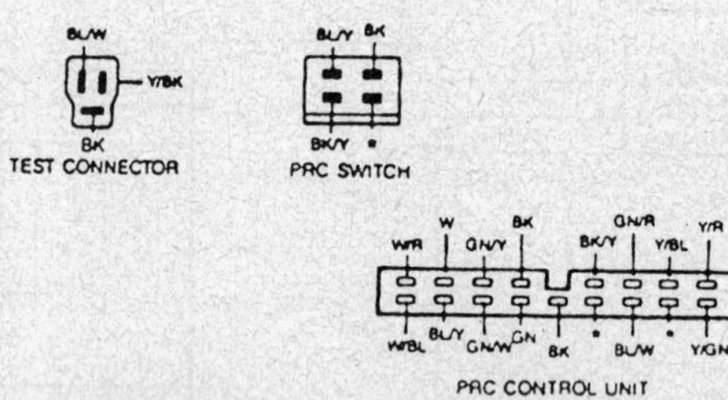


**Fig. 10 Pinpoint test, Q (Part 1 of 13). 1990–91 Probe**

| TEST STEP | | RESULT ► | ACTION TO TAKE |
|---|---|---|---|
| Q1 | SYSTEM INTEGRITY CHECK | | |
| • Visually inspect all wiring, wiring harness, connectors and components for evidence of overheating, insulation damage, looseness, shorting or other damage.<br>• Is there any cause for concern? | | Yes ►<br>No ► | SERVICE as required.<br>GO to Q2 . |

**Fig. 10 Pinpoint test, Q (Part 2 of 13). Probe**

| TEST STEP | | RESULT ► | ACTION TO TAKE |
|---|---|---|---|
| Q2 | CHECK POWER TO PRC CONTROL UNIT | | |
| • Disconnect PRC control unit connector.<br>• Key on; engine off.<br>• VOM on 20 volt scale.<br>• Measure voltage between terminal K ("BK/Y") and ground.<br>• Is voltage above 10 volts? | | Yes ►<br>No ► | GO to Q3 .<br>REPLACE 15A fuse or REPAIR "BK/Y" wire between PRC control unit and fuse box. |

**Fig. 10 Pinpoint test, Q (Part 3 of 13). Probe**

| TEST STEP | | RESULT ► | ACTION TO TAKE |
|---|---|---|---|
| Q3 | CHECK PRC CONTROL UNIT GROUNDS | | |
| • Leave PRC control unit connector disconnected.<br>• VOM on 200 ohm scale.<br>• Measure resistance as follows:<br>1. Between terminal J ("BK") and ground<br>2. Between terminal G ("BK") and ground.<br>• Are resistance readings less than 5 ohms? | | Yes ►<br>No ► | GO to Q4.<br>REPAIR "BK" wire in question between PRC control unit and chassis ground for opens. |

**Fig. 10 Pinpoint test, Q (Part 4 of 13). Probe**

| TEST STEP | | RESULT ► | ACTION TO TAKE |
|---|---|---|---|
| Q4 | CHECK TEST CONNECTOR GROUND | | |
| • Disconnect test connector from mounting.<br>• VOM on 200 ohm scale.<br>• Measure resistance between terminal "BK" wire and ground.<br>• Is resistance reading less than 5 ohms? | | Yes ►<br>No ► | GO to Q5.<br>REPAIR "BK" wire between test connector and chassis ground. |

**Fig. 10 Pinpoint test, Q (Part 5 of 13). Probe**

| TEST STEP | | RESULT ► | ACTION TO TAKE |
|---|---|---|---|
| Q5 | CHECK CONTINUITY BETWEEN PRC CONTROL UNIT AND TEST CONNECTOR | | |
| • Disconnect PRC control unit connector.<br>• VOM on 200 ohm scale.<br>• Measure resistance between PRC control unit connector terminal N ("BL/W") and test connector BL/W wire.<br>• Is resistance less than 5 ohms? | | Yes ►<br>No ► | GO to Q6.<br>REPAIR "BL/W" wire between PRC control unit and test connector for opens. |

**Fig. 10 Pinpoint test, Q (Part 6 of 13). Probe**

| TEST STEP | | RESULT ► | ACTION TO TAKE |
|---|---|---|---|
| Q6 | CHECK TEST CONNECTOR FOR SHORT TO GROUND | | |
| • Leave PRC control unit connector disconnected.<br>• Key off.<br>• VOM on 200K ohm scale.<br>• Measure resistance between PRC control unit connector terminal N ("BL/W") and ground.<br>• Is resistance greater than 10,000 ohms? | | Yes ►<br>No ► | GO to Q7.<br>REPAIR "BL/W" wire between PRC control unit and test connector for short to ground. |

**Fig. 10 Pinpoint test, Q (Part 7 of 13). Probe**

| TEST STEP | | RESULT ► | ACTION TO TAKE |
|---|---|---|---|
| Q7 | CHECK TEST CONNECTOR CIRCUIT FOR SHORT TO VPWR | | |
| • Leave PRC control unit connector disconnected.<br>• Key on; engine off.<br>• VOM on 20 volt scale.<br>• Measure voltage between PRC control unit connector terminal N ("BL/W") and ground.<br>• Is voltage reading above 0.0 volts? | | Yes ►<br><br>No ► | REPAIR "BL/W" wire between PRC control unit and test connector for short to VPWR.<br><br>GO to Q8 . |

**Fig. 10 Pinpoint test, Q (Part 8 of 13). Probe**

| TEST STEP | | RESULT ► | ACTION TO TAKE |
|---|---|---|---|
| Q8 | CHECK POWER TO PRC SWITCH | | |
| • Disconnect PRC switch connector.<br>• Key on; engine off.<br>• VOM on 20 volt scale.<br>• Measure voltage between PRC switch connector "BK/Y" wire and ground.<br>• Is voltage reading less than 10 volts? | | Yes ►<br><br>No ► | REPLACE 15A fuse or REPAIR "BK/Y" wire between fuse box and PRC switch.<br><br>GO to Q9 . |

**Fig. 10 Pinpoint test, Q (Part 9 of 13). Probe**

| TEST STEP | | RESULT ► | ACTION TO TAKE |
|---|---|---|---|
| Q9 | CHECK PRC SWITCH GROUND | | |
| • Leave PRC switch connector disconnected.<br>• VOM on 200 ohm scale.<br>• Measure resistance between PRC switch connector "BK" wire and ground.<br>• Is resistance less than 5 ohms? | | Yes ►<br>No ► | GO to Q10 .<br>REPAIR "BK" wire between PRC switch and chassis ground for opens. |

**Fig. 10 Pinpoint test, Q (Part 10 of 13). Probe**

| TEST STEP | | RESULT ► | ACTION TO TAKE |
|---|---|---|---|
| Q10 | CHECK CONTINUITY BETWEEN PRC CONTROL UNIT AND SWITCH | | |
| • PRC control unit connector and PRC switch connector disconnected.<br>• VOM on 200 ohm scale.<br>• Measure resistance between PRC control unit connector terminal D ("BL/Y") and PRC switch connector "BL/Y" wire.<br>• Is resistance less than 5 ohms? | | Yes ►<br>No ► | GO to Q11.<br>REPAIR "BL/Y" wire between PRC control unit and PRC switch for opens. |

**Fig. 10 Pinpoint test, Q (Part 11 of 13). Probe**

| TEST STEP | | RESULT ► | ACTION TO TAKE |
|---|---|---|---|
| Q11 | CHECK PRC CIRCUIT FOR SHORT TO GROUND | | |
| • PRC control unit connector and PRC switch connector disconnected.<br>• VOM on 200K ohm scale.<br>• Measure resistance between PRC control unit connector terminal D ("BL/Y") and ground.<br>• Is resistance greater than 10,000 ohms? | | Yes ►<br>No ► | GO to Q12.<br>REPAIR "BL/Y" wire between PRC control unit and PRC switch for short to ground. |

**Fig. 10 Pinpoint test, Q (Part 12 of 13). Probe**

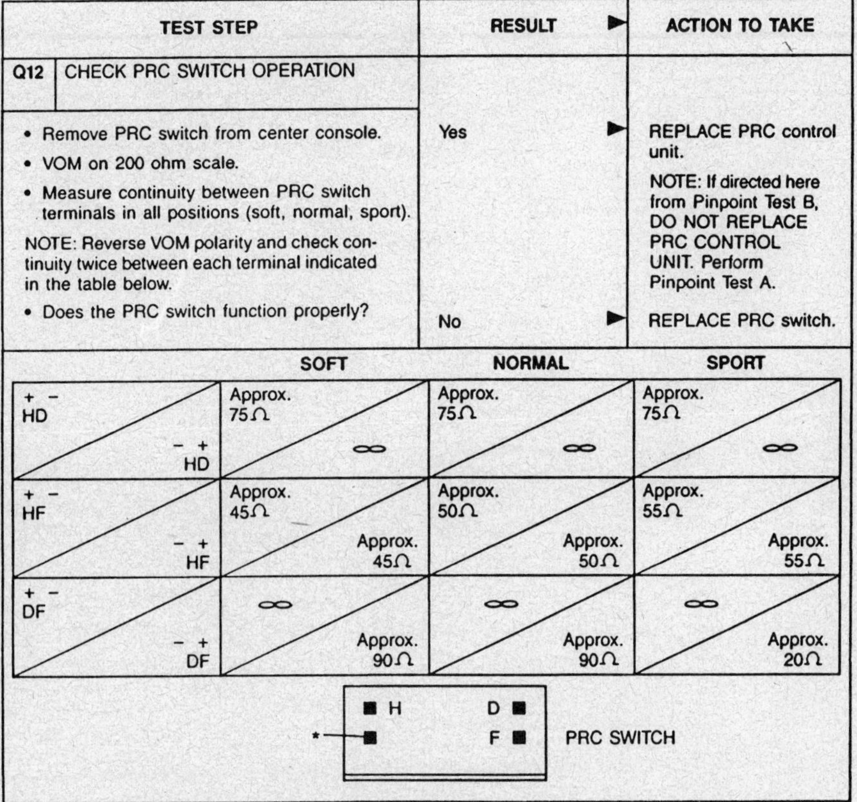

| TEST STEP | | RESULT ► | ACTION TO TAKE |
|---|---|---|---|
| Q12 | CHECK PRC SWITCH OPERATION | | |
| • Remove PRC switch from center console.<br>• VOM on 200 ohm scale.<br>• Measure continuity between PRC switch terminals in all positions (soft, normal, sport).<br>NOTE: Reverse VOM polarity and check continuity twice between each terminal indicated in the table below.<br>• Does the PRC switch function properly? | | Yes ►<br>No ► | REPLACE PRC control unit.<br>NOTE: If directed here from Pinpoint Test B, DO NOT REPLACE PRC CONTROL UNIT. Perform Pinpoint Test A.<br>REPLACE PRC switch. |

| + − / − + | SOFT | NORMAL | SPORT |
|---|---|---|---|
| + − HD / − + HD | Approx. 75Ω / ∞ | Approx. 75Ω / ∞ | Approx. 75Ω / ∞ |
| + − HF / − + HF | Approx. 45Ω / Approx. 45Ω | Approx. 50Ω / Approx. 50Ω | Approx. 55Ω / Approx. 55Ω |
| + − DF / − + DF | ∞ / Approx. 90Ω | ∞ / Approx. 90Ω | ∞ / Approx. 20Ω |



**Fig. 10 Pinpoint test, Q (Part 13 of 13). 1989 Probe**

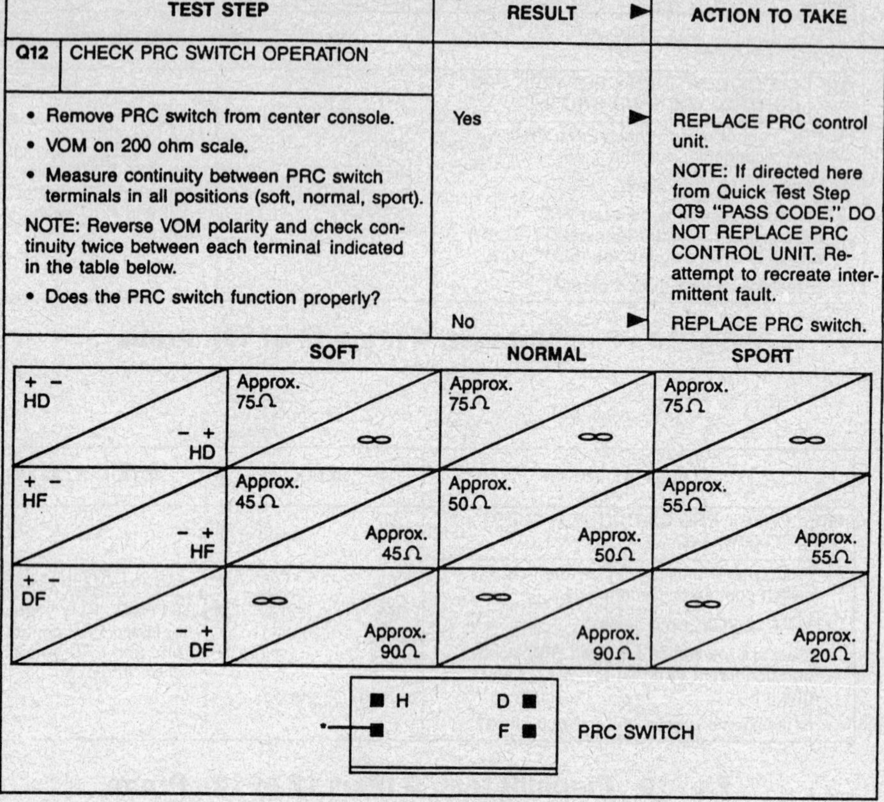

| TEST STEP | | RESULT ► | ACTION TO TAKE |
|---|---|---|---|
| Q12 | CHECK PRC SWITCH OPERATION | | |
| • Remove PRC switch from center console.<br>• VOM on 200 ohm scale.<br>• Measure continuity between PRC switch terminals in all positions (soft, normal, sport).<br>NOTE: Reverse VOM polarity and check continuity twice between each terminal indicated in the table below.<br>• Does the PRC switch function properly? | | Yes ► | REPLACE PRC control unit.<br>NOTE: If directed here from Quick Test Step QT9 "PASS CODE," DO NOT REPLACE PRC CONTROL UNIT. Re-attempt to recreate intermittent fault. |
| | | No ► | REPLACE PRC switch. |

| | SOFT | NORMAL | SPORT |
|---|---|---|---|
| + − HD / − + HD | Approx. 75Ω / ∞ | Approx. 75Ω / ∞ | Approx. 75Ω / ∞ |
| + − HF / − + HF | Approx. 45Ω / Approx. 45Ω | Approx. 50Ω / Approx. 50Ω | Approx. 55Ω / Approx. 55Ω |
| + − DF / − + DF | ∞ / Approx. 90Ω | ∞ / Approx. 90Ω | ∞ / Approx. 20Ω |



**Fig. 10 Pinpoint test, Q (Part 13 of 13). 1990–91 Probe**

# WIPER SYSTEM SERVICE

## TABLE OF CONTENTS



# Front Wiper System

## INDEX



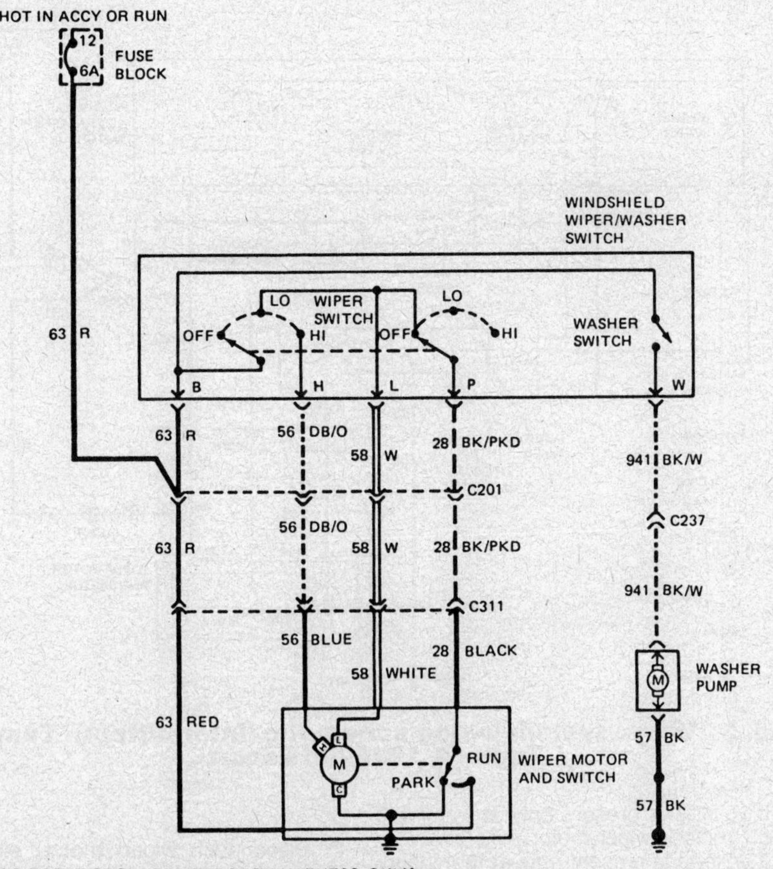


**Fig. 1 Wiper system wiring schematic (Non-Intermittent). Tempo, Topaz & 1989–90 Escort**

## DIAGNOSIS

### TEMPO, TOPAZ & 1989–90 ESCORT

Refer to **Figs. 1 through 3** for wiper system wiring schematics, and **Figs. 4 and 5** for diagnostic procedures.

### CROWN VICTORIA, GRAND MARQUIS & TOWN CAR

Refer to **Fig. 6** for wiper system wiring schematics, and **Fig. 7** for diagnostic procedures.

### CONTINENTAL, COUGAR, MARK VII, MUSTANG, SABLE, TAURUS & THUNDERBIRD

Refer to **Figs. 8 through 12** for wiper system wiring schematics, and **Fig. 13** for diagnostic procedures.

### MERKUR

Refer to **Fig. 14** for diagnostic procedures.

### PROBE

Refer to **Fig. 15** for wiper system wiring schematic, and **Fig. 16** for diagnostic and testing procedures.

### FESTIVA

Refer to **Fig. 17** for diagnostic and testing procedures.

### 1989 TRACER

Refer to **Fig. 18** for diagnostic and testing procedures.

## 1991 ESCORT & TRACER

Refer to **Fig. 19** for wiper system wiring schematic, and **Fig. 20** for diagnostic and testing procedures.

## CAPRI

Refer to **Fig. 21** for wiper system wiring schematic, and **Fig. 22** for diagnostic and testing procedures.

# TESTING

## TEMPO & TOPAZ

### WIPER MOTOR

Refer to wiring schematics **Figs. 1 through 3** when performing the following test procedures.

#### High Speed Test

1. Turn ignition switch to ON.
2. Turn wiper switch to HI.
3. Check voltage at motor connector (blue/orange wire) terminal 56. If voltage is present proceed to step 5.
4. If voltage is not present proceed as follows:
   a. Check voltage at wiper switch (red wire) terminal 63. If voltage is present, replace wiper switch.
   b. If voltage is not present at terminal 63, check circuit back to source.
5. If voltage is present at terminal 56 and motor will not run, proceed as follows:
   a. Ground motor to body.
   b. If motor runs, repair ground.
   c. If motor does not run, replace motor.

#### Low Speed Test

1. Turn ignition switch to ON.
2. Turn wiper switch to LO.
3. Check voltage at motor connector (white wire) terminal 58. If voltage is present proceed to step 5.
4. If voltage is not present proceed as follows:
   a. Check voltage at (red wire) terminal 63. If voltage is present, replace wiper switch.
   b. If voltage is not present at terminal 63, check circuit back to source.
5. If voltage is present at terminal 58 and motor will not run, proceed as follows:
   a. Ground motor to body.
   b. If motor runs, repair ground.
   c. If motor does not run, replace motor.

#### Park Operation Test

1. Turn ignition switch to ON.
2. Turn wiper switch to OFF.
3. Check voltage at motor and park switch connectors (black/pink wire) terminal 28, (white wire) terminal 58, and (red wire) terminal 63. If voltage is not present at all three terminals, proceed to steps 5 through 7.
4. If voltage is present at all three terminals and wipers are not parked, proceed as follows:
   a. Ground motor to body.
   b. If motor parks, repair ground.
   c. If motor does not park, replace motor.

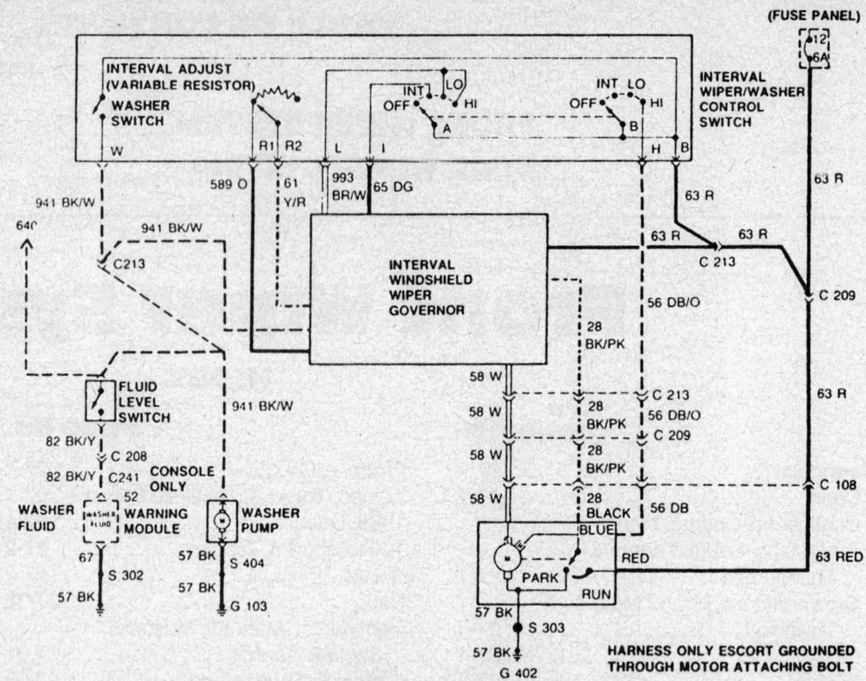


**Fig. 2 Wiper system wiring schematic (Interval). Tempo, Topaz & 1989–90 Escort**

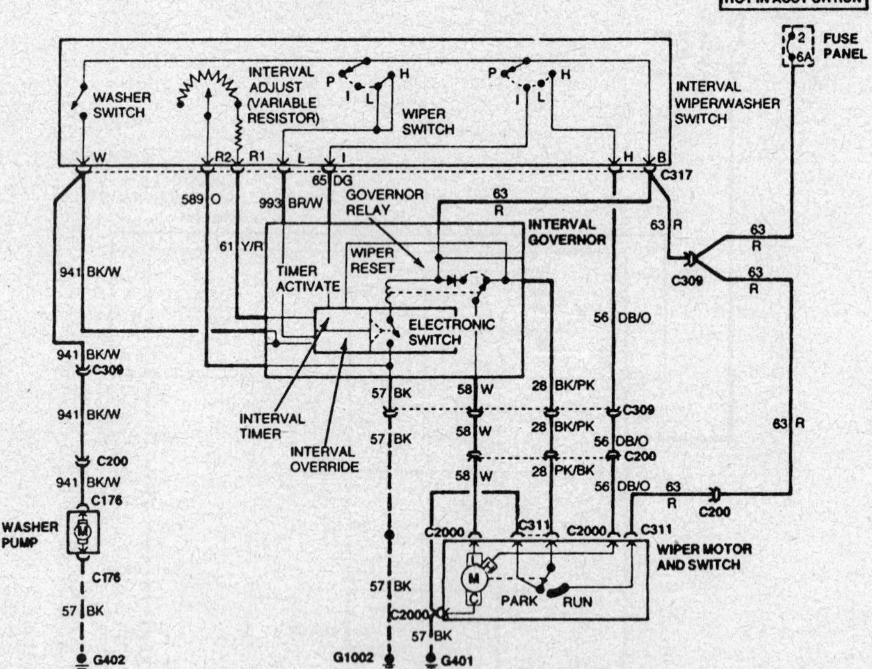


**Fig. 3 Wiper system wiring schematic (Intermittent). Tempo, Topaz & 1989–90 Escort**

5. If voltage is present only at terminal 63, replace wiper motor.
6. If voltage is present only at terminals 28 and 63, replace wiper switch.
7. If voltage still is not present at terminal 58, check terminals 28 and 58 back to wiper switch.

#### Current Draw Test

1. Disconnect wiper motor linkage.
2. Disconnect wiper motor electrical connector.
3. Make test connections as shown in **Fig. 23.** Alternately connect red test lead to wiper motor low and high speed connectors.
4. Current draw at either terminal should not exceed 3 amps.

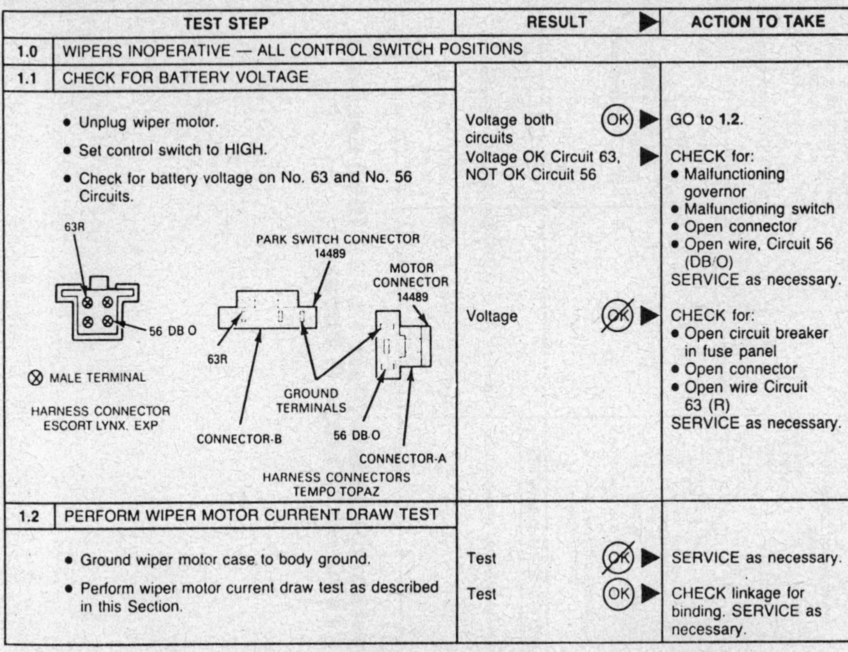

| TEST STEP | RESULT ▶ | ACTION TO TAKE |
|---|---|---|
| **1.0** WIPERS INOPERATIVE — ALL CONTROL SWITCH POSITIONS | | |
| **1.1** CHECK FOR BATTERY VOLTAGE | | |
| • Unplug wiper motor.<br>• Set control switch to HIGH.<br>• Check for battery voltage on No. 63 and No. 56 Circuits. | Voltage both circuits (OK) ▶ | GO to **1.2**. |
| | Voltage OK Circuit 63, NOT OK Circuit 56 ▶ | CHECK for:<br>• Malfunctioning governor<br>• Malfunctioning switch<br>• Open connector<br>• Open wire, Circuit 56 (DB/O)<br>SERVICE as necessary. |
| | Voltage (NOT OK) ▶ | CHECK for:<br>• Open circuit breaker in fuse panel<br>• Open connector<br>• Open wire Circuit 63 (R)<br>SERVICE as necessary. |
| **1.2** PERFORM WIPER MOTOR CURRENT DRAW TEST | | |
| • Ground wiper motor case to body ground.<br>• Perform wiper motor current draw test as described in this Section. | Test (NOT OK) ▶ | SERVICE as necessary. |
| | Test (OK) ▶ | CHECK linkage for binding. SERVICE as necessary. |



**Fig. 4 Wiper system diagnosis (Part 1 of 3). 1989 Escort, Tempo & Topaz**

| TEST STEP | RESULT ▶ | ACTION TO TAKE |
|---|---|---|
| **2.0** WIPERS INOPERATIVE OR ERRATIC, ON "INT" OR "LOW" ONLY — HI SPEED WORKS | | |
| **2.1** CHECK WIPER OPERATION | | |
| • Run wipers on HI.<br>• Do wipers hesitate when they pass through the PARK position? | YES ▶ | GO to **2.2**. |
| | NO ▶ | GO to **2.3**. |
| **2.2** CHECK GOVERNOR | | |
| • Check governor ground pigtail (under mounting screw). | (OK) ▶ | Malfunctioning governor — SERVICE as required. |
| | (NOT OK) ▶ | TIGHTEN governor mounting screws to improve ground. |
| **2.3** CHECK CIRCUIT 58 FOR BATTERY VOLTAGE | | |
| • Unplug wiper motor.<br>• Set wiper switch on LOW.<br>• Check Circuit 58 for battery voltage.<br>58W; PARK SWITCH CONNECTOR 14489; MOTOR CONNECTOR 14489; GROUND TERMINALS; CONNECTOR-B; 58W; CONNECTOR-A; HARNESS CONNECTOR ESCORT LYNX, EXP; HARNESS CONNECTORS TEMPO TOPAZ | Voltage (OK) ▶ | CHECK for malfunctioning wiper motor. PERFORM low speed current draw test. SERVICE as required. |
| | Voltage (NOT OK) ▶ | CHECK for:<br>• Open connector<br>• Malfunctioning switch<br>• Malfunctioning governor<br>• Open wire Circuit 58 (W)<br>SERVICE or REPLACE as necessary. |
| **3.0** WIPERS RUN WITH CONTROL SWITCH TURNED OFF | | |
| **3.1** CHECK WIPER SWITCH | | |
| • Unplug wiper control switch.<br>• Turn ignition key to RUN. | Wipers park ▶ | REPLACE wiper control switch. |
| | Wipers continue to run ▶ | CHECK for:<br>• Malfunctioning governor<br>• Malfunctioning wiper motor<br>SERVICE or REPLACE as required. |

**Fig. 4 Wiper system diagnosis (Part 2 of 3). 1989 Escort, Tempo & Topaz**

## WIPER SWITCH

### Continuity Test

When testing a non-intermittent wiper switch, a self-powered test lamp or an ohmmeter can be used to check continuity. When testing an intermittent wiper switch, use only an ohmmeter to check continuity.

When taking test readings move the switch lever to detect marginal switch operation.

Refer to **Fig. 24** for switch terminal identification and continuity readings.

## CIRCUIT BREAKER

1. Remove circuit breaker from fuse panel.
2. Using a suitable Volt-Amp meter, adjust current draw to equal the circuit breaker rating.
3. Connect circuit breaker to tester for 10 minutes. If circuit breaker opens within the time specified, replace it.
4. Readjust current draw to equal twice the circuit breaker rating.
5. Connect circuit breaker to tester. The ammeter current reading should drop to zero within 30 seconds. If circuit breaker does not open within the time specified, replace it.

# 1989–90 ESCORT

## NON-INTERMITTENT SYSTEM WIPER MOTOR

### High Speed Test

When performing the following test, refer to wiring schematic **Fig. 1.**

1. Turn ignition switch to ON.
2. Turn wiper switch to HI.
3. Check voltage at four-way connector (blue/orange wire) terminal 56. If voltage is present proceed to step 5.
4. If voltage is not present proceed as follows:
   a. Check voltage at wiper switch (red wire) terminal 63. If voltage is present, replace wiper switch.
   b. If voltage is not present at terminal 63, check circuit back to source.
5. If voltage is present at terminal 56 and motor will not run, proceed as follows:
   a. Ground motor case to body.
   b. If motor runs, repair ground.
   c. If motor does not run, replace motor.

### Low Speed Test

When performing the following test, refer to wiring schematic **Fig. 1.**

1. Turn ignition switch to ON.
2. Turn wiper switch to LO.
3. Check voltage at four-way connector (white wire) terminal 58. If voltage is present proceed to step 5.
4. If voltage is not present proceed as follows:
   a. Check voltage at (red wire) terminal 63. If voltage is present, replace wiper switch.
   b. If voltage is not present at terminal 63, check circuit back to source.
5. If voltage is present at terminal 58 and motor will not run, proceed as follows:

*Continued on page 27-29*

| TEST STEP | | RESULT | ACTION TO TAKE |
|---|---|---|---|
| 4.0 | WIPERS WILL NOT PARK | | |
| 4.1 | CHECK WIPER MOTOR | | |
| | • Stop wipers with ignition key so that they are not in PARK position.<br>• Unplug wiper motor and connect jumpers to motor connector as shown.<br>WHITE; RED; BLACK; ALLIGATOR CLIPS<br>NOTE: FIRST CONNECT TO BATTERY POSITIVE<br>NOTE: GROUND WIPER MOTOR CASE<br>WIPER MOTOR CONNECTOR EXCORT/LYNX,EXP<br>CONNECTOR A; 58 W; GRD; 56 BL; WIPER MOTOR; CONNECT JUMPER TO GROUND THESE TWO TERMINALS; GRD; 28 BK; 63 R; CONNECT JUMPER WIRE ACROSS THESE TWO TERMINALS; CONNECTOR B<br>WIPER MOTOR CONNECTORS TEMPO/TOPAZ | Wipers park ▶ | CHECK for:<br>• Open connection<br>• Malfunctioning governor<br>• Open wire Circuit 58 (W) or 28 (BK/PK)<br>SERVICE or REPLACE as required. |
| | | Wipers do not park ▶ | REPLACE wiper motor. |
| 5.0 | WIPERS DO NOT RUN WHEN WASHER SWITCH IS PULLED — WASHERS WORN (INTERVAL WIPERS ONLY) | | |
| 5.1 | CHECK OPERATION | | |
| | • Do wipers work OK on INT, LOW and HI? | YES ▶ | REPLACE governor. |
| | | NO ▶ | CHECK for:<br>• Malfunctioning switch<br>• Malfunctioning governor<br>SERVICE or REPLACE as required. |
| 6.0 | WASHERS INOPERATIVE | | |
| 6.1 | CHECK WIPER OPERATION | | |
| | • Check operation of wipers.<br>• Do wipers work OK? | YES ▶ | CHECK for:<br>• Low washer fluid<br>• Split, loose, pinched or kinked washer hose<br>• Malfunctioning washer pump motor<br>• Malfunctioning switch<br>• Open Circuit 941 (BK/W)<br>• Open connector<br>SERVICE or REPLACE as necessary. |
| | | NO ▶ | CHECK for:<br>• Open circuit breaker in fuse panel<br>• Open wire, Circuit 63 (R)<br>SERVICE or REPLACE as necessary. |

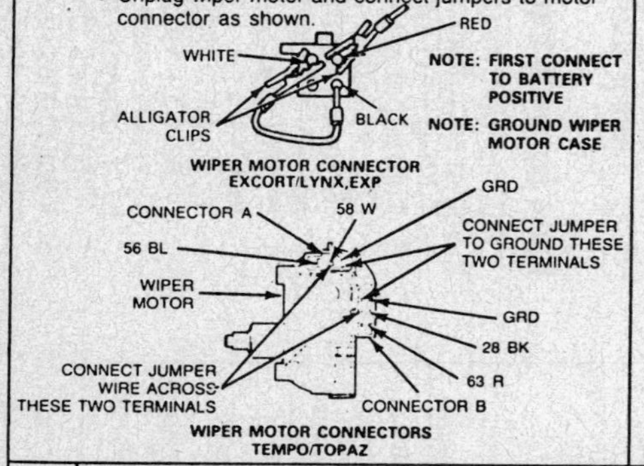

**Fig. 4 Wiper system diagnosis (Part 3 of 3). 1989 Escort, Tempo & Topaz**

| TEST STEP | | RESULT | ACTION TO TAKE |
|---|---|---|---|
| 1.0 | WIPERS INOPERATIVE — ALL CONTROL SWITCH POSITIONS | | |
| 1.1 | CHECK FOR BATTERY VOLTAGE | | |
| | • Unplug wiper motor.<br>• Set control switch to HIGH.<br>• Check for battery voltage at Circuits No. 63 and No. 56.<br>63R; 56 DB/O; ⊗ MALE TERMINAL<br>HARNESS CONNECTOR ESCORT<br>PARK SWITCH CONNECTOR 14489; MOTOR CONNECTOR 14489; 63R; GROUND TERMINALS; CONNECTOR-B; 56 DB/O; CONNECTOR-A<br>HARNESS CONNECTORS TEMPO/TOPAZ | Voltage both circuits ▶ | GO to 1.2. |
| | | Voltage OK Circuit 63, NOT OK Circuit 56 ▶ | CHECK for:<br>• Malfunctioning governor<br>• Malfunctioning switch<br>• Open connector<br>• Open wire, Circuit 56 (DB/O)<br>SERVICE as necessary. |
| | | Voltage ▶ | CHECK for:<br>• Open circuit breaker in fuse panel<br>• Open connector<br>• Open wire Circuit 63 (R)<br>SERVICE as necessary. |
| 1.2 | PERFORM WIPER MOTOR CURRENT DRAW TEST | | |
| | • Perform wiper motor current draw test as described in this Section. | Test (not OK) ▶ | SERVICE as necessary. |
| | | Test (OK) ▶ | CHECK linkage for binding. SERVICE as necessary. |

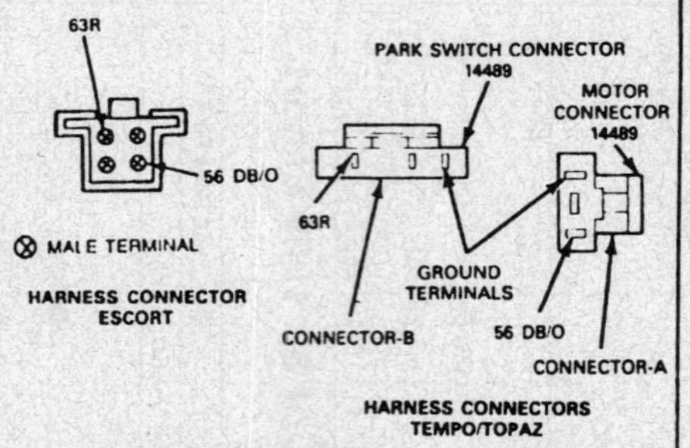

**Fig. 5 Wiper system diagnosis (Part 1 of 3). 1990 Escort & 1990—91 Tempo & Topaz**

| | TEST STEP | RESULT ▶ | ACTION TO TAKE |
|---|---|---|---|
| 2.0 | WIPERS INOPERATIVE OR ERRATIC, ON "INT" OR "LOW" ONLY — HI SPEED WORKS | | |
| 2.1 | CHECK WIPER OPERATION | | |
| | • Run wipers on HIGH.<br>• Do wipers hesitate when they pass through the PARK position? | Yes ▶<br>No ▶ | GO to **2.2**.<br>GO to **2.3**. |
| 2.2 | CHECK GOVERNOR | | |
| | • Check governor ground pigtail (under mounting screw). | OK ▶ | Malfunctioning governor — SERVICE as required. |
| | | ~~OK~~ ▶ | TIGHTEN governor mounting screws to improve ground. |
| 2.3 | CHECK CIRCUIT 58 FOR BATTERY VOLTAGE | | |
| | • Unplug wiper motor.<br>• Set wiper switch on LOW.<br>• Check Circuit 58 for battery voltage. | Voltage OK ▶ | CHECK for malfunctioning wiper motor. PERFORM low speed current draw test. GO to **4.1**. SERVICE as required. |
| | 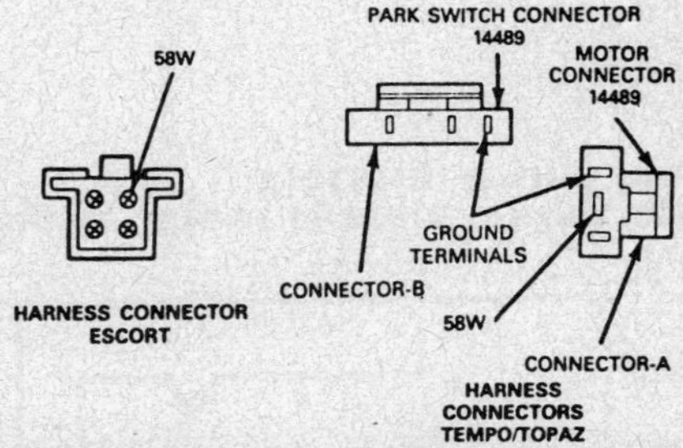 58W<br>HARNESS CONNECTOR ESCORT<br>PARK SWITCH CONNECTOR 14489<br>MOTOR CONNECTOR 14489<br>GROUND TERMINALS<br>CONNECTOR-B<br>58W<br>CONNECTOR-A<br>HARNESS CONNECTORS TEMPO/TOPAZ | Voltage ~~OK~~ ▶ | CHECK for:<br>• Open connector<br>• Malfunctioning switch<br>• Malfunctioning governor<br>• Open wire Circuit 58 (W)<br>SERVICE or REPLACE as necessary. |
| 3.0 | WIPERS RUN WITH CONTROL SWITCH TURNED OFF | | |
| 3.1 | WIPER PARK TEST | | |
| | • Perform Wiper Park Test 4.1. | Wipers fail to park ▶<br>Wipers park ▶ | REPLACE wiper motor<br>GO to **3.2**. |
| 3.2 | CHECK WIPER SWITCH | | |
| | • Unplug wiper control switch.<br>• Turn ignition switch to RUN. | Wipers stop ▶ | REPLACE wiper control switch. |
| | | Wipers continue to run ▶ | CHECK for:<br>• Malfunctioning governor<br>SERVICE or REPLACE as required. |

**Fig. 5 Wiper system diagnosis (Part 2 of 3). 1990 Escort & 1990—91 Tempo & Topaz**

| | TEST STEP | RESULT ▶ | ACTION TO TAKE |
|---|---|---|---|
| 4.0 | WIPERS WILL NOT PARK | | |
| 4.1 | CHECK WIPER MOTOR | | |
| | • Stop wipers with ignition switch so that they are not in PARK position.<br>• Unplug wiper motor and connect jumpers to motor connector as shown. | Wipers park ▶ | CHECK for:<br>• Open connection<br>• Malfunctioning governor<br>• Open wire Circuit 58 (W) or 28 (BK/PK)<br>SERVICE or REPLACE as required. |
| | 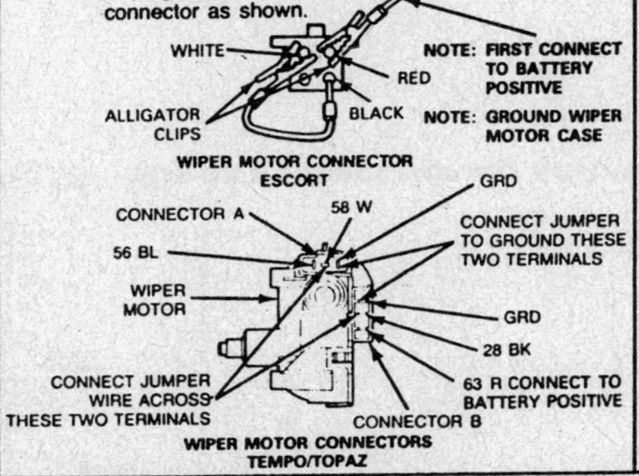 WHITE<br>RED<br>BLACK<br>ALLIGATOR CLIPS<br>NOTE: FIRST CONNECT TO BATTERY POSITIVE<br>NOTE: GROUND WIPER MOTOR CASE<br>WIPER MOTOR CONNECTOR ESCORT<br>CONNECTOR A<br>58 W<br>GRD<br>56 BL<br>CONNECT JUMPER TO GROUND THESE TWO TERMINALS<br>WIPER MOTOR<br>GRD<br>28 BK<br>CONNECT JUMPER WIRE ACROSS THESE TWO TERMINALS<br>63 R CONNECT TO BATTERY POSITIVE<br>CONNECTOR B<br>WIPER MOTOR CONNECTORS TEMPO/TOPAZ | Wipers do not park ▶ | REPLACE wiper motor. |
| 5.0 | WIPERS DO NOT RUN WHEN WASHER SWITCH IS PULLED — WASHERS WORN (INTERVAL WIPERS ONLY) | | |
| 5.1 | CHECK OPERATION | | |
| | • Do wipers work OK on INT, LOW and HIGH? | Yes ▶<br>No ▶ | REPLACE governor.<br>CHECK for:<br>• Malfunctioning switch<br>• Malfunctioning governor<br>SERVICE or REPLACE as required. |
| 6.0 | WASHERS INOPERATIVE | | |
| 6.1 | CHECK WIPER OPERATION | | |
| | • Check operation of wipers.<br>• Do wipers work OK? | Yes ▶ | CHECK for:<br>• Low washer fluid<br>• Split, loose, pinched or kinked washer hose<br>• Malfunctioning washer pump motor<br>• Malfunctioning switch<br>• Open Circuit 941 (BK/W)<br>• Open connector<br>SERVICE or REPLACE as necessary. |
| | | No ▶ | CHECK for:<br>• Open circuit breaker in fuse panel<br>• Open wire, Circuit 63 (R)<br>SERVICE or REPLACE as necessary. |

**Fig. 5 Wiper system diagnosis (Part 3 of 3). 1990 Escort & 1990–91 Tempo & Topaz**

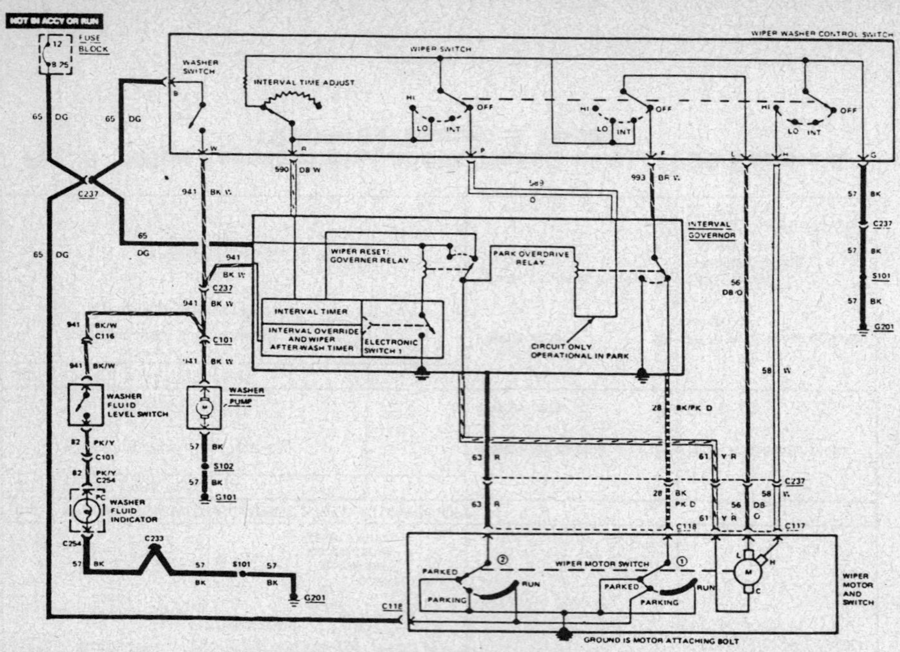

Fig. 6 Wiper system wiring schematic (Intermittent). Crown Victoria, Grand Marquis & Town Car

| CONDITION | POSSIBLE SOURCE | ACTION |
| --- | --- | --- |
| • Windshield wipers do not operate | • Open circuit breaker. | • Replace CB. If it goes again, check for short circuit. |
| | • Poor ground at wiper motor. | • Jumper motor case to car body. If motor operates, service ground. |
| | • Switch. | • Perform switch test. Service as required. |
| | • Bent or damaged linkage. | • Service or replace. |
| • Wipers will not park in off or will not pause in interval mode " | • Worn or damaged motor, switch, wiring or interval governor assembly. | • Perform Parking Test. |
| • In interval mode no wipe(s) after wash | • Circuit 941 open. | • Service as required. |
| | • Interval governor assembly inoperative. | • Replace governor. |
| • Poor ground to interval governor assembly | • Motor. | • Perform motor test. Service as required. |
| | • Open in wiring. | • Service as required. |
| | • Inoperative governor on intermittent wiper system. | • Replace governor. |

Fig. 7 Wiper system diagnosis. Crown Victoria, Grand Marquis & Town Car

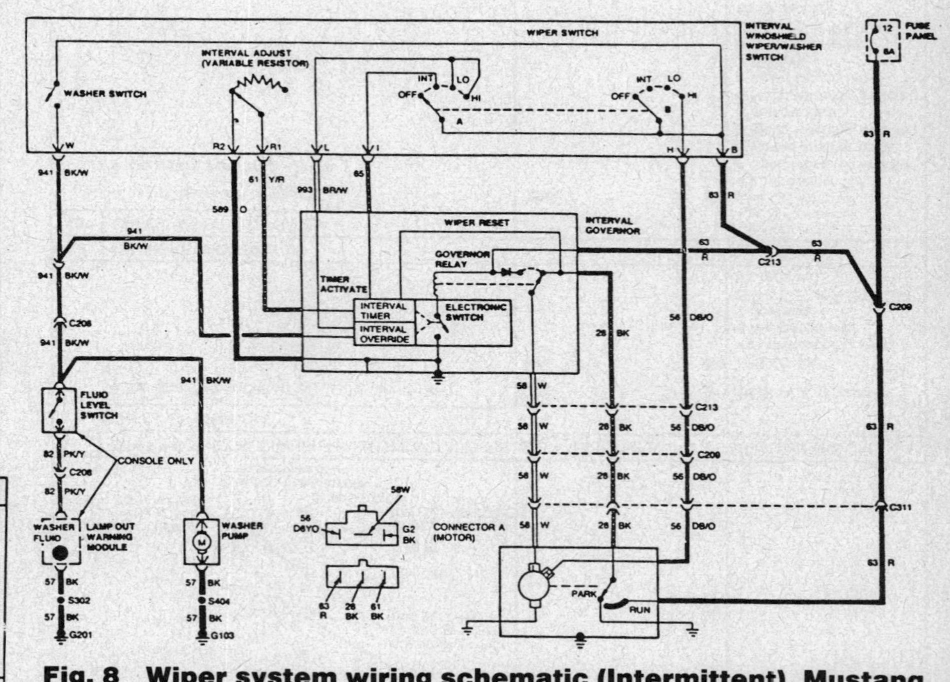


Fig. 8 Wiper system wiring schematic (Intermittent). Mustang

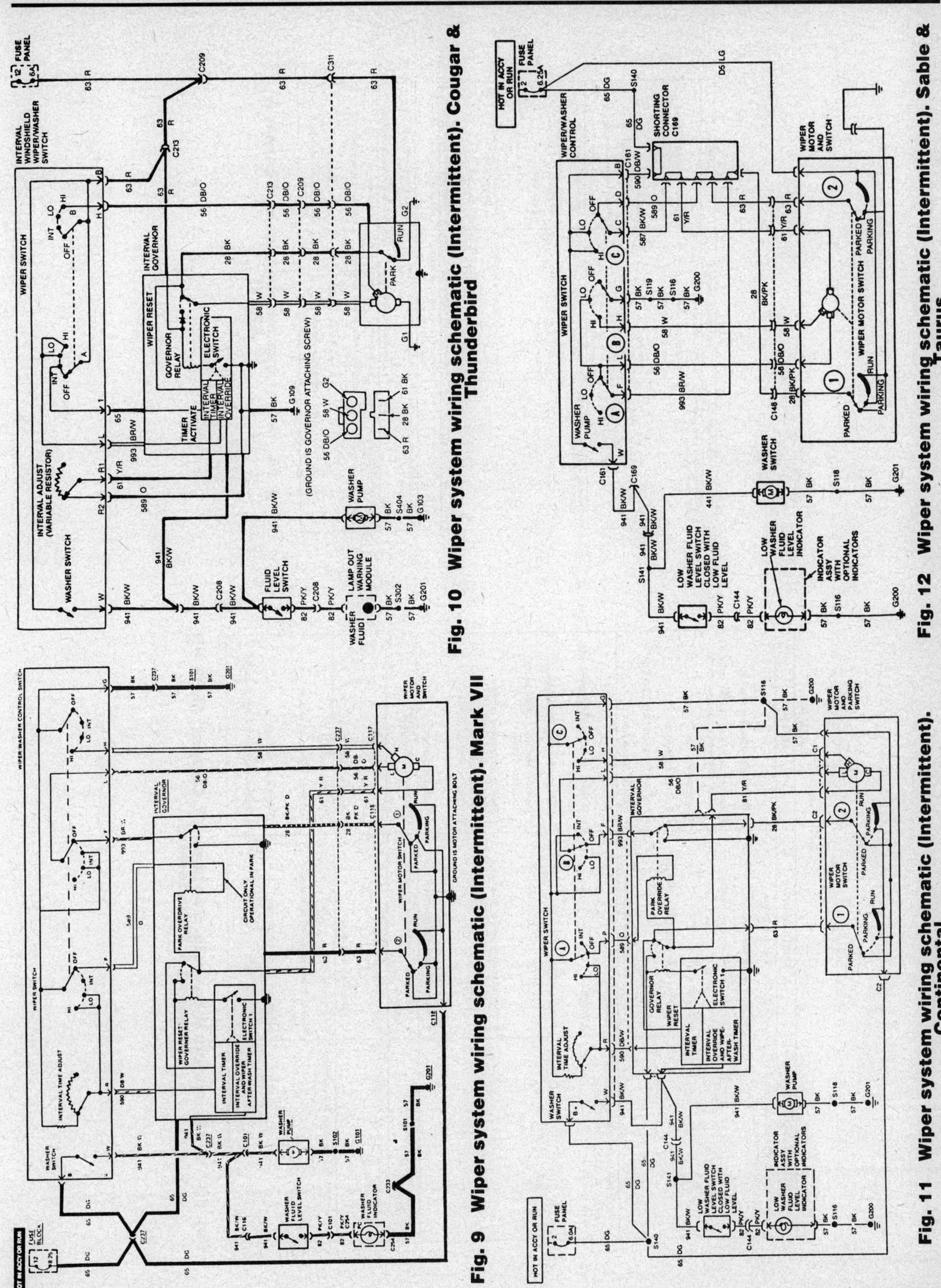

Fig. 9 Wiper system wiring schematic (Intermittent). Mark VII

Fig. 10 Wiper system wiring schematic (Intermittent). Cougar & Thunderbird

Fig. 11 Wiper system wiring schematic (Intermittent). Continental

Fig. 12 Wiper system wiring schematic (Intermittent). Sable & Taurus

| CONDITION (IGNITION ON) | POSSIBLE SOURCE | ACTION |
|---|---|---|
| • Windshield wipers inoperative in ALL switch positions. | NOTE: Check in sequence. | |
| | • Open circuit breaker. | • Check and replace if required. |
| | • Poor ground at wiper motor. | • Jumper motor case to car body. If motor now works service ground. |
| | • Switch. | • Test switch. |
| | • Bent or damaged motor linkage. | • Service as required. |
| | • Motor. | • Perform motor current draw test. |
| | • Open wire or connector. | • Service as required. |
| • Windshield wipers inoperative or erratic in LOW or INTERVAL (HIGH ok). | • Switch. | • Test switch. |
| | • Motor. | • Perform motor current draw test for low speed. |
| | • Open wiring. | • Check circuit No. 58 (White). |
| | | • Check circuit No. 61 (yellow-red) Continental only. |
| | • Poor interval governor ground. | • Service as required (tighten attaching screws). |
| | | • Check circuit No. 57 (BL) Continental only. |
| | • Inoperative interval governor. | • Replace governor. |
| • Wipers won't stop in OFF or INTERVAL | • Motor, switch, wiring or governor assembly. | • Perform parking test. |
| • Interval systems only: No wipe(s) after wash. | • Circuit No. 941 (BK/W) open. | • Service as required. |
| | • Governor inoperative. | • Replace governor. |
| Windshield washer does not operate. | • Low fluid level. | • Fill as required. |
| | • Split, loose, pinched or kinked hose. | • Inspect, service as required. |
| | • Open in wiring or switch. | • Service as required. |
| | • Washer Motor. | • Replace motor, seal and impeller assembly. |

**Fig. 13 Wiper system diagnosis. Continental, Cougar, Mark VII, Mustang & Thunderbird**

| CONDITION (IGNITION ON) | POSSIBLE SOURCE | ACTION |
|---|---|---|
| • Windshield wipers inoperative in ALL switch positions. | NOTE: Check in sequence. | |
| | • Open circuit breaker. | • Check and replace if required. |
| | • Poor ground at wiper motor. | • Jumper motor case to car body. If motor now, works service ground. |
| | • Switch. | • Test switch. |
| | • Bent or damaged motor linkage. | • Service as required. |
| | • Motor. | • Perform motor current draw test. |
| | • Open wire or connector. | • Service as required. |
| • Windshield wipers inoperative or erratic in LOW or INTERVAL (HIGH ok). | • Switch. | • Test switch. |
| | • Motor. | • Perform motor current draw test for low speed. |
| | • Open wiring. | • Check circuit |
| | • Poor interval wiper relay ground. | • Service as required (tighten attaching screws). |
| | | • Check circuit |
| | • Inoperative interval wiper. | • Replace interval wiper relay. |
| • Wipers won't stop in OFF or INTERVAL | • Motor, switch, wiring or interval wiper assembly. | • Perform parking test |
| • Interval systems only. No wipe(s) after wash. | • Circuit No. 941 (BK W) open | • Service as required |
| | • Interval wiper inoperative. | • Replace interval wiper relay. |
| Windshield washer does not operate | • Low fluid level | • Fill as required |
| | • Split, loose, pinched or kinked hose. | • Inspect, service as recuired. |
| | • Open in wiring or switch | • Service as required |
| | • Washer pump. | • Replace seal and pump assembly. |

**Fig. 14 Wiper system diagnosis. Scorpio & XR4TI**

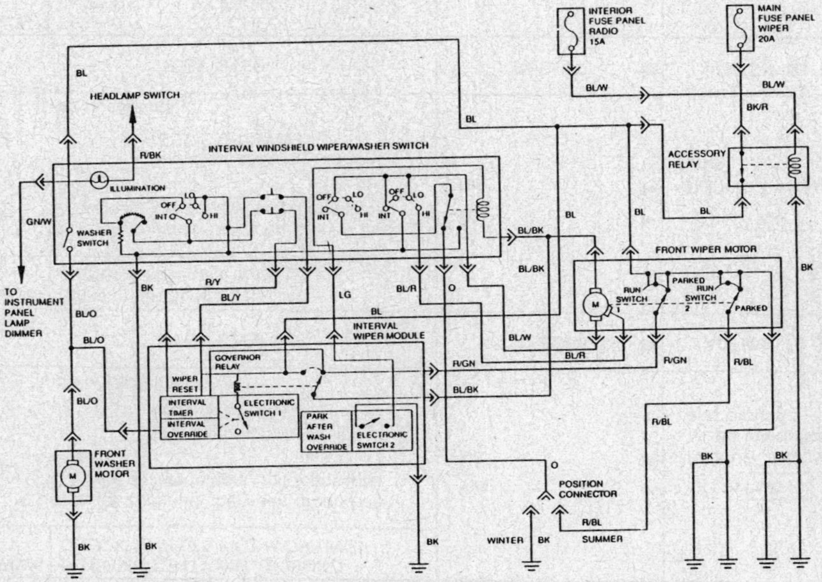

Fig. 15 Wiper system wiring schematic. Probe

| TEST STEP | RESULT ► | ACTION TO TAKE |
|---|---|---|
| **WW1** WINDSHIELD WIPER SYSTEM CHECK | | |
| **Schematics and wiring diagrams are located in the ELECTRICAL/VACUUM TROUBLE-SHOOTING MANUAL**<br>• Turn ignition key to "ON" position.<br>• Check the following wiper system operations:<br>– Low speed<br>– High speed<br>– Intermittent<br>– Mist<br>– Park | Wipers not working ►<br>Low not working ►<br>High not working ►<br>Intermittent not working ►<br>Mist not working ►<br>Park not working ► | GO to WW2 .<br>GO to WW9 .<br>GO to WW14 .<br>GO to WW16 .<br>GO to WW18 .<br>GO to WW20 . |

| TEST STEP | RESULT ► | ACTION TO TAKE |
|---|---|---|
| **WW2** WIPER FUSE CHECK (WIPERS NOT WORKING) | | |
| • Check WIPER fuse.<br>• Is fuse OK? | Yes ►<br>No ► | GO to WW3 .<br>REPLACE fuse. (Read note) |
| NOTE: If fuse blows again check for shorts to ground in "BL" wires at wiper/washer switch (connector C271), intermittent unit (connector C237), and front wiper motor (connector C900). Repair "BL" wires as needed. | | |

| TEST STEP | RESULT ► | ACTION TO TAKE |
|---|---|---|
| **WW3** INTERMITTENT SUPPLY CHECK (WIPERS NOT WORKING) | | |
| • Check for 12 volts (±1 volt) on "BL" wire at intermittent unit (connector C237).<br>• Is there 12 volts? | Yes ►<br>No ► | GO to WW4 .<br>REPAIR "BL" wire between fuse panel and intermittent unit. |

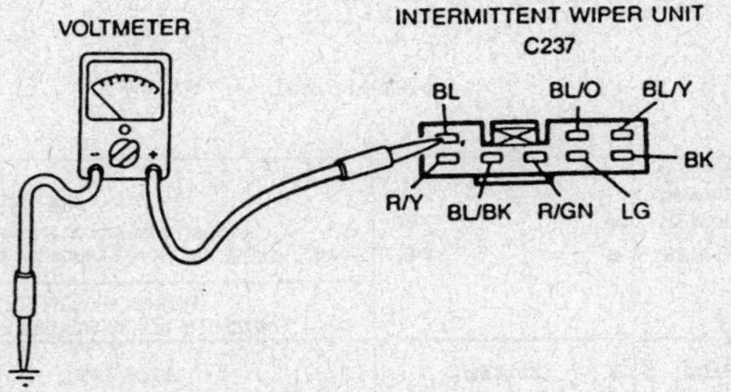

Fig. 16 Wiper system diagnosis & testing (Part 1 of 24). Probe

| TEST STEP | RESULT ► | ACTION TO TAKE |
|---|---|---|
| **WW4** WIPER MOTOR SUPPLY CHECK (WIPERS NOT WORKING) | | |
| • Check for 12 volts (±1 volt) on "BL/BK" wire at intermittent unit (connector C237). See illustration in TEST STEP WW3 • Is there 12 volts? | Yes ►<br>No ► | GO to WW8 .<br>GO to WW5 . |

| TEST STEP | RESULT ► | ACTION TO TAKE |
|---|---|---|
| **WW5** INTERMITTENT UNIT GROUND CHECK (WIPERS NOT WORKING) | | |
| • Check for continuity between ground and "BK" wire at intermittent unit (connector C237). See illustration in TEST STEP WW3 • Is there continuity? | Yes ►<br>No ► | GO to WW6 .<br>REPAIR "BK" wire between intermittent unit and ground. |

| TEST STEP | RESULT ► | ACTION TO TAKE |
|---|---|---|
| **WW6** SIGNAL GROUND CHECK (WIPERS NOT WORKING) | | |
| • Check for continuity between ground and "LG" wire at intermittent unit (connector C237). See illustration in TEST STEP WW3 • Is there continuity? | Yes ►<br>No ► | GO to WW7 .<br>REPLACE intermittent unit. |

| TEST STEP | RESULT ► | ACTION TO TAKE |
|---|---|---|
| **WW7** SIGNAL GROUND CHECK (WIPERS NOT WORKING) | | |
| • Disconnect wiper/washer switch (connector C271). • Check for continuity between ground and "LG" wire at intermittent unit (connector C237). See illustration in TEST STEP WW3 • Is there continuity? | Yes ►<br>No ► | REPAIR "LG" wire between wiper/washer switch and intermittent unit.<br>REPLACE wiper/washer switch. |

Fig. 16 Wiper system diagnosis & testing (Part 2 of 24). Probe

| TEST STEP | RESULT ► | ACTION TO TAKE |
|---|---|---|
| **WW8** WIPER MOTOR SUPPLY CHECK (WIPERS NOT WORKING) | | |
| • Check for 12 volts (± volt) on "BL/BK" wire at wiper motor (connector C900). • Is there 12 volts? | Yes ►<br>No ► | REPLACE wiper motor.<br>REPAIR "BL/BK" wire between intermittent unit and wiper motor. |



Fig. 16 Wiper system diagnosis & testing (Part 3 of 24). Probe

| TEST STEP | RESULT ► | ACTION TO TAKE |
|---|---|---|
| **WW9** WIPER MOTOR CHECK (LOW NOT WORKING) | | |
| • Turn ignition key to "OFF" position. • Disconnect wiper motor connectors C900 and C901. • Apply 12 volts (±1 volt) and ground to wiper motor as shown. • Does wiper motor work? | Yes ►<br>No ► | GO to WW10 .<br>REPLACE wiper motor. |



Fig. 16 Wiper system diagnosis & testing (Part 4 of 24). Probe

| TEST STEP | RESULT ► | ACTION TO TAKE |
|---|---|---|
| WW10 LOW SIGNAL CHECK (LOW NOT WORKING) | | |
| • Place wiper switch in "LO" position.<br>• Check for continuity between ground and "BL/W" wire at wiper/washer switch (connector C271).<br>• Is there continuity? | Yes ►<br>No ► | GO to WW11 .<br>REPLACE wiper/washer switch. |

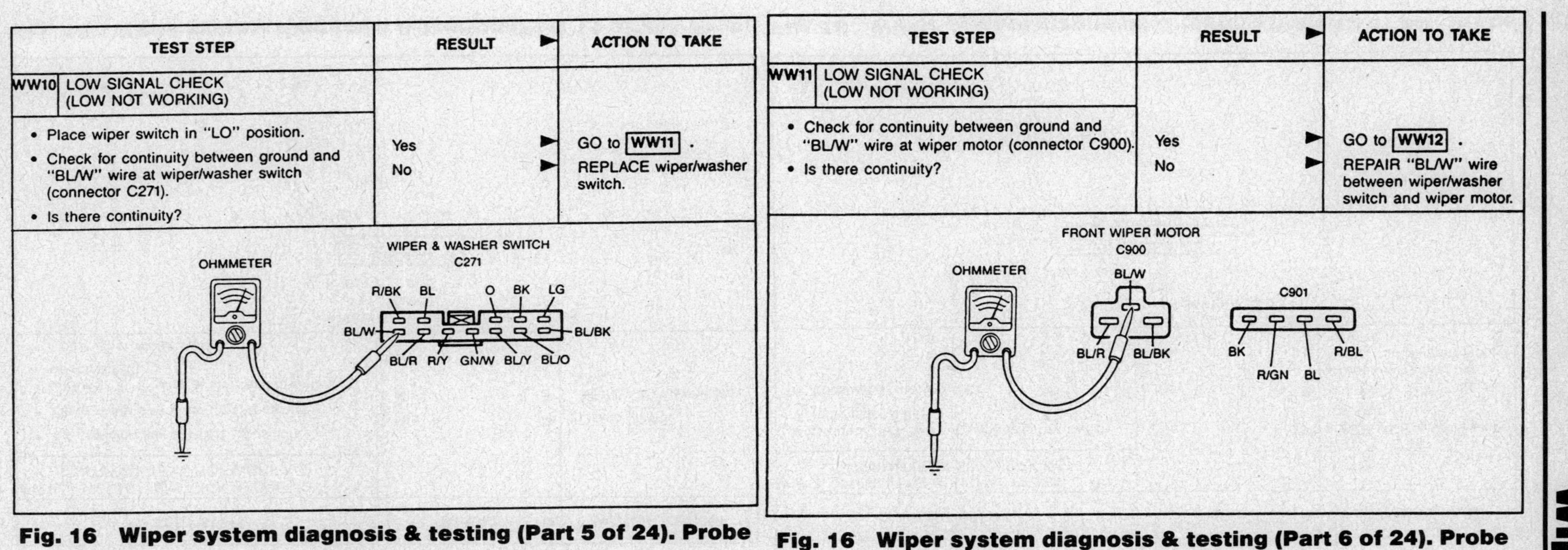


**Fig. 16 Wiper system diagnosis & testing (Part 5 of 24). Probe**

| TEST STEP | RESULT ► | ACTION TO TAKE |
|---|---|---|
| WW11 LOW SIGNAL CHECK (LOW NOT WORKING) | | |
| • Check for continuity between ground and "BL/W" wire at wiper motor (connector C900).<br>• Is there continuity? | Yes ►<br>No ► | GO to WW12 .<br>REPAIR "BL/W" wire between wiper/washer switch and wiper motor. |

**Fig. 16 Wiper system diagnosis & testing (Part 6 of 24). Probe**

| TEST STEP | RESULT ► | ACTION TO TAKE |
|---|---|---|
| WW12 INTERMITTENT SIGNAL CHECK (LOW NOT WORKING) | | |
| • Check for continuity between ground and "R/Y" wire at wiper/washer switch (connector C271).<br>See illustration in TEST STEP WW10<br>• Is there continuity? | Yes ►<br>No ► | GO to WW13 .<br>REPLACE wiper/washer switch. |

**Fig. 16 Wiper system diagnosis & testing (Part 7 of 24). Probe**

| TEST STEP | RESULT ► | ACTION TO TAKE |
|---|---|---|
| WW13 INTERMITTENT SIGNAL CHECK (LOW NOT WORKING) | | |
| • Check for continuity between ground and "R/Y" wire at intermittent unit (connector C237).<br>• Is there continuity? | Yes ►<br>No ► | REPLACE intermittent unit.<br>REPAIR "R/Y" wire between wiper/washer switch and intermittent unit. |

OHMMETER
INTERMITTENT WIPER UNIT
C237
BL BL/O BL/Y
R/Y BK
BL/BK R/GN LG

**Fig. 16 Wiper system diagnosis & testing (Part 8 of 24). Probe**

| TEST STEP | RESULT ► | ACTION TO TAKE |
|---|---|---|
| **WW14** WIPER MOTOR CHECK (HIGH NOT WORKING) | | |
| • Turn ignition key to "OFF" position.<br>• Disconnect wiper motor connectors C900 and C901.<br>• Apply 12 volts (±1 volt) and ground to wiper motor as shown.<br>• Does wiper motor work? | Yes ►<br>No ► | GO to WW15 .<br>REPLACE wiper motor. |

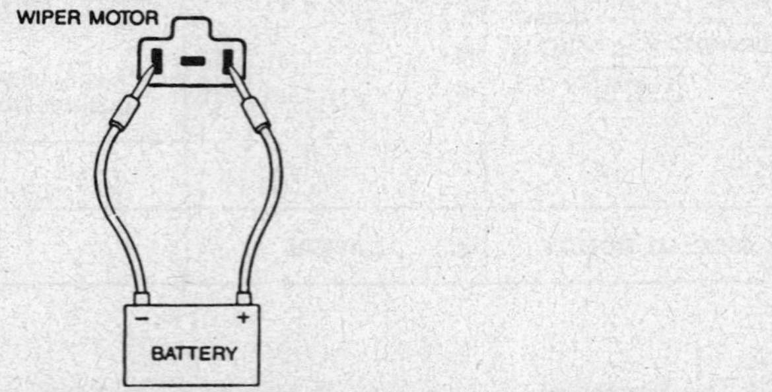

**Fig. 16 Wiper system diagnosis & testing (Part 9 of 24). Probe**

| TEST STEP | RESULT ► | ACTION TO TAKE |
|---|---|---|
| **WW15** HIGH SIGNAL CHECK (HIGH NOT WORKING) | | |
| • Place wiper switch in "HI" position.<br>• Check for continuity between ground and "BL/R" wire at wiper/washer switch (connector C271).<br>• Is there continuity? | Yes ►<br>No ► | REPAIR "BL/R" wire between wiper/washer switch and wiper motor.<br>REPLACE wiper/washer switch. |

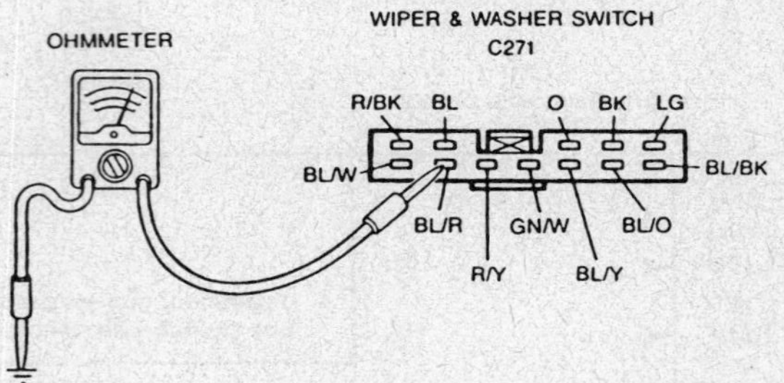

**Fig. 16 Wiper system diagnosis & testing (Part 10 of 24). Probe**

| TEST STEP | RESULT ► | ACTION TO TAKE |
|---|---|---|
| **WW16** INTERMITTENT SIGNAL CHECK (INTERMITTENT NOT WORKING) | | |
| • Turn ignition key to "OFF" position.<br>• Place wiper switch in "INT" position.<br>• Ground "R/Y" wire at intermittent unit (connector C237).<br>• Does wiper motor work? | Yes ►<br>No ► | GO to WW17 .<br>REPLACE intermittent unit. |

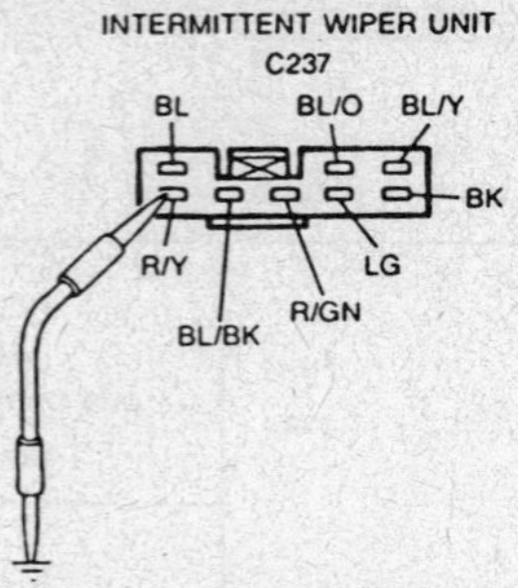

**Fig. 16 Wiper system diagnosis & testing (Part 11 of 24). Probe**

| TEST STEP | RESULT ► | ACTION TO TAKE |
|---|---|---|
| **WW17** INTERMITTENT SIGNAL CHECK (INTERMITTENT NOT WORKING) | | |
| • Ground "R/Y" wire at wiper/washer switch (connector C271).<br>• Does wiper motor work? | Yes ►<br>No ► | REPLACE wiper/washer switch.<br>REPAIR "R/Y" wire between wiper/washer switch and intermittent unit. |

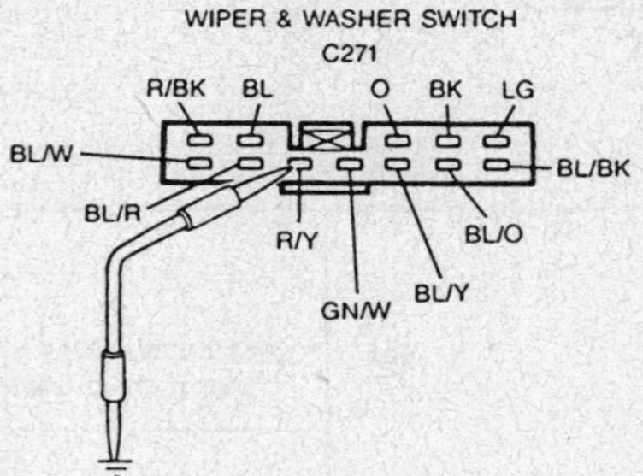

**Fig. 16 Wiper system diagnosis & testing (Part 12 of 24). Probe**

| TEST STEP | RESULT ► | ACTION TO TAKE |
|---|---|---|
| **WW18** MIST SIGNAL CHECK (MIST NOT WORKING) | | |
| • Keep ignition key in "ON" position.<br>• Ground "BL/Y" wire at intermittent unit (connector C237).<br>• Does MIST work? | Yes ►<br>No ► | GO to WW19.<br>REPLACE intermittent unit. |

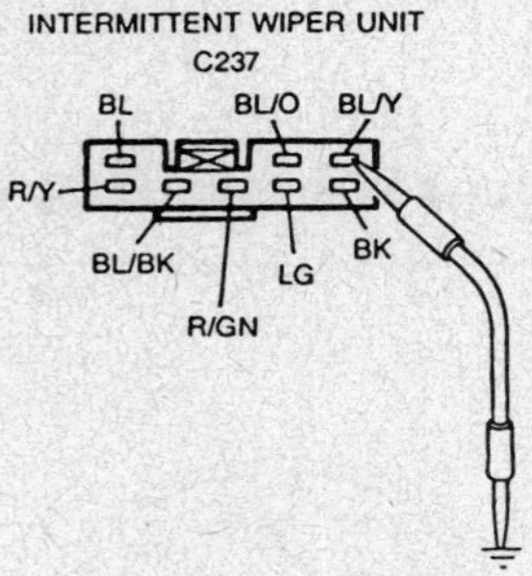

INTERMITTENT WIPER UNIT
C237
BL BL/O BL/Y R/Y BL/BK LG BK R/GN

**Fig. 16 Wiper system diagnosis & testing (Part 13 of 24). Probe**

| TEST STEP | RESULT ► | ACTION TO TAKE |
|---|---|---|
| **WW19** MIST SIGNAL CHECK (MIST NOT WORKING) | | |
| • Ground "BL/Y" wire at wiper/washer switch (connector C271).<br>• Does MIST work? | Yes ►<br>No ► | REPLACE wiper/washer switch.<br>REPAIR "BL/Y" wire between wiper/washer switch and intermittent unit. |

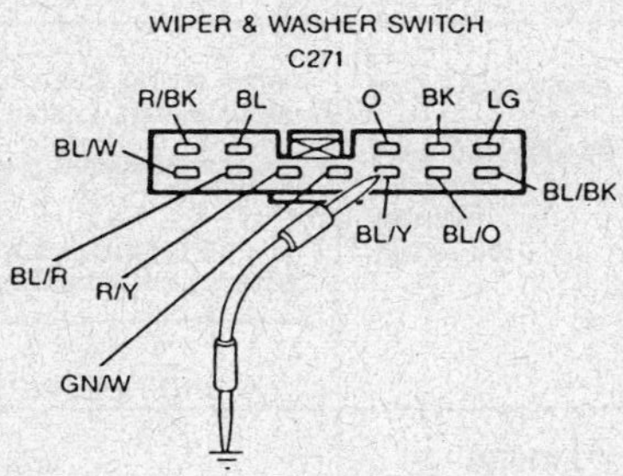

WIPER & WASHER SWITCH
C271
R/BK BL O BK LG BL/W BL/BK BL/Y BL/O BL/R R/Y GN/W

**Fig. 16 Wiper system diagnosis & testing (Part 14 of 24). Probe**

| TEST STEP | RESULT ► | ACTION TO TAKE |
|---|---|---|
| **WW20** PARK SWITCH CHECK (PARK NOT WORKING) | | |
| • Turn ignition switch to "OFF" position.<br>• Disconnect the larger of the wiper motor connectors C901.<br>• Apply 12 volts (±1 volt) to the "R/GN" wire.<br>• Does wiper park? | Yes ►<br>No ► | GO to WW24.<br>GO to WW21. |

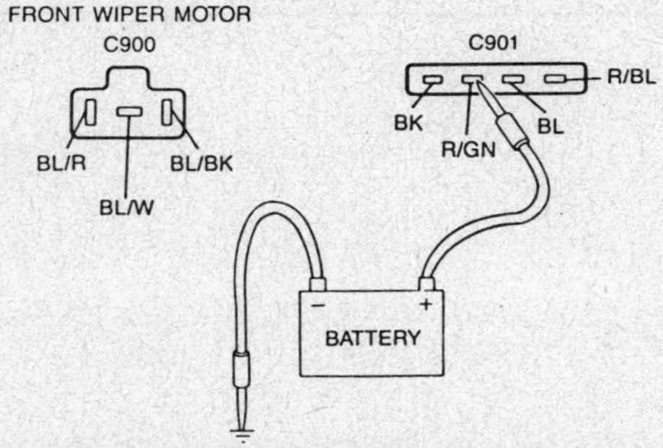

FRONT WIPER MOTOR
C900
BL/R BL/BK BL/W
C901
R/BL BK R/GN BL
BATTERY

**Fig. 16 Wiper system diagnosis & testing (Part 15 of 24). Probe**

| TEST STEP | RESULT ► | ACTION TO TAKE |
|---|---|---|
| **WW21** PARK SIGNAL CHECK (PARK NOT WORKING) | | |
| • Apply 12 volts (±1 volt) to "R/GN" wire at intermittent unit (connector C237).<br>• Does wiper park? | Yes ►<br>No ► | REPAIR "R/GN" wire between intermittent unit and wiper motor.<br>GO to WW22. |

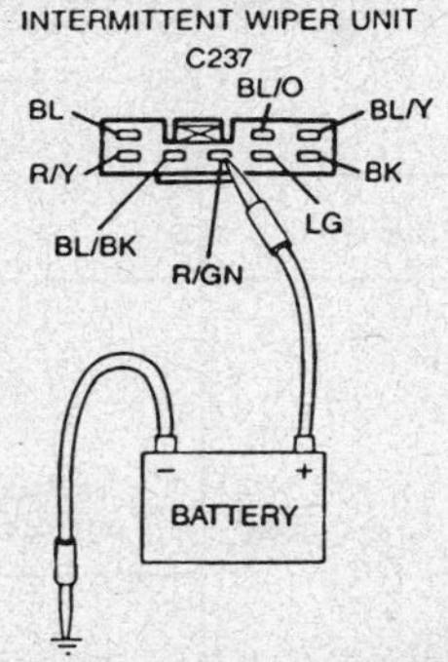

INTERMITTENT WIPER UNIT
C237
BL/O BL BL/Y R/Y BK LG BL/BK R/GN
BATTERY

**Fig. 16 Wiper system diagnosis & testing (Part 16 of 24). Probe**

| TEST STEP | RESULT ► | ACTION TO TAKE |
|---|---|---|
| **WW22** OFF SIGNAL CHECK (PARK NOT WORKING) | | |
| • Check for continuity between ground and "LG" wire at wiper/washer switch (connector C271).<br>• Is there continuity? | Yes ►<br>No ► | GO to WW23 .<br>REPLACE wiper/washer switch. |

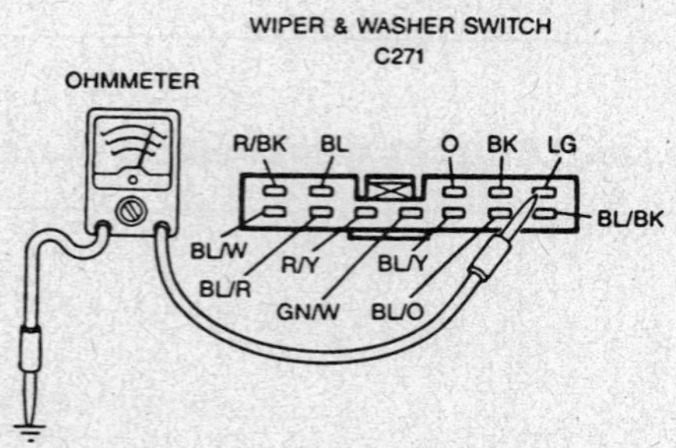

**Fig. 16 Wiper system diagnosis & testing (Part 17 of 24). Probe**

| TEST STEP | RESULT ► | ACTION TO TAKE |
|---|---|---|
| **WW23** OFF SIGNAL CHECK (PARK NOT WORKING) | | |
| • Check for continuity between ground and "LG" wire at intermittent unit (connector C237).<br>See illustration in TEST STEP WW21<br>• Is there continuity? | Yes ►<br>No ► | REPLACE intermittent unit.<br>REPAIR "LG" wire between intermittent unit and wiper/washer switch. |

| TEST STEP | RESULT ► | ACTION TO TAKE |
|---|---|---|
| **WW24** PARK SWITCH SUPPLY CHECK (PARK NOT WORKING) | | |
| • Turn ignition key to "ON" position.<br>• Check for 12 volts (±1 volt) on "BL" wire at wiper motor (connector C901).<br>See illustration in TEST STEP WW20<br>• Is there 12 volts? | Yes ►<br>No ► | GO to WW25 .<br>REPAIR "BL" wire between fuse panel and wiper motor. |

| TEST STEP | RESULT ► | ACTION TO TAKE |
|---|---|---|
| **WW25** PARK SWITCH GROUND CHECK (PARK NOT WORKING) | | |
| • Check for continuity between ground and "BK" wire at wiper motor (connector C901).<br>See illustration in TEST STEP WW20<br>• Is there continuity? | Yes ►<br>No ► | REPLACE wiper motor.<br>REPAIR "BK" wire between wiper motor and ground. |

| TEST STEP | RESULT ► | ACTION TO TAKE |
|---|---|---|
| **WW26** LIFTGATE WIPER FUNCTION CHECK | | |
| **Schematics and wiring diagrams are located in the ELECTRICAL/VACUUM TROUBLE-SHOOTING MANUAL**<br>• Turn ignition key to "ON" position.<br>• Check for proper operation of liftgate wiper by engaging and disengaging liftgate wiper switch. | Wiper not working ►<br>Park not working ►<br>Wiper won't stop ► | GO to WW27 .<br>GO to WW32 .<br>GO to WW33 . |

| TEST STEP | RESULT ► | ACTION TO TAKE |
|---|---|---|
| **WW27** LIFTGATE WIPER FUSE CHECK (WIPER NOT WORKING) | | |
| • Check liftgate wiper (rear wiper) fuse.<br>• Is fuse OK? | Yes ►<br>No ► | GO to WW28 .<br>REPLACE fuse. (Read note) |
| NOTE: If fuse blows again, check for shorts to ground in "BL/Y" wires at liftgate wiper motor (connector C402) and liftgate washer motor (connector C401). Repair "BL/Y" wires as needed. | | |

**Fig. 16 Wiper system diagnosis & testing (Part 18 of 24). Probe**

| TEST STEP | RESULT ► | ACTION TO TAKE |
|---|---|---|
| **WW28** LIFTGATE WIPER MOTOR CHECK (WIPER NOT WORKING) | | |
| • Disconnect liftgate wiper motor (connector C402).<br>• Apply 12 volts (±1 volt) and ground directly to motor as shown.<br>• Does motor operate properly? | Yes ►<br>No ► | GO to **WW29** .<br>REPLACE liftgate wiper motor. |

REAR WIPER MOTOR
B A
100°
BATTERY

**Fig. 16 Wiper system diagnosis & testing (Part 19 of 24). Probe**

| TEST STEP | RESULT ► | ACTION TO TAKE |
|---|---|---|
| **WW29** LIFTGATE WASHER CHECK (WIPER NOT WORKING) | | |
| • Turn on liftgate washer.<br>• Does washer operate properly? | Yes ►<br>No ► | GO to **WW30** .<br>REPAIR "BK" wire between liftgate wiper/washer switch and ground. |

**Fig. 16 Wiper system diagnosis & testing (Part 20 of 24). Probe**

| TEST STEP | RESULT ► | ACTION TO TAKE |
|---|---|---|
| **WW30** LIFTGATE WIPER SUPPLY CHECK (WIPER NOT WORKING) | | |
| • Check for 12 volts (±1 volt) on "BL/Y" wire at liftgate wiper motor (connector C402).<br>• Is there 12 volts? | Yes ►<br>No ► | GO to **WW31** .<br>REPAIR "BL/Y" wire between liftgate wiper motor and liftgate wiper fuse. |

VOLTMETER
REAR WIPER MOTOR C402
BL/Y BL/GN

**Fig. 16 Wiper system diagnosis & testing (Part 21 of 24). Probe**

| TEST STEP | RESULT ► | ACTION TO TAKE |
|---|---|---|
| **WW31** LIFTGATE SWITCH CONTINUITY CHECK (WIPER NOT WORKING) | | |
| • Remove rear wiper fuse.<br>• Push liftgate wiper switch to "ON" position.<br>• Check continuity between ground and liftgate wiper/washer switch "BL/GN" wire (connector C238).<br>• Is there continuity? | Yes ►<br>No ► | REPAIR "BL/GN" wire between liftgate wiper/washer switch and liftgate wiper motor.<br>REPLACE liftgate wiper/washer switch. |

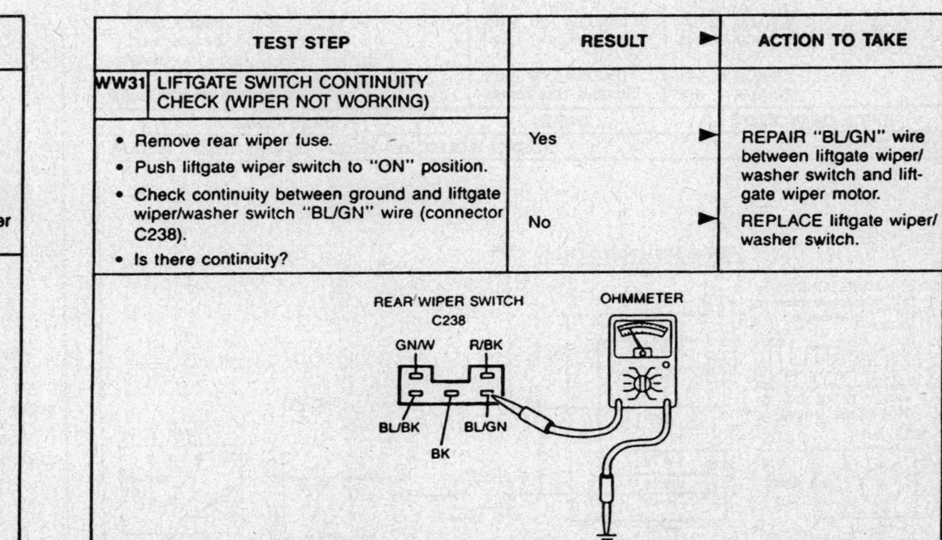


**Fig. 16 Wiper system diagnosis & testing (Part 22 of 24). Probe**

| TEST STEP | RESULT ► | ACTION TO TAKE |
|---|---|---|
| **WW32** LIFTGATE SWITCH CONTINUITY CHECK (PARK NOT WORKING) | | |
| • Place liftgate wiper out of park position by turning ignition key to "OFF" position when wiper is in the center of travel.<br>• Remove wiper fuse.<br>• Turn the liftgate wiper/washer switch to "OFF" position.<br>• Check for continuity to ground at the following places:<br>– Wiper motor case<br>– Wiper motor "BL/W" wire (connector C402) | No continuity at:<br>– Wiper motor case ►<br>– Wiper motor "BL/W" wire ► | REPAIR case ground of liftgate wiper motor.<br>REPLACE liftgate wiper motor. |



**Fig. 16 Wiper system diagnosis & testing (Part 23 of 24). Probe**

| TEST STEP | RESULT ► | ACTION TO TAKE |
|---|---|---|
| **WW33** LIFTGATE WIPER/WASHER SWITCH CHECK (WIPER WILL NOT STOP) | | |
| • Engage liftgate wiper.<br>• Disconnect liftgate wiper/washer switch (connector C238).<br>• Does wiper motor stop? | Yes ►<br>No ► | REPLACE liftgate wiper/washer switch.<br>REPAIR "BL/GN" wire between liftgate wiper motor and liftgate wiper/washer switch. |

**Fig. 16 Wiper system diagnosis & testing (Part 24 of 24). Probe**

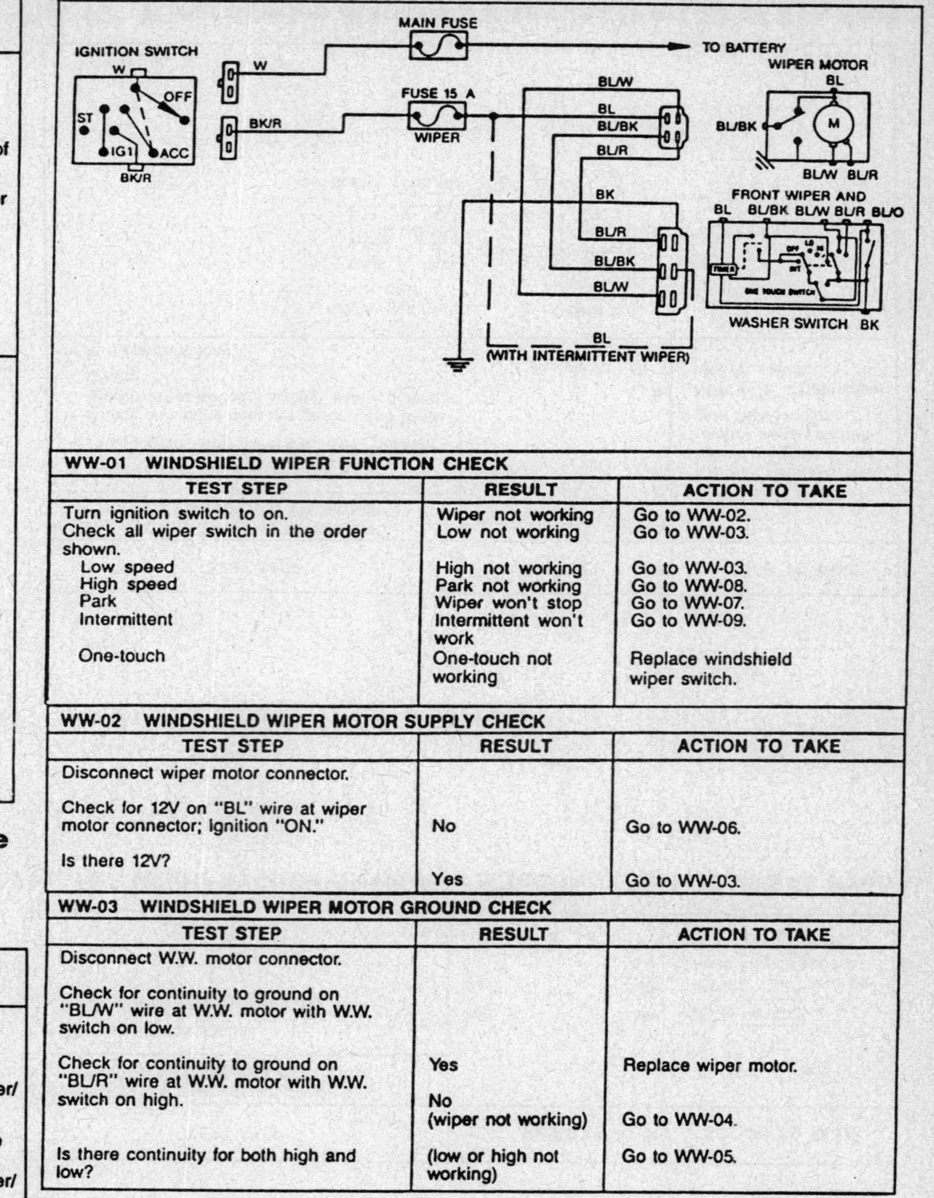


**WW-01 WINDSHIELD WIPER FUNCTION CHECK**

| TEST STEP | RESULT | ACTION TO TAKE |
|---|---|---|
| Turn ignition switch to on.<br>Check all wiper switch in the order shown. | Wiper not working<br>Low not working | Go to WW-02.<br>Go to WW-03. |
| Low speed<br>High speed<br>Park<br>Intermittent | High not working<br>Park not working<br>Wiper won't stop<br>Intermittent won't work | Go to WW-03.<br>Go to WW-08.<br>Go to WW-07.<br>Go to WW-09. |
| One-touch | One-touch not working | Replace windshield wiper switch. |

**WW-02 WINDSHIELD WIPER MOTOR SUPPLY CHECK**

| TEST STEP | RESULT | ACTION TO TAKE |
|---|---|---|
| Disconnect wiper motor connector.<br>Check for 12V on "BL" wire at wiper motor connector; Ignition "ON."<br>Is there 12V? | No | Go to WW-06. |
| | Yes | Go to WW-03. |

**WW-03 WINDSHIELD WIPER MOTOR GROUND CHECK**

| TEST STEP | RESULT | ACTION TO TAKE |
|---|---|---|
| Disconnect W.W. motor connector.<br>Check for continuity to ground on "BL/W" wire at W.W. motor with W.W. switch on low. | | |
| Check for continuity to ground on "BL/R" wire at W.W. motor with W.W. switch on high. | Yes | Replace wiper motor. |
| | No (wiper not working) | Go to WW-04. |
| Is there continuity for both high and low? | (low or high not working) | Go to WW-05. |

**Fig. 17 Wiper system diagnosis & testing (Part 1 of 3). Festiva**

| WW-04 WINDSHIELD WIPER/WASHER SWITCH GROUND CHECK | | |
|---|---|---|
| **TEST STEP** | **RESULT** | **ACTION TO TAKE** |
| Disconnect W.W. switch connector.<br><br>Check for continuity to ground on "BK" wire at W.W. switch.<br><br>Is there continuity? | Yes<br><br>No | Go to WW-05.<br><br>Service "BK" wire to ground. |

| WW-05 WINDSHIELD WIPER/WASHER SWITCH OPERATION | | |
|---|---|---|
| **TEST STEP** | **RESULT** | **ACTION TO TAKE** |
| Disconnect W.W. switch connector.<br><br>Check for continuity to "BK" terminal. | Yes | Service "BL/W" and "BL/R" from W.W. switch to W.W. motor. |
| W.W. Switch / Terminal<br>Low — "BL/W"<br>High — "BL/R"<br><br>Is there continuity between terminals? | No | Replace W.W. switch. |

| WW-06 POWER TO WIPER FUSE | | |
|---|---|---|
| **TEST STEP** | **RESULT** | **ACTION TO TAKE** |
| Remove wiper fuse at fuse panel.<br><br>Check for 12V at wiper fuse (ignition switch side). | Yes | Service fuse and/or "BL" wire to W.W. motor. |
| Is there 12V? | No | Service "BK/R" wire to ignition switch. |

| WW-07 WINDSHIELD WIPER SWITCH CHECK | | |
|---|---|---|
| **TEST STEP** | **RESULT** | **ACTION TO TAKE** |
| Disconnect wiper switch connector.<br><br>Does wiper motor stop? | No | Repair shorted wire between wiper switch and wiper motor (see note). |
| | Yes | Replace wiper switch. |
| NOTE: If wiper is running in high speed, repair "BL/R" wire. If wiper is running in low speed, repair "BL/W" wire. | | |

| WW-08 WINDSHIELD WIPER MOTOR CONTINUITY CHECK | | |
|---|---|---|
| **TEST STEP** | **RESULT** | **ACTION TO TAKE** |
| Place wipers out of park position.<br><br>Remove wiper fuse. | Yes | Go to WW-10. |
| Be sure wiper switch is off.<br><br>Disconnect wiper motor connector. | No<br>(Motor case) | Repair ground of wiper motor. |
| Check for continuity to ground at the following places:<br><br>Motor case.<br><br>Motor "BL/BK" terminal.<br><br>Is there continuity? | No<br>("BL/BK" terminal) | Replace wiper motor. |

**Fig. 17 Wiper system diagnosis & testing (Part 2 of 3). Festiva**

| WW-09 WINDSHIELD WIPER SWITCH SUPPLY CHECK | | |
|---|---|---|
| **TEST STEP** | **RESULT** | **ACTION TO TAKE** |
| Disconnect wiper switch connector. | | |
| Check for 12V at "BL" wire of wiper switch connector; ignition on. | No | Repair "BL" wire between wiper fuse and wiper switch. |
| Is there 12V? | Yes | Go to WW-10. |

| WW-10 POWER TO WIPER SWITCH "BL/BK" | | |
|---|---|---|
| **TEST STEP** | **RESULT** | **ACTION TO TAKE** |
| Disconnect wiper switch connector. | | |
| Place wipers in park position; ignition on. | | |
| Check for 12V on "BL/BK" wire to wiper switch. | Yes | Replace wiper switch. |
| Is there 12V? | No | Go to WW-11. |

| WW-11 WIPER MOTOR PARK RANGE CHECK | | |
|---|---|---|
| **TEST STEP** | **RESULT** | **ACTION TO TAKE** |
| Disconnect wiper motor connector. | | |
| Place wiper motor in park position. | | |
| Check continuity between wiper motor terminals "BL/BK" and "BL." | | |
| Is there continuity? | No | Replace wiper motor. |
| | Yes | Repair "BL/BK" wire between wiper switch and wiper motor. |

**Fig. 17 Wiper system diagnosis & testing (Part 3 of 3). Festiva**

| WW 01 WINDSHIELD WIPER FUNCTION CHECK | | |
|---|---|---|
| TEST STEP | RESULT | ACTION TO TAKE |
| • Turn ignition switch on.<br>• Check all wiper switch functions in the order shown. | Wiper not working | Go to WW 02. |
| | Low not working | Go to WW 07. |
| | High not working | Go to WW 09. |
| | Park not working | Go to WW 11. |
| | Wiper won't stop | Go to WW 12. |
| | Intermittent won't work | Go to WW 13. |
| | One-touch won't work | Replace switch. |

| WW 02 RELATED SYSTEMS CHECK (WIPER NOT WORKING) | | |
|---|---|---|
| TEST STEP | RESULT | ACTION TO TAKE |
| • Check other ignition and non-ignition systems. | Ignition working | Go to WW 03. |

| WW 03 WINDSHIELD WIPER FUSE CHECK (WIPER NOT WORKING) | | |
|---|---|---|
| TEST STEP | RESULT | ACTION TO TAKE |
| • Check wiper fuse at fuse panel. | No | Replace fuse. |
| • Is fuse OK? | Yes | Go to WW 04. |

**NOTE: If fuse blows again, check for shorts to ground in "BL" wires starting at the wiper motor. Repair or replace "BL" wires as needed.**

**Fig. 18 Wiper system diagnosis & testing (Part 1 of 7). 1989 Tracer**

**WW 04 WINDSHIELD WIPER MOTOR CHECK (WIPER NOT WORKING)**

| TEST STEP | RESULT | ACTION TO TAKE |
|---|---|---|
| • Remove wiper motor connector. • Apply 12V and ground directly to wiper motor as shown. • Is wiper motor working? | No | Replace wiper motor. |
| | Yes | Go to WW 05. |

b d a c e BAT.

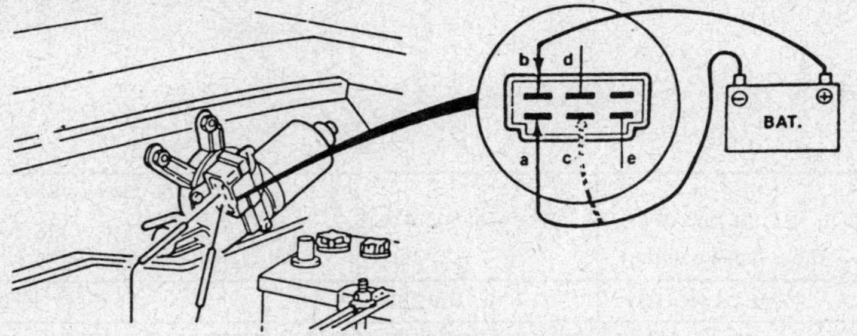

| Terminal | | Operation speed |
|---|---|---|
| + 12V | Ground | |
| b | a | Low |
| | c | High |

**WW 05 WINDSHIELD WASHER CHECK (WIPER NOT WORKING)**

| TEST STEP | RESULT | ACTION TO TAKE |
|---|---|---|
| • Turn on washer. • Is washer working? | No | Replace or repair ground wire to combination switch. |
| | Yes | Go to WW 06. |

**Fig. 18 Wiper system diagnosis & testing (Part 2 of 7). 1989 Tracer**

**WW 06 WINDSHIELD WIPER SUPPLY CHECK (WIPER NOT WORKING)**

| TEST STEP | RESULT | ACTION TO TAKE |
|---|---|---|
| • Check for 12V at wiper motor connector "BL" wire. • Is there 12V? | No | Replace or repair "BL" wire to wiper motor. |
| | Yes | Replace combination switch. |

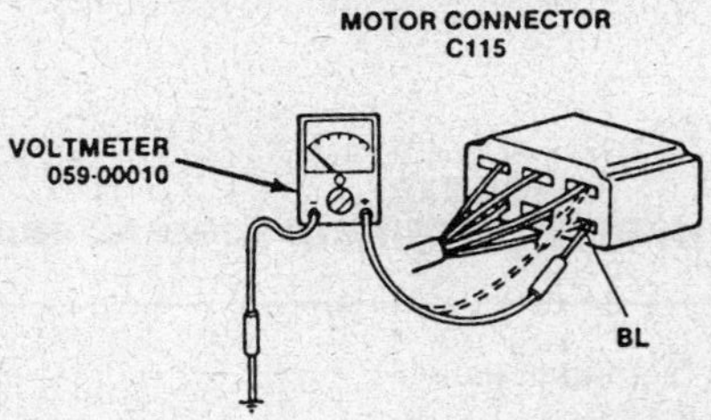

MOTOR CONNECTOR C115
VOLTMETER 059-00010
BL

**WW 07 WINDSHIELD WIPER MOTOR CHECK (LOW NOT WORKING)**

| TEST STEP | RESULT | ACTION TO TAKE |
|---|---|---|
| • Ground "BL/W" wire at wiper motor connector. • Is low speed working? | No | Replace wiper motor. |
| | Yes | Go to WW 08. |

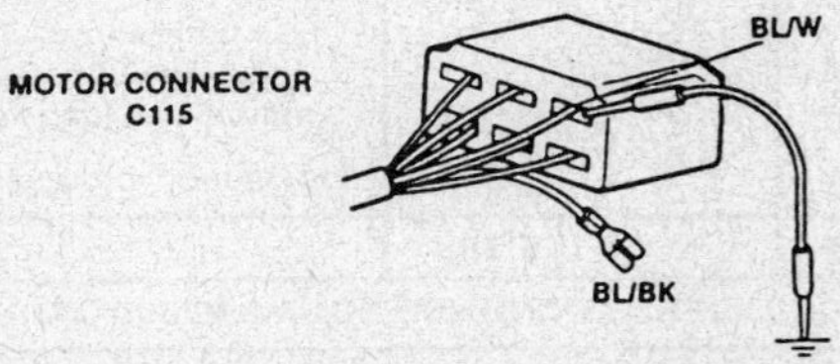

MOTOR CONNECTOR C115
BL/W
BL/BK

**Fig. 18 Wiper system diagnosis & testing (Part 3 of 7). 1989 Tracer**

| WW 08 WINDSHIELD WIPER CONTINUITY CHECK (LOW NOT WORKING) | | |
|---|---|---|
| TEST STEP | RESULT | ACTION TO TAKE |
| • Disconnect wiper motor connector.<br>• Check continuity between wiper switch and ground at "BL/W" wire with switch in low.<br>• Is there continuity? | No<br>Yes | Replace combination switch.<br>Replace or repair wire between combination switch and wiper motor. |

OHMMETER 059-00010
BL/W
SWITCH CONNECTOR C114

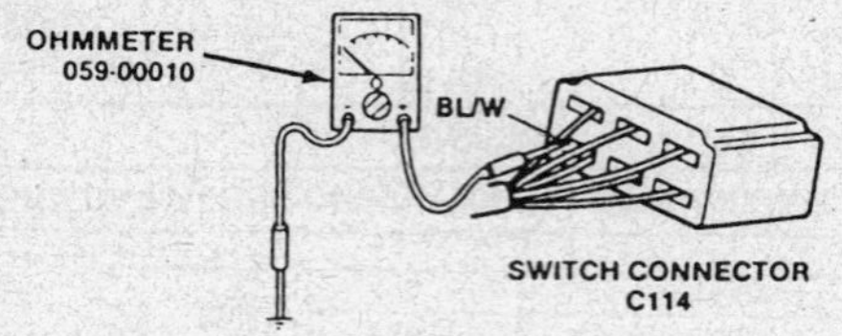

| WW 09 WINDSHIELD WIPER MOTOR CHECK (HIGH NOT WORKING) | | |
|---|---|---|
| TEST STEP | RESULT | ACTION TO TAKE |
| • Ground "BL/R" wire on wiper motor connector.<br>• Is high speed working? | No<br>Yes | Replace wiper motor.<br>Go to WW 10. |

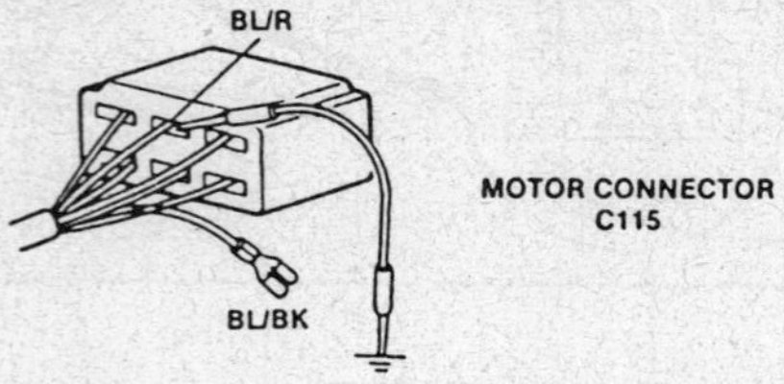

BL/R
MOTOR CONNECTOR C115
BL/BK

**Fig. 18 Wiper system diagnosis & testing (Part 4 of 7). 1989 Tracer**

| WW 10 WINDSHIELD WIPER SWITCH CONTINUITY CHECK (HIGH NOT WORKING) | | |
|---|---|---|
| TEST STEP | RESULT | ACTION TO TAKE |
| • Disconnect wiper motor connector.<br>• Check continuity between ground and "BL/R" wire at combination switch connector with switch in high.<br>• Is there continuity? | No<br>Yes | Replace combination switch.<br>Replace or repair "BL/R" wire between combination switch and wiper motor. |

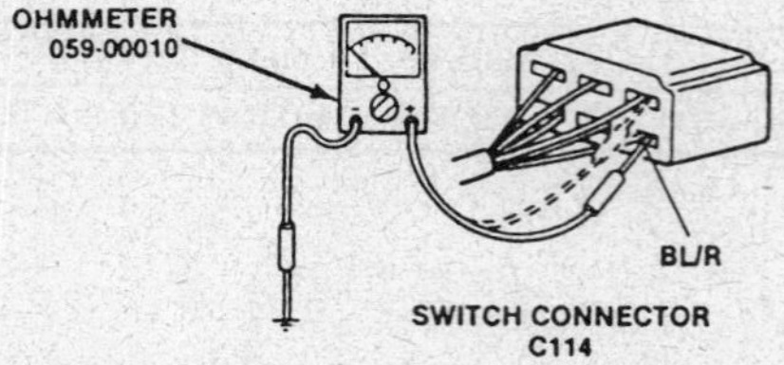

OHMMETER 059-00010
BL/R
SWITCH CONNECTOR C114

**Fig. 18 Wiper system diagnosis & testing (Part 5 of 7). 1989 Tracer**

| WW 11 WINDSHIELD WIPER MOTOR CONTINUITY CHECK (PARK NOT WORKING) | | |
|---|---|---|
| TEST STEP | RESULT | ACTION TO TAKE |
| • Place wipers out of park position.<br>• Remove wiper fuse.<br>• Be sure wiper switch is off.<br>• Check for continuity to ground at the following places:<br>—Motor "BK" wire<br>—Motor "BL/BK" wire<br>—Switch "BL/BK" wire<br>—Switch "BL/W" wire | No continuity at:<br>—Motor "BK" wire | Replace or repair ground to wiper motor. |
| | —Motor "BL/BK" wire | Replace wiper motor. |
| | —Switch "BL/BK" wire | Repair or replace wire between wiper motor and combination switch. |
| | —Switch "BL/W" wire | Replace combination switch. |

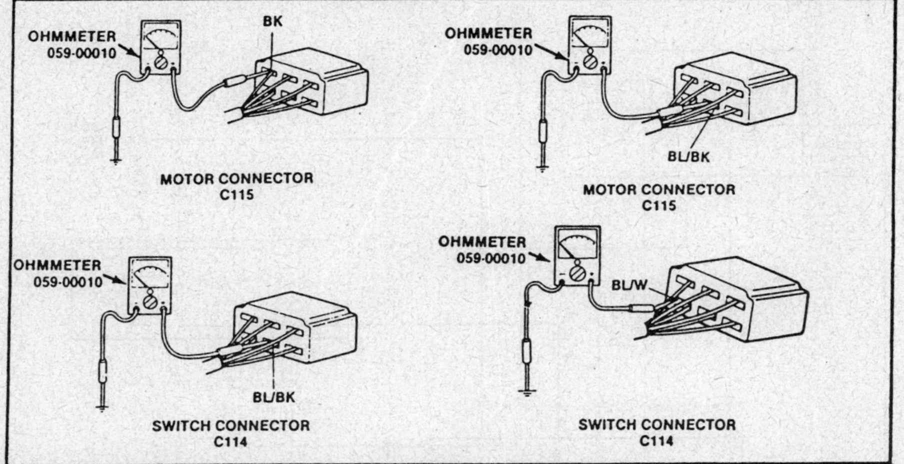

| WW 12 WINDSHIELD WIPER SWITCH CHECK (WIPER WON'T STOP) | | |
|---|---|---|
| TEST STEP | RESULT | ACTION TO TAKE |
| • Remove wiper switch connector from combination switch.<br>• Does wiper motor stop? | No | Repair shorted wire between combination switch and wiper motor. |
| | Yes | Replace combination switch. |

**Fig. 18 Wiper system diagnosis & testing (Part 6 of 7). 1989 Tracer**

| WW 13 WINDSHIELD WIPER SWITCH SUPPLY CHECK (INTERMITTENT WON'T WORK) | | |
|---|---|---|
| TEST STEP | RESULT | ACTION TO TAKE |
| • Is there 12V at "BL" wire of wiper switch? | No | Replace or repair wire between fuse panel and switch. |
| | Yes | Replace switch. |

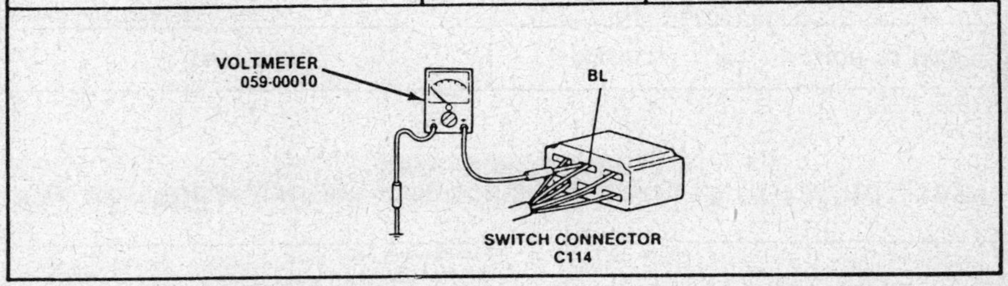

**Fig. 18 Wiper system diagnosis & testing (Part 7 of 7). 1989 Tracer**

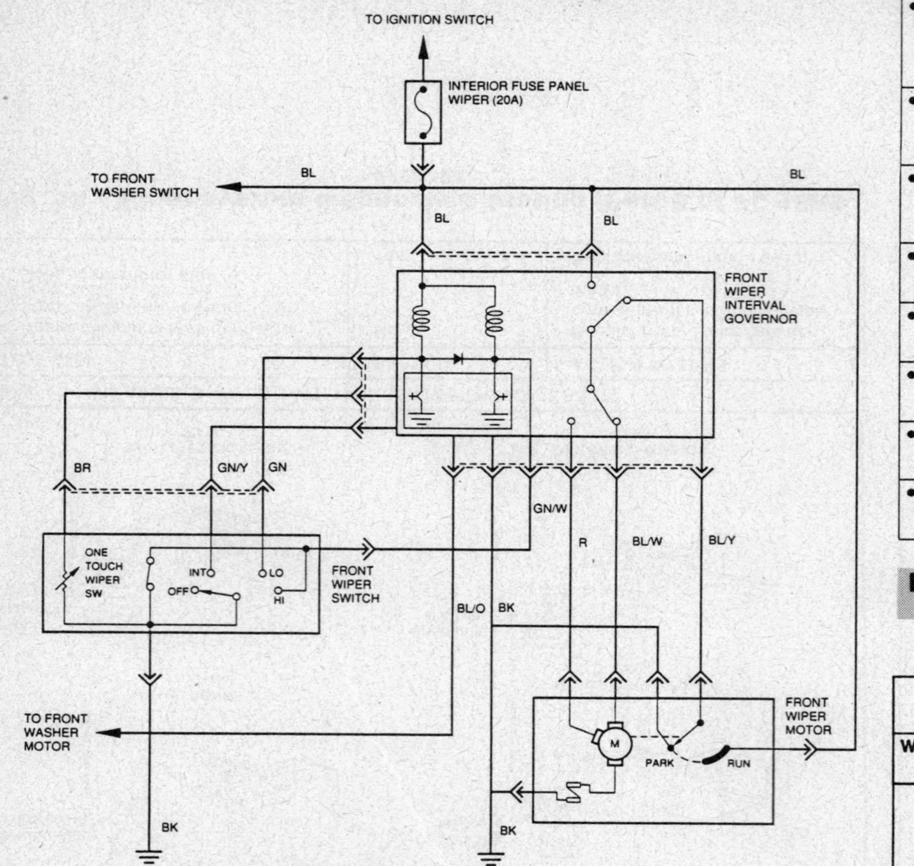


**Fig. 19 Wiper system wiring schematic. 1991 Escort & Tracer**

| CONDITION | POSSIBLE SOURCE | ACTION |
|---|---|---|
| • Wipers Not Working | • Blown fuse.<br>• Interval governor.<br>• Wiper switch.<br>• Wiper motor.<br>• Wiper circuit. | • GO to WW1. |
| • No LOW-Speed Wiper Operation | • Interval governor.<br>• Wiper switch.<br>• Wiper motor.<br>• Wiper circuit. | • GO to WW6. |
| • No HIGH-Speed Wiper Operation | • Interval governor.<br>• Wiper switch.<br>• Wiper motor.<br>• Wiper circuit. | • GO to WW6. |
| • No Intermittent Wiper Operation | • Interval governor.<br>• Wiper switch.<br>• Wiper circuit. | • GO to WW9. |
| • No MIST Operation | • Interval governor.<br>• Wiper switch.<br>• Wiper circuit. | • GO to WW9. |
| • No PARK Operation | • Interval governor.<br>• Wiper motor.<br>• Wiper circuit. | • GO to WW16. |
| • Wipers work continuously | • Interval governor.<br>• Wiper switch.<br>• Wiper circuit. | • GO to WW15. |
| • No LOW-Speed or Intermittent Operation | • Interval governor.<br>• Wiper motor.<br>• Wiper circuit. | • GO to WW6. |

**Fig. 20 Wiper system diagnosis & testing (Part 1 of 19). 1991 Escort & Tracer**

| TEST STEP | RESULT ► | ACTION TO TAKE |
|---|---|---|
| **WW1** WIPER FUSE CHECK | | |
| • Locate the interior fuse panel.<br>• Check the wiper 20 amp fuse.<br>• Is the fuse OK? | Yes ►<br>No ► | GO to WW6.<br>GO to WW2. |

**Fig. 20 Wiper system diagnosis & testing (Part 2 of 19). 1991 Escort & Tracer**

| TEST STEP | RESULT ► | ACTION TO TAKE |
|---|---|---|
| **WW2** SYSTEM CHECK | | |
| • Replace the fuse.<br>• Key ON.<br>• Check the wiper 20 amp fuse.<br>• Is the fuse OK? | Yes ►<br>No ► | GO to WW4.<br>GO to WW3. |

**Fig. 20 Wiper system diagnosis & testing (Part 3 of 19). 1991 Escort & Tracer**

| TEST STEP | RESULT ► | ACTION TO TAKE |
|---|---|---|
| **WW3** INTERVAL GOVERNOR AND WIPER MOTOR POWER SUPPLY SHORT CHECK | | |
| • Key OFF.<br>• Disconnect the interval governor and wiper motor connectors.<br>• Check the following wires for shorts to ground by touching one terminal of ohmmeter to one end of the wire and touching the other ohmmeter terminal to ground and read the resistance. | Yes ►<br>No ► | REPLACE the interval governor.<br>REPAIR/REPLACE the affected wire. |

| Wire | From | To |
|---|---|---|
| "BL" | Ignition | Interval Governor |
| "BL" | Ignition | Interval Governor |
| "BL" | Ignition | Wiper Motor |

• Is resistance greater than 10,000 ohms?

**Fig. 20 Wiper system diagnosis & testing (Part 4 of 19). 1991 Escort & Tracer**

| TEST STEP | RESULT ► | ACTION TO TAKE |
|---|---|---|
| **WW4** WIPER MOTOR SUPPLY CHECK | | |
| • Key ON.<br>• Place the wiper switch in the LOW and then in the HIGH position.<br>• Check the wiper 20 amp fuse.<br>• Is the fuse OK? | Yes ►<br>No ► | Wiper system OK.<br>GO to WW5 . |

**Fig. 20 Wiper system diagnosis & testing (Part 5 of 19). 1991 Escort & Tracer**

| TEST STEP | RESULT ► | ACTION TO TAKE |
|---|---|---|
| **WW5** WIPER MOTOR POWER SUPPLY CHECK | | |
| • Key OFF.<br>• Disconnect the interval governor and wiper motor connectors.<br>• Check the following wires for shorts to ground by touching one terminal of an ohmmeter to one end of the wire and touching the other ohmmeter terminal to ground and read resistance. | Yes ►<br>No ► | REPLACE the wiper motor.<br>REPAIR/REPLACE the affected wire. |

| Wire | From | To |
|---|---|---|
| "R" | Interval Governor | Wiper Motor |
| "BL/W" | Interval Governor | Wiper Motor |

• Is the resistance greater than 10,000 ohms?

**Fig. 20 Wiper system diagnosis & testing (Part 6 of 19). 1991 Escort & Tracer**

| TEST STEP | RESULT ► | ACTION TO TAKE |
|---|---|---|
| **WW6** INTERVAL GOVERNOR SUPPLY VOLTAGE CHECK | | |
| • Interval governor connector disconnected.<br>• Key ON.<br>• Measure the voltage on "BL" wires at the interval governor.<br>• Is voltage greater than 10 volts? | Yes ►<br>No ► | GO to WW7 .<br>REPAIR/REPLACE the "BL" wires as necessary. |

**Fig. 20 Wiper system diagnosis & testing (Part 7 of 19). 1991 Escort & Tracer**

| TEST STEP | RESULT ► | ACTION TO TAKE |
|---|---|---|
| **WW7** WIPER SWITCH GROUND CHECK | | |
| • Key OFF.<br>• Measure resistance of the "BK" wire wiper switch to ground.<br>• Is resistance less than 5 ohms? | Yes ►<br>No ► | GO to WW8 .<br>REPAIR/REPLACE the "BK" wire. |

**Fig. 20 Wiper system diagnosis & testing (Part 8 of 19). 1991 Escort & Tracer**

| TEST STEP | RESULT ► | ACTION TO TAKE |
|---|---|---|
| **WW8** WIPER MOTOR GROUND CHECK | | |
| • Measure resistance of the wiper motor body to ground.<br>• Is resistance less than 5 ohms? | Yes ►<br>No ► | GO to WW9 .<br>REPAIR ground circuit between the wiper motor body and ground. |

**Fig. 20 Wiper system diagnosis & testing (Part 9 of 19). 1991 Escort & Tracer**

| TEST STEP | RESULT ► | ACTION TO TAKE |
|---|---|---|
| **WW9** WIPER MOTOR OPERATION CHECK | | |
| • Key OFF.<br>• Wiper motor connector disconnected.<br>• Connect the negative terminal of a12-volt power source to ground.<br>• With jumper wire, apply 12 volts to the following wiper motor terminals:<br>HIGH ("R" wire)<br>LOW ("BL/W" wire)<br>• Do the wipers operate at HIGH and LOW-speeds? | Yes ►<br>No ► | GO to WW10 .<br>REPLACE the motor. |

**Fig. 20 Wiper system diagnosis & testing (Part 10 of 19). 1991 Escort & Tracer**

| TEST STEP | RESULT ► | ACTION TO TAKE |
|---|---|---|
| **WW10** WIPER MOTOR FEED CHECK | | |
| • Measure resistance of the following wires from the interval governor to the wiper motor.<br>"R" wire<br>"BL/W" wire<br>• Is the resistance less than 5 ohms? | Yes ►<br>No ► | GO to WW11 .<br>REPAIR/REPLACE the affected wire. |

**Fig. 20 Wiper system diagnosis & testing (Part 11 of 19). 1991 Escort & Tracer**

| TEST STEP | RESULT ► | ACTION TO TAKE |
|---|---|---|
| **WW11** INTERVAL GOVERNOR GROUND CHECK | | |
| • Measure resistance of the "BK" wire from wiper relay to ground.<br>• Is resistance less than 5 ohms? | Yes ►<br>No ► | GO to WW12 .<br>REPAIR/REPLACE the wire. |

**Fig. 20 Wiper system diagnosis & testing (Part 12 of 19). 1991 Escort & Tracer**

| TEST STEP | RESULT ► | ACTION TO TAKE |
|---|---|---|
| **WW12** WIPER RELAY GROUND CHECK | | |
| • Disconnect the interval governor connector.<br>• Key ON.<br>• With a jumper wire, individually ground each of the following relay connectors and note wiper operation.<br>(see table below)<br>• Do the wipers function correctly in each mode as the terminals of the relay are grounded? | Yes ►<br>No ► | GO to WW13 .<br>REPAIR/REPLACE the interval governor. |

| Relay Terminal | Wiper Function |
|---|---|
| "GN/W" | HIGH |
| "GN" | LOW |
| "GN/Y" | INT |
| "BR" | MIST |

**Fig. 20 Wiper system diagnosis & testing (Part 13 of 19). 1991 Escort & Tracer**

| TEST STEP | RESULT ► | ACTION TO TAKE |
|---|---|---|
| **WW13** WIPER SWITCH FEED CHECK | | |
| • Key OFF.<br>• Measure resistance of the following wires from the interval governor to the wiper switch:<br>"GN/W"<br>"GN"<br>"GN/Y"<br>"BR"<br>• Is the resistance of each wire less than 5 ohms? | Yes ►<br>No ► | GO to WW14 .<br>REPAIR/REPLACE the affected wire. |

**Fig. 20 Wiper system diagnosis & testing (Part 14 of 19). 1991 Escort & Tracer**

| TEST STEP | RESULT ► | ACTION TO TAKE |
|---|---|---|
| **WW14** WIPER SWITCH CHECK | | |
| • Wiper switch connector disconnected.<br>• Connect one terminal of an ohmmeter to wiper switch ground. Connect the terminal of the ohmmeter to the following wiper switch terminals with the wiper switch in the indicated positions: | Yes ► | Wiper System checks out OK — RETURN to symptom chart. |
| | No ► | REPLACE the wiper switch. |

| Switch Terminal | Switch Position |
|---|---|
| "GN/W" | HIGH |
| "GN" | LOW |
| "GN/Y" | INT |
| "BR" | MIST |

• Is the resistance of the "GN/W," "GN" and "GN/Y" terminal less than 5 ohms and is there continuity on the "BR" terminal?

**Fig. 20 Wiper system diagnosis & testing (Part 15 of 19). 1991 Escort & Tracer**

| TEST STEP | RESULT ► | ACTION TO TAKE |
|---|---|---|
| **WW15** WIPER SWITCH SUPPLY INTEGRITY CHECK | | |
| • Key OFF.<br>• Interval governor connector disconnected.<br>• Wiper switch connector disconnected.<br>• Check the following wires for shorts to ground by connecting one terminal to ground and touching the end of the indicated wire and read resistance. | Yes ► | REPLACE the wiper switch. |
| | No ► | REPAIR/REPLACE the affected wire. |

| Wire | From | To |
|---|---|---|
| "GN/W" | Interval Governor | Wiper Switch |
| "GN" | Interval Governor | Wiper Switch |
| "GN/Y" | Interval Governor | Wiper Switch |
| "BR" | Interval Governor | Wiper Switch |

• Is resistance measured at each wire greater than 10,000 ohms?

**Fig. 20 Wiper system diagnosis & testing (Part 16 of 19). 1991 Escort & Tracer**

| TEST STEP | RESULT ► | ACTION TO TAKE |
|---|---|---|
| **WW16** WIPER MOTOR PARK SUPPLY CHECK | | |
| • Key ON (will not operate in ACC).<br>• Measure voltage on the "BL" wire at the wiper motor.<br>• Is voltage greater than 10 volts? | Yes ► | GO to WW17 . |
| | No ► | REPAIR/REPLACE the "BL" wire. |

**Fig. 20 Wiper system diagnosis & testing (Part 17 of 19). 1991 Escort & Tracer**

| TEST STEP | RESULT ► | ACTION TO TAKE |
|---|---|---|
| **WW17** PARK GROUND FEED CHECK | | |
| • Key OFF.<br>• Measure resistance of the "BL/Y" wire between the interval governor and wiper motor.<br>• Is resistance less than 5 ohms? | Yes ► | GO to WW18 . |
| | No ► | REPAIR/REPLACE the "BL/Y" wire. |

**Fig. 20 Wiper system diagnosis & testing (Part 18 of 19). 1991 Escort & Tracer**

| TEST STEP | RESULT ► | ACTION TO TAKE |
|---|---|---|
| **WW18** INTERVAL GOVERNOR PARK CIRCUIT CHECK | | |
| • Disconnect the interval governor connector.<br>• Measure resistance between the "BL/Y" terminal and the "BL/W" terminal at the interval governor connector.<br>• Is the resistance less than 5 ohms? | Yes ► | REPLACE the wiper motor. |
| | No ► | REPLACE the wiper relay. |

**Fig. 20 Wiper system diagnosis & testing (Part 19 of 19). 1991 Escort & Tracer**

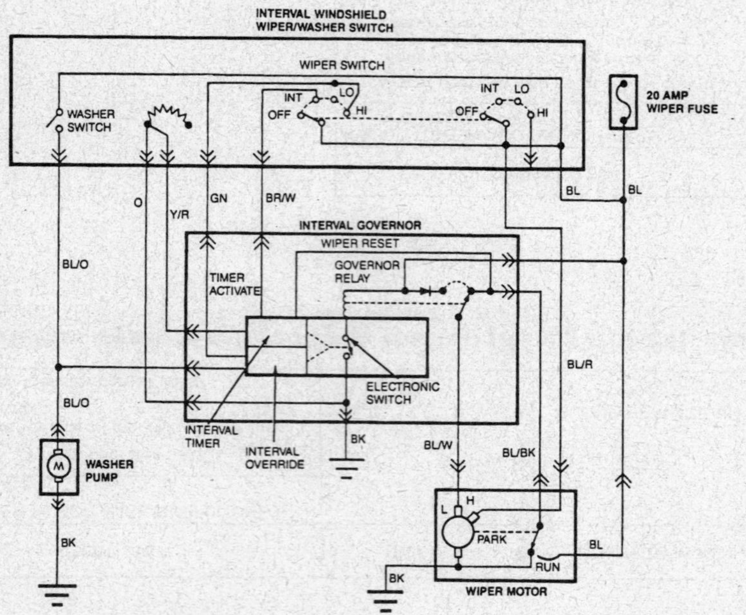


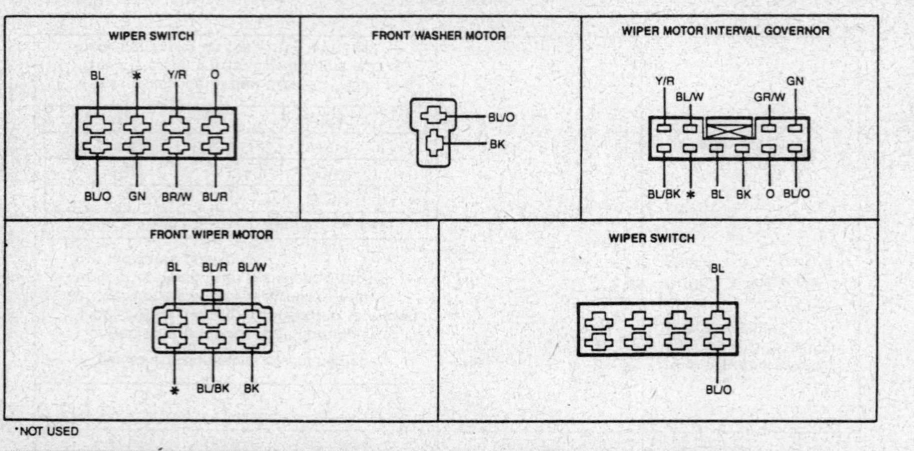


**Fig. 21 Wiper system wiring schematic. 1991 Capri**

| CONDITION | POSSIBLE SOURCE | ACTION |
|---|---|---|
| • Wiper Not Working | • Wiper fuse.<br>• Governor ground.<br>• Wiper motor ground.<br>• Circuit. | • Go to FW1.<br>• Go to FW9.<br>• Go to FW10.<br>• Go to FW4. |
| • Low Wiper Speed Not Working | • Wiper switch.<br>• Wiper governor.<br>• Wiper motor.<br>• Circuit. | • Go to FW5.<br>• Go to FW8.<br>• Go to FW12.<br>• Go to FW4. |
| • High Wiper Speed Not Working | • Wiper switch<br>• Wiper motor.<br>• Circuit. | • Go to FW5.<br>• Go to FW12.<br>• Go to FW4. |
| • Intermittent Wiper Speed Not Working | • Wiper switch.<br>• Wiper governor.<br>• Wiper motor.<br>• Circuit. | • Go to FW14.<br>• Go to FW15.<br>• Go to FW12.<br>• Go to FW4. |
| • Wiper Not Working With Washer Working | • Wiper motor.<br>• Wiper governor.<br>• Circuit. | • Go to FW12.<br>• Go to FW8.<br>• Go to FW4. |
| • Park Not Working | • Wiper switch.<br>• Wiper governor.<br>• Wiper motor.<br>• Circuit. | • Go to FW5.<br>• Go to FW8.<br>• Go to FW13.<br>• Go to FW4. |

**Fig. 22 Wiper system diagnosis & testing (Part 1 of 5). 1991 Capri**

| TEST STEP | RESULT ▶ | ACTION TO TAKE |
|---|---|---|
| **FW1** FRONT WIPER FUSE CHECK | | |
| • Check 20 amp wiper fuse.<br>• Is fuse OK? | Yes ▶<br>No ▶ | GO to **FW4.**<br>GO to **FW2.** |
| **FW2** WIPER SWITCH, GOVERNOR AND WIPER MOTOR PARK SWITCH SUPPLY CHECK | | |
| • Replace fuse.<br>• Turn key ON.<br>• Check wiper fuse.<br>• Is fuse OK? | Yes ▶<br>No ▶ | GO to **FW4.**<br>GO to **FW3.** |
| **FW3** WIPER SWITCH, GOVERNOR AND WIPER MOTOR PARK SWITCH SUPPLY SHORT CHECK | | |
| • Key OFF.<br>• Disconnect BL wire connectors from wiper switch, governor, and wiper motor.<br>• Measure resistance of BL wire between each component connector and ground.<br>  • Wiper switch<br>  • Governor<br>  • Wiper motor<br>• Is resistance greater than 10,000 ohms? | Yes ▶<br>No ▶ | GO to **FW4.**<br>SERVICE each affected BL wire between the component connector and the fuse. |
| **FW4** CHECK SUPPLY AT WIPER SWITCH, WIPER GOVERNOR AND WIPER MOTOR | | |
| • Access the wiper switch, wiper governor and the wiper motor connectors.<br>• Key ON.<br>• Measure the voltage on the BL wire at the wiper motor connectors.<br>• Is the voltage greater than 10 volts? | Yes ▶<br>No ▶ | GO to **FW5.**<br>SERVICE BL wire in question. |

**Fig. 22 Wiper system diagnosis & testing (Part 2 of 5). 1991 Capri**

| TEST STEP | RESULT ▶ | ACTION TO TAKE |
|---|---|---|
| **FW5** WIPER SWITCH CHECK | | |
| • Key OFF.<br>• Disconnect wiper switch connector.<br>• Measure resistance between the BL terminal and the following terminals at the switch:<br>**Switch Position / Terminal / Resistance**<br>OFF / All wires / Greater than 10,000 ohms<br>INT / BR/W / Less than 5 ohms<br>INT / All others / Greater than 10,000 ohms<br>LOW / GN / Less than 5 ohms<br>LOW / All others / Greater than 10,000 ohms<br>HI / GN and BL/R / Less than 5 ohms<br>HI / All others / Greater than 10,000 ohms<br>• Are the resistances correct? | Yes ▶<br>No ▶ | GO to **FW6.**<br>REPLACE wiper switch. |
| **FW6** CHECK LEADS BETWEEN WIPER SWITCH AND WIPER GOVERNOR | | |
| • Access the wiper governor.<br>• Measure the resistance of the following wires between the wiper switch and the wiper governor:<br>  • O<br>  • Y/R<br>  • GN<br>  • BR/W<br>• Are the resistances less than 5 ohms? | Yes ▶<br>No ▶ | GO to **FW7.**<br>SERVICE wires in question. |
| **FW7** CHECK WIPER GOVERNOR GROUND | | |
| • Measure the resistance of the BK wire between the governor and ground.<br>• Is the resistance less than 5 ohms? | Yes ▶<br>No ▶ | GO to **FW8.**<br>SERVICE BK wire. |

**Fig. 22 Wiper system diagnosis & testing (Part 3 of 5). 1991 Capri**

| TEST STEP | RESULT ▶ | ACTION TO TAKE |
|---|---|---|
| **FW8** CHECK WIPER GOVERNOR | | |
| • Key ON.<br>• Check the wiper governor operation by measuring the voltage on the following terminals at the wiper governor connector in the stated wiper switch position.<br><br>**Switch Position** / **Terminal Color** / **Voltage**<br>OFF — BL/W, BL/BK — Less than 1 volt<br>LOW — BL/W, BL/BK — Greater than 10 volts less than 1 volt<br>HIGH — BL/W, BL/BK, BL/R — Greater than 10 volts less than 1 volt<br>INT — BL/W, BL/BK — Greater than 10 volts less than 1 volt during each cycle<br><br>• Are the voltages correct? | Yes ▶<br>No ▶ | GO to **FW9**.<br>SERVICE wiper governor. |
| **FW9** CHECK HI-SPEED LEAD BETWEEN WIPER SWITCH AND WIPER MOTOR | | |
| • Disconnect the wiper motor connector.<br>• Measure the voltage on the BL/R wire at the harness connector.<br>• Is the voltage greater than 10 volts? | Yes ▶<br>No ▶ | GO to **FW10**.<br>SERVICE BL/R wire. |
| **FW10** CHECK LEADS BETWEEN WIPER GOVERNOR AND WIPER MOTOR | | |
| • Key OFF.<br>• Measure the resistance of the BL/W and BL/BK wires between the wiper governor and the wiper motor.<br>• Are the resistances less than 5 ohms? | Yes ▶<br>No ▶ | GO to **FW11**.<br>SERVICE wire in question. |
| **FW11** CHECK WIPER MOTOR GROUND | | |
| • Measure the resistance on the BK wire between the wiper motor and ground.<br>• Is the resistance less than 5 ohms? | Yes ▶<br>No ▶ | GO to **FW12**.<br>SERVICE BK wire. |

**Fig. 22 Wiper system diagnosis & testing (Part 4 of 5). 1991 Capri**

| TEST STEP | RESULT ▶ | ACTION TO TAKE |
|---|---|---|
| **FW12** CHECK WIPER MOTOR | | |
| • Key ON.<br>• Put the wiper switch in the low position.<br>• Do the wipers operate?<br>• Put the wiper switch in the high position.<br>• Do the wipers operate faster? | Yes ▶<br>No ▶ | GO to **FW13**.<br>SERVICE/REPLACE wiper motor. |
| **FW13** CHECK WIPER MOTOR PARK SYSTEM | | |
| • Key ON.<br>• Turn the wiper switch to low.<br>• Turn wiper switch off while wiper is not in the park position.<br>• Measure the voltage on the BL/W wire until the wiper reaches the park position.<br>• Is the voltage greater than 10 volts while not in park position? | Yes ▶<br>No ▶ | GO to **FW14**.<br>SERVICE/REPLACE wiper motor. |
| **FW14** CHECK THE INTERVAL WIPER SWITCH | | |
| • Turn the interval switch to the following positions:<br>• Measure the resistance of the Y/R terminal to the O terminal at the wiper switch for each position listed in the table.<br>• Are readings similar to these given in the following table?<br><br>**Resistance Table**<br>Slow — 1.5K ohms (± 10-15%)<br>1 — 9.3K ohms (± 10-15%)<br>2 — 7.6K ohms (± 10-15%)<br>3 — 5.8K ohms (± 10-15%)<br>4 — 4.2 ohms (± 10-15%)<br>5 — 2.4K ohms (± 10-15%)<br>Fast — 750 ohms | Yes ▶<br>No ▶ | GO to **FW15**.<br>SERVICE/REPLACE the wiper switch. |
| **FW15** CHECK WIPER GOVERNOR | | |
| • Key ON.<br>• Move the wiper switch to the INT position.<br>• Move the interval switch to the first position.<br>• Do the wipers operate intermittently?<br>• Turn the interval switch to increase the time interval.<br>• Does length of time between wipe cycles increase? | Yes ▶<br>No ▶ | RETURN to condition chart.<br>SERVICE/REPLACE wiper governor. |

**Fig. 22 Wiper system diagnosis & testing (Part 5 of 5). 1991 Capri**

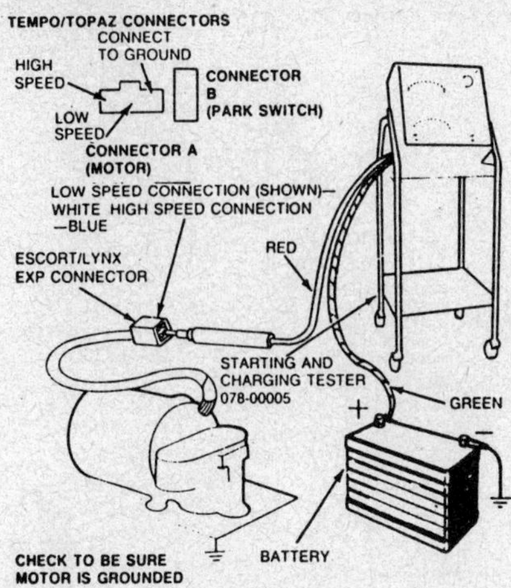


**Fig. 23 Wiper motor current draw test. Tempo, Topaz & 1989–90 Escort**

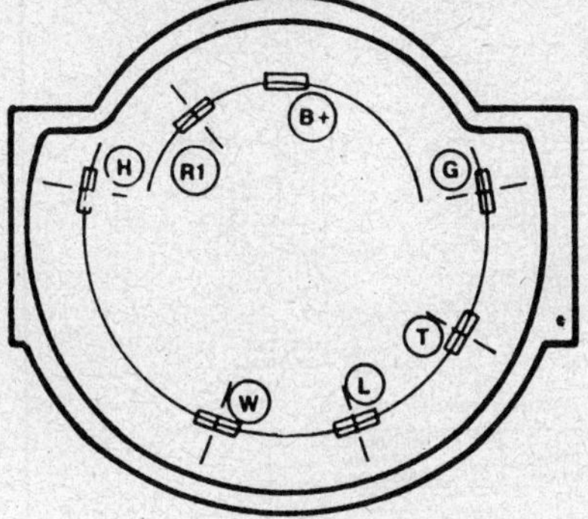


STANDARD WIPER SWITCH

| SWITCH POSITION | CONTINUITY BETWEEN TERMINALS |
|---|---|
| OFF | R1 AND L |
| LOW | B+ AND L |
| HIGH | B+ AND H |
| WASH | B+ AND W |

NOTE: T-TERMINAL IS SWITCH ILLUMINATION

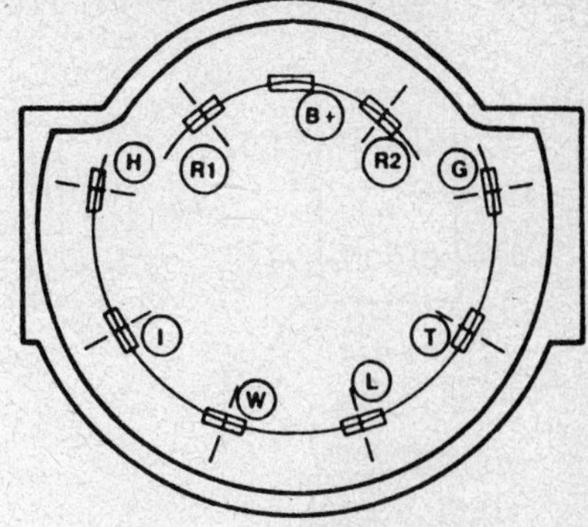


INTERVAL WIPER SWITCH

| SWITCH POSITION | CONTINUITY BETWEEN TERMINALS |
|---|---|
| OFF | NO CONTINUITY |
| INTERVAL | B+ AND I |
| LOW | B+ AND L |
| HIGH | B + AND H AND L |
| WASH | B + AND W |

NOTE: THERE SHOULD BE CONTINUITY BETWEEN TERMINALS R1 AND R2 THROUGHOUT VARIABLE RESISTANCE RANGE (MINIMUM 420 TO 880 OHMS, MAXIMUM 7,000 TO 13,000 OHMS)
T-TERMINAL IS SWITCH ILLUMINATION

**Fig. 24 Wiper switch continuity test. Tempo & Topaz**

a. Ground motor case to body.
b. If motor runs, repair ground.
c. If motor does not run, replace motor.

### Park Operation, Test

When performing the following test, refer to wiring schematic **Fig. 1.**

1. Turn ignition switch to ON.
2. Turn wiper switch to OFF.
3. Check voltage at (black/pink wire) terminal 28, (white wire) terminal 58, and (red wire) terminal 63. If voltage is not present at all three terminals, proceed to step 5.
4. If voltage is present at all three terminals and wipers are not parked, proceed as follows:
   a. Ground motor to body.
   b. If motor parks, repair ground.
   c. If motor does not park, replace motor.
5. If voltage is present only at terminal 63, replace wiper motor.
6. If voltage is present only at terminals 28 and 63, replace wiper switch.
7. If voltage still is not present at terminal 58, check terminals 28 and 58 back to wiper switch.

## INTERMITTENT SYSTEM WIPER MOTOR

When performing the following test procedures, refer to wiring schematics **Figs. 2 and 3.**

### High Speed Test

1. Turn ignition switch to ON.
2. Turn wiper switch to HI.
3. Check voltage at (blue/orange wire) terminal 56. If voltage is not present, proceed to step 5.
4. If voltage is present and motor will not run, proceed as follows:
   a. Ground motor case to body.
   b. If motor runs, repair ground.
   c. If motor does not run, replace motor.
5. Check voltage at (red wire) terminal 63. If voltage is present, replace wiper switch.
6. If voltage is not present at terminal 63, proceed as follows:
   a. Disconnect wiper switch electrical connector.
   b. Check voltage at (black/green wire) terminal 297. If voltage is present, replace wiper switch.
   c. If voltage is not present at terminal 297, check circuit back to source.

### Low Speed Test

1. Turn ignition switch to ON.
2. Turn wiper switch to LO.
3. Check voltage at (white wire) terminal 58. If voltage is not present, proceed to step 5.
4. If voltage is present at terminal 58 and motor will not run, proceed as follows:
   a. Ground motor case to body.
   b. If motor runs, repair ground.
   c. If motor does not run, replace motor.
5. Check voltage at (red wire) terminal 63. If voltage is not present, proceed to step 7.
6. If voltage is present at terminal 63, proceed as follows:
   a. Ground wiper switch connector control circuits (black/pink wire) terminal 28A, and (black wire) terminal 57A.
   b. If voltage is present at terminal 58, replace wiper switch.
   c. If voltage is not present at terminal 58, replace governor.
7. Disconnect wiper switch electrical connector.
8. Check voltage at (black/green wire) terminal 297. If voltage is present, replace wiper switch.
9. If voltage is not present at terminal 297, check circuit back to source. **If governor relay is not operative, wipers will function only in HI and PARK modes.**

### Intermittent Test

Prior to testing intermittent system operation, ensure LO and PARK wiper system operations are proper, then proceed as follows:

1. Turn ignition switch to ON.
2. Turn wiper switch to INT.
3. If wiper delay is excessive or wipers run continuously at low speed, proceed as follows:
   a. Check wiper switch continuity as described under "Wiper Switch" for these models. Replace switch as needed.
   b. If switch tests good, replace governor.

### Park Operation Test

1. Turn ignition switch to ON.
2. Turn wiper switch to OFF.
3. Check voltage at (white wire) terminal 58. If voltage is not present, proceed to step 5.
4. If voltage is present at terminal 58 and motor will not park, proceed as follows:
   a. Ground motor case to body.
   b. If motor parks, repair ground.
   c. If motor does not park, replace motor.
5. Check voltage at (black/pink wire) terminal 28, and (red wire) terminal 63. If voltage is present at both terminals, replace governor.
6. If voltage is not present at terminal 28, but present at terminal 63 and motor is not parked, replace wiper motor.
7. If voltage is not present at terminal 63, proceed as follows:
   a. Disconnect wiper switch electrical connector.
   b. Check voltage at (black/green wire) terminal 297. If voltage is present, replace wiper switch.

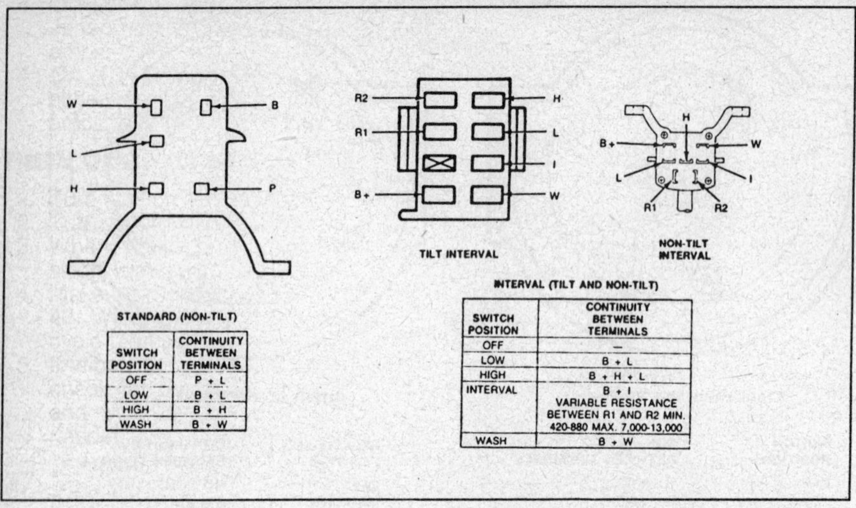


STANDARD (NON-TILT)

| SWITCH POSITION | CONTINUITY BETWEEN TERMINALS |
|---|---|
| OFF | P + L |
| LOW | B + L |
| HIGH | B + H |
| WASH | B + W |

INTERVAL (TILT AND NON-TILT)

| SWITCH POSITION | CONTINUITY BETWEEN TERMINALS |
|---|---|
| OFF | — |
| LOW | B + L |
| HIGH | B + H + L |
| INTERVAL | B + I VARIABLE RESISTANCE BETWEEN R1 AND R2 MIN. 420-880 MAX. 7,000-13,000 |
| WASH | B + W |

**Fig. 25 Wiper switch continuity test. 1989–90 Escort**

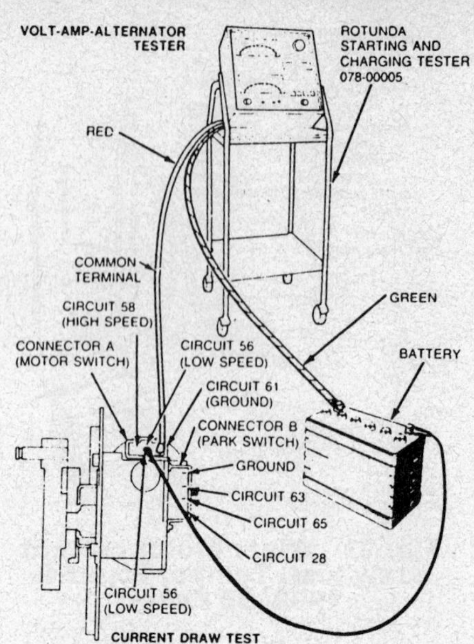


**Fig. 26 Wiper motor current draw test. Crown Victoria, Grand Marquis & Town Car**

c. If voltage is not present at terminal 297, check circuit back to source.

## ALL SYSTEMS

### Current Draw Test

1. Disconnect wiper motor linkage.
2. Disconnect wiper motor electrical connector.
3. Make test connections as shown in **Fig. 23.** Alternately connect red test lead to wiper motor low and high speed connectors.
4. Current draw at either terminal should not exceed 3 amps.

## WIPER SWITCH

### Continuity Test

When testing a non-intermittent wiper switch, a self-powered test lamp or an ohmmeter can be used to check continuity. When testing an intermittent wiper switch, use only an ohmmeter to check continuity.

When taking test readings move the switch lever to detect marginal switch operation.

Refer to **Fig. 25** for switch terminal identification and continuity readings.

## GOVERNOR

1. Ensure wiper motor current draw, and wiper switch continuity are within specifications.
2. Ensure wiper system continuity is good.
3. If steps 1 and 2 are proper, replace the electronic governor.

# CROWN VICTORIA, GRAND MARQUIS & TOWN CAR

## WIPER MOTOR

### Current Draw Test

Motor terminals may be too small to make necessary test connections. If necessary use jumper wires with suitable connector sleeves between motor and test equipment.

1. Disconnect wiper linkage from output arm and electrical connectors from motor.
2. Make test connections as shown **Fig. 26.** Alternately connect the battery negative jumper wire to high and low speed wiper motor terminals.
3. Current draw at either terminal should not exceed 3.5 amps.
4. If current draw is excessive, check output arm and wind latch assembly. If output arm assembly is satisfactory, repair or replace motor.

### Park Operation Test

Refer to wiring schematics **Fig. 6** when performing the following test procedures.

1. Turn ignition switch to ON.
2. Turn wiper switch to LO. Ensure wiper operation is proper.
3. With wipers in a vertical position turn wiper switch to OFF. Ensure wipers cycle once then park below the windshield.
4. If wipers do not function as described, perform test steps 5 through 10 according to wiper malfunction.
5. If wipers stop without cycling and parking proceed as follows:
   a. Disconnect wiper motor park switch electrical connector.
   b. With ignition switch ON, check for battery voltage at park switch electrical connector (dark green wire) terminal 65. If battery voltage is not present repair the circuit.
   c. If battery voltage is present at terminal 65, check motor housing ground. Repair as needed.
   d. If motor housing ground is good, turn ignition switch to OFF, then disconnect both wiper motor electrical connectors.
   e. Using a suitable ohmmeter, check for continuity between wiring harness terminals 28 and 56. If continuity does not exist, repair the open circuit.
   f. If continuity does exist between terminals 28 and 56, check for ground at wiper motor terminal 28. If ground is open, service the park switch.
   g. If ground is good at wiper motor terminal 28, check for continuity between wiring harness circuits 61 and 63. If continuity exists, proceed to step J.
   h. If continuity does not exist between wiring harness terminals 61 and 63, repair the open circuit. If open circuit is traced to interval governor, check for continuity between wiper switch terminals P and G. If open exists between terminals P and G, replace the wiper switch.
   i. If open does not exist between wiper switch terminals P and G, replace the interval governor.
   j. Check for continuity between wiper motor terminals 63 and 65. If open exists service wiper motor park switch.
6. **If wipers park below the windshield and the motor stays running,** service the park switch.
7. If wipers jam or stall when parking below the windshield and the motor runs in reverse, proceed as follows:
   a. Check wiper linkage. Repair as needed.
   b. If wiper linkage is satisfactory, service windlatch assembly and wiper motor arm.
8. If wipers travel into the next cycle, then park on the windshield, proceed as follows:
   a. Perform wiper switch continuity test as described under "Wiper Switch" for these models.
   b. **On non-intermittent systems,** if wiper switch continuity test is good, service wiper motor park switch.
   c. **On intermittent systems,** if wiper switch continuity test is good,

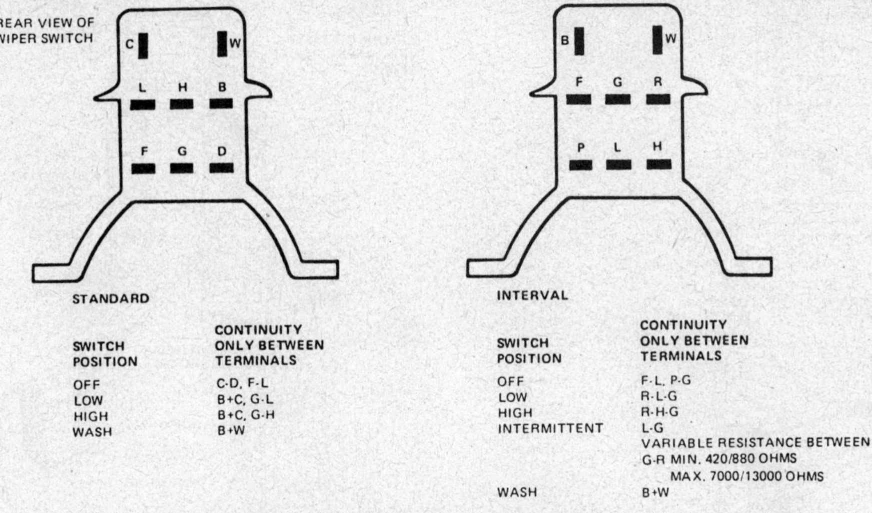


STANDARD

| SWITCH POSITION | CONTINUITY ONLY BETWEEN TERMINALS |
|---|---|
| OFF | C-D, F-L |
| LOW | B+C, G-L |
| HIGH | B+C, G-H |
| WASH | B+W |

INTERVAL

| SWITCH POSITION | CONTINUITY ONLY BETWEEN TERMINALS |
|---|---|
| OFF | F-L, P-G |
| LOW | R-L-G |
| HIGH | R-H-G |
| INTERMITTENT | L-G<br>VARIABLE RESISTANCE BETWEEN G-R MIN. 420/880 OHMS<br>MAX. 7000/13000 OHMS |
| WASH | B+W |

**Fig. 27 Wiper switch continuity test. 1989 Crown Victoria, Grand Marquis & Town Car**

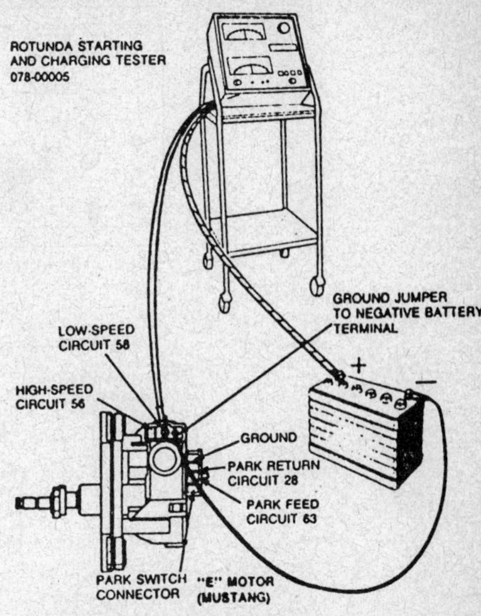


**Fig. 29 Wiper motor current draw test. Mustang**

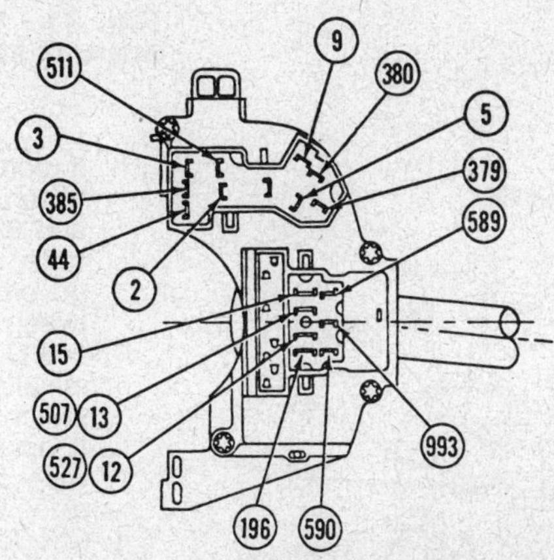


| SWITCH ACTUATOR POSITION | CONTINUITY BY CIRCUIT NUMBER |
|---|---|
| **Wiper/Washer Switching** | |
| • Wash OFF and Wiper OFF | Resistance No. 993 to 590, 103.3K ohms ± 10%.<br>No. 993 to 589, 47.6K ohms ± 10%. |
| • Wash ON and Wiper OFF | Open No. 993 to 590;<br>Resistance No. 993 to 589; 47.6K ohms ± 10%. |
| • Wiper OFF and Wash OFF | Resistance No. 993 to 590, 103.3K ohms ± 10%.<br>No. 993 to 589, 47.6K ohms ± 10%. |
| • Wiper LO or Low Speed and Wash OFF | Resistance No. 993 to 590, 3.3K ohms ± 10%.<br>No. 993 to 589, 4.08K ohms ± 10%. |
| • Wiper HI or High Speed and Wash OFF | Resistance No. 993 to 590, 3.3K ohms ± 10%.<br>Open No. 993 to 589. |
| • Wiper Interval and Wash OFF | Resistance No. 993 to 589, 11.33 K ohms ± 10%.<br>No. 993 to 590, Gradually decreasing from 103.3 K ohms to 3.3 K ohms from Maximum Delay to Minimum Delay. |

**Fig. 28 Wiper switch continuity test. 1990--91 Crown Victoria, Mark VII, Grand Marquis & Town Car**

check for voltage at washer terminal 941. If voltage is present repair as needed.

d. If voltage is not present at washer terminal 941, disconnect wiper motor electrical connectors and proceed to next step.
e. Check for continuity between terminals 61 and 63. If open exists, replace governor.
f. If continuity exist between terminals 61 and 63, service wiper motor park switch.

9. **If wipers run constantly in OFF or INT positions,** perform test procedures in step 8.
10. **If wipers stop at bottom of windshield, but do not park bellow windshield,** perform test procedures in step 8.

## WIPER SWITCH

### Continuity Test

When testing a non-intermittent wiper switch, a self-powered test lamp or an ohmmeter can be used to check continuity. When testing an intermittent wiper switch, use only an ohmmeter to check continuity.

When taking test readings move the switch lever to detect marginal switch operation.

Refer to **Fig. 27 and 28** for switch terminal identification and continuity readings.

# CONTINENTAL, MARK VII, MUSTANG, SABLE & TAURUS

## WIPER MOTOR

### Current Draw Test

1. Disconnect battery.
2. Disconnect wiper linkage from motor.
3. **On Mustang models** proceed as follows:
   a. Disconnect electrical connector from motor.
   b. Make test connections as shown **Fig. 29.** Alternately connect the red jumper wire to high and low speed wiper motor terminals.
   c. Current draw at either terminal should not exceed 3.5 amps.
4. **On Continental, Cougar, Mark VII and Sable, Taurus models** proceed as follows:
   a. Make test connections as shown **Figs. 30 and 31.** Alternately ground the high and low speed wiper motor terminals.
   b. Current draw at either terminal should not exceed 3.5 amps.

### Park Operation Test, Mustang

1. Turn ignition switch to ON.
2. Turn wiper switch to ON.
3. When wipers are in a non-parked position, turn ignition switch to OFF.
4. Make test connections as shown **Fig. 32.** Wiper motor should run one full cycle then park.
5. If wiper motor does not run to park, or will not park, replace it.

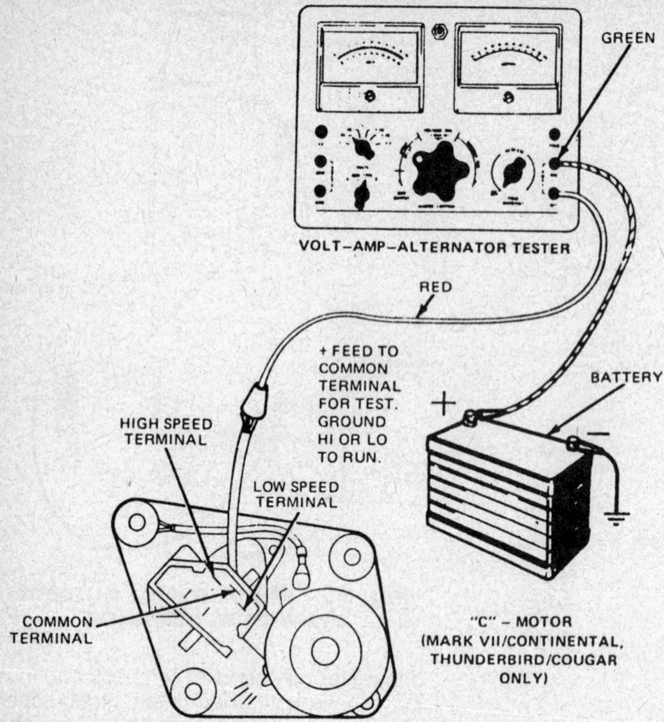


**Fig. 30 Wiper motor current draw test. Mark VII**

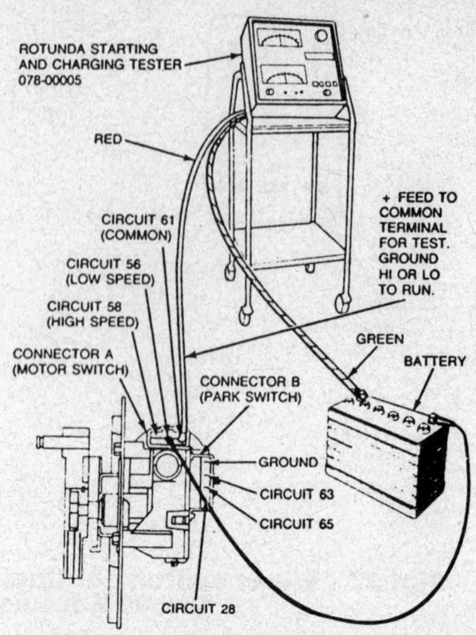


**Fig. 31 Wiper motor current draw test. Continental, Sable & Taurus**

6. If wiper motor stops, check for continuity at wiper switch and wiper system wiring. Replace or repair as needed.
7. If continuity and the wiper switch test good, and wiper motor will not stop in OFF or INT position, replace the governor.

## Park Operation Test, Continental, Cougar, Mark VII, Sable, Taurus

Refer to wiring schematics **Figs. 9, 11 or 12** when performing the following test procedures.

1. Turn ignition switch to ON.
2. Turn wiper switch to LO. Ensure wiper operation is proper.
3. With wipers in a vertical position turn wiper switch to OFF. Ensure wipers cycle once then park below the windshield.
4. If wipers do not function as described, perform test steps 5 through 10 according to wiper malfunction.
5. **If wipers stop without cycling and parking** proceed as follows:
   a. Disconnect wiper motor park switch electrical connector.
   b. With ignition switch ON, check for battery voltage at park switch electrical connector (dark green wire) terminal 65. If battery voltage is not present repair the circuit.
   c. If battery voltage is present at terminal 65, check motor housing ground. Repair as needed.
   d. If motor housing ground is good, turn ignition switch to OFF, then disconnect wiper motor electrical connectors.

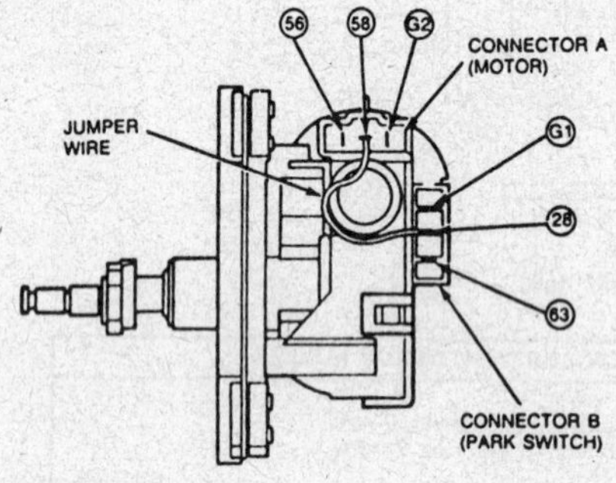


| CIRCUIT NO. | DESCRIPTION | COLOR |
|---|---|---|
| 56 | WIPER SWITCH TO MOTOR (HIGH) | DB/O |
| 58 | WIPER SWITCH TO MOTOR (LOW) | W |
| 28 | WIPER SWITCH TO MOTOR (PARK RETURN) | BLK |
| 63 | WIPER SWITCH TO MOTOR (PARK AND RETURN) | R |
| G1 | GROUND | BLK |
| G2 | GROUND | BLK |

**Fig. 32 Wiper motor park operation test (Non-Depressed). Mustang**

   e. Using a suitable ohmmeter, check for continuity between wiring harness terminals 28 and 56. If continuity does not exist, repair the open circuit.
   f. If continuity does exist between terminals 28 and 56, check for ground at wiper motor terminal 28. If ground is open, service the park switch.
   g. If ground is good at wiper motor terminal 28, check for continuity between wiring harness circuits 61 and 63. If continuity exist proceed to step J.
   h. If continuity does not exist between wiring harness terminals 61 and 63, repair the open circuit. If open circuit is traced to interval governor, check for continuity between wiper switch terminals P and G. If open exists between terminals P and G, replace the wiper switch.
   i. If open does not exist between wiper switch terminals P and G, replace the interval governor.
   j. Check for continuity between wiper motor terminals 63 and 65, if open exists service wiper motor park switch.
6. **If wipers park below the windshield and the motor stays running,** service the park switch.
7. **If wipers jam or stall when parking below the windshield and the motor runs in reverse,** proceed as follows:
   a. Check wiper linkage. Repair as needed.
   b. If wiper linkage is satisfactory, service windlatch assembly and wiper motor arm.
8. If wipers travel into the next cycle, then park on the windshield, proceed as follows:
   a. Perform wiper switch continuity test as described under "Wiper Switch" for these models.
   b. **On non-intermittent systems,** if wiper switch continuity test is good, replace wiper motor.
   c. **On intermittent systems,** if wiper switch continuity test is good, check for voltage at washer terminal 941. If voltage is present repair as needed.
   d. If voltage is not present at washer terminal 941, disconnect wiper motor electrical connectors and proceed to next step.

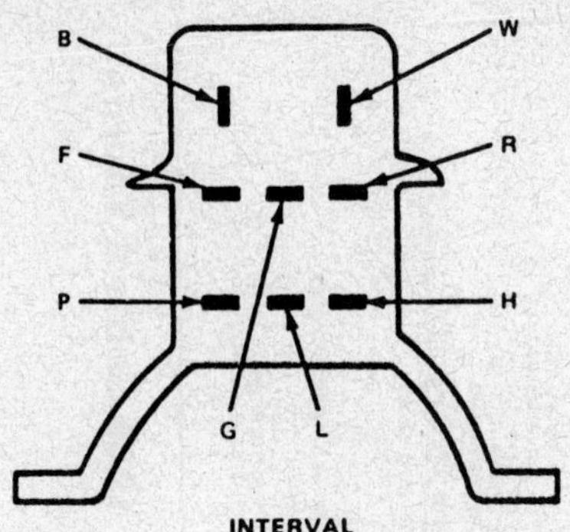


| SWITCH POSITION | CONTINUITY ONLY BETWEEN TERMINALS |
|---|---|
| OFF | F-L, P-G |
| LOW | R-L-G |
| HIGH | R-H-G |
| INTERMITTENT | L-G<br>VARIABLE RESISTANCE BETWEEN G-R:<br>MIN. 420/880 OHMS<br>MAX. 7000/13000 OHMS |
| WASH | B+W |

**Fig. 33 Wiper switch continuity test (Intermittent). 1989 Mark VII**

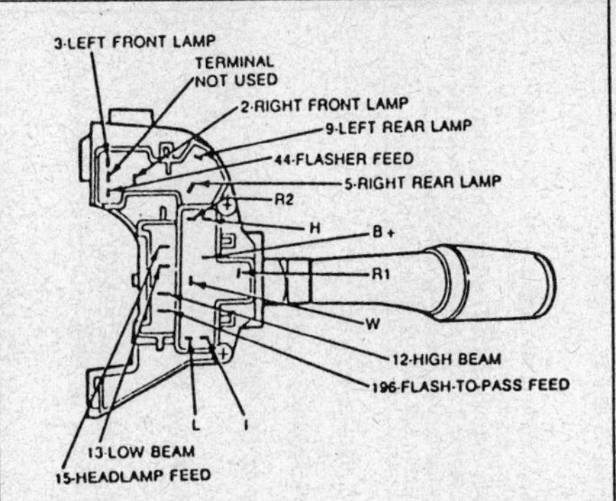


| Interval Wiper/Washer Switching; | |
|---|---|
| • Wash OFF. | Open B+ to W. |
| • Wash ON. | Closed B+ to W. |
| • Wiper O or OFF. Wash OFF. | Open B+ to H, L, I and W.<br>Resistance R1 to R2 greater than 420 ohms but less than 880 ohms. |
| • Wiper LO or low speed. Wash OFF. | Closed B+ to L.<br>Open B+ to H, I and W.<br>Resistance R1 to R2 greater than 420 ohms but less than 880 ohms. |
| • Wiper HI or high speed. Wash OFF. | Closed B+ to L and H.<br>Open B+ to W and I.<br>Resistance R1 to R2 greater than 420 ohms but less than 880 ohms. |
| • **Wiper Interval** at maximum knob travel or maximum time between wipe cycles. Wash OFF. | Closed B+ to I.<br>Open B+ to H, L and W.<br>Resistance R1 to R2 greater than 7000 ohms but less than 13,000 ohms.<br>**NOTE:** If knob is then rotated toward the OFF or minimum time between wipe cycles, then the resistance should decrease to less than 880 ohms but greater than 420 ohms. |

**Fig. 34 Wiper switch continuity test. 1989 Mustang**

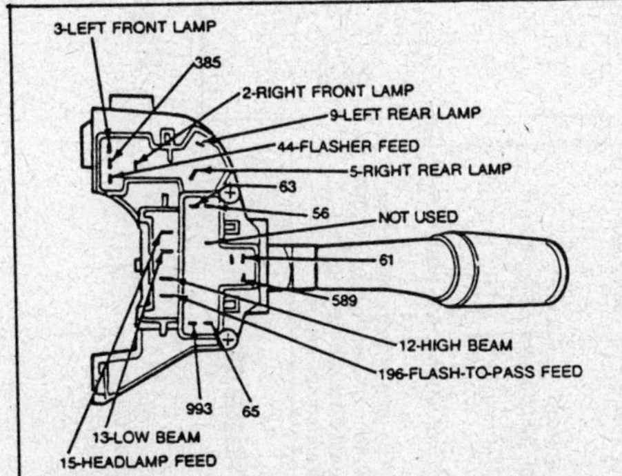


| Interval Wiper/Washer Switching; | |
|---|---|
| • Wash OFF. | Open 63 to 941. |
| • Wash ON. | Closed 63 to 941. |
| • Wiper O or OFF. Wash OFF. | Open 63 to 56, 993, 65<br>Resistance 61 to 589 greater than 420 ohms but less than 880 ohms. |
| • Wiper LO or low speed. Wash OFF. | Closed 63 to 993.<br>Open 63 to 56 and 65<br>Resistance 61 to 589 greater than 420 ohms but less than 880 ohms. |
| • Wiper HI or high speed. Wash OFF. | Closed 63 to 56 and 993<br>Open 63 to 65<br>Resistance 61 to 589 greater than 420 ohms but less than 880 ohms. |
| • **Wiper Interval** at maximum knob travel or maximum time between wipe cycles. Wash OFF. | Closed 63 to 65.<br>Open 63 to 56 and 993.<br>Resistance 61 to 589 greater than 7000 ohms but less than 13,000 ohms.<br>**NOTE:** If knob is then rotated toward the OFF or minimum time between wipe cycles, then the resistance should decrease to less than 880 ohms but greater than 420 ohms. |

**Fig. 35 Wiper switch continuity test. 1990–91 Mustang**

e. Check for continuity between terminals 61 and 63. If open exist replace governor.
f. If continuity exist between terminals 61 and 63, replace wiper motor.

9. If wipers run constantly in OFF or INT positions, perform test procedures in step 8.
10. If wipers stop at bottom of windshield, but do not park bellow windshield, perform test procedures in step 8.

## WIPER SWITCH

### Continuity Test

When testing a non-intermittent wiper switch, a self-powered test lamp or an ohmmeter can be used to check continuity. When testing an intermittent wiper switch, use only an ohmmeter to check continuity.

When taking test readings move the switch lever to detect marginal switch operation.

Refer to **Figs. 33 through 38** for switch terminal identification and continuity readings.

## CIRCUIT BREAKER

### Continental, Sable & Taurus

1. Remove circuit breaker from fuse panel.
2. Using a suitable Volt-Amp meter, adjust current draw to equal the circuit breaker rating.
3. Connect circuit breaker to tester for 10 minutes. If circuit breaker opens within the time specified, replace it.
4. Readjust current draw to equal twice the circuit breaker rating.
5. Connect circuit breaker to tester. The ammeter current reading should drop to zero within 30 seconds. If circuit breaker does not open within the time specified, replace it.

## GOVERNOR

### Continental, Sable & Taurus

1. Ensure wiper motor current draw, and wiper switch continuity are within specifications.

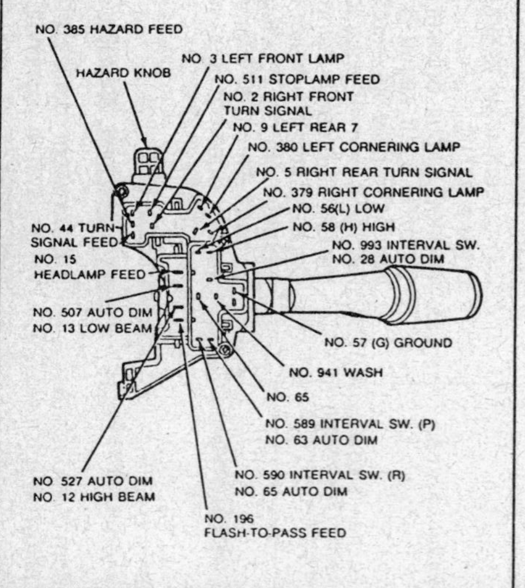

NO. 385 HAZARD FEED
HAZARD KNOB
NO. 3 LEFT FRONT LAMP
NO. 511 STOPLAMP FEED
NO. 2 RIGHT FRONT TURN SIGNAL
NO. 9 LEFT REAR 7
NO. 380 LEFT CORNERING LAMP
NO. 5 RIGHT REAR TURN SIGNAL
NO. 379 RIGHT CORNERING LAMP
NO. 56(L) LOW
NO. 58 (H) HIGH
NO. 993 INTERVAL SW.
NO. 28 AUTO DIM
NO. 44 TURN SIGNAL FEED
NO. 15 HEADLAMP FEED
NO. 507 AUTO DIM
NO. 13 LOW BEAM
NO. 57 (G) GROUND
NO. 941 WASH
NO. 65
NO. 589 INTERVAL SW. (P)
NO. 63 AUTO DIM
NO. 527 AUTO DIM
NO. 12 HIGH BEAM
NO. 590 INTERVAL SW. (R)
NO. 65 AUTO DIM
NO. 196 FLASH-TO-PASS FEED

| SWITCH ACTUATOR POSITION | CONTINUITY BY CIRCUIT NUMBER |
|---|---|
| **Interval Wiper/Washer Switching;** | |
| • Wash OFF. | Open No. 65 to 941. |
| • Wash ON. | Closed No. 65 to 941. |
| • Wiper **ON** or OFF. Wash OFF. | Closed No. 56 to 993 (i.e. Terminal No. 993/28); No. 57 to 589 (i.e. Terminal No. 589/63).<br>Open No. 57 to 56 and 58; No. 65 to 941.<br>Resistance No. 57 to 590 (Terminal No. 590/65) greater than 420 ohms but less than 880 ohms |
| • Wiper **LO** or low speed. Wash OFF | Closed No. 57 to 56 and 590 (Terminal No. 590/65).<br>Open No. 57 to 58 and 589 (i.e. Terminal No. 589/63); No. 56 to 993 (i.e. Terminal No. 993/28); No. 65 to 941. |
| • Wiper **HI** or high speed. | Closed No. 57 to 58 and 590 (Terminal No. 590/65).<br>Open No. 57 to 56 and 589 (i.e. Terminal No. 589/63); No. 56 to 993 (i.e. Terminal No. 993/28); No. 65 to 941. |
| • **Wiper Interval** at maximum knob travel or maximum time between wipe cycles. Wash **OFF**. | Closed No. 57 to 56.<br>Open No. 57 to 58 and 589 i.e. Terminal No. 589/63); No. 56 to 993 (i.e. Terminal No. 993/28); No. 65 to 941.<br>Resistance No. 57 to 590 (Terminal No. 590/65) greater than 7000 ohms but less than 13,000 ohms. **Note;** If knob is then rotated toward the OFF or minimum time between wipe cycles, then the resistance should decrease to less than 880 ohms but greater than 420 ohms. |

**Fig. 36 Wiper switch continuity test. Continental**

| SWITCH ACTUATOR POSITION | CONTINUITY BY CIRCUIT NUMBER |
|---|---|
| **Interval Wiper/Washer Switching;** | |
| • Wash OFF. | Open No. 65 to 941. |
| • Wash ON. | Closed No. 65 to 941. |
| • Wiper **ON** or OFF. Wash OFF. | Closed No. 56 to 993 (i.e. Terminal No. 993/28); No. 57 to 589 (i.e. Terminal No. 589/63).<br>Open No. 57 to 56 and 58; No. 65 to 941.<br>Resistance No. 57 to 590 (Terminal No. 590/65) greater than 420 ohms but less than 880 ohms |
| • Wiper **LO** or low speed. Wash OFF | Closed No. 57 to 56 and 590 (Terminal No. 590/65).<br>Open No. 57 to 58 and 589 (i.e. Terminal No. 589/63); No. 56 to 993 (i.e. Terminal No. 993/28); No. 65 to 941. |
| • Wiper **HI** or high speed. | Closed No. 57 to 58 and 590 (Terminal No. 590/65).<br>Open No. 57 to 56 and 589 (i.e. Terminal No. 589/63); No. 56 to 993 (i.e. Terminal No. 993/28); No. 65 to 941. |
| • **Wiper Interval** at maximum knob travel or maximum time between wipe cycles. Wash **OFF**. | Closed No. 57 to 56.<br>Open No. 57 to 58 and 589 i.e. Terminal No. 589/63); No. 56 to 993 (i.e. Terminal No. 993/28); No. 65 to 941.<br>Resistance No. 57 to 590 (Terminal No. 590/65) greater than 7000 ohms but less than 13,000 ohms. **Note;** If knob is then rotated toward the OFF or minimum time between wipe cycles, then the resistance should decrease to less than 880 ohms but greater than 420 ohms. |
| **Standard Wiper/Washer Switching;** | |
| • Wash OFF. | Open No. 65 (i.e. Terminal No. 590/65) to 941. |
| • Wash ON. | Closed No. 65 (i.e. Terminal No. 590/65) to 941. |
| • Wiper **ON** or OFF. Wash OFF. | Closed No. 61 to 63 (i.e. Terminal No. 589/63); No. 56 to 28 (i.e. Terminal No. 993/28)<br>Open No. 57 to 56 and 58; No. 65 (i.e. Terminal No. 590/65) to 61 and 941. |
| • Wiper **LO** or low speed. Wash OFF. | Closed No. 57 to 56; No. 65 (i.e. Terminal No. 590/65) to 61.<br>Open No. 57 to 58; No. 56 to 28 (i.e. Terminal no. 993/28); No. 61 to 63 (i.e. Terminal No. 589/63). |
| • Wiper **HI** or high speed. Wash OFF. | Closed No. 57 to 58; No. 65 (i.e. Terminal No. 590/65) to 61.<br>Open No. 57 to 56; No. 56 to 28 (i.e. Terminal No. 993/28); No. 61 to 63 (i.e. Terminal No. 589/63). |

NO. 3 LEFT FRONT LAMP
NO. 511 STOP LAMP FEED
HAZARD KNOB
ON
OFF
NO. 9 LEFT REAR 7
NO. 380 LEFT CORNERING LAMP
NO. 379 RIGHT CORNERING LAMP
NO. 5 RIGHT REAR TURN SIGNAL
NO. 385 HAZARD FEED
NO. 58 (H) HIGH
NO. 56 (L) LOW
NO. 993 INTERVAL SW.
NO. 28 STANDARD SW.
NO. 44 TURN SIGNAL FEED
NO. 57 (G) GROUND
NO. 2 RIGHT FRONT TURN SIGNAL
NO. 13 LOW BEAM
NO. 12 HIGH BEAM
NO. 65 INTERVAL SW ONLY
NO. 61 (C) STANDARD ONLY
NO. 941 WASH
NO. 15 HEADLAMP FEED
NO. 196 FLASH-TO-PASS FEED
NO. 590 INTERVAL SW (R)
NO. 65 STANDARD SW (B+)
NO. 589 INTERVAL SW (P)
NO. 63 STANDARD SW (D)

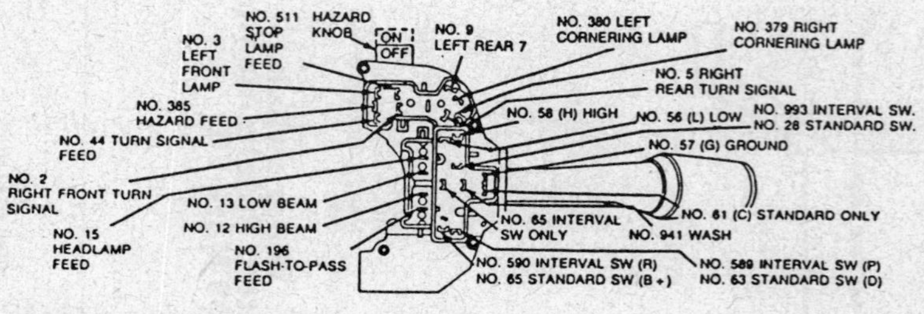

**Fig. 37 Wiper switch continuity test. 1989 Sable & Taurus**

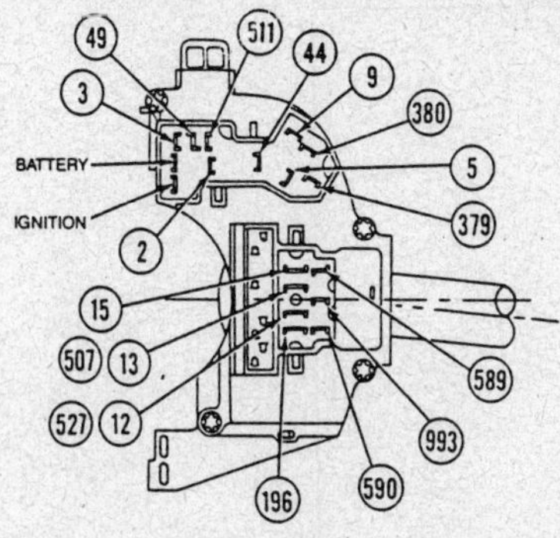


| SWITCH ACTUATOR POSITION | CONTINUITY BY CIRCUIT NUMBER |
|---|---|
| **Wiper/Washer Switching** • Wash OFF and Wiper OFF | Resistance No. 993 to 590, 103.3K ohms ± 10%. No. 993 to 589, 47.6K ohms ± 10%. |
| • Wash ON and Wiper OFF | Open No. 993 to 590; Resistance No. 993 to 589; 47.6K ohms ± 10%. |
| • Wiper OFF and Wash OFF | Resistance No. 993 to 590, 103.3K ohms ± 10%. No. 993 to 589, 47.6K ohms ± 10%. |
| • Wiper LO or Low Speed and Wash OFF | Resistance No. 993 to 590, 3.3K ohms ± 10%. No. 993 to 589, 4.08K ohms ± 10%. |
| • Wiper HI or High Speed and Wash OFF | Resistance No. 993 to 590, 3.3K ohms ± 10%. Open No. 993 to 589. |
| • Wiper Interval and Wash OFF | Resistance No. 993 to 589, 11.33 K ohms ± 10%. No. 993 to 590, Gradually decreasing from 103.3 K ohms to 3.3 K ohms from Maximum Delay to Minimum Delay. |

**Fig. 38 Wiper switch continuity test. 1990–91 Sable & Taurus**

2. Ensure wiper system continuity is good.
3. If steps 1 and 2 are proper, replace the electronic governor.

## COUGAR & THUNDERBIRD

### WIPER MOTOR

#### Current Draw Test

1. Ensure wipers are in park position.
2. Disconnect battery.
3. Remove wiper arm and blade assemblies.
4. Remove wiper module vacuum manifolds.
5. Disconnect wiper module electrical connectors.
6. Remove one nut and five screws retaining the wiper module. Remove module from vehicle
7. Remove linkage drive arm-to-motor crankpin retaining clip. Separate drive arm from crankpin.
8. Remove three wiper motor retaining screws. Remove motor.
9. Make test connections as shown **Fig. 39.** Alternately connect the red jumper wire to high and low speed wiper motor terminals.
10. Current draw at either terminal should not exceed 3.5 amps. Replace or repair as needed.
11. Install wiper motor. Ensure wiper motor is in the park position.
12. Install linkage drive arm to motor crankpin. Install retaining clip.
13. Install wiper module.
14. Connect wiper module electrical connectors.
15. Install wiper module vacuum manifolds.
16. Install wiper arm and blade assemblies.
17. Reconnect battery.

#### Park Operation Test

Refer to wiring schematics **Fig. 10** when performing the following test procedures.

1. Turn ignition switch to ON.
2. Turn wiper switch to LO. Ensure wiper operation is proper.
3. With wipers in a vertical position turn wiper switch to OFF. Ensure wipers cycle once then park below the windshield.
4. If wipers do not function as described, perform test steps 5 through 10 according to wiper malfunction.
5. **If wipers stop without cycling and parking** proceed as follows:
   a. Disconnect wiper motor park switch electrical connector.
   b. With ignition switch ON, check for battery voltage at park switch electrical connector (red wire) terminal 63. If battery voltage is not present repair the circuit.
   c. If battery voltage is present at terminal 63, check motor housing ground. Repair as needed.
   d. If motor housing ground is good, turn ignition switch to OFF, then disconnect wiper motor electrical connectors.
   e. Using a suitable ohmmeter, check for continuity between wiring harness terminals 28 and 58. If continuity does not exist, repair the open circuit.
   f. If continuity does exist between terminals 28 and 56, check for ground at wiper motor terminal 28. If ground is open, replace wiper motor.

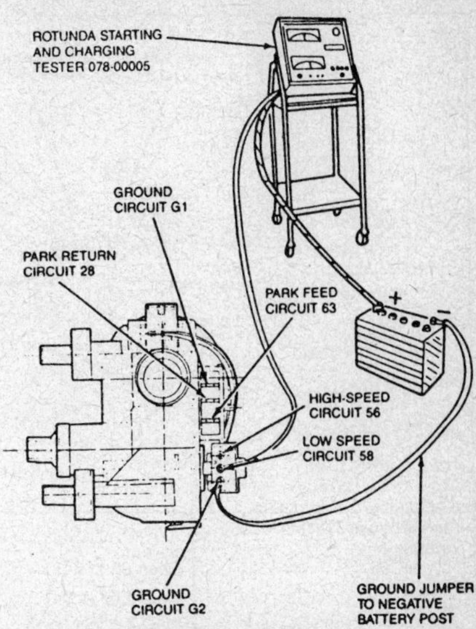


**Fig. 39 Wiper motor current draw test. Cougar & Thunderbird**

   g. If ground is good at wiper motor terminal 28, check for continuity between wiring harness circuits G2 and 63. If continuity does not exist, repair the open circuit. If open circuit is traced to interval governor, check for continuity between wiper switch terminals P and G. If open exists between terminals P and G, replace the wiper switch.
   h. If open does not exist between wiper switch terminals P and G, replace the interval governor.
6. **If wipers travel into the next cycle, then park on the windshield,** proceed as follows:
   a. Perform wiper switch continuity test as described under "Wiper Switch" for these models.
   b. **On non-intermittent systems,** if wiper switch continuity test is good, replace wiper motor.
   c. **On intermittent systems,** if wiper switch continuity test is good, check for voltage at washer terminal 941. If voltage is present repair as needed.
   d. If voltage is not present at washer terminal 941, disconnect wiper motor electrical connectors and proceed to next step.
   e. Check for continuity between terminals G2 and 63. If open exists, replace governor.
   f. If continuity exist between terminals G2 and 63, replace wiper motor.
7. **If wipers run constantly in OFF or INT positions,** perform test procedures in step 6.

### WIPER SWITCH

#### Continuity Test

When testing a non-intermittent wiper switch, a self-powered test lamp or an ohmmeter can be used to check continuity. When testing an intermittent wiper switch, use only an ohmmeter to check continuity.

When taking test readings move the

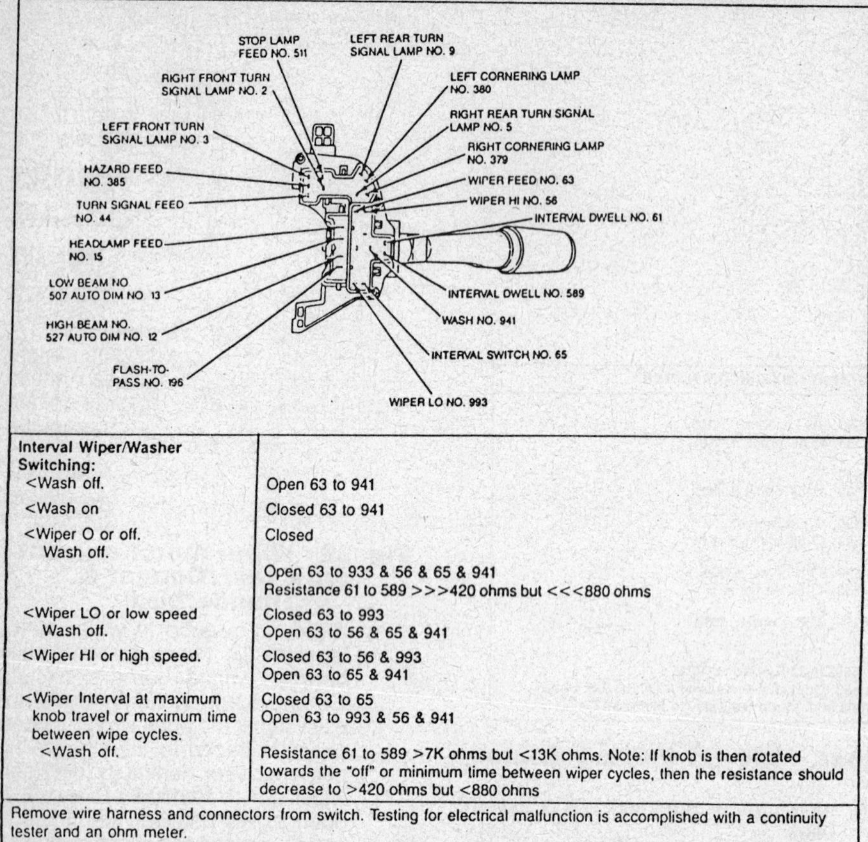


| Interval Wiper/Washer Switching: | |
|---|---|
| <Wash off. | Open 63 to 941 |
| <Wash on | Closed 63 to 941 |
| <Wiper O or off. Wash off. | Closed<br>Open 63 to 933 & 56 & 65 & 941<br>Resistance 61 to 589 >>>420 ohms but <<<880 ohms |
| <Wiper LO or low speed Wash off. | Closed 63 to 993<br>Open 63 to 56 & 65 & 941 |
| <Wiper HI or high speed. | Closed 63 to 56 & 993<br>Open 63 to 65 & 941 |
| <Wiper Interval at maximum knob travel or maximum time between wipe cycles. <Wash off. | Closed 63 to 65<br>Open 63 to 993 & 56 & 941<br>Resistance 61 to 589 >7K ohms but <13K ohms. Note: If knob is then rotated towards the "off" or minimum time between wiper cycles, then the resistance should decrease to >420 ohms but <880 ohms |
| Remove wire harness and connectors from switch. Testing for electrical malfunction is accomplished with a continuity tester and an ohm meter. | |

**Fig. 40 Wiper switch continuity test. Cougar & Thunderbird**

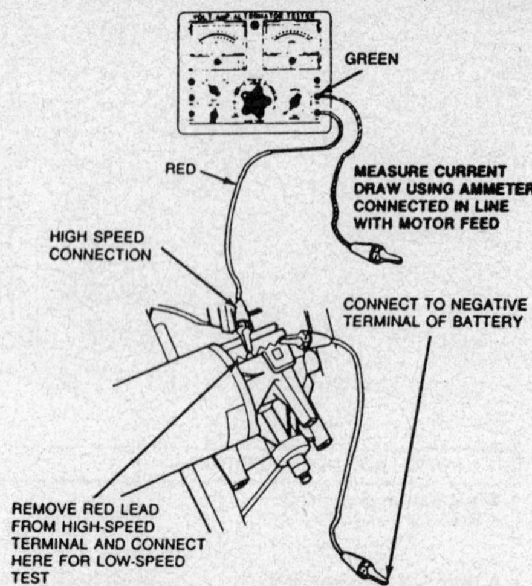


**Fig. 41 Wiper motor current draw test. Scorpio**

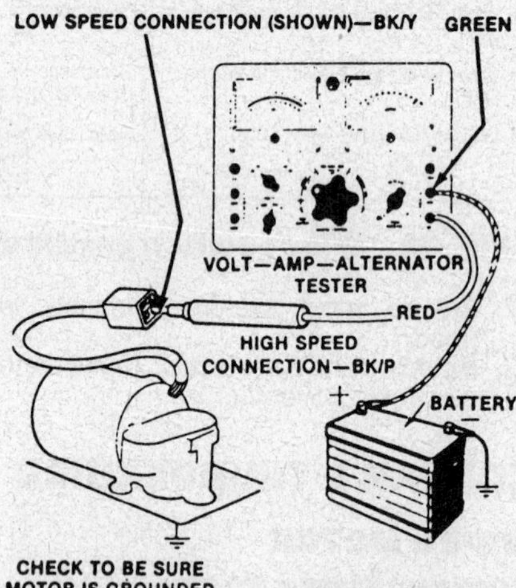


**Fig. 42 Wiper motor current draw test. XR4TI**

switch lever to detect marginal switch operation.

Refer to **Fig. 40** for switch terminal identification and continuity readings.

# MERKUR

## WIPER MOTOR

### Current Draw Test

1. Disconnect wiper motor electrical connector.
2. Make test connections as shown **Fig. 41 or 42.** Alternately connect red test lead to wiper motor low and high speed connectors.
3. **On Scorpio models,** current draw at either terminal should not exceed 3.5 amps.
4. **On XR4TI models,** current draw at either terminal should not exceed 3 amps.

### Park Operation Test

1. Turn ignition switch to ON.
2. Turn wiper switch to ON.
3. When wipers are in a non-parked position, turn ignition switch to OFF.
4. Make test connections as shown **Fig. 43.** Wiper motor should run one full cycle then park.
5. If wiper motor does not run to park, check for continuity at wiper switch and wiper system wiring. Repair as needed.

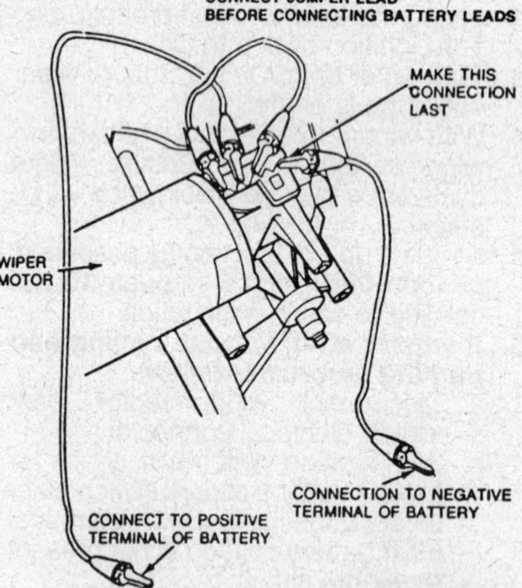


**Fig. 43 Wiper motor park operation test. Scorpio**

## WIPER SWITCH

### Continuity Test

When testing a non-intermittent wiper switch, a self-powered test lamp or an ohmmeter can be used to check continuity. When testing an intermittent wiper switch, use only an ohmmeter to check continuity.

When taking test readings move the switch lever to detect marginal switch operation.

Refer to **Fig. 44** for switch terminal identification and continuity readings.

# PROBE

Refer to **Fig. 15** for wiper system wiring schematic, and **Fig. 16** for diagnostic and testing procedures.

# FESTIVA

Refer to **Fig. 17** for diagnostic and testing procedures.

# 1989 TRACER

Refer to **Fig. 18** for diagnostic and testing procedures.

# 1991 ESCORT & TRACER

Refer to **Fig. 19** for wiper system wiring schematic, and **Fig. 20** for diagnostic and testing procedures.

# CAPRI

Refer to **Fig. 21** for wiper system wiring schematic, and **Fig. 22** for diagnostic and testing procedures.

| Switch Function① (Circuit Test) | Verify Continuity Between Pins of Switch Connector. |
|---|---|
| Windshield wiper switch lever in OFF position. | Pins 3 and 12, Pins 5 and 7, Pins 9 and 11. |
| Windshield wiper switch in INTERVAL position. | Pins 2 and 9, Pins 2 and 11, Pins 3 and 12, Pins 5 and 8 and Pins 9 and 11①. |
| Windshield wiper switch in SINGLE WIPE position. **NOTE: Switch must be held in position throughout test.** | Pins 2 and 5, Pins 3 and 12 and Pins 9 and 11. |
| Windshield wiper switch in LOW position. | Pins 2 and 5, Pins 3 and 12, and Pins 9 and 11. |
| Windshield wiper switch in HIGH position. | Pins 2 and 6, Pins 3 and 12 and Pins 9 and 11. |
| Windshield washer switch button pressed in. **NOTE: Button must be held in during test.** | Pins 1 and 4. |
| Liftgate wiper switch in ON position. | Pins 2 and 12. |
| Liftgate washer switch held in ON position. | Pins 2 and 10 and Pins 2 and 12. |
| Rotate interval wipe rheostat through positions 1 through 6. | Resistance between Pins 9 and 11 should vary between 2 and 100 ohms. |

①Interval wipe rheostat should be in position 1 during continuity tests.

**Fig. 44 Wiper switch continuity test. Scorpio**

# Rear Wiper System

## INDEX



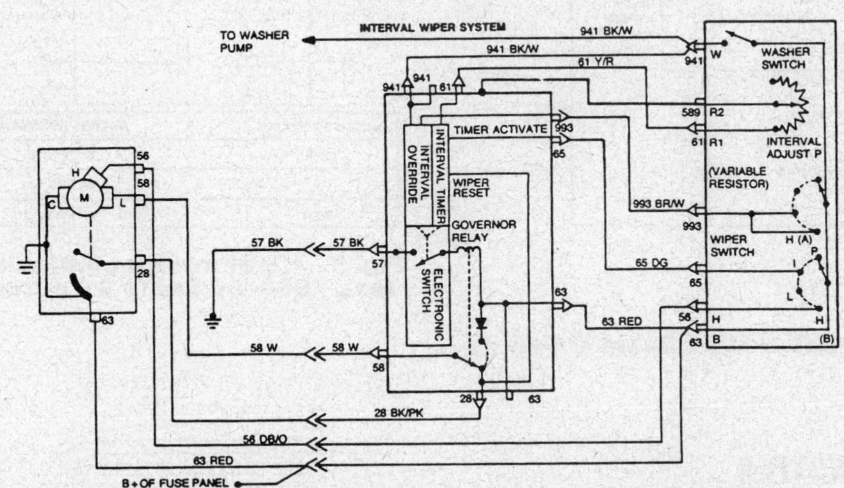


**Fig. 1 Wiper system wiring schematic. 1989–90 Escort**

## TESTING

### 1989–90 ESCORT

Refer to **Fig. 1** for rear wiper system wiring schematic.

#### WIPER MOTOR

1. **On station wagon models,** remove screws retaining license plate housing, disconnect lamp electrical connectors, then remove housing.
2. **On 3 and 5 door models,** remove liftgate inner trim panel.
3. **On all models,** remove wiper motor connector clip from retainer hole. Separate connector halves.
4. Ground the motor gear box.
5. Motor should run when 13.5 volts are applied to the white lead.
6. Motor should run and stop in park position when 13.5 volts are applied to the red lead.
7. If wiper motor operation is improper, replace or repair as needed.

#### CIRCUIT BREAKER

1. Remove circuit breaker from fuse panel.
2. Using a suitable Volt-Amp meter, adjust current draw to equal the circuit breaker rating.
3. Connect circuit breaker to tester for 10 minutes. If circuit breaker opens within the time specified, replace it.
4. Readjust current draw to equal twice the circuit breaker rating.
5. Connect circuit breaker to tester. The ammeter current reading should drop to zero within 30 seconds. If circuit breaker does not open within the time specified, replace it.

#### WIPER SWITCH

#### Continuity Test

When testing a non-intermittent wiper switch, a self-powered test lamp or an ohmmeter can be used to check continuity. When testing an intermittent wiper switch, use only an ohmmeter to check continuity.

When taking test readings move the switch lever to detect marginal switch operation.

Refer to **Figs. 2** for switch terminal identification and test readings.

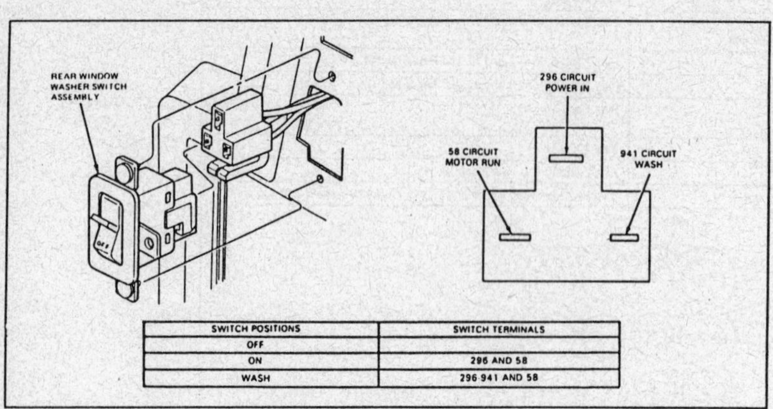


| SWITCH POSITIONS | SWITCH TERMINALS |
|---|---|
| OFF | |
| ON | 296 AND 58 |
| WASH | 296 941 AND 58 |

**Fig. 2 Wiper switch continuity test. 1989–90 Escort**

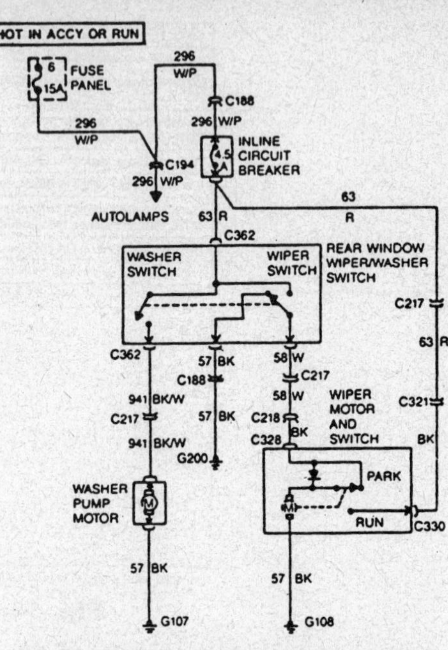


**Fig. 3 Wiper system wiring schematic. 1989-90 Sable & Taurus**

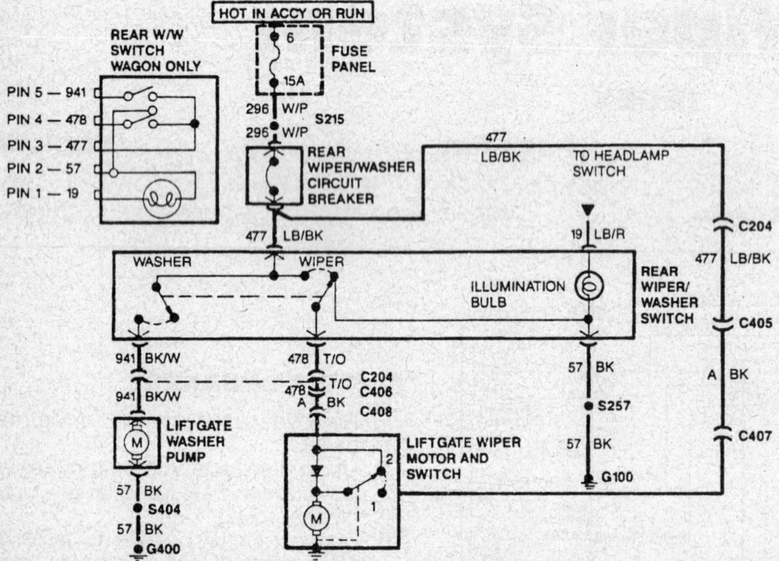


**Fig. 4 Wiper system wiring schematic. 1991 Sable & Taurus**

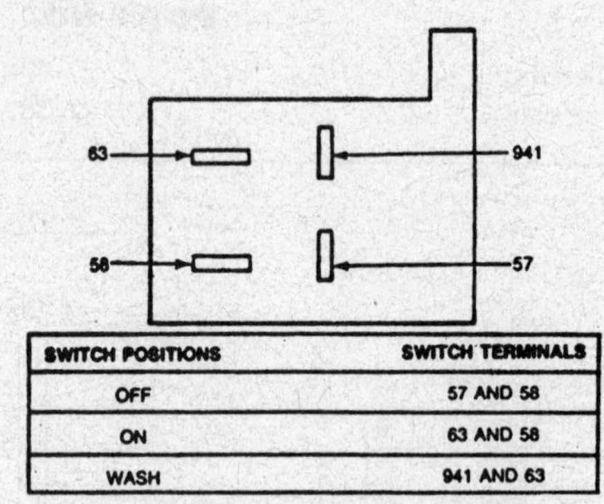


| SWITCH POSITIONS | SWITCH TERMINALS |
|---|---|
| OFF | 57 AND 58 |
| ON | 63 AND 58 |
| WASH | 941 AND 63 |

**Fig. 5 Wiper switch continuity test. 1989–90 Sable & Taurus**

## SABLE & TAURUS

### WIPER SWITCH

### Continuity Test

Refer to **Figs. 3 and 4** for rear wiper system wiring schematic. Refer to **Figs. 5 and 6** for switch terminal identification and test readings.

When testing a non-intermittent wiper switch, a self-powered test lamp or an ohmmeter can be used to check continuity. When testing an intermittent wiper switch, use only an ohmmeter to check continuity.

When taking test readings move the switch lever to detect marginal switch operation.

## FESTIVA

Refer to **Fig. 7** for diagnostic and testing procedures.

## PROBE

Refer to **Fig. 8** for rear wiper system wiring schematic, and **Fig. 9** for diagnostic and testing procedures.

## 1991 ESCORT & TRACER

Refer to **Fig. 10** for rear wiper system wiring schematic, and **Fig. 11** for diagnostic and testing procedures.

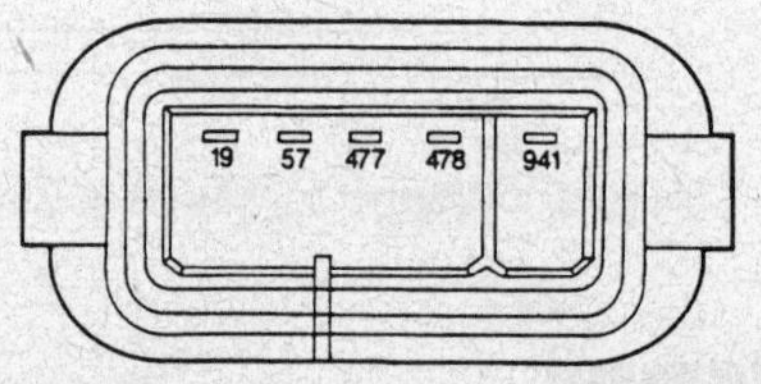


| SWITCH POSITIONS | SWITCH TERMINALS |
|---|---|
| OFF | 57 AND 478 |
| ON | 477 AND 478 |
| WASH (ON) | 477, 478 AND 941 |

**Fig. 6 Wiper switch continuity test. 1991 Sable & Taurus**

**Electrical Schematic**

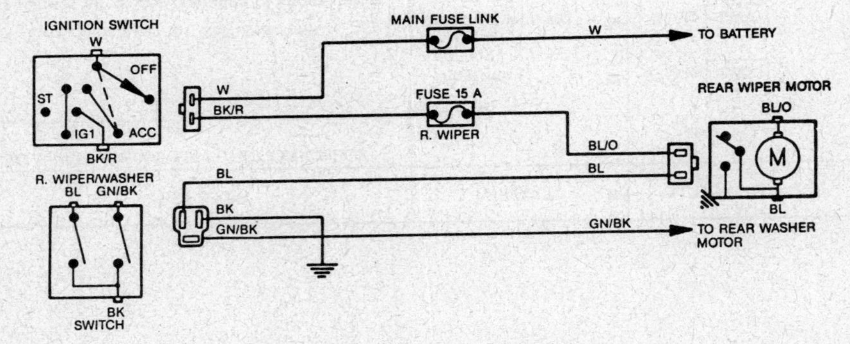

IGNITION SWITCH
W
OFF
ST
IG1
ACC
BK/R
R. WIPER/WASHER
BL GN/BK
BK
SWITCH
W
BK/R
BL
BK
GN/BK
MAIN FUSE LINK
FUSE 15 A
R. WIPER
W
TO BATTERY
BL/O
BL
GN/BK
REAR WIPER MOTOR
BL/O
BL
TO REAR WASHER MOTOR

| LW-01 SELECT SYMPTOM FROM DIAGNOSTIC MENU | | |
|---|---|---|
| **TEST STEP** | **RESULT** | **ACTION TO TAKE** |
| Turn ignition switch to "ON" position. | | |
| Turn rear wiper switch to "ON" position. | Wiper not working | Go to LW-02. |
| | Park not working | Go to LW-07. |
| | Wiper won't stop | Go to LW-03. |

| LW-02 LIFTGATE WIPER SUPPLY CHECK | | |
|---|---|---|
| **TEST STEP** | **RESULT** | **ACTION TO TAKE** |
| Disconnect wiper motor connector; turn key on. | | |
| Check for 12V on "BL/O" wire at liftgate wiper motor. | | |
| Is there 12V? | Yes | Go to LW-03. |
| | No | Go to LW-06. |

**Fig. 7 Wiper system diagnosis & testing (Part 1 of 6). Festiva**

| LW-03 LIFTGATE WIPER MOTOR GROUND CHECK | | |
|---|---|---|
| **TEST STEP** | **RESULT** | **ACTION TO TAKE** |
| Disconnect liftgate wiper motor connector. | | |
| Check for continuity to ground on "BL" wire at wiper motor. | Yes (Wiper won't stop) | Go to LW-07. |
| Operate wiper motor switch. | (Wiper not working) | Replace liftgate wiper motor. |
| Is there continuity when the switch is "ON"? | No | Go to LW-04. |

**Fig. 7 Wiper system diagnosis & testing (Part 2 of 6). Festiva**

| LW-04 LIFTGATE WIPER/WASHER SWITCH CONTINUITY CHECK | | |
|---|---|---|
| **TEST STEP** | **RESULT** | **ACTION TO TAKE** |
| Disconnect "BL" wire from wiper/washer switch. | | |
| Check continuity between liftgate wiper/washer switch "BL" terminal and ground. | | |
| Operate wiper/washer switch. | | |
| Is there continuity when the switch is "ON"? | No | Go to LW-05. |
| | Yes | Repair "BL" wire between liftgate wiper/washer switch and liftgate wiper motor. |

**Fig. 7 Wiper system diagnosis & testing (Part 3 of 6). Festiva**

| LW-05 LIFTGATE WIPER/WASHER SWITCH GROUND CHECK | | |
|---|---|---|
| **TEST STEP** | **RESULT** | **ACTION TO TAKE** |
| Disconnect wiper/washer switch connector. | | |
| Check for continuity to ground on "BK" wire at wiper/washer switch. | No | Repair "BK" wire between liftgate wiper/washer switch and ground. |
| Is there continuity? | Yes | Replace wiper/washer switch. |

**Fig. 7 Wiper system diagnosis & testing (Part 4 of 6). Festiva**

| LW-07 LIFTGATE WIPER/WASHER MOTOR CONTINUITY CHECK | | |
|---|---|---|
| **TEST STEP** | **RESULT** | **ACTION TO TAKE** |
| Place liftgate wiper out of park position by turning ignition switch to "OFF" position when wiper is in the center of travel.<br>Disconnect wiper motor connector.<br>Remove liftgate wiper fuse. Turn the liftgate wiper switch to "OFF" position.<br>Check for continuity to ground at the following places:<br>–Wiper motor case.<br>–Wiper motor "BL" terminal. | No continuity at:<br>–Wiper motor case<br><br>No continuity at:<br>–Wiper motor "BL" terminal. | Repair case ground of liftgate wiper motor.<br><br>Replace liftgate wiper motor. |

**Fig. 7 Wiper system diagnosis & testing (Part 5 of 6). Festiva**

| LW-06 POWER TO LIFTGATE WIPER FUSE | | |
|---|---|---|
| **TEST STEP** | **RESULT** | **ACTION TO TAKE** |
| Remove liftgate wiper fuse, key "ON." | No | Service "BK/R" wire to ignition switch. |
| Check for 12V on (ignition switch side) of R. wiper fuse.<br>Is there 12V? | Yes | Service fuse and/or "BL/O" wire from fuse to wiper motor. |

**Fig. 7 Wiper system diagnosis & testing (Part 6 of 6). Festiva**

| TEST STEP | | RESULT ► | ACTION TO TAKE |
|---|---|---|---|
| LW1 | LIFTGATE WIPER FUNCTION CHECK | | |
| | • Turn ignition key to "ON" position.<br>• Check for proper operation of liftgate wiper by engaging and disengaging liftgate wiper switch. | Wiper not working ►<br>Park not working ►<br>Wiper won't stop ► | GO to LW2 .<br>GO to LW7 .<br>GO to LW8 . |

**Fig. 9 Wiper system diagnosis & testing (Part 1 of 8). Probe**

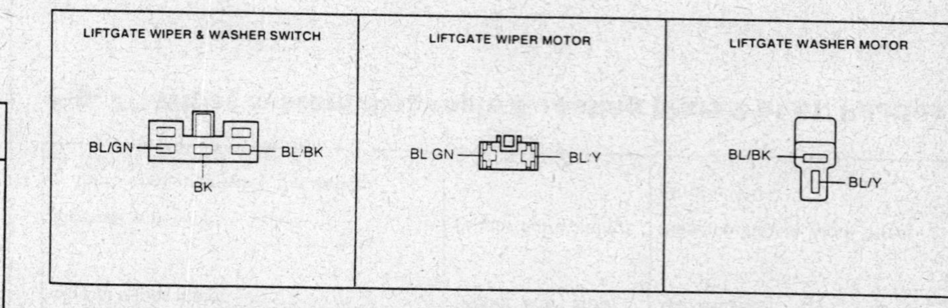


**Fig. 8 Wiper system wiring schematic. Probe**

| TEST STEP | RESULT ► | ACTION TO TAKE |
|---|---|---|
| **LW4** LIFTGATE WASHER CHECK (WIPER NOT WORKING) | | |
| • Turn on liftgate washer.<br>• Does washer operate properly? | Yes ►<br>No ► | GO to LW5 .<br>REPAIR "BK" wire between liftgate wiper/washer switch and ground. |

**Fig. 9 Wiper system diagnosis & testing (Part 2 of 8). Probe**

| TEST STEP | RESULT ► | ACTION TO TAKE |
|---|---|---|
| **LW3** LIFTGATE WIPER MOTOR CHECK (WIPER NOT WORKING) | | |
| • Disconnect liftgate wiper motor.<br>• Apply 12 volts (±1 volt) and ground directly to motor as shown.<br>• Does motor operate properly? | Yes ►<br>No ► | GO to LW4 .<br>REPLACE liftgate wiper motor. |

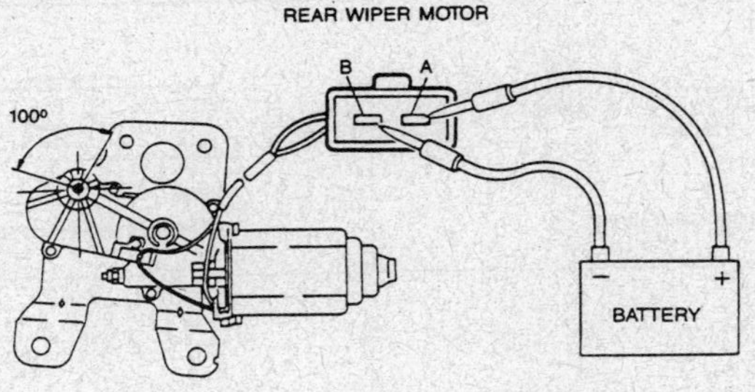

REAR WIPER MOTOR
B
A
100°
BATTERY
−
+

**Fig. 9 Wiper system diagnosis & testing (Part 3 of 8). Probe**

| TEST STEP | RESULT ► | ACTION TO TAKE |
|---|---|---|
| **LW2** LIFTGATE WIPER FUSE CHECK (WIPER NOT WORKING) | | |
| • Check liftgate wiper (rear wiper) fuse.<br>• Is fuse OK? | Yes ►<br>No ► | GO to LW3 .<br>REPLACE fuse. (Read note) |
| NOTE: If fuse blows again, check for shorts to ground in "BL/Y" wires at liftgate wiper motor and liftgate washer motor. Repair "BL/Y" wires as needed. | | |

**Fig. 9 Wiper system diagnosis & testing (Part 4 of 8). Probe**

| TEST STEP | RESULT ► | ACTION TO TAKE |
|---|---|---|
| **LW5** LIFTGATE WIPER SUPPLY CHECK (WIPER NOT WORKING) | | |
| • Check for 12 volts (±1 volt) on "BL/Y" wire at liftgate wiper motor connector.<br>• Is there 12 volts? | Yes ►<br>No ► | GO to LW6 .<br>REPAIR "BL/Y" wire between liftgate wiper motor and liftgate wiper fuse. |

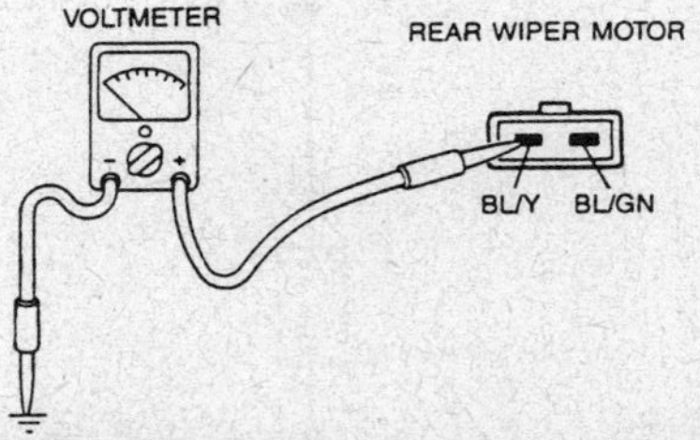

VOLTMETER
REAR WIPER MOTOR
BL/Y
BL/GN
SHOWN LOOKING INTO BACK OF CONNECTOR

**Fig. 9 Wiper system diagnosis & testing (Part 5 of 8). Probe**

| TEST STEP | RESULT ► | ACTION TO TAKE |
|---|---|---|
| **LW6** LIFTGATE SWITCH CONTINUITY CHECK (WIPER NOT WORKING) | | |
| • Remove rear wiper fuse.<br>• Push liftgate wiper switch to "ON" position.<br>• Check continuity between ground and liftgate wiper/washer switch "BL/GN" wire connector.<br>• Is there continuity? | Yes ►<br>No ► | REPAIR "BL/GN" wire between liftgate wiper/washer switch and liftgate wiper motor.<br>REPLACE liftgate wiper/washer switch. |

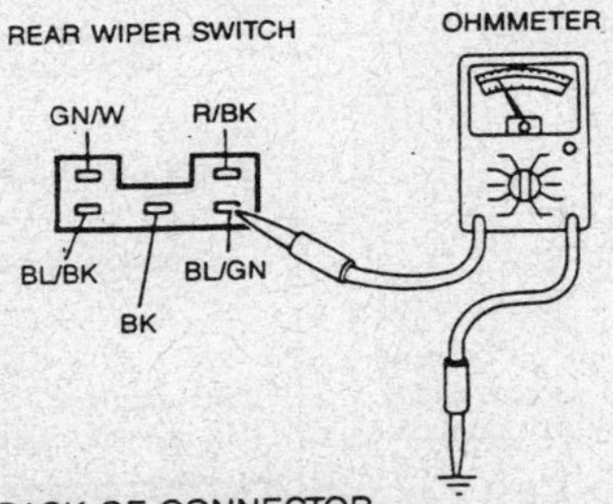

REAR WIPER SWITCH
OHMMETER
GN/W
R/BK
BL/BK
BL/GN
BK
SHOWN LOOKING INTO BACK OF CONNECTOR

**Fig. 9 Wiper system diagnosis & testing (Part 6 of 8). Probe**

| TEST STEP | RESULT ► | ACTION TO TAKE |
|---|---|---|
| **LW7** LIFTGATE SWITCH CONTINUITY CHECK (PARK NOT WORKING) | | |
| • Place liftgate wiper out of park position by turning ignition key to "OFF" position when wiper is in the center of travel.<br>• Remove wiper fuse.<br>• Turn the liftgate wiper/washer switch to "OFF" position.<br>• Check for continuity to ground at the following places:<br>– Wiper motor case<br>– Wiper motor "BL/Y" wire connector | No continuity at:<br>– Wiper motor case ►<br>– Wiper motor "BL/Y" wire ► | REPAIR case ground of liftgate wiper motor.<br>REPLACE liftgate wiper motor. |

REAR WIPER MOTOR

BL/Y

BL/GN

100°

OHMMETER

SHOWN LOOKING INTO BACK OF CONNECTOR

**Fig. 9 Wiper system diagnosis & testing (Part 7 of 8). Probe**

| TEST STEP | RESULT ► | ACTION TO TAKE |
|---|---|---|
| **LW8** LIFTGATE WIPER/WASHER SWITCH CHECK (WIPER WILL NOT STOP) | | |
| • Engage liftgate wiper.<br>• Disconnect liftgate wiper/washer switch connector.<br>• Does wiper motor stop? | Yes ►<br>No ► | REPLACE liftgate wiper/ washer switch.<br>REPAIR "BL/GN" wire between liftgate wiper motor and liftgate wiper/ washer switch. |

**Fig. 9 Wiper system diagnosis & testing (Part 8 of 8). Probe**

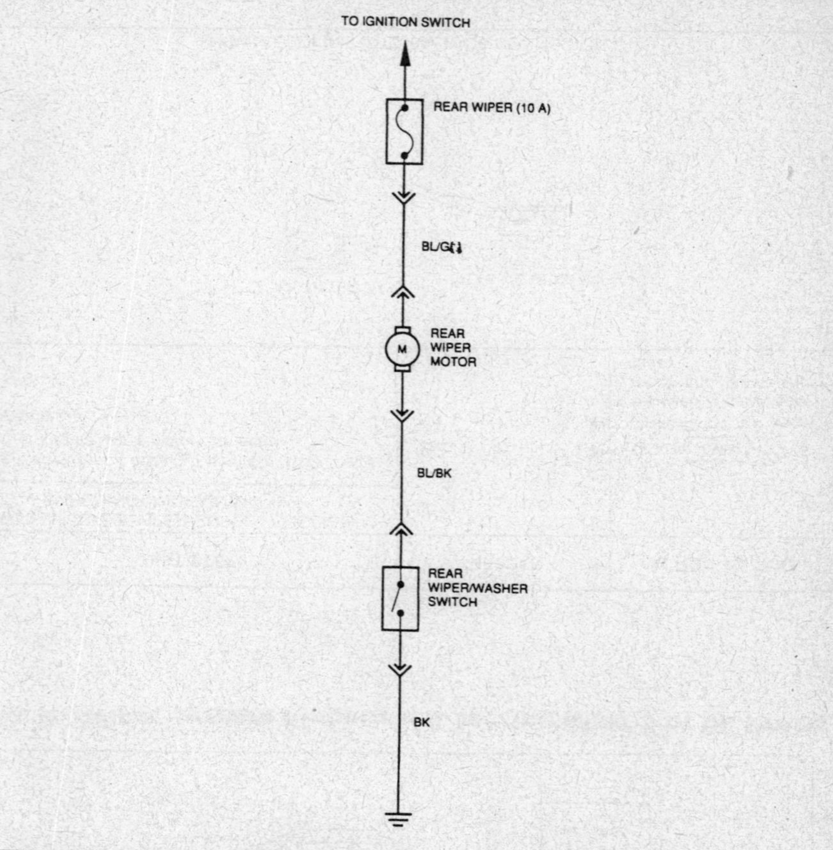


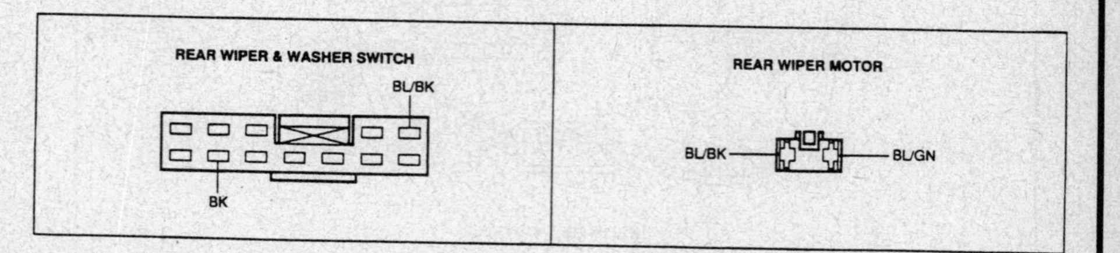


**Fig. 10 Wiper system wiring schematic. 1991 Escort & Tracer**

| SYMPTOM | POSSIBLE CAUSE | ACTION |
|---|---|---|
| • Wiper Does Not Operate | • Wiper motor.<br>• Wiper switch.<br>• Blown fuse.<br>• Wiper circuit. | • GO to **LW1.** |
| • Wiper Operates Constantly | • Wiper switch.<br>• Wiper circuit. | GO to **LW8.** |

**Fig. 11 Wiper system diagnosis & testing (Part 1 of 9). 1991 Escort & Tracer**

| TEST STEP | RESULT ► | ACTION TO TAKE |
|---|---|---|
| **LW1** REAR WIPER FUSE CHECK | | |
| • Access the fuse panel.<br>• Check the rear wiper 10 amp fuse.<br>• Is the fuse OK? | Yes ►<br>No ► | GO to LW4 .<br>GO to LW2 . |

**Fig. 11 Wiper system diagnosis & testing (Part 2 of 9). 1991 Escort & Tracer**

| TEST STEP | RESULT ► | ACTION TO TAKE |
|---|---|---|
| **LW2** REAR WIPER MOTOR SUPPLY INTEGRITY CHECK | | |
| • Replace the rear wiper fuse.<br>• Key ON.<br>• Check the rear wiper fuse.<br>• Is the fuse OK? | Yes ►<br>No ► | GO to LW3 .<br>SERVICE the "BL/GN" wire for short to ground. |

**Fig. 11 Wiper system diagnosis & testing (Part 3 of 9). 1991 Escort & Tracer**

| TEST STEP | RESULT ► | ACTION TO TAKE |
|---|---|---|
| **LW3** REAR WIPER SYSTEM CHECK | | |
| • Key ON.<br>• Rear wipers ON.<br>• Check the rear wiper fuse.<br>• Is the fuse OK? | Yes ►<br>No ► | System OK.<br>REPLACE the wiper motor. |

**Fig. 11 Wiper system diagnosis & testing (Part 4 of 9). 1991 Escort & Tracer**

| TEST STEP | RESULT ► | ACTION TO TAKE |
|---|---|---|
| **LW4** REAR WIPER MOTOR VOLTAGE CHECK | | |
| • Key ON.<br>• Rear wiper motor connector is disconnected.<br>• Measure voltage on the "BL/GN" wire at the wire motor connector.<br>• Is the voltage greater than 10 volts? | Yes ►<br>No ► | GO to LW5 .<br>SERVICE the "BL/GN" wire for an open. |

**Fig. 11 Wiper system diagnosis & testing (Part 5 of 9). 1991 Escort & Tracer**

| TEST STEP | RESULT ► | ACTION TO TAKE |
|---|---|---|
| **LW5** REAR WIPER SWITCH VOLTAGE CHECK | | |
| • Key ON.<br>• Reconnect the rear wiper motor connector.<br>• Disconnect the rear wiper switch connector.<br>• Measure the voltage on the "BL/BK" wire at the wiper switch connector.<br>• Is the voltage greater than 10 volts? | Yes ►<br>No ► | GO to LW6 .<br>SERVICE the "BL/BK" wire for an open. |

**Fig. 11 Wiper system diagnosis & testing (Part 6 of 9). 1991 Escort & Tracer**

| TEST STEP | | RESULT ► | ACTION TO TAKE |
|---|---|---|---|
| LW6 | REAR WIPER GROUND CHECK | | |
| • Key OFF.<br>• Measure the resistance of the "BK" wire from the wiper switch connector to ground.<br>• Is the resistance less than 5 ohms? | | Yes ►<br>No ► | GO to LW7 .<br>SERVICE the "BK" wire for an open or poor connection to ground. |

**Fig. 11 Wiper system diagnosis & testing (Part 7 of 9). 1991 Escort & Tracer**

| TEST STEP | | RESULT ► | ACTION TO TAKE |
|---|---|---|---|
| LW7 | REAR WIPER SWITCH CHECK | | |
| • Rear wiper switch connector is disconnected.<br>• Jumper "BL/BK" wire at wiper switch connector to ground.<br>• Key ON.<br>• Do the rear wipers operate? | | Yes ►<br>No ► | REPLACE the rear wiper switch.<br>REPLACE the rear wiper motor. |

**Fig. 11 Wiper system diagnosis & testing (Part 8 of 9). 1991 Escort & Tracer**

| TEST STEP | | RESULT ► | ACTION TO TAKE |
|---|---|---|---|
| LW8 | REAR WIPER SWITCH SUPPLY INTEGRITY CHECK | | |
| • Key OFF.<br>• Rear wiper motor connector is disconnected.<br>• Rear wiper switch connector is disconnected.<br>• Connect the ohmmeter terminal to the "BL/BK" wire. Connect other ohmmeter terminal to ground.<br>• Measure the resistance.<br>• Is resistance greater than 10,000 ohms? | | Yes ►<br>No ► | REPLACE the rear wiper switch.<br>SERVICE "BL/BK" wire for short to ground. |

**Fig. 11 Wiper system diagnosis & testing (Part 9 of 9). 1991 Escort & Tracer**

# SPEED CONTROLS

## INDEX



---

## AIRBAG SYSTEM DISARMING

**The electrical circuit necessary for system deployment is powered directly from the battery and a backup power supply. To avoid accidental deployment and possible personal injury, the airbag system must be deactivated prior to servicing or replacing any system components.**

A back-up power supply is included in the system to provide airbag deployment in the event the battery or battery cables are damaged in an accident before the sensors can close. The power supply is a capacitor that will retain a charge for approximately 15 minutes after the battery ground cable is disconnected. **Backup power supply must be disconnected to deactivate airbag system.** To remove backup power supply, refer to "Airbags" in the "Passive Restraint" section.

1. Disconnect battery ground cable.
2. Disconnect backup power supply.
3. Remove four nut and washer assemblies securing airbag module to steering wheel, then disconnect airbag electrical connector. Attach jumper wire to airbag terminals on clockspring terminals.
4. **On models equipped with passenger-side airbag,** disconnect airbag module connector located behind glove compartment. Attach a jumper wire to airbag terminals on wiring harness side of passenger airbag module connector terminals.
5. **On all models,** reconnect battery and backup power supply if necessary to perform repair procedure.
6. To reactivate, disconnect battery ground cable and backup power supply, then reverse remainder of deactivation procedure. **Torque** airbag module to 35-53 inch lbs.
7. Verify airbag lamp after reactivating system.

## ESCORT, MUSTANG, TEMPO, TOPAZ & 1991 TRACER

### SYSTEM DESCRIPTION

The speed control system is composed of On-Off, Set-Acc, Coast and Resume switches. The system contains vacuum hoses, servo (throttle actuator) assembly, speed sensor, amplifier, check valve assembly, and depending on model and year, a clutch switch, a manual lever position switch, stop light switch, or vacuum dump valve, an actuator (servo) and an actuator cable.

### SYSTEM OPERATION

To operate speed control system, engine must be running and vehicle speed must exceed 30 mph. When On-Off switch is actuated, the system is ready to accept a set speed signal. When vehicle speed stabilizes (above 30 mph), and the On switch is engaged, the operator may depress or release the Set-Acc button. This speed will be maintained until a new speed has been set, brake pedal has been depressed, or the system is turned off.

The vehicle speed may be reduced by applying the brake or clutch pedal and then resetting the speed using the method outlined above or by depressing the COAST switch. When the vehicle has slowed to the desired speed, the COAST switch is released and the new speed is set automatically. If the vehicle speed is reduced below 30 mph (48 km/h), the operator must manually increase the speed and reset the system.

### ADJUSTMENTS

#### Linkage Actuator cable, (Chain Type)

1. **On all models except Mustang,** with the engine off, set throttle linkage so throttle is closed.
2. Remove locking pin.
3. Pull bead chain through adjuster.
4. Install locking pin into the hole which keeps the chain taught, but does not open throttle.
5. **On Mustang,** remove speed control actuator cable retaining clip.
6. Push actuator cable through adjuster until slight tension is felt.
7. Insert cable retaining clip and snap into place.

#### Linkage Actuator cable, (Cable Type)

1. Remove the cable adjusting clip from the cable housing.
2. **On all models,** pull lightly on the cable until all of the slack is taken out.
3. Maintain light pressure on cable, then install the cable adjusting clip and snap into place.

#### Vacuum Dump Valve

1. Firmly depress brake pedal and hold.
2. Push dump valve in until valve collar bottoms against retaining clip.
3. Place a .05-.10 inch shim between white button on valve and pad on brake pedal.
4. Firmly pull brake pedal rearward to its normal position. Allow dump valve to move into position in retaining clip.

#### Clutch Switch

1. Secure clutch pedal in the full up position.
2. Loosen switch mounting screw, then slide switch forward toward clutch pedal, until switch plunger cap is .030 inch from contacting switch housing.
3. Release clutch pedal. Test drive vehicle and ensure proper operation of switch.

### DIAGNOSIS & TROUBLESHOOTING

Refer to "Component Testing" when performing the following procedures, also the wiring diagrams in **Figs. 1 through 4,** can be used as an diagnostic aid when following the procedures outlined below.

#### SPEED CONTROL IS INOPERATIVE

1. Apply brake pedal and ensure brake lights work. If found satisfactory, proceed to step 2. If not found satisfactory, check stop lamp circuit.
2. Check to ensure proper operation of clutch deactivator switch (manual

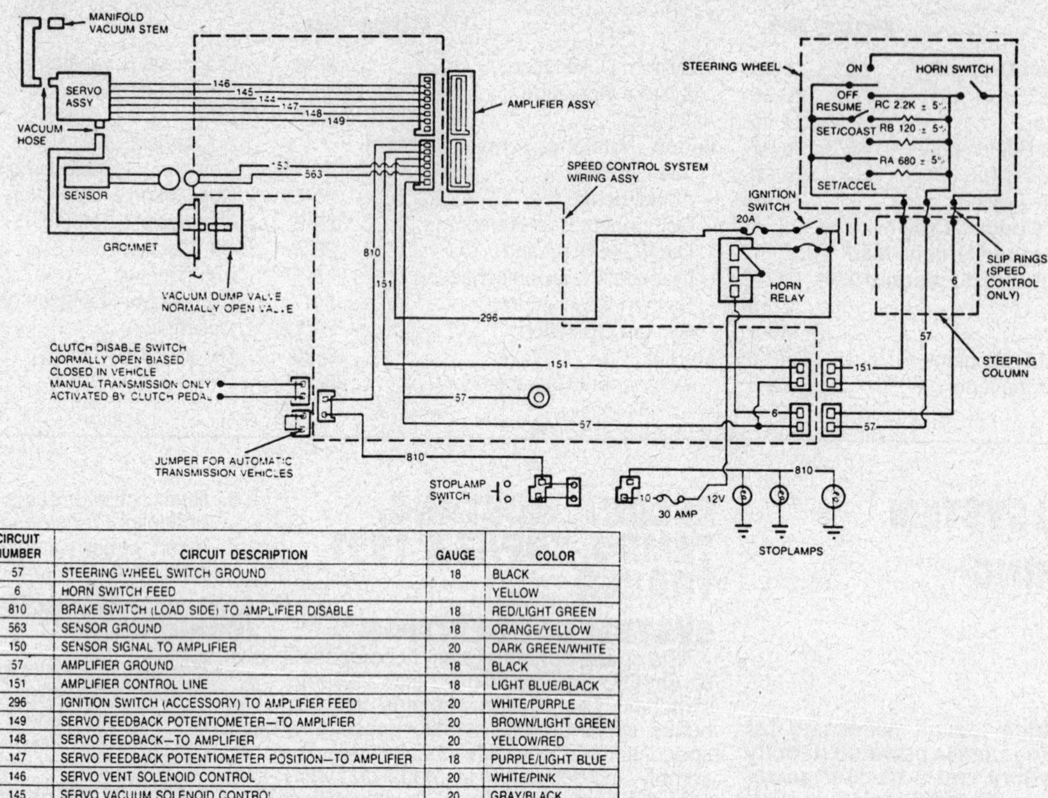


| CIRCUIT NUMBER | CIRCUIT DESCRIPTION | GAUGE | COLOR |
|---|---|---|---|
| 57 | STEERING WHEEL SWITCH GROUND | 18 | BLACK |
| 6 | HORN SWITCH FEED | | YELLOW |
| 810 | BRAKE SWITCH (LOAD SIDE) TO AMPLIFIER DISABLE | 18 | RED/LIGHT GREEN |
| 563 | SENSOR GROUND | 18 | ORANGE/YELLOW |
| 150 | SENSOR SIGNAL TO AMPLIFIER | 20 | DARK GREEN/WHITE |
| 57 | AMPLIFIER GROUND | 18 | BLACK |
| 151 | AMPLIFIER CONTROL LINE | 18 | LIGHT BLUE/BLACK |
| 296 | IGNITION SWITCH (ACCESSORY) TO AMPLIFIER FEED | 20 | WHITE/PURPLE |
| 149 | SERVO FEEDBACK POTENTIOMETER—TO AMPLIFIER | 20 | BROWN/LIGHT GREEN |
| 148 | SERVO FEEDBACK—TO AMPLIFIER | 20 | YELLOW/RED |
| 147 | SERVO FEEDBACK POTENTIOMETER POSITION—TO AMPLIFIER | 18 | PURPLE/LIGHT BLUE |
| 146 | SERVO VENT SOLENOID CONTROL | 20 | WHITE/PINK |
| 145 | SERVO VACUUM SOLENOID CONTROL | 20 | GRAY/BLACK |
| 144 | SERVO SOLENOID FEED | 20 | ORANGE/YELLOW |

**Fig. 1 Speed control wiring diagram. Mustang**

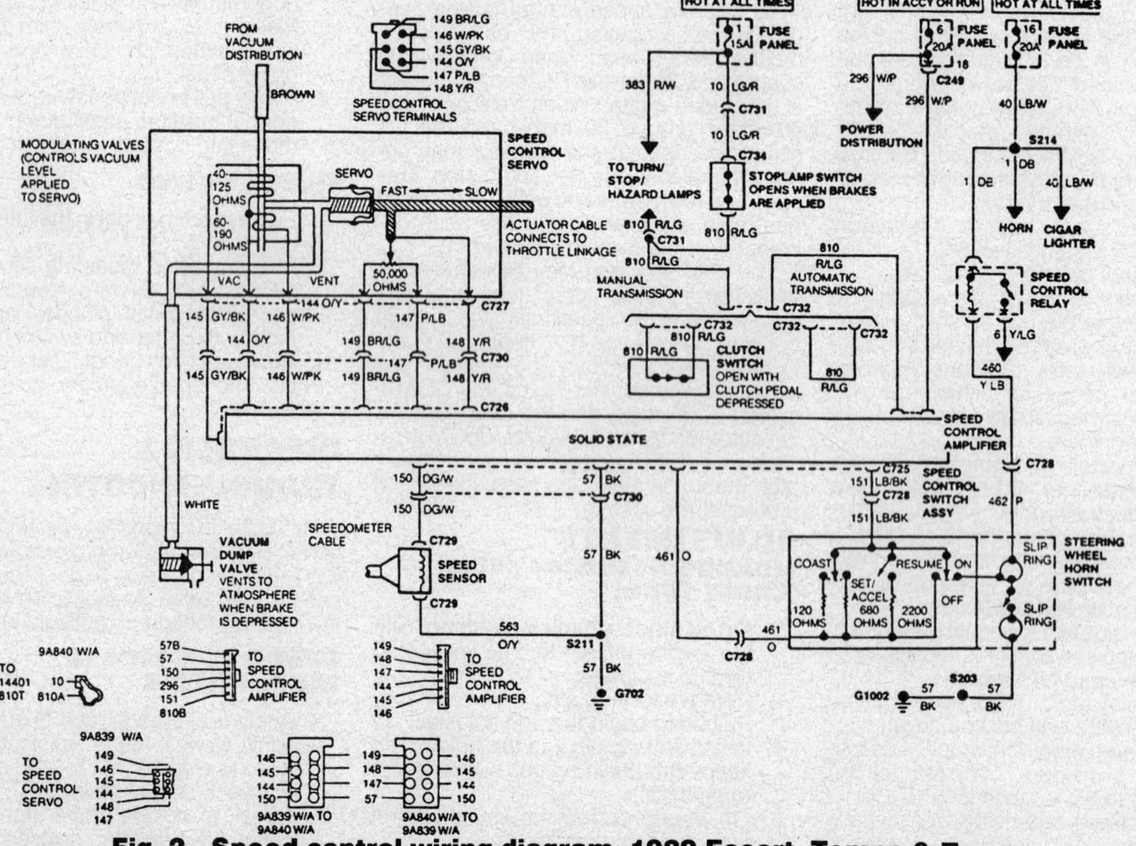


**Fig. 2 Speed control wiring diagram. 1989 Escort, Tempo & Topaz**

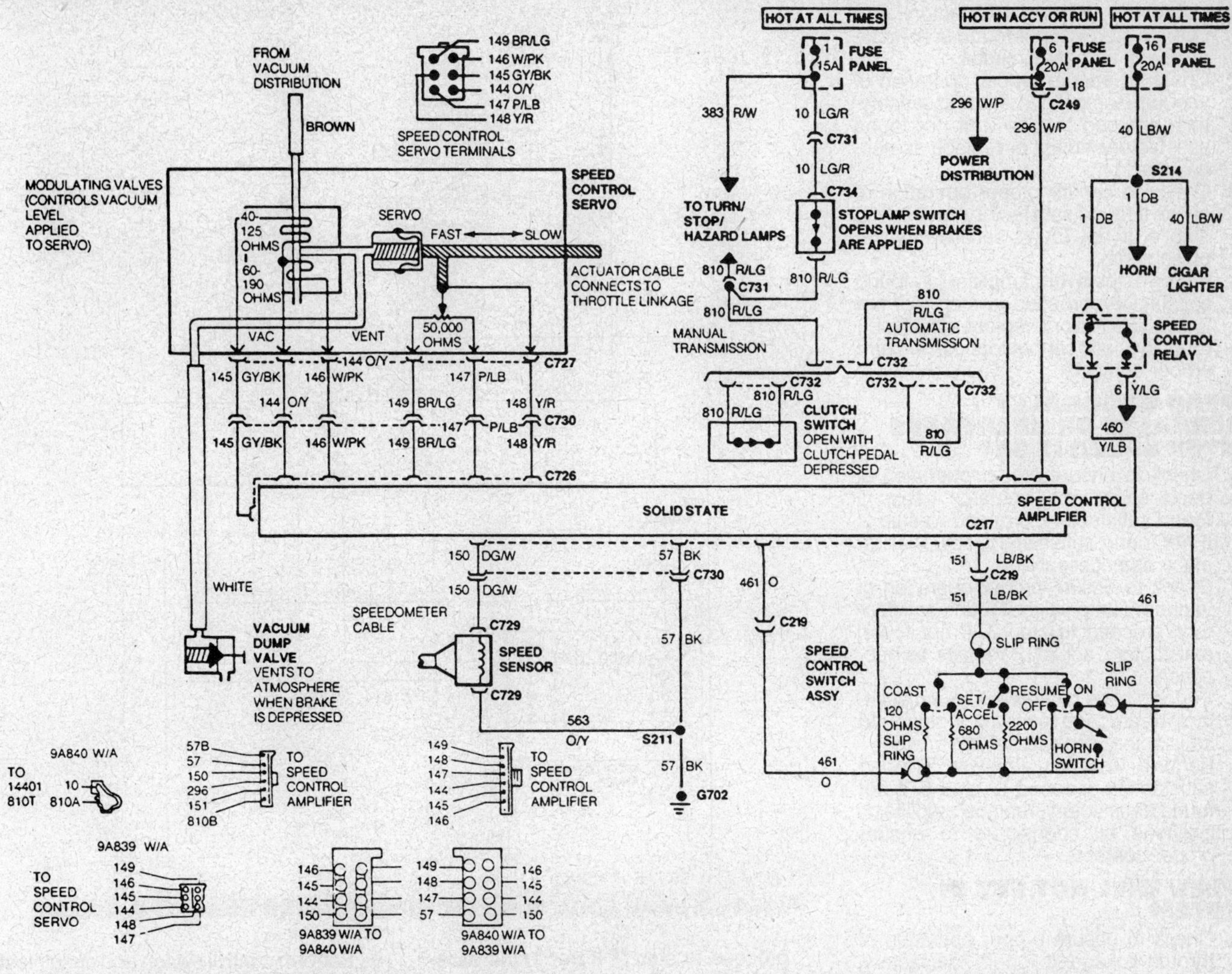


**Fig. 3 Speed control wiring diagram. 1990 Escort, 1990–91 Tempo & Topaz**

transmission only). If found satisfactory, proceed to step 3. If not found satisfactory, service or replace as necessary.

3. Check to ensure proper operation of actuator lever and throttle linkage. If found satisfactory, proceed to step 4. If not found satisfactory, service or replace actuator lever and throttle linkage.
4. Check to ensure proper vacuum at actuator. If found satisfactory, proceed to step 5. If not found satisfactory, service or replace vacuum hose and vacuum dump valve.
5. Perform tests on control switches and circuit. If found satisfactory, proceed to step 6. If not found satisfactory, service or replace switches and circuits.
6. Perform tests on servo. If found satisfactory, proceed to step 7. If not found satisfactory, replace servo.
7. Perform tests on speed sensor. If found satisfactory, proceed to step 8. If not found satisfactory, replace speed sensor.
8. Perform tests on amplifier. If found satisfactory, proceed to step 9. If not found satisfactory, replace amplifier.
9. Examine all connectors to ensure proper contacts.

## SPEED CONTINUOUSLY CHANGES UP AND DOWN

1. Check to ensure proper operation of actuator linkage. If found satisfactory, proceed to step 2. If not found satisfactory, service or replace actuator linkage.
2. Check operation of speedometer cable for proper routing and ensure no sharp bends or binding exists. If found satisfactory, proceed to step 3. If not found satisfactory, service or replace speedometer cable.
3. Check to ensure proper operation of sensor. If found satisfactory, proceed to step 4. If not found satisfactory, replace sensor.
4. Perform tests on speed sensor. If found satisfactory, proceed to step 5. If not found satisfactory, replace speed sensor.
5. Check to ensure proper operation of vacuum dump valve. If found satisfactory, proceed to step 6. If not found satisfactory, service or replace as necessary.
6. Perform tests on amplifier. If found satisfactory, proceed to step 7. If not found satisfactory, replace amplifier.
7. Examine all connectors to ensure proper contacts.

## SPEED CONTROL OPERATES BUT DOES NOT RESUME, ACCELERATE OR COAST DOWN PROPERLY

1. Check to ensure proper operation of Set-Acc switch, coast switch, resume switch and slip ring circuits. If found satisfactory, proceed to step 2. If not found satisfactory, service or replace switch and circuit as necessary.
2. Perform tests on servo. If found satisfactory, proceed to step 3. If not found satisfactory, replace servo.
3. Perform tests on the amplifier. If found satisfactory, proceed to step 4. If not found satisfactory, replace amplifier.
4. Examine all connectors to ensure proper contacts.

## SPEED CONTROL SYSTEM DOES NOT DISENGAGE WHEN BRAKES ARE APPLIED

1. Apply brake pedal and ensure brake

lights work. If found satisfactory, proceed to step 2. If not found satisfactory, check stop lamp circuit.
2. Check to ensure proper operation of vacuum dump valve. If found satisfactory, proceed to step 3. If not found satisfactory, adjust or replace as necessary.
3. Check to ensure proper operation of servo. If found satisfactory, proceed to step 4. If not found satisfactory, replace servo.
4. Perform tests on amplifier. If found satisfactory, proceed to step 5. If not found satisfactory, replace amplifier.
5. Examine all connectors to ensure proper contacts.

### SPEED GRADUALLY INCREASES OR DECREASES AFTER SPEED IS SET

1. Check to ensure proper operation of bead chain and actuator cable. If found satisfactory, proceed to step 2. If not found satisfactory, adjust or replace as necessary.
2. Check to ensure proper operation of vacuum dump valve. If found satisfactory, proceed to step 3. If not found satisfactory, adjust or replace as necessary.
3. Perform tests on servo. If found satisfactory, proceed to step 4. If not found satisfactory, replace servo.
4. Perform tests on amplifier. If found satisfactory, proceed to step 5. If not found satisfactory, replace amplifier.
5. Examine all connectors to ensure proper contacts.

### SPEED WILL NOT SET IN SYSTEM

1. Check to ensure proper operation of throttle linkage. If found satisfactory, proceed to step 2. If not found satisfactory, adjust or replace as necessary.
2. Check to ensure proper operation of switch and circuits. If found satisfactory, proceed to step 3. If not found satisfactory, service or replace as necessary.
3. Check to ensure proper operation of vacuum dump valve. If found satisfactory, proceed to step 4. If not found satisfactory, service or replace as necessary.
4. Check to ensure proper operation of stop lamp switch. If found satisfactory, proceed to step 5. If not found satisfactory, replace switch.
5. Check to ensure proper operation of stop lamps. If found satisfactory, proceed to step 6. If not found satisfactory, service lamps.
6. Check to ensure proper operation of clutch deactivator switch (manual transmission only). If found satisfactory, proceed to step 7. If not found satisfactory, service or replace as necessary.
7. Check to ensure proper operation of servo. If found satisfactory, proceed to step 8. If not found satisfactory, replace servo.
8. Check to ensure proper operation of speed sensor. If found satisfactory, proceed to step 9. If not found satisfactory, replace sensor.
9. Check to ensure proper operation of amplifier. If found satisfactory, proceed to step 10. If not found satisfactory, replace amplifier.
10. Examine all connectors to ensure proper contacts.

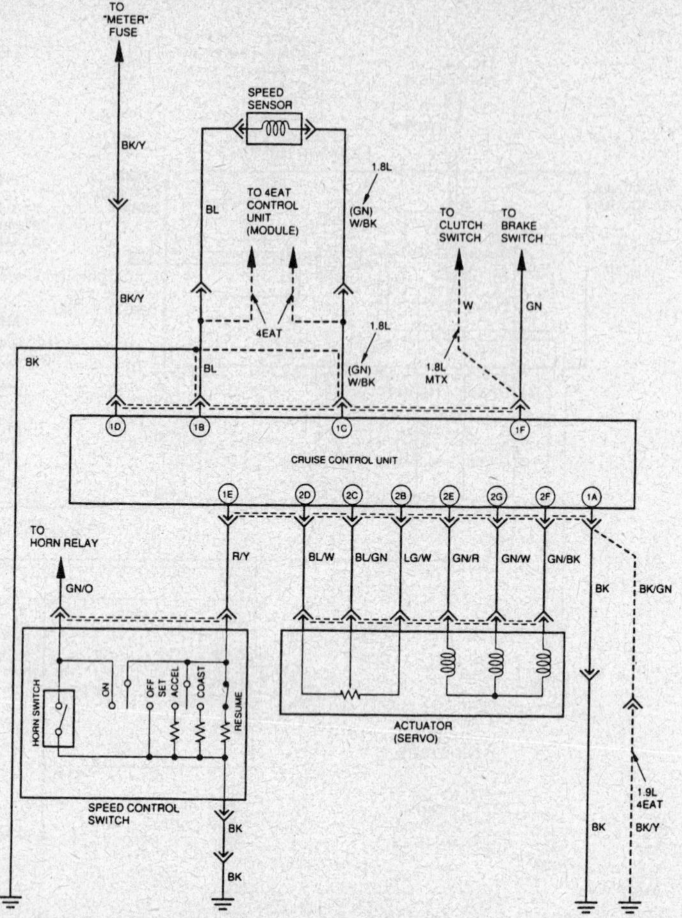


**Fig. 4 Speed control wiring diagram. 1991 Escort & Tracer**

### SPEED CONTROL DOES NOT DISENGAGE WHEN CLUTCH PEDAL IS DEPRESSED

1. Check to ensure proper operation of stop light switch. If found satisfactory, proceed to step 2. If not found satisfactory, service or replace as necessary.
2. Check to ensure proper operation of clutch switch. If found satisfactory, proceed to step 3. If not found satisfactory, replace clutch switch.
3. Examine all connectors to ensure proper contact.

### SPEED CONTROL OPERATION IS INTERMITTENT

1. Check to ensure there is proper vacuum to servo. If found satisfactory, proceed to step 2. If not satisfactory, service vacuum supply as needed.
2. Perform servo (throttle actuator) assembly test. If results are satisfactory, substitute known good amplifier. If not satisfactory, replace servo assembly.
3. Perform control switch and circuit test. If not satisfactory, replace horn pad assembly. Clean or service copper brushes and steering wheel ring.

## COMPONENT TESTING

### VISUAL INSPECTION

A visual inspection is an important part of the system test. When performing a visual inspection, check all components for abnormal conditions such as bare, broken, or disconnected wires, damaged or disconnected vacuum reserve tanks and hoses. In order for the speed control system to function properly, it is necessary that the speedometer cables be properly routed and securely attached. The servo (throttle actuator) assembly and throttle linkage should operate freely and smoothly. The bead chain should have not more than 1/4 inch freeplay.

### CONTROL SWITCH TEST

Disconnect connector at the amplifier assembly, **Figs. 1 through 4.** Perform the following checks:

1. Connect a voltmeter, part No. 014-00407 or equivalent between the light blue-black lead and ground. Depress the On button and check for battery voltage.
2. Turn ignition Off and connect an ohmmeter between the light blue-black

hash lead and ground.

3. Rotate steering wheel throughout its full range while making the following checks:
   a. Depress Off button and check for a reading between 0 and 1 ohm.
   b. Depress Set button and check for a reading between 714 and 646 ohms.
   c. Depress Coast button and check for a reading between 126 and 114 ohms.
   d. **On models which incorporate Resume, depress Resume button,** check for a reading between 2310 and 2090 ohms.
4. If resistance values are within specification but needle fluctuates, remove steering wheel and clean the brushes. Apply a light coat of lubricant ESA-M1C189A or equivalent to the slip rings. If resistance values are above the allowable limits, check the switches and ground circuit.
5. Reconnect the connector at the amplifier.

## SPEED SENSOR TEST

1. Disconnect electrical connector from speed sensor, **Figs. 1 through 4,** then connect an ohmmeter between the speed sensor terminals at speed sensor end.
2.
   a. **On 1989 Escort models,** a reading of approximately 30-100 ohms should be obtained.
   b. **On 1989 models except Escort,** a reading of approximately 200-300 ohms should be obtained.
   c. **On all 1990-91 models,** a reading of 200 ohms should be obtained.
   d. **On all models,** a reading of 0 ohms indicates a shorted coil and maximum reading indicates an open coil.
3. Replace the sensor if a correct reading has not been obtained.

## SERVO (THROTTLE ACTUATOR) ASSEMBLY TEST

### 1989 Models

1. Disconnect electrical connector from the amplifier.
2. Connect an ohmmeter between circuit 145 and circuit 144 wire leads at the electrical connector. A resistance of 40-125 ohms should be obtained.
3. Connect an ohmmeter between circuit 144 and 146 wire leads. A resistance of 60-190 ohms should be obtained.
4. Start engine.
5. Connect circuit lead 144 to positive terminal of the battery.
6. Connect circuit lead 146 to ground, and momentarily touch circuit lead 145 to ground. **The servo throttle actuator arm should pull in and engine speed should increase. The arm should also hold in position or slowly release. When circuit 146 lead is removed from ground, the servo should release.**
7. Replace servo if it fails any part of the preceding test. If circuit 144 is shorted to either circuit 146 or circuit 145 leads, it may be necessary to replace the amplifier.

### 1990–91 Models

1. Separate the eight pin connector from the amplifier.
2. Connect an ohmmeter between the orange/yellow (circuit 144) and the grey/black (circuit 145) leads at the eight pin connector, **Figs. 1 through 4.** Resistance should measure 40-75 ohms.
3. Connect an ohmmeter between the orange/yellow (circuit 144) and the white/pink (circuit 146) leads at the connector. Resistance should measure 100-150 ohms.
4. Connect an ohmmeter between the purple/light blue (circuit 147) and Yellow/Red (circuit 148) leads. Resistance should measure 20,000–30,000 ohms.
5. Connect an ohmmeter between the purple/light blue (circuit 147) and brown/light green (circuit 149) leads. Resistance should measure 40,000–60,000 ohms.
6. If proper resistance is not obtained check the wiring and servo separately for damage and replace or service as required.

## AMPLIFIER TEST

**Use only a voltmeter of 5000 ohm/volt rating or higher when performing the following amplifier test. Use of a test lamp may damage amplifier due to excess current draw.**

### "On" Circuit Test

1. Turn ignition switch to the On position.
2. Connect a voltmeter between white/purple (circuit 296) and ground in the amplifier six pin connector at the amplifier. Battery voltage should be measured.
3. If battery voltage is not measured, check fuse voltage. Repair as necessary.
4. Connect a voltmeter to light blue/black (circuit 151) and ground at the amplifier. Voltmeter should read battery voltage when speed control switch is in the On position, depressed and held. If voltage is not measured, refer to "Control Switch Test."
5. Release On button. Voltmeter should read approximately 7.8 volts, indicating the On circuit is engaged. If voltmeter reads zero, check ground and amplifier (either black wire on amplifier six pin connector). If there is no ground on the amplifier, check system ground wiring and connections. Also check the number 6, 20 amp fuse and circuit breaker.
6. If voltmeter still reads zero, substitute, but do not install a know good amplifier, then check for proper On circuit operation.

### Brake Circuit Test

1. Connect an ohmmeter between red/light green wire on the six pin connector and ground.
2. Resistance should measure less than 5 ohms.
3. If resistance is greater than 5 ohms, check for burned out stop lamps, improper wiring, or clutch malfunction.

### Horn Relay Test (Escort, Tempo, Tracer & Topaz)

1. Connect a voltmeter between yellow/light blue dot wire of relay and ground.
2. Voltmeter should indicate battery voltage.
3. If voltmeter does not indicate battery voltage, check for voltage at supply lead. **The supply lead is light blue with a white stripe on Escort and Tracer, or dark blue on Tempo and Topaz.**
4. If voltage is indicated at supply lead, replace the relay.
5. If no voltage is indicated at supply lead, check fuse and wiring for an open or short and repair or replace as necessary.

### Off Circuit Test

1. Turn ignition switch to the Run position.
2. Connect a voltmeter to the light blue/black wire (circuit 151), depress Off switch on steering wheel, then read voltage.
3. Voltage should drop to zero indicating On circuit is de-energized.
4. If voltage does not drop to zero, perform "Control Switch Test."
5. If switches are checked and found to be good, substitute a known good amplifier, then repeat procedure.

### Set-Accelerate Circuit Test

1. Turn ignition switch to the On position.
2. Connect a voltmeter between the light blue/black wire (circuit 151) in the six pin connector and ground.
3. Depress and hold Set-Acc button on steering wheel. The voltmeter should read approximately 4.5 volts.
4. Rotate steering wheel and watch the voltmeter for fluctuations. If voltage varies more than 0.5 volts, perform "Control Switch Test."

### Coast Circuit Test

1. Turn ignition switch to the On position.
2. Connect a voltmeter between light blue/black wire (circuit 151) and ground.
3. Depress and hold Coast button on steering wheel. The voltmeter should read approximately 1.5 volts.

### Resume Circuit Test

1. Turn ignition switch to the On position.
2. Connect a voltmeter between light blue/black wire (circuit 151) and ground.
3. Depress and hold Resume button on steering wheel. The voltmeter should read approximately 6.5 volts.
4. If all circuits are satisfactory, perform the "Servo Assembly Test," substituting a known good amplifier. **Do not**

**substitute a known good amplifier until the servo assembly test has been successfully completed.**

## SIMULATED ROAD TEST

1. Raise and support rear of vehicle on rear wheel drive models, or front of vehicle on front wheel drive models placing jack stands under the lower control arm assembly in order to keep halfshaft assemblies in a lateral position, then block the opposite set of wheels. **Never attempt to use the vehicle bumper jack for a test of this type.**
2. Start engine, then shift transmission to D.
3. Turn speed control system on. **If any time during the following steps the system should appear to go out of control and overspeed, be prepared to turn speed control system off at once with the Off or ignition switch.**
4. Accelerate and hold at 35 mph.
5. Press and release Set Acc button. Hold foot pressure very lightly on accelerator pedal. Speed should continue at 35 mph for a short period of time, then gradually start to surge due to lack of engine load.
6. Press Off button. The engine should decelerate to idle. Stop drive wheels with service brakes.
7. Press On button, accelerate and hold speed at 35 mph.
8. Press and hold Set-Acc button. Slowly remove foot from accelerator. The engine RPM should gradually increase.
9. When the speed reaches 50 mph, release Set-Acc button. The vehicle should maintain 50 mph for a short time before surging begins.
10. Press Coast button and hold. The engine should idle. Slow drive wheels to 35 mph.
11. Release Coast button. Speed should set at 35 mph and surging should soon start.
12. Press and release brake pedal. The system should shut off, engine should decelerate to idle.
13. Set speed at 50 mph. Using brakes, decelerate to 35 mph, then maintain with the accelerator. Depress and release Resume button. The speed should return to 50 mph.

## BRAKE STOP LAMP SWITCH & CIRCUIT TEST

Perform this test only when the brake application will not disconnect the speed control system.

1. Check operation of stop lamps by applying approximately 6 lbs. of effort to the brake pedal. If more than 6 lbs. is required, check brake pedal actuation and stop lamp switch.
2. If stop lamps do not function properly, the stop lamp switch, circuit fuse or bulbs must be checked.
3. If stop lamps function properly, check for battery voltage on white/purple wire (circuit 296) at the 6-way connector.
4. Depress brake pedal until stop lamps are lit.
5. **On all models except Escort, Tempo and Topaz,** check voltage on dark/green stripe lead at the 6-way connector. The difference between this and the voltage reading in step 3, must not exceed 1.5 volts.
6. **On Escort, Tempo and Topaz,** check voltage on red/light green lead at the 6-way connector. The difference between this and the voltage reading in step 3, must not exceed 1.5 volts.
7. If the voltage difference is greater than 1.5 volts, a high resistance in the circuit exists which must be found and corrected.
8. Perform "Vacuum Dump Valve Test."

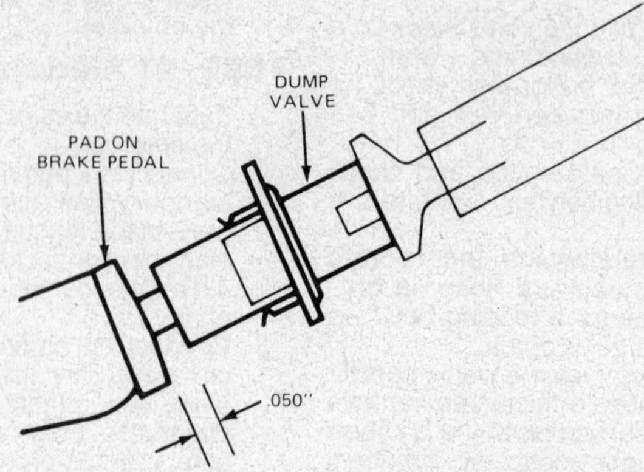
VIEW SHOWING CORRECTLY ADJUSTED DUMP VALVE
DUMP VALVE
PAD ON BRAKE PEDAL
.050"
DUMP VALVE BLACK HOUSING MUST CLEAR WHITE PLASTIC PAD ON BRAKE PEDAL WITH BRAKE PEDAL PULLED TO REARMOST POSITION.

**Fig. 5 Dump valve adjustment**

## VACUUM DUMP VALVE TEST

1. Disconnect vacuum hose (white stripe) from the servo, leading to the dump valve.
2. Connect a hand vacuum pump tool No. 021-00037 or equivalent to the hose, and draw vacuum. If a vacuum can not be obtained, the hose or dump valve is leaking, and should be replaced.
3. Depress brake pedal. Vacuum should be released. If not adjust or replace the dump valve, **Fig. 5.**

## CLUTCH SWITCH TEST

This switch functions magnetically. Do not use magnetized tools near this switch.

1. If the switch is open when the clutch pedal is released, speed control will not operate. This must be corrected before making any other tests. **Use only a voltmeter of 5000 ohm/volt rating or higher when performing the clutch switch test.**
2. Disconnect switch pigtail connector from speed control harness connector, then connect an ohmmeter to the two switch connector terminals.
3. With clutch pedal in the fully released position, the resistance should be less than 5 ohms. With clutch pedal fully depressed, the circuit should be open.
4. If switch does not function as described, remove and replace switch.

# COMPONENT REPLACEMENT

## SERVO (THROTTLE ACTUATOR) ASSEMBLY, ACTUATOR CABLE

### Except Mustang

1. Remove air cleaner assembly.
2. Remove screw or push-pin, then disconnect speed control actuator cable from accelerator cable bracket.
3. Disconnect speed control actuator cable from the accelerator cable.
4. Remove two vacuum hoses and electrical connector from the servo assembly.
5. Remove cable tie around the actuator cable, if equipped.
6. Remove two screws/nuts from servo mounting bracket.
7. Carefully remove servo and cable assembly.
8. Remove two fasteners holding cable cover to servo.
9. Pull off cover and remove cable assembly, then remove servo mounting bracket.
10. Reverse procedure to install.

### Mustang

1. Disconnect speed control actuator cable from accelerator cable bracket.
2. Disconnect servo electrical connector from inside engine compartment.
3. Apply parking brake, then raise and support left front side of vehicle.
4. Remove left front wheel, then the inner fender splash shield.
5. Remove two vacuum hoses from servo.
6. Remove two servo mounting bracket-to-pillar attaching screws.
7. Remove two actuator cable cover-to-servo attaching nuts, then the cable and cover.

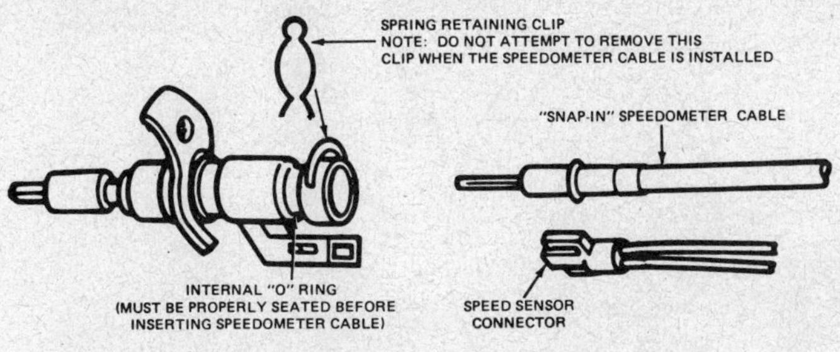


**Fig. 6 Speed sensor & speedometer cable assembly**

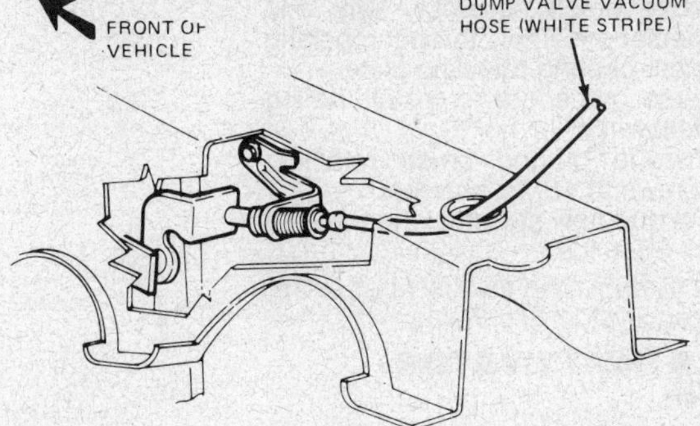


**Fig. 7 Dump valve removal (Typical)**

8. Remove servo-to-mounting bracket attaching nuts and the servo.
9. Reverse procedure to install.

## ACTUATOR CABLE

1. Remove servo assembly, and discard cable.
2. Attach new actuator cable to servo assembly.
3. Install servo assembly.

## CONTROL SWITCH OR BRUSH ASSEMBLY

### 1989 Models

1. Remove steering wheel hub Remove hub by lifting outside edges.
2. Remove steering wheel attaching nut, then steering wheel from upper shaft using tool T67L-3600-A or equivalent.
3. Remove control switches as follows:
   a. Remove steering wheel back cover, then separate control switch electrical connector from cover.
   b. Remove speed control switch assembly.
4. Remove brush assembly as follows:
   a. Remove steering column lower trim shroud, then loosen steering column mounting screws sufficiently so upper trim shroud can be removed.
   b. Separate speed control brush electrical connector.
   c. Remove brush assembly to upper bearing retainer plate attaching screws.
   d. Remove brush assembly wire and connector assembly through opening in upper bearing retainer plate.
5. Reverse procedures to install, noting the following:
   a. When installing steering wheel, align index mark on steering wheel with mark on steering shaft. **Torque** steering wheel nut to 30-40 ft. lbs.
   b. **Torque** brush assembly attaching screws to 18-26 inch lbs.
   c. **Torque** steering column mounting fasteners to 17-25 ft. lbs.

### 1990–91 Models

1. **On vehicles less air bag module,** remove two screws from rear of steering wheel to remove pad cover.
2. Remove foam insert, if equipped, then disconnect wiring connector from steering wheel.
3. Disconnect two horn wire connectors from steering wheel pad cover.
4. Remove speed control switches from steering wheel pad cover by removing two attaching screws from each side.
5. Reverse procedure to install.
6. **On vehicles equipped with air bag module,** disarm airbag system as described under "Airbag System Disarming."
7. Remove pad by removing four screws from back of steering wheel. **Place airbag module on flat surface with plastic side facing upwards.**
8. Disconnect air bag module to clockspring electrical connector. **Place air bag pad on a flat surface with the trim cover facing up.**
9. Remove speed control switches from steering wheel.
10. Reverse procedure to install.
11. Reactivate airbag as described under "Airbag System Disarming."

## SPEED SENSOR

### 1989 ESCORT

1. Separate electrical connector leading to the amplifier assembly.
2. Disconnect upper and lower speedometer cables at the speed sensor. Remove speed sensor.
3. Reverse procedure to install.

### 1989 MODELS EXCEPT ESCORT

1. Raise and support vehicle, then remove speed sensor mounting clip to transmission attaching bolt.
2. Remove the sensor and driven gear assembly from transmission, **Fig. 6.**
3. Disconnect electrical connectors from speed sensor, then speedometer cable by pulling it out of the speed sensor. **Do not remove spring retainer clip with speedometer cable in the sensor.**
4. Remove the driven gear retainer, then driven gear from sensor.
5. Reverse procedure to install.

### 1990–91 MODELS

1. Raise and support vehicle, then loosen sensor to transmission retaining nut.
2. Remove speed sensor and driven gear from transmission, then disconnect speed sensor electrical connector.
3. Disconnect speedometer cable, by pulling it from speed sensor.
4. Remove speed sensor.
5. Reverse procedure to install.

## AMPLIFIER ASSEMBLY

The amplifier is located on, or to the left of the steering column under the instrument panel.

1. Remove screws holding amplifier assembly to the mounting bracket.
2. Disconnect electrical connectors to the amplifier. Remove amplifier assembly.
3. Reverse procedure to install.

## VACUUM DUMP VALVE

1. Remove vacuum hose from valve, **Fig. 7.**
2. Remove valve from the bracket.
3. Reverse procedure to install.

## GROUND BRUSH

1. **On models less air bag module,** remove steering wheel by removing two screws from rear of steering wheel.
2. Remove foam insert, then the electrical connector from the steering wheel.
3. **On models with air bag module,** disarm airbag system as described under "Airbag System Disarming."
4. Remove four screws from rear of steering wheel, then the air bag module. **Place air bag module on a flat surface with the trim cover facing up.**
5. **On all models,** remove electrical connectors from steering wheel pad, clockspring and horn.
6. Loosen steering wheel retaining screw approximately five turns.
7. Use steering wheel puller tool No. T67L-3600-A, or equivalent, to free steering wheel from shaft. **Do not use a knock-off type puller or strike retaining bolt with a hammer as damage to the steering wheel shaft bearing may occur.**
8. Remove steering column lower trim shroud, then the straps securing brush assembly wire at ignition switch and column tube.
9. Separate speed control brush wire harness from connector, then remove screw securing brush assembly to upper bearing retainer plate.

10. Remove brush assembly wire and connector assembly through opening in upper bearing retaining plate.
11. Reverse procedure to install, noting the following:
    a. **Torque** ground brush retaining screws to 18-26 inch lbs.
    b. **Torque** new steering wheel bolt to 23-33 ft. lbs.
12. Reactivate airbag as described under "Airbag System Disarming."

### CLUTCH DEACTIVATOR SWITCH

1. Remove bracket mounting screw(s).
2. Disconnect electrical connector, then remove switch and bracket assembly.
3. Remove switch from bracket.
4. Reverse procedure to install.

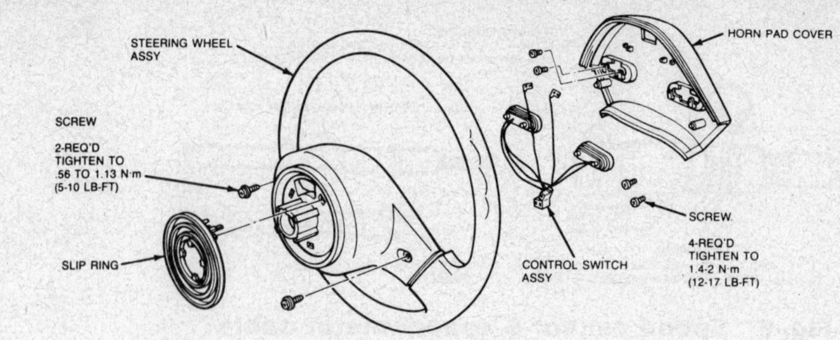


# CONTINENTAL, COUGAR, CROWN VICTORIA, GRAND MARQUIS, MARK VII, SABLE, TAURUS, THUNDERBIRD & TOWN CAR

## SYSTEM COMPONENTS

### CONTINENTAL, SABLE & TAURUS

The Integrated Vehicle Speed Control (IVSC) system for these models, **Figs. 8 and 9,** consists of operator controls, a servo (throttle actuator) assembly, a speed sensor, a clutch switch (Manual Trans.), a stop lamp switch, a vacuum dump valve, a horn relay, a vacuum reservoir, a check valve, and necessary wires and vacuum hoses.

### COUGAR, CROWN VICTORIA, GRAND MARQUIS, MARK VII, THUNDERBIRD & TOWN CAR

The Integrated Vehicle Speed Control (IVSC) system for these models consists of operator controls, a servo (throttle actuator) assembly, a speed sensor (Models with non-electronic instrument cluster only), a clutch switch (Manual Trans.), stop lamp switch, vacuum dump valve, horn relay, two check valves, aspirator (except Cougar and Thunderbird), and necessary wires and vacuum hoses. On models with an electronic instrument cluster, the electronic speedometer assembly generates the speed signal and therefore does not require a speed sensor.

## SYSTEM DESCRIPTION

### CONTINENTAL, SABLE & TAURUS

The speed control amplifier assembly function is integrated into the EEC-IV Electronic Control Assembly (ECA). The servo assembly is mounted in the engine compartment and is connected to the throttle linkage with an actuator cable. The servo is also connected to a vacuum reservoir and to a manifold vacuum source through a check valve. The speed control sensor is located on the transaxle.

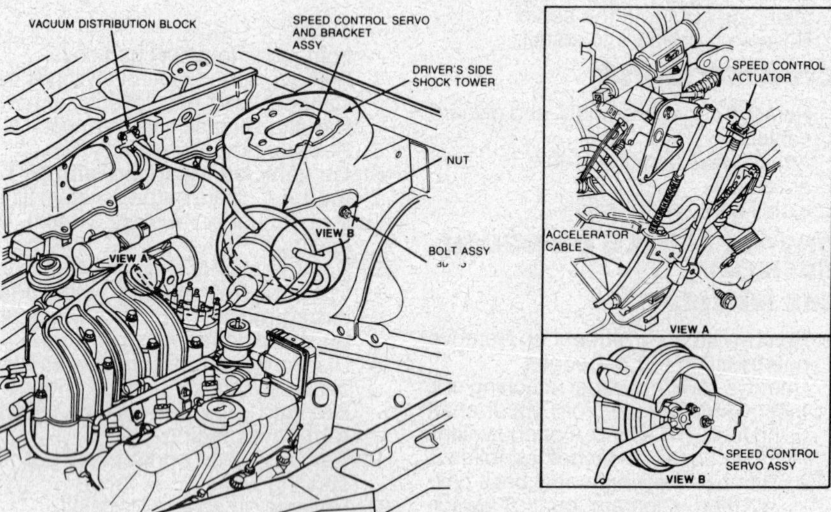


**Fig. 8 Speed control components. Sable & Taurus**

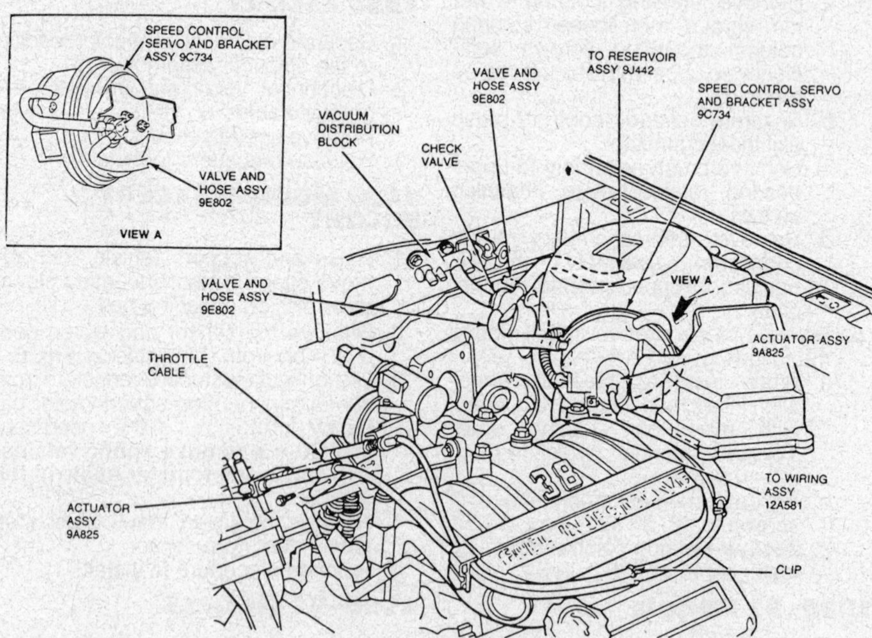


**Fig. 9 Speed control components. Continental**

The vacuum dump valve, **Fig. 10**, provides a safety feature in the system. Normally, when the brake pedal is depressed, an electrical signal from the stop lamps to the ECA will turn off the system. In addition, the vacuum dump valve will mechanically release the vacuum in the servo when the brake pedal is depressed. This releases the throttle independently of the ECA control.

### COUGAR, CROWN VICTORIA, GRAND MARQUIS, MARK VII, MUSTANG, THUNDERBIRD & TOWN CAR

The speed control amplifier assembly function is integrated into the EEC-IV Electronic Control Assembly (ECA). The servo assembly is mounted in the engine compartment and is connected to the throttle linkage with an actuator cable. The servo is also connected to an aspirator and a manifold vacuum source through check valves. The speed control sensor is located on the transmission.

The Aspirator is connected to the thermactor air pump and is used to improve speed control performance when engine load is high. The check valves switch the servo's vacuum source from the manifold to the air pump according to which has the strongest vacuum signal available. The check valves also keep vacuum from leaking back into the source not being used.

The vacuum dump valve provides an additional safety feature in the system. Normally, when the brake pedal is depressed, an electrical signal from the stop lamps to the ECA will turn off the system. In addition, the vacuum dump valve will mechanically release the vacuum in the servo when the brake pedal is depressed. This releases the throttle independently of the ECA control.

## SYSTEM OPERATION

### ACTIVATION

To operate the speed control system, vehicle speed must be no less then 26 mph for all models except Sable and Taurus with 4-153/2.5L engine, or 35 mph for Sable and Taurus models with 4-153/2.5L engine. Activate the system by pressing the ON switch on the steering wheel, then depress and release the SET ACCEL switch. This will result in the current speed being maintained until a new speed is set by the operator, the brake or clutch pedals are depressed, or the OFF switch is depressed.

### DECREASING SET SPEED

The vehicle speed may be reduced by applying the brake or clutch pedal and then resetting the speed using the forgoing method or by depressing the COAST switch. When the vehicle has slowed to the desired speed, the COAST switch is released and the new speed is set automatically. If the vehicle speed is reduced below 30 or 25 mph (as stated previously), the operator must manually increase the speed and reset the system.

### INCREASING SPEED

The vehicle set speed may be manually increased at any time by depressing the accelerator until the higher speed is reached and stabilized, then depressing and releasing the SET ACCEL button.

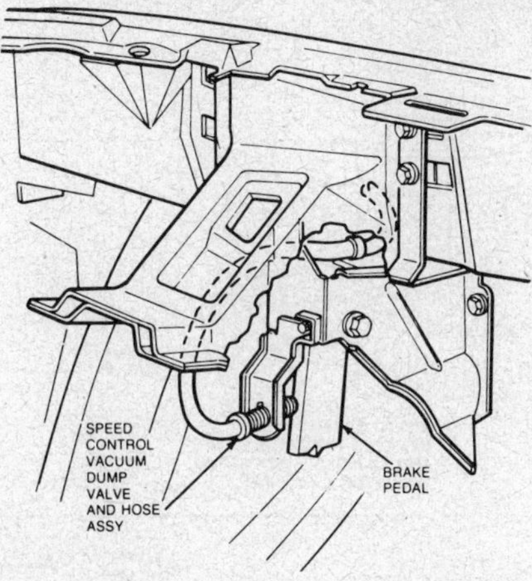


**Fig. 10 Vacuum dump valve. Continental, Sable & Taurus**

Speed may also be increased by depressing the SET ACCEL switch button at speeds over 30 or 25 mph (as stated previously) and holding it in that position. The vehicle will then automatically increase speed. When the desired rate of speed is attained and the button is released, that new set speed will be maintained.

### RESUME

When the speed control system is deactivated by depressing the brake or clutch pedal, the set speed prior to deactivation may be re-established by holding the RESUME switch for two seconds. The RESUME switch is hinged on the side closest to the SET ACCEL switch. Therefore, it should be depressed on the side farthest from the SET ACCEL switch. The resume feature will not function if the system is deactivated with the OFF switch, if the vehicle speed has been reduced to below 30 or 25 mph (as stated previously), or if the ignition switch is turned off.

## ADJUSTMENTS

### ACTUATOR CABLE, ADJUST

1. Remove speed control actuator cable retaining clip, **Figs. 11 through 14.**
2. Push actuator cable through adjuster until slight tension is felt.
3. Insert cable retaining clip and snap into place.

### BEAD CHAIN, ADJUST

1. Remove locking pin, **Fig. 15.**
2. Pull bead chain through adjuster.
3. Insert locking pin in best hole of adjuster for tight bead chain without opening throttle plate.

### VACUUM DUMP VALVE, ADJUST

The vacuum dump valve, **Figs. 10 and 16,** is adjusted in its mounting bracket. It should be adjusted closed (no vacuum leak) when the brake pedal is released, and open when the pedal is depressed. Use a hand vacuum pump to make this adjustment.

### CLUTCH SWITCH, ADJUST

1. Prop clutch pedal, **Fig. 17,** in full up position (pawl fully released from sector).
2. Loosen switch mounting screw.
3. Slide switch forward toward clutch pedal until switch plunger cap is .30 inch from contacting switch housing, then tighten attaching screw.
4. Remove prop from clutch pedal and test drive for clutch switch cancellation of a speed control.

### CLUTCH INTERLOCK THREE FUNCTION SWITCH, ADJUST

#### Cougar & Thunderbird

1. Disconnect switch electrical connector, **Fig. 18.**
2. Using a volt-ohmmeter, check for continuity at the following switch terminals.
   a. EFI switch terminals 5 and 6 should be open with clutch pedal released. Terminals 5 and 6 should show continuity, within two inches of clutch pedal travel.
   b. Speed control release switch terminals 3 and 4 should be show continuity with clutch pedal released. Terminals 3 and 4 should open within two inches of clutch pedal travel.
   c. Clutch interlock switch terminals 1 and 2 should be open with clutch pedal released. Terminals 1 and 2 should close within one inch from full clutch pedal travel.

## COMPONENT REPLACEMENT

### SERVO ASSEMBLY

#### Crown Victoria, Continental & Town Car, Grand Marquis, Sable & Taurus

1. Disconnect speed control actuator cable, **Figs. 12, 13, or 19** from accelerator cable bracket and/or intake manifold support bracket.
2. Disconnect speed control actuator cable with adjuster from accelerator cable.
3. Remove two vacuum hoses and electrical connector from servo assembly, **Figs. 20 and 21.**
4. Remove two nuts holding servo to mounting bracket.
5. Carefully remove servo and cable assembly.
6. Remove two nuts holding cable cover to servo.
7. Pull off cover, then remove cable assembly.
8. Attach cable to servo.
9. Attach cable cover to servo with two nuts.
10. **On Crown Victoria, Town Car and Grand Marquis models,**while feeding actuator cable along the dash panel, reposition the servo assembly.
11. **On all models,** attach servo to mounting bracket.

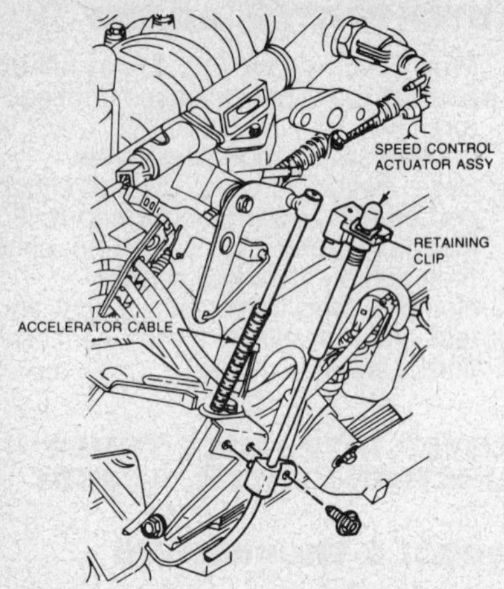


**Fig. 11 Actuator cable. Sable & Taurus w/3.0L/V6-182 engine**

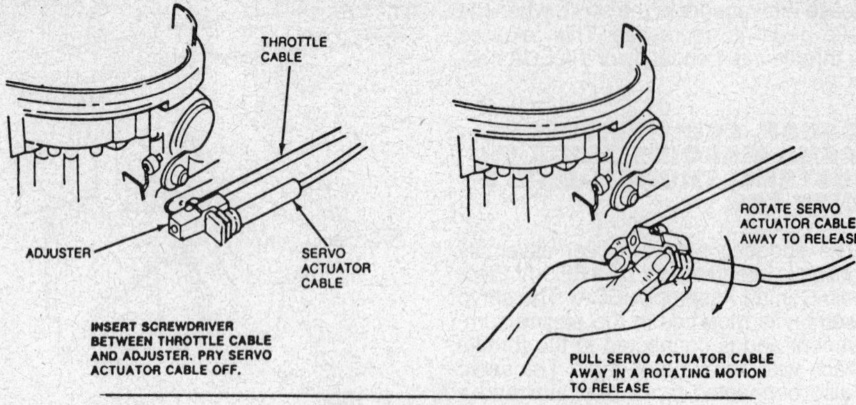


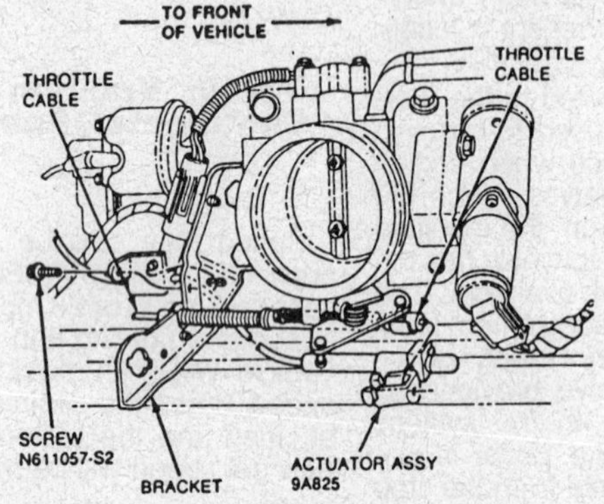


**Fig. 13 Actuator cable. Crown Victoria, Town Car, Mark VII & Grand Marquis**

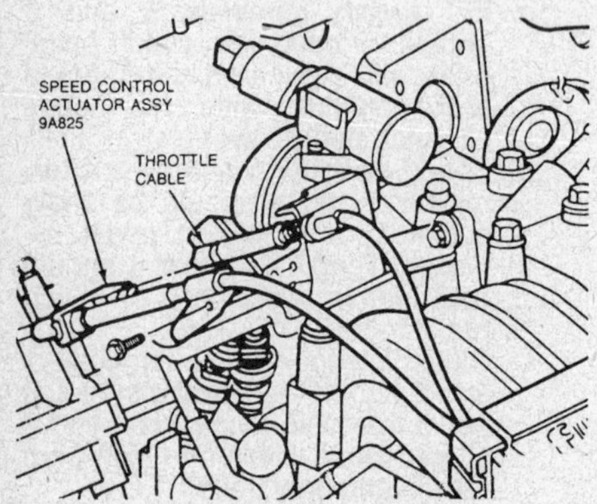


**Fig. 12 Actuator cable. Continental**

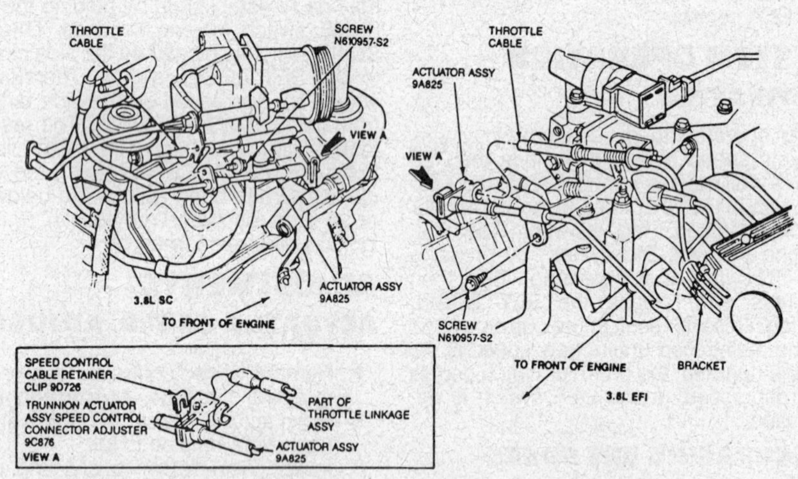


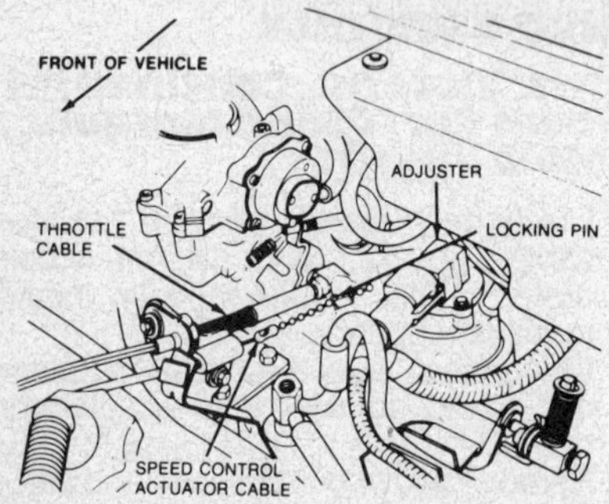


**Fig. 15 Actuator cable. Sable & Taurus w/2.5L/4-153 engine**

**Fig. 14 Actuator cable. Cougar & Thunderbird**

12. **On Continental, Sable and Taurus models,** feed actuator cable under air cleaner duct.
13. **On all models,** snap actuator cable with adjuster onto accelerator cable.
14. Connect actuator cable to accelerator cable bracket and install push pin.
15. Install two vacuum hoses and electrical connector at servo.

## Cougar, Mark VII & Thunderbird

1. Remove air cleaner assembly, and position to front of vehicle.
2. Separate speed control actuator cable from the accelerator cable.
3. **On Mark VII models,** disconnect servo electrical connector, **Fig. 22.**
4. **On Cougar and Thunderbird models,** disconnect servo electrical connector located near radiator support, **Fig. 23.**
5. **On all models,** apply parking brake.
6. Raise and support lefthand front of vehicle.
7. Remove left front wheel assembly.
8. Remove inner fender splash shield.
9. Remove two servo assembly vacuum hoses from servo.
10. **On Mark VII models,** remove two servo mounting bracket to A-pillar attaching screws.
11. **On Cougar and Thunderbird models,** remove two servo mounting bracket-to-shotgun brace attaching screws.
12. **On all models,** remove two actuator cable cover-to-servo retaining nuts, then the cover, cable, and rubber boot.
13. Remove two servo-to-mounting bracket retaining nuts.
14. Remove two bolts from front of servo.
15. Reverse procedure to install.

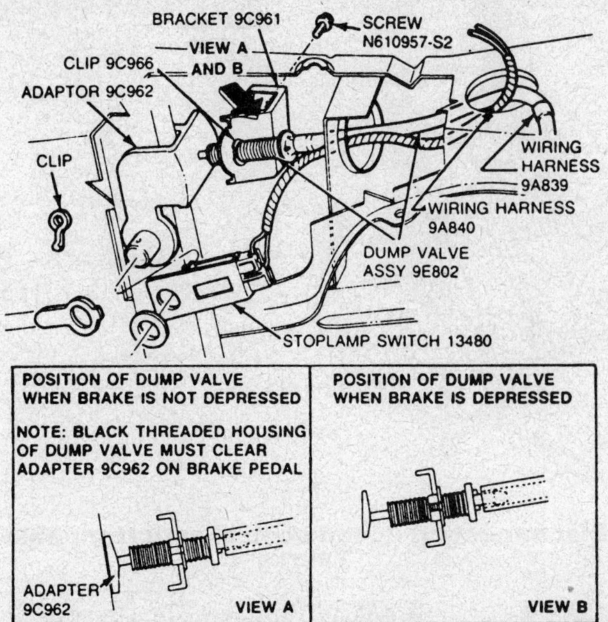


**Fig. 16 Vacuum dump valve. Crown Victoria, Town Car, Mark VII & Grand Marquis shown, Cougar, Mark VII & Thunderbird similar**

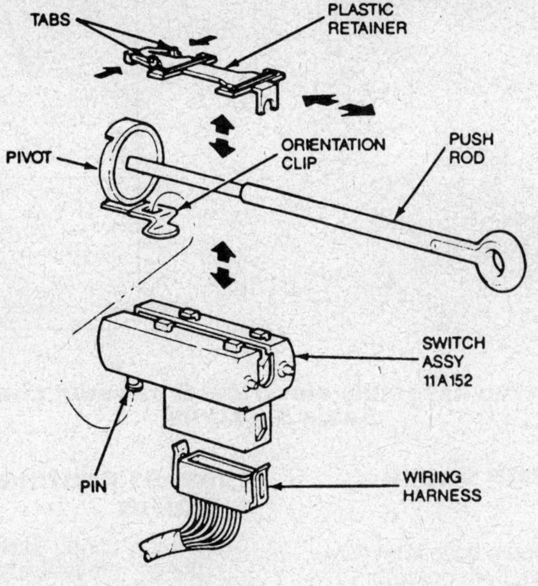


The above N.C. or N.O. contact positions are referenced with the switch installed and the clutch pedal at the up or clutch engaged position.

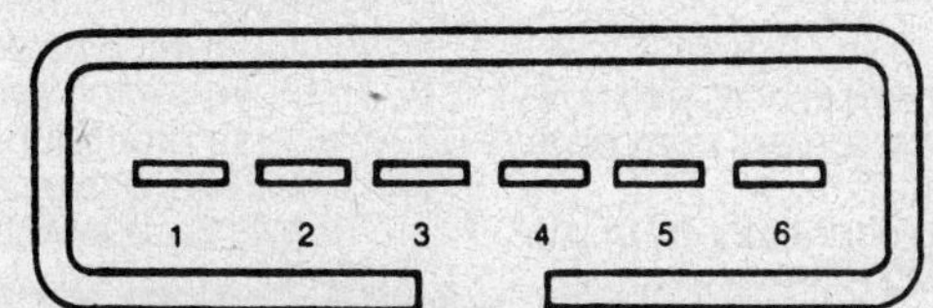


**Fig. 18 Clutch interlock three function switch. Cougar & Thunderbird**

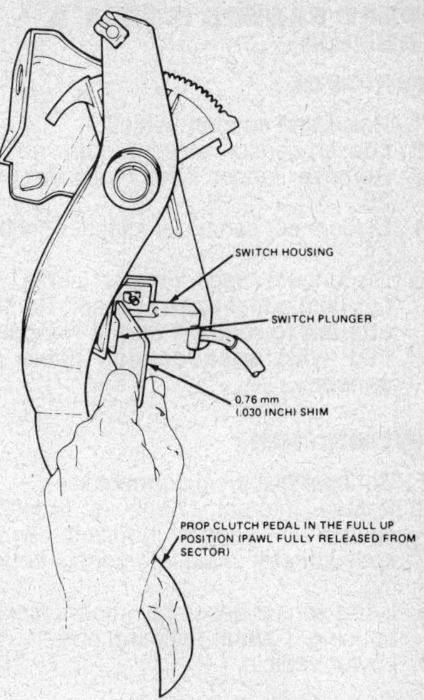


**Fig. 17 Clutch switch. Sable & Taurus**

## ACTUATOR CABLE

To replace actuator assembly, remove servo assembly, attach new actuator cable assembly to servo, and install complete assembly.

## SPEED SENSOR (CONTINENTAL, SABLE & TAURUS W/AXOD TRANSAXLE)

### Removal

1. Raise and support vehicle
2. Remove bolt retaining speed sensor mounting clip to transaxle.
3. Remove sensor and driven gear from transaxle, **Fig. 24.**
4. Disconnect electrical connector and speedometer cable from speed sensor.
5. Disconnect speedometer cable by pulling it out of speed sensor. **Do not attempt to remove spring retainer clip with speedometer cable in sensor.**
6. Remove driven gear retainer, then the driven gear from sensor.

### Installation

1. Position driven gear to speed sensor. Install gear retainer.
2. Connect electrical connector.
3. Ensure internal O-ring is properly seated in sensor housing. Snap speedometer cable into sensor housing.
4. Insert sensor assembly into transaxle housing. Install retaining bolt.
5. Lower vehicle.

## SPEED SENSOR (SABLE & TAURUS)

### Removal

1. Raise and support vehicle.
2. Loosen sensor retaining nut.
3. Remove sensor from transaxle, **Fig. 25.**
4. Disconnect sensor electrical connector.
5. Disconnect speedometer cable by pulling it out of speed sensor. **Do not attempt to remove spring retaining clip with speedometer cable in sensor.**

### Installation

1. Connect electrical connector.
2. Ensure internal O-ring is properly seated in sensor housing. Snap speedometer cable into sensor housing.
3. Insert sensor assembly into transaxle housing. Tighten retaining nut.
4. Lower vehicle.

## SPEED SENSOR (COUGAR, CROWN VICTORIA, TOWN CAR, MARK VII, GRAND MARQUIS, & THUNDERBIRD)

1. Raise and support vehicle.
2. Remove bolt retaining the sensor attaching clip, then the sensor and driven gear from transmission, **Fig. 26.**
3. Disconnect sensor electrical connector.
4. Disconnect speedometer cable by pulling it out of speed sensor, **Fig. 26. Do not attempt to remove spring retaining clip with speedometer cable in sensor.**
5. Remove retainer, then separate sensor from driven gear.
6. Position sensor to driven gear and install retainer.
7. Connect electrical connector.
8. Ensure internal O-ring is properly seated in sensor housing. Snap speedometer cable into sensor housing.
9. Install sensor to transmission.
10. Lower vehicle.

## EEC-IV ELECTRONIC CONTROL ASSEMBLY (ECA)

On Continental, Sable & Taurus models, the ECA is located behind the glove compartment, under the instrument panel.

On Crown Victoria, Town Car, Mark VII & Grand Marquis models, the ECA is located on the lefthand hinge pillar.

On Cougar and Thunderbird models, the ECA is located behind the righthand kick panel.

1. Disconnect electrical connector from ECA.
2. **On all models except Cougar and Thunderbird,** remove clip attaching ECA to dash panel.
3. **On Cougar and Thunderbird models,** remove ECA lower leg-to-cowl side sheet metal attaching screw.
4. **On all models,** remove ECA.
5. Reverse procedure to install.

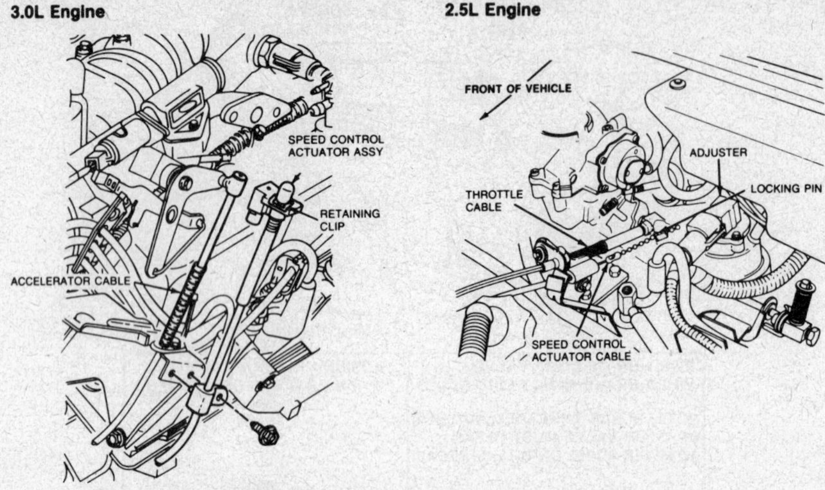


**Fig. 19 Disconnecting speed control actuator cable. Sable & Taurus**

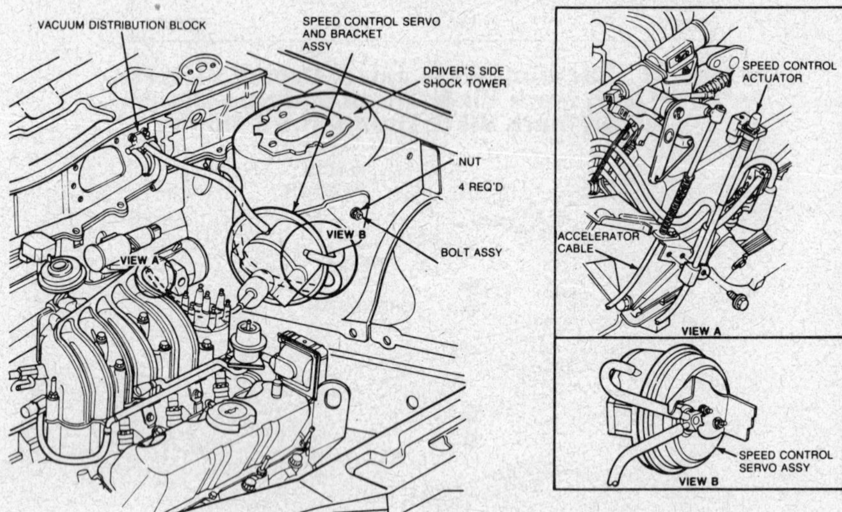


**Fig. 20 Servo assembly electrical & vacuum connections. Sable & Taurus**

## VACUUM DUMP VALVE

### Removal

1. Remove vacuum hose from valve.
2. Remove valve from bracket.

### Installation

1. Install valve to bracket.
2. Connect vacuum hose.
3. Adjust valve as described under "Adjustments."

## CONTROL SWITCHES

### 1989 Continental, Sable & Taurus

1. Remove steering wheel horn pad cover by removing two screws from back of steering wheel.
2. Disconnect wiring connector from slip ring terminal, **Fig. 27.**
3. Remove speed control switch assembly from horn pad cover by removing two attaching screws from each switch.
4. Reverse procedure to install.

### 1990–91 Continental, Sable & Taurus

1. Disarm airbag system as described under "Airbag System Disarming."
2. Remove four air bag module retaining nuts.
3. Remove module from steering wheel, then disconnect contact assembly from module. **Place air bag module on a flat surface, with the trim cover facing up.**
4. Disconnect electrical connectors from switch.
5. Remove two screws and washers retaining switch to steering wheel.
6. Remove switch and wiring assembly.
7. Reverse procedure to install.
8. Reactivate airbag as described under "Airbag System Disarming."

### 1989 Crown Victoria, Town Car & Grand Marquis

1. Remove center horn pad by inserting a punch through holes in back of steering wheel. Disconnect horn

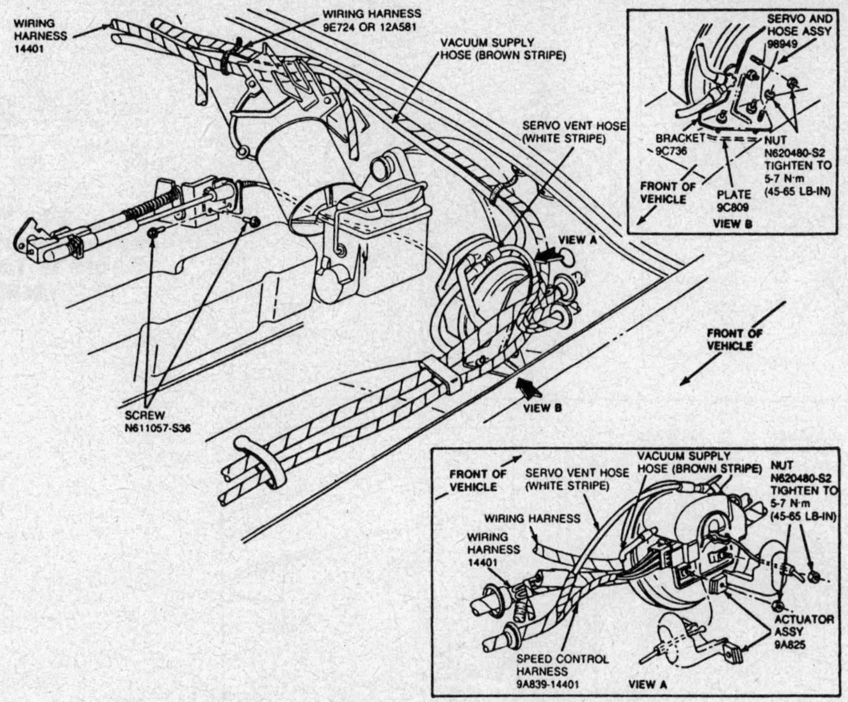


**Fig. 21 Servo assembly replacement. Crown Victoria, Town Car & Grand Marquis**

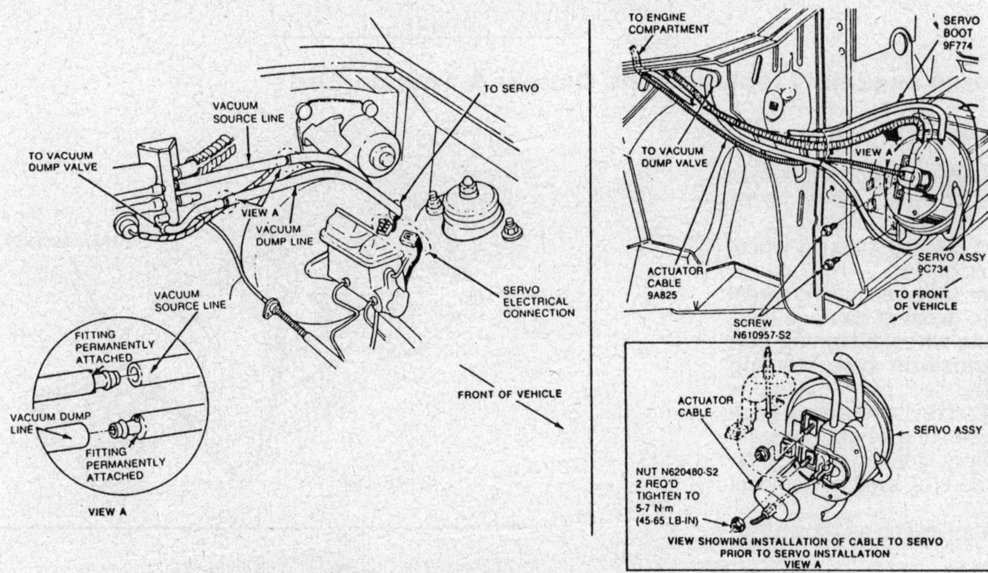


**Fig. 22 Servo assembly replacement. Mark VII**

switch electrical connectors.

2. Remove and discard steering wheel attaching bolt.
3. Using a puller, separate steering wheel from shaft.
4. Remove six screws retaining back cover to steering wheel.
5. Separate back cover from steering wheel, then disconnect control switch electrical connector.
6. Remove control switch as shown **Fig. 28.**
7. Reverse procedure to install. **Torque** new steering wheel attaching bolt to 23-33 ft. lbs.

## 1990–91 Crown Victoria, Town Car & Grand Marquis

1. Disarm airbag system as described under "Airbag System Disarming."
2. Remove four nut and washer assemblies retaining airbag module to steering wheel.
3. Remove airbag module from steering wheel. **Place airbag module on bench with trim cover facing upward.**
4. **On Town Car models,** remove horn buttons by gently prying upward with small screwdriver, then disconnect wiring harness connector.
5. **On Crown Victoria and Grand Marquis models,** pry off speed control switch bezels, then remove bezels from steering wheel.
6. **On all models,** remove Phillips head screw from speed control switch assemblies, then disconnect speed control switches from wiring harness and remove switches.
7. **On Crown Victoria and Grand Marquis models,** Remove wire organizer from steering wheel.
8. Reverse procedure to install.
9. Reactivate airbag as described under "Airbag System Disarming."

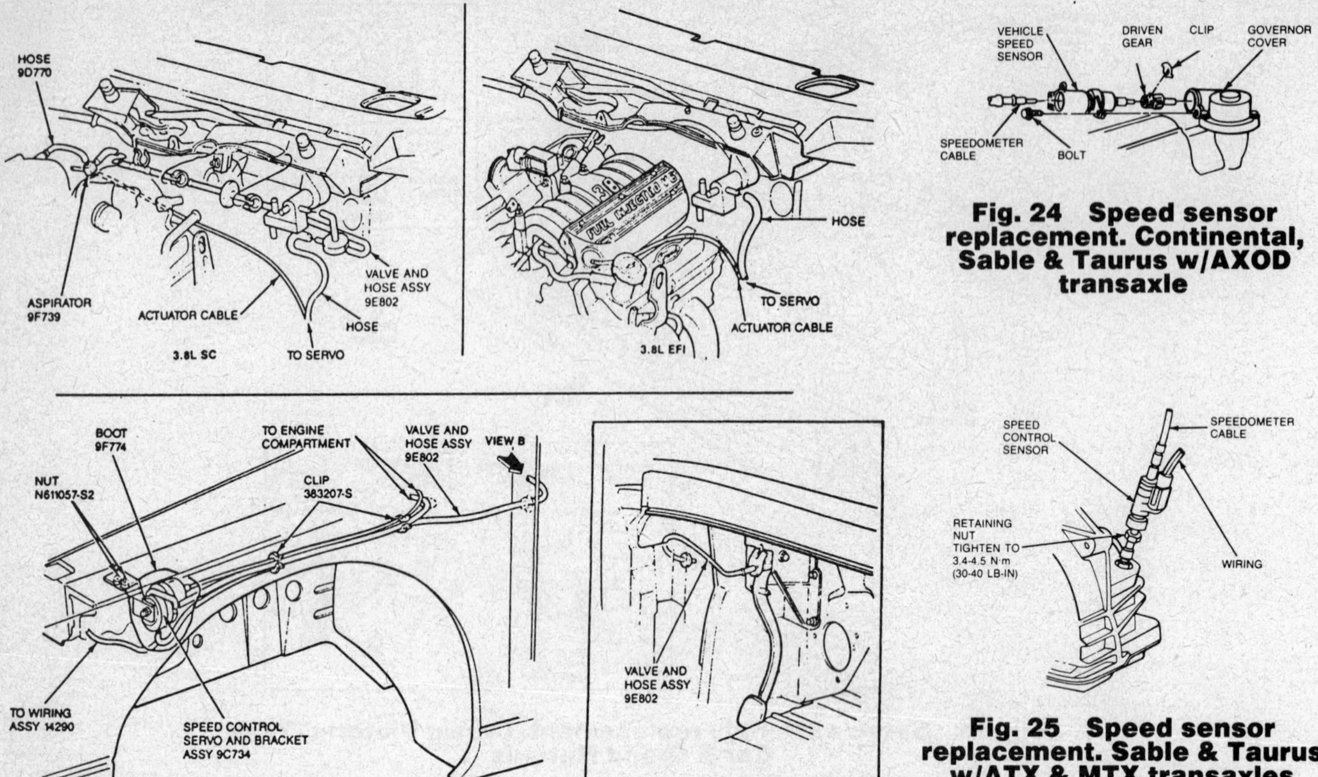


**Fig. 24 Speed sensor replacement. Continental, Sable & Taurus w/AXOD transaxle**

**Fig. 25 Speed sensor replacement. Sable & Taurus w/ATX & MTX transaxles**

**Fig. 23 Servo assembly replacement. Cougar & Thunderbird**

## 1989 Mark VII

1. Disconnect battery ground cable, then remove steering wheel center cover, **Fig. 29.**
2. Remove and discard steering wheel attaching bolt.
3. Using a puller, remove steering wheel from shaft. **To prevent damage never hit steering wheel attaching bolt or use a knock-off type steering wheel puller.**
4. Remove six screws retaining back cover to the steering wheel. Separate back cover from steering wheel, then disconnect control switch electrical connector.
5. Remove control switch as shown **Fig. 30.**
6. Reverse procedure to install. **Torque new steering wheel attaching bolt to 23-33 ft. lbs.**

## 1990–91 Mark VII

1. Disarm airbag system as described under "Airbag System Disarming."
2. Remove four nut and washers retaining air bag module to steering wheel.
3. Disconnect air bag electrical connector from clockspring contact connector, then remove air bag module from steering wheel. **Place air bag on a flat surface with the trim cover facing up.**
4. Remove horn buttons by gently prying with a small screwdriver.
5. Disconnect horn wiring harness connector.

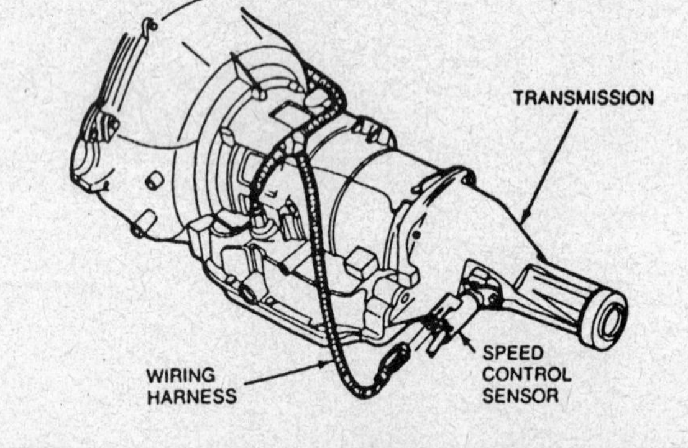


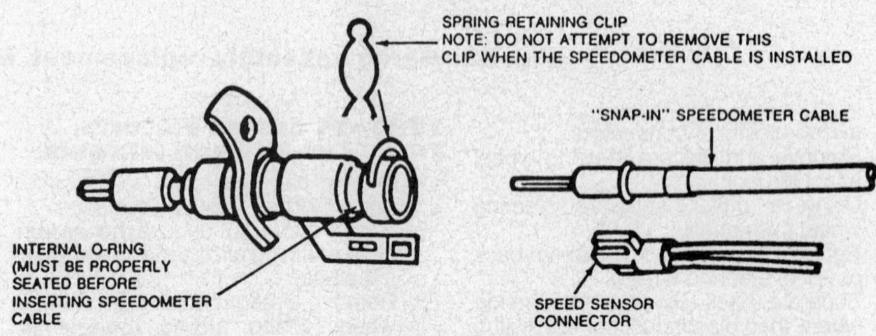


**Fig. 26 Speed sensor replacement. Cougar, Crown Victoria, Town Car, Mark VII, Grand Marquis, & Thunderbird**

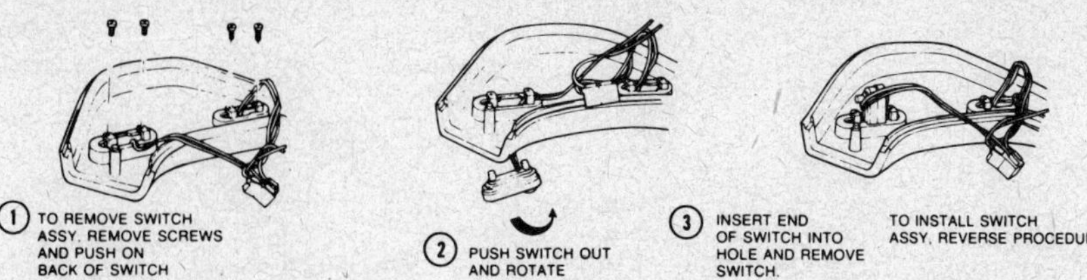


**Fig. 27 Control switch replacement. Continental, Sable & Taurus**

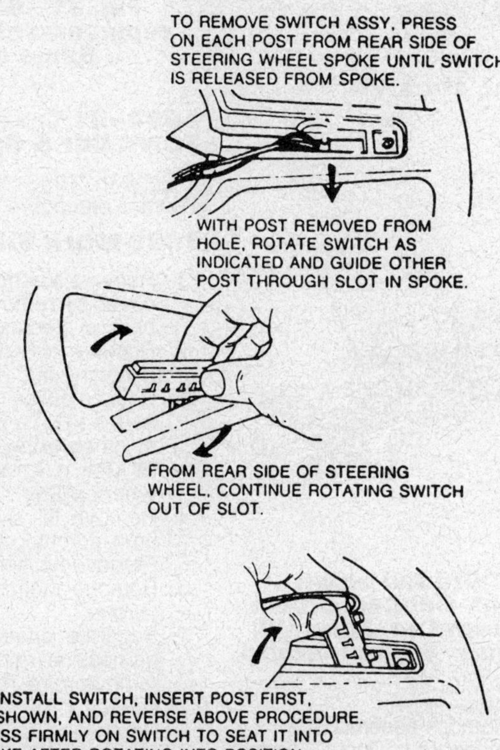

TO REMOVE SWITCH ASSY, PRESS ON EACH POST FROM REAR SIDE OF STEERING WHEEL SPOKE UNTIL SWITCH IS RELEASED FROM SPOKE.
WITH POST REMOVED FROM HOLE, ROTATE SWITCH AS INDICATED AND GUIDE OTHER POST THROUGH SLOT IN SPOKE.
FROM REAR SIDE OF STEERING WHEEL, CONTINUE ROTATING SWITCH OUT OF SLOT.
TO INSTALL SWITCH, INSERT POST FIRST, AS SHOWN, AND REVERSE ABOVE PROCEDURE. PRESS FIRMLY ON SWITCH TO SEAT IT INTO SPOKE AFTER ROTATING INTO POSITION.


**Fig. 28 Control switch replacement. Crown Victoria, Town Car & Grand Marquis**

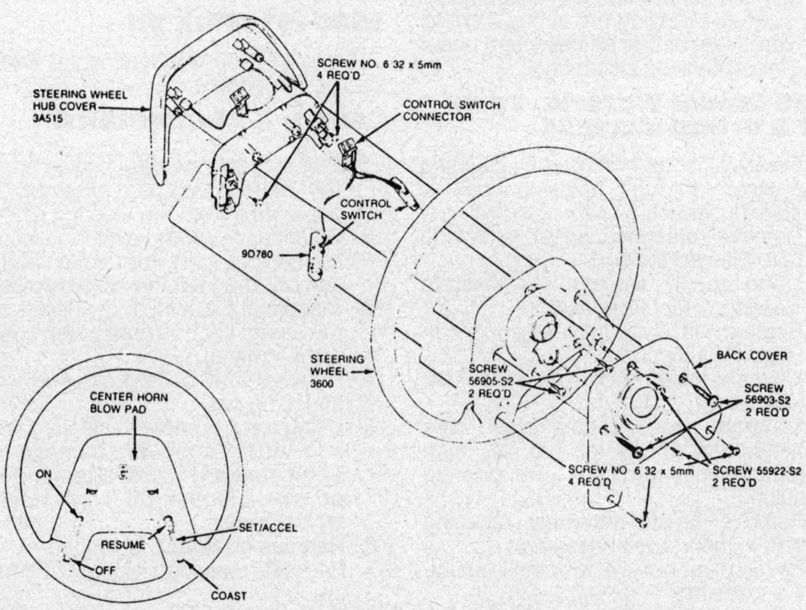


**Fig. 29 Steering wheel assembly. Mark VII**

6. Remove phillips head screws from speed control switch assemblies.
7. Disconnect speed control switches from wiring harness, then remove switches.
8. Reverse procedure to install.
9. Reactivate airbag as described under "Airbag System Disarming."

### 1989–90 Cougar & Thunderbird

1. Pull upward on upper middle edge of the horn cover/pad assembly and separate it from the steering wheel.
2. Disconnect horn switch electrical connectors from horn cover/pad assembly, then set the assembly aside.
3. Disconnect electrical connector from the speed control/horn brush contact plate terminal.
4. **On models with standard steering wheel,** use your fingers to pry out the speed control switch. Remove switch and harness assembly from steering wheel.
5. **On models with sport steering wheel,** remove four speed control switch retaining screws. Remove switch and harness assembly from steering wheel.
6. **On all models,** reverse procedure to install.

### 1991 Cougar & Thunderbird

1. Disarm airbag system as described under "Airbag System Disarming."
2. remove four nut and washer assemblies retaining the airbag module to steering wheel.
3. Disconnect airbag electrical connector from clockspring contact connector.
4. Remove airbag module from steering wheel. **Place airbag module on bench with trim cover facing up.**
5. Using a small screwdriver, remove horn buttons by gently prying upward.
6. Disconnect horn wiring harness connector.
7. Remove Phillips head screws from speed control switch assemblies.
8. Disconnect speed control switches from wiring harness, then remove switches.
9. Reverse procedure to install. **Torque** airbag retaining nuts to 3-4 ft. lbs.
10. Reactivate airbag as described under "Airbag System Disarming."

## GROUND BRUSH

### 1989 Continental, Sable & Taurus

1. Remove steering wheel hub horn pad cover by removing two screws from back of steering wheel.
2. Remove and discard steering wheel attaching nut.
3. Grasp rim of steering wheel and pull upward and away from steering shaft. Do not use steering wheel puller. **Proceed to step 5.**

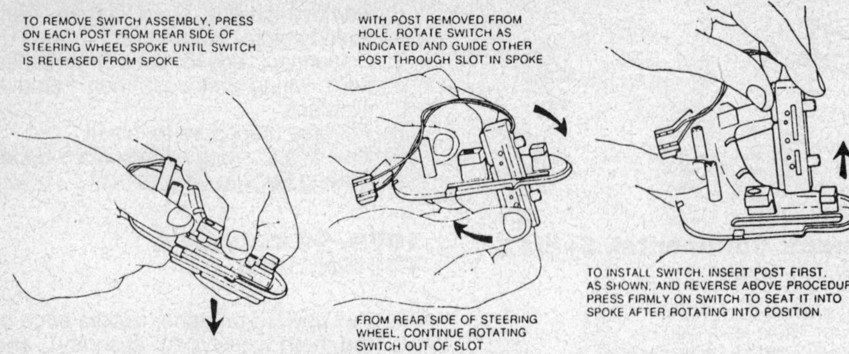
TO REMOVE SWITCH ASSEMBLY, PRESS ON EACH POST FROM REAR SIDE OF STEERING WHEEL SPOKE UNTIL SWITCH IS RELEASED FROM SPOKE
WITH POST REMOVED FROM HOLE, ROTATE SWITCH AS INDICATED AND GUIDE OTHER POST THROUGH SLOT IN SPOKE
FROM REAR SIDE OF STEERING WHEEL, CONTINUE ROTATING SWITCH OUT OF SLOT
TO INSTALL SWITCH, INSERT POST FIRST, AS SHOWN, AND REVERSE ABOVE PROCEDURE. PRESS FIRMLY ON SWITCH TO SEAT IT INTO SPOKE AFTER ROTATING INTO POSITION.

**Fig. 30 Control switch replacement. Mark VII**

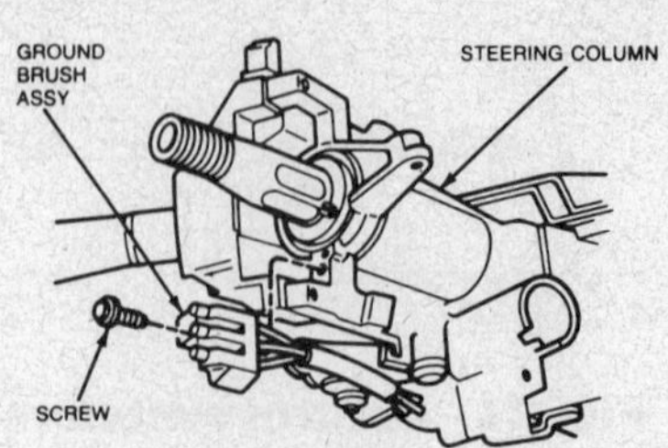
GROUND BRUSH ASSY
STEERING COLUMN
SCREW

**Fig. 31 Ground brush replacement. Continental, Sable & Taurus**

4. Remove tilt lever, if equipped.
5. Remove ignition lock cylinder, then lower steering column trim shroud.
6. Separate speed control brush wire harness at connector, **Fig. 31,** then remove wire retainers from steering column.
7. Remove brush assembly retaining screw, then brush assembly.
8. Reverse procedure to install, noting the following:
   a. **On Taurus & Sable models, torque** steering wheel retaining nut to 50-60 ft. lbs.
   b. **On Continental models, torque** steering wheel retaining nut to 23-33 ft. lbs.

## 1990–91 Continental, Sable & Taurus

1. Disarm airbag system as described under "Airbag System Disarming."
2. Center vehicle front wheels in the straight ahead position.
3. Remove four nut and washer assemblies retaining airbag module module to steering wheel.
4. Disconnect airbag electrical connector from clockspring contact connector, then remove airbag module from steering wheel. **Place airbag module on bench with trim pad facing up.**
5. Remove steering wheel retaining bolt, then discard bolt.
6. Install Steering Wheel Puller tool No. T67L-3600-A or equivalent, then remove steering wheel.
7. Remove tilt lever, if equipped.
8. **On Continental models,** remove ignition lock cylinder assembly.
9. **On Sable & Taurus models,** if a new contact assembly is to be installed, remove ignition lock mechanism.
10. **On all models,** remove lower trim panel, then lower steering column shroud.
11. Disconnect contact assembly wiring harness.
12. Apply two pieces of tape across contact assembly stator and rotor to prevent accidental rotation.
13. Remove three contact assembly retaining screw, then lift contact assembly off steering column shaft.
14. Disconnect speed control brush wiring harness at connector, then remove wiring harness retainers from steering column.
15. Remove screw retaining brush assembly to upper steering column, then brush and harness assembly.
16. Reverse procedure to install, noting the following:
   a. **Torque** contact assembly retaining screws to 18-26 inch. lbs.
   b. Ensure wiring is positioned so that no interference in encountered when installing the airbag module.
17. Reactivate airbag as described under "Airbag System Disarming."

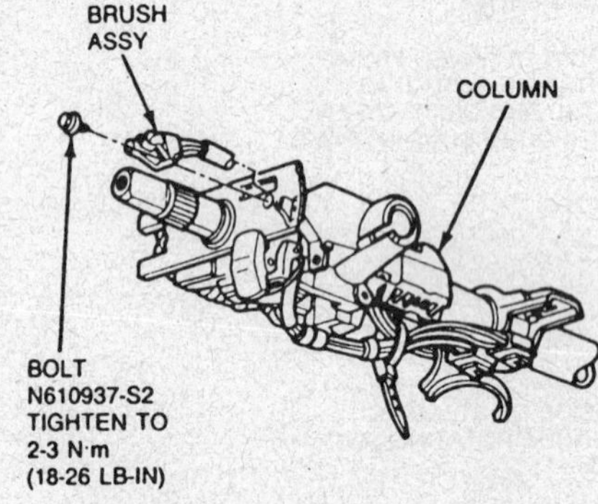
BRUSH ASSY
COLUMN
BOLT N610937-S2 TIGHTEN TO 2-3 N·m (18-26 LB-IN)

**Fig. 32 Ground brush replacement. Cougar, Crown Victoria, Town Car, Mark VII, Grand Marquis, & Thunderbird**

## 1989 Crown Victoria, Town Car & Grand Marquis

1. Remove center horn pad by inserting a punch through holes in back of steering wheel.
2. Remove steering wheel attaching bolt. Discard the bolt.
3. Using steering wheel puller, separate steering wheel from shaft.
4. Remove tilt lever from steering column, if equipped.
5. Remove steering column lower trim shroud.
6. Separate speed control brush wire harness at connector, **Fig. 32,** then remove wire retainers from steering column.
7. Remove brush assembly retaining screw, then brush assembly.
8. Reverse procedure to install, noting the following:
   a. **Torque** steering wheel retaining nut to 23-33 ft. lbs.

## 1990–91 Crown Victoria, Town Car & Grand Marquis

Refer to "1990-91 Continental, Sable & Taurus" procedure.

## 1989 Mark VII

1. Remove steering wheel hub horn pad cover by removing two screws from back of steering wheel.
2. Remove and discard steering wheel attaching nut.
3. Using a puller, remove steering wheel from shaft. **To prevent damage never hit steering wheel attaching bolt or use a knock-off type steering wheel puller.**
4. Remove tilt lever from steering column, if equipped.
5. Remove ignition lock cylinder.
6. Remove steering column lower trim shroud.
7. Separate speed control brush wire harness at connector, **Fig. 32,** then remove wire retainers from steering column.
8. Remove brush assembly retaining screw, then brush assembly.
9. Reverse procedure to install, noting the following:
   a. **Torque** steering wheel retaining nut to 23-33 ft. lbs.

## 1990–91 Mark VII

Refer to "1990-91 Continental, Sable & Taurus" procedure.

## Cougar & Thunderbird

1. Pull upward on upper middle edge of the horn cover/pad assembly and separate it from the steering wheel.
2. Disconnect horn switch electrical connectors from horn cover/pad assembly, then set the assembly aside.
3. Disconnect electrical connector from the speed control/horn brush contact plate terminal.
4. Remove and discard steering wheel attaching nut.
5. Using a puller, remove steering wheel from shaft. **To prevent damage never hit steering wheel attaching bolt or use a knock-off type steering wheel puller.**
6. Remove tilt lever, if equipped.
7. Remove steering column lower trim shroud.
8. Separate speed control brush wire harness at connector and remove

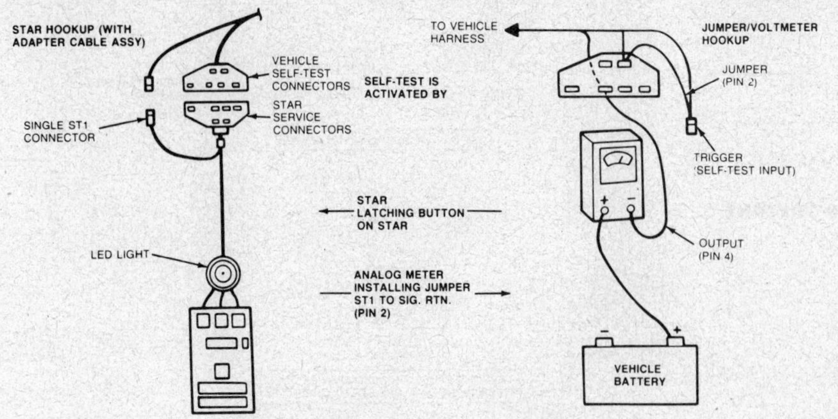


**Fig. 33 Equipment hookup**

wire retainers from steering column, **Fig. 32.**

9. Remove brush assembly retaining screw, then the brush assembly.
10. Reverse procedure to install noting the following:
    a. **Torque** new steering wheel attaching nut to 23-33 ft. lbs.

## CLUTCH SWITCH

### Removal

1. Remove screw attaching switch to bracket.
2. Disconnect electrical connector.
3. Remove switch assembly.

### Installation

1. Install switch on bracket.
2. Connect electrical connector.
3. Install attaching switch to bracket.
4. Adjust clutch switch as described under "Adjustments."

## CLUTCH INTERLOCK THREE FUNCTION SWITCH

### Cougar & Thunderbird

1. Disconnect switch electrical connector, **Fig. 18.**
2. Separate switch tab from clip by pulling downward on the clip.
3. Expose switch plastic retainer by rotating switch 1/2 turn.
4. Separate switch from retainer by pressing tabs together and allowing retainer to move rearward.
5. Remove switch from push rod.
6. Reverse procedure to install.

## SPEED CONTROL/HORN BRUSH CONTACT PLATE

### Cougar & Thunderbird

1. Pull upward on upper middle edge of the horn cover/pad assembly and separate it from the steering wheel.
2. Disconnect horn switch electrical connectors from horn cover/pad assembly, then set the assembly aside.
3. Disconnect electrical connector from the speed control/horn brush contact plate terminal.
4. Remove and discard steering wheel attaching nut.
5. Using a puller, remove steering wheel from shaft. **To prevent damage never hit steering wheel attaching bolt or use a knock-off type steering wheel puller.**
6. Working from back side of steering wheel, remove three retaining screws, then the speed control/horn brush contact plate.
7. Reverse procedure to install.

### Continental

1. Disarm airbag system as described under "Airbag System Disarming."
2. Remove four nut and washers retaining air bag module to the steering wheel.
3. Disconnect air bag electrical connector from clockspring contact connector.
4. Remove air bag module from steering wheel. **Place air bag module on a flat surface with the trim cover facing up.**
5. Remove and discard steering wheel attaching bolt.
6. Grasp rim of steering wheel at opposing points, then pull steering wheel from shaft. **Do not use steering wheel puller.**
7. Remove tilt lever, if equipped, ignition lock cylinder, then the lower trim panel and lower steering column shroud.
8. Separate speed control brush wire harness from the connector, then remove the wire harness retainers from the steering column.
9. Remove screw securing brush assembly to upper steering column.
10. Reverse procedure to install. **Torque** the new steering wheel retaining nut to 23-33 ft. lbs.
11. Reactivate airbag as described under "Airbag System Disarming."

### Mark VII

1. Disarm airbag system as described under "Airbag System Disarming."
2. Place vehicle front wheels in the straight ahead position.
3. Remove four nut and washers retaining air bag module to the steering wheel.
4. Disconnect air bag electrical connector from clockspring contact connector.
5. Remove air bag module from steering wheel. **Place air bag module on a flat surface with the trim cover facing up.**
6. Disconnect speed control and horn switches from contact assembly.
7. Remove steering wheel retaining bolt, install steering wheel puller, part No. T67L-3600-A, or equivalent, then remove steering wheel. **Route contact assembly wiring harness through steering wheel as wheel is lifted off.**
8. Remove tilt lever, if equipped, then the lower trim panel and lower steering column shroud.
9. Disconnect contact assembly wiring harness, then apply two pieces of tape across contact assembly stator and rotor, to prevent accidental rotation.
10. Remove three contact assembly retaining screws, then lift contact assembly from steering column shaft.
11. Disconnect speed control brush wiring harness from connector, then remove wiring harness retainers from steering column.
12. Remove screw, retaining brush assembly to upper steering column, then remove brush and harness assembly.
13. Reverse procedure to install. **Torque** brush retaining screw and contact assembly screws to 18-26 inch lbs., then the steering wheel retaining nut to 23-33 ft. lbs.
14. Reactivate airbag as described under "Airbag System Disarming."

## VACUUM RESERVOIR

### Continental

1. Raise and support vehicle, then remove lefthand front wheel.
2. Remove inner fender splash shield.
3. Remove hose from check valve.
4. Remove screw retaining vacuum reservoir assembly to A-pillar. Slide reservoir forward to release hook.
5. Remove vacuum reservoir assembly by pulling hose through cowl side panel.
6. Reverse procedure to install.

# TESTING

**Do not depart from the instructions provided here. Anyone who departs from the following instructions must first establish that he may compromise his personal safety and the vehicle integrity by his choice of methods, tools or parts.**

The Integrated Vehicle Speed Control (IVSC) contains a self-test capability, consisting of a Key On, Engine Off (KOEO) and Key On, Engine Running (KOER) routine, which utilizes output error codes similar to EEC-IV subsystem "Quick Tests." These "Quick Tests" then refer to Pinpoint Tests for specific components diagnosis.

Testing for the IVSC is divided into two formats: the Quick Test and the Pinpoint Tests. The Quick Test is a functional IVSC system test. The Pinpoint Tests are specific component tests.

The Quick Test checks all IVSC components except the speed sensor, which must be checked separately. To test and

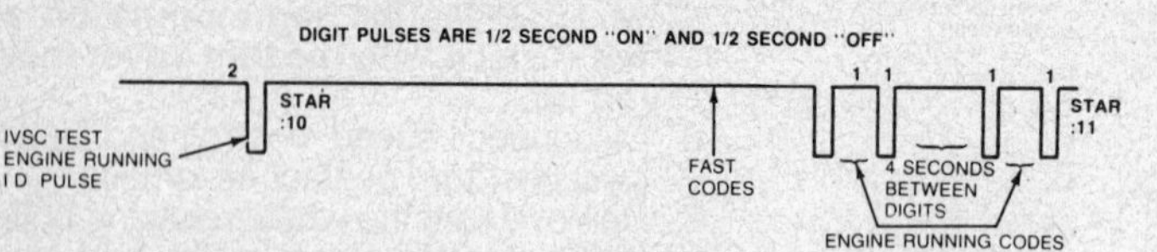


**Fig. 34 Self-Test output code format**

1 NEEDLE PULSE (SWEEP) + 1 NEEDLE PULSE (SWEEP) = 2 NEEDLE PULSES (SWEEPS) FOR 1ST DIGIT

2-SECOND PAUSE BETWEEN DIGITS

:23

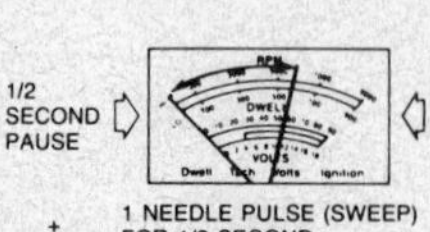


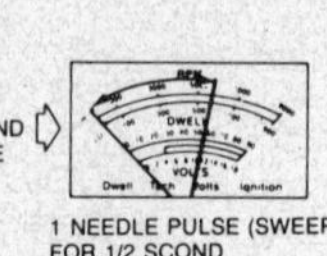


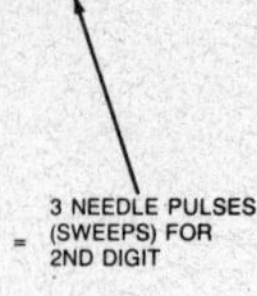

1 NEEDLE PULSE (SWEEP) FOR 1/2 SECOND + 1 NEEDLE PULSE (SWEEP) FOR 1/2 SECOND + 1 NEEDLE PULSE (SWEEP) FOR 1/2 SCOND = 3 NEEDLE PULSES (SWEEPS) FOR 2ND DIGIT

4-SECOND PAUSE BETWEEN SERVICE CODES, WHEN MORE THAN ONE CODE IS INDICATED

**Fig. 35 Reading codes with analog voltmeter**

service the IVSC system, perform the quick test first. If the system passes, check the speed sensor. If failure codes are generated, do only the Pinpoint Test specified by that particular failure code.

After all test and services have been completed, repeat the entire Quick Test to verify that the IVSC system operates properly.

## TEST EQUIPMENT

### Cougar, Crown Victoria, Continental, Town Car, Mark VII, Grand Marquis, Sable, Taurus & Thunderbird

Use Super (STAR II) Tester No. 007-00041, or Inductive Dwell-Tach-Volt-Ohmmeter (VOM) 0-20 VDC No.059-00010, or equivalent to perform the IVSC Quick Test and display error codes. A Rotunda Breakout Box 014-00322 or equivalent can also be used for convenience during Pinpoint Testing.

## EQUIPMENT HOOKUP

### Using The STAR Tester

1. Turn ignition switch to the Off position.
2. Connect color-coded adapter cable leads to STAR tester **Fig. 33.**
3. Connect two service connectors from adapter cable to vehicles appropriate Self-Test connectors.
4. After equipment hookup, proceed to Self-Testing.

### Using Analog Voltmeter

1. Turn ignition switch to the Off position.
2. Connect a jumper wire from Self-Test input (STI) to Pin 2, Signal Return on the Self-Test connector **Fig. 33.**
3. Set analog VOM on a DC voltage range to read from 0-15 volts DC. Connect VOM from battery (+) to Pin 4 Self-Test Output (STO) in the Self-Test connector.
4. After equipment hookup proceed to Self-Testing.

## QUICK TEST

### Description

The Quick Test is a functional test of the IVSC system consisting of basic Test Steps (described below). Otherwise, inaccurate diagnosis or the replacement of satisfactory components may result.

### Quick Test Steps

1. Perform a visual check for obvious faults then properly prepare the vehicle for testing.
2. Ensure proper equipment is used for gathering test data is ready prior to testing.
3. Key On, Engine Off Self Test is a static check of IVSC inputs and outputs.
4. Key On, Engine Running Self-Test is a dynamic check of the engine in operation.

### Visual Check & Vehicle Preparation

Correct test results for the Quick Test are dependent on the proper operation of related non-IVSC components systems. It may be necessary to correct faults in these areas before the IVSC will pass the Quick Test.

Before hooking up any equipment to diagnose the IVSC system, make the following checks:

1. Check all engine vacuum hoses for leaks or pinched hoses (servo to dump valve and servo to manifold vacuum).
2. Check IVSC and EEC system wiring harness electrical connections for proper connections, faulty connectors, corrosion and proper routing of harness. It may be necessary to disconnect or disassemble the connector assembly to perform some of the inspections.
3. Check EEC-IV and IVSC sensors and actuators for physical damage.
4. Perform all safety steps required to start and run operation vehicle tests.
5. Apply emergency brake. Place the shift lever in PARK (NEUTRAL for manual transmission).
6. Turn off all electrical loads.
7. Verify engine coolant is at specified level.
8. Start engine and idle until upper radiator hose is hot and pressurized and throttle is off fast idle.
9. Turn ignition key off.
10. Service items as required, then proceed to equipment hookup.

### Quick Test Self-Test

Quick Test Self-Test is divided into two specialized tests: Key On, Engine Off, and Key On, Engine Running. The Self-Test is not a conclusive test by itself, but is used as a part of the functional Quick Test diagnostic procedure. The processor stores the Self-Test program in its permanent memory. When activated, it checks the IVSC system by testing its functional capability and verifies that various sensors and actuators are connected and operating properly.

The Key On, Engine Off and Engine Running tests are functional tests which only detect faults that are present at the time of the Self-Test.

### Key On, Engine Off Test

At this time, a test of the IVSC system is conducted power applied and engine at rest. The fault must be present at the time of testing for errors to be detected in this test.

### Key On, Engine Running Test

At this time, a test of the IVSC system is conducted with the engine running. The system is checked under actual operating conditions and at normal operating temperatures. The actuators are exercised and checked for corresponding results.

### Service Codes

The EEC-IV system communicates service information by way of the Self-Test codes. These service codes are two digit numbers representing the results of the Self-Test.

The service codes are transmitted on the Self-Test output (found in the Self-Test connector) in the form of timed pulses, and read by the technician on a voltmeter or on the STAR tester, **Fig. 34.**

### Reading Codes-Analog Voltmeter

When a service code is reported on the analog voltmeter for a function test, it will represent itself as a pulsing or sweeping movement of the voltmeter's needle across the dial face of the voltmeter, **Fig. 35.** Therefore, a single-digit number of three will be reported by three needle pulses (sweeps). However as previously stated, a service code is represented by a two digit number, such as 2-3. As a result, the Self-Test service code of 2-3 will appear on the voltmeter as two needle pulses (sweeps), then, after a two second pause, the needle will pulse (sweep) three times.

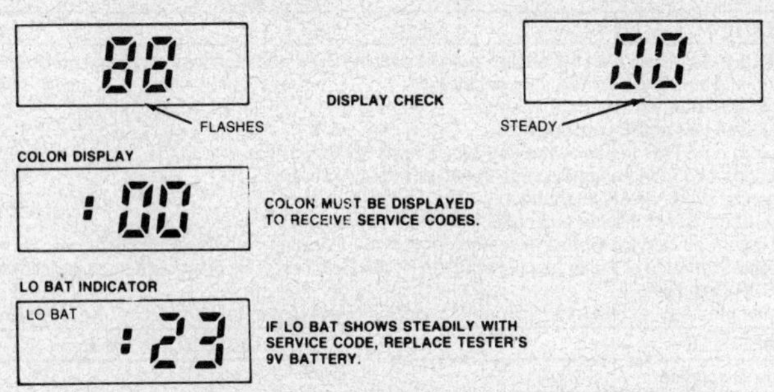


**Fig. 36 Reading codes with Self-Test Automatic Readout (STAR) tester**

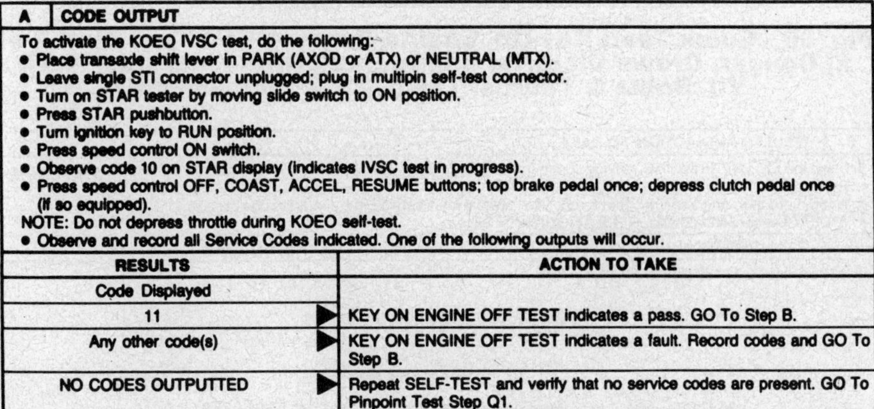

**A — CODE OUTPUT**

To activate the KOEO IVSC test, do the following:
- Place transaxle shift lever in PARK (AXOD or ATX) or NEUTRAL (MTX).
- Leave single STI connector unplugged; plug in multipin self-test connector.
- Turn on STAR tester by moving slide switch to ON position.
- Press STAR pushbutton.
- Turn ignition key to RUN position.
- Press speed control ON switch.
- Observe code 10 on STAR display (indicates IVSC test in progress).
- Press speed control OFF, COAST, ACCEL, RESUME buttons; top brake pedal once; depress clutch pedal once (if so equipped).

NOTE: Do not depress throttle during KOEO self-test.
- Observe and record all Service Codes indicated. One of the following outputs will occur.

| RESULTS | ACTION TO TAKE |
|---|---|
| Code Displayed | |
| 11 | KEY ON ENGINE OFF TEST indicates a pass. GO To Step B. |
| Any other code(s) | KEY ON ENGINE OFF TEST indicates a fault. Record codes and GO To Step B. |
| NO CODES OUTPUTTED | Repeat SELF-TEST and verify that no service codes are present. GO To Pinpoint Test Step Q1. |

**Fig. 37 Quick Test: Key On, Engine Off Self-Test (Part 1 of 2). Cougar, Crown Victoria, Continental, Grand Marquis, Mark VII, Sable, Taurus, Town Car & Thunderbird**

**B — RESULTS AND ACTION TO TAKE**

- Using the KEY ON ENGINE OFF service codes from Step A, follow the instructions in the ACTION TO TAKE column in this step.
- When more than one service code is received always start with the first code received.
- Whenever a service is made, REPEAT QUICK TEST.

NOTE: Before proceeding to the specified Pinpoint Test, read the instructions on how to use the Pinpoint Tests at the beginning of the Pinpoint Test section.

| RESULT | ACTION TO TAKE |
|---|---|
| ON DEMAND SERVICE CODES<br>23 | Check throttle position sensor. Refer to EEC-IV system diagnosis in the Auto Engine Tune Up & Electronics Manual |
| 47 | GO to Pinpoint Test Step A1. |
| 48 | Go to Pinpoint Test Step A3. |
| 49 | |
| 53 | GO to Pinpoint Test Step A5. |
| 63 | Check throttle position sensor. Refer to EEC-IV system diagnosis in the Auto Engine Tune Up & Electronics Manual |
| 74 | Check brake On/Off Circuit. Refer to EEC-IV system diagnosis in the Auto Engine Tune Up & Electronics Manual |
| 75 | GO to Pinpoint Test Step B1. |
| 67 | GO to Pinpoint Test Step B4. |
| 81 | |
| 82 | Check air management system operation. Refer to EEC-IV system diagnosis in the Auto Engine Tune Up & Electronics Manual |
| | GO to Pinpoint Test Step C1. |
| | GO to Pinpoint Test Step C5. |

NOTE: Service codes 23, 53, 63 and 67 are common with EEC-IV Diagnostics. These service codes must be diagnosed using the EEC-IV system diagnosis in the Auto Engine Tune Up & Electronics Manual.

*Can be purchased as a separate item.

**Fig. 37 Quick Test: Key On, Engine Off Self-Test (Part 2 of 2). Cougar, Crown Victoria, Continental, Grand Marquis, Mark VII, Sable, Taurus, Town Car & Thunderbird**

## Reading Codes, Self-Test Automatic Readout (STAR) Rotunda 007-00004, or STAR Rotunda 007-000717, or Equivalent

After hooking up the STAR tester and turning on its power switch, the tester will run a display check and the numerals 88 will flash in the display window, **Fig. 36.** A steady 00 will then appear to signify that the STAR tester is ready to start the Self-Test and receive the tests service codes.

To receive the service codes, press the push button at the front of the STAR tester. The button will latch down, and a colon will appear in the display window in the front of the 00 numerals. The colon must be displayed to receive the service codes.

If for any reason the technician wishes to clear the display window during the Self-Test, he must turn off the vehicle's engine, press the tester's push button once to unlatch it (colon will disappear), then press the button again to latch down the button (colon will appear again). Every time the STAR tester is turned off, the low battery indicator (LO BAT) should show briefly at the upper left corner to the tester's display window. If the LO BAT indicator shows steadily at any other time during the operation of the STAR tester with any service code, turn its power switch to OFF and replace the 9-volt battery in the tester.

The STAR tester will display the last service code received, even after it has been disconnected from the vehicle. It will hold the service code on the display until the power is turned off or the push button is unlatched and latched.

## QUICK TESTS

Refer to **Figs. 37 and 38** to perform system Quick Tests.

## PINPOINT TESTS
### Instructions For Using The Pinpoint Tests

1. Do not run any of the following Pinpoint Tests unless you are so instructed by the Quick Test. Each Pinpoint Test assumes that a fault has been detected in the system with direction to enter a specific service routine. Performing any Pinpoint Test without direction from the Quick Test may produce incorrect results and cause replacement of satisfactory components.
2. Do not replace any component unless the test result indicates that it should be replaced.
3. When more than one service code is received, always start service with the first code received.
4. Do not measure voltage or resistance at the ECA or connect any test lights to it, unless otherwise specified.
5. Isolate both ends of a circuit, and turn the ignition key off whenever checking it for shorts or continuity, unless otherwise specified.
6. Disconnect solenoids and switches from the harness before measuring for continuity, resistance or energizing by way of 12 volt source, unless otherwise instructed.

7. In using the Pinpoint Tests, follow each step in order, starting from the first step in the appropriate test. Follow each step until the fault is found.
8. After completing any service to the IVSC system, verify that all components are properly reconnected and repeat the Quick Test.
9. An open is defined as any resistance reading greater than 5 ohms, unless otherwise specified.
10. A short is defined as any resistance reading less than 10,000 ohms to ground, unless otherwise specified. **Refer to electrical wiring diagram in Fig. 39 as necessary during Pinpoint Tests. To perform Pinpoint Tests, refer to Figs. 40 through 49.**

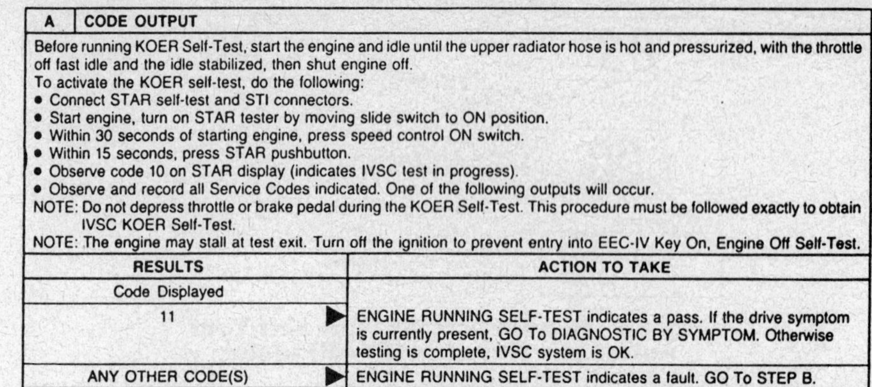

| A | CODE OUTPUT |
|---|---|
| Before running KOER Self-Test, start the engine and idle until the upper radiator hose is hot and pressurized, with the throttle off fast idle and the idle stabilized, then shut engine off.<br>To activate the KOER self-test, do the following:<br>• Connect STAR self-test and STI connectors.<br>• Start engine, turn on STAR tester by moving slide switch to ON position.<br>• Within 30 seconds of starting engine, press speed control ON switch.<br>• Within 15 seconds, press STAR pushbutton.<br>• Observe code 10 on STAR display (indicates IVSC test in progress).<br>• Observe and record all Service Codes indicated. One of the following outputs will occur.<br>NOTE: Do not depress throttle or brake pedal during the KOER Self-Test. This procedure must be followed exactly to obtain IVSC KOER Self-Test.<br>NOTE: The engine may stall at test exit. Turn off the ignition to prevent entry into EEC-IV Key On, Engine Off Self-Test. | |

| RESULTS | ACTION TO TAKE |
|---|---|
| Code Displayed | |
| 11 ▶ | ENGINE RUNNING SELF-TEST indicates a pass. If the drive symptom is currently present, GO To DIAGNOSTIC BY SYMPTOM. Otherwise testing is complete, IVSC system is OK. |
| ANY OTHER CODE(S) ▶ | ENGINE RUNNING SELF-TEST indicates a fault. GO To STEP B. |
| NO CODES OUTPUTTED ▶ | Repeat SELF-TEST and verify that no service codes are present, then GO To Pinpoint Test Step Q1. |

**Fig. 38 Quick Test: Key On, Engine Running Self-Test (Part 1 of 2).Cougar, Crown Victoria, Continental, Grand Marquis, Mark VII, Sable & Taurus, Town Car & Thunderbird**

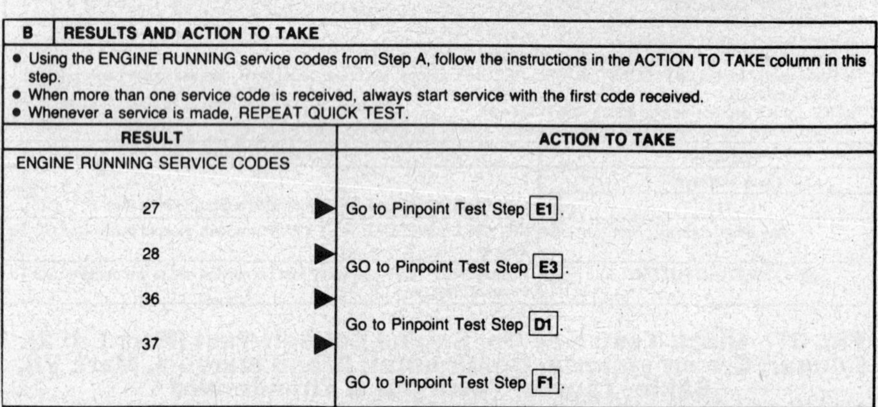

| B | RESULTS AND ACTION TO TAKE |
|---|---|
| • Using the ENGINE RUNNING service codes from Step A, follow the instructions in the ACTION TO TAKE column in this step.<br>• When more than one service code is received, always start service with the first code received.<br>• Whenever a service is made, REPEAT QUICK TEST. | |

| RESULT | ACTION TO TAKE |
|---|---|
| ENGINE RUNNING SERVICE CODES | |
| 27 ▶ | Go to Pinpoint Test Step E1. |
| 28 ▶ | GO to Pinpoint Test Step E3. |
| 36 ▶ | Go to Pinpoint Test Step D1. |
| 37 ▶ | GO to Pinpoint Test Step F1. |

**Fig. 38 Quick Test: Key On, Engine Running Self-Test (Part 2 of 2). Cougar, Crown Victoria, Continental, Grand Marquis, Mark VII, Sable & Taurus, Town Car & Thunderbird**

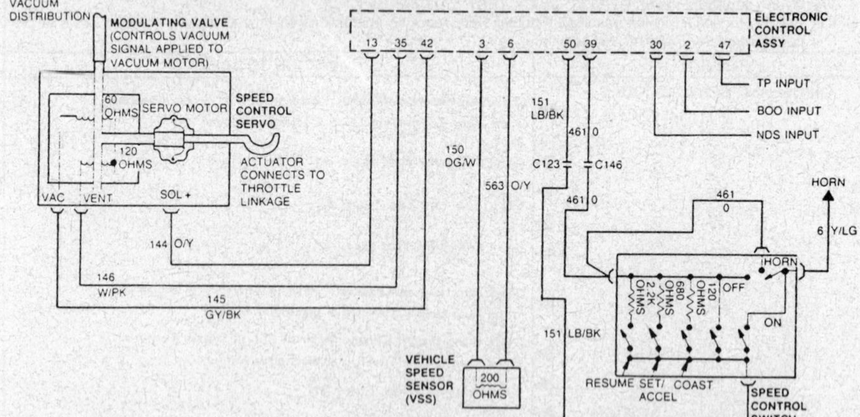


**Fig. 39 Pinpoint test wiring diagram (Part 1 of 3). Sable, Taurus & Continental**

# MERKUR

## TROUBLESHOOTING

### XR4Ti

Refer to **Fig. 50**, for system troubleshooting.

## DIAGNOSIS & TESTING

Refer to **Figs. 51 through 62**, for system diagnosis and testing.

## COMPONENT REPLACEMENT

### ON/OFF SWITCH

### XR4Ti

1. Using a thin blade screwdriver, pry switch out of instrument panel bezel then disconnect wiring from switch and remove switch.
2. Reverse procedure to install.

### CONTROL SWITCHES

### Scorpio

1. Remove steering wheel center cover, then remove three horn switch plate retaining screws.
2. Raise plate to access printed circuit board.
3. Disconnect control switch electrical from circuit board and contact plate assembly.
4. Using a flat blade screwdriver, pry switch(es) from steering wheel.
5. Reverse procedure to install.

### SPEED SENSOR

### XR4Ti

1. Disconnect speedometer cable, **Fig. 63.**
2. Remove speed sensor attaching nut, then disconnect speed sensor electrical connector and remove sensor.
3. Reverse procedure to install.

### SET/DECEL SWITCH

### XR4Ti

The set/decel switch is integral with the turn signal switch and must be replaced as a complete assembly.

1. Disconnect battery negative cable then remove steering column upper and lower trim cover.
2. Remove turn signal switch attaching screws, then disconnect the turn signal switch electrical connector and remove switch.
3. Reverse procedure to install.

### VACUUM VALVE ASSEMBLY

### XR4Ti

1. Disconnect vacuum valve hose from valve, **Fig. 64.**
2. Separate wiring connectors then remove valve attaching nuts and valve assembly
3. Reverse procedure to install.

*Continued on page 28-60*

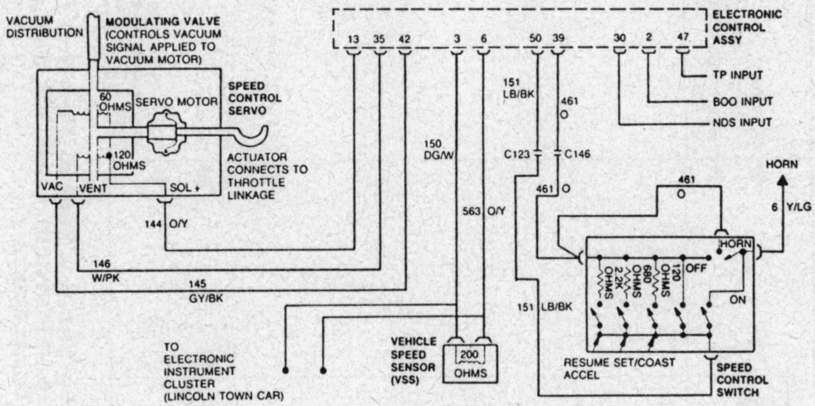


**Fig. 39 Pinpoint test wiring diagram (Part 2 of 3). Crown Victoria, Town Car & Grand Marquis**

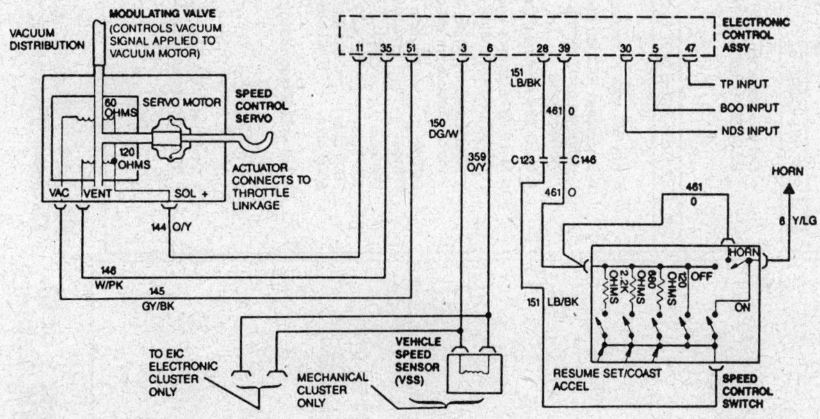


**Fig. 39 Pinpoint test wiring diagram (Part 3 of 3). Cougar & Thunderbird**

| SYMPTOM | RESULT ▶ | ACTION TO TAKE |
|---|---|---|
| • Speed control does not work.<br>• Code "11" displayed on QUICK TESTS. | ▶ | GO to G. |

**Fig. 40 Diagnostic by symptom chart (Part 1 of 2). Cougar, Crown Victoria, Continental & Town Car, Mark VII & Grand Marquis & Thunderbird**

| SYMPTOM | RESULT ▶ | ACTION TO TAKE |
|---|---|---|
| • Speed control does not work.<br>• Code "11" displayed on QUICK TESTS. | ▶ | GO to G. |
| • Clutch does not engage speed control on 2.5L MTX vehicle. | ▶ | GO to H. |

**Fig. 40 Diagnostic by symptom chart (Part 2 of 2). Sable & Taurus**

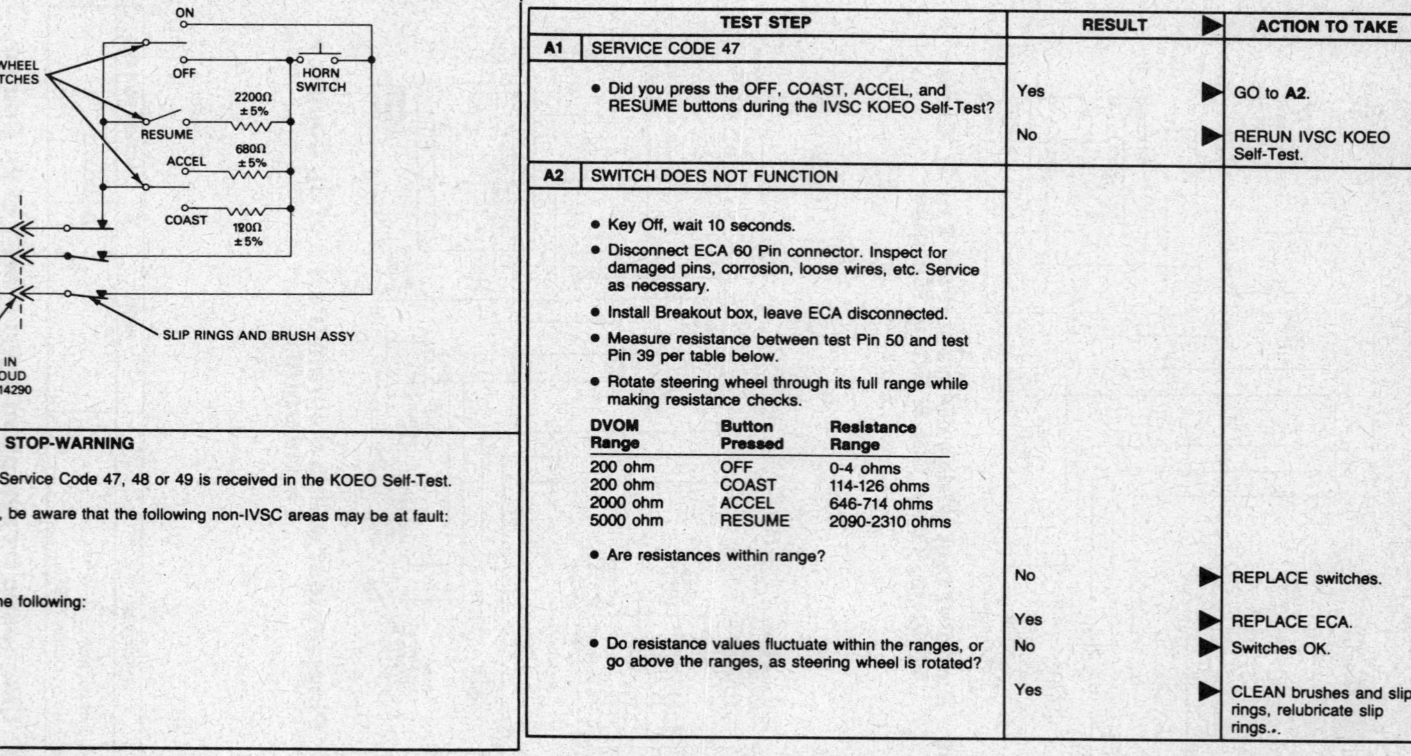


*TEST PINS LOCATED ON BREAKOUT BOX

**STOP-WARNING**

You should enter this Pinpoint Test only when a Service Code 47, 48 or 49 is received in the KOEO Self-Test.

To prevent the replacement of good components, be aware that the following non-IVSC areas may be at fault:

- Horn relay
- Fuse

This Pinpoint Test is intended to diagnose only the following:

- Speed control switches
- Brush assembly
- Slip ring assembly
- Wiring harness
- ECA

**Fig. 41 Speed control switches, Pinpoint Test A (Part 1 of 6). Crown Victoria, Continental, Grand Marquis, Mark VII, Sable, Taurus & Town Car**

| | TEST STEP | RESULT ▶ | ACTION TO TAKE |
|---|---|---|---|
| A1 | SERVICE CODE 47 | | |
| | • Did you press the OFF, COAST, ACCEL, and RESUME buttons during the IVSC KOEO Self-Test? | Yes ▶ | GO to **A2**. |
| | | No ▶ | RERUN IVSC KOEO Self-Test. |
| A2 | SWITCH DOES NOT FUNCTION | | |
| | • Key Off, wait 10 seconds.<br>• Disconnect ECA 60 Pin connector. Inspect for damaged pins, corrosion, loose wires, etc. Service as necessary.<br>• Install Breakout box, leave ECA disconnected.<br>• Measure resistance between test Pin 50 and test Pin 39 per table below.<br>• Rotate steering wheel through its full range while making resistance checks. | | |
| | **DVOM Range** / **Button Pressed** / **Resistance Range**<br>200 ohm / OFF / 0-4 ohms<br>200 ohm / COAST / 114-126 ohms<br>2000 ohm / ACCEL / 646-714 ohms<br>5000 ohm / RESUME / 2090-2310 ohms | | |
| | • Are resistances within range? | No ▶ | REPLACE switches. |
| | | Yes ▶ | REPLACE ECA. |
| | • Do resistance values fluctuate within the ranges, or go above the ranges, as steering wheel is rotated? | No ▶ | Switches OK. |
| | | Yes ▶ | CLEAN brushes and slip rings, relubricate slip rings.. |

**Fig. 41 Speed control switches, Pinpoint Test A (Part 2 of 6). Crown Victoria, Continental, Grand Marquis, Mark VII, Sable, Taurus & Town Car**

| TEST STEP | | RESULT ▶ | ACTION TO TAKE |
|---|---|---|---|
| **A3** | SERVICE CODE 48 | | |
| | • Did you press the OFF, COAST, ACCEL, and RESUME buttons during the IVSC KOEO Quick Test? | Yes ▶ | GO to **A4**. |
| | | No ▶ | RERUN IVSC KOEO QUICK TEST. |
| **A4** | SWITCH IS STUCK | | |
| | • Key off, wait 10 seconds.<br>• Disconnect ECA 60 Pin connector. Inspect for damaged pins, corrosion, loose wires, etc. Service as necessary.<br>• Install Breakout box, leave ECA disconnected.<br>• DVOM on 5000 ohm scale.<br>• Measure resistance between test Pin 50 and test Pin 39.<br>• Is resistance reading between 0 ohms and 2310 ohms? | Yes ▶ | REPLACE switches. |
| | | No ▶ | REPLACE ECA. |
| **A5** | SERVICE CODE 49 | | |
| | • Did you press the OFF, COAST, ACCEL, and RESUME buttons during the IVSC KOEO QUICK TEST? | Yes ▶ | GO to **A6**. |
| | | No ▶ | RERUN IVSC KOEO QUICK TEST. |
| **A6** | GROUND CIRCUIT TO SWITCHES OPEN | | |
| | • Key off, wait 10 seconds.<br>• Disconnect ECA 60 Pin connector. Inspect for damaged pins, corrosion, loose wires, etc. Service as necessary.<br>• Install Breakout box, leave ECA disconnected.<br>• Disconnect speed control switch plug in steering column shroud.<br>• DVOM on 200 ohm scale.<br>• Measure resistance between test Pin 39 and ground terminal in 14290 half of disconnected switch plug.<br>• Is resistance reading greater than 5 ohms? | Yes ▶ | SERVICE open circuit between EEC-IV connector Pin 39 and switch plug ground terminal. |
| | | No ▶ | REPLACE ECA. |

**Fig. 41 Speed control switches, Pinpoint Test A (Part 3 of 6). Crown Victoria, Continental, Grand Marquis, Mark VII, Sable, Taurus & Town Car**

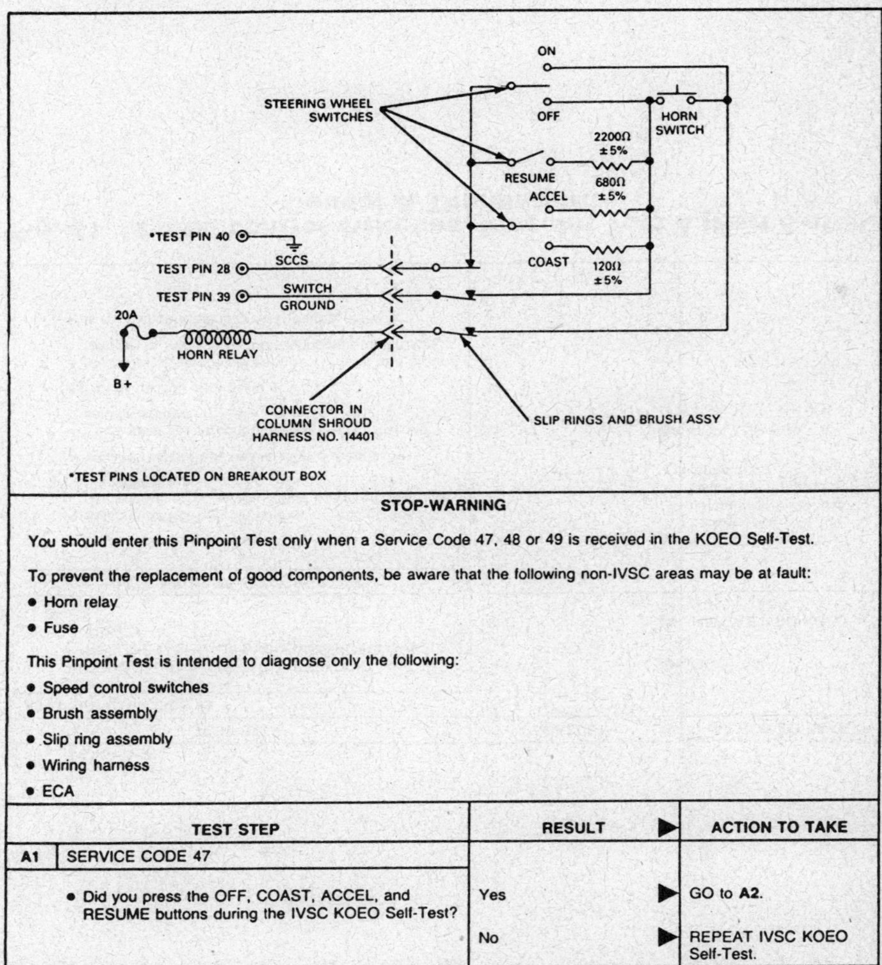


**STOP-WARNING**

You should enter this Pinpoint Test only when a Service Code 47, 48 or 49 is received in the KOEO Self-Test.

To prevent the replacement of good components, be aware that the following non-IVSC areas may be at fault:

- Horn relay
- Fuse

This Pinpoint Test is intended to diagnose only the following:

- Speed control switches
- Brush assembly
- Slip ring assembly
- Wiring harness
- ECA

| TEST STEP | | RESULT ▶ | ACTION TO TAKE |
|---|---|---|---|
| **A1** | SERVICE CODE 47 | | |
| | • Did you press the OFF, COAST, ACCEL, and RESUME buttons during the IVSC KOEO Self-Test? | Yes ▶ | GO to **A2**. |
| | | No ▶ | REPEAT IVSC KOEO Self-Test. |

**Fig. 41 Speed control switches, Pinpoint Test A (Part 4 of 6). Cougar & Thunderbird**

| TEST STEP | RESULT ▶ | ACTION TO TAKE |
|---|---|---|
| **A2** SWITCH DOES NOT FUNCTION | | |
| • Key Off, wait 10 seconds.<br>• Disconnect ECA 60 pin connector. Inspect for damaged pins, corrosion, loose wires, etc. Service as necessary.<br>• Install Breakout box, leave ECA disconnected.<br>• Measure resistance between test Pin 28 and test Pin 39 per table below.<br>• Rotate steering wheel through its full range while making resistance checks.<br>**DVOM Range / Button Pressed / Resistance Range**<br>200 ohm / OFF / 0-4 ohms<br>200 ohm / COAST / 114-126 ohms<br>2000 ohm / ACCEL / 646-714 ohms<br>5000 ohm / RESUME / 2090-2310 ohms<br>• Are resistances within range? | No ▶<br>Yes ▶ | REPLACE switches.<br>REPLACE ECA. |
| • Do resistance values fluctuate within the ranges, or go above the ranges, as steering wheel is rotated? | No ▶<br>Yes ▶ | Switches OK.<br>CLEAN brushes and slip rings, relubricate slip rings. |
| **A3** SERVICE CODE 48 | | |
| • Did you press the OFF, COAST, ACCEL, and RESUME buttons during the IVSC KOEO Quick Test? | Yes ▶<br>No ▶ | GO to **A4**.<br>REPEAT IVSC KOEO QUICK TEST. |
| **A4** SWITCH IS STUCK | | |
| • Key off, wait 10 seconds.<br>• Disconnect ECA 60 pin connector. Inspect for damaged pins, corrosion, loose wires, etc. Service as necessary.<br>• Install Breakout box, leave ECA disconnected.<br>• Rotunda Digital Volt-Ohmmeter (DVOM) 014-00407 or equivalent, on 5000 ohm scale.<br>• Measure resistance between test Pin 28 and test Pin 39.<br>• Is resistance reading between 0 ohms and 2310 ohms? | Yes ▶<br>No ▶ | REPLACE switches.<br>REPLACE ECA. |

**Fig. 41 Speed control switches, Pinpoint Test A (Part 5 of 6). Cougar & Thunderbird**

| TEST STEP | RESULT ▶ | ACTION TO TAKE |
|---|---|---|
| **A5** SERVICE CODE 49 | | |
| • Did you press the OFF, COAST, ACCEL, and RESUME buttons during the IVSC KOEO QUICK TEST? | Yes ▶<br>No ▶ | GO to **A6**.<br>REPEAT IVSC KOEO QUICK TEST. |
| **A6** GROUND CIRCUIT TO SWITCHES OPEN | | |
| • Key off, wait 10 seconds.<br>• Disconnect ECA 60 pin connector. Inspect for damaged pins, corrosion, loose wires, etc. Service as necessary.<br>• Install Breakout box, leave ECA disconnected.<br>• Disconnect speed control switch plug in steering column shroud.<br>• DVOM on 200 ohm scale.<br>• Measure resistance between test Pin 39 and ground terminal in 14290 half of disconnected switch plug.<br>• Is resistance reading greater than 5 ohms? | Yes ▶<br>No ▶ | SERVICE open circuit between EEC-IV connector Pin 39 and switch plug ground terminal.<br>REPLACE ECA. |

**Fig. 41 Speed control switches, Pinpoint Test A (Part 6 of 6). Cougar & Thunderbird**

**B**

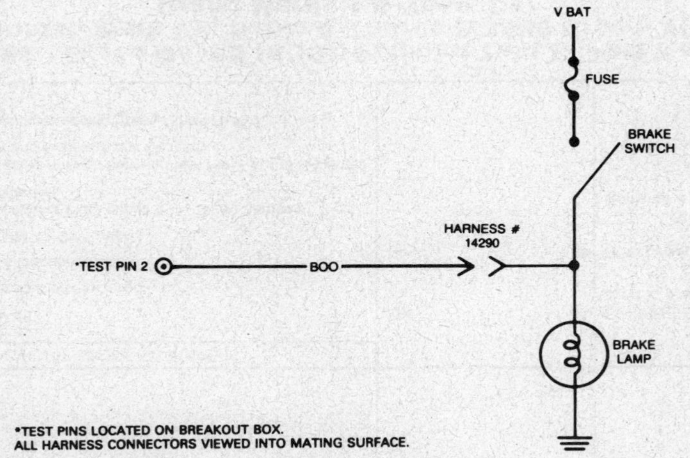

*TEST PINS LOCATED ON BREAKOUT BOX.
ALL HARNESS CONNECTORS VIEWED INTO MATING SURFACE.

**STOP-WARNING**

You should enter this Pinpoint Test only when a Service Code 74 or 75 is received in the KOEO Self-Test.

To prevent the replacement of good components, be aware that the following non-IVSC areas may be at fault:

- Brake lamp, brake switch, and fuse

This pinpoint test is intended to diagnose only the following:

- BOO circuit
- ECA

**Fig. 42 Brake On/Off (BOO), Pinpoint Test B (Part 1 of 6). Continental, Mark VII, Sable & Taurus & 1989 Crown Victoria, Grand Marquis & Town Car**

| TEST STEP | RESULT ▶ | ACTION TO TAKE |
|---|---|---|
| **B1** SERVICE CODE 74 | | |
| • Did you press brake during the KOEO Self-Test? | Yes ▶ | GO to **B2**. |
| | No ▶ | RERUN KOEO Self-Test, PRESS brake once during test. |
| **B2** BOO CIRCUIT CYCLING | | |
| • Key off, wait 10 seconds.<br>• Disconnect ECA 60 Pin connector. Inspect for damaged pins, corrosion, loose wires, etc. Service as necessary.<br>• Install Breakout box, leave ECA disconnected.<br>• DVOM on 20V scale.<br>• Measure voltage between test Pin 2 and test Pin 40 at the Breakout box while depressing and releasing brake.<br>• Does the voltage cycle? | Yes ▶ | REPLACE ECA. RETEST. |
| | No ▶ | GO to **B3**. |
| **B3** BOO CIRCUIT SHORT TO GROUND | | |
| • Key off.<br>• Breakout box installed.<br>• ECA disconnected.<br>• DVOM on 200 Ohm scale.<br>• Disconnect BOO circuit from 14290 harness (12 pin connector).<br>• Measure resistance between test Pin 2 at the Breakout box and ground.<br>• Is resistance reading greater than 5 ohms? | No ▶ | SERVICE BOO circuit short to ground. |
| | Yes ▶ | SERVICE stoplamp circuit. |

**Fig. 42 Brake On/Off (BOO), Pinpoint Test B (Part 2 of 6). Continental, Mark VII, Sable & Taurus & 1989 Crown Victoria, Grand Marquis & Town Car**

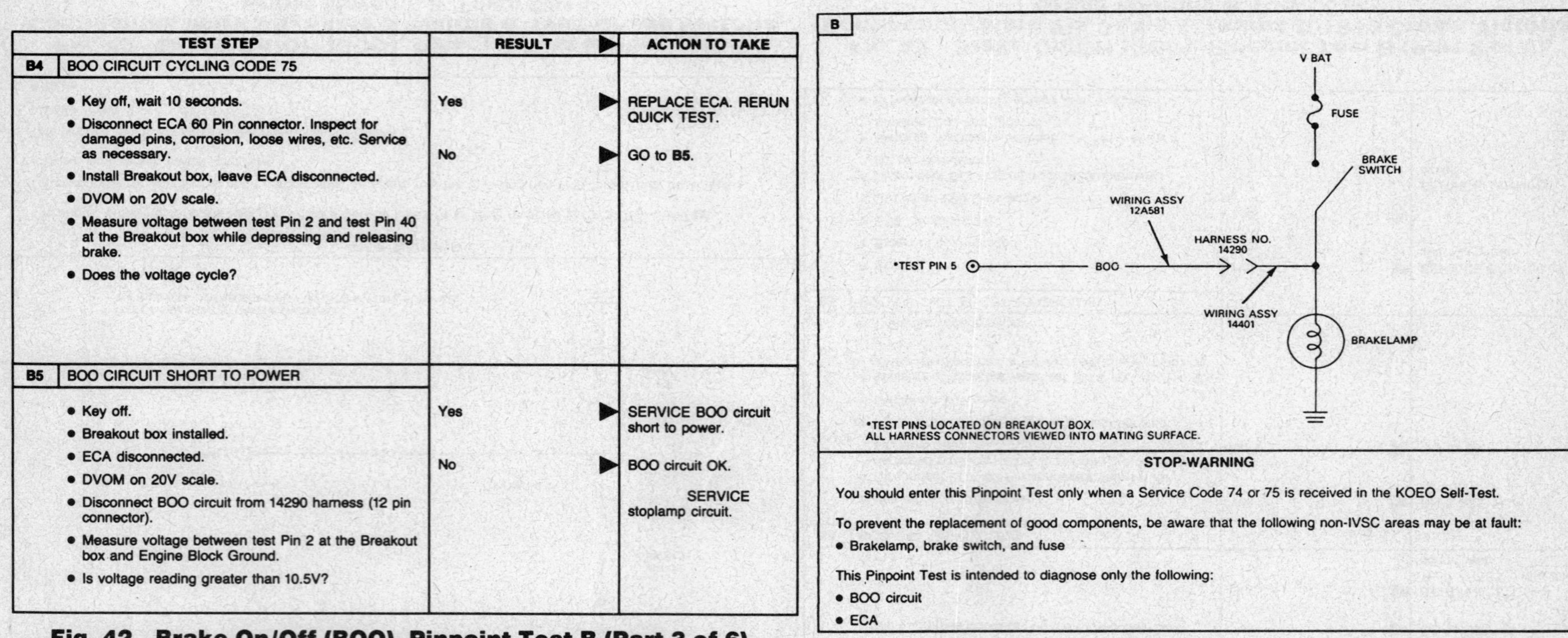

| TEST STEP | RESULT | ACTION TO TAKE |
|---|---|---|
| **B4** BOO CIRCUIT CYCLING CODE 75 | | |
| • Key off, wait 10 seconds.<br>• Disconnect ECA 60 Pin connector. Inspect for damaged pins, corrosion, loose wires, etc. Service as necessary.<br>• Install Breakout box, leave ECA disconnected.<br>• DVOM on 20V scale.<br>• Measure voltage between test Pin 2 and test Pin 40 at the Breakout box while depressing and releasing brake.<br>• Does the voltage cycle? | Yes ▶<br>No ▶ | REPLACE ECA. RERUN QUICK TEST.<br>GO to **B5**. |
| **B5** BOO CIRCUIT SHORT TO POWER | | |
| • Key off.<br>• Breakout box installed.<br>• ECA disconnected.<br>• DVOM on 20V scale.<br>• Disconnect BOO circuit from 14290 harness (12 pin connector).<br>• Measure voltage between test Pin 2 at the Breakout box and Engine Block Ground.<br>• Is voltage reading greater than 10.5V? | Yes ▶<br>No ▶ | SERVICE BOO circuit short to power.<br>BOO circuit OK.<br>SERVICE stoplamp circuit. |

**Fig. 42 Brake On/Off (BOO), Pinpoint Test B (Part 3 of 6). Continental, Mark VII, Sable & Taurus & 1989 Crown Victoria, Grand Marquis & Town Car**

**B**



•TEST PINS LOCATED ON BREAKOUT BOX.
ALL HARNESS CONNECTORS VIEWED INTO MATING SURFACE.

**STOP-WARNING**

You should enter this Pinpoint Test only when a Service Code 74 or 75 is received in the KOEO Self-Test.

To prevent the replacement of good components, be aware that the following non-IVSC areas may be at fault:

- Brakelamp, brake switch, and fuse

This Pinpoint Test is intended to diagnose only the following:

- BOO circuit
- ECA

**Fig. 42 Brake On/Off (BOO), Pinpoint Test B (Part 4 of 6). Cougar & Thunderbird & 1990 Crown Victoria, Grand Marquis & Town Car**

| | TEST STEP | RESULT | ACTION TO TAKE |
|---|---|---|---|
| **B1** | SERVICE CODE 74 | | |
| | • Did you press brake during the KOEO Self-Test? | Yes ▶ | GO to **B2**. |
| | | No ▶ | REPEAT KOEO Self-Test, PRESS brake once during test. |
| **B2** | BOO CIRCUIT CYCLING | | |
| | • Key off, wait 10 seconds.<br>• Disconnect ECA 60 pin connector. Inspect for damaged pins, corrosion, loose wires, etc. Service as necessary.<br>• Install Breakout box, leave ECA disconnected.<br>• Rotunda Digital Volt-Ohmmeter (DVOM) 014-00407 or equivalent, on 20V scale.<br>• Measure voltage between test Pin 5 and test Pin 40 at the Breakout box while depressing and releasing brake.<br>• Does the voltage cycle? | Yes ▶ | REPLACE ECA. RETEST. |
| | | No ▶ | GO to **B3**. |
| **B3** | BOO CIRCUIT SHORT TO GROUND | | |
| | • Key off.<br>• Breakout box installed.<br>• ECA disconnected.<br>• DVOM on 200 Ohm scale.<br>• Disconnect BOO circuit from 14290 harness (12 pin connector).<br>• Measure resistance between test Pin 5 at the Breakout box and ground.<br>• Is resistance reading greater than 5 ohms? | No ▶ | SERVICE BOO circuit short to ground. |
| | | Yes ▶ | SERVICE stoplamp circuit. |
| **B4** | BOO CIRCUIT CYCLING CODE 75 | | |
| | • Key off, wait 10 seconds.<br>• Disconnect ECA 60 pin connector. Inspect for damaged pins, corrosion, loose wires, etc. Service as necessary.<br>• Install Breakout box, leave ECA disconnected.<br>• Rotunda Digital Volt-Ohmmeter (DVOM) 014-00407 or equivalent, on 20V scale.<br>• Measure voltage between test Pin 5 and test Pin 40 at the Breakout box while depressing and releasing brake.<br>• Does the voltage cycle? | Yes ▶ | REPLACE ECA. REPEAT QUICK TEST. |
| | | No ▶ | GO to **B5**. |

**Fig. 42 Brake On/Off (BOO), Pinpoint Test B (Part 5 of 6). Cougar & Thunderbird & 1990–91 Crown Victoria, Grand Marquis & Town Car**

| | TEST STEP | RESULT | ACTION TO TAKE |
|---|---|---|---|
| **B5** | BOO CIRCUIT SHORT TO POWER | | |
| | • Key off.<br>• Breakout box installed.<br>• ECA disconnected.<br>• DVOM on 20V scale.<br>• Disconnect BOO circuit from 14290 harness (12 pin connector).<br>• Measure voltage between test Pin 5 at the Breakout box and engine block ground.<br>• Is voltage reading greater than 10.5 volts? | Yes ▶ | SERVICE BOO circuit short to power. |
| | | No ▶ | BOO circuit OK. SERVICE stoplamp circuit. |

**Fig. 42 Brake On/Off (BOO), Pinpoint Test B (Part 6 of 6). Cougar & Thunderbird & 1990–91 Crown Victoria, Grand Marquis & Town Car**

| | TEST STEP | RESULT | ACTION TO TAKE |
|---|---|---|---|
| | SERVICE CODE 81 OR<br>SERVICE CODES 81 AND 82 | NOTE: Correct solenoid resistance values are:<br>• VENT SOLENOID<br>Nominal - 120 ohms<br>Range - 100 to 150 ohms<br>• VACUUM SOLENOID<br>Nominal - 60 ohms<br>Range - 40-75 ohms<br>SOL+ TEST PIN<br>SCVNT TEST PIN<br>SCVAC TEST PIN<br>VENT SOLENOID<br>VACUUM SOLENOID<br>IVSC SPEED CONTROL SERVO | |
| **C** | STOP WARNING | | |
| | You should enter this Pinpoint Test only when a Service Code 81 and/or 82 is received in a KOEO Self-Test.<br><br>This Pinpoint Test is intended to diagnose only the following:<br>• Servo Vent Solenoid<br>• Servo Vacuum Solenoid<br>• SOL+, SCVNT, and SCVAC Circuits<br>• ECA. | 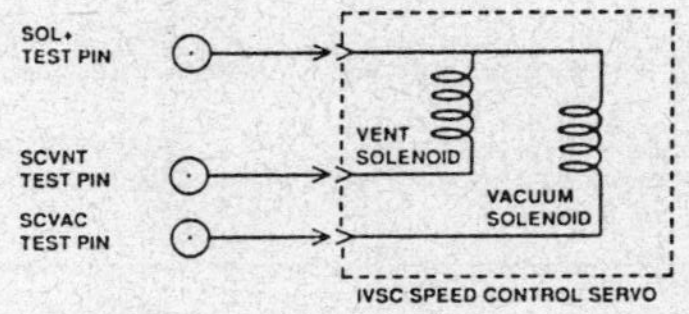 | |
| **C1** | VENT SOLENOID TEST | | |
| | • Key off.<br>• Disconnect ECA 60 pin connector. Inspect for damaged pins, corrosion, loose wires, etc. Service as necessary.<br>• Install Breakout Box (leave ECA disconnected).<br>• DVOM on 200 ohm scale.<br>• Measure resistance between the SOL+ test pin and the SCVNT test pin. | Resistance is between 100 and 150 ohms ▶ | If code 82 is also present, GO to **C6**. Otherwise, GO to **C4**. |
| | | Resistance is less than 100 ohms ▶ | REPLACE servo. REPEAT QUICK TEST. |
| | | Resistance is greater than 150 ohms ▶ | GO to **C2**. |

**Fig. 43 Servo solenoids, Pinpoint Test C (Part 1 of 3). Continental, , Crown Victoria, Grand Marquis, Mark VII, Sable, Taurus & Cougar & Thunderbird**

| TEST STEP | RESULT ▶ | ACTION TO TAKE |
|---|---|---|
| **C2** CHECK CONTINUITY OF SOL+ CIRCUIT | | |
| • Disconnect harness connector from the servo.<br>• DVOM on 200 ohm scale.<br>• Measure resistance of the SOL+ wire. | Resistance is greater than 5 ohms ▶ | SERVICE open circuit. REPEAT QUICK TEST. |
| | Resistance is less than 5 ohms ▶ | GO to **C3**. |
| **C3** CHECK CONTINUITY OF SCVNT CIRCUIT | | |
| • Disconnect harness connector from the servo.<br>• DVOM on 200 ohm scale.<br>• Measure resistance of the SCVNT wire. | Resistance is greater than 5 ohms ▶ | SERVICE open circuit. REPEAT QUICK TEST. |
| | Resistance is less than 5 ohms ▶ | REPLACE servo. REPEAT QUICK TEST. |
| **C4** SOL+ CIRCUIT SHORT TO GROUND TEST | | |
| • Disconnect harness connector from the servo.<br>• DVOM on 200,000 ohm scale.<br>• Measure resistance between the SOL+ test pin and test pin 60 (ground). | Resistance is less than 10,000 ohms ▶ | SERVICE shorted circuit. REPEAT QUICK TEST. (NOTE: Short may have damaged the ECA.) |
| | Resistance is greater than 10,000 ohms ▶ | GO to **C5**. |
| **C5** SCVNT CIRCUIT SHORT TO GROUND TEST | | |
| • Disconnect harness connector from the servo.<br>• DVOM on 200,000 ohm scale.<br>• Measure resistance between the SCVNT test pin and test pin 60 (ground). | Resistance is less than 10,000 ohms ▶ | SERVICE shorted circuit. REPEAT QUICK TEST. |
| | Resistance is greater than 10,000 ohms ▶ | REPLACE the ECA. REPEAT QUICK TEST. |
| SERVICE CODE 82 ONLY<br>**C6** VACUUM SOLENOID TEST | | |
| • Key off.<br>• Disconnect ECA 60 pin connector. Inspect for damaged pins, corrosion, loose wires, etc. Service as necessary.<br>• Install Breakout Box (leave ECA disconnected).<br>• DVOM on 200 ohm scale.<br>• Measure resistance between the SOL+ test pin and the SCVAC test pin. | Resistance is between 40 and 75 ohms ▶ | GO to **C9**. |
| | Resistance is less than 40 ohms ▶ | REPLACE servo. REPEAT QUICK TEST. |
| | Resistance is greater than 75 ohms ▶ | GO to **C7**. |

**Fig. 43 Servo solenoids, Pinpoint Test C (Part 2 of 3). Continental, , Crown Victoria, Grand Marquis, Mark VII, Sable, Taurus & Cougar & Thunderbird**

| TEST STEP | RESULT ▶ | ACTION TO TAKE |
|---|---|---|
| **C7** CHECK CONTINUITY OF SOL+ CIRCUIT | | |
| • Disconnect harness connector from the servo.<br>• DVOM on 200 ohm scale.<br>• Measure resistance of the SOL+ wire. | Resistance is greater than 5 ohms ▶ | SERVICE open circuit. REPEAT QUICK TEST. |
| | Resistance is less than 5 ohms ▶ | GO to **C8**. |
| **C8** CHECK CONTINUITY OF SCVAC CIRCUIT | | |
| • Disconnect harness connector from the servo.<br>• DVOM on 200 ohm scale.<br>• Measure resistance of the SCVAC wire. | Resistance is greater than 5 ohms ▶ | SERVICE open circuit. REPEAT QUICK TEST. |
| | Resistance is less than 5 ohms ▶ | REPLACE servo. REPEAT QUICK TEST. |
| **C9** SOL+ CIRCUIT SHORT TO GROUND TEST | | |
| • Disconnect harness connector from the servo.<br>• DVOM on 200,000 ohm scale.<br>• Measure resistance between the SOL+ test pin and test pin 60 (ground). | Resistance is less than 10,000 ohms ▶ | SERVICE shorted circuit. REPEAT QUICK TEST. (NOTE: Short may have damaged the ECA.) |
| | Resistance is greater than 10,000 ohms ▶ | GO to **C10**. |
| **C10** SCVAC CIRCUIT SHORT TO GROUND TEST | | |
| • Disconnect harness connector from the servo.<br>• DVOM on 200,000 ohm scale.<br>• Measure resistance between the SCVAC test pin and test pin 60 (ground). | Resistance is less than 10,000 ohms ▶ | SERVICE shorted circuit. REPEAT QUICK TEST. |
| | Resistance is greater than 10,000 ohms ▶ | REPLACE the ECA. REPEAT QUICK TEST. |

**Fig. 43 Servo solenoids, Pinpoint Test C (Part 3 of 3). Continental, , Crown Victoria, Grand Marquis, Mark VII, Sable, Taurus & Cougar & Thunderbird**

| D | STOP-WARNING | | |
|---|---|---|---|
| | You should enter this Pinpoint Test only when Service Code 36 is received in the KOER Self-Test.<br>This Pinpoint Test is intended to diagnose only the following:<br>• Actuator cable • ECA<br>• Vacuum hose connections • Check valve<br>• Dump valve adjustment | | |
| | **TEST STEP** | **RESULT ▶** | **ACTION TO TAKE** |
| D1 | SERVICE CODE 36 | | |
| | • Repeat KOER Self-Test of QUICK TEST. Be sure that the speed control ON button is pressed before pressing the SUPER STAR II push button. | Code 36 still present ▶<br>No Code 36 ▶ | GO to D2.<br>Increase vehicle speed test passed. SERVICE any other service code(s) as necessary. |
| D2 | CHECK ACTUATOR CABLE CONNECTION TO THROTTLE BODY | | |
| | • Is actuator cable attached to throttle body accelerator linkage? | Yes ▶<br>No ▶ | GO to D3.<br>CONNECT servo cable to throttle body accelerator linkage. REPEAT QUICK TEST. |
| D3 | CHECK VACUUM HOSES | | |
| | • Is servo vacuum supply hose tightly connected to VAC port on check valve and to the vacuum manifold, and free of cuts, cracks and kinks?<br>• Are vacuum hoses tightly connected between check valves and servo, and free of cuts, cracks and kinks?<br>• Is vacuum hose tightly connected between check valve and reservoir, and free of cuts, cracks and kinks?<br>• Is the dump valve hose tightly connected to the servo and to the dump valve, and free of cuts, cracks and kinks? | Yes ▶<br>No ▶ | GO to D4.<br>SERVICE hoses. REPEAT QUICK TEST. |
| D4 | CHECK THE CHECK VALVE | | |
| | • Disconnect the hose between check valve and servo, at the servo end.<br>• Apply 60.6 kPa (18 in-Hg) vacuum to open end of hose.<br>• Can vacuum be pumped to, and held at, 60.6 kPa (18 in-Hg) vacuum? | Yes ▶<br>No ▶ | GO to D6.<br>GO to D5. |

**Fig. 44 Speed does not increase during Dynamic Test, Pinpoint Test D (Part 1 of 4). Cougar, Crown Victoria, Continental & Town Car, Mark VII, Grand Marquis, Sable, Taurus & Thunderbird**

| | TEST STEP | RESULT ▶ | ACTION TO TAKE |
|---|---|---|---|
| D5 | CHECK VACUUM RESERVOIR | | |
| | • Disconnect hose between check valve and vacuum reservoir, at check valve end.<br>• Install vacuum pump to open end of hose to reservoir.<br>• Apply 60.6 kPa (18 in. Hg) vacuum to the reservoir.<br>• Does reservoir hold vacuum? | Yes ▶<br>No ▶ | REPLACE check valve. REPEAT QUICK TEST.<br>REPLACE vacuum reservoir. REPEAT QUICK TEST. |
| D6 | CHECK DUMP VALVE ADJUSTMENT | | |
| | • Is the dump valve adjusted properly so that the valve is closed when the brake pedal is not depressed? | Yes ▶<br>No ▶ | GO to C1.<br>ADJUST dump valve. REPEAT QUICK TEST. |

**Fig. 44 Speed does not increase during Dynamic Test, Pinpoint Test D. (Part 2 of 4) Sable & Taurus**

| | TEST STEP | RESULT ▶ | ACTION TO TAKE |
|---|---|---|---|
| D5 | CHECK ASPIRATOR CHECK VALVE | | |
| | • Disconnect hose between check valves at manifold check valve end.<br>• Apply 60.6 kPa (18 in. Hg) vacuum to open end of hose.<br>• Can vacuum be pumped to and held at 60.6 kPa (18 in. Hg) vacuum? | Yes ▶<br>No ▶ | REPLACE manifold check valve. REPEAT QUICK TEST.<br>REPLACE aspirator check valve. REPEAT QUICK TEST. |
| D6 | CHECK DUMP VALVE ADJUSTMENT | | |
| | • Is the dump valve adjusted properly so that the valve is closed when the brake pedal is not depressed? | Yes ▶<br>No ▶ | REPLACE ECA. REPEAT QUICK TEST.<br>ADJUST dump valve. REPEAT QUICK TEST. |

**Fig. 44 Speed does not increase during Dynamic Test, Pinpoint Test D (Part 3 of 4). Cougar, Crown Victoria, Town Car, Grand Marquis, & Thunderbird**

| TEST STEP | | RESULT | ACTION TO TAKE |
|---|---|---|---|
| D5 | CHECK ASPIRATOR CHECK VALVE | | |
| | • Disconnect hose between check valves at manifold check valve end.<br>• Apply 60.6 kPa (18 in-Hg) vacuum to open end of hose.<br>• Can vacuum be pumped to and held at 60.6 kPa (18 in-Hg) vacuum? | Yes ▶<br>No ▶ | REPLACE manifold check valve. REPEAT QUICK TEST.<br>REPLACE aspirator check valve. REPEAT QUICK TEST. |
| D6 | CHECK DUMP VALVE ADJUSTMENT | | |
| | • Is the dump valve adjusted properly so that the valve is closed when the brake pedal is not depressed? | Yes ▶<br>No ▶ | GO to **C1**.<br>ADJUST dump valve. REPEAT QUICK TEST. |

**Fig. 44 Speed does not increase during Dynamic Test, Pinpoint Test D (Part 4 of 4). Continental**

| E | STOP-WARNING | | |
|---|---|---|---|
| | You should enter this Pinpoint Test only when Service Codes 27 and/or 28 are received in the KOER Self-Test.<br>This Pinpoint Test is intended to diagnose only the following:<br>• Speed control servo • Vacuum reservoir<br>• Vacuum hose connections • Check valve | | |
| | **TEST STEP** | **RESULT ▶** | **ACTION TO TAKE** |
| E1 | SERVICE CODE 27 | | |
| | • Repeat Engine Running Self-Test of QUICK TEST. Be sure that the speed control ON button is pressed before pressing the STAR push button. | Code 27 still present? ▶<br>No Code 27 ▶ | GO to **E2**.<br>Servo leaks down test passed. SERVICE any other service code(s) as necessary. |
| E2 | CHECK VACUUM HOSES | | |
| | • Is vacuum supply hose tightly connected to VAC port on check valve and to vacuum manifold, and free of cuts, cracks and kinks?<br>• Is vacuum hose tightly connected between check valve and servo, and free of cuts, cracks and kinks?<br>• Is vacuum hose tightly connected between check valve and reservoir, and free of cuts, cracks and kinks?<br>• Is dump valve hose tightly connected to the servo and dump valve, and free of cuts, cracks and kinks? | Yes ▶<br>No ▶ | GO to **E3**.<br>SERVICE vacuum hoses. REPEAT QUICK TEST. |
| E3 | CHECK VACUUM RESERVOIR | | |
| | • Disconnect hose between the check valve and vacuum reservoir, at check valve end.<br>• Install vacuum pump to open end of hose to reservoir.<br>• Apply 60.6 kPa (18 in. Hg) vacuum to the reservoir.<br>• Does reservoir hold vacuum? | Yes ▶<br>No ▶ | GO to **E4**.<br>REPLACE vacuum reservoir. REPEAT QUICK TEST. |
| E4 | CHECK THE CHECK VALVE | | |
| | • Disconnect the hose between check valve and servo, at the servo end.<br>• Apply 60.6 kPa (18 in. Hg) vacuum to open end of hose.<br>• Can vacuum be pumped to, and held at, 60.6 kPa (18 in. Hg) vacuum? | Yes ▶<br>No ▶ | REPLACE servo. REPEAT QUICK TEST.<br>REPLACE check valve. REPEAT QUICK TEST. |
| E5 | SERVICE CODE 28 | | |
| | • REPEAT engine running SELF-TEST of QUICK TEST. Be sure that the speed control ON button is pressed before pressing the STAR push button. | Code 28 still present? ▶<br>No Code 27 ▶ | REPLACE servo. REPEAT QUICK TEST.<br>Servo leaks up test passed. SERVICE any other service code(s) as necessary. |

**Fig. 45 Does not hold speed during Dynamic Test, Pinpoint Test E (Part 1 of 2). Continental, Sable & Taurus**

**E — STOP-WARNING**

You should enter this Pinpoint Test only when Service Codes 27 and/or 28 are received in the KOER Self-Test.

This Pinpoint Test is intended to diagnose only the following:

- Speed control servo
- Vacuum hose connections
- Vacuum reservoir
- Check valve

| TEST STEP | RESULT ▶ | ACTION TO TAKE |
|---|---|---|
| **E1** SERVICE CODE 27 | | |
| • Repeat Engine Running Self-Test of QUICK TEST. Be sure that the speed control ON button is pressed before pressing the STAR push button. | Code 27 still present? ▶ | GO to **E2**. |
| | No Code 27 ▶ | Servo leaks down test passed. SERVICE any other service code(s) as necessary. |
| **E2** CHECK VACUUM HOSES | | |
| • Is vacuum supply hose tightly connected to VAC port on manifold check valve and to vacuum manifold, and free of cuts, cracks and kinks?<br>• Are vacuum hoses tightly connected between check valves and servo, and free of cuts, cracks and kinks?<br>• Is vacuum hose tightly connected between check valve and aspirator, and free of cuts, cracks and kinks?<br>• Is dump valve hose tightly connected to the servo and dump valve, and free of cuts, cracks and kinks? | Yes ▶ | GO to **E3**. |
| | No ▶ | SERVICE vacuum hoses. REPEAT QUICK TEST. |
| **E3** CHECK THE CHECK VALVE | | |
| • Disconnect the hose between check valve and servo, at the servo end.<br>• Apply 60.6 kPa (18 in. Hg) vacuum to open end of hose.<br>• Can vacuum be pumped to, and held at, 60.6 kPa (18 in. Hg) vacuum? | Yes ▶ | REPLACE servo. REPEAT QUICK TEST. |
| | No ▶ | REPLACE check valve. REPEAT QUICK TEST. |
| **E4** CHECK ASPIRATOR CHECK VALVE | | |
| • Disconnect hose between check valves at manifold check valve end.<br>• Apply 60.6 kPa (18 in. Hg) vacuum to open end of hose.<br>• Can vacuum be pumped to and held at 60.6 kPa (18 in. Hg) vacuum? | Yes ▶ | REPLACE manifold check valve. REPEAT QUICK TEST. |
| | No ▶ | REPLACE aspirator check valve. REPEAT QUICK TEST. |
| **E5** SERVICE CODE 28 | | |
| • REPEAT engine running SELF-TEST of QUICK TEST. Be sure that the speed control ON button is pressed before pressing the STAR push button. | Code 28 still present? ▶ | REPLACE servo. REPEAT QUICK TEST. |
| | No Code 27 ▶ | Servo leaks up test passed. SERVICE any other service code(s) as necessary. |

**Fig. 45 Does not hold speed during Dynamic Test, Pinpoint Test E (Part 2 of 2). Cougar, Crown Victoria, Town Car, Mark VII & Grand Marquis & Thunderbird**

**F — STOP-WARNING**

You should enter this Pinpoint Test only when a Service Code 37 is received in the KOER Self-Test.

This Pinpoint Test is intended to diagnose only the following:

- Actuator cable
- Throttle shaft and linkage
- Throttle position sensor
- ECA

| TEST STEP | RESULT ▶ | ACTION TO TAKE |
|---|---|---|
| **F1** SERVICE CODE 37 | | |
| • Repeat KOER Self-Test of QUICK TEST. Be sure that the speed control ON button is pressed before pressing the STAR push button. | Code 37 still present? ▶ | GO to **F2**. |
| | No Code 37 ▶ | Decrease vehicle speed test passed. SERVICE any other service code(s) as necessary. |
| **F2** CHECK FOR THROTTLE SHAFT/LINKAGE BINDING | | |
| • Is the throttle shaft or throttle linkage binding, maintaining a part throttle opening? | Yes ▶ | SERVICE to eliminate binding. REPEAT QUICK TEST. |
| | No ▶ | GO to **F3**. |
| **F3** CHECK FOR SPEED CONTROL LINKAGE BINDING | | |
| • Is the actuator cable binding? | Yes ▶ | REPLACE the actuator cable. REPEAT QUICK TEST. |
| | No ▶ | GO to **F4**. |
| **F4** CHECK FOR THROTTLE POSITION SENSOR BINDING | | |
| • Is throttle position sensor binding at a part throttle opening? | Yes ▶ | REPLACE the throttle position sensor. REPEAT QUICK TEST. |
| | No ▶ | REPLACE the ECA. REPEAT QUICK TEST. |

**Fig. 46 Speed does not increase during Dynamic Test, Pinpoint Test F. Cougar, Crown Victoria, Continental, Mark VII, Grand Marquis, Cougar, Town Car & Thunderbird**

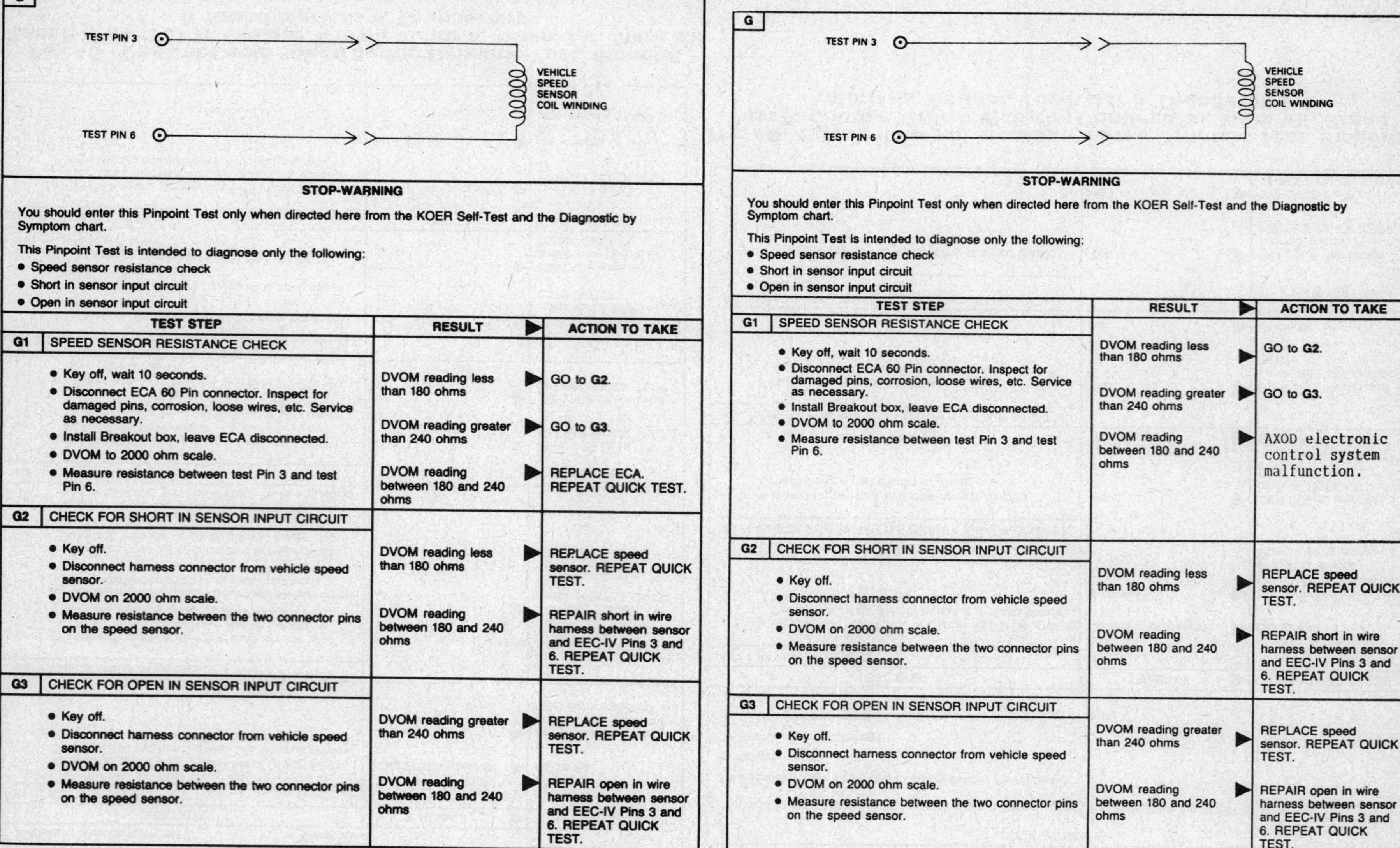

**G**



**STOP-WARNING**

You should enter this Pinpoint Test only when directed here from the KOER Self-Test and the Diagnostic by Symptom chart.

This Pinpoint Test is intended to diagnose only the following:

- Speed sensor resistance check
- Short in sensor input circuit
- Open in sensor input circuit

| TEST STEP | RESULT ▶ | ACTION TO TAKE |
|---|---|---|
| **G1** SPEED SENSOR RESISTANCE CHECK | | |
| • Key off, wait 10 seconds.<br>• Disconnect ECA 60 Pin connector. Inspect for damaged pins, corrosion, loose wires, etc. Service as necessary.<br>• Install Breakout box, leave ECA disconnected.<br>• DVOM to 2000 ohm scale.<br>• Measure resistance between test Pin 3 and test Pin 6. | DVOM reading less than 180 ohms ▶ | GO to **G2**. |
| | DVOM reading greater than 240 ohms ▶ | GO to **G3**. |
| | DVOM reading between 180 and 240 ohms ▶ | REPLACE ECA. REPEAT QUICK TEST. |
| **G2** CHECK FOR SHORT IN SENSOR INPUT CIRCUIT | | |
| • Key off.<br>• Disconnect harness connector from vehicle speed sensor.<br>• DVOM on 2000 ohm scale.<br>• Measure resistance between the two connector pins on the speed sensor. | DVOM reading less than 180 ohms ▶ | REPLACE speed sensor. REPEAT QUICK TEST. |
| | DVOM reading between 180 and 240 ohms ▶ | REPAIR short in wire harness between sensor and EEC-IV Pins 3 and 6. REPEAT QUICK TEST. |
| **G3** CHECK FOR OPEN IN SENSOR INPUT CIRCUIT | | |
| • Key off.<br>• Disconnect harness connector from vehicle speed sensor.<br>• DVOM on 2000 ohm scale.<br>• Measure resistance between the two connector pins on the speed sensor. | DVOM reading greater than 240 ohms ▶ | REPLACE speed sensor. REPEAT QUICK TEST. |
| | DVOM reading between 180 and 240 ohms ▶ | REPAIR open in wire harness between sensor and EEC-IV Pins 3 and 6. REPEAT QUICK TEST. |

**Fig. 47 Speed sensor, Pinpoint Test G (Part 1 of 3). Crown Victoria, Town Car, Mark VII & Grand Marquis**

**G**



**STOP-WARNING**

You should enter this Pinpoint Test only when directed here from the KOER Self-Test and the Diagnostic by Symptom chart.

This Pinpoint Test is intended to diagnose only the following:

- Speed sensor resistance check
- Short in sensor input circuit
- Open in sensor input circuit

| TEST STEP | RESULT ▶ | ACTION TO TAKE |
|---|---|---|
| **G1** SPEED SENSOR RESISTANCE CHECK | | |
| • Key off, wait 10 seconds.<br>• Disconnect ECA 60 Pin connector. Inspect for damaged pins, corrosion, loose wires, etc. Service as necessary.<br>• Install Breakout box, leave ECA disconnected.<br>• DVOM to 2000 ohm scale.<br>• Measure resistance between test Pin 3 and test Pin 6. | DVOM reading less than 180 ohms ▶ | GO to **G2**. |
| | DVOM reading greater than 240 ohms ▶ | GO to **G3**. |
| | DVOM reading between 180 and 240 ohms ▶ | AXOD electronic control system malfunction. |
| **G2** CHECK FOR SHORT IN SENSOR INPUT CIRCUIT | | |
| • Key off.<br>• Disconnect harness connector from vehicle speed sensor.<br>• DVOM on 2000 ohm scale.<br>• Measure resistance between the two connector pins on the speed sensor. | DVOM reading less than 180 ohms ▶ | REPLACE speed sensor. REPEAT QUICK TEST. |
| | DVOM reading between 180 and 240 ohms ▶ | REPAIR short in wire harness between sensor and EEC-IV Pins 3 and 6. REPEAT QUICK TEST. |
| **G3** CHECK FOR OPEN IN SENSOR INPUT CIRCUIT | | |
| • Key off.<br>• Disconnect harness connector from vehicle speed sensor.<br>• DVOM on 2000 ohm scale.<br>• Measure resistance between the two connector pins on the speed sensor. | DVOM reading greater than 240 ohms ▶ | REPLACE speed sensor. REPEAT QUICK TEST. |
| | DVOM reading between 180 and 240 ohms ▶ | REPAIR open in wire harness between sensor and EEC-IV Pins 3 and 6. REPEAT QUICK TEST. |

**Fig. 47 Speed sensor, Pinpoint Test G (Part 2 of 3). Continental, Sable & Taurus**

G

TEST PIN 3

TEST PIN 6

VEHICLE SPEED SENSOR COIL WINDING

**STOP-WARNING**

You should enter this Pinpoint Test only when directed here from the KOER Self-Test and the Diagnostic by Symptom chart.

This Pinpoint Test is intended to diagnose only the following:

- Speed sensor resistance check
- Short or ground in sensor input circuit
- Open in sensor input circuit

| TEST STEP | RESULT ▶ | ACTION TO TAKE |
|---|---|---|
| **G1** SPEED SENSOR RESISTANCE CHECK | | |
| • Key off, wait 10 seconds.<br>• Disconnect ECA 60 Pin connector. Inspect for damaged pins, corrosion, loose wires, etc. Service as necessary.<br>• Install Breakout box, leave ECA disconnected.<br>• DVOM to 2000 ohm scale.<br>• Measure resistance between test Pin 3 and test Pin 6. | DVOM reading less than 180 ohms ▶ | GO to **G2**. |
| | DVOM reading greater than 240 ohms ▶ | GO to **G3**. |
| | DVOM reading between 180 and 240 ohms ▶ | REPLACE ECA. REPEAT QUICK TEST. |
| **G2** CHECK FOR SHORT IN SENSOR INPUT CIRCUIT | | |
| • Key off.<br>• Disconnect harness connector from vehicle speed sensor.<br>• DVOM on 2000 ohm scale.<br>• Measure resistance between the two connector pins on the speed sensor. | DVOM reading less than 180 ohms ▶ | REPLACE speed sensor. REPEAT QUICK TEST. |
| | DVOM reading between 180 and 240 ohms ▶ | REPAIR short in wire harness between sensor and EEC-IV Pins 3 and 6 or grounded no. 150 Circuit. REPEAT QUICK TEST. |
| **G3** CHECK FOR OPEN IN SENSOR INPUT CIRCUIT | | |
| • Key off.<br>• Disconnect harness connector from vehicle speed sensor.<br>• DVOM on 2000 ohm scale.<br>• Measure resistance between the two connector pins on the speed sensor. | DVOM reading greater than 240 ohms ▶ | REPLACE speed sensor. REPEAT QUICK TEST. |
| | DVOM reading between 180 and 240 ohms ▶ | REPAIR open in wire harness between sensor and EEC-IV Pins 3 and 6. REPEAT QUICK TEST. |

**Fig. 47 Speed sensor, Pinpoint Test G (Part 3 of 3). Cougar & Thunderbird**

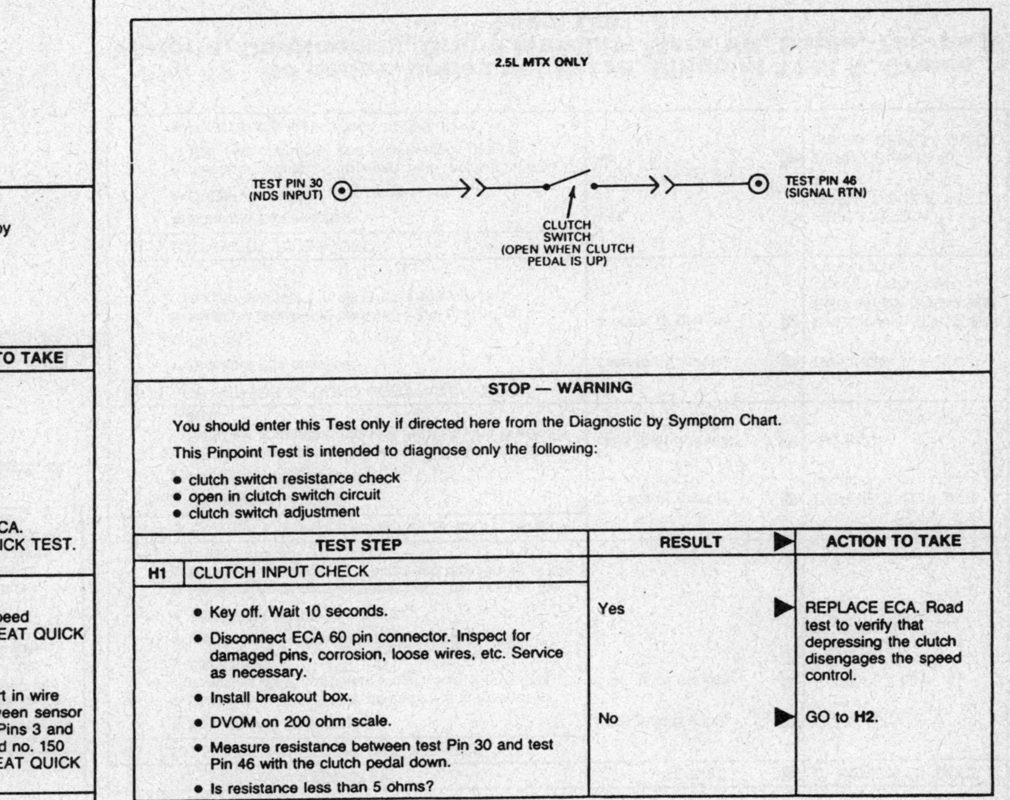


**STOP — WARNING**

You should enter this Test only if directed here from the Diagnostic by Symptom Chart.

This Pinpoint Test is intended to diagnose only the following:

- clutch switch resistance check
- open in clutch switch circuit
- clutch switch adjustment

| TEST STEP | RESULT ▶ | ACTION TO TAKE |
|---|---|---|
| **H1** CLUTCH INPUT CHECK | | |
| • Key off. Wait 10 seconds.<br>• Disconnect ECA 60 pin connector. Inspect for damaged pins, corrosion, loose wires, etc. Service as necessary.<br>• Install breakout box.<br>• DVOM on 200 ohm scale.<br>• Measure resistance between test Pin 30 and test Pin 46 with the clutch pedal down.<br>• Is resistance less than 5 ohms? | Yes ▶ | REPLACE ECA. Road test to verify that depressing the clutch disengages the speed control. |
| | No ▶ | GO to **H2**. |

**Fig. 48 Clutch switch Pinpoint Test H (Part 1 of 2). Sable & Taurus**

| TEST STEP | | RESULT | ▶ | ACTION TO TAKE |
|---|---|---|---|---|
| H2 | CHECK WIRE HARNESS | | | |
| | • Key off.<br>• Breakout box installed.<br>• DVOM on 200 ohm scale.<br>• Locate clutch switch (under the instrument panel).<br>• Measure resistance between test Pin 30 and the clutch switch harness connector.<br>• Measure resistance between test Pin 46 and the clutch switch harness connector.<br>• Are all resistance readings less than 5 ohms? | Yes | ▶ | GO to **H3**. |
| | | No | ▶ | SERVICE open circuit. Road test to verify that depressing the clutch disengages the speed control. |
| H3 | CHECK CLUTCH SWITCH ADJUSTMENT | | | |
| | • Check that clutch switch is adjusted as outlined.<br>• Is clutch switch adjusted properly? | Yes | ▶ | REPLACE clutch switch. Road test to verify that depressing the clutch disengages the speed control. |
| | | No | ▶ | READJUST clutch switch. Road test to verify that depressing the clutch disengages the speed control. |

**Fig. 48 Clutch switch Pinpoint Test H (Part 2 of 2). Sable & Taurus**

**Q**

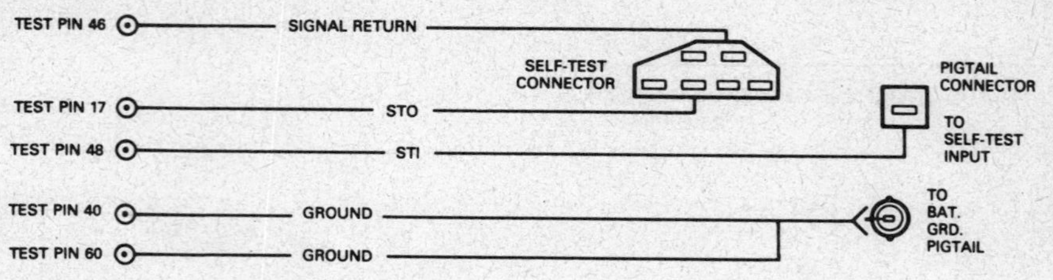

TEST PIN 46 — SIGNAL RETURN
SELF-TEST CONNECTOR
TEST PIN 17 — STO
TEST PIN 48 — STI
PIGTAIL CONNECTOR
TO SELF-TEST INPUT
TEST PIN 40 — GROUND
TEST PIN 60 — GROUND
TO BAT. GRD. PIGTAIL

TEST PINS ON BREAKOUT BOX. ALL HARNESS CONNECTORS VIEWED INTO MATING SURFACE.

**STOP-WARNING**

You should enter this Pinpoint Test only when directed here from the KOER or KOEO Self-Test.

This Pinpoint Test is intended to diagnose only the following:
- ECA
- Harness circuits: signal return, STO, STI, Ground

| TEST STEP | | RESULT | ▶ | ACTION TO TAKE |
|---|---|---|---|---|
| Q1 | SELF-TEST INPUT CONTINUITY CHECK | | | |
| | • Key off, wait 10 seconds.<br>• Disconnect ECA 60 Pin connector and inspect for damaged pins, corrosion, loose wires. Service as necessary.<br>• Install Breakout box, leave ECA disconnected.<br>• Set DVOM to 200 ohm scale.<br>• Measure resistance between Self-Test input at the Self-Test single pin connector and test Pin 48 at the Breakout box. | Less than 5 ohms | ▶ | GO to **Q2**. |
| | | 5 ohms or greater | ▶ | CORRECT open in circuit. |
| Q2 | SELF-TEST OUTPUT CIRCUIT CONTINUITY CHECK | | | |
| | • Breakout box installed.<br>• DVOM to 200 ohm scale.<br>• Measure resistance between Self-Test output at the Self-Test connector and test Pin 17 at the Breakout box. | 5 ohms or greater | ▶ | CORRECT open in circuit. |
| | | Less than 5 ohms | ▶ | GO to **Q3**. |
| Q3 | EGO SENSOR GROUND CONTINUITY CHECK | | | |
| | • Breakout box installed.<br>• Key off.<br>• Measure resistance between EGO ground on engine and test Pin 49 at the Breakout box. | Less than 5 ohms | ▶ | GO to **Q4**. |
| | | 5 ohms or greater | ▶ | CHECK and SERVICE EGO sensor ground wire or open circuit bad connection. |
| Q4 | STO SHORT TO GROUND | | | |
| | • Breakout box installed.<br>• DVOM on 200,000 ohm scale.<br>• Measure resistance between Self-Test output at Self-Test connector and engine block ground.<br>• Is resistance greater than 10,000 ohms? | Yes | ▶ | REPLACE ECA. REPEAT QUICK TEST. |
| | | No | ▶ | SERVICE shorts to ground. REPEAT QUICK TEST. |

**Fig. 49 No codes, codes not listed, Pinpoint Test Q. Crown Victoria, Continental, Grand Marquis, Mark VII, Sable, Taurus & Town Car**

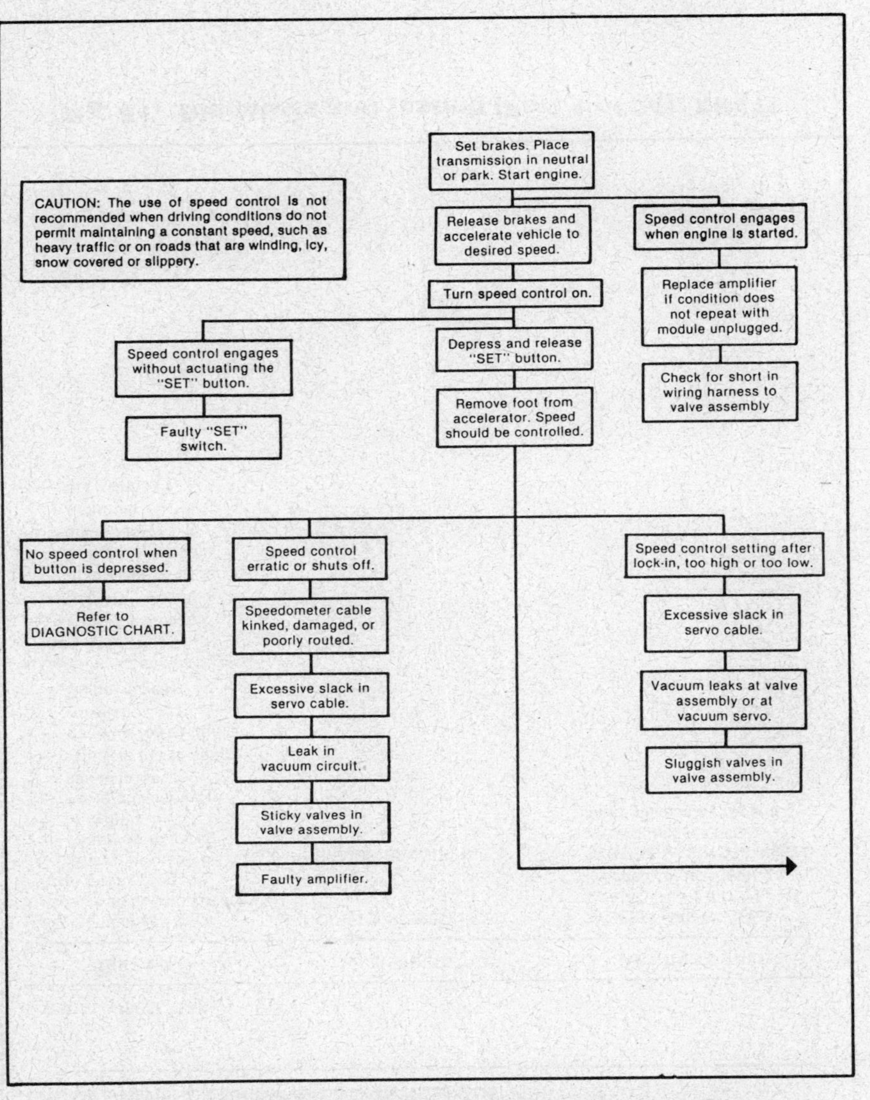


**Fig. 50 XR4Ti troubleshooting. (Part 1 of 2)**

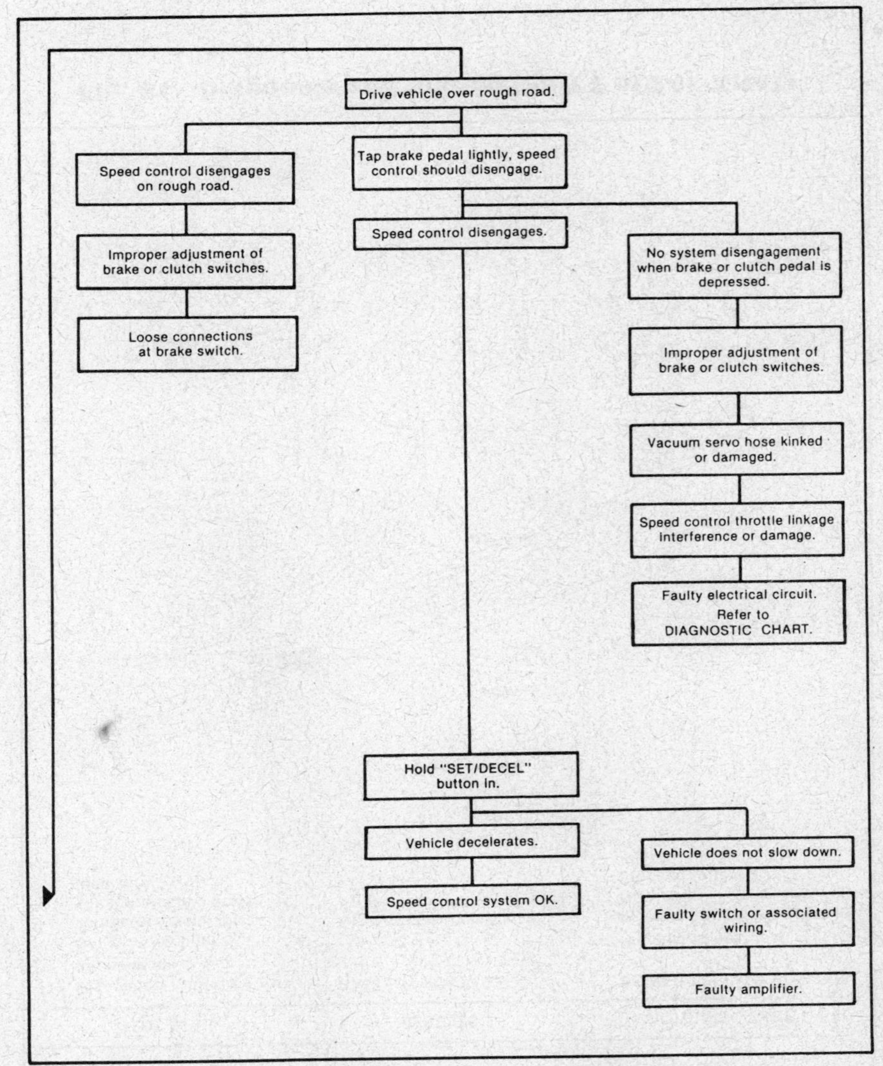


**Fig. 50 XR4Ti troubleshooting. (Part 2 of 2)**

SPEED CONTROL DIAGNOSTIC CHART

**NOTE:** The following diagnostic procedures contain mechanical and electrical tests of the speed control components. Although not specifically stated, it is assumed the ignition and speed control switches are in the ON position during all electrical tests.

**1 VISUAL INSPECTION**

| TEST STEP | RESULTS | ACTION TO TAKE |
|---|---|---|
| • Carefully check each vacuum hose and vacuum hose connection.<br>— Source to reservoir<br>— Reservoir to valve assembly<br>— Valve assembly to vacuum tee<br>— Vacuum tee to servo<br>— Vacuum tee to dump valve(s)<br>— Dump valves.<br>• Carefully check each electrical connection.<br>— Valve assembly<br>— ON/OFF switch<br>— Brake switch<br>— Clutch switch (if equipped)<br>— Amplifier<br>— Set switch | NO REPAIRS REQUIRED | SYSTEM HAS PASSED VISUAL INSPECTION.<br>Proceed to next test. |
| | REPAIRS REQUIRED | SYSTEM HAS NOT PASSED VISUAL INSPECTION.<br>Make necessary repairs. |

**Fig. 51 Diagnosis and testing (Part 1 of 24). XR4Ti**

SPEED CONTROL DIAGNOSTIC CHART

**2 POWER FEED TO SERVO**

| TEST STEP | RESULTS | ACTION TO TAKE |
|---|---|---|
| • Disconnect white/red wire at power servo.<br>• Using a test light or voltmeter, check for voltage at servo power feed wire (W/R). | BATTERY VOLTAGE | POWER FEED TO SERVO IS OK.<br>Proceed to next test. |
| | NO BATTERY VOLTAGE | POWER FEED TO SERVO IS NOT OK.<br>Proceed to test 26. |

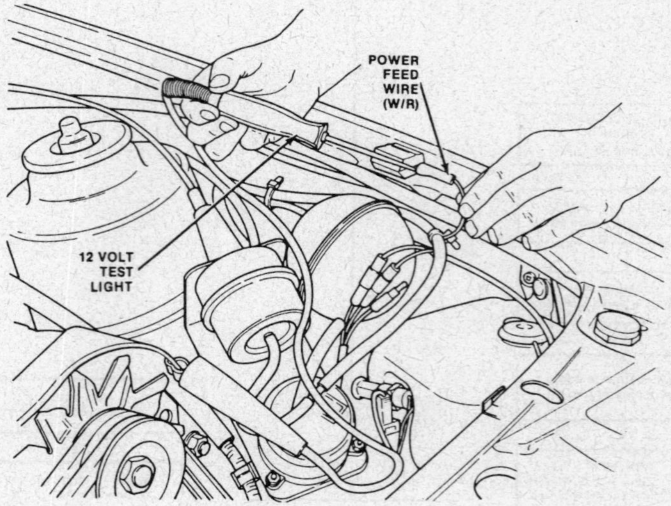

POWER FEED WIRE (W/R)

12 VOLT TEST LIGHT

**Fig. 51 Diagnosis and testing (Part 2 of 24). XR4Ti**

SPEED CONTROL DIAGNOSTIC CHART

**3 VACUUM SUPPLY LEAK TEST**

| TEST STEP | RESULTS | ACTION TO TAKE |
|---|---|---|
| • Disconnect hose from vacuum reservoir fitting marked "VAC."<br>• Using a hand vacuum pump, apply 20″ of vacuum through "VAC" hose fitting. | VACUUM HOLDS | VACUUM SUPPLY SYSTEM IS NOT LEAKING. Proceed to test 7. |
| | VACUUM DOES NOT HOLD | VACUUM SUPPLY SYSTEM IS LEAKING. Proceed to next test. |

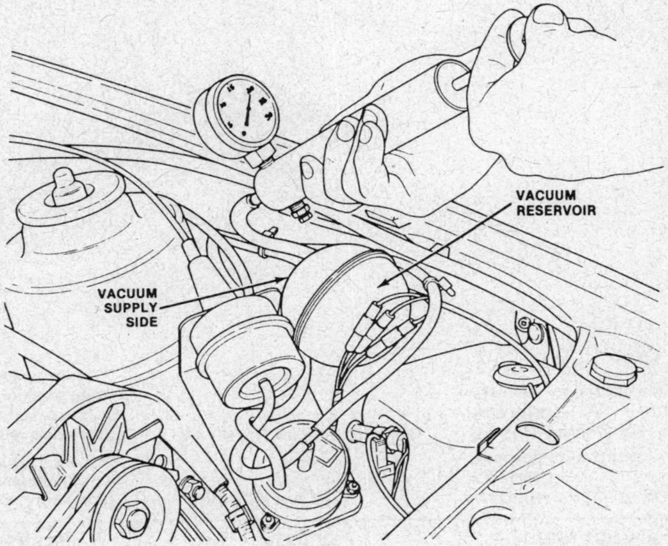

**Fig. 51 Diagnosis and testing (Part 3 of 24). XR4Ti**

SPEED CONTROL DIAGNOSTIC CHART

**4 VACUUM RESERVOIR LEAK TEST**

| TEST STEP | RESULTS | ACTION TO TAKE |
|---|---|---|
| • Disconnect hose from reservoir vacuum outlet fitting.<br>• Plug reservoir vacuum outlet fitting.<br>• Using a hand vacuum pump, apply 20″ of vacuum to reservoir through "VAC" hose fitting. | VACUUM HOLDS | VACUUM RESERVOIR IS NOT LEAKING. Proceed to next test. |
| | VACUUM DOES NOT HOLD | VACUUM RESERVOIR IS LEAKING. Replace reservoir. (Then perform test 3 again.) |

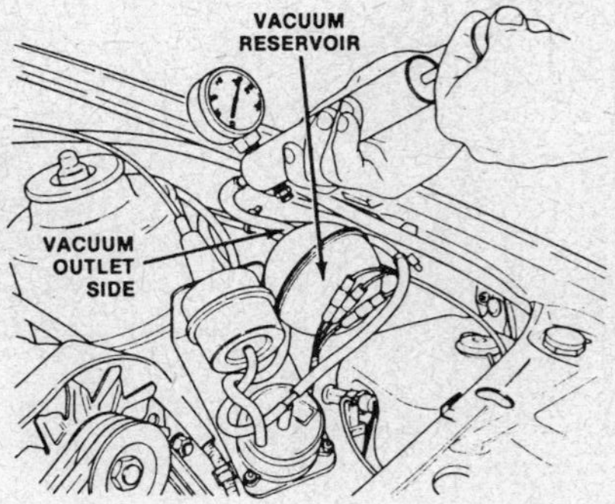

**5 VACUUM RESERVOIR CHECK VALVE TEST**

| TEST STEP | RESULTS | ACTION TO TAKE |
|---|---|---|
| • Using a hand vacuum pump, apply 20″ of vacuum to reservoir through outlet fitting. | VACUUM HOLDS | RESERVOIR CHECK VALVE IS NOT LEAKING. Proceed to next test. |
| | VACUUM DOES NOT HOLD | RESERVOIR CHECK VALVE IS LEAKING. Replace reservoir. (Then perform test 3 again.) |

**Fig. 51 Diagnosis and testing (Part 4 of 24). XR4Ti**

SPEED CONTROL DIAGNOSTIC CHART

6 VACUUM VALVE LEAK TEST

| TEST STEP | RESULTS | ACTION TO TAKE |
|---|---|---|
| • Disconnect hose from valve assembly fitting marked "VAC."<br>• Using a hand vacuum pump, apply 20" of vacuum to valve through "VAC" hose fitting. | VACUUM HOLDS | VACUUM VALVE IS NOT LEAKING. Proceed to next test. |
| | VACUUM DOES NOT HOLD | VACUUM VALVE IS LEAKING. Replace valve assembly. |

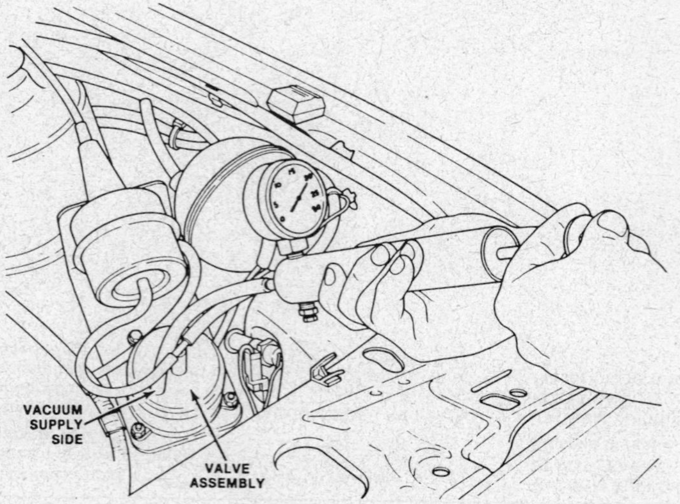

Fig. 51 Diagnosis and testing (Part 5 of 24). XR4Ti

SPEED CONTROL DIAGNOSTIC CHART

7 VACUUM VALVE ELECTRICAL TEST

| TEST STEP | RESULTS | ACTION TO TAKE |
|---|---|---|
| • Disconnect brown wire at power servo.<br>• Using a hand vacuum pump, apply 20" of vacuum to valve through "VAC" hose fitting.<br>• Connect a jumper wire from a clean chassis ground to brown wire at valve assembly. | VACUUM VENTS | VACUUM VALVE FUNCTIONS ELECTRICALLY. Proceed to next test. |
| | VACUUM DOES NOT VENT | VACUUM VALVE IS NOT FUNCTIONING ELECTRICALLY. Replace valve assembly. |

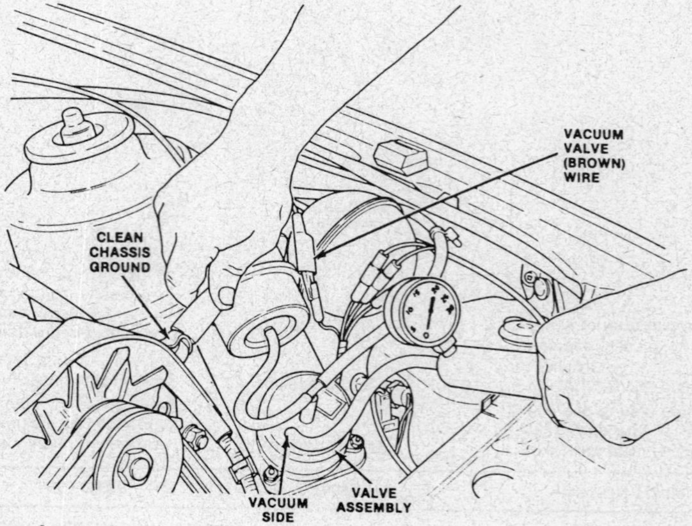

Fig. 51 Diagnosis and testing (Part 6 of 24). XR4Ti

SPEED CONTROL DIAGNOSTIC CHART

**8 SERVO VALVE ELECTRICAL/LEAK TEST**

| TEST STEP | RESULTS | ACTION TO TAKE |
|---|---|---|
| • Disconnect hose from valve assembly fitting marked "SERVO." • Disconnect yellow wire at power servo. • Connect a jumper wire from a clean chassis ground to yellow wire at valve assembly. • Using a hand vacuum pump, apply 20″ of vacuum to valve through "SERVO" hose fitting. | VACUUM HOLDS | SERVO VALVE FUNCTIONS ELECTRICALLY AND IS NOT LEAKING. Proceed to next test. |
| | VACUUM DOES NOT HOLD | SERVO VALVE IS NOT FUNCTIONING ELECTRICALLY AND/OR IS LEAKING. Replace valve assembly. |

VENT VALVE (YELLOW) WIRE
CLEAN CHASSIS GROUND
SERVO SIDE
VALVE ASSEMBLY

**Fig. 51 Diagnosis and testing (Part 7 of 24). XR4Ti**

SPEED CONTROL DIAGNOSTIC CHART

**9 SERVO LEAK TEST**

| TEST STEP | RESULTS | ACTION TO TAKE |
|---|---|---|
| • Disconnect hose from vacuum servo. • Using a hand vacuum pump, apply 20″ of vacuum to servo through hose fitting. | VACUUM HOLDS | SERVO IS NOT LEAKING. Proceed to next test. |
| | VACUUM DOES NOT HOLD | SERVO IS LEAKING. Replace servo. |

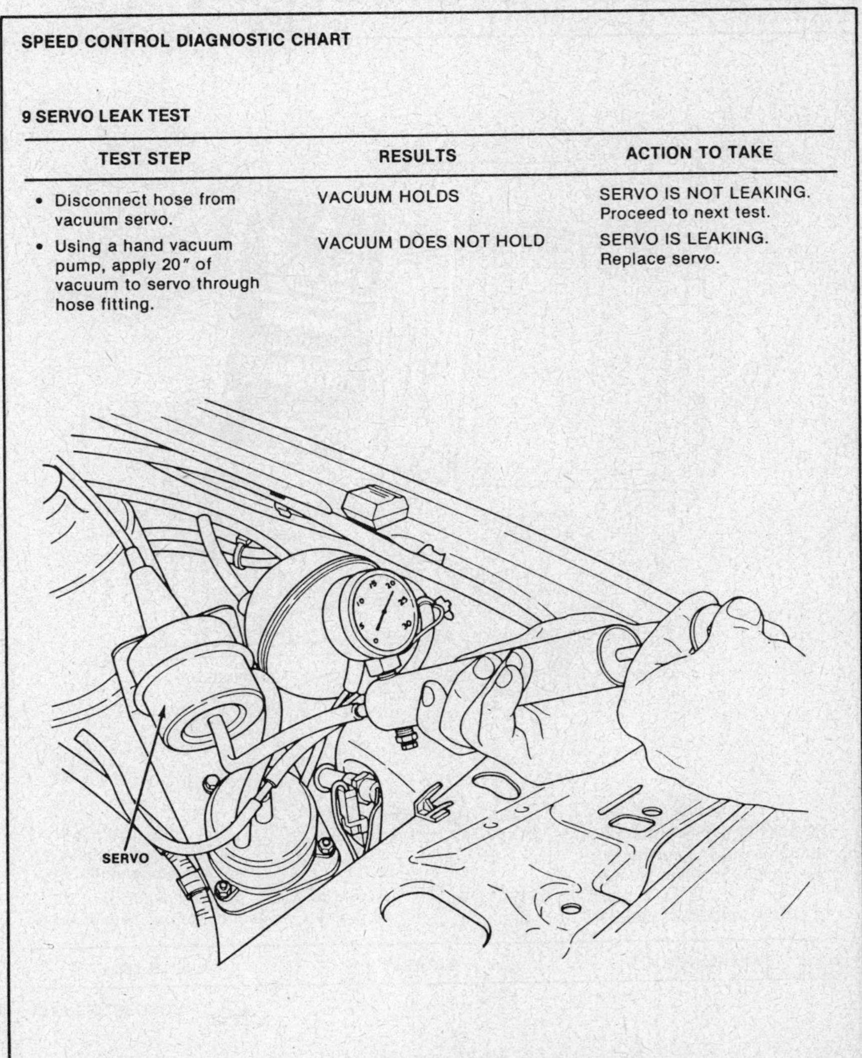


**Fig. 51 Diagnosis and testing (Part 8 of 24). XR4Ti**

SPEED CONTROL DIAGNOSTIC CHART
(Continued)

10 LINKAGE/SERVO CABLE TEST

| TEST STEP | RESULTS | ACTION TO TAKE |
|---|---|---|
| • Using a hand vacuum pump, apply 20″ of vacuum to servo through hose fitting.<br>• While applying vacuum, watch the throttle lever and servo cable. | THROTTLE LEVER MOVES SMOOTHLY TO WIDE OPEN POSITION | LINKAGE/CABLE IS OPERATING PROPERLY. Proceed to test 13. |
| | THROTTLE LEVER DOES NOT MOVE OR BINDS | LINKAGE/CABLE IS NOT OPERATING PROPERLY. Proceed to next test. |

11 THROTTLE CABLE TEST

| TEST STEP | RESULTS | ACTION TO TAKE |
|---|---|---|
| • Disconnect speed control cable from throttle lever. If necessary, refer to cable removal and installation procedure<br>• Using a hand vacuum pump, apply 20″ of vacuum to servo through hose fitting. | CABLE MOVES SMOOTHLY | CABLE IS OPERATING PROPERLY. Proceed to next test. |
| | CABLE DOES NOT MOVE OR BINDS | CABLE IS NOT OPERATING PROPERLY. Find cause and correct or replace cable. |

12 THROTTLE LEVER TEST

| TEST STEP | RESULTS | ACTION TO TAKE |
|---|---|---|
| • With the speed control cable disconnected, move the throttle lever from the idle position to wide open position. | LEVER MOVES SMOOTHLY | THROTTLE LINKAGE IS OPERATING PROPERLY. Proceed to next test. |
| | LEVER DOES NOT MOVE SMOOTHLY | THROTTLE LINKAGE IS NOT OPERATING PROPERLY. Isolate cause and repair as necessary. |

Fig. 51 Diagnosis and testing (Part 9 of 24). XR4Ti

SPEED CONTROL DIAGNOSTIC CHART

13 SPEED SENSOR

| TEST STEP | RESULTS | ACTION TO TAKE |
|---|---|---|
| • Disconnect wiring connector from speed sensor.<br>• Using an ohmmeter, measure resistance of speed sensor. | 40 OHMS ±5 OHMS | SPEED SENSOR CIRCUIT IS OK. Repair cause of high or low resistance in sensor circuit. |
| | MORE THAN 45 OHMS OR LESS THAN 35 OHMS | SPEED SENSOR IS NOT OK. Replace sensor. |

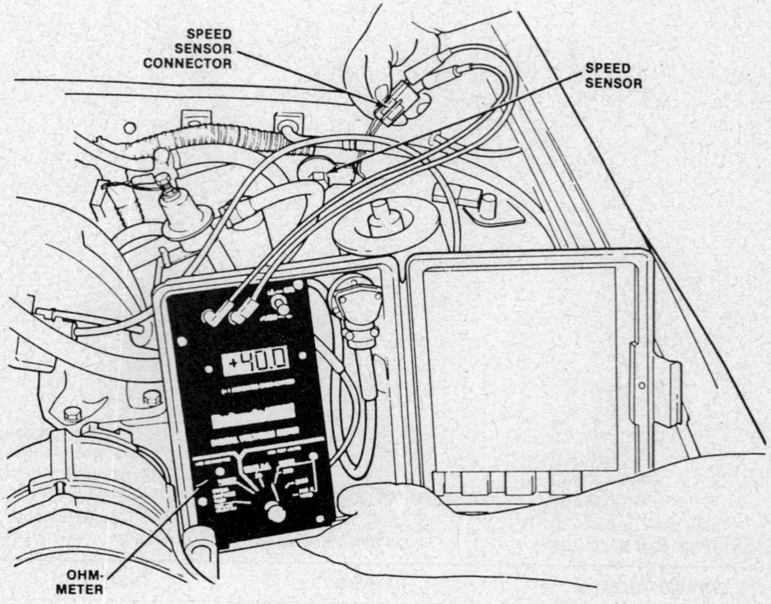

Fig. 51 Diagnosis and testing (Part 10 of 24). XR4Ti

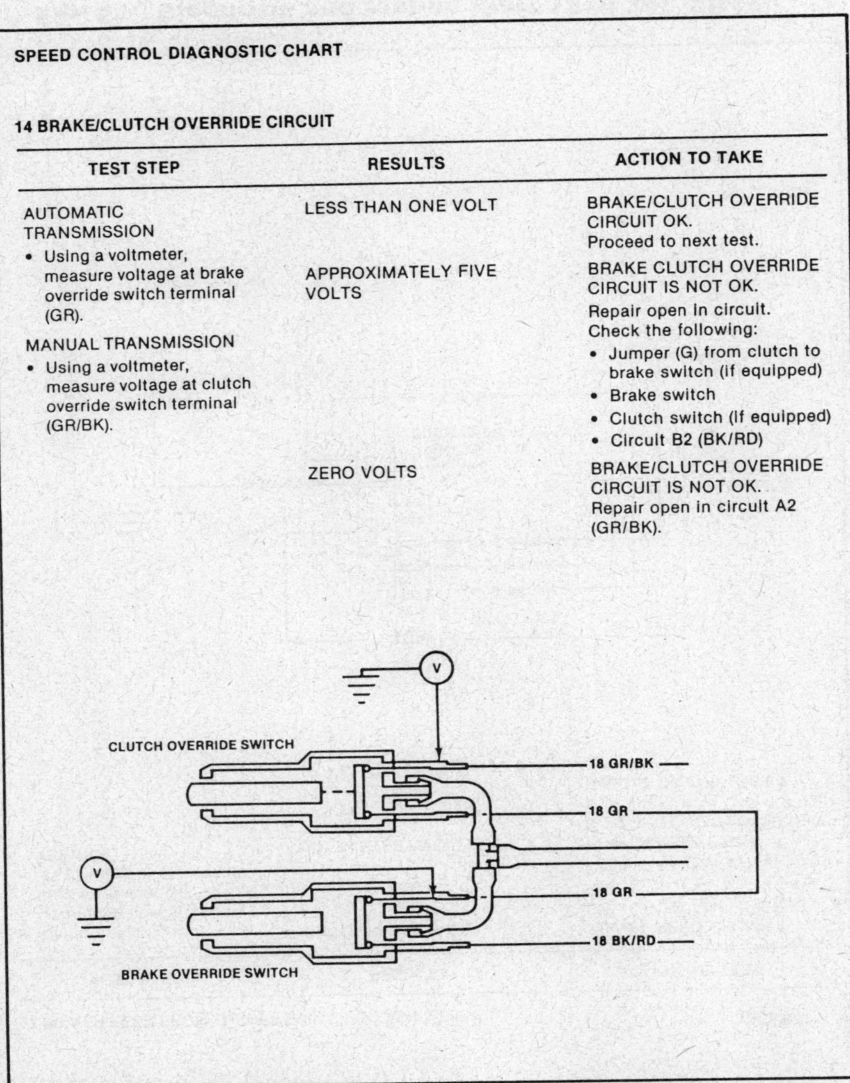

SPEED CONTROL DIAGNOSTIC CHART

14 BRAKE/CLUTCH OVERRIDE CIRCUIT

| TEST STEP | RESULTS | ACTION TO TAKE |
|---|---|---|
| AUTOMATIC TRANSMISSION<br>• Using a voltmeter, measure voltage at brake override switch terminal (GR).<br>MANUAL TRANSMISSION<br>• Using a voltmeter, measure voltage at clutch override switch terminal (GR/BK). | LESS THAN ONE VOLT | BRAKE/CLUTCH OVERRIDE CIRCUIT OK.<br>Proceed to next test. |
| | APPROXIMATELY FIVE VOLTS | BRAKE CLUTCH OVERRIDE CIRCUIT IS NOT OK.<br>Repair open in circuit. Check the following:<br>• Jumper (G) from clutch to brake switch (if equipped)<br>• Brake switch<br>• Clutch switch (If equipped)<br>• Circuit B2 (BK/RD) |
| | ZERO VOLTS | BRAKE/CLUTCH OVERRIDE CIRCUIT IS NOT OK.<br>Repair open in circuit A2 (GR/BK). |



**Fig. 51 Diagnosis and testing (Part 11 of 24). XR4Ti**

SPEED CONTROL DIAGNOSTIC CHART

15 AMPLIFIER BRAKE/CLUTCH OVERRIDE CIRCUIT SIGNAL

| TEST STEP | RESULTS | ACTION TO TAKE |
|---|---|---|
| AUTOMATIC TRANSMISSION<br>• Press and hold brake pedal. | APPROXIMATELY FIVE VOLTS | AMPLIFIER IS PROVIDING BRAKE/CLUTCH OVERRIDE SIGNAL.<br>Proceed to next test. |
| • While holding brake pedal, measure voltage at brake switch terminal (GR).<br>MANUAL TRANSMISSION<br>• Press clutch pedal approximately one inch.<br>• While holding clutch pedal, measure voltage at clutch switch terminal (GR/BK). | VOLTAGE IS NOT APPROXIMATELY FIVE VOLTS | AMPLIFIER IS NOT PROVIDING BRAKE/CLUTCH OVERRIDE SIGNAL.<br>Replace amplifier. |

16 POWER FEED TO ON/OFF SWITCH

| TEST STEP | RESULTS | ACTION TO TAKE |
|---|---|---|
| • Using a test light or voltmeter, check for voltage at ON/OFF switch ignition terminal (BK/BL). | BATTERY VOLTAGE | POWER FEED TO SWITCH IS OK.<br>Proceed to next test. |
| | NO BATTERY VOLTAGE | POWER FEED TO SWITCH IS NOT OK.<br>Repair open in wire to switch from ignition feed source. |

18 BK/BL
18 BK/WH
18 BK/WH
18 GY/GN
V
ON/OFF SWITCH CONNECTOR
18 BK/WH

**Fig. 51 Diagnosis and testing (Part 12 of 24). XR4Ti**

SPEED CONTROL DIAGNOSTIC CHART

17 POWER FEED FROM ON/OFF SWITCH TO AMPLIFIER

| TEST STEP | RESULTS | ACTION TO TAKE |
|---|---|---|
| • Using a test light or voltmeter, check for battery voltage at ON/OFF switch amplifier terminal (BK/RD). | BATTERY VOLTAGE | POWER FEED FROM SWITCH TO AMPLIFIER IS OK. Proceed to next test. |
| | NO BATTERY VOLTAGE | POWER FEED FROM SWITCH TO AMPLIFIER IS NOT OK. Replace ON/OFF switch. |

Fig. 51 Diagnosis and testing (Part 13 of 24). XR4Ti

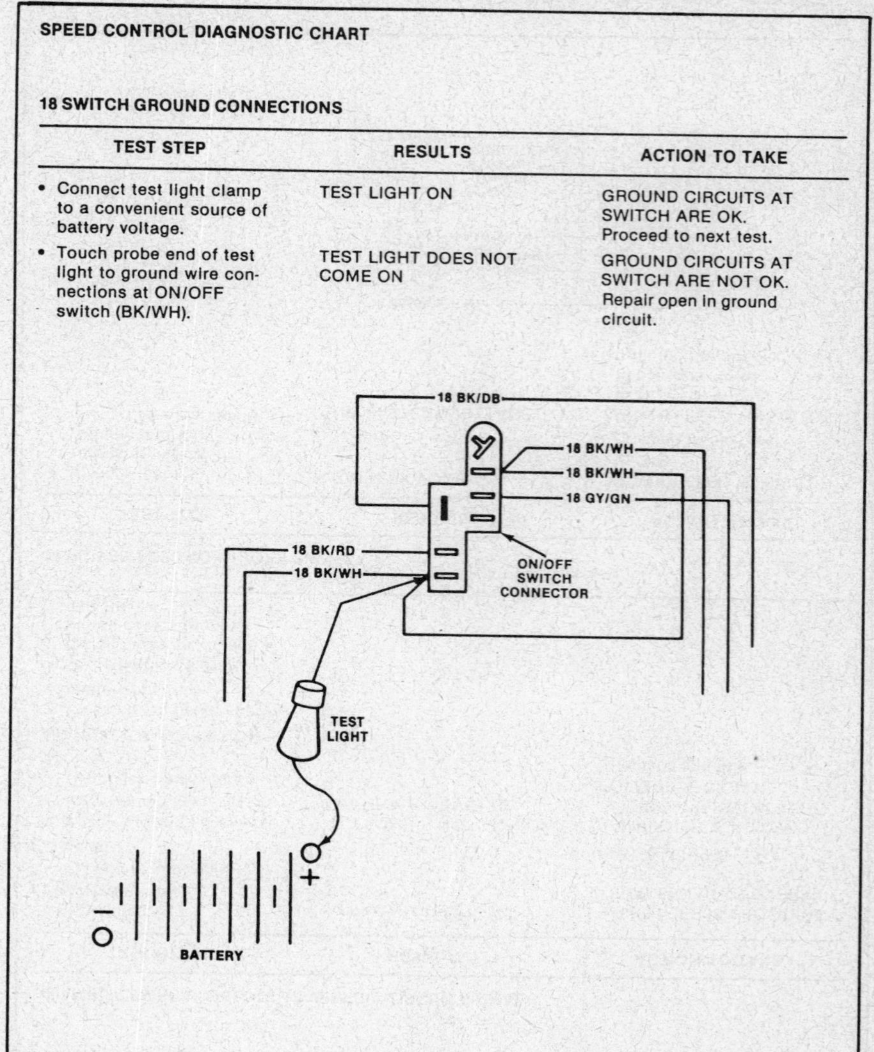

SPEED CONTROL DIAGNOSTIC CHART

18 SWITCH GROUND CONNECTIONS

| TEST STEP | RESULTS | ACTION TO TAKE |
|---|---|---|
| • Connect test light clamp to a convenient source of battery voltage.<br>• Touch probe end of test light to ground wire connections at ON/OFF switch (BK/WH). | TEST LIGHT ON | GROUND CIRCUITS AT SWITCH ARE OK. Proceed to next test. |
| | TEST LIGHT DOES NOT COME ON | GROUND CIRCUITS AT SWITCH ARE NOT OK. Repair open in ground circuit. |



Fig. 51 Diagnosis and testing (Part 14 of 24). XR4Ti

SPEED CONTROL DIAGNOSTIC CHART

**19 POWER FEED TO SET SWITCH**

| TEST STEP | RESULTS | ACTION TO TAKE |
|---|---|---|
| • Remove steering column lower trim cover.<br>• Using a test light or voltmeter, check for voltage at jumper wire supplying battery voltage to switch. | BATTERY VOLTAGE | POWER FEED CIRCUIT TO SWITCH IS OK.<br>Proceed to next test. |
| | NO BATTERY VOLTAGE | POWER FEED TO SWITCH IS NOT OK.<br>Repair open in jumper wire. |

V
SET SWITCH POWER FEED JUMPER WIRE
STEERING COLUMN

**Fig. 51 Diagnosis and testing (Part 15 of 24). XR4Ti**

SPEED CONTROL DIAGNOSTIC CHART

**20 POWER FEED FROM SET SWITCH TO AMPLIFIER**

| TEST STEP | RESULTS | ACTION TO TAKE |
|---|---|---|
| • While holding the set switch in, check for voltage at amplifier feed terminal using a voltmeter or test light. | BATTERY VOLTAGE | POWER FEED FROM SWITCH TO AMPLIFIER IS OK.<br>Proceed to next test. |
| | NO BATTERY VOLTAGE | POWER FEED FROM SWITCH TO AMPLIFIER IS NOT OK.<br>Replace switch. |

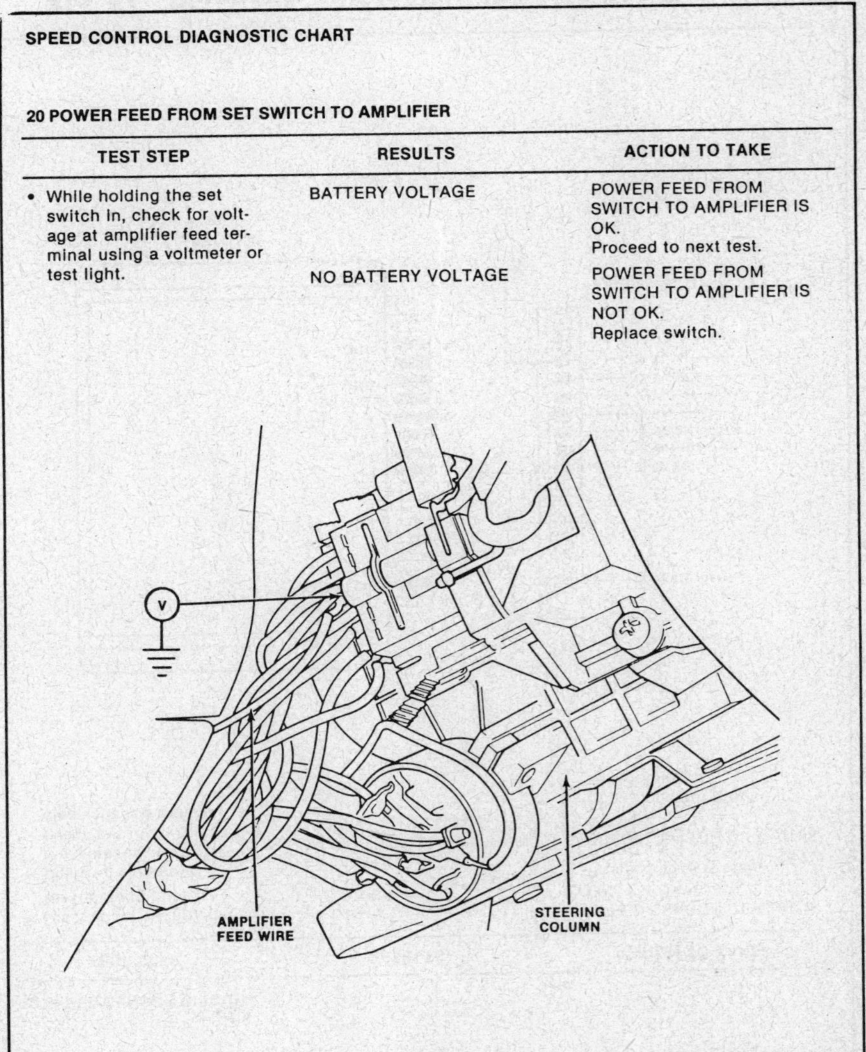


**Fig. 51 Diagnosis and testing (Part 16 of 24). XR4Ti**

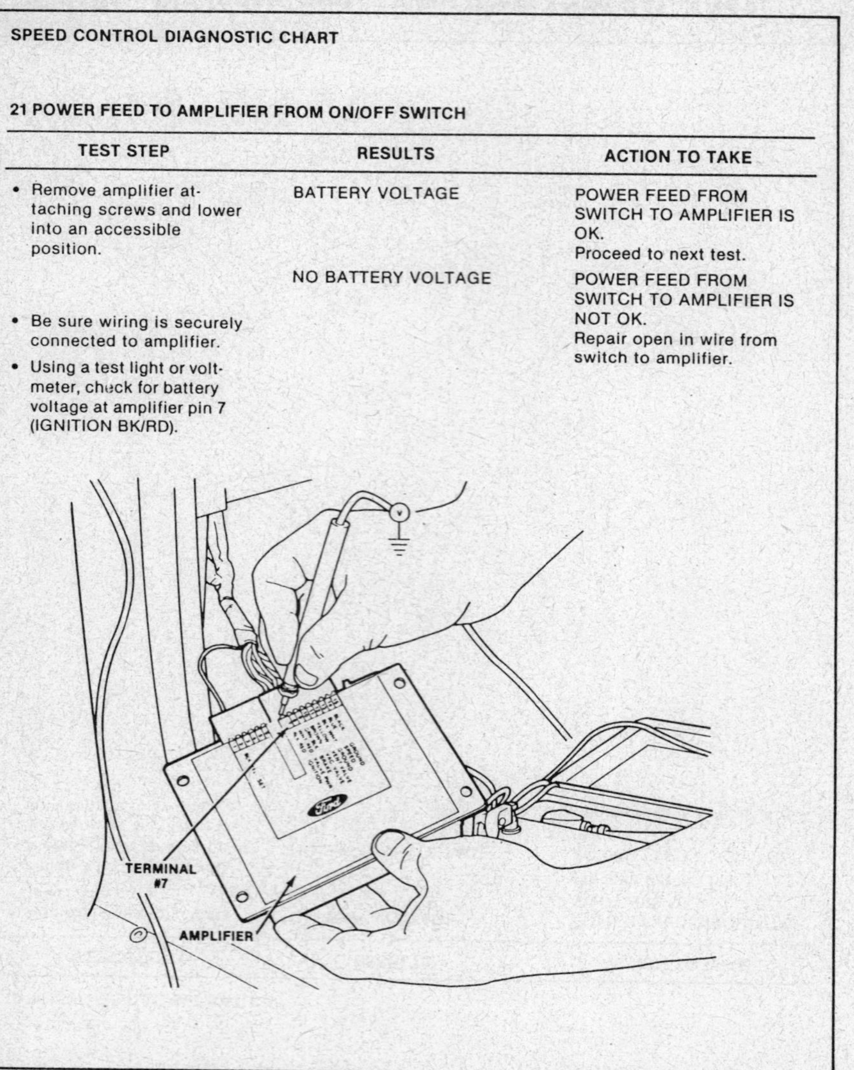

SPEED CONTROL DIAGNOSTIC CHART

21 POWER FEED TO AMPLIFIER FROM ON/OFF SWITCH

| TEST STEP | RESULTS | ACTION TO TAKE |
|---|---|---|
| • Remove amplifier attaching screws and lower into an accessible position. | BATTERY VOLTAGE | POWER FEED FROM SWITCH TO AMPLIFIER IS OK. Proceed to next test. |
| • Be sure wiring is securely connected to amplifier.<br>• Using a test light or voltmeter, check for battery voltage at amplifier pin 7 (IGNITION BK/RD). | NO BATTERY VOLTAGE | POWER FEED FROM SWITCH TO AMPLIFIER IS NOT OK. Repair open in wire from switch to amplifier. |



**Fig. 51 Diagnosis and testing (Part 17 of 24). XR4Ti**

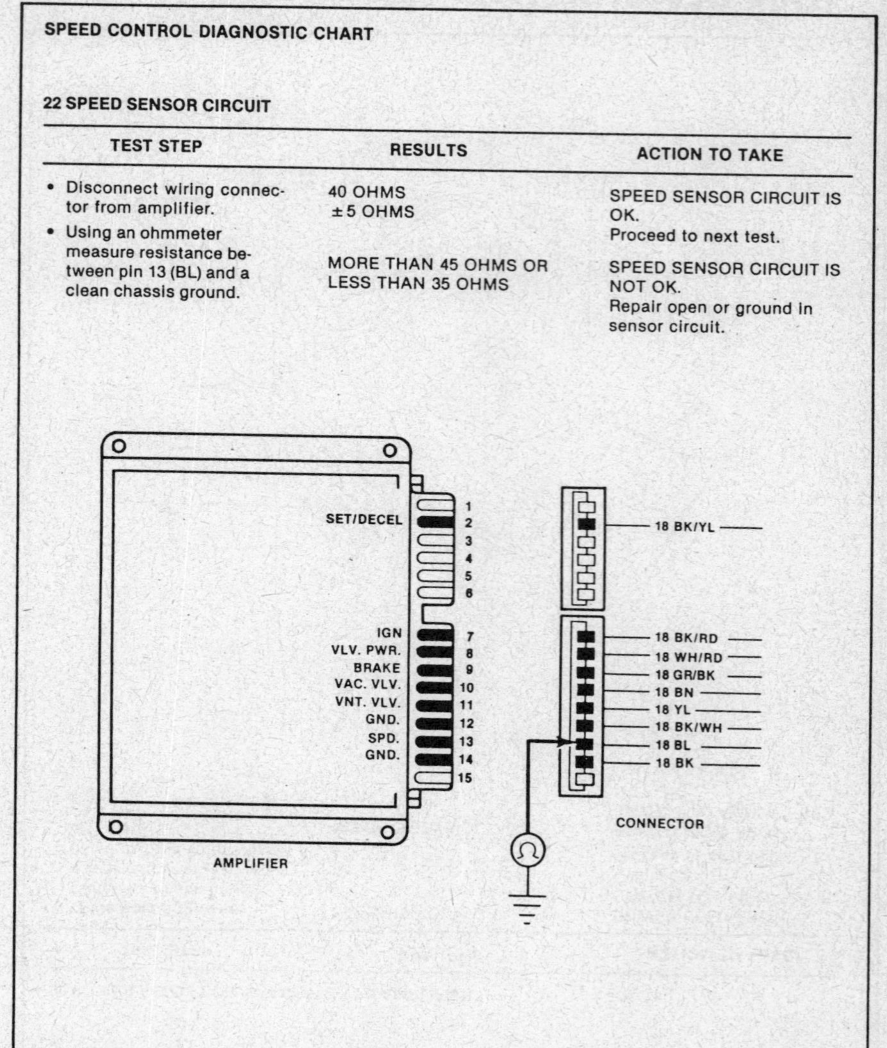

SPEED CONTROL DIAGNOSTIC CHART

22 SPEED SENSOR CIRCUIT

| TEST STEP | RESULTS | ACTION TO TAKE |
|---|---|---|
| • Disconnect wiring connector from amplifier.<br>• Using an ohmmeter measure resistance between pin 13 (BL) and a clean chassis ground. | 40 OHMS ±5 OHMS | SPEED SENSOR CIRCUIT IS OK. Proceed to next test. |
| | MORE THAN 45 OHMS OR LESS THAN 35 OHMS | SPEED SENSOR CIRCUIT IS NOT OK. Repair open or ground in sensor circuit. |



**Fig. 51 Diagnosis and testing (Part 18 of 24). XR4Ti**

SPEED CONTROL DIAGNOSTIC CHART

23 AMPLIFIER GROUND CIRCUITS

| TEST STEP | RESULTS | ACTION TO TAKE |
|---|---|---|
| • Connect test light clamp to a convenient source of battery voltage.<br>• Touch probe end of test light to terminal 14 (GND.-BK) and 12 (GND.-BK/WH) at the amplifier connector. | TEST LIGHT ON AT BOTH TERMINALS | GROUND CIRCUIT IS OK. Proceed to next test. |
| | TEST LIGHT OFF AT EITHER OR BOTH TERMINALS | GROUND CIRCUIT IS NOT OK. Repair open in ground circuit. |

SET/DECEL
IGN
VLV. PWR.
BRAKE
VAC. VLV.
VNT. VLV.
GND.
SPD.
GND.
1 2 3 4 5 6 7 8 9 10 11 12 13 14 15
18 BK/YL
18 BK/RD
18 WH/RD
18 GR/BK
18 BN
18 YL
18 BK/WH
18 BL
18 BK
CONNECTOR
AMPLIFIER
BATTERY
TEST LIGHT

Fig. 51 Diagnosis and testing (Part 19 of 24). XR4Ti

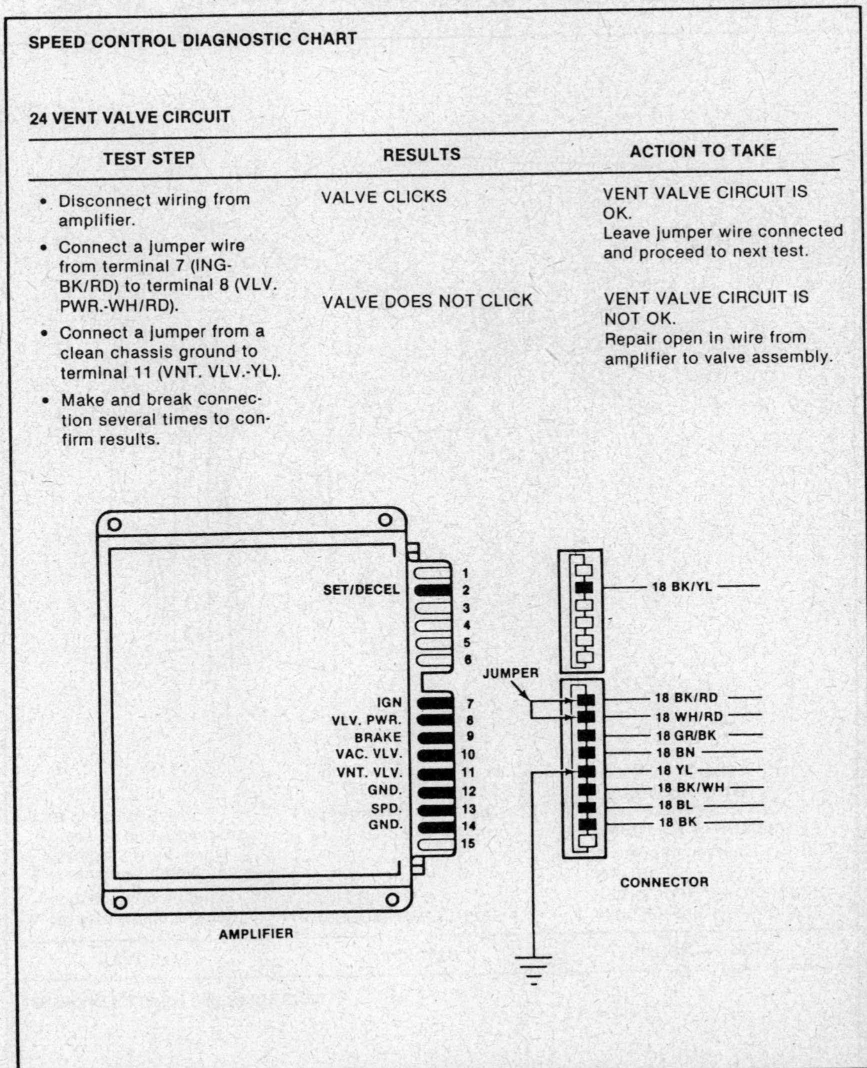

SPEED CONTROL DIAGNOSTIC CHART

24 VENT VALVE CIRCUIT

| TEST STEP | RESULTS | ACTION TO TAKE |
|---|---|---|
| • Disconnect wiring from amplifier.<br>• Connect a jumper wire from terminal 7 (ING-BK/RD) to terminal 8 (VLV. PWR.-WH/RD).<br>• Connect a jumper from a clean chassis ground to terminal 11 (VNT. VLV.-YL).<br>• Make and break connection several times to confirm results. | VALVE CLICKS | VENT VALVE CIRCUIT IS OK. Leave jumper wire connected and proceed to next test. |
| | VALVE DOES NOT CLICK | VENT VALVE CIRCUIT IS NOT OK. Repair open in wire from amplifier to valve assembly. |



Fig. 51 Diagnosis and testing (Part 20 of 24). XR4Ti

SPEED CONTROL DIAGNOSTIC CHART

**25 VACUUM VALVE CIRCUIT**

| TEST STEP | RESULTS | ACTION TO TAKE |
|---|---|---|
| • Connect jumper wire from clean chassis ground to terminal 10 (VAC. VLV.-BN).<br>• Make and break connection several times to confirm results. | VALVE CLICKS | VACUUM VALVE CIRCUIT IS OK.<br>Proceed to next test. |
| | VALVE DOES NOT CLICK | VACUUM VALVE CIRCUIT IS NOT OK.<br>Repair open in wire from amplifier to valve assembly. |

**Fig. 51 Diagnosis and testing (Part 21 of 24). XR4Ti**

SPEED CONTROL DIAGNOSTIC CHART

**26 BRAKE/CLUTCH OVERRIDE SIGNAL**

| TEST STEP | RESULTS | ACTION TO TAKE |
|---|---|---|
| • Be sure wiring is firmly connected to amplifier.<br>• Measure voltage at pin 9 (BRAKE GR/BK) while pressing either the brake or clutch pedal. | APPROXIMATELY FIVE VOLTS | AMPLIFIER IS PROVIDING BRAKE/CLUTCH OVERRIDE SIGNAL.<br>Proceed to next test. |
| | FIVE VOLTS NOT MEASURED | AMPLIFIER IS NOT PROVIDING BRAKE/CLUTCH OVERRIDE SIGNAL.<br>Replace amplifier. |

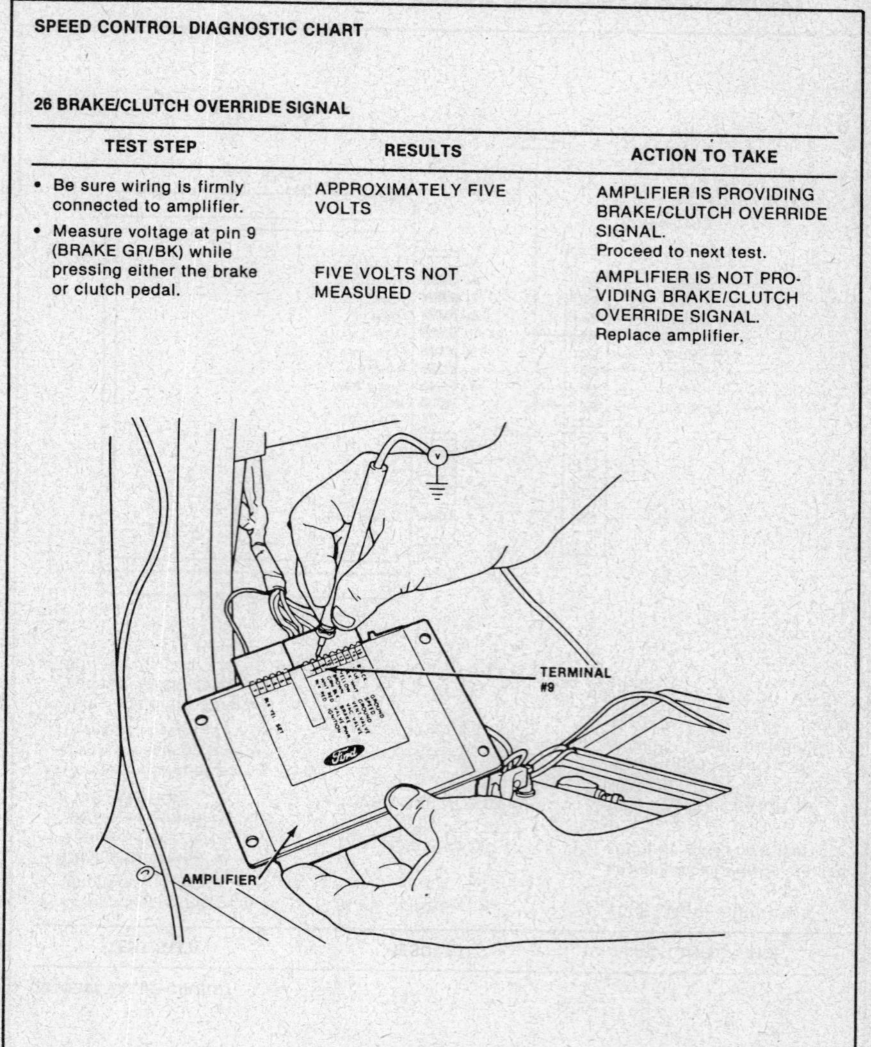


**Fig. 51 Diagnosis and testing (Part 22 of 24). XR4Ti**

SPEED CONTROL DIAGNOSTIC CHART

26 POWER FEED FROM AMPLIFIER TO SERVO

| TEST STEP | RESULTS | ACTION TO TAKE |
|---|---|---|
| • Remove amplifier attaching screws and lower into an accessible position. Do not disconnect amplifier wiring. | BATTERY VOLTAGE | AMPLIFIER IS SUPPLYING SERVO POWER FEED. Repair open in wire from amplifier to servo. |
| • Using a voltmeter, measure voltage at amplifier pin 8 (VALVE PWR WH/RD). | NO BATTERY VOLTAGE | AMPLIFIER IS NOT SUPPLYING POWER FEED. Check for voltage at amplifer pin 7 (BK/RD). — If voltage is present, replace amplifier. — If voltage is not present, go to test 16. |

Fig. 51 Diagnosis and testing (Part 23 of 24). XR4Ti

SPEED CONTROL DIAGNOSTIC CHART

27 SET/DECEL SIGNAL FROM SET SWITCH

| TEST STEP | RESULTS | ACTION TO TAKE |
|---|---|---|
| • While holding the set switch in, measure voltage at amplifier pin 2 (SET BK/YL). | BATTERY VOLTAGE | AMPLIFIER IS RECEIVING SET/DECEL SIGNAL. Proceed to next test. |
| | NO BATTERY VOLTAGE | AMPLIFIER IS NOT RECEIVING SET/DECEL SIGNAL. Repair open in wire from set switch to amplifier. |

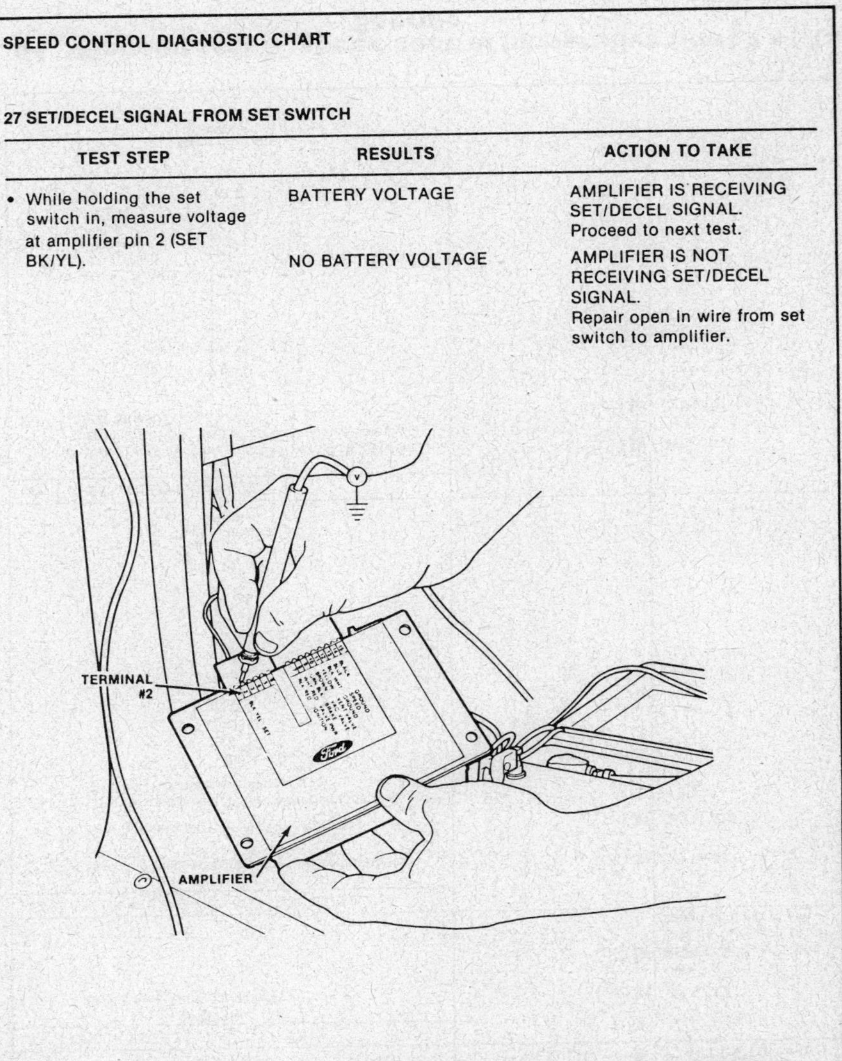


Fig. 51 Diagnosis and testing (Part 24 of 24). XR4Ti

| CONDITION | PINPOINT TEST |
|---|---|
| Speed Control System Inoperative | A |
| Speed Control Slow To Disengage When Brake Or Clutch Is Operated | B |
| Speed Control Fails To Coast Or Resume When Switch Is Operated | C |
| Speed Control Fails To Switch Off When Switch Is Operated | D |
| Vehicle Continues To Accelerate After Speed Is Set | E |
| Vehicle Speed Fluctuates Continuously | F |
| System Automatically Returns To Set Speed As Brake Pedal Is Released | G |
| System Automatically Returns To Set Speed After Release Of Clutch Pedal | H |
| Speed Control Will Not Set Or Accelerate At High Engine Speeds | J |

**Fig. 52 Speed control symptom. Scorpio**

| Terminal Number | Wire Color | Circuit Number | Function |
|---|---|---|---|
| 1 | BL/R | 9-25 | To Steering Wheel Switches |
| 2 | BK/R | 54-6 | Stop/Clutch Switch |
| 3 | — | — | Blank |
| 4 | — | — | Blank |
| 5 | BR | 31-29 | Ground |
| 6 | — | — | Blank |
| 7 | BL | 9 | From Instrument Cluster — 10.8V After 5 Sec Prove Out |
| 8 | LG | 1-3 | Ign Pulse Input from Tachometer |
| 9 | BR | 31-29 | Ground Jumper to Terminal 13 |
| 10 | BL/BK | 9-23 | Pump Common |
| 11 | BK/Y | 54-32 | Power |
| 12 | Y/BR | 2 | Speed Sensor |
| 13 | BR | 31-29 | Ground |
| 14 | BL/W | 9-26 | Vent +12V |
| 15 | BL/G | 9-24 | Pump +12V |
| 16 | — | — | Blank |

**Fig. 53 Terminal identification. Scorpio**

| | TEST STEP | RESULT ▶ | ACTION TO TAKE |
|---|---|---|---|
| A1 | CHECK FUSE 22 FOR CONTINUITY | | |
| | • Check fuse 22 for continuity. | OK ▶ | GO to **A2**. |
| | | NOT OK ▶ | REPLACE fuse 22 and CHECK operation of speed control system. |
| A2 | CHECK VOLTAGE TO CONTROL MODULE | | |
| | • Disconnect speed control module from harness connector.<br>• Turn ignition switch to RUN (position II).<br>• Using a voltmeter, test for battery voltage at terminal 11 of module connector. 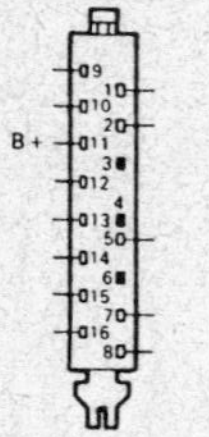<br>B+ (terminal 11)<br>SPEED CONTROL MODULE | OK ▶ | GO to **A3**. |
| | | NOT OK ▶ | GO to **A20**. |
| A3 | CHECK MODULE GROUND | | |
| | • Using an ohmmeter, check for continuity between terminals 5, 9 and 13 of control module connector and ground. 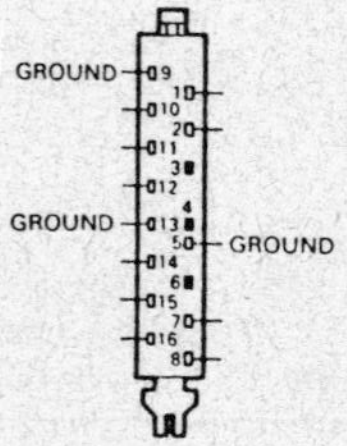<br>GROUND (terminals 9, 13, 5)<br>SPEED CONTROL MODULE | OK ▶ | GO to **A4**. |
| | | NOT OK ▶ | SERVICE open in wiring between module connector and ground. |

**Fig. 54 Pinpoint test A, speed control inoperative (Part 1 of 13). Scorpio**

| TEST STEP | RESULT ▶ | ACTION TO TAKE |
|---|---|---|
| **A4** CHECK PUMP MOTOR RESISTANCE | | |
| • Using an ohmmeter, measure resistance between terminals 10 and 14 of control module connector.<br>• Resistance reading should be between 90 and 110 ohms.<br>90-110 OHMS<br>SPEED CONTROL MODULE | OK ▶ | GO to **A5**. |
| | NOT OK ▶ | GO to **A15**. |
| **A5** CHECK PUMP SOLENOID RESISTANCE | | |
| • Using an ohmmeter, measure the resistance between terminals 10 and 15 of the control module connector.<br>• Resistance reading should be between 5 and 70 ohms.<br>5-70 OHMS<br>SPEED CONTROL MODULE | OK ▶ | GO to **A6**. |
| | NOT OK ▶ | GO to **A17**. |

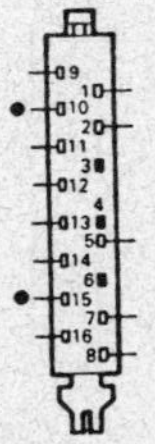

**Fig. 54 Pinpoint test A, speed control inoperative (Part 2 of 13). Scorpio**

| TEST STEP | RESULT ▶ | ACTION TO TAKE |
|---|---|---|
| **A6** CHECK PEDAL MOUNTED SWITCH CIRCUIT | | |
| • Using an ohmmeter, measure the resistance between terminal 2 of control module connector and ground.<br>• Resistance should be less than 5 ohms.<br>LESS THAN 5 OHMS<br>SPEED CONTROL MODULE | Resistance less than 5 ohms ▶ | GO to **A7**. |
| | No resistance between terminal 2 and ground ▶ | SERVICE short to ground between terminal 2 and brake pedal switch. |
| | Excessive resistance between terminal 2 and ground ▶ | GO to **A19**. |
| **A7** CHECK SPEED SENSOR OUTPUT VOLTAGE | | |
| • Turn ignition switch to RUN (position II).<br>• Place transmission in NEUTRAL.<br>• Connect positive lead of voltmeter to terminal 12 of control module connector and negative lead to ground.<br>• Slowly push vehicle forward a few feet while observing meter reading.<br>• Voltage should rise to approximately 10 volts and then fall to zero volts in regular cycle.<br>• Observe at least 8 cycles.<br>10V ZERO VOLTS<br>SPEED CONTROL MODULE | OK ▶ | GO to **A8**. |
| | NOT OK ▶ | GO to **A23**. |

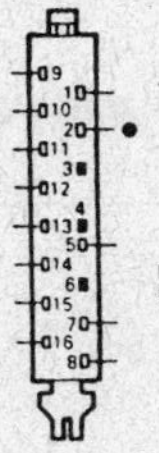

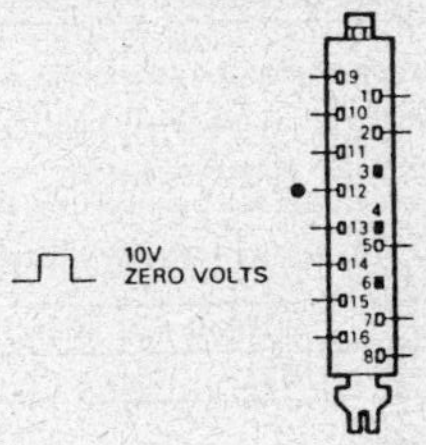

**Fig. 54 Pinpoint test A, speed control inoperative (Part 3 of 13). Scorpio**

| TEST STEP | | RESULT ▶ | ACTION TO TAKE |
|---|---|---|---|
| **A8** | CHECK SIGNAL FROM TACHOMETER | | |
| | • Connect positive lead of a test tachometer to terminal 8 of control module connector.<br>• Connect negative lead of test tachometer to vehicle ground.<br>• Set tachometer to 6 cylinder position.<br>• Start engine and observe rpm reading.<br>• Reading should be equal to engine rpm. 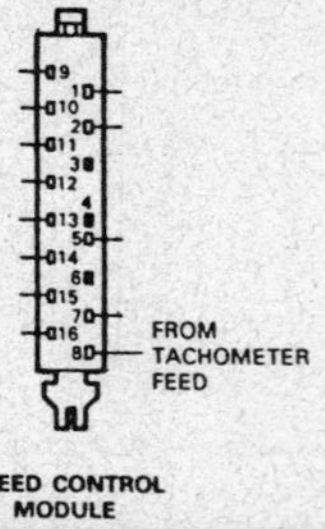<br>FROM TACHOMETER FEED<br>SPEED CONTROL MODULE | OK ▶<br>NOT OK ▶ | GO to **A9**.<br>GO to **A26**. |
| **A9** | VERIFY SIGNAL FROM CONTROL SWITCHES | | |
| | • Connect voltmeter between terminal 1 of control module connector and vehicle ground.<br>• Turn ignition switch to RUN (position II).<br>• Press speed control system ON switch while observing meter reading.<br>• Voltage reading should be approximately battery voltage. 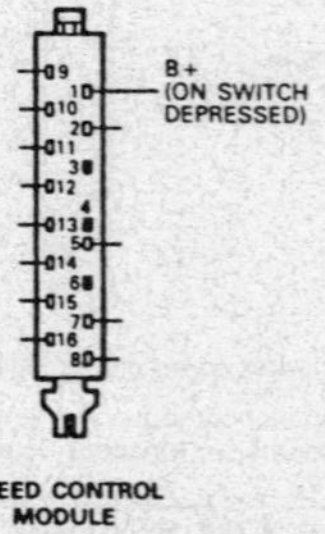<br>B+ (ON SWITCH DEPRESSED)<br>SPEED CONTROL MODULE | OK ▶<br>NOT OK ▶ | GO to **A10**.<br>GO to **A27**. |

**Fig. 54 Pinpoint test A, speed control inoperative (Part 4 of 13). Scorpio**

| TEST STEP | | RESULT ▶ | ACTION TO TAKE |
|---|---|---|---|
| **A10** | CHECK SET SWITCH | | |
| | • Turn ignition switch to OFF (position I).<br>• Connect an ohmmeter between terminal 1 of control module and ground.<br>• Depress set switch (SET position).<br>• With set switch depressed ohmmeter reading should be 400 ohms. | OK ▶<br>NOT OK ▶ | GO to **A11**.<br>SERVICE set switch. If system is still inoperative, GO to **A11**. |
| **A11** | CHECK VOLTAGE THROUGH SLIP-RING | | |
| | • Turn ignition switch to OFF (position I).<br>• Connect an ohmmeter between terminal 1 of control module and ground.<br>• Rotate steering wheel from side to side. Ohmmeter reading should only fluctuate ± 25 ohms. | OK ▶<br>NOT OK ▶ | GO to **A12**.<br>SERVICE slip ring assembly. If system is still inoperative, GO to **A12**. |

**Fig. 54 Pinpoint test A, speed control inoperative (Part 5 of 13). Scorpio**

| TEST STEP | RESULT ▶ | ACTION TO TAKE |
|---|---|---|
| **A12** CHECK PUMP ASSEMBLY — CONTROL MODULE BYPASSED | | |
| • Disconnect speed control module.<br>• Turn ignition switch to RUN (position II).<br>• Using insulated jumper leads, jump terminal 10 to terminal 11 on module connector.<br>• Connect a second jump lead between terminals 9 and 14.<br>• Pump solenoid should click.<br>• Use a third jump lead to connect terminals 9 and 15.<br>• Pump motor should run and servo should compress within 7 seconds maximum.<br>**CAUTION: Do not allow pump to run more than 10 seconds.**<br>• Remove jumper between terminals 9 and 15.<br>• Pump should stop, servo should remain compressed.<br>• Remove jumper between terminals 9 and 14.<br>• Solenoid should click, servo should relax. Maximum time 3 seconds.<br>SPEED CONTROL MODULE | OK ▶<br>NOT OK ▶ | GO to **A13**.<br>CHECK vacuum system for leak. SERVICE as necessary. |
| **A13** CHECK ACTUATOR CABLE FREEPLAY | | |
| • Check actuator cable freeplay.<br>• Freeplay should be between zero and 1mm (zero and 0.04 inch). | OK ▶<br>NOT OK ▶ | GO to **A14**.<br>ADJUST actuator cable to obtain correct freeplay. CHECK system operation. |

**Fig. 54 Pinpoint test A, speed control inoperative (Part 6 of 13). Scorpio**

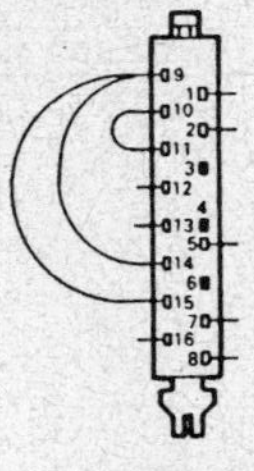

| TEST STEP | RESULT ▶ | ACTION TO TAKE |
|---|---|---|
| **A14** CHECK SERVO AND THROTTLE TRAVEL | | |
| • Compress vacuum servo using hand pressure to push servo rod all the way in (approximately 40mm [1.6 inches]).<br>• Throttle should move to near wide open position. | OK ▶<br>NOT OK ▶ | REPLACE speed control module. CHECK system operation.<br>SERVICE throttle linkage and/or actuator cable. |
| **A15** CHECK WIRING CONTINUITY | | |
| • Disconnect vacuum pump electrical connector.<br>• Using an ohmmeter with extended leads, check continuity between terminal 10 of control module connector and terminal 3 of pump connector.<br>• There should be continuity.<br>• Remove test lead from terminal 3 of pump connector and connect to vehicle ground.<br>• There should be no continuity between terminal 10 of control module connector and ground.<br>SPEED CONTROL MODULE — 0 OHMS — VACUUM PUMP (1, 2, 3) | OK ▶<br>No continuity between terminal 3 and terminal 10 ▶<br>Continuity to ground at terminal 10 ▶ | GO to **A16**.<br>SERVICE poor connection and/or open in circuit between pump connector and module connector. CHECK system operation.<br>SERVICE short to ground in circuit between pump connector and control module connector. CHECK system operation. |

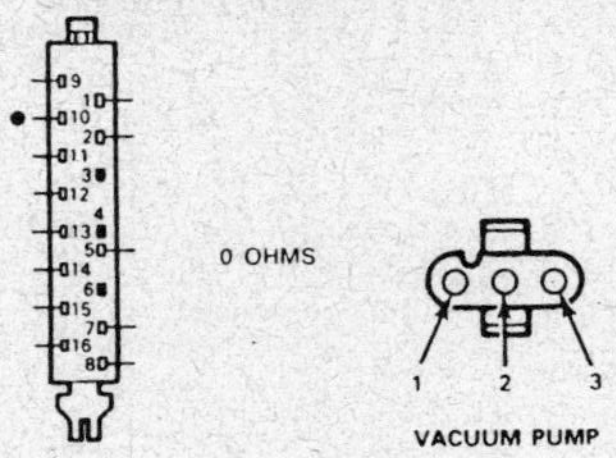

**Fig. 54 Pinpoint test A, speed control inoperative (Part 7 of 13). Scorpio**

| TEST STEP | RESULT ▶ | ACTION TO TAKE |
|---|---|---|
| **A16** CHECK WIRING CONTINUITY | | |
| • Using an ohmmeter with extended leads, check continuity between terminal 14 of control module connector and terminal 1 of vacuum pump connector.<br>• Remove test lead from terminal 1 of pump connector and connect lead to vehicle ground.<br>• There should be no continuity between terminal 14 and vehicle ground.<br>0 OHMS · SPEED CONTROL MODULE · VACUUM PUMP | OK ▶ | REPLACE vacuum pump assembly. CHECK system operation. |
| | No continuity between terminal 14 and terminal 1 ▶ | SERVICE poor connection and/or open in circuit between pump connector and module connector. CHECK system operation. |
| | Continuity to ground at terminal 14 ▶ | SERVICE short to ground in circuit between pump connector and module connector. CHECK system operation. |
| **A17** CHECK WIRING CONTINUITY | | |
| • Disconnect vacuum pump electrical connector.<br>• Using an ohmmeter with extended leads, check continuity between terminal 10 of control module connector and terminal 3 of pump connector.<br>• There should be continuity.<br>• Remove test lead from terminal 3 of pump connector and connect lead to vehicle ground.<br>• There should be no continuity between terminal 10 of module connector and ground.<br>0 OHMS · SPEED CONTROL MODULE · VACUUM PUMP | OK ▶ | GO to **A18**. |
| | No continuity between terminal 10 and terminal 3 ▶ | SERVICE poor connection and/or open in circuit between pump connector and module connector. CHECK system operation. |
| | Continuity to ground at terminal 10 ▶ | SERVICE short to ground in circuit between pump connector and control module connector. CHECK system operation. |

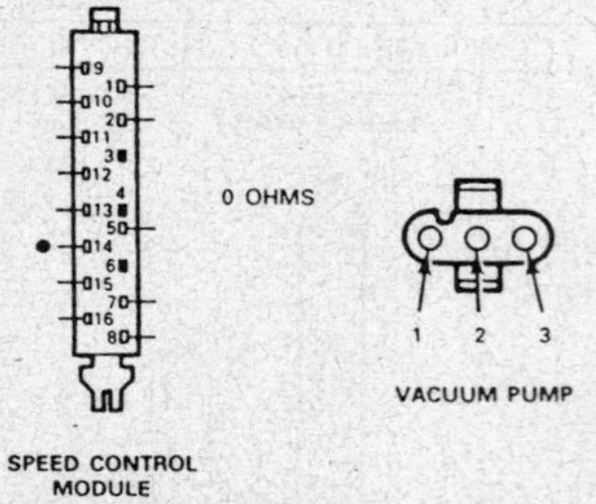

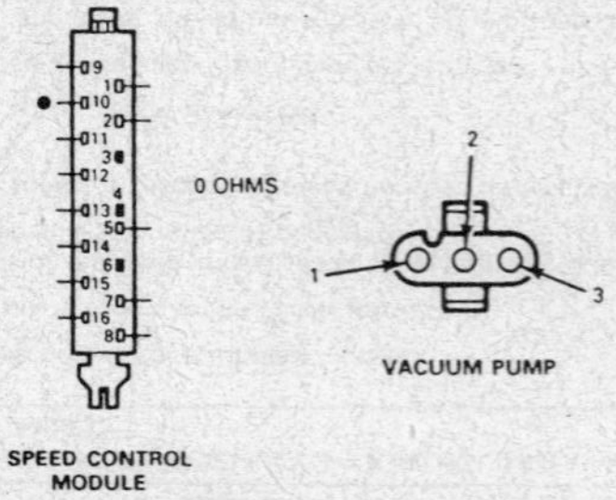

**Fig. 54 Pinpoint test A, speed control inoperative (Part 8 of 13). Scorpio**

| TEST STEP | RESULT ▶ | ACTION TO TAKE |
|---|---|---|
| **A18** CHECK WIRING CONTINUITY | | |
| • Using an ohmmeter with extended leads, check continuity between terminal 15 of control module connector and terminal 2 of pump connector.<br>• Remove test lead from terminal 2 of pump connector and connect lead to vehicle ground.<br>• There should be no continuity between terminal 15 and vehicle ground.<br>0 OHMS · SPEED CONTROL MODULE · VACUUM PUMP | OK ▶ | REPLACE vacuum pump assembly. CHECK system operation. |
| | No continuity between terminal 15 and terminal 2 ▶ | SERVICE open in circuit between pump connector and module connector. CHECK system operation. |
| | Continuity to ground at terminal 15 ▶ | SERVICE short to ground in circuit between pump connector and control module connector. CHECK system operation. |
| **A19** CHECK SWITCH CONTINUITY | | |
| • Disconnect brake pedal and clutch pedal switch connector(s).<br>• Using an ohmmeter, check continuity between terminals on switch(es) with brake and clutch pedal in normal rest position. Then check continuity with pedals depressed.<br>• There should be continuity between terminals with pedal in normal rest position and no continuity with pedal depressed. | OK ▶ | SERVICE open in circuit between stoplamp switch and terminal 2 of control module connector. CHECK system operation. |
| | NOT OK ▶ | ADJUST or REPLACE brake and/or clutch pedal switch(es). CHECK system operation. |

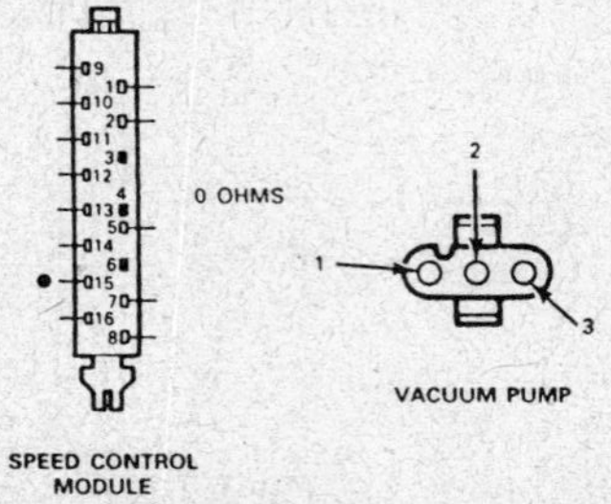

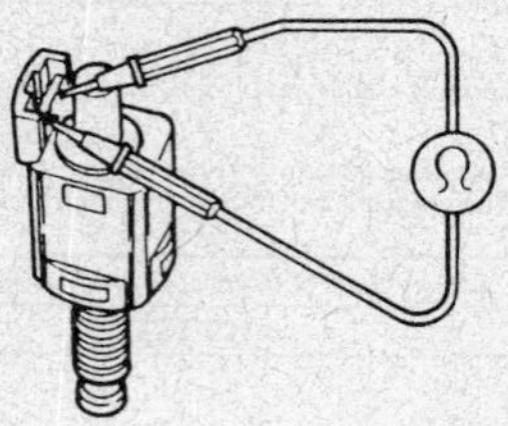

**Fig. 54 Pinpoint test A, speed control inoperative (Part 9 of 13). Scorpio**

| TEST STEP | | RESULT ▶ | ACTION TO TAKE |
|---|---|---|---|
| A20 | CHECK FUSE 22 FEED | | |
| | • Using a voltmeter, check for battery voltage at feed side of fuse 22 with ignition in RUN (position II). | OK ▶ | SERVICE open in circuit between fuse 22 and speed control module connector. |
| | | ~~OK~~ ▶ | GO to **A22**. |
| A21 | CHECK FOR CIRCUIT SHORT | | |
| | • Using an ohmmeter, check for continuity between output side of fuse 22 and vehicle ground.<br>• There should not be continuity. | OK ▶ | REPLACE fuse 22. CHECK system operation. |
| | | ~~OK~~ ▶ | SERVICE short to ground between fuse 22 and speed control module connector. |
| A22 | VERIFY FEED VOLTAGE | | |
| | • Verify power to ignition coil and EEC control module by starting engine. | OK ▶ | SERVICE open in circuit between ignition switch and fuse 22. |
| | | ~~OK~~ ▶ | SERVICE open in ignition circuit and/or open in ignition switch. |
| A23 | CHECK SPEEDOMETER OPERATION | | |
| | • Test drive vehicle. Note speedometer operation. | OK ▶ | SERVICE open in circuit between speed sensor and terminal 12 of control module connector. |
| | | ~~OK~~ ▶ | GO to **A24**. |
| A24 | CHECK CONTINUITY OF FUSE 20 | | |
| | • Check fuse 20 for continuity. | OK ▶ | SERVICE open in speed sensor circuit and/or replace speed sensor.<br>CHECK system operation. |
| | | ~~OK~~ ▶ | GO to **A25**. |

**Fig. 54 Pinpoint test A, speed control inoperative (Part 10 of 13). Scorpio**

| TEST STEP | | RESULT ▶ | ACTION TO TAKE |
|---|---|---|---|
| A25 | CHECK FOR CIRCUIT SHORT TO GROUND | | |
| | • Using an ohmmeter, test for continuity between output side of fuse 20 and vehicle ground.<br>• There should be no continuity. | OK ▶ | REPLACE fuse. CHECK system operation. |
| | | ~~OK~~ ▶ | SERVICE short to ground in speed sensor circuit. |
| A26 | VERIFY TACHOMETER OPERATION | | |
| | • Test drive vehicle. Note tachometer operation. | OK ▶ | SERVICE open in circuit between tachometer feed and terminal 8 of speed control module connector. |
| | | ~~OK~~ ▶ | SERVICE open in tachometer circuit. |
| A27 | ISOLATE STEERING WHEEL MOUNTED CONTROLS | | |
| | • Remove upper and lower steering column shrouds.<br>• Disconnect slip ring brush connector.<br>• Using an ohmmeter, test for continuity between connector terminals while holding appropriate button depressed.<br>• Continuity should exist only between the terminals stated for each position. Resistance should read zero unless otherwise noted. | OK ▶ | GO to **A28**. |
| | | ~~OK~~ ▶ | GO to **A31**. |

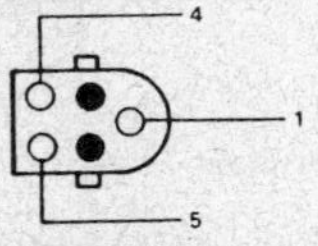

BRUSH CONNECTOR

| Hold the following switch depressed | Continuity between terminals |
|---|---|
| ON | 1 and 5* |
| OFF | 1 and 4 |
| Coast/Res. | 1 and 4 resistance should read 1000 Ω |
| Set/Acc | 1 and 4 resistance should read 330 Ω |

*** Diode in circuit. Use suitable meter and observe polarity. Positive lead of meter connected to terminal 5, negative lead connected to terminal 1.**

**Fig. 54 Pinpoint test A, speed control inoperative (Part 11 of 13). Scorpio**

| TEST STEP | | RESULT ▶ | ACTION TO TAKE |
|---|---|---|---|
| A28 | CHECK FOR BATTERY VOLTAGE AT HORN SWITCH | | |
| | • Using a voltmeter, check for battery voltage at terminal 5 of harness side of brush connector.<br>4, 1, 5 B+ V<br>SLIP RING BRUSH CONNECTOR | OK ▶<br>Not OK ▶ | SERVICE open in circuit between terminal 2 of brush connector and terminal 1 of control module connector. CHECK system operation.<br>GO to **A29**. |
| A29 | CHECK CONTINUITY OF FUSE 14 | | |
| | • Check fuse 14 for continuity. | OK ▶<br>Not OK ▶ | SERVICE open in horn relay and/or horn feed circuit between fuse 14 and terminal 1 of brush connector.<br>GO to **A30**. |
| A30 | CHECK CIRCUIT FOR SHORT TO GROUND | | |
| | • Using an ohmmeter, check for continuity to ground at output side of fuse 14.<br>• There should be no continuity. | OK ▶<br>Not OK ▶ | REPLACE fuse. CHECK system operation.<br>SERVICE short to ground in horn feed circuit. |
| A31 | CHECK CIRCUIT BOARD DIODE | | |
| | • Remove horn switch to access printed circuit board.<br>• Using an ohmmeter, check for continuity between printed circuit board terminals T1 and T2.<br>• There should be continuity only when connected with positive meter lead on terminal T1 and negative lead on T2. | OK ▶<br>Not OK ▶ | GO to **A32**.<br>REPLACE printed circuit board. CHECK system operation. |

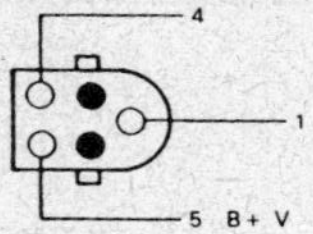

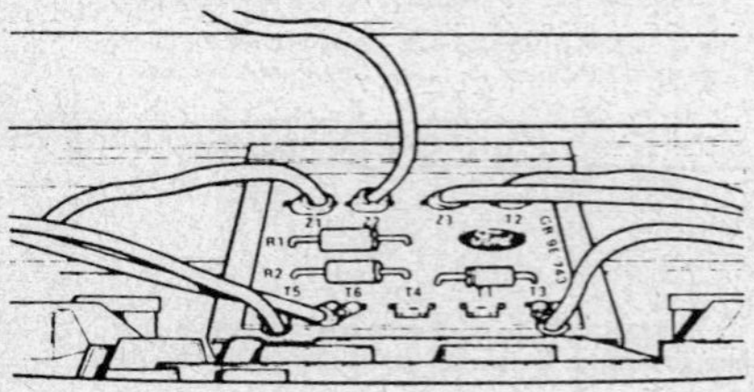

**Fig. 54 Pinpoint test A, speed control inoperative (Part 12 of 13). Scorpio**

| TEST STEP | | RESULT ▶ | ACTION TO TAKE |
|---|---|---|---|
| A32 | | | |
| | • Hold ON switch depressed.<br>• Using an ohmmeter, check for continuity between circuit board terminals T2 and Z3.<br>• There should be continuity with switch depressed only. | OK ▶<br>Not OK ▶ | SERVICE open in circuit between circuit board and pigtail connector.<br>REPLACE ON/OFF control switch. |

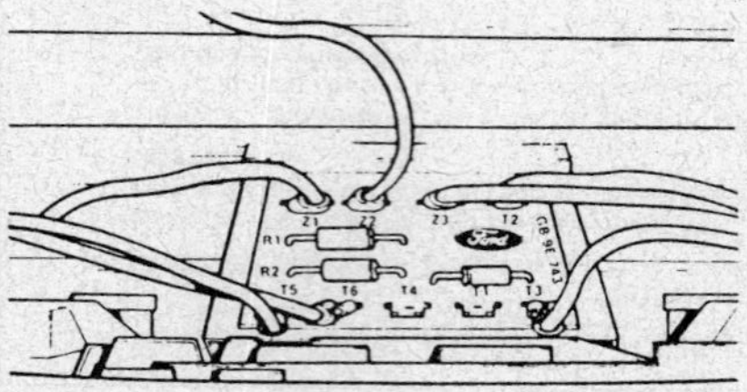

**Fig. 54 Pinpoint test A, speed control inoperative (Part 13 of 13). Scorpio**

| TEST STEP | RESULT ▶ | ACTION TO TAKE |
|---|---|---|
| **B1** CHECK PEDAL OPERATED SWITCHES | | |
| • Check brake and clutch pedal operated switches for proper adjustment. | OK ▶ | GO to **B2**. |
| | NOT OK ▶ | ADJUST and/or REPLACE switch(es). CHECK system operation. |
| **B2** CHECK BRAKELAMP OPERATION | | |
| • Depress brake pedal. Note brakelamp operation. | OK ▶ | GO to **B3**. |
| | NOT OK ▶ | SERVICE fault in brakelamp circuit and/or burned out bulbs. |
| **B3** CHECK PEDAL SWITCH(ES) FOR VACUUM DUMP | | |
| • Using hand pressure, fully compress servo and hold.<br>• Seal white port on vacuum pump and release servo.<br>• While keeping white port sealed, gently depress the brake pedal.<br>• Servo should immediately return to relaxed position.<br>• Repeat test for clutch pedal mounted switch (if applicable). | OK ▶ | GO to **B4**. |
| | NOT OK ▶ | SERVICE blocked vacuum hose and/or REPLACE blocked vacuum switch. (Switch may be tested by removing and blowing through hose port). |
| **B4** CHECK PEDAL MOUNTED SWITCH(ES) CONTINUITY | | |
| • Disconnect wiring connector from pedal mounted switch(es).<br>• Using an ohmmeter, check for continuity between switch terminals with pedal in rest position.<br>• There should be continuity.<br>• Check switch continuity with pedal depressed.<br>• There should be no continuity. | OK ▶ | GO to **B5**. |
| | NOT OK ▶ | REPLACE switch(es). CHECK system operation. |

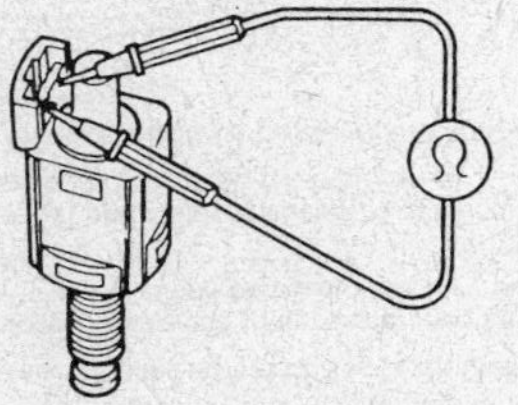

**Fig. 55 Pinpoint test B, speed control disengages slowly when clutch or brake is applied (Part 1 of 2). Scorpio**

| TEST STEP | RESULT ▶ | ACTION TO TAKE |
|---|---|---|
| **B5** CHECK PEDAL OPERATED SWITCH CIRCUIT | | |
| • Ignition switch in OFF (position 0).<br>• Disconnect harness connector from speed control module.<br>• Using an ohmmeter, measure resistance between terminals 2 and 9 of harness connector.<br>• Resistance should be less than 5 ohms.<br>LESS THAN 5 OHMS<br>SPEED CONTROL MODULE | OK ▶ | REPLACE speed control module. |
| | NOT OK ▶ | GO to **B6**. |
| **B6** VERIFY BRAKELAMP OPERATION | | |
| • Check to make sure all brakelamps are operating. | OK ▶ | SERVICE open in circuit between terminal 2 of control module connector and brakelamp. |
| | NOT OK ▶ | SERVICE brakelamp bulbs or circuit as necessary. |

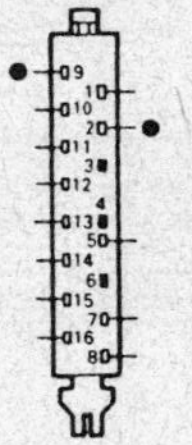

**Fig. 55 Pinpoint test B, speed control disengages slowly when clutch or brake is applied (Part 2 of 2). Scorpio**

| TEST STEP | RESULT ▶ | ACTION TO TAKE |
|---|---|---|
| **C1** CHECK CIRCUIT BOARD MOUNTED RESISTOR | | |
| • Remove upper and lower steering column shrouds.<br>• Disconnect slip ring brush pigtail connector.<br>• Remove steering wheel center cover (pulls off).<br>• Remove horn switch to access printed circuit board. Carefully pull circuit board out of cavity in steering wheel.<br>• Using an ohmmeter, measure resistance between circuit board terminals T4 and T6.<br>• Resistance should be between 940 and 1060 ohms. 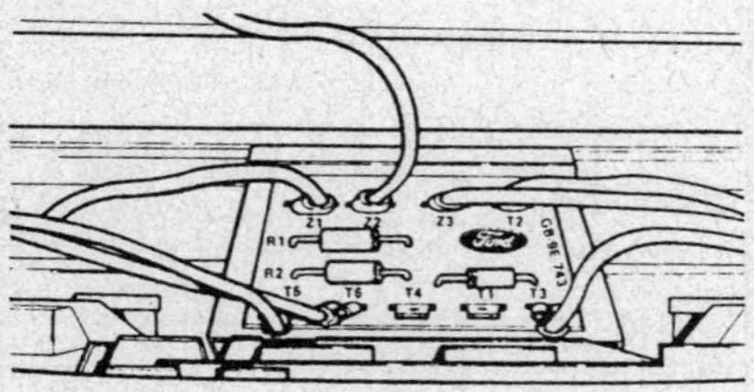 | OK ▶<br><br>NOT OK ▶ | GO to **C2**.<br><br>REPLACE printed circuit board. CHECK system operation. |
| **C2** CHECK COAST/RESUME SWITCH OPERATION | | |
| • Using an ohmmeter, check for continuity between circuit board terminals T6 and Z1 while holding coast button depressed.<br>• There should be no resistance. 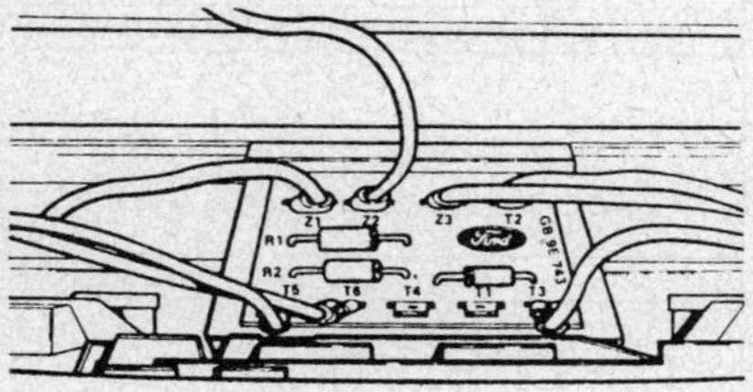 | OK ▶<br><br>NOT OK ▶ | REPLACE speed control module. CHECK system operation.<br><br>REPLACE SET/ACC — COAST/RESUME switch. CHECK system operation. |

**Fig. 56 Pinpoint test C, when operating the control switch speed control will not coast or resume. Scorpio**

| TEST STEP | RESULT ▶ | ACTION TO TAKE |
|---|---|---|
| **D1** CHECK CIRCUIT BOARD CONTINUITY | | |
| • Remove upper and lower steering column shrouds.<br>• Disconnect slip ring brush pigtail connector.<br>• Remove steering wheel center cover (pulls off).<br>• Remove horn switch assembly to expose printed circuit board. Carefully pull circuit board from cavity.<br>• Using an ohmmeter check for continuity between circuit board terminals T3 and T4. 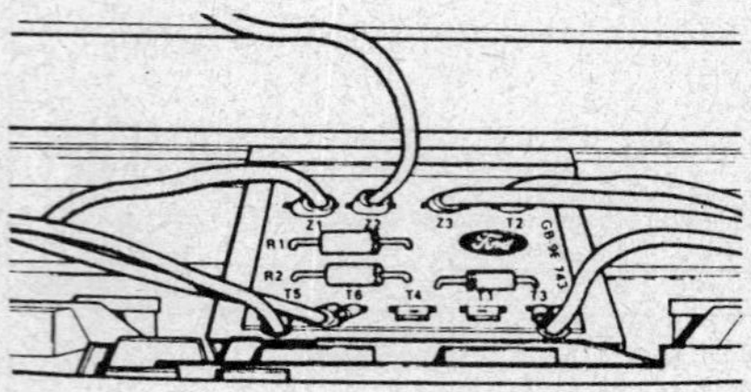 | OK ▶<br><br>NOT OK ▶ | GO to **D2**.<br><br>REPLACE printed circuit board. CHECK system operation. |
| **D2** CHECK OFF SWITCH CONTINUITY | | |
| • Using an ohmmeter, check for continuity between circuit board terminals T3 and Z3.<br>• There should be continuity when the OFF switch is depressed. 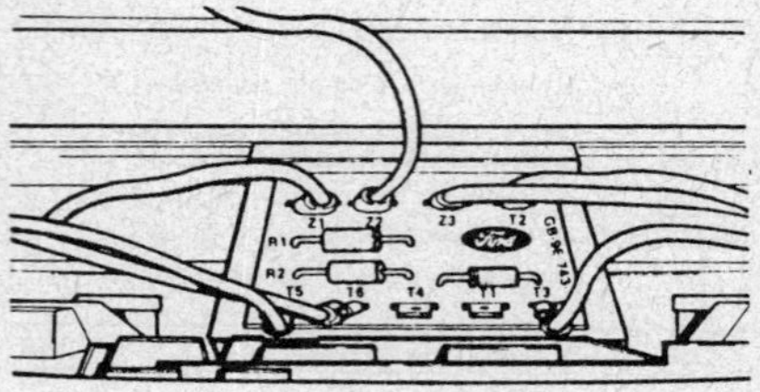 | OK ▶<br><br>NOT OK ▶ | REPLACE speed control module. CHECK system operation.<br><br>REPLACE ON/OFF switch. CHECK system operation. |

**Fig. 57 Pinpoint test D, when operating the control switch speed control will not shut off. Scorpio**

| TEST STEP | | RESULT ▶ | ACTION TO TAKE |
|---|---|---|---|
| E1 | CHECK SET/ACCEL — COAST/RESUME SWITCH | | |
| | • Remove steering wheel center cover (pulls off).<br>• Remove upper and lower steering column shrouds.<br>• Disconnect slip ring brush pigtail connector.<br>• Remove horn switch and carefully pull printed circuit board from cavity.<br>• Using an ohmmeter, check for continuity between circuit board terminals T4 and Z2.<br>• There should be no continuity.<br>• With SET/ACC switch depressed, resistance should be 330 ohms. | OK ▶ | REPLACE speed control module. CHECK system operation. |
| | | NOT OK ▶ | REPLACE SET/ACC — COAST/RESUME switch. CHECK system operation. |

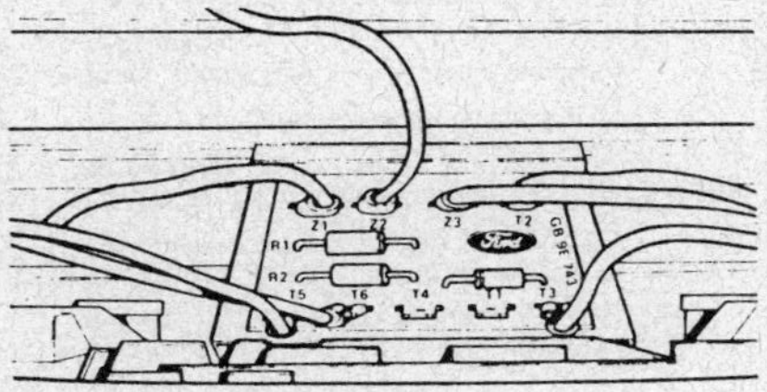

**Fig. 58 Pinpoint test E, vehicle accelerates after speed is set. Scorpio**

| TEST STEP | | RESULT ▶ | ACTION TO TAKE |
|---|---|---|---|
| F1 | CHECK ACTUATOR CABLE FREE PLAY | | |
| | • Actuator cable free play should be between 0 and 1mm. | OK ▶ | GO to **F2**. |
| | | NOT OK ▶ | ADJUST actuator cable to obtain correct free play at idle. CHECK system operation. |
| F2 | CHECK SERVO AND THROTTLE OPERATION | | |
| | • Compress vacuum servo using hand pressure.<br>• Throttle should move to wide open or near wide open position.<br>• Release hand pressure. Servo should slowly return to rest position (3 seconds maximum, 1 second minimum).<br>• Throttle should open and close smoothly without binding or sticking. | OK ▶ | GO to **F4**. |
| | | NOT OK ▶ | GO to **F3**. |
| F3 | CHECK SERVO WITH ACTUATOR CABLE DISCONNECTED | | |
| | • Disconnect actuator cable from throttle body.<br>• Compress vacuum servo using hand pressure.<br>• Servo should compress without sticking or binding.<br>• Release pressure on servo.<br>• Servo should return to relaxed position in a smooth stroke. | OK ▶ | SERVICE and/or lubricate throttle linkage. |
| | | NOT OK ▶ | CHECK for trapped/restricted vacuum hose or REPLACE servo actuator cable. CHECK system operation. |
| F4 | CHECK FOR VACUUM LEAK | | |
| | • Compress vacuum servo using hand pressure.<br>• Seal white port on vacuum pump.<br>• Release hand pressure from servo.<br>• Servo should remain compressed. | OK ▶ | GO to **F5**. |
| | | NOT OK ▶ | SERVICE vacuum leak in system. CHECK system operation. |
| F5 | CHECK SERVO RETURN | | |
| | • Repeat Test Step F4.<br>• Unblock white port on vacuum pump.<br>• Servo should slowly return to rest position, (3 seconds maximum, 1 second minimum). Throttle should close smoothly, without binding or sticking within 3 seconds maximum (WOT to idle). | OK ▶ | GO to **F7**. |
| | | NOT OK ▶ | GO to **F6**. |
| F6 | CHECK SERVO RETURN — SERVO DISCONNECTED | | |
| | • Disconnect vacuum hose and actuator cable from vacuum servo.<br>• Compress and release servo.<br>• Servo should return to rest position. | OK ▶ | CONNECT vacuum hose and actuator cable to servo. GO to **F7**. |
| | | NOT OK ▶ | REPLACE vacuum servo. CHECK system operation. |

**Fig. 59 Pinpoint test F, vehicle speed constantly fluctuates (Part 1 of 2). Scorpio**

| TEST STEP | RESULT | ACTION TO TAKE |
|---|---|---|
| **F7** CHECK PUMP AND DUMP SOLENOID — CONTROL MODULE BYPASSED | | |
| • Disconnect speed control module connector.<br>• Turn ignition switch to RUN (position II).<br>• Using insulated jumper leads, jump terminal 10 to terminal 11 on module connector.<br>• Connect second jump lead between terminals 9 and 14.<br>• Pump solenoid should click.<br>• Use third jump lead to connect terminal 9 to terminal 15.<br>• Pump motor should run and vacuum servo should compress within 7 seconds.<br>**CAUTION: Do not allow pump to run more than 10 seconds.**<br>• Remove jumper between terminals 9 and 15.<br>• Pump should stop, servo should remain compressed.<br>• Remove jumper between terminals 9 and 14.<br>• Solenoid should click, servo should relax within 3 seconds maximum (WOT to idle).<br>SPEED CONTROL MODULE | OK ▶<br>NOT OK ▶ | REPLACE speed control module.<br>REPLACE vacuum pump assembly. |

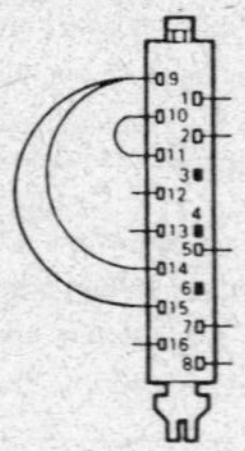

**Fig. 59 Pinpoint test F, vehicle speed constantly fluctuates (Part 2 of 2). Scorpio**

| TEST STEP | RESULT | ACTION TO TAKE |
|---|---|---|
| **G1** CHECK SWITCH CONNECTIONS | | |
| • Remove lower LH instrument trim panel to access brake and clutch (manual transmission only) mounted switch(es).<br>• Check connections on switch(es) to make sure they are not reversed. If equipped with automatic transmission the clutch switch requires jumper to complete circuit. | OK ▶<br>NOT OK ▶ | GO to **G2**.<br>INSTALL connections correctly. CHECK system operation. |
| **G2** CHECK POWER TO BRAKE PEDAL MOUNTED SWITCH | | |
| • Remove instrument panel pad.<br>• Depress brake pedal. Note brakelamp operation. | OK ▶<br>NOT OK ▶ | GO to **G3**.<br>REPLACE brakelamp switch. CHECK system operation. |
| **G3** CHECK BRAKE PEDAL OPERATED SWITCH CONTINUITY | | |
| • Disconnect wiring from brake pedal mounted switch.<br>• Using an ohmmeter check continuity of switch with brake pedal depressed and at rest.<br>• There should be continuity only with pedal depressed. | OK ▶<br>NOT OK ▶ | REPLACE speed control module. CHECK system operation.<br>REPLACE switch. CHECK system operation. |

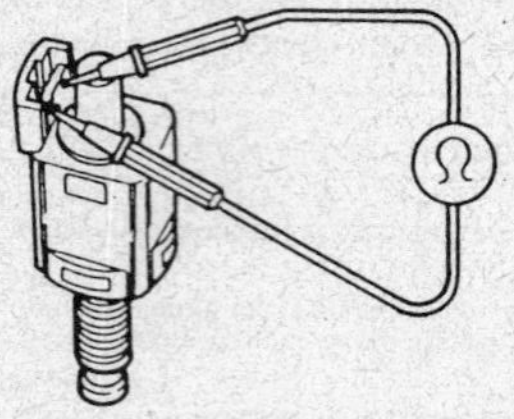

**Fig. 60 Pinpoint test G, system automatically returns to set speed as brake pedal is released. Scorpio**

| | TEST STEP | RESULT ▶ | ACTION TO TAKE |
|---|---|---|---|
| H1 | CHECK FOR BYPASS JUMP LEAD MISTAKENLY CONNECTED | | |
| | • Remove lower LH instrument trim panel.<br>• Check for second jump lead wire between brake and clutch mounted switches to be connected.<br>• Second jumper should not be connected.<br>JUMP LEAD CONNECTOR | OK ▶ | GO to **H2**. |
| | | ~~OK~~ ▶ | DISCONNECT bypass lead and tape to harness so it cannot short to ground. |
| H2 | CHECK CONTINUITY OF CLUTCH PEDAL MOUNTED SWITCH | | |
| | • Disconnect wiring connectors from clutch pedal switch.<br>• Using an ohmmeter, check switch for continuity with clutch pedal at rest and then depressed.<br>• There should be continuity only with pedal at rest. | OK ▶ | REPLACE speed control module. CHECK system operation. |
| | | ~~OK~~ ▶ | REPLACE clutch pedal switch. CHECK system operation. |

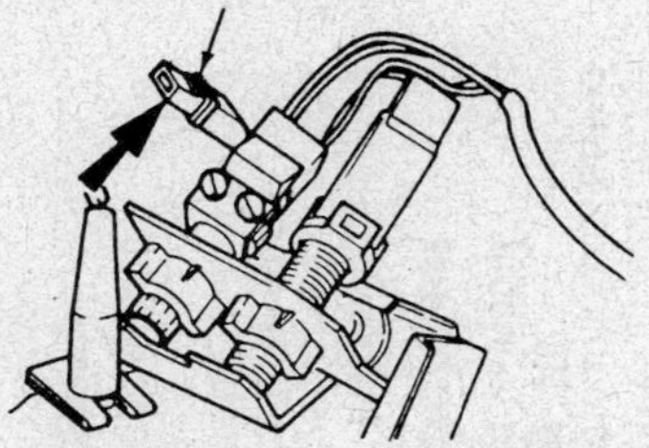

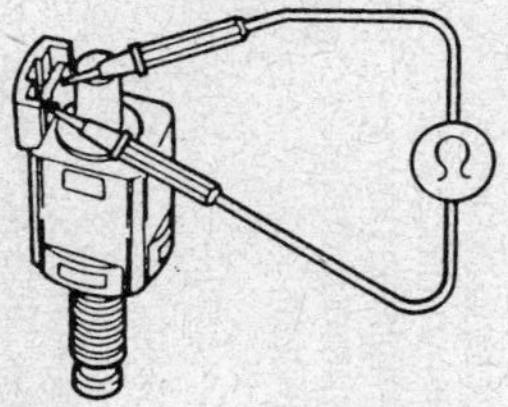

**Fig. 61 Pinpoint test H, system automatically returns to set speed as clutch pedal is released. Scorpio**

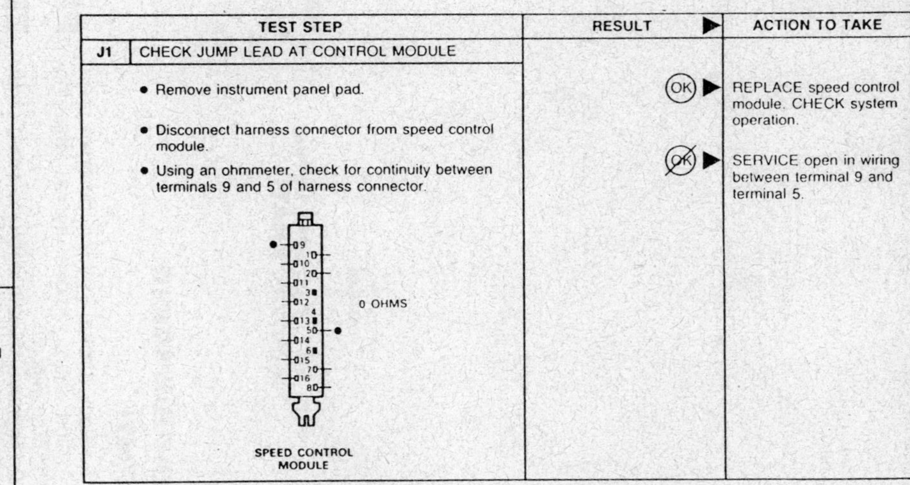

| | TEST STEP | RESULT ▶ | ACTION TO TAKE |
|---|---|---|---|
| J1 | CHECK JUMP LEAD AT CONTROL MODULE | | |
| | • Remove instrument panel pad.<br>• Disconnect harness connector from speed control module.<br>• Using an ohmmeter, check for continuity between terminals 9 and 5 of harness connector.<br>0 OHMS<br>SPEED CONTROL MODULE | OK ▶ | REPLACE speed control module. CHECK system operation. |
| | | ~~OK~~ ▶ | SERVICE open in wiring between terminal 9 and terminal 5. |

**Fig. 62 Pinpoint test J, at high engine speeds system will not set or accelerate. Scorpio**

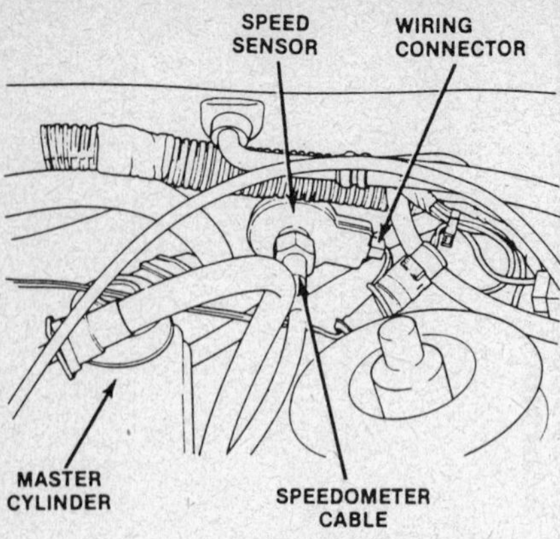


Fig. 63 Speed sensor removal. XR4Ti

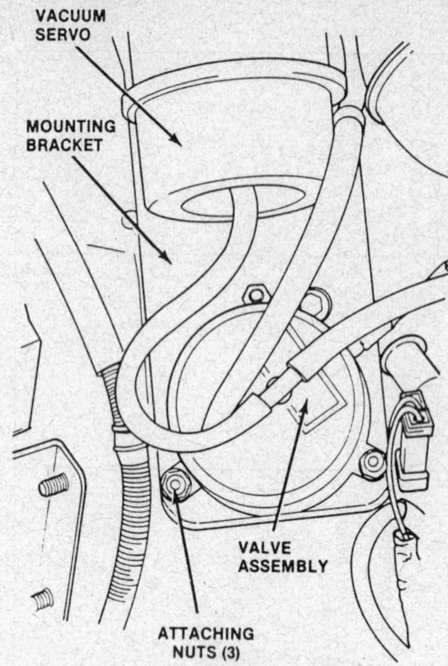


Fig. 64 Vacuum valve removal. XR4Ti

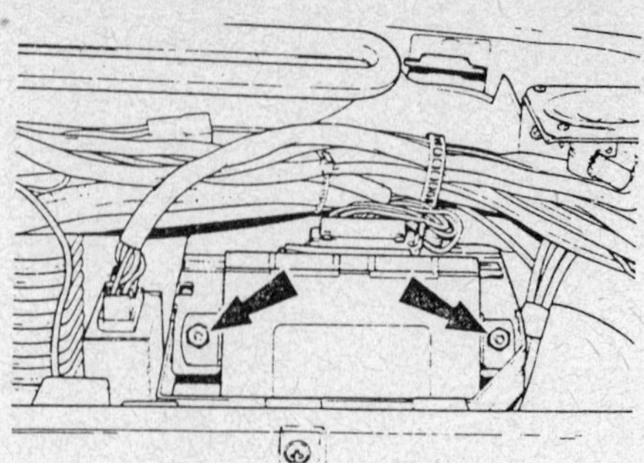

Fig. 65 Speed control module removal. Scorpio

## SPEED CONTROL MODULE

### Scorpio

1. Remove instrument cluster trim panel and instrument panel pad.
2. Remove two auxiliary warning system module-to-speed control module retaining nuts, **Fig. 65.**
3. Disconnect speed control 16 pin electrical connector, then remove module from vehicle.
4. Reverse procedure to install.

## CLUTCH/BRAKE OVERRIDE SWITCHES

### XR4Ti

1. Remove the sound deadening panel located under the instrument panel.
2. Disconnect vacuum hose from vacuum switch, **Fig. 66.**
3. Remove attaching nut and tension spring from pedal side of switch.
4. Remove remaining attaching nut from switch.
5. Reverse procedure to install.

## AMPLIFIER

### XR4Ti

1. Remove sound deadening panel located under left side of instrument panel.
2. Remove three cowl side trim panel attaching screws then pull trim panel away from body.
3. Disconnect courtesy light electrical connector then remove panel.
4. Remove amplifier attaching screws then disconnect amplifier electrical connector and lower amplifier downward and out from instrument panel.
5. Reverse procedure to install.

## SERVO CABLE

### XR4Ti

1. Remove cable attaching screws.
2. Remove routing clip attaching screw on lefthand strut tower.
3. Disconnect servo cable from throttle cable, **Fig. 67,** then remove servo attaching nuts.
4. Remove cable-to-servo shaft attaching clip, then the cable.
5. Reverse procedure to install.

## VACUUM SERVO

### XR4Ti

1. Block throttle in the wide open position then remove servo attaching nuts, **Fig. 68.**
2. Remove throttle cable-to-servo shaft retaining clip, then the servo.
3. Reverse procedure to install.

### Scorpio

1. Disconnect throttle actuator cable from servo then disconnect vacuum hose from rear of servo.
2. Remove servo unit retaining nut, then remove unit from from holding bracket.
3. Reverse procedure to install.

## VACUUM DUMP VALVE/SWITCH

### Brake Pedal Mounted

1. Remove vacuum hose and disconnect electrical connector from switch.
2. Turn switch counterclockwise to release switch from mounting collar and remove switch, **Fig. 69.**
3. Reverse procedure to install.

### Clutch Pedal Mounted

1. Hold switch and bracket assembly then disconnect vacuum hose and electrical connector from switch.
2. Push switch assembly out of spring collar.
3. Reverse procedure to install.

## SPEED SENDER UNIT

### Scorpio

1. Place drain pan under transmission at sender unit, then disconnect sender unit electrical connector.
2. Remove sender unit retaining bolt, then the sending unit, **Fig. 70.**
3. Reverse procedure to install.
4. Check transmission fluid level and add as necessary.

## VACUUM PUMP

### Scorpio

1. Disconnect vacuum pump electrical connector and vacuum hose at pump assembly.
2. Carefully pull pump assembly from rubber mountings.
3. Reverse procedure to install.

# PROBE

## DESCRIPTION & OPERATION

The speed control system consists of operator controls, an actuator (throttle actuator) assembly, speed control amplifier, clutch switch (MTX), neutral safety switch (4EAT) and brake switch.

Due to the low vacuum generated by the turbocharged engine, an electrical motor-driven actuator is used in place of a vacuum actuator.

## ADJUSTMENTS

### ACTUATOR CABLE

#### 2.2L/4-133 Engine

1. **On models equipped with electric actuator,** remove plastic cover.
2. **On all models,** loosen locknut and adjusting nuts, **Fig. 71.**
3. Carefully pull on cable housing trying not to move actuator rod.
4. Position adjusting nut A until there is 0.039-0.118 inch clearance between nut A and bracket.
5. Tighten locknut B, then replace actuator plastic cover if removed.

#### 3.0L/V6-182 Engine

1. Remove speed control actuator cable retaining clip.
2. Push actuator cable through adjuster until slight tension is felt.
3. Insert cable retaining clip, then snap into place.

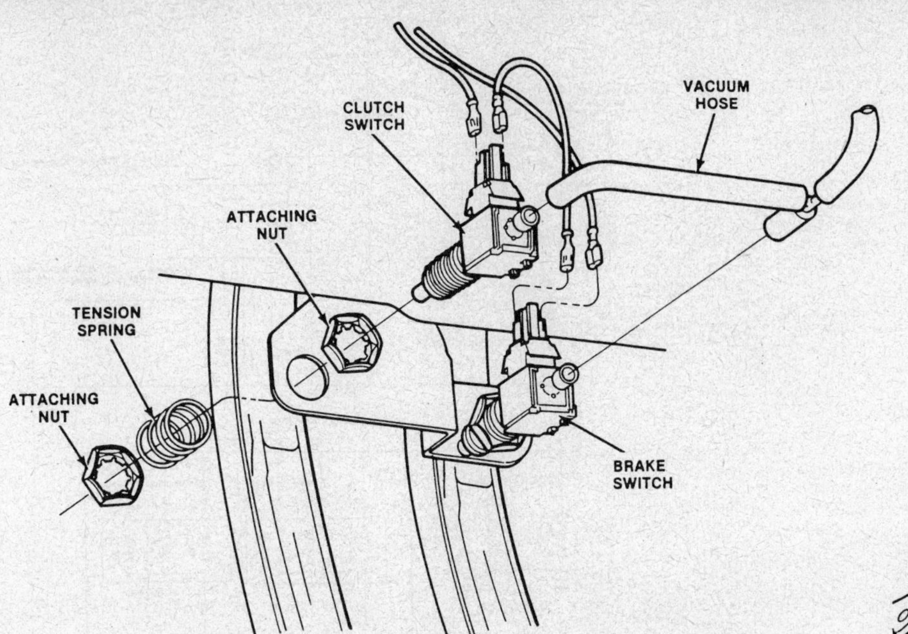


**Fig. 66 Clutch/brake switch removal. XR4Ti**

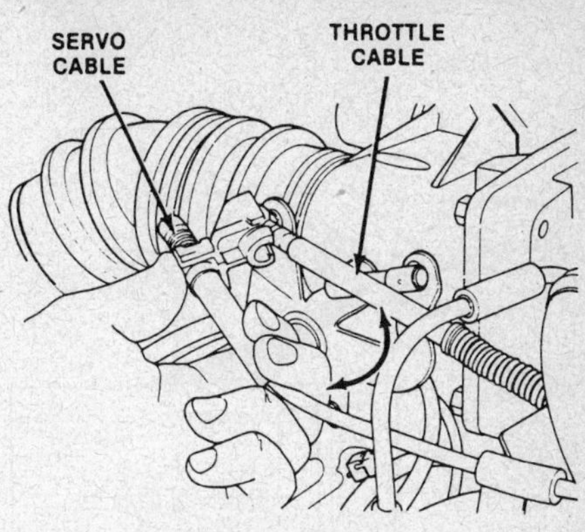


**Fig. 67 Servo cable removal. XR4Ti**

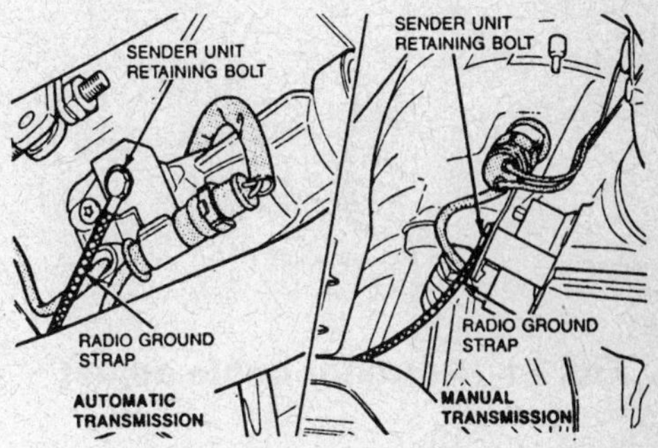


**Fig. 70 Speed sender removal. Scorpio**

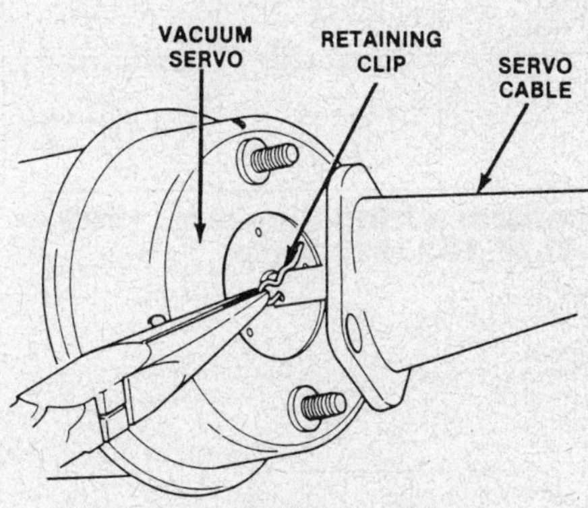


**Fig. 68 Vacuum servo removal. XR4Ti**

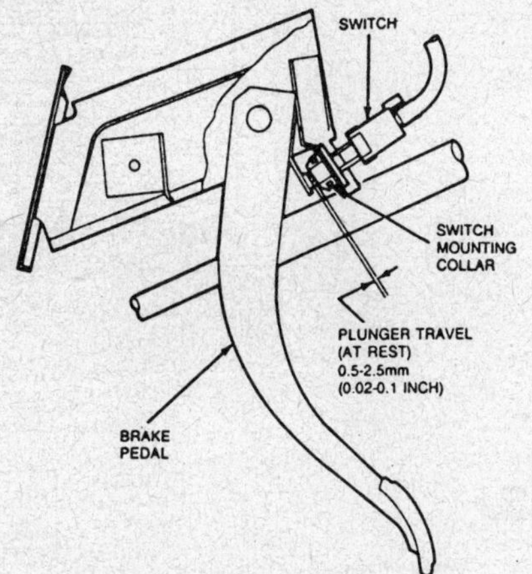


**Fig. 69 Vacuum dump valve/switch removal. Scorpio**

## DIAGNOSIS & TESTING

The wiring diagrams in **Figs. 72 through 76** may be used as a diagnostic aid when performing the testing procedures in **Figs. 77 through 79.**

### 1989

Refer to **Fig. 77**, for system diagnosis and testing.

### 1990–91 W/2.2L/4-133 Engine

Refer to **Figs. 78**, for system diagnosis and testing.

### 1990–91 W/3.0L/V6-182 Engine

Refer to **Fig. 79**, for system diagnosis and testing.

## COMPONENT REPLACEMENT

### VACUUM ACTUATOR

1. Disconnect battery negative cable.
2. Disconnect actuator electrical connector.
3. Remove actuator cable routing clip, then two actuator vacuum lines, **Fig. 80.**
4. Loosen adjusting nut and locknut then pull dust boot back to gain access to actuator rod.
5. Remove actuator cable from actuator rod and bracket.
6. Remove three actuator mounting nuts, then the actuator.
7. Reverse procedure to install.

### ELECTRIC ACTUATOR

1. Disconnect battery ground cable, then remove wiring routing clip from actuator cable.
2. Disconnect actuator electrical connector, then remove actuator bracket, **Fig. 81.**
3. Remove actuator cover, then loosen adjusting nut and locknut.
4. Remove actuator cable, two actuator mounting nuts, then the actuator.
5. Reverse procedure to install.

### ACTUATOR CABLE

1. **On models equipped with electric actuator,** remove plastic cover.
2. **On models equipped with vacuum actuator,** remove dust boot from actuator.
3. **On all models,** loosen adjusting nut and locknut, **Fig. 82.**
4. Remove actuator cable from cable bracket.
5. Remove actuator cable from cable routing clips, then squeeze lock tabs and remove cable end from pedal assembly.
6. Squeeze lock tabs securing cable housing to bulkhead, **Fig. 82,** then remove cable through engine compartment.
7. Reverse procedure to install.

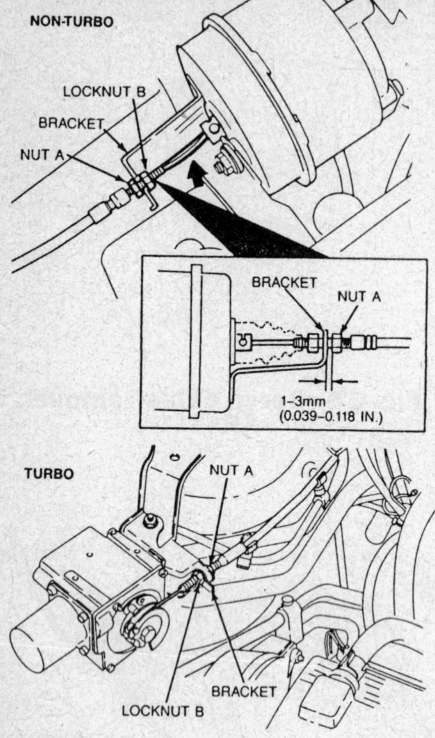


**Fig. 71 Actuator cable adjust**

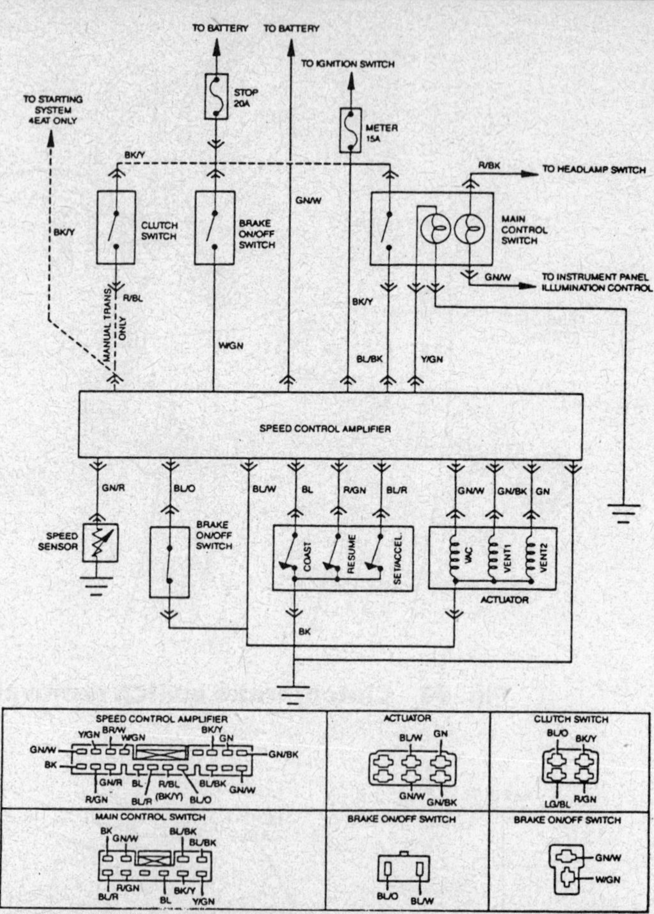


**Fig. 72 Speed control wiring diagram. 1989—90 2.2L/4-133 less turbo**

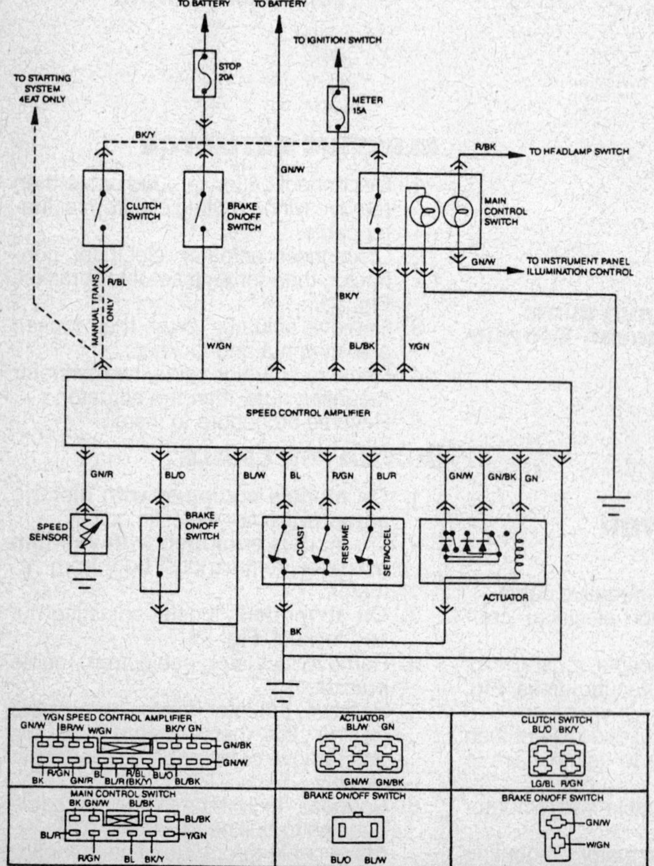


**Fig. 73 Speed control wiring diagram. 1989—90 2.2L/4-133 w/turbo**

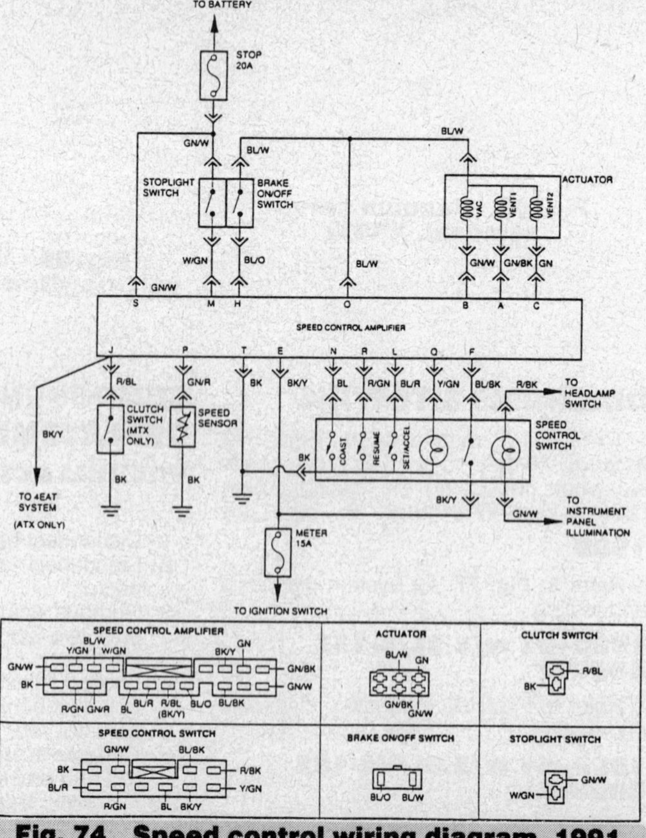


**Fig. 74 Speed control wiring diagram. 1991 2.2L/4-133 less turbo**

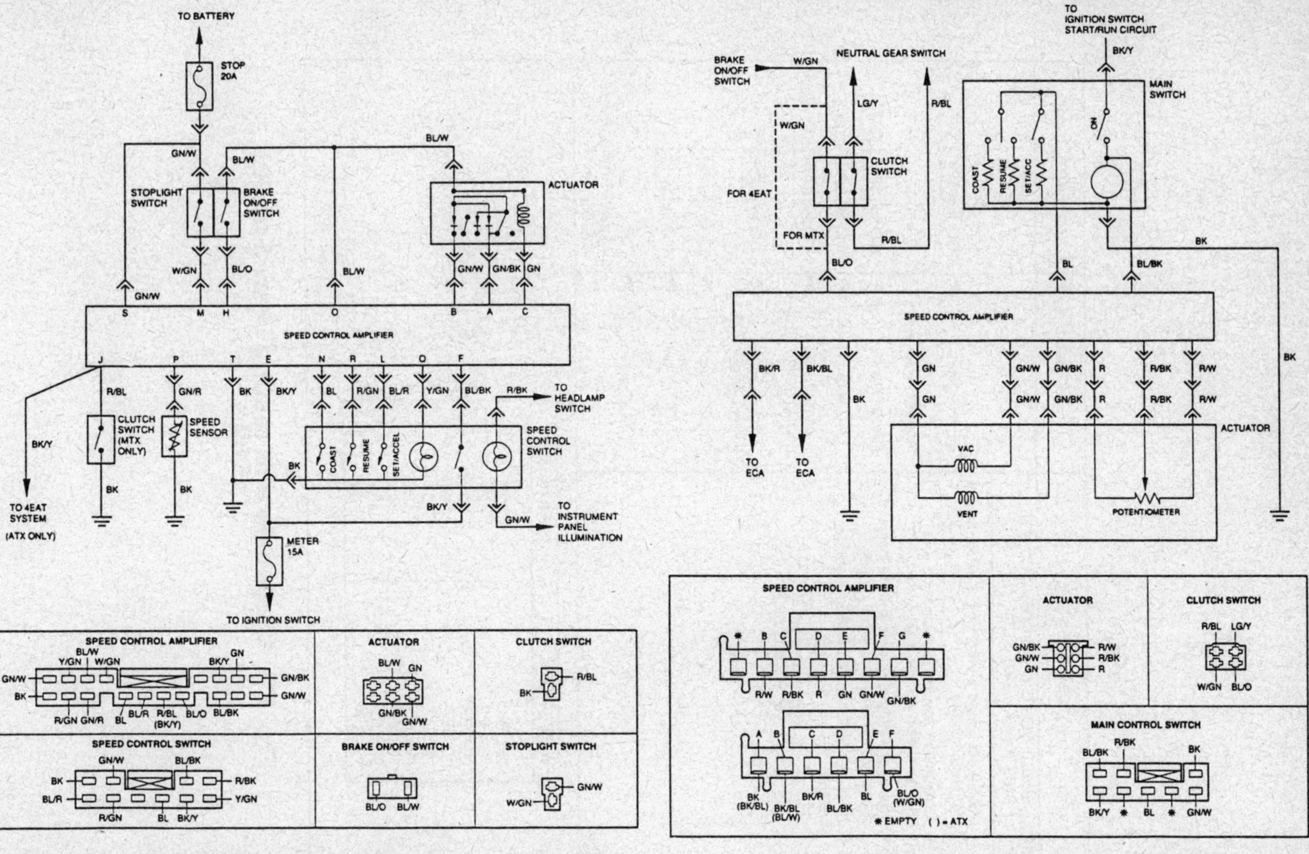

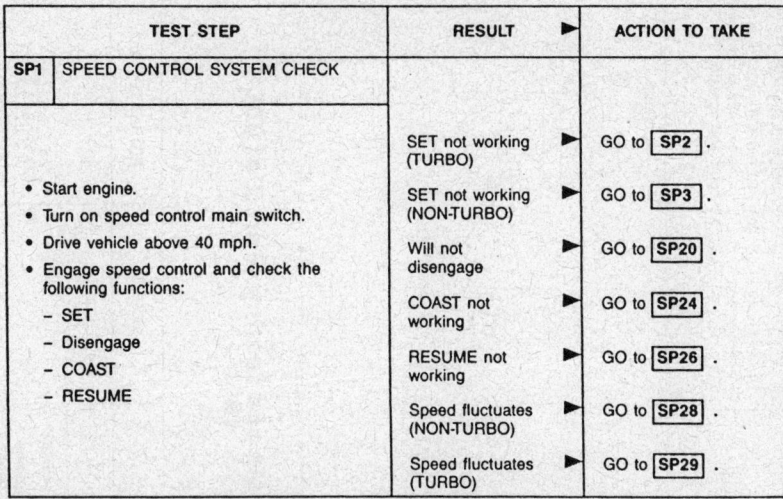

**Fig. 75 Speed control wiring diagram. 1991 2.2L/4-133 w/turbo**

**Fig. 76 Speed control wiring diagram. 3.0L/V6-182**

| TEST STEP | | RESULT ► | ACTION TO TAKE |
|---|---|---|---|
| SP1 | SPEED CONTROL SYSTEM CHECK | | |
| | • Start engine.<br>• Turn on speed control main switch.<br>• Drive vehicle above 40 mph.<br>• Engage speed control and check the following functions:<br>– SET<br>– Disengage<br>– COAST<br>– RESUME | SET not working (TURBO) ► | GO to SP2 . |
| | | SET not working (NON-TURBO) ► | GO to SP3 . |
| | | Will not disengage ► | GO to SP20 . |
| | | COAST not working ► | GO to SP24 . |
| | | RESUME not working ► | GO to SP26 . |
| | | Speed fluctuates (NON-TURBO) ► | GO to SP28 . |
| | | Speed fluctuates (TURBO) ► | GO to SP29 . |

**Fig. 77 Diagnosis and testing (Part 1 of 30). 1989**

## CLUTCH/BRAKE SWITCH

1. Disconnect battery ground cable.
2. Disconnect brake switch electrical connector.
3. Remove switch locknut, then the switch.
4. Install adjuster nut onto switch, then switch into bracket.
5. Install locknut onto switch.
6. Adjust switch so that pedal height is 8.42 inches (214 mm).
7. Tighten locknut.

## CONTROL UNIT

1. Remove instrument panel lower panel, lap duct and defrost duct.
2. Remove control unit 13 pin electrical connector, **Fig. 83.**
3. Remove control unit retaining bolt, then the control unit.
4. Reverse procedure to install.

## MAIN CONTROL SWITCH

1. Remove cluster module, if necessary, **Fig. 84.**
2. Remove two hazard switch-to-cluster module retaining screws, then the hazard switch.
3. Remove screws securing speed control switch to cluster.
4. Reverse procedure to install.

| TEST STEP | RESULT ► | ACTION TO TAKE |
|---|---|---|
| **SP2** ACTUATOR SIGNALS CHECK (TURBO ONLY) (WILL NOT SET) | | |
| • Park vehicle and shut engine off.<br>• Disconnect speed control unit (connector C268).<br>• Jump "GN/BK" and "GN/W" wires to ground at connector C268.<br>• Check for continuity between ground and "GN/BK" and "GN/W" wires at actuator (connector C186).<br>• Is there continuity? | Yes ►<br>No continuity in "GN/BK" wire ►<br>No continuity in "GN/W" wire ► | GO to SP3.<br>REPAIR "GN/BK" wire between speed control unit and actuator.<br>REPAIR "GN/W" wire between speed control unit and actuator. |



Fig. 77 Diagnosis and testing (Part 2 of 30). 1989

| TEST STEP | RESULT ► | ACTION TO TAKE |
|---|---|---|
| **SP4** SET SWITCH CHECK (WILL NOT SET) | | |
| • Press and hold speed control "SET" switch.<br>• Check for continuity between ground and "BL/R" wire at speed control unit (connector C268).<br>See illustration in TEST STEP SP2<br>• Is there continuity? | Yes ►<br><br>No ► | GO to SP7. For NON-TURBO.<br>GO to SP8. For TURBO.<br>GO to SP5. |

Fig. 77 Diagnosis and testing (Part 4 of 30). 1989

| TEST STEP | RESULT ► | ACTION TO TAKE |
|---|---|---|
| **SP3** SPEED CONTROL SYSTEM VOLTAGE CHECK (WILL NOT SET) | | |
| • Reconnect speed control unit if disconnected (connector C268).<br>• Turn ignition key to "ON" position and engage speed control main switch.<br>• Check for voltages shown in table below at speed control unit (connector C268).<br>• Go to the test step of the **first** incorrect voltage.<br>See illustration in TEST STEP SP2 | All voltages correct ►<br>Incorrect voltage at . . .<br>"BL/BK" wire ►<br>"GN" wire ►<br>"GN/BK" wire (NON-TURBO ONLY) ►<br>"GN/W" wire (NON-TURBO ONLY) ►<br>"BL/O" wire ►<br>"BL/R," "BL," or "BL/W" wires ►<br>"W/GN" wire ► | GO to SP4.<br><br>GO to SP11.<br>GO to SP13.<br>GO to SP14.<br>GO to SP15.<br>GO to SP16.<br>GO to SP18.<br>Lamps-Parking, Rear, and Marker. |

| WIRE COLOR | VOLTAGE |
|---|---|
| "BL/BK" | 12V |
| "GN" | 12V |
| "GN/BK" | 12V* |
| "GN/W" | 12V* |
| "BL/O" | 0V |
| "BL/R" | 12V |
| "BL/W" | 12V |
| "BL" | 12V |
| "W/GN" | 0V |

*NON-TURBO ONLY

12V (±1 volt)

0V (±1 volt)

Fig. 77 Diagnosis and testing (Part 3 of 30). 1989

| TEST STEP | RESULT ► | ACTION TO TAKE |
|---|---|---|
| **SP5** SET SIGNAL CHECK (WILL NOT SET) | | |
| • Ground "BL/R" wire at speed control switch (connector C269).<br>• Check for continuity between ground and "BL/R" wire at speed control unit (connector C268).<br>See illustration in TEST STEP SP2<br>• Is there continuity? | Yes ►<br>No ► | GO to SP6 .<br>REPAIR "BL/R" wire between speed control switch and speed control unit. |

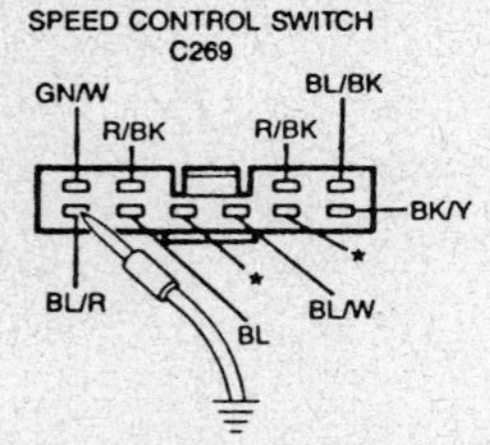

**Fig. 77 Diagnosis and testing (Part 5 of 30). 1989**

| TEST STEP | RESULT ► | ACTION TO TAKE |
|---|---|---|
| **SP6** SPEED CONTROL SWITCH GROUND CHECK (WILL NOT SET) | | |
| • Check for continuity between ground and "BK" wire at speed control switch (connector C269).<br>See illustration in TEST STEP SP5<br>• Is there continuity? | Yes ►<br>No ► | REPLACE speed control switch.<br>REPAIR "BK" wire between speed control switch and ground. |

**Fig. 77 Diagnosis and testing (Part 6 of 30). 1989**

| TEST STEP | RESULT ► | ACTION TO TAKE |
|---|---|---|
| **SP7** ACTUATOR CHECK (NON-TURBO ONLY) (WILL NOT SET) | | |
| • Start engine.<br>• Apply parking brake.<br>• Place shift lever in neutral position.<br>• Disconnect connector C268 from speed control unit.<br>• Connect "GN/BK" and "GN/W" wires (connector C268) to ground.<br>• Touch "GN" wire to ground and observe engine speed (approximately one second).<br>• Does engine speed increase to wide open throttle? | Yes ►<br>No ► | GO to SP9 .<br>ADJUST free play of speed control cable to 1–3mm as shown in illustration below. (Read note) |
| NOTE: If free play is correct and speed does not increase, replace actuator. | | |

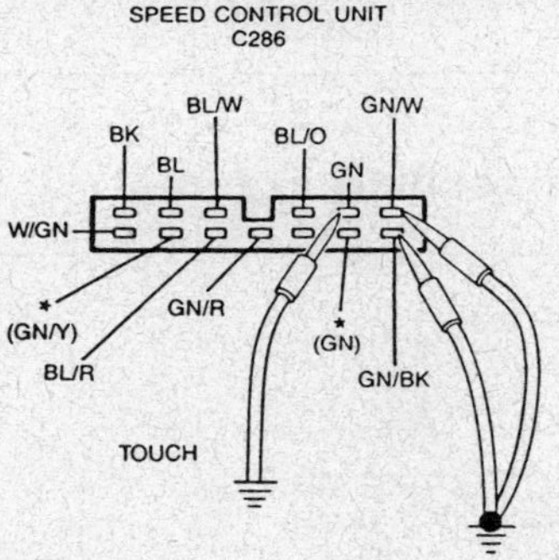

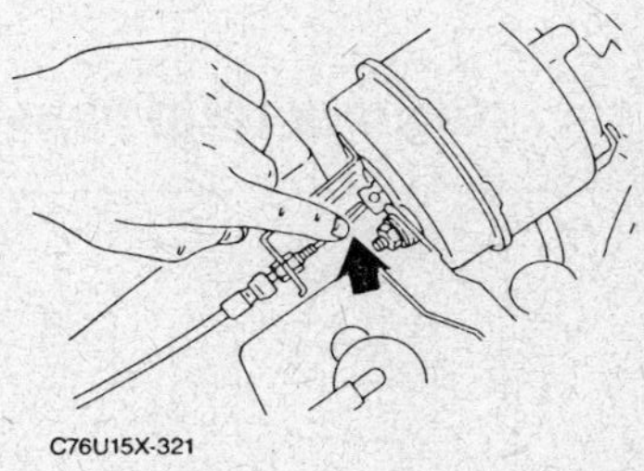

**Fig. 77 Diagnosis and testing (Part 7 of 30). 1989**

| TEST STEP | | RESULT ► | ACTION TO TAKE |
|---|---|---|---|
| SP8 | ACTUATOR CHECK (TURBO ONLY) (WILL NOT SET) | | |
| • Apply 12 volts (±1 volt) to the actuator as shown in table.<br>• Check to see that actuator responds as indicated.<br>• Is response as shown? | | Yes ►<br>No ► | GO to SP9.<br>REPLACE actuator. |

| TERMINAL CONNECTION | | | | OPERATING CONDITION OF CONTROL CABLE |
|---|---|---|---|---|
| a | b | c | d | |
| — | + | + | — | PULL CABLE |
| — | N/C | + | N/C | LOCK CABLE |
| — | — | + | + | EXTEND CABLE |
| N/C | N/C | + | N/C | RELEASE CABLE |

N/C Indicates no connections.
\+ Connect to positive battery terminal.
— Connect to negative battery terminal.

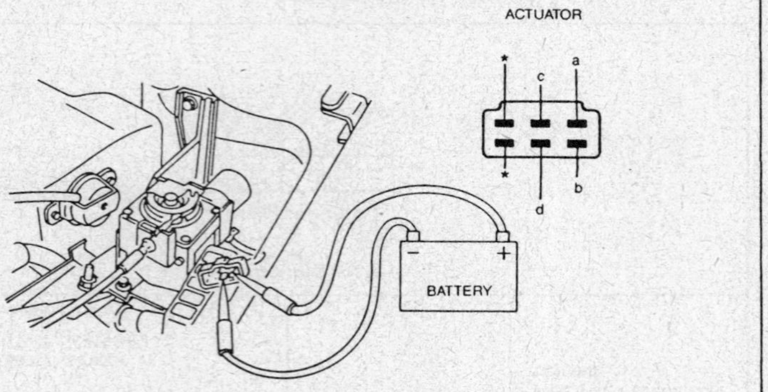

**Fig. 77 Diagnosis and testing (Part 8 of 30). 1989**

| TEST STEP | | RESULT ► | ACTION TO TAKE |
|---|---|---|---|
| SP9 | SPEED SIGNAL CHECK (WILL NOT SET) | | |
| • Place a low wattage test lamp (approximately 1.4 watts) between 12 volts and "GN/R" wire (connector C268) at speed control unit.<br>• Drive car slowly (1-5 mph).<br>• Observe test lamp. | | Test lamp:<br>Does not light ►<br>Flashes inconsistently ►<br>Flashes consistently ► | <br>GO to SP10.<br>GO to Instruments.<br>REPLACE speed control unit. |

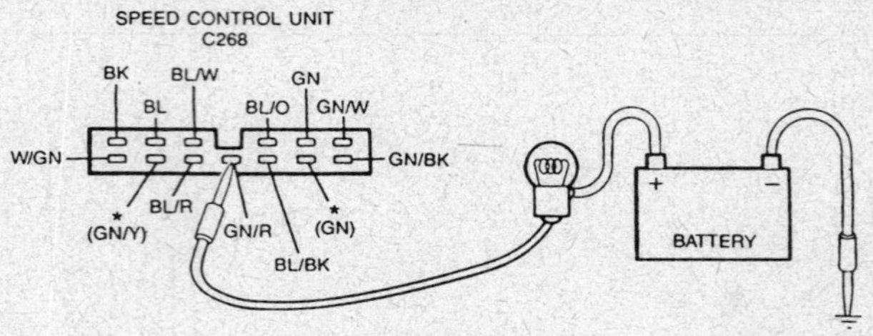

**Fig. 77 Diagnosis and testing (Part 9 of 30). 1989**

| TEST STEP | | RESULT ► | ACTION TO TAKE |
|---|---|---|---|
| SP10 | SPEED SENSOR SIGNAL CHECK (WILL NOT SET) | | |
| • Stop vehicle.<br>• Disconnect the larger of the two instrument panel connectors (C235).<br>• Place a low wattage test lamp (approximately 1.4 watts) between 12 volts and "GN/R" wire (connector C268) at speed control unit.<br>See illustration in TEST STEP SP9<br>• Touch "GN/R" wire to ground several times at instrument panel (connector C235).<br>• Does test lamp flash? | | Yes ►<br>No ► | REPLACE speed sensor.<br>REPAIR "GN/R" wire between instruments and speed control unit. |

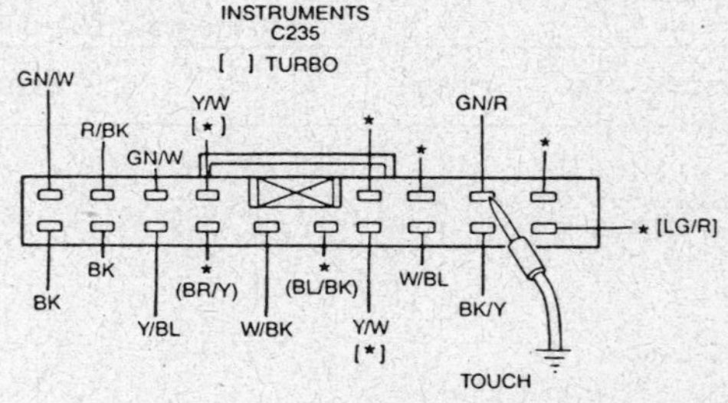

**Fig. 77 Diagnosis and testing (Part 10 of 30). 1989**

| TEST STEP | RESULT ► | ACTION TO TAKE |
|---|---|---|
| **SP11** INSTRUMENT (METER) FUSE CHECK (WILL NOT SET) | | |
| • Turn ignition key to "OFF" position.<br>• Check instrument (meter) fuse.<br>• Is fuse OK? | Yes ► | GO to SP12 . |
| | No ► | REPLACE instrument (meter) fuse. (Read note) |
| NOTE: If fuse blows again, check for shorts to ground in "BK/Y" wires at the following locations: | | |



Fig. 77 Diagnosis and testing (Part 11 of 30). 1989

| TEST STEP | RESULT ► | ACTION TO TAKE |
|---|---|---|
| **SP12** SPEED CONTROL SUPPLY CHECK (WILL NOT SET) | | |
| • Turn ignition key to "ON" position.<br>• Turn speed control main switch to "ON" position.<br>• Check for 12 volts (±1 volt) on "BL/BK" and "BK/Y" wires at speed control main switch (connector C269).<br>See illustration in TEST STEP SP11<br>• Is there 12 volts on both wires? | Yes ► | REPAIR "BL/BK" wire between speed control main switch and speed control unit. |
| | No 12 volts on "BK/Y" wire ► | REPAIR "BK/Y" wire between fuse panel and speed control main switch. |
| | No 12 volts on "BL/BK" wire only ► | REPLACE speed control main switch. |

Fig. 77 Diagnosis and testing (Part 12 of 30). 1989

| TEST STEP | RESULT ► | ACTION TO TAKE |
|---|---|---|
| **SP13** VAC SIGNAL CHECK (WILL NOT SET) | | |
| • Check for 12 volts (±1 volt) on both "BL/BK" and "GN" wires at actuator (connector C186).<br>• Is there 12 volts on both wires? | Yes ► | REPAIR "GN" wire between actuator and speed control unit. |
| | No 12 volts on "BL/BK" wire ► | REPAIR "BL/BK" wire between actuator and speed control main switch. |
| | No 12 volts on "GN" wire ► | REPLACE actuator. |



Fig. 77 Diagnosis and testing (Part 13 of 30). 1989

| TEST STEP | RESULT ► | ACTION TO TAKE |
|---|---|---|
| **SP14** VENT2 SIGNAL CHECK (NON-TURBO ONLY) (WILL NOT SET) | | |
| • Check for 12 volts (±1 volt) on "GN/BK" wire at actuator (connector C186).<br>See illustration in TEST STEP SP13<br>• Is there 12 volts? | Yes ► | REPAIR "GN/BK" wire between actuator and speed control unit. |
| | No ► | REPLACE actuator. |

Fig. 77 Diagnosis and testing (Part 14 of 30). 1989

| TEST STEP | RESULT ► | ACTION TO TAKE |
|---|---|---|
| **SP15** VENT1 SIGNAL CHECK (NON-TURBO ONLY) (WILL NOT SET) | | |
| • Check for 12 volts (±1 volt) on "GN/W" wire at actuator (connector C186).<br>See illustration in TEST STEP SP13<br>• Is there 12 volts? | Yes ► | REPAIR "GN/W" wire between actuator and speed control unit. |
| | No ► | REPLACE actuator. |

Fig. 77 Diagnosis and testing (Part 15 of 30). 1989

| TEST STEP | RESULT ► | ACTION TO TAKE |
|---|---|---|
| **SP16** CLUTCH SWITCH CHECK (WILL NOT SET) | | |
| • (If equipped with automatic transmission Go to SP17)<br>• Disconnect clutch switch (connector C231).<br>• Check for 12 volts (±1 volt) on "BL/O" wire at speed control unit (connector C268).<br>• Is there 12 volts? | Yes ►<br>No ► | GO to SP17<br>REPLACE clutch switch. |

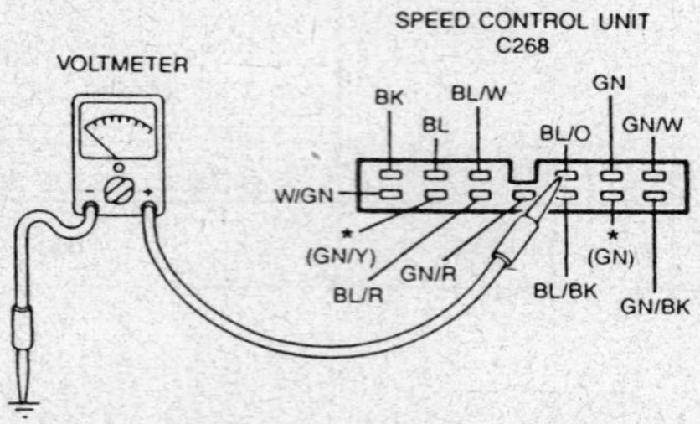

**Fig. 77 Diagnosis and testing (Part 16 of 30). 1989**

| TEST STEP | RESULT ► | ACTION TO TAKE |
|---|---|---|
| **SP17** STOP SWITCH CHECK (WILL NOT SET) | | |
| • Disconnect stop switch (connector C270).<br>• Check for 12 volts (±1 volt) on "BL/O" wire at speed control unit (connector C268).<br>See illustration in TEST STEP SP16<br>• Is there 12 volts | Yes ►<br>No ► | REPAIR "BL/O" wire between stop switch and speed control unit.<br>REPLACE stop switch. |

**Fig. 77 Diagnosis and testing (Part 17 of 30). 1989**

| TEST STEP | RESULT ► | ACTION TO TAKE |
|---|---|---|
| **SP18** SPEED CONTROL SWITCH SIGNAL CHECK (WILL NOT SET) | | |
| • Disconnect speed control switch (connector C269).<br>• Disconnect speed control unit (connector C268).<br>• Check for continuity between ground and the following wires at speed control unit (connector C268):<br>See illustration in TEST STEP SP16<br>– "BL/R" wire<br>– "BL" wire<br>– "BL/W" wire | There is continuity to ground at:<br>– "BL/R" wire ► | REPAIR "BL/R" wire between speed control unit and speed control switch. |
| | – "BL" wire ► | REPAIR "BL" wire between speed control unit and speed control switch. |
| | – "BL/W" wire ► | REPAIR "BL/W" wire between speed control unit and speed control switch. |
| | No continuity ► | GO to SP19 |

**Fig. 77 Diagnosis and testing (Part 18 of 30). 1989**

| TEST STEP | RESULT ► | ACTION TO TAKE |
|---|---|---|
| **SP19** SPEED CONTROL SWITCH CHECK (WILL NOT SET) | | |
| • Reconnect speed control switch (connector C269).<br>• Engage speed control switch and check for continuity between ground and "BL/R," "BL," and "BL/W" wires (as shown in table below) at speed control switch (connector C269).<br>• Is continuity check OK? | Yes ►<br>No ► | REPLACE speed control unit.<br>REPLACE speed control switch. |

| | GROUND | BL/R | BL | BL/W |
|---|---|---|---|---|
| SET | ● | ● | | |
| RESUME | ● | | ● | |
| COAST | ● | | | ● |

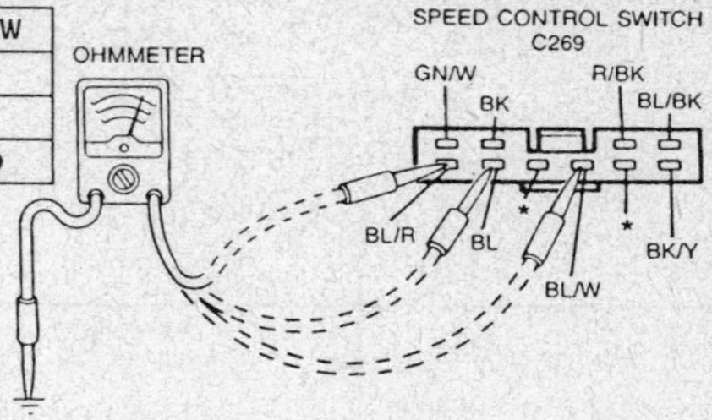

**Fig. 77 Diagnosis and testing (Part 19 of 30). 1989**

| TEST STEP | RESULT ► | ACTION TO TAKE |
|---|---|---|
| **SP20** CLUTCH SWITCH CHECK (WILL NOT DISENGAGE) | | |
| • (If equipped with automatic transmission Go to SP21)<br>• Press clutch switch.<br>• Check for 12 volts (±1 volt) on "BL/O" wire at speed control unit (connector C268).<br>• Is there 12 volts | Yes ►<br>No ► | GO to SP21 .<br>GO to SP23 . |



**Fig. 77 Diagnosis and testing (Part 20 of 30). 1989**

| TEST STEP | RESULT ► | ACTION TO TAKE |
|---|---|---|
| **SP21** STOP SWITCH CHECK (WILL NOT DISENGAGE) | | |
| • Press brake pedal.<br>• Check for 12 volts (±1 volt) on "BL/O" wire at speed control unit (connector C268).<br>See illustration in TEST STEP SP20<br>• Is there 12 volts? | Yes ►<br>No ► | CHECK speed control cable for binding and proper adjustment. (Read note)<br>GO to SP22 . |
| NOTE: If cable is not bound or improperly adjusted, replace speed control unit. | | |

**Fig. 77 Diagnosis and testing (Part 21 of 30). 1989**

| TEST STEP | RESULT ► | ACTION TO TAKE |
|---|---|---|
| **SP22** STOP SWITCH CHECK (WILL NOT DISENGAGE) | | |
| • Press brake pedal.<br>• Check for 12 volts (±1 volt) on "BK/Y" and "BL/O" wires at stop switch (connector C270).<br>• Is there 12 volts on both wires? | Yes ►<br>No 12 volts on "BK/Y" wire ►<br>No 12 volts on "BL/O" wire only ► | REPAIR "BL/O" wire between stop switch and speed control unit.<br>REPAIR "BK/Y" wire between fuse panel and stop switch.<br>REPLACE stop switch. |



**Fig. 77 Diagnosis and testing (Part 22 of 30). 1989**

| TEST STEP | RESULT ► | ACTION TO TAKE |
|---|---|---|
| **SP23** CLUTCH SWITCH CHECK (WILL NOT DISENGAGE) | | |
| • Press clutch pedal.<br>• Check for 12 volts (±1 volt) on "BK/Y" and "BL/O" wires at clutch switch (connector C231).<br>• Is there 12 volts on both wires? | Yes ►<br>No 12 volts on "BK/Y" wire ►<br>No 12 volts on "BL/O" wire only ► | REPAIR "BL/O" wire between clutch switch and speed control unit.<br>REPAIR "BK/Y" wire between fuse panel and clutch switch.<br>REPLACE clutch switch. |



**Fig. 77 Diagnosis and testing (Part 23 of 30). 1989**

| TEST STEP | RESULT ► | ACTION TO TAKE |
|---|---|---|
| **SP24** COAST SWITCH CHECK (WILL NOT COAST) | | |
| • Turn speed control switch to COAST position.<br>• Check for continuity between ground and "BL/W" wire at speed control unit (connector C268).<br>• Is there continuity? | Yes ►<br>No ► | REPLACE speed control unit.<br>GO to SP25 |

SPEED CONTROL UNIT C268

BK, BL/W, BL, GN, BL/O, GN/W, GN/BK, OHMMETER, * (GN/Y), GN/R, * (GN), W/GN, BL/R, BL/BK

**Fig. 77 Diagnosis and testing (Part 24 of 30). 1989**

| TEST STEP | RESULT ► | ACTION TO TAKE |
|---|---|---|
| **SP25** COAST SIGNAL CHECK (WILL NOT COAST) | | |
| • Ground "BL/W" wire at speed control switch (connector C269).<br>• Check for continuity between ground and "BL/W" wire at speed control unit (connector C268).<br>See illustration in TEST STEP SP24<br>• Is there continuity? | Yes ►<br>No ► | REPLACE speed control switch.<br>REPAIR "BL/W" wire between speed control switch and speed control unit. |

SPEED CONTROL SWITCH C269

GN/W, R/BK, BK, BL/BK, BL/R, BK/Y, *, BL, *, BL/W

**Fig. 77 Diagnosis and testing (Part 25 of 30). 1989**

| TEST STEP | RESULT ► | ACTION TO TAKE |
|---|---|---|
| **SP26** RESUME SWITCH CHECK (WILL NOT RESUME) | | |
| • Turn speed control switch to "RESUME" position.<br>• Check for continuity between ground and "BL" wire at speed control unit (connector C268).<br>• Is there continuity? | Yes ►<br>No ► | REPLACE speed control unit.<br>GO to SP27 . |

SPEED CONTROL UNIT C268

OHMMETER, BK, BL/W, GN, BL, BL/O, GN/W, GN/BK, W/GN, BL/R, BL/BK, * (GN/Y), GN/R, * (GN)

**Fig. 77 Diagnosis and testing (Part 26 of 30). 1989**

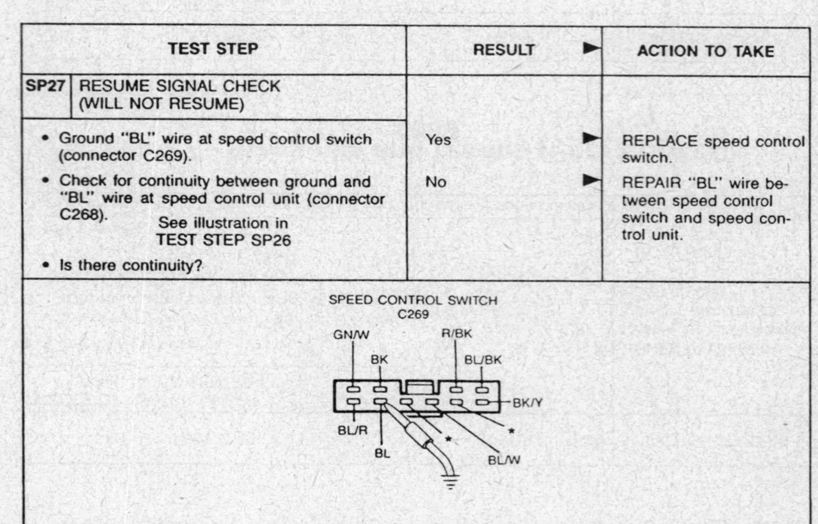

| TEST STEP | RESULT ► | ACTION TO TAKE |
|---|---|---|
| **SP27** RESUME SIGNAL CHECK (WILL NOT RESUME) | | |
| • Ground "BL" wire at speed control switch (connector C269).<br>• Check for continuity between ground and "BL" wire at speed control unit (connector C268).<br>See illustration in TEST STEP SP26<br>• Is there continuity? | Yes ►<br>No ► | REPLACE speed control switch.<br>REPAIR "BL" wire between speed control switch and speed control unit. |



**Fig. 77 Diagnosis and testing (Part 27 of 30). 1989**

| TEST STEP | RESULT ► | ACTION TO TAKE |
|---|---|---|
| **SP28** ACTUATOR CHECK (NON-TURBO ONLY) (SPEED FLUCTUATES) | | |
| • Start engine.<br>• Apply parking brake.<br>• Place shift lever in neutral position.<br>• Disconnect connector C268 from speed control unit.<br>• Connect "GN/BK" and "GN/W" wires (connector C268) to ground.<br>• Touch "GN" wire to ground and observe engine speed (approximately one second).<br>• Does engine speed increase to wide open throttle? | Yes ►<br>No ► | GO to SP30 .<br>ADJUST free play of speed control cable to 1-3mm as shown in illustration below. (Read note) |

NOTE: If free play is correct and speed does not increase, replace actuator.

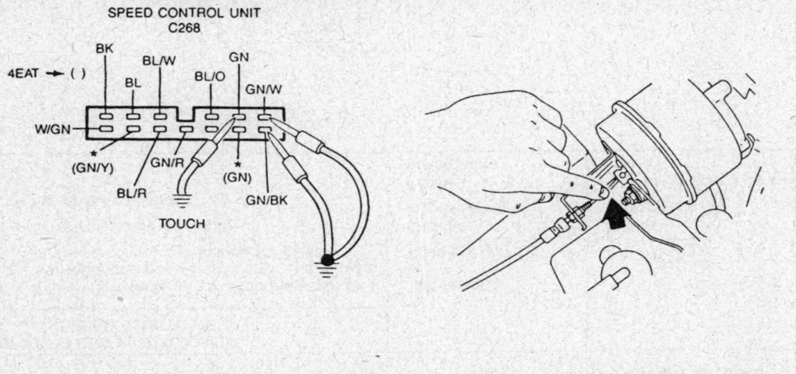

**Fig. 77 Diagnosis and testing (Part 28 of 30). 1989**

| TEST STEP | RESULT ► | ACTION TO TAKE |
|---|---|---|
| **SP29** ACTUATOR CHECK (TURBO ONLY) (SPEED FLUCTUATES) | | |
| • Apply 12 volts (±1 volt) to the actuator as shown in table.<br>• Check to see that actuator responds as indicated.<br>• Is response as shown? | Yes ►<br>No ► | GO to SP30 .<br>REPLACE actuator. |

| TERMINAL CONNECTION | | | | OPERATING CONDITION OF CONTROL CABLE |
|---|---|---|---|---|
| a | b | c | d | |
| — | + | + | — | PULL CABLE |
| — | N/C | + | N/C | LOCK CABLE |
| — | — | + | + | EXTEND CABLE |
| N/C | N/C | + | N/C | RELEASE CABLE |

N/C Indicates no connections.
\+ Connect to positive battery terminal.
— Connect to negative battery terminal.

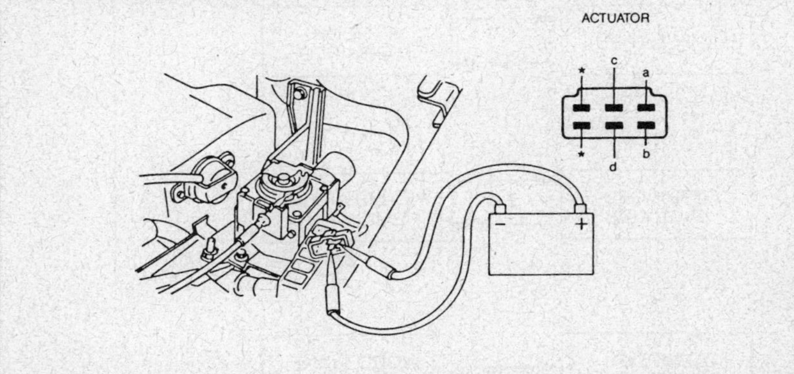

**Fig. 77 Diagnosis and testing (Part 29 of 30). 1989**

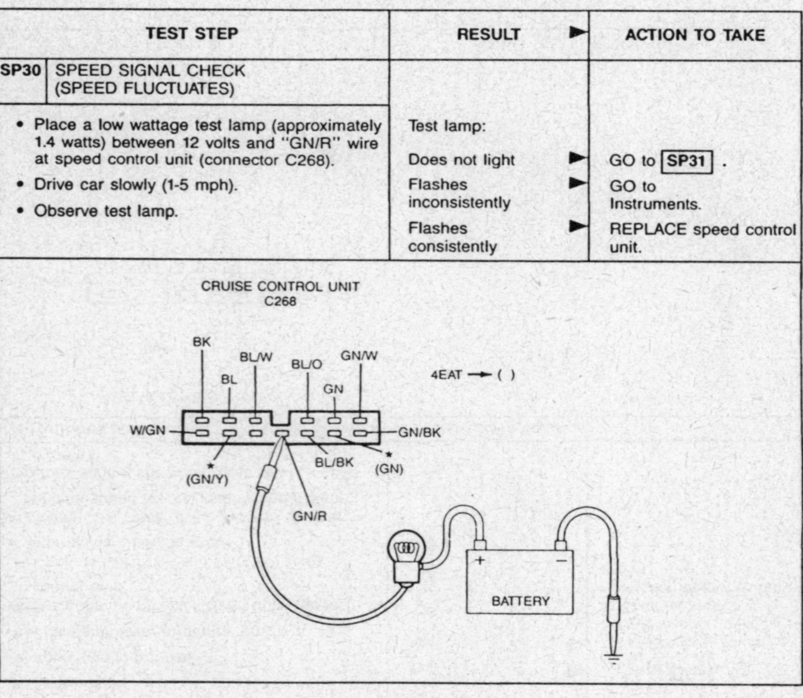

| TEST STEP | | RESULT ► | ACTION TO TAKE |
|---|---|---|---|
| SP30 | SPEED SIGNAL CHECK (SPEED FLUCTUATES) | | |
| • Place a low wattage test lamp (approximately 1.4 watts) between 12 volts and "GN/R" wire at speed control unit (connector C268).<br>• Drive car slowly (1-5 mph).<br>• Observe test lamp. | | Test lamp:<br>Does not light ►<br>Flashes inconsistently ►<br>Flashes consistently ► | <br>GO to SP31 .<br>GO to Instruments.<br>REPLACE speed control unit. |



**Fig. 77 Diagnosis and testing (Part 30 of 30). 1989**

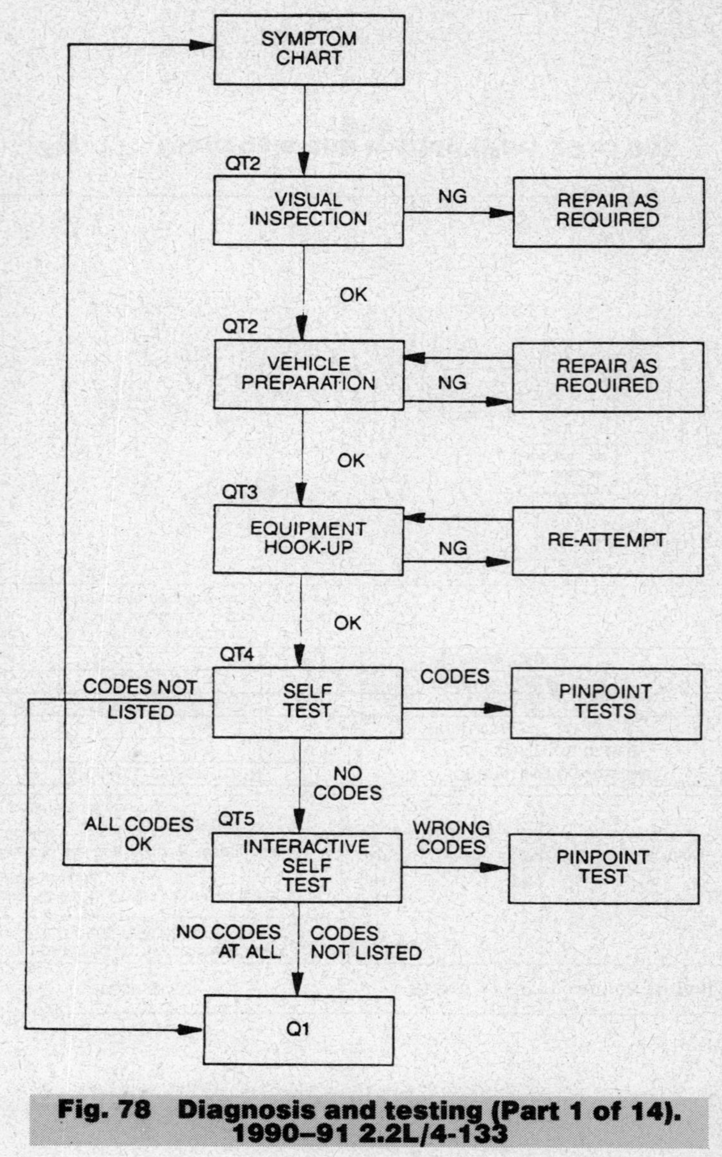



**Fig. 78 Diagnosis and testing (Part 1 of 14). 1990–91 2.2L/4-133**

| CONDITION | POSSIBLE SOURCE | ACTION |
|---|---|---|
| • Will Not Set | • Vacuum hose.<br>• Actuator cable.<br>• Switches.<br>• Control amplifier.<br>• Actuator.<br>• Circuit. | • GO to T1.<br>• GO to QT1. |
| • Intermittent Operation | • Control amplifier.<br>• Actuator.<br>• Circuit. | • GO to QT1 |
| • RESUME, COAST and/or ACCELERATION Switches Do Not Work | • Switches.<br>• Control amplifier.<br>• Circuit. | • GO to QT1. |
| • Speed Fluctuates | • Actuator cable.<br>• Control amplifier.<br>• Switches.<br>• Circuit. | • GO to T1.<br>• GO to QT1. |
| • Does Not Disengage With Brakes | • Brake ON/OFF switch(es).<br>• Control amplifier. | • GO to QT1. |
| • Does Not Disengage With Clutch | • Clutch switch.<br>• Control amplifier. | • GO to QT1. |
| • Abnormal Operation in COAST or ACCELERATION | • Steering wheel slip rings and brush assembly lubrication. | • REFER to "Steering Columns," chapter 24. |

**Fig. 78 Diagnosis and testing (Part 2 of 14). 1990–91 2.2L/4-133**

| TEST STEP | RESULT ► | ACTION TO TAKE |
|---|---|---|
| QT1 VISUAL CHECK | | |
| • Check the following components for damage:<br>—Speed Control System harness for proper connections, bent or broken pins, corrosion, loose wires and proper routing.<br>—Speed Control Amplifier, Sensors, Switches, and Actuators for physical damage.<br>—Speed Control Actuator cable for routing, corrosion, bends, and binding.<br>• Are all Speed Control System components OK? | Yes ►<br>No ► | GO to QT2 .<br>REPAIR as required. |

| TEST STEP | RESULT ► | ACTION TO TAKE |
|---|---|---|
| QT2 VEHICLE PREPARATION | | |
| • Perform all the following safety steps required to run Speed Control Quick Test:<br>—Apply Parking Brake.<br>—Place shift lever in PARK (NEUTRAL on MTX).<br>—Block drive wheels.<br>—Turn off all electrical loads such as Headlamps, Radios, A/C-Heater, Blower Fans, Wipers, etc.<br>• Have all safety steps been performed and all electrical loads turned off? | Yes ►<br>No ► | GO to QT3 .<br>Personal safety and correct diagnostic results are dependent on Test Step QT2. Do not proceed with Quick Test if vehicle preparation cannot be performed. |

**Fig. 78 Diagnosis and testing (Part 4 of 14). 1990–91 2.2L/4-133**

| TEST STEP | RESULT ► | ACTION TO TAKE |
|---|---|---|
| QT3 EQUIPMENT HOOKUP | | |
| • Turn ignition key OFF.<br>• Locate the Speed Control Amplifier.<br>• Connect a test lamp between "GN/W" and the open terminal on the Speed Control Amplifier as shown (leave the amplifier connector connected).<br>SPEED CONTROL AMPLIFIER CONNECTOR<br>GN/W<br>**NOTE:** The test lamp will function as a malfunction indicator.<br>• Is the test lamp hooked up properly? | Yes ►<br>No ► | GO to QT4 .<br>REATTEMPT Step QT3 Equipment Hookup. |

**Fig. 78 Diagnosis and testing (Part 5 of 14). 1990–91 2.2L/4-133**

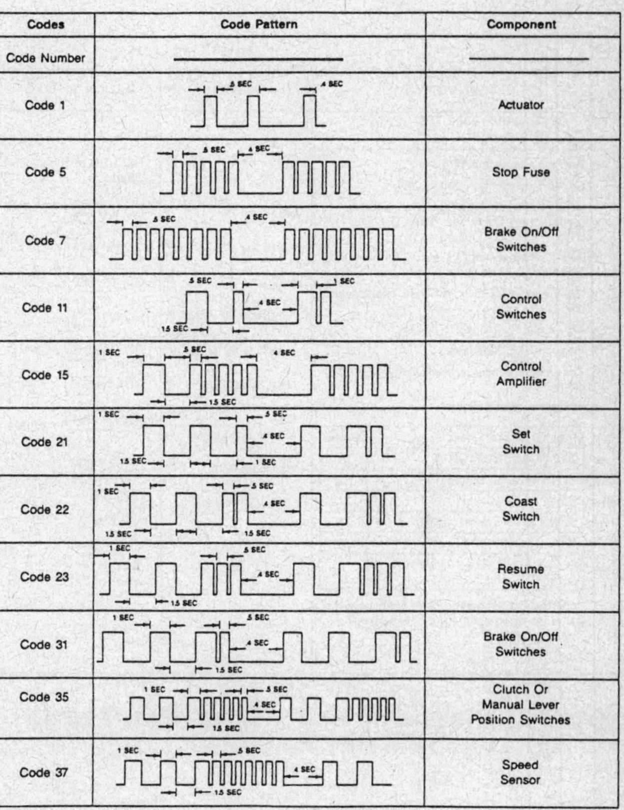

| Codes | Code Pattern | Component |
|---|---|---|
| Code Number | | |
| Code 1 | | Actuator |
| Code 5 | | Stop Fuse |
| Code 7 | | Brake On/Off Switches |
| Code 11 | | Control Switches |
| Code 15 | | Control Amplifier |
| Code 21 | | Set Switch |
| Code 22 | | Coast Switch |
| Code 23 | | Resume Switch |
| Code 31 | | Brake On/Off Switches |
| Code 35 | | Clutch Or Manual Lever Position Switches |
| Code 37 | | Speed Sensor |

**Fig. 78 Diagnosis and testing (Part 3 of 14). 1990–91 2.2L/4-133**

| TEST STEP | RESULT ► | ACTION TO TAKE |
|---|---|---|
| QT4 SELF TEST | | |
| • Turn ignition key OFF.<br>• Speed Control main switch OFF.<br>• Verify that the vehicle has been properly prepared per Quick Test Steps QT2 and QT3.<br>• Turn ignition key to the ON position.<br>• Turn Speed Control main switch ON.<br>• Move control lever upward to RESUME position and hold it more than 3 seconds.<br>• Release control lever. The test lamp should illuminate for 3 seconds, and then go out for 2 seconds.<br>• The Speed Control Unit is now in self test mode.<br>• The test lamp will now indicate any codes that have been triggered. | Code 1 (Actuator) ►<br>Code 5 (Stop Fuse) ►<br>Code 7 (Brake ON/OFF Switch) ►<br>Code 11 (Control Switch) ►<br>Code 15 (Amplifier) ►<br>No Codes ►<br>Codes Not Listed ► | GO to SP1 .<br>GO to SU1 .<br>GO to SP2 .<br>GO to SP6 .<br>GO to SU1 .<br>GO to QT5 .<br>GO to SU1 . |

**Fig. 78 Diagnosis and testing (Part 6 of 14). 1990–91 2.2L/4-133**

| TEST STEP | RESULT ► | ACTION TO TAKE |
|---|---|---|
| **QT5** INTERACTIVE SELF TEST | | |
| • Turn ignition switch OFF.<br>• Speed Control main switch OFF.<br>• Verify that the vehicle has been properly prepared per Quick Test Steps QT2 and QT3.<br>• Turn ignition switch ON. For ATX, move the shift lever to D or R position.<br>• Move control lever to RESUME position and hold it.<br>• Turn main control switch to ON.<br>• Release RESUME lever.<br>• The system is now in Interactive self test mode.<br>• Verify the chart below: | Yes ►<br>No (Code 21) ►<br>No (Code 22) ►<br>No (Code 31) ►<br>No (Code 35, ATX) ►<br>No (Code 35, MTX) ►<br>No (Code 37) ►<br>No (Codes Not Listed) ►<br>No Codes At All ► | RETURN to Symptom Chart.<br>GO to SP6.<br>GO to SP6.<br>GO to SP2.<br>GO to SP9.<br>GO to SP10.<br>GO to SP13.<br>GO to SU1.<br>GO to SU1. |

| Input/Depress/Select | Code |
|---|---|
| SET/COAST BUTTON | 21 |
| COAST/ACCEL Button | 22 |
| Brake On/Off Switch | 31 |
| Shifter in "P" or "N" (ATX) | 35 |
| Clutch Switch (MTX) | 35 |
| Drive Vehicle Above 25 MPH (Speed Sensor) | 37 |

• Does the corresponding code flash from the test lamp when each input is exercised?

**Fig. 78 Diagnosis and testing (Part 7 of 14). 1990–91 2.2L/4-133**

| TEST STEP | RESULT ► | ACTION TO TAKE |
|---|---|---|
| **SP1** ACTUATOR SIGNALS CHECK | | |
| • Key OFF.<br>• Disconnect Speed Control Amplifier and Actuator Connectors.<br>• Ground the "GN/BK", "GN/W", "GN" and "BL/W" wires at the Speed Control Amplifier leading to the Actuator.<br>• Check for continuity between ground and the "BN/BK", "GN/W", "GN" and "BL/W" wires at the Actuator.<br>• Is there continuity? | Yes ►<br>No ► | GO to SP2.<br>REPAIR the wire in question between the Speed Control Amplifier and the Actuator. |
| **SP2** BRAKE ON/OFF SIGNAL CHECK | | |
| • Disconnect the Speed Control Amplifier.<br>• Measure the resistance between the "BL/W" and "BL/O" wires at the Speed Control Amplifier.<br>• Is the resistance less than 5 Ohms with the brake released and greater than 10,000 Ohms with the brake depressed? | Yes ►<br>No ► | GO to SP5.<br>GO to SP3. |
| **SP3** BRAKE ON/OFF SIGNAL CHECK | | |
| • Disconnect the Speed Control Amplifier.<br>• Disconnect brake ON/OFF switch.<br>• Measure the resistance of the "BL/W" wire between the Speed Control Amplifier and the "BL/W" wire on the brake ON/OFF switch.<br>• Is the resistance less than 5 Ohms? | Yes ►<br>No ► | GO to SP4.<br>REPAIR "BL/W" wire between the Speed Control Amplifier and the Brake ON/OFF switch. |
| **SP4** BRAKE ON/OFF SIGNAL CHECK | | |
| • Disconnect the Speed Control Amplifier.<br>• Disconnect the brake ON/OFF switch.<br>• Measure the resistance between the "BL/O" wire at the Speed Control Amplifier and the "BL/O" wire at the brake ON/OFF switch.<br>• Is the resistance less than 5 OHMs? | Yes ►<br>No ► | REPLACE Brake ON/OFF switch.<br>REPAIR "BL/O" wire between the Speed Control Amplifier and the brake On/Off switch. |
| **SP5** BRAKE ON/OFF SIGNAL CHECK | | |
| **NOTE: Before beginning this Test Step, be sure the Brake Lamp System is operational.**<br>• Disconnect the Speed Control Amplifier connector.<br>• Measure the voltage on the "W/GN" wire at the Speed Control Amplifier connector.<br>• Is the voltage greater than 10.5V with the brake pedal depressed and less than 0.5V with the brake pedal released? | Yes 2.2L Non-Turbo ►<br>Yes 2.2L Turbo ►<br>No ► | GO to SU9.<br>GO to SU7.<br>REPAIR the "W/GN" wire between the brake ON/OFF switch and the Speed Control Amplifier. |
| **SP6** SPEED CONTROL SWITCH GROUND CHECK | | |
| • Disconnect the speed control switch.<br>• Measure the resistance between the "BK" wire at the speed control switch and ground.<br>• Is the resistance less than 5 ohms? | Yes ►<br>No ► | GO to SP7.<br>REPAIR the "BK" wire from the Speed Control Switch and ground. |

**Fig. 78 Diagnosis and testing (Part 8 of 14). 1990–91 2.2L/4-133**

| TEST STEP | RESULT ► | ACTION TO TAKE |
|---|---|---|
| **SP7** SPEED CONTROL SWITCH CHECK | | |
| • Connect the Speed Control Amplifier and Speed Control Switch.<br>• Check function of the Speed Control Switch by measuring the resistance of the following wire colors between the switch and ground. | Yes ►<br>No ► | GO to SP8.<br>REPLACE the Speed Control Switch. |

| | |
|---|---|
| **Coast:** "BL" wire | Depressed — Less than 5 ohms<br>Released — Greater than 10,000 ohms |
| **Resume:** "R/GN" | Depressed — Less than 5 ohms<br>Released — Greater than 10,000 ohms |
| **Set/Accel:** "BL/R" | Depressed — Less than 5 ohms<br>Released — Greater than 10,000 ohms |

• Are the resistances verified?

| TEST STEP | RESULT ► | ACTION TO TAKE |
|---|---|---|
| **SP8** CHECK LEAD BETWEEN SPEED CONTROL SWITCH AND SPEED CONTROL AMPLIFIER | | |
| • Key OFF.<br>• Disconnect the Speed Control Amplifier and the Speed Control Switch connectors.<br>• Measure the resistance of the following wires between the Amplifer connector and the Switch connector.<br>**Wire**<br>"BL"<br>"R/GN"<br>"BL/R"<br>• Are the resistances less than 5 ohms? | Yes ►<br>No ► | REPLACE the Speed Control Switch.<br>SERVICE the wire in question. |

**Fig. 78 Diagnosis and testing (Part 9 of 14). 1990–91 2.2L/4-133**

| TEST STEP | RESULT ► | ACTION TO TAKE |
|---|---|---|
| **SP9** PARK/NEUTRAL SIGNAL CHECK (ATX) | | |
| • Disconnect the Speed Control Amplifier connector.<br>• Measure the voltage on the "BK/Y" wire at the Speed Control Amplifier connector under the following conditions: | Yes ►<br>No ► | Check starting system electrical circuit.<br>SERVICE the "BK/Y" wire. |

| Shift Selector | Voltage |
|---|---|
| Park | 0V |
| Reverse | 10V |
| Neutral | 0V |
| Drive | 10V |
| Drive | 10V |
| Low | 10V |

• Are the approximate voltages verified?

| TEST STEP | RESULT ► | ACTION TO TAKE |
|---|---|---|
| **SP10** CLUTCH SWITCH SIGNAL CHECK | | |
| • Disconnect the Speed Control Amplifier.<br>• Measure the resistance between ground and the "R/BL" wire at the Speed Control Amplifier.<br>• Is the resistance less than 5 Ohms with the clutch pedal depressed and greater than 10,000 Ohms with the clutch pedal released? | Yes ►<br>No ► | GO to SP13.<br>GO to SP11. |
| **SP11** CLUTCH SWITCH SIGNAL CHECK | | |
| • Disconnect the Speed Control Amplifier.<br>• Measure the resistance between ground and the "R/BL" wire at the clutch switch.<br>• Is the resistance less than 5 Ohms with the clutch pedal depressed and greater than 10,000 Ohms with the clutch pedal released? | Yes ►<br>No ► | REPAIR the "R/BL" wire between the Clutch Switch and the Speed Control Amplifier.<br>GO to SP12. |
| **SP12** CLUTCH SWITCH GROUND CHECK | | |
| • Disconnect the clutch switch.<br>• Measure the resistance between the "BK" wire at the clutch switch and ground.<br>• Is the resistance less than 5 ohms? | Yes ►<br>No ► | REPLACE the Clutch Switch.<br>REPAIR the "BK" wire to ground. |

**Fig. 78 Diagnosis and testing (Part 10 of 14). 1990–91 2.2L/4-133**

| | TEST STEP | RESULT | ACTION TO TAKE |
|---|---|---|---|
| SP13 | SPEED SENSOR INPUT CHECK | | |
| | **NOTE: For vehicles equipped with conventional instrumentation, the Speed Sensor is located in the Instrument Cluster with a "GN/R" wire. For vehicles equipped with the electronic instrumentation, the Speed Sensor is located on the transaxle with a "Y/W" wire.**<br>• Disconnect the Speed Control Amplifier.<br>• Disconnect the Vehicle Speed Sensor. Refer to the illustration for analog connector location.<br>• Measure the resistance between the "GN/R" wire at the Speed Control Amplifier and the Vehicle Speed Sensor.<br>• Is the resistance less than 5 Ohms?<br>FRONT OF VEHICLE<br>INSTRUMENT PANEL<br>ANALOG CLUSTER CONNECTOR LOCATION | Yes (Conventional Cluster) ▶<br>Yes (Electronic Cluster) ▶<br>No ▶ | GO to SP15.<br>GO to SP14.<br>REPAIR the "GN/R" wire between the Speed Sensor and Speed Control Amplifier. |
| SP14 | SPEED SENSOR SIGNAL CHECK (ELECTRONIC CLUSTER) | | |
| | • Disconnect the Speed Sensor.<br>• Measure the resistance between the terminals of the Speed Sensor.<br>• Is the resistance between 175 and 225 Ohms? | Yes ▶<br>No ▶ | GO to SU1.<br>REPLACE the Speed Sensor. Refer to the NOTE in SP13 for Speed Sensor location. |

**Fig. 78 Diagnosis and testing (Part 11 of 14). 1990–91 2.2L/4-133**

| | TEST STEP | RESULT | ACTION TO TAKE |
|---|---|---|---|
| SP15 | SPEED SENSOR SIGNAL CHECK (CONVENTIONAL CLUSTER) | | |
| | • Disconnect the Speedometer Cable at the Transaxle.<br>• Disconnect the Speed Control Amplifier.<br>• Check for continuity between ground and the "GN/R" wire at the Speed Control Amplifier.<br>• Does continuity exist 4 times per one Speedometer Cable rotation? | Yes ▶<br>No ▶ | GO to SU1.<br>REPLACE the Speedometer Head. |

| | TEST STEP | RESULT | ACTION TO TAKE |
|---|---|---|---|
| SU1 | KAPWR CHECK | | |
| | • Disconnect the Speed Control amplifier.<br>• Measure the voltage on the "GN/W" wire at the Speed Control Amplifier connector.<br>• Is the voltage above 10.5 volts? | Yes ▶<br>No ▶ | GO to SU2.<br>CHECK the "STOP" fuse. If the fuse is OK, REPAIR the "GN/W" wire between the Speed Control Amplifier and Battery (+) terminal. |
| SU2 | METER FUSE CHECK | | |
| | • Locate the Interior Fuse panel.<br>• Is the 15A Meter fuse good? | Yes ▶<br>No ▶ | GO to SU5.<br>GO to SU3. |
| SU3 | CHECK SYSTEM | | |
| | • Replace the blown fuse.<br>• Key ON.<br>• Did the fuse blow again? | Yes ▶<br>No ▶ | GO to SU4.<br>GO to SU5. |
| SU4 | CHECK FOR POWER START TO GROUND | | |
| | • Key OFF.<br>• Disconnect the "BK/Y" wire from the interior fuse panel.<br>• Measure the resistance of the "BK/Y" wire between the fuse panel and ground.<br>• Is the resistance less than 5 Ohms?<br>• Reinstall the "BK/Y" wire. | Yes ▶<br>No ▶ | SERVICE the "BK/Y" wire.<br>GO to SU5. |
| SU5 | KEYPWR CHECK | | |
| | • Disconnect the Speed Control Amplifier.<br>• Measure the voltage on the "BK/Y" wire at the Speed Control Amplifier Connector.<br>• Is the voltage above 10.5V with the ignition switch on and below 1.5 volts with the ignition switch off? | Yes ▶<br>No ▶ | GO to SU6.<br>REPAIR the "BK/Y" wire between the Speed Control Unit and the ignition switch. |
| SU6 | SPEED CONTROL POWER CHECK | | |
| | • Key ON.<br>• Disconnect the Speed Control Amplifier.<br>• Measure the voltage on the "BL/BK" wire at the Speed Control Amplifier.<br>• Is the voltage greater than 10.5 volts with the main speed control switch on and less than 1.5 volts with the switch off? | Yes ▶<br>No ▶ | GO to SU9.<br>GO to SU7. |

**Fig. 78 Diagnosis and testing (Part 12 of 14). 1990–91 2.2L/4-133**

| | TEST STEP | RESULT | ACTION TO TAKE |
|---|---|---|---|
| SU7 | SPEED CONTROL POWER CHECK | | |
| | • Key ON.<br>• Measure the voltage on the "BL/BK" wire at the main speed control switch.<br>• Is the voltage above 10.5 volts with the main speed control switch on and below 1.5 volts with the switch off? | Yes ▶<br>No ▶ | REPAIR the "BL/BK" wire between the main Speed Control Switch and the Speed Control Unit.<br>GO to SU8. |
| SU8 | SPEED CONTROL POWER CHECK | | |
| | • Key ON.<br>• Disconnect the speed control switch.<br>• Measure the voltage on the "BK/Y" wire at the speed control switch.<br>• Is the voltage above 10.5 volts with the ignition switch on and below 1.5 volts with the ignition switch off? | Yes ▶<br>No ▶ | REPLACE the Speed Control Switch.<br>REPAIR the "BK/Y" wire between the Speed Control Switch and the ignition switch. |
| SU9 | SPEED CONTROL GROUND CHECK | | |
| | • Key OFF.<br>• Disconnect the Speed Control Amplifier.<br>• Measure the resistance between the "BK" wire at the Speed Control Amplifier and ground.<br>• Is the resistance less than 5 ohms? | Yes 2.2L Turbo ▶<br>Yes 2.2L Non-Turbo ▶<br>No ▶ | GO to SU11.<br>GO to SU10.<br>REPAIR the "BK" wire between the Speed Control Amplifier and ground. |
| SU10 | CHECK ACTUATOR RESISTANCE (2.2L NON-TURBO) | | |
| | • Key OFF.<br>• Disconnect the Actuator connector.<br>• Reconnect the amplifier connector.<br>• Measure the resistance between the actuator terminals as shown:<br>(see table below)<br>• Are the resistances verified? | Yes ▶<br>No ▶<br>ACTUATOR<br>GN<br>BL/W<br>GN/BK<br>GN/W | GO to SU12.<br>REPLACE the Speed Control Amplifier. |
| SU11 | CHECK ACTUATOR RESISTANCE (2.2L TURBO) | | |
| | • Disconnect the Actuator Connector.<br>• Measure resistance between terminals as shown:<br>(see table below)<br>• Are the resistances correct? | Yes ▶<br>No ▶<br>ACTUATOR<br>GN<br>BL/W<br>GN/BK<br>GN/W | GO to SU12.<br>REPLACE the Speed Control Amplifier. |

SU10:

| Terminals | Resistance |
|---|---|
| "BLW" — "GN" | 60-90 ohms |
| "BL/W" — "GN/BK" | 60-90 ohms |
| "BL/W" — "GN/W" | 60-90 ohms |
| "GN" — "GN/BK" | 160-190 ohms |
| "GN" — "GN/W" | 160-190 ohms |
| "GN/BK" — "GN/W" | 160-190 ohms |

SU11:

| Terminals | Resistance |
|---|---|
| "GN" — "BL/W" | 90-120 ohms |
| "GN" — "GN/BK" | 90-120 ohms |
| "GN" — "GN/W" | 90-120 ohms |
| "BL/W" — "GN/BK" | 5-25 ohms |
| "BL/W" — "GN/W" | 5-25 ohms |
| "GN/BK" — "GN/W" | 5-25 ohms |

**Fig. 78 Diagnosis and testing (Part 13 of 14). 1990–91 2.2L/4-133**

| | TEST STEP | RESULT | ACTION TO TAKE |
|---|---|---|---|
| SU12 | CHECK ACTUATOR OPERATION (2.2L NON-TURBO AND 2.2L TURBO) | | |
| | • Reconnect all Speed Control System related connectors.<br>• Start engine.<br>• Drive the vehicle on road or hoist at 35 mph.<br>• Verify the operation of the Speed Control System as shown below:<br>(see table below)<br>• Are functions verified? | Yes ▶<br>No ▶ | RETURN to the Symptom Chart.<br>REPLACE the Actuator. |

| Action to Take | Result |
|---|---|
| Press "ON" | "ON" indicator illuminates |
| Press "SET" | Speed holds at 35 mph |
| Press "ACCEL" | Speed increases gradually |
| Press and hold "COAST" for 5 seconds | Speed decreases until released |
| Depress brake pedal | Speed decreases |
| Press "RESUME" (above 30 mph) | Speed increases to last set speed |
| Press "OFF" | "ON" indicator shuts off and speed decreases |

2.2L Non-Turbo Only

| | TEST STEP | RESULT | ACTION TO TAKE |
|---|---|---|---|
| T1 | CHECK VACUUM SUPPLY | | |
| | • Key ON, engine idling.<br>• Connect vacuum gauge to actuator vacuum hose.<br>• Increase engine speed to 2000 RPM.<br>• Is vacuum present?<br>**NOTE: 2.5 in-Hg vacuum is minimum for normal operation.** | Yes ▶<br>No ▶ | GO to T2.<br>SERVICE vacuum hose. |
| T2 | CHECK CABLE ADJUSTMENT | | |
| | • Check cable deflection at actuator.<br>• Does cable have 1-3 mm of deflection? | Yes ▶<br>No ▶ | RETURN to Symptom Chart.<br>ADJUST cable. |

**Fig. 78 Diagnosis and testing (Part 14 of 14). 1990–91 2.2L/4-133**

Symptom Chart

| CONDITION | POSSIBLE SOURCE | ACTION |
|---|---|---|
| • Will Not Set | • Vacuum Hose.<br>• Actuator Cable.<br>• Switches.<br>• Control.<br>• Actuator.<br>• Circuit. | • GO to T1.<br>• GO to U1 |
| • Intermittent Operation | • Control Amplifier.<br>• Actuator.<br>• Circuit. | • GO to U1. |
| • RESUME, COAST and/or ACCELERATION Switches Do Not Work | • Switches.<br>• Control Amplifier.<br>• Circuit. | • GO to U6. |
| • Speed Fluctuates | • Actuator Cable.<br>• Control Amplifier.<br>• Switches.<br>• Circuit. | • GO to T1.<br>• GO to U1. |
| • Does Not Disengage With Brakes | • BOO Switch(es).<br>• Control Amplifier. | • GO to U1. |
| • Does Not Disengage With Clutch | • Clutch Switch.<br>• Control Amplifier. | • GO to U1. |

**Fig. 79 Diagnosis and Testing, Symptom Chart (Part 1 of 4). 3.0L/V6-182**

| | TEST STEP | RESULT ► | ACTION TO TAKE |
|---|---|---|---|
| T1 | CHECK VACUUM SUPPLY | | |
| | • Key on, engine idling.<br>• Connect vacuum gauge to actuator vacuum hose.<br>• Increase engine speed to 2000 RPM.<br>• Is vacuum present?<br>NOTE: 2.5 in-Hg vacuum is minimum for normal operation. | Yes ►<br>No ► | GO to T2.<br>SERVICE vacuum hose. |
| T2 | CHECK CABLE ADJUSTMENT | | |
| | • Check cable deflection at Actuator as shown.<br>• Does cable have 1-3mm of deflection? | Yes ►<br>No ► | GO to T3.<br>ADJUST cable. |
| T3 | CHECK DUMP VALVE | | |
| | • Connect Vacuum Pump to Dump Valve hose at the Actuator.<br>• Apply 5-10 in-Hg vacuum.<br>• Step on brake pedal.<br>• Is vacuum held before stepping on brake and released after stepping on brake? | Yes ►<br>No, vacuum always held ►<br>No, vacuum never held ► | RETURN to Symptom Chart.<br>ADJUST or REPLACE Dump Valve.<br>SERVICE hose at Dump Valve. |

| | TEST STEP | RESULT ► | ACTION TO TAKE |
|---|---|---|---|
| U1 | CHECK BRAKE ON/OFF SWITCH | | |
| | • Key on.<br>• Disconnect Speed Control Amplifier.<br>• Clutch pedal released (MTX).<br>• Measure voltage at Control Amplifier 8 pin connector "W/GN" (4EAT) or "BL/O" (MTX).<br>• Push brake pedal.<br>• Is voltage above 10V with brake pedal down and less than 1V with brake pedal up? | Yes, 4EAT ►<br>Yes, MTX ►<br>No, 4EAT ►<br>No, MTX ► | GO to U4.<br>GO to U3.<br>SERVICE "W/GN" wire from Control Amplifier to Brake On/Off switch.<br>GO to U2. |
| U2 | CHECK BRAKE ON/OFF TO CLUTCH SWITCH | | |
| | • Key on.<br>• Measure voltage at Clutch switch "W/GN" wire.<br>• Depress brake pedal.<br>• Is voltage above 10V with pedal depressed and less than 1V with pedal released? | Yes ►<br>No ► | GO to U3.<br>SERVICE "W/GN" wire from Brake ON/OFF to Clutch switch. |
| U3 | CHECK CLUTCH SWITCH | | |
| | • Disconnect Control Amplifier.<br>• Measure voltage at Speed Control Amplifier 8 pin connector "BL/O" wire.<br>• Key on.<br>• Depress brake pedal.<br>• Depress clutch pedal.<br>• Is voltage greater than 10V with clutch released and less than 1V with pedal depressed? | Yes ►<br>No ► | GO to U4.<br>SERVICE "BL/O" wire or clutch switch as required. |

**Fig. 79 Diagnosis and testing (Part 2 of 4). 3.0L/V6-182**

| | TEST STEP | RESULT ► | ACTION TO TAKE |
|---|---|---|---|
| U4 | CHECK POWER TO AMPLIFIER | | |
| | • Disconnect Control Amplifier.<br>• Key on.<br>• Measure voltage at Control Amplifier BL/BK wire (6 pin connector).<br>• Is 10-14 volts present with Speed Control "ON" and less than 1V present with Speed Control "OFF"? | Yes ►<br>No ► | GO to U5.<br>SERVICE "BL/BK" wire, or Speed Control On/Off Switch. |
| U5 | CHECK GROUND | | |
| | • Key off.<br>• Disconnect Control Amplifier.<br>• Measure resistance between Control Amplifier "BK" wire (6 pin connector) and ground (Battery -).<br>• Is the resistance less than 5 OHMs? | Yes ►<br>No ► | GO to U6.<br>SERVICE "BK" wire connection to ground. |
| U6 | CHECK CONTROL SWITCHES | | |
| | • Key off.<br>• Disconnect Speed Control Amplifier.<br>• Measure resistance between BL wire (6 pin connector) and ground (Battery -).<br>• Actuate switches.<br>(see switch resistance table below)<br>• Are resistances OK? | Yes ►<br>No ► | GO to U7.<br>SERVICE "BL" wire, switch ground ("BK" wire) or switch. |
| U7 | CHECK ACTUATOR | | |
| | • Key off.<br>• Disconnect Speed Control Amplifier.<br>• Measure resistance between Control Amplifier wires.<br>(see wire resistance table below)<br>• Are resistances OK? | Yes ►<br>No ► | REPLACE Control Amplifier, then GO to U8.<br>SERVICE wires in question, if all OK REPLACE Actuator. |

| Switch | Resistance (OHMs) |
|---|---|
| Set/Accel | 646-714 |
| Coast | 114-126 |
| Resume | 2090-2310 |

| Wires | Resistance (OHMs) |
|---|---|
| GN-GN/W | 40-70 |
| GN/W-GN/BK | 110-140 |
| R-R/W | 40K-60K |
| R/BK-R/W | 20K-30K |

**Fig. 79 Diagnosis and testing (Part 3 of 4). 3.0L/V6-182**

| | TEST STEP | RESULT ► | ACTION TO TAKE |
|---|---|---|---|
| U8 | CHECK ACTUATOR | | |
| | • Transmission in Neutral.<br>• Parking Brake applied.<br>• Wheels blocked.<br>• Start the engine.<br>• Main switch ON.<br>• Jump Control Amplifier GN to Battery (+).<br>• Jump Control Amplifier GN/BK to Battery (-).<br>• Momentarily jump Control Amplifier "GN/W" to Battery (-).<br>• Does the engine speed increase with "GN/W" grounded and return to normal with "GN/W" open? | Yes ►<br>No ► | TURN key OFF. GO to U9.<br>REPLACE Actuator. |
| U9 | CHECK SPEED SENSOR | | |
| | • Key off.<br>• Disconnect Speed Sensor.<br>• Measure resistance between terminals of the Speed Sensor.<br>• Is resistance 180 to 220 OHMs?<br>NOTE: For vehicles equipped with analog instrumentation, the Speed Sensor is located in the instrument cluster with a "GN/R" wire. For vehicles equipped with electronic instrumentation, the Speed Sensor is located on the transaxle with a "Y/W" wire. | Yes ►<br>No ► | SERVICE "BK/R" and/or "BK/BL" wires from Speed Sensor to ECA and Speed Control Amplifier. If all OK, REPLACE Control Amplifier.<br>REPLACE Speed Sensor. |

**Fig. 79 Diagnosis and testing (Part 4 of 4). 3.0L/V6-182**

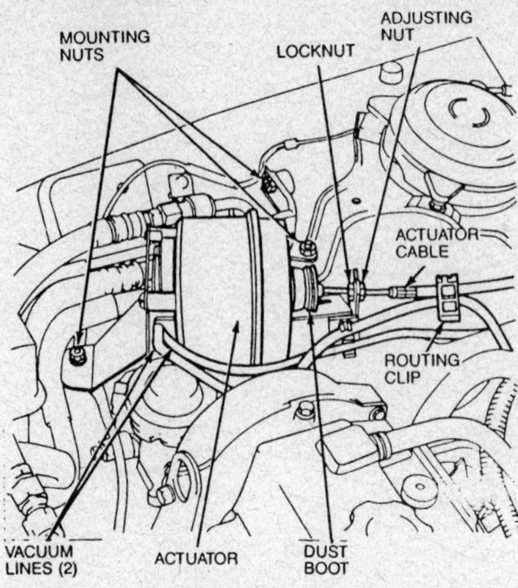


**Fig. 80 Actuator replace. Vacuum**

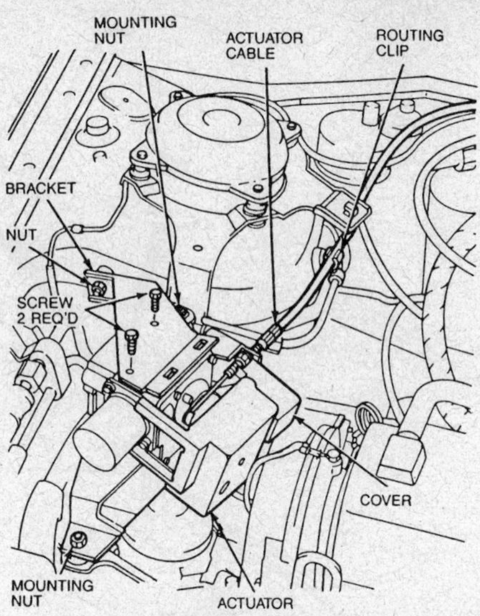


**Fig. 81 Actuator replace. Electric**

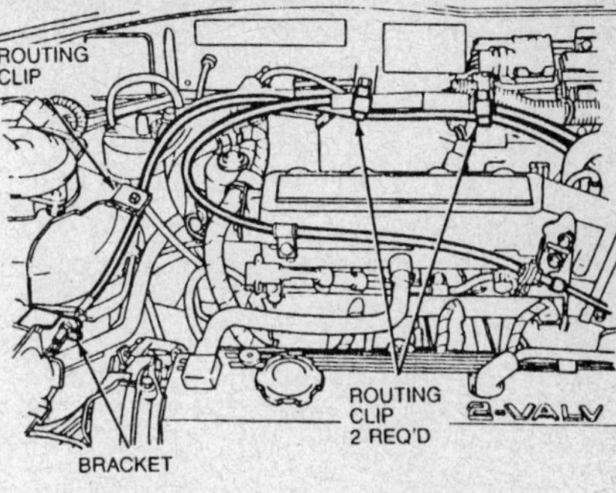


**Fig. 82 Actuator cable replace (Part 1 of 2)**

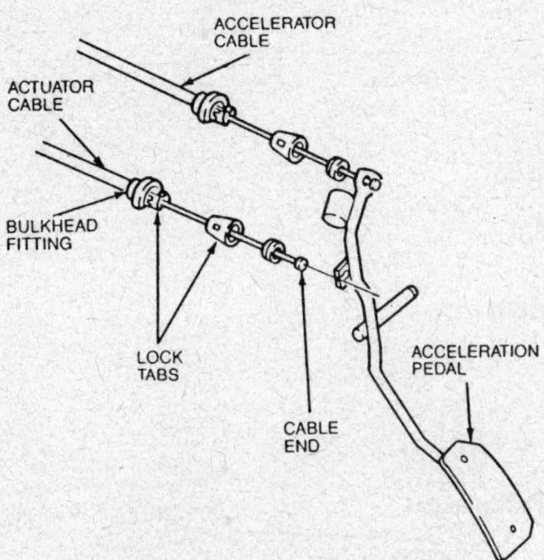


**Fig. 82 Actuator cable replace (Part 2 of 2)**

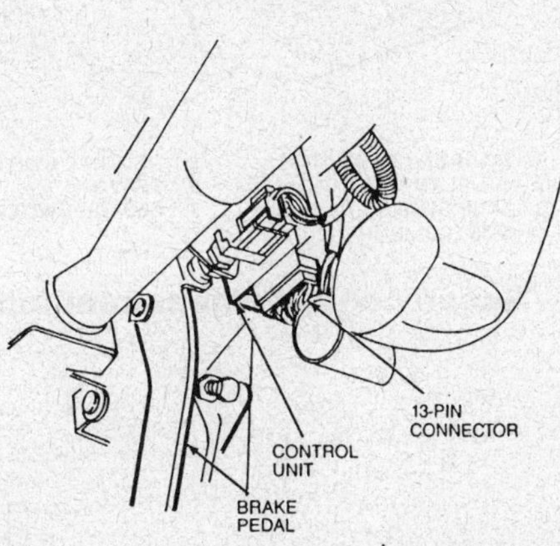


**Fig. 83 Control unit replace**

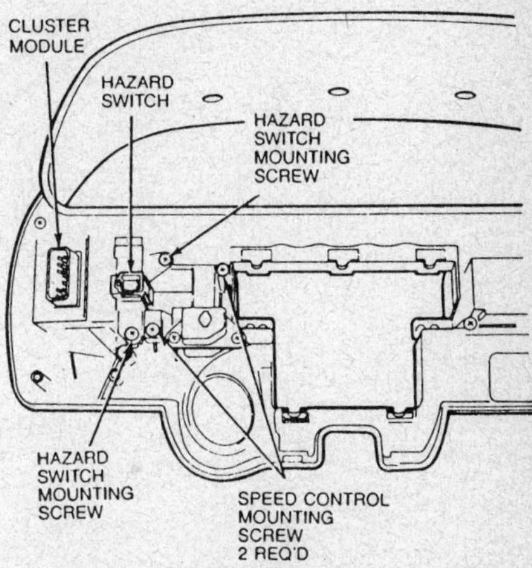


**Fig. 84 Main control switch replace**

# 1989 TRACER

## DESCRIPTION

The speed control system consists of operator controls, a servo (throttle actuator) assembly, speed sensor, main On/Off switch, clutch switch, stop lamp switch, neutral switch and the control unit.

To operate the speed control system, the engine must be running and the vehicle speed must be greater than 30 mph. When these conditions have been met, the system is ready to accept a speed signal, **Fig. 85.**

## ADJUSTMENTS

### Actuator Inner Cable Freeplay

With the engine off, remove clip, then adjust locknut while pressing down on cable until freeplay measures .04-.12 inch, **Fig. 86.**

### Clutch Pedal Height

Measure distance from center of clutch pedal to lower dash panel. Pedal height must measure 8.44-8.64 inches, **Fig. 87.** If pedal height is not within specifications, proceed as follows:

1. Remove sound deadening cover from under instrument panel.
2. Loosen locknut, then turn clutch switch until desired pedal height is obtained.
3. Tighten locknut, then measure pedal height. Repeat step 1, if pedal height is not within specifications.

## COMPONENT REPLACEMENT

### Main On/Off Switch

1. Disconnect battery negative cable.
2. Remove main On/ Off switch by gently prying outer edge from instrument panel.
3. Disconnect electrical connector from main switch terminals.
4. Reverse procedure to install.

### Control Unit

1. Disconnect battery ground cable.
2. Remove left front side trim panel.
3. Remove sound deadening cover.
4. Remove control unit to dash panel retaining screws, disconnect electrical connectors, then remove control unit.
5. Reverse procedure to install.

### Servo Assembly

1. Disconnect actuator cable from servo assembly.
2. Disconnect vacuum line from servo assembly.
3. Remove servo bracket retaining bolts, then the servo assembly.
4. Reverse procedure to install.

## DIAGNOSIS & TESTING

Refer to **Figs. 88 and 89.**

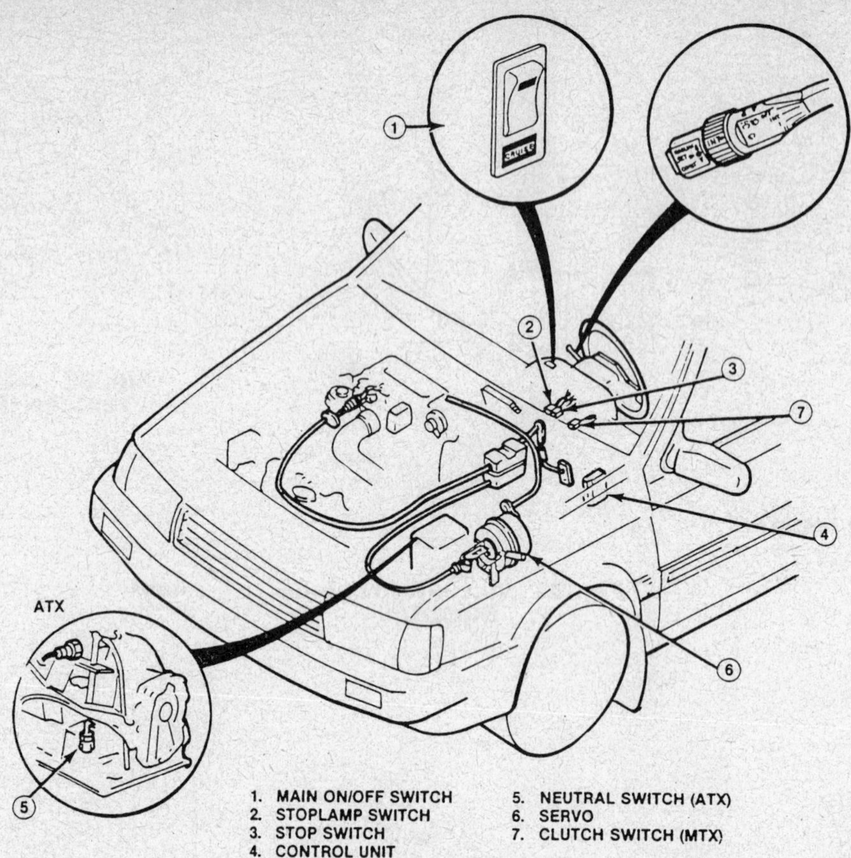


**Fig. 85 Speed control component location**

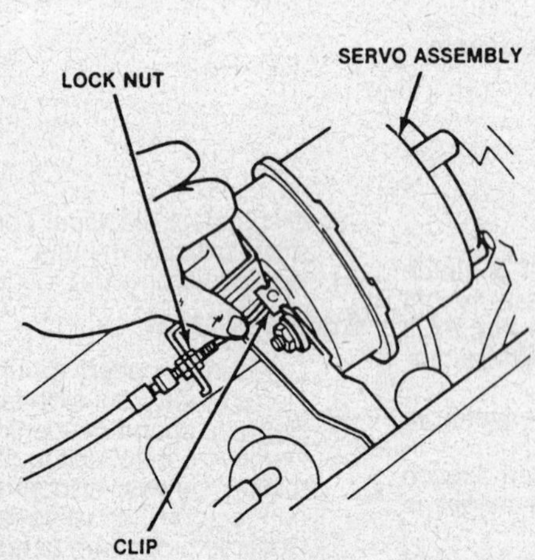


**Fig. 86 Actuator inner cable freeplay adjustment**

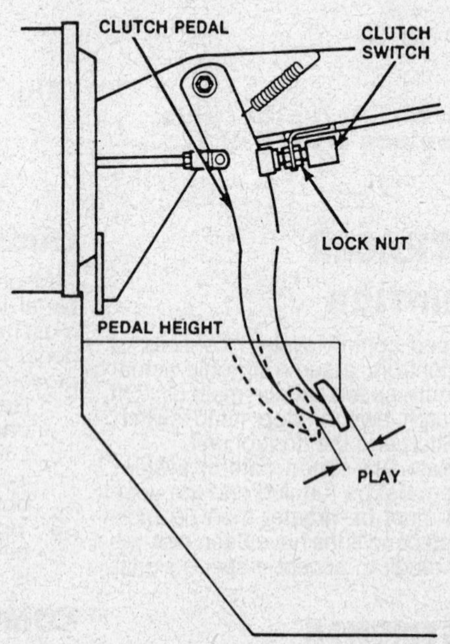


**Fig. 87 Clutch pedal height adjustment**

| SP 1 SPEED CONTROL SYSTEM CHECK | |
|---|---|
| **SYMPTOM** | **ACTION TO TAKE** |
| Schematics and wiring diagrams are illustrated in the Ford Tracer EVTM. | |
| • Speed control will not . . . | |
| —Set | Go to SP 2. |
| —Stop | Go to SP 18. |
| —Coast | Go to SP 22. |
| —Resume | Go to SP 24. |
| • Speed fluctuates | Go to SP 26. |

**Fig. 88 Speed control diagnosis (Part 1 of 28). Speed control system check**

| SP 2 SPEED CONTROL SYSTEM VOLTAGE CHECK (WILL NOT SET) | | |
|---|---|---|
| **TEST STEP** | **RESULT** | **ACTION TO TAKE** |
| • Check for voltages (Table B) at speed control unit connector C353. | All voltages correct | Go to SP 3. |
| • Go to the test step of the first incorrect voltage condition. | Incorrect voltage at . . . | |
| | "BL/BK" wire | Go to SP 9. |
| | "GR/BK" wire | Go to SP 11. |
| | "GR" wire | Go to SP 12. |
| | "GR/W" wire | Go to SP 13. |
| | "BL/O" wire | Go to SP 14. |
| | "BL/R", "BL" or "BL/W" wires | Go to SP 16. |
| | "W/GR" wire | Stoplamps. |
| | "BK/Y" wire | Ignition System. |

TABLE B

| Wire Color | Voltage |
|---|---|
| "BL/BK" | 12V |
| "GR/BK" | 12V |
| "GR" | 12V |
| "GR/W" | 12V |
| "BL/O" | 0V |
| "BL/R" | 12V |
| "BL/W" | 12V |
| "BL" | 12V |
| "W/GR" | 0V |
| "BL/Y" | 0V |

* Tolerance +/− 1 volt

**Fig. 88 Speed control diagnosis (Part 2 of 28). Speed control system voltage check (will not set)**

| SP 3 SET SWITCH CHECK (WILL NOT SET) | | |
|---|---|---|
| **TEST STEP** | **RESULT** | **ACTION TO TAKE** |
| • Press speed control set switch. | No | Go to SP 4. |
| • Is there continuity between ground and "BL/W" wire (connector C353) at speed control unit? | Yes | Go to SP 6. |

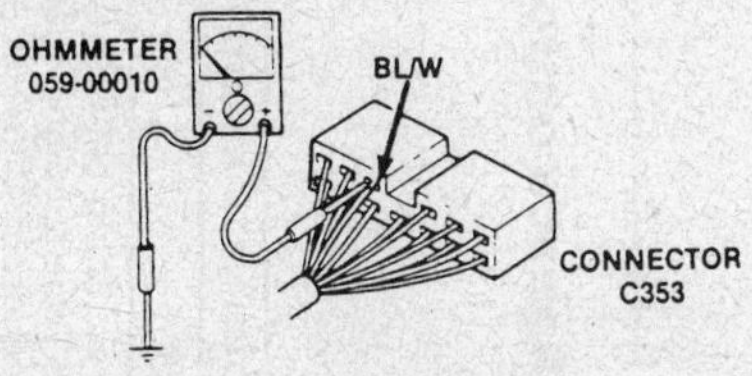

**Fig. 88 Speed control diagnosis (Part 3 of 28). Set switch check (will not set)**

**SP 4 SET SIGNAL CHECK (WILL NOT SET)**

| TEST STEP | RESULT | ACTION TO TAKE |
|---|---|---|
| • Ground "BL/W" wire at combination switch connector C358.<br>• Is there continuity between ground and "BL/W" wire (connector C353) at speed control unit? | No | Repair "BL/W" wire between combination switch and speed control unit. |
| | Yes | Go to SP 5. |

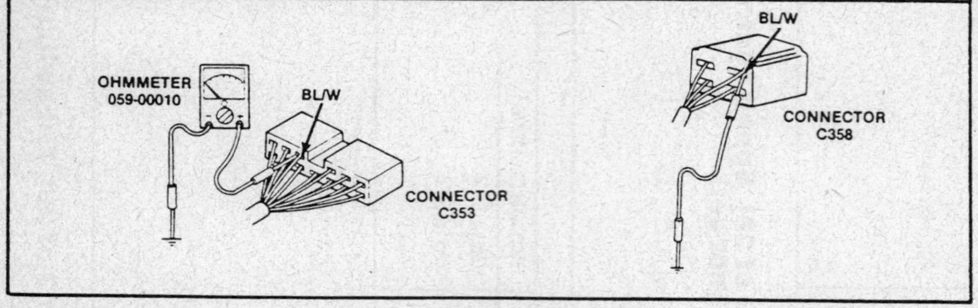

**Fig. 88 Speed control diagnosis (Part 4 of 28). Set signal check (will not set)**

**SP 5 COMBINATION SWITCH GROUND CHECK (WILL NOT SET)**

| TEST STEP | RESULT | ACTION TO TAKE |
|---|---|---|
| • Is there continuity between ground and "BK" wire at combination switch connector C358? | No | Repair "BK" wire between combination switch and ground. |
| | Yes | Replace combination switch. |

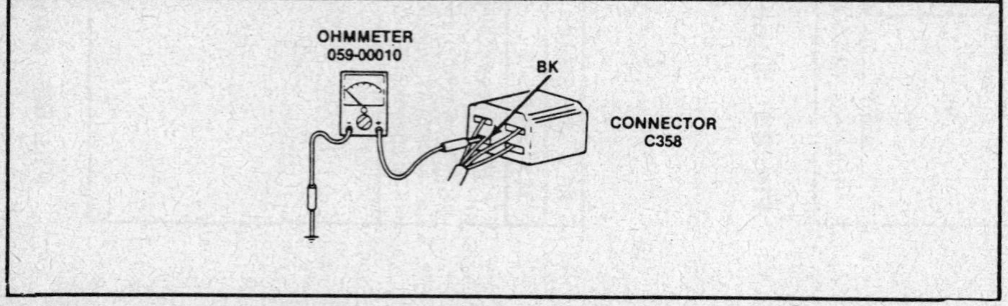

**Fig. 88 Speed control diagnosis (Part 5 of 28). Combination switch ground check (will not set)**

**SP 6 ACTUATOR SOLENOID VALVE CHECK (WILL NOT SET)**

| TEST STEP | RESULT | ACTION TO TAKE |
|---|---|---|
| • Start engine.<br>• Apply the parking brake.<br>• Place shift lever in neutral position.<br>• Remove connector C353 from speed control unit.<br>• Connect "GR" and "GR/W" wires (connector C353) to ground. Touch "GR/BK" wire to ground until engine speed reaches 1000-3000 rpm (approximately 1 sec.).<br>• Does engine speed increase and hold at 1,000-3,000 rpm? | No | Adjust free play of speed control cable to 1-3 mm. |
| | Yes | Go to SP 7. |

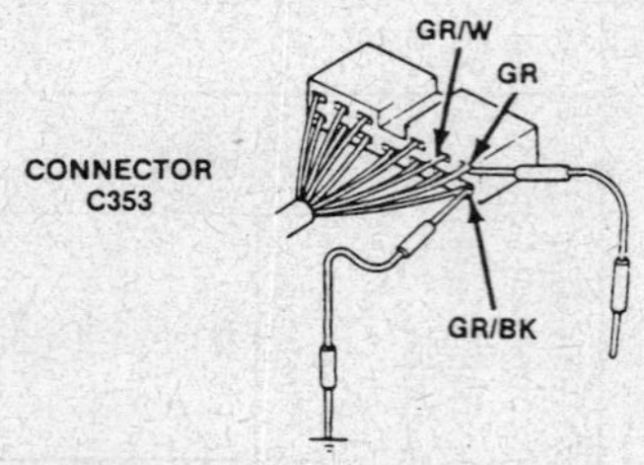

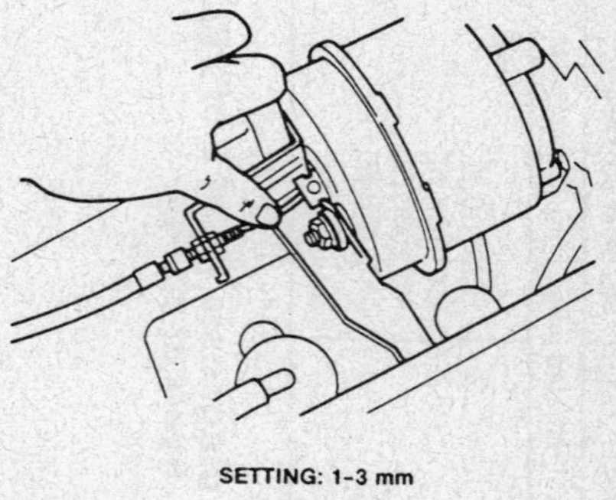

NOTE: If free play is correct and speed does not increase, replace actuator solenoid valve.

**Fig. 88 Speed control diagnosis (Part 6 of 28). Actuator solenoid valve check (will not set)**

**SP 7 SPEED SIGNAL CHECK (WILL NOT SET)**

| TEST STEP | RESULT | ACTION TO TAKE |
|---|---|---|
| • Place a low wattage test lamp (approximately 1.4 watts), between 12 V and "GR/R" wire (connector C353) at speed control unit.<br>• Drive car slowly (1-5 mph).<br>• Does test lamp flash? | No<br>Yes | Go to SP 8.<br>Replace speed control unit. |

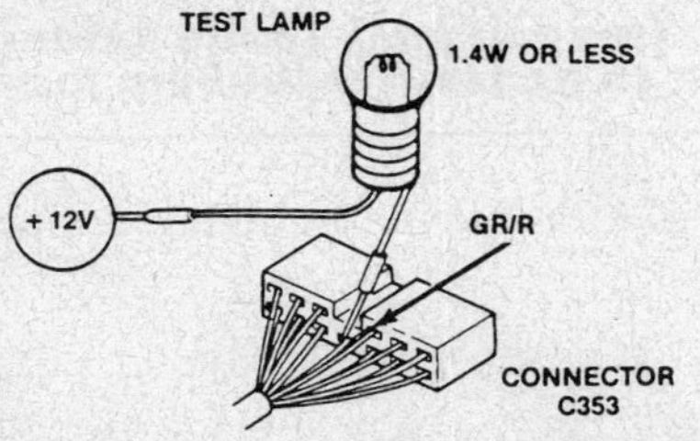

NOTE: If speedometer fluctuates when speed control is not being used, go to Instruments .

**Fig. 88 Speed control diagnosis (Part 7 of 28). Speed signal check (will not set)**

**SP 8 SPEED SENSOR SIGNAL CHECK (WILL NOT SET)**

| TEST STEP | RESULT | ACTION TO TAKE |
|---|---|---|
| • Remove instrument panel connector C127.<br>• Place a low wattage test lamp between 12V and "GR/R" wire (connector C353) at speed control unit.<br>• Touch "GR/R" wire to ground several times at instrument panel connector C127.<br>• Does test lamp flash? | No<br>Yes | Repair "GR/R" wire between instruments and speed control unit.<br>Replace speed sensor. |

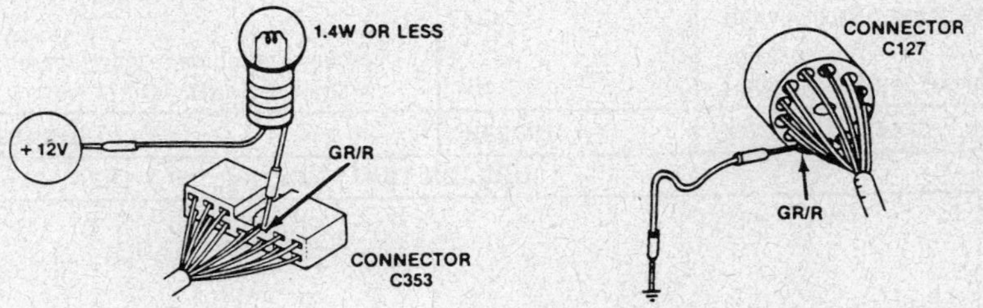

**Fig. 88 Speed control diagnosis (Part 8 of 28). Speed sensor signal check (will not set)**

**SP 9 INSTRUMENT FUSE CHECK (WILL NOT SET)**

| TEST STEP | RESULT | ACTION TO TAKE |
|---|---|---|
| • Is instrument meter fuse OK? | No<br>Yes | Replace instrument meter fuse.<br>Go to SP 10. |

NOTE: If fuse blows again, check for shorts to ground in "BK/Y" wires at clutch (connector C357), brake (connector C356), and speed control main switches (connector C354). Repair "BK/Y" wires as needed.

**Fig. 88 Speed control diagnosis (Part 9 of 28). Instrument fuse check (will not set)**

| SP 10 SPEED CONTROL SUPPLY CHECK (WILL NOT SET) | | |
|---|---|---|
| **TEST STEP** | **RESULT** | **ACTION TO TAKE** |
| • Is there 12V on both sides of speed control main switch (connector C354)? | Yes | Repair "BL/BK" wire between speed control main switch and speed control unit. |
| | No 12 volts on "BK/Y" wire | Repair "BK/Y" wire between fuse panel and speed control main switch. |
| | No 12 volts on "BL/BK" wire | Replace speed control main switch. |

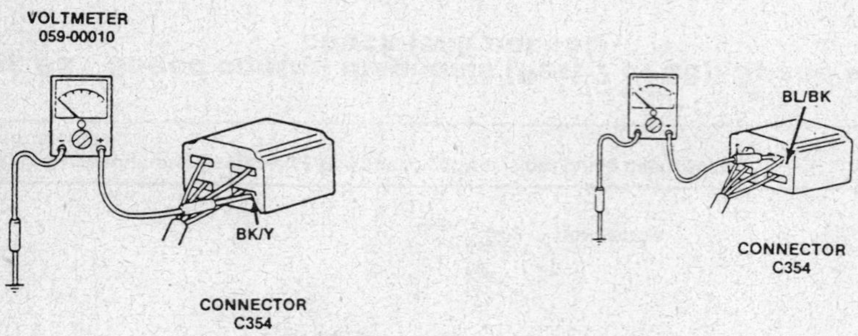

**Fig. 88 Speed control diagnosis (Part 10 of 28). Speed control supply check (will not set)**

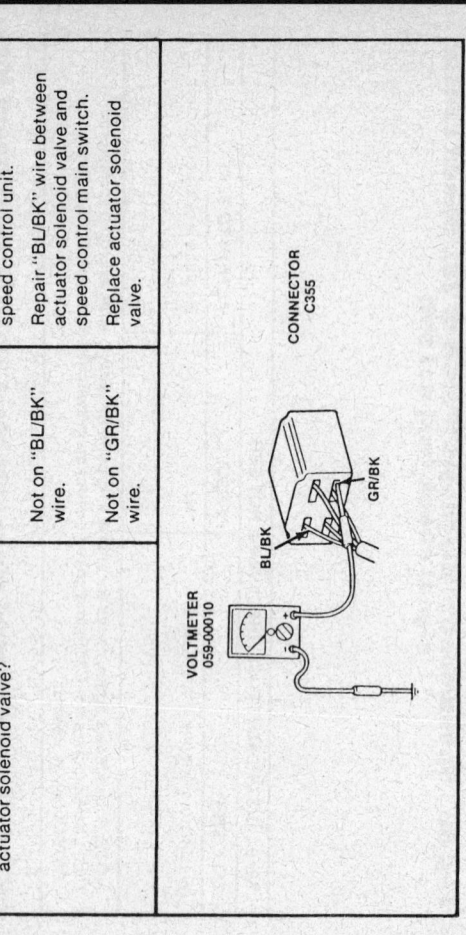

| SP 11 VAC SIGNAL CHECK (WILL NOT SET) | | |
|---|---|---|
| **TEST STEP** | **RESULT** | **ACTION TO TAKE** |
| • Is there 12V on both "BL/BK" and "GR/BK" wires (connector C355) at actuator solenoid valve? | Yes | Repair "GR/BK" wire between actuator solenoid valve and speed control unit. |
| | Not on "BL/BK" wire. | Repair "BL/BK" wire between actuator solenoid valve and speed control main switch. |
| | Not on "GR/BK" wire. | Replace actuator solenoid valve. |

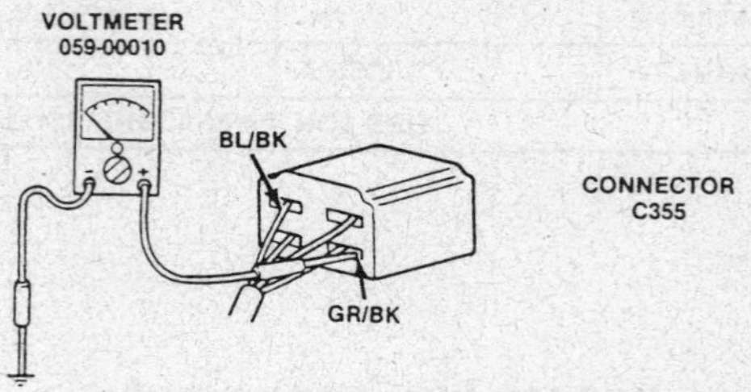

**Fig. 88 Speed control diagnosis (Part 11 of 28). VAC signal check (will not set)**

| SP 12 VENT 2 SIGNAL CHECK (WILL NOT SET) | | |
|---|---|---|
| **TEST STEP** | **RESULT** | **ACTION TO TAKE** |
| • Is there 12V on "GR" wire (connector C355) at actuator solenoid valve? | No | Replace actuator solenoid valve. |
| | Yes | Repair "GR" wire between actuator solenoid valve and speed control unit. |

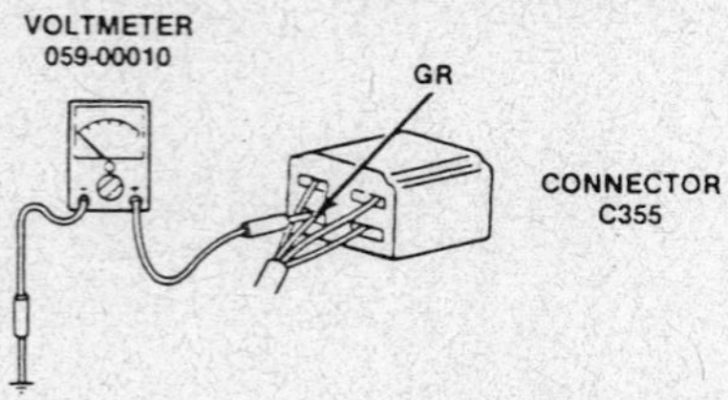

**Fig. 88 Speed control diagnosis (Part 12 of 28). Vent 2 signal check (will not set)**

| SP 13 VENT 1 SIGNAL CHECK (WILL NOT SET) | | |
|---|---|---|
| **TEST STEP** | **RESULT** | **ACTION TO TAKE** |
| • Is there 12V on "GR/W" wire (connector C355) at actuator solenoid valve? | No | Replace actuator solenoid valve. |
| | Yes | Repair "GR/W" wire between actuator solenoid valve and speed control unit. |

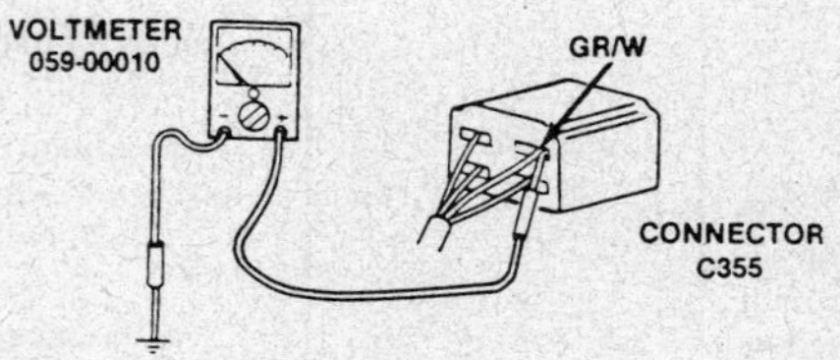

**Fig. 88 Speed control diagnosis (Part 13 of 28). Vent 1 signal check (will not set)**

| SP 14 CLUTCH SWITCH CHECK (WILL NOT SET) | | |
|---|---|---|
| **TEST STEP** | **RESULT** | **ACTION TO TAKE** |
| • (If equipped with automatic transmission, Go to SP 15.)<br>• Remove clutch switch connector.<br>• Is there 12V on "BL/O" wire (connector C353) at speed control unit? | No<br>Yes | Replace clutch switch.<br>Go to SP 15. |

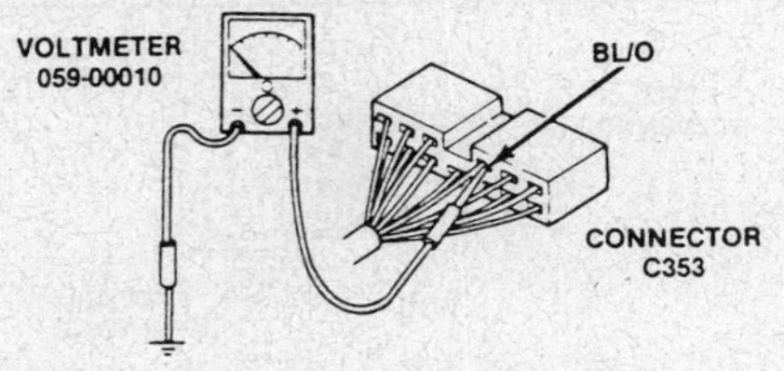

**Fig. 88 Speed control diagnosis (Part 14 of 28). Clutch switch check (will not set)**

| SP 15 STOP SWITCH CHECK (WILL NOT SET) | | |
|---|---|---|
| **TEST STEP** | **RESULT** | **ACTION TO TAKE** |
| • Remove stop switch connector.<br>• Is there 12V on "BL/O" wire (connector C353) at speed control unit? | No<br>Yes | Replace stop switch.<br>Repair "BL/O" wire between stop switch and speed control unit. |

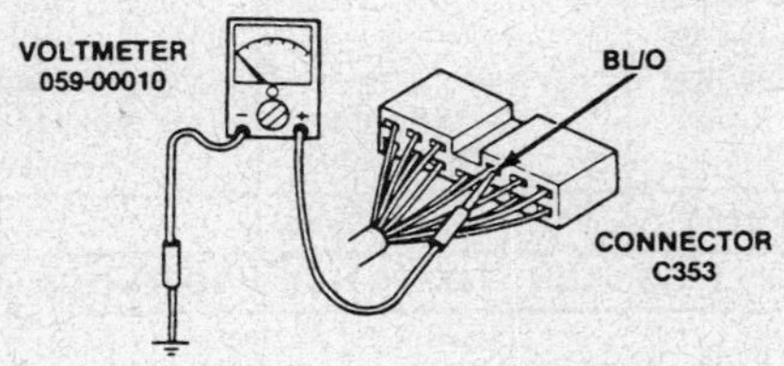

**Fig. 88 Speed control diagnosis (Part 15 of 28). Stop switch check (will not set)**

| SP 16 COMBINATION SWITCH CHECK (WILL NOT SET) | | |
|---|---|---|
| **TEST STEP** | **RESULT** | **ACTION TO TAKE** |
| • Remove combination switch connector C358.<br>• Is there continuity between ground and "BL/R", "BL", or "BL/W" wires (connector C353) at speed control unit? | No<br>Yes | Replace combination switch.<br>Go to SP 17. |

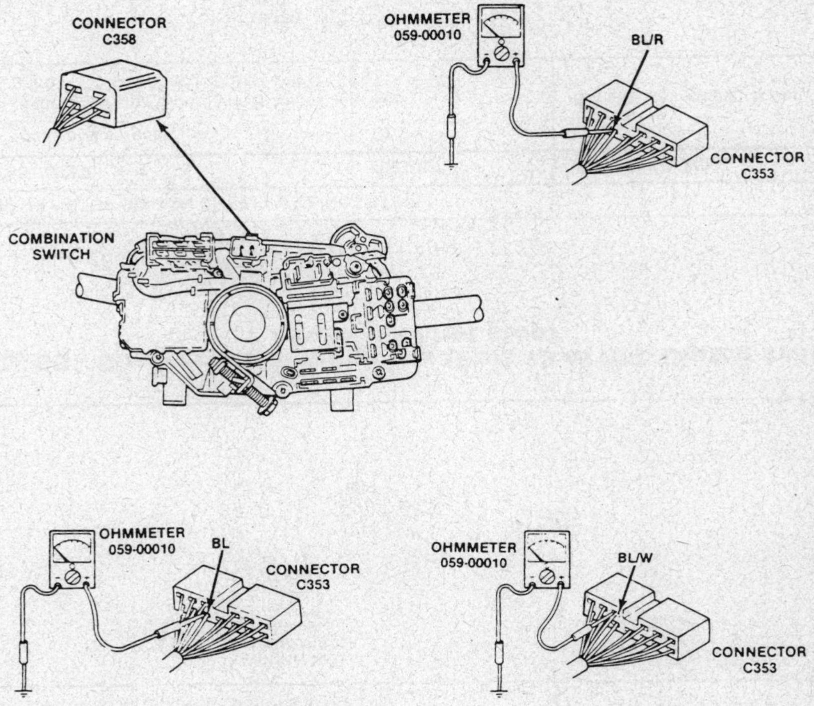

**Fig. 88 Speed control diagnosis (Part 16 of 28). Combination switch check (will not set)**

**SP 17 COMBINATION SWITCH SIGNAL CHECK (WILL NOT SET)**

| TEST STEP | RESULT | ACTION TO TAKE |
|---|---|---|
| • Check for continuity between ground and the following wires at speed control unit connector C353.<br>—"BL/R"<br>—"BL"<br>—"BL/W" | There is continuity in:<br>—"BL/R" wire | Repair "BL/R" wire between speed control unit and combination switch. |
| | —"BL" wire | Repair "BL" wire between speed control unit and combination switch. |
| | —"BL/W" wire | Repair "BL/W" wire between speed control unit and combination switch. |

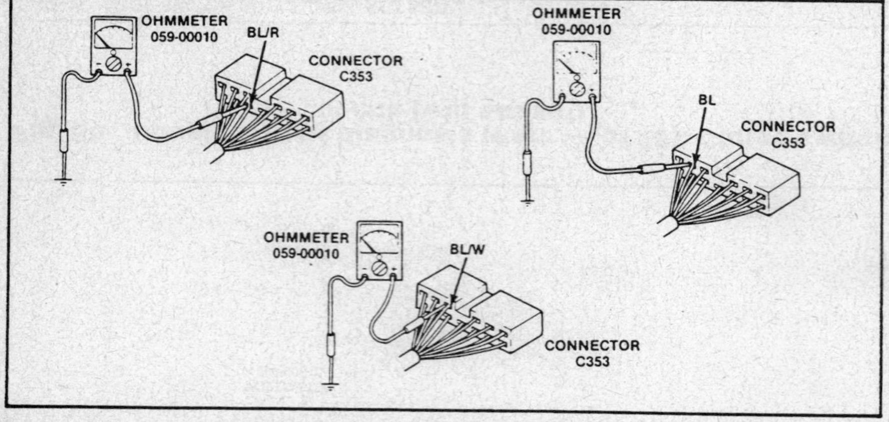

**Fig. 88 Speed control diagnosis (Part 17 of 28). Combination switch signal check (will not set)**

**SP 18 CLUTCH SWITCH CHECK (WILL NOT STOP)**

| TEST STEP | RESULT | ACTION TO TAKE |
|---|---|---|
| NOTE: If equipped with automatic transmission, Go to SP 19. | | |
| • Press clutch switch.<br>• Is there 12V on "BL/O" wire (connector C353) at speed control unit? | No<br>Yes | Go to SP 21.<br>Go to SP 19. |

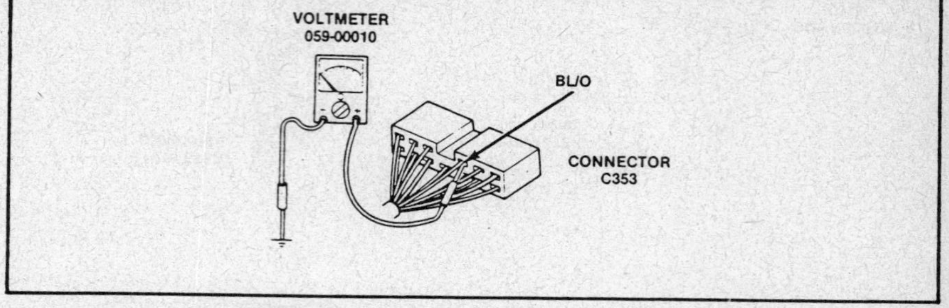

**Fig. 88 Speed control diagnosis (Part 18 of 28). Clutch switch check (will not stop)**

**SP 19 STOP SWITCH CHECK (WILL NOT STOP)**

| TEST STEP | RESULT | ACTION TO TAKE |
|---|---|---|
| • Press brake pedal.<br>• Is there 12V on "BL/O" wire (connector C353) at speed control unit? | No<br>Yes | Go to SP 20.<br>Replace speed control unit. |

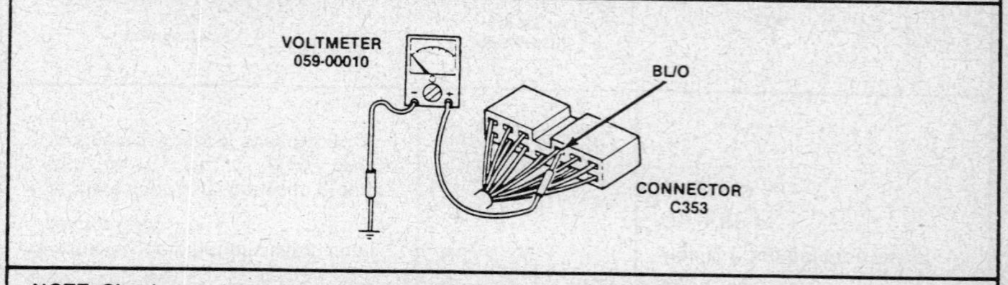

NOTE: Check speed control cable for binding and proper adjustment.

**Fig. 88 Speed control diagnosis (Part 19 of 28). Stop switch check (will not stop)**

| SP 20 STOP SWITCH CHECK (WILL NOT STOP) | | |
|---|---|---|
| **TEST STEP** | **RESULT** | **ACTION TO TAKE** |
| • Press brake pedal.<br>• Is there 12V on both sides of stop switch (connector C356)? | Yes | Repair "BL/O" wire between stop switch and speed control unit. |
| | No 12V on "BK/Y" wire | Repair "BK/Y" wire between fuse panel and stop switch. |
| | No 12V on "BL/O" wire | Replace stop switch. |

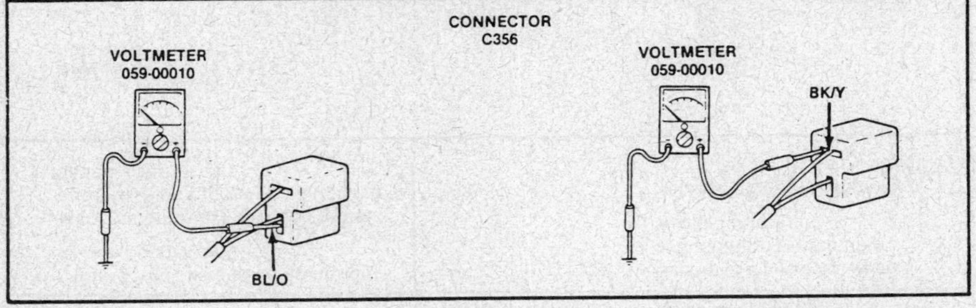

**Fig. 88 Speed control diagnosis (Part 20 of 28). Stop switch check (will not stop)**

| SP 21 CLUTCH SWITCH CHECK (WILL NOT STOP) | | |
|---|---|---|
| **TEST STEP** | **RESULT** | **ACTION TO TAKE** |
| • Press clutch pedal.<br>• Is there 12V on both sides of clutch switch (connector C357)? | Yes | Repair "BL/O" wire between clutch switch and speed control unit. |
| | No 12V on "BK/Y" wire | Repair "BK/Y" wire between fuse panel and clutch switch. |
| | No 12V on "BL/O" wire | Replace clutch switch. |

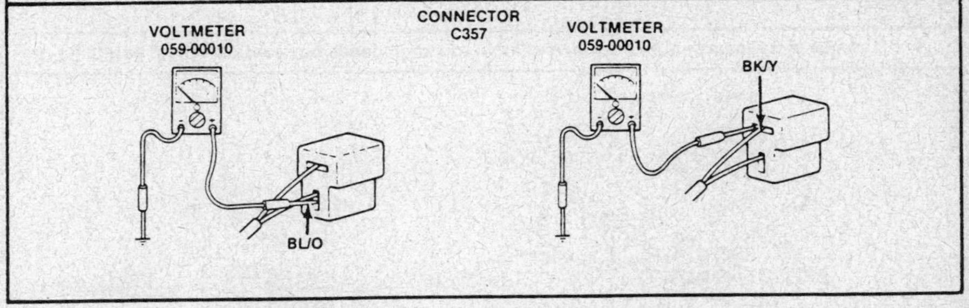

**Fig. 88 Speed control diagnosis (Part 21 of 28). Clutch switch check (will not stop)**

| SP 22 COAST SWITCH CHECK (WILL NOT COAST) | | |
|---|---|---|
| **TEST STEP** | **RESULT** | **ACTION TO TAKE** |
| • Turn speed control switch to coast position.<br>• Is there continuity between ground and "BL/R" wire (connector C353) at speed control unit? | No<br>Yes | Go to SP 23.<br>Replace speed control unit. |

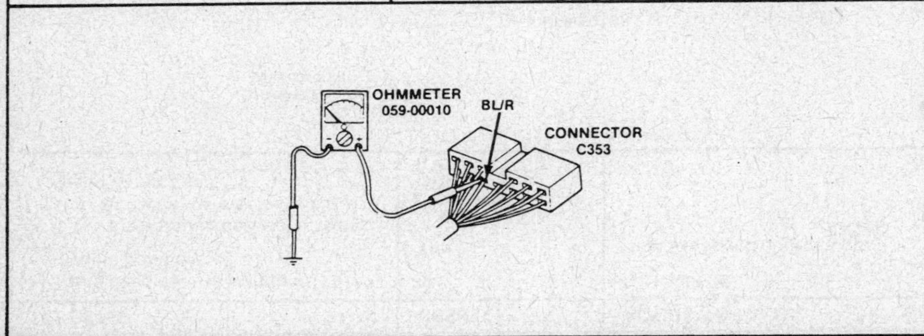

**Fig. 88 Speed control diagnosis (Part 22 of 28). Coast switch check (will not coast)**

| SP 23 COAST SIGNAL CHECK (WILL NOT COAST) | | |
|---|---|---|
| **TEST STEP** | **RESULT** | **ACTION TO TAKE** |
| • Ground "BL/R" wire at combination switch connector C358.<br>• Is there continuity between ground and "BL/R" wire (connector C353) at speed control unit? | No<br><br>Yes | Repair "BL/R" wire between combination switch and speed control unit.<br>Replace combination switch. |

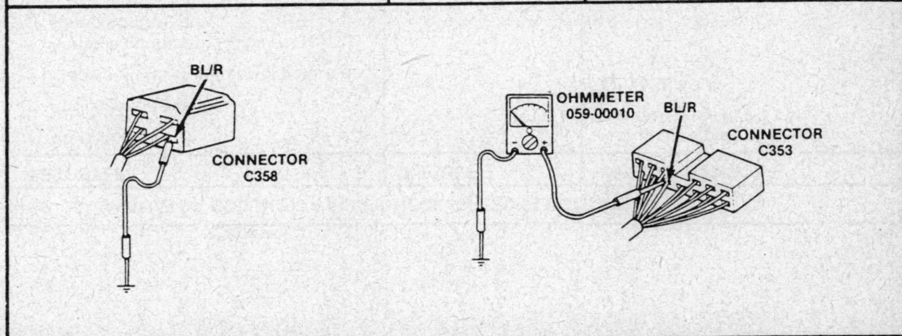

**Fig. 88 Speed control diagnosis (Part 23 of 28). Coast signal check (will not coast)**

**SP 24 RESUME SWITCH CHECK (WILL NOT RESUME)**

| TEST STEP | RESULT | ACTION TO TAKE |
|---|---|---|
| • Turn speed control switch to resume position.<br>• Is there continuity between ground and "BL" wire (connector C353) at speed control unit? | No<br>Yes | Go to SP 25.<br>Replace speed control unit. |

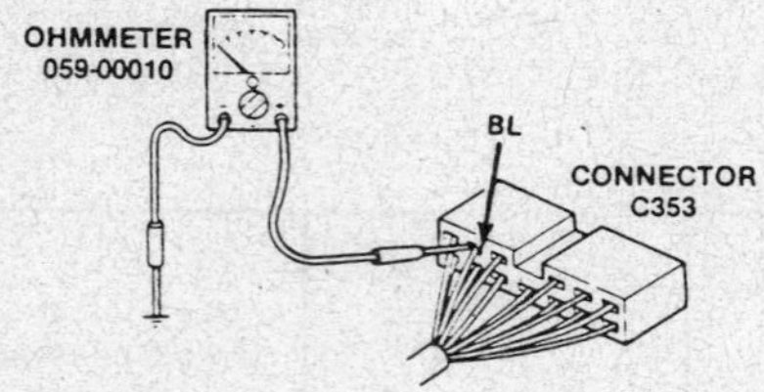

OHMMETER 059-00010
BL
CONNECTOR C353

**Fig. 88 Speed control diagnosis (Part 24 of 28). Resume switch check (will not resume)**

**SP 25 RESUME SIGNAL CHECK (WILL NOT RESUME)**

| TEST STEP | RESULT | ACTION TO TAKE |
|---|---|---|
| • Ground "BL" wire at combination switch connector C358.<br>• Is there continuity between ground and "BL" wire (connector C353) at speed control unit? | No<br>Yes | Repair "BL" wire between combination switch and speed control unit.<br>Replace combination switch. |

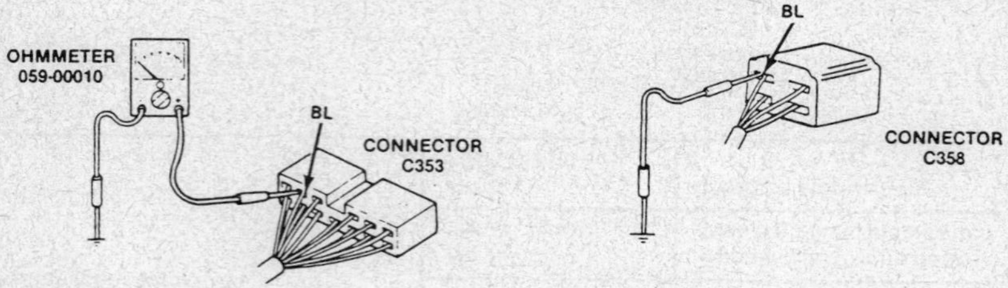

OHMMETER 059-00010
BL
CONNECTOR C353
BL
CONNECTOR C358

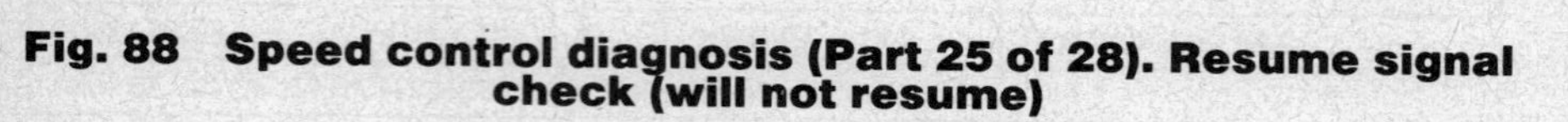

**Fig. 88 Speed control diagnosis (Part 25 of 28). Resume signal check (will not resume)**

**SP 26 ACTUATOR SOLENOID VALVE CHECK (SPEED FLUCTUATES)**

| TEST STEP | RESULT | ACTION TO TAKE |
|---|---|---|
| • Start engine.<br>• Apply parking brake.<br>• Place shift lever in neutral position.<br>• Remove connector C353 from speed control unit.<br>• Connect "GR" and "GR/W" wires (connector C353) to ground. Touch "GR/BK" wire to ground until engine speed reaches 1000-3000 rpm (approximately 1 sec.).<br>• Does engine speed increase and hold at 1,000-300 rpm? | No<br>Yes | Adjust free play of speed control cable to 1-3 mm.<br>Go to SP 7. |

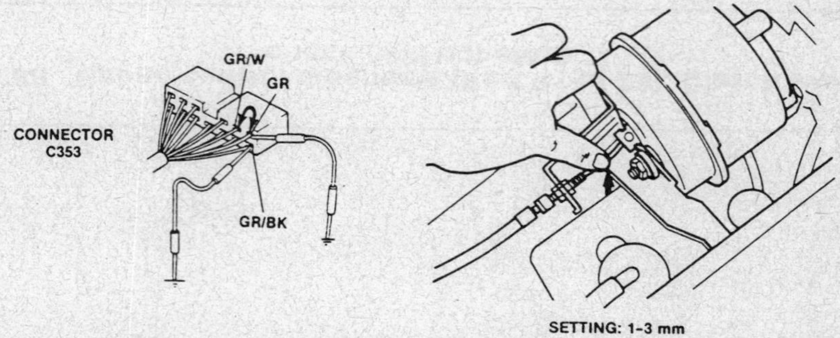

CONNECTOR C353
GR/W
GR
GR/BK
SETTING: 1-3 mm

NOTE: If free play is correct and speed does not increase, replace actuator solenoid valve.

**Fig. 88 Speed control diagnosis (Part 26 of 28). Actuator solenoid valve check (speed fluctuates)**

| SP 27 SPEED SIGNAL CHECK (SPEED FLUCTUATES) | | |
|---|---|---|
| TEST STEP | RESULT | ACTION TO TAKE |
| • Place a low wattage test lamp between 12V and "GR/R" wire (connector C353) at speed control unit.<br>• Drive car slowly (1-5 mph).<br>• Does test lamp flash? | No<br>Yes | Go to SP 8.<br>Replace speed control unit. |
| **NOTE: If speedometer fluctuates when speed control is not being used, go to Section 33-01 (Instruments).** | | |

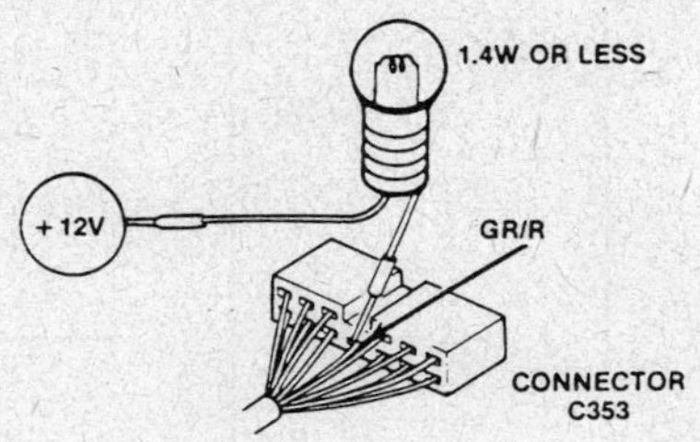

**Fig. 88 Speed control diagnosis (Part 27 of 28). Speed signal check (speed fluctuates)**

| SP 28 SPEED SENSOR SIGNAL CHECK (SPEED FLUCTUATES) | | |
|---|---|---|
| TEST STEP | RESULT | ACTION TO TAKE |
| • Remove instrument panel connector C127.<br>• Place a low wattage test lamp between 12V and "GR/R" wire (connector C353) at speed control unit.<br>• Touch "GR/R" wire to ground several times at instrument panel connector C127.<br>• Does test lamp flash? | No<br>Yes | Repair "GR/R" wire between instruments and speed control unit.<br>Replace speed sensor. |

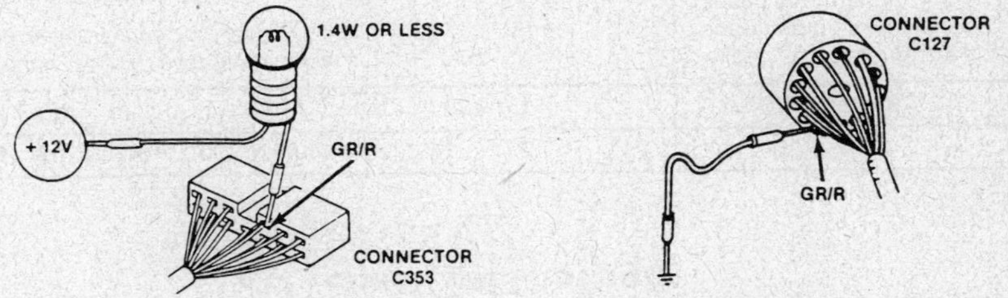

**Fig. 88 Speed control diagnosis (Part 28 of 28). Speed sensor signal check (speed fluctuates)**

| SP 1 SPEED CONTROL SYSTEM CHECK | |
|---|---|
| SYMPTOM | ACTION TO TAKE |
| Schematics and wiring diagrams are illustrated in the Ford Tracer EVTM. | |
| • Speed control will not...<br>— Set<br>— Disengage<br>— Coast<br>— Resume | <br>Go to SP 2.<br>Go to SP 17.<br>Go to SP 21.<br>Go to SP 23. |
| • Speed fluctuates | Go to SP 25. |

**Fig. 89 Speed control diagnosis (Part 1 of 27). Speed control system check**

**SP 2 SPEED CONTROL SYSTEM VOLTAGE CHECK (WILL NOT SET)**

| TEST STEP | RESULT | ACTION TO TAKE |
|---|---|---|
| • Check for voltages (Table B) at speed control unit connectors C347 and C353. | All voltages correct | Go to SP 3. |
| • Go to the test step of the first incorrect voltage condition. | Incorrect voltage at... | |
| | "BL/BK" wire | Go to SP 9. |
| | "GN/BK" wire | Go to SP 11. |
| | "GN" wire | Go to SP 12. |
| | "GN/W" wire | Go to SP 13. |
| | "BL/O" wire | Go to SP 14. |
| | | Go to SP 16. |
| | "BL/R", "BL" or "BL/W" wires | Stoplamps. |
| | "W/G" wire | Ignition System. |
| | "BK/Y" wire | |

TABLE B

| Wire Color | Voltage |
|---|---|
| "BL/BK" | 12V |
| "GN/BK" | 12V |
| "GN" | 12V |
| "GN/W" | 12V |
| "BL/O" | 0V |
| "BL/R" | 12V |
| "BL/W" | 12V |
| "BL" | 12V |
| "W/G" | 0V |
| "BK/Y" | 0V |

• Tolerance +/− 1 volt

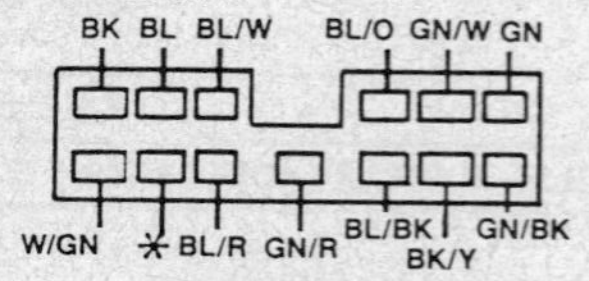

**Fig. 89 Speed control diagnosis (Part 2 of 27). Speed control system voltage check (will not set)**

**SP 3 SET SWITCH CHECK (WILL NOT SET)**

| TEST STEP | RESULT | ACTION TO TAKE |
|---|---|---|
| • Press speed control SET switch. | No | Go to SP 4. |
| • Is there continuity between ground and "BL/W" wire (connector C347) at speed control unit? | Yes | Go to SP 6. |

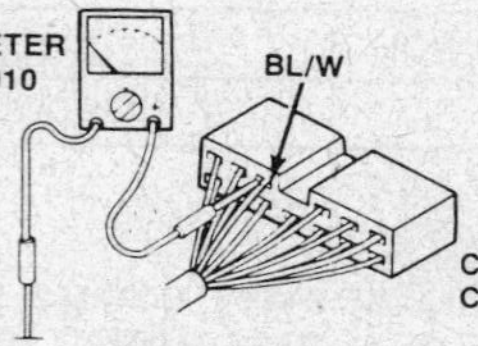

**Fig. 89 Speed control diagnosis (Part 3 of 27). Set switch check (will not set)**

**SP 4 SET SIGNAL CHECK (WILL NOT SET)**

| TEST STEP | RESULT | ACTION TO TAKE |
|---|---|---|
| • Ground "BL/W" wire at combination switch connector C352. | No | Repair "BL/W" wire between combination switch and speed control unit. |
| • Is there continuity between ground and "BL/W" wire (connector C347) at speed control unit? | Yes | Go to SP 5. |

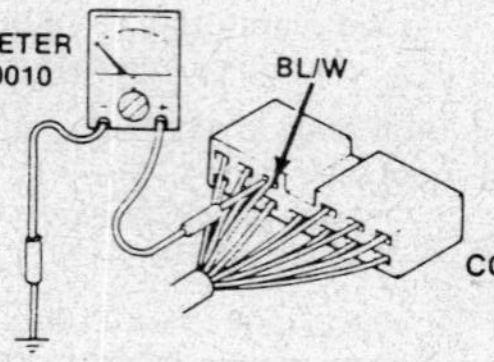

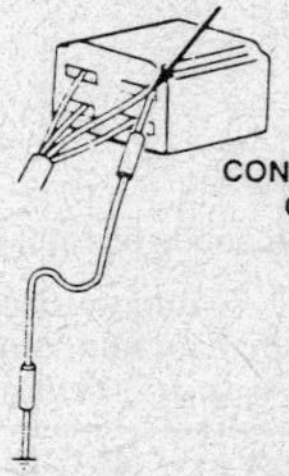

**Fig. 89 Speed control diagnosis (Part 4 of 27). Set signal Check (will not set)**

| SP 5 COMBINATION SWITCH GROUND CHECK (WILL NOT SET) | | |
|---|---|---|
| **TEST STEP** | **RESULT** | **ACTION TO TAKE** |
| • Is there continuity between ground and "BK" wire at combination switch connector C352? | No | Repair "BK" wire between combination switch and ground. |
| | Yes | Replace combination switch. |

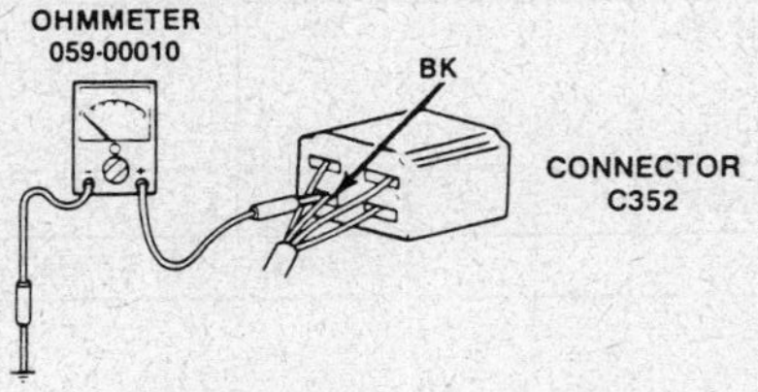

OHMMETER 059-00010
BK
CONNECTOR C352

**Fig. 89 Speed control diagnosis (Part 5 of 27). Combination switch ground check (will not set)**

| SP 7 SPEED SIGNAL CHECK (WILL NOT SET) | | |
|---|---|---|
| **TEST STEP** | **RESULT** | **ACTION TO TAKE** |
| • Place a low wattage test lamp (approximately 1.4 watts), between 12V and "GN/R" wire (connector C347) at speed control unit.<br>• Drive car slowly (1-5 mph).<br>• Does test lamp flash? | No<br>Yes | Go to SP 8.<br>Replace speed control unit. |

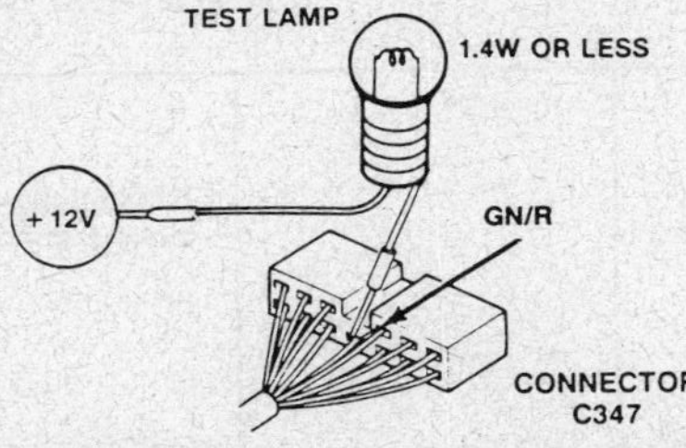

TEST LAMP
1.4W OR LESS
+ 12V
GN/R
CONNECTOR C347

NOTE: If speedometer fluctuates when speed control is not being used, go to Instruments .

**Fig. 89 Speed control diagnosis (Part 7 of 27). Speed signal check (will not set)**

| SP 6 ACTUATOR SOLENOID VALVE CHECK (WILL NOT SET) | | |
|---|---|---|
| **TEST STEP** | **RESULT** | **ACTION TO TAKE** |
| • Start engine.<br>• Apply the parking brake.<br>• Place shift lever in neutral position.<br>• Remove connector C347 from speed control unit.<br>• Connect "GN" and "GN/W" wires (connector C347) to ground. Touch "GN/BK" wire to ground until engine speed reaches 1000-3000 rpm (approximately 1 sec.).<br>• Does engine speed increase and hold at 1,000-3,000 rpm? | No | Adjust free play of speed control cable to 1-3 mm. |
| | Yes | Go to SP 7. |

GN/W
GN
CONNECTOR C347
GN/BK
SETTING: 1-3 mm 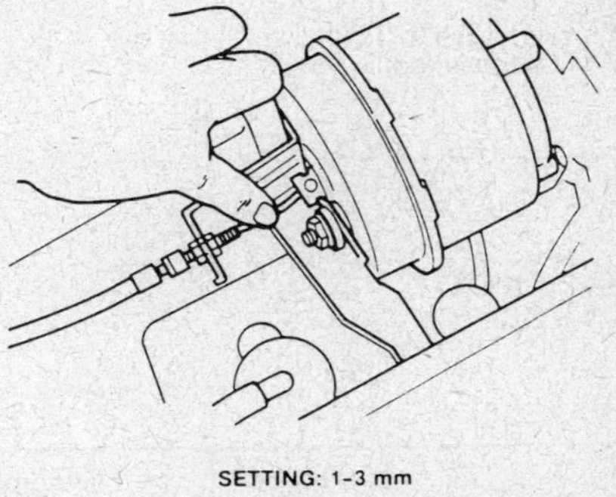

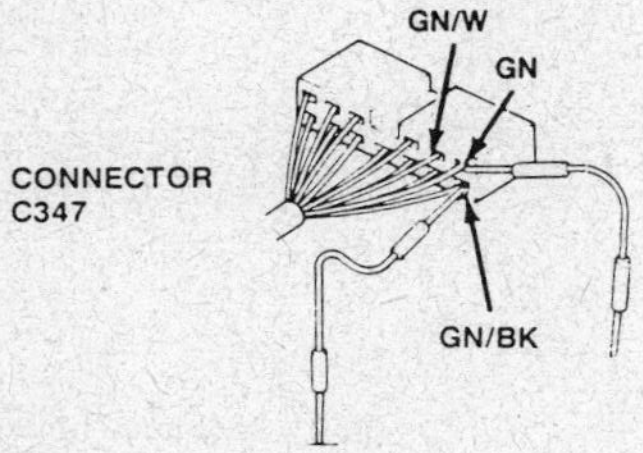

NOTE: If free play is correct and speed does not increase, replace actuator solenoid valve.

**Fig. 89 Speed control diagnosis (Part 6 of 27). Actuator solenoid valve check (will not set)**

| SP 8 SPEED SENSOR SIGNAL CHECK (WILL NOT SET) | | |
|---|---|---|
| **TEST STEP** | **RESULT** | **ACTION TO TAKE** |
| • Remove instrument panel connector C127.<br>• Place a low wattage test lamp between 12V and "GN/R" wire (connector C347) at speed control unit.<br>• Touch "GN/R" wire to ground several times at instrument panel connector C127.<br>• Does test lamp flash? | No | Repair "GN/R" wire between instruments and speed control unit. |
| | Yes | Replace speed sensor. |

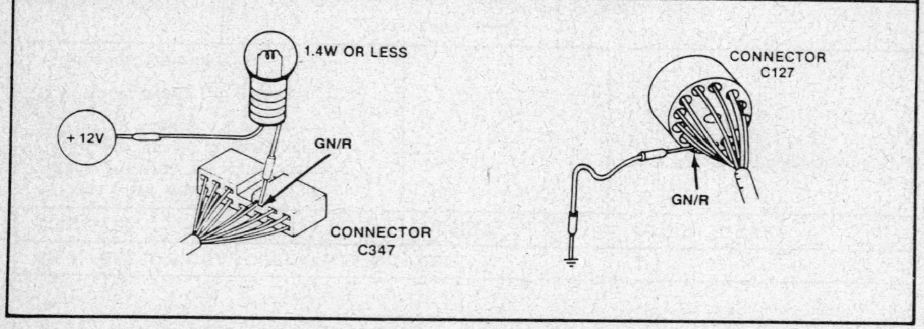

**Fig. 89 Speed control diagnosis (Part 8 of 27). Speed sensor signal check (will not set)**

| SP 9 INSTRUMENT FUSE CHECK (WILL NOT SET) | | |
|---|---|---|
| **TEST STEP** | **RESULT** | **ACTION TO TAKE** |
| • Is instrument meter fuse OK? | No | Replace instrument meter fuse. |
| | Yes | Go to SP 10. |
| NOTE: If fuse blows again, check for shorts to ground in "BK/Y" wires at clutch (connector C351), brake (connector C350), and speed control main switches (connector C348). Repair "BK/Y" wires as needed. | | |

**Fig. 89 Speed control diagnosis (Part 9 of 27). Instrument fuse check (will not set)**

| SP 10 SPEED CONTROL SUPPLY CHECK (WILL NOT SET) | | |
|---|---|---|
| **TEST STEP** | **RESULT** | **ACTION TO TAKE** |
| • Is there 12V on both "BK/Y" and "BL/BK" wires at speed control main switch connector C348? | Yes | Repair "BL/BK" wire between speed control main switch and speed control unit. |
| | No 12 volts on either wire | Repair "BK/Y" wire between fuse panel and speed control main switch. |
| | No 12 volts on one wire only | Replace speed control main switch. |

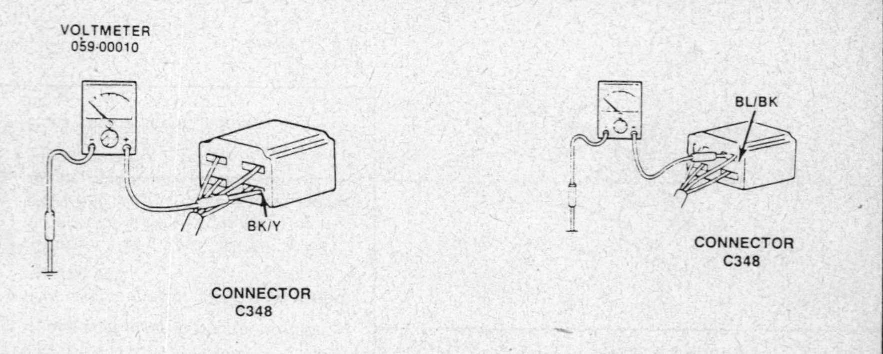

**Fig. 89 Speed control diagnosis (Part 10 of 27). Speed control supply check (will not set)**

| SP 11 VAC SIGNAL CHECK (WILL NOT SET) | | |
|---|---|---|
| TEST STEP | RESULT | ACTION TO TAKE |
| • Is there 12V on both "BL/BK" and "GN/BK" wires (connector C349) at actuator solenoid valve? | Yes | Repair "GN/BK" wire between actuator solenoid valve and speed control unit. |
| | Not on "BL/BK" wire. | Repair "BL/BK" wire between actuator solenoid valve and speed control main switch. |
| | Not on "GN/BK" wire. | Replace actuator solenoid valve. |

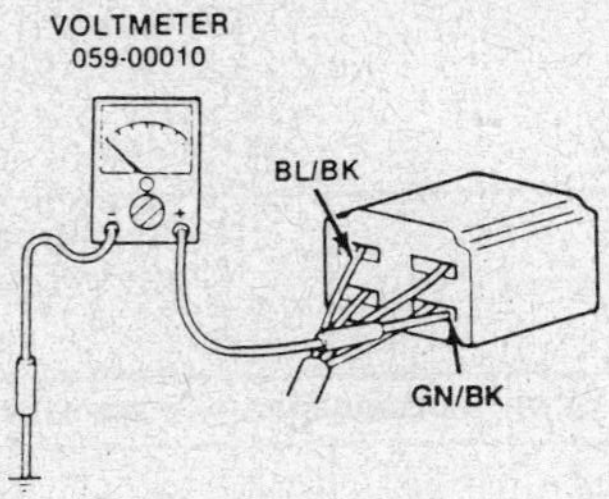

**Fig. 89 Speed control diagnosis (Part 11 of 27). VAC signal check (will not set)**

| SP 12 VENT 2 SIGNAL CHECK (WILL NOT SET) | | |
|---|---|---|
| TEST STEP | RESULT | ACTION TO TAKE |
| • Is there 12V on "GN" wire (connector C349) at actuator solenoid valve? | No | Replace actuator solenoid valve. |
| | Yes | Repair "GN" wire between actuator solenoid valve and speed control unit. |

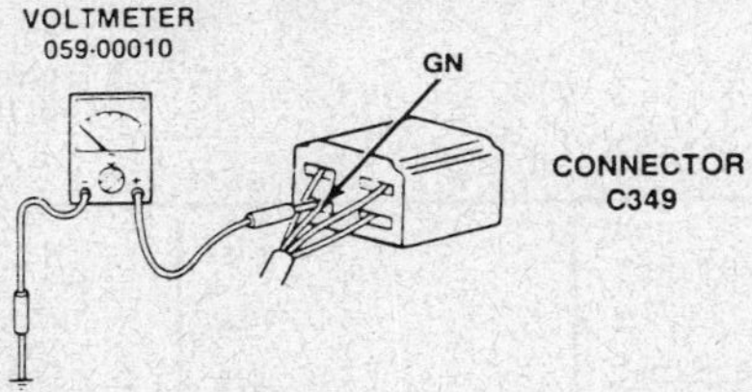

**Fig. 89 Speed control diagnosis (Part 12 of 27). Vent 2 signal check (will not set)**

| SP 13 VENT 1 SIGNAL CHECK (WILL NOT SET) | | |
|---|---|---|
| TEST STEP | RESULT | ACTION TO TAKE |
| • Is there 12V on "GN/W" wire (connector C349) at actuator solenoid valve? | No | Replace actuator solenoid valve. |
| | Yes | Repair "GN/W" wire between actuator solenoid valve and speed control unit. |

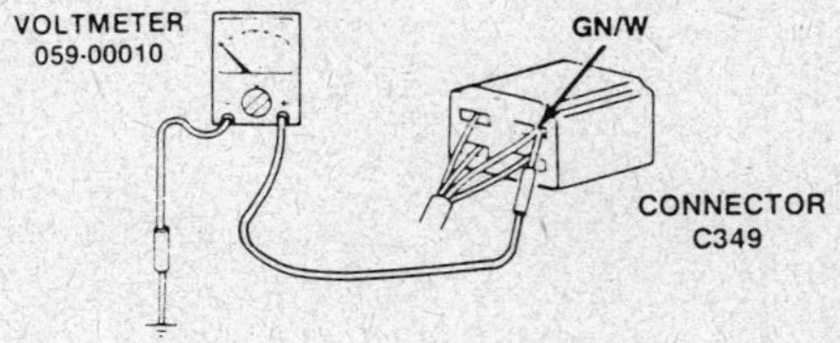

**Fig. 89 Speed control diagnosis (Part 13 of 27). Vent 1 signal check (will not set)**

| SP 14 CLUTCH SWITCH CHECK (WILL NOT SET) | | |
|---|---|---|
| TEST STEP | RESULT | ACTION TO TAKE |
| • (If equipped with automatic transmission. Go to SP 16.)<br>• Remove clutch switch connector.<br>• Is there 12V on "BL/O" wire (connector C347) at speed control unit? | No<br>Yes | Replace clutch switch.<br>Go to SP 15. |

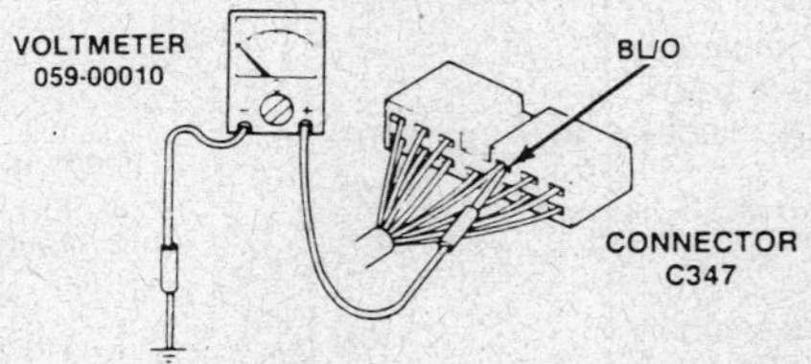

**Fig. 89 Speed control diagnosis (Part 14 of 27). Clutch switch check (will not set)**

| SP 15 STOP SWITCH CHECK (WILL NOT SET) | | |
|---|---|---|
| **TEST STEP** | **RESULT** | **ACTION TO TAKE** |
| • Remove stop switch connector.<br>• Is there 12V on "BL/O" wire (connector C347) at speed control unit? | No<br>Yes | Replace stop switch.<br>Repair "BL/O" wire between stop switch and speed control unit. |

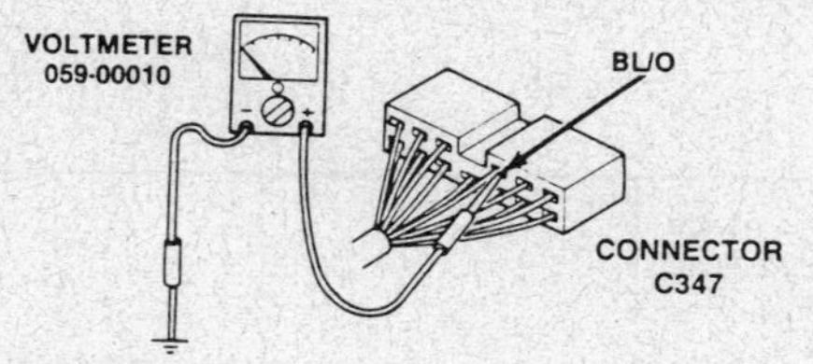

Fig. 89 Speed control diagnosis (Part 15 of 27). Stop switch check (will not set)

| SP 17 CLUTCH SWITCH CHECK (WILL NOT DISENGAGE) | | |
|---|---|---|
| **TEST STEP** | **RESULT** | **ACTION TO TAKE** |
| **NOTE: If equipped with automatic transmission, Go to SP 18.** | | |
| • Press clutch switch.<br>• Is there 12V on "BL/O" wire (connector C347) at speed control unit? | No<br>Yes | Go to SP 20.<br>Go to SP 18. |

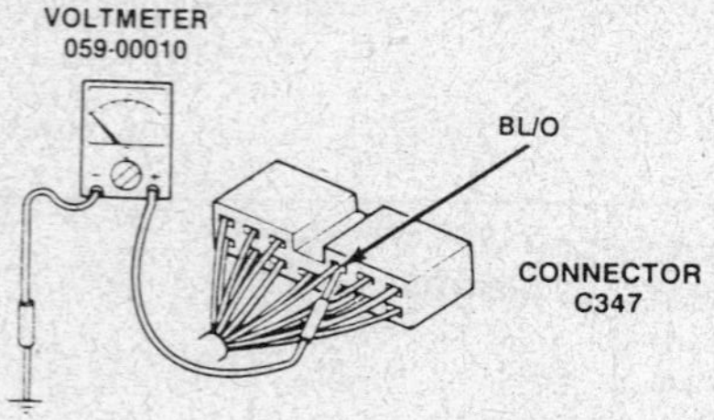

Fig. 89 Speed control diagnosis (Part 17 of 27). Clutch switch check (will not disengage)

| SP 16 COMBINATION SWITCH CHECK (WILL NOT SET) | | |
|---|---|---|
| **TEST STEP** | **RESULT** | **ACTION TO TAKE** |
| • Remove combination switch connector C352. | No | Replace combination switch. |
| • Is there continuity between ground and "BL/R", "BL", and "BL/W" wires (connector C347) at speed control unit? | There is continuity in: | |
| | —"BL/R" wire | Repair "BL/R" wire between speed control unit and combination switch. |
| | —"BL" wire | Repair "BL" wire between speed control unit and combination switch. |
| | —"BL/W" wire | Repair "BL/W" wire between speed control unit and combination switch. |

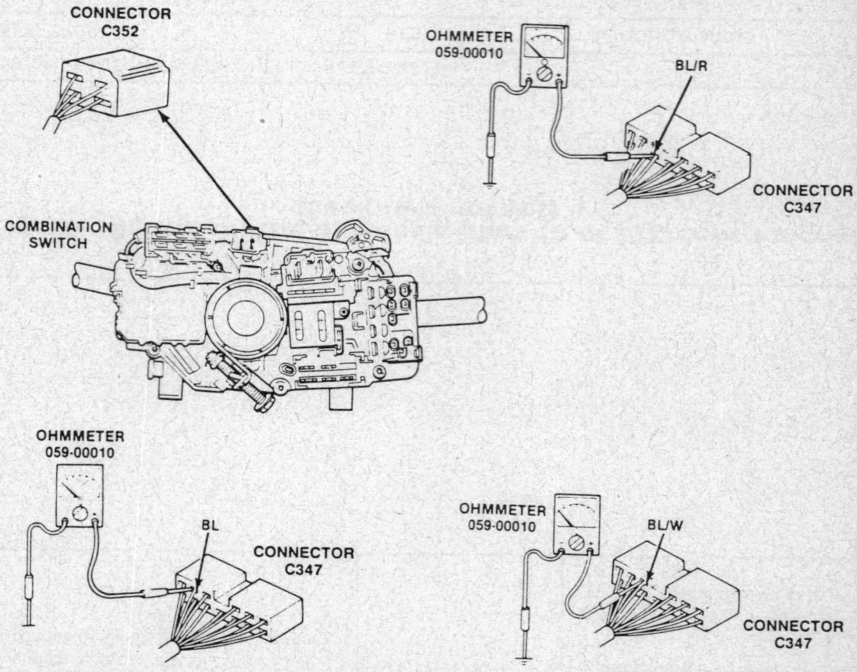

Fig. 89 Speed control diagnosis (Part 16 of 27). Combination switch check (will not set)

| SP 18 STOP SWITCH CHECK (WILL NOT DISENGAGE) | | |
|---|---|---|
| TEST STEP | RESULT | ACTION TO TAKE |
| • Press brake pedal.<br>• Is there 12V on "BL/O" wire (connector C347) at speed control unit? | No<br>Yes | Go to SP 19.<br>Replace speed control unit. |

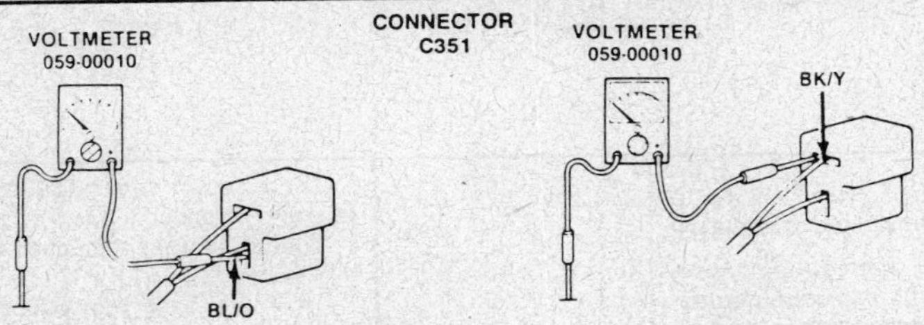

VOLTMETER 059-00010
BL/O
CONNECTOR C347

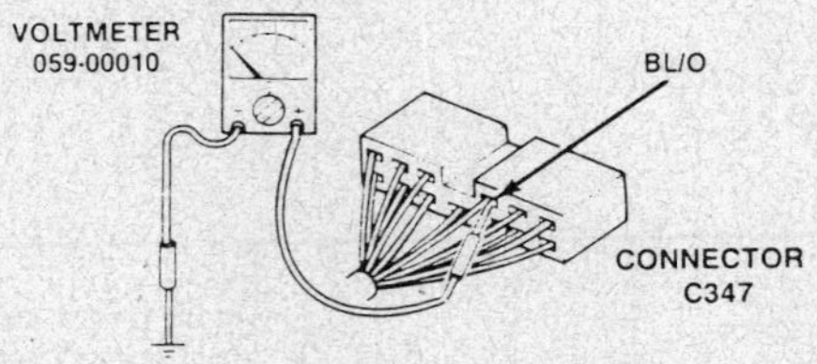

NOTE: Check speed control cable for binding and proper adjustment.

**Fig. 89 Speed control diagnosis (Part 18 of 27). Stop switch check (will not disengage)**

| SP 19 STOP SWITCH CHECK (WILL NOT DISENGAGE) | | |
|---|---|---|
| TEST STEP | RESULT | ACTION TO TAKE |
| • Press brake pedal.<br>• Is there 12V on both sides of stop switch (connector C350)? | Yes | Repair "BL/O" wire between stop switch and speed control unit. |
| | No 12V on "BK/Y" wire | Repair "BK/Y" wire between fuse panel and stop switch. |
| | No 12V on "BL/O" wire | Replace stop switch. |

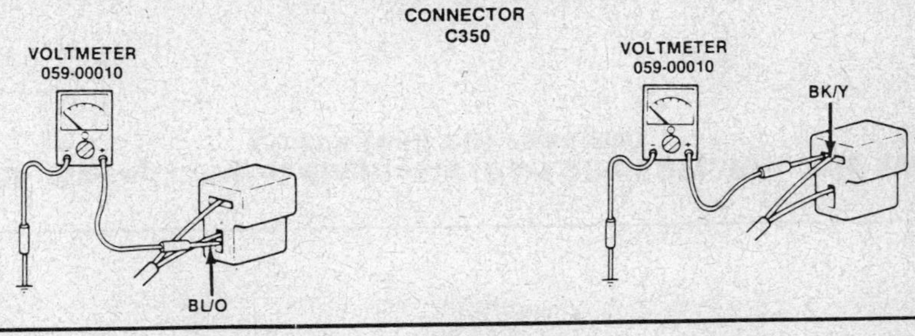

CONNECTOR C350
VOLTMETER 059-00010
VOLTMETER 059-00010
BK/Y
BL/O

**Fig. 89 Speed control diagnosis (Part 19 of 27). Stop switch check (will not disengage)**

| SP 20 CLUTCH SWITCH CHECK (WILL NOT DISENGAGE) | | |
|---|---|---|
| TEST STEP | RESULT | ACTION TO TAKE |
| • Press clutch pedal.<br>• Is there 12V on both sides of clutch switch (connector C351)? | Yes | Repair "BL/O" wire between clutch switch and speed control unit. |
| | No 12V on "BK/Y" wire | Repair "BK/Y" wire between fuse panel and clutch switch. |
| | No 12V on "BL/O" wire | Replace clutch switch. |

VOLTMETER 059-00010
CONNECTOR C351
VOLTMETER 059-00010
BK/Y
BL/O

**Fig. 89 Speed control diagnosis (Part 20 of 27). Clutch switch check (will not disengage)**

| SP 21 COAST SWITCH CHECK (WILL NOT COAST) | | |
|---|---|---|
| TEST STEP | RESULT | ACTION TO TAKE |
| • Turn speed control switch to COAST position.<br>• Is there continuity between ground and "BL/R" wire (connector C347) at speed control unit? | No<br>Yes | Go to SP 22.<br>Replace speed control unit. |

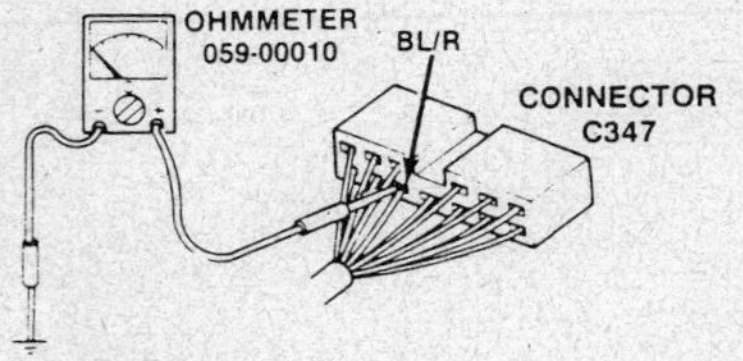

OHMMETER 059-00010
BL/R
CONNECTOR C347

**Fig. 89 Speed control diagnosis (Part 21 of 27). Coast switch check (will not coast)**

| SP 22 COAST SIGNAL CHECK (WILL NOT COAST) | | |
|---|---|---|
| TEST STEP | RESULT | ACTION TO TAKE |
| • Ground "BL/R" wire at combination switch connector C352.<br>• Is there continuity between ground and "BL/R" wire (connector C347) at speed control unit? | No | Repair "BL/R" wire between combination switch and speed control unit. |
| | Yes | Replace combination switch. |

**Fig. 89 Speed control diagnosis (Part 22 of 27). Coast signal check (will not coast)**

| SP 24 RESUME SIGNAL CHECK (WILL NOT RESUME) | | |
|---|---|---|
| TEST STEP | RESULT | ACTION TO TAKE |
| • Ground "BL" wire at combination switch connector C352.<br>• Is there continuity between ground and "BL" wire (connector C347) at speed control unit? | No | Repair "BL" wire between combination switch and speed control unit. |
| | Yes | Replace combination switch. |

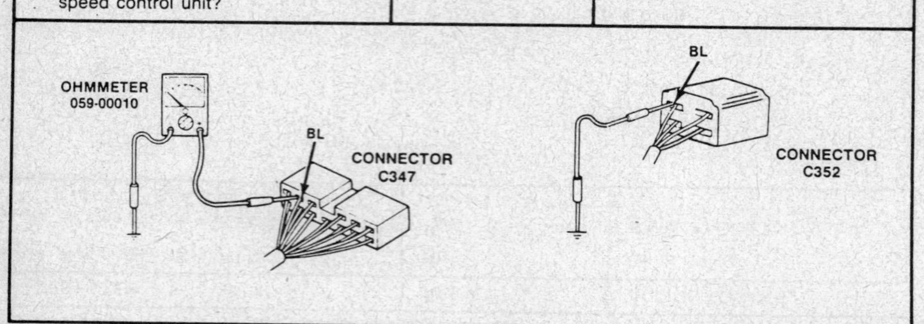


**Fig. 89 Speed control diagnosis (Part 24 of 27). Resume signal check (will not resume)**

| SP 23 RESUME SWITCH CHECK (WILL NOT RESUME) | | |
|---|---|---|
| TEST STEP | RESULT | ACTION TO TAKE |
| • Turn speed control switch to RESUME position.<br>• Is there continuity between ground and "BL" wire (connector C347) at speed control unit? | No | Go to SP 24. |
| | Yes | Replace speed control unit. |

**Fig. 89 Speed control diagnosis (Part 23 of 27). Resume switch check (will not resume)**

**SP 25 ACTUATOR SOLENOID VALVE CHECK (SPEED FLUCTUATES)**

| TEST STEP | RESULT | ACTION TO TAKE |
|---|---|---|
| • Start engine.<br>• Apply parking brake.<br>• Place shift lever in neutral position.<br>• Remove connector C347 from speed control unit.<br>• Connect "GN" and "GN/W" wires (connector C347) to ground. Touch "GN/BK" wire to ground until engine speed reaches 1000-3000 rpm (approximately 1 sec.)<br>• Does engine speed increase and hold at 1,000-3,000 rpm? | No<br>Yes | Adjust free play of speed control cable to 1-3 mm.<br>Go to SP 26. |

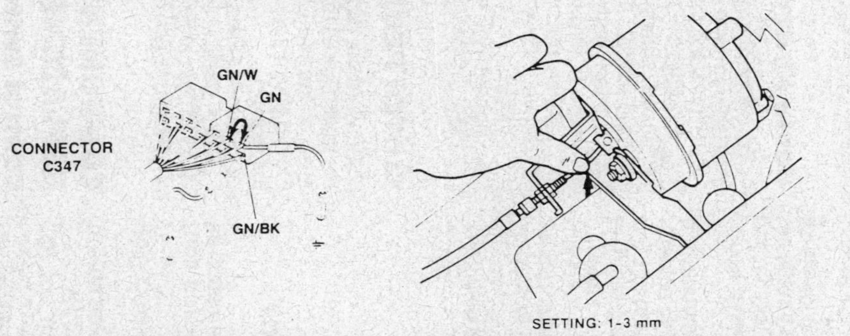

NOTE: If free play is correct and speed does not increase, replace actuator solenoid valve.

**Fig. 89 Speed control diagnosis (Part 25 of 27). Actuator solenoid valve check (speed fluctuates)**

**SP 26 SPEED SIGNAL CHECK (SPEED FLUCTUATES)**

| TEST STEP | RESULT | ACTION TO TAKE |
|---|---|---|
| • Place a low wattage test lamp between 12V and "GN/R" wire (connector C347) at speed control unit.<br>• Drive car slowly (1-5 mph).<br>• Does test lamp falsh? | No<br>Yes | Go to SP 27.<br>Replace speed control unit. |

**NOTE: If speedometer fluctuates when speed control is not being used, go to Instruments .**

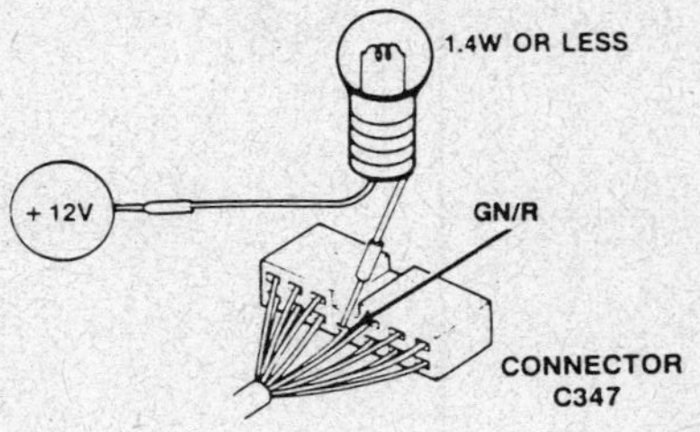

**Fig. 89 Speed control diagnosis (Part 26 of 27). Speed signal check (speed fluctuates)**

| SP 27 SPEED SENSOR SIGNAL CHECK (SPEED FLUCTUATES) | | |
|---|---|---|
| TEST STEP | RESULT | ACTION TO TAKE |
| • Remove instrument panel connector C127.<br>• Place a low wattage test lamp between 12V and "GN/R" wire (connector C347) at speed control unit.<br>• Touch "GR/R" wire to ground several times at instrument panel connector C127.<br>• Does test lamp flash? | No<br><br>Yes | Repair "GN/R" wire between instruments and speed control unit.<br><br>Replace speed sensor. |

**Fig. 89 Speed control diagnosis (Part 27 of 27). Speed sensor signal check (speed fluctuates)**

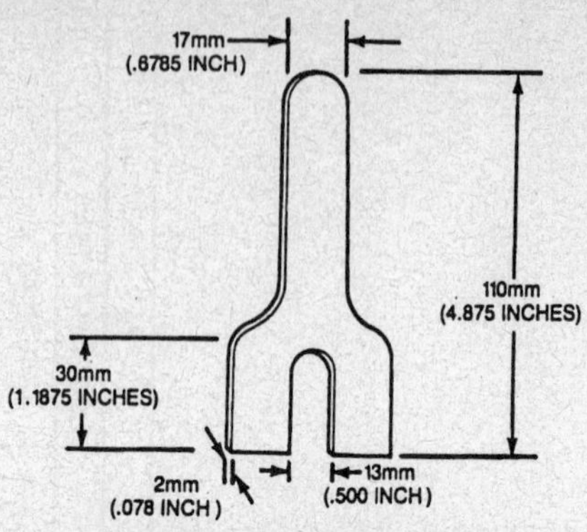


**Fig. 90 Description of tool fabrication for cable adjustments**

# CAPRI

## DESCRIPTION

The speed control system consists of operator controls, an electronic throttle actuator, electronic control unit, clutch and brake switches and an electronic speed sensor.

The operator controls are mounted in the steering wheel. The electronic actuator is mounted in the engine compartment and is connected to the throttle by a cable. The clutch and brake switches are mounted to the pedal assembly. The electronic control unit is located behind the instrument panel. The electronic speed sensor is located on the speedometer cable at the upper and lower cable connection in the engine compartment.

## ADJUSTMENTS

### ACTUATOR CABLE

#### Cable at Throttle Body

**A setting tool must be fabricated as shown in Fig. 90, to adjust speed control cables.**

1. Disconnect cable from cruise control actuator.
2. Slightly loosen cable retaining nuts at bracket on cylinder head cover.
3. Insert setting tool between nut "B" and bracket, **Fig. 91.**
4. Tighten both nuts to eliminate all cable slack.
5. Loosen nut "A" only enough to remove tool. Do not adjust nut "B."
6. Tighten nut "A" without moving nut "B."

#### Cable At Actuator

**To be performed after throttle body end adjustment.**

1. Slightly loosen cable retaining nuts at bracket.
2. Insert setting tool between bracket and nut "D," **Fig. 92.**
3. Tighten both nuts to eliminate all slack at throttle body end of cable.
4. Loosen nut "C" only enough to remove setting tool . Do not adjust nut "D."
5. Tighten nut "C" without moving nut "D."

### CLUTCH PEDAL HEIGHT

Measure the distance from the center of the clutch pedal to lower dash panel (front area of footwell). Pedal height must be 8.44-8.64 inches. Adjust if necessary as follows:

1. Loosen locknut and turn clutch switch until desired pedal height is obtained.
2. Tighten locknut when clutch pedal height is achieved.

## COMPONENT REPLACEMENT

#### Control Switches

1. Disarm airbag system as described under "Airbag Systenm Disarming."
2. Remove airbag module. **Place airbagt module on bench with trim cover facing up.**
3. Disconnect speed control harness connector.
4. Using a small flat blade screwdriver, pry out horn switches and disconnect horn wires.
5. Remove speed control switches retaining screws.
6. Remove speed control switches and harness assembly.
7. Reverse procedure to install.
8. Reactivate airbag system as described under "Airbag System Disarming."

#### Control Module

The control module is mounted under the front of the floor console. The ashtray can be removed to gain access to the module for testing.

1. Disconnect battery ground cable.
2. Remove front console side covers, then front console.
3. Remove control unit retaining screws, then disconnect electrical connector.
4. Remove control unit.
5. Reverse procedure to install.

#### Cable/Actuator Assembly

1. Remove two bolts from cable actuator.
2. Release cable from accelerator pedal, then pull cable into engine compartment.
3. Loosen locknut, then remove cable from actuator.
4. Loosen locknut, then remove cable from bracket and throttle linkage.
5. Remove cable/actuator assembly.
6. Reverse procedure to install. **Torque** cable/actuator assembly retaining bolts to 6-8 ft. lbs.

## DIAGNOSIS & TESTING

The wiring diagram in **Fig. 93.** may be used as a diagnostic aid when performing testing procedures in **Fig. 94.**

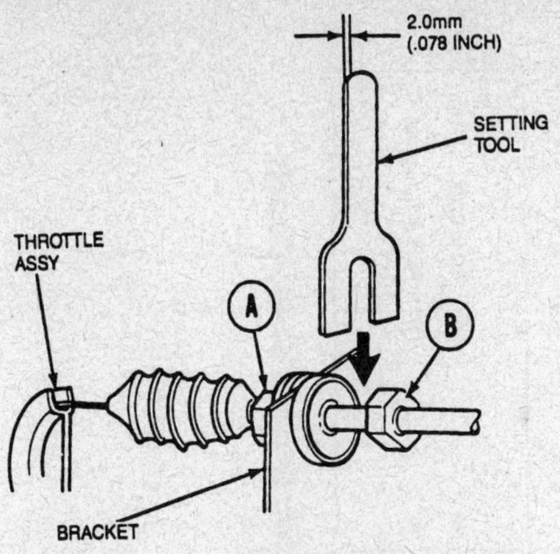


Fig. 91 Location of nut "B"

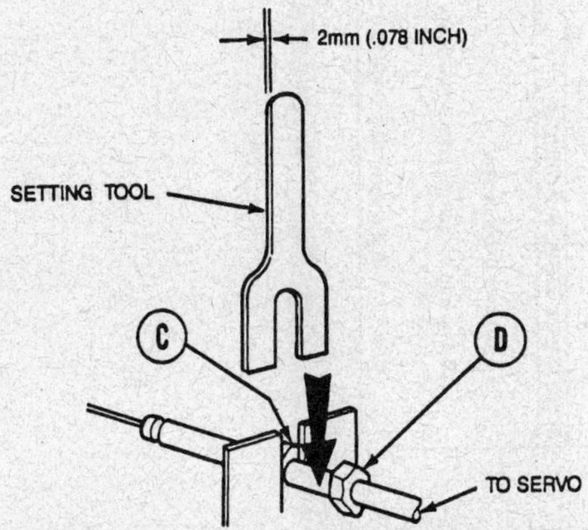


Fig. 92 Location of nut "D"

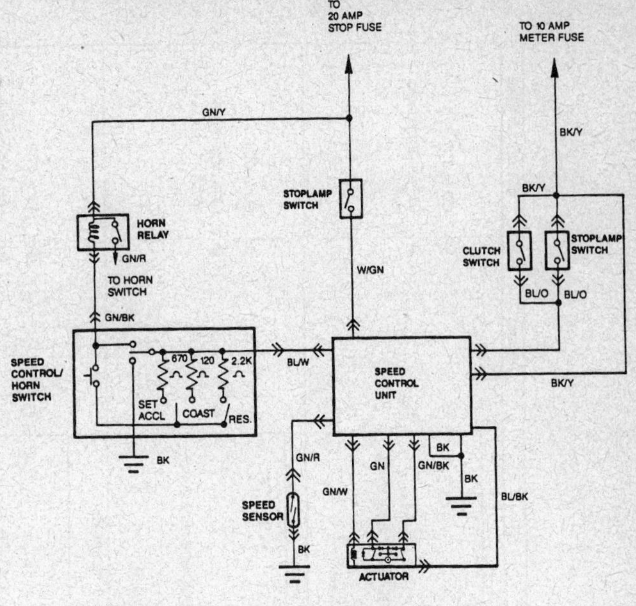


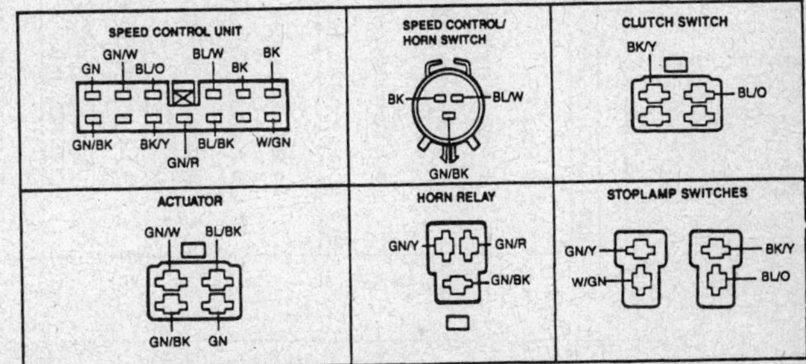


Fig. 93 Speed control wiring diagram

| CONDITION | POSSIBLE SOURCE | ACTION |
|---|---|---|
| • Speed Control System Does Not Operate | • Fuse.<br>• Speed/horn switch.<br>• Speed control unit.<br>• Actuator.<br>• Speed sensor.<br>• Circuit. | • Go to CC1.<br>• Go to CC16.<br>• Go to CC24.<br>• Go to CC23.<br>• Go to CC21.<br>• Go to CC5. |
| • Speed Control System Will Not Set Speed | • Speed/horn switch.<br>• Speed sensor.<br>• Speed control unit.<br>• Circuit. | • Go to CC16.<br>• Go to CC21.<br>• Go to CC24.<br>• Go to CC5. |
| • Speed Control System Works Intermittently | • Actuator.<br>• Speed control unit.<br>• Speed sensor.<br>• Circuit. | • Go to CC23.<br>• Go to CC24.<br>• Go to CC21.<br>• Go to CC5. |
| • Speed/Horn Switch Position Do Not Operate | • Speed/horn switch.<br>• Speed control unit.<br>• Actuator.<br>• Circuit. | • Go to CC16.<br>• Go to CC24.<br>• Go to CC23.<br>• Go to CC5. |
| • Set Speed Fluctuates | • Actuator.<br>• Speed sensor.<br>• Speed control unit.<br>• Circuit. | • Go to CC23.<br>• Go to CC21.<br>• Go to CC24.<br>• Go to CC5. |
| • Speed Control System Does Not Shut Off With Brakes Depressed | • Stoplamp switch.<br>• Speed control unit.<br>• Actuator.<br>• Circuit. | • Go to CC10.<br>• Go to CC24.<br>• Go to CC23.<br>• Go to CC5. |
| • Speed Control System Does Not Shut Off With Clutch Depressed | • Clutch switch.<br>• Speed control unit.<br>• Actuator.<br>• Circuit. | • Go to CC7.<br>• Go to CC24.<br>• Go to CC23.<br>• Go to CC5. |

Fig. 94 Diagnosis & Testing (Part 1 of 6). Capri

| TEST STEP | | RESULT | ACTION TO TAKE |
|---|---|---|---|
| CC1 | CHECK FUSES | | |
| | • Key OFF.<br>• Access interior fuse panel.<br>• Check the 20 amp stop fuse and the 10 amp meter fuse.<br>• Are the fuses good? | Yes ▶<br>No ▶ | GO to **CC4**.<br>GO to **CC2**. |
| CC2 | CHECK SYSTEM | | |
| | • Replace blown fuses.<br>• Key ON.<br>• Did the fuse(s) blow again? | Yes ▶<br>No ▶ | GO to **CC3**.<br>GO to **CC4**. |
| CC3 | CHECK FOR SHORTS TO GROUND | | |
| | • Key OFF.<br>• Disconnect the GN/Y wire from the stop fuse.<br>• Measure the resistance of the GN/Y wire to ground.<br>• Disconnect the BK/Y wire from the meter fuse.<br>• Measure the resistance of the BK/Y wire to ground.<br>• Are the resistances less than 5 ohms? | Yes ▶<br>No ▶ | SERVICE wire(s) in question.<br>GO to **CC4**. |
| CC4 | CHECK POWER SUPPLY TO SPEED CONTROL UNIT | | |
| | • Locate speed control unit.<br>• Key ON.<br>• Measure the voltage on the BK/Y wire.<br>• Is the voltage greater than 10 volts? | Yes ▶<br>No ▶ | GO to **CC5**.<br>SERVICE BK/Y wire. |
| CC5 | CHECK SUPPLY TO STOPLAMP AND CLUTCH SWITCHES | | |
| | • Locate clutch and stop switches.<br>• Measure the voltage on the BK/Y wire at each connector.<br>• Are the voltages greater than 10 volts? | Yes ▶<br>No ▶ | GO to **CC6**.<br>SERVICE BK/Y wire. |

**Fig. 94 Diagnosis & Testing (Part 2 of 6). Capri**

| TEST STEP | | RESULT | ACTION TO TAKE |
|---|---|---|---|
| CC6 | CHECK STOPLAMP SWITCH | | |
| | • Key OFF.<br>• Depress the brake pedal.<br>• Measure the voltage on the BL/O wire at the switch connector.<br>• Is the voltage greater than 10 volts? | Yes ▶<br>No ▶ | GO to **CC7**.<br>REPLACE stoplamp switch. |
| CC7 | CHECK CLUTCH SWITCH | | |
| | • Release the brake pedal.<br>• Depress the clutch.<br>• Measure the voltage on the BL/O wire at the switch connector.<br>• Is the voltage greater than 10 volts? | Yes ▶<br>No ▶ | GO to **CC8**.<br>REPLACE clutch switch. |
| CC8 | CHECK LEAD FROM SWITCHES TO SPEED CONTROL UNIT | | |
| | • Locate speed control unit.<br>• Measure the resistance of the BL/O wire between the switches and the speed control unit.<br>• Is the resistance less than 5 ohms? | Yes ▶<br>No ▶ | GO to **CC9**.<br>SERVICE BL/O wire. |
| CC9 | CHECK POWER SUPPLY TO STOPLAMP SWITCH | | |
| | • Locate stoplamp switch.<br>• Measure voltage on the GN/Y wire at the connector.<br>• Is the voltage greater than 10 volts? | Yes ▶<br>No ▶ | GO to **CC10**.<br>SERVICE GN/Y wire. |
| CC10 | CHECK STOPLAMP SWITCH | | |
| | • Depress brake pedal.<br>• Measure the voltage on the W/GN wire at the connector.<br>• Is the voltage greater than 10 volts? | Yes ▶<br>No ▶ | GO to **CC11**.<br>REPLACE stoplamp switch. |

**Fig. 94 Diagnosis & Testing (Part 3 of 6). Capri**

| TEST STEP | RESULT ▶ | ACTION TO TAKE |
|---|---|---|
| **CC11** CHECK LEAD TO SPEED CONTROL UNIT | | |
| • Key OFF.<br>• Locate the speed control unit.<br>• Measure the resistance of the W/GN wire between the stoplamp switch and the speed control unit.<br>• Is the resistance less than 5 ohms? | Yes ▶<br>No ▶ | GO to **CC12**.<br>SERVICE W/GN wire. |
| **CC12** CHECK POWER SUPPLY TO HORN RELAY | | |
| • Locate horn relay.<br>• Key ON.<br>• Measure the voltage on the GN/Y wire at the horn relay.<br>• Is the voltage greater than 10 volts? | Yes ▶<br>No ▶ | GO to **CC13**.<br>SERVICE GN/Y wire. |
| **CC13** CHECK CONTINUITY THROUGH HORN RELAY | | |
| • Measure the voltage on the GN/BK wire at the relay connector.<br>• Is the voltage greater than 10 volts? | Yes ▶<br>No ▶ | GO to **CC14**.<br>REPLACE horn relay. |
| **CC14** CHECK LEAD BETWEEN HORN RELAY AND SPEED/HORN SWITCH | | |
| • Locate the speed/horn switch.<br>• Measure the voltage on the GN/BK wire at the speed/horn switch.<br>• Is the voltage greater than 10 volts? | Yes ▶<br>No ▶ | GO to **CC15**.<br>SERVICE GN/BK wire. |
| **CC15** CHECK SPEED/HORN SWITCH GROUND | | |
| • Key OFF.<br>• Measure the resistance of the BK wire between the speed/horn switch and ground.<br>• Is the resistance less than 5 ohms? | Yes ▶<br>No ▶ | GO to **CC16**.<br>SERVICE BK wire. |

**Fig. 94 Diagnosis & Testing (Part 4 of 6). Capri**

| TEST STEP | RESULT ▶ | ACTION TO TAKE |
|---|---|---|
| **CC16** CHECK SPEED/HORN SWITCH | | |
| • Disconnect the BL/W wire from the connector.<br>• Connect the positive lead of the ohmmeter to the BL/W terminal of the connector and the negative lead to ground.<br>• Verify the resistances on the BL/W terminal of the connector while holding the speed/horn switch in the following positions:<br>**Switch Position** — **Resistance**<br>OFF — Greater than 10,000 ohms<br>ON — Greater than 10,000 ohms<br>SET — Approximately 680 ohms<br>RESUME — Approximately 2,200 ohms<br>COAST — Approximately 120 ohms<br>ACC — Approximately 680 ohms<br>• Are the resistances correct? | Yes ▶<br>No ▶ | GO to **CC17**.<br>REPLACE speed/horn switch. |
| **CC17** CHECK LEAD BETWEEN SPEED/HORN SWITCH AND SPEED CONTROL UNIT | | |
| • Key OFF.<br>• Locate the speed control unit.<br>• Measure the resistance of the BL/W wire between the speed/horn switch and the speed control unit.<br>• Is the resistance less than 5 ohms? | Yes ▶<br>No ▶ | GO to **CC18**.<br>SERVICE BL/W wire. |
| **CC18** CHECK SPEED CONTROL UNIT GROUND | | |
| • Measure the resistance of the BK wires to ground.<br>• Are the resistances less than 5 ohms? | Yes ▶<br>No ▶ | GO to **CC19**.<br>SERVICE BK wire(s). |
| **CC19** CHECK LEAD BETWEEN SPEED CONTROL UNIT AND SPEED SENSOR | | |
| • Locate speed sensor.<br>• Measure the resistance of the GN/R wire between the speed control unit and the speed sensor.<br>• Is the resistance less than 5 ohms? | Yes ▶<br>No ▶ | GO to **CC20**.<br>SERVICE GN/R wire. |

**Fig. 94 Diagnosis & Testing (Part 5 of 6). Capri**

| TEST STEP | RESULT | ACTION TO TAKE |
|---|---|---|
| **CC20** CHECK SPEED SENSOR GROUND | | |
| • Measure the resistance of the BK wire between the speed sensor and ground.<br>• Is the resistance less than 5 ohms? | Yes ▶<br>No ▶ | GO to **CC21.**<br>SERVICE BK wire. |
| **CC21** CHECK SPEED SENSOR | | |
| • Disconnect speedometer cable at the transaxle.<br>• Disconnect the GN/R wire from the speed control unit.<br>• Check for continuity between ground and the GN/R wire at the speed sensor.<br>• Does continuity exist four times per one speedometer cable rotation? | Yes ▶<br>No ▶ | GO to **CC22.**<br>REPLACE speed sensor. |
| **CC22** CHECK LEADS TO ACTUATOR | | |
| • Locate actuator connector.<br>• Measure the resistance of the GN/W, GN, BL/BK and GN/BK wires between the speed control unit and the actuator.<br>• Are the resistances less than 5 ohms? | Yes ▶<br>No ▶ | GO to **CC23.**<br>SERVICE wire in question. |
| **CC23** CHECK ACTUATOR | | |
| • Disconnect actuator connector.<br>• Apply 12 volts and ground to the following terminals.<br>• Check to see the actuator responds as indicated. | Yes ▶<br>No ▶ | GO to **CC24.**<br>REPLACE actuator. |

| GN/W | GN | GN/BK | BL/BK | Control Cable Operation |
|---|---|---|---|---|
| GND | GND | + 12 volts | + 12 volts | Pull cable |
| N/C | GND | N/C | + 12 volts | Lock cable |
| + 12 volts | GND | + 12 volts | + 12 volts | Extend cable |
| N/C | N/C | + 12 volts | + 12 volts | Release cable |

+ 12 volts — Apply 12 volts
GND — Apply Ground
N/C — No connection

• Are the control cable operations verified?

| TEST STEP | RESULT | ACTION TO TAKE |
|---|---|---|
| **CC24** CHECK SPEED CONTROL UNIT | | |
| • Start engine.<br>• Drive safely at approximately 40 mph.<br>• Operate speed control system.<br>• Does system operate correctly? | Yes ▶<br>No ▶ | RETURN to condition chart.<br>REPLACE speed control unit. |

**Fig. 94 Diagnosis & Testing (Part 6 of 6). Capri**

# TROUBLESHOOTING SUPPLEMENT

## TABLE OF CONTENTS



| TEST STEP | RESULT ▶ | ACTION TO TAKE |
|---|---|---|
| **A0** ROAD TEST | | |
| • Accelerate vehicle to the speed which the customer indicated the shake occurred. | OK ▶ | Vehicle OK. |
| | ~~OK~~ ▶ | GO to **A1**. |
| **A1** INSPECT TIRES | | |
| • Raise vehicle on hoist. Inspect tires for extreme wear or damage, cupping or flat spots. | OK ▶ | GO to **A2**. |
| | ~~OK~~ ▶ | CHECK suspension components for misalignment, abnormal wear, or damage that may have contributed to the tire wear. CORRECT suspension problems, and REPLACE damaged tires. ROAD TEST vehicle. |
| **A2** INSPECT WHEEL BEARINGS | | |
| • Spin front tires by hand to check for wheel bearing roughness. Check bearing end play. | OK ▶ | GO to **A3**. |
| | ~~OK~~ ▶ | ADJUST or REPLACE and lubricate bearings as necessary. ROAD TEST vehicle. |
| **A3** WHEEL/TIRE RUNOUT | | |
| • Spin front wheels at low speed with a wheel balance spinner, observing wheel/tire runout. | OK ▶ | BALANCE wheels. GO to **A4**. |
| | ~~OK~~ ▶ | GO to **A8**. |
| **A4** DRIVE TRAIN | | |
| • Engage drive train and carefully accelerate the drive wheels. | OK ▶ | GO to **A8**. |
| | ~~OK~~ ▶ | GO to **A5**. |
| **A5** DRIVE WHEELS | | |
| • Remove rear wheels. Secure brake drums, if so equipped, by installing the lug nuts, reversed. Carefully accelerate the drive wheels. | OK ▶ | BALANCE rear wheels. ROAD TEST. |
| | ~~OK~~ ▶ | GO to **A6**. |
| **A6** REAR DRUMS OR ROTORS | | |
| • Remove the brake drums or rotors. Carefully accelerate the drive wheels. | OK ▶ | REPLACE the drums or rotors. |
| | ~~OK~~ ▶ | GO to **A7**. |

**Fig. 1 Noise, Vibration & Harshness (NVH) (Part 1 of 7)**

| TEST STEP | RESULT ▶ | ACTION TO TAKE |
|---|---|---|
| **A7** AXLE RUNOUT | | |
| • With drum or rotor removed, check axle flange face runout, lug bolt circle radial runout, drum/rotor pilot radial runout. | OK ▶ | GO to Driveline Vibration Diagnosis. |
| | ~~OK~~ ▶ | REPLACE axle shaft or hub. |
| **A8** WHEEL RUNOUT | | |
| • Install wheels and tires in original positions. Check all wheels for total radial and lateral tire runout, 1.78mm (0.070 inches). | OK ▶ | GO to **A10**. |
| | ~~OK~~ ▶ | CHECK wheel rim runout, radial and lateral. If either exceeds 1.14mm (0.045 inches), REPLACE the wheel and recheck runout. If new rim is within limits, LOCATE and MARK the low point of rim radial runout. GO to **A9**. |
| **A9** TIRE RUNOUT | | |
| • Check total lateral and radial runout 1.78mm (0.070 inches). | OK ▶ | GO to **A10**. |
| | Lateral ~~OK~~ ▶ | REPLACE tire. |
| | Radial ~~OK~~ ▶ | MARK the highest point of tire, dismount, re-index and remount the tire with the high point aligned with the Low point of the wheel. RECHECK radial tread runout. If still out, REPLACE the tire and RECHECK runouts, re-indexing as necessary to bring radial runout within limits. GO to **A10**. |
| **A10** WHEEL BALANCE | | |
| • Balance all wheels not previously balanced. Road test vehicle. | OK ▶ | Vehicle OK. |
| | ~~OK~~ ▶ | GO to **A11**. |
| **A11** SUBSTITUTE WHEELS AND TIRES | | |
| • Substitute a known good set of wheels and tires. | OK ▶ | REINSTALL the original tire/wheel assemblies, one by one, road testing at each step, until the damaged tire(s) is identified. REPLACE tire(s) as necessary and retest. |
| | ~~OK~~ ▶ | REFER to Driveline Vibration Diagnosis. |

**Fig. 1 Noise, Vibration & Harshness (NVH) (Part 2 of 7)**

| TEST STEP | RESULT ▶ | ACTION TO TAKE |
|---|---|---|
| **B0** AIR CLEANER | | |
| • Check air cleaner for proper installation of base gasket, lid, element and air inlet duct assembly. | OK ▶ | GO to **B1**. |
| | ~~OK~~ ▶ | CORRECT condition and ROAD TEST. If moan persists, GO to **B1**. |
| **B1** POWERTRAIN RESONANCE | | |
| • Loosen all converter or clutch housing-to-engine attaching bolts 3/4 turn and road test. Retighten bolts after test. | Moan reduced or eliminated ▶ | CHECK for presence of transmission extension damper and that it is installed as required. CHANGE or INSTALL damper as indicated and RETEST. If moan still persists, GO to **B2**. |
| | ~~OK~~ ▶ | GO to **B2**. |
| **B2** ENGINE MOUNTS | | |
| • Normalize engine mounts by loosening them and, with engine running, shifting transmission from Neutral to Drive and back to Neutral. With manual transmission, load engine by slipping clutch in gear. Retighten mounting bolts and road test. | OK ▶ | Vehicle OK. |
| | ~~OK~~ ▶ | GO to **B3**. |
| **B3** EXHAUST SYSTEM | | |
| • Warm up system to normal operating temperature. Loosen all hanger attachments and reposition hangers until they hang free and straight. Then loosen all flange joints and, with engine running, shift transmission from Neutral to Drive and back to Neutral (or load engine with clutch), and retighten all hanger clamps and flanges. Road test vehicle. | OK ▶ | Vehicle OK. |
| | ~~OK~~ ▶ | REFER to Engine Accessory Vibration Diagnosis. |

**Fig. 1 Noise, Vibration & Harshness (NVH) (Part 3 of 7)**

| TEST STEP | RESULT ▶ | ACTION TO TAKE |
|---|---|---|
| **D0** UNIVERSAL JOINTS | | |
| • Raise vehicle on drive-on type hoist, or back onto a front-end alignment rack. Inspect U-joints for proper installation, seizure, or excessive wear. | OK ▶ | GO to **D1**. |
| | ~~OK~~ ▶ | INDEX-MARK driveshaft and flange, REMOVE shaft, and REPLACE the faulty U-joints. GO to **D1**. |
| **D1** RIDE HEIGHT | | |
| • Check ride height between the axle and rear bumper bracket on frame rail. | OK | GO to D2. |
| | ~~OK~~ ▶ | CHECK to make sure vehicle is not abnormally loaded. CORRECT ride height if necessary. GO to **D2**. |
| **D2** DRIVELINE ANGLES | | |
| Check driveline angles | OK ▶ | GO to **D3**. |
| | ~~OK~~ ▶ | CORRECT driveline angle |
| **D3** AXLE RING AND PINION | | |
| • If driveline angle corrections do not eliminate vibration, check ring and pinion backlash. | OK ▶ | GO to Engine Accessory Vibration Diagnosis. |
| | ~~OK~~ ▶ | ADJUST or REPLACE ring and pinion gearset. If vibration still exists, GO to Engine Accessory Vibration Diagnosis. |

**Fig. 1 Noise, Vibration & Harshness (NVH) (Part 4 of 7)**

| TEST STEP | RESULT ▶ | ACTION TO TAKE |
|---|---|---|
| **C0** WHEELS AND TIRES | | |
| • Verify that the observed condition is not a high speed shake caused by wheels/tires. | OK | REFER to High Speed Shake Diagnosis for drive-wheel runout and balance procedures. |
| | ~~OK~~ ▶ | GO to **C1**. |
| **C1** DRIVESHAFT | | |
| • Inspect driveshaft for physical damage, undercoating, or improperly seated, worn, or binding universal joints. Check index marks (paint spots) on rear of shaft and pinion yoke or companion flange. If these marks are more than 90 degrees apart, disconnect shaft and re-index to align marks as close as possible. | OK ▶ | GO to **C2**. |
| | ~~OK~~ ▶ | CLEAN shaft and REPLACE universal joints as necessary, or REPLACE shaft if damaged. RECHECK vibration at road test speed. If gone, REINSTALL wheels and road test. If vibration persists, GO to **C2**. |
| **C2** DRIVESHAFT RUNOUT | | |
| • With vehicle on hoist measure runout at front, center, and rear of driveshaft, 0.89 mm (0.035 inch). | OK ▶ | GO to **C5**. |
| | At front or center ~~OK~~ ▶ | REPLACE driveshaft. |
| | At rear ~~OK~~ ▶ | MARK the rear runout high point. GO to **C3**. |
| **C3** DRIVESHAFT RE-INDEXING | | |
| • Note or mark indexing of driveshaft to rear axle pinion flange. Disconnect the shaft, re-index 180 degrees, and reconnect. Recheck runout at rear of shaft, 0.89 mm (0.035 inch). | OK ▶ | CHECK for vibration at road-test speed. If still present, GO to **C5**. |
| | ~~OK~~ ▶ | GO to **C4**. |
| **C4** PINION YOKE OR FLANGE | | |
| • Compare the two high points marked in C2 and C3. | Marks within 25 mm (1 inch) of each other ▶ | REPLACE driveshaft. RECHECK vibration. |
| | Marks 180 degrees apart ▶ | REPLACE pinion yoke on flange. RECHECK driveshaft runout. 0.89 mm (0.035 inch). ROAD TEST for vibration. If vibration persists, GO to C5. |

**Fig. 1 Noise, Vibration & Harshness (NVH) (Part 5 of 7)**

| TEST STEP | RESULT ▶ | ACTION TO TAKE |
|---|---|---|
| **E3** ENGINE IDLING | | |
| • With engine idling, visually check all accessory drive belts and pulleys for misalignment, runout or irregular motion. Maximum runout is 3mm (1/8 inch). | OK ▶ | GO to **E4**. |
| | ~~OK~~ ▶ | If pulley(s) exceeds maximum runout, REPLACE pulley. If belt rides up and down in pulley, a variable-width condition exists. If it occurs on just one pulley, REPLACE that pulley. Otherwise, REPLACE the belt. RUN engine up to problem RPM. If belt whips, ADJUST belt tension to specifications. If belt still whips, REPLACE belt. If vibration still exists, GO to E4. |
| **E4** ACCESSORIES | | |
| • Run-up engine to problem RPM and, with stethoscope-type device, check each component.<br>• If the source cannot be detected by probing, remove each belt, one at a time, until vibration goes away. | Noisy component located ▶ | REPLACE belt. If vibration still exists, SERVICE or REPLACE component. |
| | Unable to locate vibration ▶ | Possible engine component imbalance. This situation is possible, but unlikely. |

**Fig. 1 Noise, Vibration & Harshness (NVH) (Part 6 of 7)**

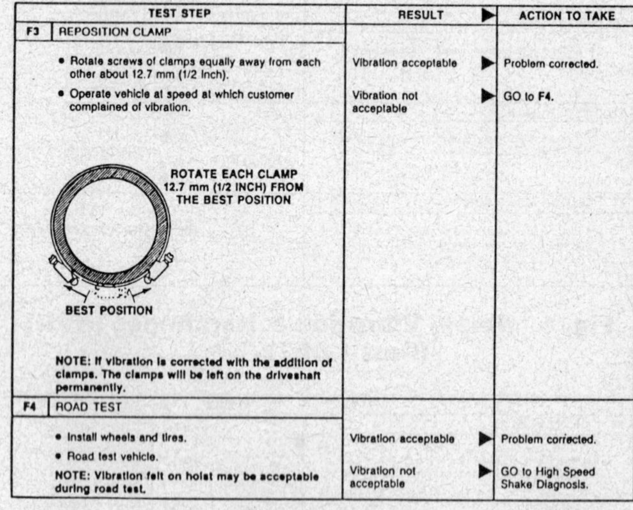

| TEST STEP | RESULT ▶ | ACTION TO TAKE |
|---|---|---|
| **F3** REPOSITION CLAMP | | |
| • Rotate screws of clamps equally away from each other about 12.7 mm (1/2 inch).<br>• Operate vehicle at speed at which customer complained of vibration. | Vibration acceptable ▶ | Problem corrected. |
| | Vibration not acceptable ▶ | GO to **F4**. |
| ROTATE EACH CLAMP 12.7 mm (1/2 INCH) FROM THE BEST POSITION<br>BEST POSITION<br>**NOTE: If vibration is corrected with the addition of clamps. The clamps will be left on the driveshaft permanently.** | | |
| **F4** ROAD TEST | | |
| • Install wheels and tires.<br>• Road test vehicle.<br>**NOTE: Vibration felt on hoist may be acceptable during road test.** | Vibration acceptable ▶ | Problem corrected. |
| | Vibration not acceptable ▶ | GO to High Speed Shake Diagnosis. |

**Fig. 1 Noise, Vibration & Harshness (NVH) (Part 7 of 7)**

| CONDITION | POSSIBLE SOURCE | ACTION |
|---|---|---|
| Loss of coolant | • Pressure cap and gasket. | • Inspect, wash gasket and test. Replace only if cap will not hold pressure test specification. |
| | • Leakage. | • Pressure test system. |
| | • External leakage. | • Inspect hose, hose connection, radiator, edges of cooling system gaskets, core plugs and drain plugs, transmission oil cooler lines, water pump, heater system components. Service or replace as required. |
| | • Radiator filler leak. | • Inspect radiator filler neck sealing surface for damage or foreign material. |
| | | • Check engine oil and transmission oil dipsticks for signs of coolant. Check coolant for signs of transmission oil. |
| | | • Check torque of head bolts, tighten if necessary. |
| | • Internal leakage. | • Disassemble engine as necessary — check for cracked intake manifold, blown head gaskets, leak at water crossover intake manifold gasket, warped head or block gasket surfaces, cracked cylinder head or engine block. |
| Engine overheats | • Low coolant level. | • Fill as required. Check for coolant loss. |
| | • Excessive rust in coolant. | • Flush system, refill with new coolant. |
| | • Loose fan belt. | • Adjust. |
| | • Pressure cap. | • Test. Replace if necessary. |
| | • Radiator or A/C condenser obstruction. | • Remove bugs, leaves, etc. |
| | • Closed thermostat. | • Test, replace if necessary. |
| | • Fan drive clutch. | • Test, replace if necessary. |
| | • Ignition. | • Check timing and advance. Adjust as required. |
| | • Temp gauge or cold light. | • Check electrical circuits and service as required. |
| | • Engine. | • Check water pump, block for blockage. |
| | • Exhaust system. | • Check for restrictions. |
| Engine fails to reach normal operating temperature | • Open thermostat. | • Test, replace if necessary. |
| | • Temperature gauge or cold light (False Reading). | • Check electrical circuits and service as required. |

**Fig. 2 Cooling System**

**NOTE: Extended cranking, because of a "No Start" condition, can load the exhaust system with raw fuel, which can ruin the catalytic converter after the engine starts. After the "No Start" condition has been repaired, disconnect the thermactor air supply, run the engine until surplus fuel is used up and reconnect the thermactor air supply.**

| System | Component |
|---|---|
| EEC | Quick Test |
| Ignition | Electrical Connections<br>Secondary Ignition Wires<br>Spark Plugs Fouled<br>Ignition Switch<br><u>DSII and TFI IV:</u><br>Ignition Coil<br>Ignition Module<br>Rotor Alignment<br>Distributor Cap, Adapter, Rotor & Stator<br><u>DIS:</u><br>Single or Dual Hall Crankshaft Sensors<br>Hall Camshaft Sensor<br>DIS Ignition Module (Low Data Rate)<br>DIS Coil(s) |
| Fuel Delivery | Filter<br>Pump<br>Water/Dirt/Rust Contamination in Fuel Lines<br>Tank (Fuel Supply)<br>Dual Tanks (Selector Switch)<br>Sender Filter<br>Fuel Pressure Regulators for EFI and CFI<br>Injectors<br>Inertia Switch |
| Basic Engine | Camshaft Timing<br>Compression |
| External Carburetor/Fuel Charging Assy./Throttle Body | Electrical Connections<br>Choke Plate and Linkage<br>Cold Enrichment Rod and Linkage (7200)<br>Venturi Valve (7200)<br>Throttle Linkages |
| Internal Carburetor | Float/Inlet Needle and Seat<br>Idle Air Bleeds and Fuel Passages |
| EGR | Valve |
| MCU | Component Diagnostics |

**Fig. 3 Engine, Cranks Normally But Will Not Start**

**NOTE: It is a good practice to confirm that the correct starting procedure was being used before proceeding with diagnosis.**

| System | Component |
|---|---|
| External Carburetor/Fuel Charging Assy/Throttle Body | Electrical and Vacuum Connections<br>Choke Plate and Linkage<br>Cold Enrichment Rod and Linkage (7200)<br>Choke Cap Indexing<br>Accelerator Pump<br>Venturi Valve (7200)<br>Bowl Vents |
| Fuel Delivery | Filter<br>Pump<br>Water/Dirt/Rust Contamination in Fuel Lines<br>Fuel Pressure Regulators for EFI and CFI<br>Sender Filter<br>Injectors |
| Internal Carburetor | Float/Inlet Needle and Seat<br>Stepper Motor (7200)<br>Cold Enrichment System (7200) |
| Ignition | Scope Engine for: Spark Plugs, Coil, Secondary Ignition Wires<br>Spark Plugs Fouled<br><br>DSII AND TFI IV:<br>Distributor Cap, Adapter & Rotor<br><br>DIS:<br>Single or Dual Hall Crankshaft Sensors<br>Hall Camshaft Senso<br>DIS Ignition Module (Low Data Rate)<br>DIS Coil(s) |
| Induction and Vacuum Distribution | Vacuum Leaks<br>Air Cleaner Element Restricted |
| Cooling | Electric Fan (Hot Start Only) |
| EGR | Valve |
| PCV | Valve |
| EVAP | Components |
| EEC | Quick Test |
| MCU | Component Diagnostics |

**Fig. 4 Engine, Cranks Normally But Slow To Start**

| System | Component |
|---|---|
| External Carburetor/Fuel Charging Assy/Throttle Body | Electrical and Vacuum Connections<br>Fast Idle Speed<br>Choke Plate and Linkage<br>Cold Enrichment Rod And Linkage (7200)<br>Choke Pulldown Adjustment & Diaphragm<br>Venturi Valve (7200)<br>Choke Cap Indexing |
| Ignition | Electrical Connections<br>Secondary Ignition Wires<br>Ignition Switch<br><br>DSII AND TFI IV:<br>Ignition Coil<br>Ignition Module<br>Rotor Alignment<br>Distributor Cap, Adapter, Rotor & Stator<br>Ballast Resistor<br><br>DIS:<br>Single or Dual Hall Crankshaft Sensors<br>Hall Camshaft Sensor<br>DIS Ignition Module (Low Data Rate)<br>DIS Coil(s) |
| EGR | Valve |
| Fuel Delivery | Filter<br>Pump<br>Water/Dirt/Rust Contamination in Fuel Lines<br>Tank (Fuel Supply)<br>Sender Filter<br>Fuel Pressure Regulators for EFI and CFI<br>Injectors<br>Inertia Switch |
| EEC | Quick Test |
| MCU | Component Diagnostics |
| Internal Carburetor | Float/Inlet Needle and Seat<br>Idle Air Bleeds and Fuel Passages |
| Exhaust | Component (Restricted) |
| Basic Engine | Camshaft and Valve Train |

**Fig. 5 Engine, Starts Normally But Will Not Run**

| System | Component |
|---|---|
| Cooling | Fan or Electric Fan (Loose or Cracked) |
| Vacuum Distribution | Vacuum Leaks |
| External Carburetor/Fuel Charging Assy/Throttle Body/Injectors | Curb or Fast Idle Speeds<br>Electrical and Vacuum Connections<br>Choke Plate and Linkage<br>Cold Enrichment Rod and Linkage (7200)<br>Venturi Valve (7200)<br>Choke Pulldown<br>Bowl Vent<br>Fuel Pressure Regulators EFI/CFI<br>Injectors<br>Fuel Rail |
| Ignition | Scope Engine For: Spark Plug, Coil, Secondary Wires, Distributor Cap, Adapter and Rotor |
| Carburetor | Idle Mixture |
| Internal Carburetor | Idle, Air Bleeds or Fuel Passages<br>Float/Inlet Needle and Seat<br>Stepper Motor (7200)<br>Hot Idle Compensator (may be external)<br>Altitude Compensator<br>Cold Enrichment System (7200) |
| EGR | Valve<br>Vacuum Regulator |
| PCV | Valve |
| EVAP | Components |
| Ignition Timing | Base plus Advance and Retard Functions |
| EEC | Quick Test |
| MCU | Component Diagnostics |
| Turbocharger | |
| Exhaust | Pipes, Muffler, Catalyst<br>Resonator, Heat Control Valve |
| Basic Engine | Compression<br>Valve Train<br>Camshaft<br>Intake Manifold Gaskets |

**Fig. 6 Engine, Rough Idle**

| System | Component |
|---|---|
| External Carburetor/Fuel Charging Assy/Throttle Body | Curb or Fast Idle Speed<br>Electrical and Vacuum Connections<br>Throttle Devices<br>Venturi Valve (7200) |
| EGR | Valve |
| Internal Carburetor | Idle Airbleeds or Fuel Passages<br>Stepper Motor (7200)<br>Hot Idle Compensator (may be external)<br>Float/Inlet Needle and Seat<br>Cold Enrichment System (7200) |
| Turbocharger | Retard Switches |
| EEC | Quick Test |
| MCU | Component Diagnostics |
| Base Transmission (E4OD Only) | Transmission Oil Level<br>Converter Clutch Control Solenoid |

**Fig. 7 Engine, Low Idle (Stalls on deceleration or or quick stop)**

**NOTE: If engine idles smoothly after being shut off, trouble is likely to be in the ignition switch, ignition harness, starter solenoid "IGN" tap, or EEC relay.**

| System | Component |
|---|---|
| External Carburetor/Fuel Charging Assy/Throttle Body | Curb or Fast Idle Speeds<br>Electrical and Vacuum Connections<br>Throttle Positioner or Dashpot<br>Throttle Plate and Linkage<br>Choke Plate and Linkage<br>Fast Idle Linkage<br>Venturi Valves (7200)<br>Speed Control Chain |
| Vacuum Distribution | Vacuum Leaks |
| Cooling | Overheating |
| Induction | Vacuum Leaks |
| Base Transmission (E4OD Only) | Coast Clutch Solenoid (starts at 3rd gear) |
| EEC (E4OD Only) | Quick Test |

**Fig. 8 Engine, High Idle (Engine diesels/run-on)**

| System | Component |
|---|---|
| Ignition | Scope Engine For: Spark Plug, Coil, Secondary Wires, Distributor Cap, Adapter and Rotor |
| EEC | Quick Test |
| MCU | Component Diagnostics |
| Fuel Delivery | Filter<br>Pump<br>Lines<br>Fuel Pressure Regulators EFI/CFI<br>Sender Filter<br>Injectors |
| External Carburetor/Fuel Charging Assy/Throttle Body | Electrical and Vacuum Connections<br>Choke and Linkage<br>Cold Enrichment Rod and Linkage (7200)<br>Venturi Valves (7200) |
| Internal Carburetor | Basic: Idle, Main, and Accelerator Pump<br>Float/Inlet Needle and Seat<br>Main Metering<br>Fuel Enrichment |
| Ignition Timing | Base plus Advance and Retard Functions |

**Fig. 9 Engine, Misses Under Load**

| System | Component |
|---|---|
| External Carburetor/Fuel Charging Assy/Throttle Body | Choke Plate and Linkage<br>Electrical & Vacuum Connections<br>Cold Enrichment Rod and Linkage (7200)<br>Accelerator Pump<br>Venturi Valve (7200) |
| Induction and Vacuum Distribution | Vacuum Leaks |
| Induction | Air Cleaner Duct, Stove Pipe, and Valve |
| Ignition | Scope Engine For: Spark Plug, Coil, Secondary Wires, Distributor Cap, Adapter and Rotor<br>Ignition Timing |
| External Carburetor/Fuel Charging Assy/Throttle Body | Curb or Fast Idle Speeds |
| EGR | Valve |
| Fuel Delivery | Filter<br>Pump<br>Water/Dirt/Rust Contamination in Fuel Lines<br>Fuel Pressure Regulators for EFI and CFI<br>Sender Filter<br>Injectors |
| Internal Carburetor | VV Diaphragm (7200)<br>Power Valve<br>Stepper Motor (7200)<br>Main System |
| EEC | Quick Test |
| MCU | Component Diagnostics |
| Turbocharger | Turbocharger Assembly |
| Exhaust (Restriction) | With Backpressure EGR System |
| Base Transmission (E4OD and A4LD) | Converter Clutch Control Solenoid<br>Converter Clutch Override<br>Converter Clutch |

**Fig. 10 Engine, Hesitates Or Stalls On Acceleration**

| System | Component |
|---|---|
| Vacuum Distribution | Vacuum Hoses, or Connections Leak(s) |
| Ignition | Scope Engine For: Spark Plug, Coil, Secondary Wires, Distributor Cap and Rotor, Crossed Wires<br>Ignition Timing |
| External Carburetor | Choke Plate and Linkage |
| Basic Engine | Intake Manifold Gaskets<br>Compression Check<br>Camshaft<br>Valves |
| Thermactor | Thermactor System Components |
| Pulse Air | Pulse Air System Components |
| EEC | Quick Test |
| MCU | Component Diagnostics |
| Exhaust | Components (Restricted) |
| Fuel Delivery | Filter<br>Pump<br>Water, Dirt, Rust, Contamination in Fuel Lines<br>Fuel Pressure Regulators EFI/CFI<br>Injectors<br>Sender Filter |

**Fig. 11 Engine, Backfire/Afterfire (Induction or exhaust)**

| System | Component |
|---|---|
| External Carburetor/Fuel Charging Assy/Throttle Body | Electrical and Vacuum Connections<br>Choke Plate and Linkage<br>Accelerator Pump<br>Venturi Valves (7200) |
| Ignition | Timing |
| Induction | Air Cleaner Duct and Valve and Element |
| Fuel Delivery | Filter<br>Pump<br>Lines<br>Fuel Pressure Regulator EFI/CFI<br>Sender Filter<br>Injectors |
| EGR | Valve |
| Internal Carburetor | Float Inlet/Needle and Seat<br>Accelerator Pump<br>Main Metering System<br>Fuel Enrichment<br>Altitude Compensator<br>Stepper Motor (7200)<br>Pullover Rod Sticking (1949) |
| Basic Engine | Compression Check<br>Camshaft<br>Valves |
| Drive Train | Clutch, Automatic Transmission, Brakes |
| EEC | Quick Test |
| MCU | Component Diagnostics |
| Turbocharger | Turbocharger Assembly |
| Exhaust | Components (Restricted) |

**Fig. 12 Engine, Lack Of Power**

| System | Component |
|---|---|
| External Carburetor/Fuel Charging Assy (Throttle Body) | Choke Plate and Linkage<br>Electrical & Vacuum Connections<br>Venturi Valves (7200) |
| Vacuum Distribution | Vacuum Leaks |
| Fuel Delivery | Filter<br>Pump<br>Lines<br>Fuel Pressure Regulator EFI/CFI<br>Sender Filter |
| Internal Carburetor | Idle, Main Systems<br>Float/Inlet Needle and Seat<br>Fuel Enrichment Systems<br>Altitude Compensator |
| EGR | Valve |
| EEC | Quick Test |
| MCU | Component Diagnostics |
| Turbocharger | Turbocharger Assembly |
| EVAP | Components |
| Basic Engine | Valve Train and Camshaft<br>Intake Manifold Gaskets |
| Thermactor | Thermactor System Components |
| Ignition | Timing |

**Fig. 13 Engine, Surge At Steady Speed**

| System | Component |
|---|---|
| Squeal, Click, or Chirp | Oil Level (low)<br>Valve Train<br>Drive Belts (loose)<br>Belt Driven Components<br>EEC Solenoids |
| Rumble, Grind | Belt Driven Components |
| Rattle | Component (loose) |
| Hiss | Thermactor System (leak)<br>Vacuum Distribution System (leak)<br>Induction System (leak)<br>Spark Plug (loose) |
| | Cooling System (leak) |
| | EVAP System (leak) |
| Snap | Secondary Ignition |
| Rap, Roar | Exhaust System (leak)<br>Pulse Air System (air cleaner) |
| Whine | Turbocharger (some whine is normal) |
| Knock | Connecting Rod Bearing (worn)<br>Main Bearing (worn)<br>Piston Pin (loose)<br>Piston to Bore Clearance (cold engine) |
| | Fuel Pump |
| | Detonation |

**Fig. 14 Engine, Noise**

**NOTE: Since fuel consumption is drastically increased for city driving, short-run operation, stop and go driving, trailer towing, extended winter warm-up periods, etc., as opposed to "trip" mileage, an attempt should be made to determine these factors when confronted with "poor mileage" conditions. However, since the operator is not always at fault, the following is appended:**

| System | Component |
|---|---|
| External Carburetor/Fuel Charging Assy/Throttle Body | Choke Plate and Linkage<br>Cold Enrichment Rod and Linkage (7200)<br>Electrical & Vacuum Connections<br>Fuel Pressure Regulators EFI/CFI |
| Induction | Air Cleaner Duct and Valve<br>Air Cleaner Element (Restricted) |
| Ignition | Scope Engine For: Spark Plug, Coil, Secondary Wires, Distributor Cap, Adapter and Rotor<br>Ignition Timing |
| Internal Carburetor | Idle, Main Systems<br>Enrichment Systems<br>Float/Inlet Needle and Seat |
| EEC | Quick Test |
| MCU | Component Diagnostics |
| Fuel Delivery | Fuel Return Line Blocked |
| Cooling | Thermostat |
| Factors External to the Engine | Tire Pressure & Type<br>Clutch Operation<br>Converter Clutch Override<br>Automatic Transmission Shift Pattern and Fluid Level<br>Brake Drag<br>Exhaust System<br>Speedometer/Odometer Gear Ratio<br>Axle Ratio<br>Vehicle Load<br>Road & Weather Conditions |
| Base Transmission (E4OD Only) | Converter Clutch Control Solenoid |

**Fig. 15 Engine, Poor Fuel Economy**

| System | Component |
|---|---|
| External Leaks | Rocker Cover Gasket, Crankshaft Seals, Engine Assembly |
| Proper Dipstick | Overfilling (sometimes accomplished by the "short stick" gas station procedure). |
| Induction | Air Cleaner Element (Sealing) |
| PCV | Valve |
| Turbocharger | Compressor/Turbine Bearing, Seals, Center Drain, Etc. |
| Internal Leaks (blue smoke from tailpipe) | Valve Guides<br>Valve Stem Seals<br>Intake Manifold and Gasket<br>Cylinder Head Drain Passages<br>Piston Rings |

**Fig. 16 Engine, High Oil Consumption**

| System | Component |
|---|---|
| EGR | Verifiy correct application, then diagnose. |
| Induction | Air Cleaner Duct and Valve Assembly |
| Vacuum Distribution | Vacuum Leaks<br>Spark Delay Valve<br>PVS |
| Basic Engine | Oil Level<br>Compression Check<br>Intake Manifold Gasket |
| Cooling | Overheating |
| EEC | Quick Test |
| MCU | Component Diagnostics |
| Turbocharger | Turbocharger Assembly |
| Thermactor | Thermactor System Components |
| Ignition | Timing |
| Base Transmission (E4OD Non-Diesel Only) | Transmission Controls |

**Fig. 17 Engine, Spark Knock/Pinging**

| System | Component |
|---|---|
| Engine Accessories | Fan<br>Belt Driven Components<br>Engine Mounts<br>Engine Vibration Damper |
| Otherwise | Non-Engine Components: Drive Line, Tires, Wheel Balance |

**Fig. 18 Engine, Vibration At Normal Speeds**

| System | Component |
|---|---|
| Gauge System | Gauge, Sender |
| Cooling | Thermostat |

**Fig. 19 Engine, Runs Cold**

| System | Component |
|---|---|
| Cooling | Coolant Level<br>Radiator or A/C Condenser<br>Pressure Cap and Overflow System<br>External Leaks<br>Belts and Belt Tension<br>Fan and Fan Clutch<br>Electric Fan (If So Equipped) |
| Gauge System | Gauge, Sender |
| Cooling | Thermostat |
| Ignition | Timing |
| Vacuum Distribution | Spark Delay Valve |
| EEC | Quick Test |
| MCU | Component Diagnostics |
| Cooling | PVS |
| Basic Engine | Oil Level<br>Internal Leak(s)<br>Core Sand in Head/Block<br>Water Pump |
| Brake | Brakes (dragging) |

**Fig. 20 Engine, Runs Hot**

**NOTE: White Smoke is normal during warm-up.**

| System | Component |
|---|---|
| Black Smoke (rich mixture) | Choke Plate and Linkage<br>Cold Enrichment Rod and Linkage (7200) |
| | Air Cleaner Element (Restricted) |
| | Internal Carburetor Components:<br>Basic: Idle, Main and Accelerator Pump<br>Metering Systems<br>Enrichment Systems<br>Fuel Inlet Needle/Seat<br>Float<br>Fuel Pressure Regulator EFI/CFI<br>Injectors |
| | EEC Components |
| | MCU Components |
| Blue Smoke (burning oil) | PCV Valve |
| | Valve Guides/Stems/Seals<br>Oil Drain Passages in Head |
| | Turbo Bearing Seals |
| | Rings (not seated, seized, gummed up, worn)<br>Cylinder bores (scuffed) |
| White Smoke (coolant in combustion) | Thermactor Vacuum Delay Valve (restricted)<br>EGR Cooler<br>Intake Manifold (cracked/porous)<br>Cylinder Head/Gasket (leaks)<br>Block (cracked/porous) |

**Fig. 21 Engine, Exhaust Smoke**

| System | Component |
|---|---|
| Fuel Delivery | Fuel Filter (leaks)<br>Fuel Line to Carburetor (leaks)<br>Injectors (leaking)<br>Fuel Pump (leaks)<br>Fuel Line, Pump to Tank (leaks)<br>Fuel Tank (leaks)<br>Fuel Tank Filler Neck/Cap (leaks)<br>Fuel Return Line (Blocked)<br>Fuel Pressure Regulator EFI/CFI |
| Internal Carburetor | Float/Inlet Needle (stuck) |
| EVAP | Carbon Canister, Solenoid, Hoses (leaks) |

**Fig. 22 Engine, Gasoline Smell**

# ENGINE REBUILDING SPECIFICATIONS

## INDEX



## CYLINDER HEAD, VALVE GUIDES & VALVE SEATS

| Engine Liter/ CID | Year | Cylinder Head Warpage Limit | Valve Guides | | | Valve Seats | | | | | |
|---|---|---|---|---|---|---|---|---|---|---|---|
| | | | Inside Diameter | Stem to Guide Clearance | | Seat Angle | Seat Width | | Run-Out | Seat Insert Bore Diameter | |
| | | | | Intake | Exhaust | | Intake | Exhaust | | Intake | Exhaust |
| 1.3L/4-80.8 | 1989-91 | .006 | .2760-.2768 | .008 | .008 | 45° | .043-.067 | .043-.067 | .0016 | — | — |
| 1.6L/4-97 | 1991 | .006 | .2366-.2374 | .0010-.0024 | .0012-.0026 | 45° | .032-.055 | .032-.055 | — | — | — |
| 1.8L/4-112 | 1991 | .004 | .2366-.2374 | .0010-.0024 | .0012-.0026 | 45° | .031-.055 | .031-.055 | — | — | — |
| 1.9L/4-116 | 1989-91 | .003 | .3174-.3187 | .0008-.0027 | .0018-.0037 | 45° | .069-.091 | .069-.091 | .003 | ④ | ⑤ |
| 2.2L/4-133 | 1989-91 | .006 | — | .008 | .008 | 45° | .047-.063 | .047-.063 | — | — | — |
| 2.3L/4-140① | 1989-91 | .006 | .3433-.3443 | .0010-.0027② | .0015-.0032② | 45° | .060-.080 | .070-.090 | .0016 | — | — |
| 2.3L/4-140③ | 1989-91 | .006 | .3433-.3442 | .0018 | .0023 | 44.5° | .060-.080 | .070-.090 | .001 | — | — |
| 2.5L/4-153③ | 1989-91 | .006 | .3433-.3442 | .0018 | .0023 | 44.5° | .060-.080 | .070-.090 | .001 | — | — |
| 2.9L/V6-177 | 1989-91 | .006 | — | .0008-.0025 | .0018-.0035 | 45° | .060-.079 | .060-.079 | .0015 | — | — |
| 3.0L/V6-182 | 1989-91 | .007 | .3140-.3150 | .0010-.0028 | .0015-.0033 | 45° | .060-.080 | .080-.100 | .001 | — | — |
| 3.0L/V6-182⑥ | 1989-91 | .008 | .2362-.2369 | .0010-.0023 | .0012-.0025 | 45° | .039-.051 | .039-.055 | — | — | — |
| 3.8L/V6-232 | 1989-91 | .007 | .3433-.3443 | .0010-.0028 | .0015-.0033 | 44.5° | .060-.080 | .060-.080 | .003 | 1.8532-1.8542 | 1.5645 |
| 4.6L/V8-281 | 1991 | — | — | .0008-.0027 | .0018-.0037 | 45° | .075-.083 | .075-.083 | .0010 | — | — |
| 5.0L/V8-302 | 1989-91 | .006 | .3433-.3443 | .0010-.0027② | .0015-.0032② | 45° | .060-.080 | .060-.080 | .002 | — | — |
| 5.8L/V8-351 | 1989-91 | .006 | .3433-.3443 | .0010-.0027② | .0015-.0032② | 45° | .060-.080 | .060-.080 | .002 | — | — |

①—Overhead Camshaft (OHC) engine.
②—Service limit: .0055 inch.
③—High Swirl Combustion (HSC) engine.
④—HO models, 1.723-1.724 inch; EFI models, 1.572-1.573 inch.
⑤—HO models, 1.506-1.507 inch; EFI models, 1.375-1.573 inch.
⑥—Super High Output (SHO) engine.

## CRANKSHAFT, BEARINGS & CONNECTING RODS

| | | Crankshaft | | | | Bearing Clearance | | | Connecting Rods | |
|---|---|---|---|---|---|---|---|---|---|---|
| Engine Liter/CID | Year | Main Bearing Journal Diameter | Connecting Rod Journal Diameter | Max. Out of Round All | Max. Taper All① | Main Bearings | Connecting Rod Bearings | Crankshaft End Play | Pin Bore Diameter | Side Clearance |
| 1.3L/4-80.8 | 1989-91 | 1.9661-1.9668 | 1.5724-1.5731 | .0020 | .0020 | — | .0009-.0017 | .0031-.0111 | .7854-.7859 | .0120 |
| 1.6L/4-97 | 1991 | 1.9661-1.9668 | 1.7693-1.7699 | .0020 | .0020 | .0010-.0017 | .0011-.0027 | .0031-.0110 | .7855-.7880 | .0043-.0103 |
| 1.8L/4-112 | 1991 | 1.9661-1.9668 | 1.7692-1.7699 | ⑪ | — | .0018-.0026 | .0008-.0026 | .0040-.0080 | .7875-.7880 | .0004-.0011 |
| 1.9L/4-116 | 1989-91 | 2.2827-2.2835 | 1.7279-1.7287 | .0003 | .0003 | .0011-.0019⑤ | .0008-.0015 | .0040-.0080 | .8106-.8114 | .0040-.0110 |
| 2.2L/4-133 | 1989-91 | 2.3597-2.3604 | 2.0055-2.0061 | .0020 | — | ⑦ | .0011-.0026 | .0031-.0071 | .8640-.8644 | .0040-.0100 |
| 2.3L/4-140③ | 1989-90 | 2.3982-2.3990 | 2.0465-2.0472 | .0006 | .0006 | .0008-.0015 | .0008-.0015 | .0040-.0080 | .9012-.9096 | .0035-.0105 |
| 2.3L/4-140 ③ | 1991 | 2.2051-2.2059 | 2.0465-2.0472 | .0006 | .0006 | .0008-.0015 | .0008-.0015 | .0040-.0080 | .9012-.9096 | .0035-.0105 |
| 2.3L/4-140④ | 1989-91 | 2.2489-2.2490 | 2.1232-2.1240 | .0004 | .0003 | .0008-.0015 | .0008-.0015 | .0040-.0080 | .9096-.9112 | .0035-.0105 |
| 2.5L/4-153 | 1989-91 | 2.2489-2.2490 | 2.1232-2.1240 | .0004 | .0003 | .0008-.0015 | .0008-.0015 | .0040-.0080 | .9096-.9112 | .0035-.0105 |
| 2.9L/V6-177 | 1989-91 | 2.2433-2.2441 | 2.1252-2.1260 | .0006 | .0006 | .0008-.0015 | .0006-.0016 | .0040-.0080 | .9450-.9562 | .0040-.0110 |
| 3.0L/V6-182 | 1989-91 | 2.5190-2.5198 | 2.1253-2.1261 | .0003② | .0006 | .0010-.0014 | .0010-.0014 | .0040-.0080 | .9096-.9112 | .0060-.0140 |
| 3.0L/V6-182⑧ | 1989-91 | 2.5187-2.5197 | 2.0463-2.0472 | .0008 | .0008 | .0011-.0022 | .0090-.0022 | .0008-.0087 | .8270-.8274 | .0063-.0123 |
| 3.8L/V6-232 | 1989-91 | ⑨ | 2.3103-2.3111 | .0006 | .0003 | ⑩ | .0010-.0014 | .0040-.0080 | .9096-.9112 | .0047-.0114 |
| 4.6L/V8-281 | 1991 | 2.657 | 2.0866 | .0019 | — | .0011-.0025 | .0011-.0027 | .0051-.0099 | .8645-.8653 | .0006-.0177 |
| 5.0L/V8-302 | 1989-90 | 2.2482-2.2490 | 2.1228-2.1236 | .0006② | ⑥ | .0004-.0015 | .0008-.0015 | .0040-.0080 | .9096-.9112 | .0100-.0200 |
| 5.0L/V8-302 | 1991 | 2.2482-2.2490 | 2.1228-2.1236 | .0006② | ⑫ | .0004-.0015 | .0008-.0015 | .0040-.0080 | .9096-.9112 | .0100-.0200 |
| 5.8L/V8-351 | 1989-91 | 2.9994-3.0002 | 2.3103-2.3111 | .0006 | ⑫ | .0004-.0015 | .0008-.0015 | .0040-.0080 | .9112-.9096 | .0100-.0200 |

①—Per inch.
②—Total journal run-out, .002 inch.
③—Overhead Camshaft (OHC) engine.
④—High Swirl Combustion (HSC) engine.
⑤—With cylinder heads installed. With cylinder heads removed, .0018-.0026 inch.
⑥—Main bearing journal, .0004 inch; connecting rod journal, .0006 inch.
⑦—No. 3, .0012-.0019 inch; others, .0010-.0017 inch.
⑧—Super High Output (SHO) engine.
⑨—EFI & SC No. 1, 2, & 3, 2.519-2.5198 inch; SC No. 4, 2.5104-2.5096 inch.
⑩—EFI, .0010-0014 inch; SC No. 1, 2, & 3, .0005-.0023 inch; SC No. 4, .0010-.0028 inch.
⑪—Main bearing, .016 inch; Rod bearing, .020 inch.
⑫—Main bearing, .0004 inch per inch; Rod bearing, .0006 inch per inch.

## CYLINDER BLOCK

| Engine Liter/ CID | Year | Cylinder Bore Diameter (Std.) | Cylinder Bore Taper Max. | Cylinder Bore Out of Round Max. |
|---|---|---|---|---|
| 1.3L/4-80.8 | 1989-91 | 2.7593-2.7960 | .0007 | .0007 |
| 1.6L/4-97 | 1991 | 3.0709-3.0717 | .0007 | .009 |
| 1.8L/4-11 | 1991 | 3.2679-3.2682 | .0005 | .005 |
| 1.9L/4-116 | 1989-91 | 3.23 | .01 | .005 |
| 2.2L/4-133 | 1989-91 | 3.3858-3.3866 | .0007 | .0007 |
| 2.3L/4-140① | 1989-91 | 3.7795-3.7825 | .010 | .005 |
| 2.3L/4-140② | 1989-91 | 3.679-3.683 | .010 | .004 |
| 2.5L/4-153② | 1989-91 | 3.679-3.683 | .010 | .004 |
| 2.9L/V6-177 | 1989-91 | 3.6614-3.6630 | .010 | .005 |
| 3.0L/V6-182 | 1989-91 | 3.504 | .002 | .002 |
| 3.0L/V6-182③ | 1989-91 | 3.5039-3.5051 | .0008 | .0008 |
| 3.8L/V6-232 | 1989-91 | 3.811 | .002 | .002 |
| 4.6L/V8-281 | 1991 | 3.551 | .0002 | .0006 |
| 5.0L/V8-302 | 1989-90 | 4.004-4.0052 | .010 | .005 |
| 5.0L/V8-302 | 1991 | 4.000-4.0048 | .010 | .005 |
| 5.8L/V8-351 | 1989-91 | 4.000-4.0048 | .010 | .005 |

①—Overhead Cam (OHC) engine.
②—High Swirl Combustion (HSC) engine.
③—Super High Output (SHO) engine.

## PISTONS, PINS, & RINGS

| Engine Liter/ CID | Year | Piston Diameter (Std.) | Piston Clearance | Piston Pin Diameter | Pin To Piston Clearance | Piston End Ring Gap ① | | Piston Ring Side Clearance | |
|---|---|---|---|---|---|---|---|---|---|
| | | | | | | Comp. | Oil | Comp. | Oil |
| 1.3L/4-80.8 | 1989-91 | 2.793-2.794 | .006 | .7864-.7866 | .0-.0010 | .006 | .008 | .001-.003 | — |
| 1.6L/4-97 | 1991 | 3.0690-3.0698 | .0010-.0026 | .7869-.7871 | .0004-.0012 | ⑬ | .008 | .0012-.0026 | .0012-.0026 |
| 1.8L/4-112 | 1991 | 3.2659-3.2667 | .0015-.0020 | .7869-.7871 | .0002-.0005 | .006-.012 | .008 | .0012-.0028 | — |
| 1.9L/4-116 | 1989-91 | ② | .0016-.0024 | .8119-.8124 | .0003-.0005 | .010 | .016 | ⑪ | — |
| 2.2L/4-133 | 1989-91 | 3.3836-3.3844 | .0014-.0030 | .8651-.8654 | — | ⑬ | ⑭ | .001-.003 | — |
| 2.3L/4-140③ | 1989-91 | ④ | .0030-.0038 | .9118-.9124 | .0003-.0005 | .010 | .015 | .002-.004 | — |
| 2.3L/4-140⑤ | 1989-91 | ⑥ | .0012-.0022 | .9119-.9124 | .0002-.0005 | .008 | .015 | .002-.004 | — |
| 2.5L/4-153 | 1989-91 | ⑥ | .0013-.0021 | .9119-.9124 | .0002-.0005 | .008 | .015 | .002-.004 | — |
| 2.9L/V6-177 | 1989-91 | ⑫ | .0011-.0019 | .9446-.9450 | .0003-.0006 | .015 | .015 | .0020-.0033 | — |
| 3.0L/V6-182 | 1989-91 | ⑦ | .0014-.0022 | .9119-.9124 | .0002-.0005 | .010 | .010 | .0012-.0031 | — |
| 3.0L/V6-182⑮ | 1989-91 | 3.5023-3.5035 | .0012-.0020 | .8267-.8271 | .00004 | .012 | .008 | ⑯ | .0024-.0059 |
| 3.8L/V6-232 | 1989-90 | ⑧ | ⑰ | .9119-.9124 | ⑱ | ⑲ | .015 | .0016-.0034 | — |
| 3.8L/V6-232 | 1991 | ⑧ | ⑳ | .9119-.9124 | .0002-.0005 | .010 | .015 | .0016-.0034 | — |
| 4.6L/V8-281 | 1991 | ㉑ | .0008-.0018 | .8659-.8661 | .0002-.0039 | .009 | .010 | ㉒ | ㉓ |
| 5.0L/V8-302 | 1989-91 | ⑩ | ⑨ | .9119-.9124 | .0002-.0004 | .010 | .015 | .002-.004 | — |
| 5.8L/V8-351 | 1989-91 | ㉔ | .0018-.0026 | .9119-.9124 | .0003-.0005 | .010 | .015 | .002-.004 | — |

① —Minimum.
② —Coded red, 3.224-3.225 inch; coded blue, 3.225-3.226 inch.
③ —Overhead cam (OHC) engine.
④ —Coded red, 3.7764-3.7770 inch; coded blue, 3.7776-3.7782 inch.
⑤ —High swirl combustion (HSC) engine.
⑥ —Coded red, 3.6783-3.6789 inch; coded blue, 3.6795-3.6801 inch; coded yellow, 3.6807-3.6811 inch.
⑦ —Coded red, 3.5024-3.5031 inch; coded blue, 3.5035-3.5041 inch; coded yellow, 3.5045-3.5051 inch.
⑧ —Coded red, 3.8095-3.8101 inch; coded blue, 3.8107-3.8113 inch; coded yellow, 3.8119-3.8125 inch.
⑨ —Except V8-302 HO engine, .0014 to .0022 inch; V8-302 HO engine, .0030-.0038 inch
⑩ —Except V8-302 HO engine, coded red, 3.9989-3.9995 inch; coded blue, 4.0001-4.0007 inch; coded yellow, 4.0013-4.0019 inch. V8-302 HO engine, coded red, 3.9972-3.9980 inch; coded blue, 3.9984-3.9992 inch; coded yellow, 3.9996-4.0004 inch.
⑪ —First ring, .0015-.0032 inch; second ring, .0015-.0035 inch.
⑫ —Coded red, 3.6605-3.6615 inch.
⑬ —First ring, .008 inch; second ring, .006 inch.
⑭ —Turbo, .006 inch; non-turbo, .012 inch.
⑮ —Super High Output (SHO) engine.
⑯ —First ring, .0008-.0024 inch; second ring, .0006-.0022 inch.
⑰ —EFI, .0014-.0032 inch; SC, .0035-.0040 inch.
⑱ —EFI, .0002-.0005 inch; SC, .0003-.0006 inch.
⑲ —First ring, .011 inch; second ring, .009 inch.
⑳ —EFI, .0014-.0032 inch; SC, .0040-.0045 inch.
㉑ —Coded red, 3.5498-3.5503 inch; coded blue, 3.5503-3.5509 inch; coded yellow, 3.5509-3.5514 inch.
㉒ —First ring, .002-.004 inch; second ring, .001-.003 inch.
㉓ —Maximum .0006 inch.
㉔ —Coded red, 3.9978–3.9984 inch; coded blue, 3.9990–3.9996 inch; coded yellow, 4.0002–4.0008 inch.

## CAMSHAFT & LIFTERS

| Engine Liter/CID | Year | Camshaft Journal Diameter | Camshaft Bearing Inside Diameter | Camshaft Bearing Clearance | Camshaft End Play | Lifter Bore Diameter | Lifter Diameter | Lifter To Bore Clearance |
|---|---|---|---|---|---|---|---|---|
| 1.3L/4-80.8 | 1989-91 | ⑨ | — | — | .0020-.0070 | — | — | — |
| 1.6L/4-97 | 1991 | 1.0213-1.0222 | — | .0014-.0032 | .0028-.0075 | — | — | .0010-.0026 |
| 1.8L/4-112 | 1991 | 1.0213-1.0220 | — | .0014-.0032 | .0028-.0075 | .876 | .8740-.8745 | .0009-.0026 |
| 1.9L/4-116 ① | 1989-91 | ⑤ | ⑥ | .0013-.0033 | .0006-.0018 | .876 | .8740-.8745 | .009-.0026④ |
| 2.2L/4-133 | 1989-91 | — | — | ⑬ | .0030-.0060 | — | — | — |
| 2.3L/4-140 ⑭ | 1989-91 | 1.7713-1.7720 | — | .001-.003 | .0010-.007⑦ | — | .8422-.8427 | .0007-.0027④ |
| 2.3L/4-140 ⑧ | 1989-91 | — | 2.009-2.010 | .001-.003 | ⑦ | — | .8740-.8744 | — |
| 2.5L/4-153 ⑧ | 1989-91 | — | 2.0094-2.0104 | .001-.003 | ⑦ | — | .8740-.8744 | ④ |
| 2.9L/V6-177 | 1989-91 | ⑩ | ⑪ | .001-.003 | .0008-.0040 | — | — | — |
| 3.0L/V6-182 | 1989-91 | 2.0074-2.0084 | 2.0094-2.0104 | .001-.003 | .0010-.0050 | .8752-.8767 | .874 | .0007-.0027④ |
| 3.0L/V6-182 ⑮ | 1989-91 | 1.2189-1.2195 | 1.2205-1.2215 | .0010-.0026 | .0120 | — | 1.2587-1.2596 | .0009-.0014 |
| 3.8L/V6-232 | 1989-90 | 2.0505-2.0515 | 2.0525-2.0535 | .001-.003 | .0250 | .8752-.8767 | .8740-.8745 | .0007-.0027④ |
| 3.8L/V6-232 | 1991 | 2.0505-2.0515 | 2.0525-2.0535 | .001-.003 | ⑫ | — | .8740-.8745 | .0007-.0027④ |
| 4.6L/V8-281 | 1991 | 1.0604-1.0614 | 1.0624-1.0635 | .0010-.0030 | .0010-.0064 | — | .6294-.6299 | .0007-.0027 |
| 5.0L/V8-302 | 1989-91 | ② | ③ | .001-.003 | .0005-.0055⑦ | .8752-.8767 | .8740-.8745 | .0007-.0027④ |
| 5.8L/V8-351 | 1989-91 | ② | ③ | .001-.003 | .001-.007 | .8752-.8767 | .8740-.8745 | .0007-.0027 |

① —Engines may be encountered with oversize tappets (all eight) and/or a n oversized camshaft. Oversize tappets will be identified by a stamping .254 OT " on the machined pad below the rocker arm rail and above the No. 1 exhaust port. Oversize camshaft will be identified by a stamping .38 O/C" on the cover rail above the No. 4 exhaust port and by stamping .38 O/S" on the distributor drive end of the camshaft.

② —No. 1, 2.0805-2.0815 inch; No. 2, 2.0655-2.0665 inch; No. 3, 2.0505-2.0515 inch; No. 4, 2.0355-2.0365 inch; No. 5, 2.0205-2.0215 inch.

③ —No. 1, 2.0825-2.0835 inch; No. 2, 2.0675-2.0685 inch; No. 3, 2.0525-2.0535 inch; No. 4, 2.0375-2.0385 inch; No. 5, 2.0225-2.0235 inch.

④ —Maximum, .0005 inch.

⑤ —Standard, 1.8007-1.8017 inch; oversize, 1.8156-1.8166 inch.

⑥ —Standard, 1.8030-1.8040 inch; oversize, No. 1, 1.7786-1.7796 inch; No. 2, 1.7884-1.7894 inch; No. 3, 1.7983-1.7993 inch; No.4, 1.8081-1.8091 inch; No. 5, 1.8179-1.8189 inch.

⑦ —Service limit: .009 inch.

⑧ —High Swirl Combustion (HSC) engine.

⑨ —No. 1 and 3, 1.7103-1.7112 inch; No. 2, 1.7091-1.7100 inch.

⑩ —No. 1, 1.7285-1.7293 inch; No. 2, 1.7135-1.7143 inch; No. 3, 1.6985-1.6992 inch; No. 4, 1.6835-1.6842 inch.

⑪ —No. 1, 1.7302-1.7310 inch; No. 2, 1.7152-1.7160 inch; No. 3, 1.7002-1.7010 inch; No. 4, 1.6852-1.6860 inch.

⑫ —No endplay. Camshaft is retained by spring.

⑬ —No. 1 and 5, .0014-.003 inch; No. 2, 3, and 4, .0026-.0045 inch.

⑭ —Overhead Camshaft (OHC) engine.

⑮ —Super High Output (SHO) engine.